Gramophone

R.E.D.
*C*lassical Collector edition 1
CATALOGUE

Retail Entertainment Data Publishing Limited
Paulton House, 8 Shepherdess Walk, London N1 7LB, UK
Tel +44 (0)171 566 8216   **Fax** +44 (0)171 566 8259

R.E.D. Classical Collector Catalogue

1st edition - November 1995

EDITOR	Philippa Bunting
ASSISTANT EDITOR	Malcolm Walker
COMPILERS	Barbara Gavrielides
	Brian Godfrey
	Kathleen McSwiney
	Mark Walker
	Richard Whitehouse
	Kathryn Wolfendale
SALES & MARKETING MANAGER	Brian Mulligan
SALES MANAGER	Marie-Clare Murray
PRODUCTION MANAGER	Keith Hawkins
PUBLISHING ASSISTANT	Becca Bailey
PUBLISHER	Brenda Daly
Cover design	Chris Spalding
Front Cover photograph supplied by	The Image Bank, London, UK
Photograph by	Hans Neleman
Database typeset by	Barbers Ltd, Wrotham, Kent, UK
Printed and bound in Great Britain by	BPC Wheatons Ltd, Exeter, Devon, UK

All enquiries:

Retail Entertainment Data Publishing Limited
Paulton House, 8 Shepherdess Walk, London N1 7LB, UK
Tel +44 (0)171 566 8216   **Fax** +44 (0)171 566 8259

ISBN 0 904520 97 8

Recording and distributing companies reserve the right to withdraw any disc without giving previous notice, and although every effort is made to obtain the latest information for inclusion in this catalogue, no guarantee can be given that all the recordings listed are immediately available. Any difficulties should be referred to the issuing company concerned. The Publishers cannot accept responsibility for the consequences of any error. When ordering, purchasers are advised to quote all relevant information in addition to catalogue numbers.

Introduction

Welcome to the first edition of the R.E.D. Classical Collector Catalogue. Included within this edition is a wealth of information for those interested in the world of recorded classical music.

Listed throughout the book are over 16,000 currently available CDs that have been reviewed in *Gramophone* magazine. Fully cross-referenced Composer, Artist and Concert indexes provide extensive recording information.

For the collector keen to explore the vast recorded repertoire, the R.E.D. Classical Collector Catalogue will prove a convenient and dependable reference source for the ever-increasing range of classical music available on CD.

Contents

How to use

Composer index

Works are listed in alphabetical order within the following sections:

   I   **Orchestral**
   II **Chamber**
  III **Instrumental**
  IV **Vocal and choral**
  V **Stage works**

The following information can be found in this index:

- Artists, who cross-reference to the Artist index

- Record Company code, full details cross-referenced in the Labels and distributors index

- Catalogue numbers

- Excerpts of the work - details are given when only part or parts of a work appear on a particular recording

- Year of recording

- The other work on the disc if only two works are on the disc. If there are three or more works then see the Concert index - listing by company, by number

see the illustrated examples on adjoining page

Artist index

All artists who appear in the Composer index are listed alphabetically here and are cross-referenced with the works on which they perform, or the title and catalogue number of the relevant entry in the Concert index.

Concert index

All recordings listed in the Composer index appear here, sorted by catalogue number within each Record Company.

Record company names and addresses

The information provided at the front of the catalogue is correct at the time of going to press according to information provided to us by the companies involved.

Abbreviations

The list provided will help identify terms presented in abbreviated form throughout the catalogue as well as shortened names for many orchestras and ensembles.

Composer index examples

ELGAR, Sir Edward William *(1857-1934) England*

Section I: ORCHESTRAL

Category of music

Title

3 Bavarian Dances—orchestra, Op. 27 (1897) (Nos. 1,3 and 6 from "Scenes from the Bavarian Highlands")

Excerpts

1. Allegretto giocoso; 2. Moderato; 3. Allegro vivace
Bournemouth Sinfonietta, N. Del Mar *Concert*

Disc contains three or more works (see Concert index by number for complete details)

(CHAN) ① **CHAN6544**

Abbreviated form of record company

Concerto for Cello and Orchestra in E minor, Op. 85 (1919)
J. Lloyd Webber, RPO, Y. Menuhin *Enigma Variations*

Year of composition

Second work on disc

(7/86) (PHIL) ① **416 354-2PH**

Catalogue number

Month and year of review in *Gramophone* magazine

Compact Disc symbol

Section IV: VOCAL AND CHORAL

The Dream of Gerontius—Oratorio, Op. 38 (1900) (Wds. Newman)
Cpte H. Watts, N. Gedda, R. Lloyd, LP Ch, New Philh, A. Boult
Music Makers

Author of text, or other notes

Complete recording

Abbreviated name of artists (expanded in Artist index)

(1/87) (EMI) ① [2] **CDS7 47208-8**

Number of discs (where more than 1)

LEHAR Franz *(1870-1848) Hungary/Austria*

Section V: STAGE WORKS

Der Graf von Luxemburg—operetta: 3 acts (1909—Vienna)

Year/place of première

Translation

(Lib. Wilner Bodansky Eng: Count of Luxembourg)
1. Hoch Evoe, Angele Didier; 2. Heut' noch werd' ich Ehefrau

1, 2. E. Schwarzkopf, Philh Chor, Philh, O. Ackermann *Concert*

Recorded excerpts

(1/86) (EMI) ① **CDC7 47284-2**

Labels and distributors index

Alongside each catalogue number in the main indexes an abbreviated code denotes the issuing company of the recording. These labels and their various distributors are listed below.

An asterisk (*) against a distributor name indicates that the company may carry only selected items.

Price codes:
Ⓕ Full price above £9.99
Ⓜ Medium price £6.99 - £9.99
Ⓑ Budget price £4.99 - £6.99
Ⓢ Super budget price below £4.99
All labels without a code are presumed to be Full price
Some label entries, displaced from their normal alphabetical positions, have been cross-referenced for ease of use.

Code	Label	Distributor

A

Code	Label	Distributor
ABBE	**Abbey Recording Co** *(Abbey* Ⓜ *, Alpha)*	Abbey Recording Co
ABBS	**Abbey Records** (SCS Music)	Conifer
ABCC	**ABC Classics**	Select
ABMU	**Abbey Music**	no current UK distributor
ACAD	**Academy Collection** Ⓜ	THE
ACAN	**Acanta**	no current UK distributor
ACCE	**Accent** *(Accent, Accent 2)*	Complete Record Co
ACCO	**Accord** (Musidisc)	Harmonia Mundi
ACNT	**Accento**	Accento
ACOU	**Acoustics Records**	Conifer
ACTA	**Acta Records**	Acta Records/Impetus
ADDA	**Adda**	no current UK distributor
ADES	**Adès**	Harmonia Mundi
AEOL	**Aeolian**	no current UK distributor
AETE	**Aeterna**	Complete Record Co
AKAD	**Akademia**	no current UK distributor
AL S	**Al Segno**	Koch International
ALBA	**Albany**	Select
ALHA	**Alhambra**	no current UK distributor
ALIE	**Alienor**	Harmonia Mundi
ALMA	**Almaviva**	Harmonia Mundi
ALPH	**Alphée**	Discovery Records
ALTA	**Altarus**	Kingdom
ALTM	**Altamira Records**	Altamira Records
ALTN	**Alta Nova**	Michael G Thomas
ALTO	**Alto Records**	Complete Record Co
AMAT	**Amati**	Complete Record Co
AMBI	**Ambitus**	RRD (Distribution)
AMCA	**AmCam Recordings**	TradeLink Music Distribution
AMGR	**American Gramaphone**	New Note
AMIA	**Amiata**	Harmonia Mundi
AMON	**Amon Ra**	Harmonia Mundi/*CM
AMPH	**Amphion Sound Recordings** Ⓜ	Priory
ANDC	**André Charlin**	Discovery Records
ANDR	**Andromeda**	Kingdom
APPL	**Applecross**	Applecross
APR	**APR** Ⓜ	Harmonia Mundi/APR
ARAB	**Arabesque**	Seaford Music
ARC	**ARC Music**	ARC Music
ARCA	**Arcana**	Koch International
ARCL	**Arc of Light**	Sony Music Entertainment
ARCH	**Archiv Produktion** *(Archiv Produktion, Archiv Produktion Galleria* Ⓜ *)*	PolyGram Record Operations
ARCI	**Archiphon**	TradeLink Music Distribution
ARCO	**Arcobaleno**	Complete Record Co
AREM	**Arembe**	Arembe
ARGO	**Argo**	PolyGram Record Operations

Code	Label	Distributor
ARHD	Archduke	no current UK distributor
ARHI	Archive Documents	Michael G Thomas
ARIO	Arion	Discovery Records
ARIS	Arista	BMG UK
ARLE	Arlecchino	no current UK distributor
ARS	Ars Produktion	RRD (Distribution)
ARSC	Ars Classicum (Vox)	Complete Record Co
ARSM	Ars Musici	Complete Record Co/Vanderbeek and Imrie
ART	Art and Music	Priory
ARVA	Arva	no current UK distributor
ARTI	Artificial Eye	FoxVideo Sales
AS D	AS Discs	Kingdom
ASPE	Aspen Music	Aspen/Impetus
ASTR	Astrée Auvidis	Harmonia Mundi
ASV	ASV	ASV/Koch International

(ASV, COE, Gaudeamus, Musicmasters, White Line Ⓜ, Quicksilva Ⓢ)

Code	Label	Distributor
ATHE	Athens	no current UK distributor
ATHN	Athene (D&J Recording)	Priory
ATLA	Atlantic Records	Warner Classics
ATRI	Atrium	Discovery Records
ATS	Arturo Toscanini Society	Michael G Thomas
ATTA	Attacca Babel	Impetus
AUDI	Audiofon	APR
AUDP	Audiophile Labs	Sound and Media
AUDT	Audite	no current UK distributor
AURO	Aurora	no current UK distributor
AUVI	Auvidis	Harmonia Mundi

(Classique, Valois, Valois Biennnale de Lyon, Travelling)

B

Code	Label	Distributor
B&L	B&L Records	no current UK distributor
B'NA	B'nai Brith	Jewish Music Distribution
BALK	Balkanton Ⓜ	Pinnacle/Impetus
BAND	Bandleader	Conifer
BARC	Barcarolle	no current UK distributor
BATO	Baton	RRD (Distribution)
BAUE	Michael Bauer Editions	Impetus
BAY	Bay Cities	no current UK distributor
BAYE	Bayer	Priory
BAYR	Concerto Bayreuth	RRD (Distribution)
BBCR	BBC Radio Classics	Carlton/Complete Record Co
BEAG	Bel Age	Target
BEEC	Sir Thomas Beecham Trust Ⓜ	Beecham
BELA	Belart Ⓑ	Karussell/PolyGram Record Operations
BELL	Belltree	Dragonsfire
BERL	Berlin Classics	Complete Record Co
BETA	Beta Productions	Beta Productions
BEUL	Beulah Ⓜ	Priory/Beulah
BIDD	Biddulph Ⓜ	Biddulph
BIRM	Birmingham Bach Choir	Birmingham Bach Choir
BIS	BIS	Conifer
BITT	Bitter and Twisted	Impetus
BLAC	Black Dragon Films	no current UK distributor
BLOC	Edition Block	Impetus
BLUE	Bluebell	no current UK distributor
BMS	British Music Society	British Music Society
BNL	BNL	no current UK distributor
BOGR	Biographies in Music (Lyric) Ⓜ	Complete Record Co
BONG	Bongiovanni	Kingdom

(Bongiovanni, Golden Age of Opera)

Code	Label	Distributor
BONT	Bonton Classics	no current UK distributor
BOST	Boston Skyline	Complete Record Co
BRAS	Bravura	no current UK distributor
BREW	Brewhouse Music	Complete Record Co
BRID	Bridge	Complete Record Co
BRIT	British Music Label	Kingdom/Forties Recording Co
BRM	BRM	Bosworth and Co
BUTT	Butterfly Music Ⓜ	RRD (Distribution)

Code	Label	Distributor
BVHA	**BVHaast**	Cadillac

C

Code	Label	Distributor
CALA	**Cala**	Complete Record Co
CALC	**Calle Classics**	Complete Record Co
CALI	**Calig**	Priory
CALL	**Calliope**	Harmonia Mundi
CAM	**CAM Productions**	Silver Sounds CD
CAMB	**Cambria**	RRD (Distribution)
CAME	**Camerata**	Impetus
CAMP	**Campion Records**	RRD (Distribution)
CNTO	*Cantoris*	*Koch International*
CANY	**Canyon Classics**	Complete Record Co
CANZ	**Canzone** (Kontrapunkt)	Impetus
CAPR	**Capriccio** *(Capriccio, Capella Edition)*	Target
CARL	**Carlton Classics**	Carlton/Complete Record Co
CPRI	*Caprice*	*Complete Record Co*
	(Caprice, Collector's Classics)	
CPRO	*Capriole* ⓜ	*Manygate Marketing*
CASC	**Cascavelle**	no current UK distributor
CAST	**Castle Vision**	BMG UK
CATA	**Catalyst**	BMG UK
CATE	**Cantate**	RRD (Distribution)
CAVA	**Cavalier** ⓜ	Kingdom
CAVE	**Cavendish Cassettes** ⓜ	Cavendish Distribution
CAW	**CAW Records**	Clive Wilkinson
CBC	**CBC Records**	Kingdom
	(Musica Viva, SM5000, Perspective)	
CBS	**CBS (Sony)**	Sony Music Entertainment
	(CBS Masterworks, Masterworks Portrait ⓜ *, Digital Masters* ⓜ *,*	
	Maestro, Odyssey ® *)*	
CBS	**CBS (France)**	Discovery Records
CCOR	**Concord Concerto**	no current UK distributor
CDM	**CdM Russian Season**	Harmonia Mundi
CEDI	**Cedille**	Seaford Music
CELE	**Celestial Harmonies**	Select
CENT	**Centaur**	Complete Record Co
EPM	*Classical Collector*	*Discovery Records*
CFM	**Classic FM**	Complete Record Co
CFP	**Classics for Pleasure** ® -	Music for Pleasure
CGP	**Covent Garden Pioneer**	Covent Garden Pioneer FSP
	(video cassettes only)	
CHAM	**Chamber Sound**	no current UK distributor
CHAN	**Chandos**	Chandos
	(Chandos, Chaconne, Brass, New Direction, Collect ⓜ *)*	
CHAR	**Charlin**	Discovery Records
CHAT	**Chatsworth**	Complete Record Co
CHES	**Chesky**	Complete Record Co
CHIE	**Chief**	Cadillac
CHNN	**Channel Classics**	Select
	(Channel Classics, Channel Crossings, Canal Grande ⓜ *)*	
CHNT	**Le Chant du Monde**	Harmonia Mundi
CHOI	**Choice Recordings**	Choice Recordings
CHOR	**Chorale Classics**	TSC Enterprises
CHRI	**Christophorus**	Select
	(Christophorus, Entree ⓜ *)*	
CHTI	**Chanticleer**	RRD (Distribution)
CIRR	**Cirrus** ⓜ	Castle Communications
CLAD	**Claddagh**	Direct Distribution
CLAI	**Classico**	no current UK distributor
CLAR	**Claremont** ⓜ	Complete Record Co
CLAS	**Classic Studio**	RRD (Distribution)
CLAT	**Clarton**	Czech Music Enterprises
CLAU	**Claudio**	Complete Record Co/Claudio
CLAV	**Claves**	Complete Record Co
	(Claves, Favor ⓜ *)*	
CLLE	**Collegium**	Koch International
CLOR	**Cleveland Orchestra**	Cleveland Orchestra
	(75th Anniversary CD Edition)	

Code	Label	Distributor
CLOU	**Cloud Nine Records**	SilvaScreen
CLRC	**Classical Recording Company**	no current UK distributor
CLRI	**Clarinet Classics**	Select
CLTS	**Collets**Ⓜ	Complete Record Co
CLUB	**Club 99**	no current UK distributor
CMC	**Canadian Music Centre**	TradeLink Music Distribution
CNCE	**Concerto**	RRD (Distribution)
CNTE	**Canterino**	TradeLink Music Distribution
CNTI	**Continuum**	Select
CNTO	**Cantoris**	Koch International
CNZO	**Canzone Italiana**	RRD (Distribution)
CLLE	*Collegium*	*Koch International*
COCE	**Consonance**Ⓜ/Ⓕ	Koch International
COLL	**Collins Classics**	Conifer
	(Collins Classics, 20th Century Plus, QuestⓂ*)*	
COLN	**Colonnade**	no current UK distributor
COLO	**Colosseum**	Pinnacle
COLU	**Columbia**	Sony Music Entertainment
CONC	**Concert Artists**	Concert Artis/Fidelio
COND	**Condon Collection**	New Note
CONI	**Conifer Classics**	Conifer
CONN	**Connoisseur Society**	Harmony Records
CONS	**Consort**	Consort Records
COOP	**Co-operative Union**	Co-operative Union
COPT	**Classical Options**	Target
CORO	**Coronata**	Presto Music
CPI	**CPI**	no current UK distributor
CPO	**CPO**	Koch International
CPRI	**Caprice**	Complete Record Co
	(Caprice, Collector's Classics)	
CPRO	**Capriole**Ⓜ	Manygate Marketing
CRAM	**Cramer Music**	Priory/Cramer Music
CRD	**CRD**	Select
CRI	**CRI**	no current UK distributor
CRYS	**Crystal**	Impetus
CSTL	**Castle**	Castle Communications
CYBE	**Cybelia**	no current UK distributor
CZEC	**Czech Radio**	Czech Music Enterprises

D

Code	Label	Distributor
MDG	***Dabringhaus und Grimm***	*Koch International*
DACA	**DaCapo** (Marco Polo)	Select
DANA	**Danacord**	Discovery Records
DANI	**Danica**	RRD (Distribution)
DANT	**Dante**	no current UK distributor
DARM	**Darmo**	Symposium Records
DATU	**Datum**	Priory
DCB	**DCB Records**	DCB Records
DECC	**Decca Classics**	PolyGram Record Operations
	(Decca, New Line, Enterprise, Entartete Musik, The British CollectionⓂ*, Jubilee*Ⓜ*, Ovation*Ⓜ*, DDD Ovation*Ⓜ*, Double Decca*Ⓜ*, Grandi Voci*Ⓜ*, Grand Opera*Ⓜ*, Opera Gala*Ⓜ*, Serenata*Ⓜ*, Historic*Ⓜ*, Cinema Gala*Ⓜ*, 100 Best Tunes*Ⓜ*, World of...*Ⓜ*, Weekend*Ⓑ*, Headline*Ⓑ*)*	
DELL	**Dell'Arte**	Symposium Records
DELO	**Delos**	Conifer
	(3000 series, 1000 seriesⓂ*)*	
DENO	**Denon**	Conifer
	(Denon, Aliare, RepertoireⓂ*)*	
DERV	**Dervorguilla**	Harmonia Mundi
DG	**Deutsche Grammophon**	PolyGram Record Operations
	(DG, DG GalleriaⓂ*, 20th Century Classics*Ⓜ*, Dokumente*Ⓜ* 3-D Classics*Ⓜ*, Doubles*Ⓜ*, Compact Editions*Ⓜ*, Compact Classics*Ⓑ*, Privilege*Ⓑ*, Classikon*Ⓑ*, Resonance*Ⓑ*)*	
DHM	**Deutsche Harmonia Mundi**	BMG UK
	(Deutsche Harmonia Mundi, Editio ClassicaⓂ*, Mozart Edition*Ⓜ*)*	
DINE	**Dinemec Classics**	no current UK distributor
DINT	**Discover International**Ⓢ/Ⓜ	Discover International
DIVA	**Divas**	Divas
DIVE	**Divertimento**	RRD (Distribution)

Code	Label	Distributor
DIVI	Divine Art	Kingdom
DIVO	Divox	Complete Record co
DIVU	Divucsa	Discovery Records
DONE	Donemus Composers' Voice	Impetus
DORE	Doremi	Priory
DORI	Dorian	Select
DORO	Doron Music	Discovery Records
DOYE	Doyen Recordings	Conifer
DPV	De Plein Vent	RRD (Distribution)
DRES	Dress Circle	no current UK distributor
DRG	DRG	New Note
DUTT	Dutton Laboratories Ⓜ/Ⓕ	Complete Record Co
DYNA	Dynamic	Priory
	(Dynamic, Il canale)	

E

Code	Label	Distributor
EAR	Ear-Rational	Impetus
EART	Earthsounds	Earthsounds
EBS	EBS	Kingdom
ECM	ECM New Series	New Note
EDA	Edition Abseits	RRD (Distribution)
EDEL	Edelweiss	Planetarium
EDIT	Edit	Czech Music Enterprises
EDL	Edel	no current UK distributor
EKLI	Eklipse	Parsifal Distribution
NONE	*Elektra Nonesuch*	*Warner Classics*
ELAN	Elan	no current UK distributor
ELCT	Electrecord	Priory
ELIT	Elite Music	Trittico
EMEC	EMEC	RRD (Distribution)
EMER	Emergo Classics	Complete Record Co
EMI	EMI Classics	EMI
	(EMI, Reflexe, Studio Ⓜ, Digital DDD Ⓜ, Références Ⓜ, Great Recordings of the Century Ⓜ, Phoenixa Ⓜ, British Composers Ⓜ, L'Esprit français Ⓜ, Klemperer Edition Ⓜ, Mozart Edition Ⓜ, Beecham Edition Ⓜ, Rouge et Noir Ⓜ, Fun with Music Ⓜ, Miles of Music Ⓜ)	
EMIL	EMI Laser	Music for Pleasure
	(EMI Laser Ⓑ, EMI Mozart '91 Ⓑ)	
EMIN	EMI Eminence Ⓜ	Music for Pleasure
ENCO	Encore	Michael G Thomas
ENGL	English Recording Co	Complete Record Co
ENSA	Ensayo	Discovery Records
ENSB	Ensemblegram	Complete Record Co
ENSE	Ensemble	Kingdom
ENSX	Ensemble XXI	no current UK distributor
ENTP	Enterprise	Priory
ENTR	Entr'acte (Fifth Continent)	Silva Screen
EPIC	Epic	Sony Music Entertainment
EPM	Classical Collector	Discovery Records
ERAS	Erasmus	Impetus
ERAT	Erato	WarnerClassics
	(Erato, MusiFrance, Bonsai Ⓜ, Emeraude Ⓜ, Libretto Ⓜ, Résidence Ⓑ)	
ERDE	Erdenklang Musikverlag	no current UK distributor
ERIE	Elysium Records	RRD (Distribution)
ERMI	Ermitage Ⓜ	no current UK distributor
ETCE	Etcetera	TradeLink Music Distribution
EUFO	Eufoda	no current UK distributor
EURM	Europa Musica	no current UK distributor
EURO	Eurodisc	BMG UK
	(Eurodisc, Mozart Year '91 Ⓑ)	
EVEN	Even Classics	RRD (Distribution)
EVER	Everest	Complete Record Co
EXTR	Extraplatte	Impetus
EYE	Eye of the Storm	Complete Record Co

F

Code	Label	Distributor
FACE	Facet (Delos) Ⓜ	Conifer

Code	Label	Distributor
FAMO	Famous and Fabulous	Famous and Fabulous
FANF	Fanfare	no current UK distributor
FERM	Fermate	RRD (Distribution)
FERT	Fert	no current UK distributor
FEST	Festivo	Priory
FIDE	Fidelio Classics	Complete Record Co
FINL	Finlandia	Warner Classics
FIRS	First Edition/Louisville	no current UK distributor
FISH	Fish Ear Records	Fish Ear Communications
FLAM	FlamencOVision	Pinnacle
FLAP	Flapper (Pavilion)	Pinnacle
FLOA	Floating Earth	Complete Record Co
FLY	Fly Records	Bucks Music
FNAC	FNAC Music	no current UK distributor
FONE	Fonè	UK Distribution
FONI	Fonitcetra Ⓜ/Ⓕ	Target
FONO	Fonoteca	no current UK distributor
FORL	Forlane	Target
FORT	The Fourties	RRD (Distribution)
FOUR	Four Hands Music	Priory
FOX	20th Century-Fox	BMG UK
FOXG	Foxglove Audio	Complete Record Co
FOYE	Foyer	RRD (Distribution)
FRAG	Fragile Records	Pinnacle
FRST	First Night Records	Pinnacle
FSM	FSM	RRD (Distribution)
FUTU	Future Classics	Complete Record Co
FY	Fy	Discovery Records
FYLK	Fylkingen Records	RER Megacorp

G

Code	Label	Distributor
GALA	Gala Ⓑ	Target
GALL	Gallo	RRD (Distribution)
GAMU	Gamut Classics	no current UK distributor
GASP	Gasparo	Complete Record Co
GEES	Geest	Cadillac
GEFF	Geffen	BMG UK
GEGA	Gega	Impetus
GEOR	Georgian Recordings	no current UK distributor
GFON	Gramofono 2000	Complete Record Co
GHA	GHA Ⓜ/Ⓕ	Koch International
GIAN	Giant Records	no current UK distributor
GIME	Gimell	Conifer
GIUL	Giulia	RRD (Distribution)
GLOB	Globe	Complete Record Co
GLOR	Gloriae Dei Cantores	Priory
GLOS	Glossa	Harmonia Mundi
GM R	GM Recording	Impetus
GME	Grande Musique d'Espagne	no current UK distributor
GNP	GNP Crescendo Records	Silva Screen
GOTH	Gothic	Gothic/Pro Organo
GRAS	Grasmere	Grasmere
GREA	Great Hall	Michael G Thomas
GREE	Greentrax	Conifer
GROS	Grosvenor Nostalgia	Grosvenor Nostalgia
GROT	Great Recordings of the Tuba	no current UK distributor
GRP	GRP	New Note
GUIL	Guild	Guild
GUIT	Guitar Masters	no current UK distributor
GVIS	Gramavision	no current UK distributor

H

Code	Label	Distributor
HANS	Hänssler	Select
HAPY	Happy Days	Conifer
HARM	Harmonia Mundi	Harmonia Mundi
	(Harmonia Mundi, Musique d'abord Ⓜ, Plus Ⓑ)	
HRMO	Harmonic	no current UK distributor

Code	Label	Distributor
HATH	Hat-Hut	Harmonia Mundi
HEAR	Hearts of Space	Ultima Thule
HENE	Heneghan and Lawson	Heneghan and Lawson
HERA	Herald	Koch International
HERI	Heritage Recordings	Mirabilis
HISP	Hispavox Zarzuela	Discovery Records
HIST	Historical Performers	Kingdom
HLCN	Helicon	Helicon
HRMO	Harmonic	no current UK distributor
HUNG	Hungaroton	Target
HUNT	Hunter's Moon	Symposium Records
HYPE	Hyperion	Select
	(Hyperion, Helios$^{\circledR}$)	

I

IKON	Ikon$^{\circledR}$	Priory
	(Ikon$^{\circledR}$, Neva Records)	
ILHA	Ilha Formosa Records	Seaford Music
IMG	IMG Records	Carlton/Complete Record Co
IMP	IMP	Carlton/Complete Record Co
	(IMP Masters$^{\circledF}$, Red Label$^{\circledM}$, Allegro$^{\circledM}$, CDI$^{\circledM}$, Duet, IMP Classics, Contour Classics$^{\circledM}$, NTI$^{\circledM}$, Discover the Classics$^{\circledR}$,IMP Collectors$^{\circledR}$, PWK Classics$^{\circledR}$)	
IMPE	Imperial Sound	Imperial Sound
INA	INA Mémoire Vive	no current UK distributor
INTA	Intaglio	no current UK distributor
INTD	Intrada	Silva Screen
INTE	Intercord	no current UK distributor
INTR	Interphon Classics	no current UK distributor
INTU	Intuition Records	New Note
IRCC	IRCC	Parsifal Distribution
IRON	Iron Needle	Kingdom
ISIS	Isis Records	Complete Record Co
ITAL	Italian Opera Rarities	RRD (Distribution)
ITM	ITM *(jazz)*	Koch International
ITM	ITM *(other titles)*	TradeLink Music Distribution

J

JADE	Jade	BMG UK
JARO	Jaro	no current UK distributor
JCR	J&C Richard Enterprise	no current UK distributor
JECK	Jecklin	no current UK distributor
JERU	Jerusalem	Jewish Music Distribution
JEWI	Jewish Music Productions	Jewish Music Distribution
JLR	JLR	KJ Associates
JMP	JMP	RRD (Distribution)
JMR	John Marks Records	May Audio Marketing
JMS	Stafford	Stafford
JOS	JOS Records	JOS Records

K

KING	Kingdom	Kingdom
KINS	Kingsway	Complete Record Co
KIWI	Kiwi-Pacific Records	no current UK distributor
KLT	KLT	Kingdom
KLVI	Klavier	UK Distribution
KOCH	Koch International	Koch International
	(Koch International Classics, Koch International$^{\circledM}$, Koch Historic, Koch Treasure$^{\circledM}$, Koch Presents$^{\circledR}$)	
SCHW	*Koch Schwann*	*Koch International*
KONT	Kontrapunkt	Impetus
KOSS	Koss Classics	HW International
K617	K617	Discovery Records

Code	Label	Distributor

L

Code	Label	Distributor
LABO	Labor Records	no current UK distributor
LAMM	Lammas	Sound Alive Music
LAND	Landor	no current UK distributor
LANS	Lansdowne	Lansdowne
LARG	Largo Records	Complete Record Co
LARR	Larrikin	no current UK distributor
LASE	LaserLight (Capriccio) Ⓢ	Target
LAUD	Laudis	no current UK distributor
LDR	LDR	no current UK distributor
L'EM	L'Empreinte Digitale	Harmonia Mundi
LEGA	Legato Classics (Lyric)	Complete Record Co
	(Legato Classics, HREⓂ*, Standing Room Only*Ⓜ*)*	
LEGE	Legend	Kingdom
LEMA	Léman Classics	no current UK distributor
LEO	Leo Records	Impetus
LHAL	London Hall	Impetus
LIBR	Libra	Griffin
LIGI	Ligia	Discovery Records
LIND	Lindenberg	Priory
LINN	Linn Records	PolyGram Record Operations
LIVE	Live Classics	Kingdom
LODI	Lodia	Lodia
LOND	London	PolyGram Record Operations
	(London, JubileeⓂ*)*	
LONG	LongMan Records	LongMan Records
L'OI	L'Oiseau-Lyre	PolyGram Record Operations
	(L'Oiseau-Lyre, FlorilegiumⓂ*)*	
LORE	Lorelt	Complete Record Co
LOTO	Lotos	RRD (Distribution)
LOTU	Lotus	Impetus
LSO	LSO Classic Masterpieces	Carlton/Complete Record Co
LUNA	Lunadisc	Complete Record Co
LYCH	Lyrichord	CM Distribution
LYRC	Lyric	Parsifal Distribution
LYRI	Lyrita	Nimbus

M

Code	Label	Distributor
MAGN	Magnum Opus	no current UK distributor
MAMI	Master Mix	New Note
MANC	Manchester Camerata	Camerata Productions
MAND	Mandala	Harmonia Mundi
MARC	Marco Polo	Select
MARQ	Marquis	Kingdom
MATE	Materiali Sonari	New Note
MATT	Musica Attacca	no current UK distributor
MAWS	Mawsom and Wareham	BMG UK
MAX	Max Sound	Max Sound
MAYA	Maya Recordings	Complete Record Co
MAYH	Kevin Mayhew	Priory
MCA	MCA Records	BMG UK
MCEG	MCEG Virgin Vision	no current UK distributor
MCI	Music Club International	VCI Distribution
MDG	Dabringhaus und Grimm	Koch International
MDIT	Mediterraneo	no current UK distributor
MEDI	Medici-Whitehall	Medici-Whitehall
MEL	Mel Recordings	Koch International
MELC	Melcot	Melcot Music Recordings
MELO	Melodiya	BMG UK
MEMO	Memories (Nuova Era) Ⓜ	Complete Record Co
MERC	Mercury Ⓜ	PolyGram Record Operations
MERI	Meridian	Nimbus
	(Meridian, DuoⓂ*)*	
MERL	Merlin	Merlin
METI	Metier	Priory
METR	Metronome	Complete Record Co
MEZH	Mezhdunarodnaya Kniga	Complete Record Co

Code	Label	Distributor
MFP	**Music for Pleasure**	Music for Pleasure
MGB	**Muzikszene Schweiz**	Complete Record Co
MILA	**Milan**	BMG UK
MIRA	**Mirabilis**	Mirabilis
MITR	**Mitra**	Priory
MKI	**MKI Disques**	no current UK distributor
MMAS	**Music Masters** (UK)	Target
MMOI	**Memoir Classics**	Target
MNTA	**Montague Music**	Montague Music
MOBS	**Musical Observations**	no current UK distributor
MODE	**Mode Records**	Harmonia Mundi
MOLE	**Molenaar**	no current UK distributor
MONR	**Monré Records**	Monré Records
MONI	**Monitor**	no current UK distributor
MONT	**Montaigne** (Auvidis)	Harmonia Mundi
MOSC	**Musica Oscura**	Complete Record Co
MOTE	**Motette**	Priory
MOZA	**Mozart Edition**	Mozart Edition
MPHO	**Musicaphon**	RRD (Distribution)
MSCM	**Music Memoria**	Discovery Records
MSVE	**Musica Sveciae**	Complete Record Co
MSOU	**Mastersound** *(Mastersound, Fanfare, Profile Ⓜ)*	RRD (Distribution)
MULT	**Multisonic** Ⓜ/Ⓕ	Priory
MUSD	**Musidisc**	Harmonia Mundi
MUSI	**Music & Arts**	Harmonia Mundi
MUSM	**Music Masters** (US)	Nimbus
MYTO	**Myto**	Parsifal Distribution

N

Code	Label	Distributor
NAIM	**Naim Audio**	no current UK distributor
NALB	**New Albion**	Harmonia Mundi
NATI	**Droffig** (National Trust)	Discovery Records
NAXO	**Naxos** Ⓢ	Select
NEAD	**Nuova as-Discs**	Kingdom
NEW	**New World**	Harmonia Mundi
NEWP	**Newport Classic** *(Newport Classic, Newport Premier)*	RRD (Distribution)
NEWT	**New Tone**	Impetus
NIGH	**Nightingale Classics**	Koch International
NIGP	**Night Pro**	President
NIMB	**Nimbus** *(Nimbus, Prima Voce Ⓜ)*	Nimbus
NKF	**NKF**	no current UK distributor
NMC	**NMC**	Complete Record Co
NMCL	**NM Classics**	Impetus
NONE	**Elektra Nonesuch**	Warner Classics
NORT	**Northeastern**	Priory
NOVA	**Novalis**	no current UK distributor
NOVE	**Novello**	no current UK distributor
NOVL	**Novelbond**	Novelbond
NUOV	**Nuova Era** *(Nuova Era, Ancient Music)*	Complete Record Co
NYOS	**National Youth Orchestra of Scotland**	National Youth Orchestra of Scotland

O

Code	Label	Distributor
O111	**Opus 111**	Harmonia Mundi
ODE	**Ode** *(Ode, Manu Classic, Voyager)*	Discovery Records
OIA	**Opera in Arabic**	no current UK distributor
OLYM	**Olympia** *(Olympia Ⓜ, Explorer)*	Priory
ONDI	**Ondine** *(Ondine, Octopus)*	Koch International
ONGA	**Ongaku Records**	no current UK distributor
ONYX	**Onyx**	RRD (Distribution)
OPAL	**Opal** (Pavilion)	Harmonia Mundi
OPRA	**Opera Rara**	Opera Rara
TRES	*Opera Tres*	*Ashley Mark Publishing*

Code	Label	Distributor
OPUS	Opus	no current UK distributor
O111	*Opus 111*	*Harmonia Mundi*
OP3	Opus 3	May Audio Marketing/Pentacone
ORCH	Orchid	Complete Record Co
ORFE	Orfeo	Koch International
OTTA	Ottavo	Priory
OXRE	OxRecs	Priory/OxRecs

P

Code	Label	Distributor
PALL	Palladio	RRD (Distribution)
PAN	Pan Classics	Vanderbeek and Imrie
PANE	Pantheon	Kingdom
PANG	Pangea	Sony Music Entertainment
PANT	Panton Ⓜ	RRD (Distribution)
PART	Partridge	Seaford Music
PASP	Past Perfect	THE
PAST	Past Times	no current UK distributor
PAUL	Paula	TradeLink Music Distnbution
PAVA	Pavane	Kingdom
PAVR	Pavarotti Collection	RRD (Distribution)
PEAR	Pearl (Pavilion)	Harmonia Mundi
PERF	Performance Recordings	no current UK distributor
PHIL	Philips Classics	PolyGram Record Operations
	(Philips, Point Music, Insignia Ⓜ, Mozart Edition Ⓜ, Silver Line Ⓜ, Musica da Camara Ⓜ, Baroque Classics Ⓜ, Duo Ⓜ, Solo Ⓜ, Legendary Classics Ⓜ, HighTech Ⓜ, Laser Line Ⓜ, Concert Classics Ⓑ)	
PHOE	Phoenix (USA)	Complete Record Co
PHOG	Phonographe (Nuova Era) Ⓜ	Complete Record Co
PHON	Phono Suecia	no current UK distributor
PP	*Pianissimo* Ⓜ	*Pianissimo*
PICK	Pickwick	Carlton/Complete Record Co
PIER	Pierre Verany Ⓕ	Kingdom
PIER	Pierre Verany Favourites Ⓜ	Discovery Records
PILZ	Pilz	no current UK distributor
PION	Pioneer	VCI Distribution
PKO	PKO	RRD (Distribution)
PLAN	Plant Life	Sympoisum Records
PLAT	Platz	Conifer
PLDO	Polydor	PolyGram Record Operations
PNT	Point Music	PolyGram Record Operations
POIN	Point Records	RRD (Distribution)
POLS	Polskie Nagrania (Muza)	Priory
POLY	Polyphonic	Conifer/Polyphonic
PP	Pianissimo Ⓜ	Pianissimo
PRAG	Praga Ⓕ/Ⓜ	Harmonia Mundi
PREA	Preamble (Fifth Continent)	Silva Screen
PREI	Preiser	Harmonia Mundi
PREL	Preludio	no current UK distributor
PRES	President	President Records
PREZ	Prezioso	Priory
PRIO	Priory	Priory
PRO	Pro Arte	no current UK distributor
PROD	ProDigital Recordings	no current UK distributor
PROM	Prometheus Records	Silva Screen
PROP	Proprius	May Audio Marketing
PROR	Pro Organo	Gothic/Pro Organo
PROU	Proudsound	Conifer
PYRA	Pyramid Records (USA)	no current UK distributor

Q

Code	Label	Distributor
QUAN	Quantum	Discovery Records
QUIN	Quintana	Harmonia Mundi

Code	Label	Distributor

R

Code	Label	Distributor
RADY	**Radio Years**	Complete Record Co
RCA	**RCA Victor**	BMG UK
	(RCA, Red Seal, Gold Seal⊕*, Victrola*®*, Silver Seal*®*)*	
RECO	**The Record Collector**	The Record Collector
RED	**Red Sky**	Direct Distribution
REDC	**Radcliffe Recordings**	Complete Record Co
REFE	**Reference Recordings**	May Audio Marketing
REGE	**Regent**	Regent
RELI	**Relief**	no current UK distributor
REM	**REM Editions**	Priory
REPL	**Replay Music**	RRD (Distribution)
RIBB	**Ribbonwood**	Discovery Records
RICE	**Ricercar**	no current UK distributor
RNCM	**RNCM**	Royal Northern College of Music
RNE	**Radio Naçional de España**	no current UK distributor
ROH	**Royal Opera House Records**	Conifer
ROMA	**Romantic Robot**	Romantic Robot
ROMO	**Romophone**	Complete Record Co
ROND	**Rondo**	RRD (Distribution)
ROSE	**Rose Collection**	no current UK distributor
ROYA	**Royal Classics**Ⓢ	Complete Record Co
RPO	**RPO**	Carlton/Complete Record Co
RUSS	**Russian Disc**	Koch International

S

Code	Label	Distributor
SAGA	**Saga Classics**⊕	Complete Record Co
SAIN	**Sain**	Sain
SAKK	**Sakkaris Records**	Pinnacle
SALA	**Salabert Actuels**	Harmonia Mundi
SALI	**Soundalive**	Koch international
SAYD	**Saydisc**	Harmonia Mundi/*CM
SCAL	**Scalen'Disc**	no current UK distributor
SCAN	**Scan'nan**	Silva Screen
SCHW	**Koch Schwann**⊕/Ⓕ	Koch International
	(Musica Mundi, Musica Sacra)	
SCOM	**Scott Music**	Scott Music
SDBD	**Soundboard Records**	Soundboard Records
SEAV	**Seaview Music**	Seaview Music
SERE	**Serendipity**	Koch Intemational
SHEF	**Sheffield Lab**	no current UK distributor
SIGN	**Signum**	TradeLink Music Distribution
SILO	**Silver Octopus**	Silver Octopus
SILV	**Silva Screen**	Silva Screen/Conifer
	(Silva Screen, Silva Classics, Silva Treasury⊕*)*	
SIMA	**Simax**	Target
SIMP	**Simply Classics**	no current UK distributor
SINE	**Sine Qua Non**	Sine Qua Non
SKAR	**Skarbo**	Discovery Records
SMIT	**Smithsonian Folkways**	Koch International
SMP	**SMP**	no current UK distributor
SOIM	**Sonic Images**	no current UK distributor
SOLE	**Solesmes**	Priory
SOLS	**Solstice**	Discovery Records
SOMM	**Somm Recordings**	Priory
SONP	**Sonpact**	Seaford Music
SONY	**Sony Classical**	Sony Music Entertainment
	(Sony Classical, Vivarte, Berlitz Passport, British Pageant⊕*, West End*⊕*, Essential Classics*®*)*	
SOUT	**Southern Cross** (Fifth Continent)	Silva Screen
SPEC	**Spectrum Records**	no current UK distributor
SPHE	**Sphemusations**	Sphemusations
SPRI	**Springthyme Records**	Direct Distribution
SPRO	**Sound Projects**	no current UK distributor
SQUI	**Squint**	no current UK distributor
STAD	**The Strad**	The Strad

Code	Label	Distributor
STAN	Stanyan	Conifer
STAR	Start Classics	Koch International
STDV	Stradivarius	Priory
STEN	Stentor	Mirabilis
STER	Sterling	Priory
STOC	Stockhausen	Stockhausen-Verlag
STOK	Stokowski Society	Stokowski Society
STRA	Stradivari Classics	Michèle International
STUD	Studio SM	Discovery Records
SUIT	Suite	RRD (Distribution)
SUMM	Summit Records	Kingdom
SUPR	Supraphon	Koch International
SUTT	Sutton Sound	Sutton Sound
SWED	Swedish Society	May Audio Marketing
SWIS	Swiss Pan	Vanderbeek and Imrie
SYMP	Symposium	Symposium Records
SYNC	Syncoop	no current UK distributor
SYPH	Symphonia	Discovery Records
SYPY	Symphony	Target

T

Code	Label	Distributor
TACT	Tactus	no current UK distributor
TAHR	Tahra	Priory
TAIZ	Taizé (Auvidis)	Harmonia Mundi
TALE	Talent	Seaford Music
TALL	Tall Poppies	Complete Record Co
TARA	Tara	Direct Distribution
TELA	Telarc	Conifer
TELD	Teldec Classics	Warner Classics
	(Teldec Classics, Das Alte Werk, Reference Ⓜ, Viva Mozart Ⓜ, Digital Experience Ⓜ, Esprit Ⓑ)	
TELS	Telstar	BMG UK
TEMP	Tempo (Auvidis)	Harmonia Mundi/Discovery Records
TER	TER Classics	Koch International
TESS	Tessitura	no current UK distributor
TEST	Testament	Complete Record Co
THIR	Third Mind	Third Mind Records
THOD	Thodey	Griffin Soundalive
THOR	Thorofon	RRD (Distribution)
TIMB	Timbre Records	Koch International
TIME	Timeless Records	no current UK distributor
TIMP	Timpani	Discovery Records
TITA	Titanic	TradeLink Music Distribution/Jewish Music Distribution
TMPL	Temple Records	Temple Records
TREM	Tremula Records	Symposium Records
TRES	Opera Tres	Ashley Mark Publishing
TREV	Trevak	no current UK distributor
TRIN	Tring International Ⓢ	Tring International/Priory
TRIT	Trittico	Trittico
TROU	Troubadisc	Complete Record Co
TUDO	Tudor	TradeLink Music Distribution
TUXE	Tuxedo Music	TradeLink Music Distribution

U

Code	Label	Distributor
ULTP	Ultraphon	Koch International
ULTR	Ultrasonic	Ultrasonic
UNIC	Unicorn-Kanchana	Harmonia Mundi
	(Unicorn-Kanchana, Souvenir Ⓜ)	
UNIT	United Recording	Complete Record Co
UPBE	Upbeat Records	Target
USK	Usk Recordings	Complete Record Co

Code	Label	Distributor

V

Code	Label	Distributor
VAI	Video Artists International	Parsifal Distribution
VANG	Vanguard Classics Ⓢ/Ⓜ	Complete Record Co
VARE	Varèse-Sarabande	Pinnacle
VENG	Vengo Records	no current UK distributor
VERO	Verona Ⓑ	Complete Record Co
VICT	Victoria	no current UK distnbutor
VIEN	Vienna Masters	no current UK distributor
VIEW	View Video	Parsifal Distribution
VIRG	Virgin Classics	EMI
	(Virgin Classics, Veritas, LCO, Duo Ⓜ, Virgo Ⓑ)	
VIR2	Virgin Records	EMI
VIRT	Virtuosi Records	Virtuosi Records
VISI	Vision Video	no current UK distnbutor
VISM	Vision Music	no current UK distributor
VITA	Vital Communications	Vital Communications
VMM	Vienna Modern Masters	TradeLink Music Distribution
VNP	VNP	no current UK distributor
VOIC	Voiceprint	Voiceprint
VOIX	Voix Celeste	Voix Celeste
VOX	Vox	Complete Record Co
	(Vox Turnabout Ⓑ, Vox Cum Laude Ⓜ, Vox Legends Ⓜ, Vox Box Ⓑ, Vox Unique Ⓜ, Allegretto Ⓑ)	
VOXA	Vox Australis	

W

Code	Label	Distributor
WALH	Walhall Records	Parsifal Distribution
WALS	Walsingham	New Note
WCOU	Watercourse	Impetus
WEA	WEA	Warner Classics
WEAL	Wealden	no current UK distributor
WERG	Wergo	Harmonia Mundi
WIEN	Wienerworld Classic	PolyGram Record Operations
WOOD	Woodmansterne	Woodmansterne
WORD	Word	no current UK distributor

Y

Code	Label	Distributor
YORE	York Records	York Records
YORK	York Ambisonic	Target
YORR	York Records	York Records
YTV	YTV	YTV Enterprises

Z

Code	Label	Distributor
ZAPP	Zappa Records	Zappa Records
ZOPF	Zopf	PolyGram Record Operations

1

Code	Label	Distributor
10 R	10 Records	EMI

3

Code	Label	Distributor
3DCL	3D Classics	Discovery Records

Record company names and addresses

Abbey Recording Company
1 Abbey Street, Eynsham,
Oxford OX8 1HR
Tel/Fax 01865 880240

Accento
61 Ravendale Road,
London N16 6TJ
Tel 0181 699 3988
Fax 0181 291 4868

Acoustics Records
PO Box 350, Reading,
Berkshire RG6 7DQ
Tel 01734 268615

Acta Records
28 Aylmer Road, London W12 9LQ
Tel/Fax 0181 740 1349

Aeterna
44 Tantallon Road,
London SW12 8DG
Tel 0181 673 1901
Fax 0181 675 0927

Albany Records (UK)
PO Box 12, Carnforth,
Lancashire LA5 9PD
Tel 01524 735873
Fax 01524 736448

Altamira Records
40 Hewitt Road, Hornsey,
London N8 0BL
Tel 0181 341 5425
Fax 0181 347 5075

Altarus Records
Easton Dene, Bailbrook Lane,
Bath BA1 7AA
Tel 01225 852323
Fax 01225 852523

Amphion Sound Recordings
Norton Lodge, 109 Beverly Road,
Norton-on Derwent, Malton,
North Yorkshire Y017 9PH
Tel 01653 698372/692044

Appian Publications
& Recordings (APR)
PO Box 1, Wark, Hexham,
Northumberland NE48 3EW
Tel 01434 220627
Fax 01434 220628

ARC Music
PO Box 111, East Grinstead,
West Sussex RH19 2FZ
Tel 01342 312161
Fax 01342 325209

Arembe
84 Filsham Road, Hastings,
East Sussex TN38 OPG
Tel/Fax 01424 423260

Ashley Mark Publishing
Olsover House, 43 Sackville Road,
Newcastle-upon-Tyne NE6 5TA
Tel 0191 276 0448
Fax 0191 276 1623

Aspen Music
51 High Street, Wells-next-the-Sea,
Norfolk NR23 1EN
Tel 01328 710552

ASV
1 Beaumont Avenue,
London W14 9LP
Tel 0171 381 8747
Fax 0171 385 2653

Athene Records
7 Felden Street, London SW6 5AE
Tel 0171 736 9485
Fax 0171 371 7087

Bandleader Records
7 Garrick Street, London WC2E 9AR
Tel 0171 240 0658

Bath University Recordings
c/o Music Office, Bath University,
Building 1, East Room 21,
Claverton Down, Bath BA2 7AY
Tel 01225 826431
Fax 01225 462508

Sir Thomas Beecham Trust
Denton House, Denton,
Harleston, Norfolk IP20 0AA
Tel 01986 788780

Beta Productions
PO Box 309 Amersham,
Buckinghamshire HP6 6DY

Beulah
The Signal Box, 1 Breach Road,
Coalville, Leicestershire LE67 3SB
Tel 01530 810828
Fax 01530 814525

Biddulph Recordings
34 St George Street, Hanover
Square, London W1R 0ND
Tel 0171 408 2458
Fax 0171 495 6501

Birmingham Bach Choir
16 Selwyn Road, Edgbaston,
Birmingham B16 OSP

Bitter and Twisted Records
22c Breakspears Road,
London SE4 1UW
Tel 0181 691 8646

BMG Classics
Bedford House, 69-79 Fulham High
Street, London SW6 3JW
Tel 0171 973 0011
Fax 0171 371 9571

BMG UK
Lyng Lane, West Bromwich,
West Midlands B70 7ST
Tel 0121 500 5545
Fax 0121 553 6880

Bosworth and Co
14-18 Heddon Street, Regent
Street, London W1R 8DP
Tel 0171 734 4961
Fax 0171 734 0475

Brewhouse Music
Breeds Farm,
57 High Street, Wicken, Ely,
Cambridgeshire CB7 5XR
Tel 01353 720309
Fax 01353 723364

British Music Society
7 Tudor Gardens, Upminster,
Essex RM14 3DE
Tel 01708 224795

Bucks Music
1a Farm Place, London W8 7SX
Tel 0171 221 4275
Fax 0171 229 6893

Cadillac Distribution
61-71 Collier Street, London N1 9DF
Tel 0171 278 7391
Fax 0171 278 7394

Cala Records
17 Shakespeare Gardens,
London N2 9LJ
Tel 0181 883 7306
Fax 0181 365 3388

Camerata Productions
30 Derby Road,
Manchester M14 6UW
Tel 0161 257 3522
Fax 0161 248 6499

Campion Records
13 Bank Square, Wilmslow,
Cheshire SK9 1AN
Tel 01625 527844
Fax 01625 536101

Cantoris Records
Exchequer Gate, Lincoln LN2 1PZ
Tel 01522 536981
Fax 01522 560550

Carlton Home Entertainment
The Waterfront, Elstree Road,
Elstree, Hertfordshire WD6 3BS
Tel 0181 207 6207
Fax 0181 207 5789

Castle Communications
A29 Barwell Business Park,
Leatherhead Road, Chessington,
Surrey KT9 2NY
Tel 0181 974 1021
Fax 0181 974 2674

Cavendish Distribution
11 Wigmore Street,
London W1H 9LB
Tel 0171 491 4117
Fax 0171 629 1966

CBS Records
see Sony Music Entertainment

Chandos Records
Chandos House, Commerce Way,
Colchester, Essex C02 8HQ
Tel 01206 794000/225200
Fax 01206 794001/225201

Choice Recordings
10a Morningside Place,
Edinburgh EH10 5ER
Tel/Fax 0131 447 7122

Claddagh Records
Dame House, Dame Street,
Dublin 2, Eire
Tel 00 353 1 677 8943
Fax 00 353 1 679 3664

Clarinet Classics
77 St Albans Avenue,
London E6 4HH
Tel/Fax 0181 472 2057

Classics for Pleasure
EMI House, 43 Brook Green,
London W6 7EF
Tel 0171 605 5000
Fax 0171 605 5050

Claudio Records
Studio 17, The Promenade,
Peacehaven, Brighton BN10 8PU
Tel 01273 580250
Fax 01273 583530

Cloud Nine Records
Silva House, 261 Royal College
Street, London NW1 9LU
Tel 0171 284 0525
Fax 0171 482 2385

CM Distribution
Hookstone Park, Harrogate, North
Yorkshire HG2 7DB
Tel 01423 888979/886696
Fax 01423 885761

Collegium Records
PO Box 172, Whittlesford,
Cambridge, CB2 4QZ
Tel 01223 832474
Fax 01223 836723

Collins Classics
Premier House, 10 Greycoat Place,
London SW1P 1SB
Tel 0171 222 1921
Fax 0171 222 1926

The Complete Record Co
12 Pepys Court, 84 The Chase,
London SW4 0NF
Tel 0171 498 9666
Fax 0171 498 1828

Concert Artist / Fidelio
Twelve Tall Trees, Newmarket Road,
Royston, Herts, SG8 7EG
Tel 01763 246747

Conifer Records
Claremont House, Horton Road,
West Drayton, Middlesex UB7 8JL
Tel 01895 447707/441422
Fax 01895 420713/441808

Consort Records
34 St Mary's Grove,
London W4 3LN
Tel 0181 995 9994
Fax 0181 995 2115

Co-operative Union
Holyoake House, Hanover Street,
Manchester M60 0AS
Tel 0161 832 4300
Fax 0161 831 7684

Covent Garden Pioneer FSP
100 Blythe Road, London W14 0HE
Tel 0171 371 6191
Fax 0171 603 0668

Cramer Music
23 Garrick Street,
London WC2E 9AX
Tel 0171 240 1612
Fax 0171 240 2639

CRD
PO Box 26, Stanmore,
Middlesex HA7 4XB
Tel 0181 958 7695
Fax 0181 958 1415

Czech Music Enterprises
5 Eversley Close, Rhyl,
Clwyd LL18 4US
Tel 01745 350645
Fax 01745 331331

Darmo Records
Arvensis, Stour Lane, Stour Row,
Shaftesbury, Dorset SP7 0QJ
Tel/Fax 01747 838318

Decca Classics
1 Sussex Place, Hammersmith,
London W6 9XS
Tel 0181 910 5000
Fax 0181 910 5411

Dell'Arte Records
PO Box 26, Hampton,
Middlesex TW12 2NL
Tel 0181 979 2479

Deutsche Grammophon
1 Sussex Place, Hammersmith,
London W6 9XS
Tel 0181 910 5000
Fax 0181 910 5411

Direct Distribution
50 Stroud Green Road,
Finsbury Park, London N4 3EF
Tel 0171 281 3465
Fax 0171 281 5671

Discover International
1 Grange House, 229 Stoke
Newington Church Street,
London N16 9HL
Tel/Fax 0171 241 6459

Discovery Records
The Old Church Mission Room,
King's Corner, Pewsey,
Wilts SN9 5BS
Tel 01672 563931
Fax 01672 563934

Discurio
9 Gillingham Street,
London SW1V 1HN
Tel/Fax 0171 828 7963

Divas Records
20 Montpelier Street,
Brighton BN1 3DJ
Tel/Fax 01273 327894

The Divine Art
Tindle House, 31 Beach Road,
South Shields, Tyne and Wear
NE33 2QX
Tel 0191 456 1837
Fax 0191 455 2954

Doreml
London House, Suite 337,
Old Court Place, London W8 4PL
Tel/Fax 0171 937 7171

Doyen Recordings
Doyen House,17 Coupland Close,
Moorside, Oldham,
Lancashire OL4 2TQ
Tel 0161 628 3799
Fax 0161 628 3799

Dragonsfire
9 Hillside Road, Ashtead,
Surrey KT2 1RZ
Tel 01372 277703
Fax 01372 278406

Dutton Laboratories
PO Box 576, Harrow,
Middlesex HA3 6YW
Tel 0181 421 1117
Fax 0181 421 2998

Earthsounds
PO Box 1, Richmond,
North Yorkshire DL10 5EB
Tel 01748 825959
Fax 01748 850218

EMI Records
Customer Services, EMI House,
43 Brook Green, London W6 7EF
Tel 0171 605 5000
Fax 0171 605 5050

EMI
Sales & Distribution Centre,
Hermes Close, Tachbrook Park,
Leamington Spa,
Warwickshire CV34 6RP
Tel 01926 888888
Fax 0181 479 5922

Erato Disques
46 Kensington Court,
London W8 5DP
Tel 0171 938 5542
Fax 0171 937 6645

First Night Records
2-3 Fitzroy Mews, London W1P 5DQ
Tel 0171 383 7767
Fax 0171 383 3020

FlamencOvision
54 Windsor Road, London N3 3SS
Tel 0181 346 4500
Fax 0181 346 2488

Floating Earth
Unit 14, 21 Wadsworth Road,
Perivale, Middlesex UB6 7JD
Tel 0181 997 4000
Fax 0181 998 5767

The Forties Recording Co
44 Challacombe, Furzton,
Milton Keynes MK4 1DP
Tel 01908 502836

Four Hands Music
15 Birchmead Close, St Albans,
Hertfordshire AL3 6BS
Tel/Fax 01727 858485

Foxglove Audio
10 Springwood Road, Little London,
Rawden, West Yorkshire LS19 6BH
Tel 0113 250 7282
Fax 0113 250 0577

FoxVideo Sales
Twentieth Century House, 31-32
Soho Square, London W1V 6AP
Tel 0171 753 8686
Fax 0171 434 2170

Gimell Records
4 Newtec Place, Magdalen Road,
Oxford OX4 1RE
Tel 01865 244557
Fax 01865 790472

Grasmere Music
62 Pont Street Mews,
Knightsbridge, London SW1X 0EF
Tel 0171 584 9765
Fax 0171 823 7100

Griffin
Church House, St Mary's Gate, 96
Church Street, Lancaster LA1 1TD
Tel 01524 844399
Fax 01524 844335

Grosvenor Records
Grosvenor Studios, 16 Birmingham
Road, Birmingham B20 3NP
Tel/Fax 0121 356 9636

Guild Records
PO Box 5, Hadleigh, Ipswich,
Suffolk IP7 6QF
Tel/Fax 01473 658026

Halcyon
Submarine Records and Tapes, 13
Gardenia Road, Bush Hill Park,
Enfield Road, Middlesex EN1 2JA

Harmonia Mundi UK
19-21 Nile Street, London N1 7LL
Tel 0171 253 0863
Fax 0171 253 3237

Harmony Records
Charborough Lodge, Charborough
Park, Wareham BH20 7EL
Tel/Fax 01929 459589

Helicon Recordings
PO Box 9, Hastings,
East Sussex TN34 3UU
Tel 01424 422061
Heneghan and Lawson
22 Pantycelyn Road,
Llandouth, Near Penarth,
South Glamorgan CF64 2PG
Tel/Fax 01222 706976
Herald Audio Visual Publications
The Studio, 29 Alfred Road,
Farnham, Surrey GU9 8ND
Tel 01252 725349
Fax 01252 735567
Heritage Recordings
50 Bessborough Place,
London SW1V 3SG
Tel 0171 828 1055
Hunters Moon Promotions
Paget's Lane, Bubbenhall,
Coventry CV8 3BJ
Tel 01926 851325
HW International
167-171 Wiloughby Lane,
Brantwood Industrial Area,
London N17 0SB
Tel 0181 808 2222
Fax 0181 808 5599
Hyperion Records
PO Box 25, Eltham,
London SE9 1AX
Tel 0181 294 1166
Fax 0181 294 1161
Ikon Records
Cathedral of the Assumption &
All Saints, Ennismore Gardens,
London, SW7 1NH
Imperial Sound
16 Stonehill Road,
London SW14 8RW
Tel 0181 876 3156
Impetus Distribution
PO Box 1324, London W5 2ZU
Tel/Fax 0181 998 6411
Isis Records
52 Argyle Street, Oxford OX4 1SS
Tel/Fax 01865 726553
Jewish Music Distribution
PO Box 2268, Hendon,
London NW4 3UW
Jewish Music Productions
PO Box 232, Harrow,
Middlesex HA1 2NN
Tel/Fax 0181 909 2445
Karussell
PO Box 1425, Chancellor's House,
72 Chancellor's Road,
Hammersmith, London W6 9QB
Tel 0181 910 5692
Fax 0181 910 5892
Kingdom Distribution
61 Collier Street, London N1 9BE
Tel 0171 713 7788
Fax 0171 713 0099
Koch International
24 Concord Road, London W3 0TH
Tel 0181 992 7177
Fax 0181 896 0817
Lammas Records
34 Carlisle Avenue, St Albans,
Hertfordshire AL3 5LU
Tel/Fax 01727 851553

Libra
Church Path, Hook, Near
Basingstoke, Hampshire RG27 9LZ
Tel 01256 762605
Fax 01256 763706
Linn Records
Floors Road, Waterfoot,
Eaglesham, Glasgow G76 0EP
Tel 0141 644 5111
Fax 0141 644 4262
Lodia
2 Rugby Street, London WC1N 3QU
Tel 0171 831 1910
Fax 0171 242 5207
LongMan Records
PO Box 2649, Brighton,
East Sussex BN2 3PP
Tel 01273 383062
London Records
Chancellors House, 72 Chancellors
Road, London W6 9RS
Tel 0181 910 5100
Fax 0181 910 5907
Lyrita
99 Green Lane, Burnham, Slough,
Buckinghamshire SL1 8EG
Tel 01628 604208
Manygate Marketing
13 Cotswold Mews, 30 Battersea
Square, London SW11 3RA
Tel 0171 223 7265
Fax 0171 585 2830
Mawson and Waeham
Midgy Hall, Sharperton, Morpeth,
Northumberland NE6S 7AS
Tel 01669 640252
Max Sound
6 Stainbeck Lane, Leeds LS7 3QY
Tel 0113 269 4807
May Audio Marketing
Aireside Mills, Cononley, Keighley,
West Yorkshire BD20 8LW
Tel 01535 632700
Fax 01535 632887
Kevin Mayhew
Rattlesden, Bury St Edmunds,
Suffolk IP30 0SZ
Tel 01449 737978
Fax 01449 737834
Melcot Music
PO Box 2404, New Milton,
Hampshire BH25 7XZ
Tel/Fax 01425 611924
Memoir Records
PO Box 66, Pinner,
Middlesex HA5 2SA
Fax 0181 866 7804
Meridian Records
PO Box 317, Eltham,
London SE9 4SF
Tel 0181 857 3213
Fax 0181 857 0731
Merlin Distribution
Fifth Floor West, Enterprise House,
Blyth Road, Hayes,
Middlesex UB3 1DD
Tel 0181 561 9099
Fax 0181 573 1643
Metier Sound and Vision
PO Box 270, Preston,
Lancashire PR2 3LZ
Tel 01772 866178

Metronome Productions
Magdalen Studio, Chapel Lane,
Farthingoe, Braekeley,
Northamptonshire NN13 5PG
Tel 01295 710641
Fax 01295 710731
Michèle International
Michèle House, The Acorn Centre,
Roebuck Road, Hainault,
Essex IG6 3TU
Tel 0181 500 1819
Fax 0181 500 1745
Mirabilis Records
5 Kings Croft Gardens,
Leeds LS17 6PB
Tel 0113 268 5123
Fax 0113 266 9063
Monré Records
PO Box 234, Richmond,
Surrey TW10 7NS
Tel/Fax 01202 659199
Montague Music
East Wing, Courtyard Cottage,
Southwick Hall,
Peterborough PE8 5BL
Tel/Fax 01832 274790
**Harold Moores
Records and Video**
2 Great Marlborough Street,
London W1V 1DE
Tel 0171 437 1576
Fax 0171 287 0377
Mozart Edition
50 Potter Street, Northwood,
Middlesex HA6 1QD
**Music Collection
International (MCI)**
Strand VCI House,
36-38 Caxton Way, Watford,
Hertfordshire WD1 8UF
Tel 01923 255558
Fax 01923 816880
Music for Pleasure
EMI House, 43 Brook Green,
London W6 7EF
Tel 0171 605 5000
Fax 0171 605 5050
Music Masters (UK)
The End House,
Gurnells Road, Seer Green,
Buckinghamshire HP9 2XJ
Tel 01494 672803
Fax 01494 678016
**National Youth Orchestra
of Scotland**
13 Somerset Place,
Glasgow G3 7JT
Tel 0141 332 8311
Fax 0141 332 3915
Naxos and Marco Polo UK
PO Box 576, Sheffield,
South Yorkshire S10 1AY
Tel 01142 678958
Fax 01142 671529
New Note
Electron House, Cray Avenue,
St Mary Cray, Orpington,
Kent BR5 3RJ
Tel 01689 877884
Fax 01689 877891
(dealers should contact Pinnacle)

Nimbus Records
Wyastone Leys, Monmouth,
Gwent NP5 3SR
Tel 01600 890682
Fax 01600 890779

NMC
Francis House, Francis Street,
London SW1P 1DE
Tel/Fax 0171 828 3432

Nonesuch
46 Kensington Court,
London W8 5DP
Tel 0171 938 5542
Fax 0171 937 6645

Novelbond
Sovereign House,
212-224 Shaftesbury Avenue,
London WC2H 8HQ

Olympia Compact Discs
31 Warple Way, London W3 0RX
Tel 0181 743 6767
Fax 0181 749 1300

Opera Rara
25 Compton Terrace, Canonbury,
London N1 2UN
Tel 0171 359 1777
Fax 0171 354 3942

OxRecs
Magdalen Farm Cottage,
Standlake, Witney,
Oxfordshire OX8 7RN
Tel 01865 300347

Parsifal Distribution
Bridge Studios, Suite No. 7,
318-326 Wandsworth Bridge Road,
London SW6 2TZ
Tel 0171 610 6725
Fax 0171 610 6729

Past Perfect
Lower Farm Barns, Bainton Road,
Bucknell, Oxfordshire OX6 9LT
Tel 01869 325052
Fax 01869 325072

Pavilion Records (Pearl)
Sparrows Green, Wadhurst,
East Sussex TN5 6SJ
Tel 01892 783591
Fax 01892 784156

Pentacone
4 Cross Bank Road, Batley,
West Yorkshire WF17 8PJ
Tel 01924 445039

Philips Classics
1 Sussex Place, Hammersmith,
London W6 9XS
Tel 0181 910 5000
Fax 0181 910 5411

Pianissimo
Ridgway Road, Pyrford, Woking,
Surrey GU22 8PR
Tel 01932 345371

Pinnacle Records
Electron House, Cray Avenue,
St Mary Cray, Orpington,
Kent BR5 3RJ
Tel 01689 870622
Fax 01689 878269

Planetarium Recordings
16 Wigmore Street,
London W1H 9DE
Tel 0171 636 5597
Fax 0171 636 5602

PolyGram Classics and Jazz
1 Sussex Place, Hammersmith,
London W6 9XS
Tel 0181 910 5000
Fax 0181 910 5412

PolyGram Record Operations
PO Box 36, Clyde Works, Grove
Road, Romford, Essex RM6 4QR
Tel 0181 910 1799
Fax 0181 910 1675

Polyphonic Reproductions
77-79 Dudden Hill Lane,
London NW10 1BD
Tel 0181 459 6194/5
Fax 0181 451 6470

President Records
Exmouth House, 11 Pine Street,
London EC1R 0JH
Tel 0171 837 5020
Fax 0171 837 4795

Presto Music
23 Portland Street,
Royal Leamington Spa,
Warwickshire CV32 5EZ
Tel 01926 334834

Priory Records
Unit 9b, Upper Wingbury
Courtyard, Wingrave,
Near Aylesbury,
Buckinghamshire HP22 4LW
Tel 01296 682255
Fax 01296 682275

ProudSound
61 Iffey Road, Oxford OX4 1EB
Tel/Fax 01865 723764

Quantum Audio
PO Box 26, Kilmarnock,
Ayrshire KA1 1BA
Tel 01563 571122
Fax 01563 571133

RCA
Bedford House, 69-79 Fulham
High Street, London SW6 3JW
Tel 0171 973 0011
Fax 0171 371 9571

The Record Collector
111 Longshots Close, Broomsfield,
Chelmsford, Essex CM1 7DU
Tel 01245 441661
Fax 01245 443642

Redcliffe Recordings
68 Barrowgate Road,
London W4 4QU
Tel 0181 995 1223

Regent Records
PO Box 528, Wolverhampton,
West Midlands WV3 9YW
Tel 01902 24377
Fax 01902 717661

ReR Megacorp
79 Beulah Road, Thornton Heath,
Surrey CR7 8JG
Tel 0181 771 1063
Fax 0181 771 3138

Romantic Robot
54 Deanscroft Avenue,
London NW9 8EN
Tel 0181 200 8870
Fax 0181 200 4075

Romophone
PO Box 717, Oxford OX2 7YU
Tel 01865 515353
Fax 01865 515335

Royal Northern College of Music
124 Oxford Road,
Manchester M13 9RD
Tel 0161 273 6283
Fax 0161 273 7611

RRD (Rare Records Distribution)
13 Bank Square, Wilmslow,
Cheshire SK9 1AN
Tel 01625 549862
Fax 01625 536101

Sain (Recordiau)
Llandwrog, Caernarfon,
Gwynedd LL54 5TG
Tel 01286 831111
Fax 01286 831497

Saydisc Records
Chipping Manor, The Chipping,
Wotton-under-Edge,
Gloucestershire GL12 7AD
Tel 01453 845036
Fax 01453 521056

Scratch Records
Hatch Farm Studios, Unit 16,
Hatch Farm, Chertsey Road,
Addlestone Moor, Surrey KT15 2EH
Tel 01932 828715
Fax 01932 828717

SCS Music
4 Newtec Place, Magdalen Road,
Oxford OX4 1RE
Tel 01865 244557
Fax 01865 790472

Seaford Music
24 Pevensey Road, Eastbourne,
East Sussex BN21 3HP
Tel 01323 732553
Fax 01323 417455

Seaview Music
42 Bateman Street,
Cambridge CB2 1NA
Tel 01223 415524
Fax 01223 415685

**Select Music and Video
Distributors**
34a Holmethorpe Avenue,
Holmethorpe Estate, Redhill,
Surrey RH1 2NN
Tel 01737 760020
Fax 01737 766316

Silva Screen
Silva House, 261 Royal College
Street, London NW1 9LU
Tel 0171 284 0525
Fax 0171 482 2385

Silver Octopus
14 Alma Street, Buxton,
Derbyshire SK17 7DY
Tel 01298 26920
Fax 01298 72292

Silver Sounds CD
Unit 7, Peerglow Estate,
Queensway, Ponders End,
Enfield, Middlesex EN3 4SN
Tel 0181 364 7711
Fax 0181 805 1135

The Sine Qua Non Society
The Old Forge, 2 Bridge Street,
Hadleigh, Suffolk IP7 6B7
Tel 01473 828494
Fax 01296 681989

Somm Recordings
13 Riversdale Road, Thames Ditton,
Surrey KT7 0QL
Tel 0181 398 1586
Fax 0181 339 0981

Sony Music Entertainment
10 Great Marlborough Street,
London W1V 2LP
Tel 0171 911 8200
Fax 0171 911 8600
Sony Music Operations
Rabans Lane, Aylesbury,
Buckinghamshire HP19 3BX
Tel 01296 395151
Fax 01296 395551
Sound and Media
Unit 3, Wells Place, Gatton Park
Business Centre, New Battlebridge
Lane, Redhill, Surrey RH1 3DR
Tel 01734 644445
Fax 01734 644213
Sphemusations
12 Northfield Road, Onehouse,
Stowmarket, Suffolk IP14 3HF
Tel 01449 613388
Springthyme Records
Balmalcolm House, Kingskettle,
Fife KY15 7TJ
Tel 01337 830773
Fax 01337 831773
J Martin Stafford
298 Blossomfield Road, Solihull,
West Midlands B91 1TH
Tel 0121 711 1975
Start Classics
Suite 20a, Canada House,
Blackburn Road, London NW6 1RZ
Tel 0171 625 7113
Fax 0171 624 3258
Stockhausen Verlag
Kettenberg 15, 51515 Kürten,
Germany
Leopold Stokowski Society
12 Market Street, Deal,
Kent CT14 6HS
The Strad
PO Box 500, Leicester LE99 0AA
Sutton Sound
26 Cleveland Square,
London W2 6DD
Tel 0171 262 9066
Fax 0171 262 3235
Symposium Records
5 High Street, Cromer,
Norfolk NR27 9HG
Tel/Fax 01263 511531
Target Records
23 Gardner Industrial Estate,
Kent House Lane, Beckenham,
Kent BR3 1QZ
Tel 0181 778 4040
Fax 0181 676 9949
Teldec Classics
46 Kensington Court,
London W8 5DP
Tel 0171 938 5542
Fax 0171 937 6645
Temple Records
Shillinghill, Temple, by Gorebridge,
Midlothian EH23 4SH
Tel 01875 830328
Fax 01875 830392
Testament Records
14 Tootswood Road, Bromley,
Kent BR2 OPD
Tel 0181 464 5947
Fax 0181 464 5352

Thames Distribution
Thames House, 63a Station Road,
Hampton, Middlesex TW12 2BT
Tel 0181 979 9033
Fax 0181 979 5055
Thats Entertainment Records
107 Kentish Town Road,
London NW1 8PD
Tel 0171 485 9593
Fax 0171 485 2282
Michael G Thomas
5a Norfolk Place, London W2 1QN
Tel 0171 723 4935/01795 536074
Top Note Music
123 Crown Street,
Aberdeen AB1 2HN
Tel/Fax 01224 210259
Total Home Entertainment (THE)
Unit 1, Rosevale Business Park,
Newcastle-under-Lyme,
Staffordshire ST5 7QT
Tel 01782 566511
Fax 01782 565400
TradeLink Music Distribution
Eastwoods House,
Church End, Potterspury,
Northamptonshire NN12 7PX
Tel 01908 543055
Fax 01908 543056
Tremula Records
63 Sandringham Road,
Maidenhead, Berkshire SL6 7PL
Tel 01628 29142
Tring International
Triangle Business Park,
Wendover Road, Aylesbury,
Buckinghamshire HP22 5BL
Tel 01296 615800
Fax 01296 614250
Trittico Distributor
34 Phillimore Walk, London W8 7SA
Tel 0171 937 2869
Fax 0171 938 1983
TSC Enterprises
5 Sanderson Street, Sheffield,
South Yorkshire S9 2UA
Tel 01142 442424
Fax 01142 434312
UK Distribution
23 Richings Way, Iver,
Buckinghamshire SL0 9DA
Tel 01753 652669
Fax 01753 654531
Ultima Thule
1 Conduit Street, Leicester LE2 0JN
Tel 0116 285 4545
Unicorn-Kanchana Records
PO Box 339, London W8 7TJ
Tel 0171 727 3881
Fax 0171 243 1701
The United Recording Company
see *Cala Records*
Upbeat Records
Sutton Business Centre, Restmor
Way, Wallington, Surrey SM6 7AH
Tel 0181 773 1223
Fax 0181 669 6752
Usk Recordings
26 Caterham Road,
London SE13 5AR
Tel/Fax 0181 318 2031

Vanderbeek and Imrie
15 Marvig, Lochs,
Isle of Lewis HS2 9QP
Tel/Fax 01851 880216
VCI Distribution
Strand VCI House,
36-38 Caxton Way, Watford,
Hertfordshire WD1 8UF
Tel 01923 255558
Fax 01923 816880
Video Artists International
158 Linwood Plaza, Suite 301,
Fort Lee, NJ 07024, USA
Tel UK Freephone 0800 892931
Virgin Records
Kensal House, 553-579 Harrow
Road, London W10 4RH
Tel 0181 964 6000
Fax 0181 964 6073
Virtuosi Records
38 York Street, London W1H 1FF
Vital Communications
38 Nevil Road, Bishopston,
Bristol BS7 9EH
Tel 01179 422830
Fax 01179 247371
Voiceprint
PO Box 5, Derwentside,
Co Durham DH9 7HR
Tel 0191 512 1103
Fax 0191 512 1104
Voix Celeste
18 Hill Close, Newmarket,
Suffolk CB8 0NR
Tel 01638 660531
Warner Classics
46 Kensington Court,
London W8 5DP
Tel 0171 938 5542
Fax 0171 937 6645
Westmoor Music
Bay G - 10, Wembley Commercial
Centre, East Lane, Wembley,
Middlesex HA9 7YH
Whitetower Records
44 Challacombe, Furzton,
Milton Keynes MK4 1DP
Tel 01908 502836
Clive Wilkinson
89 Beckfield Lane. Acomb,
York Y02 5PW
Tel 01904 794177
Woodmansterne Publications
1 The Boulevard, Blackmore Lane,
Watford, Hertfordshire WD1 8YW
Tel 01923 228236
Fax 01923 245788
WRPM
62 Woodstock Road,
Birmingham B13 9BN
Tel/Fax 0121 449 7041
York Ambisonic
PO Box 66, Lancaster LA2 6HS
Tel 01524 823020
Fax 01524 824420
York Records
30 Melbourne Street, York Y01 5AQ
Tel 01904 634172
YTV Enterprises
Television Centre, Kirkstall Road,
Leeds LS3 1JS
Tel 0113 243 8283
Fax 0113 244 5107

Abbreviations

AAM	Academy of Ancient Music	cowhn	cowhorn
alphn	alphorn	cpsd	composed
alto	counter tenor/male alto	cpsr	composer
alto fl	alto flute	cpted	completed (by)
alto sax	alto saxophone	d	died
amplified pf	amplified piano	db	double bass
AMTF	American Music Theatre Festival	dbn	double bassoon
anon	anonymous	dhp	double harp
archlte	archlute	dig pf	digital piano
arr	arranged	dir	director
ASMF	Academy of St Martin in the Fields	dncr	dancer
ATER	Associazione Teatri Emilia Romagna	EBS	English Baroque Soloists
attrib	attributed	ECCO	European Community Chamber Orchestra
b	born		
bamboo fl	bamboo flute	ECO	English Chamber Orchestra
bar	baritone	ECYO	European Community Youth Orchestra
bar hn	baritone horn		
bar sax	baritone saxophone	ed	edited (by)/edition
baroque gtr	baroque guitar	elec	electric/electronics
baroque vc	baroque cello	elec db	electric double bass
baroque vn	baroque violin	elec gtr	electric guitar
barrel org	barrel organ	elec hpd	electric harpsichord
bass cl	bass clarinet	elec kybd	electric keyboard
bass fl	bass flute	elec org	electric organ
bass gtr	bass guitar	elec pf	electric piano
bass tbn	bass trombone	Eng	English
bass tpt	bass trumpet	ENO	English National Opera
bass vn	bass violin	ens	ensemble
bass-bar	bass-baritone	EOG	English Opera Group
basset cl	basset clarinet	exc	excerpt
basset-hn	basset-horn	fest	festival
BBC PO	BBC Philharmonic Orchestra	fl	flute
BBC SO	BBC Symphony Orchestra	fl	flourished
bn	bassoon	flugel hn	flugel horn
BNOC	British National Opera Company	FNO	French National Orchestra
bp	broadcast performance	fp	fortepiano
BPDGB	Barking Pumpkin Digital Gratification Band	Fr	French
		FRNO	French Radio National Orchestra
BPO	Berlin Philharmonic Orchestra	Ger	German
BRSO	Bavarian Radio Symphony Orchestra	glock	glockenspiel
c	circa (about)	gtr	guitar
cad	cadenza	harm	harmonium
cath	cathedral	harmonic pf	harmonic piano
CBSO	City of Birmingham Symphony Orchestra	hn	horn
		hp	harp
ch	choir	hpd	harpsichord
chbr	chamber	IMS	International Musicians Seminar
chor	chorus	inc music	incidental music
cl	clarinet	inst	instrument/instrumental
clav	clavichord	intro	introduction
closed pf	closed piano	Ital	Italian
CLS	City of London Sinfonia	jew's hp	jew's harp
CO	Chamber Orchestra	kybd(s)	keyboard(s)
COE	Chamber Orchestra of Europe	LCP	London Classical Players
coll	collected (by)	lib	libretto
computer op	computer operator	LJSO	London Johann Strauss Orchestra
cond	conductor	LMP	London Mozart Players
Cons	Conservatoire	LPO	London Philharmonic Orchestra
contr	contralto (female alto)	LSC	London Symphony Chorus
cor ang	cor anglais/english horn	LSO	London Symphony Orchestra

lte	lute	RMSM	Royal Military School of Music
lte-hpd	lute-harpsichord	RNCM	Royal Northern College of Music
MCA	Munich Capella Antiqua	ROHO	Orchestra of the Royal Opera House, Covent Garden
medieval hp	medieval harp		
mez	mezzo-soprano	RPO	Royal Philharmonic Orchestra
MIDI-hn	MIDI-horn	RTE	Eire Radio Telefis
MMF	Maggio Musicale Fiorentino	ruined pf	ruined piano
mndl	mandolin	sax	saxophone
movt	movement	sinf	sinfonia
MS	manuscript	SABC	South African Broadcasting Corporation
narr	narrator		
nat	national	SCB	Schola Cantorum Basiliensis
Nat Op	National Opera	sngr	singer
NQHO	New Queen's Hall Orchestra	SNO	Royal Scottish National Orchestra
NSO	National Symphony Orchestra	sop	soprano
NYO	National Youth Orchestra of Great Britain	sop sax	soprano saxophone
		sound proj	sound projection
NYPO	New York Philharmonic Orchestra	spkr	speaker
NYPSO	New York Philharmonic Symphony Orchestra	SO	Symphony Orchestra
		sols	soloists
NZBC	New Zealand Broadcasting Corporation	Sp	Spanish
		square pf	square piano
ob	oboe	SRO	Suisse Romande Orchestra
ob d'amore	oboe d'amore	stgs	strings
ORBCB	Orchestre Regional Bayonne-Côte Basque	St Op	State Opera
		sym	symphony
op	opus/opera	synth(s)	synthesizer(s)
orch	orchestra	tangent pf	tangent piano
org	organ	tape op	tape operator
orig	original	tbn	trombone
ORR	Orchestre Révolutionnaire et Romantique	ten	tenor
		ten hn	tenor horn
OST	Original Soundtrack	ten sax	tenor saxophone
PAN	Project Ars Nova	ten tuba	tenor tuba
PAO	Pro Arte Orchestra	ten viol	tenor viol
PCA	Pro Cantione Antiqua	th	theatre
perc	percussion	timp	timpani
perf	performed/performance	tin fl	tin flute
pf	piano	toy pf	toy piano
Philadelphia	Philadelphia Orchestra	tpt	trumpet
Philh	Philharmonia Orchestra	trad	traditional
picc	piccolo	trans	transcribed/translated
PJBE	Philip Jones Brass Ensemble	traut	trautonium
PJWE	Philip Jones Wind Ensemble	treb	treble/boy soprano
PO	Philharmonic Orchestra	treb viol	treble viol
pp	public performance	va	viola
post hn	post horn	va bastarda	viola bastarda
prepared pf	prepared piano	va d'amore	viola d'amore
prod	producer/film director	va da gamba	viola da gamba
PSO	Philharmonic Symphony Orchestra	vars	variations
pub	published/publisher	vc	cello
QHLO	Queen's Hall Light Orchestra	VCA	Vienna Capella Academica
qnt	quintet	VCM	Vienna Concentus Musicus
qt	quartet	vib	vibraphone
r	recorded	vlrg	virginal
rad	radio	VJSO	Vienna Johann Strauss Orchestra
RAHO	Royal Albert Hall Orchestra	vn	violin
RCM	Royal College of Music	voc	vocalist/voice
RCS	Royal Choral Society	VPO	Vienna Philharmonic Orchestra
rec	recorder	wds	words
rev	revised	wind hp	wind harp
RLPO	Royal Liverpool Philharmonic Orchestra	WNO	Welsh National Opera
		ww	woodwind

Gramophone

Gramophone is the most influential record review magazine published today. Drawing on the skills of some of the world's most respected critics, *Gramophone* offers considered comment on more than 200 new recordings every month. In addition, there are in-depth interviews with today's leading performers and composers as well as surveys of recordings of specific works, artists and composers.

Gramophone is available at all good newsagents and record stores, or on subscription.

Single copy **£3·10** *UK annual subscription* **£34·10**

The Gramophone Classical Good CD Guide 1996

This indispensable guide is written by *Gramophone*'s panel of distinguished reviewers and is acknowledged to be the finest publication of its kind. There are nearly 880 full reviews which are new to this edition. A major feature this year is the inclusion of a rating system, which highlights those releases which are considered to be recordings of particular distinction. Other new features include listings of the winners of *The Gramophone Awards* since their inception in 1977, together with a suggested basic library.

The Gramophone Classical Good CD Guide is available through all good book and record stores, or direct from the publishers, post free.

£15·99

The Gramophone Jazz Good CD Guide

The Gramophone Jazz Good CD Guide is the essential jazz companion. It contains over 1,600 reviews, recommending the best and most representative recordings by all the major jazz artists. This indispensable guide to jazz CDs includes a basic jazz library, highlighting recordings which have become cornerstones in the evolution of jazz.

The Gramophone Jazz Good CD Guide is available through all good book and record stores, or direct from the publishers, post free.

£15·99

International Classical Record Collector

Throughout the world there is a growing interest in recorded performances as they originally existed on cylinders, piano rolls, 78s and LPs, on shellac and on vinyl. Recognising this interest *Gramophone* has recently launched *International Classical Record Collector*, a magazine which appeals to LP and CD reissue collectors, as well as audiophiles. *ICRC* covers all aspects of collecting classical music recordings from the past.

ICRC is published quarterly, in February, May, September and November. The magazine is available direct from the publishers and at selected record stores.

Single copy **£3·50** *UK annual subscription* **£14·00**

A few well-chosen words

Most of us can remember being read to – it is one of life's earliest luxuries – and it remains a pleasure in which we can indulge throughout our lives. *A few well-chosen words* is a new guide to some of the finest spoken word recordings. This unique book provides over 200 pages of reviews and recommendations for collectors, retailers, researchers and librarians. *A few well-chosen words* is available through selected record stores or direct from the publishers, post free.

£6·95

Order form overleaf

Gramophone Publications

Order form

Gramophone Subscription

Please enter my subscription to *Gramophone*, commencing with the issue dated:

Great Britain		£	Delivery	Europe		£	Delivery
☐ 1 year	Royal Mail	34·10	3-4 days	☐ 1 year	Surface	54·00	7-28 days
☐ 2 years	Royal Mail	68·20		☐ 2 years	Surface	108·00	
☐ 1 year	plus Index 73	8·00		☐ 1 year	plus Index 73	8·00	
☐ 2 years	plus Index 73+74	16·00		☐ 2 years	plus Index 73 and 74	16·00	
North America		US $	Delivery	Rest of the World		£	Delivery
☐ 1 year	Airspeeded	75·00	7-20 days	☐ 1 year	Airspeeded	71·95	7-21 days
☐ 2 years	Airspeeded	150·00		☐ 2 years	Airspeeded	143·90	
☐ 1 year	plus Index 73	12·90		☐ 1 year	plus Index 73	8·00	
☐ 2 years	plus Index 73+74	25·80		☐ 2 years	plus Index 73 and 74	16·00	

Other carriage rates are available on request

Gramophone magazine Single copies
☐ Great Britain £3·60 ☐ US $7·70 ☐ Overseas £4·75

The Gramophone Classical Good CD Guide 1996
☐ Great Britain £15·99 ☐ US $25·95 ☐ Overseas and Eire £15·99

The Gramophone Jazz Good CD Guide
☐ Great Britain £15·99 ☐ US $25·95 ☐ Overseas and Eire £15·99

A few well-chosen words
☐ Great Britain £6·95 ☐ US $13·95 ☐ Overseas £7·95

International Classical Record Collector Subscription
Please start my subscription with the Winter 1995 / Spring 1996 issue (delete as applicable)
☐ Great Britain £14·00 ☐ Europe £18·00 ☐ US $35·00 ☐ Rest of the World £20·00

International Classical Record Collector Single copy
Winter 1995 / Spring 1996 issue (delete as applicable)
☐ Great Britain £3·50 ☐ Europe £4·50 ☐ US $8·50 ☐ Rest of the World £5·00

Method of payment
☐ Cheque ☐ Sterling bank draft ☐ International Money Order
☐ British Postal Order ☐ Eurocheque ☐ Credit Card (see below)

I enclose a total payment of £ _____ or US $ (if resident in the USA) _____

Payment by credit card Please charge my
☐ Visa/Trustcard/Barclaycard ☐ Access/Mastercard/Eurocard

Total payment by credit card £ _____ or US $ (if resident in the USA) _____

Card number | | | | | | | | | | | | | | | | |

Expiry date _____

Signature _____ Date _____

Name _____

Address _____

_____

Post/Zip code _____

Prices include postage and packing. Please allow 28 days for delivery in Great Britain. Please make cheques payable, and address all correspondence to: **Gramophone Publications Limited** 177-179 Kenton Road, Harrow, Middlesex, HA3 0HA, Great Britain. **Telephone** +44 (0)181-907 4476 **Fax** +44 (0)181-909 1893

CCCAT

Gramophone Publications

Composer index

1

Stimmungen—violin and piano, Op. 32
L. Kaufman, Columbia SO, B. Herrmann (arr
Herrmann: r c1949) *Concert*
(8/92) (CAMB) ① **CD-1063**
J. Heifetz, I. Achron (r1924) *Concert*
(11/94) (RCA) ① [65] 09026 61778-2(01)

ADAM, Adolphe (Charles) (1803–1856) France

SECTION IV: VOCAL AND CHORAL

Minuit, Chrétiens
1. Cantique Noël.
1. Cambridge Sngrs, CLS, J. Rutter (arr Rutter)
Concert (12/89) (CLLE) ① **COLCD111**
1. L. Pavarotti, National PO, K.H. Adler (arr Gamley)
Concert (7/90) (DECC) ① [2] 425 681-2DM2
1. E. Caruso, orch, W.B. Rogers (r1916) *Concert*
(7/91) (RCA) ① [12] GD60495(5)
1. J.B. Faure, anon (r c1900) *Concert*
(9/91) (SYMP) ① **SYMCD1089**
1. P. Plançon, anon (r1903) *Concert*
(9/91) (PEAR) ① **GEMMCD9497**
1. E. Caruso, orch, W.B. Rogers (r1916) *Concert*
(10/91) (PEAR) ① [3] EVC3(2)
1. L. Pavarotti, National PO, K.H. Adler (arr Gamley)
Concert (12/91) (DECC) ① 433 710-2DH
1. T. Hampson, St Paul CO, H. Wolff *Concert*
(12/91) (TELD) ① 9031-73135-2
1. L. Pavarotti, National PO, K.H. Adler *Concert*
(12/91) (DECC) ① 433 010-2DM
1. G. de Chiaro (arr gtr) *Concert*
(12/91) (CENT) ① **CRC2101**
1. K. Battle, F. von Stade, Orch, A. Previn (pp1991)
Concert (12/92) (SONY) ① **SK48235**
1. R. Scotto, St Patrick's Cath Ch, St Patrick's Cath
Orch, L. Anselmi (r1981; arr Grady) *Concert*
(12/93) (VAI) ① **VAIA1013**
1. L. Quilico, Toronto SO, J.A. Bartle (r1992; arr
Cable) *Concert* (12/93) (CBC) ① **SMCD5119**
1. D. Ross, J. Carreras, P. Domingo,
Gumpoldskirchner Kinderchor, Vienna SO, V. Sutej
(pp1992; arr Schifrin) *Concert*
(12/93) (SONY) ① **SK53358**
1. K. Erb, orch, B. Seidler-Winkler (r1937) *Concert*
(6/94) (PREI) ① [2] 89208
1. P. Plançon, orch (r1906) *Concert*
(12/94) (ROMO) ① [2] 82001-2
1. P. Plançon, anon (r1903) *Concert*
(12/94) (ROMO) ① [2] 82001-2

SECTION V: STAGE WORKS

**Le chalet—opéra-comique: 1 act
(1834—Paris)** (Lib. Scribe & Mélesville)
Arrêtons-nous ici P. Plançon, anon (r1904) *Concert*
(7/93) (NIMB) ① [2] NI7840/1
Vallons de l'Helvétie P. Plançon, anon (r1904)
Concert (12/94) (ROMO) ① [2] 82001-2
Le Corsaire—ballet: 3 acts (1856—Paris)
Cpte ECO, R. Bonynge
(10/92) (DECC) ① [2] 430 286-2DH2
Giselle—ballet: 2 acts (1841—Paris)
EXCERPTS: ACT 1: 1. Introduction; 2. Les
Vendangeurs; 3. Entrée du Prince; 4. Loys seul et
entrée de Giselle; 5. Scène d'amour; 6. Retour des
vendangeurs; 7. Valse; 8. La Chasse; 9. Scène
d'Hilarion; 10. Marche des vignerons; 11. Pas seul;
12. Pas de deux des jeunes paysans; 13. Pas des
vendangeurs; 14. Galop général; 15. Finale. ACT 2:
16. Introduction; 17. Apparition et scène de Myrthe;
18. Apparition de Giselle; 19. Entrée des paysans; 20.
Entrée de Loys; 21. Pas de deux; 22. Scène de Wilis;
23. Grand pas de deux; 24. Final.
Cpte ROHO, R. Bonynge (includes music by
Burgmüller & Minkus)
(12/91) (DECC) ① [2] 433 007-2DM2
Cpte LSO, M. Tilson Thomas (American Ballet vers)
(3/92) (SONY) ① **SK42450**
Cpte ROHO, M. Ermler (r1993)
(4/94) (ROH) ① **ROH007**
Cpte Slovak RSO, A. Mogrelia (r1994)
(4/95) (NAXO) ① [2] 8 550755/6
**Les Pantins de Violette—operetta: 1 act
(1856—Paris)** (Lib. L. Battu)
EXCERPTS: 1. Le chanson du canari.
1. St. Jo, ECO, R. Bonynge (r1993) *Concert*
(9/94) (DECC) ① 440 679-2DH
**Le Postillon de Lonjumeau—opera: 3 acts,
1836 (Paris)** (Lib. de Leuven and Brunswick)
EXCERPTS: 1. Overture. ACT 1: 2. Mes amis,
3. Quoi, tous les deux!; 4. Jeunes époux, voici l'heure
fortunée; 5. Mes amis, écoutez l'histoire (Freunde,
vernehmet die Geschichte); 6. A mes désirs, il faut te
rende. ACT 2: 7. Entr'acte (Vorspiel); 8. Je vais donc
le revoir; 9. Ah! quel torment!; 10. Assis au pied d'un

hêtre; 11. Oui, des choristes du théâtre; 12. Grâce au
hasard; 13. Ah! quelle étonnante nouvelle! ACT 3:
14. Entr'acte; 15. Du vrai bonheur; 16. A la noblesse,
je m'allie; 17. Pendu!; 18. A ma douleur soyez
sensible.
5. J. Schmidt, orch (Ger: r1933) *Concert*
(4/90) (EMI) ① CDM7 69478-2
5. H. Roswaenge, Berlin St Op Orch, B. Seidler-
Winkler (r1936: Ger) *Concert*
(5/90) (PREI) ① 89018
5. H. Roswaenge, orch (r1928: Ger) *Concert*
(2/92) (PREI) ① [2] 89201
5. H.E. Groh, orch (Ger: r1932) *Concert*
(3/92) (PEAR) ① GEMMCD9419
5. H. Roswaenge, Berlin St Op Chor, Berlin St Op
Orch, B. Seidler-Winkler (Ger: r1936) *Concert*
(10/92) (TEST) ① SBT1005
5. H. Roswaenge, Berlin St Op Orch, B. Seidler-
Winkler (r1936: Ger) *Concert*
(4/95) (PREI) ① [2] 89209
**Si j'étais roi, 'If I were King'—opera: 3 acts
(1852—Paris)** (Lib. Ennery and J. Brésil)
EXCERPTS: 1. Overture; 2. Chanson à boire; 3.
Dans le sommeil; 4. De vos nobles aïeux.
1. Detroit SO, P. Paray (r1960) *Concert*
(11/93) (MERC) ① 434 332-2MM
2. G. Soulacroix, anon (r1904) *Concert*
(9/91) (SYMP) ① SYMCD1089
4. St. Jo, ECO, R. Bonynge (r1993) *Concert*
(9/94) (DECC) ① 440 679-2DH
Le Toréador—opera: 2 acts (1849—Paris)
(Lib. T. Sauvage)
EXCERPTS: 1. Ah, vous dirai-je, maman.
Cpte M. Mesplé, R. Amade, C. Clavensy, ORTF Lyric
Orch, E. Bigot (bp1963) (3/92) (MUSD) ① 20167-2
1. M. Korjus, Berlin RO, J. Müller (Ger: r1934)
Concert (10/93) (PREI) ① 89054
1. F. Hempel, orch (r1911) *Concert*
(3/94) (NIMB) ① NI7849
1. A. Galli-Curci, orch, J. Pasternack (r1921) *Concert*
(8/94) (ROMO) ① [2] 81004-2

ADAM DE LA HALLE (c1240–c1286) France

SECTION IV: VOCAL AND CHORAL

Assenés chi, Grievilier—jeu parti: 1v
Gothic Voices, C. Page (r1994) *Concert*
(8/95) (HYPE) ① CDA66773
**De ma dame vient/Dieux, comment
porroire/Omnes—motet: 3vv**
London Early Music Consort, D. Munrow *Concert*
(8/85) (ARCH) ① 415 292-2AH
J'os bien a m'amie parler—motet: 3vv
London Early Music Consort, D. Munrow *Concert*
(8/85) (ARCH) ① 415 292-2AH

ADAMS, John (b 1947) USA

SECTION I: ORCHESTRAL

**The Chairman Dances—foxtrot for orchestra
(1985)**
CBSO, S. Rattle (r1993) *Concert*
(6/94) (EMI) ① CDC5 55051-2
Baltimore SO, D. Zinman (r1994) *Concert*
(7/95) (ARGO) ① 444 454-2ZH
**Chamber Symphony—15 instruments
(1992)**
London Sinfonietta, J. Adams (r1993) *Grand Pianola
Music.* (3/95) (NONE) ① 7559-79219-2
Harmonielehre—orchestra (1984-85)
CBSO, S. Rattle (r1993) *Concert*
(6/94) (EMI) ① CDC5 55051-2
Shaker Loops—string orchestra (1983) (arr
from string septet version)
San Francisco SO, E. de Waart *Reich: Variations
(1980).* (9/86) (PHIL) ① 412 214-2PH
**Short Ride in a Fast Machine—fanfare:
orchestra (198u)**
CBSO, S. Rattle (r1993) *Concert*
(6/94) (EMI) ① CDC5 55051-2
Netherlands Wind Ens, S. Mosko (r1993/4: trans
band: L T Odorn) *Concert*
(10/95) (CHAN) ① CHAN9363
Tomba lontana—fanfare: orchestra (1986)
CBSO, S. Rattle (r1993) *Concert*
(6/94) (EMI) ① CDC5 55051-2

SECTION II: CHAMBER

**Light over Water—brass and synthesizer
(1983)**
Jim Miller, T. Wilson, W. Kingelhofer, B. McCarty, M.
Kenley, D. Kennelly, Z. Spellman, J. Adams *Shaker
Loops.* (12/90) (NALB) ① NA014CD

Shaker Loops—string septet (1978)
Ridge Qt, D. Smiley, Judiyaba, G. Lowendusky *Light
over Water.* (12/90) (NALB) ① NA014CD

SECTION III: INSTRUMENTAL

Eros Piano—piano (1989) (also for
orchestra/chamber orchestra)
P. Crossley *Concert*
(7/91) (NONE) ① 7559-79249-2
Phrygian Gates—piano (1977)
U. Oppens *Concert* (5/90) (MUSI) ① MACD-604
J. McCabe *Concert*
(6/91) (CNTI) ① [2] CCD1028/9

SECTION IV: VOCAL AND CHORAL

Bump—song: baritone and electronics
J. Adams, J. Adams *Concert*
(4/94) (NONE) ① 7559-79311-2
Cerulean—song: baritone and electronics
J. Adams, J. Adams *Concert*
(4/94) (NONE) ① 7559-79311-2
Coast—baritone and electronics
J. Adams, J. Adams *Concert*
(4/94) (NONE) ① 7559-79311-2
**Disappointment Lake—song: baritone and
electronics**
J. Adams, J. Adams *Concert*
(4/94) (NONE) ① 7559-79311-2
**Grand Pianola Music—two sopranos, two
pianos & small orchestra (1981-82)**
London Sinfonietta, J. Adams (r1993) *Chamber
Symphony.* (3/95) (NONE) ① 7559-79219-2
L. Wagstaff, K. Amps, R. Holton, E. Corver, S.
Grotenhuis, Netherlands Wind Ens, S. Mosko
(r1993/4) *Concert* (10/95) (CHAN) ① CHAN9363
**Hoodoo Zephyr—song: baritone and
electonics (1993)**
J. Adams, J. Adams *Concert*
(4/94) (NONE) ① 7559-79311-2
Tourist Song—baritone and electronics
J. Adams, J. Adams *Concert*
(4/94) (NONE) ① 7559-79311-2
Tundra—song: baritone and electronics
J. Adams, J. Adams *Concert*
(4/94) (NONE) ① 7559-79311-2

SECTION V: STAGE WORKS

**The Death of Klinghoffer—opera: prologue
& 2 acts (1991—Brussels)** (Lib. A. Goodman)
Cpte S. Sylvan, S. Friedman, J. Maddalena, T.
Hammons, T.J. Young, E. Perry, S. Nadler, London
Op Chor, Lyon Op Orch, K. Nagano
(3/93) (NONE) ① [2] 7559-79281-2
**Nixon in China—opera: 3 acts
(1987—Houston)** (Lib. A. Goodman)
Pat's Aria J. Gibson, M. Goldray, M. Riesman
(r1992; arr sax & keybds) *Concert*
(6/93) (PNT) ① 434 873-2PTH

ADAMS, Stephen (1844–1913) England

pseudonym of Michael Maybrick

SECTION IV: VOCAL AND CHORAL

The Holy City—song (pub 1892) (Wds. F. E.
Weatherly)
J. Norman, Ambrosian Sngrs, RPO, A. Gibson (arr.
Hope) *Concert* (4/83) (PHIL) ① 400 019-2PH
R. Crooks, H. Dawson, orch, J. Barbirolli (r1932)
Concert (9/93) (CLAR) ① CDGSE78-50-50
**Nirvana—I come from the silent
forest—song (pub c1892)** (Wds. F. E.
Weatherly)
R. Crooks, orch (r1933) *Concert*
(9/93) (CLAR) ① CDGSE78-50-50
The Star of Bethlehem—song (Wds. F. E.
Weatherly)
R. Crooks, H. Dawson, orch, J. Barbirolli (r1932)
Concert (9/93) (CLAR) ① CDGSE78-50-50

ADAMS, Thomas (1785–1858) England

SECTION III: INSTRUMENTAL

6 Voluntaries—organ (1824)
4. B flat.
4. Margaret Phillips *Concert*
(7/91) (GAMU) ① GAMCD522

ADDINSELL, Richard (1904–1977) England

SECTION I: ORCHESTRAL

Festival—orchestra (1946) (orig for play 'Trepass')
P. Thwaites, J. Lavender (r1989-91: arr 2 pfs: Grainger) Concert   (1/94) (PEAR) ① **SHECD9631**
P. Martin, BBC Concert Orch, K. Alwyn (r1994)
Concert   (4/95) (MARC) ① **8 223732**
The Isle of Apples—orchestra (?1960s)
BBC Concert Orch, K. Alwyn (r1994) Concert
(4/95) (MARC) ① **8 223732**
Journey to Romance—orchestra (1955) (arr from 'Invocation': 1945)
BBC Concert Orch, K. Alwyn (r1994) Concert
(4/95) (MARC) ① **8 223732**
Smokey Mountains Concerto—piano and orchestra (1950)
P. Martin, BBC Concert Orch, K. Alwyn (r1994)
Concert   (4/95) (MARC) ① **8 223732**
Tune in G—piano and orchestra (1943 rev 1952)
R. Elms, BBC Concert Orch, K. Alwyn (r1994)
Concert   (4/95) (MARC) ① **8 223732**
Warsaw Concerto—piano and orchestra (1941) (featured in the film 'Dangerous Moonlight')
M. Dichter, Philh, N. Marriner Concert
(8/84) (PHIL) ① **411 123-2PH**
C. Ortiz, RPO, M. Atzmon Concert
(9/86) (DECC) ① **414 348-2DH**
C. Ortiz, RPO, M. Atzmon Concert
(12/91) (DECC) ① **430 726-2DM**
C. Ortiz, RPO, M. Atzmon Concert
(1/92) (DECC) ① **433 616-2DSP**

SECTION V: STAGE WORKS

Blithe Spirit—film score (1945)
EXCERPTS: 1. Prelude; 2. Waltz.
1, 2. LSO, M. Mathieson (r1945) Concert
(9/94) (EMI) ① **CDGO 2059**
Fire over England—film score (1937)
Suite BBC Concert Orch, K. Alwyn (r1994) Concert
(4/95) (MARC) ① **8 223732**
Goodbye Mr Chips—film score (1939)
EXCERPTS: 1. Theme.
1. BBC Concert Orch, K. Alwyn (r1994) Concert
(4/95) (MARC) ① **8 223732**
Passionate Friends—film score (1948)
Suite Philh, M. Mathieson (r1948) Concert
(9/94) (EMI) ① **CDGO 2059**
The Prince and the Showgirl—film score (1957)
potpourri BBC Concert Orch, K. Alwyn (r1994)
Concert   (4/95) (MARC) ① **8 223732**
Ring around the moon—incidental music to C. Fry's play (1950—London)
EXCERPTS: 1. Invitation Waltz.
1. BBC Concert Orch, K. Alwyn (r1994) Concert
(4/95) (MARC) ① **8 223732**
A Tale of Two Cities—film score (1958)
EXCERPTS: 1. Theme (arr D Gamley: piano and orchestra).
1. R. Elms, BBC Concert Orch, K. Alwyn (r1994)
Concert   (4/95) (MARC) ① **8 223732**
Tom Brown's Schooldays—film score (1951)
EXCERPTS: 1. Overture.
1. BBC Concert Orch, K. Alwyn (r1994) Concert
(4/95) (MARC) ① **8 223732**
Under Capricorn—film score (1949)
Suite Prague City PO, P. Bateman (r1993) Concert
(3/94) (SILV) ① **FILMCD137**

ADDISON, John (b 1920) England

SECTION IV: VOCAL AND CHORAL

O mistress mine—song (Wds. Shakespeare)
A. Rolfe Johnson, G. Johnson Concert
(5/92) (HYPE) ① **CDA66480**

SECTION V: STAGE WORKS

A Bridge too Far—film score (1977)
EXCERPTS: 1. Overture.
1. Prague City PO, P. Bateman (r1994) Concert
(11/94) (SILV) ① **FILMCD151**
Carte blanche—ballet (1953)
Suite PAO, J. Addison (r1957) Concert
(8/94) (EMI) ① **CDM7 64718-2**

The Man Between—film score (1953)
EXCERPTS: 1. Theme.
1. Orch, R. Goodwin (r1953) Concert
(9/94) (EMI) ① **CDGO 2059**
Torn Curtain—film score (1966)
EXCERPTS: 1. Main Title.
1. Prague City PO, P. Bateman Concert
(9/95) (SILV) ① **FILMCD159**

ADDY, Obo (b 1936) Ghana

SECTION IV: VOCAL AND CHORAL

Wawshishijay (Our beginning)—percussion, vocals and string quartet (1991)
Kronos Qt, O. Addy Concert
(11/92) (NONE) ① **7559-79275-2**

ADLER, Richard (b 1921) USA

SECTION III: INSTRUMENTAL

Sonata—harpsichord (1982)
B. Harbach Concert   (3/89) (KING) ① **KCLCD2005**

ADORNO, Theodore Wiesengrund (1903–1969) Germany

SECTION I: ORCHESTRAL

Kinderjahr: sechs stücke aus Op. 68 von Robert Schumann—small orchestra (1941)
1. Frühlingsgesang; 2. Lied italiensicher Marinari; 3. Mai, lieber Mai—Bald bist du wieder da!; 4. Erinnerung (4 Nov 1847: Mendelssohns Todestag); 5. Winterzeit (II); 6. Knecht Ruprecht.
Frankfurt Op Orch, G. Bertini Concert
(6/91) (WERG) ① **WER6173-2**
6 Kurze Orchesterstücke, Op. 4 (1929)
1. Bewegt, heftig; 2. Sehr ruhig; 3. Sehr lebhaft (Gigue); 4. Äusserst langsam; 5. Leicht (walzer); 6. Sehr langsam.
Frankfurt Op Orch, G. Bertini Concert
(6/91) (WERG) ① **WER6173-2**

SECTION II: CHAMBER

2 Stücke—string quartet, Op. 2 (1925-26)
1. Bewegt; 2. Variationen.
Buchberger Qt Concert
(6/91) (WERG) ① **WER6173-2**

SECTION IV: VOCAL AND CHORAL

3 Gedichte—female vv a capella (1923-45)
(Wds. T. Däubler)
1. Dämmerung; 2. Winter; 3. Oft.
Frankfurt Chbr Ch, H.M. Beuerle Concert
(6/91) (WERG) ① **WER6173-2**

SECTION V: STAGE WORKS

Der Schatz des Indianer-Joe—Singspiel (1932-33) (fragment only)
EXCERPTS: 1. Totenlied auf den kater; 2. Hucks Auftrittslied.
M. Kiener, H. Neiser, Frankfurt Op Orch, G. Bertini
Concert   (6/91) (WERG) ① **WER6173-2**

AGOSTINI, Lodovico (1534–1590) Italy

SECTION IV: VOCAL AND CHORAL

Non t'aricordi
King's Sngrs, Tragicomedia Concert
(9/92) (EMI) ① **CDC7 54191-2**

AGRELL, Johan (1701–1765) Sweden

SECTION I: ORCHESTRAL

Concerto for Flute and Strings in D
M. Bania, Concerto Copenhagen, A. Manze (r1992)
Concert   (6/93) (CHAN) ① **CHAN0535**

AGRICOLA, Alexander (?1446–1506) Franco-Netherlands

SECTION IV: VOCAL AND CHORAL

Magnificat—4vv (one of three settings)
Chanticleer (r1990) Concert
(7/94) (CHTI) ① **CR-8808**
Nobis Sancte Spiritus—motet: 4vv
Chanticleer (r1990) Concert
(7/94) (CHTI) ① **CR-8808**

O crux ave—motet: 4vv
Chanticleer (r1990) Concert
(7/94) (CHTI) ① **CR-8808**
Regina coeli—motet: 4vv
Chanticleer (r1990) Concert
(7/94) (CHTI) ① **CR-8808**

AGRICOLA, Johann Friedrich (1720–1774) Germany

SECTION V: STAGE WORKS

Achille in Sciro—opera seria (1765—Berlin)
Del terreno, nel centro profondo J. Kowalski, Berlin
CO, M. Pommer Concert   (9/88) (CAPR) ① **10 113**

AGUADO (Y GARCÍA), Dionysio (1784–1849) Spain

SECTION III: INSTRUMENTAL

Adagio, Op. 2/1
J. Bream (r1980) Concert
(8/93) (RCA) ① **[28] 09026 61583-2(6)**
J. Bream (r1980) Concert
(6/94) (RCA) ① **09026 61607-2**
Andante—guitar
N. Kraft (r1993) Concert
(1/95) (NAXO) ① **8 553007**
Guitar Method—Lessons—guitar (pub 1825, rev 1830) (from Méthode complète pour la guitare)
EXCERPTS: 15. Lección 15; 19. Lección 19; 24. Lección 24; 26. Lección 26; 29. Lección 29.
15, 19, 24, 26, 29. N. Kraft (r1993) Concert
(1/95) (NAXO) ① **8 553007**
Guitar Method—Studies—guitar (pub 1825, rev 1830) (from Méthode complète pour la guitare)
EXCERPTS: 17. Estudio 17.
17. N. Kraft (r1993) Concert
(1/95) (NAXO) ① **8 553007**
Introduction and Rondo, Op. 2/3
J. Bream (r1980) Concert
(8/93) (RCA) ① **[28] 09026 61583-2(6)**
J. Bream (r1983) Concert
(8/93) (RCA) ① **[28] 09026 61583-2(6)**
J. Bream (r1983) Concert
(8/93) (RCA) ① **09026 61610-2**
J. Bream (r1980) Concert
(6/94) (RCA) ① **09026 61607-2**
Menuett—guitar
N. Kraft (r1993) Concert
(1/95) (NAXO) ① **8 553007**
Polonaise, Op. 2/2
J. Bream (r1980) Concert
(8/93) (RCA) ① **[28] 09026 61583-2(6)**
J. Bream (r1980) Concert
(6/94) (RCA) ① **09026 61607-2**
Variations on the Fandango—guitar
T. Kerstens Concert   (7/92) (CONI) ① **CDCF509**

AGUILERA DE HEREDIA, Sebastián (c1565–1627) Spain

SECTION II: CHAMBER

Ensalada
Hespèrion XX, J. Savall Concert
(2/92) (ASTR) ① **E8729**
Tiento de Batalla
Hespèrion XX, J. Savall Concert
(2/92) (ASTR) ① **E8729**

SECTION III: INSTRUMENTAL

Salbe de 1 tono por delasolre—organ
Y. Repérant (r1992) Concert
(9/93) (K617) ① **K617024**

AGUIRRE, Julián (1868–1924) Argentina

SECTION I: ORCHESTRAL

Huella—canción argentina: orchestra, Op. 49
J. Heifetz, E. Bay (r1945) Concert
(11/94) (RCA) ① **[65] 09026 61778-2(19)**

AHO, Kalevi (b 1949) Finland

SECTION I: ORCHESTRAL

Symphony No. 8—organ and orchestra (1993)
H-O. Ericsson, Lahti SO, O. Vänskä (r1994)
Pergamon.   (3/95) (BIS) ① **BIS-CD646**

SECTION IV: VOCAL AND CHORAL

Pergamon—4 narrators, 4 orchestral groups & organ (1990) (Wds. P Weiss)
L. Paasikivi, E-L. Saarinen, T. Nyman, M. Lehtinen, P. Pietiläinen, Lahti SO, O. Vänskä (r1994)
Symphony 8.   (3/95) (BIS) ① **BIS-CD646**

AIKEN, William (1857–1939)
England

SECTION IV: VOCAL AND CHORAL

Shall I compare thee to a summer's day?—song (1911) (Wds. Shakespeare: Sonnet XVIII)
A. Rolfe Johnson, G. Johnson *Concert*
          (5/92) (HYPE) ① **CDA66480**

AITKEN, Hugh (b 1924) USA

SECTION III: INSTRUMENTAL

Partita—violin (1968)
R. Davidovici *Concert*   (11/87) (NEW) ① **NW334-2**

ALABIEV, Alexander
Alexandrovich (1787–1851)
Russia

SECTION II: CHAMBER

Piano Trio in A minor
Borodin Trio *Tchaikovsky: Piano Trio, Op. 50.*
          (10/91) (CHAN) ① **CHAN8975**

SECTION IV: VOCAL AND CHORAL

The Nightingale—song: 1v and piano (Wds. anon)
B. Hoch, Hong Kong PO, K. Schermerhorn (arr. Richardson) *Concert*   (11/86) (CARL) ① **PCD827**
L. Pons, orch, A. Kostelanetz (Eng: r1941) *Concert*
          (4/92) (MSOU) ① **DFCDI-111**

ALAGNA

SECTION IV: VOCAL AND CHORAL

Canzuna Siciliana—song
G. Anselmi, Bettinelli (r1909) *Concert*
          (7/95) (SYMP) ① **SYMCD1170**

ALAIN, Jehan (Ariste)
(1911–1940) France

SECTION III: INSTRUMENTAL

3 Danses—organ (1937-39)
1. Joies; 2. Deuils; 3. Luttes.
K. John *Mussorgsky: Pictures.*
          (4/89) (PRIO) ① **PRCD262**
C. Crozier (r1993) *Concert*
          (2/95) (DELO) ① **DE3147**
Deuxième fantaisie—organ (1936)
P. Kee *Concert*   (10/93) (CHAN) ① **CHAN9188**
Intermezzo—organ (1935)
J. Watts *Concert*   (9/90) (PRIO) ① **PRCD286**
Le Jardin suspendu—organ (1934)
P. Kee *Concert*   (10/93) (CHAN) ① **CHAN9188**
Litanies—organ, Op. 79 (1937)
J. Watts *Concert*   (9/90) (PRIO) ① **PRCD286**
C. Curley *Concert*   (2/91) (ARGO) ① **430 200-2ZH**
C. Herrick (r1993) *Concert*
          (8/94) (HYPE) ① **CDA66676**
P. Hurford (r1982) *Concert*
          (10/95) (DECC) ① **444 567-2DM**
Piano Works, Volume 1 (pub 1944)
1. Choral; 2. Étude de Sonorité sur une double pédale (1930); 3. Un cercle d'argent; 4. Heureusement, la bonne fée sa marraine; 5. Mythologie japonaises; 6. Romance (1932); 7. Nocturne (1935); 8. Suite Facile I (1938); 9. Suite Facile II (1938).
D. Fuchs *Concert*   (3/92) (PREL) ① **PRL2153/4**
Piano Works, Volume 2 (pub 1944)
1. Thème varié à 18; 2. Ecce ancilla Domine (1930); 3. Étude sur les doubles notes (1930); 4. Togo (1929); 5. Lumière qui tombe d'un vasistas (1931); 6. Histoire d'un homme qui jouait de la trompette; 7. Prélude (1935); 8. Il pleuva toute la journée (1935); 9. Verset-choral (1939); 10. Berceuse (1936); 11. Histoire sur un tapis, entre des murs blancs; 12. Mélodie-Sandwich; 13. 26 Semptembre 1931; 14. Comme quoi les projets les plus belliqueux; 15. Nocturne (1931). 16. En devissant mes chausettes; 17. Pour le déchiffrage; 18. Chanson triste; 19. Suite Monodique (134-35); 20. Quarante variations (1930).

D. Fuchs *Concert*   (3/92) (PREL) ① **PRL2153/4**
Piano Works, Volume 3 (pub 1944)
1. Étude sur un thème de 4 notes (1929); 2. Petite Rhapsodie (1931); 3. Dans le rêve laissé par la Ballade des Pendus (1931); 4. Tarass Boulba (1936).
D. Fuchs *Concert*   (3/92) (PREL) ① **PRL2153/4**
Postlude pour l'office de Complies—organ (1930)
J. Lancelot *Concert*   (8/88) (PRIO) ① **PRCD228**
Variations sur un thème de Clément Janequin—organ (1937)
R. Noehren *Concert*   (11/87) (DELO) ① **DE3045**
M. Harris *Concert*   (3/92) (YORK) ① **CD112**

ALARD, (Jean-) Delphin
(1815–1888) France

SECTION III: INSTRUMENTAL

Estudio brillante
W. Lendle (arr Tárrega/Lendle) *Concert*
          (7/92) (TELD) ① **9031-75864-2**

ALBARTI (16th cent)
Italy/England

also known as Albert of Venice

SECTION II: CHAMBER

Pavan and Galliard—viol consort (setting of 'Belle, qui tiens ma vie')
Fretwork (r1990) *Concert*
          (7/94) (VIRG) ① **VC5 45007-2**

ALBÉNIZ, Isaac (Manuel
Francisco) (1860–1909) Spain

SECTION I: ORCHESTRAL

Catalonia—suite populaire: orchestra (1899-1908)
Mexico City PO, E. Bátiz *Concert*
          (9/91) (ASV) ① **CDDCA735**
Concierto fantástico—piano and orchestra, Op. 78 (?1887)
E.P. de Guzmán, Valencia Orch, M. Galduf *Concert.*
          (10/92) (AUVI) ① **V4661**
Iberia—orchestra (1906-8) (orch Arbós from piano suite)
1. Evocación; 3. El corpus en Sevilla; 6. Triana.
Philh, Y.P. Tortelier *Falla: Sombrero de tres picos.*
          (4/91) (CHAN) ① **CHAN8904**
Dallas SO, E. Mata *Falla: Sombrero de tres picos.*
          (9/92) (PRO) ① **CDS581**
Valencia Orch, M. Galduf *Concierto fantástico, op.78.*
          (10/92) (AUVI) ① **V4661**
1, 3, 6. Paris Cons, R. Frühbeck de Burgos *Concert*
          (7/92) (EMI) ① [2] **CZS7 67474-2**
Rapsodia española—piano and orchestra, Op. 70
A. de Larrocha, LPO, R. Frühbeck de Burgos (orch C.Halffter) *Concert*
          (10/84) (DECC) ① **410 289-2DH**

SECTION III: INSTRUMENTAL

L' automne—piano, Op. 170 (?1890)
A. Guinovart (r1993) *Concert*
          (12/94) (HARM) ① **HMI98 7007**
Azulejos—piano (incomplete: cpted Granados)
A. de Larrocha *Concert*
          (12/92) (EMI) ① **CDM7 64523-2**
Cantos de España—piano, Op. 232 (pub 1896)
1. Preludio; 2. Oriental; 3. Bajo la palmera; 4. Córdoba; 5. Seguidillas.
R. Requejo *Concert*
          (6/88) (CLAV) ① [2] **CD50-8003/4**
A. de Larrocha *Concert*
          (9/92) (DECC) ① [2] **433 923-2DM2**
R. Orozco *Iberia.*   (11/92) (AUVI) ① [2] **V4663**
A. de Larrocha *Concert*
          (12/92) (EMI) ① **CDM7 64523-2**
3. J. Bream, J. Williams (r1973; trans Llobet) *Concert*
          (11/93) (RCA) ① **09026 61452-2**
3. A. Cortot (r1926) *Concert*
          (5/95) (BIDD) ① **LHW020**
4. J. Williams (arr gtr) *Concert*
          (4/84) (SONY) ① **SK36679**
4. J. Bream (r1982; trans Bream) *Concert*
          (8/93) (RCA) ① [28] **09026 61583-2(6)**
4. A. Rubinstein (r1953) *Concert*
          (9/93) (RCA) ① **09026 61261-2**
4. J. Bream, J. Williams (r1971; arr Pujol) *Concert*
          (11/93) (RCA) ① **09026 61450-2**
4. J. Bream (r1982; trans Bream) *Concert*
          (6/94) (RCA) ① **09026 61608-2**

4, 5. T. Kropat, T. Krumeich (arr 2 gtrs) *Concert*
          (7/93) (CHNN) ① **CG9103**
5. M. Tirimo *Concert*
          (12/88) (KING) ① **KCLCD2003**
5. A. Cortot (r1919/23: 2 vers) *Concert*
          (10/94) (BIDD) ① [2] **LHW014/5**
5. A. Cortot (r1930) *Concert*
          (5/95) (BIDD) ① **LHW020**
España—piano, Op. 165 (pub 1890)
1. Preludio; 2. Tango; 3. Malagueña; 4. Serenata; 5. Capricho catalán; 6. Zortzico.
2. J. Williams (arr gtr) *Concert*
          (4/84) (SONY) ① **SK36679**
2. M. Lympany *Concert*   (1/89) (EMIL) ① **CDZ110**
2. L. Godowsky (r1920) *Concert*
          (4/89) (APR) ① [2] **APR7011**
2. F. Kreisler, C. Lamson (arr Kreisler: r1928) *Concert*   (1/90) (PEAR) ① **GEMMCD9324**
2. E. Feuermann, G. Moore (arr Kreisler: vc/pf; r1939) *Concert*   (10/91) (PEAR) ① **GEMMCD9446**
2. S. Cherkassky (arr Godowsky: pp1975) *Concert*
          (10/91) (DECC) ① **433 653-2DH**
2. A. de Larrocha *Concert*
          (11/92) (EMI) ① [2] **CMS7 64504-2**
2. S. Cherkassky (bp1985; arr Godowsky) *Concert*
          (6/93) (DECC) ① **433 651-2DH**
2. T. Kropat, T. Krumeich (arr 2 gtrs) *Concert*
          (7/93) (CHNN) ① **CG9103**
2. K. Daeshik Kang, M. Rahkonen (r1992; arr Kreisler) *Concert*   (9/93) (NIMB) ① **NI5358**
2. F. Kreisler, C. Lamson (r1928: arr Kreisler)
Concert   (12/93) (BIDD) ① **LAB080**
2. I. Perlman, S. Sanders (arr vn/pf: Kreisler) *Concert*   (6/95) (EMI) ① [20] **CZS4 83177-2(2)**
2, 3. J. Thibaud, T. Janopoulo (r1933: arr vn/pf: Kreisler) *Concert*   (10/91) (MSCM) ① **MM30321**
2, 3. A. de Larrocha *Concert*
          (9/92) (DECC) ① [2] **433 926-2DM2**
2, 3. J. Thibaud, T. Janopoulo (r1933: arr vn/pf: Kreisler) *Concert*   (12/94) (APR) ① [2] **APR7028**
3. I. Perlman, S. Sanders (arr Kreisler) *Concert*
          (11/90) (EMI) ① **CDM7 63533-2**
3. M. Lympany *Concert*   (1/92) (EMIL) ① **CDZ111**
3. I. Haendel, N. Mewton-Wood (arr Kreisler: r1941) *Concert*   (10/92) (PEAR) ① **GEMMCD9939**
3. F. Kreisler, C. Lamson (r1927: arr Kreisler) *Concert*   (12/93) (BIDD) ① **LAB075**
3. A. Cortot (r1919/23: 2 vers) *Concert*
          (10/94) (BIDD) ① [2] **LHW014/5**
Iberia—piano (pub 1909)
Book 1: 1. Evocación; 2. El puerto; 3. El Corpus en Sevilla. Book 2: 4. Rondeña; 5. Almería; 6. Triana. Book 3: 7. El Albaicín; 8. El polo; 9. Lavapiés. Book 4: 10. Málaga; 11. Jérez; 12. Eritaña.
R. Requejo *Concert*
          (6/88) (CLAV) ① [2] **CD50-8003/4**
A. de Larrocha *Concert*
          (6/88) (DECC) ① [2] **417 887-2DH2**
A. Ciccolini *Granados: Goyescas.*
          (3/92) (EMI) ① [2] **CZS7 62889-2**
A. de Larrocha *Concert*
          (9/92) (EMI) ① [2] **433 926-2DM2**
A. de Larrocha *Concert*
          (11/92) (EMI) ① [2] **CMS7 64504-2**
R. Orozco *Cantos de España.*
          (11/92) (AUVI) ① [2] **V4663**
1. A. Rubinstein (r1955) *Concert*
          (9/93) (RCA) ① **09026 61261-2**
1. J. Bream, J. Williams (r1978; trans Llobet) *Concert*   (11/93) (RCA) ① **09026 61452-2**
3. BBC PO, M. Bamert (r1994: orch Stokowski) *Concert*   (6/95) (CHAN) ① **CHAN9349**
4, 6, 7. J. Williams, LSO, P. Daniel (arr/orch S. Gray) *Concert*   (7/92) (SONY) ① **SK48480**
6. A. de Larrocha *Concert*
          (7/90) (DECC) ① **417 795-2DM**
6. M. Rosenthal (r1929) *Concert*
          (9/93) (PEAR) ① **GEMMCD9963**
6. K. Labèque, M. Labèque (r1993; trans Granados: 2 pfs) *Concert*   (9/94) (PHIL) ① **438 938-2PH**
6. A. Cortot (r1922) *Concert*
          (10/94) (BIDD) ① [2] **LHW014/5**
Mallorca—barcarola for piano, Op. 202 (pub 1890)
J. Williams (arr gtr) *Concert*
          (4/84) (SONY) ① **SK36679**
M. Kayath (arr Segovia) *Concert*
          (5/88) (CARL) ① **PCD876**
S. Isbin (trans Segovia) *Concert*
          (10/90) (VIRG) ① **VC7 59591-2**
W. Lendle (arr gtr) *Concert*
          (7/92) (TELD) ① **9031-75864-2**
A. de Larrocha *Concert*
          (12/92) (EMI) ① **CDM7 64523-2**
T. Kropat, T. Krumeich (arr 2 gtrs) *Concert*
          (7/93) (CHNN) ① **CG9103**

J. Bream (r1982; trans Bream) *Concert*
(8/93) (RCA) ① [28] **09026 61583-2(6)**
J. Bream (r1982; trans Bream) *Concert*
(6/94) (RCA) ① **09026 61608-2**
Navarra—piano (1909) (cpted de Séverac)
A. de Larrocha *Concert*
(6/88) (DECC) ① [2] **417 887-2DH2**
A. de Larrocha *Concert*
(7/90) (DECC) ① **417 795-2DM**
A. de Larrocha *Concert*
(9/92) (DECC) ① [2] **433 926-2DM2**
A. de Larrocha *Concert*
(11/92) (EMI) ① [2] **CMS7 64504-2**
A. Rubinstein (r1941) *Concert*
(9/93) (RCA) ① **09026 61261-2**
A. Rubinstein (pp1961) *Concert*
(10/93) (RCA) ① **09026 61445-2**
K. Labèque, M. Labèque (r1993; trans Marshall: 2 pfs) *Concert*
(9/94) (PHIL) ① **438 938-2PH**
Pavana capricho—piano, Op. 12 (pub 1883)
A. de Larrocha *Concert*
(9/92) (DECC) ① [2] **433 926-2DM2**
A. de Larrocha *Concert*
(11/92) (EMI) ① [2] **CMS7 64504-2**
K. Labèque, M. Labèque (r1993; trans 2 pfs) *Concert*
(9/94) (PHIL) ① **438 938-2PH**
Piano Sonata No. 3, Op. 68 (pub 1886)
1. Allegretto; 2. Andante; 3. Allegro assai.
A. Guinovart (r1993) *Concert*
(12/94) (HARM) ① **HMI98 7007**
Piano Sonata No. 4, Op. 72 (1887)
1. Allegro; 2. Scherzino; 3. Minuetto; 4. Rondo.
A. Guinovart (r1993) *Concert*
(12/94) (HARM) ① **HMI98 7007**
Piano Sonata No. 5, Op. 82 (?1888)
1. Allegro non troppo; 2. Minuetto del Gallo; 3. Rêverie; 4. Allegro.
A. Guinovart (r1993) *Concert*
(12/94) (HARM) ① **HMI98 7007**
12 Piezás características—piano, Op. 92 (1888-9)
1. Gavota; 2. Minuetto a Silvia; 3. Barcarola (Ciel sans nuages); 4. Plegeria; 5. Conchita (Polka); 6. Pilar (valse); 7. Zambra; 8. Pavana; 9. Polonesa; 10. Mazurka; 11. Staccato; 12. Torre Bermeja.
7. M. Kayath (arr Segovia) *Concert*
(5/88) (CARL) ① **PCD876**
7. A. de Larrocha *Concert*
(12/92) (EMI) ① **CDM7 64523-2**
7, 12. J. Williams (arr gtr) *Concert*
(4/84) (SONY) ① **SK36679**
12. M. Robles (arr hp: G. Bruno) *Concert*
(2/93) (DECC) ① **433 869-2DWO**
12. P. Romero (r1993; arr C. Romero) *Concert*
(4/95) (PHIL) ① **442 150-2PH**
Recuerdos de viaje—piano, Op. 71 (pub 1887)
1. En el mar; 2. Barcarola; 3. Leyenda; 4. Alborada; 5. En la alhambra; 6. Puerta de tierra: Bolero; 7. Bolero (Andalucia); 8. Rumores de la caleta : Malagueña; 9. Malagueña; 10. En la playa.
J. Byzantine (r1990; arr gtr: Byzantine) *Suite española 1.* (4/94) (CFP) ① **CD-CFP4631**
6. J. Lloyd Webber, ECO, N. Cleobury (arr C Palmer) *Concert*
(3/85) (PHIL) ① **412 231-2PH**
6. F. Kreisler, C. Lamson (arr Kreisler: r1927) *Concert*
(1/90) (PEAR) ① **GEMMCD9324**
6, 8. A. de Larrocha *Concert*
(9/92) (DECC) ① [2] **433 926-2DM2**
6, 8. A. de Larrocha *Concert*
(11/92) (EMI) ① [2] **CMS7 64504-2**
8. S. McDonald (hp) *Concert*
(10/84) (DELO) ① **DE3005**
8. M. Robles (arr hp: G. Bruno) *Concert*
(2/93) (DECC) ① **433 869-2DWO**
8. A.B. Michelangeli (r1942) *Concert*
(8/93) (EMI) ① **CDH7 64490-2**
8. A. Cortot (r1930) *Concert*
(5/95) (BIDD) ① **LHW020**
9. A. de Larrocha *Concert*
(12/92) (EMI) ① **CDM7 64523-2**
Suite española No. 1—piano, Op. 47 (pub 1886)
1. Granada; 2. Cataluna; 3. Sevilla; 4. Cádiz; 5. Asturias (added 1918); 6. Aragón (added c1918); 7. Castilla (added c1918); 8. Cuba.
R. Requejo *Concert*
(6/88) (CLAV) ① [2] **CD50-8003/4**
A. de Larrocha *Concert*
(6/88) (DECC) ① [2] **417 887-2DH2**
New Philh, R. Frühbeck de Burgos (arr Frühbeck de Burgos) (10/89) (DECC) ① **417 786-2DM**
A. de Larrocha *Concert*
(9/92) (DECC) ① [2] **433 923-2DM2**
A. de Larrocha *Concert*
(11/92) (EMI) ① [2] **CMS7 64504-2**

A. Petchersky *Concert*
(12/92) (ASV) ① **CDQS6079**
M. Barrueco (arr Barrueco) *Concert*
(3/93) (EMI) ① **CDC7 54382-2**
J. Bream (r1982; trans Bream) *Concert*
(8/93) (RCA) ① [28] **09026 61583-2(6)**
J. Byzantine (r1990; arr gtr: Byzantine) *Recuerdos de viaje.* (4/94) (CFP) ① **CD-CFP4631**
J. Bream (r1982; trans Bream) *Concert*
(6/94) (RCA) ① **09026 61608-2**
K. Labèque, M. Labèque (r1993; trans 2 pfs) *Concert*
(9/94) (PHIL) ① **438 938-2PH**
J. Heifetz, A. Sándor (r1934) *Concert*
(11/94) (RCA) ① [65] **09026 61778-2(02)**
1. LSO, R. Frühbeck de Burgos (arr de Burgos) *Concert*
(11/89) (CARL) ① **PCD924**
1. N. Hall (arr gtr) *Concert*
(5/92) (DECC) ① **430 839-2DH**
1, 3. M. Kayath (arr Kayath) *Concert*
(5/88) (CARL) ① **PCD876**
1, 3. A. Segovia (r1939) *Concert*
(5/89) (EMI) ① [2] **CHS7 61047-2**
1, 3-5. J. Williams (arr gtr) *Concert*
(4/84) (SONY) ① **SK36679**
1, 5. J. Bream (r1962; arr Bream) *Concert*
(8/93) (RCA) ① [28] **09026 61583-2(4)**
1, 5. J. Bream (r1962; arr Bream) *Concert*
(6/94) (RCA) ① **09026 61594-2**
3. Cincinnati Pops, E. Kunzel (orch Stokowski) *Concert*
(4/88) (TELA) ① **CD80129**
3. I. Perlman, S. Sanders (trans. Heifetz) *Concert*
(12/89) (EMI) ① **CDC7 49604-2**
3. A. Rubinstein (r1953) *Concert*
(9/93) (RCA) ① **09026 61261-2**
3, 5. A. de Larrocha *Concert*
(7/90) (DECC) ① **417 795-2DM**
3, 5. J. Williams (r1992: arr J Williams) *Concert*
(1/94) (SONY) ① **SK53359**
5. A. Romero (gtr) *Concert*
(4/90) (TELA) ① **CD80213**
5. S. Isbin (trans Segovia) *Concert*
(10/90) (VIRG) ① **VC7 59591-2**
5. W. Lendle (arr gtr) *Concert*
(7/92) (TELD) ① **9031-75864-2**
5. A-S. Ramírez (r1991) *Concert*
(2/94) (DENO) ① **CO-75357**
Suite española No. 2—piano (pub 1889)
1. Zaragoza; 2. Sevilla.
A. de Larrocha *Concert*
(9/92) (DECC) ① [2] **433 923-2DM2**
1. A. de Larrocha *Concert*
(12/92) (EMI) ① **CDM7 64523-2**
2. Empire Brass (r1991) *Concert*
(11/93) (TELA) ① **CD80301**
La Vega—piano (pub 1897)
A. de Larrocha *Concert*
(12/92) (EMI) ① **CDM7 64523-2**

ALBÉNIZ, Mateo (Antonio) Perez de (c1755–1831) Spain

SECTION III: INSTRUMENTAL

Sonata for Keyboard in D
S. McDonald (hp) *Concert*
(10/84) (DELO) ① **DE3005**
A. de Larrocha *Concert*
(7/90) (DECC) ① **417 795-2DM**
A. de Larrocha *Concert*
(9/92) (DECC) ① [2] **433 920-2DM2**
J. Bream (r1959; arr Pujol) *Concert*
(8/93) (RCA) ① [28] **09026 61583-2(3)**
J. Bream (r1959; arr Pujol) *Concert*
(8/93) (RCA) ① **09026 61591-2**

ALBERCH VILA, Pere (1517–1582) Spain

SECTION IV: VOCAL AND CHORAL

Con voz llorosa—madrigal
Colombina Ens (r1994) *Concert*
(11/95) (ACCE) ① **ACC94103D**
El bon jorn—ensalada
Colombina Ens (r1994) *Concert*
(11/95) (ACCE) ① **ACC94103D**
O Virgen sancta—madrigal
Colombina Ens (r1994) *Concert*
(11/95) (ACCE) ① **ACC94103D**
Reyna soberana—madrigal
Colombina Ens (r1994) *Concert*
(11/95) (ACCE) ① **ACC94103D**

ALBERO, Sebastiàn de (1722–1756) Spain

SECTION III: INSTRUMENTAL

14 Keyboard Sonatas (source: Biblioteca Marciana, Venice MS)
1. Allegro, C; 2. Allegro, C; 3. Andante, D; 4. Allegro, D minor; 5. Allegro, A minor; 6. Allegro, A minor; 7. Andante, F; 8. Allegro, F; 9. Allegro, G; 10. Allegro, G; 11. Andante, D minor; 12. Allegro, D; 13. Andante, B flat, 14. Allegro, B flat; 15. Andante, G minor; 16. Andante, G; 17. Allegro moderato, G minor; 18. Andante, E minor; 19. Allegro, E minor; 20. Andante, A; 21. Allegro, A; 22. Adagio, F; 23. Allegro, F; 24. Allegro, E flat; 25. Allegro, E flat; 26. Andante, D/D minor; 27. Allegro, C minor; 28. Andante, E minor; 29. Allegro; 30. Allegro, D.
1-14. J. Payne (1993) *Scarlatti Sonatas.*
(4/94) (BIS) ① **BIS-CD629**
3 Keyboard Sonatas (misattributed to D. Scarlatti)
1. F sharp minor, Kk142; 2. C, Kk143; 4. G, Kk144.
J. Payne (1993) *Keyboard Sonatas (Venice MS).*
(4/94) (BIS) ① **BIS-CD629**

ALBERT, Eugen (Francis Charles) d' (1864–1932) Scotland/Germany

SECTION I: ORCHESTRAL

Concerto for Piano and Orchestra No. 1 in B minor, Op. 2 (1884)
P. Lane, BBC Scottish SO, A. Francis (r1994) *Piano Concerto 2.* (5/95) (HYPE) ① **CDA66747**
Concerto for Piano and Orchestra No. 2 in E, Op. 12 (1893)
M. Ponti, Luxembourg RSO, P. Cao *Concert*
(5/93) (VOX) ① **115709-2**
P. Lane, BBC Scottish SO, A. Francis (r1994) *Piano Concerto 1.* (5/95) (HYPE) ① **CDA66747**

SECTION III: INSTRUMENTAL

Scherzo—piano, Op. 16/2
E. Joyce (r1938) *Concert*
(2/94) (PEAR) ① **GEMMCD9022**

SECTION V: STAGE WORKS

Tiefland—opera: prologue & 2 acts (1903—Prague) (Lib. Lothar)
EXCERPTS: 1. Orchestral Prelude. PROLOGUE: 2. Zwei Vaterunser bet'ich; 3. Wie ich nun gestern Abend (Träumzählung); 4. Du glabst am Ende, Weib und Glück sind eins?; 5. Ist Pedro nicht hier?; 6. Na, Mein Pedro, sag mir mal; 7. Hast du's gehört? Ich kreig und Weib; 8a. Meine Glücke zul... 8b. Ich grüss noch einmal meine Berge; 9. Interlude. ACT 1: 10. Sag uns doch, ist ed wahr?; 11. Da bin ich!; 12. An einem Abend war's, der Mond ging auf; 13. Oh, sie ist fort!; 14. Sein bin ich, sein! Sein Eigentum!; 15. Er kommt! Wo kommt er? Wo?; 16. Da ist er, seht nur!; 17. Da bin ich Herr, da bin ich schon!; 18. Marta!—Tu mit mir, was di willst; 19. Er will kein Stutzer sein!; 20. Was suchst du noch, Moruccio?; 21a. Das Fest ist vorbei; 21b. Dor Tor ist zu; 21c. Mein Leben wagt' ich drum (Wofserzählung); 22a. Wein sind allein; 22b. Schau her, das ist ein Taler; 23. So nimm das Geld, ich schenk es dir. ACT 2: 24. Die Sterne gingen zur Ruh; 25. Da ist Marta. Nun will ich gehen; 26. Wo willst du hin?; 27. Ich weiss nicht, wer mein Vater dir; 28. So kamen wir denn eines Tags hieher; 29. Ich will vom Himmel Stärke dir erflehn; 30. Ei, so mürrisch, so verdreisslich!; 31. Da Essen ist da!; 32. Ja, du hast Furcht, ein Wicht bist du; 33. Ich soll dich töten?; 34. Was gibt es Neues?; 35. Hüll in die Mantille dich roter sein; 36. Was sagt der Mensch; 37. Was wollst Ihr, he?; 38. Nun hab' ich nichts als nich mehr auf der Welt; 39. Nun soll er kommen und idch nir entreissen!; 40. He, Burschen, her! Ihr Weiber kommt!.
2, 22b T. Ralf, Berlin St Op Orch, B. Seidler-Winkler (r1942) *Concert* (10/94) (PREI) ① **89077**
8a, 8b, 21c J. Pölzer, R. Pauly, Vienna St Op Orch, K. Alwin (pp1933) *Concert*
(5/94) (SCHW) ① [2] **314512**
8b, 21c F. Völker, Berlin Staatskapelle, G. Steeger (r1940) *Concert* (8/94) (PREI) ① **89070**
27. R. Tauber, orch (r1928) *Concert*
(7/89) (PEAR) ① **GEMMCD9327**
27. Leonie Rysanek, Philh, W. Schüchter (r1952) *Concert* (2/95) (EMI) ① **CDH5 65201-2**
35. E. Marton, R. Kollo, B. Weikl, Bavarian Rad Chor, Munich RO, M. Janowski *Concert*
(3/89) (ACAN) ① **43 266**

Die Toten Augen—opera: prologue & 1 act
(1916—Dresden) (Lib. H H Ewers)
Psyche wandelt durch Säulenhallen Lotte
Lehmann, orch (r1919) *Concert*
(6/92) (PREI) ① [3] **89302**
Psyche wandelt durch Säulenhallen M. Reining,
Vienna St Op Orch, R. Moralt (r1942) *Concert*
(9/94) (PREI) ① **89065**

ALBERT, Heinrich (1604–1651) Germany

SECTION IV: VOCAL AND CHORAL

Arien—song collection (pub 1638-50) (Wds.
Dach, cpsr and others)
1. Wie ist der Mensch (Vol II/5); 2. Galathe, wo bist
du (Vol II/12); 3. O der rauchen Grausamkeit (Vol
II/18); 4. Der Mai, des Jahres Herz (Vol III/1); 5.
Phöbus jagt mit seinen Pferden (Vol III/3); 6. Wer
wegen seiner Sünden (Vol IV/3); 7. Das Lied ist hier
(Vol IV/8); 8. Bleib du nur fest (Vol IV/8); 9. Es bild
ein Mensch (Vol IV/10); 10. Der Tag beginnet zu
vergehen (Vol V/2); 11. Gott des Himmels und der
Erden (Vo. V/4); 12. O Gott aller Wohlfahrt Quell (Vol
V/9); 13. Was klagt man der Gerechten Seelen (Vol
VII/11); 14. Phyllis, die auf Blumen sass (Vol VII/21);
15. Phyllis, o mein Licht (Vol VII/24); 16. Wer das
Alter schätzt erhaben (Vol VIII/10); 17. Turpe senex
miles, tupre senilis amor; 18. Veneris miseras
resonare querelas.
Cantus Cölln, K. Junghänel (lte/dir) *Musicalische
Kürbs-Hütte.* (6/92) (DHM) ① **RD77245**
17, 18. A. Scholl, P. Valetti, A. Verzier, K. E.
Schröder, M. Märkl (r1994) *Concert*
(5/95) (HARM) ① **HMC90 1505**
**Musicalische Kürbs-Hütte—3vv and
continuo (1645)** (Eng: Musical Pumpkin
Cottage)
Cantus Cölln, K. Junghänel (lte/dir) *Arien.*
(6/92) (DHM) ① **RD77245**

ALBERT, Prince Consort (1819–1861) Germany/England

SECTION II: CHAMBER

Melody for the Violin—violin and piano
I. Brown, J. Partridge (r1968) *Concert*
(5/92) (DECC) ① **433 220-2DWO**

SECTION IV: VOCAL AND CHORAL

Grüss an der Bruder—Lied (Wds. cpsr)
J. Bowen, S. Ridgley-Whitehouse *Concert*
(8/91) (HERI) ① **HRCD901**
Grüss aus den Ferne—Lied (Wds. anon)
J. Bowen, S. Ridgley-Whitehouse *Concert*
(8/91) (HERI) ① **HRCD901**
Klage der Liebe—Lied (Wds. anon)
J. Bowen, S. Ridgley-Whitehouse *Concert*
(8/91) (HERI) ① **HRCD901**
Schmerz der Liebe—Lied (Wds. cpsr)
J. Bowen, S. Ridgley-Whitehouse *Concert*
(8/91) (HERI) ① **HRCD901**
Ständchen—Lied (Wds. anon)
J. Bowen, S. Ridgley-Whitehouse *Concert*
(8/91) (HERI) ① **HRCD901**

ALBERT, Stephen (1941–1992) USA

SECTION I: ORCHESTRAL

Concerto for Cello and Orchestra (1988-90)
Y.-Y. Ma, Baltimore SO, D. Zinman (r1993) *Concert*
(3/95) (SONY) ① **SK57961**
**In Concordium—concerto for violin and
orchestra (1986 rev 1988)**
I. Talvi, Seattle SO, G. Schwarz *TreeStone.*
(6/90) (DELO) ① **DE3059**

SECTION IV: VOCAL AND CHORAL

**TreeStone—soprano, tenor and orchestra
(1983-84)** (Wds from Joyce: 'Finnegan's
Wake')
L. Shelton, D. Gordon, NY CO, G. Schwarz *In
Concordium.* (6/90) (DELO) ① **DE3059**

ALBINONI, Tomaso Giovanni (1671–1751) Italy

SECTION I: ORCHESTRAL

Adagio in G minor—organ and strings
(spurious - cpsd R. Giazotto on orig fragment)
I Musici *Concert* (12/83) (PHIL) ① **410 606-2PH**

J. Lloyd Webber, ECO, N. Cleobury (arr C Palmer)
Concert (3/85) (PHIL) ① **412 231-2PH**
BPO, H. von Karajan *Concert*
(9/85) (DG) ① **415 301-2GH**
BPO, H. von Karajan *Concert*
(8/87) (DG) ① **419 046-2GGA**
RLPO, C. Groves *Concert*
(1/89) (EMIL) ① **CDZ114**
Solisti Italiani *Concert*
(10/89) (DENO) ① **CO-73335**
C. Curley (trans org: anon) *Concert*
(2/91) (ARGO) ① **430 200-2ZH**
I. Tracey (r1990; arr Tracey) *Concert*
(4/91) (MIRA) ① **MRCD901**
Stuttgart CO, K. Münchinger *Concert*
(8/91) (DECC) ① **430 706-2DM**
J. Galway, Munich RO, J. Georgiadis *Concert*
(12/91) (RCA) ① **RD60736**
Scottish Ens, J. Rees (r1991) *Concert*
(12/91) (VIRG) ① **VJ7 59652-2**
ECO, I. Watson (org/dir) *Concert*
(12/91) (VIRG) ① **VJ7 59656-2**
H. Hardenberger, S. Preston (arr tpt, org) *Concert*
(12/92) (PHIL) ① **434 074-2PH**
Guildhall Str Ens, R. Salter (vn/dir) (r1992) *Concert*
(2/94) (RCA) ① **09026 61275-2**
I Musici *Concert* (9/94) (PHIL) ① **442 396-2PM**
London CO, C. Warren-Green (vn/dir) (r1988)
Concert (11/94) (VIRG) ① **CUV5 61143-2**
12 Concerti a cinque—strings, Op. 5 (1707)
1. B flat; 2. F; 3. D; 4. G; 5. A minor; 6. C; 7. D; 8. F;
9. E minor; 10. A minor; 11. G minor; 12. C.
5. ASMF, N. Marriner (r1962) *Concert*
(9/93) (DECC) ① **436 224-2DM**
**12 Concerti a cinque—oboe and strings, Op.
7 (pub 1715)**
1. D; 2. C; 3. B flat; 4. G; 5. C; 6. D; 7. A; 8. D; 9. F;
10. B minor; 11. C; 12. C.
H. Holliger, M. Bourgue, K. Thunemann, I. Musici
Sinfonie, Op.2. (1/93) (PHIL) ① [2] **432 115-2PH2**
2, 3, 5, 6, 8, 9, 11, 12. H. Holliger, H. Elhorst, Berne
Camerata (4/89) (ARCH) ① **427 111-2AGA**
3. H. Läubin, ECO, S. Preston (hpd/dir) (arr tpt)
Concert (12/91) (DG) ① **431 817-2GH**
3. H. Hardenberger, I Musici (r1993; trans tpt)
Concert (5/95) (PHIL) ① **442 131-2PH**
3, 6. B. Hoff, ECO, I. Watson *Concert*
(2/90) (SIMA) ① **PSC1049**
3, 6. M. André, ECO, C. Mackerras (arr Paumgartner)
Concert (11/90) (EMI) ① **CDM7 63528-2**
3, 6, 9, 12. S. Francis, London Hpd Ens *Concerti,
Op.9.* (3/90) (UNIC) ① **DKPCD9088**
3, 6, 9, 12. M. Petri, Solisti Veneti, C. Scimone
Concerti, Op.9. (4/91) (RCA) ① **RD60207**
3, 6, 9, 12. A. Robson, Collegium Musicum 90, S.
Standage (vn/dir) (r1995) *Concerti, Op. 9.*
(5/95) (CHAN) ① **CHAN0579**
6. H. Schellenberger, Solisti Italiani *Concert*
(2/89) (DENO) ① **CO-2301**
**12 Concerti a cinque—violin or oboe(s) and
strings, Op. 9 (pub 1722)** (1,4,7 violin; 2,5,8,11
oboe; 3,6,9,12 two oboes)
1. B flat; 2. D minor; 3. F; 4. A; 5. C; 6. D; 7. G. B
minor; 9. C; 10. F; 11. B flat; 12. D.
1-3, 5, 6, 10, 11. P. Pierlot, J. Chambon, P. Toso,
Solisti Veneti, C. Scimone (r1970)
(6/93) (ERAT) ① **2292-45921-2**
2. D. Reichenberg, English Concert, T. Pinnock
(hpd/dir) *Concert* (1/86) (ARCH) ① **415 518-2AH**
2. Peterborough Stg Orch, N. Daniel (ob/dir) *Concert*
(8/89) (HYPE) ① **CDH88014**
2. B. Hoff, ECO, I. Watson *Concert*
(2/90) (SIMA) ① **PSC1049**
2. M. Messiter, Guildhall Str Ens, R. Salter (vn/dir)
Concert (9/90) (RCA) ① **RD60224**
2. G. Touvron, Slovak CO, B. Warchal *Concert*
(9/91) (OPUS) ① **9350 1710**
2 (Adagio) H. Schellenberger, M-A. Süss (arr ob/hp)
Concert (12/91) (DENO) ① **CO-76611**
2. N. Black, ECO, I. Watson (hpd/dir) *Concert*
(12/91) (VIRG) ① **VJ7 59656-2**
2, 3, 5, 8, 9, 11. A. Camden, J. Girdwood, London
Virtuosi, J. Georgiadis (r1992)
(3/94) (NAXO) ① **8 550739**
2, 5, 8, 11. S. Francis, London Hpd Ens *Concerti,
Op.7.* (3/90) (UNIC) ① **DKPCD9088**
2, 5, 8, 11. M. Petri, Solisti Veneti, C. Scimone
Concerti, Op.7. (4/91) (RCA) ① **RD60207**
2, 5, 8, 11. A. Robson, Collegium Musicum 90, S.
Standage (vn/dir) (r1995) *Concerti, Op. 7.*
(5/95) (CHAN) ① **CHAN0579**
2, 6, 9. P. Goodwin, King's Consort, R. King *Concert*
(6/91) (HYPE) ① **CDA66383**
8. H. Holliger, I Musici *Concert*
(4/88) (PHIL) ① **420 189-2PH**

---

8. H. Schellenberger, Solisti Italiani *Concert*
(2/89) (DENO) ① **CO-2301**
**Concerto for Trumpet, Oboes, Bassoon and
Strings in C**
C. Steele-Perkins, Tafelmusik, J. Lamon (vn/dir)
(r1993) *Concert* (4/95) (SONY) ① **SK53365**
**6 Sinfonie e 6 concerti a cinque—2-3 violins,
2 violas, cello and continuo, Op. 2 (pub
1705)**
3. A; 5. D; 6. G minor.
5, 6. H. Holliger, M. Bourgue, K. Thunemann, I.
Musici *Concerti, Op.7.*
(1/93) (PHIL) ① [2] **432 115-2PH2**
6. Thurston Cl Qt (arr cl qt: Thilde) *Concert*
(10/93) (ASV) ① **CDWHL2076**
6. Capella Istropolitana, J. Krechek (r1993) *Concert*
(3/95) (NAXO) ① **8 550877**

SECTION II: CHAMBER

Sonata in C—trumpet and organ
J. Freeman-Attwood, I. Simcock (r1993) *Concert*
(5/94) (PROU) ① **PROUCD135**
**6 Sonate da chiesa—violin and continuo, Op.
4 (pub 1708)**
EXCERPTS: 1. D minor; 2. E minor; 3. F; 4. G minor;
5. G minor; 6. B minor.
Locatelli Trio (r1992) *Trattenimenti, Op. 6.*
(4/95) (HYPE) ① [2] **CDA66831/2**
**12 Trattenimenti armonici per camera—violin
sonatas, Op. 6 (pub 1711)**
EXCERPTS: 1. C; 2. D; 3. B flat; 4. D minor; 5. F; 6.
A minor; 7. D; 8. E minor; 9. G; 10. C minor; 11. A;
12. B flat.
Locatelli Trio (r1992) *Sonate, Op. 4.*
(4/95) (HYPE) ① [2] **CDA66831/2**
6. Bartholdi Kuijken, W. Kuijken, R. Kohnen (arr. flute)
Concert (5/92) (ACCE) ① **ACC9177D**
11. J. Freeman-Attwood, I. Simcock (r1993; arr
tpt/org) *Concert* (5/94) (PROU) ① **PROUCD135**
**12 Trio Sonatas—two violins, cello and
continuo, Op. 1 (pub 1704)**
3. A.
3. J. Freeman-Attwood, I. Simcock (r1993; arr tpt/org)
Concert (5/94) (PROU) ① **PROUCD135**

SECTION V: STAGE WORKS

Il Nascimento dell'Aurora—festa pastorale
Cpte J. Anderson, M. Zimmermann, S. Klare, S.
Browne, Y. Yamaj, Solisti Veneti, C. Scimone (r1983)
(7/95) (ERAT) ① [2] **4509-96374-2**

ALBRICI, Vincenzo (1631–1696) Italy

SECTION II: CHAMBER

**Sonata a 5—2 trumpets, 2 violins and
continuo**
S. Keavy, C. Steele-Perkins, Parley of Instr *Concert*
(1/89) (HYPE) ① **CDA66255**

ALBRIGHT, William (b 1944) USA

SECTION III: INSTRUMENTAL

4 Fancies—harpsichord (1979)
B. Harbach *Concert* (3/89) (KING) ① **KCLCD2005**

ALCOCK, Sir Walter (Galpin) (1861–1947) England

SECTION IV: VOCAL AND CHORAL

**Psalm 90—Whoso dwelleth under the
defence of the Almighty**
Westminster Abbey Ch, I. Simcock, M. Neary
Concert (10/89) (CARL) ① **PCD919**

ALFANO, Franco (1875–1954) Italy

SECTION V: STAGE WORKS

Risurrezione—dramma: 4 acts (1904—Turin)
(Lib. C Hanau, after Tolstoy)
Cpte M. Olivero, G. Gismondo, A. Boyer, A. Di
Stasio, N. Condò, V. Magrini, P. Pace, M. Stefanoni,
Turin RAI Chor, Turin RAI Orch, E. Boncompagni
(bp1971) *Puccini: Turandot.*
(10/93) (LYRC) ① [2] **SRO839**
Dio pietoso M. Garden, orch (r1926: Fr) *Concert*
(8/93) (SYMP) ① **SYMCD1136**
Dio pietoso M. Garden, orch, R. Bourdon (r1926: 2
vers: Fr) *Concert* (8/94) (ROMO) ① **81008-2**

Glunge il treno...Dio pietoso M. Freni, Venice La
Fenice Orch, R. Abbado Concert
(9/92) (DECC) ① **433 316-2DH**

ALFONSO X (EL SÁBIO), King of Castile and León (1221–1284) Spain

SECTION II: CHAMBER

Cantiga No. 5—consort
London Musica Antiqua, M. Uridge (r1980-83)
Concert (12/93) (SYMP) ① **SYMCD1157**
Cantiga No. 10—consort
London Musica Antiqua, M. Uridge (r1980-83)
Concert (12/93) (SYMP) ① **SYMCD1157**

SECTION IV: VOCAL AND CHORAL

A Madre de Deus—cantiga
New London Consort, P. Pickett Concert
(7/92) (L'OI) ① [2] **433 148-2OH2**
Ben com'aos—cantiga
New London Consort, P. Pickett Concert
(7/92) (L'OI) ① [2] **433 148-2OH2**
De grad'a Santa Maria—cantiga
New London Consort, P. Pickett Concert
(7/92) (L'OI) ① [2] **433 148-2OH2**
De tod a chaga ben pode guarir—cantiga
(No. 126)
Catalan Capella Reial, Hespèrion XX, J. Savall
(r1993) Concert (1/94) (ASTR) ① **E8508**
En a gran coita—cantiga (No. 142)
Catalan Capella Reial, Hespèrion XX, J. Savall
(r1993) Concert (1/94) (ASTR) ① **E8508**
Mira gres fremosos faz por—cantiga (No. 37)
Catalan Capella Reial, Hespèrion XX, J. Savall
(r1993) Concert (1/94) (ASTR) ① **E8508**
Non e gran causa—cantiga
New London Consort, P. Pickett Concert
(7/92) (L'OI) ① [2] **433 148-2OH2**
Non sofre Santa María—cantiga (No. 159)
New London Consort, P. Pickett Concert
(7/92) (L'OI) ① [2] **433 148-2OH2**
Pero cantigas de loor—cantiga (No. 400)
Catalan Capella Reial, Hespèrion XX, J. Savall
(r1993) Concert (1/94) (ASTR) ① **E8508**
Pero que seja a gente—cantiga (No. 181)
Catalan Capella Reial, Hespèrion XX, J. Savall
(r1993) Concert (1/94) (ASTR) ① **E8508**
Pode por Santa Maria—cantiga (No. 163)
Catalan Capella Reial, Hespèrion XX, J. Savall
(r1993) Concert (1/94) (ASTR) ① **E8508**
Por dereito ten a Virgen—cantiga
New London Consort, P. Pickett Concert
(7/92) (L'OI) ① [2] **433 148-2OH2**
Por nos de dutta tirar—cantiga (No. 18)
Catalan Capella Reial, Hespèrion XX, J. Savall
(r1993) Concert (1/94) (ASTR) ① **E8508**
Quen a Virgen ben servira—cantiga
New London Consort, P. Pickett Concert
(7/92) (L'OI) ① [2] **433 148-2OH2**
Rosa de Rosas—cantiga (No. 330)
T. Berganza, N. Yepes Concert
(12/92) (DG) ① [2] **435 848-2GX2**
Santa Maria Sinal—cantiga (No. 123)
Catalan Capella Reial, Hespèrion XX, J. Savall
(r1993) Concert (1/94) (ASTR) ① **E8508**
Santa María, strella do dia—cantiga (No. 100)
T. Berganza, N. Yepes Concert
(12/92) (DG) ① [2] **435 848-2GX2**
Catalan Capella Reial, Hespèrion XX, J. Savall
(r1993) Concert (1/94) (ASTR) ① **E8508**
Soltar pode muit—cantiga (No. 176)
Catalan Capella Reial, Hespèrion XX, J. Savall
(r1993) Concert (1/94) (ASTR) ① **E8508**

ALFORD, Kenneth J. (1881–1945) England

Pseudonym of Kenneth J. Ricketts

SECTION I: ORCHESTRAL

Army of the Nile—march (pub 1941)
HM Royal Marines Band, Portsmouth, J.R. Mason
Concert (9/93) (CHAN) ① **CHAN6584**
By land and sea—slow march (pub 1941)
HM Royal Marines Band, Portsmouth, J.R. Mason
Concert (9/93) (CHAN) ① **CHAN6584**
Cavalry of the Clouds—march (pub 1923)
HM Royal Marines Band, Portsmouth, J.R. Mason
Concert (9/93) (CHAN) ① **CHAN6584**

Colonel Bogey—march (pub 1914) (used in
the film 'Bridge on the River Kwai')
LSO, R. Hickox Concert
(2/93) (CHAN) ① **CHAN9100**
HM Royal Marines Band, Portsmouth, J.R. Mason
Concert (9/93) (CHAN) ① **CHAN6584**
Boston Pops, A. Fiedler (r1958) Concert
(1/94) (RCA) ① **09026 61249-2**
Prague City PO, P. Bateman (r1994) Concert
(11/94) (SILV) ① **FILMCD151**
Dundein—march (pub 1928)
HM Royal Marines Band, Portsmouth, J.R. Mason
Concert (9/93) (CHAN) ① **CHAN6584**
Eagle Squadron—march (pub 1942)
HM Royal Marines Band, Portsmouth, J.R. Mason
Concert (9/93) (CHAN) ① **CHAN6584**
The Great Little Army—march (pub 1916)
HM Royal Marines Band, Portsmouth, J.R. Mason
Concert (9/93) (CHAN) ① **CHAN6584**
HM Jollies—march (pub 1929)
HM Royal Marines Band, Portsmouth, J.R. Mason
Concert (9/93) (CHAN) ① **CHAN6584**
Holyrood—march (pub 1912)
HM Royal Marines Band, Portsmouth, J.R. Mason
Concert (9/93) (CHAN) ① **CHAN6584**
The Lightning switch—fantasia
HM Royal Marines Band, Portsmouth, J.R. Mason
Concert (9/93) (CHAN) ① **CHAN6584**
The Mad Major—march (pub 1921)
HM Royal Marines Band, Portsmouth, J.R. Mason
Concert (9/93) (CHAN) ① **CHAN6584**
The Middy—march (pub 1917)
HM Royal Marines Band, Portsmouth, J.R. Mason
Concert (9/93) (CHAN) ① **CHAN6584**
A musical switch—fantasia
HM Royal Marines Band, Portsmouth, J.R. Mason
Concert (9/93) (CHAN) ① **CHAN6584**
Old Panama—march (pub 1927)
HM Royal Marines Band, Portsmouth, J.R. Mason
Concert (9/93) (CHAN) ① **CHAN6584**
On the quarter deck—march (pub 1917)
HM Royal Marines Band, Portsmouth, J.R. Mason
Concert (9/93) (CHAN) ① **CHAN6584**
The Standard of St George—march (pub 1930)
HM Royal Marines Band, Portsmouth, J.R. Mason
Concert (9/93) (CHAN) ① **CHAN6584**
The Thin Red Line—march (1908)
HM Royal Marines Band, Portsmouth, J.R. Mason
Concert (9/93) (CHAN) ① **CHAN6584**
The Vanished Army—march (pub 1919)
HM Royal Marines Band, Portsmouth, J.R. Mason
Concert (9/93) (CHAN) ① **CHAN6584**
The Vedette—march (pub 1912)
HM Royal Marines Band, Portsmouth, J.R. Mason
Concert (9/93) (CHAN) ① **CHAN6584**
Voice of the Guns—march (pub 1917)
HM Royal Marines Band, Portsmouth, J.R. Mason
Concert (9/93) (CHAN) ① **CHAN6584**

ALFVÉN, Hugo (Emil) (1872–1960) Sweden

SECTION I: ORCHESTRAL

Drapa, 'In memoriam King Oscar II'—large orchestra, Op. 27 (1908)
Stockholm PO, N. Järvi Concert
(11/89) (BIS) ① **BIS-CD395**
Herdsmaiden's dance—orchestra (?1923)
C. Lindberg, R. Pöntinen (arr. Lindberg) Concert
(9/85) (BIS) ① **BIS-CD298**
Malmö SO, J. DePreist Concert
(1/93) (BIS) ① **BIS-CD570**
A Legend of the Skerries—tone poem, Op. 20 (1904)
Iceland SO, P. Sakari (r1993) Concert
(3/95) (CHAN) ① **CHAN9313**
Swedish Rhapsody No. 1, 'Midsummer Vigil', Op. 19 (1903)
Stockholm PO, N. Järvi Symphony 2.
(7/88) (BIS) ① **BIS-CD385**
Iceland SO, P. Sakari (r1993) Concert
(3/95) (CHAN) ① **CHAN9313**
Swedish Rhapsody No. 2, 'Upsala-rapsodi'—Academic Festival Overture based on student songs, Op. 24 (1907)
Stockholm PO, N. Järvi Concert
(11/89) (BIS) ① **BIS-CD395**
Iceland SO, P. Sakari (r1993) Concert
(3/95) (CHAN) ① **CHAN9313**
Swedish Rhapsody No. 3, 'Dalarapsodi' (1931)
Iceland SO, P. Sakari (r1993) Concert
(3/95) (CHAN) ① **CHAN9313**

Symphony No. 1 in F minor, Op. 4 (1897)
Stockholm PO, N. Järvi Concert
(11/89) (BIS) ① **BIS-CD395**
Symphony No. 2 in D, Op. 11 (1897-98)
Stockholm PO, N. Järvi Midsummer Vigil, Op.19.
(7/88) (BIS) ① **BIS-CD385**
Symphony No. 4 in C minor, 'From the outskirts of the archipelago', Op. 39 (1918-19)
C. Högman, C.H. Ahnsjö, Stockholm PO, N. Järvi En
Skärgådssägen. (8/92) (BIS) ① **BIS-CD505**
Symphony No. 5 in A minor, Op. 54 (1942-53)
Stockholm PO, N. Järvi (r1992) Concert
(1/94) (BIS) ① **BIS-CD585**
A tale from the Archipelago (En Skärgådssägen)—tone poem, Op. 20 (1904)
Stockholm PO, N. Järvi Symphony 4.
(8/92) (BIS) ① **BIS-CD505**

SECTION IV: VOCAL AND CHORAL

Revelation Cantata, Op. 31 (1913)
Andante religioso Stockholm PO, N. Järvi (arr.
hp,celesta,stgs) Concert
(11/89) (BIS) ① **BIS-CD395**
7 Songs, Op. 28 (1908) (Wds. E. Thiel)
4. You are quietness (Du är stilla ro); 5. I yearn for
you (Jag längtar dig); 6. The Forest sleeps (Skogen
sofver).
6. J. Björling, Bergen SO, C. Garaguly (pp1954)
Concert (8/88) (BLUE) ① **ABCD006**
6. J. Björling, H. Ebert (r1940) Concert
(10/93) (NIMB) ① **NI7842**
6. J. Björling, H. Ebert (r1940) Concert
(12/94) (MMOI) ① **CDMOIR425**

SECTION V: STAGE WORKS

Gustav Adolf II—concert suite from incidental music, Op. 49 (1932)
1. Sarabanda; 2. Bourrée; 3. Menuett; 4. Elegi.
4. Stockholm PO, N. Järvi (r1992) Concert
(1/94) (BIS) ① **BIS-CD585**
4. Iceland SO, P. Sakari (r1993) Concert
(3/95) (CHAN) ① **CHAN9313**
The Mountain King—concert suite from ballet
1. Invocation (Besvärjelse); 2. Sorceress's Dance
(Trollflickans dans); 3. Summer Rain (Sommarregn);
4. Shepherd-girl's Dance (Vallflickans dans).
Stockholm PO, N. Järvi (r1992) Concert
(1/94) (BIS) ① **BIS-CD585**

ALISON, Richard (fl 1592–1606) England

SECTION II: CHAMBER

Alison's Knell—consort (pub 1599)
J. Bream, J. Bream Consort (r1987; ed Beck)
Concert (8/93) (RCA) ① [28] **09026 61583-2(3)**
J. Bream Consort (r1987; ed Beck) Concert
(9/94) (RCA) ① **09026 61590-2**
The Bachelar's Delight—consort (pub 1599)
J. Bream, J. Bream Consort (r1962) Concert
(8/93) (RCA) ① [28] **09026 61583-2(2)**
J. Bream, J. Bream Consort (r1987; ed Beck)
Concert (8/93) (RCA) ① [28] **09026 61583-2(3)**
J. Bream Consort (r1987; ed Beck) Concert
(9/94) (RCA) ① **09026 61590-2**
J. Bream Consort (r1962) Concert
(9/94) (RCA) ① **09026 61589-2**
De la tromba Pavin—consort (pub 1599)
J. Bream, J. Bream Consort (r1987) Concert
(8/93) (RCA) ① [28] **09026 61583-2(3)**
J. Bream, J. Bream Consort (r1962) Concert
(8/93) (RCA) ① [28] **09026 61583-2(2)**
J. Bream Consort (r1987; ed Beck) Concert
(9/94) (RCA) ① **09026 61590-2**
J. Bream Consort (r1962) Concert
(9/94) (RCA) ① **09026 61589-2**
Goe from my window—consort (pub 1599)
Musicians of Swanne Alley Concert
(2/88) (HARM) ① **HMC90 5192**
J. Bream, J. Bream Consort (r1987; ed Beck)
Concert (8/93) (RCA) ① [28] **09026 61583-2(3)**
J. Bream Consort (r1987; ed Beck) Concert
(9/94) (RCA) ① **09026 61590-2**
The Lady Frances Sidneys Almayne—consort
Musicians of Swanne Alley Concert
(2/88) (HARM) ① **HMC90 5192**
The Lady Frances Sidneys Goodnight—consort
Musicians of Swanne Alley Concert
(2/88) (HARM) ① **HMC90 5192**

Mr Allisons Almayne—consort
Musicians of Swanne Alley *Concert*
(2/88) (HARM) ① **HMC90 5192**

**ALKAN, (Charles-)Valentin
(1813–1888) France**

SECTION I: ORCHESTRAL

**Concerto da camera No. 1 in A minor—piano
and orchestra, Op. 10 (c1832)**
M-A. Hamelin, BBC Scottish So, M. Brabbins (r1993)
Concert (8/94) (HYPE) ① **CDA66717**
**Concerto da camera No. 2 in C sharp
minor—piano and orchestra (1834)**
M-A. Hamelin, BBC Scottish So, M. Brabbins (r1993)
Concert (8/94) (HYPE) ① **CDA66717**

SECTION II: CHAMBER

**Fantaisie on Mozart's 'Don Giovanni'—piano
duet, Op. 26 (pub 1844)**
A. Goldstone, C. Clemmow (r1988) *Concert*
(4/89) (SYMP) ① **SYMCD1037**
**Grand Duo Concertant in F sharp
minor—violin and piano, Op. 21 (?1840)**
R.M. Klaas, K. Lessing (r1991) *Concert*
(8/93) (MARC) ① **8 223383**
D-S. Kang, O. Gardon (r1992) *Concert*
(12/93) (TIMP) ① **1C1013**
**Sonate de Concert in E—cello and piano,
Op. 47 (1856)**
R.M. Klaas, B. Schwarz (r1991) *Concert*
(8/93) (MARC) ① **8 223383**
Y. Chiffoleau, O. Gardon (r1992) *Concert*
(12/93) (TIMP) ① **1C1013**
**Trio in G minor—piano, violin and double-
bass, Op. 30 (pub 1841)**
Alkan Trio (r1991) *Concert*
(8/93) (MARC) ① **8 223383**
D-S. Kang, Y. Chiffoleau, O. Gardon (r1992) *Concert*
(12/93) (TIMP) ① **1C1013**

SECTION III: INSTRUMENTAL

Alleluia—piano, Op. 25 (1844)
L. Martin (r1992) *Concert*
(4/95) (MARC) ① **8 223657**
**Le chemin de fer (étude)—piano, Op. 27
(pub 1844)**
L. Martin (r1990) *Concert*
(11/93) (MARC) ① **8 223500**
**Deuxième recueil de chants - Book 2, Op. 38
(1857)**
1. Assez vivement.
1. J. Gibbons (r1995) *Concert*
(11/95) (ASV) ① [2] **CDDCS227**
48 Esquisses—piano, Op. 63 (1861)
2. La staccatissimo; 4. Les cloches; 11. Les soupirs;
48. En songe.
L. Martin (r1990) (4/95) (MARC) ① **8 223352**
2, 4, 11, 48. J. Gibbons (r1995) *Concert*
(11/95) (ASV) ① [2] **CDDCS227**
3 Études—piano, Op. 76 (c1838)
1. Faintaisie (left hand); 2. Introduction, variations
and finale (right hand); 3. Étude à mouvement; 4.
Semblable et perpetuel.
L. Martin (r1992) *Concert*
(11/93) (MARC) ① **8 223500**
M-A. Hamelin (pp1994) *Concert*
(3/95) (HYPE) ① **CDA66765**
**12 Études dans les tons majeurs—piano, Op.
35 (pub 1848)**
1. A; 2. D; 3. G; 4. C; 5. F (Allegro barbaro); 6. B flat;
7. E flat (L'incendie au village voisin); 8. A flat; 9. C
sharp (Contrapunctus); 10. E flat (Chant
d'amour—Chant de mort); 11. B; 12. E.
B. Ringeissen (r1990) *Études, Op.39.*
(11/93) (MARC) ① **8 223351**
5. J. Gibbons (r1995) *Concert*
(11/95) (ASV) ① [2] **CDDCS227**
**12 Études dans les tons mineurs—piano,
Op. 39 (pub 1857)**
1. Comme le vent; 2. En rythme molossique; 3.
Scherzo diabolico; 4. Symphonie—mvt 1; 5.
Symphonie—mvt 2; 6. Symphonie—mvt 3; 7.
Symphonie—mvt 4; 8. Concerto—mvt 1; 9.
Concerto—mvt 2; 10. Concerto—mvt 3; 11. Overture;
12. Le festin d'Esope.
J. Gibbons (r1995) *Concert*
(11/95) (ASV) ① [2] **CDDCS227**
1, 2, 4-7, 11. B. Ringeissen
(4/91) (MARC) ① **8 223285**
3. B. Ringeissen *Concert*
(11/88) (HARM) ① **HMA190 927**
3, 12. B. Ringeissen (r1990) *Études, Op.35.*
(11/93) (MARC) ① **8 223351**

4-7. E. Petri (pp c1952) *Concert*
(8/94) (SYMP) ① **SYMCD1145**
8-10. M-A. Hamelin (8/93) (MUSI) ① **MACD-724**
12. M-A. Hamelin (r1994) *Concert*
(12/95) (HYPE) ① **CDA66794**
**Gigue et air ballet dans le style ancien, Op.
24 (1844)**
B. Ringeissen *Concert*
(11/88) (HARM) ① **HMA190 927**
**Grande sonate, '(Les) quatre âges'—piano,
Op. 33 (1848)**
1. Vingt ans; 2. Trente ans: quasi-Faust; 3. Quarante
ans: un heureux ménage; 4. Cinquante ans:
Prométhée enchaîné.
M-A. Hamelin (r1994) *Concert*
(12/95) (HYPE) ① **CDA66794**
**Impromptu dur le choral de
Luther—organ/pedal piano, Op. 69 (pub
c1871)**
K. Bowyer *Concert* (5/89) (NIMB) ① **NI5089**
4 Impromptus—piano, Op. 32/1 (1848)
1. Vaghezza; 2. L'amitié; 3. Fantasietta alla moresca;
4. La foi.
L. Martin (r1992) *Concert*
(4/95) (MARC) ① **8 223657**
**3 Improvisations dans le style
brillant—piano, Op. 12 (pub 1837)**
L. Martin (r1990) *Concert*
(11/93) (MARC) ① **8 223500**
**3 Marches, quasi da cavalleria, Op. 37
(1857)**
1. B. Ringeissen *Concert*
(11/88) (HARM) ① **HMA190 927**
**Les mois—12 morceaux caractéristique, Op.
74 (c1872)**
1. Une nuit d'hiver; 2. Carnaval; 3. La retraite; 4. La
Pâque; 5. Sérénade; 6. Promenade sur l'eau; 7. Nuit
d'été; 8. Les moissonneurs; 9. L'hallali; 10. Gros
temps; 11. Le mourant; 12. L'opéra.
10. J. Gibbons (r1995) *Concert*
(11/95) (ASV) ① [2] **CDDCS227**
Nocturne—piano, Op. 22 (1844)
J. Gibbons (r1995) *Concert*
(11/95) (ASV) ① [2] **CDDCS227**
2 Nocturnes—piano, Op. 57 (pub 1859)
1. B. Ringeissen *Concert*
(11/88) (HARM) ① **HMA190 927**
**Petits préludes sur les gammes du plain-
chant—organ (pub 1859)**
K. Bowyer *Concert* (5/89) (NIMB) ① **NI5089**
25 Préludes—piano, Op. 31 (1847)
EXCERPTS: 1. Lentement, C; 2. Assez lentement, F
minor; 3. Dans le genre ancien, D flat; 4. Prière du
soir, F sharp minor; 5. Psaume 150, D; 6. Ancienne
mélodie de la synagogue, G minor; 7. Librement mais
sans secousses, E flat; 8. La chanson de la folle au
bord de la mer, A flat minor; 9. Placiditas, E; 10.
Dans le style fugué, A minor; 11. Un petit rien, F; 12.
Le temps qui n'est plus, E flat minor; 13. J'étais
endormie, mais mon coeur veillait, G flat; 14.
Rapidement, B minor; 15. Dans le genre gothique, G;
16. Assez lentement, C minor; 17. Rêve d'amour, A
flat; 18. Sans trop de mouvement, C sharp minor; 19.
Prière du matin, A; 20. Modérément vite et bien
caractérisé, D minor; 21. Doucement, B flat; 22.
Anniversaire, E flat minor; 23. Assez vite; 24.
Etude de vélocité, E minor; 25. Prière, C.
L. Martin (4/91) (MARC) ① **8 223284**
O. Mustonen (r1990) *Shostakovich: Preludes, Op.
34.* (10/91) (DECC) ① **433 055-2DH**
8, 12, 13. J. Gibbons (r1995) *Concert*
(11/95) (ASV) ① [2] **CDDCS227**
**Le preux (étude de concert)—piano, Op. 17
(pub 1844)**
L. Martin (r1990) *Concert*
(11/93) (MARC) ① **8 223500**
**13 Prières—organ/pedal piano/piano 3
hands, Op. 64 (pub c1870)**
1. G; 2. A; 3. E minor; 4. B flat; 5. F; 9. E; 10. B flat;
11. E; 12. F; 13. G.
K. Bowyer *Concert* (5/89) (NIMB) ① **NI5089**
**Quatrième recueil de chants—piano, Op. 67
(pub 1873)**
6. B. Ringeissen *Concert*
(11/88) (HARM) ① **HMA190 927**
**Recueil d'impromptus—piano, Op. 32/2
(1849)**
1. Andantino; 2. Allegretto; 3. Vivace; 4. Andante.
L. Martin (r1992) *Concert*
(4/95) (MARC) ① **8 223657**
**Rondeau chromatique—piano, Op. 12
(1833)**
L. Martin (r1992) *Concert*
(4/95) (MARC) ① **8 223657**

Saltarelle—piano, Op. 23 (pub 1844)
B. Ringeissen *Concert*
(11/88) (HARM) ① **HMA190 927**
**Salut, cendre du pauvre!—paraphrase:
piano, Op. 45 (1856)**
L. Martin (r1992) *Concert*
(4/95) (MARC) ① **8 223657**
Sonatine—piano, Op. 61 (pub 1861)
B. Ringeissen *Concert*
(11/88) (HARM) ① **HMA190 927**
M-A. Hamelin (r1994) *Concert*
(12/95) (HYPE) ① **CDA66794**
**Super flumina Babylonis (variations on
Psalm 137)—piano, Op. 52 (1859)**
L. Martin (r1992) *Concert*
(4/95) (MARC) ① **8 223657**
**Transcription de Concert pour piano seul
avec cadence (Beethoven Piano Concerto in
C minor, Op. 37)**
M-A. Hamelin (pp1994) *Concert*
(3/95) (HYPE) ① **CDA66765**
**Troisième recueil de chants - Book 3, Op. 65
(c1870)**
6. Barcarolle.
Barcarolle M-A. Hamelin (r1994) *Concert*
(12/95) (HYPE) ① **CDA66794**
6. J. Gibbons (r1995) *Concert*
(11/95) (ASV) ① [2] **CDDCS227**
**Variations on a theme from Steibelt's Orage
Concerto—piano, op. 1 (1828)**
L. Martin (r1992) *Concert*
(4/95) (MARC) ① **8 223657**
**Zorcico—Spanish dance: piano (ed G.
Beck)**
B. Ringeissen *Concert*
(11/88) (HARM) ① **HMA190 927**

**ALLEGRI, Gregorio (1582–1652)
Italy**

SECTION IV: VOCAL AND CHORAL

Cantate domino—motet: 4vv & continuo
A Sei Voci, B. Fabre-Garrus, D. Ferran (1993)
Concert (9/95) (ASTR) ① **E8524**
De ore prudentis—motet: 3vv & continuo
A Sei Voci, B. Fabre-Garrus, D. Ferran (1993)
Concert (9/95) (ASTR) ① **E8524**
Miserere mei—9vv (Psalm 51)
S. Quirke, A. Wright, Westminster Cath Ch, S.
Cleobury (ed. G. Guest) *Concert*
(7/83) (ARGO) ① **410 005-2ZH**
T. Beasley-Murray, King's College Ch, S. Cleobury
Concert (5/85) (EMI) ① **CDC7 47065-2**
Westminster Abbey Ch, S. Preston *Concert*
(5/86) (ARCH) ① **415 517-2AH**
PCA, M. Brown *Concert* (7/86) (CARL) ① **PCD806**
A. Stamp, Tallis Scholars, P. Phillips *Concert*
(7/86) (GIME) ① **CDGIM339**
Taverner Consort, A. Parrott *Concert*
(8/87) (EMI) ① **CDC7 47699-2**
R. Goodman, King's College Ch, D. Willcocks
Concert (5/89) (DECC) ① **421 147-2DM**
The Sixteen, H. Christophers *Concert*
(10/90) (COLL) ① **Coll5009-2**
Tallis Scholars, P. Phillips *Concert*
(1/91) (GIME) ① **CDGIM999**
J. Budd, St Paul's Cath Ch, John Scott *Concert*
(10/91) (HYPE) ① **CDA66439**
Trinity Coll Ch, Cambridge, R. Marlow (1993)
Concert (9/94) (CONI) ① **CDCF219**
Tallis Scholars, P. Phillips (pp1994) *Concert*
(9/94) (GIME) ① **CDGIM994**
A Sei Voci, B. Fabre-Garrus (r1993; 2 versions: 1
with baroque ornamentation) *Concert*
(9/95) (ASTR) ① **E8524**
Missa Vidi turbam magnam—6vv
A Sei Voci, B. Fabre-Garrus (r1993) *Concert*
(9/95) (ASTR) ① **E8524**
Repleti sunt omnes—motet: 3vv & continuo
A Sei Voci, B. Fabre-Garrus, D. Ferran (1993)
Concert (9/95) (ASTR) ① **E8524**

**ALLEN, Georg Frederik Ferdinand
(1856–1925)**

SECTION IV: VOCAL AND CHORAL

**Sun smiles so kind and gentle—song (Wds.
J. Aakjaer)**
L. Melchior, Anon (pf) (r c1920) *Concert*
(8/88) (DANA) ① [2] **DACOCD311/2**

ALMEIDA, Francisco Antonio de (c1702–1755) Portugal

SECTION IV: VOCAL AND CHORAL

La Giuditta—oratorio (1726) (Lib. anon after Apocrypha)
Cpte L. Lootens, F. Congiu, A. Köhler, M. Hill, Cologne Concerto, R. Jacobs
(11/92) (HARM) ① [2] HMC90 1411/2

ALMEIDA, Laurindo (b 1917) Brazil

SECTION II: CHAMBER

Brazilliance—three guitars
Pro Arte Gtr Trio Concert
(1/94) (ASV) ① CDWHL2079

ALNAES, Eyvind (1872–1932) Denmark

SECTION IV: VOCAL AND CHORAL

About love (Nu brister alle de kløfter)—song (Wds. V Stuckenberg)
K. Flagstad, LSO, Ø. Fjeldstad (r1959) Concert
(12/95) (LOND) ① 440 492-2LM
K. Flagstad, LSO, Ø. Fjeldstad (r1959) Concert
(12/95) (LOND) ① [5] 440 490-2LM5(1)
A February morning at the gulf (Februarmorgen ved Golfen)—song (Wds. N C Vogt)
K. Flagstad, LSO, Ø. Fjeldstad (r1959) Concert
(12/95) (LOND) ① 440 492-2LM
K. Flagstad, LSO, Ø. Fjeldstad (r1959) Concert
(12/95) (LOND) ① [5] 440 490-2LM5(1)
Happiness between two people—song, Op. 26/1
K. Flagstad, E. McArthur (r1936) Concert
(12/95) (PEAR) ① GEMMCD9092
K. Flagstad, E. McArthur (r1936) Concert
(12/95) (NIMB) ① NI7871
K. Flagstad, E. McArthur (r1936) Concert
(12/95) (SIMA) ① [3] PSC1821(2)
K. Flagstad, E. Alnaes (r1929) Concert
(12/95) (SIMA) ① [3] PSC1821(1)
A Hundred violins (De hundrede fioliner)—song (Wds. A Øverland)
K. Flagstad, LSO, Ø. Fjeldstad (r1959) Concert
(12/95) (LOND) ① 440 492-2LM
K. Flagstad, LSO, Ø. Fjeldstad (r1959) Concert
(12/95) (LOND) ① [5] 440 490-2LM5(1)
Sidste reis, 'Last journey'—song, Op. 17/2
K. Flagstad, orch (r1930) Concert
(12/95) (SIMA) ① [3] PSC1821(1)
Yearnings of spring (Vålaengsler)—song (Wds. N C Vogt)
K. Flagstad, LSO, Ø. Fjeldstad (r1959) Concert
(12/95) (LOND) ① 440 492-2LM
K. Flagstad, LSO, Ø. Fjeldstad (r1959) Concert
(12/95) (LOND) ① [5] 440 490-2LM5(1)

ALONSO (fl 1500) Spain

SECTION IV: VOCAL AND CHORAL

La Tricotea (from the Palacio Song Book)
Hespèrion XX, J. Savall Concert
(7/92) (ASTR) ① E8762

ALONSO, Francisco (1887–1948) Spain

SECTION V: STAGE WORKS

Coplas de Ronda—zarzuela (Lib. C Amiches & J de Lucia)
Bella niñia de ojos negros P. Domingo, Madrid Zarzuela Chor, Madrid Rondalla Lírica, Madrid SO, M. Moreno-Buendia (r1987) Concert
(1/89) (EMI) ① CDC7 49148-2
La Parranda—zarzuela (Lib. F. Ardavín)
En la huerta del Segura P. Domingo, Madrid Zarzuela Chor, Madrid Rondalla Lírica, Madrid SO, M. Moreno-Buendia (r1987) Concert
(1/89) (EMI) ① CDC7 49148-2

ALPAERTS, Flor (1876–1954) Belgium

SECTION I: ORCHESTRAL

Pallieter—symphonic poem (1921-24)
3. Wedding feast (Bruiloftsfeest).
3. Belgian Rad & TV Orch, A. Rahbari (r1992) Concert
(8/94) (DINT) ① DICD920100

ALTENBURG, Johann Ernst (1734–1801) Germany

SECTION I: ORCHESTRAL

Concerto for 7 Trumpets and Timpani
G. Schwarz (tpt/dir), E. Carroll, M. Gould, R. Sirinek, N. Smith, John Miller, N. Balm, NY Y CO Concert
(10/84) (DELO) ① DE3002

ALVARADO, Diego de (c1570–1643) Spain

SECTION III: INSTRUMENTAL

Obre sobra el Pange lingua—organ
S. Farr (r1994) Concert
(11/94) (HYPE) ① CDA66725

ALVAREZ, Fermin Maria (?–1898) Spain

SECTION IV: VOCAL AND CHORAL

A Granada—song (Wds. F. Gras y Elias)
E. Caruso, orch, J. Pasternack (r1918) Concert
(12/90) (NIMB) ① NI7809
E. Caruso, orch, J. Pasternack (r1918) Concert
(7/91) (RCA) ① [12] GD60495(6)
E. Caruso, orch, J. Pasternack (r1918) Concert
(10/91) (PEAR) ① [3] EVC4(1)
Mantilla
M. Battistini, orch, C. Sabajno (r1921) Concert
(10/92) (PEAR) ① GEMMCD9936
La Partida—song (Wds. E. Blasco)
E. Caruso, G. Scognamiglio (r1914) Concert
(7/90) (CLUB) ① CL99-060
E. Caruso, orch, J. Pasternack (r1918) Concert
(12/90) (NIMB) ① NI7809
E. Caruso, orch, J. Pasternack (r1918) Concert
(7/91) (RCA) ① [12] GD60495(5)
E. Caruso, G. Scognamiglio (r1914) Concert
(7/91) (RCA) ① [12] GD60495(5)
E. Caruso, G. Scognamiglio (r1914) Concert
(10/91) (PEAR) ① [3] EVC3(1)
E. Caruso, orch, J. Pasternack (r1918) Concert
(10/91) (PEAR) ① [3] EVC4(1)
A. Galli-Curci, orch, J. Pasternack (r1916/7: two vers)
Concert
(3/94) (ROMO) ① [2] 81003-2

ALVAREZ, Javier (b 1956) Mexico

SECTION II: CHAMBER

Metro Chabacano—string quartet (1986, rev 1991) (arr from 'Cancion de Tierra')
Brodsky Qt (r1994) Concert
(10/94) (SILV) ① SILKD6001

ALWYN, William (1905–1985) England

SECTION I: ORCHESTRAL

Autumn Legend—cor anglais and strings (1954)
N. Daniel, CLS, R. Hickox Concert
(10/92) (CHAN) ① CHAN9065
O. Ellis, LPO, W. Alwyn Concert
(12/92) (LYRI) ① SRCD230
Concerto for Oboe, Harp and Strings (1944)
N. Daniel, CLS, R. Hickox Concert
(9/92) (CHAN) ① CHAN8866
Concerto for Piano and Orchestra No. 1 (1930)
H. Shelley, LSO, R. Hickox (r1992) Symphony 1.
(5/93) (CHAN) ① CHAN9155
Concerto for Piano and Orchestra No. 2 (1960)
H. Shelley, LSO, R. Hickox (r1993) Concert
(1/94) (CHAN) ① CHAN9196
Concerto for Violin and Orchestra (1938)
L. Mordkovitch, LSO, R. Hickox (r1992) Symphony 3.
(1/94) (CHAN) ① CHAN9187

Concerto Grosso No. 1 in B flat—small orchestra (1942)
CLS, R. Hickox Concert
(9/92) (CHAN) ① CHAN8866
Concerto Grosso No. 2 in G—strings (1951)
CLS, R. Hickox Concert
(9/92) (CHAN) ① CHAN8866
LPO, W. Alwyn Concert
(12/92) (LYRI) ① SRCD230
Concerto Grosso No. 3 (1964)
CLS, R. Hickox Concert
(9/92) (CHAN) ① CHAN8866
Derby Day—overture (1960)
LPO, W. Alwyn Concert
(12/92) (LYRI) ① SRCD229
LSO, R. Hickox Concert
(2/93) (CHAN) ① CHAN9093
Elizabethan Dances (1957)
LSO, R. Hickox Concert
(7/92) (CHAN) ① CHAN8902
1, 2, 4, 5. LPO, W. Alwyn Concert
(12/92) (LYRI) ① SRCD229
Fanfare for a Joyful Occasion—brass and percussion (1948)
LSO, R. Hickox Concert
(2/93) (CHAN) ① CHAN9093
Festival March (1950)
LSO, R. Hickox Concert
(7/92) (CHAN) ① CHAN8902
LPO, W. Alwyn Concert
(12/92) (LYRI) ① SRCD229
Lyra Angelica—Concerto for Harp and Strings (1954)
R. Masters, CLS, R. Hickox Concert
(10/92) (CHAN) ① CHAN9065
G. Browne, LPO, W. Alwyn Concert
(12/92) (LYRI) ① SRCD230
The Magic Island—symphonic prelude (1952)
LPO, W. Alwyn Concert
(12/92) (LYRI) ① SRCD229
LSO, R. Hickox Concert
(2/93) (CHAN) ① CHAN9093
Overture to a Masque (1940)
LSO, R. Hickox Concert
(2/93) (CHAN) ① CHAN9093
Pastoral Fantasia—viola and string orchestra (1939)
S. Tees, CLS, R. Hickox Concert
(10/92) (CHAN) ① CHAN9065
Sinfonietta for Strings (1970)
LPO, W. Alwyn Concert
(12/92) (LYRI) ① SRCD229
LSO, R. Hickox (r1993) Concert
(1/94) (CHAN) ① CHAN9196
Symphony No. 1 in D (1949)
LPO, W. Alwyn Symphony 4.
(7/92) (LYRI) ① SRCD227
LSO, R. Hickox (r1992) Piano Concerto 1.
(5/93) (CHAN) ① CHAN9155
Symphony No. 2 (1953)
LPO, W. Alwyn Concert
(10/92) (LYRI) ① SRCD228
LSO, R. Hickox Concert
(2/93) (CHAN) ① CHAN9093
Symphony No. 3 (1955-56)
LPO, W. Alwyn Concert
(10/92) (LYRI) ① SRCD228
LSO, R. Hickox (r1992) Violin Concerto.
(1/94) (CHAN) ① CHAN9187
Symphony No. 4 (1959)
LSO, R. Hickox Concert
(7/92) (CHAN) ① CHAN8902
LPO, W. Alwyn Symphony 1.
(7/92) (LYRI) ① SRCD227
Symphony No. 5, 'Hydriotaphia' (1972-73)
LPO, W. Alwyn Concert
(10/92) (LYRI) ① SRCD228
LSO, R. Hickox (r1993) Concert
(1/94) (CHAN) ① CHAN9196
Tragic Interlude—two horns, timpani and string orchestra (1936)
CLS, R. Hickox Concert
(10/92) (CHAN) ① CHAN9065

SECTION II: CHAMBER

Concerto for Flute and Eight Wind Instruments (1980)
K. Hill, London Haffner Wnd Ens, N. Daniel (ob/dir)
(r1992) Concert (10/93) (CHAN) ① CHAN9152
Music for Three Players—suite: violin, cello and piano (1950)
J. Farrall, L. Chen, J. Drake (r1992) Concert
(10/93) (CHAN) ① CHAN9152

Naiades—fantasy-sonata: flute and harp (1971)
J. Stinton, A. Brewer Concert
(4/92) (COLL) ① Coll1297-2
K. Hill, I. Jones (r1992) Concert
(10/93) (CHAN) ① CHAN9152
Rhapsody for Piano Quartet (1938)
D. Willison, Quartet of London Concert
(2/88) (CHAN) ① CHAN8440
Sonata for Clarinet and Piano (1963)
J. Farrall, J. Drake Concert
(11/94) (CHAN) ① CHAN9197
Sonata for Flute and Piano (1948)
K. Hill, J. Drake Concert
(11/94) (CHAN) ① CHAN9197
Sonata for Oboe and Piano (1930s)
N. Daniel, J. Drake Concert
(11/94) (CHAN) ① CHAN9197
Sonata Impromptu—violin and viola (1939)
L. Chen, C. MacFarlane Concert
(11/94) (CHAN) ① CHAN9197
String Quartet No. 1 in D minor (1953)
London Qt String Quartet 2.
(5/94) (CHAN) ① CHAN9219
String Quartet No. 2, 'Spring Waters' (1975)
London Qt String Quartet 1.
(5/94) (CHAN) ① CHAN9219
String Quartet No. 3 (1984)
Quartet of London Concert
(2/88) (CHAN) ① CHAN8440
String Trio (1962)
Quartet of London Concert
(2/88) (CHAN) ① CHAN8440
Suite for Oboe and Harp (1944-45)
N. Daniel, J. Drake (r1992) Concert
(10/93) (CHAN) ① CHAN9152
Trio for Flute, Cello and Piano (1951)
K. Hill, C. Dearnley, J. Drake (r1992) Concert
(10/93) (CHAN) ① CHAN9152

SECTION III: INSTRUMENTAL

Crépuscule—harp (1955)
I. Jones Concert
(11/94) (CHAN) ① CHAN9197
Divertimento—flute (1940)
K. Hill Concert
(11/94) (CHAN) ① CHAN9197
Fantasy-Waltzes (1955)
J. Ogdon Preludes.
(7/86) (CHAN) ① CHAN8399
12 Preludes (1957)
1-12. J. Ogdon Fantasy-Waltzes.
(7/86) (CHAN) ① CHAN8399

SECTION IV: VOCAL AND CHORAL

Invocations—song cycle: soprano and piano (1977) (Wds. M. Armstrong)
1. Through the centuries; 2. Holding the night; 3. Separation; 4. Drought; 5. Spring Rain; 6. Invocation to the Queen of Moonlight; 7. Our Magic Horse.
J. Gomez, J. Constable Leave-taking.
(6/94) (CHAN) ① CHAN9220
A Leave-taking—song cycle: 1v and piano (1978) (Wds. J L Warren, Baron de Tabley)
1. The Pilgrim Cranes; 2. Daffodils; 3. The Ocean Wood; 4. Fortune's Wheel; 5. Study of a Spider; 6. The Two Old Kings; 7. A Leave-taking.
A. Rolfe Johnson, G. Johnson Invocations.
(6/94) (CHAN) ① CHAN9220

SECTION V: STAGE WORKS

The Fallen Idol—film score (1948)
1. SUITE (arr C Palmer): 1a. Overture; 1b. Prelude and Opening Scene; 1c. Love Scene (part 1); 1d. Love Scene (part 2); 1e. Hide and Seek (Scherzo); 1f. Panic and Flight; 1g. Finale; 1h. Coda (End Titles).
Suite LSO, R. Hickox (r1993: arr C Palmer) Concert
(3/94) (CHAN) ① CHAN9243
The History of Mr Polly—film score (1949)
1. SUITE (arr C. Palmer): 1a. Prelude; 1b. Wedding and Funeral; 1c. Fire (Murder Arsonical); 1d. Christabel; 1e. Punting Scene (The Ferry); 1f. Utopian Sunset (Finale).
Suite LSO, R. Hickox (r1993: arr C Palmer) Concert
(3/94) (CHAN) ① CHAN9243
Miss Julie—opera: 2 acts (1977—BBC Radio) (Lib. cpsr, after Strindberg)
Cpte J. Gomez, B. Luxon, D. Jones, J. Mitchinson, Philh, V. Tausky (3/93) (LYRI) ① [2] SRCD2218
Odd Man Out—film score (1946)
1. SUITE (arr C. Palmer): 1a. Prelude; 1b. Police Chase; 1c. Delirium and Lullaby; 1d. Nemesis (Finale).
Suite LSO, R. Hickox (r1993: arr C Palmer) Concert
(3/94) (CHAN) ① CHAN9243

The Rake's Progress—film score (1945)
EXCERPTS: 1. Calypso Music.
1. LSO, R. Hickox (r1993) Concert
(3/94) (CHAN) ① CHAN9243
1. LSO, M. Mathieson (r1945) Concert
(9/94) (EMI) ① CDGO 2059

AMANI, Nikolai (1872–1904) Russia

may be spelt Amanya

SECTION IV: VOCAL AND CHORAL

Cool summer evening—song
D. Smirnov, anon (r1913) Concert
(6/93) (PEAR) ① [3] GEMMCDS9004/6(2)

AMBROSI, Alearco (b 1931) Italy

SECTION III: INSTRUMENTAL

Messa—organ (1989)
L. Benedetti (r1992) Concert
(4/95) (PRIO) ① PRCD427

AMBROSIO, Alfredo d' (1871–1914) Italy

SECTION II: CHAMBER

Canzonetta No. 1—violin and piano, Op. 6
T. Seidel, H. Kaufman (r c1924) Concert
(7/93) (APR) ① [2] APR7016
Romance in D—violin and piano, Op. 9
J. Kubelík, anon (r1902) Concert
(6/91) (BIDD) ① [2] LAB033/4
Serenade, Op. 4
J. Kubelík, anon (r1905) Concert
(6/91) (BIDD) ① [2] LAB033/4
G. Enescu, E.C. Harris (r1924) Concert
(6/93) (BIDD) ① LAB066
J. Heifetz, S. Chotzinoff (r1919) Concert
(11/94) (RCA) ① [65] 09026 61778-2(01)

AMIGIONE, Giovanni (17th Cent) Italy

SECTION II: CHAMBER

2 Sonatas—treble instrument and continuo (compiled 1613) (attrib)
J. West, P. Nicholson Concert
(4/89) (HYPE) ① [2] CDA66311/2

AMIROV, Firket (1922–1984) USSR

SECTION II: CHAMBER

6 Pieces—flute and piano
M. Wiesler, R. Pöntinen Concert
(6/90) (BIS) ① BIS-CD419

AMLIN, Martin (b 1953) USA

SECTION IV: VOCAL AND CHORAL

Time's Caravan—choir a cappella (1988) (Wds. O Khayyám, trans E Fitzgerald)
J. Oliver Chorale, J. Oliver Matthews.
(5/95) (KOCH) ① 37178-2

AMNER, John (1579–1641) England

SECTION III: INSTRUMENTAL

Variations for keyboard on 'O Lord in Thee is all my trust'
D. Price (r1994) Concert
(7/95) (HYPE) ① CDA66768

SECTION IV: VOCAL AND CHORAL

Blessed be the Lord God—anthem: 4vv
Ely Cath Ch, P. Trepte, D. Price (r1994) Concert
(7/95) (HYPE) ① CDA66768
Come, let's rejoice—anthem: 4vv (Wds. Bible)
Cambridge Sngrs, J. Rutter Concert
(4/92) (CLLE) ① COLCD113
Consider, all ye passers by—anthem: 1/5vv
Ely Cath Ch, Parley of Instr, P. Holman, P. Trepte, D. Price (r1994) Concert (7/95) (HYPE) ① CDA66768
Glory be to God on high—anthem: 1/4vv
Ely Cath Ch, P. Trepte, D. Price (r1994) Concert
(7/95) (HYPE) ① CDA66768

Hear, O Lord and have mercy—anthem: 2/4vv
Ely Cath Ch, P. Trepte, D. Price (r1994) Concert
(7/95) (HYPE) ① CDA66768
I will sing unto the Lord as long as I live—anthem: 1/5vv
Ely Cath Ch, P. Trepte, D. Price (r1994) Concert
(7/95) (HYPE) ① CDA66768
I will sing unto the Lord, for he hath triumphed gloriously—anthem: 5vv
Ely Cath Ch, P. Trepte, D. Price (r1994) Concert
(7/95) (HYPE) ① CDA66768
My Lord is hence removed—anthem: 1/6vv
Ely Cath Ch, Parley of Instr, P. Holman, P. Trepte, D. Price (r1994) Concert (7/95) (HYPE) ① CDA66768
O sing unto the Lord—anthem: 3vv
Ely Cath Ch, P. Trepte, D. Price (r1994) Concert
(7/95) (HYPE) ① CDA66768
O ye little flock—anthem: 4/6vv
Red Byrd, Rose Consort Concert
(12/91) (AMON) ① CD-SAR46
Trinity Coll Ch, Cambridge, S. Standage, R. Marlow (r1993) Concert (12/93) (CONI) ① CDCF517
Ely Cath Ch, Parley of Instr, P. Holman, P. Trepte, D. Price (r1994) Concert (7/95) (HYPE) ① CDA66768
Second Service, 'Cesar's'—4/5vv
1. Venite; 2. Te deum; 3. Jubilate; 4. Kyrie; 5. Credo; 6. Magnificat; 7. Nunc dimittis.
2, 6, 7. Ely Cath Ch, P. Trepte, D. Price (r1994) Concert (7/95) (HYPE) ① CDA66768
Sing, O heav'ns—anthem: 7vv
Ely Cath Ch, P. Trepte, D. Price (r1994) Concert
(7/95) (HYPE) ① CDA66768

ANCHIETA, Juan de (1462–1523) Spain

SECTION IV: VOCAL AND CHORAL

Con amores, la mi madre—song
C. Bott, New London Consort, P. Pickett Concert
(7/92) (LINN) ① CKD007
T. Berganza, F. Lavilla Concert
(12/92) (DG) ① [2] 435 848-2GX2
Dos ánades—3vv (from the Polacio Song Book)
Hespèrion XX, J. Savall Concert
(7/92) (ASTR) ① E8762

ANCLIFFE, Charles W. (1880–1952) England

SECTION I: ORCHESTRAL

Nights of Gladness—waltz (1912)
Southern Fest Orch, R. White Concert
(5/93) (CHAN) ① CHAN9110

ANDERSEN, Sophus (1859–1923) Denmark

SECTION IV: VOCAL AND CHORAL

Now all chasms are bursting—song (Wds. V. Stuckenberg)
L. Melchior, Anon (pf) (r c1920) Concert
(8/88) (DANA) ① [2] DACOCD311/2
So many bird are flying (Wds.B. S. Ingemann)
L. Melchior, Anon (pf) (r c1920) Concert
(8/88) (DANA) ① [2] DACOCD311/2
Waves of Kongea, what do you tell?—song (Wds. A. Jensen)
L. Melchior, Orch (r c1921) Concert
(8/88) (DANA) ① [2] DACOCD311/2

ANDERSON, Barry (1935–1989) New Zealand

SECTION II: CHAMBER

Arc—bass cl, string qt, computer tapes & electronics (1987)
H. Sparnaay, Mistry Qt, I. Dearden, J. Alvarez, S. Montague Concert (11/91) (CNTI) ① CCD1009
Domingus—spoken text and electronic tape (1978)
J.F. Robbins Concert (11/91) (CNTI) ① CCD1009
Piano Pieces 1, 2 & 3 (1969-74)
1. Piano and tape; 2. Amplified piano; 3. Piano and electronics.
1, 2, 3. S. Mays, S. Montague, S. Montague Concert
(11/91) (CNTI) ① CCD1009

Sound the Tucket Sonance ... and the Note to Mount—trombone and 2-channel tape (1980)
B. Slushin, S. Montague *Concert*
(7/90) (CNTI) ① **CCD1008**

SECTION III: INSTRUMENTAL

Electroacoustic Fanfare—computer tape (1983)
H. Sparnaay, Mistry Qt, I. Dearden, J. Alvarez, S. Montague, S. Mays, S. Montague, S. Montague, J.F. Robbins *Concert*
(11/91) (CNTI) ① **CCD1009**

SECTION IV: VOCAL AND CHORAL

Colla voce—soprano (1978) (Wds. cpsr and Hyland)
J. Manning *Concert*   (7/90) (CNTI) ① **CCD1008**
Mask—flutes, percussion, speaker, electronics and tape (1976 rev 1985) (Wds. Hyland)
K. Lukas, S. Limbrick, M. Allen, I. Dearden, J. Alvarez, P. Harlowe, S. Montague *Concert*
(7/90) (CNTI) ① **CCD1008**
Songs Penyeach—sop, amplified vn, bass cl and perc (1971) (Wds. J. Joyce)
1. Simples; 2. On the beach at Fontana.
J. Manning, G. Grey, M. Khouri, I. Dearden *Concert*
(7/90) (CNTI) ① **CCD1008**

ANDERSON, Laurie (20th Cent) USA

SECTION IV: VOCAL AND CHORAL

Cunningham Stories—1v (Wds John Cage)
EXCERPTS: 1. At the Age of Twelve... 2. Merce Cunningham Phoned His Mother; 3. Every Morning... 4. The Cunningham Company...
1-4. K. Nordine (r1993) *Concert*
(8/94) (KOCH) ① [2] **37238-2**

ANDERSON, Stefan (b 1958) Canada

SECTION IV: VOCAL AND CHORAL

A Hymn to St Cecilia (1989) (Wds. cpsr)
Wellington College Chs, T. Byram-Wigfield, S. Anderson *Concert* (10/92) (HERA) ① **HAVPCD153**

ANDREAS DE FLORENTIA (d c1415) Italy

SECTION IV: VOCAL AND CHORAL

Astio non morì mai—ballata (3vv)
Gothic Voices, C. Page *Concert*
(12/88) (HYPE) ① **CDA66286**
Per la ver'onestà—ballata (2vv)
Gothic Voices, C. Page *Concert*
(12/88) (HYPE) ① **CDA66286**

ANDREWS, Herbert (Kennedy) (1904–1965) Ireland/England

SECTION IV: VOCAL AND CHORAL

Ah see the fair chivalry—unaccompanied choir
Worcester Cath Ch, Don Hunt *Concert*
(9/90) (CARL) ① **PCD937**

ANDRIESSEN, Hendrik (1892–1981) The Netherlands

SECTION III: INSTRUMENTAL

Sonata da chiesa—organ (1927)
P. Kee *Concert* (10/93) (CHAN) ① **CHAN9188**
Theme and Variations—organ (1949)
A. Fletcher *Concert* (11/91) (MIRA) ① **MRCD903**

ANDRIESSEN, Jurriaan (b 1925) Netherlands

SECTION I: ORCHESTRAL

Concerto for Bassoon and Wind Ensemble (1963)
R. Thompson, ECO Wind Ens, G. Simon (r1981) *Concert* (10/94) (CHAN) ① **CHAN9278**

ANDRIESSEN, Louis (b 1939) The Netherlands

SECTION IV: VOCAL AND CHORAL

De Stijl—4vv and ensembles (1984-85)
G. Thoma, Schoenberg Ens, Asko Ens, R. de Leeuw (r1994) *M is for Man.*
(2/95) (NONE) ① **7559-79342-2**
De Tijd—choir and large ensemble (1980-81) (Wds. E. Schönberger)
Netherlands Chbr Ch, Schoenberg Ens, Hague Perc Ens, R. de Leeuw (r1990)
(3/94) (NONE) ① **7559-79291-2**
M is for Man, Music, Mozart—1v, wind, brass, piano and double-bass (1991)
A. Seriese, Volharding Orch, J. Hempel (r1993) *De Stijl.*
(2/95) (NONE) ① **7559-79342-2**

ANDRIEU, F. (fl late 14th Cent) France

SECTION IV: VOCAL AND CHORAL

Armes, amours/O flour des flours—double ballade: 4vv (1377) (Wds. E. Deschamps)
Organum Ens, M. Pérés *Concert*
(11/87) (HARM) ① **HMC90 1252**

ANERIO, Giovanni Francesco (c1567–1630) Italy

SECTION IV: VOCAL AND CHORAL

Dialogo pastorale al presepio di nostro signore—3vv (pub 1600)
1. Nell'apparir del sempiterno sole.
1. Gabrieli Consort, Gabrieli Players, P. McCreesh, T. Roberts (r1992-3) *Concert*
(1/94) (ARCH) ① **437 833-2AH**
Venite ad me omnes—motet
Westminster Abbey Ch, S. Preston *Concert*
(5/86) (ARCH) ① **415 517-2AH**

ANGLEBERT, Jean-Henri (1635–1691) France

SECTION III: INSTRUMENTAL

Pièces de Clavecin—keyboard (1689) (pub. with Pièces d'orgue)
1. Suite in G; 2. Suite in G minor; 3. Suite in D minor; 4. Suite in D; 5. Prélude; 6. Allemande du Vieux Gautier 'La Vestemponade'; 7. Courante de Vieux Gautier I 'La Superbe'; 8. Courante du Vieux Gautier II; 9. Courante du Vieux Gautier III; 10. Sarabande Mézangeot; 11. Chaconne du Vieux Gautier; 12. Gigue du Vieux Gautier; 13. Tombeau de Mr. de Chambonnières.
1-3. B. Tramier (9/95) (PIER) ① **PV795012**
2. J. Henry *Concert* (10/92) (VICT) ① **VCD19013**
2, 13. S. Yates (r1993) *Concert*
(11/93) (CHAN) ① **CHAN0545**
13. S. Sempé *Chambonnières: Harpsichord Suites.*
(4/93) (DHM) ① **05472 77210-2**
Pièces d'orgue (1689) (pub. with 'Pièces de Clavecin'—1689)
1. Quatuor pour le Kyrie; 2. Fugue grave I; 3. Fugue II; 4. Fugue III; 5. Fugue IV; 6. Fugue V.
1, 2. J. Payne (r1994) *Concert*
(10/95) (NAXO) ① **8 553215**
Quatuor—organ
A. Isoir *Concert* (6/90) (CALL) ① **CAL9907**

ANHALT, István (b 1919) Canada

SECTION III: INSTRUMENTAL

Fantasia—piano (1954)
G. Gould *Concert* (3/93) (SONY) ① **SMK52677**

ANKA, Paul (b 1941) Canada/USA

SECTION V: STAGE WORKS

The Longest Day—March—main theme from the film (1962) (other incidental music composed by Jarre)
Prague City PO, P. Bateman (1994; arr Townend) *Concert* (11/94) (SILV) ① **FILMCD151**
Prague City PO, P. Bateman (1994; arr Townend) *Concert* (11/94) (SILV) ① **FILMCD153**

ANNIBALE, Vincenzo d' (19th/20th cent) Italy

SECTION IV: VOCAL AND CHORAL

'O paese d' 'o sole—song (1925) (Wds. Bovio)
L. Pavarotti, Teatro Communale Orch, A. Guadagno *Concert* (8/83) (DECC) ① **410 015-2DH**
J. Carreras, P. Domingo, L. Pavarotti, MMF Orch, Rome Op Orch, Z. Mehta (pp1990) *Concert*
(10/90) (DECC) ① **430 433-2DH**

ANONYMOUS Including religious chants

For Christmas carols see separate index

SECTION I: ORCHESTRAL

Adagio and Allegro—8 timpani, 5 cellos and double-bass (18th-19th Cent)
N. Bardach, Berlin RSO, V. Handley *Concert*
(10/88) (SCHW) ① **311052**
Concerto Grosso for Two Oboes and Strings in F
Thames CO, M. Dobson *Concert*
(6/87) (CRD) ① **CRD3331**
Etenraku—Japanese ceremonial prelude
Philadelphia, L. Stokowski (r1934: arr Konoye) *Concert* (10/93) (STOK) ① **LSCD20**
Marsch der Finnländischen Reiterei (also known as 'Swedish Cavalry March')
Berlin Phil Wind Qnt, H. von Karajan (r1973: arr Voigt) *Concert* (5/94) (DG) ① **439 346-2GX2**
Petersburg March (c1817) (Prussian Army March 113)
Berlin Phil Wind Qnt, H. von Karajan (r1973) *Concert*
(5/94) (DG) ① **439 346-2GX2**

SECTION II: CHAMBER

5 Airs for Chalumeaux or Clarinets (pub 1712-15)
K. Puddy, G. Brodie (r1992) *Concert*
(10/93) (CLRI) ① **CC0004**
Alborada
R. Canter, J. Wood *Concert*
(4/87) (AMON) ① **CD-SAR22**
Allemende and Galliard—viol consort (source: Lumley Books 76 & 104)
Fretwork (r1990) *Concert*
(7/94) (VIRG) ① **VC5 45007-2**
Barafostus' Dreame—division (17th cent)
New London Consort, P. Pickett (r1992) *Concert*
(4/94) (LINN) ① **CKD011**
Canción a dos tiples (c1700—Spain)
Al Ayre Español, E. L. Banzo (r1994) *Concert*
(8/95) (DHM) ① **05472 77325-2**
Danca Amorosa—consort (14th Cent—Italy)
Dufay Collective *Concert*
(10/92) (CNTI) ① **CCD1042**
Danse d'Abroz—vielle and lute (15th Cent)
PAN Ens *Concert* (4/93) (NALB) ① **NA038CD**
2 Danses royales (14th Cent—France) (Manuscrit du Roi)
1. Dufay Collective *Concert*
(10/92) (CNTI) ① **CCD1042**
2. Sinfonye, S. Wishart *Concert*
(6/88) (HYPE) ① **CDA66283**
A Division for a trible viol to play with a virginall (17th cent) (British Library MS)
Sonnerie Trio, S. Stubbs (r1992) *Concert*
(5/94) (TELD) ① **4509-90841-2**
Du cuer je soupire—lai (15th Cent)
G. Binchois Ens, D. Vellard *Concert*
(3/92) (VIRG) ① **VC7 59043-2**
3 Ductia—two-part dances (c1240) (Reading Abbey MS)
Dufay Collective *Concert*
(10/92) (CNTI) ① **CCD1042**
Estample—consort (13th Cent—England)
Dufay Collective *Concert*
(10/92) (CNTI) ① **CCD1042**
Estampie (14th Cent) (Robertsbridge Codex)
Dufay Collective *Concert*
(10/92) (CNTI) ① **CCD1042**
8 Estampies royals—dances (14th Cent—France) (Manuscrit du Roi)
1, 2, 3. Dufay Collective *Concert*
(10/92) (CNTI) ① **CCD1042**
3, 4, 6. Sinfonye, S. Wishart *Concert*
(6/88) (HYPE) ① **CDA66283**
Faronells Ground—recorder and continuo (pub 1704)
D. Munrow, O. Brookes, C. Hogwood (r1973) *Concert*
(10/95) (DECC) ① **440 079-2DM**

Galliard—lute (16th Cent)
C. Wilson *Concert*　(11/91) (VIRG) ① **VC7 59034-2**
Galliarda—lute (16th Cent)
L. Kirchhof *Concert*　(11/92) (SONY) ① **SK48068**
Greensleeves
Circa 1500, N. Hadden (r1991) *Concert*
　　　　(8/93) (CRD) ① **CRD3487**
Ground—lute (16th Cent)
C. Wilson *Concert*　(11/91) (VIRG) ① **VC7 59034-2**
**Guillims Dumpe—lyra-viol (17th
Cent—England)**
C. Thielmann *Concert*
　　　　(11/89) (VIRG) ① **VC7 59534-2**
**3 Harpsichord Suites (17th
Century—Germany)** (Possibly by Christian
Flor?)
EXCERPTS: 1. Suite in C; 2. Suite in D minor; 3.
Suite in A.
1-3. R. Egarr (r1992) *Concert*
　　　　(7/94) (CHNN) ① **CCS5894**
Le ior—harp (14th Cent) (Faenza codex)
A. Lawrence-King *Concert*
　　　　(6/93) (HYPE) ① **CDA66619**
8 Istanpittas—monophonic dances (c1390)
(from BL Ms 29987)
1. Lamento di Tristano—La Rotta; 2. Bellicha; 3. Tre
fontane; 4. Parlamento; 5. Principio di virtù; 6.
Isabella; 7. Ghaetta; 8. In pro.
1-8. Unicorn Ens (r1994) *Concert*
　　　　(8/95) (NAXO) ① **8 553131**
Italiana—lute (16th Cent)
L. Kirchhof *Concert*　(11/92) (SONY) ① **SK48068**
Kemp's Jig
K. Ragossnig *Concert*
　　　　(2/86) (ARCH) ① **415 294-2AH**
J. Bream, J. Bream Consort (r1962) *Concert*
　　　　(8/93) (RCA) ① [28] **09026 61583-2(2)**
J. Bream Consort (r1962; arr consort) *Concert*
　　　　(9/94) (RCA) ① **09026 61589-2**
King's Morisco—keyboard
R. Aldwinckle *Concert*　(3/88) (CARL) ① **PCD873**
**Le gay playsir—chanson intabulation (14th-
15th Cent)**
C. Page *Concert*　(11/87) (HYPE) ① **CDA66238**
**Le grant playser—chanson intabulation
(14th-15th Cent)**
A. Lawrence-King *Concert*
　　　　(11/87) (HYPE) ① **CDA66238**
Le ior—harp (14th cent)
Gothic Voices, C. Page (lte/dir) *Concert*
　　　　(9/92) (HYPE) ① **CDA66588**
**Ligadoras de 3 tono para la
Elevacion—organ (17th Cent)**
M.G. Filippi, M. Henking (r1986) *Concert*
　　　　(10/89) (ARIO) ① **ARN68047**
Magnificat secundi toni—organ (1617)
J. Payne (r1994) *Concert*
　　　　(10/95) (NAXO) ① **8 553215**
Mascherade
K. Ragossnig *Concert*
　　　　(2/86) (ARCH) ① **415 294-2AH**
My Lady Carey's Dompe (16th Cent)
S. Yates (r1994) *Concert*
　　　　(12/95) (CHAN) ① **CHAN0574**
**My Lady Wynkfylds Rownde—keyboard
(16th Cent—England)**
T. Pinnock *Concert*　(11/90) (CRD) ① **CRD3307**
**My Lord of Deliem's Lamentation—lute (16th
Cent)**
C. Wilson *Concert*　(11/91) (VIRG) ① **VC7 59034-2**
Natu-Wa Kinu (Japan)
E. Kissin (arr Saegusa; pp1987) *Concert*
　　　　(11/90) (SONY) ① **SK45931**
**Niederländisch Liedgen, 'Windecken daer
het bosch af drilt'—organ
(c1610—Netherlands)**
G. Leonhardt *Concert*　(11/95) (SONY) ① **SK53371**
**Obra de sexto tom para o Levantar o
Deus—organ piece for the Elevation during
Mass (17th oent)**
S. Farr (r1994) *Concert*
　　　　(11/94) (HYPE) ① **CDA66725**
Passamezzo moderno—lute (16th Cent)
L. Kirchhof *Concert*　(11/92) (SONY) ① **SK48068**
2 Pavanas—vihuela (16th Cent—Spain)
K. Marshall (arr Marshall) *Concert*
　　　　(7/92) (AUVI) ① **V4645**
**Petrus Fabricus Lutebook (16th
Cent—Denmark)**
1. Graff van Mannsfeldts dans; 2. Polnisch Tantz I; 3.
Polnisch Tantz II; 4. Ciel turchino Gagliardo; 5.
Passamezzo—Saltarello.
1-5. J. Lindberg *Concert*　(2/89) (BIS) ① **BIS-CD390**

Praeambulum—organ (c1717) (previously
attrib Frescobaldi)
T. Roberts (r1990; ed Roberts) *Concert*
　　　　(4/93) (ARCH) ① [2] **437 552-2AH2**
Preambulum super re—keyboard (15th Cent)
(from the Buxheim keyboard manuscript)
G. Binchois Ens, D. Vellard *Concert*
　　　　(3/92) (VIRG) ① **VC7 59043-2**
Prelude—lute (17th Cent)
C. Wilson *Concert*　(11/91) (VIRG) ① **VC7 59034-2**
Romance, 'Jeux interdits' (Spain) (named
after film in which it was used)
A. Romero (arr. A.Romero) *Concert*
　　　　(4/90) (TELA) ① **CD80213**
Romanesca—lute (16th Cent)
C. Wilson *Concert*　(11/91) (VIRG) ① **VC7 59034-2**
4 Saltarelli—monophonic dances (c1390)
(from BL Ms 29987)
1. No. 1; 2. No. 2; 3. No. 3; 4. Chominciamento di
gioia.
1-4. Unicorn Ens (r1994) *Concert*
　　　　(8/95) (NAXO) ① **8 553131**
Salterello
Ulsamer Collegium, J. Ulsamer *Concert*
　　　　(2/86) (ARCH) ① **415 294-2AH**
Sarabande—lute (pub 1690) (Milleran MS)
L. Kirchhof *Concert*　(11/92) (SONY) ① **SK48068**
**Theme, Variations and Rondo
pastorale—harp** (erroneously attrib Mozart)
M. Robles *Concert*
　　　　(12/90) (DECC) ① **425 723-2DM**
Tiento Lleno 2 tono—organ (17th Cent)
M.G. Filippi, M. Henking (r1986) *Concert*
　　　　(10/89) (ARIO) ① **ARN68047**
Todai-Mori (Japan)
E. Kissin (arr Saegusa; pp1987) *Concert*
　　　　(11/90) (SONY) ① **SK45931**
Trotto—monophonic dance (c1390) (from BL
Ms 29987)
Ulsamer Collegium, J. Ulsamer *Concert*
　　　　(2/86) (ARCH) ① **415 294-2AH**
Unicorn Ens (r1994) *Concert*
　　　　(8/95) (NAXO) ① **8 553131**
Usagi (Japan)
E. Kissin (arr Saegusa; pp1987) *Concert*
　　　　(11/90) (SONY) ① **SK45931**
**Variations on 'Daphne'—organ
(c1650—Netherlands)**
G. Leonhardt *Concert*　(10/94) (SONY) ① **SK53371**
2 Verses—keyboard '(717th cent—England)
G. Leonhardt *Concert*
　　　　(11/95) (SONY) ① **SK53981**
**Voluntary for double organ in D minor (17th
Cent—England)**
R. Woolley (r1993) *Concert*
　　　　(9/94) (CHAN) ① **CHAN0553**
Voluntary for the Trumpet Stop—organ
R. Woolley (r1993) *Concert*
　　　　(9/94) (CHAN) ① **CHAN0553**
Voluntary in A minor—organ (18th Cent)
T. Koopman *Concert*　(5/91) (CAPR) ① **10 254**
**Walsingham—lyra-viol (16th
Cent—England)**
C. Thielmann *Concert*
　　　　(2/88) (HARM) ① **HMC90 5192**
Watkin's Ale
I. Watson (arr Walton) *Concert*
　　　　(4/91) (CHAN) ① **CHAN8892**
N. O'Neill *Concert*　(11/92) (CNTO) ① **CRCD2366**
The Welsh Allemaine—lute
L. Kenny *Concert*　(11/92) (CNTO) ① **CRCD2366**
**When Daphne from fair Phoebus did
fly—harp (16th Cent—England)** (arr from
ballad)
A. Lawrence-King *Concert*
　　　　(1/90) (HYPE) ① **CDA66307**

SECTION IV: VOCAL AND CHORAL

**A biente y siete de Março—song (16th
cent—Spain)**
Hespèrion XX, J. Savall (r1991-92) *Concert*
　　　　(6/93) (ASTR) ① **E8764**
A las maytines erá—cancion: 1v
C. Bott, New London Consort, P. Pickett *Concert*
　　　　(7/92) (LINN) ① **CKD007**
**A los baños de amor—song (15th
Cent—Spain)** (from the Palacio Song Book)
Hespèrion XX, J. Savall *Concert*
　　　　(7/92) (ASTR) ① **E8762**
**A vous douce debonnaire—isorhythmic
poem (13th Cent)**
Gothic Voices, C. Page *Concert*
　　　　(12/90) (HYPE) ① **CDA66423**

**Ad nutum Domini—3rd respond to the BVM
(13th cent)** (Wds. Fulbert de Chartres)
Venance Fortunat Ens, A-M. Deschamps (r1989)
Concert　(12/95) (L'EM) ① **ED13036**
**Adieu ma tres belle maistresse—rondeau
(15th Cent)** (possibly by Binchois)
G. Binchois Ens, D. Vellard *Concert*
　　　　(3/92) (VIRG) ① **VC7 59043-2**
**Adieu vous di, tres doulce
compaynie—ballade: 3vv (14th
Cent—France)** (Chantilly Codex)
Organum Ens, M. Pérès (r1987) *Concert*
　　　　(11/87) (HARM) ① **HMC90 1252**
Advent Antiphons
1. O Sapienta; 2. O Adonai; 3. O Radix Jesse; 4. O
Clavis David; 5. O Oriens; 6. O Rex Gentium; 7. O
Emmanuel; 8. O Virgo Virginum.
King's College Sngrs, E.H. Warrell *Concert*
　　　　(12/91) (REGE) ① **REGCD106**
**Agincourt Hymn—carol (14th-15th
cent—England)** (attrib Dunstable)
Gothic Voices, C. Page *Concert*
　　　　(11/87) (HYPE) ① **CDA66238**
Agnus Dei—Factus homo
Hilliard Ens (r1984) *Concert*
　　　　(3/87) (HARM) ① **HMC90 1154**
Ah, my dear son—song (15th Cent) (Fayrfax
MS)
The Sixteen, H. Christophers (r1993) *Concert*
　　　　(2/94) (COLL) ① **Coll1395-2**
Ah, silly poor Joas—Elizabethan song
M. Chance, Fretwork (r1990) *Concert*
　　　　(7/94) (VIRG) ① **VC5 45007-2**
A. Deller, SCB, A. Wenzinger (r1956: arr P Warlock)
Concert　(4/95) (VANG) ① **08.5068.71**
Ak Egartho
E. Lamandier *Concert*　(11/86) (ALIE) ① **AL1012**
Al alva venid—song (15th Cent—Spain) (from
the Palacio Song Book)
Hespèrion XX, J. Savall *Concert*
　　　　(7/92) (ASTR) ① **E8762**
C. Bott, New London Consort, P. Pickett *Concert*
　　　　(7/92) (LINN) ① **CKD007**
All creatures of our God and King—hymn
(wds St.Francis of Assisi, trans Draper)
E. Schwarzkopf, Ambrosian Sngrs, D. Vaughan,
Philh, C. Mackerras (Ger: arr Mackerras) *Concert*
　　　　(12/90) (EMI) ① **CDM7 63574-2**
All my hope on God is founded—hymn (tune
'Michael')
Truro Cath Ch, D. Briggs, H. Doughty *Concert*
　　　　(7/91) (PRIO) ① **PRCD322**
**Alle, psallite cum luya—motet: 3vv (13th
Cent—France)** (Montpelier Codex)
London Early Music Consort, D. Munrow *Concert*
　　　　(8/85) (ARCH) ① **415 292-2AH**
Westminster Abbey Ch, M. Neary, M. Baker (r1994)
Concert　(12/95) (SONY) ① **SK66614**
Alleluia: A newe work
Hilliard Ens *Concert*
　　　　(5/87) (HARM) ① **HMA190 1106**
**Alleluia dies sanctificatus—Christmas
monody (11th cent)** (Wds. Fulbert de
Chartres)
Venance Fortunat Ens, A-M. Deschamps (r1989)
Concert　(12/95) (L'EM) ① **ED13036**
Alleluia: Hic est vere martir
Hilliard Ens *Concert*
　　　　(5/87) (HARM) ① **HMA190 1106**
**Altissonis aptatis/Hin
principes—isorhythmic motet: 4vv (c1350)**
(in praise of Gaston Febus)
Huelgas Ens, P. van Nevel *Concert*
　　　　(2/93) (SONY) ① **SK48195**
L' Amanza mia—song
S. Carrington, Tragicomedia *Concert*
　　　　(9/92) (EMI) ① **CDC7 54191-2**
**Amo amas, I love a lass—partsong (19th
Cent)**
Magdalen (Oxford) Coll Ch, G. Ives *Concert*
　　　　(11/92) (CNTO) ① **CRCD2366**
Amor amaro—ballata (15th Cent)
S. Danco, E. Bellinzona (r1947) *Concert*
　　　　(4/92) (EMI) ① [7] **CHS7 69741-2(3)**
**Amor mi fa cantar a la Francesca—ballata:
3vv (13th Cent—Italy)**
Gothic Voices, C. Page *Concert*
　　　　(12/88) (HYPE) ① **CDA66286**
**Amor potest/Ad amorem—motet: 3vv (13th
Cent—France)** (Montpelier Codex)
London Early Music Consort, D. Munrow *Concert*
　　　　(8/85) (ARCH) ① **415 292-2AH**
**Amors m'art con fuoc am flamma—dansa:
1v and bagpipes**
Gothic Voices, C. Page (r1994) *Concert*
　　　　(8/95) (HYPE) ① **CDA66773**

Angelus ad Virginem (16th cent)
Westminster Abbey Ch, M. Neary, M. Baker (r1994)
Concert   (12/95) (SONY) ① **SK66614**

**Anglia, planctus itera—conductus: 1v
(1186)**
Gothic Voices, C. Page Concert
        (10/89) (HYPE) ① **CDA66336**

Annus novus in gaudio—versus (12th Cent)
(Aquitanian Polyphony)
Augsburg Early Music Ens Concert
        (3/93) (CHRI) ① **CHR74584**

**Antiphons and Responses for Saints' Days
(11th cent)** (Wds. Fulbert de Chartres; MS
Bréviaire Chartrain)
1. O martyr Domini Christi; 2. Iam super astra poli
   residens; 3. Vir Dei Leobinus; 4. Cumque gleba
   conderetur.
Venance Fortunat Ens, A-M. Deschamps (r1989)
Concert   (12/95) (L'EM) ① **ED13036**

**Antiphons for the Feast day of Our Lady of
Mount Carmel—plainchant**
Taverner Ch, A. Parrott Concert
        (6/89) (EMI) ① [2] **CDS7 49749-2**

**Aquella voz de Christo—song (16th
cent—Spain)**
Hespèrion XX, J. Savall (r1991-92) Concert
        (6/93) (ASTR) ① **E8764**

**Archangeli Michaelis
interventione—respond** (plainchant)
The Sixteen, H. Christophers Concert
        (3/91) (HYPE) ① **CDA66325**

**As I went to Walsingham—song: 1v (16th
Cent—England)**
E. Van Evera Concert
        (2/88) (HARM) ① **HMC90 5192**

Assumpta est Maria in caelum—plainsong
(Gregorian Chant)
Tallis Scholars, P. Phillips Concert
        (9/90) (GIME) ① **CDGIM020**
Tallis Scholars, P. Phillips Concert
        (1/94) (GIME) ① [4] **CDGIMB400**

Au renouvel—song (13th Cent—France)
C. A. Fulton, S. Kammen, J. Lepkoff (r1993; arr
Fulton as print piece) Concert
        (11/94) (ERAT) ① **4509-94830-2**

**Aurea personet lyra—monody in tone 1 (11th
cent)** (Wds. Fulbert de Chartres)
Venance Fortunat Ens, A-M. Deschamps (r1989)
Concert   (12/95) (L'EM) ① **ED13036**

**Avant hier en un vert pre—chanson de toile
(13th cent)**
Sinfonye, S. Wishart (r1992) Concert
        (8/93) (HYPE) ① **CDA66625**

Ave fuit prima salus—lauda (15th Cent)
(Bologna University MS. Wds. Giustiniani)
Daedalus Ens (r1992) Concert
        (11/93) (ACCE) ① **ACC9289D**

Ave Maria—3vv (12th-13th Cent—England)
Gothic Voices, C. Page (r1994) Concert
        (2/95) (HYPE) ① **CDA66739**

**Ave Maria gracia plena—conductus (14th
Cent)** (English)
Anon 4 (r1994) Concert
        (9/95) (HARM) ① **HMU90 7125**

**Ave Maria salus hominum—conductus (14th
Cent)** (English)
Anon 4 (r1994) Concert
        (9/95) (HARM) ① **HMU90 7125**

**Ave Maris Stella—Acardian melody (17th
Cent)**
Wellington College Chs, T. Byram-Wigfield, S.
Anderson (arr J. Churchill) Concert
        (10/92) (HERA) ① **HAVPCD153**
J. Payne (r1994; arr org) Concert
        (10/95) (NAXO) ① **8 553215**

**Ave, mundi rosa—Pentecost sequence: 3vv
(14th Cent)** (rediscovered 1958)
Schola Gregoriana, M. Berry (r1992) Concert
        (11/93) (HERA) ① **HAVPCD161**

**Ave parens/Ad gratie—isorhythmic motet
(13th Cent)**
Gothic Voices, C. Page Concert
        (12/90) (HYPE) ① **CDA66423**

Ave, preciosa gemma—lauda (15th Cent)
(Bologna University MS)
Daedalus Ens (r1992) Concert
        (11/93) (ACCE) ① **ACC9289D**

**Ave regina celorum—antiphon (medieval
English)**
Anon 4 (r1994) Concert
        (9/95) (HARM) ① **HMU90 7125**

**Ave, virgo, gratia, plena—motet: 4vv (15th-
16th cent)**
Gothic Voices, C. Page (r1993) Concert
        (2/94) (HYPE) ① **CDA66653**

**Avrai je ja de ma dame confort?—3vv (14th
Cent)**
Gothic Voices, C. Page (Ite/dir) Concert
        (9/92) (HYPE) ① **CDA66588**

**Ay Jesús qué mal fraile!—song (16th
cent—Spain)**
Hespèrion XX, J. Savall (r1991-92) Concert
        (6/93) (ASTR) ① **E8764**

Ay las! quant je pans—3vv (14th Cent)
Gothic Voices, C. Page, A. Lawrence-King Concert
        (6/93) (HYPE) ① **CDA66619**

Ay, que non ay!—song (15th Cent—Spain)
(from the Palacio Song Book)
Hespèrion XX, J. Savall Concert
        (7/92) (ASTR) ① **E8762**

La Badessa—ballata (14th cent) (Wds. S.
Prudenzani)
Newberry Consort, M. Springfels (r1990) Concert
        (7/93) (HARM) ① **HMU90 7038**

Beata nobis gaudia (12th-13th Cent)
Gothic Voices, C. Page (r1994) Concert
        (2/95) (HYPE) ① **CDA66739**

Before the ending of the day—hymn
Truro Cath Ch, D. Briggs, H. Doughty Concert
        (7/91) (PRIO) ① **PRCD322**

Bel fiore danza (13th Cent) (Codex Faenza)
Newberry Consort, M. Springfels (r1990) Concert
        (7/93) (HARM) ① **HMU90 7038**

**Bele Doette as fenestres se siet—chanson
de toile (12th Cent)**
Sinfonye, S. Wishart (r1992) Concert
        (8/93) (HYPE) ① **CDA66625**

Belle Doette—song (13th Cent—France)
A. Azéma, J. Lepkoff (r1993) Concert
        (11/94) (ERAT) ① **4509-94830-2**

Ben venga maggio
London Pro Musica, B. Thomas Concert
        (2/87) (CARL) ① **PCD825**

**Benedicamus Domino—monody on tone 2
(11th cent)** (Wds. Fulbert de Chartres)
Venance Fortunat Ens, A-M. Deschamps (r1989)
Concert   (12/95) (L'EM) ① **ED13036**

**Benedicamus Domino—motet on the tenor
Stirps Jesse (early 12th cent)** (Wds. Fulbert
de Chartres)
Venance Fortunat Ens, A-M. Deschamps (r1989)
Concert   (12/95) (L'EM) ① **ED13036**

Benedicta es—plainchant sequence
Tallis Scholars, P. Phillips Concert
        (7/90) (GIME) ① **CDGIM001**
Tallis Scholars, P. Phillips (r1981) Concert
        (1/94) (GIME) ① [4] **CDGIMB400**

**Bona domna, un conseil vos
deman—trobairitz song (13th cent)**
Sinfonye, S. Wishart (r1992) Concert
        (8/93) (HYPE) ① **CDA66625**

**Buelve tus claros ojos—song (16th
cent—Spain)**
Hespèrion XX, J. Savall (r1991-92) Concert
        (6/93) (ASTR) ① **E8764**

**Buenas nuevas de alegría—song (15th
cent—Spain)** (from the Colombina Song
Book)
Hespèrion XX, J. Savall Concert
        (7/92) (ASTR) ① **E8763**

**Calabaça, no sé, buen amor—villancico: 3vv
(15-16th cent)** (from 'Cancionero de Palacio')
C. Bott, New London Consort, P. Pickett Concert
        (7/92) (LINN) ① **CKD007**

**Cantigas de Santa Maria de Alfonso X el
Sabio (1252-84)**
1. Tanto son da groriosa; 2. A Madre de Jhesu-
   Cristo; 3. Mui grandes noit'e dia; 4. A que faz os
   peccadores; 5. Com' a grande enfermidade; 6. Ben
   pode Santa Maria; 7. Nenbre sse te, madre; 8. Das
   oge mais; 9. Mirages fremosos.
Alla Francesca (r c1994) Concert
        (12/95) (O111) ① **OPS30-131**

**Canto de profumieri—canti carnascialeschi
(15th cent)** (Wds. L. de' Medici)
London Pro Musica, B. Thomas Concert
        (2/87) (CARL) ① **PCD825**

Canto di capi tondi
London Pro Musica, B. Thomas Concert
        (2/87) (CARL) ① **PCD825**

Canto di lanzi suonatori di rubechine
London Pro Musica, B. Thomas Concert
        (2/87) (CARL) ① **PCD825**

Carmina Burana—songs (c12th/13th Cents)
(CB numbers after Hilka/Schumann/Bischoff:
Carmina)
1. Ecce torpet probitas CB 3; 2. Licet eger CB 8; 3.
   Ave nobilis, venerabilis CB 11 (Burana Fragments);
   4. Procurans odium CB 12; 5. O variam Fortune
   lubricum CB 14; 6. Plantus ante nescia CB 14
   (Burana Fragments); 7. Celum non animum CB 15; 8.

Michi confer venditor CB 16 (Burana Fragments); 9.
Fas et nefas CB 19; 10. Veritas veritatum CB 21; 11.
Homo, quo vigeas vide CB 22; 12. Ad cor tuum
revertere CB 26; 13. Bonum est confidere CB 27; 14.
Vite perdite CB 31; 15. Non te lusisse pudeat CB 33;
16. Deduc, Sion CB 34; 17. Nulli beneficium CB 36;
18. In Gedeonis area CB 37; 19. Crucifigat omnes
CB 47; 20. Curritur ad vocem CB 47a; 21. Nomen a
solemnibus CB 52; 22. Olim sudor Herculis CB 63;
23. A globo veteri CB 67; 24. Axe Phebus aureo CB
71; 25. Clauso Cronos CB 85; 26. Veris dulcis in
tempore CB 85; 27. Iove cum Mercurio CB 88a; 28.
Exiit dilucolo CB 90; 29. Vacillantis trutine CB 108;
30. Sic mea fata CB 116; 31. Dulce solum CB 119;
32. Dic Christi veritas CB 131; 33. Bulla fulminante
CB 131a; 34. Ecce gratum CB 143; 35. Virent prata
hiemata CB 151; 36. Tempus transit gelidum CB 153;
37. Hebet sidus CB 169; 38. Tempus est iocundum
CB 179; 39. O curus hominum CB 187; 40. Aristippe,
quamvis sero CB 189; 41. Hiemali tempore CB 203;
42. Alte clmat Epicurus CB 211. 43. Presens dies
CB21; 44. Flete, fideles anime CB4; 45. Bache, bene
venies CB200; 46. Pange lingua CB20; 47. Flete
Flenda, CB5; 48. Clauso Chronos, CB73; 49. Ich was
ein chint so wolgetan, CB185; 50. In Taberna,
CB196.
Organum Ens, M. Pérès
        (9/91) (HARM) ① **HMC90 1323/4**
1, 4, 6, 8, 11, 18, 21, 22, 24, 28, 31, 38, 41, 42, New
London Consort, P. Pickett
        (7/89) (L'OI) ① **417 373-2OH**
2, 7, 9, 12-17, 19, 23, 25, 27, 29, 36, 37, 39, 40, 43-
46. New London Consort, P. Pickett
        (3/90) (L'OI) ① [2] **425 117-2OH2**

Carro della morte
London Pro Musica, B. Thomas Concert
        (2/87) (CARL) ① **PCD825**

Carza chica
E. Lamandier Concert   (11/86) (ALIE) ① **AL1012**

Catalina, Catalina!
King's Sngrs Concert
        (9/92) (EMI) ① **CDC7 54191-2**

**Certes mout fu/Nous devons tresfort
amer—4-part isorhythmic motet, Folio 76
verso-77 recto (14-15th cent)** (Cypriot MS
Turin, Biblioteca Nazionale, J II 9)
Huelgas Ens, P. van Nevel (r1993) Concert
        (11/94) (SONY) ① **SK53976**

**C'est desoz l'olive en mi les prez—carole
(13th cent)**
Sinfonye, S. Wishart (r1992) Concert
        (8/93) (HYPE) ① **CDA66625**

**C'est la gieus en mi les prez—carole (13th
cent)**
Sinfonye, S. Wishart (r1992) Concert
        (8/93) (HYPE) ① **CDA66625**

Chi passa per 'sta strada
King's Sngrs, Tragicomedia Concert
        (9/92) (EMI) ① **CDC7 54191-2**

Chorus nove—Easter hymn: 1v (11th cent)
(Wds. Fulbert de Chartres)
Venance Fortunat Ens, A-M. Deschamps (r1989)
Concert   (12/95) (L'EM) ① **ED13036**

Civitatis nusquam conditur
Hilliard Ens Concert
        (5/87) (HARM) ① **HMA190 1106**

**Clangat tuba, martyr Thoma—carol: 3vv
(15th Cent)** (Wds. Latin and Eng)
Schola Gregoriana, M. Berry (r1992) Concert
        (11/93) (HERA) ① **HAVPCD161**

**Clap, clap, par un umile/Sus Robin—13th
century motet (3vv)** (French. Ivrea Codex)
London Early Music Consort, D. Munrow Concert
        (8/85) (ARCH) ① **415 292-2AH**

**Codex Calixtinus (Jacobus)—instrumental
and vocal collection (12th-13th cent)** (MS in
Santiago Cathedral)
1. Annua gaudia (2vv); 2. Congaudent catholici (3vv);
3. Dum pater familias (chor & instr); 4. Nostra
phalanx (2vv); 5. Regi perennis (4vv).
Excs Sequentia   (12/92) (DHM) ① **RD77199**
1-5. New London Consort, P. Pickett Concert
        (7/92) (L'OI) ① [2] **433 148-2OH2**

Codex Las Huelgas—1-4vv (12th-13th Cent)
(170 folios: Las Huelgas de Burgos Monastery
MS)
1. Alpha bovi/Domino (2vv); 2. Audi, pontus; audi,
tellus (cantio, 1v); 3. Ave Maria, gracia plena
(conductus, 2vv); 4. Belial vocatur (3vv); 5.
Benedicamus Domino cum cantico (3vv); 6.
Benedicamus—Hic est enim precursor (2vv); 7.
Benedicamus virgini matri (2vv); 8. Casta
catholica/Da, dulcis domina (conductus, 2vv); 9.
Catholicorum concio (Benedicamus, 2vv). 10. Ex
illustri nata prosapia (motet, 3vv); 11. Fa, fa mi fa mi
re/Ut re mi (solmization, 2vv); 12. In hoc festo

14

Vespers Hymn: Ave maris stella; Marian antiphon: Salve regina (monastic version) Ampleforth Abbey Monastic Ch (r1994-5) *Concert* (9/95) (CFM) ① **CFMCD1783**
Gregorian Chant Mass (performances may vary) Ite missa est Hilliard Ens (Sunday Set XI) *Concert* (5/87) (HARM) ① **HMA190 1106**
Mass for the Creator of the World Montserrat Abbey Ch, O. Cunill, I. Segarra *Concert* (3/87) (FORL) ① **UCD13919**
Mass I: Lux et Origo Burgos Santo Domingo de Silos Monastery Ch (r1956-62) *Concert* (9/95) (JADE) ① **JADC131**
Mass II: Fons Bonitatis Burgos Santo Domingo de Silos Monastery Ch (r1956-62) *Concert* (9/95) (JADE) ① **JADC131**
Mass IX: Cum Jubilo Burgos Santo Domingo de Silos Monastery Ch (r1956-62) *Concert* (9/95) (JADE) ① **JADC131**
Mass IX: Orbis Factor Burgos Santo Domingo de Silos Monastery Ch (r1956-62) *Concert* (9/95) (JADE) ① **JADC131**
Mass VIII: De Angelis Burgos Santo Domingo de Silos Monastery Ch (r1956-62) *Concert* (9/95) (JADE) ① **JADC131**
Gregorian Chant Requiem Mass (performances may vary) In paradisum Ampleforth Abbey Monastic Ch (r1994-5) *Concert* (9/95) (CFM) ① **CFMCD1783**
Requiem aeternam; Ego sum resurrectio et vita; In paradisum Kings College Ch, S. Cleobury (r1994) *Concert* (12/94) (EMI) ① **CDC5 55096-2**
Sequence: Dies irae MCA, K. Ruhland *Concert* (10/89) (RCA) ① **GD71953**
Sequence: Dies irae Wellington College Chs, T. Byram-Wigfield, S. Anderson *Concert* (10/92) (HERA) ① **HAVPCD153**
Gregorian Chants for the Church's Year (various pieces from unidentified liturgical contexts)
Evening reading: Benedictus Deus; Te Deum; Miserere; Suscipe I & II Ampleforth Abbey Monastic Ch (r1994-5) *Concert* (9/95) (CFM) ① **CFMCD1783**
Jubilate Deo; Illumina faciem tuam Oxford Camerata, J. Summerly (r1994) *Concert* (10/95) (NAXO) ① **8 553087**
Gregorian Funeral Chants (not Masses: performances may vary)
Invitatory at Matins: Regem cui; Antiphon at Benedictus (Lauds): Ego sum Ampleforth Abbey Monastic Ch (r1994-5) *Concert* (9/95) (CFM) ① **CFMCD1783**
Marian Antiphon: Salve Regina St Cecilia's Abbey, Ryde, Nuns' Ch (r1992) *Concert* (3/93) (HERA) ① **HAVPCD157**
Office for the Dead Offertory: Domine Iesu St Cecilia's Abbey, Ryde, Nuns' Ch (r1992) *Concert* (3/93) (HERA) ① **HAVPCD157**
Office for the Dead Antiphons: In paradisum; Chorus Angelorum St Cecilia's Abbey, Ryde, Nuns' Ch (r1992) *Concert* (3/93) (HERA) ① **HAVPCD157**
Procession & Vigil for the dead St Wandrille Abbey Ch, En-Calcat Abbey Ch *Concert* (3/92) (STUD) ① [2] **SM1220.02**
Procession for the funerals of Charles II & Henri II A Sei Voci, Lorraine Psallette, Toulouse Sacqueboutiers, J. Chamboux, J. Bernfeld, B. Fabre-Garrus (r1993) *Concert* (3/95) (ASTR) ① **E8521**
Guárdame las vacas—song (16th cent—Spain) Hespèrion XX, J. Savall (r1991-92) *Concert* (6/93) (ASTR) ① **E8764**
Hac in anni ianua—conductus (3vv) (12th Century) Gothic Voices, C. Page *Concert* (10/89) (HYPE) ① **CDA66336**
Harto de tanta porfía—Spanish song (15th cent) (from the Palacio Song Book) Hespèrion XX, J. Savall *Concert* (7/92) (ASTR) ① **E8762**
Gothic Voices, C. Page (r1993) *Concert* (2/94) (HYPE) ① **CDA66653**
Have your seen but a white lily grow?—song: voice and flute (Wds. B. Jonson) R. Golden, L. Rothfuss (arr Warlock) *Concert* (10/92) (KOCH) ① **37118-2**
The Heavenly Courtier (18th-19th Cent—USA) (source 'The Christian Harmony') Boston Camerata, J. Cohen (r1993) *Concert* (12/93) (ERAT) ① **4509-92874-2**
Hija mia E. Lamandier *Concert* (11/86) (ALIE) ① **AL1012**

Holy Week Chants—offices and hymns (Byzantine Chant) M. Keyrouz, Paris St Julien-le-Pauvre Ch (3/90) (HARM) ① **HMC90 1315**
Los Hombres con gran plazer—song (15th cent) T. Berganza, N. Yepes *Concert* (12/92) (DG) ① [2] **848-2GX2**
I couldn't hear nobody pray—spiritual W. White, G. McNaught (arr M. Marshall) *Concert* (6/92) (CHAN) ① **CHAN8960**
Il me convient guerpir—2vv (14th cent) Gothic Voices, C. Page, A. Lawrence-King *Concert* (6/93) (HYPE) ① **CDA66619**
Ilono E. Lamandier *Concert* (11/86) (ALIE) ① **AL1012**
In exitu Israel (15th cent) (from the Colombina Song Book) Hespèrion XX, J. Savall *Concert* (7/92) (ASTR) ① **E8763**
In mari miserie/Gemma pudiccie—13th century motet (3vv) (French. Montpelier Codex) London Early Music Consort, D. Munrow *Concert* (8/85) (ARCH) ① **415 292-2AH**
In occasu sideris—conductus (2vv) (1189) Gothic Voices, C. Page *Concert* (10/89) (HYPE) ① **CDA66336**
In Paradise—Elizabethan song M. Chance, Fretwork (r1990) *Concert* (7/94) (VIRG) ① **VC5 45007-2**
In Rama sonat gemitus—conductus (12th-13th Cent) Gothic Voices, C. Page *Concert* (2/95) (HYPE) ① **CDA66739**
In te concipitur—hymn: 3vv (14th Cent) (English) Anon 4 (r1994) *Concert* (9/95) (HARM) ① **HMU90 7125**
In those days came John the Baptist—baptismal hymn (19th Cent—USA) Boston Camerata, J. Cohen (r1993) *Concert* (12/93) (ERAT) ① **4509-92874-2**
Inter chorus paradiscolarum—motet: 4vv (14th cent—England) Amsterdam Loeki Stardust Qt (r1991; arr recorder consort) *Concert* (4/94) (L'OI) ① **436 155-2OH**
Inter densas deserti meditans/Imbribus irriguis—isorhythmic motet (3vv) (14th Century French) (Chantilly Codex) London Early Music Consort, D. Munrow *Concert* (8/85) (ARCH) ① **415 292-2AH**
Inter densas/Imbribus irriguis—motet (c1385) (in praise of Gaston Febus) Huelgas Ens, P. van Nevel *Concert* (2/93) (SONY) ① **SK48195**
Invincible Lord of Hosts—Russian liturgical chant N. Gedda, Paris Russian Orthodox Cath Ch, E. Evetz *Concert* (1/93) (PHIL) ① **434 174-2PM**
Irish lullaby—song (Wds. P. Graves) V. de los Angeles, Sinfonia of London, R. Frühbeck de Burgos (orch Gamley) *Concert* (10/88) (EMI) ① **CDM7 69502-2**
Isias cecinit—conductus (3vv) (12th Cent) Hilliard Ens, P. Hillier *Concert* (2/90) (ECM) ① **837 751-2**
Já naõ podeis ser contentes—song (16th Cent) (Wds. anon Portuguese) G. Lesne, Circa 1500, N. Hadden *Concert* (9/92) (VIRG) ① **VC7 59071-2**
Je la remire Gothic Voices, I. Barford, C. Page *Concert* (12/86) (HYPE) ① **CDA66144**
Je languis d'amere mort—virelai (14th Cent) Gothic Voices, C. Page *Concert* (3/92) (HYPE) ① **CDA66463**
Je m'en vois/Tels a mout—isorhythmic poem (13th cent) Gothic Voices, C. Page *Concert* (12/90) (HYPE) ① **CDA66423**
Je ne chant pas/Talens m'est pris—isorhythmic poem (13th cent) Gothic Voices, C. Page *Concert* (12/90) (HYPE) ① **CDA66423**
Je ne puis/Par un matin/Le premier jor/IUSTUS—motet: 4vv (12th-13th Cent) Gothic Voices, C. Page (r1994) *Concert* (2/95) (HYPE) ① **CDA66739**
Je prens plaisir en une dame—3-part ballade, Folio 104 verso (14-15th cent) (Cypriot MS Turin, Biblioteca Nazionale J II 9) Huelgas Ens, P. van Nevel (r1993) *Concert* (11/94) (SONY) ① **SK53976**

Je sui trestout d'amour raimpli—3-part virelai, Folio 155 recto (14-15th cent) (Cypriot MS Turin, Biblioteca Nazionale, J II 9) Huelgas Ens, P. van Nevel (r1993) *Concert* (11/94) (SONY) ① **SK53976**
Je vueil vivre au plaisir d'amours—4vv (15th cent) Gothic Voices, C. Page (Ite/dir) *Concert* (9/92) (HYPE) ① **CDA66588**
Jesu Christes milde moder—polyphonic sequence (c1300) Anon 4 (r1994) *Concert* (9/95) (HARM) ① **HMU90 7125**
Jour a jour la vie—4vv (14th cent) Gothic Voices, C. Page, A. Lawrence-King *Concert* (6/93) (HYPE) ① **CDA66619**
Kishmul cradle croon R. A. Morgan (Gaelic) *Concert* (12/87) (ETCE) ① **KTC1049**
Kyrie—Rex virginum Hilliard Ens (r1984) *Concert* (3/87) (HARM) ① **HMC90 1154**
La jus desouz l'olive—carole (13th century) Sinfonye, S. Wishart (r1992) *Concert* (8/93) (HYPE) ① **CDA66655**
Lamentation for Maundy Thursday (1570s) (Santa Cruz, Coimbra MS) A Capella Portvgvesa, O. Rees (r1994) *Concert* (11/94) (HYPE) ① **CDA66735**
Lamento di Tristan Ulsamer Collegium, J. Ulsamer *Concert* (2/86) (ARCH) ① **415 294-2AH**
Lamento di Tristano Dufay Collective *Concert* (10/92) (CNTI) ① **CCD1042**
Lasse, pour quoi refusai—chanson (14th Cent French) (Manuscrit du Roi) M. Kiek, Sinfonye, S. Wishart *Concert* (6/88) (HYPE) ① **CDA66283**
Latex silice—conductus (4vv) (12th Century) Gothic Voices, C. Page *Concert* (10/89) (HYPE) ① **CDA66336**
Laus detur multipharia—virelai (14th-15th Cent) Gothic Voices, C. Page *Concert* (2/95) (HYPE) ① **CDA66739**
Le Puy Manuscript—office for New Year's Day (12th-16th Cent) (plainchant and polyphony) 1. Vespers; 2. Later sections of the feast; 3. Songs. G. Binchois Ens, D. Vellard (5/93) (VIRG) ① **VC7 59238-2**
Lealtat, o lealtat—Spanish song (15th cent) (from the Colombina Song Book) Hespèrion XX, J. Savall *Concert* (7/92) (ASTR) ① **E8763**
La Légende de Marguérite—song (wds. N. Cimbal: music arr from Rossini) C. Bartoli, C. Spencer *Concert* (4/91) (DECC) ① **430 518-2DH**
Let us break bread together—song J. Norman, Ambrosian Sngrs, RPO, A. Gibson (arr. Hope) *Concert* (4/83) (PHIL) ① **400 019-2PH**
L'homme armé—chanson (15th Cent) Tallis Scholars, P. Phillips *Concert* (7/89) (GIME) ① **CDGIM019**
Oxford Camerata, J. Summerly (r1994) *Concert* (10/95) (NAXO) ① **8 553087**
Li debonnaires Dieus—chanson de toile (13th cent) Sinfonye, S. Wishart (r1992) *Concert* (8/93) (HYPE) ① **CDA66655**
Liffe, liffe London Pro Musica, B. Thomas *Concert* (2/87) (CARL) ① **PCD825**
Linstead Market—Jamaican folksong W. White, G. McNaught *Concert* (6/92) (CHAN) ① **CHAN8960**
Libre Vermell de Monserrat—pilgrim songs and dances (1399) 1. O virgo splendens; 2. Stella splendens; 3. Laudemus Virginem; 4. Mariam Matrem Virginem; 5. Polorum Regina; 6. Cuncti sinus concanentes; 7. Splendens ceptigera; 8. Los set goyts; 9. Imperayritz de la Ciutat joyosa; 10. Ad mortem festinamus. New London Consort, P. Pickett (12/95) (L'OI) ① **433 186-2OH**
Alla Francesca (r c1994) *Concert* (12/95) (O111) ① **OPS30-131**
6. Alberquerque Música Antigua *Concert* (8/93) (DORI) ① **DIS80104**
Longing R. A. Morgan (Welsh) *Concert* (12/87) (ETCE) ① **KTC1049**

O Maria virginei—conductus (3vv) (12th Cent)
Hilliard Ens, P. Hillier *Concert*
(2/90) (ECM) ① **837 751-2**

O Maria virgo pia—sequence (14th Cent) (English)
Anon 4 (r1994) *Concert*
(9/95) (HARM) ① **HMU90 7125**

O mitissima/Quant voi/Virgo virginum—13th century motet (3vv) (French. Montpelier Codex)
London Early Music Consort, D. Munrow *Concert*
(8/85) (ARCH) ① **415 292-2AH**

O mors moreris/O vita vera/Mors—motet (14th Cent) (English)
Anon 4 (r1994) *Concert*
(9/95) (HARM) ① **HMU90 7125**

O potores exquisiti
Hilliard Ens *Concert*
(5/87) (HARM) ① **HMA190 1106**

O regina seculi/Reparatrix Maria—d (MS Canonici misc 213)
Gothic Voices, C. Page *Concert*
(12/88) (HYPE) ① **CDA66286**

Occhi, non occhi—madrigal: 3vv
M. Arruabarrena, K. van Laethem, M. Valenta, J. Benet, M. van Altena, J. Cabré, T. de Zwart, A. Pols, R. Van Der Meer, K. Junghänel (lte/dir) *Concert*
(1/92) (ACCE) ① **ACC8864D**

Odorano le rose—song
C. Muzio, orch (r1922) *Concert*
(1/94) (ROMO) ① [2] **81005-2**

Oh, you must be a lover of the Lord—song (pub 1866) (Wds. I Watts; arr 'J N S')
H. Crook, R. Murcell, Harmoneion Sngrs, N. Bruce, L. Skrobacs (r1977) *Concert* (2/94) (NEW) ① **80220-2**

Old Hall Manuscript (compiled c1410-15)
Hilliard Ens (r1990) (1/92) (EMI) ① **CDC7 54111-2**

Oratio Ieremiae—motet
Hilliard Ens (r1993) *Concert*
(10/94) (ECM) ① **445 369-2**

Ovet mundus letabundus
Hilliard Ens (r1984) *Concert*
(3/87) (HARM) ① **HMC90 1154**
Amsterdam Loeki Stardust Qt (r1991; arr recorder consort) *Concert* (2/94) (L'OI) ① **436 155-2OH**

Pagginton's Pound—song: 1v and consort (17th Cent English) (aka Packington's Pound)
E. Van Evera, Musicians of Swanne Alley *Concert*
(11/89) (VIRG) ① **VC7 59534-2**

Pange melos lacrimosum—conductus (2vv) (1190)
Gothic Voices, C. Page *Concert*
(10/89) (HYPE) ① **CDA66336**

Par un martinet/Hé, bergier!—isorhythmic poem (13th cent)
Gothic Voices, C. Page *Concert*
(12/90) (HYPE) ① **CDA66423**

Pase el agoa, ma Julieta—Spanish song (from the Palacio Song Book)
Hespèrion XX, J. Savall *Concert*
(7/92) (ASTR) ① **E8762**
Gothic Voices, C. Page (r1993) *Concert*
(2/94) (HYPE) ① **CDA66653**
J. Gomez, J. Constable (r1994; arr Tarragó) *Concert*
(9/94) (CONI) ① **CDCF243**

Pater noster—plainchant
Lower Rhine Choral Soc, H. Schmitt *Concert*
(2/90) (SCHW) ① **313001**

Pe milde lomb isprad o rode—medieval English hymn
Anon 4 (r1994) *Concert*
(9/95) (HARM) ① **HMU90 7125**

Per combatter—Aria for soprano, trumpet and strings
J. Nelson, D. Ferry, K. Gohl, J. Rubin, G. Murray, C. Bianchi (r1983) *Concert*
(5/87) (HARM) ① **HMA190 5137**

Per tropo fede—ballata (14th Cent Italian)
E. Lamandier *Concert* (2/88) (ALIE) ① **AL1019**

Perdi a esperança—song (16th Cent) (Wds. anon Portuguese)
Circa 1500, N. Hadden *Concert*
(9/92) (VIRG) ① **VC7 59071-2**

Perdi la mia rueca—cancion: 1v
C. Bott, New London Consort, P. Pickett *Concert*
(7/92) (LINN) ① **CKD007**

Perspice Christicola
Hilliard Ens (r1984) *Concert*
(3/87) (HARM) ① **HMC90 1154**

Piangi, dolente anima predata—lauda (15th Cent) (Cape Town MS. Wds Giustiniani)
Daedalus Ens (r1992) *Concert*
(11/93) (ACCE) ① **ACC9289D**

Pictagore per dogmata/O terra sancta/Rosa vernans—isorhythmic motet (1374-76)
Orlando Consort (bp1994) *Concert*
(11/95) (METR) ① **METCD1008**

Plaudite tympana—16vv and instruments (17th Cent Austrian) (previously attrib O. Benevoli)
Montserrat Escolania Sols, Tolz Boys' Ch Sols, J. Griffelt, J. Lewington, H. Weber, E. Abel, B. Etheridge, D. Thomas, H. Haggenmüller, E. Wiederhut, Montserrat Escolania, Tolz Boys' Ch, Collegium Aureum, I. Segarra *Missa Salisburgensis*.
(12/91) (DHM) ① **RD77050**

Plus bele que flors/Quant revient/L'autrier jouer—isorhythmic poem (13th cent)
Gothic Voices, C. Page *Concert*
(12/90) (HYPE) ① **CDA66423**
Gothic Voices, C. Page *Concert*
(3/92) (HYPE) ① **CDA66463**

Por coi me bait mes maris?—chanson de femme (13th cent)
Sinfonye, S. Wishart (r1992) *Concert*
(8/93) (HYPE) ① **CDA66625**

Porque me naõ vês Joana—song (16th Cent) (Wds. anon Portuguese)
G. Lesne, Circa 1500, N. Hadden *Concert*
(9/92) (VIRG) ① **VC7 59071-2**

Pour vous servir—3vv (14th cent)
Gothic Voices, C. Page, A. Lawrence-King *Concert*
(6/93) (HYPE) ① **CDA66619**

Praise the Lord, the mighty King—hymn
L. Melchior, Brass Ens (Danish: r1915) *Concert*
(8/88) (DANA) ① [2] **DACOCD311/2**

Praise to the Lord, the Almighty—hymn (Stralsund Gesangbuch 1665) (Tune - Lobe den Herren)
St Paul's Cath Ch, C. Dearnley, English Brass Ens, John Scott *Concert* (7/90) (HYPE) ① **CDH88036**

Praise to Thee, Jesus Christ—Danish folktune (Wds. M. Luther)
L. Melchior, Brass Ens (Danish: r1915) *Concert*
(8/88) (DANA) ① [2] **DACOCD311/2**

Primo tempore—motet
J. Garbarek, Hilliard Ens (r1993) *Concert*
(10/94) (ECM) ① **445 369-2**

Principio di virtu (13th cent)
Newberry Consort, M. Springfels (r1990) *Concert*
(7/93) (HARM) ① **HMU90 7038**

Procedentem sponsum—motet
J. Garbarek, Hilliard Ens (r1993) *Concert*
(10/94) (ECM) ① **445 369-2**

Promat chorus hodie—versus (12th Cent) (Aquitanian Polyphony)
Augsburg Early Music Ens *Concert*
(3/93) (CHRI) ① **CHR74584**

Propiñan de Melyor—Spanish song (15th cent) (from the Colombina Song Book)
Hespèrion XX, J. Savall *Concert*
(7/92) (ASTR) ① **E8763**
C. Bott, New London Consort, P. Pickett *Concert*
(7/92) (LINN) ① **CKD007**

Prosae—discant
1. Alleluia—Gratulemur et letemur; 2. Res est admirabilis; 3. Quam dilecta tabernacula; 4. Clemens servulorum gemitus tuorum.
Discantus, B. Lesne (r1994) *Concert*
(7/95) (O111) ① **OPS30-102**

Psalm 1, 'Blessed is the man'—Anglican chant (Wds trans Coverdale. Settings/Pointing by various cpsrs)
Wells Cath Ch, A. Crossland, C. Brayne (r1990; arr W. Beale) *Concert* (10/91) (PRIO) ① **PRCD337**
St Paul's Cath Ch, John Scott, Andrew Lucas (r1993; arr Elgar) *Concert* (6/94) (HYPE) ① **CDP11001**

Psalm 2, 'Why do the heathen so furiously rage together'—Anglican chant (Wds trans Coverdale. Settings/Pointing by various cpsrs)
Norwich Cath Ch, M. Nicholas, N. Taylor (arr Statham) *Concert* (5/93) (PRIO) ① **PRCD409**
St Paul's Cath Ch, John Scott, Andrew Lucas (r1993; arr Ashfield) *Concert* (6/94) (HYPE) ① **CDP11001**

Psalm 3, 'Lord, how are they increased'—Anglican chant (Wds trans Coverdale. Settings/Pointing by various cpsrs)
Norwich Cath Ch, M. Nicholas, N. Taylor (arr M. Archer) *Concert* (5/93) (PRIO) ① **PRCD409**
St Paul's Cath Ch, John Scott, Andrew Lucas (r1993; arr Hopkins) *Concert* (6/94) (HYPE) ① **CDP11001**

Psalm 4, 'Hear me when I call, O God'—Anglican chant (Wds trans Coverdale. Settings/Pointing by various cpsrs)
St Paul's Cath Ch, John Scott, Andrew Lucas (r1993; arr Elvey) *Concert* (6/94) (HYPE) ① **CDP11001**
Rochester Cath Ch, B. Ferguson, R. Sayer (r1993; arr E.S. Carter) *Concert* (6/94) (PRIO) ① **PRCD461**

Psalm 5, 'Ponder my words, O Lord'—Anglican chant (Wds trans Coverdale. Settings/Pointing by various cpsrs)
St Paul's Cath Ch, John Scott, Andrew Lucas (r1993; arr Walford Davies) *Concert*
(6/94) (HYPE) ① **CDP11001**
York Minster Ch, P. Moore, J.S. Whiteley (r1993; arr E.C. Bairstow) *Concert* (5/95) (PRIO) ① **PRCD486**

Psalm 6, 'O Lord rebuke me not'—Anglican chant (Wds trans Coverdale. Settings/Pointing by various cpsrs)
Wells Cath Ch, A. Crossland, C. Brayne (r1990; arr S. Wesley) *Concert* (10/91) (PRIO) ① **PRCD337**
St Paul's Cath Ch, John Scott, Andrew Lucas (r1993; arr Carter) *Concert* (6/94) (HYPE) ① **CDP11001**

Psalm 7, 'O Lord my God, in Thee I have put my trust'—Anglican chant (Wds trans Coverdale. Settings/Pointing by various cpsrs)
St Paul's Cath Ch, John Scott, Andrew Lucas (r1993; arr Cooke) *Concert* (6/94) (HYPE) ① **CDP11001**

Psalm 8, 'O Lord our Governor'—Anglican chant (Wds trans Coverdale. Settings/Pointing by various cpsrs)
Guildford Cath Ch, A. Millington, G. Morgan (arr E.J. Hopkins) *Concert* (5/93) (PRIO) ① **PRCD416**
St Paul's Cath Ch, John Scott, Andrew Lucas (r1993; arr Corfe/Lawes) *Concert* (6/94) (HYPE) ① **CDP11001**

Psalm 9, 'I will give thanks unto Thee, O Lord'—Anglican chant (Wds trans Coverdale. Settings/Pointing by various cpsrs)
St Paul's Cath Ch, John Scott, Andrew Lucas (r1993; arr Stainer/Attwood) *Concert*
(6/94) (HYPE) ① **CDP11001**
York Minster Ch, P. Moore, J.S. Whiteley (r1993; arr T.A. Walmisley) *Concert*
(5/95) (PRIO) ① **PRCD486**

Psalm 10, 'Why standest thou so far off, O Lord'—Anglican chant (Wds trans Coverdale. Settings/Pointing by various cpsrs)
St Paul's Cath Ch, John Scott, Andrew Lucas (r1993; arr Attwood/Stainer) *Concert*
(6/94) (HYPE) ① **CDP11001**
Rochester Cath Ch, B. Ferguson, R. Sayer (r1993; arr R. Ashfield/P.C. Buck) *Concert*
(6/94) (PRIO) ① **PRCD461**

Psalm 11, 'In the Lord put I my trust'—Anglican chant (Wds trans Coverdale. Settings/Pointing by various cpsrs)
Lichfield Cath Ch, J. Rees-Williams (r1991; arr T. Kelway) *Concert* (4/92) (PRIO) ① **PRCD383**
St Paul's Cath Ch, John Scott, Andrew Lucas (r1993; arr Elvey) *Concert* (6/94) (HYPE) ① **CDP11001**

Psalm 12, 'Help me Lord'—Anglican chant (Wds trans Coverdale. Settings/Pointing by various cpsrs)
Wells Cath Ch, A. Crossland, C. Brayne (r1990; arr H. Stonex) *Concert* (10/91) (PRIO) ① **PRCD337**
St Paul's Cath Ch, John Scott, Andrew Lucas (r1993; arr Wilton) *Concert* (6/94) (HYPE) ① **CDP11001**

Psalm 13, 'How long wilt thou forget me, O Lord'—Anglican chant (Wds trans Coverdale. Settings/Pointing by various cpsrs)
Wells Cath Ch, A. Crossland, C. Brayne (r1990; arr H. Smart) *Concert* (10/91) (PRIO) ① **PRCD337**
St Paul's Cath Ch, John Scott, Andrew Lucas (r1993; arr Croft/Tomkins) *Concert*
(6/94) (HYPE) ① **CDP11001**

Psalm 14, '(The) fool hath said in his heart'—Anglican chant (Wds trans Coverdale. Settings/Pointing by various cpsrs)
Wells Cath Ch, A. Crossland, C. Brayne (r1990; arr T. Turle) *Concert* (10/91) (PRIO) ① **PRCD337**
St Paul's Cath Ch, John Scott, Andrew Lucas (nr1993; arr Attwood) *Concert*
(6/94) (HYPE) ① **CDP11001**

Psalm 15, 'Lord, who shall dwell in Thy tabernacle'—Anglican chant (Wds trans Coverdale. Settings/Pointing by various cpsrs)
Durham Cath Ch, J. Lancelot, I. Shaw (r1990; arr E. Hopkins) *Concert* (3/92) (PRIO) ① **PRCD343**
St Paul's Cath Ch, John Scott, Andrew Lucas (r1993; arr Gibbons) *Concert* (6/94) (HYPE) ① **CDP11001**

Psalm 16, 'Preserve me, O God'—Anglican chant (Wds trans Coverdale. Settings/Pointing by various cpsrs)
St Paul's Cath Ch, John Scott, Andrew Lucas (r1993; arr Havergal) *Concert* (6/94) (HYPE) ① **CDP11001**
Rochester Cath Ch, B. Ferguson, R. Sayer (r1993; arr H.C. Stewart) *Concert*
(6/94) (PRIO) ① **PRCD461**

Psalm 17, 'Hear the right, O Lord'—Anglican chant (Wds trans Coverdale. Settings/Pointing by various cpsrs)
St Paul's Cath Ch, John Scott, Andrew Lucas (r1993; arr Turle) *Concert* (6/94) (HYPE) ① **CDP11001**

Rochester Cath Ch, B. Ferguson, R. Sayer (r1993; arr W.N. Duckworth) *Concert* (6/94) (PRIO) ① **PRCD461**

Psalm 18, 'I will love thee, O Lord my strength'—Anglican chant (Wds trans Coverdale. Settings/Pointing by various cpsrs)
Durham Cath Ch, J. Lancelot, I. Shaw (r1990; arr B. Jacob/P. Buck/T. Walmisley/F.G. Ouseley/P. Hull) *Concert* (3/92) (PRIO) ① **PRCD343**
St Paul's Cath Ch, John Scott, Andrew Lucas (r1994; arr Walmisley/S. S. Wesley/Smart/Robinson) *Concert* (2/95) (HYPE) ① **CDP11002**

Psalm 19, '(The) heavens declare the glory of God'—Anglican chant (Wds trans Coverdale. Settings/Pointing by various cpsrs)
St Paul's Cath Ch, John Scott, Andrew Lucas (r1994; arr Walmisley) *Concert* (2/95) (HYPE) ① **CDP11002**

Psalm 20, '(The) Lord hear thee in the day of trouble'—Anglican chant (Wds trans Coverdale. Settings/Pointing by various cpsrs)
Lichfield Cath Ch, J. Rees-Williams (r1991; arr T.A. Walmisley) *Concert* (4/92) (PRIO) ① **PRCD383**
St Paul's Cath Ch, John Scott, Andrew Lucas (r1994; arr Roseingrave) *Concert* (2/95) (HYPE) ① **CDP11002**

Psalm 21, '(The) King shall rejoice in thy strength'—Anglican chant (Wds trans Coverdale. Settings/Pointing by various cpsrs)
St Paul's Cath Ch, John Scott, Andrew Lucas (r1994; arr Goss) *Concert* (2/95) (HYPE) ① **CDP11002**
York Minster Ch, P. Moore, J.S. Whiteley (r1993; arr G. Cooper) *Concert* (5/95) (PRIO) ① **PRCD486**

Psalm 22, 'My God, my God, look upon me'—Anglican chant (Wds trans Coverdale. Settings/Pointing by various cpsrs)
Wells Cath Ch, A. Crossland, C. Brayne (r1990; arr M. Camidge) *Concert* (10/91) (PRIO) ① **PRCD337**
St Paul's Cath Ch, John Scott, Andrew Lucas (r1994; arr S. Wesley/Smart) *Concert* (2/95) (HYPE) ① **CDP11002**

Psalm 23, '(The) Lord is my shepherd'—Anglican chant (Wds trans Coverdale. Settings/Pointing by various cpsrs)
St Paul's Cath Ch, John Scott, Andrew Lucas (r1994; arr Stewart) *Concert* (2/95) (HYPE) ① **CDP11002**

Psalm 24, '(The) earth is the Lord's'—Anglican chant (Wds trans Coverdale. Settings/Pointing by various cpsrs)
Durham Cath Ch, J. Lancelot, I. Shaw (r1990; arr J. Barnby) *Concert* (3/92) (PRIO) ① **PRCD343**
St Paul's Cath Ch, John Scott, Andrew Lucas (r1994; arr Barnby) *Concert* (2/95) (HYPE) ① **CDP11002**

Psalm 25, 'Unto Thee, O Lord, will I lift my soul'—Anglican chant (Wds trans Coverdale. Settings/Pointing by various cpsrs)
Rochester Cath Ch, B. Ferguson, R. Sayer (r1993; arr J. Goss) *Concert* (6/94) (PRIO) ① **PRCD461**
St Paul's Cath Ch, John Scott, Andrew Lucas (r1994; arr Turle) *Concert* (2/95) (HYPE) ① **CDP11002**

Psalm 26, 'Be thou my judge, O Lord'—Anglican chant (Wds trans Coverdale. Settings/Pointing by various cpsrs)
St Paul's Cath Ch, John Scott, Andrew Lucas (r1994; arr Sinclair) *Concert* (2/95) (HYPE) ① **CDP11002**
York Minster Ch, P. Moore, J.S. Whiteley (r1993; arr E.J. Hopkins) *Concert* (5/95) (PRIO) ① **PRCD486**

Psalm 27, '(The) Lord is my light and my salvation'—Anglican chant (Wds trans Coverdale. Settings/Pointing by various cpsrs)
Guildford Cath Ch, A. Millington, G. Morgan (arr W.H. Harris/Hylton-Stewart) *Concert* (5/93) (PRIO) ① **PRCD416**
St Paul's Cath Ch, John Scott, Andrew Lucas (r1994; arr Hopkins/Wolstenholme) *Concert* (2/95) (HYPE) ① **CDP11002**

Psalm 28, 'Unto Thee will I cry'—Anglican chant (Wds trans Coverdale. Settings/Pointing by various cpsrs)
Guildford Cath Ch, A. Millington, G. Morgan (arr E.J. Hopkins) *Concert* (5/93) (PRIO) ① **PRCD416**
St Paul's Cath Ch, John Scott, Andrew Lucas (r1994; arr Hopkins) *Concert* (2/95) (HYPE) ① **CDP11002**

Psalm 29, 'Bring unto the Lord, o ye mighty'—Anglican chant (Wds trans Coverdale. Settings/Pointing by various cpsrs)
Wells Cath Ch, A. Crossland, C. Brayne (r1990; arr Stanford) *Concert* (10/91) (PRIO) ① **PRCD337**
St Paul's Cath Ch, John Scott, Andrew Lucas (r1994; arr Ley) *Concert* (2/95) (HYPE) ① **CDP11002**

Psalm 30, 'I will magnify Thee, O Lord'—Anglican chant (Wds trans Coverdale. Settings/Pointing by various cpsrs)
Ely Cath Ch, P. Trepte, D. Price (r1993; arr Corfe/Lawes/Elgar) *Concert* (12/93) (PRIO) ① **PRCD460**
St Paul's Cath Ch, John Scott, Andrew Lucas (r1995: arr Lloyd/Scott) *Concert* (10/95) (HYPE) ① **CDP11003**

Psalm 31, 'In Thee, O Lord, I have put my trust'—Anglican chant (Wds trans Coverdale. Settings/Pointing by various cpsrs)
Ely Cath Ch, P. Trepte, D. Price (r1993; arr E. Day/Oakley/Pye) *Concert* (12/93) (PRIO) ① **PRCD460**
St Paul's Cath Ch, John Scott, Andrew Lucas (r1995: arr Lloyd) *Concert* (10/95) (HYPE) ① **CDP11003**

Psalm 32, 'Blessed is he whose unrighteousness'—Anglican chant (Wds. trans Coverdale. Settings/Pointing by various composers)
St Paul's Cath Ch, John Scott, Andrew Lucas (r1995: arr Russell) *Concert* (10/95) (HYPE) ① **CDP11003**

Psalm 33, 'Rejoice in the Lord, o ye righteous'—Anglican chant (Wds trans Coverdale. Settings/Pointing by various cpsrs)
Guildford Cath Ch, A. Millington, G. Morgan (arr Goss) *Concert* (5/93) (PRIO) ① **PRCD416**
St Paul's Cath Ch, John Scott, Andrew Lucas (r1995: arr Turle) *Concert* (10/95) (HYPE) ① **CDP11003**

Psalm 34, 'I will alway give thanks unto the Lord'—Anglican chant (Wds trans Coverdale. Settings/Pointing by various cpsrs)
Guildford Cath Ch, A. Millington, G. Morgan (arr S. Watson) *Concert* (5/93) (PRIO) ① **PRCD416**
St Paul's Cath Ch, John Scott, Andrew Lucas (r1995: arr South) *Concert* (10/95) (HYPE) ① **CDP11003**

Psalm 35, 'Plead thou my cause, O Lord'—Anglican chant (Wds trans Coverdale. Settings/Pointing by various cpsrs)
York Minster Ch, P. Moore, J.S. Whiteley (r1993; Tone i) *Concert* (5/95) (PRIO) ① **PRCD486**
St Paul's Cath Ch, John Scott, Andrew Lucas (r1995: arr Stonex) *Concert* (10/95) (HYPE) ① **CDP11003**

Psalm 36, 'My heart sheweth me the wickedness of the ungodly'—Anglican chant (Wds trans Coverdale. Settings/Pointing by various cpsrs)
Ely Cath Ch, P. Trepte, D. Price (r1993; arr Stafford Smith) *Concert* (12/93) (PRIO) ① **PRCD460**
St Paul's Cath Ch, John Scott, Andrew Lucas (r1995: arr Stewart/Hopkins) *Concert* (10/95) (HYPE) ① **CDP11003**

Psalm 37, 'Fret not thyself'—Anglican chant (Wds trans Coverdale. Settings/Pointing by various cpsrs)
York Minster Ch, P. Moore, J.S. Whiteley (r1993; arr H.J. Gauntlett/C.V. Stanford) *Concert* (5/95) (PRIO) ① **PRCD486**
St Paul's Cath Ch, John Scott, Andrew Lucas (r1995: arr Howells) *Concert* (10/95) (HYPE) ① **CDP11003**

Psalm 38, 'Put me not to rebuke, O Lord in Thy anger'—Anglican chant (Wds trans Coverdale. Settings/Pointing by various cpsrs)
York Minster Ch, P. Moore, J.S. Whiteley (r1993; arr J. Battishill) *Concert* (5/95) (PRIO) ① **PRCD486**
St Paul's Cath Ch, John Scott, Andrew Lucas (r1995: arr Barnby) *Concert* (10/95) (HYPE) ① **CDP11003**

Psalm 39, 'I said I will take heed to my ways'—Anglican chant (Wds trans Coverdale. Settings/Pointing by various cpsrs)
Durham Cath Ch, J. Lancelot, I. Shaw (r1990; arr Howells) *Concert* (3/92) (PRIO) ① **PRCD343**
St Paul's Cath Ch, John Scott, Andrew Lucas (r1995: arr Atkins) *Concert* (10/95) (HYPE) ① **CDP11003**

Psalm 40, 'I waited patiently for the Lord'—Anglican chant (Wds trans Coverdale. Settings/pointing by various cpsrs)
Rochester Cath Ch, B. Ferguson, R. Sayer (r1993; arr S.S. Wesley/J. Harrison) *Concert* (6/94) (PRIO) ① **PRCD461**
St Paul's Cath Ch, John Scott, Andrew Lucas (r1995: arr Harwood) *Concert* (10/95) (HYPE) ① **CDP11003**

Psalm 41, 'Blessed is he that considereth the poor and needy'—Anglican chant (Wds trans Coverdale. Settings/Pointing by various cpsrs)
Lichfield Cath Ch, J. Rees-Williams (r1991; arr W. Crotch) *Concert* (4/92) (PRIO) ① **PRCD383**

Psalm 44, 'We have heard with our ears, O God'—Anglican chant (Wds trans Coverdale. Settings/Pointing by various cpsrs)
Rochester Cath Ch, B. Ferguson, R. Sayer (r1993; arr J. Coward/R. Banks/B. Ferguson) *Concert* (6/94) (PRIO) ① **PRCD461**

Psalm 45, 'My heart is inditing of a good matter'—Anglican chant (Wds trans Coverdale. Settings/Pointing by various cpsrs)
Rochester Cath Ch, B. Ferguson, R. Sayer (r1993; arr B. Ferguson) *Concert* (6/94) (PRIO) ① **PRCD461**

Psalm 46, 'God is our hope and strength'—Anglican chant (Wds trans Coverdale. Settings/Pointing by various cpsrs)
Durham Cath Ch, J. Lancelot, I. Shaw (r1990; after M. Luther) *Concert* (3/92) (PRIO) ① **PRCD343**

Psalm 48, 'Great is the Lord and highly to be praised'—Anglican chant (Wds trans Coverdale. Settings/Pointing by various cpsrs)
Guildford Cath Ch, A. Millington, G. Morgan (arr G. Garrett) *Concert* (5/93) (PRIO) ① **PRCD416**

Psalm 49, 'O hear ye this, all ye people'—Anglican chant (Wds trans Coverdale. Settings/Pointing by various cpsrs)
Guildford Cath Ch, A. Millington, G. Morgan (arr Walmisley) *Concert* (5/93) (PRIO) ① **PRCD416**

Psalm 50, '(The) Lord, even the most mighty God, hath spoken'—Anglican chant (Wds trans Coverdale. Settings/Pointing by various cpsrs)
Ely Cath Ch, P. Trepte, D. Price (r1993; arr H. Murrill/Hunt) *Concert* (12/93) (PRIO) ① **PRCD460**

Psalm 51, 'Have mercy upon me, O Lord God'—Anglican chant (Wds trans Coverdale. Settings/Pointing by various cpsrs)
Ely Cath Ch, P. Trepte, D. Price (r1993; arr C.H. Wilton) *Concert* (12/93) (PRIO) ① **PRCD460**

Psalm 52, 'Why boastest thou thyself, thy tyrant'—Anglican chant (Wds trans Coverdale. Settings/Pointing by various cpsrs)
Ely Cath Ch, P. Trepte, D. Price (r1993; arr D. Cantrell) *Concert* (12/93) (PRIO) ① **PRCD460**

Psalm 53, '(The) foolish body hath said'—Anglican chant (Wds trans Coverdale. Settings/Pointing by various cpsrs)
Wells Cath Ch, A. Crossland, C. Brayne (r1990; arr L. Flintoft) *Concert* (10/91) (PRIO) ① **PRCD337**

Psalm 54, 'Save me, O God, by Thy name'—Anglican chant (Wds trans Coverdale. Settings/Pointing by various cpsrs)
Wells Cath Ch, A. Crossland, C. Brayne (r1990; arr F.W. Wadely) *Concert* (10/91) (PRIO) ① **PRCD337**

Psalm 55, 'Hear my prayer, O God'—Anglican chant (Wds trans Coverdale. Settings/Pointing by various cpsrs)
Wells Cath Ch, A. Crossland, C. Brayne (r1990; arr D.A. Cooper/F. Walker) *Concert* (10/91) (PRIO) ① **PRCD337**

Psalm 56, 'Be merciful unto me'—Anglican chant (Wds trans Coverdale. Settings/Pointing by various cpsrs)
Wells Cath Ch, A. Crossland, C. Brayne (r1990; arr Howells) *Concert* (10/91) (PRIO) ① **PRCD337**

Psalm 57, 'Be merciful unto me, O God'—Anglican chant (Wds trans Coverdale. Settings/Pointing by various cpsrs)
Lichfield Cath Ch, J. Rees-Williams (r1991; arr W. Hine) *Concert* (4/92) (PRIO) ① **PRCD383**

Psalm 58, 'Are your minds set upon righteousness?'—Anglican chant (Wds trans Coverdale. Settings/Pointing by various cpsrs)
Lichfield Cath Ch, J. Rees-Williams (r1991; arr J. Barnby) *Concert* (4/92) (PRIO) ① **PRCD383**

Psalm 59, 'Deliver me from mine enemies'—Anglican chant (Wds trans Coverdale. Settings/Pointing by various cpsrs)
Guildford Cath Ch, A. Millington, G. Morgan (arr Ouseley) *Concert* (5/93) (PRIO) ① **PRCD416**

Psalm 60, 'O God Thou hast cast us out'—Anglican chant (Wds trans Coverdale. Settings/Pointing by various cpsrs)
Wells Cath Ch, A. Crossland, C. Brayne (r1990; arr W.H. Havergal/T.A. Walmisley) *Concert* (10/91) (PRIO) ① **PRCD337**

Psalm 62, 'My soul truly waiteth still upon God'—Anglican chant (Wds trans Coverdale. Settings/Pointing by various cpsrs)
York Minster Ch, P. Moore, J.S. Whiteley (r1993; arr W. Boyce) *Concert* (5/95) (PRIO) ① **PRCD486**

Psalm 63, 'O God Thou art my God'—Anglican chant (Wds trans Coverdale. Settings/Pointing by various cpsrs)
Guildford Cath Ch, A. Millington, G. Morgan (arr A. Millington) *Concert* (5/93) (PRIO) ① **PRCD416**

Psalm 64, 'Hear my voice, O God, in my prayer'—Anglican chant (Wds trans Coverdale. Settings/Pointing by various cpsrs)
Rochester Cath Ch, B. Ferguson, R. Sayer (r1993; arr B. Ferguson/E. Edwards) *Concert* (6/94) (PRIO) ① **PRCD461**

Psalm 66, 'O be joyful in God'—Anglican chant (Wds trans Coverdale. Settings/Pointing by various cpsrs)
Durham Cath Ch, J. Lancelot, I. Shaw (r1990; arr L. Gray) *Concert* (3/92) (PRIO) ① **PRCD343**

Psalm 118, 'O give thanks unto the Lord, for he is generous'—Anglican chant (Wds trans Coverdale. Settings/Pointing by various cpsrs)
Ely Cath Ch, P. Trepte, D. Price (r1993; arr G. Elvey/Beckwith) *Concert*
(12/93) (PRIO) ① **PRCD460**
Westminster Abbey Ch, M. Neary, A. Lumsden (r1990: arr Whitlock) *Concert*
(7/95) (VIRG) ① **VC5 45036-2**

Psalm 119, 'Blessed are those that are undefiled'—Anglican chant (Wds trans Coverdale. Settings/Pointing by various cpsrs)
EXCERPTS: 1. Verse 1: Blessed are those that are undefiled; 2. Verse 33: Teach me, O Lord, the way of the statutes; 3. Verse 73: Thy hands have made me; 4. Verse 105: Thy word is a lantern unto my feet; 5. Verse 145: I call with my whole heart.
Ely Cath Ch, P. Trepte, D. Price (r1993; arr I. Atkins/West/Knight/Ware) *Concert*
(12/93) (PRIO) ① **PRCD460**
1. Gloucester Cath Ch, J. Sanders (r1991; arr Woods/W. Parratt/J. Booth/S. Matthews) *Concert*
(4/92) (PRIO) ① **PRCD387**
3. Durham Cath Ch, J. Lancelot, I. Shaw (r1990: arr J. Lemon/E. Hopkins/G. Garrett/A. Mann) *Concert*
(3/92) (PRIO) ① **PRCD343**
4. York Minster Ch, P. Moore, J.S. Whiteley (r1993; arr J. Robinson/H.J. Gauntlett/T.T. Noble/C.L. Naylor/J.L. Rogers) *Concert*
(5/95) (PRIO) ① **PRCD486**
5. Lichfield Cath Ch, J. Rees-Williams (r1991; arr E. Monk/S. Wesley/S.S. Wesley) *Concert*
(4/92) (PRIO) ① **PRCD383**

Psalm 120, 'When I was in trouble I called upon the Lord'—Anglican chant (Wds trans Coverdale. Settings/Pointing by various cpsrs)
Norwich Cath Ch, M. Nicholas, N. Taylor (arr R. Walker) *Concert* (5/93) (PRIO) ① **PRCD409**
Ely Cath Ch, P. Trepte, D. Price (r1993; arr Brooksbank) *Concert* (12/93) (PRIO) ① **PRCD460**

Psalm 121, 'I will lift up mine eyes'—Anglican chant (Wds trans Coverdale. Settings/Pointing by various cpsrs)
Wells Cath Ch, A. Crossland, C. Brayne (r1990; arr Howells) *Concert* (10/91) (PRIO) ① **PRCD337**
King's College Ch, P. Barley, S. Cleobury (r1989: arr Howells) *Concert* (7/92) (ARGO) ① **430 205-2ZH**
Westminster Abbey Ch, M. Neary, A. Lumsden (r1990: arr Walford Davies) *Concert*
(7/95) (VIRG) ① **VC5 45036-2**

Psalm 122, 'I was glad when they said unto me'—Anglican chant (Wds trans Coverdale. Settings/Pointing by various cpsrs)
Lichfield Cath Ch, J. Rees-Williams (r1991; arr W.H. Harris) *Concert* (4/92) (PRIO) ① **PRCD383**
King's College Ch, P. Barley, S. Cleobury (r1989: arr Howells) *Concert* (7/92) (ARGO) ① **430 205-2ZH**
Westminster Abbey Ch, M. Neary, A. Lumsden (r1990: arr Parratt) *Concert*
(7/95) (VIRG) ① **VC5 45036-2**

Psalm 123, 'Unto Thee lift I up mine eyes'—Anglican chant (Wds trans Coverdale. Settings/Pointing by various cpsrs)
Durham Cath Ch, J. Lancelot, I. Shaw (r1990: arr A. Culley) *Concert* (3/92) (PRIO) ① **PRCD343**
Westminster Abbey Ch, M. Neary, A. Lumsden (r1990: arr Rose) *Concert*
(7/95) (VIRG) ① **VC5 45036-2**

Psalm 124, 'If the Lord himself had not been on our side'—Anglican chant (Wds trans Coverdale. Settings/Pointing by various cpsrs)
Norwich Cath Ch, M. Nicholas, N. Taylor (arr R. Ley) *Concert* (5/93) (PRIO) ① **PRCD409**

Psalm 125, 'They that put their trust in the Lord'—Anglican chant (Wds trans Coverdale. Settings/Pointing by various cpsrs)
Ely Cath Ch, P. Trepte, D. Price (r1993; arr Mothersole) *Concert* (12/93) (PRIO) ① **PRCD460**

Psalm 127, 'Except the Lord build a house'—Anglican chant (Wds trans Coverdale. Settings/Pointing by various cpsrs)
Guildford Cath Ch, A. Millington, G. Morgan (arr P. Buck) *Concert* (5/93) (PRIO) ① **PRCD416**

Psalm 128, 'Blessed are all they that fear the Lord'—Anglican chant (Wds trans Coverdale. Settings/Pointing by various cpsrs)
Wells Cath Ch, A. Crossland, C. Brayne (r1990; arr J. Stainer) *Concert* (10/91) (PRIO) ① **PRCD337**

Psalm 129, 'Many a time have they fought against me'—Anglican chant (Wds trans Coverdale. Settings/Pointing by various cpsrs)
Lichfield Cath Ch, J. Rees-Williams (r1991; arr J.L. Rogeas) *Concert* (4/92) (PRIO) ① **PRCD383**

Psalm 130, 'Out of the deep have I called unto Thee'—Anglican chant (Wds trans Coverdale. Settings/Pointing by various cpsrs)
Lichfield Cath Ch, J. Rees-Williams (r1991; arr W. Parratt) *Concert* (4/92) (PRIO) ① **PRCD383**
Westminster Abbey Ch, M. Neary, A. Lumsden (r1990: arr Turle, from Purcell) *Concert*
(7/95) (VIRG) ① **VC5 45036-2**

Psalm 131, 'Lord I am not high-minded'—Anglican chant (Wds trans Coverdale. Settings/Pointing by various cpsrs)
Durham Cath Ch, J. Lancelot, I. Shaw (r1990; arr J. Rogers) *Concert* (3/92) (PRIO) ① **PRCD343**

Psalm 132, 'Lord, remember David'—Anglican chant (Wds trans Coverdale. Settings/Pointing by various cpsrs)
Rochester Cath Ch, B. Ferguson, R. Sayer (r1993; arr S. Vann) *Concert* (6/94) (PRIO) ① **PRCD461**

Psalm 133, 'Behold, how good and joyful'—Anglican chant (Wds trans Coverdale. Settings/Pointing by various cpsrs)
Ely Cath Ch, P. Trepte, D. Price (r1993; arr Turle) *Concert* (12/93) (PRIO) ① **PRCD460**

Psalm 134, 'Behold now, praise the Lord'—Anglican chant (Wds trans Coverdale. Settings/Pointing by various cpsrs)
Norwich Cath Ch, M. Nicholas, N. Taylor (arr M. Archer) *Concert* (5/93) (PRIO) ① **PRCD409**

Psalm 135, 'O praise the Lord, laud ye the name of the Lord'—Anglican chant (Wds trans Coverdale. Settings/Pointing by various cpsrs)
Rochester Cath Ch, B. Ferguson, R. Sayer (r1993; arr R. Ashfield/C.H. Lloyd) *Concert*
(6/94) (PRIO) ① **PRCD461**

Psalm 136, 'O give thanks unto the Lord'—Anglican chant (Wds trans Coverdale. Settings/Pointing by various cpsrs)
Wells Cath Ch, A. Crossland, C. Brayne (r1990; arr H.G. Ley) *Concert* (10/91) (PRIO) ① **PRCD337**

Psalm 137, 'By the waters of Babylon'—Anglican chant (Wds trans Coverdale. Settings/Pointing by various cpsrs)
Wells Cath Ch, A. Crossland, C. Brayne (r1990; arr P. Whitlock) *Concert* (10/91) (PRIO) ① **PRCD337**
Westminster Abbey Ch, M. Neary, A. Lumsden (r1990: arr Lloyd) *Concert*
(7/95) (VIRG) ① **VC5 45036-2**

Psalm 138, 'I will give thanks unto the Lord'—Anglican chant (Wds trans Coverdale. Settings/Pointing by various cpsrs)
Wells Cath Ch, A. Crossland, C. Brayne (r1990; arr C.H. Lloyd) *Concert* (10/91) (PRIO) ① **PRCD337**

Psalm 139, 'O Lord, Thou hast searched me out'—Anglican chant (Wds trans Coverdale. Settings/Pointing by various cpsrs)
Lichfield Cath Ch, J. Rees-Williams (r1991; arr G. Martin) *Concert* (4/92) (PRIO) ① **PRCD383**
Westminster Abbey Ch, M. Neary, A. Lumsden (r1990: arr Goss) *Concert*
(7/95) (VIRG) ① **VC5 45036-2**

Psalm 140, 'Deliver me, O Lord, from the evil man'—Anglican chant (Wds trans Coverdale. Settings/Pointing by various cpsrs)
Ely Cath Ch, P. Trepte, D. Price (r1993; arr Mothersole) *Concert* (12/93) (PRIO) ① **PRCD460**

Psalm 141, 'Lord, I call upon Thee'—Anglican chant (Wds trans Coverdale. Settings/Pointing by various cpsrs)
Norwich Cath Ch, M. Nicholas, N. Taylor (arr Anon) *Concert* (5/93) (PRIO) ① **PRCD409**

Psalm 142, 'I cried unto the Lord with my voice'—Anglican chant (Wds trans Coverdale. Settings/Pointing by various cpsrs)
Gloucester Cath Ch, J. Sanders (r1991; arr J. Barnby) *Concert* (4/92) (PRIO) ① **PRCD387**

Psalm 144, 'Blessed be the Lord my strength'—Anglican chant (Wds trans Coverdale. Settings/Pointing by various cpsrs)
Rochester Cath Ch, B. Ferguson, R. Sayer (r1993; arr E.J. Hopkins/R.W. Liddle) *Concert*
(6/94) (PRIO) ① **PRCD461**

Psalm 145, 'I will magnify Thee, O God, my King'—Anglican chant (Wds trans Coverdale. Settings/Pointing by various cpsrs)
York Minster Ch, P. Moore, J.S. Whiteley (r1993; arr C.V. Stanford) *Concert* (5/95) (PRIO) ① **PRCD486**

Psalm 146, 'Praise the Lord, O my soul'—Anglican chant (Wds trans Coverdale. Settings/Pointing by various cpsrs)
Durham Cath Ch, J. Lancelot, I. Shaw (r1990; arr O. Peasgood) *Concert* (3/92) (PRIO) ① **PRCD343**

Psalm 147, 'O praise the Lord for it is a good thing'—Anglican chant (Wds trans Coverdale. Settings/Pointing by various cpsrs)
Guildford Cath Ch, A. Millington, G. Morgan (arr Thalben-Ball) *Concert* (5/93) (PRIO) ① **PRCD416**
Westminster Abbey Ch, M. Neary, A. Lumsden (r1990: arr Stanford) *Concert*
(7/95) (VIRG) ① **VC5 45036-2**

Psalm 148, 'O praise the Lord of heaven'—Anglican chant (Wds trans Coverdale. Settings/Pointing by various cpsrs)
Wells Cath Ch, A. Crossland, C. Brayne (r1990; arr H. Monk) *Concert* (10/91) (PRIO) ① **PRCD337**
Westminster Abbey Ch, M. Neary, A. Lumsden (r1990: arr Stanford) *Concert*
(7/95) (VIRG) ① **VC5 45036-2**

Psalm 149, 'O sing unto the Lord'—Anglican chant (Wds trans Coverdale. Settings/Pointing by various cpsrs)
Wells Cath Ch, A. Crossland, C. Brayne (r1990; arr J. Turle) *Concert* (10/91) (PRIO) ① **PRCD337**
Westminster Abbey Ch, M. Neary, A. Lumsden (r1990: arr Atkins) *Concert*
(7/95) (VIRG) ① **VC5 45036-2**

Psalm 150, 'O praise God in His holiness'—Anglican chant (Wds trans Coverdale. Settings/Pointing by various cpsrs)
Durham Cath Ch, J. Lancelot, I. Shaw (r1990; arr Stanford) *Concert* (3/92) (PRIO) ① **PRCD343**
Westminster Abbey Ch, M. Neary, A. Lumsden (r1990: arr Stanford) *Concert*
(7/95) (VIRG) ① **VC5 45036-2**

150 Psalms of David (Wds. Bible)
4, 13, 16, 23, 29, 43, 48, 57, 80, 90, 91, 93, 97, 99, 104, 113, 115, 123, 129, 131, 133, 134, 138, 142, 148, 150. E. Lamandier (r1991; sung in Hebrew)
(2/93) (ALIE) ① **AL1041**

Puestos estan frente a frente—song (16th Cent)
G. Lesne, Circa 1500, N. Hadden *Concert*
(9/92) (VIRG) ① **VC7 59071-2**

Puis qu'autrement ne puis avoir—song: 2vv (14th cent)
Gothic Voices, C. Page (lte/dir) *Concert*
(9/92) (HYPE) ① **CDA66588**

Puis que l'aloe ne fine—1v (14th cent)
Gothic Voices, C. Page, A. Lawrence-King *Concert*
(6/93) (HYPE) ① **CDA66619**

Pulcherrima rosa—motet
J. Garbarek, Hilliard Ens (r1993) *Concert*
(10/94) (ECM) ① **445 369-2**

Purgator criminum—conductus (3vv) (12th Century)
Gothic Voices, C. Page *Concert*
(10/89) (HYPE) ① **CDA66336**

Puse mis amores—song (16th cent—Spain)
Hespérion XX, J. Savall (r1991-92) *Concert*
(6/93) (ASTR) ① **E8764**

Quando i oselli canta—ballata (3vv) (Italian trecentro)
Gothic Voices, C. Page *Concert*
(12/88) (HYPE) ① **CDA66286**

Quant la douce jouvencele (15th Cent)
Gothic Voices, C. Page (r1994) *Concert*
(2/95) (HYPE) ① **CDA66739**

Quant la fleur nouvele—trouvère pastourelle: 1v and bagpipes
Gothic Voices, C. Page (r1994) *Concert*
(8/95) (HYPE) ① **CDA66773**

Quant voi l'aloete/Dieux! je ne m'en partiré ja—isorhythmic poem (13th cent)
Gothic Voices, C. Page *Concert*
(12/90) (HYPE) ① **CDA66423**

Quant voi le douz tans/En mai—motet (13th Cent)
Gothic Voices, C. Page *Concert*
(3/92) (HYPE) ① **CDA66463**

Qué me queréis, cavallero?—Spanish song (15th cent) (from the Palacio Song Book)
Hespérion XX, J. Savall *Concert*
(7/92) (ASTR) ① **E8762**

The Queen's Dream
R. A. Morgan (Welsh) *Concert*
(12/87) (ETCE) ① **KTC1049**

Questro mostrasi adirata
London Pro Musica, B. Thomas *Concert*
(2/87) (CARL) ① **PCD825**

Quiconques veut d'amors joïr—rondeau (14th Cent)
Gothic Voices, C. Page *Concert*
(3/92) (HYPE) ① **CDA66463**

Quien tiene vida en espercança—Spanish song (15th cent) (from the Colombina Song Book)
Hespérion XX, J. Savall *Concert*
(7/92) (ASTR) ① **E8763**

APOLLONI, Giuseppe (1822–1889) Italy

SECTION V: STAGE WORKS

L' Ebreo—opera (1855—Venice)
Si guerrieri...Fu Dio che disse A. DiGiorgio, orch
(r1900s) *Concert*   (6/94) (IRCC) ① **IRCC-CD808**

APOSTEL, Hans Erich (1901–1972) Austria

SECTION II: CHAMBER

String Quartet No. 1, Op. 7 (1935)
LaSalle Qt *Concert*
(8/89) (DG) ① [2] **427 421-2GC2**

SECTION III: INSTRUMENTAL

Sonatina—trumpet, Op. 42a (1970)
R. Friedrich (r1992) *Concert*
(6/93) (CAPR) ① **10 439**

ARAÑÉS, Juan (d c1649) Spain

SECTION IV: VOCAL AND CHORAL

Un sarao de la Chacona
Kithara (r1993) *Concert*
(3/95) (CHAN) ① **CHAN0562**

ARAUJO, Juan de (1648–1712) Spain/South America

SECTION IV: VOCAL AND CHORAL

Dixit Dominus—1v (Wds. Psalm 109)
Cordoba Children's Ch, Elyma Ens, G. Garrido
(r1992) *Concert*   (9/93) (K617) ① **K617025**
Compañia musical, Maîtrise Nationale Ch, Grande
Ecurie, J-C. Malgoire (r1992) *Concert*
(9/93) (K617) ① **K617026**
Hola, Hala, que vienen gitanas—villancico
Cordoba Children's Ch, Elyma Ens, G. Garrido
(r1992) *Concert*   (9/93) (K617) ① **K617025**
Salve Regina
Cordoba Children's Ch, Elyma Ens, G. Garrido
(r1992) *Concert*   (9/93) (K617) ① **K617025**
Silencio, Pasito—villancico
Cordoba Children's Ch, Elyma Ens, G. Garrido
(r1992) *Concert*   (9/93) (K617) ① **K617025**

ARBAN, (Joseph) Jean-Baptiste (Laurent) (1825–1889) France

SECTION I: ORCHESTRAL

Fantasie brillante—cornet and orchestra/band
W. Marsalis, Eastman Wind Ens, D. Hunsberger (arr
D Hunsberger) *Concert* (9/87) (SONY) ① **MK42137**
Theme and Variations sur Le Carnaval de
Venise—keyed bugle and orchestra/band
W. Marsalis, Eastman Wind Ens, D. Hunsberger (arr
D Hunsberger) *Concert* (9/87) (SONY) ① **MK42137**
S. Nakarjakov, A. Markovich (arr tpt/pf) *Concert*
(5/93) (TELD) ① **9031-77705-2**

SECTION II: CHAMBER

Fantasy and Variations on themes from
Auber's 'Actéon'—cornet and piano
J. Wallace, S. Wright (r1993) *Concert*
(11/94) (EMI) ① **CDC5 55086-2**
Variations on a theme from Bellini's
'Norma'
H. Rehbenberger, R. Pöntinen *Concert*
(11/85) (BIS) ① **BIS-CD287**
S. Nakarjakov, A. Markovich (r1994: arr tpt/pf)
Concert   (6/95) (TELD) ① **4509-94554-2**
Variations on a Tyrolean Theme—cornet and
piano
S. Nakarjakov, A. Markovich (r1994: arr tpt/pf)
Concert   (6/95) (TELD) ① **4509-94554-2**

ARBEAU, Thoinot (1520–1595) France

pseudonym of Jehan Tabourot

SECTION II: CHAMBER

Orchésographie—dance manual with
examples (pub 1588/89, 1596) (examples
anonymously composed, collected by Arbeau)
Morisco; Buffons; Pavane; Bransle l'Official
London Musica Antiqua, M. Uridge (r1980-83)
Concert   (12/93) (SYMP) ① **SYMCD1157**

SECTION IV: VOCAL AND CHORAL

Belle que tiens ma vie—chanson
Scholars (r1993) *Concert*
(2/95) (NAXO) ① **8 550880**

ARCADELT, Jacques (?1505–1568) ?Flanders

SECTION IV: VOCAL AND CHORAL

Il Bianco e dolce cigno
Amaryllis Consort *Concert*
(6/86) (CARL) ① **PCD822**
Chansons
1. En ce mois délcieux; 2. Margot, labourez les
vignes; 3. Du temps que j'estois amoureux; 4. Sa
grand beauté.
Scholars (r1993) *Concert*
(2/95) (NAXO) ① **8 550880**

ARCADET France

SECTION IV: VOCAL AND CHORAL

Chanson Lorraine—song
E. Clément, F. La Forge (r1911) *Concert*
(8/95) (ROMO) ① **82002-2**

ARCHANGELSKY, Alexander (1846–1924) Russia

SECTION IV: VOCAL AND CHORAL

The Creed—unaccompanied voices (Wds
Russian Creed)
F. Chaliapin, Russian Metropolitan Church Ch, N.
Afonsky (r1932) *Concert*
(12/89) (PEAR) ① **GEMMCD9314**
F. Chaliapin, Paris Russian Met Church Ch, N.
Afonsky (r1932) *Concert*
(6/93) (PREI) ① [2] **89207**

ARDITI, Luigi (1822–1903) Italy

SECTION IV: VOCAL AND CHORAL

Il Bacio—song (Wds. Aldighieri)
A. Patti, L. Ronald (r1905) *Concert*
(4/90) (PEAR) ① **GEMMCD9312**
Leggero invisibile, 'Boléro'—song
E. Schumann-Heink, orch (r1907) *Concert*
(2/91) (NIMB) ① **NI7811**
Parla Waltz—in the style of the Italian
canzonetta
E. Teodorini, anon (r1903) *Concert*
(5/91) (SYMP) ① **SYMCD1077**
Se saran rose—song (Wds. P. Mazzoni)
N. Melba, orch, W.B. Rogers (r1910) *Concert*
(9/93) (RCA) ① **09026 61412-2**
N. Melba, orch, W.B. Rogers (r1907) *Concert*
(5/95) (ROMO) ① [3] **81011-2(1)**
N. Melba, orch, W.B. Rogers (r1910) *Concert*
(5/95) (ROMO) ① [3] **81011-2(2)**

ARENSKY, Anton Stepanovich (1861–1906) Russia

SECTION I: ORCHESTRAL

Concerto for Piano and Orchestra in F
minor, Op. 2 (1882)
S. Coombs, BBC Scottish SO, J. Maksymiuk *Concert*
(3/93) (HYPE) ① **CDA66624**
Concerto for Violin and Orchestra in A
minor, Op. 54 (1891)
Movt 2. J. Heifetz, E. Bay (r1946) *Concert*
(11/94) (RCA) ① [65] **09026 61778-2(06)**
Fantasia on Russian Folksongs—piano and
orchestra, Op. 48 (1899)
S. Coombs, BBC Scottish SO, J. Maksymiuk *Concert*
(3/93) (HYPE) ① **CDA66624**
Variations on a theme of
Tchaikovsky—string orchestra, Op. 35a
(1894)
ROHO, M. Ermler *Tchaikovsky: Nutcracker.*
(12/89) (ROH) ① **ROH304/5**
Primavera CO, P. Manley *Concert*
(3/93) (UNIC) ① **DKPCD9134**

SECTION II: CHAMBER

Concert Waltz—trumpet and piano
S. Nakarjakov, A. Markovich *Concert*
(5/93) (TELD) ① **9031-77705-2**
Piano Trio No. 1 in D minor, Op. 32 (1894)
Nash Ens *Rimsky-Korsakov: Piano and Wind
Quintet.*   (6/92) (CRD) ① **CRD3409**

H. Temianka, A. Sala, E. Joyce (r1938) *Concert*
(2/93) (BIDD) ① [2] **LAB059/60**
Solomon Trio *Tchaikovsky: Piano Trio, Op. 50.*
(5/93) (CARL) ① **MCD52**
R. Stamper, C. Jackson, Vovka Ashkenazy (r1990)
Tchaikovsky: Piano Trio, Op. 50.
(7/93) (NAXO) ① **8 550467**
C-L. Lin, G. Hoffman, Y. Bronfman (r1992)
Tchaikovsky: Piano Trio, Op. 50.
(9/94) (SONY) ① **SK53269**
Grumiaux Pf Trio (r1993) *Smetana: Piano Trio in G
minor.*   (11/94) (RICE) ① **RIS131117**
J. Heifetz, G. Piatigorsky, L. Pennario (r1963)
Concert   (11/94) (RCA) ① [65] **09026 61778-2(27)**
Beaux Arts Trio (r1994) *Piano Trio 1.*
(6/95) (PHIL) ① **442 127-2PH**
Piano Trio No. 2 in F minor, Op. 73 (1905)
Borodin Trio *Concert*
(10/91) (CHAN) ① **CHAN8924**
Beaux Arts Trio (r1994) *Piano Trio 1.*
(6/95) (PHIL) ① **442 127-2PH**
String Quartet No. 2 in A minor, Op. 35
(1894)
Raphael Ens (r1993) *Tchaikovsky: Souvenir de
Florence.*   (3/93) (HYPE) ① **CDA66648**
Suite No. 1 in F—two pianos, Op. 15
1. Romance; 2. Valse; 3. Polonaise.
2. O. Gabrilowitsch, H. Bauer (r1929) *Concert*
(4/89) (OPAL) ① **OPALCD9839**
Suite No. 2, 'Silhouettes'—two pianos, Op.
23 (1892)
1. The scholar; 2. The coquette; 3. The buffoon; 4.
The dreamer; 5. The dancer.
Danish Nat RSO, N. Järvi (arr orch) *Scriabin:
Symphony 3.*   (3/93) (CHAN) ① **CHAN8898**

SECTION III: INSTRUMENTAL

24 Characteristic Pieces—piano, Op. 36
(1894)
1. Prélude; 2. La toupe; 3. Nocturne; 4. Petite
ballade; 5. Consolation; 6. Duo; 7. Valse; 8. In modo
antico; 9. Papillon; 10. Ne m'oubliez pas; 11.
Barcarolle; 12. Intermezzo in F minor; 13. Etude; 14.
Scherzino; 15. Le ruisseau dans la forêt; 16. Elégie;
17. La rêve; 18. Inquiétude; 19. Rêverie du
printemps; 20. Mazurka; 21. Marche; 22. Tarantella;
23. Andante con variazoni; 24. Aux champs.
12, 15. M. Fingerhut (r1992) *Concert*
(4/94) (CHAN) ① **CHAN9218**
Forgotten Rhythms, 'Essais sur les rythmes
oubliés—piano, Op. 28
1. Logaédes; 2. Péans; 3. Ioniques; 4. Savi; 5.
Strophe alcéenne; 6. Strophe sapphique.
4. A. Goldenweiser (r1951) *Concert*
(8/95) (MELO) ① [11] **74321 25172-2(1)**
4. A. Goldenweiser (r1951) *Concert*
(8/95) (MELO) ① **74321 25173-2**
6 Pieces—piano, Op. 53 (1901)
1. Prélude; 2. Scherzo; 3. Elégie; 4. Mazurka; 5.
Romance; 6. Etude.
5. M. Fingerhut (r1992) *Concert*
(4/94) (CHAN) ① **CHAN9218**

SECTION IV: VOCAL AND CHORAL

I did not tell you—song, Op. 6/4 (Wds. A.
Sologub)
A. Orda, J. Lee (bp1959) *Concert*
(12/89) (SYMP) ① **SYMCD1067**
On wings of dream—song
R. Ponselle, M. Elman, R. Romani (r1939) *Concert*
(10/89) (NIMB) ① **NI7805**

SECTION V: STAGE WORKS

The Dream on the Volga—opera: 4 acts, Op.
16 (1891—Moscow) (Lib. Ostrovsky)
Cradle song E. Zbrueva, anon (r1903) *Concert*
(6/93) (PEAR) ① [3] **GEMMCDS9004/6(2)**
Raphael—opera: 1 act, Op. 37
(1894—Moscow) (Lib. A. Kryukov)
My heart trembles with passion L. Sobinov, orch
(r1911) *Concert*
(6/93) (PEAR) ① [3] **GEMMCDS9997/9(2)**

ARGENTO, Dominik (b 1927) USA

SECTION IV: VOCAL AND CHORAL

From the Diary of Virginia Woolf—song
cycle: mezzo-soprano and piano (1974)
1. Diary; 2. Anxiety; 3. Fancy; 4. Funeral; 5. Rome; 6.
War; 7. Parents; 8. Last entry.
V. Dupuy, D. Garvey *Benson: End of the World.*
(2/91) (KING) ① **KCLCD2018**

SECTION V: STAGE WORKS

The **Dream of Valentino—opera**
(1993—Washington)
EXCERPTS: 1. Tango.
1. Baltimore SO, D. Zinman (r1994) *Concert*
(7/95) (ARGO) ① **444 454-2ZH**

ARIOSTI, Attilio (Malachia) (1666–c1729) Italy

SECTION IV: VOCAL AND CHORAL

6 Cantatas (1724)
1. La rosa (1v, 2vns and continuo); 2. L'amore onesto
(1v and continuo); 3. L'olmo (1v, 2 vns and continuo);
4. Libertà acquistata in amore (1v and continuo); 5.
Naufragio vicino (1v, 2 vns and continuo); 6. La
gelosia (1v and continuo).
1. A. Monoyios, Berlin Barock Compagney (r1993)
Concert (10/95) (CAPR) ① **10 459**

ARLEN, Harold (1905–1986) USA

SECTION V: STAGE WORKS

St. Louis Woman—musical show
(1946—New York) (Lyrics J. Mercer)
EXCERPTS: 1. Come rain or come shine; 3. Any
place I hang my hat is home; 4. I had myself a true
love; 5. Legalize my name; 6. I wonder what became
of me.
Cpte P. Bailey, H. Nicholas, Orig Broadway Cast
(11/93) (EMI) ① **ZDM7 64662-2**
The **Wizard of Oz—musical film (1939)** (Wds
E.Y. Harburg. Score arr H. Stothart)
EXCERPTS: 1. Main Title; 2. Over the Rainbow; 3.
Munchkin Land; 4. Ding! Dong! The Witch is Dead; 5.
Follow the Yellow Brick Road; 6. If I Only Had a Brain
(Scarecrow); 7. We're Off to See the Wizard; 8. If I
Only Had a Heart (Tin Man); 9. We're Off to See the
Wizard (reprise); 10. If I Only Had the Nerve (Lion);
11. We're Off to See the Wizard (reprise); 12. If I
Were the King of the Forest; 13. Courage; 14. Ding!
Dong! The Witch is Dead (reprise); 15. Home Sweet
Home; 16. Over the Rainbow (instrumental).
Concert Suite Hollywood Bowl SO, J. Mauceri
(r1991; arr Stothart, ed Mauceri/Krasker) *Concert*
(9/91) (PHIL) ① **432 109-2PH**
The **Wizard of Oz—musical show based on
the film (1987—London)** (Lyrics adapted J.
Kane)
EXCERPTS: ACT ONE: 1. Overture; 2. Over the
Rainbow; 3. The Twister; 4. Munchkinland; 5. If I Only
Had a Brain; 6. We're Off to See the Wizard; 7. If I
Only Had a Heart; 8. We're Off to See the Wizard
(reprise); 9. If I Only Had the Nerve; 10. We're Off to
See the Wizard (reprise); 11. Poppies. ACT TWO:
12. Entr'acte; 13. The Merry Old Land of Oz; 14a. If I
Were King of the Forest; 14b. Courage; 15. The
Jitterbug; 16a. Winkies March; 16b. Over the
Rainbow (reprise); 17. Ding, Dong, the Witch is Dead
(reprise); 18. Finale.
1-13, 14a, 14b, 15, 16a, 16b, 17, 18. Orig London
Cast, RSC Chor, RSC Orch, J. O. Edwards (r1989)
(12/89) (TER) ① **CDTER1165**

ARNAUD, Leo (b 1904) France/USA

SECTION I: ORCHESTRAL

La Chasse
Cleveland Winds, F. Fennell *Concert*
(10/84) (TELA) ① **CD80099**
Olympiad
Cleveland Winds, F. Fennell *Concert*
(10/84) (TELA) ① **CD80099**
Olympic Theme
Cleveland Winds, F. Fennell *Concert*
(10/84) (TELA) ① **CD80099**

ARNE, Michael (c1740–1786) England

SECTION IV: VOCAL AND CHORAL

The **Lass with the Delicate Air—song
(1762)**
E. Schwarzkopf, M. Raucheisen (Ger: bp1944)
Concert (6/87) (ACAN) ① **43 801**

ARNE, Thomas Augustine (1710–1778) England

SECTION I: ORCHESTRAL

**6 Favourite Concertos—keyboard and
orchestra (1750-70s: pub 1793)**
1. C; 2. G; 3. A; 4. B flat; 5. G minor; 6. B flat.
R.B. Williams, Cantilena, A. Shepherd
(8/88) (CHAN) ① [2] **CHAN8604/5**
P. Nicholson (kybds/dir), Parley of Instr, P. Holman
(9/92) (HYPE) ① **CDA66509**
1. P. Nicholson (hpd. solo) *Concert*
(5/90) (AMON) ① **CD-SAR42**
5. English Concert, T. Pinnock (hpd/dir) (r1979)
Concert (1/93) (ARCH) ① **437 088-2AT**
5. G. Malcolm, ASMF, N. Marriner *Concert*
(9/94) (DECC) ① **440 033-2DM**
8 Overtures in eight parts (pub 1751)
1. E minor; 2. A; 3. G (from 'Henry and Emma':
1749); 4. F; 5. D; 6. B flat; 7. D (from 'Comus': 1738);
8. G minor (from 'Judgement of Paris': 1740).
1. ASMF, N. Marriner *Concert*
(9/94) (DECC) ① **440 033-2DM**

SECTION II: CHAMBER

Solo in E—violin and continuo (c1744)
Locatelli Trio *Concert* (5/93) (HYPE) ① **CDA66583**
**7 Sonatas for Two Violins and Continuo
(1757)**
Nos 2, 5, 6, 7. Nouveau Qt *Concert*
(5/90) (AMON) ① **CD-SAR42**
2. London Baroque *Concert*
(4/87) (AMON) ① **CD-SAR14**

SECTION III: INSTRUMENTAL

**8 Sonatas or Lessons—harpsichord (pub
1756)**
1. F; 2. E minor; 3. G; 4. D minor; 5. B flat; 6. G
minor; 7. A; 8. G.
1. P. Nicholson *Concert*
(5/90) (AMON) ① **CD-SAR42**
1. G. Gifford *Concert* (5/90) (LIBR) ① **LRCD156**
1, 2. M. Souter (r1994-5) *Concert*
(12/95) (ISIS) ① **ISISCD010**
2. London Baroque *Concert*
(4/87) (AMON) ① **CD-SAR14**
3. R. Aldwinckle *Concert* (7/87) (CARL) ① **PCD850**
3. T. Pinnock *Concert* (11/90) (CRD) ① **CRD3307**
3. V. Black *Concert* (5/91) (COLL) ① **Coll5024-2**
5. Daniel Smith, R. Vignoles (trans. bsn
Craxton/Mather) *Concert*
(9/89) (ASV) ① **CDDCA535**
6. T. Pinnock (r1978) *Concert*
(4/89) (CRD) ① **CRD3347**

SECTION IV: VOCAL AND CHORAL

The **British grenadiers—song** (words & music
anon: set by Arne)
L. Skeaping, J. Potter, Broadside Band, J. Barlow
(r1992; arr J. Barlow) *Concert*
(6/93) (SAYD) ① **CD-SDL400**
Cymon and Iphigenia—cantata (1753)
R. Morton, Parley of Instr, R. Goodman (vn/dir)
(reconstr. Holman) *Concert*
(5/88) (HYPE) ① **CDA66237**
6 English Cantatas (1755)
1. The School of Anacreon; 2. Lydia; 3. Frolick and
free; 4. Bacchus and Ariadne; 5. The Morning; 6.
Delia ('From golden slumbers').
3. R. Morton, Parley of Instr, R. Goodman (vn/dir)
Concert (5/88) (HYPE) ① **CDA66237**
5. E. Kirkby, Parley of Instr, R. Goodman (vn/dir)
Concert (5/88) (HYPE) ① **CDA66237**
Jenny—song (1754)
R. Morton, Parley of Instr, R. Goodman (vn/dir)
Concert (5/88) (HYPE) ① **CDA66237**
On a day, alack the day—song (c1747) (Wds.
Shakespeare: possibly spurious)
A. Rolfe Johnson, G. Johnson *Concert*
(6/87) (DUTT) ① **CDA66480**
Rule Britannia—chorus and orchestra (1740)
(Wds. Thomson. Extracted from the stage
work 'Alfred')
Britannia Building Soc Band, Desford Colliery
Caterpillar Band, CWS (Glasgow) Band, IMI
Yorkshire Imperial Band, G. Brand (pp1991: arr M
Brand) *Concert* (8/92) (POLY) ① **QPRL049D**
L. Skeaping, J. Potter, Broadside Band, J. Barlow
(r1992; arr J. Barlow) *Concert*
(6/93) (SAYD) ① **CD-SDL400**
BBC Sngrs, BBC Sym Chor, BBC SO, A. Davis
(r1994; arr Sargent) *Concert*
(2/95) (TELD) ① **4509-97868-2**

Thou soft flowing Avon—ode (1769) (upon
dedicating a building to Shakespeare)
E. Kirkby, Parley of Instr, R. Goodman (vn/dir)
Concert (5/88) (HYPE) ① **CDA66237**
The **Winter's Amusement—song collection
(1761)**
1. The Lover's Recantation; 2. Come let us all be
blithe and gay.
1. E. Kirkby, Parley of Instr, R. Goodman (vn/dir)
Concert (5/88) (HYPE) ① **CDA66237**

SECTION V: STAGE WORKS

**Artaxerxes—opera: 3 acts (1762 rev
1777—London)** (Lib. cpsr, after Metastasio)
EXCERPTS: 1. The soldier tir'd of war's alarms; 2.
Fair Aurora, prithee stay.
1. B. Hoch, Hong Kong PO, K. Schermerhorn
Concert (11/86) (CARL) ① **PCD827**
1. J. Sutherland, ROHO, F. Molinari-Pradelli *Concert*
(1/90) (DECC) ① [2] **425 493-2DM2**
**As You Like It—songs from Shakespeare's
play (1740—London)**
EXCERPTS: 1. Blow, blow, thou winter wind; 2.
Under the greenwood tree.
2. J.M. Ainsley, Orch, R. King *Concert*
(12/93) (UNIT) ① **88002-2**
The **Blind Beggar of Bethnal Green—stage
work (1744—London)** (Lib. R Dodsley. 6 songs
& 1 duet extant)
EXCERPTS: 1. Polly Millfen.
1. S.J. Langton, K. Schmidt (r1991; arr Lehmann)
Concert (12/93) (KOCH) ① **37240-2**
The **Masque of Comus—stage work
(1738—London)** (Lib. J. Datton, after Milton)
EXCERPTS: 1. Fame's an echo; 2. Not on beds of
fading flowers; 3. By the rushy-fringed bank; 4a.
Brightest Lady; 4b. Thrice upon thy Finger's Tip.
3, 4a, 4b E. Kirkby, AAM, C. Hogwood (r1991)
Concert (7/93) (L'OI) ① **436 132-2OH**
**Love in a Village—ballad opera
(1762—London)** (Lib. T. Bickerstaffe)
EXCERPTS: 1. All I wish in her obtaining; 2.
Begone, I agree; 3. Believe me, dear aunt; 4. Cease,
gay seducers; 5. Go, naughty man; 6. In love should
there meet; 7. In vain I every art essay; 8. My heart's
own; 9. Oons, neighbour, never blush; 10. Since
Hodge proves ungrateful; 12. Think, o my fairest; 13.
The Traveller benighted; 14. Well come, let us hear;
15. When once love's subtle poison; 16. When we
see a lover languish; 17. Whence can you inherit; 18.
The World is a well-furnished table; 19. The Miller of
Dee (traditional arr Arne).
19. L. Skeaping, Broadside Band, J. Barlow (r1992;
arr J. Barlow) *Concert*
(6/93) (SAYD) ① **CD-SDL400**
**Love's Labours Lost—songs from
Shakespears's play (1741—London)**
EXCERPTS: 1. The Cuckoo's Song; 2. When daisies
pied.
2. E. Schwarzkopf, G. Moore (r1947) *Concert*
(12/90) (EMI) ① **CDM7 63654-2**
**Much Ado about Nothing—songs from
Shakespeare's play (1748—London)**
EXCERPTS: 1. Sigh no more, ladies.
1. R. Morton, Parley of Instr, R. Goodman (vn/dir)
Concert (5/88) (HYPE) ① **CDA66237**
Rosamond—stage work (1733—London)
(Lib. J. Addison)
EXCERPTS: 1. Rise, Glory rise.
1. E. Kirkby, AAM, C. Hogwood (r1991) *Concert*
(7/93) (L'OI) ① **436 132-2OH**
The **Tempest—songs from Shakespeare's
play (1746—London)**
EXCERPTS: 1. Ariel's song (Where the bee sucks).
1. E. Schwarzkopf, G. Moore (r1947) *Concert*
(12/90) (EMI) ① **CDM7 63654-2**
1. E. Kirkby, AAM, C. Hogwood (r1991) *Concert*
(7/93) (L'OI) ① **436 132-2OH**
1. J.M. Ainsley, Orch, R. King *Concert*
(12/93) (UNIT) ① **88002-2**
1. I. Baillie, G. Moore (r1943) *Concert*
(7/95) (DUTT) ① **CDLX7013**
**Twelfth Night—songs from Shakespeare's
play (1741—London)**
1. Come away, death.
1. J.M. Ainsley, Orch, R. King *Concert*
(12/93) (UNIT) ① **88002-2**

ARNELL, Richard (b 1917) England

SECTION I: ORCHESTRAL

Ceremonial and Flourish—brass (1946)
Locke Brass Consort *Concert*
(12/93) (KOCH) ① **37202-2**

27

SECTION V: STAGE WORKS

The **Great detective—ballet, Op. 68 (1953)**
Suite PAO, R. Arnell (r1958) Concert
(8/94) (EMI) ① **CDM7 64718-2**
Punch and the Child—ballet (1948)
RPO, T. Beecham (r1950) Concert
(11/94) (SONY) ① **SMK46683**

ARNOLD, Ernest (19th–20th cents) ?Austria

SECTION IV: VOCAL AND CHORAL

Da draussen in der Wachau—song
E. Kunz, Kemmeter-Faltl Schrammel Ens (r1949)
Concert   (9/95) (TEST) ① **SBT1059**
Wenn der Herrgott net will—Viennese song
E. Kunz, Kemmeter-Faltl Schrammel Ens (r1948)
Concert   (9/95) (TEST) ① **SBT1059**

ARNOLD, Sir Malcolm (Henry) (b 1921) England

SECTION I: ORCHESTRAL

Beckus the Dandipratt—overture for orchestra, Op. 5 (1943)
LPO, M. Arnold Concert
(6/92) (REFE) ① **RRCD-48**
Carnival of Animals, Op. 72 (1960)
EXCERPTS: 1. The Giraffe; 2. Sheep; 3. Cows; 4.
Mice; 5. Jumbo; 6. Chiroptera (Bats).
RPO, V. Handley (r1994) Concert
(12/94) (CONI) ① **CDCF240**
Commonwealth Christmas Overture—orchestra, Op. 64 (1957)
LPO, M. Arnold Concert
(6/92) (REFE) ① **RRCD-48**
Concerto for Clarinet and Orchestra, Op. 115 (1974)
T. King, ECO, B. Wordsworth (r1992) Concert
(12/93) (HYPE) ① **CDA66634**
M. Collins, London Musici, M. Stephenson (r1993)
Concert   (12/93) (CONI) ① **CDCF228**
E. Johnson, ECO, I. Bolton (r1994) Concert
(7/95) (ASV) ① **CDDCA922**
Concerto for Clarinet and Strings No. 1, Op. 20 (1948)
M. Collins, London Musici, M. Stephenson Concert
(8/89) (CONI) ① **CDCF172**
T. King, ECO, B. Wordsworth (r1992) Concert
(12/93) (HYPE) ① **CDA66634**
E. Johnson, ECO, I. Bolton (r1994) Concert
(7/95) (ASV) ① **CDDCA922**
Concerto for Flute and Chamber Orchestra No. 2, Op. 111 (1972)
K. Jones, London Musici, M. Stephenson (r1993)
Concert   (12/93) (CONI) ① **CDCF228**
Concerto for Flute and Strings No. 1, Op. 45 (1954)
K. Jones, London Musici, M. Stephenson Concert
(8/89) (CONI) ① **CDCF172**
E. Beckett, London Fest Orch, R. Pople Concert
(3/90) (HYPE) ① **CDA66332**
Concerto for Guitar and Chamber Orchestra, Op. 67 (1959)
M. Conn, St John's Smith Square Orch, J. Lubbock
Rodrigo: Concierto de Aranjuez.
(8/87) (CARL) ① **PCD859**
J. Bream, CBSO, S. Rattle (r1991) Concert
(7/93) (EMI) ① **CDC7 54661-2**
J. Bream, Melos Ens (r1959) Concert
(8/93) (RCA) ① [28] **09026 61583-2(4)**
J. Bream, Melos Ens, M. Arnold (r1959) Concert
(6/94) (RCA) ① **09026 61598-2**
Concerto for Harmonica and Orchestra, Op. 46 (1954)
T. Reilly, Basle RSO, C. Dumont (r1976) Concert
(5/94) (CHAN) ① **CHAN9248**
Concerto for Horn and Orchestra No. 1, Op. 11 (1946)
R. Watkins, London Musici, M. Stephenson (r1993)
Concert   (12/93) (CONI) ① **CDCF228**
Concerto for Horn and Orchestra No. 2, Op. 58 (1956)
R. Watkins, London Musici, M. Stephenson Concert
(8/89) (CONI) ① **CDCF172**
Concerto for Oboe and Strings, Op. 39 (1952)
M. Messiter, London Fest Orch, R. Pople Concert
(3/90) (HYPE) ① **CDA66332**

Concerto for Piano Duet and Strings, Op. 32 (1950)
D. Nettle, Richard Markham, London Musici, M.
Stephenson (r1993) Concert
(12/93) (CONI) ① **CDCF228**
Concerto for Two Pianos (3 hands) and Orchestra, Op. 104 (1969)
C. Smith, P. Sellick, CBSO, M. Arnold Concert
(10/91) (EMI) ① **CDM7 64044-2**
D. Nettle, Richard Markham, RPO, V. Handley
(r1994) Concert   (12/94) (CONI) ① **CDCF240**
Concerto for 2 Violins and Strings, Op. 77 (1962)
K. Sillito, L. Fletcher, London Musici, M. Stephenson
Concert   (8/89) (CONI) ① **CDCF172**
I. Gruppman, V. Gruppman, San Diego CO, D. Barra
Concert   (6/92) (KOCH) ① **37134-2**
4 Cornish Dances—orchestra, Op. 91 (1966)
1. Vivace; 2. Andantino; 3. Con moto e sempre senza
parodia; 4. Allegro ma non troppo.
Philh, B. Thomson Concert
(10/90) (CHAN) ① **CHAN8867**
LPO, M. Arnold Concert
(12/90) (LYRI) ① **SRCD201**
Grimethorpe Colliery Band, E. Howarth (r1993; arr
Farr) Concert   (12/93) (CONI) ① **CDCF222**
3. Philh, M. Arnold Concert
(10/91) (EMI) ① **CDM7 64044-2**
4 English Dances—orchestra, Op. 27 (1950)
1. Andantino; 2. Vivace; 3. Mesto; 4. Allegro risoluto.
LPO, A. Boult (r1954) Concert
(9/90) (LOND) ① **425 661-2LM**
Philh, B. Thomson Concert
(10/90) (CHAN) ① **CHAN8867**
LPO, M. Arnold Concert
(12/90) (LYRI) ① **SRCD201**
Grimethorpe Colliery Band, E. Howarth (r1993; arr
Farr) Concert   (12/93) (CONI) ① **CDCF222**
3. Philh, M. Arnold Concert
(10/91) (EMI) ① **CDM7 64044-2**
4 English Dances—orchestra, Op. 33 (1951)
1. Allegro non troppo; 2. Con brio; 3. Grazioso; 4.
Giubiloso—Lento e maestoso.
LPO, A. Boult (r1954) Concert
(9/90) (LOND) ① **425 661-2LM**
Philh, B. Thomson Concert
(10/90) (CHAN) ① **CHAN8867**
LPO, M. Arnold Concert
(12/90) (LYRI) ① **SRCD201**
Grimethorpe Colliery Band, E. Howarth (r1993; arr
Farr) Concert   (12/93) (CONI) ① **CDCF222**
1. Philh, M. Arnold Concert
(10/91) (EMI) ① **CDM7 64044-2**
The Fair Field—overture for orchestra, Op. 110 (1972)
LPO, M. Arnold Concert
(6/92) (REFE) ① **RRCD-48**
Fantasy—brass band, Op. 114 (1974) (comp
for 1974 National Brass Band Championships)
Grimethorpe Colliery Band, E. Howarth (r1993)
Concert   (12/93) (CONI) ① **CDCF222**
Fantasy on a theme of John Field—piano and orchestra, Op. 116 (1975)
J. Lill, RPO, V. Handley (r1993) Concert
(2/94) (CONI) ① **CDCF224**
A Grand Grand Overture—orchestra, Op. 57 (1956)
RPO, M. Arnold (r1957) Concert
(8/94) (EMI) ① **CDM7 64718-2**
RPO, V. Handley (r1994) Concert
(12/94) (CONI) ① **CDCF240**
4 Irish Dances—orchestra, Op. 126 (1986)
1. Allegro con energico; 2. Commodo; 3. Piacevole;
4. Vivace.
Philh, B. Thomson Concert
(10/90) (CHAN) ① **CHAN8867**
LPO, M. Arnold Concert
(12/90) (LYRI) ① **SRCD201**
Little Suite No. 1—brass band, Op. 80 (1965)
Grimethorpe Colliery Band, E. Howarth (r1993)
Concert   (12/93) (CONI) ① **CDCF222**
Little Suite No. 2—bras band, Op. 93 (1967)
Grimethorpe Colliery Band, E. Howarth (r1993)
Concert   (12/93) (CONI) ① **CDCF222**
The Padstow Lifeboat—brass band, Op. 94 (1968)
Grimethorpe Colliery Band, M. Arnold (r1993)
Concert   (12/93) (CONI) ① **CDCF222**
Peterloo—overture for orchestra, Op. 97 (1968)
CBSO, M. Arnold Concert
(6/90) (EMI) ① **CDM7 63368-2**
Popular Birthday—orchestra (1972) (for
Walton's 70th birthday)
LPO, J. Latham-König (r1992) Concert
(1/94) (CHAN) ① **CHAN9148**

4 Scottish Dances—orchestra, Op. 59 (1957)
1. Pesante; 2. Vivace; 3. Allegretto; 4. Con brio.
Philh, B. Thomson Concert
(10/90) (CHAN) ① **CHAN8867**
LPO, M. Arnold Concert
(12/90) (LYRI) ① **SRCD201**
Grimethorpe Colliery Band, E. Howarth (r1993; arr
Farr) Concert   (12/93) (CONI) ① **CDCF222**
LPO, M. Arnold (r1958) Concert
(5/95) (EVER) ① **EVC9006**
Serenade—small orchestra, Op. 26 (1950)
San Diego CO, D. Barra Concert
(6/92) (KOCH) ① **37134-2**
Sinfonietta No. 1—orchestra, Op. 48 (1954)
London Fest Orch, R. Pople Concert
(3/90) (HYPE) ① **CDA66332**
San Diego CO, D. Barra Concert
(6/92) (KOCH) ① **37134-2**
Sinfonietta No. 2—orchestra, Op. 65 (1958)
London Fest Orch, R. Pople Concert
(3/90) (HYPE) ① **CDA66332**
San Diego CO, D. Barra Concert
(6/92) (KOCH) ① **37134-2**
Sinfonietta No. 3—orchestra, Op. 81 (1964)
London Fest Orch, R. Pople Concert
(3/90) (HYPE) ① **CDA66332**
The Smoke—overture for orchestra, Op. 21 (1948)
LPO, M. Arnold Concert
(6/92) (REFE) ① **RRCD-48**
The Sound Barrier—rhapsody for orchestra, Op. 38 (1952) (based on themes from film of
same name)
LSO, R. Hickox Concert
(2/93) (CHAN) ① **CHAN9100**
RPO, M. Arnold (r1957) Concert
(9/94) (EMI) ① **CDGO 2059**
A Sussex Overture—orchestra, Op. 31 (1951)
LPO, M. Arnold Concert
(6/92) (REFE) ① **RRCD-48**
Symphony No. 1, Op. 22 (1949)
Bournemouth SO, M. Arnold Concert
(10/91) (EMI) ① **CDM7 64044-2**
LSO, R. Hickox (r1994) Symphony 2.
(3/95) (CHAN) ① **CHAN9335**
Symphony No. 2, Op. 40 (1953)
Bournemouth SO, C. Groves Concert
(6/90) (EMI) ① **CDM7 63368-2**
RPO, V. Handley (r1994) Concert
(12/94) (CONI) ① **CDCF240**
LSO, R. Hickox (r1994) Symphony 1.
(3/95) (CHAN) ① **CHAN9335**
Symphony No. 3, Op. 63 (1954-57)
LSO, R. Hickox Symphony 4.
(9/94) (CHAN) ① **CHAN9290**
LPO, M. Arnold (r1959) Vaughan Williams:
Symphony 9.   (4/95) (EVER) ① **EVC9001**
Symphony No. 4, Op. 71 (1960)
LPO, M. Arnold   (11/90) (LYRI) ① **SRCD200**
LSO, R. Hickox Symphony 3.
(9/94) (CHAN) ① **CHAN9290**
Symphony No. 5, Op. 74 (1961)
CBSO, M. Arnold Concert
(6/90) (EMI) ① **CDM7 63368-2**
LSO, R. Hickox (r1995) Symphony 6.
(12/95) (CHAN) ① **CHAN9385**
Symphony No. 6, Op. 95 (1967)
RPO, V. Handley (r1993) Concert
(2/94) (CONI) ① **CDCF224**
LSO, R. Hickox (r1995) Symphony 5.
(12/95) (CHAN) ① **CHAN9385**
Symphony No. 7, Op. 113 (1973)
RPO, V. Handley Symphony 8.
(3/91) (CONI) ① **CDCF177**
Symphony No. 8, Op. 124 (1978)
RPO, V. Handley Symphony 7.
(3/91) (CONI) ① **CDCF177**
Tam O'Shanter—overture for orchestra, Op. 51 (1955)
SNO, A. Gibson Concert
(7/83) (CHAN) ① **CHAN8301**
SNO, A. Gibson Concert
(9/85) (CHAN) ① **CHAN8553**
Philh, M. Arnold Concert
(10/91) (EMI) ① **CDM7 64044-2**
RPO, V. Handley (r1993) Concert
(2/94) (CONI) ① **CDCF224**

SECTION II: CHAMBER

Divertimento—flute, oboe and clarinet, Op. 37 (1952)
J. Pearce, G. Hulse, M. Collins Concert
(1/89) (HYPE) ① **CDA66173**
J. Martin, J. Kelly, E. Johnson (r1994) Concert
(7/95) (ASV) ① **CDDCA922**

Duo—2 cellos, Op. 85 (1964)
C. van Kampen, M. Welsh *Concert*
(1/89) (HYPE) ① **CDA66171**

Duo—flute and viola, Op. 10 (1945)
J. Pearce, R. Chase *Concert*
(1/89) (HYPE) ① **CDA66173**

Piano Trio, Op. 54 (1956)
M. Crayford, C. van Kampen, I. Brown *Concert*
(1/89) (HYPE) ① **CDA66171**

5 Pieces—violin and piano, Op. 84 (1965)
M. Crayford, I. Brown *Concert*
(1/89) (HYPE) ① **CDA66171**

Quartet—oboe and strings, Op. 61 (1957)
G. Hulse, M. Crayford, R. Chase, C. van Kampen *Concert*
(1/89) (HYPE) ① **CDA66173**

Quintet—flute, violin, viola, horn and bassoon, Op. 7 (1944)
J. Pearce, M. Crayford, R. Chase, J. Pigneguy, B. Wightman *Concert*
(1/89) (HYPE) ① **CDA66173**

3 Shanties—wind quintet, Op. 4 (1943)
J. Pearce, G. Hulse, M. Collins, J. Pigneguy, B. Wightman *Concert*
(1/89) (HYPE) ① **CDA66173**
J. Martin, J. Kelly, E. Johnson, C. Briggs, S. Cohen (r1994) *Concert*
(7/95) (ASV) ① **CDDCA922**

Sonata—flute and piano, Op. 121 (1977)
J. Pearce, I. Brown *Concert*
(1/89) (HYPE) ① **CDA66173**
K. Smith, P. Rhodes *Concert*
(1/91) (ASV) ① **CDDCA739**

Sonata—viola and piano, Op. 17 (1947)
R. Chase, I. Brown *Concert*
(1/89) (HYPE) ① **CDA66171**

Sonata for Violin and Piano No. 1, Op. 15 (1947)
M. Crayford, I. Brown *Concert*
(1/89) (HYPE) ① **CDA66171**

Sonata for Violin and Piano No. 2, Op. 43 (1953)
M. Crayford, I. Brown *Concert*
(1/89) (HYPE) ① **CDA66171**

Sonatina—clarinet and piano, Op. 29 (1951)
G. de Peyer, G. Pryor *Concert*
(11/87) (CHAN) ① **CHAN8549**
M. Collins, I. Brown *Concert*
(1/89) (HYPE) ① **CDA66172**
M. Khouri, P. Pettinger *Concert*
(6/92) (CNTI) ① **CCD1038**
N. Carpenter, D. McArthur *Concert*
(10/92) (HERA) ① **HAVPCD152**
E. Jóhannesson, P. Jenkins *Concert*
(7/95) (CHAN) ① **CHAN9079**
E. Johnson, M. Martineau (r1993) *Concert*
(7/95) (ASV) ① **CDDCA922**

Sonatina—flute and piano, Op. 19 (1948)
J. Pearce, I. Brown *Concert*
(1/89) (HYPE) ① **CDA66172**

Sonatina—oboe and piano, Op. 28 (1951)
G. Hulse, I. Brown *Concert*
(1/89) (HYPE) ① **CDA66172**
J. Polmear, D. Ambache *Concert*
(9/92) (UNIC) ① **DKPCD9121**

Sonatina—recorder and piano, Op. 41 (1953)
J. Pearce, I. Brown (fl) *Concert*
(1/89) (HYPE) ① **CDA66172**

String Quartet No. 1, Op. 23 (1949)
ASMF Chbr Ens *String Quartet 2.*
(10/92) (CHAN) ① **CHAN9112**

String Quartet No. 2, Op. 118 (1975)
ASMF Chbr Ens *String Quartet 1.*
(10/92) (CHAN) ① **CHAN9112**

Trio—flute, viola and bassoon, Op. 6 (1942-43)
J. Pearce, R. Chase, B. Wightman *Concert*
(1/89) (HYPE) ① **CDA66172**

SECTION III: INSTRUMENTAL

Allegro in E minor—piano (1937)
B. Frith (r c1994) *Concert*
(2/95) (KOCH) ① **37162-2**

2 Bagatelles—piano, Op. 18 (1947)
1. Allegretto; 2. Moderato.
B. Frith (r c1994) *Concert*
(2/95) (KOCH) ① **37162-2**

8 Children's pieces—piano, Op. 36 (1952)
1. Tired bagpipes; 2. Two sad hands; 3. Across the plains; 4. Strolling tune; 5. Dancing tune; 6. Giants; 7. The Duke; 8. The Buccaneer.
B. Frith (r c1994) *Concert*
(2/95) (KOCH) ① **37162-2**

Children's Suite—piano, Op. 16
1. Prelude; 2. Carol; 3. Shepherd's lament; 4. Trumpet tune; 5. Blue tune; 6. Folk song.
B. Frith (r c1994) *Concert*
(2/95) (KOCH) ① **37162-2**

Day dreams—piano (1938)
B. Frith (r c1994) *Concert*
(2/95) (KOCH) ① **37162-2**

Fantasia—bassoon, Op. 86 (1966)
B. Wightman *Concert* (1/89) (HYPE) ① **CDA66172**

Fantasia—clarinet, Op. 87 (1966)
M. Collins *Concert* (1/89) (HYPE) ① **CDA66172**
E. Johnson (r1994) *Concert*
(7/95) (ASV) ① **CDDCA922**

Fantasia—flute, Op. 89 (1966)
J. Pearce *Concert* (1/89) (HYPE) ① **CDA66172**

Fantasia—horn, Op. 88 (1966)
J. Pigneguy *Concert* (1/89) (HYPE) ① **CDA66172**

Fantasia—oboe, Op. 90 (1966)
G. Hulse *Concert* (1/89) (HYPE) ① **CDA66172**

3 Fantasies—piano, Op. 129 (1986)
1. Lento et mesto; 2. Vivace; 3. Andante con moto.
B. Frith (r c1994) *Concert*
(2/95) (KOCH) ① **37162-2**

Fantasy—cello (1987)
J. Lloyd Webber *Concert*
(9/88) (ASV) ① **CDDCA592**

3 Piano pieces (1937)
1. Prelude; 2. Air; 3. Gigue.
B. Frith (r c1994) *Concert*
(2/95) (KOCH) ① **37162-2**

2 Piano pieces (1941)
1. Allegro; 2. Quickly.
B. Frith (r c1994) *Concert*
(2/95) (KOCH) ① **37162-2**

3 Piano pieces (1943)
1. Prelude; 2. Romance; 3. Lament.
B. Frith (r c1994) *Concert*
(2/95) (KOCH) ① **37162-2**

Piano Sonata (1942)
B. Frith (r c1994) *Concert*
(2/95) (KOCH) ① **37162-2**

Prelude—piano (1945)
B. Frith (r c1994) *Concert*
(2/95) (KOCH) ① **37162-2**

Serenade in G—piano (1937)
B. Frith (r c1994) *Concert*
(2/95) (KOCH) ① **37162-2**

Variations on a Ukrainian folksong—piano, Op. 9 (1948)
B. Frith (r c1994) *Concert*
(2/95) (KOCH) ① **37162-2**

SECTION V: STAGE WORKS

The Bridge on the River Kwai—film score (1957)
Suite LSO, R. Hickox (arr C Palmer) *Concert*
(2/93) (CHAN) ① **CHAN9100**

Hobson's Choice—film score (1953)
Suite LSO, R. Hickox (arr C Palmer) *Concert*
(2/93) (CHAN) ① **CHAN9100**

The Inn of the Sixth Happiness—film score (1958)
Suite LSO, R. Hickox (arr C Palmer) *Concert*
(2/93) (CHAN) ① **CHAN9100**

Solitaire—ballet (1956—London) (score comprises English Dances and two new pieces)
Sarabande; Polka Philh, B. Thomson *Concert*
(10/90) (CHAN) ① **CHAN8867**
Sarabande; Polka LPO, M. Arnold *Concert*
(12/90) (LYRI) ① **SRCD201**
Sarabande; Polka Bournemouth SO, M. Arnold *Concert*
(10/91) (EMI) ① **CDM7 64044-2**

Sweeney Todd—concert suite from ballet, Op. 68a (1984) (arr cpsr & D Ellis)
RPO, V. Handley (r1993) *Concert*
(2/94) (CONI) ① **CDCF224**

Whistle down the Wind—film score (1961)
Suite LSO, R. Hickox (arr C Palmer) *Concert*
(2/93) (CHAN) ① **CHAN9100**

You know what sailors are—film score (1953)
1. Scherzetto.
1. T. King, ECO, B. Wordsworth r1992; arr C. Palmer) *Concert* (12/93) (HYPE) ① **CDA66634**

ARNOLD, Samuel (1740–1802)
England

SECTION IV: VOCAL AND CHORAL

Elegy—song (1778) (Wds. anon)
R. Müller, F. Kelly *Concert*
(12/91) (HYPE) ① **CDA66497**

ARONA, Colombino (1885–?)
Italy

SECTION IV: VOCAL AND CHORAL

Campana di San Giusto—song (Wds. G. Drovetti)
T. Schipa, orch (r1926) *Concert*
(2/89) (PEAR) ① **GEMMCD9322**
E. Caruso, orch, J. Pasternack (r1919) *Concert*
(7/91) (RCA) ① [12] **GD60495(6)**
E. Caruso, orch, J. Pasternack (r1919) *Concert*
(1/91) (PEAR) ① [3] **EVC4(2)**

ARRIAGA (Y BALZOLA), Juan Crisóstomo (Jacobo Antonio) (1806–1826) Spain

SECTION I: ORCHESTRAL

Overture in F minor, 'Nonet'—small orchestra, Op. 1 (1818)
Concert des Nations, J. Savall (r1994; rev Savall) *Concert*
(10/95) (ASTR) ① **E8532**

Symphony in D (?1824)
Berlin RIAS Sinfonietta, J. Velazco *Concert*
(12/89) (SCHW) ① **311035**
Concert des Nations, Capella Reial Instr Ens, J. Savall (r1994; rev Gomez: orig vers) *Concert*
(10/95) (ASTR) ① **E8532**
Scottish CO, C. Mackerras (r1995) *Concert*
(11/95) (HYPE) ① **CDA66800**

SECTION II: CHAMBER

String Quartet No. 1 in D minor (1824)
Voces Qt *Concert* (3/89) (MDG) ① **L3236**
Chilingirian Qt *Concert*
(8/89) (CRD) ① [2] **CRD3312/3**
Sine Nomine Qt (r1994) *Concert*
(9/95) (CLAV) ① **CD50-9501**

String Quartet No. 2 in A (1824)
Voces Qt *Concert* (3/89) (MDG) ① **L3236**
Chilingirian Qt *Concert*
(8/89) (CRD) ① [2] **CRD3312/3**
Sine Nomine Qt (r1994) *Concert*
(9/95) (CLAV) ① **CD50-9501**

String Quartet No. 3 in E flat (1824)
Voces Qt *Concert* (3/89) (MDG) ① **L3236**
Chilingirian Qt *Concert*
(8/89) (CRD) ① [2] **CRD3312/3**
Sine Nomine Qt (r1994) *Concert*
(9/95) (CLAV) ① **CD50-9501**

SECTION V: STAGE WORKS

Los Esclavos felices—opera semiseria: 2 acts (1820—Bilbao) (Lib. Comella y Comella)
EXCERPTS: 1. Overture.
1. Concert des Nations, Capella Reial Instr Ens, J. Savall (r1994; rev Savall) *Concert*
(10/95) (ASTR) ① **E8532**
1. Scottish CO, C. Mackerras (r1995) *Concert*
(11/95) (HYPE) ① **CDA66800**

ARUTIUNIAN, Alexander (b 1920)
Armenia

SECTION I: ORCHESTRAL

Concerto for Trumpet and Orchestra (1950)
A. Sandoval, LSO, L. Haza (r1993) *Concert*
(1/95) (GRP) ① **GRK75002**

ASCHER, Joseph (1829–1869)
The Netherlands

SECTION IV: VOCAL AND CHORAL

Alice, where are thou?—song (1861) (Wds. W. Guernsey)
H. Nash, G. Moore (r1931) *Concert*
(11/95) (PEAR) ① **GEMMCD9175**

ASHLEY, Robert (Reynolds) (b 1930) USA

SECTION III: INSTRUMENTAL

Factory Preset—computer (1993)
R. Ashley (r1993) *Concert*
(8/94) (KOCH) ① [2] **37238-2**

ASHMORE, Lawrence (b 1930) England

SECTION I: ORCHESTRAL

4 Seasons—folksong arrangements: clarinet and strings (1989)
R. Stoltzman, Guildhall Str Ens *Concert*
(9/91) (RCA) ① **RD60437**

ASSMAYER, Ignaz (1790–1862) Austria

SECTION II: CHAMBER

Octet in E flat—wind octet with double-bass
Consortium Classicum *Concert*
(9/90) (SCHW) ① **310002**

ASTON, Hugh (c1485–1558) England

SECTION II: CHAMBER

High Ashton's Maske—consort (possibly by W. Whytbroke)
Amsterdam Loeki Stardust Qt (r1991) *Concert*
(2/94) (L'OI) ① **436 155-2OH**
Amsterdam Loeki Stardust Qt *Concert*
(10/94) (L'OI) ① **440 207-2OM**

SECTION III: INSTRUMENTAL

A Hornepype—keyboard
S. Yates (r1994) *Concert*
(12/95) (CHAN) ① **CHAN0574**

ASTON, Peter George (b 1938) England

SECTION IV: VOCAL AND CHORAL

Alleluya Psallat II—4vv unaccompanied (1971)
Worcester Cath Ch, Don Hunt *Concert*
(9/90) (CARL) ① **PCD937**
Evening Service in F
Gloucester Cath Ch, J. Sanders, M. Lee (r1994)
Concert (4/95) (PRIO) ① **PRCD494**

ATKINS, Sir Ivor (1869–1953) England

SECTION IV: VOCAL AND CHORAL

Praise ye the Lord—Psalm 146 (Wds. Bible)
Truro Cath Ch, D. Briggs, H. Doughty *Concert*
(7/91) (PRIO) ① **PRCD322**

ATTAINGNANT, Pierre (c1494–1551/2) France

SECTION II: CHAMBER

Basse danse La Brosse/Tripla/Tourdion
Ulsamer Collegium, J. Ulsamer *Concert*
(2/86) (ARCH) ① **415 294-2AH**
Basse danse La Gatta
Ulsamer Collegium, J. Ulsamer *Concert*
(2/86) (ARCH) ① **415 294-2AH**
Basse danse La Magdalena
Ulsamer Collegium, J. Ulsamer *Concert*
(2/86) (ARCH) ① **415 294-2AH**
Dance collection—consort (pub 1530)
(various anon basse dances & branles)
1. Cortège; 2. Bransle simple; 3. Anonymous Ronde;
4. Bransle double; 5. La saltarelle du jeu d'amour; 6.
Anonymous Galliarde; 7. Anonymous Basse danse;
8. Tourdion Estampie; 9. Anonymous Branle; 10.
Branle gay, 'C'est mon amy'; 11. Two Haulberroys;
12. Branle de Poictou; 13. Sansserre.
8. London Musica Antiqua, M. Uridge (r1980-83)
Concert (12/93) (SYMP) ① **SYMCD1157**

SECTION III: INSTRUMENTAL

Magnificat quarti toni—organ
J. Payne (r1994) *Concert*
(10/95) (NAXO) ① **8 553215**
Parce Domine—organ (after J Obrecht)
J. Payne (r1994) *Concert*
(10/95) (NAXO) ① **8 553215**
Prélude—lute (pub 1529)
Baltimore Consort (r1992; arr Baltimore Consort)
Concert (4/95) (DORI) ① **DOR90177**

Sanctus and Benedictus—organ
J. Payne (r1994) *Concert*
(10/95) (NAXO) ① **8 553215**

ATTERBERG, Kurt (Magnus) (1887–1974) Sweden

SECTION I: ORCHESTRAL

Ballad without words—orchestra, Op. 56 (1957-58)
Norrköping SO, J. Hirokami (r1992) *Concert*
(8/92) (BIS) ① **BIS-CD553**
Concerto for Horn and Orchestra in A, Op. 28 (1926)
A. Linder, Gothenburg SO, G. Oskamp *Symphony 3.*
(10/89) (CPRI) ① **CAP21364**
Rondeau rétrospectif—orchestra, Op. 26 (1925)
I. Prunyi, S. Falvay (r1990; arr 2 pfs) *Concert*
(9/94) (MARC) ① **8 223404**
Suite No. 3—violin, viola and string orchestra, Op. 19/1 (1917)
A. Lysy, P. Coletti, Camerata Lysy *Concert*
(3/87) (CLAV) ① **CD50-8507**
Symphony No. 3, 'West Coast Pictures', Op. 10 (1914-16)
Stockholm PO, S. Ehrling *Horn Concerto, Op. 28.*
(10/89) (CPRI) ① **CAP21364**
Symphony No. 5 in D minor, 'Sinfonia funebre', Op. 20 (1919-22)
Stockholm PO, S. Westerberg *Concert*
(8/92) (MSVE) ① **MSCD620**
Symphony No. 6 in C, Op. 31 (1927-28)
NBC SO, A. Toscanini (bp1943) *Sibelius: Symphony 2.*
(1/90) (DELL) ① **CDDA9019**
Norrköping SO, J. Hirokami (r1992) *Concert*
(8/92) (BIS) ① **BIS-CD553**
A Värmland Rhapsody, Op. 36 (1933)
Norrköping SO, J. Hirokami (r1992) *Concert*
(8/92) (BIS) ① **BIS-CD553**

SECTION II: CHAMBER

Piano Quintet, Op. 31 bis (1927-28) (arr cpsr from Symphony 6)
I. Prunyi, New Budapest Qt (r1990) *Concert*
(9/93) (MARC) ① **8 223405**
Sonata for Cello/Viola/Violin and Piano in B minor, Op. 27 (1925)
E. Pérényi, I. Prunyi (r1990; vn/pf) *Concert*
(9/94) (MARC) ① **8 223404**
Sonata for Horn and Piano in B minor, Op. 27 (1955)
I. Magyari, I. Prunyi (r1990) *Concert*
(9/93) (MARC) ① **8 223405**
Suite No. 1, 'Orientale'—two violins, cello and piano (1948) (arr from orch suite)
A. Kiss, F. Balogh, G. Kertész, I. Prunyi (r1990)
Concert (9/93) (MARC) ① **8 223405**
Trio concertante in G minor/C—violin, cello and harp, Op. 57 (1966)
A. Kiss, G. Kertész, D. Sipkay (r1991) *Concert*
(9/94) (MARC) ① **8 223404**

SECTION III: INSTRUMENTAL

Autumn Ballads—piano, Op. 15 (1918)
1. B minor; 2. C minor.
I. Prunyi (r1990) *Concert*
(9/94) (MARC) ① **8 223404**
Valse monotone in C—piano (arr from last movt of Suite No. 3)
I. Prunyi (r1990) *Concert*
(9/94) (MARC) ① **8 223404**

ATTWOOD, Thomas (1765–1838) England

SECTION IV: VOCAL AND CHORAL

Blessed is the man—hymn (Wds. Psalm I)
Jesus College Ch, D. Phillips, T. Horton *Concert*
(7/93) (CNTO) ① **CRCD2367**
Come, Holy Ghost
Magdalen Oxford Coll Ch, J. Harper *Concert*
(11/91) (ABBE) ① **CDCA912**
St Paul's Cath Ch, John Scott, Adrian Lucas (r1991)
Concert (8/93) (HYPE) ① **CDA66618**
Coronach, 'He is gone on the mountain'—1v & harp (1810) (Wds Scott)
Invocation (r1994) *Concert*
(3/95) (HYPE) ① **CDA66740**
Ellen's Song, 'Ave Maria'—1v & piano (c1810) (Wds Scott)
Invocation (r1994) *Concert*
(3/95) (HYPE) ① **CDA66740**

The Soldier's Dream—1v & harp (c1810) (Wds T. Campbell)
Invocation (r1994) *Concert*
(3/95) (HYPE) ① **CDA66740**
Teach me, O Lord—anthem (Wds. Pslam 119, verse 33)
St Paul's Cath Ch, John Scott, Andrew Lucas (r1993)
Concert (6/94) (HYPE) ① **CDA66678**

AUBER, Daniel-François-Esprit (1782–1871) France

SECTION V: STAGE WORKS

Le Domino noir, '(The) Black domino'—opéra-comique: 3 acts (1837)
Overture Black Dyke Mills Band, D. Hurst (arr brass band) *Concert* (9/93) (CHAN) ① **CHAN4514**
Fra Diavolo—opéra-comique: 3 acts (1830—Paris) (Lib. Scribe)
EXCERPTS: 1. Overture; 2. ACT 1: Voyez sur cette roche. ACT 2: 3. Quel bonheur; 4. Agnès la jouvencelle. ACT 3: 5. O Sainte Vierge; 6. Pour toujours, disait-elle.
Cpte N. Gedda, M. Mesplé, T. Dran, J. Berbié, R. Corazza, J. Bastin, M. Trempont, M. Hamel, J Laforge Choral Ens, Monte Carlo PO, M. Soustrot (r1983/4) (1/94) (EMI) ① [2] **CDS7 54810-2**
1. Berlin St Op Orch, O. Klemperer (r1929) *Concert*
(2/89) (SYMP) ① **SYMCD1042**
3. E. Berger, Berlin St Op Orch, L. Blech (Ger: r1934)
Concert (12/91) (PREI) ① **89035**
3. A. Nezhdanova, orch (r1910: Russ) *Concert*
(6/93) (PEAR) ① [3] **GEMMCDS9007/9(2)**
3. A. Nezhdanova, orch (r1910; Russ) *Concert*
(3/95) (NIMB) ① **NI7865**
4. N. Figner, anon (r1901: Russ) *Concert*
(6/93) (PEAR) ① [3] **GEMMCDS9997/9(1)**
4. D. Yuzhin, anon (r1902: Russ) *Concert*
(6/93) (PEAR) ① [3] **GEMMCDS9001/3(1)**
6. H. Roswaenge, Berlin St Op Orch, B. Seidler-Winkler (r1936: Ger) *Concert*
(5/90) (PREI) ① **89018**
6. H. Roswaenge, Berlin St Op Chor, Berlin St Op Orch, B. Seidler-Winkler (Ger: r1936) *Concert*
(10/92) (TEST) ① **SBT1005**
6. H. Roswaenge, Berlin St Op Orch, B. Seidler-Winkler (r1936: Ger) *Concert*
(4/95) (PREI) ① [2] **89209**
Grand Pas Classique—pas de deux (Paris) (arr from various works)
English Concert Orch, R. Bonynge *Concert*
(11/90) (DECC) ① [2] **421 818-2DH2**
Gustav III, ou le Bal masqué—opéra-historique: 5 acts (1833—Paris)
1. Overture; 2. Ballet Music; 2a. Allemande; 2b. Pas des folies; 2c. Pas des paysans; 2d. Menuet; 2e. Marche I; 2f. Marche II; 2g. Galop.
Cpte L. Dale, R. Tawil, C. Treguier, B. Lafon, V. Marestin, R. Pujol, G. Dubernet, P. Foucher, F. Leguérinel, Intermezzo Voc Ens, French Lyrique Orch, M. Swierczewski (pp1991)
(9/93) (ARIO) ① [3] **ARN368220**
Manon Lescaut—opéra-comique: 3 acts (1856—Paris) (Lib. Scribe, after Prévost)
C'est l'histoire amoureuse A. Galli-Curci, orch (r1917) *Concert* (2/89) (PEAR) ① **GEMMCD9308**
C'est l'histoire amoureuse A. Galli-Curci, orch, R. Bourdon (r1917) *Concert* (5/90) (NIMB) ① **NI7806**
C'est l'histoire amoureuse A. Galli-Curci, orch, J. Pasternack (r1917) *Concert*
(3/94) (ROMO) ① [2] **81003-2**
La Muette de Portici—opera: 5 acts (1828—Paris) (Lib. Scribe and Delavigne)
EXCERPTS: 1. Overture; 2. Amis, la matinée; 3. Du pauvre seul ami fidèle!; 4. Voyez du haut des rivages.
1. Lamoureux Orch, I. Markevitch *Concert*
(7/95) (DG) ① **447 406-2GOR**
3. L. Slezak, orch (r1908) *Concert*
(2/91) (PREI) ① **89020**

AUBERT, Louis François Marie (1867–1968) France

SECTION III: INSTRUMENTAL

Hommage à Gabriel Fauré—piano
M. Fingerhut *Concert* (9/88) (CHAN) ① **CHAN8578**

SECTION IV: VOCAL AND CHORAL

Cache-cache—duet (Wds. A. de Bengy Puyvallée)
F. Lott, A. Murray, G. Johnson (r1991) *Concert*
(7/92) (EMI) ① **CDC7 54411-2**

AUDEFROI (fl 1190–1230)
France

SECTION IV: VOCAL AND CHORAL
Au novel tens pascor—chanson de toile: 1v
Gothic Voices, C. Page (r1994) *Concert*
(8/95) (HYPE) ① **CDA66773**
Bele Emmelos—chanson de femme
Sinfonye, S. Wishart (r1992) *Concert*
(8/93) (HYPE) ① **CDA66625**

AUDRAN, Edmond (1840–1901)
France

SECTION V: STAGE WORKS
Miss Helyett—operetta: 3 acts (1890—Paris)
(Wds. M. Boucheron)
Cpte L. Dachary, C. Collart, G. Ristori, L. Arseguet,
A. Doniat, D. Tirmont, M. Hamel, R. Lenoty, G. Rey,
ORTF Lyric Chorale, ORTF Lyric Orch, M. Cariven
(bp1963) *Poupée*. (11/93) (MUSD) ① [2] **20240-2**
La Poupée—operetta: 4 acts (1896—Paris)
(Lib. Ordonneau)
Excs H. Hennetier, J. Peyron, R. Massard, Duvaleix,
R. Lenoty, Génio, G. Ristori, P. Roi, J. Pruvost,
French Rad Lyric Chor, French Rad Lyric Orch, M.
Cariven (bp1958) *Miss Helyett*.
(11/93) (MUSD) ① [2] **20240-2**

AUFSCHNAITER, Benedikt Anton (1662–1742) Austria

SECTION IV: VOCAL AND CHORAL
Improperium exspectavit—motet
Niederaltaicher Scholaren, K. Ruhland (r1992)
Concert (10/93) (SONY) ① **SK53117**

AULIN, Tor (1866–1914)
Sweden

SECTION II: CHAMBER
4 Aquarelles (Akvareller)—violin and piano (1899)
1. Iydll; 2. Humoresque; 3. Cradle Song; 4.
Polonaise.
2. E. Zimbalist, S. Chotzinoff (r1911) *Concert*
(7/93) (APR) ① [2] **APR7016**

AURIC, Georges (1899–1983)
France

SECTION I: ORCHESTRAL
La Seine au Matin—piano and orchestra (1937)
B. Lerner (pf version) *Concert*
(1/89) (ETCE) ① **KTC1061**

SECTION II: CHAMBER
5 Bagatelles—piano duet (1925) (from 'La
femme silencieuse' & 'Le dompteur')
1. Ouverture; 2. Petite Marche; 3. Valse; 4. Rêveries;
5. Retraite.
P. Corre, E. Exerjean *Concert*
(5/94) (PIER) ① **PV786091**
Imaginées II—cello and piano (1969)
N. Fischer, J.K. Fischer *Concert*
(9/91) (NORT) ① **NR238-CD**
Imaginées III—clarinet and piano (1973)
R. Samuels, F. Renzi (r1993) *Concert*
(7/95) (KOCH) ① **37186-2**
Sonata for Violin and Piano in G (1936)
F.P. Zimmermann, A. Lonquich (r1991) *Concert*
(1/95) (EMI) ① **CDC7 54541-2**
Trio—oboe, clarinet and bassoon (1936)
Pro Arte Wind Quintet *Concert*
(1/93) (NIMB) ① **NI5327**

SECTION IV: VOCAL AND CHORAL
Marie Laurencin—song (1919) (Wds. J.
Cocteau)
S. Varcoe, G. Johnson *Concert*
(6/88) (HYPE) ① **CDA66248**

AUSTIN, Larry Don (b 1930) USA

SECTION II: CHAMBER
**art is self-alteration is Cage is...—four
double bass quartets (1983)**
R. Black (1983) *Concert*
(8/94) (KOCH) ① [2] **37238-2**

AVISON, Charles (1709–1770)
England

SECTION I: ORCHESTRAL
12 Concerti grossi after D. Scarlatti—strings (1744)
1. A; 2. G; 3. D minor; 4. A minor; 5. D minor; 6. D; 7.
G minor; 8. E minor; 9. C; 10. D; 11. G; 12. D.
I. Brown, M. Latchem, D. Vigay, N. Kraemer, ASMF,
N. Marriner (r1978)
(8/94) (PHIL) ① [2] **438 806-2PM2**
Brandenburg Consort, R. Goodman (r1994)
(4/95) (HYPE) ① [2] **CDA66891/2**
1-6. Berlin Ens (3/92) (SCHW) ① **316015**
7-12. Berlin Ens (3/92) (SCHW) ① **316029**
9. English Concert, T. Pinnock (hpd/dir) *Concert*
(1/86) (ARCH) ① **415 518-2AH**
9. English Concert, T. Pinnock (hpd/dir) (r1984)
Concert (1/93) (ARCH) ① **437 088-2AT**

SECTION II: CHAMBER
Sonata for Violin and Keyboard in F
Daniel Smith, R. Vignoles (trans bsn Atkinson)
Concert (9/89) (ASV) ① **CDDCA535**
**6 Sonatas for 2 Violins, Harpsichord and
Cello (1756)**
2. London Baroque *Concert*
(4/87) (AMON) ① **CD-SAR14**

AYLEWARD, Robert (1626–1669)
England

SECTION IV: VOCAL AND CHORAL
Evening (Short) Service—choir
Chichester Cath Ch, A. Thurlow, J. Thomas (r1994)
Concert (5/95) (PRIO) ① **PRCD511**

AZZAIOLO, Filippo (fl 1557–69)
Italy

SECTION IV: VOCAL AND CHORAL
Chi passa per 'sta strada—madrigal
E. Van Evera, Musicians of Swanne Alley *Concert*
(11/89) (VIRG) ① **VC7 59534-2**

BABBITT, Milton (Byron) (b 1916)
USA

SECTION I: ORCHESTRAL
Concerto for Piano and Orchestra (1985)
A. Feinberg, American Cpsrs Orch, C. Wuorinen
Head of the Bed. (12/87) (NEW) ① **NW346-2**
**Correspondences—string orchestra and
synthesized tape (1967)**
Chicago SO, James Levine (r1990) *Concert*
(7/94) (DG) ① **431 698-2GH**
Relata I (1965)
Juilliard Orch, P. Zukofsky *Concert*
(7/91) (NEW) ① **80396-2**

SECTION IV: VOCAL AND CHORAL
The Head of the Bed (1981)
J. Bettina, Parnassus, A. Korf *Piano Concerto.*
(12/87) (NEW) ① **NW346-2**

BABELL, William (c1690–1723)
England

SECTION I: ORCHESTRAL
**Concerto a 7 for Recorder and Strings in D,
from Op. 3 (pub 1730)**
F. Brüggen, M. Leonhardt, A. Stuurop, A. van den
Hombergh, L. van Dael, A. Bylsma, F. Nijenhuis, G.
Leonhardt (r1971) *Concert*
(10/95) (TELD) ① **4509-97465-2**
**Concerto for Recorder and Strings in E
minor, Op. 3/3 (pub 1730)**
C. Pehrsson, Drottningholm Baroque Ens *Concert*
(10/88) (BIS) ① **BIS-CD249**

SECTION II: CHAMBER
**Sonata for Oboe and Continuo No. 1 in B flat
(pub 1723)**
P. Dombrecht, W. Kuijken, R. Kohnen *Concert*
(9/86) (ACCE) ① **ACC57804D**

SECTION III: INSTRUMENTAL
The **Lady's Entertainment, or Banquet of
Musick—keyboard arrangements of popular
Opera arias (pub 1709 & 1716)**
EXCERPTS: 3. VOLUME THREE: 3a. Man in
Imagination (from Clotildo by F. B. Conti); 3b.
Rimiravi (from Clotildo); 3c. Kindly Cupid (from
Pyrrhus by A. Scarlatti); 3d. Rise O Sun (from
Pyrrhus); 4. VOLUME FOUR: 4a. Ritorno gia (from
Hydaspes by F. Mancini); 4b. Se credi (from
Hydaspes); 4c. Vi fara (from Hydaspes); 4d. In non
voglio (from Hydaspes); 4e. Mostro crudel (from
Hydaspes); 4f. Perte sol (from Almahide by G.
Bononcini); 4g. Alvariar (from Almahide).
3, 3a-d, 4, 4a-g J. Chapman (r1995) *Handel Pieces,
Op. 8.* (12/95) (COLL) ① **Coll1456-2**
**Pièces de clavecin de Mr Handel—keyboard
arrangements of Handel arias, Op. 8 (pub
c1745)**
EXCERPTS: 1. Arias from Rinaldo: 1a. Vo far
guerra; 1b. Lascia ch'io pianga; 1c. Bel piacere; 1d.
Sulla routa di fortuna; 1e. Overture; 1f. Hor la
Trumba; 2. Se in Ombre Nacosta (attrib. Handel); 3.
Questo Conforto Solo (from Antiochus).
1, 1a-f, 2, 3. J. Chapman (r1995) *Lady's
Entertainment.* (12/95) (COLL) ① **Coll1456-2**

BACCUSI, Ippolito (c1550–1609)
Italy

SECTION IV: VOCAL AND CHORAL
Io son bell'e delicata—madrigal: 5vv
M. Arruabarrena, K. van Laethem, M. Valenta, J.
Benet, M. van Altena, J. Cabré, T. de Zwart, A. Pols,
R. Van Der Meer, K. Junghänel (lte/dir) *Concert*
(1/92) (ACCE) ① **ACC8864D**
Mentre ti fui mi grato—madrigal: 5vv
M. Arruabarrena, K. van Laethem, M. Valenta, J.
Benet, M. van Altena, J. Cabré, T. de Zwart, A. Pols,
R. Van Der Meer, K. Junghänel (lte/dir) *Concert*
(1/92) (ACCE) ① **ACC8864D**

BACEWICZ, Grażyna (1909–1969)
Poland

SECTION I: ORCHESTRAL
Concerto for String Orchestra (1948)
Polish CO, J. Maksymiuk (r1975) *Concert*
(12/93) (OLYM) ① **OCD392**
Cracow PO, R. Bader (r1991) *Symphony 3.*
(2/95) (SCHW) ① **311432**
**Concerto for Violin and Orchestra No. 7
(1965)**
P. Janowski, Warsaw PO, A. Markowski (r1969)
Concert (12/93) (OLYM) ① **OCD392**
Symphony No. 3 (1952)
Cracow PO, R. Bader (r1991) *String Orchestra
Concerto.* (2/95) (SCHW) ① **311432**

SECTION II: CHAMBER
Oberek No. 2—violin and piano (1952)
Midori, R. McDonald (r1992) *Concert*
(6/93) (SONY) ① **SK52568**
Piano Quintet No. 2 (1965)
Warsaw Pf Qnt (r1971) *Concert*
(8/93) (OLYM) ① **OCD387**
Sonata for Violin and Piano No. 4 (1949)
E. Statkiewicz, A. Utrecht (r1968) *Concert*
(12/93) (OLYM) ① **OCD392**
String Quartet No. 3 (1947)
Wilanów Qt (r1978) *Concert*
(8/93) (OLYM) ① **OCD387**
String Quartet No. 4 (1950)
Maggini Qt (r1993) *Concert*
(2/95) (ASV) ① **CDDCA908**
String Quartet No. 5 (1955)
Wilanów Qt (r1978) *Concert*
(8/93) (OLYM) ① **OCD387**

SECTION III: INSTRUMENTAL
Sonata for Piano No. 2 (1953)
S. Marin *Concert* (4/93) (RNE) ① **M3/03**
K. Zimerman (r1977) *Concert*
(12/93) (OLYM) ① **OCD392**

Heilig, 'Herr, werth das Schaaren'—1v,
double chorus and orchestra, H778 (Wq217)
(1776) (Wds. Isaiah 6:3)
H. Helling, Rheinische Kantorei, Kleine Konzert, H.
Max *Concert* (10/88) (CAPR) ① **10 208**
Magnificat in D minor—soli, chorus and
orchestra, H772 (Wq215) (1749)
EXCERPTS: 1. Magnificat anima mea Dominum; 2.
Quia respexit humilitatem; 3. Quia fecit mihi magna;
4. Et misericordiae; 5. Fecit potentiam; 6. Deposuit;
7. Suscepit Israel; 8. Gloria Patri; 9. Sicut cervus.
2. E. Ameling, Collegium Aureum, G. Schmidt-Gaden
(r1966) *Concert*
(12/95) (DHM) ① [4] 74321 26617-2(1)
Morgengesang am Schöpfungsfeste—ode,
H779 (Wq239) (1783) (Wds. Klopstock)
B. Schlick, J. Koslowsky, Rheinische Kantorei, Kleine
Konzert, H. Max *Concert* (10/88) (CAPR) ① **10 208**
Phillis und Thirsis—cantata: SS, 2 flutes and
continuo, H697 (Wq232) (1765)
R. Hofmann, N. Rogers, H-M. Linde, C. Huntgeburth,
P. Carrai, R. Junghanns (r1981) *Concert*
(4/92) (DHM) ① **RD77188**

BACH, Georg Christoph
(1642–1697) Germany

SECTION IV: VOCAL AND CHORAL

Siehe, wie fein und lieblich ist—Vocal
Concerto: 3vv and strings (1689)
P. Elliott, H. Meens, S. Varcoe, Cologne Musica
Antiqua, R. Goebel (r1986) *Concert*
(1/93) (ARCH) ① **437 090-2AT**

BACH, Johann Bernhard (bap
1676–1749) Germany

SECTION III: INSTRUMENTAL

Du Friedefürst, Herr Jesu Christ—partita
sopra: organ
W. Krumbach (r1968-9) *Concert*
(1/95) (TELD) ① [2] 4509-92176-2
Passacaglia in B flat—organ
W. Krumbach (r1968-9) *Concert*
(1/95) (TELD) ① [2] 4509-92176-2

BACH, Johann Christian
(1735–1782)
Germany/Italy/England

T Nos—C.S. Terry, J.C. Bach

SECTION I: ORCHESTRAL

Concerto for Keyboard and Strings in A
(?1754-55) (also attrib C.P.E. Bach)
G. Malcolm, ASMF, N. Marriner *Concert*
(9/94) (DECC) ① **440 033-2DM**
Concerto for Oboe, 2 Horns and Strings in F,
T290/7
B. Glaetzner, Berlin CO, M. Pommer *Concert*
(10/88) (CAPR) ① **10 069**
6 Concertos for Keyboard and Strings,
T293/4 (Op. 7) (pub 1770)
1. C; 2. F; 3. D; 4. B flat; 5. E flat; 6. G.
5. London Baroque *Concert*
(11/92) (HARM) ① **HMC90 1395**
6 Concertos for Keyboard and Strings,
T295/1 (Op. 13) (pub 1777)
1. C; 2. D; 3. F; 4. B flat; 5. G; 6. E flat.
2. Lukas Consort, V. Lukas (fp/dir) (r1990) *Concert*
(10/95) (CAMP) ① **RRCD1334**
4. M. Flipse, Concertgebouw, W. Mengelberg
(pp1943) *Concert* (5/95) (ARHI) ① **ADCD112**
6 Favourite Overtures, T272/2 (pub 1763)
EXCERPTS: 1. Orione; 2. La calamità; 3. Artaserse;
4. Il tutore; 5. La cascina; 6. Astarto (Alessandro
nell'Indie).
2. Netherlands CO, D. Zinman (r1976) *Concert*
(10/94) (PHIL) ① [2] 442 275-2PM2
2-6. Hanover Band, A. Halstead (r1994) *Concert*
(11/95) (CPO) ① **CPO999 129-2**
6 Grand Overtures, Op. 18 (T269/4) (c1781)
1. E flat; 2. B flat; 3. D; 4. D; 5. E; 6. D.
English SO, W. Boughton (1992)
(9/94) (NIMB) ① **NI5403**
Netherlands CO, D. Zinman (r1974) *Concert*
(10/94) (PHIL) ① [2] 442 275-2PM2
1. St Paul CO, P. Zukerman *Concert*
(2/88) (SONY) ① **SK39964**
1, 4. AAM, S. Standage (vn/dir) (r1993) *Concert*
(12/93) (CHAN) ① **CHAN0540**
4. Lukas Consort, V. Lukas (r c1990) *Concert*
(10/95) (CAMP) ① **RRCD1334**

Overture in D—for Gassmann's opera 'Gli
Uccellatori', T277/4 (1759, rev & pub 1763)
Hanover Band, A. Halstead (r1994) *Concert*
(11/95) (CPO) ① **CPO999 129-2**
An Overture in 8 Parts—from Lampugnani's
pasticcio 'La Giulia', T275/3 (pub 1766)
(corrected vers of Periodical Ov.)
Hanover Band, A. Halstead (r1994) *Concert*
(11/95) (CPO) ① **CPO999 129-2**
Sinfonia Concertante in A major—violin,
cello and orchestra, T284/4 (1773)
E. Turovsky, Y. Turovsky (vc/dir), Montreal I Musici
Concert (1/87) (CHAN) ① **CHAN8470**
P. Zukerman (vn/dir), Y-Y. Ma, St Paul CO *Concert*
(2/88) (SONY) ① **SK39964**
Budapest Camerata, H. Gmür (r1994) *Concert*
(7/95) (NAXO) ① 8 553085
Sinfonia Concertante in C—flute, oboe,
violin, cello and orchestra, T289/4
AAM, S. Standage (vn/dir) (r1993; ed Maunder)
Concert (12/93) (CHAN) ① **CHAN0540**
Sinfonia Concertante in E flat—2 vns/obs, 2
fls, 2 hns & strings, T284/6 (1774)
Budapest Camerata, H. Gmür (r1994) *Concert*
(7/95) (NAXO) ① 8 553085
Lukas Consort, V. Lukas (r c1990) *Concert*
(10/95) (CAMP) ① **RRCD1334**
6 Symphonies, Op. 3 (T262/1) (1765)
1. C; 2. D; 3. E flat; 4. B flat; 5. F; 6. G.
Budapest Camerata, H. Gmür (r1994)
(7/95) (NAXO) ① 8 553083
Hanover Band, A. Halstead (r1994)
(11/95) (CPO) ① **CPO999 268-2**
6 Symphonies, Op. 6 (T264/1) (pub 1770)
1. G; 2. D; 3. E flat; 4. B flat; 5. E flat; 6. G minor.
Netherlands CO, D. Zinman (r1976) *Concert*
(10/94) (PHIL) ① [2] 442 275-2PM2
Budapest Camerata, H. Gmür (r1994)
(7/95) (NAXO) ① 8 553084
6. AAM, S. Standage (vn/dir) (r1993) *Concert*
(12/93) (CHAN) ① **CHAN0540**
6. Lukas Consort, V. Lukas (r c1990) *Concert*
(10/95) (CAMP) ① **RRCD1334**
3 Symphonies, Op. 9 (T268/3) (pub 1773)
1. B flat; 2. E flat; 3. B flat.
Netherlands CO, D. Zinman (r1976) *Concert*
(10/94) (PHIL) ① [2] 442 275-2PM2
Budapest Camerata, H. Gmür (r1994)
(7/95) (NAXO) ① 8 553085
2. Lukas Consort, V. Lukas (r c1990) *Concert*
(10/95) (CAMP) ① **RRCD1334**

SECTION II: CHAMBER

Duets—Four Sonatas and Two Duetts,
Op.18/T326/3 (1781)
Nos 5, 6. H. Fagius, D. Sanger *Concert*
(10/85) (BIS) ① **BIS-CD273**
6 Quintets for flute, oboe, violin, viola and
continuo, Op. 11
1. C; 2. G; 3. F; 4. E flat; 5. A; 6. D.
2, 3. Adieux *Concert* (7/91) (DHM) ① **RD77250**
6. VCM, N. Harnoncourt (r1963) *Concert*
(7/93) (TELD) ① **4509-91002-2**
6 Sonatas—violin and keyboard, T329/1 (Op.
20) (c1785) (doubtful)
1. C; 2. G; 3. F; 4. G; 5. A; 6. B flat.
2. London Baroque *Concert*
(11/92) (HARM) ① **HMC90 1395**
4 Sonatas for Keyboard, Violin and Cello,
T323/5 (Op. 15) (pub 1778)
1. C; 2. A; 3. D; 4. B flat.
1, 2. Trio 1790 (r1993) *Sonatas, T313/1.*
(7/95) (CPO) ① **CPO999 254-2**
6 Sonatas for Keyboard, Violin/Flute and
Cello, T313/1 (Op. 2) (pub 1764)
1. F; 2. G; 3. D; 4. C; 5. D; 6. E flat.
Trio 1790 (r1993) *Sonatas, T323/5.*
(7/95) (CPO) ① **CPO999 254-2**

SECTION III: INSTRUMENTAL

6 Keyboard Sonatas, Op. 5 (T338/1) (pub
1766)
EXCERPTS: 1. B flat; 2. D; 3. G; 4. E flat; 5. E; 6. C
minor.
1. G. Gifford *Concert* (5/90) (LIBR) ① **LRCD156**
2. M. Souter (r1994-5) *Concert*
(12/95) (ISIS) ① **ISISCD010**
5, 6. V. Black *Keyboard Sonatas, Op. 17.*
(2/90) (CRD) ① **CRD3453**
6. T. Pinnock *Concert* (11/90) (CRD) ① **CRD3307**
6 Sonatas for Keyboard, Op. 17 (T341/1) (pub
c1779)
1. G; 2. C minor; 3. E flat; 4. G; 5. A; 6. B flat.
R. Woolley *Concert* (12/93) (CHAN) ① **CHAN0543**
2. I. Hobson *Concert* (3/89) (ARAB) ① **Z6594**

2, 3, 5. V. Black *Keyboard Sonatas, Op. 5.*
(2/90) (CRD) ① **CRD3453**

SECTION IV: VOCAL AND CHORAL

Canata a 3 voci—for the birthday of Charles
III of Spain (1762) (Wds. ?Passeri)
EXCERPTS: 1. Overture (original of 'Il tutore'
Overture, T273/2).
1. Hanover Band, A. Halstead (r1994) *Concert*
(11/95) (CPO) ① **CPO999 129-2**
6 Canzonette—two sopranos and continuo,
Op. 4 (T259/1) (1765)
1. Già la notte s'avvicine; 2. Ah rammenta oh bella
Irene; 3. Pur nel sonno almen talora; 4. T'intenda si
mio cor; 5. Che ciascun per te sospiri; 6. Ascoltami,
oh Clori.
2. V. de los Angeles, D. Fischer-Dieskau, G. Moore
(r1960: arr Reichert) *Concert*
(4/94) (EMI) ① [4] CMS5 65061-2(2)

SECTION V: STAGE WORKS

Adriano in Siria—opera, T211
(1976—London) (Lib after Metastasio)
EXCERPTS: 1. Overture.
1. AAM, S. Standage (vn/dir) (r1993) *Concert*
(12/93) (CHAN) ① **CHAN0540**
Amadis de Gaule—opera: 3 acts, T215
(1779—Paris) (Lib. de Vismes, after Quinault)
Cpte J. Wagner, U. Sonntag, I. Verebics, W. Schöne,
E. Hobarth, Stuttgart Gächinger Kantorei, Stuttgart
Bach Collegium, H. Rilling
(9/93) (HANN) ① [2] 98 963
Catone in Utica—opera: 3 acts (Naples) (Lib
after Metastasio)
EXCERPTS: 1. Overture; 2. Fiumicel che son de
appena.
1. Hanover Band, A. Halstead (r1994) *Concert*
(11/95) (CPO) ① **CPO999 129-2**

BACH, Johann Christoph
(1642–1703) Germany

SECTION III: INSTRUMENTAL

Aus meines Herzens Grunde—chorale:
organ
W. Krumbach (r1968-9) *Concert*
(1/95) (TELD) ① [2] 4509-92176-2
Prelude and Fugue in E flat—organ
W. Krumbach (r1968-9) *Concert*
(1/95) (TELD) ① [2] 4509-92176-2
Wach auf, mein Herz, und singe—chorale:
organ
W. Krumbach (r1968-9) *Concert*
(1/95) (TELD) ① [2] 4509-92176-2
Warum betrübst du dich, mein
Herz—chorale: organ
W. Krumbach (r1968-9) *Concert*
(1/95) (TELD) ① [2] 4509-92176-2

SECTION IV: VOCAL AND CHORAL

Ach, das ich Wassers g'nug hätte—lament:
contralto, violin, 3 violas and continuo
J. Bowman, King's Consort, R. King *Concert*
(3/87) (MERI) ① **CDE84126**
R. Jacobs, Kuijken Consort *Concert*
(4/88) (ACCE) ① **ACC77912D**
Fürchte dich nicht—motet: 5vv and
continuo
Cantus Cölln, K. Junghänel (lte/dir) (r1993) *Concert*
(7/94) (DHM) ① **05472 77305-2**
Der Gerechte, ob er gleich zu zeitlich
stirbt—motet: 5vv (1676)
Cantus Cölln, K. Junghänel (lte/dir) (r1993) *Concert*
(7/94) (DHM) ① **05472 77305-2**
Herr, wende dich—dialogue: 4vv, 2 violins, 2
violas and continuo
D. Cordier, H. Meens, P. Elliott, M. Schopper,
Cologne Musica Antiqua, R. Goebel (r1986) *Concert*
(1/93) (ARCH) ① **437 090-2AT**
Ich lasse dich nicht—motet: 8vv
Cantus Cölln, K. Junghänel (lte/dir) (r1993) *Concert*
(7/94) (DHM) ① **05472 77305-2**
Meine Freundin, du bist schön—dialogue:
4vv, 4 violins, 3 violas and continuo
(Wedding piece)
M. Zedelius, D. Cordier, P. Elliott, M. Schopper,
Rheinische Kantorei, Cologne Musica Antiqua, R.
Goebel (r1986) *Concert*
(1/93) (ARCH) ① **437 090-2AT**

BACH, Johann Christoph Friedrich (1732–1795) Germany

HW—Numbers from catalogue by H. Wohlfarth

SECTION II: CHAMBER

6 Quartets—flute, violin, viola and cello, HWVI (c1768)
3. C.
3. Adieux Concert   (7/91) (DHM) ① **RD77250**

SECTION III: INSTRUMENTAL

Sonata in A—cello piccola (pub 1770) (pub in 'Musikalisches Vielerley')
A. Bylsma, B. van Asperen Bach: Viola da gamba Sonatas, BWV1027-9.   (3/91) (SONY) ① **SK45945**

SECTION IV: VOCAL AND CHORAL

Die Amerikanerin—cantata: soprano and orchestra, HWXVIII/3 (pub 1776) (Wds. H. W. von Gerstenberg)
B. Schlick, Kleine Konzert, H. Max Concert
          (10/90) (CAPR) ① **10 303**
Ino—cantata: soprano and orchestra, HWXVIII/4 (pub 1780) (Wds. C. W. Rambler)
B. Schlick, Kleine Konzert, H. Max Concert
          (10/90) (CAPR) ① **10 303**
Pygmalion—cantata: bass and orchestra, HWXVIII/5 (Wds. C. W. Ramler)
H. van der Kamp, Kleine Konzert, H. Max Concert
          (10/90) (CAPR) ① **10 303**

BACH, Johann Ernst (1722–1777) Germany

SECTION III: INSTRUMENTAL

Fantasie and Fugue in F—organ
W. Krumbach (r1968-9) Concert
          (1/95) (TELD) ① [2] **4509-92176-2**

SECTION IV: VOCAL AND CHORAL

Meine Seele erhebt den Herrn—motet: soloists, chorus, strings and continuo
M. Lins, S. Weisheit, M. Schmitz, H-G. Wimmer, Rheinische Kantorei, Kleine Konzert, H. Max (r1989) Concert   (11/90) (CAPR) ① [2] **10 310/1**
Passionaoratorium—soloists, chorus and orchestra (c1764)
B. Schlick, D. Cordier, C. Prégardien, S. Varcoe, Rheinische Kantorei, Kleine Konzert, H. Max (r1989) Concert   (11/90) (CAPR) ① [2] **10 310/1**
Vertrauen der Christen auf Gott—ode: tenor, chorus and orchestra (Wds. Psalm 77)
C. Prégardien, Rheinische Kantorei, Kleine Konzert, H. Max (r1989) Concert
          (11/90) (CAPR) ① [2] **10 310/1**

BACH, Johann Lorenz (1695–1773) Germany

SECTION III: INSTRUMENTAL

Prelude and Fugue in D—organ
W. Krumbach (r1968-9) Concert
          (1/95) (TELD) ① [2] **4509-92176-2**

BACH, Johann Michael (1648–1694) Germany

SECTION III: INSTRUMENTAL

Allein Gott in der Höh sei Ehr—chorale: organ
W. Krumbach (r1968-9) Concert
          (1/95) (TELD) ① [2] **4509-92176-2**
Wenn wir in höchsten Nöten sein—chorale: organ
W. Krumbach (r1968-9) Concert
          (1/95) (TELD) ① [2] **4509-92176-2**

SECTION IV: VOCAL AND CHORAL

Ach bleib bei uns, Herr Jesu Christ—vocal concerto: 4vv and strings
Rheinische Kantorei, Cologne Musica Antiqua, R. Goebel (r1986) Concert
          (1/93) (ARCH) ① **437 090-2AT**
Ach, wie sehnlich wart ich der Zeit—aria: 1v, strings and continuo
M. Zedelius, Cologne Musica Antiqua, R. Goebel (r1986) Concert   (1/93) (ARCH) ① **437 090-2AT**
Fürtet euch nicht—motet: 8vv and continuo
Cantus Cölln, K. Junghänel (lte/dir) (r1993) Concert
          (7/94) (DHM) ① **05472 77305-2**

Halt, was du hast—motet: 8vv and continuo
Cantus Cölln, K. Junghänel (lte/dir) (r1993) Concert
          (7/94) (DHM) ① **05472 77305-2**
Liebster Jesu, hör mein Flehen—cantata
M. Zedelius, D. Cordier, P. Elliott, H. Meens, M. Schopper, Cologne Musica Antiqua, R. Goebel (r1986) Concert   (1/93) (ARCH) ① **437 090-2AT**

BACH, Johann Sebastian (1685–1750) Germany

BWV–Numbers used in W. Schmieder, Bach-Werke-Verzeichnis

SECTION I: ORCHESTRAL

Brandenburg Concertos, BWV1046-51 (1708-21)
1. F, BWV1046 (vn picc, obs, hns, bns & stgs: 1717); 1a. (without tempo indication); 1b. Adagio; 1c. Allegro; 1d. Menuetto; 1e. Trio I; 1f. Polacca; 1g. Trio II; 2. F, BWV1047 (rec/fl, ob, tpt, vn & stgs: 1718-18); 2a. (without tempo indication); 2b. Andante; 2c. Allegro assai; 3. G, BWV1048 (stgs: 1711-13); 3a. (without tempo indication); 3b. Adagio; 3c. Allegro; 4. G, BWV1049 (vn, 2 recs/fls & stgs—cf Hpd Conc, BWV1057); 4a. Allegro; 4b. Andante; 4c. Presto; 5. D, BWV1050 (hpd, vn, fl & stgs: 1720-21); 5a. Allegro; 5b. Affettuoso; 5c. Allegro; 6. B flat, BWV1051 (vas, vcs & d-b: 1708-10); 6a. (without tempo indication); 6b. Adagio, ma non tanto; 6c. Allegro.
AAM, C. Hogwood   (4/85) (L'OI) ① [2] **414 187-2OH2**
BPO, H. von Karajan (r1978/9)
          (3/86) (DG) ① [2] **415 374-2GH2**
ASMF, N. Marriner Suites, BWV1066-9.
          (7/87) (EMI) ① [3] **CDS7 47881-8**
Cologne Musica Antiqua, R. Goebel Triple Concerto, BWV1044.   (3/88) (ARCH) ① [2] **423 116-2AH2**
English Concert, T. Pinnock (hpd/dir) Suites, BWV1066-9.   (10/88) (ARCH) ① [3] **423 492-2AX3**
OAE   (7/89) (VIRG) ① [2] **VCD7 59260-2**
Vienna Academy Orch, M. Haselböck
          (1/90) (NOVA) ① [2] **150 035-2**
COE (r1990)   (5/91) (DG) ① [2] **431 660-2GH2**
A. Busch Chbr Plyrs, A. Busch (r1935) Suites, BWV1066-9.   (12/91) (EMI) ① [3] **CHS7 64047-2**
Concert des Nations, Capella Reial Instr Ens, J. Savall   (2/92) (ASTR) ① [2] **E8737**
Philh, O. Klemperer Concert
          (9/92) (EMI) ① [3] **CMS7 64150-2**
Brandenburg Consort, R. Goodman
          (12/92) (HYPE) ① [2] **CDA66711/2**
Collegium Aureum (r1965-7) Suites, BWV1066-9.
          (3/93) (DHM) ① **05472 77251-2**
VCM, N. Harnoncourt
          (7/93) (TELD) ① [2] **9031-77611-2**
Paris Ecole Normale CO, A. Cortot (r1932) Concert
          (11/93) (KOCH) ① [2] **37705-2**
CPE Bach Orch, P. Schreier (r1991/2) Concert
          (4/94) (PHIL) ① [2] **434 918-2PH2**
Scottish Ens, J. Rees (r1991/2)
          (11/94) (VIRG) ① [2] **CUD5 61114-2**
New London Consort, P. Pickett (r1992)
          (1/95) (L'OI) ① [2] **440 675-2OH2**
Tafelmusik, J. Lamon (vn/dir) (r1993)
          (4/95) (SONY) ① [2] **S2K66289**
VCM, N. Harnoncourt (r1981) Suites, BWV1066-9.
          (5/95) (TELD) ① [2] **4509-95980-2**
Petite Bande, S. Kuijken (r1993/4)
          (6/95) (DHM) ① **05472 77308-2**
ECO, B. Britten (r1968) Concert
          (7/95) (DECC) ① [2] **443 847-2DF2**
Bath Fest Orch, Y. Menuhin (r1959)
          (11/95) (EMI) ① [2] **CES5 68516-2**
1, 2, 4. VCM, N. Harnoncourt Suites, BWV1066-9.
          (9/92) (TELD) ① **9031-75858-2**
1-3. ASMF, N. Marriner
          (3/83) (PHIL) ① **400 076-2PH**
1-3. English Concert, T. Pinnock (hpd/dir)
          (1/84) (ARCH) ① **410 500-2AH**
1-3. Berlin CO, P. Wohlert Harpsichord Concerto, BWV1054.   (5/90) (LASE) ① **15 508**
1-3. Capella Istropolitana, B. Warchal (r1987)
          (10/90) (NAXO) ① **8 550047**
1-3. Brandenburg Consort, R. Goodman
          (12/92) (HYPE) ① **CDA66611**
1-3. ECO, R. Leppard (r1975) Concert
          (12/94) (PHIL) ① **442 386-2PM**
1-3. ECO, P. Ledger (r c1986)
          (10/95) (CARL) ① **PCD2006**
1, 3, 4. Hanover Band, A. Halstead (hpd/dir)
          (2/93) (EMIN) ① **CD-EMX2200**
2. M. André, Philh, R. Muti Concert
          (1/86) (EMI) ① **CDC7 47311-2**

---

2. Stuttgart CO, K. Münchinger Concert
          (10/91) (DECC) ① **430 499-2DWO**
2. Philh, Edwin Fischer (r1953) Concert
          (6/94) (EMI) ① **CDH7 64928-2**
2, 5. Cologne Musica Antiqua, R. Goebel (r1986/7) Suites, BWV1066-9. (1/94) (DG) ① **439 401-2GCL**
2, 5, 6. Hanover Band, A. Halstead (hpd/dir)
          (2/93) (EMIN) ① **CD-EMX2201**
3. BPO, W. Furtwängler (r1930) Concert
          (4/92) (KOCH) ① [2] **37059-2**
3. H. Snell Brass, H. Snell (r1991 arr Mowat: brass ens) Concert   (8/92) (POLY) ① **QPRL007D**
3. British SO, Henry Wood (r1932) Concert
          (9/94) (DUTT) ① [2] **2CDAX2002**
3c Amsterdam Loeki Stardust Qt Concert
          (10/94) (L'OI) ① **440 207-2OM**
3, 5, 6. VCM, N. Harnoncourt Suites, BWV1066-9.
          (9/92) (TELD) ① **9031-75859-2**
4-6. ASMF, N. Marriner
          (3/83) (PHIL) ① **400 077-2PH**
4-6. English Concert, T. Pinnock (hpd/dir)
          (1/84) (ARCH) ① **410 501-2AH**
4-6. Berlin CO, P. Wohlert   (5/90) (LASE) ① **15 509**
4-6. Capella Istropolitana, B. Warchal (r1987)
          (10/90) (NAXO) ① **8 550048**
4-6. Brandenburg Consort, R. Goodman
          (12/92) (HYPE) ① **CDA66612**
4-6. ECO, R. Leppard (r1975) Triple Concerto, BWV1044.   (12/94) (PHIL) ① **442 387-2PM**
4-6. ECO, P. Ledger (r c1986)   (10/95) (CARL) ① **PCD2009**
5. Edwin Fischer (pf/dir), G. Morris, M. Parikian, R. Clarke, Philh (r1952) Concert
          (11/89) (EMI) ① **CDH7 63039-2**
5. J. Thibaud, A. Cortot, R. Cortet, Paris Cons CO (r1932) Concert   (9/91) (BIDD) ① **LAB028**
5. Paris Ecole Normale CO, A. Cortot (pf/dir) (r1930) Concert   (10/91) (MSCM) ① **MM30321**
5. Prades Fest Orch, P. Casals (r1950) Concert
          (5/94) (SONY) ① **SMK58982**
Concerto for Flute and Strings in E minor, BWV1059/BWV35
J. Galway (fl/dir), Zagreb Sols Concert
          (11/87) (RCA) ① **GD86517**
Concerto for Flute and Strings in G, BWV1056 (perf version: Hogwood)
W. Bennett, ASMF, N. Marriner Concert
          (7/87) (DECC) ① **417 715-2DM**
W. Bennett, ASMF, N. Marriner (r1973/4) Concert
          (7/95) (DECC) ① [2] **443 847-2DF2**
Concerto for Flute, Violin, Harpsichord and Strings in A minor, BWV1044 (?after 1730) (adapted from organ works)
L. Beznosiuk, S. Standage, T. Pinnock (hpd/dir), English Concert Concert
          (1/85) (ARCH) ① **413 731-2AH**
W. Hazelzet, A. Staier, R. Goebel (vn/dir), Cologne Musica Antiqua Brandenburg Concertos.
          (3/88) (ARCH) ① [2] **423 116-2AH2**
L. Beznosiuk, S. Standage, T. Pinnock (hpd/dir), English Concert Suites, BWV1066-9.
          (4/89) (ARCH) ① **427 112-2AGA**
V. Spivakov (vn/dir), E. Duran, S. Bezrodny, Moscow Virtuosi Concert   (6/90) (RCA) ① **RD87991**
C. Krueger, D. Stepner, J. Gibbons, Boston Early Music Fest Orch, A. Parrott (r1992) Suites, BWV1066-9.   (5/93) (EMI) ① [2] **CDS7 54653-2**
J. Galway, R. Wolters, U. Duetschler, Württemberg CO, J. Faerber Concert
          (6/93) (RCA) ① **09026 60900-2**
T. Rosenbusch, I. Grafenauer, S. Preston, CPE Bach Orch, P. Schreier (r1992) Concert
          (4/94) (PHIL) ① [2] **434 918-2PH2**
R. Adeney, J-L. Garcia, R. Leppard (hpd/dir), ECO (r1983) Brandenburg Concertos.
          (12/94) (PHIL) ① **442 387-2PM**
Concert Français, P. Hantaï (hpd/dir) (r1993) Concert
          (1/95) (ASTR) ① **E8523**
F. Brüggen, Leonhardt Consort (r1967) Concert
          (5/95) (ARCH) ① **4509-97473-2**
Concerto for Harpsichord and Strings in A, BWV1055 (recons from lost Ob d'amore Conc)
A. Schiff, ECO, G. Malcolm (cnd) Concert
          (5/85) (DENO) ① **C37-7236**
T. Pinnock (hpd/dir), English Concert Concert
          (2/87) (ARCH) ① **415 992-2AH**
I. Bolton (hpd/dir), St James's Baroque Plyrs Concert
          (11/87) (CARL) ① **PCD864**
Edwin Fischer (pf/dir), E. Fischer CO (r1936) Concert
          (11/89) (EMI) ① **CDH7 63039-2**
J-P. Rampal, Ars Rediviva, M. Munclinger (arr fl/stgs: Munclinger) Concert
          (8/92) (SONY) ① [2] **SK48184**
M-J. Pires, Lisbon Gulbenkian Orch, M. Corboz (r1974: pf) Concert
          (12/93) (ERAT) ① **4509-92864-2**

S. Sempé, Capriccio Stravagante (r1993) *Concert* (1/94) (DHM) ① **05472 77222-2**
C. Rousset, AAM, C. Hogwood (r1993) *Concert* (10/95) (L'OI) ① **443 326-2OH**
G. Leonhardt (hpd/dir), Leonhardt Consort (r c1968) *Concert* (11/95) (TELD) ① [3] **4509-97452-2**

Concerto for Harpsichord and Strings in D, BWV1054 (c1738-39) (from Violin Concerto, BWV1042)
T. Pinnock (hpd/dir), English Concert *Concert* (9/87) (ARCH) ① **415 991-2AH**
Berlin CO, P. Wohlert *Brandenburg Concertos.* (5/90) (LASE) ① **15 508**
B. van Asperen, Amsterdam Melante (r1991) *Concert* (6/93) (EMI) ① **CDC7 54478-2**
S. Sempé, Capriccio Stravagante (r1993) *Concert* (1/94) (DHM) ① **05472 77222-2**
Concert Français, P. Hantaï (hpd/dir) (r1993) *Concert* (1/95) (ASTR) ① **E8523**
G. Leonhardt (hpd/dir), Leonhardt Consort (r c1966) *Concert* (11/95) (TELD) ① [3] **4509-97452-2**

Concerto for Harpsichord and Strings in D minor, BWV1052 (reconstructed from lost Violin Concerto)
A. Schiff, ECO, G. Malcolm (pf) *Concert* (5/85) (DENO) ① **C37-7236**
T. Pinnock (hpd/dir), English Concert *Concert* (9/87) (ARCH) ① **415 991-2AH**
I. Bolton (hpd/dir), St James's Baroque Plyrs *Concert* (11/87) (CARL) ① **PCD864**
Edwin Fischer (pf/dir), E. Fischer CO (r1933) *Concert* (11/89) (EMI) ① **CDH7 63039-2**
D. Lipatti, Concertgebouw, E. van Beinum (pp1947) *Concert* (4/90) (JECK) ① **JD541-2**
O. Maione, ECCO, E. Aadland (pf) *Concert* (3/92) (CARL) ① **PCD964**
B. van Asperen, Amsterdam Melante (r1991) *Concert* (6/93) (EMI) ① **CDC7 54478-2**
M-J. Pires, Lisbon Gulbenkian Orch, M. Corboz (r1974; pf) *Concert* (12/93) (ERAT) ① **4509-92864-2**
G. Gould, Toronto SO, E. MacMillan (bp1955) *Concert* (7/94) (CBC) ① **PSCD2005**
Concert Français, P. Hantaï (hpd/dir) (r1993) *Concert* (1/95) (ASTR) ① **E8523**
H. Tachezi, VCM, N. Harnoncourt (r c1968) *Concert* (11/95) (TELD) ① [3] **4509-97452-2**

Concerto for Harpsichord and Strings in D minor, BWV1059 (from lost Oboe Concerto)
G. Leonhardt (hpd/dir), Leonhardt Consort (r c1966) *Concert* (11/95) (TELD) ① [3] **4509-97452-2**

Concerto for Harpsichord and Strings in E, BWV1053 (c1738-39) (from lost ?Oboe Concerto)
T. Pinnock (hpd/dir), English Concert *Concert* (9/87) (ARCH) ① **415 991-2AH**
B. van Asperen, Amsterdam Melante (r1991) *Concert* (6/93) (EMI) ① **CDC7 54478-2**
Edwin Fischer (pf/dir), Philh (r1950) *Concert* (6/94) (EMI) ① **CDH7 64928-2**
C. Rousset, AAM, C. Hogwood (r1994) *Concert* (10/95) (L'OI) ① **443 326-2OH**
G. Leonhardt (hpd/dir), Leonhardt Consort (r c1968) *Concert* (11/95) (TELD) ① [3] **4509-97452-2**

Concerto for Harpsichord and Strings in F, BWV1057 (c1738-39) (from Brandenburg Concerto, BWV1049)
T. Pinnock (hpd/dir), English Concert *Concert* (2/87) (ARCH) ① **415 992-2AH**
I. Bolton (hpd/dir), St James's Baroque Plyrs *Concert* (11/87) (CARL) ① **PCD864**
F. Brüggen, Leonhardt Consort (r1967) *Concert* (10/95) (TELD) ① **4509-97473-2**
G. Leonhardt (hpd/dir), Leonhardt Consort (r c1966) *Concert* (11/95) (TELD) ① [3] **4509-97452-2**

Concerto for Harpsichord and Strings in F minor, BWV1056 (2 movts from lost Oboe Concerto)
A. Schiff, ECO, G. Malcolm (pf) *Concert* (5/85) (DENO) ① **C37-7236**
T. Pinnock (hpd/dir), English Concert *Concert* (2/87) (ARCH) ① **415 992-2AH**
I. Bolton (hpd/dir), St James's Baroque Plyrs *Concert* (11/87) (CARL) ① **PCD864**
Edwin Fischer (pf/dir), E. Fischer CO (r1938) *Concert* (11/89) (EMI) ① **CDH7 63039-2**
Scottish Ens, J. Rees (vn/dir) (arr Vn) *Concert* (12/91) (VIRG) ① **VJ7 59641-2**
J-P. Rampal, Ars Rediviva, M. Munclinger (arr fl/stgs: Munclinger) *Concert* (8/92) (SONY) ① [2] **SK48184**
M-J. Pires, Lisbon Gulbenkian Orch, M. Corboz (r1974; pf) *Concert* (12/93) (ERAT) ① **4509-92864-2**
C. Haskil, Prades Fest Orch, P. Casals (r1950) *Concert* (5/94) (SONY) ① **SMK58982**
A. Jambor, Concertgebouw, W. Mengelberg (pp1939) *Concert* (5/95) (ARHI) ① **ADCD112**
G. Leonhardt (hpd/dir), Leonhardt Consort (r c1968) *Concert* (11/95) (TELD) ① [3] **4509-97452-2**
Arioso Britannia Building Soc Band, H. Snell (r1990; arr Snell: brass band) *Concert* (8/92) (DOYE) ① **DOYCD004**
Largo I. Biret (trans Kempff) *Concert* (5/93) (MARC) ① **8 223452**
Movt 2. W. Kempff (r1975: arr pf: Kempff) *Concert* (11/94) (DG) ① [2] **439 672-2GX2**
Movt 2. A. Cortot (r1937: arr pf: Cortot) *Concert* (5/95) (BIDD) ① **LHW020**
Movt 2. J. Starker, G. Moore (r1958: arr vc/pf: Franko) *Concert* (12/95) (EMI) ① [6] **CZS5 68485-2**

Concerto for Harpsichord and Strings in G minor, BWV1058 (c1738-39) (from Violin Concerto, BWV1041)
T. Pinnock (hpd/dir), English Concert *Concert* (2/87) (ARCH) ① **415 992-2AH**
C. Rousset, AAM, C. Hogwood (r1993) *Concert* (10/95) (L'OI) ① **443 326-2OH**
G. Leonhardt (hpd/dir), Leonhardt Consort (r c1966) *Concert* (11/95) (TELD) ① [3] **4509-97452-2**

Concerto for Oboe and Strings in A, BWV1055 (reconstructed from lost Oboe d'amore Concerto)
H. Holliger, ASMF, I. Brown *Concert* (1/86) (PHIL) ① **412 851-2PH**
P. Goodwin, King's Consort, R. King *Concert* (7/88) (HYPE) ① **CDA66267**
D. Boyd (ob/dir), COE *Concert* (4/90) (DG) ① **429 225-2GH**

Concerto for Oboe and Strings in D minor, BWV1059 (reconstructed from lost Oboe Concerto)
1. Allegro; 2. Siciliano; 3. Presto.
H. Holliger, ASMF, I. Brown *Concert* (1/86) (PHIL) ① **412 851-2PH**
D. Boyd (ob/dir), COE *Concert* (4/90) (DG) ① **429 225-2GH**

Concerto for Oboe and Strings in F minor, BWV1053 (reconstructed from lost ?Oboe Concerto)
H. Holliger, ASMF, I. Brown *Concert* (1/86) (PHIL) ① **412 851-2PH**
P. Goodwin, King's Consort, R. King *Concert* (7/88) (HYPE) ① **CDA66267**
D. Boyd (ob/dir), COE *Concert* (4/90) (DG) ① **429 225-2GH**
N. Black, ASMF, N. Marriner (r1973-4) *Concert* (1/94) (DECC) ① **440 037-2DM**

Concerto for Oboe and Strings in G minor, BWV1056/156 (movt 2 from Cantata No. 156)
M. Messiter, Guildhall Str Ens, R. Salter (vn/dir) *Concert* (9/90) (RCA) ① **RD60224**

Concerto for Oboe d'amore and Strings in A, BWV1055
D. Reichenberg, English Concert, T. Pinnock *Concert* (1/85) (ARCH) ① **413 731-2AH**
N. Black, ASMF, N. Marriner (r1973-4) *Concert* (1/94) (DECC) ① **440 037-2DM**
A. Robson (ob/dir), OAE (r1991) *Concert* (11/94) (VIRG) ① **VC5 45095-2**

Concerto for Oboe, Violin and Strings in C minor, BWV1060 (reconstruction of lost Oboe and Violin Concerto)
1. Allegro; 2. Adagio; 3. Allegro.
S. Standage, D. Reichenberg, English Concert, T. Pinnock *Concert* (1/85) (ARCH) ① **413 731-2AH**
I. Perlman (vn/dir), R. Still, Israel PO *Concert* (4/85) (EMI) ① **CDC7 47073-2**
M. Blankestijn, D. Boyd, COE, A. Schneider (pp1984) *Concert* (3/87) (ASV) ① **CDCOE803**
C. Kaine, T. Miller, ASMF, N. Marriner (perf ed. Hogwood) *Concert* (7/87) (DECC) ① **417 715-2DM**
A. Grumiaux, H. Holliger, New Philh, E. de Waart (r1970: recons F Giegling) *Concert* (5/88) (PHIL) ① **420 700-2PSL**
D. Sitkovetsky (vn/dir), N. Black, ECO *Concert* (5/88) (NOVA) ① **150 017-2**
C. Mackintosh, S. Hammer, AAM, C. Hogwood *Concert* (9/89) (L'OI) ① **421 500-2OH**
F.P. Zimmermann, N. Black, ECO, J. Tate *Concert* (3/90) (EMI) ① **CDC7 49862-2**
Elizabeth Wallfisch, P. Goodwin, King's Consort, R. King *Concert* (4/90) (HYPE) ① **CDA66380**
V. Spivakov (vn/dir), A. Utkin, Moscow Virtuosi *Concert* (6/90) (RCA) ① **RD87991**
R. Michelucci, L. Driehuys, I Musici *Concert* (11/91) (PHIL) ① **426 075-2PCC**
G. Kremer, H. Holliger (ob/dir), ASMF *Concert* (11/91) (PHIL) ① **426 462-2PBQ2**
O. Shumsky (vn/dir), R. Miller, Scottish CO *Concert* (9/92) (NIMB) ① **NI5325**
G. Schmalfuss, Varga Fest Orch, T. Varga (vn/dir) (r1969) *Concert* (11/93) (CLAV) ① [4] **CD50-9300/4**
T Varga (vn/dir), G. Schmalfuss, Varga Fest Orch (r1969) *Concert* (11/93) (CLAV) ① **CD50-9311**
I. Stern, M. Tabuteau, Prades Fest Orch, P. Casals (r1950) *Concert* (5/94) (SONY) ① **SMK58982**
D. Walter, M-A. Nicolas, Toulouse Nat CO, J-C. Malgoire (r1993) *Concert* (6/94) (AUVI) ① **V4697**
Elizabeth Wallfisch (vn/dir), A. Robson, OAE (r1991) *Concert* (11/94) (VIRG) ① **VC5 45095-2**
A. Harnoncourt, J. Schaeftlein, VCM, N. Harnoncourt (r c1970) *Concert* (5/95) (TELD) ① **4509-95518-2**
I. Perlman (vn/dir), R. Still, Israel PO *Concert* (6/95) (EMI) ① [20] **CZS4 83177-2(1)**
T. Miller, C. Kaine, ASMF, N. Marriner (r1973/4) *Concert* (7/95) (DECC) ① [2] **443 847-2DF2**
Y. Menuhin (vn/dir), L. Goossens, Bath Fest Orch *Concert* (11/95) (EMI) ① [2] **CES5 68517-2**

Concerto for Violin and Strings in A, BWV1052 (reconstructed from lost Violin Concerto)
I. Perlman (vn/dir), Israel PO *Concert* (4/85) (EMI) ① **CDC7 47073-2**
J. Szigeti, New Friends of Music Orch, F. Stiedry (r1940) *Concert* (11/92) (BIDD) ① **LAB064**
S. Standage (vn/dir), Collegium Musicum 90 (r1992) *Concert* (5/93) (CHAN) ① **CHAN0530**
R. Ricci (vn/dir), City of London Ens (r1969) *Concert* (10/94) (UNIC) ① **UKCD2067**
Elizabeth Wallfisch (vn/dir), OAE (r1991) *Concert* (11/94) (VIRG) ① **VC5 45095-2**

Concerto for Violin and Strings in A minor, BWV1041 (1717-23)
1. (Allegro moderato); 2. Andante; 3. Allegro assai.
J. Schröder, AAM, C. Hogwood *Concert* (3/83) (L'OI) ① **400 080-2OH**
A-S. Mutter, ECO, S. Accardo (r1982) *Concert* (2/84) (EMI) ① **CDC7 47005-2**
S. Standage, English Concert, T. Pinnock *Concert* (8/84) (ARCH) ① **410 646-2AH**
J. Laredo (vn/dir), Scottish CO *Concert* (5/86) (CARL) ① **PCD808**
I. Perlman, ECO, D. Barenboim *Concert* (12/87) (EMI) ① **CDC7 47856-2**
V. Spivakov (vn/dir), Moscow Virtuosi *Concert* (12/87) (CIRR) ① **CICD1004**
A. Grumiaux, Solistes Romands, A. Gerecz (r1978) *Concert* (5/88) (PHIL) ① **420 700-2PSL**
D. Sitkovetsky (vn/dir), ECO *Concert* (5/88) (NOVA) ① **150 017-2**
Y. Menuhin, Paris SO, G. Enescu (r1936) *Concert* (3/89) (EMI) ① **CDH7 61018-2**
B. Huberman, VPO, I. Dobroven (r1934) *Concert* (8/89) (PEAR) ① **GEMMCD9341**
F.P. Zimmermann, ECO, J. Tate *Concert* (3/90) (EMI) ① **CDC7 49862-2**
C. Mackintosh, King's Consort, R. King *Concert* (4/90) (HYPE) ① **CDA66380**
R. Michelucci, I Musici *Concert* (11/91) (PHIL) ① **426 075-2PCC**
P. Zukerman, ECO *Concert* (11/91) (RCA) ① **RD60718**
Polish CO, J. Stanienda (vn/dir) (pp1990) *Concert* (12/91) (LINN) ① **CKD001**
O. Shumsky (vn/dir), Scottish CO *Concert* (9/92) (NIMB) ① **NI5325**
I. Stern, Prades Fest Orch, P. Casals (r1950) *Concert* (5/94) (SONY) ① **SMK58982**
M-A. Nicolas, Toulouse Nat CO, J-C. Malgoire (r1993) *Concert* (6/94) (AUVI) ① **V4697**
R. Ricci (vn/dir), City of London Ens (r1969) *Concert* (10/94) (UNIC) ① **UKCD2067**
J. Heifetz, Los Angeles PO, A. Wallenstein (r1953) *Concert* (11/94) (RCA) ① [65] **09026 61778-2(24)**
A. Grumiaux, ECO, R. Leppard (r1964) *Concert* (12/94) (PHIL) ① **442 386-2PM**
A. Harnoncourt, VCM, N. Harnoncourt (r c1967) *Concert* (5/95) (TELD) ① **4509-95518-2**
D. Oistrakh (vn/dir), Vienna SO (r1962) *Concert* (6/95) (DG) ① [2] **447 427-2GOR2**
J. Schröder, AAM, C. Hogwood (r1981) *Concert* (10/95) (L'OI) ① **443 326-2OH**
Y. Menuhin (vn/dir), Bath Fest Orch *Concert* (11/95) (EMI) ① [2] **CES5 68517-2**

Concerto for Violin and Strings in E, BWV1042 (1717-23)
1. Allegro; 2. Adagio; 3. Allegro assai.
J. Schröder, AAM, C. Hogwood *Concert* (3/83) (L'OI) ① **400 080-2OH**
A-S. Mutter, ECO, S. Accardo (r1982) *Concert* (2/84) (EMI) ① **CDC7 47005-2**
S. Standage, English Concert, T. Pinnock *Concert* (8/84) (ARCH) ① **410 646-2AH**
J. Laredo (vn/dir), Scottish CO *Concert* (5/86) (CARL) ① **PCD808**

R.Thomas (vn/dir), Soloists of Australia (pp1986) *Concert* (4/87) (CHAN) ① **CHAN8498**
I. Perlman, ECO, D. Barenboim *Concert* (12/87) (EMI) ① **CDC7 47856-2**
V. Spivakov (vn/dir), Moscow Virtuosi *Concert* (12/87) (CIRR) ① **CICD1004**
A. Grumiaux, Solistes Romands, A. Gerecz (r1978) *Concert* (5/88) (PHIL) ① **420 700-2PSL**
D. Sitkovetsky (vn/dir), ECO *Concert* (5/88) (NOVA) ① **150 017-2**
Y. Menuhin, Paris SO, G. Enescu (r1933) *Concert* (3/89) (EMI) ① **CDH7 61018-2**
B. Huberman, VPO, I. Dobroven (r1935) *Concert* (8/89) (PEAR) ① **GEMMCD9341**
F.P. Zimmermann, ECO, J. Tate *Concert* (3/90) (EMI) ① **CDC7 49862-2**
C. Mackintosh, King's Consort, R. King *Concert* (4/90) (HYPE) ① **CDA66380**
R. Michelucci, I Musici *Concert* (11/91) (PHIL) ① **426 075-2PCC**
P. Zukerman, ECO *Concert* (11/91) (RCA) ① **RD60718**
Scottish Ens, J. Rees (vn/dir) *Concert* (12/91) (VIRG) ① **VJ7 59641-2**
O. Shumsky (vn/dir), Scottish CO *Concert* (9/92) (NIMB) ① **NI5325**
T Varga (vn/dir), Varga CO (r1973) *Concert* (11/93) (CLAV) ① **CD50-9311**
Varga CO, T. Varga (vn/dir) (r1973) *Concert* (11/93) (CLAV) ① [4] **CD50-9300/4**
M-A. Nicolas, Toulouse Nat CO, J-C. Malgoire (r1993) *Concert* (6/94) (AUVI) ① **V4697**
R. Ricci (vn/dir), City of London Ens (r1969) *Concert* (10/94) (UNIC) ① **UKCD2067**
J. Heifetz, Los Angeles PO, A. Wallenstein (r1953) *Concert* (11/94) (RCA) ① [65] **09026 61778-2(24)**
A. Grumiaux, ECO, R. Leppard (r1964) *Concert* (12/94) (PHIL) ① **442 386-2PM**
A. Harnoncourt, VCM, N. Harnoncourt (r c1967) *Concert* (5/95) (TELD) ① **4509-95518-2**
D. Oistrakh (vn/dir), Vienna SO (r1962) *Concert* (6/95) (DG) ① [2] **447 427-2GOR2**
I. Perlman, ECO, D. Barenboim *Concert* (6/95) (EMI) ① [20] **CZS4 83177-2(1)**
Y. Menuhin (vn/dir), Bath Fest Orch *Concert* (11/95) (EMI) ① [2] **CES5 68517-2**

Concerto for Violin and Strings in F minor, BWV1056 (transc from Harpsichord Concerto, BWV1056)
I. Perlman (vn/dir), Israel PO *Concert* (4/85) (EMI) ① **CDC7 47073-2**
I. Perlman, ECO, D. Barenboim *Concert* (12/87) (EMI) ① **CDC7 47856-2**
P. Zukerman, ECO *Concert* (11/91) (RCA) ① **RD60718**
S. Standage (vn/dir), Collegium Musicum 90 (r1992) *Concert* (5/93) (CHAN) ① **CHAN0530**
I. Perlman (vn/dir), Israel PO (r1982) *Concert* (5/93) (EMI) ① [4] **CMS7 64617-2**
Elizabeth Wallfisch (vn/dir), OAE (r1991) *Concert* (11/94) (VIRG) ① **VC5 45095-2**
A. Harnoncourt, VCM, N. Harnoncourt (r c1977) *Concert* (5/95) (TELD) ① **4509-95518-2**
I. Perlman, ECO, D. Barenboim *Concert* (6/95) (EMI) ① [20] **CZS4 83177-2(1)**

Concerto for Violin, Oboe, Flute and Strings in D minor, BWV1063
C. Kaine, N. Black, W. Bennett, ASMF, N. Marriner (r1973-4) *Concert* (1/94) (DECC) ① **440 037-2DM**

Concerto for 2 Violins and Strings in D minor, BWV1043 (1717-23)
1. Vivace; 2. Largo ma non tanto; 3. Allegro.
J. Schröder, C. Hirons, AAM, C. Hogwood *Concert* (3/83) (L'OI) ① **400 080-2OH**
A-S. Mutter, S. Accardo, ECO, S. Accardo (r1982) *Concert* (2/84) (EMI) ① **CDC7 47005-2**
S. Standage, E. Wilcock, English Concert, T. Pinnock *Concert* (8/84) (ARCH) ① **410 646-2AH**
J. Laredo (vn/dir), J. Tunnell, Scottish CO *Concert* (5/86) (CARL) ① **PCD808**
I. Perlman, P. Zukerman, ECO, D. Barenboim *Concert* (12/87) (EMI) ① **CDC7 47856-2**
A. Futer, V. Spivakov (vn/dir), Moscow Virtuosi *Concert* (12/87) (CIRR) ① **CICD1004**
A. Grumiaux, H. Krebbers, Solistes Romands, A. Gerecz (r1978) *Concert* (5/88) (PHIL) ① **420 700-2PSL**
D. Sitkovetsky (vn/dir), J-L. Garcia, ECO *Concert* (5/88) (NOVA) ① **150 017-2**
Y. Menuhin (vn/dir), C. Ferras, Festival CO *Concert* (1/89) (EMIL) ① **CDZ114**
Y. Menuhin, G. Enescu, Paris SO, P. Monteux (r1932) *Concert* (3/89) (EMI) ① **CDH7 61018-2**
C. Mackintosh, Elizabeth Wallfisch, King's Consort, R. King *Concert* (4/90) (HYPE) ① **CDA66380**
V. Spivakov (vn/dir), A. Futer *Concert* (6/90) (RCA) ① **RD87991**
R. Michelucci, F. Ayo, I Musici *Concert* (11/91) (PHIL) ① **426 075-2PCC**
H. Szeryng, M. Hasson, ASMF, N. Marriner *Concert* (11/91) (PHIL) ① **426 462-2PBQ2**
Y. Menuhin (vn/dir), C. Ferras, Bath Fest Orch *Concert* (11/91) (EMI) ① [3] **CZS7 67310-2**
P. Zukerman, J-L. Garcia, ECO *Concert* (11/91) (RCA) ① **RD60718**
J. Murdoch, Scottish Ens, J. Rees (vn/dir) *Concert* (12/91) (VIRG) ① **VJ7 59641-2**
G. Enescu, Y. Menuhin, Paris SO, P. Monteux (r1932) *Concert* (12/91) (MSCM) ① **MM30322**
R. Manning, B. Shaw, Capital Virtuosi *Concert* (1/92) (SPRO) ① **SPCV1001**
O. Shumsky (vn/dir), J. Tunnell, Scottish CO *Concert* (9/92) (NIMB) ① **NI5325**
Arnold Rosé, Alma Rosé, CO (r1928) *Concert* (12/92) (BIDD) ① [2] **LAB056/7**
F. Kreisler, E. Zimbalist, Stg Qt (r1915) *Concert* (9/93) (PEAR) ① [2] **GEMMCDS9996**
G. Varga, Varga CO, T. Varga (vn/dir) (r1973) *Concert* (11/93) (CLAV) ① [4] **CD50-9300/4**
T Varga (vn/dir), G. Varga, Varga CO (r1973) *Concert* (11/93) (CLAV) ① **CD50-9311**
M-A. Nicolas, A. Moglia, Toulouse Nat CO, J-C. Malgoire (r1993) *Concert* (6/94) (AUVI) ① **V4697**
J. Heifetz, E. Friedman, New SO, M. Sargent (r1961) *Concert* (11/94) (RCA) ① [65] **09026 61778-2(11-15)**
J. Heifetz, RCA Victor CO, F. Waxman (r1946; Heifetz plays both parts) *Concert* (11/94) (RCA) ① [65] **09026 61778-2(06)**
A. Harnoncourt, W. Pfeiffer, VCM, N. Harnoncourt (r c1967) *Concert* (5/95) (TELD) ① **4509-95518-2**
D. Oistrakh, I. Oistrakh, RPO, E. Goossens (r1961) *Concert* (6/95) (DG) ① [2] **447 427-2GOR2**
I. Perlman, P. Zukerman, ECO, D. Barenboim *Concert* (6/95) (EMI) ① [20] **CZS4 83177-2(1)**
Y. Menuhin (vn/dir), C. Ferras, Bath Fest Orch *Concert* (11/95) (EMI) ① [2] **CES5 68517-2**
J. Schröder, C. Hirons, AAM, C. Hogwood *Concert* (9/89) (L'OI) ① **421 500-2OH**
J. Suk, M. Kosina, Suk CO, J. Vlach *Vivaldi: Concerti, Op. 8.* (11/91) (SUPR) ① **11 0281-2**
3. Solisti Italiani *Concert* (10/89) (DENO) ① **CO-73335**

Concerto for 3 Violins and Strings in D, BWV1064 (orig lost: recons from keyboard ver, BWV1064)
V. Spivakov (vn/dir), A. Futer, B. Garlitski, Moscow Virtuosi *Concert* (6/90) (RCA) ① **RD87991**
C. Kaine, R. Thomas, R. Studt, ASMF, N. Marriner (arr/recons Hogwood) *Concert* (1/94) (DECC) ① **440 037-2DM**
T. Rosenbusch, U. Eschenburg, S. Schergaut, CPE Bach Orch, P. Schreier (r1992) *Concert* (4/94) (PHIL) ① [2] **434 918-2PH2**
Freiburg Baroque Orch, T. Hengelbrock (r1992) *Concert* (4/94) (DHM) ① **05472 77289-2**

Concerto for 4 Harpsichords and Strings in A minor, BWV1065 (transc from Vivaldi: 4-Violin Concerto, Op. 3/10)
T. Pinnock (hpd/dir), K. Gilbert, L.U. Mortensen, N. Kraemer, English Concert *3-Harpsichord Concerti.* (4/83) (ARCH) ① **400 041-2AH**
M. Béroff, J-P. Collard, G. Tacchino, B. Rigutto, Paris Orch Ens, J-P. Wallez (pfs) *3-Harpsichord Concerti.* (5/85) (EMI) ① **CDC7 47063-2**
C. Eschenbach, J. Frantz, G. Oppitz, H. Schmitt, Hamburg PO (pfs) *Concert* (12/85) (DG) ① **415 655-2GH**
D. Moroney, C. Rousset, C. Tilney, C. Hogwood (hpd/dir), AAM *Concert* (3/92) (L'OI) ① **433 053-2OH**
G. Leonhardt (hpd/dir), A. Uittenbosch, E. Müller, J. van Wering, Leonhardt Consort (r c1966) *Concert* (11/95) (TELD) ① [3] **4509-97452-2**

3 Concertos for Two Harpsichords and Strings, BWV1060-62
1. C minor; 2. C; 3. C minor.
G. Leonhardt, B. van Asperen (hpd/dir), Amsterdam Melante (r1993) (10/95) (VIRG) ① **VC5 45054-2**
1, 2. C. Eschenbach, J. Frantz, Hamburg PO (pfs) *Concert* (12/85) (DG) ① **415 655-2GH**
1, 3. C. Rousset, C. Hogwood (hpd/dir), AAM *Concert* (9/89) (L'OI) ① **421 500-2OH**
1, 3. G. Leonhardt (hpd/dir), E. Müller, Leonhardt Consort (r c1966) *Concert* (11/95) (TELD) ① [3] **4509-97452-2**
2. A. Schnabel, K.U. Schnabel, LSO, A. Boult (r1936) *Brahms: Piano Concerto 2.* (2/91) (PEAR) ① **GEMMCD9399**
2. G. Leonhardt (hpd/dir), A. Uittenbosch, Leonhardt Consort (r c1968) *Concert* (11/95) (TELD) ① [3] **4509-97452-2**

2 Concertos for 3 Harpsichords and Strings, BWV1063-64
1. D minor; 2. C.
G. Leonhardt (hpd/dir), A. Uittenbosch, A. Curtis, Leonhardt Consort (r c1966) *Concert* (11/95) (TELD) ① [3] **4509-97452-2**
T. Pinnock (hpd/dir), K. Gilbert, L.U. Mortensen, English Concert *4-Harpsichord Concerto.* (4/83) (ARCH) ① **400 041-2AH**
M. Béroff, J-P. Collard, G. Tacchino, B. Rigutto, Paris Orch Ens, J-P. Wallez (pfs) *4-Harpsichord Concerto.* (5/85) (EMI) ① **CDC7 47063-2**
1. C. Eschenbach, J. Frantz, G. Oppitz, Hamburg PO (pfs) *Concert* (12/85) (DG) ① **415 655-2GH**
1. D. Moroney, C. Rousset, C. Tilney, AAM, C. Hogwood *Concert* (3/92) (L'OI) ① **433 053-2OH**
2. C. Hirons, M. Huggett, C. Mackintosh, C. Hogwood (hpd/dir), AAM (arr Hogwood: 3 vns) *Concert* (3/92) (L'OI) ① **433 053-2OH**
2. D. Moroney, C. Rousset, C. Hogwood (hpd/dir), AAM *Concert* (3/92) (L'OI) ① **433 053-2OH**
2. Edwin Fischer (pf/dir), R. Smith, D. Matthews, Philh (r1950) *Concert* (6/94) (EMI) ① **CDH7 64928-2**

4 Orchestral Suites, BWV1066-9 (c1717-23)
1. C, BWV1066 (2 oboes, bassoon and strings): 1a. Ouverture; 1b. Courante; 1c. Gavotte; 1d. Forlane; 1e. Menuetto; 1f. Bourrée; 1g. Passepied; 2. B minor, BWV1067 (flute and strings): 2a. Ouverture; 2b. Rondeau; 2c. Sarabande; 2d. Bourrée; 2e. Polonaise; 2f. Menuet; 2g. Badinerie; 3. D, BWV1068 (2 oboes, 3 trumpets, strings and timpani): 3a. Ouverture; 3b. Air ('Air on a G String'); 3c. Gavotte; 3d. Bourrée; 3e. Gigue; 4. D, BWV1069 (3 oboes, 3 trumpets, strings and timpani): 4a. Ouverture; 4b. Bourrée; 4c. Gavotte; 4d. Réjouissance.
Cologne Musica Antiqua, R. Goebel *Suite, BWV1070.* (10/86) (ARCH) ① [2] **415 671-2AH2**
ASMF, N. Marriner *Brandenburg Concertos.* (7/87) (EMI) ① [3] **CDS7 47881-8**
English Concert, T. Pinnock (hpd/dir) *Brandenburg Concertos.* (10/88) (ARCH) ① [3] **423 492-2AX3**
Amsterdam Baroque Orch, T. Koopman (r1988) (1/90) (DHM) ① [2] **RD77864**
Moscow Virtuosi, V. Spivakov (5/91) (RCA) ① [2] **RD60360**
Concert des Nations, J. Savall (6/91) (ASTR) ① [2] **E8727/8**
W. Bennett, ASMF, N. Marriner (7/91) (DECC) ① **430 378-2DM**
Boston Early Music Sols, W. Malloch (r1989) (10/91) (KOCH) ① **37037-2**
ASMF, N. Marriner *Concert* (11/91) (PHIL) ① **426 462-2PBQ2**
A. Busch Chbr Plyrs, A. Busch (r1936) *Brandenburg Concertos.* (12/91) (EMI) ① [3] **CHS7 64047-2**
New Philh, O. Klemperer *Concert* (9/92) (EMI) ① [3] **CMS7 64150-2**
Collegium Aureum (r1969) *Brandenburg Concertos.* (3/93) (DHM) ① [3] **05472 77251-2**
Boston Early Music Fest Orch, A. Parrott (r1992) *Triple Concerto, BWV1044.* (5/93) (EMI) ① [2] **CDS7 54653-2**
VCM, N. Harnoncourt (r1966) (2/94) (TELD) ① [2] **4509-92174-2**
English Concert, T. Pinnock (r1993-4) *Concert* (12/95) (ARCH) ① [2] **439 780-2AH2**
1, 2. Brandenburg Consort, R. Goodman *Concert* (7/91) (HYPE) ① **CDA66501**
1-3. ECO, P. Ledger (12/91) (VIRG) ① **VJ7 59640-2**
1-3. Bath Fest Orch, Y. Menuhin *Concert* (11/95) (EMI) ① [2] **CES5 68517-2**
2. Zagreb Sols, J. Galway (fl/dir) *Concert* (11/87) (RCA) ① **GD86517**
2. P. Evison, Drottningholm Baroque Ens *Concert* (10/88) (BIS) ① **BIS-CD249**
2. J-P. Rampal, Stuttgart CO, K. Münchinger *Musikalisches Opfer, BWV1079.* (7/91) (DECC) ① **430 266-2DM**
2. VCM, N. Harnoncourt *Brandenburg Concertos.* (9/92) (TELD) ① **9031-75858-2**
2. Württemberg CO, J. Faerber *Concert* (6/93) (RCA) ① **09026 60900-2**
2. Cologne Musica Antiqua, R. Goebel (r1982) *Brandenburg Concertos.* (1/94) (DG) ① **439 401-2GCL**
2. I Musici *Concert* (9/94) (PHIL) ① **442 396-2PM**
2. Concertgebouw, W. Mengelberg (pp1939) *Concert* (5/95) (ARHI) ① **ADCD112**
2f, 2g, 3b ASMF, N. Marriner *Concert* (10/91) (DECC) ① **430 499-2DWO**

2g I. Tracey (arr Tracey) *Concert*
(1/90) (CFP) ① **CD-CFP4558**
2g, 3b O.E. Antonsen, W. Marshall (r1992: arr tpt/org: Antonsen/Marshall) *Concert*
(10/94) (EMI) ① **CDC5 55048-2**
2, 3. ASMF, N. Marriner *Concert*
(7/87) (DECC) ① **417 715-2DM**
2, 3. S. Preston, English Concert, T. Pinnock *Triple Concerto, BWV1044.*
(4/89) (ARCH) ① **427 112-2AGA**
2, 3. Stuttgart CO, K. Münchinger *Concert*
(8/91) (DECC) ① **430 706-2DM**
2, 3. VCM, N. Harnoncourt (r1983) *Brandenburg Concertos.* (5/95) (TELD) ① [2] **4509-95980-2**
3. BRSO, O. Klemperer (pp1957) *Brahms: Symphony 4.* (8/90) (ORFE) ① **C201891A**
3. VCM, N. Harnoncourt *Brandenburg Concertos.*
(9/92) (TELD) ① **9031-75859-2**
3. Leipzig Gewandhaus, H. Abendroth (bp1944) *Concert* (9/94) (TAHR) ① [2] **TAH106/7**
3a S. Cleobury (r1979: arr S Cleobury) *Concert*
(6/93) (DECC) ① **436 402-2DWO**
3b Cantilena, A. Shepherd *Concert*
(9/84) (CHAN) ① **CHAN8319**
3b Scottish CO, K. Montgomery *Concert*
(1/89) (EMIL) ① **CDZ114**
3b Solisti Italiani *Concert*
(10/89) (DENO) ① **CO-73335**
3b F. Kreisler, anon (r1904: arr Wilhelmj) *Concert*
(7/90) (BIDD) ① [2] **LAB009/10**
3b W. Burmester, anon (arr Burmester: r1909) *Concert* (8/90) (SYMP) ① **SYMCD1071**
3b NBC SO, A. Toscanini (r1946) *Concert*
(1/91) (RCA) ① **GD60308**
3b J. Hubay, Budapest Cons Orch, Mr Zsolt (arr Wilhelmj: r1929) *Concert*
(12/91) (BIDD) ① **LAB045**
3b K. Parlow, Anon (pf) (arr Wilhelmj: r1909) *Concert* (12/91) (APR) ① [2] **APR7015**
3b Scottish Ens, J. Rees (r1991) *Concert*
(12/91) (VIRG) ① **VJ7 59652-2**
3b BPO, W. Furtwängler (r1929) *Concert*
(4/92) (KOCH) ① [2] **37059-2**
3b M. Kliegel, R. Havenith (arr L. Rose) *Concert*
(9/92) (MARC) ① **8 223403**
3b Rosé Qt (arr Wilhelmj: r1927) *Concert*
(12/92) (BIDD) ① [2] **LAB056/7**
3b Guildhall Str Ens, R. Salter (vn/dir) (r1992) *Concert* (2/94) (RCA) ① **09026 61275-2**
3b B. Huberman, P. Frenkel (r1921: arr Wilhelmj) *Concert* (3/94) (BIDD) ① [2] **LAB077/8**
3b BBC PO, M. Bamert (r1993: orch Stokowski) *Concert* (5/94) (EMI) ① [6] **ZDMF7 64830-2**
3b N. Milstein, L. Pommers (r1957: arr Wilhelmj) *Concert* (5/94) (EMI) ① [6] **ZDMF7 64830-2**
3b B. Huberman, S. Schultze (r1929: arr Wilhelmj) *Concert* (9/94) (BIDD) ① [2] **LAB081/2**
3b M. Maisky, D. Hovora (r1993: arr vc/pf: Maisky) *Concert* (9/94) (DG) ① **439 863-2GH**
3b J. Starker, G. Moore (r1958: arr vc/pf: Delsart) *Concert* (12/95) (EMI) ① [6] **CZS5 68485-2**
4. Freiburg Baroque Orch, T. Hengelbrock (r1991) *Concert* (4/94) (DHM) ① **05472 77289-2**
Suite in G—strings, BWV1070 (spurious: possibly by W F Bach)
1. Larghetto—Un poco Allegro; 2. Torneo; 3. Aria. Adagio; 4. Menuetto alternativo—Trio; 5. Capriccio.
Cologne Musica Antiqua, R. Goebel *Suites, BWV1066-9.* (10/86) (ARCH) ① [2] **415 671-2AH2**

The Art of Fugue, '(Die) Kunst der Fuge', BWV1080 (c1745-50)
Cologne Musica Antiqua, R. Goebel *Concert*
(4/85) (ARCH) ① [3] **413 642-2AH3**
D. Moroney (5/86) (HARM) ① [2] **HMC90 1169/70**
Hespèrion XX, J. Savall
(11/88) (ASTR) ① [2] **E2001**
H. Walcha *Concert*
(10/89) (ARCH) ① [12] **419 904-2AX12(2)**
K. Gilbert (4/90) (ARCH) ① **427 673-2AH**
G. Leonhardt, B. van Asperen *Concert*
(12/90) (DHM) ① [2] **GD77010**
Juilliard Qt (6/92) (SONY) ① [2] **S2K45937**
T. Nikolaieva *Concert*
(2/93) (HYPE) ① [2] **CDA66631/2**
G. Leonhardt (r1953)
(10/93) (VANG) ① **08.2012.72**
ASMF, N. Marriner (r1974) *Musikalisches Opfer, BWV1079.* (5/94) (PHIL) ① [2] **442 556-2PM2**
Amsterdam Bach Sols (Bärenreiter ed)
(8/89) (OTTA) ① **OTRC48503**
Contrapunctus 18. H. Walcha (cptd Walcha) *Concert*
(10/89) (ARCH) ① [12] **419 904-2AX12(1)**

Contrapunctus 13, 17-19. W. Rübsam (r1992) *Concert* (1/94) (NAXO) ① **8 550704**
Contrapunctus 1-12, 14, 15. W. Rübsam (r1992) *Concert* (1/94) (NAXO) ① **8 550703**
Contrapunctus 1. Amsterdam Loeki Stardust Qt *Concert* (10/94) (L'OI) ① **440 207-2OM**
Canon concordia discors a 2—canon in contrary motion, BWV1086 (?c1731)
Cpte Cologne Musica Antiqua, R. Goebel *Concert*
(4/85) (ARCH) ① [3] **413 642-2AH3**
7 Canons, BWV1072-78
1. Canon trias harmonica a 8, BWV1072 (pub 1754); 2. Canon a 4 perpetus, BWV1073 (1713); 3. Canon a 4 (completely invertible puzzle canon: 1727), BWV1074; 4. Canon a 2 perpetus, BWV1075 (1734); 5. Canon triplex a 6, BWV1076; 6. Canone doppio sopr'il soggetto, BWV1077 (1747); 7. Canon super fa mi a 7 post tempus musicum, BWV1078 (1749).
Cpte Cologne Musica Antiqua, R. Goebel *Concert*
(4/85) (ARCH) ① [3] **413 642-2AH3**
Musikalisches Opfer, 'Musical Offering'—flute, 2 violins and continuo, BWV1079 (1747)
1. Ricercar a 3; 2. Canon 1, a 2; 3. Canon 2, a 2; 4. Canon 3, a 2; 5. Canon 4, a 2; 6. Canon 5, a 2; 7. Fuga canonica in epidiapente; 8. Ricercar a 6; 9. Canon a 2; 10. Canon a 4; 11. Trio Sonata in C minor (Sonata sopr'il soggetto reale); 12. Canon perpetuus.
Cologne Musica Antiqua, R. Goebel *Concert*
(4/85) (ARCH) ① [3] **413 642-2AH3**
D. Moroney, M. Cook, J. See, J. Holloway, J. ter Linden (8/88) (HARM) ① **HMC90 1260**
J-P. Rampal, Stuttgart CO, K. Münchinger *Suites, BWV1066-9.* (7/91) (DECC) ① [2] **430 266-2DM**
ASMF, N. Marriner (r1978) *Art of Fugue.*
(5/95) (PHIL) ① [2] **442 556-2PM2**
1, 8. T. Nikolaieva *Concert*
(2/93) (HYPE) ① [2] **CDA66631/2**
8. LSO, P. Boulez (orch Webern: r1969) *Concert*
(6/91) (SONY) ① [3] **SM3K45845**
8. VPO, C. Abbado (r1990: orch Webern) *Concert*
(5/93) (DG) ① **431 774-2GH**
8. Cleveland Orch, C. von Dohnányi (orch Webern) *Bruckner: Symphony 6.*
(10/94) (DECC) ① **436 153-2DH**
11. J. Galway, K-W. Chung, P. Moll, M. Welsh *Concert* (11/87) (RCA) ① **GD86517**
Sonata for Violin and Harpsichord in G, BWV1019a (additional earlier movements for Sonata, BWV1019)
1. Adagio; 2. Cantabile.
E. Blumenstock, J. Butt (r1991-92) *Concert*
(3/93) (HARM) ① [2] **HMU90 7084/5**
6 Sonatas for Flute and Harpsichord, BWV1030-35
EXCERPTS: 1. B minor; 2. E flat (doubtful: possibly by C.P.E. Bach); 2b. Siciliano; 3. A; 4. C (doubtful); 5. E minor; 6. E.
J. Solum, I. Kipnis, B. Bogatin
(2/89) (ARAB) ① **Z6589**
M. Jurkovič, Z. Růžičková, J. Alexander
(12/89) (OPUS) ① **9351 1758**
S. Preston, T. Pinnock, J. Savall *Partita, BWV1013.*
(1/90) (CRD) ① [2] **CRD3314/5**
M. Arita, C. Arita, H. Suzuki *Concert*
(5/90) (DENO) ① [2] **CO-73868/9**
J. See, M. Springfels, D. Moroney *Concert*
(11/91) (HARM) ① [2] **HMU90 7024/5**
M. Petri, K. Jarrett (2/93) (RCA) ① **09026 61274-2**
W. Bennett, G. Malcolm, M. Evans (r1978)
(3/94) (ASV) ① **CDQS6108**
M. Larrieu, W. Kuijken, R. Puyana (r1967) *Viola da Gamba Sonatas, BWV1027-9.*
(4/94) (PHIL) ① [2] **438 809-2PM2**
1. S. Kuijken, J. van Dael, W. Kuijken, A. Glatt, A. Woodrow, G. Leonhardt (arr. in D minor by F. Brüggen for 2 vn, 2 va da gamba and bc) *Concert* (5/90) (RCA) ① [2] **GD71964**
1, 2. H. Schellenberger, R. Koehne, J. Fink (trans ob) *Concert* (8/88) (DENO) ① **CO-2142**
1, 2, 4-6. J. Galway, S. Cunningham, P. Moll (r1993) *Violin Sonatas, BWV1020-25.*
(6/95) (RCA) ① **09026 62555-2**
1-3. A. Nicolet, K. Richter *Concert*
(9/89) (ARCH) ① **427 113-2AGA**
1, 3-5. Barthold Kuijken, G. Leonhardt, W. Kuijken *Concert* (1/90) (DHM) ① [2] **RD77026**
1, 3, 5, 6. F. Brüggen, G. Leonhardt, A. Bylsma *Concert* (5/90) (RCA) ① [2] **GD71964**
2. E. Talmi, Y. Talmi *Concert*
(6/90) (CARL) ① **PWK1133**
2. Barthold Kuijken, B. van Asperen (r1993) *Concert* (5/94) (SONY) ① [2] **S2K53964**

2. M. Verbruggen, M. Meyerson (r1993) *Trio Sonatas, BWV525-530.*
(2/95) (HARM) ① **HMU90 7119**
2b D. Lipatti (arr Kempff: r1950) *Concert*
(6/89) (EMI) ① **CDH7 69800-2**
2b G. Fergus-Thompson (trans Kempff) *Concert*
(10/91) (ASV) ① **CDDCA759**
2b H. Schellenberger, M-A. Süss *Concert*
(12/91) (DENO) ① **CO-76611**
2b T. Nikolaieva (pf) *Concert*
(9/92) (MEZH) ① **MK418024**
2b I. Biret (trans Kempff) *Concert*
(5/93) (MARC) ① **8 223452**
2b W. Kempff (r1975: arr pf: Kempff) *Concert*
(11/94) (DG) ① [2] **439 672-2GX2**
3. M. Petri, H. Petri (trans rec) *Concert*
(10/88) (RCA) ① **RD87749**
3. J. Galway, Württemberg CO, J. Faerber (arr & orch Mohr) *Concert* (6/93) (RCA) ① **09026 60900-2**
4. J. See, M. Springfels, D. Moroney (fl solo) *Concert* (11/91) (HARM) ① [2] **HMU90 7024/5**
5. M. Verbruggen, Sonnerie Trio *Concert*
(2/90) (ASV) ① **CDGAU113**
5. P. E. Davies, J. Alley, A. Shulman *Concert*
(7/94) (EMI) ① **CDC5 55085-2**
3 Sonatas for Viola da gamba and Harpsichord, BWV1027-29 (c1720)
1. G; 2. D; 3. G minor.
Y-Y. Ma, K. Gilbert (12/85) (SONY) ① **MK37794**
M. Maisky, M. Argerich
(1/86) (DG) ① **415 471-2GH**
A. Bylsma, B. van Asperen *J. C. F. Bach: Cello Sonata in A.* (3/91) (SONY) ① **SK45945**
P. Casals, P. Baumgartner (r1950)
(10/91) (SONY) ① **MPK46445**
M. Cervera, R. Puyana (r1969) *Flute Sonatas, BWV1030-5.* (4/94) (PHIL) ① [2] **438 809-2PM2**
P. Tortelier, R. Veyron-Lacroix *Concert*
(8/94) (ERAT) ① [2] **4509-95359-2**
K. Kashkashian, K. Jarrett (r1991)
(1/95) (ECM) ① **445 230-2**
3 Sonatas for Violin and Continuo, BWV1020-25
1. G minor, BWV1020 (doubtful: now thought to be by C P E Bach); 2. G, BWV1021 (c1721); 3. F, BWV1022 (doubtful); 4. E minor, BWV1023 (c1975); 5. G minor, BWV1024 (doubtful); 6. A, BWV1025 (doubtful).
1. A. Nicolet, K. Richter *Concert*
(9/89) (ARCH) ① **427 113-2AGA**
1. M. Arita, C. Arita *Concert*
(5/90) (DENO) ① [2] **CO-73868/9**
1. J. See, M. Springfels, D. Moroney *Concert*
(11/91) (HARM) ① [2] **HMU90 7024/5**
1. Barthold Kuijken, B. van Asperen (fl) *Concert*
(5/94) (SONY) ① [2] **S2K53964**
1. J. Galway, S. Cunningham, P. Moll (r1993; arr fl) *Flute Sonatas, BWV1030-5.*
(6/95) (RCA) ① **09026 62555-2**
2. A. Busch, R. Serkin (r1929) *Concert*
(12/92) (PEAR) ① **GEMMCD9942**
2. A. Busch, R. Serkin (r1929) *Concert*
(3/95) (SYMP) ① **SYMCD1109**
2, 4. E. Blumenstock, E. Le Guin, S. Lehning, J. Butt (r1991-92) *Concert*
(10/93) (HARM) ① [2] **HMU90 7084/5**
6 Sonatas for Violin and Harpsichord, BWV1014-19.
EXCERPTS: 1. B minor; 1c. Andante; 2. A; 2c. Andante; 2d. Presto; 3. E; 4. C minor, 4a. Siciliano; Largo; 5. F minor; 6. G.
J. Suk, Z. Růžičková
(8/88) (SUPR) ① [2] **COS-1370/1**
S. Kuijken, G. Leonhardt
(10/90) (DHM) ① [2] **GD77170**
S. Lautenbacher, K. Klinckerfuss
(10/90) (BAYE) ① [2] **BR100086/7**
E. Blumenstock, J. Butt (r1991-92) *Concert*
(10/93) (HARM) ① [2] **HMU90 7084/5**
1, 2, 6. V. Mullova, B. Canino (1992) *C.P.E. Bach: Sonata, H514.* (7/93) (PHIL) ① **434 084-2PH**
4. Y. Menuhin, G. Gould (bp1965) *Concert*
(10/93) (SONY) ① **SMK52688**
4a H. Temianka, J. Graudan (r1937) *Concert*
(2/93) (BIDD) ① [2] **LAB059/60**
4a BBC PO, M. Bamert (r1993: orch Stokowski) *Concert* (3/94) (CHAN) ① **CHAN9259**
4 Trio Sonatas, BWV1036-39
1. D minor, BWV1036 (2 vns, hpd: spurious); 2. C, BWV1037 (2 vns, hpd: doubtful: possibly by J G Goldberg); 3. G, BWV1038 (fl, vn & cont: after Vn Son, BWV1021—prob by a Bach son); 4. G, BWV1039 (2 fl, continuo: c1720).
London Baroque (6/86) (HARM) ① **HMC90 1173**

12. S. Feinberg (r1952; arr Feinberg) *Concert*
(8/95) (MELO) ① **[11] 74321 25172-2(1)**
12. S. Feinberg (r1952; arr Feinberg) *Concert*
(8/95) (MELO) ① **74321 25175-2**
12, 13a S. Feinberg (r1962; arr Feinberg) *Concert*
(8/95) (MELO) ① **[11] 74321 25172-2(1)**
12, 13a S. Feinberg (r1962; arr Feinberg) *Concert*
(8/95) (MELO) ① **74321 25175-2**
13a P. Kee *Concert* (10/89) (CHAN) ① **CHAN0506**
13a, 13b, 14a, 14b, 15a, 15b, 16-18. M. Souter
(r1993) *Concert* (5/95) (ISIS) ① **ISISCD008**
13a, 14a, 15a, 15b, 16. L. Antonini (r1991) *Concert*
(10/94) (SONY) ① **SK57487**
18. E. Petri (pp1958: arr pf: Petri) *Concert*
(3/94) (MUSI) ① **[4] MACD-772**
Christ lag in Todesbanden—organ,
BWV695
H. Fagius *Concert*
(10/91) (BIS) ① **[2] BIS-CD343/4**
A. Isoir *Concert*
(2/93) (CALL) ① **[15] CAL9703/17(2)**
L. Rogg *Concert*
(2/93) (HARM) ① **[12] HMX290 772/83(3)**
Christ lag in Todesbanden—chorale prelude,
BWV718 (before 1708)
G. Leonhardt *Concert* (12/90) (DHM) ① **RD77868**
A. Isoir *Concert*
(2/93) (CALL) ① **[15] CAL9703/17(1)**
L. Rogg *Concert*
(2/93) (HARM) ① **[12] HMX290 772/83(3)**
Christe, der du bist der helle Tag—partite
diverse, BWV766 (c1704-15)
C. Herrick *Concert* (5/92) (HYPE) ① **CDA66455**
A. Isoir *Concert*
(2/93) (CALL) ① **[15] CAL9703/17(1)**
L. Rogg *Concert*
(2/93) (HARM) ① **[12] HMX290 772/83(1)**
Christum wir sollen loben schon, BWV696
(?1739-42)
H. Fagius *Concert*
(10/91) (BIS) ① **[2] BIS-CD343/4**
A. Isoir *Concert*
(2/93) (CALL) ① **[15] CAL9703/17(2)**
L. Rogg *Concert*
(2/93) (HARM) ① **[12] HMX290 772/83(2)**
L. Ghielmi (r1992) *Concert*
(7/93) (DHM) ① **05472 77278-2**
Christus, der uns selig macht, BWV747
(spurious)
H. Fagius *Concert* (10/91) (BIS) ① **BIS-CD445**
A. Isoir *Concert*
(2/93) (CALL) ① **[15] CAL9703/17(2)**
Chromatic Fantasia and Fugue in D minor,
BWV903 (c1720 rev c1730)
R. Aldwinckle *Concert* (6/86) (CARL) ① **PCD817**
A. Schiff (pf) *Concert*
(12/87) (HUNG) ① **HCD11690**
I. Kipnis *Concert* (1/88) (ARAB) ① **Z6577**
W. Landowska (r1935) *Concert*
(5/88) (EMI) ① **CDH7 61008-2**
L.U. Mortensen (1/89) (KONT) ① **32012**
C. Arrau (r1945; pf) *Concert*
(7/89) (RCA) ① **[2] GD87841**
A. Staier (r1990) *Concert* (10/89) (DHM) ① **RD77039**
S. Barere (pp1946) *Concert*
(11/89) (APR) ① **[2] APR7008**
W. Gieseking (bp1950) *Concert*
(11/90) (MUSI) ① **MACD-612**
M. Tipo *Concert* (11/91) (EMI) ① **CDC7 54147-2**
C. Rousset *Concert* (5/92) (L'OI) ① **433 054-2OH**
R. Tureck (bp1992) *Concert*
(8/93) (VAI) ① **[2] VAIA1024**
Edwin Fischer (r1931) *Concert*
(6/94) (EMI) ① **CDH7 64928-2**
C. Booth (r1993) *Concert*
(10/94) (OLYM) ① **OCD437**
W. Rübsam (r1991) *Concert*
(10/94) (NAXO) ① **8 550709**
A. Hewitt (r1994) *Concert*
(11/94) (HYPE) ① **CDA66746**
G. Malcolm (r1960) *Concert*
(11/95) (DECC) ① **444 390-2DWO**
Chromatic Fantasia in D minor—keyboard,
BWV903a (c1720)
I. Kipnis *Concert* (1/88) (ARAB) ① **Z6577**
Clavier-Übung III—chorale preludes,
BWV669-689
1. Kyrie, Gott Vater in Ewigkeit, BWV669; 2. Christe,
aller Welt Trost, BWV670; 3. Kyrie, Gott heiliger
Geist, BWV671; 4. Kyrie, Gott Vater in Ewigkeit,
BWV672; 5. Christe, aller Welt Trost, BWV673; 6.
Kyrie, Gott heiliger Geist, BWV674; 7. Allein Gott in
der Höh' sei Ehr', BWV675; 8. Allein Gott in der Höh'
sei Ehr', BWV676; 9. Allein Gott in der Höh',
BWV676a; 10. Fughetta: Allein Gott in der Höh',
BWV677; 11. Dies sind die heil'gen zehn Gebot',

BWV678; 12. Fughetta: Dies sind die heil'gen,
BWV679; 13. Wir glauben all'an einen Gott,
BWV680; 14. Fughetta: Wir glauben all'an einen
Gott, BWV681; 15. Vater unser im Himmelreich,
BWV682; 16. Vater unser im Himmelreich, BWV683;
17. Vater unser in Himmelreich, BWV683a; 18.
Christ, unser Herr, zum Jordan kam, BWV684; 19.
Christ, unser Herr, zum Jordan kam, BWV685; 20.
Aus tiefer Not, BWV686; 21. Aus tiefer Not, BWV687;
22. Jesus Christus unser Heiland, BWV688; 23.
Fuga: Jesus Christus unser Heiland, BWV689.
H. Walcha *Concert*
(10/89) (ARCH) ① **[12] 419 904-2AX12(2)**
1-3, 7, 10, 12, 14, 16, 18, 21, 23. G. Leonhardt
Concert (12/90) (DHM) ① **RD77868**
1-8, 10-14. W. Rübsam (r1993) *Prelude and Fugue,*
BWV552. (12/94) (NAXO) ① **8 550929**
1-8, 10-16, 18-23. M-C. Alain *Concert*
(4/92) (ERAT) ① **[2] 2292-45664-2**
1-8, 10-16, 18-23. A. Isoir *Concert*
(2/93) (CALL) ① **[15] CAL9703/17(4)**
1-8, 10-16, 18-23. L. Rogg *Concert*
(2/93) (HARM) ① **[12] HMX290 772/83(3)**
1-8, 16-18, 23. M. Radulescu *Concert*
(4/93) (DHM) ① **[2] 05472 77276-2**
8. P. Guillot *Concert* (9/89) (SCAL) ① **ARI139**
13. J-P. Brosse *Concert* (3/90) (PIER) ① **PV789104**
13. Sydney SO, R. Pickler (orch Stokowski) *Concert*
(10/91) (CHAN) ① **CHAN6532**
13. BBC PO, M. Bamert (r1993: orch Stokowski)
Concert (3/94) (CHAN) ① **CHAN9259**
13. P. Hurford (r1993) *Concert*
(3/94) (EMIN) ① **CD-EMX2218**
15. K. John *Concert* (4/90) (PRIO) ① **PRCD264**
15, 16, 18-23. W. Rübsam (r1993) *Concert*
(12/94) (NAXO) ① **8 550930**
15, 22. T. Koopman *Concert*
(8/89) (NOVA) ① **150 036-2**
20, 22. F-H. Houbart (r1984) *Concert*
(3/86) (PIER) ① **PV784061**
Concerto in the Italian Style, 'Italian
Concerto', BWV971 (1735)
T. Pinnock *Concert*
(11/84) (ARCH) ① **413 591-2AH**
R. Aldwinckle *Concert* (6/86) (CARL) ① **PCD817**
W. Landowska (r1935/6) *Concert*
(5/88) (EMI) ① **CDH7 61008-2**
K. Haugsand *Concert* (9/88) (SIMA) ① **PSC1032**
G. Leonhardt *Concert* (10/89) (RICA) ① **GD71952**
K. Gilbert (r1988) *Concert*
(2/90) (HARM) ① **HMA190 1278**
G. Leonhardt *Concert*
(12/90) (DHM) ① **[2] GD77013**
V. Black *Concert* (5/91) (COLL) ① **Coll5024-2**
M. Tipo *Concert* (11/91) (EMI) ① **CDC7 54147-2**
C. Rousset *Concert* (5/92) (L'OI) ① **433 054-2OH**
D. Moroney *Concert* (9/92) (VIRG) ① **VC7 59272-2**
L.U. Mortensen *French Overture, BWV831.*
(12/92) (KONT) ① **32113**
A. Schiff *Concert*
(10/93) (DECC) ① **[2] 433 313-2DH2**
G. Gould (bp1955) *Concert*
(7/94) (CBC) ① **PSCD2005**
S. Richter (r1991) *Concert*
(8/94) (PHIL) ① **[3] 438 613-2PH3**
W. Rübsam (r1991) *Concert*
(10/94) (NAXO) ① **8 550709**
A. Staier (r1995) (DHM) ① **[3] 05472 77306-2**
Solomon (pp1956) *Concert*
(4/95) (APR) ① **[2] APR7030**
S. Richter (pp1948) *Concert*
(8/95) (MELO) ① **[11] 74321 25172-2(1)**
S. Richter (pp1948) *Concert*
(8/95) (MELO) ① **74321 25178-2**
G. Malcolm (r1960) *Concert*
(11/95) (DECC) ① **444 390-2DWO**
6 Concertos—transcriptions for organ,
BWV592-7 (1708-17) (works by other
composers)
1. G (after Concerto by Johann Ernst); 2. A minor
(after Vivaldi, Op. 3 No. 8); 3. C (after Vivaldi, Op. 7
No. 11); 4. C (after Johann Ernst); 5. D minor (after
Vivaldi, Op. 3 No. 11); 5a. No tempo indication; 5b.
Grave; 5c. Fugue; 5d. Largo; 5e. Finale; 6. E flat
(after unknown composer).
W. Rübsam (r1993) *Concert*
(12/94) (NAXO) ① **8 550936**
1. M. Murray *Concert* (8/89) (TELA) ① **CD80179**
1. K. John *Concert* (4/90) (PRIO) ① **PRCD264**
1. K. Bowyer *Concert* (10/92) (NIMB) ① **NI5280**
1-5. S.Preston (9/88) (DG) ① **423 087-2GH**
1-5. A. Isoir *Concert*
(2/93) (CALL) ① **[15] CAL9703/17(2)**
2. M. Murray *Concert* (10/84) (TELA) ① **CD80088**

2. H. Fagius *Concert*
(10/91) (BIS) ① **[2] BIS-CD343/4**
2, 3, 5. B. Foccroulle *Concert*
(10/91) (RICE) ① **RIC086069**
4, 6. H. Fagius *Concert*
(10/91) (BIS) ① **[2] BIS-CD439/40**
5. K. Bowyer (r1992) *Concert*
(6/93) (NIMB) ① **NI5290**
5. A. Brailowsky (r1938) *Concert*
(8/94) (APR) ① **APR5501**
5. P. Hurford (r1993) *Concert*
(3/94) (EMIN) ① **CD-EMX2226**
5. A. Cortot (r1937: arr pf: Cortot) *Concert*
(5/95) (BIDD) ① **LHW020**
5d J. Thibaud, T. Janopoulo (r1930: arr vn/pf:
Pochon) *Concert* (12/94) (APR) ① **[2] APR7028**
16 Concertos—transciptions for organ,
BWV972-987 (1713-16) (works by other
composers)
1. D, BWV972 (Vivaldi: Concerto, Op. 3/9—RV230);
2. G, BWV973 (Vivaldi: Concerto, Op. 7/8—RV299);
3. D minor, BWV974 (A. Marcello—Oboe Concerto);
4. G minor, BWV975 (Vivaldi: Concerto, Op.
4/6—RV316); 5. C, BWV976 (Vivaldi: Concerto, Op.
3/12—RV265); 6. C, BWV977 (source unknown); 7.
F, BWV978 (Vivaldi: Concerto, Op. 3/3—RV310); 8.
B minor, BWV979 (source unknown); 9. G, BWV980
(Vivaldi: Concerto, Op. 4/1—RV381); 10. C minor,
BWV981 (source unknown); 11. B flat, BWV982
(concerto by Duke Johann Ernst of Saxe-Weimar);
12. G minor, BWV983 (source unknown); 13. C,
BWV984 (concerto by Duke Johann Ernst of Saxe-
Weimar); 14. G minor, BWV985 (violin concerto by
Telemann); 15. G, BWV986 (source unknown); 16. D
minor, BWV987 (concerto by Duke Johann Ernst of
Saxe-Weimar).
H. Dreyfus (10/91) (DENO) ① **[2] CO-76497/8**
1. W. Landowska (r1946) *Concert*
(3/93) (RCA) ① **[2] GD60919**
1-6, 8, 10, 13. I. Bolton (7/90) (ASV) ① **CDGAU116**
5. C. Booth (r1993) *Concert*
(10/94) (OLYM) ① **OCD437**
7. K. Gilbert *Concert* (6/88) (NOVA) ① **150 018-2**
Das Jesulein soll doch mein Trost, BWV702
(doubtful)
H. Fagius *Concert*
(10/91) (BIS) ① **[2] BIS-CD343/4**
A. Isoir *Concert*
(2/93) (CALL) ① **[15] CAL9703/17(2)**
Du Friedefürst, Herr Jesu Christ—chorale
prelude
G. Barber *Concert* (7/91) (ASV) ① **CDGAU121**
4 Duets, BWV802-805 (Clavier-Übung III)
1. E minor; 2. F; 3. G; 4. A minor.
H. Walcha (10/89) (ARCH) ① **[12] 419 904-2AX12(1)**
K. Gilbert (r1988) *Concert*
(2/90) (HARM) ① **HMA190 1278**
M-C. Alain *Concert*
(4/92) (ERAT) ① **[2] 2292-45664-2**
C. Rousset *Concert* (5/92) (L'OI) ① **433 054-2OH**
D. Moroney *Concert* (9/92) (VIRG) ① **VC7 59272-2**
A. Isoir *Concert*
(2/93) (CALL) ① **[15] CAL9703/17(5)**
T. Nikolaieva *Concert*
(2/93) (HYPE) ① **[2] CDA66631/2**
M. Radulescu *Concert*
(4/93) (DHM) ① **[2] 05472 77276-2**
S. Richter (r1991) *Concert*
(8/94) (PHIL) ① **[3] 438 613-2PH3**
W. Rübsam (r1993) *Concert*
(12/94) (NAXO) ① **8 550930**
Palladian Ens (r1994: arr vn/va da gamba) *Concert*
(8/95) (LINN) ① **CKD036**
Durch Adams Fall ist ganz verderbt, BWV705
(doubtful)
A. Isoir *Concert* (8/89) (CALL) ① **CAL9710**
H. Fagius *Concert*
(10/91) (BIS) ① **[2] BIS-CD343/4**
A. Isoir *Concert*
(2/93) (CALL) ① **[15] CAL9703/17(2)**
Ein feste Burg ist unser Gott, BWV720
(1709)
B. Foccroulle *Concert* (3/90) (RICE) ① **RIC064042**
H. Fagius *Concert*
(10/91) (BIS) ① **[2] BIS-CD439/40**
A. Isoir *Concert*
(2/93) (CALL) ① **[15] CAL9703/17(2)**
L. Rogg *Concert*
(2/93) (HARM) ① **[12] HMX290 772/83(2)**
K. Bowyer *Concert* (3/93) (NIMB) ① **NI5289**
6 English Suites—keyboard, BWV806-811
(by 1724-25)
EXCERPTS: 1. A: 1a. Prelude; 1b. Allemande; 1c.
Courante I; 1d. Courante II & Doubles; 1e.
Sarabande; 1f. Bourrée I; 1g. Bourrée II; 1h. Gigue;

2. A MINOR: 2a. Prelude; 2b. Allemande; 2c.
Courante; 2d. Sarabande; 2e. Bourrée I; 2f. Bourrée
II; 2g. Gigue; 3. G MINOR: 3a. Prelude; 3b.
Allemande; 3c. Courante; 3d. Sarabande; 3e.
Gavotte I; 3f. Gavotte II (Musette); 3g. Gigue; 4. F:
4a. Prelude; 4b. Allemande; 4c. Courante; 4d.
Sarabande; 4e. Menuet I; 4f. Menuet II; 4g. Gigue;
5. E MINOR: 5a. Prelude; 5b. Allemande; 5c.
Courante; 5d. Sarabande; 5e. Passepied I &
Rondeau; 5f. Passepied II; 5g. Gigue; 6. D MINOR:
6a. Prelude; 6b. Allemande; 6c. Courante; 6d.
Sarabande; 6e. Double; 6f. Gavotte I; 6g. Gavotte II;
6h. Gigue.
A. Schiff   (12/88) (DECC) ① [2] 421 640-2DH2
C. Tilney (r1990s)   (2/94) (MUSI) ① [2] MACD-777
2. M. Argerich Concert
                     (12/88) (DG) ① 423 880-2GGA
2, 3. I. Pogorelich   (7/87) (DG) ① 415 480-2GH
2, 4, 6. Safri Duo (r1994: trans perc) French Suites,
BWV812-17.   (5/95) (CHAN) ① CHAN9339
3. J. Henry Concert   (10/92) (VICT) ① VCD19013
3. W. Kempff (r1975) Concert
                  (11/94) (DG) ① [2] 439 672-2GX2
3d, 3e, 3f J. Heifetz, A. Sándor (arr Heifetz: r1934)
Concert   (2/94) (EMI) ① CDH7 64494-2
3e, 3f J. Heifetz, A. Sándor (r1934) Concert
                 (11/94) (RCA) ① [65] 09026 61778-2(02)
3, 4, 6. S. Richter (r1991) Concert
                     (8/94) (PHIL) ① [3] 438 613-2PH3
4. A. Schiff (pf) Concert
                     (12/87) (HUNG) ① HCD11690
5. M. Horszowski (r1980s) Concert
                  (12/93) (NONE) ① [3] 7559-79261-2
6e, 6f P. Casals, N. Mednikoff (r1928; arr Pollain)
Concert   (10/91) (BIDD) ① LAB017
6f, 6g J. Heifetz, E. Bay (r1946) Concert
                 (11/94) (RCA) ① [65] 09026 61778-2(06)
Erbarm' dich mein, O Herre Gott—chorale,
BWV721 (?1707-17)
R. Noehren Concert   (3/87) (DELO) ① DE3028
P. Kee Concert   (10/89) (CHAN) ① CHAN0506
J-P. Brosse Concert   (3/90) (PIER) ① PV789104
K. Bowyer Concert   (10/92) (NIMB) ① NI5280
H. Hardenberger, S. Preston (arr tpt, org) Concert
                     (12/92) (PHIL) ① 434 074-2PH
A. Isoir Concert
                     (2/93) (CALL) ① [15] CAL9703/17(1)
P. Hurford (r1993) Concert
                     (3/94) (EMIN) ① CD-EMX2218
B. Foccroulle Concert
                     (10/91) (RICE) ① RIC086069
Fantasia and Fugue in A minor, BWV561
(spurious)
P. Hurford Concert
                     (2/90) (DECC) ① [3] 421 337-2DM3
A. Isoir Concert
                     (2/93) (CALL) ① [15] CAL9703/17(1)
Fantasia and Fugue in A minor, BWV904
(c1725)
I. Kipnis Concert   (1/88) (ARAB) ① Z6577
A. Staier Concert   (10/89) (DHM) ① RD77039
A. Isoir Concert
                     (2/93) (CALL) ① [15] CAL9703/17(1)
Edwin Fischer (r1937) Concert
                     (6/94) (EMI) ① CDH7 64928-2
W. Krumbach (1968-9) Concert
                     (1/95) (TELD) ① [2] 4509-92176-2
Fantasia and Fugue in A minor—keyboard,
BWV944 (early vers of BWV543)
I. Kipnis Concert   (1/88) (ARAB) ① Z6577
G. Leonhardt Concert (10/89) (RCA) ① GD71952
S. Richter (pp1948) Concert
                     (8/95) (MELO) ① [11] 74321 25178-2
S. Richter (pp1948) Concert
                     (8/95) (MELO) ① [11] 74321 25172-2(1)
Fantasia and Fugue in C minor, BWV537
(1708-17)
R. Noehren Concert   (3/87) (DELO) ① DE3028
H. Walcha Concert
                 (10/89) (ARCH) ① [12] 419 904-2AX12(1)
P. Hurford Concert
                     (2/90) (DECC) ① [3] 421 337-2DM3
RAHO, E. Elgar (trans Elgar: r1921/3) Concert
                 (9/92) (PEAR) ① [5] GEMMCDS9951/5
M. Murray Concert   (10/92) (TELA) ① CD80286
A. Isoir Concert
                     (2/93) (CALL) ① [15] CAL9703/17(2)
L. Rogg Concert
                 (2/93) (HARM) ① [12] HMX290 772/83(2)
RAHO, E. Elgar (trans Elgar: r1926) Concert
                 (2/94) (BIDD) ① [3] CDS7 54564-2
LSO, A. Coates (arr Elgar: r1928) Concert
                     (4/93) (KOCH) ① [2] 37704-2
C. Herrick (r1993) Concert
                     (4/94) (HYPE) ① [2] CDA66791/2

L. Ghielmi (r1993) Concert
                     (9/94) (DHM) ① 05472 77312-2
P. Hurford (r1970s) Concert
                     (12/94) (DECC) ① [2] 443 485-2DF2
N. Danby (r1993) Concert
                     (5/95) (SONY) ① SMK64239
Fantasia and Fugue in C minor, BWV562
(c1730: fugue c1740-45)
P. Hurford (r1970s) Concert
                     (12/94) (DECC) ① [2] 443 485-2DF2
Fantasia and Fugue in G minor, BWV542
(1708-23)
M. Murray Concert   (1/84) (TELA) ① CD80049
T. Koopman Concert   (4/88) (NOVA) ① 150 005-2
H. Walcha Concert
                 (10/89) (ARCH) ① [12] 419 904-2AX12(1)
P. Kee Concert   (10/89) (CHAN) ① CHAN0506
P. Hurford Concert
                     (2/90) (DECC) ① [3] 421 337-2DM3
John Scott (r1989) Concert
                     (4/91) (REGE) ① REGCD105
S. Preston Concert   (6/92) (DG) ① 435 381-2GH
K. Bowyer Concert   (10/92) (NIMB) ① NI5280
A. Isoir Concert
                     (2/93) (CALL) ① [15] CAL9703/17(2)
L. Rogg Concert
                 (2/93) (HARM) ① [12] HMX290 772/83(2)
P. Grainger (r1931: arr Liszt) Concert
                     (2/94) (BIDD) ① LHW010
C. Herrick (r1993) Concert
                     (4/94) (HYPE) ① [2] CDA66791/2
L. Ghielmi (r1993) Concert
                     (9/94) (DHM) ① 05472 77312-2
M. Souter (r1991) Concert
                     (10/94) (ISIS) ① ISISCD002
P. Hurford (r1970s) Concert
                     (12/94) (DECC) ① [2] 443 485-2DF2
W. Krumbach (1968-9) Concert
                     (1/95) (TELD) ① [2] 4509-92176-2
T. Koopman Concert
                     (8/95) (TELD) ① 4509-94458-2
P. Hurford (r1977) Concert
                     (10/95) (DECC) ① 444 569-2DM
Fantasia con imitazione in B minor, BWV563
(before 1707)
H. Fagius Concert
                     (10/91) (BIS) ① [2] BIS-CD343/4
A. Isoir Concert
                     (2/93) (CALL) ① [15] CAL9703/17(2)
K. Bowyer (r1992) Concert   (2/94) (NIMB) ① NI5377
Fantasia in C minor, BWV562 (c1730)
H. Walcha Concert
                 (10/89) (ARCH) ① [12] 419 904-2AX12(1)
P. Hurford Concert
                     (2/90) (DECC) ① [3] 421 337-2DM3
A. Isoir Concert
                     (2/93) (CALL) ① [15] CAL9703/17(2)
L. Rogg Concert
                 (2/93) (HARM) ① [12] HMX290 772/83(2)
C. Herrick (r1993) Concert
                     (4/94) (HYPE) ① [2] CDA66791/2
T. Koopman Concert
                     (8/95) (TELD) ① 4509-94458-2
Fantasia in C minor, BWV906 (c1738)
I. Kipnis Concert   (1/88) (ARAB) ① Z6577
G. Leonhardt Concert (10/89) (RCA) ① GD71952
A. Staier Concert   (10/89) (DHM) ① RD77039
W. Landowska (r1957) Concert
                     (3/93) (RCA) ① [2] GD60919
Edwin Fischer (r1949) Concert
                     (6/94) (EMI) ① CDH7 64928-2
S. Richter (r1991) Concert
                     (8/94) (PHIL) ① [3] 438 613-2PH3
A. Hewitt Concert
                     (11/94) (HYPE) ① CDA66746
Fantasia in C minor, BWV919 (doubtful)
I. Kipnis Concert   (1/88) (ARAB) ① Z6577
A. Staier Concert   (10/89) (DHM) ① RD77039
W. Landowska (r1946) Concert
                     (3/93) (RCA) ① [2] GD60919
Fantasia in C minor (no BWV number)
T. Koopman Concert   (10/91) (NOVA) ① 150 052-2
Harald Vogel Concert   (8/92) (DHM) ① RD77202
Fantasia in G, BWV570 (1708)
H. Otto Concert   (5/84) (DENO) ① C37-7004
P. Hurford Concert
                     (2/90) (DECC) ① [3] 421 337-2DM3
M-C. Alain (r1990) Concert
                     (7/93) (ERAT) ① 4509-91702-2
T. Koopman Concert
                     (8/95) (TELD) ① 4509-94458-2
Fantasia in G, BWV572 (1708)
Cleveland Winds, F. Fennell (orch. version) Concert
                     (12/83) (TELA) ① CD80038
T. Koopman Concert   (8/89) (NOVA) ① 150 036-2
M. Murray Concert   (8/89) (TELA) ① CD80179

H. Walcha Concert
                 (10/89) (ARCH) ① [12] 419 904-2AX12(1)
P. Hurford Concert
                     (2/90) (DECC) ① [3] 421 337-2DM3
S. Preston Concert   (3/90) (DG) ① 427 668-2GH
J-P. Brosse Concert   (3/90) (PIER) ① PV789104
H. Fagius Concert
                     (10/91) (BIS) ① [2] BIS-CD439/40
D. Wagler Concert   (10/91) (PRIO) ① PRCD332
N. Rawsthorne Concert
                     (6/92) (CFP) ① CD-CFP4479
Harald Vogel Concert   (8/92) (DHM) ① RD77202
A. Isoir Concert
                     (2/93) (CALL) ① [15] CAL9703/17(2)
L. Rogg Concert
                 (2/93) (HARM) ① [12] HMX290 772/83(2)
C. Herrick (r1993) Concert
                     (4/94) (HYPE) ① [2] CDA66791/2
P. Hurford (r1970s) Concert
                     (12/94) (DECC) ① [2] 443 485-2DF2
T. Koopman Concert
                     (8/95) (TELD) ① 4509-94458-2
Fantasia in G minor, BWV917 (doubtful)
I. Kipnis Concert   (1/88) (ARAB) ① Z6577
A. Staier Concert   (10/89) (DHM) ① RD77039
Fantasia on a rondo in C minor, BWV918
(doubtful)
I. Kipnis Concert   (1/88) (ARAB) ① Z6577
Fantasia super Jesu, meine Freude, BWV713
(1708-17)
B. Foccroulle Concert
                     (10/91) (RICE) ① RIC085068
A. Isoir Concert
                     (2/93) (CALL) ① [15] CAL9703/17(2)
L. Rogg Concert
                 (2/93) (HARM) ① [12] HMX290 772/83(3)
Fantasia super Valet will ich dir geben,
BWV735 (after 1723)
P. Hurford (r1989) Concert
                     (4/91) (REGE) ① REGCD105
A. Isoir Concert
                     (2/93) (CALL) ① [15] CAL9703/17(1)
P. Hurford (r1993) Concert
                     (12/94) (EMIN) ① CD-EMX2226
K. Bowyer (r1993) Concert   (7/95) (NIMB) ① NI5423
6 French Suites, BWV812-17
1. D minor; 2. C minor; 3. B minor; 4. E flat; 5. G; 6.
E.
C. Hogwood Concert
                     (8/86) (L'OI) ① [2] 411 811-2OH2
G. Leonhardt Concert   (5/90) (RCA) ① GD71963
D. Moroney Concert
                     (4/91) (VIRG) ① [2] VCD7 59011-2
A. Schiff Concert
                     (10/93) (DECC) ① [2] 433 313-2DH
J. MacGregor (r1993)   (2/94) (COLL) ① Coll1371-2
K. Jarrett (r1991)   (4/94) (ECM) ① [2] 437 955-2
G. Gould (1971-73: pf) French Overture, BWV831.
                     (7/95) (SONY) ① [2] SM2K52609
A. Gavrilov (r1993)
                     (7/95) (DG) ① [2] 445 840-2GH2
1(Allemande; Sarabande) R. Veyron-Lacroix
(r1978) Concert   (12/93) (ERAT) ① 4509-92135-2
1, 2. W. Rübsam (r1991) Concert
                     (10/94) (NAXO) ① 8 550709
2, 4, 6. S. Richter (r1991) Concert
                     (8/94) (PHIL) ① [3] 438 613-2PH3
3-6. W. Rübsam (r1991)
                     (10/94) (NAXO) ① 8 550710
5. R. Aldwinckle Concert   (6/86) (CARL) ① PCD817
5 (Gigue) M. Hess (r1928) Concert
                     (5/91) (PEAR) ① GEMMCD9462
5. W. Kempff (r1975) Concert
                     (11/94) (DG) ① [2] 439 672-2GX2
5(Gigue) M. Hess (r1928) Concert
                     (3/95) (BIDD) ① LHW024
5. G. Malcolm (r1960) Concert
                     (11/95) (DECC) ① 444 390-2DWO
6. M. Horszowski (r1991) Concert
                     (10/91) (NONE) ① 7559-79264-2
6. Safri Duo (r1994: trans perc) English Suites,
BWV806-811.   (5/95) (CHAN) ① CHAN9339
Fughetta in C minor—keyboard, BWV961
(spurious)
I. Kipnis Concert   (1/88) (ARAB) ① Z6577
M. Tipo Concert   (11/91) (EMI) ① CDC7 54147-2
G. Gould (1980) Concert
                     (11/94) (SONY) ① [2] SM2K52597
Fugue, BWV946
P. Hurford Concert
                     (2/90) (DECC) ① [3] 421 337-2DM3
Fugue in C—organ, BWVAnh90
A. Isoir Concert
                     (2/93) (CALL) ① [15] CAL9703/17(1)
Fugue in C, BWV952 (doubtful)
M. Tipo Concert   (11/91) (EMI) ① CDC7 54147-2

G. Gould (r1979) *Concert*
(11/94) (SONY) ① [2] **SM2K52597**
Prelude and Fugue in G minor, BWV535
(1708-17)
H. Otto *Concert* (5/84) (DENO) ① **C37-7004**
M. Murray *Concert* (8/89) (TELA) ① **CD80179**
H. Walcha *Concert*
(10/89) (ARCH) ① [12] **419 904-2AX12(1)**
P. Hurford *Concert*
(2/90) (DECC) ① [3] **421 337-2DM3**
G. Barber *Concert* (7/91) (ASV) ① **CDGAU121**
Harald Vogel *Concert* (8/92) (DHM) ① **RD77202**
A. Isoir *Concert*
(2/93) (CALL) ① [15] **CAL9703/17(2)**
L. Rogg *Concert*
(2/93) (HARM) ① [12] **HMX290 772/83(1)**
K. Bowyer (r1993) *Concert* (7/95) (NIMB) ① **NI5423**
W. Rübsam (r1994) *Concert*
(10/95) (NAXO) ① **8 553033**
Prelude and Fugue in G minor, BWV558
(probably spurious: ? by Krebs)
D. Sanger *Concert* (3/87) (MERI) ① **ECD84081**
K. John *Concert* (5/89) (PRIO) ① **PRCD235**
P. Kee *Concert* (12/92) (CHAN) ① **CHAN0527**
K. Bowyer (r1992) *Concert* (2/94) (NIMB) ① **NI5377**
Prelude, Fugue and Allegro in E flat—lute or
keyboard, BWV998 (1740s)
E.M. Meckmann *Concert* (10/89) (RCA) ① **GD71958**
G. Leonhardt *Concert*
(12/90) (DHM) ① **GD77013**
M. Barrueco (gtr) *Concert*
(2/91) (EMI) ① **CDC7 49980-2**
L. Kirchhof *Concert*
(3/91) (SONY) ① [2] **S2K45858**
D. Moroney *Concert* (9/92) (VIRG) ① **VC7 59272-2**
W. Landowska (r1946) *Concert*
(3/93) (RCA) ① [2] **GD60919**
E. Petri (pp1958: arr pf: Busoni) *Concert*
(3/94) (MUSI) ① [4] **MACD-772**
J. Bream (r1992: arr gtr: Bream) *Concert*
(1/95) (EMI) ① **CDC5 55123-2**
Prelude in A minor, BWV569 (?before 1707)
A. Isoir *Concert*
(2/93) (CALL) ① [15] **CAL9703/17(1)**
Prelude (Fantasia) in A minor—keyboard,
BWV922 (doubtful)
I. Kipnis *Concert* (1/88) (ARAB) ① **Z6577**
A. Staier *Concert* (10/89) (DHM) ① **RD77039**
Prelude in C, BWV567 (by Krebs)
M. Murray *Concert* (8/89) (TELA) ① **CD80179**
Prelude (Fantasia) in C minor, BWV921
(doubtful)
A. Staier *Concert* (10/89) (DHM) ① **RD77039**
Prelude in C minor—lute, BWV999 (c1725)
N. North *Concert* (6/86) (AMON) ① **CD-SAR23**
J. Lindberg (r1986; arr lte) *Concert*
(11/87) (BIS) ① **BIS-CD327**
A. Segovia (arr Segovia; r1928) *Concert*
(5/89) (EMI) ① [2] **CHS7 61047-2**
L. Kirchhof *Concert*
(3/91) (SONY) ① [2] **S2K45858**
M. Tipo *Concert* (11/91) (EMI) ① **CDC7 54147-2**
J. Bream (r1966) *Concert*
(8/93) (RCA) ① [28] **09026 61583-2(3)**
J. Bream (r1966) *Concert*
(6/94) (RCA) ① **09026 61592-2**
Prelude in G, BWV568 (before 1708)
H. Fagius *Concert*
(10/91) (BIS) ① [2] **BIS-CD439/40**
A. Isoir *Concert*
(2/93) (CALL) ① [15] **CAL9703/17(1)**
9 Preludes (Pieces from Clavier-Büchlein for
W F Bach)—keyboard, BWV924-932 (1720)
1. Praeambulum, C; 2. Prelude, D (? by W. F. Bach);
3. Prelude, D minor; 4. Praeambulum, F; 5. Prelude,
F; 6. Trio, G minor; 7. Praeambulum, G minor; 8.
Prelude, A minor (spurious); 9. Prelude, E minor
(spurious).
1-5, 7. M. Tipo *Concert*
(11/91) (EMI) ① **CDC7 54147-2**
1-5, 7. G. Gould (r1980) *Concert*
(11/94) (SONY) ① [2] **SM2K52597**
6. L. Rév *Concert* (7/87) (HYPE) ① **CDA66185**
6 Little Preludes, BWV933-38
1. C; 2. C minor; 3. D minor; 4. D; 5. E; 6. E minor.
T. Koopman *Concert* (6/88) (CAPR) ① **10 210**
M. Tipo *Concert* (11/91) (EMI) ① **CDC7 54147-2**
G. Gould (r1979) *Concert*
(11/94) (SONY) ① [2] **SM2K52597**
5. L. Rév *Concert* (7/87) (HYPE) ① **CDA66185**
5 Preludes, BWV939-43
1. C; 2. D minor; 3. C minor; 4. A minor; 5. C.
M. Tipo *Concert* (11/91) (EMI) ① **CDC7 54147-2**
5. H. Fagius *Concert*
(10/91) (BIS) ① [2] **BIS-CD439/40**

5. A. Isoir *Concert*
(2/93) (CALL) ① [15] **CAL9703/17(4)**
Ricercar a 3, BWV1079a: 5a (1747) (transc
from *Musikalisches Opfer*, BWV1079)
A. Isoir *Concert*
(2/93) (CALL) ① [15] **CAL9703/17(5)**
Sarabande con Partite in C—keyboard,
BWV990 (after 'Bellérphon' Overture (Lully)
Harald Vogel *Concert* (8/92) (DHM) ① **RD77202**
Schübler Chorales, BWV645-650 (c1748-49)
1. Wachet auf, ruft uns die Stimme; 2. Wo soll ich
fliehen hin; 3. Wer nur den lieben Gott lässt walten; 4.
Meine Seele erhebet den Herren; 5. Ach blieb' bei
uns, Herr Jesu Christ; 6. Kommst du nun, Jesu, vom
Himmel herunter.
H. Otto *Concert* (5/84) (DENO) ① **C37-7004**
A. Isoir *Concert* (8/89) (CALL) ① **CAL9710**
H. Walcha *Concert*
(10/89) (ARCH) ① [12] **419 904-2AX12(2)**
T. Koopman *Concert*
(12/89) (DG) ① **427 801-2GDC**
S. Preston *Concert* (6/92) (DG) ① **435 381-2GH**
P. Hurford, M. Laird Brass Ens (r1990: arr Hurford)
Concert (9/92) (ARGO) ① **433 451-2ZH**
A. Isoir *Concert*
(2/93) (CALL) ① [15] **CAL9703/17(2)**
L. Rogg *Concert*
(2/93) (HARM) ① [12] **HMX290 772/83(3)**
M-C. Alain (r1981) *Concert*
(6/93) (ERAT) ① **2292-45922-2**
M. Souter (r1993) *Concert*
(5/95) (ISIS) ① **ISISCD008**
1. T. Koopman *Concert*
(4/88) (NOVA) ① **150 005-2**
1.-J-P. Brosse *Concert* (3/90) (PIER) ① **PV789104**
1. R. Marlow *Concert* (12/90) (CONI) ① **CDCF501**
1. D. Flood *Concert* (4/91) (YORK) ① **CD108**
1. S. Preston *Concert*
(6/91) (DECC) ① **430 091-2DWO**
1. G. Fergus-Thompson (trans Busoni) *Concert*
(10/91) (ASV) ① **CDDCA759**
1. T. Nikolaieva (pf) *Concert*
(9/92) (MEZH) ① **MK418024**
1. I. Biret (trans Kempff) *Concert*
(5/93) (MARC) ① **8 223452**
1. O.E. Antonsen, W. Marshall (r1992: arr tpt/org)
Concert (10/94) (EMI) ① **CDC5 55048-2**
1. P. Hurford (1970s) *Concert*
(12/94) (DECC) ① [2] **443 485-2DF2**
1. BBC PO, E. Downes (r1994: orch Respighi)
Concert (1/95) (CHAN) ① **CHAN9311**
1. G. Cziffra (r1968: arr Busoni) *Concert*
(3/95) (EMI) ① **CDM5 65255-2**
1. E. Petri (r1942: arr Busoni) *Concert*
(8/95) (APR) ① [2] **APR7027**
1. P. Hurford (1978) *Concert*
(10/95) (DECC) ① **444 569-2DM**
1, 5. N. Rawsthorne *Concert*
(6/92) (CFP) ① **CD-CFP4479**
3. S. Feinberg (r1962: arr Feinberg) *Concert*
(8/95) (MELO) ① **74321 25175-2**
3. S. Feinberg (r1962: arr Feinberg) *Concert*
(8/95) (MELO) ① [11] **74321 25172-2(1)**
Sei gegrüsset, Jesu gütig—Partita diverse
sopra..., BWV768
A. Isoir *Concert* (8/89) (CALL) ① **CAL9710**
T. Koopman *Concert* (8/89) (NOVA) ① **150 036-2**
H. Walcha *Concert*
(10/89) (ARCH) ① [12] **419 904-2AX12(2)**
C. Herrick *Concert* (5/92) (HYPE) ① **CDA66455**
A. Isoir *Concert*
(2/93) (CALL) ① [15] **CAL9703/17(2)**
L. Rogg *Concert*
(2/93) (HARM) ① [12] **HMX290 772/83(1)**
K. Bowyer (r1992) *Concert* (6/93) (NIMB) ① **NI5290**
M-C. Alain (r1990) *Concert*
(7/93) (ERAT) ① **4509-91702-2**
W. Rübsam (r1992) *Concert*
(1/94) (NAXO) ① **8 550704**
Sonata in A minor—keyboard (1702-10) (arr
from Reinken: Hortus musicus)
B. van Asperen (r1990) *Concert*
(3/91) (SONY) ① **SK46349**
Sonata in D minor—keyboard, BWV964 (arr
of Vn Sonata, BWV1003 by ?W. F. Bach)
K. Haugsand *Concert* (9/88) (SIMA) ① **PSC1032**
C. Booth (r1993) *Concert*
(10/94) (OLYM) ① **OCD437**
3 Sonatas and 3 Partitas—violin, BWV1001-
1006 (1720)
EXCERPTS: 1. SONATA No.1 in G MINOR,
BWV1001: 1a. Adagio; 1b. Fuga; 1c. Siciliano; 1d.
Presto; 2. PARTITA No. 1 in B MINOR, BWV1002:
2a. Allemande; 2b. Double I; 2c. Courante; 2d.
Double II; 2e. Sarabande; 2f. Double III; 2g. Tempo di
Bourrée; 2h. Double IV; 3. SONATA No. 2 in A

MINOR, BWV1003: 3a. Grave; 3b. Fuga; 3c.
Andante; 3d. Allegro; 4. PARTITA No. 2 in D MINOR,
BWV1004: 4a. Allemande; 4b. Courante; 4c.
Sarabande; 4d. Gigue; 4e. Chaconne; 5. SONATA
No. 3 in C, BWV1005: 5a. Adagio; 5b. Fuga; 5c.
Largo; 5d. Allegro assai; 6. PARTITA No. 3 in E,
BWV1006: 6a. Preludio; 6b. Loure; 6c. Gavotte en
rondeu; 6d. Menuett I; 6e. Menuett II; 6f. Bourrée; 6g.
Gigue.
D. Sitkovetsky (3/87) (ORFE) ① [3] **C130852H**
O. Shumsky (9/87) (ASV) ① [2] **CDDCD454**
N. Milstein (12/88) (DG) ① [2] **423 294-2GCM2**
Y. Menuhin (r1934-6)
(8/89) (EMI) ① [2] **CHS7 63035-2**
L. Mordkovitch
(12/90) (CHAN) ① [2] **CHAN8835/6**
O. Kagan (pp1989)
(4/93) (ERAT) ① [2] **2292-45805-2**
A. Grumiaux (r1960-1)
(2/94) (PHIL) ① [2] **438 736-2PM2**
N. Milstein (r1950s)
(5/94) (EMI) ① [2] **ZDMB7 64793-2**
J. Heifetz (r1952)
(11/94) (RCA) ① [65] **09026 61778-2(17)**
S. Mintz (1/95) (DG) ① [2] **445 526-2GMA2**
I. Perlman (12/88) (EMI) ① [2] **CDS7 49483-2**
S. Végh (12/88) (AUVI) ① [2] **V4427**
1. J. Szigeti (r1931) *Concert*
(1/90) (BIDD) ① [2] **LAB005/6**
1. J. Szigeti (r1931) *Concert*
(10/91) (MSCM) ① **MM30320**
1. J. Szigeti (bp1946) *Solo Violin Partitas and*
Sonatas. (8/94) (MUSI) ① **MACD-774**
1a F. Kreisler (r1926) *Concert*
(9/92) (BIDD) ① [2] **LAB049/50**
1a N. Milstein (r1936) *Concert*
(10/92) (BIDD) ① **LAB055**
1a Arnold Rosé (r1928) *Concert*
(12/92) (BIDD) ① [2] **LAB056/7**
1a, 2g J. Joachim (r1903) *Concert*
(8/90) (SYMP) ① **SYMCD1071**
1b A. Segovia (r1928; arr Segovia) *Concert*
(5/89) (EMI) ① [2] **CHS7 61047-2**
1, 2, 4. N. North (r1993: arr lte: North)
(9/89) (LINN) ① **CKD013**
1, 2, 5. N. Goluses (r1994; trans gtr)
(12/95) (NAXO) ① **8 553193**
1, 3, 5. F. Bungarten (r1987; trans gtr: Bungarten)
(9/89) (MDG) ① **L3306**
1, 4, 5. J. Heifetz (r1935) *Concert*
(2/94) (EMI) ① **CDH7 64494-2**
1, 5. J. Heifetz (r1935) *Concert*
(11/94) (RCA) ① [65] **09026 61778-2(03)**
2. M. Barrueco (trans gtr) *Concert*
(2/91) (EMI) ① **CDC7 49980-2**
2d S. Mayor (trans mand ens: Mayor) *Concert*
(3/92) (ACOU) ① **CDACS012**
2e, 2f, 3c B. Huberman (r1934) *Concert*
(9/94) (BIDD) ① [2] **LAB081/2**
2g J. Szigeti (r1927) *Concert*
(1/90) (BIDD) ① [2] **LAB005/6**
2g J. Szigeti (r1941) *Concert*
(7/94) (BIDD) ① [2] **LAB070/1**
2, 4, 6. V. Mullova (r1992/3)
(6/94) (PHIL) ① **434 075-2PH**
3. J. Szigeti (r1933) *Concert*
(1/90) (BIDD) ① [2] **LAB005/6**
3. J. Szigeti (r1933) *Concert*
(10/91) (MSCM) ① **MM30320**
3, 5, 6. N. North (r1993: arr lte: North)
(4/95) (LINN) ① **CKD029**
3, 6. A. Bylsma (arr Bylsma: vc piccolo) *Partita,*
BWV1013. (3/89) (DHM) ① **RD77998**
3, 6. J. Szigeti (bp1949) *Solo Violin Partitas and*
Sonatas. (8/94) (MUSI) ① **MACD-774**
4. Celedonio Romero (trans gtr: P Romero) *Concert*
(2/87) (DELO) ① **DE1005**
4. A. Busch (r1929) *Concert*
(8/90) (EMI) ① **CDH7 63494-2**
4. M. Seiffge (trans Seiffge) *Concert*
(2/91) (BAYE) ① **BR100095**
4. N. Hali (trans gtr) *Concert*
(5/92) (DECC) ① **430 839-2DH**
4. N. Milstein (r1935) *Concert*
(10/92) (BIDD) ① **LAB055**
4. A. Busch (r1929) *Concert*
(12/92) (PEAR) ① **GEMMCD9942**
4. J. Heifetz (r1935) *Concert*
(11/94) (RCA) ① [65] **09026 61778-2(18)**
4. D. Garrett (r1993) *Concert*
(4/95) (DG) ① **445 657-2GH**
4d A. Busch (r1929) *Concert*
(6/93) (SYMP) ① **SYMCD1109**
4e R. Smith (arr Busoni) *Liszt: Beethoven*
Symphonies, S464. (9/85) (NIMB) ① **NI5013**

L. Rogg *Concert*
(2/93) (HARM) ① [12] **HMX290 772/83(1)**
M-C. Alain (r1981) *Concert*
(6/93) (ERAT) ① **2292-45922-2**
L. Ghielmi (r1992) *Concert*
(7/93) (DHM) ① **05472 77278-2**
P. Grainger (r1931: arr Grainger) *Concert*
(2/94) (BIDD) ① **LHW010**
BBC PO, M. Bamert (r1993: orch Stokowski) *Concert*
(3/94) (CHAN) ① **CHAN9259**
P. Hurford (r1993) *Concert*
(3/94) (EMIN) ① **CD-EMX2218**
M. Souter (r1991) *Concert*
(10/94) (ISIS) ① **ISISCD002**
P. Hurford (r1970s) *Concert*
(12/94) (DECC) ① [2] **443 485-2DF2**
W. Krumbach (r1968-9) *Concert*
(1/95) (TELD) ① [2] **4509-92176-2**
BBC SO, A. Davis (r1994: arr Wood) *Concert*
(2/95) (TELD) ① **4509-97868-2**
P. Hurford (r1979) *Concert*
(10/95) (DECC) ① **444 569-2DM**
Toccata and Fugue in D minor,
'Dorian'—keyboard, BWV538 (1708-17)
T. Koopman *Concert* (8/89) (NOVA) ① **150 036-2**
H. Walcha *Concert*
(10/89) (ARCH) ① [12] **419 904-2AX12(1)**
P. Hurford *Concert*
(2/90) (DECC) ① [3] **421 337-2DM3**
B. Foccroulle *Concert* (3/90) (RICE) ① **RIC064042**
C. Herrick *Concert* (4/91) (HYPE) ① **CDA66434**
M. Murray *Concert* (10/92) (TELA) ① **CD80286**
A. Isoir *Concert*
(2/93) (CALL) ① [15] **CAL9703/17(2)**
L. Rogg *Concert*
(2/93) (HARM) ① [12] **HMX290 772/83(1)**
L. Antonini (r1991) *Concert*
(10/94) (SONY) ① **SK57487**
P. Hurford (r1970s) *Concert*
(12/94) (DECC) ① [2] **443 485-2DF2**
Toccata and Fugue in E—organ, BWV566
(before 1708)
K. Bowyer (r1993) *Concert* (7/95) (NIMB) ① **NI5423**
Toccata and Fugue in F, BWV540 (?1708-
10)
M. Murray *Concert* (1/84) (TELA) ① **CD80049**
H. Walcha *Concert*
(10/89) (ARCH) ① [12] **419 904-2AX12(1)**
P. Hurford *Concert*
(2/90) (DECC) ① [3] **421 337-2DM3**
C. Herrick *Concert* (4/91) (HYPE) ① **CDA66434**
H. Fagius *Concert*
(10/91) (BIS) ① [2] **BIS-CD439/40**
B. Foccroulle *Concert*
(10/91) (RICE) ① **RIC085068**
S. Preston *Concert* (6/92) (DG) ① **435 381-2GH**
A. Isoir *Concert*
(2/93) (CALL) ① [15] **CAL9703/17(2)**
L. Rogg *Concert*
(2/93) (HARM) ① [12] **HMX290 772/83(1)**
Toccata (and Fugue) in E—organ, BWV566
(1707)
G. Barber *Concert* (7/91) (ASV) ① **CDGAU121**
A. Isoir *Concert*
(2/93) (CALL) ① [15] **CAL9703/17(1)**
L. Rogg *Concert*
(2/93) (HARM) ① [12] **HMX290 772/83(1)**
M-C. Alain (r1981) *Concert*
(6/93) (ERAT) ① **2292-45922-2**
7 Toccatas, BWV910-16 (before 1708-10)
1. F sharp minor; 2. C minor; 3. D; 4. D minor; 5. E
minor; 6. G minor; 7. G.
W. Rübsam (r1989) (8/94) (NAXO) ① **8 550708**
1, 2, 6. K. Gilbert (r1992) *Concert*
(6/93) (ARCH) ① **437 555-2AH**
1, 3, 4. G. Gould (r1976) *Concert*
(9/94) (SONY) ① [2] **SM2K52612**
2. M. Argerich *Concert*
(12/88) (DG) ① **423 880-2GGA**
2, 3. A. Schnabel (r1937) *Brahms: Piano Concerto 1.*
(2/91) (PEAR) ① **GEMMCD9376**
2, 6, 7. G. Gould (r1979) *Concert*
(9/94) (SONY) ① [2] **SM2K52612**
3. A. Schiff (pf) *Concert*
(12/87) (HUNG) ① **HCD11690**
3. W. Kempff (r1975) *Concert*
(11/94) (DG) ① [2] **439 672-2GX2**
3. G. Malcolm (r1960) *Concert*
(11/95) (DECC) ① **444 390-2DWO**
3, 4. G. Leonhardt *Concert*
(10/89) (RCA) ① **GD71952**
3-5, 7. L.U. Mortensen *Concert*
(1/89) (KONT) ① **32012**
4. G. Leonhardt *Concert*
(12/90) (DHM) ① **RD77868**

4, 7. S. Richter (r1991) *Concert*
(8/94) (PHIL) ① [3] **438 613-2PH3**
5. G. Gould (r1963) *Concert*
(9/94) (SONY) ① [2] **SM2K52612**
6. K. Bowyer (r1992) *Concert*
(2/94) (NIMB) ① **NI5377**
7. K. Bowyer (r1992) *Concert*
(2/94) (NIMB) ① **NI5377**
7(Allegro) M. Hess (r1929) *Concert*
(3/95) (BIDD) ① **LHW024**
Trio in C minor, BWV585 (by Fasch)
P. Hurford *Concert*
(2/90) (DECC) ① [3] **421 337-2DM3**
W. Rübsam (r1993) *Concert*
(12/94) (NAXO) ① **8 550936**
Trio in D minor, BWV583
H. Otto *Concert* (5/84) (DENO) ① **C37-7004**
P. Hurford *Concert*
(2/90) (DECC) ① [3] **421 337-2DM3**
H. Fagius *Concert*
(10/91) (BIS) ① [2] **BIS-CD439/40**
A. Isoir *Concert*
(2/93) (CALL) ① [15] **CAL9703/17(4)**
L. Rogg *Concert*
(2/93) (HARM) ① [12] **HMX290 772/83(3)**
N. Danby (r1993: 2 vers) *Concert*
(5/95) (SONY) ① **SMK64239**
Trio in G, BWV586 (Telemann transc Bach)
H. Otto *Concert* (5/84) (DENO) ① **C37-7004**
H. Fagius *Concert*
(10/91) (BIS) ① [2] **BIS-CD343/4**
W. Rübsam (r1993) *Concert*
(12/94) (NAXO) ① **8 550936**
Trio in G, BWV1027a (transc Vla da gamba
Sonata, BWV1027, movt iii)
A. Isoir *Concert*
(2/93) (CALL) ① [15] **CAL9703/17(4)**
Trio in G minor, BWV584 (spurious)
A. Isoir *Concert* (8/89) (CALL) ① **CAL9710**
A. Isoir *Concert*
(2/93) (CALL) ① [15] **CAL9703/17(2)**
K. Bowyer (r1993) *Concert* (7/95) (NIMB) ① **NI5423**
W. Rübsam (r1994) *Concert*
(10/95) (NAXO) ① **8 553033**
6 Trio Sonatas—organ, BWV525-530
(c1727)
1. E flat, BWV525; 2. C minor, BWV526; 3. D minor,
BWV527; 4. E minor, BWV528; 5. C, BWV529; 6. G,
BWV530.
H. Walcha *Concert*
(10/89) (ARCH) ① [12] **419 904-2AX12(1)**
C. Herrick (11/90) (HYPE) ① **CDA66390**
J. Butt (9/92) (HARM) ① **HMU90 7055**
A. Isoir *Concert*
(2/93) (CALL) ① [15] **CAL9703/17(4)**
L. Rogg *Concert*
(2/93) (HARM) ① [12] **HMX290 772/83(3)**
S. Preston (r1993) (5/94) (DG) ① **437 835-2GH**
1. Barthold Kuijken, S. Kuijken, W. Kuijken, R.
Kohnen (trans for fl, vn and cont) *Concert*
(3/86) (ACCE) ① **ACC58019D**
1. K. Bowyer *Concert* (10/92) (NIMB) ① **NI5280**
1(Allegro) G. Weir *Concert*
(12/94) (KOSS) ① **KC1013**
1-3. W. Rübsam (r1989) *Prelude and Fugue,*
BWV543. (5/94) (NAXO) ① **8 550651**
1, 3, 5, 6. M. Verbruggen, M. Meyerson (r1993; transc
Verbruggen) *Flute Sonatas, BWV1030-5.*
(2/95) (HARM) ① **HMU90 7119**
1, 3, 5, 6. Palladian Ens (r1994: arr vn/rec/va da
gamba/continuo) *Concert* (1/95) (LINN) ① **CKD036**
1, 5. J. Bream, G. Malcolm (r1969: arr lte/hpd)
Concert (8/93) (RCA) ① [28] **09026 61583-2(5)**
1, 5. J. Bream, G. Malcolm (r1969: arr lte/hpd)
Concert (8/93) (RCA) ① **09026 61603-2**
2. H. Fagius *Concert*
(10/91) (BIS) ① [2] **BIS-CD343/4**
2. K. Bowyer (r1992) *Concert*
(6/93) (NIMB) ① **NI5290**
3. M. Verbruggen, Sonnerie Trio *Concert*
(2/90) (ASV) ① **CDGAU113**
3. K. John *Concert* (4/90) (PRIO) ① **PRCD264**
3-5. L. Ghielmi (r1993) *Concert*
(9/94) (DHM) ① **05472 77312-2**
4-6. W. Rübsam (r1989) *Prelude and Fugue,*
BWV547. (5/94) (NAXO) ① **8 550653**
5. R. Noehren *Concert* (3/87) (DELO) ① **DE3028**
5. K. Bowyer *Concert* (3/93) (NIMB) ① **NI5289**
5. G. Barber (r1990) *Concert*
(11/93) (PRIO) ① **PRCD315**
5. P. Hurford (r1993) *Concert*
(12/94) (EMIN) ① **CD-EMX2226**
5(Largo) S. Feinberg (r1962: arr Feinberg) *Concert*
(8/95) (MELO) ① [11] **74321 25175-2**
5(Largo) S. Feinberg (r1962: arr Feinberg) *Concert*
(8/95) (MELO) ① [11] **74321 25172-2(1)**

6. T. Koopman *Concert*
(8/89) (NOVA) ① **150 036-2**
6. H. Fagius *Concert* (10/91) (BIS) ① **BIS-CD445**
6(pt) T. Kropat, T. Krumeich (arr 2 gtrs) *Concert*
(7/93) (CHNN) ① **CG9103**
6. K. Bowyer (r1993) *Concert*
(7/95) (NIMB) ① **NI5423**
Valet will ich dir geben, BWV736 (1708-17)
H. Walcha *Concert*
(10/89) (ARCH) ① [12] **419 904-2AX12(2)**
G. Leonhardt *Concert* (12/90) (DHM) ① **RD77868**
A. Isoir *Concert*
(2/93) (CALL) ① [15] **CAL9703/17(4)**
L. Rogg *Concert*
(2/93) (HARM) ① [12] **HMX290 772/83(2)**
K. Bowyer (r1993) *Concert* (7/95) (NIMB) ① **NI5423**
W. Rübsam (r1994) *Concert*
(10/95) (NAXO) ① **8 553033**
Vater unser im Himmelreich—Chorale
Prelude, BWV737 (1708-17)
M. Murray *Concert* (1/84) (TELA) ① **CD80049**
A. Isoir *Concert*
(2/93) (CALL) ① [15] **CAL9703/17(1)**
P. Hurford (r1993) *Concert*
(12/94) (EMIN) ① **CD-EMX2226**
Vater unser im Himmelreich, BWV762
(spurious)
H. Fagius *Concert* (10/91) (BIS) ① **BIS-CD445**
A. Isoir *Concert*
(2/93) (CALL) ① [15] **CAL9703/17(1)**
Vom Himmel hoch, da komm ich her,
BWV700 (before 1708 rev 1740s)
H. Walcha *Concert*
(10/89) (ARCH) ① [12] **419 904-2AX12(2)**
H. Fagius *Concert*
(10/91) (BIS) ① [2] **BIS-CD343/4**
Harald Vogel *Concert* (8/92) (DHM) ① **RD77202**
N. Danby (r1993) *Concert*
(5/95) (SONY) ① **SMK64239**
Vom Himmel hoch, da komm ich her,
BWV701 (?1739-42)
L. Rogg (r1966) *Concert*
(4/88) (HARM) ① **HMA190 717**
A. Isoir *Concert* (8/89) (CALL) ① **CAL9710**
H. Fagius *Concert*
(10/91) (BIS) ① [2] **BIS-CD343/4**
Harald Vogel *Concert* (8/92) (DHM) ① **RD77202**
A. Isoir *Concert*
(2/93) (CALL) ① [15] **CAL9703/17(2)**
L. Rogg *Concert*
(2/93) (HARM) ① [12] **HMX290 772/83(2)**
L. Ghielmi (r1992) *Concert*
(7/93) (DHM) ① **05472 77278-2**
N. Danby (r1993) *Concert*
(5/95) (SONY) ① **SMK64239**
Vom Himmel hoch, da komm ich her,
BWV738 (1708-17)
H. Fagius *Concert*
(10/91) (BIS) ① [2] **BIS-CD439/40**
A. Isoir *Concert*
(2/93) (CALL) ① [15] **CAL9703/17(1)**
L. Rogg *Concert*
(2/93) (HARM) ① [12] **HMX290 772/83(2)**
K. Bowyer (r1993) *Concert* (3/93) (NIMB) ① **NI5289**
Vom Himmel hoch da komm ich
her—canonic variations: keyboard, BWV769
(1747)
L. Rogg (r1966) *Concert*
(4/88) (HARM) ① **HMA190 717**
H. Walcha *Concert*
(10/89) (ARCH) ① [12] **419 904-2AX12(2)**
S. Preston *Concert* (3/90) (DG) ① **427 668-2GH**
H. Fagius *Concert*
(10/91) (BIS) ① [2] **BIS-CD439/40**
M-C. Alain *Concert*
(4/92) (ERAT) ① [2] **2292-45664-2**
C. Herrick *Concert* (5/92) (HYPE) ① **CDA66455**
A. Isoir *Concert*
(2/93) (CALL) ① [15] **CAL9703/17(5)**
L. Rogg *Concert*
(2/93) (HARM) ① [12] **HMX290 772/83(3)**
Wenn wir in höchsten Nöten
sein—Partita—chorale with 7 variations:
organ, BWV Anh78
W. Krumbach (r1968-9) *Concert*
(1/95) (TELD) ① [2] **4509-92176-2**
K. Bowyer (r1993) *Concert* (7/95) (NIMB) ① **NI5423**
Wer nur den lieben Gott lässt walten,
BWV690 (1708-17)
A. Isoir *Concert* (8/89) (CALL) ① **CAL9710**
B. Foccroulle *Concert* (3/90) (RICE) ① **RIC064042**
A. Isoir *Concert*
(2/93) (CALL) ① [15] **CAL9703/17(2)**
L. Rogg *Concert*
(2/93) (HARM) ① [12] **HMX290 772/83(2)**

wohlgetan (chor).

P. Esswood, K. Equiluz, M. van Egmond, Tolz Boys' Ch, King's College Ch, Leonhardt Consort, G. Leonhardt *Concert* (9/85) (TELD) Ⓓ [2] **2292-42500-2**

A. Reynolds, P. Schreier, T. Adam, Munich Bach Ch, Munich Bach Orch, K. Richter (r1973-4) *Concert* (7/94) (ARCH) Ⓓ [5] **439 374-2AX5**

P. Esswood, K. Equiluz, M. van Egmond, Tolz Boys' Ch, King's College Ch, Leonhardt Consort, G. Leonhardt *Concert* (2/95) (TELD) Ⓓ [6] **4509-91755-2**

H. Watts, Adalbert Kraus, W. Schöne, Stuttgart Gächinger Kantorei, Stuttgart Bach Collegium, H. Rilling *Concert* (2/95) (HANS) Ⓓ **98 883**

1. SRO, E. Ansermet *Concert* (10/91) (DECC) Ⓓ **430 499-2DWO**

Cantata No. 13, 'Meine Seufzer, meine Tränen', BWV13 (1726) (Epiphany II)

EXCERPTS: 1. Aria: Meine Seufzer, meine Tränen (T); 2. Recit: Mein liebster Gott lässt mich (A); 3. Choral: Der Gott, der mir hat versprochen (A); 4. Recit: Mein Kummer nimmet zu (S); 5. Aria: Ächzen und erbärmlich weinen (B); 6. Choral: So sei nun, Seele deine (chor).

W. Gampert, P. Esswood, K. Equiluz, M. van Egmond, Tolz Boys' Ch, King's College Ch, Leonhardt Consort, G. Leonhardt *Concert* (9/85) (TELD) Ⓓ [2] **2292-42500-2**

E. Mathis, A. Reynolds, P. Schreier, D. Fischer-Dieskau, Munich Bach Ch, Munich Bach Orch, K. Richter (r1971) *Concert* (3/94) (ARCH) Ⓓ [4] **439 369-2AX4**

A. Auger, C. Watkinson, Adalbert Kraus, W. Heldwein, Stuttgart Gächinger Kantorei, Stuttgart Bach Collegium, H. Rilling *Concert* (2/95) (HANS) Ⓓ **98 874**

W. Gampert, P. Esswood, K. Equiluz, M. van Egmond, Tolz Boys' Ch, King's College Ch, Leonhardt Consort, G. Leonhardt *Concert* (2/95) (TELD) Ⓓ [6] **4509-91755-2**

Cantata No. 14, 'Wär Gott nicht mit uns deise Zeit', BWV14 (1735) (Epiphany IV)

EXCERPTS: 1. Chorus: Wär Gott nicht mit uns diese Zeit; 2. Aria: Unsre Stärke heisst zu schwach (S); 3. Recit: Ja, hätt es Gott nur zugegeben (T); 4. Aria: Gott, bei deinem starken Schützen (B); 5. Choral: Gott Lob und Dank, der nicht zugab (chor).

P. Hinterreiter, M. van Altena, M. van Egmond, Tolz Boys' Ch, King's College Ch, Leonhardt Consort, G. Leonhardt *Concert* (9/85) (TELD) Ⓓ [2] **2292-42500-2**

K. Laki, A. Baldin, P. Huttenlocher, Stuttgart Gächinger Kantorei, Württemberg CO, H. Rilling (r1984) *Concert* (2/95) (HANS) Ⓓ **98 859**

P. Hinterreiter, M. van Altena, M. van Egmond, Tolz Boys' Ch, King's College Ch, Leonhardt Consort, G. Leonhardt *Concert* (2/95) (TELD) Ⓓ [6] **4509-91755-2**

Cantata No. 16, 'Herr Gott, dich loben wir', BWV16 (1726) (New Year)

EXCERPTS: 1. Chorus: Herr Gott, dich loben wir; 2. Recit: So stimmen wir bei dieser frohen Zeit (B); 3. Aria & Chorus: Lasst uns jauchzen, lasst uns freueun (B, chor); 4. Recit: Ach treuer Hort (A); 5. Aria: Geliebter Jesu, du allein (T); 6. Choral: All solch dein Güt wir preisen (chor).

P. Esswood, M. van Altena, M. van Egmond, Tolz Boys' Ch, King's College Ch, Leonhardt Consort, G. Leonhardt *Concert* (9/85) (TELD) Ⓓ [2] **2292-42500-2**

G. Schreckenbach, P. Schreier, P. Huttenlocher, Stuttgart Gächinger Kantorei, Stuttgart Bach Collegium, H. Rilling *Concert* (2/95) (HANS) Ⓓ **98 871**

P. Esswood, M. van Altena, M. van Egmond, Tolz Boys' Ch, King's College Ch, Leonhardt Consort, G. Leonhardt *Concert* (2/95) (TELD) Ⓓ [6] **4509-91755-2**

Cantata No. 17, 'Wer Dank opfert, der preiset mich', BWV17 (1726) (Trinity XIV)

EXCERPTS: PART ONE: 1. Chorus: Wer Dank opfert, der preiset mich; 2. Recit: Es muss die ganze Welt (A); 3. Aria: Herr, deine Güte (S). PART TWO: 4. Recit: Einer aber unter ihnen (T); 5. Aria: Welch Übermass der Güte (T); 6. Recit: Sieh meinen Willen an (B); 7. Choral: Wie sich ein vat'r erbarmet (chor).

P. Esswood, K. Equiluz, M. van Egmond, Vienna Boys' Ch, Chorus Viennensis, VCM, N. Harnoncourt *Concert* (9/85) (TELD) Ⓓ [2] **2292-42501-2**

E. Mathis, J. Hamari, P. Schreier, D. Fischer-Dieskau, Munich Bach Ch, Munich Bach Orch, K. Richter (r1976/7) *Concert* (1/95) (ARCH) Ⓓ [6] **439 387-2AX6**

A. Auger, G. Schreckenbach, Adalbert Kraus, W. Heldwein, Stuttgart Gächinger Kantorei, Stuttgart Bach Collegium, H. Rilling *Concert* (2/95) (HANS) Ⓓ **98 868**

anon, P. Esswood, K. Equiluz, M. van Egmond, Vienna Boys' Ch, Chorus Viennensis, VCM, N. Harnoncourt *Concert* (2/95) (TELD) Ⓓ [6] **4509-91755-2**

Cantata No. 18, 'Gleich wie der Regen und Schnee', BWV18 (c1714) (Sexagesima)

EXCERPTS: 1. Sinfonia; 2. Recit: Gleich wie der Regen und Schnee (B); 3. Recit & Chorus: Mein Gott, hier wird mein Herze sein (S,T,B, chor); 4. Aria: Mein Seelenschatz ist Gottes Wort (S); 5. Choral: Ich bitt', o Herr, aus Herzens Grund (chor).

K. Equiluz, M. van Egmond, Vienna Boys' Ch, Chorus Viennensis, VCM, N. Harnoncourt *Concert* (9/85) (TELD) Ⓓ [2] **2292-42501-2**

anon, K. Equiluz, M. van Egmond, Vienna Boys' Ch, Chorus Viennensis, VCM, N. Harnoncourt *Concert* (2/95) (TELD) Ⓓ [6] **4509-91755-2**

E. Csapó, G. Schnaut, Adalbert Kraus, W. Schöne, Stuttgart Gächinger Kantorei, Inst Ens, H. Rilling *Concert* (2/95) (HANS) Ⓓ **98 877**

Cantata No. 19, 'Es erhub sich ein Streit', BWV19 (1726) (St Michael)

EXCERPTS: 1. Chorus: Es erhub sich ein Streit; 2. Recit: Gottlob, der Drache liegt (B); 3. Aria: Gott schickt uns Mahanaim zu (S); 4. Recit: Was ist der schnöde mensch (T); 5. Aria: Bleibet, ihr Engel, bleibt bei mir (T); 6. Recit: Lasst uns das Angesicht (S); 7. Choral: Lass dein' Engel mit mir fahren (chor).

K. Equiluz, M. van Egmond, Vienna Boys' Ch, Chorus Viennensis, VCM, N. Harnoncourt *Concert* (9/85) (TELD) Ⓓ [2] **2292-42501-2**

B. Rondelli, Adalbert Kraus, S. Nimsgern, Stuttgart Gächinger Kantorei, Stuttgart Bach Collegium, H. Rilling *Concert* (2/95) (HANS) Ⓓ **98 869**

anon, K. Equiluz, M. van Egmond, Vienna Boys' Ch, Chorus Viennensis, VCM, N. Harnoncourt *Concert* (2/95) (TELD) Ⓓ [6] **4509-91755-2**

Cantata No. 20, 'O Ewigkeit, du Donnerwort', BWV20 (1724) (Trinity I)

EXCERPTS: PART ONE: 1. Chorus: O Ewigkeit, du Donnerwort; 2. Recit: Kein Unglück ist in aller Welt zu finden (T); 3. Aria: Ewigkeit, du machst mir bange (T); 4. Recit: Gesetzt, es dau'rte der Verdammten Qual (B); 5. Aria: Gott ist gerecht (B); 6. Aria: O Mensch, errette deine Seele (A); 7. Choral: Solang ein Gott im Himmel lebt (chor). PART TWO: 8. Aria: Wacht auf, verlornen Schafe (B); 9. Recit: Verlass, o Mensch, die Wollust dieser Welt (A); 10. Duet: O Menschenkind, hör auf geschwind (A,T); 11. Choral: O Ewigkeit, du Donnerwort (chor).

P. Esswood, K. Equiluz, M. van Egmond, Vienna Boys' Ch, Chorus Viennensis, VCM, N. Harnoncourt *Concert* (9/85) (TELD) Ⓓ [2] **2292-42501-2**

P. Esswood, K. Equiluz, M. van Egmond, Vienna Boys' Ch, Chorus Viennensis, VCM, N. Harnoncourt *Concert* (2/95) (TELD) Ⓓ [6] **4509-91756-2**

V. Gohl, M. Kessler, T. Altmeyer, Adalbert Kraus, W. Schöne, Frankfurt Kantorei, Stuttgart Bach Collegium, H. Rilling (r1970) *Concert* (2/95) (HANS) Ⓓ **98 801**

Cantata No. 21, 'Ich hatte viel Bekümmernis', BWV21 (c1714) (Trinity III)

EXCERPTS: PART ONE: 1. Sinfonia; 2. Chorus: Ich hatte viel Bekümmernis; 3. Aria: Seufzer, Tränen, Kummer, Not (S); 4. Recit: Wie hast du dich, mein Gott (T); 5. Aria: Bäche von gesalz'nen Zähren (T); 6. Chorus: Was betrübst du dich, meine Seele. PART TWO: 7. Recit: Ach Jesu, meine Ruh', mein Licht, wo bleibest du? (S,B); 8. Duet: Komm, mein Jesu, und erquikke (S,B); 9. Chorus: Sei nun wieder zufrieden, meine Seele; 10. Aria: Erfreue dich, Seele erfreue dich, Herze (T); 11. Chorus: Das Lamm, das erwürget ist.

P. Esswood, K. Equiluz, W. Wyatt, Vienna Boys' Ch, Chorus Viennensis, VCM, N. Harnoncourt *Concert* (1/86) (TELD) Ⓓ [2] **2292-42502-2**

G. de Reyghere, C. Prégardien, P. Lika, Netherlands Chbr Ch, Petite Bande, S. Kuijken *Magnificat, BWV243.* (2/90) (VIRG) Ⓓ **VC7 59528-2**

B. Schlick, G. Lesne, H. Crook, P. Harvey, Ghent Collegium Vocale, Paris Chapelle Royale Chor, Paris Chapelle Royale Orch, P. Herreweghe (r1990) *Cantata 42.* (5/91) (HARM) Ⓓ **HMC90 1328**

E. Mathis, E. Haefliger, D. Fischer-Dieskau, Munich Bach Ch, Munich Bach Orch, K. Richter (r1969) *Concert* (7/94) (ARCH) Ⓓ [6] **439 380-2AX6**

A. Auger, Adalbert Kraus, W. Schöne, N. Amini, K. Hagerman, D. Robinson, N. Anderson, Indiana Univ Chbr Sngrs, Stuttgart Bach Collegium, H. Rilling *Cantata 93.* (2/95) (HANS) Ⓓ **98 865**

anon, P. Esswood, K. Equiluz, W. Wyatt, Vienna Boys' Ch, Chorus Viennensis, VCM, N. Harnoncourt *Concert* (2/95) (TELD) Ⓓ [6] **4509-91756-2**

B. Schlick, K. Wessel, G. de Mey, K. Mertens, Amsterdam Baroque Ch, Amsterdam Baroque Orch, T. Koopman (r1994) *Concert* (9/95) (ERAT) Ⓓ [3] **4509-98536-2**

3. K. Battle, W. Marsalis, St Luke's Orch, J. Nelson *Concert* (8/92) (SONY) Ⓓ **SK46672**

3. E. Ameling, H. de Vries, R. van der Meer, A. de Klerk (r1983) *Concert* (7/94) (EMI) Ⓓ **CDC5 55000-2**

Cantata No. 22, 'Jesus nahm zu sich die Zwölfe', BWV22 (1723) (Quinquagesima)

EXCERPTS: 1. Arioso & Chorus: Jesus nahm zu sich die Zwölfe; 2. Aria: Mein Jesu, ziehe mich nach dir (A); 3. Recit: Mein Jesu, ziehe mich so werd'ich laufen (B); 4. Aria: Mein Alles in Allein, mein ewiges Gut (T); 5. Choral: Ertöt' uns durch dein' Güte (chor).

P. Esswood, K. Equiluz, M. van Egmond, Tolz Boys' Ch, King's College Ch, Leonhardt Consort, G. Leonhardt *Concert* (1/86) (TELD) Ⓓ [2] **2292-42502-2**

P. Esswood, K. Equiluz, M. van Egmond, Tolz Boys' Ch, Kings College Ch, Leonhardt Consort, G. Leonhardt *Concert* (2/95) (TELD) Ⓓ [6] **4509-91756-2**

H. Watts, Adalbert Kraus, W. Schöne, Stuttgart Gächinger Kantorei, Stuttgart Bach Collegium, H. Rilling *Concert* (2/95) (HANS) Ⓓ **98 879**

5. M. André, H. Bilgram (arr tpt/org) *Concert* (1/93) (EMI) Ⓓ **CDC7 54330-2**

Cantata No. 23, 'Du wahrer Gott und Davids Sohn', BWV23 (1723) (Quinquagesima)

EXCERPTS: 1. Duet: Du wahrer Gott und Davids Sohn (S,A); 2. Recit: Ach, gehe nicht vorüber, ach gehe nicht (T); 3. Chorus: Aller Augen warten, Herr, du allmächt'ger; 4. Choral: Christe, du Lamm Gottes (chor).

W. Gampert, P. Esswood, M. van Altena, Tolz Boys' Ch, King's College Ch, Leonhardt Consort, G. Leonhardt *Concert* (1/86) (TELD) Ⓓ [2] **2292-42502-2**

E. Mathis, A. Reynolds, P. Schreier, Munich Bach Ch, Munich Bach Orch, K. Richter (r1973-4) *Concert* (7/94) (ARCH) Ⓓ [5] **439 374-2AX5**

W. Gampert, P. Esswood, M. van Altena, Tolz Boys' Ch, Kings College Ch, Leonhardt Consort, G. Leonhardt *Concert* (2/95) (TELD) Ⓓ [6] **4509-91756-2**

A. Auger, H. Watts, A. Baldin, N. Tüller, Stuttgart Gächinger Kantorei, Stuttgart Bach Collegium, H. Rilling *Concert* (2/95) (HANS) Ⓓ **98 879**

Cantata No. 24, 'Ein ungefärbt Gemüte', BWV24 (1723) (Trinity IV)

EXCERPTS: 1. Aria: Ein ungefärbt Gemüte (A); 2. Recit: Die Redlichkeit ist eine von den Gottesgaben (T); 3. Chorus: Alles nun, das ihr wollet; 4. Recit: Die Heuchelei ist eine Brut (B); 5. Aria: Treu und Wahrheit sei der Grund (T); 6. Choral: O Gott, du frommer Gott (chor).

P. Esswood, K. Equiluz, M. van Egmond, Vienna Boys' Ch, Chorus Viennensis, VCM, N. Harnoncourt *Concert* (1/86) (TELD) Ⓓ [2] **2292-42503-2**

A. Reynolds, P. Schreier, D. Fischer-Dieskau, Munich Bach Ch, Munich Bach Orch, K. Richter (r1974-5) *Concert* (7/94) (ARCH) Ⓓ [6] **439 380-2AX6**

anon, P. Esswood, K. Equiluz, M. van Egmond, Vienna Boys' Ch, Chorus Viennensis, VCM, N. Harnoncourt *Concert* (2/95) (TELD) Ⓓ [6] **4509-91756-2**

A. Auger, H. Watts, K. Pugh, Adalbert Kraus, W. Heldwein, W. Schöne, Stuttgart Gächinger Kantorei, Stuttgart Bach Collegium, H. Rilling (r1977/8) *Concert* (2/95) (HANS) Ⓓ **98 803**

Cantata No. 25, 'Es ist nicht Gesundes an meinem Liebe', BWV25 (1723) (Trinity XIV)

EXCERPTS: 1. Chorus: Es ist nichts Gesundes an meinem Leibe; 2. Recit: Die ganze Welt ist nur ein Hospital (T); 3. Aria: Ach, wo hol'ich Armer Rat? (B); 4. Recit: O Jesu, lieber Meister (S); 5. Aria: Öffne meinen schlechten Liedern (S); 6. Choral: Ich will alle meine Tage (chor).

K. Equiluz, M. van Egmond, Vienna Boys' Ch, Chorus Viennensis, VCM, N. Harnoncourt *Concert* (1/86) (TELD) Ⓓ [2] **2292-42503-2**

anon, K. Equiluz, M. van Egmond, Vienna Boys' Ch, Chorus Viennensis, VCM, N. Harnoncourt *Concert* (2/95) (TELD) Ⓓ [6] **4509-91756-2**

A. Auger, Adalbert Kraus, P. Huttenlocher, Stuttgart Gächinger Kantorei, Stuttgart Bach Collegium, H. Rilling (r1977/8) *Concert* (2/95) (HANS) Ⓓ **98 810**

Cantata No. 26, 'Ach wie flüchtig, ach wie nichtig', BWV26 (1724) (Trinity XXIV)

EXCERPTS: 1. Chorus: Ach wie flüchtig, ach wie nichtig; 2. Aria: So schnell ein rauschend Wasser

schiesst (T); 3. Recit: Die Freude wird zur Traurigkeit (A); 4. Aria: An iridische Schätze das herze zu hängen (B); 5. Recit: Die höchste Herrlichkeit und Pracht (S); 6. Choral: Ach wie flüchtig, ach wie nichtig (chor).

P. Esswood, K. Equiluz, S. Nimsgern, Vienna Boys' Ch, Chorus Viennensis, VCM, N. Harnoncourt *Concert* (1/86) (TELD) ① [2] **2292-42503-2**

U. Buckel, H. Töpper, E. Haefliger, T. Adam, Munich Bach Ch, Munich Bach Orch, K. Richter (r1966) *Concert* (1/95) (ARCH) ① [5] **439 394-2AX5**

anon, P. Esswood, K. Equiluz, S. Nimsgern, Vienna Boys' Ch, Chorus Viennensis, VCM, N. Harnoncourt *Concert* (2/95) (TELD) ① [6] **4509-91756-2**

A. Auger, D. Soffel, Adalbert Kraus, P. Huttenlocher, Stuttgart Gächinger Kantorei, Stuttgart Bach Collegium, H. Rilling (r1979/80) *Concert* (2/95) (HANS) ① **98 821**

F. Sailer, C. Hellmann, H. Krebs, E. Wenk, Heilbronn Schütz Ch, Pforzheim CO, F. Werner (r1961) *Concert* (5/95) (ERAT) ① [2] **4509-97407-2**

Cantata No. 27, 'Wer weiss, wie nahe mir mein Ende!', BWV27 (1726) (Trinity XVI)

EXCERPTS: 1. Chorus: Wer weiss, wie nahe mir mein Ende; 2. Recit: Mein Leben hat kein ander Ziel (T); 3. Aria: Willkommen! will ich sagen (A); 4. Recit; Ach wer doch schon im Himmel wär! (S); 5. Aria: Gute Nacht, du Weltgetümmel! (B); 6. Choral: Welt ade! ich bin dein müde (chor).

P. Esswood, K. Equiluz, S. Nimsgern, Vienna Boys' Ch, Chorus Viennensis, VCM, N. Harnoncourt *Concert* (1/86) (TELD) ① [2] **2292-42503-2**

R. Hansmann, H. Watts, K. Equiluz, M. van Egmond, Monteverdi Ch, Concerto Amsterdam, J. Jürgens (r1966/7) *Concert* (10/94) (TELD) ① **4509-93687-2**

E. Mathis, J. Hamari, P. Schreier, D. Fischer-Dieskau, Munich Bach Ch, Munich Bach Orch, K. Richter (r1976/7) *Concert* (1/95) (ARCH) ① [6] **439 387-2AX6**

anon, P. Esswood, anon, K. Equiluz, S. Nimsgern, Vienna Boys' Ch, Chorus Viennensis, VCM, N. Harnoncourt *Concert* (2/95) (TELD) ① [6] **4509-91756-2**

E. Wiens, G. Schreckenbach, L-M. Harder, W. Heldwein, Stuttgart Gächinger Kantorei, Stuttgart Bach Collegium, H. Rilling (r1982) *Concert* (2/95) (HANS) ① **98 813**

Cantata No. 28, 'Gottlob! nun geht das Jahr zu Ende', BWV28 (1725) (Christmas I)

EXCERPTS: 1. Aria: Gottlob! nun geht das Jahr zu Ende (S); 2. Chorus: Nun lob, mein Seel, den Herren; 3. Recit & Arioso: So spricht der Herr (B); 4. Recit: Gott ist ein Quell (T); 5. Duet: Gott hat uns im heurigen Jahre gesegnet (A,T); 6. Choral: All solch dein Güt wir preisen (chor).

P. Esswood, K. Equiluz, S. Nimsgern, Vienna Boys' Ch, Chorus Viennensis, VCM, N. Harnoncourt *Concert* (1/86) (TELD) ① [2] **2292-42504-2**

E. Mathis, H. Töpper, P. Schreier, D. Fischer-Dieskau, Munich Bach Ch, Munich Bach Orch, K. Richter (r1970-2) *Concert* (3/94) (ARCH) ① [4] **439 369-2AX4**

anon, P. Esswood, K. Equiluz, S. Nimsgern, Vienna Boys' Ch, Chorus Viennensis, VCM, N. Harnoncourt *Concert* (2/95) (TELD) ① [6] **4509-91756-2**

A. Auger, G. Schreckenbach, Adalbert Kraus, W. Heldwein, Stuttgart Gächinger Kantorei, Stuttgart Bach Collegium, H. Rilling (r1981/2) *Cantata 194.* (2/95) (HANS) ① **98 827**

Cantata No. 29, 'Wir danken dir, Gott, wir danken dir', BWV29 (1731) (Town Council Inauguration)

EXCERPTS: 1. Sinfonia; 2. Chorus: Wir danken dir, Gott; 3. Aria: Halleluja, Stärk und Macht (T); 4. Recit: Gottlob! Es geht uns wohl! (B); 5. Aria: Gedenk an uns mit deiner Liebe (S); 6. Recit: Vergiss es ferner nicht (A, chor); 7. Aria: Halleluja, Stärk und Macht (A); 8. Choral: Sei Lob und Preis mit Ehren (chor).

P. Esswood, K. Equiluz, M. van Egmond, Vienna Boys' Ch, Chorus Viennensis, VCM, N. Harnoncourt *Concert* (1/86) (TELD) ① [2] **2292-42504-2**

U. Sonntag, E. Graf, A. Baldin, P. Huttenlocher, Stuttgart Gächinger Kantorei, Württemberg CO, H. Rilling (r1984) *Concert* (2/95) (HANS) ① **98 857**

anon, P. Esswood, K. Equiluz, M. van Egmond, Vienna Boys' Ch, Chorus Viennensis, VCM, N. Harnoncourt *Concert* (2/95) (TELD) ① [6] **4509-91756-2**

1. Taverner Plyrs, A. Parrott *Concert* (12/88) (EMI) ① **CDM7 69853-2**

1. I. Tracey (r1990; arr Tracey) *Concert* (4/91) (MIRA) ① **MRCD901**

1. I. Biret (trans Kempff) *Concert* (5/93) (MARC) ① **8 223452**

1. W. Kempff (r1975: arr pf: Kempff) *Concert* (11/94) (DG) ① [2] **439 672-2GX2**

Cantata No. 30, 'Freue dich, erlöste Schar', BWV30 (1738 or later) (St John)

EXCERPTS: PART ONE: 1. Chorus: Freue dich erlöste Schar; 2. Recit: Wir haben Rast (B); 3. Aria: Gelobet sei Gott, gelobet sein Name (B); 4. Recit: Der Herold kömmt (A); 5. Aria: Kommt, ihr angefochtnen Sünder (A); 6. Choral: Eine Stimme lässt sich hören (chor). PART TWO: 7. Recit: So bist du denn, mein Heill, bedacht (B); 8. Aria: Ich will nun hassen (B); 9. Recit: Und ob wohl sonst der Unbestand (S); 10. Aria: Eilt, ihr Stunden, kommt herbei (S); 11. Recit: Geduld, der angenehme Tag (T); 12. Chorus: Freue dich, geheilgte Schar.

P. Esswood, K. Equiluz, M. van Egmond, Vienna Boys' Ch, Chorus Viennensis, VCM, N. Harnoncourt *Concert* (1/86) (TELD) ① [2] **2292-42504-2**

E. Mathis, A. Reynolds, P. Schreier, D. Fischer-Dieskau, Munich Bach Ch, Munich Bach Orch, K. Richter (r1974-5) *Concert* (7/94) (ARCH) ① [6] **439 380-2AX6**

C. Cuccaro, M. Georg, A. Baldin, P. Huttenlocher, Stuttgart Gächinger Kantorei, Württemberg CO, H. Rilling (r1984) *Cantata 112.* (2/95) (HANS) ① **98 860**

anon, P. Esswood, K. Equiluz, M. van Egmond, Vienna Boys' Ch, Chorus Viennensis, VCM, N. Harnoncourt *Concert* (2/95) (TELD) ① [6] **4509-91756-2**

Cantata No. 31, '(Der) Himmel lacht! die Erde jubilliert', BWV31 (1715) (Wds. Franck. Easter)

EXCERPTS: 1. Sonata; 2. Chorus: Der Himmel lacht, die Erde jubilieret; 3. Recit: Erwünschter Tag! Sei, Seele, wieder froh (B); 4. Aria: Fürst des Lebens, starker Streiter (B); 5. Recit: So stehe denn, du gottergebne Seele (T); 6. Aria: Adam muss in uns verwesen (T); 7. Recit: Weill denn das Haupt sein Glied (S); 8. Aria: Letze Stunde, brich herein (S); 9. Choral: So fahr ich hin zu Jesu Christ (chor).

K. Equiluz, S. Nimsgern, Vienna Boys' Ch, Chorus Viennensis, VCM, N. Harnoncourt *Concert* (1/88) (TELD) ① [2] **2292-42505-2**

anon, anon, K. Equiluz, S. Nimsgern, Vienna Boys' Ch, Chorus Viennensis, VCM, N. Harnoncourt *Concert* (2/95) (TELD) ① [6] **4509-91756-2**

A. Auger, Adalbert Kraus, W. Schöne, Indiana Univ Chbr Sngrs, Stuttgart Bach Collegium, H. Rilling *Cantata 134.* (2/95) (HANS) ① **98 881**

I. Reichelt, H. Töpper, H. Krebs, F. Kelch, Heilbronn H. Schütz Ch, Pforzheim CO, F. Werner (r1964) *Concert* (6/95) (ERAT) ① [2] **4509-98525-2**

B. Schlick, K. Wessel, G. de Mey, K. Mertens, Amsterdam Baroque Ch, Amsterdam Baroque Orch, T. Koopman (r1994) *Concert* (9/95) (ERAT) ① [3] **4509-98536-2**

1. Taverner Plyrs, A. Parrott *Concert* (12/88) (EMI) ① **CDM7 69853-2**

Cantata No. 32, 'Liebster Jesu, mein Verlangen', BWV32 (1726) (Wds. Lehms. Epiphany I)

EXCERPTS: 1. Aria: Liebster Jesu, mein Verlangen (S); 2. Recit: Was ist's, dass du mich gesuchet? (B); 3. Aria: Hier, in meines Vaters Stätte (B); 4. Recit: Ach! heiliger und grosser Gott (S,B); 5. Duet: Nun verschwinden alle Plagen (S,B); 6. Choral: Mein Gott, öffne mir die Pforten (chor).

W. Gampert, M. van Egmond, Hanover Boys' Ch, Leonhardt Consort, G. Leonhardt *Concert* (1/88) (TELD) ① [2] **2292-42505-2**

A. Auger, W. Heldwein, Stuttgart Gächinger Kantorei, Stuttgart Bach Collegium, H. Rilling *Concert* (2/95) (HANS) ① **98 873**

W. Gampert, M. van Egmond, Hanover Boys' Ch, Leonhardt Consort, G. Leonhardt *Concert* (2/95) (TELD) ① [6] **4509-91756-2**

Cantata No. 33, 'Allein zu dir, Herr Jesu Christ', BWV33 (1724) (Trinity XIII)

EXCERPTS: 1. Chorus: Allein zu dir, Herr Jesu Christ; 2. Recit: Mein Gott und Richter (B); 3. Aria: Wie furchtsam wankten meine Schritte (A); 4. Recit: Mein Gott, verwirf mich nicht (T); 5. Duet: Gott, der du die Liebe heisst (T,B); 6. Choral: Ehr sei Gott in dem höchsten Thron (chor).

R. Jacobs, M. van Altena, M. van Egmond, Hanover Boys' Ch, Leonhardt Consort, G. Leonhardt *Concert* (1/88) (TELD) ① [2] **2292-42505-2**

J. Hamari, P. Schreier, D. Fischer-Dieskau, Munich Bach Ch, Munich Bach Orch, K. Richter (r1976/7) *Concert* (1/95) (ARCH) ① [6] **439 387-2AX6**

R. Jacobs, M. van Altena, M. van Egmond, Hanover Boys' Ch, Leonhardt Consort, G. Leonhardt *Concert* (2/95) (TELD) ① [6] **4509-91756-2**

H. Watts, F. Lang, P. Huttenlocher, Stuttgart Gächinger Kantorei, Stuttgart Bach Collegium, H. Rilling (r1979) *Concert* (2/95) (HANS) ① **98 811**

Cantata No. 34, 'O ewiges Feuer, O Ursprung der Liebe', BWV34 (c1740) (Whit Sunday)

EXCERPTS: 1. Chorus: O ewiges Feuer, o Ursprung der Liebe; 2. Recit: Herr! unsre Herzen halten dir (T); 3. Aria: Wohl euch, ihr auserwählten Seelen (A); 4. Recit: Erwählt sich Gott die heil'gen Hütten (B); 5. Chorus: Friede über Israel! Dankt den höchsten Wunderhänden.

P. Esswood, K. Equiluz, S. Nimsgern, Vienna Boys' Ch, Chorus Viennensis, VCM, N. Harnoncourt *Concert* (1/88) (TELD) ① [2] **2292-42505-2**

A. Reynolds, P. Schreier, D. Fischer-Dieskau, Munich Bach Ch, Munich Bach Orch, K. Richter (r1974-5) *Concert* (7/94) (ARCH) ① [6] **439 380-2AX6**

P. Esswood, K. Equiluz, S. Nimsgern, Vienna Boys' Ch, Chorus Viennensis, VCM, N. Harnoncourt *Concert* (2/95) (TELD) ① [6] **4509-91756-2**

H. Watts, Adalbert Kraus, W. Schöne, Stuttgart Gächinger Kantorei, Stuttgart Bach Collegium, H. Rilling (r1972) *Concert* (2/95) (HANS) ① **98 887**

Cantata No. 35, 'Geist und Seele wird verwirret', BWV35 (1726) (Trinity XII)

EXCERPTS: PART ONE: 1. Sinfonia; 2. Aria: Geist und Seele wird verwirret (A); 3. Recit: Ich wundre mich, denn alles was man sieht (A); 4. Gott hat alles wohlgemacht (A). PART TWO: 5. Sinfonia; 6. Recit: Ach, starker Gott, lass mich doch dieses (A); 7. Aria: Ich wünsche mir, bei Gott zu leben (A).

P. Esswood, VCM, N. Harnoncourt *Concert* (1/88) (TELD) ① [2] **2292-42506-2**

R. Jacobs, Ens 415, C. Banchini *Concert* (10/88) (HARM) ① **HMC90 1273**

J. van Nes, Amsterdam Bach Sols, L. Van Doeselaar *Cantata 170.* (9/90) (OTTA) ① **OTRC108506**

P. Esswood, VCM, N. Harnoncourt *Concert* (2/95) (TELD) ① [6] **4509-91756-2**

J. Hamari, Stuttgart Bach Collegium, H. Rilling (r1982) *Concert* (2/95) (HANS) ① **98 811**

Cantata No. 36, 'Schwingt freudig euch empor', BWV36 (1731) (Advent I)

EXCERPTS: PART ONE: 1. Chorus: Schwingt freudig euch empor; 2. Choral: Nun komm, der heiden Heiland (S,A); 3. Aria: Die Liebe zieht mit sanften Schritten; 4. Choral: Zwingt die Saiten in Cythara (chor). PART TWO: 5. Aria: Willkommen, werter Schatz (B); 6. Choral: Der du bist dem Vater gleich (T); 7. Aria: Auch mit gedämpften, schwachten Stimmen (S); 8. Choral: Lob sei Gott dem Vater g'ton (chor).

P. Esswood, K. Equiluz, R. van der Meer, Vienna Boys' Ch, Chorus Viennensis, VCM, N. Harnoncourt *Concert* (1/88) (TELD) ① [2] **2292-42506-2**

N. Argenta, P. Lang, A. Rolfe Johnson, O. Bär, Monteverdi Ch, EBS, J.E. Gardiner *Concert* (2/93) (ARCH) ① **437 327-2AH**

anon, P. Esswood, K. Equiluz, R. van der Meer, Vienna Boys' Ch, Chorus Viennensis, VCM, N. Harnoncourt *Concert* (2/95) (TELD) ① [6] **4509-91756-2**

A. Auger, G. Schreckenbach, P. Schreier, W. Heldwein, Stuttgart Gächinger Kantorei, Stuttgart Bach Collegium, H. Rilling (r1980-2) *Cantata 63.* (2/95) (HANS) ① **98 823**

7. K. Battle, I. Perlman, St Luke's Orch, J. Nelson (r1989/90) *Concert* (3/92) (DG) ① **429 737-2GH**

Cantata No. 37, 'Wer da gläubet und getauft wird', BWV37 (1724) (Ascension)

EXCERPTS: 1. Chorus: Wer da gläubet und getauft wird; 2. Aria: Der glaube ist das Pfand der Liebe (T); 3. Choral: Herr Gott Vater, mein starker Held (S,A); 4. Recit: Ihr Sterblichen, verlanget ihr mit mir (B); 5. Aria: Der Glaube schafft der Seele Flügel (B); 6. Choral: Den Glauben mir verleihe (chor).

P. Esswood, K. Equiluz, R. van der Meer, Vienna Boys' Ch, Chorus Viennensis, VCM, N. Harnoncourt *Concert* (1/88) (TELD) ① [2] **2292-42506-2**

anon, P. Esswood, K. Equiluz, R. van der Meer, Vienna Boys' Ch, Chorus Viennensis, VCM, N. Harnoncourt *Concert* (2/95) (TELD) ① [6] **4509-91757-2**

A. Auger, C. Watkinson, Adalbert Kraus, P. Huttenlocher, Stuttgart Gächinger Kantorei, Stuttgart Bach Collegium, H. Rilling (r1979) *Concert* (2/95) (HANS) ① **98 886**

Cantata No. 38, 'Aus tiefer Not schrei ich zu dir', BWV38 (1724) (Trinity XXI)

EXCERPTS: 1. Chorus: Aus tiefer Not schrei' ich zu dir; 2. Recit: In Jesu Gnade wird allein (A); 3. Aria: Ich höre mitten in den Leiden (T); 4. Recit a battuta: Ach! dass mein Glaube (S); 5. Terzetto: Wenn meine Trübsal als mit Ketten (S,A,B); 6. Choral: Ob bei uns ist der Sünden viel (chor).

P. Esswood, K. Equiluz, R. van der Meer, Vienna Boys' Ch, Chorus Viennensis, VCM, N. Harnoncourt *Concert* (1/88) (TELD) ① [2] **2292-42506-2**

E. Mathis, T. Schmidt, P. Schreier, D. Fischer-Dieskau, Munich Bach Ch, Munich Bach Orch, K. Richter (r1977/8) *Concert*
(1/95) (ARCH) ① [5] **439 394-2AX5**
anon, P. Esswood, K. Equiluz, R. van der Meer, Vienna Boys' Ch, Chorus Viennensis, VCM, N. Harnoncourt *Concert*
(2/95) (TELD) ① [6] **4509-91757-2**
A. Auger, H. Watts, L-M. Harder, P. Huttenlocher, Stuttgart Gächinger Kantorei, Stuttgart Bach Collegium, H. Rilling (r1980) *Concert*
(2/95) (HANS) ① **98 818**

Cantata No. 39, 'Brich dem Hungrigen dein Brot', BWV39 (1726) (Trinity I)
EXCERPTS: PART ONE: 1. Chorus: Brich dem Hungrigen dein Brot; 2. Recit: Der reiche Gott (B); 3. Aria: Seinem Schöpfer noch auf Erden (A). PART TWO: 4. Aria: Wohlzutun und mitzuteilen (B); 5. Aria: Höchster, was ich habe (S); 6. Recit: Wie soll ich dir, o Herr (A); 7. Choral: Selig sind, die aus Erbarmen (chor).
R. Jacobs, M. van Egmond, Hanover Boys' Ch, Leonhardt Consort, G. Leonhardt *Concert*
(1/88) (TELD) ① [2] **2292-42556-2**
Collegium Vocale, P. Herreweghe (r1991) *Concert*
(3/94) (VIRG) ① **VC7 59320-2**
E. Mathis, A. Reynolds, D. Fischer-Dieskau, Munich Bach Ch, Munich Bach Orch, K. Richter (r1974-5) *Concert* (7/94) (ARCH) ① [6] **439 380-2AX6**
anon, R. Jacobs, M. van Egmond, Hanover Boys' Ch, Leonhardt Consort, G. Leonhardt *Concert*
(2/95) (TELD) ① [6] **4509-91757-2**
A. Auger, G. Schreckenbach, F. Gerihsen, Stuttgart Gächinger Kantorei, Stuttgart Bach Collegium, H. Rilling (r1982) *Concert* (2/95) (HANS) ① **98 802**

Cantata No. 40, 'Dazu ist erschienen der Sohn Gottes', BWV40 (1723) (2nd day of Christmas)
EXCERPTS: 1. Chorus: Dazu ist erschienen der Sohn Gottes; 2. Recit: Das Wort ward Fleisch und wohnet in der Welt (T); 3. Choral: Die Sünd'macht Leid (chor); 4. Aria: Höllische Schlange, wird dir nicht bange (B); 5. Recit: Die Schlange, so im Paradise (A); 6. Choral: Schüttle deinen Kopf und sprich (chor); 7. Aria: Christenkinder, freuet euch (T); 8. Choral: Jesu, nimm dich deiner Glieder (chor).
R. Jacobs, M. van Altena, M. van Egmond, Hanover Boys' Ch, Leonhardt Consort, G. Leonhardt *Concert*
(1/88) (TELD) ① [2] **2292-42556-2**
R. Jacobs, M. van Altena, M. van Egmond, Hanover Boys' Ch, Leonhardt Consort, G. Leonhardt *Concert*
(2/95) (TELD) ① [6] **4509-91757-2**
V. Gohl, Adalbert Kraus, S. Nimsgern, Stuttgart Gedächtniskirche Ch, Stuttgart Bach Collegium, H. Rilling (r1970) *Concert* (2/95) (HANS) ① **98 824**

Cantata No. 41, 'Jesu, nun sei gepreiset', BWV41 (1725) (New Year)
EXCERPTS: 1. Chorus: Jesu, nun sei gepreist; 2. Aria: Lass uns, o höchster Gott (S); 3. Recit: Herr! Deine Hand, dein Segen muss allein (A); 4. Aria: Woferne du den edlen Frieden (T); 5. Recit: Doch weil der Feind bei Tag und Nacht (S,A,T,B); 6. Choral: Dein ist allein die Ehre (chor).
P. Esswood, K. Equiluz, R. van der Meer, Vienna Boys' Ch, Chorus Viennensis, VCM, N. Harnoncourt *Concert* (1/88) (TELD) ① [2] **2292-42556-2**
H. Donath, M. Höffgen, Adalbert Kraus, S. Nimsgern, Stuttgart Gächinger Kantorei, Stuttgart Bach Collegium, H. Rilling *Concert*
(2/95) (HANS) ① **98 870**
anon, P. Esswood, K. Equiluz, R. van der Meer, Vienna Boys' Ch, Chorus Viennensis, VCM, N. Harnoncourt *Concert*
(2/95) (TELD) ① [6] **4509-91757-2**

Cantata No. 42, 'Am Abend aber desselbigen Sabbats', BWV42 (1725) (Easter I)
EXCERPTS: 1. Sinfonia; 2. Recit: Am Abend aber desselbigen Sabbaths (T); 3. Aria: Wo Zwei und Drei versammlet (A); 4. Choral: Verzage nicht (S,T); 5. Recit: Man kann hiervon ein schön Exempel sehen (B); 6. Aria: Jesus ist ein Schild der Seinen (B); 7. Choral: Verleih' uns Frieden gnädiglich (chor).
P. Esswood, K. Equiluz, R. van der Meer, Vienna Boys' Ch, Chorus Viennensis, VCM, N. Harnoncourt *Concert* (1/88) (TELD) ① [2] **2292-42556-2**
B. Schlick, G. Lesne, H. Crook, P. Kooy, Ghent Collegium Vocale, Paris Chapelle Royale Chor, Paris Chapelle Royale Orch, P. Herreweghe (r1990) *Cantata 21.* (5/91) (HARM) ① **HMC90 1328**
anon, P. Esswood, K. Equiluz, R. van der Meer, Vienna Boys' Ch, Chorus Viennensis, VCM, N. Harnoncourt *Concert*
(2/95) (TELD) ① [6] **4509-91757-2**
A. Auger, J. Hamari, P. Schreier, P. Huttenlocher, Stuttgart Gächinger Kantorei, Stuttgart Bach Collegium, H. Rilling *Concert*
(2/95) (HANS) ① **98 882**
1. Brandenburg Consort, R. Goodman *Concert*
(7/91) (HYPE) ① **CDA66501**
1. Freiburg Baroque Orch, T. Hengelbrock (r1992) *Concert* (4/94) (DHM) ① **05472 77289-2**
1. English Concert, T. Pinnock (r1993-4) *Concert*
(12/95) (ARCH) ① [2] **439 780-2AH2**

Cantata No. 43, 'Gott fähret auf mit Jauchzen', BWV43 (1726) (Ascension)
EXCERPTS: PART ONE: 1. Chorus: Gott fähret auf mit Jauchzen; 2. Recit: Es will der Höchste (T); 3. Aria: Ja, tausendmal tausend (T); 4. Recit: Und der Herr (S); 5. Aria: Mein Jesus hat nunmehr (S). PART TWO: 6. Recit: Es kommt der Helden Held (B); 7. Aria: Er ists, der ganz allein (B); 8. Recit: Der Vater hat ihm ja (A); 9. Aria: Ich sehe schon im geist (A); 10. Recit: Er will mir neben sich (S); 11. Choral: Du Lebensfürst, Herr Jesu Christ (chor).
P. Jelosits, P. Esswood, K. Equiluz, R. van der Meer, Vienna Boys' Ch, Chorus Viennensis, VCM, N. Harnoncourt *Concert*
(1/88) (TELD) ① [2] **2292-42559-2**
B. Schlick, C. Patriasz, C. Prégardien, P. Kooy, Collegium Vocale, P. Herreweghe (r1993) *Concert*
(3/94) (HARM) ① **HMC90 1479**
P. Jelosits, P. Esswood, K. Equiluz, R. van der Meer, Vienna Boys' Ch, Chorus Viennensis, VCM, N. Harnoncourt *Concert*
(2/95) (TELD) ① [6] **4509-91757-2**
A. Auger, J. Hamari, L-M. Harder, P. Huttenlocher, Stuttgart Gächinger Kantorei, Stuttgart Bach Collegium, H. Rilling (r1981/2) *Concert*
(2/95) (HANS) ① **98 885**
F. Sailer, C. Hellmann, H. Krebs, J. Stämpfli, Heilbronn Schütz Ch, Pforzheim CO, F. Werner (r1961) *Concert*
(5/95) (ERAT) ① [2] **4509-97407-2**

Cantata No. 44, 'Sie werden euch in den Bann tun', BWV44 (1724) (Ascension I)
EXCERPTS: 1. Duet: Sie werden euch in den Bann tun (T,B); 2. Chorus: Es kömmt aber die Zeit; 3. Aria: Christen müssen auf der Erden (A); 4. Choral: Ach Gott, wie manches Herzelied (T); 5. Recit: Es sucht der Antichrist (B); 6. Aria: Es ist und bleibt der Christen Trost (S); 7. Choral: So sei nun, Seele (chor).
P. Jelosits, P. Esswood, K. Equiluz, R. van der Meer, Vienna Boys' Ch, Chorus Viennensis, VCM, N. Harnoncourt *Concert*
(1/88) (TELD) ① [2] **2292-42559-2**
B. Schlick, C. Patriasz, C. Prégardien, P. Kooy, Collegium Vocale, P. Herreweghe (r1993) *Concert*
(3/94) (HARM) ① **HMC90 1479**
E. Mathis, A. Reynolds, D. Fischer-Dieskau, Munich Bach Ch, Munich Bach Orch, K. Richter (r1973-5) *Concert* (7/94) (ARCH) ① [6] **439 380-2AX6**
P. Jelosits, P. Esswood, K. Equiluz, R. van der Meer, Vienna Boys' Ch, Chorus Viennensis, VCM, N. Harnoncourt *Concert*
(2/95) (TELD) ① [6] **4509-91757-2**
A. Auger, H. Watts, A. Baldin, W. Schöne, Stuttgart Gächinger Kantorei, Stuttgart Bach Collegium, H. Rilling (r1979) *Concert* (2/95) (HANS) ① **98 886**

Cantata No. 45, 'Es ist dir gesagt, Mensch, was gut ist', BWV45 (1726) (Trinity VIII)
EXCERPTS: PART ONE: 1. Chorus: Es ist gesagt, mensch, was gut ist; 2. Recit: Der Höchste lässt mich (T); 3. Aria: Weiss ich Gottes Rechte (T). PART TWO: 4. Arioso: Es werden Viele zu mir sagen (B); 5. Aria: Wer Gott bekennt aus wahrem Herzensgrund (A); 6. Recit: So wird denn Herz und Mund (A); 7. Choral: Gib, dass ich tu' mit Fleiss (chor).
R. Jacobs, K. Equiluz, H-F. Kunz, Hanover Boys' Ch, Leonhardt Consort, G. Leonhardt *Concert*
(1/88) (TELD) ① [2] **2292-42559-2**
H. Töpper, E. Haefliger, K. Engen, Munich Bach Ch, Ansbach Bach Week Sols Ens, K. Richter (r1959) *Concert* (1/95) (ARCH) ① [6] **439 387-2AX6**
R. Jacobs, K. Equiluz, H-F. Kunz, Hanover Boys' Ch, Leonhardt Consort, G. Leonhardt *Concert*
(2/95) (TELD) ① [6] **4509-91757-2**
J. Hamari, A. Baldin, P. Huttenlocher, Stuttgart Gächinger Kantorei, Stuttgart Bach Collegium, H. Rilling (r1982) *Concert* (2/95) (HANS) ① **98 807**

Cantata No. 46, 'Schauet doch und sehet', BWV46 (1723) (Trinity X)
EXCERPTS: 1. Chorus: Schauet doch und sehet; 2. Recit: So klage du, zerstörte Gottesstadt (T); 3. Aria: Dein Wetter zog sich auf von weiten (B); 4. Recit: Doch bildet euch, o Sünder (A); 5. Aria: Doch Jesus will auch bei der Strafe (A); 6. Choral: O grosser Gott der Treu (chor).
R. Jacobs, K. Equiluz, H-F. Kunz, Hanover Boys' Ch, Leonhardt Consort, G. Leonhardt *Concert*
(1/88) (TELD) ① [2] **2292-42559-2**
R. Jacobs, K. Equiluz, H-F. Kunz, Hanover Boys' Ch, Leonhardt Consort, G. Leonhardt *Concert*
(2/95) (TELD) ① [6] **4509-91757-2**
H. Watts, Adalbert Kraus, W. Schöne, Stuttgart Gächinger Kantorei, Stuttgart Bach Collegium, H. Rilling (r1977/8) *Concert* (2/95) (HANS) ① **98 808**

Cantata No. 47, 'Wer sich selbst erhöhet', BWV47 (1726) (Wds J.F. Helbig. Trinity XVII)
EXCERPTS: 1. Chorus: Wer sich selbst erhöhet; 2. Aria: Wer ein wahrer Christ will heissen (S); 3. Recit: Der Mensch ist Kot, Stank, Asch und Erde (B); 4. Aria: Jesu beuge doch mein Herze (B); 5. Choral Der zeitlichen Ehr will ich gern entbehrn (chor).
P. Jelosits, R. van der Meer, Vienna Boys' Ch, Chorus Viennensis, VCM, N. Harnoncourt *Concert*
(1/88) (TELD) ① [2] **2292-42560-2**
P. Jelosits, R. van der Meer, Vienna Boys' Ch, Chorus Viennensis, VCM, N. Harnoncourt *Concert*
(2/95) (TELD) ① [6] **4509-91757-2**
A. Auger, P. Huttenlocher, Stuttgart Gächinger Kantorei, Stuttgart Bach Collegium, H. Rilling (r1982) *Concert* (2/95) (HANS) ① **98 815**

Cantata No. 48, 'Ich elender Mensch, wer wird mich erlösen', BWV48 (1723) (Trinity XIX)
EXCERPTS: 1. Chorus: Ich elender Mensch, wer wird mich erlösen; 2. Recit: O Schmerz, o Elend, so mich trifft (A); 3. Choral: Soll's ja so sein (chor); 4. Aria: Ach, lege das Sodom der sündlichen Glieder (A); 5. Recit: Hier aber tut des Heilands hand (T); 6. Aria: Vergiebt uns Jesus unsre Sünden (T); 7. Choral: Herr Jesu Christ, einiger Trost (chor).
P. Esswood, K. Equiluz, Vienna Boys' Ch, Chorus Viennensis, VCM, N. Harnoncourt *Concert*
(1/88) (TELD) ① [2] **2292-42560-2**
P. Esswood, K. Equiluz, Vienna Boys' Ch, Chorus Viennensis, VCM, N. Harnoncourt *Concert*
(2/95) (TELD) ① [6] **4509-91757-2**

Cantata No. 49, 'Ich gehe und suche mit Verlangen', BWV49 (1726) (Trinity XX)
EXCERPTS: 1. Sinfonia; 2. Aria: Ich geh' und suche mit Verlangen (B); 3. Recit: Mein Mahl ist zubereit (B,S); 4. Aria: Ich bin herrlich, ich bin schön (S); 5. Recit: Mein Glaube hat mich selbst so angezogen (S,B); 6. Duet: Dich hab ich je und je geliebet (S,B).
P. Jelosits, R. van der Meer, Vienna Boys' Ch, Chorus Viennensis, VCM, N. Harnoncourt *Concert*
(1/88) (TELD) ① [2] **2292-42560-2**
N. Argenta, K. Mertens, Petite Bande, S. Kuijken (vn/dir) (r1993) *Concert*
(3/94) (ACCE) ① **ACC9395D**
P. Jelosits, R. van der Meer, VCM, N. Harnoncourt *Concert* (2/95) (TELD) ① [6] **4509-91757-2**
B. Schlick, A. Scholl, C. Prégardien, G. Schwarz, Concerto Vocale, Limoges Baroque Ens, C. Coin (vc/dir) (r1993) *Concert* (2/95) (ASTR) ① **E8530**
A. Auger, P. Huttenlocher, Stuttgart Bach Collegium, H. Rilling (r1982) *Concert* (2/95) (HANS) ① **98 817**

Cantata No. 50, 'Nun ist das Heil und die Kraft', BWV50 (1726) (fragment. St Michael)
Vienna Boys' Ch, Chorus Viennensis, VCM, N. Harnoncourt *Concert*
(1/88) (TELD) ① [2] **2292-42560-2**
Vienna St Op Chor, Vienna St Op Orch, F. Prohaska (r1957) *Concert* (9/93) (VANG) ① **08.2010.71**
Stuttgart Gächinger Kantorei, Württemberg CO, H. Rilling (r1984) *Concert* (2/95) (HANS) ① **98 857**
Vienna Boys' Ch, Chorus Viennensis, VCM, N. Harnoncourt *Concert*
(2/95) (TELD) ① [6] **4509-91757-2**

Cantata No. 51, 'Jauchzet Gott in allen Landen!', BWV51 (1730) (Trinity XV)
EXCERPTS: 1. Aria: Jauchzet Gott in allen Landen (S); 2. Recit: Wir beten zu dem Tempel an (S); 3. Aria: Höchster, mache deine Güter ferner (S); 4. Choral: Sei Lob und Preis mit Ehren (S); 5. Aria: Alleluja (S).
E. Kirkby, C. Steele-Perkins, English Baroque Ens, J.E. Gardiner *Magnificat, BWV243.*
(9/85) (PHIL) ① **411 458-2PH**
M. Kweksilber, Leonhardt Consort, G. Leonhardt *Concert* (11/88) (TELD) ① [2] **2292-42422-2**
A. Auger, Stuttgart Gächinger Kantorei, Stuttgart Bach Collegium, Württemberg CO, H. Rilling *Concert*
(1/89) (NOVA) ① **150 029-2**
B. Hendricks, CPE Bach Orch, P. Schreier *Concert*
(7/90) (EMI) ① **CDC7 49843-2**
E. Schwarzkopf, Philh, P. Gellhorn (r1950) *Concert*
(7/90) (EMI) ① **CDH7 63201-2**
J. Baird, B. Baugess, American Bach Sols, J. Thomas (r1990) *Concert*
(12/92) (KOCH) ① **37138-2**

Cantata No. 65, 'Sie werden aus Saba alle kommen', BWV65 (1724) (Epiphany)
EXCERPTS: 1. Chorus: Sie werden aus Saba alle kommen; 2. Choral: Die Kön'ge aus Saba kamen dar (chor); 3. Recit: Was dort Jesaias vorhergesehn (B); 4. Aria: Gold und Ophir ist zu schlecht (B); 5. Recit: Verschmähe nicht (T); 6. Aria: Nimm mich dir zu eigen hin (T); 7. Choral: Ei nun, mein Gott (chor).
K. Equiluz, R. van der Meer, Tolz Boys' Ch, VCM, N. Harnoncourt Concert
(2/89) (TELD) ① [2] **2292-42571-2**
E. Haefliger, T. Adam, Munich Bach Ch, Munich Bach Orch, K. Richter (r1967) Concert
(3/94) (ARCH) ① [4] **439 369-2AX4**
Adalbert Kraus, W. Schöne, Stuttgart Gächinger Kantorei, Stuttgart Bach Collegium, H. Rilling Concert
(2/95) (HANS) ① **98 872**
K. Equiluz, R. van der Meer, Tolz Boys' Ch, VCM, N. Harnoncourt Concert
(2/95) (TELD) ① [6] **4509-91758-2**

Cantata No. 66, 'Erfreut euch, ihr Herzen', BWV66 (1724) (Easter Monday)
EXCERPTS: 1. Chorus: Erfreut euch, ihr Herzen!; 2. Recit: Es bricht das Grab und damit unsre Not (B); 3. Aria: Lasset dem Höchsten ein Danklied (B); 4. Recit: Bei Jesu Leben freudig sein (A,T); 5. Recit: Ich fürchte zwar des Grabes Finsternissen (A,T); 6. Choral: Alleluja! (chor).
P. Esswood, K. Equiluz, M. van Egmond, Hanover Boys' Ch, Ghent Collegium Vocale, Leonhardt Consort, G. Leonhardt Concert
(2/89) (TELD) ① [2] **2292-42571-2**
P. Esswood, K. Equiluz, M. van Egmond, Hanover Boys' Ch, Ghent Collegium Vocale, Leonhardt Consort, G. Leonhardt Concert
(2/95) (TELD) ① [6] **4509-91758-2**
G. Schreckenbach, Adalbert Kraus, P. Huttenlocher, Stuttgart Gächinger Kantorei, Stuttgart Bach Collegium, H. Rilling Cantata 182.
(2/95) (HANS) ① **98 880**
B. Schlick, K. Wessel, J. Taylor, P. Kooy, Collegium Vocale, P. Herreweghe (r1994) Easter Oratorio, BWV249.
(5/95) (HARM) ① **HMC90 1513**

Cantata No. 67, 'Halt im Gedächtnis Jesum Christ', BWV67 (1724) (Easter I)
EXCERPTS: 1. Chorus: Halt im Gedächtnis Jesum Christ; 2. Aria: Mein Jesus ist erstanden (T); 3. Recit: Mein Jesu, heissest du des Todes Gift (A); 4. Choral: Erschienen ist der herrlich' Tag (chor); 5. Recit: Doch scheinet fast (A); 6. Aria: Friede sei mit euch (chor); 7. Choral: Du Friede fürst, Herr Jesu Christ (chor).
P. Esswood, K. Equiluz, M. van Egmond, Hanover Boys' Ch, Ghent Collegium Vocale, Leonhardt Consort, G. Leonhardt Concert
(2/89) (TELD) ① [2] **2292-42571-2**
E. Ameling, H. Watts, W. Krenn, T. Krause, Lausanne Pro Arte Ch, SRO, E. Ansermet Concert
(5/92) (DECC) ① **433 175-2DM**
L. Benningsen, P. Pears, K. Engen, Munich Bach Ch, Munich St Op Orch, K. Richter (r1958) Concert
(5/93) (TELD) ① **9031-77614-2**
A. Reynolds, P. Schreier, D. Fischer-Dieskau, Munich Bach Ch, Munich Bach Orch, K. Richter (r1973-4) Concert
(7/94) (ARCH) ① [5] **439 374-2AX5**
P. Esswood, K. Equiluz, M. van Egmond, Hanover Boys' Ch, Ghent Collegium Vocale, Leonhardt Consort, G. Leonhardt Concert
(2/95) (TELD) ① [6] **4509-91758-2**
A. Auger, T. Mitsui, A. Murray, Adalbert Kraus, W. Heldwein, Stuttgart Gächinger Kantorei, Stuttgart Bach Collegium, H. Rilling Concert
(2/95) (HANS) ① **98 882**
I. Reichelt, H. Töpper, H. Krebs, F. Kelch, Heilbronn H. Schütz Ch, Pforzheim CO, F. Werner (r1961) Concert
(6/95) (ERAT) ① [3] **4509-98525-2**

Cantata No. 68, 'Also hat Gott die Welt geliebt', BWV68 (1725) (Whit Monday)
EXCERPTS: 1. Chorus: Also hat Gott die Welt geliebt; 2. Aria: Mein gläubiges Herze (S) (Eng: My heart ever faithful); 3. Recit: Ich bin mit Petro nicht vermessen (B); 4. Aria: Du bist geboren mir zu Gute (B); 5. Chorus: Wer an ihn glaubet, der wird nicht gerichtet.
P. Jelosits, R. van der Meer, Tolz Boys' Ch, VCM, N. Harnoncourt Concert
(2/89) (TELD) ① [2] **2292-42571-2**
E. Mathis, D. Fischer-Dieskau, Munich Bach Ch, Munich Bach Orch, K. Richter (r1974-5) Concert
(7/94) (ARCH) ① [5] **439 380-2AX6**
P. Jelosits, R. van der Meer, Tolz Boys' Ch, VCM, N. Harnoncourt Concert
(2/95) (TELD) ① [6] **4509-91758-2**
A. Auger, P. Huttenlocher, Stuttgart Gächinger Kantorei, Stuttgart Bach Collegium, H. Rilling (r1980/1) Concert
(2/95) (HANS) ① **98 890**

Mein gläubiges Herz E. Schwarzkopf, Inst Ens (r1950) Concert
(7/90) (EMI) ① **CDH7 63201-2**
2. G. Lubin, J. Krieger (French: r1930s) Concert
(5/91) (CLUB) ① **CL99-022**
2. I. Baillie, CBO, B. Cameron (r1941: Eng) Concert
(7/95) (DUTT) ① **CDLX7013**

Cantata No. 69, 'Lobe den Herrn, meine Seele', BWV69 (1740s) (adaptation of 69a. Town council inauguration)
EXCERPTS: 1. Chorus: Lobe den Herrn, meine Seele; 2. Recit: Wie gross ist Gottes Güte doch! (S); 3. Aria: Meine Seele, auf! erzähle (A); 4. Recit: Der Herr hat grosse Ding' an uns getan (T); 5. Aria: Mein Erlöser und Erhalter (B); 6. Choral: Es danke, Gott und lobe dich (chor).
W. Wiedl, P. Esswood, K. Equiluz, Tolz Boys' Ch, VCM, N. Harnoncourt Concert
(9/89) (TELD) ① [2] **2292-42572-2**
W. Wiedl, P. Esswood, K. Equiluz, Tolz Boys' Ch, VCM, N. Harnoncourt Concert
(2/95) (TELD) ① [6] **4509-91758-2**
H. Donath, J. Hamari, Adalbert Kraus, W. Schöne, Stuttgart Gächinger Kantorei, Stuttgart Bach Collegium, H. Rilling (r1973/82) Concert
(2/95) (HANS) ① **98 829**

Cantata No. 69a, 'Lobe den Herrn, meine Seele', BWV69a (1723) (Trinity XII)
EXCERPTS: 1. Chorus: Lobe den Herrn, meine Seele; 2. Recit: Ach, dass ich tausend Zungen hätte (S); 3. Aria: Meine Seele, auf erzähle (T); 4. Recit: Gedenk ich nur zurück (A); 5. Aria: Mein Erlöser und Erhalter (B); 6. Choral: Was Gott tut, das ist wohlgetan (chor).
W. Wiedl, P. Esswood, K. Equiluz, R. van der Meer, Tolz Boys' Ch, VCM, N. Harnoncourt Concert
(9/89) (TELD) ① [2] **2292-42572-2**
W. Wiedl, P. Esswood, K. Equiluz, R. van der Meer, Tolz Boys' Ch, VCM, N. Harnoncourt Concert
(2/95) (TELD) ① [6] **4509-91758-2**

Cantata No. 70, 'Wachet, betet, seid bereit allezeit', BWV70 (1723) (Wds. partly Franck. Trinity XXVI)
EXCERPTS: PART ONE: 1. Chorus: Wachet, betet, seid bereit allezeit; 2. Recit: Erschrecket, ihr verstockten Sünder! (B); 3. Aria: Wann kommt der Tag (A); 4. Recit: Auch bei dem himmlischen Verlangen (T); 5. Aria: Lass der Spötter Zungen schmähen (S); 6. Recit: Jedoch! bei dem unartigen Geschlechte (T); 7. Choral: Freu' dich sehr, o meine Seele (chor). PART TWO: 8. Aria: Hebt euer Haupt empor (T); 9. Recit: Ach, soll nicht dieser grosse Tag (B); 10. Aria: Seliger Erquickungs Tag (B); 11. Choral: Nicht nach Welt, nach Himmel (chor).
W. Wiedl, P. Esswood, K. Equiluz, R. van der Meer, Tolz Boys' Ch, VCM, N. Harnoncourt Concert
(9/89) (TELD) ① [2] **2292-42572-2**
A. Felbermayer, E. Wien, H. Meyer-Welfing, N. Foster, Vienna St Op Chor, Vienna St Op Orch, F. Prohaska (r1957) Concert
(9/93) (VANG) ① **08.2010.71**
E. Mathis, T. Schmidt, P. Schreier, D. Fischer-Dieskau, Munich Bach Ch, Munich Bach Orch, K. Richter (r1977/8) Concert
(1/95) (ARCH) ① [5] **439 394-2AX5**
A. Auger, V. Gohl, L-M. Harder, S. Nimsgern, Stuttgart Gächinger Kantorei, Stuttgart Bach Collegium, H. Rilling Concert
(2/95) (HANS) ① **98 866**
W. Wiedl, P. Esswood, K. Equiluz, R. van der Meer, Tolz Boys' Ch, VCM, N. Harnoncourt Concert
(2/95) (TELD) ① [6] **4509-91758-2**

Cantata No. 71, 'Gott ist mein König', BWV71 (1708) (Town council inauguration)
EXCERPTS: 1. Chorus: Gott ist mein König; 2. Aria: Ich bin nun achtzig Jahr (S,T); 3. Chorus: Dein Alter sei wie deine Jugend; 4. Arioso: Tag und Nacht (B); 5. Chorus: Du wollest dem Feinde; 7. Chorus: Das neue Regiment.
W. Wiedl, P. Esswood, K. Equiluz, L. Visser, Tolz Boys' Ch, VCM, N. Harnoncourt Concert
(9/89) (TELD) ① [2] **2292-42572-2**
K. Graf, A. Auger, H. Gardow, H. Schwarz, G. Schreckenbach, A. Senger, Adalbert Kraus, L-M. Harder, N. Tüller, P. Huttenlocher, Stuttgart Gächinger Kantorei, Stuttgart Bach Collegium, H. Rilling (r1975/82) Concert (2/95) (HANS) ① **98 863**
W. Wiedl, P. Esswood, K. Equiluz, L. Visser, Tolz Boys' Ch, VCM, N. Harnoncourt Concert
(2/95) (TELD) ① [6] **4509-91758-2**
B. Schlick, K. Wessel, G. de Mey, K. Mertens, Amsterdam Baroque Ch, Amsterdam Baroque Orch, T. Koopman (r1994) Concert
(9/95) (ERAT) ① [3] **4509-98536-2**

Cantata No. 72, 'Alles nur nach Gottes Willen', BWV72 (1726) (Wds. Franck. Epiphany III)
EXCERPTS: 1. Chorus: Alles nur nach Gottes Willen; 2. Recit, Arioso & Aria: O sel'ger Christ (A); 3. Recit: Se glaube nun! (B); 4. Aria: Mein Jesus will es tun (S); 5. Choral: Was mein Gott will (chor).
W. Wiedl, P. Esswood, R. van der Meer, Tolz Boys' Ch, VCM, N. Harnoncourt Concert
(9/89) (TELD) ① [2] **2292-42572-2**
A. Auger, H. Laurich, W. Schöne, Stuttgart Gächinger Kantorei, Stuttgart Bach Collegium, H. Rilling Concert
(2/95) (HANS) ① **98 875**

Cantata No. 73, 'Herr, wie du willt, so schicks mit mir', BWV73 (1724) (Epiphany III)
EXCERPTS: 1. Chorus: Herr, wie du willt, so schicks mit mir; 2. Aria: Ach, senke doch den Geist der Freuden (T); 3. Recit: Ach, unser Wille bleibt verkehrt (B); 4. Aria: Herr, so du willt (B); 5. Choral: Das ist des Vaters Wille (chor).
J. Erler, K. Equiluz, M. van Egmond, Hanover Boys' Ch, Ghent Collegium Vocale, Leonhardt Consort, G. Leonhardt Concert (9/89) (TELD) ① [2] **2292-42573-2**
B. Schlick, G. Lesne, H. Crook, P. Kooy, Ghent Collegium Vocale, Ghent Collegium Vocale Orch, P. Herreweghe Concert
(5/93) (VIRG) ① **VC7 59237-2**
M. Schreiber, Adalbert Kraus, W. Schöne, Stuttgart Gächinger Kantorei, Stuttgart Bach Collegium, H. Rilling Concert
(2/95) (HANS) ① **98 874**
J. Erler, K. Equiluz, M. van Egmond, Hanover Boys' Ch, Ghent Collegium Vocale, Leonhardt Consort, G. Leonhardt Concert
(2/95) (TELD) ① [6] **4509-91758-2**

Cantata No. 74, 'Wer mich liebet, der wird mein Wort halten', BWV74 (1723) (Wds. Ziegler. Whit Sunday)
EXCERPTS: 1. Chorus: Wer mich liebet, der wird mein Wort halten; 2. Aria: Komm, mein Herze steht (S); 3. Recit: Die Wohnung ist bereit (A); 4. Aria: Ich gehe hin (B); 5. Aria: Kommt! eilet (T); 6. Recit: Es ist nichts Verdamm (B); 7. Aria: Nichts kann mich erretten (A); 8. Choral: Kein Menschenkind hier (chor).
J. Erler, P. Esswood, K. Equiluz, M. van Egmond, Hanover Boys' Ch, Ghent Collegium Vocale, Leonhardt Consort, G. Leonhardt Concert
(9/89) (TELD) ① **2292-42573-2**
J. Erler, P. Esswood, K. Equiluz, M. van Egmond, Hanover Boys' Ch, Ghent Collegium Vocale, Leonhardt Consort, G. Leonhardt Concert
(2/95) (TELD) ① [6] **4509-91758-2**
H. Donath, M. Laurich, Adalbert Kraus, P. Huttenlocher, Stuttgart Gächinger Kantorei, Stuttgart Bach Collegium, H. Rilling (r1972) Concert
(2/95) (HANS) ① **98 887**
2. E. Ameling, H. de Vries, R. van der Meer, A. de Klerk (r1983) Concert
(7/94) (EMI) ① **CDC5 55000-2**

Cantata No. 75, '(Die) Elenden sollen essen', BWV75 (1723) (Trinity I)
EXCERPTS: PART ONE: 1. Chorus: Die Elenden sollen essen; 2. Recit: Was hilft des Purpurs Majestät (B); 3. Aria: Mein Jesus soll mein Alles sein (T); 4. Recit: Gott stürzet und erhöhet (T); 5. Aria: Ich nehme mein Leiden mit Freuden (S); 6. Recit: In dess schenkt Gott ein gut Gewissen (S); 7. Choral: Was Gott tut, das ist wohlgetan (chor). PART TWO: 8. Sinfonia; 9. Recit: Nur eines kränkt (A); 10. Aria: Jesus macht mich geistlich reich (A); 11. Recit: Wer nur in Jesu bleibt (B); 12. Aria: Mein Herze glaubt (B); 13. Recit: O Armut, der kein Reichtum gleicht! (T); 14. Choral: Was Gott tut, das ist wohlgetan (chor).
M. Klein, P. Esswood, Adalbert Kraus, M. van Egmond, Hanover Boys' Ch, Ghent Collegium Vocale, Leonhardt Consort, G. Leonhardt Concert
(9/89) (TELD) ① **2292-42573-2**
M. Klein, P. Esswood, Adalbert Kraus, M. van Egmond, Hanover Boys' Ch, Ghent Collegium Vocale, Leonhardt Consort, G. Leonhardt Concert
(2/95) (TELD) ① [6] **4509-91758-2**
I. Reichelt, V. Gohl, J. Hamari, Adalbert Kraus, A. Baldin, H-F. Kunz, Frankfurt Kantorei, Stuttgart Bach Collegium, H. Rilling (r1970/83) Concert
(2/95) (HANS) ① **98 891**
5. E. Ameling, H. de Vries, R. van der Meer, A. de Klerk (r1983) Concert
(7/94) (EMI) ① **CDC5 55000-2**
7. M. André, H. Bilgram (arr tpt/org) Concert
(1/93) (EMI) ① **CDC7 54330-2**

Cantata No. 76, '(Die) Himmel erzählen die Ehre Gottes', BWV76 (1723) (Trinity II)
EXCERPTS: PART ONE: 1. Chorus: Die Himmel erzählen die Ehre Gottes; 2. Recit: So lässt sich Gott nicht unbezeuget! (T); 3. Aria: Hört, ihr Völker (S); 4. Recit: Wer aber hört (B); 5. Aria: Fahr'hin, abgöttische Zunft (B); 6. Recit: Du hast uns, Herr (A); 7. Choral: Es woll' uns Gott genädig sein (chor). PART TWO: 8. Sinfonia; 9. Recit: Gott segne noch die treue Schar (B); 10. Aria: Hasse nur, hasse mich recht (B); 11. Recit: Ich fühle schon im Geist (A); 12. Aria: Liebt, ihr Christen, in der Tat (A); 13. Recit: So soll die Christenheit (T); 14. Choral: Es danke, Gott, und lobe dich (chor).
W. Wiedl, P. Esswood, K. Equiluz, R. van der Meer, Tolz Boys' Ch, VCM, N. Harnoncourt *Concert* (9/89) (TELD) ① [2] **2292-42576-2**
E. Mathis, A. Reynolds, P. Schreier, K. Moll, Munich Bach Ch, Munich Bach Orch, K. Richter (r1974-5) *Concert* (7/94) (ARCH) ① [6] **439 380-2AX6**
A. Auger, H. Watts, Adalbert Kraus, S. Nimsgern, Stuttgart Gächinger Kantorei, Stuttgart Bach Collegium, H. Rilling *Concert* (2/95) (HANS) ① **98 869**
W. Wiedl, P. Esswood, K. Equiluz, R. van der Meer, Tolz Boys' Ch, VCM, N. Harnoncourt *Concert* (2/95) (TELD) ① [6] **4509-91758-2**
I. Reichelt, H. Töpper, H. Krebs, F. Kelch, Heilbronn H. Schütz Ch, Pforzheim CO, F. Werner (r1960) *Concert* (6/95) (ERAT) ① [2] **4509-98525-2**

Cantata No. 77, 'Du sollst Gott, deinen Herren, lieben', BWV77 (1723) (Trinity XIII)
EXCERPTS: 1. Chorus: Du sollst Gott, deinen Herren, lieben; 2. Recit: So muss es sein! (B); 3. Aria: Mein Gott, ich liebe dich (S); 4. Recit: Gib mir dabei, mein Gott! (T); 5. Aria: Ach, es bleibt in meiner Liebe (A); 6. Choral: Du stellst, mein Jesu (chor).
D. Bratschke, P. Esswood, Adalbert Kraus, M. van Egmond, Hanover Boys' Ch, Ghent Collegium Vocale, Leonhardt Consort, G. Leonhardt *Concert* (9/89) (TELD) ① [2] **2292-42576-2**
D. Bratschke, P. Esswood, Adalbert Kraus, M. van Egmond, Hanover Boys' Ch, Ghent Collegium Vocale, Leonhardt Consort, G. Leonhardt *Concert* (2/95) (TELD) ① [6] **4509-91758-2**
H. Donath, J. Hamari, Adalbert Kraus, W. Schöne, Stuttgart Gächinger Kantorei, Stuttgart Bach Collegium, H. Rilling (r1972/83) *Concert* (2/95) (HANS) ① **98 809**

Cantata No. 78, 'Jesu, der du meine Seele', BWV78 (1724) (Trinity XIV)
EXCERPTS: 1. Chorus: Jesu, der du meine Seele; 2. Aria (Duet): Wir eilen mit schwachen (S,A); 3. Recit: Ach! ich bin ein Kind der Sünden (T); 4. Aria: Dein Blut, so meine Schuld durch streicht (T); 5. Recit: Die Wunden, Nägel, Kron' und Grab (B); 6. Aria: Nun, du wirst mein Gewissen stillen (B); 7. Choral: Herr! ich glaube, hilf mir Schwachen (chor).
I. Schmithüsen, C. Brett, H. Crook, P. Kooy, Paris Chapelle Royale Chor, Paris Chapelle Royale Orch, P. Herreweghe *Cantata 198.* (10/88) (HARM) ① **HMC90 1270**
W. Wiedl, P. Esswood, K. Equiluz, R. van der Meer, Tolz Boys' Ch, VCM, N. Harnoncourt *Concert* (9/89) (TELD) ① [2] **2292-42576-2**
T. Stich-Randall, D. Hermann, A. Dermota, H. Braun, Vienna Bach Guild Ch, Vienna Bach Guild Orch, F. Prohaska (r1954) *Cantata 106.* (9/93) (VANG) ① **08.2009.71**
U. Buckel, H. Töpper, J. van Kesteren, K. Engen, Munich Bach Ch, Ansbach Bach Week Sols Ens, K. Richter (r1961) *Concert* (1/95) (ARCH) ① [6] **439 387-2AX6**
A. Auger, C. Watkinson, A. Baldin, W. Schöne, Stuttgart Gächinger Kantorei, Stuttgart Bach Collegium, H. Rilling (r1979) *Concert* (2/95) (HANS) ① **98 861**
W. Wiedl, P. Esswood, K. Equiluz, R. van der Meer, Tolz Boys' Ch, VCM, N. Harnoncourt *Concert* (2/95) (TELD) ① [6] **4509-91758-2**

Cantata No. 79, 'Gott, der Herr, ist Sonn und Schild', BWV79 (1725) (Reformation Festival)
EXCERPTS: 1. Chorus: Gott, der Herr, ist Sonn' und Schild; 2. Aria: Gott ist unser Sonn' und Schild! (A); 3. Choral: Nun danket Alle Gott (chor); 4. Recit: Gott Lob! Wir wissen den (B); 5. Aria (a due): Gott, ach Gott, verlass (S,B); 6. Choral: Erhalt uns in der Wahrheit (chor).
D. Bratschke, P. Esswood, M. van Egmond, Hanover Boys' Ch, Ghent Collegium Vocale, Leonhardt Consort, G. Leonhardt *Concert* (9/89) (TELD) ① [2] **2292-42576-2**
A. Auger, J. Hamari, P. Huttenlocher, Stuttgart Gächinger Kantorei, Stuttgart Bach Collegium, H. Rilling *Concert* (2/95) (HANS) ① **98 866**
D. Bratschke, P. Esswood, M. van Egmond, Hanover Boys' Ch, Ghent Collegium Vocale, Leonhardt Consort, G. Leonhardt *Concert* (2/95) (TELD) ① [6] **4509-91759-2**

Cantata No. 80, 'Ein feste Burg ist unser Gott', BWV80 (1724) (Reformation Festival)
EXCERPTS: 1. Chorus: Ein' feste Burg ist unser Gott; 2. Aria: Mit unsrer Macht (S,B); 3. Recit: Erwägedoch, Kind Gottes (B); 4. Aria: Komm in mein Herzenshaus (B); 5. Choral: Und wenn die Welt voll Teufel war' (chor); 6. Recit: So stehe denn bei CHristi blutgefärbter Fahne (T); 7. Duet: Wie selig sind doch sie (A,T); 8. Choral: Das Wort sie sollen lassen strahn (chor).
W. Wiedl, P. Esswood, K. Equiluz, R. van der Meer, Tolz Boys' Ch, VCM, N. Harnoncourt *Concert* (12/89) (TELD) ① [2] **2292-42577-2**
B. Schlick, G. Lesne, H. Crook, P. Kooy, Ghent Collegium Vocale, Chapelle Royale Orch, P. Herreweghe *Magnificat, BWV243.* (1/91) (HARM) ① **HMC90 1326**
I. Kertesi, J. Németh, J. Mukk, I. Gáti, Hungarian Rad Chor, Failoni CO, M. Antal *Cantata 147.* (12/92) (NAXO) ① **8 550642**
E. Mathis, T. Schmidt, P. Schreier, D. Fischer-Dieskau, Munich Bach Ch, Munich Bach Orch, K. Richter (r1977/8) *Concert* (1/95) (ARCH) ① [5] **439 394-2AX5**
W. Wiedl, P. Esswood, K. Equiluz, R. van der Meer, Tolz Boys' Ch, VCM, N. Harnoncourt *Concert* (2/95) (TELD) ① [6] **4509-91759-2**
A. Auger, G. Schreckenbach, L-M. Harder, P. Huttenlocher, Stuttgart Gächinger Kantorei, Württemberg CO, H. Rilling (r1976/83) *Concert* (2/95) (HANS) ① **98 819**
I. Reichelt, H. Töpper, H. Krebs, F. Kelch, Heilbronn H. Schütz Ch, Pforzheim CO, F. Werner (r1961) *Concert* (6/95) (ERAT) ① [2] **4509-98525-2**

Cantata No. 81, 'Jesus schläft, was soll ich hoffen?', BWV81 (1724) (Epiphany IV)
EXCERPTS: 1. Aria: Jesus schläft, was soll ich hoffen (A); 2. Recit: Herr! warum bleibest du so ferne? (T); 3. Aria: Die schäumenden Wellen von Belials Bächen (T); 4. Arioso: Ihr Kleingläubigen (B); 5. Aria: Schweig', aufgetürmtes Meer! (B); 6. Recit: Wohl mir! mein Jesus spricht (A); 7. Choral: Unter deinen Schirmen (chor).
P. Esswood, K. Equiluz, R. van der Meer, Tolz Boys' Ch, VCM, N. Harnoncourt *Concert* (12/89) (TELD) ① [2] **2292-42577-2**
A. Reynolds, D. Fischer-Dieskau, Munich Bach Ch, Munich Bach Orch, K. Richter (r1972) *Concert* (3/94) (ARCH) ① [4] **439 369-2AX4**
P. Esswood, K. Equiluz, R. van der Meer, Tolz Boys' Ch, VCM, N. Harnoncourt *Concert* (2/95) (TELD) ① [6] **4509-91759-2**
J. Hamari, Adalbert Kraus, S. Nimsgern, Stuttgart Gächinger Kantorei, Stuttgart Bach Collegium, H. Rilling *Concert* (2/95) (HANS) ① **98 876**

Cantata No. 82, 'Ich habe genug', BWV82 (1727) (Purification)
EXCERPTS: 1. Aria: Ich habe genug (B); 2. Recit: Ich habe genug! (B); 3. Aria: Schlummert ein (B); 4. Recit: Mein Gott! wann kommt das schöne Nun! (B); 5. Aria: Ich freue mich auf meinen Tod (B).
D. Thomas, Taverner Plyrs, A. Parrott *Cantata 202.* (9/88) (HYPE) ① **CDA66036**
R. Jacobs, Ens 415, C. Banchini *Concert* (10/88) (HARM) ① **HMC90 1273**
D. Fischer-Dieskau, Württemberg CO, H. Rilling *Concert* (1/89) (NOVA) ① **150 028-2**
H. van der Kamp, Fiori Musicali, T. Albert *Cantata 56.* (10/89) (MDG) ① **L3297**
M. van Egmond, Baroque Instr Ens, F. Brüggen (r1977) *Cantata 56.* (10/89) (RCA) ① **GD71956**
P. Huttenlocher, VCM, N. Harnoncourt *Concert* (12/89) (TELD) ① [2] **2292-42577-2**
M. van Egmond, Ricercar Consort *Concert* (1/90) (RICE) ① **RIC061041**
H. Hotter, Philh, Anthony Bernard (r1950) *Concert* (4/90) (EMI) ① **CDH7 63198-2**
B. Hendricks, CPE Bach Orch, P. Schreier *Concert* (7/90) (EMI) ① **CDC7 49843-2**
J. Shirley-Quirk, ASMF, N. Marriner *Concert* (7/91) (DECC) ① **430 260-2DM**
P. Kooy, Chapelle Royale Ch, Chapelle Royale Orch, P. Herreweghe *Concert* (10/92) (HARM) ① **HMC90 1365**
W. Sharp, J. Abberger, American Bach Sols, J. Thomas (r1990) *Concert* (12/92) (KOCH) ① **37138-2**
O. Bär, Scottish CO, P. Schreier *Concert* (6/93) (EMI) ① **CDC7 54453-2**
N. Argenta, K. Mertens, Petite Bande, S. Kuijken (vn/dir) (r1993) *Concert* (3/94) (ACCE) ① **ACC9395D**
D. Fischer-Dieskau, Munich Bach Orch, K. Richter (r1968) *Concert* (3/94) (ARCH) ① [4] **439 369-2AX4**
N. Argenta, Sonnerie Ens, M. Huggett (r1993) *Concert* (12/94) (VIRG) ① **VC5 45038-2**
D. Fischer-Dieskau, Stuttgart Bach Collegium, H. Rilling (r1983) *Concert* (2/95) (HANS) ① **98 855**
P. Huttenlocher, VCM, N. Harnoncourt *Concert* (2/95) (TELD) ① [6] **4509-91759-2**
2, 3. E. Ameling, A. May, G. Leonhardt (r1966) *Concert* (12/95) (DHM) ① [4] **74321 26617-2(1)**

Cantata No. 83, 'Erfreute Zeit im neuen Bunde', BWV83 (1724) (Purification)
EXCERPTS: 1. Aria: Erfreute Zeit, im neuen Bunde (A); 2. Intonation & Recit: Herr, nun lässest du deinen (B); 3. Aria: Eile, eile (T); 4. Recit: Ja, merkt dein Glaube noch (A); 5. Choral: Er ist das Heil und selig' Licht (chor).
K. Equiluz, M. van Egmond, Vienna Boys' Ch, Chorus Viennensis, VCM, N. Harnoncourt *Concert* (12/89) (TELD) ① [2] **2292-42577-2**
anon, K. Equiluz, M. van Egmond, Vienna Boys' Ch, Chorus Viennensis, VCM, N. Harnoncourt *Concert* (2/95) (TELD) ① [6] **4509-91759-2**
H. Watts, Adalbert Kraus, W. Heldwein, Stuttgart Gächinger Kantorei, Stuttgart Bach Collegium, H. Rilling *Concert* (2/95) (HANS) ① **98 875**

Cantata No. 84, 'Ich bin vergnügt mit meinem Glücke', BWV84 (1727) (Wds. Pisander. Septuagesima)
EXCERPTS: 1. Aria: Ich bin vergnügt mit meinem Glücke (S); 2. Recit: Gott ist mir ja nichts schuldig (S); 3. Aria: Ich esse mit Freuden mein weniges Brot (S); 4. Recit: Im Schweisse meines Angesichts (S); 5. Choral: Ich leb' indess in dir vergnüget (chor).
V. Hruba-Freiberger, Leipzig Univ Ch, Leipzig New Bach Collegium Musicum, M. Pommer *Concert* (9/89) (CAPR) ① **10 151**
W. Wiedl, Tolz Boys' Ch, VCM, N. Harnoncourt *Concert* (12/89) (TELD) ① [2] **2292-42578-2**
W. Wiedl, Tolz Boys' Ch, VCM, N. Harnoncourt *Concert* (2/95) (TELD) ① [6] **4509-91759-2**
A. Auger, Stuttgart Gächinger Kantorei, Württemberg CO, H. Rilling *Concert* (2/95) (HANS) ① **98 877**
N. Argenta, Sonnerie Ens, M. Huggett *Concert* (6/95) (VIRG) ① **VC5 45059-2**
3. K. Battle, I. Perlman, St Luke's Orch, J. Nelson (r1989/90) *Concert* (3/92) (DG) ① **429 737-2GH**

Cantata No. 85, 'Ich bin ein guter Hirt', BWV85 (1725) (Easter II)
EXCERPTS: 1. Aria: Ich bin ein guter Hirt (B); 2. Aria: Jesus ist ein guter Hirt (A); 3. Choral: Der Herr ist mein getreuer Hirt (S); 4. Recit: Wenn die Miethlinge schlafen (T); 5. Aria: Seht, was die Liebe tut! (T); 6. Choral: Ist Gott mein Schutz und treuer Hirt (chor).
W. Wiedl, P. Esswood, K. Equiluz, R. van der Meer, Tolz Boys' Ch, VCM, N. Harnoncourt *Concert* (12/89) (TELD) ① [2] **2292-42578-2**
A. Auger, G. Schreckenbach, Adalbert Kraus, W. Heldwein, Stuttgart Gächinger Kantorei, Stuttgart Bach Collegium, H. Rilling (r1980/1) *Concert* (2/95) (HANS) ① **98 864**
W. Wiedl, P. Esswood, K. Equiluz, R. van der Meer, Tolz Boys' Ch, VCM, N. Harnoncourt *Concert* (2/95) (TELD) ① [6] **4509-91759-2**
I. Reichelt, H. Töpper, H. Krebs, F. Kelch, Heilbronn Schütz Ch, Pforzheim CO, F. Werner (r1959) *Concert* (5/95) (ERAT) ① [2] **4509-97407-2**
B. Schlick, A. Scholl, C. Prégardien, G. Schwarz, Concerto Vocale, Limoges Baroque Ens, C. Coin (vc/dir) (r1994) *Concert* (12/95) (ASTR) ① **E8544**

Cantata No. 86, 'Warlich, warlich, ich sage euch', BWV86 (1724) (Easter V)
EXCERPTS: 1. Aria: Wahrlich, wahrlich, ich sage euch (B); 2. Aria: Ich will doch wohl Rosen brechen (A); 3. Chroal: Und was der ewig güt'ge Gott (S); 4. Recit: Gott macht es nicht (T); 5. Aria: Gott hilft gewiss (T); 6. Choral: Die Hoffnung wart't der rechter Zeit (chor).
W. Wiedl, P. Esswood, K. Equiluz, R. van der Meer, Tolz Boys' Ch, VCM, N. Harnoncourt *Concert* (12/89) (TELD) ① [2] **2292-42578-2**
W. Wiedl, P. Esswood, K. Equiluz, R. van der Meer, Tolz Boys' Ch, VCM, N. Harnoncourt *Concert* (2/95) (TELD) ① [6] **4509-91759-2**
A. Auger, H. Watts, Adalbert Kraus, W. Heldwein, Stuttgart Gächinger Kantorei, Stuttgart Bach Collegium, H. Rilling (r1979) *Concert* (2/95) (HANS) ① **98 885**

Cantata No. 87, 'Bisher habt ihr nichts gebeten', BWV87 (1725) (Wds. Ziegler. Easter V)
EXCERPTS: 1. Aria: Bisher habt ihr nichts gebeten (B); 2. Recit: O Wort, das Geist und Seel'erschreckt! (A); 3. Aria: Vergib, o Vater, vergib unsre Schuld (A);

4. Recit: Wenn unsre Schuld bis an den Himmel steigt (T); 5. Aria: In der Welt habt ihr Angst (B); 6. Aria: Ich will leiden (T); 7. Choral: Muss ich sein betrübet? (chor).
P. Esswood, K. Equiluz, R. van der Meer, Tolz Boys' Ch, VCM, N. Harnoncourt *Concert*
(12/89) (TELD) ① [2] 2292-42578-2
A. Reynolds, P. Schreier, D. Fischer-Dieskau, Munich Bach Ch, Munich Bach Orch, K. Richter (r1973-4) *Concert* (7/94) (ARCH) ① [5] 439 374-2AX5
P. Esswood, K. Equiluz, R. van der Meer, Tolz Boys' Ch, VCM, N. Harnoncourt *Concert*
(2/95) (TELD) ① [6] 4509-91759-2
J. Hamari, A. Baldin, W. Heldwein, Stuttgart Gächinger Kantorei, Stuttgart Bach Collegium, H. Rilling (r1980/1) *Concert* (2/95) (HANS) ① 98 885
I. Reichelt, H. Töpper, H. Krebs, F. Kelch, Heilbronn H. Schütz Ch, Pforzheim CO, F. Werner (r1961) *Concert* (6/95) (ERAT) ① [2] 4509-98525-2

Cantata No. 88, 'Siehe, ich will viel Fischer aussenden', BWV88 (1726) (Trinity V)
EXCERPTS: PART ONE: 1. Aria: Siehe, ich will viel Fischer aussenden (B); 2. Recit: Wie leichtlich könnte doch (T); 3. Aria: Nein! Gott ist alle zeit geflissen (T). PART TWO: 4. Aria: Jesus sprach zu Simon (T,B); 5. Duet: Beruft Gott selbst (S,A); 6. Recit: Was kann dich denn (S); 7. Choral: Sing', bet' und geh' auf Gottes Wegen (chor).
M. Klein, P. Esswood, K. Equiluz, M. van Egmond, Hanover Boys' Ch, Ghent Collegium Vocale, Leonhardt Consort, G. Leonhardt *Concert*
(12/89) (TELD) ① [2] 2292-42578-2
M. Klein, P. Esswood, K. Equiluz, M. van Egmond, Hanover Boys' Ch, Ghent Collegium Vocale, Leonhardt Consort, G. Leonhardt *Concert*
(2/95) (TELD) ① [6] 4509-91759-2
I. Reichelt, V. Gohl, Adalbert Kraus, W. Schöne, Stuttgart Gedächtniskirche Ch, Stuttgart Bach Collegium, H. Rilling (r1970) *Concert*
(2/95) (HANS) ① 98 804

Cantata No. 89, 'Was soll ich aus dir machen, Ephraim?', BWV89 (1723) (Trinity XXII)
EXCERPTS: 1. Aria: Was soll ich aus dir machen, Ephraim? (B); 2. Recit: Ja, freilich sollte Gott (A); 3. Aria: Ein unbarmherziges Gerichte (A); 4. Recit: Wohlan! mein Herze legt (S); 5. Aria: Gerechter Gott, ach, rechnest du (S); 6. Choral: Mir mangelt zwar sehr viel (chor).
M. Klein, P. Esswood, M. van Egmond, Hanover Boys' Ch, Ghent Collegium Vocale, Leonhardt Consort, G. Leonhardt *Concert*
(12/89) (TELD) ① [2] 2292-42578-2
M. Klein, P. Esswood, M. van Egmond, Hanover Boys' Ch, Ghent Collegium Vocale, Leonhardt Consort, G. Leonhardt *Concert*
(2/95) (TELD) ① [6] 4509-91759-2
A. Auger, H. Watts, P. Huttenlocher, Stuttgart Gächinger Kantorei, Stuttgart Bach Collegium, H. Rilling (r1977) *Concert* (2/95) (HANS) ① 98 818
5. E. Ameling, H. de Vries, R. van der Meer, A. de Klerk (r1983) *Concert*
(7/94) (EMI) ① CDC5 55000-2

Cantata No. 90, 'Es reifet euch ein schrecklich Ende', BWV90 (1723) (Trinity XXV)
EXCERPTS: 1. Aria: Es reifet euch ein schrecklich Ende (T); 2. Recit: Des Höchsten Güte wird von Tag (A); 3. Aria: So löschet im Eifer (B); 4. Recit: Doch Gottes Auge sieht (T); 5. Chora: Leit' uns mit deiner rechten Hand (chor).
P. Esswood, K. Equiluz, M. van Egmond, Hanover Boys' Ch, Ghent Collegium Vocale, Leonhardt Consort, G. Leonhardt *Concert*
(12/89) (TELD) ① [2] 2292-42578-2
P. Esswood, K. Equiluz, M. van Egmond, Hanover Boys' Ch, Ghent Collegium Vocale, Leonhardt Consort, G. Leonhardt *Concert*
(2/95) (TELD) ① [6] 4509-91759-2
H. Adalbert Kraus, S. Nimsgern, Stuttgart Gächinger Kantorei, Stuttgart Bach Collegium, H. Rilling (r1977/8) *Concert* (2/95) (HANS) ① 98 821

Cantata No. 91, 'Gelobet seist du, Jesu Christ', BWV91 (1724) (Christmas)
EXCERPTS: 1. Chorus: Gelobet seist du, Jesu Christ; 2. Recit & Choral: Der Glanz der höchsten Herrlichkeit (S); 3. Aria: Gott, dem der Erdenkreis zu klein (T); 4. Recit: O Christenheit! (B); 5. Aria (Duet): Die Armut, so Gott auf sich nimmt (S,A); 6. Choral: Das hat er Alles uns getan (chor).
D. Bratschke, P. Esswood, K. Equiluz, M. van Egmond, Hanover Boys' Ch, Ghent Collegium Vocale, Leonhardt Consort, G. Leonhardt *Concert*
(12/89) (TELD) ① [2] 2292-42582-2

D. Bratschke, P. Esswood, K. Equiluz, M. van Egmond, Hanover Boys' Ch, Ghent Collegium Vocale, Leonhardt Consort, G. Leonhardt *Concert*
(2/95) (TELD) ① [6] 4509-91759-2
H. Donath, H. Watts, Adalbert Kraus, W. Schöne, Stuttgart Gächinger Kantorei, Frankfurt Kantorei, Stuttgart Bach Collegium, Württemberg CO, H. Rilling (r1972/84) *Concert* (2/95) (HANS) ① 98 822

Cantata No. 92, 'Ich habe in Gottes Herz und Sinn', BWV92 (1724) (Septuagesima)
EXCERPTS: 1. Chorus: Ich hab in Gottes Herz und Sinn; 2. Recit & Choral: Es kann mir fehlen nimmermehr (B); 3. Aria: Seht, seht! wie bricht (T); 4. Choral: Zudem ist Weisheit und Verstand (A); 5. Recit: Wir wollen nun licht länger zagen (T); 6. Aria: Das Brausen (B); 7. Choral & Recit: Ei nun, mein Gott, so fall' ich dir (chor); 8. Aria: Meinem Hirten bleib' ich treu (S); 9. Choral: Soll ich denn auch des Todes Weg (chor).
D. Bratschke, P. Esswood, K. Equiluz, M. van Egmond, Hanover Boys' Ch, Ghent Collegium Vocale, Leonhardt Consort, G. Leonhardt *Concert*
(2/95) (TELD) ① [2] 2292-42582-2
E. Mathis, P. Schreier, D. Fischer-Dieskau, Munich Bach Ch, Munich Bach Orch, K. Richter (r1973-4) *Concert* (7/94) (ARCH) ① [5] 439 374-2AX5
D. Bratschke, P. Esswood, K. Equiluz, M. van Egmond, Hanover Boys' Ch, Ghent Collegium Vocale, Leonhardt Consort, G. Leonhardt *Concert*
(2/95) (TELD) ① [6] 4509-91759-2
A. Auger, H. Watts, Stuttgart Gächinger Kantorei, Stuttgart Bach Collegium, H. Rilling *Concert*
(2/95) (HANS) ① 98 877

Cantata No. 93, 'Wer nur den lieben Gott lässt walten', BWV93 (1724) (Trinity V)
EXCERPTS: 1. Chorus: Wer nur den lieben Gott lässt walten; 2. Recit & Choral: Was helfen uns die schweren Sorgen? (B); 3. Aria: Man halte nur ein wenig stille (T); 4. Aria (Duet) & Choral: Er kennt die rechten (S,A); 5. Recit & Choral: Denk' nicht in deiner Drangsalshitze (T); 6. Aria: Ich will auf den Herren (S); 7. Choral: Sing', bet' und geh' auf Gottes Wegen (chor).
W. Wiedl, P. Esswood, K. Equiluz, R. van der Meer, Tolz Boys' Ch, VCM, N. Harnoncourt *Concert*
(12/89) (TELD) ① [2] 2292-42582-2
Collegium Vocale, P. Herreweghe (r1991) *Concert*
(3/94) (VIRG) ① VC7 59320-2
E. Mathis, A. Reynolds, P. Schreier, D. Fischer-Dieskau, Munich Bach Ch, Munich Bach Orch, K. Richter (r1974-5) *Concert*
(7/94) (ARCH) ① [6] 439 380-2AX6
A. Auger, A. Murray, Adalbert Kraus, W. Heldwein, Stuttgart Gächinger Kantorei, Stuttgart Bach Collegium, H. Rilling *Cantata 21.*
(2/95) (HANS) ① 98 865
W. Wiedl, P. Esswood, K. Equiluz, R. van der Meer, Tolz Boys' Ch, VCM, N. Harnoncourt *Concert*
(2/95) (TELD) ① [6] 4509-91759-2
6. E. Ameling, H. de Vries, R. van der Meer, A. de Klerk (r1983) *Concert*
(7/94) (EMI) ① CDC5 55000-2

Cantata No. 94, 'Was frag ich nach der Welt', BWV94 (1724) (Trinity IX)
EXCERPTS: 1. Chorus: Was frag ich nach der Welt; 2. Aria: Die Welt ist wie ein Rauch (B); 3. Recit & Choral: Die Welt sucht Ehr' und Ruhm (T); 4. Aria: Betörte Welt (A); 5. Recit & Choral: Die Welt bekümmert sich (A); 6. Aria: Die Welt kann ihre Lust und Freud' (T); 7. Es halt' es mit der blinden Welt (S); 8. Choral: Was frag' ich nach der elt! (chor).
W. Wiedl, P. Esswood, K. Equiluz, P. Huttenlocher, Tolz Boys' Ch, VCM, N. Harnoncourt *Concert*
(12/89) (TELD) ① [2] 2292-42582-2
W. Wiedl, P. Esswood, K. Equiluz, P. Huttenlocher, Tolz Boys' Ch, VCM, N. Harnoncourt *Concert*
(2/95) (TELD) ① [6] 4509-91759-2
H. Donath, E. Paaske, A. Baldin, H-F. Kunz, W. Schöne, Stuttgart Gächinger Kantorei, Stuttgart Bach Collegium, H. Rilling (r1974) *Concert*
(2/95) (HANS) ① 98 808
7. E. Ameling, H. de Vries, R. van der Meer, A. de Klerk (r1983) *Concert*
(7/94) (EMI) ① CDC5 55000-2

Cantata No. 95, 'Christus, der ist mein Leben', BWV95 (1723) (Trinity XVI)
EXCERPTS: 1. Chorus: Christus, der ist mein Leben; 2. Recit & Choral: Nun, falsche welt (S); 3. Recit: Ach, könnte mir doch bald (T); 4. Aria: Ach, schlage doch bald (T); 5. Recit: Denn ich weiss dies (B); 6. Choral: Weil du vom Tod erstanden (chor).
W. Wiedl, K. Equiluz, P. Huttenlocher, Tolz Boys' Ch, VCM, N. Harnoncourt *Concert*
(12/89) (TELD) ① 2292-42583-2

W. Wiedl, K. Equiluz, P. Huttenlocher, Tolz Boys' Ch, VCM, N. Harnoncourt *Concert*
(2/95) (TELD) ① [6] 4509-91759-2
A. Auger, Adalbert Kraus, W. Heldwein, Stuttgart Gächinger Kantorei, Stuttgart Bach Collegium, H. Rilling (r1977/8) *Concert* (2/95) (HANS) ① 98 812

Cantata No. 96, 'Herr Christ, der ein'ge Gottes-Sohn', BWV96 (1724) (Trinity XVIII)
EXCERPTS: 1. Chorus: Herr Christ, der ein'ge Gottes-Sohn; 2. Recit: O Wunderkraft der Liebe (A); 3. Aria: Ach, ziehe die Seele (T); 4. Recit: Ach, führe mich, o Gott (S); 5. Aria: Bald zur Rechtem, bald zur Linken (B); 6. Choral: Ertöt' uns durch dein' Güte (chor).
W. Wiedl, P. Esswood, K. Equiluz, P. Huttenlocher, Tolz Boys' Ch, VCM, N. Harnoncourt *Concert*
(12/89) (TELD) ① 2292-42583-2
E. Mathis, T. Schmidt, P. Schreier, D. Fischer-Dieskau, Munich Bach Ch, Munich Bach Orch, K. Richter (r1977/8) *Concert*
(1/95) (ARCH) ① [5] 439 394-2AX5
W. Wiedl, P. Esswood, K. Equiluz, P. Huttenlocher, Tolz Boys' Ch, VCM, N. Harnoncourt *Concert*
(2/95) (TELD) ① [6] 4509-91759-2
H. Donath, M. Höffgen, Adalbert Kraus, S. Nimsgern, Stuttgart Gächinger Kantorei, Stuttgart Bach Collegium, H. Rilling (r1973) *Concert*
(2/95) (HANS) ① 98 814

Cantata No. 97, 'In allen meinen Taten', BWV97 (1734)
EXCERPTS: 1. Chorus: In allen meinen Taten; 2. Aria: Nichts ist espat und frühe (A); 3. Recit: Es kann mir nichts geschehen (T); 4. Aria: Ich traue seiner Gnaden (T); 5. Recit: Er wolle meiner Sünden (A); 6. Aria: Leg' ich mich späte nieder (A); 7. Duet: Hat er es denn beschlossen (S,B); 8. Aria: Ihm hab' ich mich ergeben (S); 9. Choral: So sei nun, Seele (chor).
W. Wiedl, P. Esswood, K. Equiluz, R. van der Meer, P. Huttenlocher, Tolz Boys' Ch, VCM, N. Harnoncourt *Concert* (12/89) (TELD) ① 2292-42583-2
W. Wiedl, P. Esswood, K. Equiluz, R. van der Meer, P. Huttenlocher, Tolz Boys' Ch, VCM, N. Harnoncourt *Concert*
(2/95) (TELD) ① [6] 4509-91759-2
H. Donath, H. Gardow, Adalbert Kraus, P. Huttenlocher, Stuttgart Gächinger Kantorei, Stuttgart Bach Collegium, H. Rilling (r1974) *Concert*
(2/95) (HANS) ① 98 835
4. K. Battle, I. Perlman, St Luke's Orch, J. Nelson (r1989/90) *Concert* (3/92) (DG) ① 429 737-2GH

Cantata No. 98, 'Was Gott tut, das ist wohlgetan', BWV98 (1726) (Trinity XXI)
EXCERPTS: 1. Chorus: Was Gott tut, das ist wohlgetan; 2. Recit: Ach Gott! wann wirst du mich (T); 3. Aria: Hört, ihr Augen, auf zu weinen (A); 4. Recit: Gott hat ein Herz (A); 5. Aria: Meinen Jesum lass' ich nicht (A).
C. Lengert, P. Esswood, K. Equiluz, M. van Egmond, Hanover Boys' Ch, Ghent Collegium Vocale, Leonhardt Consort, G. Leonhardt *Concert*
(12/89) (TELD) ① 2292-42583-2
C. Lengert, P. Esswood, K. Equiluz, M. van Egmond, Hanover Boys' Ch, Ghent Collegium Vocale, Leonhardt Consort, G. Leonhardt *Concert*
(2/95) (TELD) ① [6] 4509-91759-2
A. Auger, J. Hamari, L-M. Harder, W. Heldwein, Stuttgart Gächinger Kantorei, Stuttgart Bach Collegium, H. Rilling (r1982/3) *Concert*
(2/95) (HANS) ① 98 817
3. E. Ameling, H. de Vries, R. van der Meer, A. de Klerk (r1983) *Concert*
(7/94) (EMI) ① CDC5 55000-2

Cantata No. 99, 'Was Gott tut, das ist wohlgetan', BWV99 (1724) (Trinity XV)
EXCERPTS: 1. Chorus: Was Gott tut, das ist wohlgetan; 2. Recit: Sein Wort der Wahrheit stehet (B); 3. Aria: Erschütt're dich nur nicht (T); 4. Recit: Nun, der von Ewigkeit geschloss'ne (A); 5. Aria (Duet): Wenn des Kreuzes Bitter (S,A); 6. Choral: Was Gott tut, das ist wohlgetan (chor).
W. Wiedl, P. Esswood, K. Equiluz, P. Huttenlocher, Tolz Boys' Ch, VCM, N. Harnoncourt *Concert*
(12/89) (TELD) ① [2] 2292-42584-2
W. Wiedl, P. Esswood, K. Equiluz, P. Huttenlocher, Tolz Boys' Ch, VCM, N. Harnoncourt *Concert*
(2/95) (TELD) ① [6] 4509-91759-2
A. Auger, H. Watts, L-M. Harder, J. Bröcheler, Stuttgart Gächinger Kantorei, Stuttgart Bach Collegium, H. Rilling (r1979) *Concert*
(2/95) (HANS) ① 98 813

Cantata No. 100, 'Was Gott tut, das ist wohlgetan', BWV100 (c1732-35)
EXCERPTS: 1. Chorus: Was Gott tut, das ist wohlgetan; 2. Duet: (A,T); 3. Aria: (S); 4. Aria (B); 5. Aria: (A); 6. Choral: (chor).

D. Bratschke, P. Esswood, K. Equiluz, M. van Egmond, Hanover Boys' Ch, Ghent Collegium Vocale, Leonhardt Consort, G. Leonhardt *Concert* (12/89) (TELD) ⓘ [2] **2292-42584-2**

E. Mathis, J. Hamari, P. Schreier, D. Fischer-Dieskau, Munich Bach Ch, Munich Bach Orch, K. Richter (r1976/7) *Concert* (1/95) (ARCH) ⓘ [6] **439 387-2AX6**

A. Auger, J. Hamari, Adalbert Kraus, P. Huttenlocher, Stuttgart Gächinger Kantorei, Württemberg CO, H. Rilling (r1983/4) *Concert* (2/95) (HANS) ⓘ **98 858**

D. Bratschke, P. Esswood, K. Equiluz, M. van Egmond, Hanover Boys' Ch, Ghent Collegium Vocale, Leonhardt Consort, G. Leonhardt *Concert* (2/95) (TELD) ⓘ [6] **4509-91760-2**

Cantata No. 101, 'Nimm von uns, Herr, du treuer Gott', BWV101 (1724) (Trinity X)

EXCERPTS: 1. Chorus: Nimm von uns, Herr, du treuer Gott; 2. Aria: Handle nicht nach deinen Rechten (T); 3. Recit & Choral: Ach! Herr Gott, durch die Treue (S); 4. Aria: Warum willst du so zornig sein (B); 5. Recit & Choral: Die Sünd' ha uns verderbet (T); 6. Aria (Duet): Gedenk' an Jesu bittern Tod (S,A); 7. Choral: Leit' uns mit deiner rechten Hand (chor).

W. Wiedl, P. Esswood, K. Equiluz, P. Huttenlocher, Tolz Boys' Ch, VCM, N. Harnoncourt *Concert* (12/89) (TELD) ⓘ [2] **2292-42584-2**

W. Wiedl, P. Esswood, K. Equiluz, P. Huttenlocher, Tolz Boys' Ch, VCM, N. Harnoncourt *Concert* (2/95) (TELD) ⓘ [6] **4509-91760-2**

A. Auger, H. Watts, A. Baldin, J. Bröcheler, Stuttgart Gächinger Kantorei, Stuttgart Bach Collegium, H. Rilling (r1979) *Concert* (2/95) (HANS) ⓘ **98 809**

Cantata No. 102, 'Herr, deine Augen sehen nach dem Glauben', BWV102 (1726) (Trinity X)

EXCERPTS: PART ONE: 1. Chorus: Herr, deine Augen sehen nach dem Glauben; 2. Recit: Wo ist das Ebenbild (B); 3. Aria: Weh! der Seele (A); 4. Arioso: Verachtest du den Reichtum (B). PART TWO: 5. Aria: Erschrecke doch (T); 6. Recit: Beim Warten ist Gefar (A); 7. Choral: Heut' lebst du (chor).

P. Esswood, K. Equiluz, P. Huttenlocher, Tolz Boys' Ch, VCM, N. Harnoncourt *Concert* (12/89) (TELD) ⓘ [2] **2292-42584-2**

J. Hamari, P. Schreier, D. Fischer-Dieskau, Munich Bach Ch, Munich Bach Orch, K. Richter (r1975-7) *Concert* (1/95) (ARCH) ⓘ [6] **439 387-2AX6**

P. Esswood, K. Equiluz, P. Huttenlocher, Tolz Boys' Ch, VCM, N. Harnoncourt *Concert* (2/95) (TELD) ⓘ [6] **4509-91760-2**

E. Randová, K. Equiluz, W. Schöne, Stuttgart Gächinger Kantorei, Stuttgart Bach Collegium, H. Rilling (r1972) *Concert* (2/95) (HANS) ⓘ **98 809**

Cantata No. 103, 'Ihr werdet weinen und heulen', BWV103 (1725) (Easter III)

EXCERPTS: 1. Chorus: Ihr werdet weinen und heulen; 2. Recit: Wer sollte nicht in Klagen untergehn (T); 3. Aria: Kein Arzt ist ausser dir (A); 4. Recit: Du wirst mich nach der Angst (A); 5. Aria: Erholet euch (T); 6. Choral: Ich hab' dich einen Augenblick (chor).

P. Esswood, K. Equiluz, M. van Egmond, Hanover Boys' Ch, Ghent Collegium Vocale, Leonhardt Consort, G. Leonhardt *Concert* (2/90) (TELD) ⓘ **2292-42602-2**

P. Esswood, K. Equiluz, M. van Egmond, Hanover Boys' Ch, Ghent Collegium Vocale, Leonhardt Consort, G. Leonhardt *Concert* (2/95) (TELD) ⓘ [6] **4509-91760-2**

D. Soffel, P. Schreier, W. Heldwein, Stuttgart Gächinger Kantorei, Stuttgart Bach Collegium, H. Rilling *Concert* (2/95) (HANS) ⓘ **98 883**

Cantata No. 104, 'Du Hirte Israel, höre', BWV104 (1724) (Easter II)

EXCERPTS: 1. Chorus: Du Hirte Israel, höre; 2. Recit: Der höchste Hüter sorgt für mich (T); 3. Aria: Verbirgt mein Hirte sich zulange (T); 4. Recit: Ja, dieses Wort ist meiner Seelen Speise (B); 5. Aria: Beglückte Herde, Jesu Schafe (B); 6. Choral: Der Herr ist mein getreuer Hirt (chor).

K. Equiluz, P. Huttenlocher, Tolz Boys' Ch, VCM, N. Harnoncourt *Concert* (2/90) (TELD) ⓘ **2292-42602-2**

P. Schreier, D. Fischer-Dieskau, Munich Bach Ch, Munich Bach Orch, K. Richter (r1973) *Concert* (7/94) (ARCH) ⓘ [5] **439 374-2AX5**

Adalbert Kraus, W. Schöne, Stuttgart Gächinger Kantorei, Stuttgart Bach Collegium, H. Rilling *Concert* (2/95) (HANS) ⓘ **98 869**

K. Equiluz, P. Huttenlocher, Tolz Boys' Ch, VCM, N. Harnoncourt *Concert* (2/95) (TELD) ⓘ [6] **4509-91760-2**

Cantata No. 105, 'Herr, gehe nicht ins Gericht', BWV105 (1723) (Trinity IX)

EXCERPTS: 1. Chorus: Herr, gehe nicht ins Gericht; 2. Recit: Mein Gott, verwirf mich nicht (A); 3. Aria: Wie zittern und wanken der Sünden Gedanken (S); 4. Recit: Wohl aber dem (B); 5. Aria: Kann ich nur Jesum (T); 6. Choral: Nun, ich weiss, du wirst mir stillen (chor).

W. Wiedl, P. Esswood, K. Equiluz, R. van der Meer, Tolz Boys' Ch, VCM, N. Harnoncourt *Concert* (2/90) (TELD) ⓘ **2292-42602-2**

B. Schlick, G. Lesne, H. Crook, P. Kooy, Ghent Collegium Vocale, Ghent Collegium Vocale Orch, P. Herreweghe *Concert* (5/93) (VIRG) ⓘ **VC7 59237-2**

E. Mathis, J. Hamari, P. Schreier, D. Fischer-Dieskau, Munich Bach Ch, Munich Bach Orch, K. Richter (r1976/7) *Concert* (1/95) (ARCH) ⓘ [6] **439 387-2AX6**

W. Wiedl, P. Esswood, K. Equiluz, R. van der Meer, Tolz Boys' Ch, VCM, N. Harnoncourt *Concert* (2/95) (TELD) ⓘ [6] **4509-91760-2**

A. Auger, H. Watts, Adalbert Kraus, W. Heldwein, Stuttgart Gächinger Kantorei, Stuttgart Bach Collegium, H. Rilling (r1977/8) *Concert* (2/95) (HANS) ⓘ **98 807**

5. K. Battle, I. Perlman, St Luke's Orch, J. Nelson (r1989/90) *Concert* (3/92) (DG) ⓘ **429 737-2GH**

Cantata No. 106, 'Gottes Zeit ist die allerbeste Zeit', BWV106 (1707) (Funeral)

EXCERPTS: 1. Sonatina; 2. Chorus: Gottes Zeit ist die allerbeste Zeit; 3. Duet: In deine Hände (A,B); 4. Chorus: Glorie, Lob, Ehr' und Herrlichkeit.

M. Klein, R. Harten, M. van Altena, M. van Egmond, Hanover Boys' Ch, Ghent Collegium Vocale, Leonhardt Consort, G. Leonhardt *Concert* (2/90) (TELD) ⓘ **2292-42602-2**

N. Argenta, M. Chance, A. Rolfe Johnson, S. Varcoe, Monteverdi Ch, EBS, J.E. Gardiner *Concert* (5/91) (ARCH) ⓘ **429 782-2AH**

G. de Reyghere, J. Bowman, G. de Mey, M. van Egmond, Ricercar Consort *Concert* (7/91) (RICE) ⓘ **RIC079061**

T. Stich-Randall, D. Hermann, A. Dermota, H. Braun, Vienna Bach Guild Ch, Vienna Bach Guild Orch, F. Prohaska (r1954) *Cantata 78.* (9/93) (VANG) ⓘ **08.2009.71**

C. Brandes, D. Minter, Jeffrey Thomas, W. Sharp, American Bach Sols, J. Thomas (r1993) *Concert* (4/94) (KOCH) ⓘ **37164-2**

H. Töpper, E. Haefliger, T. Adam, Munich Bach Ch, Munich Bach Orch, K. Richter (r1966) *Concert* (1/95) (ARCH) ⓘ [5] **439 394-2AX5**

M. Klein, R. Harten, M. van Altena, M. van Egmond, Hanover Boys' Ch, Ghent Collegium Vocale, Leonhardt Consort, G. Leonhardt *Concert* (2/95) (TELD) ⓘ [6] **4509-91760-2**

E. Csapó, H. Schwarz, Adalbert Kraus, W. Schöne, Stuttgart Gächinger Kantorei, Inst Ens, H. Rilling (r1975) *Cantata 198.* (2/95) (HANS) ⓘ **98 830**

B. Schlick, K. Wessel, G. de Mey, K. Mertens, Amsterdam Baroque Ch, Amsterdam Baroque Orch, T. Koopman (r1994) *Concert* (9/95) (ERAT) ⓘ [3] **4509-98536-2**

1. Taverner Plyrs, A. Parrott *Concert* (12/88) (EMI) ⓘ **CDM7 69853-2**

1. F. Brüggen, Leonhardt Consort (r1967) *Concert* (10/95) (TELD) ⓘ **4509-97473-2**

Cantata No. 107, 'Was willst du dich betrüben', BWV107 (1724) (Trinity VII)

EXCERPTS: 1. Chorus: Was willst du dich betrüben; 2. Recit: Denn Gott verlässet Keinen (B); 3. Aria: Auf ihn magst du es wagen (B); 4. Aria: Wenn auch gleich aus der Höllen (T); 5. Aria: Er richt't's zu seinen Ehren (S); 6. Aria: Drum ich mich ihm ergebe (T); 7. Choral: Herr, gib, dass ich dein' Ehre ja (chor).

M. Klein, K. Equiluz, M. van Egmond, Hanover Boys' Ch, Ghent Collegium Vocale, Leonhardt Consort, G. Leonhardt *Concert* (2/90) (TELD) ⓘ [2] **2292-42603-2**

Collegium Vocale, P. Herreweghe (r1991) *Concert* (3/94) (VIRG) ⓘ **VC7 59320-2**

M. Klein, K. Equiluz, M. van Egmond, Hanover Boys' Ch, Ghent Collegium Vocale, Leonhardt Consort, G. Leonhardt *Concert* (2/95) (TELD) ⓘ [6] **4509-91760-2**

A. Auger, A. Baldin, J. Bröcheler, Stuttgart Gächinger Kantorei, Stuttgart Bach Collegium, H. Rilling (r1979) *Concert* (2/95) (HANS) ⓘ **98 805**

Cantata No. 108, 'Es ist euch gut, dass ich hingehe', BWV108 (1725) (Easter IV)

EXCERPTS: 1. Aria: Es ist euch gut, dass ich hingehe (B); 2. Aria: Mich kann kein Zweifel stören (T); 3. Recit: Dein Geist wird mich (T); 4. Chorus: Wenn aber jener, der Geist der Wahrheit; 5. Aria: Was mein Herz von dir begehrt (A); 6. Choral: Dein Geist, den Gott vom Himmel gibt (chor).

P. Esswood, K. Equiluz, R. van der Meer, Tolz Boys' Ch, VCM, N. Harnoncourt *Concert* (2/90) (TELD) ⓘ [2] **2292-42603-2**

L. Benningsen, P. Pears, K. Engen, Munich Bach Ch, Munich St Op Orch, K. Richter (r1958) *Concert* (5/93) (TELD) ⓘ **9031-77614-2**

H. Töpper, E. Haefliger, T. Adam, Munich Bach Ch, Munich Bach Orch, K. Richter (r1967) *Concert* (7/94) (ARCH) ⓘ [5] **439 374-2AX5**

P. Esswood, K. Equiluz, R. van der Meer, Tolz Boys' Ch, VCM, N. Harnoncourt *Concert* (2/95) (TELD) ⓘ [6] **4509-91760-2**

C. Watkinson, P. Schreier, P. Huttenlocher, Stuttgart Gächinger Kantorei, Stuttgart Bach Collegium, H. Rilling (r1980/1) *Cantata 146.* (2/95) (HANS) ⓘ **98 884**

Cantata No. 109, 'Ich glaube, lieber Herr, hilf meinem Unglauben!', BWV109 (1723) (Trinity XXI)

EXCERPTS: 1. Chorus: Ich glaube, lieber Herr; 2. Recit: Des Herren Hand ist ja (T); 3. Aria: Wie zweifelhaftig ist mein Hoffen (T); 4. Recit: O fasse dich (A); 5. Aria: Der Heiland kennet ja (A); 6. Choral: Wer hofft in Gott und dem vertraut (chor).

P. Esswood, K. Equiluz, Tolz Boys' Ch, VCM, N. Harnoncourt *Concert* (2/90) (TELD) ⓘ [2] **2292-42603-2**

P. Esswood, K. Equiluz, Tolz Boys' Ch, VCM, N. Harnoncourt *Concert* (2/95) (TELD) ⓘ [6] **4509-91760-2**

G. Schreckenbach, K. Equiluz, Stuttgart Gächinger Kantorei, Stuttgart Bach Collegium, H. Rilling (r1971/81) *Concert* (2/95) (HANS) ⓘ **98 818**

Cantata No. 110, 'Unser Mund sei voll Lachens', BWV110 (1725) (Christmas)

EXCERPTS: 1. Chorus: Unsert Mund sei voll Lachens; 2. Aria: Ihr Gedanken und ihr Sinnen (T); 3. Recit: Dir, Herr, ist Niemand gleich (B); 4. Aria: Ach Herr! was ist ein Menschenkind (A); 5. Duet: Ehre sei Gott (S,T); 6. Aria: Wacht auf! (B); 7. Choral: Alleluja! gelobt sei Gott (chor).

W. Wiedl, S. Frangoulis, P. Esswood, K. Equiluz, S. Lorenz, R. van der Meer, Tolz Boys' Ch, VCM, N. Harnoncourt *Concert* (2/90) (TELD) ⓘ [2] **2292-42603-2**

W. Wiedl, S. Frangoulis, P. Esswood, K. Equiluz, S. Lorenz, R. van der Meer, Tolz Boys' Ch, VCM, N. Harnoncourt *Concert* (2/95) (TELD) ⓘ [6] **4509-91760-2**

K. Graf, H. Gardow, A. Baldin, W. Schöne, Stuttgart Gächinger Kantorei, Stuttgart Bach Collegium, H. Rilling (r1974) *Concert* (2/95) (HANS) ⓘ **98 824**

1. English Concert Ch, English Concert, T. Pinnock (r1993-4) *Concert* (12/95) (ARCH) ⓘ [2] **439 780-2AH2**

Cantata No. 112, '(Der) Herr ist mein getreuer Hirt', BWV112 (1731) (Easter II)

EXCERPTS: 1. Chorus: Der Herr ist mein getreuer Hirt; 2. Aria: Zum reinen Wasser ermich weist (A); 3. Recit: Und ob ich wandert (B); 4. Duet: Du bereitest für mir einen Tisch (S,T); 5. Choral: Gutes und die Barmherzigkeit (chor).

M. Huber, P. Esswood, K. Equiluz, R. van der Meer, Tolz Boys' Ch, VCM, N. Harnoncourt *Concert* (2/90) (TELD) ⓘ [2] **2292-42606-2**

I. Nielsen, G. Schreckenbach, A. Baldin, W. Heldwein, Stuttgart Gächinger Kantorei, Stuttgart Bach Collegium, H. Rilling (r1981) *Cantata 30.* (2/95) (HANS) ⓘ **98 860**

M. Huber, P. Esswood, K. Equiluz, R. van der Meer, Tolz Boys' Ch, VCM, N. Harnoncourt *Concert* (2/95) (TELD) ⓘ [6] **4509-91760-2**

Cantata No. 113, 'Herr Jesu Christ, du höchstes Gut', BWV113 (1724) (Trinity XI)

EXCERPTS: 1. Chorus: Herr Jesu Christ, du höchstes Gut; 2. Choral: Erbarm' dich mein in solcher Last (A); 3. Aria: Fürwahr, wenn mir das kömmet ein (B); 4. Recit & Choral: Jedoch dein heilsam Wort (B); 5. Aria: Jesus nimmt die Sünder an (T); 6. Recit: Der Heiland nimmt die Sünder an (T); 7. Aria (Duet): Ach Herr, mein Gott (S,A); 8. Choral: Stärk' mich mit deinem Freudengeist (chor).

S. Hennig, D. Bratschke, R. Jacobs, K. Equiluz, M. van Egmond, Hanover Boys' Ch, Ghent Collegium Vocale, Leonhardt Consort, G. Leonhardt *Concert* (2/90) (TELD) ⓘ [2] **2292-42606-2**

S. Hennig, D. Bratschke, R. Jacobs, K. Equiluz, M. van Egmond, Hanover Boys' Ch, Ghent Collegium Vocale, Leonhardt Consort, G. Leonhardt *Concert* (2/95) (TELD) ⓘ [6] **4509-91760-2**

A. Auger, G. Schreckenbach, Adalbert Kraus, N. Tüller, Frankfurt Kantorei, Stuttgart Bach Collegium, H. Rilling (r1973/81) *Concert* (2/95) (HANS) ⓘ **98 810**

Cantata No. 114, 'Ach, lieben Christen, seid getrost', BWV114 (1724) (Trinity XVII)

EXCERPTS: 1. Chorus: Ach, lieben Christen, seid getrost; 2. Aria: Wo wird in diesem Jammertale (T); 3. Recit: O Sünder trage mit Geduld (B); 4. Choral: Kein

Frucht das Weizenkörnlein bringt (S); 5. Aria: Du machst, o Tod (A); 6. Recit: Indess bedenke deine Seele (T); 7. Choral: Wir wachen oder schlafen ein (chor).

S. Hennig, R. Jacobs, K. Equiluz, M. van Egmond, Hanover Boys' Ch, Ghent Collegium Vocale, Leonhardt Consort, G. Leonhardt *Concert* (2/90) (TELD) ① [2] **2292-42606-2**

S. Hennig, R. Jacobs, K. Equiluz, M. van Egmond, Hanover Boys' Ch, Ghent Collegium Vocale, Leonhardt Consort, G. Leonhardt *Concert* (2/95) (TELD) ① [6] **4509-91760-2**

G. Schnaut, J. Hamari, K. Equiluz, W. Schöne, Frankfurt Kantorei, Stuttgart Gächinger Kantorei, Stuttgart Bach Collegium, H. Rilling (r1974/81) *Concert* (2/95) (HANS) ① **98 814**

Cantata No. 115, 'Mache dich, mein Geist bereit', BWV115 (1724) (Trinity XXII)

EXCERPTS: 1. Chorus: Mache dich, mein Geist bereit; 2. Aria: Ach schläfrige Seele (A); 3. Recit: Gott, so vor deine Seele wacht (B); 4. Aria: Bete aber auch (S); 5. Recit: Er sehnet sich nach unserm (T); 6. Choral: Drum so lasst uns immer dar (chor).

M. Huber, P. Esswood, K. Equiluz, P. Huttenlocher, Tolz Boys' Ch, VCM, N. Harnoncourt *Concert* (2/90) (TELD) ① [2] **2292-42608-2**

E. Mathis, T. Schmidt, P. Schreier, D. Fischer-Dieskau, Munich Bach Ch, Munich Bach Orch, K. Richter (r1977/8) *Concert* (1/95) (ARCH) ① [5] **439 394-2AX5**

M. Huber, P. Esswood, K. Equiluz, P. Huttenlocher, Tolz Boys' Ch, VCM, N. Harnoncourt *Concert* (2/95) (TELD) ① [6] **4509-91760-2**

B. Schlick, A. Scholl, C. Prégardien, G. Schwarz, Concerto Vocale, Limoges Baroque Ens, C. Coin (vc/dir) (r1993) *Concert* (2/95) (ASTR) ① **E8530**

A. Auger, H. Watts, L-M. Harder, W. Schöne, Stuttgart Gächinger Kantorei, Stuttgart Bach Collegium, H. Rilling (r1980) *Concert* (2/95) (HANS) ① **98 819**

4. K. Battle, I. Perlman, St Luke's Orch, J. Nelson (r1989/90) *Concert* (3/92) (DG) ① **429 737-2GH**

Cantata No. 116, 'Du Friedefürst, Herr Jesus Christ', BWV116 (1724) (Trinity XXV)

EXCERPTS: 1. Chorus: Du Friedefürst, Herr Jesu Christ; 2. Aria: Ach, unaussprechlich (A); 3. Recit: Gedenke doch, o Jesu (T); 4. Aria (Terzett): Ach, wir bekennen unsre Schuld (STB); 5. Recit: Ach, lass uns durch die scharfen (A); 6. Choral: Erleucht' auch unsern Sinn und Herz (chor).

M. Huber, P. Esswood, K. Equiluz, P. Huttenlocher, Tolz Boys' Ch, VCM, N. Harnoncourt *Concert* (2/90) (TELD) ① [2] **2292-42608-2**

E. Mathis, T. Schmidt, P. Schreier, D. Fischer-Dieskau, Munich Bach Ch, Munich Bach Orch, K. Richter (r1977/8) *Concert* (1/95) (ARCH) ① [5] **439 394-2AX5**

M. Huber, P. Esswood, K. Equiluz, P. Huttenlocher, Tolz Boys' Ch, VCM, N. Harnoncourt *Concert* (2/95) (TELD) ① [6] **4509-91760-2**

A. Auger, H. Watts, L-M. Harder, P. Huttenlocher, Stuttgart Gächinger Kantorei, Stuttgart Bach Collegium, H. Rilling (r1980) *Concert* (2/95) (HANS) ① **98 820**

Cantata No. 117, 'Sei Lob und Ehr dem höchsten Gut', BWV117 (c1728-31)

EXCERPTS: 1. Chorus: Sei Lob und Ehr' dem höchsten Gut; 2. Recit: Es danken dir die Himmelsheer (B); 3. Aria: Was unser Gott geschaffen hat (T); 4. Choral: Ich rief dem Herrn in meiner Not (chor); 5. Recit: Der Herr ist noch und nimmer nicht (A); 6. Aria: Wenn trost und Hülf' ermangeln muss (B); 7. Aria: Ich will dich all mein Leben lang (A); 8. Recit: Ihr, die inr Christi Namen nennt (T); 9. Chorus: So kommet vor sein Angesicht.

M. Georg, Adalbert Kraus, A. Schmidt, Stuttgart Gächinger Kantorei, Stuttgart Bach Collegium, Württemberg CO, H. Rilling *Concert* (1/89) (NOVA) ① **150 028-2**

R. Jacobs, K. Equiluz, M. van Egmond, Hanover Boys' Ch, Ghent Collegium Vocale, Leonhardt Consort, G. Leonhardt *Concert* (2/90) (TELD) ① [2] **2292-42608-2**

M. Georg, Adalbert Kraus, A. Schmidt, Stuttgart Gächinger Kantorei, Württemberg CO, H. Rilling (r1984) *Concert* (2/95) (HANS) ① **98 856**

R. Jacobs, K. Equiluz, M. van Egmond, Hanover Boys' Ch, Ghent Collegium Vocale, Leonhardt Consort, G. Leonhardt *Concert* (2/95) (TELD) ① [6] **4509-91760-2**

Cantata No. 118, 'O Jesu Christ, mein's Leben Licht'—motet movement, BWV118

Monteverdi Ch, EBS, J.E. Gardiner (2nd vers) *Concert* (5/91) (ARCH) ① **429 782-2AH**

Cantata No. 119, 'Preise Jerusalem, den Herrn', BWV119 (1723) (town council inauguration)

EXCERPTS: 1. Chorus: Preise, Jerusalem, den Herrn; 2. Recit: Gesegnet Land! (T); 3. Aria: Wohl dir (T); 4. Recit: So herrlich stehst du (B); 5. Aria: Die Obrigkeit its Gottes Gabe (A); 7. Chorus: Der Herr hat gut's an uns getan; 8. Recit: Zuletzt! (A); 9. Choral: Hilf deinem Volk (chor).

M. Huber, P. Esswood, K. Equiluz, R. Holl, Tolz Boys' Ch, VCM, N. Harnoncourt *Concert* (2/90) (TELD) ① [2] **2292-42608-2**

M. Huber, P. Esswood, K. Equiluz, R. Holl, Tolz Boys' Ch, VCM, N. Harnoncourt *Concert* (2/95) (TELD) ① [6] **4509-91761-2**

A. Auger, A. Murray, Adalbert Kraus, W. Schöne, Stuttgart Gächinger Kantorei, Stuttgart Bach Collegium, H. Rilling (r1977/8) *Concert* (2/95) (HANS) ① **98 828**

Cantata No. 120, 'Gott, man lobet dich in der Stille', BWV120 (1728-29) (Town council inauguration)

EXCERPTS: 1. Aria: Gott, man lobet dich in der Stille (A); 2. Chorus: Jauchzet, ihr erfreuten Stimmen; 3. Recit: Auf, du geliebte Lindenstadt! (B); 4. Aria: Heil und Segen (S); 5. Recit: Nun, Herr, so weihe selbst dein Regiment (T); 6. Choral: Nun hilf uns, Herr, den Dienern dein (chorus).

M. Huber, P. Esswood, K. Equiluz, P. Huttenlocher, Tolz Boys' Ch, VCM, N. Harnoncourt *Concert* (3/90) (TELD) ① [2] **2292-42609-2**

M. Huber, P. Esswood, K. Equiluz, P. Huttenlocher, Tolz Boys' Ch, VCM, N. Harnoncourt *Concert* (2/95) (TELD) ① [6] **4509-91761-2**

H. Donath, H. Laurich, Adalbert Kraus, W. Schöne, Stuttgart Gächinger Kantorei, Stuttgart Bach Collegium, H. Rilling (r1973) *Concert* (2/95) (HANS) ① **98 829**

Cantata No. 121, 'Christum wir sollen loben schon', BWV121 (1724) (2nd day of Christmas)

EXCERPTS: 1. Chorus: Christum wir sollen loben schon; 2. Aria: O du von Gott erhöhte Creatur (T); 3. Recit: Der Gnade unermesslich's Wesen (A); 4. Aria: Johannis freudenvolles Springen (B); 5. Recit: Doch wie erblickt es dich in deiner Krippe? (S); 6. Choral: Lob, Ehr' und Dank sei dirgesagt (chor).

M. Huber, P. Esswood, K. Equiluz, P. Huttenlocher, Tolz Boys' Ch, VCM, N. Harnoncourt *Concert* (3/90) (TELD) ① [2] **2292-42609-2**

E. Mathis, A. Reynolds, P. Schreier, D. Fischer-Dieskau, Munich Bach Ch, Munich Bach Orch, K. Richter (r1971/2) *Concert* (3/94) (ARCH) ① [4] **439 369-2AX4**

M. Huber, P. Esswood, K. Equiluz, P. Huttenlocher, Tolz Boys' Ch, VCM, N. Harnoncourt *Concert* (2/95) (TELD) ① [6] **4509-91761-2**

A. Auger, D. Soffel, Adalbert Kraus, W. Schöne, Stuttgart Gächinger Kantorei, Stuttgart Bach Collegium, H. Rilling (r1980) *Concert* (2/95) (HANS) ① **98 824**

Cantata No. 122, '(Das) neugeborne Kindelein', BWV122 (1724) (Christmas I)

EXCERPTS: 1. Chorus: Das neugebor'ne Kindelein; 2. Aria: O Menschen, die ihr täglich sündigt (B); 3. Recit: Die Engel, welche sich zuvor vor euch (S); 4. Aria (Terzett): Ist Gott versöhnt und unser Freund (SAT); 5. Recit: Dies ist ein Tag (B); 6. Choral: Es bringt das rechte Jubeljahr (chor).

M. Huber, T. Schilling, K. Equiluz, P. Huttenlocher, Tolz Boys' Ch, VCM, N. Harnoncourt *Concert* (3/90) (TELD) ① [2] **2292-42609-2**

M. Huber, T. Schilling, K. Equiluz, P. Huttenlocher, Tolz Boys' Ch, VCM, N. Harnoncourt *Concert* (2/95) (TELD) ① [6] **4509-91761-2**

H. Donath, H. Watts, Adalbert Kraus, N. Tüller, Frankfurt Kantorei, Stuttgart Bach Collegium, H. Rilling (r1972) *Concert* (2/95) (HANS) ① **98 826**

Cantata No. 123, 'Liebster Immanuel, Herzog der Frommen', BWV123 (1725) (Epiphany)

EXCERPTS: 1. Chorus: Liebster Immanuel, Herzog der Frommen; 2. Recit: Die Himmels-Süssigkeit (A), 3. Aria: Auch die harte Kreuzesreise (T); 4. Recit: Kein Höllenfeind kann mich verschlingen (B); 5. Aria: Lass', o Welt, mich aus Verachtung (B); 6. Choral: Drum fahrt nur immerhin (chor).

S. Rampf, K. Equiluz, R. Holl, Tolz Boys' Ch, VCM, N. Harnoncourt *Concert* (3/90) (TELD) ① [2] **2292-42609-2**

H. Watts, Adalbert Kraus, P. Huttenlocher, Stuttgart Gächinger Kantorei, Stuttgart Bach Collegium, H. Rilling *Concert* (2/95) (HANS) ① **98 872**

S. Rampf, K. Equiluz, R. Holl, Tolz Boys' Ch, VCM, N. Harnoncourt *Concert* (2/95) (TELD) ① [6] **4509-91761-2**

Cantata No. 124, 'Meinen Jesum lass ich nicht', BWV124 (1725) (Epiphany I)

EXCERPTS: 1. Chorus: Meinen Jesum lass' ich nicht; 2. Recit: So lange sich ein Tropfen Blut (T); 3. Aria: Undwenn der harte Todeschlag (T); 4. Recit: Doch, ach! welch' schweres Ungemach (B); 5. Aria (Duet): Entziehe dich eilends (S,A); 6. Choral: Jesum lass' ich nicht von mir (chor).

A. Bergius, S. Rampf, K. Equiluz, T. Thomaschke, Tolz Boys' Ch, VCM, N. Harnoncourt *Concert* (3/90) (TELD) ① **2292-42615-2**

L. Schädle, H. Töpper, E. Haefliger, T. Adam, Munich Bach Ch, Munich Bach Orch, K. Richter (r1967) *Concert* (3/94) (ARCH) ① [4] **439 369-2AX4**

A. Auger, H. Watts, A. Baldin, W. Schöne, Stuttgart Gächinger Kantorei, Stuttgart Bach Collegium, H. Rilling *Concert* (2/95) (HANS) ① **98 872**

A. Bergius, S. Rampf, K. Equiluz, T. Thomaschke, Tolz Boys' Ch, VCM, N. Harnoncourt *Concert* (2/95) (TELD) ① [6] **4509-91761-2**

Cantata No. 125, 'Mit Fried und Freud ich fahrt dahin', BWV125 (1725) (Purification)

EXCERPTS: 1. Chorus: Mit Fried' und Freud' ich fahr' dahin; 2. Aria: Ich will auch mit gebroch'nen Augen nach dir (A); 3. Recit: O Wunder, dass ein Herz (B); 4. Aria (Duet): Ein unbegreiflich Licht (T,B); 5. Recit: O unerschöpfter Schatz (A); 6. Choral: Er sit das Heil und sel'ge Licht (chor).

P. Esswood, K. Equiluz, T. Thomaschke, Tolz Boys' Ch, VCM, N. Harnoncourt *Concert* (3/90) (TELD) ① **2292-42615-2**

P. Esswood, K. Equiluz, T. Thomaschke, Tolz Boys' Ch, VCM, N. Harnoncourt *Concert* (2/95) (TELD) ① [6] **4509-91761-2**

M. Höffgen, K. Equiluz, W. Schöne, Stuttgart Gedächtniskirche Ch, Stuttgart Bach Collegium, H. Rilling *Concert* (2/95) (HANS) ① **98 876**

Cantata No. 126, 'Erhalt uns, Herr, bei deinen Wort', BWV126 (1725) (Sexagesima)

EXCERPTS: 1. Chorus: Erhalt' uns, Herr, bei deinem Wort; 2. Aria: Sende deine Macht (T); 3. Recit: Der Menschen Gunst und Macht (A,T); 4. Aria: Stürze zu Boden (B); 5. Recit: So wird dein Wort und Wahrheot offen bar (T); 6. Choral: Verleih uns Frieden gnädiglich (chor).

P. Esswood, K. Equiluz, T. Thomaschke, Tolz Boys' Ch, VCM, N. Harnoncourt *Concert* (3/90) (TELD) ① **2292-42615-2**

A. Reynolds, P. Schreier, T. Adam, Munich Bach Ch, Munich Bach Orch, K. Richter (r1973-4) *Concert* (7/94) (ARCH) ① [5] **439 374-2AX5**

P. Esswood, K. Equiluz, T. Thomaschke, Tolz Boys' Ch, VCM, N. Harnoncourt *Concert* (2/95) (TELD) ① [6] **4509-91761-2**

H. Watts, Adalbert Kraus, W. Schöne, Stuttgart Gächinger Kantorei, Stuttgart Bach Collegium, H. Rilling *Concert* (2/95) (HANS) ① **98 878**

Cantata No. 127, 'Herr Jesu Christ, wahr' Mensch und Gott', BWV127 (1725) (Quinquagesima)

EXCERPTS: 1. Chorus: Herr Jesu Christ, wahr'r Mensch und Gott; 2. Recit: Wenn Alles sich zur letzten Zeit (T); 3. Aria: Die Seele ruht in Jesu Händen (S); 4a. Recit: Wenn einstens die Posaunen (B); 4b. Aria: Fürwahr, euch sage ich (B); 5. Choral: Ach Herr, vergib all' unsre Schuld (chor).

S. Hennig, K. Equiluz, M. van Egmond, Hanover Boys' Ch, Ghent Collegium Vocale, Leonhardt Consort, G. Leonhardt *Concert* (3/90) (TELD) ① **2292-42615-2**

A. Fahberg, P. Pears, K. Engen, Munich Bach Ch, Munich St Op Orch, K. Richter (r1958) *Concert* (5/93) (TELD) ① **9031-77614-2**

S. Hennig, K. Equiluz, M. van Egmond, Hanover Boys' Ch, Ghent Collegium Vocale, Leonhardt Consort, G. Leonhardt *Concert* (2/95) (TELD) ① [6] **4509-91761-2**

A. Auger, L-M. Harder, W. Schöne, Stuttgart Gächinger Kantorei, Stuttgart Bach Collegium, H. Rilling *Concert* (2/95) (HANS) ① **98 878**

Cantata No. 128, 'Auf Christi Himmelfahrt allein', BWV128 (1725) (Ascension)

EXCERPTS: 1. Chorus: Auf Christi Himmelfahrt allein; 2. Recit: Ich bin bereit, komm (T); 3. Aria: Auf, mit hellem Schall (B); 4. Aria (Duet): Sein' Allmacht zu ergründen (A,T); 5. Choral: Alsdann so wirst du mich zu deiner Rechten stellen (chor).

R. Jacobs, K. Equiluz, M. van Egmond, Hanover Boys' Ch, Ghent Collegium Vocale, Leonhardt Consort, G. Leonhardt *Concert* (3/90) (TELD) ① [2] **2292-42617-2**

R. Jacobs, K. Equiluz, M. van Egmond, Hanover Boys' Ch, Ghent Collegium Vocale, Leonhardt Consort, G. Leonhardt *Concert* (2/95) (TELD) ① [6] **4509-91761-2**

G. Schreckenbach, A. Baldin, W. Schöne, Stuttgart Gächinger Kantorei, Stuttgart Bach Collegium, H. Rilling (r1980/1) *Concert* (2/95) (HANS) Ⓓ **98 886**

Cantata No. 129, 'Gelobet sei der Herr, mein Gott', BWV129 (1724) (Trinity)

EXCERPTS: 1. Chorus: Gelobet sei der Herr, mein Gott; 2. Aria: (B); 3. Aria: (S); 4. Aria (A); 5. Choral: Dem wir das Heilig itzt mit Freuden lassen klingen (chor).

S. Hennig, R. Jacobs, M. van Egmond, Hanover Boys' Ch, Ghent Collegium Vocale, Leonhardt Consort, G. Leonhardt *Concert* (3/90) (TELD) Ⓓ [2] **2292-42617-2**

E. Mathis, A. Reynolds, D. Fischer-Dieskau, Munich Bach Ch, Munich Bach Orch, K. Richter (r1974-5) *Concert* (7/94) (ARCH) Ⓓ [6] **439 380-2AX6**

A. Auger, G. Schreckenbach, P. Huttenlocher, Stuttgart Gächinger Kantorei, Stuttgart Bach Collegium, H. Rilling (r1982) *Concert* (2/95) (HANS) Ⓓ **98 861**

S. Hennig, R. Jacobs, M. van Egmond, Hanover Boys' Ch, Ghent Collegium Vocale, Leonhardt Consort, G. Leonhardt *Concert* (2/95) (TELD) Ⓓ [6] **4509-91761-2**

5. Trinity Coll Ch, Cambridge, R. Marlow (r1993; Eng) *Concert* (2/94) (CONI) Ⓓ **CDCF219**

Cantata No. 130, 'Herr Gott, dich loben alle wir', BWV130 (1724) (St Michael)

EXCERPTS: 1. Chorus: Herr Gott, dich loben alle wir; 2. Recit: Ihr heller Glanz (A); 3. Aria: Der alte Drache brennt vor Neid (B); 4. Recit: Wohl aber uns (S,T); 5. Aria: Lass, o Fürst der Cherubinen (T); 6. Choral: Darum wir billig loben dich (chor).

A. Bergius, S. Rampf, K. Equiluz, W. Heldwein, Tolz Boys' Ch, VCM, N. Harnoncourt *Concert* (3/90) (TELD) Ⓓ [2] **2292-42617-2**

E. Ameling, H. Watts, W. Krenn, T. Krause, Lausanne Pro Arte Ch, SRO, E. Ansermet *Concert* (5/92) (DECC) Ⓓ **433 175-2DM**

E. Mathis, T. Schmidt, P. Schreier, D. Fischer-Dieskau, Munich Bach Ch, Munich Bach Orch, K. Richter (r1975/6/8) *Concert* (1/95) (ARCH) Ⓓ [5] **439 394-2AX5**

K. Graf, G. Schnaut, Adalbert Kraus, W. Schöne, Stuttgart Gedächtniskirche Ch, Stuttgart Bach Collegium, H. Rilling *Concert* (2/95) (HANS) Ⓓ **98 868**

A. Bergius, S. Rampf, K. Equiluz, W. Heldwein, Tolz Boys' Ch, VCM, N. Harnoncourt *Concert* (2/95) (TELD) Ⓓ [6] **4509-91761-2**

F. Sailer, C. Hellmann, H. Krebs, E. Wenk, Heilbronn Schütz Ch, Pforzheim CO, F. Werner (r1961) *Concert* (5/95) (ERAT) Ⓓ [2] **4509-97407-2**

Cantata No. 131, 'Aus der Tiefen rufe ich, Herr, zu dir', BWV131 (1707)

EXCERPTS: 1. Chorus: Aus der Tiefe rufe ich, Herr, zu dir; 2. Aria: So du willst, Herr, Sünde zurechnen (B,S); 3. Chorus: Ich harre des Herrn; 4. Aria: Meine Seele wartet (T,A); 5. Chorus: Israel, hoffe auf den Herrn.

A. Bergius, P. Esswood, K. Equiluz, R. Holl, Tolz Boys' Ch, VCM, N. Harnoncourt *Concert* (3/90) (TELD) Ⓓ [2] **2292-42617-2**

B. Schlick, G. Lesne, H. Crook, P. Kooy, Ghent Collegium Vocale, Ghent Collegium Vocale Orch, P. Herreweghe *Concert* (5/93) (VIRG) Ⓓ **VC7 59237-2**

Adalbert Kraus, W. Schöne, Stuttgart Gächinger Kantorei, Stuttgart Bach Collegium, H. Rilling *Concert* (2/95) (HANS) Ⓓ **98 866**

A. Bergius, P. Esswood, K. Equiluz, R. Holl, Tolz Boys' Ch, VCM, N. Harnoncourt *Concert* (2/95) (TELD) Ⓓ [6] **4509-91761-2**

B. Schlick, K. Wessel, G. de Mey, K. Mertens, Amsterdam Baroque Ch, Amsterdam Baroque Orch, T. Koopman (r1994) *Concert* (9/95) (ERAT) Ⓓ [3] **4509-98536-2**

Cantata No. 132, 'Bereitet die Wege, bereitet die Bahn!', BWV132 (1715) (Advent IV)

EXCERPTS: 1. Aria: Bereitet die Wege, bereitet die Bahn (S); 2. Recit: Willst du dich Gottes Kind (T); 3. Aria: Wer bist du? (B); 4. Recit: Ich will, mein Gott (A); 5. Aria: Christi Glieder, ach, bedenket (A); 6. Choral: Ertöt' uns durch dein' Güte (chor).

S. Hennig, R. Jacobs, M. van Altena, M. van Egmond, Hanover Boys' Ch, Ghent Collegium Vocale, Leonhardt Consort, G. Leonhardt *Concert* (3/90) (TELD) Ⓓ [2] **2292-42618-2**

E. Mathis, A. Reynolds, P. Schreier, T. Adam, Munich Bach Ch, Munich Bach Orch, K. Richter (r1972) *Concert* (3/94) (ARCH) Ⓓ [4] **439 369-2AX4**

S. Hennig, R. Jacobs, M. van Altena, M. van Egmond, Hanover Boys' Ch, Ghent Collegium Vocale, Leonhardt Consort, G. Leonhardt *Concert* (2/95) (TELD) Ⓓ [6] **4509-91761-2**

A. Auger, H. Watts, K. Equiluz, W. Schöne, Stuttgart Gächinger Kantorei, Stuttgart Bach Collegium, H. Rilling (r1976/7) *Concert* (2/95) (HANS) Ⓓ **98 822**

Cantata No. 133, 'Ich freue mich in dir', BWV133 (1724) (3rd day of Christmas)

EXCERPTS: 1. Chorus: Ich freue mich in dir; 2. Aria: Getrost! es fasst ein heil'ger Leib (A); 3. Recit: Ein Adam mag sich voller Schrecken (T); 4. Aria: Wie lieblich klingt es in den Ohren (S); 5. Recit: Wohlan! Des Todes Furcht und Schmerz erwägt nicht (B); 6. Choral: Wohlan! so will ich mich an dich, o Jesu, halten (chor).

S. Hennig, R. Jacobs, M. van Altena, M. van Egmond, Hanover Boys' Ch, Ghent Collegium Vocale, Leonhardt Consort, G. Leonhardt *Concert* (3/90) (TELD) Ⓓ [2] **2292-42618-2**

S. Hennig, R. Jacobs, M. van Altena, M. van Egmond, Hanover Boys' Ch, Ghent Collegium Vocale, Leonhardt Consort, G. Leonhardt *Concert* (2/95) (TELD) Ⓓ [6] **4509-91761-2**

A. Auger, D. Soffel, A. Baldin, P. Huttenlocher, Stuttgart Gächinger Kantorei, Stuttgart Bach Collegium, H. Rilling (r1980) *Concert* (2/95) (HANS) Ⓓ **98 826**

Cantata No. 134, '(Ein) Herz, das seinen Jesum lebend weiss', BWV134 (1724) (Easter Tuesday)

EXCERPTS: 1. Recit: Ein Herz, das seinen Jesum lebend weiss (T,A); 2. Aria: Auf, Gläubige! (T); 3. Recit: Wohl dir, Gott hat an dich gedacht (T,A); 4. Aria (Duet): Wir danken, wir preisen (A,T); 5. Recit: Doch wirke selbst den dank (T,A); 6. Chorus: Erschallet, ihr Himmel.

R. Jacobs, M. van Altena, Hanover Boys' Ch, Ghent Collegium Vocale, Leonhardt Consort, G. Leonhardt *Concert* (3/90) (TELD) Ⓓ [2] **2292-42618-2**

R. Jacobs, M. van Altena, Hanover Boys' Ch, Ghent Collegium Vocale, Leonhardt Consort, G. Leonhardt *Concert* (2/95) (TELD) Ⓓ [6] **4509-91761-2**

H. Watts, Adalbert Kraus, Stuttgart Gächinger Kantorei, Stuttgart Bach Collegium, H. Rilling *Cantata 31.* (2/95) (HANS) Ⓓ **98 881**

Cantata No. 135, 'Ach Herr, mich armen Sünder', BWV135 (1724) (Trinity III)

EXCERPTS: 1. Chorus: Ach Herr, mich armen Sünder; 2. Recit: Ach heile mich (T); 3. Aria: Tröste mir, Jesu mein Gemüte (T); 4. Recit: Ich bin von Seufzen müde (A); 5. Aria: Weicht all', ihr Übeltäter, weicht! (B); 6. Choral: Ehr' sei in's Himmels Throne (chor).

R. Jacobs, M. van Altena, M. van Egmond, Hanover Boys' Ch, Ghent Collegium Vocale, Leonhardt Consort, G. Leonhardt *Concert* (3/90) (TELD) Ⓓ [2] **2292-42618-2**

A. Reynolds, P. Schreier, D. Fischer-Dieskau, Munich Bach Ch, Munich Bach Orch, K. Richter (r1974-5) *Concert* (7/94) (ARCH) Ⓓ [6] **439 380-2AX6**

R. Jacobs, M. van Altena, M. van Egmond, Hanover Boys' Ch, Ghent Collegium Vocale, Leonhardt Consort, G. Leonhardt *Concert* (2/95) (TELD) Ⓓ [6] **4509-91761-2**

H. Watts, Adalbert Kraus, P. Huttenlocher, Stuttgart Gächinger Kantorei, Stuttgart Bach Collegium, H. Rilling (r1979) *Concert* (2/95) (HANS) Ⓓ **98 802**

Cantata No. 136, 'Erforsche mich, Gott, und erfahre mein Herz', BWV136 (1723) (Trinity VIII)

EXCERPTS: 1. Chorus: Erforsche mich, Gott, und erfahre mein Herz; 2. Recit: Ach, dass Fluch (T); 3. Aria: Es kommt ein Tag (A); 4. Recit: Die Himmel selber sind nicht rein (B); 5. Aria (Duet): Uns treffen zwarder Sünden Flecken (T,B); 6. Choral: Dein Blut, der edle Saft (chor).

P. Esswood, K. Equiluz, W. Heldwein, Tolz Boys' Ch, VCM, N. Harnoncourt *Concert* (2/95) (TELD) Ⓓ [6] **4509-91761-2**

H. Watts, K. Equiluz, N. Tüller, Stuttgart Gächinger Kantorei, Stuttgart Bach Collegium, H. Rilling (r1977/8) *Concert* (2/95) (HANS) Ⓓ **98 806**

Cantata No. 137, 'Lobe den Herren, den mächtigen König der ehren' (1725) (Trinity XII)

EXCERPTS: 1. Chorus: Lobe den Herren, den mächtigen König der Ehren; 2. Aria: Lobe den Herren, der Alles so herrlich regieret (A); 3. Aria (Duet): Lobe den Herren, der künst und fein (S,B); 4. Aria: Lobe den Herre (T); 5. Choral: Lobe den Herren, was in mir ist (chor).

E. Mathis, J. Hamari, P. Schreier, D. Fischer-Dieskau, Munich Bach Ch, Munich Bach Orch, K. Richter (r1975-7) *Concert* (1/95) (ARCH) Ⓓ [6] **439 387-2AX6**

A. Auger, G. Schreckenbach, Adalbert Kraus, W. Heldwein, Stuttgart Gächinger Kantorei, Stuttgart Bach Collegium, H. Rilling (r1980-2) *Concert* (2/95) (HANS) Ⓓ **98 861**

A. Bergius, P. Esswood, K. Equiluz, A. Hartinger, Tolz Boys' Ch, VCM, N. Harnoncourt *Concert* (2/95) (TELD) Ⓓ [6] **4509-91761-2**

Cantata No. 138, 'Warum betrübst du dich, mein Herz?', BWV138 (1723) (Trinity XV)

EXCERPTS: 1. Chorus: Warum betrübst du dich, mein Herz; 2. Recit: Ich bin veracht't (B); 3. Chorus: Ach! wie? Gott sorget freilich für das Vieh; 4. Recit: Ach süsser Trost! (T); 5. Aria: Auf Gott steht meine Zuversicht (B); 6. Choral: Weil du mein Gott und Vater bist (chor).

A. Bergius, S. Rampf, K. Equiluz, R. Holl, Tolz Boys' Ch, VCM, N. Harnoncourt *Concert* (2/95) (TELD) Ⓓ [6] **4509-91762-2**

A. Auger, R. Bollen, A. Baldin, P. Huttenlocher, Stuttgart Gächinger Kantorei, Stuttgart Bach Collegium, H. Rilling (r1977/8) *Concert* (2/95) (HANS) Ⓓ **98 812**

Cantata No. 139, 'Wohl dem, der sich auf seinen Gott', BWV139 (1724) (Trinity XXIII)

EXCERPTS: 1. Chorus: Wohl dem, der sich auf seinen Gott; 2. Aria: Gott ist mein Freund (T); 3. Recit: Der Heiland sendet (A); 4. Aria: Das Unglück schlägt (B); 5. Recit: Ja, trag'ich gleich (S); 6. Choral: Dahero Trotz der Höllen Heer! (chor).

E. Mathis, T. Schmidt, P. Schreier, D. Fischer-Dieskau, Munich Bach Ch, Munich Bach Orch, K. Richter (r1977/8) *Concert* (1/95) (ARCH) Ⓓ [5] **439 394-2AX5**

A. Bergius, P. Esswood, K. Equiluz, R. Holl, Tolz Boys' Ch, VCM, N. Harnoncourt *Concert* (2/95) (TELD) Ⓓ [6] **4509-91762-2**

I. Nielsen, H. Watts, Adalbert Kraus, P. Huttenlocher, Stuttgart Gächinger Kantorei, Stuttgart Bach Collegium, H. Rilling (r1979/80) *Concert* (2/95) (HANS) Ⓓ **98 820**

Cantata No. 140, 'Wachet auf, ruft uns die Stimme', BWV140 (1731) (Trinity XXVII)

EXCERPTS: 1. Chorus: Wachet auf! wachet auf! ruft uns die Stimme; 2. Recit: Er kommt, er koomt, der Bräut'gam kommt! (T); 3. Aria (Duet): Wann kommst du, mein Heil? (S,B); 4. Choral: Zion hört die Wächter singen (T); 5. Recit: So geh'herein zu mir (B); 6. Aria (Duet): Mein Freund ist mein! (S,B); 7. Choral: Gloria sei dir gesungen (chor).

A. Auger, A. Baldin, P. Huttenlocher, Stuttgart Gächinger Kantorei, Stuttgart Bach Collegium, Württemberg CO, H. Rilling *Concert* (1/89) (NOVA) Ⓓ **150 029-2**

M. Petri, Westminster Abbey Ch, National PO, M. Neary *Concert* (12/91) (RCA) Ⓓ **RD60060**

G. de Chiaro (arr gtr: De Chiaro) *Concert* (12/91) (CENT) Ⓓ **CRC2101**

R. Holton, M. Chance, A. Rolfe Johnson, S. Varcoe, Monteverdi Ch, EBS, J.E. Gardiner *Cantata 147.* (6/92) (ARCH) Ⓓ **431 809-2AH**

L. Dutoit, K. Equiluz, H. Braun, Vienna Chbr Ch, Vienna St Op Orch, F. Prohaska (r1959) *Cantata 4.* (9/93) (VANG) Ⓓ **08.2001.71**

E. Mathis, P. Schreier, D. Fischer-Dieskau, Munich Bach Ch, Munich Bach Orch, K. Richter (r1977/8) *Concert* (1/95) (ARCH) Ⓓ [5] **439 394-2AX5**

A. Auger, A. Baldin, P. Huttenlocher, Stuttgart Gächinger Kantorei, Württemberg CO, H. Rilling (r1983/4) *Concert* (2/95) (HANS) Ⓓ **98 857**

A. Bergius, K. Equiluz, T. Hampson, Tolz Boys' Ch, VCM, N. Harnoncourt *Concert* (2/95) (TELD) Ⓓ [6] **4509-91762-2**

1. P. Hurford *Concert* (10/91) (DECC) Ⓓ **430 499-2DWO**

1. G. Fergus-Thompson (arr Busoni) *Concert* (10/92) (ASV) Ⓓ **CDWHL2066**

1. Prince of Wales Brass (arr Warren) *Concert* (12/93) (ASV) Ⓓ **CDWHL2083**

1. Tragicomedia, S. Stubbs (r1991) *Anna magdalena Notenbuch (1725).* (12/94) (TELD) Ⓓ **4509-91183-2**

3, 6. T. Hampson, A. Bergius, VCM, N. Harnoncourt *Concert* (4/92) (TELD) Ⓓ **9031-74798-2**

4. W. Kempff (r1975: arr pf: Kempff) *Concert* (11/94) (DG) Ⓓ [2] **439 672-2GX2**

Cantata No. 143, 'Lobe den Herr, meine Seele', BWV143 (spurious)

EXCERPTS: 1. Chorus: Lobe den Herrn, meine Seele; 2. Choral: Du Friedefürst, Herr Jesu Christ (S); 3. Recit: Wohl dem, dass Hülfe der Gott Jakobs ist (T); 4. Aria: Tausendfaches Unglück (T); 5. Aria: Der Herr ist König (B); 6. Aria & Chorale: Jesu, Retter deiner Herde (T); 7. Chorus: Halleluja.

E. Csapó, Adalbert Kraus, W. Schöne, Frankfurt Kantorei, Stuttgart Bach Collegium, H. Rilling *Concert* (2/95) (HANS) Ⓓ **98 870**

R. Cericius, K. Equiluz, M. van Egmond, Hanover Boys' Ch, Ghent Collegium Vocale, Leonhardt Consort, G. Leonhardt *Concert* (2/95) (TELD) Ⓓ [6] **4509-91762-2**

Cantata No. 144, 'Nimm, was dein ist, und gehe hin', BWV144 (1724) (Septuagesima)
EXCERPTS: 1. Chorus: Nimm, was dein ist, und gehe hin; 2. Aria: Murre nicht, lieber Christ (A); 3. Choral: Was Gott tut, das ist wohlgetan (chor); 4. Recit: Wo die Genügsamkeit regiert (T); 5. Aria: Genügsamkeit (S); 6. Choral: Was mein Gott will (chor).
A. Pfeiffer, P. Esswood, K. Equiluz, Hanover Boys' Ch, Ghent Collegium Vocale, Leonhardt Consort, G. Leonhardt Consort, G. Leonhardt
(2/95) (TELD) ① [6] 4509-91762-2
A. Auger, H. Watts, Adalbert Kraus, Stuttgart Gächinger Kantorei, Stuttgart Bach Collegium, H. Rilling Concert (2/95) (HANS) ① 98 876
5. E. Ameling, H. de Vries, R. van der Meer, A. de Klerk (r1983) Concert
(7/94) (EMI) ① CDC5 55000-2

Cantata No. 145, 'Ich lebe, mein Herze, zu deinem Ergötzen', BWV145 (?1729) (Easter Tuesday)
EXCERPTS: 1. Choral: Auf, mein Herz, des Herrn Tag (chor); 2. Chorus: So du mit deinem Munde; 3. Aria (Duet): Ich lebe, mein Herze, zu deinem Ergötzen (S,T); 4. Recit: Nun höre, Moses (T); 5. Aria: Merke, mein Herze (B); 6. Recit: Mein Jesus lebt (S); 7. Choral: Drum wir auch billig fröhlich sein (chor).
C. Cuccaro, Adalbert Kraus, A. Schmidt, Stuttgart Gächinger Kantorei, Stuttgart Bach Collegium, Württemberg CO, H. Rilling Concert
(1/89) (NOVA) ① 150 029-2
C. Cuccaro, Adalbert Kraus, A. Schmidt, Stuttgart Gächinger Kantorei, Württemberg CO, H. Rilling (r1984) Concert (2/95) (HANS) ① 98 856
A. Bergius, K. Equiluz, T. Hampson, Tolz Boys' Ch, VCM, N. Harnoncourt Concert
(2/95) (TELD) ① [6] 4509-91762-2

Cantata No. 146, 'Wir müssen durch viel Trübsal', BWV146 (c1726-8) (Easter III)
EXCERPTS: 1. Sinfonia; 2. Chorus: Wir müssen durch viel Trübsal; 3. Aria: Ich will nach dem Himmel zu (A); 4. Recit: Ach! wer doch schon im Himmel wär! (S); 5. Aria: Ich säe meine Zähren mit bangem Herzen (S); 6. Recit: Ich bin bereit mein Kreuzgeduldig (T); 7. Duet: Wie will ich mich freuen (T,B); 8. Choral: Denn wer selig dahin fähret (chor).
A. Bergius, P. Esswood, K. Equiluz, T. Hampson, Tolz Boys' Ch, VCM, N. Harnoncourt Concert
(2/95) (TELD) ① [6] 4509-91762-2
H. Donath, M. Höffgen, K. Equiluz, H-F. Kunz, Stuttgart Gächinger Kantorei, Stuttgart Bach Collegium, H. Rilling (r1973) Cantata 108.
(2/95) (HANS) ① 98 884
7. T. Hampson, K. Equiluz, VCM, N. Harnoncourt Concert (4/92) (TELD) ① 9031-74798-2

Cantata No. 147, 'Herz und Mund und Tat und Leben', BWV147 (1723) (Visitation)
EXCERPTS: PART ONE: 1. Chorus: Herz und Mund und Tat und Leben; 2. Recit: Gebene dieter Mund! (T); 3. Aria: Schäme dich, O Seele nicht (A); 4. Recit: Verstokkung kann Gewaltverfallenden (B); 5. Aria: Bereite dir, Jesu, noch itzo die Bahn (S); 6. Choral: Wohl mir, dass ich Jesum habe (chor). PART TWO: 7. Aria: Hilf, Jesu, hilf (T); 8. Recit: Der höchsten Allmacht Wunderhand (A); 9. Aria: Ich will von Jesu Wunden (B); 10. Choral: Jesu bleibet meine Freude (Jesu, joy of man's desiring).
A. Bergius, S. Rampf, K. Equiluz, T. Hampson, Tolz Boys' Ch, VCM, N. Harnoncourt Concert
(2/86) (TELD) ① [2] 2292-42631-2
G. de Chiaro (arr gtr: De Chiaro) Concert
(12/91) (CENT) ① CRC2101
R. Holton, M. Chance, A. Rolfe Johnson, S. Varcoe, Monteverdi Ch, EBS, J.E. Gardiner Cantata 140.
(6/92) (ARCH) ① 431 809-2AH
I. Kertesi, J. Németh, J. Mukk, I. Gáti, Hungarian Rad Chor, Failoni CO, M. Antal Cantata 80.
(12/92) (NAXOS) ① 8 550642
U. Buckel, H. Töpper, J. van Kesteren, K. Engen, Munich Bach Ch, Ansbach Bach Week Sols Ens, K. Richter (r1961) Concert
(7/94) (ARCH) ① 439 380-2AX6
A. Auger, H. Watts, W. Schöne, Frankfurt Kantorei, Stuttgart Bach Collegium, H. Rilling (r1976/7) Concert (2/95) (HANS) ① 98 863
A. Bergius, S. Rampf, K. Equiluz, T. Hampson, Tolz Boys' Ch, VCM, N. Harnoncourt Concert
(2/95) (TELD) ① [6] 4509-91762-2
5. J. Sutherland, G. Jones Orch, Geraint Jones Concert (8/89) (CFP) ① CD-CFP4532
9. T. Hampson, VCM, N. Harnoncourt Concert
(4/92) (TELD) ① 9031-74798-2
10. St Paul's Cath Ch, ECO, Barry Rose Concert
(5/85) (PHIL) ① 412 629-2PH

10. J. Lloyd Webber, RPO, N. Cleobury (arr vc) Concert (3/87) (PHIL) ① 416 698-2PH
10. Salisbury Cath Ch, C. Walsh, R. Seal Concert
(9/87) (MERI) ① CDE84025
10. A. Stringer, N. Rawsthorne (r1974) Concert
(11/87) (CRD) ① CRD3308
10. Taverner Consort, Taverner Plyrs, A. Parrott Concert (12/88) (EMI) ① CDM7 69853-2
10. N. Hooper (arr gtr) Solo Cello Suites.
(5/89) (ABBS) ① SCSCD2831
10. D. Lipatti (arr Hess: r1950) Concert
(6/89) (EMI) ① CDH7 69800-2
10. Solisti Italiani Concert
(10/89) (DENO) ① CO-73335
10. King's College Ch, ASMF, D. Willcocks Concert
(1/91) (CFP) ① CD-CFP4570
10. M. Hess (arr Hess: r1928) Concert
(5/91) (PEAR) ① GEMMCD9462
10. St. John's College Ch, P. White, G. Guest (Eng) Concert (10/91) (DECC) ① 430 499-2DWO
10. G. Fergus-Thompson (trans Hess) Concert
(10/91) (ASV) ① CDDCA759
10. M. Tipo (arr Hess) Concert
(11/91) (EMI) ① CDC7 54147-2
10. J. Galway, Munich RO, J. Georgiadis Concert
(12/91) (RCA) ① RD60736
10. M. Lympany (arr Hess) Concert
(1/92) (EMIL) ① CDZ111
10. T. Nikolaieva (pf) Concert
(9/92) (MEZH) ① MK418024
10. P. Hurford, M. Laird Brass Ens (r1990: arr Hurford) Concert (9/92) (ARGO) ① 433 451-2ZH
10. G. Fergus-Thompson (arr Hess) Concert
(10/92) (ASV) ① CDWHL2066
10. J. McCormack, G. Moore (r1941) Concert
(1/93) (MMOI) ① CDMOIR411
10. I. Biret (trans Kempff) Concert
(5/93) (MARC) ① 8 223452
10. St John's College Ch, P. White, G. Guest (r1958) Concert (6/93) (DECC) ① 436 402-2DWO
10. H. Bauer (r1928: arr Bauer) Concert
(9/93) (BIDD) ① LHW007
10. Prince of Wales Brass (arr Harrison) Concert
(12/93) (ASV) ① CDWHL2083
10. M. Hess (r1940: arr pf: Hess) Concert
(2/94) (DUTT) ① CDLX7005
10. Westminster Cath Ch, J. O'Donnell, I. Simcock (r1993; arr Whittaker) Concert
(3/94) (HYPE) ① CDA66669
10. O.E. Antonsen, W. Marshall (r1992: arr tpt/org: Alain) Concert (10/94) (EMI) ① CDC5 55048-2
10. W. Kempff (r1975: arr pf: Kempff) Concert
(11/94) (DG) ① [2] 439 672-2GX2
10. M. Hess (r1928: arr pf: Hess) Concert
(3/95) (BIDD) ① LHW024
10. D. Lipatti (r1941: arr pf: Hess) Concert
(10/95) (ARCI) ① [2] ARC112/3

Cantata No. 148, 'Bringet dem Herrn Ehre seines Namens', BWV148 (1723) (Trinity XVII)
EXCERPTS: 1. Concerto: Bringet dem Herrn Ehre seines Namens (chor); 2. Aria: Ich eile die Lehre des Lebens (T); 3. Recit: So wie der Hirsch (A); 4. Aria: Mund und Herze steht dir offen (A); 5. Recit: Bleib' auch, mein Gott (T); 6. Choral: Führ' auch mein Herz und Sinn (chor).
P. Esswood, K. Equiluz, Tolz Boys' Ch, VCM, N. Harnoncourt Concert
(2/86) (TELD) ① 2292-42631-2
J. Hamari, P. Schreier, Munich Bach Ch, Munich Bach Orch, K. Richter (r1977/8) Concert
(1/95) (ARCH) ① [6] 439 387-2AX6
P. Esswood, K. Equiluz, Tolz Boys' Ch, VCM, N. Harnoncourt Concert
(2/95) (TELD) ① [6] 4509-91762-2
H. Watts, K. Equiluz, Stuttgart Gächinger Kantorei, Stuttgart Bach Collegium, H. Rilling (1977) Concert
(2/95) (HANS) ① 98 814

Cantata No. 149, 'Man singet mit Freuden vom Sieg', BWV149 (1728) (St Michael)
EXCERPTS: 1. Chorus: Man singet mit Freuden vom Sieg; 2. Aria: Kraft und Stärke seingesungen Gott (B); 3. Recit: Ich fürchte mich vor tausend Feinden nicht (A); 4. Aria: Gottes Engel weichen nie (S); 5. Recit: Ich danke dir (T); 6. Aria (Duet): Seid wachsam, ihr heiligen Wächter (A,T); 7. Choral: Ach Herr, lass dein' lieb' Engelein (chor).
S. Hennig, P. Esswood, K. Equiluz, M. van Egmond, Hanover Boy's Ch, Ghent Collegium Vocale, Leonhardt Consort, G. Leonhardt Concert
(2/86) (TELD) ① 2292-42631-2
S. Hennig, P. Esswood, K. Equiluz, M. van Egmond, Hanover Boy's Ch, Ghent Collegium Vocale, Leonhardt Consort, G. Leonhardt Concert
(2/95) (TELD) ① [6] 4509-91762-2

A. Auger, M. Georg, A. Baldin, P. Huttenlocher, Stuttgart Gächinger Kantorei, Stuttgart Bach Collegium, H. Rilling (r1983/4) Concert
(2/95) (HANS) ① 98 815

Cantata No. 150, 'Nach dir, Herr, verlanget mich', BWV150 (1708)
EXCERPTS: 1. Sinfonia; 2. Chorus: Nach dir, Herr, verlanget mich; 3. Aria: Doch bin und bleibe ich vergnügt (S); 4. Chorus: Lente mich, leite mich; 5. Aria (Terzett): Cedern müssen von den Winden (A,T,B); 6. Chorus: Meine Augen sehen stets; 7. Chorus (Ciacona): Meine Tage in den Leiden.
A. Pfeiffer, P. Esswood, K. Equiluz, M. van Egmond, Hanover Boy's Ch, Ghent Collegium Vocale, Leonhardt Consort, G. Leonhardt Concert
(2/86) (TELD) ① [2] 2292-42631-2
A. Pfeiffer, P. Esswood, K. Equiluz, M. van Egmond, Hanover Boy's Ch, Ghent Collegium Vocale, Leonhardt Consort, G. Leonhardt Concert
(2/95) (TELD) ① [6] 4509-91762-2
M. Schreiber, M. Jetter, P. Maus, H-F. Kunz, Stuttgart Gächinger Kantorei, Stuttgart Bach Collegium, H. Rilling (r1970) Concert (2/95) (HANS) ① 98 835
B. Schlick, K. Wessel, G. de Mey, K. Mertens, Amsterdam Baroque Ch, Amsterdam Baroque Orch, T. Koopman (r1994) Concert
(2/95) (ERAT) ① [3] 4509-98536-2

Cantata No. 151, 'Süsser Trost, mein Jesus kommt', BWV151 (1725) (3rd day of Christmas)
EXCERPTS: 1. Aria: Süsser Trost, mein Jesus kommt (S); 2. Recit: Erfreue dich, mein Herz (B); 3. Aria: In Jesu Demut kann ich Trost (A); 4. Recit: Du teurer Gottes sohn (T); 5. Choral: Heut' schleusst er wieder auf die Tür (chor).
S. Hennig, P. Esswood, K. Equiluz, M. van Egmond, Hanover Boy's Ch, Ghent Collegium Vocale, Leonhardt Consort, G. Leonhardt Concert
(2/86) (TELD) ① [2] 2292-42631-2
S. Hennig, P. Esswood, K. Equiluz, M. van Egmond, Hanover Boy's Ch, Ghent Collegium Vocale, Leonhardt Consort, G. Leonhardt Concert
(2/95) (TELD) ① [6] 4509-91762-2
N. Gamo-Yamamoto, H. Laurich, Adalbert Kraus, H-F. Kunz, Frankfurt Kantorei, Stuttgart Bach Collegium, H. Rilling (1971) Concert
(2/95) (HANS) ① 98 825

Cantata No. 152, 'Tritt auf die Glaubensahn', BWV152 (1714) (Wds. Franck. Christmas I)
EXCERPTS: 1. Concerto; 2. Aria: Tritt auf die Glaubensbahn (S); 3. Recit: Der heiland ist gesetzt in Israel zum (B); 4. Aria: Stein, der über alle Schätze (S); 5. Recit: Es ärg're sich die kluge Welt (B); 6. Duet: Wie soll ich dich, Liebster der Seelen (S,B).
C. Wegmann, T. Hampson, Tolz Boys' Ch, VCM, N. Harnoncourt Concert
(4/86) (TELD) ① [2] 2292-42632-2
G. de Reyghere, M. van Egmond, Ricercar Consort Concert (1/90) (RICE) ① RIC061041
C. Brandes, W. Sharp, American Bach Sols, J. Thomas (1993) Concert (4/94) (KOCH) ① 37164-2
C. Wegmann, T. Hampson, Tolz Boys' Ch, VCM, N. Harnoncourt Concert
(2/95) (TELD) ① [6] 4509-91762-2
A. Auger, W. Schöne, Inst Ens, H. Rilling (r1976)
(2/95) (HANS) ① 98 826
2, 6. T. Hampson, C. Wegmann, VCM, N. Harnoncourt Concert
(4/92) (TELD) ① 9031-74798-2

Cantata No. 153, 'Schau, lieber Gott, wie meine Feind', BWV153 (1724) (New Year I)
EXCERPTS: 1. Choral: Schau, lieber Gott, wie meine Feind (chor); 2. Recit: Mein liebster Gott (A); 3. Aria: Fürchte dich nicht, ich bin mit dir (B); 4. Recit: Du sprichst zwar, lieber Gott (T); 5. Choral: Und obgleich alle Teufel (chor); 6. Aria: Stürmt nur, stürmt, ihr Trübsals wetter (T); 7. Recit: Getrost, mein Herz (B); 8. Aria: Soll ich meinen Lebenslauf (A); 9. Choral: Drum will ich, weil ich lebe noch (chor).
S. Rampf, K. Equiluz, T. Hampson, Tolz Boys' Ch, VCM, N. Harnoncourt Concert
(4/86) (TELD) ① [2] 2292-42632-2
A. Murray, Adalbert Kraus, W. Heldwein, Stuttgart Gächinger Kantorei, Stuttgart Bach Collegium, H. Rilling Concert (2/95) (HANS) ① 98 871
S. Rampf, K. Equiluz, T. Hampson, Tolz Boys' Ch, VCM, N. Harnoncourt Concert
(2/95) (TELD) ① [6] 4509-91762-2
3. T. Hampson, VCM, N. Harnoncourt Concert
(4/92) (TELD) ① 9031-74798-2

Cantata No. 154, 'Mein liebster Jesus ist verloren', BWV154 (1724) (Epiphany I)
EXCERPTS: 1. Aria (Concerto): Mein liebster Jesus ist verloren (T); 2. Recit: Wo treff' ich meinen Jesus an (T); 3. Choral: Jesu, mein Hort und Erretter (chor); 4. Aria: Jesu, lass dich finden (A); 5. Arioso: Wisset

ihr nichr, dass ich sein muss in dem (B); 6. Recit: Dies ist die Stimme meines Freundes (T); 7. Aria (Duet): Wohl mir, jesus ist gefunden (A,T); 8. Choral: Meinen Jesum lass ich nicht (chor).

P. Esswood, K. Equiluz, T. Hampson, Tolz Boys' Ch, VCM, N. Harnoncourt *Concert* (4/86) (TELD) ① [2] **2292-42632-2**

A. Murray, A. Baldin, W. Heldwein, Stuttgart Gächinger Kantorei, Stuttgart Bach Collegium, H. Rilling *Concert* (2/95) (HANS) ① **98 872**

P. Esswood, K. Equiluz, T. Hampson, Tolz Boys' Ch, VCM, N. Harnoncourt *Concert* (2/95) (TELD) ① [6] **4509-91762-2**

5. T. Hampson, VCM, N. Harnoncourt *Concert* (4/92) (TELD) ① **9031-74798-2**

Cantata No. 155, 'Mein Gott, wie lang, ache lange', BWV155 (1716) (Wds. Franck. Epiphany II)

EXCERPTS: 1. Recit (Concerto): Mein Gott, wie lang', ach lange (S); 2. Aria (Duet): Du musst glauben, du musst hoffen (A,T); 3. Recit: So sei, o Seele, sei zufrieden! (B); 4. Aria: Wirf, mein Herze, wirf dich noch in des Höchsten Liebesarme (S); 5. Choral: Ob sich's anliess', als wollt' er nicht (chor).

A. Bergius, P. Esswood, K. Equiluz, T. Hampson, Tolz Boys' Ch, VCM, N. Harnoncourt *Concert* (4/86) (TELD) ① [2] **2292-42632-2**

I. Reichelt, N. Lerer, F. Melzer, H-F. Kunz, Stuttgart Gächinger Kantorei, Stuttgart Bach Collegium, H. Rilling *Concert* (2/95) (HANS) ① **98 873**

A. Bergius, P. Esswood, K. Equiluz, T. Hampson, Tolz Boys' Ch, VCM, N. Harnoncourt *Concert* (2/95) (TELD) ① [6] **4509-91762-2**

Cantata No. 156, 'Ich steh mit einem Fuss im Grabe', BWV156 (1729) (Wds. Picander. Epiphany III)

EXCERPTS: 1. Sinfonia; 2. Aria & Choral: Ich steh' mit einem Fuss im Grabe (S,T); 3. Recit: mein' Angst und Not (B); 4. Aria: Herr, was du willst soll mirgefallen (A); 5. Recit: Und willst du, dass ich nicht soll kranken (B); 6. Choral: Herr, wie du willt (chor).

C. Wegmann, P. Esswood, K. Equiluz, T. Hampson, Tolz Boys' Ch, VCM, N. Harnoncourt *Concert* (4/86) (TELD) ① [2] **2292-42632-2**

S. Rickards, Jeffrey Thomas (ten/dir), J. Weaver, American Bach Sols *Concert* (4/93) (KOCH) ① **37163-2**

C. Wegmann, P. Esswood, K. Equiluz, T. Hampson, Tolz Boys' Ch, VCM, N. Harnoncourt *Concert* (2/95) (TELD) ① [6] **4509-91762-2**

H. Laurich, K. Equiluz, W. Schöne, Stuttgart Gedächtniskirche Ch, Stuttgart Bach Collegium, H. Rilling *Concert* (2/95) (HANS) ① **98 875**

1. Taverner Plyrs, A. Parrott *Concert* (12/88) (EMI) ① **CDM7 69853-2**

1. J. Szigeti, Orch, W. Goehr (r1937: arr Szigeti) *Concert* (11/92) (BIDD) ① **LAB064**

1. J. Lloyd Webber, J. Lenehan (r1992: arr vc/pf) *Concert* (10/93) (PHIL) ① **434 917-2PH**

Cantata No. 157, 'Ich lasse dich nicht, du segnest mich denn', BWV157 (1729) (Wds. Picander. Funeral/Purification)

EXCERPTS: 1. Duet: Ich lasse dich nicht, du segnest mich denn (T,B); 2. Aria: Ich halte meinen Jesum feste (T); 3. Recit: Mein lieber Jesu du (T); 4. Aria: Ja, ich halte Jesum feste (B); 5. Choral: Meinem Jesum lass' ich nicht (chor).

K. Equiluz, M. van Egmond, Tolz Boys' Ch, Ghent Collegium Vocale, Leonhardt Consort, G. Leonhardt *Concert* (4/87) (TELD) ① [2] **2292-42633-2**

K. Equiluz, M. van Egmond, Tolz Boys' Ch, Ghent Collegium Vocale, Leonhardt Consort, G. Leonhardt *Concert* (2/95) (TELD) ① [6] **4509-91762-2**

Adalbert Kraus, P. Huttenlocher, Stuttgart Gächinger Kantorei, Inst Ens, H. Rilling (r1982/3) *Concert* (2/95) (HANS) ① **98 835**

Cantata No. 158, '(Der) Friede sei mit dir', BWV158 (1727) (Easter Tuesday/Purification)

EXCERPTS: 1. Recit: Der Friede sei mit dir (B); 2. Aria & Choral: Welt, ade! ich bin dein müde (S,B); 3. Recit: Nun Herr, regiere meinen Sinn (B); 4. Choral: Hier ist das rechte Osterlamm (chor).

C. Wegmann, M. van Egmond, Tolz Boys' Ch, Ghent Collegium Vocale, Leonhardt Consort, G. Leonhardt *Concert* (4/87) (TELD) ① [2] **2292-42633-2**

P. Kooy, Chapelle Royale Ch, Chapelle Royale Orch, P. Herreweghe *Concert* (10/92) (HARM) ① **HMC90 1365**

O. Bär, Scottish CO, P. Schreier *Concert* (6/93) (EMI) ① **CDC7 54453-2**

D. Fischer-Dieskau, Munich Bach Ch, Munich Bach Orch, K. Richter (r1969) *Concert* (7/94) (ARCH) ① [5] **439 374-2AX5**

M. van Egmond, Monteverdi Ch, Concerto Amsterdam, J. Jürgens (r1966/7) *Concert* (10/94) (TELD) ① **4509-93687-2**

C. Wegmann, M. van Egmond, Tolz Boys' Ch, Ghent Collegium Vocale, Leonhardt Consort, G. Leonhardt *Concert* (2/95) (TELD) ① [6] **4509-91762-2**

P. Huttenlocher, Stuttgart Gächinger Kantorei, Inst Ens, H. Rilling *Concert* (2/95) (HANS) ① **98 882**

Cantata No. 159, 'Sehet, wir gehn hinauf gen Jerusalem', BWV159 (1729) (Wds. Picander. Quinquagesima)

EXCERPTS: 1. Recit & Arioso: Sehet, wir geh'n hinauf gen Jerusalem (A,B); 2. Aria & Choral: Ich folge dir nach (S,A); 3. Recit: Nun will ich mich (T); 4. Aria: Es ist vollbracht (B); 5. Choral: Jesu, deine Passion ist mir lauter Freude (chor).

T. Eiwanger, P. Esswood, K. Equiluz, M. van Egmond, Tolz Boys' Ch, Ghent Collegium Vocale, Leonhardt Consort, G. Leonhardt *Concert* (4/87) (TELD) ① [2] **2292-42633-2**

J. Baker, R. Tear, J. Shirley-Quirk, St Anthony Sngrs, ASMF *Concert* (7/91) (DECC) ① **430 260-2DM**

T. Eiwanger, P. Esswood, K. Equiluz, M. van Egmond, Tolz Boys' Ch, Ghent Collegium Vocale, Leonhardt Consort, G. Leonhardt *Concert* (2/95) (TELD) ① [6] **4509-91762-2**

J. Hamari, A. Baldin, P. Huttenlocher, Stuttgart Gächinger Kantorei, Stuttgart Bach Collegium, H. Rilling *Concert* (2/95) (HANS) ① **98 879**

4. E. Schumann, orch, K. Alwin (r1927) *Concert* (6/91) (PREI) ① **89031**

Cantata No. 161, 'Komm, du süsse Todesstunde', BWV161 (1715) (Wds. Franck. Trinity XVI/Purification)

EXCERPTS: 1. Aria: Komm, du süsse Todesstunde (A); 2. Recit: Welt, deine Lust ist Last (T); 3. Aria: Mein Verlangen ist, den Heiland zu umfangen (T); 4. Recit: Der Schluss ist schon gemacht (A); 5. Chorus: Wenn es meines Gottes Wille; 6. Choral: Der Leib zwar in der Erden (chor).

P. Esswood, K. Equiluz, Tolz Boys' Ch, VCM, N. Harnoncourt *Concert* (4/87) (TELD) ① [2] **2292-42633-2**

C. Brandes, D. Minter, Jeffrey Thomas, W. Sharp, American Bach Sols, J. Thomas (r1993) *Concert* (4/94) (KOCH) ① **37164-2**

P. Esswood, K. Equiluz, Tolz Boys' Ch, VCM, N. Harnoncourt *Concert* (2/95) (TELD) ① [6] **4509-91762-2**

H. Laurich, Adalbert Kraus, Frankfurt Kantorei, Stuttgart Bach Collegium, H. Rilling (r1975/6) *Concert* (2/95) (HANS) ① **98 812**

Cantata No. 162, 'Ach! ich sehe, jetzt, da ich zur Hochzeit gehe', BWV162 (1715) (Wds. Franck. Trinity XX)

EXCERPTS: 1. Aria: Ach, ich sehe, itzt da ich zur Hochzeit gehe (B); 2. Recit: O grosses Hochzeitfest (T); 3. Aria: Jesu, Brunnquellaller Gnaden (S); 4. Recit: Mein Jesu, lass mich nicht zur Hochzeit unbekleidet kommen (A); 5. Aria (Duet): In meinem Gott bin icherfreut (A,T); 6. Choral: Ach, ich habe schonerblikket (chor).

T. Eiwanger, P. Esswood, K. Equiluz, R. Holl, Tolz Boys' Ch, VCM, N. Harnoncourt *Concert* (4/87) (TELD) ① [2] **2292-42633-2**

T. Eiwanger, P. Esswood, K. Equiluz, R. Holl, Tolz Boys' Ch, VCM, N. Harnoncourt *Concert* (2/95) (TELD) ① [6] **4509-91762-2**

A. Auger, A. Rogers, K. Equiluz, W. Schöne, Frankfurt Kantorei, Stuttgart Bach Collegium, H. Rilling (r1975/6) *Concert* (2/95) (HANS) ① **98 816**

Cantata No. 163, 'Nur jedem das Seine', BWV163 (1715) (Wds. Franck. Trinity XXIII)

EXCERPTS: 1. Aria: Nur jedem das Seine (T); 2. Recit: Du bist mein Gott (B); 3. Aria: Lass mein Herz die Münze sein (B); 4. Recit: Ich wollte dir, o Gott (S,A); 5. Aria (Duet): Nimm mich mir und gibmich dir (S,A); 6. Choral: Führ' auch mein Herz und Sinn.

T. Eiwanger, P. Iconomou, K. Equiluz, R. Holl, Tolz Boys' Ch, VCM, N. Harnoncourt *Concert* (4/87) (TELD) ① [2] **2292-42633-2**

T. Eiwanger, P. Iconomou, K. Equiluz, R. Holl, Tolz Boys' Ch, VCM, N. Harnoncourt *Concert* (2/95) (TELD) ① [6] **4509-91763-2**

A. Auger, H. Watts, Adalbert Kraus, N. Tüller, Stuttgart Gächinger Kantorei, Stuttgart Bach Collegium, H. Rilling (r1976/7) *Concert* (2/95) (HANS) ① **98 820**

Cantata No. 164, 'Ihr, die ihr euch Christo nennet', BWV164 (1725) (Wds. Franck. Trinity XIII)

EXCERPTS: 1. Aria: Ihr, die irh euch von Christo nennet (T); 2. Recit: Wir hören zwar (B); 3. Aria: Nur durch Lieb' und durch Erbarmen werden (A); 4. Recit: Ach, schmelze doch durch deinen Liebesstrahl (T); 5. Aria (Duet): Händen, die sich nicht verschliessen (S,B); 6. Choral: Ertöt' uns durch dein' Gütte (chor).

C. Wegmann, P. Esswood, K. Equiluz, M. van Egmond, Tolz Boys' Ch, Ghent Collegium Vocale, Leonhardt Consort, G. Leonhardt *Concert* (9/87) (TELD) ① [2] **2292-42634-2**

C. Wegmann, P. Esswood, K. Equiluz, M. van Egmond, Tolz Boys' Ch, Ghent Collegium Vocale, Leonhardt Consort, G. Leonhardt *Concert* (2/95) (TELD) ① [6] **4509-91763-2**

E. Wiens, J. Hamari, L-M. Harder, W. Heldwein, Stuttgart Gächinger Kantorei, Stuttgart Bach Collegium, H. Rilling (r1981/2) *Concert* (2/95) (HANS) ① **98 811**

Cantata No. 165, 'O heilges Geist-und Wasserbad', BWV165 (1715) (Wds. Franck. Trinity)

EXCERPTS: 1. Aria (Concerto): O heil'ges Geist-und Wasserbad (S); 2. Recit: Die sündige Geburt verdammter Adams-Erben (B); 3. Aria: Jesu, der aus grosser Liebe (A); 4. Recit: Ich habe ja, mein Seelen bräutigam (B); 5. Aria: Jesu, meines Todes Tod (T); 6. Choral: Sein Wort, sein' Taufe (chor).

T. Eiwanger, P. Esswood, K. Equiluz, M. van Egmond, Tolz Boys' Ch, Ghent Collegium Vocale, Leonhardt Consort, G. Leonhardt *Concert* (9/87) (TELD) ① [2] **2292-42634-2**

T. Eiwanger, P. Esswood, K. Equiluz, M. van Egmond, Tolz Boys' Ch, Ghent Collegium Vocale, Leonhardt Consort, G. Leonhardt *Concert* (2/95) (TELD) ① [6] **4509-91763-2**

A. Auger, A. Rogers, K. Equiluz, W. Schöne, Frankfurt Kantorei, Stuttgart Bach Collegium, H. Rilling (r1975/6) *Concert* (2/95) (HANS) ① **98 891**

Cantata No. 166, 'Wo gehest du hin?', BWV166 (1724) (Easter IV)

EXCERPTS: 1. Aria: Wo gehest du hin?; 2. Aria: Ich will an den Himmel denken (T); 3. Choral: Ich bitte dich, Herr Jesu Christ (S); 4. Recit: Gleichwie die Regenwasser bald verfliessen (B); 5. Aria: Man nehme sich in Acht (A); 6. Choral: Wer weiss, wie nahe mir mein Ende (chor).

C. Wegmann, P. Esswood, K. Equiluz, M. van Egmond, Tolz Boys' Ch, Ghent Collegium Vocale, Leonhardt Consort, G. Leonhardt *Concert* (9/87) (TELD) ① [2] **2292-42634-2**

C. Wegmann, P. Esswood, K. Equiluz, M. van Egmond, Tolz Boys' Ch, Ghent Collegium Vocale, Leonhardt Consort, G. Leonhardt *Concert* (2/95) (TELD) ① [6] **4509-91763-2**

H. Watts, A. Baldin, W. Schöne, Stuttgart Gächinger Kantorei, Stuttgart Bach Collegium, H. Rilling *Concert* (2/95) (HANS) ① **98 883**

Cantata No. 167, 'Ihr Menschen, rühmet Gottes Liebe', BWV167 (1723) (St John)

EXCERPTS: 1. Aria: Ihr Menschen, rühmet Gottes Liebe (T); 2. Recit: Gelobet sei der Herr Gott Israel (A); 3. Duet: Gottes Wort (S,A); 4. Recit: Des Weibes Samen kam (B); 5. Choral: Sei Lob und Preis mit Ehren (chor).

H. Wittek, P. Iconomou, K. Equiluz, R. Holl, Tolz Boys' Ch, VCM, N. Harnoncourt *Concert* (9/87) (TELD) ① [2] **2292-42634-2**

H. Wittek, P. Iconomou, K. Equiluz, R. Holl, Tolz Boys' Ch, VCM, N. Harnoncourt *Concert* (2/95) (TELD) ① [6] **4509-91763-2**

K. Graf, H. Gardow, Adalbert Kraus, N. Tüller, Stuttgart Gedächtniskirche Ch, Stuttgart Bach Collegium, H. Rilling (r1974) *Concert* (2/95) (HANS) ① **98 803**

Cantata No. 168, 'Tue Rechnung! Donnerwort', BWV168 (1725) (Wds. Franck. Trinity IX)

EXCERPTS: 1. Aria: Tue Rechnung! Donnerwort (B); 2. Recit: Es ist nur fremdes Gut (T); 3. Aria: Capital und Interessen (T); 4. Recit: Jedoch, erschrock'nes Herz (B); 5. Aria (Duet): Herz, zerreiss' des Mammons Kette (S,A); 6. Choral: Stärk' mich mit deinem Freudengeist (chor).

H. Wittek, C. Immler, K. Equiluz, R. Holl, Tolz Boys' Ch, VCM, N. Harnoncourt *Concert* (9/87) (TELD) ① [2] **2292-42634-2**

H. Wittek, C. Immler, K. Equiluz, R. Holl, Tolz Boys' Ch, VCM, N. Harnoncourt *Concert* (2/95) (TELD) ① [6] **4509-91763-2**

N. Burns, V. Gohl, T. Altmeyer, S. Nimsgern, Frankfurt Kantorei, Stuttgart Bach Collegium, H. Rilling (r1970) *Concert* (2/95) (HANS) ① **98 807**

Cantata No. 169, 'Gott soll allein mein Herze haben', BWV169 (1726) (Trinity XVIII)

EXCERPTS: 1. Sinfonia; 2. Arioso: Gott soll allein mein Herze haben (A); 3. Aria: Gott soll allein mein Herze haben (A); 4. Recit: Was ist die Liebe Gottes? (A); 5. Aria: Stirb in mir (A); 6. Recit: Doch meint es auch dabei (A); 7. Choral: Du süsse Liebe, schenk' uns deine Gunst (chor).

P. Esswood, Tolz Boys' Ch, VCM, N. Harnoncourt *Concert* (9/87) (TELD) ① [2] **2292-42634-2**

A. Reynolds, P. Schreier, T. Adam, Munich Bach Ch, Munich Bach Orch, K. Richter (r1974-5) *Concert* (7/94) (ARCH) Ⓓ [5] **439 374-2AX5**

P. Esswood, K. Equiluz, R. Holl, Tolz Boys' Ch, VCM, N. Harnoncourt *Concert* (2/95) (TELD) Ⓓ [6] **4509-91763-2**

D. Soffel, A. Baldin, P. Huttenlocher, Stuttgart Gächinger Kantorei, Stuttgart Bach Collegium, H. Rilling *Cantata 66.* (2/95) (HANS) Ⓓ **98 880**

F. Sailer, C. Hellmann, H. Krebs, E. Wenk, Heilbronn Schütz Ch, Pforzheim CO, F. Werner (r1961) *Concert* (5/95) (ERAT) Ⓓ [2] **4509-97407-2**

1. F. Brüggen, Leonhardt Consort (r1967) *Concert* (10/95) (TELD) Ⓓ **4509-97473-2**

Cantata No. 183, 'Sie werden euch in den Bann tun', BWV183 (1725) (Wds. Ziegler. Ascension I)

EXCERPTS: 1. Recit: Sie werden euch in den Bann tun (B); 2. Aria: Ich fürchte nicht des Todes Schrecken (T); 3. Recit: Ich bin bereit (A); 4. Aria: Höchster Tröster, heil'ger Geist (S); 5. Choral: Du bist ein Geist (chor).

H. Wittek, P. Esswood, K. Equiluz, T. Hampson, Tolz Boys' Ch, VCM, N. Harnoncourt *Concert* (2/89) (TELD) Ⓓ [2] **2292-42738-2**

H. Wittek, P. Esswood, K. Equiluz, T. Hampson, Tolz Boys' Ch, VCM, N. Harnoncourt *Concert* (2/95) (TELD) Ⓓ [6] **4509-91764-2**

A. Auger, J. Hamari, P. Schreier, W. Heldwein, Stuttgart Gächinger Kantorei, Stuttgart Bach Collegium, H. Rilling (r1981) *Concert* (2/95) (HANS) Ⓓ **98 887**

B. Schlick, A. Scholl, C. Prégardien, G. Schwarz, Concerto Vocale, Limoges Baroque Ens, C. Coin (vc/dir) (r1994) *Concert* (12/95) (ASTR) Ⓓ **E8544**

Cantata No. 184, 'Erwünschtes Freudenlicht', BWV184 (1724) (Whit Tuesday)

EXCERPTS: 1. Recit: Erwünschtes Freudenlicht (T); 2. Aria (Duet): Gesegnete Christen, glückselige Herde (S,A); 3. Recit: So freuet euch (T); 4. Aria: Glück und Segen sind bereit (T); 5. Choral: Herr, ich hoff' je, du werdest die in keiner Not verlassen (chor); 6. Chorus: Guter Hirte, Trost der Deinen.

A. Raymann, P. Esswood, K. Equiluz, M. van Egmond, Hanover Boys' Ch, Ghent Collegium Vocale, Leonhardt Consort, G. Leonhardt *Concert* (2/89) (TELD) Ⓓ [2] **2292-42738-2**

A. Raymann, P. Esswood, K. Equiluz, M. van Egmond, Hanover Boys' Ch, Ghent Collegium Vocale, Leonhardt Consort, G. Leonhardt *Concert* (2/95) (TELD) Ⓓ [6] **4509-91764-2**

A. Auger, G. Schnaut, Adalbert Kraus, N. Tüller, Stuttgart Gächinger Kantorei, Stuttgart Bach Collegium, H. Rilling (r1976/7) *Concert* (2/95) (HANS) Ⓓ **98 890**

Cantata No. 185, 'Barmherziges Herze der ewigen Liebe', BWV185 (1715) (Wds. Franck. Trinity IV)

EXCERPTS: 1. Aria (Duet): Barmherziges Herze der ewigen Liebe (S,T); 2. Recit: Ihr Herzen (A); 3. Aria: Sei bemüht in dieser Zeit (A); 4. Recit: Die Eigenliebe schmeichelt sich (B); 5. Aria: Das ist der Christen Kunst (B); 6. Choral: Ich ruf zu dir, Herr Jesu Christ (chor).

H. Wittek, P. Esswood, K. Equiluz, T. Hampson, Tolz Boys' Ch, VCM, N. Harnoncourt *Concert* (9/89) (TELD) Ⓓ [2] **2292-44179-2**

H. Wittek, P. Esswood, K. Equiluz, T. Hampson, Tolz Boys' Ch, VCM, N. Harnoncourt *Concert* (2/95) (TELD) Ⓓ [6] **4509-91764-2**

A. Auger, H. Laurich, A. Baldin, P. Huttenlocher, Frankfurt Kantorei, Stuttgart Bach Collegium, H. Rilling (r1976) *Concert* (2/95) (HANS) Ⓓ **98 804**

B. Schlick, K. Wessel, G. de Mey, K. Mertens, Amsterdam Baroque Ch, Amsterdam Baroque Orch, T. Koopman (r1994) *Concert* (9/95) (ERAT) Ⓓ [3] **4509-98536-2**

5. T. Hampson, VCM, N. Harnoncourt *Concert* (4/92) (TELD) Ⓓ **9031-74798-2**

Cantata No. 186, 'Ärge dich, o Seele, nicht', BWV186 (1723) (Trinity VII)

EXCERPTS: PART ONE: 1. Chorus: Ärge dich, o Seele, nicht; 2. Recit: Die Knechtsgestalt, die Not (B); 3. Aria: Bist du, der mir helfen soll (B); 4. Recit: Ach, dass ein Christ (T); 5. Aria: Mein Heiland lässt sich merken (T); 6. Choral: Ob sich's anliess' (chor). PART TWO: 7. Recit: Es ist die Welt (B); 8. Aria: Die Armen will der Herr umarmen (S); 9. Recit: Nun mag die Welt mit ihrer Lust vergehen (A); 10. Aria (Duet): Lass, Seele, kein Leiden von Jesu dich scheiden (S,A).

H. Wittek, P. Esswood, K. Equiluz, R. Holl, Tolz Boys' Ch, VCM, N. Harnoncourt *Concert* (9/89) (TELD) Ⓓ [2] **2292-44179-2**

H. Wittek, P. Esswood, K. Equiluz, R. Holl, Tolz Boys' Ch, VCM, N. Harnoncourt *Concert* (2/95) (TELD) Ⓓ [6] **4509-91764-2**

A. Auger, H. Watts, K. Equiluz, P. Huttenlocher, Stuttgart Gächinger Kantorei, Stuttgart Bach Collegium, H. Rilling (r1977) *Concert* (2/95) (HANS) Ⓓ **98 805**

Cantata No. 187, 'Es wartet alles auf dich', BWV187 (1726) (Trinity VII)

EXCERPTS: PART ONE: 1. Chorus: es wartet alles auf dich; 2. Recit: Was Creaturen hält das grosse Rund der Welt! (B); 3. Aria: Du Herr, du krönst allein (A). PART TWO: 4. Aria: Darum sollt ihr nicht sorgen (B); 5. Aria: Gott versorget (S); 6. Recit: Halt' ich nur fest (S); 7. Choral: Gott hat dei Erd' schön zugericht't (chor).

M. Emmermann, P. Esswood, M. van Egmond, Hanover Boys' Ch, Ghent Collegium Vocale, Leonhardt Consort, G. Leonhardt *Concert* (9/89) (TELD) Ⓓ [2] **2292-44179-2**

E. Mathis, J. Hamari, D. Fischer-Dieskau, Munich Bach Ch, Munich Bach Orch, K. Richter (r1976/7) *Concert* (1/95) (ARCH) Ⓓ [6] **439 387-2AX6**

M. Emmermann, P. Esswood, M. van Egmond, Hanover Boys' Ch, Ghent Collegium Vocale, Leonhardt Consort, G. Leonhardt *Concert* (2/95) (TELD) Ⓓ [6] **4509-91764-2**

M. Friesenhausen, H. Laurich, W. Schöne, Stuttgart Gächinger Kantorei, Stuttgart Bach Collegium, H. Rilling (r1971) *Concert* (2/95) (HANS) Ⓓ **98 806**

5. K. Battle, I. Perlman, St Luke's Orch, J. Nelson (r1989/90) *Concert* (3/92) (DG) Ⓓ **429 737-2GH**

5. E. Ameling, H. de Vries, R. van der Meer, A. de Klerk (r1983) *Concert* (7/94) (EMI) Ⓓ **CDC5 55000-2**

Cantata No. 188, 'Ich habe meine Zuversicht', BWV188 (c1728) (Wds. Picander. Trinity XXI)

EXCERPTS: 1. Aria: Ich habe meine Zuversicht (T); 2. Recit: Gott meint es gut mit jedermann (B); 3. Aria: Unerforschlich ist die Weise (A); 4. Recit: Die Macht der Welt verlieret sich (S); 5. Choral: Auf meinen lieben Gott (chor).

H. Wittek, P. Esswood, K. Equiluz, R. Holl, Tolz Boys' Ch, VCM, N. Harnoncourt *Concert* (9/89) (TELD) Ⓓ [2] **2292-44179-2**

H. Wittek, P. Esswood, K. Equiluz, R. Holl, Tolz Boys' Ch, VCM, N. Harnoncourt *Concert* (2/95) (TELD) Ⓓ [6] **4509-91764-2**

A. Auger, J. Hamari, A. Baldin, W. Heldwein, Stuttgart Gächinger Kantorei, Württemberg CO, H. Rilling (r1983) *Concert* (2/95) (HANS) Ⓓ **98 817**

Cantata No. 190, 'Singet dem Herrn ein neues Lied!', BWV190 (1724) (New Year)

EXCERPTS: 1. Chorus: Singet dem Herrn ein neues Lied; 2. Choral: Herr Gott, dich loben wir! (chor); 3. Aria: Lobe, Zion, deinen Gott (A); 4. Recit: Es wünsche sich die Welt (B); 5. Aria (Duet): Jesus soll mein Alles sein (T,B); 6. Recit: Nun, Jesus gebe (T); 7. Choral: Lass uns das Jahr vollbringen (chor).

H. Watts, K. Equiluz, N. Tüller, Stuttgart Gächinger Kantorei, Stuttgart Bach Collegium, H. Rilling *Concert* (2/95) (HANS) Ⓓ **98 870**

Cantata No. 191, 'Gloria in excelsis Deo', BWV191 (after 1740) (Christmas. adapt from Mass, BWV232)

EXCERPTS: 1. Chorus: Gloria in excelsis Deo; 2. Duet: Gloria Patri (S,T); 3. Chorus: Sicut erat in principio.

N. Gamo-Yamamoto, Adalbert Kraus, Stuttgart Gächinger Kantorei, Stuttgart Bach Collegium, H. Rilling *Concert* (2/95) (HANS) Ⓓ **98 867**

Cantata No. 192, 'Nun danket alle Gott', BWV192 (1730)

EXCERPTS: 1. Chorus: Nun danket alle Gott; 2. Duet: Der ewig reiche Gott (S,B); 3. Chorus: Lob, Ehr' und Preis sei Gott.

H. Wittek, T. Hampson, Tolz Boys' Ch, VCM, N. Harnoncourt *Concert* (5/90) (TELD) Ⓓ **2292-44193-2**

H. Donath, N. Tüller, Frankfurt Kantorei, Stuttgart Bach Collegium, H. Rilling (r1974) *Concert* (2/95) (HANS) Ⓓ **98 863**

H. Wittek, T. Hampson, Tolz Boys' Ch, VCM, N. Harnoncourt *Concert* (2/95) (TELD) Ⓓ [6] **4509-91764-2**

2. T. Hampson, H. Wittek, VCM, N. Harnoncourt *Concert* (4/92) (TELD) Ⓓ **9031-74798-2**

Cantata No. 193, 'Ihr Tore zu Zion', BWV193 (c1727) (Town council inauguration)

EXCERPTS: 1. Chorus: Ihr Tore zu Zion; 2. Recit: Der Hüter Israel (S); 3. Aria: Gott, wir danken deiner Güte (S); 4. Recit: O Leipziger Jerusalem (A); 5. Aria: Sende, Herr, den Segen ein (A); 6. Recit (T/B); 7. Chorus.

A. Auger, J. Hamari, Stuttgart Gächinger Kantorei, Stuttgart Bach Collegium, H. Rilling (r1983: arr R Kubik) *Concert* (2/95) (HANS) Ⓓ **98 829**

Cantata No. 194, 'Höchsterwünschtes Freudenfest', BWV194 (1723) (Störmthal church & organ consecration)

EXCERPTS: PART ONE: 1. Chorus: Höchsterwünschtes Freudenfest; 2. Recit: Unendlich grosser Gott (B); 3. Aria: Was des Höchsten Glanz erfüllt (B); 4. Recit: Wie könnte dir (S); 5. Aria: Hilf, Gott, dass es uns gelingt (S); 6. Choral: Heil'ger Geist ins Himmels Throne (chor). PART TWO: 7. Recit: Ihr Heiligen, erfreuet euch (T); 8. Aria: Des Höchsten Gegenwart allein (T); 9. Recit (Duet): Kann wohl ein Mensch (S,B); 10. Aria (Duet): O wie wohl ist uns gescheh'n (S,B); 11. Wohlan dem nach (B); 12. Choral: Sprich Jazu meinen Taten (chor).

H. Stricker, S. Gienger, K. Equiluz, T. Hampson, Tolz Boys' Ch, VCM, N. Harnoncourt *Concert* (5/90) (TELD) Ⓓ **2292-44193-2**

H. Stricker, S. Gienger, K. Equiluz, T. Hampson, Tolz Boys' Ch, VCM, N. Harnoncourt *Concert* (2/95) (TELD) Ⓓ [6] **4509-91764-2**

J. Beckmann, Adalbert Kraus, W. Heldwein, Stuttgart Gächinger Kantorei, Stuttgart Bach Collegium, H. Rilling (r1976/7) *Cantata 28.* (2/95) (HANS) Ⓓ **98 827**

3, 10. T. Hampson, S. Gienger, VCM, N. Harnoncourt *Concert* (4/92) (TELD) Ⓓ **9031-74798-2**

Cantata No. 195, 'Dem Gerechten muss das Licht', BWV195 (after 1737) (Wedding)

EXCERPTS: 1. Chorus: Dem Gerechten muss das Licht; 2. Recit: Dem Freuden Licht (B); 3. Aria: Rühmet Gottes Güt' und Treu' (B); 4. Recit: Wohlan, so knüpfet denn ein Band (S); 5. Chorus: Wir kommen, deine Heiligkeit; 6. Choral: Nun danket all' und bringet Ehr' (chor).

J.P. O'Farrell, R. Jacobs, J. Elwes, H. van der Kamp, Hanover Boys' Ch, Ghent Collegium Vocale, Leonhardt Consort, G. Leonhardt *Concert* (5/90) (TELD) Ⓓ **2292-44193-2**

S. Inou-Heller, E. Graf, O. Pfaff, A. Schmidt, Stuttgart Gächinger Kantorei, Württemberg CO, H. Rilling (r1984) *Concert* (2/95) (HANS) Ⓓ **98 859**

J.P. O'Farrell, R. Jacobs, J. Elwes, H. van der Kamp, Hanover Boys' Ch, Ghent Collegium Vocale, Leonhardt Consort, G. Leonhardt *Concert* (2/95) (TELD) Ⓓ [6] **4509-91764-2**

Cantata No. 196, '(Der) Herr denket an uns', BWV196 (?1708) (Wedding)

EXCERPTS: 1. Sinfonia; 2. Chorus: Der Herr denket an uns; 3. Aria: Er segnet (S); 4. Duet: Der Herr segne euch (T,B); 5. Chorus: Ihr seid die Gesegneten.

H. Wittek, K. Equiluz, T. Hampson, Tolz Boys' Ch, VCM, N. Harnoncourt *Concert* (5/90) (TELD) Ⓓ [2] **2292-44194-2**

H. Wittek, K. Equiluz, T. Hampson, Tolz Boys' Ch, VCM, N. Harnoncourt *Concert* (2/95) (TELD) Ⓓ [6] **4509-91764-2**

D. Soffel, A. Baldin, N. Tüller, Stuttgart Gächinger Kantorei, Stuttgart Bach Collegium, H. Rilling (r1975) *Concert* (2/95) (HANS) Ⓓ **98 828**

B. Schlick, K. Wessel, G. de Mey, K. Mertens, Amsterdam Baroque Ch, Amsterdam Baroque Orch, T. Koopman (r1994) *Concert* (9/95) (ERAT) Ⓓ [3] **4509-98536-2**

4. T. Hampson, K. Equiluz, VCM, N. Harnoncourt *Concert* (4/92) (TELD) Ⓓ **9031-74798-2**

Cantata No. 197, 'Gott ist unsre Zuversicht', BWV197 (c1742) (Wedding)

EXCERPTS: 1. Chorus: Gott ist unsre Zuversicht; 2. Recit: Gott ist und bleibt de beste Sorger (B); 3. Aria: Schläfert aller Sorgen kummer (A); 4. Recit: Drum folget Gott und seinem Triebe (B); 5. Choral: Du süsse Lieb' (chor); 6. Aria: O du angenehmes Paar (B); 7. Recit: So wie es Gott mit dir getreu (S); 8. Aria: Vergnügen und Lust (S); 9. Recit: Und dieser frohe Lebenslauf (B); 10. Choral: So wandelt froh auf Gottes Wegen (chor).

J.P. O'Farrell, R. Jacobs, H. van der Kamp, Hanover Boys' Ch, Ghent Collegium Vocale, Leonhardt Consort, G. Leonhardt *Concert* (5/90) (TELD) Ⓓ [2] **2292-44194-2**

J.P. O'Farrell, R. Jacobs, H. van der Kamp, Hanover Boys' Ch, Ghent Collegium Vocale, Leonhardt Consort, G. Leonhardt *Concert* (2/95) (TELD) Ⓓ [6] **4509-91764-2**

C. Cuccaro, M. Georg, P. Huttenlocher, Stuttgart Gächinger Kantorei, Württemberg CO, H. Rilling (r1984) *Concert* (2/95) (HANS) Ⓓ **98 828**

8. K. Battle, I. Perlman, St Luke's Orch, J. Nelson (r1989/90) *Concert* (3/92) (DG) Ⓓ **429 737-2GH**

Cantata No. 198, 'Lass, Fürstin, lass noch einen Strahl' (Trauer Ode)—secular cantata, BWV198 (1727) (Wds. J. C. Gottsched)
EXCERPTS: PART ONE: 1. Chorus: Lass Fürstin, lass noch einen Strahl; 2. Recit: Dein Sachsen (S); 3. Aria: Verstummt ihr holden Saiten (S); 4. Recit: Der Glocken bebendes Getön (A); 5. Aria: Wie starb die Heldin (A); 6. Recit: Ihr Leben liess die Kunst (T); 7. Chorus: An dir, du Vorbild grosser Frauen. PART TWO: 8. Recit: Aria: Der Ewigkeit saphirnes Haus (T); 9. Recit: Was Wunder ist's? (B); 10. Chorus: Doch, Königin!.
I. Schmithüsen, C. Brett, H. Crook, P. Kooy, Paris Chapelle Royale Chor, Paris Chapelle Royale Orch, P. Herreweghe *Cantata 78.* (10/88) (HARM) ① **HMC90 1270**
J.P. O'Farrell, R. Jacobs, J. Elwes, H. van der Kamp, Hanover Boys' Ch, Ghent Collegium Vocale, Leonhardt Consort, G. Leonhardt *Concert* (5/90) (TELD) ① [2] **2292-44194-2**
N. Argenta, M. Chance, A. Rolfe Johnson, S. Varcoe, Monteverdi Ch, EBS, J.E. Gardiner *Concert* (5/91) (ARCH) ① **429 782-2AH**
J. Nelson, J. Malafronte, Jeffrey Thomas (ten/dir), W. Sharp, American Bach Sols *Concert* (4/93) (KOCH) ① **37163-2**
R. Hansmann, H. Watts, K. Equiluz, M. van Egmond, Monteverdi Ch, Concerto Amsterdam, J. Jürgens (r1966) *Concert* (10/94) (TELD) ① **4509-93687-2**
J.P. O'Farrell, R. Jacobs, J. Elwes, H. van der Kamp, Hanover Boys' Ch, Ghent Collegium Vocale, Leonhardt Consort, G. Leonhardt *Concert* (2/95) (TELD) ① [6] **4509-91764-2**
A. Auger, G. Schreckenbach, A. Baldin, P. Huttenlocher, Stuttgart Gächinger Kantorei, Württemberg CO, H. Rilling (r1983) *Cantata 106.* (2/95) (HANS) ① **98 830**

Cantata No. 199, 'Mein Herze schwimmt im Blut', BWV199 (1714) (Wds. Lehms. Trinity XI)
EXCERPTS: 1. Recit: Mein Herze schwimmt im Blut (S); 2. Aria: Stumme Seufzer, stille Klagen (S); 3. Recit: Doch Gott muss mir genädig sein (S); 4. Aria: Tiefgebückt und voller Reue (S); 5. Recit: Auf die Schmerzens (S); 6. Choral: Ich Dein betrübtes Kind; 7. Recit: Ich lege mich in diese Wunden (S); 8. Aria: Wie freudig ist mein Herz (S).
V. Hruba-Freiberger, Leipzig Univ Ch, Leipzig New Bach Collegium Musicum, M. Pommer *Concert* (9/89) (CAPR) ① **10 151**
B. Bonney, VCM, N. Harnoncourt *Concert* (5/90) (TELD) ① [2] **2292-44194-2**
E. Schwarzkopf, Philh, T. Dart (r1958) *Concert* (12/90) (EMI) ① **CDM7 63655-2**
F. Wagner, Capella Istropolitana, C. Brembeck *Concert* (9/92) (NAXO) ① **8 550431**
N. Argenta, Sonnerie Ens, M. Huggett (r1993) *Concert* (12/94) (VIRG) ① **VC5 45038-2**
E. Mathis, Munich Bach Ch, Munich Bach Orch, K. Richter (r1971/2) *Concert* (1/95) (ARCH) ① [6] **439 387-2AX6**
B. Bonney, VCM, N. Harnoncourt *Concert* (2/95) (TELD) ① [6] **4509-91764-2**
A. Auger, Stuttgart Bach Collegium, H. Rilling (r1976) *Concert* (2/95) (HANS) ① **98 810**
B. Schlick, Concerto Vocale, Limoges Baroque Ens, C. Coin (vc/dir) (r1994) *Concert* (12/95) (ASTR) ① **E8544**
2. E. Ameling, H. de Vries, R. van der Meer, A. de Klerk (r1983) *Concert* (7/94) (EMI) ① **CDC5 55000-2**

Cantata No. 200, 'Bekennen will ich seinen Namen', BWV200 (?1742) (fragment only. Purification)
M. Georg, Württemberg CO, H. Rilling (r1984) *Concert* (2/95) (HANS) ① **98 858**
J. Kowalski, ASMF, K. Sillito *Concert* (6/95) (CAPR) ① **10 523**

Cantata No. 201, 'Geschwinde, ihr wirbeln den Winde' (Phoebus und Pan'—secular cantata, BWV201 (?1729) (Wds. Picander)
EXCERPTS: 1. Chorus: Geschwinde ihr wirbelnden Winde; 2. Recit: Und du bist doch; 3. Aria: Patron, Patron; 4. Recit: Was braucht ihr euch zu zanken?; 5. Aria: Mit Verlangen; 6. Recit: Pan, rücke deine Kehle; 7. Aria: Zu Tanze, zu Sprunge; 8. Recit: Nunmehro Richter her!; 9. Aria: Phoebus, deine Melodei; 10. Komm, Mydas; 11. Aria: Pan ist Meister; 12. Recit: Wie, Mydas, bist du toll?; 13. Aria: Aufgeblas'ne Hitze; 14. Recit: Du guter Mydas; 15. Chorus: Labt das Herz, ihr holden Saiten.
Patron, patron I. Baillie, CBO, B. Cameron (r1941: Eng: arr Mottl) *Concert* (7/95) (DUTT) ① **CDLX7013**

Cantata No. 202, 'Weichet nur, betrübte Schatten' (Wedding Cantata)—secular cantata, BWV202 (?1718-23)
EXCERPTS: 1. Aria: Weichet nur, betrübte Schatten (S); 2. Recit: Die Welt wird wieder neu (S); 3. Aria: Phoebus eilt mit schnellen Pferden (S); 4. Recit: Drumsucht auch Amor (S); 5. Aria: Wenn die Frühlingslüfte (S); 6. Recit: Und dieses ist das Glükke (S); 7. Aria: Sich üben im Lieben (S); 8. Recit: So sei das Band (S); 9. Gavotte: Sehet in Zufriedenheit (S).
E. Kirkby, Taverner Plyrs, A. Parrott *Cantata 82.* (9/88) (HYPE) ① **CDA66036**
G. de Reyghere, Ricercar Consort *Concert* (1/90) (RICE) ① **RIC061041**
B. Hendricks, CPE Bach Orch, P. Schreier *Concert* (7/90) (EMI) ① **CDC7 49843-2**
E. Ameling, Collegium Aureum *Concert* (10/90) (DHM) ① [2] **GD77151**
M. Zádori, Capella Savaria, P. Németh (fl/dir) *Concert* (7/91) (QUIN) ① **QUI90 3010**
F. Wagner, Capella Istropolitana, C. Brembeck *Concert* (9/92) (NAXO) ① **8 550431**
M. Zádori, Capella Savaria, P. Németh (fl/dir) (r1990) *Concert* (8/94) (HARM) ① **HMA190 3010**
A. Felbermayer, H. Rössl-Majdan, W. Kmentt, Vienna Bach Guild Ch, Vienna Bach Guild Orch, F. Prohaska (r1953) *Concert* (10/94) (VANG) ① **08.2028.71**
N. Argenta, Sonnerie Ens, M. Huggett *Concert* (6/95) (VIRG) ① **VC5 45059-2**
E. Ameling, Collegium Aureum, F. Maier (vn/dir) (r1964/8) *Concert* (12/95) (DHM) ① [4] **74321 26617-2(1)**
1, 7. A. Auger, Mostly Mozart Orch, G. Schwarz *Concert* (11/86) (DELO) ① **DE3026**
5. K. Battle, I. Perlman, St Luke's Orch, J. Nelson (r1989/90) *Concert* (3/92) (DG) ① **429 737-2GH**
7. E. Kirkby, D. Reichenberg, Taverner Plyrs, A. Parrott *Concert* (9/87) (HYPE) ① **CDA66227**
7. E. Ameling, H. de Vries, R. van der Meer, A. de Klerk (r1983) *Concert* (7/94) (EMI) ① **CDC5 55000-2**
7. L. Garrett, RPO, P. Robinson (r1994) *Concert* (4/95) (SILV) ① **SILKD6004**

Cantata No. 204, 'Ich bin in mir vergnügt'—secular cantata, BWV204 (1726-27) (Wds. Hunold)
EXCERPTS: 1. Recit: Ich bin in mir vergnügt (S); 2. Aria: Ruhig und in sich zufrieden (S); 3. Recit: Ihr Seelen, die ihrausser euch (S); 4. Aria: Die Schätzbarkeit der weiten Erden (S); 5. Recit: Schwer ist es zwar (S); 6. Aria: Meine Seele sei vergnügt (S); 7. Recit: Ein edler Mensch (S); 8. Aria: Himmlische Vergnügsasmkeit (S).
D. Röschmann, Québec Violons du Roy (r1994) *Cantata 210.* (10/95) (DORI) ① **DOR90207**
4. K. Battle, I. Perlman, St Luke's Orch, J. Nelson (r1989/90) *Concert* (3/92) (DG) ① **429 737-2GH**

Cantata No. 206, 'Schleicht, spielende Wellen'—secular cantata, BWV206 (1736) (Birthday & name day of August III)
EXCERPTS: 1. Chorus: Schleicht, spielende Wellen; 2. Recit: O glückliche Veränderung! (B); 3. Aria: Schleuss des Janustempels Türen (B); 4. Recit: So recht! (T); 5. Aria: Jede Wogemeiner Wellen (T); 6. Recit: Ich nehm' zugleich an (A); 7. Aria: Reis, von Habsburgs hohem Stamme (A); 8. Recit: Verzeiht, bemooste (S); 9. Aria: Hört doch!; 10. Recit: Ich muss, ich will gehorsam sein (B); 11. Chorus: Die himmlische Vorsicht.
R. Ziesak, M. Chance, C. Prégardien, P. Kooy, Stuttgart Chbr Ch, Concerto Cologne, F. Bernius *Cantata 207a.* (9/91) (SONY) ① **SK46492**

Cantata No. 207a, 'Auf, schmetternde Töne'—secular cantata, BWV207a (1734) (Name day of August III)
EXCERPTS: 1. Chorus: Auf, schmetternde Töne; 2. Recit: Die stille Pleisse spielt (T); 3. Aria: Augustus' Namenstages Schimmer (T); 4. Recit: Augustus' Wohl ist der treuen Sachsen (S,B); 5. Duet: Mich kann die süsse Ruhe laben; 6. Recit: Augustus schützt die frohen Felder (A); 7. Aria: Preiset, späte Eolgezeiten; 8. Recit: Ihr Fröhlichen; 9. Chorus: August lebe.
R. Ziesak, M. Chance, C. Prégardien, P. Kooy, Stuttgart Chbr Ch, Concerto Cologne, F. Bernius *Cantata 206.* (9/91) (SONY) ① **SK46492**

Cantata No. 208, 'Was mir behagt, ist nur die muntre Jagd' (Hunt Cantata)—secular cantata, BWV208 (1713) (Wds. Franck. Birthday of Duke Christian of Saxe-Weissenfels)
EXCERPTS: 1. Recit: Was mir behagt, ist nur die muntre Jagd!; 2. Aria: Jagen ist die Lust der Götter; 3. Recit: Wie, schönste Göttin, wie?; 4. Aria: Willst du dich nur mehr ergötzen; 5. Recit: Ich liebe dich zwar noch!; 6. Aria: Ich, der ich sonst ein Gott in diesen Feldern bin; 7. Aria: Ein Fürst ist seines Landes Pan!; 8. Recit: Soll den der Pales Opfer hier das letzte sein?; 9. Aria: Schafe können sicher weiden; 10. Recit: So stimmt mit ein; 11. Chorale: Lebe, Sonne dieser Erden; 12. Duet: Entzücket uns beide; 13. Aria: Weil die wollenreichen Herden; 14. Aria: Ihr Felder und Auen; 15. Chorale: Ihr lieblichste Blikke!.
J. Smith, E. Kirkby, S. Davies, M. George, Parley of Instr, R. Goodman (12/86) (HYPE) ① **CDA66169**
J. Pászthy, J. Németh, J. Mukk, I. Gáti, Hungarian Rad Chor, Failoni CO, M. Antal *Cantata 51.* (12/92) (NAXO) ① **8 550643**
9. E. Kirkby, Parley of Instr, R. Goodman *Concert* (9/87) (HYPE) ① **CDA66227**
9. G. Fisher, King's Consort, R. King *Concert* (8/88) (CARL) ① **PCD894**
9. B. Hendricks, CPE Bach Orch, P. Schreier *Concert* (7/90) (EMI) ① **CDC7 49843-2**
9. E. Schwarzkopf, Inst Ens (r1946) *Concert* (7/90) (EMI) ① **CDH7 63201-2**
9. G. Fergus-Thompson (trans Le Fleming) *Concert* (10/91) (ASV) ① **CDDCA759**
9. M. Petri, Westminster Abbey Ch, National PO, M. Neary *Concert* (12/91) (RCA) ① **RD60060**
9. P. Hurford, M. Laird Brass Ens (r1990: arr Hazell) *Concert* (9/92) (ARGO) ① **433 451-2ZH**
9. E. Schwarzkopf, M. Raucheisen, Inst Ens (bp1944) *Concert* (5/93) (ACAN) ① **43 128**
9. Toronto Children's Chor, Toronto SO, J.A. Bartle (r1992; arr Cable) *Concert* (12/93) (CBC) ① **SMCD5119**
9. E. Petri (pp1958: arr pf: Petri) *Concert* (3/94) (MUSI) ① [4] **MACD-772**
9. BBC PO, M. Bamert (r1993: orch Stokowski) *Concert* (3/94) (CHAN) ① **CHAN9259**

Cantata No. 209, 'Non sa che sia dolore'—secular cantata, BWV209 (?1734) (Departure of a scholar)
EXCERPTS: 1. Sinfonia; 2. Recit: non sa che sia dolore (S); 3. Aria: Parti pur, e con dolore (S); 4. Recit: Tuo saver al tempo (S); 5. Aria: Riceti gramezza e pavento (S).
E. Ameling, Collegium Aureum *Concert* (10/90) (DHM) ① [2] **GD77151**
M. Zádori, Capella Savaria, P. Németh (fl/dir) *Concert* (7/91) (QUIN) ① **QUI90 3010**
F. Wagner, Capella Istropolitana, C. Brembeck *Concert* (9/92) (NAXO) ① **8 550431**
M. Zádori, Capella Savaria, P. Németh (fl/dir) (r1990) *Concert* (8/94) (HARM) ① **HMA190 3010**
T. Stich-Randall, Vienna St Op Orch, A. Heiller (r1954) *Concert* (10/94) (VANG) ① **08.2028.71**
N. Argenta, Sonnerie Ens, M. Huggett *Concert* (6/95) (VIRG) ① **VC5 45059-2**
E. Ameling, Collegium Aureum, F. Maier (vn/dir) (r1964/8) *Concert* (12/95) (DHM) ① [4] **74321 26617-2(1)**
1. Brandenburg Consort, R. Goodman *Concert* (7/91) (HYPE) ① **CDA66501**
2. A. Auger, Mostly Mozart Orch, G. Schwarz *Concert* (11/86) (DELO) ① **DE3026**

Cantata No. 210, 'O holder Tag, erwünschte Zeit'—secular cantata, BWV210 (?1742) (Wedding)
EXCERPTS: 1. Recit: O holder Tag (S); 2. Aria: Spielet, ihr beseelten Lieder (S); 3. Recit: Doch haltet ein (S); 4. Aria: Ruhet hie, matte Töne (S); 5. Recit: So glaubt man denn (S); 6. Aria: Schweigt, ihr Flöten (S); 7. Recit: Was Luft? (S); 8. Aria: Grosser Göner (S); 9. Recit: Hochteurer Mann (S); 10. Aria: Seid beglückt (S).
M. Zádori, Capella Savaria, P. Németh (fl/dir) *Concert* (7/91) (QUIN) ① **QUI90 3010**
M. Zádori, Capella Savaria, P. Németh (fl/dir) (r1990) *Concert* (8/94) (HARM) ① **HMA190 3010**
D. Röschmann, Québec Violons du Roy (r1994) *Cantata 204.* (10/95) (DORI) ① **DOR90207**

Cantata No. 211, 'Schweigt stille, plaudert nicht' (Coffee Cantata)—secular cantata, BWV211 (c1734-35) (Wds. Picander)
EXCERPTS: 1. Recit: Schweigt stille, plaudert nict (T); 2. Aria: Hat man nicht mit seinen Kindern (B); 3. Recit: Du böses Kind (S); 4. Aria: Ei! wie schmeckt der Coffee süsse (S); 5. Recit: Wenn du mir nicht den Coffee läss'st (S); 6. Aria: Mädchen, die von harten Sinnen (B); 7. Recit: nun folge (S); 8. Aria: Heute noch (S); 9. Recit: Nun geht und sucht (T); 10. Chorus: Die Katze lässt das Mausen nicht.
L. Dawson, N. Robertson, S. Alder, Friends of Apollo *Cantata 212.* (10/86) (MERI) ① **ECD84110**
E. Kirkby, R. Covey-Crump, D. Thomas, AAM, C. Hogwood (hpd/dir) *Cantata 212.* (10/89) (L'OI) ① **417 621-2OH**
E. Ameling, G. English, S. Nimsgern, Collegium Aureum *Concert* (10/90) (DHM) ① [2] **GD77151**

I. Kertesi, J. Mukk, I. Gáti, Failoni CO, M. Antal *Cantata 212.* (3/93) (NAXO) ① **8 550641**
B. Bonney, R. Popken, C. Prégardien, D. Wilson-Johnson, Age of Enlightenment Ch, OAE, G. Leonhardt (r1994) *Cantata 213.* (7/95) (PHIL) ① **442 779-2PH**
7, 8. E. Ameling, Collegium Aureum, F. Maier (vn/dir) (r1964/8) *Concert* (12/95) (DHM) ① [4] **74321 26617-2(1)**

Cantata No. 212, 'Mer hahn en neue Oberkeet' (Peasant Cantata)—secular cantata, BWV212 (1733) (Wds. Picander)
EXCERPTS: 1. Instrumental; 2. Aria (Duet): Mer hahn en neue Oberkeet (S,B); 3. Recit: Nu, miecke (S,B); 4. Aria: Ach es schmeckt doch gar zu gut (S); 5. Recit: Der Herr ist gut (B); 6. Aria: Ach Herr Schösser (B); 7. Recit: Es bleibt dabei (S); 8. Aria: Unser trefflicher lieber (S); 9. Recit: Er hilft uns allen alt und jung (S,B); 10. Aria: Das ist galant (S); 11. Recit: Und unsre gnäd'ge Frau (B); 12. Aria: Fünfzig Taler bares Geld (B); 13. Recit: Im Ernst ein Wort! (S); 14. Aria: Kleinzschocher müsse (S); 15. Recit: Das ist zu klug (B); 16. Aria: Es nehme zehntausend Ducaten (B); 17. Recit: Das klingt zu liederlich (S); 18. Aria: Gib, Schöne (S); 19. Recit: Du hast wohl recht (B); 20. Aria: Dein Wachstum (B); 21. Recit: Und damit sei (S,B); 22. Aria: Und dass ihr's alle wisst (S); 23. Recit: Mein Schatz (S,B); 24. Chorus: Wir gehn nun wo der Tudelsack.
L. Dawson, S. Alder, Friends of Apollo *Cantata 211.* (10/86) (MERI) ① **ECD84110**
E. Kirkby, D. Thomas, AAM, C. Hogwood (hpd/dir) *Cantata 211.* (10/89) (L'OI) ① **417 621-2OH**
E. Ameling, G. English, S. Nimsgern, Collegium Aureum *Concert* (10/90) (DHM) ① [2] **GD77151**
I. Kertesi, J. Mukk, I. Gáti, Failoni CO, M. Antal *Cantata 211.* (3/93) (NAXO) ① **8 550641**
13, 14. E. Ameling, Collegium Aureum, F. Maier (vn/dir) (r1964/8) *Concert* (12/95) (DHM) ① [4] **74321 26617-2(1)**

Cantata No. 213, 'Hercules auf dem Scheidewege'—secular cantata, BWV213 (1733) (Wds. Picander. Birthday of Prince F. Christian)
EXCERPTS: 1. Chorus: Lasst uns sorgen; 2. Recit: Und wo? (A); 3. Aria: Schlafe, mein Liebster (S); 4. Recit: Auf! folge meiner Bahn (S,T); 5. Aria: Treues Echo (A,A); 6. Recit: Mein hoffnungsvoller Held! (T); 7. Aria: Auf meinen Flügeln (T); 8. Recit: Die weiche Wollust (T); 9. Aria: Ich will dich nicht hören (A); 10. Recit: Geliebte Tugend (A); 11. Aria (Duet): Ich bin deine (A,T); 12. Recit: Schaut, Götter (B); 13. Chorus: Lust der Völker.
B. Bonney, R. Popken, C. Prégardien, D. Wilson-Johnson, Age of Enlightenment Ch, OAE, G. Leonhardt (r1994) *Cantata 211.* (7/95) (PHIL) ① **442 779-2PH**

Cantata No. 217, 'Gedenke, Herr, wie es uns gehet'—spurious cantata, BWV219 (composer unknown)
J. Koslowsky, K. Wessel, H. Geraerts, P. Langshaw, Alsfeld Voc Ens, Steintor Barock, W. Helbich *Concert* (9/92) (CPO) ① [2] **CPO999 139-2**

Cantata No. 218, 'Gott der Hoffnung erfülle euch'—spurious cantata, BWV218 (comp Telemann; Wds. Neumeister)
J. Koslowsky, K. Wessel, H. Geraerts, P. Langshaw, Alsfeld Voc Ens, Steintor Barock, W. Helbich *Concert* (9/92) (CPO) ① [2] **CPO999 139-2**

Cantata No. 219, 'Siehe, es hat überwunden der Löwe'—spurious cantata, BWV219 (comp Telemann; Wds. Neumeister)
J. Koslowsky, K. Wessel, H. Geraerts, P. Langshaw, Alsfeld Voc Ens, Steintor Barock, W. Helbich *Concert* (9/92) (CPO) ① [2] **CPO999 139-2**

Cantata No. 220, 'Lobt ihn mit Herz und Munde'—spurious cantata, BWV220 (composer unknown)
J. Koslowsky, K. Wessel, H. Geraerts, P. Langshaw, Alsfeld Voc Ens, Steintor Barock, W. Helbich *Concert* (9/92) (CPO) ① [2] **CPO999 139-2**

Cantata No. 221, 'Wer suchet die Pracht, wer wünscht den Glanz'—spurious cantata, BWV221 (composer unknown)
J. Koslowsky, K. Wessel, H. Geraerts, P. Langshaw, Alsfeld Voc Ens, Steintor Barock, W. Helbich *Concert* (9/92) (CPO) ① [2] **CPO999 139-2**

Cantata No. 222, 'Mein Odem ist schwach'—spurious cantata, BWV222 (comp J E Bach)
J. Koslowsky, K. Wessel, H. Geraerts, P. Langshaw, Alsfeld Voc Ens, Steintor Barock, W. Helbich *Concert* (9/92) (CPO) ① [2] **CPO999 139-2**

Christmas Oratorio—soloists, chorus & orchestra, BWV248 (1734)
CANTATA 1: 1. Jauchzet, frohlocket!; 2. Es begab sich aber zu der Zeit; 3. Nun wird mein liebster Bräutigam; 4. Bereite dich, Zion; 5. Wie soll ich dich empfangen; 6. Und sie gebar ihren ersten Sohn; 7. Er ist auf Erden kommen arm; 8. Grosser Herr und starker König; 9. Ach mein herzliebes Jesulein!. CANTATA 2: 10. Sinfonia; 11. Und es waren Hirten; 12. Brich an, o schönes Morgenlicht; 13. Und der Engel sprach; 14. Was Gott dem Abraham verheissen; 15. Frohe Hirten, eilt; 16. Und das habt zum Zeichen; 17. Schaut hin!; 18. Sp geht denn hin!; 19. Schlafe, mein Liebster; 20. Und alsobald war da bei dem Engel; 21. Ehre sei Gott in der Höhe; 22. So recht, ihr Engel; 23. Wir singen dir in deinem Heer. CANTATA 3: 24. Herrscher des Himmels; 25. Und da die Engel von ihnen gen Himmel; 26. Lasset uns nun gehen gen Bethlehem; 27. Er hat sein Volk getröst't; 28. Dies hat er alles uns getan; 29. Herr, dein Mitleid, dein Erbarmen; 30. Und sie kamen eilend; 31. Schliesse, mein Herze; 32. Ja, ja, mein Herz soll es bewahren; 33. Ich will dich mit Fleiss bewahren; 34. Und die Hirten; 35. Seid froh dieweil. CANTATA 4: 36. Fallt mit Danken; 37. Und da acht Tage; 38. Immanuel, o süsses Wort!; 39. Flösst, mein Heiland; 40. Wohlan! Dein Name soll allein; 41. Ich will nur dir zu Ehren leben; 42. Jesus richte mein Beginnen. CANTATA 5: 43. Ehre sei dir, Gott, gesungen; 44. Da Jesus geboren; 45. Wo ist der neugeborene König der Jüden?; 46. Dein Glanz all' Finsternis verzehrt; 47. Erleucht' auch meine finstre Sinnen; 48. Da das der König Herodes; 49. Warum wollt ihr erschrecken?; 50. Und liess versammeln alle Hohenpriester; 51. Ach! Wann wird die Zeit erscheinen?; 52. Mein Liebster herrschet schon; 53. Zwar ist solche Herzensstube. CANTATA 6: 54. Herr, wenn die stolzen Feinde; 55. Da berief Herodes; 56. Du Falsche, suche nur den Herrn zu fällen; 57. Nur ein Wink; 58. Als sie nun den König; 59. Ich steh an deiner Krippen hier; 60. Und Gott befahl ihnen im Traum; 61. So geht! genug, mein Schatz; 62. Nun mögt ihr stolzen Feinde; 63. Was will der Höllen Schrecken nun; 64. Nun seid ihr wohl gerochen.
Cpte P. Esswood, K. Equiluz, S. Nimsgern, Vienna Boys' Ch, Chorus Viennensis, VCM, N. Harnoncourt (12/86) (TELD) ① [2] **9031-77610-2**
Cpte N. Argenta, A.S. von Otter, A. Rolfe Johnson, H-P. Blochwitz, O. Bär, Monteverdi Ch, EBS, J.E. Gardiner (12/87) (ARCH) ① [2] **423 232-2AH2**
Cpte H. Donath, A. Ihle, M. Lipovšek, E. Büchner, R. Holl, Leipzig Rad Chor, L. Güttler Brass Ens, Staatskapelle Dresden, P. Schreier (ten/dir) (12/87) (PHIL) ① [3] **420 204-2PH3**
Cpte G. Janowitz, C. Ludwig, F. Wunderlich, F. Crass, Munich Bach Ch, Munich Bach Orch, K. Richter (r1965) (3/89) (ARCH) ① [3] **427 236-2AX3**
Cpte B. Schlick, M. Chance, H. Crook, P. Kooy, Ghent Collegium Vocale, Ghent Collegium Vocale Orch, P. Herreweghe (12/89) (VIRG) ① [2] **VCD7 59530-2**
Cpte R. Ziesak, M. Groop, C. Prégardien, K. Mertens, Frankfurt Voc Ens, Cologne Concerto, R. Otto (4/92) (CAPR) ① [2] **60 025-2**
Cpte I. Kertesi, J. Németh, J. Mukk, J. Tóth, Hungarian Rad Chor, Failoni CO, G. Oberfrank (4/93) (NAXO) ① [3] **8 550428/30**
Cpte Lynda Russell, C. Wyn-Rogers, M. Padmore, M. George, The Sixteen, The Sixteen Orch, H. Christophers (r1993) (12/93) (COLL) ① [2] **Coll7028-2**
Cpte A. Auger, C. Muckenheim, J. Hamari, P. Schreier, W. Schöne, Stuttgart Gächinger Kantorei, Stuttgart Bach Collegium, H. Rilling (r1984) (2/95) (HANS) ① [3] **98 851/3**
1. K. Münchinger, Lübecker Kantorei, Stuttgart CO *Concert* (10/91) (DECC) ① **430 499-2DWO**
5. Ex Cathedra Chbr Ch, J. Skidmore (r c1994) *Concert* (12/94) (ASV) ① **CDDCA912**
10. Taverner Plyrs, A. Parrott *Concert* (12/88) (EMI) ① **CDM7 69853-2**
10. Virtuosi Saxoniae, L. Güttler *Concert* (12/89) (CAPR) ① **10 225**
15. U. Heilmann, Leipzig Gewandhaus, P. Schreier (r1993) *Concert* (3/95) (DECC) ① **440 680-2DH**
39. C. Studer, LSO, I. Marin *Concert* (11/92) (DG) ① **435 387-2GH**
39. E. Ameling, H. de Vries, R. van der Meer, A. de Klerk (r1983) *Concert* (7/94) (EMI) ① **CDC5 55000-2**

Easter Oratorio—soloists, chorus & orchestra, BWV249 (1725)
1. Sinfonia.
Cpte M. Frimmer, R. Popken, C. Prégardien, D. Wilson-Johnson, Age of Enlightenment Ch, OAE, G. Leonhardt (r1993) *Cantata 11.* (10/94) (PHIL) ① **442 119-2PH**
Cpte A. Auger, J. Hamari, Adalbert Kraus, P. Huttenlocher, Stuttgart Gächinger Kantorei, Stuttgart Bach Collegium, H. Rilling (r1980/1) *Cantata 6.* (2/95) (HANS) ① **98 862**
E. Van Evera, C. Trevor, C. Daniels, P. Kooy, Taverner Consort, Taverner Plyrs, A. Parrott (r1993) *Cantata 4.* (7/94) (VIRG) ① **VC5 45011-2**
B. Schlick, K. Wessel, J. Taylor, P. Kooy, Collegium Vocale, P. Herreweghe (r1994) *Cantata 66.* (5/95) (HARM) ① **HMC90 1513**
1. English Concert, T. Pinnock (r1993-4) *Concert* (12/95) (ARCH) ① [2] **439 780-2AH2**

Es ist gewisslich an der Zeit—chorale: 4vv, BWV307
I. Biret (trans Kempff) *Concert* (5/93) (MARC) ① **8 223452**
W. Kempff (r1975: arr pf: Kempff) *Concert* (11/94) (DG) ① [2] **439 672-2GX2**

Gerecht kommt um—motet (by c1740: ?c1730) (spurious: reworking of Tristis est (Kuhnau)
Stuttgart Gächinger Kantorei, Stuttgart Bach Collegium, H. Rilling *Concert* (10/91) (HANS) ① [2] **98 965**

Ich lasse dich nicht—motet, BWVAnh159 (spurious: possibly by J. Christoph Bach)
Stuttgart Gächinger Kantorei, Stuttgart Bach Collegium, H. Rilling *Concert* (10/91) (HANS) ① [2] **98 965**
Alsfeld Voc Ens, W. Helbich (r1993) *Concert* (1/95) (CPO) ① **CPO999 235-2**

Jauchzet dem Herrn, alle Welt—motet, BWV Anh160 (spurious: probably by Telemann)
Stuttgart Gächinger Kantorei, Stuttgart Bach Collegium, H. Rilling *Concert* (10/91) (HANS) ① [2] **98 965**
Alsfeld Voc Ens, W. Helbich (r1993) *Concert* (1/95) (CPO) ① **CPO999 235-2**

Lob und Ehre und Weisheit und Dank—motet, BWV Anh162 (spurious: comp G. G. Wagner)
Alsfeld Voc Ens, W. Helbich (r1993) *Concert* (1/95) (CPO) ① **CPO999 235-2**

Magnificat in D—soloists, chorus & orchestra, BWV243 (c1728-31)
1. Magnificat; 2. Et exultavit spiritus meus; 3. Quia respexit humilitatem; 4. Omnes generationes; 5. Quia fecit mihi magna; 6. Et misericordia; 7. Fecit potentiam; 8. Deposuit; 9. Esurientes implevit bonis; 10. Suscepit Israel; 11. Sicut locutus est; 12. Gloria.
N. Argenta, P. Kwella, C. Brett, A. Rolfe Johnson, D. Thomas, Monteverdi Ch, English Baroque Ens, J.E. Gardiner *Cantata 51.* (9/85) (PHIL) ① **411 458-2PH**
D. Upshaw, P. Jensen, M. Simpson, D. Gordon, W. Stone, Atlanta Sym Chbr Chor, Atlanta SO, Robert Shaw (r1988) *Vivaldi: Gloria, RV589.* (8/89) (TELA) ① **CD80194**
G. de Reyghere, R. Jacobs, C. Prégardien, P. Lika, Netherlands Chbr Ch, Petite Bande, S. Kuijken *Cantata 21.* (2/90) (VIRG) ① **VC7 59528-2**
B. Schlick, A. Mellon, G. Lesne, H. Crook, P. Kooy, Ghent Collegium Vocale, Chapelle Royale Orch, P. Herreweghe *Cantata 80.* (1/91) (HARM) ① **HMC90 1326**
E. Kirkby, T. Bonner, M. Chance, J.M. Ainsley, S. Varcoe, Collegium Musicum 90 Chor, Collegium Musicum 90, R. Hickox *Concert* (7/91) (CHAN) ① **CHAN0518**
B. Hendricks, A. Murray, J. Rigby, U. Heilmann, J. Hynninen, ASMF Chor, ASMF, N. Marriner *Vivaldi: Gloria, RV589.* (3/92) (EMI) ① **CDC7 54283-2**
E. Ameling, H. van Bork, H. Watts, W. Krenn, T. Krause, Vienna Academy Ch, Stuttgart CO, K. Münchinger *Concert* (5/92) (DECC) ① **433 175-2DM**
Lynda Russell, G. Fisher, A. Browner, I. Partridge, M. George, The Sixteen, The Sixteen Orch, H. Christophers *Concert* (12/92) (COLL) ① **Coll1320-2**
L. Popp, A. Pashley, J. Baker, R. Tear, T. Hemsley, New Philh Chor, New Philh, D. Barenboim *Concert* (3/93) (EMI) ① **CDM7 64634-2**
J. Smith, R. Yakar, B. Finnilä, A. Rolfe Johnson, J. Van Dam, Lausanne Voc Ens, Lausanne CO, M. Corboz *Concert* (6/93) (ERAT) ① **2292-45923-2**
M. Coertse, M. Sjöstedt, H. Rössl-Majdan, A. Dermota, F. Guthrie, Vienna St Op Chor, Vienna St Op Orch, F. Prohaska (r1957) *Concert* (9/93) (VANG) ① **08.2010.71**

B. Bonney, B. Remmert, R. Trost, O. Bär, Berlin RIAS Chbr Ch, CPE Bach CO, P. Schreier *Concert*
(2/95) (PHIL) ① [2] **438 873-2PH2**

Mass in A, BWV234 (?late 1730s)
A. Mellon, G. Lesne, C. Prégardien, P. Kooy, Ghent Collegium Vocale, Ghent Collegium Vocale Orch, P. Herreweghe *Concert*
(1/91) (VIRG) ① **VC7 59587-2**
B. Bonney, B. Remmert, R. Trost, O. Bär, Berlin RIAS Chbr Ch, CPE Bach CO, P. Schreier *Concert*
(2/95) (PHIL) ① [2] **438 873-2PH2**

Mass in B minor—soloists, chorus & orchestra, BWV232 (assembled c1747-9)
1. Kyrie eleison; 2. Christe eleison; 3. Kyrie eleison; 4. Gloria in excelsis; 5. Laudamus te; 6. Gratias agimus tibi; 7. Dominus Deus; 8. Qui tollis peccata mundi; 9. Qui sedes; 10. Quoniam tu solus; 11. Cum sancto spiritu; 12. Credo; 13. Credo; 14. Et in unum Dominum; 15. Et incarnatus est; 16. Crucifixus; 17. Et resurrexit; 18. Et in spiritum sanctum; 19. Confiteor; 20. Et expecto; 21. Sanctus; 22. Hosanna; 23. Benedictus; 24. Agnus Dei; 25. Dona nobis pacem.
Cpte L. Dawson, C. Hall, N. Argenta, H. Milner, M. Chance, S. Varcoe, P. Kwella, M. Nichols, R.L. Morgan, W. Evans, Monteverdi Ch, EBS, J.E. Gardiner (2/86) (ARCH) ① [2] **415 514-2AH2**
Cpte M. Marshall, J. Baker, R. Tear, S. Ramey, ASMF Chor, ASMF, N. Marriner (r1977)
(7/86) (PHIL) ① [2] **416 415-2PH2**
Cpte E. Kirkby, E. Van Evera, P. Iconomou, C. Immler, M. Kilian, R. Covey-Crump, D. Thomas, Taverner Consort, Taverner Plyrs, A. Parrott
(8/86) (EMI) ① [2] **CDS7 47293-8**
Cpte B. Schlick, C. Patriasz, C. Brett, H. Crook, P. Kooy, Ghent Collegium Vocale, Ghent Collegium Vocale Orch, P. Herreweghe
(8/89) (VIRG) ① [2] **VCD7 59517-2**
Cpte J. Smith, M. Chance, N. van der Meel, H. van der Kamp, Netherlands Chbr Ch, Eighteenth Century Orch, F. Brüggen (pp1989)
(2/90) (PHIL) ① [2] **426 238-2PH2**
Cpte I. Poulenard, G. Laurens, R. Jacobs, J. Elwes, M. van Egmond, H. van der Kamp, Netherlands Bach Soc Collegium Musicum, Petite Bande, G. Leonhardt
(6/90) (DHM) ① [2] **GD77040**
Cpte A. Giebel, J. Baker, N. Gedda, H. Prey, F. Crass, BBC Chor, New Philh, O. Klemperer
(4/91) (EMI) ① [2] **CMS7 63364-2**
Cpte S. McNair, D. Ziegler, M. Simpson, J. Aler, W. Stone, T. Paul, Atlanta Sym Chbr Chor, Atlanta SO, Robert Shaw (4/91) (TELA) ① [2] **CD80233**
Cpte F. Lott, A.S. von Otter, H-P. Blochwitz, W. Shimell, G. Howell, Chicago Sym Chor, Chicago SO, G. Solti (pp1990)
(5/91) (DECC) ① [2] **430 353-2DH2**
Cpte A. Auger, A. Murray, M. Lipovšek, P. Schreier, A. Scharinger, Leipzig Rad Chor, Staatskapelle Dresden, P. Schreier
(6/92) (PHIL) ① [2] **432 972-2PH2**
Cpte F. Wagner, F. Schäfer-Subrata, M. Koppelstetter, M. Schäfer, H. Elbert, Slovak Phil Chor, Capella Istropolitana, C. Brembeck
(1/93) (NAXO) ① [2] **8 550585/6**
Cpte N. Argenta, C. Denley, M. Tucker, S. Varcoe, Collegium Musicum 90 Chor, Collegium Musicum 90, R. Hickox (1/93) (CHAN) ① [2] **CHAN0533/4**
Cpte American Bach Sols, J. Thomas
(4/93) (KOCH) ① [2] **37194-2**
Cpte C. Dubosc, C. Denley, J. Bowman, J. M. Ainsley, M. George, The Sixteen, The Sixteen Orch, H. Christophers (r1994)
(11/94) (COLL) ① [2] **Coll7032-2**
Cpte E. Ameling, Y. Minton, H. Watts, W. Krenn, T. Krause, Vienna Singakademie Chor, Stuttgart CO, K. Münchinger (r1970)
(12/94) (DECC) ① [2] **440 609-2DF2**
Cpte G. Janowitz, C. Ludwig, P. Schreier, R. Kerns, K. Ridderbusch, Vienna Singverein, BPO, H. von Karajan (r1973) (3/95) (DG) ① [2] **439 696-2GX2**
Cpte R. Ziesak, R. Alexander, J. Van Nes, K. Lewis, D. Wilson-Johnson, Bavarian Rad Chor, BRSO, C. M. Giulini (pp1994)
(3/95) (SONY) ① [2] **S2K66354**
Cpte R. Hansmann, E. Iiyama, H. Watts, K. Equiluz, M. van Egmond, Vienna Boys' Ch, Viennensis Chor, VCM, N. Harnoncourt (r1968)
(4/95) (TELD) ① [2] **4509-95517-2**
Cpte B. Schlick, K. Wessel, G. de Mey, K. Mertens, Amsterdam Baroque Ch, Amsterdam Baroque Orch, T. Koopman (r1994)
(5/95) (ERAT) ① [2] **4509-98478-2**
2(pt), 5, 14(pt) E. Schwarzkopf, K. Ferrier, Vienna SO, H. von Karajan (pp1950) *Concert*
(12/90) (EMI) ① **CDM7 63655-2**
5, 23. K. Battle, I. Perlman, St Luke's Orch, J. Nelson (r1989/90) *Concert* (3/92) (DG) ① **429 737-2GH**
7. W. Widdop, E. Schumann, LSO, A. Coates (r1929) *Concert* (11/92) (CLAR) ① **CDGSE78-50-46**
9, 24. K. Ferrier, Vienna SO, H. von Karajan (pp1950) *Concert*
(4/92) (EMI) ① [7] **CHS7 69741-2(1)**
9, 24. K. Ferrier, LPO, A. Boult (r1952) *Concert*
(6/92) (DECC) ① **433 474-2DM**
9, 24. J. Kowalski, ASMF, N. Marriner (r1993) *Concert* (8/94) (CAPR) ① **10 532**
24. K. Ferrier, LPO, A. Boult *Concert*
(10/91) (DECC) ① **430 499-2DWO**
24. A. Deller, Leonhardt Baroque Ens, G. Leonhardt (org/dir) (r1954) *Concert*
(1/95) (VANG) ① **08.5069.71**

Mass in F, BWV233 (?late 1730s)
A. Mellon, G. Lesne, P. Kooy, Ghent Collegium Vocale, Ghent Collegium Vocale Orch, P. Herreweghe *Mass, BWV236.*
(9/91) (VIRG) ① **VC7 59634-2**
B. Bonney, B. Remmert, R. Trost, O. Bär, Berlin RIAS Chbr Ch, CPE Bach CO, P. Schreier *Concert*
(2/95) (PHIL) ① [2] **438 873-2PH2**
Qui tollis peccata mundi E. Ameling, H. de Vries, R. van der Meer, A. de Klerk (r1983) *Concert*
(7/94) (EMI) ① **CDC5 55000-2**

Mass in G, BWV236 (?late 1730s)
A. Mellon, G. Lesne, C. Prégardien, P. Kooy, Ghent Collegium Vocale, Ghent Collegium Vocale Orch, P. Herreweghe *Mass, BWV233.*
(9/91) (VIRG) ① **VC7 59634-2**
R. Ziesak, I. Danz, C. Prégardien, M. Brodard, Stuttgart Gächinger Kantorei, Stuttgart CO, H. Rilling (r1992) *Mass, BWV235.* (10/93) (HANS) ① **98 962**
B. Bonney, B. Remmert, R. Trost, O. Bär, Berlin RIAS Chbr Ch, CPE Bach CO, P. Schreier *Concert*
(2/95) (PHIL) ① [2] **438 873-2PH2**

Mass in G minor, BWV235 (?late 1730s)
A. Mellon, G. Lesne, C. Prégardien, P. Kooy, Ghent Collegium Vocale, Ghent Collegium Vocale Orch, P. Herreweghe *Concert*
(1/91) (VIRG) ① **VC7 59587-2**
I. Danz, C. Prégardien, T. Quasthoff, Stuttgart Gächinger Kantorei, Stuttgart Bach Collegium, H. Rilling (r1992) *Mass, BWV236.*
(10/93) (HANS) ① **98 962**
B. Bonney, B. Remmert, R. Trost, O. Bär, Berlin RIAS Chbr Ch, CPE Bach CO, P. Schreier *Concert*
(2/95) (PHIL) ① [2] **438 873-2PH2**

Merk auf, mein Herz, und sieh dorthin—motet, BWV Anh163 (spurious: possibly by Bach of Eisenach)
Alsfeld Voc Ens, W. Helbich (r1993) *Concert*
(1/95) (CPO) ① **CPO999 235-2**

Motets, BWV225-230
1. Singet dem Herrn, BWV225; 2. Geist hilft unsrer Schwachheit, BWV226; 3. Jesu, meine Freude, BWV227; 4. Fürchte dich nicht, BWV228; 5. Komm, Jesu, komm!, BWV229; 6. Lobet den Herrn, BWV230.
Cpte A. Mellon, G. de Reyghere, V. Darras, H. Crook, P. Kooy, Ghent Collegium Vocale, Paris Chapelle Royale Chor, Paris Chapelle Royale Orch, P. Herreweghe (12/86) (HARM) ① **HMC90 1231**
Cpte Trinity Coll Ch, Cambridge, R. Marlow
(12/88) (CONI) ① **CDCF158**
Cpte Augsburg Cath Boys' Ch, R. Kammler
(10/89) (DHM) ① **RD77031**
Cpte The Sixteen, H. Christophers
(11/90) (HYPE) ① **CDA66369**
Cpte A. Egeler, I. Fischer, M. van der Zeyst, M. Brutscher, T. Herberich, Stuttgart Chbr Ch, Stuttgart Baroque Orch, F. Bernius
(2/91) (SONY) ① **SK45859**
Cpte Stuttgart Gächinger Kantorei, Stuttgart Bach Collegium, H. Rilling *Concert*
(10/91) (HANS) ① [2] **98 965**
Cpte G. de Reyghere, K. van Laethem, M. van der Zeijst, S. Buwalda, H.H. Jansen, J-C. Happel, Petite Bande Chor, Petite Bande, S. Kuijken (pp1992)
(5/93) (ACCE) ① **ACC9287D**
Cpte Netherlands Chbr Ch, T. Koopman (r1986-7)
(5/93) (PHIL) ① **434 165-2PH**
1, 3, 4, 6. Oxford Christ Church Cath Ch, F. Grier
(11/90) (ASV) ① **CDGAU118**

Musicalisches Gesang-Buch G. C. Schemelli—sacred songs: 1v and continuo, BWV439-488 (pub 1736) (only continuo comp Bach, unless stated)
1. Ach, dass nicht die letzte Stunde, BWV439; 2. Auf, Auf! die rechte Zeit ist hier, BWV440; 3. Auf, Auf! mein Herz, mit Freuden, BWV441; 4. Beglückter Stand getreuer Seelen, BWV442; 5. Beschränkt, ihr Weisen dieser Welt, BWV443; 6. Brich entzwei, mein armes Herze, BWV444; 7. Brunnquell aller Güter, BWV445; 8. Der lieben Sonne Licht und Pracht, BWV446; 9. Der Tag ist hin, die Sonne gehet nieder, BWV447; 10. Der Tag mit seinem Lichte, BWV448; 11. Dich bet'ich an, mein höchster Gott, BWV449; 12. Die bittre Leidenszeit beginnet abermal, BWV450; 13. Die goldene Sonne, voll Freud' und Wonne, BWV451; 14. Dir, dir Jehovah, will ich singen, BWV452 (melody by Bach); 15. Eins ist Not! ach Herr, dies Eine, BWV453; 16. Ermuntre dich, mein schwacher Geist, BWV454; 17. Erwürgtes Lamm, das die verwahrten Siegel, BWV455; 18. Es glänzet der Christen, BWV456; 19. Es ist nun aus mit meinem Leben, BWV457; 20. Es is vollbracht! vergiss ja nicht, BWV458; 21. Es kostet viel, ein Christ zu sein, BWV459; 22. Gieb dich zufrieden und sei stille, BWV460; 23. Gott lebet noch, was verzagst du doch?, BWV461; 24. Gott, wie gross ist deine Güte, BWV462; 25. Herr, nicht schicke deine Rache, BWV463; 26. Ich bin ja, Herr, in deiner Macht, BWV464; 27. Ich freue mich in der, BWV465; 28. Ich halte treulich still und liebe, BWV466; 29. Ich lass' dich nicht, BWV467; 30. Ich liebe Jesum alle Stund', BWV468; 31. Ich steh' an deiner Krippen hier, BWV469; 32. Ihr Gestirn', ihr hohen Lüfte, BWV476; 33. Jesu, deine Liebeswunden, BWV471; 34. Jesu, Jesu, du bist mein, BWV470; 35. Jesu, meines Glaubens Zier, BWV472; 36. Jesu, meines Herzens Freu, BWV473; 37. Jesus ist das schönste Licht, BWV474; 38. Jesus, unser Trost und Leben, BWV475; 39. Kein Stündlein geht dahin, BWV477; 40. Komm, süsser Tod, BWV478 (melody by Bach); 41. Kommt, Seelen, dieser Tag, BWV479; 42. Kommt wieder aus der finstern Gruft, BWV480; 43. Lasset uns mit Jesu ziehen, BWV481; 44. Liebes Herz, bedenke doch, BWV482; 45. Liebster Gott, wann werd'ich sterben?, BWV483; 46. Liebster Herr Jesu! wo bleibest du so lange?, BWV484; 47. Liebster Immanuel, Herzog der Frommen, BWV485; 48. Meines Lebens letzte Zeit, BWV488; 49. Mein Jesu, dem die Seraphinen, BWV486; 50. Mein Jesu! was für Seelenweh, BWV487; 51. Meines Lebens letzte Zeit, BWV488.
1. K. Ferrier, J. Newmark (bp1949) *Concert*
(6/92) (DECC) ① **433 473-2DM**
31. Quink *Concert* (12/89) (TELA) ① **CD80202**
40. Sydney SO, R. Pickler (orch Stokowski) *Concert*
(10/91) (CHAN) ① **CHAN6532**
40, 50. BBC PO, M. Bamert (r1993: orch Stokowski) *Concert* (3/94) (CHAN) ① **CHAN9259**

Musikalisches Gesang-Buch von G. C. Schemelli—sacred songs: 1v and continuo, BWV489-507 (only continuo by Bach, unless stated)
1. Nicht so traurig, nicht so sehr, BWV489; 2. Nur mein Jesus ist mein Leben, BWV490; 3. O du Liebe meine Liebe, BWV491; 4. O finstre Nacht, BWV492; 5. O Jesulein süss, o Jesulein mild, BWV493; 6. O liebe Seele, sieh' die Sinnen, BWV494; 7. O wie selig seid ihr doch, ihr Frommen, BWV495; 8. Seelen-Bräutigam, Jesu, Gottes Lamm!, BWV495; 9. Seelenweide, meine Freude, BWV497; 10. Sei gegrüsset, Jesu gütig, BWV499; 11. Selig, wer an Jesum denkt, BWV498; 12. So gehst du nun, mein Jesu, hin, BWV500; 13. So giebst du nun, mein Jesu, gute Nacht, BWV501; 14. So wünsch' ich mir zu guter Letzt, BWV502; 15. Steh' ich bei meinem Gott, BWV503; 16. Vergiss mein nicht, dass ich dein nicht, BWV504; 17. Vergiss mein nicht, mein allerliebster Gott, BWV505 (melody by Bach); 18. Was bist du moch, o Seele, so betrübet, BWV506; 19. Wo ist mein Schäflein, das ich liebe, BWV507.
5. Quink *Concert* (12/89) (TELA) ① **CD80202**
5. K. Erb, B. Seidler-Winkler (r1934) *Concert*
(6/94) (PREI) ① [2] **89208**
17. K. Ferrier, J. Newmark (bp1949) *Concert*
(6/92) (DECC) ① **433 473-2DM**

Nun danket alle Gott—motet, BWV Anh164 (spurious: comp J. C. Altnickol)
Alsfeld Voc Ens, W. Helbich (r1993) *Concert*
(1/95) (CPO) ① **CPO999 235-2**

O Jesu Christ, mein's Lebens Licht—motet, BWV118 (1736-37) (Wds. M. Böhme)
Stuttgart Gächinger Kantorei, Stuttgart Bach Collegium, H. Rilling *Concert*
(10/91) (HANS) ① [2] **98 965**

O Jesulein süss, BWV493
Taverner Ch, Taverner Consort, Taverner Plyrs, A. Parrott *Concert* (12/89) (EMI) ① **CDC7 49809-2**

Sanctus in D, BWV238 (1723)
A. Mellon, G. Lesne, C. Prégardien, P. Kooy, Ghent Collegium Vocale, Ghent Collegium Vocale Orch, P. Herreweghe *Concert*
(1/91) (VIRG) ① **VC7 59587-2**

St. John Passion—soloists, chorus and orchestra, BWV245 (1724 rev c1730 and late 1740s)
PART 1: 1. Herr, unser Herrscher; 2. Jesus ging (Recit); 3. Jesum von Nazareth!; 4. Jesus spricht

(Recit); 5. Jesum von Nazareth!; 6. Jesus antwortete (Recit); 7. O grosse Lieb; 8. Auf dass das Wort (Recit); 9. Dein Will gescheh; 10. Die Schar aber (Recit); 11. Von den Stricken; 12. Simon Petrus aber (Recit); 13. Ich folge dir; 14. Derselbige Jünger (Recit); 15. Wer hat dich so geschlagen; 16. Und Hannas sandte (Recit); 17. Bist du nicht seiner Jünger einer?; 18. Er leugnete aber (Recit); 19. Ach, mein Sinn; 20. Petrus, der nicht denkt zurück. PART 2: 21. Christus, der uns selig macht; 22. Da führeten sie Jesum (Recit); 23. Wäre dieser nicht ein Übeltäter; 24. Da sprach Pilatus (Recit); 25. Wir dürfen niemand töten; 26. Auf dass erfüllet (Recit); 27. Ach grosser König; 28. Das sprach Pilatus (Recit); 29. Nicht diesen; 30. Barrabas aber (Recit); 31. Betrachte, meine Seel; 32. Erwäge; 33. Und die Kriegsknechte (Recit); 34. Sei gegrüsset; 35. Und gaben ihm Backenstreiche (Recit); 36. Kreuzige!; 37. Pilatus sprach zu ihnen (Recit); 38. Wir haben ein Gesetz; 39. Da Pilatus (Recit); 40. Durch dein Gefängnis; 41. Die Juden aber (Recit); 42. Lässest du diesen los; 43. Da Pilatus (Recit); 44. Weg, weg; 45. Spricht Pilatus (Recit); 46. Wir haben keinen König; 47. Da überantwortete (Recit); 48. Eilt, ihr angefochtnen Seelen; 49. Allda kreuzigten sie ihn (Recit); 50. Schreibe nicht; 51. Pilatus antwortet (Recit); 52. In meines Herzens Grunde; 53. Die Kriegsknechte aber (Recit); 54. Lasset uns; 55. Auf dass erfüllet (Recit); 56. Er nahm alles; 57. Und von Stund (Recit); 58. Es ist vollbracht!; 59. Und neigte (Recit); 60. Mein teurer Heiland; 61. Und siehe da (Recit); 62. Mein Herz, indem die ganze Welt; 63. Zerfliesse, mein Herze; 64. Die Juden aber (Recit); 65. O hilfe, Christe; 66. Darnach bat Pilatum (Recit); 67. Ruht wohl; 68. Ach Herr, lass dein lieb Engelein.

Cpte A. Rolfe Johnson, S. Varcoe, N. Argenta, R. Holton, M. Chance, N. Archer, R. Müller, C. Hauptmann, Monteverdi Ch, EBS, J.E. Gardiner (2/87) (ARCH) ① [2] **419 324-2AH2**

Cpte H. Crook, P. Lika, B. Schlick, C. Patriasz, W. Kendall, P. Kooy, Ghent Collegium Vocale, Paris Chapelle Royale Orch, P. Herreweghe (5/88) (HARM) ① [2] **HMC90 1264/5**

Cpte C. Prégardien, H. van der Kamp, B. Schlick, R. Jacobs, N. van der Meel, M. van Egmond, Petite Bande Chor, Petite Bande, S. Kuijken (6/90) (DHM) ① [2] **GD77041**

Cpte I. Nielsen, N. Stutzmann, C.H. Ahnsjö, R. Swensen, A. Scharinger, T. Quasthoff, Neubeuern Chor, Munich Bach Collegium, E. zu Guttenberg (10/92) (RCA) ① [2] **RD60903**

Cpte A. Stumphius, J. Bowman, N. van der Meel, C. Prégardien, K. Sigmundsson, P. Kooy, Netherlands Chbr Ch, Eighteenth Century Orch, F. Brüggen (r1992) (5/93) (PHIL) ① [2] **434 905-2PH2**

Cpte Scholars Baroque Ens (r1993) (5/95) (NAXO) ① [2] **8 550664/5**

Cpte P. Pears, G. Howell, H. Harper, A. Hodgson, R. Tear, J. Shirley-Quirk, J. Hill, R. Burgess, J. Tobin, Adrian Thompson, Wandsworth Sch Boys' Ch, ECO, B. Britten (r1971: Eng) (7/95) (DECC) ① [2] **443 859-2DF2**

19. U. Heilmann, Leipzig Gewandhaus, P. Schreier (r1993) *Concert* (3/95) (DECC) ① **440 680-2DH**

58. K. Ferrier, LPO, A. Boult (Eng: r1952) *Concert* (6/92) (DECC) ① **433 474-2DM**

58. C. Ludwig, Berlin SO, K. Forster *Concert* (9/92) (EMI) ① [4] **CMS7 64074-2(2)**

St Matthew Passion—soloists, chorus and orchestra, BWV244 (1727) (Passio secundum Matthaeum)

PART 1: 1. Kommt, ihr Töchter; 2. Da Jesus diese Rede vollendet; 3. Herzliebster Jesu; 4. Da versammleten sich die Hohenpriester; 5. Ja nicht auf das Fest; 6. Da nun Jesus war zu Bethanien; 7. Wozu dienet dieser Unrat?; 8. Da das Jesus merkete; 9. Du lieber Heiland du; 10. Buss' und Reu'; 11. Da ging hin der Zwölfen einer; 12. Blute nur; 13. Aber am ersten Tage; 14. Wo willst du?; 15a. Er sprach; 15b. Gehet hin in die Stadt; 16. Ich bin's ich sollte büssen; 17. Er antwortete und sprach; 18. Wiewohl mein Herz; 19. Ich will dir mein Herze schenken; 20. Und da sie den Lobgesang gesprochen hatten; 21. Erkenne mich; 22. Petrus aber; 23. Ich will hier bei dir stehen; 24. Da kam Jesus mit ihnen; 25. O Schmerz!; 26. Ich will bei meinem Jesu wachen; 27. Und ging hin ein wenig; 28. Der Heiland fällt vor seinem Vater nieder; 29. Gerne will ich; 30. Und er kam zu seinen Jüngern; 31. Was mein Gott will; 32. Und er kam und fand; 33. So ist mein Jesus; 34. Und siehe, einer aus denen; 35. O Mensch, bewein' dein' Sünde gross. PART 2: 36. Ach, nun ist mein Jesus hin!; 37. Die aber Jesum gegriffen hatten; 38. Mir hat die Welt; 39. Und wiewohl viel falsche Zeugen; 40. Mein Jesus schweigt; 41. Geduld, Geduld; 42. Und der Hohepriester antwortete; 43. Da speieten sie aus in sein Angesicht; 44. Wer hat dich so geschlagen; 45. Petrus aber sass draussen; 46. Wahrlich, du bist auch einer von denen; 47. Erbarme dich; 48. Bin ich gleich von dir gewichen; 49. Des Morgens aber hielten alle Hohenpriester; 50. Und er warf die Silberlinge in den Tempel; 51. Gebt mir meinen Jesum wieder!; 52. Sie hielten aber einen Rat; 53. Befiehl du deine Wege; 54. Auf das Fest aber hatte der Landpfleger; 55. Wie wunderbarlich; 56. Der Landpfleger sagte; 57. Er hat uns allen wohlgetan; 58. Aus Liebe will mein Heiland sterben;; 59. Sie schrieen aber noch; 60. Erbarm' es Gott!; 61. Können Tränen meiner Wangen; 62. Da nahmen die Kriegsknechte; 63. O Haupt voll Blut; 64. Und da sie ihn verspottet hatten; 65. Ja! freilich will; 66. Komm, süsses Kreuz; 67. Und da sie an die Stätte; 68. Desgleichen schmäheten; 69. Ach, Golgotha; 70. Sehet, Jesus hat die Hand; 71. Und von der sechsten Stunde; 72. Wenn ich einmal soll scheiden; 73. Und siehe da; 74. Am Abend, da es kühle war; 75. Mache dich, mein Herze; 76. Und Joseph nahm den Leib; 77. Nun ist der Herr; 78. Wir setzen uns mit Tränen nieder.

Cpte T. Adam, L. Popp, M. Lipovšek, E. Büchner, R. Holl, A. Scheibner, E. Wlaschiha, H.C. Polster, O. Bär, J. Schneiderheinze, E. Wegner, A. Ihle, E. Wilke, H. Terner, H-J. Ribbe, K. Henkel, Dresdner Kapellknaben, Leipzig Rad Chor, Staatskapelle Dresden, P. Schreier (ten/dir) (8/85) (PHIL) ① [3] **412 527-2PH3**

Cpte H. Crook, U. Cold, B. Schlick, R. Jacobs, H-P. Blochwitz, P. Kooy, Paris Chapelle Royale Chor, Ghent Collegium Vocale, St Niklaas In Dulci Jubilo Children's Ch, Paris Chapelle Royale Orch, P. Herreweghe (11/85) (HARM) ① [3] **HMC90 1155/7**

Cpte K. Equiluz, K. Ridderbusch, P. Esswood, T. Sutcliffe, J. Bowman, N. Rogers, M. van Egmond, M. Schopper, Regensburg Cath Ch (Boys' Voices), King's College Male Voice Ch, VCM, N. Harnoncourt (9/87) (TELD) ① [3] **2292-42509-2**

Cpte P. Schreier, D. Fischer-Dieskau, G. Janowitz, C. Ludwig, H. Laubenthal, W. Berry, A. Diakov, Berlin Cath. Boys' Ch, Berlin St Boys' Ch, Vienna Singverein, Berlin Deutsche Op Chor, BPO, H. von Karajan (3/88) (DG) ① [3] **419 789-2GH3**

Cpte H-P. Blochwitz, O. Bär, K. Te Kanawa, A.S. von Otter, A. Rolfe Johnson, T. Krause, Glen Ellyn Children's Chor, Chicago Sym Chor, Chicago SO, G. Solti (4/88) (DECC) ① [3] **421 177-2DH3**

Cpte A. Rolfe Johnson, A. Schmidt, B. Bonney, A. Monoyios, A.S. von Otter, M. Chance, H. Crook, O. Bär, C. Hauptmann, London Oratory Jnr Ch, Monteverdi Ch, EBS, J.E. Gardiner (10/89) (ARCH) ① [3] **427 648-2AH3**

Cpte C. Prégardien, M. van Egmond, C. Fliegner, M. Kiener, R. Jacobs, D. Cordier, M. Schäfer, J. Elwes, K. Mertens, P. Lika, Tolz Boys' Ch, Petite Bande Chor, Petite Bande, G. Leonhardt (5/90) (DHM) ① [3] **RD77848**

Cpte M. Marshall, J. van Nes, C.H. Ahnsjö, A. Baldin, H. Prey, A. Scharinger, C. Dobmeier, T. Hamberger, Tolz Boys' Ch, Neubeuern Chor, Munich Bach Collegium, E. zu Guttenberg (pp1990) (9/91) (EURO) ① [3] **RD69303**

Cpte G. de Mey, P. Kooy, B. Schlick, K. Wessel, C. Prégardien, K. Mertens, Breda Sacraments Ch, Netherlands Bach Soc Ch, Amsterdam Baroque Orch, T. Koopman (r1992) (5/93) (ERAT) ① [3] **2292-45814-2**

Cpte W. Jochens, P. Lika, A. Kazimierczuk, A. Browner, M. Schäfer, F-J. Selig, Chorus Musicus, Neue Orch, C. Spering (r1992; arr Mendelssohn) (9/93) (O111) ① [2] **OPS30-72/3**

Cpte F. Lott, A. Hodgson, R. Tear, N. Jenkins, J. Shirley-Quirk, S. Roberts, St Paul's Cath Boys' Ch, Bach Ch, Thames CO, D. Willcocks (r1978: Eng: rev Elgar/Atkins) (7/94) (ASV) ① [3] **CDQSS324**

Cpte I. Verebits, R. Kiss, J. Németh, A. Csenki, J. Mukk, I. Gáti, P. Cser, P. Köves, F. Korpás, Hungarian Fest Chor, Hungarian Rad Children's Ch, Hungarian St PO, G. Oberfrank (r1993) (8/94) (NAXO) ① [3] **8 550832/4**

C. Oelze, I. Danz, M. Schade, M. Görne, T. Quasthoff, Stuttgart Gächinger Kantorei, Stuttgart Bach Collegium, H. Rilling (rc1994) (4/95) (HANS) ① [3] **98 925**

Abridged T. Lemnitz, F. Beckmann, K. Erb, G. Hüsch, S. Schulze, Leipzig St Thomas Church Ch, Leipzig Gewandhaus, G. Ramin (r1941) (10/91) (CALI) ① [2] **CAL50859/60**

Abridged E. Grümmer, M. Höffgen, A. Dermota, D. Fischer-Dieskau, O. Edelmann, Vienna Boys' Ch, Vienna Singakademie Chor, VPO, W. Furtwängler (pp1954) (10/95) (EMI) ① [2] **CHS5 65509-2**

Excs E. Suddaby, K. Ferrier, E. Greene, W. Parsons, Bach Ch, Jacques Orch, R. Jacques (Eng: r1947/8) (6/92) (DECC) ① **433 469-2DM**

1, 3, 12, 23, 26, 28, 29, 33, 47, 51, 58, 72, 75, 78. E. Schwarzkopf, C. Ludwig, N. Gedda, W. Berry, Hampstead Church Boys' Ch, Philh Ch, Philh, O. Klemperer (r1961) (9/94) (EMIN) ① **CD-EMX2223**

9, 10, 47, 60, 61. J. Kowalski, ASMF, N. Marriner (r1993) *Concert* (8/94) (CAPR) ① **10 532**

10. K. Ferrier, LPO, A. Boult (Eng: r1952) *Concert* (6/92) (DECC) ① **433 474-2DM**

12, 19. A. Auger, Mostly Mozart Orch, G. Schwarz *Concert* (11/86) (DELO) ① **DE3026**

40, 41. U. Heilmann, Leipzig Gewandhaus, P. Schreier (r1993) *Concert* (3/95) (DECC) ① **440 680-2DH**

47. M. Anderson, Victor Sinfonietta, Robert Shaw (r1946) *Concert* (1/90) (RCA) ① **GD87911**

47. K. Ferrier, National SO, M. Sargent (Eng: r1946) *Concert* (6/91) (DECC) ① **430 096-2DWO**

47. R. Anday, Vienna St Op Orch, K. Alwin (r1929) *Concert* (5/92) (PREI) ① **89046**

47. K. Ferrier, National SO, M. Sargent (r1946: Eng) *Concert* (6/92) (DECC) ① **433 470-2DM**

47. K. Flagstad, Philh, W. Susskind (r1950) *Concert* (7/93) (TEST) ① **SBT1018**

58. E. Schumann, orch, K. Alwin (r1927) *Concert* (6/91) (PREI) ① **89031**

78. Stuttgart Hymnus Boys' Ch, Stuttgart CO, K. Münchinger *Concert* (10/91) (DECC) ① **430 499-2DWO**

Unser Wandel ist im Himmel—motet, BWV Anh165 (spurious: comp J. E. Bach)

Alsfeld Voc Ens, W. Helbich (r1993) *Concert* (1/95) (CPO) ① **CPO999 235-2**

BACH, Wilhelm Friedemann *(1710–1784) Germany*

F—Numbers used in M. Falck, W.F. Bach (rev 1919)

SECTION I: ORCHESTRAL

Concerto for Keyboard and Orchestra in E minor, F43 (?pre 1767)

G. Penson, Ricercar Consort, A. Chamorro *Concert* (9/90) (RICE) ① **RIC069049**

Concerto for Keyboard and Orchestra in F minor, F44 (1733-46)

G. Penson, Ricercar Consort, A. Chamorro *Concert* (9/90) (RICE) ① **RIC069049**

Sinfonia in D, F64 (1746-64) (introduction to the cantata 'Dies ist der tag', F85)

Kleine Konzert, H. Max (r1991) *Concert* (11/94) (CAPR) ① **10 426**

Sinfonia in D minor—2 flutes and strings, F65

Ricercar Consort, A. Chamorro *Concert* (9/90) (RICE) ① **RIC069049**

SECTION III: INSTRUMENTAL

7 Chorale Preludes—organ, F38/1

1. Nun komm der Heiden Heiland; 2. Christe, der du bist Tag und Licht; 3. Jesu meine Freude; 4. Durch Adams Fall ist ganz verderbt; 5. Was mein Gott will; 6. Wir Christenleut han jetzund Freud; 7. Wir danken dir.

L. Van Doeselaar *Concert* (10/89) (ETCE) ① **KTC2003-1**

10 Fantasias—harpsichord, F14-23 (1733-84)

1-8, 10. H. Dreyfus (8/89) (DENO) ① **CO-72588**

Fugue in B flat—organ, F34 (1735)

L. Van Doeselaar *Concert* (10/89) (ETCE) ① **KTC2003-2**

Fugue in C minor—organ, F32 (1734)

L. Van Doeselaar *Concert* (10/89) (ETCE) ① **KTC2003-1**

Fugue in C minor—organ with pedals

L. Van Doeselaar *Concert* (10/89) (ETCE) ① **KTC2003-2**

Fugue in D—organ with pedals

L. Van Doeselaar *Concert* (10/89) (ETCE) ① **KTC2003-2**

Fugue in F—organ, F33 (before 1733)

L. Van Doeselaar *Concert* (10/89) (ETCE) ① **KTC2003-2**

Fugue in F—organ: 2 keyboards and pedals, F36

L. Van Doeselaar *Concert* (10/89) (ETCE) ① **KTC2003-2**

Fugue in G minor—organ, F37

L. Van Doeselaar *Concert* (10/89) (ETCE) ① **KTC2003-2**

8 Fugues—keyboard, F31 (1778)
1. C; 2. C minor; 3. D; 4. D minor; 5. E flat; 6. E minor; 7. B flat; 8. F minor.
L. Van Doeselaar *Concert*
(10/89) (ETCE) ① **KTC2003-1**
C. Rousset (r1989) *Concert*
(8/94) (HARM) ① **HMA190 1305**

3 Fugues—organ: 2 keyboards and pedals
1. A minor; 2. C minor; 3. B flat.
L. Van Doeselaar *Concert*
(10/89) (ETCE) ① **KTC2003-2**

Keyboard Sonata in G, F7 (before 1745)
C. Rousset (r1989) *Concert*
(8/94) (HARM) ① **HMA190 1305**

Keyboard Sonata No. 2 in A, F8 (1731-46)
C. Rousset (r1989) *Concert*
(8/94) (HARM) ① **HMA190 1305**

Keyboard Sonata No. 7 in C—keyboard, F2 (c1778)
C. Rousset (r1989) *Concert*
(8/94) (HARM) ① **HMA190 1305**

March—keyboard, F30
C. Rousset (r1989) *Concert*
(8/94) (HARM) ① **HMA190 1305**

12 Polonaises—keyboard, F12 (c1765)
1. C; 2. C minor; 3. D; 4. D minor; 5. E flat; 6. E flat minor; 7. E; 8. E minor; 9. F; 10. F minor; 11. G; 12. G minor.
8. V. Black *Concert* (5/91) (COLL) ① **Coll5024-2**

Prelude—keyboard, F29
C. Rousset (r1989) *Concert*
(8/94) (HARM) ① **HMA190 1305**

Suite in G minor—keyboard, F24 (pub 1893)
C. Rousset (r1989) *Concert*
(8/94) (HARM) ① **HMA190 1305**

SECTION IV: VOCAL AND CHORAL

Dies ist der Tag—cantata, F85 (Whitsun)
B. Schlick, C. Schubert, W. Jochens, S. Schreckenberger, Rheinische Kantorei, Kleine Konzert, H. Max (r1991) *Concert*
(11/94) (CAPR) ① **10 426**

Erzittert und fallet—cantata, F83 (Easter Sunday)
B. Schlick, C. Schubert, W. Jochens, S. Schreckenberger, Rheinische Kantorei, Kleine Konzert, H. Max (r1991) *Concert*
(11/94) (CAPR) ① **10 426**

Es ist eine Stimme eines Predigers in der Wüste—cantata, F89 (Advent/Feast of John the Baptist)
B. Schlick, C. Schubert, W. Jochens, S. Schreckenberger, Rheinische Kantorei, Kleine Konzert, H. Max (r1991) *Lasset uns ablegen, F80.*
(11/94) (CAPR) ① **10 425**

Lasset uns ablegen die Werke der Finsternis—cantata, F80 (1749) (Advent I)
B. Schlick, C. Schubert, W. Jochens, S. Schreckenberger, Rheinische Kantorei, Kleine Konzert, H. Max (r1991) *Es ist eine Stimme, F89.*
(11/94) (CAPR) ① **10 425**

BACHELER, Daniel (?c1574–after 1610) England

SECTION II: CHAMBER

Daniells Amlayne—consort (pub 1609)
J. Bream, J. Bream Consort (r1987) *Concert*
(8/93) (RCA) ① [28] **09026 61583-2(3)**
J. Bream Consort (r1987) *Concert*
(9/94) (RCA) ① **09026 61590-2**

SECTION III: INSTRUMENTAL

Miscellaneous pieces in Lord Herbert of Cherbury's Lute Book—lute
1. Prelude; 2. Fantasie; 3. Pavin; 4. 3 Courantes.
P. O'Dette *Concert* (4/93) (HARM) ① **HMU07 7068**

Monsieur's Almaine—lute (pub 1610)
J. Bream (r1960) *Concert*
(8/93) (RCA) ① [28] **09026 61583-2(1)**
J. Bream (r1960) *Concert*
(8/93) (RCA) ① **09026 61584-2**

Variations on Dowland's 'Earl of Essex Galliard'—lute (in Lord Herbert of Cherbury's Lute Book)
P. O'Dette *Concert* (4/93) (HARM) ① **HMU07 7068**

Variations on 'La jeune fillette'—lute (in Lord Herbet of Cherbury's Lute Book)
P. O'Dette *Concert* (4/93) (HARM) ① **HMU07 7068**
Baltimore Consort (r1992; arr Baltimore Consort) *Concert* (4/95) (DORI) ① **DOR90177**

BACHELET, Alfred (1864–1944) France

SECTION IV: VOCAL AND CHORAL

Chère nuit
C. Muzio, orch (r1920) *Concert*
(5/90) (BOGR) ① [2] **BIM705-2**
L. Pons, orch, M. Abravanel (r1946) *Concert*
(7/90) (SONY) ① **MPK45694**
C. Muzio, orch (r1920) *Concert*
(1/94) (ROMO) ① [2] **81005-2**

BACHMANN, Robert C. (b 1944) Switzerland

SECTION I: ORCHESTRAL

Rotation 90 degrees North—low strings (1990)
RPO, R.C. Bachmann (r1991) *Concert*
(2/94) (ARVA) ① **CD-390004-2**

BACH/VIVALDI

SECTION I: ORCHESTRAL

Concerto for Organ and Strings in A minor, BWV593/RV522 (Op. 3 No. 8) (Organ part transc Bach from Vivaldi's Concerto Op. 3 No. 8; original string parts by Vivaldi: arr. Redel)
P. Bardon, Munich Pro Arte, K. Redel (arr. Redel) *Concert* (5/84) (PIER) ① **PV79801**

Concerto for Organ and Strings in C, BWV594/RV285a (Op. 7 No. 5) (Organ part transc Bach from Vivaldi's Concerto Op. 7 No. 5; original string parts by Vivaldi: arr. Redel)
P. Bardon, Munich Pro Arte, K. Redel (arr. Redel) *Concert* (5/84) (PIER) ① **PV79801**

Concerto for Organ and Strings in D, BWV972/RV230 (Op. 3 No. 9) (Organ part transc Bach from Vivaldi's Concerto Op. 3 No. 9; original string parts by Vivaldi: arr. Redel)
P. Bardon, Munich Pro Arte, K. Redel (arr. Redel) *Concert* (5/84) (PIER) ① **PV79801**

Concerto for Organ and Strings in G minor, BWV975/RV316a (Op. 4 No. 6) (Organ part transc Bach from Vivaldi's Concerto Op. 4 No. 6; original string parts by Vivaldi: arr. Redel)
P. Bardon, Munich Pro Arte, K. Redel (arr. Redel) *Concert* (5/84) (PIER) ① **PV79801**

BADAJÓZ EL MÚSICO (fl c1520) Spain

also known as João de Badajos

SECTION IV: VOCAL AND CHORAL

O desdichado de mi (from the Palacio Song Book)
Hespèrion XX, J. Savall *Concert*
(7/92) (ASTR) ① **E8762**

BADARZEWSKA-BARANOWSKA, Tekla (1834–1861) Poland

SECTION III: INSTRUMENTAL

The Maiden's Prayer—piano
A. Etherden *Concert*
(7/93) (HUNT) ① **HMPCD0589**

BAELZ, John (20th Cent) England

SECTION IV: VOCAL AND CHORAL

Ring Christ, Ring Mary, Benedict and Bede—hymn (1980)
Durham Cath Ch, J. Lancelot, I. Shaw *Concert*
(7/91) (PRIO) ① **PRCD296**

BAERMANN, C. (19th Cent) Germany

SECTION I: ORCHESTRAL

Duo concertant—two clarinets and band, Op. 33
A. Giammatteo, F.J. Brissett, wind band (r1926) *Concert* (2/94) (CLRI) ① **CC0005**

BAËRMANN, Heinrich (Joseph) (1784–1847) Germany

SECTION II: CHAMBER

Air varié—clarinet and piano
V. Soames, J. Drake (r1990s) *Concert*
(8/93) (CLRI) ① **CC0003**

Quintet (Septet) in E flat—clarinet and string quartet, Op. 23 (two obbligato horns optional)
2. Adagio (previously attrib Wagner).
Movt 2. J. Cohler, J. Gordon (r1992;arr cl/pf) *Concert*
(11/94) (ONGA) ① **024-101**
2. E. Johnson, ECO, C. Groves *Concert*
(11/94) (ASV) ① **CDDCA559**
2. A. Boskovsky, Vienna Octet *Concert*
(9/88) (DECC) ① **417 643-2DM**
2. V. Soames, Duke Qt (r1990s) *Concert*
(8/93) (CLRI) ① **CC0003**

BAINBRIDGE, Simon (b 1952) England

SECTION I: ORCHESTRAL

Concerto for Viola and Orchestra (1976)
W. Trampler, London Sinfonietta, M. Tilson Thomas *Concert* (5/91) (CNTI) ① **CCD1020**

Fantasia for Double Orchestra (1983-84)
BBC SO, S. Bainbridge *Concert*
(5/91) (CNTI) ① **CCD1020**

SECTION II: CHAMBER

Concertante in moto perpetuo—oboe and chamber ensemble (1983)
N. Daniel, Composers Ens, S. Bainbridge *Concert*
(5/91) (CNTI) ① **CCD1020**

SECTION IV: VOCAL AND CHORAL

A Song from Michelangelo (Wds. Michelangelo)
M. Wiegold, Composers Ens, D. Muldowney *Concert*
(4/92) (NMC) ① **NMCD003**

BAINTON, Edgar (Leslie) (1880–1956) England/Australia

SECTION IV: VOCAL AND CHORAL

And I saw a new heaven—anthem (Wds. Book of Revelation)
New College Ch, E. Higginbottom *Concert*
(3/87) (PROU) ① **PROUCD114**
Guildford Cath Ch, A. Millington, P. Wright *Concert*
(5/89) (PRIO) ① **PRCD257**
St Bride's Ch, Fleet St, C. Etherington, R. Jones *Concert* (2/91) (REGE) ① **REGSB701CD**
St Paul's Cath Ch, John Scott *Concert*
(4/92) (HYPE) ① **CDA66519**
Dundee Cath Ch, R. Lightband (org/dir) *Concert*
(8/92) (ABBE) ① **CDCA926**
Wellington College Chs, T. Byram-Wigfield, S. Anderson *Concert* (10/92) (HERA) ① **HAVPCD153**
King's College Ch, S. Cleobury, C. Hughes (r1991) *Concert* (6/93) (EMI) ① **CDC7 54418-2**
Jesus College Ch, D. Phillips, T. Horton *Concert*
(7/93) (CNTO) ① **CRCD2367**

BAIRSTOW, Sir Edward C(uthbert) (1874–1946) England

SECTION III: INSTRUMENTAL

Elegy—organ
F. Jackson (r1990) *Concert*
(4/91) (MIRA) ① **MRCD902**

Evening Song—organ
F. Jackson (r1990) *Concert*
(4/91) (MIRA) ① **MRCD902**

Legend—organ
F. Jackson (r1990) *Concert*
(4/91) (MIRA) ① **MRCD902**

Meditation—organ
F. Jackson (r1990) *Concert*
(4/91) (MIRA) ① **MRCD902**

Nocturne in D flat—organ (1903)
F. Jackson (r1990) *Concert*
(4/91) (MIRA) ① **MRCD902**

Organ Sonata in E flat
F. Jackson (r1990) *Concert*
(4/91) (MIRA) ① **MRCD902**
John Scott (r1992) *Concert*
(8/94) (PRIO) ① **PRCD401**

Prelude in C—organ
F. Jackson (r1990) *Concert*
(4/91) (MIRA) ① **MRCD902**

Prelude on 'Vexilla Regis'—organ
F. Jackson (r1990) *Concert*
(4/91) (MIRA) ① **MRCD902**
Scherzo in A flat—organ
F. Jackson (r1990) *Concert*
(4/91) (MIRA) ① **MRCD902**
3 Short Preludes—organ
F. Jackson (r1990) *Concert*
(4/91) (MIRA) ① **MRCD902**
Toccata and Prelude on 'Pange Lingua'—organ
F. Jackson (r1990) *Concert*
(4/91) (MIRA) ① **MRCD902**

SECTION IV: VOCAL AND CHORAL

Blessed City, heavenly Salem—anthem
Guildford Cath Ch, A. Millington, P. Wright *Concert*
(5/89) (PRIO) ① **PRCD257**
New College Ch, E. Higginbottom *Concert*
(3/90) (PROU) ① **PROUCD125**
St Paul's Cath Ch, Andrew Lucas, John Scott
Concert (9/90) (HYPE) ① **CDA66374**
Magdalen Oxford Coll Ch, G. Webber *Concert*
(11/91) (ABBE) ① **CDCA914**
T. Barber, Winchester Cath Ch, Waynflete Sngrs, T. Byram-Wigfield, Bournemouth SO, D. Hill *Concert*
(4/92) (ARGO) ① **430 836-2ZH**
York Minster Ch, P. Moore, J.S. Whiteley (r1991)
Concert (6/93) (PRIO) ① **PRCD365**
Jesus College Ch, D. Phillips, T. Horton *Concert*
(7/93) (CNTO) ① **CRCD2367**
Truro Cath Ch, D. Briggs, S. Morley (r1992) *Concert*
(7/94) (PRIO) ① **PRCD429**
A Blessed Virgin's Cradle Song (Wds. E. Rogers)
Lichfield Cath Ch, J. Rees-Williams *Concert*
(12/90) (ABBE) ① **CDCA903**
York Minster Ch, P. Moore, J.S. Whiteley (r1991)
Concert (6/93) (PRIO) ① **PRCD365**
Evening Service in D
1. Magnificat; 2. Nunc dimittis.
York Minster Ch, P. Moore, J.S. Whiteley (r1991)
Concert (6/93) (PRIO) ① **PRCD365**
I sat down under his shadow—anthem: 4vv (1925) (Wds. Bible)
Cambridge Sngrs, J. Rutter *Concert*
(4/92) (CLLE) ① **COLCD113**
If the Lord had not helped me (1910) (Wds. Psalm 94)
York Minster Ch, P. Moore, J.S. Whiteley (r1991)
Concert (6/93) (PRIO) ① **PRCD365**
Jesu, grant me this I pray—anthem (1924) (fauxbourdon setting of 'Song 13' by O. Gibbons)
York Minster Ch, P. Moore, J.S. Whiteley (r1991)
Concert (6/93) (PRIO) ① **PRCD365**
St Paul's Cath Ch, John Scott, Andrew Lucas (r1993)
Concert (6/94) (HYPE) ① **CDA66678**
Jesu, the very thought of Thee—anthem (Wds. St Bernard of Clairvaux, trans Caswall)
York Minster Ch, P. Moore, J.S. Whiteley (r1991)
Concert (6/93) (PRIO) ① **PRCD365**
The Lamentation (1942) (Wds. Bible)
Ely Cath Ch, P. Trepte *Concert*
(2/92) (GAMU) ① **GAMCD527**
York Minster Ch, P. Moore, J.S. Whiteley (r1991)
Concert (6/93) (PRIO) ① **PRCD365**
Let all mortal flesh keep silence—anthem (1925)
Guildford Cath Ch, A. Millington, P. Wright *Concert*
(5/89) (PRIO) ① **PRCD257**
St Paul's Cath Ch, Andrew Lucas, John Scott
Concert (9/90) (HYPE) ① **CDA66374**
Magdalen Oxford Coll Ch *Concert*
(11/91) (ABBE) ① **CDCA914**
King's College Sngrs, E.H. Warrell *Concert*
(12/91) (REGE) ① **REGCD106**
St John's Evangelist Cath Ch, D. Pearson *Concert*
(10/92) (DELO) ① **DE3125**
York Minster Ch, P. Moore, J.S. Whiteley (r1991)
Concert (6/93) (PRIO) ① **PRCD365**
Lord, I call upon Thee (1916) (Wds. Psalm 141 & 38)
York Minster Ch, P. Moore, J.S. Whiteley (r1991)
Concert (6/93) (PRIO) ① **PRCD365**
Southwark Cath Ch, P. Wright, S. Layton (r1992)
Concert (7/94) (PRIO) ① **PRCD435**
Lord, Thou hast been our refuge—anthem: choir and orchestra (1917)
York Minster Ch, P. Moore, J.S. Whiteley (r1991)
Concert (6/93) (PRIO) ① **PRCD365**
Lincoln Cath Ch, J. Vivian, C. Walsh (r1993) *Concert*
(7/94) (PRIO) ① **PRCD454**

Music, when soft voices die—part-song (Wds. Shelley)
King's Sngrs *Concert*
(6/88) (EMI) ① **CDC7 49765-2**
The Oak and the Ash—English folksong arrangement
M. Padmore, Cambridge Sngrs, J. Rutter *Concert*
(4/87) (CLLE) ① **COLCD104**
Save us, O Lord—anthem; choir and organ
St Paul's Cath Ch, John Scott *Concert*
(4/92) (HYPE) ① **CDA66519**
York Minster Ch, P. Moore, J.S. Whiteley (r1991)
Concert (6/93) (PRIO) ① **PRCD365**
Though I speak with the tongues of men—anthem (1934)
Lincoln Cath Ch, J. Vivian, C. Walsh (r1993) *Concert*
(7/94) (PRIO) ① **PRCD454**
When Israel came out of Egypt (1929) (Wds. Psalm 114)
York Minster Ch, P. Moore, J.S. Whiteley (r1991)
Concert (6/93) (PRIO) ① **PRCD365**

BAKER, Philip E. *(20th Cent)* USA

SECTION IV: VOCAL AND CHORAL

Easter anthem—chorus (Wds. adapted from ancient hymnary)
St John's Episcopal Cath Ch, D. Pearson *Concert*
(10/92) (DELO) ① **DE3125**

BAKFARK, Bálint *(1507–1576)* Hungary

SECTION III: INSTRUMENTAL

Fantasia—lute
J. Bream (r1966) *Concert*
(8/93) (RCA) ① **[28] 09026 61583-2(1)**
J. Bream (r1966) *Concert*
(6/94) (RCA) ① **09026 61585-2**

BALAKAUSKAS, Osvaldas *(b 1937)* Lithuania/USSR

SECTION I: ORCHESTRAL

Ostrobothnian Symphony (1990)
Ostrobothnian CO, J. Kangas (r1994) *Concert*
(11/95) (FINL) ① **4509-97892-2**

BALAKIREV, Mily Alexeyevich *(1837–1910)* Russia

SECTION I: ORCHESTRAL

Concerto for Piano and Orchestra in E flat (1861-62) (cpted Lyapunov)
M. Ponti, Westphalian SO, S. Landau *Concert*
(5/93) (VOX) ① **115714-2**
Concerto for Piano and Orchestra No. 1 in F sharp, Op. 1 (1855-56)
M. Binns, English Northern Philh, D. Lloyd-Jones
Concert (7/93) (HYPE) ① **CDA66640**
I. Zhukov, USSR TV & Rad Orch, A. Dmitriev (r1973)
Concert (2/94) (MEZH) ① **MK417087**
Concerto for Piano and Orchestra No. 2 in E flat, Op. posth (1861-62) (unfinished: cpted Lyapunov)
M. Binns, English Northern Philh, D. Lloyd-Jones
Concert (7/93) (HYPE) ① **CDA66640**
Overture on the Themes of three Russian songs—orchestra (1858 rev 1881)
Philh, E. Svetlanov *Concert*
(9/92) (HYPE) ① **CDA66586**
Philh, D.V. Yu (r1993) *Concert*
(1/95) (CARL) ① **MCD82**
Second Overture on Russian Themes, 'Russia'—orchestra (1863-64 rev 1884)
Philh, E. Svetlanov (Symphonic poem Rus - pub 1890 with minor alterations) *Symphony 1.*
(12/91) (HYPE) ① **CDA66493**
LPO, H. Harty (r1933) *Concert*
(11/93) (DUTT) ① **CDAX8005**
Russian St SO, I. Golovshin (r1993) *Symphony 2.*
(10/94) (NAXO) ① **8 550793**
Symphony No. 1 in C (1864-66, 1893-97)
RPO, T. Beecham (r1955) *Tamara.*
(7/90) (EMI) ① **CDM7 63375-2**
Philh, E. Svetlanov *Russian Ov. II.*
(12/91) (HYPE) ① **CDA66493**
Russian St SO, I. Golovshin (r1993) *Concert*
(10/94) (NAXO) ① **8 550792**
Symphony No. 2 in D minor (1900-08)
Philh, E. Svetlanov *Concert*
(9/92) (HYPE) ① **CDA66586**

Russian St SO, I. Golovshin (r1993) *Russian Ov II.*
(9/94) (NAXO) ① **8 550793**
Tamara—symphonic poem (1867-82)
RPO, T. Beecham (r1954) *Symphony 1.*
(7/90) (EMI) ① **CDM7 63375-2**
Philh, E. Svetlanov *Concert*
(9/92) (HYPE) ① **CDA66586**
Russian St SO, I. Golovshin (r1993) *Concert*
(10/94) (NAXO) ① **8 550792**

SECTION III: INSTRUMENTAL

Au jardin—piano (1884)
M. Fingerhut *Concert* (6/87) (CHAN) ① **CHAN8439**
Berceuse in D flat—piano (1901)
M. Campanella *Concert* (12/90) (NUOV) ① **6826**
Islamey—oriental fantasy (1869 rev 1902)
USSR Academy SO, E. Svetlanov (orch Lyapunov)
Concert (7/89) (OLYM) ① **OCD129**
D. Ciani (pp) *Concert* (8/89) (DYNA) ① **CDS55**
S. Barere (pp1947) *Concert*
(11/89) (APR) ① **[2] APR7008**
M. Campanella *Concert* (12/90) (NUOV) ① **6826**
S. Barere (r1935 & 1936: 2 versions) *Concert*
(5/91) (APR) ① **[2] APR7001**
A. Gavrilov (r1977) *Concert*
(11/92) (EMI) ① **CDM7 64329-2**
O. Mustonen *Concert*
(2/93) (DECC) ① **436 255-2DH**
S. Cherkassky (bp1982) *Concert*
(6/93) (DECC) ① **433 651-2DH**
G. Cziffra (r1954) *Concert*
(11/93) (APR) ① **[2] APR7021**
Russian St SO, I. Golovshin (r1993: orch Lyapunov)
Concert (10/94) (NAXO) ① **8 550792**
Philh, D.V. Yu (orch Lyapunov) *Concert*
(1/95) (CARL) ① **MCD82**
The Lark—piano (c1864 version 1); 1900 (version 2) (based on Glinka's song)
G. Fergus-Thompson *Concert*
(6/88) (KING) ① **KCLCD2001**
7 Mazurkas—piano
1. A flat (1861 rev c1884); 2. C sharp minor (1861 rev c1884); 3. B minor (1886); 4. G flat (1886); 5. D (1900); 6. A flat (1902); 7. E flat minor (1906).
J. Banowetz (r1986) *Scherzi.*
(11/87) (MARC) ① **8 220447**
Polka in F sharp minor—piano (1859)
M. Fingerhut *Concert* (6/87) (CHAN) ① **CHAN8439**
3 Scherzi—piano
1. B minor (1856); 2. B flat minor (1900); 3. F sharp (1901).
J. Banowetz (r1986) *Mazurkas.*
(11/87) (MARC) ① **8 220447**
Sonata for Piano in B flat minor (1900-05)
D. Amato *Dutilleux: Piano Sonata (1947).*
(9/87) (ARHD) ① **DARC2**
G. Fergus-Thompson *Concert*
(6/88) (KING) ① **KCLCD2001**
R. Smith *Concert* (8/89) (NIMB) ① **NI5187**
Spanish Melody—piano (1902)
A. Etherden *Concert*
(7/93) (HUNT) ① **HMPCD0589**
Toccata in C sharp minor—piano (1902)
M. Fingerhut *Concert* (6/87) (CHAN) ① **CHAN8439**

SECTION IV: VOCAL AND CHORAL

3 Forgotten songs—1v & piano (1855)
1. Thou art so captivating (Wds. Golovinsky); 2. The link (Wds. Tumansky); 3. Spanish song (Wds. Mikhaylov).
1, 3, O. Borodina, L. Gergieva (r1994) *Concert*
(8/95) (PHIL) ① **442 780-2PH**
20 Songs—1v and piano (1858-64)
1. Brigand's song (wds. Kol'tsov); 2. Embrace, kiss (wds. Kol'tsov); 3. Barcarolle (wds. Arsen'yev after Heine); 4. Cradle Song (wds. Arsen'yev); 5. The bright moon (wds. Yetsevich); 6. When thou playest, carefree child (wds. Vil'de); 7. The knight (wds. Vil'de); 8. I'm a fine fellow (wds. Kol'tsov); 9. My heart is torn (wds. Kol'tsov); 10. Come to me (wds. Kol'tsov); 11. Song of Selim (wds. Lermontov); 12. Lead me, o night (wds. Maykov); 13. Hebrew melody (wds. Lermontov, after Byron); 14. Rapture (wds. Kol'tsov); 15. Why (wds. Lermontov); 16. Song of the golden fish (wds. Lermontov); 17. Old man's song (wds. Kol'tsov); 18. When I hear thy voice (wds. Lermontov); 19. Georgian song (wds. Pushkin); 20. The dream (wds. Mikhaylov, after Heine).
5, 9, 11, 18. O. Borodina, L. Gergieva (r1994)
Concert (8/95) (PHIL) ① **442 780-2PH**
10 Songs—1v and piano (1895-96)
1. Over the lake (wds. Goleníshchev-Kutuzov); 2. The wilderness (wds. Zhemchuzhnikov); 3. The sea does not foam (wds. Tolstoy); 4. When the yellow cornfield waves (wds. Lermontov); 5. I loved him (wds. Kol'stov); 6. The pine-tree (wds. Lermontov); 7.

Nachstück (wds. Khomyakov); 8. The putting-right (wds. May); 9. 'Mid autumn flowers (wds. Axakov); 10. The rosy sunset fades (wds. Kul'chinsky).
1, 5. O. Borodina, L. Gergieva (r1994) *Concert*
(8/95) (PHIL) ① **442 780-2PH**

BALBASTRE, Claude-Béninge (1727–1799) France

SECTION II: CHAMBER

4 Sonates en quatuor—hpd/pf, with 2 vns, 2 hns & bass ad lib, Op. 3 (pub 1734)
EXCERPTS: 1. B flat; 2. F; 3. C; 4. D.
Concerto Rococo (r1993)
(3/95) (PIER) ① **PV794043**

SECTION III: INSTRUMENTAL

Air Gay—keyboard (1759)
J. Henry *Concert* (10/92) (VICT) ① **VCD19013**
Noëls en variations—organ (pub ?1770)
Suite I in D; 1. Prelude; 2. A la venue de Noël; 3. Joseph est bien marié; 4. Où s'en vont ces gais bergers; 5. Ah, ma voisine, est-tu fâchée; 6. Tous les bourgeois de Châtre; 7. Quand Jesus naquit à Noël. Suite II in A: 8. Votre bonté Grand Dieu; 9. Il est un petit l'ange; 10. Joseph revenant un jour; 11. Au jô deu de pubelle; 12. Grand dé, ribon, ribeine; 13. A cei-ci le moître de tô l'univar. Suite III in G; 14. Qué tu grô Jan, quei fôlie; 15. Divine princesse; 16. O jour ton div flambeau; 17. Quel désordre dans la nature; 18. Vé Noei Blaizôte; 19. Fanne, coraige, le diale à mor. Suite IV in C: 20. Or dites-nous Maie; 21. Je rend graces à mon Dieu; 22. Qui a peu cve machuret; 23. Comment tu oze petite Rose; 24. Laissés paltvros bêtes; 25a. Il n'est rien de plus tendre; 25b. Si c'est pour ôter la vie; 25c. A minuit fut fait un réveil.
11. J. van Oortmerssen *Concert*
(11/87) (BIS) ① **BIS-CD316**
12. J. van Oortmerssen *Concert*
(11/87) (BIS) ① **BIS-CD316**
Premier livre de pièces de clavecin (pub 1759)
1. La de Caze; 2. La d'Héricourt; 3. La Ségur; 4. La Montmartel ou la Brunoy; 5. La Boullongne; 6. La Castelmore; 7. La Courteille; 8. La Bellaud; 9. La Lamarck; 10. La Berville; 11. La Lugeac; 12. La Suzanne; 13. La Genty; 14. La Malesherbe; 15. La Berryer ou La Lamoignon; 16. La Laporte; 17. La Morisseau.
12. T. Pinnock *Concert*
(11/84) (ARCH) ① **413 591-2AH**
12. V. Black *Concert* (5/91) (COLL) ① **Coll5024-2**

BALCOMBE, Richard (b 1955) England

SECTION I: ORCHESTRAL

Greensleeves Suite—cello orchestra (1993)
LPO Vcs, RPO Vcs, BBC SO Vcs, Philh Vcs, G. Simon (r1993) *Concert*
(9/95) (CALA) ① **CACD0104**

BALDASSARE, Pietro (before 1690–after 1768) Italy

SECTION I: ORCHESTRAL

Sonata for Cornett (Trumpet), Strings and Continuo in F
A. Stringer, N. Rawsthorne (r1974) *Concert*
(11/87) (CRD) ① **CRD3308**
G. Touvron, Slovak CO, B. Warchal *Concert*
(9/91) (OPUS) ① **9350 1710**
H. Hardenberger, I Musici (r1994) *Concert*
(5/95) (PHIL) ① **442 131-2PH**

BALDOMIR, José (1869–?) Spain

SECTION IV: VOCAL AND CHORAL

Meus Amores, 'Ballada gallega'—song
(Wds. S. Wolpe)
C. Supervia, CO (r1929) *Concert*
(3/93) (NIMB) ① [2] **NI7836/7**

BALDUCCI, Giuseppe (1796–?) Italy

SECTION V: STAGE WORKS

Tazia—dramma: 1 act (1826—Naples) (Lib. L. Ricciuti)
Che vedol...Numa immenso...Non più veggio J. Rhys-Davies, P. Nilon, Philh, D. Parry *Concert*
(8/95) (OPRA) ① [3] **ORCH104**

BALDWIN, John (before 1560–1615) England

SECTION II: CHAMBER

In Nomine a 4—consort (4 parts)
Fretwork *Concert* (3/88) (AMON) ① **CD-SAR29**
Upon in nomine—consort: 4 parts
Amsterdam Loeki Stardust Qt (r1991) *Concert*
(2/94) (L'OI) ① **436 155-2OH**
Upon salva nos—consort: 4 parts
Amsterdam Loeki Stardust Qt (r1991) *Concert*
(2/94) (L'OI) ① **436 155-2OH**
4 vocum—consort: 4 parts
Amsterdam Loeki Stardust Qt (r1991) *Concert*
(2/94) (L'OI) ① **436 155-2OH**

BALFE, Michael William (1808–1870) Ireland

SECTION IV: VOCAL AND CHORAL

Killarney—song (1862) (Wds. E. Falconer)
A. Campoli, Orch, W. Goehr *Concert*
(10/91) (PEAR) ① **PASTCD9744**
Trust her not—duet (Wds. Longfellow)
F. Lott, A. Murray, G. Johnson (r1991) *Concert*
(7/92) (EMI) ① **CDC7 54411-2**

SECTION V: STAGE WORKS

The Bohemian Girl—opera: 3 acts (1843—London) (Lib. A Bunn, after Saint Georges)
EXCERPTS: 1. Overture. ACT 1: 2. Up with the banner; 3. A soldier's life; 4. 'Tis sad to leave our fatherland; 5. In the gipsy's life you read; 6. Comrade, your hand; 7. Is no succour near at hand?; 8. What means this alarm?; 9. Waltz; 10. Down with the daring slave; 11. Galop; 12. What sounds break on the ear? ACT 2: 13. Silence, silence! The lady moon; 14. I dreamt I dwelt in marble halls; 15. The wound upon thy arm; 16. What is the spell hath yet effaced; 17. Listen, when I relate the hope of a Gipsy's fate; 18. In the gipsy's life you read; 19. 'Tis gone - the past was all a dream; 20. This is thy deed; 21b. Come with the gypsy bride; 22. Life itself is at the best; 23. My dear uncle, it delights me to see you; 24a. What'er the scenes; 24b. The heart bow'd down; 25. Hold! hold! ACT 3: 26a. Introduction; 26b. The past appears to me but a dream; 27. When other lips and other hearts; 28. Through the world with thou fly, love; 29. Welcome the present; 30. Through every hope be fled; 31. See at your feet a suppliant one; 32. When the fair land of Poland; 33. Let not the soul for sorrows grieve; 34. Oh! what full delight.
Cpte N. Thomas, P. Power, B. Cullen, J. Summers, T. German, RTE Phil Ch, Ireland National SO, R. Bonynge (8/92) (ARGO) ① [2] **433 324-2ZH2**
24b H. Scott, Orig Broadway Cast (r1913) *Concert*
(5/94) (PEAR) ① [3] **GEMMCDS9059/61**
27. H. Nash, orch (r1926) *Concert*
(8/89) (PEAR) ① **GEMMCD9319**
Le Puits d'amour—opéra-comique: 3 acts (1843—Paris) (Lib. E Scribe & A de Leuven)
EXCERPTS: 1. Rêves d'amour, rêves de gloire.
1. S. Jo, ECO, R. Bonynge (r1993) *Concert*
(9/94) (DECC) ① **440 679-2DH**

BALL, Eric (1903–1989) England

SECTION I: ORCHESTRAL

Journey into freedom—rhapsody: brass band
Black Dyke Mills Band, P. Parkes (pp1987) *Concert*
(11/93) (CHAN) ① **CHAN4513**
The Kingdom Triumphant—tone poem: brass band
Sellers Engin Band, N. Law (r1993) *Concert*
(11/95) (CHAN) ① **CHAN4531**
Rhapsody on Negro Spirituals No. 1—brass band
Black Dyke Mills Band, R. Newsome (r1977) *Concert*
(1/94) (CHAN) ① **CHAN4528**

Rhapsody on Negro Spirituals No. 2—brass band
Black Dyke Mills Band, R. Newsome *Concert*
(10/91) (CHAN) ① **CHAN6539**
Sinfonietta—The Wayfarer—brass band (1976)
Black Dyke Mills Band, R. Newsome *Concert*
(7/93) (CHAN) ① **CHAN4508**
Softly sounds the little bell—brass band
Glasgow CWS Band, H. Snell *Concert*
(9/92) (DOYE) ① **DOYCD005**
Star Lake—brass band
Glasgow CWS Band, H. Snell *Concert*
(9/92) (DOYE) ① **DOYCD005**

BALL, Ernest R (1878–1927) USA

SECTION V: STAGE WORKS

Barry of Ballymore—musical show (1911)
(Music & lyrics collab with Chauncey Olcott)
EXCERPTS: 1. I Love the Name of Mary (Lyrics Graff); 2. Mother Machree (Lyrics Young).
1, 2. C. Olcott, Orig Broadway Cast (r1913) *Concert*
(5/94) (PEAR) ① [3] **GEMMCDS9053/5**
2. J. McCormack, E. Schneider (r1927) *Concert*
(5/93) (MMOI) ① **CDMOIR418**
2. A. Murray, G. Johnson (r1992) *Concert*
(8/93) (HYPE) ① **CDA66627**
The Isle o' Dreams—musical show (1913)
(Music collab with Chauncey Olcott)
EXCERPTS: 1. When Irish Eyes are Smiling (Lyrics Graff).
1. C. Olcott, Orig Broadway Cast (r1913) *Concert*
(5/94) (PEAR) ① [3] **GEMMCDS9053/5**
Macushla—musical show (1912—New York)
(Music & lyrics collab Chauncey Olcott)
EXCERPTS: 1. That's How the Shannon Flows (Lyrics Brennan); 2. I'll Miss You Old Ireland, God Bless You, Goodbye; 3. 'Tis an Irish Gil I Love (music Brennan; lyrics Dubin); 4. Macushla Asthore (Lyrics Brennan).
1-4. C. Olcott, Orig Broadway Cast (r1920) *Concert*
(5/94) (PEAR) ① [3] **GEMMCDS9053/5**
Trilby—songs for the musical show (1895, revived 1915—New York) (Lyrics Brennan)
EXCERPTS: 1. To the Lass We Love, a Toast; 2. A Breath o' Blooming Heather.
1, 2. G. MacFarlane, Orig Broadway Cast (r1915) *Concert* (5/94) (PEAR) ① [3] **GEMMCDS9056/8**

BALLARD, Robert (c1575–in or after 1650) France

SECTION III: INSTRUMENTAL

Branles de village—lute
L. Kirchhof *Concert* (11/92) (SONY) ① **SK48068**
Baltimore Consort (r1992; arr Baltimore Consort) *Concert* (4/95) (DORI) ① **DOR90177**

BALLET, William (17th Cent)

SECTION IV: VOCAL AND CHORAL

Lute-book lullaby, 'Sweet was the song the virgin sang'—1v, lute (Wds. cpsr)
Cambridge Sngrs, J. Rutter (choral arr G Shaw) *Concert* (12/87) (CLLE) ① **COLCD106**
King's College Ch, D. Willcocks (arr G. Shaw) *Concert* (12/89) (DECC) ① **425 499-2DM**
Quink *Concert* (12/89) (TELA) ① **CD80202**

BALLETTI, Bernardino (fl 1554) Italy

SECTION III: INSTRUMENTAL

Intabolatura di lauto, libro primo (pub 1554)
1. La moretta; 2. Represe.
1, 2. J. Lindberg (r1991) *Concert*
(11/93) (BIS) ① **BIS-CD599**

BALOGH, Ernő (b 1897) Hungary/USA

SECTION III: INSTRUMENTAL

Caprice antique—piano
F. Kreisler, C. Lamson (r1925: arr Kreisler) *Concert*
(9/93) (BIDD) ① [2] **LAB068/9**
Dirge of the north—piano
F. Kreisler, C. Lamson (r1924: arr Kreisler) *Concert*
(9/93) (BIDD) ① [2] **LAB068/9**

BALTZAR, Thomas (c1630–1663) Germany/England

SECTION II: CHAMBER

Divisions on 'John Come Kiss me Now'—violin and piano (pub 1685) (in Playford's 'The Division Violin')
Sonnerie Trio, S. Stubbs, A. Lawrence-King (r1992)
   Concert (5/94) (TELD) ① **4509-90841-2**
Scaramouche (r1992) *Concert*
   (5/94) (CHNN) ① **CCS4792**
Pavan and Galliard in C—3 violins, bass and continuo
Parley of Instr, R. Goodman, P. Holman *Concert*
   (11/88) (HYPE) ① **CDA66108**

SECTION III: INSTRUMENTAL

A Prelude for the Violin by Senior Balshar, a Germaine (pub 1685) (in Playford's 'The Division Violin')
M. Huggett (r1992) *Concert*
   (5/94) (TELD) ① **4509-90841-2**

BANCHIERI, Adriano (1568–1634) Italy

SECTION III: INSTRUMENTAL

L' organo Suonarino—organ (pub 1605)
1. Suonata prima; 2. Dialogo secondo.
1, 2. T. Roberts (r1990; ed Roberts) *Concert*
   (4/93) (ARCH) ① [2] **437 552-2AH2**

SECTION IV: VOCAL AND CHORAL

Barca di Venetia per Padova—madrigals (5vv and continuo), Op. 12 (pub 1605 rev 1623)
C. Janequin Ens *Concert*
   (11/90) (HARM) ① **HMC90 1281**
Contrappunto bestiale alla mente—madrigal comedy (1608)
Magdalen (Oxford) Coll Ch, G. Ives *Concert*
   (11/92) (CNTO) ① **CRCD2366**

BAND, Richard (20th Cent) USA

SECTION V: STAGE WORKS

Bride of the Re-Animator—film score (1991)
EXCERPTS: 1. Prologue & Main Title.
1. OST *Concert* (5/93) (SILV) ① **SILVAD3003**

BANISTER, John (d ?1735) England

SECTION II: CHAMBER

The Musick att the Bath—suite (recons Holman)
Parley of Instr, P. Holman (r1993) *Concert*
   (6/94) (HYPE) ① **CDA66667**

BANTOCK, Sir Granville (1868–1946) England

SECTION I: ORCHESTRAL

Celtic Symphony—six harps and strings (1940)
RPO, V. Handley *Concert*
   (5/91) (HYPE) ① **CDA66450**
Fifine at the Fair—tone poem: orchestra (1901)
RPO, T. Beecham (r1949) *Concert*
   (6/92) (EMI) ① **CDM7 63405-2**
RPO, V. Handley *Concert*
   (3/93) (HYPE) ① **CDA66630**
Hebridean Symphony (1915)
Košice St PO, A. Leaper *Concert*
   (10/90) (MARC) ① **8 223274**
RPO, V. Handley *Concert*
   (5/91) (HYPE) ① **CDA66450**
2 Heroic Ballads—orchestra (1944)
1. Cuchullin's Lament; 2. Kishmul's Gallery.
RPO, V. Handley *Concert*
   (3/93) (HYPE) ① **CDA66630**
Old English Suite—small orchestra (1909)
Košice St PO, A. Leaper *Concert*
   (10/90) (MARC) ① **8 223274**
Pagan Symphony (1923-28)
RPO, V. Handley *Concert*
   (3/93) (HYPE) ① **CDA66630**
Russian Scenes (1899)
Košice St PO, A. Leaper *Concert*
   (10/90) (MARC) ① **8 223274**

The Sea Reivers (1920) (orig Scherzo of 'Hebridean Symphony')
RPO, V. Handley *Concert*
   (5/91) (HYPE) ① **CDA66450**
The Witch of Atlas—tone poem (1902)
RPO, V. Handley *Concert*
   (5/91) (HYPE) ① **CDA66450**

BARBELLA, Emanuele (1718–1777) Italy

SECTION II: CHAMBER

Duetto IV—two mandolins/violins (c1770)
1. First movement; 2. A charming shepherdess in the country; 3. The God Bacchus infuses mirth.
A. Stephens, S. Mossop *Concert*
   (3/92) (AMON) ① **CD-SAR53**

BARBER, Charlie (b 1949) England

SECTION II: CHAMBER

Kantilgan Karangan—six pianos (1992-93)
Piano Circus (r1992-93) *Concert*
   (2/95) (ARGO) ① **443 527-2ZH**

BARBER, Samuel (1910–1981) USA

SECTION I: ORCHESTRAL

Adagio for Strings, Op. 11 (1938) (arr from 2nd movt of String Quartet)
St Louis SO, L. Slatkin *Concert*
   (12/83) (TELA) ① **CD80059**
Los Angeles PO, L. Bernstein (pp 1982) *Concert*
   (10/84) (DG) ① **413 324-2GH**
LSO, A. Schenck *Concert*
   (6/86) (ASV) ① **CDDCA534**
Montreal I Musici, Y. Turovsky *Concert*
   (7/87) (CHAN) ① **CHAN8515**
ASMF, N. Marriner *Concert*
   (11/87) (ARGO) ① **417 818-2ZH**
Israel CO, Y. Talmi *Concert*
   (8/88) (CHAN) ① **CHAN8593**
NZ SO, A. Schenck *Concert*
   (8/89) (STRA) ① **SCD8012**
St Louis SO, L. Slatkin *Concert*
   (10/89) (EMI) ① **CDC7 49463-2**
Scottish CO, J-P. Saraste *Concert*
   (10/89) (VIRG) ① **VC7 59565-2**
CLS, R. Hickox *Concert*
   (11/89) (VIRG) ① **VC7 59520-2**
Atlanta SO, Y. Levi *Concert*
   (5/92) (TELA) ① **CD80250**
Zagreb Sols, A. Janigro *Concert*
   (8/92) (VANG) ① **08.4016.71**
NBC SO, A. Toscanini (r1942) *Concert*
   (11/92) (RCA) ① **GD60307**
Baltimore SO, D. Zinman *Concert*
   (1/93) (ARGO) ① **436 288-2ZH**
NYPO, L. Bernstein *Concert*
   (5/93) (SONY) ① **SMK47567**
Boston SO, C. Munch (r1957) *Concert*
   (9/93) (RCA) ① **09026 61424-2**
Detroit SO, N. Järvi (r1993) *Concert*
   (10/93) (CHAN) ① **CHAN9169**
Guildhall Str Ens, R. Salter (vn/dir) (r1992) *Concert*
   (2/94) (RCA) ① **09026 61275-2**
BPO, S. Bychkov *Concert*
   (3/94) (PHIL) ① **434 108-2PH**
NZ SO, J. Sedares (r1993) *Concert*
   (9/94) (KOCH) ① **37243-2**
LSO, M. Tilson Thomas (r1994) *Concert*
   (8/95) (CBS) ① **CDC5 55358-2**
OST (recorded for the film 'Platoon') *Concert*
   (9/95) (VIR2) ① **CDV2774**
Smithsonian Chbr Plyrs, K. Slowik (r1994) *Concert*
   (9/95) (DHM) ① **05472 77343-2**
Commando March—band (1943)
Cleveland Winds, F. Fennell *Concert*
   (10/84) (TELA) ① **CD80099**
Concerto for Cello and Orchestra, Op. 22 (1945)
R. Wallfisch, ECO, G. Simon (r1982) *Shostakovich: Cello Concerto 1.*
   (2/85) (CHAN) ① **CHAN8322**
R. Kirshbaum, Scottish CO, J-P. Saraste *Concert*
   (10/89) (VIRG) ① **VC7 59565-2**
Concerto for Piano and Orchestra, Op. 38 (1962)
T. Joselson, LSO, A. Schenck *Concert*
   (6/86) (ASV) ① **CDDCA534**
J. Browning, St Louis SO, L. Slatkin *Concert*
   (11/91) (RCA) ① **RD60732**

A. Ruskin, MIT SO, D. Epstein *Gershwin: Piano Concerto.*
   (5/93) (VOX) ① **115719-2**
Concerto for Violin and Orchestra, Op. 14 (1939-40)
L. Kaufman, Lucerne Fest Orch, W. Goehr (r1951) *Concert*
   (1/92) (MUSI) ① **MACD-667**
H. Kun, English SO, W. Boughton *Bernstein: Serenade.*
   (6/92) (NIMB) ① **NI5329**
J. Stinton, Philh, S. Bedford (r1992; arr Stinton: fl/orch) *Khachaturian: Violin Concerto.*
   (9/93) (COLL) ① **Coll1383-2**
G. Shaham, LSO, A. Previn (r1993) *Concert*
   (9/94) (DG) ① **439 886-2GH**
I. Perlman, Boston SO, S. Ozawa *Concert*
   (6/95) (EMI) ① **CDC5 55360-2**
Die natali—chorale preludes for Christmas, Op. 37 (1960)
Louisville Orch, J. Mester *Concert*
   (6/90) (ALBA) ① **TROY021-2**
Essay for Orchestra No. 1, Op. 12 (1937)
Moscow PO, D. Kitaienko *Concert*
   (2/88) (SHEF) ① **CD26**
NZ SO, A. Schenck *Concert*
   (8/89) (STRA) ① **SCD8012**
St Louis SO, L. Slatkin *Concert*
   (10/89) (EMI) ① **CDC7 49463-2**
Detroit SO, N. Järvi *Concert*
   (3/92) (CHAN) ① **CHAN9053**
Atlanta SO, Y. Levi *Concert*
   (5/92) (TELA) ① **CD80250**
Baltimore SO, D. Zinman *Concert*
   (1/93) (ARGO) ① **436 288-2ZH**
Essay for Orchestra No. 2, Op. 17 (1942)
St Louis SO, L. Slatkin *Concert*
   (10/89) (EMI) ① **CDC7 49463-2**
Detroit SO, N. Järvi *Concert*
   (3/92) (CHAN) ① **CHAN9053**
Atlanta SO, Y. Levi *Concert*
   (5/92) (TELA) ① **CD80250**
Sym of the Air, V. Golschmann *Concert*
   (8/92) (VANG) ① **08.4016.71**
Baltimore SO, D. Zinman *Concert*
   (1/93) (ARGO) ① **436 288-2ZH**
Essay for Orchestra No. 3, Op. 47 (1978)
NYPO, Z. Mehta *Corigliano: Clarinet Concerto.*
   (5/88) (NEW) ① **NW309-2**
St Louis SO, L. Slatkin *Concert*
   (10/89) (EMI) ① **CDC7 49463-2**
NZ SO, A. Schenck (r1989) *Concert*
   (1/91) (KOCH) ① **37010-2**
Detroit SO, N. Järvi *Concert*
   (3/92) (CHAN) ① **CHAN9053**
Fadograph of a Yestern Scene—orchestra, Op. 44 (1971)
NZ SO, A. Schenck (r1989) *Concert*
   (1/91) (KOCH) ① **37010-2**
Intermezzo
Detroit SO, N. Järvi *Concert*
   (10/94) (CHAN) ① **CHAN9253**
Medea's Meditation and Dance of Vengeance, Op. 23a (1955) (originally from the ballet)
LSO, A. Schenck *Concert*
   (6/86) (ASV) ① **CDDCA534**
St Louis SO, L. Slatkin *Concert*
   (10/89) (EMI) ① **CDC7 49463-2**
Atlanta SO, Y. Levi *Concert*
   (5/92) (TELA) ① **CD80250**
Boston SO, C. Munch (r1957) *Concert*
   (9/93) (RCA) ① **09026 61424-2**
Detroit SO, N. Järvi *Concert*
   (10/94) (CHAN) ① **CHAN9253**
Music for a scene from Shelley—orchestra, Op. 7 (1935)
NZ SO, A. Schenck *Concert*
   (8/89) (STRA) ① **SCD8012**
Sym of the Air, V. Golschmann *Concert*
   (8/92) (VANG) ① **08.4016.71**
Baltimore SO, D. Zinman *Concert*
   (1/93) (ARGO) ① **436 288-2ZH**
Detroit SO, N. Järvi *Concert*
   (10/94) (CHAN) ① **CHAN9253**
Mutations from Bach—brass and timpani (1967)
LSO Brass Ens, E. Crees *Concert*
   (1/92) (COLL) ① **Coll1288-2**
London Gabrieli Brass Ens, C. Larkin *Concert*
   (8/92) (HYPE) ① **CDA66517**
The School for Scandal Overture, Op. 5 (1931-33)
NZ SO, A. Schenck *Concert*
   (8/89) (STRA) ① **SCD8012**
St Louis SO, L. Slatkin *Concert*
   (10/89) (EMI) ① **CDC7 49463-2**
Seattle SO, G. Schwarz *Concert*
   (9/90) (DELO) ① **DE3078**

Detroit SO, N. Järvi *Concert*
(10/91) (CHAN) ① **CHAN8958**
Atlanta SO, Y. Levi *Concert*
(5/92) (TELA) ① **CD80250**
Baltimore SO, D. Zinman *Concert*
(1/93) (ARGO) ① **436 288-2ZH**
Symphony No. 1, Op. 9 (1936 rev 1942)
Detroit SO, N. Järvi *Concert*
(10/91) (CHAN) ① **CHAN8958**
St Louis SO, L. Slatkin *Concert*
(11/91) (RCA) ① **RD60732**
Baltimore SO, D. Zinman *Concert*
(1/93) (ARGO) ① **436 288-2ZH**
NYPO, B. Walter (r1945) *Concert*
(8/95) (SONY) ① **SMK64466**
Symphony No. 2, Op. 19 (rev 1944 rev 1947)
NZ SO, A. Schenck *Concert*
(8/89) (STRA) ① **SCD8012**
Detroit SO, N. Järvi (r1993) *Concert*
(10/93) (CHAN) ① **CHAN9169**
Under the Willow Tree
Detroit SO, N. Järvi *Concert*
(10/94) (CHAN) ① **CHAN9253**

SECTION II: CHAMBER

Canzone—flute and piano, Op. 38 (1962) (arr from Piano Concerto—movt 2)
P. Robison, T. Hester *Concert*
(11/90) (MMAS) ① **MMD 60195A**
A. Still, S. De Witt Smith (r1992) *Concert*
(4/94) (KOCH) ① **37144-2**
J. Baxtresser, I. Margalit (r1994) *Concert*
(8/95) (EMI) ① **CDC5 55400-2**
Serenade—string quartet/string orchestra, Op. 1 (1929)
Sym of the Air, V. Golschmann *Concert*
(8/92) (VANG) ① **08.4016.71**
Endellion Qt (r1990) *Concert*
(10/94) (VIRG) ① **VC5 45033-2**
Sonata for Cello and Piano, Op. 6 (1932)
R. Kirshbaum, R. Vignoles *Concert*
(10/89) (VIRG) ① **VC7 59565-2**
Y. Hanani, M. Levin (r1990) *Concert*
(10/93) (KOCH) ① **37070-2**
A. Stepansky, I. Margalit (r1994) *Concert*
(8/95) (EMI) ① **CDC5 55400-2**
Souvenirs—piano: four hands, Op. 28 (1952)
(suite arr from ballet)
Pas de deux B. Eden, A. Tamir *Concert*
(6/90) (CARL) ① **PWK1134**
String Quartet, Op. 11 (1936)
Chester Qt *Concert* (11/92) (KOCH) ① **37069-2**
Lindsay Qt (bp1988) *Concert*
(1/93) (ASV) ① **CDDCA825**
Emerson Qt (r1990) *Concert*
(4/93) (DG) ① **435 864-2GH**
Duke Qt (r1993) *Concert*
(1/94) (COLL) ① **Coll1386-2**
Tokyo Qt (r1992) *Concert*
(2/94) (RCA) ① **09026 61387-2**
Endellion Qt (r1990) *Concert*
(10/94) (VIRG) ① **VC5 45033-2**
Summer Music—wind quintet, Op. 31 (1956)
Bergen Wind Qnt *Concert*
(9/86) (BIS) ① **BIS-CD291**
Vienna/Berlin Ens *Concert*
(11/92) (SONY) ① **SK48052**
Reykjavik Wind Qnt (r1992) *Concert*
(11/93) (CHAN) ① **CHAN9174**
J. Baxtresser, J. Robinson, S. Drucker, J. Le Clair, P. Myers (r1994) *Concert*
(8/95) (EMI) ① **CDC5 55400-2**

SECTION III: INSTRUMENTAL

Ballade—piano, Op. 46 (1972)
B. Lerner *Concert* (12/88) (ETCE) ① **KTC1019**
P. Jablonski *Concert*
(7/91) (DECC) ① **430 542-2DH**
E. Parkin (r1992) *Concert*
(10/93) (CHAN) ① **CHAN9177**
M. Legrand *Concert*
(7/95) (ERAT) ① **4509-96386-2**
Excursions—piano, Op. 20 (1942-44)
1. Un poco allegro; 2. In slow blues tempo; 3. Allegretto; 4. Allegro molto.
E. Parkin *Concert* (1/89) (PREA) ① **PRCD1776**
J. MacGregor *Concert* (3/92) (COLL) ① **Coll1107-2**
E. Parkin (r1992) *Concert*
(10/93) (CHAN) ① **CHAN9177**
I. Margalit (r1994) *Concert*
(8/95) (EMI) ① **CDC5 55400-2**
Love Song—piano
B. Lerner *Concert* (12/89) (ETCE) ① **KTC1036**

Nocturne, 'Homage to John Field'—piano, Op. 33 (1959)
E. Parkin (r1992) *Concert*
(10/93) (CHAN) ① **CHAN9177**
I. Margalit (r1994) *Concert*
(8/95) (EMI) ① **CDC5 55400-2**
Sonata for Piano, Op. 26 (1949)
W. Delony *Prokofiev: Piano Sonata 6.*
(3/91) (CENT) ① **CRC2064**
V. Cliburn *Concert* (5/91) (RCA) ① **GD60415**
P. Lawson *Concert* (5/91) (VIRG) ① **VC7 59008-2**
J. MacGregor *Concert* (3/92) (COLL) ① **Coll1107-2**
V. Horowitz (r1950) *Concert*
(6/92) (RCA) ① **GD60377**
E. Parkin (r1992) *Concert*
(10/93) (CHAN) ① **CHAN9177**
Souvenirs—piano, Op. 28
E. Parkin (r1992) *Concert*
(10/93) (CHAN) ① **CHAN9177**

SECTION IV: VOCAL AND CHORAL

Agnus Dei—chorus, organ/piano, Op. 11 (1967) (arr of Adagio, Op. 11)
Corydon Sngrs, M. Best *Concert*
(9/87) (HYPE) ① **CDA66219**
The Sixteen, H. Christophers *Concert*
(11/93) (GAMU) ① **Coll1287-2**
St John's Episcopal Cath Ch, D. Pearson *Concert*
(10/92) (DELO) ① **DE3125**
Cambridge Univ Chbr Ch, T. Brown (r1992) *Concert*
(11/93) (GAMU) ① **GAMCD535**
Trinity Coll Ch, Cambridge, R. Marlow (r1993) *Concert*
(2/94) (CONI) ① **CDCF219**
Andromache's Farewell—soprano and orchestra, Op. 39 (1962) (Wds. Euripides, trans J. P. Creagh)
M. Arroyo, NYPO, T. Schippers (r1963) *Concert*
(10/91) (SONY) ① **MPK46727**
R. Alexander, Netherlands PO, E. de Waart (r1992) *Concert*
(6/93) (ETCE) ① **KTC1145**
The Beggar's song—song: 1v and piano (1936) (Wds. W H Davies)
T. Hampson, J. Browning (r1991-2) *Concert*
(5/94) (DG) ① [2] **435 867-2GH2**
Despite and Still—songs, Op. 41 (1968-69) (Wds. various)
1. A Last Song (Wds. Graves); 2. My Lizard (Wds. Roethke); 3. In the Wilderness (Wds. Graves); 4. Solitary Hotel (Wds. Joyce); 5. Despite and Still (Wds. Graves).
Cpte R. Alexander, T. Crone *Concert*
(9/88) (ETCE) ① **KTC1055**
Cpte T. Hampson, J. Browning (r1991) *Concert*
(5/94) (DG) ① [2] **435 867-2GH2**
4. T. Allen, R. Vignoles (r1993) *Concert*
(10/94) (VIRG) ① **VC5 45033-2**
Dover Beach—baritone and string quartet, Op. 3 (1931) (Wds. M. Arnold)
D. Fischer-Dieskau, Juilliard Qt (r1967) *Concert*
(10/91) (SONY) ① **MPK46727**
T. Hampson, Emerson Qt (r1992) *Concert*
(5/94) (DG) ① [2] **435 867-2GH2**
T. Allen, Endellion Qt (r1990) *Concert*
(10/94) (VIRG) ① **VC5 45033-2**
Hermit Songs—voice and piano, Op. 29 (1952-53) (Wds. from 8th-13th Irish texts)
1. At Saint Patrick's Purgatory; 2. Church Bell at Night; 3. St Ita's Vision; 4. The Heavenly Banquet; 5. The Crucifixion; 6. Sea-Snatch; 7. Promiscuity; 8. The Monk and his Cat; 9. The Praises of God; 10. The Desire for Hermitage.
Cpte R. Alexander, T. Crone *Concert*
(9/88) (ETCE) ① **KTC1055**
Cpte L. Price, S. Barber (r1954) *Concert*
(10/91) (SONY) ① **MPK46727**
Cpte C. Studer, J. Browning (r1992) *Concert*
(5/94) (DG) ① [2] **435 867-2GH2**
L. Price, S. Barber (pp1953) *Concert*
(8/94) (RCA) ① **09026 61983-2**
8. Cambridge Univ Chbr Ch, T. Brown (r1992: arr chorus: cpsr) *Concert*
(11/93) (GAMU) ① **GAMCD535**
In the dark pinewood—song: 1v and piano (1937) (Wds. J Joyce)
T. Hampson, J. Browning (r1991-2) *Concert*
(5/94) (DG) ① [2] **435 867-2GH2**
Knoxville: Summer of 1915—soprano and orchestra, Op. 24 (1947) (Wds. J. Agee)
J. Gomez, CLS, R. Hickox *Concert*
(11/89) (VIRG) ① **VC7 59520-2**
E. Steber, Dumbarton Oaks CO, W. Strickland (r1950) *Concert* (10/91) (SONY) ① **MPK46727**
S. McNair, Atlanta SO, Y. Levi *Concert*
(5/92) (TELA) ① **CD80250**
R. Alexander, Netherlands PO, E. de Waart (r1992) *Concert* (6/93) (ETCE) ① **KTC1145**

L. Price, New Philh, T. Schippers (r1968) *Concert*
(8/94) (RCA) ① **09026 61983-2**
B. Hendricks, LSO, M. Tilson Thomas (r1994) *Concert* (8/95) (EMI) ① **CDC5 55358-2**
Let down the bars, O Death—4vv a cappella, Op. 8/2 (1936) (Wds. E. Dickinson)
Cambridge Univ Chbr Ch, T. Brown (1992) *Concert*
(11/93) (GAMU) ① **GAMCD535**
Love at the door—song: 1v and piano (1934) (Wds. Meleager, trans J A Symonds)
T. Hampson, J. Browning (r1991-2) *Concert*
(5/94) (DG) ① [2] **435 867-2GH2**
The Lovers—baritone, chorus and orchestra, Op. 43 (1971) (Wds. P. Neruda)
D. Duesing, Chicago Sym Chor, Chicago SO, A. Schenck (pp1991) *Prayers of Kierkegaard.*
(3/92) (KOCH) ① **37125-2**
Love's Caution—song: 1v and piano (1935) (Wds. W H Davies)
C. Studer, J. Browning (r1992) *Concert*
(5/94) (DG) ① [2] **435 867-2GH2**
Mélodies passagères—songs, Op. 27 (1950-51) (Wds. Rilke)
1. Puisque tout passe; 2. Un cygne; 3. Tombeau dans un parc; 4. Le clocher chante; 5. Départ.
Cpte T. Hampson, J. Browning (r1991) *Concert*
(5/94) (DG) ① [2] **435 867-2GH2**
P. Robison, T. Hester (fl/pf) *Concert*
(11/90) (MMAS) ① **MMD 60195A**
Night Wanderers—song: 1v and piano (1935) (Wds. W H Davies)
T. Hampson, J. Browning (r1991-2) *Concert*
(5/94) (DG) ① [2] **435 867-2GH2**
Nuvoletta—voice and piano, Op. 25 (1947) (Wds. J. Joyce)
R. Alexander, T. Crone *Concert*
(9/88) (ETCE) ① **KTC1055**
C. Studer, T. Browning (r1992) *Concert*
(5/94) (DG) ① [2] **435 867-2GH2**
L. Price, S. Barber (pp1953) *Concert*
(8/94) (RCA) ① **09026 61983-2**
Oh that so sweet imprisonment—song: 1v and piano (1935) (Wds. J Joyce)
C. Studer, J. Browning (r1992) *Concert*
(5/94) (DG) ① [2] **435 867-2GH2**
Prayers of Kierkegaard—sop, cont (ad lib), ten (ad lib), chorus and orch, Op. 30 (1954)
G. Capone, S. Bap Theo Sem Chor, Louisville Orch, J. Mester *Concert* (6/90) (ALBA) ① **TROY021-2**
S. Reese, Chicago Sym Chor, Chicago SO, A. Schenck (pp1991) *Lovers.*
(3/92) (KOCH) ① **37125-2**
Reincarnation—4vv, Op. 16 (1937-40) (Wds. Stephens)
1. Mary Hynes; 2. Anthony O'Daly; 3. The Coolin'.
The Sixteen, H. Christophers *Concert*
(4/92) (COLL) ① **Coll1287-2**
Cambridge Univ Chbr Ch, T. Brown (r1992) *Concert*
(11/93) (GAMU) ① **GAMCD535**
Serenades—song: 1v and piano (1934) (Wds. G Dillon)
T. Hampson, J. Browning (r1991-2) *Concert*
(5/94) (DG) ① [2] **435 867-2GH2**
A Slumber Song of the Madonna—song: 1v and organ (1925) (Wds. A Noyes)
C. Studer, J. Browning (r1992) *Concert*
(5/94) (DG) ① [2] **435 867-2GH2**
3 Songs—voice and piano, Op. 2 (1927-34)
1. The daisies (wds. J. Stephens); 2. With rue my heart is laden (wds. A. E. Housman); 3. Bessie Bobtail (wds. J. Stephens).
Cpte R. Alexander, T. Crone *Concert*
(9/88) (ETCE) ① **KTC1055**
Cpte T. Hampson, J. Browning (r1991) *Concert*
(5/94) (DG) ① [2] **435 867-2GH2**
T. Allen, R. Vignoles (r1993) *Concert*
(10/94) (VIRG) ① **VC5 45033-2**
1. L. Price, S. Barber (pp1953) *Concert*
(8/94) (RCA) ① **09026 61983-2**
2. A. Rolfe Johnson, G. Johnson (r c1994) *Concert*
(8/95) (HYPE) ① [2] **CDA66471/2**
3 Songs—voice and piano, Op. 10 (1936) (Wds. J. Joyce)
1. Rain has fallen; 2. Sleep now; 3. I hear an army.
Cpte R. Alexander, T. Crone *Concert*
(9/88) (ETCE) ① **KTC1055**
Cpte T. Hampson, J. Browning (r1991) *Concert*
(5/94) (DG) ① [2] **435 867-2GH2**
T. Allen, R. Vignoles (r1993) *Concert*
(10/94) (VIRG) ① **VC5 45033-2**
1. L. Price, S. Barber (pp1953) *Concert*
(8/94) (RCA) ① **09026 61983-2**
3. R. Alexander, Netherlands PO, E. de Waart (r1992) *Concert* (6/93) (ETCE) ① **KTC1145**

4 Songs—voice and piano, Op. 13 (1937-40)
1. A nun takes the veil (wds. G. M. Hopkins); 2. The secrets of the old (wds. W. B. Yeats); 3. Sure on this shining night (wds. J. Agee); 4. Nocturne (wds. F. Prokosch).
Cpte R. Alexander, T. Crone *Concert*
(9/88) (ETCE) ① **KTC1055**
Cpte C. Studer, J. Browning (r1992) *Concert*
(5/94) (DG) ① [2] **435 867-2GH2**
1, 3. Cambridge Univ Chbr Ch, T. Brown (r1992: arr chorus: cpsr) *Concert*
(11/93) (GAMU) ① **GAMCD535**
3, 4. R. Alexander, Netherlands PO, E. de Waart (r1992) *Concert*　　(6/93) (ETCE) ① **KTC1145**
3, 4. T. Allen, R. Vignoles (r1993) *Concert*
(10/94) (VIRG) ① **VC5 45033-2**
3, 4. B. Hendricks, LSO, M. Tilson Thomas (r1994) *Concert*　　(8/95) (EMI) ① **CDC5 55358-2**
4. L. Price, S. Barber (pp1953) *Concert*
(8/94) (RCA) ① **09026 61983-2**

2 Songs—voice and piano, Op. 18 (1942-43)
1. The Queen's face on a summery coin (wds. R. Horan); 2. Monks and Raisins (wds. J. Garcia Villa).
Cpte R. Alexander, T. Crone *Concert*
(9/88) (ETCE) ① **KTC1055**
Cpte C. Studer, J. Browning (r1992) *Concert*
(5/94) (DG) ① [2] **435 867-2GH2**

3 Songs, Op. 45 (1972)
1. Now have I Fed and Eaten up; 2. A Green Lowland of Pianos; 3. O Boundless, Boundless Evening.
Cpte T. Hampson, J. Browning (r1991) *Concert*
(5/94) (DG) ① [2] **435 867-2GH2**
T. Allen, R. Vignoles (r1993) *Concert*
(10/94) (VIRG) ① **VC5 45033-2**

A Stopwatch and an ordnance map—male vv, 3 timpani, Op. 15 (1940) (Wds. Spender)
Orphei Drängar Ch, E. Ericson *Concert*
(7/88) (BIS) ① **BIS-CD383**
R. DeCormier Chorale, Sym of the Air, V. Golschmann *Concert*　(8/92) (VANG) ① **08.4016.71**
Cambridge Univ Chbr Ch, T. Brown (r1992) *Concert*
(11/93) (GAMU) ① **GAMCD535**

Strings in the Earth and Air—song: 1v and piano (1935) (Wds. J Joyce)
C. Studer, J. Browning (r1992) *Concert*
(5/94) (DG) ① [2] **435 867-2GH2**

There's Nae Lark—song: 1v and piano (1927) (Wds. A Swinburne)
T. Hampson, J. Browning (r1991-2) *Concert*
(5/94) (DG) ① [2] **435 867-2GH2**

To be sung on the water—4vv a cappella, Op. 42/2 (1968) (Wds. L. Brogan)
Cambridge Univ Chbr Ch, T. Brown (r1992) *Concert*
(11/93) (GAMU) ① **GAMCD535**

Twelfth Night—4vv a cappella, Op. 42/1 (1968) (Wds. Laurie Lee)
Cambridge Univ Chbr Ch, T. Brown (r1992) *Concert*
(11/93) (GAMU) ① **GAMCD535**

The Virgin Martyrs—female chorus, Op. 8/1 (1935-36)
1. The Virgin Martyrs; 2. Let down the bars, O Death.
Cambridge Univ Chbr Ch, T. Brown (r1992) *Concert*
(11/93) (GAMU) ① **GAMCD535**
2. Washington Cath Ch, P. Callaway *Concert*
(8/92) (VANG) ① **08.4016.71**

SECTION V: STAGE WORKS

Antony and Cleopatra—opera: 3 acts, Op. 40 (1966—New York) (Lib. Zeffirelli, after Shakespeare)
ACT ONE: 1. Prologue: From Alexandria; 2. These strong Egyptian fetters; 3. I am sick and sullen; 4. Orchestral Interlude; 5. Ah! Hail, Marcus Antonius!; 6. Give me some music; 7. The most infectious pestilence upon you!; 8. A sister I bequeath thee; 9. When first she met Mark Antony; 10. Where's my serpent of old Nile? ACT TWO: 11. Contemning Rome, he has done all this; 12. Lord Alexas, sweet Alexas; 13. Hush, here come the Queen and Antony; 14. The night is shiny; 15a. Inside the tent; 15b. Oh take, oh take those lips away; 16. On to our ships; 17. Hark! the land bids me tread no more upon it; 18. Most kind ambassador; 19. Oh, bear me witness; 20. O sov'reign mistress of true melancholy; 21. Orchestral Interlude; 22. The last she spoke; 23. Where's Antony? ACT THREE: 24. O Charmian, I will never go from hence; 25. My lord, my lord! (On the death of Antony); 26. The breaking of so great a thing; 27. Prelude; 28. He words me, girls; 29. Here is a rural fellow; 30. Give me my robe; 31. Death of Cleopatra: She looks like sleep.
6, 30. L. Price, New Philh, T. Schippers (r1968) *Concert*　　(8/94) (RCA) ① **09026 61983-2**
6, 31. R. Alexander, Netherlands PO, E. de Waart (r1992) *Concert*　　(6/93) (ETCE) ① **KTC1145**

25, 31. Cambridge Univ Chbr Ch, T. Brown (r1992) *Concert*　　(11/93) (GAMU) ① **GAMCD535**
30. C. Vaness, NY Met Op Orch, J. Conlon (pp1991) *Concert*　　(6/93) (RCA) ① **09026 61509-2**
30. L. Price, New Philh, T. Schippers (r1968) *Concert*
(4/94) (RCA) ① [6] **09026 61580-2(7)**

A Hand of Bridge—opera: 1 act, Op. 35 (1958—Spoleto)
P. Neway, E. Alberts, W. Lewis, P. Maero, Sym of the Air, V. Golschmann *Concert*
(8/92) (VANG) ① **08.4016.71**

Medea—ballet, Op. 23 (1946, rev 1947—New York) (rev vers entitled 'The Cave of the Heart')
Atlantic Sinfonietta, A. Schenck (r1990) *Copland: Appalachian Spring Suite.*
(4/92) (KOCH) ① **37019-2**

Medea—concert suite from ballet (1947)
NZ SO, A. Schenck (r1989) *Concert*
(1/91) (KOCH) ① **37010-2**

Souvenirs—concert suite from ballet, Op. 28
EXCERPTS: 1. Waltz; 2. Schottische; 3. Pas de deux; 4. Two-step; 5. Hesitation-Tango; 6. Galop.
NZ SO, A. Schenck (r1989) *Concert*
(9/90) (KOCH) ① **37005-2**
St Louis SO, L. Slatkin *Concert*
(11/91) (RCA) ① **RD60732**

Vanessa—opera: 4 acts, Op. 32 (1958—New York) (Lib. G Menotti)
EXCERPTS: ACT 1: 1. Portage crème aux perles; 2. No, I cannot understand; 3. Must the winter come so soon?; 4. Listen!...They are here; 5. Do not utter a word, Anatol; 6. Yes, I believe I shall love you; 7. Where are you? ACT 2: 8. And then?—He made me drink; 9. No, you are not as good a skater; 10. 'Under the willow tree...'; 11. Erika, I am so happy; 12. Our arms are entwined; 13. Did you hear her?; 14. Outside this house the world has changed; 15. Orchestral Interlude (Hymn). ACT 3: 16. The Count and Countess d'Albany; 17. I should never have been a doctor; 19. At last I found you; 20. Nothing to worry about. ACT 4: 21. Why did no one warm me?; 22. Why must the greatest sorrows; 23. There, look!; 24. Grandmother!—Yes, Erika; 27. Interlude; 28. By the time we arrive; 29. For every love there is a last farewell; 30. And you, my friend; 31. To leave, to break (Quintet); 32. Goodbye, Erika.
Cpte E. Steber, R. Elias, R. Resnik, N. Gedda, G. Tozzi, G. Cehanovsky, R. Nagy, NY Met Op Chor, NY Met Op Orch, D. Mitropoulos
(7/90) (RCA) ① [2] **GD87899**
3. F. von Stade, NY Met Op Orch, J. Conlon (pp1991) *Concert*　　(6/93) (RCA) ① **09026 61509-2**
3, 5. R. Alexander, Netherlands PO, E. de Waart (r1992) *Concert*　　(6/93) (ETCE) ① **KTC1145**
5. L. Price, RCA Italiana Op Orch, F. Molinari-Pradelli *Concert*　　(12/92) (RCA) ① [4] **09026 61236-2**
10. Cambridge Univ Chbr Ch, T. Brown (r1992) *Concert*　　(11/93) (GAMU) ① **GAMCD535**
31. E. Steber, R. Elias, R. Resnik, N. Gedda, G. Tozzi, G. Cehanovsky, NY Met Op Orch, D. Mitropoulos (r1958) *Concert*
(4/94) (RCA) ① [6] **09026 61580-2(5)**

BARBERIIS, Melchiore de *(fl c1545–1550) Italy*

SECTION IV: VOCAL AND CHORAL

Madonna qual certezza
Kithara (r1993) *Concert*
(3/95) (CHAN) ① **CHAN0562**

BARBETTA, Giulio Cesare *(c1540–after 1603) Italy*

SECTION III: INSTRUMENTAL

Fantasia—lute (pub 1569) (from 'Il libro primo dell'intavolatura')
J. Lindberg (r1991) *Concert*
(11/93) (BIS) ① **BIS-CD599**

Intabolatura di liuto (pub 1585)
1. GAGLIARDE: 1a. detto lo Zacarij; 1b. detto il Barbetino; 2. PAVANE: 2a. detta la Porcelina; 2b. detta la Barbarina; 3. MORESCHE: 3a. detta il Mattacino; 3b. detta la Bergamasca; 3c. detta la Canarie; 4. BALLETTI: 4a. de Contadini Lombardi; 4b. de Russia detto l'orso; 5. Padovana detta Zo per la Brenta; 6. Saltarello detto O la val cerca.
1-4. J. Lindberg (r1991) *Concert*
(11/93) (BIS) ① **BIS-CD599**

BARBIERI, Francisco Asenjo *(1823–1894) Spain*

SECTION V: STAGE WORKS

El Barberillo de Lavapiès—zarzuela: 3 acts (1874—Madrid) (Lib. Larra)
EXCERPTS: 1. Preludio: Dicen que en El Pardo; 2. Tirana: No hay que guitar; 3. Seguidillas manchegas: En el templo; 4. Canción de la paloma.
Cpte M.C. Ramirez, D. Perez, L. Sagi-Vela, F. Saura, R. Alonso, L. Frutos, Madrid Coros Cantores, Spanish Lyric Orch, F. Moreno Torroba
(10/92) (HISP) ① **CDZ7 67454-2**
Exc P. Perez Inigo, Madrid SO, E. G. Asensio (pp1991) *Concert*　　(11/92) (CARL) ① **MCD45**
No hay que quitar los hilvanes J. Carreras, I. Rey, ECO, E. Ricci (r1994) *Concert*
(2/95) (ERAT) ① **4509-95789-2**

BARCHET, Siegfried *(1918–1982) Germany*

SECTION II: CHAMBER

Images de Menton—cello and piano
Boulevard de Garavan M. Kliegel, R. Havenith *Concert*　　(9/92) (MARC) ① **8 223403**

BARDI, Giovanni de' *(1534–1612) Italy*

SECTION IV: VOCAL AND CHORAL

Miseri abitator—madrigal (5vv) - Intermedio 4, La Pellegrina (c1589) (Wds. Strozzi)
Taverner Consort, Taverner Plyrs, A. Parrott *Concert*
(8/88) (EMI) ① **CDC7 47998-2**

BARGIEL, Woldemar *(1828–1897) Germany*

SECTION II: CHAMBER

Octet in C minor—strings, Op. 15a (pub 1877)
Divertimenti (r1989) *Mendelssohn: Octet, Op.20.*
(4/90) (HYPE) ① **CDA66356**

BARIÉ, Augustin *(1884–1915) France*

SECTION III: INSTRUMENTAL

3 Pièces—organ, Op. 7 (pub 1911)
EXCERPTS: 1. Marche; 2. Lamento; 3. Toccata.
P. Wright (r1992) *Concert*
(10/94) (PRIO) ① **PRCD406**
M-B. Dufourcet (r1992) *Concert*
(6/95) (PRIO) ① **PRCD422**
3. N. Kynaston *Concert*
(4/89) (HYPE) ① **CDA66265**

Symphonie in B flat minor—organ, Op. 5 (1907, pub 1911)
P. Wright (r1992) *Concert*
(10/94) (PRIO) ① **PRCD406**

BARLOW, Wayne *(b 1912) USA*

SECTION II: CHAMBER

The Winter's Past—oboe and piano (arr from Rhapsody for ob & stgs)
H. Lucarelli, Brooklyn PO, M. Barrett (r1993) *Concert*
(7/94) (KOCH) ① **37187-2**

BARNBY, Sir Joseph *(1838–1896) England*

SECTION IV: VOCAL AND CHORAL

The Kiss—partsong
PCA, M. Brown *Concert*　　(3/87) (CONI) ① **CDCF145**
Sweet and low—glee
PCA, M. Brown *Concert*　　(3/87) (CONI) ① **CDCF145**

BARRERA, Josef *(18th Cent) Spain*

SECTION II: CHAMBER

Sonata—two organs (1782)
M.G. Filippi, M. Henking (r1986) *Concert*
(10/89) (ARIO) ① **ARN68047**

Sonata—two organs (1784)
M.G. Filippi, M. Henking (r1986) *Concert*
(10/89) (ARIO) ① **ARN68047**

BARRETT, John (c1676–?1719) England

SECTION II: CHAMBER

Sonata for Two Trumpets, Oboe and Strings (c1700)
English Tpt Virtuosi, A. Hoskins (tpt/dir), M. Hoskins (tpt/dir) (r1994) *Concert* (10/95) (MOSC) ① **070979**

BARRIOS MANGORÉ, (Pio) Agustín (1885–1944) Paraguay

SECTION III: INSTRUMENTAL

Las Abejas—guitar (1921) (Eng: The Bees)
J. Williams (r1994) *Concert*
(9/95) (SONY) ① **SK64396**

Aconquija Maxima—guitar
J. Williams *Concert* (8/89) (SONY) ① **SK44898**
J. Williams (r1994) *Concert*
(9/95) (SONY) ① **SK64396**

Aire de Zamba—guitar
A. Romero (arr. A.Romero) *Concert*
(4/90) (TELA) ① **CD80213**
J. Williams (r1994) *Concert*
(9/95) (SONY) ① **SK64396**

Le Catedral—guitar (1921)
S. Isbin *Concert* (10/90) (VIRG) ① **VC7 59591-2**
J. Williams (r1994) *Concert*
(9/95) (SONY) ① **SK64396**

Choro da saudade—guitar
M. Kayath (arr. Stover) *Concert*
(9/87) (CARL) ① **PCD853**
A. Romero (arr. A.Romero) *Concert*
(4/90) (TELA) ① **CD80213**
J. Williams (r1994) *Concert*
(9/95) (SONY) ① **SK64396**

Cueca—guitar (c1925)
J. Williams *Concert* (8/89) (SONY) ① **SK44898**
J. Williams (r1994) *Concert*
(9/95) (SONY) ① **SK64396**

Julia florida—guitar (1938)
M. Kayath (arr. Stover) *Concert*
(9/87) (CARL) ① **PCD853**
J. Williams (r1994) *Concert*
(9/95) (SONY) ① **SK64396**

Una Limosna por el amor de Dios (El ultimo canto)—guitar (1944)
J. Williams *Concert* (8/89) (SONY) ① **SK44898**
J. Williams (r1994) *Concert*
(9/95) (SONY) ① **SK64396**

Maxixa—guitar
J. Williams (r1994) *Concert*
(9/95) (SONY) ① **SK64396**

Mazurka appassionata—guitar (1919)
J. Williams (r1994) *Concert*
(9/95) (SONY) ① **SK64396**

Medallon antiquo—guitar
J. Williams (r1994) *Concert*
(9/95) (SONY) ① **SK64396**

Prelude in C minor—guitar
J. Williams (r1994) *Concert*
(9/95) (SONY) ① **SK64396**

Prelude in G minor—guitar
J. Williams (r1994) *Concert*
(9/95) (SONY) ① **SK64396**

Un Sueno en la Floresta—guitar (1918)
A. Romero (arr. A.Romero) *Concert*
(4/90) (TELA) ① **CD80213**
J. Williams (r1992) *Concert*
(1/94) (SONY) ① **SK53359**
J. Williams (r1994) *Concert*
(9/95) (SONY) ① **SK64396**

Villancico de Navidad—guitar
J. Williams (r1994) *Concert*
(9/95) (SONY) ① **SK64396**

Waltzes—guitar, Op. 8
3. No 3 (c1919); 4. No 4 (1923).
3. M. Kayath (arr. Stover) *Concert*
(9/87) (CARL) ① **PCD853**
3, 4. J. Williams (r1994) *Concert*
(9/95) (SONY) ① **SK64396**

BARRY, Darrol (20th cent) England

SECTION I: ORCHESTRAL

A Salford Sinfonietta—brass band (1992)
1. Intrada; 2. Threnody (in memoriam Colin Rice); 3. Danza.

BNFL Band, R. Evans (r1993) *Concert*
(5/94) (POLY) ① **QPRL062D**

BARRY, Gerald (b 1952) Ireland

SECTION II: CHAMBER

'........'—untitled work for chamber ensemble (1979)
Nua Nós, D. N. Mheadhra (r1993) *Concert*
(4/95) (NMC) ① **NMCD022**

Bob—2 cl/bass cl, vn, vc, marimba, pf (1989)
Nua Nós, D. N. Mheadhra (r1993) *Concert*
(4/95) (NMC) ① **NMCD022**

Piano Quartet—vn, va, vc, pf (1992)
Nua Nós, D. N. Mheadhra (r1993) *Concert*
(4/95) (NMC) ① **NMCD022**

Sextet—cl/bass cl, tpt, db, 2 marimbas, pf (1992-3)
Nua Nós, D. N. Mheadhra (r1993) *Concert*
(4/95) (NMC) ① **NMCD022**

SECTION III: INSTRUMENTAL

Au Milieu—piano (1981)
N. Kawai (r1993) *Concert*
(4/95) (NMC) ① **NMCD022**

Sur les Pointes—piano (1981)
N. Kawai (r1993) *Concert*
(4/95) (NMC) ① **NMCD022**

Swinging Tripes and Trillibubkins—piano (1986)
N. Kawai (r1993) *Concert*
(4/95) (NMC) ① **NMCD022**

Triorchic Blues—piano/violin (1990)
M. d'Arcy (r1993) *Concert*
(4/95) (NMC) ① **NMCD022**
N. Kawai (r1993) *Concert*
(4/95) (NMC) ① **NMCD022**

BARRY, John (b 1933) England

SECTION V: STAGE WORKS

Body Heat—film score (1981)
EXCERPTS: 1. Main Theme.
1. Prague City PO, N. Raine (r1993; arr Raine) *Concert* (8/94) (SILV) ① **FILMCD141**
1. Hollywood Bowl SO, J. Mauceri (r1993) *Concert*
(1/95) (PHIL) ① **442 425-2PH**

Born Free—film score (1966)
EXCERPTS: 1. Main Theme; 2. Lions at Play.
1, 2. Prague City PO, N. Raine (r1993; arr Raine) *Concert* (8/94) (SILV) ① **FILMCD141**

Chaplin—film score (1992)
EXCERPTS: 1. Main Theme; 2. Early Days in London/The Honeysuckle and the Bee; 3. Charlie Proposes; 4. To California/The Cutting Room; 5. Discovering the Tramp/The Wedding Chase; 6. Chaplin's Studio Opening; 7. Salt Lake City Episode; 8. The Roll Dance; 9. News of Hetty's Death; 10. Smile; 11. From London to L.A. 12. Joan Barry Trouble/Oona Arrives; 13. Remembering Hetty; 14. Smile; 15. The Roll Dance (reprise); 16. Chaplin—Main Theme; 17. Smile (with Robert Downey Jr).
1. Prague City PO, N. Raine (r1993; arr Raine) *Concert* (8/94) (SILV) ① **FILMCD141**

Dances With Wolves—film score (1990)
EXCERPTS: 1. The John Dunbar Theme; 2. Main Title; 3. Looks Like a Suicide; 4. Journey to Fort Sedgewick; 5. Ride to Fort Hayes; 6. The Death of Timmons; 7. Two Socks—The Wolf Theme; 8. Pawnee Attack; 9. Kicking Bird's Gift; 10. Journey to the Buffalo Killing Ground; 11. The Buffalo Hunt; 12. Stands With a Fist Remembers; 13. Love Theme; 14. The John Dunbar Theme (2nd version); 15. Two Socks at Play; 16. The Death of Cisco; 17. Rescue of Dances With Wolves; 18. Loss of the Journal & Return to Winter Camp; 19. Dances With Wolves: Farewell & End Title.
1. Hollywood Bowl SO, J. Mauceri (r1991) *Concert*
(9/91) (PHIL) ① **432 109-2PH**
1. Prague City PO, N. Raine (r1993) *Concert*
(8/94) (SILV) ① **FILMCD141**

Eleanor and Franklin—film score (1976)
EXCERPTS: 1. Main Theme.
1. Prague City PO, N. Raine (r1993; arr Raine) *Concert* (8/94) (SILV) ① **FILMCD141**

Hanover Street—film score (1979)
EXCERPTS: 1. Opening Titles; 2. Closing Titles.
1, 2. Prague City PO, N. Raine (r1993; arr Raine) *Concert* (8/94) (SILV) ① **FILMCD141**

High Road to China—film score (1983)
EXCERPTS: 1. Waziri Village Attack & Escape.
1. OST *Concert* (5/93) (SILV) ① **SILVAD3001**

Indecent Proposal—film score (1993)
EXCERPTS: 1. Main Theme.
1. Prague City PO, N. Raine (r1993; arr Raine) *Concert* (8/94) (SILV) ① **FILMCD141**

King Rat—film score (1965)
OST, J. Barry (r1965) (9/95) (COLU) ① **JK57894**

The Last Valley—film score (1970)
EXCERPTS: 1. Main Title; 2. Death of the Captain; 3. End Title.
1-3. Prague City PO, N. Raine (r1993; arr Raine) *Concert* (8/94) (SILV) ① **FILMCD141**

The Lion in Winter—film score (1968)
EXCERPTS: 1. The Lion in Winter; 2. Eleanor's Arrival; 3. We're Jungle Creatures.
1-3. Prague City PO, N. Raine (r1993; arr Raine) *Concert* (8/94) (SILV) ① **FILMCD141**

Midnight Cowboy—film score (1969)
EXCERPTS: 1. Rizzo's Death.
1. Prague City PO, N. Raine (r1993; arr Raine) *Concert* (8/94) (SILV) ① **FILMCD141**

Out of Africa—film score (1985)
EXCERPTS: 1. Main Theme; 2. Have You Got a Story for Me?.
1. Prague City PO, N. Raine (r1993; arr Raine) *Concert* (8/94) (SILV) ① **FILMCD141**

The Persuaders—television score
EXCERPTS: 1. Main Theme.
1. Prague City PO, N. Raine (r1993; arr Raine) *Concert* (8/94) (SILV) ① **FILMCD141**

Raise the Titanic—film score (1980)
Suite Prague City PO, N. Raine (r1993; arr Raine) *Concert* (8/94) (SILV) ① **FILMCD141**

Robin and Marian—film score (1976)
EXCERPTS: 1. Theme; 2. Dawn; 3. This Way; 4. The End.
2-4. Prague City PO, N. Raine (r1993; arr Raine) *Concert* (8/94) (SILV) ① **FILMCD141**

Somewhere in Time—film score (1980)
EXCERPTS: 1. Main Theme; 2. End Titles; 3. We're Losing Him (Love Theme).
2. Prague City PO, N. Raine (r1993; arr Raine) *Concert* (8/94) (SILV) ① **FILMCD141**

Zulu—film score (1964)
EXCERPTS: 1. Main Title—Isandhlwana 1879; 2. News of the Massacre/Rorke's Drift Threatened; 3. Wagons Over; 4. First Zulu Appearance and Assault; 5. Durnford's Horses Arrive & Depart/The Third Assault; 6. Zulu's Final Appearance and Salute; 7. The V.C. Roll and 'Men of Harlech'; 8. Zulu Dances: 8a. Tetha Leyanto (D. Bethela, arr Barry); 8b. High Grass; 8c. Zulu Stamp; 8d. Big Shield; 8e. Ngenzini (B. Knoza, arr Barry); 9. Monkey Feathers (arrangement of Main Title).
1. Prague City PO, N. Raine (r1993; arr Raine) *Concert* (8/94) (SILV) ① **FILMCD141**

BARSANTI, Francesco (1690–1772) Italy/England

SECTION I: ORCHESTRAL

Concerto grosso in D, Op. 3/4 (pub 1743)
M. Rimon (hn/dir), Israel PO *Concert*
(2/92) (CARL) ① **MCD31**

SECTION II: CHAMBER

6 Sonatas—violin/recorder and continuo (pub 1724-27)
1. G minor; 2. C; 3. C minor.
2. F. Brüggen, A. Bylsma, G. Leonhardt (r1967) *Concert* (7/94) (TELD) ① **4509-93669-2**
3. E. Haupt, C. Schornsheim *Concert*
(2/90) (CAPR) ① **10 234**

BART, Lionel (b 1930) England

SECTION V: STAGE WORKS

Oliver!—musical show (1960—London)
(Book & Lyrics cpsr)
EXCERPTS: 1. Overture; 2. Food Glorious Food; 3. Oliver!, 4. I Shall Scream; 5. Boy For Sale; 6. That's Your Funeral; 7. Where Is Love?; 8. Consider Yourself; 9. Pick a Pocket Or Two; 10. It's a Fine Life; 11. I'll Do Anything; 12. Be Back Soon; 13. Oom-Pah-Pah; 14. As Long As He Needs Me; 15. Where Is Love? (reprise); 16. Who Will Buy?; 17. It's a Fine Life (reprise); 18. Reviewing the Situation. 20. Reprises: 20a. Oliver!; 20b. As Long As He Needs Me; 20c. Reviewing the Situation; 21. Finale.
Cpte J. Pryce, London Cast, M. Koch (r1994/5; orch W. D. Brohn) (8/95) (FRST) ① **CASTCD47**

BARTHÉLEMY, Richard (19th/20th Cent) Italy

SECTION IV: VOCAL AND CHORAL

Adorables tourments—song (Wds. R. Gäel: comp with E. Caruso)
E. Caruso, orch (r1908) *Concert*
(12/90) (PEAR) ① [3] **EVC1(2)**
E. Caruso, orch (r1908) *Concert*
(7/91) (RCA) ① [12] **GD60495(2)**
Chi se nne scorda occhiu!—song (wds. Marvasi)
T. Schipa, orch (r1928) *Concert*
(2/89) (PEAR) ① **GEMMCD9322**
Triste ritorno—song (Wds. F. Forzati)
E. Caruso, orch (r1906) *Concert*
(12/90) (PEAR) ① [3] **EVC1(2)**
E. Caruso, orch (r1906) *Concert*
(7/91) (RCA) ① [12] **GD60495(2)**

BARTLET, John (fl 1606–10) England

SECTION IV: VOCAL AND CHORAL

Sweete birdes deprive us never—ayre
E. Kirkby, A. Rooley *Concert*
(8/91) (L'OI) ① **425 892-2OH**

BARTLETT, James Carroll (1850–1929) USA

SECTION IV: VOCAL AND CHORAL

A Dream—song (wds. C. B. Cory)
E. Caruso, orch, J. Pastemack (r1920) *Concert*
(7/91) (RCA) ① [12] **GD60495(6)**
E. Caruso, orch, J. Pastemack (r1920) *Concert*
(10/91) (PEAR) ① [3] **EVC4(2)**

BARTÓK, Béla (1881–1945) Hungary/USA

Sz-numbers from A. Szöllösy's Bibliographie....
Bartók pub 1956

SECTION I: ORCHESTRAL

Concerto for Orchestra, Sz116 (?1942, 1943 rev 1945)
Los Angeles PO, A. Previn (r1988) *Janáček: Sinfonietta.* (3/89) (TELA) ① **CD80174**
Berlin RIAS Orch, F. Fricsay (r1957) *Concert*
(5/89) (DG) ① [2] **427 410-2GDO2**
Czech PO, K. Ančerl *Janáček: Sinfonietta.*
(12/89) (SUPR) ① **11 0604-2**
Chicago SO, F. Reiner (r1955) *Music for Strings, Percussion and Celesta.* (1/90) (RCA) ① **GD60175**
Hungarian St Orch, A. Fischer *Miraculous Mandarin.*
(6/90) (NIMB) ① **NI5229**
Oslo PO, M. Jansons *Music for Strings, Percussion and Celesta.* (1/91) (EMI) ① **CDC7 54070-2**
LSO, A. Dorati *Concert*
(11/91) (MERC) ① **432 017-2MM**
SNO, N. Järvi *Enescu: Romanian Rhapsodies, Op. 11.* (2/92) (CHAN) ① **CHAN8947**
NYPO, L. Bernstein (r1959) *Music for Strings, Percussion and Celesta.*
(11/92) (SONY) ① **SMK47510**
Boston SO, R. Kubelík *Miraculous Mandarin.*
(1/93) (DG) ① **437 247-2GGA**
Philadelphia, E. Ormandy (r1963) *Concert*
(5/93) (SONY) ① **SBK48263**
Hungarian Nat PO, T. Ferenc *Concert*
(7/93) (CARL) ① **PCD1013**
BPO, L. Maazel (r1979) *Music for Strings, Percussion and Celesta.* (1/94) (DG) ① **439 402-2GCL**
Concertgebouw, B. Haitink (r1960) *Concert*
(2/94) (PHIL) ① [2] **438 812-2PM2**
Chicago SO, F. Reiner (r1955) *Concert*
(3/94) (RCA) ① **09026 61504-2**
Chicago SO, P. Boulez *Pieces, Sz51.*
(3/94) (DG) ① **437 826-2GH**
Philh, H. Wolff (r1993) *Concert*
(9/94) (TELD) ① **9031-76350-2**
St Louis SO, L. Slatkin (r1991) *Miraculous Mandarin.*
(9/94) (RCA) ① **09026 61702-2**
RPO, R. Kubelík (r1958) *Concert*
(11/94) (EMI) ① [2] **CZS5 68223-2**
CBSO, S. Rattle (r1992) *Miraculous mandarin.*
(1/95) (EMI) ① **CDC5 55094-2**
Houston SO, L. Stokowski (r c1960) *Kodály: Psalmus Hungaricus.* (4/95) (EMI) ① **EVC9008**
San Francisco SO, H. Blomstedt (r1993) *Kossuth.*
(7/95) (DECC) ① **443 773-2DH**

Boston SO, S. Ozawa (r1994) *Miraculous Mandarin.*
(8/95) (PHIL) ① **442 783-2PH**
Concerto for Piano and Orchestra No. 1, Sz83 (1926)
M. Pollini, Chicago SO, C. Abbado *Piano Concerto 2.*
(9/86) (DG) ① **415 371-2GH**
Z. Kocsis, Budapest Fest Orch, I. Fischer *Concert*
(1/88) (PHIL) ① [3] **416 831-2PH3**
G. Anda, Berlin RIAS Orch, F. Fricsay *Concert*
(5/89) (DG) ① [2] **427 410-2GDO2**
S. Kovacevich, LSO, Colin Davis *Concert*
(5/91) (PHIL) ① **426 660-2PSL**
P. Donohoe, CBSO, S. Rattle (r1992) *Concert*
(11/93) (EMI) ① **CDC7 54871-2**
G. Sandór, South-West German RSO, R. Reinhardt (r1958-9) *Concert*
(11/93) (VOX) ① [2] **CDX2 5506**
S. Kovacevich, LSO, Colin Davis (r1975) *Concert*
(2/94) (PHIL) ① [2] **438 812-2PM2**
J. Jandó, Budapest SO, A. Ligeti (r1994) *Concert*
(2/95) (NAXO) ① **8 550771**
G. Anda, Berlin RSO, F. Fricsay (r1960) *Concert*
(5/95) (DG) ① **447 399-2GOR**
Z. Kocsis, Budapest Fest Orch, I. Fischer (r1985) *Concert* (12/95) (PHIL) ① **446 366-2PH**
Concerto for Piano and Orchestra No. 2, Sz95 (1930-31)
M. Pollini, Chicago SO, C. Abbado *Piano Concerto 1.*
(9/86) (DG) ① **415 371-2GH**
Z. Kocsis, Budapest Fest Orch, I. Fischer *Concert*
(1/88) (PHIL) ① [3] **416 831-2PH3**
G. Anda, Berlin RIAS Orch, F. Fricsay *Concert*
(5/89) (DG) ① [2] **427 410-2GDO2**
T. Barto, LPO, C. Eschenbach *Rachmaninov: Piano Concerto 3.* (1/90) (EMI) ① **CDC7 49861-2**
S. Kovacevich, BBC SO, Colin Davis *Concert*
(5/91) (PHIL) ① **426 660-2PSL**
A. Foldes, Lamoureux Orch, E. Bigot (r1948) *Rhapsody 1, Sz87.* (11/91) (JECK) ① **JD648-2**
P. Entremont, NYPO, L. Bernstein (r1967) *Concert*
(11/92) (SONY) ① [2] **SM2K47511**
P. Donohoe, CBSO, S. Rattle (r1990) *Concert*
(11/93) (EMI) ① **CDC7 54871-2**
G. Sandór, Vienna Pro Musica Orch, M. Gielen (r1958-9) *Concert*
(11/93) (VOX) ① [2] **CDX2 5506**
S. Kovacevich, BBC SO, Colin Davis (r1968) *Concert*
(2/94) (PHIL) ① [2] **438 812-2PM2**
J. Jandó, Budapest SO, A. Ligeti (r1994) *Concert*
(2/95) (NAXO) ① **8 550771**
G. Anda, Berlin RSO, F. Fricsay (r1959) *Concert*
(5/95) (DG) ① **447 399-2GOR**
Z. Kocsis, Budapest Fest Orch, I. Fischer (r1987) *Concert* (12/95) (PHIL) ① **446 366-2PH**
Concerto for Piano and Orchestra No. 3, Sz119 (1945) (final 17 bars scored by T. Serly)
1. Allegretto; 2. Adagio religioso; 3. Allegro vivace.
Z. Kocsis, Budapest Fest Orch, I. Fischer *Concert*
(1/88) (PHIL) ① [3] **416 831-2PH3**
G. Anda, Berlin RIAS Orch, F. Fricsay *Concert*
(5/89) (DG) ① [2] **427 410-2GDO2**
A. Fischer, BRSO, F. Fricsay (pp1960) *Tchaikovsky: Symphony 6.* (8/90) (ORFE) ① **C200891A**
S. Kovacevich, LSO, Colin Davis *Concert*
(5/91) (PHIL) ① **426 660-2PSL**
P. Entremont, NYPO, L. Bernstein (r1967) *Concert*
(11/92) (SONY) ① [2] **SM2K47511**
P. Donohoe, CBSO, S. Rattle (r1992) *Concert*
(11/93) (EMI) ① **CDC7 54871-2**
G. Sandór, Vienna Pro Musica Orch, M. Gielen (r1958-9) *Concert*
(11/93) (VOX) ① [2] **CDX2 5506**
S. Kovacevich, LSO, Colin Davis (r1975) *Concert*
(2/94) (PHIL) ① [2] **438 812-2PM2**
J. Jandó, Budapest SO, A. Ligeti (r1994) *Concert*
(2/95) (NAXO) ① **8 550771**
G. Anda, Berlin RSO, F. Fricsay (r1959) *Concert*
(5/95) (DG) ① **447 399-2GOR**
G. Anda, Staatskapelle Dresden, H. von Karajan (pp1972) *Schumann: Symphony 4.*
(10/95) (DG) ① **447 666-2GDO**
Z. Kocsis, Budapest Fest Orch, I. Fischer (r1984) *Concert* (12/95) (PHIL) ① **446 366-2PH**
Movt 2. D. Lipatti, SW German Rad Orch, P. Sacher (pp1948) *Concert* (10/95) (ARCI) ① **ARC112/3**
Concerto for Viola and Orchestra, Sz120 (1945) (cpted T. Serly)
R. Golani, BRSO, A. Ligeti *Concert*
(2/91) (CONI) ① **CDCF189**
Y. Menuhin, New Philh, A. Dorati *Concert*
(4/91) (EMI) ① **CDM7 63985-2**
T. Zimmermann, BRSO, D. Shallon *Hindemith: Schwanendreher.* (3/93) (EMI) ① **CDC7 54101-2**
W. Christ, BPO, S. Ozawa (r1989) *Music for Strings, Percussion and Celesta.*
(4/94) (DG) ① **437 993-2GH**

Y-Y. Ma, Baltimore SO, D. Zinman (r1993) *Concert*
(3/95) (SONY) ① **SK57961**
Concerto for Violin and Orchestra No. 1, Sz36 (1907-08)
N. Gotkovsky, National PO, C. Gerhardt *Violin Concerto 2.* (3/87) (PYRA) ① **PYR13486**
J. Suk, Czech PO, J. Ferencsik (pp1979) *Berg: Violin Concerto.* (5/90) (SUPR) ① **11 0706-2**
K-W. Chung, Chicago SO, G. Solti *Violin Concerto 2.*
(2/91) (DECC) ① **425 015-2DM**
Midori, BPO, Z. Mehta *Violin Concerto 2.*
(2/91) (SONY) ① **SK45941**
Y. Menuhin, New Philh, A. Dorati *Concert*
(4/91) (EMI) ① **CDM7 63985-2**
G. Hetzel, Hungarian St SO, A. Fischer *Violin Concerto 2.* (7/93) (NIMB) ① **NI5333**
Concerto for Violin and Orchestra No. 2, Sz112 (1937-38)
N. Gotkovsky, National PO, C. Gerhardt *Violin Concerto 1.* (3/87) (PYRA) ① **PYR13486**
P. Hofer, Radio Lille Orch, M. Suzan (pp1971) *Prokofiev: Violin Concerto 1.*
(12/87) (INA) ① **MHC291059**
Y. Menuhin, Philh, W. Furtwängler (r1953) *Solo Violin Sonata.* (10/89) (EMI) ① **CDH7 69804-2**
K-W. Chung, LPO, G. Solti *Violin Concerto 1.*
(2/91) (DECC) ① **425 015-2DM**
Midori, BPO, Z. Mehta *Violin Concerto 1.*
(2/91) (SONY) ① **SK45941**
A-S. Mutter, Boston SO, S. Ozawa *Moret: En rêve.*
(11/91) (DG) ① **431 626-2GH**
I. Stern, NYPO, L. Bernstein (r1958) *Concert*
(11/92) (SONY) ① [2] **SM2K47511**
G. Hetzel, Hungarian St SO, A. Fischer *Violin Concerto 1.* (7/93) (NIMB) ① **NI5333**
I. Gitlis, Vienna Pro Musica orch, J. Horenstein (r1950s) *Concert* (11/93) (VOX) ① [2] **CDX2 5505**
K. Takezawa, LSO, M. Tilson Thomas (r1992) *Concert* (12/93) (RCA) ① [3] **09026 61677-2**
K. Takezawa, LSO, M. Tilson Thomas (r1992) *Concert* (12/93) (RCA) ① **09026 61675-2**
H. Szeryng, Concertgebouw, B. Haitink (r1969) *Concert* (2/94) (PHIL) ① [2] **438 812-2PM2**
K-W. Chung, CBSO, S. Rattle (r1990) *Concert*
(6/94) (EMI) ① **CDC7 54211-2**
T. Varga, BPO, F. Fricsay (r1951) *Concert*
(11/94) (DG) ① **445 402-2GDO**
T. Varga, BPO, F. Fricsay (r c1950) *Concert*
(11/94) (DG) ① [11] **445 400-2GDO10**
A-S. Mutter, Boston SO, S. Ozawa (r1991) *Concert*
(12/94) (DG) ① [3] **445 487-2GX3**
I. Perlman, LSO, A. Previn *Concert*
(6/95) (EMI) ① [20] **CZS4 83177-2(2)**
Y. Menuhin, Minnesota Orch, A. Dorati (r1957) *Suite 2.* (2/91) (SONY) ① **434 350-2MM**
Concerto for 2 Pianos and Orchestra, Sz115 (1940) (arr cpsr from Sonata for 2 Pianos and Percussion)
K. Labèque, M. Labèque, S. Gualda, J-P. Drouet, CBSO, S. Rattle *Sonata for 2 Pianos and Percussion.* (9/87) (EMI) ① **CDC7 47446-2**
A. Gold, R. Fizdale, NYPO, L. Bernstein (r1966) *Concert* (11/92) (SONY) ① **SM2K47511**
Dance Suite—orchestra, Sz77 (1923)
Philh Hungarica, A. Dorati *Concert*
(11/91) (MERC) ① **432 017-2MM**
Hungarian Nat PO, T. Ferenc *Concert*
(5/93) (CARL) ① **PCD1021**
LPO, F. Welser-Möst (r1992/3) *Concert*
(10/93) (EMI) ① **CDC7 54858-2**
Berlin RIAS Orch, F. Fricsay (r c1952) *Concert*
(11/94) (DG) ① [11] **445 400-2GDO10**
Berlin RIAS Orch, F. Fricsay (r1953) *Concert*
(11/94) (DG) ① **445 402-2GDO**
LPO, J. Ferencsik (r c1958) *Falla: Sombrero de tres picos.* (4/95) (EVER) ① **EVC9000**
NYPO, P. Boulez (r1972) *Concert*
(9/95) (SONY) ① [2] **SM2K64100**
Chicago SO, P. Boulez (r1992) *Concert*
(9/95) (DG) ① **445 825-2GH**
Divertimento—strings, Sz113 (1939)
F. Liszt CO, J. Rolla *Music for Strings, Percussion and Celesta.* (9/85) (HUNG) ① **HCD12531**
Montreal I Musici, Y. Turovsky *Concert*
(7/87) (CHAN) ① **CHAN8515**
Polish CO, J. Maksymiuk *Britten: Frank Bridge Variations.* (11/87) (MDG) ① **L3180**
Chicago SO, G. Solti *Concert*
(5/91) (DECC) ① **430 352-2DH**
Polish CO, J. Stanienda (vn/dir) (pp1990) *Concert*
(12/91) (LINN) ① **CKD001**
Zagreb Sols, T. Ninič *Concert*
(11/92) (CARL) ① **PCD1000**
Hungarian St SO, A. Fischer (r1992) *Concert*
(7/93) (NIMB) ① [2] **NI5362/3**

G. Sandór (r1993) *Concert*
(11/95) (SONY) ① [4] **SX4K68275**
1, 3, 5, 13, 15, 25, 35, 36. A. Vardi *Concert*
(6/90) (CARL) ① **PWK1132**
3, 5, 10, 12, 16, 18, 19, 21, 25, 30, 36. G. Tozer
Concert (12/92) (TALL) ① **TP001**
26, 27, 32, 40. L. Rév *Concert*
(7/87) (HYPE) ① **CDA66185**
66. M. Tirimo *Concert*
(12/88) (KING) ① **KCLCD2003**
3 Hungarian folksongs from the Csík
district—piano, Sz35a (1907)
Z. Kocsis (r1993) *Concert*
(11/94) (PHIL) ① **442 016-2PH**
G. Sandór (r1994) *Concert*
(11/95) (SONY) ① [4] **SX4K68275**
Hungarian Folktunes—piano, Sz66 (c1914-
18)
1. The peacock; 2. At the Jánoshida fairground; 3.
White Lily.
Z. Kocsis (r1991) *Concert*
(1/94) (PHIL) ① **434 104-2PH**
S. Stanzeleit, G. Fenyö (arr Szigeti) *Concert*
(6/94) (ASV) ① **CDDCA883**
G. Sandór (r1994) *Concert*
(11/95) (SONY) ① [4] **SX4K68275**
15 Hungarian Peasant Songs—piano, Sz71
(1914-18)
1. Old Tune No. 1; 2. Old Tune No. 2; 3. Old Tune
No. 3; 4. Old Tune No. 4; 5. Scherzo; 6. Ballade
(Tema con variazoni); 7. Old Dance Tune No. 1; 8.
Old Dance Tune No. 2; 9. Old Dance Tune No. 3; 10.
Old Dance Tune No. 4; 11. Old Dance Tune No. 5;
12. Old Dance Tune No. 6; 13. Old Dance Tune No.
7; 14. Old Dance Tune No. 8; 15. Old Dance Tune
No. 9.
A. Schiff *Concert* (7/85) (DENO) ① **C37-7092**
R. Hagopian *Concert* (11/89) (ETCE) ① **KTC1012**
P. Frankl *Concert* (6/90) (ASV) ① **CDDCA687**
M. Béroff (r1976-8) *Concert*
(1/95) (EMI) ① [2] **CZS5 68101-2**
G. Sandór (r1994) *Concert*
(11/95) (SONY) ① [4] **SX4K68275**
excs S. Stanzeleit, G. Fenyö *Concert*
(6/94) (ASV) ① **CDDCA883**
8 Improvisations on Hungarian Peasant
Songs—piano, Sz74 (Op. 20) (1920)
G. Sandór (r1994) *Concert*
(11/95) (SONY) ① [4] **SX4K68275**
9 Little Pieces—piano, Sz82 (1926)
1. Dialogue 1; 2. Dialogue 2; 3. Dialogue 3; 4.
Dialogue 4; 5. Menuetto; 6. Air; 7. Marcia delle
bestie; 8. Tambourine; 9. Preludio—All'ungherese.
G. Sandór (r1995) *Concert*
(11/95) (SONY) ① [4] **SX4K68275**
Mikrokosmos, Book 1—progressive pieces
for piano (6 vols), Sz107 (1926, 1932-39)
1. Unison melody 1; 2. Unison melody 2; 4. Unison
melody 4; 5. Unison melody 5; 6. Unison melody 6; 7.
Dotted note; 8. Repitition; 9. Syncopation; 10. With
alternate hands; 11. Parallel motion; 12. Reflection;
13. Change of position; 14. Question and answer. 15.
Village song; 16. Parallel motion and change of
position; 17. Contrary motion; 18. Unison melody 7;
19. Unison melody 8; 20. Unison melody 9; 21.
Unison melody 10; 22. Imitation and counterpoint; 23.
Imitation and inversion; 24. Pastorale; 25. Imitation
and inversion; 26. Repitition; 27. Syncopation; 28.
Canon at the octave; 29. Imitation reflected; 30.
Canon at the lower fifth; 31. Little dance in canon
form; 32. In Dorian mode; 33. Slow dance; 34. In
Phrygian mode; 35. Chorale; 36. Free Chorale.
D. Ránki *Concert*
(10/92) (TELD) ① [3] **9031-76139-2**
Mikrokosmos, Book 2—progressive pieces
for piano (6 vols), Sz107 (1926, 1932-39)
(Numbers is brackets relate to complete
edition)
1. In Lydian mode (37); 2. Staccato and legato 1 (38);
3. Staccato and legato 2 (39); 4. In Yugoslav mode
(40); 5. Melody with accompaniment (41); 6.
Accompaniment in broken triads (42); 7. In Hungarian
style: 2 pfs (43); 8. Contrary motion: 2pfs (44); 9.
Meditation (45); 10. Increasing-diminishing (46); 11.
Big fair (47); 12. In Mixolydian mode (48); 13.
Crescendo-diminuendo (49); 14. Minuetto (50); 15.
Waves (51); 16. Unison divided (52); 17. In
Transylvanian style (53); 18. Chromatic (54); 19.
Triplets in Lydian mode: 2 pfs (55); 20. Melody in
tenths (56); 21. Accents (57); 22. In Oriental style
(58); 23. Major and minor (59); 24. Canon with
sustained notes (60); 25. Pentatonic melody (61); 26.
Minor sixths in parallel motion (62); 27. Buzzing (63);
28. Line and point (64); 29. Dialogue: 1v and pf (65);
30. Melody divided (66).

D. Ránki *Concert*
(10/92) (TELD) ① [3] **9031-76139-2**
Mikrokosmos, Book 3—progressive pieces
for piano (6 vols), Sz107 (1926, 1932-39)
(numbers in brackets relate to complete
edition)
1. Thirds against a single voice (67); 2. Hungarian
dance: 2 pfs (68); 3. Chord study (69); 4. Melody
against double notes (70); 5. Thirds (71); 6. Dragon's
dance (72); 7. Sixths and triads (73); 8. Hungarian
song: 1v and pf (74); 9. Triplets (75); 10. In three
parts (76); 11. Little study (77); 12. Five-tone scale
(78); 13. Hommage à JSB (79); 14. Hommage à R.
Sch (80); 15. Wandering (81); 16. Scherzo (82); 17.
Melody with interruptions (83); 18. Merriment (84);
19. Broken chords (85); 20. Two major pentachords
(86); 21. Variations (87); 22. Duets for pipes (88); 23.
In four parts (89); 24. In Russian style (90); 25.
Chromatic Invention 1 (91); 26. Chromatic Invention 2
(92); 27. In four parts (93); 28. Tale (94); 29. Song of
the fox: 1v and pf (95); 30. Stumblings (96).
D. Ránki *Concert*
(10/92) (TELD) ① [3] **9031-76139-2**
Mikrokosmos, Book 4—progressive pieces
for piano (6 vols), Sz107 (1926, 1932-38)
(numbers in brackets relate to complete
edition)
1. Notturno (97); 2. Thumb under (98); 3. Crossed
hands (99); 4. In the style of a folksong (100); 5.
Diminished fifth (101); 6. Harmonics (102); 7. Minor
and major (103); 8. Through the keys (104); 9.
Playsong (105); 10. Children's song (106); 11.
Melody in the mist (107); 12. Wrestling (108); 13.
From the island of Bali (109); 14. Clashing sounds
(110); 15. Intermezzo (111); 16. Variations on a
folktune (112); 17. Bulgarian rhythm 1 (113); 18.
Theme and inversion (114); 19. Bulgarian rhythm 2
(115); 20. Melody (116); 21. Bourrée (117); 22.
Triplets in 9/8 time (118); 23. Dance in 3/4 time (119);
24. Fifth chords (120); 25. Two-part study (121).
D. Ránki *Concert*
(10/92) (TELD) ① [3] **9031-76139-2**
21. Philh Hungarica, A. Dorati (orch Serly) *Concert*
(11/91) (MERC) ① **432 017-2MM**
Mikrokosmos, Book 5—progressive pieces
for piano (6 vols), Sz107 (1926, 1932-39)
(numbers in brackets relate to complete
edition)
1. Chords together and opposed (122); 2. Staccato
and legato (123); 3. Staccato (124); 4. Boating (125);
5. Change of time (126); 6. New Hungarian folksong:
1v and pf (127); 7. Peasant dance (128); 8.
Alternating thirds (129); 9. Village joke (130); 10.
Fourths (131); 11. Major seconds broken and
together (132); 12. Syncopation (133); 13. Three
studies in double notes (134); 14. Perpetuum mobile
(135); 15. Whole-tone scale (136); 16. Unison (137);
17. Bagpipe (138); 18. Merry Andrew (139).
D. Ránki *Concert*
(10/92) (TELD) ① [3] **9031-76139-2**
3. B. Bartók (r1937) *Concert*
(5/94) (EMI) ① **CDC5 55031-2**
7, 11, 16. M. Yudina (1964) *Concert*
(8/95) (MELO) ① [11] **74321 25172-2(1)**
7, 11, 16. M. Yudina (1964) *Concert*
(8/95) (MELO) ① [11] **74321 25176-2**
7, 18. G. Tozer *Concert* (12/92) (TALL) ① **TP001**
Mikrokosmos, Book 6—progressive pieces
for piano (6 vols), Sz107 (1926, 1932-39)
(numbers in brackets relate to complete
edition)
1. Free variations (140); 2. Subject and reflection
(141); 3. From the diary of a fly (142); 4. Divided
arpeggios (143); 5. Minor seconds, major sevenths
(144); 6. Chromatic invention (145); 7. Ostinato (146);
8. March (147); 9. Dance in Bulgarian rhythm 1 (148);
10. Dance in Bulgarian rhythm 2 (149); 11. Dance in
Bulgarian rhythm 3 (150); 12. Dance in Bulgarian
rhythm 4 (151); 13. Dance in Bulgarian rhythm 5
(152); 14. Dance in Bulgarian rhythm 6 (153).
D. Ránki *Concert*
(10/92) (TELD) ① [3] **9031-76139-2**
3. Philh Hungarica, A. Dorati (orch Serly) *Concert*
(11/91) (MERC) ① **432 017-2MM**
3, 5-7, 10. M. Yudina (1964) *Concert*
(8/95) (MELO) ① [11] **74321 25172-2(1)**
3, 5-7, 10. M. Yudina (1964) *Concert*
(8/95) (MELO) ① [11] **74321 25176-2**
7. B. Bartók (r1937) *Concert*
(5/94) (EMI) ① **CDC5 55031-2**
9, 10, 11, 12, 13, 14. J. MacGregor (r1993) *Concert*
(8/94) (COLL) ① **Coll1404-2**
9-14. M. Béroff (r1976-8) *Concert*
(1/95) (EMI) ① [2] **CZS5 68101-2**

Out of doors—piano, Sz81 (1926)
J. MacGregor (r1993) *Concert*
(8/94) (COLL) ① **Coll1404-2**
M. Béroff (r1976-8) *Concert*
(1/95) (EMI) ① [2] **CZS5 68101-2**
G. Sandór (r1995) *Concert*
(11/95) (SONY) ① [4] **SX4K68275**
Petite Suite—piano, Sz105 (arr cpsr from 44
Duos)
1. Slow tune—Valachain dance; 2. Whirling dance; 3.
Quasi pizzicato; 4. Ruthenian; 5. Bagpipes.
G. Sandór (r1994) *Concert*
(11/95) (SONY) ① [4] **SX4K68275**
Romanian Christmas Carols—piano, Sz57
Z. Kocsis (r1993) *Concert*
(11/94) (PHIL) ① **442 016-2PH**
G. Sandór (r1994) *Concert*
(11/95) (SONY) ① [4] **SX4K68275**
2 Romanian Dances—piano, Sz43 (1909-10,
rev 1945)
P. Frankl *Concert* (6/90) (ASV) ① **CDDCA687**
Z. Kocsis (r1993) *Concert*
(11/94) (PHIL) ① **442 016-2PH**
G. Sandór (r1994) *Concert*
(11/95) (SONY) ① [4] **SX4K68275**
1. B. Bartók (r1929) *Concert*
(5/94) (EMI) ① **CDC5 55031-2**
6 Romanian Folkdances—piano, Sz56
(1915)
A. Schiff *Concert* (7/85) (DENO) ① **C37-7092**
J. Szigeti, B. Bartók (arr Székely: r1930) *Concert*
(1/90) (BIDD) ① [2] **LAB007/8**
P. Frankl *Concert* (6/90) (ASV) ① **CDDCA687**
K. Nikkanen (arr Székely) *Concert*
(10/91) (COLL) ① **Coll1203-2**
S. Stanzeleit, G. Fenyö (r1992; arr Székely) *Concert*
(6/93) (ASV) ① **CDDCA852**
Midori, R. McDonald (r1992) *Concert*
(6/93) (SONY) ① **SK52568**
Z. Kocsis (r1991) *Concert*
(1/94) (PHIL) ① **434 104-2PH**
J. Szigeti, B. Bartók (r1930: arr vn/pf: Székely)
Concert (5/94) (EMI) ① **CDC5 55031-2**
M. Kaplan, B. Canino (r1993; arr Székely: vn/pf)
Concert (12/94) (ARAB) ① **Z6649**
M. Béroff (r1976-8) *Concert*
(1/95) (EMI) ① [2] **CZS5 68101-2**
G. Sandór (r1994) *Concert*
(11/95) (SONY) ① [4] **SX4K68275**
3 Rondos on (Slovak) Folktunes—piano,
Sz84 (1916-27)
A. Schiff *Concert* (7/85) (DENO) ① **C37-7092**
P. Frankl *Concert* (6/90) (ASV) ① **CDDCA687**
Budapest SO, A. Ligeti (arr Dorati) *Concert*
(2/91) (CONI) ① **CDCF189**
Z. Kocsis (r1993) *Concert*
(11/94) (PHIL) ① **442 016-2PH**
G. Sandór (r1994) *Concert*
(11/95) (SONY) ① [4] **SX4K68275**
7 Sketches—piano, Sz44 (1908-10)
1. Portrait of a girl; 2. See-saw, dickory-daw; 3.
Lento; 4. Non troppo lento; 5. Romanian folksong; 6.
In Wallachian style; 7. Poco lento.
G. Sandór (r1994) *Concert*
(11/95) (SONY) ① [4] **SX4K68275**
Sonata for Piano, Sz80 (1926)
M. Béroff (r1976-8) *Concert*
(1/95) (EMI) ① [2] **CZS5 68101-2**
G. Sandór (r1994) *Concert*
(11/95) (SONY) ① [4] **SX4K68275**
Sonata for Solo Violin, Sz117 (1944)
N. Kennedy Ellington: Mainly Black.
(5/87) (EMI) ① **CDC7 47621-2**
Y. Menuhin (r1947) *Violin Concerto 2.*
(10/89) (EMI) ① **CDH7 69804-2**
K. Ososotowicz *Concert*
(4/91) (HYPE) ① **CDA66415**
K. Nikkanen *Concert* (10/91) (COLL) ① **Coll1203-2**
K. Takezawa *Concert*
(2/93) (RCA) ① **09026 60704-2**
S. Stanzeleit (1992) *Concert*
(6/93) (ASV) ① **CDDCA852**
I. Gitlis (r1950s) *Concert*
(11/93) (VOX) ① [2] **CDX2 5505**
H. Schneeberger (r1993) *Concert*
(11/94) (DECC) ① **443 893-2DH**
M. Kaplan (r1993) *Concert*
(12/94) (ARAB) ① **Z6649**
R. Hillyer (r1989; arr va) *Concert*
(5/95) (SCHW) ① **311612**
Sonatina—piano, Sz55 (1915)
Z. Kocsis (r1991) *Concert*
(1/94) (PHIL) ① **434 104-2PH**
S. Stanzeleit, G. Fenyö (arr Gertier) *Concert*
(6/94) (ASV) ① **CDDCA883**

M. Béroff (r1976-8) *Concert*
    (1/95) (EMI) ① [2] **CZS5 68101-2**
G. Anda (r1954) *Concert*
    (10/95) (TEST) ① **SBT1067**
G. Sandór (r1993) *Concert*
    (11/95) (SONY) ① [4] **SX4K68275**
3 Studies—piano, Sz72 (Op. 18) (1918)
Z. Kocsis (r1993) *Concert*
    (11/95) (PHIL) ① **442 016-2PH**
G. Sandór (r1995) *Concert*
    (11/95) (SONY) ① [4] **SX4K68275**
Suite—piano, Sz62 (Op. 14) (1916)
P. Frankl (incl. Andante) *Concert*
    (6/90) (ASV) ① **CDDCA687**
B. Bartók (r1929) *Concert*
    (5/94) (EMI) ① **CDC5 55031-2**
Z. Kocsis (r1993) *Concert*
    (11/94) (PHIL) ① **442 016-2PH**
G. Sandór (r1994) *Concert*
    (11/95) (SONY) ① [4] **SX4K68275**

SECTION IV: VOCAL AND CHORAL

**Cantata profana—tenor, baritone, chorus
and orchestra, Sz94 (1930)** (Wds. various
trans cpsr)
J. Aler, J. Tomlinson, Chicago Sym Chor, Chicago
SO, P. Boulez *Wooden Prince.*
    (3/93) (DG) ① **435 863-2GH**
H. Krebs, D. Fischer-Dieskau, Berlin RIAS Chbr Ch,
Berlin St Hedwig's Cath Ch, Berlin RIAS Orch, F.
Fricsay (bp1950s) *Concert*
    (11/94) (DG) ① [11] **445 400-2GDO10**
H. Krebs, D. Fischer-Dieskau, Berlin RIAS Chbr Ch,
Berlin St Hedwig's Cath Ch, Berlin RIAS Orch, F.
Fricsay (bp1951) *Concert*
    (11/94) (DG) ① **445 402-2GDO**
**5 Hungarian Folk Tunes—1v and piano
(1928)** (rev version of Bartók/Kodály collection)
  1. Far behind I left my country; 2. Crossing the river;
  3. In the summer fields; 4. The horseman; 5. Walking
  through the home.
V. Medgyaszay, B. Bartók (r1928) *Concert*
    (5/94) (EMI) ① **CDC5 55031-2**
**8 Hungarian Folksongs—1v and piano, Sz64
(1907-17)**
  1. Black is the earth; 2. My God, my God; 3. Wives,
  let me be one of your company; 4. So much sorrow;
  5. If I climb the rocky mountains; 6. They are
  mending the great forest highway; 7. Up to now my
  work; 8. The snow is melting.
1-3, 5. M. Basilides, B. Bartók (r1928) *Concert*
    (5/94) (EMI) ① **CDC5 55031-2**
1-5. J. Hamari, I. Prunyi (r1992) *Concert*
    (7/93) (HUNG) ① **HCD31535**
6-8. F. Székelyhídy, B. Bartók (r1928) *Concert*
    (5/94) (EMI) ① **CDC5 55031-2**
**5 Hungarian Folksongs—1v and orchestra,
Sz101** (orch cpsr from Sz92)
  1. In prison; 2. Old lament; 3. Nuptial lament I; 4.
  Complaint; 5. Nuptial lament II.
J. Hamari, Hungarian St Orch, J. Kovács (r1992)
    (7/93) (HUNG) ① **HCD31535**
**4 Old Hungarian Folksongs—4 male vv,
Sz50**
  1. Long ago I told you; 2. O God, why am I waiting?;
  3. In my sister-in-law's garden; 4. Farmboy, load the
  cart well.
Orphei Drängar Ch, E. Ericson *Concert*
    (7/88) (BIS) ① **BIS-CD383**
**5 Songs—1v and piano, Sz61 (Op. 15)
(1916)**
  1. Spring: My love (wds. Gombossy); 2. Summer
  (wds. Gombossy); 3. Night of desire (wds. Gleiman);
  4. Winter: In vivid dream (wds. Gombossy); 5.
  Autumn: In the valley (wds. Gombossy).
J. Hamari, I. Prunyi (r1992) *Concert*
    (7/93) (HUNG) ① **HCD31535**
J. Hamari, Hungarian St Orch, J. Kovács (r1992; orch
Kodály) *Concert* (7/93) (HUNG) ① **HCD31535**
5 Songs, Sz63 (Op. 16) (1916) (Wds. Ady)
  1. Autumn tears; 2. Autumn echoes; 3. Lost content;
  4. Alone with the sea; 5. I cannot come to you.
J. Hamari, I. Prunyi (r1992) *Concert*
    (7/93) (HUNG) ① **HCD31535**
**3 Village Scenes—chorus and
orchestra/piano, Sz79 (1926)**
  1. Wedding; 2. Lullaby; 3. Lad's Dance.
I. Seefried, E. Werba (Ger: pp1953) *Concert*
    (7/93) (DG) ① [2] **437 348-2GDO2**

SECTION V: STAGE WORKS

**Duke Bluebeard's castle—opera: 1 act, Sz48
(Op. 11) (1918—Budapest)** (Lib. B. Balázs)
Cpte D. Fischer-Dieskau, J. Varady, Bavarian St
Orch, W. Sawallisch (r1979)
    (9/88) (DG) ① **423 236-2GC**

Cpte S. Ramey, E. Marton, Hungarian St Orch, A.
Fischer   (9/88) (SONY) ① **MK44523**
Cpte K. Kováts, S. Sass, I. Sztankay, LPO, G. Solti
(r1979)   (5/92) (DECC) ① **433 082-2DM**
Cpte M. Székely, O. Szönyi, LSO, A. Dorati (r1962)
Berg: Wozzeck.   (7/93) (MERC) ① **434 325-2MM**
Cpte S. Nimsgern, T. Troyanos, BBC SO, P. Boulez
(r1976)   (3/95) (SONY) ① **SMK64110**
Cpte W. Berry, C. Ludwig, LSO, I. Kertész (r1965)
    (4/95) (DECC) ① **443 571-2DCS**
Cpte F. Struckmann, K. Szendrényi, Frankfurt RSO,
E. Inbal (r1992)   (10/95) (DENO) ① **CO-78932**
Cpte D. Fischer-Dieskau, H. Töpper, Berlin RSO, F.
Fricsay (r1958: Ger) *Stravinsky: Oedipus Rex.*
    (11/95) (DG) ① [2] **445 445-2GX2**
**The Miraculous mandarin—pantomime: 1
act, Sz73 (Op. 19) (1926—Cologne)**
Cpte Philh, N. Järvi *Leó Weiner: Suite, Op. 18.*
    (3/92) (CHAN) ① **CHAN9029**
Cpte LP Ch, LPO, F. Welser-Möst (r1992) *Concert*
    (10/93) (EMI) ① **CDC7 54858-2**
Cpte Montreal Sym Chor, Montreal SO, C. Dutoit
(r1991) *Concert* (3/94) (DECC) ① **436 210-2DH**
Cpte St Louis Sym Chor, St Louis SO, L. Slatkin
(r1992-3) *Concerto for Orchestra.*
    (9/94) (RCA) ① **09026 61702-2**
Cpte Ambrosian Sngrs, LSO, C. Abbado (r1982)
Concert   (12/94) (DG) ① **445 501-2GMA**
Cpte CBSO, S. Rattle (r1992) *Concerto for
Orchestra.*   (1/95) (EMI) ① **CDC5 55094-2**
Cpte Tanglewood Fest Chor, Boston SO, S. Ozawa
(r1994) *Concerto for Orchestra.*
    (8/95) (PHIL) ① **442 783-2PH**
Suite Hungarian St Orch, A. Fischer *Concerto for
Orchestra.*   (6/90) (NIMB) ① **NI5229**
Suite Chicago SO, G. Solti *Concert*
    (5/91) (DECC) ① **430 352-2DH**
Suite Boston SO, S. Ozawa *Concerto for Orchestra.*
    (1/93) (DG) ① **437 247-2GGA**
Suite Philadelphia, E. Ormandy *Concert*
    (5/93) (SONY) ① **SBK48263**
Suite Hungarian Nat PO, T. Ferenc *Concert*
    (7/93) (CARL) ① **PCD1013**
Suite Philadelphia, E. Ormandy (r1978) *Concert*
    (9/94) (EMI) ① **CDM5 65175-2**
Suite Philh, H. Wolff (1992) *Concert*
    (9/94) (TELD) ① **9031-76350-2**
**The Wooden Prince—ballet: 1 act, Sz60 (Op.
13) (1917—Budapest)**
Cpte Philh, N. Järvi *Hungarian Sketches.*
    (10/91) (CHAN) ① **CHAN8895**
Cpte NYPO, P. Boulez (r1975) *Concert*
    (9/95) (SONY) ① [2] **SM2K64100**
Chicago SO, P. Boulez *Cantata profana.*
    (3/93) (DG) ① **435 863-2GH**
**The Wooden Prince—concert suite from
ballet, Sz60 (1921-24)**
Hungarian St SO, A. Fischer (r1991) *Concert*
    (7/93) (NIMB) ① [2] **NI5362/3**

BARTOLINO DA PADOVA *(fl 1365-1405) Italy*

SECTION IV: VOCAL AND CHORAL

Alba columba—ballata
Newberry Consort, M. Springfels (r1990) *Concert*
    (7/93) (HARM) ① **HMU90 7038**

BARTOLOMEO DA BOLOGNA *(fl 1409-1425) Italy*

SECTION IV: VOCAL AND CHORAL

Arte psalentes—ballade: 3vv
Orlando Consort (bp1994) *Concert*
    (11/95) (METR) ① **METCD1008**
Que pena maior—virelai: 3vv
P. Memelsdorff, K. Boeke, S. Fomina, C. Designes,
K-E. Schröder, J. Feldman, H. Rodriguez (r1993)
Concert   (4/95) (ARCA) ① **A21**

BARVYNSKY, Vasyl' Oleksandrovich *(1888-1963) Russia*

SECTION IV: VOCAL AND CHORAL

Oh fields!—song (Wds. A. Konysky)
P. Plishka, T. Hrynkiv *Concert*
    (11/92) (FORL) ① **UCD16645**

BASS, George

SECTION IV: VOCAL AND CHORAL

Chansonette—song
F. Kreisler, C. Lamson (r1924: arr Kreisler) *Concert*
    (9/93) (BIDD) ① [2] **LAB068/9**

BASSANI, Giovanni Battista *(c1657-1716) Italy*

SECTION IV: VOCAL AND CHORAL

Nascere, dive puellule—cantata (1v)
M. van Egmond, Ricercar Consort *Concert*
    (1/90) (RICE) ① **RIC054032**
Posate, dormite
G. Souzay, J. Bonneau (r1948) *Concert*
    (4/92) (EMI) ① [7] **CHS7 69741-2(3)**

BASSANO, Augustine *(?-1604) Italy*

SECTION II: CHAMBER

Pavan
His Majesties Sagbutts and Cornetts, P. Bassano
(r1990) *Concert* (5/91) (ASV) ① **CDGAU122**

BASSANO, Giovanni *(c1528-1617) Italy*

SECTION II: CHAMBER

**Amor che col partire—recorder, violin and
continuo** (arr of chanson by Cipriono de Rore)
M. Verbruggen, Sonnerie Trio *Concert*
    (2/90) (ASV) ① **CDGAU113**
**Frais et gaillard—recorder, violin and
continuo** (arr of chanson by Clemens non
Papa)
M. Verbruggen, Sonnerie Trio *Concert*
    (2/90) (ASV) ① **CDGAU113**
His Majesties Sagbutts and Cornetts, P. Bassano
(r1990) *Concert* (5/91) (ASV) ① **CDGAU122**
Baltimore Consort (r1992: arr Baltimore Consort)
Concert (4/95) (DORI) ① **DOR90177**
Ung gay bergère—consort (pub 1575) (arr of
chanson by Crecquillon)
Baltimore Consort (r1992: arr Baltimore Consort)
Concert (4/95) (DORI) ① **DOR90177**

SECTION IV: VOCAL AND CHORAL

Ave Regina—motet
Wren Orch, J. Iveson, S. Saunders, R. Gowman, R.
Gowman, Bernard Rose (r1977) *Concert*
    (7/91) (DECC) ① **430 359-2DM**
Canite Tuba in Syon—motet
Gentlemen of the Chappell, His Majesties Sagbutts
and Cornetts, P. Bassano (r1990) *Concert*
    (5/91) (ASV) ① **CDGAU122**
Deus qui Beatum Marcum—motet
E. van Evera, Gentlemen of the Chappell, His
Majesties Sagbutts and Cornetts, P. Bassano (r1990)
Concert   (5/91) (ASV) ① **CDGAU122**
**Motetti, madrigali et canzone francese di
diversi eccellenti autori—4-6vv (1591)**
  1. Caro dolce ben mio (Gabrieli); 2. Oncques amour
  (Crecquillon).
1, 2. B. Dickey, Tragicomedia *Concert*
    (6/92) (ACCE) ① **ACC9173D**
Vestiva i colli
Kithara (r1993) *Concert*
    (3/95) (CHAN) ① **CHAN0562**

BASSANO, Jeronimo *(1559-1635) Italy*

SECTION II: CHAMBER

5 Fantasias a 5 (Christ Church MSS716-720)
  1. No. 1; 3. No. 3.
1, 3. His Majesties Sagbutts and Cornetts, P.
Bassano (r1990) *Concert*
    (5/91) (ASV) ① **CDGAU122**

BASSI, Luigi *(1833-1871) Italy*

SECTION II: CHAMBER

**Fantasia di concerto: variations on 'Caro
nome' from Verdi's 'Rigoletto'—clarinet and
piano**
M. Gomez, anon (r1904) *Concert*
    (2/94) (CLRI) ① **CC0005**

Mélodie d' 'I Puritani' (Bellini)—clarinet and
piano
9, 18. M. Gomez, C. Draper, H.P. Draper, Renard Cl
Qt, R. Kell, F. Thurston, R. Clarke, Griller Qt, A.
Umbach, C. Esberger, R. Quaranta, A. Giammatteo,
F.J. Brissett, B. Goodman, G. Hamelin, A. Périer, H.
Lefèbvre, anon, wind band, SO, C. Raybould, G.
Moore, Budapest Qt, orch, P. Coppola, Garde
Republicaine Band (r1898) Concert
(2/94) (CLRI) ① CC0005

BATAILLE, Gabriel (c1575–1630) France

SECTION IV: VOCAL AND CHORAL

Cachez, beaux yeux—song
G. Souzay, J. Bonneau (r1953) Concert
(7/91) (DECC) ① 425 975-2DM
Ma bergère non légère
G. Souzay, J. Bonneau (r1953) Concert
(7/91) (DECC) ① 425 975-2DM
Tambourin—song
G. Souzay, J. Bonneau (r1953) Concert
(7/91) (DECC) ① 425 975-2DM

BATH, Hubert (1883–1945) England

SECTION I: ORCHESTRAL

Honour and Glory—brass band
Wingates Temperance Band, H. Moss (r1931)
Concert (11/93) (BEUL) ① 1PD2

BATISTE, Antoine-Edouard (1820–1876) France

SECTION III: INSTRUMENTAL

Grand Offertoire in D—organ
C. Herrick Concert (10/92) (HYPE) ① CDA66605
Offertoire in D minor—organ
C. Herrick Concert (9/91) (HYPE) ① CDA66457
The Pilgrim's Song of Hope—organ
J.A. Meale (r c1927) Concert
(9/94) (BEUL) ① 1PD5

BATTISHILL, Jonathan (1738–1801) England

SECTION IV: VOCAL AND CHORAL

O Lord, look down from heaven—anthem
(7vv, org)
Magdalen Oxford Coll Ch, J. Harper Concert
(11/91) (ABBE) ① CDCA912
St Paul's Cath Ch, John Scott Concert
(4/92) (HYPE) ① CDA66519
Llandaff Cath Ch, M. Smith, M. Hoeg (r1994) Concert
(10/95) (PRIO) ① PRCD510
Sylvia blushes when I woo her—glee
Hilliard Ens, L-L. Kiesel Concert
(12/91) (MERI) ① DUOCD89009

BAUER, Harold (1873–1951) USA

SECTION III: INSTRUMENTAL

Eighteenth Century Tunes
1. Barberini's Minuet; 2. Motley & Flourish.
1, 2. H. Bauer (r1924) Concert
(9/93) (BIDD) ① LHW007

BAULD, Alison (b 1944) Australia

SECTION IV: VOCAL AND CHORAL

Farewell Already—song: soprano and string
quartet (1993) (Wds. after Shakespeare. Arr
from Richard III, 1985)
J. Manning, Jane's Minstrels, R. Montgomery (r1993)
Concert (10/95) (NMC) ① NMCD025

BAX, Sir Arnold (Edward Trevor) (1883–1953) England

SECTION I: ORCHESTRAL

Christmas Eve on the Mountains—tone
poem (1911 rev c1933)
LPO, B. Thomson Symphony 1.
(2/87) (CHAN) ① CHAN8480
LPO, B. Thomson (r1986) Concert
(2/94) (CHAN) ① CHAN9168

Concerto for Cello and Orchestra (1932)
R. Wallfisch, LPO, B. Thomson Concert
(11/87) (CHAN) ① CHAN8494
Concerto for Violin and Orchestra (1938)
L. Mordkovitch, LPO, B. Thomson Concert
(4/92) (CHAN) ① CHAN9003
Coronation March—orchestra (1952) (written
for the Coronation of Elizabeth II)
LSO, M. Sargent (r1953) Concert
(7/95) (BEUL) ① 1PD13
Cortège—orchestra (1925)
LPO, B. Thomson Concert
(11/87) (CHAN) ① CHAN8494
Fanfare for the Wedding of Princess
Elizabeth (1948)
PJBE (r1970) Concert
(6/93) (DECC) ① 436 403-2DWO
Festival Overture (1911 rev 1918)
LPO, B. Thomson Symphony 6.
(7/88) (CHAN) ① CHAN8586
LPO, B. Thomson (r1987) Concert
(2/94) (CHAN) ① CHAN9168
The Garden of Fand—tone poem (1913-16)
Ulster Orch, B. Thomson (r1982) Concert
(1/84) (CHAN) ① CHAN8307
RPO, T. Beecham (r1947) Concert
(6/92) (EMI) ① CDM7 63405-2
LPO, A. Boult Concert (9/92) (LYRI) ① SRCD231
The Happy Forest—tone poem (1914-21)
Ulster Orch, B. Thomson (r1982) Concert
(1/84) (CHAN) ① CHAN8307
In the faery hills—tone poem (1909)
Ulster Orch, B. Thomson Concert
(9/85) (CHAN) ① CHAN8367
Into the twilight—tone poem (1908)
Ulster Orch, B. Thomson Concert
(9/85) (CHAN) ① CHAN8367
A Legend—tone poem (1944)
LPO, B. Thomson Concert
(4/92) (CHAN) ① CHAN9003
Mediterranean (1922) (arr of 1920 piano
work)
LPO, B. Thomson Concert
(11/87) (CHAN) ① CHAN8494
LPO, B. Thomson Concert
(10/91) (CHAN) ① CHAN6538
LPO, A. Boult Concert (9/92) (LYRI) ① SRCD231
J. Heifetz, E. Bay (r1946) Concert
(11/94) (RCA) ① [65] 09026 61778-2(06)
Morning Song, 'Maytime in Sussex'—piano
and orchestra (c1946)
M. Fingerhut, LPO, B. Thomson Symphonic
Variations. (2/88) (CHAN) ① CHAN8516
Northern Ballad No. 1—1920
LPO, A. Boult Concert (9/92) (LYRI) ① SRCD231
Northern Ballad No. 2 (1934)
RPO, V. Handley Concert
(9/86) (CHAN) ① CHAN8464
November Woods—tone poem (1917)
Ulster Orch, B. Thomson (r1982) Concert
(1/84) (CHAN) ① CHAN8307
LPO, A. Boult Concert (9/92) (LYRI) ① SRCD231
Nympholept—tone poem (1912-15)
LPO, B. Thomson Symphony 2.
(9/87) (CHAN) ① CHAN8493
LPO, B. Thomson (r1986) Concert
(2/94) (CHAN) ① CHAN9168
On the Sea-Shore—tone poem (incomplete)
Ulster Orch, V. Handley (ed./orch. Parlett) Concert
(3/87) (CHAN) ① CHAN8473
4 Orchestral Sketches (1912-13)
1. Pensive Twilight; 2. Dance in the Sun; 3. In the
Hills of Home; 4. Dance of Wild Irravel.
4. LPO, B. Thomson Concert
(12/86) (CHAN) ① CHAN8454
4. LPO, B. Thomson (r1986) Concert
(2/94) (CHAN) ① CHAN9168
Overture, Elegy and Rondo—orchestra
(1927)
Slovak PO, A. Wordsworth (r1987) Sinfonietta.
(7/88) (MARC) ① 8 223102
Overture to a Picaresque
Comedy—orchestra (1930)
LPO, B. Thomson Concert
(11/87) (CHAN) ① CHAN8494
LPO, H. Harty (r1935) Concert
(9/95) (DUTT) ① CDLX7016
Paean (1920 orch 1938)
LPO, B. Thomson Concert
(12/86) (CHAN) ① CHAN8454
LPO, B. Thomson (r1986) Concert
(2/94) (CHAN) ① CHAN9168
Phantasy—viola and orchestra (1920)
R. Golani, RPO, V. Handley Concert
(4/89) (CONI) ① CDCF171

Prelude for a Solemn Occasion—orchestra
(1927-33)
LPO, B. Thomson Concert
(11/87) (CHAN) ① CHAN8494
Romantic Overture—chamber orchestra
(1926)
LPO, B. Thomson Concert
(4/92) (CHAN) ① CHAN9003
Roscatha—tone poem (1910)
Ulster Orch, B. Thomson Concert
(9/85) (CHAN) ① CHAN8367
Russian Suite—orchestra (1919) (arr cpsr
from various piano works)
LPO, B. Thomson Symphony 5.
(8/89) (CHAN) ① CHAN8669
Saga Fragment—piano and chamber
orchestra (1932) (arr cpsr from piano quartet
movement)
M. Fingerhut, LPO, B. Thomson Winter Legends.
(2/87) (CHAN) ① CHAN8484
Sinfonietta—orchestra (1932)
Slovak PO, B. Wordsworth (r1987) Overture, Elegy
and Rondo. (7/88) (MARC) ① 8 223102
Spring Fire—symphony (1913)
RPO, V. Handley Concert
(9/86) (CHAN) ① CHAN8464
Summer Music (1917-20 rev 1932)
Ulster Orch, B. Thomson (r1982) Concert
(1/84) (CHAN) ① CHAN8307
Symphonic Scherzo (orch 1917 rev 1933)
RPO, V. Handley Concert
(9/86) (CHAN) ① CHAN8464
Symphonic Variations in E—piano and
orchestra (1918)
M. Fingerhut, LPO, B. Thomson Morning Song.
(2/88) (CHAN) ① CHAN8516
Symphony No. 1 in E flat (1921-22)
LPO, B. Thomson Christmas Eve.
(2/87) (CHAN) ① CHAN8480
LPO, M. Fredman Symphony 7.
(12/92) (LYRI) ① SRCD232
Symphony No. 2 in E minor/C (1926)
LPO, B. Thomson Nympholept.
(9/87) (CHAN) ① CHAN8493
Symphony No. 3 (1929)
LPO, B. Thomson Concert
(12/86) (CHAN) ① CHAN8454
Symphony No. 4 (1931)
Ulster Orch, B. Thomson Tintagel.
(8/84) (CHAN) ① CHAN8312
Symphony No. 5 in C sharp minor (1931-32)
LPO, B. Thomson Russian Suite.
(8/89) (CHAN) ① CHAN8669
Symphony No. 6 (1934)
LPO, B. Thomson Festival Overture.
(7/88) (CHAN) ① CHAN8586
Symphony No. 7 (1939)
LPO, B. Thomson Concert
(12/88) (CHAN) ① CHAN8628
LPO, R. Leppard Symphony 1.
(12/92) (LYRI) ① SRCD232
The Tale the pine tress knew—tone poem
(1931)
Ulster Orch, B. Thomson Concert
(9/85) (CHAN) ① CHAN8367
Tintagel—tone poem (1917-19)
Ulster Orch, B. Thomson Symphony 4.
(8/84) (CHAN) ① CHAN8312
Ulster Orch, B. Thomson Concert
(10/91) (CHAN) ① CHAN6538
LPO, A. Boult Concert (9/92) (LYRI) ① SRCD231
Ulster Orch, B. Thomson (r1983) Concert
(2/94) (CHAN) ① CHAN9168
LSO, J. Barbirolli (r1965) Vaughan Williams:
Symphony 5. (3/95) (EMI) ① CDM5 65110-2
Winter Legends—Sinfonia concertante for
piano and orchestra (1930)
M. Fingerhut, LPO, B. Thomson Saga Fragment.
(2/87) (CHAN) ① CHAN8484

SECTION II: CHAMBER

The Devil that tempted Sir Anthony—piano
duet (1929)
Jeremy Brown, S. Tanyel Concert
(7/89) (CHAN) ① CHAN8603
Folk-Tale—cello and piano (1918)
B. Gregor-Smith, Y. Wrigley (r1993) Concert
(8/94) (ASV) ① CDDCA896
Hardanger—piano duet (1927)
Jeremy Brown, S. Tanyel Concert
(7/89) (CHAN) ① CHAN8603
Legend for Viola and Piano (1929)
P. Coletti, L. Howard (r1993) Concert
(10/94) (HYPE) ① CDA66687

Legend-Sonata in F sharp minor—cello and piano (1943)
B. Gregor-Smith, Y. Wrigley (r1993) *Concert*
(8/94) (ASV) ① **CDDCA896**

Moy Mell, 'The Pleasant Plain'—piano duet (1917)
Jeremy Brown, S. Tanyel *Concert*
(7/89) (CHAN) ① **CHAN8603**

Nonet—fl, ob, cl, hp, db, stg qt (1930)
J. Slater, L. Goossens, F. Thurston, M. Korchinska, V. Watson, Griller Qt (r1937) *Concert*
(12/95) (DUTT) ① **CDAX8014**

Piano Quartet (1922)
J. McCabe, English Qt *Concert*
(4/87) (CHAN) ① **CHAN8391**

Piano Trio in B flat (1946)
Borodin Trio *Bridge: Piano Trio 2.*
(4/87) (CHAN) ① **CHAN8495**
Pirasti Trio (r1994) *Concert*
(9/95) (ASV) ① **CDDCA925**

The Poisoned fountain—piano duet (1928)
Jeremy Brown, S. Tanyel *Concert*
(7/89) (CHAN) ① **CHAN8603**

Quartet for Strings No. 2 in E minor (1925)
Mistry Qt *Piano Quintet.*
(4/91) (CHAN) ① **CHAN8795**

Quintet for Harp and Strings (1919)
S. Kanga, English Qt *Concert*
(4/87) (CHAN) ① **CHAN8391**

Quintet for oboe and strings (1921)
S. Francis, English Qt *Concert*
(7/87) (CHAN) ① **CHAN8392**
P. Woods, Audubon Qt *Concert*
(10/89) (TELA) ① **CD80205**

Quintet for Piano and Strings (1922)
D.O. Norris, Mistry Qt *String Quartet 2.*
(4/91) (CHAN) ① **CHAN8795**

Red Autumn—piano duet (1931)
Jeremy Brown, S. Tanyel *Concert*
(7/89) (CHAN) ① **CHAN8603**

Sonata for Cello and Piano (1923)
B. Gregor-Smith, Y. Wrigley (r1993) *Concert*
(8/94) (ASV) ① **CDDCA896**

Sonata for Clarinet and Piano (1934)
J. Hilton, K. Swallow *Concert*
(2/89) (CHAN) ① **CHAN8683**
M. Khouri, P. Pettinger *Concert*
(6/92) (CNTI) ① **CCD1038**
E. Johnson, M. Martineau *Concert*
(7/94) (ASV) ① **CDDCA891**

Sonata for two pianos (1929)
Jeremy Brown, S. Tanyel *Concert*
(7/89) (CHAN) ① **CHAN8603**

Sonata for Viola and Piano (1922)
W. Primrose, H. Cohen (r1937) *Concert*
(10/91) (PEAR) ① **GEMMCD9453**

Sonata for Violin and Piano No. 1 in E (1910)
E. Gruenberg, J. McCabe *Violin Sonata 2.*
(9/90) (CHAN) ① **CHAN8845**

Sonata for Violin and Piano No. 2 in D (1915)
E. Gruenberg, J. McCabe *Violin Sonata 1.*
(9/90) (CHAN) ① **CHAN8845**

Sonata for Violin and Piano No. 3 (1927)
May Harrison, C. Lynch (bp1936; incomplete) *Concert*
(12/90) (SYMP) ① **SYMCD1075**

Sonatina for Cello and Piano in D (1933)
B. Gregor-Smith, Y. Wrigley (r1993) *Concert*
(8/94) (ASV) ① **CDDCA896**

String Quartet No. 1 (1918)
English Qt *Concert*
(4/87) (CHAN) ① **CHAN8391**

SECTION III: INSTRUMENTAL

Apple Blossom—piano (1915)
E. Parkin *Concert*
(7/90) (CHAN) ① **CHAN8732**

Burlesque—piano (1920)
E. Parkin *Concert*
(7/90) (CHAN) ① **CHAN8732**

Country-Tune—piano (1920)
E. Parkin *Concert*
(12/87) (CHAN) ① **CHAN8496**

A Hill Tune—piano (1920)
E. Parkin *Concert*
(8/88) (CHAN) ① **CHAN8497**

In a Vodka Shop—piano (1915)
E. Parkin *Concert*
(8/88) (CHAN) ① **CHAN8497**

Legend—piano (1935)
J. McCabe *Concert*
(11/92) (CNTI) ① **CCD1045**

Lullaby—piano (1920)
E. Parkin *Concert*
(12/87) (CHAN) ① **CHAN8496**

The Maiden with the Daffodil—piano (1915)
E. Parkin *Concert*
(12/87) (CHAN) ① **CHAN8496**

Nereid—piano (1916)
E. Parkin *Concert*
(7/90) (CHAN) ① **CHAN8732**

O Dame get up and Bake your pies—piano (1945)
E. Parkin *Concert*
(7/90) (CHAN) ① **CHAN8732**

On a May Evening—piano (1918)
E. Parkin *Concert*
(7/90) (CHAN) ① **CHAN8732**

The Princess's Rose Garden—piano (1915)
E. Parkin *Concert*
(7/90) (CHAN) ① **CHAN8732**

Rhapsodic Ballad—cello solo
R. Wallfisch (r1986) *Concert*
(4/87) (CHAN) ① **CHAN8499**

Romance—piano
E. Parkin *Concert*
(7/90) (CHAN) ① **CHAN8732**

2 Russian Tone Pictures—piano (1912)
1. May Night in the Ukraine; 2. Gopak.
E. Parkin *Concert*
(7/90) (CHAN) ① **CHAN8732**

Sleepy Head—piano (1915)
E. Parkin *Concert*
(7/90) (CHAN) ① **CHAN8732**

Sonata for Piano No. 1 in F sharp minor (1910 rev 1921)
E. Parkin *Concert*
(12/87) (CHAN) ① **CHAN8496**

Sonata for Piano No. 2 in G (1919)
E. Parkin *Concert*
(12/87) (CHAN) ① **CHAN8496**
J. McCabe *Concert*
(11/92) (CNTI) ① **CCD1045**

Sonata for Piano No. 3 in G sharp minor (1926)
E. Parkin *Concert*
(8/88) (CHAN) ① **CHAN8497**

Sonata for Piano No. 4 in G (1932)
E. Parkin *Concert*
(8/88) (CHAN) ① **CHAN8497**

Sonata in E flat—piano (1919) (first version of Symphony No. 1)
J. McCabe *Concert*
(11/92) (CNTI) ① **CCD1045**

Water Music—piano (1920)
E. Parkin *Concert*
(8/88) (CHAN) ① **CHAN8497**

Winter Waters—piano (1915)
E. Parkin *Concert*
(12/87) (CHAN) ① **CHAN8496**

SECTION IV: VOCAL AND CHORAL

Enchanted Summer—2 sopranos, chorus and orchestra (1910) (Wds. Shelley)
A. Williams-King, L. McWhirter, Brighton Fest Chor, RPO, V. Handley *Concert*
(10/89) (CHAN) ① **CHAN8625**

Epithalamium—unison chorus and organ (1947)
Rodolfus Ch, R. Allwood, C. Hughes (r1993) *Concert*
(9/95) (HERA) ① **HAVPCD176**

Eternity—song (1925) (Wds. R. Herrick)
M. Hill, LPO, B. Thomson *Concert*
(12/88) (CHAN) ① **CHAN8628**
P. Wright, R. Barnes *Concert*
(5/93) (CNTI) ① **CCD1046**

Far in a Western Brookland—song (1918) (Wds. A. E. Housman)
C. Keyte, R. Barnes *Concert*
(5/93) (CNTI) ① **CCD1046**

Fatherland—tenor, chorus, orchestra (1907 rev 1934) (Wds. Runeberg, trans C. Bax)
M. Hill, Brighton Fest Chor, RPO, V. Handley *Concert*
(10/89) (CHAN) ① **CHAN8625**

The Flute—song (1907) (Wds. B. Bjørnson, trans E. Gosse)
P. Wright, R. Barnes *Concert*
(5/93) (CNTI) ① **CCD1046**

Glamour—song (1921) (Wds. cpsr)
M. Hill, LPO, B. Thomson (orch R.Newton) *Concert*
(12/88) (CHAN) ① **CHAN8628**

5 Greek Folk Songs—chorus a capella: 4vv (1944)
1. The miracle of Saint Basil; 2. The bridesmaid's song; 3. In far-off Malta; 4. The happy tramp; 5. A pilgrim's chant.
Finzi Sngrs, P. Spicer (r1991) *Concert*
(6/93) (CHAN) ① **CHAN9139**

I have house and land in Kent—song (1918) (Wds. trad)
C. Keyte, R. Barnes *Concert*
(5/93) (CNTI) ① **CCD1046**

I sing of a maiden—unaccompanied partsong (5vv) (1926) (Wds. Anon)
Finzi Sngrs, P. Spicer (r1991) *Concert*
(6/93) (CHAN) ① **CHAN9139**
Rodolfus Ch, R. Allwood (r1993) *Concert*
(9/95) (HERA) ① **HAVPCD176**

5 Irish Songs (1921)
1. The Pigeons (wds. P. Colum); 2. As I came over the grey, grey hills (wds. J. Campbell); 3. I heard a piper piping (wds. J. Campbell); 4. Across the door (wds. P. Colum); 5. Beg-Innish (wds. J. M. Synge).
3. P. Wright, R. Barnes *Concert*
(5/93) (CNTI) ① **CCD1046**

3 Irish Songs (1922) (Wds. P. Colum)
1. Cradle Song; 2. Rann of Exile; 3. Rann of Wandering.
2. C. Keyte, R. Barnes *Concert*
(5/93) (CNTI) ① **CCD1046**

Lord, thou hast told us—choir a cappella (1931) (Wds. T Washbourne)
Rodolfus Ch, R. Allwood (r1993) *Concert*
(9/95) (HERA) ① **HAVPCD176**

A Lyke-wake—song (1908) (Wds. Border Ballad (Anon: 15th Cent)
M. Hill, LPO, B. Thomson *Concert*
(12/88) (CHAN) ① **CHAN8628**

Magnificat—choir, organ (1948)
P. Wright, R. Barnes *Concert*
(5/93) (CNTI) ① **CCD1046**
Rodolfus Ch, R. Allwood, C. Hughes (r1993) *Concert*
(9/95) (HERA) ① **HAVPCD176**

The Market Girl—song (1922) (Wds. T. Hardy)
R. Greager, R. Barnes *Concert*
(5/93) (CNTI) ① **CCD1046**

Mater ora filium—unaccompanied chorus (1921)
Finzi Sngrs, P. Spicer (r1991) *Concert*
(6/93) (CHAN) ① **CHAN9139**
Rodolfus Ch, R. Allwood (1993) *Concert*
(9/95) (HERA) ① **HAVPCD176**

A Milking Sian—song (1907) (Wds. F. Macleod)
P. Wright, R. Barnes *Concert*
(5/93) (CNTI) ① **CCD1046**

O dear! what can the matter be?—song (1918) (Wds. trad)
P. Wright, R. Barnes *Concert*
(5/93) (CNTI) ① **CCD1046**

Out and Away—song (1926) (Wds. J. Stephens)
R. Greager, R. Barnes *Concert*
(5/93) (CNTI) ① **CCD1046**

Shieling Song (1908) (Wds. F. Macleod)
P. Wright, R. Barnes *Concert*
(5/93) (CNTI) ① **CCD1046**

Slumber Song (1910) (Wds. cpsr. Pub 1920 as 'A Lullaby')
M. Hill, LPO, B. Thomson *Concert*
(12/88) (CHAN) ① **CHAN8628**

The Song in the Twilight (1905) (Wds. F. Bax)
P. Wright, R. Barnes *Concert*
(5/93) (CNTI) ① **CCD1046**

This worldes joie—unaccompanied chorus (1923)
Finzi Sngrs, P. Spicer (r1991) *Concert*
(6/93) (CHAN) ① **CHAN9139**
Rodolfus Ch, R. Allwood (r1993) *Concert*
(9/95) (HERA) ① **HAVPCD176**

To Eire—song (1910) (Wds. J. H. Cousins)
P. Wright, R. Barnes *Concert*
(5/93) (CNTI) ① **CCD1046**

5 Traditional Songs of France (1920)
1. Sarabande—Amours, tant tu me fais de mal; 2. Langueo d'amours; 3. Me suis mise en danse; 4. Femmes, battez vos-marys; 5. La targo.
1, 2, 4, 5. P. Wright, C. Keyte, R. Barnes *Concert*
(5/93) (CNTI) ① **CCD1046**

Walsinghame—tenor, chorus and orchestra (1926) (Wds. 16th cent.)
M. Hill, L. McWhirter, Brighton Fest Chor, RPO, V. Handley *Concert*
(10/89) (CHAN) ① **CHAN8625**

What is it like to be young and fair—SSAAT, Wds. C. Bax (1953)
Cambridge Univ Chbr Ch, T. Brown *Concert*
(4/92) (GAMU) ① **GAMCD529**

The White peace—song (1907) (Wds. Macleod)
P. Wright, R. Barnes *Concert*
(5/93) (CNTI) ① **CCD1046**

SECTION V: STAGE WORKS

Between Dusk and Dawn—ballet (1917)
LPO, B. Thomson *Truth about the Russian Dancers.*
(10/90) (CHAN) ① **CHAN8863**

Golden Eagle—incidental music to C. Bax's play (1946)
EXCERPTS—; 1. Prelude; 2. Rizzio's Song of Ronsard; 3. Dance; 4. Pavane: Prelude, Act 2 Scene 1; 5. Rizzio; 6. Song (Rizzio); 7. Prelude, Act 2 Scene 2; 8. Act 3 Scene 1; 9. Prelude, Act 3 Scene 2; 10. Mary Stuart's Prayer.
LPO, B. Thomson *Concert*
(4/92) (CHAN) ① **CHAN9003**

Malta GC—film score (1942)
SUITE: 1. Fanfare and Prelude; 2. Convoy; 3. Old Valetta; 4. Air Raid; 5. Ruins; 6. Quick March; 7. Intermezzo; 8. Reconstruction; 9. Finale (pt 1); 10. Finale (pt 2).
1-10. RPO, K. Alwyn (r1986) *Oliver Twist.*
(10/87) (CLOU) ① **ACN7012**
10. RPO, K. Alwyn *Concert*
(5/93) (SILV) ① **SILVAD3002**

Oliver Twist—film score (1948)
EXCERPTS: 1. Prelude; 2. The Fight; 4. Oliver's Sleepless Night; 5. Oliver and the Artful Dodger; 6. Fagin's Romp; 7. The Chase; 8. Oliver

and Brownlow; 9. Nancy and Brownlow; 10. Finale.
1-10. E. Parkin, RPO, K. Alwyn (r1986) *Malta GC.*
(10/87) (CLOU) ① **ACN7012**
6. RPO, K. Alwyn *Concert*
(5/93) (SILV) ① **SILVAD3002**
The **Truth about the Russian
Dancers**—incidental music (1920, rev 1926)
LPO, B. Thomson *Between Dusk and Dawn.*
(10/90) (CHAN) ① **CHAN8863**

BAYES, Nora *(1880–1928)* USA

SECTION V: STAGE WORKS

Ladies First—Nora Bayes' songs from the
show (1918—New York)
EXCERPTS: 1. Without You (Bayes/Fisher); 2.
Prohibition Blues (Sloane/Smith); 3. Just Like a
Gypsy (Simons/Bayes).
1-3. N. Bayes, Orig Broadway Cast (r1918-19)
Concert (5/94) (PEAR) ① [3] **GEMMCDS9059/61**

BAYNES, Sydney *(1879–1938)*
England

SECTION I: ORCHESTRAL

Destiny—waltz (1912)
Southern Fest Orch, R. White *Concert*
(5/93) (CHAN) ① **CHAN9110**

BAZIN, François (Emmanuel-
Joseph) *(1816–1878)* France

SECTION V: STAGE WORKS

Maître Pathelin—opéra comique: 3 acts
(1856—Paris) (Lib. de Leuven and Langlé)
EXCERPTS: 1. Overture; 2. Pauvre avocat dans ton
état; 3. Nous ferons ripaille; 4. Veux-te bien ranger la
boutique; 5. Quel air de probité; 6. Quel triste sort; 7.
Je pense a vous quand je m'éveille; 8. Je suis un
avocat d'ithaque; 9. Quand on alliat te faire pendre;
10. C'est effroyable.
Cpte C. Harbell, M. Stiot, L. Felder, B. Plantey, G.
Friedmann, M. Jarry, J. Peyron, M. Hamel, French
Rad Lyric Chor, French Rad Lyric Orch, J. Brebion
(bp1971) *Voyage en Chine.*
(4/94) (MUSD) ① [2] **202552**
Le **Voyage en Chine**—opéra comique: 3 acts
(1865—Paris) (Lib. E Labiche and A Delacour)
EXCERPTS: 1. Overture. ACT 1: 2. Qu'a-t-elle
donc?; 3. C'est jour de fête; 4. Je vous présente ici
ma femme; 5. Ah! je vais donc la revoir; 6. Ah! quelle
amusante folie; 7. C'est jour de fête. ACT 2: 8. Ah!
quelle heureuse destinée; 9. Six cailloux, cinq
cailloux; 10. Quel temps effroyable!; 11. Je suis
breton; 12. Fille dénaturée. ACT 3: 13. Voguons, la
mer est belle; 14. Quand le soleil sur notre monde;
15. En chine, en chine; 16. Faut-il hisser, capitaine.
Cpte C. Collart, M. Sénéchal, L. Dachary, A. Balbon,
A. Martineau, G. Rey, R. Lenoty, Duvaleix, French
Rad Lyric Chor, French Rad Lyric Orch, M. Cariven
(bp1968) *Maître Pathelin.*
(4/94) (MUSD) ① [2] **202552**

BAZZINI, Antonio *(1818–1897)*
Italy

SECTION I: ORCHESTRAL

Saul—overture to Alfieri's work (1866)
NBC SO, A. Toscanini (bp1939) *Concert*
(5/94) (ATS) ① [2] **ATCD100**

SECTION II: CHAMBER

La **Ronde des lutins**—scherzo fantastique:
violin and piano, Op. 25 (1852)
J. Heifetz, A. Benoist (r1917) *Concert*
(1/91) (BIDD) ① **LAB015**
I. Perlman, J.G. Guggenheim (pp1990) *Concert*
(2/91) (EMI) ① **CDC7 54108-2**
J. Kubelík, anon (r1904) *Concert*
(6/91) (BIDD) ① **LAB033/4**
J. Kubelík, anon (r1905) *Concert*
(6/91) (BIDD) ① **LAB033/4**
Y. Menuhin, M. Gazelle (r1934) *Concert*
(9/91) (TEST) ① **SBT1003**
J. Heifetz, A. Benoist (r1917) *Concert*
(12/91) (APR) ① [2] **APR7015**
K. Daeshik Kang, M. Rahkonen (r1992) *Concert*
(9/93) (NIMB) ① **NI5358**
B. Huberman, P. Frenkel (r1922) *Concert*
(3/94) (BIDD) ① [2] **LAB077/8**
M. Vengerov, I. Golan (r1993) *Concert*
(4/94) (TELD) ① **9031-77351-2**

J. Heifetz, A. Benoist (r1917) *Concert*
(11/94) (RCA) ① [65] **09026 61778-2(01)**
J. Heifetz, E. Bay (r1937) *Concert*
(11/94) (RCA) ① [65] **09026 61778-2(03)**

BEACH, Amy Marcy (Cheney)
(1867–1944) USA

also known as Mrs. H.H.A. Beach

SECTION I: ORCHESTRAL

**Concerto for Piano and Orchestra in C sharp
minor, Op. 45 (1889)**
M.L. Boehm, Westphalian SO, S. Landau *Macdowell:
Piano Concerto 2.* (5/93) (VOX) ① **115718-2**
Symphony in E minor, 'Gaelic', Op. 32
(1896)
Detroit SO, N. Järvi *Concert*
(10/91) (CHAN) ① **CHAN8958**

SECTION II: CHAMBER

3 Compositions—violin and piano, Op. 40
(1898)
J. Silverstein, V. Eskin *Concert*
(1/90) (NORT) ① **NR9004-CD**
3 Compositions—cello and piano, Op. 40
(1903) (arr cpsr from vn/pf vers)
P. Frame, R. Weirich (r1994) *Concert*
(3/95) (KOCH) ① **37281-2**
Lento espressivo—violin and piano (1920s)
J. Silverstein, V. Eskin *Concert*
(1/90) (NORT) ① **NR9004-CD**
Pastorale—wind quintet (1942)
Reykjavik Wind Qnt (r1992) *Concert*
(11/93) (CHAN) ① **CHAN9174**
Piano Trio in A minor, Op. 150 (1938)
Hartley Trio *Concert* (6/94) (GAMU) ① **GAMCD536**
Macalester Trio *Concert*
(10/94) (VOX) ① [2] **115845-2**
**Quintet for Piano and Strings in F sharp, Op.
67 (1907)**
M. Roscoe, Endellion Qt (r1994) *Concert*
(10/95) (ASV) ① **CDDCA932**
Romance—violin and piano, Op. 23 (1893)
J. Silverstein, V. Eskin *Concert*
(1/90) (NORT) ① **NR9004-CD**
E. Skorodin, K. Schmidt (r1991) *Concert*
(12/93) (KOCH) ① **37240-2**
Sonata for Violin and Piano, Op. 34 (1896)
P. Frame, B. Snyder (r1994: arr vc/pf) *Concert*
(3/95) (KOCH) ① **37281-2**
C. Macomber, D. Walsh (r1994) *Corigliano: Violin
Sonata.* (8/95) (KOCH) ① **37223-2**

SECTION III: INSTRUMENTAL

By the still waters—piano (1932)
V. Eskin *Concert* (1/90) (NORT) ① **NR9004-CD**
From Grandmother's Garden—piano, Op. 97
(1922)
V. Eskin *Concert* (1/90) (NORT) ① **NR9004-CD**
The **Hermit Thrush at Eve**—piano, Op. 92/1
(1922)
C. O'Riley *Concert* (12/95) (DELO) ① **DE3170**
A **Humming Bird**—piano (1932)
V. Eskin *Concert* (1/90) (NORT) ① **NR9004-CD**
5 Improvisations—piano, Op. 148
M. Legrand (r1994) *Concert*
(7/95) (ERAT) ① **4509-96386-2**
4 Sketches—piano, Op. 15 (1892)
1. In Autumn; 2. Phantoms; 3. Dreaming; 4. Fireflies.
1. K. Schmidt (r1991) *Concert*
(12/93) (KOCH) ① **37240-2**

SECTION IV: VOCAL AND CHORAL

3 Browning Songs—1v and piano, Op. 44
(1900)
1. The year's at the spring; 2. Ah, love, but a day; 3. I
send my heart up to Thee.
1. E. Eames, anon (r1908) *Concert*
(11/93) (ROMO) ① [2] **81001-2**
1. E. Eames, anon (r1905) *Concert*
(11/93) (ROMO) ① [2] **81001-2**
2. D. Fortunato, V. Eskin *Concert*
(1/90) (NORT) ① **NR9004-CD**
5 Burns Songs—1v and piano, Op. 43
(1899)
1. Dearie; 2. Scottish cradle song; 3. Oh were my
love thin yon lilac fair!; 4. Far awa'; 5. My lassie.
1. D. Fortunato, V. Eskin *Concert*
(1/90) (NORT) ① **NR9004-CD**
Dark Garden—song, Op. 131 (1932) (Wds.
Speyer)
D. Fortunato, V. Eskin *Concert*
(1/90) (NORT) ① **NR9004-CD**

Give me not love—2vv & piano, Op. 61 (1905)
(Wds. Coates)
L. Flanigan, P. Groves, C. O'Riley (r1995) *Concert*
(12/95) (DELO) ① **DE3170**
Hymn of Trust—song, Op. 13 (1891) (Wds.
Holmes)
D. Fortunato, V. Eskin *Concert*
(1/90) (NORT) ① **NR9004-CD**
In the Twilight—1v & piano, Op. 85 (1922)
(Wds. Longfellow)
C. Hellekant, C. O'Riley (r1995) *Concert*
(12/95) (DELO) ① **DE3170**
Rendezvous—song with violin obbligato,
Op. 120 (1928) (Wds. Speyer)
D. Fortunato, J. Silverstein, V. Eskin *Concert*
(1/90) (NORT) ① **NR9004-CD**
3 Shakespeare Songs—1v and piano, Op. 37
(1897)
1. O mistress mine; 2. Take, o take those lips away;
3. Fairy lullaby.
1. D. Fortunato, V. Eskin *Concert*
(1/90) (NORT) ① **NR9004-CD**
1. P. Groves, C. O'Riley (r1995) *Concert*
(12/95) (DELO) ① **DE3170**
Singing Joyfully—duet: soprano, mezzo-
soprano and piano
S.J. Langton, S. Mentzer, K. Schmidt (r1991) *Concert*
(12/93) (KOCH) ① **37240-2**
4 Songs—1v and piano, Op. 1 (1885-87)
1. With Violets (wds. K. Vannah); 2. Die vier Brüder
(wds. Schiller); 3. Jeune fille et jeune fleur (wds.
Chateaubriand); 4. Ariette (wds. Shelley).
3. T. Paul, C. O'Riley (r1995) *Concert*
(12/95) (DELO) ① **DE3170**
4. D. Fortunato, V. Eskin *Concert*
(1/90) (NORT) ① **NR9004-CD**
3 Songs—1v and piano, Op. 11 (1889-90)
(Wds. W E Henley)
1. Dark is the Night; 2. The Western Wind; 3. The
Blackbird.
1. D. Fortunato, V. Eskin *Concert*
(1/90) (NORT) ① **NR9004-CD**
1. L. Flanigan, C. O'Riley (r1995) *Concert*
(12/95) (DELO) ① **DE3170**
3 Songs—1v and piano, Op. 12 (1887) (Wds.
R. Burns)
1. Wilt thou be my Dearie?; 2. Ye Banks and Braes o'
Bonnie Doon; 3. My Luv is Like a Red, Red Rose.
2. D. Fortunato, V. Eskin *Concert*
(1/90) (NORT) ① **NR9004-CD**
4 Songs—1v and piano, Op. 14 (1890)
1. The Summer Wind (wds. W. Learned); 2. Le secret
(wds. J. de Resseguier); 3. Sweetheart, Sigh no more
(wds. T. B. Aldrich); 4. The Trush (wds. E. R. Sill).
3. S.J. Langton, K. Schmidt (r1991) *Concert*
(12/93) (KOCH) ① **37240-2**
3 Songs—1v and piano, Op. 19 (1893)
1. For me the Jasmine Buds Unfold (wds. F. E
Coates); 2. Ecstasy (with violin obbligato: wds. cpsr);
3. Golden Gates.
2. D. Fortunato, V. Eskin *Concert*
(1/90) (NORT) ① **NR9004-CD**
3 Songs—1v and piano, Op. 21 (1893)
1. Chanson d'amour (wds. V. Hugo); 2. Extase (wds.
V. Hugo); 3. Elle et moi (wds. F. Bovet).
2, 3. D. Fortunato, V. Eskin *Concert*
(1/90) (NORT) ① **NR9004-CD**
4 Songs—1v and piano, Op. 26 (1894)
1. My Star (wds. C. Fabbri); 2. Just for This (Wds. C.
Fabbri); 3. Spring (wds. C. Fabbri); 4. Wouldn't that
be Queer (wds. E. J. Cooley).
2. D. Fortunato, V. Eskin *Concert*
(1/90) (NORT) ① **NR9004-CD**
4 Songs—1v and piano, Op. 51 (1903)
1. Ich sagete nicht (wds. E. Wissman); 2. Wir drei
(wds. H. Eschelbach); 3. Juni (wds. E. Jansen); 4. Je
demande a l'oiseau (wds. Sylvestre).
3. D. Fortunato, V. Eskin *Concert*
(1/90) (NORT) ① **NR9004-CD**

SECTION V: STAGE WORKS

Cabildo—chamber opera: 1 act, Op. 149
(1932, fp 1945—Athens) (Lib. N B Stephens)
Cpte S. M. Hanan, A. D. Griffey, C. Hellekant, E.
Perry, P. Groves, T. Paul, L. Flanigan, New York
Concert Sngrs, M. Peskanov, C. Brey, C. O'Riley
(r1995) *Concert* (12/95) (DELO) ① **DE3170**

BEALE, William *(1784–1854)*
England

SECTION IV: VOCAL AND CHORAL

Come, let us join the roundelay—partsong
PCA, M. Brown *Concert* (3/87) (CONI) ① **CDCF145**

Hilliard Ens, L-L. Kiesel *Concert*
(12/91) (MERI) ① **DUOCD89009**

BEAMISH, Sally *(b 1956)* England

SECTION IV: VOCAL AND CHORAL

Tuscan lullaby—song (Wds. trad)
M. Wiegold, Composers Ens, D. Muldowney *Concert*
(4/92) (NMC) ① **NMCD003**

BEASER, Robert *(b 1954)* USA

SECTION I: ORCHESTRAL

Chorale Variations—orchestra (1992)
American Cpsrs Orch, D. R. Davies (r1992) *Concert*
(8/94) (ARGO) ① **440 337-2ZH**
Concerto for Piano and Orchestra (1990)
P. M. Paul, American Cpsrs Orch, D. R. Davies
(r1992) *Concert* (8/94) (ARGO) ① **440 337-2ZH**

SECTION II: CHAMBER

Variations for Flute and Piano (1981)
P. Robison, T. Hester *Concert*
(11/90) (MMAS) ① **MMD 60195A**

SECTION IV: VOCAL AND CHORAL

7 Deadly Sins—bass and orchestra (1984)
(Wds. A Hecht)
1. Pride; 2. Envy; 3. Wrath; 4. Sloth; 5. Avarice; 6.
Gluttony; 7. Lust.
J. Opalach, American Cpsrs Orch, D. R. Davies
(r1992) *Concert* (8/94) (ARGO) ① **440 337-2ZH**

BEATRIZ, Comtessa de Dia *(fl late 12th Cent)* France

SECTION IV: VOCAL AND CHORAL

A chanter m'er de so qu'eu no
volria—chanson
M. Kiek *Concert* (6/88) (HYPE) ① **CDA66283**
Sinfonye, S. Wishart (r1992; Estampie arr Wishart)
Concert (8/93) (HYPE) ① **CDA66625**
Estat ai en greu cossirier—trobairitz canso
Sinfonye, S. Wishart (r1992) *Concert*
(8/93) (HYPE) ① **CDA66625**

BEAVER, Jack *(1900–1963)* England

SECTION I: ORCHESTRAL

Sovereign Heritage—symphonic overture
(1930s)
Black Dyke Mills Band, G. Brand (arr F. Wright)
Concert (9/93) (RSR) ① **RSRD1002**

SECTION V: STAGE WORKS

The **Thirty Nine Steps**—film score (1935)
(collab with Louis Levy)
EXCERPTS: 1. The Thirty Nine Steps; 2. Highland
Hotel; 3. Mr Memory; 4. Finale.
1-4. Prague City PO, P. Bateman (recons & orch
Philip Lane) *Concert* (9/95) (SILV) ① **FILMCD159**

BECHGAARD, Julius *(1843–1917)* Denmark

SECTION IV: VOCAL AND CHORAL

A Sailor's Farewell—song
L. Melchior, Anon (pf) (r1913: HMV) *Concert*
(8/88) (DANA) ① [2] **DACOCD311/2**
L. Melchior, Orch (r1913: Odeon) *Concert*
(8/88) (DANA) ① [2] **DACOCD311/2**

BECK, Conrad *(b 1901)* Switzerland

SECTION III: INSTRUMENTAL

3 Epigramme für Paul Sacher—cello (1975)
P. Demenga (r1993) *Concert*
(8/95) (ECM) ① [2] **445 234-2**
Foxtrot—piano
M. Fingerhut *Concert* (9/88) (CHAN) ① **CHAN8578**

BECKER, John *(1886–1961)* USA

SECTION IV: VOCAL AND CHORAL

Frühlingszeit—song
E. Schumann-Heink, orch (r1907) *Concert*
(2/91) (NIMB) ① **NI7811**

BECKETT, Walter *(b 1914)* Ireland

SECTION II: CHAMBER

String Quartet No. 1 (1980)
Vanbrugh Qt (r1993) *Concert*
(10/94) (CHAN) ① **CHAN9295**

BEDFORD, David (Vickerman) *(b 1937)* England

SECTION II: CHAMBER

Fridiol Kennings—saxophone quartet and
percussion (1980)
Apollo Sax Qt, M. Hamnett (r1993) *Concert*
(8/95) (ARGO) ① **443 903-2ZH**

SECTION IV: VOCAL AND CHORAL

Even Now—song: 1v, 2 cls,va, vc & db (1990)
(Wds. E Dowson)
M. Wiegold, Composers Ens, D. Muldowney *Concert*
(4/92) (NMC) ① **NMCD003**

BEDYNGHAM, Johannes *(d c1459/60)* England

SECTION IV: VOCAL AND CHORAL

Gentil madonna, de non
m'abandonare—lauda (in Mellon Chaçonnier.
Wds. Giustiniani)
Daedalus Ens (r1992) *Concert*
(11/93) (ACCE) ① **ACC9289D**

BEETHOVEN, Ludwig van *(1770–1827)* Germany

Works with opus numbers are identified by
Kinsky's Thematic Catalogue

SECTION I: ORCHESTRAL

Concerto for Piano and Orchestra in D, Op.
61 (1807) (arr cpsr from Violin Concerto)
D. Barenboim (pf/dir), ECO *Romances.*
(4/90) (DG) ① **429 179-2GGA**
Concerto for Piano and Orchestra in E flat,
WoO4 (1784) (orch Willy Hess from surviving
piano part & orchestral cues)
L. Grychtolowna, Folkwang CO, H. Dressel (r c1966)
Concert (8/95) (PHIL) ① [2] **442 580-2PM2**
Concerto for Piano and Orchestra No. 1 in C,
Op. 15 (1797)
R. Serkin, Boston SO, S. Ozawa *Concert*
(5/85) (TELA) ① [3] **CD80061**
M. Perahia, Concertgebouw, B. Haitink *Piano
Concerto 2.* (4/87) (SONY) ① **SK42177**
C. Ortiz, CLS, R. Hickox *Piano Concerto 1.*
(8/87) (CARL) ① **PCD854**
D. Barenboim (pf/dir), BPO *Concert*
(12/87) (EMI) ① [3] **CDS7 47974-8**
A.B. Michelangeli, Vienna SO, C.M. Giulini (r1979)
Piano Sonata 4. (2/88) (DG) ① **419 248-2GH**
W. Kempff, BPO, F. Leitner *Piano Concerto 2.*
(9/88) (DG) ① **419 856-2GGA**
A. Brendel, LPO, B. Haitink (r1975) *Piano Concerto
2.* (9/88) (PHIL) ① **420 882-2PSL**
M. Pollini, VPO, E. Jochum (pp1982) *Concert*
(1/89) (DG) ① [3] **419 793-2GH3**
C. Arrau, Staatskapelle Dresden, Colin Davis *Concert*
(1/89) (PHIL) ① [3] **422 149-2PH3**
W. Kempff, BPO, F. Leitner *Concert*
(1/89) (DG) ① [3] **427 237-2GX3**
Vladimir Ashkenazy (pf/dir), Cleveland Orch *Concert*
(3/89) (DECC) ① [3] **421 718-2DH3**
Vladimir Ashkenazy (pf/dir), Cleveland Orch *Piano
Concerto 2.* (3/89) (DECC) ① **433 320-2DH**
D. Barenboim, New Philh, O. Klemperer *Concert*
(3/90) (EMI) ① [3] **CMS7 63360-2**
S. Vladar, Capella Istropolitana, B. Wordsworth *Piano
Rondo, WoO6.* (12/90) (NAXO) ① **8 550190**
C. Arrau, Philh, A. Galliera *Concert*
(1/92) (EMI) ① [5] **CZS7 67379-2**
L. Bernstein (pf/dir), NYPO (r1960) *Mozart: Piano
Concerto 25.* (11/92) (SONY) ① **SMK47519**

A. Dorfman, NBC SO, A. Toscanini (r1945) *Piano
Concerto 4.* (11/92) (RCA) ① **GD60268**
K. Zimerman (pf/dir), VPO (r1991) *Concert*
(11/92) (DG) ① [3] **435 467-2GH3**
K. Zimerman (pf/dir), VPO (r1991) *Piano Concerto 2.*
(11/92) (DG) ① **437 545-2GH**
J. Lill, CBSO, W. Weller *Concert*
(1/93) (CHAN) ① [3] **CHAN9084/6**
Emil Gilels, Czech PO, K. Sanderling (bp1958)
Concert (4/93) (MULT) ① [3] **310106-2**
W. Kempff, BPO, P. Van Kempen (r1953) *Concert*
(4/93) (DG) ① [3] **435 744-2GDO3**
G. Gould, Columbia SO, V. Golschmann *Concert*
(4/93) (SONY) ① [3] **SM3K52632**
A. Rubinstein, Sym of the Air, J. Krips *Concert*
(4/93) (RCA) ① [3] **09026 61260-2**
Solomon, Philh, H. Menges (r1956) *Concert*
(9/93) (EMI) ① [2] **CZS7 67735-2**
A. de Larrocha, LSO, M. Tilson Thomas (r1992)
Concert (12/93) (RCA) ① **09026 61677-2**
A. de Larrocha, LSO, M. Tilson Thomas (r1992)
Piano Sonata 15. (12/93) (RCA) ① **09026 61676-2**
M. Pollini, BPO, C. Abbado (pp1992) *Concert*
(1/94) (DG) ① [3] **439 770-2GH3**
S. Richter, Schleswig-Holstein Music Fest Orch, C.
Eschenbach (pp1988) *Chopin: Etudes.*
(6/94) (DG) ① **09026 61534-2**
M. Argerich, Philh, G. Sinopoli (r1985) *Piano
Concerto 2.* (12/94) (DG) ① **445 504-2GMA**
W. Gieseking, Berlin St Op Orch, H. Rosbaud (r1937)
Concert (5/95) (APR) ① **APR5511**
S. Kovacevich, BBC SO, Colin Davis (r1970) *Concert*
(8/95) (PHIL) ① [2] **442 577-2PM2**
Concerto for Piano and Orchestra No. 2 in B
flat, Op. 19 (1793 rev 1794-95)
M. Pollini, VPO, E. Jochum *Piano Concerto 4.*
(10/84) (DG) ① **413 445-2GH**
R. Serkin, Boston SO, S. Ozawa *Concert*
(5/85) (TELA) ① [3] **CD80061**
M. Perahia, Concertgebouw, B. Haitink *Piano
Concerto 1.* (4/87) (SONY) ① **SK42177**
E. Westenholz, Copenhagen Collegium Musicum, M.
Schønwandt *Piano Concerto 4.*
(8/87) (BIS) ① **BIS-CD349**
C. Ortiz, CLS, R. Hickox *Piano Concerto 1.*
(8/87) (CARL) ① **PCD854**
D. Barenboim (pf/dir), BPO *Concert*
(12/87) (EMI) ① [3] **CDS7 47974-8**
W. Kempff, BPO, F. Leitner *Piano Concerto 1.*
(9/88) (DG) ① **419 856-2GGA**
A. Brendel, LPO, B. Haitink (r1977) *Piano Concerto
1.* (9/88) (PHIL) ① **420 882-2PSL**
M. Pollini, VPO, E. Jochum *Concert*
(1/89) (DG) ① [3] **419 793-2GH3**
C. Arrau, Staatskapelle Dresden, Colin Davis *Concert*
(1/89) (PHIL) ① [3] **422 149-2PH3**
W. Kempff, BPO, F. Leitner *Concert*
(1/89) (DG) ① [3] **427 237-2GX3**
Vladimir Ashkenazy (pf/dir), Cleveland Orch *Concert*
(3/89) (DECC) ① [3] **421 718-2DH3**
Vladimir Ashkenazy (pf/dir), Cleveland Orch *Piano
Concerto 1.* (3/89) (DECC) ① **433 320-2DH**
D. Barenboim, New Philh, O. Klemperer *Concert*
(3/90) (EMI) ① [3] **CMS7 63360-2**
S. Vladar, Capella Istropolitana, B. Wordsworth *Piano
Concerto 5.* (10/90) (NAXO) ① **8 550121**
C. Arrau, Philh, A. Galliera *Concert*
(1/92) (EMI) ① [5] **CZS7 67379-2**
K. Zimerman (pf/dir), VPO (r1991) *Concert*
(11/92) (DG) ① [3] **435 467-2GH3**
K. Zimerman (pf/dir), VPO (r1991) *Piano Concerto 1.*
(11/92) (DG) ① **437 545-2GH**
J. Lill, CBSO, W. Weller *Concert*
(1/93) (CHAN) ① [3] **CHAN9084/6**
Emil Gilels, Czech PO, K. Sanderling (bp1958)
Concert (4/93) (MULT) ① [3] **310106-2**
W. Kempff, BPO, P. Van Kempen (r1953) *Concert*
(4/93) (DG) ① [3] **435 744-2GDO3**
G. Gould, Columbia SO, L. Bernstein (r1957) *Concert*
(4/93) (SONY) ① [3] **SM3K52632**
A. Rubinstein, Sym of the Air, J. Krips *Concert*
(4/93) (RCA) ① **09026 61260-2**
A. Schnabel, Philh, I. Dobroven (r1946) *Piano
Concerto 5.* (3/94) (TEST) ① **SBT1020**
M. Pollini, BPO, C. Abbado (pp1992) *Concert*
(6/94) (DG) ① [3] **439 770-2GH3**
M. Kazakevich, ECO, C. Mackerras (r1993: ed B
Cooper) *Piano Concerto 4.*
(10/94) (CONI) ① **CDCF237**
M. Argerich, Philh, G. Sinopoli (r1985) *Piano
Concerto 1.* (12/94) (DG) ① **445 504-2GMA**
S. Kovacevich, BBC SO, Colin Davis (r1974) *Concert*
(8/95) (PHIL) ① [2] **442 577-2PM2**
T. Fellner, ASMF, N. Marriner (r1994) *Piano
Concerto 3.* (9/95) (ERAT) ① **4509-98539-2**

Solomon, Philh, A. Cluytens (r1952) Concert
(11/95) (EMI) ① [2] CHS5 65503-2

Concerto for Piano and Orchestra No. 3 in C minor, Op. 37 (?1800)

R. Serkin, Boston SO, S. Ozawa (r1982) Choral Fantasia.
(12/83) (TELA) ① CD80063
R. Serkin, Boston SO, S. Ozawa Concert
(5/85) (TELA) ① [3] CD80061
D. Barenboim (pf/dir), BPO Concert
(12/87) (EMI) ① [3] CDS7 47974-8
A.B. Michelangeli, Vienna SO, C.M. Giulini (pp1979)
(2/88) (DG) ① 423 230-2GH
C. Ortiz, CLS, R. Hickox Piano Concerto 4.
(4/88) (CARL) ① PCD879
Vladimir Ashkenazy, Chicago SO, G. Solti Piano Concerto 4.
(5/88) (DECC) ① 417 740-2DM
A. Brendel, LPO, B. Haitink Piano Concerto 4.
(5/88) (PHIL) ① 420 861-2PSL
M. Pollini, VPO, K. Böhm Concert
(1/89) (DG) ① [3] 419 793-2GH3
W. Kempff, BPO, F. Leitner Concert
(1/89) (DG) ① [3] 427 237-2GX3
C. Arrau, Staatskapelle Dresden, Colin Davis Concert
(1/89) (PHIL) ① [3] 422 149-2PH3
Vladimir Ashkenazy (pf/dir), Cleveland Orch Concert
(3/89) (DECC) ① [3] 421 718-2DH3
Vladimir Ashkenazy (pf/dir), Cleveland Orch Piano Concerto 4.
(3/89) (DECC) ① 433 321-2DH
S. Kovacevich, BBC SO, Colin Davis Piano Concerto 4.
(12/89) (PHIL) ① 426 062-2PCC
D. Barenboim, New Philh, O. Klemperer Concert
(3/90) (EMI) ① [3] CMS7 63360-2
RPO, Vladimir Ashkenazy (pf/dir) (pp1989) Concert
(5/90) (RPO) ① CDRPO7014
S. Vladar, Capella Istropolitana, B. Wordsworth Piano Concerto 4.
(10/90) (NAXO) ① 8 550122
A. Rubinstein, NBC SO, A. Toscanini (pp1944) Violin Concerto.
(1/91) (RCA) ① GD60261
C. Arrau, Philh, A. Galliera Concert
(1/92) (EMI) ① [5] CZS7 67373-2
R. Serkin, NYPO, L. Bernstein (r1964) Piano Concerto 5.
(11/92) (SONY) ① SMK47520
K. Zimerman, VPO, L. Bernstein (pp1989) Concert
(11/92) (DG) ① [3] 435 467-2GH3
J. Lill, CBSO, W. Weller Concert
(1/93) (CHAN) ① [3] CHAN9084/6
Emil Gilels, Czech PO, K. Sanderling (bp1958) Concert
(4/93) (MULT) ① [3] 310106-2
W. Kempff, BPO, P. Van Kempen (r1953) Concert
(4/93) (DG) ① [3] 435 744-2GDO3
G. Gould, Columbia SO, L. Bernstein (r1959) Concert
(4/93) (SONY) ① SM3K3632
A. Rubinstein, Sym of the Air, J. Krips Concert
(4/93) (RCA) ① [3] 09026 61260-2
Vladimir Ashkenazy, VPO, Z. Mehta (r1983) Concert
(7/93) (DECC) ① 436 471-2DM
Solomon, Philh, H. Menges (1956) Concert
(9/93) (EMI) ① [2] CZS7 67735-2
A. Schnabel, Philh, I. Dobroven (r1947) Piano Concerto 4.
(3/94) (TEST) ① SBT1021
M. Pollini, BPO, C. Abbado (pp1992) Concert
(6/94) (DG) ① [3] 439 770-2GH3
G. Gould, CBC SO, H. Unger (bp1955) Concert
(7/94) (CBC) ① PSCD2004
M. Hambourg, SO, M. Sargent (r1929) Concert
(6/95) (PEAR) ① GEMMCD9147
S. Kovacevich, BBC SO, Colin Davis (r1971) Concert
(8/95) (PHIL) ① [2] 442 577-2PM2
J. Katchen, LSO, P. Gamba (r1958) Concert
(9/95) (DECC) ① [2] 440 839-2DF2
T. Fellner, ASMF, N. Marriner (r1994) Piano Concerto 2.
(9/95) (ERAT) ① 4509-98539-2
C. Haskil, Lamoureux Concerts Orch, I. Markevitch (r1959) Concert
(11/95) (PHIL) ① [12] 442 685-2PM12
C. Haskil, Lamoureux Concerts Orch, I. Markevitch (r1959) Concert
(11/95) (PHIL) ① [4] 442 631-2PM4
Solomon, BBC SO, A. Boult (r1944) Concert
(11/95) (EMI) ① [2] CHS5 65503-2
Solomon, BBC SO, A. Boult (r1944) Piano Trios.
(11/95) (DUTT) ① CDLX7015

Concerto for Piano and Orchestra No. 4 in G, Op. 58 (1805-6)

1. Allegro moderato; 2. Andante con moto; 3. Rondo (Vivace).

M. Pollini, VPO, K. Böhm Piano Concerto 2.
(10/84) (DG) ① 413 445-2GH
R. Serkin, Boston SO, S. Ozawa Concert
(5/85) (TELA) ① [3] CD80061
C. Rosenberger, LSO, G. Schwarz Symphony 5.
(9/86) (DELO) ① DE3027
E. Westenholz, Copenhagen Collegium Musicum, M. Schønwandt Piano Concerto 2.
(8/87) (BIS) ① BIS-CD349

D. Barenboim (pf/dir), BPO Concert
(12/87) (EMI) ① [3] CDS7 47974-8
C. Ortiz, CLS, R. Hickox Piano Concerto 3.
(4/88) (CARL) ① PCD879
Vladimir Ashkenazy, Chicago SO, G. Solti Piano Concerto 3.
(5/88) (DECC) ① 417 740-2DM
A. Brendel, LPO, B. Haitink Piano Concerto 3.
(5/88) (PHIL) ① 420 861-2PSL
M. Pollini, VPO, K. Böhm Concert
(1/89) (DG) ① [3] 419 793-2GH3
C. Arrau, Staatskapelle Dresden, Colin Davis Concert
(1/89) (PHIL) ① [3] 422 149-2PH3
W. Kempff, BPO, F. Leitner Concert
(1/89) (DG) ① [3] 427 237-2GX3
Vladimir Ashkenazy (pf/dir), Cleveland Orch Concert
(3/89) (DECC) ① [3] 421 718-2DH3
Vladimir Ashkenazy (pf/dir), Cleveland Orch Concert
(3/89) (DECC) ① 433 321-2DH
S. Kovacevich, BBC SO, Colin Davis Piano Concerto 3.
(12/89) (PHIL) ① 426 062-2PCC
D. Barenboim, New Philh, O. Klemperer Concert
(3/90) (EMI) ① [3] CMS7 63360-2
S. Vladar, Capella Istropolitana, B. Wordsworth Piano Concerto 3.
(10/90) (NAXO) ① 8 550122
Vladimir Ashkenazy, VPO, Z. Mehta Piano Concerto 5.
(8/91) (DECC) ① 430 704-2DM
G. Bachauer, LSO, A. Dorati Piano Concerto 5.
(11/91) (MERC) ① 432 018-2MM
C. Arrau, Philh, A. Galliera (r1955) Concert
(1/92) (EMI) ① [5] CZS7 67373-2
R. Serkin, NBC SO, A. Toscanini (pp1944) Piano Concerto 1.
(11/92) (RCA) ① GD60268
K. Zimerman, VPO, L. Bernstein (pp1989) Concert
(11/92) (DG) ① [3] 435 467-2GH3
J. Lill, CBSO, W. Weller Concert
(1/93) (CHAN) ① [3] CHAN9084/6
Emil Gilels, Czech PO, K. Sanderling (bp1958) Concert
(4/93) (MULT) ① [3] 310106-2
W. Kempff, BPO, P. Van Kempen (r1953) Concert
(4/93) (DG) ① [3] 435 744-2GDO3
G. Gould, NYPO, L. Bernstein (r1961) Concert
(4/93) (SONY) ① SM3K3632
A. Rubinstein, Sym of the Air, J. Krips Concert
(4/93) (RCA) ① [3] 09026 61260-2
A. Schnabel, Philh, I. Dobroven (r1946) Piano Concerto 3.
(3/94) (TEST) ① SBT1021
M. Pollini, BPO, C. Abbado (pp1992) Concert
(6/94) (DG) ① [3] 439 770-2GH3
M. Kazakevich, ECO, C. Mackerras (r1993: ed B Cooper) Piano Concerto 2.
(10/94) (CONI) ① CDCF237
F. Ts'ong, Sinfonia Varsovia, J. Swoboda Haydn: Keyboard Concerto, HobXVIII/11.
(11/94) (CARL) ① MCD87
E. Ax, RPO, A. Previn (r1986) Piano Concerto 5.
(1/95) (RCA) ① 74321 17890-2
W. Kempff, BPO, F. Leitner (r1961) Piano Concerto 5.
(5/95) (DG) ① [2] 447 402-2GOR
S. Kovacevich, BBC SO, Colin Davis (r1974) Concert
(8/95) (PHIL) ① [2] 442 577-2PM2
J. Katchen, LSO, P. Gamba (r1963) Concert
(9/95) (DECC) ① [2] 440 839-2DF2
Solomon, Philh, A. Cluytens (1952) Concert
(11/95) (EMI) ① [2] CHS5 65503-2
1. R. Serkin, Danish RSO, F. Busch (bp1933) Concert
(8/92) (DANA) ① DACOCD303

Concerto for Piano and Orchestra No. 5 in E flat, 'Emperor', Op. 73 (1809)

1. Allegro; 2. Adagio un poco mosso; 3. Rondo (Allegro).

R. Serkin, Boston SO, S. Ozawa (r1981)
(12/83) (TELA) ① CD80065
M. Pollini, VPO, K. Böhm
(11/84) (DG) ① 413 447-2GH
R. Serkin, Boston SO, S. Ozawa Concert
(5/85) (TELA) ① [3] CD80061
C. Arrau, Staatskapelle Dresden, Colin Davis
(8/86) (PHIL) ① 416 215-2PH
M. Perahia, Concertgebouw, B. Haitink
(11/87) (SONY) ① SK42330
D. Barenboim (pf/dir), BPO Concert
(12/87) (EMI) ① [3] CDS7 47974-8
W. Kempff, BPO, F. Leitner Piano Sonata 32.
(12/87) (DG) ① 419 468-2GGA
A.B. Michelangeli, Vienna SO, C.M. Giulini (pp1979)
(2/88) (DG) ① 419 249-2GH
Edwin Fischer, Philh, W. Furtwängler (r1951) Piano Sonata 7.
(3/88) (EMI) ① CDH7 61005-2
C. Ortiz, CLS, R. Hickox (r1987) Piano Sonata 21.
(8/88) (CARL) ① PCD895
M. Pollini, VPO, K. Böhm Concert
(1/89) (DG) ① [3] 419 793-2GH3
C. Arrau, Staatskapelle Dresden, Colin Davis Concert
(1/89) (PHIL) ① [3] 422 149-2PH3
W. Kempff, BPO, F. Leitner Concert
(1/89) (DG) ① [3] 427 237-2GX3

Vladimir Ashkenazy (pf/dir), Cleveland Orch Concert
(3/89) (DECC) ① [3] 421 718-2DH3
Vladimir Ashkenazy (pf/dir), Cleveland Orch Fantasia.
(3/89) (DECC) ① 433 322-2DH
S. Kovacevich, LSO, Colin Davis (r1969) Piano Sonata 30.
(12/89) (PHIL) ① 422 482-2PCC
D. Barenboim, New Philh, O. Klemperer Concert
(3/90) (EMI) ① [3] CMS7 63360-2
M. Tan, LCP, R. Norrington (r1989) Choral Fantasia.
(4/90) (EMI) ① CDC7 49965-2
S. Vladar, Capella Istropolitana, B. Wordsworth Piano Concerto 2.
(10/90) (NAXO) ① 8 550121
S. Vladar, Capella Istropolitana, B. Wordsworth Piano Sonata 15.
(10/90) (NAXO) ① 8 550290
A. Dikov, Sofia PO, E. Tabakov Concert
(10/90) (LASE) ① 15 523
V. Horowitz, RCA Victor SO, F. Reiner (r1952) Tchaikovsky: Piano Concerto 1.
(12/90) (RCA) ① GD87992
Vladimir Ashkenazy, VPO, Z. Mehta Piano Concerto 4.
(8/91) (DECC) ① 430 704-2DM
L. Fleisher, Cleveland Orch, G. Szell Triple Concerto.
(8/91) (SONY) ① SBK46549
B. Moiseiwitsch, LPO, G. Szell (r1938) Concert
(1/91) (KOCH) ① 37035-2
G. Bachauer, LSO, S. Skrowaczewski Piano Concerto 4.
(11/91) (MERC) ① 432 018-2MM
C. Eschenbach, Boston SO, S. Ozawa Concert
(12/91) (DG) ① [2] 413 145-2GW2
C. Arrau, Philh, A. Galliera Concert
(1/92) (EMI) ① [5] CZS7 67373-2
S. Kovacevich (pf/dir), Australian CO Grosse Fuge.
(3/92) (EMIN) ① CD-EMX2184
A. Brendel, LPO, B. Haitink Choral Fantasia.
(7/92) (PHIL) ① 434 148-2PM
R. Serkin, NYPO, L. Bernstein (r1962) Piano Concerto 3.
(11/92) (SONY) ① SMK47520
K. Zimerman, VPO, L. Bernstein (pp1989) Concert
(11/92) (DG) ① [3] 435 467-2GH3
J. Lill, CBSO, W. Weller Concert
(1/93) (CHAN) ① [3] CHAN9084/6
Emil Gilels, Czech PO, K. Sanderling (bp1958) Concert
(4/93) (MULT) ① [3] 310106-2
W. Kempff, BPO, P. Van Kempen (r1953) Concert
(4/93) (DG) ① [3] 435 744-2GDO3
G. Gould, American SO, L. Stokowski Concert
(4/93) (SONY) ① [3] SM3K3632
A. Rubinstein, Sym of the Air, J. Krips Concert
(4/93) (RCA) ① [3] 09026 61260-2
A. Benedetti-Michelangeli, Prague SO, V. Smetáček (pp1957) Symphony 4.
(10/93) (PRAG) ① PR250 021
A. Schnabel, Philh, A. Galliera (r1947) Piano Concerto 2.
(3/94) (TEST) ① SBT1020
M. Pollini, BPO, C. Abbado (pp1993) Concert
(6/94) (DG) ① [3] 439 770-2GH3
Edwin Fischer, Staatskapelle Dresden, K. Böhm (r1939) Piano Sonata 31.
(12/94) (DANT) ① HPC007
E. Ax, RPO, A. Previn (r1986) Piano Concerto 4.
(1/95) (RCA) ① 74321 17890-2
W. Gieseking, Berlin RO, A. Rother (r1944) Schumann: Piano Concerto.
(5/95) (MUSI) ① MACD-815
W. Kempff, BPO, F. Leitner (r1961) Piano Concerto 4.
(5/95) (DG) ① [2] 447 402-2GOR
S. Kovacevich, LSO, Colin Davis (r1969) Concert
(8/95) (PHIL) ① [2] 442 580-2PM2
J. Katchen, LSO, P. Gamba (r1963) Concert
(9/95) (DECC) ① [2] 440 839-2DF2
A.B. Michelangeli, Rome RAI Orch, M. Freccia (pp1960) Concert
(10/95) (MEMR) ① [4] 999001
Solomon, Philh, H. Menges (1956) Concert
(11/95) (EMI) ① [2] CHS5 65503-2

Concerto for Piano and Orchestra in C, WoO5 (1800) (sketch)

G. Kremer, LSO, E. Tchakarov Concert
(1/91) (DG) ① 431 168-2GGA

Concerto for Violin and Orchestra in D, Op. 61 (1806)

1. Allegro ma non troppo; 2. Larghetto; 3. Rondo (Allegro).

I. Perlman, Philh, C.M. Giulini
(2/84) (EMI) ① CDC7 47002-2
A-S. Mutter, BPO, H. von Karajan (r1979)
(5/85) (DG) ① 413 818-2GH
J-J. Kantorow, Netherlands CO, A. Ros-Marbà
(6/86) (DENO) ① C37-7508
A-S. Mutter, BPO, H. von Karajan Concert
(3/88) (DG) ① [4] 415 565-2GX4
S. Mintz, Philh, G. Sinopoli Romances.
(5/88) (DG) ① 423 064-2GH
F.P. Zimmermann, ECO, J. Tate Romances.
(7/88) (EMI) ① CDC7 49737-2
R. Thomas (vn/dir), Bournemouth Sinfonietta Romances.
(9/89) (CRD) ① CRD3353

Y. Menuhin, Philh, W. Furtwängler (r1953)
Mendelssohn: Violin Concerto, Op.64.
(10/89) (EMI) ① **CDH7 69799-2**
W. Schneiderhan, BPO, E. Jochum *Romances.*
(10/89) (DG) ① **427 197-2GR**
A. Grumiaux, Concertgebouw, Colin Davis
Romances. (11/89) (PHIL) ① **420 348-2PM**
A. Grumiaux, New Philh, A. Galliera *Romances.*
(11/89) (PHIL) ① **426 064-2PCC**
I. Perlman, BPO, D. Barenboim (pp1986) *Romances.*
(11/89) (EMI) ① **CDC7 49567-2**
J. Heifetz, NBC SO, A. Toscanini (r1940) *Piano
Concerto 3.* (1/91) (RCA) ① **GD60261**
M. Szenthelyi, Hungarian St. Orch, G. Györiványi-
Ráth *Concert* (3/91) (LASE) ① **15 515**
J. Szigeti, British SO, B. Walter (r1932) *Concert*
(10/91) (MSCM) ① **MM30272**
Y. Menuhin, VPO, C. Silvestri *Concert*
(11/91) (EMI) ① **[3] CZS7 67310-2**
W. Schneiderhan, BPO, E. Jochum *Concert*
(12/91) (DG) ① **[2] 413 145-2GW2**
Scottish CO, J. Laredo (vn/dir) *Romances.*
(4/92) (CARL) ① **PCD977**
K-W. Chung, Concertgebouw, K. Tennstedt (pp1989)
Bruch: Violin Concerto 1.
(6/92) (EMI) ① **CDC7 54072-2**
F. Kreisler, Berlin St Op Orch, L. Blech (r1926)
Concert (9/92) (BIDD) ① **[2] LAB049/50**
I. Stern, NYPO, L. Bernstein (r1959) *Concert*
(11/92) (SONY) ① **SMK47521**
Vanessa-Mae, LSO, K. Bakels *Tchaikovsky: Violin
Concerto.* (11/92) (TRIT) ① **TCMA27103**
P. Zukerman, Los Angeles PO, Z. Mehta *Violin
Sonata 10.* (11/92) (RCA) ① **09026 61219-2**
O. Shumsky, Philh, A. Davis *Romances.*
(12/92) (ASV) ① **CDQS6080**
N. Kennedy, N German RSO, K. Tennstedt (pp1992)
Bach: Solo Violin Partitas and Sonatas.
(12/92) (EMI) ① **CDC7 54574-2**
K-W. Chung, VPO, K. Kondrashin *Mendelssohn:
Violin Concerto, Op. 64.*
(2/93) (DECC) ① **430 752-2DM**
F. Kreisler, Berlin St Op Orch, L. Blech (r1926)
Concert (9/93) (PEAR) ① **GEMMCDS9996**
L. Kogan, Paris Cons, C. Silvestri (r1959) *Concert*
(9/93) (EMI) ① **[2] CZS7 67732-2**
G. Kulenkampff, BPO, H. Schmidt-Isserstedt (r1936)
Bruch: Violin Concerto 1.
(11/93) (TELD) ① **9031-76443-2**
G. Kremer, COE, N. Harnoncourt *Romances.*
(12/93) (TELD) ① **9031-74881-2**
S. Chase, Hanover Band, R. Goodman (r1992)
Romances. (12/93) (CALA) ① **CACD1013**
D. Sitkovetsky, ASMF, N. Marriner (r1991)
Romances. (3/94) (VIRG) ① **VC5 45001-2**
I. Perlman, Philh, C.M. Giulini (r1980) *Concert*
(4/94) (EMI) ① **[3] CMS7 64922-2**
M. Huggett, OAE, C. Mackerras (r1992)
Mendelssohn: Violin Concerto, Op.64.
(4/94) (EMIN) ① **CD-EMX2217**
N. Milstein, Philh, E. Leinsdorf (r1961) *Concert*
(6/94) (EMI) ① **[6] ZDMF7 64830-2**
D. Oistrakh, Stockholm Fest Orch, S. Ehrling (r1954)
Sibelius: Violin Concerto.
(7/94) (TEST) ① **SBT1032**
H. Szeryng, Concertgebouw, B. Haitink *Romances.*
(9/94) (PHIL) ① **442 398-2PM**
A. Grumiaux, Concertgebouw, Colin Davis (r1974)
Concert (9/94) (PHIL) ① **[2] 442 287-2PM2**
J-P. Wallez, Lille Nat Orch, J-C. Casadesus (r1985)
Romances. (9/94) (FORL) ① **FF054**
J. Heifetz, Boston SO, C. Munch (r1955) *Concert*
(11/94) (RCA) ① **[65] 09026 61778-2(11-15)**
J. Heifetz, NBC SO, A. Toscanini (r1940) *Concert*
(11/94) (RCA) ① **[65] 09026 61778-2(05)**
S. Accardo, Milan La Scala PO, C.M. Giulini (r1992)
(1/95) (SONY) ① **SK53287**
I. Perlman, BPO, D. Barenboim (pp1986) *Concert*
(6/95) (EMI) ① **[20] CZS4 83177-2(1)**
H. Krebbers, Concertgebouw, B. Haitink (r1974)
Concert (8/95) (PHIL) ① **[2] 442 580-2PM2**
A. Campoli, LSO, J. Krips (r1952) *Bruch: Scottish
Fantasy.* (9/95) (BEUL) ① **2PD10**
W. Schneiderhan, BPO, E. Jochum (r1962) *Mozart:
Violin Concerto, K219.*
(9/95) (DG) ① **447 403-2GOR**
J. Heifetz, NBC SO, A. Toscanini (r1940) *Concert*
(11/95) (PEAR) ① **[2] GEMMCDS9157**
3(pt) C. Flesch, orch (r1930s) *Concert*
(8/90) (SYMP) ① **SYMCD1071**
**Concerto for Violin, Cello, Piano and
Orchestra in C, Op. 56 (1803-04)**
A-S. Mutter, Y-Y. Ma, M. Zeltser, BPO, H. von
Karajan (r1979) *Concert*
(8/85) (DG) ① **415 276-2GH**

U. Hoelscher, H. Schiff, C. Zacharias, Leipzig
Gewandhaus, K. Masur *Romances.*
(5/87) (EMI) ① **CDC7 47427-2**
C. Funke, J. Timm, P. Rösel, Dresden PO, H. Kegel
Choral Fantasia. (9/87) (CAPR) ① **10 150**
J-J. Kantorow, M. Fujiwara, J. Rouvier, Netherlands
CO, E. Krivine *Romances.*
(9/87) (DENO) ① **CO-1407**
Zingara Trio, ECO, H. Eath (r1988) *Boccherini:
Cello Concerto, G480.* (6/89) (CARL) ① **PCD917**
Barcelona Trio, ECO, E. Colomer *Piano Trios.*
(10/89) (HARM) ① **HMP 3905205**
R. Serkin, J. Laredo, L. Parnas, Marlboro Fest Orch,
A. Schneider *Brahms: Double Concerto.*
(11/89) (SONY) ① **MPK44842**
Suk Trio, Czech PO, K. Masur *Piano Trios.*
(5/90) (SUPR) ① **11 0707-2**
W. Schneiderhan, P. Fournier, G. Anda, Berlin RSO,
F. Fricsay (r1960) *Brahms: Double Concerto.*
(12/90) (DG) ① **429 934-2GDO**
H. Szeryng, J. Starker, C. Arrau, New Philh, E. Inbal
Brahms: Double Concerto.
(12/90) (PHIL) ① **426 631-2PSL**
I. Stern, L. Rose, E. Istomin, Philadelphia, E.
Ormandy *Piano Concerto 5.*
(8/91) (SONY) ① **SBK46549**
D. Oistrakh, M. Rostropovich, S. Richter, BPO, H.
von Karajan (r1969) *Brahms: Double Concerto.*
(7/93) (EMI) ① **CDM7 64744-2**
Beaux Arts Trio, Leipzig Gewandhaus, K. Masur
(r1992) *Choral Fantasia.*
(6/94) (PHIL) ① **438 005-2PH**
Fontenay Trio, Philh, E. Inbal (r1990) *Piano Trios.*
(7/95) (TELD) ① **4509-97447-2**
H. Szeryng, J. Starker, C. Arrau, New Philh, E. Inbal
(r1970) *Concert*
(8/95) (PHIL) ① **[2] 442 580-2PM2**
I. Perlman, Y-Y. Ma, D. Barenboim (pf/dir), BPO
(pp1995) *Choral Fantasia.*
(12/95) (EMI) ① **CDC5 55516-2**
**The Consecration of the House—overture to
Meisl's play, Op. 124 (1822)**
Philadelphia, R. Muti *Concert*
(1/89) (EMI) ① **[6] CDS7 49487-2**
NYPO, L. Bernstein (r1962) *Concert*
(11/92) (SONY) ① **SMK47521**
NBC SO, A. Toscanini (r1947) *Concert*
(11/92) (RCA) ① **GD60267**
BPO, P. van Kempen (r1953) *Concert*
(3/94) (PHIL) ① **[2] 438 533-2PM2**
Leipzig Gewandhaus, K. Masur (r1974) *Concert*
(5/94) (PHIL) ① **[2] 438 706-2PM2**
12 Contredanses, WoO14 (1802)
ASMF, N. Marriner (r1978) *Concert*
(5/94) (PHIL) ① **[2] 438 706-2PM2**
No 1 in C M. Elman, A. Loesser (arr Elman; r1921)
Concert (12/91) (APR) ① **[2] APR7015**
11 Contredanses, WoO17 (1819)
LPO, F. Weingartner (r1938) *Symphony 9.*
(5/91) (PEAR) ① **GEMMCD9407**
LPO, F. Weingartner (r1938) *Concert*
(11/93) (DUTT) ① **CDAX8005**
**Coriolan—overture to Von Collins' play, Op.
62 (1807)**
BPO, H. von Karajan (r1965) *Concert*
(8/85) (DG) ① **415 276-2GH**
VPO, C. Abbado (pp1985) *Symphony 3.*
(3/87) (DG) ① **419 597-2GH**
BPO, H. von Karajan *Concert*
(4/87) (DG) ① **415 833-2GGA**
LSO, W. Morris (1988) *Symphony 3.*
(12/88) (CARL) ① **PCD900**
Berlin St Op Orch, O. Klemperer (r1927) *Concert*
(2/89) (SYMP) ① **SYMCD1042**
VPO, L. Bernstein (pp1981) *Concert*
(3/89) (DG) ① **[6] 423 481-2GX6**
CBSO, W. Weller *Concert*
(5/89) (CHAN) ① **[6] CHAN8712/7**
VPO, C. Abbado (pp1985) *Concert*
(3/89) (DG) ① **[6] 427 306-2GH6**
LCP, R. Norrington *Concert*
(11/89) (EMI) ① **CDC7 49816-2**
Philh, H. von Karajan (r1953) *Concert*
(11/89) (EMI) ① **[6] CMS7 63310-2**
Dresden PO, H. Kegel *Concert*
(10/90) (LASE) ① **15 523**
VPO, K. Böhm *Concert*
(10/90) (DG) ① **429 509-2GR**
Chicago SO, G. Solti *Concert*
(4/92) (DECC) ① **[6] 430 792-2DC6**
NBC SO, A. Toscanini (r1945) *Concert*
(11/92) (RCA) ① **GD60267**
Chicago SO, F. Reiner (r1959) *Concert*
(12/92) (RCA) ① **09026 60962-2**
Leipzig Gewandhaus, K. Masur (r1973) *Concert*
(5/94) (PHIL) ① **[2] 438 706-2PM2**

Milan La Scala PO, C. M. Giulini (r1993) *Concert*
(5/94) (SONY) ① **SK53974**
LSO, B. Walter (r1938) *Concert*
(8/94) (DUTT) ① **CDLX7008**
VPO, L. Bernstein (pp1981) *Concert*
(12/94) (DG) ① **445 505-2GMA**
BPO, W. Furtwängler (pp1943) *Concert*
(3/95) (TAHR) ① **[4] FURT1004/7**
VPO, K. Böhm (r1971) *Concert*
(4/95) (DG) ① **[2] 437 368-2GX2**
BPO, H. von Karajan (r1965) *Symphony 9.*
(5/95) (DG) ① **447 401-2GOR**
Columbia SO, B. Walter (r1959) *Concert*
(8/95) (SONY) ① **SMK64460**
**Ecossaise in D—wind ensemble, WoO22
(1810)**
Berlin Phil Wind Qnt, H. Priem-Bergrath *Concert*
(10/87) (DG) ① **419 624-2GH**
**12 German Dances—orchestra, WoO8
(1795)**
EXCERPTS: 1. C; 2. A; 3. F; 4. B flat; 5. E flat; 6. G;
7. C; 8. A; 9. F; 10. D; 11. G; 12. C.
ASMF, N. Marriner (r1978) *Concert*
(5/94) (PHIL) ① **[2] 438 706-2PM2**
6. J. Heifetz, E. Bay (r1946) *Concert*
(11/94) (RCA) ① **[65] 09026 61778-2(06)**
**March in B flat—wind ensemble, WoO29
(1798)**
Berlin Phil Wind Qnt, H. Priem-Bergrath *Concert*
(10/87) (DG) ① **419 624-2GH**
Mozzafiato, C. Neidich (r1992/3) *Concert*
(8/94) (SONY) ① **SK53367**
March in D—wind ensemble, WoO24 (1816)
Berlin Phil Wind Qnt, H. Priem-Bergrath *Concert*
(10/87) (DG) ① **419 624-2GH**
March in F—wind ensemble, WoO19 (1810)
Berlin Phil Wind Qnt, H. Priem-Bergrath *Concert*
(10/87) (DG) ① **419 624-2GH**
**March in F, 'für die böhmische
Landwehr'—wind ensemble, WoO18 (1809)**
Berlin Phil Wind Qnt, H. Priem-Bergrath *Concert*
(10/87) (DG) ① **419 624-2GH**
Berlin Phil Wind Qnt, H. von Karajan (r1973: arr
Schade) *Concert* (8/93) (DG) ① **439 346-2GX2**
**March with Trio in C—wind ensemble,
WoO20 (before 1823)**
Berlin Phil Wind Qnt, H. Priem-Bergrath *Concert*
(10/87) (DG) ① **419 624-2GH**
12 Menuets, WoO7 (1795)
ASMF, N. Marriner (r1978) *Concert*
(5/94) (PHIL) ① **[2] 438 706-2PM2**
Namensfeier—overture, Op. 115 (1814-15)
(Eng: Name-Day)
Leipzig Gewandhaus, K. Masur (r1973) *Concert*
(5/94) (PHIL) ① **[2] 438 706-2PM2**
**Polonaise in D—wind ensemble, WoO21
(1810)**
Berlin Phil Wind Qnt, H. Priem-Bergrath *Concert*
(10/87) (DG) ① **419 624-2GH**
Romances—violin and orchestra
1. G, Op. 40 (c1802); 2. F, Op. 50 (c1798).
U. Hoelscher, Leipzig Gewandhaus, K. Masur *Triple
Concerto.* (5/87) (EMI) ① **CDC7 47427-2**
St. Paul CO, P.Zukerman (vn/dir) *Concert*
(11/87) (PHIL) ① **420 168-2PH**
S. Mintz, Philh, G. Sinopoli *Violin Concerto.*
(5/88) (DG) ① **423 064-2GH**
F.P. Zimmermann, J. Tate *Violin Concerto.*
(7/88) (EMI) ① **CDC7 49737-2**
R. Thomas (vn/dir), Bournemouth Sinfonietta *Violin
Concerto.* (9/89) (CRD) ① **CRD3353**
D. Oistrakh, RPO, E. Goossens *Violin Concerto.*
(10/89) (EMI) ① **427 197-2GR**
A. Grumiaux, New Philh, E. De Waart *Violin
Concerto.* (11/89) (PHIL) ① **420 348-2PM**
A. Grumiaux, Concertgebouw, B. Haitink *Violin
Concerto.* (11/89) (PHIL) ① **426 064-2PCC**
I. Perlman, BPO, D. Barenboim (r1986) *Violin
Concerto.* (11/89) (EMI) ① **CDC7 49567-2**
P. Zukerman, LPO, D. Barenboim *Piano Concerto,
Op.61.* (4/90) (DG) ① **429 179-2GGA**
M. Szenthelyi, Hungarian St. Orch, G. Györiványi-
Ráth *Concert* (3/91) (LASE) ① **15 515**
D. Oistrakh, RPO, E. Goossens *Concert*
(4/92) (CARL) ① **[2] 413 844-2GW2**
Scottish CO, J. Laredo (vn/dir) *Violin Concerto.*
(4/92) (CARL) ① **PCD977**
G. Kremer, COE, N. Harnoncourt *Violin Concerto.*
(12/93) (TELD) ① **9031-74881-2**
S. Chase, Hanover Band, R. Goodman *Violin
Concerto.* (12/93) (CALA) ① **CACD1013**
D. Sitkovetsky, ASMF, N. Marriner (r1991) *Violin
Concerto.* (3/94) (VIRG) ① **VC5 45001-2**
H. Szeryng, Concertgebouw, B. Haitink *Violin
Concerto.* (9/94) (PHIL) ① **442 398-2PM**

J-P. Wallez, Lille Nat Orch, J-C. Casadesus (r1985)
Violin Concerto. (11/94) (FORL) ① **FF054**
J. Heifetz, RCA Victor SO, W. Steinberg (r1951)
Concert (11/94) (RCA) ① [65] **09026 61778-2(08)**
S. Accardo, Milan La Scala PO, C.M. Giulini (r1992)
Violin Concerto. (1/95) (SONY) ① **SK53287**
D. Oistrakh, RPO, E. Goossens (r1961) *Concert*
(6/95) (DG) ① [2] **447 427-2GOR2**
A. Grumiaux, Concertgebouw, B. Haitink (r1960)
Concert (8/95) (PHIL) ① [2] **442 577-2PM2**
1. J-J. Kantorow, Netherlands CO, E. Krivine *Triple
Concerto.* (9/87) (DENO) ① **CO-1407**
1. G. Kremer, LSO, E. Tchakarov *Concert*
(1/91) (DG) ① **431 168-2GGA**
2. D. Oistrakh, Czech PO, K. Ančerl (r1954) *Concert*
(12/91) (SUPR) ① **11 0582-2**
2. W. Boskovsky (vn/dir), Vienna Mozart Ens (r1969)
Concert (5/92) (DECC) ① **433 220-2DWO**
2. O. Shumsky, Philh, A. Davis *Violin Concerto.*
(12/92) (ASV) ① **CDQS6080**
2. A. Grumiaux, Concertgebouw, B. Haitink (r1960)
Concert (9/94) (PHIL) ① [2] **442 287-2PM2**
2. H. Bean, BBC SO, A. Boult (pp1972) *Concert*
(3/95) (BBCR) ① **BBCRD9114**

Rondo in B flat—piano and orchestra, WoO6
(?1794) (orig finale of Pf Conc, Op 19)
S. Vladar, Capella Istropolitana, B. Wordsworth *Piano
Concerto 1.* (12/90) (NAXO) ① **8 550190**

Symphony No. 1 in C, Op. 21 (1800)
EXCERPTS: 1. Adagio molto—Allegro con brio; 2.
Andante cantabile con moto; 3. Menuetto; 4.
Adagio—Allegro molto e vivace.
Los Angeles CO, G. Schwarz *Concert*
(6/87) (DELO) ① **DE3013**
Dresden PO, H. Kegel *Concert*
(12/87) (CAPR) ① [5] **10 451/5**
BPO, H. von Karajan (r1975) *Concert*
(4/88) (DG) ① **419 048-2GGA**
LCP, R. Norrington *Symphony 6.*
(9/88) (EMI) ① **CDC7 49746-2**
Philadelphia, R. Muti *Concert*
(1/89) (EMI) ① [6] **CDS7 49487-2**
Hanover Band, M. Huggett *Concert*
(1/89) (NIMB) ① [5] **NI5144/8**
VPO, L. Bernstein (pp1977) *Concert*
(3/89) (DG) ① [6] **423 481-2GX6**
VPO, C. Abbado (pp1988) *Symphony 4.*
(5/89) (DG) ① **427 301-2GH**
FNO, C. Schuricht (pp1965) *Symphony 3.*
(5/89) (MONT) ① **TCE8841**
CBSO, W. Weller *Concert*
(5/89) (CHAN) ① [6] **CHAN8712/7**
Cleveland Orch, C. von Dohnányi (r1988) *Symphony
2.* (6/89) (TELA) ① **CD80187**
VPO, C. Abbado (pp1988) *Concert*
(9/89) (DG) ① [6] **427 306-2GH6**
BPO, H. von Karajan (r1961) *Concert*
(1/90) (DG) ① [5] **429 036-2GX5**
Philh, H. von Karajan (r1953) *Concert*
(1/90) (EMI) ① [5] **CMS7 63310-2**
NBC SO, A. Toscanini (r1951) *Concert*
(5/90) (RCA) ① [5] **GD60324**
Philh, O. Klemperer (r1957) *Symphony 7.*
(8/90) (EMI) ① **CDM7 63354-2**
COE, N. Harnoncourt (pp1990) *Concert*
(11/91) (TELD) ① [5] **2292-46452-2**
VPO, H. Schmidt-Isserstedt *Symphony 3.*
(1/92) (DECC) ① **433 619-2DSP**
Chicago SO, G. Solti *Concert*
(4/92) (DECC) ① [6] **430 792-2DC6**
Leningrad PO, E. Mravinsky (pp1983) *Symphony 3.*
(6/92) (ERAT) ① **2292-45759-2**
Leningrad PO, E. Mravinsky (pp1983) *Concert*
(6/92) (ERAT) ① [11] **2292-45763-2**
NYPO, L. Bernstein (r1964) *Symphony 3.*
(11/92) (SONY) ① **SMK47514**
Milan La Scala PO, C.M. Giulini (r1991) *Symphony 7.*
(12/92) (SONY) ① **SK48236**
Leipzig Gewandhaus, K. Masur *Concert*
(5/93) (PHIL) ① [5] **426 290-2PH5**
BBC SO, A. Toscanini (r1937) *Concert*
(5/94) (BIDD) ① [2] **WHL008/9**
Concertgebouw, B. Haitink (1987) *Concert*
(9/94) (PHIL) ① [5] **442 073-2PB5**
ORR, J.E. Gardiner (pp1993) *Symphony 3.*
(11/94) (ARCH) ① [5] **439 900-2AH5**
ORR, J.E. Gardiner (pp1993) *Symphony 2.*
(11/94) (ARCH) ① [5] **447 049-2AH**
NYPSO, W. Mengelberg (r1930) *Symphony 3.*
(12/94) (BIDD) ① **WHL020**
VPO, P. Monteux (r1960) *Concert*
(12/94) (DECC) ① [2] **440 627-2DF2**
N. German RSO, G. Wand (r1986) *Concert*
(5/95) (RCA) ① [5] **74321 20277-2**
Concertgebouw, W. Sawallisch (r1993) *Symphony 3.*
(6/95) (EMI) ① **CDC7 54501-2**

Columbia SO, B. Walter (r1959) *Concert*
(8/95) (SONY) ① **SMK64460**
RPO, B. Wordsworth (r1994) *Symphony 7.*
(8/95) (TRIN) ① **TRP033**
Munich PO, R. Kempe *Concert*
(11/95) (EMI) ① [2] **CES5 68518-2**
Staatskapelle Dresden, Colin Davis (r1993) *Concert*
(12/95) (PHIL) ① [6] **446 067-2PH6**
4. La Scala Orch, A. Toscanini (r1921) *Concert*
(11/92) (RCA) ① **GD60315**

Symphony No. 2 in D, Op. 36 (1801-2)
LCP, R. Norrington *Symphony 8.*
(3/87) (EMI) ① **CDC7 47698-2**
BPO, H. von Karajan (r1977) *Symphony 7.*
(12/87) (DG) ① **419 050-2GGA**
Dresden PO, H. Kegel *Concert*
(12/87) (CAPR) ① [5] **10 451/5**
VPO, C. Abbado (pp1987) *Symphony 5.*
(4/88) (DG) ① **423 590-2GH**
Philadelphia, R. Muti *Concert*
(1/89) (EMI) ① [6] **CDS7 49487-2**
Hanover Band, M. Huggett *Concert*
(1/89) (NIMB) ① [5] **NI5144/8**
VPO, L. Bernstein (pp1978) *Concert*
(3/89) (DG) ① [6] **423 481-2GX6**
CBSO, W. Weller *Concert*
(5/89) (CHAN) ① [6] **CHAN8712/7**
Cleveland Orch, C. von Dohnányi (r1988) *Symphony
1.* (6/89) (TELA) ① **CD80187**
VPO, C. Abbado (pp1987) *Concert*
(9/89) (DG) ① [6] **427 306-2GH6**
N. German RSO, G. Wand (1988) *Symphony 4.*
(9/89) (RCA) ① **RD60058**
BPO, H. von Karajan (r1961/2) *Concert*
(1/90) (DG) ① [5] **429 036-2GX5**
Philh, H. von Karajan (r1953/5) *Concert*
(1/90) (EMI) ① [5] **CMS7 63310-2**
NBC SO, A. Toscanini (r1949/51) *Concert*
(5/90) (RCA) ① [5] **GD60324**
Philh, O. Klemperer (r1957) *Symphony 4.*
(8/90) (EMI) ① **CDM7 63355-2**
COE, N. Harnoncourt (pp1990) *Concert*
(11/91) (TELD) ① [5] **2292-46452-2**
VPO, H. Schmidt-Isserstedt *Symphony 7.*
(1/92) (DECC) ① **433 605-2DSP**
Chicago SO, G. Solti *Concert*
(4/92) (DECC) ① [6] **430 792-2DC6**
NYPO, L. Bernstein (r1962) *Symphony 7.*
(11/92) (SONY) ① **SMK47515**
Leipzig Gewandhaus, K. Masur *Concert*
(5/93) (PHIL) ① [5] **426 290-2PH5**
Milan La Scala PO, C. M. Giulini (r1991) *Symphony
8.* (3/94) (SONY) ① **SK48238**
Concertgebouw, B. Haitink (1987) *Concert*
(9/94) (PHIL) ① [5] **442 073-2PB5**
Concertgebouw, W. Sawallisch (r1993) *Symphony 8.*
(9/94) (EMI) ① **CDC7 54502-2**
ORR, J.E. Gardiner (pp1991) *Concert*
(11/94) (ARCH) ① [5] **439 900-2AH5**
ORR, J.E. Gardiner (pp1991) *Symphony 1.*
(11/94) (ARCH) ① [5] **447 049-2AH**
LSO, P. Monteux (r1960) *Concert*
(12/94) (DECC) ① [2] **443 479-2DF2**
N. German RSO, G. Wand (1988) *Concert*
(5/95) (RCA) ① [5] **74321 20277-2**
Columbia SO, B. Walter (r1959) *Concert*
(8/95) (SONY) ① **SMK64460**
RPO, J. Lockhart (r1994) *Symphony 8.*
(8/95) (TRIN) ① **TRP039**
Staatskapelle Dresden, Colin Davis (r1992) *Concert*
(12/95) (PHIL) ① [6] **446 067-2PH6**

Symphony No. 3 in E flat, 'Eroica', Op. 55
(1803)
EXCERPTS: 1. Allegro con brio; 2. Marcia funebre;
3. Scherzo; 4. Allegro molto.
Cleveland Orch, C. von Dohnányi (r1983)
(9/84) (TELA) ① **CD80090**
VPO, C. Abbado (pp1985) *Coriolan.*
(3/87) (DG) ① **419 597-2GH**
BPO, H. von Karajan (r1976) *Leonore.*
(4/87) (DG) ① **419 049-2GGA**
Dresden PO, H. Kegel *Concert*
(12/87) (CAPR) ① [5] **10 451/5**
LSO, W. Morris (1988) *Coriolan.*
(12/88) (CARL) ① **PCD900**
Philadelphia, R. Muti *Concert*
(1/89) (EMI) ① [6] **CDS7 49487-2**
Hanover Band, R. Goodman *Concert*
(1/89) (NIMB) ① [5] **NI5144/8**
VPO, L. Bernstein (pp1978) *Concert*
(3/89) (DG) ① [6] **423 481-2GX6**
LCP, R. Norrington (1987) *Prometheus.*
(4/89) (EMI) ① **CDC7 49101-2**
FNO, C. Schuricht (pp1963) *Symphony 1.*
(5/89) (MONT) ① **TCE8841**

CBSO, W. Weller *Concert*
(5/89) (CHAN) ① [6] **CHAN8712/7**
VPO, C. Abbado (pp1985) *Concert*
(9/89) (DG) ① [6] **427 306-2GH6**
BPO, H. von Karajan (r1962) *Concert*
(1/90) (DG) ① [5] **429 036-2GX5**
Philh, H. von Karajan (r1952) *Concert*
(1/90) (EMI) ① [5] **CMS7 63310-2**
NBC SO, A. Toscanini (r1949) *Concert*
(5/90) (RCA) ① [5] **GD60324**
Philh, O. Klemperer (r1959) *Grosse Fuge.*
(8/90) (EMI) ① **CDM7 63356-2**
Cleveland Orch, G. Szell *Symphony 8.*
(3/91) (SONY) ① **SBK46328**
N German RSO, G. Wand (pp1989) *Leonore.*
(10/91) (RCA) ① **RD60755**
COE, N. Harnoncourt (pp1990) *Concert*
(11/91) (TELD) ① [5] **2292-46452-2**
VPO, H. Schmidt-Isserstedt *Symphony 1.*
(1/92) (DECC) ① **433 619-2DSP**
Philh, O. Klemperer (r1955) *Leonore.*
(4/92) (EMI) ① **CDM7 63855-2**
Chicago SO, G. Solti *Concert*
(4/92) (DECC) ① [6] **430 792-2DC6**
Leningrad PO, E. Mravinsky (pp1968) *Symphony 1.*
(6/92) (ERAT) ① **2292-45759-2**
Leningrad PO, E. Mravinsky (pp1968) *Concert*
(6/92) (ERAT) ① [11] **2292-45763-2**
NBC SO, A. Toscanini (bp1953) *Mozart: Symphony
40.* (10/92) (RCA) ① **GD60271**
Scottish CO, J-P. Saraste *Serenade, Op. 8.*
(10/92) (VIRG) ① **VJ7 59674-2**
NBC SO, A. Toscanini (bp1939) *Symphony 8.*
(11/92) (RCA) ① **GD60269**
NYPO, L. Bernstein (r1964) *Symphony 1.*
(11/92) (SONY) ① **SMK47514**
VPO, F. Weingartner (r1936) *Symphony 8.*
(11/92) (PREI) ① **90113**
Chicago SO, F. Reiner (r1954) *Concert*
(12/92) (RCA) ① **09026 60962-2**
Staatskapelle Dresden, Colin Davis (r1991) *Egmont.*
(3/93) (PHIL) ① **434 120-2PH**
Leipzig Gewandhaus, K. Masur *Concert*
(5/93) (PHIL) ① [5] **426 290-2PH5**
BPO, P. van Kempen (r1950s) *Concert*
(3/94) (PHIL) ① [2] **438 533-2PM2**
BPO, H. Knappertsbusch (r1943) *Liszt: Préludes.*
(5/94) (PREI) ① **90976**
SO, A. Coates (r1926) *Mozart: Symphony 41.*
(6/94) (CLAR) ① **CDGSE78-50-55**
Concertgebouw, W. Mengelberg (pp1940) *Concert*
(7/94) (MUSI) ① [4] **MACD-780**
Concertgebouw, B. Haitink (1987) *Concert*
(9/94) (PHIL) ① [5] **442 073-2PB5**
NY Met Op Orch, James Levine *Schubert: Symphony
8.* (9/94) (DG) ① **439 862-2GH**
LPO, K. Tennstedt (pp1991) *Mussorgsky: Night on
the Bare Mountain.* (11/94) (EMI) ① **CDC5 55186-2**
ORR, J.E. Gardiner (pp1993) *Concert*
(11/94) (ARCH) ① [5] **439 900-2AH5**
ORR, J.E. Gardiner (pp1993) *Symphony 4.*
(11/94) (ARCH) ① [5] **447 050-2AH**
NYPSO, W. Mengelberg (r1930) *Symphony 1.*
(12/94) (BIDD) ① **WHL020**
Concertgebouw, P. Monteux (r1962) *Concert*
(12/94) (PHIL) ① [5] **442 544-2PM5**
VPO, P. Monteux (1957) *Concert*
(12/94) (DECC) ① [2] **440 627-2DF2**
BPO, W. Furtwängler (pp1952) *Concert*
(5/94) (TAHR) ① **FURT1008/11**
Milan La Scala PO, C. M. Giulini (r1992)
(4/95) (SONY) ① **SK58974**
VPO, K. Böhm (r1971) *Concert*
(4/95) (DG) ① [2] **437 368-2GX2**
N. German RSO, G. Wand (r1985) *Concert*
(5/95) (RCA) ① [5] **74321 20277-2**
Concertgebouw, W. Sawallisch (r1993) *Symphony 1.*
(6/95) (EMI) ① **CDC7 54501-2**
RPO, G. Herbig (r1994) *Fidelio.*
(6/95) (TRIN) ① **TRP026**
Columbia SO, B. Walter (r1958) *Symphony 8.*
(8/95) (SONY) ① **SMK64461**
Munich PO, R. Kempe *Concert*
(11/95) (EMI) ① [2] **CES5 68518-2**
Staatskapelle Dresden, Colin Davis (r1991) *Concert*
(12/95) (PHIL) ① [6] **446 067-2PH6**

Symphony No. 4 in B flat, Op. 60 (1806)
EXCERPTS: 1. Adagio—Allegro vivace; 2. Adagio;
3. Allegro vivace; 4. Allegro ma non troppo.
Bavarian St Orch, C. Kleiber (pp1982)
(6/85) (ORFE) ① **C100841H**
Dresden PO, H. Kegel *Concert*
(12/87) (CAPR) ① [5] **10 451/5**
BPO, H. von Karajan (r1976) *Concert*
(4/88) (DG) ① **419 048-2GGA**

Philadelphia, R. Muti *Concert*
(1/89) (EMI) ① [6] **CDS7 49487-2**
Hanover Band, R. Goodman *Concert*
(1/89) (NIMB) ① [5] **NI5144/8**
VPO, L. Bernstein (pp1978) *Concert*
(3/89) (DG) ① [6] **423 481-2GX6**
VPO, C. Abbado (pp1988) *Symphony 1.*
(5/89) (DG) ① **427 301-2GH**
CBSO, W. Weller *Concert*
(5/89) (CHAN) ① [6] **CHAN8712/7**
Cleveland Orch, C. von Dohnányi (r1988) *Symphony 8.*
(6/89) (TELA) ① **CD80198**
VPO, C. Abbado (pp1988) *Concert*
(9/89) (DG) ① [6] **427 306-2GH6**
N. German RSO, G. Wand (r1988) *Symphony 2.*
(9/89) (RCA) ① **RD60058**
LCP, R. Norrington *Symphony 5.*
(11/89) (EMI) ① **CDC7 49656-2**
BPO, H. von Karajan (r1962) *Concert*
(1/90) (DG) ① [5] **429 036-2GX5**
Philh, H. von Karajan (r1953) *Concert*
(1/90) (EMI) ① [5] **CMS7 63310-2**
NBC SO, A. Toscanini (bp1951) *Concert*
(5/90) (RCA) ① [5] **GD60324**
Philh, O. Klemperer (r1957) *Symphony 2.*
(8/90) (EMI) ① **CDM7 63355-2**
COE, N. Harnoncourt (pp1990) *Concert*
(11/91) (TELD) ① [5] **2292-46452-2**
Chicago SO, G. Solti *Concert*
(4/92) (DECC) ① [6] **430 792-2DC6**
NYPO, L. Bernstein (r1962) *Concert*
(11/92) (SONY) ① **SMK47516**
Concertgebouw, W. Sawallisch *Symphony 7.*
(12/92) (EMI) ① **CDC7 54503-2**
Leipzig Gewandhaus, K. Masur *Concert*
(5/93) (PHIL) ① [5] **426 290-2PH5**
Leningrad PO, E. Mravinsky (pp1955) *Piano Concerto 5.*
(10/93) (PRAG) ① **PR250 021**
BBC SO, A. Toscanini (r1939) *Concert*
(5/94) (BIDD) ① [2] **WHL008/9**
Concertgebouw, B. Haitink (r1987) *Concert*
(9/94) (PHIL) ① [5] **442 073-2PB5**
San Francisco SO, P. Monteux (r1952) *Concert*
(9/94) (RCA) ① [15] **09026 61893-2**
ORR, J.E. Gardiner (r1993) *Concert*
(11/94) (ARCH) ① [5] **439 900-2AH5**
ORR, J.E. Gardiner (r1993) *Symphony 3.*
(11/94) (ARCH) ① **447 050-2AH**
LSO, P. Monteux (r1960) *Concert*
(12/94) (DECC) ① [2] **443 479-2DF2**
BPO, W. Furtwängler (pp1943) *Concert*
(3/95) (MUSI) ① [2] **MACD-824**
N. German RSO, G. Wand (r1988) *Concert*
(5/95) (RCA) ① [5] **74321 20277-2**
Columbia SO, B. Walter (r1958) *Symphony 6.*
(8/95) (SONY) ① **SMK64462**
Milan La Scala PO, C. M. Giulini (r1993) *Symphony 5.*
(11/95) (SONY) ① **SK58921**
Staatskapelle Dresden, Colin Davis (r1993) *Concert*
(12/95) (PHIL) ① [6] **446 067-2PH6**
Movt 2: rehearsal Leipzig RSO, H. Abendroth
(bp1949) *Concert* (9/94) (TAHR) ① [2] **TAH102**
rehearsal sequences Columbia SO, B. Walter
(r1958) *Concert* (8/95) (SONY) ① **SMK64465**

Symphony No. 5 in C minor, Op. 67 (1807)
EXCERPTS: 1. Allegro con brio; 2. Andante con
moto; 3. Allegro; 4. Allegro.
LSO, G. Schwarz *Piano Concerto 4.*
(9/86) (DELO) ① **DE3027**
Philh, G. Simon *Concert*
(3/87) (CALA) ① [2] **CACD0101**
BPO, H. von Karajan (r1976) *Concert*
(8/87) (DG) ① **419 051-2GGA**
Dresden PO, H. Kegel *Concert*
(12/87) (CAPR) ① [5] **10 451/5**
VPO, C. Abbado (pp1987) *Concert*
(4/88) (DG) ① **423 590-2GH**
Cleveland Orch, C. von Dohnányi (r1987) *Symphony 7.*
(9/88) (TELA) ① **CD80163**
Philadelphia, R. Muti *Concert*
(1/89) (EMI) ① [6] **CDS7 49487-2**
Hanover Band, R. Goodman *Concert*
(1/89) (NIMB) ① [5] **NI5144/8**
VPO, L. Bernstein (pp1977) *Concert*
(3/89) (DG) ① [6] **423 481-2GX6**
CBSO, W. Weller *Concert*
(5/89) (CHAN) ① [6] **CHAN8712/7**
VPO, C. Abbado (pp1987) *Concert*
(9/89) (DG) ① [6] **427 306-2GH6**
LCP, R. Norrington *Symphony 4.*
(11/89) (EMI) ① **CDC7 49656-2**
BPO, H. von Karajan (r1962) *Concert*
(1/90) (DG) ① [5] **429 036-2GX5**
Philh, H. von Karajan (r1954) *Concert*
(1/90) (EMI) ① [5] **CMS7 63310-2**

NYPSO, A. Toscanini (pp1933) *Concert*
(3/90) (PEAR) ① [3] **GEMMCDS9373**
NBC SO, A. Toscanini (bp1952) *Concert*
(5/90) (RCA) ① [5] **GD60324**
Philh, O. Klemperer (r1959) *Symphony 8.*
(8/90) (EMI) ① **CDM7 63357-2**
Philh, Vladimir Ashkenazy *Symphony 7.*
(8/91) (DECC) ① **430 701-2DM**
COE, N. Harnoncourt (pp1990) *Concert*
(11/91) (TELD) ① [5] **2292-46452-2**
VPO, O. Klemperer (pp1968) *Schubert: Symphony 8.*
(2/92) (DG) ① **435 327-2GWP**
VPO, O. Klemperer (pp1968) *Concert*
(2/92) (DG) ① [12] **435 321-2GWP12**
Philh, O. Klemperer (r1955) *Symphony 7.*
(4/92) (EMI) ① **CDM7 63868-2**
Chicago SO, G. Solti *Concert*
(4/92) (DECC) ① [6] **430 792-2DC6**
BPO, W. Furtwängler (r1926) *Concert*
(4/92) (KOCH) ① [2] **37059-2**
NYPSO, A. Toscanini (pp1931) *Concert*
(4/92) (PEAR) ① [3] **GEMMCDS9922**
Leningrad PO, E. Mravinsky (pp1974) *Concert*
(6/92) (ERAT) ① [11] **2292-45763-2**
Berlin St Op Orch, R. Strauss (1928) *Symphony 7.*
(10/92) (KOCH) ① **37115-2**
NYPO, L. Bernstein (r1961) *Concert*
(11/92) (SONY) ① **SMK47516**
NBC SO, A. Toscanini (r1939) *Concert*
(11/92) (RCA) ① **GD60270**
Concertgebouw, W. Sawallisch *Symphony 6.*
(4/93) (EMI) ① **CDC7 54504-2**
Leipzig Gewandhaus, K. Masur *Concert*
(5/93) (PHIL) ① [5] **426 290-2PH5**
RLPO, C. Mackerras (1992) *Symphony 7.*
(12/93) (EMIN) ① **CD-EMX2212**
NYPO, K. Masur (pp1992) *Egmont.*
(1/94) (TELD) ① **9031-77313-2**
BPO, H. von Karajan (r1962) *Symphony 6.*
(1/94) (DG) ① **439 403-2GCL**
N German RSO, G. Wand (pp1992) *Symphony 6.*
(5/94) (RCA) ① **09026 61930-2**
BPO, W. Furtwängler (1937) *Concert*
(7/94) (BIDD) ① [2] **WHL006/7**
BPO, H. Abendroth (1939) *Concert*
(9/94) (TAHR) ① [2] **TAH102**
Concertgebouw, B. Haitink (r1986) *Concert*
(9/94) (PHIL) ① [5] **442 073-2PB5**
Queen's Hall Orch, Henry Wood (r1935) *Concert*
(9/94) (DUTT) ① [2] **2CDAX2002**
LPO, F. Welser-Möst (pp1992)
(10/94) (EMI) ① **CDU5 65390-2**
ORR, J.E. Gardiner (pp1994) *Concert*
(11/94) (ARCH) ① [5] **439 900-2AH5**
Concertgebouw, B. Haitink (r1986) *Symphony 6.*
(12/94) (PHIL) ① **442 404-2PM**
LSO, P. Monteux (r1961) *Concert*
(12/94) (DECC) ① [2] **443 479-2DF2**
Los Angeles PO, C.M. Giulini *Schumann: Symphony 3.*
(1/95) (DG) ① **445 502-2GMA**
BPO, W. Furtwängler (pp1954) *Concert*
(3/95) (TAHR) ① [4] **FURT1008/11**
BPO, W. Furtwängler (pp1943) *Concert*
(3/95) (MUSI) ① [2] **MACD-824**
N. German RSO, G. Wand (r1987) *Concert*
(5/95) (RCA) ① [5] **74321 20277-2**
VPO, C. Kleiber (r1974) *Symphony 7.*
(5/95) (DG) ① **447 400-2GOR**
RPO, C. Gibault (r1994) *Schubert: Symphony 8.*
(7/95) (TRIN) ① **TRP022**
Columbia SO, B. Walter (r1958) *Symphony 7.*
(8/95) (SONY) ① **SMK64463**
Munich PO, R. Kempe *Concert*
(11/95) (EMI) ① [2] **CES5 68518-2**
Concertgebouw, G. Szell (r1966) *Concert*
(11/95) (PHIL) ① [2] **442 727-2PM2**
Milan La Scala PO, C. M. Giulini (r1993) *Symphony 4.*
(11/95) (SONY) ① **SK58921**
Staatskapelle Dresden, Colin Davis (r1992) *Concert*
(12/95) (PHIL) ① [6] **446 067-2PH6**
rehearsal sequences Columbia SO, B. Walter
(r1958) *Concert* (8/95) (SONY) ① **SMK64465**
2. NYPO, J. Stransky (r1917) *Concert*
(4/92) (PEAR) ① [3] **GEMMCDS9922**
2-4. Philh, G. Cantelli (r1956) *Concert*
(11/94) (TEST) ① **SBT1034**
4. La Scala Orch, A. Toscanini (r1920) *Concert*
(11/92) (RCA) ① **GD60315**

Symphony No. 6 in F, 'Pastoral', Op. 68 (1808)
EXCERPTS: 1. Allegro ma non troppo (Awakening
of cheerful feelings...in the country); 2. Andante molto
mosso (By the brook); 3. Allegro (Merry gathering of
country folk); 4. Allegro (Thunderstorm); 5. Allegretto
(Shepherds' Song. Happy & thankful feelings after
the Storm).

NY Y CO, G. Schwarz (9/86) (DELO) ① **DE3017**
BPO, H. von Karajan (r1976) *Concert*
(4/87) (DG) ① **415 833-2GGA**
Cleveland Orch, C. von Dohnányi (r1986) *Leonore.*
(11/87) (TELA) ① **CD80145**
Dresden PO, H. Kegel *Concert*
(12/87) (CAPR) ① [5] **10 451/5**
VPO, C. Abbado *Concert*
(4/88) (DG) ① **419 779-2GH**
LCP, R. Norrington *Symphony 1.*
(9/88) (EMI) ① **CDC7 49746-2**
Philadelphia, R. Muti *Concert*
(1/89) (EMI) ① [6] **CDS7 49487-2**
Hanover Band, R. Goodman *Concert*
(1/89) (NIMB) ① [5] **NI5144/8**
VPO, L. Bernstein (pp1978) *Concert*
(3/89) (DG) ① [6] **423 481-2GX6**
CBSO, W. Weller (with rehearsal sequence) *Concert*
(5/89) (CHAN) ① [6] **CHAN8712/7**
LSO, W. Morris (r1988) *Egmont.*
(5/89) (CARL) ① **PCD912**
VPO, C. Abbado *Concert*
(9/89) (DG) ① [6] **427 306-2GH6**
BPO, H. von Karajan (r1962) *Concert*
(1/90) (DG) ① [5] **429 036-2GX5**
Philh, H. von Karajan (r1953) *Concert*
(1/90) (EMI) ① [5] **CMS7 63310-2**
NBC SO, A. Toscanini (r1952) *Concert*
(5/90) (RCA) ① [5] **GD60324**
Philh, O. Klemperer (r1957) *Concert*
(8/90) (EMI) ① **CDM7 63358-2**
COE, N. Harnoncourt (pp1990) *Concert*
(11/91) (TELD) ① [5] **2292-46452-2**
Philh, Vladimir Ashkenazy *Concert*
(12/91) (DECC) ① **430 721-2DM**
Chicago SO, G. Solti *Concert*
(4/92) (DECC) ① [6] **430 792-2DC6**
Leningrad PO, E. Mravinsky (pp1982) *Concert*
(6/92) (ERAT) ① [11] **2292-45763-2**
Leningrad PO, E. Mravinsky (pp1982)
(6/92) (ERAT) ① **2292-45761-2**
NYPO, L. Bernstein (r1963) *Concert*
(11/92) (SONY) ① **SMK47517**
VPO, F. Schalk (r1928) *Symphony 6.*
(11/92) (PREI) ① **90111**
Munich PO, R. Kempe
(12/92) (CFP) ① **CD-CFP4419**
Concertgebouw, W. Sawallisch *Symphony 5.*
(4/93) (EMI) ① **CDC7 54504-2**
Leipzig Gewandhaus, K. Masur *Concert*
(5/93) (PHIL) ① [5] **426 290-2PH5**
BPO, H. von Karajan (r1962) *Symphony 5.*
(1/94) (DG) ① **439 403-2GCL**
BBC SO, A. Toscanini (r1937) *Concert*
(5/94) (BIDD) ① [2] **WHL008/9**
RPO, M. Ermler (r1992) *Egmont.*
(5/94) (TRIN) ① **TRP001**
Milan La Scala PO, C. M. Giulini (r1993) *Concert*
(5/94) (SONY) ① **SK53974**
N German RSO, G. Wand (pp1992) *Symphony 5.*
(5/94) (RCA) ① **09026 61930-2**
VPO, B. Walter (r1936) *Concert*
(8/94) (PREI) ① **90157**
Concertgebouw, B. Haitink (r1986) *Concert*
(9/94) (PHIL) ① [5] **442 073-2PB5**
Boston SO, S. Koussevitzky (r1928) *Concert*
(9/94) (BIDD) ① **WHL019**
BPO, A. Cluytens (r1960) *Concert*
(11/94) (EMI) ① [2] **CZS5 68220-2**
ORR, J.E. Gardiner (r1992) *Concert*
(11/94) (ARCH) ① [5] **439 900-2AH5**
Concertgebouw, B. Haitink (r1986) *Symphony 5.*
(12/94) (PHIL) ① **442 404-2PM**
VPO, P. Monteux (r1958) *Concert*
(12/94) (DECC) ① [2] **440 627-2DF2**
BPO, W. Furtwängler (pp1944) *Concert*
(3/95) (TAHR) ① [4] **FURT1004/7**
BPO, W. Furtwängler (pp1954) *Concert*
(3/95) (TAHR) ① [4] **FURT1008/11**
BPO, W. Furtwängler (pp1944) *Concert*
(3/95) (MUSI) ① [2] **MACD-824**
BBC SO, A. Boult (pp1972) *Concert*
(3/95) (BBCR) ① **BBCRD9114**
VPO, K. Böhm (r1971) *Concert*
(4/95) (DG) ① [2] **437 928-2GX2**
VPO, W. Furtwängler (r1943) *Brahms: Haydn Variations.*
(5/95) (PREI) ① **90199**
N. German RSO, G. Wand (r1987) *Concert*
(5/95) (RCA) ① [5] **74321 20277-2**
Columbia SO, B. Walter (r1958) *Symphony 4.*
(8/95) (SONY) ① **SMK64462**
Munich PO, R. Kempe *Concert*
(11/95) (EMI) ① [2] **CES5 68519-2**
Staatskapelle Dresden, Colin Davis (r1992) *Concert*
(12/95) (PHIL) ① [6] **446 067-2PH6**

Symphony No. 7 in A, Op. 92 (1812)
EXCERPTS: 1. Poco sostenuto—Vivace; 2.
Allegretto; 3. Presto; 4. Allegro con brio.
BPO, H. von Karajan (r1976) *Symphony 2.*
        (12/87) (DG) ① **419 050-2GGA**
Dresden PO, H. Kegel *Concert*
        (12/87) (CAPR) ① [5] **10 451/5**
VPO, C. Abbado (pp1987) *Symphony 8.*
        (4/88) (DG) ① **423 364-2GH**
Philh, O. Klemperer (stereo: r1955) *Prometheus.*
        (4/88) (EMI) ① **CDM7 69183-2**
Cleveland Orch, C. von Dohnányi (r1987) *Symphony
5.*
        (9/88) (TELA) ① **CD80163**
Philadelphia, R. Muti *Concert*
        (1/89) (EMI) ① [6] **CDS7 49487-2**
Hanover Band, R. Goodman *Concert*
        (1/89) (NIMB) ① [5] **NI5144/8**
VPO, L. Bernstein (pp1977) *Concert*
        (3/89) (DG) ① [6] **423 481-2GX6**
CBSO, W. Weller *Concert*
        (5/89) (CHAN) ① [6] **CHAN8712/7**
VPO, C. Abbado (pp1987) *Concert*
        (9/89) (DG) ① [6] **427 306-2GH6**
LCP, R. Norrington *Concert*
        (11/89) (EMI) ① **CDC7 49816-2**
BPO, H. von Karajan (r1962) *Concert*
        (1/90) (DG) ① [5] **429 036-2GX5**
Philh, H. von Karajan (r1951/2) *Concert*
        (1/90) (EMI) ① [5] **CMS7 63310-2**
NYPSO, A. Toscanini (r1936) *Concert*
        (3/90) (PEAR) ① [3] **GEMMCDS9373**
NBC SO, A. Toscanini (r1951) *Concert*
        (5/90) (RCA) ① [5] **GD60324**
Philh, O. Klemperer (r1960) *Symphony 1.*
        (8/90) (EMI) ① **CDM7 63354-2**
VPO, K. Böhm *Concert*
        (10/90) (DG) ① **429 509-2GR**
VPO, F. Weingartner (r1936) *Concert*
        (5/91) (MSCM) ① **MM30269**
Philh, Vladimir Ashkenazy *Symphony 5.*
        (8/91) (DECC) ① **430 701-2DM**
COE, N. Harnoncourt (pp1990) *Concert*
        (11/91) (TELD) ① [5] **2292-46452-2**
VPO, H. Schmidt-Isserstedt *Symphony 2.*
        (1/92) (DECC) ① **433 605-2DSP**
Philh, O. Klemperer (mono: r1955) *Symphony 5.*
        (4/92) (EMI) ① **CDM7 63868-2**
Chicago SO, G. Solti *Concert*
        (4/92) (DECC) ① [6] **430 792-2DC6**
Leningrad PO, E. Mravinsky (pp1964) *Concert*
        (6/92) (ERAT) ① [11] **2292-45763-2**
Berlin St Op Orch, R. Strauss (r1926) *Symphony 5.*
        (10/92) (KOCH) ① **37115-2**
NYPO, L. Bernstein (r1964) *Symphony 2.*
        (11/92) (SONY) ① **SMK47515**
NYPO, A. Toscanini (r1936) *Concert*
        (11/92) (RCA) ① **GD60316**
Milan La Scala PO, C.M. Giulini *Symphony 1.*
        (11/92) (SONY) ① **SK48236**
Boston SO, L. Bernstein (pp1990) *Britten: Sea
Interludes, Op. 33a.* (12/92) (DG) ① **431 768-2GH**
Concertgebouw, W. Sawallisch *Symphony 4.*
        (12/92) (EMI) ① **CDC7 54503-2**
Leipzig Gewandhaus, K. Masur *Concert*
        (5/93) (PHIL) ① [5] **426 290-2PH5**
Berlin RO, M. Mengelberg (bp1939) *Concert*
        (12/93) (ARHI) ① **ADCD111**
RLPO, C. Mackerras (r1992) *Symphony 5.*
        (12/93) (EMIN) ① **CD-EMX2212**
BPO, P. van Kempen (r1953) *Concert*
        (3/94) (PHIL) ① [2] **438 533-2PM2**
Concertgebouw, O. Klemperer (pp1951) *Concert*
        (8/94) (ARCI) ① **ARC109**
Concertgebouw, B. Haitink (r1985) *Concert*
        (9/94) (PHIL) ① [5] **442 073-2PB5**
Philh, G. Cantelli (r1956) *Concert*
        (11/94) (EMI) ① [2] **CZS5 68217-2**
ORR, J.E. Gardiner (r1992) *Concert*
        (11/94) (ARCH) ① [5] **439 900-2AH5**
LSO, P. Monteux (r1961) *Concert*
        (12/94) (DECC) ① [2] **443 479-2DF2**
BPO, W. Furtwängler (bp1943) *Concert*
        (3/95) (MUSI) ① [2] **MACD-824**
VPO, K. Böhm (r1971) *Concert*
        (4/95) (DG) ① [2] **437 928-2GX2**
N. German RSO, G. Wand (r1987) *Concert*
        (5/95) (RCA) ① [5] **74321 20277-2**
VPO, C. Kleiber (r1976) *Symphony 5.*
        (5/95) (DG) ① **447 400-2GOR**
Saito Kinen Orch, S. Ozawa (pp1993) *Schubert:
Symphony 8.* (7/95) (PHIL) ① **442 424-2PH**
Columbia SO, B. Walter (r1958) *Symphony 5.*
        (8/95) (SONY) ① **SMK64463**
RPO, B. Wordsworth (r1994) *Symphony 1.*
        (8/95) (TRIN) ① **TRP033**

Philadelphia, L. Stokowski (r1927) *Concert*
        (11/95) (BIDD) ① **WHL033**
Staatskapelle Dresden, Colin Davis (r1992) *Concert*
        (12/95) (PHIL) ① [6] **446 067-2PH6**
rehearsal sequences Columbia SO, B. Walter
        (r1958) *Concert*   (8/95) (SONY) ① **SMK64465**
1(pt) SO, T. Beecham (pp1936) *Concert*
        (11/91) (SYMP) ① [2] **SYMCD1096/7**
Symphony No. 8 in F, Op. 93 (1812)
Cleveland Orch, C. von Dohnányi (r1983) *Schubert:
Symphony 8.*   (10/84) (TELA) ① **CD80091**
LCP, R. Norrington *Symphony 2.*
        (3/87) (EMI) ① **CDC7 47698-2**
Los Angeles CO, G. Schwarz *Concert*
        (6/87) (DELO) ① **DE3013**
BPO, H. von Karajan (r1976) *Concert*
        (8/87) (DG) ① **419 051-2GGA**
Dresden PO, H. Kegel *Concert*
        (12/87) (CAPR) ① [5] **10 451/5**
VPO, C. Abbado (pp1987) *Symphony 7.*
        (4/88) (DG) ① **423 364-2GH**
Philadelphia, R. Muti *Concert*
        (1/89) (EMI) ① [6] **CDS7 49487-2**
Hanover Band, R. Goodman *Concert*
        (1/89) (NIMB) ① [5] **NI5144/8**
VPO, L. Bernstein (pp1978) *Concert*
        (3/89) (DG) ① [6] **423 481-2GX6**
CBSO, W. Weller *Concert*
        (5/89) (CHAN) ① [6] **CHAN8712/7**
Cleveland Orch, C. von Dohnányi (r1983) *Symphony
4.*   (6/89) (TELA) ① **CD80198**
VPO, C. Abbado (pp1987) *Concert*
        (9/89) (DG) ① [6] **427 306-2GH6**
BPO, H. von Karajan (r1962) *Concert*
        (1/90) (DG) ① [5] **429 036-2GX5**
Philh, H. von Karajan *Concert*
        (1/90) (EMI) ① [5] **CMS7 63310-2**
NBC SO, A. Toscanini (r1952) *Concert*
        (5/90) (RCA) ① [5] **GD60324**
Philh, O. Klemperer (r1957) *Symphony 9.*
        (8/90) (EMI) ① **CDM7 63357-2**
Cleveland Orch, G. Szell *Symphony 3.*
        (3/91) (SONY) ① **SBK46328**
VPO, F. Weingartner (r1936) *Concert*
        (5/91) (MSCM) ① **MM30269**
COE, N. Harnoncourt (pp1990) *Concert*
        (11/91) (TELD) ① [5] **2292-46452-2**
Chicago SO, G. Solti *Concert*
        (4/92) (DECC) ① [6] **430 792-2DC6**
NBC SO, A. Toscanini (r1939) *Symphony 3.*
        (4/92) (RCA) ① **GD60269**
NYPO, L. Bernstein (r1963) *Concert*
        (11/92) (SONY) ① **SMK47517**
VPO, F. Schalk (r1928) *Symphony 6.*
        (11/92) (PREI) ① **90111**
VPO, F. Weingartner (r1936) *Symphony 3.*
        (11/92) (PREI) ① **90113**
Leipzig Gewandhaus, K. Masur *Concert*
        (5/93) (PHIL) ① [5] **426 290-2PH5**
Milan La Scala PO, C. M. Giulini (r1992) *Symphony
2.*   (3/94) (SONY) ① **SK48238**
BPO, P. van Kempen (r1953) *Concert*
        (3/94) (PHIL) ① [2] **438 533-2PM2**
Concertgebouw, B. Haitink (r1987) *Concert*
        (9/94) (PHIL) ① [5] **442 073-2PB5**
Concertgebouw, W. Sawallisch (pp1992) *Symphony
2.*   (9/94) (EMI) ① **CDC7 54502-2**
San Francisco SO, P. Monteux (r1950) *Concert*
        (9/94) (RCA) ① [15] **09026 61893-2**
ORR, J.E. Gardiner (r1992) *Concert*
        (11/94) (ARCH) ① [5] **439 900-2AH5**
VPO, P. Monteux (r1960) *Concert*
        (12/94) (DECC) ① [2] **440 627-2DF2**
BBC SO, A. Boult (r1932) *Concert*
        (2/95) (BEUL) ① **1PD12**
VPO, K. Böhm (r1971) *Concert*
        (5/95) (RCA) ① [2] **437 928-2GX2**
N. German RSO, G. Wand (r1987) *Concert*
        (5/95) (RCA) ① [5] **74321 20277-2**
Munich PO, R. Kempe *Concert*
        (11/95) (EMI) ① [2] **CES5 68519-2**
RPO, J. Lockhart (r1994) *Symphony 2.*
        (11/95) (TRIN) ① **TRP039**
Staatskapelle Dresden, Colin Davis (r1993) *Concert*
        (12/95) (PHIL) ① [6] **446 067-2PH6**
**Symphony No. 9 in D minor, 'Choral', Op.
125 (1822-4)**
1. Allegro ma non troppo, un poco maestoso; 2.
Molto vivace; 3. Adagio e cantabile—Andante
moderato; 4. Presto—Allegro assai; 4a. Ode to Joy.
C. Vaness, J. Taylor, S. Jerusalem, R. Lloyd,
Cleveland Oratorio Chor, Cleveland Orch, C. von
Dohnányi (r1985)   (2/86) (TELA) ① **CD80120**

A. Tomowa-Sintow, A. Baltsa, P. Schreier, J. Van
Dam, Vienna Singverein, BPO, H. von Karajan
(r1976)   (4/87) (DG) ① **415 832-2GGA**
G. Beňačková, M. Lipovšek, G. Winbergh, H. Prey,
Vienna St. Op. Concert Ch, VPO, C. Abbado
(pp1986)   (6/87) (DG) ① **419 598-2GH**
Y. Kenny, Sarah Walker, P. Power, P. Salomaa,
London Schütz Ch, LCP, R. Norrington (r1987)
        (10/87) (EMI) ① **CDC7 49221-2**
J. Norman, R. Runkel, R. Schunk, H. Sotin, Chicago
Sym Chor, Chicago SO, G. Solti
        (10/87) (DECC) ① **417 800-2DH**
P. Curtin, F. Kopleff, J. McCollum, D. Gramm,
Chicago Sym Chor, Chicago SO, F. Reiner
        (11/87) (RCA) ① **GD86532**
A. Hargan, U. Walther, E. Büchner, K. Kováts, Berlin
Rad Chor, Leipzig Rad Chor, Dresden PO, H. Kegel
Concert   (12/87) (CAPR) ① [5] **10 451/5**
E. Schwarzkopf, E. Höngen, J. Patzak, H. Hotter,
Vienna Singverein, VPO, H. von Karajan (r1947)
        (9/88) (EMI) ① **CDH7 61076-2**
I. Wenglor, A. Burmeister, M. Ritzmann, R. Kühne,
Czech Phil Chor, Czech PO, P. Kletzki
        (12/88) (SUPR) ① **2SUP0026**
C. Studer, D. Ziegler, P. Seiffert, J. Morris,
Westminster Ch, Philadelphia, R. Muti *Concert*
        (1/89) (EMI) ① [6] **CDS7 49487-2**
E. Harrhy, J. Bailey, A. Murgatroyd, M. George, Oslo
Cath Ch, Hanover Band, R. Goodman *Concert*
        (1/89) (NIMB) ① [5] **NI5144/8**
G. Jones, H. Schwarz, R. Kollo, K. Moll, Vienna St
Op Chor, VPO, L. Bernstein (pp1979) *Concert*
        (3/89) (DG) ① [6] **423 481-2GX6**
J. Barstow, L. Finnie, D. Rendall, J. Tomlinson,
CBSO Chor, CBSO, W. Weller *Concert*
        (5/89) (CHAN) ① [6] **CHAN8712/7**
G. Beňačková, M. Lipovšek, G. Winbergh, H. Prey,
Vienna St Op Concert Ch, VPO, C. Abbado (pp1986)
        (9/89) (DG) ① [6] **427 306-2GH6**
A. Auger, C. Robbin, A. Rolfe Johnson, G. Reinhart,
LSC, AAM, C. Hogwood
        (11/89) (L'OI) ① **425 517-2OH**
G. Janowitz, H. Rössl-Majdan, W. Kmentt, W. Berry,
Vienna Singverein, BPO, H. von Karajan (r1962)
Concert   (1/90) (DG) ① [5] **429 036-2GX5**
E. Schwarzkopf, E. Höngen, E. Haefliger, O.
Edelmann, Vienna Singverein, Philh, H. von Karajan
(r1955) *Concert*   (1/90) (EMI) ① [5] **CMS7 63310-2**
J. Anderson, Sarah Walker, K. König, J-H. Rootering,
Bavarian Rad Chor, Berlin Rad Chor, Dresden Phil
Chor (Children's Voices), BRSO, Staatskapelle
Dresden, Paris Chors, LSO, NYPO, Leningrad Kirov
Th Orch, L. Bernstein (pp1989)
        (3/90) (DG) ① **429 861-2GH**
E. Farrell, N. Merriman, J. Peerce, N. Scott, R. Shaw
Chorale, NBC SO, A. Toscanini (r1952) *Concert*
        (5/90) (RCA) ① [5] **GD60324**
H. Donath, B. Fassbaender, H. Laubenthal, H. Sotin,
Bavarian Rad Chor, BRSO, R. Kubelík (pp1982)
        (8/90) (ORFE) ① **C207891A**
A. Nordmo-Løvberg, C. Ludwig, W. Kmentt, H.
Hotter, Philh Chor, Philh, O. Klemperer (r1957)
        (8/90) (EMI) ① **CDM7 63359-2**
J. Varady, J. van Nes, K. Lewis, S. Estes, Ernst Senff
Chor, BPO, C.M. Giulini
        (1/91) (DG) ① **427 655-2GH**
B. Poschner-Klebel, M. Hintermeier, R. Tear, R.
Lloyd, Vienna Singakademie Chor, Viennensis Chor,
Vienna SO, E. Inbal (pp1989/90)
        (3/91) (DENO) ① **CO-76646**
R. Falcon, K. McKellar-Ferguson, R. Margison, T.
Thomaschke, Brighton Fest Chor, RPO, Y. Menuhin
        (4/91) (RPO) ① **CDRPO7001**
L. Helletsgruber, R. Anday, G. Maikl, R. Mayr, Vienna
St Op Chor, VPO, F. Weingartner (r1935)
Contredanses, WoO17.
        (5/91) (PEAR) ① **GEMMCD9407**
P. Lorengar, Y. Minton, S. Burrows, M. Talvela,
Chicago Sym Chor, Chicago SO, G. Solti
        (5/91) (DECC) ① **430 438-2DM**
L. Helletsgruber, R. Anday, G. Maikl, R. Mayr, Vienna
St Op Chor, VPO, F. Weingartner (r1035)
        (5/91) (MSCM) ① **MM30270**
C. Margiono, B. Remmert, R. Schasching, R. Holl, A.
Schoenberg Ch, COE, N. Harnoncourt (pp1991)
Concert   (11/91) (TELD) ① [5] **2292-46452-2**
J. Rodgers, D. Jones, P. Bronder, B. Terfel, Liverpool
Phil Ch, RLPO, C. Mackerras
        (12/91) (EMIN) ① **CD-EMX2186**
J. Sutherland, M. Horne, J. King, M. Talvela, Vienna
St Op Chor, VPO, H. Schmidt-Isserstedt
        (1/92) (DECC) ① **433 617-2DSP**
I. Seefried, R. Anday, A. Dermota, P. Schoeffler,
Vienna Singakademie Chor, VPO, W. Furtwängler
(pp1953)   (2/92) (DG) ① **435 325-2GWP**

I. Seefried, R. Anday, A. Dermota, P. Schoeffler,
Vienna Singakademie Chor, VPO, W. Furtwängler
(pp1953) *Concert*
    (2/92) (DG) ① [12] **435 321-2GWP12**
P. Lorengar, Y. Minton, S. Burrows, M. Talvela,
Chicago Sym Chor, Chicago SO, G. Solti *Concert*
    (4/92) (DECC) ① [6] **430 792-2DC6**
G. Beňačková, A. Gjevang, G. Neumann, A. Korn,
Czech Phil Chor, Czech PO, V. Neumann (pp1989)
    (4/92) (SUPR) ① **11 1174-2**
D. Labelle, D. Fortunato, B. Cresswell, D. Arnold,
Boston Pro Musica Chor, Boston PO, B. Zander
    (9/92) (CARL) ① **MCD40**
M. Arroyo, R. Sarfaty, N. di Virgilio, N. Scott, Juilliard
Chor, NYPO, L. Bernstein (r1964) *Fidelio*.
    (11/92) (SONY) ① **SMK47518**
S. McNair, U. Heilmann, J. van Nes, B. Weikl, Leipzig
Rad Chor, Leipzig Gewandhaus, K. Masur *Concert*
    (5/93) (PHIL) ① [5] **426 290-2PH5**
M. Price, M. Lipovšek, P. Seiffert, J-H. Rootering,
Düsseldorf Musikverein, Concertgebouw, W.
Sawallisch (pp1992) (1/94) (EMI) ① **CDC7 54505-2**
H. Schymberg, L. Tunell, G. Bäckelin, S. Björling,
Stockholm Phil Ch, Stockholm Concert Soc Orch, W.
Furtwängler (pp1943)
    (5/94) (MUSI) ① **MACD-2002**
T. Briem, E. Höngen, P. Anders, R. Watzke, Bruno
Kittel Ch, BPO, W. Furtwängler (pp1942)
    (5/94) (MUSI) ① **MACD-653**
A. Marc, I. Vermillion, S. Jerusalem, F. Struckmann,
Berlin St Op Chor, Berlin Staatskapelle, D.
Barenboim (r1992) (7/94) (ERAT) ① **4509-94353-2**
P. Curtin, F. Kopleff, J. McCollum, D. Gramm,
Chicago Sym Chor, CSO, F. Reiner (r1961)
    (7/94) (RCA) ① **09026 61795-2**
L. Popp, C. Watkinson, P. Schreier, R. Holl,
Netherlands Rad Chor, Concertgebouw, B. Haitink
(r1987) *Concert*
    (9/94) (PHIL) ① [5] **442 073-2PB5**
I. Seefried, M. Forrester, E. Haefliger, D. Fischer-
Dieskau, Berlin St Hedwig's Cath Ch, BPO, F.
Fricsay (r1957/8) (11/94) (DG) ① **445 401-2GDO**
I. Gonzalez, O. Dominguez, F. Becerra, R. Bañuelas,
Mexico City Chor, Mexico City PO, F. Lozano
    (11/94) (FORL) ① **FF018**
I. Seefried, M. Forrester, E. Haefliger, D. Fischer-
Dieskau, Berlin St Hedwig's Cath Ch, BPO, F.
Fricsay (r1957/8) *Concert*
    (11/94) (DG) ① [11] **445 400-2GDO10**
L. Orgonášová, A.S. von Otter, A. Rolfe Johnson, G.
Cachemaille, Monteverdi Ch, ORR, J.E. Gardiner
(r1992) *Concert*
    (11/94) (ARCH) ① [5] **439 900-2AH5**
J. Norman, B. Fassbaender, P. Domingo, W. Berry,
Vienna St Op Concert Ch, VPO, K. Böhm (r1980)
    (12/94) (DG) ① **445 503-2GMA**
E. Schwarzkopf, E. Cavelti, E. Haefliger, O.
Edelmann, Lucerne Festival Chor, Philh, W. Furtwängler
(pp1954) (3/95) (TAHR) ① **FURT1003**
T. Briem, E. Höngen, P. Anders, R. Watzke, Bruno
Kittel Ch, BPO, W. Furtwängler (pp1942) *Concert*
    (3/95) (TAHR) ① [4] **FURT1004/7**
G. Jones, T. Troyanos, Jess Thomas, K.
Ridderbusch, Vienna St Op Chor, VPO, K. Böhm
(r1970) *Concert* (4/95) (DG) ① [2] **437 368-2GX2**
R. Alexander, F. Cunar, G. Lakes, P. Plishka,
Ambrosian Sngrs, RPO, A. Previn (r1989-90)
    (4/95) (RCA) ① **09026 60363-2**
T. van der Sluys, S. Luger, L. van Tulder, W. Ravelli,
Amsterdam Toonkunst Ch, Concertgebouw, W.
Mengelberg (pp1938) (5/95) (ARHI) ① **ADCD113**
E. Wiens, H. Hartwig, K. Lewis, R. Hermann,
Hamburg St Op Chor, N. German Rad Chor, N.
German RSO, G. Wand (r1986) *Concert*
    (5/95) (RCA) ① [5] **74321 20277-2**
G. Janowitz, H. Rössl-Majdan, W. Kmentt, W. Berry,
Vienna Singverein, BPO, H. von Karajan (r1962)
Coriolan.   (5/95) (DG) ① **447 401-2GOR**
E. Cundari, N. Rankin, A. da Costa, W. Wilderman,
Westminster Ch, Columbia SO, B. Walter (r1959)
    (8/95) (SONY) ① **SMK64464**
S. Armstrong, A. Reynolds, R. Tear, J. Shirley-Quirk,
LSO, LSO, C.M. Giulini (r1972) *Concert*
    (11/95) (EMI) ① [2] **CES5 68519-2**
S. Sweet, J. Rappé, P. Frey, F. Grundheber, Dresden
St Op Chor, Staatskapelle Dresden, Colin Davis
(r1993) *Concert*
    (12/95) (PHIL) ① [6] **446 067-2PH6**
rehearsal sequences Columbia SO, B. Walter
(r1958) *Concert* (8/95) (SONY) ① **SMK64465**
**Symphony "No. 10' in E flat (first movement
sketches)** (realised/cpted B. Cooper, 1988)
LSO, W. Morris (includes lecture by Dr Barry Cooper)
    (1/89) (CARL) ① **PCD911**
CBSO, W. Weller (with rehearsal sequence) *Concert*
    (5/89) (CHAN) ① [6] **CHAN8712/7**

**Wellingtons Sieg, '(Die) Schlacht bei
Vittoria', Op. 91** (1813) (Battle Symphony)
BPO, H. von Karajan *Concert*
    (10/87) (DG) ① **419 624-2GH**
Octophoros, P. Dombrecht *Concert*
    (2/90) (ACCE) ① **ACC8860D**
LSO, A. Dorati (r1960) *Concert*
    (12/95) (MERC) ① **434 360-2MM**

    SECTION II: CHAMBER

Adagio in E flat—mandolin & piano, Wo043/2
(1796)
A. Stephens, R. Burnett *Concert*
    (3/92) (AMON) ① **CD-SAR53**
**Andantino con variazioni—piano &
mandolin, Wo44/2 (1796)**
A. Stephens, R. Burnett *Concert*
    (3/92) (AMON) ① **CD-SAR53**
**3 Duets—clarinet & bassoon, Wo027 (?1810-
15)** (probably spurious)
1. C; 2. F; 3. B flat.
1. S. Milan, S. Azzolini *Concert*
    (4/93) (CHAN) ① **CHAN9108**
1. Mozzafiato, C. Neidich (r1992/3) *Concert*
    (8/94) (SONY) ① **SK53367**
3. K. Puddy, A. Mitchell (r1992) *Concert*
    (10/93) (CLRI) ① **CC0004**
**Duo in E flat—viola & cello, Wo032 (1796-
97)**
W. Primrose, E. Feuermann (r1941) *Concert*
    (9/94) (BIDD) ① **LAB088**
3 Equale—4 trombones, Wo030 (1812)
1. D minor; 2. D; 3. B flat.
London Gabrieli Brass Ens, C. Larkin *Concert*
    (4/92) (HYPE) ① **CDA66470**
**Grosse Fuge in B flat—string quartet, Op.
133 (1826)**
Alban Berg Qt *Concert*
    (8/85) (EMI) ① [4] **CDS7 47135-8**
Melos Qt *Concert*
    (10/86) (DG) ① [3] **415 676-2GH3**
Talich Qt *Concert* (3/87) (CALL) ① **CAL9635**
Lindsay Qt *Concert*
    (1/89) (ASV) ① [4] **CDDCS403**
Amadeus Qt *Concert*
    (1/89) (DG) ① [7] **423 473-2GX7**
Talich Qt *Concert* (1/89) (CALL) ① [7] **CAL9633/9**
Végh Qt *String Quartet 13*.
    (11/89) (AUVI) ① **V4407**
Quartetto Italiano *Concert*
    (2/90) (PHIL) ① [4] **426 050-2PM4**
Britten Qt *Concert* (4/90) (LDR) ① **LDRCD1008**
Britten Qt *Concert* (4/90) (COLL) ① **Coll1298-2**
Philh, O. Klemperer (r1956) *Symphony 3*.
    (8/90) (EMI) ① **CDM7 63356-2**
Arditti Qt *Concert* (11/90) (GVIS) ① **GV79440-2**
IMS Sols, S. Végh *String Quartet 14*.
    (9/91) (CAPR) ① **10 356**
Pražák Qt *String Quartet 13*.
    (10/91) (NUOV) ① **6861**
VPO, W. Furtwängler (pp1954) *Concert*
    (2/92) (DG) ① [12] **435 321-2GWP12**
VPO, W. Furtwängler (pp1954) *Concert*
    (2/92) (DG) ① [4] **435 324-2GWP**
Australian CO, S. Kovacevich (arr str orch) *Piano
Concerto 5*.   (3/92) (EMIN) ① **CD-EMX2184**
Vlach Qt (pp1962) *Concert*
    (4/93) (PRAG) ① [7] **PR254 009/15**
Alban Berg Qt (pp1989) *Concert*
    (10/93) (EMI) ① [4] **CDS7 54592-2**
Borodin Qt (pp1991) *Concert*
    (10/93) (RUSS) ① **RDCD11087**
Hagen Qt (r1993) *Schubert: String Quintet*.
    (11/94) (DG) ① **439 774-2GH**
Orford Qt *Concert*
    (9/95) (DELO) ① **DE3038**
Orford Qt *Concert*
    (9/95) (DELO) ① [8] **DE3039**
**6 Ländler—two violins & cello, Wo015 (1801-
02)**
V. Beths, G. Beths, A. Bylsma *Concert*
    (12/91) (CHNN) ① **CCS1491**
**10 National Airs with Variations—piano &
flute/violin, Op. 107 (c1818)**
EXCERPTS: 1. I bin a Tiroler Bua; 2. Bonny Laddie,
Highland Laddie; 3. Volkslied aus Kleinrussland; 4. St
Patrick's Day; 5. A Madel, ja a Madel; 6. Peggy's
Daughter; 7. Schöne Minka; 8. O Mary, at thy
Window be; 9. Oh, Thou art the Lad of my Heart; 10.
The Highland Watch.
2. Scottish Early Music Consort (r1987) *Concert*
    (10/95) (CHAN) ① **CHAN0581**
Notturno in D—violin & piano, Op. 42 (1803)
(arr from Serenade, Op. 8: trans anon)
N. Imai, R. Vignoles *Schubert: Arpeggione Sonata,
D821*.   (4/90) (CHAN) ① **CHAN8664**

G. Caussé, F-R. Duchâble (r1994) *Concert*
    (7/95) (EMI) ① **CDC5 55166-2**
**Octet in E flat—2 oboes, 2 clarinets, 2 horns
& 2 bassoons, Op. 103 (?1792-3)**
Classical Winds (r1986) *Concert*
    (5/87) (AMON) ① **CD-SAR26**
COE Wind Sols *Concert*
    (9/88) (ASV) ① **CDCOE807**
Mozzafiato, C. Neidich (r1992/3) *Concert*
    (8/94) (SONY) ① **SK53367**
Vienna Wind Sols (r1992) *Concert*
    (3/95) (DECC) ① **436 654-2DH**
3 Piano Quartets, Wo036 (1785)
1. E flat; 2. D; 3. C.
A. Goldstone, Cummings Trio
    (9/87) (MERI) ① **CDE84098**
P. Cassard, R. Oleg, M. da Silva, M. Coppey (r1994)
Piano Quartet, Op. 16. (5/95) (AUVI) ① [2] **V4715**
Piano Trios
1. E flat, Op. 1:1; 2. G, Op. 1:2; 3. C minor, Op. 1:3;
4. B flat, Op. 11 (clarinet, piano and cello); 5. D, Op.
70:1 (Ghost); 6. E flat, Op. 70:2; 7. B flat, Op. 97
(Archduke); 8. E flat, Wo038; 9. B flat, Wo039; 10. E
flat, Op. 44 (Variations on an original theme); 11. G,
Op. 121a (Kakudu Variations); 12. E flat, Hess 48.
Vladimir Ashkenazy, I. Perlman, L. Harrell *Allegretto,
Hess48*.   (3/87) (EMI) ① [4] **CDS7 47455-8**
Borodin Trio   (7/87) (CHAN) ① [4] **CHAN8352/5**
Beaux Arts Trio
    (3/92) (PHIL) ① [5] **432 381-2PM5**
1. J. Fuchs, P. Casals, E. Istomin (r1953) *Schubert:
Piano Trio 2*.   (5/93) (SONY) ① **SMK58988**
1. J. Heifetz, G. Piatigorsky, J. Lateiner (r1964)
Concert (11/94) (RCA) ① [65] **09026 61778-2(30)**
1-11. Czech Pf Trio, V. Riha (r1964)
    (6/92) (CHNT) ① [4] **LDC278 1076/9**
1-11. Beaux Arts Trio (r1965)
    (11/94) (PHIL) ① [3] **438 948-2PM3**
1, 2. London Fp Trio (11/87) (HYPE) ① **CDA66197**
1, 2. E. Hobarth, C. Coin, P. Cohen
    (3/94) (HARM) ① **HMC90 1361**
1, 2. Stuttgart Pf Trio (r1992-3)
    (7/94) (NAXO) ① **8 550946**
1-3, 5-7. H. Szeryng, P. Fournier, W. Kempff
    (6/87) (DG) ① [3] **415 879-2GCM3**
1-3, 5-7, 9-11. P. Zukerman, J. Du Pré, D. Barenboim
Allegretto, Hess48.
    (8/89) (EMI) ① [3] **CMS7 63124-2**
1, 5. Chung Trio (r1991)
    (8/93) (EMI) ① **CDC7 54579-2**
1-7, 10, 11. Fontenay Trio (r1990/2)
    (3/94) (TELD) ① [3] **9031-73281-2**
2. A. Schneider, P. Casals, E. Istomin (r1951)
Schubert: Piano Trio 1.
    (5/94) (SONY) ① **SMK58989**
2, 4, 8. Castle Trio (11/92) (VIRG) ① **VC7 59220-2**
3. C. Mackintosh, S. Comberti, C. Kite *Concert*
    (8/89) (CDE) ① **CDE84145**
3. Barcelona Trio *Triple Concerto*.
    (10/89) (HARM) ① **HMP 3905205**
3, 4. English Piano Trio, A. Mackay *Concert*
    (4/94) (MERI) ① **CDE84253**
3, 4, 9. W. Meyer, E. Hobarth, C. Coin, P. Cohen
(r1993)   (1/95) (HARM) ① **HMC90 1475**
3, 8, 10, 12. Stuttgart Pf Trio (r1992-3)
    (7/94) (NAXO) ① **8 550947**
4. E. Eban, M. Bergman, A. Shkolov *Brahms: Clarinet
Trio*.   (3/87) (MERI) ① **CDE84122**
4. Borodin Trio, J. Campbell *Concert*
    (6/89) (CHAN) ① **CHAN8655**
4. R. Kell, A. Pini, D. Matthews (r1944) *Concert*
    (3/92) (TEST) ① **SBT1022**
4. Nash Ens (r1989) *Septet, Op.20*.
    (10/95) (VIRG) ① **CUV5 61233-2**
4. W. Boeykens Ens (r1995) *Septet, Op.20*.
    (12/95) (HARM) ① **HMC90 1518**
4, 7. A. Schneider, P. Casals, E. Istomin (r1951)
    (5/94) (SONY) ① **SMK58990**
4, 7. Chung Trio (1/95) (EMI) ① **CDC5 55187-2**
5. P. Zukerman, J. Du Pré, D. Barenboim *Concert*
    (3/89) (EMI) ① [2] **CMS7 69707-2**
5. A. Busch, H. Busch, R. Serkin (r1947) *Brahms:
Piano Trio 2*.   (12/91) (SONY) ① **MPK46447**
5. J. Fuchs, P. Casals, E. Istomin (r1951) *Concert*
    (5/94) (SONY) ① **SMK58991**
5. Fontenay Trio (r1989) *Triple Concerto*.
    (7/95) (TELD) ① **4509-97447-2**
5, 6. Solomon Trio (5/94) (CARL) ① **MCD44**
5, 6. Stuttgart Pf Trio (r1989)
    (12/94) (NAXO) ① **8 550948**
5, 7. Beaux Arts Trio
    (11/86) (PHIL) ① **412 891-2PH**
5, 7. Mirecourt Trio (3/89) (MUSI) ① **MACD-265**
5, 7. H. Szeryng, P. Fournier, W. Kempff
    (9/90) (DG) ① **429 712-2GGA**

6. A. Schneider, P. Casals, E. Istomin (r1951)
Concert   (5/94) (SONY) ① SMK58991
6. J. Heifetz, G. Piatigorsky, L. Pennario (r1963)
Concert   (11/94) (RCA) ① [65] 09026 61778-2(28)
7. J. Thibaud, P. Casals, A. Cortot (r1928) Schubert:
Piano Trio 1.   (10/89) (EMI) ① CDH7 61024-2
7. Suk Trio Triple Concerto.
        (5/90) (SUPR) ① 11 0707-2
7. J. Thibaud, P. Casals, A. Cortot (r1928) Concert
         (12/91) (EMI) ① [3] CHS7 64057-2
7. S. Richter, Borodin Qt Concert
        (8/94) (PHIL) ① [2] 438 624-2PH2
7. J. Heifetz, E. Feuermann, A. Rubinstein (r1941)
Schubert: Piano Trio 1.
       (11/94) (RCA) ① [65] 09026 61778-2(29)
7. I. Perlman, L. Harrell, Vladimir Ashkenazy Concert
       (6/95) (EMI) ① [20] CZS4 83177-2(1)
7. H. Holst, A. Pini, Solomon (r1943) Concert
        (7/95) (APR) ① APR5503
7. A. Previn, V. Mullova, H. Schiff Brahms: Piano Trio
1.   (8/95) (PHIL) ① 442 123-2PH
7. H. Holst, A. Pini, Solomon (r1943) Piano Concerto
3.   (11/95) (DUTT) ① CDLX7015
7, 11. G. Oppitz, D. Sitkovetsky, D. Geringas
        (8/87) (NOVA) ① 150 008-2
7, 11. Kalichstein/Laredo/Robinson Trio
        (1/88) (CARL) ① PCD874
7, 11, 12. Solomon Trio (r1992)
        (3/94) (CARL) ① MCD69
7, 9. I. Perlman, L. Harrell, Vladimir Ashkenazy
       (11/84) (EMI) ① CDC7 47010-2
7, 9, 11. Castle Trio   (3/92) (VIRG) ① VC7 59044-2
9. V. Beths, A. Bylsma, S. Hoogland Concert
        (12/91) (CHNN) ① CCS1491
9, 11. Raphael Trio Trio, Op. 38.
        (4/92) (UNIC) ① DKPCD9118
11. J. Thibaud, P. Casals, A. Cortot (r1926) Concert
        (12/91) (EMI) ① [3] CHS7 64057-2

Quartet for Piano and Strings, Op. 16 (arr
cpsr from Piano & Wind Quintet)
Jerusalem Stg Trio, N. Ben-Or Serenade, op 8.
        (6/90) (MERI) ① CDE84154
I. Stern, J. Laredo, Y-Y. Ma, E. Ax (r1992)
Schumann: Piano Quartet, Op. 47.
        (10/94) (SONY) ① SK53339
P. Cassard, R. Oleg, M. da Silva, M. Coppey (r1994)
Piano Quartets, WoO36.
        (5/95) (AUVI) ① [2] V4715

**Quintet in E flat—oboe, clarinet, bassoon,
horn & piano, Op. 16 (1796)**
A. Previn, Vienna Wind Sols (r1985) Mozart: Piano
and Wind Quintet, K452.
        (6/86) (TELA) ① CD80114
M. Perahia, N. Black, T. King, A. Halstead, G. Sheen
Mozart: Piano and Wind Quintet, K452.
        (12/86) (SONY) ① SK42099
Nash Ens Mozart: Piano and Wind Quintet, K452.
        (6/87) (CRD) ① CRD3367
Vladimir Ashkenazy, London Wind Sols Mozart:
Piano and Wind Quintet, K452.
        (7/89) (DECC) ① 421 151-2DM
V. Perlemuter, Albion Ens Mozart: Piano and Wind
Quintet, K452.   (7/89) (NIMB) ① NI5157
C. Kite, C. Lawson, P. Goodwin, A. Halstead, J. Ward
Concert   (8/89) (MERI) ① CDE84145
A. Vogel, D. Shifrin, R. Graham, K. Munday, C.
Rosenberger Mozart: Piano and wind quintet, K452.
        (2/91) (DELO) ① DE3024
C. Eschenbach, Rhineland-Pfalz State PO Chbr Sols
Mozart: Piano and Wind Quintet, K452.
        (10/92) (SIGN) ① SIGX06-00
J. Jandó, J. Kiss, B. Kovács, J. Kev,eházi, J. Vajda
Concert   (4/93) (NAXO) ① 8 550511
S. Richter, Moraguès Qnt Concert
        (8/94) (PHIL) ① [2] 438 624-2PH2
D. Barenboim, D. Clevenger, L. Combs, D. Damiano,
H. Schellenberger (r1993) Mozart: Piano and Wind
Quintet, K452.   (12/94) (ERAT) ① [2] 4509-96359-2

**Quintet in E flat—oboe, bassoon & 3 horns,
Hess19 (?1793)** (fragment)
COE Wind Sols Concert
        (9/88) (ASV) ① CDCOE807
Z. Tylšar, B. Tylšar, R. Beránek, J. Mihule, F.
Herman Concert   (3/93) (SUPR) ① 11 1445-2
O. Rácz, J. Vajda, J. Kev¸eházi, János Kev¸eházi, S.
Berki (r1994) Concert (11/95) (NAXO) ① 8 553090

**Rondino in E flat—2 oboes, 2 clarinets, 2
horns & 2 bassoons, Wo025 (1793)**
Classical Winds (r1986) Concert
        (5/87) (AMON) ① CD-SAR26
COE Wind Sols Concert
        (9/88) (ASV) ① CDCOE807
Mozzafiato, C. Neidich (r1992/3) Concert
        (8/94) (SONY) ① SK53367

**Rondo in G—violin & piano, WoO41 (1793-
94)**
Y. Menuhin, W. Kempff Concert
       (6/87) (DG) ① [4] 415 874-2GCM4
**Septet in E flat—cl, hn, bn, vn, va, vc & db,
Op. 20 (1799-1800)**
Vienna Octet Mendelssohn: Octet, Op.20.
       (5/88) (DECC) ① 421 093-2DM
Berlin Phil Octet (r1972) Sextet, Op.81b.
       (5/90) (PHIL) ① 426 091-2PC
Gaudier Ens Sextet, Op.81b.
       (7/92) (HYPE) ① CDA66513
NBC SO, A. Toscanini (r1951) Concert
       (11/92) (RCA) ① GD60270
Hausmusik (r1992) String Quintet, Op.29.
       (6/93) (EMI) ① CDC7 54656-2
Vienna Chbr Ens (r1992) Sextet, Op.81b.
       (11/93) (DENO) ① CO-75373
AAM Chbr Ens (r1990) Weber: Clarinet Quintet,
J182.   (7/94) (L'OI) ① 433 044-2OH
Berlin Sols (r1990) Mozart: Horn Quintet, K407.
       (6/95) (TELD) ① 4509-97451-2
Nash Ens (r1989) Piano Trios.
       (10/95) (VIRG) ① CUV5 61233-2
J. Balogh, J. Vajda, J. Kev¸eházi, I. Hegyi, G. Máthé,
Peter Szabó, I. Tóth (r1994) Concert
       (11/95) (NAXO) ① 8 553090
W. Boeykens Ens (r1995) Piano Trios.
       (12/95) (HARM) ① HMC90 1518
**Serenade in D—violin, viola & cello, Op. 8
(1796-97)**
Mozart Trio String Trio, Op.3.
       (9/88) (DENO) ① CO-2251
A-S. Mutter, B. Giuranna, M. Rostropovich Concert
       (7/89) (DG) ① [2] 427 687-2GH2
Jerusalem Stg Trio Piano Quartet, op 16.
       (6/90) (MERI) ① CDE84154
J. Galway, P. Moll (arr Böhm) Concert
       (7/90) (RCA) ① RD87756
S. Goldberg, P. Hindemith, E. Feuermann (r1934)
Concert   (10/91) (PEAR) ① GEMMCD9443
S. Goldberg, P. Hindemith, E. Feuermann (r1934)
Concert   (5/92) (EMI) ① CDH7 64250-2
D. Sitkovetsky, G. Caussé, D. Geringas Symphony 3.
       (10/92) (VIRG) ① VJ7 59674-2
I. Perlman, P. Zukerman, L. Harrell (pp1990) Concert
       (2/93) (EMI) ① [2] CDS7 54198-2
Archibudelli (r1992) String Trio, Op. 3.
       (5/94) (SONY) ① SK53961
J. Heifetz, W. Primrose, G. Piatigorsky (r1960)
Concert   (11/94) (RCA) ① [65] 09026 61778-2(25)
**Serenade in D—flute, violin & viola, Op. 25
(1801)**
Israel Fl Ens Concert   (6/90) (CARL) ① PWK1139
J. Galway, J. Swensen, P. Neubauer Concert
       (7/90) (RCA) ① RD87756
S. Milan, L. Chilingirian, L. Williams Concert
       (4/93) (CHAN) ① CHAN9108
**Serenade in D—piano & flute/violin, Op. 41
(1803)** (arr of Op. 25)
E. Pahud, E. Lesage (r1993) Concert
       (9/93) (AUVI) ① V4693
**Sextet in E flat—2 clarinets, 2 horns & 2
bassoons, Op. 71 (1796)**
Classical Winds (r1986) Concert
       (5/87) (AMON) ① CD-SAR26
COE Wind Sols Concert
       (9/88) (ASV) ① CDCOE807
Z. Tylšar, B. Tylšar, V. Kyzivát, Z. Tesař, F. Herman,
V. Horák Concert   (3/93) (SUPR) ① 11 1445-2
Mozzafiato, C. Neidich (r1992/3) Concert
       (8/94) (SONY) ① SK53367
**Sextet in E flat—two horns, two violins, viola
& cello, Op. 81b (?1795)**
Berlin Phil Octet (r1968) Septet, Op.20.
       (5/90) (PHIL) ① 426 091-2PC
Gaudier Ens Septet, Op.20.
       (7/92) (HYPE) ① CDA66513
Vienna Chbr Ens (r1992) Septet, Op.20.
       (11/93) (DENO) ① CO-75373
J. Kev¸eházi, János Kev¸eházi, I. Hegyi, P. Popa, G.
Máthé, Peter Szabó (r1994) Concert
       (11/95) (NAXO) ① 8 553090
**Sonata for Cello and Piano in E flat, Op. 64
(pub 1807)** (arr of String Trio, Op. 3)
A. Karttunen, T. Hakkila (r1992) Concert
       (11/95) (FINL) ① 4509-95584-2
**Sonata for Cello and Piano No. 1 in F, Op. 5/1
(1796)**
Y-Y. Ma, E. Ax Cello Sonata 2.
       (11/85) (SONY) ① SK37251
A. Pleeth, M. Tan Concert
       (12/88) (HYPE) ① CDA66281
J. Du Pré, D. Barenboim (pp1970) Concert
       (8/89) (EMI) ① [2] CMS7 63015-2

M. Maisky, M. Argerich (r1990) Concert
       (2/92) (DG) ① 431 801-2GH
P. Fournier, F. Gulda (r1959) Concert
       (6/93) (DG) ① [2] 437 352-2GDO2
P. Casals, R. Serkin (r1953) Concert
       (5/94) (SONY) ① [2] SM2K58985
T. Hugh, Y. Solomon (r1993) Concert
       (9/94) (CARL) ① MCD80
P. Casals, M. Horszowski (r1939) Concert
       (10/94) (EMI) ① [2] CHS5 65185-2
M. Maisky, M. Argerich (r1990) Concert
       (2/95) (DG) ① [2] 439 934-2GH2
A. Karttunen, T. Hakkila (r1992) Concert
       (11/95) (FINL) ① 4509-95584-2
**Sonata for Cello and Piano No. 2 in G minor,
Op. 5/2 (1796)**
Y-Y. Ma, E. Ax Cello Sonata 1.
       (11/85) (SONY) ① SK37251
A. Pleeth, M. Tan Concert
       (12/88) (HYPE) ① CDA66281
J. Du Pré, D. Barenboim (pp1970) Concert
       (8/89) (EMI) ① [2] CMS7 63015-2
G. Piatigorsky, A. Schnabel (r1934) Concert
       (10/91) (PEAR) ① GEMMCD9447
M. Maisky, M. Argerich (r1990) Concert
       (2/92) (DG) ① 431 801-2GH
G. Piatigorsky, A. Schnabel (r1934) Concert
       (3/92) (MUSI) ① MACD-674
P. Fournier, F. Gulda (r1959) Concert
       (6/93) (DG) ① [2] 437 352-2GDO2
P. Casals, R. Serkin (r1951) Concert
       (5/94) (SONY) ① [2] SM2K58985
T. Hugh, Y. Solomon (r1993) Concert
       (9/94) (CARL) ① MCD80
P. Casals, M. Horszowski (r1939) Concert
       (10/94) (EMI) ① [2] CHS5 65185-2
M. Maisky, M. Argerich (r1990) Concert
       (2/95) (DG) ① [2] 439 934-2GH2
**Sonata for Cello and Piano No. 3 in A, Op. 69
(1807-08)**
A. Pleeth, M. Tan Concert
       (12/88) (HYPE) ① CDA66282
J. Du Pré, D. Barenboim (pp1970) Concert
       (3/89) (EMI) ① [2] CMS7 69707-2
J. Du Pré, S. Kovacevich (r1965) Cello Sonata 5.
       (8/89) (EMI) ① CDM7 69179-2
J. Du Pré, D. Barenboim (pp1970) Concert
       (8/89) (EMI) ① [2] CMS7 63015-2
E. Feuermann, M. Hess (r1937) Concert
       (5/91) (PEAR) ① GEMMCD9462
E. Feuermann, M. Hess (r1937) Concert
       (10/91) (PEAR) ① GEMMCD9446
E. Feuermann, M. Hess (r1937) Concert
       (5/92) (EMI) ① CDH7 64250-2
P. Fournier, F. Gulda (r1959) Concert
       (6/93) (DG) ① [2] 437 352-2GDO2
M. Maisky, M. Argerich (r1992) Concert
       (12/93) (DG) ① 437 514-2GH
P. Casals, R. Serkin (r1953) Concert
       (5/94) (SONY) ① [2] SM2K58985
J. Du Pré, S. Kovacevich (r1965) Concert
       (8/94) (EMI) ① [6] CZS5 68132-2
T. Hugh, Y. Solomon (r1993) Concert
       (9/94) (CARL) ① MCD80
P. Casals, O. Schulhof (r1930) Concert
       (10/94) (EMI) ① [2] CHS5 65185-2
M. Maisky, M. Argerich (r1992) Concert
       (2/95) (DG) ① [2] 439 934-2GH2
**Sonata for Cello and Piano No. 4 in C, Op.
102/1 (1815)**
A. Pleeth, M. Tan Concert
       (12/88) (HYPE) ① CDA66282
J. Du Pré, D. Barenboim (pp1970) Concert
       (8/89) (EMI) ① [2] CMS7 63015-2
P. Fournier, F. Gulda (r1959) Concert
       (6/93) (DG) ① [2] 437 352-2GDO2
M. Maisky, M. Argerich (r1992) Concert
       (12/93) (DG) ① 437 514-2GH
P. Casals, R. Serkin (r1953) Concert
       (5/94) (SONY) ① [2] SM2K58985
P. Casals, M. Horszowski (r1936) Concert
       (10/94) (EMI) ① [2] CHS5 65185-2
M. Maisky, M. Argerich (r1992) Concert
       (2/95) (DG) ① [2] 439 934-2GH2
**Sonata for Cello and Piano No. 5 in D, Op.
102/2 (1815)**
A. Pleeth, M. Tan Concert
       (12/88) (HYPE) ① CDA66282
J. Du Pré, S. Kovacevich (r1965) Cello Sonata 3.
       (8/89) (EMI) ① CDM7 69179-2
J. Du Pré, D. Barenboim (pp1970) Concert
       (8/89) (EMI) ① [2] CMS7 63015-2
P. Fournier, F. Gulda (r1959) Concert
       (6/93) (DG) ① [2] 437 352-2GDO2
M. Maisky, M. Argerich (r1992) Concert
       (12/93) (DG) ① 437 514-2GH

25. Vladimir Ashkenazy (r1984) *Concert*
          (7/93) (DECC) ① **430 759-2DM**
Ecossaise in E flat—piano, WoO86 (1825)
A. Schiff *Concert*   (4/89) (HUNG) ① **HCD11885**
M. Levitzki (r1927) *Concert*
          (6/92) (APR) ① **[2] APR7020**
6 Ecossaises—piano, WoO83 (authenticity
doubtful)
A. Brendel *Concert*   (8/85) (PHIL) ① **412 227-2PH**
J. Lhévinne (r1920: arr Busoni) *Concert*
          (10/92) (APR) ① **[2] APR7013**
Scotch Step F. Busoni (r1922: arr Busoni) *Concert*
          (4/90) (PEAR) ① **GEMMCD9347**
Scotch Step F. Busoni (r1922: arr Busoni) *Concert*
          (8/94) (SYMP) ① **SYMCD1145**
Fantasia in G minor/B flat, Op. 77 (1809)
M. Tan *Concert*   (12/92) (EMI) ① **CDC7 54526-2**
Menuet in G, WoO10 No. 2 (c1795)
I Musici *Concert*   (12/83) (PHIL) ① **410 606-2PH**
M. Lympany *Concert*   (1/89) (EMIL) ① **CDZ110**
J. Szigeti, K. Ruhrseitz (arr vn/pf: r1926) *Concert*
          (1/90) (BIDD) ① **LAB005/6**
F. Kreisler, H. Kreisler, C. Keith (r1923: arr. Kreisler)
          Concert   (7/90) (BIDD) ① **[2] LAB009/10**
Hungarian St. Orch, G. Győriványi-Ráth (arr orch)
          Concert   (3/91) (LASE) ① **15 515**
S. Koussevitzky, P. Luboshutz (r1929: arr db/pf)
          Concert   (9/94) (BIDD) ① **WHL019**
P. Casals, O. Schulhof (r1930: arr vc/pf) *Concert*
          (10/94) (PEAR) ① **[2] CHS5 65185-2**
2 Movements of a Sonata in F—piano,
WoO50 (c1790-92) (pub posth)
D. Blumenthal (r1991) *Concert*
          (10/93) (ETCE) ① **[2] KTC2018**
Piano Piece, 'Lustig-Traurig', WoO54
(?1802)
C. Kite *Concert*   (8/89) (MERI) ① **CDE84145**
Polonaise in C—piano, Op. 89 (1814)
A. Schiff *Concert*   (4/89) (HUNG) ① **HCD11885**
Presto in C minor—piano, WoO52 (?1795)
J. Lill *Concert*   (1/93) (CHAN) ① **[3] CHAN9084/6**
Rondo a capriccio in G, 'Rage over a lost
penny', Op. 129 (1795)
M. Lympany *Concert*   (1/92) (EMIL) ① **CDZ111**
A. Ugorski *Concert*   (2/93) (DG) ① **435 881-2DH**
A. Brailowsky (r1938) *Concert*
          (8/94) (APR) ① **APR5501**
Rondos, Op. 51 (c1797/98)
1. C; 2. G.
L. Lortie *Concert*   (10/90) (CHAN) ① **CHAN8616**
W. Kempff (r1950s) *Concert*
          (4/93) (DG) ① **[3] 435 744-2GDO3**
S. Richter (r1986) *Concert*
          (8/94) (PHIL) ① **[2] 438 624-2PH2**
1. B. Moiseiwitsch (r1942) *Concert*
          (9/90) (APR) ① **[2] APR7005**
Sonata for Piano No. 1 in F minor, Op. 2/1
(1793-95)
1. Allegro; 2. Adagio; 3. Menuetto; 4. Prestissimo.
A. Brendel (r1977) *Concert*
          (1/85) (PHIL) ① **[11] 412 575-2PH11**
D. Barenboim *Concert*
          (7/85) (DG) ① **[6] 413 759-2GX6**
I. Margalit *Concert*   (3/88) (CHAN) ① **CHAN8582**
J. O'Conor (r1989) *Concert*
          (9/90) (TELA) ① **CD80214**
D. Barenboim *Concert*
          (10/90) (EMI) ① **[10] CZS7 62863-2**
J. Jandó *Concert*   (12/90) (NAXO) ① **8 550150**
W. Kempff (r1964) *Concert*
          (3/91) (DG) ① **[9] 429 306-2GX9**
A. Schnabel (r1934) *Concert*
          (7/91) (EMI) ① **[8] CHS7 63765-2**
C. Arrau *Concert*
          (1/92) (PHIL) ① **[11] 432 301-2PM11**
J. Lill *Concert*   (12/92) (ASV) ① **CDQS6055**
S. Richter *Concert*
          (3/93) (EMI) ① **[4] CMS7 64429-2**
I. Hobson (r1992) *Concert*   (7/93) (ARAB) ① **Z6637**
J-B. Pommier *Concert*
          (9/93) (ERAT) ① **[3] 2292-45598-2**
A. Brendel (r1960s) *Concert*
          (9/93) (VOX) ① **[2] 115772-2**
R. Goode *Concert*
          (3/94) (NONE) ① **[10] 7559-79328-2**
Z. Kocsis *Concert*   (9/94) (PHIL) ① **442 405-2PM**
T. Nikolaieva (pp1983) *Concert*
          (1/95) (OLYM) ① **[10] 7559-79328-2**
A. Brendel *Concert*   (7/95) (PHIL) ① **442 124-2PH**
C. Arrau (r1988) *Concert*
          (7/95) (PHIL) ① **[2] 432 173-2PH2**
M. Perahia (r1994) *Concert*
          (8/95) (SONY) ① **SK64397**

Sonata for Piano No. 2 in A, Op. 2/2 (1794-
95)
A. Brendel (r1977) *Concert*
          (1/85) (PHIL) ① **[11] 412 575-2PH11**
D. Barenboim *Concert*
          (7/85) (DG) ① **[6] 413 759-2GX6**
J. O'Conor (r1989) *Concert*
          (9/90) (TELA) ① **CD80214**
D. Barenboim *Concert*
          (10/90) (EMI) ① **[10] CZS7 62863-2**
J. Jandó *Concert*   (12/90) (NAXO) ① **8 550150**
W. Kempff (r1964) *Concert*
          (3/91) (DG) ① **[9] 429 306-2GX9**
A. Schnabel (r1933) *Concert*
          (7/91) (EMI) ① **[8] CHS7 63765-2**
C. Arrau *Concert*
          (1/92) (PHIL) ① **[11] 432 301-2PM11**
J. Lill *Concert*   (12/92) (ASV) ① **CDQS6055**
I. Hobson (r1992) *Concert*   (7/93) (ARAB) ① **Z6637**
J-B. Pommier *Concert*
          (9/93) (ERAT) ① **[3] 2292-45598-2**
M. Horszowski (r1980s) *Concert*
          (12/93) (NONE) ① **[3] 7559-79261-2**
R. Goode *Concert*
          (3/94) (NONE) ① **[10] 7559-79328-2**
T. Nikolaieva (pp1983) *Concert*
          (1/95) (OLYM) ① **OCD561**
A. Brendel *Concert*   (7/95) (PHIL) ① **442 124-2PH**
C. Arrau (r1990) *Concert*
          (7/95) (PHIL) ① **[2] 432 173-2PH2**
M. Perahia (r1994) *Concert*
          (8/95) (SONY) ① **SK64397**

Sonata for Piano No. 3 in C, Op. 2/3 (1794-
95)
A. Brendel (r1977) *Concert*
          (1/85) (PHIL) ① **[11] 412 575-2PH11**
D. Barenboim *Concert*
          (7/85) (DG) ① **[6] 413 759-2GX6**
B-L. Gelber *Concert*   (9/88) (DENO) ① **CO-2203**
J. O'Conor (r1989) *Concert*
          (9/90) (TELA) ① **CD80214**
D. Barenboim *Concert*
          (10/90) (EMI) ① **[10] CZS7 62863-2**
J. Jandó *Concert*   (12/90) (NAXO) ① **8 550150**
W. Kempff (r1964) *Concert*
          (3/91) (DG) ① **[9] 429 306-2GX9**
A. Schnabel (r1934) *Concert*
          (7/91) (EMI) ① **[8] CHS7 63765-2**
C. Arrau *Concert*
          (1/92) (PHIL) ① **[11] 432 301-2PM11**
I. Hobson (r1992) *Concert*   (7/93) (ARAB) ① **Z6637**
A.B. Michelangeli (r1941) *Concert*
          (8/93) (EMI) ① **CDH7 64490-2**
J-B. Pommier *Concert*
          (9/93) (ERAT) ① **[3] 2292-45598-2**
S. Richter *Concert*
          (1/94) (OLYM) ① **OCD336**
R. Goode *Concert*
          (3/94) (NONE) ① **[10] 7559-79328-2**
T. Nikolaieva (pp1983) *Concert*
          (1/95) (OLYM) ① **OCD561**
Solomon (pp1956) *Concert*
          (4/95) (APR) ① **[2] APR7030**
A. Brendel *Concert*   (7/95) (PHIL) ① **442 124-2PH**
M. Perahia (r1990) *Concert*
          (8/95) (SONY) ① **SK64397**
A.B. Michelangeli (pp1987) *Concert*
          (10/95) (MEMR) ① **[4] 999001**
Finale M. Hambourg (r1926) *Concert*
          (4/89) (OPAL) ① **OPALCD9839**
Sonata for Piano No. 4 in E flat, Op. 7 (1797-
98)
A. Brendel (r1977) *Concert*
          (1/85) (PHIL) ① **[11] 412 575-2PH11**
D. Barenboim *Concert*
          (7/85) (DG) ① **[6] 413 759-2GX6**
A.B. Michelangeli *Piano Concerto 1.*
          (2/88) (DG) ① **419 248-2GH**
D. Barenboim *Concert*
          (10/90) (EMI) ① **[10] CZS7 62863-2**
J. Jandó *Concert*   (12/90) (NAXO) ① **8 550167**
W. Kempff (r1964) *Concert*
          (3/91) (DG) ① **[9] 429 306-2GX9**
A. Schnabel (r1935) *Concert*
          (7/91) (EMI) ① **[8] CHS7 63765-2**
C. Arrau *Concert*
          (1/92) (PHIL) ① **[11] 432 301-2PM11**
J-B. Pommier *Concert*
          (9/93) (ERAT) ① **[3] 2292-45598-2**
S. Richter (r1975) *Concert*
          (1/94) (OLYM) ① **OCD336**
R. Goode *Concert*
          (3/94) (NONE) ① **[10] 7559-79328-2**
J. O'Conor (r1993) *Concert*
          (8/94) (TELA) ① **CD80363**

T. Nikolaieva (pp1983) *Concert*
          (1/95) (OLYM) ① **OCD562**
Sonata for Piano No. 5 in C minor, Op. 10/1
(?1795-97)
A. Brendel (r1977) *Concert*
          (1/85) (PHIL) ① **[11] 412 575-2PH11**
D. Barenboim *Concert*
          (7/85) (DG) ① **[6] 413 759-2GX6**
Emil Gilels *Concert*   (11/87) (DG) ① **419 172-2GH**
B-L. Gelber *Concert*   (9/88) (DENO) ① **CO-2203**
D. Barenboim *Concert*
          (10/90) (EMI) ① **[10] CZS7 62863-2**
J. Jandó *Concert*   (12/90) (NAXO) ① **8 550161**
J. O'Conor *Concert*   (12/90) (TELA) ① **CD80237**
W. Kempff (r1964) *Concert*
          (3/91) (DG) ① **[9] 429 306-2GX9**
A. Schnabel (r1935) *Concert*
          (7/91) (EMI) ① **[8] CHS7 63765-2**
C. Arrau *Concert*
          (1/92) (PHIL) ① **[11] 432 301-2PM11**
R. Goode *Concert*   (4/92) (NONE) ① **7559-79213-2**
L. Lortie *Concert*   (3/93) (CHAN) ① **CHAN9101**
J. Lill *Concert*   (3/93) (ASV) ① **CDQS6057**
J-B. Pommier *Concert*
          (9/93) (ERAT) ① **[3] 2292-45598-2**
A. Brendel (r1960s) *Concert*
          (9/93) (VOX) ① **[2] 115772-2**
R. Goode *Concert*
          (3/94) (NONE) ① **[10] 7559-79328-2**
T. Fellner (r1993) *Concert*
          (9/94) (CLAV) ① **CD50-9328**
Z. Kocsis *Concert*   (9/94) (PHIL) ① **442 405-2PM**
T. Nikolaieva (pp1983) *Concert*
          (1/95) (OLYM) ① **OCD562**
Sonata for Piano No. 6 in F, Op. 10/2 (1796-
97)
A. Brendel (r1975) *Concert*
          (1/85) (PHIL) ① **[11] 412 575-2PH11**
D. Barenboim *Concert*
          (7/85) (DG) ① **[6] 413 759-2GX6**
D. Barenboim *Concert*
          (10/90) (EMI) ① **[10] CZS7 62863-2**
J. Jandó *Concert*   (12/90) (NAXO) ① **8 550161**
J. O'Conor *Concert*   (12/90) (TELA) ① **CD80237**
W. Kempff (r1964) *Concert*
          (3/91) (DG) ① **[9] 429 306-2GX9**
S. Richter (pp1980) *Concert*
          (3/91) (PYRA) ① **[2] PYR13500/1**
A. Schnabel (r1933) *Concert*
          (7/91) (EMI) ① **[8] CHS7 63765-2**
C. Arrau *Concert*
          (1/92) (PHIL) ① **[11] 432 301-2PM11**
R. Goode *Concert*   (4/92) (NONE) ① **7559-79213-2**
L. Lortie *Concert*   (3/93) (CHAN) ① **CHAN9101**
J. Lill *Concert*   (3/93) (ASV) ① **CDQS6057**
J-B. Pommier *Concert*
          (9/93) (ERAT) ① **[3] 2292-45598-2**
A. Brendel (r1960s) *Concert*
          (9/93) (VOX) ① **[2] 115772-2**
M. Horszowski (r1980s) *Concert*
          (12/93) (NONE) ① **[3] 7559-79261-2**
R. Goode *Concert*
          (3/94) (NONE) ① **[10] 7559-79328-2**
T. Nikolaieva (pp1983) *Concert*
          (1/95) (OLYM) ① **OCD562**
Sonata for Piano No. 7 in D, Op. 10/3 (1797-
98)
A. Brendel (r1972) *Concert*
          (1/85) (PHIL) ① **[11] 412 575-2PH11**
D. Barenboim *Concert*
          (7/85) (DG) ① **[6] 413 759-2GX6**
Emil Gilels *Concert*   (12/87) (DG) ① **423 136-2GH**
Edwin Fischer (r1954) *Piano Concerto 5.*
          (3/88) (EMI) ① **CDH7 61005-2**
D. Barenboim *Concert*
          (10/90) (EMI) ① **[10] CZS7 62863-2**
J. Jandó *Concert*   (12/90) (NAXO) ① **8 550161**
J. O'Conor *Concert*   (12/90) (TELA) ① **CD80237**
W. Kempff (r1964) *Concert*
          (3/91) (DG) ① **[9] 429 306-2GX9**
S. Richter (pp1980) *Concert*
          (3/91) (PYRA) ① **[2] PYR13500/1**
A. Schnabel (r1935) *Concert*
          (7/91) (EMI) ① **[8] CHS7 63765-2**
C. Arrau *Concert*
          (1/92) (PHIL) ① **[11] 432 301-2PM11**
R. Goode *Concert*   (4/92) (NONE) ① **7559-79213-2**
S. Richter *Concert*
          (3/93) (EMI) ① **[4] CMS7 64429-2**
L. Lortie *Concert*   (3/93) (CHAN) ① **CHAN9101**
J. Lill *Concert*   (3/93) (ASV) ① **CDQS6057**
J-B. Pommier *Concert*
          (9/93) (ERAT) ① **[3] 2292-45598-2**
R. Goode *Concert*
          (3/94) (NONE) ① **[10] 7559-79328-2**

Emil Gilels *Piano Sonata 17.*
    (8/86) (DG) ① **419 161-2GH**
W. Kempff (r1965) *Concert*
    (8/87) (DG) ① **415 834-2GGA**
B-L. Gelber *Concert*   (1/89) (DENO) ① **CO-72539**
J. Jandó *Piano Concerto 5.*
    (10/90) (NAXO) ① **8 550290**
D. Barenboim *Concert*
    (10/90) (EMI) ① [10] **CZS7 62863-2**
W. Kempff (r1965) *Concert*
    (3/91) (DG) ① [9] **429 306-2GX9**
A. Schnabel (r1933) *Concert*
    (7/91) (EMI) ① [8] **CHS7 63765-2**
C. Arrau *Concert*
    (1/92) (PHIL) ① [11] **432 301-2PM11**
M. Horszowski (pp1986) *Concert*
    (4/92) (LYRN) ① **LYRCD070**
M. Pollini *Concert*   (4/92) (DG) ① **427 770-2GH**
J-B. Pommier *Concert*
    (9/93) (ERAT) ① [3] **2292-45812-2**
A. Brendel (r1960s) *Concert*
    (9/93) (VOX) ① [2] **115772-2**
A. de Larrocha (r1992) *Piano Concerto 1.*
    (12/93) (RCA) ① **09026 61676-2**
R. Goode *Concert*
    (3/94) (NONE) ① [10] **7559-79328-2**
A. Brendel (r1977) *Concert*
    (4/94) (PHIL) ① [2] **438 730-2PM2**
A. Schnabel (r1933) *Concert*
    (11/94) (PEAR) ① [2] **GEMMCDS9123**
G. Oppitz (r1993) *Concert*
    (5/95) (RCA) ① **09026 61969-2**
T. Nikolaieva (pp1983) *Concert*
    (6/95) (OLYM) ① **OCD565**

Sonata for Piano No. 16 in G, Op. 31/1 (1802)
A. Brendel (r1977) *Concert*
    (1/85) (PHIL) ① [11] **412 575-2PH11**
D. Barenboim *Concert*
    (7/85) (DG) ① [6] **413 766-2GX6**
R. Goode *Concert*   (9/90) (NONE) ① **7559-79212-2**
D. Barenboim *Concert*
    (10/90) (EMI) ① [10] **CZS7 62863-2**
W. Kempff (r1964) *Concert*
    (3/91) (DG) ① [9] **429 306-2GX9**
J. Jandó *Concert*   (6/91) (NAXO) ① **8 550166**
A. Schnabel (r1935) *Concert*
    (7/91) (EMI) ① [8] **CHS7 63765-2**
C. Arrau *Concert*
    (1/92) (PHIL) ① [11] **432 301-2PM11**
A. Brendel (r1992) *Concert*
    (7/93) (PHIL) ① **438 134-2PH**
J-B. Pommier *Concert*
    (9/93) (ERAT) ① [3] **2292-45812-2**
R. Goode *Concert*   (3/94) (NONE) ① [10] **7559-79328-2**
A. Schnabel (r1935) *Concert*
    (11/94) (PEAR) ① [2] **GEMMCDS9123**
T. Nikolaieva (pp1983) *Concert*
    (6/95) (OLYM) ① **OCD565**
M. Chung (r1994) *Concert*
    (6/95) (CHNN) ① **CCS7195**
C. Arrau (r1990) *Concert*
    (7/95) (PHIL) ① [2] **432 173-2PH2**
S. Kovacevich *Concert*
    (11/95) (EMI) ① **CDC5 55226-2**

Sonata for Piano No. 17 in D minor, 'Tempest', Op. 31/2 (1802)
A. Brendel (r1977) *Concert*
    (1/85) (PHIL) ① [11] **412 575-2PH11**
D. Barenboim *Concert*
    (7/85) (DG) ① [6] **413 766-2GX6**
Emil Gilels *Piano Sonata 15.*
    (8/86) (DG) ① **419 161-2GH**
M. Perahia *Concert*   (2/88) (SONY) ① **MK42319**
J. O'Conor *Concert*   (5/88) (TELA) ① **CD80160**
W. Kempff *Piano Sonata 29.*
    (9/88) (DG) ① **419 857-2GGA**
M. Pollini *Concert*   (5/89) (DG) ① **427 642-2GH**
D. Barenboim *Concert*
    (12/89) (DG) ① **427 803-2GDC**
R. Goode *Concert*   (9/90) (NONE) ① **7559-79212-2**
D. Barenboim *Concert*
    (10/90) (EMI) ① [10] **CZS7 62863-2**
J. Jandó *Concert*   (2/91) (NAXO) ① **8 550054**
W. Kempff (r1964) *Concert*
    (3/91) (DG) ① [9] **429 306-2GX9**
S. Richter (pp1980) *Concert*
    (3/91) (PYRA) ① [2] **PYR13500/1**
A. Schnabel (r1934) *Concert*
    (7/91) (EMI) ① [8] **CHS7 63765-2**
C. Arrau *Concert*
    (1/92) (PHIL) ① [11] **432 301-2PM11**
S. Richter *Concert*
    (3/93) (EMI) ① [4] **CMS7 64429-2**

A. Brendel (r1992) *Concert*
    (7/93) (PHIL) ① **438 134-2PH**
J-B. Pommier *Concert*
    (9/93) (ERAT) ① [3] **2292-45812-2**
B-L. Gelber (r1992) *Concert*
    (1/94) (DENO) ① **CO-75245**
R. Goode *Concert*
    (3/94) (NONE) ① [10] **7559-79328-2**
A. Brendel (r1977) *Concert*
    (4/94) (PHIL) ① [2] **438 730-2PM2**
Z. Kocsis *Concert*   (9/94) (PHIL) ① **442 405-2PM**
A. Schnabel (r1934) *Concert*
    (11/94) (PEAR) ① [2] **GEMMCDS9123**
G. Oppitz (r1993) *Concert*
    (5/95) (RCA) ① **09026 61969-2**
T. Nikolaieva (pp1983) *Concert*
    (6/95) (OLYM) ① **OCD565**
C. Ortiz (r1994) *Concert*   (10/95) (TRIN) ① **TRP027**
C. Haskil (r1960) *Concert*
    (11/95) (PHIL) ① [12] **442 685-2PM12**
C. Haskil (r1960) *Concert*
    (11/95) (PHIL) ① [3] **442 635-2PM3**
C. Haskil (r1955) *Concert*
    (11/95) (PHIL) ① [3] **442 635-2PM3**
C. Haskil (r1955) *Concert*
    (11/95) (PHIL) ① [12] **442 685-2PM12**
S. Kovacevich *Concert*
    (11/95) (EMI) ① **CDC5 55226-2**

Sonata for Piano No. 18 in E flat, Op. 31/3 (1802)
A. Brendel (r1975) *Concert*
    (1/85) (PHIL) ① [11] **412 575-2PH11**
D. Barenboim *Concert*
    (7/85) (DG) ① [6] **413 766-2GX6**
Emil Gilels *Concert*   (12/87) (DG) ① **423 136-2GH**
M. Perahia *Concert*   (2/88) (SONY) ① **MK42319**
B-L. Gelber *Concert*   (6/89) (DENO) ① **CO-73006**
R. Goode *Concert*   (9/90) (NONE) ① **7559-79212-2**
D. Barenboim *Concert*
    (10/90) (EMI) ① [10] **CZS7 62863-2**
W. Kempff (r1964) *Concert*
    (3/91) (DG) ① [9] **429 306-2GX9**
S. Richter (pp1980) *Concert*
    (3/91) (PYRA) ① [2] **PYR13500/1**
J. Jandó *Concert*   (6/91) (NAXO) ① **8 550166**
A. Schnabel (r1932) *Concert*
    (7/91) (EMI) ① [8] **CHS7 63765-2**
C. Arrau *Concert*
    (1/92) (PHIL) ① [11] **432 301-2PM11**
C. Arrau (r1947) *Concert*
    (1/92) (EMI) ① [5] **CZS7 67379-2**
A. Rubinstein (r1954) *Concert*
    (4/93) (RCA) ① **09026 61260-2**
A. Brendel (r1992) *Concert*
    (7/93) (PHIL) ① **438 134-2PH**
J-B. Pommier *Concert*
    (9/93) (ERAT) ① [3] **2292-45812-2**
R. Goode *Concert*
    (3/94) (NONE) ① [10] **7559-79328-2**
Vladimir Ashkenazy (pp1963) *Concert*
    (5/94) (RUSS) ① **RDCD11208**
S. Richter (r1992) *Concert*
    (8/94) (PHIL) ① [2] **438 624-2PH2**
A. Schnabel (r1932) *Concert*
    (11/94) (PEAR) ① [2] **GEMMCDS9123**
T. Nikolaieva (pp1983) *Concert*
    (6/95) (OLYM) ① **OCD566**
C. Haskil (r1960) *Concert*
    (11/95) (PHIL) ① [3] **442 635-2PM3**
C. Haskil (r1955) *Concert*
    (11/95) (PHIL) ① [12] **442 685-2PM12**
C. Haskil (r1960) *Concert*
    (11/95) (PHIL) ① [12] **442 685-2PM12**
C. Haskil (r1955) *Concert*
    (11/95) (PHIL) ① [3] **442 635-2PM3**
S. Kovacevich *Concert*
    (11/95) (EMI) ① **CDC5 55226-2**
Movt 2. J. Hofmann *Concert*
    (10/92) (APR) ① [2] **APR7013**

Sonata for Piano No. 19 in G minor, Op. 49/1 (?1797)
A. Brendel (r1975) *Concert*
    (1/85) (PHIL) ① [11] **412 575-2PH11**
D. Barenboim *Concert*
    (7/85) (DG) ① [6] **413 766-2GX6**
Emil Gilels *Concert*   (11/87) (DG) ① **419 172-2GH**
D. Barenboim *Concert*
    (10/90) (EMI) ① [10] **CZS7 62863-2**
J. Jandó *Concert*   (12/90) (NAXO) ① **8 550167**
W. Kempff (r1964) *Concert*
    (3/91) (DG) ① [9] **429 306-2GX9**
A. Schnabel (r1932) *Concert*
    (7/91) (EMI) ① [8] **CHS7 63765-2**
C. Arrau *Concert*
    (1/92) (PHIL) ① [11] **432 301-2PM11**
J. Lill *Concert*   (12/92) (ASV) ① **CDQS6055**

J. O'Conor *Concert*   (5/93) (TELA) ① **CD80293**
J-B. Pommier *Concert*
    (9/93) (ERAT) ① [3] **2292-45812-2**
R. Goode *Concert*
    (3/94) (NONE) ① [10] **7559-79328-2**
S. Richter (r1992) *Concert*
    (8/94) (PHIL) ① [2] **438 486-2PH2**
A. Brendel (r1994) *Concert*
    (12/94) (PHIL) ① **438 863-2PH**
T. Nikolaieva (pp1983) *Concert*
    (6/95) (OLYM) ① **OCD566**

Sonata for Piano No. 20 in G, Op. 49/2 (1795-97)
A. Brendel (r1977) *Concert*
    (1/85) (PHIL) ① [11] **412 575-2PH11**
D. Barenboim *Concert*
    (7/85) (DG) ① [6] **413 766-2GX6**
Emil Gilels *Concert*   (11/87) (DG) ① **419 172-2GH**
B-L. Gelber *Concert*   (9/88) (DENO) ① **CO-2203**
D. Barenboim *Concert*
    (10/90) (EMI) ① [10] **CZS7 62863-2**
J. Jandó *Concert*   (12/90) (NAXO) ① **8 550167**
W. Kempff (r1964) *Concert*
    (3/91) (DG) ① [9] **429 306-2GX9**
A. Schnabel (r1933) *Concert*
    (7/91) (EMI) ① [8] **CHS7 63765-2**
C. Arrau *Concert*
    (1/92) (PHIL) ① [11] **432 301-2PM11**
J. Lill *Concert*   (12/92) (ASV) ① **CDQS6055**
J. O'Conor *Concert*   (5/93) (TELA) ① **CD80293**
J-B. Pommier *Concert*
    (9/93) (ERAT) ① [3] **2292-45812-2**
R. Goode *Concert*
    (3/94) (NONE) ① [10] **7559-79328-2**
S. Richter (r1992) *Concert*
    (8/94) (PHIL) ① [2] **438 486-2PH2**
T. Nikolaieva (pp1983) *Concert*
    (6/95) (OLYM) ① **OCD566**

Sonata for Piano No. 21 in C, 'Waldstein', Op. 53 (1803-04)
A. Brendel (r1973) *Concert*
    (1/85) (PHIL) ① [11] **412 575-2PH11**
D. Barenboim *Concert*
    (7/85) (DG) ① [6] **413 766-2GX6**
Emil Gilels *Concert*   (8/86) (DG) ① **419 162-2GH**
Vladimir Ashkenazy *Concert*
    (12/87) (DECC) ① **417 732-2DM**
J. O'Conor *Concert*   (5/88) (TELA) ① **CD80160**
C. Ortiz *Piano Concerto 5.*
    (8/88) (CARL) ① **PCD895**
Y. Nat (r1954) *Concert*
    (1/89) (EMI) ① **CDH7 61012-2**
M. Pletnev *Concert*   (4/89) (VIRG) ① **VC7 59247-2**
M. Pollini *Concert*   (5/89) (DG) ① **427 642-2GH**
W. Kempff *Concert*   (6/89) (DG) ① **419 053-2GGA**
B-L. Gelber *Concert*   (9/90) (DENO) ① **CO-74653**
D. Barenboim *Concert*
    (10/90) (EMI) ① [10] **CZS7 62863-2**
J. Jandó *Concert*   (2/91) (NAXO) ① **8 550054**
W. Kempff (r1964) *Concert*
    (3/91) (DG) ① [9] **429 306-2GX9**
Vladimir Ashkenazy *Concert*
    (4/91) (DECC) ① **425 838-2DH**
A. Schnabel (r1934) *Concert*
    (7/91) (EMI) ① [8] **CHS7 63765-2**
C. Arrau *Concert*
    (1/92) (PHIL) ① [11] **432 301-2PM11**
C. Arrau (r1956/7) *Concert*
    (1/92) (EMI) ① [5] **CZS7 67379-2**
L. Lortie *Concert*   (4/92) (CHAN) ① **CHAN9024**
A. Brendel (r1993) *Concert*
    (11/93) (PHIL) ① **438 472-2PH**
S. Kovacevich (r1992) *Concert*
    (2/94) (EMI) ① **CDC7 54896-2**
R. Goode *Concert*
    (3/94) (NONE) ① [10] **7559-79328-2**
A. Brendel (r1973) *Concert*
    (4/94) (PHIL) ① [2] **438 730-2PM2**
Barry Douglas (r1992) *Concert*
    (6/94) (RCA) ① **09026 61280-2**
V. Horowitz (r1956) *Concert*
    (7/94) (RCA) ① **GD60375**
V. Horowitz (r1972) *Concert*
    (7/94) (SONY) ① **SK43467**
M. Tan (r1987) *Concert*
    (2/95) (VIRG) ① **VER5 61160-2**
T. Nikolaieva (pp1983) *Concert*
    (6/95) (OLYM) ① **OCD566**
W. Kempff (r1964) *Concert*
    (9/95) (DG) ① **447 404-2GOR**

Sonata for Piano No. 22 in F, Op. 54 (1804)
A. Brendel (r1977) *Concert*
    (1/85) (PHIL) ① [11] **412 575-2PH11**
D. Barenboim *Concert*
    (7/85) (DG) ① [6] **413 766-2GX6**

D. Barenboim *Concert*
(10/90) (EMI) ① [10] **CZS7 62863-2**
J. Jandó *Concert* (12/90) (NAXO) ① **8 550167**
W. Kempff (r1964) *Concert*
(3/91) (DG) ① [9] **429 306-2GX9**
A. Schnabel (r1933) *Concert*
(7/91) (EMI) ① [8] **CHS7 63765-2**
C. Arrau *Concert*
(1/92) (PHIL) ① [11] **432 301-2PM11**
C. Arrau *Concert*
(1/92) (EMI) ① [5] **CZS7 67379-2**
J. O'Conor *Concert* (5/93) (TELA) ① **CD80293**
A. Brendel (r1993) *Concert*
(11/93) (PHIL) ① **438 472-2PH**
R. Goode *Concert*
(3/94) (NONE) ① [10] **7559-79328-2**
S. Richter (r1992) *Concert*
(8/94) (PHIL) ① [2] **438 486-2PH2**
G. Cziffra (r1958) *Concert*
(3/95) (EMI) ① **CDM5 65254-2**
T. Nikolaieva (pp1983) *Concert*
(6/95) (OLYM) ① **OCD566**
C. Arrau (r1990) *Concert*
(7/95) (PHIL) ① [2] **432 173-2PH2**

**Sonata for Piano No. 23 in F minor,
'Appassionata', Op. 57 (1804)**
Vladimir Ashkenazy *Concert*
(5/84) (DECC) ① **410 260-2DH**
A. Brendel (r1970) *Concert*
(1/85) (PHIL) ① [11] **412 575-2PH11**
D. Barenboim *Concert*
(7/85) (DG) ① [6] **413 766-2GX6**
C. Rosenberger *Piano Sonata 32.*
(8/85) (DELO) ① **DE3009**
Emil Gilels *Concert* (8/86) (DG) ① **419 162-2GH**
J. Ogdon *Concert* (11/86) (CARL) ① **PCD828**
D. Barenboim *Concert* (6/87) (DG) ① **419 602-2GH**
J. O'Conor *Concert* (7/87) (TELA) ① **CD80118**
Vladimir Ashkenazy *Concert*
(12/87) (DECC) ① **417 732-2DM**
I. Margalit *Concert* (3/88) (CHAN) ① **CHAN8582**
Y. Nat (r1955) *Concert*
(1/89) (EMI) ① **CDH7 61012-2**
M. Pletnev *Concert* (4/89) (VIRG) ① **VC7 59247-2**
W. Kempff *Concert* (6/89) (DG) ① **419 053-2GGA**
B-L. Gelber *Concert* (6/89) (DENO) ① **CO-73006**
D. Barenboim *Concert*
(10/90) (EMI) ① [10] **CZS7 62863-2**
J. Jandó *Concert* (2/91) (NAXO) ① **8 550045**
W. Kempff (r1964) *Concert*
(3/91) (DG) ① [9] **429 306-2GX9**
R. Casadesus *Concert*
(3/91) (SONY) ① **SBK46345**
Vladimir Ashkenazy *Concert*
(4/91) (DECC) ① **425 838-2DH**
A. Schnabel (r1933) *Concert*
(7/91) (EMI) ① [8] **CHS7 63765-2**
C. Arrau *Concert*
(1/92) (PHIL) ① [11] **432 301-2PM11**
C. Arrau *Concert*
(1/92) (EMI) ① [5] **CZS7 67379-2**
A. Rubinstein (pp1975) *Concert*
(3/93) (RCA) ① **09026 61160-2**
H. Bauer (r1927) *Concert* (9/93) (BIDD) ① **LHW007**
A. Rubinstein (r1963) *Concert*
(10/93) (RCA) ① **09026 61443-2**
R. Goode *Concert*
(3/94) (NONE) ① [10] **7559-79328-2**
A. Brendel (r1970) *Concert*
(4/94) (PHIL) ① [2] **438 730-2PM2**
Barry Douglas (r1991) *Concert*
(6/94) (RCA) ① **09026 61280-2**
V. Horowitz *Concert* (7/94) (RCA) ① **GD60375**
V. Horowitz (r1972) *Concert*
(7/94) (SONY) ① **SK53467**
S. Richter (r1992) *Concert*
(8/94) (PHIL) ① [2] **438 486-2PH2**
Edwin Fischer (r1935) *Concert*
(12/94) (APR) ① **APR5502**
M. Tan (r1987) *Concert*
(2/95) (VIRG) ① **VER5 61160-2**
T. Nikolaieva (pp1983) *Concert*
(6/95) (OLYM) ① **OCD567**
W. Kempff (r1964) *Concert*
(9/95) (DG) ① **447 404-2GOR**
A. Brendel (r1994) *Concert*
(11/95) (PHIL) ① **442 787-2PH**

**Sonata for Piano No. 24 in F sharp, Op. 78
(1809)**
A. Brendel (r1970) *Concert*
(1/85) (PHIL) ① [11] **412 575-2PH11**
D. Barenboim *Concert*
(7/85) (DG) ① [6] **413 766-2GX6**
W. Kempff (r1965) *Concert*
(8/87) (DG) ① **415 834-2GGA**

D. Barenboim *Concert*
(10/90) (EMI) ① [10] **CZS7 62863-2**
J. Jandó *Concert* (12/90) (NAXO) ① **8 550162**
W. Kempff (r1965) *Concert*
(3/91) (DG) ① [9] **429 306-2GX9**
R. Casadesus *Concert*
(3/91) (SONY) ① **SBK46345**
A. Schnabel (r1932) *Concert*
(7/91) (EMI) ① [8] **CHS7 63765-2**
C. Arrau *Concert*
(1/92) (PHIL) ① [11] **432 301-2PM11**
J. O'Conor *Concert* (5/93) (TELA) ① **CD80293**
G. Gould (r1968) *Piano Sonata 29.*
(10/93) (SONY) ① **SMK52645**
S. Kovacevich (r1992) *Concert*
(2/94) (EMI) ① **CDC7 54896-2**
E. Petri (r1936) *Concert*
(3/94) (APR) ① [2] **APR7024**
R. Goode *Concert*
(3/94) (NONE) ① [10] **7559-79328-2**
T. Nikolaieva (pp1983) *Concert*
(6/95) (OLYM) ① **OCD567**
C. Arrau (r1990) *Concert*
(7/95) (PHIL) ① [2] **432 173-2PH2**
A. Brendel (r1994) *Concert*
(11/95) (PHIL) ① **442 787-2PH**

Sonata for Piano No. 25 in G, Op. 79 (1809)
A. Brendel (r1972) *Concert*
(1/85) (PHIL) ① [11] **412 575-2PH11**
D. Barenboim *Concert*
(7/85) (DG) ① [6] **413 766-2GX6**
M. Pollini *Concert* (5/89) (DG) ① **427 642-2GH**
D. Barenboim *Concert*
(10/90) (EMI) ① [10] **CZS7 62863-2**
J. Jandó *Concert* (12/90) (NAXO) ① **8 550161**
W. Kempff (r1964) *Concert*
(3/91) (DG) ① [9] **429 306-2GX9**
A. Schnabel (r1935) *Concert*
(7/91) (EMI) ① [8] **CHS7 63765-2**
C. Arrau *Concert*
(1/92) (PHIL) ① [11] **432 301-2PM11**
J. O'Conor *Concert* (5/93) (TELA) ① **CD80293**
A. Brendel (r1960s) *Concert*
(9/93) (VOX) ① [2] **115772-2**
B-L. Gelber (r1992) *Concert*
(1/94) (DENO) ① **CO-75245**
R. Goode *Concert*
(3/94) (NONE) ① [10] **7559-79328-2**
T. Nikolaieva (pp1983) *Concert*
(6/95) (OLYM) ① **OCD567**
C. Arrau (r1990) *Concert*
(7/95) (PHIL) ① [2] **432 173-2PH2**
A. Brendel (r1994) *Concert*
(11/95) (PHIL) ① [2] **442 787-2PH**

**Sonata for Piano No. 26 in E flat, 'Les
adieux', Op. 81a (1809-10)**
A. Brendel (r1977) *Concert*
(1/85) (PHIL) ① [11] **412 575-2PH11**
D. Barenboim *Concert*
(7/85) (DG) ① [6] **413 766-2GX6**
Emil Gilels *Concert* (8/86) (DG) ① **419 162-2GH**
M. Perahia *Concert* (2/88) (SONY) ① **MK42319**
J. O'Conor *Concert* (5/88) (TELA) ① **CD80160**
L. Godowsky (r1929) *Concert*
(4/89) (APR) ① [2] **APR7010**
M. Pollini *Concert* (5/89) (DG) ① **427 642-2GH**
W. Kempff *Concert* (6/89) (DG) ① **419 053-2GGA**
B-L. Gelber *Concert* (6/89) (DENO) ① **CO-73006**
D. Barenboim *Concert*
(12/89) (DG) ① **427 803-2GDC**
D. Barenboim *Concert*
(10/90) (EMI) ① [10] **CZS7 62863-2**
J. Jandó *Concert* (2/91) (NAXO) ① **8 550054**
W. Kempff (r1964) *Concert*
(3/91) (DG) ① [9] **429 306-2GX9**
R. Casadesus *Concert*
(3/91) (SONY) ① **SBK46345**
A. Schnabel (r1933) *Concert*
(7/91) (EMI) ① [8] **CHS7 63765-2**
C. Arrau *Concert*
(1/92) (PHIL) ① [11] **432 301-2PM11**
C. Arrau (r1958) *Concert*
(1/92) (EMI) ① [5] **CZS7 67379-2**
L. Lortie *Concert* (4/92) (CHAN) ① **CHAN9024**
A. Rubinstein (r1962) *Concert*
(10/93) (RCA) ① **09026 61443-2**
M. Horszowski (pp1982) *Diabelli Variations.*
(12/93) (RELI) ① **CR911020**
R. Goode *Concert*
(3/94) (NONE) ① [10] **7559-79328-2**
A. Brendel (r1977) *Concert*
(4/94) (PHIL) ① [2] **438 730-2PM2**
M. Tan (r1987) *Concert*
(2/95) (VIRG) ① **VER5 61160-2**
G. Oppitz (r1993) *Concert*
(5/95) (RCA) ① **09026 61969-2**

T. Nikolaieva (pp1983) *Concert*
(6/95) (OLYM) ① **OCD567**
**Sonata for Piano No. 27 in E minor, Op. 90
(1814)**
A. Brendel (r1975) *Concert*
(1/85) (PHIL) ① [11] **412 575-2PH11**
D. Barenboim *Concert*
(7/85) (DG) ① [6] **413 766-2GX6**
B-L. Gelber *Concert* (9/90) (DENO) ① **CO-74653**
D. Barenboim *Concert*
(10/90) (EMI) ① [10] **CZS7 62863-2**
J. Jandó *Concert* (12/90) (NAXO) ① **8 550162**
W. Kempff (r1965) *Concert*
(3/91) (DG) ① [9] **429 306-2GX9**
S. Barere (pp1949) *Concert*
(5/91) (APR) ① [2] **APR7009**
A. Schnabel (r1932) *Concert*
(7/91) (EMI) ① [8] **CHS7 63765-2**
C. Arrau *Concert*
(1/92) (PHIL) ① [11] **432 301-2PM11**
S. Kovacevich *Concert*
(10/92) (EMI) ① **CDC7 54599-2**
Solomon (r1956) *Concert*
(7/93) (EMI) ① **CHS7 64708-2**
J. O'Conor (r1992) *Concert*
(8/93) (TELA) ① **CD80335**
A. Brendel (r1975) *Concert*
(8/93) (PHIL) ① [2] **438 374-2PM2**
Solomon (r1956) *Concert*
(9/93) (EMI) ① [2] **CZS7 67735-2**
S. Richter (r1971) *Concert*
(1/94) (OLYM) ① **OCD336**
E. Petri (pp1959) *Concert*
(3/94) (MUSI) ① [4] **MACD-772**
E. Petri (r1936) *Concert*
(3/94) (APR) ① [2] **APR7024**
R. Goode *Concert*
(3/94) (NONE) ① [10] **7559-79328-2**
Barry Douglas (r1991) *Concert*
(6/94) (RCA) ① **09026 61280-2**
S. Richter *Concert*
(8/94) (PHIL) ① [2] **438 617-2PH2**
C. Rosen (r1968/9) *Concert*
(11/94) (SONY) ① [2] **SB2K53531**
T. Nikolaieva (pp1983) *Concert*
(6/95) (OLYM) ① **OCD567**
A. Brendel (r1995) *Concert*
(11/95) (PHIL) ① **442 787-2PH**
Sonata for Piano No. 28 in A, Op. 101 (1816)
A. Brendel (r1975) *Concert*
(1/85) (PHIL) ① [11] **412 575-2PH11**
D. Barenboim *Concert*
(7/85) (DG) ① [6] **413 766-2GX6**
M. Pollini *Concert*
(12/86) (DG) ① [2] **419 199-2GH2**
A. Ciccolini *Concert* (3/90) (NUOV) ① [2] **6797/8**
M. Pollini *Piano Sonata 29.*
(7/90) (DG) ① **429 569-2GH**
D. Barenboim *Concert*
(10/90) (EMI) ① [10] **CZS7 62863-2**
J. Jandó *Concert* (12/90) (NAXO) ① **8 550162**
W. Kempff (r1964) *Concert*
(3/91) (DG) ① [9] **429 306-2GX9**
A. Schnabel (r1934) *Concert*
(7/91) (EMI) ① [8] **CHS7 63765-2**
C. Arrau *Concert*
(1/92) (PHIL) ① [11] **432 301-2PM11**
C. Arrau (r1956) *Concert*
(1/92) (EMI) ① [5] **CZS7 67379-2**
S. Kovacevich *Concert*
(10/92) (EMI) ① **CDC7 54599-2**
Solomon (r1954) *Concert*
(7/93) (EMI) ① [2] **CHS7 64708-2**
A. Brendel (r1975) *Concert*
(8/93) (PHIL) ① [2] **438 374-2PM2**
J. O'Conor (r1992) *Concert*
(8/93) (TELA) ① **CD80335**
A. Brendel (r1992) *Concert*
(11/93) (PHIL) ① **438 472-2PH**
M. Horszowski (pp1970) *Piano Sonata 29.*
(12/93) (RELI) ① **CR911021**
B-L. Gelber (r1992) *Concert*
(1/94) (DENO) ① **CO-75245**
R. Goode *Concert*
(3/94) (NONE) ① [10] **7559-79328-2**
V. Horowitz (pp1967) *Concert*
(7/94) (SONY) ① **SK53466**
P. Donohoe *Diabelli Variations.*
(8/94) (EMI) ① **CDC7 54792-2**
S. Richter (r1986) *Concert*
(8/94) (PHIL) ① [2] **438 624-2PH2**
C. Rosen (r1968/9) *Concert*
(11/94) (SONY) ① [2] **SB2K53531**
T. Nikolaieva (pp1983) *Piano Sonata 29.*
(6/95) (OLYM) ① **OCD568**

6, 12, 13. E. Woods, C. Watkinson, J. Protschka, R. Salter, C. Altenburger, J. Berger, H. Deutsch (r1987) *Concert* (12/95) (SONY) ① **SK64301**

12 Irish Songs—folksong arrangements, WoO154 (1816)
1. The Elfin Fairies; 2. Oh harp of Erin; 3. The Farewell Song; 4. The pulse of an Irishman; 5. Oh! who, my dear Dermot; 6. Put round the bright wine; 7. From Garyone, my happy home; 8. Save me from the grave and wise (with chorus); 9. Oh! would I were but that sweet linnet (duet); 10. The hero may perish (duet); 11. The Soldier in a Foreign Land (duet); 12. He promised me at parting (duet).
1, 9. F. Lott, A. Murray, G. Johnson, G. Solodchin, J. Williams *Concert* (11/90) (EMI) ① **CDC7 49930-2**
4, 8, 12. E. Woods, C. Watkinson, J. Protschka, R. Salter, C. Altenburger, J. Berger, H. Deutsch (r1987) *Concert* (12/95) (SONY) ① **SK64301**
9, 12. V. de los Angeles, D. Fischer-Dieskau, G. Moore (r1960) *Concert* (4/94) (EMI) ① [4] **CMS5 65061-2(2)**

Der Kuss—Lied, Op. 128 (?1822) (Wds. Weisse)
F. Wunderlich, H. Giesen *Concert* (11/90) (DG) ① **429 933-2GDO**
O. Bär, G. Parsons (r1992) *Concert* (11/93) (EMI) ① **CDC7 54879-2**
D. Fischer-Dieskau, H. Klust (r1955) *Concert* (10/95) (TEST) ① **SBT1057**

Der Liebende—Lied, WoO139 (1809) (Wds. Reissig)
O. Bär, G. Parsons (r1992) *Concert* (11/93) (EMI) ① **CDC7 54879-2**

Lied aus der Ferne—Lied, WoO137 (1809) (Wds. Reissig)
O. Bär, G. Parsons (r1992) *Concert* (11/93) (EMI) ① **CDC7 54879-2**
D. Fischer-Dieskau, H. Klust (r1955) *Concert* (10/95) (TEST) ① **SBT1057**

6 Lieder, Op. 48 (1802-03) (Wds. Gellert)
1. Bitten; 2. Die Liebe des Nächsten; 3. Vom Tode; 4. Die Ehre Gottes aus der Natur; 5. Gottes Macht und Vorsehung; 6. Busslied.
Cpte D. Fischer-Dieskau, G. Moore (pp1965) *Concert* (6/87) (ORFE) ① **C140501A**
Cpte J. Kowalski, S. Katz *Concert* (12/92) (CAPR) ① **10 359**
Cpte O. Bär, G. Parsons (r1992) *Concert* (11/93) (EMI) ① **CDC7 54879-2**
Cpte D. Fischer-Dieskau, H. Klust (r1955) *Concert* (10/95) (TEST) ① **SBT1057**
4. H. Hotter, H. Dokoupil (r1968-9) *Concert* (8/89) (PREI) ① **93390**
4. O. Natzke, H. Greenslade (Eng: r1947) *Concert* (12/92) (ODE) ① **CDODE1365**
4. H. Schlusnus, Berlin St Op Orch, H. Weigert (r1930) *Concert* (1/94) (PREI) ① [2] **89205**
4. K. Flagstad, E. McArthur (r1936) *Concert* (12/95) (PEAR) ① **GEMMCD9092**
4. K. Flagstad, E. McArthur (r1936) *Concert* (12/95) (NIMB) ① **NI7871**
4. K. Flagstad, E. McArthur (r1936) *Concert* (12/95) (SIMA) ① [3] **PSC1821(2)**

8 Lieder, Op. 52 (pub 1805)
1. Urians Reise um die Welt (with chorus) (wds. Claudius); 2. Feuerfarb (wds. Mereau); 3. Das Liedchen von der Ruhe (wds. Ueltzen); 4. Maigesang: Mailied (wds. Goethe); 5. Mollys Abschied (wds. Bürger); 6. Die Liebe (wds. Lessing); 7. Marmotte (wds. Goethe); 8. Das Blümchen Wunderhold (wds. Bürger).
3, 4, 6, 7. D. Fischer-Dieskau, H. Klust (r1955) *Concert* (10/95) (TEST) ① **SBT1057**
4. D. Fischer-Dieskau, J. Demus *Concert* (9/85) (DG) ① **415 189-2GH**
4. D. Fischer-Dieskau, G. Moore (pp1965) *Concert* (6/87) (ORFE) ① **C140501A**
4. O. Bär, G. Parsons (r1992) *Concert* (11/93) (EMI) ① **CDC7 54879-2**

6 Lieder, Op. 75 (pub 1809)
1. Mignons Lied (wds. Goethe); 2. Neue Liebe, neues Leben (wds. Goethe); 3. Aus Goethes Faust: Es war einmal ein König (wds. Goethe); 4. Gretels Warnung (wds. von Harlem); 5. An den fernen Geliebten (wds. Reissig); 6. Der Zufriedene (wds. Reissig).
2. H. Prey, L. Hokanson *Concert* (6/87) (DENO) ① **CO-1254**
2. O. Bär, G. Parsons (r1992) *Concert* (11/93) (EMI) ① **CDC7 54879-2**
2, 3. D. Fischer-Dieskau, G. Moore (pp1965) *Concert* (6/87) (ORFE) ① **C140501A**
2, 3, 6. D. Fischer-Dieskau, H. Klust (r1955) *Concert* (10/95) (TEST) ① **SBT1057**
3. D. Fischer-Dieskau, J. Demus *Concert* (9/85) (DG) ① **415 189-2GH**

3 Lieder, Op. 83 (pub 1810) (Wds. Goethe)
1. Wonne der Wehmut; 2. Sehnsucht; 3. Mit einem gemalten Band.
Cpte O. Bär, G. Parsons (r1992) *Concert* (11/93) (EMI) ① **CDC7 54879-2**
Cpte D. Fischer-Dieskau, H. Klust (r1955) *Concert* (10/95) (TEST) ① **SBT1057**
1. E. Schwarzkopf, G. Moore (r1954) *Concert* (12/90) (EMI) ① **CDM7 63654-2**
1. I. Seefried, E. Werba (pp1957) *Concert* (9/93) (ORFE) ① **C297921B**
1, 2. D. Fischer-Dieskau, G. Moore (pp1965) *Concert* (6/87) (ORFE) ① **C140501A**

Mass in C—SATB, chorus and orchestra, Op. 86 (1807)
M. Hajóssyová, J. Zerhauová, P. Oswald, P. Mikuláš, Slovak Phil Chor, Slovak PO, A. Nanut (6/90) (OPUS) ① **9352 1947**
G. Janowitz, J. Hamari, H. Laubenthal, E.G. Schramm, Munich Bach Ch, Munich Bach Orch, K. Richter (r1970) *Mozart: Mass, K317.* (6/90) (DG) ① **429 510-2GR**
H. Schellenberg, M. Simpson, J. Humphrey, M. Myers, Atlanta Sym Chor, Atlanta SO, Robert Shaw *Concert* (2/91) (TELA) ① **CD80248**
C. Eda-Pierre, P. Payne, R. Tear, K. Moll, LSC, LSO, Colin Davis (r1977) *Missa Solemnis.* (8/93) (PHIL) ① [2] **438 362-2PM2**
K. van Kampen, I. Danz, K. Lewis, M. Brodard, Stuttgart Gächinger Kantorei, Stuttgart Bach Collegium, H. Rilling (r1994) *Christus am Oelberge, Op. 85.* (11/94) (HANS) ① [2] **98 993**

Mass in D, 'Missa Solemnis'—SATB, chorus, orchestra and organ, Op. 123 (1818-23)
Cpte J. Varady, I. Vermillion, V. Cole, R. Pape, Berlin Rad Chor, BPO, G. Solti (pp1994) (6/95) (DECC) ① **444 337-2DH**
G. Janowitz, A. Baltsa, P. Schreier, J. Van Dam, Vienna Singverein, BPO, H. von Karajan (4/88) (EMI) ① [2] **CMS7 69246-2**
M. Hirsti, C. Watkinson, A. Murgatroyd, M. George, Oslo Cath Ch, Hanover Band, T. Kvam (8/88) (NIMB) ① **NI5109**
T. Kiberg, R. Lang, W. Cochran, M. Krutikov, Maryland Univ Chor, European SO, A. Dorati (pp1988; includes rehearsal excs) (11/88) (BIS) ① [2] **BIS-CD406/7**
S. McNair, J. Taylor, J. Aler, T. Krause, Atlanta Sym Chor, Atlanta SO, Robert Shaw (r1987) *Mozart: Mass, K427.* (11/88) (TELA) ① [2] **CD80150**
E. Söderström, M. Höffgen, W. Kmentt, M. Talvela, New Philh Chor, New Philh, O. Klemperer (r1965) *Choral Fantasia.* (12/88) (EMI) ① [2] **CMS7 69538-2**
G. Janowitz, C. Ludwig, F. Wunderlich, W. Berry, Vienna Singverein, BPO, H. von Karajan *Mozart: Mass, K317.* (2/89) (DG) ① [2] **423 913-2GGA2**
C. Vaness, W. Meier, H-P. Blochwitz, H. Tschammer, Tallis Chbr Ch, ECO, J. Tate (1989) (4/90) (EMI) ① **CDC7 49950-2**
P. Coburn, F. Quivar, A. Baldin, A. Schmidt, Stuttgart Gächinger Kantorei, Stuttgart Bach Collegium, H. Rilling (4/90) (HANS) ① [2] **98 956**
L. Marshall, M. Merriman, E. Conley, J. Hines, R. Shaw Chorale, NBC SO, A. Toscanini (r1953) *Cherubini: Requiem 1.* (3/91) (RCA) ① [2] **GD60272**
C. Margiono, C. Robbin, W. Kendall, A. Miles, Monteverdi Ch, EBS, J.E. Gardiner (3/91) (ARCH) ① **429 779-2AH**
T. Eipperle, L. Willer, J. Patzak, G. Hann, Vienna St Op Chor, VPO, C. Krauss (pp1944) (2/92) (DG) ① [12] **435 321-2GWP12**
E. Farrell, C. Smith, Richard Lewis, K. Borg, Westminster Ch, NYPO, L. Bernstein (r1960) *Concert* (11/92) (SONY) ① [2] **SM2K47522**
C. Studer, J. Norman, P. Domingo, K. Moll, Leipzig Rad Chor, Swedish Rad Chor, E Ericson Chbr Ch, VPO, James Levine (11/92) (DG) ① [2] **435 770-2GH2**
E. Mei, M. Lipovšek, A. Rolfe Johnson, R. Holl, A. Schoenberg Ch, COE, N. Harnoncourt (pp1992) (4/93) (TELD) ① [2] **9031-74884-2**
A. Tomowa-Sintow, P. Payne, R. Tear, R. Lloyd, LSC, LSO, Colin Davis (r1977) *Mass in C.* (8/93) (PHIL) ① [2] **438 362-2PM2**
L. Orgonášová, J. Rappé, U. Heilmann, J-H. Rootering, Bavarian Rad Chor, BRSO, Colin Davis (r1992) *Choral Fantasia.* (3/94) (RCA) ① [2] **09026 60967-2**
T. Kiberg, W. Meier, J. Aler, R. Holl, Chicago Sym Chor, Chicago SO, D. Barenboim (pp1993) (6/94) (ERAT) ① [2] **4509-91731-2**
M. Arroyo, M. Forrester, Richard Lewis, C. Siepi, Singing City Chs, Philadelphia, E. Ormandy (r1967) (10/94) (SONY) ① **SBK53517**

R. Mannion, B. Remmert, J. Taylor, C. Hauptmann, Chapelle Royale Ch, Collegium Vocale, Paris Champs-Élysées Orch, P. Herreweghe (pp1995) (12/95) (HARM) ① **HMC90 1557**

Meeresstille und glückliche Fahrt—cantata, Op.112 (1814-15) (Wds. Goethe)
Vienna St. Op. Concert Ch, VPO, C. Abbado *Concert* (4/88) (DG) ① **419 779-2GH**
Ambrosian Sngrs, LSO, M. Tilson Thomas *Concert* (11/88) (SONY) ① **MK76404**
Vienna St Op Concert Ch, VPO, C. Abbado *Concert* (9/89) (DG) ① [6] **427 306-2GH6**
Atlanta Sym Chor, Atlanta SO, Robert Shaw *Concert* (2/91) (TELA) ① **CD80248**

Opferlied—soprano, chorus and orchestra, Op. 121b (1823-24)
L. Haywood, Ambrosian Sngrs, LSO, M. Tilson Thomas *Concert* (11/88) (SONY) ① **MK76404**

La Partenza—Lied, WoO124 (1797) (Wds. Metastasio)
C. Bartoli, A. Schiff (r1992) *Concert* (11/93) (DECC) ① **440 297-2DH**

Resignation—Lied, WoO149 (1817) (Wds. von Haugwitz)
F. Wunderlich, H. Giesen *Concert* (11/90) (DG) ① **429 933-2GDO**
D. Fischer-Dieskau, H. Klust (r1955) *Concert* (10/95) (TEST) ① **SBT1057**

25 Scottish Songs—folksong arrangements, Op. 108 (1818)
1. Music, Love and Wine (with chorus); 2. Sunset; 3. Oh! sweet were the hours; 4. The Maid of Isla; 5. The Sweetest lad was Jamie; 6. Dim, dim is my eye; 7. Bonnie laddie, highland laddie; 8. The lovely lass of Inverness; 9. Behold my love how green the groves (duet); 10. Sympathy; 11. Oh! thou art the lad; 12. Oh, had my fate; 13. Come fill, fill, my good fellow (with chorus); 14. O, how can I be blithe; 15. O cruel was my father; 16. Could this ill world; 17. O Mary, at thy window be; 18. Enchantress, farewell; 19. O swiftly glides the bonny boat (with chorus); 20. Faithfu' Johnie; 21. Jeanie's Distress; 22. The Highland Watch (with chorus); 23. The Shepherd's Song; 24. Again, my lyre; 25. Sally in our Alley.
1-3, 5, 7, 9, 13, 18-20, 23. E. Woods, C. Watkinson, J. Protschka, R. Salter, C. Altenburger, J. Berger, H. Deutsch (r1987) *Concert* (12/95) (SONY) ① **SK64301**
2, 3, 5, 7, 8, 17, 20, 24, 25. M. Kweksilber, V. Bethes, A. Bylsma, S. Hoogland *Concert* (12/91) (CHNN) ① **CCS1491**
5, 6, 11, 14, 20, 21. English Piano Trio, A. Mackay *Concert* (4/94) (MERI) ① **CDE84253**
8. Scottish Early Music Consort (r1987) *Concert* (10/95) (CHAN) ① **CHAN0581**

12 Scottish Songs—folksong arrangements, WoO156 (1822-41)
1. The Banner of Buccleuch (trio); 2. Duncan Gray (trio); 3. Up quit thy bower (trio); 4. Ye shepherds of this pleasant vale (trio); 5. Cease your running; 6. Highland Harry; 7. Polly Stewart; 8. Womankind (trio); 9. Lochnager (trio); 10. Glencoe (trio); 11. Auld lang syne (trio with chorus); 12. The Quaker's Wife (trio).
2. Scottish Early Music Consort (r1987) *Concert* (10/95) (CHAN) ① **CHAN0581**
2, 5. E. Woods, C. Watkinson, J. Protschka, R. Salter, C. Altenburger, J. Berger, H. Deutsch (r1987) *Concert* (12/95) (SONY) ① **SK64301**
5. English Piano Trio, A. Mackay *Concert* (4/94) (MERI) ① **CDE84253**

Sehnsucht—Lied, WoO146 (1815-16) (Wds. Reissig)
O. Bär, G. Parsons (r1992) *Concert* (11/93) (EMI) ① **CDC7 54879-2**
D. Fischer-Dieskau, H. Klust (r1955) *Concert* (10/95) (TEST) ① **SBT1057**

12 Songs of various nationality—folksong arrangements, WoO157 (1816-39)
1. God Save the King (with chorus) (Eng); 2. The Soldier (Irish); 3. O Charlie is my darling (trio) (Scots); 4. O sanctissima (trio) (Sicilian); 5. The Miller of Dee (trio) (Eng); 6. A health to the brave (duet) (Irish); 7. Since all thy vows false maid (trio) (Irish); 8. By the side of the Shannon (Irish); 9. Highlander's Lament (with chorus) (Scots); 10. Sir Johnie Cope (?Scots); 11. The Wandering Minstrel (with chorus) (Irish); 12. La gondoletta (Venetian).
3, 7. E. Woods, C. Watkinson, J. Protschka, R. Salter, C. Altenburger, J. Berger, H. Deutsch (r1987) *Concert* (12/95) (SONY) ① **SK64301**

23 Songs of various nationality—folksong arrangements, WoO158a
1. Ridder Stig synger i Congens Gaard (Danish); 2. Horch auf, mein Liebchen (Ger); 3. Wegen meiner bleib d'Fräula (Ger); 4. Wann i in der Früh aufstehn (Tirolean); 5. I bin a Tyroler Bua (Tirolean); 6. A

Madel, ja a Madel (Tirolean); 7. Wer solche Buema afipackt (Tirolean); 8. Ih mag di nit (Tirolean); 9. Oj upiłem sie w karczmie (Polish); 10. Poszla bab po popiół (Polish); 11. Yo no quiero embarcarme (?Por); 12. Seus lindos olhos (duet) (Port); 13. Im Walde sind viele Mücklein geboren (Russ); 14. Ach Bächlein, Bächlein, kühle Wasser (Russ); 15. Unsere Mädchen gingen in den Wald (Russ); 16. Schöne Minka, ich muss scheiden (Ukrainian); 17. Lilla Carl, sov sött i frid (Swed); 18. An ä Bergli bi i gesässe (?Swiss); 19. Una paloma blanca (Sp); 20. Como la mariposa (duet) (Sp); 21. La tiranna se embarca (Sp); 22. Édes kinos emlékezet (Hung); 23. Da brava, Catina (Venetian).

23. A. Rolfe Johnson, B. Brooks, J. Pearson, G. Johnson *Concert* (3/88) (HYPE) ① **CDA66112**

6 Songs of various nationality—folksong arrangements, WoO158c

1. When my hero in court appears (from 'The Beggar's Opera'); 2. Non, non, Collette n'est point trompeuse (from 'Le devin du village'); 3. Mark yonder pomp of costly fashion (Scots); 4. Bonnie wee thing (trio) (Scots); 5. From thee, Eliza, I must go (trio) (Scots); 6. unidentified.

4. Scottish Early Music Consort (r1987) *Concert* (10/95) (CHAN) ① **CHAN0581**

Der **Wachtelschlag—Lied, WoO129 (1803)** (Wds. Sauter)

D. Fischer-Dieskau, G. Moore (pp1965) *Concert* (6/87) (ORFE) ① **C140501A**

O. Bär, G. Parsons (r1992) *Concert* (11/93) (EMI) ① **CDC7 54879-2**

K. Erb, B. Seidler-Winkler (r1939) *Concert* (6/94) (PREI) ① [2] **89208**

D. Fischer-Dieskau, H. Klust (r1955) *Concert* (10/95) (TEST) ① **SBT1057**

26 Welsh Songs—folksong arrangements, WoO155 (1817)

1. Sion, the son of Evan (duet); 2. The Monks of Bangor's March (duet); 3. The Cottage Maid; 4. Love without Hope; 5. A golden robe my love shall wear; 6. The Maids of Mona; 7. Oh let the night my blushes hide; 8. Farewell, thou noisy town; 9. To the Aeolian Harp; 10. Ned Pugh's Farewell; 11. Merch Megan; 12. Waken lords and ladies gay; 13. Helpless Woman; 14. The Dream (duet); 15. When mortals all to rest retire; 16. The Damsels of Cardigan; 17. The Dairy House; 18. Sweet Richard; 19. The Vale of Clwyd; 20. To the Blackbird; 21. Cupid's Kindness; 22. Constancy (duet); 23. The Old Strain; 24. Three Hundred Pounds; 25. The Parting Kiss; 26. Good Night.

2, 4, 8, 9, 20. E. Woods, C. Watkinson, J. Protschka, R. Salter, C. Altenburger, J. Berger, H. Deutsch (r1987) *Concert* (12/95) (SONY) ① **SK64301**

14. V. de los Angeles, D. Fischer-Dieskau, G. Moore (r1960) *Concert* (4/94) (EMI) ① [4] **CMS5 65061-2(2)**

Zärtliche Liebe, 'Ich liebe dich'—Lied, WoO123 (?1795) (Wds. Herrosee)

D. Fischer-Dieskau, J. Demus *Concert* (9/85) (DG) ① **415 189-2GH**

H. Prey, L. Hokanson *Concert* (6/87) (DENO) ① **CO-1254**

H. Hotter, H. Dokoupil (r1968-9) *Concert* (8/89) (PREI) ① **93390**

F. Wunderlich, H. Giesen *Concert* (11/90) (DG) ① **429 933-2GDO**

O. Natzke, H. Greenslade (Eng: r1947) *Concert* (12/92) (ODE) ① **CDODE1365**

F. Wunderlich, H. Giesen *Concert* (5/93) (DG) ① **431 110-2GB**

O. Bär, G. Parsons (r1992) *Concert* (11/93) (EMI) ① **CDC7 54879-2**

H. Schlusnus, F. Rupp (r1932) *Concert* (1/94) (PREI) ① [2] **89205**

K. Erb, B. Seidler-Winkler (r1939) *Concert* (6/94) (PREI) ① [2] **89208**

C. Ludwig, C. Spencer (pp1994) *Concert* (3/95) (RCA) ① **09026 62652-2**

D. Fischer-Dieskau, H. Klust (r1955) *Concert* (10/95) (TEST) ① **SBT1057**

K. Flagstad, E. McArthur (r1936) *Concert* (12/95) (PEAR) ① **GEMMCD9092**

K. Flagstad, E. McArthur (r1936) *Concert* (12/95) (NIMB) ① **NI7871**

K. Flagstad, E. McArthur (r1936) *Concert* (12/95) (SIMA) ① [3] **PSC1821(2)**

SECTION V: STAGE WORKS

Egmont—incidental music, Op. 84 (1810)

EXCERPTS: 1. Overture; 2. Die Trommel gerühret!; 3. Zwischenakt I (Andante); 4. Zwischenakte II (Larghetto); 5. Freudvoll und leidvoll; 6. Zwischenakte III (Allegro); 7. Zwischenakte IV (Poco sostenuto e risoluto); 8. Klärchen's Tod; 9. Süsser Schlaf (Melodrama); 10. Siegessymphonie.

Cpte G. Janowitz, E. Schellow, BPO, H. von Karajan *Concert* (10/87) (DG) ① **419 624-2GH**

Cpte S. McNair, W. Quadflieg, NYPO, K. Masur (pp1992) *Symphony 5.* (1/94) (TELD) ① **9031-77313-2**

1. BPO, H. von Karajan (r1969) *Concert* (8/85) (DG) ① **415 276-2GH**

1. BPO, H. von Karajan (r1969) *Concert* (4/88) (DG) ① **419 048-2GGA**

1. VPO, L. Bernstein *Concert* (3/89) (DG) ① [6] **423 481-2GX6**

1. LSO, W. Morris (r1988) *Symphony 6.* (5/89) (CARL) ① **PCD912**

1. VPO, C. Abbado *Concert* (9/89) (DG) ① [6] **427 306-2GH6**

1. LCP, R. Norrington *Concert* (11/89) (EMI) ① **CDC7 49816-2**

1. Philh, H. von Karajan (r1953) *Concert* (1/90) (EMI) ① [5] **CMS7 63310-2**

1. NYPSO, W. Mengelberg (r1930) *Concert* (7/90) (SYMP) ① **SYMCD1078**

1. VPO, K. Böhm *Concert* (10/90) (DG) ① **429 509-2GR**

1. Philh, Vladimir Ashkenazy *Concert* (12/91) (DECC) ① **430 721-2DM**

1. Chicago SO, G. Solti *Concert* (4/92) (DECC) ① [6] **430 792-2DC6**

1. BPO, W. Furtwängler (r1933) *Concert* (4/92) (KOCH) ① [2] **37059-2**

1. NYPO, L. Bernstein (r1970) *Concert* (11/92) (SONY) ① **SMK47516**

1. NBC SO, A. Toscanini (bp1939) *Concert* (11/92) (RCA) ① **GD60267**

1. NBC SO, A. Toscanini (r1953) *Concert* (11/92) (RCA) ① **GD60270**

1. Staatskapelle Dresden, Colin Davis (r1991) *Symphony 3.* (3/93) (PHIL) ① **434 120-2PH**

1. RPO, M. Ermler (r1992) *Symphony 6.* (5/94) (TRIN) ① **TRP001**

1. Leipzig Gewandhaus, K. Masur (r1972) *Concert* (5/94) (PHIL) ① [2] **438 706-2PM2**

1. Milan La Scala PO, C. M. Giulini (r1993) *Concert* (5/94) (SONY) ① **SK53974**

1. Concertgebouw, W. Mengelberg (pp1943) *Concert* (7/94) (MUSI) ① [4] **MACD-780**

1. Concertgebouw, B. Haitink (r1985) *Concert* (9/94) (PHIL) ① [5] **442 073-2PB5**

1. VPO, L. Bernstein (pp1981) *Concert* (12/94) (DG) ① **445 505-2GMA**

1. LSO, P. Monteux (r1961) *Concert* (12/94) (DECC) ① [2] **443 479-2DF2**

1. BBC SO, A. Boult (pp1972) *Concert* (3/95) (BBCR) ① **BBCRD9114**

1. VPO, K. Böhm (r1971) *Concert* (4/95) (DG) ① [2] **437 368-2GX2**

1. BPO, R. Kempe (r c1958) *Concert* (11/95) (EMI) ① [2] **CES5 68518-2**

1. Staatskapelle Dresden, Colin Davis (r1991) *Concert* (12/95) (PHIL) ① [6] **446 067-2PH6**

1, 2, 5, 8. B. Nilsson, Philh, O. Klemperer (r1957) *Concert* (8/90) (EMI) ① **CDM7 63358-2**

1, 3-10. C. Studer, B. Ganz, BPO, C. Abbado (pp1991) *Concert* (5/92) (DG) ① **435 617-2GH**

2, 5. I. Seefried, E. Werba (pp1957) *Concert* (9/93) (ORFE) ① **C297921B**

2, 5. C. Ludwig, C. Spencer (pp1994) *Concert* (3/95) (RCA) ① **09026 62652-2**

Fidelio—opera: 2 acts, Op. 72 (1814—Vienna) (Lib. Sonnleithner and Treitschke)

EXCERPTS: 1. Overture; 2. ACT 1: Jetzt, Schätzchen, jetzt; 3. Oh, wär' ich schon; 4. Mir ist so wunderbar; 5. Hat man nicht auch Gold; 6. Gut, Söhnchen, gut; 7. March; 8. Ha! Welch ein Augenblick; 9. Jetzt, Alter; 10a. Abscheulicher!; 10b. Komm, Hoffnung; 11. O, welche Lust!; 12a. Nun sprecht, wie ging's?; 12b. Ach! Vater, eilt!. ACT 2: 13a. Gott! Welch Dunkel hier!; 13b. In des Lebens; 14a. Melodrama; 14b. Nur hurtig fort; 15. Euch werde Lohn; 16. Er sterbe!; 17. O, namen, namenlose Freude!; 18. Heil sei dem Tag; 19. Des besten Königs Wink und Wille; 20. Wer ein holdes Weib errungen.

Cpte H. Dernesch, P. Hofmann, T. Adam, H. Sotin, S. Ghazarian, D. Kuebler, G. Howell, R. Johnson, P. Kraus, Chicago Sym Chor, Chicago SO, G. Solti (with dialogue) (3/85) (DECC) ① [2] **410 227-2DH2**

Cpte G. Janowitz, R. Kollo, H. Sotin, M. Jungwirth, L. Popp, A. Dallapozza, D. Fischer-Dieskau, K. Terkal, A. Sramek, Vienna St Op Chor, VPO, L. Bernstein (with dialogue) (6/87) (DG) ① [2] **419 436-2GH2**

Cpte H. Dernesch, J. Vickers, Z. Kélémen, K. Ridderbusch, H. Donath, H. Laubenthal, J. Van Dam, W. Hollweg, S.R. Frese, Berlin Deutsche Op Chor, BPO, H. von Karajan (with dialogue) (4/88) (EMI) ① [2] **CMS7 69290-2**

Cpte J. Norman, R. Goldberg, E. Wlaschiha, K. Moll, P. Coburn, H-P. Blochwitz, A. Schmidt, Dresden St Op Chor, Staatskapelle Dresden, B. Haitink (r1989: with dialogue) (1/91) (PHIL) ① [2] **426 308-2PH2**

Cpte K. Flagstad, R. Maison, F. Schorr, E. List, M. Farell, K. Laufkötter, A. Gabor, NY Met Op Chor, NY Met Op Orch, A. Bodanzky (pp1938: with recits!) (5/91) (MUSI) ① [2] **MACD-619**

Cpte R. Bampton, J. Peerce, H. Janssen, S. Belarsky, E. Steber, J. Laderoute, N. Moscona, Chor, NBC SO, A. Toscanini (omits dialogue: bp1944/r1945) (10/92) (RCA) ① [2] **GD60273**

Cpte M. Mödl, W. Windgassen, O. Edelmann, G. Frick, S. Jurinac, R. Schock, A. Poell, A. Hendriks, F. Bierbach, Vienna St Op Chor, VPO, W. Furtwängler (r1953: omits dialogue) (5/93) (EMI) ① [2] **CHS7 64496-2**

Cpte Leonie Rysanek, E. Haefliger, D. Fischer-Dieskau, G. Frick, I. Seefried, F. Lenz, K. Engen, Bavarian St Op Chor, Bavarian St Orch, F. Fricsay (r1957: with dialogue) *Leonore.* (5/93) (DG) ① [2] **437 345-2GDO2**

Cpte G. Schnaut, J. Protschka, H. Welker, K. Rydl, R. Ziesak, U. Heilmann, T. Krause, F. Struckmann, Vienna St Op Concert Ch, VPO, C. von Dohnányi (r1991: with dialogue) (7/93) (DECC) ① [2] **436 627-2DHO2**

Cpte K. Flagstad, J. Patzak, P. Schoeffler, J. Greindl, E. Schwarzkopf, A. Dermota, H. Braun, H. Gallos, L. Pantscheff, Vienna St Op Chor, VPO, W. Furtwängler (pp1950: with dialogue) (12/93) (EMI) ① [2] **CHS7 64901-2**

Cpte H. Konetzni, T. Ralf, P. Schoeffler, H. Alsen, I. Seefried, P. Klein, T. Neralič, H. Gallos, H. Schweiger, Vienna St Op Chor, Vienna St Op Orch, K. Böhm (pp1944: with dialogue) *Weber: Oberon.* (8/94) (PREI) ① [2] **90195**

Cpte C. Margiono, P. Seiffert, S. Leiferkus, L. Polgár, B. Bonney, D. van der Walt, B. Skovhus, R. Macias, R. Florianschütz, A. Schoenberg Ch, COE, N. Harnoncourt (r1994) (10/95) (TELD) ① [2] **4509-94560-2**

1. BPO, H. von Karajan (r1965) *Concert* (8/85) (DG) ① **415 276-2GH**

1. BPO, H. von Karajan *Concert* (8/87) (DG) ① **419 051-2GGA**

1. Philadelphia, R. Muti *Concert* (1/89) (EMI) ① [6] **CDS7 49487-2**

1. VPO, L. Bernstein (pp1978) *Concert* (3/89) (DG) ① [6] **423 481-2GX6**

1. Staatskapelle Dresden, K. Böhm *Concert* (12/91) (DG) ① [2] **413 145-2GW2**

1. M. Arroyo, R. Sarfaty, N. di Virgilio, N. Scott, Juilliard Chor, NYPO, L. Bernstein (r1961) *Symphony 9.* (11/92) (SONY) ① **SMK47518**

1. Leipzig Gewandhaus, K. Masur (r1973-4) *Concert* (5/94) (PHIL) ① [2] **438 706-2PM2**

1. Staatskapelle Dresden, K. Böhm (r1969) *Concert* (4/95) (DG) ① [2] **437 928-2GX2**

1. RPO, G. Herbig (r1994) *Symphony 3.* (6/95) (TRIN) ① **TRP026**

1. BPO, R. Kempe (r c1958) *Concert* (11/95) (EMI) ① [2] **CES5 68518-2**

3. E. Schwarzkopf, Philh, A. Galliera (r1950) *Concert* (4/92) (EMI) ① [7] **CHS7 69741-2(4)**

3. I. Seefried, Bavarian St Orch, F. Fricsay (r1957) *Concert* (9/93) (DG) ① [2] **437 677-2GDO2**

4. P. Anders, T. Eipperle, M. Fuchs, G. Hann, Berlin RSO, A. Rother (bp1944) *Concert* (8/93) (ACAN) ① **43 268**

4. E. Berger, H. Gottlieb, M. Wittrisch, W. Domgraf-Fassbaender, Berlin St Op Orch, F. Zweig (r1930s) *Concert* (10/93) (NIMB) ① **NI7848**

5. M. Salminen, Lahti SO, E. Klas *Concert* (8/92) (BIS) ① **BIS-CD520**

8. F. Schorr, New SO, A. Coates (r1930) *Concert* (9/91) (PEAR) ① **GEMMCD9398**

8. P. Schoeffler, Vienna St Op Chor, Vienna St Op Orch, K. Böhm (r1944) *Concert* (4/92) (EMI) ① [7] **CHS7 69741-2(4)**

10a, 10b F. Leider, orch, J. Barbirolli (r1928) *Concert* (2/90) (PREI) ① **89004**

10a, 10b E. Schwarzkopf, Philh, H. von Karajan (r1954) *Concert* (7/90) (EMI) ① **CDH7 63201-2**

10a, 10b F. Leider, orch (r1921) *Concert* (5/91) (PREI) ① [3] **89301**

10a, 10b K. Flagstad, Philadelphia, E. Ormandy (r1937) *Concert* (2/92) (MMOI) ① **CDMOIR408**

10a, 10b Lilli Lehmann, orch (r1907) *Concert* (7/92) (PEAR) ① [3] **GEMMCDS9923(2)**

10a, 10b K. Flagstad, Philadelphia, E. Ormandy
(r1937) *Concert* (7/93) (NIMB) ① **NI7847**
10a, 10b H. Konetzni, Berlin St Op Orch, H. Schmidt-
Isserstedt (r1937) *Concert* (1/95) (PREI) ① **90078**
10a, 10b R. Hunter, Tasmanian SO, D. Franks
(r1989) *Concert* (10/95) (ABCC) ① **8 7000 10**
10a, 10b K. Flagstad, Philadelphia, E. Ormandy
(r1937) *Concert* (12/95) (SIMA) ① [3] **PSC1821(2)**
10b Lotte Lehmann, orch, M. Gurlitt (r1927) *Concert*
(10/89) (NIMB) ① **NI7802**
11. Berlin Deutsche Op Chor, Berlin Deutsche Op
Orch, G. Sinopoli *Concert*
(10/85) (DG) ① **415 283-2GH**
11. F. Wunderlich, H.G. Nöcker, Stuttgart Rad Chor,
Stuttgart RSO, A. Rischner (bp1957) *Concert*
(10/89) (ACAN) ① **43 267**
11. J.M. Ainsley, A. Miles, ROH Chor, ROHO, B.
Haitink *Concert* (12/89) (EMI) ① **CDC7 49849-2**
13a H. Roswaenge, Berlin St Op Orch, B. Seidler-
Winkler (r1938) *Concert*
(5/90) (PEAR) ① **GEMMCD9394**
13a H. Roswaenge, Berlin St Op Orch, B. Seidler-
Winkler (r1938) *Concert*
(7/92) (PEAR) ① [3] **GEMMCDS9926(2)**
13a, 13b H. Roswaenge, Berlin St Op Orch, B.
Seidler-Winkler (r1938) *Concert*
(4/87) (PREI) ① **89018**
13a, 13b F. Völker, Berlin Staatskapelle, A. Melichar
(r1933) *Concert* (8/94) (PREI) ① **89070**
13a, 13b, 17. P. Anders, W. Wegner, N German
RSO, H. Schmidt-Isserstedt (bp1948) *Concert*
(8/93) (ACAN) ① **43 268**
Der **Geschöpfe des Prometheus, '(The)**
Creatures of Prometheus'—incidental music
for Vigano's play, Op. 43 (1801—Vienna)
EXCERPTS: 1. Overture; 2. Introduction (La
tempesta); 3. Poco adagio; 4. Adagio—allegro con
brio; 5. Allegro vivace; 6. Maestoso—andante; 7.
Adagio—andante quasi allegretto; 8. Un poco
adagio—allegro; 9. Grave; 10. Allegro con brio; 11.
Adagio; 12. Pastorale. Allegro; 13. Andante; 14.
Maestoso—adagio; 15. Allegro; 16.
Andante—adagio; 17. Andantino—adagio; 18. Finale.
Allegretto.
Cpte Orpheus CO (4/87) (DG) ① **419 608-2GH**
Cpte Scottish CO, C. Mackerras (r1994)
(11/94) (HYPE) ① **CDA66748**
1. COE, J. Judd *Concert* (8/85) (CARL) ① **PCD805**
1. BPO, H. von Karajan *Concert*
(4/87) (DG) ① **415 833-2GGA**
1. LSO, G. Schwarz *Concert*
(6/87) (DELO) ① **DE3013**
1. Philh, O. Klemperer *Symphony 7.*
(4/88) (EMI) ① **CDM7 69183-2**
1. VPO, L. Bernstein (pp1978) *Concert*
(3/89) (DG) ① [6] **423 481-2GX6**
1. LCP, R. Norrington (r1987) *Symphony 3.*
(4/89) (EMI) ① **CDC7 49101-2**
1. CBSO, W. Weller *Concert*
(5/89) (CHAN) ① [6] **CHAN8712/7**
1. New Philh, O. Klemperer (r1969) *Concert*
(8/90) (EMI) ① **CDM7 63358-2**
1. VPO, K. Böhm *Concert*
(10/90) (DG) ① **429 509-2GR**
1. VPO, F. Weingartner (1936) *Concert*
(5/91) (MSCM) ① **MM30269**
1. NBC SO, A. Toscanini (r1944) *Concert*
(11/92) (RCA) ① **GD60267**
1. Leipzig Gewandhaus, K. Masur (r1973) *Concert*
(5/94) (PHIL) ① [2] **438 706-2PM2**
1. BBC SO, A. Boult (pp1969) *Concert*
(3/95) (BBCR) ① **BBCRD9114**
1. VPO, K. Böhm (r1971) *Concert*
(4/95) (DG) ① [2] **437 368-2GX2**
1. BPO, R. Kempe (r c1958) *Concert*
(11/95) (EMI) ① [2] **CES5 68518-2**
2, 3, 11, 12, 17, 18. BPO, C. Abbado (pp1992)
Concert (1/95) (SONY) ① **SK53978**
König Stefan—incidental music, Op. 117
(1812—Vienna) (Wds. A. von Kotzebue)
EXCERPTS: 1. Overture; 2. Ruhend von seinen
Taten; 3. Auf dunklem Irrweg; 4. Siegesmarsch; 5.
Wo die Unschuld Blumen streute; 6. Melodrama 1; 7.
Eine neue strahlende Sonne; 8. Melodrama 2; 9. Heil
unserm Königel; 10. Heil unserm Enkelnl.
1. VPO, L. Bernstein (pp1978) *Concert*
(3/89) (DG) ① [6] **423 481-2GX6**
1. NYPO, L. Bernstein (1967) *Concert*
(11/92) (SONY) ① **SMK47517**
1. Leipzig Gewandhaus, K. Masur (r1973) *Concert*
(5/94) (PHIL) ① [2] **438 706-2PM2**
1. LSO, P. Monteux (r1960) *Concert*
(12/94) (DECC) ① [2] **443 479-2DF2**
1-5, 7-10. Ambrosian Sngrs, LSO, M. Tilson Thomas
Concert (11/88) (SONY) ① **MK76404**

Leonore—opera: 3 acts, Op. 72
(1805—Vienna) (Lib. J Sonnleither)
EXCERPTS: 1a. Leonore Overture No. 1, Op. 138;
1b. Leonore Overture No. 2; 1c. Leonore Overture
No. 3. ACT 1:
1a Concertgebouw, W. Mengelberg (r1931) *Concert*
(7/90) (SYMP) ① **SYMCD1078**
1a Philh, O. Klemperer (r1954) *Concert*
(8/92) (EMI) ① **CDM7 64143-2**
1a BBC SO, A. Toscanini (r1939) *Concert*
(5/94) (BIDD) ① [2] **WHL008/9**
1a-c Leipzig Gewandhaus, K. Masur (r1973-4)
Concert (5/94) (PHIL) ① [2] **438 706-2PM2**
1b VPO, C. Abbado *Concert*
(9/89) (DG) ① [6] **427 306-2GH6**
1b Dresden PO, H. Kegel *Concert*
(10/90) (LASE) ① **15 523**
1b BPO, E. Jochum *Concert*
(12/91) (DG) ① [2] **413 145-2GW2**
1b NBC SO, A. Toscanini (bp1939) *Concert*
(11/92) (RCA) ① **GD60267**
1b Chicago SO, F. Reiner (r1955) *Concert*
(12/92) (RCA) ① **09026 60962-2**
1b, 1c Philh, O. Klemperer (r1954) *Symphony 3.*
(4/92) (EMI) ① **CDM7 63855-2**
1c BPO, H. von Karajan *Symphony 3.*
(4/87) (DG) ① **419 049-2GGA**
1c Cleveland Orch, C. von Dohnányi (r1986)
Symphony 6. (11/87) (TELA) ① **CD80145**
1c Philadelphia, R. Muti *Concert*
(1/89) (EMI) ① [6] **CDS7 49487-2**
1c VPO, L. Bernstein (pp1978) *Concert*
(3/89) (DG) ① [6] **423 481-2GX6**
1c NBC SO, A. Toscanini (bp1939) *Concert*
(5/90) (RCA) ① [5] **GD60324**
1c VPO, B. Walter (r1936) *Concert*
(1/91) (KOCH) ① **37011-2**
1c N German RSO, G. Wand (pp1990) *Symphony 3.*
(10/91) (RCA) ① **RD60755**
1c Staatskapelle Dresden, K. Böhm *Concert*
(12/91) (DG) ① [2] **413 145-2GW2**
1c Philh, Vladimir Ashkenazy *Concert*
(12/91) (DECC) ① **430 721-2DM**
1c VPO, W. Furtwängler (pp1944) *Concert*
(2/92) (DG) ① [12] **435 321-2GWP12**
1c VPO, W. Furtwängler (pp1944) *Concert*
(2/92) (DG) ① **435 324-2GWP**
1c National PO, L. Stokowski *Concert*
(4/92) (EMI) ① **CDM7 64140-2**
1c Chicago SO, G. Solti *Concert*
(4/92) (DECC) ① [6] **430 792-2DC6**
1c BPO, C. Abbado (pp1991) *Concert*
(5/92) (DG) ① **435 617-2GH**
1c NYPO, L. Bernstein (r1960) *Concert*
(11/92) (SONY) ① **SMK47521**
1c NBC SO, A. Toscanini (r1945) *Concert*
(11/92) (RCA) ① **GD60267**
1c BPO, F. Fricsay (r1958) *Fidelio.*
(5/93) (DG) ① [2] **437 345-2GDO2**
1c VPO, B. Walter (r1936) *Concert*
(8/94) (PREI) ① **90157**
1c Staatskapelle Dresden, K. Böhm (r1969) *Concert*
(4/95) (DG) ① [2] **437 928-2GX2**
1c Staatskapelle Dresden, Colin Davis (r1993)
Concert (12/95) (PHIL) ① [4] **446 067-2PH6**

5. Boston Pops, A. Fiedler (r1958) *Concert*
(1/94) (RCA) ① **09026 61249-2**

BEIDERBECKE, Bix (1903-1976)
USA

SECTION III: INSTRUMENTAL

Candlelights: A Modern Piano Solo
A. Feinberg (r1994) *Concert*
(11/95) (ARGO) ① **444 457-2ZH**

BELLA, Ján Levoslav
(1843-1936) Slovakia

SECTION III: INSTRUMENTAL

4 Little pieces—piano (1866-69)
1. Caprice; 2. Vivace; 3. Fairy Dance; 4. Capriccietto.
D. Ruso (r1993) *Concert*
(6/95) (MARC) ① **8 223644**
Piece in C minor—piano (movt 1 of unfinished
Pf Son)
D. Ruso (r1993) *Concert*
(6/95) (MARC) ① **8 223644**
Sonata for Piano in B flat minor (1882)
D. Ruso (r1993) *Concert*
(6/95) (MARC) ① **8 223644**
Sonatina in E minor—piano (1870)
D. Ruso (r1993) *Concert*
(6/95) (MARC) ① **8 223644**
Variations in C sharp minor on 'A swarm, a
swarm in flying' (Letí, Letí roj)—piano, Op.
21
(6/95) (MARC) ① **8 223644**
Variations on 'In Pressburg by the Danube'
(Pri Prešporku na Danuji)—piano, Op. 9 (pub
1866)
D. Ruso (r1993) *Concert*
(6/95) (MARC) ① **8 223644**

BELLINI, Vincenzo (1801-1835)
Italy

SECTION I: ORCHESTRAL

Concerto for Oboe and Orchestra in E flat
Peterborough Stg Orch, N. Daniel (ob/dir) *Concert*
(8/89) (HYPE) ① **CDH88014**
R. Smedvig, Scottish CO, J. Ling (tpt) *Concert*
(8/90) (TELA) ① **CD80232**
H. Schellenberger, BPO, James Levine *Concert*
(5/91) (DG) ① **429 750-2GH**
M. André, Zurich CO, E. de Stoutz (trans tpt) *Concert*
(9/91) (EMI) ① **CDC7 54086-2**
R. Lord, ASMF, N. Marriner (r1964) *Concert*
(7/95) (DECC) ① [2] **443 838-2DF2**

SECTION IV: VOCAL AND CHORAL

Dolente imagine di figlia mia—arietta (1821)
(Wds. Genoino)
J. Carreras, Martin Katz *Concert*
(9/90) (SONY) ① **SK45863**
Il Fervido desiderio—arietta
J. Carreras, Martin Katz *Concert*
(9/90) (SONY) ① **SK45863**
G. Gatti, G. Moore (r1949) *Concert*
(4/92) (EMI) ① [7] **CHS7 69741-2(7)**
Malinconia, ninfa gentile—arietta
J. Carreras, Martin Katz *Concert*
(9/90) (SONY) ① **SK45863**
R. Tebaldi, R. Bonynge (r1972) *Concert*
(9/93) (DECC) ① **436 202-2DM**
Per pietà, bell'idol mio—aria da camera: 1v &
piano (Wds. P. Metastasio)
J. Carreras, Martin Katz *Concert*
(9/90) (SONY) ① **SK45863**
La Ricordanza—song (1834) (Wds. Pepoli)
J. Carreras, Martin Katz *Concert*
(9/90) (SONY) ① **SK45863**
Vaga luna che inargenti—aria da camera: 1v
& piano (Wds. anon)
J. Carreras, Martin Katz *Concert*
(9/90) (SONY) ① **SK45863**
Vanne, o rosa fortunata—arietta (?1829)
L. Pavarotti, Bologna Teatro Comunale Orch, R.
Bonynge *Concert*
(7/86) (DECC) ① [2] **417 011-2DH2**

SECTION V: STAGE WORKS

Adelson e Salvini—opera: 3 acts
(1825—Naples) (Lib. A.L. Tottola)
Cpte F. Previati, B. Williams, A. Nafé, A. Tomicich, L.
Rizzi, E. Jankovic, R. Coviello, G. Tosi, Bellini Th
Chor, Bellini Th Orch, A. Licata (pp1992)
(2/94) (NUOV) ① [2] **7154/5**

Cpte J. Sutherland, L. Pavarotti, P. Cappuccilli, N.
Ghiaurov, A. Caminada, G. Luccardi, R. Cazzaniga,
ROH Chor, LSO, R. Bonynge
(4/89) (DECC) ① [3] **417 588-2DH3**
Cpte M. Callas, G. di Stefano, R. Panerai, N. Rossi-
Lemeni, A. Mercuriali, C. Forti, A. Cattelani, La Scala
Chor, La Scala Orch, T. Serafin (r1953)
(4/89) (EMI) ① [2] **CDS7 47308-8**
Cpte M. Devia, W. Matteuzzi, C. Robertson, P.
Washington, E. Jankovic, F. Federici, Catania Teatro
Massimo Bellini Chor, Catania Teatro Massimo
Bellini Orch, R. Bonynge (pp1989)
(10/91) (NUOV) ① [3] **6842/4**
Cpte E. Gruberová, J. Lavender, E. Kim, F.E.
D'Artegna, K. Lytting, D. Siegele, C. Tuand, Bavarian
Rad Chor, Munich RO, F. Luisi (pp1993)
(12/94) (NIGH) ① [3] **NC070562-2**
4a C. Tagliabue, La Scala Orch, U. Berrettoni (r1946)
Concert (11/90) (PREI) ① **89015**
4b G. De Luca, orch (r1922) Concert
(1/92) (PREI) ① **89036**
4b M. Battistini, orch, C. Sabajno (r1911) Concert
(7/92) (PEAR) ① [3] **GEMMCDS9923(1)**
4b D. Hvorostovsky, Philh, I. Marin (r1992) Concert
(9/94) (PHIL) ① **434 912-2PH**
7. J. Sutherland, L. Pavarotti, G. Luccardi, N.
Ghiaurov, ROH Chor, ROHO, R. Bonynge Concert
(7/86) (DECC) ① [2] **417 011-2DH2**
7. G. Sabbatini, Berlin RSO, R. Paternostro Concert
(10/89) (CAPR) ① **10 247**
7. Alfredo Kraus, M. Caballé, A. Ferrin, S. Elenkov,
Ambrosian Op Chor, Philh, R. Muti Concert
(10/89) (EMI) ① **CDM7 63104-2**
7. G. Lauri-Volpi, orch (r1928) Concert
(10/89) (NIMB) ① **NI7801**
7. M. Fleta, orch (r1923) Concert
(2/90) (PREI) ① **89002**
7. G. Lauri-Volpi, orch, R. Bourdon (r1928) Concert
(9/90) (PREI) ① **89012**
7. G. Morino, Warmia Nat PO, B. Amaducci Concert
(10/90) (NUOV) ① **6851**
7. D. Borgioli, orch (r c1923) Concert
(12/90) (CLUB) ① **CL99-014**
7. A. Bonci, anon (r1905) Concert
(11/92) (MEMO) ① [2] **HR4408/9(1)**
7. G. Lauri-Volpi, orch (r1922) Concert
(7/93) (NIMB) ① **NI7845**
7. G. Lauri-Volpi, orch, R. Bourdon (r1928) Concert
(7/93) (NIMB) ① **NI7845**
7. A. Auger, R. Bunger, H. Lackner, Vienna Op Orch,
N. Rescigno (r1969) Concert
(12/93) (DECC) ① **433 437-2DA**
7. A. Bonci, anon (r1905) Concert
(4/94) (EMI) ① [3] **CHS7 64860-2(1)**
7. A. Pertile, La Scala Orch, C. Sabajno (r1930)
Concert (10/94) (PREI) ① **89072**
7. A. Giorgini, orch (r1905) Concert
(4/95) (RECO) ① **TRC3**
7. M. Freni, L. Pavarotti, B. Giaiotti, chor, Rome SO,
R. Muti (pp1969) Concert
(10/95) (RCA) ① **09026 68014-2**
7, 18a, 18b R. Giménez, S.C. Dyson, Scottish Phil
Sngrs, Scottish CO, M. Veltri Concert
(5/90) (NIMB) ① **NI5224**
9. M. André, Toulouse Capitole Orch, M. Plasson (arr
tpt) Concert (1/89) (EMI) ① **CDC7 49219-2**
9. L. Aliberti, Berlin RSO, R. Paternostro Concert
(10/89) (CAPR) ① **10 247**
9. A. Galli-Curci, orch, G. Polacco (r1923) Concert
(10/89) (NIMB) ① **NI7801**
9. F. Toresella, anon (r1900) Concert
(12/89) (SYMP) ① **SYMCD1065**
9. J. Sutherland, ROHO, F. Molinari-Pradelli Concert
(1/90) (DECC) ① [2] **425 493-2DM2**
9. E. Gruberová, V. Walterová, L.M. Vodička, P.
Horáček, Smetana Th Chor, Czech PO, F. Haider
Concert (5/90) (SONY) ① **SK45633**
9. L. Pons, Columbia SO, A. Kostelanetz (r1949)
Concert (7/90) (SONY) ① **MPK45694**
9. Dilbèr, Estonia Op Orch, E. Klas Concert
(9/92) (ONDI) ① **ODE768-2**
9. A. Galli-Curci, orch, R. Bourdon (r1923) Concert
(8/94) (ROMO) ① [2] **81004-2**
9, 16a-c J. Sutherland, M. Elkins, P. Duval, R.
Capecchi, E. Flagello, MMF Chor, MMF Orch, R.
Bonynge Concert
(2/93) (DECC) ① [3] **433 706-2DMO3**
14. E. Pinza, orch (r1924) Concert
(2/89) (PEAR) ① **GEMMCD9306**
16a-c M. Caballé, M. Manuguerra, A. Ferrin, Philh, R.
Muti Concert (10/88) (EMI) ① **CDM7 69500-2**
16a-c M. Freni, Rome Op Orch, F. Ferraris Concert
(10/89) (EMI) ① **CDM7 63110-2**
16a-c M. Callas, R. Panerai, N. Rossi-Lemeni, La
Scala Chor, La Scala Orch, T. Serafin (r1953)
Concert (2/90) (EMI) ① [4] **CMS7 63244-2**

16b L. Aliberti, Munich RO, L. Gardelli Concert
(11/86) (ORFE) ① **C119841A**
16b A. Galli-Curci, orch (r1917) Concert
(2/89) (PEAR) ① **GEMMCD9308**
16b A. Galli-Curci, orch, R. Bourdon (r1917) Concert
(5/90) (NIMB) ① **NI7806**
16b L. Orgonášová, Bratislava RSO, W. Humburg
Concert (2/93) (NAXO) ① **8 550605**
16b M. Sembrich, orch (r1907) Concert
(7/93) (NIMB) ① [2] **NI7840/1**
16b M. Carosio, orch, A. Erede (r1948) Concert
(4/94) (EMI) ① [3] **CHS7 64864-2(2)**
16b I. Mula-Tchako, Paris Opéra-Bastille Orch, E.
Kohn (pp1992) Concert (6/94) (SONY) ① **SK46691**
16b, 16c A. Galli-Curci, orch, J. Pasternack (r1917)
Concert (3/94) (ROMO) ① [2] **81003-2**
16b, 16c A. Galli-Curci, orch, J. Pasternack (r1920)
Concert (8/94) (ROMO) ① [2] **81004-2**
16b, 16c M. Devia, Svizzera Italiana Orch, M. Rota
(pp1992) Concert (10/94) (BONG) ① **GB2513-2**
16c L. Tetrazzini, orch (r1912) Concert
(9/92) (EMI) ① [3] **CHS7 63802-2(2)**
16c L. Tetrazzini, orch (r1912) Concert
(9/92) (PEAR) ① **GEMMCD9223**
18b A. Giorgini, orch (r1908) Concert
(4/95) (RECO) ① **TRC3**
19a L. Pavarotti, Catania Teatro Massimo Bellini
Orch, A. Quadri (pp1968) Concert
(10/95) (RCA) ① **09026 62541-2**
19b, 19c, 20. M. Callas, G. di Stefano, La Scala
Orch, T. Serafin Concert
(10/88) (EMI) ① **CDM7 69543-2**
20. F. Marconi, M. Galvany, orch (r1908) Concert
(10/90) (SYMP) ① **SYMCD1069**
20. D. Borgioli, E. Surinach, orch (r c1923) Concert
(12/90) (CLUB) ① **CL99-014**

La Sonnambula—opera: 2 acts
(1831—Milan) (Lib. F. Romani)
EXCERPTS - ACT 1: 1. Viva Amina!; 2. Tutto è
gioia; 3. In Elvezia non v'ha rosa; 4a. Care
compagne; 4b. A te, diletta tenera madre; 4c. Come
per me sereno; 4d. Sovra il sen; 5. Io più di tutti, o
Amina; 6a. Perdono, o mia diletta; 6b. Elvin, che
rechi?; 6c. Prendi: l'anel ti dono; 6d. Ah! vorrei trovar
parole; 7a. Qual rumore; 7b. Il mulino!; 7c. Vi ravviso,
o luoghi ameni; 7d. Tu non sai con quei begli occhi;
8a. Contezza del paese avete voi, Signor; 8b. A
questa colsa, o notte bruna; 8c. Basta così; 8a. Elvino!
E me tu lasci; 9b. Son geloso del zefiro errante; 10.
Davver, non mi dispiace; 11. Che veggio?; 12.
Osservate! L'uscio è aperto; 13. È menzogna; 14a.
D'un pensiero e d'un accento; 14b. Non più nozze.
ACT 2: 15. Qui la selva è più folta; 16a. Reggimi, o
buono madre; 16b. Tutto è sciolto; 16c. Pasci il
guardo e appaga l'alma; 17a. Viva il Conte!; 17b. Ah!
perchè non posso odiarti; 18a. Lasciami: aver
compreso; 18b. De'lieti auguri a voi son grato; 19a.
Signor Conte, agli occhi miei; 19b. V'han certuni che
dormendo; 19c. Piano, amici, non gridate; 20. Lisa
mendace anch'essa!; 21a. Signor, che creder
deggio?; 21b. Chi? Mira...ella stessa; 22a. Oh! se
una volta sola; 22b. Ah! non creda mirarti; 22c. Ah!
non giunge.
Cpte M. Callas, N. Monti, N. Zaccaria, E. Ratti, F.
Cossotto, G. Morresi, F. Ricciardi, La Scala Chor, La
Scala Orch, A. Votto (1957)
(9/86) (EMI) ① [2] **CDS7 47378-8**
Cpte J. Sutherland, L. Pavarotti, N. Ghiaurov, I.
Buchanan, D. Jones, J. Tomlinson, P. de Palma,
London Op Chor, National PO, R. Bonynge
(4/87) (DECC) ① [2] **417 424-2DH2**
Cpte J. Valásková, J. Kundlák, P. Mikuláš, E.
Antoličová, J. Saparová, J. Galla, V. Schrenkel,
Slovak Phil Chor, Bratislava RSO, O. Lenárd
(10/89) (OPUS) ① [2] **9356 1928/9**
4a-c Dilbèr, Estonia Op Orch, E. Klas Concert
(9/92) (ONDI) ① **ODE768-2**
4a-d J. Sutherland, ROH Chor, ROHO, F. Molinari-
Pradelli Concert
(1/90) (DECC) ① [2] **425 493-2DM2**
4a-d M. Callas, La Scala Chor, La Scala Orch, A.
Votto (1957) Concert
(2/90) (EMI) ① [4] **CMS7 63244-2**
4a, 4b, 4c, 4d M. Devia, Svizzera Italiana Orch, M.
Rota (pp1992) Concert
(10/94) (BONG) ① **GB2513-2**
4c L. Orgonášová, Bratislava RSO, W. Humburg
Concert (2/93) (NAXO) ① **8 550605**
4c A. Galli-Curci, orch, J. Pasternack (r1920) Concert
(3/94) (ROMO) ① [2] **81003-2**
4c, 4d L. Tetrazzini, orch (r1912) Concert
(9/92) (EMI) ① [3] **CHS7 63802-2(2)**
4c, 4d L. Tetrazzini, orch (r1912) Concert
(9/92) (PEAR) ① **GEMMCD9223**
4c, 4d, 22b A. Galli-Curci, orch (r1917-20) Concert
(2/89) (PEAR) ① **GEMMCD9308**

4c, 22b, 22c M. Callas, La Scala Orch, T. Serafin
(r1955) Concert (12/87) (EMI) ① **CDC7 47966-2**
4d A. Galli-Curci, orch, R. Bourdon (r1919) Concert
(5/90) (NIMB) ① **NI7806**
4d A. Galli-Curci, orch, J. Pasternack (r1919) Concert
(3/94) (ROMO) ① [2] **81003-2**
6b T. Dal Monte, T. Schipa, La Scala Chor, La Scala
Orch, F. Ghione (r1933) Concert
(4/90) (EMI) ① **CDH7 63200-2**
6c T. Schipa, T. dal Monte, La Scala Chor, La Scala
Orch, F. Ghione (r1933) Concert
(10/90) (MSCM) ① [2] **MM30231**
6c Ferruccio Tagliavini, EIAR Orch, U. Tansini
(r1940) Concert (3/94) (CENT) ① **CRC2164**
6c A. Giorgini, orch (r1905) Concert
(4/95) (RECO) ① **TRC3**
6c, 9b F. de Lucia, M. Galvany, anon (r1908) Concert
(1/95) (SYMP) ① **SYMCD1149**
7b, 7c P. Plançon, anon (Fr: r1903) Concert
(9/91) (PEAR) ① **GEMMCD9497**
7b, 7c P. Plançon, anon (r1903) Concert
(12/94) (ROMO) ① [2] **82001-2**
7b, 7c P. Plançon, anon (r1903) Concert
(1/95) (NIMB) ① **NI7860**
7c F. Chaliapin, orch, R. Bourdon (r1927) Concert
(12/89) (EMI) ① **GEMMCD9314**
7c L. Sibiriakov, orch (r1911: Russ) Concert
(6/93) (PEAR) ① [3] **GEMMCDS9007/9(2)**
7c T. Pasero, Rome Teatro Reale Orch, L. Ricci
(r1943) Concert (4/95) (PREI) ① **89074**
7c, 7d R. Arié, LSO, J. Krips (r1949) Concert
(4/92) (EMI) ① [7] **CHS7 69741-2(7)**
7d T. Pasero, orch, L. Molajoli (r1928) Concert
(6/90) (PREI) ① **89010**
9b A. Galli-Curci, T. Schipa, orch, R. Bourdon (r1923)
Concert (12/89) (RCA) ① **GD87969**
9b A. Galli-Curci, T. Schipa, orch, R. Bourdon (r1923)
Concert (5/90) (NIMB) ① **NI7806**
9b T. Schipa, A. Galli-Curci, orch, R. Bourdon (r1923)
Concert (10/90) (MSCM) ① [2] **MM30231**
9b A. Galli-Curci, T. Schipa, orch, R. Bourdon (r1923)
Concert (3/94) (CONI) ① **CDHD201**
9b A. Galli-Curci, T. Schipa, orch, R. Bourdon (r1923)
Concert (8/94) (ROMO) ① [2] **81004-2**
9b, 14a D. Borgioli, E. Surinach, orch (r c1923)
Concert (12/90) (CLUB) ① **CL99-014**
11(pt) T. Pasero, G. Bernelli, Rome Teatro Reale
Orch, L. Ricci (r1943) Concert
(4/95) (PREI) ① **89074**
14a, 22b T. dal Monte, A. Sinnone, Vienna St Op
Chor, Vienna St Op Orch, G. del Campo (pp1935)
Concert (7/94) (SCHW) ① [2] **314512**
16b, 16c, 17b R. Giménez, S.C. Dyson, Scottish Phil
Sngrs, Scottish CO, M. Veltri Concert
(5/90) (NIMB) ① **NI5224**
17b F. de Lucia, anon (r1908) Concert
(1/95) (SYMP) ① **SYMCD1149**
22a-c K. Battle, R. Stene, R. Croft, M.S. Doss, LPO,
B. Campanella (r1991) Concert
(12/93) (DG) ① **435 866-2GH**
22b E. Gruberová, Munich RO, L. Gardelli Concert
(11/86) (ORFE) ① **C101841A**
22b T. dal Monte, La Scala Orch, C. Sabajno (r1929)
Concert (2/90) (PREI) ① **89001**
22b A. Barili (r1906) Concert
(4/90) (PEAR) ① **GEMMCD9312**
22b C. Muzio, orch, L. Molajoli (r1935) Concert
(4/91) (NIMB) ① **NI7814**
22b A. Patti, A. Barili (r1906) Concert
(7/92) (PEAR) ① [3] **GEMMCDS9923(1)**
22b L. Tetrazzini, orch, P. Pitt (r1909) Concert
(9/92) (EMI) ① [3] **CHS7 63802-2(1)**
22b L. Tetrazzini, orch, P. Pitt (r1909) Concert
(9/92) (PEAR) ① **GEMMCD9221**
22b L. Tetrazzini, orch (r1911) Concert
(9/92) (PEAR) ① **GEMMCD9223**
22b A. Patti, A. Barili (r1906) Concert
(7/93) (NIMB) ① [2] **NI7840/1**
22b A. Galli-Curci, orch, J. Pasternack (r1917)
Concert (3/94) (ROMO) ① [2] **81003-2**
22b A. Galli-Curci, orch (r1917) Concert
(3/94) (CONI) ① **CDHD201**
22b A. Patti, A. Barili (r1906) Concert
(4/94) (EMI) ① [3] **CHS7 64860-2(1)**
22b T. dal Monte, La Scala Orch, C. Sabajno (r1929)
Concert (4/94) (EMI) ① [3] **CHS7 64864-2(1)**
22b A. Pendachanska, Sofia SO, M. Angelov (r1994)
Concert (12/95) (CAPR) ① **10 706**
22b, 22c L. Aliberti, Munich RO, L. Gardelli Concert
(11/86) (ORFE) ① **C119841A**
22b, 22c L. Tetrazzini, orch (r1911) Concert
(10/90) (NIMB) ① **NI7808**
22b, 22c J. Sutherland, N. Monti, F. Corena, MMF
Chor, MMF Orch, R. Bonynge Concert
(2/93) (DECC) ① [3] **433 706-2DMO3**

22b, 22c S. Jo, Monte Carlo PO, P. Olmi (r1994)
Concert   (6/95) (ERAT) ① 4509-97239-2
22c L. Tetrazzini, orch (r1911) Concert
                       (10/89) (NIMB) ① NI7801
22c M. Sembrich, orch (r1904) Concert
                       (7/92) (PEAR) ① [3] GEMMCDS9923(1)
22c L. Tetrazzini, anon (r c1904) Concert
                       (9/92) (PEAR) ① GEMMCD9225
22c L. Tetrazzini, orch (r1911) Concert
                       (9/92) (PEAR) ① GEMMCD9224
22c L. Tetrazzini, orch (r1911) Concert
                       (12/93) (NIMB) ① NI7851
22c M. Ivogün, orch (r1916) Concert
                       (1/94) (CLUB) ① CL99-020
22c A. Galli-Curci, orch (r1924) Concert
                       (3/94) (CONI) ① CDHD201
22c R. Peters, RCA SO, R. Cellini (r1958) Concert
                       (4/94) (RCA) ① [6] 09026 61580-2(6)
22c A. Galli-Curci, orch, R. Bourdon (r1924) Concert
                       (8/94) (ROMO) ① [2] 81004-2
Zaira—opera seria: 2 acts (1829—Milan) (Lib.
    F. Romani)
Cpte K. Ricciarelli, S. Alaimo, R. Vargas, A.
    Papadjiakou, S. Silbano, R. de Candia, L. Roni, G.B.
    Palmieri, Catania Teatro Massimo Bellini Chor,
    Catania Teatro Massimo Bellini Orch, P. Olmi
    (pp1990)   (7/91) (NUOV) ① [2] 6982/3
Amo ed amata in sono Y. Kenny, L. Davies, G.
    Mitchell Ch, Philh, D. Parry Concert
                       (8/95) (OPRA) ① [3] ORCH104

BELLINZANI, Paolo Benedetto (1690–1772) Italy

SECTION II: CHAMBER

**12 Sonatas for Flute and Continuo, Op. 3
    (pub 1728)**
    EXCERPTS: 1. No 1 in B flat; 3. No 3 in C; 4. No 4 in
    G minor; 5. No 5 in F; 6. No 6 in A minor; 8. No 8 in C
    minor; 12. No 12 in D minor, 'La Follia'.
3. E. Haupt, C. Schornsheim Concert
                       (2/90) (CAPR) ① 10 234

BELLSTEDT, Herman (1858–1926) Germany/USA

SECTION I: ORCHESTRAL

**Napoli—Variations on a Neapolitan
    song—cornet and wind orchestra**
3. W. Marsalis, Eastman Wind Ens, D. Hunsberger
    (arr D Hunsberger) Concert
                       (9/87) (SONY) ① MK42137

BELMONTE (15th–16th Cent) Spain

SECTION IV: VOCAL AND CHORAL

Nunca fue pena mayor (from the Colombina
    Song Book)
    Hespèrion XX, J. Savall Concert
                       (7/92) (ASTR) ① E8763

BEMBERG, Herman (1859–1931) France

SECTION IV: VOCAL AND CHORAL

Un ange est venue—song
    N. Melba, C. Gilibert, orch, W.B. Rogers (r1907)
    Concert   (5/95) (ROMO) ① [3] 81011-2(1)
Les Anges pleurent—song (Wds. G.
    Audigier)
    N. Melba, G. Lapierre (r1913) Concert
                       (9/93) (RCA) ① 09026 61412-2
    N. Melba, G. Lapierre (r1913) Concert
                       (5/95) (ROMO) ① [3] 81011-2(2)
Ça fait peur aux oiseaux—song
    E. Clément, F. La Forge (r1911) Concert
                       (8/95) (ROMO) ① 82002-2
Chanson de baisers—song
    E. Eames, anon (r1908) Concert
                       (11/93) (ROMO) ① [2] 81001-2
Chant hindou—song (Wds. Ocampo)
    . E. Zbrueva, anon, anon (r1913: Russ) Concert
                       (6/93) (PEAR) ① [3] GEMMCDS9004/6(2)
Chant vénitien—song (Wds. G. Roussel)
    N. Melba, G. Lapierre (r1913) Concert
                       (9/93) (RCA) ① 09026 61412-2
    N. Melba, G. Lapierre (r1913) Concert
                       (5/95) (ROMO) ① [3] 81011-2(2)
Il neige—song
    E. Clément, F. La Forge (r1911) Concert
                       (8/95) (ROMO) ① 82002-2

E. Clément, anon (r1910s) Concert
                       (8/95) (PEAR) ① GEMMCD9161
Le Soupir—song
    P. Plançon, anon (r1905) Concert
                       (12/94) (ROMO) ① [2] 82001-2

BEN HAIM, Paul (1897–1974) Germany/Israel

SECTION I: ORCHESTRAL

Concerto for Violin and Orchestra (1960)
    I. Perlman, Israel PO, Z. Mehta (pp1990)
    Castelnuovo-Tedesco: Violin Concerto 2.
                       (5/93) (EMI) ① CDC7 54296-2
**The Sweet Psalmist of Israel—harpsichord
    and orchestra (1956)**
    S. Marlowe, NYPO, L. Bernstein (r1959) Concert
                       (11/92) (SONY) ① [2] SM2K47533

SECTION II: CHAMBER

Berceuse sfaradite—violin and piano
    I. Perlman, S. Sanders Concert
                       (6/95) (EMI) ① [20] CZS4 83177-2(3)

BENATZKY, Ralph (1884–1957) Austria/Germany

SECTION V: STAGE WORKS

**Im weissen Rössl, 'White Horse
    Inn'—operetta: 3 acts (1930—Berlin)** (some
    songs by Stolz & others; Lib Gilbert)
    EXCERPTS: 1. Auf wiedersehen; 2. Mein Liebeslied
    muss ein Walzer sein (comp Stolz).
    Excs E. Köth, I. Hallstein, R. Schock, P. Alexander,
    W. Hufnagel, chor, SO, J. Fehring
                       (2/91) (EURO) ① GD69028
    2. M. Hill Smith, P. Morrison, Chandos Concert Orch,
    S. Barry (Eng) Concert
                       (7/88) (CHAN) ① CHAN8561

BENDA, František (1709–1786) Bohemia

SECTION I: ORCHESTRAL

Concerto for Flute and Strings in E minor
    P. Gallois, CPE Bach CO, P. Schreier (r1993)
    Concert   (2/95) (DG) ① 439 895-2GH
Symphony in C
    Slovak CO, B. Warchal Concert
                       (11/89) (OPUS) ① 9350 1812

BENDA, Georg (Anton) (1722–1795) Bohemia

baptised Jiří Antonín

SECTION II: CHAMBER

**Sonata for Violin/Flute and Continuo in A
    minor**
    J. Coe, L.U. Mortensen, S. Standage (vn/dir) Concert
                       (5/94) (CHAN) ① CHAN0541

SECTION III: INSTRUMENTAL

Sonatinas for Piano (pub 1780-87) (from
    'Sammlung vermischter Clavierstücke')
    3. A minor; 9. A minor; 16. G minor; 21. F; 29. E flat;
    32. Rondo in A.
    Five Sonatinas C. Schornsheim (r1991) Concert
                       (4/95) (CAPR) ① 10 424
    3, 9, 16, 21, 29, 32. T. Roberts (r1993) Concert
                       (1/94) (HYPE) ① CDA66649

SECTION IV: VOCAL AND CHORAL

**Das Andenken—Lied: 1v and piano (pub
    1780-87)**
    E. Kirkby, T. Roberts (r1993) Concert
                       (1/94) (HYPE) ① CDA66649
**Belise starb, und sprach im Scheiden—Lied:
    1v and piano (pub 1780-87)**
    E. Kirkby, T. Roberts (r1993) Concert
                       (1/94) (HYPE) ① CDA66649
**Cephalus und Aurore—cantata: 1v and
    piano/orchestra** (pf vers pub in 'Sammlung
    vermischter Clavier-und Gesangstücke')
    E. Kirkby, T. Roberts (r1993) Concert
                       (1/94) (HYPE) ① CDA66649
**Du fehlest mir—Lied: 1v and piano (pub
    1780-87)**
    E. Kirkby, T. Roberts (r1993) Concert
                       (1/94) (HYPE) ① CDA66649
**Du, kleine Blondine, bezauberst ja
    schon!—Lied: 1v and piano (pub 1780-87)**
    R. Müller, T. Roberts (r1993) Concert
                       (1/94) (HYPE) ① CDA66649

**Ein trunkner Dichter leerte—Lied: 1v and
    piano (pub 1780-87)**
    R. Müller, T. Roberts (r1993) Concert
                       (1/94) (HYPE) ① CDA66649
**Faulheit, itzo will ich dir—Lied: 1v and piano
    (pub 1780-87)**
    R. Müller, T. Roberts (r1993) Concert
                       (1/94) (HYPE) ① CDA66649
**Ich liebte nur Ismenen—Lied: 1v and piano
    (pub 1780-87)**
    R. Müller, T. Roberts (r1993) Concert
                       (1/94) (HYPE) ① CDA66649
**Lieber Amor, leihe mir—Lied: 1v and piano
    (pub 1780-87)**
    R. Müller, T. Roberts (r1993) Concert
                       (1/94) (HYPE) ① CDA66649
**Mein Geliebter hat versprochen—Lied: 1v
    and piano (pub 1780-87)**
    E. Kirkby, T. Roberts (r1993) Concert
                       (1/94) (HYPE) ① CDA66649
**Mein Thyrsis! dürft ich dir doch
    sagen—Lied: 1v and piano (pub 1780-87)**
    E. Kirkby, T. Roberts (r1993) Concert
                       (1/94) (HYPE) ① CDA66649
**Mir Armen, den des Fiebers kraft—Lied: 1v
    and piano (pub 1780-87)**
    R. Müller, T. Roberts (r1993) Concert
                       (1/94) (HYPE) ① CDA66649
**Philint ist still, und flieht die Schönen—Lied:
    1v and piano (pub 1780-87)**
    R. Müller, T. Roberts (r1993) Concert
                       (1/94) (HYPE) ① CDA66649
**Philint stand jüngst vor Babets Thür—Lied:
    1v and piano (pub 1780-87)**
    R. Müller, T. Roberts (r1993) Concert
                       (1/94) (HYPE) ① CDA66649
**Venus, wenn du willst mich rühren—Lied: 1v
    and piano (pub 1780-87)**
    E. Kirkby, T. Roberts (r1993) Concert
                       (1/94) (HYPE) ① CDA66649
**Von nun an, O Liebe verlass' ich dein
    Reich—Lied: 1v and piano (pub 1780-87)**
    R. Müller, T. Roberts (r1993) Concert
                       (1/94) (HYPE) ① CDA66649

BENDINELLI, Cesare (c1542–1617) Italy

SECTION II: CHAMBER

Fanfare, 'Sarasinetta'—brass (c1614)
    Gabrieli Players, P. McCreesh Concert
                       (5/90) (VIRG) ① VC7 59006-2
Sonata 333—brass and drums (c1614)
    Gabrieli Players, P. McCreesh Concert
                       (5/90) (VIRG) ① VC7 59006-2

BENEDICT, Sir Julius (1804–1885) Germany/England

SECTION II: CHAMBER

Carnevale di Venezia—clarinet and piano
    R. Quaranta, anon (r1902) Concert
                       (2/94) (CLRI) ① CC0005

SECTION IV: VOCAL AND CHORAL

La Capinera—song
    A. Galli-Curci, orch, J. Pasternack (r1918) Concert
                       (3/94) (ROMO) ① [2] 81003-2
**Variations de concert sur le Carnaval de
    Venise—song (pub 1865)**
    L. Tetrazzini, orch, P. Pitt (r1909) Concert
                       (9/92) (EMI) ① [3] CHS7 63802-2(1)
    L. Tetrazzini, orch, P. Pitt (r1909) Concert
                       (9/92) (PEAR) ① GEMMCD9221
    L. Tetrazzini, orch (r1911) Concert
                       (9/92) (PEAR) ① GEMMCD9223
    T. dal Monte, Vienna St Op Orch, G. del Campo
    (pp1935) Concert   (7/94) (SCHW) ① [2] 314512
**The Wren—soprano, flute and
    orchestra/piano**
    B. Hoch, Hong Kong PO, K. Schermerhorn Concert
                       (11/86) (CARL) ① PCD827
    L. Pons, orch, A. Kostelanetz (r1939) Concert
                       (4/92) (MSOU) ① DFCDI-111

SECTION V: STAGE WORKS

**Lily of Killarney—opera: 3 acts
    (1862—London)** (Lib. J Oxenford, after D
    Boucicault)
    EXCERPTS—; 1. The moon hath raised her lamp
    above; 2. 'Tis charming girl I love; 3. I'm alone; 4. Eily
    Mavoureen.
    1. Hilliard Ens, L-L. Kiesel Concert
                       (12/91) (MERI) ① DUOCD89009

BENEKEN, Friedrich Burkhard (1760–1818) Germany

SECTION IV: VOCAL AND CHORAL

Oh, how peacefully—song
J. Björling, Inst Ens (r1920) *Concert*
(8/92) (BLUE) ① **ABCD016**

BENGUEREL, Xavier (b 1931) Spain

SECTION I: ORCHESTRAL

Tempo—guitar and strings (1983)
W. Weigel, European Master Orch, P. Schmelzer
(r1992) *Concert* (5/95) (SCHW) ① **312362**

BENJAMIN, Arthur (1893–1960) Australia/England

SECTION I: ORCHESTRAL

2 Jamaican Pieces—small orchestra (1938)
1. Jamaican Song; 2. Jamaican Rumba.
RTE Concert Orch, E. Tomlinson (r1993) *Concert*
(12/95) (MARC) ① **8 223522**
Overture to an Italian Comedy (1937)
Chicago SO, F. Stock (r1941) *Concert*
(12/93) (BIDD) ① **WHL016**
Romantic Fantasy—violin, viola & orchestra (1935)
J. Heifetz, W. Primrose, RCA Victor SO, I. Solomon
(r1956) *Concert*
(11/94) (RCA) ① [65] **09026 61778-2(31)**

SECTION II: CHAMBER

Jamaican Rumba—two pianos (1938)
I. Stern, Columbia SO, M. Katims (arr Harris) *Concert*
(7/90) (SONY) ① **SK45816**
J. Heifetz, M. Kaye (r1944) *Concert*
(11/94) (RCA) ① [65] **09026 61778-2(19)**

BENJAMIN, George (b 1960) England

SECTION I: ORCHESTRAL

Antara—orchestra (1987 rev 1989)
London Sinfonietta, G. Benjamin *Concert*
(10/89) (NIMB) ① **NI5167**

BENNET, John (b ?c1575/80; fl 1599–1614) England

SECTION IV: VOCAL AND CHORAL

All creatures now—ayre
Amaryllis Consort, C. Brett *Concert*
(3/88) (CARL) ① **PCD873**
Round about in a fair ring—madrigal (6vv) (pub 1599)
Cambridge Sngrs, J. Rutter *Concert*
(11/87) (CLLE) ① **COLCD105**
Venus' birds—ayre (1v and consort)
D. Cordier, Tragicomedia, S. Stubbs *Concert*
(1/90) (HYPE) ① **CDA66307**
Weep, o mine eyes—madrigal (4vv) (pub 1599)
Hilliard Ens, P. Hillier *Concert*
(2/89) (EMI) ① **CDC7 49197-2**

BENNETT, John (c1725–1784) England

SECTION III: INSTRUMENTAL

Voluntary in G minor—organ (pub 1758)
Margaret Phillips *Concert*
(5/91) (GAMU) ① **GAMCD514**

BENNETT, Richard Rodney (b 1936) England

SECTION I: ORCHESTRAL

Concerto for Guitar and Chamber Orchestra (1970)
J. Bream, Melos Ens (r1972) *Concert*
(8/93) (RCA) ① [28] **09026 61583-2(4)**
J. Bream, Melos Ens, D. Atherton (r1972) *Concert*
(6/94) (RCA) ① **09026 61598-2**
Concerto for Saxophone and Orchestra (1988)
J. Harle, ASMF, N. Marriner *Concert*
(1/92) (EMI) ① **CDC7 54301-2**

Concerto for Solo Percussion and Chamber Orchestra (1989-90)
E. Glennie, Scottish CO, P. Daniel *Concert*
(4/93) (RCA) ① **09026 61277-2**
Concerto for Stan Getz—soprano saxophone and orchestra (1990)
J. Harle, BBC Concert Orch, B. Wordsworth (r1993)
Concert (7/95) (ARGO) ① **443 529-2ZH**

SECTION II: CHAMBER

Summer Music—flute and piano
1. Summer Music; 2. Siesta; 3. Games.
K. Smith, P. Rhodes *Concert*
(1/91) (ASV) ① **CDDCA739**

SECTION III: INSTRUMENTAL

Impromptus—guitar (1974)
1. Recitativo; 2. Agitato; 3. Elegiaco; 4. Con fuoco; 5.
Arioso.
J. Bream (r1981-2) *Concert*
(8/93) (RCA) ① [28] **09026 61583-2(4)**
J. Bream (r1981-2) *Concert*
(9/94) (RCA) ① **09026 61597-2**
C. Ogden (r1994) *Concert* (6/95) (NIMB) ① **NI5390**
Noctuary: Variations on a theme by Scott Joplin—piano (1981)
J. McCabe *Concert*
(6/91) (CNTI) ① [2] **CCD1028/9**

SECTION IV: VOCAL AND CHORAL

The Aviary—song cycle: unison vv (1965)
1. The Lark.
1. Magdalen (Oxford) Coll Ch, G. Ives *Concert*
(11/92) (CNTO) ① **CRCD2366**
3 Verses—chorus and organ (1965)
Magdalen Oxford Coll Ch, J. Harper *Concert*
(11/91) (ABBE) ① **CDCA915**

SECTION V: STAGE WORKS

Murder on the Orient Express—film score (1974)
EXCERPTS: 1. Waltz.
1. Hollywood Bowl SO, J. Mauceri (r1993) *Concert*
(6/94) (PHIL) ① **438 685-2PH**

BENNETT, Robert Russell (1894–1981) USA

SECTION I: ORCHESTRAL

Symphonic Songs—wind orchestra (1957)
1. Serenade; 2. Spiritual; 3. Celebration.
Eastman Wind Ens, F. Fennell *Concert*
(12/91) (MERC) ① **432 009-2MM**

SECTION II: CHAMBER

Hexapoda—5 studies in Jitteroptera (1941)
J. Heifetz, E. Bay (r1945) *Concert*
(11/94) (RCA) ① [65] **09026 61778-2(19)**
A Song Sonata—violin and piano
J. Heifetz, B. Smith (r1955) *Concert*
(11/94) (RCA) ① [65] **09026 61778-2(35)**

BENSON, Warren (b 1924) USA

SECTION IV: VOCAL AND CHORAL

Songs for the End of the World—mez, cor ang, hn, vc and marimba (1980) (Wds. J. Gardner)
1. Awakening; 2. Two Step; 3. Lullaby; 4. Spring; 5.
Siciliana; 6. Nocturne.
V. Dupuy, T. Bacon, R. Russell, D. Howard, B. Sills,
D. Welcher *Argento: Virginia Woolf.*
(2/91) (KING) ① **KCLCD2018**

BENTZON, Jørgen (1897–1951) Denmark

SECTION II: CHAMBER

Racconto No. 3—oboe, clarinet and bassoon
Selandia Ens *Concert* (6/90) (KONT) ① **32032**

BERBERIAN, Cathy (1925–1983) USA

SECTION IV: VOCAL AND CHORAL

Stripsody—1v (1966) (Wds. cpsr)
C. Berberian (pp1970) *Concert*
(7/89) (WERG) ① **WER60054-50**

BERG, Alban (Maria Johannes) (1885–1935) Austria

SECTION I: ORCHESTRAL

Concerto for Violin and Orchestra, 'To the memory of an angel' (1935)
I. Perlman, Boston SO, S. Ozawa *Stravinsky: Violin Concerto.*
(12/84) (DG) ① **413 725-2GH**
J. Suk, Czech PO, V. Neumann *Bartók: Violin Concerto 1.*
(5/90) (SUPR) ① **11 0706-2**
Y. Menuhin, BBC SO, P. Boulez *Bloch: Violin Concerto.*
(4/91) (EMI) ① **CDM7 63989-2**
L. Krasner, BBC SO, A. Webern (bp1936) *Lyric Suite.*
(6/91) (TEST) ① **SBT1004**
F.P. Zimmermann, Stuttgart RSO, G. Gelmetti
Concert (3/92) (EMI) ① **CDC7 54248-2**
Y. Menuhin, SRO, E. Ansermet (pp1964) *Concert*
(11/92) (CASC) ① **VEL2003**
A-S. Mutter, Chicago SO, James Levine *Rihm: Gesungene Zeit.* (1/93) (DG) ① **437 093-2GH**
A-S. Mutter, Chicago SO, James Levine (r1992)
Concert (12/94) (DG) ① [3] **445 487-2GX3**
T. Zehetmair, Philh, H. Holliger (r1991) *Concert*
(6/95) (TELD) ① **4509-97449-2**
Lulu—Symphonie—soprano and orchestra (1934)
1. Rondo (Andante und Hymne); 2. Ostinato
(Allegro); 3. Lied der Lulu (Comodo); 4. Variationen;
5. Adagio.
M. Price, LSO, C. Abbado *Concert*
(8/88) (DG) ① **423 238-2GC**
A. Auger, CBSO, S. Rattle (r1987/8) *Concert*
(11/89) (EMI) ① **CDC7 49857-2**
J. Blegen, NYPO, P. Boulez *Concert*
(12/90) (SONY) ① **SMK45838**
H. Pilarczyk, LSO, A. Dorati *Concert*
(3/91) (MERC) ① **432 006-2MM**
A. Réaux, NYPO, K. Masur *Weill: Sieben Todsünden.*
(12/94) (TELD) ① **4509-95029-2**
Lyric Suite—3 pieces for string orchestra (1928) (movts. 2-4 of Lyric Suite for string quartet)
BPO, H. von Karajan *Concert*
(9/89) (DG) ① [3] **427 424-2GC3**
NYPO, P. Boulez *Concert*
(12/90) (SONY) ① **SMK45838**
Berlin SO, Vladimir Ashkenazy (r1991) *Concert*
(2/94) (DECC) ① **436 567-2DH**
3 Orchestral Pieces, Op. 6 (1914-15)
1. Präludium; 2. Reigen; 3. Marsch.
BPO, James Levine *Concert*
(8/87) (DG) ① **419 781-2GH**
LSO, C. Abbado *Concert*
(8/88) (DG) ① **423 238-2GC**
BPO, H. von Karajan *Concert*
(9/89) (DG) ① [3] **427 424-2GC3**
LSO, A. Dorati *Concert*
(3/91) (MERC) ① **432 006-2MM**
SRO, E. Ansermet (pp1959) *Concert*
(11/92) (CASC) ① **VEL2003**
Berlin SO, Vladimir Ashkenazy (r1990) *Concert*
(2/94) (DECC) ① **436 567-2DH**

SECTION II: CHAMBER

Chamber Concerto for Piano, Violin amd 13 Wind Instruments (Kammerkonzert) (1923-25)
W. Marschner, C. Seemann, BRSO, P. Hindemith
(pp1959) *Concert* (8/90) (ORFE) ① **C197891A**
S. Schmidt, O. Kagan, Moscow Cons Instr Ens, Y.
Nikolaevsky (pp1977) *Concert*
(3/93) (EMI) ① [4] **CMS7 64429-2**
E.H. Smebye, Norwegian Wind Ens, O.K. Ruud
(r1991) *Weill: Violin Concerto.*
(8/93) (SIMA) ① **PSC1090**
P. Zukerman, D. Barenboim, Paris
InterContemporain Ens, P. Boulez (r1977) *Concert*
(7/95) (DG) ① **447 405-2GOR**
Lyric Suite—string quartet (1925-26)
LaSalle Qt *Concert*
(4/88) (DG) ① [4] **419 994-2GCM4**
Schoenberg Qt *String Quartet.*
(12/89) (SCHW) ① **310005**
Galimir Qt (r1936) *Violin Concerto.*
(6/91) (TEST) ① **SBT1004**
Arditti Qt *String Quartet.* (12/91) (MONT) ① **789001**
Vogler Qt *Verdi: String Quartet.*
(12/91) (RCA) ① **RD60855**
Alban Berg Qt *String Quartet.*
(11/94) (EMI) ① **CDC5 55190-2**
String Quartet, Op. 3 (1910)
LaSalle Qt *Concert*
(4/88) (DG) ① [4] **419 994-2GCM4**

Schoenberg Qt *Lyric Suite.*
(12/89) (SCHW) ① 310005
Arditti Qt *Lyric Suite.* (12/91) (MONT) ① 789001
Alban Berg Qt *Lyric Suite.*
(11/94) (EMI) ① CDC5 55190-2
Petersen Qt (r1989/91) *Concert*
(2/95) (CAPR) ① 10 511
Brindisi Qt (r1994) *Concert*
(6/95) (METR) ① METCD1007

SECTION III: INSTRUMENTAL

Sonata for Piano, Op. 1 (1907-08)
Barry Douglas *Concert*
(12/92) (RCA) ① 09026 61221-2
N. Demidenko (pp1993) *Concert*
(1/94) (HYPE) ① [2] CDA66781/2
M. Pollini (r1992) *Debussy: Etudes.*
(3/94) (DG) ① 423 678-2GH
M. Bratke (r1993) *Concert*
(4/94) (OLYM) ① OCD431
M. Kazakevich (r1993) *Concert*
(9/94) (CONI) ① CDCF235
M. Yudina (1964) *Concert*
(8/95) (MELO) ① [11] 74321 25172-2(1)
M. Yudina (1964) *Concert*
(8/95) (MELO) ① 74321 25176-2

SECTION IV: VOCAL AND CHORAL

Am Abend—Lied (c1904-05) (Wds. Geibel)
M. Shirai, H. Höll *Concert*
(11/92) (CAPR) ① 10 419
Am Strande—song (c1902) (Wds. G.
Scherer)
D. Fischer-Dieskau, A. Reimann *Concert*
(9/90) (EMI) ① CDM7 63570-2
An Leukon—song (1908) (Wds. Gleim)
D. Dorow, T. Crone *Concert*
(12/88) (ETCE) ① KTC1051
M. Shirai, H. Höll *Concert*
(11/92) (CAPR) ① 10 419
**3 Bruchstücke aus 'Wozzeck'—soprano and
orchestra (1924)**
1. Tchin bum! Soldaten ... 2. Und ist kein Betrug ... 3.
Ringel, Ringel ...
S. Danco, SRO, E. Ansermet (pp1953) *Concert*
(11/92) (CASC) ① VEL2003
7 Early songs (1905-08 rev and orch 1928)
1. Nacht (wds. Hauptmann); 2. Schilflied (wds.
Lenau); 3. Die Nachtigall (wds. Storm); 4.
Traumgekrönt (wds. Rilke); 5. Im Zimmer (wds.
Schlaf); 6. Liebesode (wds. Hartleben); 7.
Sommertage (wds. Hohenberg).
D. Dorow, T. Crone *Concert*
(12/88) (ETCE) ① KTC1051
E. Speiser, I. Gage *Concert*
(1/89) (JECK) ① JD561-2
L. Popp, I. Gage *Concert* (4/92) (RCA) ① RD60950
M. Shirai, H. Höll *Concert*
(11/92) (CAPR) ① 10 419
M. Marshall, G. Parsons (r1984) *Concert*
(8/93) (DG) ① 437 719-2GC
K. Lövaas, N German RSO, H. Blomstedt (bp)
Concert (8/93) (DG) ① 437 719-2GC
B. Balleys, Berlin SO, Vladimir Ashkenazy (r1992)
Concert (2/94) (DECC) ① 436 567-2DH
A.S. von Otter, B. Forsberg (r1991) *Concert*
(6/94) (DG) ① 437 515-2GH
C. Ludwig, E. Werba (pp1968) *Concert*
(7/94) (ORFE) ① C331931A
J. Norman, LSO, P. Boulez (r1987/88) *Concert*
(3/95) (SONY) ① SK66826
**Er klagt, dass der Frühling so kortz
blüht—song (c1902)** (Wds. A. Holz)
D. Fischer-Dieskau, A. Reimann *Concert*
(9/90) (EMI) ① CDM7 63570-2
M. Shirai, H. Höll *Concert*
(11/92) (CAPR) ① 10 419
J. Norman, A. Schein (r1994) *Concert*
(3/95) (SONY) ① SK66826
Erster Verlust—song (c1904-05) (Wds.
Goethe)
D. Fischer-Dieskau, A. Reimann *Concert*
(9/90) (EMI) ① CDM7 63570-2
M. Shirai, H. Höll *Concert*
(11/92) (CAPR) ① 10 419
**Es wandelt, was wir schauen—song (c1904-
05)** (Wds. Eichendorff)
D. Fischer-Dieskau, A. Reimann *Concert*
(9/90) (EMI) ① CDM7 63570-2
Ferne Lieder—song (c1904-05) (Wds.
Rückert)
D. Fischer-Dieskau, A. Reimann *Concert*
(9/90) (EMI) ① CDM7 63570-2
M. Shirai, H. Höll *Concert*
(11/92) (CAPR) ① 10 419

J. Norman, A. Schein (r1994) *Concert*
(3/95) (SONY) ① SK66826
Fraue, du Süsse—Lied (Wds. Finckh)
M. Shirai, H. Höll *Concert*
(11/92) (CAPR) ① 10 419
Geliebte Schöne—song (c1904-05) (Wds.
Heine)
D. Fischer-Dieskau, A. Reimann *Concert*
(9/90) (EMI) ① CDM7 63570-2
J. Norman, A. Schein (r1994) *Concert*
(3/95) (SONY) ① SK66826
Grabschrift—song (c1904-05) (Wds.
Jakobowski)
D. Fischer-Dieskau, A. Reimann *Concert*
(9/90) (EMI) ① CDM7 63570-2
M. Shirai, H. Höll *Concert*
(11/92) (CAPR) ① 10 419
J. Norman, A. Schein (r1994) *Concert*
(3/95) (SONY) ① SK66826
Herbstgefühl—Lied (c1902) (Wds. S.
Fleischer)
M. Shirai, H. Höll *Concert*
(11/92) (CAPR) ① 10 419
Ich liebe dich—song (c1904-05) (Wds.
Grabbe)
D. Fischer-Dieskau, A. Reimann *Concert*
(9/90) (EMI) ① CDM7 63570-2
Ich will die Fluren meiden—Lied (c1904-05)
(Wds. Rückert)
M. Shirai, H. Höll *Concert*
(11/92) (CAPR) ① 10 419
Im Morgengrauen—song (c1904-05) (Wds.
Stieler)
D. Fischer-Dieskau, A. Reimann *Concert*
(9/90) (EMI) ① CDM7 63570-2
M. Shirai, H. Höll *Concert*
(11/92) (CAPR) ① 10 419
Liebe—Lied (c1904-05) (Wds. Rilke)
J. Norman, A. Schein (r1994) *Concert*
(3/95) (SONY) ① SK66826
Lied des Schiffermädels—Lied (c1904-05)
(Wds. O J Bierbaum)
J. Norman, A. Schein (r1994) *Concert*
(3/95) (SONY) ① SK66826
Mignon—Lied (c1904-05) (Wds. Goethe)
M. Shirai, H. Höll *Concert*
(11/92) (CAPR) ① 10 419
J. Norman, A. Schein (r1994) *Concert*
(3/95) (SONY) ① SK66826
Die Näherin—Lied (c1904-05) (Wds. Rilke)
M. Shirai, H. Höll *Concert*
(11/92) (CAPR) ① 10 419
**5 Orchesterlieder nach Ansichtskartentexten
von Peter Altenberg, Op. 4 (1912)**
1. Seele, wir bist du schöner; 2. Sahst du nach dem
Gewitterregen; 3. Über die Grenzen des All; 4. Nichts
ist gekommen; 5. Hier ist Friede.
M. Price, LSO, C. Abbado *Concert*
(8/88) (DG) ① 423 238-2GC
B. Balleys, Berlin SO, Vladimir Ashkenazy (r1992)
Concert (2/94) (DECC) ① 436 567-2DH
J. Norman, LSO, P. Boulez (r1984) *Concert*
(3/95) (SONY) ① SK66826
Regen—Lied (1905-09) (Wds. J. Schlaf)
D. Fischer-Dieskau, A. Reimann *Concert*
(9/90) (EMI) ① CDM7 63570-2
M. Shirai, H. Höll *Concert*
(11/92) (CAPR) ① 10 419
Schattenleben—song (c1904-05) (Wds.
Graf)
D. Fischer-Dieskau, A. Reimann *Concert*
(9/90) (EMI) ① CDM7 63570-2
J. Norman, A. Schein (r1994) *Concert*
(3/95) (SONY) ① SK66826
**Schleisse mir die augen beide—song (Wds.
Storm)**
1. 1907 (first setting); 2. 1925 (second setting).
D. Dorow, T. Crone *Concert*
(12/88) (ETCE) ① KTC1051
E. Speiser, I. Gage *Concert*
(1/89) (JECK) ① JD561-2
M. Shirai, H. Höll *Concert*
(11/92) (CAPR) ① 10 419
J. Norman, A. Schein (r1994) *Concert*
(3/95) (SONY) ① SK66826
Schlummerlose Nächte—song (c1904-05)
(Wds. Greif)
D. Fischer-Dieskau, A. Reimann *Concert*
(9/90) (EMI) ① CDM7 63570-2
Sehnsucht I—Lied (c1902) (Wds.
Hohenberg)
M. Shirai, H. Höll *Concert*
(11/92) (CAPR) ① 10 419

Sehnsucht II—song (c1902) (Wds.
Hohenberg)
D. Fischer-Dieskau, A. Reimann *Concert*
(9/90) (EMI) ① CDM7 63570-2
J. Norman, A. Schein (r1994) *Concert*
(3/95) (SONY) ① SK66826
4 Songs, Op. 2 (?1909-10)
1. Schlafen, schlafen (wds. Hebbel); 2. Schlafend
trägt man mich (wds. Mombert); 3. Nun ich der
Riesen Stärksten (wds. Mombert); 4. Warum die
Lüfte (wds. Mombert).
B. Fassbaender, J. Wustman *Concert*
(9/88) (ACAN) ① 43 579
D. Dorow, T. Crone *Concert*
(12/88) (ETCE) ① KTC1051
E. Speiser, I. Gage *Concert*
(1/89) (JECK) ① JD561-2
M. Zakai, Yonathan Zak *Concert*
(5/91) (KOCH) ① 37021-2
M. Shirai, H. Höll *Concert*
(11/92) (CAPR) ① 10 419
Spaziergang—Lied (c1902) (Wds. A.
Mombert)
D. Fischer-Dieskau, A. Reimann *Concert*
(9/90) (EMI) ① CDM7 63570-2
M. Shirai, H. Höll *Concert*
(11/92) (CAPR) ① 10 419
Sternenfall—Lied (c1902) (Wds. Wilhelm)
M. Shirai, H. Höll *Concert*
(11/92) (CAPR) ① 10 419
Tiefe Sehnsucht—duet (c1904) (Wds.
Liliencron)
D. Fischer-Dieskau, A. Reimann *Concert*
(9/90) (EMI) ① CDM7 63570-2
Traurigkeit—Lied (c1902) (Wds. P.
Altenberg)
D. Fischer-Dieskau, A. Reimann *Concert*
(9/90) (EMI) ① CDM7 63570-2
Über den Bergen—song (c1902) (Wds.
Busse)
D. Fischer-Dieskau, A. Reimann *Concert*
(9/90) (EMI) ① CDM7 63570-2
M. Shirai, H. Höll *Concert*
(11/92) (CAPR) ① 10 419
Vielgeliebte, schöne Frau—song
D. Fischer-Dieskau, A. Reimann *Concert*
(9/90) (EMI) ① CDM7 63570-2
J. Norman, A. Schein (r1994) *Concert*
(3/95) (SONY) ① SK66826
Vorüber!—Lied (c1904-05) (Wds. F
Wisbacher)
J. Norman, A. Schein (r1994) *Concert*
(3/95) (SONY) ① SK66826
**Der Wein—concert aria for soprano and
orchestra (1929)** (Wds. Baudelaire, trans S.
George)
J. Norman, NYPO, P. Boulez *Concert*
(12/90) (SONY) ① SMK45838
S. Hass, Vienna SO, G. Rozhdestvensky (pp1982)
Concert (8/93) (DG) ① 437 719-2GC
Winter—Lied (c1902) (Wds.J. Schlaf)
D. Fischer-Dieskau, A. Reimann *Concert*
(9/90) (EMI) ① CDM7 63570-2
Wo der Goldregen steht—song (c1902) (Wds.
Lorenz)
J. Norman, A. Schein (r1994) *Concert*
(3/95) (SONY) ① SK66826

SECTION V: STAGE WORKS

Lulu—opera: 3 acts (1937—Zurich) (Wds.
cpsr after Wedekind. Act 3 incomplete: cpted)
Cpte T. Stratas, F. Mazura, K. Riegel, Y. Minton, R.
Tear, T. Blankenheim, G. Nienstedt, H. Pampuch, J.
Bastin, H. Schwarz, J. Manning, U. Boese, A.
Ringart, C. Meloni, P-Y. Le Maigat, Paris Op. Orch,
P. Boulez (r1979)
(11/86) (DG) ① [3] 415 489-2GH3
Cpte E. Lear, D. Fischer-Dieskau, D. Grobe, P.
Johnson, L. Driscoll, J. Greindl, W.W. Dicks, G.
Feldhoff, K-E. Mercker, L. Clam, A. Oelke, B.
Scherler, Berlin Deutsche Op Orch, K. Böhm
Wozzeck. (1/93) (DG) ① [3] 435 705-2GX3
Cpte P. Wise, W. Schöne, P. Straka, B.
Fassbaender, G. Clark, H. Hotter, E. Gutstein, B.
Schwanbeck, S. Kale, B. Moland, G. Knight, H.
Estourelle, L. Zannini, M. Kobayashi, F. Dudziak, H.
Hennequin, FNO, J. Tate (pp1991)
(1/93) (EMI) ① [3] CDS7 54622-2
**Wozzeck—opera: 3 acts/15 scenes, Op. 7
(1925—Berlin)** (Lib. Büchner)
Cpte E. Waechter, A. Silja, H. Winkler, H.
Laubenthal, H. Zednik, A. Malta, G. Jahn, Vienna St
Op Chor, VPO, C. von Dohnányi *Schoenberg:
Erwartung.* (2/89) (DECC) ① [2] 417 348-2DH2

Cpte F. Grundheber, H. Behrens, W. Raffeiner, P. Langridge, H. Zednik, A. Haugland, A. Gonda, Vienna Boys' Ch, Vienna St Op Chor, VPO, C. Abbado (pp1987)
(2/89) (DG) ① [2] **423 587-2GH2**
Cpte D. Fischer-Dieskau, E. Lear, H. Melchert, F. Wunderlich, G. Stolze, K.C. Kohn, A. Oelke, Berlin Deutsche Op Chor, Berlin Deutsche Op Orch, K. Böhm *Lulu*.
(1/93) (DG) ① [3] **435 705-2GX3**
Excs H. Pilarczyk, LSO, A. Dorati (r1961) *Bartók: Duke Bluebeard's castle*.
(7/93) (MERC) ① **434 325-2MM**

BERGGREEN, Andreas Peter (1801–1880) Denmark

SECTION IV: VOCAL AND CHORAL

Just think one day the fog will go—song
(Wds. W. A. Wexels)
L. Melchior, Brass Ens (r1915) *Concert*
(8/88) (DANA) ① [2] **DACOCD311/2**
Welcome again, God's little angels—song
(Wds. N. F. S. Grundtvig)
L. Melchior, Anon (harm) (r1915) *Concert*
(8/88) (DANA) ① [2] **DACOCD311/2**

BERGMAN, Erik (Valdemar) (b 1911) Finland

SECTION IV: VOCAL AND CHORAL

Bim Bam Boom (Bim Bam Bum)—tenor, chorus and ensemble, Op. 80 (1976) (Wds. Morgenstern)
J. Potter, New London Chmbr Ch, J. Wood *Concert*
(1/88) (CHAN) ① **CHAN8478**
The Birds (Fåglarna)—baritone, male chorus, percussion and celeste, Op. 56a (1962) (Wds. Von Schoultz)
S. Varcoe, New London Chmbr Ch, J. Wood *Concert*
(1/88) (CHAN) ① **CHAN8478**
Hathor Suite—chorus and orchestra, Op. 70 (1971) (Wds. Schott, after ancient Egyptian)
P. Walmsley-Clarke, S. Varcoe, New London Chmbr Ch, J. Wood *Concert* (1/88) (CHAN) ① **CHAN8478**
Nox—baritone, chorus, flute, cor anglais and percussion, Op. 65 (1970)
S. Varcoe, New London Chmbr Ch, J. Wood *Concert*
(1/88) (CHAN) ① **CHAN8478**

SECTION V: STAGE WORKS

The Singing Tree—opera: 2 acts, Op. 110 (1986-88—Helsinki) (Lib. B. Carpelan)
Cpte P. Lindroos, C. Hellekant, K. Hannula, P. Salomaa, S. Tiilikainen, M. Wallén, A-L. Jakobson, M. Harju, T-M. Tuomela, E-K. Vilke, T. Nyman, P. Lindroos, Dominante Ch, Tapiola Chbr Ch, Finnish Nat Op Orch, U. Söderblom (r1992)
(5/93) (ONDI) ① [2] **ODE794-2D**

BERIO, Luciano (b 1925) Italy

SECTION I: ORCHESTRAL

Continuo—orchestra (1990)
Chicago SO, D. Barenboim (pp1993) *Concert*
(8/95) (TELD) ① **4509-99596-2**
Eindrücke—orchestra (1973-74)
FNO, P. Boulez *Sinfonia*.
(7/88) (ERAT) ① **2292-45228-2**
Formazioni—orchestra (1987)
Concertgebouw, R. Chailly *Concert*
(8/90) (DECC) ① **425 832-2DH**

SECTION II: CHAMBER

Corale—violin, two horns and 23 strings (1981) (based on Sequenza VIII)
Accademia Bizantina, C. Chiarappa (vn/dir) (r1992) *Concert* (5/94) (DENO) ① **CO-75448**
34 Duetti—two violins (1979-82)
A. Gjezi, D. Berio, Accademia Bizantina (r1992) *Concert* (5/94) (DENO) ① **CO-75448**
Notturno—string quartet (1993)
Alban Berg Qt (pp1994) *Haydn: String Quartets, Op.77.* (10/95) (EMI) ① **CDC5 55191-2**
Opus Number Zoo—wind quintet (1970)
Vienna/Berlin Ens *Concert*
(11/92) (SONY) ① **SK48052**
2 Pezzi—violin and piano (1951 rev 1966)
C. Chiarappa, R. Valentini (r1992) *Concert*
(5/94) (DENO) ① **CO-75448**
Sequenza X—trumpet in C and piano resonance (1984)
R. Friedrich, T. Duis (r1991-2) *Concert*
(6/93) (CAPR) ① **10 482**

SECTION III: INSTRUMENTAL

Les mots sont allés—cello (1976-78)
T. Demenga (r1993) *Concert*
(8/95) (ECM) ① [2] **445 234-2**
M. Haimovitz (r1994) *Concert*
(12/95) (DG) ① **445 834-2GH**
Lied per clarinetto solo (1983)
P. Meyer (r1993) *Concert*
(7/95) (DENO) ① **CO-78917**
Sequenza IXa—clarinet (1980)
P. Meyer (r1993) *Concert*
(7/95) (DENO) ① **CO-78917**
Sequenza V—trombone (1966)
C. Lindberg *Concert* (10/89) (BIS) ① **BIS-CD388**
Sequenza VIII—percussion (1975)
C. Chiarappa (r1992) *Concert*
(5/94) (DENO) ① **CO-75448**
Sequenza X—trumpet (1984)
G. Ashton (r1991) *Concert*
(4/94) (VIRG) ① **VC5 45003-2**

SECTION IV: VOCAL AND CHORAL

Coro—voices and instruments (1975-76 rev 1977) (Wds. various)
Cologne Rad Chor, Cologne RSO, L. Berio
(10/88) (DG) ① **423 902-2GC**
11 Folk Songs—1v and 7 instrs (1964 rev 1973)
1. Black is the colour (USA); 2. I wonder as I wander (USA); 3. Loosin yelav (Armenia); 4. Rossignolet du bois (France); 5. A la femminisca (Sicily); 6. La donna ideale (Italy); 7. Ballo (Italy); 8. Mottetu de tristura (Sardinia); 9. Malurous qu'on uno fenno (Auvergne); 10. Lo fiolaire (Auvergne); 11. Azerbaijan love song (Azerbaijan).
J. van Nes, Concertgebouw, R. Chailly *Concert*
(8/90) (DECC) ① **425 832-2DH**
C. Berberian, Juilliard Ens, L. Berio (r1968) *Concert*
(7/95) (RCA) ① **09026 62540-2**
Recital I for Cathy—song recital (1971)
1. Se i languidi miei sguardi (Monteverdi); 2. Amor, dov'é la fé (Monteverdi); 3. 'ah! he hadn't been there before...'; 4. 'clarinet that's the sound that's been haunting me...'; 5. Avendo gran desio (Berio-da Lentini); 6. 'Who hasn't taken a piece out of my life'; 7. Musician Exchange: 'these 5 men...'; 8. Excerpts: Mahler, Delibes, Rossini etc. 9. Calmo e lontano: 'libera nos'.
C. Berberian, London Sinfonietta, L. Berio (r1972) *Concert* (7/95) (RCA) ① **09026 62540-2**
Sinfonia—8vv and orchestra (1968 rev 1969) (Wds. various)
R. Pasquier, New Swingle Sngrs, FNO, P. Boulez *Eindrücke*. (7/88) (ERAT) ① **2292-45228-2**
Electric Phoenix, Concertgebouw, R. Chailly *Concert*
(8/90) (DECC) ① **425 832-2DH**

SECTION V: STAGE WORKS

Laborintus II—opera (1965—Paris) (Wds. E. Sanguineti)
C. Legrand, J. Baucomont, C. Meunier, E. Sanguineti, Chorale Expérimentale, Musique Vivante Ens, L. Berio (12/87) (HARM) ① **HMA190 764**

BERKELEY, Sir Lennox (Randall Francis) (1903–1989) England

SECTION I: ORCHESTRAL

Concerto for Guitar and Orchestra, Op. 88 (1974)
J. Bream, Monteverdi Orch, J.E. Gardiner (r1975) *Concert* (8/93) (RCA) ① [28] **09026 61583-2(5)**
J. Bream, Monteverdi Orch, J. E. Gardiner (r1975) *Concert* (9/94) (RCA) ① **09026 61605-2**
Divertimento in B flat—chamber orchestra, Op. 18 (1943)
LPO, L. Berkeley *Concert*
(3/93) (LYRI) ① **SRCD226**
Partita—chamber orchestra, Op. 66 (1964-65)
LPO, L. Berkeley *Concert*
(3/93) (LYRI) ① **SRCD226**
Serenade—string orchestra, Op. 12 (1939)
ASMF, K. Sillito *Concert*
(10/91) (COLL) ① **Coll1234-2**
LPO, L. Berkeley *Concert*
(3/93) (LYRI) ① **SRCD226**
Sinfonia Concertante—oboe and orchestra, Op. 84 (1973)
Canzonetta R. Winfield, LPO, L. Berkeley *Concert* (3/93) (LYRI) ① **SRCD226**
Symphony No. 3 (in one movement)—1969, Op. 74
LPO, L. Berkeley *Concert*
(3/93) (LYRI) ① **SRCD226**

SECTION II: CHAMBER

Palm Court Waltz—piano duet, Op. 81/2 (1971)
R. Terroni, N. Beedie (r1993) *Concert*
(3/94) (BMS) ① **BMS416CD**
Sonatina for Piano Duet, Op. 39 (c1954)
R. Terroni, N. Beedie (r1993) *Concert*
(3/94) (BMS) ① **BMS416CD**
Theme and Variations—piano duet, Op. 73 (1968)
R. Terroni, N. Beedie (r1993) *Concert*
(3/94) (BMS) ① **BMS416CD**

SECTION III: INSTRUMENTAL

Improvisation on a Theme of Manuel de Falla—piano, Op. 55/2 (1960)
C. Headington *Concert*
(6/89) (KING) ① **KCLCD2012**
Mazurka—piano, Op. 101/2 (1982)
C. Headington *Concert*
(6/89) (KING) ① **KCLCD2012**
3 Mazurkas—piano, Op. 32/1 (1949)
C. Headington *Concert*
(6/89) (KING) ① **KCLCD2012**
Paysage—piano (1944)
C. Headington *Concert*
(6/89) (KING) ① **KCLCD2012**
3 Pieces—piano, Op. 2 (1935)
1. Etude; 2. Berceuse; 3. Capriccio.
C. Headington *Concert*
(6/89) (KING) ① **KCLCD2012**
Polka—piano, Op. 5a (1934)
C. Headington *Concert*
(6/89) (KING) ① **KCLCD2012**
6 Preludes—piano, Op. 23 (1945)
C. Headington *Concert*
(6/89) (KING) ① **KCLCD2012**
A. Goldstone *Concert*
(3/92) (GAMU) ① **GAMCD526**
R. Terroni (r1993) *Concert*
(3/94) (BMS) ① **BMS416CD**
5 Short Pieces—piano, Op. 4 (1936)
C. Headington *Concert*
(6/89) (KING) ① **KCLCD2012**
R. Terroni (r1993) *Concert*
(3/94) (BMS) ① **BMS416CD**
Sonata for Piano, Op. 20 (1940-45)
C. Headington *Concert*
(6/89) (KING) ① **KCLCD2012**
R. Terroni (r1993) *Concert*
(3/94) (BMS) ① **BMS416CD**
Sonatina for Guitar, Op. 52/1 (1957)
J. Savijoki *Concert* (1/93) (ONDI) ① **ODE779-2**
J. Bream (r1959) *Concert*
(8/93) (RCA) ① [28] **09026 61583-2(4)**
J. Bream (r1959) *Concert*
(6/94) (RCA) ① **09026 61595-2**
C. Ogden (r1994) *Concert* (6/95) (NIMB) ① **NI5390**
Theme and Variations—guitar, Op. 77 (1970)
J. Savijoki *Concert* (1/93) (ONDI) ① **ODE779-2**
J. Bream (r1973) *Concert*
(8/93) (RCA) ① [28] **09026 61583-2(4)**
J. Bream (r1973) *Concert*
(6/94) (RCA) ① **09026 61595-2**

SECTION IV: VOCAL AND CHORAL

Because I Liked You Better—song: 1v and piano (early 1940s) (Wds. A E Housman)
A. Rolfe Johnson, G. Johnson (r1994) *Concert*
(8/95) (HYPE) ① [2] **CDA66471/2**
He would not stay for me—song: 1v and piano (early 1940s) (Wds. A E Housman)
A. Rolfe Johnson, G. Johnson (r1994) *Concert*
(8/95) (HYPE) ① [2] **CDA66471/2**
In wintertime—4vv a capella, Op. 103 (1983)
Elysian Sngrs, M. Greenall *Concert*
(12/91) (CNTI) ① **CCD1043**
The Lord is my shepherd—4vv and organ, Op. 91/1 (1975)
King's College Ch, S. Cleobury, C. Hughes (r1991) *Concert* (6/93) (EMI) ① **CDC7 54418-2**
St Paul's Cath Ch, John Scott, Andrew Lucas (r1994) *Concert* (5/95) (HYPE) ① **CDA66758**
5 Poems, Op. 53 (1958) (Wds. W. H. Auden)
1. Lauds; 2. O lurcher-loving collier; 3. What's in your mind; 4. Eyes look into the well; 5. Carry her over the water.
2. F. Lott, G. Johnson *Concert*
(7/90) (CHAN) ① **CHAN8722**
Songs of the half-light—soprano/tenor and guitar, Op. 65 (1964) (Wds. W. de la Mare)
1. Rachel; 2. Full moon; 3. All that's past; 4. The moth; 5. The fleeting.

I. Partridge, J. Savijoki *Concert*
(1/93) (ONDI) ① **ODE779-2**
Spring at this hour—6vv a capella, Op. 37/2
(1953) (Wds. P. Dehn)
Cambridge Univ Chbr Ch, T. Brown *Concert*
(4/92) (GAMU) ① **GAMCD529**
Thou hast made me—4vv and organ, Op.
55/1 (1960) (Wds. J. Donne)
Magdalen Oxford Coll Ch, J. Harper *Concert*
(11/91) (ABBE) ① **CDCA915**

BERKELEY, Michael (b 1948) England

SECTION I: ORCHESTRAL

Concerto for Clarinet and Orchestra (1991)
E. Johnson, Northern Sinfonia, S. Edwards *Concert*
(2/94) (ASV) ① **CDDCB1101**
Music from Chaucer—brass ensemble
PJBE *Concert* (2/88) (CHAN) ① **CHAN8490**

SECTION III: INSTRUMENTAL

Flighting—clarinet (1985)
E. Johnson *Concert* (2/94) (ASV) ① **CDDCB1101**
Impromptu—guitar (1983)
A. Gifford (r1990) *Concert*
(12/92) (NATI) ① **NTCD001**
Worry Beads—guitar (1979)
A. Gifford (r1990) *Concert*
(12/92) (NATI) ① **NTCD001**

SECTION IV: VOCAL AND CHORAL

Père du doux répos—baritone (1985) (Wds.
P. de Tyard)
H. Herford *Concert* (2/94) (ASV) ① **CDDCB1101**

SECTION V: STAGE WORKS

Baa Baa Black Sheep—opera: 3 acts
(1993—Cheltenham) (Lib. D Marouf, after R
Kipling)
Cpte M. Lorimer, W. Dazeley, A. Taylor-Morley, G.
Mosley, E. Hulse, H. Newman, F. Kimm, P. Sheffield,
M. Holland, C. Bayley, P. McCann, B. Cookson, Op
North Chor, English Northern Philh, P. Daniel
(pp1993) (4/95) (COLL) ① [2] **Coll7036-2**

BERLIN, Irving (1888–1989) USA

SECTION I: ORCHESTRAL

Berlin Goes to Hollywood—concert overture
(arr & orch Larry Wilcox from various songs)
1. Let Me Sing and I'm Happy; 2. Blue Skies; 3.
Puttin' On the Ritz.
Hollywood Bowl Orch, J. Mauceri (r1994) *Concert*
(11/95) (PHIL) ① **446 406-2PH**
Patriotic Overture—concert overture (arr &
orch Sid Ramin from various songs)
1. This is the Army Mr Jones; 2. Give Me Your Tired,
Your Poor; 3. Oh, How I Hate to Get Up in the
Morning; 4. God Bless America.
Hollywood Bowl Orch, J. Mauceri (r1994) *Concert*
(11/95) (PHIL) ① **446 406-2PH**

SECTION II: CHAMBER

Suite—brass ensemble (arr Snell)
1. Anything you can do; 2. A pretty girl is like a
melody; 3. It's a lovely day tomorrow; 4. Putting on
the Ritz.
H. Snell Brass, H. Snell *Concert*
(9/91) (POLY) ① **QPRZ005D**

SECTION IV: VOCAL AND CHORAL

Always—song (1925) (wds. cpsr)
M. Patinkin, Orch, E. Stern (r1990; orch Troob, arr
Ford) *Concert* (11/94) (NONE) ① **7559-79330-2**
P. LuPone, Hollywood Bowl Orch, J. Mauceri (r1994;
orch Warner) *Concert*
(11/95) (PHIL) ① **446 406-2PH**
Blue Skies—song (1927) (Lyrics cpsr. Later
used in 1946 film of same name)
F. Kreisler, C. Lamson (r1927; arr Kreisler) *Concert*
(12/93) (BIDD) ① **LAB075**
Dance and Grow Thin—song for the show
'Dance and Grow Thin' (1917) (Lyrics
Meyer)
Van & Schenck, Orig Broadway Cast (r1917) *Concert*
(5/94) (PEAR) ① [3] **GEMMCDS9056/8**
Follow the Crowd—song for the show
'Queen of the Movies' (1914) (Lyrics cpsr)
I. Berlin, Orig Broadway Cast (r1914) *Concert*
(5/94) (PEAR) ① [3] **GEMMCDS9056/8**
God Bless America—song (1918 rev 1938)
M. Horne, NY Met Op Orch, J. Conlon (pp1991)
Concert (6/93) (RCA) ① **09026 61509-2**

Woodman, Spare That Tree—song for Bert
Williams (1911) (Lyrics Bryan)
Bert Williams, Orig Broadway Cast (r1913) *Concert*
(5/94) (PEAR) ① [3] **GEMMCDS9053/5**

SECTION V: STAGE WORKS

Annie get your Gun—musical show, later
film (1946; film 1950—New York) (Lyrics
cpsr)
EXCERPTS: 1. Overture; 2. Doin' what comes
natur'lly; 3. Anything you can do; 4. The girl that I
marry; 5. I got lost in his arms; 6. I got the sun in the
morning; 7. I'm an Indian too; 8. Who do you love, I
hope; 9. You can't get a man with a gun; 10. They
say it's wonderful; 11. My defenses are down; 12.
There's no business like show busines; 13.
Moonshine lullaby; 14. I'm a bad, bad man.
DISCARDED ITEM: 15. Let's go West again.
Cpte K. Criswell, T. Hampson, J. Graae, R. Luker, D.
Garrison, D. Healy, A. Marks, G. Jbara, S. Green, P.
Bartlett, C. Buckfield, J. McGlinn, B. Ogston,
Ambrosian Chor, London Sinfonietta, J. McGlinn
(11/91) (EMI) ① **CDC7 54206-2**
Cpte Mary Martin, J. Raitt, US TV Cast (bp1957)
(11/93) (EMI) ① **ZDM7 64765-2**
2, 5, 12. P. LuPone, Hollywood Bowl Orch, J.
Mauceri (r1994; orch R Warner & R R Bennett)
Concert (11/95) (PHIL) ① **446 406-2PH**
10. V. Masterson, T. Allen, Philh, J.O. Edwards
(r1990) *Concert* (5/94) (TER) ① **CDVIR8317**
15. K. Criswell, Ambrosian Sngrs, London
Sinfonietta, J. McGlinn (r1992) *Concert*
(4/94) (EMI) ① **CDC7 54802-2**
As Thousands Cheer—musical revue (1933)
(Lyrics Hart)
EXCERPTS: 1. Easter Parade; 2. Heat Wave; 3.
Lonely Heart.
2. P. LuPone, Hollywood Bowl Orch, J. Mauceri
(r1994; trans McGurty from film 'Alexander's Ragtime
Band') *Concert* (11/95) (PHIL) ① **446 406-2PH**
3. P. LuPone, Hollywood Bowl Orch, J. Mauceri
(r1994; orch Schwartz) *Concert*
(11/95) (PHIL) ① **446 406-2PH**
Call Me Madam—musical show (1950—New
York) (Lyrics cpsr)
EXCERPTS: 1. Overture; 2. Mrs Sally Adams; 3.
The Hostess With the Mostes' on the Ball; 4.
Washington Square Dance; 5. Can You Use Any
Lichtenburg; 6. Can You Use Any Money Today?; 7.
Marrying for Love; 8. The Ocarina; 9. It's a Lovely
Day Today; 10. The Best Thing for You; 11.
Something to Dance About; 12. Once Upon a Time
Today; 13. They Like Ike; 14. You're Just in Love.
3, 10. P. LuPone, Hollywood Bowl Orch, J. Mauceri
(r1994) *Concert* (11/95) (PHIL) ① **446 406-2PH**
8, 9, 11. Hollywood Bowl Orch, J. Mauceri (r1994;
orch Hagen, Mayers & Spencer; ed Krasker &
Mauceri) *Concert* (11/95) (PHIL) ① **446 406-2PH**
Easter Parade—musical film (1948)
EXCERPTS: 1. Better Luck Next Time; 2. It Only
Happens When I Dance; 3. Steppin' Out With My
Baby.
3. P. LuPone, Hollywood Bowl Orch, J. Mauceri
(r1994; adapted L Wilcox) *Concert*
(11/95) (PHIL) ① **446 406-2PH**
Follow the Fleet—musical film (1936) (Lyrics
cpsr)
EXCERPTS: 1. Main Title; 2. We Saw the Sea; 3.
Let Yourself Go; 4. Get These Behind Me; 5. Dance
Contest; 6. I'd Rather Lead a Band; 7. But Where Are
You?; 8. I'm Putting All My Eggs in One Basket; 9.
Let's Face the Music and Dance; 10. We Saw the
Sea (instrumental); 11. The Monte Carlo Ballet (instr
vers of 'Let's Face the Music').
3. P. LuPone, Hollywood Bowl Orch, J. Mauceri
(r1994; adapted L Wilcox) *Concert*
(11/95) (PHIL) ① **446 406-2PH**
9. P. LuPone, Hollywood Bowl Orch, J. Mauceri (r1994; orch
Steiner & DePackh) *Concert*
(11/95) (PHIL) ① **446 406-2PH**
Top Hat—musical film (1935) (Lyrics cpsr)
EXCERPTS: 1. Cheek to Cheek; 2. Isn't This a
Lovely Day?; 3. Piccolino; 4. Top Hat, White Tie and
Tails; 5. No Strings.
5. P. LuPone, Hollywood Bowl Orch, J. Mauceri
(r1994; orch R Warner, after L Reisman) *Concert*
(11/95) (PHIL) ① **446 406-2PH**
Watch Your Step—musical show
(1914—New York) (Lyrics cpsr)
EXCERPTS: 1. Chatter Chatter; 2. I Love to Have
the Boys Around Me; 3. I've Gotta Go Back to Texas;
4. Lead Me to Love; 5. Let's Go Around; 6. Look Me
in Your Harem and Throw Me Away; 7. Look At
Them Doing It!; 8. Metropolitan Nights; 9. Minstrel
Parade; 10. Move Over; 11. Office Hours; 12. Opera
Burlesque; 13. Play a Simple Melody; 14. Settle

Down in a One-Horse Town; 15. Show Me How to Do
the Fox Trot; 16. Syncopated Walk; 17. They Always
Follow Me Around; 18. Watch Your Step; 19. What is
Love?; 20. When I Discovered You.
3. E. Brice, C. King, Orig Broadway Cast (r1916)
Concert (5/94) (PEAR) ① [3] **GEMMCDS9056/8**
White Christmas—musical film (1954)
(remake of 'Holiday Inn')
EXCERPTS: 1. White Christmas; 2. Mandy; 3.
Snow; 4. Gee, I Wish I Was Back in the Army; 5.
Love, You Didn't Do Right By Me; 6. Sisters; 7. The
Best Things Happen While You're Dancing; 8. Count
Your Blessings Instead of Sheep.
8. P. LuPone, B. Motley, J. Powell, G. Van Buren, J.
West, Hollywood Bowl Orch, J. Mauceri (r1994; trans
McGurty) *Concert* (11/95) (PHIL) ① **446 406-2PH**
Ziegfeld Follies of 1919—songs for the
musical revue (1919—New York)
EXCERPTS: 1. Mandy; 2. You'd Be Surprised; 3.
I've Got My Captain Working for Me Now; 4. A Pretty
Girl is Like a Melody.
1-4. E. Cantor, J. Steel, Van & Schenck, Orig
Broadway Cast (r1919) *Concert*
(5/94) (PEAR) ① [3] **GEMMCDS9059/61**

BERLIOZ, (Louis-)Hector (1803–1869) France

SECTION I: ORCHESTRAL

Le Carnaval romain—overture, Op. 9 (1844)
(based on material from Benvenuto Cellini)
SNO, A. Gibson *Concert*
(8/84) (CHAN) ① **CHAN8316**
LSO, Colin Davis *Concert*
(9/86) (PHIL) ① **416 430-2PH**
World PO, L. Maazel (pp1986) *Concert*
(7/88) (AUVI) ① **AV6113**
Concertgebouw, W. Mengelberg (r1937) *Concert*
(7/90) (SYMP) ① **SYMCD1078**
Toulouse Capitole Orch, M. Plasson *Concert*
(9/90) (EMI) ① **CDC7 54010-2**
Polish St PO, K. Jean *Concert*
(1/91) (NAXO) ① **8 550231**
Boston SO, C. Munch *Concert*
(3/91) (RCA) ① **VD60478**
Baltimore SO, D. Zinman *Concert*
(11/91) (TELA) ① **CD80271**
Cleveland Orch, L. Maazel *Symphonie fantastique.*
(1/92) (DECC) ① **433 611-2DSP**
National PO, L. Stokowski *Concert*
(4/92) (EMI) ① **CDM7 64140-2**
BPO, James Levine *Concert*
(7/92) (DG) ① [2] **429 724-2GH2**
Concertgebouw, M. Jansons *Symphonie fantastique.*
(10/92) (EMI) ① **CDC7 54479-2**
NYPO, L. Bernstein (r1959) *Concert*
(11/92) (SONY) ① **SMK47525**
NBC SO, A. Toscanini (r1953) *Concert*
(11/92) (RCA) ① **GD60322**
BPO, L. Blech (r1927) *Concert*
(2/93) (KOCH) ① **37072-2**
LSO, A. Previn *Concert*
(3/93) (EMI) ① **CDM7 64630-2**
Strasbourg PO, A. Lombard *Concert*
(6/93) (ERAT) ① **2292-45925-2**
Paris Orch, D. Barenboim (r1980) *Concert*
(7/93) (DG) ① [2] **437 638-2GGA2**
Detroit SO, P. Paray (r1958) *Concert*
(9/93) (MERC) ① **434 328-2MM**
Boston SO, C. Munch (r1958) *Concert*
(11/93) (RCA) ① **09026 61400-2**
RPO, E. Bátiz (r1987) *Concert*
(7/94) (IMG) ① **IMGCD1606**
LPO, Henry Wood (r1940) *Concert*
(9/94) (DUTT) ① **CDAX8008**
LSO, Colin Davis (r1965) *Concert*
(10/94) (PHIL) ① [2] **442 290-2PM2**
LPO, T. Beecham (r1936) *Concert*
(10/94) (DUTT) ① **CDLX7009**
Paris Orch, S. Bychkov (r1993) *Symphonie
fantastique.* (11/94) (PHIL) ① **438 939-2PH**
NYPO, P. Boulez (r1972) *Concert*
(3/95) (SONY) ① [3] **SM3K45103**
Boston SO, S. Koussevitzky (r1944) *Concert*
(7/95) (BIDD) ① **WHL028**
VPO, R. Kempe (r c1959) *Concert*
(11/95) (EMI) ① [2] **CES5 68525-2**
Le Corsaire—overture, Op. 21 (1844)
SNO, A. Gibson *Concert*
(8/84) (CHAN) ① **CHAN8316**
LSO, Colin Davis *Concert*
(9/86) (PHIL) ① **416 430-2PH**
FNO, C. Munch (pp1967) *Concert*
(11/88) (MONT) ① **MUN2011**

Baltimore SO, D. Zinman (r1987) *Concert*
(12/88) (TELA) ① **CD80164**
Toulouse Capitole Orch, M. Plasson *Concert*
(9/90) (EMI) ① **CDC7 54010-2**
Polish St PO, K. Jean *Concert*
(1/91) (NAXO) ① **8 550231**
Boston SO, C. Munch *Concert*
(3/91) (RCA) ① **VD60478**
SNO, A. Gibson *Concert*
(10/91) (CHAN) ① **CHAN6538**
Brno St PO, P. Vronský *Concert*
(10/91) (SUPR) ① **11 0388-2**
RPO, A. Previn *Symphonie fantastique.*
(5/92) (RPO) ① **CDRPO7016**
BPO, James Levine *Concert*
(7/92) (DG) ① [2] **429 724-2GH2**
Stockholm PO, G. Rozhdestvensky *Symphonie fantastique.*
(8/92) (CHAN) ① **CHAN9052**
RPO, Y. Temirkanov *Concert*
(11/92) (RCA) ① **09026 61203-2**
LSO, A. Previn *Concert*
(3/93) (EMI) ① **CDM7 64630-2**
Black Dyke Mills Band, G. Brand (arr G. Brand)
Concert (9/93) (RSR) ① **RSRD1002**
Detroit SO, P. Paray (r1958) *Concert*
(9/93) (MERC) ① **434 328-2MM**
Boston SO, C. Munch (r1958) *Concert*
(11/93) (RCA) ① **09026 61400-2**
RPO, E. Bátiz (r1987) *Concert*
(7/94) (IMG) ① **IMGCD1606**
LSO, Colin Davis (r1965) *Concert*
(10/94) (PHIL) ① [2] **442 290-2PM2**
Les Francs-juges—overture, Op. 3 (1836)
LSO, Colin Davis *Concert*
(9/86) (PHIL) ① **416 430-2PH**
Baltimore SO, D. Zinman *Concert*
(11/91) (TELA) ① **CD80271**
Harold in Italy—symphony for viola and orchestra, Op. 16 (1834)
N. Imai, LSO, Colin Davis *Concert*
(12/86) (PHIL) ① **416 431-2PH**
Y. Bashmet, Frankfurt RSO, E. Inbal
(12/89) (DENO) ① **CO-73207**
J. Suk, Czech PO, D. Fischer-Dieskau *Rêverie et caprice.*
(5/90) (SUPR) ① **11 0708-2**
Y. Menuhin, Philh, Colin Davis (r1962) *Rêverie et Caprice.*
(11/90) (EMI) ① **CDM7 63530-2**
G. Caussé, Toulouse Capitole Orch, M. Plasson
Concert (2/92) (EMI) ① **CDC7 54237-2**
C. Cooley, NBC SO, A. Toscanini (bp1953) *Roméo et Juliette.*
(11/92) (RCA) ① **GD60275**
J. de Pasquale, Philadelphia, E. Ormandy (r1965)
Concert (8/94) (SONY) ① **SBK53255**
N. Imai, LSO, Colin Davis (r1975) *Concert*
(10/94) (PHIL) ① [2] **442 290-2PM2**
W. Primrose, Boston SO, C. Munch (r1958) *Indy: Symphonie, Op.25.* (5/95) (RCA) ① **09026 62582-2**
W. Primrose, Boston SO, S. Koussevitzky (r1944)
Concert (7/95) (BIDD) ① **WHL028**
King Lear—overture, Op. 4 (1831)
SNO, A. Gibson *Concert*
(8/84) (CHAN) ① **CHAN8316**
LSO, Colin Davis *Concert*
(9/86) (PHIL) ① **416 430-2PH**
Prague SO, V. Smetáček *Symphonie fantastique.*
(12/90) (SUPR) ① **11 1103-2**
Polish St PO, K. Jean *Concert*
(1/91) (NAXO) ① **8 550231**
Brno St PO, P. Vronský *Concert*
(10/91) (SUPR) ① **11 0388-2**
Philh, J-P. Rouchon (r1993) *Concert*
(8/94) (ASV) ① **CDDCA895**
Marche troyenne, 'Trojan March'—orchestra (arr cpsr 'Les Troyens', act 1)
Baltimore SO, D. Zinman (r1987) *Concert*
(12/88) (TELA) ① **CD80164**
Detroit SO, P. Paray (r1959) *Concert*
(9/93) (MERC) ① **434 328-2MM**
Philadelphia, E. Ormandy (r1968) *Concert*
(8/94) (SONY) ① **SBK53255**
Rêverie et caprice—romance for violin and orchestra, Op. 8 (1841)
A. Dumay, Monte Carlo PO, A. Dumay *Concert*
(6/87) (EMI) ① **CDC7 47544-2**
J. Suk, Prague SO, V. Smetáček *Harold in Italy.*
(5/90) (SUPR) ① **11 0708-2**
Y. Menuhin, Philh, J. Pritchard (r1964) *Harold in Italy.*
(11/90) (EMI) ① **CDM7 63530-2**
I. Perlman, Paris Orch, D. Barenboim (r1980)
Concert (7/95) (DG) ① **445 549-2GMA**
Rob Roy—overture (1831)
SNO, A. Gibson *Concert*
(8/84) (CHAN) ① **CHAN8316**
Brno St PO, P. Vronský *Concert*
(10/91) (SUPR) ① **11 0388-2**

Symphonie fantastique, Op. 14 (1830)
1. Rêveries; 2. Un bal; 3. Scène aux champs; 4. Marche au supplice; 5. Songe d'une nuit du Sabbat.
Chicago SO, C. Abbado
(5/84) (DG) ① **410 895-2GH**
Concertgebouw, Colin Davis
(12/84) (PHIL) ① **411 425-2PH**
Cleveland Orch, L. Maazel (r1982)
(10/85) (TELA) ① **CD80076**
BPO, D. Barenboim (1/86) (SONY) ① **SK39859**
Paris Orch, C. Munch (r1968)
(5/86) (EMI) ① **CDC7 47372-2**
BPO, H. von Karajan (r1974)
(5/86) (DG) ① **415 325-2GH**
LSO, R. Williams (1/88) (CARL) ① **PCD870**
Boston SO, C. Munch *Grande messe des morts.*
(2/88) (RCA) ① [2] **RD86210**
FNO, C. Munch (pp1963) *Concert*
(11/88) (MONT) ① **MUN2011**
LCP, R. Norrington (4/89) (EMI) ① **CDC7 49541-2**
Frankfurt RSO, E. Inbal (r1987)
(7/89) (DENO) ① **CO-73208**
FRNO, J. Martinon *Lélio.*
(12/89) (EMI) ① [2] **CZS7 62739-2**
LSO, S. Skrowaczewski
(6/90) (CHAN) ① **CHAN8727**
Toulouse Capitole Orch, M. Plasson *Concert*
(9/90) (EMI) ① **CDC7 54010-2**
Czech PO, C. Zecchi *King Lear.*
(12/90) (SUPR) ① **11 1103-2**
BPO, H. von Karajan (r1964) *Damnation de Faust.*
(12/90) (DG) ① **429 511-2GR**
Bratislava RSO, P. Steinberg
(1/91) (NAXO) ① **8 550093**
Boston SO, S. Ozawa (r1973) *Roméo et Juliette.*
(1/91) (DG) ① **431 169-2GGA**
Boston SO, C. Munch *Concert*
(3/91) (RCA) ① **VD60478**
Philadelphia, E. Ormandy *Concert*
(3/91) (SONY) ① **SBK46329**
Baltimore SO, D. Zinman *Concert*
(11/91) (TELA) ① **CD80271**
VPO, B. Haitink *Carnaval Romain.*
(1/92) (DECC) ① **433 611-2DSP**
RPO, A. Previn *Concert*
(5/92) (RPO) ① **CDRPO7016**
VPO, Colin Davis (r1990)
(5/92) (PHIL) ① **432 151-2PH**
Philh, O. Klemperer *Concert*
(8/92) (EMI) ① **CDM7 64143-2**
Stockholm PO, G. Rozhdestvensky *Corsaire.*
(8/92) (CHAN) ① **CHAN9052**
Concertgebouw, M. Jansons *Carnaval Romain.*
(10/92) (EMI) ① **CDC7 54479-2**
NYPO, L. Bernstein (r1968) *Concert*
(11/92) (SONY) ① **SMK47525**
RPO, Y. Temirkanov *Concert*
(11/92) (RCA) ① **09026 61203-2**
FNO, L. Bernstein *Concert*
(3/93) (EMI) ① **CDM7 64630-2**
Strasbourg PO, A. Lombard *Concert*
(6/93) (ERAT) ① **2292-45925-2**
ORR, J.E. Gardiner (r1991)
(6/93) (PHIL) ① **434 402-2PH**
Detroit SO, P. Paray (r1959) *Concert*
(9/93) (MERC) ① **434 328-2MM**
Philh, E. Bátiz (r1993) *Concert*
(7/94) (IMG) ① **IMGCD1606**
San Francisco SO, P. Monteux (r1945) *Concert*
(9/94) (RCA) ① [15] **09026 61893-2**
LSO, Colin Davis (r1963) *Concert*
(10/94) (PHIL) ① [2] **442 290-2PM2**
Paris Orch, S. Bychkov (r1993) *Carnaval romain.*
(12/94) (DENO) ① **CO-78902**
LSO, P. Boulez (r1967) *Concert*
(3/95) (SONY) ① [3] **SM3K64103**
Lamoureux Orch, I. Markevitch (r1961) *Concert*
(7/95) (DG) ① **447 406-2GOR**
BPO, R. Kempe (r c1958) *Concert*
(11/95) (EMI) ① [2] **CES5 68525-2**
4. Locke Brass Consort, J. Stobart (arr Stobart)
(9/92) (CRD) ① **CRD3402**
Symphonie funèbre et triomphale—orchestra and chorus, Op. 15 (1840)
John Alldis Ch, LSO, Colin Davis *Grande messe des morts.* (4/86) (PHIL) ① [2] **416 283-2PH2**
Montreal Sym Chor, Montreal SO, C. Dutoit *Roméo et Juliette* (r1980)
(4/92) (DECC) ① **417 302-2DH2**
Gardiens de la Paix Orch, D. Dondeyne *Concert*
(8/88) (CALL) ① **CAL9859**
Leeds Fest Chor, Wallace Collection, J. Wallace
Concert (7/89) (NIMB) ① **NI5175**

Montreal Sym Chor, Montreal SO, C. Dutoit *Roméo et Juliette.* (7/90) (DECC) ① **425 001-2DM**
Czech PO, C. Eschenbach *Mort de Cléopâtre.*
(5/92) (SUPR) ① **11 0389-2**
John Alldis Ch, LSO, Colin Davis (r1969) *Concert*
(10/94) (PHIL) ① [2] **442 290-2PM2**
Movt 3. BBC SO, J. Pritchard (pp1983) *Concert*
(10/95) (BBCR) ① [2] **DMCD98**
Waverley—overture, Op. 1 (1828)
SNO, A. Gibson *Concert*
(9/85) (CHAN) ① **CHAN8379**
LSO, Colin Davis *Concert*
(9/86) (PHIL) ① **416 430-2PH**
Toulouse Capitole Orch, M. Plasson *Concert*
(2/92) (EMI) ① **CDC7 54237-2**

SECTION IV: VOCAL AND CHORAL

Amitié, reprends ton empire—2 sopranos, baritone and piano (?1818-22) (Wds. Florian)
F. Pollet, A.S. Von Otter, T. Allen, C. Garben (r1991)
Concert (7/94) (DG) ① [2] **435 860-2GH2**
Aubade—song (1839) (Wds. A Musset)
H. Crook, Lyon Op Orch, J.E. Gardiner *Concert*
(2/91) (ERAT) ① **2292-45517-2**
La Belle Isabeau, conte pendant l'orage—song. Op. 19/5 (1843 or earlier) (Wds. A. Dumas)
A.S. Von Otter, Stockholm Royal Op Chor, C. Garben (r1991) *Concert* (7/94) (DG) ① [2] **435 860-2GH2**
Canon libre à la quinte—2 voices and pianos (?1818-22) (Wds. Bourgerie)
F. Pollet, A.S. Von Otter, C. Garben (r1991) *Concert*
(7/94) (DG) ① [2] **435 860-2GH2**
La captive—song, Op. 12 (1832, orch 1848) (Wds. V Hugo)
C. Robbin, Lyon Op Orch, J.E. Gardiner *Concert*
(2/91) (ERAT) ① **2292-45517-2**
A.S. Von Otter, T. Thedéen, C. Garben (r1991)
Concert (7/94) (DG) ① [2] **435 860-2GH2**
J. Baker, CLS, R. Hickox (r1990) *Concert*
(11/94) (VIRG) ① **CUV5 61118-2**
Les champs—tenor and piano, Op. 19/2 (1834) (Wds. P J de Béranger)
J. Aler, C. Garben (r1991) *Concert*
(7/94) (DG) ① [2] **435 860-2GH2**
Chansonette—1v and piano (1835) (Wds. L de Wally)
J. Aler, C. Garben (r1991) *Concert*
(7/94) (DG) ① [2] **435 860-2GH2**
Le Chant des Bretons—chorus and piano, Op. 13/5 (1834) (Wds. A. Brizeux)
J. Aler, C. Garben (r1991) *Concert*
(7/94) (DG) ① [2] **435 860-2GH2**
Le Chasseur danois—song, Op. 19/6 (1845) (Wds. A. de Leuven)
G. Cachemaille, Lyon Op Orch, J.E. Gardiner
Concert (2/91) (ERAT) ① **2292-45517-2**
T. Allen, C. Garben (r1991) *Concert*
(7/94) (DG) ① [2] **435 860-2GH2**
Le Cinq mai (chant sur la mort de Napoléon)—bass, chorus and orchestra, Op. 6 (1835) (Wds. P J de Béranger)
L. Visser, Netherlands Rad Chor, Dutch RSO, J. Fournet (pp1987) *Concert*
(5/89) (DENO) ① **CO-72886**
La Damnation de Faust—dramatic legend: 4 parts, Op. 24 (1854-56) (Wds. cpsr, Gondonnière & de Nerval)
PART 1: 1. Le viel hiver (Introduction); 2. Les bergers quittent; 3a. Mais d'un éclat guerrier; 3b. Hungarian March. PART 2: 4. Sans regrets j'ai quitté; 5a. Christ vient de ressusciter; 5b. Hélas! doux chants de ciel; 6a. O pure émotion!; 6b. A boire encor!; 7. Certain rat; 8. Amen (fugue); 9a. Vrai Dieu, Messieurs!; 9b. Une puce gentille; 10. Voici des roses; 11. Dors, heureux Faust; 12a. Ballet des Sylphes; 12b. Quelle céleste image; 13. Villes entourées...Jam nox stellata. PART 3: 14. La retraite; 15a. Merci doux crépuscule; 15b. Je l'entends; 16a. Que l'air est étouffant!; 16b. Autrefois un roi de Thulé; 17. Esprits des flammes (Evocation); 18. Menuet des Follets, 'Will-o'-the-wisp'; 19. Devant la maison (Sérénade); 20. Grands dieux! que vois-je!; 21. Allons, il est trop tard. PART 4: 22a. D'amour l'ardente flamme; 22b. Au son des trompettes; 23. Nature immense (Invocation); 24. A la voûte azurée; 25. Dans mon coeur retentit; 26a. Hop! Irimiru Karabrao (Pandemonium); 26b. Alors l'Enfer se tut (Epilogue); 27a. Laus! Hosanna!; 27b. Remonte au ciel (Apotheosis).
Cpte J. Veasey, N. Gedda, J. Bastin, R. Van Allan, G. Knight, Ambrosian Sngrs, Wandsworth Sch Boys' Ch, LSC, LSO, Colin Davis (r1973)
(1/87) (PHIL) ① [2] **416 395-2PH2**

J. Tourel, NYPO, L. Bernstein (r1961) *Concert*
(11/92) (SONY) ① [2] **SM2K47526**
R. Plowright, Philh, J-P. Rouchon (r1993) *Concert*
(8/94) (ASV) ① **CDDCA895**
A. Pashley, ECO, Colin Davis (r1967) *Concert*
(12/94) (DECC) ① [2] **443 461-2DF2**
Y. Minton, BBC SO, P. Boulez (r1976) *Concert*
(3/95) (SONY) ① [3] **SM3K64103**
La **Mort d'Orphée (monologue et
bacchanale)—tenor, female vv and orchestra**
(1827) (Wds. Berton)
G. Garino, Netherlands Rad Chor, Dutch RSO, J.
Fournet (pp1987) *Concert*
(5/89) (DENO) ① **CO-72886**
Nocturne—2 sopranos and guitar (?1825-30)
(Wds. anon)
F. Pollet, A.S. Von Otter, G. Söllscher (r1991)
Concert   (7/94) (DG) ① [2] **435 860-2GH2**
Les **Nuits d'été—solo voice and orchestra,
Op. 7 (1840-41, orch 1843 (No. 4) and 1856)**
(Wds. T Gautier)
1. Villanelle; 2. Le spectre de la rose; 3. Sur les
lagunes; 4. Absence; 5. Au cimetière; 6. L'île
inconnue.
J. Norman, LSO, Colin Davis *Ravel: Shéhérazade.*
(3/85) (PHIL) ① **412 493-2PH**
E. Ameling, Atlanta SO, Robert Shaw (r1983) *Fauré:
Pelléas et Mélisande Suite.*
(10/85) (TELA) ① **CD80084**
J. Baker, New Philh, J. Barbirolli *Concert*
(11/88) (EMI) ① **CDM7 69544-2**
R. Crespin, SRO, E. Ansermet *Concert*
(11/88) (DECC) ① **417 813-2DH**
B. Greevy, Ulster Orch, Y.P. Tortelier *Concert*
(1/90) (CHAN) ① **CHAN8735**
J. Van Dam, J-P. Collard *Concert*
(1/90) (HARM) ① **CDC7 49288-2**
D. Montague, C. Robbin, H. Crook, G. Cachemaille,
Lyon Op Orch, J.E. Gardiner *Concert*
(2/91) (ERAT) ① **2292-45517-2**
C. Alliot-Lugaz, Monte Carlo PO, C. Bardon
Chausson: Poème de l'amour et de la mer.
(4/91) (REM) ① **REM311074**
L. Price, Chicago SO, F. Reiner *Enfance du Christ.*
(12/92) (RCA) ① [2] **09026 61234-2**
V. de los Angeles, Boston SO, C. Munch (r1955)
Roméo et Juliette. (4/93) (RCA) ① [2] **GD60661**
B. Hendricks, ECO, Colin Davis (r1993) *Britten:
Illuminations.* (8/94) (EMI) ① **CDC5 55053-2**
J. Baker, CLS, R. Hickox (r1990) *Concert*
(11/94) (VIRG) ① **CUV5 61118-2**
Y. Minton, S. Burrows, BBC SO, P. Boulez (r1976)
Concert   (3/95) (SONY) ① [3] **SM3K64103**
V. Kasarova, Austrian RSO, P. Steinberg (r1994)
Concert   (7/95) (RCA) ① **09026 68008-2**
B. Balleys, Paris Champs-Élysées Orch, P.
Herreweghe (r1994) *Herminie.*
(10/95) (HARM) ① **HMC90 1522**
1. S. Mayor, H. James, H. James (arr Mayor:
mandolin ens) *Concert*
(3/92) (ACOU) ① **CDACS012**
2, 4. M. Teyte, LSO, L. Heward (r1940) *Concert*
(10/94) (EMI) ① [2] **CHS5 65198-2**
2, 4. M. Teyte, LPO, L. Heward (r1940) *Concert*
(11/95) (PEAR) ① **GEMMCD9134**
6. Sarah Walker, R. Vignoles *Concert*
(11/87) (HYPE) ① **CDA66165**
L' **origine de la harpe—song, Op. 2/7 (1829)**
(Wds. T Gounet after T Moore)
T. Hampson, G. Parsons (r1993) *Concert*
(5/94) (EMI) ① **CDC5 55047-2**
F. Pollet, C. Garben (r1991) *Concert*
(7/94) (DG) ① [2] **435 860-2GH2**
**Pleure, pauvre Colette—romance: 2sops/2
tens and piano (?1818-22)** (Wds. Bourgerie)
F. Lott, A. Murray, G. Johnson *Concert*
(11/90) (EMI) ① **CDC7 49930-2**
F. Pollet, A.S. Von Otter, C. Garben (r1991) *Concert*
(7/94) (DG) ① [2] **435 860-2GH2**
**Prière du matin—female chorus and piano,
Op. 19/4 (1848 or earlier)** (Wds. Lamartine)
F. Pollet, A.S. Von Otter, C. Garben (r1991) *Concert*
(7/94) (DG) ① [2] **435 860-2GH2**
La **Révolution grecque—2 basses, chorus
and orchestra (1825-26)** (Wds. H Ferrand)
R. van der Meer, L. Visser, Netherlands Rad Chor,
Dutch RSO, J. Fournet (pp1987) *Concert*
(5/89) (DENO) ① **CO-72886**
**Roméo et Juliette—dramatic symphony:
soloists, chorus and orchestra, Op. 17 (1839)**
(Wds. Deschamps after Shakespeare)
1. Premier transports (Strophes); 2. Roméo alone; 3.
Capulet's ball; 4. Love scene; 5. Queen Mab scherzo;
6. Juliette's funeral procession; 7. Roméo at the
tomb; 8. Friar Laurence's air.

Cpte F. Quivar, A. Cupido, T. Krause, Montreal
Tudor Vocal Ens, Montreal SO, C. Dutoit *Symphonie
funèbre et triomphale.*
(12/86) (DECC) ① **417 302-2DH2**
Cpte B. Fassbaender, N. Gedda, J. Shirley-Quirk,
Austrian Rad Chor, Austrian RSO, L. Gardelli
(6/88) (ORFE) ① [2] **C087842H**
Cpte N. Denize, V. Cole, R. Lloyd, Cologne Rad
Chor, Stuttgart Rad Chor, Berlin RIAS Chbr Ch,
Frankfurt RSO, E. Inbal
(6/90) (DENO) ① [2] **CO-73210/1**
Cpte Y. Minton, F. Araiza, J. Bastin, Paris Orch Chor,
Paris Orch, D. Barenboim *Concert*
(1/93) (DG) ① [2] **437 244-2GGA2**
Cpte M. Roggero, L. Chabay, Yi-Kwei-Sze, Harvard
Glee Club, Radcliffe Choral Soc, Boston SO, C.
Munch (r1953) *Nuits d'été.*
(4/93) (RCA) ① [2] **GD60661**
1, 2, 3, 4, 5, 7. San Diego Master Chorale, San Diego
SO, Y. Talmi (r1994) *Troyens.*
(11/95) (NAXO) ① **8 553195**
2, 3. LPO, H. Harty (r1933) *Concert*
(9/95) (DUTT) ① **CDLX7016**
2-4. NBC SO, A. Toscanini (r1947) *Harold in Italy.*
(11/92) (RCA) ① **GD60275**
2-5. Montreal Sym Chor, Montreal SO, C. Dutoit
Symphonie funèbre et triomphale.
(7/90) (DECC) ① **425 001-2DM**
2-5. NYPO, L. Bernstein (r1959) *Concert*
(11/92) (SONY) ① [2] **SM2K47526**
4. Baltimore SO, D. Zinman (r1987) *Concert*
(12/88) (TELA) ① **CD80164**
4. Polish St PO, K. Jean *Concert*
(1/91) (NAXO) ① **8 550231**
4. New England Cons Orch, Boston SO, S. Ozawa
(r1975) *Symphonie fantastique.*
(1/91) (DG) ① **431 169-2GGA**
5. Philadelphia, A. Toscanini (r1942) *Concert*
(6/91) (RCA) ① [4] **GD60328**
5. NBC SO, A. Toscanini (bp1951) *Concert*
(11/92) (RCA) ① **GD60322**
5. Boston SO, C. Munch (r1961) *Concert*
(11/93) (RCA) ① **09026 61400-2**
**Sara la baigneuse—chorus and
orchestra/piano, Op. 11 (1834 rev 1850)**
(Wds. V Hugo)
F. Pollet, A.S. Von Otter, C. Garben (r1991) *Concert*
(7/94) (DG) ① [2] **435 860-2GH2**
St Anthony Sngrs, ECO, Colin Davis (r1967) *Concert*
(12/94) (DECC) ① [2] **443 461-2DF2**
**8 Scènes de Faust—voices and
orchestra/piano, Op. 1 (later withdrawn)
(1828-29)** (Wds. G de Nerval, after Goethe)
1. Chant de la fête de Pâques (chorus); 2. Paysans
sous les tilleuls danse et chant (chorus); 3. Concert
de sylphes (6vv); 4. Écot de joyeux compagnons
(Song of the rat: bass and chorus); 5. Chanson de
Méphistophélès (Song of the flea: tenor and chorus);
6. Le roi de Thulé (soprano); 7. Romance de
Marguérite, choeur de soldats (soprano and chorus);
8. Sérénade de Méphistophélès (tenor).
6. F. Pollet, C. Garben (r1993) *Concert*
(7/94) (DG) ① [2] **435 860-2GH2**
8. J. Aler, G. Söllscher (r1993) *Concert*
(7/94) (DG) ① [2] **435 860-2GH2**
**Te Deum—tenor, chorus and orchestra, Op.
22 (1849)**
F. Araiza, M. Haselböck, LSC, LP Ch, Wooburn
Sngrs, St Alban's Sch Ch, Haberdashers' Aske's Sch
Ch, Southend Boys' Ch, Desborough School Ch,
Forest School Ch, Winnersh, High Wycombe Parish
Church Ch, ECYO, C. Abbado (pp1981)
(2/84) (DG) ① **410 696-2GH**
Franco Tagliavini, N. Kynaston, Wandsworth Sch
Boys' Ch, LSC, LSO, Colin Davis (r1969)
(4/88) (PHIL) ① **416 660-2PH**
Le **Trébuchet—soprano, soprano/tenor,
baritone and piano, Op. 13/3 (1849 or earlier)**
(Wds. T Gounet, after T Moore)
F. Lott, A. Murray, G. Johnson *Concert*
(11/90) (EMI) ① **CDC7 49930-2**
V. de los Angeles, D. Fischer-Dieskau, G. Moore
(r1960) *Concert*
(4/94) (EMI) ① [4] **CMS5 65061-2(2)**
J. Aler, T. Allen, C. Garben (r1991) *Concert*
(7/94) (DG) ① [2] **435 860-2GH2**
**Tristia—chorus and orchestra, Op. 18 (1831
(No. 1), 1848 (Nos. 2 and 3)** (Wds Moore and
after Shakespeare)
1. Méditation religieuse; 2. La mort d'Ophélie; 3.
Marche funèbre pour la dernière scène d'Hamlet.
John Alldis Ch, LSO, Colin Davis *Concert*
(8/86) (PHIL) ① **416 431-2PH**
1, 2. St Anthony Sngrs, ECO, Colin Davis (r1967)
Concert   (12/94) (DECC) ① [2] **443 461-2DF2**

2. C. Robbin, Lyon Op Orch, J.E. Gardiner *Concert*
(2/91) (ERAT) ① **2292-45517-2**
2. A.S. Von Otter, C. Garben (r1991) *Concert*
(7/94) (DG) ① [2] **435 860-2GH2**
3. LPO, H. Harty (r1935) *Concert*
(9/95) (DUTT) ① **CDLX7016**
Zaïde—song, Op. 19/1 (1845) (Wds de
Beauvoir)
B. Fournier, Lyon Op Orch, J.E. Gardiner *Concert*
(2/91) (ERAT) ① **2292-45517-2**
F. Pollet, T. Lutz, C. Garben (r1991) *Concert*
(7/94) (DG) ① [2] **435 860-2GH2**
J. Baker, CLS, R. Hickox (r1990) *Concert*
(11/94) (VIRG) ① **CUV5 61118-2**

SECTION V: STAGE WORKS

**Béatrice et Bénédict—opera: 2 acts
(1862—Baden-Baden)** (Lib. cpsr, after
Shakespeare)
EXCERPTS: 1. Overture. ACT 1: 2. La More est en
fuite; 3. Je vais le voir; 4. Comment le dédain
pourrait-il mourir?; 5. Me marier? Dieu me pardonne!;
6. Mourez, tendres époux (épithalame); 7. Ah! je vais
l'aimer; 8. Vous soupirez, madame? (nocturne); 9.
Entr'acte. ACT 2: 10. Le vin de Syracuse; 11a. Non!
que viens-je d'entendre?; 11b. Il m'en souvient; 12.
Je vais d'un coeur aimant (trio); 13. Viens, de
l'hyménée; 14. Dieu qui guidas nos bras; 15. Ici l'on
voit Bénédict; 16. L'amour est un flambeau.
Cpte J. Baker, R. Tear, C. Eda-Pierre, H. Watts, T.
Allen, J. Bastin, R. Lloyd, R. Van Allan, John Alldis
Ch, LSO, Colin Davis (with dialogue)
(9/87) (PHIL) ① [2] **416 952-2PH2**
Cpte S. Graham, J-L. Viala, S. McNair, C. Robbin, G.
Cachemaille, G. Bacquier, V. le Texier, P. Magnant,
Lyon Op Chor, Lyon Op Orch, J. Nelson (with
dialogue)   (6/92) (ERAT) ① [2] **2292-45773-2**
1. SNO, A. Gibson *Concert*
(8/84) (CHAN) ① **CHAN8316**
1. Boston SO, C. Munch *Concert*
(3/89) (RCA) ① **GD86805**
1. RPO, Y. Temirkanov *Concert*
(11/92) (RCA) ① **09026 61203-2**
1. LSO, A. Previn *Concert*
(3/93) (EMI) ① **CDM7 64630-2**
1. Boston SO, C. Munch (r1958) *Concert*
(11/93) (RCA) ① **09026 61400-2**
1. Philh, J-P. Rouchon (r1993) *Concert*
(8/94) (ASV) ① **CDDCA895**
1, 9. NYPO, P. Boulez (r1971) *Concert*
(3/95) (SONY) ① [3] **SM3K64103**
**Benvenuto Cellini—opera: 2 acts
(1838—Paris)** (Lib. de Wailly and Barbier)
EXCERPTS: 1. Overture. ACT 1 SCENE 1: 2.
Teresa...mais où peut-elle être?; 3. Tra la la la, De
profundis!; 4a. Les belles fleurs!; 4b. Entre l'amour et
le devoir; 5. O Teresa, vous que j'aime; 6. Ah! mourir,
chère belle; 7. Ah! maître drôle, ah! libertin! ACT 1
SCENE 2: 8a. Une heure encore; 8b. La gloire était
ma seule idole; 9a. A boire, à boire; 9b. Si la terre
aux beaux jours se couronne; 10. Que voulez-vous?;
11. Cette somme t'est due; 12. Ah! qui pourrait me
résister?; 13. Vous voyer, j'espère; 14. Venez, venez,
peuple de Rome. ACT 2 SCENE 1: 15. Ah, qu'est il
devenu?; 16. Rosa purpurea; 17. Ma dague en main;
18. Ah! le ciel, cher époux; 19. Quand des sommets
de la montagne; 20. Ah! mille excuses; 21. Le
Pape voit de la prudence!; 22. Justice à nous; 23. Ah!
ça, démon!; 24. Ah! maintenant de sa folle
impudence. ACT 2 SCENE 2: 25. Tra la la...Mais
qu'ai-je donc?; 26a. Seul pour lutter; 26b. Sur les
monts; 27. Bienheureux les matelots; 28. Peuple
ouvrier; 29. Du métal! du métal!.
Cpte N. Gedda, J. Bastin, R. Massard, R. Soyer, D.
Blackwell, R. Herincx, C. Eda-Pierre, H.
Cuénod, J. Berbié, ROH Chor, BBC SO, Colin Davis
(11/88) (PHIL) ① [3] **416 955-2PH3**
1. FNO, C. Munch (pp1966) *Concert*
(11/88) (MONT) ① **MUN2011**
1. Baltimore SO, D. Zinman (r1987) *Concert*
(12/88) (TELA) ① **CD80164**
1. Polish St PO, K. Jean *Concert*
(1/91) (NAXO) ① **8 550231**
1. Brno St PO, P. Vronský *Concert*
(10/91) (SUPR) ① **11 0388-2**
1. Toulouse Capitole Orch, M. Plasson *Concert*
(2/92) (EMI) ① **CDC7 54237-2**
1. BPO, James Levine *Concert*
(7/92) (DG) ① **429 724-2GH2**
1. NYPO, L. Bernstein *Concert*
(11/92) (SONY) ① **SMK45525**
1. Strasbourg PO, A. Lombard *Concert*
(11/93) (ERAT) ① **2292-45925-2**
1. Black Dyke Mills Band, G. Brand (arr F. Wright)
Concert   (9/93) (RSR) ① **RSRD1002**

1. Boston SO, C. Munch (r1959) *Concert*
      (11/93) (RCA) ① **09026 61400-2**
1. San Francisco SO, P. Monteux (r1952) *Concert*
      (9/94) (RCA) ① **[15] 09026 61893-2**
1. NYPO, P. Boulez (r1972) *Concert*
      (3/95) (SONY) ① **[3] SM3K64103**
8a, 8b P. Domingo, National PO, E. Kohn *Concert*
      (11/90) (EMI) ① **CDC7 54053-2**
Les **Troyens, '(The) Trojans'—opera: 5 acts
(Acts 1-2: 1890; Acts 3-5: 1863—Acts 1-2:
Karlsruhe; Acts 3-5: Paris)** (Lib cpsr, after
Virgil)
PART I: LA PRISE DE TROIE. ACT 1: 1. Après dix
ans; 2a. Les Grecs ont disparu!; 2b. Malheureux Roi!;
3a. Chorèbe! il faut qu'il; 3b. Reviens à toi, vierge
adoré!; 3c. Si tu m'aimes, va-t-en; 4. Dieux
protecteurs; 5. Combat de ceste et Pas de lutteurs; 6.
Andromaque et son fils!; 7. Du peuple et des soldats,
ô roil; 8. Châtiment effroyable!; 9. Que la déesse
nous protège; 10. Non, je ne verrai pas; 11a. Du roi
des dieux, ô fille aimée (Trojan March); 11b. Arrêtez!
Oui, la flamme! la hache!. ACT 2: 12a. À lumière de
Troie!; 12b. Ah!...fuis, fils de Vénus; 13. La ville
ensanglantée; 14. Ah! Puissante Cybèle; 15a. Tous
ne périront pas; 15b. O digne soeur d'Hector!; 16.
Complices de sa gloire. PART 2: LES TROYENS À
CARTHAGE. ACT 3: 17a. Prelude; 17b. De Carthage
les cieux semblent bénir la fête; 18. Gloire à Didon;
19a. Nous avons vu finir; 19b. Chers Tyriens; 19c.
Cette belle journée; 20. Entrée des constructeurs; 21.
Entrée des matelots; 22. Entrée des laboureurs; 23.
Peuple! tous les honneurs; 24a. Les chants joyeux;
24b. Sa voix fait naître dans mon sein; 25a. La porte
du palais; 25b. Errante sur les mers; 26. Trojan
March; 27. Auguste reine; 28. Reine, je suis Enéel.
ACT 4: 29. Royal Hunt and Storm; 30a. Dites, Narbal;
30b. Pour de ce côte rien; 31. De quels revers;
32. Marche. BALLETS: 33a. Pas des Almées; 33b.
Danse des Esclaves; 33c. Pas d'Esclaves nubiennes;
34. O blonde Cérès; 35a. Pardonne, Iopas; 35b. O
pudeur! Tout conspire; 36a. Mais bannissons ces
tristes souvenirs; 36b. Tout n'est que paix et charme;
37. Nuits d'ivresse! ACT 5: 38. Vallon sonore; 39.
Préparez tout; 40. Par Bacchus! ils sont tous; 41a.
Inutiles regrets!; 41b. Ah! quand viendra l'instant; 42.
Encor ces voix! 43. Debout, Troyens; 44. Errante sur
tes pas; 45. Va, ma soeur, l'implorer; 46a. En mer,
voyez!; 46b. Dieux immortels!; 47. Je vais mourir; 48.
Adieu, fière cité; 49. Dieux de l'oubli; 50a. D'un
malheureux amour; 50b. Mon souvenir vivra; 51.
Quels cris!; 52a. Imprécation; 52b. Haine éternelle.
Cpte J. Veasey, J. Vickers, B. Lindholm, P. Glossop,
H. Begg, R. Soyer, A. Raffell, A. Howells, I. Partridge,
P. Thau, E. Bainbridge, R. Davies, R. Herincx, D.
Wicks, D. Lennox, Wandsworth Sch Boys' Ch, ROH
Chor, ROHO, Colin Davis (r1969)
      (12/86) (PHIL) ① **[4] 416 432-2PH4**
Cpte F. Pollet, G. Lakes, D. Voigt, G. Quilico, H.
Perraguin, J-P. Courtis, M. Philippe, C. Dubosc, J-L.
Maurette, R. Schirrer, C. Carlson, J. M. Ainsley, M.
Belleau, G. Cross, M. Beauchemin, Montreal Sym
Chor, Montreal SO, C. Dutoit (r1993)
      (12/94) (DECC) ① **[4] 443 693-2DH4**
17a LSO, Colin Davis *Concert*
      (12/86) (PHIL) ① **416 431-2PH**
17a San Francisco SO, P. Monteux (r1945) *Concert*
      (9/94) (RCA) ① **[15] 09026 61893-2**
17a, 29. San Diego Master Chorale, San Diego SO,
Y. Talmi (r1994) *Roméo et Juliette*.
      (11/95) (NAXO) ① **8 553195**
29. Baltimore SO, D. Zinman (r1987) *Concert*
      (12/88) (TELA) ① **CD80164**
29. ROH Chor, ROHO, B. Haitink *Concert*
      (12/89) (EMI) ① **CDC7 49849-2**
29. RPO, K.H. Adler (pp1982) *Concert*
      (8/91) (DECC) ① **430 716-2DM**
29. Boston SO, C. Munch (r1959) *Concert*
      (11/93) (RCA) ① **09026 61400-2**
29. Paris Orch, D. Barenboim (r1976) *Concert*
      (8/94) (SONY) ① **SBK53255**
29. Lyon Nat Orch, E. Krivine (r1993) *Symphonie
fantastique*. (12/94) (DENO) ① **CO-78902**
29. NYPO, P. Boulez (r1971) *Concert*
      (3/95) (SONY) ① **[3] SM3K64103**
41a, 41b G. Thill, Orch, E. Bigot (r1934) *Concert*
      (1/89) (EMI) ① **CDM7 69548-2**
47-49. J. Baker, B. Greevy, K. Erwen, G. Howell,
Ambrosian Op Chor, LSO, A. Gibson *Concert*
      (11/88) (EMI) ① **CDM7 69544-2**
48. R. Gorr, Philh, T. Collingwood (r1958) *Concert*
      (4/92) (EMI) ① **[7] CHS7 69741-2(3)**

BERNARD, (Jean) Emile (Auguste) (1843-1902) France

SECTION IV: VOCAL AND CHORAL
Ca fait peur—song, Op. 108
E. Clément, anon (r1911) *Concert*
      (8/95) (PEAR) ① **GEMMCD9161**

BERNARD, Felix (1897-1944) USA

written in collaboration with Johnny Black (b 1896)
USA

SECTION I: ORCHESTRAL
Dardanella—orchestra
London Sinfonietta, S. Rattle *Concert*
      (12/87) (EMI) ① **CDC7 47991-2**

BERNARD, James (20th Cent) England

SECTION V: STAGE WORKS
**Dracula Has Risen from the Grave—film
score (1968)**
EXCERPTS: 1. Finale.
1. Philh, N. Richardson *Concert*
      (5/93) (SILV) ① **SILVAD3003**

BERNARDI, Steffano (1585-1636) Italy

SECTION IV: VOCAL AND CHORAL
Magnificat anima mea Dominum—motet
Niederaltaicher Scholaren, K. Ruhland (r1992)
Concert   (10/93) (SONY) ① **SK53117**

BERNART DE VENTADORN (?c1130/40–c1190/1200) France

SECTION IV: VOCAL AND CHORAL
**Amics Bernart de Ventadorn—troubadour
song**
Camerata Mediterranea, J. Cohen (r1993; arr Cohen)
Concert   (11/94) (ERAT) ① **4509-94825-2**
**Be m'au perdut lai enves
Ventadorn—chanson**
P. Hillier, S. Stubbs, A. Lawrence-King, E. Headley
Concert   (7/89) (ECM) ① **837 360-2**
**Bel m'es can eu vei la brolha—troubadour
song**
Camerata Mediterranea, J. Cohen (r1993; arr Cohen)
Concert   (11/94) (ERAT) ① **4509-94825-2**
**Can l'erba fresch'el folha par—troubadour
song**
Camerata Mediterranea, J. Cohen (r1993; arr Cohen)
Concert   (11/94) (ERAT) ① **4509-94825-2**
Can vei la lauzta mover—troubadour song
Gothic Voices, C. Page *Concert*
      (12/90) (HYPE) ① **CDA66423**
**Cantarai d'aqueszt trobadors—troubadour
song**
Camerata Mediterranea, J. Cohen (r1993; arr Cohen)
Concert   (11/94) (ERAT) ① **4509-94825-2**
En Cossirer en en esmai—troubadour song
Camerata Mediterranea, J. Cohen (r1993; arr Cohen)
Concert   (11/94) (ERAT) ① **4509-94825-2**
**Era.m cosselhatz, senhor—troubadour
song**
Camerata Mediterranea, J. Cohen (r1993; arr Cohen)
Concert   (11/94) (ERAT) ① **4509-94825-2**
Lanquan vei la foilla—chanson
Camerata Mediterranea, J. Cohen (r1993; arr Cohen)
Concert   (11/94) (ERAT) ① **4509-94825-2**
**Lo gens temps de pascor—troubadour
song**
Camerata Mediterranea, J. Cohen (r1993; arr Cohen)
Concert   (11/94) (ERAT) ① **4509-94825-2**
Non es meravilla s'eu chan—chanson
Sinfonye, S. Wishart (r1992) *Concert*
      (8/93) (HYPE) ① **CDA66625**
**Per melhs cobrir lo mal pes—troubadour
song**
Camerata Mediterranea, J. Cohen (r1993; arr Cohen)
Concert   (11/94) (ERAT) ① **4509-94825-2**
Pos me pregatz seignor—chanson
Camerata Mediterranea, J. Cohen (r1993; arr Cohen)
Concert   (11/94) (ERAT) ① **4509-94825-2**

Quan l'erba fresc e.l foilla par—chanson
E. Lamandier *Concert* (2/88) (ALIE) ① **AL1019**
Quan vei la lauzeta mover—chanson
P. Hillier, S. Stubbs, A. Lawrence-King, E. Headley
Concert   (7/89) (ECM) ① **837 360-2**
Tant ai mo cor ple de joya—chanson
Camerata Mediterranea, J. Cohen (r1993; arr Cohen)
Concert   (11/94) (ERAT) ① **4509-94825-2**

BERNERS, (Sir Gerald Hugh Tyrwhitt-Wilson, Baronet) Lord (1883-1950) England

SECTION I: ORCHESTRAL
Fantaisie espagnole—orchestra (1920)
RLPO, B. Wordsworth (r1986) *Concert*
      (8/94) (EMI) ① **CDM5 65098-2**
Fugue—orchestra (1928)
RLPO, B. Wordsworth (r1986) *Concert*
      (8/94) (EMI) ① **CDM5 65098-2**
3 Morceaux—orchestra (1919)
1. Chinoiserie; 2. Valse sentimentale; 3. Kasatchok.
RLPO, B. Wordsworth (r1986) *Concert*
      (8/94) (EMI) ① **CDM5 65098-2**
Nicholas Nickleby—film score (1947)
RLPO, B. Wordsworth (r1986) *Concert*
      (8/94) (EMI) ① **CDM5 65098-2**

SECTION IV: VOCAL AND CHORAL
Red Roses and Red Noses—song (Wds.
cpsr)
F. Lott, G. Johnson *Concert*
      (7/90) (CHAN) ① **CHAN8722**

SECTION V: STAGE WORKS
**The Triumph of Neptune—ballet
(1926—London)**
EXCERPTS: 1. Harlequinade; 2. Dance of the Fairy
Princess; 3. Schottische; 4. Cloudland; 5. Sunday
morning (Intermezzo); 6. Polka; 7. Hompipe; 8. The
Frozen Forest; 9. Apotheosis of Neptune.
R. Grooters, Philadelphia, T. Beecham (r1952)
Concert   (11/94) (SONY) ① **SMK46683**
1, 2, 3, 4, 5, 6, 7, 8, 9. RLPO, B. Wordsworth (r1986)
Concert   (8/94) (EMI) ① **CDM5 65098-2**
1-3, 5-7, 9. R. Alva, LPO, T. Beecham (r1937)
Concert   (6/92) (EMI) ① **CDM7 63405-2**

BERNSTEIN, Elmer (b 1922) USA

SECTION V: STAGE WORKS
The Age of Innocence—film score (1993)
EXCERPTS: 1. Main Theme; 2. At the Opera
(Gounod's Faust); 3. Radetzky March (J. Strauss I);
4. Emperor Waltz - excerpt (J. Strauss II); 5. Tales
from the Vienna Woods - excerpt (J. Strauss II); 6.
Mrs Mingott; 7. Dangerous Conversation; 8. Slighted;
9. Van Der Luydens; 10. First Visit; 11. Roses
Montage; 12. Ellen's Letter; 13. Archer's Books; 14.
Mrs Mingott's Help; 15. Archer Pleads; 16. Passage
of Time; 17. Archery; 18. Ellen at the Shore; 19.
Blenker Farm; 20. Boston Common; 21. Parker
House; 22. Pick Up Ellen; 23. Conversation with
Letterblair; 24. Archer Leaves; 25. Farewell Dinner;
26. Ellen Leaves; 27. In the Train; 28. Ellen's House; 29.
Madame Olenska; 30. End Credits.
1. OST (r1993) *Concert* (9/95) (VIRG2) ① **CDV2774**
The Bridge at Remagen—film score (1968)
EXCERPTS: 1. Main Theme.
1. Prague City PO, P. Bateman (1994; arr J. Bell)
Concert   (11/94) (SILV) ① **FILMCD151**
The Comancheros—film score (1961)
EXCERPTS: 1. Main Title; 2. Escort; 3. McBaine and
the Prairie; 4. Jake Surveys the Camp; 5. Pursuit; 6.
Mexican Dance; 7. Indian Attack; 8. Finale.
1-8. Utah SO, E. Bernstein (r1985) *True Grit*.
      (3/87) (VARE) ① **VCD47236**
Ghostbusters—film score (1984)
EXCERPTS: 1. Prague City PO, W. Motzing (r1993) *Concert*
      (8/94) (SILV) ① **FILMCD146**
The Great Escape—film score (1963)
EXCERPTS: 1. Main Title (March); 2. Premature
Plans; 3. Cooler and the mole; 4. Blythe; 5.
Discovery; 6. Various Troubles; 7. On the Road; 8.
Betrayal; 9. Hendley's Risk; 10. Road's End; 11.
More Action; 12. The Chase; 13. Finale.
1. Prague City PO, P. Bateman (r1994) *Concert*
      (11/94) (SILV) ① **FILMCD151**
1-13. OST, E. Bernstein (r1963)
      (5/93) (INTD) ① **MAF7025D**

The **Hallelujah Trail—overture for chorus and orchestra (1965)** (arr cpsr from film score. Wds E. Sheldon)
Arizona St Uni Concert Ch, Phoenix SO, J. Sedares (r1993) *Magnificent Seven.*
(11/94) (KOCH) ① 37222-2
Kings Go Forth—film score (1958)
EXCERPTS: 1. Kings Go Forth; 2. The Riviera; 3. Monique's Theme; 4. The Bunker; 5. Sam's Theme; 6. Sam and Monique; 7. Sam's Return; 8. Monique's Theme (reprise); 9. Le Chat Noir; 10. Quiet Drive; 11. Britt's Kiss; 12. Monique's Despair; 13. Displaced; 14. Finale.
1-14. OST, E. Bernstein (r1959) *Some Came Running.*
(5/93) (CLOU) ① CNS5004
The **Magnificent Seven—film score (1960)**
EXCERPTS: 1. Theme; 2. Main Titles & Calvera's Visit: Allegro con fuoco; 3. Council of War: Allegro molto marcato; 4. Strange Funeral: Moderato; 5. After the Brawl: Allegro; 6. The Journey: Allegro vigoroso; 7. Toreador: Moderato; 8. Training; 9. Fiesta & Celebration; 10. Calvera's Return: Allegro brutale; 11. Calvera Routed & Petra's Declaration; 12. Ambush: Moderato; 13. Surprise & Crossroads: Allegro energico; 14. Enemy Camp & Nightmare; 15. Defeat: Slow & Dark; 16. Showdown & Finale: Allegro con fuoco.
2-16. Phoenix SO, J. Sedares (r1993; ed & arr E. Bernstein & C. Palmer) *Hallelujah Trail Overture.*
(11/94) (KOCH) ① 37222-2
Some Came Running—film score (1959)
EXCERPTS: 1. Prelude; 2. To Love and Be Loved; 3. Dave's Double Life; 4. Dave and Gwen; 5. Fight; 6. Gwen's Theme; 7. Ginny; 8. Short Noise; 9. Live It Up; 10. Tryst; 11. Seduction; 12. Smitty's Place; 13. Rejection; 14. Pursuit; 15. Finale.
1-15. OST, E. Bernstein (r1959) *Kings Go Forth.*
(5/93) (CLOU) ① CNS5004
True Grit—film score (1969)
EXCERPTS: 1. Main Title; 2. Rooster and Runaway; 3. Bald Mountain; 4. Pony Mine and Papa's Thing; 5. The Dying Moon; 6. Big Trail; 7a. Sad Departure; 7b. The Pace that kills; 8. Warm Wrap-Up.
1-6, 7a, 7b, 8. Utah SO, E. Bernstein (1985) *Comancheros.*
(3/87) (VARE) ① VCD47236
2, 8. Prague City PO, P. Bateman (r1994; arr Shuken & Hayes) *Concert*
(11/94) (SILV) ① FILMCD153

BERNSTEIN, Leonard (1918–1990) USA

SECTION I: ORCHESTRAL

Divertimento—orchestra/band (1980)
BRSO, L. Bernstein (pp1983) *Concert*
(12/86) (HUNG) ① HCD12631
Fanfare for JFK—brass ensemble (1961)
LPO, J. Mester *Concert* (7/91) (KOCH) ① 37012-2
Fanfare for the 25th Anniversary of the High School of Music and Art, New York City—brass ensemble (1961)
LPO, J. Mester *Concert* (7/91) (KOCH) ① 37012-2
Halil—nocturne: flutes, percussion, harp and strings (1981)
M. Faust, Cologne RSO, A. Francis (r1992) *Concert*
(12/94) (CAPR) ① 10 495
Jubilee Games—concerto for orchestra
Israel PO, L. Bernstein (pp1988/9) *Concert*
(1/92) (DG) ① 429 231-2GH
3 Meditations from 'Mass'—cello and orchestra (1971)
M. Rostropovich, Israel PO, L. Bernstein (pp1981) *Concert*
(10/94) (DG) ① [2] 437 952-2GX2
On the Town—three dance episodes from the musical (1944)
1. The great lover displays himself; 2. Lonely town—pas de deux; 3. Times Square, 1944.
NYPO, L. Bernstein (r1963) *Concert*
(5/92) (SONY) ① [3] SM3K47154
NYPO, L. Bernstein *Concert*
(11/92) (SONY) ① SMK47530
Overture to 'Candide'—orchestra (arr cpsr from overture to stage work)
Los Angeles PO, L. Bernstein (pp1982) *Concert*
(10/84) (DG) ① 413 324-2GH
NYPO, L. Bernstein (r1963) *Concert*
(5/92) (SONY) ① [3] SM3K47154
NYPO, L. Bernstein (r1959) *Concert*
(11/92) (SONY) ① SMK47529
J. Kahane, Bournemouth SO, A. Litton (r1990) *Concert* (11/94) (VIRG) ① CUV5 61119-2
Prelude, Fugue and Riffs—clarinet and jazz ensemble (1949 rev 1955)
B. Goodman, Columbia Jazz Combo, L. Bernstein *Concert* (5/87) (SONY) ① MK42227

M. Collins, P. Donohoe, London Sinfonietta, S. Rattle *Concert* (12/87) (EMI) ① CDC7 47991-2
LSO Brass Ens, E. Crees *Concert*
(1/92) (COLL) ① Coll1288-2
B. Goodman, Columbia Jazz Combo, L. Bernstein (r1963) *Concert* (3/92) (SONY) ① [3] SM3K47162
H. de Boer, Netherlands Wind Ens, R. Dufallo (r1993) *Concert* (3/94) (CHAN) ① CHAN9210
Serenade—violin, strings, harp and percussion (1954) (after Plato's "Symposium")
Z. Francescatti, NYPO, L. Bernstein (r1965) *Concert* (3/92) (SONY) ① [3] SM3K47162
H. Kun, English SO, W. Boughton *Barber: Violin Concerto.* (6/92) (NIMB) ① NI5329
I. Perlman, Boston SO, S. Ozawa *Concert*
(6/95) (EMI) ① CDC5 55360-2
Shivaree—double brass ensemble and percussion (1969)
LPO, J. Mester *Concert* (7/91) (KOCH) ① 37012-2
Symphony No. 1, 'Jeremiah'—mezzo-soprano and orchestra (1943) (Wds. Book of Lamentations)
J. Tourel, NYPO, L. Bernstein (r1961) *Concert*
(3/92) (SONY) ① [3] SM3K47162
N. Merriman, St Louis SO, L. Bernstein (r1945) *Concert* (6/94) (RCA) ① 09026 61581-2
Symphony No. 2, '(The) Age of Anxiety'—piano & orchestra (1949)
P. Entremont, NYPO, L. Bernstein (r1965) *Concert* (3/92) (SONY) ① [3] SM3K47162
J. Kahane, Bournemouth SO, A. Litton (r1990) *Concert* (11/94) (VIRG) ① CUV5 61119-2
Symphony No. 3, 'Kaddish'—soprano, narrator, chorus and orchestra (1961-63 rev 1977) (spoken text cpsr: prayer in Aramaic & Hebrew)
F. Montealegre, J. Tourel, Camerata Sngrs, NYPO, L. Bernstein (r1964) *Concert*
(3/92) (SONY) ① [3] SM3K47162
Exc B. Hendricks, E. Ericson Chbr Ch, Swedish RSO, E. Ericson *Concert*
(4/91) (EMI) ① CDC7 54098-2

SECTION II: CHAMBER

Rondo for Lifey—trumpet and piano (1949)
S. Nakarjakov, A. Markovich *Concert*
(5/93) (TELD) ① 9031-77705-2
W. Marsalis, J.L. Stillman (r1992) *Concert*
(5/94) (SONY) ① SK47193
Sonata for Clarinet and Piano (1941-42)
R. Stoltzman, LSO, E. Stern (r1993; orch Ramin) *Concert* (12/93) (RCA) ① 09026 61790-2
Y-Y. Ma, J. Kahane (r1992) *Concert*
(4/94) (SONY) ① SK53126

SECTION III: INSTRUMENTAL

7 Anniversaries—piano (1942-43)
1. For Aaron Copland; 2. For my sister, Shirley; 3. In Memoriam: Alfred Eisner; 4. For Paul Bowles; 5. In Memoriam: Nathalie Koussevitzky; 6. For Sergei Koussevitzky; 7. For William Schuman.
5. L. Slatkin (r1992) *Concert*
(6/94) (RCA) ① 09026 61581-2
5 Anniversaries—piano (1949/51)
1. For Elizabeth Rudolf; 2. For Lukas Foss; 3. Elizabeth B. Ehrman; 4. For Sandy Gelhorn; 5. For Susanna Kyle.
M. Legrand (r1994) *Concert*
(7/95) (ERAT) ① 4509-96386-2
Touches—chorale, 8 variations & coda: piano (1981 rev 1983)
D. Achatz *Concert* (9/87) (BIS) ① BIS-CD352
B. Lerner *Concert* (12/88) (ETCE) ① KTC1019

SECTION IV: VOCAL AND CHORAL

Arias and Barcarolles—mezzo-soprano, baritone and piano duet (1988)
1. Prelude; 2. Love Duet; 3. Little Smary; 4. The Love of my Life; 5. Greeting; 6. Oif Mayn Khas'neh (At my wedding); 7. Mr and Mrs Webb say Goodnight; 8. Nachspiel (In memoriam).
J. Kaye, W. Sharp, M. Barrett, S. Blier (r1989) *Concert* (6/90) (KOCH) ① 37000-2
J. Bunnell, D. Duesing, Seattle SO, G. Schwarz (orch B. Sheng) *Concert* (9/90) (DELO) ① DE3078
La Bonne cuisine—four recipes: voice and piano (1947) (Wds. E. Dutoit, trans cpsr)
1. Plum pudding; 2. Queues de boeuf (Ox tails); 3. Tavouk Guenksis; 4. Civet à toute vitesse (Rabbit at top speed).
1, 2. R. Alexander, T. Crone *Concert*
(2/87) (ETCE) ① KTC1037

Chichester Psalms—treble, chorus and orchestra (1965) (Wds. Bible)
1. Urah, haneval, v'chinor! (wds. Psalms 100 and 108); 2. Adonai ro-i, lo ehsar (wds. Psalms 2 and 23); 3. Adonai, Adonai (wds. Psalms 131 and 133).
Vienna Jeunesse Ch, Israel PO, L. Bernstein (pp1977) *Songfest.* (5/86) (DG) ① 415 965-2GH
A. Jones, LSC, RPO, R. Hickox *Fauré: Requiem.*
(1/87) (RPO) ① CDRPO7007
D. Martelli, R. Masters, G. Kettel, T. Trotter, Corydon Sngrs, M. Best *Concert*
(9/87) (HYPE) ① CDA66219
D.L. Ragin, Atlanta Sym Chor, Atlanta SO, Robert Shaw (r1988-9) *Concert* (3/90) (TELA) ① CD80181
J. Bogart, Camerata Sngrs, NYPO, L. Bernstein (r1965) *Concert* (3/92) (SONY) ① [3] SM3K47162
1. Collegiate Chorale, NY Met Op Orch, J. Conlon (pp1991) *Concert* (6/93) (RCA) ① 09026 61509-2
I hate music—song cycle (1943) (Wds. cpsr)
1. My name is Barbara; 2. Jupiter has seven moons; 3. I hate music; 4. A Big Indian and a Little Indian (Riddle Song); 5. I'm a Person too.
R. Alexander, T. Crone *Concert*
(2/87) (ETCE) ① KTC1037
3. C. Ludwig, C. Spencer (pp1994) *Concert*
(3/95) (RCA) ① 09026 62652-2
Mass—theatre piece: sngrs, players, dancers & orch (1971) (Wds. Roman Mass and cpsr & S. Schwartz)
Cpte A. Titus, N. Scribner Ch, Berkshire Boy Ch, orch, L. Bernstein (r1971) *Dybbuk.*
(5/92) (SONY) ① [3] SM3K47158
Simple Song; I go on R. Alexander, T. Crone *Concert* (2/87) (ETCE) ① KTC1037
Simple Song C. Studer, LSO, I. Marin *Concert*
(11/92) (DG) ① 435 387-2GH
Warm up St John's Episcopal Cath Ch, D. Pearson *Concert* (10/92) (DELO) ① DE3125
Missa brevis—alto, chorus a capella and perc (1988) (based on choruses from 'The Lark' (1955)
D.L. Ragin, Atlanta Sym Chor, Atlanta SO, Robert Shaw (r1988-9) *Concert* (3/90) (TELA) ① CD80181
Piccola Serenata—vocalise for Karl Böhm's 85th birthday (1979)
R. Alexander, T. Crone *Concert*
(2/87) (ETCE) ① KTC1037
Silhouette—song (1951) (Wds. cpsr)
R. Alexander, T. Crone *Concert*
(2/87) (ETCE) ① KTC1037
So pretty—song (1968) (Wds Comden and Green: extracted from musical "West Side Story")
R. Alexander, T. Crone *Concert*
(2/87) (ETCE) ① KTC1037
Songfest—cycle of American poems for six soloists and orchestra (1977) (Wds. various)
1. Sextet: To the poem (wds. F O'Hara); 2. Solo: The Pennycandystore beyond the El (wds. L. Ferlinghetti); 3. Solo: A Julia de Burgos (wds. J. de Burgos); 4. Solo: To what you said... (wds. W. Whitman); 5. Duet: I, too, sing America—Okay 'Negroes' (wds. L Hughes/J Jordan); 6. Trio: To my dear and loving husband (wds. A. Bradstreet); 7. Duet: Storyette H. M. (wds. G. Stein); 8. Sextet: if you can't eat you got to (wds. e. e. cummings); 9. Solo: Music I heard with you (wds. C. Aitken); 10. Solo: Zizi's Lament (wds. G. Corso); 11. Solo—Sonnet: What lips my lips have kissed (wds. E. St. Vincent Millay); 12. Sextet: Israfel (wds. E. A. Poe).
C. Dale, R. Elias, N. Williams, N. Rosenshein, J. Reardon, D. Gramm, Washington NSO, L. Bernstein *Chichester Psalms.* (5/86) (DG) ① 415 965-2GH
L. Hohenfeld, W. White, P. Spence, W. Planté, V. Hartman, J. Cheek, St Louis SO, L. Slatkin (r1992) *Concert* (6/94) (RCA) ① 09026 61581-2
4, 7. J. Kaye, W. Sharp, M. Barrett, S. Sant'Ambrogio (r1989) *Concert* (6/90) (KOCH) ① 37000-2
Two Love Songs—voice and piano (1949) (Wds. R. M. Rilke, trans J. Lamont)
1. Extinguish my eyes; 2. When my soul touches yours.
R. Alexander, T. Crone *Concert*
(2/87) (ETCE) ① KTC1037

SECTION V: STAGE WORKS

Candide—operetta: 2 acts (1956—New York) (Wds. various)
EXCERPTS—; 1. Overture. ACT 1: 2. The best of all possible worlds; 3. Oh, happy we; 4. Wedding Procession, Chorale and Battle Scene; 5. Candide begins her travels; 6. It must be so; 7. Lisbon Sequence; 8. Paris Waltz; 9. Glitter and be gay; 10. You were dead, you know; 11. Pilgrim's procession; 12. My Love; 13. I am easily assimilated (Buenos Aires); 14. Finale (Quartet). ACT 2: 15. Quiet; 16.

The Ballade of Eldorado; 17. Bon Voyage; 18. Raft Sequence; 19. Venice Gambling Scene; 20. What's the use?; 21. The Venice Gavotte; 22. Return to Westphalia; 23. Make our garden grow. ADDITIONAL ITEM FOR LONDON PRODUCTION, 1959—; 24. We are women.

1. Czech PO, A. Copland (pp1973) *Concert* (6/93) (ROMA) ① **RR1973**

8. Hollywood Bowl SO, J. Mauceri (r1993) *Concert* (6/94) (PHIL) ① **438 685-2PH**

9. M. Hill Smith, Scottish Op Orch, J. Brown (r1989-91) *Concert* (10/91) (TER) ① **CDVIR8314**

9. S. Jo, Monte Carlo PO, P. Olmi (r1994) *Concert* (6/95) (ERAT) ① **4509-97239-2**

Candide (opera house version)—comic operetta: 2 acts (1982—New York) (Wds. various)

EXCERPTS: 1. Overture. ACT 1: 2. Life is happiness indeed; 3. The Best of all possible worlds; 4. O happy we; 5. It must be so; 6. Fanfare, Chorale and Battle; 7. Glitter and be gay; 8. Dear boy; 9. Auto da Fé scene; 10. Candide's Lament; 12. I am easily assimilated; 13. Finale (Quartet). ACT 2: 14. To the New World; 15. My Love; 16. The Old Lady's Tale (Barcarolle); 17. Alleluia; 18. Sheep Song; 19. Governor's Waltz; 20. Bon Voyage; 21. Quiet; 22. What's the use; 23. Make our garden grow.

Cpte D. Eisler, E. Mills, J. Langston, S. Reeve, M. Clement, J. Castle, J. Billings, J. Harrold, NYC Op Chor, NYC Op Orch, J. Mauceri (10/86) (NEW) ① [2] **NW340/1-2**

5, 10. R. Alexander, T. Crone *Concert* (2/87) (ETCE) ① **KTC1037**

Candide—comic operetta: 2 acts (1988 final version—Glasgow) (Wds. various)

EXCERPTS—ACT 1: 1. Overture; 1a. Westphalia chorale (wds. Bernstein/Wells); 2. Life is happiness indeed (wds. Sondheim); 3. The best of all possible worlds (wds. La Touche); 3a. Universal good (wds. Bernstein/Wells); 4. Oh, happy we (wds. Wilbur); 5. It must be so (wds. Wilbur); 6. Westphalia (wds. Bernstein/Wells); 6a. Battle music; 7. Candide's lament (wds. La Touche); 8. Dear Boy (wds. Wilbur); 9. Auto-da-fée (wds. La Touche/Wilbur); 10. Candide begins his travels; 10a. It must be me (wds. Wilbur); 11. The Paris waltz; 12. Glitter and be gay (wds. Wilbur); 13. You were dead, you know (wds. La Touche); 14. I am easily assimilated (wds. Bernstein); 15. Quartet finale (wds. Wilbur). ACT 2: 16. Universal good (wds. Bernstein/Wells); 17. My love (wds. Wilbur/La Touche); 18. We are women (wds. Bernstein); 19. The pilgrims' procession/Alleluia (wds. Wilbur); 20. Quiet (wds. Wilbur); 21. Introduction to Eldorado; 22. The ballad of Eldorado (wds. Hellman); 23. Words, words, words (wds. Bernstein); 24. Bon voyage (wds. Wilbur); 25. The kings' barcarolle (wds. Wilbur); 26. Money, money, money (wds. Wilbur); 27. What's the use (wds. Wilbur); 28. The Venice gavotte (wds. Wilbur/Parker); 29. Nothing more than this (wds. Bernstein); 30. Universal good (wds. Hellman/Bernstein); 31. Make our garden grow (wds. Wilbur).

Cpte J. Hadley, J. Anderson, A. Green, C. Ludwig, N. Gedda, D. Jones, K. Ollmann, N. Jenkins, R. Suart, J. Treleaven, L. Benson, C. Bayley, LSC, LSO, L. Bernstein (8/91) (DG) ① [2] **429 734-2GH2**

1. Empire Brass (r1992; arr. R. Smedvig) *Concert* (1/94) (TELA) ① **CD80305**

1, 12. T. Dahl, Calgary PO, M. Bernardi (r1992) *Concert* (12/94) (CBC) ① **SMCD5125**

1, 3-5, 7, 11-14, 17, 21, 24, 27, 28, 31. N. Grace, M. Beudert, M. Hill Smith, A. Howard, M. Tinkler, G. Miles, B. Bottone, Scottish Op Chor, SNO, J. Brown (8/88) (TER) ① **CDTER1156**

12. D. Upshaw, orch, E. Stern (r1993) *Concert* (12/94) (NONE) ① **7559-79345-2**

31. R. Fleming, J. Hadley, Collegiate Chorale, NY Met Op Orch, J. Conlon (pp1991) *Concert* (6/93) (RCA) ① **09026 61509-2**

Dybbuk—ballet (1974—New York)

Cpte D. Johnson, J. Ostendorf, NY City Ballet Orch, L. Bernstein (r1974) *Mass.* (5/92) (SONY) ① [3] **SM3K47158**

Facsimile—ballet (1946—New York)

NYPO, L. Bernstein (r1963) *Concert* (5/92) (SONY) ① [3] **SM3K47154**

RCA Victor Orch, L. Bernstein (r1947) *Concert* (7/94) (RCA) ① **09026 61650-2**

Fancy Free—ballet (1944—New York)

Cpte NYPO, L. Bernstein (r1963) *Concert* (5/92) (SONY) ① [3] **SM3K47154**

Cpte NYPO, L. Bernstein *Concert* (11/92) (SONY) ① **SMK47530**

D. Achatz (arr. piano) *Concert* (9/87) (BIS) ① **BIS-CD352**

J. Kahane, Bournemouth SO, A. Litton (r1990) *Concert* (11/94) (VIRG) ① **CUV5 61119-2**

The **Lark—incidental music: 7vv (1955—Boston)** (Wds. L. Hellman, after Anouilh)

EXCERPTS: 1a. Spring song; 1b. Court song; 1c. Soldier's song; 2. PART 2: 2a. Prelude; 2b. Benedictus; 2c. Sanctus; 2d. Requiem; 2e. Gloria.

Cpte The Sixteen, H. Christophers *Concert* (4/92) (COLL) ① **Coll1287-2**

Madwoman of Central Park West (1979)

EXCERPTS: 1. My new friends.

1. D. Upshaw, orch, E. Stern (r1993: orch L Wilcox) *Concert* (12/94) (NONE) ① **7559-79345-2**

On the Town—musical comedy: 2 acts (1944—Boston) (lyrics A. Green & B. Comden)

EXCERPTS. ACT 1: 1. I feel like I'm not out of bed yet; 2. New York, New York; 3. Chase music; 4. Miss Turnstiles Variations—She's a home loving girl; 5. Taxi number—Come up to my place; 6. Carried away; 7. Lonely town; 8. Carnegie Hall Pavane; 9. Do-Do-Re-Do; 10. Dance—Lonely town (originally: Sailor's on the town); 11. I can cook too; 12. Lucky to be me; 13. Dance—Times Square (Finale). ACT 2: 14. Night Club Sequence—So long baby; 15. Night Club Sequence—I wish I was dead; 16. Night Club Sequence—I'm blue; 17. Night Club Sequence—You got me; 18. Night Club Sequence—I understand (Pitkin's song); 19. Ballet—Imaginary Coney Island; 20. Some other time; 21. Dance: The real Coney Island; 22. Finale.

Cpte B. Comden, A. Green, N. Walker, J. Reardon, C. Alexander, G. Gaynes, R. Striboneen, chor, orch, L. Bernstein *Concert* (5/92) (SONY) ① [3] **SM3K47154**

Cpte F. von Stade, T. Daly, M. McLaughlin, T. Hampson, K. Ollmann, D. Garrison, S. Ramey, E. Lear, C. Laine, London Voices, LSO, M. Tilson Thomas (pp1992) (10/93) (DG) ① **437 516-2GH**

5-7, 12. J. Kaye, W. Sharp, M. Barrett (r1989) *Concert* (6/90) (KOCH) ① **37000-2**

6, 8. J. Norman, J.T. Williams (r1989) *Concert* (4/92) (PHIL) ① **422 401-2PH**

On the Waterfront—film score (1954)

Love theme Hollywood Bowl SO, J. Mauceri (r1991) *Concert* (9/91) (PHIL) ① **432 109-2PH**

On the Waterfront—concert suite from film score (1954 rev 1955)

Israel PO, L. Bernstein (pp1981) *West Side Story.* (4/85) (DG) ① [2] **415 253-2GH2**

NYPO, L. Bernstein (r1960) *Concert* (5/92) (SONY) ① [3] **SM3K47154**

NYPO, L. Bernstein *Concert* (11/92) (SONY) ① **SMK47530**

Peter Pan—incidental music to Barrie's play (1954—New York) (Lyrics cpsr)

EXCERPTS: SONGS: 1. Who am I?; 2. My house; 3. Peter, Peter; 4. Never-Land. CHORUSUS: 5. Pirate song; 6. Plank round. SONG: 7. Dream with me.

1-4. R. Alexander, T. Crone *Concert* (2/87) (ETCE) ① **KTC1037**

4. J. Kaye, M. Barrett, S. Sant'Ambrogio (r1989) *Concert* (6/90) (KOCH) ① **37000-2**

7. K. Criswell, London Sinfonietta, J. McGlinn (r1992) *Concert* (4/94) (EMI) ① **CDC7 54802-2**

Trouble in Tahiti—opera: 7 scenes (1952—Waltham) (Lib. cpsr)

Cpte J. Reardon, J. Patrick, A. Butler, M. Clark, M. Brown, Columbia Wind Ens, L. Bernstein (r1973) *Concert* (5/92) (SONY) ① [3] **SM3K47154**

West Side Story—musical show: 2 acts (1957—New York) (Book A. Laurents, lyrics S. Sondheim)

EXCERPTS: 1. Prologue. ACT 1: 2. Jet Song; 3. Something's coming; 4. The Dance at the Gym; 4a. Blues; 4b. Promenade; 4c. Mambo; 4d. Cha-Cha; 4e. Meeting; 4f. Jump; 5. Maria; 6. Tonight (Balcony scene); 7. America; 8. Cool; 9. One hand, one heart; 10. Tonight (Quintet); 11. The Rumble. ACT 2: 12. I feel pretty; 13a. Ballet sequence; 13b. transition to Scherzo; 13c. Scherzo; 13d. Somewhere; 13e. Procession and Nightmare; 14. Gee, Officer Krupke; 15. A boy like that/I have a love; 16. Taunting scene; 17. Finale. ADDITIONAL ITEMS FOR FILM VERSION—1960: 18. Overture; 19. End credits.

Cpte K. Te Kanawa, N. Bernstein, J. Carreras, A. Bernstein, T. Troyanos, M. Horne, K. Ollmann, L. Edeiken, S. Zambalis, A. Réaux, D. Livingstone, M. Nelson, S. Bogardus, P. Thom, T. Lester, R. Harrell, Broadway Chor, Broadway Orch, L. Bernstein (r1984) *On the Waterfront Suite.* (4/85) (DG) ① [2] **415 253-2GH2**

Cpte M. Nixon, J. Bryant, R. Tamblyn, Orig Film Cast, J. Green (r1960) (8/93) (SONY) ① **SK48211**

Cpte B. Bonney, M. Ball, L. Williams, C. Howard, M. Carewe, L. Gibson, J. O'Grady, D. Chessor, L. Benson, A. Busher, J. Graeme, M. Pearn, Royal Phil Chor, RPO, B. Wordsworth (r1993) (10/93) (IMG) ① **IMGCD1801**

Cpte T. Olafimihan, P. Manuel, C. O'Connor, S. Burgess, N. Warnford, J. Paton, E. Stephenson, N. Carty, K. Daniels, M. Michaels, A. Sarple, A. Edmeads, G. Stevens, N. Ferranti, Chor, National SO, J.O. Edwards (r1993) (2/94) (TER) ① [2] **CDTER2 1197**

Medley Tetra (r1989-91: arr gtr qt: Storry) *Concert* (11/93) (CONI) ① **CDCF903**

Medley R. Stoltzman, LSO, E. Stern (r1993; arr Bennett: 'Variants') *Concert* (12/93) (RCA) ① **09026 61790-2**

1, 2, 4c, 5, 7, 8, 13c, 13d Netherlands Wind Ens, R. Dufallo (r1993: arr brass: E Crees) *Concert* (3/94) (CHAN) ① **CHAN9210**

1, 3, 4c, 5, 7, 8, 13c, 13d LSO Brass Ens, E. Crees (arr brass: Cress) *Concert* (1/92) (COLL) ① **Coll1288-2**

2, 3, 5, 7, 9, 10, 12, 15. K. Labèque, M. Labèque (arr Kostal) *West Side Story Symphonic Dances.* (1/90) (SONY) ① **SK45531**

3. M. Patinkin, Orch, E. Stern (r1993; orch Troob, arr Ford) *Concert* (11/94) (NONE) ① **7559-79330-2**

5. F. Araiza, Munich RSO, R. Weikert (arr Mattes) *Concert* (3/93) (RCA) ① **09026 61163-2**

5. J. Hadley, NY Met Op Orch, J. Conlon (pp1991) *Concert* (6/93) (RCA) ① **09026 61509-2**

5. P. Bertin, A. Scholl, D. Visse, F. Couturier (r1995: arr R Wagner) *Concert* (8/95) (HARM) ① **HMC90 1552**

5, 10. J. Carreras, P. Domingo, L. Pavarotti, MMF Orch, Rome Op Orch, Z. Mehta (pp1990) *Concert* (10/90) (DECC) ① **430 433-2DH**

6. V. Masterson, T. Allen, Philh, J.O. Edwards (r1990) *Concert* (5/94) (TER) ① **CDVIR8317**

6. LPO Vcs, RPO Vcs, BBC SO Vcs, Philh Vcs, G. Simon (r1993; arr Balcombe) *Concert* (9/95) (CALA) ① **CACD0104**

6. S. Bullock, A. Davies, A. Bryn Parri (r1994) *Concert* (11/95) (SAIN) ① **SCDC2070**

7, 12, 13d Chee-Yun, A. Eguchi (arr vn/pf: Penaforte) *Concert* (12/93) (DENO) ① **CO-75118**

12. D. Upshaw, E. Stern, L. Stifelman (r1993: arr E Stern) *Concert* (12/94) (NONE) ① **7559-79345-2**

13d J. Lloyd Webber, RPO, N. Cleobury (arr vc) *Concert* (3/87) (PHIL) ① **416 698-2PH**

West Side Story—symphonic dances from musical show (1960)

1. Prologue; 2. Somewhere; 3. Scherzo; 4. Mambo; 5. Cha-Cha; 6. Meeting Scene; 7. 'Cool' Fugue; 8. Rumble; 9. Finale.

Los Angeles PO, L. Bernstein (pp1982) *Concert* (8/83) (DG) ① **410 025-2GH**

D. Achatz (arr. piano) *Concert* (9/87) (BIS) ① **BIS-CD352**

K. Labèque, M. Labèque, J-P. Drouet, S. Gualda, T. Gurtu (arr Kostal) *West Side Story.* (1/90) (SONY) ① **SK45531**

San Francisco SO, S. Ozawa *Concert* (12/91) (DG) ① [2] **413 851-2GW2**

NYPO, L. Bernstein (r1961) *Concert* (5/92) (SONY) ① [3] **SM3K47154**

NYPO, L. Bernstein (r1959) *Concert* (11/92) (SONY) ① **SMK47529**

4. Baltimore SO, D. Zinman (r1994: 2 perfs) *Concert* (7/95) (ARGO) ① **444 454-2ZH**

Wonderful Town—musical comedy: 2 acts (1953—New York) (Book and lyrics Green and Comden)

EXCERPTS: ACT 1: 1. Christopher Street; 2. Ohio; 3. Conquering the city; 4. One hundred easy ways; 5. What a waste; 6. Story Vignettes—Rexford; Mr Mallory; Danny; Trent; 7. A little bit in love; 8. Pass that football; 9. Conversation piece; 10. A quiet girl; 12. Conga! ACT 2: 13. My darlin' Eileen; 13. Swing; 14. It's love; 15. Ballet at the Village Vortex; 16. The wrong note rag.

7. J. Kaye, M. Barrett (r1989) *Concert* (6/90) (KOCH) ① **37000-2**

1600 Pennsylvania Avenue—musical: 2 acts (1976—Philadelphia) (Book and lyrics A. J. Lerner)

EXCERPTS: ACT 1: 1. Rehearsel; 2. On ten square miles by the Potomac River; 3. If I was adove; 4. Welcome home, Miz Adams; 5. Take care of this house; 6. The President Jefferson Sunday Luncheon Party March; 7. Seene; 8. Sonatina; 9. Lud's wedding—I love my wife; 10. Auctions—The little white lie; 11. Mark of a man; 12. We must have a ball; 13. The ball. ACT 2: 14. Bright and black; 15. Duet for One (The first lady of the land); 16. The Robber-Baron Minstrel Parade; 17. Pity the poor; 18.

Red White and Blues; 19. Proud.
5. R. Alexander, T. Crone *Concert*
(2/87) (ETCE) ① **KTC1037**
6, 15. J. Kaye, L. Richardson, T. Miller, K. Colson, D.
Gaines, Ambrosian Sngrs, London Sinfonietta, J.
McGlinn *Concert* (8/93) (EMI) ① **CDC7 54586-2**

BERR, José *(1874–1947)* Germany

SECTION II: CHAMBER

Fantasia on Rossini's 'Una voce poco fa'—bassoon and piano
K. Walker, J. Drake *Concert*
(10/89) (REGE) ① **REGCD104**

BERTÉ, Heinrich *(1857–1924)* Hungary

SECTION V: STAGE WORKS

Das Dreimäderlhaus—operetta
(1916—Vienna) (based on works by Schubert)
Zu jeder Zeit; Nicht klagen R. Tauber, orch (r1926)
Concert (12/92) (NIMB) ① **NI7833**

BERTI, Oscar *Venezuela*

SECTION III: INSTRUMENTAL

Alegres Rincones—piano
A. Gifford (r1990; trans Lauro) *Concert*
(12/92) (NATI) ① **NTCD001**

BERTOLUSI, Vincenzo *(1550–1608) Italy/Denmark*

also known as Vincentius Bertholusius

SECTION IV: VOCAL AND CHORAL

Ego flos campi (from Sacrae Cantiones I)
Hilliard Ens, P. Hillier *Concert*
(2/89) (BIS) ① **BIS-CD389**

BERTONI, Ferdinando (Gaspare) *(1725–1813) Italy*

SECTION III: INSTRUMENTAL

Organ Sonata in F—organ
R. Micconi *Concert* (3/90) (MOTE) ① **CD10561**

BERTRAND, Anthoine de *(1530/40–1580/82) France*

SECTION IV: VOCAL AND CHORAL

De nuit, le bien—chanson
Scholars (r1993) *Concert*
(2/95) (NAXO) ① **8 550880**
Premier Livre des amours de Pierre de
Ronsard—chansons: 4vv (1576)
1. Las! Pleust à dieu n'avoir jamais tasté; 2.
Avecques moy pleurer vous devriez bien; 3. Ha
signeur dieu, que de graces écloses; 4. Dans le
serain de sa jumelle flamme; 5. Qui voudra voir
dedans une jeunesse; 6. Nature ornant la dame; 7.
Oeil q ui mes pleurs de tes rayons essuye; 8. Tout
me déplait, mais rien ne m'est si grief; 9. Las, je me
plains de mile et mile et mile; 10. Mon dieu, que ma
maistresse est belle; 11. Ie vy ma nymphe entre cent
damoiselles; 12. Amour archer d'une tirade ront; 13.
Ie parangonne á ta jeune beauté; 14. Ce ris plus
dous de l'ouuvre d'un abeille; 15. Doux fut le trait;
16. Amour me tue, et si je ne veux dire; 17. Telle
qu'elle est dedans ma souvenance; 18. Ie voudrois
estre ixion et tantale; 19. Ces deux yeux bruns; 20. Ie
veux mourir pour tes beautez, maistresse; 21. Beauté
dont la douceur pourroit vaincre les Roys; 22. Quand
en songeant ma folastre j'acole; 23. Tes yeux divins
me promettent le don; 24. Ce ne sont qu'uains,
qu'amorces et qu'apas; 25. Le ciel ne veut, dame,
que je joüisse.
C. Janequin Ens (r1984)
(5/87) (HARM) ① **HMA190 1147**

BERWALD, Franz (Adolf) *(1796–1868) Sweden*

SECTION I: ORCHESTRAL

Concerto for Piano and Orchestra in D
(1855)
M. Migdal, RPO, U. Björlin (r1976) *Concert*
(6/94) (EMI) ① **CDM5 65073-2**

Concerto for Violin and Orchestra in C sharp
minor, Op. 2 (1820) (ed. H. Marteau (Leipzig,
1911)
A. Tellefsen, RPO, U. Björlin (r1976) *Concert*
(6/94) (EMI) ① **CDM5 65073-2**
Festival of the Bayadères—symphonic poem
(1842)
RPO, U. Björlin (r1976) *Concert*
(6/94) (EMI) ① **CDM5 65073-2**
Serious and joyful fancies—symphonic
poem (1842)
RPO, U. Björlin (r1976) *Concert*
(6/94) (EMI) ① **CDM5 65073-2**
Symphony No. 1 in G minor, 'Sinfonie
sérieuse' (1842)
Gothenburg SO, N. Järvi *Concert*
(12/85) (DG) ① [2] **415 502-2GH2**
San Francisco SO, H. Blomstedt (r1992) *Symphony*
4. (1/94) (DECC) ① **436 597-2DH**
Symphony No. 2 in D, 'Sinfonie capricieuse'
(1842) (only short score survives: realized
Castegren)
Gothenburg SO, N. Järvi *Concert*
(12/85) (DG) ① [2] **415 502-2GH2**
Symphony No. 3 in C, 'sinfonie singulière'
(1845)
Gothenburg SO, N. Järvi *Concert*
(12/85) (DG) ① [2] **415 502-2GH2**
LSO, S. Ehrling *Symphony 4.*
(8/92) (BLUE) ① **ABCD037**
Symphony No. 4 in E flat (1845)
Gothenburg SO, N. Järvi *Concert*
(12/85) (DG) ① [2] **415 502-2GH2**
LSO, S. Ehrling *Symphony 3.*
(8/92) (BLUE) ① **ABCD037**
San Francisco SO, H. Blomstedt (r1991) *Symphony*
1. (1/94) (DECC) ① **436 597-2DH**

SECTION II: CHAMBER

Piano Quintet No. 1 in C minor (1853)
S. Lindgren, Berwald Qt *Concert*
(10/93) (MSVE) ① **MSCD521**
Piano Trio in C (1845)
J. Modrian, vn, G. Kertész, vc, K. Drafi (r1991)
Concert (10/93) (MARC) ① **8 223430**
Piano Trio in C (c1850) (fragment: rev of Pf
Trio (1845)
J. Modrian, vn, G. Kertész, vc, K. Drafi (r1991)
Concert (10/93) (MARC) ① **8 223430**
Piano Trio in E flat (1849) (incomplete: sketch
for Pf Trio 1)
J. Modrian, vn, G. Kertész, vc, K. Drafi (r1991)
Concert (10/93) (MARC) ① **8 223430**
Piano Trio No. 1 in E flat (1849)
A. Kiss, C. Onczay, I. Prunyi *Concert*
(10/93) (MARC) ① **8 223170**
L. Negro, B. Lysell, O. Karlsson *Concert*
(10/93) (MSVE) ① **MSCD521**
Piano Trio No. 2 in F minor (1851)
A. Kiss, C. Onczay, I. Prunyi *Concert*
(10/93) (MARC) ① **8 223170**
Piano Trio No. 3 in D minor (1851)
A. Kiss, C. Onczay, I. Prunyi *Concert*
(10/93) (MARC) ① **8 223170**
L. Negro, B. Lysell, O. Karlsson *Concert*
(10/93) (MSVE) ① **MSCD521**
Piano Trio No. 4 in C (c1853)
J. Modrian, vn, G. Kertész, vc, K. Drafi (r1991)
Concert (10/93) (MARC) ① **8 223430**
Septet in B flat—cl, bn, hn, vn, va, vc, db
(?1828)
Nash Ens *Hummel: Septet, Op.74.*
(6/89) (CRD) ① **CRD3344**
String Quartet No. 1 in G minor (1818)
Chilingirian Qt (r1979) *Wikmanson: String Quartet 2.*
(3/95) (CRD) ① **CRD3361**

SECTION V: STAGE WORKS

The Queen of Golconda—opera: 3 acts
(1868—Stockholm) (Lib. after J B C Vial & E G
F de Favières)
EXCERPTS: 1. Overture.
1. RPO, U. Björlin (r1976) *Concert*
(6/94) (EMI) ① **CDM5 65073-2**

BESARD, Jean-Baptiste *(c1567–after 1617) Burgundy*

SECTION II: CHAMBER

Bransles de village—two lutes (pub 1604)
N. North, P. O'Dette *Concert*
(4/88) (HYPE) ① **CDA66228**

SECTION III: INSTRUMENTAL

Air de cour—lute
J. Bream (r1966) *Concert*
(8/93) (RCA) ① [28] **09026 61583-2(1)**
J. Bream (r1966) *Concert*
(6/94) (RCA) ① **09026 61585-2**
Branle
K. Ragossnig *Concert*
(2/86) (ARCH) ① **415 294-2AH**
J. Bream (r1966) *Concert*
(8/93) (RCA) ① [28] **09026 61583-2(1)**
J. Bream (r1966) *Concert*
(6/94) (RCA) ① **09026 61585-2**
Guillemette—lute
J. Bream (r1966) *Concert*
(8/93) (RCA) ① [28] **09026 61583-2(1)**
J. Bream (r1966) *Concert*
(6/94) (RCA) ① **09026 61585-2**
Volte—lute
J. Bream (r1966) *Concert*
(8/93) (RCA) ① [28] **09026 61583-2(1)**
J. Bream (r1966) *Concert*
(6/94) (RCA) ① **09026 61585-2**

SECTION IV: VOCAL AND CHORAL

Airs de Cour—1v and lute (pub 1603)
1. C'est malheur; 2. Adieu bergère; 3. Beaux yeux; 4.
La viola la nacelle d'amour; 5. Quelle divinité; 6. Si
c'est pour mon pucellage.
R. Covey-Crump, P. O'Dette *Concert*
(4/88) (HYPE) ① **CDA66228**

BEST, Peter *(20th Cent)* Australia

SECTION V: STAGE WORKS

Crocodile Dundee—film score (1986)
EXCERPTS: 1. Theme; 2. Mick & His Mate; 3. Cyril;
4. Walkabout Bounce; 5. Goodnight Walter; 6. In the
Truck; 7. The Buffalo; 8. In the Boat; 9. Never Never
Land; 10. The Death Roll; 11. Sunset; 12. Nice One,
Skippy; 13. Walk in the Bush; 14. Would You Mind?;
15. Mick Meets New York; 16. G'Day; 17. Yessir; 18.
Mad, Bad & Dangerous; 19. The Pimp; 20. Stone the
Crows; 21. That's Not a Knife; 22. Oh Richard; 23.
The Pimp Returns.
1. OST *Concert* (5/93) (SILV) ① **SILVAD3001**
Heroes—television score (1990)
EXCERPTS: 1. Main Title Theme; 2. Townsville
Raid/Not You, Bill; 3. He Worries Me/Boarding In One
Hour/Canoe Race; 4. Riptide; 5. Bathtime; 6. Let's
Get Out/Watchtower/The Dinghy's Back; 7.
Destroyer; 8. Gentelmen, Relax.
1. OST *Concert* (5/93) (SILV) ① **SILVAD3001**

BEST, W(illiam) T(homas) *(1826–1897) England*

SECTION III: INSTRUMENTAL

Air with Variations—organ
Margaret Phillips *Concert*
(7/91) (GAMU) ① **GAMCD522**
4 Choral Preludes on old English psalm
tunes—organ
1. Lord, hear the voice of my complaint; 2. Through
all the changing scenes of life; 3. My Soul for ehlp pn
God relies; 4. My Soul, praise the Lord.
Margaret Phillips *Concert*
(7/91) (GAMU) ① **GAMCD522**

BETTINELLI, Bruno *(b 1913)* Italy

SECTION III: INSTRUMENTAL

Toccata Fantasia—organ (1958)
L. Benedetti (r1992) *Concert*
(4/95) (PRIO) ① **PRCD427**

BÉVENOT, (Dom) Laurence *(20th cent) France*

SECTION IV: VOCAL AND CHORAL

Compline—plainchant (sung in English)
1. English psalmody; 2. Compline hymn; 3. Verse; 4.
Nunc dimittis; 5. Final prayers and blessing.
1-5. Ampleforth Abbey Monastic Ch (r1994-5)
Concert (9/95) (CFM) ① **CFMCD1783**

BIBALO, Antonio (b 1922) Norway/Italy

SECTION I: ORCHESTRAL

The **Savage** (1983)
Borealis Ens, C. Eggen (r1990s) *Concert*
(9/93) (AURO) ① **ACD4973**

SECTION III: INSTRUMENTAL

Study in blue—guitar (1983)
S-E. Olsen *Concert* (9/88) (SIMA) ① **PSC1031**

BIBER, Carl Heinrich (?–c1750) Bohemia

SECTION I: ORCHESTRAL

Sonata—8 trumpets, strings, continuo and 2 timpani (1744)
J. Wallace, Philh, S. Wright *Concert*
(4/89) (NIMB) ① **NI5121**
Sonata for Trumpet and Violin with 4 trumpets, violins, continuo and timpani (1729)
J. Wallace, P. Thomas, Philh, S. Wright *Concert*
(4/89) (NIMB) ① **NI5121**
Sonata Paschalis for solo trumpet, violins, 4 trumpets, timpani and continuo (1729)
J. Wallace, Philh, S. Wright *Concert*
(4/89) (NIMB) ① **NI5121**

BIBER, Heinrich Ignaz Franz von (1644–1704) Bohemia

SECTION I: ORCHESTRAL

Battalia a 10 in D—10-part strings (pub 1673)
VCM, N. Harnoncourt (r1965) *Concert*
(1/93) (ARCH) ① **437 081-2AT**
New London Consort, P. Pickett (r1992) *Concert*
(6/94) (L'OI) ① **436 460-2OH**
Fidicunium Sacro-profanum—12 Sonatas (1683)
1. B minor a 8; 2. F a 8; 3. D minor a 5; 4. C (Concerto) a 5; 5. E minor a 6; 6. A minor.
1–6. Cantilena, A. Shepherd *Concert*
(4/88) (CHAN) ① [2] **CHAN8448/9**
4. C. Steele-Perkins, Tafelmusik, J. Lamon (vn/dir)
(r1993) *Concert* (4/95) (SONY) **SK53365**
8. VCM, N. Harnoncourt (r1965) *Concert*
(1/93) (ARCH) ① **437 081-2AT**
Sonata, 'Sancti Polycarpi'—8 tpts, timp, org & violine
G. Schwarz (tpt/dir), E. Carroll, M. Gould, R. Sirinek, N. Smith, John Miller, N. Balm, R. Mase, NY Y CO *Concert* (10/84) (DELO) ① **DE3002**
W. Marsalis, ECO, R. Leppard *Concert*
(6/88) (SONY) ① **SK42478**
Sonatae tam aris quam aulis servientes (pub 1676)
1. Sonata I in C; 2. Sonata II in D; 3. Sonata III in G minor; 4. Sonata IV in C; 5. Sonata V in E minor; 6. Sonata VI in F; 7. Sonata VII in C; 8. Sonata VIII in G; 9. Sonata IX in B flat; 10. Sonata X in G minor; 11. Sonata XI in A; 12. Sonata XII in C.
1, 10. C. Steele-Perkins, J. Thiessen, Tafelmusik, J. Lamon (vn/dir) (r1993) *Concert*
(4/95) (SONY) **SK53365**
2, 3, 5, 9. Freiburg Baroque Orch Consort (r1993)
Georg Muffat: Armonico tributo sonatas.
(10/94) (DHM) ① **05472 77303-2**

SECTION II: CHAMBER

Ballettae a 4 violettae—strings and continuo
New London Consort, P. Pickett (r1992) *Concert*
(6/94) (L'OI) ① **436 460-2OH**
Duets—two trumpets
1. C; 5. C; 11. G minor; 13. A minor.
1, 5, 11, 13. C. Steele-Perkins, J. Thiessen (r1993)
Concert (4/95) (SONY) **SK53365**
Harmonia artificioso–ariosa: deversimodè accordata (1712)
1. Partita in D minor: 1a. Adagio—Presto—Adagio; 1b. Allemenade; 1c. Gigue; 1d. Aria; 1e. Sarabande; 1f. Finale. 2. Partita in B minor: 2a. Praeludium; 2b. Allamande—Variatio; 2c. Balletto—Allegro; 2d. Aria—Presto; 2e. Gigue—Presto. 3. Partita in A: 3a. Praeludium—Allegro; 3b. Allamande; 3c. Amener—Presto; 3d. Balletto; 3e. Gigue; 3f. Ciacona (Canon in unisono). 4. Partita in E flat: 4a. Adagio—Allegro—Adagio; 4b. Allamande; 4c. Trezza: Presto; 4d. Aria; 4e. Canario; 4f. Gigue—Presto; 4g. Pollicinello—Presto; 5. Partita in

G minor: 5a. Intrada: Alla breva; 5b. Aria: Adagio; 5c. Balletto: Presto; 5d. Gigue; 5e. Passacaglia: (Adagio)—Allegro—Adagio. 6. Partita No 6: 6a. Praeludium—Adagio—Allegro; 6b. Aria—Variatio I-XIII; 6c. Finale—Adagio—Allegro. 7. Partita in C minor: 7a. Praeludium; 7b. Allamande; 7c. Sarabande; 7d. Gigue—Presto; 7e. Aria; 7f. Trezza; 7g. Arietta variata.
Purcell Qt, Elizabeth Wallfisch (vn/dir) (r1994)
(11/94) (CHAN) ① [2] **CHAN0575/6**
Tafelmusik, J. Lamon (vn/dir) (r1993)
(5/95) (SONY) **SK58920**
Mensa sonara—sonatas da camera (4 strings and continuo) (pub 1683)
1. D; 2. F; 3. A minor; 4. B flat; 5. E; 6. G minor.
Cologne Musica Antiqua, R. Goebel *Sonata violino solo.* (11/89) (ARCH) ① **423 701-2AH**
Mystery (Rosary) Sonatas and Passacaglia—violin and continuo (c1676)
THE JOYFUL MYSTERIES: 1. D minor: The Annunciation; 2. A: Mary's visit to Elizabeth; 3. B minor: The Nativity; 4. D minor: Presentation of Jesus in the temple; 5. A: 12 Year-old Jesus in the temple. THE SORROWFUL MYSTERIES: 6. C minor: Christ's Agony in the Garden; 7. F: The Scourging of Jesus; 8. B flat: The Crowing with Thorns; 9. A minor: The Carrying of the Cross; 10. G minor: The Crucifixion. The Glorious Mysteries: 11. G: The Resurrection; 12. C: The Ascension; 13. D Minor: The Descent of the Holy Ghost; 14. D: The Assumption of the Virgin; 16. G minor: Passacaglia.
Cpte Cologne Musica Antiqua, R. Goebel
(10/91) (ARCH) ① [2] **431 656-2AH2**
F. Maier, F. Lehrndorfer, M. Engel, K. Junghänel
(5/91) (DHM) ① [2] **GD77102**
J. Holloway, D. Moroney, Tragicomedia
(5/91) (VIRG) ① [2] **VCD7 59551-2**
1–9. E. Johnson, L. O'Sullivan, E. Milnes
(10/91) (NEWP) ① **NC60035/1**
10–16. E. Johnson, L. O'Sullivan, E. Milnes
(10/91) (NEWP) ① **NC60035/2**
16. A. Manze (r1993–4) *Concert*
(2/95) (HARM) ① **HMU90 7134/5**
Sonata a 6 in B, '(Die) Pauern Kirchfahrt genandt'
VCM, N. Harnoncourt (r1965) *Concert*
(1/93) (ARCH) ① **437 081-2AT**
New London Consort, P. Pickett (r1992) *Concert*
(6/94) (L'OI) ① **436 460-2OH**
Sonata in D minor—two violins, trombone and continuo
VCM, N. Harnoncourt (r1965) *Concert*
(1/93) (ARCH) ① **437 081-2AT**
Sonata, '(La) Pastorella'—violin and continuo
Romanesca (r1993-4) *Concert*
(2/95) (HARM) ① **HMU90 7134/5**
Sonata violino solo representativa in A—violin and continuo (1669)
R. Goebel, Cologne Musica Antiqua *Mensa sonara.*
(11/89) (ARCH) ① **423 701-2AH**
Romanesca (r1993-4) *Concert*
(2/95) (HARM) ① **HMU90 7134/5**
8 Sonatae for Violin and Continuo (pub 1681)
3. F; 4. D; 6. C minor.
Romanesca (r1993-4) *Concert*
(2/95) (HARM) ① **HMU90 7134/5**

SECTION III: INSTRUMENTAL

Passacaglia for Lute (anon arr of Sonata VI from Sonatae, 1681)
N. North (r1993-4) *Concert*
(2/95) (HARM) ① **HMU90 7134/5**

SECTION IV: VOCAL AND CHORAL

Missa alleluja—8/8vv & intruments (1698)
Vienna Hofburgkapelle Schola, Concerto Palatino, Gradus ad Parnassum, K. Junghänel (1994) *Concert*
(7/95) (DHM) ① **05472 77326-2**
Ne cedite mentes—motet: chorus and continuo
Niederaltaicher Scholaren, K. Ruhland (r1992)
Concert (10/93) (SONY) **SK53117**
Requiem a 15 in A (1687)
E. Bongers, A. Grimm, K. Wessel, S. Davies, R. Steur, K-J. de Koning, Amsterdam Baroque Orch, Amsterdam Baroque Ch, T. Koopman (r1992)
Vesperae. (9/94) (ERAT) ① **4509-91725-2**

Requiem in F minor—SSATB, chorus, strings, tbns (ad lib)
S. Piau, M. van der Sluis, B. Lettinga, D. Cordier, J. Elwes, H. van der Kamp, Netherlands Bach Soc Ch, Netherlands Bach Soc Baroque Orch, G. Leonhardt (r1992) *Valls: Missa Scala Aretina.*
(8/93) (DHM) ① **05472 77277-2**
C. Bott, T. Bonner, C. Robson, J. M. Ainsley, M. George, New London Consort, P. Pickett (r1992)
Concert (6/94) (L'OI) ① **436 460-2OH**
Serenada in C, '(Der) Nachtwächter'—bass and strings
S. Grant, New London Consort, P. Pickett (r1992)
Concert (6/94) (L'OI) ① **436 460-2OH**
Vesperae a 32—8 sols, chor, stgs, brass and timp (1674)
E. Bongers, A. Grimm, K. Wessel, P. de Groot, M. Reyans, S. Davies, R. Steur, K-J. de Koning, Amsterdam Baroque Orch, Amsterdam Baroque Ch, T. Koopman (r1992) *Requiem in A.*
(9/94) (ERAT) ① **4509-91725-2**

SECTION V: STAGE WORKS

Arminio—opera: 3 acts (1691-2—Salzburg)
(Lib. F M Raffaelini)
Cpte B. Schlick, G. Schwarz, G. Türk, X. Meijer, G. Kenda, B. Landauer, M. Forster, H. Oswald, O. Rastbichler, I. Troupova, R. Schwarzer, F. Mehltretter, Salzburg Hofmusik, W. Brunner (r1994)
(6/95) (CPO) ① [3] **CPO999 258-2**

BIDAOLA, Guridi (20th Cent) Spain

SECTION III: INSTRUMENTAL

Viejo zortzico—guitar
M. Robles *Concert*
(2/93) (DECC) ① **433 869-2DWO**

BIEBL, Franz (b 1906) Germany

SECTION IV: VOCAL AND CHORAL

Ave Maria—baritone and chorus
Chanticleer (r1990) *Concert*
(12/94) (CHTI) ① **CR-8803**

BIENERT, Olaf (20th Cent) Germany

SECTION IV: VOCAL AND CHORAL

Parc Monceau—Lied: 1v and piano (c1924)
(Wds. Tucholsky)
W. Sharp, S. Blier (r1991) *Concert*
(7/93) (KOCH) ① **37086-2**

BIGAGLIA, Diogenio (c1676–c1745) Italy

SECTION II: CHAMBER

Sonata for Recorder and Continuo in A minor, Op. 1 (pub c1722)
M. Petri, G. Malcolm *Concert*
(10/86) (PHIL) ① **412 632-2PH**
F. Brüggen, A. Bylsma, G. Leonhardt (1967) *Concert*
(7/94) (TELD) ① **4509-93669-2**

BILLI, Vincenzo (1869–1938) Italy

SECTION IV: VOCAL AND CHORAL

Campane a sera—song (wds. E. Caruso)
E. Caruso, orch, J. Pasternack (r1918) *Concert*
(12/90) (NIMB) ① **NI7809**
E. Caruso, orch, J. Pasternack (arr Malfetti: r1918)
Concert (7/91) (RCA) ① [12] **GD60495(6)**
E. Caruso, orch, J. Pasternack (arr Malfetti: r1918)
Concert (10/91) (PEAR) ① [3] **EVC4(1)**

SECTION V: STAGE WORKS

Tizianello—operetta
E canta Il grillo T. Ruffo, orch (r1929) *Concert*
(2/93) (PREI) ① [3] **89303(2)**

BILLINGS, William (1746–1800) USA

SECTION IV: VOCAL AND CHORAL

The **Continental Harmony—collection (pub 1794)**
1. Creation; 2. O Praise the Lord (Thanksgiving Hymn).

1, 2. His Majestie's Clerkes, P. Hillier *Concert*
(10/92) (HARM) ① **HMU90 7048**
The **Lord is ris'n included—anthem for Easter (pub 1787)**
His Majestie's Clerkes, P. Hillier *Concert*
(10/92) (HARM) ① **HMU90 7048**
The **New-England Psalm-Singer—collection (pub 1770)**
1. Africa; 2. Boston; 3. Brookfield; 4. As the hart panteth; 5. When Jesus wept.
1, 3, 4. His Majestie's Clerkes, P. Hillier *Concert*
(10/92) (HARM) ① **HMU90 7048**
The **Psalm-Singer's Amusement—collection (pub 1781)**
1. Rutland; 2. They that go down to the sea (Euroclydon).
1, 2. His Majestie's Clerkes, P. Hillier *Concert*
(10/92) (HARM) ① **HMU90 7048**
The **Singing Master's Assistant, or Key to Practical Music—collection (pub 1778)**
1. Emmaus; 2. Judea; 3. David the King was grieved (David's Lament); 4. Hear my prayer, o Lord; 5. I am the rose of Sharon; 6. Is any afflicted.
1, 3-6. His Majestie's Clerkes, P. Hillier *Concert*
(10/92) (HARM) ① **HMU90 7048**
The **Suffolk Harmony—collection (pub 1786)**
1. Jordan; 2. Shiloh; 3. Samuel the priest (Funeral Anthem).
1-3. His Majestie's Clerkes, P. Hillier *Concert*
(10/92) (HARM) ① **HMU90 7048**

BINCHOIS, Gilles de Bins dit (c1400–1460) Belgium

SECTION II: CHAMBER

Chanson
G. Binchois Ens, D. Vellard *Concert*
(3/92) (VIRG) ① **VC7 59043-2**

SECTION IV: VOCAL AND CHORAL

A solis ortus cardine—Hymnus and Laudes in Nativitate Domini (polyphonic set)
PCA *Concert* (12/91) (DHM) ① **GD77228**
Deo gracias
G. Binchois Ens, D. Vellard *Concert*
(3/92) (VIRG) ① **VC7 59043-2**
Gloria, laus et honor—processional hymn (Wds. Bishop Theodulf of Orleans)
G. Binchois Ens, D. Vellard *Concert*
(3/92) (VIRG) ① **VC7 59043-2**
Je ne vis onques la pareille
G. Binchois Ens, D. Vellard *Concert*
(3/92) (VIRG) ① **VC7 59043-2**
Seule esgaree (Wds. Christine de Pizan?)
G. Binchois Ens, D. Vellard *Concert*
(3/92) (VIRG) ① **VC7 59043-2**
Vostre tres doulx regart (1430s)
G. Binchois Ens, D. Vellard *Concert*
(3/92) (VIRG) ① **VC7 59043-2**

BINGE, Ronald (1910–1979) England

SECTION I: ORCHESTRAL

Las **Castañuelas—orchestra** (ENg: The Castanets)
Bratislava RSO, E. Tomlinson (r1992) *Concert*
(11/94) (MARC) ① **8 223515**
Concerto for Saxophone and Orchestra (1956)
K. Edge, Bratislava RSO, E. Tomlinson (r1992) *Concert* (11/94) (MARC) ① **8 223515**
Dance of the snowflakes—orchestra
Bratislava RSO, E. Tomlinson (r1992) *Concert* (11/94) (MARC) ① **8 223515**
Elizabethan Serenade—orchestra (1951)
Bratislava RSO, E. Tomlinson (r1992) *Concert* (11/94) (MARC) ① **8 223515**
Faire Frou-Frou—orchestra
Bratislava RSO, E. Tomlinson (r1992) *Concert* (11/94) (MARC) ① **8 223515**
High Stepper—orchestra
Bratislava RSO, E. Tomlinson (r1992) *Concert* (11/94) (MARC) ① **8 223515**
Madrugado—orchestra (1950s) (Eng: Daybreak)
Bratislava RSO, E. Tomlinson (r1992) *Concert* (11/94) (MARC) ① **8 223515**
Miss Melanie—orchestra (1950s)
Bratislava RSO, E. Tomlinson (r1992) *Concert* (11/94) (MARC) ① **8 223515**

Prelude, The Whispering Valley—piano and orchestra
S. Cápová, Bratislava RSO, E. Tomlinson (r1992) *Concert* (11/94) (MARC) ① **8 223515**
The **Red sombrero—orchestra**
Bratislava RSO, E. Tomlinson (r1992) *Concert* (11/94) (MARC) ① **8 223515**
Sailing by—orchestra (1960s)
Bratislava RSO, E. Tomlinson (r1992) *Concert* (11/94) (MARC) ① **8 223515**
Scherzo: Allegro molto—orchestra (1951)
Bratislava RSO, E. Tomlinson (r1992) *Concert* (11/94) (MARC) ① **8 223515**
Scottish Rhapsody—orchestra
Bratislava RSO, E. Tomlinson (r1992) *Concert* (11/94) (MARC) ① **8 223515**
String Song—orchestra (1955)
Bratislava RSO, E. Tomlinson (r1992) *Concert* (11/94) (MARC) ① **8 223515**
Trade winds—orchestra
Bratislava RSO, E. Tomlinson (r1992) *Concert* (11/94) (MARC) ① **8 223515**
Venetian Carnival—orchestra
Bratislava RSO, E. Tomlinson (r1992) *Concert* (11/94) (MARC) ① **8 223515**
The **Watermill—oboe, harp and string orchestra (1958)**
Bratislava RSO, E. Tomlinson (r1992) *Concert* (11/94) (MARC) ① **8 223515**

BIRTWISTLE, Sir Harrison (b 1934) England

SECTION I: ORCHESTRAL

Antiphonies—piano and orchestra (1993)
J. Macgregor, Netherlands Rad PO, M. Gielen (r1994) *Concert* (3/94) (COLL) ① **Coll1414-2**
Carmen Arcadiae Mechanicae Perpetuum (1978)
London Sinfonietta, E. Howarth *Concert*
(4/88) (ETCE) ① **KTC1052**
Endless Parade—trumpet, vibraphone and strings (1986-87)
H. Hardenberger, P. Patrick, BBC PO, E. Howarth *Concert* (6/91) (PHIL) ① **432 075-2PH**
Gawain's Journey—orchestra (1991) (based on themes from opera 'Gawain')
Philh, E. Howarth (r1993) *Triumph of Time.*
(7/93) (COLL) ① **Coll1387-2**
An **Imaginary Landscape—orchestra (1971)**
BBC SO, P. Daniel (r1994) *Concert*
(12/94) (COLL) ① **Coll1414-2**
Melencolia I—clarinet, harp and two string orchestra (1976)
A. Pay, H. Tunstall, London Sinfonietta, O. Knussen (r1991) *Concert* (8/93) (NMC) ① **NMCD009**
Nomos—orchestra (1968)
BBC SO, P. Daniel (r1994) *Concert*
(12/94) (COLL) ① **Coll1414-2**
Ritual Fragment—15 players, unconducted (1990)
London Sinfonietta (r1991) *Concert*
(8/93) (NMC) ① **NMCD009**
Secret Theatre (1984)
London Sinfonietta, E. Howarth *Concert*
(4/88) (ETCE) ① **KTC1052**
Paris InterContemporain Ens, P. Boulez (r1994) *Concert* (9/95) (DG) ① **439 910-2GH**
Silbury Air—small orchestra (1977)
London Sinfonietta, E. Howarth *Concert*
(4/88) (ETCE) ① **KTC1052**
Tragoedia—orchestra (1965)
1. Prologue; 2. Parados; 3. Episodion: Strophe I—Anapaest I; 4. Antistrophe I; 5. Stasimon; 6. Episodion: Strophe II—Anapaest II; 7. Antistrophe II; 8. Exodus.
Paris InterContemporain Ens, P. Boulez (r1994) *Concert* (9/95) (DG) ① **439 910-2GH**
The **Triumph of Time—orchestra (1972)**
Philh, E. Howarth (r1993) *Gawain's Journey.*
(7/93) (COLL) ① **Coll1387-2**
Verses for Ensembles—wind quintet, brass quintet and percussion (1968-69)
Netherland Wind Ens, Hague Perc Ens, J. Wood (pp1991) *Concert* (7/92) (ETCE) ① **KTC1130**

SECTION II: CHAMBER

5 Distances—five instruments
Paris InterContemporain Ens, P. Boulez (r1994) *Concert* (9/95) (DG) ① **439 910-2GH**
For O, for O, the Hobby-horse is Forgot—ceremony: six percussionists (1976)
Hague Perc Ens (pp1991) *Concert*
(7/92) (ETCE) ① **KTC1130**

Refrains and Choruses—wind quintet (1957)
Netherland Wind Ens (pp1991) *Concert*
(7/92) (ETCE) ① **KTC1130**

SECTION IV: VOCAL AND CHORAL

Meridian—mez, hn, vc, six sops & inst ens (1970-71)
M. King, M. Thompson, C. van Kampen, London Sinfonietta Voices, London Sinfonietta, O. Knussen (r1991) *Concert* (8/93) (NMC) ① **NMCD009**
3 Settings of Celan—soprano & five instruments (Wds. P Celan)
1. White and Light; 2. Night; 3. Tenebrae.
C. Whittlesey, Paris InterContemporain Ens, P. Boulez (r1994) *Concert*
(9/95) (DG) ① **439 910-2GH**
White and Light—song (Wds. P. Celan)
M. Wiegold, Composers Ens, D. Muldowney *Concert* (4/92) (NMC) ① **NMCD003**

SECTION V: STAGE WORKS

Punch and Judy—opera: 1 act (1968—Aldeburgh) (Lib. S. Pruslin)
Cpte S. Roberts, J. DeGaetani, P. Bryn-Julson, P. Langridge, D. Wilson-Johnson, J. Tomlinson, London Sinfonietta, D. Atherton
(12/89) (ETCE) ① ‡ **KTC2014**

BISHOP, Sir Henry R(owley) (1786–1855) England

SECTION IV: VOCAL AND CHORAL

By the simplicity of Venus' doves—glee (Wds. F. Reynolds, after Shakespeare)
Hilliard Ens, L-L. Kiesel (arr G Bush) *Concert*
(12/91) (MERI) ① **DUOCD89009**
Echo Song
A. Galli-Curci, orch (r1921) *Concert*
(3/94) (CONI) ① **CDHD201**
A. Galli-Curci, orch, J. Pasternack (r1921) *Concert* (8/94) (ROMO) ① [2] **81004-2**
Forester sound the cheerful horn—catch
PCA, M. Brown *Concert* (3/87) (CONI) ① **CDCF145**
Magdalen (Oxford) Coll Ch, G. Ives *Concert*
(11/92) (CNTO) ① **CRCD2366**
Home, sweet home—song (included in opera 'Clari')
N. Melba, L. Ronald (r1921) *Concert*
(3/89) (LARR) ① **CDLRH221**
L. Godowsky (arr Godowsky: r1921) *Concert*
(4/89) (APR) ① [2] **APR7015**
A. Patti, L. Ronald (r1905) *Concert*
(4/90) (PEAR) ① **GEMMCD9312**
L. Tetrazzini, orch (r1912) *Concert*
(9/92) (EMI) ① [3] **CHS7 63802-2(2)**
L. Tetrazzini, orch (r1912) *Concert*
(9/92) (PEAR) ① **GEMMCD9223**
E. Albani, anon (r1904) *Concert*
(10/92) (SYMP) ① **SYMCD1093**
S. Adams, anon (r1902) *Concert*
(3/93) (SYMP) ① **SYMCD1100**
L. Skeaping, Broadside Band, J. Barlow (r1992; arr J. Barlow) (6/93) (SAYD) ① **CD-SDL400**
A. Patti, L. Ronald (r1905) *Concert*
(7/93) (NIMB) ① [2] **NI7840/1**
A. Galli-Curci, orch, J. Pasternack (r1917) *Concert*
(3/94) (ROMO) ① [2] **81003-2**
R. Ponselle, orch, J. Pasternack (r1925) *Concert* (11/94) (ROMO) ① [2] **81006-2**
E. Rethberg, anon, stg qt (r1926) *Concert*
(2/95) (ROMO) ① [2] **81012-2**
K. Flagstad, orch (r1914: Norw) *Concert*
(12/95) (SIMA) ① [3] **PSC1821(1)**
Lo, here the gentle lark—song (from opera 'The Comedy of Errors') (1819) (Wds. Reynolds, after Shakspeare)
N. Melba, J. Lemmoné, orch, W.B. Rogers (r1910) *Concert* (3/89) (LARR) ① **CDLRH221**
T. dal Monte, La Scala Orch, La Scala Chor, G. Nastrucci (r1929) *Concert* (2/90) (PREI) ① **89001**
M. Ivogün, orch (r c1925) *Concert*
(8/92) (NIMB) ① **NI7832**
A. Galli-Curci, orch, J. Pasternack (r1919) *Concert* (3/94) (ROMO) ① [2] **81003-2**
A. Galli-Curci, orch (r1919) *Concert*
(3/94) (CONI) ① **CDHD201**
K. Battle, J-P. Rampal, M. Garrett (pp1991) *Concert* (9/94) (SONY) ① **SK53106**
N. Melba, orch, W.B. Rogers (r1910) *Concert*
(5/95) (ROMO) ① [3] **81011-2(2)**
N. Melba, orch, W.B. Rogers (r1907) *Concert*
(5/95) (ROMO) ① [3] **81011-2(1)**

My pretty Jane, '(The) bloom is on the rye'—song (Wds. Fitzball)
H. Nash, G. Moore (r1931) *Concert*
(9/91) (PEAR) ① **GEMMCD9473**
O happy fair!—song (Wds. Shakespeare)
A. Rolfe Johnson, G. Johnson *Concert*
(5/92) (HYPE) ① **CDA66480**
Pretty Mocking Bird—song
A. Galli-Curci, orch, R. Bourdon (r1924) *Concert*
(5/90) (NIMB) ① **NI7806**
A. Galli-Curci, orch, R. Bourdon (r1924) *Concert*
(8/94) (ROMO) ① [2] **81004-2**

BISKUP, Josef *Bohemia*

SECTION I: ORCHESTRAL

Vorwärts March
Czech PO, V. Neumann *Concert*
(6/87) (ORFE) ① **C107101A**

BISSELL, Keith *(b 1912) Canada*

SECTION IV: VOCAL AND CHORAL

6 Folk Songs from Eastern Canada (1970)
4. Quand j'étais une fille de quinze ans.
4. C. Robbin, M. McMahon (r1985) *Concert*
(7/94) (MARQ) ① **ERAD113**
6 Maritime Folk Songs (1969)
1. C. Robbin, M. McMahon (r1985) *Concert*
(7/94) (MARQ) ① **ERAD113**

BIXIO, Cesare Andrea *(1898–1978) Italy*

SECTION IV: VOCAL AND CHORAL

La Canzone dell'amore—song (Wds. B. Cherubini)
B. Gigli, La Scala Orch, D. Olivieri (r1934) *Concert*
(6/93) (MMOI) ① **CDMOIR417**
Cuore diglielo anche tu—song
G. Lugo, orch, D. Olivieri (r1939) *Concert*
(2/92) (PREI) ① **89034**
Mamma—song (Wds. Cherubini)
L. Pavarotti, orch, H. Mancini (arr Mancini) *Concert*
(7/90) (DECC) ① [2] **425 681-2DM2**
La Mia canzone al vento—song (Wds. Cherubini)
G. Lugo, orch, D. Olivieri (r1939) *Concert*
(2/92) (PREI) ① **89034**
L. Pavarotti, NYPO, L. Magiera (pp1993) *Concert*
(2/95) (DECC) ① **444 450-2DH**

BIZET, Georges (Alexandre César Léopold) *(1838–1875) France*

SECTION I: ORCHESTRAL

Jeux d'enfants (Petite Suite) (1871) (orch cpsr from 2 pf vers)
1. Marche (Trompette et Tambour); 2. Berceuse (La poupée); 3. Impromptu (La toupie); 4. Duo (Petit mari, petite femme); 5. Galop (Le bal).
Concertgebouw, B. Haitink *Concert*
(10/86) (PHIL) ① **416 437-2PH**
Montreal SO, C. Dutoit *Concert*
(6/89) (DECC) ① **421 527-2DH**
Consort of London, R. Haydon Clark *Arlésienne.*
(10/91) (COLL) ① **Coll1141-2**
Paris Bastille Orch, Myung-Whun Chung *Concert*
(11/91) (DG) ① **431 778-2GH**
LPO, A. Dorati (r1937) *Concert*
(11/93) (DUTT) ① **CDAX8005**
LSO, R. Benzi (r1965) *Concert*
(10/94) (PHIL) ① [2] **442 272-2PM2**
FRNO, J. Martinon (r c1971) *Concert*
(5/95) (DG) ① [2] **437 371-2GX2**
RPO, A. Licata *Concert* (11/95) (TRIN) ① **TRP046**
3. L. Rév (arr. Garbon) *Concert*
(7/87) (HYPE) ① **CDA66185**
Patrie—Overture, Op. 19 (1873)
RPO, T. Beecham (r1956) *Concert*
(9/92) (EMI) ① **CDM7 63401-2**
Detroit SO, P. Paray (r1958) *Concert*
(8/93) (MERC) ① **434 321-2MM**
Toulouse Capitole Orch, M. Plasson (r1993) *Concert*
(5/95) (DENO) ① **CDC5 55057-2**
Roma—symphony (1860-68 rev 1871)
Munich RO, L. Gardelli (r1984) *Symphony.*
(1/90) (ORFE) ① **C184891A**
Toulouse Capitole Orch, M. Plasson (r1993) *Concert*
(5/95) (DENO) ① **CDC5 55057-2**
Carnaval RPO, T. Beecham (r1957) *Concert*
(9/92) (EMI) ① **CDM7 63401-2**

Symphony in C (1855)
Concertgebouw, B. Haitink *Concert*
(10/86) (PHIL) ① **416 437-2PH**
FRNO, T. Beecham (r1959) *Arlésienne Suites.*
(11/87) (EMI) ① **CDC7 47794-2**
Orpheus CO *Concert* (1/89) (DG) ① **423 624-2GH**
Munich RO, L. Gardelli (r1984) *Roma.*
(1/90) (ORFE) ① **C184891A**
Cincinnati SO, J. López-Cobos *Concert*
(11/90) (TELA) ① **CD80224**
Scottish CO, J-P. Saraste (r1988) *Concert*
(12/91) (VIRG) ① **VJ7 59657-2**
NYPO, L. Bernstein (r1963) *Concert*
(11/92) (SONY) ① **SMK47532**
St Paul CO, H. Wolff (r1992) *Concert*
(2/94) (TELD) ① **9031-77309-2**
Lyon Nat Orch, E. Krivine (r1992) *Arlésienne Suites.*
(2/94) (DENO) ① **CO-75471**
ASMF, N. Marriner (r1992) *Arlésienne Suites.*
(8/94) (EMI) ① **CDC5 55118-2**
LSO, R. Benzi (r1965) *Concert*
(10/94) (PHIL) ① [2] **442 272-2PM2**
FRNO, J. Martinon (r c1971) *Concert*
(5/95) (DG) ① [2] **437 371-2GX2**
Toulouse Capitole Orch, M. Plasson (r1993) *Concert*
(5/95) (DENO) ① **CDC5 55057-2**

SECTION II: CHAMBER

Jeux d'enfants, 'Children's Games'—12 pieces: piano duet (1871)
1. L'escarpolette; 2. La toupie; 3. La poupée; 4. Les chevaux de bois; 5. Le volant; 6. Trompette et tambour; 7. Les bulles de savon; 8. Les quatre coins; 9. Colin-Maillard; 10. Saute-Mouton; 11. Petit mari, petite femme; 12. Le bal.
K. Labèque, M. Labèque *Concert*
(11/87) (PHIL) ① **420 159-2PH**
I. Beyer, H. Dagul *Concert*
(10/92) (FOUR) ① **FHMD9212**

SECTION III: INSTRUMENTAL

Là ci darem la mano—after Mozart's'Don Giovanni'—piano
C. Katsaris (r1992) *Concert*
(6/93) (SONY) ① **SK52551**
Nocturne in D—piano (1868)
G. Gould (r1971) *Concert*
(3/93) (SONY) ① [2] **S2M2K52654**
Variations chromatiques de concert—piano (1868)
G. Gould (r1971) *Concert*
(3/93) (SONY) ① **SM2K52654**
M-F. Bucquet (r1980) *Concert*
(10/94) (PHIL) ① [2] **442 272-2PM2**

SECTION IV: VOCAL AND CHORAL

Adieux de l'hôtesse arabe—mélodie (1866) (Wds. V. Hugo)
F. Lott, G. Johnson (r1984) *Concert*
(5/87) (HARM) ① **HMA190 1138**
Agnus Dei (orch Guiraud: vocal arr of Intermezzo from 'L'Arlésienne')
L. Pavarotti, National PO, K.H. Adler (arr Gamley) *Concert* (7/90) (DECC) ① [2] **425 681-2DM2**
E. Caruso, S. Scognamiglio (r1913) *Concert*
(7/91) (RCA) ① [12] **GD60495(4)**
E. Caruso, S. Scognamiglio (r1913) *Concert*
(10/91) (PEAR) ① [3] **EVC3(1)**
L. Pavarotti, National PO, K.H. Adler (arr Gamley) *Concert* (12/91) (DECC) ① **433 710-2DH**
G. Thill, orch, Anthony Bernard (r1932) *Concert*
(1/93) (MMOI) ① **CDMOIR411**
J. Carreras, Vienna Boys' Ch, Vienna SO, U. C. Harrer (r1983; arr Maarse) *Concert*
(10/94) (PHIL) ① [2] **442 272-2PM2**
Chanson d'avril—mélodie (1866) (Wds. L. Bouilhet)
G. Souzay, D. Baldwin (r1963) *Concert*
(10/94) (PHIL) ① [2] **442 272-2PM2**
G. Souzay, D. Baldwin (r1963) *Concert*
(3/95) (PHIL) ① [4] **438 964-2PM4(2)**
La Chanson du fou—mélodie (1868) (Wds. V. Hugo)
D. Fischer-Dieskau, H. Höll (r c1987) *Concert*
(12/95) (TELD) ① **4509-97457-2**
Douce mer—mélodie (1866) (Wds. A. de Lamartine)
S. Varcoe, G. Johnson *Concert*
(6/88) (HYPE) ① **CDA6248**
La Fuite—duet (1872) (wds. T. Gautier)
C. Alliot-Lugaz, F. Le Roux, J. Cohen *Concert*
(4/91) (REM) ① **REM311086**
Guitare—mélodie (1866) (Wds. V. Hugo)
F. Lott, G. Johnson (r1984) *Concert*
(5/87) (HARM) ① **HMA190 1138**

J. Gomez, J. Constable (r1994) *Concert*
(9/94) (CONI) ① **CDCF243**
Pastorale—song (1868)
E. Orel, anon (Russ: r c1902) *Concert*
(7/93) (SYMP) ① **SYMCD1105**
E. Rethberg, orch (r1920) *Concert*
(7/94) (PREI) ① **89051**

SECTION V: STAGE WORKS

L' Arlésienne—incidental music to Daudet's play (1872—Paris)
Cpte Orféon Donostiarra, Toulouse Capitole Orch, M. Plasson (reconstr. Riffaud)
(10/88) (EMI) ① **CDC7 47460-2**
Cpte Consort of London, R. Haydon Clark *Jeux d'enfants.* (10/91) (COLL) ① **Coll1141-2**
2. G. Cziffra (r1971; trans Rachmaninov: pf) *Concert*
(3/95) (EMI) ① **CDM5 65255-2**
L' Arlésienne—concert suites from incidental music (1872) (Suite 1 orch cpsr; Suite 2 arr Guiraud)
SUITE NO. 1: 1. Prélude; 2. Menuet; 3. Adagietto; 4. Carillon. SUITE NO. 2: 5. Pastorale; 6. Intermezzo; 7. Minuet (from 'La jolie fille de Perth'); 8. Farandole.
RPO, T. Beecham *Symphony.*
(11/87) (EMI) ① **CDC7 47794-2**
Montreal SO, C. Dutoit *Carmen Suites.*
(6/88) (DECC) ① **417 839-2DH**
LSO, C. Abbado *Carmen Suites.*
(12/88) (DG) ① **423 472-2GGA**
LSO, R. Frühbeck de Burgos *Carmen Suites.*
(1/89) (CARL) ① **PCD905**
Slovak PO, A. Bramall *Carmen Suites.*
(10/90) (LASE) ① **8 550061**
Budapest PO, J. Sándor *Carmen Suites.*
(10/90) (LASE) ① **15 614**
BPO, H. von Karajan *Concert*
(8/91) (DG) ① **431 160-2GH**
Paris Bastille Orch, Myung-Whun Chung *Concert*
(11/91) (DG) ① **431 778-2GH**
NYPO, L. Bernstein (r1968) *Carmen Suites.*
(11/92) (SONY) ① **SMK47531**
Detroit SO, P. Paray (r1964) *Carmen Suites.*
(8/93) (MERC) ① **434 321-2MM**
Lyon Nat Orch, E. Krivine (r1992) *Symphony.*
(2/94) (DENO) ① **CO-75471**
ASMF, N. Marriner (r1992) *Symphony.*
(8/94) (EMI) ① **CDC5 55118-2**
Lamoureux Concerts Orch, A. Dorati (r1959) *Concert*
(10/94) (PHIL) ① [2] **442 272-2PM2**
Paris Orch, S. Bychkov (r1993) *Carmen Suites.*
(12/94) (PHIL) ① **442 128-2PH**
1-3, 8. National SO, Sidney Beer (r1944) *Concert*
(5/95) (DUTT) ① **CDK1200**
1, 3, 8. Hallé, J. Barbirolli (r1950) *Concert*
(7/95) (DUTT) ① **CDSJB1002**
1-4. Cincinnati SO, J. López-Cobos *Concert*
(11/90) (TELA) ① **CD80224**
1-4. Philadelphia, L. Stokowski (r1929) *Concert*
(8/95) (BIDD) ① **WHL012**
2. H. Shelley (r1991: arr pf: Rachmaninov) *Concert*
(3/92) (HYPE) ① **CDA66486**
2. S. Rachmaninov (arr Rachmaninov: r1922) *Concert* (3/93) (RCA) ① [10] **09026 61265-2(3)**
2. H. Shelley (r1991: arr pf: Rachmaninov) *Concert*
(3/94) (HYPE) ① [8] **CDS44041/8**
2. J. Bálint, M. Mercz (r1992: fl/hp: Mercz) *Concert*
(12/94) (NAXO) ① **8 550741**
6. F. Kreisler, H. Kreisler, M. Raucheisen (arr Kreisler: vn/pf; r1928) *Concert*
(1/90) (PEAR) ① **GEMMCD9324**
6. F. Kreisler, H. Kreisler, M. Raucheisen (arr Kreisler: r1927) *Concert*
(9/92) (BIDD) ① [2] **LAB049/50**
8. Cincinnati Pops, E. Kunzel *Concert*
(10/89) (TELA) ① **CD80170**
8. La Scala Orch, A. Toscanini (r1921) *Concert*
(11/92) (RCA) ① **GD60315**
8. Empire Brass (1992: arr. R. Smedvig) *Concert*
(3/94) (TELA) ① **CD80305**
Carmen—opera: 4 acts (1875—Paris) (Lib. Meilhac and Halévy)
EXCERPTS; 1. Prélude; 2. ACT 1: Sur la place, chacun place; 3. Avec la garde montante; 4a. La cloche a sonné; 4b. La voilà!; 5. L'amour est un oiseau rebelle (Habanera); 6. Carmen! sur les pas; 7. Parle-moi de ma mère; 8. Au secours!; 9. Voyons, brigadier; 10a. Près des remparts de Séville (Séguidille); 10b. Voici l'ordre. ACT 2: 11a. Entr'acte; 11b. Les tringles des sistres (Gypsy Song); 11c. Danse bohemienne; 11d. Vous avez quelque chose; 12a. Vivat, vivat le torero!; 12b. Votre toast (Toreador's Song); 13. Nous avons en tête une affaire!; 14. Halte-là! ACT 3; 15a. Je vais danser en votre honneur; 15b. Au quartier!; 15c. La fleur que tu m'avais jetée; 15d. Non! tu ne m'aimes pas!; 16.

Holà! Carmen!. ACT 3: 17a. Entr'acte; 17b. Écoute
compagnon; 17c. Notre métier est bon; 18a. Mêlons!
Coupons! (Card Scene); 18b. Voyons, que j'essaie à
mon tour; 18c. En vain, pour éviter; 19. Quant au
douanier; 20. Je dis que rien ne
m'épouvante(Micaëla's aria); 21. Je suis Escamillo.
ACT 4: 22a. Entr'acte; 22b. A deux cuartos!; 23. Les
voici; 24. Si tu m'aimes, Carmen; 25. C'est toi!
(Finale).
Cpte A. Baltsa, J. Carreras, K. Ricciarelli, J. Van
Dam, C. Barbaux, J. Berbié, G. Quilico, H. Zednik, M.
Melbye, A. Malta, Schöneberg Boys' Ch, Paris Op.
Chor, BPO, H. von Karajan (r1982: with dialogue)
(12/83) (DG) ① [3] 410 088-2GH3
Cpte J. Migenes, P. Domingo, F. Esham, R.
Raimondi, L. Watson, S. Daniel, J-P. Lafont, G.
Garino, F. Le Roux, J.P. Bogart, J. Guiomar, A. di
Leo, French Rad Chor, FNO, L. Maazel (with
dialogue)   (9/85) (ERAT) ① [3] 2292-45207-2
Cpte T. Troyanos, P. Domingo, K. Te Kanawa, J.
Van Dam, N. Burrowes, J. Berbié, M. Roux, M.
Sénéchal, T. Allen, P. Thau, J. Loreau, G. Berbié,
John Alldis Ch, Haberdashers' Aske's Sch Ch, LPO,
G. Solti (with dialogue)
(9/85) (DECC) ① [3] 414 489-2DH3
Cpte T. Berganza, P. Domingo, I. Cotrubas, S.
Milnes, Y. Kenny, A. Nafé, G. Bacquier, G. Pogson,
S. Harling, R. Lloyd, Watson Coll Boys' Chor,
Ambrosian Sngrs, LSO, C. Abbado (r1977: with
dialogue)   (2/88) (DG) ① [3] 419 636-2GH3
Cpte V. de los Angeles, N. Gedda, J. Micheau, E.
Blanc, D. Monteil, M. Croisier, M. Linval, J-C. Benoit,
M. Hamel, B. Plantey, X. Depraz, Petits Chanteurs de
Versailles, French Rad Maîtrise, French Rad Chor,
FRNO, T. Beecham (r1958/9: with recits)
(6/88) (EMI) ① [3] CDS7 49240-2
Cpte L. Price, F. Corelli, M. Freni, R. Merrill, M.
Linval, G. Macaux, J-C. Benoit, M. Besançon, B.
Demigny, F. Schooten, Vienna Boys' Ch, Vienna St
Op Chor, VPO, H. von Karajan (r1963: with recits)
(10/88) (RCA) ① [3] GD86199
Cpte R. Stevens, J. Peerce, L. Albanese, R. Merrill,
P. Lenchner, M. Roggero, G. Cehanovsky, A. de
Paolis, H. Thompson, O. Hawkins, NY Lycée
Français Children's Ch, R. Shaw Chorale, RCA Victor
Orch, F. Reiner (r1951; with recits)
(5/89) (RCA) ① [3] GD87981
Cpte J. Norman, N. Shicoff, M. Freni, S. Estes, G.
Raphanel, J. Rigby, F. Le Roux, G. Garino, N.
Rivenq, J-P. Courtis, French Rad Maîtrise, French
Rad Chor, FNO, S. Ozawa (with dialogue)
(8/89) (PHIL) ① [3] 422 366-2PH3
Cpte M. Horne, J. McCracken, A. Maliponte, T.
Krause, C. Boky, M. Baldwin, R. Christopher, A.
Velis, R. Gibbs, D. Gramm, NY Met Op Children's
Ch, Manhattan Op Chor, NY Met Op Orch, L.
Bernstein (r1972: with dialogue)
(9/91) (DG) ① [3] 427 440-2GX3
Cpte M. Callas, N. Gedda, A. Guiot, R. Massard, N.
Sautereau, J. Berbié, J-P. Vauquelin, J. Pruvost, M.
Maievski, C. Calès, J. Mars, R. Duclos Ch, J.
Pesneaud Children's Ch, Paris Op Orch, G. Prêtre
(r1964: with recits)
(5/92) (EMI) ① [2] CDS7 54368-2
Cpte E. Destinn, O. Metzger, K. Jörn, M. Nast, H.
Bachmann, M. Dietrich, D. Parbs, J. Lieban, R.
Krasa, F. Dahn, Berlin Court Op Chor, orch, B.
Seidler-Winkler (r1908: Ger) Concert
(12/94) (SUPR) ① [12] 11 2136-2(3)
Cpte R. Resnik, M. del Monaco, J. Sutherland, T.
Krause, G. Spanellys, Y. Minton, J. Prudent, A.
Hallett, C. Calès, R. Geay, Geneva Grand Th Chor,
SRO, T. Schippers (r1963)
(7/95) (DECC) ① [2] 443 871-2DF2
Cpte S. Michel, R. Jobin, M. Angelici, M. Dens, G.
Chellet, R. Notti, J. Vieuille, F. Leprin, J. Thirache, X.
Smati, Paris Opéra-Comique Chor, Paris Opéra-
Comique Orch, A. Cluytens (r1950: with dialogue)
(9/95) (EMI) ① [2] CMS5 65318-2
Cpte B. Uría-Monzon, C. Papis, L. Vaduva, V. le
Texier, M. Castets, M. Olmeda, F. Leguérinel, T.
Trégan, O. Lallouette, L. Sarrazin, P. Renard,
Bordeaux CNR Children's Ch, Bordeaux Th Chor,
Bordeaux Aquitaine Orch, A. Lombard (r1994)
(10/95) (AUVI) ① [2] V4734
Excs J. Migenes, P. Domingo, R. Raimondi, F.
Esham, S. Daniel, L. Watson, J.P. Bogart, F. Le
Roux, French Rad Chor, FNO, L. Maazel
(12/84) (ERAT) ① [2] 2292-45209-2
Excs T. Mazaroff, E. Réthy, E. Brems, A. Arnold, P.
Pierotic, G. Monthy, D. Komarek, O. Levko-Antosch,
M. Bokor, Vienna St Op Chor, Vienna St Op Orch, B.
Walter (pp1937: Ger) Concert
(2/95) (SCHW) ① [2] 314572

Excs P. Gallois, London Fest Orch, R. Pople (r1993:
arr fl: de Borne/Pierre) Concert
(5/95) (DG) ① 445 822-2GH
Fantasy C. Arrau (r1928: arr Busoni) Concert
(9/92) (PEAR) ① GEMMCD9928
1. Vienna St Op Orch, B. Walter (pp1937) Concert
(6/94) (SCHW) ① 314502
1-3, 5, 7, 10a, 11b, 11d, 12a, 12b, 15c, 18c, 22b, 25.
A. Baltsa, J. Carreras, K. Ricciarelli, J. Van Dam, C.
Barbaux, J. Berbié, G. Quilico, H. Zednik, M. Melbye,
A. Malta, Paris Op. Chor, BPO, H. von Karajan
(r1982)   (2/85) (DG) ① 413 322-2GH
1, 4a, 4b, 5, 10a, 11b, 12b, 13, 15b, 15c, 18a-c, 20,
25. R. Resnik, M. del Monaco, G. Spanellys, Y.
Minton, T. Krause, J. Prudent, A. Hallett, J.
Sutherland, Geneva Grand Th Chor, SRO, T.
Schippers   (1/92) (DECC) ① 433 626-2DSP
3. J. Bálint, N. Mercz (r1992: arr fl/hp: Mercz) Concert
(12/94) (NAXO) ① 8 550741
4b, 10a, 15c J. Rhodes, A. Lance, Paris Op Orch, R.
Benzi (r1959) Concert
(10/94) (PHIL) ① [2] 442 272-2PM2
5. J. Lloyd Webber, RPO, N. Cleobury (arr vc)
Concert   (3/87) (PHIL) ① 416 698-2PH
5. C. Supervia, orch, G. Cloëz (r1930) Concert
(10/89) (NIMB) ① NI7801
5. I. Minghini-Cattaneo, orch, J. Barbirolli (Ital: r1929)
Concert   (6/90) (PREI) ① 89008
5. E. Teodorini, anon (r1903) Concert
(3/95) (SYMP) ① SYMCD1077
5. J. Tourel, Philh, W. Susskind (r1951) Concert
(4/92) (EMI) ① [7] CHS7 69741-2(1)
5. E. Calvé, anon (r1902) Concert
(3/93) (SYMP) ① SYMCD1100
5. D. Soffel, Swedish CO, M. Liljefors (pp1986)
Concert   (4/93) (CPRI) ① CAP21428
5. E. Calvé, anon (r1907) Concert
(7/93) (NIMB) ① NI7840/1
5. F. Litvinne, orch (r1907) Concert
(12/94) (SYMP) ① SYMCD1128
5. A. Scholl, Camargue PO, Reinhardt Wagner
(r1995: arr R Wagner) Concert
(8/95) (HARM) ① HMC90 1552
5, 10a M. Callas, FRNO, G. Prêtre Concert
(2/88) (EMI) ① CDC7 49059-2
5, 10a M. Lipovšek, Munich RO, G. Patanè Concert
(6/90) (ORFE) ① C179891A
5, 10a C. Supervia, orch, A. Albergoni (Ital: r1927)
Concert   (9/90) (CLUB) ① CL99-074
5, 10a C. Supervia, orch, A. Albergoni (Ital: r1927)
Concert   (9/90) (PREI) ① 89023
5, 10a E. Destinn, anon (r1908: Ger) Concert
(12/94) (SUPR) ① [12] 11 2136-2(1)
5, 10a E. Destinn, orch, F. Kark (r1906: Ger) Concert
(12/94) (SUPR) ① [12] 11 2136-2(1)
5, 10a, 10b M. Callas, N. Gedda, R. Duclos Ch, Paris
Op Orch, G. Prêtre Concert
(2/90) (EMIN) ① CD-EMX2123
5, 10a, 11b S. Onegin, orch (r1927) Concert
(2/91) (PREI) ① 89027
5, 10a, 11b, 15a(pt), 15b-d, 18a, 18c, 25. C.
Supervia, A. Vavon, A. Bernadet, G. Micheletti, orch,
G. Cloëz (r1930) Concert
(3/93) (NIMB) ① [2] NI7836/7
5, 10a, 18c M. Klose, Berlin Deutsche Op Orch, O.
Steeger (r1941: Ger) Concert
(7/95) (PREI) ① 89082
5, 12b V. Masterson, A. Michaels-Moore, ROH Chor,
RPO, R. Stapleton Concert
(10/90) (CARL) ① MCD15
5, 18c R. Anday, Vienna St Op Orch, K. Alwin (Ger:
r1931) Concert   (5/92) (PREI) ① 89046
5, 18c K. Branzell, orch (Ger: r1928) Concert
(8/92) (PREI) ① 89039
5, 18c D. Giannini, La Scala Orch, C. Sabajno
(r1932) Concert   (4/93) (PREI) ① 89044
5, 18c K. Thorborg, Berlin St Op Orch, F. Weissmann
(r1933: Ger) Concert   (4/94) (PREI) ① 89084
7. M. Fleta, L. Bori, orch (r1924) Concert
(3/91) (PREI) ① 89002
7. E. Caruso, F. Alda, orch, W.B. Rogers (r1914)
Concert   (7/90) (CLUB) ① CL99-060
7. F. Ansseau, F. Heldy, orch, P. Coppola (r1927)
Concert   (1/91) (PREI) ① 89022
7. F. Alda, E. Caruso, orch, W.B. Rogers (r1914)
Concert   (7/91) (RCA) ① [12] GD60495(5)
7. E. Caruso, F. Alda, orch, W.B. Rogers (r1914)
Concert   (10/91) (PEAR) ① [3] EVC3(1)
7. A. Cortis, A. Rozsa, La Scala Orch, C. Sabajno
(Ital: r1930) Concert   (10/91) (PREI) ① 89043
7. F. Hempel, H. Jadlowker, orch (Ger: r1900s)
Concert   (12/90) (CLUB) ① CL99-042
7. G. Zenatello, E. Cervi-Caroli, anon (r1907: Ital)
Concert   (5/94) (SYMP) ① SYMCD1168
7. G. Zenatello, E. Cervi-Caroli, anon (r1907: Ital)
Concert   (5/94) (PEAR) ① [4] GEMMCDS9073(1)

7(pt) E. Rethberg, R. Tauber, orch (r1921: Ger)
Concert   (7/94) (PREI) ① 89051
7. F. de Lucia, J. Huguet, orch (r1907: Ital) Concert
(1/95) (SYMP) ① SYMCD1149
7. H. Roswaenge, H. von Debička, Berlin St Op Orch,
H. Weigert (r1931: Ger) Concert
(4/95) (PREI) ① [2] 89209
7. W. Ludwig, M. Perras, Berlin St Op Orch, B.
Seidler-Winkler (r1937: Ger) Concert
(11/95) (PREI) ① 89088
7. S. Bullock, A. Davies, A. Bryn Parri (r1994)
Concert   (11/95) (SAIN) ① SCDC2070
7(pt) 15c J. Kiepura, E. Réthy, Vienna St Op Orch,
K. Alwin (pp1938: Fr/Ger) Concert
(3/95) (SCHW) ① [2] 314602
10a B. Fassbaender, Stuttgart RSO, H. Graf Concert
(11/86) (ORFE) ① C096841A
10a M. André, Toulouse Capitole Orch, M. Plasson
(arr tpt) Concert   (1/89) (EMI) ① CDC7 49219-2
10a V. de los Angeles, G. Parsons (pp1990) Concert
(12/91) (COLL) ① Coll1247-2
10a E. Calvé, anon (r1902) Concert
(7/92) (PEAR) ① [3] GEMMCDS9923(1)
10a B. Castagna, orch, W. Pelletier (r1938) Concert
(4/94) (RCA) ① [6] 09026 61580-2(4)
10a E. Destinn, orch, F. Kark (r1906: Ger) Concert
(12/94) (SUPR) ① 11 1337-2
10a E. Destinn, anon (r1901-2: Ger) Concert
(12/94) (SUPR) ① [12] 11 2136-2(1)
10a, 11b, 18c E. Destinn, orch, B. Seidler-Winkler
(r1906: Ger) Concert
(12/94) (SUPR) ① [12] 11 2136-2(1)
11b E. Calvé, anon (r1908) Concert
(7/92) (PEAR) ① [3] GEMMCDS9923(1)
11b M. Mei-Figner, anon (r1902: Russ) Concert
(6/93) (PEAR) ① [3] GEMMCDS9997/9(1)
11b E. Calvé, anon (r1908) Concert
(4/94) (RCA) ① [6] 09026 61580-2(1)
11b, 18a M. Callas, N. Sautereau, J. Berbié, Paris
Op Orch, G. Prêtre Concert
(2/90) (EMI) ① CDM7 63182-2
11b, 18c E. Destinn, orch, F. Kark (r1908: Ger)
Concert   (12/94) (SUPR) ① [12] 11 2136-2(2)
11c L. Howard (arr Moszkowski) Concert
(12/86) (HYPE) ① CDA66090
12b L. Tibbett, L.M. Belleri, F. Cingolani, NY Met Op
Chor, NY Met Op Orch, G. Setti (r1929) Concert
(3/90) (RCA) ① GD87808
12b H. Schlusnus, Berlin St Op Orch, A. Melichar
(Ger: r1931) Concert   (8/90) (PREI) ① 89006
12b C. Tagliabue, Turin EIAR Orch, A. la Rosa
Parodi (Ital: r1942) Concert
(11/90) (PREI) ① 89015
12b A. Scotti, anon (Ital: r1902) Concert
(3/93) (SYMP) ① SYMCD1100
12b L. Warren, orch, W. Pelletier (r1940) Concert
(8/93) (VAI) ① VAIA1017
12b G. Viviani, orch (r1924: Ital) Concert
(12/94) (BONG) ① GB1043-2
13. C. Supervia, A. Apolloni, I. Mannarini, G. Nessi,
A. Baracchi, orch, A. Albergoni (Ital: r1927) Concert
(9/90) (PREI) ① 89023
15a-d L. Pavarotti, Vienna Volksoper Orch, L.
Magiera Concert
(7/90) (DECC) ① [2] 425 681-2DM2
15c L. Pavarotti, Vienna Volksoper Orch, L. Magiera
Concert   (7/86) (DECC) ① [2] 417 011-2DH2
15c P. Domingo, Los Angeles PO, C.M. Giulini
Concert   (7/86) (DG) ① 415 366-2GH
15c J. Björling, Hilversum RO, F. Weissmann
(pp1939) Concert   (8/88) (BLUE) ① ABCD091
15c B. Gigli, La Scala Orch, F. Ghione (Ital: r1935)
Concert   (9/88) (EMI) ① CDH7 61051-2
15c G. Thill, Orch, P. Gaubert (r1927) Concert
(1/89) (EMI) ① CDM7 69548-2
15c R. Tauber, orch (Ger: r1923) Concert
(7/89) (PEAR) ① GEMMCD9327
15c M. Fleta, orch (Ital: r1922: Ital) Concert
(3/90) (PREI) ① 89002
15c H. Roswaenge, Berlin St Op Orch, B. Seidler-
Winkler (Ger: r1938) Concert
(5/90) (PEAR) ① GEMMCD9394
15c H. Roswaenge, Berlin St Op Orch, B. Seidler-
Winkler (Ger: r1938) Concert
(5/90) (PREI) ① 89018
15c G. Lauri-Volpi, orch, R. Bourdon (r1930) Concert
(9/90) (PREI) ① 89012
15c E. Caruso, anon (Ital: r1905) Concert
(12/90) (PEAR) ① [3] EVC1(1)
15c F. Ansseau, orch, P. Coppola (r1927) Concert
(1/91) (PREI) ① 89022
15c E. Caruso, anon (r1909) Concert
(3/91) (PEAR) ① [3] EVC2
15c E. Caruso, orch (Ital: r1909) Concert
(3/91) (PEAR) ① [3] EVC2

2b E. Barham, A. Michaels-Moore, RPO, R.
Stapleton *Concert* (10/90) (CARL) ① **MCD15**
2b E. Caruso, M. Ancona, orch, W.B. Rogers (Ital:
r1907) *Concert* (12/90) (PEAR) ① [3] **EVC1(2)**
2b D. Borgioli, B. Franci, orch (Ital: r c1923) *Concert*
(12/90) (CLUB) ① **CL99-014**
2b E. Caruso, M. Ancona, orch, W.B. Rogers (r1907:
Ital) *Concert* (7/91) (RCA) ① [12] **GD60495(2)**
2b B. Lazzaretti, R. Servile, Berlin RSO, H.M.
Schneidt *Concert* (5/92) (CAPR) ① **10 380**
2b R. Childs, N. Childs, Britannia Building Soc Band,
G. Brand (pp1991: arr K Wilkinson) *Concert*
(8/92) (POLY) ① **QPRL049D**
2b B. Gigli, G. De Luca, orch, R. Bourdon (Ital:
r1927) *Concert* (6/93) (MMOI) ① **CDMOIR417**
2b J. Hadley, T. Hampson, WNO Orch, C. Rizzi
(r1992) *Concert* (11/93) (TELD) ① **9031-73283-2**
2b B. Gigli, G. De Luca, orch, R. Bourdon (r1927:
Ital) *Concert* (10/94) (PREI) ① **89073**
2b E. Caruso, M. Ancona, orch (r1907: Ital) *Concert*
(10/94) (NIMB) ① **NI7859**
2b L. Simoneau, R. Bianco, Lamoureux Concerts
Orch, J. Fournet (r1953) *Concert*
(10/94) (PHIL) ① [2] **442 272-2PM2**
2b J. Lotrič, I. Morozov, Slovak RSO, J. Wildner
(r1994) *Concert* (2/95) (NAXO) ① **8 553030**
2b A. Giorgini, F. Federici, orch (r1909: Ital) *Concert*
(4/95) (RECO) ① **TRC3**
2b E. Clément, M. Journet, orch, R. Bourdon (r1912)
Concert (8/95) (ROMO) ① **82002-2**
2b E. Clément, M. Journet, orch, R. Bourdon (r1912)
Concert (8/95) (PEAR) ① **GEMMCD9161**
2b R. Hutt, H. Schlusnus, orch (r1921: Ger) *Concert*
(12/95) (PREI) ① **89110**
6a, 6b G. Anselmi, anon (r1907: Ital) *Concert*
(7/95) (SYMP) ① **SYMCD1170**
6a, 6b, 11. E. Caruso, F. Lapitino, orch, J.
Pasternack (r1916) *Concert*
(10/91) (PEAR) ① [3] **EVC4(1)**
6b E. Gigli, orch, E. Goossens (Ital: r1931) *Concert*
(9/88) (EMI) ① **CDH7 61051-2**
6b E. Caruso, S. Cottone (Ital: r1904) *Concert*
(5/89) (EMI) ① **CDH7 61046-2**
6b M. Fleta, orch (r1927: Ital) *Concert*
(2/90) (PREI) ① **89002**
6b B. Gigli, orch, R. Bourdon (Ital: r1929) *Concert*
(5/90) (PEAR) ① **GEMMCD9367**
6b D. Smirnov, orch (Ital: r1909) *Concert*
(7/90) (CLUB) ① **CL99-031**
6b G. Morino, Warmia Nat PO, B. Amaducci (Ital)
Concert (10/90) (NUOV) ① **6851**
6b B. Gigli, orch, R. Bourdon (Ital: r1929) *Concert*
(10/90) (RCA) ① **GD87811**
6b E. Caruso, S. Cottone (Ital: r1904) *Concert*
(12/90) (PEAR) ① [3] **EVC1(1)**
6b D. Borgioli, orch (Ital: r c1923) *Concert*
(12/90) (CLUB) ① **CL99-014**
6b E. Caruso, S. Cottone (Ital: r1904) *Concert*
(7/91) (RCA) ① [12] **GD60495(1)**
6b H.E. Groh, orch (Ger: r1932) *Concert*
(3/92) (PEAR) ① **GEMMCD9419**
6b N. Gedda, Philh, A. Galliera (r1953) *Concert*
(4/92) (EMI) ① [7] **CHS7 69741-2(5)**
6b A. Bonci, anon (Ital: r1906) *Concert*
(7/92) (PEAR) ① [3] **GEMMCDS9924(2)**
6b E. Caruso, anon (Ital: r1904) *Concert*
(11/92) (MEMO) ① [2] **HR4408/9(1)**
6b J. McCormack, orch (Ital: r1912) *Concert*
(5/93) (MMOI) ① **CDMOIR418**
6b L. Sobinov, orch (r1910: Russ) *Concert*
(6/93) (PEAR) ① [3] **GEMMCDS9997/9(2)**
6b B. Gigli, orch, E. Goossens (Ital: r1931) *Concert*
(6/93) (MMOI) ① **CDMOIR417**
6b A. Davidov, anon (r1901: Russ) *Concert*
(6/93) (PEAR) ① [3] **GEMMCDS9007/9(1)**
6b J. Björling, Stockholm Royal Op Orch, N.
Grevillius (r1945) *Concert*
(10/93) (EMI) ① **CDH7 64707-2**
6b H. Nash, Liverpool PO, M. Sargent (r1944: Eng)
Concert (11/95) (PEAR) ① **GEMMCD9175**
6b, 11. E. Caruso, F. Lapitino, orch, J. Pasternack
(r1916) *Concert* (7/91) (RCA) ① [12] **GD60495(5)**
6b, 11. G. Lugo, orch, A. Wolff (r1932) *Concert*
(2/92) (PREI) ① **89034**
6b, 11. E. Caruso, orch (r1916) *Concert*
(10/94) (NIMB) ① **NI7859**
6b, 11. A. Giorgini, orch (r1908: Ital) *Concert*
(4/95) (RECO) ① **TRC3**
8a T. dal Monte, La Scala Orch, La Scala Chor, G.
Nastrucci (r1929: Ital) *Concert*
(2/90) (PEAR) ① **89001**
8a A. Nezhdanova, anon (r1907: Russ) *Concert*
(6/93) (PEAR) ① [3] **GEMMCDS9007/9(1)**
8a, 8b L. Tetrazzini, orch, P. Pitt (Ital: r1909) *Concert*
(9/92) (PEAR) ① **GEMMCD9222**

8a, 10b L. Tetrazzini, orch, P. Pitt (Ital: r1909)
Concert (9/92) (EMI) ① [3] **CHS7 63802-2(1)**
10. K. Te Kanawa, ROHO, J. Tate *Concert*
(2/90) (EMI) ① **CDC7 49863-2**
10a, 10b M. Callas, Paris Cons, G. Prêtre *Concert*
(2/88) (EMI) ① **CDC7 49059-2**
10a, 10b M. Freni, La Scala Orch, A. Votto *Concert*
(2/89) (EMI) ① **CDM7 63110-2**
10a, 10b P. Alarie, Lamoureux Orch, P. Dervaux
(r1953) *Concert*
(11/94) (PHIL) ① [2] **438 953-2PM2**
10b A. Galli-Curci, orch (r1921) *Concert*
(2/89) (PEAR) ① **GEMMCD9308**
10b T. dal Monte, La Scala Orch, C. Sabajno (r1929:
Ital) *Concert* (2/90) (PREI) ① **89001**
10b E. Berger, Berlin St Op Orch, L. Blech (Ger:
r1934) *Concert* (12/91) (PREI) ① **89035**
10b A. Noni, orch (Ital: r1951) *Concert*
(4/92) (EMI) ① [7] **CHS7 69741-2(7)**
10b L. Tetrazzini, orch, P. Pitt (Ital: r1909) *Concert*
(9/92) (PEAR) ① **GEMMCD9221**
10b A. Nezhdanova, U. Masetti (r1906: Russ)
Concert (6/93) (PEAR) ① [3] **GEMMCDS9007/9(1)**
10b A. Galli-Curci, orch (r1921) *Concert*
(8/94) (NIMB) ① **NI7852**
10b A. Galli-Curci, orch, J. Pasternack (r1921)
Concert (8/94) (ROMO) ① [2] **81004-2**
14a C. Tagliabue, orch, U. Berrettoni (Ital: r1946)
Concert (11/90) (PREI) ① **89015**

BJÖRKLUND, Steffan *(b 1944)* Sweden

BJÖRNSSON, Árni *(b 1905)* Iceland

BLACHER, Boris *(1903–1975)* Germany

**Dance Scenes, '(La) Vie'—ballet (1938; perf
1979)** (score rediscovered 1976)
LPO, N. Sheriff (r1994) *Concert*
(7/95) (LARG) ① [2] **Largo5130**

BLACK, J.M. *(19th–20th Cent)* USA

BLACKWOOD, Easley *(b 1933)* USA

BLAIR, Hugh *(1864–1932)* England

BLAKE, Howard *(b 1938)* England

BLAKE WATKINS, Michael *(b 1948) England*

BLANC, Frédéric *(20th Cent)* France

BLAND, James A(llen) (1854–1911) USA

SECTION IV: VOCAL AND CHORAL

Carry me back to old Virginny—song (1878) (Wds. cpsr)
E. Mason, Male Trio, orch, F. Black (r1928) *Concert*
  (8/94) (ROMO) ① **81009-2**
R. Ponselle, Male Qt, orch, J. Pasternack (r1925)
Concert (11/94) (ROMO) ① [2] **81006-2**
E. Steber, orch, H. Barlow (bp1950) *Concert*
  (11/95) (VAI) ① **VAIA1072**

BLANGINI, Felice (1781–1841) France

SECTION IV: VOCAL AND CHORAL

Per valli, per boschi—song
N. Melba, C. Gilibert, orch, W.B. Rogers (r1907)
Concert (5/95) (ROMO) ① [3] **81011-2(1)**

BLAVET, Michel (1700–1768) France

SECTION I: ORCHESTRAL

Concerto for Flute and Strings in A minor
E-B. Hilse, Berlin Ancient Music Academy *Concert*
  (7/87) (CAPR) ① **10 134**

SECTION II: CHAMBER

6 Sonatas—flute and continuo, Op. 3 (pub. 1740)
2. B minor; 3. E minor; 4. A; 6. D.
2-4. P. Allain-Dupré, M. Muller, M. Tallet, Y. Le
Gaillard *Flute Sonatas, Op. 2.*
  (8/86) (CHNT) ① **LDC278 798**
2, 6. M. Arita, W. Kuijken, C. Arita *Flute Sonatas, Op.2.* (9/92) (DENO) ① **CO-79550**
6 Sonates mélées de pièces—flute and continuo, Op. 2 (pub 1732)
2. D minor; 3. G minor; 4. G minor; 5. D; 6. A minor.
2. R. Brown, J. Johnstone *Concert*
  (2/94) (CHAN) ① **CHAN0544**
2, 4, 5. M. Arita, W. Kuijken, C. Arita *Flute Sonatas, Op.3.* (9/92) (DENO) ① **CO-79550**
3. Royal Trio (r1991) *Concert*
  (8/93) (DHM) ① **05472 77176-2**
4-6. P. Allain-Dupré, M. Muller, M. Tallet, Y. Le
Gaillard *Flute Sonatas, Op. 3.*
  (8/86) (CHNT) ① **LDC278 798**

BLEICHMAN, Julius Ivanovich (1860–1910 or 1868–1909) Russia

may be spelt Bleichmann

SECTION IV: VOCAL AND CHORAL

Far off, far off—song
A. Bogdanovich, anon (r1903) *Concert*
  (6/93) (PEAR) ① [3] **GEMMCDS9007/9(1)**
My lips are silent—song
L. Sibiriakov, anon (r1906) *Concert*
  (6/93) (PEAR) ① [3] **GEMMCDS9001/3(2)**

SECTION V: STAGE WORKS

La Princess lointaine—opera
Love is a delightful dream A. Bogdanovich, anon
(r1905) *Concert*
  (6/93) (PEAR) ① [3] **GEMMCDS9007/9(1)**

BLISS, Sir Arthur (Drummond) (1891–1975) England

T-Numbers from Thompson 1966, 1971

SECTION I: ORCHESTRAL

Antiphonal Fanfare—three brass choirs, T115 (1969) (for Investiture of the Prince of Wales)
PJBE (r1970) *Concert*
  (6/93) (DECC) ① **436 403-2DWO**
Baraza—piano and orchestra with men's voices, T65 (1945) (expanded from film 'Men of Two Worlds')
S. Cápová, Slovak Phil Chor, Bratislava RSO,
Adriano *Concert* (12/91) (MARC) ① **8 223315**
A Colour Symphony, T24 (1921-22 rev 1932)
1. Purple (Andante maestoso); 2. Red (Allegro
vivace); 3. Blue (Gently flowing); 4. Green
(Moderato).

Ulster Orch, V. Handley *Checkmate.*
  (4/87) (CHAN) ① **CHAN8503**
LSO, A. Bliss (r1955) *Concert*
  (8/95) (DUTT) ① **CDLXT2501**
Concerto for Cello and Orchestra, T120 (1970)
R. Wallfisch, Ulster Orch, V. Handley *Concert*
  (7/91) (CHAN) ① **CHAN8818**
R. Cohen, RPO, B. Wordsworth *Concert*
  (9/94) (ARGO) ① **443 170-2ZH**
Concerto for Piano and Orchestra, T58 (1938)
P. Fowke, RLPO, D. Atherton *Homage March, T99.*
  (8/90) (UNIC) ① **UKCD2029**
Concerto for Violin and Orchestra, T79 (1955)
A. Campoli, LPO, A. Bliss (r1955) *Concert*
  (9/95) (BEUL) ① **3PD10**
Hymn to Apollo—orchestra, T41 (1926 rev 1965)
Ulster Orch, V. Handley *Concert*
  (7/91) (CHAN) ① **CHAN8818**
LSO, A. Bliss *Concert* (9/92) (LYRI) ① **SRCD225**
Introduction and Allegro—orchestra, T40 (1926 rev 1937)
RPO, B. Wordsworth *Concert*
  (9/94) (ARGO) ① **443 170-2ZH**
LSO, A. Bliss (r1955) *Concert*
  (8/95) (DUTT) ① **CDLXT2501**
Investiture Antiphonal Fanfare—brass (1969) (for the Investiture of the Prince of Wales)
LPO, M. Kibblewhite *Concert*
  (2/93) (CALA) ① **CACD1010**
Kenilworth—suite: brass band, T55 (1936)
Black Dyke Mills Band, P. Parkes *Concert*
  (9/93) (CHAN) ① **CHAN4506**
Fodens Motor Works Band, F. Mortimer (r1936)
Concert (11/93) (BEUL) ① **1PD2**
March, 'Homage to a Great Man'—orchestra, T99 (1964) (for the State Funeral of Sir Winston Churchill)
RLPO, D. Atherton *Piano Concerto.*
  (8/90) (UNIC) ① **UKCD2029**
Meditations on a theme by John Blow—orchestra, T80 (1955)
RPO, B. Wordsworth *Concert*
  (9/94) (ARGO) ① **443 170-2ZH**
Mêlée fantasque—orchestra, T22 (1921 rev 1965)
LSO, A. Bliss *Concert* (9/92) (LYRI) ① **SRCD225**
Music for strings, T54 (1935)
Northern Sinfonia, R. Hickox *Pastoral.*
  (7/91) (CHAN) ① **CHAN8886**
6 Royal Fanfares—brass ensemble, T88 (1960)
1. The Sovereign's Fanfare; 2. Fanfare for the Bride;
3. Interlude; 4. Royal Fanfare; 5. Wedding Fanfare; 6.
Fanfare (Finale).
1, 2. Locke Brass Consort *Concert*
  (12/93) (KOCH) ① **37202-2**
4, 5. London Brass *Concert*
  (10/89) (CARL) ① **PCD919**
Theme and Cadenza—violin and orchestra (1946) (from music for radio play by Trudy Bliss)
A. Campoli, LPO, A. Bliss (r1955) *Concert*
  (9/95) (BEUL) ① **3PD10**
Welcome the Queen—march, T78 (1954) (for the film of same name)
LSO, A. Bliss (r1959) *Concert*
  (6/93) (DECC) ① **436 403-2DWO**
LSO, A. Bliss (r1954) *Concert*
  (5/94) (BELA) ① **450 143-2**

SECTION II: CHAMBER

Conversation—chamber ensemble, T15 (1920)
1. The Committee Meeting; 2. In the Wood; 3. In the
Ball Room; 4. Soliloquy; 5. In the Tube at Oxford
Circus.
Nash Ens, L. Friend *Concert*
  (9/88) (HYPE) ① **CDA66137**
Pastoral—clarinet and piano (pub posth)
E. Jóhannesson, P. Jenkins *Concert*
  (1/93) (CHAN) ① **CHAN9079**
E. Johnson, M. Martineau *Concert*
  (7/94) (ASV) ① **CDDCA891**
2 Pieces—clarinet and piano, T9 (c1916)
1. Rhapsody; 2. Pastoral.
2. T. King, C. Benson *Concert*
  (11/89) (HYPE) ① **CDA66044**
Quintet for Clarinet and Strings, T50 (1931)
J. Hilton, Lindsay Qt *Concert*
  (2/89) (CHAN) ① **CHAN8683**
Movt 4. F. Thurston, Griller Qt (r1935) *Concert*
  (2/94) (CLRI) ① **CC0005**

Quintet for Oboe and Strings, T44 (1927)
Nash Ens, L. Friend *Concert*
  (9/88) (HYPE) ① **CDA66137**
P. Woods, Audubon Qt *Concert*
  (10/89) (TELA) ① **CD80205**
Sonata for Viola and Piano, T52 (1933)
E. Vardi, K. Sturrock *Concert*
  (7/91) (CHAN) ① **CHAN8770**
String Quartet No. 1 in B flat, T60 (1941)
Delmé Qt (r1985) *String Quartet 2.*
  (11/89) (HYPE) ① **CDA66178**
String Quartet No. 2, T70 (1950)
Delmé Qt (r1985) *String Quartet 1.*
  (11/89) (HYPE) ① **CDA66178**

SECTION III: INSTRUMENTAL

Bliss (A one-step)—piano, T28 (1923)
P. Fowke *Concert* (1/92) (CHAN) ① **CHAN8979**
2 Interludes—piano, T35 (1925)
K. Sturrock *Concert* (7/91) (CHAN) ① **CHAN8770**
4 Masks—piano, T34 (1924)
K. Sturrock *Concert* (7/91) (CHAN) ① **CHAN8770**
Miniature Scherzo—piano, T114 (1969) (for
125th anniversary of 'The Musical Times')
P. Fowke *Concert* (1/92) (CHAN) ① **CHAN8979**
The Rout Trot—piano, T42 (1927)
P. Fowke *Concert* (1/92) (CHAN) ① **CHAN8979**
Sonata for Piano, T72 (1952)
P. Fowke *Concert* (1/92) (CHAN) ① **CHAN8979**
Study—piano, T43 (1927)
P. Fowke *Concert* (1/92) (CHAN) ① **CHAN8979**
Suite—piano, T36 (1925)
1. Overture; 2. Polonaise: Alla polacca; 3. Elegy:
Grave; 4. Variations.
Toccata—piano, T37 (c1925)
K. Sturrock *Concert* (7/91) (CHAN) ① **CHAN8770**
Triptych—piano, T122 (1971)
K. Sturrock *Concert* (7/91) (CHAN) ① **CHAN8770**
P. Fowke *Concert* (1/92) (CHAN) ① **CHAN8979**

SECTION IV: VOCAL AND CHORAL

Aubade for Coronation Morning—SS and chorus, T76 (1953) (Wds. H. Reed)
Cambridge Univ Chbr Ch, T. Brown *Concert*
  (4/92) (GAMU) ① **GAMCD529**
A Birthday Song for a Royal Child (for the birth of HRH Prince Andrew)—chorus a capella, T87 (1960) (Wds. C. Lewis Day)
Finzi Sngrs, P. Spicer *Concert*
  (11/91) (CHAN) ① **CHAN8980**
The Enchantress—scena: mezzo-soprano and orchestra, T71 (1951-52) (Wds. H Reed, after Theocritus)
L. Finnie, Ulster Orch, V. Handley *Concert*
  (7/91) (CHAN) ① **CHAN8818**
Madame Noy—soprano and chamber ensemble, T10 (1918) (Wds. E H W Meyerstein)
E. Gale, Nash Ens, L. Friend *Concert*
  (9/88) (HYPE) ① **CDA66137**
Mar Portugues—chorus a capella (1973) (Wds. F. Pessoa, trans A. Goodison)
R. Hay, S. Carter, J. Bowen, Finzi Sngrs, P. Spicer
Concert (11/91) (CHAN) ① **CHAN8980**
Morning Heroes—orator, chorus and orchestra, T48 (1930) (Wds. various)
J. Westbrook, Liverpool Phil Ch, RLPO, C. Groves
  (10/91) (EMI) ① **CDM7 63906-2**
B. Blessed, East London Chor, Harlow Chor, E. Herts
Chor, LPO, M. Kibblewhite *Concert*
  (2/93) (CALA) ① **CACD1010**
2 Nursery Rhymes—1v, clarinet and piano, T20 (1921) (Wds. F Comford)
1. The Ragwort; 2. The Dandelion.
E. Johnson, J. Howarth *Concert*
  (7/94) (ASV) ① **CDDCA891**
Pastoral, 'Lie strewn the white flocks'—mezzo-soprano, chorus, flute, timpani and strings, T46 (1928) (Wds. various)
S. Minty, J. Pearce, Holst Sngrs, Holst Orch, H.D.
Wetton *Concert* (11/88) (HYPE) ① **CDA66175**
D. Jones, D. Haslam, Sinfonia Chor, Northern
Sinfonia, R. Hickox *Music for Strings.*
  (7/91) (CHAN) ① **CHAN8886**
A Prayer of St. Francis of Assisi—four female vv (1973)
East London Chor, M. Kibblewhite *Concert*
  (2/93) (CALA) ① **CACD1010**
Rhapsody—mezzo-soprano, tenor and chamber ensemble, T13 (1919) (wordless)
E. Gale, A. Rolfe Johnson, Nash Ens, L. Friend
Concert (9/88) (HYPE) ① **CDA66137**

River Music—chorus a capella (1967) (Wds.
C. Lewis Day)
Finzi Sngrs, P. Spicer *Concert*
(11/91) (CHAN) ① **CHAN8980**
Rout—soprano and chamber ensemble, T14
(1920 orch 1921)
E. Gale, Nash Ens, L. Friend *Concert*
(9/88) (HYPE) ① **CDA66137**
R. Woodland, LSO, A. Bliss *Concert*
(9/92) (LYRI) ① **SRCD225**
Serenade—baritone and orchestra, T47
(1936) (Wds. Spenser and Wotton)
J. Shirley-Quirk, LSO, B. Priestman *Concert*
(9/92) (LYRI) ① **SRCD225**
The Shield of Faith—SB, chorus and organ
(1974) (Wds. various)
A. Crookes, R. Williams, A. Lumsden, Finzi Sngrs, P.
Spicer *Concert* (11/91) (CHAN) ① **CHAN8980**
Women of Yueh—song cycle with chamber
ensemble, T32 (1923-24) (Wds. Li-Tai-Po)
E. Gale, Nash Ens, L. Friend *Concert*
(9/88) (HYPE) ① **CDA66137**
The World is charged with the grandeur of
God—cantata, T116 (1969) (Wds. Hopkins)
Finzi Wind Ens, Finzi Sngrs, P. Spicer *Concert*
(11/91) (CHAN) ① **CHAN8980**
Ambrosian Sngrs, LSO, P. Ledger *Concert*
(9/92) (LYRI) ① **SRCD225**

SECTION V: STAGE WORKS

Adam Zero—ballet, T67 (1946—London)
EXCERPTS: 1. Fanfare Overture; 2. The Stage; 3.
Birth of Adam; 4. Adam's Fates; 5. Dance of Spring;
6. Love Dance; 7. Bridal Ceremony; 8. Adam
achieves Power; 9. Re-entry of Adam's FAtes; 10.
Dance of Summer; 11. Approach of Autumn; 12.
Night Club Scene; 13. Destruction of Adam's World;
14. Approach of Winter; 15. Dance with Death; 16.
Finale.
5, 7, 10. LSO, A. Bliss *Concert*
(9/92) (LYRI) ① **SRCD225**
Checkmate—ballet, T57 (1937—London)
EXCERPTS: 1. Prologue:The Players; 2. Dance of
the Pawns; 3. Dance of the Four Knights; 4. Entry of
the Black Queen; 5. Red Knight's Mazurka; 6.
Ceremony of the Bishops; 7. Entry of the Red
Castles; 8. Entry of the Red King and Queen; 9. The
Attack; 10. The Duel; 11. The Black Queen Dances;
12. Finale: Checkmate.
1, 3-6, 12. Ulster Orch, V. Handley *Colour
Symphony.* (4/87) (CHAN) ① **CHAN8503**
1, 3-6, 12. English Northern Philh, D. Lloyd-Jones
Concert (3/91) (HYPE) ① **CDA66436**
2-6, 12. Sinfonia of London, A. Bliss (r1960) *Concert*
(8/94) (EMI) ① **CDM7 64718-2**
3-6, 12. W. Australian SO, H-H. Schönzeler *Concert*
(6/92) (CHAN) ① **CHAN6576**
Christopher Columbus—film score, T68a
(1949)
Suite Bratislava RSO, Adriano (arr Adriano) *Concert*
(12/91) (MARC) ① **8 223315**
Conquest of the Air—film score, T56 (1936)
SUITE: 1. The Wind; 2. The Vision of Leonard da
Vinci; 3. Stunting; 4. Gliding; 5. March—Conquest of
the Air.
Philh, K. Alwyn *Concert*
(2/91) (SILV) ① **FILMCD713**
3. Philh, K. Alwyn *Concert*
(5/93) (SILV) ① **SILVAD3002**
Men of Two Worlds—film score, T65 (1945)
EXCERPTS -; 1. Return to Tanganyika; 2. The
Challenge; 3. Kisenga's Family; 4. Village Fire and
Finale.
Baraza E. Joyce, National SO, M. Mathieson (r1946)
Concert (8/95) (DUTT) ① **CDLXT2501**
1-4. Slovak Phil Chor, Bratislava RSO, Adriano
Concert (12/91) (MARC) ① **8 223315**
Seven Waves Away—film score (1956)
Bratislava RSO, Adriano *Concert*
(12/91) (MARC) ① **8 223315**
Things to come—film score, T53 (1934-35)
EXCERPTS: 1. Prologue; 2. Ballet for Children; 3.
Attack; 4. Pestilence; 5. The World in Ruins; 6.
Machines; 7. March; 8. Epilogue—later renamed as
'Theme and Reconstruction'; 9. Building the New
World (recons. C Palmer); 10. Attack on the Moon
Gun (recons. C Palmer); 11. Epilogue (recons. C
Palmer).
2-4, 6-8. LSO, A. Bliss (r1957) *Concert*
(5/94) (BELA) ① **450 143-2**
2-4, 6-8. LSO, A. Bliss (r1957) *Concert*
(8/95) (DUTT) ① **CDLXT2501**
2-5. LSO, A. Bliss (r1935) *Concert*
(8/95) (DUTT) ① **CDLXT2501**

BLITHEMAN, John (c1525–1591) England

SECTION IV: VOCAL AND CHORAL

In pace—Compline respond: 4vv
Worcester Cath Ch, Don Hunt, R. Johnston (r1993)
Concert (2/95) (ABBE) ① **CDCA957**

BLITZSTEIN, Marc (1905–1964) USA

SECTION IV: VOCAL AND CHORAL

The Airborne Symphony—tenor, bass,
narrator, male chorus and orchestra (1943-
46) (Wds. cpsr)
C. Holland, W. Scheff, R. Shaw, Victor Chorale, NY
City SO, L. Bernstein (r1946) *Native Land.*
(7/95) (RCA) ① **09026 62568-2**
Emily (Ballad of the Bombadier) W. Sharp, S. Blier
Concert (10/91) (KOCH) ① **37050-2**
From Marion's Book—song cycle (1960)
(Wds. e.e. cummings)
1. O by the by; 2. Until and I heard; 3. Open your
heart.
1-3. W. Sharp, S. Blier *Concert*
(10/91) (KOCH) ① **37050-2**
Jimmie's Got a Goil—song (1935) (Wds. e.e.
cummings)
W. Sharp, S. Blier *Concert*
(10/91) (KOCH) ① **37050-2**
Stay in my Arms—song (1935) (Wds. cpsr)
W. Sharp, S. Blier *Concert*
(10/91) (KOCH) ① **37050-2**
This is the Garden—chorus and orchestra
(1957) (Wds. cpsr)
In Twos K. Holvik, W. Sharp, S. Blier *Concert*
(10/91) (KOCH) ① **37050-2**
Zipperfly (The New Suit)—song (1945) (Wds.
cpsr)
W. Sharp, S. Blier *Concert*
(10/91) (KOCH) ① **37050-2**

SECTION V: STAGE WORKS

The cradle will rock—play in music: 10
scenes (1936-37—New York) (Lib. cpsr)
The Cradle will Rock; Croon-Spoon; Nickel under
the Foot K. Holvik, W. Sharp, S. Blier *Concert*
(10/91) (KOCH) ① **37050-2**
Goloopchik—musical play (1945) (Lib. cpsr)
Displaced W. Sharp, S. Blier *Concert*
(10/91) (KOCH) ① **37050-2**
The Guests—ballet (1949—New York)
Excs B. Lerner *Concert*
(12/89) (ETCE) ① **KTC1036**
Juno—musical play: 2 acts (1957-59—New
York) (Lib. cpsr/Stein after O'Casey)
Bird on a Tree; I wish it so K. Holvik, W. Sharp, S.
Blier *Concert* (10/91) (KOCH) ① **37050-2**
I wish it so D. Upshaw, E. Stern (r1993) *Concert*
(12/94) (NONE) ① **7559-79345-2**
The Magic Barrel—opera: 1 act (1963) (Lib.
cpsr after Malamud)
Then W. Sharp, S. Blier *Concert*
(10/91) (KOCH) ① **37050-2**
Native Land—film score (1940-41)
EXCERPTS: 1. Dusty sun.
1. W. Scheff, L. Bernstein (r1946) *Airborne
Symphony.* (7/95) (RCA) ① **09026 62568-2**
No for an Answer—opera: 2 acts (1938-
40—New York) (Lib. cpsr)
In the clear; Penny Candy W. Sharp, S. Blier
Concert (10/91) (KOCH) ① **37050-2**
In the clear D. Upshaw, E. Stern (r1993: arr E Stern)
Concert (12/94) (NONE) ① **7559-79345-2**
Regina—opera: 3 acts (1946-49—New York)
(Lib. cpsr after Hellmann)
Blues; What will it be me K. Holvik, W. Sharp,
S. Blier *Concert* (10/91) (KOCH) ① **37050-2**
Reuben, Reuben—musical play: 2 acts
(1950-55—Boston) (Lib. cpsr)
Monday Morning Blues; Rose Song W. Sharp, S.
Blier *Concert* (10/91) (KOCH) ① **37050-2**
Never get lost D. Upshaw, E. Stern (r1993) *Concert*
(12/94) (NONE) ① **7559-79345-2**

BLOCH, Ernest (1880–1959) Switzerland/USA

SECTION I: ORCHESTRAL

America—epic rhapsody: chorus and
orchestra (1925-27)
Seattle Sym Chorale, Seattle SO, G. Schwarz
(r1993) *Concerto Grosso 1.*
(8/94) (DELO) ① **DE3135**
Baal Shem (1923 orch 1939)
1. Vidui; 2. Nigun; 3. Simchan Torah.
M. Guttman, RPO, J. Serebrier *Concert*
(5/92) (ASV) ① **CDDCA785**
Concerto for Violin and Orchestra—1937-38
Y. Menuhin, Philh, P. Kletzki *Berg: Violin Concerto.*
(4/91) (EMI) ① **CDM7 63989-2**
M. Guttman, RPO, J. Serebrier *Concert*
(5/92) (ASV) ① **CDDCA785**
Concerto grosso No. 1—strings and piano
obbligato (1924-25)
I. Rob, Israel CO, Y. Talmi *Concert*
(8/88) (CHAN) ① **CHAN8593**
Eastman-Rochester Orch, H. Hanson *Concert*
(11/91) (MERC) ① **432 718-2MM**
P. Michaelian, Seattle SO, G. Schwarz (r1992)
America. (8/94) (DELO) ① **DE3135**
San Diego CO, D. Barra (r1992) *Concert*
(12/94) (KOCH) ① **37196-2**
Concerto grosso No. 2—string orchestra and
string quartet (1952)
Eastman-Rochester Orch, H. Hanson *Concert*
(11/91) (MERC) ① **432 718-2MM**
San Diego CO, D. Barra (r1992) *Concert*
(12/94) (KOCH) ① **37196-2**
Evocations—orchestra (1937)
NZ SO, J. Sedares (r1993) *Concert*
(9/94) (KOCH) ① **37232-2**
3 Jewish Poems—orchestra (1913)
1. Danse; 2. Rite; 3. Cortège funèbre.
NZ SO, J. Sedares (r1993) *Concert*
(9/94) (KOCH) ① **37232-2**
2 Last Poems ... (Maybe ...)—flute and
orchestra (1958)
A. Still, NZ SO, J. Sedares (r1993) *Concert*
(9/94) (KOCH) ① **37232-2**
Schelomo—cello and orchestra (1915-16)
M. Maisky, Israel PO, L. Bernstein (pp1988) *Dvořák:
Cello Concerto.* (1/90) (DG) ① **427 347-2GH**
P. Fournier, BPO, A. Wallenstein *Concert*
(5/90) (DG) ① **429 155-2GR**
G. Miquelle, Eastman-Rochester Orch, H. Hanson
Concert (11/91) (MERC) ① **432 718-2MM**
E. Feuermann, Philadelphia, L. Stokowski (r1940) *R.
Strauss: Don Quixote.* (12/91) (BIDD) ① **LAB042**
O. Harnoy, LPO, C. Mackerras *Concert*
(12/91) (RCA) ① **RD60757**
L. Rose, Philadelphia, E. Ormandy (r1961) *Concert*
(5/93) (SONY) ① **SBK48278**
T. Thedéen, Malmö SO, L. Markiz (r1990) *Symphony
(1903).* (5/93) (BIS) ① **BIS-CD576**
S. Isserlis, LSO, R. Hickox (r1988) *Elgar: Cello
Concerto.* (11/94) (VIRG) ① **CUV5 61125-2**
M. Kliegel, Ireland National SO, G. Markson (r1993)
Concert (11/94) (NAXO) ① **8 550519**
Y-Y. Ma, Baltimore SO, D. Zinman (r1993) *Concert*
(3/95) (SONY) ① **SK57961**
Sinfonia breve (1952)
Minneapolis SO, A. Dorati (r1960) *Concert*
(7/93) (MERC) ① **434 329-2MM**
Symphony in C sharp minor (1903)
Malmö SO, L. Markiz (r1992) *Schelomo.*
(5/93) (BIS) ① **BIS-CD576**

SECTION II: CHAMBER

Baal Shem—violin and piano (1923)
1. Vidui; 2. Nigun; 3. Simchas Torah.
Lionel Friedman, A. Schiller *Concert*
(8/90) (ASV) ① **CDDCA714**
J. Szigeti, A. Foldes (r1940) *Concert*
(7/94) (BIDD) ① **LAB070/1**
2. J. Szigeti, K. Ruhrseitz (r1926) *Concert*
(1/90) (BIDD) ① **LAB005/6**
2. Y. Turovsky (arr Purich) *Concert*
(7/90) (CHAN) ① **CHAN8800**
2. I. Perlman, J.G. Guggenheim (pp1990) *Concert*
(2/91) (EMI) ① **CDC7 54108-2**
2. Y. Menuhin, L. Persinger (r1929) *Concert*
(4/91) (BIDD) ① **LAB031**
2. P. Berman, L. Berman (pp1990) *Concert*
(8/92) (AUDI) ① **CD72040**
2. M. Vengerov, I. Golan (r1993) *Concert*
(5/94) (TELD) ① **9031-77351-2**
2. M. Maisky, D. Hovora (r1993: arr vc/pf: Schuster)
Concert (9/94) (DG) ① **439 863-2GH**

2. J. Heifetz, B. Smith (r1972) *Concert*
(11/94) (RCA) ① [65] 09026 61778-2(46)
2. N. Milstein, L. Mittman (r1938) *Concert*
(9/95) (BIDD) ① LAB096
From Jewish Life—cello and piano (1924)
1. Prayer; 2. Supplication; 3. Jewish Song.
Y. Turovsky (arr Antonini/Purich) *Concert*
(7/90) (CHAN) ① CHAN8800
1. A. Lysy, Camerata Lysy (arr Kindler) *Concert*
(3/87) (CLAV) ① CD50-8507
2 Last Poems—flute and piano (1958) (arr
cpsr from fl/orch vers)
1. Funeral Music; 2. 'Life Again?...'.
A. Still, S. De Witt Smith (r1992) *Concert*
(4/92) (KOCH) ① 37144-2
**Meditation and Processional—viola and
piano (1951)**
S. Rowland-Jones, N. Immelman *Concert*
(4/92) (ETCE) ① KTC1112
**Méditation hébraïque—cello and piano
(1924)**
Y. Turovsky (arr Purich) *Concert*
(7/90) (CHAN) ① CHAN8800
Night—string quartet (1925)
Rasumovsky Qt *Concert*
(12/92) (IMPE) ① RAZCD901
3 Nocturnes—piano trio (1924)
Hartley Trio *Concert* (6/94) (GAMU) ① GAMCD536
Sonata for Violin and Piano No. 1 (1920)
Lionel Friedman, A. Schiller *Concert*
(8/90) (ASV) ① CDDCA714
J. Heifetz, E. Bay (r1953) *Concert*
(11/94) (RCA) ① [65] 09026 61778-2(08)
**Sonata for Violin and Piano No. 2, 'Poème
mystique' (1924)**
Lionel Friedman, A. Schiller *Concert*
(8/90) (ASV) ① CDDCA714
J. Heifetz, B. Smith (r1955) *Concert*
(11/94) (RCA) ① [65] 09026 61778-2(08)
String Quartet No. 3 (1952)
New World Qt (r1978) *Concert*
(10/93) (VOX) ① [2] 115775-2
Suite—viola and piano (1919)
W. Primrose, F. Kitzinger (r1939) *Concert*
(10/91) (PEAR) ① GEMMCD9453
S. Rowland-Jones, N. Immelman *Concert*
(4/92) (ETCE) ① KTC1112
Suite hébraïque—viola and piano (1950)
S. Rowland-Jones, N. Immelman *Concert*
(4/92) (ETCE) ① KTC1112

---SECTION III: INSTRUMENTAL---

4 Circus Pieces—piano (1922)
1. The two 'Burlington' Brothers; 2. The Clown; 3.
The Homeliest Woman; 4. Dialogue and Dance of the
Heavy-weight and the Dwarf.
I. Kassai *Concert* (6/90) (MARC) ① 8 223288
Danse sacrée—piano (1923)
I. Kassai *Concert* (6/90) (MARC) ① 8 223289
**Enfantines—piano: 10 pieces for children
(1923)**
1. Lullaby; 2. The Joyous Party; 3. With Mother; 4.
Elves; 5. Joyous March; 6. Melody; 7. Pastorale; 8.
Rainy Day; 9. Teasing; 10. Dream.
I. Kassai *Concert* (6/90) (MARC) ① 8 223288
Ex-voto—piano (1914)
I. Kassai *Concert* (6/90) (MARC) ① 8 223289
In the Night—piano (1922)
I. Kassai *Concert* (6/90) (MARC) ① 8 223288
N. Immelman *Concert* (4/92) (ETCE) ① KTC1112
Nirvana—poem for piano (1923)
I. Kassai *Concert* (6/90) (MARC) ① 8 223288
Poems of the Sea—piano (1922)
1. Waves; 2. Chanty; 3. At Sea.
I. Kassai *Concert* (6/90) (MARC) ① 8 223288
5 Sketches in Sepia—piano (1923)
1. Prélude; 2. Fumées; 3. Lucioles; 4. Incertitide; 5.
Epilogue.
I. Kassai *Concert* (6/90) (MARC) ① 8 223288
N. Immelman *Concert* (4/92) (ETCE) ① KTC1112
Sonata for Piano (1935)
I. Kassai *Concert* (6/90) (MARC) ① 8 223289
Visions and Prophecies—piano (1936)
I. Kassai *Concert* (6/90) (MARC) ① 8 223289

---SECTION IV: VOCAL AND CHORAL---

**Sacred Service—baritone, chorus and
orchestra (1933)**
L. Berkman, Zemel Ch, LSO, G. Simon
(5/89) (CHAN) ① CHAN8418
R. Merrill, NY Met Synagogue Ch, NYPO, L.
Bernstein (r1960) *Concert*
(11/92) (SONY) ① [2] SM2K47533

**BLOCKX, Jan (1851–1912)
Belgium**

---SECTION V: STAGE WORKS---

**Milenka—ballet-pantomime
(1888—Brussels)**
1. Flemish Fair.
1. Belgian Rad & TV Orch, A. Rahbari (r1992)
Concert (8/94) (DINT) ① DICD920100

**BLODEK, Vilém (1834–1874)
Czechoslovakia**

---SECTION V: STAGE WORKS---

In the Well—opera: 1 act (1867—Prague) (Lib.
K. Sabina)
Intermezzo Czech PO, V. Neumann *Concert*
(9/90) (ORFE) ① C180891A

**BLOMDAHL, Karl-Birger
(1916–1968) Sweden**

---SECTION I: ORCHESTRAL---

Symphony No. 1 (1943)
Swedish RSO, L. Segerstam (r1993) *Concert*
(8/94) (BIS) ① BIS-CD611
Symphony No. 2 (1947)
Swedish RSO, L. Segerstam (r1993) *Concert*
(8/94) (BIS) ① BIS-CD611
Symphony No. 3, 'Facetter' (Facets) (1950)
Swedish RSO, L. Segerstam (r1991) *Concert*
(8/94) (BIS) ① BIS-CD611

**BLONDEL DE NESLE (fl
1180–1200) France**

---SECTION IV: VOCAL AND CHORAL---

**L' Amours dont sui espris—chanson (1v)
(c1180-1200)**
Gothic Voices, C. Page *Concert*
(10/89) (HYPE) ① CDA66336
**En tous tans que vente bise—isorhythmic
poem (13th cent)**
Gothic Voices, C. Page *Concert*
(12/90) (HYPE) ① CDA66423
**Ma joie me semont—chanson (1v) (?before
1179)**
Gothic Voices, C. Page *Concert*
(10/89) (HYPE) ① CDA66336

BLOOM, Robert (b 1908) USA

---SECTION I: ORCHESTRAL---

Narrative—oboe and strings
H. Lucarelli, Brooklyn PO, M. Barrett (r1993) *Concert*
(7/94) (KOCH) ① 37187-2
Requiem—oboe and strings (1951)
H. Lucarelli, Brooklyn PO, M. Barrett (r1993) *Concert*
(7/94) (KOCH) ① 37187-2

BLOOM, Rube (1902–1976) USA

---SECTION III: INSTRUMENTAL---

Silhouette—piano (1927)
A. Feinberg (r1994) *Concert*
(11/95) (ARGO) ① 444 457-2ZH
Spring Fever—piano (1926)
A. Feinberg (r1994) *Concert*
(11/95) (ARGO) ① 444 457-2ZH

**BLOW, John (1649–1708)
England**

---SECTION II: CHAMBER---

**Chaconne in G—2 violins, viola and
continuo** (also in keyboard version in F)
Parley of Instr, R. Goodman, P. Holman *Concert*
(11/88) (HYPE) ① CDA66108
**Ground in G minor—two violins and
continuo**
Parley of Instr (r1993) *Concert*
(1/94) (HYPE) ① CDA66658
Sonata in A—two violins and continuo
Palladian Ens (r1992) *Concert*
(7/93) (LINN) ① CKD010
Parley of Instr (r1993) *Concert*
(1/94) (HYPE) ① CDA66658

---SECTION III: INSTRUMENTAL---

**A Choice Collection of Lessons—four
suites: harpsichord/spinet (pub 1698)**
EXCERPTS: 1. Suite No. 1 in D minor; 1a. Alman; 2.
Suite No. 3 in A minor; 4. Suite No. 4 in C.
1a F. Kelly (r1992) *Concert*
(9/94) (MOSC) ① 070987
1, 3. T. Roberts (r1993) *Concert*
(10/93) (HYPE) ① CDA66646
**Ground in C—keyboard (unpub: Christ Church
Library, Oxford)**
T. Roberts (r1993) *Concert*
(10/93) (HYPE) ① CDA66646
**Ground in G minor—keyboard (unpub: Christ
Church Library, Oxford)**
T. Roberts (r1993) *Concert*
(10/93) (HYPE) ① CDA66646
**Morlake Ground—keyboard (unpub: Christ
Church Library, Oxford)**
T. Roberts (r1993) *Concert*
(10/93) (HYPE) ① CDA66646
Mortlack's Ground—keyboard (pub 1687)
(from 'Musick's Hand-Maid', pt 2)
T. Pinnock (r1978) *Concert*
(4/89) (CRD) ① CRD3347
6 Organ Voluntaries (ed Cooper)
1. D minor; 2. A; 3. G; 4. C; 5. G minor; 6. Double
Voluntary in D minor.
J. Butt (r1992) *Concert*
(6/94) (HARM) ① HMU90 7103
J. Butt (r1992) *Concert*
(7/95) (HARM) ① [6] HMX290 1528/33(2)
**Prelude in G—keyboard (unpub: Christ Church
Library, Oxford)**
T. Roberts (r1993) *Concert*
(10/93) (HYPE) ① CDA66646
Verse for the Double Organ in G
R. Woolley (r1993) *Concert*
(9/94) (CHAN) ① CHAN0553
Verse in A minor—organ
R. Woolley (r1993) *Concert*
(9/94) (CHAN) ① CHAN0553
Verse in C—organ
R. Woolley (r1993) *Concert*
(9/94) (CHAN) ① CHAN0553
Verse in G—organ
R. Woolley (r1993) *Concert*
(9/94) (CHAN) ① CHAN0553
Verse in G minor—organ
R. Woolley (r1993) *Concert*
(9/94) (CHAN) ① CHAN0553
Verset in D minor—organ
T. Dart (r1957) *Concert* (5/95) (JMS) ① JMSCD1
Voluntary for the Cornet and Echo—organ
R. Woolley (r1993) *Concert*
(9/94) (CHAN) ① CHAN0553
**Voluntary in A—The 100th Psalm Tune, set
as a Lesson**
T. Koopman *Concert* (5/91) (CAPR) ① 10 254
**Voluntary in G minor (unpub: British Library
anon MS)**
T. Roberts (r1993) *Concert*
(10/93) (HYPE) ① CDA66646

---SECTION IV: VOCAL AND CHORAL---

**Ah, Heav'n! What is't I hear?—duet (pub
1700)**
M. Chance, J. Bowman, King's Consort, R. King
Concert (7/88) (HYPE) ① CDA66253
Awake, awake, my lyre—secular ode (c1676)
(Wds. A. Cowley)
Red Byrd, Parley of Instr (r1993) *Concert*
(1/94) (HYPE) ① CDA66658
Begin the song—St Cecilia's Day ode (1684)
(Wds. J. Oldham)
1. Music's the cordial.
1. Red Byrd, Parley of Instr (r1993) *Concert*
(1/94) (HYPE) ① CDA66658
**Behold, O God, our defender—anthem for
the coronation of James II (1685)**
Westminster Abbey Ch, orch, S. Preston (r1986)
Concert (7/95) (ARCH) ① 447 155-2AP
**Blessed is the man that hath not
walked—verse anthem: AABB, chor, strings
& org (1680-3)** (Wds. Psalms)
King's College Ch, ASMF, D. Willcocks (r1974)
(8/93) (DECC) ① 436 259-2DM
**Bring the shepherds, bring the
kids—marriage ode**
P. Todd, M. Bevan, Deller Consort, Stour Music Fest
CO, A. Deller (alto/dir) *Concert*
(1/89) (HARM) ① HMA190 201

Chloe found Amintas—secular song (2vv)
(Wds. d'Urfey)
P. Todd, M. Bevan, Deller Consort, A. Deller (alto/dir)
Concert (1/89) (HARM) ① **HMA190 201**
Red Byrd, Parley of Instr (r1993) Concert
(1/94) (HYPE) ① **CDA66658**

Cry aloud, and spare not—verse anthem:
TTB, chor, strings & org (1683) (for discovery
of the Rye House Plot. Wds. Isaiah)
ECO, ASMF, D. Willcocks (r1974) Concert
(8/93) (DECC) ① **436 256-2DM**

The Curse, 'Go, perjur'd man'—secular
song: 2vv (Wds. R. Herrick)
Red Byrd, Parley of Instr (r1993) Concert
(1/94) (HYPE) ① **CDA66658**

Fairest work of happy nature—secular song:
1v and continuo (pub 1689)
J.M. Ainsley, P. Chateauneuf (r1993) Concert
(10/93) (HYPE) ① **CDA66646**

Flavia grown old, 'Why, Flavia, why so
wanton still'—secular song: 1v and continuo
(pub 1700) (from 'Amphion Anglicus')
J.M. Ainsley, T. Roberts (r1993) Concert
(1/94) (HYPE) ① **CDA66658**

Gloria patri, qui creavit nos—motet: 5vv
Red Byrd, Parley of Instr (r1993) Concert
(1/94) (HYPE) ① **CDA66658**

God spake sometime in visions—Coronation
anthem for James II (1685)
King's College Ch, ASMF, D. Willcocks (r1974)
Concert (8/93) (DECC) ① **436 259-2DM**
Westminster Abbey Ch, orch, S. Preston (r1986)
(7/95) (ARCH) ① **447 155-2AP**

Help, Father Abraham—dialogue between
Dives and Abraham
Red Byrd, Parley of Instr (r1993) Concert
(1/94) (HYPE) ① **CDA66658**

I little thought—song (pub 1687) (Wds
Cowley)
Consort of Musicke, A. Rooley (lte/dir) (r1993)
Concert (1/95) (MOSC) ① **070986**

I was glad when they said unto me—verse
anthem: AATTB, chor & orch (1697) (for the
opening of the Choir of St Paul's Cathedral)
ECO, ASMF, D. Willcocks (r1974) Concert
(8/93) (DECC) ① **436 256-2DM**

Let thy hand be strengthened—anthem
(Coronation of James II) (1685)
Westminster Abbey Ch, orch, S. Preston (r1986)
Concert (7/95) (ARCH) ① **447 155-2AP**

Lovely Selina, innocent and free—incidental
song from 'The Princess of Cleve' (1689)
(Wds. Lee)
J.M. Ainsley, T. Roberts, P. Chateauneuf (r1993)
Concert (10/93) (HYPE) ① **CDA66646**
E. Kirkby, A. Rooley (r1994) Concert
(10/95) (MOSC) ① **070979**

Mark how the lark and linnet sing—ode on
the death of Mr Henry Purcell (1695) (Wds
Dryden)
M. Chance, J. Bowman, King's Consort, R. King
Concert (7/88) (HYPE) ① **CDA66253**
M. Deller, Deller Consort, A. Deller (alto/dir) Concert
(1/89) (HARM) ① **HMA190 201**
R. Holton, R. Covey-Crump, C. Daniels, S. Birchall,
Parley of Instr Ch, Parley of Instr, R. Goodman, P.
Holman Concert (3/93) (HYPE) ① **CDA66578**

My God, my God, look upon me—ful anthem:
chorus & organ (1697)
Magdalen Oxford Coll Ch, J. Harper Concert
(11/91) (ABBE) ① **CDCA912**

No more, the dear, lovely nymph's no
more—secular song: 1v and continuo (pub
1692) (Wds. P. Motteux)
J.M. Ainsley, T. Roberts, P. Chateauneuf (r1993)
Concert (10/93) (HYPE) ① **CDA66646**

O all the torments, all the cares—secular
song: 1v and continuo (pub 1700) (from
'Amphion Anglicus')
J.M. Ainsley, T. Roberts, P. Chateauneuf
(r1993) Concert (1/94) (HYPE) ① **CDA66658**

O mighty God, who sit'st on high—sacred
song: 1v and continuo (pub 1693)
J.M. Ainsley, T. Roberts, P. Chateauneuf (r1993)
Concert (10/93) (HYPE) ① **CDA66646**

O sing unto the Lord a new song: let the
congregation—verse anthem: ATTB, chor,
strings & org (1684) (Wds. Psalm 149)
ECO, ASMF, D. Willcocks (r1974) Concert
(8/93) (DECC) ① **436 256-2DM**

O that mine eyes would melt into a
flood—sacred song: 1v and continuo (pub
1688)
J.M. Ainsley, T. Roberts, P. Chateauneuf (r1993)
Concert (10/93) (HYPE) ① **CDA66646**

O turn not these fine eyes away—secular
songs: 1v and continuo (pub 1700) (from
'Amphion Anglicus')
J.M. Ainsley, T. Roberts (r1993) Concert
(10/93) (HYPE) ① **CDA66646**

Paratum cor meum—2vv
Red Byrd, Parley of Instr (r1993) Concert
(1/94) (HYPE) ① **CDA66658**

Poor Celadon, he sighs in vain—secular
song: 1v (pub 1700)
Red Byrd, Parley of Instr (r1993) Concert
(1/94) (HYPE) ① **CDA66658**

The Queen's Epicedium, 'No, Lesbia, no,
you ask in vain'—secular song: 1v and
continuo (pub 1695)
J.M. Ainsley, T. Roberts, P. Chateauneuf (r1993)
Concert (10/93) (HYPE) ① **CDA66646**

Sabina has a thousand charms—secular
song: 1v and continuo (pub 1700) (from
'Amphion Anglicus')
J.M. Ainsley, T. Roberts (r1993) Concert
(10/93) (HYPE) ① **CDA66646**

Salvator mundi—motet (5vv)
Norwich Cath Ch, M. Nicholas, N. Taylor Concert
(3/92) (PRIO) ① **PRCD351**
Oxford Christ Church Cath Ch, S. Darlington Concert
(10/92) (NIMB) ① **NI5328**
Red Byrd, Parley of Instr (r1993) Concert
(1/94) (HYPE) ① **CDA66658**
Westminster Abbey Ch, M. Neary, M. Baker (r1994)
Concert (12/95) (SONY) ① **SK66614**

The Self-banished—secular song
J.M. Ainsley, P. Chateauneuf (r1993) Concert
(10/93) (HYPE) ① **CDA66646**

Septimnius and Acme, 'Whilst on
Septiminius's panting breast'—secular song:
2vv (pub 1685 & 1700) (Wds. A. Cowley)
Red Byrd, Parley of Instr (r1993) Concert
(1/94) (HYPE) ① **CDA66658**

Sing unto the Lord, O ye Saints of
his—anthem (doubtful)
J. Bowman, J.M. Ainsley, M. George, Winchester
Quiristers, King's Consort Ch, Orch, R. King Concert
(12/93) (UNIT) ① **88002-2**

Sing ye Muses—4v (pub 1700)
Red Byrd, Parley of Instr (r1993) Concert
(1/94) (HYPE) ① **CDA66658**

Stay, gentle Echo—dialogue between
Philander and the Echo (c1670s)
Red Byrd, Parley of Instr (r1993) Concert
(1/94) (HYPE) ① **CDA66658**

The Sullen years are past—song from
incomplete New Year's Day Ode (1694) (Wds.
P Motteux)
E. Kirkby, E. Tubb, M. Chance, I. Bostridge, S.
Richardson, S. Birchall, Westminster Abbey Ch, New
London Consort, M. Neary (r1994) Concert
(3/95) (SONY) ① **SK66243**

Tell me no more—song: 1v (pub 1700) (from
Amphion Anglicus)
E. Tubb, F. Kelly (r1992) Concert
(9/94) (MOSC) ① **070987**

Welcome, every guest—song: 1v (pub 1700)
(from Amphion Anglicus)
E. Tubb, F. Kelly (r1992) Concert
(9/94) (MOSC) ① **070987**

What is't to us—song: 1v (pub 1700) (from
Amphion Anglicus)
E. Tubb, F. Kelly (r1992) Concert
(9/94) (MOSC) ① **070987**

Whilst he abroad does like the sun—song
from incomplete ode (1692)
E. Kirkby, E. Tubb, M. Chance, I. Bostridge, S.
Richardson, S. Birchall, Westminster Abbey Ch, New
London Consort, M. Neary (r1994) Concert
(3/95) (SONY) ① **SK66243**

SECTION V: STAGE WORKS

Venus and Adonis—masque
(?1681—Oxford)
Cpte N. Argenta, L. Dawson, S. Varcoe, E. van
Evera, J.M. Ainsley, C. Daniels, Gordon Jones, R.
Covey-Crump, Chor, London Baroque, C. Medlam
(r1987) (9/88) (HARM) ① **HMA190 1276**
Cpte C. Bott, M. George, L. Crabtree, J. Gooding, A.
King, S. Grant, C. Robson, P. Agnew, Westminster
Abbey Sch Chor, New London Consort, P. Pickett
(r1992) (7/94) (L'OI) ① **440 220-2OH**

BLUMENFELD, Felix
(Mikhaylovich) (1863–1931)
Russia

SECTION III: INSTRUMENTAL

Etude de concert in F sharp minor—piano,
Op. 24 (1897)
D. Blumenthal (r1993) Concert
(12/95) (MARC) ① **8 223656**

Etude for the left hand in A flat—piano, Op.
36
S. Barere (pp1947) Concert
(11/89) (APR) ① [2] **APR7008**
S. Barere (r1935) Concert
(5/91) (APR) ① [2] **APR7001**
D. Blumenthal (r1993) Concert
(12/95) (MARC) ① **8 223656**

Etude in F sharp—piano, Op. 54 (1927)
D. Blumenthal (r1993) Concert
(12/95) (MARC) ① **8 223656**

Etude, 'Sur mer'—piano, Op. 14 (1890)
D. Blumenthal (r1993) Concert
(12/95) (MARC) ① **8 223656**

Etude-Fantaisie in F minor—piano, Op. 48
(1916)
D. Blumenthal (r1993) Concert
(12/95) (MARC) ① **8 223656**

4 Etudes—piano, Op. 2
1. A.
1. D. Blumenthal (r1993) Concert
(12/95) (MARC) ① **8 223656**

3 Etudes—piano, Op. 3
1. D flat; 2. E minor; 3. A minor.
D. Blumenthal (r1993) Concert
(12/95) (MARC) ① **8 223656**

2 Etudes—piano, Op. 29 (1898)
1. D; 2. A.
D. Blumenthal (r1993) Concert
(12/95) (MARC) ① **8 223656**

4 Etudes—piano, Op. 44 (1912)
1. G flat; 2. D flat; 3. E minor; 4. A minor.
D. Blumenthal (r1993) Concert
(12/95) (MARC) ① **8 223656**

2 Etudes-fantaisies—piano, Op. 25 (1898)
1. G minor; 2. E flat minor.
D. Blumenthal (r1993) Concert
(12/95) (MARC) ① **8 223656**

Valse-Etude in F—piano, Op. 4
D. Blumenthal (r1993) Concert
(12/95) (MARC) ① **8 223656**

BLUNDEVILLE, John (17th Cent)
England

SECTION IV: VOCAL AND CHORAL

Beneath this gloomy shade—song (Wds
Cowley)
Consort of Musicke, A. Rooley (lte/dir) (r1993)
Concert (1/95) (MOSC) ① **070986**

BOCCHERINI, Luigi (1743–1805)
Italy

G—Gérard Nos; B—Original autograph Nos

SECTION I: ORCHESTRAL

Concerto for Cello and Orchestra No. 1 in E
flat, G474 (? by 1770-72)
D. Geringas, Padua CO, B. Giuranna Concert
(7/89) (CLAV) ① [3] **CD50-8814/6**
J. Berger, South-West German CO, V. Czarnecki
Concert (9/92) (EBS) ① [3] **EBS6058**

Concerto for Cello and Orchestra No. 2 in A,
G475
D. Geringas, Padua CO, B. Giuranna Concert
(7/89) (CLAV) ① [3] **CD50-8814/6**
J. Berger, South-West German CO, V. Czarnecki
Concert (9/92) (EBS) ① [3] **EBS6058**

Concerto for Cello and Orchestra No. 3 in D,
G476
D. Geringas, Padua CO, B. Giuranna Concert
(7/89) (CLAV) ① [3] **CD50-8814/6**
J. Berger, South-West German CO, V. Czarnecki
Concert (9/92) (EBS) ① [3] **EBS6058**
A. Bylsma, Tafelmusik, J. Lamon (r1992) Concert
(7/93) (SONY) ① **SK53121**
C. Coin (vc/dir), Limoges Baroque Ens (r1994)
Concert (4/94) (ASTR) ① **E8517**

Concerto for Cello and Orchestra No. 4 in C,
G477 (pub 1770)
D. Geringas, Padua CO, B. Giuranna Concert
(7/89) (CLAV) ① [3] **CD50-8814/6**

A. Bylsma, Concerto Amsterdam, J. Schröder (r1965)
Concert   (7/93) (TELD) ① 9031-77624-2
Concerto for Cello and Orchestra No. 5 in D, G478 (? authentic)
D. Geringas, Padua CO, B. Giuranna Concert
          (7/89) (CLAV) ① [3] CD50-8814/6
J. Berger, South-West German CO, V. Czarnecki
          (9/92) (EBS) ① [3] EBS6058
Concerto for Cello and Orchestra No. 6 in D, G479 (pub 1770)
D. Geringas, Padua CO, B. Giuranna Concert
          (7/89) (CLAV) ① [3] CD50-8814/6
M. Rostropovich, Zurich Collegium Musicum, P.
          Sacher Concert   (4/90) (DG) ① 429 098-2GGA
J. Berger, South-West German CO, V. Czarnecki
Concert   (9/92) (EBS) ① [3] EBS6058
A. Bylsma, Concerto Amsterdam, J. Schröder (r1965)
Concert   (7/93) (TELD) ① 9031-77624-2
M. Rostropovich, Zurich Collegium Musicum, P.
          Sacher Concert (10/94) (DG) ① [2] 437 952-2GX2
Concerto for Cello and Orchestra No. 7 in G, G480 (pub 1771)
F. Schmidt, ECO, E. Heath (r1988) Beethoven: Triple
          Concerto.   (6/89) (CARL) ① PCD917
D. Geringas, Padua CO, B. Giuranna Concert
          (7/89) (CLAV) ① [3] CD50-8814/6
L. Claret, ECO, G. Malcolm Haydn: Cello Concerto in
C.   (10/89) (HARM) ① HMP390 5204
A. Bylsma, Tafelmusik, J. Lamon Concert
          (2/90) (DHM) ① RD77867
S. Isserlis, Ostrobothnian CO, J. Kangas Concert
          (7/92) (VIRG) ① VC7 59015-2
J. Berger, South-West German CO, V. Czarnecki
Concert   (9/92) (EBS) ① [3] EBS6058
A. Bylsma, Concerto Amsterdam, J. Schröder (r1965)
Concert   (7/93) (TELD) ① 9031-77624-2
C. Coin (vc/dir), Limoges Baroque Ens (r1993)
Concert   (4/94) (ASTR) ① E8517
Concerto for Cello and Orchestra No. 8 in C, G481 (pub 1771)
D. Geringas, Padua CO, B. Giuranna Concert
          (7/89) (CLAV) ① [3] CD50-8814/6
J. Berger, South-West German CO, V. Czarnecki
          (9/92) (EBS) ① [3] EBS6058
A. Bylsma, Concerto Amsterdam, J. Schröder (r1965)
Concert   (7/93) (TELD) ① 9031-77624-2
Concerto for Cello and Orchestra No. 9 in B flat, G482 (arr Grützmacher unless indicated)
Y. Turovsky (vc/dir), Montreal I Musici Concert
          (1/87) (CHAN) ① CHAN8470
J. Du Pré, ECO, D. Barenboim (r1967) Haydn: Cello
          Concerto in D. (12/87) (EMI) ① CDC7 47840-2
Y-Y. Ma, St Paul CO, P. Zukerman Concert
          (2/88) (SONY) ① SK39964
P. Casals, LSO, L. Ronald (r1936) Concert
          (5/89) (PEAR) ① GEMMCD9349
D. Geringas, Padua CO, B. Giuranna Concert
          (7/89) (CLAV) ① [3] CD50-8814/6
M. Haimovitz, ECO, A. Davis Concert
          (4/90) (DG) ① 429 219-2GH
S. Isserlis, Ostrobothnian CO, J. Kangas Concert
          (7/92) (VIRG) ① VC7 59015-2
J. Berger, South-West German CO, V. Czarnecki
Concert   (9/92) (EBS) ① [3] EBS6058
O. Harnoy, Solisti Veneti, C. Scimone (r1991)
          (8/93) (RCA) ① 09026 61228-2
C. Coin (vc/dir), Limoges Baroque Ens (r1993)
Concert   (4/94) (ASTR) ① E8517
J. Starker, Philh, C.M. Giulini (1958) Concert
          (12/95) (EMI) ① [6] CZS5 68485-2
Concerto for Cello and Orchestra No. 10 in D, G483 (c1782)
D. Geringas, Padua CO, B. Giuranna Concert
          (7/89) (CLAV) ① [3] CD50-8814/6
A. Bylsma, Tafelmusik, J. Lamon Concert
          (2/90) (DHM) ① RD77867
J. Berger, South-West German CO, V. Czarnecki
          (9/92) (EBS) ① [3] EBS6058
Concerto for Cello and Orchestra No. 11 in C, G573
D. Geringas, Padua CO, B. Giuranna Concert
          (7/89) (CLAV) ① [3] CD50-8814/6
J. Berger, South-West German CO, V. Czarnecki
Concert   (9/92) (EBS) ① [3] EBS6058
A. Bylsma, Tafelmusik, J. Lamon (r1992) Concert
          (7/93) (SONY) ① SK53121
Concerto for Cello and Orchestra No. 12 in E flat (? authentic)
D. Geringas, Padua CO, B. Giuranna Concert
          (7/89) (CLAV) ① [3] CD50-8814/6
J. Berger, South-West German CO, V. Czarnecki
Concert   (9/92) (EBS) ① [3] EBS6058
Concerto (Sinfonia concertante) for 2 Violins and Orchestra in C, G491 (Op. 7) (1769)
Neuss German Chbr Acad, J. Goritzki (r1992-3)
          Concert   (12/94) (CPO) ① CPO999 084-2

6 Symphonies, G493-498 (Op. 21) (pub 1775)
1. B flat; 2. E flat; 3. C; 4. D; 5. B flat; 6. A.
1-5. Neuss German Chbr Acad, J. Goritzki
          (1/94) (CPO) ① CPO999 174-2
5. Tafelmusik, J. Lamon Concert
          (2/90) (DHM) ① RD77867
6. Neuss German Chbr Acad, J. Goritzki (r1993)
          Symphonies, G509-14.
          (1/94) (CPO) ① CPO999 175-2
6 Symphonies, G503-508 (Op. 12) (pub 1771)
1. D; 2. E flat; 3. C; 4. D minor (La Casa del Diavolo);
          5. B flat; 6. A.
1-3. Neuss German Chbr Acad, J. Goritzki (r1993)
          (8/94) (CPO) ① CPO999 172-2
4. Ens 415, C. Banchini Concert
          (4/89) (HARM) ① HMC90 1291
4. Tafelmusik, J. Lamon Concert
          (2/90) (DHM) ① RD77867
4. AAM, C. Hogwood (r1992) Concert
          (2/95) (L'OI) ① 436 993-2OH
4-6. Neuss German Chbr Acad, J. Goritzki (r1990 &
          1993)   (1/94) (CPO) ① CPO999 173-2
6 Symphonies, G509-514 (Op. 35) (pub 1782)
1. D; 2. E flat; 3. A; 4. F; 5. E flat; 6. B flat.
1-3. Neuss German Chbr Acad, J. Goritzki
          Symphonies, G493-8.
          (1/94) (CPO) ① CPO999 175-2
3, 4. Ens 415, C. Banchini Concert
          (4/89) (HARM) ① HMC90 1291
4. AAM, C. Hogwood (r1992) Concert
          (2/95) (L'OI) ① 436 993-2OH
4-6. Neuss German Chbr Acad, J. Goritzki (r1991-2)
          Symphonies, G515-8.
          (1/94) (CPO) ① CPO999 176-2
6. ECCO, J. Faerber Concert
          (10/86) (HYPE) ① CDA66156
4 Symphonies, G515-518 (Op. 37) (pub 1787)
1. C; 2. D; 3. D minor; 4. A.
1. Neuss German Chbr Acad, J. Goritzki (r1991-2)
          Symphonies, G509-14.
          (1/94) (CPO) ① CPO999 176-2
1, 3, 4. New Berlin CO, M. Erxleben (vn/dir) (r1992)
          (5/93) (CAPR) ① 10 457
3, 4. Neuss German Chbr Acad, J. Goritzki (r1993)
          Symphony, G519.   (8/94) (CPO) ① CPO999 177-2
Symphony in C—guitar, 2 violins & orchestra, G523 (c1798) (arr of Quintet, G268)
Neuss German Chbr Acad, J. Goritzki (r1992-3)
Concert   (12/94) (CPO) ① CPO999 084-2
Symphony in C minor, G519 (Op. 41) (1788)
New Berlin CO, M. Erxleben (vn/dir) (r1992) Concert
          (5/93) (CAPR) ① 10 458
Tafelmusik, J. Lamon (r1992) Concert
          (7/93) (SONY) ① SK53121
Neuss German Chbr Acad, J. Goritzki (r1993)
          Symphonies, G515-8.
          (8/94) (CPO) ① CPO999 177-2
AAM, C. Hogwood (r1992) Concert
          (2/95) (L'OI) ① 436 993-2OH
Symphony in D, G490 (pub ?c1775)
Ens 415, C. Banchini Concert
          (4/89) (HARM) ① HMC90 1291
Neuss German Chbr Acad, J. Goritzki (r1992-3)
Concert   (12/94) (CPO) ① CPO999 084-2
Symphony in D, G500 (1767)
Neuss German Chbr Acad, J. Goritzki (r1993)
Concert   (1/95) (CPO) ① CPO999 178-2
Symphony in D, G520 (Op. 42) (1789)
New Berlin CO, M. Erxleben (vn/dir) (r1992)
          (5/93) (CAPR) ① 10 458
Neuss German Chbr Acad, J. Goritzki (r1993)
Concert   (1/95) (CPO) ① CPO999 178-2
Symphony in D, G521 (Op. 43) (1790)
New Berlin CO, M. Erxleben (vn/dir) (r1992)
          (5/93) (CAPR) ① 10 458
Tafelmusik, J. Lamon (r1992) Concert
          (7/93) (SONY) ① SK53121
Symphony in D minor, G522 (Op. 45) (1792)
New Berlin CO, M. Erxleben (vn/dir) (r1992)
          (5/93) (CAPR) ① 10 458
Concert   (1/95) (CPO) ① CPO999 178-2

SECTION II: CHAMBER

Duet for Two Violins in E flat, '(La) bona notte', G62
M. Seiler, S. Walch (r1993) Concert
          (4/94) (CAPR) ① 10 453

6 Duets—2 harpsichords, G76 (anon arrs of String Quartets, G195-200)
EXCERPTS: 1. B flat; 2. G minor; 3. E flat; 4. A; 5. F;
          6. F minor.
W. Christie, C. Rousset String Quintets, G340-5.
          (4/87) (HARM) ① HMC90 1233
6 Fugues—2 cellos/bassoons, G73
EXCERPTS: 1. C; 2. F; 3. B flat; 4. E flat; 5. A; 6. E.
2, 3, 5. A. Bylsma, K. Slowik (r1992) Concert
          (3/94) (SONY) ① SK53362
Guitar Quintets—guitar, 2 violins, viola and cello, G445-453 (1798) (arr cpsr from other qnts)
EXCERPTS: 1. D minor; 2. E; 3. B flat; 4. D; 4c.
          Grave assai (from G341); 4d. Fandango (from G341);
          5. D; 6. G; 7. E minor; 8. lost; 9. C, 'La ritrata di
          Madrid'.
P. Romero, ASMF Chbr Ens (r1978-80)
          (4/94) (PHIL) ① [2] 438 769-2PM2
1-3. Z. Tokos, Danubius Qt
          (10/92) (NAXO) ① 8 550551
4. N. Kraft, B. Silver (arr cpsr) Concert
          (11/91) (CHAN) ① CHAN8937
4. J. Bream, G. Malcolm (r1967; ed Bream) Concert
          (8/93) (RCA) ① [28] 09026 61583-2(4)
4a J. Bream, G. Malcolm (r1967; ed Bream) Concert
          (7/94) (RCA) ① 09026 61599-2
4d J. Bream (1983; arr Bream) Concert
          (8/93) (RCA) ① [28] 09026 61583-2(6)
4d J. Bream (1983; arr Bream) Concert
          (8/93) (RCA) ① 09026 61610-2
4-6. R. Savino, Artaria Qt
          (11/90) (HARM) ① HMU90 7026
4-6. Z. Tokos, Danubius Qt
          (10/92) (NAXO) ① 8 550552
4, 7, 9. N. Yepes, Melos Qt
          (6/90) (DG) ① 429 512-2GR
7. J. Bream, Cremona Qt (r1967) Concert
          (8/93) (RCA) ① [28] 09026 61583-2(4)
7. J. Bream, Cremona Qt (r1967) Concert
          (7/94) (RCA) ① 09026 61599-2
7, 9. R. Savino, Artaria Qt (1991) Giuliani: Gran
          Quintetto, Op. 65. (2/94) (HARM) ① HMU90 7069
6 Notturni—wind and strings, G467-72 (1787) (5 sextets, 1 octet)
EXCERPTS: 1. Sextet (Nocturne) in E flat; 2. Sextet
          (lost); 3. Sextet (lost); 4. Octet (Nocturne) in G; 5.
          Sextet (Nocturne) in E flat; 6. Sextet (Nocturne) in B
          flat.
4. Tafelmusik, J. Lamon (1992) Concert
          (7/93) (SONY) ① SK53121
6 Piano Quintets—piano, 2 violins, viola and cello, G407-412 (Op. 56) (1797)
EXCERPTS: 1. E minor; 2. F; 3. C; 4. E flat; 5. D; 6.
          A minor.
1, 2, 5. P. Cohen, Mosaïques Qt (1993)
          (4/94) (ASTR) ① E8518
6 Piano Quintets—piano, 2 violins, viola and cello, G413-418 (Op. 57) (1799)
EXCERPTS: 1. A; 2. B flat; 3. C; 4. D minor; 5.
          E; 6. C.
2, 3, 6. P. Cohen, Mosaïques Qt
          (12/92) (ASTR) ① E8721
6 Quartets—2 violins, viola and cello, G242-247 (Op. 58) (pub 1789)
1. C; 2. E flat; 3. B flat; 4. B minor; 5. D;
          6. E flat.
2. Talich Qt (r1985) Concert
          (11/95) (CALL) ① CAL6698
6 Quintets—oboe/flute and strings, G431-436 (Op. 55) (pub 1774)
EXCERPTS: 1. G; 2. F; 3. D; 4. A; 5. E flat; 6. D
          minor.
L. Lencses, Parisii Qt (1992)
          (4/94) (CAPR) ① 10 454
6 Sextets, 'Divertimentos'—flute, 2 violins, viola and 2 cellos, G461-466 (Op. 16) (1773)
EXCERPTS: 1. A; 2. A; 3. A; 4. E flat; 5. A; 6. C.
1, 4-6. H. Haupt, M-K. Lee, S. Walch, D. Poppen, L.
          Quandt, G. Teutsch, E. Laine (r1992)
          (3/94) (CAPR) ① 10 456
Sonata for Cello and Continuo No. 2 in C minor, G2
A. Bylsma, B. van Asperen (r1992) Concert
          (3/94) (SONY) ① SK53362
Sonata for Cello and Continuo No. 2 in C minor, G2b (second version)
S. Isserlis, M. Cole Concert
          (7/92) (VIRG) ① VC7 59015-2
Sonata for Cello and Continuo No. 5 in G, G5
S. Isserlis, M. Cole Concert
          (7/92) (VIRG) ① VC7 59015-2

Sonata for Cello and Continuo No. 6 in C, G6
S. Isserlis, M. Cole *Concert*
(7/92) (VIRG) ① **VC7 59015-2**
Sonata for Cello and Continuo No. 8 in B flat, G8
A. Bylsma, B. van Asperen (r1992) *Concert*
(3/94) (SONY) ① **SK53362**
Sonata for Cello and Continuo No. 9 in F, G9
A. Bylsma, B. van Asperen (r1992) *Concert*
(3/94) (SONY) ① **SK53362**
Sonata for Cello and Continuo No. 9 in G, G15
A. Bylsma, B. van Asperen (r1992) *Concert*
(3/94) (SONY) ① **SK53362**
Sonata for Cello and Continuo No. 10 in E flat, G10
A. Bylsma, B. van Asperen (r1992) *Concert*
(3/94) (SONY) ① **SK53362**
Sonata in D—violin and piano (unidentified)
J. Heifetz, G. Piatigorsky (r1964) *Concert*
(11/94) (RCA) ① [65] **09026 61778-2(28)**
String Quartet in A—2 violins, viola and cello, G213 (Op. 39) (1787)
Petersen Qt (r1991) *Concert*
(5/93) (CAPR) ① **10 451**
Revolutionary Drawing Room (r1993) *String Quartets, G214-5.* (8/95) (CPO) ① **CPO999 205-2**
6 String Quartets, G165-170 (Op. 8) (1769)
EXCERPTS: 1. D; 2. C minor; 3. E flat; 4. G minor; 5. F; 6 A.
3. Nuovo Quartetto *Concert*
(11/86) (DENO) ① **CO-1029**
6 String Quartets, G177-182 (Op. 15) (1772)
EXCERPTS: 1. D; 2. F; 3. E; 4. F; 5. E flat; 6. C minor.
1. Petersen Qt (r1991) *Concert*
(5/93) (CAPR) ① **10 451**
6 String Quartets, G189-194 (Op. 24) (1776-78)
EXCERPTS: 1. D; 2. A; 3. E flat; 4. C; 5. C minor; 6. G minor.
6. Petersen Qt (r1991) *Concert*
(5/93) (CAPR) ① **10 451**
6 String Quartets—2 violins, viola and cello, G201-206 (Op. 32) (1780)
EXCERPTS: 1. E flat; 2. E minor; 3. D; 4. C; 5. G minor; 6. A.
Esterházy Qt (r1976)
(10/95) (TELD) ① [2] **4509-95988-2**
6 String Quartets—2 violins, viola and cello, G207-12 (Op. 33) (1781)
EXCERPTS: 1. E; 2. C; 3. G; 4. B flat; 5. E minor; 6. E flat.
Revolutionary Drawing Room (r1994)
(8/95) (CPO) ① **CPO999 206-2**
2 String Quartets—2 violins, viola and cello, G214-5 (Op. 41) (1788)
EXCERPTS: 1. C minor; 2. C.
Revolutionary Drawing Room (r1993) *String Quartet, G213.* (8/95) (CPO) ① **CPO999 205-2**
6 String Quartets—2 violins, viola and cello, G220-225 (Op. 44) (1792)
EXCERPTS: 1. B flat; 2. E minor; 3. F; 4. G, 'La Tiranna'; 5. E; 6. E flat.
4. Nuovo Quartetto *Concert*
(11/86) (DENO) ① **CO-1029**
4. Ens 415 *String Quintets, G337-9.*
(6/91) (HARM) ① **HMC90 1334**
4. M. Seiler, S. Walch, D. Poppen, R. Lester (r1993) *Concert* (4/94) (CAPR) ① **10 453**
2 String Quartets, G248-249 (Op. 64) (1804)
EXCERPTS: 1. F; 2. D (incomplete—Allegro only).
1. Petersen Qt (r1991) *Concert*
(5/93) (CAPR) ① **10 451**
6 String Quintets, G271-276 (Op. 11) (pub 1771)
EXCERPTS: 1. B flat; 2. A; 3. C; 4. F minor; 5. E; 5a. Minuet; 6. D, 'L'uccelliera'.
4-6. Smithsonian Chbr Plyrs
(4/92) (DHM) ① **RD77159**
5. Berlin Philh Ens *Concert*
(9/88) (DENO) ① **CO-2199**
5a I Musici *Concert* (12/83) (PHIL) ① **410 606-2PH**
5a Cincinnati Pops, E. Kunzel (arr Stokowski) *Concert* (4/88) (TELA) ① **CD80129**
5a Guildhall Str Ens, R. Salter (vn/dir) (r1992) *Concert* (2/94) (RCA) ① **09026 61275-2**
5a NBC SO, A. Toscanini (bp1943) *Concert*
(5/94) (ATS) ① [2] **ATCD100**
5a M. Maisky, D. Hovora (r1993: arr vc/pf: Maisky) *Concert* (9/94) (DG) ① **439 863-2GH**

6 String Quintets—two violins, viola, two cellos, G277-82 (Op. 13) (1772)
EXCERPTS: 1. E flat; 2. C; 3. F; 4. D minor; 5. A; 6. E.
4. Berlin Philh Ens *Concert*
(9/88) (DENO) ① **CO-2199**
4. Petersen Qt, U. Knörzer, G. Schiefen (r1992) *Concert* (4/94) (CAPR) ① **10 452**
6 String Quintets—two violins, viola and two cellos, G319-324 (Op 30) (1780)
EXCERPTS: 1. B flat; 2. A minor; 3; C; 4. E flat; 5. E minor; 6. C, 'La musica nottuma delle strade di Madrid'.
6. M. Seiler, S. Walch, D. Poppen, R. Lester, H. Penny (r1993) *Concert* (4/94) (CAPR) ① **10 453**
6 String Quintets—2 violins, viola and 2 cellos, G325-330 (Op. 31) (1780)
EXCERPTS: 1. E flat; 2. G; 3. B flat; 4. C minor; 5. A; 6. F.
2. Petersen Qt, U. Knörzer, G. Schiefen (r1992) *Concert* (4/94) (CAPR) ① **10 452**
4. Ens 415 *Stabat Mater (1781).*
(9/92) (HARM) ① **HMC90 1378**
6 String Quintets—2 violins, viola and 2 cellos, G331-336 (Op. 36) (pub 1786)
EXCERPTS: 1. E flat; 2. D; 3. G; 4. A minor; 5. G minor; 6. F.
6. M. Seiler, S. Walch, D. Poppen, R. Lester, H. Penny (r1993) *Concert* (4/94) (CAPR) ① **10 453**
3 String Quartets—two violins, viola, cello and double-bass, G337-339 (Op. 39) (1787)
EXCERPTS: 1. B flat; 2. F; 3. D.
Ens 415 *String Quartets, G220-5.*
(6/91) (HARM) ① **HMC90 1334**
3. Berlin Philh Ens *Concert*
(9/88) (DENO) ① **CO-2199**
6 String Quintets—two violins, viola and two cellos, G340-345 (Op. 40) (1788)
EXCERPTS: 1. A; 2. D, 'Fandango'; 2b. Fandango; 3. D; 4. C; 5. E minor; 6. B flat.
2b W. Christie, C. Rousset (arr anon: 2 hpds) *Duets, G76.* (4/87) (HARM) ① **HMC90 1233**
2 String Quintets—two violins, viola, two cellos, G376-377 (Op. 51) (1795)
EXCERPTS: 1. E flat; 2. C minor.
2. Berlin Philh Ens *Concert*
(9/88) (DENO) ① **CO-2199**
6 String Quintets—two violins, two viola and cello, G391-396 (Op. 60) (pub 1801)
EXCERPTS: 1. C; 2. B flat; 3. A; 4. E flat; 5. G; 6. F.
1, 5. Ens 415 (r1992) *String Quintets, G397-402.*
(8/93) (HARM) ① **HMC90 1402**
3. Petersen Qt, U. Knörzer, G. Schiefen (r1992) *Concert* (4/94) (CAPR) ① **10 452**
6 String Quintets—2 violins, 2 violas and cello, G397-402 (Op. 62) (pub 1802)
EXCERPTS: 1. C; 2. E flat; 3. F; 4. B flat; 5. D; 6. E.
1. Ens 415 (r1992) *String Quintets, G391-6.*
(8/93) (HARM) ① **HMC90 1402**
5. Petersen Qt, U. Knörzer, G. Schiefen (r1992) *Concert* (4/94) (CAPR) ① **10 452**
6 String Sextets—2vns, 2vas, 2 vcs, G454-59 (Op. 23) (1776)
EXCERPTS: 1. E flat; 2. B flat; 3. E; 4. F minor; 5. D; 6. F.
1, 2, 5. Ens 415 (r1993)
(6/94) (HARM) ① **HMC90 1478**
1, 3, 4, 6. M. Seiler, I. Juda, D. Poppen, W. Dickel, R. Lester, H. Penny *Concert* (4/94) (CAPR) ① **10 450**
6 String Trios—violin, viola & cello, G107-112 (Op. 47) (1793)
EXCERPTS: 1. A; 2. G; 3. B flat; 4. E flat; 5. D; 6. F.
Europa Galante Trio (5/92) (O111) ① **OPS41-9105**

SECTION IV: VOCAL AND CHORAL
---

15 Concert Arias—soprano or soprano/tenor and orchestra, G544-558 (Wds. Metastasio, except Nos 7 & 13 where anon)
1. Ah non lasciarmi, no; 2. Deh respirar lasciatemi; 3. Deh respirar lasciatemi; 4. Caro, son tua cosi; 5. Ah no son io che pario; 6. Care luci che regnate; 7. Infelice in van mi lagno; 8. Numi, se giusti, siete; 9. Caro Padre, a me non dei; 10. Ah che nel dirti addio; 11. Per qual paterno amplesso; 12. Tu di saper procura; 13. Mi dona, mi rende quell'alma pietosa; 14. M. Almajano, Limoges Baroque Ens, C. Coin (r1993) *Concert* (4/94) (ASTR) ① **E8517**
Stabat Mater—soprano and strings/3vv and strings, G532 (1781, 1800)
M. Matsumoto, Pforzheim SW German CO, V. Czamecki (1781 vers)
(10/91) (AMAT) ① **SRR8903/1**
A. Mellon, Ens 415 (1781 vers) *String Quintets, G325-30.* (9/92) (HARM) ① **HMC90 1378**

BOCHSA, (Robert) Nicolas Charles *(1789–1856) France*

SECTION II: CHAMBER

Nocturne in F—oboe/clarinet and harp, Op. 50/2
H. Schellenberger, M-A. Süss *Concert*
(12/91) (DENO) ① **CO-76611**

SECTION III: INSTRUMENTAL

Etude—harp (unidentified)
L. Laskine (r1975) *Concert*
(12/93) (ERAT) ① **4509-92131-2**

BOCK, Jerry (b 1928) USA

SECTION V: STAGE WORKS

Fiddler on the Roof—musical show (1964—New York) (Lyrics S. Harnick; based on Sholem Aleichem's stories)
EXCERPTS: 1. Tradition; 2. Matchmaker, Matchmaker; 3. If I Were A Rich Man; 4. Sabbath Prayer; 5. To Life; 6. Miracle of Miracles; 7. Tevye's Dream; 8. Sunrise, Sunset; 9. Bottle Dance; 10. Now I Have Everything; 11. Do You Love Me?; 12. Far From the Home I Love; 13. Anatevka. ADDITIONAL ITEMS: 14. Wedding Dance; 15. The Rumor.
Medley Tetra (1989-91; arr Storry: gtr qt) *Concert*
(11/93) (CONI) ① **CDCF903**

BOËLLMANN, Léon *(1862–1897) France*

SECTION II: CHAMBER

Piano Quartet in F minor, Op. 10 (c1890)
B. Bánfalvi, J. Fejérvári, K. Botvay, I. Prunyi (r1991) *Piano Trio, Op. 19.* (11/93) (MARC) ① **8 223524**
Piano Trio in G, Op. 19 (c1895)
B. Bánfalvi, K. Botvay, I. Prunyi (r1991) *Piano Quartet, Op. 10.* (11/93) (MARC) ① **8 223524**

SECTION III: INSTRUMENTAL

Deuxième Suite—organ, Op. 27 (1896)
1. Prélude pastoral; 2. Allegretto con moto; 3. Andantino; 4. Final-Marche.
P. Caire *Concert* (7/89) (REM) ① **REM311053**
D.M. Patrick *Concert* (5/93) (PRIO) ① **PRCD371**
12 Pièces—organ, Op. 16 (c1890)
1. Prélude; 2. Fugue; 3. Marche religieuse; 4. Intermezzo; 5. Canon; 6 Chant; 7. Élégie; 8. Verset de procession I sur Adoro te; 9. Verset de procession II sur Adoro te; 10. Canzona dans la tonalité grégorienne; 11. Adagietti; 12. Paraphrase sur Laudate Dominum.
P. Caire *Concert* (7/89) (REM) ① **REM311053**
Suite gothique—organ, Op. 25 (1895)
1. Introduction-Choral; 2. Menuet gothique; 3. Prière à Notre-Dame; 4. Toccata.
C. Herrick *Concert* (3/89) (MERI) ① **CDE84148**
P. Caire *Concert* (7/89) (REM) ① **REM311053**
P. Hurford *Concert* (8/91) (DECC) ① **430 710-2DM**
S. Lindley *Concert* (3/93) (NAXO) ① **8 550581**
P. Hurford (r1987) *Concert*
(10/95) (DECC) ① **444 567-2DM**
4. John Scott *Concert* (12/87) (CIRR) ① **CICD1007**

BOËLY, Alexandre (Pierre François) *(1785–1858) France*

SECTION II: CHAMBER

String Quartet No. 1, Op. 27 (1857)
E. Popa, Paris String Trio *Concert*
(8/87) (CHNT) ① **LDC278 821**
String Quartet No. 3, Op. 29 (1857)
E. Popa, Paris String Trio *Concert*
(8/87) (CHNT) ① **LDC278 821**
String Trio No. 1, Op. 5/1 (1808)
E. Popa, Paris String Trio *Concert*
(8/87) (CHNT) ① **LDC278 821**

SECTION III: INSTRUMENTAL

Offertoire sur les grandes jeux—organ (pub. 1842)
J. van Oortmerssen *Concert*
(11/87) (BIS) ① **BIS-CD316**

BOESMANS, Philippe (b 1936) Belgium

SECTION I: ORCHESTRAL

Concerto for Piano and Orchestra (1978)
M. Mercenier, Liège PO, P. Bartholomée (pp1978)
Concert   (10/89) (RICE) ① **RIC014024**
Concerto for Violin and Orchestra (1979)
R. Pieta, Liège PO, P. Bartholomée *Concert*
(10/89) (RICE) ① **RIC014024**
Conversions—orchestra (1980)
Liège PO, P. Bartholomée *Concert*
(10/89) (RICE) ① **RIC014024**
Extase—piano, tuba and small ensemble (1985)
G. Foccroulle, M. Massot, Synonymes Ens, P. Davin
Attitudes.   (10/90) (RICE) ① **RIC002040**

SECTION IV: VOCAL AND CHORAL

Attitudes—spectacle musical (1977) (concert version; text M. Blondel)
E. Ross, Musique Nouvelle Ens, G-E. Octors *Extase.*
(10/90) (RICE) ① **RIC002040**

BOËSSET, Antoine (de) (1586–1643) France

SECTION IV: VOCAL AND CHORAL

Divine Amaryllis—air de cour (pub 1636)
R. Covey-Crump, P. O'Dette *Concert*
(4/88) (HYPE) ① **CDA66228**
Me veux-tu voir mourir—song
G. Souzay, J. Bonneau (r1953) *Concert*
(7/91) (DECC) ① **425 975-2DM**

BÖHM, Carl (1844–1920) Germany

SECTION II: CHAMBER

6 Pieces—violin and piano, Op. 314
3. Gavotte.
3. M. Elman, P. Kahn (r1906) *Concert*
(12/91) (APR) ① [2] **APR7015**

SECTION IV: VOCAL AND CHORAL

143 Lieder, Op. 326
27. Stille wie die Nacht (1913: wds cpsr).
27. J. McCormack, F. Kreisler, L. Schwab (Eng: r1915) *Concert*   (9/89) (PEAR) ① **GEMMCD9315**
27. E. Schumann-Heink, orch (r1921) *Concert*
(2/91) (NIMB) ① **NI7811**
27. E. Eames, anon (r1905) *Concert*
(11/93) (ROMO) ① [2] **81001-2**
27. E. Eames, orch (r1906) *Concert*
(11/93) (ROMO) ① [2] **81001-2**

BÖHM, Georg (1661–1733) Germany

SECTION III: INSTRUMENTAL

Capriccio in D—keyboard
G. Leonhardt *Concert*   (9/93) (SONY) ① **SK53114**
10 Chorale Partite and Variations—keyboard, WK ii
1. Ach wie nichtig, ach wie flüchtig, WK ii 74 (hpd); 2. Auf meinen lieben Gott, WK ii 80; 3. Aus tiefer Not schrei ich zu dir, WK ii 87; 4. Christe der du bist Tag und Licht, WK ii 91; 5. Freu dich sehr, o meine Seele, WK ii 115 (?hpd); 6. Gelobet seist du, Jesu Christ, WK ii 115 (?hpd); 7. Herr Jesu Christ, dich zu uns wend, WK ii 121; 8. Jesu du bist allzu schöne, WK i 69 ((?hpd); 9. Vater unser im Himmelreich, WK ii 132; 10. Wer nur den lieben Gott lässt walten, WK ii 143 (?hpd).
R. Alessandrini (r1994) *Keyboard Suites.*
(8/95) (ASTR) ① **E8526**
1, 10. G. Leonhardt *Concert*
(9/93) (SONY) ① **SK53114**
Chorales—organ, WK ii
1. Allein Gott in der Höh sei Ehr, Wk ii 78; 2. Christ lag in Todesbanden—fantasia, Wk ii 98; 3. Christ lag in Todesbanden, Wk ii 102; 4. Christum wir sollen loben schon, Wk ii 104; 5. Gelobet seist du, Jesu Christ, WK ii 119; 6. Nun bitten wir den heiligen Geist, WK ii 130; 7. Vater unser im Himmelreich, Wk ii 138; 8. Vom Himmel hoch, WK ii 141.
7. G. Leonhardt *Concert*
(10/94) (SONY) ① **SK53371**
Prelude, Fugue and Postlude in G minor—keyboard
G. Leonhardt *Concert*   (9/93) (SONY) ① **SK53114**

---

11 Suites—keyboard
1. C minor; 2. D; 3. D minor; 4. D minor; 5. E flat (doubtful); 6. E flat; 7. F; 8. F minor; 9. F minor; 10. G; 11. A minor.
1, 2, 6, 8. G. Leonhardt *Concert*
(9/93) (SONY) ① **SK53114**
1, 3, 4, 5, 11. R. Alessandrini (r1994) *Chorale Partite and Variations.*   (8/95) (ASTR) ① **E8526**
2 (Ouverture a 5) Parley of Instr, R. Goodman, P. Holman (reconstructed Holman) *Concert*
(9/91) (HYPE) ① **CDA66074**

BOÏELDIEU, (François) Adrien (1775–1834) France

SECTION I: ORCHESTRAL

Concerto for Harp and Orchestra in C (1801)
M. Robles, ASMF, I. Brown *Concert*
(12/90) (DECC) ① **425 723-2DM**
M. Nordmann, F. Liszt CO, J-P. Rampal (r1993)
Concert   (10/95) (SONY) ① **SK58919**

SECTION V: STAGE WORKS

Le Calife de Bagdad, '(The) Caliph of Baghdad'—opéra-comique (1800—Paris) (Lib. Saint-Just)
Cpte L. Dale, L. Mayo, J. Michelini, C. Cheriez, H. Rhys-Evans, Camerata de Provence Chor, Camerata de Provence Orch, A. de Almeida (r1992)
(9/94) (SONP) ① **SPT93007**
La Dame blanche—opéra-comique: 3 acts (1825—Paris) (Lib. Scribe)
EXCERPTS: 1. Overture; 2. Viens, gentille dane.
Cpte A. Legros, F. Louvay, M. Sénéchal, A. Doniat, J. Berbié, G. Bacquier, P. Héral, Paris Sym Chor, Paris SO, P. Stoll   (11/90) (ACCO) ① **22086-2**
Ah, quel plaisir E. Clément, anon (r1905) *Concert*
(8/95) (ROMO) ① **82002-2**
Overture Detroit SO, P. Paray (r1960) *Concert*
(11/93) (MERC) ① **434 332-2MM**
Rêverie de Georges Brown D. Devriès, orch, G. Cloëz (r1928) *Concert*   (9/94) (NIMB) ① **NI7856**
Viens, gentille dame H. Roswaenge, Berlin St Op Orch, F. Weissmann (Ger: r1928) *Concert*
(5/90) (PEAR) ① **GEMMCD9394**
Viens, gentille Dame H. Roswaenge, orch (r1928: Ger) *Concert*   (2/92) (PREI) ① [2] **89201**
La Fête du village voisin—opéra-comique: 3 acts (1816—Paris) (Lib. C Serwin)
EXCERPTS: ACT 1: 1. Profitez de la vie (Boléro).
1. S. Jo, ECO, R. Bonynge (r1993) *Concert*
(9/94) (DECC) ① **440 679-2DH**
Les Voitures Versées—opéra-comique: 1 act (1808—St Petersburg) (Lib. E. Dupaty)
Cpte C. Collart, L. Dachary, D. Boursin, H. Hennetier, C. Petit, A. Doniat, B. Demigny, A. Mallabrera, J. Peyron, French Rad Lyric Orch, J. Brebion (bp1971)
(3/92) (MUSD) ① **20152-2**

BOISDEFFRE, René de (1834–1906) France

SECTION II: CHAMBER

Chanson Neapolitan—clarinet and piano
1, 18. M. Gomez, C. Draper, H.P. Draper, Renard Cl Qt, R. Kell, F. Thurston, R. Clarke, Griller Qt, A. Umbach, C. Esberger, R. Quaranta, A. Giammatteo, F.J. Brissett, B. Goodman, G. Hamelin, A. Périer, H. Lefèbvre, anon, wind band, SC, G. Raybould, G. Moore, Budapest Qt, orch, P. Coppola, Garde Republicaine Band (rc1904) *Concert*
(2/94) (CLRI) ① **CC0005**

BOISMORTIER, Joseph Bodin de (1689–1755) France

SECTION II: CHAMBER

Diverses pièces—viola da gamba and continuo, Op. 31 (pub 1730)
1. Prélude; 2. Gavotte; 3. Le suppliant; 4. Allemande; 5. L'adulateur; 6. Sarabande; 7. Menuet; 8. Rigaudon.
B. Re, R. Kohnen *Concert*
(9/88) (PIER) ① **PV788012**
6 Sonatas en trio—3 flutes, Op. 7 (1725)
1. D minor; 3. C (A); 6. G minor (F minor).
1. F. Brüggen, K. Boeke, W. van Hauwe (r1970)
Concert   (11/95) (TELD) ① **4509-97469-2**
5 Sonatas for Cello/Viol/Bassoon and Continuo, Op. 26 (pub 1729)
4. E minor; 6. D.
4. K. Walker, D. Nixon, C. Stein *Sonatas, Op.50.*
(5/88) (GALL) ① **CD-367**

---

6 Sonatas for Keyboard and Flute, Op. 91 (pub 1741-42)
1. D; 2. G minor; 6. C minor.
6. M. André, H. Bilgram (tpt/org) *Concert*
(1/93) (EMI) ① **CDC7 54330-2**
6 Sonatas for Two Cellos/Bassoons/Viols, Op. 50 (pub 1734) (No.6 with continuo)
EXCERPTS: 1. E minor; 2. G; 3. D; 4. D minor; 5. C minor.
1, 2, 4, 5. K. Walker, D. Nixon, C. Stein *Sonatas, Op.26.*   (5/88) (GALL) ① **CD-367**
6 Sonates à quatre parties différentes—3 flutes/violins and continuo, Op. 34 (pub 1731)
1. B minor (G minor); 2. B flat (G); 3. E minor; 4. D; F minor (D minor); 6. C minor (A minor).
1. Florilegium Ens, S. Pauley (r1994) *Concert*
(12/95) (CHNN) ① **CCS7595**

BOITO, Arrigo (1842–1918) Italy

SECTION V: STAGE WORKS

Mefistofele—opera: prologue & 4 acts (1868—Milan) (Lib. cpsr)
EXCERPTS: PROLOGUE: 1. Prelude; 2. Ave Signor degli angeli; 3. Ave Signor! Perdona se il mio gergo; 4a. T'è noto Faust?; 4b. Siam nimbi; 4c. Salve Regina!. ACT 1: 5. Perchè di là?; 6. Al soave raggiar; 7. Sediam sovra quel sasso; 8. Dai campi, dai prati; 9a. Olà! chi urla?; 9b. Che baccano!; 10a. Sono lo spirito che nega; 10b. Strano figlio del Caos; 11a. Se tu mi doni; 11b. Fin da stanotte. ACT 2: 12. Cavaliero illustre e saggio; 13a. Dimmi se credi, Enrico; 13b. Colma il tuo cor; 14. Dio clemente (Walpurgis Night); 15a. Su, cammina; 15b. Folletto; 15c. Ascoltai; 16a. Popoli! E scettro e clamide; 16b. Ecco il mondo; 16c. Ah! sul riddiamo. ACT 3: 17. L'altra notte; 18. Dio di pietà!; 19. Lontano, lontano; 20. Sorge il dì!; 21. Spunta l'aurora pallida. ACT 4: 22. La notte immobile; 23. Ecco la notte del classico Sabba; 24. Danza; 25. Notte cupa, truce; 26. Forma ideal, purissima; 27. O incantesimo!. EPILOGUE: 28. Cammina, cammina; 29a. Ogni mortal; 29b. Giunto sul passo estremo; 30. Ave Signor.
Cpte N. Ghiaurov, L. Pavarotti, M. Freni, M. Caballé, N. Condò, P. de Palma, D. Jones, R. Leggate, Trinity Boys' Ch, National PO, O. de Fabritiis
(12/85) (DECC) ① [3] **410 175-2DH3**
Cpte S. Ramey, P. Domingo, E. Marton, T. Takács, S. Tedesco, E. Farkas, A. Pataki, Hungaroton Op Chor, Nyíregyházi Boys' Ch, Hungarian St Orch, G. Patané   (4/91) (SONY) ① [2] **S2K44983**
Cpte C. Siepi, M. del Monaco, R. Tebaldi, F. Cavalli, L. Danieli, P. de Palma, Santa Cecilia Academy Chor, Santa Cecilia Academy Orch, T. Serafin (r1958)   (4/94) (DECC) ① [2] **440 054-2DMO2**
1-4c J. Cheek, Morehouse-Spelman Chor, Callanwolde Young Sngrs, Atlanta Sym Chor, Atlanta SO, Robert Shaw Chorale
(9/85) (TELA) ① [2] **CD80109**
1-4c N. Moscona, Columbus Boychoir, R. Shaw Chorale, NBC SO, A. Toscanini (bp1954) *Concert*
(6/91) (RCA) ① **GD60276**
3. E. Pinza, orch (r1924) *Concert*
(2/89) (PEAR) ① **GEMMCD9306**
3. F. Chaliapin, orch, R. Bourdon (r1927) *Concert*
(12/89) (PEAR) ① **GEMMCD9314**
3. A. Didur, anon (r1906) *Concert*
(7/92) (PEAR) ① [3] **GEMMCD9925(1)**
3. F. Chaliapin, orch, V. Bellezza (pp1926) *Concert*
(7/92) (PEAR) ① [3] **GEMMCD9925(2)**
3. J. Van Dam, Loire PO, M. Soustrot (r1992)
Concert   (8/93) (FORL) ① **UCD16681**
3. A. Didur, anon (r1906) *Concert*
(1/94) (CLUB) ① **CL99-089**
3. F. Chaliapin, La Scala Orch, C. Sabajno (r1912)
Concert   (4/94) (EMI) ① [3] **CHS7 64860-2(2)**
3, 10a, 10b, 16b T. Pasero, orch, L. Molajoli (r1927)
Concert   (6/90) (PREI) ① **89010**
3, 10, 16b N. de Angelis, orch, L. Molajoli (r1927)
Concert   (7/92) (PREI) ① **89042**
8. L. Pavarotti, National PO, O. de Fabritiis *Concert*
(7/90) (DECC) ① **425 681-2DM2**
8. E. Caruso, S. Cottone (r1902) *Concert*
(7/90) (CLUB) ① **CL99-060**
8. F. Marconi, S. Cottone (r1903) *Concert*
(10/90) (SYMP) ① **SYMCD1069**
8. F. Marconi, orch (r1908) *Concert*
(10/90) (SYMP) ① **SYMCD1069**
8. G. Malipiero, orch, U. Berrettoni (r1940) *Concert*
(4/92) (EMI) ① [7] **CHS7 69741-2(7)**
8. B. Gigli, orch (r1921) *Concert*
(6/93) (MMOI) ① **CDMOIR417**
8. G. Zenatello, anon (r1906) *Concert*
(5/94) (SYMP) ① **SYMCD1168**

8. G. Zenatello, anon (r1906) *Concert*
(5/94) (PEAR) ① [4] **GEMMCDS9073(1)**
8. P. Domingo, LSO, J. Rudel (r1973) *Concert*
(6/94) (EMI) ① **CDC5 55017-2**
8. L. Escalais, anon (r1906: Fr) *Concert*
(12/94) (SYMP) ① **SYMCD1128**
8, 29b B. Gigli, orch, R. Bourdon (r1927) *Concert*
(9/88) (PEAR) ① **GEMMCD9316**
8, 29b E. Caruso, S. Cottone (r1902) *Concert*
(5/89) (EMI) ① **CDH7 61046-2**
8, 29b B. Gigli, orch (r1921) *Concert*
(5/90) (NIMB) ① **NI7807**
8(2 vers), 29b E. Caruso, S. Cottone (r1902) *Concert*
(12/90) (PEAR) ① [3] **EVC17(1)**
8(2 vers), 29b E. Caruso, S. Cottone (r1902) *Concert*
(7/91) (RCA) ① [12] **GD60495(1)**
8, 29b G. Zenatello, orch (r1906) *Concert*
(5/94) (PEAR) ① [4] **GEMMCDS9073(1)**
8, 29b A. Giorgini, orch (r c1913) *Concert*
(4/95) (RECO) ① **TRC3**
10. E. Pinza, orch, C. Sabajno (r1923) *Concert*
(2/89) (PEAR) ① **GEMMCD9306**
10a A. Didur, anon (r1901) *Concert*
(6/93) (PEAR) ① [3] **GEMMCDS9997/9(2)**
10a, 10b A. Didur, S. Cottone (r1903) *Concert*
(6/93) (PEAR) ① [3] **GEMMCDS9997/9(2)**
10a, 10b A. Didur, orch (r1906) *Concert*
(1/94) (CLUB) ① **CL99-089**
10a, 10b, 16b T. Pasero, SO, D. Marzollo (r1944)
Concert (4/95) (PREI) ① **89074**
10a, 16b A. Didur, anon (r1900) *Concert*
(6/93) (PEAR) ① [3] **GEMMCDS9997/9(2)**
10a, 16b L. Sibiriakov, orch (r1908: Russ) *Concert*
(5/94) (PEAR) ① [3] **GEMMCDS9001/3(2)**
11b G. Zenatello, A. Didur, anon (r1906) *Concert*
(5/94) (PEAR) ① [4] **GEMMCDS9073(1)**
11b G. Zenatello, A. Didur, anon (r1906) *Concert*
(5/94) (SYMP) ① **SYMCD1168**
12. G. Cigna, I. Mannarini, P. Civil, T. Pasero, orch,
L. Molajoli (r1932) *Concert* (11/90) (PREI) ① **89016**
15a G. Mansueto, G. De Tura, chor, orch (r1909)
Concert (4/94) (EMI) ① [3] **CHS7 64860-2(2)**
16a N. de Angelis, orch, L. Molajoli (r1929) *Concert*
(7/92) (PREI) ① **89042**
17. M. Callas, Philh, T. Serafin (r1954) *Concert*
(11/86) (EMI) ① **CDC7 47282-2**
17. C. Muzio, orch, L. Molajoli (r1935) *Concert*
(10/89) (NIMB) ① **NI7802**
17. C. Muzio, orch (r1922) *Concert*
(5/90) (ROMO) ① [2] **BIM705-2**
17. G. Bellincioni, S. Cottone (r1903) *Concert*
(6/90) (SYMP) ① **SYMCD1073**
17. V. de los Angeles, Rome Op Orch, G. Morelli
(r1954) *Concert* (8/90) (EMI) ① **CDH7 63495-2**
17. K. Te Kanawa, LSO, Myung-Whun Chung
Concert (11/90) (EMI) ① **CDC7 54062-2**
17. E. Burzio, orch (r1913) *Concert*
(1/91) (CLUB) ① [2] **CL99-587/8**
17. C. Muzio, orch, L. Molajoli (r1935) *Concert*
(4/91) (NIMB) ① **NI7814**
17. C. Ferrani, anon (r1902) *Concert*
(5/91) (SYMP) ① **SYMCD1077**
17. R. Tebaldi, Santa Cecilia Academy Orch, F.
Molinari-Pradelli
(8/91) (DECC) ① [2] **430 481-2DX2**
17. L. Price, RCA Italiana Op Orch, F. Molinari-
Pradelli *Concert*
(12/92) (RCA) ① [4] **09026 61236-2**
17. R. Raisa, orch (r1924) *Concert*
(1/94) (CLUB) ① **CL99-052**
17. C. Muzio, orch (r1922) *Concert*
(1/94) (ROMO) ① [2] **81005-2**
17. P. Tassinari, La Scala Orch, F. Ghione (r1933)
Concert (4/94) (EMI) ① [3] **CHS7 64864-2(2)**
17. M. Freni, Ater Orch, L. Magiera (pp: Ital) *Concert*
(5/94) (DECC) ① [2] **443 018-2DF2**
17. C. Muzio, orch (r1917) *Concert*
(1/95) (ROMO) ① [2] **81010-2**
17. K. Vayne, orch (bp1958-9) *Concert*
(6/95) (PREI) ① **89996**
17. I. Galante, Latvian Nat SO, A. Vilumanis (r1994)
Concert (11/95) (CAMP) ① **RRCD1335**
19. E. Clément, G. Farrar, orch, R. Bourdon (r1913)
Concert (8/95) (ROMO) ① **82002-2**
19. E. Clément, G. Farrar, orch, R. Bourdon (r1913)
Concert (8/95) (PEAR) ① **GEMMCD9161**
21. E. Burzio, orch (r c1907) *Concert*
(1/91) (CLUB) ① [2] **CL99-587/8**
21. T. Arkel, anon (r1910) *Concert*
(11/92) (MEMO) ① [2] **HR4408/9(1)**
29a, 29b R. Alagna, LPO, R. Armstrong *Concert*
(12/95) (EMI) ① **CDC5 55540-2**
29b D. Smirnov, orch (r1909) *Concert*
(7/90) (CLUB) ① **CL99-031**
29b D. Borgioli, orch (r c1923) *Concert*
(12/90) (CLUB) ① **CL99-014**

29b G. Lauri-Volpi, orch (r1922) *Concert*
(7/93) (NIMB) ① **NI7845**
29b B. Gigli, orch, C. Sabajno (r1918) *Concert*
(4/94) (EMI) ① [3] **CHS7 64864-2(1)**
29b G. Zenatello, orch (r1908) *Concert*
(5/94) (SYMP) ① **SYMCD1168**
29b D. Smirnov, orch (r1910: Russ) *Concert*
(3/95) (NIMB) ① **NI7865**
Nerone—opera: 5 acts (1924—Milan) (Lib.
cpsr)
EXCERPTS: ACT 1: 1. Canto d'amore, vola col
vento; 2. Queste ad un lido fatal; 3. Se côlta (È il mio
Nume l'adoro); 4. Padre Nostro; 5. Fanuèl!...Non
t'alzar; 6. Gloria al tuo Dio (La Simonia); 7. Nessun ci
segue?; 8. Egli è là; 9. Apollo torne. ACT 2: 10.
Stupor! Portanto; 11. Tu qua ti nascondi; 12.
Nell'antro ov'io m'ascondo tutto vedro2; 13. Ecco il
magico specchio; 14. Ahimè! Non m'acciecar; 15.
Ecco, la Dea si china; 16. Cieca la santa nell'error
ripiomba; 17. Spiato son, là!... 18. Quesdta dagli
angui amor. ACT 3: 19. E vedendo le turbe ad udir
pronte; 20. A me i ligustri, a te gli allor; 21. Oh date a
piene mani; 22. Di pace una dolente a lor favella; 23.
Fanuèl, parla ti desta. Salvati per riddi? ACT 4: 24. Va
guardingo, attento espolra; 25. Vivete in pace, in
concento soave d'amor; 26. Qui sola resti? ACT 4:
27. Vittoria! Infamia! Morte!; 28. I verdi han vinto, è
salva Roma; 29. Che vuoi dir? Una congiura; 30.
Stande Vesta che la man che riscatta le vite; 31. E
tu, non voli?; 32. Scendi, cerchiam fra i morti; 33. Ah!
Non temer, son con te; 34. Fanuèl...Morirò?—Vivrai;
35. Sento che ascende (Laggiù tra i giunchi di
Genezaret); 36. Quella che il mio truce Iddio ghermi
sull'ara?
11, 12. M. Journet, orch (r1924) *Concert*
(4/94) (EMI) ① [3] **CHS7 64864-2(1)**
15. A. Pertile, orch (r1924) *Concert*
(4/94) (EMI) ① [3] **CHS7 64864-2(1)**

BOLCOM, William (Elden) *(b 1938) USA*

SECTION I: ORCHESTRAL

**Orphée-Sérénade—chamber orchestra
(1984)**
1. Overture; 2. Romance; 3. Pas de Bacchantes; 4.
Hurlubertu; 5. Elégie; 6. Energique.
Orpheus CO (r1990) *Concert*
(7/93) (DG) ① **435 389-2GH**
**Symphony No. 4—mezzo-soprano and
orchestra (1987)** (Wds. T. Roethke)
J. Morris, St Louis SO, L. Slatkin *Sessions I.*
(10/88) (NEW) ① **NW356-2**

SECTION II: CHAMBER

Sessions I—instrumental ensemble (1965)
J. Berg, J. Gippo, P. Bowman, B. Herr, G. Berry, T.
Myers, T. Dumm, J. Sant'Ambrogio, R. O'Donnell
Symphony 4. (10/88) (NEW) ① **NW356-2**
Sonata for Violin and Piano No. 2 (1978)
M. Bachmann, J. Klibonoff (r1994) *Concert*
(5/95) (CATA) ① **09026 62668-2**

SECTION III: INSTRUMENTAL

Dead Moth Tango—piano (1983-84)
U. Oppens *Concert* (5/90) (MUSI) ① **MACD-604**

SECTION IV: VOCAL AND CHORAL

12 Cabaret songs—1v and piano (1977-83)
(Wds. A. Weinstein)
VOLUME 1. Over the piano; 2. Fur (Murray the
furrier); 3. He tipped the waiter; 4. Waitin'; 5. Song of
Black Max (as told by the de Kooning boys); 6. Amor.
VOLUME 2: 7. Places to live; 8. Toothbrush time; 9.
Surprise!; 10. The actor; 11. Oh close the curtain; 12.
George.
6. F. von Stade, Martin Katz (pp1994) *Concert*
(1/95) (RCA) ① **09026 62547-2**
The Tyger—chorus and orchestra
Collegiate Chorale, NY Met Op Orch, J. Conlon
(pp1991) *Concert* (6/93) (RCA) ① **09026 61509-2**

BOLZONI, Giovanni *(1841–1919) Italy*

SECTION I: ORCHESTRAL

**Al castello medioevale No. 1—serenade:
orchestra**
NBC SO, A. Toscanini (bp1943) *Concert*
(5/94) (ATS) ① [2] **ATCD100**
Minuetto—strings
NBC SO, A. Toscanini (bp1943) *Concert*
(5/94) (ATS) ① [2] **ATCD100**
Detroit SO, N. Järvi (r1992) *Concert*
(8/94) (CHAN) ① **CHAN9227**

BOND, Capel *(1730–1790) England*

SECTION I: ORCHESTRAL

6 Concertos in Seven Parts (pub 1766)
1. D (trumpet and strings); 2. A minor (strings); 3. E
minor (strings); 4. C minor (strings); 5. G minor
(strings); 6. B flat (bassoon and strings).
Parley of Instr, R. Goodman (hpd/dir)
(2/93) (HYPE) ① **CDA66467**

BOND, Carrie Jacobs *(1862–1946) USA*

SECTION IV: VOCAL AND CHORAL

A Perfect Day—song (Wds. cpsr)
R. Ponselle, orch, J. Pasternack (r1925) *Concert*
(10/89) (NIMB) ① **NI7805**
V. Masterson, J. Constable *Concert*
(4/92) (GAMU) ① **GAMD506**
R. Ponselle, orch, J. Pasternack (r1925) *Concert*
(11/94) (ROMO) ① [2] **81006-2**

BONI, Guillaume *(d c1594) France*

SECTION IV: VOCAL AND CHORAL

Comment au départir—chanson: 4vv (Wds
Ronsard)
C. Janequin Ens, D. Visse (r1993) *Concert*
(2/95) (HARM) ① **HMC90 1491**
Ha, bel accueil—chanson: 4vv (Wds
Ronsard)
C. Janequin Ens, D. Visse (r1993) *Concert*
(2/95) (HARM) ① **HMC90 1491**
Las! sans espoir—chanson: 4vv (Wds
Ronsard)
C. Janequin Ens, D. Visse (r1993) *Concert*
(2/95) (HARM) ① **HMC90 1491**
Quand je dors—chanson: 5vv (Wds
Ronsard)
C. Janequin Ens, D. Visse (r1993) *Concert*
(2/95) (HARM) ① **HMC90 1491**
Rossignol mon mignon—chanson: 4vv (Wds
Ronsard)
C. Janequin Ens, D. Visse (r1993) *Concert*
(2/95) (HARM) ① **HMC90 1491**

BONNÉN, Helge *(1896–1983) Denmark*

SECTION IV: VOCAL AND CHORAL

When peace came over the land—song
L. Melchior, Orch (r c1921) *Concert*
(8/88) (DANA) ① [2] **DACOCD311/2**

BONNET, Joseph *(1884–1944) France*

SECTION III: INSTRUMENTAL

**12 Pièces nouvelles—organ, Op. 7 (pub
1910)**
1. Clair de lune; 2. Etude de Concert; 3. Pastorale; 4.
Caprice Héroïque; 11. Elfes.
1-4. J. Watts *Concert* (8/94) (PRIO) ① **PRCD377**
2. C. Herrick *Concert* (10/92) (HYPE) ① **CDA66605**
2. D.M. Patrick *Concert* (5/93) (PRIO) ① **PRCD371**
11. J. Parker-Smith *Concert*
(4/86) (ASV) ① **CDDCA539**
11. C. Herrick *Concert* (5/89) (HYPE) ① **CDA66258**
11. G. Weir *Concert* (12/92) (KOSS) ① **KC1013**
Romance sans paroles—organ
S. Lindley *Concert* (3/93) (NAXO) ① **8 550581**
Variations de concert—organ, Op. 1 (1908)
C. Herrick *Concert* (7/86) (HYPE) ① **CDA66121**

BONONCINI, Antonio Maria *(1677–1726) Italy*

SECTION IV: VOCAL AND CHORAL

**Stabat mater—soloists, chorus & orchestra
(c1720s)**
F. Palmer, P. Esswood, P. Langridge, C. Keyte, St
John's College Ch, Philomusica of London, G. Guest
(r1977) *Concert*
(7/95) (DECC) ① [2] **443 868-2DF2**

BONONCINI, Giovanni
(1670–1747) Italy

SECTION I: ORCHESTRAL

**12 Sinfonias—strings and continuo, Op. 3
(pub 1685)** (Nos.5, 8-10 with 1-2 tpts)
10. No 10 in D; 12. No 12.
10. S. Keavy, C. Steele-Perkins, Parley of Instr
Concert (1/89) (HYPE) ① **CDA66255**

SECTION II: CHAMBER

**8 Divertimenti da camera—violin/flute and
continuo (pub 1722)**
1. A minor; 2. G minor; 3. E minor; 4. G; 5. F; 6. C
minor; 7. D minor; 8. B flat.
6. M. Petri, G. Malcolm Concert
  (10/86) (PHIL) ① **412 632-2PH**
6. E. Haupt, C. Schornsheim Concert
  (2/90) (CAPR) ① **10 234**
**Sonata for Cello and Continuo in A minor
(pub 1748)**
Seminario Musicale (r1992) Concert
  (12/94) (VIRG) ① **VC5 45000-2**
**Sonata for 2 Violins and Continuo in D minor
(pub 172)**
Seminario Musicale (r1992) Concert
  (12/94) (VIRG) ① **VC5 45000-2**

SECTION IV: VOCAL AND CHORAL

**Cantate e duetti—1-2vv and instruments
(pub 1721)** (12 solo cantatas and 2 duets)
1. Barbara ninfa ingrata; 2. Care luci del mio bene; 3.
Da te che pasci ogn'ora; 4. Dolente e mesta; 5. Ecco
Dorinda il giorno; 6. Già la stagion d'amore; 7.
Lasciami un sol momento; 8. Le tenui ruggiade; 9.
Misero pastorello; 10. O frondoso arboscello; 11. O
mesta tortorella; 12. Siedi Amarilli mia; 13. Luci
barbare spietate (duet); 14. Pietoso nume arcier
(duet).
2, 12. R. Jacobs, S. Kuijken, L. van Dael, W. Kuijken,
R. Kohnen (r1979) Concert
  (1/93) (ARCH) ① **437 082-2AT**
6, 7, 9, 12. G. Lesne, Seminario Musicale (r1992)
Concert (12/94) (VIRG) ① **VC5 45000-2**
**Del più a me non v'ascondete—air: 1v and
continuo**
J. Baker, ASMF, N. Marriner Concert
  (1/93) (PHIL) ① **434 173-2PM**

SECTION V: STAGE WORKS

**Cefalo e Procride—pastorella: 1 act
(1702—Berlin)** (Lib. A Guridi)
EXCERPTS: 1a. Cintia, il tuo nome invòco; 1b.
Sacro dardo, in te confido; 2a. Numi del cielpietos;
2b. Bella auretta.
1a, 1b, 2a, 2b A. Monoyios, Berlin Barock
Compagney (r1993) Concert
  (10/95) (CAPR) ① **10 459**
**Griselda—dramma per musica: 3 acts
(1722—London)** (Lib. Rolli)
Per la gloria d'adoravi J. Kowalski, Berlin CO, M.
Pommer (r1993) Concert (9/88) (CAPR) ① **10 113**
Per la gloria d'adoravi J. Carreras, ECO, V. Sutej
(r1992; arr Agostinelli) Concert
  (6/93) (PHIL) ① **434 926-2PH**
**Muzio Scevola—dramma per musica: 3 acts
(1710—Vienna)** (Lib. ?Stampaglia, after
Minato)
EXCERPTS: 1. Pupille amate; 2. Come quando.
1, 2. J. Baird, F. Urrey, Brewer CO, R. Palmer
Concert (3/93) (NEWP) ① **NPD85540**
**Muzio Scevola (Act II)—dramma per musica:
3 acts (1721—London)** (Lib. Rolli. Act 1 by
Amadei; Act 3 by Handel)
EXCERPTS: 1. Overture; 2. Dolce pensier; 3. E pure
in mezzo all'armi; 4. Si, t'ama, o cara.
1-4. J. Ostendorf, E. Mills, Brewer CO, R. Palmer
Concert (3/93) (NEWP) ① **NPD85540**
**Polifemo—dramma per musica: 1 act
(1702—Berlin)** (Lib. A Ariostl)
1a. Respira, alma, respira; 1b. Dove sei, dove
t'ascondi; 2a. Non soffrir-a2, mai Circe; 2b. Pensiero
di vendetta; 3. Voi del ciel numi clementi.
1a, 1b, 2a, 2b A. Monoyios, Berlin Barock
Compagney (r1993) Concert
  (10/95) (CAPR) ① **10 459**
3. J. Kowalski, Berlin CO, M. Pommer Concert
  (9/88) (CAPR) ① **10 113**
**Il Trionfo di Camilla—dramma per musica: 3
acts (1696—Naples)** (Lib. S Stampiglia)
Pupille nere E. Pinza, F. Kitzinger (r1940) Concert
  (9/93) (RCA) ① **09026 61245-2**

BONPORTI, Francesco Antonio
(1672–1749) Italy

SECTION I: ORCHESTRAL

10 Concerti a Quattro, Op. 11 (after 1727)
4. B flat; 5. F; 6. F; 7. F; 8. D; 9. E; 10. A.
5(Rezitativo; Adagio assai) Solisti Italiani Concert
  (10/89) (DENO) ① **CO-73335**
5. S. Standage (vn/dir), Collegium Musicum 90
(r1992) Concert (5/93) (CHAN) ① **CHAN0530**

BORCHGREVINCK, Melchior
(c1570–1632) Denmark

SECTION III: INSTRUMENTAL

Paduana and Galliard—lute (pub 1607)
J. Lindberg Concert (2/89) (BIS) ① **BIS-CD390**

SECTION IV: VOCAL AND CHORAL

**Baci amorosi e cari—madrigal: 5vv (pub
1606)**
Consort of Musicke, A. Rooley (lte/dir) Concert
  (2/89) (BIS) ① **BIS-CD392**

BORGANOFF

SECTION IV: VOCAL AND CHORAL

Zigeunerweisen—song
R. Tauber, Dajos Bela Orch (r1928) Concert
  (7/89) (EMI) ① **CDM7 69476-2**

BORNE, Fernande Le
(1862–1929)

SECTION II: CHAMBER

**Fantasia brillante sur Carmen
(Bizet)—variations for flute and piano**
K. Jones, C. Edwards (r1993) Concert
  (10/94) (CONI) ① [2] **CDCF905**
A. Griminelli, NYPO, L. Magiera (pp1993) Concert
  (2/95) (DECC) ① **444 450-2DH**

BORODIN, Alexander Porfir'yevich
(1833–1887) Russia

SECTION I: ORCHESTRAL

**In the Steppes of Central Asia—musical
picture (1880)**
St. Louis SO, L. Slatkin Concert
  (12/83) (TELA) ① **CD80072**
Gothenburg SO, N. Järvi Concert
  (3/91) (DG) ① **429 984-2GH**
Slovak PO, D. Nazareth Concert
  (7/91) (NAXO) ① **8 550051**
Gothenburg SO, N. Järvi Concert
  (9/92) (DG) ① [2] **435 757-2GH2**
LSO, A. Coates (r1929) Concert
  (12/92) (KOCH) ① **37700-2**
Concertgebouw, W. Mengelberg (r1941) Concert
  (6/93) (ARHI) ① **ADCD108**
Philh, G. Simon (r1992) Concert
  (3/94) (CALA) ① **CACD1011**
RPO, Vladimir Ashkenazy Concert
  (8/94) (DECC) ① **436 651-2DH**
SRO, E. Ansermet (r1961) Concert
  (9/95) (DECC) ① **444 389-2DWO**
Boston Pops, A. Fiedler (r1957) Concert
  (12/95) (RCA) ① **09026 68132-2**
Symphony No. 1 in E flat (1862-67)
Rome RAI Orch, J. Serebrier Concert
  (6/90) (ASV) ① **CDDCA706**
Bratislava RSO, S. Gunzenhauser Concert
  (8/91) (NAXO) ① **8 550238**
Gothenburg SO, N. Järvi Concert
  (9/92) (DG) ① [2] **435 757-2GH2**
Russian St SO, E. Svetlanov (r1992) Concert
  (1/94) (RCA) ① **09026 61674-2**
RPO, Vladimir Ashkenazy Concert
  (8/94) (DECC) ① **436 651-2DH**
Stockholm PO, G. Rozhdestvensky (r1992) Concert
  (9/94) (CHAN) ① **CHAN9199**
Symphony No. 2 in B minor (1869-76)
Rome RAI Orch, J. Serebrier Concert
  (6/90) (ASV) ① **CDDCA706**
Bratislava RSO, S. Gunzenhauser Concert
  (8/91) (NAXO) ① **8 550238**
Gothenburg SO, N. Järvi Concert
  (9/92) (DG) ① [2] **435 757-2GH2**
Russian St SO, E. Svetlanov (r1993) Petite Suite.
  (8/94) (RCA) ① **09026 62505-2**

RPO, Vladimir Ashkenazy Concert
  (8/94) (DECC) ① **436 651-2DH**
VPO, R. Kubelík (r1960) Concert
  (11/94) (EMI) ① [2] **CZS5 68223-2**
Hallé, C. Lambert (r1943) Concert
  (2/95) (DUTT) ① **CDAX8010**
Philh, P. Kletzki (r1954) Tchaikovsky: Manfred
Symphony. (3/95) (TEST) ① **SBT1048**
LSO, J. Martinon (r1960) Concert
  (9/95) (DECC) ① **444 389-2DWO**
Symphony No. 3 in A minor (1882, 1886-87)
(orch Glazunov)
Rome RAI Orch, J. Serebrier Concert
  (6/90) (ASV) ① **CDDCA706**
Bratislava RSO, S. Gunzenhauser Concert
  (8/91) (NAXO) ① **8 550238**
Gothenburg SO, N. Järvi Concert
  (9/92) (DG) ① [2] **435 757-2GH2**
Russian St SO, E. Svetlanov (r1992) Concert
  (1/94) (RCA) ① **09026 61674-2**
Stockholm PO, G. Rozhdestvensky (r1993) Concert
  (9/94) (CHAN) ① **CHAN9199**

SECTION II: CHAMBER

Piano Quintet in C minor (1862)
Monte Carlo Pro Arte Qnt (r1993) Shostakovich:
Piano Quintet, Op.57. (10/94) (AUVI) ① **V4702**
String Quartet No. 1 in A (1875-78)
Borodin Qt String Quartet 2.
  (5/88) (EMI) ① **CDC7 47795-2**
String Quartet No. 2 in D (1885)
1. Allegro; 2. Scherzo; 3. Notturno; 4. Finale.
Borodin Qt String Quartet 1.
  (5/88) (EMI) ① **CDC7 47795-2**
Talich Qt (r1986) Tchaikovsky: String Quartet 1.
  (5/88) (CALL) ① **CAL6202**
S. Accardo, M. Batjer, T. Hoffman, P. Wiley Verdi:
String Quartet. (5/89) (DYNA) ① **CDS47**
Cleveland Qt Smetana: String Quartet 1.
  (10/89) (TELA) ① **CD80178**
Borodin Qt Concert (5/90) (DECC) ① **425 541-2DM**
Hollywood Qt (r1952) Concert
  (8/95) (TEST) ① **SBT1061**
Lafayette Qt (r1994) Concert
  (9/95) (DORI) ① **DOR90203**
3. St Louis SO, L. Slatkin Concert
  (1/84) (TELA) ① **CD80080**
3. Quartetto Italiano (r1968) Concert
  (3/89) (PHIL) ① **420 876-2PSL**
3. I. Stern, Columbia SO, F. Brieff (arr Harris)
Concert (7/90) (SONY) ① **SK45816**
3. English Gtr Qt (arr Gallery) Concert
  (10/90) (SAYD) ① **CD-SDL379**
3. Gothenburg SO, N. Järvi Concert
  (9/92) (DG) ① [2] **435 757-2GH2**
3. BBC Sym Chor, Philh, G. Simon (r1992; orch
Rimsky-Korsakov) Concert
  (3/94) (CALA) ① **CACD1011**
3. Borodin Qt (r1962) Concert
  (9/95) (DECC) ① **444 389-2DWO**

SECTION III: INSTRUMENTAL

Petite Suite—piano (1885)
1. Au couvent; 2. Intermezzo; 3. Mazurka; 4.
Mazurka; 5. Rêverie; 6. Sérénade; 7. Nocturne.
Gothenburg SO, N. Järvi (orch Glazunov) Concert
  (9/92) (DG) ① [2] **435 757-2GH2**
Philh, G. Simon (r1992; orch Glazunov) Concert
  (3/94) (CALA) ① **CACD1011**
Russian St SO, E. Svetlanov (r1993; orch Glazunov)
Symphony 2. (8/94) (RCA) ① **09026 62505-2**
In the monastery; Nocturne M. Fingerhut Concert
  (6/87) (CHAN) ① **CHAN8439**
3. A. Goldenweiser (r1946) Concert
  (8/95) (MELO) ① [11] **74321 25172-2(1)**
3. A. Goldenweiser (r1946) Concert
  (8/95) (MELO) ① **74321 25173-2**
Scherzo in A flat—piano (1885)
M. Fingerhut Concert (6/87) (CHAN) ① **CHAN8439**
S. Rachmaninov (r1935) Concert
  (3/93) (RCA) ① [10] **09026 61265-2(2)**
Vladimir Ashkenazy (r1993) Concert
  (9/95) (DECC) ① **444 389-2DWO**

SECTION IV: VOCAL AND CHORAL

Arabian melody—song (1881) (Wds. Trad.,
trans. cpsr)
B. Christoff, A. Tcherepnin Concert
  (6/90) (EMI) ① [3] **CMS7 63386-2**
The False note—song (1868) (Wds. cpsr)
B. Christoff, A. Tcherepnin Concert
  (6/90) (EMI) ① [3] **CMS7 63386-2**
O. Borodina, L. Gergieva (r1994) Concert
  (8/95) (PHIL) ① **442 780-2PH**

The **Fishermaiden—song with cello obbligato (c1854)** (Wds. Heine, trans. D. Kropotkin)
B. Christoff, M. Tortelier, A. Tcherepnin *Concert*
(6/90) (EMI) ① [3] **CMS7 63386-2**

For the shores of thy far native land—song (1881) (Wds. Pushkin)
B. Christoff, M. Tortelier, Lamoureux Orch, G. Tzipine *Concert* (6/90) (EMI) ① [3] **CMS7 63386-2**
T. Wallström, Stockholm PO, G. Rozhdestvensky (r1993) *Concert* (9/94) (CHAN) ① **CHAN9199**
D. Hvorostovsky, M. Arkadiov *Concert*
(2/95) (PHIL) ① **442 536-2PH**
N. Ghiaurov, Z. Ghiaurov (r1971) *Concert*
(9/95) (DECC) ① **444 389-2DWO**

From my tears—song (1870-71) (Wds. Heine, trans. Mey)
B. Christoff, A. Tcherepnin *Concert*
(6/90) (EMI) ① [3] **CMS7 63386-2**

Listen to my song, little friend—song with cello obbligato (c1854) (Wds. E. von Kruse)
B. Christoff, M. Tortelier, A. Tcherepnin *Concert*
(6/90) (EMI) ① [3] **CMS7 63386-2**

The **Magic garden—song (1885)** (Wds. G. Collin, trans. cpsr)
B. Christoff, A. Tcherepnin *Concert*
(6/90) (EMI) ① [3] **CMS7 63386-2**

My songs are poisoned—song (1868) (Wds. Heine, trans L. A. Mey)
B. Christoff, A. Tcherepnin *Concert*
(6/90) (EMI) ① [3] **CMS7 63386-2**

The **Pretty girl no longer loves me—song with cello obbligato (c1854)** (Wds. Vinogradov)
B. Christoff, M. Tortelier, A. Tcherepnin *Concert* (6/90) (EMI) ① [3] **CMS7 63386-2**

Pride—song (1884-85) (Wds. A.K. Tolstoy)
B. Christoff, A. Tcherepnin *Concert*
(6/90) (EMI) ① [3] **CMS7 63386-2**

Requiem—male chorus and orchestra (arr Stokowski from pf work 'Chopsticks')
BBC Sym Chor, Philh, G. Simon (r1992) *Concert*
(3/94) (CALA) ① **CACD1011**

The **Sea—song (1870)** (Wds. cpsr)
T. Allen, R. Vignoles *Concert*
(11/87) (HYPE) ① **CDA66165**
B. Christoff, J. Reiss *Concert*
(6/90) (EMI) ① [3] **CMS7 63386-2**

The **Sea Princess—song (1868)** (Wds. cpsr)
Sarah Walker, R. Vignoles *Concert*
(11/87) (HYPE) ① **CDA66165**
B. Christoff, A. Tcherepnin *Concert*
(6/90) (EMI) ① [3] **CMS7 63386-2**
O. Borodina, L. Gergieva (r1994) *Concert*
(8/95) (PHIL) ① **442 780-2PH**

The **Sleeping Princess—song (1867)** (Wds. cpsr)
B. Christoff, A. Tcherepnin *Concert*
(6/90) (EMI) ① [3] **CMS7 63386-2**
B. Christoff, G. Moore (r1950) *Concert*
(4/92) (EMI) ① [7] **CHS7 69741-2(6)**

Song of the dark forest (1868) (Wds. cpsr)
B. Christoff, A. Tcherepnin *Concert*
(6/90) (EMI) ① [3] **CMS7 63386-2**

Those folk—song (1881) (Wds. Nekrasov)
B. Christoff, Lamoureux Orch, G. Tzipine *Concert*
(6/90) (EMI) ① [3] **CMS7 63386-2**
L. Dyadkova, Stockholm PO, G. Rozhdestvensky (r1993) *Concert* (9/94) (CHAN) ① **CHAN9199**

Why are thou so early, dawn?—song (1852-55) (Wds. S. Solov'yov)
B. Christoff, A. Tcherepnin *Concert*
(6/90) (EMI) ① [3] **CMS7 63386-2**

SECTION V: STAGE WORKS

Prince Igor—opera: prologue & 4 acts (1890—St Petersburg) (Lib. cpsr)
EXCERPTS—PROLOGUE: 1. Overture; 2. To the sun in his glory. ACT 1: 3. I hate a dreary life (Galitzky's Aria); 4. For long past (Yaroslavna's Aria). ACT 2: 5. The prairie floweret (Song of the Polovtsi maidens); 6. Dance of the Polovtsi maidens; 7. Daylight is fading (Vladimir's Aria); 8. Do you love? (Duet); 9. No sleep, no rest (Igor's Aria); 10. How goes it Prince? (Konchak's Aria); 11. Polovtsian Dances. ACT 3: 12. Polovtsian March. ACT 4: 13. I shed bitter tears (Yaroslavna's Lament).
Cpte C. Chekerliski, J. Wiener, T. Todorov, B. Christoff, R. Penkova, L. Mihailov, K. Dulguarov, Sofia National Op Chor, Sofia National Op Orch, J. Semkow (omits Act 3) *Concert*
(6/90) (EMI) ① [3] **CMS7 63386-2**

Cpte B. Martinovich, S. Evstatieva, K. Kaludov, N. Ghiuselev, N. Ghiaurov, A. Milcheva, M. Popov, S. Georgiev, Anton Petkov, Sofia National Op Chor, Sofia Fest Orch, E. Tchakarov
(6/90) (SONY) ① **S3K44878**

Cpte M. Kit, G. Gorchakova, G. Grigorian, V. Ognovenko, B. Minzhilkiev, O. Borodina, N. Gassiev, G. Selezniev, K. Pluzhnikov, E. Perlasova, T. Novikova, Kirov Th Chor, Kirov Th Orch, V. Gergiev (r1994) (4/95) (PHIL) ① [3] **442 537-2PH3**

Konchakovna's cavatina E. Zbrueva, orch (r1911) *Concert*
(6/93) (PEAR) ① [3] **GEMMCDS9004/6(2)**

Suite M. Field, I. Boughton, BBC Sym Chor, Philh, G. Simon (r1992; orch Glazunov/Rimsky-Korsakov) *Concert* (3/94) (CALA) ① **CACD1011**
1. Russian St SO, E. Svetlanov (r1992; orch Glazunov) *Concert* (1/94) (RCA) ① **09026 61674-2**
1. Philh, C. Silvestri (r1959) *Concert*
(1/94) (EMI) ① [2] **CZS5 68229-2**
1. Russian Nat Orch, M. Pletnev (orch Glazunov) *Concert* (12/94) (DG) ① **439 892-2GH**
1. Hallé, L. Heward (r1942) *Concert*
(2/95) (DUTT) ① **CDAX8010**
1, 11. London Sym Chor, LSO, G. Solti (r1966: arr Rimsky-Korsakov) *Concert*
(9/95) (DECC) ① **444 389-2DWO**
1, 11. Boston Pops, A. Fiedler (r1957) *Concert*
(12/95) (RCA) ① **09026 68132-2**
1, 6, 11. Gothenburg Sym Chor, Gothenburg SO, N. Järvi *Concert* (9/92) (DG) ① [2] **435 757-2GH2**
3. A. Kipnis, Victor SO, N. Berezowski (r1945) *Concert* (9/92) (RCA) ① **GD60522**
3. L. Sibiriakov, orch (r1908) *Concert*
(6/93) (PEAR) ① [3] **GEMMCDS9001/3(2)**
3. A. Jerger, Vienna St Op Chor, Vienna St Op Orch, L. Ludwig (pp1941: Ger) *Concert*
(6/94) (SCHW) ① **314502**
3. N. Ghiaurov, London Sym Chor, LSO, E. Downes (r1965; orch Rimsky-Korsakov) *Concert*
(9/95) (DECC) ① **444 389-2DWO**
3, 10. B. Christoff, Philh, I. Dobroven (r1950) *Concert* (6/93) (EMI) ① **CDH7 64252-2**
4. N. Koshetz, orch (r1928) *Concert*
(10/89) (NIMB) ① **NI7802**
4, 13. K. Vayne, anon (r1949) *Concert*
(6/95) (PREI) ① **89996**
6. Philadelphia, L. Stokowski (r1937: arr Glazunov/Rimsky-Korsakov/Stokowski) *Concert*
(11/94) (DUTT) ① **CDAX8009**
6, 11. BPO, H. von Karajan *Rimsky-Korsakov: Scheherazade*. (4/87) (DG) ① **419 063-2GGA**
6, 11. LPO, W. Susskind *Concert*
(11/87) (CFP) ① **CD-CFP9000**
7. J. Björling, orch, N. Grevillius (r1933: Swed) *Concert* (8/92) (BLUE) ① **ABCD016**
7. L. Sobinov, anon (r1901) *Concert*
(6/93) (PEAR) ① [3] **GEMMCDS9997/9(1)**
7. D. Yuzhin, anon (r1902) *Concert*
(6/93) (PEAR) ① [3] **GEMMCDS9001/3(1)**
7. D. Smirnov, orch, J. Harrison (r1923) *Concert*
(6/93) (PEAR) ① [3] **GEMMCDS9004/6(1)**
7. J. Björling, orch, N. Grevillius (r1933: Swed) *Concert* (10/93) (EMI) ① **CDH7 64707-2**
7. C. Kullman, orch (Ger: r1935) *Concert*
(11/93) (PREI) ① **89057**
7. W. Widdop, orch, L. Collingwood (r1926: Eng) *Concert* (5/94) (CLAR) ① **CDGSE78-50-52**
9. H. Schlusnus, Berlin St Op Orch, A. Melichar (Ger: r c1931) *Concert* (9/90) (PREI) ① **89006**
9. O. Kamionsky, anon (r1905) *Concert*
(6/93) (PEAR) ① [3] **GEMMCDS9001/3(1)**
9. V. Kastorsky, orch (r1908) *Concert*
(6/93) (PEAR) ① [3] **GEMMCDS9001/3(1)**
9. D. Hvorostovsky, Kirov Th Orch, V. Gergiev (r1993) *Concert* (5/94) (PHIL) ① **438 872-2PH**
9, 10. K. Borg, Berlin RSO, H. Stein (r1963) *Concert* (12/94) (FINL) ① [3] **4509-95606-2**
10. F. Chaliapin, orch, A. Coates (r1927) *Concert*
(6/88) (EMI) ① **CDH7 61009-2**
10. M. Reizen, Bolshoi Th Orch, A. Melik-Pashayev (r1951) *Concert* (12/92) (PREI) ① **89059**
11. Beecham Choral Soc, RPO, T. Beecham (r1956) *Rimsky-Korsakov: Scheherazade.*
(9/87) (EMI) ① **CDC7 47717-2**
11. LSC, LSO, R. Hickox *Concert*
(4/89) (CARL) ① **PCD908**
11. T. Sporsén, Gothenburg Sym Chor, Gothenburg SO, N. Järvi *Concert* (3/91) (DG) ① **429 984-2GH**
11. Slovak PO, D. Nazareth *Concert*
(7/91) (NAXO) ① **8 550051**
11. Royal Phil Chor, WNO Chor, RPO, L. Stokowski *Concert* (4/92) (DECC) ① **433 625-2DSP**
11. Glasgow CWS Band, R. Tennant (arr Snell) *Concert* (9/92) (DOYE) ① **DOYCD005**

11. Black Dyke Mills Band, J. Watson (r1992: arr Huckridge) *Concert* (9/93) (POLY) ① **QPRL053D**
11. NYPO, L. Bernstein (r1963) *Concert*
(9/93) (SONY) ① **SMK47600**
11. Leeds Fest Chor, LPO, T. Beecham (r1934) *Concert* (6/94) (DUTT) ① **CDLX7003**
11. Chicago SO, F. Reiner (r1959) *Concert*
(8/94) (RCA) ① **09026 61958-2**
11. Paris Cons, C. Silvestri (r1961) *Concert*
(11/94) (EMI) ① [2] **CZS5 68229-2**
11. Philadelphia, L. Stokowski (r1937) *Concert*
(11/95) (BIDD) ① **WHL027**
11, **Villagers' chorus, Be firm Countess** Bolshoi Th Chor, Bolshoi SO, A. Lazarev (r1993) *Concert*
(5/94) (ERAT) ① **4509-91723-2**
11, 12. Kirov Th Chor, Kirov Th Orch, V. Gergiev (r1993) *Concert* (4/94) (PHIL) ① **442 011-2PH**
12. LSO, A. Coates (r1932) *Concert*
(12/92) (KOCH) ① **37700-2**
12. Russian St SO, E. Svetlanov (r1992; orch Rimsky-Korsakov) *Concert*
(1/94) (RCA) ① **09026 61674-2**
12. LPO, T. Beecham (r1938) *Concert*
(6/94) (DUTT) ① **CDLX7003**

BORRONO DA MILANO, Pietro Paolo *(fl 1530–40) Italy*

SECTION III: INSTRUMENTAL

Fantasias without names—lute
Fantasia P. O'Dette (r1990-2) *Concert*
(10/95) (HARM) ① **HMU90 7043**

Pavana ditta la Desparata—lute
P. O'Dette (r1990-2) *Concert*
(10/95) (HARM) ① **HMU90 7043**

Pavana la Gombertina—lute
P. O'Dette (r1990-2) *Concert*
(10/95) (HARM) ① **HMU90 7043**

Saltarello chiamato el Mazolo—lute
P. O'Dette (r1990-2) *Concert*
(10/95) (HARM) ① **HMU90 7043**

Saltarellos without names—lute
Two saltarellos P. O'Dette (r1990-2) *Concert*
(10/95) (HARM) ① **HMU90 7043**

Tocha tocha la Canella—lute intabulation
P. O'Dette (r1990-2) *Concert*
(10/95) (HARM) ① **HMU90 7043**

BORTKIEWICZ, Sergei *(1877–1952) Austria/USSR*

SECTION I: ORCHESTRAL

Concerto for Piano and Orchestra No. 1 in B flat, Op. 16 (1912)
S. Coombs, BBC Scottish SO, J. Maksymiuk *Concert*
(3/93) (HYPE) ① **CDA66624**

BORTNYANSKY, Dmitry Stepanovich *(1751–1825) Ukraine*

SECTION IV: VOCAL AND CHORAL

Come o ye people—sacred concerto (Wds. from Orthodox poetry)
St Petersburg Glinka Acad Ch, V. Chernushenko (r1993) *Concert* (4/95) (TELD) ① **4509-93856-2**
Glory be to God in the highest—sacred concerto: choir (text from Vigil on the Eve of Christ's Nativity)
St Petersburg Glinka Acad Ch, V. Chernushenko (r1993) *Concert* (4/95) (TELD) ① **4509-93856-2**
The **Hymn of the Cherubim No. 7—chorus a cappella**
St Petersburg Glinka Acad Ch, V. Chernushenko (r1993) *Concert* (4/95) (TELD) ① **4509-93856-2**
I cried unto God with my voice—sacred concerto (Wds. from Psalms 76 & 17)
St Petersburg Glinka Acad Ch, V. Chernushenko (r1993) *Concert* (4/95) (TELD) ① **4509-93856-2**
In this day the Lord has made—Russian liturgical chant
N. Gedda, Paris Russian Orthodox Cath Ch, E. Evetz *Concert* (1/93) (PHIL) ① **434 174-2PM**
Let God arise—sacred concerto (Wds. from Psalm 67)
St Petersburg Glinka Acad Ch, V. Chernushenko (r1993) *Concert* (4/95) (TELD) ① **4509-93856-2**
Lord, make me know mine end—sacred concerto (Wds. from Psalm 38)
St Petersburg Glinka Acad Ch, V. Chernushenko (r1993) *Concert* (4/95) (TELD) ① **4509-93856-2**

Make a joyful noise unto the Lord—sacred concerto (Wds. from Psalm 65 & 80)
St Petersburg Glinka Acad Ch, V. Chernushenko
(r1993) *Concert*   (4/95) (TELD) ① **4509-93856-2**
Many years—choir
Bolshoi Children's Ch, A. Zaboronok (r1994) *Concert*
(7/95) (COLL) ① **Coll1443-2**
Mnogaya lieta—chorus a capella
Tallis Scholars, P. Phillips (arr Philips) *Concert*
(6/91) (GIME) ① **CDGIM002**
Te Deum
Moscow Patriarchal Ch, A. Grindenko (r1992) *Anon: Early Russian Plain Chant.*
(4/94) (O111) ① **OPS30-79**
St Petersburg Glinka Acad Ch, V. Chernushenko
(r1993) *Concert*   (4/95) (TELD) ① **4509-93856-2**

BOSSI, Marco Enrico (1861–1925) Italy

SECTION I: ORCHESTRAL

Intermezzi goldoniani—string orchestra, Op. 127 (1905)
2. Gagliarda; 5. Serenatina; 6. Burlesca.
2, 5, 6. NBC SO, A. Toscanini (bp1944) *Concert*
(5/94) (ATS) ① [2] **ATCD100**

SECTION III: INSTRUMENTAL

Entrée pontificale—organ
C. Walsh *Concert*   (9/87) (MERI) ① **CDE84025**
Giga—?piano, Op. 73
G. Weir (arr R. Bossi) *Concert*
(12/92) (KOSS) ① **KC1013**
Noël—organ, Op. 94/2
N. Kynaston *Concert*   (4/89) (HYPE) ① **CDA66265**
Pièce héroïque—organ, Op. 128
C. Herrick *Concert*   (9/91) (HYPE) ① **CDA66457**
Scherzo in G minor—organ, Op. 49/2
I. Tracey *Concert*   (1/90) (CFP) ① **CD-CFP4558**
C. Herrick *Concert*   (9/91) (HYPE) ① **CDA66457**
G. Weir *Concert*   (12/92) (KOSS) ① **KC1013**
Stunde der Freude—organ, Op. 132/5
L. Benedetti (r1992) *Concert*
(4/95) (PRIO) ① **PRCD427**
Stunde der Wehie—organ, Op. 132/4
L. Benedetti (r1992) *Concert*
(4/95) (PRIO) ① **PRCD427**
Toccata di Concerto—organ, Op. 118/5
N. Kynaston *Concert*   (4/89) (HYPE) ① **CDA66265**

SECTION IV: VOCAL AND CHORAL

Il Brivido—chorus
Orphei Drängar Ch, E. Ericson *Concert*
(7/88) (BIS) ① **BIS-CD383**

BOTSFORD, George (1874–1949) USA

SECTION III: INSTRUMENTAL

Black and White Rag—piano (1908)
Britannia Building Soc Band, H. Snell (r1990; arr Snell: xylophone duet) *Concert*
(8/92) (DOYE) ① **DOYCD004**

BOTTEGARI, Cosimo (1554–1620) Italy

SECTION IV: VOCAL AND CHORAL

Non si vedde giamai
Kithara (r1993) *Concert*
(3/95) (CHAN) ① **CHAN0562**

BOTTERMUND, Hans (c1860–?) Germany

SECTION III: INSTRUMENTAL

Variations on a Theme by Paganini—solo cello
J. Starker (trans Starker: vc) *Concert*
(1/89) (DELO) ① **DE1015**

BOTTESINI, Giovanni (1821–1889) Italy

SECTION I: ORCHESTRAL

Andante sostenuto—strings
ECO, A. Litton *Concert*   (6/87) (ASV) ① **CDDCA563**
Concertino for Double Bass and Strings in C minor
T. Martin, LSO, F. Petracchi *Concert*
(3/95) (ASV) ① **CDDCA907**

Duetto for Clarinet, Double Bass and Orchestra
E. Johnson, T. Martin, ECO, A. Litton *Concert*
(6/87) (ASV) ① **CDDCA563**
Duo Concertant for Cello, Double Bass and Orchestra on themes from Bellini's 'I Puritani'
Overture T. Martin, M. Welsh, LSO, F. Petracchi *Concert*   (3/95) (ASV) ① **CDDCA907**
Gran Concerto for Double Bass and Orchestra in F
T. Martin, ECO, A. Litton *Concert*
(6/87) (ASV) ① **CDDCA563**
Gran Duo Concertante for Violin, Double Bass and Orchestra (1880)
J-L. Garcia, T. Martin, ECO, A. Litton *Concert*
(3/95) (ASV) ① **CDDCA907**

SECTION II: CHAMBER

Concerto for Double Bass and Piano No. 2 in B minor
M. Hanskov, N.E. Aggesen *Concert*
(3/92) (DANA) ① **DACOCD378**
Elegie in D—double bass and piano
M. Hanskov, T. Lønskov *Concert*
(3/92) (DANA) ① **DACOCD378**
T. Martin, LSO, F. Petracchi *Concert*
(3/95) (ASV) ① **CDDCA907**
Passione Amorosa—double bass and piano
(orig pt of Concerto di bravura for db & pf)
T. Martin, F. Petracchi, LSO, M. Gibson *Concert*
(3/95) (ASV) ① **CDDCA907**

SECTION V: STAGE WORKS

Alì Babà—comic opera: 4 acts (1871)
Overture LSO, F. Petracchi *Concert*
(3/95) (ASV) ① **CDDCA907**
Il diavolo della notte—opera: 4 acts (1858)
Sinfonia LSO, F. Petracchi *Concert*
(3/95) (ASV) ① **CDDCA907**
Ero e Leandro—opera: 3 acts (1879—Turin)
(Lib. A. Boito)
Prelude LSO, F. Petracchi *Concert*
(3/95) (ASV) ① **CDDCA907**
Romanza d'Ero A. Pinto, anon (r1902) *Concert*
(8/93) (SYMP) ① **SYMCD1111**
Splendi! erma facella A. Pinto, anon (r1902) *Concert*   (6/94) (IRCC) ① **IRCC-CD808**

BOTTRIGARI, Ercole (1531–1612) Italy

SECTION IV: VOCAL AND CHORAL

Mi parto
R. Jacobs, K. Junghänel (r1985) *Concert*
(5/87) (HARM) ① **HMA190 1183**
So ben mi c'ha bon tempo
R. Jacobs, K. Junghänel (r1985) *Concert*
(5/87) (HARM) ① **HMA190 1183**

BOUGHTON, Rutland (1878–1960) England

SECTION I: ORCHESTRAL

Concerto for Oboe and Orchestra No. 1 in C (1936)
S. Francis, RPO, V. Handley (r1988) *Symphony 3.*
(1/90) (HYPE) ① **CDA66343**
Symphony No. 3 in B minor (1937)
RPO, V. Handley (r1988) *Oboe Concerto 1.*
(1/90) (HYPE) ① **CDA66343**

SECTION V: STAGE WORKS

Bethlehem—choral drama (1915—Street)
(Text cpsr, after Coventry Nativity Play)
Cpte H. Field, R. Bryan, R. Bryson, R. Evans, J. Bowen, A. Peacock, A. Opie, J. MacDougall, R. Van Allan, C. Seaton, C. Campbell, I. Boughton, G. Matheson-Bruce, Holst Sngrs, New London Children's Ch, CLS, A. Melville (r1993)
(4/94) (HYPE) ① **CDA66690**
The Immortal Hour—music drama: 2 acts (1914—Glastonbury) (Lib. F Macleod)
EXCERPTS: 1. Introduction. ACT 1 2. By dim moon-glimmering coasts and sad sea wastes; 3. Though you have travelled from one darkness of another; 4. Ye know not who I am; 5. I have come hither, led by dreams and visions; 6. Hail, Son of Shadow!; 7. I am old; more old more ancient; 8. Brother and kin to all the twilit gods; 9. Laugh not, ye outcasts of the invisible world; 10. Fair is the moonlight; 11. Hail, daughter of kings, and star among dreams; 12. Have you forgot the delicate smiling land; 13. I have forgotten all; 14. A king of men has wooed the Immortal Hour; 15. Led here by

---

dreams; 16. I will go back to the Country of the Young; 17. Sir, I am glad; 18. I have come to this lone wood; 19. Look, O king!; 20. There is no backward way for such as I; 21. I have heard you calling, Dalua, Dalual; 22. I've seen that man before who came tonight; 23. Yes, woman, yes, I know; 24. But sometimes...Tell me: have you heard; 25. Good folk, I gave you greeting; 26. Good sir, you are most welcome; 27. At last I know why dreams have led me hither; 28. And your name, fair lord?; 29. Truly, I now know full well; 30. I, too, am lifted with the breath; 31. Who laughed?; 32. Dear Lord, sit here; 33. How beautiful they are (Unseen Voices). ACT 2 34. By the Voice in the corries; 35. The The Bells of Youth are ringing; 36. But this was in the old, old far-off days; 37. Hail, Eochaidh, High King of Eire, hail!; 38. Green fire of Joy, green fire of Life; 39. Etain, speak, my Queen; 40. No, no, my Queen; 41. I, too, have heard strange, delicate music; 42. The Queen!; 43. Hail, Eochaidh, King of Eirel; 44. I am the king's first son; 45. Dagda, Lord of Thunder and Silence; 46. Fair lord, my thanks I give; 47. Have not great poets sung; 48. In the days of the Great Fires; 49. Hear us, Oengus, beautiful, terrible, Sun-Lord!; 50. But now, fair lord, tell me the boon you crave; 51. I have seen all things pass and all things go; 52. This nameless lord; 53. How beautiful they are (The Faery Song); 54. I have heard...I have dreamed that song; 55. I am a song in the Land of the Young; 56. I am a small leaf in a great wood; 57. O do not leave me, Star of my Desire!; 58. Hasten, lost love, found love!; 59. In the Land of Youth there are pleasant places; 60. They sleep with many lances.
Cpte R. Kennedy, P. Taylor, Anne Dawson, D. Wilson-Johnson, V. Hill, R. Bryson, P. Taylor, R. Bryson, M. Davies, G. Mitchell Ch, ECO, A. Melville (r1983)   (8/87) (HYPE) ① [2] **CDA66101/2**
53. Webster Booth, J. Cockerill (r1939) *Concert*
(4/92) (EMI) ① [7] **CHS7 69741-2(2)**

BOULANGER, Lili (1893–1918) France

SECTION I: ORCHESTRAL

D'un matin du printemps (1918)
Women's PO, J. Falletta *Concert*
(2/93) (KOCH) ① **37169-2**
D'un soir triste (1918)
Women's PO, J. Falletta *Concert*
(2/93) (KOCH) ① **37169-2**

SECTION II: CHAMBER

3 Pieces—violin and piano
1. Nocturne (1911); 2. Cortège (1914); 3. D'un matin de printemps (1918).
Y. Menuhin, C. Curzon *Concert*
(8/92) (EMI) ① **CDM7 64281-2**
1, 2. O. Charlier, E. Naoumoff (r1993) *Concert*
(9/94) (MARC) ① **8 223636**
1, 2. J. Roche, P. Freed *Concert*
(10/94) (VOX) ① [2] **115845-2**
1, 2. J. Heifetz, I. Achron (r1924) *Concert*
(11/94) (RCA) ① [65] **09026 61778-2(01)**

SECTION III: INSTRUMENTAL

Cortège—piano
S. Marin *Concert*   (4/93) (RNE) ① **M3/03**
D'un jardin clair—piano (1914)
S. Marin *Concert*   (4/93) (RNE) ① **M3/03**
E. Naoumoff (r1993) *Concert*
(9/94) (MARC) ① **8 223636**
Thème et Variations—piano (1914) (cpted E Naoumoff)
E. Naoumoff (r1993) *Concert*
(9/94) (MARC) ① **8 223636**
D'un vieux jardin—piano (1914)
S. Marin *Concert*   (4/93) (RNE) ① **M3/03**
E. Naoumoff (r1993) *Concert*
(9/94) (MARC) ① **8 223636**

SECTION IV: VOCAL AND CHORAL

Attente—mélodie (1911) (Wds. M. Maeterlinck)
M. Shirai, H. Höll *Concert*
(4/90) (BAYE) ① **BR100041**
Clairières dans le ciel—song cycle: tenor and piano (1914) (Wds. F. Jammes)
1. Elle était descendue; 2. Elle est gravement gaie; 3. Parfois je suis triste; 4. Un poète disait; 5. Au pied de mon lit; 6. Si tout ceci n'est qu'un pauvre rêve; 7. Nous nous aimerons tant; 8. Vous m'avez regardé avec toute votre; 9. Les lilas qui avaient fleuri; 10. Deux ancolies; 11. Par ce que j'ai souffert; 12. Je garde une médaille d'elle; 13. Demain fera un an.
1, 6, 7, 13. I. Sabrié, E. Naoumoff (r1993) *Concert*
(9/94) (MARC) ① **8 223636**

Dans l'immense Tristesse—mélodie (1916)
(Wds. B. Galéron de Calone)
M. Shirai, H. Höll Concert
(4/90) (BAYE) ① **BR100041**
Doris Reinhardt, E. Naoumoff (r1993) Concert
(9/94) (MARC) ① **8 223636**
Du fond de l'abîme—contralto, tenor, chorus and organ
O. Dominguez, R. Amade, E. Brasseur Chorale,
Lamoureux Orch, I. Markevitch Concert
(8/92) (EMI) ① **CDM7 64281-2**
Hymne au Soleil—contralto, choir and piano (1912) (Wds. C. Delavigne)
R. Böhm, Heidelberg Madrigal Ch, S. Eberspächer,
G. Kegelmann Concert
(4/90) (BAYE) ① **BR100041**
Pie Jesu—mezzo-soprano, string quartet, harp and organ (1918)
A. Fauqueur, J-J. Grunenwald, Lamoureux Orch, I.
Markevitch Concert (8/92) (EMI) ① **CDM7 64281-2**
I. Sabrié, Francis Pierre, E. LeBrun, O. Charlier, A. P.
Dureau, M. Demesse, R. Semezis, E. Naoumoff
(r1993) Concert (9/94) (MARC) ① **8 223636**
Psalm 24—chorus and orchestra (1916)
(Wds. Bible)
M. Sénéchal, J-J. Grunenwald, E. Brasseur Chorale,
Lamoureux Orch, I. Markevitch Concert
(8/92) (EMI) ① **CDM7 64281-2**
Psalm 129—baritone, male chorus and orchestra (1916)
P. Mollet, E. Brasseur Chorale, Lamoureux Orch, I.
Markevitch Concert (8/92) (EMI) ① **CDM7 64281-2**
Reflets—mélodie (1911) (Wds. M.
Maeterlinck)
M. Shirai, H. Höll Concert
(4/90) (BAYE) ① **BR100041**
Renouveau—soloists, choir and piano (1911)
(Wds. A. Silvestre)
C. Friedek, R. Böhm, Heidelberg Madrigal Ch, S.
Eberspächer, G. Kegelmann Concert
(4/90) (BAYE) ① **BR100041**
Le Retour—mélodie (1912) (Wds. G.
Delaquys)
M. Shirai, H. Höll Concert
(4/90) (BAYE) ① **BR100041**
Doris Reinhardt, E. Naoumoff (r1993) Concert
(9/94) (MARC) ① **8 223636**
Les Sirènes—soprano, choir and piano (1911) (Wds. Grandmougin)
C. Friedek, Heidelberg Madrigal Ch, S. Eberspächer,
G. Kegelmann Concert
(4/90) (BAYE) ① **BR100041**
Soir sur la Plaine—soprano, tenor, choir and piano (1913) (Wds. A. Samain)
C. Friedek, B. Gärtner, Heidelberg Madrigal Ch, S.
Eberspächer, G. Kegelmann Concert
(4/90) (BAYE) ① **BR100041**
Vieille prière bouddhique—tenor, chorus and orchestra (1917)
M. Sénéchal, E. Brasseur Chorale, Lamoureux Orch,
I. Markevitch Concert
(8/92) (EMI) ① **CDM7 64281-2**

BOULANGER, Nadia (1887–1979) France

SECTION II: CHAMBER

3 Pièces—cello and piano (1915)
1. Modéré; 2. Sans vitesse et à l'aise; 3. Vite et
nerveusement rythmé.
N. Fischer, J.K. Fischer Concert
(9/91) (NORT) ① **NR238-CD**
1, 2. R. Pidoux, E. Naoumoff (r1993) Concert
(9/94) (MARC) ① **8 223636**

SECTION III: INSTRUMENTAL

Vers la vie nouvelle—piano (1919)
E. Naoumoff (r1993) Concert
(9/94) (MARC) ① **8 223636**

SECTION IV: VOCAL AND CHORAL

Le Cocteau—1v and piano (1922) (Wds
adapted C Mauclair)
1, 2. S. Robert, E. Naoumoff (r1993) Concert
(9/94) (MARC) ① **8 223636**
Lux aeterna—soprano, harp, violin and cello (1918)
I. Sabrié, Francis Pierre, O. Charlier, R. Semezis, E.
Naoumoff (r1993) Concert
(9/94) (MARC) ① **8 223636**

BOULEZ, Pierre (b 1925) France

SECTION I: ORCHESTRAL

Dérive (1984)
London Sinfonietta, G. Benjamin Concert
(10/89) (NIMB) ① **NI5167**
Eclat/Multiples—15 instruments/orchestra (1965-70)
Paris InterContemporain Ens, P. Boulez Rituel in
memoriam Maderna. (8/90) (SONY) ① **SMK45839**
...explosante-fixe...—computer-transformed flutes & chamber orchestra (1991-93)
S. Cherrier, E. Ophèle, P-A. Valade, Paris
InterContemporain Ens, P. Boulez (r1994) Concert
(12/95) (DG) ① **445 833-2GH**
Figures, Doubles, Prismes—orchestra (1957 rev 1963-68)
BBC SO, P. Boulez Concert
(12/90) (ERAT) ① **2292-45494-2**
Memoriale—flute and chamber orchestra (1976)
S. Bell, London Sinfonietta, G. Benjamin Concert
(10/89) (NIMB) ① **NI5167**
12 Notations—orchestra (1945 rev 1978)
P-L. Aimard, Paris InterContemporain Ens, P. Boulez
(r1993) Concert (12/95) (DG) ① **445 833-2GH**
1-4. VPO, C. Abbado (pp1988) Concert
(4/90) (DG) ① **429 260-2GH**
1-4. Paris Orch, D. Barenboim Concert
(10/90) (ERAT) ① **2292-45493-2**
Rituel in memoriam Bruno Maderna (1974)
BBC SO, P. Boulez Eclat/Multiples.
(8/90) (SONY) ① **SMK45839**
Paris Orch, D. Barenboim Concert
(10/90) (ERAT) ① **2292-45493-2**

SECTION II: CHAMBER

Domaines for clarinet and 21 instruments (1968)
M. Portal, Musique Vivante Ens, D. Masson
(3/89) (HARM) ① **HMA190 930**
Messagesquisse—7 celli (1977)
Paris Orch, D. Barenboim Concert
(10/90) (ERAT) ① **2292-45493-2**
T. Demenga, Cello Ens, J. Wyttenbach (r1993)
Concert (8/95) (ECM) ① **[2] 445 234-2**
Structures pour deux pianos, Livre 1 (1952)
Alfons Kontarsky, Aloys Kontarsky Structures, Bk 2.
(6/93) (WERG) ① **WER6011-2**
Structures pour deux pianos, Livre 2 (1956-61)
Alfons Kontarsky, Aloys Kontarsky Structures, Bk 1.
(6/93) (WERG) ① **WER6011-2**
P-L. Aimard, F. Boffard, Paris InterContemporain
Ens, P. Boulez (r1994) Concert
(12/95) (DG) ① **445 833-2GH**

SECTION III: INSTRUMENTAL

Domaines—clarinet (1968) (original version for
solo clarinet)
P. Meyer (r1993) Concert
(7/95) (DENO) ① **CO-78917**
Sonata for Piano No. 1 (1946)
C. Helffer Concert (8/88) (ASTR) ① **E7716**
I. Biret (r1995) Concert
(11/95) (NAXO) ① **8 553353**
Sonata for Piano No. 2 (1948)
C. Helffer Concert (8/88) (ASTR) ① **E7716**
M. Pollini (1976) Concert
(6/95) (DG) ① **447 431-2GOR**
I. Biret (r1995) Concert
(11/95) (NAXO) ① **8 553353**
Sonata for Piano No. 3 (1955-57)
C. Helffer Concert (8/88) (ASTR) ① **E7716**
I. Biret (r1995) Concert
(11/95) (NAXO) ① **8 553353**

SECTION IV: VOCAL AND CHORAL

Improvisation sur Mallarmé I—soprano and chamber ensemble/orchestra (1957)
E. Sziklay, Budapest Chbr Ens, A. Mihály Concert
(10/87) (HUNG) ① **HCD11385**
Improvisation sur Mallarmé II—soprano and chamber ensemble (1957)
E. Sziklay, Budapest Chbr Ens, A. Mihály Concert
(10/87) (HUNG) ① **HCD11385**
Pli selon pli (1957-62)
P. Bryn-Julson, BBC SO, P. Boulez (r1981)
(12/90) (ERAT) ① **2292-45376-2**
Les Soleil des eaux—soprano, chorus and orchestra (1948 rev 1958, 1965) (Wds. R.
Char: org music for radio play)
P. Bryn-Julson, BBC Sngrs, BBC SO, P. Boulez
Concert (12/90) (ERAT) ① **2292-45494-2**

J. Nendick, L. Devos, B. McDaniel, BBC Chor, BBC
SO, P. Boulez Concert
(3/92) (EMI) ① **CDM7 63948-2**
Le visage nuptial—soprano, contralto, chorus and orchestra (1946 rev 1951, 1988-89) (Wds. R.Char)
P. Bryn-Julson, E. Laurence, BBC Sngrs, BBC SO,
P. Boulez Concert (12/90) (ERAT) ① **2292-45494-2**

BOURGAULT-DUCOUDRAY, Louis (Albert) (1840–1910) France

SECTION V: STAGE WORKS

Thamara—opera: 2 acts (1891—Paris) (Lib. L.
Gallet)
Belle d'une beauté fatale A. Affre, orch (r1907-8)
Concert (8/92) (IRCC) ① **IRCC-CD802**

BOURGEOIS, Derek (David) (b 1941) England

SECTION I: ORCHESTRAL

Concerto for Trombone and Orchestra, Op. 114b
C. Lindberg, City of London Wind Ens, G. Brand
Concert (3/90) (LDR) ① **LDRCD1012**
C. Lindberg, BBC Nat Orch of Wales, G. Llewellyn
(r1993) Concert (10/95) (BIS) ① **BIS-CD658**

SECTION III: INSTRUMENTAL

Serenade—organ, Op. 22
C. Herrick Concert (5/89) (HYPE) ① **CDA66258**
City of London Wind Ens, G. Brand (r1991: arr
concert band) Concert
(7/89) (LDR) ① **LDRCD1001**
Variations on a theme of Herbert Howells—organ, Op. 87 (1984)
C. Herrick Concert (10/92) (HYPE) ① **CDA66605**

BOURGEOIS, Emile (?–1922) France

SECTION IV: VOCAL AND CHORAL

La véritable manola—song
L. David, anon (r1905) Concert
(12/94) (SYM?) ① **SYMCD1172**

BOURGEOIS, Louis (c1510–1561) France

SECTION IV: VOCAL AND CHORAL

Psalm 137—Estans assis aux rives aquatiques (pub 1547)
Baltimore Consort (r1992; arr Baltimore Consort)
Concert (4/95) (DORI) ① **DOR90177**

BOUZIGNAC, Guillaume (before 1592–after 1641) France

SECTION IV: VOCAL AND CHORAL

Alleluja, Deus dixit—motet: 5vv
C. de Corbiac, F. Gédéon, O. Flusin, S. Maciejewski,
R. Taylor, Contrepoint Voc Ens, Brussels Ludi Musici
Ens, O. Schneebeli Concert
(1/89) (AUVI) ① **AV6108**
Alleluia, Fundite rores—motet: 6vv
C. de Corbiac, F. Gédéon, O. Flusin, S. Maciejewski,
R. Taylor, Contrepoint Voc Ens, Brussels Ludi Musici
Ens, O. Schneebeli Concert
(1/89) (AUVI) ① **AV6108**
Alleluia, Venite amici—motet: 5vv
C. de Corbiac, F. Gédéon, O. Flusin, S. Maciejewski,
R. Taylor, Contrepoint Voc Ens, Brussels Ludi Musici
Ens, O. Schneebeli Concert
(1/89) (AUVI) ① **AV6108**
Pages de la Chapelle, Arts Florissants Chor, O.
Gibbons Viol Ens, Arts Florissants Instr Ens, W.
Christie (r1993) Concert
(6/94) (HARM) ① **HMC90 1471**
Ave Maria—motet
Pages de la Chapelle, Arts Florissants Chor, O.
Gibbons Viol Ens, Arts Florissants Instr Ens, W.
Christie (r1993) Concert
(6/94) (HARM) ① **HMC90 1471**
Cantate Domino, omnis Francia—motet: 5vv
C. de Corbiac, F. Gédéon, O. Flusin, S. Maciejewski,
R. Taylor, Contrepoint Voc Ens, Brussels Ludi Musici
Ens, O. Schneebeli Concert
(1/89) (AUVI) ① **AV6108**

Chère Phylis—chanson
C. de Corbiac, F. Gédéon, O. Flusin, S. Maciejewski,
R. Taylor, Contrepoint Voc Ens, Brussels Ludi Musici
Ens, O. Schneebeli *Concert*
(1/89) (AUVI) ① **AV6108**
Clamant clavi—motet
Pages de la Chapelle, Arts Florissants Chor, O.
Gibbons Viol Ens, Arts Florissants Instr Ens, W.
Christie (r1993) *Concert*
(6/94) (HARM) ① **HMC90 1471**
Dum silentium—motet
Pages de la Chapelle, Arts Florissants Chor, O.
Gibbons Viol Ens, Arts Florissants Instr Ens, W.
Christie (r1993) *Concert*
(6/94) (HARM) ① **HMC90 1471**
Ecce aurora—motet
Pages de la Chapelle, Arts Florissants Chor, O.
Gibbons Viol Ens, Arts Florissants Instr Ens, W.
Christie (r1993) *Concert*
(6/94) (HARM) ① **HMC90 1471**
Ecce festivitas amoris—5vv
C. de Corbiac, F. Gédéon, O. Flusin, S. Maciejewski,
R. Taylor, Contrepoint Voc Ens, Brussels Ludi Musici
Ens, O. Schneebeli *Concert*
(1/89) (AUVI) ① **AV6108**
Pages de la Chapelle, Arts Florissants Chor, O.
Gibbons Viol Ens, Arts Florissants Instr Ens, W.
Christie (r1993) *Concert*
(6/94) (HARM) ① **HMC90 1471**
Ecce homo—motet
Pages de la Chapelle, Arts Florissants Chor, O.
Gibbons Viol Ens, Arts Florissants Instr Ens, W.
Christie (r1993) *Concert*
(6/94) (HARM) ① **HMC90 1471**
Ego gaudebo in Domino—motet: 5vv
C. de Corbiac, F. Gédéon, O. Flusin, S. Maciejewski,
R. Taylor, Contrepoint Voc Ens, Brussels Ludi Musici
Ens, O. Schneebeli *Concert*
(1/89) (AUVI) ① **AV6108**
Flos in floris tempore—motet
Pages de la Chapelle, Arts Florissants Chor, O.
Gibbons Viol Ens, Arts Florissants Instr Ens, W.
Christie (r1993) *Concert*
(6/94) (HARM) ① **HMC90 1471**
**Gaudeamus omnes in die
Assumptionis—motet: 8vv**
C. de Corbiac, F. Gédéon, O. Flusin, S. Maciejewski,
R. Taylor, Contrepoint Voc Ens, Brussels Ludi Musici
Ens, O. Schneebeli *Concert*
(1/89) (AUVI) ① **AV6108**
Ha, plange, filia Jerusalem—motet
Pages de la Chapelle, Arts Florissants Chor, O.
Gibbons Viol Ens, Arts Florissants Instr Ens, W.
Christie (r1993) *Concert*
(6/94) (HARM) ① **HMC90 1471**
A. Azéma, F. Jodry, W. Hite, C. Kale, D. McCabe, P.
Guttry, Boston Schola Cantorum, Boston Camerata,
J. Cohen (r1994) *Concert*
(11/95) (ERAT) ① **4509-98480-2**
**Heureux séjour de Parthénisse—chanson:
4vv**
C. de Corbiac, F. Gédéon, O. Flusin, S. Maciejewski,
R. Taylor, Contrepoint Voc Ens, Brussels Ludi Musici
Ens, O. Schneebeli *Concert*
(1/89) (AUVI) ① **AV6108**
Hodie cum gaudio—motet: 5vv
C. de Corbiac, F. Gédéon, O. Flusin, S. Maciejewski,
R. Taylor, Contrepoint Voc Ens, Brussels Ludi Musici
Ens, O. Schneebeli *Concert*
(1/89) (AUVI) ① **AV6108**
In pace in idipsum—motet: 4vv
Pages de la Chapelle, Arts Florissants Chor, O.
Gibbons Viol Ens, Arts Florissants Instr Ens, W.
Christie (r1993) *Concert*
(6/94) (HARM) ① **HMC90 1471**
Jubilate Deo—motet
Pages de la Chapelle, Arts Florissants Chor, O.
Gibbons Viol Ens, Arts Florissants Instr Ens, W.
Christie (r1993) *Concert*
(6/94) (HARM) ① **HMC90 1471**
Noë, noë, pastores, cantate Domino—5vv
C. de Corbiac, F. Gédéon, O. Flusin, S. Maciejewski,
R. Taylor, Contrepoint Voc Ens, Brussels Ludi Musici
Ens, O. Schneebeli *Concert*
(1/89) (AUVI) ① **AV6108**
O mors, ero mors tua—5vv
C. de Corbiac, F. Gédéon, O. Flusin, S. Maciejewski,
R. Taylor, Contrepoint Voc Ens, Brussels Ludi Musici
Ens, O. Schneebeli *Concert*
(1/89) (AUVI) ① **AV6108**
Pages de la Chapelle, Arts Florissants Chor, O.
Gibbons Viol Ens, Arts Florissants Instr Ens, W.
Christie (r1993) *Concert*
(6/94) (HARM) ① **HMC90 1471**

Quaerem quem diligit—motet: 5vv
C. de Corbiac, F. Gédéon, O. Flusin, S. Maciejewski,
R. Taylor, Contrepoint Voc Ens, Brussels Ludi Musici
Ens, O. Schneebeli *Concert*
(1/89) (AUVI) ① **AV6108**
Ruisseau qui cours—chanson: 4vv
C. de Corbiac, F. Gédéon, O. Flusin, S. Maciejewski,
R. Taylor, Contrepoint Voc Ens, Brussels Ludi Musici
Ens, O. Schneebeli *Concert*
(1/89) (AUVI) ① **AV6108**
Salve Jesus piissime—motet: 5vv
C. de Corbiac, F. Gédéon, O. Flusin, S. Maciejewski,
R. Taylor, Contrepoint Voc Ens, Brussels Ludi Musici
Ens, O. Schneebeli *Concert*
(1/89) (AUVI) ① **AV6108**
Pages de la Chapelle, Arts Florissants Chor, O.
Gibbons Viol Ens, Arts Florissants Instr Ens, W.
Christie (r1993) *Concert*
(6/94) (HARM) ① **HMC90 1471**
Te Deum—8vv
C. de Corbiac, F. Gédéon, O. Flusin, S. Maciejewski,
R. Taylor, Contrepoint Voc Ens, Brussels Ludi Musici
Ens, O. Schneebeli *Concert*
(1/89) (AUVI) ① **AV6108**
Pages de la Chapelle, Arts Florissants Chor, O.
Gibbons Viol Ens, Arts Florissants Instr Ens, W.
Christie (r1993) *Concert*
(6/94) (HARM) ① **HMC90 1471**
Tota pulchra es—motet
Pages de la Chapelle, Arts Florissants Chor, O.
Gibbons Viol Ens, Arts Florissants Instr Ens, W.
Christie (r1993) *Concert*
(6/94) (HARM) ① **HMC90 1471**
Unus ex vobis—motet: 5vv
Pages de la Chapelle, Arts Florissants Chor, O.
Gibbons Viol Ens, Arts Florissants Instr Ens, W.
Christie (r1993) *Concert*
(6/94) (HARM) ① **HMC90 1471**
D. McCabe, Boston Schola Cantorum, Boston
Camerata, J. Cohen (r1994) *Concert*
(11/95) (ERAT) ① **4509-98480-2**
Vulnerasti cor meum—motet
Pages de la Chapelle, Arts Florissants Chor, O.
Gibbons Viol Ens, Arts Florissants Instr Ens, W.
Christie (r1993) *Concert*
(6/94) (HARM) ① **HMC90 1471**

BOVICELLI, Giovanni Battista (fl 1592–1594) Italy

SECTION IV: VOCAL AND CHORAL

**Regole, passaggi di musica, madrigali et
motetti passeggiati (1594)** (treatise on
improvisation & ornamentation)
1. Angelus ad pastores (Rore); 2. Io son ferito ahi
lasso (Palestrina).
1, 2. B. Dickey, Tragicomedia *Concert*
(6/92) (ACCE) ① **ACC9173D**

BOVIO, L. (19th Cent) Italy

SECTION IV: VOCAL AND CHORAL

Cara piccina—song
L. Tetrazzini, orch (r1922) *Concert*
(9/92) (PEAR) ① **GEMMCD9225**

BOWEN, Brian

SECTION I: ORCHESTRAL

**Euphonium Music—euphonium and brass
band (1978)**
R. Childs, Britannia Building Soc Band, H. Snell
Concert (2/91) (DOYE) ① **DOYCD002**

BOWEN, (Edwin) York (1884–1961) England

SECTION II: CHAMBER

Sonata for Oboe and Piano, Op. 85 (1930)
J. Polmear, D. Ambache *Concert*
(9/92) (UNIC) ① **DKPCD9121**

SECTION III: INSTRUMENTAL

Berceuse in D—piano, Op. 93 (1928)
M-C. Girod (r1994) *Concert*
(12/95) (3DCL) ① **3D8012**
Nocturne in A flat—piano, Op. 78 (1925)
M-C. Girod (r1994) *Concert*
(12/95) (3DCL) ① **3D8012**
Partita in D minor—piano, Op. 156 (1957)
M-C. Girod (r1994) *Concert*
(12/95) (3DCL) ① **3D8012**

**24 Preludes in All Keys—piano, Op. 102
(1940)**
M-C. Girod (r1994) *Concert*
(12/95) (3DCL) ① **3D8012**
Rêverie in B—piano, Op. 86 (1928)
M-C. Girod (r1994) *Concert*
(12/95) (3DCL) ① **3D8012**

BOWLES, Paul (b 1910) USA

SECTION II: CHAMBER

Cross-Country—piano
B. Lerner *Concert* (12/89) (ETCE) ① **KTC1036**
Music for a Farce—suite (1938) (arr from
stage music to play 'Too Much Johnson')
Chicago Pro Musica *Concert*
(8/89) (REFE) ① **RRCD-29**

SECTION III: INSTRUMENTAL

Dance—piano
B. Lerner *Concert* (12/89) (ETCE) ① **KTC1036**
6 Latin-American Pieces—piano (1937-48)
1. Huapango; 2. El Bejuco; 3. Tierra Mojado; 4.
Orosi; 5. La Cuelga; 6. Huapango 2.
B. Lerner *Concert* (12/88) (ETCE) ① **KTC1019**
6 Preludes—piano (1934-35)
B. Lerner *Concert* (12/88) (ETCE) ① **KTC1019**
Sonatina—piano (1932/5)
B. Lerner *Concert* (12/89) (ETCE) ① **KTC1036**

BOXBERG, Christian Ludwig (1670–1729) Germany

SECTION IV: VOCAL AND CHORAL

Bestelle dein haus—funeral cantata: 4vv
(Wds. Bible)
G. de Reyghere, J. Bowman, G. de Mey, M. van
Egmond, Ricercar Consort *Concert*
(7/91) (RICE) ① **RIC079061**

BOYCE, William (1711–1779) England

SECTION I: ORCHESTRAL

Concerto Grosso in B flat
Cantilena, A. Shepherd *Concert*
(6/92) (CHAN) ① **CHAN6541**
**Concerto grosso in B minor—2 violins, cello
and strings**
Thames CO, M. Dobson *Concert*
(6/87) (CRD) ① **CRD3331**
Cantilena, A. Shepherd *Concert*
(6/92) (CHAN) ① **CHAN6541**
Concerto Grosso in E flat
Cantilena, A. Shepherd *Concert*
(6/92) (CHAN) ① **CHAN6541**
**Concerto grosso in E minor—2 violins, cello
and strings**
Thames CO, M. Dobson *Concert*
(6/87) (CRD) ① **CRD3331**
12 Overtures (pub 1770) (orig sources in
parentheses)
1. D (Birthday Ode, 1762); 2. G (Birthday Ode, 1765);
3. B flat (New Year Ode, 1763); 4. D (St James's
Park Ode, 1763); 5. F (New Year Ode, 1762); 6. D
minor (Secular Masque, 1746); 7. G (New Year Ode,
1765); 8. D (Birthday Ode, 1761); 9. D (New Year
Ode, 1768); 10. F (Birthday Ode, 1764); 11. D
(Birthday Ode, 1766); 12. G (New Year Ode, 1767).
1-9. Cantilena, A. Shepherd
(10/91) (CHAN) ① **CHAN6531**
10-12. Cantilena, A. Shepherd *Concert*
(6/92) (CHAN) ① **CHAN6541**
8 Symphonies, Op. 2 (pub 1760) (orig sources
in parentheses)
1. B flat (New Year Ode, 1756); 2. A (Birthday Ode,
1756); 3. C (The Chaplet, 1749); 4. F (Shepherds'
Lottery, 1751); 5. D (St Cecilia' Day Ode, 1739); 6. F
(Solomon, 1742); 7. B flat (Pythian Ode, 1740); 8. D
minor (Worcester Overture, ?1737 or 1755).
AAM, C. Hogwood (1992)
(4/94) (L'OI) ① **436 761-2OH**
Bournemouth Sinfonietta, R. Thomas (vn/dir)
(5/86) (CRD) ① **CRD3356**
English Concert, T. Pinnock
(9/87) (ARCH) ① **419 631-2AH**
1. English Concert, T. Pinnock (hpd/dir) (r1979)
Concert (1/93) (ARCH) ① **437 088-2AT**
4. H. Snell Brass, H. Snell (arr Snell) *Concert*
(9/91) (POLY) ① **QPRZ005D**
5(Gavotte) I. Tracey (r1990; arr Tracey) *Concert*
(4/91) (MIRA) ① **MRCD901**

SECTION II: CHAMBER

12 Sonatas—two violins and continuo (1747)
EXCERPTS: 3. A; 12. G; 12a. Gavotte.
12a I. Scharrer (r c1927: arr Craxton: pf) *Concert*
(7/94) (PEAR) ① **GEMMCD9978**

SECTION III: INSTRUMENTAL

10 Voluntaries—keyboard (pub 1779)
1. No 1 in D; 7. No 7.
Nos. 1, 2, 4, 10. A. Wills *Concert*
(4/92) (SAGA) ① **EC3379-2**
Nos. 1, 4, 7. G. Cooper *Concert*
(10/92) (CRD) ① **CRD3483**
1. A. Stringer, N. Rawsthorne (r1994) *Concert*
(11/87) (CRD) ① **CRD3308**
1. Margaret Phillips *Concert*
(5/91) (GAMU) ① **GAMCD514**
1. J. Bate *Concert* (11/91) (UNIC) ① **DKPCD9106**
7. T. Dart (r1957) *Concert* (5/95) (JMS) ① **JMSCD1**

SECTION IV: VOCAL AND CHORAL

By the waters of Babylon—verse anthem (c1740)
Ely Cath Ch, A. Wills *Concert*
(4/92) (SAGA) ① **EC3379-2**
New College Ch, E. Higginbottom *Concert*
(10/92) (CRD) ① **CRD3483**
I have surely built thee an house—verse anthem (1759)
Ely Cath Ch, A. Wills *Concert*
(4/92) (SAGA) ① **EC3379-2**
New College Ch, E. Higginbottom *Concert*
(10/92) (CRD) ① **CRD3483**
The Lord is King be the people never so impatient—verse anthem (1763) (thanksgiving for the piece)
New College Ch, E. Higginbottom *Concert*
(10/92) (CRD) ① **CRD3483**
O give thanks—verse anthem (1762) (for the birth of Prince George)
New College Ch, E. Higginbottom *Concert*
(10/92) (CRD) ① **CRD3483**
O praise the Lord—verse anthem (c1763)
New College Ch, E. Higginbottom *Concert*
(10/92) (CRD) ① **CRD3483**
O where shall wisdom be found?—anthem (?1769)
New College Ch, D. Burchell, E. Higginbottom *Concert* (10/89) (MERI) ① **CDE84151**
Magdalen Oxford Coll Ch, J. Harper *Concert*
(11/91) (ABBE) ① **CDCA912**
Norwich Cath Ch, M. Nicholas, N. Taylor *Concert*
(3/92) (PRIO) ① **PRCD351**
New College Ch, E. Higginbottom *Concert*
(10/92) (CRD) ① **CRD3483**
Solomon—serenata: soprano, tenor, chorus and orchestra (1743) (Wds. E. Moore)
PART ONE: 1. Overture; 2. Behold, Jerusalem; 3. From the mountains, lo! he comes; 4. Tell me, lovely shepherd; 5. Fairest of the virgin throng; 6. As the rich apple, on whose boughs; 7. Beneath this ample shade I lay; 8. Who quits the lily's fleecy white; 9. Balmy sweetness, ever flowing; 10a. Let not my prince; 10b. Ah, simple mel; 11. Fair and comely is my love; 12. Forbear, O charming swain; 13. Fill with cooling juice the bowl! PART TWO: 14. Sinfonia; 15a. The cheerful spring; 15b. Arise, my fair, and come away; 16. Together let us range the fields; 17. How lovely art thou to the sight; 18. Let me, love, thy bole ascending; 19. O, that a sister's specious name; 20. Soft, I adjure you, by the fawns; 21. My fair's a garden of delight; 22. Softly rise, O southern breeze! PART THREE: 23. Arise, my fair, the doors unfold; 24. Obedient to thy voice I hie; 25. Ye blooming virgins; 26. Who is thy love, O charming maid!; 27. On his face the vernal rose; 28. This, O ye virgins; 29. Sweet nymph, whom nudder charms adorn; 30. O take me! stamp me on thy breast!; 31a. Thou soft invader of the soul (duet); 31b. In vain we trace the globe (chorus).
Cpte B. Mills, H. Crook, Parley of Instr Ch, Parley of Instr, R. Goodman (11/90) (HYPE) ① **CDA66378**
4. L. Garrett, RPO, P. Robinson (r1994) *Concert*
(4/95) (SILV) ① **SILKD6004**
Spring Gardens—song: 1v
E. Tubb, F. Kelly (r1992) *Concert*
(9/94) (MOSC) ① **070987**
Tell me, ye brooks—cantata: 1v (pub 1748) (in Lyra Britannica III)
E. Tubb, F. Kelly (r1992) *Concert*
(9/94) (MOSC) ① **070987**
Turn Thee unto me—anthem (?1736)
New College Ch, D. Burchell, E. Higginbottom *Concert* (10/89) (MERI) ① **CDE84151**

Ely Cath Ch, A. Wills *Concert*
(4/92) (SAGA) ① **EC3379-2**
New College Ch, E. Higginbottom *Concert*
(10/92) (CRD) ① **CRD3483**
Wherewithal shall a young man—verse anthem (1743)
New College Ch, E. Higginbottom *Concert*
(10/92) (CRD) ① **CRD3483**

BOYDELL, Brian (b 1917) Ireland

SECTION II: CHAMBER

String Quartet No. 2, Op. 44 (1959)
Vanbrugh Qt (r1993) *Concert*
(10/94) (CHAN) ① **CHAN9295**

BOYLE, Malcolm (1902–1976) England

SECTION IV: VOCAL AND CHORAL

Thou, O God, art praised in Sion—anthem
Southwark Cath Ch, P. Wright, S. Layton (r1992)
Concert (7/94) (PRIO) ① **PRCD435**

BOYVIN, Jacques (c1649–1706) France

SECTION III: INSTRUMENTAL

Livre d'orgue contenant les huit tons à l'usage ordinaire de l'Eglise—Book 2—organ (pub 1700)
1. Premier ton: 3. Troisième ton: 3a. Concert de Flûtes; 4. Quartième ton: 4a. Suite; 5. Quinzième ton: 5a. Prélude-Grand Plein Jeu; 5b. Récit; 5c. Grand Dialogue à quatre coeurs.
4a A. Isoir *Concert* (6/90) (CALL) ① **CAL9916**

BOZZA, Eugène (1905–1991) France

SECTION II: CHAMBER

En forêt—horn and piano (1941)
B. Tuckwell, D. Blumenthal *Concert*
(11/92) (ETCE) ① **KTC1135**
3 Impressions—flute and piano (1953)
R. Aitken, R. McCabe *Concert*
(9/89) (BIS) ① **BIS-CD184**
3 Pièces pour une musique de nuit—flute, oboe, clarinet and bassoon (1954)
Selandia Ens *Concert* (6/90) (KONT) ① **32032**
Pulcinella—clarinet and piano (1944)
J. Cohler, J. Gordon (r1993) *Concert*
(5/95) (CRYS) ① **Crystal CD733**
Rustiques—trumpet and piano
W. Marsalis, J.L. Stillman (r1992) *Concert*
(5/94) (SONY) ① **SK47193**
Scherzo—wind quintet
Berlin Phil Wind Qnt *Concert*
(4/93) (BIS) ① **BIS-CD536**
Sonata for Oboe and Piano (1971)
N. Daniel, J. Drake (1990) *Concert*
(11/94) (VIRG) ① **CUV5 61141-2**

BRACCO, C.A (fl 1885–1894) Italy

SECTION IV: VOCAL AND CHORAL

Serenata—song (Wds. Caruso)
E. Caruso, orch, J. Pasternack (r1919) *Concert*
(7/91) (RCA) ① **[12] GD60495(6)**
E. Caruso, orch, J. Pasternack (r1919) *Concert*
(10/91) (PEAR) ① **[3] EVC4(2)**

BRACHROGGE, Hans (d c1638) Denmark

SECTION IV: VOCAL AND CHORAL

Io ardo in vivo foco—madrigal: 3vv (pub 1619)
Consort of Musicke, A. Rooley (Ite/dir) *Concert*
(2/89) (BIS) ① **BIS-CD392**

BRADE, William (1560–1630) England

SECTION II: CHAMBER

Coral—violin and piano
New London Consort, P. Pickett (1992) *Concert*
(4/94) (LINN) ① **CKD011**

Sonnerie Trio (r1992) *Concert*
(5/94) (TELD) ① **4509-90841-2**
Newe ausserlesene liebliche Branden—dances (pub 1617)
Masque Dance London Musica Antiqua, M. Uridge (r1980-83) *Concert*
(12/93) (SYMP) ① **SYMCD1157**
Newe ausserlesene Paduanen, Galliarden, Canzonen, Allmand und Coranten—consort pieces in five parts (pub 1609)
Excs Lautten Compagney (r1990/1) *Concert*
(6/93) (CAPR) ① **10 431**

SECTION III: INSTRUMENTAL

Paduana and Galliard—lute (pub 1607)
J. Lindberg *Concert* (2/89) (BIS) ① **BIS-CD390**
Toulon Musica Antiqua, C. Mendoze *Concert*
(9/93) (PIER) ① **PV787092**

BRAEIN, Edvard Fliflet (1924–1976) Norway

SECTION V: STAGE WORKS

Anne Pedersdotter—opera: 4 acts (1971—Oslo) (Lib H. Kristiansen, after H. Wiers-Jensen)
Cpte K. Ekeberg, S. Carlsen, V. Hanssen, K. M. Sandve, R. Eriksen, S. A. Thorsen, T. Stensvold, C. Ehrstedt, G. Oskarsson, A. Helleland, I. M. Brekke, T. Gilje, R. Nygård, Norwegian Nat Op Chor, Norwegian Nat Op Orch, P. Å. Andersson (r1991)
(12/94) (SIMA) ① **[2] PSC3121**

BRAGA, Gaetano (1829–1907) Italy

SECTION IV: VOCAL AND CHORAL

7 Melodies (1867)
5. La serenata (Angel's serenade: wds. M. M. Marcello).
5. J. McCormack, F. Kreisler, V. O'Brien (Eng: r1914) *Concert* (9/89) (PEAR) ① **GEMMCD9315**
5. F. Alda, M. Elman, F. La Forge (r1915) *Concert*
(10/91) (BIDD) ① **LAB039**
5. L. Tetrazzini, inst ens (r1914) *Concert*
(9/92) (EMI) ① **[3] CHS7 63802-2(2)**
5. L. Tetrazzini, inst ens (r1914) *Concert*
(9/92) (PEAR) ① **GEMMCD9223**
5. A. Adini, anon (r1905) *Concert*
(1/95) (SYMP) ① **SYMCD1172**
5. C. Muzio, orch (r1918: Eng) *Concert*
(1/95) (ROMO) ① **[2] 81010-2**
5. E. Rethberg, M. Rosen, F. Persson (r1926: Eng) *Concert* (2/95) (ROMO) ① **[2] 81012-2**
5. E. Rethberg, F. Fradkin, anon (r1925: Eng) *Concert* (2/95) (ROMO) ① **[2] 81012-2**

BRAHMS, Johannes (1833–1897) Germany

SECTION I: ORCHESTRAL

Academic Festival Overture, Op. 80 (1880)
VPO, L. Bernstein (pp1982) *Double Concerto.*
(11/84) (DG) ① **410 031-2GH**
VPO, L. Bernstein (pp) *Concert*
(11/88) (DG) ① **[4] 415 570-2GX4**
BRSO, Colin Davis (r1988) *Symphony 2.*
(9/89) (RCA) ① **RD87980**
Philh, O. Klemperer *Concert*
(1/90) (EMI) ① **CDM7 69651-2**
NBC SO, A. Toscanini (bp1948) *Concert*
(5/90) (RCA) ① **[4] GD60325**
Belgian Rad & TV Orch, A. Rahbari *Concert*
(10/90) (NAXO) ① **8 550281**
VPO, J. Barbirolli *Concert*
(11/90) (EMI) ① **CDM7 63537-2**
Cleveland Orch, G. Szell *Concert*
(3/91) (SONY) ① **SBK46330**
Philh, F. d'Avalos *Concert*
(9/91) (ASV) ① **CDDCA744**
Chicago SO, G. Solti *Concert*
(4/92) (DECC) ① **[4] 430 799-2DC4**
RPO, A. Litton *Symphony 1.*
(10/92) (VIRG) ① **VJ7 59673-2**
NYPO, L. Bernstein (r1963) *Concert*
(11/92) (SONY) ① **SMK47538**
BBC PO, G. Herbig *Symphony 1.*
(12/92) (COLL) ① **Coll3049-2**
LPO, W. Sawallisch *Symphony 3.*
(4/93) (EMI) ① **CDC7 54523-2**
Curtis Inst Student Orch, F. Reiner (pp1937) *Concert*
(5/93) (VAI) ① **[2] VAIA1020**
NYPO, K. Masur (pp1992) *Symphony 2.*
(5/93) (TELD) ① **9031-77291-2**

RPO, A. Previn (r1987) *Symphony 4.*
(1/94) (TELA) ① **CD82006**
Vienna SO, W. Sawallisch (r1961) *Concert*
(5/94) (PHIL) ① [2] **438 760-2PM2**
Concertgebouw, B. Haitink (r1972) *Concert*
(9/94) (PHIL) ① [4] **442 068-2PB4**
Chicago SO, D. Barenboim (r1993) *Concert*
(11/94) (ERAT) ① [4] **4509-94817-2**
Chicago SO, D. Barenboim (r1993) *Symphony 4.*
(11/94) (ERAT) ① **4509-95194-2**
LSO, P. Monteux (r1962) *Concert*
(12/94) (PHIL) ① [5] **442 544-2PM5**
VPO, L. Bernstein (pp1982) *Symphony 2.*
(12/94) (DG) ① **445 506-2GMA**
Hallé, S. Skrowaczewski (r1987) *Symphony 1.*
(10/95) (CARL) ① **PCD2014**
Concerto for Piano and Orchestra No. 1 in D
minor, Op. 15 (1854-58)
Vladimir Ashkenazy, Concertgebouw, B. Haitink
(7/83) (DECC) ① **410 009-2DH**
K. Zimerman, VPO, L. Bernstein (pp)
(5/86) (DG) ① **413 472-2GH**
Emil Gilels, BPO, E. Jochum *Concert*
(9/86) (DG) ① [2] **419 158-2GH2**
M. Pollini, VPO, K. Böhm
(8/87) (DG) ① **419 470-2GGA**
A. Brendel, BPO, C. Abbado
(11/87) (PHIL) ① **420 071-2PH**
Barry Douglas, LSO, S. Skrowaczewski (r1988)
(3/89) (RCA) ① **RD87780**
I. Margalit, LSO, B. Thomson *Mendelssohn:*
Capriccio brillant, Op. 22.
(11/89) (CHAN) ① **CHAN8724**
D. Barenboim, New Philh, J. Barbirolli (r1967) *Haydn*
Variations. (11/90) (EMI) ① **CDM7 63536-2**
A. Schnabel, LPO, G. Szell (r1938) *Bach: Toccatas,*
BWV910-16. (2/91) (PEAR) ① **GEMMCD9376**
H. Gutiérrez, RPO, A. Previn (r1990) *Tragic Overture.*
(11/91) (TELA) ① **CD80252**
S. Kovacevich, LPO, W. Sawallisch *Lieder, Op.91.*
(10/92) (EMI) ① **CDC7 54578-2**
A. Rubinstein, Chicago SO, F. Reiner (r1954)
Concert (2/93) (RCA) ① **09026 61263-2**
L. Berman, Prague SO, P. Altrichter (pp1992) *Violin*
Concerto. (10/93) (SUPR) ① [2] **11 1832-2**
G. Oppitz, BRSO, Colin Davis (r1993) *Concert*
(7/94) (RCA) ① **09026 61620-2**
W. Backhaus, BBC SO, A. Boult (r1932) *Concert*
(9/94) (BIDD) ① **LHW017**
Solomon, Philh, R. Kubelik (r1954) *Handel*
Variations. (10/94) (TEST) ① **SBT1041**
Emil Gilels, BPO, E. Jochum (r1972) *Ballades.*
(3/95) (DG) ① [2] **419 158-2GH2**
M. Anderson, Hungarian St SO, A. Fischer (r1994)
Dohnányi: Nursery Variations.
(3/95) (NIMB) ① **NI5349**
C. Curzon, LSO, G. Szell (r1962) *Concert*
(4/95) (DECC) ① **425 082-2DCS**
J. Katchen, LSO, P. Monteux (r1959) *Concert*
(10/95) (DECC) ① [2] **440 612-2DF2**
D. Sgouros, Sofia PO, E. Tabakov (r1993) *Piano*
Concerto 2. (11/95) (CAPR) ① [2] **10 650**
Concerto for Piano and Orchestra No. 2 in B
flat, Op. 83 (1878-81)
1. Allegro non troppo; 2. Allegro appassionata; 3.
Andante; 4. Allegretto grazioso.
Vladimir Ashkenazy, VPO, B. Haitink
(7/84) (DECC) ① **410 199-2DH**
K. Zimerman, VPO, L. Bernstein (pp)
(1/86) (DG) ① **415 359-2GH**
Emil Gilels, BPO, E. Jochum *Concert*
(9/86) (DG) ① [2] **419 158-2GH2**
H. Gutiérrez, RPO, A. Previn (r1988) *Haydn*
Variations. (7/89) (TELA) ① **CD80197**
D. Barenboim, New Philh, J. Barbirolli *Concert*
(11/90) (EMI) ① **CDM7 63537-2**
A. Schnabel, BBC SO, A. Boult (r1935) *Bach: 2-*
Harpsichord Concerti.
(2/91) (PEAR) ① **GEMMCD9399**
A. Brendel, BPO, C. Abbado
(6/92) (PHIL) ① **432 975-2PH**
V. Horowitz, NBC SO, A. Toscanini (r1940) *Concert*
(7/92) (RCA) ① **GD60523**
Emil Gilels, BPO, E. Jochum *Piano Pieces, Op.116.*
(9/92) (DG) ① **435 588-2GGA**
J. Watts, NYPO, L. Bernstein (r1968) *Haydn*
Variations. (11/92) (SONY) ① **SMK47539**
A. Rubinstein, LSO, A. Coates (r1929) *Tchaikovsky:*
Piano Concerto 1.
(11/92) (CLAR) ① **CDGSE78-50-41**
C. Katsaris, Philh, E. Inbal
(12/92) (TELD) ① **9031-77599-2**
V. Horowitz, NBC SO, A. Toscanini (r1940)
Tchaikovsky: Piano Concerto 1.
(9/93) (RCA) ① **GD60319**

J. Jandó, Brussels BRT PO, A. Rahbari (r1992)
Schumann: Introduction and Allegro, Op.92.
(9/93) (NAXO) ① **8 550506**
A. Rubinstein, RCA Victor SO, J. Krips (r1958)
Concert (10/93) (RCA) ① **09026 61442-2**
S. Richter, Leningrad PO, E. Mravinsky (pp1961)
(2/94) (RUSS) ① **RDCD11158**
R. Serkin, Cleveland Orch, G. Szell (r1966) *R.*
Strauss: Burleske. (3/94) (SONY) ① **SBK53262**
G. Oppitz, BRSO, Colin Davis (r1993) *Concert*
(7/94) (RCA) ① [2] **09026 61620-2**
W. Backhaus, Saxon St Orch, K. Böhm (r1939)
Concert (9/94) (BIDD) ① **LHW018**
Solomon, Philh, I. Dobroven (r1947) *Concert*
(10/94) (TEST) ① **SBT1042**
S. Kovacevich, LPO, W. Sawallisch *Lieder, Op.105.*
(10/94) (EMI) ① **CDC5 55218-2**
V. Cliburn, Moscow PO, K. Kondrashin (pp1972)
Rachmaninov: Paganini Rhapsody.
(2/95) (RCA) ① **09026 62695-2**
A. Aeschbacher, BPO, W. Furtwängler (pp1943)
Concert (3/95) (TAHR) ① [4] **FURT1004/7**
Emil Gilels, BPO, E. Jochum *Ballades.*
(5/95) (DG) ① **439 466-2GCL**
C. Ousset, Leipzig Gewandhaus, K. Masur (r1974)
(7/95) (BERL) ① **0021 612BC**
E. Leonskaja, Leipzig Gewandhaus, K. Masur
(pp1994) (7/95) (TELD) ① **4509-94544-2**
G. Bachauer, LSO, S. Skrowaczewski (r1962)
Concert (9/95) (MERC) ① **434 340-2MM**
J. Katchen, LSO, J. Ferencsik (r1960) *Concert*
(10/95) (DECC) ① [2] **440 612-2DF2**
D. Sgouros, Sofia PO, E. Tabakov (r1993) *Piano*
Concert 1. (11/95) (CAPR) ① [2] **10 650**
Concerto for Violin and Orchestra in D, Op.
77 (1878)
1. Allegro non troppo; 2. Adagio; 3. Allegro giocoso.
G. Kremer, VPO, L. Bernstein
(8/83) (DG) ① **410 029-2GH**
I. Perlman, Chicago SO, C.M. Giulini (r1976)
(1/87) (EMI) ① **CDC7 47166-2**
A-S. Mutter, BPO, H. von Karajan *Concert*
(3/88) (DG) ① [4] **415 565-2GX4**
G. Neveu, Philh, I. Dobroven (r1946) *Sibelius: Violin*
Concerto. (3/88) (EMI) ① **CDH7 61011-2**
H. Krebbers, Concertgebouw, B. Haitink (r1973)
Tragic Overture. (5/90) (PHIL) ① **422 972-2PCC**
C. Ferras, BPO, H. von Karajan *Violin Sonata 1.*
(5/90) (DG) ① **429 513-2GR**
U. Ughi, Philh, W. Sawallisch *Bruch: Violin Concerto*
1. (3/91) (RCA) ① **VD60479**
I. Stern, Philadelphia, E. Ormandy *Double Concerto.*
(3/91) (SONY) ① **SBK46335**
N. Kennedy, LPO, K. Tennstedt
(4/91) (EMI) ① **CDC7 54187-2**
X. Wei, LPO, I. Bolton *Mendelssohn: Violin Concerto,*
Op. 64. (4/91) (ASV) ① **CDDCA748**
H. Udagawa, LSO, C. Mackerras (r1989) *Bruch:*
Violin Concerto 1. (9/91) (CHAN) ① **CHAN8974**
J. Heifetz, Boston SO, S. Koussevitzky (r1939)
Double Concerto. (10/91) (BIDD) ① **LAB041**
Y. Menuhin, BPO, R. Kempe *Concert*
(11/91) (EMI) ① [3] **CZS7 67310-2**
C. Ferras, BPO, H. von Karajan *Concert*
(12/91) (DG) ① [2] **413 844-2GW2**
B. Belkin, LSO, I. Fischer *Massenet: Thaïs.*
(1/92) (DECC) ① **433 604-2DSP**
R. Ricci, Sinfonia of London, N. del Mar (with 16
cadenzas) (2/92) (BIDD) ① **LAW002**
F. Kreisler, Berlin St Op Orch, L. Blech (r1927)
(9/92) (BIDD) ① [2] **LAB049/50**
Z. Francescatti, NYPO, L. Bernstein (r1961) *Sibelius:*
Violin Concerto. (11/92) (SONY) ① **SMK47540**
H. Szeryng, LSO, A. Dorati *Khachaturian: Violin*
Concerto. (3/93) (MERC) ① **434 318-2MM**
I. Perlman, BPO, D. Barenboim (pp1992)
(2/93) (EMI) ① **CDC7 54580-2**
T. Little, RLPO, V. Handley *Sibelius: Violin Concerto.*
(2/93) (EMIN) ① **CD-EMX2203**
D. Oistrakh, FRNO, O. Klemperer *Mozart: Sinfonia*
Concertante, K364. (3/93) (EMI) ① **CDM7 64632-2**
J. Heifetz, Chicago SO, F. Reiner (r1955)
Tchaikovsky: Violin Concerto.
(4/93) (RCA) ① **09026 61495-2**
T. Zehetmair, Cleveland Orch, C. von Dohnányi
(r1989) *Schumann: Fantasie, Op. 131.*
(7/93) (TELD) ① **4509-91443-2**
F. Kreisler, Berlin St Op Orch, L. Blech (r1926)
Concert (9/93) (PEAR) ① [2] **GEMMCDS9996**
C. Ferras, ORTF PO, C. Bruck (pp1966) *Violin*
Concerto. (9/93) (INA) ① **262007**
D. Oistrakh, ORTF PO, C. Bruck (pp1967) *Violin*
Concerto. (9/93) (INA) ① **262007**
L. Kogan, Philh, K. Kondrashin (r1959) *Concert*
(9/93) (EMI) ① [2] **CZS7 67732-2**

P. Berman, Prague SO, P. Altrichter (pp1992) *Piano*
Concerto 1. (10/93) (SUPR) ① [2] **11 1832-2**
P. Zukerman, Paris Orch, D. Barenboim (r1979)
Violin Sonata 1. (1/94) (DG) ① **439 405-2GCL**
I. Perlman, Chicago SO, C.M. Giulini (r1976) *Concert*
(4/94) (EMI) ① [3] **CMS7 64922-2**
T. Wanami, LPO, A. Leaper (r1992) *Schumann:*
Violin Concerto. (4/94) (CARL) ① **PCD1062**
N. Milstein, Philh, A. Fistoulari (r1960) *Concert*
(5/94) (EMI) ① [6] **ZDMF7 64830-2**
H. Krebbers, Concertgebouw, W. Mengelberg
(pp1943) *Concert* (7/94) (MUSI) ① [4] **MACD-780**
J. Martzy, Philh, P. Kletzki (r1954) *Mendelssohn:*
Violin Concerto, Op.64. (9/94) (TEST) ① **SBT1037**
A. Grumiaux, New Philh, Colin Davis (r1971) *Concert*
(9/94) (PHIL) ① [2] **442 287-2PM2**
I. Haendel, LSO, S. Celibidache (r1952) *Tchaikovsky:*
Violin Concerto. (10/94) (TEST) ① **SBT1038**
V. Mullova, BPO, C. Abbado (pp1992)
(11/94) (PHIL) ① **438 998-2PH**
J. Heifetz, Chicago SO, F. Reiner (r1955) *Concert*
(11/94) (RCA) ① [65] **09026 61778-2(11-15)**
J. Heifetz, Boston SO, S. Koussevitzky (r1939)
Concert (11/94) (RCA) ① [65] **09026 61778-2(04)**
A-S. Mutter, BPO, H. von Karajan (r1981)
Mendelssohn: Violin Concerto, Op.64.
(12/94) (DG) ① **445 515-2GMA**
D. Oistrakh, Staatskapelle Dresden, F. Konwitschny
(r1954) *Concert*
(6/95) (DG) ① [2] **447 427-2GOR2**
I. Perlman, Chicago SO, C.M. Giulini (r1976) *Concert*
(6/95) (EMI) ① [20] **CZS4 83177-2(1)**
J. Heifetz, Boston SO, S. Koussevitzky (r1939)
Concert (11/95) (PEAR) ① [2] **GEMMCDS9167**
3. A. Busch, NBC SO, F. Black (pp1942) *Concert*
(6/93) (SYMP) ① **SYMCD1109**
Concerto for Violin, Cello and Orchestra in A
minor, Op. 102 (1887)
G. Kremer, M. Maisky, VPO, L. Bernstein (pp1982)
Academic Festival Overture.
(11/84) (DG) ① **410 031-2GH**
I. Perlman, M. Rostropovich, Concertgebouw, B.
Haitink *Mendelssohn: Violin Concerto, Op.64.*
(5/89) (EMI) ① **CDC7 49486-2**
L. Mordkovitch, R. Wallfisch, LSO, N. Järvi *Bruch:*
Violin Concerto 1. (6/89) (CHAN) ① **CHAN8667**
I. Stern, L. Rose, Philadelphia, E. Ormandy
Beethoven: Triple Concerto.
(11/89) (SONY) ① **MPK44842**
P. Novšak, S. Basler, Bamberg SO, H. Wallberg
String Sextet 2. (3/90) (CLAV) ① **CD50-8014**
M. Mischakoff, F. Miller, NBC SO, A. Toscanini
(bp1948) *Concert* (9/90) (RCA) ① [4] **GD60235**
W. Schneiderhan, J. Starker, Berlin RSO, F. Fricsay
(r1961) *Beethoven: Triple Concerto.*
(12/90) (DG) ① **429 934-2GDO**
H. Szeryng, J. Starker, Concertgebouw, B. Haitink
Beethoven: Triple Concerto.
(12/90) (PHIL) ① **426 631-2PSL**
I. Stern, L. Rose, Philadelphia, E. Ormandy *Violin*
Concerto. (3/91) (SONY) ① **SBK46335**
J. Heifetz, E. Feuermann, Philadelphia, E. Ormandy
(r1939) *Violin Concerto.* (10/91) (BIDD) ① **LAB041**
J. Thibaud, P. Casals, Barcelona Casals Orch, A.
Cortot (r1929) *Concert*
(11/91) (EMI) ① [3] **CHS7 64057-2**
D. Oistrakh, M. Rostropovich, Cleveland Orch, G.
Szell (r1969) *Beethoven: Triple Concerto.*
(7/93) (EMI) ① **CDM7 64744-2**
N. Milstein, G. Piatigorsky, Philadelphia Robin Hood
Dell Orch, F. Reiner (r1951) *R. Strauss: Don Quixote.*
(10/93) (RCA) ① **09026 61485-2**
J. Thibaud, P. Casals, Barcelona Casals Orch, A.
Cortot (r1929) *Concert*
(11/93) (KOCH) ① [2] **37705-2**
J. Heifetz, E. Feuermann, Philadelphia, E. Ormandy
(r1939) *Concert*
(11/94) (RCA) ① [65] **09026 61778-2(05)**
J. Heifetz, G. Piatigorsky, RCA Victor SO, A.
Wallenstein (1960) *Concert*
(11/94) (RCA) ① [65] **09026 61778-2(11-15)**
I. Kaler, M. Kliegel, Ireland National SO, A.
Constantine (1994) *Schumann: Cello Concerto.*
(10/95) (NAXO) ① **8 550938**
21 Hungarian Dances (1852-69) (originally for
piano, four hands: orch versions)
1. G minor (orch Brahms); 2. D minor (orch Hallén);
3. F sharp minor (orch Juon); 5.
G minor (orch Schmeling); 6. D (orch Schmeling); 7.
F (orch Schmeling); 8. A minor (orch Gál); 9. E minor
(orch Gál); 10. F (orch Brahms); 11. D minor (orch
Parlow); 12. D minor (orch Parlow); 13. D (orch
Parlow); 14. D minor (orch Parlow); 15. B flat (orch
Parlow); 16. F minor (orch Dvořák); 17. F sharp minor
(orch Dvořák); 18. D (orch Dvořák); 19. B minor (orch
Dvořák); 20. E minor (orch Dvořák); 21. E minor (orch

Dvořák).
VPO, C. Abbado (9/84) (DG) ① **410 615-2GH**
Berlin Staatskapelle, O. Suitner (r1989)
(3/91) (DENO) ① **CO-74597**
LSO, N. Järvi (3/91) (CHAN) ① **CHAN8885**
1. LSO, C. Mackerras (r1961) *Concert*
(12/95) (MERC) ① **434 352-2MM**
1, 10. BPO, W. Furtwängler (r1930) *Concert*
(4/92) (KOCH) ① [2] **37073-2**
1, 17, 20, 21. NBC SO, A. Toscanini (r1953) *Concert*
(5/90) (RCA) ① [4] **GD60325**
1, 2, 5-7, 11, 21. LSO, A. Dorati (r1957) *Concert*
(8/93) (MERC) ① **434 326-2MM**
1-3. Philh, F. d'Avalos *Concert*
(9/91) (ASV) ① **CDDCA746**
1, 3, 10. Concertgebouw, B. Haitink (r1980) *Concert*
(9/94) (PHIL) ① [4] **442 068-2PB4**
1, 3, 10, 17. NYPO, B. Walter (r1951) *Concert*
(8/95) (SONY) ① **SMK64467**
1, 3, 5, 10, 16, 18-21. N German RSO, J.E. Gardiner
(r1992) *Concert* (6/93) (DG) ① **437 506-2GH**
1, 3, 5, 6, 10, 12, 13, 19, 21. LSO, W. Boskovsky
(r1974) *Dvořák: Slavonic Dances.*
(5/94) (BELA) ① **450 061-2**
2. N. Milstein, L. Pommers (r1956: arr Joachim)
Concert (5/94) (EMI) ① [6] **ZDMF7 64830-2**
3, 4, 10, 12, 15, 17-20. LSO, A. Dorati (r1965)
Concert (8/93) (MERC) ① **434 326-2MM**
5. I. Stern, Columbia SO, M. Katims (arr Harris)
Concert (7/90) (SONY) ① **SK45816**
5, 6. LPO, T. Beecham (bp1939) *Concert*
(11/91) (SYMP) ① [2] **SYMCD1096/7**
5, 6. NYPO, L. Bernstein *Concert*
(5/93) (SONY) ① **SMK47572**
6. BRSO, L. Bernstein (pp1983) *Concert*
(12/86) (HUNG) ① **HCD12631**
17-20. BPO, H. von Karajan *Concert*
(5/90) (DG) ① **429 156-2GR**
17-21. RPO, R. Kubelik (r1957) *Concert*
(11/94) (EMI) ① [2] **CZS5 68223-2**
17-21. Chicago SO, F. Stock (r1926) *Concert*
(2/95) (BIDD) ① [2] **WHL021/2**

Serenade No. 1 in D, Op. 11 (1857-58)
1. Allegro molto; 2. Scherzo; 3. Adagio non troppo;
4a. Menuetto I; 4b. Menuetto II; 5. Scherzo; 6. Rondo
(Allegro).
Ulster Orch, V. Handley *Haydn Variations.*
(11/89) (CHAN) ① **CHAN8612**
Vienna SO, G. Bertini (r1982) *Serenade 2.*
(6/90) (ORFE) ① **C008101A**
Philh, F. d'Avalos *Symphony 3.*
(9/91) (ASV) ① **CDDCA745**
Berlin Scharoun Ens (recons Rotter)
(9/91) (SCHW) ① **311114**
Brussels BRT PO, A. Rahbari *Symphony 3.*
(1/92) (NAXO) ① **8 550280**
W. German Sinf, D. Joeres *Serenade 2.*
(5/93) (CARL) ① **PCD1024**
Atlanta SO, Y. Levi (r1993) *Haydn Variations.*
(11/93) (TELA) ① **CD80349**
Concertgebouw, B. Haitink (r1976) *Concert*
(9/94) (PHIL) ① [4] **442 068-2PB4**
Milan La Scala PO, R. Muti (r1993) *Elgar: In the
South.* (1/95) (SONY) ① **SK57973**
1, 4. NBC SO, A. Toscanini (bp1943/48) *Concert*
(6/90) (DELL) ① **CDDA9022**

**Serenade No. 2 in A—small orchestra
(without violins), Op. 16 (1858-59 rev 1875)**
Linos Ens *Wagner: Siegfried Idyll.*
(12/89) (SCHW) ① **310000**
Vienna SO, G. Bertini (r1982) *Serenade 1.*
(6/90) (ORFE) ① **C008101A**
Brussels BRT PO, A. Rahbari *Symphony 2.*
(9/91) (NAXO) ① **8 550279**
Philh, F. d'Avalos *Concert*
(9/91) (ASV) ① **CDDCA746**
NYPO, L. Bernstein (r1966) *Symphony 1.*
(11/92) (SONY) ① **SMK47536**
NBC SO, A. Toscanini (bp1942) *Symphony 1.*
(11/92) (RCA) ① **GD60277**
W. German Sinf, D. Joeres *Serenade 2.*
(5/93) (CARL) ① **PCD1024**
Concertgebouw, B. Haitink (r1980) *Concert*
(9/94) (PHIL) ① [4] **442 068-2PB4**

Symphony No. 1 in C minor, Op. 68 (1855-76)
1. Un poco sostenuto—Allegro; 2. Andante
sostenuto; 3. Un poco allegretto e grazioso; 4.
Adagio—Allegro non troppo ma con brio.
BPO, H. von Karajan (r1987)
(12/87) (DG) ① **423 141-2GH**
VPO, L. Bernstein (pp) *Concert*
(11/88) (DG) ① [4] **415 570-2GX4**
LSO, N. Järvi *Schumann: Manfred.*
(5/89) (CHAN) ① **CHAN8653**

BPO, H. von Karajan (r1977) *Haydn Variations.*
(8/89) (DG) ① **427 253-2GGA**
Philh, O. Klemperer (r1989)
(1/90) (EMI) ① **CDM7 69651-2**
NBC SO, A. Toscanini (r1951) *Concert*
(5/90) (RCA) ① [4] **GD60325**
BPO, H. von Karajan (r1987) *Concert*
(7/90) (DG) ① [3] **427 602-2GH3**
BPO, H. von Karajan (r1977) *Concert*
(7/90) (DG) ① [3] **429 644-2GSE3**
Belgian Rad & TV Orch, A. Rahbari *Haydn
Variations.* (10/90) (NAXO) ① **8 550278**
Chicago SO, G. Wand (pp1989)
(4/91) (RCA) ① **RD60428**
Czech PO, J. Bělohlávek
(8/91) (SUPR) ① **11 0394-2**
BPO, H. von Karajan (r1963) *Schumann: Overture,
Scherzo and Finale.* (8/91) (DG) ① **431 161-2GR**
BRSO, Colin Davis (r1989) *Haydn Variations.*
(8/91) (RCA) ① **RD60382**
Philh, F. d'Avalos *Tragic Overture.*
(9/91) (ASV) ① **CDDCA729**
LCP, R. Norrington *Haydn Variations.*
(10/91) (EMI) ① **CDC7 54286-2**
BPO, C. Abbado *Gesang der Parzen, Op. 89.*
(10/91) (DG) ① **431 790-2GH**
Berlin St Op Orch, O. Klemperer (r1928) *Concert*
(11/91) (KOCH) ① **37053-2**
BPO, K. Böhm *Concert*
(12/91) (DG) ① [2] **413 424-2GW2**
LPO, W. Sawallisch *Schicksalslied, Op. 54.*
(2/92) (EMI) ① **CDC7 54359-2**
Chicago SO, G. Solti *Concert*
(4/92) (DECC) ① [4] **430 799-2DC4**
RPO, A. Litton *Academic Festival Overture.*
(10/92) (VIRG) ① **VJ7 59673-2**
VPO, C.M. Giulini (10/92) (DG) ① **435 347-2GH**
NYPO, L. Bernstein (r1960) *Serenade 2.*
(11/92) (SONY) ① **SMK47536**
VPO, B. Walter (r1937) *Concert*
(11/92) (PREI) ① **90114**
NBC SO, A. Toscanini (r1941) *Serenade 2.*
(11/92) (RCA) ① **GD60277**
BBC PO, G. Herbig *Academic Festival Overture.*
(12/92) (COLL) ① **Coll3049-2**
Philh, G. Cantelli (r1953) *Concert*
(2/93) (TEST) ① **SBT1012**
Czech PO, G. Albrecht (pp1992) *Concert*
(6/93) (SUPR) ① **11 1830-2**
RLPO, M. Janowski (9/93) (ASV) ① **CDQS6101**
Leningrad PO, E. Mravinsky (r1950) *Concert*
(3/94) (MEMR) ① [2] **991006**
Philadelphia, L. Stokowski (r1927: with theme outline)
Concert (8/94) (BIDD) ① [2] **WHL017/8**
BPO, H. Abendroth (r1941) *Concert*
(9/94) (TAHR) ① [2] **TAH102**
Concertgebouw, B. Haitink (r1972) *Concert*
(9/94) (PHIL) ① [4] **442 068-2PB4**
Chicago SO, D. Barenboim (r1993) *Concert*
(11/94) (ERAT) ① [4] **4509-94817-2**
Chicago SO, D. Barenboim (r1993)
(11/94) (ERAT) ① **4509-95191-2**
VPO, L. Bernstein (pp1981) *Concert*
(12/94) (DG) ① **445 506-2GMA**
N German RSO, W. Furtwängler (pp1951) *Haydn
Variations.* (3/95) (TAHR) ① **FURT1001**
BPO, R. Kempe (r1959) *Concert*
(4/95) (TEST) ① [3] **SBT3054**
N. German RSO, G. Wand (r1982) *Concert*
(5/95) (RCA) ① [2] **74321 20283-2**
BPO, H. von Karajan (r1963) *Schumann: Symphony
1.* (7/95) (DG) ① **447 408-2GOR**
Hallé, S. Skrowaczewski (r1987) *Academic Festival
Overture.* (10/95) (CARL) ① **PCD2014**
Movt 4. BPO, W. Furtwängler (pp1945) *Concert*
(3/95) (TAHR) ① [4] **FURT1004/7**

Symphony No. 2 in D, Op. 73 (1877)
1. Allegro non troppo; 2. Adagio non troppo; 3.
Allegretto grazioso; 4. Allegro con spirito.
Hallé, S. Skrowaczewski *Tragic Overture.*
(8/87) (CARL) ① **PCD857**
BPO, H. von Karajan (r1986) *Haydn Variations.*
(11/87) (DG) ① **423 142-2GH**
VPO, L. Bernstein (pp) *Concert*
(11/88) (DG) ① [4] **415 570-2GX4**
FNO, C. Munch (pp1965) *Schumann: Symphony 4.*
(11/88) (MONT) ① **MUN2021**
LSO, N. Järvi *Schumann: Julius Cäsar.*
(4/89) (CHAN) ① **CHAN8649**
FNO, B. Walter (r1955) *Mozart: Symphony 38.*
(5/89) (MONT) ① **TCE8831**
BRSO, Colin Davis (r1988) *Academic Festival
Overture.* (9/89) (RCA) ① **RD87980**
Philh, O. Klemperer (r1956) *Alto Rhapsody, Op. 53.*
(1/90) (EMI) ① **CDM7 69650-2**

BPO, H. von Karajan (r1963) *Symphony 3.*
(2/90) (DG) ① **429 153-2GR**
BPO, C. Abbado (r1988) *Alto Rhapsody, Op. 53.*
(2/90) (DG) ① **427 643-2GH**
NBC SO, A. Toscanini (r1952) *Concert*
(5/90) (RCA) ① [4] **GD60325**
BPO, H. von Karajan (r1986) *Concert*
(7/90) (DG) ① [3] **427 602-2GH3**
BPO, H. von Karajan (r1977) *Concert*
(7/90) (DG) ① [3] **429 644-2GSE3**
Concertgebouw, B. Haitink *Symphony 3.*
(11/90) (PHIL) ① **426 632-2PSL**
LPO, W. Sawallisch *Haydn Variations.*
(12/90) (EMI) ① **CDC7 54059-2**
Philh, F. d'Avalos *Concert*
(9/91) (ASV) ① **CDDCA744**
Brussels BRT PO, A. Rahbari *Serenade 2.*
(9/91) (NAXO) ① **8 550279**
Danish RSO, J. Horenstein (pp1972) *Horenstein:
Blyth Interview.* (9/91) (UNIC) ① **UKCD2036**
BPO, H. von Karajan *Schumann: Symphony 2.*
(11/91) (DG) ① **435 067-2GGA**
VPO, W. Furtwängler (pp1945) *Concert*
(2/92) (DG) ① [12] **435 321-2GWP12**
VPO, W. Furtwängler (pp1945) *Concert*
(2/92) (DG) ① **435 324-2GWP**
Chicago SO, G. Solti *Concert*
(4/92) (DECC) ① [4] **430 799-2DC4**
VPO, C.M. Giulini (7/92) (DG) ① **435 348-2GH**
Boston SO, B. Haitink *Tragic Overture.*
(10/92) (PHIL) ① **432 094-2PH**
NYPO, L. Bernstein (r1962) *Symphony 3.*
(11/92) (SONY) ① **SMK47537**
BBC SO, A. Toscanini (pp1938) *Concert*
(4/93) (TEST) ① **SBT1015**
NYPO, K. Masur (pp1992) *Academic Festival
Overture.* (5/93) (TELD) ① **9031-77291-2**
RLPO, M. Janowski *Tragic Overture.*
(11/93) (ASV) ① **CDQS6102**
LCP, R. Norrington (r1992) *Tragic Overture.*
(12/93) (EMI) ① **CDC7 54875-2**
Leningrad PO, E. Mravinsky (pp1978) *Concert*
(3/94) (MEMR) ① [2] **991006**
Philadelphia, L. Stokowski (r1929) *Concert*
(8/94) (BIDD) ① [2] **WHL017/8**
Concertgebouw, B. Haitink (r1978) *Concert*
(9/94) (PHIL) ① [4] **442 068-2PB4**
San Francisco SO, P. Monteux (r1945) *Concert*
(9/94) (RCA) ① [15] **09026 61893-2**
Chicago SO, D. Barenboim (r1993) *Concert*
(11/94) (ERAT) ① [4] **4509-94817-2**
Chicago SO, D. Barenboim (r1993) *Tragic Overture.*
(11/94) (ERAT) ① **4509-95192-2**
Mexico City PO, F. Lozano *Tragic Overture.*
(11/94) (FORL) ① **FF017**
VPO, F. Fricsay (pp1961) *Concert*
(11/94) (DG) ① **445 407-2GDO**
VPO, F. Fricsay (pp1961) *Concert*
(11/94) (DG) ① [11] **445 400-2GDO10**
LSO, P. Monteux (r1962) *Concert*
(12/94) (PHIL) ① [5] **442 544-2PM5**
VPO, L. Bernstein (pp1982) *Academic Festival
Overture.* (12/94) (DG) ① **445 506-2GMA**
LPO, T. Beecham (r1936) *Concert*
(3/95) (DUTT) ① [2] **2CDAX2003**
BPO, R. Kempe (r1955) *Concert*
(4/95) (TEST) ① [3] **SBT3054**
N. German RSO, G. Wand (r1982) *Concert*
(5/95) (RCA) ① [2] **74321 20283-2**
Movt 2. BPO, W. Furtwängler (bp1947: rehearsal)
Concert (3/95) (TAHR) ① [4] **FURT1008/11**

Symphony No. 3 in F, Op. 90 (1883)
1. Allegro con brio; 2. Andante; 3. Poco allegretto; 4.
Allegro.
VPO, L. Bernstein (pp) *Concert*
(11/88) (DG) ① [4] **415 570-2GX4**
LSO, N. Järvi *Schumann: Overture, Scherzo and
Finale.* (3/89) (CHAN) ① **CHAN8646**
Hallé, S. Skrowaczewski (r1987) *Haydn Variations.*
(4/89) (CARL) ① **PCD906**
BPO, H. von Karajan (r1988) *Tragic Overture.*
(9/89) (DG) ① **427 496-2GH**
Philh, O. Klemperer (r1957) *Symphony 4.*
(1/90) (EMI) ① **CDM7 69649-2**
BPO, H. von Karajan (r1964) *Symphony 2.*
(2/90) (DG) ① **429 153-2GR**
BRSO, Colin Davis (1988) *Tragic Overture.*
(5/90) (RCA) ① **RD60118**
NBC SO, A. Toscanini (r1952) *Concert*
(5/90) (RCA) ① [4] **GD60325**
BPO, H. von Karajan (r1988) *Concert*
(7/90) (DG) ① [3] **427 602-2GH3**
BPO, H. von Karajan (r1977) *Concert*
(7/90) (DG) ① [3] **429 644-2GSE3**
BRSO, E. Ansermet (pp1966) *Honegger: Symphony
3.* (8/90) (ORFE) ① **C202891A**

Concertgebouw, B. Haitink Symphony 2.
(11/90) (PHIL) ① 426 632-2PSL
BPO, C. Abbado Concert
(1/91) (DG) ① 429 765-2GH
VPO, C.M. Giulini (pp1990) Haydn Variations.
(8/91) (DG) ① 431 681-2GH
Philh, F. d'Avalos Serenade 1.
(9/91) (ASV) ① CDDCA745
Concertgebouw, W. Mengelberg (bp1944) Concert
(12/91) (ARHI) ① ADCD107
Brussels BRT PO, A. Rahbari Serenade 1.
(1/92) (NAXO) ① 8 550280
Chicago SO, G. Solti Concert
(4/92) (DECC) ① [4] 430 799-2DC4
NYPO, L. Bernstein (r1964) Symphony 2.
(11/92) (SONY) ① SMK47537
VPO, B. Walter (r1936) Symphony 4.
(11/92) (KOCH) ① 37120-2
LPO, W. Sawallisch Academic Festival Overture.
(4/93) (EMI) ① CDC7 54523-2
VPO, C. Krauss (r1930) Concert
(5/93) (KOCH) ① 37129-2
BPO, H. von Karajan (r1977/8) Symphony 4.
(8/93) (DG) ① 437 645-2GGA
Leningrad PO, E. Mravinsky (pp1965) Concert
(3/94) (MEMR) ① [2] 991006
BPO, H. Knappertsbusch (r1942) Haydn: Symphony
94.
(5/94) (PREI) ① 90121
Concertgebouw, W. Mengelberg (pp1944) Concert
(7/94) (MUSI) ① [4] MACD-780
Philadelphia, L. Stokowski (r1928) Concert
(8/94) (BIDD) ① [2] WHL017/8
Concertgebouw, B. Haitink (r1970) Concert
(9/94) (PHIL) ① [4] 442 068-2PB4
Chicago SO, D. Barenboim (r1993) Concert
(11/94) (ERAT) ① [4] 4509-94817-2
Chicago SO, D. Barenboim (r1993) Haydn Variations.
(11/94) (ERAT) ① 4509-95193-2
VPO, L. Bernstein (pp) Haydn Variations.
(1/95) (DG) ① 445 507-2GMA
Boston SO, B. Haitink (r1993) Alto Rhapsody, Op.
53.
(3/95) (PHIL) ① 442 120-2PH
BPO, R. Kempe (r1960) Concert
(4/95) (TEST) ① [3] SBT3054
N. German RSO, G. Wand (r1983) Concert
(5/95) (RCA) ① [2] 74321 20283-2
VPO, James Levine (pp1992) Concert
(6/95) (DG) ① 439 887-2GH
Chicago SO, F. Reiner (r1957) Concert
(RCA) ① 09026 61793-2
Symphony No. 4 in E minor, Op. 98 (1884-5)
1. Allegro non troppo; 2. Andante moderato; 3.
Allegro giocoso; 4. Allegro energico e passionato.
VPO, C. Kleiber (r1980)
(9/85) (DG) ① 400 037-2GH
VPO, L. Bernstein (pp) Concert
(11/88) (DG) ① [4] 415 570-2GX4
LSO, N. Järvi Schumann: Genoveva.
(12/88) (CHAN) ① CHAN8595
FNO, J. Krips (pp1954) Mozart: Symphony 40.
(5/89) (MONT) ① TCE8821
BPO, H. von Karajan (1988)
(12/89) (DG) ① 427 497-2GH
Philh, O. Klemperer (r1956/7) Symphony 3.
(1/90) (EMI) ① CDM7 69649-2
NBC SO, A. Toscanini (r1951) Concert
(5/90) (RCA) ① [4] GD60325
BPO, H. von Karajan (1988)
(7/90) (DG) ① [3] 427 602-2GH3
BPO, H. von Karajan (r1977)
(7/90) (DG) ① 429 644-2GSE3
BRSO, O. Klemperer (pp1957) Bach: Suites,
BWV1066-9.
(8/90) (ORFE) ① C201891A
Belgian Rad & TV Orch, A. Rahbari Concert
(10/90) (NAXO) ① 8 550281
VPO, C.M. Giulini Tragic Overture.
(12/90) (DG) ① 429 403-2GH
BRSO, Colin Davis (1989)
(12/90) (RCA) ① RD60383
LPO, W. Sawallisch Tragic Overture.
(12/90) (EMI) ① CDC7 54060-2
Cleveland Orch, G. Szell Concert
(3/91) (SONY) ① SBK46330
Philh, F. d'Avalos Concert
(9/91) (ASV) ① CDDCA746
VPO, K. Böhm Concert
(12/91) (DG) ① 413 424-2GW2
Chicago SO, G. Solti Concert
(4/92) (DECC) ① [4] 430 799-2DC4
BPO, C. Abbado Concert
(4/92) (DG) ① 435 349-2GH
NYPO, L. Bernstein (r1962) Concert
(11/92) (SONY) ① SMK47538
BBC SO, B. Walter (r1934) Symphony 3.
(11/92) (KOCH) ① 37120-2

BPO, H. von Karajan (r1977/8) Symphony 3.
(8/93) (DG) ① 437 645-2GGA
RPO, A. Previn (r1987) Academic Festival Overture.
(1/94) (TELA) ① CD82006
Leningrad PO, E. Mravinsky (pp1973) Concert
(3/94) (MEMR) ① [2] 991006
Philadelphia, L. Stokowski (r1933) Concert
(8/94) (BIDD) ① [2] WHL017/8
Concertgebouw, B. Haitink (r1972) Concert
(9/94) (PHIL) ① [4] 442 068-2PB4
LSO, H. Abendroth (r1927) Concert
(9/94) (TAHR) ① [2] TAH102
Boston SO, B. Haitink (r1992) Haydn Variations.
(9/94) (PHIL) ① 434 991-2PH
Chicago SO, D. Barenboim (r1993) Concert
(11/94) (ERAT) ① [4] 4509-94817-2
Chicago SO, D. Barenboim (r1993) Academic
Festival Overture. (11/94) (ERAT) ① 4509-95194-2
Cleveland Orch, Vladimir Ashkenazy (r1992) Handel
Variations. (11/94) (DECC) ① 436 853-2DH
VPO, L. Bernstein (pp) Tragic Overture.
(1/95) (DG) ① 445 508-2GMA
New Philh, L. Stokowski (pp1974) Concert
(3/95) (BBCR) ① BBCRD9107
BPO, R. Kempe (r1956) Concert
(4/95) (TEST) ① [3] SBT3054
N. German RSO, G. Wand (r1983) Concert
(5/95) (RCA) ① [2] 74321 20283-2
Tragic Overture, Op. 81 (1880 rev 1881)
Hallé, S. Skrowaczewski Symphony 2.
(9/87) (CARL) ① PCD857
VPO, L. Bernstein (pp) Concert
(11/88) (DG) ① [4] 415 570-2GX4
BPO, H. von Karajan (r1983) Symphony 3.
(12/89) (DG) ① 427 496-2GH
Philh, O. Klemperer Concert
(1/90) (EMI) ① CDM7 69651-2
Concertgebouw, B. Haitink (r1970) Violin Concerto.
(5/90) (PHIL) ① 422 972-2PCC
BRSO, Colin Davis (1988) Symphony 3.
(5/90) (RCA) ① RD60118
NBC SO, A. Toscanini (bp1953) Concert
(5/90) (RCA) ① [4] GD60325
BPO, H. von Karajan Concert
(7/90) (DG) ① [3] 427 602-2GH3
Belgian Rad & TV Orch, A. Rahbari Concert
(10/90) (NAXO) ① 8 550281
VPO, J. Barbirolli Concert
(11/90) (EMI) ① CDM7 63537-2
VPO, C.M. Giulini Symphony 4.
(12/90) (DG) ① 429 403-2GH
LPO, W. Sawallisch Symphony 4.
(12/90) (EMI) ① CDC7 54060-2
BPO, C. Abbado Concert
(1/91) (DG) ① 429 765-2GH
Cleveland Orch, G. Szell Concert
(3/91) (SONY) ① SBK46330
Philh, F. d'Avalos Symphony 1.
(9/91) (ASV) ① CDDCA729
RPO, A. Previn (r1990) Piano Concerto 1.
(11/91) (TELA) ① CD80252
BPO, L. Maazel Concert
(12/91) (DG) ① [2] 413 424-2GW2
Chicago SO, G. Solti Concert
(4/92) (DECC) ① [4] 430 799-2DC4
Boston SO, B. Haitink Symphony 2.
(10/92) (PHIL) ① 432 094-2PH
NYPO, L. Bernstein (r1964) Concert
(11/92) (SONY) ① SMK47538
RLPO, M. Janowski Concert
(11/93) (ASV) ① CDQS6102
LCP, R. Norrington (r1992) Symphony 2.
(12/93) (EMI) ① CDC7 54875-2
BBC SO, A. Toscanini (r1937) Concert
(5/94) (BIDD) ① [2] WHL008/9
Vienna SO, W. Sawallisch (r1961) Concert
(5/94) (PHIL) ① 438 760-2PM2
Leipzig Gewandhaus, H. Abendroth (bp1945)
Concert (9/94) (TAHR) ① [2] TAH106/7
Concertgebouw, B. Haitink (r1970) Concert
(9/94) (PHIL) ① [4] 442 068-2PB4
LPO, T. Beecham (r1937) Concert
(10/94) (DUTT) ① CDLX7009
Chicago SO, D. Barenboim (r1994) Concert
(11/94) (ERAT) ① [4] 4509-94817-2
Chicago SO, D. Barenboim (r1994) Symphony 2.
(11/94) (ERAT) ① 4509-95192-2
Luxembourg Rad & TV SO, L. Hager Symphony 2.
(11/94) (FORL) ① FF017
LSO, P. Monteux (r1962) Concert
(12/94) (PHIL) ① [5] 442 544-2PM5
VPO, L. Bernstein (pp) Symphony 4.
(1/95) (DG) ① 445 508-2GMA
BPO, R. Kempe Concert
(4/95) (TEST) ① [3] SBT3054

VPO, James Levine (r1992) Concert
(6/95) (DG) ① 439 887-2GH
**Variations on a Theme by Haydn, 'St Antoni
Chorale', Op. 56a (1873)** (Theme is from a
wind partita probably not by Haydn but possibly
by Pleyel)
BPO, H. von Karajan (r1983) Symphony 2.
(11/87) (DG) ① 423 142-2GH
VPO, L. Bernstein (pp) Concert
(11/88) (DG) ① [4] 415 570-2GX4
Hallé, S. Skrowaczewski (r1987) Symphony 3.
(4/89) (CARL) ① PCD906
RPO, A. Previn (r1988) Piano Concerto 2.
(7/89) (TELA) ① CD80197
BPO, H. von Karajan (r1964) Symphony 1.
(8/89) (DG) ① 427 253-2GGA
Ulster Orch, V. Handley Serenade 1.
(11/89) (CHAN) ① CHAN8612
NYPSO, A. Toscanini (r1936) Concert
(3/90) (PEAR) ① [3] GEMMCDS9373
NBC SO, A. Toscanini (r1952) Concert
(5/90) (RCA) ① [4] GD60325
BPO, H. von Karajan Concert
(7/90) (DG) ① [3] 427 602-2GH3
Belgian Rad & TV Orch, A. Rahbari Symphony 1.
(10/90) (NAXO) ① 8 550278
VPO, J. Barbirolli (r1967) Piano Concerto 1.
(11/90) (EMI) ① CDM7 63536-2
LPO, W. Sawallisch Symphony 2.
(12/90) (EMI) ① CDC7 54059-2
BRSO, Colin Davis (r1989) Symphony 1.
(8/91) (RCA) ① RD60382
VPO, C.M. Giulini Symphony 3.
(8/91) (DG) ① 431 681-2GH
Philh, F. d'Avalos Concert
(9/91) (ASV) ① CDDCA744
LCP, R. Norrington Symphony 1.
(10/91) (EMI) ① CDC7 54286-2
LSO, E. Jochum Concert
(12/91) (DG) ① [2] 413 424-2GW2
NYPSO, A. Toscanini (r c1927) Concert
(4/92) (PEAR) ① [3] GEMMCDS9922
BPO, C. Abbado Concert
(4/92) (DG) ① 435 349-2GH
NYPO, L. Bernstein (r1971) Piano Concerto 2.
(11/92) (SONY) ① SMK47539
NYPO, A. Toscanini (r1936) Concert
(11/92) (RCA) ① GD60317
NYPO, K. Masur (pp1991) Concert
(12/92) (TELD) ① 9031-74007-2
LSO, A. Dorati (r1957) Concert
(8/93) (MERC) ① 434 326-2MM
Atlanta SO, Y. Levi (r1993) Serenade 1.
(11/93) (TELA) ① CD80349
Vienna SO, W. Sawallisch (r1959) Concert
(5/94) (PHIL) ① [2] 438 760-2PM2
Concertgebouw, B. Haitink (r1973) Concert
(9/94) (PHIL) ① [4] 442 068-2PB4
Boston SO, B. Haitink (r1992) Symphony 4.
(9/94) (PHIL) ① 434 991-2PH
Queen's Hall Orch, Henry Wood (r1935) Concert
(9/94) (DUTT) ① [2] 2CDAX2002
Chicago SO, D. Barenboim (r1993) Concert
(11/94) (ERAT) ① [4] 4509-94817-2
Chicago SO, D. Barenboim (r1993) Symphony 3.
(11/94) (ERAT) ① 4509-95193-2
Berlin RSO, F. Fricsay (r1957) Concert
(11/94) (DG) ① [11] 445 400-2GDO10
Berlin RSO, F. Fricsay (r1957) Concert
(11/94) (DG) ① 445 407-2GDO
VPO, L. Bernstein (pp) Symphony 3.
(1/95) (DG) ① 445 507-2GMA
N German RSO, W. Furtwängler (pp1951) Symphony
3. (3/95) (TAHR) ① FURT1001
BPO, R. Kempe (r1956) Concert
(4/95) (TEST) ① [3] SBT3054
VPO, W. Furtwängler (r1943) Beethoven: Symphony
6. (5/95) (PREI) ① 90199
Solti Orchestral Project, G. Solti (pp1994) Concert
(12/95) (DECC) ① 444 458-2DH

SECTION II: CHAMBER

**Academic Festival Overture—piano duet
(1881)** (arr cpsr)
T. Lønskov, R. Llambias Symphony 2.
(2/93) (KONT) ① 32120
**21 Hungarian Dances—piano duet (1852-
69)**
1. G minor; 2. D minor; 3. F; 4. F minor; 5. F sharp
minor; 6. D flat; 7. A; 8. A minor; 9. E minor; 10. E;
11. A minor; 12. D minor; 13. D; 14. D minor; 15. D
minor; 16. F minor; 17. F sharp minor; 18. D; 19. B
minor; 20. E minor; 21. E minor.
K. Labèque, M. Labèque
(9/86) (PHIL) ① 416 459-2PH

J-P. Collard, M. Béroff *Waltzes, Op. 39.*
(5/88) (EMI) ① **CDC7 47642-2**
J. Katchen, J-P. Marty (r1964/5) *Concert*
(2/91) (DECC) ① [6] **430 053-2DM6**
A. Rosand, H. Sung (arr Joachim) *Joachim: Romance in B flat.* (3/93) (BIDD) ① **LAW003**
Y. Tal, A. Groethuysen (r1992) *Waltzes, Op. 39.*
(4/94) (SONY) ① **SK53285**
N. Green, F. Moyer (r1993: arr vc/pf: Piatti) *Schmidt: Phantasiestücke.* (5/95) (BIDD) ① **LAW010**
1. K-W. Chung, P. Moll (arr vn/pf: Joachim) *Concert*
(9/87) (DECC) ① **417 289-2DH**
1. L. Auer, anon (r1920: arr vn/pf: Joachim) *Concert*
(8/90) (SYMP) ① **SYMCD1071**
1. Y. Menuhin, M. Gazelle (r1936: arr vn/pf: Joachim) *Concert* (9/91) (TEST) ① **SBT1003**
1. L. Auer, W. Bogutskahein (r1920: arr vn/pf: Joachim) (12/91) (APR) ① [2] **APR7015**
1. S. Mayor, S. Price (arr mandolin ens: Mayor) *Concert* (3/92) (ACOU) ① **CDACS014**
1. K. Takezawa, P. Moll (arr vn/pf) *Concert*
(2/93) (RCA) ① **09026 60704-2**
1. T. Seidel, E. Kusmiak (r c1940: arr vn/pf: Joachim) *Concert* (7/93) (APR) ① [2] **APR7016**
1. B. Huberman, P. Frenkel (r1922: arr Joachim) *Concert* (3/94) (BIDD) ① [2] **LAB077/8**
1. B. Huberman, S. Schultze (r1932: arr Joachim) *Concert* (9/94) (BIDD) ① [2] **LAB081/2**
1. J. Heifetz, S. Chotzinoff (r1920) *Concert*
(11/94) (RCA) ① [65] **09026 61778-2(01)**
1, 2, 4, 7. S. Chang, J. Feldman (r1993: arr vn/pf: Joachim) *Tchaikovsky: Violin Concerto.*
(12/93) (EMI) ① **CDC7 54753-2**
1, 2, 7, 9. I. Perlman, Vladimir Ashkenazy (r1983: arr vn/pf: Joachim) *Concert*
(5/93) (EMI) ① [4] **CMS7 64617-2**
2, 20. A. Busch, B. Seidler-Winkler (r1919: arr vn/pf: Joachim) *Concert* (6/93) (SYMP) ① **SYMCD1109**
4. C. Hansen, B. Zakharoff (r1924: arr vn/pf: Auer) *Concert* (12/91) (APR) ① [2] **APR7015**
4, 6. B. Eden, A. Tamir *Concert*
(6/90) (CARL) ① **PWK1134**
5. F. Kreisler, H. Squire (r1911: arr vn/pf: Joachim) *Concert* (7/90) (BIDD) ① **LAB009/10**
5. A. Busch, B. Seidler-Winkler (r1922: arr vn/pf: Joachim) *Concert* (6/93) (SYMP) ① **SYMCD1109**
5. K. Daeshik Kang, M. Rahkonen (r1992: arr vn/pf: Joachim) (9/93) (NIMB) ① **NI5358**
5. J. Szigeti, A. Foldes (r1941: arr vn/pf: Joachim) *Concert* (7/94) (BIDD) ① [2] **LAB070/1**
6, 9. V. Spivakov, S. Bezrodny (r1991-2) *Concert*
(5/95) (RCA) ① **09026 62524-2**
7. I. Menges, H. Harty (r1914: arr vn/pf: Joachim) *Concert* (12/91) (APR) ① [2] **APR7015**
7. B. Huberman, P. Frenkel (r1923: arr vn/pf: Joachim) *Concert* (3/94) (BIDD) ① [2] **LAB077/8**
7. J. Heifetz, Los Angeles PO, A. Wallenstein (r1953) *Concert* (11/94) (RCA) ① [65] **09026 61778-2(31)**
7. J. Heifetz, E. Bay (r1945) *Concert*
(11/94) (RCA) ① [65] **09026 61778-2(19)**
11, 17, 20. J. Heifetz, B. Smith (r1956: arr vn/pf: Joachim/Heifetz) *Concert*
(7/89) (RCA) ① **GD87965**
11, 17, 20. J. Heifetz, B. Smith (r1956) *Concert*
(11/94) (RCA) ① [65] **09026 61778-2(41)**
12. Y. Menuhin, F. Webster (r1938: arr vn/pf: Joachim) *Concert* (9/91) (TEST) ① **SBT1003**
17. X. Wei, Pam Nicholson (arr vn/pf: Joachim) *Concert* (9/90) (ASV) ① **CDDCA698**
17. F. Kreisler, M. Raucheisen (arr Kreisler: r1926) *Concert* (9/92) (BIDD) ① **LAB049/50**

Hymn in Veneration of the Great Joachim—waltz: 2 violins and double-bass/cello (1853)
V. Spivakov, R. Salter, C. West (r1991-2) *Concert*
(5/95) (RCA) ① **09026 62524-2**

15 Neue Liebeslieder Waltzes—piano duet, Op. 65a (1877) (arr cpsr from vocal version)
B. Eden, A. Tamir *Concert*
(5/91) (CRD) ① **CRD3413**

Piano Quartet No. 1 in G minor, Op. 25 (1861)
M. Perahia, Amadeus Qt
(12/87) (SONY) ① **SK42361**
Domus *Piano Quartet 3.*
(6/88) (VIRG) ① **VC7 59248-2**
A. Rubinstein, Guarneri Qt (r1967) *Piano Quartet 3.*
(5/89) (RCA) ① **GD85677**
Villiers Pf Qt *Mahler: Piano Quartet Movement.*
(11/89) (ETCE) ① **KTC1072**
Borodin Trio, R. Golani *Concert*
(4/90) (CHAN) ① **CHAN8809/10**
Cologne RSO, H. Wakasugi (orch Schoenberg) *Schoenberg: Chamber Symphony 1.*
(9/90) (SCHW) ① **311034**

A. Rubinstein, Pro Arte Qt (r1932) *Piano Quartet 2.*
(11/90) (BIDD) ① **LAB027**
LSO, N. Järvi (orch Schoenberg) *Handel Variations.*
(2/91) (CHAN) ① **CHAN8825**
I. Stern, J. Laredo, Y-Y. Ma, E. Ax *Concert*
(3/91) (SONY) ① [2] **S2K45846**
LSO, G. Simon (orch Schoenberg) *Clarinet Sonata 1.*
(3/93) (CALA) ① **CACD1006**
Kandinsky Qt (r1991) *Piano Quartet 3.*
(1/94) (FNAC) ① **592094**
R. Serkin, Busch Qt (r1949) *String Quartet 3.*
(11/94) (EMI) ① **CDH5 65190-2**
Emil Gilels, Amadeus Qt (r1970) *Ballades.*
(6/95) (DG) ① **447 407-2GOR**

Piano Quartet No. 2 in A, Op. 26 (1861-62)
Domus *Mahler: Piano Quartet Movement.*
(1/89) (VIRG) ① **VC7 59144-2**
Borodin Trio, R. Golani *Concert*
(4/90) (CHAN) ① [2] **CHAN8809/10**
R. Serkin, Busch Qt (r1932) *Piano Quartet 1.*
(11/90) (BIDD) ① **LAB027**
I. Stern, J. Laredo, Y-Y. Ma, E. Ax *Concert*
(3/91) (SONY) ① [2] **S2K45846**

Piano Quartet No. 3 in C minor, Op. 60 (1855-75)
Domus *Piano Quartet 1.*
(6/88) (VIRG) ① **VC7 59248-2**
A. Rubinstein, Guarneri Qt *Piano Quintet.*
(5/89) (RCA) ① **GD85677**
J. Panenka, Kocian Qt (1988) *Piano Quintet.*
(3/90) (DENO) ① **CO-73536**
Borodin Trio, R. Golani *Concert*
(4/90) (CHAN) ① [2] **CHAN8809/10**
J. Lateiner, J. Heifetz, S. Schonbach, G. Piatigorsky *Concert* (9/90) (RCA) ① **GD87873**
I. Stern, J. Laredo, Y-Y. Ma, E. Ax *Concert*
(3/91) (SONY) ① [2] **S2K45846**
Kandinsky Qt (r1991) *Piano Quartet 1.*
(1/94) (FNAC) ① **592094**
J. Heifetz, S. Schonbach, G. Piatigorsky, J. Lateiner (r1965) *Concert*
(11/94) (RCA) ① [65] **09026 61778-2(42)**

Piano Trio in A, Op. posth (pub 1938) (attrib Brahms)
Beaux Arts Trio *Concert*
(1/88) (PHIL) ① [2] **416 838-2PH2**
Fontenay Trio *Concert*
(11/92) (TELD) ① [2] **9031-76036-2**
Odeon Trio (r1990s) *Concert*
(7/93) (CAPR) ① [3] **10 633**
Beaux Arts Trio (r1960s) *Concert*
(8/93) (PHIL) ① [2] **438 365-2PM2**
Vienna Pf Trio (r1993) *Piano Trio 3.*
(9/94) (NAXO) ① **8 550747**
I. Perlman, L. Harrell, Vladimir Ashkenazy (r1991) *Concert* (2/95) (EMI) ① [2] **CDS7 54725-2**

Piano Trio No. 1 in B, Op. 8 (1853-4 rev 1889)
Borodin Trio *Concert*
(2/85) (CHAN) ① **CHAN8334/5**
Israel Pf Trio *Piano Trio 3.*
(9/86) (CRD) ① **CRD3432**
Beaux Arts Trio *Concert*
(1/88) (PHIL) ① [2] **416 838-2PH2**
A. Rubinstein, H. Szeryng, P. Fournier *Piano Trio 2.*
(4/88) (RCA) ① **RD86260**
J. Suk, J. Starker, J. Katchen *Piano Trio 2.*
(12/88) (DECC) ① **421 152-2DM**
M. Kaplan, C. Carr, D. Golub *Horn Trio.*
(4/90) (ARAB) ① **Z6607**
Fontenay Trio *Concert*
(11/92) (TELD) ① [2] **9031-76036-2**
Dussek Pf Trio *Concert*
(11/92) (MERI) ① [2] **CDE84227/8**
Guarneri Trio *Concert*
(11/92) (OTTA) ① [2] **OTRC29134**
Trieste Trio *Concert* (2/93) (DG) ① **437 131-2GX2**
Odeon Trio (r1990s) *Concert*
(7/93) (CAPR) ① [3] **10 633**
Beaux Arts Trio (r1960s) *Concert*
(8/93) (PHIL) ① [2] **438 365-2PM2**
I. Stern, P. Casals, M. Hess (r1952) *String Sextet 1.*
(5/94) (SONY) ① **SMK58994**
Vienna Pf Trio (r1993) *Piano Trio 2.*
(10/94) (NAXO) ① **8 550746**
J. Heifetz, E. Feuermann, A. Rubinstein (r1941) *Concert* (11/94) (RCA) ① [65] **09026 61778-2(32)**
I. Perlman, L. Harrell, Vladimir Ashkenazy (r1991) *Concert* (2/95) (EMI) ① [2] **CDS7 54725-2**
K-W. Chung, Myung-Wha Chung, Myung-Whun Chung (1987) *Mendelssohn: Piano Trio 1.*
(4/95) (DECC) ① **421 425-2DH**
Bekova Trio *Piano Trio 2.*
(5/95) (CHAN) ① **CHAN9340**
A. Previn, V. Mullova, H. Schiff *Beethoven: Piano Trios.* (8/95) (PHIL) ① **442 123-2PH**

Piano Trio No. 2 in C, Op. 87 (1880-82)
Borodin Trio *Concert*
(2/85) (CHAN) ① [2] **CHAN8334/5**
Israel Pf Trio *Schumann: Piano Trio 1.*
(9/86) (CRD) ① **CRD3433**
Beaux Arts Trio *Concert*
(1/88) (PHIL) ① [2] **416 838-2PH2**
A. Rubinstein, H. Szeryng, P. Fournier *Piano Trio 1.*
(4/88) (RCA) ① **RD86260**
J. Suk, J. Starker, J. Katchen *Piano Trio 1.*
(12/88) (DECC) ① **421 152-2DM**
M. Kaplan, C. Carr, D. Golub *Concert*
(4/90) (ARAB) ① **Z6608**
M. Hess, J. D'Aranyi, G. Cassadó (r1935) *Concert*
(8/90) (APR) ① [2] **APR7012**
A. Busch, H. Busch, R. Serkin (r1951) *Beethoven: Piano Trios.* (12/91) (SONY) ① **MPK46447**
Fontenay Trio *Concert*
(11/92) (TELD) ① [2] **9031-76036-2**
Dussek Pf Trio *Concert*
(11/92) (MERI) ① [2] **CDE84227/8**
Guarneri Trio *Concert*
(11/92) (OTTA) ① [2] **OTRC29134**
Trieste Trio *Concert* (2/93) (DG) ① **437 131-2GX2**
Odeon Trio (r1990s) *Concert*
(7/93) (CAPR) ① [3] **10 633**
Beaux Arts Trio (r1960s) *Concert*
(8/93) (PHIL) ① [2] **438 365-2PM2**
Vienna Pf Trio (r1993) *Piano Trio 1.*
(10/94) (NAXO) ① **8 550746**
J. Heifetz, G. Piatigorsky, L. Pennario (r1963) *Schubert: Piano Trio 2.*
(11/94) (RCA) ① [65] **09026 61778-2(38)**
I. Perlman, L. Harrell, Vladimir Ashkenazy (r1991) *Concert* (2/95) (EMI) ① [2] **CDS7 54725-2**
Bekova Trio *Piano Trio 1.*
(5/95) (CHAN) ① **CHAN9340**

Piano Trio No. 3 in C minor, Op. 101 (1886)
Borodin Trio *Concert*
(2/85) (CHAN) ① **CHAN8334/5**
Israel Pf Trio *Piano Trio 1.*
(9/86) (CRD) ① **CRD3432**
Beaux Arts Trio *Concert*
(1/88) (PHIL) ① [2] **416 838-2PH2**
M. Kaplan, C. Carr, D. Golub *Concert*
(4/90) (ARAB) ① **Z6608**
Fontenay Trio *Concert*
(11/92) (TELD) ① [2] **9031-76036-2**
Guarneri Trio *Concert*
(11/92) (MERI) ① [2] **CDE84227/8**
Trieste Trio *Concert* (2/93) (DG) ① **437 131-2GX2**
Odeon Trio (r1990s) *Concert*
(7/93) (CAPR) ① [3] **10 633**
Beaux Arts Trio (r1960) *Concert*
(8/93) (PHIL) ① [2] **438 365-2PM2**
Vienna Pf Trio (r1993) *Piano Trio, Op. posth.*
(9/94) (NAXO) ① **8 550747**
I. Perlman, L. Harrell, Vladimir Ashkenazy (r1991) *Concert* (2/95) (EMI) ① [2] **CDS7 54725-2**

Quintet for Clarinet and Strings in B minor, Op. 115 (1891)
Nash Ens *Mozart: Clarinet Quintet, K581.*
(6/87) (CRD) ① **CRD3445**
T. King, Gabrieli Qt *Clarinet Trio.*
(12/87) (HYPE) ① **CDA66107**
K. Leister, Amadeus Qt *Clarinet Trio.*
(12/87) (DG) ① [3] **419 875-2GCM3**
K. Puddy, Delmé Qt *Dvořák: String Quartet 12.*
(3/88) (CARL) ① **PCD883**
A. Boskovsky, Vienna Octet *String Quartet 3.*
(9/88) (DECC) ① **417 643-2DM**
G. de Peyer, Melos Ens (r1964) *Mozart: Clarinet Quintet, K581.* (11/89) (EMI) ① **CDM7 63116-2**
Chbr Music NW *String Quintet 2.*
(3/90) (DELO) ① **DE3066**
Berlin Sols *Mozart: Clarinet Quintet, K581.*
(9/90) (TELD) ① **2292-46429-2**
O. Oppenheim, Budapest Qt *String Quartet 3.*
(11/90) (SONY) ① **MPK45553**
P. Moraguès, Talich Qt *String Quartet 3.*
(11/90) (PYRA) ① **PYR13489**
R. Kell, Busch Qt (r1937) *Horn Trio.*
(6/91) (TEST) ① **SBT1001**
M. Portal, Melos Qt *String Quintet 2.*
(7/91) (HARM) ① **HMC90 1349**
S. Meyer, Vienna Stg Sextet *Yun: Clarinet Quintet.*
(11/91) (EMI) ① **CDC7 54304-2**
E. Daniels, Composers Qt *Weber: Clarinet Quintet, J182.* (12/91) (REFE) ① **RRCD-40**
J. Campbell, Allegri Qt *Piano Quintet.*
(12/92) (CALA) ① **CACD1009**
J. Balogh, Danubius Qt (r1991) *Clarinet Trio.*
(9/93) (NAXO) ① **8 550391**

H. Wright, Boston Sym Chbr Players (r1993) Mozart: Clarinet Quintet, K581.
(9/94) (PHIL) ① 442 149-2PH
Berlin Phil Octet (r1972) Concert
(8/95) (PHIL) ① [2] 446 172-2PM2
R. Stoltzman, Tokyo Qt (r1993) Weber: Clarinet Quintet, J182. (8/95) (RCA) ① 09026 68033-2
C. Neidich, Juilliard Qt (r1994) Concert
(9/95) (SONY) ① [2] S2K66285

Quintet for Piano and Strings in F minor, Op. 34 (1861-4)
M. Pollini, Quartetto Italiano
(6/87) (DG) ① 419 673-2GH
Rome Fauré Qnt (11/87) (CLAV) ① CD50-8702
C. Eschenbach, Amadeus Qt Concert
(12/87) (DG) ① [3] 419 875-2GCM3
Barry Douglas, Tokyo Qt Concert
(12/87) (RCA) ① RD86673
E. Leonskaja, Alban Berg Qt (pp1987) Dvořák: Piano Quintet, Op.81. (10/88) (EMI) ① CDC7 49024-2
J. Panenka, Kocian Qt (r1988) Piano Quartet 3.
(3/90) (DENO) ① CO-73536
P. Frankl, Lindsay Qt Schumann: Piano Quintet, Op.44. (12/90) (ASV) ① CDDCA728
J. Jandó, Kodály Qt Schumann: Piano Quintet, Op. 44. (2/91) (NAXO) ① 8 550406
A. Schiff, Takács Qt String Quartet 3.
(11/91) (DECC) ① 430 529-2DH
R. de Waal, Allegri Qt Clarinet Quintet.
(12/92) (CALA) ① CACD1009
P. Lane, New Budapest Qt String Quartet 3.
(4/93) (HYPE) ① CDA66652
G. Gould, Montreal Qt (bp1957) Schumann: Piano Quartet, Op. 47. (10/93) (SONY) ① SMK52684
P. Gulda, Hagen Qt (r1992) Schoenberg: Chamber Symphony 1. (10/93) (DG) ① 437 804-2GH
Nash Ens (r1991) Horn Trio.
(9/94) (CRD) ① CRD3489
S. Vladar, Artis Qt (r1993) Schumann: Piano Quintet, Op. 44. (10/94) (SONY) ① SK58954
Borodin Qt, E. Virzaladze (r1990) String Quartet 2.
(5/95) (TELD) ① 4509-97461-2
W. Haas, Berlin Phil Octet (r1973) Concert
(8/95) (PHIL) ① [2] 446 172-2PM2

Scherzo in C minor, 'FAE Sonata'—violin and piano, Op. 5 (1853) (mvt from Vn Son in A min (coll Schumann/Dietrich))
J. Laredo, J-B. Pommier Concert
(12/91) (VIRG) ① VJ7 59642-2
O. Renardy, W. Robert (r1940) Concert
(12/92) (BIDD) ① [2] LAB061/2
P. Zukerman, D. Barenboim Concert
(1/93) (DG) ① 437 248-2GGA
I. Stern, Y. Bronfman (pp1991) Concert
(3/94) (SONY) ① SK53107

Sonata for Cello and Piano in D (?1890s) (arr from Violin Sonata, Op. 78)
J. Starker, S. Neriki Concert
(4/92) (RCA) ① RD60598
C. Dearnley, J. Drake Cello Sonata 2.
(10/93) (MERI) ① CDE84223
M. Kliegel, K. Merscher (r1992) Concert
(12/93) (NAXO) ① 8 550656
K. Georgian, P. Gililov (r1989) Concert
(9/94) (BIDD) ① [2] LAW014

Sonata for Cello and Piano No. 1 in E minor, Op. 38 (1862-65)
M. Rostropovich, R. Serkin Cello Sonata 2.
(9/83) (DG) ① 410 510-2GH
S. Isserlis, Peter Evans Cello Sonata 2.
(4/86) (HYPE) ① CDA66159
R. Wallfisch, P. Wallfisch Cello Sonata 2.
(8/88) (CHAN) ① CHAN8615
C. Henckel, E. Westenholz Cello Sonata 2.
(12/88) (BIS) ① BIS-CD192
T. Mørk, J. Lagerspetz Concert
(8/89) (SIMA) ① PSC1029
E. Feuermann, T. Van der Pas (r1934) Concert
(6/90) (BIDD) ① LAB011
C. Starck, C. Eschenbach Cello Sonata 2.
(4/91) (CLAV) ① CD50-9005
G. Piatigorsky, A. Rubinstein (r1936) Concert
(10/91) (PEAR) ① GEMMCD9447
E. Feuermann, T. van der Pas (r1934) Concert
(10/91) (PEAR) ① GEMMCD9443
G. Piatigorsky, R. Stewart (pp1947) Concert
(10/91) (MUSI) ① MACD-644
G. Piatigorsky, A. Rubinstein (r1936) Concert
(3/92) (MUSI) ① MACD-674
Y-Y. Ma, E. Ax Concert
(11/92) (SONY) ① SK48191
B. Harrison, G. Moore (r1927) Concert
(3/93) (CLAR) ① CDGSE78-50-47
B. Harrison, G. Moore (r1926/7) Concert
(3/93) (SYMP) ① SYMCD1140

M. Kliegel, K. Merscher (r1992) Concert
(12/93) (NAXO) ① 8 550656
P. Wispelwey, P. Komen (r1992) Cello Sonata 2.
(1/94) (CHNN) ① CCS5493
K. Georgian, P. Gililov (r1990) Concert
(9/94) (BIDD) ① [2] LAW014
D. Yablonski, O. Yablonskaya Cello Sonata 2.
(11/94) (DINT) ① DICD920186
J. Starker, R. Buchbinder (r1993) Concert
(11/94) (RCA) ① 09026 61562-2
N. Rosen, D. Stevenson Concert
(3/95) (JMR) ① JMR5
J. Starker, G. Sebok (r1959) Cello Sonata 2.
(7/95) (ERAT) ① 4509-96950-2

Sonata for Cello and Piano No. 2 in F, Op. 99 (1886)
M. Rostropovich, R. Serkin Cello Sonata 1.
(9/83) (DG) ① 410 510-2GH
S. Isserlis, Peter Evans Cello Sonata 1.
(4/86) (HYPE) ① CDA66159
R. Wallfisch, P. Wallfisch Cello Sonata 1.
(8/88) (CHAN) ① CHAN8615
C. Henckel, E. Westenholz Cello Sonata 1.
(12/88) (BIS) ① BIS-CD192
T. Mørk, J. Lagerspetz Concert
(8/89) (SIMA) ① PSC1029
J. Du Pré, E. Lush (pp1962) Concert
(9/89) (EMI) ① CDM7 63166-2
C. Starck, C. Eschenbach Cello Sonata 1.
(4/91) (CLAV) ① CD50-9005
Y-Y. Ma, E. Ax Concert
(11/92) (SONY) ① SK48191
C. Dearnley, J. Drake Cello Sonata in D.
(10/93) (MERI) ① CDE84223
M. Kliegel, K. Merscher (r1992) Concert
(12/93) (NAXO) ① 8 550656
P. Wispelwey, P. Komen (r1992) Cello Sonata 1.
(1/94) (CHNN) ① CCS5493
K. Georgian, P. Gililov (r1990) Concert
(9/94) (BIDD) ① [2] LAW014
P. Casals, M. Horszowski (r1936) Concert
(10/94) (EMI) ① [2] CHS5 65185-2
D. Yablonski, O. Yablonskaya Cello Sonata 1.
(11/94) (DINT) ① DICD920186
J. Starker, R. Buchbinder (r1993) Concert
(11/94) (RCA) ① 09026 61562-2
N. Rosen, D. Stevenson Concert
(3/95) (JMR) ① JMR5
J. Starker, G. Sebok (r1959) Cello Sonata 1.
(7/95) (ERAT) ① 4509-96950-2

Sonata for Clarinet and Piano No. 1 in F minor, Op. 120/1 (1894)
1. Allegro appassionato; 2. Andante, un poco adagio; 3. Allegretto grazioso; 4. Vivace.
T. King, C. Benson Clarinet Sonata 2.
(10/87) (HYPE) ① CDA66202
G. de Peyer, G. Pryor Clarinet Sonata 2.
(3/88) (CHAN) ① CHAN8563
R. Stoltzman, R. Goode Clarinet Sonata 2.
(9/89) (RCA) ① GD60036
A. Hacker, R. Burnett Concert
(4/90) (AMON) ① CD-SAR37
J. Campbell, LSO, G. Simon (orch Berio) Piano Quartet 1. (3/93) (CALA) ① CACD1006
M. Portal, M. Rudy Concert
(5/93) (EMI) ① CDC7 54466-2
M. Khouri, J. McCabe (r1990) Concert
(8/93) (CNTI) ① CCD1027
F. Cohen, Vladimir Ashkenazy (r1991) Concert
(10/93) (DECC) ① 430 149-2DH
E. Petrov, V. Pyasetsky (r1993) Concert
(9/94) (ETCE) ① KTC1177
J. Cohler, J. Gordon (r1992) Concert
(11/94) (ONGA) ① 024-101

Sonata for Clarinet and Piano No. 2 in E flat, Op. 120/2 (1894)
T. King, C. Benson Clarinet Sonata 1.
(10/87) (HYPE) ① CDA66202
G. de Peyer, G. Pryor Clarinet Sonata 1.
(3/88) (CHAN) ① CHAN8563
R. Stoltzman, R. Goode Clarinet Sonata 1.
(9/89) (RCA) ① GD60036
A. Hacker, R. Burnett Concert
(4/90) (AMON) ① CD-SAR37
M. Portal, M. Rudy Concert
(5/93) (EMI) ① CDC7 54466-2
M. Khouri, J. McCabe (r1990) Concert
(8/93) (CNTI) ① CCD1027
F. Cohen, Vladimir Ashkenazy (r1991) Concert
(10/93) (DECC) ① 430 149-2DH
E. Petrov, V. Pyasetsky (r1993) Concert
(9/94) (ETCE) ① KTC1177
J. Cohler, J. Hodgkinson (r1992) Concert
(11/94) (ONGA) ① 024-102

Sonata for Two Pianos in F minor, Op. 34b (1864) (arr of Piano Quintet, Op. 34)
M. Argerich, A. Rabinovitch (r1993) Concert
(1/95) (TELD) ① 4509-92257-2

Sonata for Viola and Piano No. 1 in F minor, Op. 120/1 (1894)
N. Imai, R. Vignoles Concert
(10/87) (CHAN) ① CHAN8550
R. Golani, K. Bogino Concert
(9/92) (CONI) ① CDCF199
P. Zukerman, D. Barenboim Concert
(1/93) (DG) ① 437 248-2GGA
L.A. Tomter, L.O. Andsnes (r1991) Concert
(11/93) (VIRG) ① VC7 59309-2
P. Zukerman, M. Neikrug (r1991) Concert
(9/94) (RCA) ① 09026 61276-2

Sonata for Viola and Piano No. 2 in E flat, Op. 120/2 (1894)
N. Imai, R. Vignoles Concert
(10/87) (CHAN) ① CHAN8550
W. Primrose, G. Moore (r1937) Concert
(6/90) (BIDD) ① LAB011
R. Golani, K. Bogino Concert
(9/92) (CONI) ① CDCF199
P. Zukerman, D. Barenboim Concert
(1/93) (DG) ① 437 248-2GGA
L.A. Tomter, L.O. Andsnes (r1991) Concert
(11/93) (VIRG) ① VC7 59309-2
W. Primrose, G. Moore (r1937) Concert
(9/94) (PEAR) ① GEMMCD9045
P. Zukerman, M. Neikrug (r1991) Concert
(9/94) (RCA) ① 09026 61276-2

Sonata for Violin and Piano No. 1 in G, Op. 78 (1878-79)
I. Perlman, Vladimir Ashkenazy Concert
(2/87) (EMI) ① CDC7 47403-2
N. Gotkovsky, I. Gotkovsky Concert
(4/87) (PYRA) ① PYR13487
J. Suk, J. Katchen Concert
(5/88) (DECC) ① 421 092-2DM
N-E. Sparf, E. Westenholz Concert
(12/88) (BIS) ① BIS-CD212
H. Szeryng, A. Rubinstein Concert
(4/89) (RCA) ① GD86264
C. Ferras, P. Barbizet Violin Concerto.
(5/90) (DG) ① 429 513-2GR
T. Seidel, A. Loesser (r1926) Concert
(6/90) (BIDD) ① LAB013
I. Perlman, D. Barenboim (pp1989) Concert
(12/90) (SONY) ① SK45819
K. Ososotowicz, S. Tomes Concert
(11/91) (HYPE) ① CDA66465
J. Laredo, J-B. Pommier Concert
(12/91) (VIRG) ① VJ7 59642-2
A. Dumay, M-J. Pires Concert
(3/93) (DG) ① 435 800-2GH
N. Wakabayashi, K. Sturrock (r1991) Concert
(10/93) (CARL) ① PCD1050
G. de Vito, Edwin Fischer (r1954) Concert
(12/93) (TEST) ① SBT1024
P. Zukerman, D. Barenboim (r1974) Violin Concerto.
(1/94) (DG) ① 439 405-2GCL
I. Stern, Y. Bronfman (pp1991) Concert
(3/94) (SONY) ① SK53107
I. Perlman, Vladimir Ashkenazy Concert
(4/94) (EMI) ① [20] CZS4 83177-2(2)

Sonata for Violin and Piano No. 2 in A, Op. 100 (1886)
I. Perlman, Vladimir Ashkenazy Concert
(2/87) (EMI) ① CDC7 47403-2
N. Gotkovsky, I. Gotkovsky Concert
(4/87) (PYRA) ① PYR13487
J. Suk, J. Katchen Concert
(5/88) (DECC) ① 421 092-2DM
N-E. Sparf, E. Westenholz Concert
(12/88) (BIS) ① BIS-CD212
J. Heifetz, E. Bay (r1936) Concert
(6/90) (BIDD) ① LAB011
T. Seidel, A. Loesser (r1926) Concert
(6/90) (BIDD) ① LAB013
I. Perlman, D. Barenboim (pp1989) Concert
(12/90) (SONY) ① SK45819
K. Ososotowicz, S. Tomes Concert
(11/91) (HYPE) ① CDA66465
J. Laredo, J-B. Pommier Concert
(12/91) (VIRG) ① VJ7 59642-2
M. Vengerov, A. Markovich Beethoven: Violin Sonata 9. (5/92) (TELD) ① 9031-74001-2
A. Busch, R. Serkin (r1932) Concert
(12/92) (PEAR) ① GEMMCD9942
A. Dumay, M-J. Pires Concert
(3/93) (DG) ① 435 800-2GH
N. Wakabayashi, K. Sturrock (r1991) Concert
(10/93) (CARL) ① PCD1050
I. Menges, H. Samuel (r1929) Concert
(11/93) (BIDD) ① LAB076

6 Pieces—piano, Op. 118 (1892)
1. Intermezzo, A minor; 2. Intermezzo, A; 3. Ballade,
G minor; 4. Intermezzo, F minor; 5. Romance, F; 6.
Intermezzo, E flat minor.
R. Lupu *Concert*   (8/87) (DECC) ① **417 599-2DH**
S. Kovacevich *Concert*
     (4/88) (PHIL) ① **420 750-2PH**
W. Backhaus (r1933) *Concert*
     (3/90) (PEAR) ① **GEMMCD9385**
L. Hokanson *Concert*   (9/90) (BAYE) ① **BR100035**
E. Knardahl *Concert*   (9/90) (SIMA) ① **PSC1059**
G. Oppitz *Concert*
     (10/90) (EURO) ① [5] **RD69245**
J. Katchen (r1962) *Concert*
     (2/91) (DECC) ① [6] **430 053-2DM6**
L. Zilberstein *Concert*   (3/91) (DG) ① **431 123-2GH**
I. Biret *Concert*   (5/92) (NAXO) ① **8 550354**
H. Grimaud *Piano Sonata 3.*
     (9/92) (DENO) ① **CO-79782**
E. Ax (r1991) *Concert*   (10/92) (SONY) ① **SK48046**
W. Kempff *Concert*   (1/93) (DG) ① **437 249-2GGA**
V. Afanassiev *Concert*   (4/93) (DENO) ① **CO-75090**
W. Backhaus (r1932) *Concert*
     (9/94) (BIDD) ① **LHW019**
1, 2, 4, 6. L. Edlina *Concert*
     (11/86) (CHAN) ① **CHAN8467**
2. A. Servadei *Concert*   (7/91) (CARL) ① **PCD949**
2. G. Fergus-Thompson *Concert*
     (10/92) (ASV) ① **CDWHL2066**
2. I. Pogorelich *Concert*
     (1/93) (DG) ① **437 460-2GH**
3. S. Richter *Concert*
     (8/94) (PHIL) ① [3] **438 477-2PH3**
5. A. Rubinstein *Concert*   (2/88) (RCA) ① **RD85672**
5. W. Gieseking (r1940) *Concert*
     (3/94) (PEAR) ① **GEMMCD9038**
5. A. Rubinstein (r1959) *Concert*
     (9/94) (RCA) ① **09026 61862-2**
6. M. Perahia *Concert*   (10/91) (SONY) ① **SK47181**
6. A. Rubinstein *Concert*
     (2/93) (RCA) ① **09026 61263-2**
6. M. Kazakevich (r1993) *Concert*
     (9/94) (CONI) ① **CDCF235**
6. Solomon (pp1956) *Concert*
     (4/95) (APR) ① **APR7030**

4 Pieces—piano, Op. 119 (1892)
1. Intermezzo, B minor; 2. Intermezzo, E minor; 3.
Intermezzo, C; 4. Rhapsody, E flat.
R. Lupu *Concert*   (8/87) (DECC) ① **417 599-2DH**
L. Hokanson *Concert*   (9/90) (BAYE) ① **BR100035**
G. Oppitz *Concert*
     (10/90) (EURO) ① [5] **RD69245**
G. Oppitz *Piano Sonata 3.*
     (10/90) (ORFE) ① **C020821A**
J. Katchen (r1962) *Concert*
     (2/91) (DECC) ① [6] **430 053-2DM6**
I. Biret *Concert*   (5/92) (NAXO) ① **8 550354**
L. Vogt *Concert*   (5/92) (EMI) ① **CDC7 54446-2**
W. Kempff *Concert*   (1/93) (DG) ① **437 249-2GGA**
V. Afanassiev *Concert*   (4/93) (DENO) ① **CO-75090**
1. A. Servadei *Concert*   (7/91) (CARL) ① **PCD949**
1-3. L. Edlina *Concert*
     (11/86) (CHAN) ① **CHAN8467**
1-3. W. Backhaus (r1935) *Concert*
     (9/94) (BIDD) ① **LHW019**
3. Solomon (r1952) *Concert*
     (10/94) (TEST) ① **SBT1042**
3. M. Hess (r1928) *Concert*
     (3/95) (BIDD) ① **LHW024**
4. M. Perahia *Concert*   (10/91) (SONY) ① **SK47181**
4. E. Petri (r1940) *Concert*
     (3/94) (APR) ① [2] **APR7024**
4. S. Richter *Concert*
     (8/94) (PHIL) ① [3] **438 477-2PH3**

Prelude and Fugue in A minor—organ (1856-57)
K. Bowyer *Concert*   (11/90) (NIMB) ① **NI5262**
N. Danby *Concert*   (6/92) (CRD) ① **CRD3404**
R. Parkins (r1994) *Concert*
     (12/94) (NAXO) ① **8 550824**

Prelude and Fugue in G minor—organ (1856-57)
K. Bowyer *Concert*   (11/90) (NIMB) ① **NI5262**
N. Danby *Concert*   (6/92) (CRD) ① **CRD3404**
R. Parkins (r1994) *Concert*
     (12/94) (NAXO) ① **8 550824**

Rákóczy March—piano transcription (1853)
I. Biret (r1993) *Concert*   (5/92) (NAXO) ① **8 550958**

2 Rhapsodies—piano, Op. 79 (1879)
1. B minor; 2. G minor.
R. Lupu *Concert*   (8/87) (DECC) ① **417 599-2DH**
S. Kovacevich *Concert*
     (4/88) (PHIL) ① **420 750-2PH**
W. Backhaus (r1933) *Concert*
     (3/90) (PEAR) ① **GEMMCD9385**
E. Knardahl *Concert*   (9/90) (SIMA) ① **PSC1059**

J. Plowright *Concert*
     (10/90) (KING) ① **KCLCD2016**
G. Oppitz *Concert*
     (10/90) (EURO) ① [5] **RD69245**
J. Katchen (r1960s) *Concert*
     (2/91) (DECC) ① [6] **430 053-2DM6**
P. Katin *Concert*   (5/91) (OLYM) ① **OCD263**
E. Ax (r1991) *Concert*   (10/92) (SONY) ① **SK48046**
I. Pogorelich *Concert*   (1/93) (DG) ① **437 460-2GH**
M. Argerich *Concert*   (2/93) (DG) ① **437 252-2GGA**
M. Rudy (r1991/2) *Concert*
     (5/93) (EMI) ① **CDC7 54233-2**
E. Petri (r1940) *Concert*
     (3/94) (APR) ① [2] **APR7024**
W. Backhaus (r1932) *Concert*
     (9/94) (BIDD) ① **LHW019**
L.D. Alvanis *Concert*   (3/95) (MERI) ① **CDE84268**
A. Lubimov (r1994) *Concert*
     (5/95) (ERAT) ① **4509-98474-2**
M. Argerich (r1960) *Concert*
     (6/95) (DG) ① **447 430-2GOR**
V. Afanassiev (r1993) *Concert*
     (7/95) (DENO) ① **CO-78906**
1. M. Perahia *Concert*   (10/91) (SONY) ① **SK47181**
1. A. Rubinstein *Concert*
     (2/93) (RCA) ① **09026 61263-2**
1. Solomon (pp1956) *Concert*
     (4/95) (APR) ① [2] **APR7030**
1, 2. G. Oppitz (r1989) *Concert*
     (9/94) (RCA) ① **09026 61811-2**
2. A. Servadei *Concert*   (7/91) (CARL) ① **PCD949**
2. A. Rubinstein (r1970) *Concert*
     (10/93) (RCA) ① **09026 61442-2**
2. W. Gieseking (r1924) *Concert*
     (3/94) (PEAR) ① **GEMMCD9038**
2. Solomon (r1944) *Concert*
     (10/94) (TEST) ① **SBT1042**

2 Sarabandes—piano (1855)
1. A minor; 2. B minor.
I. Biret (r1993) *Concert*   (5/95) (NAXO) ① **8 550958**

Scherzo in E flat minor, Op. 4 (1851)
W. Backhaus (r1933) *Concert*
     (3/90) (PEAR) ① **GEMMCD9385**
L. Hokanson *Concert*   (9/90) (BAYE) ① **BR100035**
G. Oppitz *Concert*
     (10/90) (EURO) ① [5] **RD69245**
J. Katchen (r1960s) *Concert*
     (2/91) (DECC) ① [6] **430 053-2DM6**
I. Biret *Concert*   (5/92) (NAXO) ① **8 550354**
W. Backhaus (r1932) *Concert*
     (9/94) (BIDD) ① **LHW017**

Sonata for Piano No. 1 in C, Op. 1 (1852-53)
E. Knardahl *Concert*   (4/88) (SIMA) ① **PSC1021**
G. Oppitz *Concert*
     (10/90) (EURO) ① [5] **RD69245**
J. Katchen (r1960s) *Concert*
     (2/91) (DECC) ① [6] **430 053-2DM6**
S. Richter (pp1988) *Concert*
     (4/92) (RCA) ① **RD60859**
I. Biret *Piano Sonata 3.*   (5/92) (NAXO) ① **8 550351**
E. Leonskaja *Piano Sonata 3.*
     (6/92) (TELD) ① **9031-73184-2**
S. Richter (pp1987) *Piano Sonata 2.*
     (3/93) (DECC) ① **436 457-2DH**
S. Richter *Concert*
     (8/94) (PHIL) ① [3] **438 477-2PH3**

Sonata for Piano No. 2 in F sharp minor, Op. 2 (1852)
H. Grimaud (r1988) *Schumann: Kreisleriana.*
     (9/89) (DENO) ① **CO-73336**
G. Oppitz *Concert*
     (10/90) (EURO) ① [5] **RD69245**
J. Katchen (r1960s) *Concert*
     (2/91) (DECC) ① [6] **430 053-2DM6**
I. Biret *Piano Sonata 1.*   (5/92) (NAXO) ① **8 550351**
S. Richter (pp1987) *Piano Sonata 1.*
     (3/93) (DECC) ① **436 457-2DH**
S. Richter *Concert*
     (8/94) (PHIL) ① [3] **438 477-2PH3**

Sonata for Piano No. 3 in F minor, Op. 5 (1853)
A. Rubinstein *Concert*   (2/88) (RCA) ① **RD85672**
G. Oppitz *Concert*
     (10/90) (EURO) ① [5] **RD69245**
J. Plowright *Concert*
     (10/90) (KING) ① **KCLCD2016**
G. Oppitz *Piano Pieces, Op.119.*
     (10/90) (ORFE) ① **C020821A**
J. Katchen (r1960s) *Concert*
     (2/91) (DECC) ① [6] **430 053-2DM6**
M. Perahia *Concert*   (10/91) (SONY) ① **SK47181**
E. Leonskaja *Piano Sonata 1.*
     (6/92) (TELD) ① **9031-73184-2**
H. Grimaud *Piano Pieces, Op.118.*
     (9/92) (DENO) ① **CO-79782**

J-F. Heisser *Schumann Variations.*
     (10/92) (ERAT) ① **2292-45633-2**
I. Biret *Ballades.*   (12/92) (NAXO) ① **8 550352**
P. Grainger (r1926) *Concert*
     (4/93) (BIDD) ① **LHW008**
H. Bauer (r1939) *Concert*   (4/94) (BIDD) ① **LHW009**
A. Bonatta (r1992) *Concert*   (7/94) (ASTR) ① **E8752**
A. Rubinstein (r1959) *Concert*
     (9/94) (RCA) ① **09026 61862-2**
B-L. Gelber (r1992) *Handel Variations.*
     (11/94) (DENO) ① **CO-75959**
G. Sokolov (pp1993) *Ballades.*
     (3/95) (O111) ① **OPS30-103**
M. Anderson (r1993) *Concert*
     (7/95) (NIMB) ① **NI5422**

Study on Impromptu in E flat, D935/2 (Schubert)—piano transcription: left-hand (c1855)
I. Biret (r1993) *Concert*   (5/95) (NAXO) ① **8 550958**

Theme and Variations in D minor—piano (1860)
I. Biret (r1993) *Concert*   (5/95) (NAXO) ① **8 550958**
M. Rudy (r1994) *Concert*
     (7/95) (EMI) ① **CDC5 55167-2**

25 Variations and Fugue on a Theme by G.F. Handel—piano, Op. 24 (1861)
NBC SO, A. Toscanini (orch Rubbra: bp1939)
Concert   (1/90) (DELL) ① **CDDA9020**
E. Knardahl *Concert*   (9/90) (SIMA) ① **PSC1059**
G. Oppitz *Concert*
     (10/90) (EURO) ① [5] **RD69245**
J. Katchen (r1962) *Concert*
     (2/91) (DECC) ① [6] **430 053-2DM6**
LSO, N. Järvi (orch Rubbra) *Piano Quartet 1.*
     (2/91) (CHAN) ① **CHAN8825**
P. Katin *Concert*   (5/91) (OLYM) ① **OCD263**
J. Colom *Concert*
     (5/92) (CHNT) ① [2] **LDC278 1064/5**
E. Ax (r1991) *Concert*   (10/92) (SONY) ① **SK48046**
R. Tureck (pp1992) *Concert*
     (8/93) (VAI) ① [2] **VAIA1024**
B. Moiseiwitsch (r1953) *Concert*
     (1/94) (TEST) ① **SBT1023**
E. Petri (r1938) *Concert*
     (3/94) (APR) ① [2] **APR7024**
G. Oppitz (r1989) *Concert*
     (9/94) (RCA) ① **09026 61811-2**
Solomon (r1942) *Piano Concerto 1.*
     (10/94) (TEST) ① **SBT1041**
B-L. Gelber (r1992) *Piano Sonata 3.*
     (11/94) (DENO) ① **CO-75959**
Cleveland Orch, Vladimir Ashkenazy (r1992: orch E
Rubbra) *Symphony 4.*
     (11/94) (DECC) ① **436 853-2DH**
A. Lubimov (r1994) *Concert*
     (5/95) (ERAT) ① **4509-98474-2**
Solomon (r1942) *Piano Concerto 1.*
     (7/95) (APR) ① **APR5503**
M. Rudy (r1994) *Concert*
     (7/95) (EMI) ① **CDC5 55167-2**
J. Katchen (r1965) *Concert*
     (10/95) (DECC) ① [2] **440 612-2DF2**
A. Schiff (pp1994) *Concert*
     (11/95) (TELD) ① **4509-99051-2**

Variations in F sharp minor on a Theme by R. Schumann—piano, Op. 9 (1854)
G. Oppitz *Concert*
     (10/90) (EURO) ① [5] **RD69245**
J. Katchen (r1960s) *Concert*
     (2/91) (DECC) ① [6] **430 053-2DM6**
J. Colom *Concert*
     (5/92) (CHNT) ① [2] **LDC278 1064/5**
J-F. Heisser *Piano Sonata 3.*
     (10/92) (ERAT) ① **2292-45633-2**
A. Bonatta (r1992) *Concert*   (7/94) (ASTR) ① **E8752**
L. Lortie (r1993) *Concert*
     (8/94) (CHAN) ① **CHAN9289**
M. Rudy (r1994) *Concert*
     (7/95) (EMI) ① **CDC5 55167-2**

Variations on a Hungarian song in D—piano, Op. 21/2 (1853)
G. Oppitz *Concert*
     (10/90) (EURO) ① [5] **RD69245**
J. Katchen (r1960s) *Concert*
     (2/91) (DECC) ① [6] **430 053-2DM6**
J. Colom *Concert*
     (5/92) (CHNT) ① [2] **LDC278 1064/5**
A. Bonatta (r1992) *Concert*   (7/94) (ASTR) ① **E8752**
I. Biret (r1993) *Concert*   (8/94) (NAXO) ① **8 550959**
M. Rudy (r1994) *Concert*
     (7/95) (EMI) ① **CDC5 55167-2**

28 Variations on a Theme by Paganini—piano, Op. 35 (1862-63)
M. Ponti *Liszt: Paganini Studies, S140.*
     (1/87) (MERI) ① **CDE84101**

G. Oppitz *Concert*
(10/90) (EURO) ① [5] **RD69245**
J. Katchen (r1965) *Concert*
(2/91) (DECC) ① [6] **430 053-2DM6**
L. Zilberstein *Concert* (3/91) (DG) ① **431 123-2GH**
J. Colom *Concert*
(5/92) (CHNT) ① [2] **LDC278 1064/5**
M. Raekallio *Concert* (8/92) (ONDI) ① **ODE777-2**
E. Petri (r1937) *Concert*
(3/94) (APR) ① [2] **APR7024**
S. Richter *Concert*
(8/94) (PHIL) ① [3] **438 477-2PH3**
G. Oppitz (r1989) *Concert*
(9/94) (RCA) ① **09026 61811-2**
W. Backhaus (r1929) *Concert*
(9/94) (BIDD) ① **LHW018**
J. Katchen (r1965) *Concert*
(10/95) (DECC) ① [2] **440 612-2DF2**
J-Y. Thibaudet (r1994) *Concert*
(10/95) (DECC) ① **444 338-2DH**
Book II G. Bachauer (r1963) *Concert*
Vars.1-8, 10-22, 24-27. A.B. Michelangeli (r1948)
Concert (8/93) (EMI) ① **CDH7 64490-2**
Variations on an original theme in D—piano,
Op. 21/1 (1857)
W. Backhaus (r1935) *Concert*
(3/90) (PEAR) ① **GEMMCD9385**
G. Oppitz *Concert*
(10/90) (EURO) ① [5] **RD69245**
J. Katchen (r1960s) *Concert*
(2/91) (DECC) ① [6] **430 053-2DM6**
J. Colom *Concert*
(5/92) (CHNT) ① [2] **LDC278 1064/5**
I. Biret (r1993) *Concert* (8/94) (NAXO) ① **8 550509**
W. Backhaus (r1935) *Concert*
(9/94) (BIDD) ① **LHW018**
16 Waltzes—piano, Op. 39 (1865)
1. B; 2. E; 3. G sharp minor; 4. E minor; 5. E; 6. C
sharp; 7. C sharp minor; 8. B flat; 9. D minor; 10. G;
11. B minor; 12. E; 13. B; 14. G sharp minor; 15. A
flat; 16. C sharp minor.
S. Kovacevich *Concert*
(4/88) (PHIL) ① **420 750-2PH**
G. Oppitz *Concert*
(10/90) (EURO) ① [5] **RD69245**
J. Katchen (r1960s) *Concert*
(2/91) (DECC) ① [6] **430 053-2DM6**
M. Rudy (r1991/2) *Concert*
(5/93) (EMI) ① **CDC7 54233-2**
W. Backhaus (r1935) *Concert*
(9/94) (BIDD) ① **LHW019**
I. Biret (r1992) *Hungarian Dances.*
(10/94) (NAXO) ① **8 550355**
1, 2, 15. W. Backhaus (r1932) *Concert*
(9/94) (BIDD) ① **LHW017**
2, 15. A. Servadei *Concert*
(7/91) (CARL) ① **PCD949**
15. M. Tirimo *Concert*
(12/88) (KING) ① **KCLCD2003**
15. M. Lympany *Concert* (1/89) (EMIL) ① **CDZ110**
15. V. Horowitz (r1950) *Concert*
(1/93) (RCA) ① **GD60463**
15. P. Grainger (r1926) *Concert*
(4/93) (BIDD) ① **LHW008**
15. F. Kreisler, C. Lamson (r1921: arr Hochstein)
Concert (9/93) (BIDD) ① [2] **LAB068/9**
15. B. Huberman, S. Schultze (r1929: arr Hochstein)
Concert (9/94) (BIDD) ① [2] **LAB081/2**
15, 16. H. Bauer (r1939) *Concert*
(4/93) (BIDD) ① **LHW009**

SECTION IV: VOCAL AND CHORAL

Ave Maria—4 female vv, orchestra/organ,
Op. 12 (1858) (Wds. liturgical)
Trinity Coll Ch, Cambridge, R. Pearce, R. Marlow
Concert (2/90) (CONI) ① **CDCF178**
4 Balladen und Romanzen—2vv and piano,
Op. 75 (pub 1878)
1. Edward (AT) (trad Scots); 2. Guter Rat (SA) (from
Des Knaben Wunderhorn); 3. So lass uns wandern!
(ST) (trad Czech); 4. Walpurgisnacht (SS) (wds.
Alexis).
2. J. Banse, B. Fassbaender, C. Garben (r1993)
Concert (8/95) (SCHW) ① **312592**
Begräbnisgesang—5vv, wind ensemble and
timpani, Op. 13 (1858) (Wds. M. Weisse)
Bavarian Rad Chor, BRSO, B. Haitink *Concert*
(4/84) (ORFE) ① **C025821A**
London Schütz Ch, LCP, R. Norrington (r1992)
Deutsches Requiem, Op.45.
(4/93) (EMI) ① **CDC7 54658-2**
49 Deutsche Volkslieder—voice and piano,
WoO33 (1894)
BOOK 1: 1. Sagt mir, o schönste Schäf'rin mein; 2.
Erlaube mir, fein's Mädchen; 3. Gar lieblich hast sich

gesellet; 4. Guten Abend, mein tausiger Schatz; 5.
Die Sonne scheint nicht mehr; 6. Da unten im Tale; 7.
Gunhilde lebt' gar stille und fromm. BOOK 2: 8. Ach,
englische Schäferin; 9. Es war eine schöne Jüdin; 10.
Es ritt ein Ritter; 11. Jungfräulein, soll ich mit euch
geh'n; 12. Feinsliebchen, du sollst mir nicht barfuss
geh'n; 13. Wach' auf, mein Hort; 14. Maria ging aus
wandern. BOOK 3: 15. Schwesterlein, Schwesterlein;
16. Wach' auf mein' Herzensschöne; 17. Ach Gott,
wie weh tut Scheiden; 18. So wünsch' ich ihr ein'
gute Nacht; 19. Nur ein Gesicht auf Erden lebt; 20.
Schönster Schatz, mein Engel; 21. Es ging ein
Maidlein zarte. BOOK 4: 22. Wo gehst du hun, du
Stolze?; 23. Der Reiter spreitet seinen Mantel aus;
24. Mir ist ein schön's braun's Maidelein; 25. Mein
Mädel hat ein Rosenmund; 26. Ach könnt' ich
deisen Abend; 27. Ich stand auf hohem Berge; 28. Es
reit' ein Herr und auch sein Knecht. BOOK 5: 29. Es
war ein Markgraf über'm Rhein; 30. All' mein'
Gedanken; 31. Dort in den Weiden steht ein Haus;
32. So will ich frisch und fröhlich sein; 33. Och
Moder, ich well ein Ding han; 34. Wie komm't ich denn
zur Tür herein?; 35. Soll sich der Mond nicht heller
scheinen. BOOK 6: 36. Es steht ein Fiedler; 37. Du
mein einzig Licht; 38. Des Abends kann ich nicht
schlafen geh'n; 39. Schöner Augen schöne Strahlen;
40. Ich weiss mir'n Maidlein hübsch und fein; 41. Es
steht ein' Lind'; 42. In stiller Nacht, zur ersten Wacht.
BOOK 7 (chorus ad lib): 43. Es standen drei Rosen;
44. Dem Himmel will ich klagen; 45. Es sass ein
schneeweiss Vögelein; 46. Es war einmal ein
Zimmergesell; 47. Es ging sich unsre Fraue; 48.
Nachtigall, sag, was für Grüss; 49. Verstohlen geht
der Mond auf.
1-42. E. Schwarzkopf, D. Fischer-Dieskau, G. Moore
(11/89) (EMI) ① [2] **CDS7 49525-2**
2, 3, 15, 25, 41. P. Schreier, K. Ragossnig *Concert*
(10/89) (NOVA) ① **150 039-2**
2, 6, 12. Lotte Lehmann, P. Ulanowsky (r1941)
Concert (11/95) (CLAR) ① **CDGSE78-50-57**
6. K. Livingstone, N. Mackie, J.J. Blakely (Eng)
Concert (1/90) (MERI) ① **DUOCD89002**
6, 10, 41. E. Parcells, F. Justen (arr Krause) *Concert*
(5/92) (SCHW) ① **314063**
6, 15, 37. M. Price, G. Johnson (r1992) *Concert*
(5/94) (RCA) ① **09026 60901-2**
6, 31, 33. M. Lipovšek, C. Spencer (r1992) *Concert*
(9/93) (SONY) ① **SK52490**
6, 33. E. Schwarzkopf, G. Moore (r1965) *Concert*
(12/90) (EMI) ① **CDM7 63654-2**
12, 15, 33, 41, 42. E. Ameling, J. Demus (r1967)
Concert (12/95) (DHM) ① [4] **74321 26617-2(1)**
15, 42. C. Ludwig, G. Parsons *Concert*
(9/92) (EMI) ① [4] **CMS7 64074-2(1)**
25. H. Rehfuss, F. Martin (bp1964) *Concert*
(5/94) (CLAV) ① **CD50-9327**
33, 34. C. Ludwig, G. Moore *Concert*
(9/92) (EMI) ① [4] **CMS7 64074-2(1)**
34, 41, 42. L. Popp, G. Parsons (pp1981) *Concert*
(6/95) (ORFE) ① **C363941B**
42. B. Fassbaender, I. Gage *Concert*
(9/87) (ACAN) ① **43 507**
42. E. Schwarzkopf, G. Moore (r1965) *Concert*
(12/90) (EMI) ① **CDM7 63654-2**
Ein Deutsches Requiem, 'German
Requiem'—soprano, baritone, 4vv, orchestra
(& organ ad lib), Op. 45 (1857-68) (Wds. Bible
trans Luther)
1. Selig sind die da Leid tragen; 2. Denn alles
Fleisch; 3. Herr, lehre doch mich; 4. Wie lieblich sind
deine Wohnungen; 5. Ihr habt nun Traurigkeit; 6.
Denn wir haben hie; 7. Selig sind die Toten.
Cpte A. Auger, R. Stilwell, Atlanta Sym Chor, Atlanta
SO, Robert Shaw (r1983)
(1/86) (TELA) ① **CD80092**
Cpte E. Schwarzkopf, D. Fischer-Dieskau, Philh
Chor, Philh, O. Klemperer (r1961)
(6/87) (EMI) ① **CDC7 47238-2**
Cpte M. Price, T. Allen, Munich Hochschule Chbr Ch,
Bavarian Rad Chor, BRSO, W. Sawallisch
(6/87) (ORFE) ① **C039101A**
Cpte M.A. Häggander, S. Lorenz, Leipzig Rad Chor,
Leipzig GO, H. Kegel (6/87) (CAPR) ① **10 095**
Cpte A. Tomowa-Sintow, J. van Dam, Vienna
Singverein, BPO, H. von Karajan (1976)
(6/88) (EMI) ① **CDM7 69229-2**
Cpte E. Schwarzkopf, H. Rehfuss, Vienna Singverein,
VPO, H. von Karajan (r1947)
(1/90) (EMI) ① **CDH7 61010-2**
Cpte L. Popp, W. Brendel, Prague Phil Chor, Czech
PO, G. Sinopoli (r1982)
(6/90) (DG) ① **429 486-2GDC**
Cpte C. Margiono, R. Gilfry, Monteverdi Ch, ORR,
J.E. Gardiner (4/91) (PHIL) ① [2] **432 140-2PH**
Cpte F. Lott, D. Wilson-Johnson, LSC, LSO, R.
Hickox (1/92) (CHAN) ① **CHAN8942**

Cpte D. Brown, G. Cachemaille, Stuttgart Gächinger
Kantorei, Stuttgart Bach Collegium, H. Rilling
(1/92) (HANS) ① **98 966**
Cpte L. Dawson, O. Bär, London Schütz Ch, LCP, R.
Norrington (r1992) *Begräbnisgesang, Op.13.*
(4/93) (EMI) ① **CDC7 54658-2**
Cpte C. Studer, A. Schmidt, Swedish Rad Chor, E.
Ericson Chbr Ch, BPO, C. Abbado (pp1992)
(5/93) (DG) ① **437 517-2GH**
Cpte A.M. Blasi, B. Terfel, Bavarian Rad Chor,
BRSO, Colin Davis (r1992)
(5/93) (RCA) ① **09026 60868-2**
Cpte Janet Williams, T. Hampson, Chicago Sym
Chor, Chicago SO, D. Barenboim (r1992-3)
(11/93) (ERAT) ① **4509-92856-2**
Cpte M. Stader, H. Prey, Stuttgart Südfunkchor,
Hesse Rad Chor, Stuttgart RSO, C. Schuricht (r1959)
(11/93) (ARCI) ① **ARCH2.2**
Cpte E. Grümmer, D. Fischer-Dieskau, Berlin St
Hedwig's Cath Ch, BPO, R. Kempe (r1955)
(1/94) (EMI) ① **CDH7 64705-2**
Cpte J. Norman, J. Hynninen, LP Ch, BBC Sym
Chor, LPO, K. Tennstedt (r1984) *Concert*
(5/94) (EMI) ① [2] **CZS7 67819-2**
Cpte W. Lipp, F. Crass, Vienna Singverein, Vienna
SO, W. Sawallisch (r1962) *Concert*
(5/94) (PHIL) ① [2] **438 760-2PM2**
Cpte M. Gauci, E. Tumagian, Slovak Phil Chor,
Bratislava RSO, A. Rahbari (r1992)
(5/94) (NAXO) ① **8 550213**
Cpte E. Norberg-Schulz, W. Holzmair, San Francisco
Sym Chor, San Francisco SO, H. Blomstedt (r1993)
(7/95) (DECC) ① **443 771-2DH**
Cpte I. Seefried, G. London, Westminster Ch, NYPO,
B. Walter (r1954) *Alto Rhapsody, Op. 53.*
(8/95) (SONY) ① **SMK64469**
1. Salisbury Cath Ch, C. Walsh, R. Seal (Eng)
Concert (9/87) (MERI) ① **CDE84025**
1. St Bride's Ch, Fleet St, C. Etherington, R. Jones
(Eng) *Concert* (2/91) (REGE) ① **REGSB701CD**
4. Truro Cath Ch, D. Briggs, H. Doughty (Eng)
Concert (7/91) (PRIO) ① **PRCD322**
5. K. Te Kanawa, Chicago Sym Chor, Chicago SO,
G. Solti *Concert* (11/87) (DECC) ① **417 645-2DH**
5. J. Budd, St Paul's Ch, Adrian Lucas, John
Scott *Concert* (10/91) (HYPE) ① **CDA66439**
3 Duets—soprano, contralto and piano, Op.
20 (pub 1861)
1. Weg der Liebe I (from Herder: Stimmen der
Völker); 2. Weg der Liebe II; 3. Die Meere (wds. trad
Ital).
J. Banse, B. Fassbaender, C. Garben (r1993)
Concert (8/95) (SCHW) ① **312592**
3. Sarah Walker, T. Allen, R. Vignoles *Concert*
(11/87) (HYPE) ① **CDA66165**
4 Duets—contralto, baritone and piano, Op.
28 (pub 1864)
1. Die Nonne und der Ritter (wds. Eichendorff); 2. Vor
der Tür (wds. old Ger); 3. Es rauscht das Wasser
(wds. Goethe); 4. Der Jäger und sein Liebchen (wds.
von Fallersleben).
1-3. B. Fassbaender, H. Komatsu, C. Garben
Concert (11/93) (HARM) ① **HMC90 5210**
4 Duets—soprano, contralto and piano, Op.
61 (pub 1874)
1. Die Schwestern (wds. Mörike); 2. Klosterfräulein
(wds. Kerner); 3. Phänomen (from Goethe); 4. Die
Boten der Liebe (trad Czech trans Wenzig).
J. Banse, B. Fassbaender, C. Garben (r1993)
Concert (8/95) (SCHW) ① **312592**
1-4. F. Lott, A. Murray, G. Johnson *Concert*
(11/90) (EMI) ① **CDC7 49930-2**
5 Duets—soprano, contralto and piano, Op.
66 (pub 1875)
1. Klänge I (wds. Groth); 2. Klänge II; 3. Am Strande
(wds. Hölty); 4. Jägerlied (wds. Candidus); 5. Hüt du
dich! (from Des Knaben Wunderhorn).
3, 4. J. Banse, B. Fassbaender, C. Garben (r1993)
Concert (8/95) (SCHW) ① **312592**
4 Ernste Gesänge, 'Four Serious
Songs'—bass and piano, Op. 121 (1896)
(Wds. Bible).
1. Denn es gehet dem Menschen; 2. Ich wandte mich
und sahe; 3. O Tod, wie bitter; 4. Wenn ich mit
Menschen-und mit Engelzungen.
Cpte D. Fischer-Dieskau, J. Demus *Concert*
(9/85) (DG) ① **415 189-2GH**
Cpte D. Fischer-Dieskau, G. Moore (pp1958)
Concert (6/87) (ORFE) ① **C140201A**
Cpte R. Holl, Golders Orkest, Y. Talmi (orch
Leinsdorf) *Concert* (7/87) (OTTA) ① **OTRC98402**
Cpte J. DeGaetani, G. Kalish *Concert*
(1/90) (ARAB) ① **Z6141**
Cpte H. Hotter, G. Moore (r1951) *Concert*
(4/90) (EMI) ① **CDH7 63198-2**

Cpte J. Hynninen, R. Gothóni (pp1985) *Schumann: Dichterliebe, Op. 48*. (10/90) (ONDI) ① **ODE738-2**
Cpte L. Finnie, A. Legge *Concert*
(9/91) (CHAN) ① **CHAN8786**
Cpte K. Moll, C. Garben *Concert*
(8/93) (ACAN) ① **44 2093-2**
Cpte B. Fassbaender, E. Leonskaja (r1992) *Concert*
(10/94) (TELD) ① **9031-74872-2**
K. Borg, E. Werba (r1959) *Concert*
(12/94) (FINL) ① [3] **4509-95606-2**
K. Flagstad, E. McArthur (r1956) *Concert*
(12/95) (LOND) ① [5] **440 490-2LM5(2)**
K. Flagstad, E. McArthur (r1956) *Concert*
(12/95) (LOND) ① **440 494-2LM**

**Fest- und Gedenksprüche—8vv, Op. 109
(1886-88)** (Wds. Bible)
1. Unsere Väter hofften auf dich; 2. Wenn ein starker Gewappneter; 3. Wo ist ein so herrlich Volk.
Paris Chapelle Royale Chor, Ghent Collegium Vocale, P. Herreweghe *Concert*
(3/88) (HARM) ① **HMC90 1122**
Trinity Coll Ch, Cambridge, R. Marlow *Concert*
(2/90) (CONI) ① **CDCF178**

Geistliches Lied—4vv and organ/piano, Op. 30 (1856) (Wds. P. Flemming)
Trinity Coll Ch, Cambridge, J. Morgan, R. Marlow *Concert* (2/90) (CONI) ① **CDCF178**
Bristol Cath Ch, A. Pinel, M. Archer *Concert*
(4/90) (MERI) ① **CDE84188**
King's College Ch, S. Cleobury, C. Hughes (r1990) *Concert* (3/94) (ARGO) ① **433 452-2ZH**

Gesang der Parzen—6vv and orchestra, Op. 89 (1882) (Wds. Goethe)
Bavarian Rad Chor, BRSO, B. Haitink *Concert*
(4/84) (ORFE) ① **C025821A**
Atlanta Sym Chor, Atlanta SO, Robert Shaw *Concert* (3/89) (TELA) ① **CD80176**
R. Shaw Chorale, NBC SO, A. Toscanini (bp1948)
Concert (5/90) (RCA) ① [4] **GD60325**
Berlin Rad Chor, BPO, C. Abbado *Symphony 1*.
(10/91) (DG) ① **431 790-2GH**
Bavarian Rad Chor, BRSO, Colin Davis (r1992)
Concert (5/93) (RCA) ① **09026 61201-2**

4 Gesänge—3 female vv, 2 horns and harp, Op. 17 (pub 1862)
1. Es tönt ein voller (wds. Ruperti); 2. Lied von Shakespeare (Twelfth Night); 3. Der Gärtner (wds. J. Eichendorff); 4. Gesang aus Fingal (wds. Ossian).
D. Wynne, A. Halstead, C. Rutherford, Monteverdi Ch, J.E. Gardiner *Concert*
(8/92) (PHIL) ① **432 152-2PH**

3 Gesänge—6vv, Op. 42 (pub 1868)
1. Abendständchen (wds. Brentano); 2. Vineta (wds. W. Müller); 3. Darthulas Grabesgesang (wds. Ossian, trans Herder).
Monteverdi Ch, J.E. Gardiner *Concert*
(8/92) (PHIL) ① **432 152-2PH**
1. R. Shaw Fest Sngrs, Robert Shaw, N. Mackenzie (r1992) *Concert* (11/93) (TELA) ① **CD80326**

7 Gesänge—4-6vv, Op. 62 (1874)
1. Rosmarin (wds. Des knaben Wunderhorn); 2. Von alten Liebesliedern (wds. Des knaben Wunderhorn); 3. Waldesnacht (wds. P. Heyse); 4. Dein Herzlein mild (wds. P. Heyse); 5. All meine Herzgedanken (wds. P. Heyse); 6. Es geht ein Wehen (wds. P. Heyse); 7. Vergangen ist mir Glück (Volkslied).
3. R. Shaw Fest Sngrs, Robert Shaw, N. Mackenzie (r1992) *Concert* (11/93) (TELA) ① **CD80326**

5 Gesänge—4-6vv unaccompanied, Op. 104 (pub 1889)
1. Nachtwache I (wds. Rückert); 2. Nachtwache II (wds. Rückert); 3. Letzes Glück (wds. M. Kalbeck); 4. Verlorene Jugend (wds. trad, trans Wenzig); 5. Im Herbst (wds. K. Groth).
Monteverdi Ch, J.E. Gardiner *Concert*
(8/92) (PHIL) ① **432 152-2PH**

18 Liebeslieder—waltzes for 4vv and piano duet, Op. 52 (1868-69) (Wds. G. F. Daumer)
1. Rede, Mädchen, allzu liebes; 2. Am Gesteine rauscht die Flut; 3. O die Frauen; 4. Wie des Abends schöne Rote; 5. Die grüne Hopfenranke; 6. Ein kleiner, hübscher Vogel; 7. Wohl schön bewandt war es; 8. Wenn so lind dein Auge mir; 9. Am Donaustrande; 10. O wie sanft die Quelle; 11. Nein, es ist nicht Auszukommen; 12. Schlosser auf; 13. Vögelein durchrauscht die Luft; 14. Sieh, wie ist die Welle klar; 15. Nachtigall, sie singt so schön; 16. Ein duneler Schacht ist Liebe; 17. Nacht wandle, ein Licht; 18. Es bebet das Gesträuche.
E. Mathis, B. Fassbaender, P. Schreier, D. Fischer-Dieskau, K. Engel, W. Sawallisch *Concert*
(12/88) (DG) ① **423 133-2GH**
chor, A. Balsam, J. Kahn, A. Toscanini (bp1948)
Concert (5/90) (RCA) ① [4] **GD60325**

T. Shaw, P. Salmon, R. Levin, J. Perry, Monteverdi Ch, J.E. Gardiner *Concert*
(8/92) (PHIL) ① **432 152-2PH**
I. Seefried, K. Ferrier, J. Patzak, H. Günter, C. Curzon, H. Gál (pp1952) *Concert*
(9/92) (DECC) ① **425 995-2DM**
R. Shaw Fest Sngrs, Robert Shaw, N. Mackenzie, J. Wustman (r1992) *Concert*
(11/93) (TELA) ① **CD80326**
B. Bonney, A.S. von Otter, K. Streit, O. Bär, B. Forsberg, H. Deutsch (pp1994) *Concert*
(10/95) (EMI) ① **CDC5 55430-2**
7. I. Seefried, H. von Nordberg, F. Wührer (r1947)
Concert (4/92) (EMI) ① [7] **CHS7 69741-2(4)**

6 Lieder—tenor/soprano and piano, Op. 3 (pub 1854)
1. Liebestreu (wds. Reinick); 2. Liebe und Frühling I - Wie sich Rebenranken schwingen (wds.Fallersleben); 3. Liebe und Frühling II - Ich muss hinaus (wds. Fallersleben); 4. Lied aus dem Gedicht 'Ivan' (wds. Bodenstedt); 5. In der Fremde (wds. Eichendorff); 6. Lindes Rauschen in den Wipfeln (wds. Eichendorff).
1. M. Price, J. Lockhart *Concert*
(2/87) (ORFE) ① **C058831A**
1. J. Norman, D. Barenboim *Concert*
(9/87) (DG) ① **413 311-2GH**
1. B. Fassbaender, I. Gage *Concert*
(9/87) (ACAN) ① **43 507**
1. T. Mørk, J. Lagerspetz (arr vc/pf) *Concert*
(8/89) (SIMA) ① **PSC1029**
1. E. Ameling, R. Jansen *Concert*
(6/91) (HYPE) ① **CDA66444**
1. C. Ludwig, G. Moore *Concert*
(9/92) (EMI) ① [4] **CMS7 64074-2(1)**
1. F. Pollet, R. Vignoles *Concert*
(12/95) (ACCO) ① **20441-2**

6 Lieder—soprano/tenor and piano, Op. 6 (pub 1853)
1. Spanische Lied (wds. anon); 2. Der Frühling (wds. Rousseau); 3. Nachwirkung (wds. Meissner); 4. Juchhel (wds. Reinick); 5. Wie die Wolke nach der Sonne (wds. Fallersleben); 6. Nachtigallen schwingen lustig (wds. Fallersleben).
1. E. Mathis, G. Wyss (r1994) *Concert*
(11/95) (DENO) ① **CO-78947**
1. F. Pollet, R. Vignoles *Concert*
(12/95) (ACCO) ① **20441-2**

6 Lieder, Op. 7 (pub 1854)
1. Treue Liebe (wds. Ferrand); 2. Parole (wds. Eichendorff); 3. Anklänge (wds. Eichendorff); 4. Volkslied (wds. trad); 5. Die Trauernde (wds. trad); 6. Heimkehr (wds. Uhland).
1. K. Flagstad, E. McArthur (r1956) *Concert*
(12/95) (LOND) ① **440 494-2LM**
1. K. Flagstad, E. McArthur (r1956) *Concert*
(12/95) (LOND) ① [5] **440 490-2LM5(2)**
3. F. Pollet, R. Vignoles *Concert*
(12/95) (ACCO) ① **20441-2**
3, 4, 5. E. Mathis, G. Wyss (r1994) *Concert*
(11/95) (DENO) ① **CO-78947**
5. L. Popp, G. Parsons (pp1981) *Concert*
(6/95) (ORFE) ① **C363941B**

5 Lieder, Op. 19 (pub 1862)
1. Der Kuss (wds. Hölty); 2. Scheiden und Meiden (wds. Uhland); 3. In der Ferne (wds. Uhland); 4. Der Schmied (wds. Uhland); 5. An eine Äolsharfe (wds. Mörike).
4. M. Price, J. Lockhart *Concert*
(2/87) (ORFE) ① **C058831A**
4. J. Norman, D. Barenboim *Concert*
(9/87) (DG) ① **413 311-2GH**
4. C. Ludwig, G. Moore *Concert*
(9/92) (EMI) ① [4] **CMS7 64074-2(1)**
4, 5. C. Ludwig, G. Spencer (pp1993) *Concert*
(10/93) (RCA) ① **09026 61547-2**
5. B. Fassbaender, I. Gage *Concert*
(9/87) (ACAN) ① **43 507**
5. M. Shirai, H. Höll *Concert*
(9/88) (CAPR) ① **10 204**
5. D. Fischer-Dieskau, H. Höll *Concert*
(1/90) (BAYE) ① **BR100006**

9 Lieder, Op. 32 (pub 1865)
1. Wie rafft ich mich auf in der Nacht (wds. Platen); 2. Nicht mehr zu dir zu gehen (wds. Daumer); 3. Ich schleich umher betrübt (wds. Platen); 4. Der Storm, der neben mir verrauschte (wds. Platen); 5. Wie, so willst du mich wieder (wds. Platen); 6. Du sprichst, dass sich mich täuschte (wds. Platen); 7. Bitteres zu sagen denkst du (wds. Daumer); 8. So stehn wir, ich und meine Weide (wds. Daumer); 9. Wie bist du, meine Königin (wds. Daumer).
1. A.S. von Otter, B. Forsberg *Concert*
(4/91) (DG) ① **429 727-2GH**
1, 2, 4, 5, 9. D. Fischer-Dieskau, H. Höll *Concert*
(1/90) (BAYE) ① **BR100006**

1, 4, 5, 9. D. Fischer-Dieskau, G. Moore (pp1958) *Concert* (6/87) (ORFE) ① **C140201A**
2. M. Shirai, H. Höll *Concert*
(9/88) (CAPR) ① **10 204**
2. F. Pollet, R. Vignoles *Concert*
(12/95) (ACCO) ① **20441-2**
3. N. Mackie, J.J. Blakely (Eng) *Concert*
(1/90) (MERI) ① **DUOCD89002**
5. B. Fassbaender, I. Gage *Concert*
(9/87) (ACAN) ① **43 507**
9. A. Kipnis, anon (r c1916) *Concert*
(10/91) (PEAR) ① **GEMMCD9451**
9. M. Lipovšek, C. Spencer (r1992) *Concert*
(9/93) (SONY) ① **SK52490**
9. P. Schoeffler, E. Lush (r1947) *Concert*
(1/95) (PREI) ① **90190**
9. Lotte Lehmann, P. Ulanowsky (r1941) *Concert*
(11/95) (CLAR) ① **CDGSE78-50-57**

4 Lieder, Op. 43 (pub 1868)
1. Von ewiger Liebe (wds. Fallersleben); 2. Die Mainacht (wds. Hölty); 3. Ich schnell mein Horn ins Jammertal (wds. Uhland); 4. Das Lied vom Herrn von Falkenstein (wds. Uhland).
1. M. Price, J. Lockhart *Concert*
(2/87) (ORFE) ① **C058831A**
1. K. Ferrier, B. Walter (pp1949) *Concert*
(9/92) (DECC) ① **433 476-2DM**
1. C. Ludwig, G. Parsons *Concert*
(9/92) (EMI) ① [4] **CMS7 64074-2(1)**
1. M. Horne, Martin Katz (pp1994) *Concert*
(1/95) (RCA) ① **09026 62547-2**
1. E. Mathis, G. Wyss (r1994) *Concert*
(11/95) (DENO) ① **CO-78947**
1. E. Ameling, J. Demus (r1967) *Concert*
(12/95) (DHM) ① [4] **74321 26617-2(1)**
1, 2. B. Fassbaender, I. Gage *Concert*
(9/87) (ACAN) ① **43 507**
1, 2. A.S. von Otter, B. Forsberg *Concert*
(4/91) (DG) ① **429 727-2GH**
1, 2. J. Baker, M. Isepp *Concert*
(3/92) (SAGA) ① **EC3361-2**
1, 2. M. Lipovšek, C. Spencer (r1992) *Concert*
(9/93) (SONY) ① **SK52490**
1, 2. C. Ludwig, E. Werba (pp1963) *Concert*
(7/94) (ORFE) ① **C331931A**
1, 2. C. Robbin, M. McMahon (r1985) *Concert*
(7/94) (MARQ) ① **ERAD113**
1, 2. F. Pollet, R. Vignoles *Concert*
(12/95) (ACCO) ① **20441-2**
2. M. Shirai, H. Höll *Concert*
(9/88) (CAPR) ① **10 204**
2. E. Ameling, R. Jansen *Concert*
(6/91) (HYPE) ① **CDA66444**
2. A. Kipnis, G. Moore (r1936) *Concert*
(10/91) (PEAR) ① **GEMMCD9451**
2. C. Ludwig, G. Moore *Concert*
(9/92) (EMI) ① [4] **CMS7 64074-2(1)**
2. P. Schoeffler, E. Lush (r1947) *Concert*
(1/95) (PREI) ① **90190**
2. Lotte Lehmann, P. Ulanowsky (r1941) *Concert*
(11/95) (CLAR) ① **CDGSE78-50-57**

4 Lieder, Op. 46 (pub 1868)
1. Die Kränze (wds. Daumer); 2. Magyarisch (wds. Daumer); 3. Die Schale der Vergessenheit (wds. Hölty); 4. An die Nachtigall (wds. Hölty).
4. K. Livingstone, N. Mackie, J.J. Blakely (Eng) *Concert* (1/90) (MERI) ① **DUOCD89002**
4. E. Ameling, R. Jansen *Concert*
(6/91) (HYPE) ① **CDA66444**
4. H. Hagegård, T. Schuback (r1976) *Concert*
(5/94) (BIS) ① **BIS-CD054**
4. Lotte Lehmann, P. Ulanowsky (r1941) *Concert*
(11/95) (CLAR) ① **CDGSE78-50-57**
4. E. Mathis, G. Wyss (r1994) *Concert*
(11/95) (DENO) ① **CO-78947**

5 Lieder, Op. 47 (pub 1868)
1. Botschaft (wds. Daumer after Hafis); 2. Liebesglut (wds. Daumer after Hafis); 3. Sonntag (wds. Uhland); 4. O liebliche Wangen (wds. Flemming); 5. Die Liebende schreibt (wds. Daumer).
1. D. Fischer-Dieskau, G. Moore (pp1958) *Concert*
(6/87) (ORFE) ① **C140201A**
1. H. Hotter, G. Moore (r1956) *Concert*
(4/90) (EMI) ① **CDH7 63198-2**
1. K. Ferrier, P. Spurr (r1949) *Concert*
(6/91) (DECC) ① **430 096-2DWO**
1. E. Ameling, R. Jansen *Concert*
(6/91) (HYPE) ① **CDA66444**
1. K. Ferrier, B. Walter (pp1949) *Concert*
(6/92) (DECC) ① **433 476-2DM**
1. K. Ferrier, J. Newmark (r1950) *Concert*
(6/92) (DECC) ① **433 471-2DM**
3. H. Prey, L. Hokanson *Concert*
(6/87) (DENO) ① **CO-1254**
3. A.S. von Otter, B. Forsberg *Concert*
(4/91) (DG) ① **429 727-2GH**

1. H. Hotter, G. Moore (r1956) *Concert*
  (4/90) (EMI) ① **CDH7 63198-2**
1. E. Schwarzkopf, G. Parsons (r1970) *Concert*
  (12/90) (EMI) ① **CDM7 63654-2**
1. A.S. von Otter, B. Forsberg *Concert*
  (4/91) (DG) ① **429 727-2GH**
1. C. Ludwig, G. Parsons *Concert*
  (9/92) (EMI) ① **[4] CMS7 64074-2(1)**
1. I. Seefried, E. Werba (pp1953) *Concert*
  (7/93) (DG) ① **[2] 437 348-2GDO2**
1. C. Ludwig, C. Spencer (pp1993) *Concert*
  (10/93) (RCA) ① **09026 61547-2**
1. H. Schlusnus, F. Rupp (r1931) *Concert*
  (1/94) (PREI) ① **[2] 89205**
1. C. Ludwig, E. Werba (pp1963) *Concert*
  (7/94) (ORFE) ① **C331931A**
1. R. Streich, G. Weissenborn (r1961) *Concert*
  (10/94) (DG) ① **[2] 437 680-2GDO2**
1. F. Pollet, R. Vignoles *Concert*
  (12/95) (ACCO) ① **20441-2**
1. E. Ameling, J. Demus (r1967) *Concert*
  (12/95) (DHM) ① **[4] 74321 26617-2(1)**
1, 3, 4. B. Fassbaender, I. Gage *Concert*
  (9/87) (ACAN) ① **43 507**
1, 4. M. Shirai, H. Höll *Concert*
  (9/88) (CAPR) ① **10 204**
3. E. Ameling, R. Jansen *Concert*
  (6/91) (HYPE) ① **CDA66444**
5 Lieder, Op. 107 (pub 1889)
1. An die Stolze (wds. Flemming); 2. Salamander (wds. Remcke); 3. Das Mädchen spricht (wds. Gruppe); 4. Maienkätzchen (wds. Liliencron); 5. Mädchenlied (wds. Heyse).
2. D. Fischer-Dieskau, G. Moore (pp1958) *Concert*
  (6/87) (ORFE) ① **C140201A**
3. J. Norman, D. Barenboim *Concert*
  (9/87) (DG) ① **413 311-2GH**
3. K. Livingstone, J.J. Blakely (Eng) *Concert*
  (1/90) (MERI) ① **DUOCD89002**
3. J. Baker, M. Isepp *Concert*
  (3/92) (SAGA) ① **EC3361-2**
3. B. Fassbaender, E. Leonskaja (r1992) *Concert*
  (10/94) (TELD) ① **9031-74872-2**
3, 5. M. Price, J. Lockhart *Concert*
  (2/87) (ORFE) ① **C058831A**
3, 5. C. Ludwig, G. Parsons *Concert*
  (9/92) (EMI) ① **[4] CMS7 64074-2(1)**
3, 5. Sarah Walker, R. Vignoles *Concert*
  (4/94) (MERI) ① **CDE84232**
3, 5. E. Ameling, J. Demus (r1967) *Concert*
  (12/95) (DHM) ① **[4] 74321 26617-2(1)**
4. D. Fischer-Dieskau, H. Höll *Concert*
  (1/90) (BAYE) ① **BR100006**
5. B. Fassbaender, I. Gage *Concert*
  (9/87) (ACAN) ① **43 507**
5. A.S. von Otter, B. Forsberg *Concert*
  (4/91) (DG) ① **429 727-2GH**
5. R. Streich, G. Weissenborn (r1961) *Concert*
  (10/94) (DG) ① **[2] 437 680-2GDO2**
5. E. Mathis, G. Wyss (r1994) *Concert*
  (11/95) (DENO) ① **CO-78947**
5. F. Pollet, R. Vignoles *Concert*
  (12/95) (ACCO) ① **20441-2**
8 Lieder und Romanzen, Op. 14 (pub 1861) (Wds. trad)
1. Vor dem Fenster; 2. Vom vervundeten Knaben; 3. Murrays Ermordung (from Percy: Reliques); 4. Ein Sonett (attrib. Count Thibault); 5. Trennung; 6. Gang zur Liebsten; 7. Ständchen; 8. Sehnsucht.
1. M. Price, J. Lockhart *Concert*
  (2/87) (ORFE) ① **C058831A**
1, 2, 7, 8. M. Price, G. Johnson (r1992) *Concert*
  (5/94) (RCA) ① **09026 60901-2**
8. L. Popp, G. Parsons (pp1981) *Concert*
  (6/95) (ORFE) ① **C363941B**
8. E. Mathis, G. Wyss (r1994) *Concert*
  (11/95) (DENO) ① **CO-78947**
5 Lieder und Romanzen—1/2 female vv and piano, Op. 84 (pub 1882)
1. Sommerabend (wds. Schmidt); 2. Der Kranz (wds. Schmidt); 3. In den Beeren (wds. Schmidt); 4. Vergebliches Ständchen (wds. trad); 5. Spannung (wds. trad).
1-5. J. Norman, D. Barenboim *Concert*
  (9/87) (DG) ① **413 311-2GH**
4. H. Prey, L. Hokanson *Concert*
  (6/87) (DENO) ① **CO-1254**
4. L. Tetrazzini, orch (Ital: r1911) *Concert*
  (10/90) (NIMB) ① **NI7808**
4. A.S. von Otter, B. Forsberg *Concert*
  (4/91) (DG) ① **429 727-2GH**
4. E. Ameling, R. Jansen *Concert*
  (6/91) (HYPE) ① **CDA66444**
4. V. de los Angeles, G. Parsons (pp1990) *Concert*
  (12/91) (COLL) ① **Coll1247-2**

4. C. Ludwig, G. Parsons *Concert*
  (9/92) (EMI) ① **[4] CMS7 64074-2(1)**
4. C. Ludwig, C. Spencer (pp1993) *Concert*
  (10/93) (RCA) ① **09026 61547-2**
4. V. de los Angeles, G. Moore (r1960) *Concert*
  (4/94) (EMI) ① **[4] CMS5 65061-2(2)**
4. H. Rehfuss, F. Martin (bp1964) *Concert*
  (5/94) (CLAV) ① **CD50-9327**
4. R. Streich, G. Weissenborn (r1961) *Concert*
  (10/94) (DG) ① **[2] 437 680-2GDO2**
4. B. Fassbaender, E. Leonskaja (r1992) *Concert*
  (10/94) (TELD) ① **9031-74872-2**
4. E. Rethberg, K. Ruhrseitz (r1932) *Concert*
  (10/95) (ROMO) ① **[2] 81014-2**
4. E. Ameling, J. Demus (r1967) *Concert*
  (12/95) (DHM) ① **[4] 74321 26617-2(1)**
4, 5. M. Price, G. Johnson (r1992) *Concert*
  (5/94) (RCA) ① **09026 60901-2**
12 Lieder und Romanzen—4 female vv (and piano ad lib), Op. 44 (1859-66) (Wds. various)
1. Minnelied (wds. J. H. Voss); 2. Der Bräutigam (wds. Eichendorff); 3. Barcarole (wds. trad Italian); 4. Fragen (wds. trad Slav); 5. Die Müllerin (wds. A. von Chamisso); 6. Die Nonne (wds. L. Uhland); 7. Nun stehn die Rosen (wds. P. Heyse); 8. Die Berge sind spitze (wds. P. Heyse); 9. Am Wildbach die Weiden (wds. P. Heyse); 10. Und gehst du über den Kirchhof (wds. P. Heyse); 11. Die Braut (wds. Müller); 12. Märznacht (wds. L. Uhland).
7-10. Cambridge Sngrs, J. Rutter (r1992) *Concert*
  (11/93) (CLLE) ① **COLCD119**
Marienlieder—4vv, Op. 22 (1859) (Wds. trad)
1. Der englische Gruss; 2. Marias Kirchgang; 3. Marias Wallfahrt; 4. Der Jäger; 5. Ruf zu Maria; 6. Magdalena; 7. Marias Lob.
Bavarian Rad Chor, BRSO, Colin Davis (r1992) *Concert*
  (5/93) (RCA) ① **09026 61201-2**
2 Motets—5vv, Op. 29 (?1860)
1. Es ist das Heil uns kommen her (wds. P. Speratus); 2. Schalfe in mir, Gott (wds. Bible: Psalm 51).
Paris Chapelle Royale Chor, Ghent Collegium Vocale, P. Herreweghe *Concert*
  (3/88) (HARM) ① **HMC90 1122**
Trinity Coll Ch, Cambridge, R. Marlow *Concert*
  (2/90) (CONI) ① **CDCF178**
King's College Ch, S. Cleobury (r1990) *Concert*
  (3/94) (ARGO) ① **433 452-2ZH**
3 Motets—4 female vv, Op. 37 (pub 1866)
1. O bone Jesu; 2. Adoramus te, Christe; 3. Regina coeli laetare.
Trinity Coll Ch, Cambridge, R. Marlow *Concert*
  (2/90) (CONI) ① **CDCF178**
2 Motets—4-6vv, Op. 74 (pub 1879)
1. Warum ist das Licht gegeben (Wds. Bible: trans Luther); 2. O Heiland, reiss die Himmel auf (Wds. Anon).
Paris Chapelle Royale Chor, Ghent Collegium Vocale, P. Herreweghe *Concert*
  (3/88) (HARM) ① **HMC90 1122**
Trinity Coll Ch, Cambridge, R. Marlow *Concert*
  (2/90) (CONI) ① **CDCF178**
King's College Ch, S. Cleobury (r1990) *Concert*
  (3/94) (ARGO) ① **433 452-2ZH**
3 Motets—4-8vv, Op. 110 (1889)
1. Ich aber bin elend (Wds. Bible); 2. Ach, arme Welt (Wds. Anon); 3. Wenn wir in höchsten Nöten sein (wds. P. Eber).
Paris Chapelle Royale Chor, Ghent Collegium Vocale, P. Herreweghe *Concert*
  (3/88) (HARM) ① **HMC90 1122**
Trinity Coll Ch, Cambridge, R. Marlow *Concert*
  (2/90) (CONI) ① **CDCF178**
2. Bristol Cath Ch, M. Archer *Concert*
  (4/90) (MERI) ① **CDE84188**
Nänie—4vv and orchestra, Op. 82 (1880-81) (Wds. Schiller)
Bavarian Rad Chor, BRSO, B. Haitink *Concert*
  (4/84) (ORFE) ① **C025821A**
Atlanta Sym Chor, Atlanta SO, Robert Shaw *Concert*
  (3/89) (TELA) ① **CD80176**
Prague Phil Chor, Czech PO, G. Sinopoli *Concert*
  (11/91) (DG) ① **435 066-2GGA**
Berlin Rad Chor, BPO, C. Abbado *Concert*
  (4/92) (DG) ① **435 349-2GH**
Bavarian Rad Chor, BRSO, Colin Davis *Concert*
  (5/93) (RCA) ① **09026 61201-2**
15 Neue Liebeslieder—waltzes for 4vv and piano duet, Op. 65 (1874) (Wds. Daumer & Goethe)
E. Mathis, B. Fassbaender, P. Schreier, D. Fischer-Dieskau, K. Engel, W. Sawallisch *Concert*
  (12/88) (DG) ① **423 133-2GH**

R. Shaw Fest Sngrs, Robert Shaw, N. Mackenzie, J. Wustman (r1992) *Concert*
  (11/93) (TELA) ① **CD80326**
B. Bonney, A.S. von Otter, K. Streit, O. Bär, B. Forsberg, H. Deutsch (pp1994) *Concert*
  (10/95) (EMI) ① **CDC5 55430-2**
Zum Schluss I. Seefried, K. Ferrier, J. Patzak, H. Günter, C. Curzon, H. Gál (pp1952) *Concert*
  (9/92) (DECC) ① **425 995-2DM**
Psalm 13—3 female vv, piano/organ and strings ad lib, Op. 27 (1859) (Wds. Bible)
Trinity Coll Ch, Cambridge, R. Pearce, R. Marlow *Concert*
  (2/90) (CONI) ① **CDCF178**
3 Quartets—SATB and piano, Op. 64 (pub 1874)
1. An die Heimat (wds. Sternau); 2. Der Abend (wds. Schiller); 3. Fragen (wds. Daumer).
E. Mathis, B. Fassbaender, P. Schreier, D. Fischer-Dieskau, K. Engel, W. Sawallisch *Concert*
  (12/88) (DG) ① **423 133-2GH**
2. R. Shaw Fest Sngrs, Robert Shaw, N. Mackenzie (r1992) *Concert*
  (11/93) (TELA) ① **CD80326**
4 Quartets—SATB and piano, Op. 92 (pub 1884)
1. O schöne Nacht (wds. Daumer); 2. Spätherbst (wds. Allmers); 3. Abendlied (wds. Hebbel); 4. Warum? (wds. J. W. Goethe).
R. Levin, Monteverdi Ch, J.E. Gardiner *Concert*
  (8/92) (PHIL) ① **432 152-2PH**
1, 3. R. Shaw Fest Sngrs, Robert Shaw, N. Mackenzie (r1992) *Concert*
  (11/93) (TELA) ① **CD80326**
6 Quartets—SATB and piano, Op. 112 (1870-1891)
1. Sehsucht (wds. F. Kugler); 2. Nächtens (wds. F. Kugler); 3. Himmel strahlt so helle und klar (wds. Hungarian trad); 4. Rote Rosenknopspen künden (wds. Hungarian trad); 5. Brennessel steht an Wegesrand (wds. Hungarian trad); 6. Liebe Schwalbe, kleine Schwalbe (wds. Hungarian trad).
2. R. Shaw Fest Sngrs, Robert Shaw, N. Mackenzie (r1992) *Concert*
  (11/93) (TELA) ① **CD80326**
Rhapsody—contralto, 4 male vv and orchestra, Op. 53 (1869) (Wds. Goethe)
A. Hodgson, Bavarian Rad Chor, BRSO, B. Haitink *Concert*
  (4/84) (ORFE) ① **C025821A**
M. Horne, Atlanta Sym Chor, Atlanta SO, Robert Shaw *Concert*
  (3/89) (TELA) ① **CD80176**
M. Anderson, San Francisco Municipal Chor, San Francisco SO, P. Monteux (r1945) *Concert*
  (1/90) (RCA) ① **GD87911**
C. Ludwig, Philh Chor, Philh, O. Klemperer (1962) *Symphony 3.* (1/90) (EMI) ① **CDM7 69650-2**
M. Lipovšek, Ernst Senff Chor, BPO, C. Abbado (r1988) *Symphony 2.* (2/90) (DG) ① **427 643-2GH**
S. Onegin, Berlin Doctors' Ch, Berlin St Op Orch, K. Singer (r1929) *Concert* (2/91) (PREI) ① **89027**
B. Fassbaender, Prague Phil Chor, Czech PO, G. Sinopoli *Concert* (11/91) (DG) ① **435 066-2GGA**
K. Ferrier, LP Ch, LPO, C. Krauss (r1947) *Concert*
  (6/92) (DECC) ① **433 477-2DM**
N. Stutzmann, Bavarian Rad Chor, BRSO, Colin Davis (r1992) *Concert*
  (5/93) (RCA) ① **09026 61201-2**
A. Heynis, Vienna Singverein, Vienna SO, W. Sawallisch (r1962) *Concert*
  (5/94) (PHIL) ① **[2] 438 760-2PM2**
M. Forrester, Berlin RIAS Chbr Ch, Berlin RSO, F. Fricsay (r1957) *Concert*
  (11/94) (DG) ① **445 407-2GDO**
M. Forrester, Berlin RIAS Chbr Ch, Berlin RSO, F. Fricsay (r1957) *Concert*
  (11/94) (DG) ① **[11] 445 400-2GDO10**
J. van Nes, Tanglewood Fest Chor, Boston SO, B. Haitink (r1993) *Symphony 3.*
  (3/95) (PHIL) ① **442 120-2PH**
A.S. von Otter, A. Schoenberg Ch, VPO, James Levine (pp1992) *Concert*
  (6/95) (DG) ① **439 887-2GH**
M. Miller, Occidental Coll Concert Ch, Columbia SO, B. Walter (r1958) *Deutsches Requiem, Op. 45.*
  (3/95) (SONY) ① **SMK64469**
15 Romanzen aus 'Die schöne Magelone', Op. 33 (1861) (Wds. L. Tieck)
SET 1: 1. Keinen hat es noch gereut; 2. Traun! Bogen und Pfeil sind gut; 3. Sind es Schmerzen, sind es Freuden. SET 2: 4. Liebe kam aus fernen Landen; 5. So willst du des Armen; 6. Wie soll ich die Freude. SET 3: 7. War es dir, dir; 8. Wir müssen uns trennen; 9. Ruhe, Süssliebchen. SET 4: 10. Verzweiflung; 11. Wie schnell verschwindet; 12. Muss es eine Trennung geben. SET 5: 13. Sulima; 14. Wie froh und frisch; 15. Treue Liebe dauert lange.
Cpte B. Fassbaender, E. Leonskaja (also Tieck's Poems which comprise Die Schöne Magelone) (10/94) (TELD) ① **4509-90854-2**

9, 12. E. Ameling, R. Jansen *Concert*
(6/91) (HYPE) ① **CDA66444**
Schicksalslied—4vv and orchestra, Op. 54
(1868-71) (Wds. Hölderlin)
Atlanta Sym Chor, Atlanta SO, Robert Shaw *Concert*
(3/89) (TELA) ① **CD80176**
Ernst Senff Chor, BPO, C. Abbado *Concert*
(1/91) (DG) ① **429 765-2GH**
Prague Phil Chor, Czech PO, G. Sinopoli *Concert*
(11/91) (DG) ① **435 066-2GGA**
Ambrosian Sngrs, LPO, W. Sawallisch *Symphony 1.*
(2/92) (EMI) ① **CDC7 54359-2**
Bavarian Rad Chor, BRSO, Colin Davis (r1992)
Concert (5/93) (RCA) ① **09026 61201-2**
Vienna Singverein, Vienna SO, W. Sawallisch
(r1962) *Concert*
(5/94) (PHIL) ① [2] **438 760-2PM2**
Stanford Univ Chor, San Francisco SO, P. Monteux
(r1949) *Concert*
(9/94) (RCA) ① [15] **09026 61893-2**
Leipzig Rad Chor, BPO, C. Abbado (pp1993) *Concert*
(3/95) (SONY) ① **SK53975**
Triumphlied—baritone, 8vv and orchestra,
Op. 55 (1870-71) (Wds. Bible)
W. Brendel, Prague Phil Chor, Czech PO, G. Sinopoli
Concert (11/91) (DG) ① **435 066-2GGA**
14 Volks-Kinderlieder—voice and piano
(1858)
1. Dornröschen; 2. Die Nachtigall; 3. Die Henne; 4.
Sandmännchen; 5. Der Mann; 6. Heidenröslein; 7.
Das Schlaraffenland; 8a. Beim Ritt auf dem Knie (Uli
Mann will reiden); 8b. Beim Ritt auf dem Knie (Alt
Mann wollt reiten); 9. Der Jäger im Walde; 10. Das
Mädchen und die Hasel; 11. Wiegenlied; 12.
Weihnachten; 13. Marienwürmchen; 14. Dem
Schutzengel.
4. H. Spani, orch, G. Nastrucci (r1930) *Concert*
(9/90) (CLUB) ① [2] **CL99-509/10**
4. E. Schwarzkopf, Philh, C. Mackerras (arr
Mackerras) *Concert*
(12/90) (EMI) ① **CDM7 63574-2**
4. E. Parcells, F. Justen (arr Faust) *Concert*
(5/92) (SCHW) ① **314063**
11. P. McCann, I. Robertson (r1984: arr P McCann)
Concert (11/92) (CHAN) ① **CHAN4501**
11 Zigeunerlieder—4vv and piano, Op. 103
(1887) (Wds. trad Hungarian, trans Conrat)
1. He, Zigeuner, greife; 2. Hochgetürmte Rimaflut; 3.
Wisst ihr, wann mein Kindchen; 4. Lieber Gott, du
weisst; 5. Brauner Bursche führt zum Tanze; 6.
Röslein dreie in der Reihe; 7. Kommt dir manchmal;
8. Horch, der Wind klagt; 9. Weit und breit schaut
niemand; 10. Mond verhüllt sein Angesicht; 11. Rote
Abendwolken ziehn.
1-7, 11. J. Norman, D. Barenboim *Concert*
(9/87) (DG) ① **413 311-2GH**
1-7, 11. J. DeGaetani, G. Kalish *Concert*
(1/90) (ARAB) ① **Z6141**
1-7, 11. A.S. von Otter, B. Forsberg *Concert*
(4/91) (DG) ① **429 727-2GH**
1-7, 11. C. Ludwig, G. Moore *Concert*
(9/92) (EMI) ① [4] **CMS7 64074-2(1)**
1-7, 11. Sarah Walker, R. Vignoles *Concert*
(4/94) (MERI) ① **CDE84232**
1-7, 11. M. Price, G. Johnson (r1992) *Concert*
(5/94) (RCA) ① **09026 60901-2**
11. R. Shaw Fest Sngrs, Robert Shaw, M. Mackenzie
(r1992) *Concert* (11/93) (TELA) ① **CD80326**

BRANDL, Johann *(1835–1913)*
Austria

SECTION V: STAGE WORKS

Der Liebe Augustin—operetta: 3 acts
(1887—Vienna) (Lib. H. Klein)
EXCERPTS: 1. Du alter Stephansturm (The Old
Refrain).
1. F. Kreisler, C. Lamson (1924: arr Kreisler)
Concert (9/93) (BIDD) ① **LAB068/9**
1. F. Kreisler, M. Raucheisen (r1930: arr Kreisler)
Concert (12/93) (EMI) ① **CDH7 64701-2**

BRANDT, Willi *(19th cent (late)*
?Germany

SECTION II: CHAMBER

Concert Piece No. 2—trumpet and piano
S. Nakarjakov, A. Markovich (r1994) *Concert*
(6/95) (TELD) ① **4509-94554-2**

152

BRASSART, Johannes *(fl*
1420–1445) France

SECTION IV: VOCAL AND CHORAL

Te dignitas presularis—motet: 3vv
Orlando Consort (bp1994) *Concert*
(11/95) (METR) ① **METCD1008**

BRATTON, John W. *(1867–1947)*
USA

SECTION V: STAGE WORKS

The Man From China—musical show
(1904—New York) (Lyrics West)
EXCERPTS: 1. Fifty-Seven Ways to Catch a Man.
1. S. Mayhew, Broadway Cast (r1910) *Concert*
(5/94) (PEAR) ① [3] **GEMMCDS9050/2(2)**

BRAUN, Johannes Georg
(1656–1687) Germany

SECTION II: CHAMBER

Canzonata—organ and brass ensemble
A. Ross, His Majesties Sagbutts and Cornetts
Concert (9/87) (MERI) ① **CDE84096**

BRAUNFELS, Walter *(1882–1954)*
Germany

SECTION V: STAGE WORKS

Verkündigung—opera: prologue & 4 acts,
Op. 50 (1948—Cologne) (Lib. P Claudel)
Cpte S. Nimsgern, C. Rüggeberg, A. Trauboth, C.
Shirasaka-Teratani, J. Bröcheler, C. Bladin, C.
Brüggemann, A. Kajiyama, S. Sevenich, B. Dommer,
R-D. Krüll, Cologne Sym Chor, Cologne SO, D.R.
Davies (pp1992)
(7/94) (EMI) ① [2] **CDS5 55104-2**

BREDICEANU, Tiberiu
(1877–1968) Romania

SECTION IV: VOCAL AND CHORAL

Vai, mindruto, dragi ne-aven—song
H. Darclée, anon (r1928) *Concert*
(11/92) (MEMO) ① [2] **HR4408/9(1)**

BRETAN, Nicolae *(1887–1968)*
Romania

SECTION V: STAGE WORKS

Arald—opera: 1 act (1982—Iaşi) (Lib. cpsr,
after M. Eminescu)
Cpte D. Zancu, A. Agache, I. Voineag, S. Şandru,
Moldova PO, C. Mandeal (r1987) *Golem.*
(10/95) (NIMB) ① **NI5424**
Golem—opera: 1 act (1923—Cluj) (Lib. cpsr,
after I. Kaczév)
Cpte A. Agache, T. Daróczi, S. Şandru, D. Zancu,
Chor, Moldova PO, C. Mandeal (r1987) *Arald.*
(10/95) (NIMB) ① **NI5424**

BRETÓN, Tomás *(1850–1923)*
Spain

SECTION II: CHAMBER

String Quartet in D (pub c1910)
New Budapest Qt (1992) *Piano Trio in E.*
(6/95) (MARC) ① **8 223745**
Trio in E—piano, violin and cello (pub
c1891)
G. Oravecz, New Budapest Qt (1992) *String Quartet*
in D. (6/95) (MARC) ① **8 223745**

SECTION V: STAGE WORKS

La Dolores—ópera: 3 acts (1895—Madrid)
EXCERPTS: 1. Aragón la más famasa; 2. Di que es
verdad que me llamas.
Jota T. P. Domingo, Madrid SO, E. G. Asensio
(pp1991) *Concert* (11/92) (CARL) ① **MCD45**
1. P. Domingo, Madrid Zarzuela Chor, Madrid
Rondalla Lírica, Madrid SO, M. Moreno-Buendia
(r1987) *Concert* (1/89) (EMI) ① **CDC7 49148-2**
La Verbena de La Paloma—sainte lírico: 1
act (1894—Madrid) (Lib. R de la Vega)
EXCERPTS—: 1. El aceite de ricino; 2. El niño está
dormido; 3. Seguidillas: Por ser la Virgen de la
Paloma.

Cpte T. Tourné, D. Ripolles, E. Garcia, R. Cesari,
A.P. Bayod, A. Armentia, M. del Carmen Andres, M.
del Pilar Alonso, J. Bermejo, A. Fernandez, J.
Portillo, J.R. Henche, J.L. Cancela, Madrid Coros
Cantores, Madrid Concerts Orch, F. Moreno Torroba
Chapí: Revoltosa. (10/92) (HISP) ① **CDZ7 67328-2**
Cpte M. Bayo, P. Domingo, R. Pierotti, S. Tro, R.
Castejon, J. Castejón, A. M. Amengual, Milagros
Martin, E. Baquerizo, Madrid Comunidad Chor,
Madrid SO, A. R. Marbà (r1994)
(9/95) (AUVI) ① **V4725**

BREVI, Giovanni Battista
(c1650–after 1725) Italy

SECTION IV: VOCAL AND CHORAL

Catenae terrenae—cantata (1v)
M. van Egmond, Ricercar Consort *Concert*
(1/90) (RICE) ① **RIC054032**

BREWER, Sir (Alfred) Herbert
(1865–1928) England

SECTION III: INSTRUMENTAL

Marche héroïque—organ (c1914)
C. Herrick *Concert* (7/86) (HYPE) ① **CDA66121**
J. Parker-Smith *Concert*
(9/90) (ASV) ① **CDDCA702**

SECTION IV: VOCAL AND CHORAL

Evening Canticles in D (1927)
1. Magnificat; 2. Nunc dimittis.
Gloucester Cath Ch, J. Sanders, M. Lee (r1994)
Concert (4/95) (PRIO) ① **PRCD494**
1, 2. St Paul's Cath Ch, C. Dearnley, John Scott
Concert (3/88) (HYPE) ① **CDA66249**

BRIAN, Havergal *(1876–1972)*
England

SECTION I: ORCHESTRAL

Burlesque Variations on an Original
Theme—theme and seven variations (1903)
Hull Youth SO, G. Heald-Smith (r1981) *Concert*
(5/95) (CAMP) ① [2] **RR2CD1331/2**
Concerto for Violin and Orchestra in C (1934-
35)
M. Bisengaliev, BBC Scottish SO, L. Friend (r1993)
Concert (8/94) (MARC) ① **8 223479**
Doctor Merryheart—comedy overture No. 1
(1911-12)
Hull Youth SO, G. Heald-Smith (r1979) *Concert*
(5/95) (CAMP) ① [2] **RR2CD1331/2**
English Suite No. 1—orchestra (1899-1904)
1. Characteristic march; 2. Valse; 3. Under the beech
tree; 4. Interlude; 5. Hymn; 6. Carnival.
Hull Youth SO, G. Heald-Smith (r1979) *Concert*
(5/95) (CAMP) ① [2] **RR2CD1331/2**
Fantastic Variations on an Old
Rhyme—orchestra with organ (1907)
A. Smith, Hull Youth SO, G. Heald-Smith (r1979)
Concert (5/95) (CAMP) ① [2] **RR2CD1331/2**
Festal dance—orchestra (1907-08) (movt 3
of 'A Fantastic Symphony')
Ireland National SO, A. Leaper *Concert*
(2/93) (MARC) ① **8 223481**
D. Martin, Hull Youth SO, G. Heald-Smith (r1980)
Concert (5/95) (CAMP) ① [2] **RR2CD1331/2**
For valour—orchestra with organ (1902-06)
A. Smith, Hull Youth SO, G. Heald-Smith (r1980)
Concert (5/95) (CAMP) ① [2] **RR2CD1331/2**
In Memoriam—tone poem (?1911-12)
Ireland National SO, A. Leaper *Concert*
(2/93) (MARC) ① **8 223481**
Hull Youth SO, G. Heald-Smith (r1980) *Concert*
(5/95) (CAMP) ① [2] **RR2CD1331/2**
The Jolly Miller—concert overture (1962)
BBC Scottish SO, L. Friend (r1993) *Concert*
(8/94) (MARC) ① **8 223479**
Symphony No. 1, 'Gothic'—soloists, chorus,
brass bands and orchestra (1919-27) (Wds.
Roman Liturgy)
E. Jenisová, D. Pecková, V. Doležal, P. Mikuláš,
Slovak Phil Chor, Slovak Op Chor, Slovak Folk Ens
Chor, Lucnica Chor, Bratislava City Ch, Youth Echo
Ch, Czech RSO, Slovak PO, O. Lenárd (r1989)
(7/90) (MARC) ① [2] **8 223280/1**
Symphony No. 3 in C sharp minor (1931-32)
BBC SO, L. Friend (r1988)
(8/89) (HYPE) ① **CDA66334**

Symphony No. 4, '(Das) Siegeslied'—S,
double chorus and orchestra (1932-33) (Wds.
Psalm LXVIII)
J. Valásková, Slovak Phil Chor, Brno Phil Chor,
Cantus Ch, Slovak Op Chor, Youth Echo Ch,
Bratislava RSO, A. Leaper *Symphony 12.*
(2/93) (MARC) ① **8 223447**
Symphony No. 7 in C (1948)
RLPO, C. Mackerras (r1987) *Concert*
(9/93) (EMI) ① **CDM7 64717-2**
Symphony No. 12 (1957)
Bratislava RSO, A. Leaper *Symphony 4.*
(2/93) (MARC) ① **8 223447**
Symphony No. 17 (1960-61)
Ireland National SO, A. Leaper *Concert*
(2/93) (MARC) ① **8 223481**
Symphony No. 18 (1961)
BBC Scottish SO, L. Friend (r1993) *Concert*
(8/94) (MARC) ① **8 223479**
Symphony No. 31 (1968)
RLPO, C. Mackerras (r1987) *Concert*
(9/93) (EMI) ① **CDM7 64717-2**
Symphony No. 32 in A flat (1968)
Ireland National SO, A. Leaper *Concert*
(2/93) (MARC) ① **8 223481**
The Tinker's Wedding—comedy overture
(1947-8)
RLPO, C. Mackerras (r1987) *Concert*
(9/93) (EMI) ① **CDM7 64717-2**

SECTION IV: VOCAL AND CHORAL

2 Herrick songs—chorus and orchestra
(1911-12)
1. Requiem for the rose; 2. The hag.
St Nicholas Sngrs, Hull Youth SO, G. Heald-Smith
(r1981) *Concert*
(5/95) (CAMP) ① [2] **RR2CD1331/2**

BRICCIALDI, Giulio *(1818–1881)*
Italy

SECTION II: CHAMBER

Wind Quintet—fl, ob, cl, hn, bn, Op. 124
Aulos Wind Qnt *Concert*
(10/91) (SCHW) ① **310087**

BRICUSSE, Leslie *(b 1931)*
England

SECTION V: STAGE WORKS

Scrooge—musical show, based on the 1970
film (1991) (Lyrics cpsr, after Dickens)
EXCERPTS: ACT ONE: 1. A Christmas Carol; 2. I
Hate Christmas; 3. No Better Life; 4. Christmas
Children; 5. I Hate Christmas (reprise); 6. Father
Christmas; 7. Make the Most of This World; 8. It's Not
My Fault; 9. You...You; 12. It's Not My Fault
(reprise); 13. I Like Life. ACT TWO: 14. Entr'Acte; 15.
Good Times; 16. The Beautiful Day; 17. The
Minister's Cat; 18. A Better Life; 19. Thank You Very
Much; 20. I'll Begin Again; 21. Finale (medley).
Cpte A. Newley, T. Watt, J. Wallington, J. Pertwee, J.
Teal, S. Johns, J. Clay, Orig Cast (r1992)
(7/93) (TER) ① **CDTER1194**

BRIDGE, Frank *(1879–1941)*
England

H—numbers used in Paul Hindmarsh's catalogue

SECTION I: ORCHESTRAL

Cherry Ripe—strings, H119b (1916) (No. 2 of
'Two Old English Songs')
New Zealand CO, N. Braithwaite *Concert*
(11/92) (KOCH) ① **37139-2**
English Stg Orch, W. Boughton (r1992) *Concert*
(8/93) (NIMB) ① **NI5366**
2 Entr'actes (1906, 1926 orch 1936) (orch cpsr
from piano works)
1 Rosemary (H68h); 2 Canzonetta (H169)
English Stg Orch, W. Boughton (r1992) *Concert*
(8/93) (NIMB) ① **NI5366**
Lament—strings, H117 (1915)
English Stg Orch, W. Boughton (r1992) *Concert*
(8/93) (NIMB) ① **NI5366**
Oration, 'Concerto elegiaco'—cello and
orchestra, H180 (1930)
S. Isserlis, CLS, R. Hickox *Britten: Cello Symphony.*
(2/92) (EMI) ① **CDM7 63909-2**
Phantasm—piano and orchestra, H182
(1931)
K. Stott, RPO, V. Handley *Concert*
(1/90) (CONI) ① **CDCF175**

2 Poems—orchestra, H118 (1916)
1. The open air; 2. The story of my heart.
BBC Northern SO, N. Del Mar (r1977) *Concert*
(10/95) (BBCR) ① **BBCRD9129**
Sally in our Alley—string orchestra, H119a
(1916)
English Stg Orch, W. Boughton (r1992) *Concert*
(8/93) (NIMB) ① **NI5366**
The Sea—suite for large orchestra, H100
(1910-11)
1. Seascape; 2. Sea Foam; 3. Moonlight; 4. Storm.
Ulster Orch, V. Handley *Concert*
(3/87) (CHAN) ① **CHAN8473**
1. Ulster Orch, V. Handley *Concert*
(10/91) (CHAN) ① **CHAN6538**
Sir Roger de Coverley—a Christmas dance
for string orchestra, H155 (1922)
English Stg Orch, W. Boughton (r1992) *Concert*
(8/93) (NIMB) ① **NI5366**
Suite—string orchestra, H93 (1908)
1. Prelude; 2. Intermezzo; 3. Nocturne; 4. Finale.
ECO, D. Garforth *Concert*
(5/87) (CHAN) ① **CHAN8390**
English Stg Orch, W. Boughton *Concert*
(10/88) (NIMB) ① **NI5068**
New Zealand CO, N. Braithwaite *Concert*
(11/92) (KOCH) ① **37139-2**
There is a willow grows aslant a
brook—impression for orchestra, H174
(1928)
New Zealand CO, N. Braithwaite *Concert*
(11/92) (KOCH) ① **37139-2**
English Stg Orch, W. Boughton (r1992) *Concert*
(8/93) (NIMB) ① **NI5366**

SECTION II: CHAMBER

Allegro appassionato—viola and piano, H82
(1908)
P. Coletti, L. Howard (r1993) *Concert*
(10/94) (HYPE) ① **CDA66687**
Cherry ripe—string quartet, H119b (1916)
Delmé Qt *Concert* (9/87) (CHAN) ① **CHAN8426**
Rasumovsky Qt *Concert*
(12/92) (IMPE) ① **RAZCD901**
Cradle song—violin/cello and piano, H96
(1902)
L. McAslan, J.J. Blakely *Concert*
(4/92) (CNTI) ① **CCD1022**
H. Temianka, J. Graudan (r1937) *Concert*
(2/93) (BIDD) ① [2] **LAB059/60**
Elegy—cello and piano, H47 (1904)
J. Lloyd Webber, J. McCabe *Concert*
(2/93) (ASV) ① **CDDCA807**
Hearts ease—violin and piano, H161a
(1912)
L. McAslan, J.J. Blakely *Concert*
(4/92) (CNTI) ① **CCD1022**
3 Idylls—string quartet, H67 (1906)
1. Adagio molto espressivo—Allegretto moderato e
rubato; 2. Allegretto poco lento; 3. Allegro con moto.
Brindisi Qt *Concert* (5/91) (CONI) ① **CDCF196**
Coull Qt (r1993) *Concert*
(10/94) (HYPE) ① **CDA66718**
2. Rasumovsky Qt *Concert*
(12/92) (IMPE) ① **RAZCD901**
An Irish melody, 'Londonderry air'—string
quartet, H86 (1908)
Delmé Qt *Concert* (9/87) (CHAN) ① **CHAN8426**
English Stg Orch, W. Boughton (r1992) *Concert*
(8/93) (NIMB) ① **NI5366**
Moto perpetuo—violin/cello and piano, H4c
(1900, rev 1911)
H. Temianka, J. Graudan (r1937) *Concert*
(2/93) (BIDD) ① [2] **LAB059/60**
Norse Legend—violin and piano, H60
(1905)
L. McAslan, J.J. Blakely *Concert*
(4/92) (CNTI) ① **CCD1022**
Pensiero—viola and piano, H53a (1905)
P. Coletti, L. Howard (r1993) *Concert*
(10/94) (HYPE) ① **CDA66687**
Phantasy in C minor—violin, cello and piano,
H79 (1907)
Dartington Trio *Concert*
(11/88) (HYPE) ① **CDA66279**
Hartley Trio *Concert* (3/92) (GAMU) ① **GAMCD516**
Phantasy in F sharp minor—violin, viola,
cello and piano, H94 (1910)
Dartington Trio, P. Ireland *Concert*
(11/88) (HYPE) ① **CDA66279**
Piano Trio No. 2, H178 (1928-29)
Borodin Trio *Bax: Piano Trio in B flat.*
(4/87) (CHAN) ① **CHAN8495**
Dartington Trio *Concert*
(11/88) (HYPE) ① **CDA66279**

Romanze—violin and piano, H45
L. McAslan, J.J. Blakely *Concert*
(4/92) (CNTI) ① **CCD1022**
Sally in our alley—string quartet, H119a
(1916)
Delmé Qt *Concert* (9/87) (CHAN) ① **CHAN8426**
Scherzetto—cello and piano, H19 (c1901-
02)
J. Lloyd Webber, J. McCabe *Concert*
(2/93) (ASV) ① **CDDCA807**
Serenade—violin and piano, H23 (1903)
L. McAslan, J.J. Blakely *Concert*
(4/92) (CNTI) ① **CCD1022**
4 Short Pieces—violin and piano, H104
(1912) (Nos 1 and 2 also cello and piano)
1. Meditation; 2. Spring Song; 3. Lullaby; 4. Country
Dance.
1, 2. B. Gregor-Smith, Y. Wrigley *Concert*
(9/92) (ASV) ① **CDDCA796**
Sir Roger de Coverley—string quartet, H155
(1922)
Delmé Qt *Concert* (9/87) (CHAN) ① **CHAN8426**
New Zealand CO, N. Braithwaite *Concert*
(11/92) (KOCH) ① **37139-2**
Sonata for Cello and Piano in D minor, H125
(1913-17)
R. Wallfisch, P. Wallfisch (r1986) *Concert*
(4/87) (CHAN) ① **CHAN8499**
B. Gregor-Smith, Y. Wrigley *Concert*
(9/92) (ASV) ① **CDDCA796**
K. Scholes, E. Blackwood *Blackwood: Cello Sonata.*
(11/92) (CEDI) ① **CDR90000 008**
M. Rostropovich, B. Britten (r1968) *Schubert:
Arpeggione Sonata, D821.*
(4/95) (DECC) ① **443 575-2DCS**
Sonata for Violin and Piano, H183 (1932)
L. McAslan, J.J. Blakely *Concert*
(4/92) (CNTI) ① **CCD1022**
String Quartet No. 1 in E minor, 'Bologna'
(1906)
Brindisi Qt *String Quartet 1.*
(5/92) (CNTI) ① **CCD1035**
String Quartet No. 2 in G minor, H115
(1915)
Delmé Qt *Concert* (9/87) (CHAN) ① **CHAN8426**
Brindisi Qt *String Quartet 4.*
(5/92) (CNTI) ① **CCD1036**
String Quartet No. 3, H175 (1925-27)
Brindisi Qt *String Quartet 3.*
(5/92) (CNTI) ① **CCD1035**
String Quartet No. 4 (1937)
Brindisi Qt *String Quartet 2.*
(5/92) (CNTI) ① **CCD1036**

SECTION III: INSTRUMENTAL

Arabesque—piano, H112d (1916)
Peter Jacobs *Concert* (9/90) (CNTI) ① **CCD1016**
Berceuse—piano, H8 (1901)
Peter Jacobs *Concert* (6/91) (CNTI) ① **CCD1018**
Canzonetta, 'Happy South'—piano, H169
(1926)
Peter Jacobs *Concert* (6/91) (CNTI) ① **CCD1018**
Capriccio No. 1 in A minor—piano, H52
(1905)
Peter Jacobs *Concert* (9/90) (CNTI) ① **CCD1016**
K. Stott *Concert* (9/91) (CONI) ① **CDCF186**
Capriccio No. 2 in F sharp minor—piano,
H54b (1905)
Peter Jacobs *Concert* (9/90) (CNTI) ① **CCD1016**
K. Stott *Concert* (9/91) (CONI) ① **CDCF186**
4 Characteristic Pieces—piano, H126 (1917)
1. Water Nymphs; 2. Fragrance; 3. Bittersweet; 4.
Fireflies.
Peter Jacobs *Concert* (6/91) (CNTI) ① **CCD1018**
Come Sweet Death,
'Todessehnsucht'—piano, H181 (1931) (arr
of Bach chorale 'Komm, susser Tod')
Peter Jacobs *Concert* (6/91) (CNTI) ① **CCD1019**
A Dedication—piano, H171 (1926)
Peter Jacobs *Concert* (6/91) (CNTI) ① **CCD1018**
Dramatic Fantasia—piano, H66 (1906)
A. Goldstone *Concert*
(3/92) (GAMU) ① **GAMCD526**
Etude rhapsodique—piano, H58 (1905)
Peter Jacobs *Concert* (6/91) (CNTI) ① **CCD1018**
A Fairy Tale—suite for piano, H116 (1917)
1. The Princess; 2. The Ogre; 3. The Spell; 4. The
Prince.
Peter Jacobs *Concert* (9/90) (CNTI) ① **CCD1016**
Gargoyle—piano, H177 (1928)
Peter Jacobs *Concert* (9/90) (CNTI) ① **CCD1016**
A. Goldstone *Concert*
(3/92) (GAMU) ① **GAMCD526**
Graziella—piano, H170 (1926)
Peter Jacobs *Concert* (6/91) (CNTI) ① **CCD1019**

Hidden Fires—piano, H172 (1927)
Peter Jacobs *Concert*   (9/90) (CNTI) ① CCD1016
The Hour Glass—suite for piano, H148 (1919-20)
1. Dusk; 2. The Dew Fairy; 3. The Midnight Tide.
Peter Jacobs *Concert*   (6/91) (CNTI) ① CCD1019
K. Stott *Concert*   (9/91) (CONI) ① CDCF186
3 Improvisations—piano, left-hand, H134 (1918)
1. At Dawn; 2. A Vigil; 3. A Revel.
Peter Jacobs *Concert*   (9/90) (CNTI) ① CCD1016
In Autumn—piano, H162 (1924)
1. Retrospect; 2. Through the Eaves.
Peter Jacobs *Concert*   (9/90) (CNTI) ① CCD1016
Lament—piano, H117 (1915)
Peter Jacobs *Concert*   (6/91) (CNTI) ① CCD1018
3 Lyrics—piano, H161 (1921-24)
1. Heartsease; 2. Dainty Rogue; 3. The Hedgerow.
Peter Jacobs *Concert*   (6/91) (CNTI) ① CCD1019
3 Miniature Pastorals, Set 1—piano, H127 (1917)
1. Allegretto con moto; 2. Tempo de valse; 3. Allegretto ben moderato.
Peter Jacobs *Concert*   (9/90) (CNTI) ① CCD1016
3 Miniature Pastorals, Set 2—piano, H149 (1921)
1. Allegro giusto; 2. Andante con moto; 3. Allegro ma non troppo.
Peter Jacobs *Concert*   (9/90) (CNTI) ① CCD1016
3 Miniature Pastorals, Set 3—piano, H150 (1921)
Peter Jacobs (ed Hindmarsh) *Concert*
     (6/91) (CNTI) ① CCD1019
Miniature Suite—piano (pub 1990)
1. Chorale; 2. Impromptu; 3. Caprice; 4. March.
Peter Jacobs (ed Hindmarsh) *Concert*
     (6/91) (CNTI) ① CCD1019
Moderato—piano, H29 (1903)
Peter Jacobs *Concert*   (6/91) (CNTI) ① CCD1018
Penseés fugitives 1—piano, H16 (1902)
Peter Jacobs *Concert*   (6/91) (CNTI) ① CCD1018
3 Pieces—organ, H63 (1905)
1. Andante moderato, C minor; 2. Adagio, E; 3. Allegro con spirito, B flat.
2. A. Lumsden *Concert*
     (4/91) (GUIL) ① GRCD7025
2. J. Bielby *Concert*   (5/91) (PRIO) ① PRCD298
2. A. Fletcher *Concert*   (11/91) (MIRA) ① MRCD903
3 Pieces—piano, H108 (1912)
1. Minuet; 2. Columbine; 3. Romance.
Peter Jacobs *Concert*   (6/91) (CNTI) ① CCD1018
3 Poems—piano, H112a-c (1914-15)
1. Solitude; 2. Ecstasy; 3. Sunset.
Peter Jacobs *Concert*   (6/91) (CNTI) ① CCD1018
2. K. Stott *Concert*   (9/91) (CONI) ① CDCF186
Scherzettino—piano, H20 (c1900-02)
Peter Jacobs *Concert*   (6/91) (CNTI) ① CCD1018
A Sea Idyll—piano, H54a (1905)
Peter Jacobs *Concert*   (9/90) (CNTI) ① CCD1016
K. Stott *Concert*   (9/91) (CONI) ① CDCF186
3 Sketches—piano, H68 (1906)
1. April; 2. Rosemary; 3. Valse capricieuse.
Peter Jacobs *Concert*   (6/91) (CNTI) ① CCD1019
Sonata—piano, H160 (1921-24)
Peter Jacobs *Concert*   (6/91) (CNTI) ① CCD1019
K. Stott *Concert*   (9/91) (CONI) ① CDCF186
Vignettes de Marseille—suite for piano, H166 (1925)
1. Carmelita; 2. Nicolette; 3. Zoraida; 4. En fête.
Peter Jacobs *Concert*   (6/91) (CNTI) ① CCD1018
K. Stott *Concert*   (9/91) (CONI) ① CDCF186
Winter Pastoral—piano, H168 (1925)
Peter Jacobs *Concert*   (9/90) (CNTI) ① CCD1016

SECTION IV: VOCAL AND CHORAL

The Bee—4vv a capella, H110 (1913) (Wds. Tennyson)
King's Sngrs *Concert*
     (6/88) (EMI) ① CDC7 49765-2
Day after day—song: 1v and piano, Wds. R Tagore (1922)
S. Leonard, M. Martineau (r1993) *Concert*
     (3/95) (UNIT) ① 88016-2
Dweller in my deathless dreams—song: 1v and piano (1925) (Wds. R Tagore)
S. Leonard, M. Martineau (r1993) *Concert*
     (3/95) (UNIT) ① 88016-2
Go not, happy day—song, H34 (1916) (Wds. A. Tennyson)
L. Finnie, A. Legge *Concert*
     (4/90) (CHAN) ① CHAN8749
F. Lott, G. Johnson *Concert*
     (4/90) (CHAN) ① CHAN8722
K. Ferrier, F. Stone (bp1952) *Concert*
     (6/91) (DECC) ① 430 096-2DWO

K. Ferrier, F. Stone (bp1952) *Concert*
     (7/91) (LOND) ① 430 061-2LM
K. Ferrier, F. Stone (bp1952) *Concert*
     (6/92) (DECC) ① 433 473-2DM
Hilli-ho!—4vv a capella, H91 (1909) (Wds. T. Moore)
King's Sngrs *Concert*
     (6/88) (EMI) ① CDC7 49765-2
Isobel—song, H102 (1912) (Wds. D. Goddard-Fenwick)
Sarah Walker, R. Vignoles *Concert*
     (10/92) (CRD) ① CRD3473
Journey's End—song: 1v and piano (1925) (Wds. H Wolfe)
S. Leonard, M. Martineau (r1993) *Concert*
     (3/95) (UNIT) ① 88016-2
Love went a-riding—song, H114 (1914) (Wds. M.E. Coleridge)
K. Flagstad, E. McArthur (r1937) *Concert*
     (12/95) (NIMB) ① NI7871
O weary hearts! O slumbering eyes—4vv a capella, H92 (1913) (Wds. Tennyson)
King's Sngrs *Concert*
     (6/88) (EMI) ① CDC7 49765-2
Speak to me my love—song: 1v and piano (1924) (Wds. R Tagore)
S. Leonard, M. Martineau (r1993) *Concert*
     (3/95) (UNIT) ① 88016-2

BRIDGE, Sir (John) Frederick (1844–1924) England

SECTION IV: VOCAL AND CHORAL

The Goslings—partsong (Wds. Weatherly)
PCA, M. Brown *Concert*   (3/87) (CONI) ① CDCF145
Two snails—partsong (Wds. Braine)
PCA, M. Brown *Concert*   (3/87) (CONI) ① CDCF145

BRIQUET (fl c1420) France

SECTION IV: VOCAL AND CHORAL

Ma seul amour—rondeau
Gothic Voices, I. Barford, C. Page *Concert*
     (12/86) (HYPE) ① CDA66144

BRISTOW, George Frederick (1825–1898) USA

SECTION I: ORCHESTRAL

Symphony No. 2 in F sharp minor, Op. 26 (1858)
Detroit SO, N. Järvi (r1993) *Concert*
     (10/93) (CHAN) ① CHAN9169

BRITO, Estêvão (c1575–1641) Portugal

SECTION IV: VOCAL AND CHORAL

Lamentationes Jeremiae—4vv
Oxford Camerata, J. Summerly *Concert*
     (4/93) (NAXO) ① 8 550572
Salve Regina—motet: 4vv
A Capella Portvgvesa, O. Rees (r1994) *Concert*
     (1/94) (HYPE) ① CDA66725

BRITTEN, (Edward) Benjamin (Lord Britten of Aldeburgh) (1913–1976) England

SECTION I: ORCHESTRAL

An American Overture, Op. 27 (1941) (orig 'An Occasional Overture': posth renamed: pub 1985)
CBSO, S. Rattle *Concert*
     (11/91) (EMI) ① [2] CDS7 54270-2
NZ SO, M. Fredman (r1994) *Concert*
     (10/95) (NAXO) ① 8 553107
The Building of the House—overture: chorus and orchestra, Op. 79 (1967)
CBSO Chor, CBSO, S. Rattle *Concert*
     (11/91) (EMI) ① [2] CDS7 54270-2
Canadian Carnival—overture, Op. 19 (1939)
ECO, S. Bedford *Concert*
     (12/90) (COLL) ① Coll1123-2
CBSO, S. Rattle *Concert*
     (11/91) (EMI) ① [2] CDS7 54270-2
Concerto for Piano and Orchestra in D, Op. 13 (1938 rev 1945)
S. Richter, ECO, B. Britten (r1970) *Violin Concerto.*
     (10/89) (DECC) ① 417 308-2LM
J. MacGregor, ECO, S. Bedford (1938 vers) *Concert*
     (2/91) (COLL) ① Coll1102-2

J. MacGregor, ECO, S. Bedford *Violin Concerto.*
     (9/92) (COLL) ① Coll1301-2
G. Lin, Melbourne SO, J. Hopkins *Copland: Piano Concerto.*   (11/92) (CHAN) ① CHAN6580
R. Gothóni, Helsingborg SO, O. Kamu (r1994) *Concert*   (1/95) (ONDI) ① ODE825-2
Concerto for Violin and Orchestra in D minor, Op. 15 (1939 rev 1958)
M. Lubotsky, ECO, B. Britten (r1970) *Piano Concerto.*
     (10/89) (DECC) ① 417 308-2LM
L. McAslan, ECO, S. Bedford *Concert*
     (12/90) (COLL) ① Coll1123-2
L. McAslan, ECO, S. Bedford *Piano Concerto.*
     (9/92) (COLL) ① Coll1301-2
Diversions—piano (left-hand) and orchestra, Op. 21 (1940 rev 1954)
P. Donohoe, CBSO, S. Rattle *Concert*
     (11/91) (EMI) ① [2] CDS7 54270-2
L. Fleisher, Boston SO, S. Ozawa *Concert*
     (4/93) (SONY) ① SK47188
Lachrymae—Reflections on a song of Dowland for viola and strings, Op. 48a (1976) (orch cpsr from work for viola and piano)
G. Caussé, Toulouse Nat CO, B. Bratoev *Concert*
     (7/88) (AUVI) ① A6124
N-E. Sparf, Stockholm PO, P. Csaba (r1988) *Concert*
     (8/89) (BIS) ① BIS-CD435
R. Golani, Montreal I Musici, Y. Turovsky *Concert*
     (2/91) (CHAN) ① CHAN8817
Y. Bashmet (va/dir), Moscow Sols Ens *Concert*
     (6/91) (RCA) ① RD60464
K. Kashkashian, Stuttgart CO, D.R. Davies (r1992) *Concert*   (11/93) (ECM) ① 439 611-2
L. A. Tomter, Norwegian CO, I. Brown (r1990) *Concert*   (10/95) (VIRG) ① VC5 45121-2
Mont Juic—suite of Catalan dances, Op. 12 (1937) (composed with Sir Lennox Berkeley (Op. 9)
1. Andante maestoso, Op. 9/1 (Berkeley); 2. Allegro grazioso, Op. 9/2 (Berkeley); 3. Lament—Andante moderato, Op. 14/1 (Britten); 4. Allegro moderato, Op. 14/2 (Britten).
ECO, S. Bedford *Concert*
     (12/90) (COLL) ① Coll1123-2
LPO, L. Berkeley *Concert*
     (3/93) (LYRI) ① SRCD226
Movement for Clarinet and Orchestra (1942-43) (fragment only)
T. King, ECO, B. Wordsworth (r1992; orch C. Matthews) *Concert*   (12/93) (HYPE) ① CDA66634
Occasional Overture—orchestra, Op. 38 (1946)
CBSO, S. Rattle *Concert*
     (11/91) (EMI) ① [2] CDS7 54270-2
Passacaglia, Op. 33b (1945) (from opera 'Peter Grimes')
Ulster Orch, V. Handley *Concert*
     (3/87) (CHAN) ① CHAN8473
LSO, S. Bedford *Concert*
     (2/90) (COLL) ① Coll1019-2
BBC SO, A. Davis *Concert*
     (8/91) (TELD) ① 9031-73126-2
NYPO, L. Bernstein (1973) *Concert*
     (11/92) (SONY) ① SMK47541
LPO, L. Slatkin (1990) *Concert*
     (3/94) (RCA) ① 09026 61226-2
NZ SO, M. Fredman (r1994) *Concert*
     (10/95) (NAXO) ① 8 553107
BBC SO, G. Rozhdestvensky (pp1978) *Concert*
     (10/95) (BBCR) ① BBCRD9129
Prelude and Fugue—18-part string orchestra, Op. 29 (1943)
Northern Sinfonia, R. Hickox *Concert*
     (3/88) (ASV) ① CDDCA591
Bournemouth Sinfonietta, R. Thomas (r1977) *Concert*
     (11/93) (CHAN) ① CHAN6592
Norwegian CO, I. Brown (r1991) *Concert*
     (10/95) (VIRG) ① VC5 45121-2
Russian Funeral—march for brass and percussion (1936) (pub 1981)
London Brass Virtuosi, D. Honeyball *Concert*
     (7/87) (HYPE) ① CDA66189
London Collegiate Brass, J. Stobart *Concert*
     (9/87) (CRD) ① CRD3444
Wallace Collection, J. Wallace *Concert*
     (3/92) (COLL) ① Coll1229-2
CBSO, S. Rattle (r1994) *Shostakovich: Symphony 4.*
     (11/95) (EMI) ① CDC5 55476-2
Scottish Ballad—two pianos and orchestra, Op. 26 (1941)
P. Donohoe, C. Fowke, CBSO, S. Rattle *Concert*
     (11/91) (EMI) ① [2] CDS7 54270-2

4 Sea Interludes—orchestra, Op. 33a (1945)
(from opera 'Peter Grimes')
1. Dawn; 2. Sunday Morning; 3. Moonlight; 4. Storm.
Ulster Orch, V. Handley Concert
(3/87) (CHAN) ① **CHAN8473**
LSO, A. Previn (r1974) Spring Symphony.
(4/87) (EMI) ① **CDM7 64736-2**
Bergen PO, N. Järvi Concert
(6/89) (BIS) ① **BIS-CD420**
LSO, S. Bedford Concert
(2/90) (COLL) ① **Coll1019-2**
BBC SO, A. Davis Concert
(8/91) (TELD) ① **9031-73126-2**
NYPO, L. Bernstein (r1973) Concert
(11/92) (SONY) ① **SMK47541**
Boston SO, L. Bernstein (pp1990) Beethoven:
Symphony 7.   (12/92) (DG) ① **431 768-2GH**
Philh, C.M. Giulini (r1962) Concert
(9/93) (EMI) ① [2] **CZS7 67723-2**
LPO, L. Slatkin (r1990) Concert
(3/94) (RCA) ① **09026 61226-2**
Bournemouth SO, R. Hickox (r1993) Concert
(3/94) (CHAN) ① **CHAN9221**
Concertgebouw, E. van Beinum (r1953) Concert
(9/94) (DECC) ① **440 063-2DM**
RLPO, T. Yuasa (r1994) Concert
(3/95) (EMIN) ① **CD-EMX2231**
NZ SO, M. Fredman (r1994) Concert
(10/95) (NAXO) ① **8 553107**
2, 4. Ulster Orch, V. Handley Concert
(10/91) (CHAN) **CHAN6538**
**Simple Symphony—string orchestra, Op. 4
(1933-34)**
1. Boisterous Bourrée; 2. Playful Pizzicato; 3.
Sentimental Sarabande; 4. Frolicsome Finale.
Northern Sinfonia, R. Hickox Concert
(3/88) (ASV) ① **CDDCA591**
Orpheus CO Concert   (1/89) (DG) ① **423 624-2GH**
J-W. Audoli Inst Ens, J-W. Audoli Concert
(6/89) (ARIO) ① **ARN68035**
Slovak CO, B. Warchal Concert
(10/89) (OPUS) ① **9350 1773**
ECO, G. Levine Concert   (1/90) (ARAB) ① **Z6603**
Montreal I Musici, Y. Turovsky Concert
(2/91) (CHAN) ① **CHAN8817**
Britten Qt Concert   (5/91) (COLL) ① **Coll1115-2**
ASMF, K. Sillito Concert
(10/91) (COLL) ① **Coll1234-2**
Slovak CO, B. Warchal Concert
(3/92) (CAMP) ① **RRCD1313**
Wallace Collection, J. Wallace (arr Matthews &
Wright) Concert   (3/92) (COLL) ① **Coll1229-2**
ECO, B. Britten (r1968) Concert
(6/93) (DECC) ① **436 990-2DWO**
Bournemouth Sinfonietta, R. Thomas (r1977) Concert
(11/93) (CHAN) ① **CHAN6592**
Boyd Neel Orch, B. Neel (r1939) Concert
(5/94) (DUTT) ① **CDAX8007**
Bournemouth Sinfonietta, R. Studt (vn/dir) (r1993)
Concert   (10/94) (NAXO) ① **8 550979**
Norwegian CO, I. Brown (r1990) Concert
(10/95) (VIRG) ① **VC5 45121-2**
Orpheus CO (r1987) Concert
(12/95) (DG) ① **445 561-2GMA**
Sinfonia da Requiem, Op. 20 (1940)
1. Lacrimosa; 2. Dies irae; 3. Requiem aeternam.
New Philh, B. Britten (r1964) Concert
(9/89) (LOND) ① **425 100-2LM**
LSO, S. Bedford Concert
(2/90) (COLL) ① **Coll1019-2**
LSO, R. Hickox Concert
(11/91) (CHAN) ① [2] **CHAN8983/4**
CBSO, S. Rattle Concert
(11/91) (EMI) ① [2] **CDS7 54270-2**
Stuttgart RSO, N. Marriner (r1984) Concert
(1/94) (CAPR) ① **10 428**
CBSO, S. Rattle (r1984) Shostakovich: Symphony
10.   (3/94) (EMI) ① **CDM7 64870-2**
LPO, L. Slatkin (r1990) Concert
(3/94) (RCA) ① **09026 61226-2**
NZ SO, M. Fredman (r1994) Concert
(10/95) (NAXO) ① **8 553104**
BBC SO, G. Rozhdestvensky (pp1981) Concert
(10/95) (BBCR) ① **BBCRD9129**
**Sinfonietta—chamber orchestra, Op. 1
(1933)**
1. Poco presto ed agitato; 2. Variations: Andante
lento; 3. Tarantella: Presto vivace.
LMP, J. Glover Concert
(5/90) (ASV) ① **CDDCA682**
Vienna Octet Concert
(9/90) (LOND) ① **425 715-2LM**
Tapiola Sinfonietta, O. Vänskä Concert
(8/92) (BIS) ① **BIS-CD540**
Stuttgart RSO, N. Marriner (r1986) Concert
(1/94) (CAPR) ① **10 428**

**Suite on English Folk Tunes, 'A time there
was...', Op. 90 (1966 and 1974)**
1. Cakes and Ale; 2. The Bitter Withy; 3. Hankin
Booby (1966); 4. Hunt the Squirrel; 5. Lord
Melbourne.
CBSO, S. Rattle Concert
(11/91) (EMI) ① [2] **CDS7 54270-2**
NYPO, L. Bernstein (r1976) Concert
(11/92) (SONY) ① **SMK47541**
Bournemouth SO, R. Hickox (r1994) Concert
(3/94) (CHAN) ① **CHAN9221**
**Symphony for Cello and Orchestra, Op. 68
(1963)**
R. Wallfisch, ECO, S. Bedford Death in Venice Suite.
(1/86) (CHAN) ① **CHAN8363**
T. Mørk, Bergen PO, N. Järvi Concert
(6/89) (BIS) ① **BIS-CD420**
M. Rostropovich, ECO, B. Britten (r1964) Concert
(9/89) (LOND) ① **425 100-2LM**
S. Isserlis, CLS, R. Hickox Bridge: Oration.
(2/92) (EMI) ① **CDM7 63909-2**
**Variation on an Elizabethan Theme,
'Sellinger's Round'—orchestra (1953 pub
1973)** (Variation No. 4 in complete work)
Toulouse Nat CO, B. Bratoev Concert
(7/88) (AUVI) ① **A6124**
**Variations on a theme of Frank
Bridge—string orchestra, Op. 10 (1937)**
1. Introduction and Theme; 2. Adagio; 3. March; 4.
Romance; 5. Aria italiana; 6. Bourrée classique; 7.
Winer Walzer; 8. Moto perpetuo; 9. Funeral March;
10. Chant; 11. Fugue and Finale.
Polish CO, J. Maksymiuk Bartók: Divertimento.
(11/87) (MDG) ① **L3180**
Northern Sinfonia, R. Hickox Concert
(3/88) (ASV) ① **CDDCA591**
Toulouse Nat CO, B. Bratoev Concert
(7/88) (AUVI) ① **A6124**
Norwegian CO, I. Brown Concert
(1/89) (SIMA) ① **PSC1035**
ASMF, N. Marriner Concert
(8/89) (LOND) ① **421 391-2LM**
Stockholm PO, P. Csaba (r1988) Concert
(8/89) (BIS) ① **BIS-CD435**
ECO, G. Levine Concert   (1/90) (ARAB) ① **Z6603**
Montreal I Musici, Y. Turovsky Concert
(2/91) (CHAN) ① **CHAN8817**
BBC SO, A. Davis Concert
(8/91) (TELD) ① **9031-73126-2**
Slovak CO, B. Warchal Concert
(3/92) (CAMP) ① **RRCD1313**
RPO, C. Groves (r1989) Concert
(9/92) (CARL) ① **CDRPO5005**
ECO, A. Gibson Concert
(12/92) (CFP) ① **CD-CFP4598**
Bournemouth Sinfonietta, R. Thomas (r1977) Concert
(11/93) (CHAN) ① **CHAN6592**
Boyd Neel Orch, B. Neel (r1938) Concert
(5/94) (DUTT) ① **CDAX8007**
Bournemouth Sinfonietta, R. Studt (vn/dir) (r1993)
Concert   (10/94) (NAXO) ① **8 550823**
Norwegian CO, I. Brown (r1988) Concert
(10/95) (VIRG) ① **VC5 45121-2**
**Young Apollo—piano and string orchestra,
Op. 16 (1939)**
P. Stewart, E. Turovsky, C. Prévost, S. Careau, D.
Ellis, Montreal I Musici, Y. Turovsky Concert
(2/91) (CHAN) ① **CHAN8817**
P. Donohoe, CBSO, S. Rattle Concert
(11/91) (EMI) ① [2] **CDS7 54270-2**
**The Young Person's Guide to the
Orchestra—Variations and Fugue on a
Theme by Purcell, Op. 34 (1946)** (Wds
Crozier. Spoken text only on recordings with
narrator)
RPO, A. Previn Concert
(10/87) (TELA) ① **CD80126**
FRNO, L. Maazel Concert
(11/88) (DG) ① **423 239-2GC**
Bergen PO, N. Järvi Concert
(6/89) (BIS) ① **BIS-CD420**
LSO, B. Britten Concert
(12/90) (LOND) ① **425 659-2LM**
LPO, S. Edwards Concert
(2/91) (EMIN) ① **CD-EMX2165**
BBC SO, A. Davis Concert
(8/91) (TELD) ① **9031-73126-2**
NYPO, L. Bernstein (r1961) Concert
(11/92) (SONY) ① **SMK47541**
E. Shilling, Czech PO, K. Ančerl (r1963) Concert
(3/93) (SUPR) ① **11 1945-2**
LSO, B. Britten (r1963) Concert
(6/93) (DECC) ① **436 990-2DWO**
Philh, C.M. Giulini (r1962) Concert
(9/93) (EMI) ① [2] **CZS7 67723-2**

LPO, L. Slatkin (r1989) Concert
(3/94) (RCA) ① **09026 61226-2**
Bournemouth SO, R. Hickox (r1993) Concert
(3/94) (CHAN) ① **CHAN9221**
Minnesota Orch, N. Marriner Concert
(7/94) (EMI) ① **CDM7 64300-2**
Concertgebouw, E. van Beinum (r1953) Concert
(9/94) (DECC) ① **440 063-2DM**
RLPO, C. Groves (pp1977) Concert
(5/95) (BBCR) ① **BBCRD9111**
H. Downs, Boston Pops, A. Fiedler (r1961/6) Concert
(12/95) (RCA) ① **09026 68131-2**

┌─────────────────────────────────────┐
│   **SECTION II: CHAMBER**   │
└─────────────────────────────────────┘

Alla marcia—string quartet (1933)
Gabrieli Qt (r1982) Concert
(6/93) (UNIC) ① **UKCD2060**
Endellion Qt (r1986) Concert
(7/95) (EMI) ① [3] **CMS5 65115-2**
Courtly Dances from 'Gloriana'—consort
(arr Bream)
Music from Act 2 Scene 3; 1. March (No. 11); 2.
Corante (No. 14); 3. Pavan (No. 1); 4. Galliard (No.
3); 5. Galliard (No. 3); 6. La Volta (No. 5); 7. March:
Finale (No. 11).
J. Bream, J. Bream Consort (r1963) Concert
(8/93) (RCA) ① [28] **09026 61583-2(3)**
J. Bream Consort (r1963) Concert
(9/94) (RCA) ① **09026 61589-2**
3 Divertimenti—string quartet (1936)
1. March; 2. Waltz; 3. Burlesque.
Gabrieli Qt (r1982) Concert
(6/93) (UNIC) ① **UKCD2060**
Endellion Qt (r1986) Concert
(7/95) (EMI) ① [3] **CMS5 65115-2**
2. Rasumovsky Qt Concert
(12/92) (IMPE) ① **RAZCD901**
**Fanfare for St Edmundsbury—3 trumpets
(1959)**
Wallace Collection, J. Wallace Concert
(3/92) (COLL) ① **Coll1229-2**
**Gemini Variations (12 Variations and Fugue
on an Epigram of Kodály)—flute, violin and
piano duet, Op. 73 (1965)**
G. Jeney, Z. Jeney (r1966) Concert
(11/93) (LOND) ① **436 393-2LM**
2 Insect Pieces—oboe and piano (1935)
1. The Grasshopper; 2. The Wasp.
S. Watkins, P.Ledger Concert
(12/87) (MERI) ① **CDE84119**
D. Wickens, J. Constable (r1982) Concert
(6/93) (UNIC) ① **UKCD2060**
H. Holliger, A. Schiff (r1991) Concert
(12/94) (PHIL) ① **434 076-2PH**
**Introduction and Rondo alla burlesca—2
pianos, Op. 23/1 (1940)**
B. Britten, C. Curzon (r1944) Concert
(10/95) (PEAR) ① **GEMMCD9177**
**Lachrymae—Reflections on a song of
Dowland for viola and piano, Op. 48 (1950)**
K. Kashkashian, R. Levin Concert
(9/86) (ECM) ① **827 744-2**
T. Zimmermann, H. Höll Concert
(3/92) (EMI) ① **CDC7 54394-2**
N. Imai, N. Yoshino (r1993; arr va & hp) Concert
(12/94) (PHIL) ① **442 012-2PH**
**Mazurka elegiaca—2 pianos, Op. 23/2
(1941)**
B. Britten, C. Curzon (r1944) Concert
(10/95) (PEAR) ① **GEMMCD9177**
**Phantasy—oboe and string trio, Op. 2
(1932)**
G. Zubicky, T. Tønnesen, L.A. Tomter, T. Mørk
Concert   (11/88) (SIMA) ① **PSC1022**
P. Woods, Audubon Qt Concert
(10/89) (TELA) ① **CD80205**
D. Wickens, Gabrieli Qt (r1982) Concert
(6/93) (UNIC) ① **UKCD2060**
H. Holliger, T. Zehetmair, T. Zimmermann, T.
Demenga (r1992) Concert
(12/94) (PHIL) ① **434 076-2PH**
D. Boyd, Endellion Qt (r1986) Concert
(7/95) (EMI) ① [3] **CMS5 65115-2**
Phantasy in F minor—string quintet (1932)
Gabrieli Qt, K. Essex (r1982) Concert
(6/93) (UNIC) ① **UKCD2060**
Endellion Qt, N. Logie (r1986) Concert
(7/95) (EMI) ① [3] **CMS5 65115-2**
Quartettino—string quartet (1930)
Endellion Qt (r1986) Concert
(7/95) (EMI) ① [3] **CMS5 65115-2**
Reveille—violin and piano (1937)
L. McAslan, J.J. Blakely Concert
(4/92) (CNTI) ① **CCD1022**

Rhapsody—string quartet (1929)
Endellion Qt (r1986) *Concert*
(7/95) (EMI) ① [3] **CMS5 65115-2**
Sonata for Cello and Piano, Op. 65 (1961)
A. Baillie, I. Brown *Concert*
(6/88) (ETCE) ① [2] **KTC2006**
A. Baillie, I. Brown *Cello Suite 1.*
(6/88) (ETCE) ① **KTC2006(1)**
M. Rostropovich, B. Britten *Concert*
(10/89) (LOND) ① **421 859-2LM**
K.B. Dinitzen, P. Salo *Concert*
(2/93) (KONT) ① [2] **32101/2**
M. Welsh, J. Lenehan (r1994) *Concert*
(7/95) (EMI) ① **CDC5 55398-2**
Scherzo; Marcia J. Du Pré, S. Kovacevich (bp1965)
Concert (9/89) (EMI) ① **CDM7 63165-2**
String Quartet in D (1931)
Britten Qt *Concert* (5/91) (COLL) ① **Coll1115-2**
Endellion Qt (r1986) *Concert*
(7/95) (EMI) ① [3] **CMS5 65115-2**
String Quartet No. 1 in D, Op. 25 (1941)
Alberni Qt *Shostakovich: Piano Quintet, Op.57.*
(3/89) (CRD) ① **CRD3351**
Britten Qt *Concert* (5/91) (COLL) ① **Coll1115-2**
Endellion Qt (r1986) *Concert*
(7/95) (EMI) ① [3] **CMS5 65115-2**
String Quartet No. 2 in C, Op. 36 (1945)
1. Allegro calmo, senza rigore; 2. Vivace; 3.
Chacony: Sostenuto.
Alberni Qt *String Quartet 3.*
(3/89) (CRD) ① **CRD3395**
Amadeus Qt *Concert*
(9/90) (LOND) ① **425 715-2LM**
Britten Qt *String Quartet 3.*
(12/90) (COLL) ① **Coll1025-2**
Brindisi Qt *Concert* (5/91) (CONI) ① **CDCF196**
Tokyo Qt (r1992) *Concert*
(2/94) (RCA) ① **09026 61387-2**
Endellion Qt (r1986) *Concert*
(7/95) (EMI) ① [3] **CMS5 65115-2**
Chacony Toulouse Nat CO, B. Bratoev *Concert*
(8/94) (AUVI) ① **A6124**
String Quartet No. 3, Op. 94 (1975)
Lindsay Qt *Tippett: String Quartet 4.*
(5/88) (ASV) ① **CDDCA608**
Alberni Qt *String Quartet 2.*
(3/89) (CRD) ① **CRD3395**
Amadeus Qt *Concert*
(9/90) (LOND) ① **425 715-2LM**
Britten Qt *String Quartet 2.*
(12/90) (COLL) ① **Coll1025-2**
Endellion Qt (r1986) *Concert*
(7/95) (EMI) ① [3] **CMS5 65115-2**
Suite—violin and piano, Op. 6 (1934-35)
L. McAslan, J. Blakely *Concert*
(4/92) (CNTI) ① **CCD1022**
A. Barantschik, J. Alley (r1994) *Concert*
(7/95) (EMI) ① **CDC5 55398-2**
**Temporal Variations—oboe and piano (1936
pub 1980)**
P. Bree, P. Komen *Concert*
(2/90) (ETCE) ① **KTC1074**
D. Wickens, J. Constable (r1982) *Concert*
(6/93) (UNIC) ① **UKCD2060**
H. Holliger, A. Schiff (r1991) *Concert*
(12/94) (PHIL) ① **434 076-2PH**

SECTION III: INSTRUMENTAL

Elegy—viola (1930)
G. Caussé *Concert* (7/88) (AUVI) ① **A6124**
P. Coletti (r1993) *Concert*
(10/94) (HYPE) ① **CDA66687**
G. Jackson (r1986) *Concert*
(7/95) (EMI) ① [3] **CMS5 65115-2**
P. Silverthorne (r1994) *Concert*
(7/95) (EMI) ① **CDC5 55398-2**
L. A. Tomter (r1991) *Concert*
(10/95) (VIRG) ① **VC5 45121-2**
Holiday Diary—piano, Op. 5 (1934)
1. Early Morning Bathe; 2. Sailing; 3. Funfair; 4.
Night.
C. Headington *Concert*
(11/90) (KING) ① **KCLCD2017**
2, 4. A. Gavrilov (r1992) *Concert*
(3/94) (DG) ① **439 778-2GH**
**6 Metamorphoses after Ovid—oboe, Op. 49
(1951)**
S. Watkins *Concert* (12/87) (MERI) ① **CDE84119**
G. Zubicky *Concert* (11/88) (SIMA) ① **PSC1022**
J. Polmear *Concert* (9/92) (UNIC) ① **DKPCD9121**
H. Holliger (r1991) *Concert*
(12/94) (PHIL) ① **434 076-2PH**
R. Carter (r1995) *Concert*
(7/95) (EMI) ① **CDC5 55398-2**

Night Piece, 'Notturno'—piano (1963)
A. Goldstone *Concert*
(3/92) (GAMU) ① **GAMCD526**
**Nocturnal after John Dowland—guitar, Op.
70 (1963) (ed J. Bream)**
S-E. Olsen *Concert* (9/88) (SIMA) ① **PSC1031**
N. Kraft *Concert* (1/90) (CHAN) ① **CHAN8784**
M. Seifige *Concert* (2/91) (BAYE) ① **BR100095**
J. Savijoki *Concert* (1/93) (ONDI) ① **ODE779-2**
J. Bream (r1966) *Concert*
(8/93) (RCA) ① [28] **09026 61583-2(5)**
J. Bream (r1992) *Concert*
(4/94) (EMI) ① **CDC7 54901-2**
S. Isbin (r c1992) *Concert*
(7/94) (VIRG) ① **VC5 45024-2**
J. Bream (r1966) *Concert*
(9/94) (RCA) ① **09026 61601-2**
C. Ogden (r1994) *Concert* (6/95) (NIMB) ① **NI5390**
**Prelude and Fugue on a Theme of
Vittoria—organ (1946)**
M. Kleinschmidt (r1990) *Concert*
(5/91) (KOCH) ① **37030-2**
Suite—harp, Op. 83 (1969)
O. Ellis *Concert* (12/87) (MERI) ① **CDE84119**
Suite No. 1—cello, Op. 72 (1964)
A. Baillie *Cello Sonata.*
(6/88) (ETCE) ① **KTC2006(1)**
A. Baillie *Concert* (6/88) (ETCE) ① [2] **KTC2006**
T. Hugh *Concert* (6/88) (HYPE) ① **CDA66274**
M. Rostropovich *Concert*
(10/89) (LOND) ① **421 859-2LM**
T. Thedéen *Concert* (5/90) (BIS) ① **BIS-CD446**
M. Haimovitz *Concert* (1/92) (DG) ① **431 813-2GH**
P. Wispelwey *Concert* (8/92) (GLOB) ① **GLO5074**
K.B. Dinitzen *Concert*
(2/93) (KONT) ① [2] **32101/2**
Suite No. 2—cello, Op. 80 (1967)
A. Baillie *Concert* (6/88) (ETCE) ① [2] **KTC2006**
A. Baillie *Cello Suite 3.*
(6/88) (ETCE) ① **KTC2006(2)**
T. Hugh *Concert* (6/88) (HYPE) ① **CDA66274**
M. Rostropovich *Concert*
(10/89) (LOND) ① **421 859-2LM**
T. Thedéen *Concert* (5/90) (BIS) ① **BIS-CD446**
P. Wispelwey *Concert* (8/92) (GLOB) ① **GLO5074**
K.B. Dinitzen *Concert*
(2/93) (KONT) ① [2] **32101/2**
Suite No. 3—cello, Op. 87 (1972)
A. Baillie *Concert* (6/88) (ETCE) ① [2] **KTC2006**
A. Baillie *Cello Suite 2.*
(6/88) (ETCE) ① **KTC2006(2)**
T. Hugh *Concert* (6/88) (HYPE) ① **CDA66274**
T. Thedéen *Concert* (5/90) (BIS) ① **BIS-CD446**
S. Isserlis *Concert* (3/92) (VIRG) ① **VC7 59052-2**
P. Wispelwey *Concert* (8/92) (GLOB) ① **GLO5074**
K.B. Dinitzen *Concert*
(2/93) (KONT) ① [2] **32101/2**
M. Haimovitz (r1993) *Concert*
(12/95) (DG) ① **445 834-2GH**
Tema-Sacher—cello (1976)
J. Lloyd Webber *Concert*
(9/88) (ASV) ① **CDDCA592**
K.B. Dinitzen *Concert*
(2/93) (KONT) ① [2] **32101/2**
T. Demenga (r1993) *Concert*
(8/95) (ECM) ① [2] **445 234-2**
**5 Walztes (Waltzes)—piano (1923-25: recomp
1969)**
1. Rather fast and nervous; 2. Quick, with wit; 3.
Dramatic; 4. Rhythmic: not fast; 5. Variations: quiet
and simple.
A. Goldstone *Concert*
(3/92) (GAMU) ① **GAMCD526**

SECTION IV: VOCAL AND CHORAL

A.M.D.G.—chorus a cappella (1939) (Wds.
G.M. Hopkins)
1. Heaven-Haven; 2. O deus, ego amo te; 3. Rosa
Mystica; 4. The Soldier; 5. Prayer II; 6. God's
Grandeur; 7. Prayer I.
Cambridge Univ Chbr Ch, T. Brown *Concert*
(4/92) (GAMU) ① **GAMCD529**
**Advance Democracy—chorus a cappella
(1938)** (Wds. R. Swingler)
The Sixteen, H. Christophers (r1992) *Concert*
(6/93) (COLL) ① **Coll1343-2**
Antiphon—4vv and organ, Op. 56b (1956)
(Wds. G. Herbert)
The Sixteen, Margaret Phillips, H. Christophers
(r1992) *Concert* (6/93) (COLL) ① **Coll1343-2**
**Ballad of Heroes—tenor/soprano, chorus
and orchestra, Op. 14 (1939)** (Wds. Swingler &
W. H. Auden)
1. Funeral March; 2. Scherzo (Dance of Death); 3.
Recitative and Choral.

M. Hill, LSC, LSO, R. Hickox *Concert*
(11/91) (CHAN) ① [2] **CHAN8983/4**
R. Tear, CBSO Chor, CBSO, S. Rattle *Concert*
(11/91) (EMI) ① [2] **CDS7 54270-2**
**The Ballad of Little Musgrave and Lady
Barnard—male vv and piano (1943)** (Wds.
anon)
The Sixteen, S. Westrop, H. Christophers (r1992)
Concert (6/93) (COLL) ① **Coll1343-2**
Chorus Viennensis, A. Gavrilov (r1992) *Concert*
(3/94) (DG) ① **439 778-2GH**
2 Ballads—2vv and piano (1937)
1. Mother Comfort (wds. M. Slater); 2. Underneath
the abject willow (wds. W. H. Auden).
K. Livingstone, N. Mackie, J.J. Blakely *Concert*
(2/89) (UNIC) ① **UKCD2009**
F. Lott, A. Murray, G. Johnson (r1991) *Concert*
(7/92) (EMI) ① **CDC7 54411-2**
**A Birthday Hansel—1v and harp, Op. 92
(1975)** (Wds. Burns)
1. Birthday song; 2. My early walk; 3. Wee Willie; 4.
My Hoggie; 5. Afton Water; 6. The Winter; 7. Leezie
Lindsay.
Y. Kenny, T. Crone (arr. C. Matthews) *Concert*
(6/87) (ETCE) ① **KTC1046**
P. Pears, O. Ellis *Concert*
(9/90) (LOND) ① **425 716-2LM**
**A Boy is Born—choral variations on old
carols—mixed vv and organ (ad lib), Op. 3
(1932-33)**
1. Theme—A boy was born; 2. Lullaby, Jesu; 3.
Herod; 4. Jesus, as Thou art our Saviour; 5. The
Three kings; 6. In the bleak mid-winter; 7. Noël.
R. Unwin, Westminster Cath Ch, Corydon Sngrs, M.
Best *Concert* (5/86) (HYPE) ① **CDA66126**
T. Rose, Cambridge Univ Ladies' Ch, King's College
Ch, S. Cleobury *Concert*
(12/91) (ARGO) ① **433 215-2ZH**
The Sixteen, H. Christophers *Concert*
(8/92) (COLL) ① **Coll1286-2**
M. Harnett, Purcell Sngrs, All Saints Ch, B. Britten
(r1957) *Concert* (9/93) (LOND) ① **436 394-2LM**
1. Quink *Concert* (3/89) (TELA) ① **CD80202**
4 Cabaret songs—1v and piano (1937-39)
(Wds. W. H. Auden)
1. Tell me the truth about love; 2. Funeral blues; 3.
Johnny; 4. Calypso.
Sarah Walker, R. Vignoles (pp1982) *Concert*
(3/89) (MERI) ① **CDE84167**
J. Gomez, Martin Jones (r1992) *Concert*
(9/93) (UNIC) ① **DKPCD9138**
**Cantata Academica, 'Carmen
basiliense'—soloists, chorus and orchestra,
Op. 62 (1959)** (Wds. compiled B. Wyss)
1. Bonorum summum omnium; 2. quae bene
beateque vivendi; 3. At huius caelestis doni; 4.
Maiorum imprimis virtus; 5. nam vero Aeneas Sylvius;
6. Et gubernacula mundi qui tenet; 7. ut ad longaeva
tempora; 8. Docendi ac discendi aeuitati; 9. Rhenana
erga omnes urbs; 10. Ut iustissime Basilea; 11. O
cives Basiliensi; 12. Nos autem cuncti hoc festo die;
13. vigeatque academia libera.
J. Vyvyan, H. Watts, P. Pears, O. Brannigan, London
Sym Chor, LSO, G. Malcolm (r1964) *Concert*
(9/93) (LOND) ① **436 396-2LM**
**Cantata misericordium—tenor, baritone,
chorus and orchestra, Op. 69 (1963)** (Wds. P.
Wilkinson)
P. Pears, D. Fischer-Dieskau, London Sym Chor,
LSO, B. Britten (r1964) *Concert*
(9/89) (LOND) ① **425 100-2LM**
Britten Sngrs, CLS, R. Hickox *Concert*
(3/94) (CHAN) ① **CHAN8997**
**Canticle No. 1 - My beloved is
mine—soprano/tenor and piano, Op. 40
(1947)** (Wds. F. Quarles)
A. Rolfe Johnson, G. Johnson *Concert*
(5/90) (HYPE) ① **CDA66209**
P. Pears, B. Britten (r1961) *Concert*
(9/90) (LOND) ① **425 716-2LM**
A. Rolfe Johnson, R. Vignoles *Concert*
(5/92) (HYPE) ① **CDA66498**
**Canticle No. 2—Abraham and
Isaac—alto/contralto, tenor and piano, Op.
51 (1952)** (Wds. Chester miracle play)
P. Pears, J. Hahessy, B. Britten (r1961) *Concert*
(9/90) (LOND) ① **425 716-2LM**
A. Rolfe Johnson, M. Chance, R. Vignoles *Concert*
(5/92) (HYPE) ① **CDA66498**
P. Esswood, J. Griffett, J. Ridgway (r1992) *Concert*
(1/94) (CARL) ① **MCD57**
**Canticle No. 3 - Still falls the rain—tenor,
horn and piano, Op. 55 (1954)** (Wds. E.
Sitwell)
P. Pears, B. Tuckwell, B. Britten (r1961) *Concert*
(9/90) (LOND) ① **425 716-2LM**

A. Rolfe Johnson, R. Vignoles, M. Thompson *Concert*
(5/92) (HYPE) ① **CDA66498**
**Canticle No. 4—The Journey of the
Magi—alto, tenor, baritone and piano, Op. 86
(1971)** (Wds. T. S. Eliot)
P. Pears, J. Bowman, J. Shirley-Quirk, B. Britten
(r1972) *Concert* (9/90) (LOND) ① **425 716-2LM**
A. Rolfe Johnson, M. Chance, A. Opie, R. Vignoles
Concert (5/92) (HYPE) ① **CDA66498**
**Canticle No. 5—The Death of St
Narcissus—tenor and harp, Op. 89 (1974)**
(Wds. T. S. Eliot)
P. Pears, O. Ellis (r1976) *Concert*
(9/90) (LOND) ① **425 716-2LM**
A. Rolfe Johnson, S. Williams *Concert*
(5/92) (HYPE) ① **CDA66498**
**A Ceremony of Carols—treble vv and harp,
Op. 28 (1942)** (Wds. various)
1. Procession; 2. Wolcom Yole!; 3. There is no rose;
4a. That youngë child; 4b. Balulalow; 5. As dew in
Aprille; 6. This little Babe; 7. Interlude (harp); 8. In
freezing winter night; 9. Spring carol; 10. Adam lay i-
bounden; 11. Recession.
Westminster Cath Ch, S. Williams, D. Hill *Concert*
(2/88) (HYPE) ① **CDA66220**
P. Winn, R. Johnston, J. McFadzean, M. Body, T.
Rose, M. Pearce, R. Masters, King's College Ch, S.
Cleobury *Concert* (12/91) (ARGO) ① **433 215-2ZH**
Elysian Sngrs, M. Greenall *Concert*
(12/91) (CNTI) ① **CCD1043**
The Sixteen, S. Williams, H. Christophers (r1992)
Concert (7/93) (COLL) ① **Coll1370-2**
Copenhagen Boys Ch, E. Simon, B. Britten (r1953)
Concert (9/93) (LOND) ① **436 394-2LM**
3. King's College Ch, D. Willcocks, O. Ellis *Concert*
(1/91) (CFP) ① **CD-CFP4570**
7. M. Robles *Concert*
(2/93) (DECC) ① **433 869-2DWO**
10. St John's College Ch, M. Robles, G. Guest
(r1964) *Concert* (6/93) (DECC) ① **436 990-2DWO**
**4 Chansons françaises—soprano and
orchestra (1928)** (Wds. V. Hugo and P.
Verlaine)
1. Nuits de Juin (wds. V Hugo); 2. Sagesse (wds. P
Verlaine); 3. L'Enfance (Wds. V Hugo); 4. Chanson
d'Automne (wds. P Verlaine).
F. Lott, SNO, B. Thomson *Concert*
(6/89) (CHAN) ① **CHAN8657**
J. Gomez, CBSO, S. Rattle *Concert*
(11/91) (EMI) ① [2] **CDS7 54270-2**
F. Lott, ECO, S. Bedford (r1994) *Concert*
(12/94) (COLL) ① [2] **Coll7037-2**
**A Charm of Lullabies—song cycle: mezzo
and piano, Op. 41 (1947)** (Wds. various)
C. Watkinson, T. Crone *Concert*
(6/87) (ETCE) ① **KTC1046**
**Children's Crusade
(Kinderkreuzzug)—ballad: children's vv,
perc, 2 pfs & org, Op. 82 (1969)** (Wds. B.
Brecht)
Wandsworth Sch Boys' Ch, chbr ens, B. Britten, R.
Burgess (r1970) *Concert*
(11/93) (LOND) ① **436 393-2LM**
**6 Chinese Songs—1v and guitar, Op. 58
(1957)** (trans. A. Waley)
1. The big chariot; 2. The old lute; 3. The autumn
wind; 4. The herd-boy; 5. Depression; 6. Dance
Song.
I. Partridge, J. Savijoki *Concert*
(1/93) (ONDI) ① **ODE779-2**
P. Pears, J. Bream (r1963-4) *Concert*
(8/93) (RCA) ① [28] **09026 61583-2(5)**
J. Griffett, T. Walker (r1992) *Concert*
(1/94) (CARL) ① **MCD57**
P. Pears, J. Bream (r1963-4) *Concert*
(9/94) (RCA) ① **09026 61601-2**
**Choral Dances from 'Gloriana'—tenor,
chorus and harp** (Wds. W Plomer)
1. Time; 2. Concord; 3. Time and Concord; 4.
Country girls; 5. Rustics and Fishermen; 6. Final
dance of homage.
M Hill, T. Owen, Holst Sngrs, H.D. Wetton (rev ver)
Concert (11/88) (HYPE) ① **CDA66175**
1. I. Partridge, H. Tunstall, The Sixteen, H.
Christophers *Concert* (8/92) (COLL) ① **Coll1286-2**
Chorale on an Old French Carol
Britten Sngrs, CLS, R. Hickox *Concert*
(3/92) (CHAN) ① **CHAN8997**
**Corpus Christi carol—treble and organ
(1961)** (arr cpsr from 'A Boorn is born')
J. Baker, G. Moore (r1967) *Concert*
(11/94) (EMI) ① **CDM5 65009-2**
Fancie—song (1961) (Wds. Shakespeare)
A. Rolfe Johnson, G. Johnson *Concert*
(5/92) (HYPE) ① **CDA66480**

**Festival Te Deum—4vv and organ, Op. 32
(1944)**
M. Seers, Westminster Cath Ch, Corydon Sngrs, M.
Best *Concert* (5/86) (HYPE) ① **CDA66126**
J. Budd, St Paul's Cath Ch, Adrian Lucas, John Scott
Concert (10/91) (HYPE) ① **CDA66439**
The Sixteen, Margaret Phillips, H. Christophers
(r1992) *Concert* (7/93) (COLL) ① **Coll1370-2**
Hereford Cath Ch, R. Massey, G. Bowen (r1994)
Concert (2/95) (PRIO) ① **PRCD507**
**Fish in the unruffled lakes—song: 1v and
piano (1937)** (Wds. W. H. Auden)
F. Lott, G. Johnson *Concert*
(7/90) (CHAN) ① **CHAN8722**
**5 Flower Songs—chorus a cappella, Op. 47
(1950)** (Wds. various)
1. To daffodils (wds. Herrick); 2. The succession of
the four sweet months (wds. Herrick); 3. Marsh
flowers (wds. Crabbe); 4. The evening primrose (wds.
Clare); 5. Ballad of green broom (wds. Anon).
Cpte Cambridge Sngrs, J. Rutter *Concert*
(4/87) (CLLE) ① **COLCD104**
The Sixteen, H. Christophers *Concert*
(8/92) (COLL) ① **Coll1286-2**
**Folk Song Arrangements—1v and piano
(unless otherwise stated)**
VOLUME 1—BRITISH pub 1943; 1. The Salley
Gardens (also unison vv and piano); 2. Little Sir
William; 3. The Bonny Earl o' Moray; 4. O can ye sew
cushions?; 5. The trees they grow so high; 6. The
ash grove; 7. Oliver Cromwell (also unison vv and
piano). VOLUME 2—FRENCH (pub 1946): 8. La noël
passée; 9. Voici le printemps; 10. Fileuse; 11. Le roi
s'en va-t-en chasse (The King goes a-hunting); 12. La
belle est au jardin d'amour; 13. Il est quelqu'un sur
terre; 14. Eho! Eho!; 15. Quand j'étais chez mon
père. VOLUME 3—BRITISH (pub 1947): 16. The
plough boy; 17. There's none to soothe; 18. Sweet
Polly Oliver; 19. The Miller of Dee; 20. The foggy
foggy dew; 21. O waly waly; 22. Come you not from
Newcastle? VOLUME 4—IRISH (pub 1960): 23.
Avenging and bright; 24. Sail on, sail on; 25. How
sweet the answer; 26. The minstrel boy; 27. At the
mid hour of night; 28. Rich and rare; 29. Dear harp of
my country; 30. Oft in the stilly night; 31. The last
rose of summer; 32. O the sight entrancing. VOLUME
5—BRITISH (pub 1961): 33. The brisk young widow;
34. Salley in our alley; 35. The Lincolnshire poacher;
36. Early one morning; 37. Ca' the yowes. VOLUME
6—BRITISH (guitar: pub 1961): 38. I will give my love
an apple; 39. Sailor-boy; 40. Master Kilby; 41. Bonny
at morn; 42. The soldier and the sailor; 43. The
shooting of his dear. EIGHT FOLK SONG
ARRANGEMENTS (hp/gtr: 1976): 44. Lord, I married
me a wife; 45. She's like a swallow; 46. Lemady; 47.
Bonny at morn; 48. I was lonely and forlorn; 49.
David of the white rock; 50. The false knight; 51. Bird
scarer's song. UNPUBLISHED FOLK SONGS: 52.
Greensleeves; 53. I wonder as I wander; 54. The
crocodile; 55. Pray Goody; 56. The Holly and the Ivy;
57. Soldier, won't you marry me?; 58. The Deaf
Woman's Courtship; 59. The stream in the valley; 60.
Unidentified folk song setting; 61. The bitter withy.
Cpte F. Lott, P. Langridge, T. Allen, C. Bonnell, O.
Ellis, C. van Kampen, G. Johnson (r1995) *Concert*
(11/95) (COLL) ① [3] **Coll7039-2**
1, 15, 21, 22. C. Watkinson, T. Crone *Concert*
(6/87) (ETCE) ① **KTC1046**
1, 21. L. Finnie, A. Legge *Concert*
(4/90) (CHAN) ① **CHAN8749**
1, 2, 5, 21. A. Rolfe Johnson, G. Johnson *Concert*
(5/90) (HYPE) ① **CDA66209**
1, 2, 6, 7. P. Pears, B. Britten (r1944) *Concert*
(10/95) (PEAR) ① **GEMMCD9177**
1-3, 6, 7, 15, 17, 18. P. Pears, B. Britten (r1944-6)
Concert (2/94) (EMI) ① [2] **CMS7 64727-2**
1-51. L. Anderson, R. Nathan, J. MacDougall, B.
Lewis, C. Ogden, M. Martineau (r1994)
(2/95) (HYPE) ① [2] **CDA66941/2**
1, 6, 17, 20, 21. P. Esswood, J. Ridgway (r1992)
Concert (1/94) (CARL) ① **MCD57**
2, 3, 7, 16. J. Griffett, J. Ridgway (r1992) *Concert*
(1/94) (CARL) ① **MCD57**
2, 3, 7, 16, 21, 22. E. Söderström, WNO Orch, R.
Armstrong (r1982) *Concert*
(12/88) (EMI) ① **CDM7 69522-2**
4-6, 25, 26, 31. Y. Kenny, T. Crone *Concert*
(6/87) (ETCE) ① **KTC1046**
5. C. Robbin, M. McMahon (r1994) *Concert*
(7/94) (MARQ) ① **ERAD113**
9-12, 15. S. Wyss, B. Britten (r1943) *Concert*
(2/94) (EMI) ① [2] **CMS7 64727-2**
10-12, 14, 15. F. Palmer, Endymion Ens, J. Whitfield
(r1986) *Concert* (7/95) (EMI) ① **CDM5 65114-2**
11. P. Pears, B. Britten (r1950) *Concert*
(4/92) (EMI) ① **CHS7 69741-2(2)**

11, 16, 20-22. P. Pears, B. Britten (r1947/50) *Concert*
(2/94) (EMI) ① [2] **CMS7 64727-2**
16, 36. P. Pears, B. Britten (r1961) *Concert*
(6/93) (DECC) ① **436 990-2DWO**
21. S. Bullock, A. Bryn Parri (r1994) *Concert*
(11/95) (SAIN) ① **SCDC2070**
21, 22. F. Lott, G. Johnson *Concert*
(7/90) (CHAN) ① **CHAN8722**
21, 22. K. Ferrier, F. Stone (bp1952) *Concert*
(7/91) (LOND) ① **430 061-2LM**
21, 22. K. Ferrier, F. Stone (bp1952) *Concert*
(6/92) (DECC) ① **433 473-2DM**
21, 37. K. Ferrier, J. Newmark (r1950) *Concert*
(6/92) (DECC) ① **433 475-2DM**
22. K. Ferrier, F. Stone (bp1952) *Concert*
(6/91) (DECC) ① **430 096-2DWO**
25, 30-32. A. Murray, G. Johnson (r1992) *Concert*
(8/93) (HYPE) ① **CDA66627**
38-40, 42, 43. P. Pears, J. Bream (r1963-4) *Concert*
(8/93) (RCA) ① [28] **09026 61583-2(5)**
38-40, 42, 43. P. Pears, J. Bream (r1963-4) *Concert*
(9/94) (RCA) ① **09026 61601-2**
38-43. I. Partridge, J. Savijoki *Concert*
(1/93) (ONDI) ① **ODE779-2**
38-43. J. Griffett, T. Walker (r1992) *Concert*
(1/94) (CARL) ① **MCD57**
44-47, 49, 51. J. Shirley-Quirk, O. Ellis *Concert*
(12/87) (MERI) ① **CDE84119**
Folk Song Arrangements—1v & orchestra
EXCERPTS: 1. VOLUME 1 (1942): 1a. the bonny
Earl o' Moray; 1b. The salley gardens (string
orchestra); 1c. the salley gardens (strings, bassoon
& harp); 1d. Little Sir William; 1e. Oliver Cromwell; 1f.
O can ye sew cushions?; 2. VOLUME 2 (1948): 2a.
Le roi s'en va-t'en chasse; 2b. Fileuse; 2c. Eho! Eho!;
2d. La belle est au jardin d'amour; 2e. Quand j'étais
chez mon père; 3. VOLUME 3 (1950s): 3a. The
plough boy; 3b. O waly, waly; 3c. Come you not from
Newcastle?.
Cpte P. Langridge, T. Allen, Northern Sinfonia, S.
Bedford (r1995) *Concert*
(11/95) (COLL) ① [3] **Coll7039-2**
**Friday Afternoons—12 songs: children's vv
and piano, Op. 7 (1933-35)**
1. Begone, dull care!; 2. A Tragic Story; 3. Cuckoo!;
4. Ee-oh!; 5. A New Year Carol; 6. I must be married
on Sunday; 7. There was a man of Newington; 8.
Fishing Song; 9. The Useful Plough; 10. Jazz-Man;
11. There was a monkey; 12. Old Abram Brown.
Vienna Boys' Ch, A. Gavrilov (r1992) *Concert*
(3/94) (DG) ① **439 778-2GH**
1. Magdalen (Oxford) Coll Ch, G. Ives *Concert*
(11/92) (CNTO) ① **CRCD2366**
1-3, 5-12. Downside School Boys Ch, V. Tunnard, B.
Britten (r1966) *Concert*
(9/93) (LOND) ① **436 394-2LM**
**The Golden Vanity—boys' vv and piano, Op.
78 (1966)** (Wds. C. Graham)
Wandsworth Sch Boys' Ch, B. Britten, R. Burgess
(r1966) *Noye's Fludde*.
(11/93) (LOND) ① **436 397-2LM**
Vienna Boys' Ch, A. Gavrilov, P. Marschik (r1992)
Concert (3/94) (DG) ① **439 778-2GH**
**6 Hölderlin Fragments—song cycle: 1v and
piano, Op. 61 (1958)**
EXCERPTS: 1. Menschenbeifall; 2. Die Heimat; 3.
Sokrates und Alcibiades; 4. Die Jugend; 5. Hälfte des
Lebens; 6. Die Linien des Lebens.
P. Pears, B. Britten (r1961) *Concert*
(11/93) (LOND) ① [2] **433 200-2LHO2**
5. M. Shirai, H. Höll *Concert*
(12/94) (CAPR) ① **10 534**
**The Holy Sonnets of John Donne—song
cycle: tenor and piano, Op. 35 (1945)**
P. Pears, B. Britten (r1947) *Concert*
(4/93) (EMI) ① **CDC7 54605-2**
**A Hymn of St Columba, 'Regis regum
rectissimi'—4vv and organ (1962)**
Westminster Cath Ch, D. Hill *Concert*
(2/88) (HYPE) ① **CDA66220**
St Thomas Ch, G. Hancock (1990) *Concert*
(5/91) (KOCH) ① **37030-2**
Wellington College Chs, T. Byram-Wigfield, S.
Anderson *Concert* (10/92) (HERA) ① **HAVPCD153**
King's College Ch, S. Cleobury, C. Hughes (r1991)
Concert (6/93) (EMI) ① **CDC7 54418-2**
The Sixteen, Margaret Phillips, H. Christophers
Concert (7/93) (COLL) ① **Coll1370-2**
**Hymn to St Cecilia—chorus a cappella, Op.
27 (1942)** (Wds. W H Auden)
1. In a garden shady; 2. I cannot grow; 3. O ear
whose creatures cannot wish to fall; 4. O cry created
as the bow of sin.
Corydon Sngrs, M. Best *St Nicolas*.
(5/89) (HYPE) ① **CDA66333**

St Thomas Ch, G. Hancock (r1990) *Concert*
(5/91) (KOCH) ① **37030-2**
The Sixteen, H. Christophers *Concert*
(8/92) (COLL) ① **Coll1286-2**
London Sym Chor, G. Malcolm (r1961) *Concert*
(9/93) (LOND) ① **436 396-2LM**
Cambridge Sngrs, J. Rutter (r1992) *Concert*
(11/93) (CLLE) ① **COLCD119**
Hymn to St Peter—treble, choir and organ, Op. 56a (1955)
P. Berry, St Thomas Ch, M. Kleinschmidt, G.
Hancock (r1990) *Concert*
(5/91) (KOCH) ① **37030-2**
Magdalen Oxford Coll Ch, G. Webber *Concert*
(11/91) (ABBE) ① **CDCA914**
The Sixteen, Margaret Phillips, H. Christophers
(r1992) *Concert* (7/93) (COLL) ① **Coll1370-2**
Jesus College Ch, D. Phillips, T. Horton *Concert*
(7/93) (CNTO) ① **CRCD2367**
A Hymn to the Virgin—chorus a cappella (1930 rev 1934) (Wds. c1300 anon)
Westminster Cath Ch, D. Hill *Concert*
(2/88) (HYPE) ① **CDA66220**
Cambridge Sngrs, J. Rutter *Concert*
(6/88) (CLLE) ① **COLCD107**
The Sixteen, H. Christophers *Concert*
(12/90) (COLL) ① **Coll1270-2**
St John's College Ch, G. Guest (r1962) *Concert*
(6/93) (DECC) ① **436 990-2DWO**
The Sixteen, H. Christophers (r1992) *Concert*
(7/93) (COLL) ① **Coll1370-2**
Jesus College Ch, D. Phillips, T. Horton *Concert*
(7/93) (CNTO) ① **CRCD2367**
Trinity Coll Ch, Cambridge, R. Marlow (r1993)
Concert (12/93) (CONI) ① **CDCF517**
Chanticleer (r1990) *Concert*
(12/94) (CHTI) ① **CR-8803**
Les Illuminations—soprano/tenor and strings, Op. 18 (1939) (Wds. A Rimbaud)
1. Fanfare; 2. Villes; 3. Phrase; 4. Antique; 5.
Royauté; 6. Marine; 7. Interlude; 8. Being beauteous;
9. Parade; 10. Départ.
R. Tear, Philh, C.M. Giulini *Concert*
(11/88) (DG) ① **423 239-2GC**
F. Lott, SNO, B. Thomson *Concert*
(6/89) (CHAN) ① **CHAN8657**
C. Eda-Pierre, J-W. Audoli Inst Ens, J-W. Audoli
Concert (6/89) (ARIO) ① **ARN68035**
C. Högman, Stockholm PO, P. Csaba (r1988)
(8/89) (BIS) ① **BIS-CD435**
E. Söderström, ECO, G. Levine *Concert*
(1/90) (ARAB) ① **Z6603**
A. Rolfe Johnson, LMP, J. Glover *Concert*
(5/90) (ASV) ① **CDDCA682**
J. Hadley, English Stg Orch, W. Boughton *Concert*
(9/90) (NIMB) ① **NI5234**
S. Danco, SRO, E. Ansermet (bp1953) *Concert*
(1/93) (CASC) ① **VEL2010**
P. Pears, ECO, B. Britten (r1966) *Concert*
(9/93) (LOND) ① **436 395-2LM**
B. Hendricks, ECO, Colin Davis (r1993) *Berlioz: Nuits
d'été*. (8/94) (EMI) ① **CDC5 55053-2**
F. Lott, ECO, S. Bedford (r1994) *Concert*
(12/94) (COLL) ② **Coll7037-2**
J. Gomez, Endymion Ens, J. Whitfield (r1986)
Concert (7/95) (EMI) ① **CDM5 65114-2**
J. Micheau, Lamoureux Orch, P. Sacher (r1954)
Concert (12/95) (PHIL) ② **438 970-2PM2**
Jubilate Deo in C—4vv and organ (1961)
Worcester Cath Ch, A. Partington, Don Hunt *Concert*
(9/90) (CARL) ① **PCD937**
St Thomas Ch, M. Kleinschmidt, G. Hancock (r1990)
Concert (5/91) (KOCH) ① **37030-2**
St John's Episcopal Cath Ch, D. Pearson *Concert*
(10/92) (DELO) ① **DE3125**
The Sixteen, Margaret Phillips, H. Christophers
(r1992) *Concert* (7/93) (COLL) ① **Coll1370-2**
Southwark Cath Ch, P. Wright, S. Layton (r1992)
Concert (7/94) (PRIO) ① **PRCD435**
Jubilate Deo in E flat—4vv and organ
Westminster Cath Ch, D. Hill *Concert*
(2/88) (HYPE) ① **CDA66220**
King Herod and the Cock—choir & piano (1962)
P. Langridge, Wenhaston Boys' Ch, C. Barnett, D. O.
Norris (r1995) *Concert*
(11/95) (COLL) ③ **Coll7039-2**
Missa brevis in D—boys' vv and organ, Op. 63 (1959)
New College Ch, E. Higginbottom *Concert*
(3/87) (PROU) ① **PROUCD114**
Westminster Cath Ch, D. Hill *Concert*
(2/88) (HYPE) ① **CDA66220**
The Sixteen, Margaret Phillips, H. Christophers
(r1992) *Concert* (7/93) (COLL) ① **Coll1370-2**

A New Year Carol—female vv and piano (1971) (arr cpsr from No. 5 of 'Friday Afternoons', Op. 7)
Cambridge Sngrs, CLS, J. Rutter *Concert*
(12/89) (CLLE) ① **COLCD111**
The Sixteen, S. Westrop, H. Christophers (r1992)
Concert (7/93) (COLL) ① **Coll1370-2**
Nocturne—tenor, seven obbligato instruments and strings, Op. 60 (1958) (Wds. various)
1. On a poet's lips I slept (wds. P B Shelley); 2.
Below the thunders of the upper deep (wds. A
Tennyson); 3. Encinctured with a twive of leaves
(wds S Taylor Coleridge); 4. Midnight's bell going ting
(wds. T Middleton); 5. When that night on my bed I
lay (wds W Wordsworth); 6. She sleeps on soft, last
breaths (wds W Owen); 7. WHat is more gentle than
a wind in summer? (wds. J Keats); 8. When most I
wink, then do mine eyes best see (wds
Shakespeare).
A. Rolfe Johnson, LMP, J. Glover *Concert*
(5/90) (ASV) ① **CDDCA682**
J. Hadley, English Stg Orch, W. Boughton *Concert*
(9/90) (NIMB) ① **NI5234**
C. Prégardien, Tapiola Sinfonietta, O. Vänskä
Concert (8/92) (BIS) ① **BIS-CD540**
P. Pears, LSO, B. Britten (r1959) *Concert*
(9/93) (LOND) ① **436 395-2LM**
P. Langridge, Northern Sinfonia, S. Bedford (r1994)
Concert (12/94) (COLL) ② **Coll7037-2**
Now sleeps the crimson petal—song: 1v and piano (Wds. A Tennyson: discarded from Serenade, Op 31)
C. Prégardien, I. Lanzky-Otto, Tapiola Sinfonietta, O.
Vänskä *Concert* (8/92) (BIS) ① **BIS-CD540**
On this Island—song cycle: 1v and piano, Op. 11 (1937) (Wds. W H Auden)
1. Let the florid music praise!; 2. Now the leaves are
falling fast; 3. Seascape; 4. Nocturne; 5. As it is,
plenty.
1. R. Fleming, W. Jones (pp1994) *Concert*
(1/95) (RCA) ① **09026 62547-2**
5. J. Gomez, Martin Jones (r1992) *Concert*
(9/93) (UNIC) ① **DKPCD9138**
Our Hunting Fathers—symphonic cycle: 1v and orchestra, Op. 8 (1936) (Wds. W H
Auden)
1. Prologue; 2. Rats away!; 3. Messaline; 4. Dance of
Death (Hawking for the partridge); 5. Epilogue and
Funeral Music.
E. Söderström, WNO Orch, R. Armstrong (r1982)
Concert (12/88) (EMI) ① **CDM7 69522-2**
P. Bryn-Julson, ECO, S. Bedford *Concert*
(4/92) (COLL) ① **Coll1192-2**
P. Bryn-Julson, ECO, S. Bedford (r1994) *Concert*
(12/94) (COLL) ② **Coll7037-2**
Phaedra—mezzo-soprano and ensemble, Op. 93 (1975) (Wds. Racine trans R. Lowell)
C. Eda-Pierre, J-W. Audoli Inst Ens, J-W. Audoli
Concert (6/89) (ARIO) ① **ARN68035**
J. Baker, ECO, S. Bedford (r1977) *Rape of Lucretia*.
(5/90) (LOND) ① ② **425 666-2LH2**
A. Murray, ECO, S. Bedford (r1994) *Concert*
(12/94) (COLL) ② **Coll7037-2**
F. Palmer, Endymion Ens, J. Whitfield (r1986)
Concert (7/95) (EMI) ① **CDM5 65114-2**
The Poet's Echo—song cycle: 1v and piano, Op. 76 (1965) (Wds. Pushkin, trans Pears)
G. Vishnevskaya, M. Rostropovich (r1968) *Concert*
(11/93) (LOND) ① ② **433 200-2LHO2**
Praise we great men—soloists, chorus and orchestra (1976) (fragments: ed & orch C.
Matthews)
A. Hargan, M. King, R. Tear, W. White, CBSO Chor,
CBSO, S. Rattle *Concert*
(11/91) (EMI) ① ② **CDS7 54270-2**
Psalm 150—children's choir and ensemble, Op. 67 (1962) (Wds. Bible)
City of London Girls, City of London Boys, K-H.
Goedicke, R. Hickox *Concert*
(4/91) (CHAN) ① **CHAN8855**
Downside School Boys Ch, B. Britten (r1966) *Concert*
(9/93) (LOND) ① **436 394-2LM**
Rejoice in the Lamb—Festival Cantata—soloists, chorus and organ, Op. 30 (1943) (Wds. C Smart)
1. Rejoice in God, O ye Tongues; 2. Let Nimrod, the
mighty hunter; 3. For I will consider my Cat Jeoffry;
4. For the Mouse; 5. For the flowers are great blessings;
6. For I am under the same accusation; 7. For H is
the spirit; 8. For at that time malignity ceases.
M. Seers, M. Chance, P. Salmon, G. Hayes,
Westminster Cath Ch, B. Britten (r1966) *Concert*
(5/86) (HYPE) ① **CDA66126**

O. Johnston, W. Missin, P. Cave, J. Bernays, New
College Ch, Fiori Musicali, E. Higginbottom *Concert*
(3/90) (PROU) ① **PROUCD125**
M. Hartnett, J. Steele, P. Todd, D. Francke, G.
Malcolm, Purcell Sngrs, B. Britten (r1957) *St Nicolas*.
(9/90) (DECC) ① **425 714-2LM**
St Thomas Ch, M. Kleinschmidt, G. Hancock (r1990)
Concert (5/91) (KOCH) ① **37030-2**
R. Johnston, J. Crookes, S. Williams, D. Sladden, P.
Barley, King's College Ch, S. Cleobury *Concert*
(12/91) (ARGO) ① **433 215-2ZH**
The Sixteen, Margaret Phillips, H. Christophers
(r1992) *Concert* (6/93) (COLL) ① **Coll1343-2**
S. Channing, J. Bowman, R. Morton, M. Creed, J.
Lancelot, D. Corkhill, King's College Ch, P. Ledger
(r1974) *Little Sweep*.
(7/95) (EMI) ① **CDM5 65111-2**
Sacred and Profane—eight medieval lyrics: 5vv a cappella, Op. 91 (1974-75)
1. St Godric's Hymn; 2. Imon waxe wood; 3. Lenton
is come; 4. The long night; 5. Yific of luve can; 6.
Carol; 7. Ye that pasen by; 8. A death.
Cambridge Univ Chbr Ch, T. Brown *Concert*
(4/92) (GAMU) ① **GAMCD529**
The Sixteen, H. Christophers (r1992) *Concert*
(6/93) (COLL) ① **Coll1343-2**
Serenade—tenor, horn and strings, Op. 31 (1943) (Wds. various)
1. Prologue; 2. Pastoral: The day's grown old (wds C
Cotton); 3. Nocturne: The splendour falls on castle
walls (wds A Tennyson); 4. Elegy: O Rose, thou art
sick (wds W Blake); 5. Dirge: This ae nighte (wds
15th cent anon); 6. Hymn: Queen and huntress (wds
B Jonson); 7. Sonnet: O soft embalmer of the still
night (wds J Keats); 8. Epilogue.
R. Tear, D. Clevenger, Chicago SO, C.M. Giulini
Concert (11/88) (DG) ① **423 239-2GC**
R. Tear, A. Civil, Northern Sinfonia, N. Marriner
(r1970) *Concert* (12/88) (EMI) ① **CDM7 69522-2**
A. Rolfe Johnson, M. Thompson, SNO, B. Thomson
Concert (6/89) (CHAN) ① **CHAN8657**
J. Hadley, A. Halstead, English Stg Orch, W.
Boughton *Concert* (9/90) (NIMB) ① **NI5234**
M. Hill, J. Bryant, RPO, Vladimir Ashkenazy *Concert*
(1/91) (RPO) ① **CDRPO7015**
P. Schreier, P. Damm, Slovak CO, B. Warchal
Concert (3/92) (CAMP) ① **RRCD1313**
C. Prégardien, I. Lanzky-Otto, Tapiola Sinfonietta, O.
Vänskä *Concert* (8/92) (BIS) ① **BIS-CD540**
P. Pears, D. Brain, Boyd Neel Orch, B. Britten
(r1944) *Concert* (9/92) (DECC) ① **425 996-2DM**
P. Pears, B. Tuckwell, LSO, B. Britten (r1963)
Concert (9/93) (LOND) ① **436 395-2LM**
M. Hill, F. Lloyd, CLS, R. Hickox (r1988) *Noye's
Fludde*. (11/94) (VIRG) ① **CUV5 61122-2**
P. Langridge, F. Lloyd, ECO, S. Bedford (r1994)
Concert (12/94) (COLL) ② **Coll7037-2**
P. Pears, D. Brain, Boyd Neel String Orch, B. Britten
(r1944) *Concert* (10/95) (PEAR) ① **GEMMCD9177**
3. P. Pears, B. Tuckwell, LSO, B. Britten (r1963)
Concert (6/93) (DECC) ① **436 990-2DWO**
A Shepherd's Carol—chorus a cappella (1944) (Wds W H Auden)
The Sixteen, H. Christophers (r1992) *Concert*
(7/93) (COLL) ① **Coll1370-2**
7 Sonnets of Michelangelo—tenor and piano, Op. 22 (1940)
1. Si come nella penna (XVI); 2. A che più debb'io
mai l'intensa voglia (XXXI); 3. Veggio co' bei vastri
occhi (XXX); 4. Tu sa' ch'io so (LV); 5. Rendete agli
occhi miei (XXXVIII); 6. S'un castro amor (XXXII); 7.
Spiro ben nato (XXIV).
A. Rolfe Johnson, G. Johnson *Concert*
(5/90) (HYPE) ① **CDA66209**
P. Pears, B. Britten (r1954) *Concert*
(9/92) (DECC) ① **425 996-2DM**
P. Pears, B. Britten (r1942) *Concert*
(4/93) (EMI) ① **CDC7 54605-2**
P. Pears, B. Britten (r1942) *Concert*
(10/95) (PEAR) ① **GEMMCD9177**
A Spring Symphony—soloists, chorus and orchestra, Op. 44 (1949) (Wds. various)
1. Introduction: Shine out (wds 16th cent anon); 2.
The merry cuckoo (wds E Spencer); 3. Spring, the
sweet Spring (wds T Nashe); 4. When as the rye,
'The Driving Boy' (wds G Peele and J Clare); 5. Now
the bright morning star (wds J Milton); 6. Welcome
Maids of Honour (wds R Herrick); 7. Waters above
(wds H Vaughan); 8. Out of the lawn lie in bad (wds
W H Auden); 9. When will my May come (wds
Barnefield); 10. Fair and fair (wds. G Peele); 11.
Sound the flute (wds W Blake); 12. Finale—London,
to thee I do present (wds anon, J Beaumont, J
Fletcher).

S. Armstrong, J. Baker, R. Tear, St Clement Danes
Sch Ch, LSC, LSO, A. Previn (r1978) *Sea Interludes*,
Op. 33a.   (4/87) (EMI) ① **CDM7 64736-2**
E. Gale, A. Hodgson, M. Hill, Southend Boys' Ch,
LSC, LSO, R. Hickox *Concert*
                                      (4/91) (CHAN) ① **CHAN8855**
J. Vyvyan, N. Procter, P. Pears, Emanuel School
Boys' Ch, ROH Chor, ROHO, B. Britten (r1960)
Concert   (9/93) (LOND) ① **436 396-2LM**
J. Vincent, K. Ferrier, P. Pears, St Willibrord's Boys'
Ch, Netherlands Rad Chor, Concertgebouw, E. van
Beinum (pp1949) *Concert*
                                      (9/94) (DECC) ① **440 063-2DM**
Spring, the sweet spring J. Vyvyan, N. Procter, P.
Pears, ROH Chor, ROHO, B. Britten (r1960) *Concert*
                                      (6/93) (DECC) ① **436 990-2DWO**
**St Nicolas—voices, piano duet, orchestra
and organ, Op. 42 (1948)** (Wds. E Crozier)
1. Introduction: Our eyes are blinded by the holiness
you bear; 2. The Birth of Nicolas; 3. Nicolas devotes
himself to God; 4. He journeys to Palestine; 5.
Nicolas comes to Myra and is chosen Bishop; 6.
Nicolas from prison; 7. Nicolas and the pickled boys;
8. His Piety and Marvellous Works; 9. The Death of
Nicolas.
H. Briggs, A. Rolfe Johnson, Corydon Sngrs, St
George's Chapel Ch, Warwick Univ Chbr Ch,
Sevenoaks School Ch, Tonbridge Sch Ch, Southgate
Christ Church Ch, Penshurst Choral Soc, Occasional
Ch, C. Edwards, J. Alley, John Scott, ECO, M. Best
Hymn to St Cecilia.   (5/89) (HYPE) ① **CDA66333**
P. Pears, D. Hemmings, R. Downes, Beccles J.
Leman Sch Ch, Ipswich School Prep Dept Ch,
Aldeburgh Fest Ch, Aldeburgh Fest Orch, B. Britten
(r1954) *Rejoice in the Lamb.*
                                      (9/90) (DECC) ① **425 714-2LM**
King's College Ch, ASMF, D. Willcocks, R. Tear
Concert   (1/91) (CFP) ① **CD-CFP4570**
**Sweet was the Song the Virgin sang—4
female vv a cappella (1931 rev 1966)** (Wds.
W. Ballet)
The Sixteen, H. Christophers (r1992) *Concert*
                                      (7/93) (COLL) ① **Coll1370-2**
Sweeter than Roses—Purcell realisation
J. Bowman, B. Britten *Concert*
                                      (9/90) (LOND) ① **425 716-2LM**
The **Sycamore tree—4vv (1930 rev 1967)**
(Wds. trad)
The Sixteen, H. Christophers (r1992) *Concert*
                                      (6/93) (COLL) ① **Coll1343-2**
Te Deum in C—chorus and organ (1934)
Worcester Cath Ch, A. Partington, Don Hunt *Concert*
                                      (9/90) (CARL) ① **PCD937**
St Thomas Ch, M. Kleinschmidt, G. Hancock (r1990)
Concert   (5/91) (KOCH) ① **37030-2**
The Sixteen, Margaret Phillips, H. Christophers
(r1992) *Concert*   (6/93) (COLL) ① **Coll1343-2**
Norwich Cath Ch, M. Nicholas, N. Taylor (r1993)
Concert   (10/94) (PRIO) ① **PRCD470**
**Tit for Tat—song cycle: 1v and piano (1928-
30 rev 1970)** (Wds. W. de la Mare)
J. Shirley-Quirk, P.Ledger *Concert*
                                      (12/87) (MERI) ① **CDE84119**
The **Twelve Apostles—choir and piano
(1962)**
P. Langridge, Wenhaston Boys' Ch, C. Barnett, D. O.
Norris (r1995) *Concert*
                                      (11/95) (COLL) ① **[3] Coll7039-2**
**War Requiem—soloists, choirs, organ and
orchestras, Op. 66 (1961)** (Wds. Requiem
Mass and W. Owen)
1. REQUIEM AETERNAM: 1a. Requiem aeternam;
1b. What passing bells for these who die as cattle?;
2. DIES IRAE: 2a. Dies irae; 2b. Bugles sang,
saddening the evening air; 2c. Liber scriptus profetur;
2d. Out there, we've walked quite friendly up to
Death; 2e. Recordare Jesu pie; 2f. Be slowly lifted
up; 2g. Dies irae; 2h. Lacrimosa dies illa; 2i. Move
him into the sun; 3. OFFERTORIUM: 3a. Domine
Jesu Christe; 3b. So Abram rose, and clave the
wood; 4. SANCTUS: 4a. Sanctus, sanctus, sanctus;
4b. After the blast of lightning from the East; 5.
AGNUS DEI: 5a. One ever hangs where shelled
roads part; 6. LIBERA ME: 6a. Libera me, Domine;
6b. It seemed that out of battle I escaped; 6c. Let us
sleep now...In paradisium.
E. Söderström, R. Tear, T. Allen, Oxford Christ
Church Cath Ch, CBSO Chor, CBSO, S. Rattle
                                      (12/84) (EMI) ① **[2] CDS7 47034-8**
G. Vishnevskaya, P. Pears, D. Fischer-Dieskau, S.
Preston, Bach Ch, Highgate Sch Ch, London Sym
Chor, Melos Ens, LSO, B. Britten
                                      (4/85) (DECC) ① **[2] 414 383-2DH2**
L. Haywood, A. Rolfe Johnson, B. Luxon, Atlanta Boy
Ch, Atlanta Sym Chor, Atlanta SO, Robert Shaw
(r1988)   (11/89) (TELA) ① **[2] CD80157**

H. Harper, P. Langridge, J. Shirley-Quirk, St Paul's
Cath Boys' Ch, LSC, LSO, R. Hickox *Concert*
                                      (11/91) (CHAN) ① **[2] CHAN8983/4**
L. Orgonášová, A. Rolfe Johnson, B. Skovhus,
Monteverdi Ch, Tolz Boys' Ch, N German Rad Chor,
N German RSO, J. E. Gardiner (pp1992)
                                      (11/93) (DG) ① **[2] 437 801-2GH2**
Lacrimosa G. Vishnevskaya, Bach Ch, LSC,
Highgate Sch Ch, LSO, B. Britten (r1963) *Concert*
                                      (6/93) (DECC) ① **436 990-2DWO**
A **Wedding Anthem, 'Amo ergo
sum'—chorus and organ, Op. 46 (1949)**
(Wds. R.Duncan)
M. Seers, J. Coxwell, P. Salmon, Westminster Cath
Ch, Corydon Sngrs, M. Best *Concert*
                                      (5/86) (HYPE) ① **CDA66126**
The Sixteen, Margaret Phillips, H. Christophers
(r1992) *Concert*   (6/93) (COLL) ① **Coll1343-2**
**Welcome Ode—youth choir and orchestra,
Op. 95b (1976)** (wds. various)
City of London Girls, City of London Boys, LSO, R.
Hickox *Concert*   (4/91) (CHAN) ① **CHAN8855**
**When you're feeling like expressing your
affection—song: 1v and piano (1930s)**
(unpub: wds. ?W. H. Auden)
J. Gomez, Martin Jones (r1992) *Concert*
                                      (9/93) (UNIC) ① **DKPCD9138**
**Winter Words—song cycle: 1v and piano,
Op. 52 (1953)** (Wds. T. Hardy)
A. Rolfe Johnson, G. Johnson *Concert*
                                      (5/90) (HYPE) ① **CDA66209**
P. Pears, B. Britten (r1954) *Concert*
                                      (9/92) (DECC) ① **425 996-2DM**

┌──┐
│   **SECTION V: STAGE WORKS**   │
└──┘

**Albert Herring—chamber opera: 3 acts, Op.
39 (1947—Glyndebourne)** (Lib. E Crozier, after
G de Maupassant)
Cpte P. Pears, S. Fisher, J. Peters, J. Noble, O.
Brannigan, E. Evans, A. Cantelo, S. Rex, J. Ward, C.
Wilson, S. Amit, A. Pashley, S. Terry, ECO, B. Britten
                                      (6/89) (DECC) ① **[2] 421 849-2LH2**
**Billy Budd—opera: 4 acts, Op. 50
(1951—London)** (Lib. E M Forster & E Crozier,
after H Melville)
Interlude and Sea Shanties P. Glossop, D.
Bowman, G. Dempsey, Ambrosian Op Chor, LSO, B.
Britten (r1967) *Concert*
                                      (6/93) (DECC) ① **436 990-2DWO**
The **Burning Fiery Furnace—church
parable: 1 act, Op. 77 (1966—Orford)** (Lib. W
Plomer)
Cpte P. Pears, B. Drake, J. Shirley-Quirk, R. Tear, S.
Dean, P. Leeming, EOG Chor, EOG Orch, B. Britten
(r1967)   (10/90) (DECC) ① **414 663-2LM**
**Curlew River—church parable: 1 act, Op. 71
(1964—Orford)** (Wds. W. Plomer)
Cpte P. Pears, J. Shirley-Quirk, H. Blackburn, B.
Drake, B. Webb, EOG Chor, EOG Orch, B. Britten
                                      (9/89) (DECC) ① **421 858-2LM**
**Death in Venice—opera: 2 acts, Op. 88
(1973—Aldeburgh)** (Lib. M Piper, after T
Mann)
Cpte P. Pears, J. Shirley-Quirk, J. Shirley-Quirk, J.
Shirley-Quirk, J. Shirley-Quirk, J. Shirley-Quirk, J.
Bowen, P. Leeming, N. Williams, P. MacKay, I.
Saunders, EOG Chor, ECO, S. Bedford (r1974)
                                      (5/90) (LOND) ① **[2] 425 669-2LH2**
Death in Venice—concert suite from opera
(arr S. Bedford)
Cpte ECO, S. Bedford *Cello Symphony.*
                                      (1/86) (CHAN) ① **CHAN8363**
**Gloriana—opera: 3 acts, Op. 53
(1953—London)** (Lib. W. Plomer)
EXCERPTS: 13. Second Lute Song of the Earl of
Essex; 17a. On rivalries 'tis safe for kings; 17b. O
God, my King, sole ruler of the world.
Cpte J. Barstow, P. Langridge, D. Jones, J.
Summers, A. Opie, Y. Kenny, R. Van Allan, B. Terfel,
J. Watson, W. White, J. Shirley-Quirk, J.M. Ainsley,
P. Hoare, WNO Chor, WNO Orch, C. Mackerras
                                      (7/93) (ARGO) ① **[2] 440 213-2ZHO2**
13. P. Pears, J. Bream (r1963-4) *Concert*
                                      (8/93) (RCA) ① **[28] 09026 61583-2(5)**
13. P. Pears, J. Bream (r1963-4) *Concert*
                                      (9/94) (RCA) ① **09026 61601-2**
17a, 17b L. Price, Philh, H. Lewis (r1979) *Concert*
                                      (12/92) (RCA) ① **[4] 09026 61236-2**
Gloriana—concert suite from opera, Op. 53a
(arr cspr)
1. The Tournament; 2. The Lute Song; 3. The Courtly
Dances; 4. Gloriana moritura.
LSO, S. Bedford *Concert*
                                      (2/90) (COLL) ① **Coll1019-2**
RLPO, T. Yuasa (r1994) *Concert*
                                      (3/95) (EMIN) ① **CD-EMX2231**

BBC Northern SO, N. Del Mar (r1977) *Concert*
                                      (10/95) (BBCR) ① **BBCRD9129**
3. RPO, A. Previn *Concert*
                                      (10/87) (TELA) ① **CD80126**
**Instruments of the Orchestra—music for
educational film (1946)** (Text M. Slater)
LSO, M. Sargent (r1946) *Concert*
                                      (7/95) (BEUL) ① **1PD13**
**Johnson over Jordan—incidental music to J.
B. Priestley's play (1939)**
SUITE (arr P Hindmarsh: 1988): 1. Overture; 2.
Introduction; 3. Incinerators' Ballet; 4. The Spider and
the Fly; 5. Approach of Death; 6. End Music.
ECO, S. Bedford (arr Hindmarsh) *Concert*
                                      (4/92) (COLL) ① **Coll1192-2**
Bournemouth SO, R. Hickox (r1993) *Concert*
                                      (3/94) (CHAN) ① **CHAN9221**
The **Spider & the Fly** Ens (r1992; arr Runswick: instr
ens) *Concert*   (9/93) (UNIC) ① **DKPCD9138**
The **Little Sweep—chamber opera: 1 act, Op.
45 (1949—Aldeburgh)** (Lib. E Crozier: Act 3 of
'Let's Make An Opera')
Cpte D. Hemmings, J. Vyvyan, N. Evans, A. Cantelo,
T. Anthony, P. Pears, M. Ingram, Marilyn Baker, R.
Fairhurst, L. Vaughan, G. Soskin, Alleyn's Sch Ch,
EOG Orch, B. Britten (r1955) *Concert*
                                      (11/93) (LOND) ① **436 393-2LM**
Cpte R. Lloyd, R. Tear, S. Monck, H. Begg, C.
Benson, C. Fordham, C. Wearing, M. Wells, D. Glick,
C. Huehns, K. Willis, J. Constable, F. Grier, T. Fry,
Finchley Children's Music Group, King's College Ch,
Medici Qt, P. Ledger (r1977) *Rejoice in the Lamb.*
                                      (7/95) (EMI) ① **CDM5 65111-2**
**Matinées musicales—ballet suite, Op. 24
(1941)** (from misc pieces by Rossini, orch
Britten)
1. March; 2. Nocturne; 3. Waltz; 4. Pantomime; 5.
Moto perpetuo.
National PO, R. Bonynge *Concert*
                                      (12/90) (LOND) ① **425 659-2LM**
ECO, A. Gibson *Concert*
                                      (12/92) (CFP) ① **CD-CFP4598**
Helsingborg SO, O. Kamu (r1994) *Concert*
                                      (1/95) (ONDI) ① **ODE825-2**
A **Midsummer Night's Dream—opera: 3 acts,
Op. 64 (1960—Aldeburgh)** (Lib. cpsr & P.
Pears, after Shakespeare)
Cpte A. Deller, E. Harwood, P. Pears, T. Hemsley, J.
Veasey, H. Harper, J. Shirley-Quirk, H. Watts, O.
Brannigan, N. Lumsden, K. Macdonald, D. Kelly, R.
Tear, K. Raggett, R. Dakin, J. Prior, I. Wodehouse,
G. Clark, S. Terry, Downside School Boys' Ch,
Emanuel School Boys' Ch, LSO, B. Britten (r1966)
                                      (5/90) (LOND) ① **[2] 425 663-2LH2**
Cpte J. Bowman, L. Watson, J. Graham-Hall, H.
Herford, D. Jones, J. Gomez, N. Bailey, P. Walker, D.
Maxwell, R. Bryson, Adrian Thompson, A. Gallacher,
R. Horn, R. Suart, S. Hart, G. Pierre, A. Mead, N.
Watson, D. Fletcher, Trinity Boys' Ch, CLS, R. Hickox
(r1990)   (8/93) (VIRG) ① **[2] VCD7 59305-2**
**Noye's Fludde—Chester miracle play, Op. 59
(1958—Orford)** (Chester miracle play.)
Cpte O. Brannigan, S. Rex, D. Pinto, D. Angadi, S.
Alexander, T. Anthony, C. Clack, M-T. Pinto, E.
O'Donovan, Chor, E. Suffolk Children's Orch, EOG
Orch, N. del Mar (pp1961) *Golden Vanity.*
                                      (11/93) (LOND) ① **436 397-2LM**
Cpte D. Maxwell, J. Ormiston, A. Gallifant, T. Lamb,
N. Berry, R. Pasco, C. Johnson, P. Hewetson, J.
Brown, CLS, R. Hickox (r1989) *Serenade.*
                                      (11/94) (VIRG) ① **CUV5 61122-2**
**Noye, Noye, take thou thy company ... Still I heare
are lions** T. Anthony, O. Brannigan, D. Pinto, D.
Angadi, S. Alexander, C. Clack, M-T. Pinto, E.
O'Donovan, E Suffolk Children's Orch, ECO, N. del
Mar (pp1961) *Concert*
                                      (6/93) (DECC) ① **436 990-2DWO**
**On the Frontier—incidental music
(1938—Cambridge)** (Wds. W H Auden & C
Isherwood)
EXCERPTS: 1. The clock on the wall gives an
electric tick; 2. The papers say there'll be war before
long.
1. Ens (r1992; arr Runswick: instr ens) *Concert*
                                      (9/93) (UNIC) ① **DKPCD9138**
**Owen Wingrave—opera: 2 acts, Op. 85
(1971—BBC TV, London)** (Lib. M Piper, after
H. James)
Cpte B. Luxon, J. Shirley-Quirk, N. Douglas, S.
Fisher, H. Harper, J. Vyvyan, J. Baker, P. Pears,
Wandsworth Sch Boys' Ch, ECO, B. Britten (r1970)
Concert   (11/93) (LOND) ① **[2] 433 200-2LHO2**

Pas de Six (The Prince of the Pagodas)—concert suite from ballet, Op. 57a (1954-56)
1. Entrée; 2. Variation I—Pas de deux; 3. Variation II—Girl's solo; 4. Variation III—Boy's solo; 5. Pas de trois; 6. Coda.
RLPO, T. Yuasa (r1994) *Concert*
(3/95) (EMIN) ① **CD-EMX2231**

Paul Bunyan—operetta: prologue and 2 acts, Op. 17 (1941—New York) (Lib. W.H. Auden)
EXCERPTS: 1. Overture; 2. Lullaby of Dream Shadows; 3. Inkslinger's Love; 4. Song.
Cpte P. Wagner, J. Lawless, D. Dressen, E.C. Nelson, C. Ware, V. Sutton, M. Fristad, J. Bohn, P. Jorgenson, T. Dahl, T. Shaffer, L. Weller, J. McKee, J. Westbrock, M. Jette, S. Herber, J. Hardy, Plymouth Music Series Chor, Plymouth Music Series Orch, P. Brunelle (8/88) (VIRG) ① [2] **VCD7 59249-2**
Blues Ens (r1992; arr Runswick: instr ens) *Concert*
(9/93) (UNIC) ① **DKPCD9138**
Overture ECO, S. Bedford *Concert*
(2/91) (COLL) ① **Coll1102-2**

Peter Grimes—opera: prologue & 3 acts, Op. 33 (1945—London) (Lib. M Slater, after G Crabbe's 'The Borough')
EXCERPTS: 1. Prologue; ACT 1; 2. Interlude (Dawn); 3. Oh, hang at open doors the net; 4. Good morning, good morning!; 5. I have to go from pub to pub; 6. Let her among you without fault; 7. And do you prefer the storm; 8. Picture what that day was like; 9. They listen to money; 10. What harbour shelters peace; 11. Interlude (Storm); 12a. Past time to close!; 12b. A joke's a joke; 13. We live and let live; 14. Now the Great Bear and Pleiades; 15. Old Joe has gone fishing. ACT 2: 16. Interlude (Sunday morning); 17. Glitter of waves; 18. Grimes is at his exercise; 19. We planned that our lives should have a new start; 20. From the gutter; 21. Passacaglia; 22. Go there!; 23. In dreams I've built myself some kindlier home; 24. The whole affair. ACT 3: 25. Interlude (Moonlight); 26a. Assign your prettiness to me; 26b. Mr Keene! Can you spare a moment?; 27. Good night! It's time for bed; 28. Embroidery in childhood; 29. Mister Swallow; 30. Who holds himself apart; 31. Interlude; 32. Steady! There you are!; 33. Final Scene.
Cpte P. Pears, C. Watson, J. Pease, J. Watson, R. Nilsson, O. Brannigan, L. Elms, G. Evans, J. Lanigan, D. Kelly, M. Studholme, I. Kells, ROH Chor, ROHO, B. Britten (4/86) (DECC) ① **414 577-2DH3**
Cpte J. Vickers, H. Harper, J. Summers, E. Bainbridge, J. Dobson, F. Robinson, P. Payne, T. Allen, J. Lanigan, R. Van Allan, T. Cahill, A. Pashley, ROH Chor, ROHO, Colin Davis
(11/91) (PHIL) ① [2] **432 578-2PM2**
Cpte A. Rolfe Johnson, F. Lott, T. Allen, P. Payne, S. Kale, S. Dean, Sarah Walker, S. Keenlyside, N. Jenkins, D. Wilson-Johnson, M. Bovino, G. Webster, ROH Chor, ROHO, B. Haitink (r1992)
(7/93) (EMI) ① [2] **CDS7 54832-2**
2. ROHO, B. Britten (r1958) *Concert*
(6/93) (DECC) ① **436 990-2DWO**
2, 11, 16, 21, 25. ROHO, B. Britten *Concert*
(12/90) (LOND) ① **425 659-2LM**
6, 14, 16, 17, 23, 28, 31, 32. P. Pears, J. Cross, T. Culbert, BBC Th Chor, ROHO, R. Goodall (r1948) *Concert*
(2/94) (EMI) ① [2] **CMS7 64727-2**

The Prince of the Pagodas—ballet: 3 acts, Op. 57 (1957—London)
Prelude and Dances, Op. 57a (arr Del Mar); 1. Prelude; 2. March and Gavotte; 3. The Four Kings (a. North; b. East; c. West; d. South); 4. Belle Epine and Belle Rose; 5. Variations of the Prince and Belle Rose; 6. Finale.
Cpte London Sinfonietta, O. Knussen
(7/90) (VIRG) ① [2] **VCD7 59578-2**

The Prodigal Son—church parable: 1 act, Op. 81 (1968) (Lib. W. Plomer)
Cpte P. Pears, J. Shirley-Quirk, B. Drake, R. Tear, EOG Chor, EOG Orch, B. Britten (r1969)
(9/90) (DECC) ① **425 713-2LM**

The Rape of Lucretia—chamber opera: 2 acts, Op. 37 (1946—Glyndebourne) (Lib. R Duncan, after A Obey)
Cpte J. Baker, P. Pears, H. Harper, B. Luxon, J. Shirley-Quirk, B. Drake, J. Hall, E. Bainbridge, ECO, B. Britten (r1970) *Phaedra.*
(5/90) (LOND) ① [2] **425 666-2LH2**
Abridged N. Evans, P. Pears, J. Cross, F. Sharp, N. Lumsden, D. Dowling, M. Ritchie, F. Nielsen, EOGCO, R. Goodall (r1947) *Concert*
(2/94) (EMI) ① [2] **CMS7 64727-2**
Cpte J. Rigby, H. Mason, C. Pierard, D. Maxwell, A. Miles, A. Opie, P. Rozario, A. Gunson, CLS, R. Hickox (r1993) (3/94) (CHAN) ① [2] **CHAN9254/5**

Soirées musicales—ballet suite, Op. 9 (1936) (from misc pieces by Rossini, orch Britten)
1. March; 2. Canzonetta; 3. Tirolese; 4. Bolero; 5. Tarantella.
National PO, R. Bonynge *Concert*
(12/90) (LOND) ① **425 659-2LM**
ECO, A. Gibson *Concert*
(12/92) (CFP) ① **CD-CFP4598**
Helsingborg SO, O. Kamu (r1994) *Concert*
(1/95) (ONDI) ① **ODE825-2**

This way to the Tomb—incidental music for Ronald Duncan's masque (1945)
EXCERPTS: 1. Deus in adjutorium meum; 2. soprano solo; 3. St Anthony's Meditation; 4. Evening; 5. Morning; 6. Night.
Boogie-Woogie Ens (r1992; arr Runswick: instr ens) *Concert*
(2/88) (HYPE) ① **CDA66220**
1. Westminster Cath Ch, D. Hill *Concert*
(3/92) (CHAN) ① **CHAN8997**

The Turn of the Screw—chamber opera: prologue and 2 acts, Op. 54 (1954—Venice) (Lib. M. Piper, after H. James)
Cpte P. Pears, J. Vyvyan, D. Hemmings, O. Dyer, J. Cross, A. Mandikian, EOG Orch, B. Britten
(5/90) (LOND) ① [2] **425 672-2LH2**
Cpte P. Langridge, F. Lott, S. Pay, E. Hulse, P. Cannan, N. Secunde, Aldeburgh Fest Ens, S. Bedford (6/94) (COLL) ① [2] **Coll7030-2**

BRIXI, František Xaver (1732-1771) Bohemia

5 Concertos—organ and orchestra
1. F; 2. D; 3. G; 4. C; 5. C.
S-J. Bleicher, South-West German RSO, J. Berger *Concert* (9/92) (EBS) ① [2] **EBS6065**
2, 4, 5. J. Hora, Prague CO, F. Vajnar
(9/92) (SUPR) ① **10 3029-2**

Fugues—organ
1. G minor; 2. C; 3. A.
S-J. Bleicher *Concert*
(9/92) (EBS) ① [2] **EBS6065**
Preludes—organ
1. F; 2. A minor; 3. F.
S-J. Bleicher *Concert*
(9/92) (EBS) ① [2] **EBS6065**

BROADBENT, Derek (20th Cent) England

British Bandsman—march (1987)
Besses o' the Barn Band, Black Dyke Mills Band, Yorkshire Imperial Band, H. Mortimer (pp1987) *Concert* (11/93) (CHAN) ① **CHAN4513**

BROD, Henri (1801-1838) France

Nocturne in the form of variations on motifs from Rossini's opera 'Le siège de Corinthe'—oboe and harp, Op. 16
H. Schellenberger, M-A. Süss *Concert*
(12/91) (DENO) ① **CO-76611**

BRODSZKY, Nicholas (1905-1958) Germany/USA

Carnival—film score (1946) (orch S. Torch)
EXCERPTS: 1. Intermezzo.
1. Two Cities SO, C. Williams (r1945) *Concert*
(9/94) (EMI) ① **CDGO 2059**
The Way to the Stars—film score (1945) (collab with C. Williams)
Suite Two Cities SO, C. Williams (r1945) *Concert*
(9/94) (EMI) ① **CDGO 2059**

BROGI, Renato (1873-1924) Italy

Fior di Campo—song
C. Formichi, orch (r1932) *Concert*
(11/94) (PREI) ① **89055**

Visione veneziana—song
T. Ruffo, orch (r1929) *Concert*
(2/93) (PREI) ① [3] **89303(2)**
T. Ruffo, orch (r1912) *Concert*
(2/93) (PREI) ① [3] **89303(1)**

Volontario—song
C. Formichi, orch (r1932) *Concert*
(11/94) (PREI) ① **89055**

BROLLO, Bartolomeus (fl c1430-1450) Italy

Qui le sien—rondeau (3vv) (Originally Anonymous - atrrib Brollo by Reaney, 1969)
Gothic Voices, I. Barford, C. Page *Concert*
(12/86) (HYPE) ① **CDA66144**

BRONSART (VON SCHELLENDORF), Hans (1830-1913) Germany

Concerto for Piano and Orchestra in F sharp minor, Op. 10 (pub 1873)
M. Ponti, Westphalian SO, R. Kapp *Concert*
(5/93) (VOX) ① **115709-2**

BROSSARD, Sébastien de (1655-1730) France

Dialogus poenitentis animae cum Deo—oratorio: 2vv and 2 vns
N. Rime, J-P. Fouchécourt, I. Honeyman, B. Delétré, Parlement de Musique, M. Gester (r1992) *Elévations (1698).* (9/93) (0111) ① **OPS30-69**
Elévations et motets—1-3vv, 2vns/fls and continuo (pub 1698)
1. Salve Rex Christe; 2. O Domine quia refugium; 3. Qui non diligat te; 4. Festis laeta sonent; 5. Psallite superi; 6. Templa nunc fument.
N. Rime, J-P. Fouchécourt, I. Honeyman, B. Delétré, Parlement de Musique, M. Gester (r1992) *Dialogus.*
(9/93) (0111) ① **OPS30-69**

BROUWER, Leo (b 1939) Cuba

Concerto for Guitar and Orchestra No. 3, 'Concerto elegiaco'—1986
J. Bream, RCA Victor CO, L. Brouwer (r1987) *Concert* (8/93) (RCA) ① [28] **09026 61583-2(5)**
J. Bream, RCA Victor CO, L. Brouwer (r1987) *Concert* (9/94) (RCA) ① **09026 61605-2**

Canción de cuna, 'Berceuse'—guitar
M. Kayath *Concert* (9/87) (CARL) ① **PCD853**
J. Williams *Concert* (8/89) (SONY) ① **SK44898**
Danza caracteristica—guitar (1957)
J. Williams *Concert* (8/89) (SONY) ① **SK44898**
Decamerón negro—guitar (1981)
1. El arpa del guerrero; 2. Huida de los amantes; 3. Balada de la doncella.
S. Isbin *Concert* (10/90) (VIRG) ① **VC7 59591-2**
La Espiral Eterna—guitar (1971)
T. Korhonen *Concert* (8/90) (ONDI) ① **ODE730-2**
Ojos brujos—guitar
M. Kayath *Concert* (9/87) (CARL) ① **PCD853**
Paisaje Cubano con Campanas—guitar (1986)
T. Korhonen *Concert* (8/90) (ONDI) ① **ODE730-2**
Sonata for Guitar (1990)
J. Bream (r1992) *Concert*
(4/94) (EMI) ① **CDC7 54901-2**
Tarantos—guitar (1974)
T. Korhonen *Concert* (8/90) (ONDI) ① **ODE730-2**

BROWN, Christopher (Roland) (b 1943) England

Fanfare to welcome Sir Michael Tippett—string quartet
Lindsay Qt (r1992) *Concert*
(1/94) (ASV) ① **CDDCA879**

BROWN, William *(fl 1782–1787)* USA

SECTION III: INSTRUMENTAL

Rondos—piano (1787)
1. W. Naboré (r1992) *Concert*
(8/94) (DORO) ① **DRC3001**

BROWNE, John *(1426–1498)* England

SECTION IV: VOCAL AND CHORAL

Jhesu mercy—carol: 4vv
The Sixteen, H. Christophers *Concert*
(4/92) (COLL) ① **Coll1316-2**
Cambridge Taverner Ch, O. Rees (r1993) *Concert*
(12/93) (PAST) ① **3589**
O Maria Salvatoris mater—motet: 8vv
The Sixteen, H. Christophers *Concert*
(2/94) (COLL) ① **Coll1395-2**
Salve regina—motet: 5vv
The Sixteen, H. Christophers *Concert*
(11/89) (MERI) ① **CDE84175**
The Sixteen, H. Christophers (r1993) *Concert*
(2/94) (COLL) ① **Coll1395-2**
Stabat iuxta Christi crucem—antiphon: 6vv
The Sixteen, H. Christophers *Concert*
(4/92) (COLL) ① **Coll1314-2**
Stabat mater dolorosa—motet: 6vv
The Sixteen, H. Christophers *Concert*
(11/89) (MERI) ① **CDE84175**
The Sixteen, H. Christophers (r1993) *Concert*
(4/92) (COLL) ① **Coll1316-2**

BROWNE, William Charles Denis *(1888–1915) England*

SECTION IV: VOCAL AND CHORAL

Arabia—song (1914) (Wds. de la Mare)
M. Hill, C. Benson *Concert*
(6/88) (HYPE) ① **[2] CDA66261/2**
Diaphenia—song (1912) (Wds. H. Constable)
M. Hill, C. Benson *Concert*
(6/88) (HYPE) ① **[2] CDA66261/2**
Epitaph on Salathiel Pavy—song (1913)
(Wds. B Johnson)
M. Hill, C. Benson *Concert*
(6/88) (HYPE) ① **[2] CDA66261/2**
**To Gratiana dancing and singing—song
(1912-14)** (Wds. R. Lovelace)
M. Hill, C. Benson *Concert*
(6/88) (HYPE) ① **[2] CDA66261/2**

BRUBECK, Dave *(b 1920) USA*

SECTION II: CHAMBER

It's a Raggy Waltz—jazz chamber ensemble
Brodsky Qt (arr M. Thomas) *Concert*
(4/92) (TELD) ① **2292-46015-2**
**Strange Meadow Lark—jazz chamber
ensemble**
Brodsky Qt (arr M. Thomas) *Concert*
(4/92) (TELD) ① **2292-46015-2**

BRUCH, Max (Karl August) *(1838–1920) Germany*

SECTION I: ORCHESTRAL

**Adagio appassionato—violin and orchestra,
Op. 57 (1891)**
S. Accardo, Leipzig Gewandhaus, K. Masur *Concert*
(7/91) (PHIL) ① **[3] 432 282-2PSL3**
**Concerto for Clarinet, Viola and Orchestra in
E minor, Op. 88 (1911)**
T. King, N. Imai, LSO, A. Francis (r1980) *Concert*
(1/88) (HYPE) ① **CDA66022**
E. Brunner, T. Zimmermann, Bamberg SO, L.
Zagrosek *Concert* (4/90) (SCHW) ① **311065**
**Concerto for Two Pianos and Orchestra, Op.
88a**
K. Labèque, M. Labèque, Philh, S. Bychkov (r1990)
Mendelssohn: 2-Piano Concerto in E.
(7/93) (PHIL) ① **432 095-2PH**
**Concerto for Violin and Orchestra No. 1 in G
minor, Op. 26 (1868)**
1. Allegro moderato: 2. Adagio: 3. Allegro energico.
A-S. Mutter, BPO, H. von Karajan *Mendelssohn:
Violin Concerto, Op. 64.*
(3/83) (DG) ① **400 031-2GH**

I. Perlman, Concertgebouw, B. Haitink (r1983)
Mendelssohn: Violin Concerto, Op. 64.
(12/85) (EMI) ① **CDC7 47074-2**
C-L. Lin, Chicago SO, L. Slatkin *Scottish Fantasy.*
(7/87) (SONY) ① **SK42315**
S. Mintz, Chicago SO, C. Abbado *Concert*
(12/87) (DG) ① **419 629-2GH**
A-S. Mutter, BPO, H. von Karajan *Concert*
(3/88) (DG) ① **[4] 415 565-2GX4**
J. Bell, ASMF, N. Marriner *Mendelssohn: Violin
Concerto, Op.64.* (5/88) (DECC) ① **421 145-2DH**
S. Ishikawa, Brno St PO, J. Bělohlávek *Sibelius:
Violin Concerto.* (9/88) (SUPR) ① **2SUP0002**
Y. Menuhin, Philh, W. Susskind (r1956)
Mendelssohn: Violin Concerto, Op.64.
(1/89) (EMI) ① **CDM7 69003-2**
N. Kennedy, ECO, J. Tate *Concert*
(1/89) (EMI) ① **CDC7 49663-2**
L. Mordkovitch, LSO, N. Järvi *Brahms: Double
Concerto.* (6/89) (CHAN) ① **CHAN8667**
X. Wei, Philh, K. Bakels *Saint-Saëns: Violin Concerto
3.* (2/90) (ASV) ① **CDDCA680**
G. Shaham, Philh, G. Sinopoli *Mendelssohn: Violin
Concerto, op 64.* (3/90) (DG) ① **427 656-2GH**
F. Kreisler, RAHO, E. Goossens (r1924/5) *Concert*
(7/90) (BIDD) ① **[2] LAB009/10**
T. Little, RLPO, V. Handley (r1989) *Dvořák: Violin
Concerto.* (7/90) (CFP) ① **CD-CFP4566**
M. Szenthelyi, Budapest PO, J. Sándor
Mendelssohn: Violin Concerto, Op. 64.
(3/91) (LASE) ① **15 615**
U. Ughi, LSO, G. Prêtre *Brahms: Violin Concerto.*
(3/91) (RCA) ① **VD60479**
Y. Menuhin, LSO, L. Ronald (r1931) *Concert*
(4/91) (BIDD) ① **LAB031**
S. Accardo, Leipzig Gewandhaus, K. Masur *Concert*
(7/91) (PHIL) ① **[3] 432 282-2PSL3**
H. Udagawa, LSO, C. Mackerras (r1989) *Brahms:
Violin Concerto.* (9/91) (CHAN) ① **CHAN8974**
Y. Menuhin, Philh, W. Susskind *Concert*
(11/91) (EMI) ① **[3] CZS7 67310-2**
Y.U. Kim, Bamberg SO, O. Kamu *Concert*
(12/91) (DG) ① **[2] 413 844-2GW2**
K-W. Chung, LPO, K. Tennstedt (r1990) *Beethoven:
Violin Concerto.* (6/92) (EMI) ① **CDC7 54072-2**
G. Kulenkampff, BPO, J. Keilberth (r1941)
Beethoven: Violin Concerto.
(11/93) (TELD) ① **9031-76443-2**
T. Varga, Vienna Fest Orch, J-M. Auberson (r1965)
Concert (11/93) (CLAV) ① **[4] CD50-9300/4**
T. Varga, Vienna Fest Orch, J-M. Auberson (r1965)
Tchaikovsky: Violin Concerto.
(11/93) (CLAV) ① **CD50-9313**
I. Gitlis, Vienna Pro Musica orch, J. Horenstein
(r1950s) *Concert* (11/93) (VOX) ① **[2] CDX2 5505**
I. Perlman, Concertgebouw, B. Haitink (r1983)
Concert (4/94) (EMI) ① **[3] CMS7 64922-2**
M. Vengerov, Leipzig Gewandhaus, K. Masur (r1993)
Mendelssohn: Violin Concerto, Op.64.
(4/94) (TELD) ① **4509-90875-2**
G. Bustabo, Concertgebouw, W. Mengelberg
(pp1940) *Concert* (7/94) (MUSI) ① **[4] MACD-780**
J-P. Wallez, Luxembourg Rad & TV SO, D. Chorafas
(r1981) *Mendelssohn: Violin Concerto, Op. 64.*
(11/94) (FORL) ① **FF041**
J. Heifetz, New SO, M. Sargent (1962) *Concert*
(11/94) (RCA) ① **[65] 09026 61778-2(11-15)**
J. Heifetz, LSO, M. Sargent (r1951) *Concert*
(11/94) (RCA) ① **[65] 09026 61778-2(08)**
I. Perlman, Concertgebouw, B. Haitink (r1983)
Concert (6/95) (EMI) ① **[20] CZS4 83177-2(1)**
A. Campoli, SO, W. Goehr (r1937) *Concert*
(9/95) (PEAR) ① **GEMMCD9151**
N. Milstein, NYPSO, J. Barbirolli (r1942) *Concert*
(9/95) (BIDD) ① **LAB096**
J. Laredo (vn/dir), Scottish CO (r c1986)
Mendelssohn: Violin Concerto, Op.64.
(10/95) (CARL) ① **PCD2005**
B. Belkin, RPO, J. Hirokami (r1994) *Sibelius: Violin
Concerto.* (10/95) (DENO) ① **CO-78951**
L. Chen, Arnhem PO, R. Benzi (r1994) *Elgar: Violin
Concerto.* (11/95) (UPBE) ① **URCD115**
**Concerto for Violin and Orchestra No. 2 in D
minor, Op. 44 (1878)**
I. Perlman, Israel PO, Z. Mehta *Scottish Fantasy.*
(6/88) (EMI) ① **CDC7 49071-2**
S. Accardo, Leipzig Gewandhaus, K. Masur *Concert*
(7/91) (PHIL) ① **[3] 432 282-2PSL3**
J. Heifetz, RCA Victor SO, I. Solomon (r1954)
Concert (11/94) (RCA) ① **[65] 09026 61778-2(20)**
I. Perlman, Israel PO, Z. Mehta (r1986) *Concert*
(6/95) (EMI) ① **[20] CZS4 83177-2(1)**
N-Y. Hu, Seattle SO, G. Schwarz (r1993/4)
Goldmark: Violin Concerto 1.
(12/95) (DELO) ① **DE3156**

**Concerto for Violin and Orchestra No. 3 in D
minor, Op. 58 (1891)**
S. Accardo, Leipzig Gewandhaus, K. Masur *Concert*
(7/91) (PHIL) ① **[3] 432 282-2PSL3**
**In memoriam (adagio)—violin and orchestra,
Op. 65 (1893)**
S. Accardo, Leipzig Gewandhaus, K. Masur *Concert*
(7/91) (PHIL) ① **[3] 432 282-2PSL3**
**Kol Nidrei—adagio on Hebrew melodies, Op.
47 (1881)**
P. Casals, LSO, L. Ronald (r1936) *Concert*
(5/89) (PEAR) ① **GEMMCD9349**
M. Haimovitz, Chicago SO, James Levine *Concert*
(6/89) (DG) ① **427 323-2GH**
P. Fournier, Lamoureux Orch, J. Martinon *Concert*
(5/90) (DG) ① **429 155-2GR**
P. Casals, LSO, L. Ronald (r1936) *Concert*
(8/90) (EMI) ① **CDH7 63498-2**
Y. Bashmet, M. Muntain (arr va/pf) *Concert*
(2/90) (RCA) ① **RD60112**
J. Starker, LSO, A. Dorati *Concert*
(3/91) (MERC) ① **432 001-2MM**
P. Casals, N. Mednikoff (r1928) *Concert*
(10/91) (BIDD) ① **LAB017**
B. Huberman, S. Schultze (r1930) *Concert*
(10/91) (EPM) ① **150 032**
O. Harnoy, LPO, C. Mackerras *Concert*
(12/91) (RCA) ① **RD60757**
M. Maisky, Paris Orch, S. Bychkov *Concert*
(10/92) (DG) ① **435 781-2GH**
B. Huberman, P. Frenkel (r1922) *Concert*
(3/94) (BIDD) ① **[2] LAB077/8**
J. Du Pré, G. Moore (r1962) *Concert*
(8/94) (EMI) ① **[6] CZS5 68132-2**
B. Huberman, S. Schultze (r1930) *Concert*
(9/94) (BIDD) ① **[2] LAB081/2**
M. Kliegel, Ireland National SO, G. Markson (r1993)
Concert (11/94) (NAXO) ① **8 550519**
J. Du Pré, G. Moore (r1962) *Concert*
(11/95) (EMI) ① **CDC5 55529-2**
**Konzertstück in F sharp minor—violin and
orchestra, Op. 84 (1911)**
S. Accardo, Leipzig Gewandhaus, K. Masur *Concert*
(7/91) (PHIL) ① **[3] 432 282-2PSL3**
**Romance in A minor—violin and orchestra,
Op. 41 (1874)**
S. Accardo, Leipzig Gewandhaus, K. Masur *Concert*
(7/91) (PHIL) ① **[3] 432 282-2PSL3**
**Scottish Fantasy—violin and orchestra, Op.
46 (1880)**
C-L. Lin, Chicago SO, L. Slatkin *Violin Concerto 1.*
(7/87) (SONY) ① **SK42315**
I. Perlman, Israel PO, Z. Mehta *Violin Concerto 2.*
(6/88) (EMI) ① **CDC7 49071-2**
S. Accardo, Leipzig Gewandhaus, K. Masur *Concert*
(7/91) (PHIL) ① **[3] 432 282-2PSL3**
A.A. Meyers, RPO, J. López-Cobos *Lalo: Symphonie
espagnole.* (9/92) (RCA) ① **RD60942**
J. Heifetz, RCA Victor SO, W. Steinberg (r1947)
Concert (11/94) (RCA) ① **[65] 09026 61778-2(06)**
J. Heifetz, New SO, M. Sargent (r1961) *Concert*
(11/94) (RCA) ① **[65] 09026 61778-2(11-15)**
Midori, Israel PO, Z. Mehta (r1993) *Sibelius: Violin
Concerto.* (2/95) (SONY) ① **SK58967**
I. Perlman, Israel PO, Z. Mehta (r1986) *Concert*
(6/95) (EMI) ① **[20] CZS4 83177-2(1)**
A. Campoli, LPO, A. Boult (r1958) *Beethoven: Violin
Concerto.* (9/95) (BEUL) ① **2PD10**
**Serenade in A minor—violin and orchestra,
Op. 75 (1900)**
S. Accardo, Leipzig Gewandhaus, K. Masur *Concert*
(7/91) (PHIL) ① **[3] 432 282-2PSL3**
**Suite on Russian Theme—orchestra, Op. 79b
(pub 1905)**
Hungarian St Orch, M. Honeck (1987) *Symphony 3.*
(10/88) (MARC) ① **8 223104**
Swedish Dances, Op. 63 (pub 1892) (orch
cpsr from violin/piano work)
Leipzig Gewandhaus, K. Masur *Concert*
(3/89) (PHIL) ① **[2] 420 932-2PH2**
Symphony No. 1 in E flat, Op. 28 (pub 1870)
Leipzig Gewandhaus, K. Masur *Concert*
(3/89) (PHIL) ① **[2] 420 932-2PH2**
Cologne Gürzenich Orch, J. Conlon (1992) *Concert*
(4/94) (EMI) ① **[2] CDS5 55046-2**
**Symphony No. 2 in F minor, Op. 36 (pub
1870)**
Leipzig Gewandhaus, K. Masur *Concert*
(3/89) (PHIL) ① **[2] 420 932-2PH2**
Cologne Gürzenich Orch, J. Conlon (1993) *Concert*
(4/94) (EMI) ① **[2] CDS5 55046-2**
Symphony No. 3 in E, Op. 51 (pub 1887)
Hungarian St Orch, M. Honeck (1987) *Russian
Suite.* (10/88) (MARC) ① **8 223104**
Leipzig Gewandhaus, K. Masur *Concert*
(3/89) (PHIL) ① **[2] 420 932-2PH2**

Cologne Gürzenich Orch, J. Conlon (r1993) *Concert*
(4/94) (EMI) ① [2] **CDS5 55046-2**

SECTION II: CHAMBER

Piano Trio in C minor, Op. 5 (1858)
Göbel Trio, Berlin *Concert*
(7/88) (THOR) ① **CTH2002**

8 Pieces—clarinet, viola and piano, Op. 83 (pub 1910)
1. A minor; 2. B minor; 3. C sharp minor; 4. D minor;
5. F minor; 6. G minor; 7. B; 8. E flat minor.
J. Hilton, N. Imai, R. Vignoles *Concert*
(4/91) (CHAN) ① **CHAN8776**
H. de Graaf, I. Shimon, D. Wayenberg *Concert*
(4/93) (CHNN) ① **CG9107**
1, 2, 5, 6. S. Meyer, T. Zimmermann, H. Höll *Concert*
(8/89) (EMI) ① **CDC7 49736-2**

String Quartet No. 1 in C minor, Op. 9 (pub 1859)
Academica Qt *String Quartet 2.*
(5/94) (DYNA) ① **CDS29**

String Quartet No. 2 in E, Op. 10 (pub 1860)
Academica Qt *String Quartet 1.*
(5/94) (DYNA) ① **CDS29**

SECTION III: INSTRUMENTAL

Adagio on Celtic Themes—cello, Op. 56 (1891)
O. Harnoy *Concert*
(12/91) (RCA) ① **RD60757**

Ave Maria—cello, Op. 61 (1892)
O. Harnoy *Concert*
(12/91) (RCA) ① **RD60757**

Canzone—cello, Op. 55 (1891)
O. Harnoy *Concert*
(12/91) (RCA) ① **RD60757**

SECTION IV: VOCAL AND CHORAL

Jubilate—soprano, chorus and orchestra, Op. 3 (1858) (Wds. T. Moore trans Freiligrath)
C. Studer, Ambrosian Sngrs, LSO, I. Marin *Concert*
(11/92) (DG) ① **435 387-2GH**

BRUCKNER, (Joseph) Anton (1824–1896) Austria

SECTION I: ORCHESTRAL

Overture in G minor (1862-63)
Berlin RSO, R. Chailly *Symphony 0.*
(1/90) (DECC) ① **421 593-2DH**
South-West German RSO, L. Hager *Concert*
(10/91) (AMAT) ① **SRR8904/1**
Queen's Hall Orch, Henry Wood (r1937) *Concert*
(1/94) (BEUL) ① **1PD3**
Queen's Hall Orch, Henry Wood (r1937) *Concert*
(9/94) (DUTT) ① [2] **2CDAX2002**
Philh, L. von Matačić (r1956) *Symphony 4.*
(2/95) (TEST) ① **SBT1050**

Symphony No. 0 in D minor, 'Nullte' (1863-64)
Berlin RSO, R. Chailly *Overture in G minor.*
(1/90) (DECC) ① **421 593-2DH**
Chicago SO, D. Barenboim *Concert*
(1/93) (DG) ① **437 250-2GGA**
Chicago SO, D. Barenboim (r1979) *Concert*
(8/94) (DG) ① [10] **429 025-2GX10**
Concertgebouw, B. Haitink (r1966) *Concert*
(8/94) (PHIL) ① [9] **442 040-2PB9**

Symphony No. 1 in C minor (Linz version: 1865-66; Vienna version: 1890-91)
Bavarian St Orch, W. Sawallisch (Linz vers.)
(12/86) (ORFE) ① **C145851A**
BPO, E. Jochum (Linz vers.) *Concert*
(2/90) (DG) ① [9] **429 079-2GX9**
Cologne RSO, G. Wand (Vienna vers.) *Concert*
(2/90) (RCA) ① [10] **GD60075**
BPO, H. von Karajan (Linz vers) *Concert*
(3/91) (DG) ① [9] **429 648-2GSE9**
Staatskapelle Dresden, E. Jochum (r1978) *Concert*
(3/91) (EMI) ① [9] **CZS7 62935-2**
Chicago SO, D. Barenboim *Te Deum.*
(12/91) (DG) ① **435 068-2GGA**
Chicago SO, D. Barenboim (r1980) *Concert*
(8/94) (DG) ① [10] **429 025-2GX10**
Concertgebouw, B. Haitink (r1972) *Concert*
(8/94) (PHIL) ① [9] **442 040-2PB9**

Symphony No. 2 in C minor (1871-72 rev 1875-76)
BPO, H. von Karajan (r1981: orig vers)
(2/87) (DG) ① **415 988-2GH**
BRSO, E. Jochum (ed. Haas) *Concert*
(2/90) (DG) ① [9] **429 079-2GX9**
Cologne RSO, G. Wand (ed. Haas) *Concert*
(2/90) (RCA) ① [10] **GD60075**
BPO, H. von Karajan (ed Nowak) *Concert*
(3/91) (DG) ① [9] **429 648-2GSE9**
Staatskapelle Dresden, E. Jochum (r1980) *Concert*
(3/91) (EMI) ① [9] **CZS7 62935-2**

Chicago SO, G. Solti (r1991: ed Nowak)
(8/93) (DECC) ① **436 844-2DH**
Concertgebouw, R. Chailly (r1991)
(3/94) (DECC) ① **436 154-2DH**
Chicago SO, D. Barenboim (r1981) *Concert*
(8/94) (DG) ① [10] **429 025-2GX10**
Concertgebouw, B. Haitink (r1969) *Concert*
(8/94) (PHIL) ① [9] **442 040-2PB9**

Symphony No. 3 in D minor (1873-77 rev 1888-89)
BRSO, E. Jochum (ed. Nowak) *Concert*
(2/90) (DG) ① [9] **429 079-2GX9**
Cologne RSO, G. Wand (ed. Nowak) *Concert*
(2/90) (RCA) ① [10] **GD60075**
BPO, H. von Karajan (ed. Nowak) *Concert*
(3/91) (DG) ① [9] **429 648-2GSE9**
Staatskapelle Dresden, E. Jochum (r1977) *Concert*
(3/91) (EMI) ① [9] **CZS7 62935-2**
VPO, B. Haitink (1877 vers)
(3/91) (PHIL) ① **422 411-2PH**
Staatskapelle Dresden, G. Sinopoli
(10/91) (DG) ① **431 684-2GH**
VPO, K. Böhm (3/93) (DECC) ① **425 032-2DM**
N German RSO, G. Wand (pp1992)
(3/93) (RCA) ① **09026 61374-2**
Frankfurt RSO, E. Inbal (r1982)
(9/93) (TELD) ① **4509-91445-2**
Chicago SO, G. Solti (r1992: ed Nowak)
(4/94) (DECC) ① **440 316-2DH**
Chicago SO, D. Barenboim (r1980) *Concert*
(8/94) (DG) ① [10] **429 025-2GX10**
Concertgebouw, B. Haitink (r1963) *Concert*
(8/94) (PHIL) ① [9] **442 040-2PB9**
Cleveland Orch, G. Szell (r1966: ed Nowak)
Symphony 8. (1/95) (SONY) ① [2] **SB2K53519**
Concertgebouw, N. Harnoncourt (pp1994)
(9/94) (TELD) ① **4509-98405-2**

Symphony No. 4 in E flat, 'Romantic' (1874 rev 1878-80 & 1886)
BPO, H. von Karajan (r1970)
(9/87) (EMI) ① **CDM7 69006-2**
Philh, O. Klemperer (r1965)
(12/88) (EMI) ① **CDM7 69127-2**
Staatskapelle Dresden, G. Sinopoli
(12/88) (DG) ① **423 677-2GH**
BPO, E. Jochum (9/89) (DG) ① **427 200-2GR**
BPO, E. Jochum *Concert*
(2/90) (DG) ① [9] **429 079-2GX9**
Cologne RSO, G. Wand *Concert*
(2/90) (RCA) ① [10] **GD60075**
Royal Flanders PO, G. Newbold
(10/90) (NAXO) ① **8 550154**
Cincinnati SO, J. López-Cobos (r1990)
(12/90) (TELA) ① **CD80244**
BPO, H. von Karajan *Concert*
(3/91) (DG) ① [9] **429 648-2GSE9**
Staatskapelle Dresden, E. Jochum (r1975) *Concert*
(3/91) (EMI) ① [9] **CZS7 62935-2**
VPO, C. Abbado (4/91) (DG) ① **431 719-2GH**
N German RSO, G. Wand (pp1990)
(7/91) (RCA) ① **RD60784**
Frankfurt RSO, E. Inbal (orig vers)
(2/93) (TELD) ① **9031-77597-2**
VPO, K. Böhm (3/93) (DECC) ① **425 036-2DM**
Hamburg PO, E. Jochum (r1939) *Symphony 7.*
(7/93) (DANT) ① [2] **LYS007/8**
BPO, H. von Karajan (r1975)
(1/94) (DG) ① **439 522-2GGA**
BPO, D. Barenboim (r1992)
(3/94) (TELD) ① **9031-73272-2**
BPO, H. Knappertsbusch (pp1943-4)
(9/94) (MUSI) ① **MACD-249**
Chicago SO, D. Barenboim (r1972) *Concert*
(8/94) (DG) ① [10] **429 025-2GX10**
Concertgebouw, B. Haitink (r1965) *Concert*
(8/94) (PHIL) ① [9] **442 040-2PB9**
Philadelphia, W. Sawallisch (r1993)
(9/94) (EMI) ① **CDC5 55119-2**
NYPO, K. Masur (pp1993)
(12/94) (TELD) ① **4509-93332-2**
NBC SO, B. Walter (pp1940) *Concert*
(2/95) (PEAR) ① **GEMMCD9131**
Philh, L. von Matačić (r1954: ed Loewe/Schalk)
Overture in G minor. (2/95) (TEST) ① **SBT1050**
San Francisco SO, H. Blomstedt (r1993: ed Hass)
(7/95) (DECC) ① **443 327-2DH**

Symphony No. 5 in B flat (1875-76)
Czech PO, L. von Matačić
(6/86) (SUPR) ① **C37-7418**
BRSO, E. Jochum *Concert*
(2/90) (DG) ① [9] **429 079-2GX9**
Cologne RSO, G. Wand *Concert*
(2/90) (RCA) ① [10] **GD60075**
BPO, H. von Karajan *Concert*
(3/91) (DG) ① [9] **429 648-2GSE9**

N German RSO, G. Wand (pp1989)
(3/91) (RCA) ① **RD60361**
Staatskapelle Dresden, E. Jochum (r1980) *Concert*
(3/91) (EMI) ① [9] **CZS7 62935-2**
New Philh, O. Klemperer
(3/91) (EMI) ① **CDM7 63612-2**
Vienna SO, H. von Karajan (pp1954)
(3/91) (ORFE) ① **C231901A**
VPO, C. Schuricht (pp1963)
(2/92) (DG) ① **435 332-2GWP**
VPO, C. Schuricht (pp1963) *Concert*
(2/92) (DG) ① [2] **435 321-2GWP12**
BPO, D. Barenboim (orig vers: pp1991)
(3/93) (TELD) ① **9031-73271-2**
Concertgebouw, R. Chailly (r1991)
(11/93) (DECC) ① **433 819-2DH**
Chicago SO, D. Barenboim (r1977) *Concert*
(8/94) (DG) ① [10] **429 025-2GX10**
Concertgebouw, B. Haitink (r1971) *Concert*
(8/94) (PHIL) ① [9] **442 040-2PB9**
LPO, F. Welser-Möst (pp1993)
(4/95) (EMI) ① **CDC5 55125-2**

Symphony No. 6 in A (1879-81)
Bavarian St Orch, W. Sawallisch
(6/84) (ORFE) ① **C024821A**
BRSO, E. Jochum *Concert*
(2/90) (DG) ① [9] **429 079-2GX9**
Cologne RSO, G. Wand *Concert*
(2/90) (RCA) ① [10] **GD60075**
New Philh, O. Klemperer (r1964)
(3/90) (EMI) ① **CDM7 63351-2**
N. German RSO, G. Wand (pp1988)
(2/91) (RCA) ① **RD60061**
BPO, H. von Karajan *Concert*
(3/91) (DG) ① [9] **429 648-2GSE9**
Staatskapelle Dresden, E. Jochum (r1978) *Concert*
(3/91) (EMI) ① [9] **CZS7 62935-2**
San Francisco SO, H. Blomstedt (r1990) *Wagner:*
Siegfried Idyll. (5/93) (DECC) ① **436 129-2DH**
Chicago SO, D. Barenboim (r1978) *Concert*
(8/94) (DG) ① [10] **429 025-2GX10**
Concertgebouw, B. Haitink (r1970) *Concert*
(8/94) (PHIL) ① [9] **442 040-2PB9**
Cleveland Orch, C. von Dohnányi *Bach:*
Musikalisches Opfer, BWV1079.
(10/94) (DECC) ① **436 153-2DH**
BPO, D. Barenboim (r1994)
(9/95) (TELD) ① **4509-94556-2**
Movts 2-4. BPO, W. Furtwängler (pp1943) *Concert*
(3/95) (TAHR) ① [4] **FURT1004/7**

Symphony No. 7 in E (1881-83)
Czech PO, L. von Matačić
(6/86) (SUPR) ① **C37-7419**
VPO, K. Böhm (11/88) (DG) ① **419 858-2GGA**
BPO, O. Klemperer (r1960)
(11/88) (EMI) ① **CDM7 69126-2**
BPO, H. von Karajan (r1970/1)
(6/89) (EMI) ① **CDM7 69923-2**
BPO, E. Jochum *Concert*
(2/90) (DG) ① [9] **429 079-2GX9**
Cincinnati SO, J. López-Cobos (r1989)
(12/90) (TELA) ① **CD80188**
Cologne RSO, G. Wand *Concert*
(2/90) (RCA) ① [10] **GD60075**
VPO, H. von Karajan (r1989)
(5/90) (DG) ① **429 226-2GH**
BRSO, Colin Davis (pp1987)
(8/90) (ORFE) ① **C208891A**
BPO, H. von Karajan *Concert*
(3/91) (DG) ① [9] **429 648-2GSE9**
Staatskapelle Dresden, E. Jochum (r1976) *Concert*
(3/91) (EMI) ① [9] **CZS7 62935-2**
BPO, J. Horenstein (1928)
(7/91) (KOCH) ① **37022-2**
LPO, F. Welser-Möst (pp1987)
(5/92) (EMI) ① **CDC7 54434-2**
VPO, E. Jochum (r1939) *Symphony 4.*
(7/93) (DANT) ① [2] **LYS007/8**
BPO, D. Barenboim (r1992)
(9/93) (TELD) ① **9031-77118-2**
N German RSO, G. Wand (pp1992)
(9/93) (RCA) ① **09026 61398-2**
Staatskapelle Dresden, G. Sinopoli (r1991)
(9/93) (DG) ① **435 786-2GH**
Frankfurt RSO, E. Inbal (1985)
(2/94) (TELD) ① **4509-92686-2**
South-West German RSO, M. Gielen (1986)
(5/94) (INTE) ① **INT860 901**
VPO, C. Abbado (r1992)
(5/94) (DG) ① **437 518-2GH**
Chicago SO, D. Barenboim (r1979) *Concert*
(8/94) (DG) ① [10] **429 025-2GX10**
Concertgebouw, B. Haitink (r1966) *Concert*
(8/94) (PHIL) ① [9] **442 040-2PB9**
VPO, G. Szell (pp1968)
(1/95) (SONY) ① **SMK47646**

Pange lingua, 'Tantum ergo'—chorus (1868)
Corydon Sngrs, M. Best *Concert*
(7/86) (HYPE) ① **CDA66062**
Bavarian Rad Chor, E. Jochum *Concert*
(9/88) (DG) ① [4] **423 127-2GX4**
St Bride's Ch, Fleet St, R. Jones, M. Morley (r1994)
(7/95) (NAXO) ① **8 550956**
Psalm 112 in B flat—double chorus and orchestra (1863) (Wds. Bible)
Corydon Sngrs, ECO, M. Best *Concert*
(1/88) (HYPE) ① **CDA66245**
Psalm 114 in G—5vv chorus and 3 trombones (1852) (Wds. Bible)
R. Brenner, P. Brown, C. Sheen, Corydon Sngrs, M. Best (ed. Best) *Concert*
(1/88) (HYPE) ① **CDA66245**
Psalm 150 in C—soprano, chorus and orchestra (1892) (Wds. Bible)
M. Stader, Berlin Deutsche Op Chor, BPO, E. Jochum *Concert* (9/88) (DG) ① [4] **423 127-2GX4**
R. Welting, Chicago Sym Chor, Chicago SO, D. Barenboim (r1993) (DG) ① **437 250-2GGA**
J. Booth, J. Rigby, J.M. Ainsley, G. Howell, Corydon Sngrs, Corydon Orch, M. Best (r1992) *Mass in F minor.* (3/93) (HYPE) ① **CDA66599**
R. Welting, Chicago Sym Chor, Chicago SO, D. Barenboim (r1979) *Concert*
(8/94) (DG) ① [10] **429 025-2GX10**
Requiem in D minor—soloists, chorus and orchestra (1848-49)
J. Rodgers, C. Denley, M. Davies, M. George, T. Trotter, Corydon Sngrs, ECO, M. Best *Concert*
(1/88) (HYPE) ① **CDA66245**
Salvum fac populum—antiphon (1884)
St Bride's Ch, Fleet St, R. Jones, M. Morley (r1994) *Concert* (7/95) (NAXO) ① **8 550956**
Te Deum in C—soloists, chorus and orchestra (1881-84)
M. Stader, S. Wagner, E. Haefliger, P. Lagger, Berlin Deutsche Op Chor, BPO, E. Jochum *Concert* (9/88) (DG) ① [4] **423 127-2GX4**
A. Kupper, R. Siewert, L. Fehenberger, K. Borg, Bavarian Rad Chor, BRSO, E. Jochum (pp1954) *Verdi: Requiem.* (8/90) (ORFE) ① [2] **C195892H**
J. Norman, Y. Minton, D. Rendall, S. Ramey, Chicago Sym Chor, Chicago SO, D. Barenboim *Symphony 1.* (12/91) (DG) ① **435 068-2GGA**
J. Rodgers, C. Wyn-Rogers, K. Lewis, A. Miles, Corydon Sngrs, Corydon Orch, M. Best, J. O'Donnell (r1993) *Mass in D minor.*
(11/93) (HYPE) ① **CDA66650**
J. Norman, Y. Minton, D. Rendall, S. Ramey, Chicago Sym Chor, Chicago SO, D. Barenboim (r1981) *Concert*
(8/94) (DG) ① [10] **429 025-2GX10**
A. Giebel, M. Höffgen, J. Traxel, G. Frick, Berlin St Hedwig's Cath Ch, BPO, K. Forster (r1956) *Mozart: Requiem.* (10/94) (EMI) ① **CDH5 65202-2**
Tota pulchra es—tenor, chorus and organ (1878)
Corydon Sngrs, M. Best *Concert*
(7/86) (HYPE) ① **CDA66062**
Richard Holm, Bavarian Rad Chor, A. Nowakowski, E. Jochum *Concert*
(9/88) (DG) ① [4] **423 127-2GX4**
Bristol Cath Ch, M. Archer *Concert*
(4/90) (MERI) ① **CDE84188**
Lincoln Cath Ch, C. Walsh (r1993) *Concert*
(7/94) (PRIO) ① **PRCD454**
St Bride's Ch, Fleet St, R. Jones, M. Morley (r1994) *Concert* (7/95) (NAXO) ① **8 550956**
Vexilla regis—hymn (chorus) (1892)
Corydon Sngrs, M. Best, T. Trotter *Concert*
(7/86) (HYPE) ① **CDA66062**
Bavarian Rad Chor, E. Jochum *Concert*
(9/88) (DG) ① [4] **423 127-2GX4**
Chapelle Royale Ch, Ghent Collegium Vocale, P. Herreweghe *Concert*
(8/92) (HARM) ① **HMC90 1322**
St Bride's Ch, Fleet St, R. Jones, M. Morley (r1994) *Concert* (7/95) (NAXO) ① **8 550956**
Virga Jesse floruit—gradual in E minor (chorus) (1885)
Corydon Sngrs, M. Best *Concert*
(7/86) (HYPE) ① **CDA66062**
Bavarian Rad Chor, E. Jochum *Concert*
(9/88) (DG) ① [4] **423 127-2GX4**
Stuttgart Chbr Ch, F. Bernius *Concert*
(8/92) (SONY) ① **SK48037**
St Bride's Ch, Fleet St, R. Jones, M. Morley (r1994) *Concert* (7/95) (NAXO) ① **8 550956**

BRUDIEU, Joan (c1520–1591) France/Catalonia

SECTION IV: VOCAL AND CHORAL

Madrigal XIII, 'Fantasiant, amor a mi descobre' (Wds. A March)
Colombina Ens (r1994) *Concert*
(11/95) (ACCE) ① **ACC94103D**
Madrigal XV, 'Ma voluntat amb la rahó s'envelopa' (Wds. A March)
Colombina Ens (r1994) *Concert*
(11/95) (ACCE) ① **ACC94103D**
Madrigal XVI, 'Si l'amor en un ser dura' (Wds. A March)
Colombina Ens (r1994) *Concert*
(11/95) (ACCE) ① **ACC94103D**

BRUHNS, Nicolaus (1665–1697) Germany

SECTION III: INSTRUMENTAL

Nun komm der Heiden Heiland—chorale prelude
B. Coudurier *Concert* (10/89) (BNL) ① **BNL112754**
B. Foccroulle *Concert*
(1/90) (RICE) ① [3] **RIC048035/7**
P. Kee *Concert* (10/93) (CHAN) ① **CHAN0539**
Prelude and Fugue in E minor No. 1—organ
H. Balli *Concert* (9/85) (DENO) ① **C37-7068**
B. Coudurier *Concert* (10/89) (BNL) ① **BNL112754**
B. Foccroulle *Concert*
(1/90) (RICE) ① [3] **RIC048035/7**
P. Kee *Concert* (10/93) (CHAN) ① **CHAN0539**
Andrew Lucas (r1991) *Concert*
(2/94) (MIRA) ① **MRCD905**
Prelude and Fugue in E minor No. 2—organ
B. Coudurier *Concert* (10/89) (BNL) ① **BNL112754**
B. Foccroulle *Concert*
(1/90) (RICE) ① [3] **RIC048035/7**
P. Kee *Concert* (10/93) (CHAN) ① **CHAN0539**
Prelude and Fugue in G—organ
B. Coudurier *Concert* (10/89) (BNL) ① **BNL112754**
B. Foccroulle *Concert*
(1/90) (RICE) ① [3] **RIC048035/7**
P. Kee *Concert* (10/93) (CHAN) ① **CHAN0539**
Prelude and Fugue in G minor—organ
B. Coudurier *Concert* (10/89) (BNL) ① **BNL112754**
B. Foccroulle *Concert*
(1/90) (RICE) ① [3] **RIC048035/7**
P. Kee *Concert* (10/93) (CHAN) ① **CHAN0539**

SECTION IV: VOCAL AND CHORAL

Alleluja, Paratum cor meum—3vv, strings and continuo
G. de Mey, I. Honeyman, M. van Egmond, Ricercar Consort *Concert* (1/90) (RICE) ① [3] **RIC048035/7**
De profundis clamavi—1v, 2 violins and continuo (?1689-91)
M. van Egmond, Ricercar Consort *Concert*
(1/90) (RICE) ① [3] **RIC048035/7**
M. Schopper, Cologne Musica Antiqua, R. Goebel (1/93) (ARCH) ① **437 079-2AT**
Erstanden ist der heilige Christ—cantata (2vv, strings and continuo)
G. de Mey, I. Honeyman, Ricercar Consort *Concert*
(1/90) (RICE) ① [3] **RIC048035/7**
Hemmt eure Trähnenfluth—cantata (4vv, strings and continuo)
G. de Reyghere, J. Bowman, G. de Mey, M. van Egmond, Ricercar Consort *Concert*
(1/90) (RICE) ① [3] **RIC048035/7**
Der Herr hat seinen Stuhl im Himmel bereitet—cantata (1v, strings and continuo) (?1689-91)
M. van Egmond, Ricercar Consort *Concert*
(1/90) (RICE) ① [3] **RIC048035/7**
Ich liege und schlaffe—cantata (4vv, strings, bassoon and continuo)
G. de Reyghere, J. Bowman, G. de Mey, M. van Egmond, Ricercar Consort *Concert*
(1/90) (RICE) ① [3] **RIC048035/7**
Jauchzet dem Herren alle Welt—cantata (1v, strings, bassoon and continuo)
G. de Mey, Ricercar Consort *Concert*
(1/90) (RICE) ① [3] **RIC048035/7**
Mein Herz ist bereit—cantata (1v, strings and continuo) (?1689-91)
M. van Egmond, Ricercar Consort *Concert*
(1/90) (RICE) ① [3] **RIC048035/7**

Muss nicht der Mensch auff dieser Erden in steten Streite seyn—cantata (4vv, strings, wind and continuo)
G. de Reyghere, J. Bowman, G. de Mey, M. van Egmond, Ricercar Consort *Concert*
(1/90) (RICE) ① [3] **RIC048035/7**
O werter heil'ger Geist—4vv, strings, bassoon, brass and continuo
G. de Reyghere, J. Bowman, G. de Mey, M. van Egmond, Ricercar Consort *Concert*
(1/90) (RICE) ① [3] **RIC048035/7**
Woll dem, der den Herren fürchtet—cantata (3vv, strings, basson and continuo)
G. de Reyghere, J. Feldman, M. van Egmond, Ricercar Consort *Concert*
(1/90) (RICE) ① [3] **RIC048035/7**
Der Zeit meines Abscheids ist vorhanden—cantata (4vv, strings, bassoon and continuo)
G. de Reyghere, J. Bowman, G. de Mey, M. van Egmond, Ricercar Consort *Concert*
(1/90) (RICE) ① [3] **RIC048035/7**

BRÜLL, Ignaz (1846–1907) Austria

SECTION II: CHAMBER

3 Morceaux—violin and piano, Op. 90
1. Scène espagnole.
1. M. Elman, P. Kahn (r1906) *Concert*
(12/91) (APR) ① [2] **APR7015**

BRUMEL, Antoine (c1460–after 1520) France

SECTION IV: VOCAL AND CHORAL

Lamentation: Heth. Cogitavit Dominus—4vv
Tallis Scholars, P. Phillips *Concert*
(9/92) (GIME) ① **CDGIM026**
Chanticleer (r1987) *Concert*
(7/94) (CHTI) ① **CR-8805**
Lauda Sion Salvatorem—motet: 4vv
Chanticleer (r1987) *Concert*
(7/94) (CHTI) ① **CR-8805**
Laudate Dominum de caelis—motet: 4vv
Chanticleer (r1987) *Concert*
(7/94) (CHTI) ① **CR-8805**
Magnificat secundi toni—4vv
Tallis Scholars, P. Phillips *Concert*
(9/92) (GIME) ① **CDGIM026**
Mater Patris et filia—motet: 3vv (rhymed office antiphon)
Chanticleer (r1990) *Concert*
(7/94) (CHTI) ① **CR-8808**
Missa, 'Berzerette savoyenne'—4vv (parody of Josquin's chanson)
Chanticleer (r1987) *Concert*
(7/94) (CHTI) ① **CR-8805**
Missa, 'Et ecce terrae motus'—12vv ('Earthquake' Mass)
Huelgas Ens, P. van Nevel *Missa pro defunctis.*
(5/91) (SONY) ① **SK46348**
Tallis Scholars, P. Phillips *Concert*
(9/92) (GIME) ① **CDGIM026**
Missa pro defunctis—4vv
Dies irae Huelgas Ens, P. van Nevel *Missa Et ecce terrae motus.* (5/91) (SONY) ① **SK46348**
Nato canunt omnia—motet: 5vv (compilation of various Christmas texts)
New London Chmbr Ch, J. Wood *Concert*
(3/93) (AMON) ① **CD-SAR56**
Sicut lilium inter spinas—antiphon: 4vv
Chanticleer (r1987) *Concert*
(7/94) (CHTI) ① **CR-8805**

BRUNEAU, (Louis Charles Bonaventure) Alfred (1857–1934) France

SECTION V: STAGE WORKS

L' Attaque du Moulin—opera: 4 acts (1893—Paris) (Lib. L Gallet, after E Zola)
EXCERPTS: 1. Prélude et Lied; 2. La guerre, la forêt; 3. Les fiançailles au moulin; 4. Les Adieux à la forêt.
4. A. Affre, orch (r1905) *Concert*
(8/92) (IRCC) ① **IRCC-CD802**
4. G. Thill, orch, A. Bruneau (r1930) *Concert*
(8/95) (FORL) ① **UCD16727**

Virginie—opera: 3 acts (1931—Paris) (Lib. H.
Duvernois)
Quand j'avais la taille fine; Ah! mon Dieu, quelle
aventure! G. Féraldy, orch (r1931) *Concert*
(8/92) (IRCC) ① **IRCC-CD802**

BRUNETTI, Gaetano (1744–1798) Italy/Spain

SECTION I: ORCHESTRAL

Symphony No. 22 in G minor (1783)
Cologne Concerto (r1993) *Concert*
(7/95) (CAPR) ① **10 489**
Symphony No. 26 in B flat (1782)
Cologne Concerto (r1993) *Concert*
(7/95) (CAPR) ① **10 489**
Symphony No. 36 in A
Cologne Concerto (r1993) *Concert*
(7/95) (CAPR) ① **10 489**

BRUSSELMANS, Michel (1886–1960) Belgium

SECTION I: ORCHESTRAL

Flemish rhapsody—orchestra (1931)
Belgian Rad & TV Orch, A. Rahbari (r1992) *Concert*
(8/94) (DINT) ① **DICD920101**

BRUSTAD, Bjarne (1895–1978) Norway

SECTION II: CHAMBER

Capricci—violin and viola (1931)
T. Tønnesen, L.A. Tomter *Concert*
(10/91) (VICT) ① **VCD19006**

SECTION III: INSTRUMENTAL

Eventyr, 'Fairytale'—suite: violin (1932)
T. Tønnesen *Concert* (10/91) (VICT) ① **VCD19006**

BRYARS, Gavin (b 1943) England

SECTION I: ORCHESTRAL

The Green Ray—saxophone and orchestra
J. Harle, Bournemouth Sinfonietta, I. Bolton *Concert*
(7/92) (ARGO) ① **433 847-2ZH**

SECTION II: CHAMBER

After the Requiem—electric guitar, 2 violas
and cello (1990)
B. Frisell, A. Balanescu, K. Musker, A. Hinnigan
Concert (9/91) (ECM) ① **847 537-2**
Alaric I or II—saxophone quartet (1989)
E. Parker, S. Sulzmann, R. Warleigh, J. Argüelles
Concert (9/91) (ECM) ① **847 537-2**
Allegrasco—cl, vn, pf, elec gtr, db and perc
(1983)
R. Heaton, A. Balanescu, B. Frisell, G. Bryars, M.
Allen, S. Limbrick *Concert*
(9/91) (ECM) ① **847 537-2**
4 Elements—chamber ensemble (1990)
EXCERPTS: 1. Water; 2. Earth; 3. Air; 4. Fire.
Chbr Ens *Concert* (5/94) (ECM) ① **445 351-2**
Sub Rosa—chamber ensemble (1986)
G. Bryars Ens *Concert* (5/94) (ECM) ① **445 351-2**
The Tower of Löbenicht—vn, bass cl, ten
hn, db, pf, gtr and perc (1987)
A. Balanescu, R. Heaton, Dave Smith, G. Bryars,
Dave Smith, B. Frisell, M. Allen, S. Limbrick *Concert*
(9/91) (ECM) ① **847 537-2**

SECTION IV: VOCAL AND CHORAL

The Black River—1v and organ (1991) (Wds.
J. Verne '20000 Leagues under the Sea')
S. Leonard, C. Bowers-Broadbent (r1992) *Concert*
(5/93) (ECM) ① **437 956-2**
Glorious Hill—choir a cappella (1988) (Wds.
P. della Mirandola)
Hilliard Ens *Concert* (5/94) (ECM) ① **445 351-2**
Incipit Vita Nova—male alto and string trio
(1989) (Wds. Dante)
D. James, A. Dreyer, U. Lachner, R. Firth *Concert*
(5/94) (ECM) ① **445 351-2**
Jesus' Blood never failed me yet—tramp,
chorus, string quartet and orchestra (1971
rev 1993)
T. Waits, Hampton Qt, Chor, Orch, M. Riesman
(r1993) (10/93) (PNT) ① **438 823-2PTH**

The Sinking of the Titanic (1969, various
later revs)
Westhaston Boys' Ch, C. Thornton, Z. Bryars, O.
Bryars, L. Thornion, G. Bryars Ens (r1990)
(2/95) (PNT) ① **446 061-2PTH**

BUCALOSSI, Procida Ernest Luigi (1863–1933) England

SECTION I: ORCHESTRAL

The Grasshopper's Dance—characteristic
piece (1905)
A. Campoli, Orch, W. Goehr *Concert*
(10/91) (PEAR) ① **PASTCD9744**
Southern Fest Orch, R. White *Concert*
(5/93) (CHAN) ① **CHAN9110**

BUCK, Dudley (1839–1909) USA

SECTION III: INSTRUMENTAL

Variations on 'The Star-Spangled
Banner'—organ, Op. 23
C. Herrick *Concert* (10/92) (HYPE) ① **CDA66605**

SECTION IV: VOCAL AND CHORAL

Rock of Ages—choir anthem (1873) (Wds. A.
M. Toplady)
M. Stewart, Harmoneion Sngrs, N. Bruce, L.
Skrobacs (r1977) *Concert* (2/94) (NEW) ① **80220-2**

BULL, John (?1562/3–1628) England

SECTION II: CHAMBER

In Nomine a 5—consort (5 parts)
C. Wilson, Fretwork *Concert*
(3/88) (AMON) ① **CD-SAR29**

SECTION III: INSTRUMENTAL

Almans—keyboard
EXCERPTS: 1. Dallying; 2. Duke of Brunswick's; 3.
French; 4. Germain; 5. Ionic; 6. Untitled (6).
2, 4. P. Hantaï (r1994) *Concert*
(9/95) (ASTR) ① **E8543**
4. B. van Asperen *Concert*
(2/95) (TELD) ① **4509-95532-2**
Dr Bull's Goodnight—keyboard
P. Hantaï (r1994) *Concert* (9/95) (ASTR) ① **E8543**
Canon in subdiapente, two parts in one with
a running base ad placitum
B. van Asperen *Concert*
(2/95) (TELD) ① **4509-95532-2**
Dutch Dance—keyboard
B. van Asperen *Concert*
(2/95) (TELD) ① **4509-95532-2**
P. Hantaï (r1994) *Concert* (9/95) (ASTR) ① **E8543**
Een kindeken is ons geboren in G—organ
(melodic variations on a carol)
T. Koopman *Concert* (5/91) (CAPR) ① **10 254**
Fantasias—keyboard (nos from Musica
Britannica)
EXCERPTS: 10. Fantasia X; 12. Fantasia XII; 15.
Fantasia XV.
10, 12. B. van Asperen *Concert*
(2/95) (TELD) ① **4509-95532-2**
10, 15. P. Hantaï (r1994) *Concert*
(9/95) (ASTR) ① **E8543**
Galliards—keyboard
EXCERPTS: 1. Charlotte de la Haye's; 2. Italian; 3.
Lady Lucy's; 4. Lord Hunsdon's; 5. Quadran (3
versions); 6. Regina (3 versions); 7. The Prince's; 8.
Vaulting (Thumping; Dancing); 9. Untitled (4).
9. P. Hantaï (r1994; Musica Britannica no 78) *Concert*
(9/95) (ASTR) ① **E8543**
A Gigge, 'Dr Bull's my selfe'—keyboard
N. O'Neill *Concert* (11/92) (CNTO) ① **CRCD2366**
B. van Asperen *Concert*
(2/95) (TELD) ① **4509-95532-2**
In Nomine—keyboard
Z. Růžičková *Concert*
(10/89) (ORFE) ① **C139861A**
S. Yates (r1994) *Concert*
(12/95) (CHAN) ① **CHAN0574**
In Nomines—keyboard (nos from Musica
Britnnica)
EXCERPTS: 4. In Nomine IV; 5. In Nomine V; 9. In
Nomine IX; 12. In Nomine XII.
4, 5, 9, 12. P. Hantaï (r1994) *Concert*
(9/95) (ASTR) ① **E8543**
9, 12. B. van Asperen *Concert*
(2/95) (TELD) ① **4509-95532-2**
The King's Hunt—keyboard
Z. Růžičková *Concert*
(10/89) (ORFE) ① **C139861A**

N. O'Neill *Concert* (11/92) (CNTO) ① **CRCD2366**
B. van Asperen *Concert*
(2/95) (TELD) ① **4509-95532-2**
P. Hantaï (r1994) *Concert* (9/95) (ASTR) ① **E8543**
My Jewel—keyboard
Z. Růžičková *Concert*
(10/89) (ORFE) ① **C139861A**
Pavans—keyboard
EXCERPTS: 1. Pavan in the second tone; 2.
Quadran (3 versions); 3. Spanish; 4. Untitled.
1. P. Hantaï (r1994) *Concert*
(9/95) (ASTR) ① **E8543**
Pavans and galliards—keyboard
1. Chromatic (Queen Elizabeth's); 2. Fantastic; 3.
Lord Lumley's; 4. Melancholy; 5. St Thomas Wake; 6.
Symphony; 7. Trumpet; 8. (Four) untitled.
1, 2. B. van Asperen *Concert*
(2/95) (TELD) ① **4509-95532-2**
1-4. P. Hantaï (r1994) *Concert*
(9/95) (ASTR) ① **E8543**
Salvator Mundi Deus—keyboard
T. Dart (r1957) *Concert* (5/95) (JMS) ① **JMSCD1**
P. Hantaï (r1994) *Concert* (9/95) (ASTR) ① **E8543**
3 Toys—keyboard
1. Duchess of Brunswick (Most sweet and fair); 2.
English; 3. Irish.
2, 3. P. Hantaï (r1994) *Concert*
(9/95) (ASTR) ① **E8543**
Untitled Fantasia—keyboard
T. Dart (r1957) *Concert* (5/95) (JMS) ① **JMSCD1**
Walsingham—keyboard
Z. Růžičková *Concert*
(10/89) (ORFE) ① **C139861A**
Why ask you—keyboard (3 settings)
P. Hantaï (r1994) *Concert* (9/95) (ASTR) ① **E8543**

SECTION IV: VOCAL AND CHORAL

Starre Anthem, 'Almighty God, who by the
leading'—anthem: 5-6vv
Red Byrd, Rose Consort *Concert*
(12/91) (AMON) ① **CD-SAR46**

BULL, Ole (Bornemann) (1810–1880) Norway

SECTION IV: VOCAL AND CHORAL

Saeterjentens Søndag, 'The Herd-girls'
Sunday'—song
K. Flagstad, orch (r1929) *Concert*
(12/95) (SIMA) ① [3] **PSC1821(1)**
K. Flagstad, orch (r1923) *Concert*
(12/95) (SIMA) ① [3] **PSC1821(1)**

BULLA, Stephen (20th cent)

SECTION I: ORCHESTRAL

Chorale and Toccata—brass band
BNFL Band, R. Evans (r1993) *Concert*
(5/94) (POLY) ① **QPRL062D**

BULLER, John (b 1927) England

SECTION I: ORCHESTRAL

The Theatre of Memory (1981)
D. Butt, J. Marshall, A. Jennings, W. Houghton, R.
Pople, J. Marson, M. Hicks, BBC SO, M. Elder
Proença. (11/92) (UNIC) ① **UKCD2049**

SECTION IV: VOCAL AND CHORAL

Proença—mezzo-soprano, electric guitar
and orchestra (1977)
Sarah Walker, T. Walker, BBC SO, M. Elder *Theatre
of Memory*. (11/92) (UNIC) ① **UKCD2049**

BULLOCK, Sir Ernest (1890–1979) England

SECTION IV: VOCAL AND CHORAL

Give us the wings of faith—anthem
Guildford Cath Ch, A. Millington, P. Wright *Concert*
(5/89) (PRIO) ① **PRCD257**
Wellington College Chs, T. Byram-Wigfield, S.
Anderson *Concert* (10/92) (HERA) ① **HAVPCD153**
St Paul's Cath Ch, John Scott, Andrew Lucas (r1993)
Concert (6/94) (HYPE) ① **CDA66678**

BULMAN, Barick *(fl c1600)* England

SECTION III: INSTRUMENTAL

Pavan—lute
J. Bream (r1960) *Concert*
(8/93) (RCA) ① [28] **09026 61583-2(1)**
J. Bream (r1960) *Concert*
(8/93) (RCA) ① **09026 61584-2**

BÜLOW, Hans (Guido) von *(1830–1894) Germany*

SECTION III: INSTRUMENTAL

Arabesques sur un Thème de l'opéra 'Rigoletto' (Verdi)—piano, Op. 2 (pub 1852)
D. Blumenthal (r1991) *Concert*
(10/93) (MARC) ① **8 223421**
Iphigenie in Aulis (Gluck)—Tanzweisen: piano
D. Blumenthal (r1991) *Concert*
(10/93) (MARC) ① **8 223421**
Paraphrase of the Quintet from Act 3 of 'Die Meistersinger von Nürnberg (Wagner)—piano
D. Blumenthal (r1991) *Concert*
(10/93) (MARC) ① **8 223421**
Rêverie Fantastique—piano, Op. 7
D. Blumenthal (r1991) *Concert*
(10/93) (MARC) ① **8 223421**
Tarantella—piano, Op. 19 (pub 1860)
D. Blumenthal (r1991) *Concert*
(10/93) (MARC) ① **8 223421**
3 Valses caractéristiques—piano, Op. 18 (pub 1860)
1. L'ingénu.
1. D. Blumenthal (r1991) *Concert*
(10/93) (MARC) ① **8 223421**

BUONAMENTE, Giovanni Battista *(late 16th Cent–1642) Italy*

SECTION II: CHAMBER

Sonata a tre violini
J. Holloway, S. Ritchie, A. Manze, N. North, M. Springfels, J. Toll (r1993) *Concert*
(2/94) (HARM) ① **HMU90 7091**
Suite—3 instruments (pub 1626)
EXCERPTS: 1. Gagliarda seconda; 2. Corrente terza e quarta; 3. Brando terza; 4. Avanti il Brando; 5. Brando Quarto.
Palladian Ens (r1993) *Concert*
(1/95) (LINN) ① **CKD015**

BUONO, Gioan Pietro del *(17th cent) Italy*

SECTION III: INSTRUMENTAL

Sonata quinta—keyboard (1641)
R. Alessandrini (r1994) *Concert*
(4/95) (O111) ① **OPS30-118**

BURGMÜLLER, (August Joseph) Norbert *(1810–1836) Germany*

SECTION I: ORCHESTRAL

Symphony No. 2 in D, Op. 11
Berlin RSO, G. Schmöhe *Schumann: Symphony 4.*
(11/89) (SCHW) ① **311010**

SECTION II: CHAMBER

Duo in E flat—clarinet and piano, Op. 15
E. Johnson, G. Back *Concert*
(5/91) (ASV) ① **CDDCA732**

BURGON, Geoffrey *(b 1941)* England

SECTION IV: VOCAL AND CHORAL

Nunc dimittis—treble, trumpet and strings (1979) (orig used in 'Tinker, Tailor, Soldier, Spy')
L. Garrett, Philh, G. Burgon (r1992) *Concert*
(5/93) (SILV) ① **FILMCD117**
Trinity Coll Ch, Cambridge, R. Marlow (r1993) *Concert*
(2/94) (CONI) ① **CDCF219**

SECTION V: STAGE WORKS

Bleak House—television score (1985)
EXCERPTS: 1. Bleak House: main title; 2. The streets of London; 3. Dedlock versus Boythorn; 4. Lady Dedlock's quest; 5. Finale.
1-5. Philh, G. Burgon (r1992) *Concert*
(5/93) (SILV) ① **FILMCD117**
Brideshead Revisited—televison score (1981)
1. Brideshead Revisited—main title; 2. Julia; 3. Julia's Theme; 4. The Hunt; 5. Fading Light; 6. Farewell to Brideshead.
1-6. Philh, G. Burgon (r1992) *Concert*
(5/93) (SILV) ① **FILMCD117**
The Chronicles of Narnia—television score (1988-89)
1. Aslan's theme; 2. The great battle; 3. Mr Tumnus' tune; 4. The storm at sea; 5. Aslan sacrificed; 6. The journey to Harfang; 7. Farewell to Narnia.
1-7. Philh, G. Burgon (r1992) *Concert*
(5/93) (SILV) ① **FILMCD117**
Robin Hood—film score (1991)
EXCERPTS: 1. Attack on the Castle; 2. The Wedding.
OST, G. Burgon (r1991)
(11/91) (SILV) ① **FILMCD083**
1, 2. OST *Concert*
(5/93) (SILV) ① **SILVAD3001**
Testament of Youth—television score (1979)
1. Testament of Youth—main title; 2. Intimation of War; 3. Elegy; 4. Finale.
1-4. Philh, G. Burgon (r1992) *Concert*
(5/93) (SILV) ① **FILMCD117**
Tinker, Tailor, Soldier, Spy—television score (1979) (see also Nunc dimittis)
EXCERPTS: 1. Opening Music.
1. Philh, G. Burgon (r1992) *Concert*
(5/93) (SILV) ① **FILMCD117**

BURLEIGH, Cecil *(1885–1980) USA*

SECTION II: CHAMBER

Pictures—violin and piano, Op. 30
EXCERPTS: 4. Hills.
4. J. Heifetz, E. Bay (r1946) *Concert*
(11/94) (RCA) ① [65] **09026 61778-2(19)**
Plantation (Southland) Sketches—violin and piano, Op. 36
Margaret Harrison, R. Paul (r1929) *Concert*
(3/93) (SYMP) ① **SYMCD1140**
Small Concert Pieces—violin and piano, Op. 21
EXCERPTS: 4. Moto perpetuo.
4. J. Heifetz, E. Bay (r1946) *Concert*
(11/94) (RCA) ① [65] **09026 61778-2(19)**

BURLEIGH, Henry Thacker *(1866–1949) USA*

SECTION IV: VOCAL AND CHORAL

Jean—song (1903)
C. Muzio, orch (r1918) *Concert*
(1/95) (ROMO) ① [2] **81010-2**

BURNEY, Charles *(1726–1814)* England

SECTION III: INSTRUMENTAL

Cornet Piece in D—keyboard (pub 1751)
T. Koopman (trans org) *Concert*
(5/91) (CAPR) ① **10 254**
6 Cornet Pieces and a Fugue—keyboard (pub 1751)
1. E minor; 7. Fugue in F minor.
1. J. Bate *Concert*
(5/91) (UNIC) ① **DKPCD9101**
7. J. Bate *Concert*
(7/91) (UNIC) ① **DKPCD9105**

BURTON, Eldin *(1913–1985) USA*

SECTION II: CHAMBER

Sonatina—flute and piano (1946)
J. Stinton, S. Mitchell *Concert*
(12/91) (COLL) ① **Coll1103-2**
A. Still, S. De Witt Smith (r1992) *Concert*
(4/94) (KOCH) ① **37144-2**

BURTON, John *(1730–1785)* England

SECTION III: INSTRUMENTAL

Piano Sonata No. 1 in D (1776)
I. Hobson *Concert*
(3/89) (ARAB) ① **Z6594**

BUSBY, Thomas *(1755–1838)* England

SECTION III: INSTRUMENTAL

Sonata for Piano in E, Op. 1/4
I. Hobson *Concert*
(3/89) (ARAB) ① **Z6594**

BUSCH, Adolf (George Wilhelm) *(1891–1952) Germany*

SECTION IV: VOCAL AND CHORAL

Aus den Himmelsaugen—Lied: 1v, viola & piano (Wds. H Heine)
M. Shirai, T. Zimmermann, H. Höll (r1993-4) *Concert*
(9/95) (CAPR) ① **10 462**
Nun die Schatten dunkeln—Lied: 1v, viola & piano (Wds. E. Geibel)
M. Shirai, T. Zimmermann, H. Höll (r1993-4) *Concert*
(9/95) (CAPR) ① **10 462**
Wonne der Wehmut—Lied: 1v, viola & piano (Wds. J W Goethe)
M. Shirai, T. Zimmermann, H. Höll (r1993-4) *Concert*
(9/95) (CAPR) ① **10 462**

BUSCH, William *(1901–1945)* England

SECTION IV: VOCAL AND CHORAL

Rest—song
J. Baker, G. Moore (r1967) *Concert*
(11/94) (EMI) ① **CDM5 65009-2**

BUSH, Alan (Dudley) *(b 1900)* England

SECTION I: ORCHESTRAL

English Suite—string orchestra, Op. 28 (1946)
Northern CO, N. Ward (r1994) *Concert*
(4/95) (REDC) ① **RR008**

SECTION II: CHAMBER

Lyric Interlude—violin & piano, Op. 26 (1944)
C. Gould, S. Rahman (r1994) *Concert*
(4/95) (REDC) ① **RR008**

SECTION III: INSTRUMENTAL

Nocturne—piano, Op. 46 (1957)
P. Lane (r1994) *Concert*
(4/95) (REDC) ① **RR008**
Relinquishment—piano, Op. 11 (1928)
P. Lane (r1994) *Concert*
(4/95) (REDC) ① **RR008**

SECTION IV: VOCAL AND CHORAL

Voices of the Prophets—cantata: tenor & piano, Op. 41 (1953) (Wds. various)
1. From the 65th chapter of Isaiah (Wds. Bible); 2. From 'Against the scholastic philosophy' (Wds. Milton); 3. From the preface to 'Milton' (Wds. Blake); 4. From 'My song is for all men' (Wds. P. Blackmore).
P. Langridge, L. Friend (1986) *Concert*
(4/95) (REDC) ① **RR008**

BUSH, Geoffrey *(b 1920)* England

SECTION IV: VOCAL AND CHORAL

3 Elizabethan songs (1947)
1. Sigh no more, ladies (wds. Shakespeare).
1. F. Lott, G. Johnson *Concert*
(7/90) (CHAN) ① **CHAN8722**
1. A. Rolfe Johnson, G. Johnson *Concert*
(5/92) (HYPE) ① **CDA66480**
The End of love—song cycle: baritone and piano (Wds. K. Raine)
B. Luxon, G. Bush *Concert*
(9/92) (CHAN) ① **CHAN8830**
Farewell, Earth's Bliss—baritone and string orchestra (1950)
S. Varcoe, CLS, R. Hickox *Concert*
(1/91) (CHAN) ① **CHAN8864**

Greek Love Songs—baritone and piano
(1964) (Wds. Meleager, trans Fitts)
B. Luxon, G. Bush *Concert*
(9/92) (CHAN) ① **CHAN8830**
In Praise of Mary—soprano solo, chorus and
string orchestra (1955)
V. Hill, J. Watts, RCM Chbr Ch, RPO, D. Willcocks
Concert (12/86) (UNIC) ① **DKPCD9057**
A Little Love-music—soprano, tenor and
piano (1976)
T. Cahill, I. Partridge, G. Bush *Concert*
(9/92) (CHAN) ① **CHAN8830**
A Menagerie—unaccompanied choir (1969)
Westminster Sngrs, R. Hickox *Concert*
(1/91) (CHAN) ① **CHAN8864**
4 Songs from 'The Hesperides'—baritone
and string orchestra (1949) (Wds. R. Herrick)
S. Varcoe, CLS, R. Hickox *Concert*
(1/91) (CHAN) ① **CHAN8864**
3 Songs of Ben Jonson—tenor and piano
I. Partridge, G. Bush *Concert*
(9/92) (CHAN) ① **CHAN8830**
Songs of Wonder—tenor and piano (1959)
I. Partridge, G. Bush *Concert*
(9/92) (CHAN) ① **CHAN8830**
A Summer Serenade—tenor, chorus, piano
and orchestra (1948)
Adrian Thompson, E. Parkin, Westminster Sngrs,
CLS, R. Hickox *Concert*
(1/91) (CHAN) ① **CHAN8864**

BUSNOIS, Antoine (c1430–1492) France

SECTION IV: VOCAL AND CHORAL

A que ville—rondeau: 3vv
Pomerium Musices, A. Blachly (r1993) *Concert*
(4/95) (DORI) ① **DOR90184**
Anthoni usque limina—motet: 4vv
New London Chmbr Ch, J. Wood *Concert*
(3/93) (AMON) ① **CD-SAR56**
Pomerium Musices, A. Blachly (r1993) *Concert*
(4/95) (DORI) ① **DOR90184**
Bel acueil—rondeau: 3vv
Pomerium Musices, A. Blachly (r1993) *Concert*
(4/95) (DORI) ① **DOR90184**
Fortuna disperata—motet: 4vv
Daedalus Ens *Concert*
(12/92) (ACCE) ① **ACC9176D**
In hydraulis—secular motet: 4vv
New London Chmbr Ch, J. Wood *Concert*
(3/93) (AMON) ① **CD-SAR56**
Pomerium Musices, A. Blachly (r1993) *Concert*
(4/95) (DORI) ① **DOR90184**
Je ne puis vivre ainsi—bergerette: 3vv
Pomerium Musices, A. Blachly (r1993) *Concert*
(4/95) (DORI) ① **DOR90184**
Missa, 'O crux lignum'—4vv
Pomerium Musices, A. Blachly (r1993) *Concert*
(4/95) (DORI) ① **DOR90184**
Regina coeli (first setting)—Marian antiphon:
4vv
Pomerium Musices, A. Blachly (r1993) *Concert*
(4/95) (DORI) ① **DOR90184**
Victimae Paschali laudes—Easter sequence:
4vv
Clerk's Group, E. Wickham (r1994) *Concert*
(3/95) (ASV) ① **CDGAU139**
Pomerium Musices, A. Blachly (r1993) *Concert*
(4/95) (DORI) ① **DOR90184**

BUSONI, Ferruccio (Dante Michelangiolo Benvenuto) (1866–1924) Italy/Germany

SECTION I: ORCHESTRAL

Berceuse élégiaque—orchestra, Op. 42
(1909)
Versailles Camerata, A. du Closel (arr Schoenberg)
Concert (9/88) (AUVI) ① **AV6110**
Schoenberg Ens, R. De Leeuw (r1991: arr Stein)
Concert (5/94) (SCHW) ① **312632**
NBC SO, A. Toscanini (bp1948) *Concert*
(5/94) (ATS) ① [2] **ATCD100**
Concertino for Clarinet and Small Orchestra,
Op. 48 (1919)
P. Meyer, ECO, D. Zinman (r1992) *Concert*
(11/93) (DENO) ① **CO-75289**
U. Rodenhäuser, Berlin RSO, G. Albrecht (r1991-2)
Concert (6/94) (CAPR) ① **10 479**

Concerto for Piano and Orchestra, Op. 39
(1903-04) (male chorus in finale: wds. A.
Oehlensläger)
V. Banfield, Bavarian Rad Chor, BRSO, L. Herbig
(7/89) (CPO) ① **CPO999 017-2**
G. Ohlsson, Cleveland Orch Chor, Cleveland Orch,
C. von Dohnányi (r1989)
(4/90) (TELA) ① **CD80207**
V. Postnikova, French Rad Chor, FNO, G.
Rozhdestvensky *Fantasia contrappuntistica.*
(4/92) (ERAT) ① [2] **2292-45478-2**
D. Lively, Freiburg Voc Ens, South-West German
RSO, M. Gielen (4/92) (SCHW) ① **311160**
Concerto for Violin and Orchestra in D, Op.
35a (1896-97)
J. Szigeti, Little Orch Soc, T. Scherman (r1954) *Violin
Sonata 2.* (5/93) (SONY) ① **MPK52537**
Divertimento for Flute and Orchestra, Op. 52
(1920)
J-C. Gérard, Berlin RSO, G. Albrecht (r1991-2)
Concert (6/94) (CAPR) ① **10 479**
Konzertstück in D minor—piano and
orchestra, Op. 31a (1890)
J-F. Antonioli, Lausanne CO, L. Foster *Concert*
(8/89) (CLAV) ① **CD50-8806**
Nocturne symphonique—orchestra, Op. 43
(1912)
Berlin RSO, G. Albrecht (r1991-2) *Concert*
(6/94) (CAPR) ① **10 479**
Rondo arlecchinesco—suite from
'Arlecchino', Op. 46 (1915)
J. Peerce, NBC SO, A. Toscanini (bp1938) *Concert*
(5/94) (ATS) ① [2] **ATCD100**
Berlin RSO, G. Albrecht (r1991-2) *Concert*
(6/94) (CAPR) ① **10 479**
2 Studies from 'Doktor Faust', Op. 51 (1918-
19)
1. Sarabande; 2. Cortège.
Berlin RSO, G. Albrecht (r1991-2) *Concert*
(6/94) (CAPR) ① **10 479**
Tanzwalzer—orchestra, Op. 53 (1920)
Berlin RSO, G. Albrecht (r1991-2) *Concert*
(6/94) (CAPR) ① **10 479**

SECTION II: CHAMBER

Fantasia contrappuntistica (version IV)—two
pianos (1922)
E. Petri, C. Bussotti (pp1959) *Concert*
(3/94) (MUSI) ① [4] **MACD-772**
Sonata for Violin and Piano No. 1 in E minor,
Op. 29 (1890)
C. Edinger, G. Puchelt *Violin Sonata 2.*
(10/89) (THOR) ① **CTH2045**
Sonata for Violin and Piano No. 2 in E minor,
Op. 36a (1898)
C. Edinger, G. Puchelt *Violin Sonata 1.*
(10/89) (THOR) ① **CTH2045**
J. Szigeti, M. Horszowski (r1956) *Violin Concerto,
Op. 35a.* (5/93) (SONY) ① **MPK52537**

SECTION III: INSTRUMENTAL

3 Albumblätter—piano (1917-23)
1. Zürich; 2. Rome; 3. Berlin.
3. E. Petri (r1938) *Concert*
(8/95) (APR) ① [2] **APR7027**
An die Jugend—piano (pub 1909)
1. Preludio, fughetta ed esercizio; 2. Preludio, fuga e
fuga figurata (study after Bach); 3. Giga, bolero e
variazione (study after Mozart); 4. Introduzione e
capriccio (Paganinesco).
3. E. Petri (r1938) *Concert*
(8/95) (APR) ① [2] **APR7027**
7 Elegien—piano (1907)
1. Nach der Wendung; 2. All'Italia (in modo
napoletano); 3. Meine Seele bangt und hofft zu dir
(Chorale Prelude); 4. Turandots Frauengemach
(Intermezzo); 5. Die Nächtlichen (Waltz); 6.
Erscheinung (Notturno); 7. Berceuse élégiaque (arr
cpsr from orch version, Op. 42).
B. Wolosoff *Piano Sonata, Op.20a.*
(10/89) (MUSI) ① **MACD-293**
1, 7. W. Stephenson (r1993) *Concert*
(11/94) (OLYM) ① **OCD461**
2. E. Petri (r1938) *Concert*
(4/90) (PEAR) ① **GEMMCD9347**
2. E. Petri (pp1959) *Concert*
(3/94) (MUSI) ① [4] **MACD-772**
2. E. Petri (r1938) *Concert*
(8/95) (APR) ① [2] **APR7027**
Fantasia after J. S. Bach—piano (1909)
J. Ogdon *Concert* (7/89) (CNTI) ① **CCD1006**
E. Petri (r1937) *Concert*
(4/90) (PEAR) ① **GEMMCD9347**
E. Petri (r1937) *Concert*
(8/95) (APR) ① [2] **APR7027**

Fantasia contrappuntistica—piano (1910 (rev
1910 & 1912)
J. Ogdon *Concert* (7/89) (CNTI) ① **CCD1006**
P. Guillot (trans org Middelschulte) *Concert*
(9/89) (SCAL) ① **ARI139**
C. O'Riley *Concert* (10/89) (CENT) ① **CRC2036**
V. Postnikova *Piano Concerto, Op. 39.*
(4/92) (ERAT) ① [2] **2292-45478-2**
Indianisches Tagebuch I (4 studies on Red
Indian motives)—piano (1915)
1. Corn blossom; 2. Song of Victory; 3. Bluebird
song; Corngrinding song; 4. Passamaquoddy dance
song; The broad Mississippisave.
E. Petri (r1937) *Concert*
(4/90) (PEAR) ① **GEMMCD9347**
E. Petri (pp1959) *Concert*
(3/94) (MUSI) ① [4] **MACD-772**
E. Petri (r1937) *Concert*
(8/95) (APR) ① [2] **APR7027**
Macchietti medioeval—piano (pub 1883)
1. Dama; 2. Cavaliere; 3. Paggio; 4. Guerriero; 5.
Astrologo; 6. Trovatore.
W. Stephenson (r1993) *Concert*
(11/94) (OLYM) ① **OCD461**
Perpetuum mobile—piano (1921) (transcr
from Concertino, Op. 54 (pt 2)
E. Petri (pp1959) *Concert*
(3/94) (MUSI) ① [4] **MACD-772**
Sonata for Piano in F minor, Op. 20a (1883)
B. Wolosoff *Elegien.* (10/89) (MUSI) ① **MACD-293**
Sonatina No. 3, 'ad usum infantis'—piano
(1916)
E. Petri (r1938) *Concert*
(4/90) (PEAR) ① **GEMMCD9347**
E. Petri (r1938) *Concert*
(8/95) (APR) ① [2] **APR7027**
Sonatina No. 4 in die Nativitas Christi
MCMXVII—piano (1917)
1. Allegretto; 2. Calmo; 3. Sostenuto ala breve; 4.
Moderamente vivace—Sostenuto; 5. Un poco meno
del I. Tempo.
W. Stephenson (r1993) *Concert*
(11/94) (OLYM) ① **OCD461**
Sonatina No. 6 super Carmen
(Kammerfantasie)—piano (1920)
P. Fowke *Concert* (8/89) (CRD) ① **CRD3396**
E. Petri (r1936) *Concert*
(4/90) (PEAR) ① **GEMMCD9347**
W. Stephenson (r1993) *Concert*
(11/94) (OLYM) ① **OCD461**
M-A. Hamelin (pp1994) *Concert*
(3/95) (HYPE) ① **CDA66765**
E. Petri (r1935/6) *Concert*
(8/95) (APR) ① [2] **APR7027**
6 Stücke—piano, Op. 33b (pub 1896)
1. Schwermut; 2. Frohsinn; 3. Scherzino; 4. Fantasia
in modo antico; 5. Finnische Ballade; 6. Exeunt
omnes.
4. W. Stephenson (r1993) *Concert*
(11/94) (OLYM) ① **OCD461**
Suite Campestre—piano, Op. 3 (1877)
W. Stephenson (r1993) *Concert*
(11/94) (OLYM) ① **OCD461**
Toccata: Preludio, Fantasia, Ciacona—piano
(1921)
J. Ogdon *Concert* (7/89) (CNTI) ① **CCD1006**

SECTION IV: VOCAL AND CHORAL

2 Lieder—voice and piano, Op. 18 (pub
1885)
1. Wohlauf, der Kühle Winter ist vergangen (wds. N.
von Reuenthal); 2. Unter der Linden (wds. W. von der
Vogelweide).
2. E. Schwarzkopf, M. Raucheisen (bp1944) *Concert*
(5/93) (ACAN) ① **43 128**
Zigeunerlied—baritone and orchestra, Op.
55/2 (1923) (Wds. Goethe)
W. Sharp, S. Blier (r1991) *Concert*
(7/93) (KOCH) ① **37086-2**

SECTION V: STAGE WORKS

Arlecchino, oder Die Fenster—opera: 1 act,
Op. 50 (1917—Zurich) (Lib. cpsr)
Cpte E. T. Richter, S. Mentzer, T. Mohr, W. Holzmair,
P. Huttenlocher, S. Dahlberg, Lyon Op Chor, Lyon
Op Orch, K. Nagano (r1992) *Turandot.*
(11/93) (VIRG) ① [2] **VCD7 59313-2**
Cpte R. Wörle, M. Bellamy, R. Pape, S. Lorenz, P.
Lika, Berlin RSO, G. Albrecht (r1992)
(11/94) (CAPR) ① **60 038**

Doktor Faust—poem for music: 6 sections
(1925—Dresden) (Lib. cpsr: cpted/ed P.
Jarnach)
Cpte D. Fischer-Dieskau, W. Cochran, A. de Ridder,
H. Hillebrecht, K.C. Kohn, F. Grundheber, M.
Schmidt, M. Rintzler, H. Sotin, Bavarian Rad Chor,
BRSO, F. Leitner (r1969)
(8/89) (DG) ① [3] **427 413-2GC3**
Turandot—opera: 2 acts (1917—Zurich) (Lib.
cpsr, after Gozzi)
Cpte M. Gessendorf, S. Dahlberg, F-J. Selig, G.
Sima, F. Struckmann, A-M. Rodde, M. Schäfer, M.
Kraus, W. Holzmair, Lyon Op Chor, Lyon Op Orch, K.
Nagano (r1991) Arlecchino.
(11/93) (VIRG) ① [2] **VCD7 59313-2**
Cpte L. Plech, J. Protschka, R. Pape, G.
Schreckenbach, F. Molsberger, C. Lindsley, R.
Wörle, J.W. Prein, G. Schwarz, Berlin RIAS Chbr Ch,
Berlin RSO, G. Albrecht (r1992)
(11/93) (CAPR) ① **60 039**
Turandot—concert suite from incidental
music, Op. 41 (1904)
Milan La Scala PO, R. Muti (r1992) Concert
(4/94) (SONY) ① **SK53280**
Berlin RSO, G. Albrecht (r1991-2) Concert
(6/94) (CAPR) ① **10 479**

BÜSSER, (Paul-)Henri (1872–1973) France

SECTION II: CHAMBER

Prélude et Scherzo—flute and piano
S. Milan, I. Brown Concert
(11/88) (CHAN) ① **CHAN8609**
P. Lloyd, R. Holt Concert (9/92) (CARL) ① **PCD991**

BUSSOTTI, Sylvano (b 1931) Italy

SECTION V: STAGE WORKS

La Passion selon Sade—chamber mystery-
play: 1 act (1969—Stockholm) (Lib. L. Loulié)
'O'—Atti Vocali (transcr Berberian)
C. Berberian Concert
(7/89) (WERG) ① **WER60054-50**

BUSTIJN, Pieter (d 1729) The Netherlands

SECTION III: INSTRUMENTAL

9 Harpsichord Suites (c1712)
EXCERPTS: 5. Suite V in G minor.
5. B. van Asperen (r1990) Concert
(3/91) (SONY) ① **SK46349**

BUTLER, Martin (b 1960) England

SECTION II: CHAMBER

Going with the Grain—marimba, fls, cls, vn,
va & vc (1991)
Lontano, O. de la Martinez Concert
(5/94) (LORE) ① **LNT104**
Jazz Machines—fls, cls, va, vc, pf & vib
(1990)
Lontano, O. de la Martinez Concert
(5/94) (LORE) ① **LNT104**
Songs and Dances from a Haunted
Place—string quartet (1988)
Bingham Qt Concert (11/92) (NMC) ① **NMCD006**
Tin-Pan Ballet—fls, tbn, vc, pf, synth & perc
(1986)
Lontano, O. de la Martinez Concert
(5/94) (LORE) ① **LNT104**

SECTION III: INSTRUMENTAL

Bluegrass Variations—violin (1987)
R. Crouch Concert (5/94) (LORE) ① **LNT104**
On the Rocks—piano (1992)
M. Butler Concert (5/94) (LORE) ① **LNT104**

BUTTERFIELD, James Austin (1837–1891) USA

SECTION IV: VOCAL AND CHORAL

When you and I were young, Maggie—song
(1866) (Wds. G. W. Johnson)
W. Oakland, Orig Broadway Cast (r1908) Concert
(5/94) (PEAR) ① [3] **GEMMCDS9053/5**

BUTTERWORTH, Arthur (b 1926) England

SECTION I: ORCHESTRAL

Sinfonia for Brass, 'Maoriana', Op. 85
(1990)
BNFL Band, R. Evans (r1993) Concert
(5/94) (POLY) ① **QPRL062D**

BUTTERWORTH, George (Sainton Kaye) (1885–1916) England

SECTION I: ORCHESTRAL

The Banks of green willow—idyll: orchestra
(1913)
English Stg Orch, W. Boughton Concert
(10/88) (NIMB) ① **NI5068**
ASMF, N. Marriner Concert
(5/89) (DECC) ① **417 778-2DM**
ASMF, N. Marriner Concert
(8/89) (LOND) ① **421 391-2LM**
RLPO, G. Llewellyn (r1992) Concert
(6/93) (ARGO) ① **436 401-2ZH**
English Sinfonia, C. Groves (r1988) Concert
(10/95) (CARL) ① **PCD2017**
Two English Idylls—orchestra (1911)
English Stg Orch, W. Boughton Concert
(10/88) (NIMB) ① **NI5068**
ASMF, N. Marriner Concert
(8/89) (LOND) ① **421 391-2LM**
RLPO, G. Llewellyn (r1992) Concert
(6/93) (ARGO) ① **436 401-2ZH**
A Shropshire Lad—Rhapsody (1912)
English Stg Orch, W. Boughton Concert
(10/88) (NIMB) ① **NI5068**
ASMF, N. Marriner Concert
(8/89) (LOND) ① **421 391-2LM**
RLPO, G. Llewellyn (r1992) Concert
(6/93) (ARGO) ① **436 401-2ZH**

SECTION IV: VOCAL AND CHORAL

Bredon Hill and other songs from 'A
Shropshire Lad' (1912) (Wds. A. E Housman)
1. Bredon Hill; 2. O fair enough are sky and plain; 3.
When the lad for longing sighs; 4. On the idle hill of
summer; 5. With rue my heart is laden.
B. Luxon, D. Willison Concert
(11/90) (CHAN) ① **CHAN8831**
B. Terfel, M. Martineau (r1994) Concert
(8/95) (DG) ① **445 946-2GH**
1, 3, 4. A. Rolfe Johnson, G. Johnson (r c1994)
(8/95) (HYPE) ① [2] **CDA66471/2**
Love Blows as the Wind Blows—song
collection (Wds. W. E. Henley)
1. Love blows as the wind blows; 2. Life in her
creaking shoes; 3. Coming up from Richmond.
Cpte S. Varcoe, CLS, R. Hickox Concert
(1/90) (CHAN) ① **CHAN8743**
R. Tear, CBSO, V. Handley (r1979) Concert
(3/94) (EMI) ① **CDM7 64731-2**
Requiescat—song (1911) (Wds. O. Wilde)
S. Varcoe, C. Benson Concert
(6/88) (HYPE) ① [2] **CDA66261/2**
A Shropshire Lad—song cycle (1911) (Wds.
A. E. Housman)
1. Loveliest of trees; 2. When I was one-and-twenty;
3. Look not in my eyes; 4. Think no more, lad; 5. The
lads are their hundreds; 6. Is my team ploughing?.
Cpte S. Varcoe, CLS, R. Hickox (orch L.Baker)
Concert (1/90) (CHAN) ① **CHAN8743**
Cpte B. Luxon, D. Willison Concert
(11/90) (CHAN) ① **CHAN8831**
Cpte G. Trew, R. Vignoles, Coull Qt Concert
(11/90) (MERI) ① **CDE84185**
Cpte A. Rolfe Johnson, G. Johnson (r c1994)
Concert (8/95) (HYPE) ① [2] **CDA66471/2**
B. Terfel, M. Martineau (r1994) Concert
(8/95) (DG) ① **445 946-2GH**

BUTTOLPH, David (b 1902) USA

SECTION V: STAGE WORKS

Rope—film score (1948)
EXCERPTS: 1. Main Title (based on a theme by
Poulenc).
1. Prague City PO, P. Bateman (recons & orch Philip
Lane) Concert (9/95) (SILV) ① **FILMCD159**

BUXTEHUDE, Dietrich (c1637–1707) Germany/Denmark

BuxWV—Numbers used in G. Karstädt, Buxtehude-
Werke-Verzeichnis, 1974

SECTION II: CHAMBER

7 Sonatas—2 vns, va da gamba & hpd, Op. 1
(BuxWV252-8) (pub ?1694)
EXCERPTS: 1. F, BuxWV252; 2. G, BuxWV253; 3.
A minor, BuxWV254; 4. B flat, BuxWV255; 5. C,
BuxWV256; 6. D minor, BuxWV257; 7. E minor,
BuxWV258.
1, 2, 6. Capriccio Stravagante, S. Sempé (hpd/dir)
(r1992) Concert (2/95) (DHM) ① **05472-77300-2**
7 Sonatas—2 vns, va da gamba & hpd, Op. 2
(BuxWV259-65) (pub 1696)
EXCERPTS: 1. B flat, BuxWV259; 2. D, BuxWV260;
3. G minor, BuxWV261; 4. C minor, BuxWV262; 5. A,
BuxWV263; 6. E, BuxWV264; 7. F, BuxWV265.
3. Capriccio Stravagante, S. Sempé (hpd/dir) (r1992)
Concert (2/95) (DHM) ① **05472-77300-2**
Trio Sonata in B flat—violin, viola da gamba
and continuo, BuxWV273
Cologne Musica Antiqua, R. Goebel Concert
(6/89) (ARCH) ① **427 118-2AGA**
Cologne Musica Antiqua, R. Goebel (r1980) Concert
(1/93) (ARCH) ① **437 089-2AT**
Trio Sonata in C—2 violins, viola da gamba
and continuo, BuxWV266
Cologne Musica Antiqua, R. Goebel Concert
(6/89) (ARCH) ① **427 118-2AGA**
Capriccio Stravagante, S. Sempé (hpd/dir) (r1992)
Concert (2/95) (DHM) ① **05472-77300-2**
Trio Sonata in D—va da gamba, vc &
continuo, BuxWV267
Capriccio Stravagante, S. Sempé (hpd/dir) (r1992)
Concert (2/95) (DHM) ① **05472-77300-2**
Trio Sonata in G—2 violins, viola da gamba
and continuo, BuxWV271
Cologne Musica Antiqua, R. Goebel Concert
(6/89) (ARCH) ① **427 118-2AGA**

SECTION III: INSTRUMENTAL

Ach Gott und Herr—chorale variations,
BuxWV177
M. Chapuis Concert (12/89) (AUVI) ① **V4431**
Ach Herr mich armen Sünder—chorale
prelude, BuxWV178
M. Chapuis Concert (12/89) (AUVI) ① **V4431**
N. Danby Concert (2/91) (VIRG) ① **VC7 59212-2**
Auf meinen lieben Gott—organ, BuxWV179
P. Kee Concert (10/93) (CHAN) ① **CHAN0539**
Canzona in C—organ, BuxWV166
M. Chapuis Concert (12/89) (AUVI) ① **V4431**
Margaret Phillips (r1989) Concert
(4/91) (REGE) ① **REGCD105**
Canzona in G—organ, BuxWV170
M. Chapuis Concert (12/89) (AUVI) ① **V4432**
Canzonetta in A minor—organ, BuxWV225
N. Danby Concert (2/91) (VIRG) ① **VC7 59212-2**
Canzonetta in C—organ, BuxWV167
M. Chapuis Concert (12/89) (AUVI) ① **V4431**
Canzonetta in D minor—organ, BuxWV168
M. Chapuis Concert (12/89) (AUVI) ① **V4431**
Canzonetta in E minor—organ, BuxWV169
M. Chapuis Concert (12/89) (AUVI) ① **V4431**
Canzonetta in G—organ, BuxWV172
M. Chapuis Concert (12/89) (AUVI) ① **V4432**
Canzonetta in G minor—organ, BuxWV173
M. Chapuis Concert (12/89) (AUVI) ① **V4432**
La Capricciosa—keyboard: 32 variations,
BuxWV250
M. Meyerson Concert (2/87) (ASV) ① **CDGAU102**
Christ, unser Herr, zum Jordan
kam—chorale prelude, BuxWV180
R. Saorgin Concert (8/89) (HARM) ① **HMA190 942**
Ciacona in C minor—organ, BuxWV159
M. Chapuis Concert (12/89) (AUVI) ① **V4431**
H. Walcha Concert
(3/90) (ARCH) ① **427 133-2AGA**
Ciacona in E minor—organ, BuxWV160
H. Walcha Concert
(3/90) (ARCH) ① **427 133-2AGA**
John Scott (r1989) Concert
(4/91) (REGE) ① **REGCD105**
Capriccio Stravagante, S. Sempé (hpd/dir) (r1992; arr
2 hpds) Concert (2/95) (DHM) ① **05472-77300-2**
Durch Adams Fall ist ganz verderbt—chorale
prelude, BuxWV183
R. Saorgin Concert (8/89) (HARM) ① **HMA190 942**
Ein feste Burg ist unser Gott—chorale
prelude, BuxWV184
R. Saorgin Concert (8/89) (HARM) ① **HMA190 942**

SECTION IV: VOCAL AND CHORAL

Ich halte es dafür—cantata (2vv, strings and
continuo), BuxWV48
G. de Reyghere, M. van Egmond, Ricercar Consort
Concert   (1/90) (RICE) ① **RIC041016**
Ich suchte des Nachts—cantata (2vv,
strings, oboes and continuo), BuxWV50
G. de Mey, M. van Egmond, Ricercar Consort
Concert   (1/90) (RICE) ① **RIC041016**
Jesu, meine Freud und Lust—1v, strings and
continuo, BuxWV59
J. Bowman, King's Consort, R. King Concert
          (3/87) (MERI) ① **CDE84126**
Jesu, meines Lebens Leben—cantata: 3vv,
strings & continuo, BuxWV62
C. McFadden, F. Dukel, J. Kenny, M. van Altena, S.
MacLeod, Collegium Vocale, Royal Consort, Anima
Eterna, J. van Immerseel (r1994) Concert
          (7/95) (CHNN) ① **CCS7895**
Jubilate Domino, omnis terra—1v, viola da
gamba and continuo, BuxWV64 (?1667)
J. Bowman, King's Consort, R. King Concert
          (3/87) (MERI) ① **CDE84126**
R. Jacobs, Kuijken Consort Concert
          (4/88) (ACCE) ① **ACC77912D**
Laudate pueri Dominum—concerto (2vv, 5
violas da gamba, cello and continuo),
BuxWV69
G. de Reyghere, A. Mellon, Ricercar Consort Concert
          (1/90) (RICE) ① **RIC046023**
Das Neugeborne Kindelein—cantata (4vv,
strings and continuo), BuxWV13
G. de Reyghere, H. Ledroit, G. de Mey, M. van
Egmond, Ricercar Consort Concert
          (1/90) (RICE) ① **RIC041016**
Nichts soll uns scheiden—cantata (3vv,
strings and continuo), BuxWV77
G. de Reyghere, H. Ledroit, M. van Egmond,
Ricercar Consort Concert
          (1/90) (RICE) ① **RIC041016**
Nimm von uns, Herr—cantata: 4vv, strings,
bn & continuo, BuxWV98
C. McFadden, F. Dukel, J. Kenny, M. van Altena, S.
MacLeod, Collegium Vocale, Royal Consort, Anima
Eterna, J. van Immerseel (r1994) Concert
          (7/95) (CHNN) ① **CCS7895**
Singet dem Herrn ein neues Lied—cantata
(1v, strings and continuo), BuxWV98
G. de Reyghere, Ricercar Consort Concert
          (1/90) (RICE) ① **RIC046023**

BUZZI-PECCIA, Arturo (1854–1943) Italy

SECTION IV: VOCAL AND CHORAL

Baciami!—song
C. Muzio, orch (r1918) Concert
          (1/95) (ROMO) ① [2] **81010-2**
Colombetta—song
C. Muzio, orch, L. Molajoli (r1934) Concert
          (4/91) (NIMB) ① **NI7814**
Little birdies—song
A. Galli-Curci, orch, J. Pasternack (r1917) Concert
          (1/92) (RCA) ① [2] **81003-2**
Lolita, '(The) Spanish Serenade'—song
(Wds. cpsr)
E. Caruso, orch (r1908) Concert
          (3/91) (PEAR) ① [3] **EVC2**
E. Caruso, orch (r1908) Concert
          (7/91) (RCA) ① [12] **GD60495(2)**
T. Ruffo, orch (r1923) Concert
          (2/93) (PREI) ① [3] **89303(2)**
Mal d'amore—song
C. Muzio, Anon (pf) (r1923) Concert
          (5/90) (BOGR) ① [2] **BIM705-2**
C. Muzio, anon (r1923) Concert
          (1/94) (ROMO) ① [2] **81005-2**
Povero Pulcinella—song
B. Gigli, orch (r1924) Concert
          (5/90) (NIMB) ① **NI7807**
Torna amore—song
B. Gigli, orch, N. Shilkret (r1926) Concert
          (5/90) (PEAR) ① **GEMMCD9367**

BYRD, Charlie (b 1926) USA

SECTION III: INSTRUMENTAL

3 Blues—guitar
1. Spanish guitar blues; 2. Blues for Felix; 3. Swing
59.
J. Williams Concert   (8/89) (SONY) ① **SK44898**

BYRD, William (1543–1623) England

BK—Numbers used in A. Brown (ed), William Byrd:
Keyboard Music (rev 1976)

SECTION II: CHAMBER

Browning a 5—variations for consort: 5
parts, BE17/10
Rose Consort Concert
          (12/91) (AMON) ① **CD-SAR46**
F. Brüggen, Brüggen Consort (r1967/79) Concert
          (10/95) (TELD) ① **4509-97465-2**
Fretwork Concert   (11/89) (VIRG) ① **VC7 59539-2**
Christe qui lux es l a 4—consort hymn,
BE17/24
Rose Consort Concert
          (12/91) (AMON) ① **CD-SAR46**
Rose Consort Concert
          (12/91) (WOOD) ① **WOODM001-2**
Fantasia a 3, C No. 1—consort: 3 parts,
BE17/1
J. Bream, J. Bream Consort (r1987; ed Beck)
Concert   (8/93) (RCA) ① [28] **09026 61583-2(3)**
Rose Consort Concert
          (10/93) (WOOD) ① **WOODM002-2**
J. Bream Consort (r1987; ed Beck) Concert
          (9/94) (RCA) ① **09026 61590-2**
Fretwork Concert   (11/89) (VIRG) ① **VC7 59539-2**
Fantasia a 3, C No. 2—consort: 3 parts,
BE17/2
Rose Consort Concert
          (10/93) (WOOD) ① **WOODM002-2**
Fretwork Concert   (11/89) (VIRG) ① **VC7 59539-2**
Fantasia a 3, C No. 3—consort: 3 parts,
BE17/3
Fretwork Concert   (3/88) (AMON) ① **CD-SAR29**
Fretwork Concert   (11/89) (VIRG) ① **VC7 59539-2**
Fantasia a 4, G minor—consort: 4 parts,
BE17/4
Amsterdam Loeki Stardust Qt (r1991) Concert
          (2/94) (L'OI) ① **436 155-2OH**
SCB, A. Wenzinger (r1956) Concert
          (4/95) (VANG) ① **08.5068.71**
Rose Consort, Red Byrd, T. Roberts, T. Bonner
(r1992) Concert   (6/95) (NAXO) ① **8 550604**
Fretwork Concert   (11/89) (VIRG) ① **VC7 59539-2**
Fantasia a 5, C(Canon 2 in 1)—consort: 5
parts, BE17/8 (?1580s)
Rose Consort Concert
          (12/91) (AMON) ① **CD-SAR46**
Fantasia a 6, G minor No. 1—consort: 6
parts, BE17/12
Fretwork Concert   (11/89) (VIRG) ① **VC7 59539-2**
Fantasia a 6, G minor No. 2—consort: 6
parts, BE17/13
Rose Consort, Red Byrd, T. Roberts, T. Bonner
(r1992) Concert   (6/95) (NAXO) ① **8 550604**
Fretwork Concert   (11/89) (VIRG) ① **VC7 59539-2**
Fantasia a 6 No. 3—six viols
Rose Consort, Red Byrd, T. Roberts, T. Bonner
(r1992) Concert   (6/95) (NAXO) ① **8 550604**
In Nomine a 4 No. 2—consort: 4 parts,
BE17/17
C. Wilson, Fretwork Concert
          (3/88) (AMON) ① **CD-SAR29**
Rose Consort Concert
          (12/91) (WOOD) ① **WOODM001-2**
Rose Consort Concert
          (10/93) (WOOD) ① **WOODM002-2**
Rose Consort, Red Byrd, T. Roberts, T. Bonner
(r1992) Concert   (6/95) (NAXO) ① **8 550604**
5 In Nomines a 5—consort: 5 parts, BE17/18-
22
Fretwork Concert   (3/91) (VIRG) ① **VC7 59586-2**
In Nomine F. Brüggen, Brüggen Consort (r1967/79)
Concert   (10/95) (TELD) ① **4509-97465-2**
5. Rose Consort, Red Byrd, T. Roberts, T. Bonner
(r1992) Concert   (6/95) (NAXO) ① **8 550604**
Pavan and Galliard a 6, C—consort: 6 parts,
BE17/15
Rose Consort, Red Byrd, T. Roberts, T. Bonner
(r1992) Concert   (6/95) (NAXO) ① **8 550604**
C. Wilson, Fretwork Concert
          (11/89) (VIRG) ① **VC7 59539-2**
Sermone blando a 3—consort hymn,
BE17/23
Amsterdam Loeki Stardust Qt Concert
          (10/94) (L'OI) ① **440 207-2OM**

SECTION III: INSTRUMENTAL

All in a garden green—variations for
keyboard, BK56
U. Duetschler Concert
          (10/90) (CLAV) ① **CD50-9001**

S. Yates (r1994) Concert
          (8/95) (CHAN) ① **CHAN0578**
Barley Break—keyboard, BK92
S. Yates (r1994) Concert
          (12/95) (CHAN) ① **CHAN0574**
The Battle—keyboard, BK94 (?1570s/80s)
1. The soldiers' summons; 2. The march of footmen;
3. The march of horsemen; 4. The trumpets; 5. The
Irish march; 6. The bagpipe and the drone; 7. The
flute and the drum; 8. The march to the fight; 9. The
retreat.
1, 2, 6, 7. Z. Růžičková Concert
          (10/89) (ORFE) ① **C139861A**
The Bells—ground for keyboard, BK98 (after
1590s)
R. Aldwinckle Concert   (7/87) (CARL) ① **PCD850**
U. Duetschler Concert
          (10/90) (CLAV) ① **CD50-9001**
T. Pinnock Concert   (11/90) (CRD) ① **CRD3307**
S. Yates (r1994) Concert
          (12/95) (CHAN) ① **CHAN0574**
The Burying of the dead—keyboard, BK113
(spurious addition to The Battle, BK94)
Z. Růžičková Concert
          (10/89) (ORFE) ① **C139861A**
The Carman's Whistle—variations for
keyboard, BK36
U. Duetschler Concert
          (10/90) (CLAV) ① **CD50-9001**
E. Thornburgh Concert   (4/92) (KOCH) ① **37057-2**
Clarifica me, Pater—first setting—keyboard,
BK47
C. Bowers-Broadbent (r1992) Concert
          (9/94) (ECM) ① **439 172-2**
Clarifica me, Pater—second
setting—keyboard, BK48
C. Bowers-Broadbent (r1992) Concert
          (9/94) (ECM) ① **439 172-2**
Clarifica me, Pater—third setting—keyboard,
BK49
C. Bowers-Broadbent (r1992) Concert
          (9/94) (ECM) ① **439 172-2**
Fantasia, C No. 1—keyboard, Bk26
T. Dart (r1957) Concert   (5/95) (JMS) ① **JMSCD1**
Fantasia, C No. 2—keyboard, BK25
U. Duetschler Concert
          (10/90) (CLAV) ① **CD50-9001**
T. Dart (r1957) Concert   (5/95) (JMS) ① **JMSCD1**
Fantasia, G No. 1, 'A Voluntary for My Ladye
Nevell'—keyboard (BK61)
G. Gould (r1967) Concert
          (11/93) (SONY) ① **SMK52589**
Fantasia, G No. 2—keyboard, BK62
U. Duetschler Concert
          (10/90) (CLAV) ① **CD50-9001**
Fantasia in A minor—keyboard, BK13
S. Yates (r1994) Concert
          (12/95) (CHAN) ① **CHAN0574**
Fortune my foe—variations for keyboard,
BK6 (1570s)
E. Thornburgh Concert   (4/92) (KOCH) ① **37057-2**
Galliard—keyboard, BK55 (arr from work by
Harding)
S. Yates (r1994) Concert
          (12/95) (CHAN) ① **CHAN0574**
Galliard, G No. 10, 'for the
victory'—keyboard, BK95 (addition to The
Battle, BK94)
Z. Růžičková Concert
          (10/89) (ORFE) ① **C139861A**
Gloria tibi Trinitas—keyboard, BK50
C. Bowers-Broadbent (r1992) Concert
          (9/94) (ECM) ① **439 172-2**
Hugh Ashton's Ground—keyboard, BK20
E. Thornburgh Concert   (4/92) (KOCH) ① **37057-2**
G. Gould (r1971) Concert
          (11/93) (SONY) ① **SMK52589**
S. Yates (r1994) Concert
          (12/95) (CHAN) ① **CHAN0574**
John come kiss me now—variations:
keyboard, BK81
E. Thornburgh Concert   (4/92) (KOCH) ① **37057-2**
G. Cooper (r1992) Concert
          (5/94) (TELD) ① **4509-90841-2**
Rose Consort, Red Byrd, T. Roberts, T. Bonner
(r1992) Concert   (6/95) (NAXO) ① **8 550604**
Lavolta No. 1 in G, 'Lady Morley'—keyboard,
BK90
S. Yates (r1994) Concert
          (8/95) (CHAN) ① **CHAN0578**
The March before the Battle of The Earl of
Oxford's March—keyboard, BK93
Britannia Building Soc Band, H. Snell (arr Howarth)
Concert   (7/93) (DOYE) ① **DOYCD011**

O clap your hands—anthem: 5vv
R. Graham-Campbell, King's College Ch, S. Cleobury
Concert   (12/89) (EMI) ① CDC7 47771-2
O dear life—consort: 1v and 4 viols (pub
1589) (Wds. P. Sidney)
E. Van Evera, Musicians of Swanne Alley Concert
        (2/88) (HARM) ① HMC90 5192
O God, the proud are risen against me—full
anthem: 6vv
Tallis Scholars, P. Phillips Concert
        (6/87) (GIME) ① CDGIM011
Tallis Scholars, P. Phillips (r1987) Concert
        (7/93) (GIME) ① [2] CDGIM343/4
O Lord how vain are all our
delights—consort song: 1v and 4 viols (Wds.
P. Sidney)
E. Van Evera, Musicians of Swanne Alley Concert
        (2/88) (HARM) ① HMC90 5192
I Fagiolini, Fretwork (r1994) Concert
        (8/95) (CHAN) ① CHAN0578
O Lord make thy servant—full anthem: 6vv
Tallis Scholars, P. Phillips Concert
        (6/87) (GIME) ① CDGIM011
R. Graham-Campbell, King's College Ch, S. Cleobury
Concert   (12/89) (EMI) ① CDC7 47771-2
Tallis Scholars, P. Phillips Concert
        (1/91) (GIME) ① CDGIM999
Tallis Scholars, P. Phillips (r1987) Concert
        (7/93) (GIME) ① [2] CDGIM343/4
O Lord, turn thy wrath—anthem: 5vv (pub
1641) (contrafactum of 'Ne irascaris Domine'
(part 1)
Magdalen Oxford Coll Ch, J. Harper Concert
        (11/91) (ABBE) ① CDCA901
O quam gloriosum est regnum—motet: 5vv
(pub 1589)
New College Ch, E. Higginbottom Concert
        (12/91) (CRD) ① CRD3420
O that most rare breast—consort song: 5vv
(Wds. attrib E. Dyer)
A. Tysall, Rose Consort Concert
        (10/93) (WOOD) ① WOODM002-2
Plorans plorabit—motet: 5vv (pub 1605)
(non-liturgical: from Gradualia 1/i)
Cambridge Sngrs, J. Rutter Concert
        (4/90) (CLLE) ① COLCD110
Praise our Lord all ye Gentiles—anthem: 5vv
(pub 1611)
Cambridge Sngrs, J. Rutter Concert
        (4/90) (CLLE) ① COLCD110
Prevent us, O lord—full anthem: 5vv
Quink Concert   (9/90) (ETCE) ① KTC1031
Psalmes, Sonets and Songs—5vv (pub
1588)
EXCERPTS: 1. O God give ear and do apply; 5. O
Lord, how long wilt Thou forget; 8. Blessed is he that
fears the Lord; 11. I joy not in no earthly bliss; 12.
Though Amaryllis dance in green; 13. Who likes to
love; 14. My mind is like a kingdom is; 17. If women
could be fair; 19. What pleasure have great princes?;
22. In fields abroad; 23. Constant Penelope; 24. La
virginella; 25. Farewell, false love; 26. The match
that's made; 28. All as a sea; 29. Susanna fair; 30. If
that sinner's sigh; 31. Care for thy soul; 32. Lullaby,
my sweet little baby; 33. Why do I use my paper, ink
and pen?; 34. Come to me, grief, for ever; 35. O that
most rare breast.
13, 14. I Fagiolini, Fretwork (r1994) Concert
        (8/95) (CHAN) ① CHAN0578
29. Rose Consort, Red Byrd, T. Roberts, T. Bonner
(r1992) Concert   (6/95) (NAXO) ① 8 550604
31. A. Deller, SCB, A. Wenzinger (r1956: arr E
Fellowes) Concert   (4/95) (VANG) ① 08.5068.71
Rejoice unto the Lord—consort song: 1v and
4 viols
Rose Consort, Red Byrd, T. Roberts, T. Bonner
(r1992) Concert   (6/95) (NAXO) ① 8 550604
Retire, my soul—anthem: 5vv (pub 1611)
Quink Concert   (9/90) (ETCE) ① KTC1031
Short Service—6vv
1. Venite; 2. Te Deum; 3. Benedictus; 4. Kyrie; 5.
Creed; 6. Magnificat; 7. Nunc dimittis.
1. Worcester Cath Ch, Don Hunt Concert
        (9/90) (CARL) ① PCD937
Siderum rector—motet: 5vv (pub 1575)
Cambridge Sngrs, J. Rutter Concert
        (4/90) (CLLE) ① COLCD110
Sing joyfully unto God our strength—full
anthem: 6vv
Tallis Scholars, P. Phillips Concert
        (6/87) (GIME) ① CDGIM011
R. Graham-Campbell, King's College Ch, S. Cleobury
Concert   (12/89) (EMI) ① CDC7 47771-2
Cambridge Sngrs, J. Rutter Concert
        (4/90) (CLLE) ① COLCD110

Magdalen Oxford Coll Ch, J. Harper Concert
        (11/91) (ABBE) ① CDCA912
R. Johnston, Worcester Cath Ch, Don Hunt Concert
        (5/93) (ABBE) ① CDCA943
Tallis Scholars, P. Phillips (r1987) Concert
        (7/93) (GIME) ① [2] CDGIM343/4
Teach me, O Lord—anthem
Magdalen Oxford Coll Ch, J. Harper Concert
        (11/91) (ABBE) ① CDCA901
R. Johnston, Worcester Cath Ch, Don Hunt Concert
        (5/93) (ABBE) ① CDCA943
Lincoln Cath Ch, J. Vivian, C. Walsh (r1993) Concert
        (7/94) (PRIO) ① PRCD454
This day Christ was born—anthem: 6vv (pub
1611)
Oxford Christ Church Cath Ch, S. Preston Concert
        (2/90) (GAMU) ① GOUPCD153
Cambridge Taverner Ch, O. Rees (r1993) Concert
        (12/93) (PAST) ① 3589
This sweet and merry month of May—4vv
(pub 1611)
Cambridge Sngrs, J. Rutter Concert
        (11/87) (CLLE) ① COLCD105
Though Amaryllis dance in green—madrigal:
5vv (pub 1588)
Cambridge Sngrs, J. Rutter Concert
        (11/87) (CLLE) ① COLCD105
Amaryllis Consort, C. Brett Concert
        (3/88) (CARL) ① PCD873
A. Tysall, Rose Consort Concert
        (10/93) (WOOD) ① WOODM002-2
Tribulatio proxima est—motet: 5vv (pub
1591)
New College Ch, E. Higginbottom Concert
        (7/87) (CRD) ① CRD3439
Tristitia et anxietas—motet: 5vv (pub 1589)
New College Ch, E. Higginbottom Concert
        (12/91) (CRD) ① CRD3420
Triumph with pleasant melody—1-2vv:
consort song
Rose Consort, Red Byrd, T. Roberts, T. Bonner
(r1992) Concert   (6/95) (NAXO) ① 8 550604
I Fagiolini, Fretwork (r1994) Concert
        (8/95) (CHAN) ① CHAN0578
Truth at the First—song: 1v and viols
I Fagiolini, Fretwork (r1994) Concert
        (8/95) (CHAN) ① CHAN0578
Turn our captivity—anthem: 6vv (pub 1611)
Cambridge Sngrs, J. Rutter Concert
        (4/90) (CLLE) ① COLCD110
Vide Domine afflictionem—motet: 5vv (pub
1589)
New College Ch, E. Higginbottom Concert
        (12/91) (CRD) ① CRD3420
Vigilate—motet: 5vv (pub 1589)
Salisbury Cath Ch, R. Seal Concert
        (11/90) (MERI) ① CDE84180
New College Ch, E. Higginbottom Concert
        (12/91) (CRD) ① CRD3420
La Virginella—consort song: 5vv
A. Tysall, Rose Consort Concert
        (10/93) (WOOD) ① WOODM002-2
Ye sacred muse—consort song: 1v and 4
viols (1585) (Elegy for Thomas Tallis)
A. Tysall, Rose Consort Concert
        (10/93) (WOOD) ① WOODM002-2
A. Deller, SCB, A. Wenzinger (r1956: arr E Fellowes)
Concert   (4/95) (VANG) ① 08.5068.71
M. Chance, Fretwork Concert
        (3/91) (VIRG) ① VC7 59586-2

BYRNE, David (b 1952) Scotland

SECTION II: CHAMBER

High Life for nine instruments
Balanescu Qt (r1992) Concert
        (3/93) (ARGO) ① 436 565-2ZH

SECTION V: STAGE WORKS

The Last Emperor—film score (1987) (collab
with Ryiuchi Sakamoto)
EXCERPTS: 1. Main Title.
1. OST (r1987) Concert   (9/95) (VIR2) ① CDV2774

BYRON, John (b 1958) England

SECTION IV: VOCAL AND CHORAL

Verba—soprano and chorus (1990) (Wds.
Bible)
Oxford Schola Cantorum, J. Summerly Concert
        (4/92) (PREL) ① PROUCD129

CABALLERO, Manuel Fernández
(1835–1906) Spain

SECTION V: STAGE WORKS

El Dúo de la Africana—zarzuela: 1 act
(1893—Madrid) (Lib. Echegaray)
EXCERPTS: 1. Dúo-Jota.
1. J. Carreras, I. Rey, ECO, E. Ricci (r1994) Concert
        (2/95) (ERAT) ① 4509-95789-2

CABANILLES, Juan Bautista José
(1644–1712) Spain

SECTION III: INSTRUMENTAL

Corrente Italiana—harpsichord
Hespèrion XX, J. Savall Concert
        (2/92) (ASTR) ① E8729
Paseos—organ
J. Butt Concert   (7/92) (HARM) ① HMU90 7047
Passacalles—keyboard
EXCERPTS: 1. del primero tono; 5. Passacalles V.
1. J. Butt Concert   (7/92) (HARM) ① HMU90 7047
1. S. Yates (r1993) Concert
        (11/94) (CHAN) ① CHAN0560
5. Hespèrion XX, J. Savall Concert
        (2/92) (ASTR) ① E8729
Tientos—keyboard (some 200 works in total)
EXCERPTS: 1. Tientos de primer tono; 2. Tientos de
falsas; 3. Tientos de cuarto tono; 4. Tientos de quinto
tono; 4a. Tiento XVII de Pange Lingua, quinto tono
punto alto; 5. Tienos de segundo tono; 6. Tientos de
batallas; 7. Tiento lleno; 8. Untitled Tientos.
1, 2, 3(de mano derecha), 4(por gesolreut), 6(de
octavo tono), 7(de quinto tono por Bequadrado)
J. Butt Concert   (7/92) (HARM) ① HMU90 7047
2. M.G. Filippi, M. Henking (r1986) Concert
        (10/89) (ARIO) ① ARN68047
6. S. Yates (r1993; Octavo Tono) Concert
        (11/94) (CHAN) ① CHAN0560
7. Hespèrion XX, J. Savall Concert
        (2/92) (ASTR) ① E8729
Xácara—organ
J. Butt Concert   (7/92) (HARM) ① HMU90 7047

CABEZÓN, Antonio de
(1510–1566) Spain

SECTION II: CHAMBER

Fantasia a 5 on 'Susanne un jour' (after
Lassus's chanson)
Hespèrion XX, J. Savall (r1991-92) Concert
        (6/93) (ASTR) ① E8764

SECTION III: INSTRUMENTAL

Ave Maria—motet glosas for organ (pub
1578) (after Josquin Desprez's Pater noster)
K. Marshall Concert   (7/92) (AUVI) ① V4645
Ave maris stella—intermedios on the hymn
strophes for organ
K. Marshall Concert   (7/92) (AUVI) ① V4645
Ave maris stella a 2—hymn for organ (pub
1578)
K. Marshall Concert   (7/92) (AUVI) ① V4645
Diferencias sobre el Canto llano del
Caballero—organ
S. Yates (r1993) Concert
        (11/94) (CHAN) ① CHAN0560
Diferencias sobre 'Guárdame las
vacas'—organ (pub 1578)
K. Marshall Concert   (7/92) (AUVI) ① V4645
Diferencias sobre 'La dama le
demanda'—chanson for organ (pub 1578)
S. Yates (r1993) Concert
        (11/94) (CHAN) ① CHAN0560
Diferencias sobre la Gallarda
Milanesa—organ (pub 1578)
S. Yates (r1993) Concert
        (11/94) (CHAN) ① CHAN0560
Discante sobre la Pavana Italiana—organ
(pub 1578)
K. Marshall Concert   (7/92) (AUVI) ① V4645
Du vien sela—chanson for organ (pub 1578)
(after de Sermisy)
K. Marshall Concert   (7/92) (AUVI) ① V4645
Farbordón y glosas del sexto tono—organ
K. Marshall Concert   (7/92) (AUVI) ① V4645
Farbordones del primer tono—organ (pub
1578)
S. Yates (r1993) Concert
        (11/94) (CHAN) ① CHAN0560
Obra sobre Cantus firmus—keyboard
S. Yates (r1993) Concert
        (11/94) (CHAN) ① CHAN0560

Pange lingua—hymn for organ
K. Marshall *Concert* (7/92) (AUVI) ① **V4645**
Pange lingua—interludium for organ
K. Marshall *Concert* (7/92) (AUVI) ① **V4645**
Pavana con su glosa—organ (pub 1578)
S. Yates (r1993) *Concert*
(11/94) (CHAN) ① **CHAN0560**
Tiento del cuarto tono—organ (pub 1578)
K. Marshall *Concert* (7/92) (AUVI) ① **V4645**
Tiento del segundo tono—organ
City of London Wind Ens, G. Brand (r1991: arr concert band: Grainger) *Concert*
(7/89) (LDR) ① **LDRCD1001**
Tiento del séptimo tono, 'Cum Sancto Spíritu'—organ (pub 1578) (after Josquin Desprez's Missa de Beata Virgine)
K. Marshall *Concert* (7/92) (AUVI) ① **V4645**
Tiento del tercer tono, 'Fugas al contrario'—organ
K. Marshall *Concert* (7/92) (AUVI) ① **V4645**
Tiento sobre 'Qui la dirá'—organ (after Willaert)
K. Marshall *Concert* (7/92) (AUVI) ① **V4645**
Tientos III (primer tono)—organ (pub 1578)
S. Yates (r1993) *Concert*
(11/94) (CHAN) ① **CHAN0560**
Un gay bergier—chanson for organ (pub 1578) (after Crecquillon)
K. Marshall *Concert* (7/92) (AUVI) ① **V4645**

CABEZÓN, Hernando de (1541–1602) Spain

SECTION III: INSTRUMENTAL

Dulce memoria glosada—keyboard (pub 1578)
S. Yates (r1993) *Concert*
(11/94) (CHAN) ① **CHAN0560**

CACCINI, Francesca (1587–1640) Italy

SECTION IV: VOCAL AND CHORAL

O che nuovo stupor—madrigal (1v) (pub 1618)
M. van Egmond, Ricercar Consort *Concert*
(1/90) (RICE) ① **RIC054032**

CACCINI, Giulio (c1545–1618) Italy

SECTION IV: VOCAL AND CHORAL

Ave Maria
I. Galante, Latvian Nat SO, A. Vilumanis (r1994: arr Brinums) *Concert* (11/95) (CAMP) ① **RRCD1335**
Bella ragion—madrigal (1v)
J. Bowman, S. Sempé, J. Bernfeld *Concert*
(9/89) (ARIO) ① **ARN68046**
Io che dal Ciel cader—aria (1vv) - Intermedio 4, La Pellegrina (c1589) (Wds. ?Strozzi)
E. Van Evera, Taverner Plyrs, A. Parrott *Concert*
(8/88) (EMI) ① **CDC7 47998-2**
Le nuove musiche—song collection: 1v (pub 1602)
1. Ah, dispietato amor (wds. B. Tasso); 2. Amarilli mia bella (wds. G. B. or A. Guarini); 3. Amor, io parto; 4. Ardi, cor mio (wds. Rinuccini); 5. Ard'il mio petto misero (wds. Chiabrera); 6. Belle rose porporine (wds. Chiabrera); 7. Deh, dove son fuggiti (wds. Chiabrera); 8. Dolcissimo sospiro (wds. Rinuccini); 9. Dovro dunque morire; 10. Fere selvaggie (wds. Cini); 11. Fillide mia, se di belta (wds. Rinuccini); 12. Filli, mirandoli cielo (wds. ?Rinuccini); 13. Fortunato augellino (wds. Rinuccini); 14. Io parto, amati luni (wds. ?Rinuccini); 15. Movetevi a pieta; 16. Non più guerra, pietate (wds. G. B. Guarini); 17. Occh'immortali (wds. Rinuccini); 18. Odi, Euterpe; 19. Perfidissimo volto (wds. G. B. Guarini); 20. Queste l'agrim'amare; 21. Stogova con le stelle (wds. Rinuccini); 22. Udite, udite amanti (wds. Rinuccini); 23. Vedro 'l mio sol (wds. G. B. or A. Guarini).
2. R. Jacobs, K. Junghänel (r1989) *Concert*
(5/87) (HARM) ① **HMA190 1183**
2. A. Lawrence-King (trans. Lawrence-King) *Concert*
(9/87) (HYPE) ① **CDA66229**
2. J. Bowman, S. Sempé, J. Bernfeld *Concert*
(9/89) (ARIO) ① **ARN68046**
2. H. Spani, orch, G. Nastrucci (r1929) *Concert*
(9/90) (CLUB) ② **CL99-509/10**
2. H. Jadlowker, orch (r1927) *Concert*
(12/91) (CLUB) ① **CL99-042**
2. C. Bartoli, G. Fischer *Concert*
(12/92) (DECC) ① **436 267-2DH**

---

2. J. Baker, ASMF, N. Marriner *Concert*
(1/93) (PHIL) ① **434 173-2PM**
2, 18, 22. M. van Egmond, C. Farr *Concert*
(1/90) (ETCE) ① **KTC1056**
2, 6, 19, 22. N. Rogers, C. Tilney, A. Bailes, J. Savall, P. Ros (r1975) *Concert*
(1/93) (ARCH) ① **437 075-2AT**
Nuove musiche e nuova maniera de scriverle—song collection: 1v (pub 1614)
1. Al fonte al prato (wds. Cini); 2. Alma luci beate; 3. Amor, ch'attendi, amor, che fai? (wds. ?Rinuccini); 4. Amor l'ali m'impenna (wds. T. Tasso); 5. A quei sospir'ardenti (wds. ?Rinuccini); 6. Aur'amorosa che dolcemente spiri; 7. Ch'io non t'ami, cor mio (wds. G. B. Guarini); 8. Con le luci d'un bel ciglio; 9. Dalla porta d'oriente (wds. M. Menadori); 10. Deh, chi d'alloro (wds. Rinuccini); 11. Dite, o del foco mio; 12. Hor che lungi da voi (wds. Chiabrera); 13. In tristo umor (wds. Petrarch); 14. Io che l'eta solea (wds. G. della Casa); 15. La bella ma vi stringo (wds. G. B. Guarini); 16. Lasso che pur d'un'o e a l'altro (wds. Petrarch); 17. Mentre che fra doglie e pene (wds. Rinuccini); 18. Non ha 'l ciel costanti (wds. Rinuccini); 19. O che felice giorno; 20. O dolce fonte del mio pianto; 21. Ohime, begli occhi; 22. O piante, o selve ombrose (wds. ?Rinuccini); 23. Pien d'amoroso affetto; 24. Più l'altrui fallo (wds. Petrarch); 25. Se in questo scolorito (wds. ?Rinuccini or Chiabrera); 26. Se ridete gioise (wds. Chiabrera); 27. S'io vivo, anima mia; 28. Torna, deh torna, pargoletto mio (wds. Rinuccini); 29. Tu ch'hai le penne (wds. ?Rinuccini); 30. Tutto 'l di piano (wds. Chiabrera); 31. Vaga su spin'ascosa (wds. Chaibrera).
3, 26. M. van Egmond, C. Farr *Concert*
(1/90) (ETCE) ① **KTC1056**
29. C. Bartoli, G. Fischer *Concert*
(12/92) (DECC) ① **436 267-2DH**
Ragion sempre addita—song
J. Baker, ASMF, N. Marriner *Concert*
(1/93) (PHIL) ① **434 173-2PM**

CADMAN, Charles Wakefield (1881–1946) USA

SECTION II: CHAMBER

Legend of the Canyon—violin and piano
F. Kreisler, C. Lamson (r1925) *Concert*
(9/93) (BIDD) ① [2] **LAB068/9**

SECTION IV: VOCAL AND CHORAL

4 American Indian songs, Op. 45 (1909)
1. From the land of the sky-blue water; 2. Far off I heara lover's flute.
1. E. Mason, orch (r1928) *Concert*
(8/93) (SYMP) ① **SYMCD1136**
1. F. Kreisler, C. Lamson (r1925: arr Kreisler) *Concert* (9/93) (BIDD) ① [2] **LAB068/9**
1. E. Mason, orch, F. Black (r1924) *Concert*
(8/94) (ROMO) ① **81009-2**
1. E. Mason, orch, F. Black (r1928) *Concert*
(8/94) (ROMO) ① **81009-2**
2. E. Mason, orch (r1925) *Concert*
(8/93) (SYMP) ① **SYMCD1136**
2. E. Mason, orch, F. Black (r1925) *Concert*
(8/94) (ROMO) ① **81009-2**
At dawning, 'I love you'—song, Op. 29/1 (pub 1906) (Wds. N. E. Eberhardt)
F. Kreisler, C. Lamson (r1926: arr Rissland) *Concert*
(9/93) (BIDD) ① **LAB075**
M. Garden, J. Dansereau (r1926) *Concert*
(8/94) (ROMO) ① **81008-2**
Moonlight Song, Op. 42/2
E. Rethberg, orch (r1928-9) *Concert*
(2/95) (ROMO) ① [2] **81012-2**

CAGE, John (1912–1992) USA

SECTION I: ORCHESTRAL

Atlas Eclipticalis—any combination of up to 86 instruments (1961-62) (to be performed with/without 'Winter Music')
E. Blum (1992) (12/93) (HATH) ① **ARTCD6111**
Barton Workshop (r1992) *Concert*
(12/93) (ETCE) ① [3] **KTC3002**
S.E.M. Ens Orch, P. Kotik (r1992) *Concert for Piano.*
(12/93) (WERG) ① **WER6216-2**
Chicago SO, James Levine (r1990) *Concert*
(7/94) (DG) ① **431 698-2GH**
E. Blum (r1992; with Winter Music for 4 pianos superimposed) *Winter Music.*
(10/94) (HATH) ① **ARTCD6141**

Concert for Piano and Orchestra—63 pages (1957-58) (to be played in whole or in part, in any order)
EXCERPTS: 1. Three Solos for Trumpet.
Barton Workshop (r1992) *Concert*
(12/93) (ETCE) ① [3] **KTC3002**
J. Kubera, S.E.M. Ens Orch, P. Kotik (r1992) *Atlas Eclipticalis.* (12/93) (WERG) ① **WER6216-2**
cello solo F-M. Uitti *Concert*
(3/92) (ETCE) ① [2] **KTC2016**
1. E. Brown *Concert* (8/94) (KOCH) ① [2] **37238-2**
Fifty-eight—58 instruments (1992)
Pannonic Wind Orch, W. van Zutphen (1992)
(6/94) (HATH) ① **ARTCD6135**
Winter Music—1-20 pianists (1957)
M. Persson, S. Schleiermacher, K. Scholz, N. Vigeland (r1993) *Atlas Eclipticalis.*
(10/94) (HATH) ① **ARTCD6141**

SECTION II: CHAMBER

Amores—two solo prepared pianos and two percussion trios (1943)
M. Wiesler, R. Pilat, Kroumata Perc Ens *Concert*
(2/86) (BIS) ① **BIS-CD272**
Z. Kocsis, Amadinda Perc Group *Concert*
(11/90) (HUNG) ① **HCD12991**
Hélios Qt *Concert* (9/92) (WERG) ① **WER6203-2**
3 Dances—two amplified prepared pianos (1944-45)
1. Dance No. 1.
1. P. Moraz, C. Turner *Concert*
(8/94) (KOCH) ① [2] **37238-2**
A Dip in the Lake, for Chicago and Vicinity—427 addresses (1978) (chance operations)
1. Ten Quicksteps; 2. Sixty-one Waltzes; 3. Fifty-six marches.
F-M. Uitti (vers for vc and incp instr) *Concert*
(3/92) (ETCE) ① [2] **KTC2016**
Double Music—4 percussionists (1941) (in collaboration with Lou Harrison)
Amadinda Perc Group *Concert*
(11/90) (HUNG) ① **HCD12991**
Hélios Qt *Concert* (9/92) (WERG) ① **WER6203-2**
First Construction (In Metal)—6 percussion (1939)
Hélios Qt *Concert* (9/92) (WERG) ① **WER6203-2**
Five—5vv or 5 instruments (1988)
Barton Workshop (r1992) *Concert*
(12/93) (ETCE) ① [3] **KTC3002**
13 Harmonies—violin & keyboard instruments (1986) (harmonies taken from 'Apartment House, 1776')
1. Old North (W. Billings); 2. Rapture (S. Belcher); 3. Judea (W. Billings); 4. Heath (W. Billings); 5. New York (A. Law); 6. The Lord descended (W. Billings); 7. Wheeler's Point (W. Billings); 8. Brunswick (J. Lyon); 9. Bellingham (W. Billings); 10. Greenwich (A. Law); 11. Framingham (W. Billings); 12. The Lord is risen (W. Billings); 13. Bloomfield (A. Law).
R. Zahab, E. Moe (r1994) *Concert*
(11/95) (KOCH) ① **37130-2**
R. Zahab, E. Moe (r1994; vers determined by chance operations) *Concert* (11/95) (KOCH) ① **37130-2**
Hymnkus—14 parts: 11 performers (1986)
Barton Workshop (r1992) *Concert*
(12/93) (ETCE) ① [3] **KTC3002**
Imaginary Landscape No. 2 (March No. 1)—five percussion (1942)
Hélios Qt *Concert* (9/92) (WERG) ① **WER6203-2**
Music for....—title to be cpted by no. of additional performers (1984)
Barton Workshop (r1992: six players) *Concert*
(12/93) (ETCE) ① [3] **KTC3002**
Music for Four—string quartet (1987 rev 1988)
Arditti Qt (pp1988) *Pieces for String Quartet.*
(12/89) (MODE) ① **Mode 17**
Arditti Qt (r1989) *String Quartet.*
(12/93) (MODE) ① **Mode 27**
Arditti Qt (r1991-92) *Concert*
(12/93) (MONT) ① **782010**
30 Pieces for String Quartet (1983)
Arditti Qt (pp1988) *Music for Four.*
(12/89) (MODE) ① **Mode 17**
Excs Kronos Qt (pp) *Concert*
(8/94) (KOCH) ① [2] **37238-2**
Second Construction—four percussion (1940)
Kroumata Perc Ens (pp1983) *Concert*
(1/84) (BIS) ① **BIS-CD232**
Hélios Qt *Concert* (9/92) (WERG) ① **WER6203-2**
Seven 2—bass-fl, cl, tbn, vc, db and 2 perc
Barton Workshop (r1992) *Concert*
(12/93) (ETCE) ① [3] **KTC3002**

She is Asleep—voice, prepared pf/quartet of 12 tom-toms (1943)
Hélios Qt *Concert*   (9/92) (WERG) ① **WER6203-2**

Some of 'The Harmony of Maine' (Supply Belcher)—organ and six assistants (1978) (subsidiary of 'Apartment House, 1776')
1. Alpha C. M. 2. Majesty C. M. 3. Harmony C. M. 4. Creation L. M; 5. Hallowell S. M. 6. Advent C. M. 7. Turner C. M. 8. Sunday C. M. 9. St. John's C. M. 10. Invitation L. M. 11. Transmigration; 12. Chester L. M; 13. The Lilly P. M.
H-O. Ericsson, K. Johansson, K. Andersson, G. Sjöström, B. Tribukait, P. Grundberg, K. M. Jansson *Concert*   (4/93) (BIS) ① **BIS-CD510**

Sonata for two voices—2 or more instruments (1933)
Barton Workshop (r1992) *Concert*   (12/93) (ETCE) ① [3] **KTC3002**

String Quartet in four parts (1950)
LaSalle Qt *Concert*   (8/88) (DG) ① **423 245-2GC**
Arditti Qt (r1989) *Music for Four.*   (12/93) (MODE) ① **Mode 27**

Third Construction—four percussion (1941)
Amadinda Perc Group *Concert*   (11/90) (HUNG) ① **HCD12991**
Hélios Qt *Concert*   (9/92) (WERG) ① **WER6203-2**

Variations I-VII
1. Variations I (1958): Any number of players, any means; 2. Variations II (1961): Any number of players and sound producing means; 3. Variations III (1963): Any number of people performing any actions; 4. Variations IV (1964): Any number of players, any produced sounds; 5. Variations V (1965): 37 remarks for an audio-visual performance; 6. Variations VI (1966): plurality of sound systems; 7. Variations VII (1966): various means.
F-M. Uitti (vers for multiple celli) *Concert*   (3/92) (ETCE) ① [2] **KTC2016**

4'33'—tacet for any instrument/instruments (1952)
Amadinda Perc Group *Concert*   (11/90) (HUNG) ① **HCD12991**
F. Zappa *Concert*   (8/94) (KOCH) ① [2] **37238-2**

26'1. 1499' for a string player—any four-stringed instruments (1953-55)
F-M. Uitti *Concert*   (3/92) (ETCE) ① [2] **KTC2016**

SECTION III: INSTRUMENTAL

Bacchanale—prepared piano (1940)
M. Legrand (r1994) *Concert*   (7/95) (ERAT) ① **4509-96386-2**
M. Leng Tan (r1993) *Concert*   (7/95) (NALB) ① **NA070CD**
S. Drury (r1994) *Concert*   (7/95) (CATA) ① **09026 61980-2**

Cheap Imitation—piano: violin vers, 1977 (1969)
P. Zukofsky *Concert*   (7/92) (MOBS) ① **CP2103**

Chorals—violin (1978)
P. Zukofsky *Concert*   (7/92) (MOBS) ① **CP2103**

Daughters of the Lonesome Isle—prepared piano (1945)
M. Leng Tan (r1993) *Concert*   (7/95) (NALB) ① **NA070CD**

Dream—piano (1948)
S. Drury (r1994) *Concert*   (7/95) (CATA) ① **09026 61980-2**

Etudes australes, Books I-IV—piano (1974-75)
G. Sultan (r1978/82)   (7/93) (WERG) ① [3] **WER6152-2**

Etudes Boreales—cello/piano/violin (1978)
F-M. Uitti *Concert*   (3/92) (ETCE) ① [2] **KTC2016**

Freeman Etudes—violin (1978—)
P. Zukofsky *Concert*   (7/92) (MOBS) ① **CP2103**

Imitations II—clarinet (1976)
Barton Workshop (r1992) *Concert*   (12/93) (ETCE) ① [3] **KTC3002**

In a Landscape—harp/piano (1948)
M. Leng Tan (r1993; pf vers) *Concert*   (7/95) (NALB) ① **NA070CD**
S. Drury (r1994) *Concert*   (7/95) (CATA) ① **09026 61980-2**

In the Name of the Holocaust—prepared piano (1942)
M. Leng Tan (r1993; string pf vers) *Concert*   (7/95) (NALB) ① **NA070CD**

Music for Marcel Duchamp—prepared piano (1947)
P. Roggenkamp *Concert*   (9/92) (WERG) ① **WER6074-2**
N. Butterley (r1992) *Concert*   (10/94) (TALL) ① **TP025**
S. Drury (r1994) *Concert*   (7/95) (CATA) ① **09026 61980-2**

Music for Piano No. 2 (1953)
M. Leng Tan (r1993; arr bowed pf: M. Leng Tan) *Concert*   (7/95) (NALB) ① **NA070CD**

Music of Changes—piano (1951)
H. Henck   (8/89) (WERG) ① **WER60099-50**

Ophelia—piano (1946)
M. Leng Tan (r1993) *Concert*
     (7/95) (NALB) ① **NA070CD**

The Perilous Night—prepared piano (1944)
M. Leng Tan *Four Walls.*
     (1/92) (NALB) ① **NA037CD**

Prelude for Meditation—prepared piano (1944)
S. Drury (r1994) *Concert*
     (7/95) (CATA) ① **09026 61980-2**

Sliding Trombone (1957-58)
C. Lindberg *Concert*   (10/89) (BIS) ① **BIS-CD388**

Sonata for Clarinet (1933)
Barton Workshop (r1992) *Concert*
     (12/93) (ETCE) ① [3] **KTC3002**

Sonatas and Interludes—prepared piano (1946-48)
G. Fremy   (9/88) (ETCE) ① **KTC2001**
N. Butterley (r1992) *Concert*
     (10/94) (TALL) ① **TP025**
Sonata XIII P. Roggenkamp *Concert*
     (9/92) (WERG) ① **WER6074-2**

Souvenir—organ (1983)
S. Drury (r1994) *Concert*
     (7/95) (CATA) ① **09026 61980-2**

Suite—toy piano/piano (1948)
M. Leng Tan (r1993; toy pf vers) *Concert*
     (7/95) (NALB) ① **NA070CD**
S. Drury (r1994) *Concert*
     (7/95) (CATA) ① **09026 61980-2**

Totem Ancestor—prepared piano (1943)
Barton Workshop (r1992) *Concert*
     (12/93) (ETCE) ① [3] **KTC3002**

A Valentine out of season—prepared piano (1944)
Barton Workshop (r1992) *Concert*
     (12/93) (ETCE) ① [3] **KTC3002**
S. Drury (r1994) *Concert*
     (7/95) (CATA) ① **09026 61980-2**

SECTION IV: VOCAL AND CHORAL

Aria—1v (1958)
M. Monk (pp1985) *Concert*
     (8/94) (KOCH) ① [2] **37238-2**

Eight Whiskus—voice (1984) (texts derived from Chris Mann)
J. La Barbara *Concert*   (9/91) (NALB) ① **NA035CD**

Empty Words III (non-syntactic mixture of spoken sounds)
Stuttgart Schola Cantorum, C. Gottwald *Concert*
     (9/92) (WERG) ① **WER6074-2**

A Flower—1v and closed pf (1950)
C. Berberian, B. Canino *Concert*
     (7/89) (WERG) ① **WER60054-50**
J. La Barbara, W. Winant *Concert*
     (9/91) (NALB) ① **NA035CD**

Forever and Sunsmell—1v and 2 perc (1942) (Wds. e. e. cummings)
J. La Barbara, S. Evans *Concert*
     (9/91) (NALB) ① **NA035CD**

Laughtears—conversation on 'Roaratorio' (1979)
J. Cage, K. Schöning *Concert*
     (10/94) (MODE) ① **Mode 28/9**

Lecture on nothing—solo voice (1959)
F-M. Uitti *Concert*   (3/92) (ETCE) ① [2] **KTC2016**

Living Room Music—objects 'to be found in a living room' (1940)
D. van Tieghem (r1976) *Concert*
     (8/94) (KOCH) ① [2] **37238-2**

Mirakus—voice (1984) (texts derived from Marcel Duchamp)
J. La Barbara *Concert*   (9/91) (NALB) ① **NA035CD**

Music for....—title to be cpted by no. of additional performers (1984)
2 players J. La Barbara *Concert*
     (9/91) (NALB) ① **NA035CD**

New York City—sounds recorded outside Cage's apartment
S. Smith *Concert*   (8/94) (KOCH) ① [2] **37238-2**

Nowth upon Nacht—voice and piano (1984) (Wds. J. Joyce)
J. La Barbara, W. Winant *Concert*
     (9/91) (NALB) ① **NA035CD**

Roaratorio: An Irish Circus on Finnegans Wake—speaker, Irish musicians and 62-track tape (1979)
J. Cage, J. Heaney, S. Ennis, P. Glackin, M. Malloy, P. Mercier, M. Mercier *Concert*
     (10/94) (MODE) ① [2] **Mode 28/9**

Solo for Voice 49—1v, any range (1958) (Wds. H. D. Thoreau)
J. La Barbara *Concert*   (9/91) (NALB) ① **NA035CD**

Solo for Voice 52 (Aria No. 2)—song (1970)
J. La Barbara *Concert*   (9/91) (NALB) ① **NA035CD**

Solo for Voice 67—song with electronics (1970)
J. La Barbara *Concert*   (9/91) (NALB) ① **NA035CD**

Song Books I-II—solos for voice (1970-72) (Bk I: Nos 3-59; Bk 2: Nos 59-93)
Stuttgart Schola Cantorum, C. Gottwald *Concert*
     (9/92) (WERG) ① **WER6074-2**
22, 79. Barton Workshop (r1992) *Concert*
     (12/93) (ETCE) ① [3] **KTC3002**

Sonnekus—voice and piano (1985) (Wds. Genesis)
1. 1; 2. 2; 3. 3; 4. Je te veux (E. Satie: 1902); 5. 4; 6. 5; 7. La Diva de l'Empire (E. Satie: 1919); 8. 6; 9. 7; 10. 8; 11. Tendrement (E. Satie: 1903); 12. 9.
J. La Barbara, L. Stein *Concert*
     (9/91) (NALB) ① **NA035CD**

The Wonderful widow of eighteen springs—1v and closed pf (1942) (Wds. J. Joyce)
C. Berberian, B. Canino *Concert*
     (7/89) (WERG) ① **WER60054-50**
J. La Barbara, W. Winant *Concert*
     (9/91) (NALB) ① **NA035CD**
G. English, N. Butterley (r1992) *Concert*
     (10/94) (TALL) ① **TP025**

Writing for the Second Time through Finnegans Wake—speaker (1976-79) (radio play text for 'Roaratorio')
J. Cage *Concert*
     (10/94) (MODE) ① [2] **Mode 28/9**

SECTION V: STAGE WORKS

Four Walls—dance-play: 2 acts: soprano and piano (1944) (play by M. Cunningham)
J. La Barbara, M. Leng Tan *Perilous Night (1944.*
     (1/92) (NALB) ① **NA037CD**

The Seasons—ballet for orchestra: 1 act (1947)
EXCERPTS: 1. Prelude I; 2. Winter; 3. Prelude II; 4. Spring; 5. Prelude III; 6. Summer; 7. Prelude IV; 8. Fall; 9. Finale (Prelude I).
M. Leng Tan (r1993; pf vers) *Concert*
     (7/95) (NALB) ① **NA070CD**

Sixteen Dances—soloist and company of 3 (1950-51)
Modern Ens, I. Metzmacher (r1992)
     (4/95) (RCA) ① **09026 61574-2**

CAIMO, Gioseppe (c1545–1584)
Italy

SECTION IV: VOCAL AND CHORAL

Piangete valli—madrigal
Amaryllis Consort *Concert*
     (6/86) (CARL) ① **PCD822**

CALACE, Raffaele (1863–1934)
Italy

SECTION I: ORCHESTRAL

Bolero—plectrum orchestra, Op. 26
Brescia Mndl and Gtr Orch, C. Mandonico (r1990) *Concert*   (12/93) (FONE) ① **91F02**

Impressioni Orientali—plectrum orchestra, Op. 132
Brescia Mndl and Gtr Orch, C. Mandonico (r1990) *Concert*   (12/93) (FONE) ① **91F02**

Impressionismo, 'Momento lirico'—plectrum orchestra, Op. 145
Brescia Mndl and Gtr Orch, C. Mandonico (r1990) *Concert*   (12/93) (FONE) ① **91F02**

Intermezzo, 'Mesto pensiero'—plectrum orchestra, Op. 146
Brescia Mndl and Gtr Orch, C. Mandonico (r1990) *Concert*   (12/93) (FONE) ① **91F02**

Mazurka—plectrum orchestra, Op. 141
Brescia Mndl and Gtr Orch, C. Mandonico (r1990) *Concert*   (12/93) (FONE) ① **91F02**

Pavana—plectrum orchestra, Op. 54
Brescia Mndl and Gtr Orch, C. Mandonico (r1990) *Concert*   (12/93) (FONE) ① **91F02**

Tarantella—plectrum orchestra, Op. 18
Brescia Mndl and Gtr Orch, C. Mandonico (r1990) *Concert*   (12/93) (FONE) ① **91F02**

SECTION II: CHAMBER

Concerto a plettro—mandolin quartet and guitar, Op. 155
Calace Qnt (r1990) *Concert*
     (12/93) (FONE) ① **91F02**

Danza Spagnola—mandolin quartet and guitar, Op. 105
Calace Qnt (r1990) *Concert*
(12/93) (FONE) ① **91F02**
Mattino d'autunno—mandolin quartet, Op. 164
Calace Qnt (r1990) *Concert*
(12/93) (FONE) ① **91F02**
Suite No. 3, Op. 98—two mandolins, Op. 98 (c1900)
1. Adagio; 2. Marziale allegretto; 3. Minuetto: 4. Scherzoso.
A. Stephens, S. Mossop *Concert*
(3/92) (AMON) ① **CD-SAR53**

CALDARA, Antonio (c1670–1736) Italy

SECTION II: CHAMBER

12 Suonate da camera—2 violins and continuo, Op. 1 (1693)
5. E minor.
5. Seminario musicale *Concert*
(11/91) (VIRG) ① **VC7 59058-2**
12 Suonate da camera—2 violins and continuo, Op. 2 (1699)
3. D.
3. Seminario musicale *Concert*
(11/91) (VIRG) ① **VC7 59058-2**

SECTION IV: VOCAL AND CHORAL

Come raggio di sol—arietta
J. Baker, ASMF, N. Marriner *Concert*
(1/93) (PHIL) ① **434 173-2PM**
J. Carreras, ECO, V. Sutej (r1992; arr Agostinelli) *Concert*
(6/93) (PHIL) ① **434 926-2PH**
Crucifixus
The Sixteen, H. Christophers, L. Cummings, R. Jeffrey (r1992) *Concert*
(10/93) (COLL) ① **Coll1360-2**
St John's College Ch, G. Guest (r1977) *Concert*
(7/95) (DECC) ① [2] **443 868-2DF2**
Dario, 'Piangerò sin ch'avro vita'—cantata: 1v and continuo (after 1716)
Wren Baroque Sols, M. Elliott *Concert*
(2/93) (UNIC) ① **DKPCD9130**
De piaceri foriera giunge la Primavera—madrigal: 5vv (1731-32) (Wds. A. M. Lucchini)
Wren Baroque Sols, M. Elliott *Concert*
(2/93) (UNIC) ① **DKPCD9130**
Dell'uom la vita è un sogno—madrigal: 4vv (1731-32) (Wds. A. M. Lucchini)
Wren Baroque Sols, M. Elliott *Concert*
(2/93) (UNIC) ① **DKPCD9130**
D'improvviso—solo cantata (1712) (Wds. P. Ottoboni)
G. Lesne, Seminario musicale *Concert*
(11/91) (VIRG) ① **VC7 59058-2**
La forriera del giorno—cantata: 1v and continuo (pub 1701-02)
Wren Baroque Sols, M. Elliott *Concert*
(2/93) (UNIC) ① **DKPCD9130**
Fra pioggie, nevi e gelo—madrigal: 5vv (1731-32) (Wds. A. M. Lucchini)
Wren Baroque Sols, M. Elliott *Concert*
(2/93) (UNIC) ① **DKPCD9130**
Fugge di Lot la Moglie—madrigal: 4vv (1731-32) (Wds. A. M. Lucchini)
Wren Baroque Sols, M. Elliott *Concert*
(2/93) (UNIC) ① **DKPCD9130**
Il Gelsomino—cantata: 1v and continuo (c1709-16)
Wren Baroque Sols, M. Elliott *Concert*
(2/93) (UNIC) ① **DKPCD9130**
Là su morbide piume—madrigal: 4vv (1731-32) (Wds. A. M. Lucchini)
Wren Baroque Sols, M. Elliott *Concert*
(2/93) (UNIC) ① **DKPCD9130**
Laudate pueri Dominum (1720)
Fiori Musicali Ch, Fiori Musicali, P. Rapson *Purcell: St Cecilia's Day Ode, Z328.*
(10/91) (UNIC) ① **DKPCD9109**
Lungi dall'Idol mio—cantata: 1v and continuo (c1709-16)
Wren Baroque Sols, M. Elliott *Concert*
(2/93) (UNIC) ① **DKPCD9130**
Medea in Corinto—solo cantata
G. Lesne, Seminario musicale *Concert*
(11/91) (VIRG) ① **VC7 59058-2**
Sebben crudele me fai languir—aria
C. Bartoli, G. Fischer *Concert*
(12/92) (DECC) ① **436 267-2DH**
J. Baker, ASMF, N. Marriner *Concert*
(1/93) (PHIL) ① **434 173-2PM**

J. Carreras, ECO, V. Sutej (r1992; arr Agostinelli) *Concert*
(6/93) (PHIL) ① **434 926-2PH**
Selve amiche—aria
C. Bartoli, G. Fischer *Concert*
(12/92) (DECC) ① **436 267-2DH**
J. Baker, ASMF, N. Marriner *Concert*
(1/93) (PHIL) ① **434 173-2PM**
Soffri, mio caro Alcino—solo cantata (1715)
G. Lesne, Seminario musicale *Concert*
(11/91) (VIRG) ① **VC7 59058-2**
Stabat Mater—SATB, chorus and orchestra
G. Fisher, C. Trevor, I. Partridge, M. George, The Sixteen, The Sixteen Orch, H. Christophers *Concert*
(12/92) (COLL) ① **Coll1320-2**
Stella ria—cantata: 1v and continuo (c1709-16)
Wren Baroque Sols, M. Elliott *Concert*
(2/93) (UNIC) ① **DKPCD9130**
Vedi co'l crine sciolto—madrigal: 4vv (1731-32) (Wds. A. M. Lucchini)
Wren Baroque Sols, M. Elliott *Concert*
(2/93) (UNIC) ① **DKPCD9130**
Vicino a un rivoletto—solo cantata (1729)
G. Lesne, Seminario musicale *Concert*
(11/91) (VIRG) ① **VC7 59058-2**

CALE, John J. (b 1942) Wales/USA

SECTION III: INSTRUMENTAL

In Memoriam John Cage—Call Waiting—tape (1992)
J. Cale (r1992) *Concert*
(8/94) (KOCH) ① [2] **37238-2**

CALESTANI, Vincenzo (1589–c1617) Italy

SECTION IV: VOCAL AND CHORAL

Damigella tutta bella—madrigal: 1v and continuo (pub 1617) (Wds. G. Chiabrera)
N. Rogers, C. Tilney, A. Bailes, J. Savall, P. Ros (r1975) *Concert*
(1/93) (ARCH) ① **437 075-2AT**

CALIFONA

SECTION IV: VOCAL AND CHORAL

Vieni sul mar'—song (Wds. anon)
E. Caruso, orch, J. Pasternack (r1919) *Concert*
(12/90) (NIMB) ① **NI7809**
E. Caruso, orch, J. Pasternack (r1919) *Concert*
(7/91) (RCA) ① [12] **GD60495(6)**
E. Caruso, orch, J. Pasternack (r1919) *Concert*
(10/91) (PEAR) ① [3] **EVC4(2)**

CALLEJA, Rafael (Gómez) (1874–1938) Spain

SECTION V: STAGE WORKS

Emigrantes—zarzuela: 1 act (1905—Madrid) (comp with Barrera)
Granadinas J. Carreras, ECO, E. Ricci (r1994) *Concert*
(2/95) (ERAT) ① **4509-95789-2**

CALVERT, Morley (b 1928) Canada

SECTION I: ORCHESTRAL

Introduction, Elegy and Caprice—brass band (1978)
Black Dyke Mills Band, P. Parkes (pp1978/9) *Concert*
(3/94) (CHAN) ① **CHAN4522**

CALVI, Carlo (fl 1646) Italy

SECTION III: INSTRUMENTAL

Aria di Firenze—guitar
B. Mason *Concert*　　(10/90) (AMON) ① **CD-SAR45**
Corrente—guitar
B. Mason *Concert*　　(10/90) (AMON) ① **CD-SAR45**
Passamezzo—guitar
B. Mason *Concert*　　(10/90) (AMON) ① **CD-SAR45**
Ruggiero—guitar
B. Mason *Concert*　　(10/90) (AMON) ① **CD-SAR45**

CAMBINI, Giuseppe Maria (1746–1825) Italy

SECTION II: CHAMBER

Quintet for wind instruments No. 3 in F—cl, fl, ob, hn and hn (pub c1802)
Aulos Wind Qnt *Concert*
(10/89) (SCHW) ① **310011**

CAMILLERI, Charles (b 1931) Malta

SECTION I: ORCHESTRAL

Concerto for Piano and Orchestra No. 1, 'Mediterranean' (1948, rec 1978)
A. de Groote, Bournemouth SO, M. Laus (r1993) *Concert*
(9/94) (UNIC) ① **DKPCD9150**
Concerto for Piano and Orchestra No. 2, 'Maqam' (1967-8)
A. de Groote, Bournemouth SO, M. Laus (r1993) *Concert*
(9/94) (UNIC) ① **DKPCD9150**
Concerto for Piano and Orchestra No. 3, 'Leningrad' (1985)
A. de Groote, Bournemouth SO, M. Laus (r1993) *Concert*
(9/94) (UNIC) ① **DKPCD9150**

SECTION III: INSTRUMENTAL

L' Amour de Dieu—organ (1980)
K. Bowyer (r1993) *Concert*
(11/95) (UNIC) ① **DKPCD9151**
Invocation to the Creator—organ (1976)
K. Bowyer (r1993) *Concert*
(11/95) (UNIC) ① **DKPCD9151**
Morphogenesis—organ (1978)
K. Bowyer (r1993) *Concert*
(11/95) (UNIC) ① **DKPCD9151**
Wine of Peace—organ (1976)
K. Bowyer (r1993) *Concert*
(11/95) (UNIC) ① **DKPCD9151**

SECTION IV: VOCAL AND CHORAL

Amen—chorus a cappella (1979)
Joyful Company of Sngrs, P. Broadbent (r1994) *Concert*
(3/95) (UNIC) ① **DKPCD9157**
Celestial Voices—chorus a cappella
Joyful Company of Sngrs, P. Broadbent (r1994) *Concert*
(3/95) (UNIC) ① **DKPCD9157**
Lumen nivis, '(The) light of snow'—chorus a cappella (1992)
Joyful Company of Sngrs, P. Broadbent (r1994) *Concert*
(3/95) (UNIC) ① **DKPCD9157**
Malta Yok!—chorus a cappella (Wds. P Serracino-Inglott)
Joyful Company of Sngrs, P. Broadbent (r1994) *Concert*
(3/95) (UNIC) ① **DKPCD9157**
Missa brevis—chorus a cappella (1975)
Joyful Company of Sngrs, P. Broadbent (r1994) *Concert*
(3/95) (UNIC) ① **DKPCD9157**
Pacem in Maribus—chorus a cappella (1989) (Wds. P. Serracino-Inglott)
Joyful Company of Sngrs, P. Broadbent (r1994) *Concert*
(3/95) (UNIC) ① **DKPCD9157**
Requiem—chorus a cappella (1990)
Joyful Company of Sngrs, P. Broadbent (r1994) *Concert*
(3/95) (UNIC) ① **DKPCD9157**
Sonus Spiritus—chorus a cappella (1991)
Joyful Company of Sngrs, P. Broadbent (r1994) *Concert*
(3/95) (UNIC) ① **DKPCD9157**
Unum Deum—tenor, baritone and chorus a cappella (1981)
Joyful Company of Sngrs, P. Broadbent (r1994) *Concert*
(3/95) (UNIC) ① **DKPCD9157**

CAMPANA, Fabio (1819–1882) Italy

SECTION V: STAGE WORKS

Esmeralda—opera: 4 acts (1869—St Petersburg) (Lib. G T Cimino)
Plango ma questo lagrimar E. Foggi, anon (r1910s) *Concert*
(6/94) (IRCC) ① **IRCC-CD808**

CAMPBELL, Sidney (1910–1974) England

SECTION IV: VOCAL AND CHORAL

Sing we merrily unto God our strength—anthem
St John's Episcopal Cath Ch, D. Pearson *Concert*
(10/92) (DELO) ① **DE3125**

CAMPION, Thomas (1567–1620) England

SECTION II: CHAMBER

What if a day—consort
Musicians of Swanne Alley *Concert*
(11/89) (VIRG) ① **VC7 59534-2**

SECTION IV: VOCAL AND CHORAL

21 Ayres—1v, lute, orpharion and bass viol **(pub 1601)** (in Rosseter's collection 'A Booke of Ayres')
1. Blame noy my cheekes, though pale with love they be; 2. Come let us sound with melodie the praises; 3. Faire if you expect admiring; 4. Followe thy faire sunne, unhappy shaddowe; 5. Follow your saint, follow with accents sweet; 6. Harke all you ladies that doo sleepe; 7. I care not for these ladies; 8. It fell on a sommers daie; 9. Mistris since you so much desire; 10. My love hath vowed hee will forska mee; 11. My sweetest Lesbia, let us live and love; 12. See where she flies enrag'd from me; 13. The man of life upright; 14. The sypres curten of the night (The Cypress Curtain); 15. Thus art not faire, for all thy red and white; 16. Though you are yoong and I am olde; 17. Turne backe you wanton flier; 18. When the god of merrie love; 19. When thou must home to shades of under ground; 20. When to her lute Corrina sings; 21. Your faire lookes enflame my desire.
E. Kirkby, A. Rooley (pp1985) *Concert*
(6/87) (HYPE) ① **CDA66186**
2, 20. E. Kirkby, A. Rooley *Concert*
(8/91) (L'OI) ① **425 892-2OH**
3, 7, 8, 12, 14, 21. D. Minter, P. O'Dette *Concert*
(6/91) (HARM) ① **HMU90 7023**
8. J. Bream, J. Bream Consort (r1962) *Concert*
(8/93) (RCA) ① **[28] 09026 61583-2(3)**
8. J. Bream Consort (r1962; arr consort) *Concert*
(9/94) (RCA) ① **09026 61589-2**
14. M. Chance, C. Wilson (r1992) *Concert*
(10/94) (CHAN) ① **CHAN0538**

First Booke of Ayres, 'Divine and Morall Songs'—lute-songs: 1v **(pub 1613)** (alternative vv arrs in brackets)
1. All lookes be pale, harts cold as stone (2vv); 2. As by the streames of Babilon (4vv); 3. Author of light, revive my dying spright (4vv); 4. Awake thou heavy spright (4vv); 5. Bravely deckt come forth bright day; 6. Come chearfull day (3vv); 7. Jack and Jone they thinke no ill (3vv); 8. Lift up to heaven sad wretch thy heavy spright (3vv); 9. Lighten heavy heart thy spright (3vv); 10. Loe, when backe mine eye (4vv); 11. Most sweet and pleasing are thy waes O God (4vv); 12. Never-weather-beaten saile more willing bent to shore; 13. Out of my soules depth to thee my cryes have sounded (4vv); 14. Seeke the Lord, and in his waies perseuer; 15. Sing a song of joy (4vv); 16. The man of life upright, whose cheerfull minde is free (4vv); 17. To musicke bent is my retyred minde (4vv); 18. Tune thy musicke to thy hart (4vv); 19. View me Lord a worke of thine (4vv); 20. Where are all thy beauties now, all harts enchaining? (4vv); 21. Wise men patience never want (4vv).
3. J. Bowman, D. Miller, King's Consort *Concert*
(10/91) (HYPE) ① **CDA66447**
3, 12. D. Minter, P. O'Dette *Concert*
(6/91) (HARM) ① **HMU90 7023**
3, 12. M. Chance, C. Wilson (r1992) *Concert*
(10/94) (CHAN) ① **CHAN0538**
6. E. Kirkby, A. Rooley (pp1985) *Concert*
(6/87) (HYPE) ① **CDA66186**
7. C. Keyte, R. Barnes (arr Bax) *Concert*
(5/93) (CNTI) ① **CCD1046**
15. Kings College Ch, C. van Kampen, R. Spencer, D. Willcocks (arr Fellowes) *Concert*
(12/91) (EMI) ① **CDM7 64130-2**

Fourth Booke of Ayres—lute-songs: 1v **(pub 1617)**
1. Are you what your faire lookes expresse?; 2. Beauty but a painted hell; 3. Beauty since you so much desire; 4. Deare if I with guile would guild a true intent; 5. Every dame affects good fame; 6. Faine would I wed a faire young man; 7. Her fayre inflaming eyes; 8. If any hath the heart to kill; 9. I must complain, yet doe enjoy my love; 10. Love prolonging thy distresse; 11. Love me or not, love her I must or dye; 12. O love, where are thy shafts, thy quiver, and thy bow?; 13. Respect my faith, regard my service past; 14. Since shee, even shee, for whom I liv'd; 15. So sweet is thy discourse to me; 16. There is a garden in her face; 17. Thinkest thou to seduce me then; 18. Thou joy'st fond boy, to be my many loved; 19. To his sweete lute Apollo sung the motions of the spheares; 20. Vayle love mine yes, O

hide from me; 21. What means this folly, now to brave it so?; 22. Young and simple though I am; 23. Your fayre lookes my desire.
1-3, 11. D. Minter, P. O'Dette *Concert*
(6/91) (HARM) ① **HMU90 7023**
6. C. Bott, New London Consort, P. Pickett (r1992) *Concert*
(4/94) (LINN) ① **CKD011**

Move now with measured sound—ayre **(pub 1607)**
E. Kirkby, Consort of Musicke, A. Rooley *Concert*
(9/87) (HYPE) ① **CDA66227**

Now hath Flora robb'd her bower—ayre **(pub 1607)**
E. Kirkby, Consort of Musicke, A. Rooley *Concert*
(9/87) (HYPE) ① **CDA66227**

Second Booke of Ayres, 'Light Conceits of Lovers'—lute-songs: 1-3vv **(pub 1613)**
1. A secret love or two I must confesse; 2. Come away, armed with loves delights; 3. Come you pretty false-ey'd wanton; 4. Faine would I my love disclose; 5. Give beauty all her right; 6. Good men shew if you can tell; 7. Harden then thy hart with more than flinty rage; 8. Her rosie cheekes, her ever smiling eyes; 9. How easi'y wert thou chaind?; 10. O deare that I with thee might live; 11. O what unhpt for sweet supply; 12. Pin'd I am and like to dye; 13. So many loves have I neglected; 14. Sweet exclude me not nor be divided; 15. The peacefull westerne winde; 16. There is none, O none but you; 17. Tough your strangenesse frets my hart; 18. Vaine men whose follies make a god of love; 19. What harvest halfe so sweet is?; 20. Where shall I refuge seek, if you refuse me (2vv); 21. Where she her sacred bowre adornes.
3, 12, 14. D. Minter, P. O'Dette *Concert*
(6/91) (HARM) ① **HMU90 7023**

Third Booke of Ayres—lute-songs: 1v **(pub 1617)**
1. Awake thou spring of speaking grace; 2. Be thou then my deauty named; 3. Breake now my heart and dye; 4. Come, o come my lifes delight; 5. Could my heart have more tongues imploy; 6. Fire, fire, fire loe here I burne; 7. Fire that must flame is with apt fuell fed; 8. If love loves truth, then women do not love; 9. If thou long'st so much to learne; 10. Kinde are her answers; 11. Maids are simple some men say; 12. Never love unlesse you can; 13. Now let her change and spare not; 14. Thou winter nights enlarge; 15. Oft have I sigh'd for him that heares me not; 16. O griefe, O spight, to see poor vertue scorn'd; 17. O never to be moved; 18. O sweet delight, O more than humane blisse; 19. Shall I come sweet love to thee?; 20. Shall I then hope when faith is fled?; 21. Silly boy 'tis ful moone yet; 22. Sleepe angry beautie sleep, and feare not me; 23. So quirke, so hot, so mad is thy fond sute; 24. So try'd are all my thoughts; 25. Thrice tosse these oaken ashes in the ayre; 26. Thus I resolve, and time hath taught me so; 27. Turne all thy thoughts to eyes; 28. Were my hart as some mens are; 29. What is it that all men possesse?; 30. Why presumes thy pride on that?.
1, 6, 10, 12, 17, 19, 24. D. Minter, P. O'Dette *Concert*
(6/91) (HARM) ① **HMU90 7023**
14, 25. J. Elwes, S. Stubbs *Concert*
(9/93) (HYPE) ① **PV787092**
15. J. Bowman, D. Miller, King's Consort *Concert*
(10/91) (HYPE) ① **CDA66447**

CAMPRA, André (1660–1744) France

SECTION IV: VOCAL AND CHORAL

Achille oisif—cantata (1v and ens) **(pub 1714)**
J. Nicolas, D. Cuiller, P. Allain-Dupré, J. Bernfeld, M. Chapuis *Concert* (5/87) (PIER) ① **PV786101**
Arion—cantata: 1v and ensemble **(pub 1708)**
J. Nicolas, D. Cuiller, P. Allain-Dupré, J. Bernfeld, M. Chapuis *Concert* (5/87) (PIER) ① **PV786101**
J. Feldman, Arts Florissants Voc Ens, Arts Florissants Instr Ens (r1986) *Concert*
(5/87) (HARM) ① **HMA190 1238**
Daphné—cantata: 1v and ensemble **(pub 1708)**
J. Nicolas, D. Cuiller, P. Allain-Dupré, J. Bernfeld, M. Chapuis *Concert* (5/87) (PIER) ① **PV786101**
Didon—cantata: 1v and ensemble **(pub 1708)**
J. Nicolas, D. Cuiller, P. Allain-Dupré, J. Bernfeld, M. Chapuis *Concert* (5/87) (PIER) ① **PV786101**

La Dispute de l'amour et de l'hymen—cantata: 1v and ensemble **(pub 1714)**
D. Visse, Arts Florissants Voc Ens, Arts Florissants Instr Ens (r1986) *Concert*
(5/87) (HARM) ① **HMA190 1238**
Enée et Didon—cantata: 1v and ensemble **(pub 1714)**
J. Feldman, J-F. Gardeil, Arts Florissants Voc Ens, Arts Florissants Instr Ens (r1986) *Concert*
(5/87) (HARM) ① **HMA190 1238**
Les Femmes—cantata: 1v and ensemble **(pub 1708)** (Wds. Roy)
J-F. Gardeil, Arts Florissants Voc Ens, Arts Florissants Instr Ens (r1985) *Concert*
(5/87) (HARM) ① **HMA190 1238**
Hébé—cantat: 1v and ensemble **(pub 1708)**
J. Nicolas, D. Cuiller, P. Allain-Dupré, J. Bernfeld, M. Chapuis *Concert* (5/87) (PIER) ① **PV786101**
Messe de Requiem (c1722)
E. Baudry, M. Zanetti, J. Benet, J. Elwes, S. Varcoe, Paris Chapelle Royale Chor, Paris Chapelle Royale Orch, P. Herreweghe
(9/87) (HARM) ① **HMC90 1251**

SECTION V: STAGE WORKS

L' Europe galante—opéra-ballet: prologue & 4 acts **(1697—Paris)**
R. Yakar, M. Kweksilber, R. Jacobs, Petite Bande, G. Leonhardt (r1973) *Lully: Bourgeois Gentilhomme.*
(2/91) (DHM) ① **[2] GD77059**
Idoménée—tragédie lyrique: prologue and 5 acts **(1712 rev 1731)** (Lib. A Dachet)
EXCERPTS: 1. Ouverture. PROLOGUE: 2. Laissez nous sortir d'esclavage; 3. Quelle douce harmonie; 4. Sarabande; 5a. Chantez le dieu charmant; 5b. Air des Tritons; 6. Coulez Ruisseaux; 7. Jeunes Beautez. ACT ONE: 8. Venez, Gloire, Fierté; 9. Rassemblez les Troyens; 10. Marche; 11. Quittez vos fers; 12. Chantons, celebrons sa victoire; 13a. Rondeau; 13b. Tout se rend aux traits de la Beauté; 14. Seigneur, à tous les Grecs; 15. Son Pere ne vit plus!. ACT TWO: 16. O Dieux!; 17. Cessez de souleuer les ondes; 18. La paix regne par tout; 19. Soyez témoins de mon inquiétude; 20. Il me fuit le Cruel!; 21. Vous, des tendres amours; 22. Nous obeissons à ta voix; 23. D'un amour qui s'éteint. ACT THREE: 24. Ne condamne point mes transports; 25. Je dois être jaloux; 26. Que d'immoler mon fils; 27. Votre bonté s'interesse pour moy; 28a. Symphonie; 28b. Je vois des Argiens; 29a. Premier & Deuxième Riguadons; 29b. Aimable espérance; 30. Allez, Prince, partez; 31. Je viens des vastes mers. ACT FOUR: 32. Espoir des Malheureux; 33. Princesse, à vos regards j'ose encore m'offrir; 34. Ciel! que vois-jel; 35. O Neptune, reçoy tes voeux; 36. Triomphez, remportez une immortelle gloire; 37. Musette. 38. Voiez au son de nos musettes; 39. Riguadon. Menuets; 40. La Paix & les Plaisirs tranquiles; 41. Premier & Deuxième Passepieds; 42. Neptune a calmé sa colere. ACT FIVE: 43. Il est donc vray, Seigneur; 44. Ah! quel bonheur; 45. Peuples, pour la derniere fois; 46. Passacaille. Bourrées; 47. Gloire brillante, charmants plaisirs; 48. Je remets entre vos mains ces marques éclatantes; 49. Du Souverain des mers; 50. Quel feu dans mon sein se rallume!; 51. Quel pouvoir m'a conduit sur ce bord écarté?.
Cpte B. Delétré, S. Piau, M. Zanetti, J-P. Fouchécourt, M. Boyer, J. Corréas, R. Dugay, J-C. Sarragosse, M. Saint-Palais, A. Pichard, A. Mopin, Arts Florissants Chor, Arts Florissants Orch, W. Christie (r1991)
(9/92) (HARM) ① **[3] HMC90 1396/8**

CANNING, Thomas (b 1911) USA

SECTION I: ORCHESTRAL

Fantasy on a Hymn Tune (Amanda) by Justin Morgan—double string quartet and string orchestra **(1944)**
Houston SO, L. Stokowski (r c1959) *Concert*
(4/95) (EVER) ① **EVC9004**

CANNIO, Enrico (19th/20th Cent) Italy

SECTION IV: VOCAL AND CHORAL

'O surdato 'nnammurato—Song **(1915)** (Wds. Califano)
L. Pavarotti, Teatro Communale Orch, A. Guadagno *Concert* (8/83) (DECC) ① **410 015-2DH**
B. Gigli, orch. O. Sabajno (r1918) *Concert*
(5/90) (NIMB) ① **NI7807**

CANTELOUBE (DE CALARET), (Marie) Joseph (1879–1957) France

SECTION II: CHAMBER

Danse—horn and piano (1953)
B. Tuckwell, D. Blumenthal *Concert*
(11/92) (ETCE) ① **KTC1135**

SECTION IV: VOCAL AND CHORAL

Chants d'Auvergne—1v and orchestra (1923-30) (trad Auvergne melodies harm Canteloube)
Serie 1: 1. La pastoura als camps; 2. Baïlèro; 3a. L'ïo dè rotso; 3b. Ound' onorèn gorda; 3c. Obal, din lou Limouzi. Serie 2: 4. Pastourelle; 5. L'Antouèno; 6. La pastroulleta è lo chibaliè; 7. La delïssado; 8a. N'aï pas iéu de mïo; 8b. Lo calhé. Serie 3: 9. Lo fiolairé; 10. Passo pel prat; 11. Lou boussu; 12. Brezairola; 13. Malurous qu'o uno fenno. Serie 4: 14. Jou l'pount d'o Mirabel; 15. Oï, ayaï; 16. Pour l'enfant; 17. Chut, chut; 18. Pastorale; 19. Lou coucut. Serie 5: 20. Postouro sé tu m'aymo; 21. Quand z-èyro petituono; 22. Tè, l'co, tèl; 23. Uno jionto postouro; 24. Hé! beyla-z-y-dau fél; 25. Obal, din lo combuèlo; 26. Là-haut, sur le rocher; 27. Lou diziou bé.
Cpte N. Davrath, orch, P. de la Roche *Concert*
(10/91) (VANG) ① [2] **08.8002.72**
1, 2, 3a-c, 4-7, 8a, 8b, 9-13. K. Te Kanawa, ECO, J. Tate
(7/83) (DECC) ① **410 004-2DH**
1, 2, 3a-c, 4-7, 8a, 8b, 9-19, 22, 23. F. von Stade, RPO, A. de Almeida (6/91) (SONY) ① **MDK46509**
1-7, 8a, 8b, 9-13. Marvis Martin, Auvergne Orch, J-J. Kantorow (1992) (11/94) (DENO) ① **CO-75862**
2. K. Te Kanawa, ECO, J. Tate *Concert*
(11/87) (DECC) ① **417 645-2DH**
2. L. Garrett, Philh, A. Greenwood (1990-1) *Concert*
(11/91) (SILV) ① **SONGCD903**
2. Ex Cathedra Chbr Ch, J. Skidmore (r c1994) *Concert* (12/94) (ASV) ① **CDDCA912**
2, 3a-c, 4, 5, 7, 9-13, 17, 19, 20, 22, 23. J. Gomez, RLPO, V. Handley (10/87) (EMIN) ① **CD-EMX9500**
2, 3a-c, 4, 6, 7, 9, 11-15, 17, 19, 20, 22, 23. A. Auger, ECO, Y.P. Tortelier
(11/94) (VIRG) ① **CUV5 61120-2**
2, 3a, 4, 5, 10, 12, 13. A. Moffo, American SO, L. Stokowski *Concert* (6/89) (RCA) ① **GD87831**
2, 3a, 7, 8a, 9, 11, 13, 14, 16, 17, 19, 20, 23. P. Rozario, Philh, J. Pritchard
(10/90) (CARL) ① **PCD938**
2, 4, 7, 9-12, 14, 15, 17, 19, 20, 22, 23, 25. D. Upshaw, Lyon Op Orch, K. Nagano (r1994)
(2/95) (ERAT) ① **4509-96559-2**
3a, 4. L. Garrett, RPO, P. Robinson (r1994) *Concert*
(4/95) (SILV) ① **SILKD6004**
3c I. Watson, C. Nicklin (arr Walton) *Concert*
(4/91) (CHAN) ① **CHAN8892**
12, 13. G. Souzay, J. Bonneau (r1953) *Concert*
(7/91) (DECC) ① **425 975-2DM**
14-27. K. Te Kanawa, ECO, J. Tate (r1983) *Villa-Lobos: Bachianas Brasileiras 5.*
(1/85) (DECC) ① **411 730-2DH**
Chants des Pays Basques—French folksongs arrangements (1947)
1. Comment donc savoir; 2. Le premier de tous les oiseaux; 3. J'ai un douce amie; 4. Dans le tombeau; 5. Allons, beau rossignol.
1-5. N. Davrath, orch, G. Kingsley *Concert*
(10/91) (VANG) ① [2] **08.8002.72**
Chants du Languedoc—French folksong arrangements (1947)
1. La fille d'un paysan; 2. Mon père m'a plasée; 3. O up!; 4. Moi j'ai un homme; 5. Quand Marion va au moulin.
1-5. N. Davrath, orch, G. Kingsley *Concert*
(10/91) (VANG) ① [2] **08.8002.72**
Chants paysans—French folksong arrangements
1. La mère Antoine; 2. Oh! Madelon, je dois partir; 3. Rossignolet qui chants; 4. Lorsque le meunier; 5. Reveillez-vous, belle endormie.
1-5. N. Davrath, orch, G. Kingsley *Concert*
(10/91) (VANG) ① [2] **08.8002.72**

CAPIO, Iseut de (fl early 13th Cent) France

SECTION IV: VOCAL AND CHORAL

Domna N'Almucs, si-us plages—trobairitz song (with Almuc de Castelnau?)
Sinfonye, S. Wishart (r1992) *Concert*
(8/93) (HYPE) ① **CDA66625**

CAPIROLA, Vincenzo (1474–after 1548) Italy

SECTION III: INSTRUMENTAL

Capirola Lutebook—42 lute works (copied c 1517 by Capirola's student Vidal)
RICERCARI: 1. Ricercare I; 2. Ricercare II; 3. Ricercare IV; 4. Ricercare V; 5. Ricercare V; 6. Ricercare VI; 7. Ricercare VII; 8. Ricercare VIII; 9. Ricercare IX; 10. Ricercare XI; 11. Ricercare XI; 12. Ricercare XII; 13. Ricercare XIII. DANCES: 14. Bassa danse; 15. La Spagna I; 16. La Spagna II; 17. Padoana 'alla francesca' I; 18. Padoana 'alla francesca' II; 19. Padoana descorda; 20. Balletto. INTABULATIONS: 21. Sit Nomen Domini Benedictum (after Prioris); 22. Sncta Trinitas (after Fevin); 23. Allez regrets (after von Ghizeghem); 24. Nunca fue pena major (after Urrede); 25. O florens rosa (after Ghiselin); 26. Stavasi amor dormendo (after Tromboncini); 27. La Villanella; 28. Gentil prince; 29. De tous biens pleine (after von Ghizeghem); 30. Et in terra (after Josquin); 31. Qui tollis (after Josquin).
6, 15, 19, 20, 29-31. J. Lindberg *Concert*
(10/89) (BIS) ① **BIS-CD399**

CAPLET, André (1878–1925) France

SECTION I: ORCHESTRAL

Légende pour orchestre (1905)
Rhineland-Pfalz State PO, L. Segerstam (r1987)
(9/95) (MARC) ① **8 223751**
Marche triomphale et pompière—orchestra
Rhineland-Pfalz State PO, L. Segerstam (r1987)
(9/95) (MARC) ① **8 223751**
Le Masque de la mort rouge—harp and string orchestra (1908)
F. Cambreling, Monte Carlo PO, G. Prêtre (r1983) *Concert* (9/93) (EMI) ① **CDM7 64687-2**
Suite Persane—orchestra (1901)
1. Sharki; 2. Nihavend; 3. Iskia Samasi.
Rhineland-Pfalz State PO, L. Segerstam (r1987)
(9/95) (MARC) ① **8 223751**

SECTION II: CHAMBER

Conte fantastique—harp and string quartet (1919)
A. Giles, R. Kaminkovsky, R. Mozes, Y. Kaminkovsky, Y. Alperin *Concert*
(6/90) (CARL) ① **PWK1141**
L. Cabel, Musique Oblique Ens *Concert*
(2/93) (HARM) ① **HMC90 1417**
Rêverie et Petite Valse—flute and piano (1905)
R. Aitken, R. McCabe *Concert*
(9/89) (BIS) ① **BIS-CD184**
P. Lloyd, R. Holt *Concert* (9/92) (CARL) ① **PCD991**
P. E. Davies, J. Alley *Concert*
(7/94) (EMI) ① **CDC5 55085-2**

SECTION III: INSTRUMENTAL

2 Divertissements—harp (1924)
1. A la française; 2. A l'espagnole.
L. Cabel *Concert* (2/93) (HARM) ① **HMC90 1417**

SECTION IV: VOCAL AND CHORAL

Inscriptions champêtre—chorus (1914) (Wds. R. de Gourmont)
Lyon Nat Orch Chor, B. Tetu (r1992) *Miroir de Jésus.*
(9/93) (ACCO) ① **20233-2**
Le miroir de Jésus—mezzo-soprano, female vv, harp and strings (1923) (Wds. H Ghéon)
1. Miroir de Joie; 1a. Prélude; 1b. Annonciation; 1c. Visitation; 1d. Nativité; 1e. Présentation; 1f. Recouvrement; 2. Miroir de Peine; 2a. Prélude; 2b. Agonie au jardin; 2c. Flagellation; 2d. Couronnement d'épines; 2e. Portement de croix; 2f. Crucifixion; 3. Miroir de Gloire; 3a. Prélude; 3b. Résurrection; 3c. Ascension; 3d. Pentecôte; 3e. Assomption; 3f. Couronnement au ciel.
H. Schaer, Lyon Nat Orch Chor, Ravel Qt, M. Chanu, I. Moretti, B. Tetu (r1992) *Inscriptions champêtre.*
(9/93) (ACCO) ① **20233-2**
Myrrha—cantata (1901) (Wds. F Beisser)
S. Coste, M. Duguay, J-F. Lapointe, Paris Sorbonne Chor, Paris Sorbonne Orch, J. Grimbert (r1993/4) *Concert* (10/95) (MARC) ① **8 223755**
Prières—1v, harp and string quartet (1914)
1. O nascro dominicale; 2. Salutation angélique; 3. Symbole des apôtres.
S. Coste, Musique Oblique Ens, L. Cabel *Concert*
(2/93) (HARM) ① **HMC90 1417**

Septet—three wordless female voices and string quartet (1909)
S. Coste, S. Piau, S. Deguy, Musique Oblique Ens *Concert* (2/93) (HARM) ① **HMC90 1417**
2 Sonnets—soprano and harp (1924)
1. Quand reverrai-je hélas (wds. Du Bellay); 2. Doux fut le trait (wds. Ronsard).
S. Piau, L. Cabel *Concert*
(2/93) (HARM) ① **HMC90 1417**
Tout est lumière—cantata (1901) (Wds. V Hugo)
B. Desnoues, Paris Sorbonne Chor, Paris Sorbonne Orch, J. Grimbert (r1993/4) *Concert*
(10/95) (MARC) ① **8 223755**
Le Vieux coffret—four songs (1917) (Wds. de Gourmont)
4. Forêt.
4. C. Panzéra, SO, P. Coppola (r1928) *Concert*
(3/93) (DANT) ① [2] **LYS003/4**
4. C. Panzéra, orch, P. Coppola (r1928) *Concert*
(3/93) (EMI) ① **CDH7 64254-2**

CAPOLONGO, G. ?Italy

SECTION IV: VOCAL AND CHORAL

Suonno è fantasia—song
T. Ruffo, orch (r1912) *Concert*
(2/93) (PREI) ① [3] **89303(1)**
T. Ruffo, orch (r1929) *Concert*
(2/93) (PREI) ① [3] **89303(2)**

CARAFA DI COLOBRANO, Michele (Enrico-Francesco-Vincenzo-Aloisio-Paolo) (1787–1872) Italy

SECTION V: STAGE WORKS

Gabriella di Vergy—opera: 2 acts (1816—Naples) (Lib. Tottola)
Ah! fermate...Raoul!...Perchè non chiusi al di. Y. Kenny, P. Doghan, G. Mitchell Ch, Philh, D. Parry (r1987) *Concert* (10/90) (OPRA) ① [3] **ORCH103**
Le Nozze di Lammermoor—drama: 2 acts (1829—Paris) (Lib. L Balocchi)
D'un orribile tempesta S. McCulloch, T. Goble, I. Thompson, J. Viera, A. Thorburn, Philh, D. Parry *Concert* (8/95) (OPRA) ① [3] **ORCH104**

CARDILLO, Salvatore (19th/20th Cent) Italy

SECTION IV: VOCAL AND CHORAL

Core 'ngrato—song (1911) (Wds. R. Cordiferro)
L. Pavarotti, National PO, G. Chiaramello (arr Chiarmello) *Concert*
(7/90) (DECC) ① [2] **425 681-2DM2**
J. Carreras, MMF Orch, Rome Op Orch, Z. Mehta (pp1990) *Concert* (9/90) (DECC) ① **430 433-2DH**
E. Caruso, orch (r1911) *Concert*
(3/91) (PEAR) ① [3] **EVC2**
E. Caruso, orch (r1911) *Concert*
(7/91) (RCA) ① [12] **GD60495(4)**
E. Caruso, orch (r1911) *Concert*
(10/92) (TEST) ① **SBT1005**
P. Domingo, LSO, M. Peeters *Concert*
(5/93) (DG) ① **431 104-2GB**

CARDON, Jean-Baptiste (1760–1803) France

SECTION III: INSTRUMENTAL

Variations on 'Ah, vous dirai-je, maman'—harp
F. Kelly *Concert* (12/91) (HYPE) ① **CDA66497**

CARDOSO, Manuel (1566–1650) Portugal

SECTION IV: VOCAL AND CHORAL

Magnificat (Secundi Toni)—5vv (pub 1613)
Tallis Scholars, P. Phillips *Concert*
(10/90) (GIME) ① **CDGIM021**
Missa Pro defunctis—6vv (pub 1625)
Tallis Scholars, P. Phillips *Concert*
(10/90) (GIME) ① **CDGIM021**
Missa Regina caeli (1636)
The Sixteen, H. Christophers (r1993) *Concert*
(8/94) (COLL) ① **Coll1407-2**

Mulier quae erat—motet (5vv) (pub 1648)
Tallis Scholars, P. Phillips *Concert*
(10/90) (GIME) ① **CDGIM021**
Non mortui—motet (6vv) (pub 1625)
Tallis Scholars, P. Phillips *Concert*
(10/90) (GIME) ① **CDGIM021**
The Sixteen, H. Christophers (r1993) *Concert*
(8/94) (COLL) ① **Coll1407-2**
Nos autem gloriari—motet (5vv) (pub 1648)
Tallis Scholars, P. Phillips *Concert*
(10/90) (GIME) ① **CDGIM021**
Sitivit anima mea—motet (6vv) (pub 1625)
Tallis Scholars, P. Phillips *Concert*
(10/90) (GIME) ① **CDGIM021**
The Sixteen, H. Christophers (r1993) *Concert*
(8/94) (COLL) ① **Coll1407-2**
Tantum ergo sacramentum—motet
Circa 1500, N. Hadden *Concert*
(9/92) (VIRG) ① **VC7 59071-2**
Tulerunt lapides—motet (4vv) (pub 1648)
The Sixteen, H. Christophers (r1993) *Concert*
(8/94) (COLL) ① **Coll1407-2**

CAREY, Henry *(1687–1743)* England

SECTION IV: VOCAL AND CHORAL

Sally in our alley—song
H. Nash, orch (r1926) *Concert*
(8/89) (PEAR) ① **GEMMCD9319**
J. Potter, Broadside Band, J. Barlow (r1992; arr J.
Barlow) *Concert* (6/93) (SAYD) ① **CD-SDL400**

CARISSIMI, Giacomo *(1605–1674)* Italy

SECTION IV: VOCAL AND CHORAL

A piè d'un verde alloro, '(I)
Filosofi'—cantata: 2vv (before 1650) (Wds.
Benigni)
E. Schwarzkopf, I. Seefried, G. Moore (r1955)
Concert (3/89) (EMI) ① **CDH7 69793-2**
Amante sdegnato, 'Amor mio, che cosa è
questa'—cantata: 1v
E. Speiser, H.L. Hirsch *Concert*
(3/89) (JECK) ① **JD5004-2**
Il Ciarlatano, 'Poichè lo sdegno
intese'—cantata: 3vv
Consort of Musicke, A. Rooley *Concert*
(12/91) (DHM) ① **RD77154**
Deh memoria e che più chiedi—cantata (1v)
E. Speiser, H.L. Hirsch *Concert*
(3/89) (JECK) ① **JD5004-2**
Del giudizio universale, 'Suonerà l'ultima
tromba'—cantata: 1v (Wds. Benigni)
E. Speiser, H.L. Hirsch *Concert*
(3/89) (JECK) ① **JD5004-2**
Desiderata nobis—motet: 3vv and continuo
(pub 1667)
Gabrieli Consort, Gabrieli Players, P. McCreesh, T.
Roberts (r1992-3) *Concert*
(1/94) (ARCH) ① **437 833-2AH**
E pur vuole in cielo, 'Destava la cativa sorte
in amore'—cantata: 2 sopranos (1656)
E. Schwarzkopf, I. Seefried, G. Moore (r1955)
Concert (3/89) (EMI) ① **CDH7 69793-2**
Exulta gaude, filia Sion—motet: 2vv and
continuo (pub 1675)
Gabrieli Consort, Gabrieli Players, P. McCreesh, T.
Roberts (r1992-3) *Concert*
(1/94) (ARCH) ① **437 833-2AH**
Il mio core è un mar—cantata (2vv)
E. Schwarzkopf, I. Seefried, G. Moore (r1955)
Concert (3/89) (EMI) ① **CDH7 69793-2**
In un mar di pensieri—cantata (1v)
E. Speiser, H.L. Hirsch *Concert*
(3/89) (JECK) ① **JD5004-2**
Jephte, 'Historia di Jephte'—oratorio (before
1650)
N. Robson, S.H. Jones, Monteverdi Ch, EBS, J.E.
Gardiner *Concert* (11/90) (ERAT) ① **2292-45466-2**
Cantus Cölln (r1994) *Concert*
(10/95) (DHM) ① **05472 77322-2**
Jonas, 'Histoire de Jonas'—oratorio
M. Tucker, S. Varcoe, Monteverdi Ch, EBS, J.E.
Gardiner (r1988) *Concert*
(11/90) (ERAT) ① **2292-45466-2**
Judicium Extremum (Judicium Dei
extremum)—oratorio
S. Varcoe, His Majesties Sagbutts and Cornetts,
Monteverdi Ch, EBS, J.E. Gardiner *Concert*
(11/90) (ERAT) ① **2292-45466-2**

Il Lamento in morte di Maria Stuarda,
'Ferma, lascia ch'io parli—cantata: 1v
E. Speiser, H.L. Hirsch *Concert*.
(3/89) (JECK) ① **JD5004-2**
Lungi omai deh spiega—cantata: 2vv (before
1672)
E. Schwarzkopf, I. Seefried, G. Moore (r1955)
Concert (3/89) (EMI) ① **CDH7 69793-2**
O vulnera doloris—motet: 1-3vv
M. van Egmond, Ricercar Consort *Concert*
(1/90) (RICE) ① **RIC054032**
Vittoria! Vittoria!—arietta
H. Jadlowker, anon (r1927) *Concert*
(12/91) (CLUB) ① **CL99-042**
M. Battistini, C. Sabajno (r1921) *Concert*
(10/92) (PEAR) ① **GEMMCD9936**
C. Bartoli, G. Fischer *Concert*
(12/92) (DECC) ① **436 267-2DH**

CARLSTEDT, Jan *(b 1926)* Sweden

SECTION I: ORCHESTRAL

Metamorphosis—string orchestra, Op. 42
(1987)
Musica Vitae CO, W. Rajski *Concert*
(6/90) (BIS) ① **BIS-CD460**

SECTION II: CHAMBER

Divertimento for oboe quartet (1962)
G. Zubicky, T. Tønnesen, L.A. Tomter, T. Mørk
(r1988) (SIMA) ① **PSC1022**

CARLTON, Nicholas *(c1570–1630) England*

SECTION III: INSTRUMENTAL

A Verse for two to play in D
minor—keyboard
T. Koopman, T. Mathot *Concert*
(5/91) (CAPR) ① **10 254**

CAROSO, Fabritio *(c1527/35–after 1605) Italy*

SECTION II: CHAMBER

Il Ballarino—dance collection (pub 1581)
1. Cascarda allegrezza d'amore; 2. Dolce amoroso
fuoco.
1, 2. Broadside Band, J. Barlow *Concert*
(3/88) (HYPE) ① **CDA66244**
Barriera
Ulsamer Collegium, J. Ulsamer *Concert*
(2/86) (ARCH) ① **415 294-2AH**
Celeste Giglio
Ulsamer Collegium, J. Ulsamer *Concert*
(2/86) (ARCH) ① **415 294-2AH**
Laura soave—Balletto con Gagliarda,
Saltarello e Canario—3-part consort (1589)
J. Holloway, P. O'Dette, C. Thielmann *Concert*
(4/88) (HYPE) ① **CDA66228**
Nobilità di Dame—dance collection (pub
1600)
1. Balletto celeste giglio; 2. Balletto forza d'amore; 3.
Balletto alta gonzaga.
1-3. Broadside Band, J. Barlow *Concert*
(3/88) (HYPE) ① **CDA66244**

CAROUBEL, Pierre Francisque *(d 1611) Italy/France*

SECTION II: CHAMBER

Courante I
Ulsamer Collegium, J. Ulsamer *Concert*
(2/86) (ARCH) ① **415 294-2AH**
Courante II
Ulsamer Collegium, J. Ulsamer *Concert*
(2/86) (ARCH) ① **415 294-2AH**
Pavana de Spaigne
Ulsamer Collegium, J. Ulsamer *Concert*
(2/86) (ARCH) ① **415 294-2AH**
Volte I
Ulsamer Collegium, J. Ulsamer *Concert*
(2/86) (ARCH) ① **415 294-2AH**
Volte II
Ulsamer Collegium, J. Ulsamer *Concert*
(2/86) (ARCH) ① **415 294-2AH**

CARPENTER, John *(b 1948)* USA

SECTION V: STAGE WORKS

Big Trouble In Little China—film score
(1986)
EXCERPTS: 1. Pork Chop Express—Main Title.
1. D. Caine *Concert* (5/93) (SILV) ① **SILVAD3001**
Dark Star—film score (1974)
EXCERPTS: 1. Suite.
1. D. Caine *Concert* (5/93) (SILV) ① **SILVAD3003**
Halloween—film score (1978)
EXCERPTS: 1. Main Title.
1. D. Caine *Concert* (5/93) (SILV) ① **SILVAD3003**
They Live—film score (1988) (collab with Alan
Howarth)
EXCERPTS: 1. End Title.
1. D. Caine *Concert* (5/93) (SILV) ① **SILVAD3003**

CARPENTER, John Alden *(1876–1951) USA*

SECTION I: ORCHESTRAL

Adventures in a Perambulator—suite (1914)
EXCERPTS: 1. En Voiture!; 2. The Policeman; 3.
The Hurdy-Gurdy; 4. The Lake; 5. Dogs; 6. Dreams.
Eastman-Rochester Orch, H. Hanson (r1956)
Concert (2/93) (MERC) ① **434 319-2MM**

SECTION III: INSTRUMENTAL

Danza—piano (1947) (trans from orchestral
work, 1937)
D. Oldham *Concert* (7/88) (NEW) ① **NW328/9-2**
5 Diversions—piano (1922)
1. Lento; 2. Allegretto con moto; 3. Animato; 4.
Moderato; 5. Adagio.
D. Oldham *Concert* (7/88) (NEW) ① **NW328/9-2**
Impromptu—piano (1913)
D. Oldham *Concert* (7/88) (NEW) ① **NW328/9-2**
Little Dancer—piano (1917)
D. Oldham *Concert* (7/88) (NEW) ① **NW328/9-2**
Little Indian—piano (1917)
D. Oldham *Concert* (7/88) (NEW) ① **NW328/9-2**
Minuet—piano (1893)
D. Oldham *Concert* (7/88) (NEW) ① **NW328/9-2**
Nocturne—piano (1898)
D. Oldham *Concert* (7/88) (NEW) ① **NW328/9-2**
Polonaise américaine—piano (1912)
D. Oldham *Concert* (7/88) (NEW) ① **NW328/9-2**
Sonata for Piano (1897)
D. Oldham *Concert* (7/88) (NEW) ① **NW328/9-2**
Tango américain—piano (1920)
D. Oldham *Concert* (7/88) (NEW) ① **NW328/9-2**
Twilight Reverie—piano (1894)
D. Oldham *Concert* (7/88) (NEW) ① **NW328/9-2**

CARPENTRAS, Elzéar Genet de *(c1470–1548) France*

SECTION IV: VOCAL AND CHORAL

Vexilla regis—alternatim motet: 4vv
A. Azéma, F. Jodry, W. Hite, C. Kale, D. McCabe, P.
Guttry, Boston Schola Cantorum, Boston Camerata,
J. Cohen (r1994) *Concert*
(11/95) (ERAT) ① **4509-98480-2**

CARR, Robert *(fl 1684–87)* England

SECTION II: CHAMBER

Divisions upon an Italian ground—recorder
& continuo (pub 1686) (from 'The Delightful
Companion')
F. Brüggen, A. Bylsma (r1967/79) *Concert*
(11/95) (TELD) ① **4509-97465-2**

CARREIRA, António *(c1530–before 1597) Portugal*

SECTION III: INSTRUMENTAL

Canção a Quatro glosada—keyboard
S. Yates (r1993) *Concert*
(11/94) (CHAN) ① **CHAN0560**
Tento—organ
S. Farr (r1994) *Concert*
(11/94) (HYPE) ① **CDA66725**

SECTION IV: VOCAL AND CHORAL

Stabat mater
Taverner Ch, O. Rees (r1992) *Concert*
(1/94) (HERA) ① **HAVPCD155**

CARREÑO, Teresa (1853–1917)
Venezuela

SECTION II: CHAMBER

String Quartet in B minor (1896)
J. Roche, R. Zelnick, T. Strasser, C. Heller *Concert*
(10/94) (VOX) ① [2] **115845-2**

CARRERA Y LANCHARES, Pedro (fl 1786–1815) Spain

SECTION III: INSTRUMENTAL

Versos a 4 tono (Clasicos)—psalm versets for organ
1. no tempo marking; 2. Allegretto; 3. Andante; 4.
Poco andante; 5. Allegro comodo; 6. Allgretto.
J. van Oortmerssen *Concert*
(11/87) (BIS) ① **BIS-CD316**

CARROLL, Earl (1893–1948) USA

SECTION V: STAGE WORKS

So Long, Letty—musical show (1916—New York) (Lyrics cpsr)
EXCERPTS: 1. Patrick Henry Must Have Been a Married Man.
1. B. Linn, Orig Broadway Cast (r1917) *Concert*
(5/94) (PEAR) ① [3] **GEMMCDS9056/8**

CARROLL, Harry (19th–20th Cent) USA

SECTION V: STAGE WORKS

Oh, Look!—musical show (1918—New York) (Lyrics McCarthy)
EXCERPTS: 1. I'm Always Chasing Rainbows.
1. H. Fox, Orig Broadway Cast (r1918) *Concert*
(5/94) (PEAR) ① [3] **GEMMCDS9059/61**

CARTER, Elliott (Cook) (b 1908) USA

SECTION I: ORCHESTRAL

Concerto for Piano and Orchestra (1964-65)
U. Oppens, Cincinnati SO, M. Gielen (pp1984)
Variations for Orchestra. (4/87) (NEW) ① **NW347-2**
Partita—orchestra (1993)
Chicago SO, D. Barenboim (pp1994) *Concert*
(8/95) (TELD) ① **4509-99596-2**
Variations for Orchestra (1954-55)
Cincinnati SO, M. Gielen (pp1985) *Piano Concerto.*
(4/87) (NEW) ① **NW347-2**
Chicago SO, James Levine (r1990) *Concert*
(7/94) (DG) ① **431 698-2GH**

SECTION II: CHAMBER

Brass Quintet—2 trumpets, horn and 2 trombones (1974)
Wallace Collection, J. Wallace *Concert*
(3/92) (COLL) ① **Coll1229-2**
Canon for 3: In Memoriam Igor Stravinski—3 equal instruments (1971)
R. Friedrich, W. Bauer, M. Mester (r1992) *Concert*
(6/93) (CAPR) ① **10 439**
Con Leggerezza Pensosa: Omaggio a Italo Calvino—clarinet, violin and cello (1990)
Group for Contemporary Music (r1993) *Concert*
(12/94) (BRID) ① **BCD9044**
Duo—violin and piano (1973-74)
Group for Contemporary Music (r1993) *Concert*
(12/94) (BRID) ① **BCD9044**
Duo—violin and piano (1973-74)
R. Mann, C. Oldfather *Concert*
(4/92) (SONY) ① [2] **S2K47229**
Elegy—cello and piano (1943)
K. Kashkashian, R. Levin *Concert*
(9/86) (ECM) ① **827 744-2**
Elegy—string quartet (1946) (arr from work for vc and pf)
Arditti Qt (5/89) (ETCE) ① **KTC1066**
Arditti Qt (r1991-92) *Concert*
(12/93) (MONT) ① **782010**
Enchanted Preludes—flute and cello (1988)
P. Racine, T. Demenga *Concert*
(12/90) (ECM) ① **839 617-2**
Group for Contemporary Music (r1993) *Concert*
(12/94) (BRID) ① **BCD9044**

Esprit rude/Esprit doux—flute and clarinet (1985)
P. Racine, E. Molinari *Concert*
(12/90) (ECM) ① **839 617-2**
A Fantasy about Purcell's 'Fantasia Upon One Note'—2 trumpets, horn & 2 trombone (1974)
London Gabrieli Brass Ens. C. Larkin *Concert*
(5/92) (HYPE) ① **CDA66517**
Sonata for Cello and Piano (1948)
Group for Contemporary Music (r1992) *Concert*
(12/94) (BRID) ① **BCD9044**
String Quartet No. 1 (1950-51)
Arditti Qt *String Quartet 4.*
(5/89) (ETCE) ① **KTC1065**
Juilliard Qt *Concert*
(4/92) (SONY) ① [2] **S2K47229**
String Quartet No. 2 (1959)
Arditti Qt *Concert* (5/89) (ETCE) ① **KTC1066**
Juilliard Qt *Concert*
(4/92) (SONY) ① [2] **S2K47229**
String Quartet No. 3 (1971)
Arditti Qt *Concert* (5/89) (ETCE) ① **KTC1066**
Juilliard Qt *Concert*
(4/92) (SONY) ① [2] **S2K47229**
String Quartet No. 4 (1986)
Arditti Qt *String Quartet 1.*
(5/89) (ETCE) ① **KTC1065**
Juilliard Qt *Concert*
(4/92) (SONY) ① [2] **S2K47229**
Triple Duo—chamber ensemble (1982-83)
H. Schneeberger, T. Demenga, P. Racine, E.
Molinari, P. Cleemann, G. Huber, J. Wyttenbach
Concert (12/90) (ECM) ① **839 617-2**

SECTION III: INSTRUMENTAL

Changes—guitar (1983)
Group for Contemporary Music (r1994) *Concert*
(12/94) (BRID) ① **BCD9044**
Gra—clarinet (1993)
Group for Contemporary Music (r1993) *Concert*
(12/94) (BRID) ① **BCD9044**
Night Fantasies—piano (1980)
A. Karis *Concert* (1/87) (BRID) ① **BCD9001**
U. Oppens *Concert* (5/90) (MUSI) ① **MACD-604**
Riconoscenza per Goffredo Petrassi—violin (1984)
H. Schneeberger *Concert*
(12/90) (ECM) ① **839 617-2**
Group for Contemporary Music (r1992) *Concert*
(12/94) (BRID) ① **BCD9044**
Scrivo in Vento—flute (1991)
Group for Contemporary Music (r1993) *Concert*
(12/94) (BRID) ① **BCD9044**
Sonata for Piano (1945-46)
P. Lawson *Concert* (5/91) (VIRG) ① **VC7 59008-2**
J. McCabe *Concert*
(6/91) (CNTI) ① [2] **CCD1028/9**

SECTION IV: VOCAL AND CHORAL

Emblems—men's vv and piano (1947) (Wds. A Tate)
J. Oliver Chorale, J. Oliver (r1992) *Concert*
(5/95) (KOCH) ① **37178-2**
The Harmony of Morning—women's vv and chamber orch (1945) (Wds. M Van Doren)
J. Oliver Chorale, J. Oliver (r1992) *Concert*
(5/95) (KOCH) ① **37178-2**
Heart not so heavy as mine—choir a cappella (1938) (Wds. E Dickinson)
J. Oliver Chorale, J. Oliver (r1992) *Concert*
(5/95) (KOCH) ① **37178-2**
In Sleep, In Thunder—tenor and 14 players (1981) (Wds. R. Lowell)
J. Garrison, Speculum Musicae, R. Black *Concert*
(2/90) (BRID) ① **BCD9014**
A Mirror on which to dwell—soprano and chamber ensemble (1975) (Wds. E Bishop)
C. Schadeberg, Speculum Musicae, D. Palma
Concert (2/90) (BRID) ① **BCD9014**
Musicians wrestle everywhere—choir a cappella (1945) (Wds. E Dickinson)
J. Oliver Chorale, J. Oliver (r1992) *Concert*
(5/95) (KOCH) ① **37178-2**
3 Poems of Robert Frost—mezzo-soprano, baritone and piano (1943)
P. Mason, Speculum Musicae, D. Starobin (1980
version: bar & orch) *Concert*
(2/90) (BRID) ① **BCD9014**
Syringa—mezzo-soprano, bass and 11 instruments (1978)
Katherine Ciesinski, J. Opalach, Speculum Musicae,
W. Purvis *Concert* (2/90) (BRID) ① **BCD9014**

CARULLI, Ferdinando (1770–1841) Italy

SECTION II: CHAMBER

Duo—two guitars, Op. 34
J. Bream, J. Williams (r1971) *Concert*
(11/93) (RCA) ① **09026 61450-2**
Serenade—two guitars, Op. 96/1
J. Bream, J. Williams (r1973) *Concert*
(11/93) (RCA) ① **09026 61452-2**
Variations de Beethoven arranges pour le Piano et Guitarre, Op. 169
N. North, M. Cole *Concert*
(6/87) (AMON) ① **CD-SAR18**

CARUSO, Enrico (1873–1921) Italy

SECTION IV: VOCAL AND CHORAL

Dreams of long ago—song (Wds. E. Carroll)
E. Caruso, orch. W.B. Rogers (r1912) *Concert*
(7/91) (RCA) ① [12] **GD60495(4)**
E. Caruso, orch. W.B. Rogers (r1912) *Concert*
(10/91) (PEAR) ① [3] **EVC3(1)**
Tiempo antico—song (Wds. cpsr)
E. Caruso, orch. W.B. Rogers (r1916) *Concert*
(7/91) (RCA) ① [12] **GD60495(5)**
E. Caruso, orch. W.B. Rogers (r1916) *Concert*
(10/91) (PEAR) ① [3] **EVC4(1)**

CARVER, Robert (c1490–1550) Scotland

SECTION IV: VOCAL AND CHORAL

Gaude flore virginali—motet (5vv)
Cappella Nova, A. Tavener *Concert*
(10/91) (ASV) ① **CDGAU124**
Mass for 5 voices, 'Fera pessima' (?mid 1520s)
Cappella Nova, A. Tavener *Missa Pater creator omnium.* (5/92) (ASV) ① **CDGAU127**
Mass for 6 voices
Cappella Nova, A. Tavener *Missa L'homme armé.*
(10/91) (ASV) ① **CDGAU126**
Missa Dum sacrum mysterium—10vv (1513)
Cappella Nova, A. Tavener *Concert*
(10/91) (ASV) ① **CDGAU124**
Missa L'homme armé—4vv (c1520)
Cappella Nova, A. Tavener *Mass for 6 voices.*
(10/91) (ASV) ① **CDGAU126**
Agnus Dei from Amsterdam Loeki Stardust Qt (1991; arr recorder consort) *Concert*
(2/94) (L'OI) ① **436 155-2OH**
Missa Pater creator omnium—4vv (1546)
Cappella Nova, A. Tavener *Mass for 5 voices.*
(5/92) (ASV) ① **CDGAU127**
O bone Jesu—motet (19vv)
Cappella Nova, A. Tavener *Concert*
(10/91) (ASV) ① **CDGAU124**

CARYLL, Ivan (1861–1921) Belgium/England
nom-de-plum of Félix Tilkin

SECTION V: STAGE WORKS

Chin-Chin—musical show (1914—New York) (Lyrics Caldwell, Burnside & O'Dea)
EXCERPTS: 1. Chin-Chin.
1. Six Brown Brothers (r1916) *Concert*
(5/94) (PEAR) ① [3] **GEMMCDS9056/8**
The Pink Lady—musical show (London)
Waltz Southern Fest Orch, R. White *Concert*
(5/93) (CHAN) ① **CHAN9110**
A Runaway Girl—musical show (1898—London) (Lyrics Hopwood & Greenbank; music collab with Lionel Monckton)
EXCERPTS: 1. Not the Sort of Girl I Care About; 2. I Thought it My Business to Say So; 3. I Love Society; 4. For There's No-One in the World Like You; 5. The Boy Guessed Right; 6. The Piccaninnies; 7. The Soldiers in the Park; 8. Sea-Girl Land of My Home; 9. The Man from Cook's; 10. The Singing Girl.
7. E. Jackson, Broadway Cast (r1899) *Concert*
(5/94) (PEAR) ① [3] **GEMMCDS9050/2(1)**
The Toreador—musical show (1901—London) (Lyrics Ross & Greenbank; Monckton & Rubens)
EXCERPTS: 1. Maud; 2. When I Marry Amelia; 3. Captivating Cora; 4. I'm Romantic; 5. España; 6. Toreador's Song; 7. Keep Off the Grass; 8.

Everybody's Awfully Good to Me; 9. Archie.
6. W. H. Thompson, Broadway Cast (r1902) *Concert*
(5/94) (PEAR) ① [3] **GEMMCDS9050/2(1)**

CASADESUS, Henri (Gustave) (1879–1947) France

SECTION I: ORCHESTRAL

Concerto for Cello and Strings in C minor
(spuriously attrib to J C Bach)
Y. Turovsky (vc/dir), Montreal I Musici *Concert*
(1/87) (CHAN) ① **CHAN8470**
Concerto for Viola and Orchestra in B minor
(incorrectly attrib. Handel)
W. Primrose, CO, W. Goehr (r1937) *Concert*
(9/94) (BIDD) ① **LAB088**
W. Primrose, CO, W. Goehr (r1937) *Concert*
(9/94) (PEAR) ① **GEMMCD9045**

CASALS, Pablo (1876–1973) Spain

SECTION I: ORCHESTRAL

Sardana—cello orchestra (1927)
LPO Vcs, RPO Vcs, BBC SO Vcs, Philh Vcs, G.
Simon (r1993) *Concert*
(9/95) (CALA) ① **CACD0104**

SECTION IV: VOCAL AND CHORAL

Cançó a la verge—2 trebles (1942)
Montserrat Escolania, I. Segarra *Concert*
(1/92) (SCHW) ① **313062**
Eucaristica—3 trebles and chorus (1934)
Montserrat Escolania, I. Segarra *Concert*
(1/92) (SCHW) ① **313062**
Nigra sum—3 trebles and men's chorus
(1942)
Montserrat Escolania, I. Segarra *Concert*
(1/92) (SCHW) ① **313062**
O vos omnes—chorus (?1932) (various
versions, pub 1953-54 & 1965)
Montserrat Escolania, I. Segarra *Concert*
(1/92) (SCHW) ① **313062**
Oracio a La Verge de Montserrat—chorus
(1959) (Wds. Gubern)
Montserrat Escolania, I. Segarra *Concert*
(1/92) (SCHW) ① **313062**
Recordare, virgo mater—chorus (1942)
Montserrat Escolania, I. Segarra *Concert*
(1/92) (SCHW) ① **313062**
Rosarium beatae virginis—chorus (1932)
Montserrat Escolania, I. Segarra *Concert*
(1/92) (SCHW) ① **313062**
Salve, Montserratina—chorus (1932)
Montserrat Escolania, I. Segarra *Concert*
(1/92) (SCHW) ① **313062**
Tota pulchra es—chorus with tenor (ad lib)
(1943)
Montserrat Escolania, I. Segarra *Concert*
(1/92) (SCHW) ① **313062**

CASELLA, Alfredo (1883–1947) Italy

SECTION I: ORCHESTRAL

Paganiniana—orchestra, Op. 65 (1942)
Santa Cecilia Academy Orch, G. Cantelli (r1949)
Concert   (7/93) (TEST) ① **SBT1017**
Milan La Scala PO, R. Muti (r1992) *Concert*
(4/94) (SONY) ① **SK53280**

SECTION III: INSTRUMENTAL

Sonatina—piano, Op. 28 (1916)
W. Gieseking (pp1947) *Concert*
(3/94) (PEAR) ① **GEMMCD9038**

CASHIAN, Philip (b 1963) England

SECTION II: CHAMBER

String Quartet No. 1 (1987)
Bingham Qt *Concert*   (11/92) (NMC) ① **NMCD006**

CASKEN, John (b 1949) England

SECTION I: ORCHESTRAL

Darting the Skiff—string orchestra (1992/3)
Northern Sinfonia, J. Casken (r1994) *Concert*
(5/95) (COLL) ① **Coll1424-2**
Maharal Dreaming (1989)
Northern Sinfonia, J. Casken (r1994) *Concert*
(5/95) (COLL) ① **Coll1424-2**

Vaganza—large ensemble (1985)
Northern Sinfonia, J. Casken (r1994) *Concert*
(5/95) (COLL) ① **Coll1424-2**

CASSADÓ, Gaspar (1896–1966) Spain

SECTION II: CHAMBER

Dance of the Green Devil—cello and piano
M. Kliegel, R. Havenith *Concert*
(9/92) (MARC) ① **8 223403**

SECTION III: INSTRUMENTAL

Suite for Cello
M. Kliegel (r1993) *Concert*
(1/95) (NAXO) ① **8 550785**

CASTELLO, Dario (1590–1644) Italy

SECTION II: CHAMBER

Sonate concertate in stil moderno—two
violins and continuo (libro primo pub 1621,
libro secondo pub 1629)
EXCERPTS: 1. Sonata prima; 2. Sonata seconda; 3.
Sonata terza; 4. Sonata quarta; 5. Sonata quinta; 9.
Sonata nona; 10. Sonata decima; 12. Sonata
duodecima; 15. Sonata quindicesima; 17. Sonata
decimosettima, 'in ecco'.
2. Taverner Plyrs, A. Parrott *Concert*
(8/91) (EMI) ① **CDC7 54117-2**
12. Palladian Ens (r1993) *Concert*
(1/95) (LINN) ① **CKD015**
15. Capriccio Stravagante, S. Sempé (hpd/dir)
Concert   (10/91) (DHM) ① **RD77220**

CASTELNUOVO-TEDESCO, Mario (1895–1968) Italy/USA

SECTION I: ORCHESTRAL

Concerto for Guitar and Orchestra No. 1 in
D, Op. 99 (1939)
N. Hall, LMP, A. Litton (r1992) *Concert*
(3/94) (DECC) ① **440 293-2DH**
N. Kraft, Northern CO, N. Ward (r1992) *Concert*
(4/94) (NAXO) ① **8 550729**
Concerto for Violin and Orchestra No. 2, 'I
profeti', Op. 66 (1931)
J. Heifetz, Los Angeles PO, A. Wallenstein (r1954)
Concert   (9/90) (RCA) ① **GD87872**
I. Perlman, Israel PO, Z. Mehta (pp1990) *Ben Haim:
Violin Concerto.*   (5/93) (EMI) ① **CDC7 54296-2**
J. Heifetz, Los Angeles PO, A. Wallenstein (r1954)
Concert (11/94) (RCA) ① [65] **09026 61778-2(43)**
I. Perlman, Israel PO, Z. Mehta (pp1990) *Concert*
(6/95) (EMI) ① [20] **CZS4 83177-2(2)**

SECTION II: CHAMBER

The Lark—poem in the form of a Rondo, Op.
64 (1930)
J. Heifetz, E. Bay (r1953-4) *Concert*
(11/94) (RCA) ① [65] **09026 61778-2(31)**
Sea murmurs—violin and piano, Op. 24a
(1938) (arr cpsr from Shakespeare Songs,
1932)
J. Lloyd Webber, J. Lenehan (r1992: arr vn/pf:
Heifetz) *Concert*   (10/93) (PHIL) ① **434 917-2PH**
J. Heifetz, B. Smith (r1972) *Concert*
(11/94) (RCA) ① [65] **09026 61778-2(46)**
J. Heifetz, A. Sándor (r1934) *Concert*
(11/94) (RCA) ① [65] **09026 61778-2(02)**
J. Heifetz, E. Bay (r1946) *Concert*
(11/94) (RCA) ① [65] **09026 61778-2(06)**
Sonata—flute and guitar, Op. 205 (1965)
V. Taylor, T. Kain *Concert*   (11/94) (TALL) ① **TP003**
Tango—violin and piano, Op. 24b (1933) (arr
cpsr from Shakespeare Songs, Vol. VIII)
J. Heifetz, E. Bay (r1946) *Concert*
(11/94) (RCA) ① [65] **09026 61778-2(06)**

SECTION III: INSTRUMENTAL

Alt Wien—piano rhapsody, Op. 30 (1923)
EXCERPTS: 1. Valse.
1. J. Heifetz, A. Sándor (r1934) *Concert*
(11/94) (RCA) ① [65] **09026 61778-2(02)**
Capriccio Diabolico, 'omaggi a
Paganini'—guitar, Op. 85 (1935)
N. Kraft *Concert*   (8/93) (CHAN) ① **CHAN9033**
Etudes d'ondes—piano
X. Wei, Pam Nicholson (arr Heifetz as Sea Murmurs)
Concert   (9/90) (ASV) ① **CDDCA698**

3 Preludi Mediterranei—guitar, Op. 176
(1955)
1. Sernatella; 2. Nenia; 3. Danza.
D. Hoogeveen (r1992) *Concert*
(4/94) (ETCE) ① **KTC1150**
Sonata, 'omaggio a Boccherini'—guitar, Op.
77 (1934)
N. Kraft *Concert*   (8/93) (CHAN) ① **CHAN9033**
Vivo e energico A. Segovia (r1936) *Concert*
(5/89) (EMI) ① [2] **CHS7 61047-2**
Variazioni à travers les siècles—guitar, Op.
71 (1932)
D. Hoogeveen (r1992) *Concert*
(4/94) (ETCE) ① **KTC1150**

SECTION IV: VOCAL AND CHORAL

Divan of Moses-ibn-Ezra—song cycle:
soprano and guitar, Op. 207 (1966)
PART 1: 1. When the morning of life has passed; 2.
The dove that nests in the tree-tops; 3. Wrung with
anguish. PART 2: 4. Sorrow shatters my heart; 5.
Fate has blocked the way; 6. O brook. PART 3: 7.
Drink deep, my friend; 8. Dull and sad is the sky; 9.
The garden dons a coat of many. PART 4: 10. Men
and children of this world; 11. The world is like a
woman of folly; 12. Only in God I trust. PART 5: 14. I
have seen upon the face; 15. Let man remember all
his days; 16. Come now, to the Court of Death; 17.
Peace upon them; 18. I behold ancient graves; 19.
Wouldst thou look upon me in my grave?.
R. Alexander, D. Hoogeveen (r1992) *Concert*
(4/94) (ETCE) ① **KTC1150**

CASTILLO, Ricardo (1891–1966) Guatemala

SECTION I: ORCHESTRAL

Guatemala I—orchestra (1934)
Moscow SO, A. de Almeida (r1994) *Concert*
(5/95) (MARC) ① **8 223710**
Sinfonieta para Orquesta (1948)
1. Allegramente; 2. Moto espressivo e moderato; 3.
Allegro.
Moscow SO, A. de Almeida (r1994) *Concert*
(5/95) (MARC) ① **8 223710**
Xibalbá—symphonic poem (1944)
1. Invocación; 2. Evocación.
Moscow SO, A. de Almeida (r1994) *Concert*
(5/95) (MARC) ① **8 223710**

SECTION III: INSTRUMENTAL

Guatemala II—serie de impresiones: piano
(1936)
Moscow SO, A. de Almeida (r1994: orch R Asturias)
Concert   (5/95) (MARC) ① **8 223710**

CASTILLON (DE SAINT-VICTOR), (Marie-) Alexis (1838–1873) France

SECTION I: ORCHESTRAL

Concerto for Piano and Orchestra in D, Op.
12 (1871)
A. Ciccolini, Monte Carlo PO, G. Prêtre *Esquisses
symphoniques.*   (3/92) (EMI) ① **CDM7 63943-2**
Esquisses symphoniques, Op. 15 (1877)
Monte Carlo PO, G. Prêtre *Piano Concerto in D.*
(3/92) (EMI) ① **CDM7 63943-2**

CASTRO, Jean de (c1540–c1600) Netherlands

SECTION IV: VOCAL AND CHORAL

De peu de bien—chanson: 6vv (pub 1576)
(Wds Ronsard)
C. Janequin Ens, D. Visse (r1993) *Concert*
(2/95) (HARM) ① **HMC90 1491**
Je suis tellement langoureux—chanson: 5vv
(pub 1576) (Wds Ronsard)
C. Janequin Ens, D. Visse (r1993) *Concert*
(2/95) (HARM) ① **HMC90 1491**
Quand tu tournes tes yeux—chanson: 3vv
(pub 1576) (Wds Ronsard)
C. Janequin Ens, D. Visse (r1993) *Concert*
(2/95) (HARM) ① **HMC90 1491**

CASTRO, Juan Blas de (c1560–1631) Spain

SECTION IV: VOCAL AND CHORAL

Desdelas torres del alma
M. Figueras, Hespèrion XX, J. Savall *Concert*
(2/92) (ASTR) ① **E8729**

Entre dos Alamos verdes
M. Figueras, Hespèrion XX, J. Savall *Concert*
(2/92) (ASTR) ① **E8729**

CATALÁN, Maria (b 1951) Spain

SECTION III: INSTRUMENTAL

las Iruñeako Taldea—piano variations (1986)
2, 7. S. Marin *Concert* (4/93) (RNE) ① **M3/03**

CATALANI, Alfredo (1854–1893) Italy

SECTION V: STAGE WORKS

Loreley—azione romantica: 4 acts (1890—Rome) (Lib. Zanardini. after D'Ormeville)
Amor, celeste abbrezza M. Freni, Venice La Fenice Orch, R. Abbado *Concert*
(9/92) (DECC) ① **433 316-2DH**
Dove son? C. Muzio, orch (r1922) *Concert*
(5/90) (BOGR) ① [2] **BIM705-2**
Dove son? C. Muzio, orch (r1922) *Concert*
(1/94) (ROMO) ① [2] **81005-2**
Nel verde maggio B. Gigli, orch, R. Bourdon (r1923) *Concert* (5/90) (NIMB) ① **NI7807**
La **Wally—opera: 4 acts (1892—Milan)** (Lib. Illica)
EXCERPTS: ACT 1: 1. Tr la la la...Bravo Gellner; 2. Un di verso il Murzoll; 3a. S'ode echeggiar; 3b. Su per l'erto sentier; 4. Ma si direbbe; 5. Chi osò levar sul padre; 6. L'Hagenbach l'abborro; 7a. Sei tu che domandato hai; 7b. T'amo ben io; 8. Ebben?...Ne andrò lontana; 9. Ad ora così tarda. ACT 2: 10. Entro la folla che intorno s'aggira; 11. Suona la squilla mattutina; 12. No!...coll'amor tu non dei scherzar; 13. Eccola qua; 14. Finor non m'han baciata; 15a. Sei tu?...Son io; 15b. Cantava un di mia nonna; 15c. Se tu, Wally, sapessi; 16. Che brami, Wally?; 17a. Già il canto fervido; 17b. No! parla! vo'saper. ACT 3: 18. Interlude and Orchestral Introduction; 19. Fa cor, Wally; 20. Non v'è maggior piacer; 21. Ebben...Dunque; 22. L'Hagenbach qui?; 23. Nè mai dunque avrò pace; 24. Buio è il sentier; 25. A me soccorso. ACT 4: 26. Orchestral Interlude; 27. Luogo sicura questo non è più; 28. Prendi, fanciul, e serbala; 29a. Eterne a me dintorno; 29b. Sì, come te, fanciulla del mio canto; 30a. Wally! Wally!...Come sei triste; 30b. Ah! sono, ahimè!; 30c. M'hai salvato...Quando a Sölden; 30d. Vieni, una placida vita.
Cpte R. Tebaldi, M. del Monaco, P. Cappuccilli, J. Diaz, L. Marimpietri, S. Malagù, A. Mariotti, Turin Lyric Chor, Monte Carlo Nat Op Orch, F. Cleva (2/90) (DECC) ① [2] **425 417-2DM2**
Cpte E. Marton, F.E. d'Artegna, A. Titus, F. Araiza, J. Kaufman, B. Calm, M. Pertusi, Bavarian Rad Chor, Munich RO, P. Steinberg
(9/90) (EURO) ① [2] **RD69073**
7b G. Bechi, La Scala Orch, U. Berrettoni (r1941) *Concert* (2/90) (PREI) ① **89009**
8. G. Bumbry, Stuttgart RSO, S. Soltesz *Concert* (11/86) (ORFE) ① **C081841A**
8. M. Callas, Philh, T. Serafin (r1954) *Concert* (11/86) (EMI) ① **CDC7 47282-2**
8. C. Muzio, orch (r1920) *Concert* (5/90) (BOGR) ① [2] **BIM705-2**
8. N. Miricioiu, D. Harper (pp1985) *Concert* (5/90) (ETCE) ① **KTC1041**
8. V. de los Angeles, Rome Op Orch, G. Morelli (r1954) *Concert* (8/90) (EMI) ① **CDH7 63495-2**
8. H. Spani, orch, C. Sabajno (r1928) *Concert* (9/90) (CLUB) ① [2] **CL99-509/10**
8. R. Tebaldi, Monte Carlo Nat Op Orch, F. Cleva *Concert* (8/91) (DECC) ① [2] **430 481-2DX2**
8. L. Garrett, Philh, A. Greenwood (r1990-1) *Concert* (11/91) (SILV) ① **SONGCD903**
8. H. Spani, La Scala Orch, C. Sabajno (r1928) *Concert* (2/92) (MMOI) ① **CDMOIR408**
8. A. Marc, NZ SO, H. Wallberg *Concert* (6/92) (DELO) ① **DE3108**
8. M. Gauci, Belgian Rad & TV Orch, A. Rahbari *Concert* (11/92) (NAXO) ① **8 550606**
8. H. Spani, La Scala Orch, C. Sabajno (r1928) *Concert* (12/92) (PREI) ① **89037**

8. J. Hammond, Philh, W. Susskind (r1949) *Concert* (12/92) (TEST) ① **SBT1013**
8. R. Pampanini, orch, L. Molajoli (r1927) *Concert* (8/93) (PREI) ① **89063**
8. R. Tebaldi, Monte Carlo Op Orch, F. Cleva (r1968) *Concert* (10/93) (DECC) ① **436 461-2DM**
8. C. Muzio, orch (r1920) *Concert* (1/94) (ROMO) ① [2] **81005-2**
8. N. Stemme, Paris Opéra-Bastille Orch, E. Kohn (pp1992) *Concert* (6/94) (SONY) ① **SK46691**
8. C. Muzio, orch (r1917) *Concert* (1/95) (ROMO) ① [2] **81010-2**
8, 23. M. Freni, Venice La Fenice Orch, R. Abbado *Concert* (9/92) (DECC) ① **433 316-2DH**
23. G. Cigna, orch, L. Molajoli (r1932) *Concert* (11/90) (PREI) ① **89016**
23. G. Cigna, orch, L. Molajoli (r1932) *Concert* (11/90) (LYRC) ① **SRO805**

CATO, Diomedes (before 1570–?after 1607) Italy

SECTION III: INSTRUMENTAL

Fantasia sopra 'la canzon degli Ucelli' (Janequin)—lute (in Lord Herbert of Cherbury's Lute Book)
P. O'Dette *Concert* (4/93) (HARM) ① **HMU90 7068**

CATURLA, Alejandro García (1906–1940) Cuba

SECTION I: ORCHESTRAL

3 Danzas cubanas—orchestra (1928)
1. Danza del tambor; 2. Motivos de danzas; 3. Danza lucumi.
New World Sym, M. Tilson Thomas (r1992) *Concert* (6/93) (ARGO) ① **436 737-2ZH**

CAUDIOSO, Domenico (18th Cent)

SECTION I: ORCHESTRAL

Concerto for Mandolin and Strings in G
B. Bianchi, Solisti Veneti, C. Scimone *Concert* (12/93) (ERAT) ① **4509-92132-2**

CAVALIERI, Emilio de (c1550–1602) Italy

SECTION IV: VOCAL AND CHORAL

Dalle pie alte sfere—aria (1v) - Intermedio 1, La Peligrina (c1589) (Wds. Bardi)
E. Kirkby, Taverner Plyrs, A. Parrott *Concert* (8/88) (EMI) ① **CDC7 47998-2**
Godi, turba mortal—aria (1v) - Intermedio 6, La Peligrina (c1589) (Wds. Rinuccini)
E. Van Evera, Taverner Plyrs, A. Parrott *Concert* (8/88) (EMI) ① **CDC7 47998-2**
O che nuovo miracolo—madrigal (8vv) - Intermedio 6, La Peligrina (c1589) (Wds. Lucchesini)
Taverner Consort, Taverner Ch, Taverner Plyrs, A. Parrott *Concert* (8/88) (EMI) ① **CDC7 47998-2**

CAVALLI, (Pietro) Francesco (1602–1676) Italy

SECTION II: CHAMBER

Canzoni (Musiche Sacrae)—3-12vv
1. 3vv; 2. 4vv; 3. 6vv; 4. 8vv; 5. 10vv; 6. 12vv.
1. R. Micconi (arr org) *Concert* (3/90) (MOTE) ① **CD10561**
1. Palladian Ens (r1993) *Concert* (1/95) (LINN) ① **CKD015**

SECTION IV: VOCAL AND CHORAL

Donzelle fuggite
E. Pinza, F. Kitzinger (r1940) *Concert* (9/93) (RCA) ① **09026 61245-2**
Lauda Jerusalem—double choir (pub 1656) (from 'Musiche sacre')
Gabrieli Consort, Gabrieli Players, P. McCreesh (r1990; ed Bartlett) *Concert* (4/93) (ARCH) ① [2] **437 552-2AH2**
Salve Regina
A. Wright, Westminster Cath Ch, S. Cleobury (ed. Raymond) *Concert* (7/83) (ARGO) ① **410 005-2ZH**
Monteverdi Ch, EBS, J.E. Gardiner *Concert* (7/85) (ERAT) ① **2292-45219-2**
The Sixteen, H. Christophers, L. Cummings, R. Jeffrey (r1992) *Concert* (10/93) (COLL) ① **Coll1360-2**

SECTION V: STAGE WORKS

Calisto—opera: prologue & 3 acts (1652—Venice) (Lib. Faustini)
Cpte M. Bayo, M. Lippi, S. Keenlyside, G. Pushee, A. Mantovani, S. Theodoridou, G. Ragon, B. Banks, D. Visse, D. Pittsinger, J. Vindevogel, Concerto Vocale, R. Jacobs (r1994; realised Jacobs) (9/95) (HARM) ① [3] **HMC90 1515/7**
Giasone—opera: prologue and 3 acts (1649—Venice)
EXCERPTS: 1. Delizie contente.
1. C. Bartoli, G. Fischer *Concert* (12/92) (DECC) ① **436 267-2DH**
L' **Ormindo—opera: 2 acts (1644—Venice)** (Lib. G Faustini)
EXCERPTS: 1. Sinfonia. ACT ONE: 2a. Miracolo d'amore; 2b. Quel che creduto io non avrei pur vidi; 2c. Huat, hanat, Ista; 2d. Perfidissimo Amida; 3. Verginella infelice; 4a. Se nel sen di giovinetti; 4b. Eccola appunto, Ormindo; 4c. Oh dell'anima mia; 5. Se del Perù le vene; 6a. Auree trecce inanellate; 6b. Dove, mia bella Aurora; 7. Volevo amar anch'io; 8. No, non vo' più amare. ACT TWO: 9. Che città; 10a. Quanto esclamasti; 10b. E' questo, s'io non erro; 10c. Che miro? Oh stupore; 11. Che dirà, che farà; 12. Ah pigri! Che tardate?; 13. In grembo al caro amato; 14a. Conosco gl'apparati; 14b. Ahi, spirò la mia vita; 14c. Son morti questi adulteri?; 14d. Un talamo ed un letto.
Cpte J. Wakefield, P.-C. Runge, I. Garcisanz, H. van Bork, J. Allister, H. Cuénod, A. Howells, J. Berbié, F. Davià, R. Van Allan, LPO, R. Leppard (r1968) (9/95) (DECC) ① [2] **444 529-2DMO2**

CAZZATI, Maurizio (c1620–1677) Italy

SECTION II: CHAMBER

Sonate a due, tre, quattro, e cinque, con alcune per tromba, Op. 35 (pub 1665)
11. C.
11. S. Keavy, Parley of Instr *Concert* (1/89) (HYPE) ① **CDA66255**

SECTION IV: VOCAL AND CHORAL

Factum est praelium magnum—cantata (1v)
M. van Egmond, Ricercar Consort *Concert* (1/90) (RICE) ① **RIC054032**
In Calvaria ruppe—cantata (1v)
M. van Egmond, Ricercar Consort *Concert* (1/90) (RICE) ① **RIC054032**

CEBRIÁN (16th cent) Spain

SECTION IV: VOCAL AND CHORAL

Lágrimas di mi consuelo—song
Hespèrion XX, J. Savall (r1991-92) *Concert* (6/93) (ASTR) ① **E8764**

CEREROLS, Joan (1618–1676) Spain

SECTION IV: VOCAL AND CHORAL

Missa de batalla—12vv and continuo
Capella Reial Voc Ens, Capella Reial Instr Ens, J. Savall *Missa pro defunctis a 7.* (7/89) (ASTR) ① **E8704**
Missa pro defunctis—7vv and continuo
Capella Reial Voc Ens, Capella Reial Instr Ens, J. Savall *Missa de batalla.* (7/89) (ASTR) ① **E8704**

CERHA, Friedrich (b 1926) Austria

SECTION IV: VOCAL AND CHORAL

Eine Art Chansons—60 short songs (1986-7) (Wds various)
EXCERPTS: 1. Statt Overtüre; 2. sonnett; 3. synopsis einer politischen rede; 4. der wein; 5. stiegen steigen; 6. ich weiss nicht; 7. ich glaub' sie sind klein kavalier; 8. wenn es stinkt; 9. Polka mit Satie); 10. Da Frieden auf der Wöd; 11. Puppenmarsch; 12. Die Utopie der Solidarität; 13. Achleitner; 14. Gigözzn; 15. Aria buffa für Nali; 16. klassisch; 17. ein deutsches denkmal; 18. sieben kinder; 19. etüde in f; 20. der (ale-)xander; 21. zwergenparade; 22. ich bekreuzige mich; 23. lichtung; 24. fragment; 25. österreiches fragment; 26. ich brech dich; 27. thechdthehn jahr; 28. falamalaekum; 29. loch; 30. wien: heldenplatz; 31. 13. märz; 32. keiner schliessich; 33. vater komm erzähl vom krieg; 34. was können sie dir tun?; 35.

koexistenz; 36. Minipotpourri; 37. sieben weltwunder; 38. ich haben einen sessel; 39. kleeblattgasse; 40. tür auf; 41. haiku; 42. ich was not yet in brasilien; 43. Wenn der Puls der Frau Schulz.
1-43. H. K. Gruber, Martin Jones, R. McGee, J. Holland (pp1993; disc includes poetry recitals by Gerhard Rühm and H.C. Artmann)
(9/94) (LARG) ① **Largo 5126**

ČERNÝ, Frantisek *(1861–1940) Czechoslovakia*

SECTION II: CHAMBER

Mazurka—double-bass and piano
M. Hanskov, N.E. Aggesen *Concert*
(3/92) (DANA) ① **DACOCD378**

CERTON, Pierre *(c1510–1572) France*

SECTION IV: VOCAL AND CHORAL

La, la, la, je ne l'ose dire—chanson
C. Janequin Ens, D. Visse (r1994) *Concert*
(5/95) (HARM) ① **HMC90 1453**
O madame, pers-je mon tems—chanson (pub 1552)
Baltimore Consort (r1992; arr Baltimore Consort)
Concert (4/95) (DORI) ① **DOR90177**

CERVANTES (KAWANAG), Ignacio *(1847–1905) Cuba*

SECTION III: INSTRUMENTAL

Por qué, eh?—piano
A. Feinberg (r1994) *Concert*
(11/95) (ARGO) ① **444 457-2ZH**

CESARIS, Johannes *(fl c1385–1420) France*

SECTION IV: VOCAL AND CHORAL

Mon seul voloir/Certes m'amour—double rondeau: 3vv
Gothic Voices, C. Page (lte/dir) *Concert*
(9/92) (HYPE) ① **CDA66588**
Se vous scaviez, ma tres douce maistresse—rondeau: 3vv
Gothic Voices, C. Page (lte/dir) *Concert*
(9/92) (HYPE) ① **CDA66588**

CESTI, Antonio *(1623–1669) Italy*

SECTION V: STAGE WORKS

Orontea—opera: 3 acts (1649—Venice) (Lib. G.A. Cicognini)
EXCERPTS: 1. Intorno all'idol mio.
1. C. Bartoli, G. Fischer *Concert*
(12/92) (DECC) ① **436 267-2DH**
1. J. Baker, ASMF, N. Marriner *Concert*
(1/93) (PHIL) ① **434 173-2PM**

CHABRIER, (Alexis-)Emmanuel *(1841–1894) France*

SECTION I: ORCHESTRAL

Bourrée fantasque (1891) (orch. Mottl)
Toulouse Capitole Orch, M. Plasson (r1987) *Concert*
(9/88) (EMI) ① **CDC7 49652-2**
España—rapsodie (1883)
Hallé, J. Loughran *Concert*
(3/88) (CFP) ① **CD-CFP9011**
Toulouse Capitole Orch, M. Plasson (r1987) *Concert*
(9/88) (EMI) ① **CDC7 49652-2**
Montreal SO, C. Dutoit *Concert*
(6/89) (DECC) ① **421 527-2DH**
Cincinnati Pops, E. Kunzel *Concert*
(10/89) (TELA) ① **CD80170**
Ulster Orch, Y.P. Tortelier *Concert*
(2/91) (CHAN) ① **CHAN8852**
Black Dyke Mills Band, G. Brand (arr G Langford)
Concert (10/91) (CHAN) ① **CHAN6539**
National PO, L. Stokowski *Concert*
(4/92) (EMI) ① **CDM7 64140-2**
Paris Cons, P. Dervaux *Concert*
(7/92) (EMI) ① [2] **CZS7 67474-2**
LPO, T. Beecham (r1939) *Concert*
(10/92) (EMI) ① **CDM7 63401-2**
LSO, A. Argenta (r1956) *Concert*
(6/93) (DECC) ① [2] **433 911-2DM2**

Warsaw Nat PO, J. Semkow *Concert*
(5/94) (BELA) ① **450 129-2**
G. Rabol, S. Dugas (r1994; arr 2 pfs) *Concert*
(2/95) (NAXO) ① **8 553080**
LSO, A. Argenta (r1957) *Concert*
(5/95) (DECC) ① **443 580-2DCS**
National SO, V. Olof (r1944) *Concert*
(5/95) (DUTT) ① **CDK1200**
Habanera—orchestra (pub 1885) (orch cpsr from piano work)
Toulouse Capitole Orch, M. Plasson *Concert*
(2/91) (EMI) ① **CDC7 54004-2**
Joyeuse marche—marche française (1888)
Hallé, J. Loughran *Concert*
(3/88) (CFP) ① **CD-CFP9011**
Toulouse Capitole Orch, M. Plasson (r1987) *Concert*
(9/88) (EMI) ① **CDC7 49652-2**
Montreal SO, C. Dutoit *Concert*
(6/89) (DECC) ① **421 527-2DH**
Black Dyke Mills Band, G. Brand (arr G Langford)
Concert (10/91) (CHAN) ① **CHAN6539**
G. Rabol, S. Dugas (r1994) *Concert*
(2/95) (NAXO) ① **8 553080**
Larghetto—horn and orchestra (1875)
P. del Vescovo, Toulouse Capitole Orch, M. Plasson
Concert (2/91) (EMI) ① **CDC7 54004-2**
Prélude pastorale—orchestra (1888)
Toulouse Capitole Orch, M. Plasson (r1987) *Concert*
(9/88) (EMI) ① **CDC7 49652-2**
G. Rabol, S. Dugas (r1994) *Concert*
(2/95) (NAXO) ① **8 553080**
Suite pastorale (1888) (arr. from 10 piéces pittoresques, Nos. 6, 7, 4 and 10)
Toulouse Capitole Orch, M. Plasson (r1987) *Concert*
(9/88) (EMI) ① **CDC7 49652-2**
Ulster Orch, Y.P. Tortelier *Concert*
(2/91) (CHAN) ① **CHAN8852**

SECTION II: CHAMBER

Cortège burlesque—piano duet (1883-88) (orig for one pf)
G. Rabol, S. Dugas (r1994) *Concert*
(2/95) (NAXO) ① **8 553080**
Souvenirs de Munich—quadrille on themes from 'Tristan und Isolde' (Wagner)—piano: four hands (1885-86)
G. Rabol, S. Dugas (r1994) *Concert*
(2/95) (NAXO) ① **8 553080**
3 Valses romantiques—two pianos (pub 1883)
1. Très vite et impétueusement; 2. Mouvement modéré de Valse; 3. Animé.
Toulouse Capitole Orch, M. Plasson (orch Mottl)
Concert (2/91) (EMI) ① **CDC7 54004-2**
G. Rabol, S. Dugas (r1994) *Concert*
(2/95) (NAXO) ① **8 553080**
K. Stott, E. Burley (r1994: arr A Cortot) *Concert*
(5/95) (UNIC) ① **DKPCD9158**

SECTION III: INSTRUMENTAL

Air de ballet—piano (1883-88)
A. D'Arco *Concert* (9/88) (CALL) ① **CAL9828**
A. Planès (r1993) *Concert*
(5/94) (HARM) ① **HMC90 1465**
G. Rabol, S. Dugas (r1994) *Concert*
(2/95) (NAXO) ① **8 553080**
Bourrée fantasque—piano (pub 1891)
A. D'Arco *Concert* (9/88) (CALL) ① **CAL9828**
R. McMahon *Concert* (8/92) (PP) ① **PP10792**
A. Planès (r1993) *Concert*
(5/94) (HARM) ① **HMC90 1465**
G. Rabol (r1993) *Concert*
(2/95) (NAXO) ① **8 553009**
Capriccio in C sharp minor (1883) (cpted M Le Boucher)
(2/95) (NAXO) ① **8 553010**
Habanera—piano (1885)
A. Planès (r1993) *Concert*
(5/94) (HARM) ① **HMC90 1465**
G. Rabol (r1993) *Concert*
(2/95) (NAXO) ① **8 553009**
Impromptu in C—piano (1873)
A. D'Arco *Concert* (9/88) (CALL) ① **CAL9828**
R. McMahon *Concert* (8/92) (PP) ① **PP10792**
A. Planès (r1993) *Concert*
(5/94) (HARM) ① **HMC90 1465**
G. Rabol (r1994) *Concert*
(2/95) (NAXO) ① **8 553010**
K. Stott (r1994) *Concert*
(5/95) (UNIC) ① **DKPCD9158**
Julia—piano: valse, Op. 1 (1857)
G. Rabol (r1994) *Concert*
(2/95) (NAXO) ① **8 553010**
Marche des Cipayes—piano (1863)
A. D'Arco *Concert* (9/88) (CALL) ① **CAL9828**

G. Rabol (r1994) *Concert*
(2/95) (NAXO) ① **8 553010**
Petite valse—piano (unidentified)
G. Rabol (r1993) *Concert*
(2/95) (NAXO) ① **8 553009**
10 Pièces pittoresques—piano (1881)
1. Paysage; 2. Mélancolie; 3. Tourbillon; 4. Sous-bois; 5. Mauresque; 6. Idylle; 7. Danse villageoise; 8. Improvisation; 9. Menuet pompeux; 10. Scherzo-valse.
A. D'Arco *Concert* (9/88) (CALL) ① **CAL9828**
R. McMahon *Concert* (8/92) (PP) ① **PP10792**
A. Planès (r1993) *Concert*
(5/94) (HARM) ① **HMC90 1465**
G. Rabol (r1993) *Concert*
(2/95) (NAXO) ① **8 553009**
K. Stott (r1994) *Concert*
(5/95) (UNIC) ① **DKPCD9158**
7. C. Ortiz *Concert* (6/87) (CARL) ① **PCD846**
9. European CO Per Musica, J. Reynolds (orch. Ravel) *Concert* (10/87) (ETCE) ① **KTC1040**
9. Toulouse Capitole Orch, M. Plasson (r1987: orch Ravel) *Concert* (9/88) (EMI) ① **CDC7 49652-2**
10. J. Szigeti, N. Magaloff (arr vn/pf: r1933) *Concert*
(1/90) (BIDD) ① [2] **LAB007/8**
10. A. Rubinstein (r1963) *Concert*
(10/93) (RCA) ① **09026 61446-2**
5 Pièces posthumes—piano (1897)
1. Aubade; 2. Ballabile; 3. Caprice; 4. Feuillet d'album; 5. Ronde Champêtre.
K. Stott (r1994) *Concert*
(5/95) (UNIC) ① **DKPCD9158**
1, 5. G. Rabol (r1994) *Concert*
(2/95) (NAXO) ① **8 553010**
2-4. G. Rabol (r1993) *Concert*
(2/95) (NAXO) ① **8 553009**
2, 4, 5. A. Planès (r1993) *Concert*
(5/94) (HARM) ① **HMC90 1465**
3. A. D'Arco *Concert* (9/88) (CALL) ① **CAL9828**
Souvenirs de Brunehaut—waltzes: piano (1862)
G. Rabol (r1994) *Concert*
(2/95) (NAXO) ① **8 553010**
Suite de valses—piano (1872)
G. Rabol, S. Dugas (r1994) *Concert*
(2/95) (NAXO) ① **8 553080**

SECTION IV: VOCAL AND CHORAL

Ballade des gros dindons—song (1890) (Wds. Rostand)
C. Castelli, H. Boschi (r1950s) *Concert*
(8/92) (CHNT) ① **LDC278 1068**
Chanson pour Jeanne—song (1886)
C. Castelli, H. Boschi (r1950s) *Concert*
(8/92) (CHNT) ① **LDC278 1068**
G. Souzay, D. Baldwin (r1963) *Concert*
(3/95) (PHIL) ① [4] **438 964-2PM4(2)**
L' île heureuse—song (1897) (Wds. Mikhaël)
S. Varcoe, G. Johnson *Concert*
(6/88) (HYPE) ① **CDA66248**
C. Castelli, H. Boschi (r1950s) *Concert*
(8/92) (CHNT) ① **LDC278 1068**
D. Fischer-Dieskau, H. Höll (r c1987) *Concert*
(12/95) (TELD) ① **4509-97457-2**
Les cigales—song (1890) (Wds. Gérard)
G. Souzay, D. Baldwin (r1963) *Concert*
(3/95) (PHIL) ① [4] **438 964-2PM4(2)**
D. Fischer-Dieskau, H. Höll (r c1987) *Concert*
(12/95) (TELD) ① **4509-97457-2**
Ode à la musique for soprano, female chorus and orchestra (1890) (Wds. Rostand)
B. Hendricks, Toulouse Capitole Orch, M. Plasson *Concert*
(2/91) (EMI) ① **CDC7 54004-2**
Pastorale des cochons roses—song (1890) (Wds. Rostand)
C. Castelli, H. Boschi (r1950s) *Concert*
(8/92) (CHNT) ① **LDC278 1068**
Sulamite—mezzo, female voices and orchestra (1884) (wds. J. Richepin)
S. Mentzer, Toulouse Mid-Pyrénées Chor, Toulouse Capitole Orch, M. Plasson *Concert*
(2/91) (EMI) ① **CDC7 54004-2**
S. Danco, Piantoni Cercle Choral, SRO, E. Ansermet
(bp1945) *Concert* (1/93) (CASC) ① **VEL2010**
Villanelle des petits canards—song (1890) (Wds. Gérard)
D. Fischer-Dieskau, H. Höll (r c1987) *Concert*
(12/95) (TELD) ① **4509-97457-2**

SECTION V: STAGE WORKS

Briséïs, ou Les amants de Corinthe—drame lyrique: 1 act of unfinished opera (1888-91; perf 1897—Paris) (Lib. Mendès & Mikhaël, after Goethe)
Cpte J. Rodgers, M. Padmore, S. Keenlyside. M. George, K. Harries, Scottish Op Chor, BBC Scottish SO, J. Y. Ossonce (pp1994)
(8/95) (HYPE) ① CDA66803

Une **Éducation manquée—operetta: 1 act (1879—Paris)** (Lib. E. Leterrier & A. Vanloo)
Cpte C. Castelli, C. Collart, X. Depraz, Orch. C. Bruck (with dialogue: r1950s) *Concert*
(8/92) (CHNT) ① LDC278 1068

Gwendoline—opera: 2 acts (1886—Brussels) (Lib. C. Mendes)
EXCERPTS: 1. Overture.
Blonde aux yeux de pervenche C. Castelli, H. Boschi (r1950s) *Concert*
(8/92) (CHNT) ① LDC278 1068
Ne riez pas B. Hendricks, Toulouse Capitole Orch, M. Plasson *Concert* (2/91) (EMI) ① CDC7 54004-2
Overture Toulouse Capitole Orch, M. Plasson *Concert* (2/91) (EMI) ① CDC7 54004-2
1. FRNO, T. Beecham (r1957) *Concert*
(8/92) (EMI) ① CDM7 63401-2

Le **Roi malgré lui—opéra-comique: 3 acts (1887—Paris)** (Lib. de Najac and Burani, rev Richepin)
EXCERPTS: 1. Sextor des serves; 2. Chanson tzigane; 3. Danse slave; 4. Fête polonaise; 5. Beau pays (Romance du roi).
Couplets du polonais; Couplets des Gondoles L. Fugère, orch (r1930) *Concert*
(6/93) (SYMP) ① SYMCD1125
Hélas, à l'esclavage C. Castelli, H. Boschi (r1950s) *Concert* (8/92) (CHNT) ① LDC278 1068
Le polonais est triste et grave; Je suis du pays des gondoles L. Fugère, orch (r1930) *Concert*
(9/91) (SYMP) ① SYMCD1089
3, 4. Toulouse Capitole Orch, M. Plasson (r1987) *Concert* (9/88) (EMI) ① CDC7 49652-2
4. Detroit SO, N. Järvi (r1992) *Concert*
(8/94) (CHAN) ① CHAN9227
4. San Francisco SO, P. Monteux (r1947) *Concert*
(9/94) (RCA) ① [15] 09026 61893-2

CHADWICK, George Whitefield (1854–1931) USA

SECTION I: ORCHESTRAL

Symphonic Sketches—orchestra (1895-1904)
1. Jubilee (1895); 2. Noël (1895); 3. Hobgoblin (1904); 4. A Vagrom Ballad (1896).
Detroit SO, N. Järvi (r1994) *Symphony 2.*
(4/95) (CHAN) ① CHAN9334

Symphony No. 2 in B flat (1885)
Albany SO, J. Heygi H. Parker: *Northern Ballad.*
(9/87) (NEW) ① NW339-2
Detroit SO, N. Järvi (r1994) *Symphonic Sketches.*
(4/95) (CHAN) ① CHAN9334

Symphony No. 3 in F (1893-94)
Detroit SO, N. Järvi *Concert*
(10/94) (CHAN) ① CHAN9253

SECTION II: CHAMBER

String Quartet No. 1 in G minor (1878)
Portland Qt *String Quartet 2.*
(10/90) (NORT) ① NR236-CD

String Quartet No. 2 in C (1878)
Portland Qt *String Quartet 1.*
(10/90) (NORT) ① NR236-CD

CHAMBONNIÈRES, Jacques Champion de (1601/02–1672) France

Works numbering by Brunold-Tessier

SECTION III: INSTRUMENTAL

Allemandes—harpsichord
1. F, BT46; 2. C, BT62; 3. C, BT63; 4. F, 'L'Affligée', BT124.
1-4. F. Lengellé *Concert*
(9/87) (LYRN) ① LYRCD066
Autre brusque in F—harpsichord, BT115
F. Lengellé *Concert* (9/87) (LYRN) ① LYRCD066
Autre in C—harpsichord, BT65
F. Lengellé *Concert* (9/87) (LYRN) ① LYRCD066
Chaconne et Rondeau in F—harpsichord
W. Landowska (r1934) *Concert*
(10/92) (MSCM) ① MM30444

Chaconne in F—harpsichord, BT116
F. Lengellé *Concert* (9/87) (LYRN) ① LYRCD066
Courantes—harpsichord
1. F, BT102; 2. C, BT64; 3. G, BT117.
1-3. F. Lengellé *Concert*
(9/87) (LYRN) ① LYRCD066
La **Drollerie—harpsichord, BT129**
F. Lengellé *Concert* (9/87) (LYRN) ① LYRCD066
Gaillarde and Double in B flat—harpsichord, BT141 & 141bis
F. Lengellé *Concert* (9/87) (LYRN) ① LYRCD066
Gigues—harpsichord
1. C, BT76; 2. G, BT127 (Canaris).
1, 2. F. Lengellé *Concert*
(9/87) (LYRN) ① LYRCD066
Pavanes—harpsichord
1. D minor, BT87; 2. G minor, BT128.
1, 2. F. Lengellé *Concert*
(9/87) (LYRN) ① LYRCD066
Le **Printemps in A minor—passacaglia, BT142**
F. Lengellé *Concert* (9/87) (LYRN) ① LYRCD066
Rondeau in F—harpsichord, BT116
F. Lengellé *Concert* (9/87) (LYRN) ① LYRCD066
Sarabandes—harpsichord
1. F, BT23; 2. C, BT74; 3. G, BT120.
1-3. F. Lengellé *Concert*
(9/87) (LYRN) ① LYRCD066
4 Suites—harpsichord (compiled Sempé from various MSS)
1. Suite, C; 2. Suite, G; 3. Suite, A; 4. Suite, D.
S. Sempé, B. Feehan (some movts with theorbo continuo) *Anglebert: Harpsichord Works.*
(4/93) (DHM) ① 05472 77210-2

CHAMINADE, Cécile (Louise Stèphanie) (1857–1944) France

SECTION I: ORCHESTRAL

Concertino for flute and orchestra, Op. 107 (1902)
S. Milan, CLS, R. Hickox *Concert*
(10/90) (CHAN) ① CHAN8840

SECTION II: CHAMBER

Piano Trio No. 1 in G minor, Op. 11 (1880)
Macalester Trio *Concert*
(10/94) (VOX) ① [2] 115845-2

SECTION III: INSTRUMENTAL

Air à danser—piano, Op. 164
E. Parkin *Concert* (8/91) (CHAN) ① CHAN8888
Air de Ballet—piano, Op. 30
E. Parkin *Concert* (8/91) (CHAN) ① CHAN8888
Peter Jacobs *Concert* (9/92) (HYPE) ① CDA66584
Arlequine—piano, Op. 53
Peter Jacobs (r1993) *Concert*
(11/94) (HYPE) ① CDA66706
Au pays dévasté—piano, Op. 155 (pub 1919)
Peter Jacobs (r1993) *Concert*
(11/94) (HYPE) ① CDA66706
Callirhoë—ballet—piano, Op. 37 (1890)
3. Pas des écharpes; 4. Callirhoë.
3. E. Parkin *Concert* (8/91) (CHAN) ① CHAN8888
Chaconne—piano, Op. 8
Peter Jacobs *Concert* (9/92) (HYPE) ① CDA66584
Chanson Brétonne—piano
K. Schmidt (r1991) *Concert*
(12/93) (KOCH) ① 37240-2
Peter Jacobs (r1993) *Concert*
(11/94) (HYPE) ① CDA66706
Contes bleus No. 2—piano, Op. 122
E. Parkin *Concert* (8/91) (CHAN) ① CHAN8888
Danse créole—piano, Op. 94
E. Parkin *Concert* (8/91) (CHAN) ① CHAN8888
Deuxième Valse—piano, Op. 77
Peter Jacobs *Concert* (9/92) (HYPE) ① CDA66584
Divertissement—piano, Op. 105 (1901)
Peter Jacobs (r1993) *Concert*
(11/94) (HYPE) ① CDA66706
Etude mélodique in G flat—piano, Op. 118
Peter Jacobs *Concert* (9/92) (HYPE) ① CDA66584
Etude Pathétique—piano, Op. 124
Peter Jacobs *Concert* (9/92) (HYPE) ① CDA66584
Etude scholastique—piano, Op. 139
Peter Jacobs *Concert* (9/92) (HYPE) ① CDA66584
Etude symphonique—piano, Op. 28 (1895)
Peter Jacobs (r1993) *Concert*
(11/94) (HYPE) ① CDA66706
6 Etudes de concert—piano, Op. 35
1. Scherzo in C; 2. Automne; 3. Fileuse; 5. Impromptu; 6. Tarantella.
1, 2. Peter Jacobs *Concert*
(9/92) (HYPE) ① CDA66584

2. M. Lympany *Concert* (1/89) (EMI) ① CDZ110
2. E. Parkin *Concert* (8/91) (CHAN) ① CHAN8888
2. M. Guttman, RPO, J. Serebrier (arr Uy: vn/orch) *Concert* (10/93) (ASV) ① CDDCA855
5, 6. Peter Jacobs (r1993) *Concert*
(11/94) (HYPE) ① CDA66706
Feuillets d'Album—piano, Op. 98
3. Elégie; 4. Valse arabesque.
3. Peter Jacobs (r1993) *Concert*
(11/94) (HYPE) ① CDA66706
4. E. Parkin *Concert* (8/91) (CHAN) ① CHAN8888
Gigue in D—piano, Op. 43
Peter Jacobs (r1993) *Concert*
(11/94) (HYPE) ① CDA66706
Guitare—piano, Op. 32
E. Parkin *Concert* (8/91) (CHAN) ① CHAN8888
Libellules—piano, Op. 24
Peter Jacobs (r1993) *Concert*
(11/94) (HYPE) ① CDA66706
Lisonjera (L'Enjôleuse)—piano, Op. 50
E. Parkin *Concert* (8/91) (CHAN) ① CHAN8888
Peter Jacobs *Concert* (9/92) (HYPE) ① CDA66584
Lolita—caprice espagnol: piano, Op. 54
E. Parkin *Concert* (8/91) (CHAN) ① CHAN8888
Minuetto—piano, Op. 23
E. Parkin *Concert* (8/91) (CHAN) ① CHAN8888
Nocturne—piano, Op. 165 (pub 1925)
Peter Jacobs (r1993) *Concert*
(11/94) (HYPE) ① CDA66706
L' **Ondine—piano, Op. 101**
Peter Jacobs *Concert* (9/92) (HYPE) ① CDA66584
Pas des sylphes: intermezzo—piano
E. Parkin *Concert* (8/91) (CHAN) ① CHAN8888
Passacaille in E—piano, Op. 130
Peter Jacobs (r1993) *Concert*
(11/94) (HYPE) ① CDA66706
Pastorale—piano, Op. 114 (1904)
Peter Jacobs (r1993) *Concert*
(11/94) (HYPE) ① CDA66706
6 Pièces humoristiques—piano, Op. 87
2. Sous bois; 4. Autrefois; 5. Consolation.
2, 5. Peter Jacobs (r1993) *Concert*
(11/94) (HYPE) ① CDA66706
4. E. Parkin *Concert* (8/91) (CHAN) ① CHAN8888
4. Peter Jacobs *Concert*
(9/92) (HYPE) ① CDA66584
Pierrette—piano, Op. 41
E. Parkin *Concert* (8/91) (CHAN) ① CHAN8888
Poème romantique—piano, Op. 7/1
Peter Jacobs (r1993) *Concert*
(11/94) (HYPE) ① CDA66706
Poèmes Provençales—piano, Op. 127
1. Dans la Lande; 2. Solitude; 3. Le passé; 4. Pêcheurs de Nuit.
2, 4. Peter Jacobs *Concert*
(9/92) (HYPE) ① CDA66584
Romance in D—piano, Op. 137
Peter Jacobs *Concert* (9/92) (HYPE) ① CDA66584
6 Romances sans paroles—piano, Op. 76
1. Souvenance; 2. Elévation; 3. Idylle; 4. Eglogue; 5. Chanson bretonne; 6. Méditation.
1, 2. Peter Jacobs *Concert*
(9/92) (HYPE) ① CDA66584
1, 3, 6. E. Parkin *Concert*
(8/91) (CHAN) ① CHAN8888
Scherzo-Valse—piano, Op. 148
Peter Jacobs (r1993) *Concert*
(11/94) (HYPE) ① CDA66706
Sérénade—piano, Op. 29
E. Parkin *Concert* (8/91) (CHAN) ① CHAN8888
Peter Jacobs *Concert* (9/92) (HYPE) ① CDA66584
Sérénade espagnole—piano
K-W. Chung, P. Moll (arr Kreisler) *Concert*
(9/87) (DECC) ① 417 289-2DH
H. Kreisler, F. Kreisler (r1921) *Concert*
(7/90) (BIDD) ① [2] LAB009/10
A. Campoli, S. Crooke (arr Kreisler) *Concert*
(10/91) (PEAR) ① PASTCD9744
K. Takezawa, P. Moll (arr Kreisler) *Concert*
(2/93) (RCA) ① 09026 60704-2
I. Perlman, S. Sanders (arr vn/pf: Kreisler) *Concert* (6/95) (EMI) ① [20] CZS4 83177-2(2)
Sous le masque—piano, Op. 116
E. Parkin *Concert* (8/91) (CHAN) ① CHAN8888
Thème varié in A—piano, Op. 89
Peter Jacobs *Concert* (9/92) (HYPE) ① CDA66584
Toccata—piano, Op. 39
E. Parkin *Concert* (8/91) (CHAN) ① CHAN8888
Tristesse in C sharp minor—piano, Op. 104
Peter Jacobs (r1993) *Concert*
(11/94) (HYPE) ① CDA66706
Valse romantique—piano, Op. 115
Peter Jacobs *Concert* (9/92) (HYPE) ① CDA66584
Valse tendre—piano, Op. 119 (pub 1906)
Peter Jacobs (r1993) *Concert*
(11/94) (HYPE) ① CDA66706

SECTION IV: VOCAL AND CHORAL

L' anneau d'argent—song
L. Fugère, anon (r1928) *Concert*
(6/93) (SYMP) ① **SYMCD1125**

L' Été—song: 1v and piano
S.J. Langton, K. Schmidt (r1991) *Concert*
(12/93) (KOCH) ① **37240-2**

Ronde d'amour—song
L. Fugère, anon (r1928) *Concert*
(6/93) (SYMP) ① **SYMCD1125**

Rosemonde—song: 1v and piano
S. Mentzer, K. Schmidt (r1991) *Concert*
(12/93) (KOCH) ① **37240-2**

CHAMPION, Thomas *(d 1580)* France

SECTION IV: VOCAL AND CHORAL

Psalm 137—Estans assis aux rives aquatiques (pub 1571)
Baltimore Consort (r1992; arr Baltimore Consort)
Concert (4/95) (DORI) ① **DOR90177**

CHANLER, Theodore (Ward) *(1902–1961) USA*

SECTION IV: VOCAL AND CHORAL

8 Epitaphs—voice and piano (1937) (Wds. W. de la Mare)
1. Alice Rodd; 2. Susannah Fry; 3. Three Sisters; 4. Thomas Logge; 5. A Midget; 6. 'No voice to scold'; 7. Ann Poverty; 8. 'Be very quiet now'.
G. Maurice, G. Johnson (pp1988) *Concert*
(5/92) (ETCE) ① **KTC1099**

CHAPÍ (Y LORENTE), Ruperto *(1851–1909) Spain*

SECTION V: STAGE WORKS

La Bruja—comic opera: 3 acts (1887—Madrid) (Lib. M R Carrión)
No extrañéis que se escapen P. Domingo, Madrid Zarzuela Chor, Madrid SO, M. Moreno-Buendia (r1987) *Concert* (1/89) (EMI) ① **CDC7 49148-2**

Las Hijas del Zebedeo—zarzuela: 2 acts (1889—Madrid) (Lib. Estremera)
Al pensar en el dueño L. Tetrazzini, orch, P. Pitt (r1909) *Concert*
(9/92) (EMI) ① [3] **CHS7 63802-2(1)**
Al pensar en el dueño L. Tetrazzini, orch, P. Pitt (r1909) *Concert* (9/92) (PEAR) ① **GEMMCD9222**
Carceleras V. de los Angeles, Sinfonia of London, R. Frühbeck de Burgos (orch Gamley) *Concert* (10/88) (EMI) ① **CDM7 69502-2**
Carceleras L. Tetrazzini, orch (r1911) *Concert* (9/92) (PEAR) ① **GEMMCD9223**
El Milagro de la Virgen—zarzuela: 3 acts (1884—Madrid) (Lib. M. Pina Dominguez)
Flores purisimas E. Caruso, G. Scognamiglio (r1914) *Concert* (7/91) (RCA) ① [12] **GD60495(5)**
Flores purisimas E. Caruso, G. Scognamiglio (r1914) *Concert* (10/91) (PEAR) ① [3] **EVC3(1)**
El Puñado de Rosas—zarzuela: 1 act (1902—Madrid) (Lib. Arniches & R. Asensio Más)
Duo de Rosario y Pepe G. Sanchez, P. Domingo, Madrid SO, E. G. Asensio (pp1991) *Concert* (7/91) (CARL) ① **MCD45**
La Revoltosa—sainete lírico: 1 act (1897—Madrid) (Lib. F. Shaw and Silva)
Cpte T. Tourné, M. R. Gabriel, A.M. Higueras, R. Cesari, M. Hernandez, R. Diez, S. Garcia, A. Viñes, Madrid Coros Cantores, Madrid Concerts Orch, P. Sorozábal Bretón: Verbena de la Paloma.
(10/92) (HISP) ① **CDZ7 67328-2**

CHAPIN, Harry *(1942–1981) USA*

SECTION IV: VOCAL AND CHORAL

Taxi—song
M. Patinkin, Orch, E. Stern (r1993; orch Troob, arr Ford) *Concert* (11/94) (NONE) ① **7559-79330-2**

CHAPLIN, Sir Charles *(1899–1977) England*

SECTION V: STAGE WORKS

City Lights—film score (1931)
EXCERPTS: 1. Overture/Unveiling the Statue; 2. The Flower Girl (Violetera); 3. Evening/Meeting the

Millionaire; 4. At the Millionaire's Home; 5. The Nightclub—Dance Suite; 6. The Limousine; 7. The Sober Dawn; 8. The Party & The Morning After; 9. Eviction/The Road Sweeper/At the Girl's Home; 10. The Boxing Match; 11. The Burglars; 12. Reunited.
1-12. City Lights Orch, Carl Davis (r1991)
(11/91) (SILV) ① **FILMCD078**

CHAPMAN, Edward T *(b 1902)* England

SECTION IV: VOCAL AND CHORAL

The Three Ravens—traditional ballad arrangement
N. Sears, Cambridge Sngrs, J. Rutter *Concert*
(4/87) (CLLE) ① **COLCD104**

CHARDAVOINE, Jehan *(1538–c1580) France*

SECTION IV: VOCAL AND CHORAL

Une jeune fillette—chanson (pub 1576)
Baltimore Consort (r1992; arr Baltimore Consort)
Concert (4/95) (DORI) ① **DOR90177**
Mignonne, allons voir si la rose—chanson (pub 1576)
Baltimore Consort (r1992; arr Baltimore Consort)
Concert (4/95) (DORI) ① **DOR90177**

CHARLES, Ernest *(1895–1984)* USA

SECTION IV: VOCAL AND CHORAL

When I have sung my songs—song
R. Ponselle, R. Romani (r1939) *Concert*
(1/90) (RCA) ① **GD87810**
R. Ponselle, R. Romani (r1939) *Concert*
(10/93) (NIMB) ① **NI7846**
K. Flagstad, E. McArthur (r1936) *Concert*
(12/95) (PEAR) ① **GEMMCD9092**
K. Flagstad, E. McArthur (r1936) *Concert*
(12/95) (NIMB) ① **NI7871**

CHARPENTIER, Gustave *(1860–1950) France*

SECTION V: STAGE WORKS

Louise—opera: 4 acts (1900—Paris) (Lib. cpsr)
EXCERPTS: 1. Prelude. ACT 1: 2a. O coeur ami! ô coeur promis!; 2b. Prêtez l'oreille!; 3. Moi, je vous avais remarqué; 4. C'était mon adorée!; 5. Bonsoir! La soupe est prête?; 6. Une lettre?; 7. O mon enfant, ma Louise. ACT 2: 8. Prelude; 9. Dire qu'en c'moment y a des femmes; 10. Les bons lits! les belles robes!; 11. C'est ici? C'est là qu'elle travaille?; 12. Ella va paraître, ma joie, ma plante; 13. Bonjour! Bonjour! Comment vas-tu?; 14. Pourquoi te retourner?; 15. Laissez-moi, ah! de grâce!; 16. Marchand d'habits! avez-vous des habits à vendr'?; 17. Interlude; 18a. La! la! la! C'est énervant!; 18b. Oh! moi quand je suis dans la ruse; 19. Un!...Quell drôl' de fanfare!; 20. Dans la cité lointaine; 21. Qu'est-c' qui lui prend?. ACT 3: 22. Prelude; 23. Depuis le jour où je me suis donnée; 24. Louise!...Quelle belle vie?; 25. Ainsi tout enfant a le droit de choisir; 26. Julien! Louise!; 27. Ah! Prends-moi vite, vite; 28a. Ils sont là?; 28b. Choeur des gens de la butte; 29. Par Mercure aux pieds légers; 30. O jolie! Soeur choisie!; 31. Je ne viens pas en ennemie. ACT 4: 33a. Tu devrais te rapprocher de la fenêtre; 33b. Les pauvres gens peuvent-ils être heureux?; 34. Voir naître un enfant; 35. Louise! Louise! Quoi? Viens m'aider!; 36a. Bonsoir, père; 36b. Reste...repose-toi; 36c. L'enfant serait sage; 37. Tout le droit de d'être libre!; 38. Qu'il vienne vite, vite, mon bien-aimé; 39. Louise!...Louise!...
Cpte I. Cotrubas, P. Domingo, G. Bacquier, J. Berbié, M. Sénéchal, L. Guitton, E. Manchet, L. Reid, J. Jarvis, S. Minty, A. Butier, M. Midgley, L. Richardson, P. Clark, G. Jennings, P. Bartlett, M. Cable, M. Dickinson, D. Murray, J. Noble, L. Fyson, P. Bamber, W. Mason, V. Midgley, J. Lewington, P. Halstead, O. Broome, P. Bedford, N. Jenkins, E. Fleet, M. Brown, C. Parker, J. Brown, M. Clark, U. Connors, A. MacGregor, I. Thompson, Ambrosian Op Chor, New Philh, G. Prêtre
(6/91) (SONY) ① [3] **S3K46429**
Cpte B. Monmart, A. Laroze, L. Musy, S. Michel, L. Rialland, P. Giannotti, J. Fournet, Paris Opéra-Comique Chor, Paris Opéra-Comique Orch, J. Fournet (r1956)
(9/94) (PHIL) ① [3] **442 082-2PM3**

Cpte B. Sills, N. Gedda, J. Van Dam, M. Dunn, M. Hill, E. Lublin, Maîtrise de la Résurrection, Paris Op Chor, Paris Op Orch, J. Rudel (r1977)
(2/95) (EMI) ① [3] **CMS5 65299-2**
23. G. Bumbry, Stuttgart RSO, S. Soltesz *Concert*
(11/86) (ORFE) ① **C081841A**
23. M. Callas, FRNO, G. Prêtre *Concert*
(2/88) (EMI) ① **CDC7 49059-2**
23. M. Freni, Rome Op Orch, F. Ferraris *Concert*
(10/89) (EMI) ① **CDM7 63110-2**
23. M. Callas, FRNO, G. Prêtre *Concert*
(2/90) (EMIN) ① **CD-EMX2123**
23. K. Te Kanawa, ROHO, J. Tate *Concert*
(2/90) (EMI) ① **CDC7 49863-2**
23. E. Steber, Philh, W. Susskind (r1947) *Concert*
(4/92) (EMI) ① [7] **CHS7 69741-2(1)**
23. A. Marc, NZ SO, H. Wallberg *Concert*
(6/92) (DELO) ① **DE3108**
23. K. Battle, M. Garrett (pp1991) *Concert*
(7/92) (DG) ① **435 440-2GH**
23. L. Edvina, orch (r1919) *Concert*
(7/92) (PEAR) ① [3] **GEMMCDS9925(1)**
23. L. Price, RCA Italiana Op Orch, F. Molinari-Pradelli *Concert*
(12/92) (RCA) ① [4] **09026 61236-2**
23. M. Caballé, New Philh, R. Giovaninetti (r1970) *Concert*
(5/93) (DG) ① **431 103-2GB**
23. M. Garden, orch (r1926) *Concert*
(8/93) (SYMP) ① **SYMCD1136**
23. M. Garden, orch (r1912) *Concert*
(8/93) (SYMP) ① **SYMCD1136**
23. N. Melba, G. Lapierre (r1913) *Concert*
(9/93) (RCA) ① **09026 61412-2**
23. G. Moore, RCA SO, W. Pelletier (r1940) *Concert*
(4/94) (RCA) ① [6] **09026 61580-2(4)**
23. M. Garden, orch, R. Bourdon (r1926: 2 vers) *Concert*
(8/94) (ROMO) ① **81008-2**
23. M. Garden, J. Dansereau (r1927) *Concert*
(8/94) (ROMO) ① **81008-2**
23. E. Mason, orch, F. Black (r1928) *Concert*
(8/94) (ROMO) ① **81009-2**
23. A. Roocroft, LPO, F. Welser-Möst *Concert*
(10/94) (EMI) ① **CDC5 55090-2**
23. M. Devia, Svizzera Italiana Orch, M. Rota (pp1992) *Concert* (10/94) (BONG) ① **GB2513-2**
23. C. Muzio, orch (r1918) *Concert*
(1/95) (ROMO) ① [2] **81010-2**
23. N. Melba, orch, W.B. Rogers (r1913) *Concert*
(5/95) (ROMO) ① [3] **81011-2(2)**
23. N. Melba, G. Lapierre (r1913) *Concert*
(5/95) (ROMO) ① [3] **81011-2(2)**
34. L. Fugère, orch (r1928) *Concert*
(6/93) (SYMP) ① **SYMCD1125**
36b M. Journet, SO, R. Bourdon (r1926) *Concert*
(1/94) (CLUB) ① **CL99-034**
36b Vanni-Marcoux, orch (r1934) *Concert*
(1/94) (CLUB) ① **CL99-101**

CHARPENTIER, Marc-Antoine *(1643–1704) France*

H–Numbers from H.W. Hitchcock's catalogue

SECTION I: ORCHESTRAL

Messe pour plusieurs instruments au lieu des orgues—woodwind, strings and continuo, H513 (?early 1670s)
Excs Grande Ecurie, J-C. Malgoire (r1992) *Concert*
(9/93) (K617) ① **K617026**

SECTION II: CHAMBER

3 Noëls—flute, strings and continuo, H531 (?late 1680s)
1. O Créateur; 2. Vous qui désirez sans fin; 3. À la venue de Noël.
1. J-L. Bindi, Nantes Voc Ens, Nantes Instr Ens, P. Colleaux (arr Colleaux) *Concert*
(4/88) (ARIO) ① **ARN68015**
1, 2. German Baroque sols, R. Ewerhart (org/dir) *Concert* (12/91) (FSM) ① **FCD91220**
2, 3. English Concert, T. Pinnock (hpd/dir) *Concert*
(12/91) (ARCH) ① **435 262-2AH**
Noëls sur les instruments—flute, strings and continuo, H534 (?early 1690s)
1. Où s'en vont ces gays bergers; 2. Or, nous dites Marie; 3. Joseph est bien marié; 4. Les Bourgeois de Chastre; 5. Une jeune pucelle; 6. Laissez paître vos bêtes.
1. English Concert, T. Pinnock (hpd/dir) *Concert*
(12/91) (ARCH) ① **435 262-2AH**
1, 2, 3, 6. German Baroque sols, R. Ewerhart (org/dir) *Concert* (12/91) (FSM) ① **FCD91220**
1-4. J-L. Bindi, Nantes Voc Ens, Nantes Instr Ens, P. Colleaux (arr Visse) *Concert*
(4/88) (ARIO) ① **ARN68015**

Prélude in D minor—strings and continuo, H510 (?early 1670s)
Seminario Musicale (r1993) *Concert*
(9/95) (VIRG) ① VC5 45075-2

Prélude in G minor—flute, strings and continuo, H528 (?late 1680s)
Seminario Musicale (r1993) *Concert*
(9/95) (VIRG) ① VC5 45075-2

Prélude pour ce qu'on voudra—strings, H521 (1679)
Seminario Musicale (r1993) *Concert*
(9/95) (VIRG) ① VC5 45075-2

Prelude pour le 2de Magnificat (H80)—strings and continuo, H533 (?early 1690s)
Concert des Nations, J. Savall *Concert*
(2/90) (ASTR) ① E8713

Sonate a 8—2 flutes, 4 strings, harpsichord and theorbo, H548
Ricercar Consort *Concert*
(10/88) (RICE) ① RIC037011

Symphonie devant Regina coeli—strings and continuo, H509 (?early 1670s)
Concert des Nations, J. Savall *Concert*
(2/90) (ASTR) ① E8713

Tenebare Ritornelles pour 1ere lecon du mercredi—2 vns & 2 viols in alternation with continuo, H100 (? early 1670s)
Seminario musicale (r1990s) *Concert*
(9/95) (VIRG) ① VC7 59295-2

SECTION IV: VOCAL AND CHORAL

Ah, qu'on est malheureux—air (1v and continuo), H443
H. Ledroit, Ricercar Consort *Concert*
(10/88) (RICE) ① RIC037011

3 Airs on Verses from 'Le Cid'—1v and continuo (pub 1681) (Wds. Corneille)
1. Percé jusques au fond du coeur; 2. Père, maîtresse, honneur, amour; 3. Que je sens de rudes combats.
H. Ledroit, Ricercar Consort *Concert*
(10/88) (RICE) ① RIC037011

Amour, vous avez beau redoubler mes alarmes—air: 1v and continuo, H445
H. Ledroit, Ricercar Consort *Concert*
(10/88) (RICE) ① RIC037011

Auprès du feu l'on fait l'amour—air: 1v and continuo, H446
H. Ledroit, Ricercar Consort *Concert*
(10/88) (RICE) ① RIC037011

Autre leçon de ténèbres, 'Ego vir videns'—2vv and continuo, H92 (early 1670s)
Parlement de Musique, M. Gester (hpd/dir) *Concert*
(9/92) (O111) ① OPS55-9119

Ave maris stella—treble, alto, three basses and continuo, H67 (? late 1680s)
Compañía musical, Maîtrise Nationale Ch, Grande Ecurie, J-C. Malgoire (r1992) *Concert*
(9/93) (K617) ① K617026

Le Bavolet—air: 1v and continuo, H499a (1679) (Wds. de Visé)
H. Ledroit, Ricercar Consort *Concert*
(10/88) (RICE) ① RIC037011

Beatus vir—psalm: 8/8vv and instruments, H224 (?mid-1690s)
E. Brunner, H. Viera, A. Zaepffel, A. Ramirez, P. Huttenlocher, Lisbon Gulbenkian Orch, M. Corboz
(r1980) *Concert* (6/93) (ERAT) ① 2292-45926-2

Caecilia virgo et martyr, 'Est secretum Valerianae'—dramatic motet: 6/8vv and instruments, H397 (?mid-1670s)
Arts Florissants Voc Ens, Arts Florissants Instr Ens, W. Christie *Concert* (10/85) (HARM) ① HMC90 066

Canticum in honorem BVM, 'Annuntiae superi narrate coeli'—dramatic motet: 5vv and continuo, H400 (c1680)
Concert des Nations, J. Savall *Concert*
(2/90) (ASTR) ① E8713

Canticum in honorem Sancti Zaverii, 'Vidi angelum volantem'—motet: 5/4vv and instruments, H355 (?late 1680s)
E. Baudry, C. Dune, G. Ragon, Nantes Voc Ens, Stradivaria Ens, P. Colleaux *Judicium Salomonis, H422.* (11/89) (ARIO) ① ARN68037

Canticum in nativitatem Domini, 'Frigidae noctis umbra'—dramatic motet: 6/6vv and instruments, H414 (1683-85)
Arts Florissants Voc Ens, Arts Florissants Instr Ens, W. Christie *Pastorale, H483.*
(3/85) (HARM) ① HMC90 1082

Canticum in nativitatem Domini, 'Quem vidistis pastores'—motet: 4vv and instruments, H314 (?early 1670s)
D. Ferran, Nantes Voc Ens, Nantes Instr Ens, P. Colleaux *Concert* (4/88) (ARIO) ① ARN68015

Canticum in nativitatem Domini, 'Usquequo avertis faciem tuam'—dramatic motet: 8/4vv and instruments, H416 (?late 1680s)
Arts Florissants Voc Ens, Arts Florissants Instr Ens, W. Christie *Pastorale, H482.*
(12/86) (HARM) ① HMC90 5130

Canticum pro pace, 'Totus orbis personet tubarem clangore'—dramatic motet: 8vv, strings and continuo, H392 (?mid 1670s)
B. Schlick, N. Zijlstra, K. Wessel, D. Visse, C. Prégardien, H. van Berne, P. Kooy, K. Mertens, Amsterdam Baroque Orch, T. Koopman *Concert*
(12/92) (ERAT) ① [2] 2292-45822-2

Dixit Dominus (pour le Port Royal)—3/2vv and continuo, H226 (?late 1690s)
G. de Reyghere, I. Poulenard, J. Feldman, B. Mernier, Capella Ricercar, J. Léjeune *Concert*
(1/89) (RICE) ① RIC052034

Elévation à 5 sans dessus de violon, 'Transfige dulcissime Jesu'—motet: 5vv, H251 (1683)
Concert Spirituel Voc Ens, H. Niquet (r1994) *Concert*
(6/95) (NAXO) ① 8 553173

Filius prodigus, 'Homo quidam duos habebat filios'—dramatic motet: 4/4vv, 2 violins and continuo, H399 (1680)
Arts Florissants Voc Ens, Arts Florissants Instr Ens, W. Christie *Concert* (10/85) (HARM) ① HMC90 066

Josue, 'cum audisset Adonisedec rex Jerusalem'—dramatic motet: 6/4vv, strings and continuo, H404 (early 1680s)
B. Schlick, N. Zijlstra, K. Wessel, D. Visse, C. Prégardien, H. van Berne, P. Kooy, K. Mertens, Amsterdam Baroque Orch, T. Koopman *Concert*
(12/92) (ERAT) ① [2] 2292-45822-2

Judicium Salomonis, 'Confortatum est regnum Israel'—dramatic motet: 8/4vv and instruments, H422 (1702)
A. Zaepffel, J. Benet, G. Ragon, J. Elwes, J. Cabré, G. Reinhart, Nantes Voc Ens, Stradivaria Ens, P. Colleaux *In honorem sancti Xaverii canticum, H355.*
(11/89) (ARIO) ① ARN68037

Laudate Dominum omnes gentes—psalm: 8/8vv, flute, strings and continuo, H223 (?mid-1690s) (Wds. Psalm 116)
B. Degelin, J. Nirouët, J. Caals, K. Widmer, Ghent Madrigal Ch, Ghent Cantabile, Musica Polyphonica, L. Devos (12/84) (ERAT) ① 2292-45202-2

Laudate Dominum omnes gentes (pour le Port Royal)—3/2vv and continuo, H227 (?late 1690s)
G. de Reyghere, I. Poulenard, J. Feldman, B. Mernier, Capella Ricercar, J. Léjeune *Concert*
(1/89) (RICE) ① RIC052034

Litanies de la Vierge—6/6vv, two treble viols and continuo, H83 (1683-85)
Arts Florissants Voc Ens, Arts Florissants Instr Ens, W. Christie *Concert* (9/89) (HARM) ① HMC90 1298

Litanies de la Vierge—8/4vv and continuo, H89 (?early 1690s)
Concert Spirituel Voc Ens, H. Niquet (r1994) *Concert*
(6/95) (NAXO) ① 8 553173

Magnificat—3vv, 2 violins and continuo, H73 (?early 1670s)
Arts Florissants Voc Ens, Arts Florissants Instr Ens, W. Christie *Concert* (10/85) (HARM) ① HMC90 066

Magnificat—8vv and 8 instruments, H74
D. Upshaw, A. Murray, J. Aler, K. Moll, ASMF Chor, ASMF, N. Marriner (ed A Boustead) *Te Deum, H146.*
(12/91) (EMI) ① CDC7 54284-2
Compañía musical, Maîtrise Nationale Ch, Grande Ecurie, J-C. Malgoire (r1992) *Concert*
(9/93) (K617) ① K617026

Magnificat—8/4vv, 2 flutes, strings and continuo, H79 (1690s)
J. Nirouët, J. Caals, K. Widmer, Ghent Madrigal Ch, Ghent Cantabile, Musica Polyphonica, L. Devos *Concert* (12/84) (ERAT) ① 2292-45202-2

Magnificat—4/4vv, flutes, strings and continuo, H80 (1690s)
Concert des Nations, J. Savall *Concert*
(2/90) (ASTR) ① E8713

Magnificat (pour le Port Royal)—6vv and continuo, H81 (?late 1690s)
G. de Reyghere, I. Poulenard, J. Feldman, B. Foccroulle, Capella Ricercar, J. Léjeune *Concert*
(1/89) (RICE) ① RIC052034

Messe de minuit pour Noël—6vv and instruments, H9 (?early 1690s)
M-C. Vallin, E. Le Piniec, G. Ragon, E. Lestrigant, J-L. Bindi, D. Ferran, Nantes Voc Ens, Nantes Instr Ens, P. Colleaux *Concert*
(4/88) (ARIO) ① ARN68015
A. Walker, A. Flutter, J. Turnbull, B. Cooper, A. Rupp, St John's College Ch, CLS, G. Guest *Concert*
(3/89) (CHAN) ① CHAN8658
A. Cantelo, H. Gelmar, J. Bowman, I. Partridge, C. Keyte, King's College Ch, ECO, D. Willcocks (r1967) *Te Deum H146.* (1/90) (EMI) ① CDM7 63135-2

Messe des morts—4vv and continuo, H7 (?early 1690s)
Concert Spirituel Voc Ens, H. Niquet (r1994) *Concert*
(6/95) (NAXO) ① 8 553173

Messe pour le Port Royal—3/1vv and continuo, H5 (?late 1680s)
G. de Reyghere, I. Poulenard, J. Feldman, L. Van Gijsegem, B. Foccroulle, Capella Ricercar, J. Léjeune *Concert* (1/89) (RICE) ① RIC052034

Miserere—2vv, 2 flutes and continuo, H157 (early 1670s)
Parlement de Musique, M. Gester (hpd/dir) *Concert*
(9/92) (O111) ① OPS55-9119

Miserere mei—psalm: 8/4vv, flute, strings and continuo, H219 (?early 1690s) (Wds. Psalm 50)
Paris Chapelle Royale Chor, Paris Chapelle Royale Orch, P. Herreweghe *Concert*
(5/86) (HARM) ① HMC90 1185

Missa Assumpta est Maria—8/6vv, 2 flutes, strings and continuo, H11 (1698-1702)
Arts Florissants Voc Ens, Arts Florissants Instr Ens, W. Christie *Concert* (9/89) (HARM) ① HMC90 1298

Mors Saulis et Jonathae, 'Cum essent congregata ad praelium'—dramatic motet: 8/4vv, 2 tpts, stgs & cont, H403 (early 1680s)
B. Schlick, N. Zijlstra, K. Wessel, D. Visse, C. Prégardien, H. van Berne, P. Kooy, K. Mertens, Amsterdam Baroque Orch, T. Koopman *Concert*
(12/92) (ERAT) ① [2] 2292-45822-2

Nativité de la vierge, 'Sicut spina rosam genuit'—motet: 2vv and continuo, H309 (?early 1670s)
Concert des Nations, J. Savall *Concert*
(2/90) (ASTR) ① E8713

Nisi Dominus—two sopranos, bass, two violins and continuo, H231 (Wds. Psalm 126)
Parlement de Musique, M. Gester *Concert*
(9/92) (O111) ① OPS30-9005

Notus in Judea—two sopranos, bass, two violins and continuo (1681) (Wds. Psalm 75)
Parlement de Musique, M. Gester *Concert*
(9/92) (O111) ① OPS30-9005

O clementissime Domine Jesu—elevation motet: 3vv and continuo, H256 (1683-85)
G. de Reyghere, I. Poulenard, J. Feldman, B. Foccroulle, J. Léjeune *Concert*
(1/89) (RICE) ① RIC052034

O Deus, O Salvator noster—motet: 5/4vv, strings and continuo, H372 (?mid-1690s)
Paris Chapelle Royale Chor, Paris Chapelle Royale Orch, P. Herreweghe *Concert*
(5/86) (HARM) ① HMC90 1185

O salutaris hostia—motet: 3vv and continuo, H261 (?early ?1690s)
D. Collot, E. Gall, F. Masset, S. Vatillon (r1992) *Concert* (10/93) (ERAT) ① [2] 4509-91722-2

Oculi omnium in te speravi—motet pour le saint sacrement au reposoir, H346 (?late 1680s)
Paris Chapelle Royale Chor, Paris Chapelle Royale Orch, P. Herreweghe *Concert*
(5/86) (HARM) ① HMC90 1185

Orphée descendant aux enfers—cantata: 3vv and instruments, H471 (1683)
H. Ledroit, G. de Mey, J. Bona, Ricercar Consort *Concert* (10/88) (RICE) ① RIC037011

Paravit Dominus in judicio thronum suum—motet pour une longue offrande:8/4vv & instr, H434 (1698-99)
Paris Chapelle Royale Chor, Paris Chapelle Royale Orch, P. Herreweghe *Concert*
(5/86) (HARM) ① HMC90 1185

Pastorale sur la naissance de notre Seigneur Jésus Christ—cantata: 6/5vv, two violins and continuo, H482 (1683-85)
Arts Florissants Voc Ens, Arts Florissants Instr Ens, W. Christie *In nativitatem Domini canticum, H416.*
(12/86) (HARM) ① HMC90 5130

Pastorale sur la naissance de notre Seigneur Jésus Christ—cantata: 6/5vv, two flutes, two violins & continuo, H483 (1683-85)
Arts Florissants Voc Ens, Arts Florissants Instr Ens, W. Christie *In nativitatem Domini canticum, H414*.
(3/85) (HARM) ① **HMC90 1082**

Pour la conception de la vierge, 'Conceptio tuo Dei genitrix virgo'—motet: 2vv and continuo, H313 (?early 1670s)
Concert des Nations, J. Savall *Concert*
(2/90) (ASTR) ① **E8713**

Pour la fête de l'Epiphanie, 'Cum natum esset Jesus in Bethlehem'—dramatic motet: 3vv, strings and continuo, H395 (?mid-1670s)
Concert des Nations, J. Savall *Concert*
(2/90) (ASTR) ① **E8713**

Praelium Michaelis archengeli factum in coelo cum dracone—dramatic motet: 6-8vv, 2 tpts, stgs & continuo, H410 (1683)
B. Schlick, N. Zijlstra, K. Wessel, D. Visse, C. Prégardien, H. van Berne, P. Kooy, K. Mertens, Amsterdam Baroque Orch, T. Koopman *Concert*
(12/92) (ERAT) ① [2] **2292-45822-2**

Psalm 50, 'Miserere'—2 trebles, alto & continuo, H173 (?late 1670s)
C. Greuillet, C. Pelon, G. Lesne, Seminario Musicale (r1994) *Concert*
(9/95) (VIRG) ① **VC5 45107-2**

Psalmus David 110us, 'Confitebor tibi'—psalm: 4vv and continuo, H220 (?early 1690s)
Concert Spirituel Voc Ens, H. Niquet (r1994) *Concert*
(6/95) (NAXO) ① **8 553173**

Psalmus David 112us, 'Laudate pueri'—psalm: 6/4vv and continuo, H203 (?late 1680s)
Concert Spirituel Voc Ens, H. Niquet (r1994) *Concert*
(6/95) (NAXO) ① **8 553173**

Psalmus 126us, 'Nisi Dominus'—psalm: 4vv and continuo, H160 (?early 1670s)
Concert Spirituel Voc Ens, H. Niquet (r1994) *Concert*
(6/95) (NAXO) ① **8 553173**

Quam dilecta—8vv, flute, strings and continuo, H167 (Wds. Psalm 83)
B. Schlick, N. Zijlstra, K. Wessel, D. Visse, C. Prégardien, H. van Berne, P. Kooy, K. Mertens, Amsterdam Baroque Orch, T. Koopman *Concert*
(12/92) (ERAT) ① [2] **2292-45822-2**

Quatuor anni tempestatis, H335-38 (1685)
1. Ver; 2. Aestas; 3. Autumnus; 4. Hyenis.
Parlement de Musique, M. Gester *Concert*
(9/91) (O111) ① **OPS30-9005**

Quemadmodum desiderat cervus—two sopranos, bass, two violins and continuo, H174 (1679-80) (Wds. Psalm 41)
Parlement de Musique, M. Gester *Concert*
(9/91) (O111) ① **OPS30-9005**

Quid audio, quid murmur (Epitaphium Carpentarij)—cantata: 6vv and continuo, H474
H. Ledroit, G. de Reyghere, M. Ledroit, G. de Mey, J. Bona, Ricercar Consort *Concert*
(10/88) (RICE) ① **RIC037011**

Rendez-moi mes plaisirs—air: 1v and continuo, H463
H. Ledroit, Ricercar Consort *Concert*
(10/88) (RICE) ① **RIC037011**

Répons après la 1ère leçon du jeudi—tenor, 2 flutes, continuo, H144 (?mid-1690s)
I. Honeyman, Seminario Musicale (r1993) *Concert*
(9/95) (VIRG) ① **VC5 45075-2**

Répons après la 1ère leçon du mercredi—alto and continuo, H117 (?c1680)
G. Lesne, Seminario Musicale (r1994) *Concert*
(9/95) (VIRG) ① **VC5 45107-2**

Répons après la 2de leçon du jeudi—3/4vv, flute, strings and continuo, H128 (?early 1690s)
S. Piau, G. Lesne, I. Honeyman, P. Harvey, Seminario Musicale (r1993) *Concert*
(9/95) (VIRG) ① **VC5 45075-2**

Répons après la 2nde leçon du mercredi—2 tenors and continuo, H126 (?early 1690s)
G. Lesne, C. Purves, Seminario Musicale (r1994) *Concert*
(9/95) (VIRG) ① **VC5 45107-2**

Répons après la 3ème leçon du jeudi—bass, flute, strings and continuo, H129 (?early 1690s)
P. Harvey, Seminario Musicale (r1993) *Concert*
(9/95) (VIRG) ① **VC5 45075-2**

Répons après la 3ème leçon du mercredi—alto, strings & continuo, H131 (?early 1690s)
G. Lesne, Seminario Musicale (r1994) *Concert*
(9/95) (VIRG) ① **VC5 45107-2**

Salve regina—3vv and continuo, H23 (?mid-1670s)
Concert des Nations, J. Savall *Concert*
(2/90) (ASTR) ① **E8713**

Salve regina—antiphon: 3/8vv and continuo, H24 (?mid-1670s)
Lisbon Gulbenkian Chor, Lisbon Gulbenkian Orch, M. Corboz (r1977) *Concert*
(6/93) (ERAT) ① **2292-45926-2**

Stabat Mater (pour des religieuses)—1/1v and continuo, H15
J. Feldman, B. Mernier, Capella Ricercar, J. Léjeune *Concert*
(1/89) (RICE) ① **RIC052034**
Concert des Nations, J. Savall *Concert*
(2/90) (ASTR) ① **E8713**

Te Deum—8/4vv and instruments, H146 (?early 1690s)
1. Prélude.
B. Degelin, L. Jansen, J. Nirouët, J. Caals, K. Widmer, Ghent Madrigal Ch, Ghent Cantabile, Musica Polyphonica, L. Devos *Concert*
(12/84) (ERAT) ① **2292-45202-2**
Arts Florissants Voc Ens, Arts Florissants Instr Ens, W. Christie *Concert* (9/89) (HARM) ① **HMC90 1298**
F. Lott, E. Harrhy, C. Brett, I. Partridge, S. Roberts, King's College Ch, ASMF, P. Ledger (r1977) *Messe de minuit, H9.* (1/90) (EMI) ① **CDC7 63135-2**
D. Upshaw, A. Murray, E. Robinson, J. Aler, K. Moll, ASMF Chor, ASMF, N. Marriner *Magnifical, H74.*
(12/91) (EMI) ① **CDC7 54284-2**
E. Saque, J. Silva, J. Williams, F. Serafim, J.O. Lopes, Lisbon Gulbenkian Chor, Lisbon Gulbenkian Orch, M. Corboz (r1977) *Concert*
(6/93) (ERAT) ① **2292-45926-2**
1. A. Stringer, N. Rawsthorne (r1974) *Concert*
(11/87) (CRD) ① **CRD3308**
1. P. Hurford, M. Laird Brass Ens (r1990: arr Hazell) *Concert* (9/92) (ARGO) ① **433 451-2ZH**
1. S. Lindley *Concert* (3/93) (NAXO) ① **8 550581**
1. O.E. Antonsen, W. Marshall (r1992: arr tpt/org: Antonsen/Marshall)
(10/94) (EMI) ① **CDC5 55048-2**

Tenebrae leçon du jeudi No. 1—bass, woodwind, strings & continuo, H121 (?late 1680s)
P. Harvey, Seminario Musicale (r1993) *Concert*
(9/95) (VIRG) ① **VC5 45075-2**

Tenebrae leçon du jeudi No. 2—alto and continuo, H139 (?early 1690s)
G. Lesne, Seminario Musicale (r1993) *Concert*
(9/95) (VIRG) ① **VC5 45075-2**

Tenebrae leçon du jeudi No. 3—3/6vv, flute, strings and continuo, H136 (?early 1690s)
S. Piau, G. Lesne, I. Honeyman, P. Harvey, Seminario Musicale (r1993) *Concert*
(9/95) (VIRG) ① **VC5 45075-2**

Tenebrae leçon du mercredi No. 1—bass, woodwind, strings and continuo, H120 (?late 1680s)
C. Purves, Seminario Musicale (r1994) *Concert*
(9/95) (VIRG) ① **VC5 45107-2**

Tenebrae leçon du mercredi No. 2—alto and continuo, H138 (?early 1690s)
G. Lesne, Seminario Musicale (r1994) *Concert*
(9/95) (VIRG) ① **VC5 45107-2**

Tenebrae leçon du mercredi No. 3—bass, strings and continuo, H141 (?early 1690s)
C. Purves, Seminario Musicale (r1994) *Concert*
(9/95) (VIRG) ① **VC5 45107-2**

Tenebrae Lesson (JOD. Manum suam)—2vv and continuo, H92 (? early 1670s) (3eme du mecredi saint)
Parlement de Musique, M. Gester (hpd/dir) *Concert*
(9/92) (O111) ① **OPS55-9119**

Tenebrae Lesson (Incipit oratio Jeremaie)—2vv, two trumpets, strings and continuo, H95 (? early 1670s) (3eme leçon du vendredi saint)
Parlement de Musique, M. Gester (hpd/dir) *Concert*
(9/92) (O111) ① **OPS55-9119**
3. A. Mellon, G. Lesne, Seminario musicale (r1990s) *Concert* (9/95) (VIRG) ① **VC7 59295-2**

3 Tenebrae Lessons—3-6vv, flute, strings and continuo, H135-137 (? early 1690s)
1. 3eme lecon di mercredi (JOD. Manum suam); 2. 3eme lecon du jeudi (ALEPH. Ego vir videns); 3. 3eme lecon du vendredi (Incipit oratio Jeremaie).
B. Schlick, N. Zijlstra, K. Wessel, D. Visse, C. Prégardien, H. van Berne, P. Kooy, K. Mertens, Amsterdam Baroque Orch, T. Koopman *Concert*
(12/92) (ERAT) ① [2] **2292-45822-2**

3 Tenebrae Lessons—contralto and continuo, H138-140 (? early 1690s)
1. 2de lecon du mercredi (VAU. Et egrussus est); 2. 2de lecon du jeudi (LAMED. Matribus suis); 3. 2de lecon du vendredi (ALEPH. Quomodo obscuratum

est).
3. G. Lesne, Seminario musicale (r1990s) *Concert*
(9/95) (VIRG) ① **VC7 59295-2**

Tenebrae Lessons du vendredi saint—1-3vv and continuo (? early 1670s)
1. Lettres hebriques de la 1ere lecon, H99; 2. 1ere lecon (De lamentatione Jeremiae), H105; 3. 2de lecon (ALEPH. Quomodo obscuratum est), H106; 4. 3eme lecon (Incipit oratio Jermeiae), H110.
1, 2. A. Mellon, G. Lesne, I. Honeyman, Seminario musicale (r1990s) *Concert*
(9/95) (VIRG) ① **VC7 59295-2**

9 Tenebrae Responsories—1-3vv and continuo, H111-119 (c1680)
1. In nomte Oliveti; 2. Tristis est anima mea; 3. Amicus meus; 4. Unus ex discipulis meis; 5. Eram quasi agnus; 6. Una hora non potuistis; 7. Seniores populi; 8. Revelabunt coeli; 9. O Juda.
5, 9. Parlement de Musique, M. Gester (hpd/dir) *Concert*
(9/92) (O111) ① **OPS55-9119**

9 Tenebrae Responsories—1-4vv and continuo, H126-134 (? early 1690s)
1. Tristis est anima mea; 2. Amicus meus; 3. Velum templi; 4. Tenebrae factae sunt; 5. Jerusalem surge; 6. Ecce quomodo; 7. Unus ex discipulis meis; 8. Tanquam ad latronem; 9. O vos omnes.
4. J.O. Lopes, Lisbon Gulbenkian Chor, Lisbon Gulbenkian Orch, M. Corboz (r1977) *Concert*
(6/93) (ERAT) ① **2292-45926-2**
6, 8. I. Honeyman, J. Bona, Seminario musicale (r1990s) *Concert* (9/95) (VIRG) ① **VC7 59295-2**
9. Parlement de Musique, M. Gester (hpd/dir) *Concert* (9/92) (O111) ① **OPS55-9119**

Tristes déserts, sombre retraie—air: 1v and continuo, H469
H. Ledroit, Ricercar Consort *Concert*
(10/88) (RICE) ① **RIC037011**

SECTION V: STAGE WORKS

Les Arts Florissants—opera, H487 (1685-86)
Cpte J. Feldman, A. Mellon, G. Reinhart, C. Dussaut, G. Laurens, D. Visse, P. Cantor, Arts Florissants Voc Ens, Arts Florissants Instr Ens, W. Christie (r1981)
(12/87) (HARM) ① **HMA190 1083**

Le Malade Imaginaire—Prologue and Intermèdes—6-5vv, 2 flutes, strings and continuo, H495 (1673) (Play by Molière)
M. Zanetti, N. Rime, C. Brua, D. Visse, H. Crook, J-F. Gardeil, Arts Florissants Voc Ens, Arts Florissants Orch, W. Christie
(4/91) (HARM) ① [2] **HMC90 1336**

Médée—tragédie lyrique, H491 (1693) (Text P. Corneille)
Cpte J. Feldman, J. Bona, A. Mellon, G. Ragon, P. Cantor, S. Boulin, Arts Florissants Chor, Arts Florissants Orch, W. Christie
(3/85) (HARM) ① [3] **HMC90 1139/41**
Cpte L. Hunt, B. Delétré, M. Zanetti, M. Padmore, J-M. Salzmann, N. Rime, Arts Florissants Chor, Arts Florissants Orch, W. Christie (r1994)
(6/95) (ERAT) ① [3] **4509-96558-2**

CHAUSSON, (Amedée-)Ernest (1855–1899) France

SECTION I: ORCHESTRAL

Poème—violin and orchestra, Op. 25 (1896)
A. Dumay, Monte Carlo PO, A. Dumay *Concert*
(6/87) (EMI) ① **CDC7 47544-2**
I. Perlman, Paris Orch, J. Martinon *Concert*
(12/87) (EMI) ① **CDC7 47725-2**
I. Perlman, NYPO, Z. Mehta *Concert*
(12/87) (DG) ① **423 063-2GH**
G. Neveu, Philh, I. Dobroven (r1946) *Concert*
(8/90) (EMI) ① **CDH7 63493-2**
L. Mordkovitch, M. Gusak-Grin (arr vn/pf) *Concert*
(11/90) (CHAN) ① **CHAN8748**
Y. P. Tortelier (vn/dir), Ulster Orch *Concert*
(12/91) (CHAN) ① **CHAN8952**
G. Enescu, S. Schlüssel (arr vn/pf: r1929) *Concert*
(12/91) (MSCM) ① **MM30322**
J. Bell, RPO, A. Litton *Concert*
(1/92) (DECC) ① **433 519-2DH**
C. Pavlík, Dvořák CO, V. Válek *Concert*
(4/92) (SUPR) ① **11 0111-2**
Z. Francescatti, NYPO, L. Bernstein *Concert*
(5/93) (SONY) ① **SMK47548**
G. Enescu, S. Schlüssel (r1929) *Concert*
(6/93) (BIDD) ① **LAB066**
E. Friedman, LSO, M. Sargent *Concert*
(9/93) (RCA) ① **09026 61210-2**
J. Heifetz, RCA Victor SO, I. Solomon (r1952) *Concert* (11/94) (RCA) ① [65] **09026 61778-2(22)**

Soir de fête—symphonic poem, Op. 32 (1897/8)
RTBF New SO, J. Serebrier *Concert*
(9/85) (CHAN) ① **CHAN8369**
Symphony in B flat, Op. 20 (1889/90)
RTBF New SO, J. Serebrier *Concert*
(9/85) (CHAN) ① **CHAN8369**
Czech PO, Z. Košler (r1982) *Roussel: Festin de l'araignée.*
(8/88) (SUPR) ① **CO-1472**
Philh, F. d'Avalos *Franck: Symphony.*
(8/90) (ASV) ① **CDDCA708**
Netherlands Rad PO, J. Fournet (r1988) *Fauré: Pelléas et Mélisande Suite.*
(9/90) (DENO) ① **CO-73675**
Loire PO, M. Soustrot (r1992) *Concert*
(6/94) (PIER) ① **PV792051**
San Francisco SO, P. Monteux (r1950) *Concert*
(9/94) (RCA) ① **[15] 09026 61893-2**
The Tempest—incidental music to Shakespeare play, Op. 18 (1888)
RTBF New SO, J. Serebrier *Concert*
(9/85) (CHAN) ① **CHAN8369**

SECTION II: CHAMBER

Andante et Allegro—clarinet and piano (1881)
P. Meyer, E. Le Sage *Concert*
(9/92) (DENO) ① **CO-79282**
Concert for Violin, Piano and String Quartet in D, Op. 21 (1889-91)
J. Suk, J. Hála, Suk Qt *Fauré: Violin Sonata 2.*
(1/91) (SUPR) ① **11 0269-2**
J. Thibaud, A. Cortot, Stg Qt (r1931) *Concert*
(11/91) (BIDD) ① **LAB029**
C. Ferras, P. Barbizet, Parrenin Qt *Concert*
(4/93) (EMI) ① **CDM7 64365-2**
J. Heifetz, J-M. Sanromá, Musical Art Qt (r1941)
Concert (11/94) (RCA) ① **[65] 09026 61778-2(05)**
Piano Quartet in A, Op. 30 (1897)
Musiciens (r1982) *Piano Trio.*
(9/87) (HARM) ① **HMA190 1115**
Piano Trio in G minor, Op. 3 (1881)
Beaux Arts Trio *Ravel: Piano Trio.*
(4/85) (PHIL) ① **411 141-2PH**
Musiciens (r1982) *Piano Quartet.*
(9/87) (HARM) ① **HMA190 1115**
String Quartet, Op. 35 (1899) (incomplete)
Athenaeum-Enescu Qt *Franck: Piano Quintet.*
(12/92) (PIER) ① **PV792032**

SECTION IV: VOCAL AND CHORAL

Chanson perpétuelle—soprano and orch, Op. 37 (1898) (Wds. Cros)
J. Norman, M. Dalberto, R. Patterson, S. Sansalone, J-P. Pigerre, L. Anderson *Concert*
(10/88) (ERAT) ① **2292-45368-2**
A. Esposito, P. Barbizet, Parrenin Qt *Concert*
(4/93) (EMI) ① **CDM7 64365-2**
M. Teyte, G. Moore, Blech Qt (r1943) *Concert*
(10/94) (EMI) ① **[2] CHS5 65198-2**
4 Chansons de Shakespeare, Op. 28 (Wds. trans Bouchor)
1. Chanson de Clown (1v and pf: from 'Twelfth Night': 1890); 2. Chanson d'amour (1v and pf: from 'Measure for Measure': 1891); 3. Chanson d'Ophélie (1v and pf: from 'Hamlet': 1896); 4. Chant funèbre (4 female vv and pf: from 'Much Ado about Nothing': 1897).
2. G. Souzay, D. Baldwin (r1977) *Concert*
(9/94) (EMI) ① **CDM5 65161-2**
2 Duos—two voices and piano, Op. 11 (1883)
1. La nuit (wds. T. de Banville); 2. Le réveil (wds. H. Balzac).
F. Lott, A. Murray, G. Johnson *Concert*
(11/90) (EMI) ① **CDC7 49930-2**
C. Alliot-Lugaz, F. Le Roux, J. Cohen *Concert*
(4/91) (REM) ① **REM311086**
7 Mélodies—voice and piano, Op. 2 (1879-82) (Wds. various)
1. Nanny (wds. Leconte de Lisle); 2. Le charme (wds. Silvestre); 3. Les papillons (wds. Gautier); 4. La dernière (wds. Gautier); 5. Sérénade italienne (wds. P. Bourget); 6. Hébé (wds. L. Ackermann); 7. Le colibri (wds. Leconte de Lisle).
1-3, 5, 7. G. Souzay, J. Bonneau (r1955) *Concert*
(7/91) (DECC) ① **425 975-2DM**
1-3, 5, 7. G. Souzay, D. Baldwin (r1977) *Concert*
(9/94) (EMI) ① **CDM5 65161-2**
2-5, 7. J. Norman, M. Dalberto *Concert*
(10/88) (ERAT) ① **2292-45368-2**
3. M. Teyte, G. Moore (r1944) *Concert*
(10/94) (EMI) ① **[2] CHS5 65198-2**
3. D. Fischer-Dieskau, H. Höll (r c1987) *Concert*
(12/95) (TELD) ① **4509-97457-2**

---

7. M. Teyte, G. Moore (r1943) *Concert*
(10/94) (EMI) ① **[2] CHS5 65198-2**
4 Mélodies—1v & piano, Op. 8 (Wds. Bouchor)
1. Nocturne (1886); 2. Amour d'antan (1882); 3. Printemps triste (1883-88); 4. Nos souvenirs (1888).
4. G. Souzay, D. Baldwin (r1977) *Concert*
(9/94) (EMI) ① **CDM5 65161-2**
2 Mélodies—1v & piano, Op. 36
1. Cantique à l'épouse (wds A Jounet: 1896); 2. Dans la forêt du charme et de l'enchantement (wds J Moréas: 1898).
1. G. Souzay, J. Bonneau (r1955) *Concert*
(7/91) (DECC) ① **425 975-2DM**
1. G. Souzay, D. Baldwin (r1977) *Concert*
(9/94) (EMI) ① **CDM5 65161-2**
2. S. Varcoe, G. Johnson *Concert*
(6/88) (HYPE) ① **CDA66248**
2. P. Frijsh, C. Dougherty (r1940) *Concert*
(4/95) (PEAR) ① **[2] GEMMCDS9095(1)**
Poème de l'amour et de la mer—1v & orchestra, Op. 19 (1882-90) (Wds. Bouchor)
1. La fleur des eaux; 2. Interlude; 3. La mort de l'amour.
J. Norman, L. Anderson, Monte Carlo PO, A. Jordan *Concert*
(10/88) (ERAT) ① **2292-45368-2**
C. Alliot-Lugaz, Monte Carlo PO, C. Bardon *Berlioz: Nuits d'été.*
(4/91) (REM) ① **REM311074**
L. Finnie, Ulster Orch, Y. P. Tortelier *Concert*
(12/91) (CHAN) ① **CHAN8952**
V. de los Angeles, Lamoureux Orch, J-P. Jacquillat *Concert*
(4/93) (EMI) ① **CDM7 64365-2**
V. de los Angeles, Lamoureux Orch, J-P. Jacquillat (r1969) *Concert*
(4/94) (EMI) ① **[4] CMS5 65061-2(1)**
W. Meier, Philadelphia, R. Muti (r1993) *Concert*
(7/94) (EMI) ① **CDC5 55120-2**
G. Swarthout, RCA Victor SO, P. Monteux (r1952)
(9/94) (RCA) ① **[15] 09026 61893-2**
V. Kasarova, Austrian RSO, P. Steinberg (r1994)
Concert (9/95) (RCA) ① **09026 68008-2**
1, 3a, 3b M. Teyte, orch, L. Lucas (r1946) *Concert*
(10/94) (EMI) ① **[2] CHS5 65198-2**
3b G. Souzay, J. Bonneau (r1955) *Concert*
(7/91) (DECC) ① **425 975-2DM**
3b C. Panzéra, SO, P. Coppola (r1935) *Concert*
(3/93) (DANT) ① **[2] LYS003/4**
3b C. Panzéra, orch, P. Coppola (r1935) *Concert*
(3/93) (EMI) ① **CDH7 64254-2**
3b D. Fischer-Dieskau, H. Höll (r c1987) *Concert*
(12/95) (TELD) ① **4509-97457-2**
Serres chaudes—1v & piano, Op. 24 (Wds. M Maeterlinck)
1. Serre chaude (1896); 2. Serre d'ennui (1893); 3. Lassitude (1893); 4. Fauves las (1896); 5. Oraison (1895).
5. G. Souzay, D. Baldwin (r1977) *Concert*
(9/94) (EMI) ① **CDM5 65161-2**
Le Temps des lilas—song (1877) (Wds. Bouchor: orig 2nd song of 'Poème de l'amour')
P. Frijsh, P. James Orch, P. James (bp1936) *Concert*
(4/95) (PEAR) ① **[2] GEMMCDS9095(2)**

SECTION V: STAGE WORKS

Le Roi Arthus—drama lyrique: 3 acts, Op. 23 (1903—Brussels) (Lib. cpsr)
Cpte G. Quilico, T. Zylis-Gara, G. Winbergh, R. Massis, G. Friedmann, F. Loup, G. Cachemaille, T. Dran, R. Schirrer, A. Laiter, French Rad Chor, French Rad New PO, A. Jordan
(10/91) (ERAT) ① **[3] 2292-45407-2**

CHÁVEZ (Y RAMÍREZ), Carlos (Antonio de Padua) (1899–1978) Mexico

SECTION I: ORCHESTRAL

Sinfonia de Antigona (1933)
RPO, E. Bátiz *Concert* (8/89) (ASV) ① **CDDCA653**
Symphony No. 2, 'Sinfonia India' (1935-36)
New World Sym, M. Tilson Thomas (1992) *Concert*
(6/93) (ARGO) ① **436 737-2ZH**
Xalapa SO, H. de la Fuente *Concert*
(12/93) (CARL) ① **MCD63**
Symphony No. 4, 'Romantic' (1953)
RPO, E. Bátiz *Concert* (8/89) (ASV) ① **CDDCA653**

SECTION II: CHAMBER

Energia—nine instruments (1925)
Camerata, Tambuco, E. Mata (r1994) *Concert*
(9/95) (DORI) ① **DOR90215**
Suite for Double Quartet (1943) (adapted cpsr from ballet 'Daughter of Colchis')
Camerata, Tambuco, E. Mata (r1994) *Concert*
(9/95) (DORI) ① **DOR90215**

Tambuco—six percussion (1964)
Camerata, Tambuco, E. Mata (r1994) *Concert*
(9/95) (DORI) ① **DOR90215**
Toccata—six percussion (1942)
Amadinda Perc Group *Concert*
(11/90) (HUNG) ① **HCD12991**
Camerata, Tambuco, E. Mata (r1994) *Concert*
(9/95) (DORI) ① **DOR90215**
Xochipilli—an imanined Aztec music—four wind instruments & percussion (1940)
Camerata, Tambuco, E. Mata (r1994) *Concert*
(9/95) (DORI) ① **DOR90215**

SECTION V: STAGE WORKS

Suite de Caballos de vapor, 'Horse-Power Suite'—ballet (1926-27)
S. Bolívar SO, E. Mata (r1994) *Concert*
(8/95) (DORI) ① **DOR90211**

CHERKASSKY, Shura (b 1911) Russia/USA

SECTION III: INSTRUMENTAL

Prélude pathétique—piano (1922)
S. Cherkassky (bp1982) *Concert*
(6/93) (DECC) ① **433 651-2DH**

CHERUBINI, Luigi (Carlo Zanobi Salvadore Maria) (1760–1842) Italy

SECTION I: ORCHESTRAL

Concert Overture
ASMF, N. Marriner *Concert*
(9/92) (EMI) ① **CDC7 54438-2**
Marche religieuse (orchestral appendix to Coronation Mass)
Philh, R. Muti *Coronation Mass in A.*
(4/89) (EMI) ① **CDC7 49302-2**
2 Sonatas in F—horn and orchestra (1804)
2. B. Tuckwell, ASMF, N. Marriner (r1964) *Concert*
(9/95) (DECC) ① **[2] 443 838-2DF2**

SECTION II: CHAMBER

8 Marches—wind instruments (c1800-1820)
1. Prefect of Eure-et-Loire (1800); 2. Prefect's Return (1800); 3. March (1805); 4. March (1808); 5. March (1809); 6. March (1810); 7. National Guard (1814); 8. Funeral (1812).
8. Neue Orch, C. Spering (1994) *Concert*
(2/95) (O111) ① **OPS30-116**
6 redoublés et (2) marches—trumpet, 3 horns and trombone (1814)
London Gabrieli Brass Ens, C. Larkin *Concert*
(4/94) (HYPE) ① **CDA66470**
String Quartet No. 1 in E flat (1814)
Melos Qt *Concert*
(4/90) (DG) ① **[3] 429 185-2GCM3**
Movt 3. NBC SO, A. Toscanini (bp1943) *Concert*
(4/90) (ATS) ① **ATCD100**
String Quartet No. 2 in C
Melos Qt *Concert*
(4/90) (DG) ① **[3] 429 185-2GCM3**
String Quartet No. 3 in D minor (1834)
Melos Qt *Concert*
(4/90) (DG) ① **[3] 429 185-2GCM3**
String Quartet No. 4 in E (1835)
Melos Qt *Concert*
(4/90) (DG) ① **[3] 429 185-2GCM3**
String Quartet No. 5 in F (1835)
Melos Qt *Concert*
(4/90) (DG) ① **[3] 429 185-2GCM3**
String Quartet No. 6 in A minor (1837)
Melos Qt *Concert*
(4/90) (DG) ① **[3] 429 185-2GCM3**

SECTION III: INSTRUMENTAL

Capriccio—study: piano (1789)
P. Spada *Concert* (4/92) (EURM) ① **[2] 350225**
Fantasia in C—piano (1810)
P. Spada *Concert* (4/92) (EURM) ① **[2] 350225**
6 Sonatas—harpsichord (1780)
1. F; 2. C; 3. B flat; 4. G; 5. D; 6. E flat.
P. Spada (pf) *Concert*
(4/92) (EURM) ① **[2] 350225**

SECTION IV: VOCAL AND CHORAL

Hymne à la victoire (1796)
Leeds Fest Chor, Wallace Collection, J. Wallace *Concert* (7/89) (NIMB) ① **NI5175**
In Paradisium—choir & orchestra (1820)
Cologne Chorus Musicus, Neue Orch, C. Spering (r1994) *Concert* (2/95) (O111) ① **OPS30-116**

Mass in A, 'Coronation' (1825)
Philh Chor, Philh, R. Muti *Marche religieuse.*
(4/89) (EMI) ① CDC7 49302-2
Mass in D minor—SATB, chorus and orchestra (1811 rev 1822)
P. Coburn, G. Burandt, C. Kallisch, M. Thompson, M. Wanner, J. Will, Stuttgart Gächinger Kantorei, Stuttgart Bach Collegium, H. Rilling (r1992) *Haydn: Mass 10.* (5/93) (HANS) ① [2] 98 981
Mass in G, 'Coronation' (1819)
LP Chor, LPO, R. Muti
(4/89) (EMI) ① CDC7 49553-2
Requiem Mass No. 1 in C minor—chorus and orchestra (1816)
Berlin Rad Chor, Berlin RSO, C.P. Flor
(11/89) (RCA) ① RD60059
R. Shaw Chorale, NBC SO, A. Toscanini (bp1950) *Beethoven: Missa Solemnis.*
(3/91) (RCA) ① [2] GD60272
Cologne Chorus Musicus, Neue Orch, C. Spering (r1994) *Concert* (2/95) (O111) ① OPS30-116
Requiem Mass No. 2 in D minor—chorus and orchestra (1836)
Ambrosian Sngrs, New Philh, R. Muti
(4/89) (EMI) ① CDC7 49301-2

SECTION V: STAGE WORKS

Les Abencérages—opera: 3 acts (1813—Paris) (Lib. V. J. E. de Jouy, after Chateaubriand)
EXCERPTS: 1. Overture.
1. ASMF, N. Marriner *Concert*
(9/92) (EMI) ① CDC7 54438-2
Anacréon—opéra-ballet: 2 acts (1803—Paris) (Lib. C. R. Mendouze)
Overture ASMF, N. Marriner *Concert*
(9/92) (EMI) ① CDC7 54438-2
Overture Concertgebouw, W. Mengelberg (pp1943) *Concert* (12/93) (ARHI) ① ADCD111
Overture Lamoureux Orch, I. Markevitch *Concert*
(7/95) (DG) ① 447 406-2GOR
Les Deux journées—opera: 3 acts (Paris) (Lib. J. N. Bouilly)
EXCERPTS: 1. Overture.
1. ASMF, N. Marriner *Concert*
(9/92) (EMI) ① CDC7 54438-2
Elisa—opera: 2 acts (1794—Paris) (Lib. J. A. de R. Saint-Cyr)
Overture ASMF, N. Marriner *Concert*
(9/92) (EMI) ① CDC7 54438-2
Faniska—opera: 3 acts (1806—Vienna) (Lib. J. Sonnleithner)
Overture ASMF, N. Marriner *Concert*
(9/92) (EMI) ① CDC7 54438-2
L' Hôtellerie portugaise—opera: 1 act (1798—Paris) (Lib. E. Aignan)
EXCERPTS: 1. Overture.
1. ASMF, N. Marriner *Concert*
(9/92) (EMI) ① CDC7 54438-2
Lodoïska—opera: 3 acts (1791—Paris)
Cpte M. Devia, F. Pedaci, B. Lombardo, T. Moser, A. Corbelli, W. Shimell, M. Luperi, D. Serraiocco, P. Spina, E. Panariello, E. Capuano, R. Cazzaniga, A. Bramante, La Scala Chor, La Scala Orch, R. Muti (pp1991) (10/91) (SONY) ① [2] S2K47290
Medea—opera: 3 acts (1797—Paris) (Lib. F.B. Hoffman)
ACT 1: 1a. Overture; 1b. Che? Quando già corona; 1c. Io cedo alla buona preghiera; 1d. O Amore, vieni a me; 1e. No, non temer; 2a. O bella Glauce; 2b. Colco! Pensier; 3a. Or che più non vedrò; 3b. Ah, già troppo turbò; 4a. Pronube dive; 4b. Signor! Ferma una donna; 5a. Qui tremar devi tu; 5b. Taci, Giason; 6a. Dei tuoi figli la madre; 6b. Son vane qui minacce; 7. Nemici senza cor. ACT 2: 8a. Introduction; 8b. Soffrir non posso; 9a. Data almen, per pietà; 9b. Medea! o Medea!; 10a. Solo un pianto; 10b. Creonte a me solo; 11a. Figli miei; 11b. Hai dato pronto ascolto; 12. Ah! Triste canto...Dio dell' Amor!. ACT 3: 13a. Introduction; 13b. Numi, venite a me; 14a. Del fiero duol; 14b. D'amore il raggio ancora; 15. E che? Io son Medea!.
Cpte M. Callas, M. Picchi, R. Scotto, G. Modesti, M. Pirazzini, L. Marimpietri, E. Galassi, A. Giacomotti, La Scala Chor, La Scala Orch, T. Serafin *Beethoven: Ah! perfido, Op.65.*
(2/91) (EMI) ① [2] CMS7 63625-2
1a ASMF, N. Marriner *Concert*
(9/92) (EMI) ① CDC7 54438-2
1c, 1d E. Gruberová, Munich RO, L. Gardelli *Concert* (11/86) (ORFE) ① C101841A
6a, 6b G. Bumbry, Stuttgart RSO, S. Soltesz *Concert* (11/86) (ORFE) ① C081841A
6a, 6b M. Callas, La Scala Orch, T. Serafin (r1955) *Concert* (11/86) (EMI) ① CDC7 47282-2

6a, 6b M. Callas, La Scala Orch, T. Serafin (r1955) *Concert* (2/90) (EMI) ① [4] CMS7 63244-2

CHESNOKOV, Paul Grigor'yevich (1877–1944) Russia

SECTION IV: VOCAL AND CHORAL

Bless the Lord, o my soul—chorus a capella, Op. 27/1 (Wds. Psalm 103 (104)
Bolshoi Children's Ch, A. Zaboronok (r1994) *Concert* (7/95) (COLL) ① Coll1443-2
Come, let us entreat Joseph—double choir, Op. 9/9
Bolshoi Children's Ch, A. Zaboronok (r1994) *Concert* (7/95) (COLL) ① Coll1443-2
Joyous light—double choir, Op. 9/21
Bolshoi Children's Ch, A. Zaboronok (r1994) *Concert* (7/95) (COLL) ① Coll1443-2
Let us, mystically representing the Cherubim—double choir (from the 'Liturgy', Op. 16)
Bolshoi Children's Ch, A. Zaboronok (r1994) *Concert* (7/95) (COLL) ① Coll1443-2
Praise ye the name of the Lord in heaven—double choir (from the 'Liturgy', Op. 16)
Bolshoi Children's Ch, A. Zaboronok (r1994) *Concert* (7/95) (COLL) ① Coll1443-2

CHILCOT, Thomas (c1700–1766) England

SECTION I: ORCHESTRAL

---

6 Concertos for the Harpsichord, Op. 2 (pub 1765)
EXCERPTS: 2. No 2 in A; 6. No 6 in G.
2. P. Nicholson (kybds/dir), Parley of Instr, P. Holman (r1993; recons R. Langley) *Concert*
(8/94) (HYPE) ① CDA66700

SECTION III: INSTRUMENTAL

---

6 Suites of Lessons—harpsichord (pub 1734)
EXCERPTS: 1. Suite in G minor; 2. Suite in E minor (numbering conjectural); 3. Suite in B flat.
2. M. Souter (r1994-5) *Concert*
(12/95) (ISIS) ① ISISCD010
3. G. Gifford *Concert* (5/90) (LIBR) ① LRCD156

CHILD, William (1606/7–1697) England

SECTION IV: VOCAL AND CHORAL

O Lord, grant the King a long life—Coronation anthem for King James II: 5vv
Westminster Abbey Ch, orch, S. Preston (r1986) *Concert* (7/95) (ARCH) ① 447 155-2AP

CHIPP, Edmund Thomas (1823–1886) ?England

SECTION III: INSTRUMENTAL

---

24 Sketches for the organ, Op. 11
Canzonet Margaret Phillips *Concert*
(7/91) (GAMU) ① GAMCD522
Twilight fancies—piano (1857)
2. A; 7. F.
2, 7. I. Hobson *Concert* (3/89) (ARAB) ① Z6596

CHOPIN, Fryderyk Franciszek (1810–1849) Poland

SECTION I: ORCHESTRAL

Andante spianato and Grande Polonaise in E flat—piano and orchestra, Op. 22 (1830-1; 1834)
I. Birot, Košice St PO, R. Stankovsky *Concert*
(4/92) (NAXO) ① 8 550368
R. Yassa *Ballades.* (10/95) (PAVA) ① ADW7173
Concerto for Piano and Orchestra No. 1 in E minor, Op. 11 (1830)
1. Allegro maestoso; 2. Larghetto; 3. Rondo (Vivace).
M. Argerich, LSO, C. Abbado *Liszt: Piano Concerto 1.* (4/85) (DG) ① 415 061-2GH
K. Zimerman, Los Angeles PO, C.M. Giulini (pp1978) *Piano Concerto 2.* (9/86) (DG) ① 415 970-2GH
A. Rubinstein, New SO, S. Skrowaczewski *Piano Concerto 2.* (9/87) (RCA) ① RD85612
M. Rosenthal, Orch, F. Weissmann (r1930/1) *Concert* (4/89) (PEAR) ① GEMMCD9339

D. Lipatti, Zurich Tonhalle Orch, O. Ackermann (pp1950) *Concert* (4/90) (JECK) ① JD541-2
T. Vásáry, BPO, J. Semkow *Piano Concerto 2.*
(6/90) (DG) ① 429 515-2GR
M. Perahia, Israel PO, Z. Mehta (pp1989) *Piano Concerto 2.* (6/90) (SONY) ① SK44922
I. Székely, Budapest SO, G. Németh *Piano Concerto 2.* (10/90) (NAXO) ① 8 550123
I. Székely, Budapest SO, G. Németh *Liszt: Piano Concerto 1.* (10/90) (NAXO) ① 8 550292
C. Arrau, Cologne RSO, O. Klemperer (pp1954) *Liszt: Piano Concerto 2.*
(10/90) (MUSI) ① MACD-625
M. Setrak, Baltic Phil SO, W. Rajski (arr/ed. Tausig) *J. Wieniawski: Piano Concerto, Op. 20.*
(11/90) (CHNT) ① LDC278 902
Emil Gilels, Philadelphia, E. Ormandy *Piano Concerto 2.* (3/91) (SONY) ① SBK46336
J. Hofmann, orch (pp1930s) *Piano Concerto 2.*
(2/92) (DANT) ① HPC002
I. Biret, Košice St PO, R. Stankovsky *Concert*
(4/92) (NAXO) ① 8 550368
C. Arrau, LPO, E. Inbal *Piano Concerto 2.*
(7/92) (PHIL) ① 434 145-2PM
M. Pollini, Philh, P. Kletzki *Concert*
(11/92) (EMI) ① CDM7 64354-2
M-J. Pires, Monte Carlo Nat Op Orch, A. Jordan *Piano Concerto 2.* (6/93) (ERAT) ① 2292-45927-2
A. Rubinstein, LSO, J. Barbirolli (r1937) *Concert*
(7/93) (EMI) ① [2] CHS7 64491-2
N. Demidenko, Philh, H. Schiff (r1993) *Piano Concerto 2.* (11/93) (HYPE) ① CDA66647
M. Horszowski, Vienna St Op Orch, H. Swarowsky (r1952) *Concert* (12/93) (RELI) ① CR911023
E. Wild, RPO, M. Sargent (r1962) *Concert*
(2/94) (CHES) ① Chesky CD93
B. Rigutto, Budapest PO, E. Bergel (r1992) *Piano Concerto 2.* (10/94) (DENO) ① CO-75637
E. Ax, Philadelphia, E. Ormandy *Piano Concerto 2.*
(1/95) (RCA) ① 74321 17892-2
G. Cziffra, Paris Orch, G. Cziffra Jnr (r1968) *Concert* (3/95) (EMI) ① CDM5 65251-2
M. Tirimo, Philh, F. Glushchenko (r1994) *Piano Concerto 2.* (6/95) (CONI) ① 75605 51247-2
H. Nakamura, LSO, A. Fistoulari (r1984) *Piano Concerto 2.* (7/95) (SONY) ① SMK64241
G. Anda, Philh, A. Galliera (r1956) *Concert*
(10/95) (TEST) ① SBT1066
A. Brailowsky, BPO, J. Prüwer (r1928) *Piano Concerto 2.* (11/95) (DANA) ① [2] DACOCD336/7
O. Mustonen, San Francisco SO, H. Blomstedt (r1994) *Grieg: Piano Concerto.*
(11/95) (DECC) ① 444 518-2DH
Romanza M-A. Hamelin (pp1994; trans Balakirev: pf) *Concert* (3/95) (HYPE) ① CDA66765
Concerto for Piano and Orchestra No. 2 in F minor, Op. 21 (1829)
1. Maestoso; 2. Larghetto; 3. Allegro vivace.
I. Pogorelich, Chicago SO, C. Abbado *Polonaises.*
(2/84) (DG) ① 410 507-2GH
K. Zimerman, Los Angeles PO, C.M. Giulini *Piano Concerto 1.* (9/86) (DG) ① 415 970-2GH
A. Rubinstein, Sym of the Air, A. Wallenstein *Piano Concerto 1.* (9/87) (RCA) ① RD85612
Vladimir Ashkenazy, LSO, D. Zinman *Tchaikovsky: Piano Concerto 1.* (1/89) (DECC) ① 417 750-2DM
T. Vásáry, BPO, J. Kulka *Piano Concerto 1.*
(6/90) (DG) ① 429 515-2GR
M. Perahia, Israel PO, Z. Mehta (pp1989) *Piano Concerto 1.* (6/90) (SONY) ① SK44922
I. Székely, Budapest SO, G. Németh *Piano Concerto 1.* (10/90) (NAXO) ① 8 550123
M. Setrak, Polish Chmbr PO, W. Rajski (arr *Concert* (11/90) (CHNT) ① LDC278 962
C. Rosen, New Philh, J. Pritchard *Piano Concerto 1.* (3/91) (SONY) ① SBK46336
J. Hofmann, orch (pp1930s) *Piano Concerto 1.*
(2/92) (DANT) ① HPC002
I. Biret, Košice St PO, R. Stankovsky *Concert*
(4/92) (NAXO) ① 8 550368
A. Cortot, orch, J. Barbirolli (r1935) *Concert*
(6/92) (EMI) ① [6] CZS7 67359-2
C. Arrau, LPO, E. Inbal *Piano Concerto 1.*
(7/92) (PHIL) ① 434 145-2PM
L. Lortie, Philh, N. Järvi *Schumann: Piano Concerto.*
(11/92) (CHAN) ① CHAN9061
M-J. Pires, Monte Carlo Nat Op Orch, A. Jordan *Piano Concerto 1.* (6/93) (ERAT) ① 2292-45927-2
A. Rubinstein, LSO, J. Barbirolli (r1931) *Concert*
(7/93) (EMI) ① [2] CHS7 64491-2
N. Demidenko, Philh, H. Schiff (r1993) *Piano Concerto 1.* (11/93) (HYPE) ① CDA66647
B. Rigutto, Budapest PO, E. Bergel (r1992) *Piano Concerto 1.* (10/94) (DENO) ① CO-75637
M-J. Pires, RPO, A. Previn *Preludes.*
(10/94) (DG) ① 437 817-2GH

P. Katin *Fantasie, Op.49.*
(1/89) (UNIC) ① **UKCD2008**
N. Demidenko *Concert*
(1/92) (HYPE) ① **CDA66514**
M. Pollini *Concert* (3/92) (DG) ① **431 623-2GH**
H. Shelley *Concert* (7/92) (CHAN) ① **CHAN9018**
A. Rubinstein (r1932) *Concert*
(10/93) (EMI) ① **[3] CHS7 64697-2**
S. Richter (r1977) *Schumann: Bunte Blätter.*
(4/94) (OLYM) ① **OCD338**
C. Arrau *Polonaises.* (9/94) (PHIL) ① **442 407-2PM**
C. Katsaris *Concert*
(1/95) (TELD) ① **[2] 4509-95499-2**
1. V. Horowitz *Concert* (5/86) (DG) ① **419 045-2GH**
1. V. Horowitz (r1951) *Concert*
(11/91) (RCA) ① **GD60376**
1. V. Horowitz (pp1953) *Concert*
(7/93) (RCA) ① **09026 60987-2**
1. V. Horowitz (r1963) *Concert*
(7/94) (SONY) ① **[2] S2K53457**
1, 2. V. Sofronitzky (pp1960) *Concert*
(8/95) (MELO) ① **[2] 74321 25177-2**
1, 2. V. Sofronitzky (pp1960) *Concert*
(8/95) (MELO) ① **[11] 74321 25172-2(1)**
1, 3. J. Hofmann (pf roll) *Concert*
(12/95) (NIMB) ① **NI8803**
2. A.B. Michelangeli *Concert*
(11/84) (DG) ① **413 449-2GH**
2. M. Argerich *Concert*
(4/88) (DG) ① **415 836-2GGA**
2. M. Pletnev *Concert*
(4/90) (VIRG) ① **VC7 59252-2**
2. Vladimir Ashkenazy *Concert*
(7/90) (DECC) ① **417 798-2DM**
2. V. Horowitz (r1957) *Concert*
(7/93) (RCA) ① **09026 60987-2**
2. A. Friedheim (r1912) *Concert*
(8/93) (PEAR) ① **GEMMCD9993**
2. S. Tanyel (r1992) *Concert*
(4/94) (COLL) ① **Coll1330-2**
2. E. Kissin (pp1993) *Concert*
(5/94) (RCA) ① **09026 60445-2**
2. I. Scharrer (r1932) *Concert*
(7/94) (PEAR) ① **GEMMCD9978**
2. M. Pletnev (r1988) *Concert*
(3/95) (VIRG) ① **VC5 45076-2**
2. Solomon (pp1956) *Concert*
(4/95) (APR) ① **[2] APR7030**
2. C. Licad *Concert* (10/95) (MUSM) ① **67124-2**
3. Vladimir Ashkenazy *Concert*
(3/84) (DECC) ① **410 180-2DH**
3. I. Pogorelich *Concert*
(5/85) (DG) ① **415 123-2GH**
3. C. Ortiz *Concert* (12/87) (CARL) ① **PCD872**
3. S. Barere (r1935) *Concert*
(5/91) (APR) ① **[2] APR7001**
3. S. Barere (pp1949) *Concert*
(5/91) (APR) ① **[2] APR7009**
3. M. Levitzki (r1929) *Concert*
(6/92) (APR) ① **APR7020**
3. C. Arrau (r1939) *Concert*
(9/92) (PEAR) ① **GEMMCD9928**
3. S. Barere (bp1920s/30s) *Concert*
(1/93) (APR) ① **[2] APR7014**
3. V. Horowitz (r1957) *Concert*
(1/93) (RCA) ① **GD60463**
3. S. Rachmaninov (r1924) *Concert*
(3/93) (RCA) ① **[10] 09026 61265-2(3)**
3. M. Argerich (r1960) *Concert*
(6/95) (DG) ① **447 430-2GOR**
4. L. Godowsky (r1930) *Concert*
(4/89) (APR) ① **[2] APR7011**
4. V. Horowitz (r1936) *Concert*
(3/90) (EMI) ① **[3] CHS7 63538-2**
4. S. Tanyel *Concert* (12/91) (COLL) ① **Coll1219-2**
**Sonata for Piano No. 1 in C minor, Op. 4
(1828)**
L.O. Andsnes *Concert*
(6/92) (VIRG) ① **[2] VCK7 59072-2**
C. Katsaris *Concert* (6/93) (SONY) ① **SK48483**
G. Ohlsson (r1990) *Concert*
(10/93) (ARAB) ① **Z6628**
**Sonata for Piano No. 2 in B flat minor,
'Funeral March', Op. 35 (1839)**
1. Grave—doppio movimento; 2. Scherzo; 3. Marche
funèbre; 4. Presto.
J. Bingham *Concert* (3/85) (MERI) ① **ECD84070**
I. Pogorelich *Concert* (5/85) (DG) ① **415 123-2GH**
M. Pollini *Piano Sonata 3.*
(8/86) (DG) ① **415 346-2GH**
A. Rubinstein *Concert* (2/87) (RCA) ① **RD89812**
H. Shelley *Preludes.* (10/87) (CARL) ① **PCD862**
P. Katin *Concert* (5/88) (OLYM) ① **OCD193**
M. Uchida *Piano Sonata 3.*
(2/89) (PHIL) ① **420 949-2PH**

M. Perahia *Piano Sonata 3.*
(3/89) (SONY) ① **MK76242**
L. Godowsky (r1930) *Concert*
(4/89) (APR) ① **[2] APR7010**
M. Pletnev *Concert* (4/90) (VIRG) ① **VC7 59252-2**
C. Rosen *Concert* (4/91) (MUSI) ① **MACD-609**
S. Rachmaninov (r1930) *Concert*
(11/91) (MSCM) ① **MM30271**
V. Horowitz (r1950) *Concert*
(11/91) (RCA) ① **GD60376**
S. Tanyel *Concert* (12/91) (COLL) ① **Coll1219-2**
A. Cortot (r1928) *Concert* (6/92) (BIDD) ① **LHW001**
A. Cortot (r1933) *Concert*
(6/92) (EMI) ① **[6] CZS7 67359-2**
L.O. Andsnes *Concert*
(6/92) (VIRG) ① **[2] VCK7 59072-2**
A. Gavrilov (r1991) *Ballades.*
(6/92) (DG) ① **435 622-2GH**
S. Rachmaninov (r1930) *Concert*
(3/93) (RCA) ① **[10] 09026 61265-2(2)**
A. Lear *Concert* (4/93) (KING) ① **KCLCD2031**
C. Katsaris *Concert* (6/93) (SONY) ① **SK48483**
P. Badura-Skoda (r1992) *Piano Sonata 3.*
(6/93) (AUVI) ① **V4671**
G. Ohlsson (r1990) *Concert*
(10/93) (ARAB) ① **Z6628**
G. Sokolov (pp1985) *Etudes.*
(1/94) (O111) ① **OPS30-83**
P. Grainger (r1928) *Concert*
(2/94) (BIDD) ① **LHW010**
V. Horowitz (r1962) *Concert*
(7/94) (SONY) ① **[2] S2K53457**
F-R. Duchâble (r1984) *Concert*
(10/94) (ERAT) ① **[3] 4509-92403-2**
M. Pletnev (r1988) *Concert*
(3/95) (VIRG) ① **VC5 45076-2**
A. Brailowsky (r1932) *Concert*
(11/95) (DANA) ① **[2] DACOCD336/7**
B. Rigutto (r1990-92) *Concert*
(12/95) (DENO) ① **CO-78927**
J. Hofmann (pf roll) *Concert*
(12/95) (NIMB) ① **NI8803**
1. V. Horowitz (r1936) *Concert*
(1/93) (APR) ① **[2] APR7014**
3. W. Kempff *Concert*
(10/91) (DECC) ① **433 070-2DWO**
3. A. Friedheim (two versions: r1912/3) *Concert*
(8/93) (PEAR) ① **GEMMCD9993**
3. BBC PO, M. Bamert (r1994: orch Stokowski)
(6/95) (CHAN) ① **CHAN9349**
3, 4. I. Paderewski (r1928) *Concert*
(3/93) (RCA) ① **GD60923**
**Sonata for Piano No. 3 in B minor, Op. 58
(1844)**
1. Allegro maestoso; 2. Scherzo; 3. Largo; 4. Presto,
non tanto.
M. Pollini *Piano Sonata 2.*
(8/86) (DG) ① **415 346-2GH**
A. Rubinstein *Concert* (2/87) (RCA) ① **RD89812**
J. Ogdon *Concert* (3/87) (CARL) ① **PCD834**
P. Katin *Concert* (10/87) (OLYM) ① **OCD186**
M. Uchida *Piano Sonata 2.*
(2/89) (PHIL) ① **420 949-2PH**
M. Perahia *Piano Sonata 2.*
(3/89) (SONY) ① **MK76242**
D. Lipatti (r1947) *Concert*
(11/89) (EMI) ① **CDH7 63038-2**
M. Frager *Concert* (6/91) (TELA) ① **CD80280**
A. Cortot (r1931) *Concert* (6/92) (BIDD) ① **LHW001**
A. Cortot (r1931) *Concert*
(6/92) (EMI) ① **[6] CZS7 67359-2**
L.O. Andsnes *Concert*
(6/92) (VIRG) ① **[2] VCK7 59072-2**
A. Lear *Concert* (4/93) (KING) ① **KCLCD2031**
C. Katsaris *Concert* (6/93) (SONY) ① **SK48483**
P. Badura-Skoda (r1992) *Piano Sonata 2.*
(6/93) (AUVI) ① **V4671**
G. Ohlsson (r1990) *Concert*
(10/93) (ARAB) ① **Z6628**
H. Shelley *Concert* (11/93) (CHAN) ① **CHAN9175**
N. Demidenko (r1993) *Ballades.*
(11/93) (HYPE) ① **CDA66577**
P. Grainger (r1926) *Concert*
(2/94) (BIDD) ① **LHW010**
E. Petri (pp1959) *Concert*
(3/94) (MUSI) ① **[4] MACD-772**
E. Nebolsin (r1993) *Concert*
(7/94) (DECC) ① **440 935-2DH**
P. Grainger (r1925) *Concert*
(8/94) (SYMP) ① **SYMCD1145**
A. Brailowsky (r1938) *Concert*
(8/94) (APR) ① **APR5501**
F-R. Duchâble (r1984) *Concert*
(10/94) (ERAT) ① **[3] 4509-92403-2**
W. Małcużyński (r1961) *Concert*
(11/94) (EMI) ① **[2] CZS5 68226-2**

E. Kissin (pp1993) *Mazurkas.*
(11/94) (RCA) ① **09026 62542-2**
**Souvenir de Paganini (Variations in
A)—piano (1829)**
I. Biret *Concert* (5/93) (NAXO) ① **8 550367**
F. Ts'Ong (r1985) *Concert*
(12/94) (SONY) ① **SBK53515**
Tarantelle in A flat—piano, Op. 43 (1841)
A. Rubinstein *Concert* (12/86) (RCA) ① **RD89911**
K. Stott *Concert* (9/89) (CONI) ① **CDCF169**
B. d'Ascoli *Concert* (9/90) (NIMB) ① **NI5249**
A. Cortot (r1933) *Concert*
(6/92) (EMI) ① **[6] CZS7 67359-2**
N. Demidenko *Concert*
(11/92) (HYPE) ① **CDA66597**
S. Cherkassky (pp1991) *Concert*
(1/93) (DECC) ① **433 654-2DH**
A. Cortot (r1919/20/23: 3 vers) *Concert*
(10/94) (BIDD) ① **[2] LHW014/5**
Variations (No. 6) in E—piano (1837)
(variations on March from Bellini's 'I puritani')
I. Biret *Concert* (5/93) (NAXO) ① **8 550367**
Waltzes—piano
1. E flat, Op. 18; 2. A flat, Op. 34/1; 3. A minor, Op.
34/2; 4. F, Op. 34/3; 5. A flat, Op. 42; 6. D flat, Op.
64/1 (Minute); 7. C sharp minor, Op. 64/2; 8. A flat,
Op. 64/3; 9. A flat, Op. 69/1; 10. E minor, Op. 69/2;
11. G flat, Op. 70/1; 12. F minor, Op. 70/2; 13. D flat,
Op 70/3; 14. E minor, Op. posth. 15. E, Op. posth.
16. A flat, Op. posth. 17. E flat, Op. posth. 18. E flat,
Op. posth. (pub. 1925); 19. A minor, Op. posth.
Vladimir Ashkenazy
(12/86) (DECC) ① **414 600-2DH**
C. Katsaris (6/92) (TELD) ① **9031-75857-2**
J-B. Pommier (r1993)
(3/94) (ERAT) ① **4509-92887-2**
C. Katsaris *Concert*
(1/95) (TELD) ① **[2] 4509-95499-2**
P. Katin (r1994) *Polonaises.*
(1/95) (OLYM) ① **[2] OCD289**
1. A. Brailowsky (r1938) *Concert*
(8/94) (APR) ① **APR5501**
1, 10. Vladimir Ashkenazy (r1981/3) *Concert*
(7/93) (DECC) ① **430 759-2DM**
1-14. D. Lipatti (r1950) *Concert*
(7/89) (EMI) ① **CDH7 69802-2**
1-14. A. Cortot (r1943) *Concert*
(6/92) (EMI) ① **[6] CZS7 67359-2**
1-14. W. Małcużyński (r1959) *Concert*
(11/94) (EMI) ① **[2] CZS5 68226-2**
1-17. J-M. Luisada (r1990) ① **431 779-2GH**
1-17. A. Schiller (r1994) *Polonaises.*
(4/95) (ASV) ① **CDQS6149**
1, 3. Vladimir Ashkenazy *Concert*
(7/90) (DECC) ① **417 798-2DM**
1, 3-14. D. Lipatti (pp1950) *Concert*
(12/94) (EMI) ① **CDH5 65166-2**
1, 3-5, 9-14. Vladimir Ashkenazy *Nocturnes.*
(2/93) (DECC) ① **430 751-2DM**
1, 5, 10, 14. A. Cortot (r1934) *Concert*
(6/92) (EMI) ① **[6] CZS7 67359-2**
1, 5, 7. M. Perahia (r1994) *Concert*
(12/94) (SONY) ① **SK64399**
1, 6, 11. S. Rachmaninov (r1921) *Concert*
(3/93) (RCA) ① **[10] 09026 61265-2(3)**
1, 7, 10. Vladimir Ashkenazy *Concert*
(10/91) (DECC) ① **433 070-2DWO**
2. C. Sheppard *Concert*
(12/87) (CIRR) ① **CICD1010**
2. M. Tirimo *Concert*
(12/88) (KING) ① **KCLCD2003**
2. J. Hofmann (pp1945) *Concert*
(5/93) (VAI) ① **VAIA1020**
2. A. Rubinstein (r1928) *Concert*
(10/93) (EMI) ① **[3] CHS7 64697-2**
2, 3, 5. E. Kissin (pp1993) *Concert*
(5/94) (RCA) ① **09026 60445-2**
2, 5. L. Godowsky (r1924) *Concert*
(4/89) (APR) ① **[2] APR7011**
2, 7. A. Brailowsky (r1928) *Concert*
(11/95) (DANA) ① **[2] DACOCD336/7**
3. I. Friedman (r1926) *Concert*
(1/93) (APR) ① **[2] APR7014**
3. V. Horowitz (r1945) *Concert*
(7/93) (RCA) ① **09026 60987-2**
3. V. Horowitz (pp1953) *Concert*
(7/94) (RCA) ① **09026 60986-2**
3. V. Horowitz (r1971) *Concert*
(7/94) (SONY) ① **[2] S2K53468**
4. C. Arrau (r1928) *Concert*
(9/92) (PEAR) ① **GEMMCD9928**
4. S. Rachmaninov (r1920) *Concert*
(3/93) (RCA) ① **[10] 09026 61265-2(3)**
4. E. von Sauer (r c1940) *Concert*
(8/93) (PEAR) ① **GEMMCD9993**

5. S. Barere (r1934) *Concert*
(5/91) (APR) ① [2] **APR7001**
5. S. Barere (pp1949) *Concert*
(5/91) (APR) ① [2] **APR7009**
5. M. Rosenthal (r1929) *Concert*
(10/92) (APR) ① [2] **APR7013**
5. J. Hofmann (r1935) *Concert*
(10/92) (APR) ① [2] **APR7013**
5. S. Barere (bp1920s/30s) *Concert*
(1/93) (APR) ① [2] **APR7014**
5. S. Barere (r1929) *Concert*
(1/93) (APR) ① [2] **APR7014**
5. M. Rosenthal (r1934) *Concert*
(9/93) (APR) ① [2] **APR7002**
5. M. Rosenthal (r1935) *Concert*
(9/93) (APR) ① [2] **APR7002**
5. M. Rosenthal (r1935) *Concert*
(9/93) (PEAR) ① **GEMMCD9963**
5. E. Petri (r1929) *Concert*
(11/93) (APR) ① [2] **APR7023**
5. J. Hofmann (pf roll) *Concert*
(12/95) (NIMB) ① **NI8803**
5, 13. E. Nebolsin (r1993) *Concert*
(7/94) (DECC) ① **440 935-2DH**
5, 6. J. Hofmann (pp1937) *Concert*
(5/93) (VAI) ① **VAIA1020**
5, 8. S. Rachmaninov (r1919) *Concert*
(10/92) (APR) ① [2] **APR7013**
5, 8. S. Rachmaninov (r1919) *Concert*
(3/93) (RCA) ① [10] **09026 61265-2(3)**
6. J. Bolet *Concert*
(10/91) (DECC) ① **433 070-2DWO**
6. E. Zimbalist, S. Chotzinoff (r1912: arr Zimbalist)
Concert (9/93) (APR) ① [2] **APR7016**
6. A. Galli-Curci, orch, J. Pasternack (r1919: arr
Buzzi-Peccia) *Concert*
(3/94) (ROMO) ① [2] **81003-2**
6, 10. S. Rachmaninov (r1923) *Concert*
(3/93) (RCA) ① [10] **09026 61265-2(3)**
6, 7. Vladimir Ashkenazy *Concert*
(3/84) (DECC) ① **410 180-2DH**
6, 7, 9. C. Ortiz *Concert* (12/87) (CARL) ① **PCD872**
7. L. Godowsky (r1913) *Concert*
(4/89) (APR) ① [2] **APR7011**
7. E. Kissin (pp1990) *Concert*
(3/91) (RCA) ① [2] **RD60443**
7. B. Huberman, S. Schultze (arr Huberman: r1932)
Concert (10/91) (EPM) ① **150 032**
7. A. Cortot (r1925) *Concert*
(6/92) (EMI) ① [6] **CZS7 67359-2**
7. A. Rubinstein (r1930) *Concert*
(7/93) (EMI) ① [2] **CHS7 64491-2**
7. M. Rosenthal (r1936) *Concert*
(9/93) (APR) ① [2] **APR7002**
7. M. Rosenthal (r1936) *Concert*
(9/93) (PEAR) ① **GEMMCD9963**
7. V. Horowitz (r1946) *Concert*
(7/94) (RCA) ① **09026 60986-2**
7. V. Horowitz (pp1968) *Concert*
(7/94) (SONY) ① [2] **S2K53468**
7. B. Huberman, S. Schultze (r1929: arr Huberman)
Concert (9/94) (BIDD) ① [2] **LAB081/2**
7. B. Huberman, S. Schultze (r c1932: arr Huberman)
Concert (9/94) (BIDD) ① [2] **LAB081/2**
7. G. Cziffra (r1974) *Concert*
(3/95) (EMI) ① **CDM5 65251-2**
7. A. Cortot (r1925) *Concert*
(5/95) (BIDD) ① **LHW020**
7, 11. M. Lympany *Concert*
(1/92) (EMIL) ① **CDZ111**
7, 14. M. Rosenthal (r1930) *Concert*
(4/89) (PEAR) ① **GEMMCD9339**
7, 8. S. Rachmaninov (r1927) *Concert*
(11/91) (MSCM) ① **MM30271**
7, 8. S. Rachmaninov (r1927) *Concert*
(3/93) (RCA) ① [10] **09026 61265-2(2)**
8, 11. M. Levitzki (r1928) *Concert*
(6/92) (APR) ① [2] **APR7020**
9. V. Horowitz (pp1981) *Concert*
(9/90) (RCA) ① **GD87752**
9. V. Horowitz (pp1981) *Concert*
(5/93) (RCA) ① **09026 61416-2**
9. A. Brailowsky (r1932) *Concert*
(11/95) (DANA) ① [2] **DACOCD336/7**
9, 11. Vladimir Ashkenazy *Concert*
(7/90) (DECC) ① **417 798-2DM**
10. Vladimir Ashkenazy *Concert*
(7/90) (DECC) ① **417 798-2DM**
11. M. Levitzki (r1923) *Concert*
(1/93) (APR) ① [2] **APR7014**
11. E. Zimbalist, E. Bay (r1925: arr Spalding) *Concert*
(7/93) (APR) ① [2] **APR7016**
11. B. Huberman, S. Schultze (r1935: arr Huberman)
Concert (9/94) (BIDD) ① [2] **LAB081/2**
14. S. Rachmaninov (r1930) *Concert*
(11/91) (MSCM) ① **MM30271**

14. M. Levitzki (two versions: r1924) *Concert*
(1/93) (APR) ① [2] **APR7014**
14. S. Rachmaninov (r1930) *Concert*
(3/93) (RCA) ① [10] **09026 61265-2(2)**
14. S. Cherkassky (bp1979) *Concert*
(6/93) (DECC) ① **433 651-2DH**
14. I. Scharrer (r c 1926) *Concert*
(7/94) (PEAR) ① **GEMMCD9978**
14. A. Brailowsky (r1931) *Concert*
(11/95) (DANA) ① [2] **DACOCD336/7**
15-17. P. Frankl *Concert*
(5/92) (ASV) ① **CDDCA781**

SECTION IV: VOCAL AND CHORAL

Aspiration—song (arr unknown: from
Nocturne, Op. 9/2)
C. Muzio, orch (r1921) *Concert*
(5/90) (BOGR) ① [2] **BIM705-2**
C. Muzio, orch (r1921) *Concert*
(1/94) (ROMO) ① [2] **81005-2**
**Messagero amoroso (Waltz, Op 64/1)—song
transcription** (voc arr. Buzzi-Peccia)
A. Galli-Curci, orch (r1919) *Concert*
(2/89) (PEAR) ① **GEMMCD9308**
19 Polish songs—voice and piano, Op. 74
(1829-47) (Wds. various)
1. The wish (wds. S. Witwicki: 1829); 2. Spring (wds.
S. Witwicki: 1838); 3. The sad stream (wds. S.
Witwicki: 1831); 4. Merrymaking (wds. S. Witwicki:
1830); 5. There where she loves (wds. S. Witwicki:
1829); 6. Out of my sight! (wds. A. Mickiewicz: 1829);
7. The envoy (wds. S. Witwicki: 1830); 8. Handsome
lad (wds. B. Zaleski: 1841); 9. Melodya (wds. Z.
Krasiński: 1847); 10. The warrior (wds. S. Witwicki:
1830); 11. The double end (wds. B. Zaleski: 1845);
12. My darling (wds. A. Mickiewicz: 1837); 13. I want
what I have not (wds. B. Zaleski: 1845); 14. The ring
(wds. S. Witwicki: 1836); 15. The bridegroom (wds.
S. Witwicki: 1831); 16. Lithuanian song (wds. S.
Witwicki: 1831); 17. Hymn from the tomb (wds. W.
Pol: 1836); 18. Charms (wds. B. Zaleski: 1830); 19.
Reverie (wds. B. Zaleski: 1840).
3, 7, 10, 15. A. Orda, J. Lee (bp1961) *Concert*
(12/89) (SYMP) ① **SYMCD1067**
12. A. Cortot (arr pf: r1923) *Concert*
(6/92) (EMI) ① [6] **CZS7 67359-2**

SECTION V: STAGE WORKS

**Les Sylphides—ballet conceived by M.
Fokin (1909—Paris)**
orch version by R. Douglas: 1936. 1. Prelude (Op.
28:7); 2. Nocturne (Op. 32:2); 3. Waltz (Op. 70:1); 4.
Mazurka (Op. 33:2); 5. Mazurka (Op. 67:3); 6.
Prelude (Op. 28:7); 7. Waltz 2 (Op. 64:2); 8. Waltz
(Op. 18).
Cpte BPO, H. von Karajan (r1961) *Concert*
(10/94) (DG) ① [2] **437 404-2GX2**
Berlin RSO, H. Fricke *Delibes: Coppélia.*
(12/86) (CAPR) ① **10 073**
BPO, H. von Karajan *Concert*
(5/90) (DG) ① **429 163-2GR**
Bratislava RSO, O. Lenárd (orch Glazunov)
Tchaikovsky: Nutcracker.
(9/91) (NAXO) ① [2] **8 550324/5**

**CHRISTINÉ, Henri *(1867–1941)*
Switzerland/France**

SECTION V: STAGE WORKS

Phi-Phi—operetta: 3 acts (1918—Paris) (Lib.
A. Willemetz & F. Solar)
EXCERPTS: 1. Overture. ACT 1: 2. Ensemble; 3.
C'est une gamine charmante; 4. Maître, lorsque l'on a
vingt ans; 5. Je connais toutes les historiettes; 6.
Vertu, Verturon, Verturonnette; 7. J'sortais des portes
de Trézène; 8. Pour l'amour (Finale 1). ACT 2: 9. Ah!
cher monsieri; 10. Prière à Pallas; 11. Tout tombe;
12. Ah! tais-toi! (Valse et Finale 2). ACT 3: 13. Duo
des souvenirs; 14. Bien chapeautée; 15. Chanson
des petits Païens; 16. Quintette; 17. Finale.
13. B. Hendricks, G. Quilico, Lyon Op Orch, L. Foster
(r1993) *Concert* (6/95) (EMI) ① **CDC5 55151-2**

**CHUECA, Federico *(1846–1908)*
Spain**

SECTION V: STAGE WORKS

El Bateo—zarzuela
Prelude Madrid SO, E. G. Asensio (pp1991) *Concert*
(11/92) (CARL) ① **MCD45**
La Gran Vía—zarzuela (1886—Madrid) (Lib.
F. Perez G: comp with Valverde)
Schottisch del Eliseo Madrileño T. Verdera, Madrid
SO, E. G. Asensio (pp1991) *Concert*
(11/92) (CARL) ① **MCD45**

**CHUKHADJIAN, Tigran
(1837–1898) Armenia**
may also be spelt Tchukhadzhan

SECTION V: STAGE WORKS

Arshak II—opera (1868) (Lib. T. T'erzyan)
Arshak's arioso P. Lisitsian, Bolshoi Th Orch, A.
Orlov (r1948) *Concert* (8/93) (PREI) ① **89061**

**CHURCHILL, Frank E.
(1901–1942) USA**

SECTION V: STAGE WORKS

Bambi—musical film (1942) (Lyrics Larry
Morey; music collab with Ed Plumb)
EXCERPTS: 1. Main Title; 2. Little April Shower; 3.
Gallop of the Stags; 4. Love is a Song; 5. Wintry
Winds; 6. Let's Sing a Gay Little Spring Song; 7. I
Bring You a Song; 8. Finale.
2. Anthony Newman (r1994-5; arr Fraser) *Concert*
(12/95) (DELO) ① **DE3186**
**Snow White and the Seven Dwarfs—musical
film (1937)** (Lyrics Larry Morey; underscore
Leigh Harline & Paul Smith)
EXCERPTS: 1. Overture; 2. I'm Wishing; 3. One
Song; 4. With a Smile and a Song; 5. Whistle While
You Work; 6. Heigh-Ho; 7. Bluddle-Uddle-Um-Dum
(The Washing Song); 8. A Silly Song; 9. Some Day
My Prince Will Come; 10. Finale.
4. C. Rosenberger (r1994-5; arr Fraser) *Concert*
(12/95) (DELO) ① **DE3186**
6. E. Zukerman, Shanghai Qt (r1994-5; arr Fraser)
Concert (12/95) (DELO) ① **DE3186**
The **Three Little Pigs—musical film (1933)**
(Lyrics Ann Ronell)
EXCERPTS: 1. Who's Afraid of the Big Bad Wolf.
1. ECO, D. Fraser (r1994-5; arr Fraser) *Concert*
(12/95) (DELO) ① **DE3186**

**CIAMPI, Vincenzo *(1719–1762)*
Italy**

SECTION V: STAGE WORKS

Tre cicisbei ridicoli—opera (Lib. Contini)
Fanciullina H. Spani, orch, G. Nastrucci (r1929)
Concert (9/90) (CLUB) ① [2] **CL99-509/10**

**CICONIA, Johannes *(c1335–1411)*
France**

SECTION IV: VOCAL AND CHORAL

Aler m'en veus—virelai (2vv)
PAN Ens *Concert* (5/93) (NALB) ① **NA048CD**
Alla Francesca, Alta (r1993) *Concert*
(9/94) (O111) ① **OPS30-101**
Amor per ti sempre—ballata (doubtful: attrib
Ciconia)
PAN Ens (arr. Kammen) *Concert*
(5/93) (NALB) ① **NA048CD**
Ben che da vui donna—ballata (2vv)
PAN Ens *Concert* (5/93) (NALB) ① **NA048CD**
Alla Francesca, Alta (r1993) *Concert*
(9/94) (O111) ① **OPS30-101**
Caçando un giorno—madrigal: 2vv
PAN Ens *Concert* (5/93) (NALB) ① **NA048CD**
Alla Francesca, Alta (r1993) *Concert*
(9/94) (O111) ① **OPS30-101**
Che nel servir anticho—ballata (3vv)
PAN Ens *Concert* (5/93) (NALB) ① **NA048CD**
Alla Francesca, Alta (r1993) *Concert*
(9/94) (O111) ① **OPS30-101**
Chi vole amar—ballata: 2vv (attrib Ciconia)
Alla Francesca, Alta (r1993) *Concert*
(9/94) (O111) ① **OPS30-101**
Deduto sey—ballata: 3vv
Alla Francesca, Alta (r1993) *Concert*
(9/94) (O111) ① **OPS30-101**
**Doctorum principem/ Melodia suavissima/
Vir mitis—isorhythmic motet: 4vv**
PAN Ens *Concert* (5/93) (NALB) ① **NA048CD**
Gli atti col dançar frances—ballata (3vv)
(Anon, attrib. Ciconia)
PAN Ens *Concert* (5/93) (NALB) ① **NA048CD**
Alla Francesca, Alta (r1993) *Concert*
(9/94) (O111) ① **OPS30-101**
Gloria—mass movement (3vv) (unidentified)
Alla Francesca, Alta (r1993) *Concert*
(9/94) (O111) ① **OPS30-101**
**Gloria, 'Suscipe trinitas'—single mass
movement: 3vv**
Orlando Consort (bp1994) *Concert*
(11/95) (METR) ① **METCD1008**

CIKKER, Ján (1911–1990) Czechoslovakia

SECTION I: ORCHESTRAL

CILEA, Francesco (1866–1950) Italy

SECTION V: STAGE WORKS

CIMA, Giovanni Paolo (b c1570; fl until 1662) Italy

SECTION II: CHAMBER

CIMARA, Pietro (1887–1967) Italy

SECTION IV: VOCAL AND CHORAL

CIMAROSA, Domenico (1749–1801) Italy

SECTION I: ORCHESTRAL

Peterborough Stg Orch, N. Daniel (ob/dir) *Concert*
(8/89) (HYPE) ① **CDH88014**

Sinfonia Concertante in G—2 flutes and orchestra (1793)
P-L. Graf, G. Guéneux, Zurich Camerata, R. Tschupp
Concert (11/87) (JECK) ① **JD506-2**
J-P. Rampal (fl/dir), S. Kudo, Salzburg Mozarteum
Orch *Concert* (2/92) (SONY) ① **SK45930**

SECTION III: INSTRUMENTAL

Sonata for Keyboard in A minor
(unidentified)
R. Veyron-Lacroix (r1989) *Concert*
(12/93) (ERAT) ① **4509-92135-2**
Sonata for Keyboard in G minor
(unidentified)
R. Veyron-Lacroix (r1989) *Concert*
(12/93) (ERAT) ① **4509-92135-2**
31 Sonatas for Keyboard (ed. V. Vitale)
Numbers in brackets indicate those of MS source.
VOL. 1: 1. C—Tempo di Menuetto (No. 7); 2.
C—Andantino (No. 14); 3. A—Allegro (No. 19); 4.
A—Allegro (No. 21); 5. B flat—Largo (No. 26); 6. B
flat—Allegro (No. 27); 7. D—Allegretto (No. 30); 8.
F—Allegro (No. 31); 9. G—Allegro (No. 32); 10. D
minor—Andantino (No. 42); 11. F—Allegro (No. 43);
12. B flat—Allegro (No. 1); 13. A minor—Andantino
(No. 2); 14. A—Minuè (No. 3); 15. C—Allegretto (No.
5); 16. C—Allegro (No. 50). VOL. 2: 17. D
minor—Andantino (No. 9); 18. D—Allegro (No. 13);
19. A minor—Andantino (No. 46); 20. A—Allegro (No.
47); 21. G—Allegro (No. 15); 22. C minor—Allegro
(No. 66); 23. E flat—Andantino (No. 67); 24. C
minor—Allegro (No. 68); 25. E flat—Allegro (No. 44);
26. A minor—Andante (No. 20); 27. A—Allegro (No.
57); 28. D—Rondo: Allegro (No. 76); 29. A—Allegro
(No. 73); 30. E flat—Largo-Allegro-Allegro moderato
(No. 74); 31. B flat—Allegro brioso (No. 78).
C sharp minor; A J. Bream (r1959; arr Bream)
Concert (8/93) (RCA) ① **[28] 09026 61583-2(4)**
C sharp minor; A J. Bream (r1959; arr Bream)
Concert (6/94) (RCA) ① **09026 61592-2**

SECTION IV: VOCAL AND CHORAL

Il **Maestro di cappella—intermezzo: baritone and orchestra (c1786-93)**
Cpte F. Corena, ROHO, A. Quadri *Donizetti: Don Pasquale.* (10/92) (DECC) ① **[2] 433 036-2DM2**
Requiem in G minor—soloists, chorus and orchestra (1787)
E. Ameling, B. Finnilä, R. Van Vrooman, K. Widmer,
Montreux Fest Chor, Lausanne CO, V. Negri (r1969;
rev Negri) *Flute and Oboe Concertante in G.*
(7/95) (PHIL) ① **442 657-2PM**
Il **Sacrificio d'Abramo—oratorio: 2 parts (1786)**
EXCERPTS: 1a. Chi per pietà mi dice; 1b. Deh
parlate.
1a, 1b A. Roocroft, ASMF, N. Marriner *Concert*
(12/95) (EMI) ① **CDC5 55396-2**

SECTION V: STAGE WORKS

Artemisia—opera: 3 acts (1801—Venice) (Lib.
C Jamejo)
EXCERPTS: 1. Entro quest'anima.
1. A. Roocroft, ASMF, N. Marriner *Concert*
(12/95) (EMI) ① **CDC5 55396-2**
Il **Matrimonio segreto—opera: 2 acts (1792—Vienna)** (Lib. G. Bertati)
EXCERPTS: 1. Overture.
Cpte A. Auger, J. Varady, D. Fischer-Dieskau, J.
Hamari, R. Davies, A. Rinaldi, ECO, D. Barenboim
(r1975/6) (8/93) (DG) ① **[3] 437 696-2GX3**

CIOCIANO, M.S

SECTION IV: VOCAL AND CHORAL

Cielo turchino—song (Wds. C. Capaldo)
E. Caruso, orch, W.B. Rogers (r1915) *Concert*
(12/90) (NIMB) ① **NI7809**
E. Caruso, orch, W.B. Rogers (r1915) *Concert*
(7/91) (RCA) ① **[12] GD60495(5)**
E. Caruso, orch, W.B. Rogers (r1915) *Concert*
(10/91) (PEAR) ① **[3] EVC3(2)**

CIRINO, Chuck (20th cent) USA

SECTION V: STAGE WORKS

Transylvania Twist—film score (1991)
Suite OST, C. Cirino (r1991) *Concert*
(10/93) (SILV) ① **FILMCD127**

198

ČIURLIONIS, Mikolajus Konstantinas (1875–1911) Lithuania

SECTION I: ORCHESTRAL

In the Forest—symphonic poem (1900)
Slovak PO, J. Domarkas *Concert*
(6/91) (MARC) ① **8 223323**
USSR TV & Rad Orch, V. Fedoseyev *Concert*
(6/91) (CDM) ① **LDC288 004**
5 Preludes—string orchestra (arr from piano works)
1. Dainele; 2. Tranquilo; 3. Andante; 4. Con moto,
Op. 7/2; 5. Lento, Op. 12/1.
Slovak PO, J. Domarkas *Concert*
(6/91) (MARC) ① **8 223323**
The Sea—symphonic poem (1903-07)
Slovak PO, J. Domarkas *Concert*
(6/91) (MARC) ① **8 223323**
USSR TV & Rad Orch, V. Fedoseyev *Concert*
(6/91) (CDM) ① **LDC288 004**

SECTION II: CHAMBER

Quartet for Strings in C minor (1901-02)
Vilnius Qt *Concert* (6/91) (CDM) ① **LDC288 004**
M. Rubackyté (r1993; trans Rubackyté: pf) *Concert*
(2/95) (MARC) ① **8 223550**

SECTION III: INSTRUMENTAL

Autumn—piano, VL264
M. Rubackyté (r1993) *Concert*
(2/95) (MARC) ① **8 223550**
Chansonette—piano, VL199
M. Rubackyté (r1993) *Concert*
(2/95) (MARC) ① **8 223549**
Fugue in B flat minor—piano, VL345
M. Rubackyté (r1993) *Concert*
(2/95) (MARC) ① **8 223550**
Humoresque—piano, VL162
M. Rubackyté (r1993) *Concert*
(2/95) (MARC) ① **8 223549**
Impromptu—piano, VL181
M. Rubackyté (r1993) *Concert*
(2/95) (MARC) ① **8 223549**
Mazurka—piano, VL222
M. Rubackyté (r1993) *Concert*
(2/95) (MARC) ① **8 223549**
Mazurka—piano, VL234
M. Rubackyté (r1993) *Concert*
(2/95) (MARC) ① **8 223549**
Nocturne—piano, VL178
M. Rubackyté (r1993) *Concert*
(2/95) (MARC) ① **8 223549**
Nocturne—piano, VL183
M. Rubackyté (r1993) *Concert*
(2/95) (MARC) ① **8 223549**
Pater Noster—piano, VL260
M. Rubackyté (r1993) *Concert*
(2/95) (MARC) ① **8 223550**
3 Pieces on a Theme—piano
EXCERPTS: 1. VL271; 2. VL270; 3. VL269.
M. Rubackyté (r1993) *Concert*
(2/95) (MARC) ① **8 223550**
Preludes—piano
EXCERPTS: 1. VL164; 2. VL169; 3. VL182a; 4.
VL184; 5. VL185; 6. VL186; 7. VL187; 8. VL188; 9.
VL197; 10. VL230; 11. VL239; 12. VL241; 13. VL256;
14. VL259; 15. VL294; 16. VL295; 17. VL298; 18.
VL304; 19. VL325; 20. VL327; 21. VL330; 22. VL335;
23. VL338; 24. VL340; 25. VL343; 26. VL344.
1-10. M. Rubackyté (r1993) *Concert*
(2/95) (MARC) ① **8 223549**
11-26. M. Rubackyté (r1993) *Concert*
(2/95) (MARC) ① **8 223550**
Sonata for Piano, VL155
M. Rubackyté (r1993) *Concert*
(2/95) (MARC) ① **8 223549**

CLARIBEL (1830–1869) England

pseudonym of Charlotte A. Barnard

SECTION IV: VOCAL AND CHORAL

Come back to Erin—song (Wds. cpsr)
N. Melba, Coldstream Guards Band, M. Rogan
(r1905) *Concert* (3/89) (LARR) ① **CDLRH221**

CLARKE, Herbert Lincoln (1867–1945) USA

SECTION I: ORCHESTRAL

The Débutante—cornet and wind orchestra
W. Marsalis, Eastman Wind Ens, D. Hunsberger (arr
D Hunsberger) *Concert* (9/87) (SONY) ① **MK42137**
Showers of Gold—cornet and band
R. Webster, Britannia Building Soc Band, G. Brand
(pp1991: arr Horn) *Concert*
(8/92) (POLY) ① **QPRL049D**
Sounds from the Hudson—valse brillant: cornet and wind orchestra
W. Marsalis, Eastman Wind Ens, D. Hunsberger (arr
D Hunsberger) *Concert* (9/87) (SONY) ① **MK42137**

CLARKE, Jeremiah (c1674–1707) England

SECTION I: ORCHESTRAL

Suite in D—trumpet and strings
1. Duke of Gloster's March; 2. Minuet; 3. Cebell; 4.
Rondo—Prince of Denmark's March (Trumpet
Voluntary); 5. Serenade; 6. Bourée; 7. Ecossaise; 8.
Hornpipe; 9. Gigue.
H. Hardenberger, S. Preston (arr tpt, org) *Concert*
(12/92) (PHIL) ① **434 074-2PH**
1. P. Hurford, M. Laird Brass Ens (r1990: arr Hurford)
Concert (9/92) (ARGO) ① **433 451-2ZH**
4. A. Stringer, N. Rawsthorne (r1974) *Concert*
(11/87) (CRD) ① **CRD3308**
4. I. Tracey (r1990; arr org) *Concert*
(4/91) (MIRA) ① **MRCD901**
4. S. Preston *Concert*
(6/91) (DECC) ① **430 091-2DWO**
4. S. Preston (r1964: arr S Preston) *Concert*
(6/93) (DECC) ① **436 402-2DWO**
4. R. Woolley *Concert*
(9/94) (CHAN) ① **CHAN0553**
4. O.E. Antonsen, W. Marshall (r1992: arr tpt/org:
Antonsen/Marshall) *Concert*
(10/94) (EMI) ① **CDC5 55048-2**

SECTION III: INSTRUMENTAL

Trumpet Tune and Air—organ, T438
R. Woolley (r1993) *Concert*
(9/94) (CHAN) ① **CHAN0553**
Trumpet tune H. Hardenberger, S. Preston *Concert*
(12/92) (PHIL) ① **434 074-2PH**

SECTION IV: VOCAL AND CHORAL

Blest be these sweet regions—anthem
Concerto Vocale *Concert*
(3/86) (HARM) ① **HMC90 1133**
Come, come along for a dance and a song—ode on the death of Purcell (1695-96)
(Wds. anon)
R. Holton, C. Daniels, S. Birchall, Parley of Instr Ch,
Parley of Instr, R. Goodman *Concert*
(3/93) (HYPE) ① **CDA66578**

CLARKE, Rebecca (1886–1979) England

SECTION II: CHAMBER

Chinese Puzzle—violin and piano
J. Rees, K. Sturrock (r1992) *Concert*
(5/93) (GAMU) ① **GAMCD534**
Epilogue—cello and piano (1921)
P. Frame, R. Weirich (r1994) *Concert*
(5/93) (KOCH) ① **37281-2**
Lullaby—viola and cello (1918)
J. Rees, K. Sturrock (r1992: arr vn/pf) *Concert*
(5/93) (GAMU) ① **GAMCD534**
P. Coletti, L. Howard (r1993) *Concert*
(10/94) (HYPE) ① **CDA66687**
Midsummer Moon—violin and piano (1924)
J. Rees, K. Sturrock (r1992) *Concert*
(5/93) (GAMU) ① **GAMCD534**
Morpheus—viola and piano (1918)
P. Coletti, L. Howard (r1993) *Concert*
(10/94) (HYPE) ① **CDA66687**
Piano Trio—violin, viola & piano (1921)
Cologne Clementi Trio *Mendelssohn-Hensel: Piano Trio.*
(3/87) (LARG) ① **Largo 5103**
Hartley Trio *Concert* (9/91) (GAMU) ① **GAMCD518**
A. Watkinson, G. Jackson, M. Roscoe (1994)
Concert (10/95) (ASV) ① **CDDCA932**
Sonata for Cello and Piano (1921) (arr cpsr
from Viola Sonata)
P. Frame, B. Snyder (r1994) *Concert*
(3/95) (KOCH) ① **37281-2**

3. B. Szokolay (r1990) *Concert*
(9/95) (NAXO) ① **8 550452**
3 Keyboard Sonatas, Op. 40 (1802)
1. G; 2. B minor; 3. D.
2, 3. N. Demidenko (r1994) *Concert*
(10/95) (HYPE) ① **CDA66808**
3. M. Tipo (r1992) *Concert*
(2/94) (EMI) ① **CDC7 54766-2**
3 Keyboard Sonatas, Op. 50 (1821)
1. A; 2. D minor; 3. G minor (Didone abbandonata).
1(Adagio sostenuto) V. Horowitz (r1963) *Concert*
(11/92) (SONY) ① **SK48093**
1 (Adagio sostenuto) V. Horowitz (r1963) *Concert*
(7/94) (SONY) ① **SK53466**
6 Keyboard Sonatinas, Op. 36 (1797)
1. C; 2. G; 3. C; 4. F; 5. G; 6. D.
D. Blumenthal (r1991) *Concert*
(10/93) (ETCE) ① [2] **KTC2018**
B. Szokolay (r1990) *Concert*
(9/95) (NAXO) ① **8 550452**

CLÉRAMBAULT, Louis-Nicolas (1676–1749) France

SECTION II: CHAMBER

Sonata, '(La) Magnifique'—violin and continuo
Music's Re-creation *Concert*
(1/91) (MERI) ① **CDE84182**

SECTION III: INSTRUMENTAL

Largo in C minor—harpsichord
J. Heifetz, E. Bay (arr Dandelot; r1932) *Concert*
(12/91) (APR) ① [2] **APR7015**
J. Heifetz, A. Sándor (r1934) *Concert*
(11/94) (RCA) ① [65] **09026 61778-2(02)**
Premier Livre d'Orgue (pub c1710)
1. Suite de premier ton; 2. Suite de deuxième ton.
G.C. Baker *Mage: Livre d'orgue.*
(3/92) (FY) ① **FYCD043**
1. D. Wagler *Concert* (10/91) (PRIO) ① **PRCD332**
1(Dialogue sur les grands jeux) M. Dupré (r c1926)
Concert (9/94) (BEUL) ① **1PD5**
1, 2. P. Bardon *Concert* (5/84) (PIER) ① **PV784011**
1, 2. J. Boyer (r1993; interpolated with Magnificat & Benedictus) *Concert* (2/95) (FNAC) ① [2] **592316**

SECTION IV: VOCAL AND CHORAL

Apollon and Doris—cantata: 2vv and simphonie (1720) (Cantates françoises: Livre 4)
I. Poulenard, G. Ragon, Amalia Ens *Concert*
(10/91) (O111) ① **OPS39-9103**
Benedictus
Demoiselles de Saint-Cyr, E. Mandrin, S. Moquet
(r1993; with deuxième organ suite interpolated)
Concert (2/95) (FNAC) ① [2] **592316**
Cantate Vincentium—motet: 2vv
Demoiselles de Saint-Cyr, E. Mandrin (r1993)
Concert (2/95) (FNAC) ① [2] **592316**
De profundis clamavi—motet: 2vv
Demoiselles de Saint-Cyr, E. Mandrin, S. Moquet
(r1993) *Concert* (2/95) (FNAC) ① [2] **592316**
Domine ante te—motet: 2vv
Demoiselles de Saint-Cyr, E. Mandrin, S. Moquet
(r1993) *Concert* (2/95) (FNAC) ① [2] **592316**
Domine salvum fac Regem—motet: 2vv (pub 1725)
Demoiselles de Saint-Cyr, E. Mandrin (r1993)
Concert (2/95) (FNAC) ① [2] **592316**
Exultate Deo—motet: 2vv
Demoiselles de Saint-Cyr, E. Mandrin, S. Moquet
(r1993) *Concert* (2/95) (FNAC) ① [2] **592316**
Exultet in Domino—motet (from 4th book of motets)
Demoiselles de Saint-Cyr, E. Mandrin (r1993)
Concert (2/95) (FNAC) ① [2] **592316**
Factum est silentium—motet: 1v
Demoiselles de Saint-Cyr, E. Mandrin, S. Moquet
(r1993) *Concert* (2/95) (FNAC) ① [2] **592316**
Gloria in excelsis Deo—motet: 1v
Demoiselles de Saint-Cyr, E. Mandrin (r1993)
Concert (2/95) (FNAC) ① [2] **592316**
Hodie Christus natus est—motet: 2vv (pub 1725)
Demoiselles de Saint-Cyr, E. Mandrin, S. Moquet
(r1993) *Concert* (2/95) (FNAC) ① [2] **592316**
Hodie Maria virgo caelos ascendit—motet: 2vv
Demoiselles de Saint-Cyr, E. Mandrin, S. Moquet
(r1993) *Concert* (2/95) (FNAC) ① [2] **592316**
Immolabit haedum—motet: 2vv
Demoiselles de Saint-Cyr, E. Mandrin, S. Moquet
(r1993) *Concert* (2/95) (FNAC) ① [2] **592316**

L' isle de Délos—cantata: voice and simphonie (1716) (Cantates françoises: Livre 3)
I. Poulenard, Amalia Ens *Concert*
(10/91) (O111) ① **OPS39-9103**
Justificeris Domine—antiphon
Demoiselles de Saint-Cyr, E. Mandrin (r1993)
Concert (2/95) (FNAC) ① [2] **592316**
Léandre et Héro—cantata: voice and instrumental ensemble (1713) (Cantates françoises: Livre 2)
J. Baird, Music's Re-creation *Concert*
(1/91) (MERI) ① **CDE84182**
I. Poulenard, Amalia Ens *Concert*
(10/91) (O111) ① **OPS39-9103**
Magnificat
Demoiselles de Saint-Cyr, E. Mandrin (r1993; with premier organ suite interpolated) *Concert*
(2/95) (FNAC) ① [2] **592316**
Médée—cantata: 1v (pub 1710)
J. Baird, American Baroque, S. Schultz *Concert*
(9/92) (KOCH) ① **37096-2**
Miserere mei Deus—motet: 3vv
Demoiselles de Saint-Cyr, E. Mandrin (r1993)
Concert (2/95) (FNAC) ① [2] **592316**
O felix Maria—motet: 2vv
Demoiselles de Saint-Cyr, E. Mandrin (r1993)
Concert (2/95) (FNAC) ① [2] **592316**
O salutaris hostia—motet: 2vv
Demoiselles de Saint-Cyr, E. Mandrin (r1993)
Concert (2/95) (FNAC) ① [2] **592316**
Orphée—cantata: voice and instrumental ensemble (1710) (Cantates françoises: Livre 1)
J. Baird, Music's Re-creation *Concert*
(1/91) (MERI) ① **CDE84182**
Pirâme et Tisbé—cantata: voice and simphonie (1713) (Cantates françoises: Livre 2)
G. Ragon, Amalia Ens *Concert*
(10/91) (O111) ① **OPS39-9103**
Regina caeli laetare—motet: 1v
Demoiselles de Saint-Cyr, E. Mandrin, S. Moquet
(r1993) *Concert* (2/95) (FNAC) ① [2] **592316**
Zéphire et Flore—cantata: voice and instrumental ensemble (1716) (Cantates françoises: Livre 3)
J. Baird, Music's Re-creation *Concert*
(1/91) (MERI) ① **CDE84182**

CLIFTON, John (1781–1841) England

SECTION IV: VOCAL AND CHORAL

If music be the food of love—canzonet: 1v, pf/hp (1802) (Wds. Shakespeare)
A. Rolfe Johnson, G. Johnson *Concert*
(5/92) (HYPE) ① **CDA66480**

CLUTSAM, George H. (1866–1951) Australia

SECTION IV: VOCAL AND CHORAL

I know of two bright eyes—song (Wds. Abdul-Mejid from 'Songs of the Turkish Hills')
W. Widdop, P. Kahn (r1926) *Concert*
(5/94) (CLAR) ① **CDGSE78-50-52**

COATES, Eric (1886–1957) England

SECTION I: ORCHESTRAL

Ballad—string orchestra (1904) (unpub)
East England Orch, M. Nabarro *Concert*
(9/92) (ASV) ① **CDWHL2053**
By the Sleepy Lagoon—valse serenade (1930)
LSO, C. Mackerras (r1955) *Concert*
(9/89) (CFP) ① [2] **CD-CFPD4456**
East England Orch, M. Nabarro *Concert*
(9/92) (ASV) ① **CDWHL2053**
Calling all Workers—march (1940)
CBSO, R. Kilbey (r1971) *Concert*
(9/89) (CFP) ① [2] **CD-CFPD4456**
Bratislava RSO, A. Leaper (r1992) *Concert*
(1/94) (MARC) ① **8 223445**
BBC Concert Orch, A. Boult (bp1975) *Concert*
(3/95) (BBCR) ① **BBCRD9106**
Cinderella—phantasy (1929)
RLPO, C. Groves *Concert* (7/86) (ARAB) ① **Z8036**
RLPO, C. Groves (r1971) *Concert*
(9/89) (CFP) ① [2] **CD-CFPD4456**

Bratislava RSO, A. Leaper (r1992) *Concert*
(1/94) (MARC) ① **8 223445**
The Dam Busters—march for the film (1954)
(other incidental music by Leighton Lucas)
RLPO, C. Groves (r1968) *Concert*
(9/89) (CFP) ① [2] **CD-CFPD4456**
Bratislava RSO, A. Leaper (r1992) *Concert*
(1/94) (MARC) ① **8 223445**
Prague City PO, P. Bateman (r1994) *Concert*
(11/94) (SILV) ① **FILMCD151**
BBC Concert Orch, A. Boult (bp1975) *Concert*
(3/95) (BBCR) ① **BBCRD9106**
Four Centuries—suite (1941)
1. Prelude and Hornpipe (17th cent); 2. Pavane and Tambourin (18th cent); 3. Valse (19th cent); 4. Rhythm (20th cent).
East England Orch, M. Nabarro *Concert*
(8/93) (ASV) ① **CDWHL2075**
From Meadow to Mayfair—suite for orchestra (1931)
1. In the country; 2. A song by the way; 3. Evening in town.
RLPO, C. Groves (r1968) *Concert*
(9/89) (CFP) ① [2] **CD-CFPD4456**
London—suite for orchestra (1932)
1. Covent Garden: tarantelle; 2. Westminter: meditation; 3. Knightsbridge: march.
RLPO, C. Groves *Concert* (7/86) (ARAB) ① **Z8036**
RLPO, C. Groves (r1970) *Concert*
(9/89) (CFP) ① [2] **CD-CFPD4456**
East England Orch, M. Nabarro *Concert*
(9/92) (ASV) ① **CDWHL2053**
Bratislava RSO, A. Leaper (r1992) *Concert*
(1/94) (MARC) ① **8 223445**
Queen's Hall Orch, Henry Wood (r1935) *Concert*
(9/94) (DUTT) ① **CDAX8008**
BBC Concert Orch, A. Boult (bp1975) *Concert*
(3/95) (BBCR) ① **BBCRD9106**
London Again—suite for orchestra (1936)
1. Oxford Street: march; 2. Langham Place: elegie; 3. Mayfair: valse.
RLPO, C. Groves *Concert* (7/86) (ARAB) ① **Z8036**
RLPO, C. Groves (r1970) *Concert*
(9/89) (CFP) ① [2] **CD-CFPD4456**
Bratislava RSO, A. Leaper (r1992) *Concert*
(1/94) (MARC) ① **8 223445**
London Bridge—march (1934)
Queen's Hall Orch, Henry Wood (r1935) *Concert*
(9/94) (DUTT) ① **CDAX8008**
The Merrymakers—overture (1922)
LSO, C. Mackerras (r1955) *Concert*
(9/89) (CFP) ① [2] **CD-CFPD4456**
Bratislava RSO, A. Leaper (r1992) *Concert*
(1/94) (MARC) ① **8 223445**
BBC Concert Orch, A. Boult (bp1975) *Concert*
(3/95) (BBCR) ① **BBCRD9106**
Music Everywhere—march for Rediffusion (1948)
RLPO, C. Groves (r1968) *Concert*
(9/89) (CFP) ① [2] **CD-CFPD4456**
Saxo-Rhapsody in A minor—alto saxophone and orchestra (1936)
J. Brymer, RLPO, C. Groves (r1968) *Concert*
(9/89) (CFP) ① [2] **CD-CFPD4456**
The Selfish Giant—phantasy (1925)
Bratislava RSO, A. Leaper (r1992) *Concert*
(1/94) (MARC) ① **8 223445**
Summer Days—suite for orchestra (1919)
1. In a country lane; 2. On the edge of the lake; 3. At the dance.
3. LSO, C. Mackerras (r1955) *Concert*
(9/89) (CFP) ① [2] **CD-CFPD4456**
The Three Bears—a phantasy (1926)
RLPO, C. Groves *Concert* (7/86) (ARAB) ① **Z8036**
LSO, C. Mackerras (r1955) *Concert*
(9/89) (CFP) ① [2] **CD-CFPD4456**
East England Orch, M. Nabarro *Concert*
(9/92) (ASV) ① **CDWHL2053**
The Three Elizabeths—suite for orchestra (1940-44)
1. Halcyon Days: Elizabeth Tudor; 2. Springtime in Angus: Elizabeth of Glamis; 3. Youth of Britain: The Princess Elizabeth.
CBSO, R. Kilbey (r1971) *Concert*
(9/89) (CFP) ① [2] **CD-CFPD4456**
East England Orch, M. Nabarro *Concert*
(9/92) (ASV) ① **CDWHL2053**
London Pops Orch, F. Fennell (r1965) *Concert*
(11/93) (MERC) ① **434 330-2MM**
BBC Concert Orch, A. Boult (bp1975) *Concert*
(3/95) (BBCR) ① **BBCRD9106**
The Three Men—suite for orchestra (1935)
1. The man from the country; 2. The man-about-town; 3. The man from the sea.
3. LSO, C. Mackerras (r1955) *Concert*
(9/89) (CFP) ① [2] **CD-CFPD4456**

Wood Nymphs—valsette (1917)
RLPO, C. Groves (r1968) *Concert*
(9/89) (CFP) ① [2] **CD-CFPD4456**

SECTION IV: VOCAL AND CHORAL

Birdsongs at Eventide—song (1926) (Wds. R. Barrie)
V. Masterson, J. Constable *Concert*
(4/92) (GAMU) ① **GAMD506**
R. Crooks, F. Schauwecker (r1937) *Concert*
(9/93) (CLAR) ① **CDGSE78-50-50**
The Green Hills o' Somerset—song (1916) (Wds. F. E. Weatherly)
I. Wallace, BBC Concert Orch, A. Boult (bp1975) *Concert*
(3/95) (BBCR) ① **BBCRD9106**
I heard you singing—song (1923) (Wds. R. Barrie)
J. Hislop, M. Hayward, P. Kahn (r1926) *Concert*
(1/93) (PEAR) ① **GEMMCD9956**
Stonecracker John—song (1909) (Wds. F. E. Weatherly)
I. Wallace, BBC Concert Orch, A. Boult (bp1975) *Concert*
(3/95) (BBCR) ① **BBCRD9106**

SECTION V: STAGE WORKS

The Jester at the Wedding—concert suite from ballet (1930)
1. March: The Princess arrives; 2. Minuet: Dance of the Pages; 3. Humoresque: The Jester; 4. Valse: The Dance of the Orange Blossoms; 5. Caprice: The Princess; 6. The Princess and the Jester.
East England Orch, M. Nabarro *Concert*
(8/93) (ASV) ① **CDWHL2075**
BBC Concert Orch, A. Boult (bp1975) *Concert*
(3/95) (BBCR) ① **BBCRD9106**
The seven dwarfs—ballet sequence for revue (1930) (later re-orch as 'The Enchanted Garden')
Cpte East England Orch, M. Nabarro *Concert*
(8/93) (ASV) ① **CDWHL2075**

COBBOLD, William (1560–1639) England

SECTION IV: VOCAL AND CHORAL

New fashions—quodlibet: 1v and 4 viols
Red Byrd, Circa 1500, N. Hadden (r1991) *Concert*
(8/93) (CRD) ① **CRD3487**
Ye mortal wights—consort song: 1v and viol consort
J. Budd, Fretwork (r1990) *Concert*
(7/94) (VIRG) ① **VC5 45007-2**

COBERT, Robert (b 1924) USA

SECTION V: STAGE WORKS

Dracula—film score (1973)
Suite OST, R. Cobert (r1973) *Concert*
(10/93) (SILV) ① **FILMCD127**

COCCHI, Gioacchino (c1720–after 1788) Italy

SECTION V: STAGE WORKS

Per la patria—opera
M. Battistini, orch (r1911) *Concert*
(2/92) (PREI) ① **89045**

COCCIA, Carlo (1782–1873) Italy

SECTION V: STAGE WORKS

Clotilde—opera: 2 acts (1815—Venice) (Lib. Rossi)
Io servir! Oh avvillemento! E. Harrhy, J. Cashmore, Philh, D. Parry *Concert*
(10/90) (OPRA) ① [3] **ORCH103**
Maria Stuart, Regina di Scozia—opera seria (1827—London) (Lib. Giannone)
Vieno... o Grande!...Ecco l'Indegna B. Mills, J. Rhys-Davies, A. Mason, B. Ford, P. Nilon, I. Sharpe, C. Bayley, M. Glanville, A. Miles, G. Mitchell Ch, Philh, D. Parry *Concert* (8/95) (OPRA) ① [3] **ORCH104**
Rosmonda—melodramma serio: 2 acts (1829—Venice) (Lib. F Romani)
Volgon tre lune...Perchè non ho del vento? Y. Kenny, D. Montague, Philh, D. Parry *Concert*
(8/95) (OPRA) ① [3] **ORCH104**

COCHEREAU, Pierre Charles (1924–1984) France

SECTION III: INSTRUMENTAL

Improvisations oAlouette, gentille Alouette'—organ (improvised 1970) (transc Briggs)
2, 7. D. Briggs *Concert* (9/90) (PRIO) ① **PRCD284**

COCKER, Norman (1880–1953) England

SECTION III: INSTRUMENTAL

Tuba Tune—organ
I. Tracey (ed Ley) *Concert*
(1/90) (CFP) ① **CD-CFP4558**
G. Green *Concert* (3/93) (NAXO) ① **8 550582**

COCTEAU, Jean (1889–1963) France

SECTION V: STAGE WORKS

Le bel indifférent—monodrama (1940—Paris)
E. Piaf, Inst Ens (r1953) Poulenc: Voix Humaine.
(10/94) (EMI) ① **CDM5 65156-2**

CODAX, Martin (fl c1230) Galicia

SECTION IV: VOCAL AND CHORAL

Aj deus se sab'ora meu amigo—cantiga de amigo
M. Kiek, Sinfonye, S. Wishart *Concert*
(6/88) (HYPE) ① **CDA66283**
New London Consort, P. Pickett *Concert*
(7/92) (L'OI) ① [2] **433 148-2OH2**
Aj ondas que eu vin veer—cantiga de amigo
M. Kiek, Sinfonye, S. Wishart *Concert*
(6/88) (HYPE) ① **CDA66283**
New London Consort, P. Pickett *Concert*
(7/92) (L'OI) ① [2] **433 148-2OH2**
Atlas undas que venez sur la mar—cantiga de amigo (Wds. Anon, 12th Cent Catalan)
New London Consort, P. Pickett *Concert*
(7/92) (L'OI) ① [2] **433 148-2OH2**
Eno sagrado en vigo—cantiga de amigo (Music: A Lawrence-King)
M. Kiek, Sinfonye, S. Wishart *Concert*
(6/88) (HYPE) ① **CDA66283**
New London Consort, P. Pickett *Concert*
(7/92) (L'OI) ① [2] **433 148-2OH2**
Esperanza de totz ferms esperans—cantiga de amigo (Wds. Guillaume d'Autpol)
New London Consort, P. Pickett *Concert*
(7/92) (L'OI) ① [2] **433 148-2OH2**
Mia jrmana fremosa treides comigo—cantiga de amigo
M. Kiek, Sinfonye, S. Wishart *Concert*
(6/88) (HYPE) ① **CDA66283**
New London Consort, P. Pickett *Concert*
(7/92) (L'OI) ① [2] **433 148-2OH2**
Mundad' ei comigo—cantiga de amigo
M. Kiek, Sinfonye, S. Wishart *Concert*
(6/88) (HYPE) ① **CDA66283**
New London Consort, P. Pickett *Concert*
(7/92) (L'OI) ① [2] **433 148-2OH2**
Ondas do mar de vigo—cantiga de amigo
M. Kiek, Sinfonye, S. Wishart *Concert*
(6/88) (HYPE) ① **CDA66283**
New London Consort, P. Pickett *Concert*
(7/92) (L'OI) ① [2] **433 148-2OH2**
Quantas sabedes amar amigo—cantiga de amigo
M. Kiek, Sinfonye, S. Wishart *Concert*
(6/88) (HYPE) ① **CDA66283**
New London Consort, P. Pickett *Concert*
(7/92) (L'OI) ① [2] **433 148-2OH2**

COEHLO, Manuel Rodrigues (c1555–1635) Portugal

SECTION III: INSTRUMENTAL

Flores de música—keyboard/harp collection (pub 1620)
EXCERPTS: 1. Verso sobre Ave maris stella; 2. Ave maris stella (verset); 3. Deo gratias; 4. Segunda Susana grosada a 4 sobre a de 5; 5. Segunda Tento do primeiro tom.
1-3. S. Farr (r1994) *Concert*
(11/94) (HYPE) ① **CDA66725**

4, 5. S. Yates (r1993) *Concert*
(11/94) (CHAN) ① **CHAN0560**

COHAN, George (Michael) (1878–1942) USA

SECTION IV: VOCAL AND CHORAL

Over there—song (1917) (Wds. cpsr: French wds. F. Delamarre)
E. Caruso, orch, J. Pasternack (r1918) *Concert*
(12/90) (NIMB) ① **NI7809**
E. Caruso, orch, J. Pasternack (r1918) *Concert*
(7/91) (RCA) ① [12] **GD60495(6)**
E. Caruso, orch, J. Pasternack (r1918) *Concert*
(10/91) (PEAR) ① [3] **EVC4(1)**

SECTION V: STAGE WORKS

Fifty Miles from Boston—musical show (1908—New York) (Lyrics cpsr)
EXCERPTS: 1. The Small Town Gal.
1. G. M. Cohan, Orig Broadway Cast (r1911) *Concert*
(5/94) (PEAR) ① [3] **GEMMCDS9053/5**
George Washington Jnr—musical show (1906—New York) (Lyrics cpsr)
EXCERPTS: 1. You're a Grand Old Flag; 2. All Aboard for Broadway; 3. I Was Born in Virginia.
3. E. Levey (r1911) *Concert*
(5/94) (PEAR) ① [3] **GEMMCDS9050/2(2)**
Little Johnny Jones—musical revue (1904—New York) (Wds. cpsr)
EXCERPTS: 1. Yankee Doodle Boy; 2. Give my Regards to Broadway; 3. I'm Mighty Glad I'm Living, That's All; 4. Life's a Funny Proposition After All.
1. Cincinnati Uni Sngrs, Cincinnati Uni Th Orch, E. Rivers (r1978) *Concert* (4/94) (NEW) ① **80221-2**
3, 4. G. M. Cohan, Broadway Cast (r1911) *Concert*
(5/94) (PEAR) ① [3] **GEMMCDS9050/2(2)**
Mother Goose—musical show (1903—New York) (Lyrics cpsr)
EXCERPTS: 1. Hey There! May There!; 2. I Want to Hear a Yankee Doodle Tune.
1, 2. G. M. Cohan, Broadway Cast (r1911) *Concert*
(5/94) (PEAR) ① [3] **GEMMCDS9050/2(1)**

COKKEN

SECTION II: CHAMBER

Fantasia on Rossini's William Tell—bassoon and piano, Op. 34
K. Walker, J. Drake *Concert*
(10/89) (REGE) ① **REGCD104**

COLAHAN, Arthur (20th Cent)

SECTION IV: VOCAL AND CHORAL

Galway Bay—song (1948) (Wds. cpsr)
A. Murray, G. Johnson (r1992) *Concert*
(8/93) (HYPE) ① **CDA66627**

COLE, Bob (1863–1911) USA

pseudonym of Robert Allen

SECTION IV: VOCAL AND CHORAL

The Maiden With the Dreamy Eyes—song used in the show 'The Supper Club' (1901) (Lyrics J Rosamond Johnson)
T. Q. Seabrooke, Broadway Cast (r1904) *Concert*
(5/94) (PEAR) ① [3] **GEMMCDS9050/2(1)**

COLEMAN, Charles (c1605–1664) England

SECTION IV: VOCAL AND CHORAL

Did you not once, Lucinda, vow?—dialogue between a nymph and a shepherd
C. Bott, M. George, New London Consort, P. Pickett (r1992) *Concert* (4/94) (LINN) ① **CKD011**

COLERIDGE TAYLOR, Samuel (1875–1912) England

SECTION I: ORCHESTRAL

Ballade in A minor—orchestra, Op. 33 (1898)
RLPO, G. Llewellyn (r1992) *Concert*
(11/93) (ARGO) ① **436 401-2ZH**
Ballade in D minor—violin and orchestra, Op. 4 (1895)
M. Ludwig, V. Eskin (arr cpsr) *Concert*
(10/92) (KOCH) ① **37056-2**

Petite Suite de Concert—orchestral suite, Op. 77 (1910)
1. La caprice de Nanette; 2. Demande et réponse; 3. Un sonnet d'amour; 4. La tarantelle's frétillante.
V. Eskin (arr cpsr) *Concert*
(10/92) (KOCH) ① **37056-2**

Symphonic Variations on an African air—orchestra, Op. 63 (1906)
RLPO, G. Llewellyn (r1992) *Concert*
(6/93) (ARGO) ① **436 401-2ZH**

SECTION II: CHAMBER

Quintet in F sharp minor—clarinet and strings, Op. 10 (1895)
M. Ludwig, Hawthorne Qt *Concert*
(10/92) (KOCH) ① **37056-2**

SECTION III: INSTRUMENTAL

24 Negro Melodies—piano transcriptions, Op. 59/1 (1905)
1. At the dawn of day; 2. The stones are very hard; 3. Take Nabandji; 4. They will not lend me a child; 5. Song of Conquest; 6. Warrior's Song; 7. Obala; 8. The Bamboula; 9. The angels changed my name; 10. Deep River; 11. Didn't my Lord deliver Daniel?; 12. Don't be weary, traveller; 13. Going up; 14. I'm troubled in mind; 15. I was a way down a-yonder; 16. Let us cheer the weary throne; 17. Many thousand gone; 18. My Lord delivered Daniel; 19. Oh, he raised a poor Lazarus; 20. Pilgrim's Song; 21. Run, Mary, run; 22. Sometimes I feel like a motherless child; 23. Steal away; 24. Wade in the water.
3, 8, 10, 13, 21, 22. V. Eskin *Concert*
(10/92) (KOCH) ① **37056-2**

SECTION IV: VOCAL AND CHORAL

Scenes from 'The Song of Hiawatha'—cantata: sop, ten, bar, chorus & orchestra, Op. 30 (1898-1900) (Wds. H. W. Longfellow)
1. Hiawatha's Wedding Feast (1898); 1a. Onaway, awake, beloved; 2. The Death of Minnehaha (1898); 3. Overture to 'The Song of Hiawatha' (1899); 4. Hiawatha's Departure (1900); 4a. Hiawatha's vision.
1a Webster Booth, Liverpool PO, M. Sargent (r1944) *Concert*
(5/95) (DUTT) ① **CDAX8012**

SECTION V: STAGE WORKS

Othello—incidental music to Shakespeare's play, Op. 79 (1911—London)
EXCERPTS: 1. Dance; 2. Children's Intermezzo; 3. Funeral March; 4. The Willow Song; 5. Military March.
1-5. New SO, M. Sargent (r1932) *Concert*
(7/95) (BEUL) ① **1PD13**

COLIN, Jean (d after 1694) France

SECTION IV: VOCAL AND CHORAL

Missa pro defunctis—6vv (pub 1688)
Sagittarius Ens, La Fenice, M. Laplénie, A. Pumir (pp1993) *Helfer: Missa pro defunctis.*
(3/95) (CALL) ① **CAL9891**

COLLARD, Edward (fl c1595–1599) England

SECTION III: INSTRUMENTAL

Walsingham—lute
P. O'Dette *Concert* (2/88) (HARM) ① **HMC90 5192**

COLLASSE, Pascal (1649–1709) France

SECTION IV: VOCAL AND CHORAL

Cantiques spirituels tirez de l'Ecriture Sainte (1695) (Wds. J. Racine)
1. A la louange de la Charité; 2. Sur le bonheur des Justes et sur le malheur des réprouvés; 3. Plaintes d'un Chrétien sur les contrariétés qu'il éprouve; 4. Sur les Vaines occupations des gens du siècle.
I. Poulenard, M. Ruggeri, J. Mayeur, Concert Royal, P. Bismuth (vn/dir) (r1992) *Rebel: Suite en D La Ré B mol II.* (4/94) (ASTR) ① **E8756**
A. Mellon, S. Piau, B. Thivel, Talens Lyriques, C. Rousset (hpd/dir) (r1991)
(9/94) (ERAT) ① **4509-92860-2**

COLLET, Henri (1885–1951) France

SECTION III: INSTRUMENTAL

Los Amantes de Galicia—folksong: piano solo (1942)
R. Yakar, C. Lavoix (r1994) *Concert*
(10/95) (CLAV) ① **CD50-9506**

Cantos de Castilla—piano solo, Op. 42 (1920-22)
VOLUME 1: 1. Al parao; 2. Para aguinaldos; 3. Vendimia; 4. Pasacalle; 5. Pito. VOLUME 2: 6. Amorosa; 7. Romanza; 8. Ronda; 9. Bolero; 10. Humorada.
C. Lavoix (r1994) *Concert*
(10/95) (CLAV) ① **CD50-9506**

SECTION IV: VOCAL AND CHORAL

5 Canciones populares castellanas—1v and piano, Op. 69 (1923)
R. Yakar, C. Lavoix (r1994) *Concert*
(10/95) (CLAV) ① **CD50-9506**

7 Canciones populares de Burgos—1v and piano, Op. 80 (1926)
R. Yakar, C. Lavoix (r1994) *Concert*
(10/95) (CLAV) ① **CD50-9506**

La Pena—song
R. Yakar, C. Lavoix (r1994) *Concert*
(10/95) (CLAV) ① **CD50-9506**

Poema de un día—1v and piano, Op. 48
R. Yakar, C. Lavoix (r1994) *Concert*
(10/95) (CLAV) ① **CD50-9506**

COLLINS, Anthony (Vincent Benedictus) (1893–1963) England

SECTION I: ORCHESTRAL

Vanity Fair—orchestra
RTE Concert Orch, E. Tomlinson (r1993) *Concert*
(12/95) (MARC) ① **8 223522**

COLLINS, Mr (fl 1780) England

SECTION IV: VOCAL AND CHORAL

The Chapter of Kings—comic song (1785) (in 'The Evening Brush')
L. Skeaping, Broadside Band, J. Barlow (r1992; arr J. Barlow) *Concert* (6/93) (SAYD) ① **CD-SDL400**

COMMETTE, Edouard (1883–1967) France

SECTION III: INSTRUMENTAL

Offertoire sur des Noëls—organ
J.S. Whiteley *Concert* (12/91) (YORK) ① **CD846**

COMPÈRE, Loyset (c1445–1518) France

SECTION III: INSTRUMENTAL

Ave Maria gratia plena—organ
J. Payne (r1994) *Concert*
(10/95) (NAXO) ① **8 553214**

Paranymphus salutat virginem—organ
J. Payne (r1994) *Concert*
(10/95) (NAXO) ① **8 553214**

SECTION IV: VOCAL AND CHORAL

Alons fere nos barbes—chanson: 4vv
Orlando Consort (r1993) *Concert*
(6/94) (METR) ① **METCD1002**

Asperges me, Domine—motet: 4vv
Orlando Consort (r1993) *Concert*
(6/94) (METR) ① **METCD1002**

Ave Maria, gratia plena—motet: 4vv
Orlando Consort (r1993) *Concert*
(6/94) (METR) ① **METCD1002**

Che fa la ramacina—frottola: 4vv
Orlando Consort (r1993) *Concert*
(6/94) (METR) ① **METCD1002**

Missa in Nativitate, 'Hodie nobis de virgine'—4vv
Orlando Consort (r1993) *Concert*
(6/94) (METR) ① **METCD1002**

Ne vous hastez pas—chanson: 3vv
Orlando Consort (r1993) *Concert*
(6/94) (METR) ① **METCD1002**

Nous sommes de l'ordre de Saint Babouys—chanson: 4vv
C. Janequin Ens, D. Visse (r1994) *Concert*
(5/95) (HARM) ① **HMC90 1453**

Omnium bonorum plena—motet: 4vv (?1742)
Orlando Consort (r1993) *Concert*
(6/94) (METR) ① **METCD1002**

Scaramella fa la galla—frottola: 4vv
Hilliard Ens, P. Hillier *Concert*
(3/89) (EMI) ① **CDC7 49209-2**
Orlando Consort (r1993) *Concert*
(6/94) (METR) ① **METCD1002**

Se j'ay parlé—chanson: 3vv (Wds. H Baude)
Orlando Consort (r1993) *Concert*
(6/94) (METR) ① **METCD1002**

Seray je vostre mieulx amée—chanson
Orlando Consort (r1993) *Concert*
(6/94) (METR) ① **METCD1002**

CONFORTI, Giovanni Battista (fl 1550–1570) Italy

SECTION II: CHAMBER

Il Primo libro di ricercari—four instruments (pub 1558)
1. Ricercar del quarto tono.
Amsterdam Loeki Stardust Qt *Concert*
(10/94) (L'OI) ① **440 207-2OM**

CONFREY, Edward Elezear (1895–1971) USA

SECTION III: INSTRUMENTAL

Kitten on the Keys—piano rag
A. Feinberg (r1994) *Concert*
(11/95) (ARGO) ① **444 457-2ZH**

CONINGSBY CLARKE, Robert (1879–1934) England

SECTION IV: VOCAL AND CHORAL

The Blind Ploughman—song
F. Chaliapin, orch, R. Bourdon (r1927) *Concert*
(6/93) (PREI) ① [2] **89207**

CONNOLLY, Justin (b 1933) England

SECTION IV: VOCAL AND CHORAL

Poems of Wallace Stevens II—soprano, clarinet and piano, Op. 14 (1970)
1. Earthy Anecdote; 2. The Place of the Solitaires; 3. Life is Motion.
J. Manning, Jane's Minstrels (r1993) *Concert*
(10/95) (NMC) ① **NMCD025**

CONRAD, Con (1891–1938) USA
pseudonym of Conrad K. Dober

SECTION IV: VOCAL AND CHORAL

Memory Lane—song
A. Galli-Curci, orch, R. Bourdon (r1924) *Concert*
(8/94) (ROMO) ① [2] **81004-2**

CONSTANT, Marius (b 1925) France

SECTION I: ORCHESTRAL

Hämeenlinna (1990)
Helsinki PO, S. Comissiona *Concert*
(4/92) (ONDI) ① **ODE767-2**

SECTION II: CHAMBER

Alleluias—trumpet and organ
G. Touvron, E. Krapp (r1992) *Concert*
(9/93) (RCA) ① **09026 61186-2**

CONSTANTIN, Louis (c1585–1657) France

SECTION II: CHAMBER

Pavan—3 violins and continuo (from "t Uitnemend Kabinet')
J. Holloway, S. Ritchie, A. Manze, N. North, M. Springfels, J. Toll (r1993) *Concert*
(2/94) (HARM) ① **HMU90 7091**

CONTI, Bill (b 1942) USA

SECTION V: STAGE WORKS

Masters of the Universe—film score (1987)
EXCERPTS: 1. He-Man Victorious; 2. End Titles.
1, 2. OST *Concert* (5/93) (SILV) ① **SILVAD3003**

CONTI, Carlo (1796–1868) Italy

SECTION V: STAGE WORKS

Giovanna Shore—melodramma serio: 3 acts
(1829—Milan) (Lib. F Romani)
A che di fiore e lagrime M. Hill Smith, C. Bayley, A.
Miles, Philh, D. Parry *Concert*
(8/95) (OPRA) ① **[3] ORCH104**

CONUS, Julius (1869–1942) Russia

SECTION I: ORCHESTRAL

Concerto for Violin and Orchestra in E minor
(1896–97)
J. Heifetz, RCA Victor SO, I. Solomon (r1952)
Concert (11/94) (RCA) ① **[65] 09026 61778-2(20)**
I. Perlman, Pittsburgh SO, A. Previn *Concert*
(6/95) (EMI) ① **[20] CZS4 83177-2(2)**

CONVERSI, Girolamo (fl 1571–5) Italy

SECTION IV: VOCAL AND CHORAL

Io canterò—madrigal: 5vv
M. Arruabarrena, K. van Laethem, M. Valenta, J.
Benet, M. van Altena, J. Cabré, T. de Zwart, A. Pols,
R. Van Der Meer, K. Junghänel (lte/dir) *Concert*
(1/92) (ACCE) ① **ACC8864D**

CONYNGHAM, Barry (b 1944) Australia

SECTION I: ORCHESTRAL

Monuments—Concerto for Piano, DX7
(Yamaha synth) & Orchestra (1989)
R. Davidovici, LSO, G. Simon (r1990) *Southern*
Cross. (2/94) (CALA) ① **CACD1008**
Southern Cross—Double Concerto for
Violin, Piano and Orchestra (1981)
1. Magnitude; 2. Velocity; 3. Duration; 4. Collisions; 5.
Distance.
R. Davidovici, T. Ungár, LSO, G. Simon (r1990)
Monuments. (2/94) (CALA) ① **CACD1008**

COOKE, Arnold (Atkinson) (b 1906) England

SECTION II: CHAMBER

Sonata for Clarinet and Piano (1962)
T. King, C. Benson *Concert*
(11/89) (HYPE) ① **CDA66044**

COOKE, Benjamin (1734–1793) England

SECTION IV: VOCAL AND CHORAL

Epitaph on a dormouse—glee
PCA, M. Brown *Concert* (3/87) (CONI) ① **CDCF145**

COOKE, J(ohn) (d 1419) England

SECTION IV: VOCAL AND CHORAL

Gloria (Old Hall MS)
Gothic Voices, C. Page (r1994) *Concert*
(2/95) (HYPE) ① **CDA66739**

COOKE, James Francis (1875–1960) USA

SECTION IV: VOCAL AND CHORAL

Ol' Car'lina—song
A. Galli-Curci, orch, J. Pastemack (r1921) *Concert*
(8/94) (ROMO) ① **[2] 81004-2**

COOKE, Thomas (1782–1848) England

SECTION IV: VOCAL AND CHORAL

Strike the lyre—partsong (Wds. anon)
PCA, M. Brown *Concert* (3/87) (CONI) ① **CDCF145**

COOPER, Lindsay (20th Cent) England

SECTION IV: VOCAL AND CHORAL

The road is wider than long (1991) (Wds. R.
Penrose)
Lontano, O. de la Martinez *Concert*
(9/92) (LORE) ① **LNT101**

COPLAND, Aaron (1900–1990) USA

SECTION I: ORCHESTRAL

Ceremonial Fanfare—brass ensemble
(1969)
Cincinnati Pops, E. Kunzel *Concert*
(10/87) (TELA) ① **CD80117**
LPO, J. Mester *Concert* (7/91) (KOCH) ① **37012-2**
LSO Brass Ens, E. Crees *Concert*
(1/92) (COLL) ① **Coll1288-2**
Concerto—piano and orchestra (1926)
N. Lee, FNO, A. Copland *Concert*
(6/91) (ETCE) ① **KTC1098**
E. Wild, Sym of the Air, A. Copland *Menotti: Piano*
Concerto. (2/92) (VANG) ① **08.4029.71**
G. Lin, Melbourne SO, J. Hopkins *Britten: Piano*
Concerto. (11/92) (CHAN) ① **CHAN6580**
Concerto for Clarinet and String Orchestra
with Harp and Piano (1947–48)
B. Goodman, Columbia SO, A. Copland *Concert*
(5/87) (SONY) ① **MK42227**
G. Macdonald, Northern Sinfonia, S. Bedford *Concert*
(2/88) (ASV) ① **CDDCA568**
J. Hilton, SNO, M. Bamert *Concert*
(10/88) (CHAN) ① **CHAN8618**
R. Hosford, COE, T. Fischer *Concert*
(10/89) (ASV) ① **CDCOE811**
G. de Peyer, NY Virtuosi, K. Klein *Concert*
(3/91) (COLL) ① **Coll1097-2**
B. Goodman, Columbia SO, A. Copland (r1963)
Concert (7/91) (SONY) ① **[3] SM3K46559**
S. Drucker, NYPO, L. Bernstein *Concert*
(8/91) (DG) ① **431 672-2GH**
J. Campbell, Canadian Nat Arts Centre Orch, F-P.
Decker *Concert* (9/92) (CBC) ① **SMCD5096**
P. Meyer, ECO, D. Zinman (r1992) *Concert*
(11/93) (DENO) ① **CO-75289**
R. Stoltzman, LSO, M. Tilson Thomas (r1992)
Concert (12/93) (RCA) ① **09026 61790-2**
R. Stoltzman, LSO, M. Tilson Thomas (r1992)
Concert (12/93) (RCA) ① **09026 61677-2**
Connotations—orchestra (1961–62)
NYPO, L. Bernstein *Concert*
(8/91) (DG) ① **431 672-2GH**
Dance Symphony—orchestra (1930)
Detroit SO, A. Dorati *Concert*
(8/91) (DECC) ① **430 705-2DM**
Danzón cubano—orchestra (1942 orch 1945)
(orch cpsr from piano work)
J. Pierce, D. Jonas (r1989: arr Gold/Fizdale) *Concert*
(10/90) (KOCH) ① **37002-2**
New Philh, A. Copland (r1970) *Concert*
(7/91) (SONY) ① **[3] SM3K46559**
NYPO, L. Bernstein (r1963) *Concert*
(5/93) (SONY) ① **SMK47544**
New World Sym, M. Tilson Thomas (r1992) *Concert*
(6/93) (ARGO) ① **436 737-2ZH**
Baltimore SO, D. Zinman (r1993) *Concert*
(10/94) (ARGO) ① **440 639-2ZH**
Fanfare for the Common Man—brass and
percussion (1942)
Atlanta SO, L. Lane *Concert*
(12/83) (TELA) ① **CD80078**
London Brass Virtuosi, D. Honeyball *Concert*
(7/87) (HYPE) ① **CDA66189**
English SO, W. Boughton *Concert*
(10/90) (NIMB) ① **NI5246**
LPO, J. Mester *Concert* (7/91) (KOCH) ① **37012-2**
LSO, A. Copland (r1968) *Concert*
(7/91) (SONY) ① **[3] SM3K46559**
Detroit SO, A. Dorati *Concert*
(8/91) (DECC) ① **430 705-2DM**
LPO, Carl Davis *Concert*
(12/91) (VIRG) ① **VJ7 59654-2**

LSO Brass Ens, E. Crees *Concert*
(1/92) (COLL) ① **Coll1288-2**
Seattle SO, G. Schwarz (r1992) *Concert*
(5/93) (DELO) ① **DE3140**
NYPO, L. Bernstein (r1966) *Concert*
(5/93) (SONY) ① **SMK47543**
Netherlands Wind Ens, R. Dufallo (r1993) *Concert*
(3/94) (CHAN) ① **CHAN9210**
RPO, P. Ellis (r1994) *Concert*
(12/95) (TRIN) ① **TRP040**
Inaugural Fanfare—wind and percussion
(1969)
LPO, J. Mester *Concert* (7/91) (KOCH) ① **37012-2**
Inscape—orchestra (1967)
FNO, A. Copland *Concert*
(6/91) (ETCE) ① **KTC1098**
Czech PO, A. Copland (pp1973) *Concert*
(6/93) (ROMA) ① **RR1973**
John Henry—chamber orchestra (1940 rev
1952)
Cincinnati Pops, E. Kunzel *Concert*
(10/87) (TELA) ① **CD80117**
LSO, A. Copland (r1968) *Concert*
(7/91) (SONY) ① **[3] SM3K46559**
Jubilee Variation on a theme by (Sir) Eugene
Goossens—orchestra (1945)
Cincinnati Pops, E. Kunzel *Concert*
(10/87) (TELA) ① **CD80117**
3 Latin-American sketches—orchestra (1959–
71)
1. Estribillo; 2. Paisaje Mexicano; 3. Danza de
Jalisco.
Orpheus CO *Concert* (8/89) (DG) ① **427 335-2GH**
NY Virtuosi, K. Klein *Concert*
(3/91) (COLL) ① **Coll1097-2**
Phoenix SO, J. Sedares (r1991) *Concert*
(4/92) (KOCH) ① **37092-2**
Letter from Home—orchestra (1944 rev
1962)
LSO, A. Copland (r1968) *Concert*
(7/91) (SONY) ① **[3] SM3K46559**
Lincoln Portrait—narrator and orchestra
(1942)
K. Hepburn, Cincinnati Pops, E. Kunzel *Concert*
(10/87) (TELA) ① **CD80117**
H. Fonda, LSO, A. Copland (r1971) *Concert*
(7/91) (SONY) ① **[3] SM3K46559**
J. E. Jones, Seattle SO, G. Schwarz (r1992) *Concert*
(5/93) (DELO) ① **DE3140**
Music for a Great City—orchestra (1963–64)
(based on music for film 'Something Wild')
1. Skyline; 2. Night Thoughts; 3. Subway Jam; 4.
Toward the Bridge.
St Louis SO, L. Slatkin *Symphony 3.*
(2/91) (RCA) ① **RD60149**
Music for Radio, 'Prairie Journal'—orchestra
(1937)
St Louis SO, L. Slatkin (1991) *Concert*
(11/94) (RCA) ① **09026 61699-2**
Music for the Theatre—suite: small
orchestra (1925)
1. Prologue; 2. Dance; 3. Interlude; 4. Burlesque; 5.
Epilogue.
Atlanta SO, Y. Levi (1989) *Symphony 3.*
(1/90) (TELA) ① **CD80201**
NYPO, L. Bernstein *Concert*
(8/91) (DG) ① **431 672-2GH**
An Outdoor Overture—orchestra (1937)
Cincinnati Pops, E. Kunzel *Concert*
(10/87) (TELA) ① **CD80117**
LSO, A. Copland (r1969) *Concert*
(7/91) (SONY) ① **[3] SM3K46559**
Seattle SO, G. Schwarz (r1992) *Concert*
(5/93) (DELO) ① **DE3140**
Prelude—chamber orchestra (1924 rev
1934)
London Sinfonietta, O. Knussen (r1993) *Concert*
(10/94) (ARGO) ① **443 203-2ZH**
Quiet city—cor anglais, trumpet and strings
(1939) (arr from incid music to I Shaw's play)
Philip Smith, T. Stacy, NYPO, L. Bernstein (pp 1985)
Symphony 3. (11/86) (DG) ① **419 170-2GH**
C. Nicklin, M. Laird, ASMF, N. Marriner *Concert*
(11/87) (ARGO) ① **417 818-2ZH**
R. Mase, S. Taylor, Orpheus CO *Concert*
(8/89) (DG) ① **427 335-2GH**
H. McQueen, C. Steele-Perkins, CLS, R. Hickox
Concert (11/89) (VIRG) ① **VC7 59520-2**
English SO, W. Boughton *Concert*
(10/90) (NIMB) ① **NI5246**
NY Virtuosi, K. Klein *Concert*
(3/91) (COLL) ① **Coll1097-2**
LSO, A. Copland (r1965) *Concert*
(7/91) (SONY) ① **[3] SM3K46559**
LSO, M. Tilson Thomas (r1994) *Concert*
(8/95) (EMI) ① **CDC5 55358-2**

El salón México—orchestra (1933-36)
J. Pierce, D. Jonas (r1989: arr Gold/Fizdale) *Concert*
(10/90) (KOCH) ① **37002-2**
New Philh, A. Copland (r1972) *Concert*
(7/91) (SONY) ① [3] **SM3K46559**
P. Jablonski (trans pf: L Bernstein) *Concert*
(7/91) (DECC) ① **430 542-2DH**
Detroit SO, A. Dorati *Concert*
(8/91) (DECC) ① **430 705-2DM**
NYPO, L. Bernstein *Concert*
(8/91) (DG) ① **431 672-2GH**
Boston SO, S. Koussevitzky (r1938) *Concert*
(12/91) (PEAR) ① **GEMMCD9492**
LSO Brass Ens, E. Crees (arr brass: Crees) *Concert*
(1/92) (COLL) ① **Coll1288-2**
NYPO, L. Bernstein (r1961) *Concert*
(5/93) (SONY) ① **SMK47544**
Baltimore SO, D. Zinman (r1993) *Concert*
(10/94) (ARGO) ① **440 639-2ZH**
RPO, P. Ellis (r1994) *Concert*
(12/95) (TRIN) ① **TRP040**
Short Symphony (No. 2)—orchestra (1932-33)
Orpheus CO *Concert* (8/89) (DG) ① **427 335-2GH**
Statements—orchestra (1932-35)
1. Militant; 2. Cryptic; 3. Dogmatic; 4. Subjective; 5. Jingo; 6. Prophetic.
5. RCA Victor Orch, L. Bernstein (r1949) *Concert*
(7/94) (RCA) ① **09026 61650-2**
Symphony No. 1 (1928) (arr from Organ Symphony, 1924)
FNO, A. Copland *Concert*
(6/91) (ETCE) ① **KTC1098**
Symphony No. 3—orchestra (1944-46)
NYPO, L. Bernstein (pp 1985) *Quiet city.*
(11/86) (DG) ① **419 170-2GH**
Atlanta SO, Y. Levi (r1989) *Music for the Theatre.*
(1/90) (TELA) ① **CD80201**
St Louis SO, L. Slatkin *Music for a Great City.*
(2/91) (RCA) ① **RD60149**
New Philh, A. Copland (r1976) *Concert*
(7/91) (SONY) ① [3] **SM3K46559**

SECTION II: CHAMBER

Duo—flute and piano (1971)
M-U. Senn, H. Göbel *Concert*
(4/88) (THOR) ① **CTH2012**
M. Cox, N. Clayton *Concert*
(3/90) (KING) ① **KCLCD2013**
F. Smith, R. Hodgkinson *Concert*
(9/90) (NORT) ① **NR227-CD**
P. Robison, T. Hester *Concert*
(11/90) (MMAS) ① **MMD 60195A**
A. Still, S. De Witt Smith (r1992) *Concert*
(4/94) (KOCH) ① **37144-2**
Nocturne—violin and piano (1928)
M. Bachmann, J. Klibonoff (r1994) *Concert*
(5/95) (CATA) ① **09026 62668-2**
Nonet—3 violins, 3 violas and 3 cellos (1960)
English SO, W. Boughton *Concert*
(10/90) (NIMB) ① **NI5246**
2 Pieces—violin and piano (1926)
1. Nocturne; 2. Ukelele Serenade.
R. Davidovici, S. de Groote *Concert*
(11/87) (NEW) ① **NW334-2**
Sextet—clarinet, piano and strings (1937) (arr from Short Symphony)
BPO Academy *Concert* (4/88) (THOR) ① **CTH2012**
Sonata—clarinet and piano (1986) (arr cpsr from Violin Sonata)
V. Soames, J. Drake *Concert*
(9/92) (CLRI) ① **CC0001**
Sonata for Violin and Piano (1942-43)
H. Maile, H. Göbel *Concert*
(4/88) (THOR) ① **CTH2012**
Threnody I (Igor Stravinsky, in memoriam)—flute, violin, viola and cello (1971)
F. Smith, S. Chase, K. Murdoch, Ronald Thomas *Concert* (9/90) (NORT) ① **NR227-CD**
Threnody II (Beatrice Cunningham, in memoriam)—flute, violin, viola and cello (1973)
F. Smith, S. Chase, K. Murdoch, Ronald Thomas *Concert* (9/90) (NORT) ① **NR227-CD**
Vitebsk, 'Study on a Jewish Theme'—piano trio (1929)
Göbel Trio, Berlin *Concert*
(4/88) (THOR) ① **CTH2012**
Hartley Trio *Concert* (6/94) (GAMU) ① **GAMCD536**
Vocalise—flute and piano (1972) (arr cpsr from song: 1928)
F. Smith, R. Hodgkinson *Concert*
(9/90) (NORT) ① **NR227-CD**

A. Still, S. De Witt Smith (r1992) *Concert*
(4/94) (KOCH) ① **37144-2**

SECTION III: INSTRUMENTAL

The cat and the mouse—piano (1920)
E. Parkin (r1991) *Concert*
(8/93) (SILV) ① **SONGCD906**
L. Smit (r1978) *Concert*
(2/95) (SONY) ① [2] **SM2K66345**
Down a country lane—piano (1962)
E. Parkin (r1991) *Concert*
(8/93) (SILV) ① **SONGCD906**
L. Smit (r1978) *Concert*
(2/95) (SONY) ① [2] **SM2K66345**
Episode—organ (1940)
H-O. Ericsson *Concert* (4/93) (BIS) ① **BIS-CD510**
In evening air—piano (1966) (arr from film score 'The Cummington Story')
E. Parkin (r1991) *Concert*
(8/93) (SILV) ① **SONGCD906**
L. Smit (r1993) *Concert*
(2/95) (SONY) ① [2] **SM2K66345**
Midsummer Nocturne—piano (1947)
E. Parkin (r1991) *Concert*
(8/93) (SILV) ① **SONGCD906**
L. Smit (r1978) *Concert*
(2/95) (SONY) ① [2] **SM2K66345**
Moods—three esquisses: piano (1920-21)
1. Embittered; 2. Wistful; 3. Jazzy.
B. Lerner *Concert* (12/89) (ETCE) ① **KTC1036**
L. Smit (r1993) *Concert*
(2/95) (SONY) ① [2] **SM2K66345**
Night Thoughts (Homage to Ives)—piano (1972)
C. Fierro *Concert* (11/90) (DELO) ① **DE1013**
L. Smit (r1978) *Concert*
(2/95) (SONY) ① [2] **SM2K66345**
Our Town—piano (1944) (arr film score)
1. Story of Our Town; 2. Conversation at the Soda Fountain; 3. The Resting-Place on the Hill.
E. Parkin *Concert* (1/89) (PREA) ① **PRCD1776**
E. Parkin (r1991) *Concert*
(8/93) (SILV) ① **SONGCD906**
Passacaglia—piano (1921-22)
C. Fierro *Concert* (11/90) (DELO) ① **DE1013**
E. Parkin (r1991) *Concert*
(8/93) (SILV) ① **SONGCD906**
L. Smit (r1978) *Concert*
(2/95) (SONY) ① [2] **SM2K66345**
Le petit portrait (ABE)—piano (1921)
B. Lerner *Concert* (12/89) (ETCE) ① **KTC1036**
L. Smit (r1993) *Concert*
(2/95) (SONY) ① [2] **SM2K66345**
4 Piano Blues (1926-48)
1. Freely poetic (1947); 2. Soft and languid (1934); 3. Muted and sensuous (1948); 4. With bounce (1928).
E. Parkin (r1991) *Concert*
(8/93) (SILV) ① **SONGCD906**
L. Smit (r1978) *Concert*
(2/95) (SONY) ① [2] **SM2K66345**
M. Legrand (r1994) *Concert*
(7/95) (ERAT) ① **4509-96386-2**
2, 3. J. MacGregor *Concert*
(8/89) (COLL) ① **Coll1299-2**
3. P. Jablonski (trans pf: L Bernstein) *Concert*
(7/91) (DECC) ① **430 542-2DH**
Piano Fantasy—piano (1955-57)
C. Fierro *Concert* (11/90) (DELO) ① **DE1013**
L. Smit (r1978) *Concert*
(2/95) (SONY) ① [2] **SM2K66345**
2 Pieces—piano (1944-82)
1. Midday Thoughts (1944-82); 2. Proclamation (1973-82).
B. Lerner *Concert* (12/88) (ETCE) ① **KTC1019**
E. Parkin *Concert* (1/89) (PREA) ① **PRCD1776**
L. Smit (r1993) *Concert*
(2/95) (SONY) ① [2] **SM2K66345**
Preamble, 'for a solemn occasion'—organ (1949)
H-O. Ericsson *Concert* (4/93) (BIS) ① **BIS-CD510**
Sentimental Melody (Slow dance)—piano (1926)
B. Lerner *Concert* (12/89) (ETCE) ① **KTC1036**
L. Smit (r1993) *Concert*
(2/95) (SONY) ① [2] **SM2K66345**
Sonata for Piano (1939-41)
P. Lawson *Concert* (5/91) (VIRG) ① **VC7 59008-2**
J. McCabe *Concert*
(6/91) (CNTI) ① [2] **CCD1028/9**
E. Parkin (r1991) *Concert*
(8/93) (SILV) ① **SONGCD906**
L. Smit (r1978) *Concert*
(2/95) (SONY) ① [2] **SM2K66345**
Sonnet II—piano (1918-20)
B. Lerner *Concert* (12/89) (ETCE) ① **KTC1036**

Sunday afternoon music—piano (1935)
L. Smit (r1978) *Concert*
(2/95) (SONY) ① [2] **SM2K66345**
Variations—piano (1930)
J. MacGregor *Concert* (8/89) (COLL) ① **Coll1299-2**
C. Fierro *Concert* (11/90) (DELO) ① **DE1013**
E. Parkin (r1991) *Concert*
(8/93) (SILV) ① **SONGCD906**
L. Smit (r1978) *Concert*
(2/95) (SONY) ① [2] **SM2K66345**
The Young Pioneers—piano (1935)
L. Smit (r1978) *Concert*
(2/95) (SONY) ① [2] **SM2K66345**

SECTION IV: VOCAL AND CHORAL

Las Agachadas, '(The) Shake-down Song'—8vv a cappella (1942) (wds. Spanish trad)
New England Cons Chor, A. Copland (r1965) *Concert* (7/91) (SONY) ① [3] **SM3K46559**
Alone—song (1923) (Wds. E P Mathers)
R. Alexander, R. Vignoles *Concert*
(3/92) (ETCE) ① **KTC1100**
Canticle of Freedom—chorus and orchestra (1955) (Wds. J Barbour)
Seattle Sym Chorale, Seattle SO, G. Schwarz
(1992) *Concert* (5/93) (DELO) ① **DE3140**
In the Beginning—mezzo-soprano, 4vv (1947) (Wds. Bible)
C. Denley, Corydon Sngrs, M. Best *Concert*
(9/87) (HYPE) ① **CDA66219**
4 Motets—4vv a capella (1921) (Wds. Bible arr cpsr)
1. Help us, O Lord; 2. Have mercy on us, O my Lord; 3. Sing ye praises to our King.
Corydon Sngrs, M. Best *Concert*
(9/87) (HYPE) ① **CDA66219**
The Sixteen, H. Christophers *Concert*
(4/92) (COLL) ① **Coll1287-2**
My heart is in the East—song (1918) (Wds. A. Schaffer: unpub)
R. Alexander, R. Vignoles *Concert*
(3/92) (ETCE) ① **KTC1100**
Night—song (1918) (Wds. A. Schaffer: unpub)
R. Alexander, R. Vignoles *Concert*
(3/92) (ETCE) ① **KTC1100**
Old American Songs—Set 1—voice and piano/small orchestra (1950 orch 1954)
1. The boatmen's dance (D. Emmett, 1843); 2. The dodger (coll. Lomax); 3. Long time ago (1830s); 4. Simple gifts (Shaker, 1840); 5. I bought me a cat.
Cpte R. Alexander, R. Vignoles *Concert*
(3/92) (ETCE) ① **KTC1100**
S. Milnes, Cincinnati Pops, E. Kunzel *Concert*
(10/87) (TELA) ① **CD80117**
W. White, G. McNaught *Concert*
(6/92) (CHAN) ① **CHAN8960**
3, 4. Y. Kenny, L. Skrobacs (pp1984) *Concert*
(7/90) (ETCE) ① **KTC1029**
Old American Songs—Set 2—voice and piano/orchestra (1952 orch 1958)
1. The little horses (coll. Lomax); 2. Zion's walls (attrib. McCarry); 3. The golden willow tree; 4. At the river (Lowry, 1865); 5. Ching-a-ring (1830s).
Cpte R. Alexander, R. Vignoles *Concert*
(3/92) (ETCE) ① **KTC1100**
W. White, G. McNaught *Concert*
(6/92) (CHAN) ① **CHAN8960**
4. Y. Kenny, L. Skrobacs (pp1984) *Concert*
(7/90) (ETCE) ① **KTC1029**
4. T. Troyanos, NY Met Op Orch, J. Conlon (pp1991) *Concert* (6/93) (RCA) ① **09026 61509-2**
4. M. Horne, Martin Katz (pp1994) *Concert*
(1/95) (RCA) ① **09026 62547-2**
Old Poem—song (1920) (Wds. Chinese trad, trans A. Waley)
R. Alexander, R. Vignoles *Concert*
(3/92) (ETCE) ① **KTC1100**
Pastorale—song (1921) (Wds. E. P. Mathers)
R. Alexander, R. Vignoles *Concert*
(3/92) (ETCE) ① **KTC1100**
12 Poems of Emily Dickinson—songs (1944-50)
1. Nature, the gentlest mother; 2. There came a wind like a bugle; 3. Why do they shut me out of heaven; 4. The world feels dusty; 5. Heart, we will forget him; 6. Dear March, come in; 7. Sleep is supposed to be; 8. When they come back; 9. I felt a funeral in my brain; 10. I've heard an organ talk sometimes; 11. Going to heaven; 12. The chariot.
Cpte R. Alexander, R. Vignoles *Concert*
(3/92) (ETCE) ① **KTC1100**
1, 2, 4-7, 11, 12. B. Hendricks, LSO, M. Tilson Thomas (r1994) *Concert*
(8/95) (EMI) ① **CDC5 55358-2**

Poet's Song—voice and piano (1927) (Wds.
e. e. cummings)
R. Alexander, R. Vignoles *Concert*
(3/92) (ETCE) ① **KTC1100**
A **Summer vacation**—song (1918) (Wds. A.
Schaffer: unpub)
R. Alexander, R. Vignoles *Concert*
(3/92) (ETCE) ① **KTC1100**

SECTION V: STAGE WORKS

Appalachian Spring—ballet
(1944—Washington) (orig 13 instruments, later
orch)
LSO, W. Susskind (r c1958) *Concert*
(4/95) (EVER) ① **EVC9003**
Appalachian Spring—concert suite from
ballet (1945 & 1970)
Atlanta SO, L. Lane *Concert*
(12/83) (TELA) ① **CD80078**
Los Angeles PO, L. Bernstein (pp 1982) *Concert*
(10/84) (DG) ① **413 324-2GH**
Moscow PO, D. Kitaienko *Concert*
(2/88) (SHEF) ① **CD27**
Orpheus CO *Concert* (8/89) (DG) ① **427 335-2GH**
CLS, R. Hickox *Concert*
(11/89) (VIRG) ① **VC7 59520-2**
English SO, W. Boughton *Concert*
(10/90) (NIMB) ① **NI5246**
NY Virtuosi, K. Klein *Concert*
(3/91) (COLL) ① **Coll1097-2**
LSO, A. Copland (r1970) *Concert*
(7/91) (SONY) ① [3] **SM3K46559**
Detroit SO, A. Dorati *Concert*
(8/91) (DECC) ① **430 705-2DM**
Atlantic Sinfonietta, A. Schenck (r1990) *Barber:
Medea.* (4/92) (KOCH) ① **37019-2**
NYPO, L. Bernstein (r1961) *Concert*
(5/93) (SONY) ① **SMK47543**
RPO, P. Ellis (r1994) *Concert*
(12/95) (TRIN) ① **TRP040**
Billy the Kid—ballet (1938—Chicago)
Cpte Baltimore SO, D. Zinman (r1993) *Concert*
(10/94) (ARGO) ① **440 639-2ZH**
Billy the Kid—concert suite from ballet
(1939)
1. Introduction; 2. Open Pairie; 2. Street in a
Frontier Town; 3. Mexican Dance and Finale; 4.
Prairie Night: Card Game; 5. Gun Battle; 6.
Celebration: After Billy's capture; 7. Billy's Death; 8.
The Open Prairie again.
LSO, A. Copland (r1969) *Concert*
(7/91) (SONY) ① [3] **SM3K46559**
NYPO, L. Bernstein (r1959) *Concert*
(5/93) (SONY) ① **SMK47543**
Czech PO, A. Copland (pp1973) *Concert*
(6/93) (ROMA) ① **RR1973**
Morton Gould Orch, M. Gould (r1957) *Concert*
(2/94) (RCA) ① **09026 61667-2**
Bournemouth SO, J. Farrer (r1993) *Concert*
(8/94) (CARL) ① **MCD75**
RPO, P. Ellis (r1994) *Concert*
(12/95) (TRIN) ① **TRP040**
Dance panels—ballet (1963—Munich)
Lehigh Valley CO, D. Spieth, C. Brey (r1993) *Lipkis:
Scaramouche.* (7/94) (KOCH) ① **37166-2**
Grohg—ballet: 1 act (1925—Rochester)
EXCERPTS: 1. Introduction, Cortège and Entrance
of Grohg; 2. Dance of the Adolescent; 3. Dance of
the Opium-eater; 4. Dance of the Streetwalker; 5.
Grohg imagines the Dead are mocking him; 6.
Illumination and Disappearance of Grohg.
Cpte Cleveland Orch., O. Knussen (r1993) *Concert*
(10/94) (ARGO) ① **443 203-2ZH**
Hear Ye! Hear Ye!—ballet: 1 act (1934) (arr
small orchestra: 1935)
EXCERPTS: 1. Prelude; 2. The Courtroom; 3. Dance
of the Prosecuting Attorney; 4. Dance of the Defense
Attorney; 5. Quarrel; 6. The Nightclub hostess sworn
in; 7. First Pas-de-deux; 8. Pas-de-deux continued;
First murder; 9. The Courtroom; 10. The Honeymoon
Couple return; 11. The Chorus-girls' dance with
doves; 12. Second Pas de deux and Murder; 13. The
Courtroom; 14. The Waiter is sworn in; 15. The
Chorus-girls' third dance; 16. Third Pas-de-deux and
Murder; 17. The Verdict; 18. The Courtroom.
Cpte London Sinfonietta, O. Knussen (r1993)
Concert (10/94) (ARGO) ① **443 203-2ZH**
The Heiress—film score (1948)
EXCERPTS: 1. Prelude; 2. Catherine's Engagement;
3. Cherry Red Dress; 4. Departure; 5. Morris
Suggests Love; 6. The Proposal; 7. Finale.
1-7. St Louis SO, L. Slatkin (r1992; reconstructed A.
Freed) *Concert* (11/94) (RCA) ① **09026 61699-2**

Music for Movies—concert suite from film
scores (1942) (from The City, Of Mice and
Men, and Our Town)
1. New England Countryside (The City); 2. Sunday
Traffic (The City); 3. Barley Waggons (Of Mice and
Men); 4. Story of Grovers (Our Town); 5. Threshing
Machines(Of Mice and Men).
New Philh, A. Copland (r1974) *Concert*
(7/91) (SONY) ① [3] **SM3K46559**
St Louis SO, L. Slatkin (r1991) *Concert*
(11/94) (RCA) ① **09026 61699-2**
Our Town—concert suite from film score
(1940)
LSO, A. Copland (r1967) *Concert*
(7/91) (SONY) ① [3] **SM3K46559**
St Louis SO, L. Slatkin (r1991) *Concert*
(11/94) (RCA) ① **09026 61699-2**
The Red Pony—concert suite from film
score (1948)
EXCERPTS: 1. Morning on the Ranch; 2. The Gift;
3a. Dream March; 3b. Circus March; 4. Walk to the
Bunkhouse; 5. Grandfather's Story; 6. Happy Ending.
Phoenix SO, J. Sedares (r1991) *Concert*
(4/92) (KOCH) ① **37092-2**
St Louis SO, L. Slatkin (r1992) *Concert*
(11/94) (RCA) ① **09026 61699-2**
Rodeo—ballet (1942—New York)
1. Buckaroo Spring; 2. Corral Nocturne; 3. Saturday
Night Waltz; 4. Hoe-Down.
Cpte Baltimore SO, D. Zinman (r1993) *Concert*
(10/94) (ARGO) ① **440 639-2ZH**
Atlanta SO, L. Lane *Concert*
(12/83) (TELA) ① **CD80078**
English SO, W. Boughton *Concert*
(10/90) (NIMB) ① **NI5246**
LSO, A. Copland (r1968) *Concert*
(7/91) (SONY) ① [3] **SM3K46559**
Detroit SO, A. Dorati *Concert*
(8/91) (DECC) ① **430 705-2DM**
NYPO, L. Bernstein (r1960) *Concert*
(5/93) (SONY) ① **SMK47543**
Minneapolis SO, A. Dorati (r1957) *Concert*
(7/93) (MERC) ① **434 329-2MM**
Morton Gould Orch, M. Gould (r1957; includes
Honky-Tonk Interlude) *Concert*
(2/94) (RCA) ① **09026 61667-2**
1-4. Bournemouth SO, J. Farrer (r1993) *Concert*
(8/94) (CARL) ① **MCD75**
3. Empire Brass (1992; arr. Pilafian) *Concert*
(1/94) (TELA) ① **CD80305**
3, 4. J. Pierce, D. Jonas (1989: arr Bernstein)
Concert (10/94) (KOCH) ① **37002-2**
4. I. Stern, Columbia SO, M. Katims (arr Harris)
Concert (7/90) (SONY) ① **SK45816**
4. Brodsky Qt (arr M. Thomas) *Concert*
(4/92) (TELD) ① **2292-46015-2**
4. RPO, P. Ellis (r1994) *Concert*
(12/95) (TRIN) ① **TRP040**
The Tender Land—opera: 2 acts (1954—New
York) (Lib. H. Everett, after E. Johns)
Cpte E. Comeaux, J. Hardy, M. Jette, L. Lehr, D.
Dressen, J. Bohn, V. Sutton, A. Smuda, M. Fristad,
S. Herber, Plymouth Music Series Chor, Plymouth
Music Series Orch, P. Brunelle
(8/90) (VIRG) ① [2] **VCD7 59253-2**
The Promise of Living Cincinnati Pops, E. Kunzel
Concert (10/87) (TELA) ① **CD80117**
The Tender Land—concert suite from opera
(1956)
1. Introduction and Love Music; 2. Party Scene; 3.
Finale: The Promise of Living.
Phoenix SO, J. Sedares (r1991) *Concert*
(4/92) (KOCH) ① **37092-2**

**COPPIN, Johnny (20th Cent)
England**

SECTION II: CHAMBER

The Glastonbury Thorn—theme
Coppin ens *Concert* (12/91) (RED) ① **RSKCD111**

**COPPINI, Alessandro
(c1465–1527) Italy**

SECTION IV: VOCAL AND CHORAL

Lanzi maine far chaxon—4vv
London Pro Musica, B. Thomas *Concert*
(2/87) (CARL) ① **PCD825**

**COPRARIO, John
(?c1570/80–1626) England**
also known as John Cooper

SECTION II: CHAMBER

Almaine—three viols
Circa 1500, N. Hadden (r1991) *Concert*
(8/93) (CRD) ① **CRD3487**

SECTION IV: VOCAL AND CHORAL

In darkness let me dwell—song
M. Chance, D. Cordier, Tragicomedia, S. Stubbs
Concert (8/93) (HYPE) ① **CDA66335**

**CORBETTA, Francesco
(c1615–1681) Italy**

SECTION II: CHAMBER

Sinfonia a 2
N. North, M. Cole *Concert*
(6/87) (AMON) ① **CD-SAR18**

SECTION III: INSTRUMENTAL

Ciaconna—guitar
B. Mason *Concert* (10/90) (AMON) ① **CD-SAR45**
Preludio—guitar
B. Mason *Concert* (10/90) (AMON) ① **CD-SAR45**

**CORDELLA, Giacomo (1786–1846
or 1847) Italy**

SECTION V: STAGE WORKS

Lo **Sposo di provincia**—commedia per
musica: 2 acts (1821—Rome) (Lib. G
Schmidt)
Oh soave mia speranza N. Focile, F. Kimm, P.
Nilon, Philh, D. Parry *Concert*
(8/95) (OPRA) ① [3] **ORCH104**

**CORDER, Frederick (1852–1932)
England**

SECTION I: ORCHESTRAL

Prospero—overture
English Northern Philh, D. Lloyd-Jones *Concert*
(1/92) (HYPE) ① **CDA66515**

**CORDIER, Baude (fl early 15th
Cent) France**

SECTION IV: VOCAL AND CHORAL

Belle, bonne, sage, plaisant—rondeau (3vv)
Organum Ens, M. Pérès *Concert*
(11/87) (HARM) ① **HMC90 1252**
Ce jour de l'an—New Year song: 3vv
Gothic Voices, C. Page (lte/dir) *Concert*
(9/92) (HYPE) ① **CDA66588**
Tout par compas suy composés—rondeau
(3vv)
Organum Ens, M. Pérès *Concert*
(11/87) (HARM) ① **HMC90 1252**

COREA, Chick (b 1941) USA

SECTION III: INSTRUMENTAL

Children's Songs—piano
Nos 2-6, 6, 7, 9, 11, 16, 18. Apollo Sax Qt, J. Harle,
M. Hamnett (r1993: arr Apollo Sax Qt) *Concert*
(4/95) (ARGO) ① **443 903-2ZH**

**CORELLI, Arcangelo (1653–1713)
Italy**

SECTION I: ORCHESTRAL

12 Concerti Grossi—strings, Op. 6 (pub
1714)
1. D; 2. F; 3. C minor; 4. D; 5. B flat; 6. F; 7. D; 8. G
minor (Christmas Concerto); 9. F; 10. C; 11. B flat;
12. F.
English Concert, T. Pinnock
(1/89) (ARCH) ① [2] **423 626-2AH2**
Slovak CO, B. Warchal
(1/90) (OPUS) ① [2] **9350 1977/8**
Solisti Italiani (r1989)
(5/90) (DENO) ① [2] **CO-74168/9**
I Musici (9/90) (PHIL) ① [2] **426 453-2PBQ2**
Petite Bande, S. Kuijken (r1976-8)
(9/90) (DHM) ① [2] **GD77007**

C. Chiarappa (vn/dir), Accademia Bizantina *Concert*
(5/91) (EURM) ① [9] **350202**
Ens 415, C. Banchini (vn/dir), J. Christensen
(6/92) (HARM) ① [2] **HMC90 1406/7**
Guildhall Str Ens   (9/92) (RCA) ① [2] **RD60071**
Brandenburg Consort, R. Goodman (r1992)
(9/93) (HYPE) ① [2] **CDA66741/2**
ASMF, N. Marriner (r1973/4)
(7/95) (DECC) ① [2] **443 862-2DF2**
1, 3, 7-9, 11. Tafelmusik, J. Lamon
(12/89) (DHM) ① **RD77908**
1-6. Philh Baroque Orch, N. McGegan
(2/90) (HARM) ① **HMU90 7014**
2. Y. Menuhin (vn/dir), R. Masters, Derek Simpson,
Bath Fest Orch *Concert*
(11/89) (CFP) ① **CD-CFP4557**
2. ECO, I. Watson (hpd/dir) *Concert*
(12/91) (VIRG) ① **VJ7 59656-2**
4. Scottish Ens, J. Rees (vn/dir) (r1991) *Concert*
(12/91) (VIRG) ① **VJ7 59652-2**
4. Capella Istropolitana, J. Krechek (r1993) *Concert*
(3/95) (NAXO) ① **8 550877**
7. ASMF, N. Marriner (r1961) *Concert*
(9/93) (DECC) ① **436 224-2DM**
7-12. Philh Baroque Orch, N. McGegan
(4/91) (HARM) ① **HMU90 7015**
8. M. Schwalbé, BPO, H. von Karajan *Concert*
(9/85) (DG) ① **415 301-2GH**
8. BPO, H. von Karajan *Concert*
(8/87) (DG) ① **419 046-2GGA**
8. Virtuosi Saxoniae, L. Güttler *Concert*
(12/89) (CAPR) ① **10 225**
8. M. Petri, National PO, M. Neary (arr. Petri) *Concert*
(12/91) (RCA) ① **RD60060**
8. English Concert, T. Pinnock (hpd/dir) *Concert*
(12/91) (ARCH) ① **435 262-2AH**
8. Giardino Armonico Ens *Concert*
(12/91) (TELD) ① **2292-46013-2**
8. ASMF, N. Marriner (r1973) *Concert*
(9/93) (DECC) ① **436 224-2DM**
8(**Pastorale**) Prince of Wales Brass (arr Quirk)
Concert   (12/93) (ASV) ① **CDWHL2083**
8. Pantaleon Ens, K-H. Schickhaus (dulcimer/dir)
(r1991) (12/93) (TUDO) ① **Tudor 767**
8. English Concert, T. Pinnock (r1992) *Concert*
· (3/94) (ARCH) ① **437 834-2AH**
8. LSO, B. Walter (r1938) *Concert*
(8/94) (DUTT) ① **CDLX7008**
8. I Musici *Concert*   (9/94) (PHIL) ① **442 396-2PM**
8(**Pastorale**) Solisti Italiani (r1973) *Concert*
(12/94) (DENO) ① **CO-78912**
Concerto for Oboe and Strings in F (arr
Barbirolli from Violin Sonatas Op. 5/10 (movts
1,2,4 and 5) and Op. 5/7 (movt 3)
B. Hoff, ECO, I. Watson *Concert*
(2/90) (SIMA) ① **PSC1049**
M. André, H. Bilgram (arr tpt/org) *Concert*
(1/93) (EMI) ① **CDC7 54330-2**
Overture to S Beatrice d'Este, WoO1 (1689)
C. Chiarappa (vn/dir), Accademia Bizantina *Concert*
(5/91) (EURM) ① [9] **350202**
Sonata for Trumpet and Strings in D
S. Keavy, Parley of Instr *Concert*
(1/89) (HYPE) ① **CDA66255**
H. Hardenberger, I Musici (r1993) *Concert*
(5/95) (PHIL) ① **442 131-2PH**

SECTION II: CHAMBER

Fuga a quattro voci, Anh15 (doubtful)
C. Chiarappa (vn/dir), Accademia Bizantina *Concert*
(5/91) (EURM) ① [9] **350202**
**Sonata in A—violin and continuo, Anh33
(pub 1704)** (doubtful)
C. Chiarappa (vn/dir), Accademia Bizantina *Concert*
(5/91) (EURM) ① [9] **350202**
**Sonata in D—trumpet, 2 violins and
continuo, WoO4**
C. Chiarappa (vn/dir), Accademia Bizantina *Concert*
(5/91) (EURM) ① [9] **350202**
2 Sonatas—2 violins, viola and continuo
1. G minor, WoO2.
1. C. Chiarappa (vn/dir), Accademia Bizantina
Concert   (5/91) (EURM) ① [9] **350202**
1. Berlin Barock Compagney (r1993) *Concert*
(10/95) (CAPR) ① **10 459**
**12 Sonatas for Violin/Recorder and
Continuo, Op. 5 (pub 1700)**
1. D; 2. B flat; 3. C; 4. F; 5. G minor; 6. A; 7. D minor;
8. E minor; 9. A; 9a. A—elab by Geminiani; 10. F; 11.
E; 12. D minor (La Follia).
Locatelli Trio (incl 9a)
(3/95) (HYPE) ① [2] **CDA66381/2**
C. Chiarappa (vn/dir), Accademia Bizantina *Concert*
(5/91) (EURM) ① [9] **350202**
1-6. C. Banchini, J. Christensen, L. Contini, K. Gohl
(9/90) (HARM) ① **HMC90 1307**

3, 12. Purcell Qt *Concert*
(9/87) (HYPE) ① **CDA66226**
4, 12. F. Brüggen, A. Bylsma, G. Leonhardt (r1967,
1972) *Concert*   (7/94) (TELD) ① **4509-93669-2**
5(**Adagio**) A. Busch, various (r1919) *Concert*
(6/93) (SYMP) ① **SYMCD1109**
8. Barthold Kuijken, W. Kuijken, R. Kohnen *Concert*
(5/92) (ACCE) ① **ACC9177D**
9. M. Petri, G. Malcolm *Concert*
(10/86) (PHIL) ① **412 632-2PH**
11. R. Campbell (trans Anon for vla and gamba)
Concert   (9/87) (HYPE) ① **CDA66226**
12. B. Kol, A. Brodo, D. Shemer *Concert*
(6/90) (CARL) ① **PWK1138**
12. Y. Menuhin, H. Giesen (r1930) *Concert*
(4/91) (BIDD) ① **LAB032**
12. G. Enescu, S. Schlüssel (arr David, rev Pethie:
r1929) *Concert*   (12/91) (MSCM) ① **MM30322**
12. J. Szigeti, A. Farkas (arr Léonard: r1940) *Concert*
(5/93) (SONY) ① **MPK52569**
12. G. Enescu, S. Schlüssel (r1929) *Concert*
(6/93) (BIDD) ① **LAB066**
12. A. Grumiaux, R. Castagnone (r1956; arr
Castagnone) *Concert*
(11/93) (PHIL) ① [3] **438 516-2PM3**
12. N. Milstein, L. Pommers (r1959) *Concert*
(5/94) (EMI) ① [6] **ZDMF7 64830-2**
12. J. Szigeti, A. Foldes (r1940: arr Léonard) *Concert*
(7/94) (BIDD) ① [2] **LAB070/1**
**Sonate ... composta da Arcangelo Corelli ed
altri autori—violin and continuo (pub 1697)**
(doubtful)
1. D, Anh34; 2. A minor, Anh35; 3. D, Anh36; 4. D,
Anh37.
1-4. C. Chiarappa (vn/dir), Accademia Bizantina
Concert   (5/91) (EURM) ① [9] **350202**
**6 Trio Sonatas—2 violins and continuo, Op.
posth (WoO5-10) (pub 1715)**
1. A; 2. D; 3. D; 4. D; 5. G minor; 6. G minor.
C. Chiarappa (vn/dir), Accademia Bizantina *Concert*
(5/91) (EURM) ① [9] **350202**
**12 Trio Sonatas—2 violins and continuo, Op.
1 (pub 1681)**
1. F; 2. E minor; 3. A; 4. A minor; 5. B flat; 6. B minor;
7. C; 8. C minor; 9. G; 10. G minor; 11. D minor; 12.
D.
C. Chiarappa (vn/dir), Accademia Bizantina *Concert*
(5/91) (EURM) ① [9] **350202**
Purcell Qt *Trio Sonatas, Op. 2.*
(6/91) (CHAN) ① **CHAN0516**
London Baroque *Trio Sonatas, Op. 3.*
(10/91) (HARM) ① [2] **HMC90 1344/5**
Purcell Qt, J. Lindberg *Trio Sonatas, Op. 2.*
(6/92) (CHAN) ① **CHAN0515**
1, 3, 7, 9, 11, 12. English Concert *Trio Sonatas, Op.
2.*   (6/87) (ARCH) ① **419 614-2AH**
9. Purcell Qt *Concert*   (9/87) (HYPE) ① **CDA66226**
**12 Trio Sonatas—2 violins and continuo, Op.
2 (pub 1685)**
1. D; 2. D minor; 3. C; 4. E minor; 5. B flat; 6. G
minor; 7. F; 8. B minor; 9. F sharp minor; 10. E; 11. E
flat; 12. G.
C. Chiarappa (vn/dir), Accademia Bizantina *Concert*
(5/91) (EURM) ① [9] **350202**
Purcell Qt *Trio Sonatas, Op. 1.*
(6/91) (CHAN) ① **CHAN0516**
London Baroque *Trio Sonatas, Op. 4.*
(10/91) (HARM) ① [2] **HMC90 1342/3**
Purcell Qt, J. Lindberg *Trio Sonatas, Op. 1.*
(6/92) (CHAN) ① **CHAN0515**
1(**Adagio**) F. Kreisler, H. Kreisler, M. Raucheisen (arr
Kreisler: r1927) *Concert*
(9/92) (BIDD) ① [2] **LAB049/50**
4, 12. Purcell Qt *Concert*
(9/87) (HYPE) ① **CDA66226**
4, 6, 9, 12. English Concert *Trio Sonatas, Op. 1.*
(6/87) (ARCH) ① **419 614-2AH**
6. English Gtr Qt (arr Gallery) *Concert*
(11/91) (SAYD) ① **CD-SDL386**
12. Berlin Barock Compagney (r1993) *Concert*
(10/95) (CAPR) ① **10 459**
**12 Trio Sonatas—2 violins and continuo, Op.
3 (pub 1689)**
1. F; 2. D; 3. B flat; 4. B minor; 5. D minor; 6. G; 7. E
minor; 8. C; 9. F minor; 10. A minor; 11. G minor; 12.
A minor.
C. Chiarappa (vn/dir), Accademia Bizantina *Concert*
(5/91) (EURM) ① [9] **350202**
London Baroque *Trio Sonatas, Op. 1.*
(10/91) (HARM) ① [2] **HMC90 1344/5**
1. English Gtr Qt (arr Gallery) *Concert*
(11/91) (SAYD) ① **CD-SDL386**
1, 2, 3, 4, 5, 6. Purcell Qt, J. Lindberg *Trio Sonatas,
Op.4.*   (12/92) (CHAN) ① **CHAN0526**

7-12. C. Mackintosh, Elizabeth Wallfisch, R. Boothby,
R. Woolley, J. Lindberg *Trio Sonatas, Op. 4.*
(8/93) (CHAN) ① **CHAN0532**
12. Purcell Qt *Concert*   (9/87) (HYPE) ① **CDA66226**
**12 Trio Sonatas—2 violins and continuo, Op.
4 (pub 1694)**
1. C; 2. G minor; 3. A; 4. D; 5. A minor; 6. E; 7. F; 8.
D minor; 9. B flat; 10. G; 11. C minor; 12. B minor.
C. Chiarappa (vn/dir), Accademia Bizantina *Concert*
(5/91) (EURM) ① [9] **350202**
London Baroque *Trio Sonatas, Op. 2.*
(10/91) (HARM) ① [2] **HMC90 1342/3**
1, 2, 3, 4, 5, 6. Purcell Qt *Trio Sonatas, Op.3.*
(12/92) (CHAN) ① **CHAN0526**
3. Purcell Qt *Concert*   (9/87) (HYPE) ① **CDA66226**
7-12. C. Mackintosh, C. Weiss, R. Boothby, R.
Woolley *Trio Sonatas, Op. 3.*
(8/93) (CHAN) ① **CHAN0532**

CORFE, Joseph (1740–1820) England

SECTION IV: VOCAL AND CHORAL

**Lady Anne Bothwell's Lament—glee: 4vv
(1791)** (Wds Trad Scottish)
Invocation (r1994)
(3/95) (HYPE) ① **CDA66740**

CORGHI, Azio (b 1937) Italy

SECTION V: STAGE WORKS

**Divara—Wasser und Blut—opera: 3 act
(1993—Münster)** (Lib. cpsr & José Saramago)
Cpte S. von der Burg, C. Krieg, H. Hildmann, M.
Holm, H. Fitz, R. Schwarts, E. L. Thingboe, S.
McLeod, G. Wunderer, D. Midboe, M. Baba, G.
Kiefer, M. Coles, B. Trottmann, Münster City Th
Chor, Münster SO, W. Humburg (r1993)
(10/95) (MARC) ① [2] **8 223706/7**

CORIGLIANO, John (Paul) (b 1938) USA

SECTION I: ORCHESTRAL

Aria—oboe and strings (1985) (arr cpsr from
Oboe Concerto movt)
H. Lucarelli, Brooklyn PO, M. Barrett (r1993) *Concert*
(7/94) (KOCH) ① **37187-2**
Concerto for Clarinet and Orchestra (1977)
S. Drucker, NYPO, Z. Mehta *Barber: Essay for
Orchestra 3.*   (5/88) (NEW) ① **NW309-2**
Symphony No. 1 (1990)
Chicago SO, D. Barenboim (pp1990)
(7/91) (ERAT) ① **2292-45601-2**

SECTION II: CHAMBER

Sonata for Violin and Piano (1963)
M. Bachmann, J. Klibonoff (r1993) *Concert*
(12/93) (CATA) ① **09026 61824-2**
C. Macomber, D. Walsh (1994) *Beach: Violin
Sonata, Op. 34.*   (8/95) (KOCH) ① **37223-2**

CORKINE, William (fl 1610–12) England

SECTION IV: VOCAL AND CHORAL

**What booteth love?—ayre: 1v and viols (pub
1610)**
A. Deller, SCB, A. Wenzinger (r1956: arr T Dart)
Concert   (4/95) (VANG) ① **08.5068.71**

CORNAGO, Johannes (fl 1455–1485) Spain

SECTION IV: VOCAL AND CHORAL

Qu'es mi vida—chanson
London Medieval Ens *Concert*
(9/93) (L'OI) ① [2] **436 194-2OH2**
Ques mi vida preguntáys (comp with
Ockeghem: Colombina Song Book)
Hespèrion XX, J. Savall *Concert*
(7/92) (ASTR) ① **E8763**
Señora, qual soy venido (comp with Triana:
Columbina Song Book)
Hespèrion XX, J. Savall *Concert*
(7/92) (ASTR) ① **E8763**

CORNELIUS, (Carl August) Peter (1824–1874) Germany

SECTION IV: VOCAL AND CHORAL

Am Meer—sop, bass & pf (1866) (Wds. Eichendorff)
E. Mathis, H. Komatsu, C. Garben (r1994) *Concert*
(11/95) (CPO) ① **CPO999 262-2**

4 Duets—soprano, bass and piano, Op. 16 (1866-67)
1. Heimatgedenken (wds. A. Becker); 2. Brennende Liebe (wds. Mosen); 3. Komm herbei, Tod (wds. Shakespeare); 4. Scheiden (wds. H. von Fallersleben).
E. Mathis, H. Komatsu, C. Garben (r1994) *Concert*
(11/95) (CPO) ① **CPO999 262-2**
1, 4. E. Schwarzkopf, J. Greindl, M. Raucheisen
(bp1944) *Concert* (5/93) (ACAN) ① **43 128**

Ich und Du—duet (1861) (Wds. Hebbel)
B. Fassbaender, K. Moll, C. Garben *Concert*
(9/91) (HARM) ① **HMC90 5210**
E. Mathis, H. Komatsu, C. Garben (r1994) *Concert*
(11/95) (CPO) ① **CPO999 262-2**

3 Lieder—1v & piano, Op. 4 (1854) (Wds. cpsr)
1. In Lust und Schmerzen; 2. Komm, wir wandel zusammen; 3. Möcht' im Walde mit dir gehen.
2. H. Hotter, H. Dokoupil (r1968-9) *Concert*
(8/89) (PREI) ① **93390**

Sonnenuntergang—Lied (Wds Hölderlin)
M. Shirai, H. Höll *Concert*
(12/94) (CAPR) ① **10 534**

Trauer und Trost—song cycle, Op. 3 (1854) (wds. cpsr)
1. Trauer; 2. Angedenken; 3. Ein Ton; 4. An den Traum; 5. Treue; 6. Trost.
M. Price, G. Johnson (r1993) *Concert*
(2/95) (FORL) ① **UCD16728**

Zu den Bergen hebt sich ein Augenpaar—duet (1866) (Wds. cpsr, after Psalm 121)
B. Fassbaender, H. Komatsu, C. Garben *Concert*
(9/91) (HARM) ① **HMC90 5210**
E. Mathis, H. Komatsu, C. Garben (r1994) *Concert*
(11/95) (CPO) ① **CPO999 262-2**

3 zweistimmige Lieder—sop, bar & piano, Op. 6 (1861-2) (Wds. Hebbel & W von Tegernsee)
1. Liebesprobe; 2. Der beste Liebesbrief; 3. Ein Wort der Liebe.
E. Mathis, H. Komatsu, C. Garben (r1994) *Concert*
(11/95) (CPO) ① **CPO999 262-2**

SECTION V: STAGE WORKS

Der Barbier von Bagdad, '(The) Barber of Baghdad'—opera: 2 acts (1858—Weimar) (Lib. cpsr)
EXCERPTS: 1. Overture; 2. Ach, das Leid hab' ich getragen; 3. Mein Sohn, sei Allahs Frieden; 4. O holdes Bild; 5. O wüsstest du, Verehrter; 6. Salam aleikum; 7. Sanfter Schlummer; 8. So leb ich noch; 9. Vor deinem Fenster.
3. F. Wunderlich, K. Böhme, Stuttgart RSO, H. Müller-Kray (bp1957) *Concert*
(10/89) (ACAN) ① **43 267**
4. H.E. Groh, E. Bettendorf, orch (r1933) *Concert*
(3/92) (PEAR) ① **GEMMCD9419**
4. M. Ivogün, K. Erb, orch (r1917) *Concert*
(1/94) (CLUB) ① **CL99-020**
4. H. Roswaenge, I. Roswaenge, Berlin St Op Orch, B. Seidler-Winkler (r1939) *Concert*
(4/95) (PREI) ① **[2] 89209**
7. H.E. Groh, orch (r1932) *Concert*
(3/92) (PEAR) ① **GEMMCD9419**
8. A. Piccaver, orch (r1920) *Concert*
(8/93) (PREI) ① **89060**

CORNET, Séverin (c1530–1582) The Netherlands

SECTION IV: VOCAL AND CHORAL

Parmi di star
King's Sngrs, Tragicomedia *Concert*
(9/92) (EMI) ① **CDC7 54191-2**

CORNYSH, William (1468–1523) England

SECTION II: CHAMBER

Fa la sol a 3—consort (3 parts)
Fretwork *Concert* (3/88) (AMON) ① **CD-SAR29**

SECTION IV: VOCAL AND CHORAL

Adieu, adieu, my heartes lust—partsong (3vv)
Tallis Scholars, P. Phillips *Concert*
(4/89) (GIME) ① **CDGIM014**

Adieu courage—partsong (3vv)
Tallis Scholars, P. Phillips *Concert*
(4/89) (GIME) ① **CDGIM014**

Ah, Robin, gentle Robin—partsong (3vv)
Tallis Scholars, P. Phillips *Concert*
(4/89) (GIME) ① **CDGIM014**
Magdalen (Oxford) Coll Ch, G. Ives *Concert*
(11/92) (CNTO) ① **CRCD2366**

Ave Maria, mater Dei—motet (4vv)
Tallis Scholars, P. Phillips *Concert*
(4/89) (GIME) ① **CDGIM014**
The Sixteen, H. Christophers *Concert*
(11/96) (MERI) ① **CDE84175**
The Sixteen, H. Christophers *Concert*
(7/93) (COLL) ① **Coll1342-2**
Westminster Abbey Ch, M. Neary, M. Baker (r1994) *Concert* (12/95) (SONY) ① **SK66614**

Gaude virgo mater Christi—motet (4vv)
Tallis Scholars, P. Phillips *Concert*
(4/89) (GIME) ① **CDGIM014**

Magnificat—5vv
Tallis Scholars, P. Phillips *Concert*
(4/89) (GIME) ① **CDGIM014**

Salve regina—motet (5vv)
Tallis Scholars, P. Phillips *Concert*
(4/89) (GIME) ① **CDGIM014**
Tallis Scholars, P. Phillips *Concert*
(1/91) (GIME) ① **CDGIM999**
The Sixteen, H. Christophers *Concert*
(4/92) (COLL) ① **Coll1314-2**

Stabat mater—motet (5vv)
Tallis Scholars, P. Phillips *Concert*
(4/89) (GIME) ① **CDGIM014**
The Sixteen, H. Christophers *Concert*
(4/92) (COLL) ① **Coll1316-2**

Woefully arrayed—partsong (4vv)
Tallis Scholars, P. Phillips *Concert*
(4/89) (GIME) ① **CDGIM014**

CORREA DE ARAUXO, Francisco (c1583/4–1654) Spain

SECTION II: CHAMBER

Batalla des Morales
Hespèrion XX, J. Savall *Concert*
(2/92) (ASTR) ① **E8729**

SECTION III: INSTRUMENTAL

Libro de Tientos y Discursos de Música Práctica y Theórica de Organo—organ (pub 1626) (also known as 'Facultad organica'; 69 pieces)
2. Tiento y discurso de Segundo Tono; 8. Tiento de Octavo Tono; 10. Tiento de Décima Tono; 14. Segundo tiento de Primer Tono; 15. Tiento de Quarto Tono; 16. Segundo tiento de Quarto Tono; 18. Cuarto tiento de Cuarto Tono; 19. Quinto tiento de Cuarto Tono; 22. Segundo tiento de Sexto Tono; 23. Tiento tercero de Sexto Tono; 27. Tiento de medio registro de tiple de Séptimo Tono; 28. Quarto Tiento de medio registro; 29. Quinto tiento de tiple de Séptimo Tono; 34. Quinto Tiento de medio registro de baxones de Primero Tono; 37. 47. Tiento de medio registro de tiple de Octavo Tono; 49. Tiento de medio registro de baxón de Duodécimo Tono; 51. Tiento de medio registro de baxón de Décimo Tono; 52. Tiento de registro entero de Primero Tono; 53. Tiento de medio registro de dos tiples de Segundo Tono; 54. Tiento de medio registro de dos tiples de Séptimo Tono; 57. Tiento y discurso de medio registro de dos baxones de Octavo Tono; 59. Tiento de medio registro de tiple de Segundo Tono; 68. Canto Llano de la Inmaculada Concepción de la Virgen María; 69. Tres glosas sobre el Canto Llano de la Inmaculada Concepción.
8, 14, 15, 16, 19, 22, 23, 29, 47, 49, 51, 57, 59. B. Foccroulle (7/92) (AUVI) ① **V4646**
10, 15, 16, 28, 34, 37, 47, 52, 54. G. Mersiovsky
(7/92) (DHM) ① **GD77226**

CORRETTE, Gaspard (d before 1733) France/Holland

SECTION III: INSTRUMENTAL

Messe du huitième ton à l'usage des dames réligieuses—organ (1703)
J. Payne (r1994) *Concert*
(10/95) (NAXO) ① **8 553214**

CORRETTE, Michel (1709–1795) France

SECTION I: ORCHESTRAL

Concerto comique No. 25, '(Les) Sauvages et la Furstemberg'
Florilegium Ens, J. Rogers, S. Pauley (r1994) *Concert* (12/95) (CHNN) ① **CCS7595**

6 Organ Concertos, Op. 26 (pub 1756)
1. G; 2. A; 3. D; 4. C; 5. F; 6. D minor.
6: Noël Allemand German Baroque sols, R. Ewerhart (org/dir) *Concert*
(12/91) (FSM) ① **FCD91220**

SECTION III: INSTRUMENTAL

Nouveau livre de Noëls avec un carillon—harpsichord/organ (pub 1753)
M. Chapuis (12/89) (ASTR) ① **E7745**

CORTIS, Antonio (1891–1952) Spain

SECTION IV: VOCAL AND CHORAL

Calabazas—song
A. Cortis, orch (r1927) *Concert*
(3/94) (NIMB) ① **NI7850**

Tropezón—song
A. Cortis, orch (r1927) *Concert*
(3/94) (NIMB) ① **NI7850**

COSENTINO (19th–20th cent) Italy

SECTION IV: VOCAL AND CHORAL

Mattinata—song
G. Zenatello, orch (r1911) *Concert*
(5/94) (PEAR) ① **[4] GEMMCDS9073(2)**

COSTA, Pasquale Mario (1858–1933) Italy

SECTION IV: VOCAL AND CHORAL

Munasterio—song
T. Ruffo, orch (r1920) *Concert*
(2/93) (PREI) ① **[3] 89303(1)**

Sei morta nella vita mia—song (Wds. G. Capitelli)
E. Caruso, V. Bellezza (r1918) *Concert*
(7/90) (CLUB) ① **CL99-060**
E. Caruso, V. Bellezza (r1918) *Concert*
(7/91) (RCA) ① **[12] GD60495(6)**
E. Caruso, V. Bellezza (r1918) *Concert*
(10/91) (PEAR) ① **[3] EVC4(1)**
T. Ruffo, orch (r1920) *Concert*
(2/93) (PREI) ① **[3] 89303(1)**
T. Ruffo, orch (r1929) *Concert*
(2/93) (PREI) ① **[3] 89303(2)**

COSTE, Gabriel (?c1500–c1540) France

SECTION IV: VOCAL AND CHORAL

Chansons—4vv (1538-43)
1. A mos avis (wds. Héroet: 1541); 2. Cette fillette (wds. Molinet: 1540); 3. Il n'est pas vray (wds. M de St-Gelais: 1543); 4. Je ne scay combien (wds. C Marot: 1540-41); 5. Jusques à la mort (wds. C Marot: 1538); 6. Le corps ravy (wds. P du Guillet: 1541); 7. O de doulceur (wds. anon: 1540); 8. Pour faire plus tost mal (wds. C Marot: 1538); 9. Retirez vous petits vers (wds. anon: 1541); 10. Rigueur me tient (wds. anon: 1539); 11. Si du proces d'amour (wds. anon: 1538); 12. Si les oyseaulx (wds. anon: 1539); 13. Si souvenir pouvoit (wds. anon: 1538); 14. Sus donc fascheux (wds. anon: 1540); 15. Ung pauvre ayment (wds. anon: 1539); 16. Viens soulas (wds. Des Périers: 1540).
2. C. Janequin Ens, D. Visse (r1994) *Concert*
(5/95) (HARM) ① **HMC90 1453**

COSTE, Napoléon (1806–1883) France

SECTION II: CHAMBER

Le Montagnard—divertissement pastoral: oboe/violin and guitar, Op. 34
V. Taylor, T. Kain (fl/gtr) *Concert*
(9/92) (TALL) ① **TP003**

amour; 14b. La Linote éfarouchée; 14c. Les Fauvétes
Plaintives; 14d. Le Rossignol-vainqueur; 14e. La
Julliet (2 hpds); 14f. Le Carillon de Cithére; 14g. Le
Petit-Rien. (15th Ordre: A minor-major); 15a. La
Régente, ou La Minerve; 15b. Le Dodo, ou L'Amour
en berceau; 15c. L'Evaporée; 15d. Muséte de Choisi
(2 hpds); 15e. Muséte de Taverni (2 hpds); 15f. Les
Vergers Fleũris; 15g. La Douce et Piquante; 15h. La
Princesse de Chabeuil, ou La Muse de Monaco.
(16th Ordre: G major-min; 16a. Les Graces
incomparables, ou La Conti; 16b. L'Himen-Amour;
16c. Les Vestales; 16d. L'Aimable Thérése; 16e. Le
Drõle de Corps; 16f. La Distraite; 16g. La Létiville (2
hpds). (17th Ordre: E minor); 17a. La Superbe, ou La
Forqueray; 17b. Les Petits Moulins à Vent; 17c. Les
Timbres; 17d. Courante; 17e. Les Petites Chrémiéres
de Bagnolet. (18th Ordre: F minor-; 18a. Allemande,
La Verneũil; 18b. La Verneuilléte; 18c. Soeur
Monique; 18d. Le Turbulent; 18e. L'Attendrissante;
18f. Le Tic-Toc-Choc, ou Les Maillotins; 18g. Le
Gaillard-Boĩteux. (19th Ordre: D minor-major); 19a.
Les Calotins et Les Calotines, ou La Piéce à tretous;
19b. L'Ingénue; 19c. L'Artiste; 19d. Les Culbutes
Jxcxbxnxs (Jacobines); 19e. La Muse-Plantine; 19f.
L'Enjouée.
K. Gilbert   (10/89) (HARM) ① [2] HMA190 357/8
C. Rousset, B. Rannou (r1992) Concerts Royaux.
                (9/93) (HARM) ① [3] HMC90 1442/4
O. Baumont, D. Moroney (r1992)
                (2/94) (ERAT) ① [2] 4509-92859-2
13d, 14a, 15b, 15d, 15f, 18c, 19a W. Landowska
(r1930s) Concert   (10/92) (MSCM) ① MM30444
13d, 14c, 15b, 18f, 19e M. Meyer (r1946) Concert
                (6/95) (EMI) ① [4] CZS5 68092-2
13d, 17b, 18f G. Cziffra (r1980-81) Concert
                (3/95) (EMI) ① CDM5 65253-2
14a F. Brũggen, G. Leonhardt (r1978) Concert
                (10/95) (TELD) ① 4509-97469-2
14a, 14f G. Malcolm (r1969) Concert
                (11/95) (DECC) ① 444 390-2DWO
14e, 15d, 16g W. Christie, C. Rousset Concert
                (1/89) (HARM) ① HMC90 1269
14f I. Paderewski (r1914) Concert
                (3/93) (PEAR) ① GEMMCD9943
14f S. Assad, O. Assad (r1991; arr 2 gtrs) Concert
                (10/93) (NONE) ① 7559-79292-2
14f H. Bauer (r1939) Concert
                (4/94) (BIDD) ① LHW009
14f, 18c R. Veyron-Lacroix (r1967) Concert
                (12/93) (ERAT) ① 4509-92135-2
15b S. Sempé Concert   (1/91) (DHM) ① RD77219
15d, 15e Smithsonian Chbr Plyrs, K. Slowik (r1987)
Concert   (4/95) (DHM) ① 05472 77327-2
15e, 18f V. Black Concert
                (5/91) (COLL) ① Coll5024-2
16g G. Leonhardt Concert
                (10/92) (SONY) ① SK48080
17. K. Gilbert Concert   (6/88) (NOVA) ① 150 018-2
17b J. Heifetz, I. Achron (r1925) Concert
                (11/94) (RCA) ① [65] 09026 61778-2(02)
**Livre de clavecin, Book 4—Ordres 20-27
(pub 1730)**
(20th Ordre: G major-minor); 20a. La Princesse
Marie; 20b. La Boufone; 20c. Les Chérubins, ou
L'Aimable Lazarue; 20d. La Croũlli, ou La
Couperinéte (2 hpds; hpd/gamba); 20e. La Fine
Madelon; 20f. La Douce Janneton; 20g. La Sézile;
20h. Les Tambourins. (21st Ordre: E minor); 21a. La
Reine des Coeurs; 21b. La Bondissante; 21c. La
Couperin; 21d. La Harpée: Piéce dans le Goũt de la
Harpe; 21e. La Petite Pince-sans-rire. (22nd Ordre: D
major-minor); 22a. La Trophée; 22b. Le Point du
Jour; 22c. L'Anguille; 22d. Le Croc-en-jambe; 22e.
Menuets Croisées; 22f. Les Tours de Passe-passe.
(23rd Ordre: F major); 23a. L'Audacieuse; 23b. Les
Tricoteuses; 23c. L'Arlequine; 23d. Les Gondoles de
Délos; 23e. Les Satires, Chèvres-pieds. (24th Ordre:
A minor-major); 24a. Allemande grave, Les Vieux
Seigneurs; 24b. Les Jeunes Seigneurs, cy-devant les
Petits Maĩtres; 24c. Les Dars-homicides; 24d. Les
Guirlandes; 24e. Les Brinborions; 24f. La Divine
Babiche ou Les Amours badins; 24g. La Belle Javotte
autre fois L'Infante; 24h. L'Amphibie. (25th Ordre: C
major-minor); 25a. La Visionnaire; 25b. La
Misterieuse; 25c. La Monflambert; 25d. La Muse
Victorieuse; 25e. Les Ombres Errantes. (26th Ordre:
F sharp minor); 26a. La Convalescente; 26b.
Gavotte; 26c. La Sophie; 26d. L'Epineuse; 26e. La
Pantomime. (27th Ordre: B minor); 27a. L'Exquise;
27b. Les Pavots; 27c. Les Chinois; 27d. Saillie.
K. Gilbert   (10/89) (HARM) ① [2] HMA190 359/60
O. Baumont (r1992)
                (8/93) (ERAT) ① 2292-45824-2
C. Rousset (r1993)
                (10/94) (HARM) ① HMC90 1445/6

Exc W. Landowska (r1930s) Concert
                (10/92) (MSCM) ① MM30444
Excs J. Henry Concert
                (10/92) (VICT) ① VCD19013
20h L. Fugère, anon (arr Tiersot: r1929) Concert
                (6/93) (SYMP) ① SYMCD1125
22c G. Cziffra (r1980-81) Concert
                (3/95) (EMI) ① CDM5 65253-2
23c, 24a S. Sempé Concert
                (1/91) (DHM) ① RD77219
23c, 25e M. Meyer (r1946) Concert
                (6/95) (EMI) ① [4] CZS5 68092-2
**Messe à l'usage ordinaire des
paroisses—organ (pub 1690)**
P. Bardon Concert
                (3/87) (PIER) ① [2] PV785051/2
A. Isoir Concert   (6/90) (CALL) ① CAL9907
J-C. Ablitzer, Organum Ens, M. Pérès (with
plainchant)   (9/91) (HRMO) ① H/CD8613
R. Saorgin, M. Carey (with plainchant) Messe pour
les couvents.   (3/92) (REM) ① [2] REM311104
**Messe pour les convents de religieux et
religieuses—organ (pub 1690)** (recordings
may included Gregorian Chant)
P. Bardon Concert
                (3/87) (PIER) ① [2] PV785051/2
A. Isoir Titelouze: Hymnes de l'Eglise.
                (6/90) (CALL) ① CAL9908
R. Saorgin, M. Carey (with plainchant) Messe à
l'usage ordinaire des paroisses.
                (3/92) (REM) ① [2] REM311104
Demoiselles de Saint-Cyr, E. Mandrin, M. Bouvard
(r1991)   (8/94) (SONY) ① SK57486

SECTION IV: VOCAL AND CHORAL

Domine salvum fac regem—motet (2vv)
J. Feldman, I. Poulenard, G. Reinhart, J. ter Linden,
D. Moroney (r1984) Concert
                (12/87) (HARM) ① HMA190 1150
**Jucunda vox Ecclesiae—motet de Saint
Augustin (3vv)**
J. Feldman, I. Poulenard, G. Reinhart, J. ter Linden,
D. Moroney (r1984) Concert
                (12/87) (HARM) ① HMA190 1150
**Laetentur coeli et exultet—motet de Saint
Barthélemy (2vv)**
J. Feldman, I. Poulenard, G. Reinhart, J. ter Linden,
D. Moroney (r1984) Concert
                (12/87) (HARM) ① HMA190 1150
J. Bowman, M. Chance, M. Caudle, R. King Concert
                (3/92) (HYPE) ① CDA66474
**Lauda Sion salvatorem—elevation motet
(2vv)**
J. Feldman, I. Poulenard, G. Reinhart, J. ter Linden,
D. Moroney (r1984) Concert
                (12/87) (HARM) ① HMA190 1150
**3 Leçons de ténèbres—1-2vv (pub ?1713-
17)**
1. Premier Leçon; 2. Deuxième Leçon; 3. Troisième
Leçon.
Concerto Vocale Concert
                (3/86) (HARM) ① HMC90 1133
M. van der Sluis, G. Laurens, P. Monteilhet, M.
Muller, L. Boulay Concert
                (8/90) (ERAT) ① 2292-45012-2
J. Bowman, M. Chance, M. Caudle, R. King Concert
                (3/92) (HYPE) ① CDA66474
G. Lesne, Seminario musicale Ens (r1991)
                (4/94) (HRMO) ① H/CD9140
Magnificat anima mea—2vv
J. Feldman, I. Poulenard, G. Reinhart, J. ter Linden,
D. Moroney (r1984) Concert
                (12/87) (HARM) ① HMA190 1150
M. van der Sluis, G. Laurens, P. Monteilhet, M.
Muller, L. Boulay Concert
                (8/90) (ERAT) ① 2292-45012-2
J. Bowman, M. Chance, M. Caudle, R. King Concert
                (3/92) (HYPE) ① CDA66474
**O misterium ineffabile—elevation motet
(2vv)**
J. Feldman, I. Poulenard, G. Reinhart, J. ter Linden,
D. Moroney (r1984) Concert
                (12/87) (HARM) ① HMA190 1150
Regina coeli laetare—motet (2vv)
J. Feldman, I. Poulenard, G. Reinhart, J. ter Linden,
D. Moroney (r1984) Concert
                (12/87) (HARM) ① HMA190 1150
Tantum ergo sacramentum—motet (3vv)
J. Feldman, I. Poulenard, G. Reinhart, J. ter Linden,
D. Moroney (r1984) Concert
                (12/87) (HARM) ① HMA190 1150
Venite exultemus Domino—motet (2vv)
J. Feldman, I. Poulenard, G. Reinhart, J. ter Linden,
D. Moroney (r1984) Concert
                (12/87) (HARM) ① HMA190 1150

J. Bowman, M. Chance, M. Caudle, R. King Concert
                (3/92) (HYPE) ① CDA66474
**Victoria! Christo resurgenti—motet for
Easter Day: 2vv & bc**
J. Feldman, I. Poulenard, G. Reinhart, J. ter Linden,
D. Moroney (r1984) Concert
                (12/87) (HARM) ① HMA190 1150
M. van der Sluis, G. Laurens, P. Monteilhet, M.
Muller, L. Boulay Concert
                (8/90) (ERAT) ① 2292-45012-2

**COUPERIN, Louis (c1626–1661)
France**

nos for harpsichord works from B. Gustafson, 1983

SECTION III: INSTRUMENTAL

Fantaisies—organ
1. Fantaisie; 2. Fantaisie sur la tierce du grand clavier
avec le tremblant lent; 3. Fantaisie en basse; 4.
Fantaisie en quatuor; 5. Duo; 6. Fantaisie sur le
cromhorne.
1. A. Isoir Concert   (6/90) (CALL) ① CAL9907
1, 5. J. Payne (r1994) Concert
                (10/95) (NAXO) ① 8 553215
Harpsichord Works I (pieces in keys of C and
C minor)
PRELUDES IN C: 1a. Prelude 9; 1b. Prelude 10; 1c.
Prelude II. ALLEMANDES IN C: 2a. Allemande 15;
2b. Allemande 126, 'Le Moutier and Double'.
COURANTES IN C: 3a. Courante 16; 3b. Courante
17; 3c. Courante 18; 3d. Courante 19.
SARABANDES IN C: 4a. Sarabande 20; 4b.
Sarabande 21; 4c. Sarabande 22; 4d. Sarabande 23;
4f. Sarabande 24; 4g. Sarabande 25; 4h. Sarabande
28. OTHER PIECES IN C: 5a. Gavotte and Double
131; 5b. Menuet 29; 5c. Passacaille 27; 5d. Rigaudon
et Double 127; 5e. Chaconne 26. PIECES IN C
MINOR: 6a. Prelude 128; 6b. Allemande 30, 'La La
Précieuse'; 6c. Courante 31; 6d. Sarabande 32; 6e.
Gigue 33; 6f. Chaconne 34, 'La Bergeronnette'.
Cpte D. Moroney (r1983) Concert
                (4/90) (HARM) ① [4] HMA190 1124/7
1a, 2b, 3b, 4f, 4b, 3c B. Verlet (r1992) Concert
                (4/93) (ASTR) ① E8733
1b, 3d, 4c, 5b, 5d, 5a, 6b, 6c, 6d, 6e, 6f B. Verlet
Concert   (4/93) (ASTR) ① E8734
1c, 2a, 3a, 4g, 5c B. Verlet (r1986) Concert
                (7/91) (ASTR) ① E8731
1(pt), 2(pt), 3(pt), 4(pt), 5c L. Cummings (r1993)
Concert   (3/95) (NAXO) ① 8 550922
4h, 4a, 4d B. Verlet (r1991) Concert
                (4/93) (ASTR) ① E8735
Harpsichord Works II (pieces in keys of D and
D minor)
PIECES IN D: 1a. Prelude 2; 1b. Allemande 58; 1c.
Courante 59; 1d. Sarabande 60; 1e. Gallarde 61; 1f.
Chaconne 62; 2. Prelude 1 in D minor.
ALLEMANDES IN D MINOR: 3a. Allemande 35; 3b.
Allemande 36. COURANTES IN D MINOR: 4a.
Courante 38; 4b. Courante 39; 4c. Courante 40; 4d.
Courante 41; 4e. Courante 42; 4f. Courante 43.
SARABANDES IN D MINOR: 5a. Sarabande 44; 5b.
Sarabande 45; 5c. Sarabande 46; 5d. Sarabande en
canon 47; 5e. Sarabande 49; 5f. Sarabande 49; 5g.
Sarabande 50; 5h. Sarabande 51; 5i. Sarabande 56.
CHACONES IN D MINOR: 6a. Chaconne 55; 6b.
Chaconne 57, 'La Complaignatie'. OTHER PIECES
IN D MINOR: 7a. Gigue 122; 7b. Gavotte 124; 7c.
Canaries 52; 7d. Piéces de trois sortes de
mouvements 37; 7e. La Pastourelles 54; 7f. Volte 53.
Cpte D. Moroney (r1983) Concert
                (4/90) (HARM) ① [4] HMA190 1124/7
1a-f L. Cummings (r1993) Concert
                (3/95) (NAXO) ① 8 550922
1a, 1b, 1c, 1d, 1e, 1f, 7d, 4b, 4d, 5a, 5e, 7b B. Verlet
(r1992) Concert   (4/93) (ASTR) ① E8733
2, 3b, 7a, 4c, 5d, 4e, 6a B. Verlet (r1989) Concert
                (7/91) (ASTR) ① E8732
5b, 7c, 4f, 7e, 3a, 4a, 5c, 7f B. Verlet (r1991)
Concert   (4/93) (ASTR) ① E8735
5f, 5h, 5i B. Verlet (r1991) Concert
                (4/93) (ASTR) ① E8734
6a R. Aldwinckle Concert
                (7/87) (CARL) ① PCD850
6a I. Isoir (trans org) Concert
                (6/90) (CALL) ① CAL9907
Harpsichord Works III (pieces in keys of E and
F)
PIECES IN E MINOR: 1a. Prelude 14; 1b. Prelude
13; 1c. Courante 64; 1d. Sarabande 65. PRELUDES
IN F: 2a. Prelude 12; 2b. Prelude 13. ALLEMANDES
IN F: 3a. Allemande 66; 3b. Allemande grave 67.
COURANTES IN F: 4a. Courante 68; 4b. Courante
69; 4c. Courante 70; 4d. Courante 71.
SARABANDES IN F: 5a. Sarabande 72; 5b.

Sarabande 74; 5c. Sarabande 75. GIGUES IN F: 6a.
Gigue 76; 6b. Gigue 79. CHACONNES IN F: 7a.
Chaconne 78; 7b. Chaconne 80. OTHER PIECES IN
F: 8a. Bransle de Basque 73; 9. Pavanne 120 in F
sharp minor; 10. Tombeau de M. de Blancrocher; 11.
Galliarde.

Cpte D. Moroney (r1983) *Concert*
　　　　　　　(4/90) (HARM) ① **[4] HMA190 1124/7**
1a, 1b, 1c, 1d B. Verlet (r1991) *Concert*
　　　　　　　(4/93) (ASTR) ① **E8735**
1a, 3a, 4d, 5b, 6b, 7b B. Verlet (r1986) *Concert*
　　　　　　　(7/91) (ASTR) ① **E8731**
1c, 5a B. Verlet (r1991) *Concert*
　　　　　　　(4/93) (ASTR) ① **E8734**
2b, 3b, 4c, 4a, 8a, 6a, 7a, 5c, 9. B. Verlet (r1989)
Concert (7/91) (ASTR) ① **E8732**
2(pt), 3b, 4(pt), 5(pt), 6(pt), 7(pt), 8a, 10, 11. L.
Cummings (r1993) *Concert*
　　　　　　　(3/95) (NAXO) ① **8 550922**
8a A. Isoir (trans org) *Concert*
　　　　　　　(6/90) (CALL) ① **CAL9907**
Harpsichord Works IV (pieces in keys of G
and G minor)
PIECES IN G: 1a. Prelude 129; 1b. Sarabande 87;
1c. Galliarde 88; 1d. Chaconne 89. ALLEMANDES IN
G: 2a. Allemande 82; 2b. Allemande 83.
COURANTES IN G: 3a. Courante 84; 3b. Courante
85; 3c. Courante 86; 3d. Courante 90; 3e. Courante
91; 3f. Courante 92. PRELUDES IN G MINOR: 4a.
Prelude 3; 4b. Prelude 4; 4c. Prelude 5.
SARABANDES IN G MINOR: 5a. Sarabande 95; 5b.
Sarabande 97. OTHER PIECES IN G MINOR: 6a.
Allemande 93; 6b. Courante 94; 6c. Chaconne ou
Passacaille 96; 6d. Chaconne 121; 6e. Passacaglia
98.

Cpte D. Moroney (r1983) *Concert*
　　　　　　　(4/90) (HARM) ① **[4] HMA190 1124/7**
1a, 2a, 3b, 3e, 1b, 1c, 1d B. Verlet (r1991) *Concert*
　　　　　　　(4/93) (ASTR) ① **E8734**
3d, 3e, 3c B. Verlet (r1992) *Concert*
　　　　　　　(4/93) (ASTR) ① **E8733**
4b, 6a, 6b, 5a, 6e B. Verlet (r1986) *Concert*
　　　　　　　(7/91) (ASTR) ① **E8731**
5b, 6d, 4c B. Verlet (r1989) *Concert*
　　　　　　　(7/91) (ASTR) ① **E8732**
6d A. Isoir (trans org) *Concert*
　　　　　　　(6/90) (CALL) ① **CAL9907**
Harpsichord Works V (pieces in keys of A and
B)
PIECES IN A: 1a. Prelude 8; 1b. Courante 112; 1c.
Courante 113; 1d. Gigue 114. PRELUDES IN A
MINOR: 2a. Prélude 6 à l'imitation de M. Froberger;
2b. Prelude 7. ALLEMANDES IN A MINOR: 3a.
Allemande 99; 3b. Allemande 100; 3c. Allemande 101,
'L'Amiable'; 3d. Allemande 132. COURANTES IN A
MINOR: 4a. Courante 103; 4b. Courante 104; 4c.
Courante 105, 'La Mignonne'; 4d. Courante 106; 4e.
Courante 133; 4f. Autre Courante 134.
SARABANDES IN A MINOR: 5a. Sarabande 107; 5b.
Sarabande 108; 5c. Sarabande 109; 5d. Sarabande
110. OTHER PIECES IN A MINOR: 6a. Menuet de
Poitou et Double 111; 6b. Gavotte et Double 125; 6c.
La Piémontoise 102. PIECES IN B MINOR: 7a.
Allemande 115; 7b. Courante 116; 7c. Sarabande
117. PIECES IN B FLAT: 8a. Allemande 118; 9.
Courante 119.

Cpte D. Moroney (r1983) *Concert*
　　　　　　　(4/90) (HARM) ① **[4] HMA190 1124/7**
1a-d, 8a B. Verlet (r1989) *Concert*
　　　　　　　(7/91) (ASTR) ① **E8732**
2a, 3c, 4c, 5a, 6c, 6a B. Verlet (r1986) *Concert*
　　　　　　　(7/91) (ASTR) ① **E8731**
2a, 3c, 4c, 5(pt), 6a, 6c L. Cummings (r1993)
Concert (3/95) (NAXO) ① **8 550922**
2b, 3a, 3b, 4a, 4b, 5a, 5b, 6b B. Verlet (r1991)
Concert (4/93) (ASTR) ① **E8735**
3b, 4e, 4f, 5d, 7a, 7b, 7c B. Verlet (r1992) *Concert*
　　　　　　　(4/93) (ASTR) ① **E8733**
6c R. Aldwinckle *Concert*
　　　　　　　(7/87) (CARL) ① **PCD850**

COWARD, Sir Noel (Pierce)
(1899–1973) England

SECTION IV: VOCAL AND CHORAL

World Weary—song (Wds. cpsr)
Sarah Walker, R. Vignoles (pp1982) *Concert*
　　　　　　　(3/89) (MERI) ① **CDE84167**

SECTION V: STAGE WORKS

Bitter Sweet—operetta: 3 acts
(1929—London) (Lib. cpsr)
EXCERPTS: ACT ONE: 1. Opening—That
Wonderful Melody; 2. The Call of Life; 3. If You Could
Only Come With Me; 4. I'll See You Again; 5. Polka;

---

6. What is Love?; 7. The Last Dance; 8. Finale. ACT
TWO: 9. Opening Chorus: Life In the Morning; 10.
Ladies of the Town; 11. If Love Were All; 12. Dear
Little Café; 13. Bitter Sweet Waltz; 14. Officers'
Chorus: We Wish to Order Wine; 15. Tokey; 16.
Bonne nuit, merci; 17. Kiss Me. ACT THREE: 18. Ra-
Ra-Ra-Boom-De-Ay; 19. Alas! The Time is Past; 20.
We All Wear a Green Carnation; 21. Zigeuner; 22.
Finale.

Cpte V. Masterson, M. Smith, R. Ashe, D. Maxwell,
New Sadlers Wells Op Chor, New Sadlers Wells Op
Orch, M. Reed (r1988)
　　　　　　　(11/89) (TER) ① **[2] CDTER2 1160**
Conversation Piece—musical show
(1934—London) (Book & Lyrics cpsr)
EXCERPTS: 1. Brighton Parade; 2. Danser, Danser;
3. I'll Follow My Secret Heart; 4. There's Always
Something; 5. Regency Rakes; 6. Nevermore; 7.
Dear Little Soldiers; 8. The English Lesson; 9. Lady
Julia's Theme; 10. Melanie's Aria; 11. Charming,
Charming.

3. M. Hill Smith, Philh, J.O. Edwards (r1989-91)
Concert (10/91) (TER) ① **CDVIR8314**
Sail Away—musical show (1961—New York)
(Book & Lyrics cpsr)
EXCERPTS: 1. Come to Me; 2. Sail Away; 3. Where
Shall I Find Him?; 4. Beatnik Love Affair; 5. Later
Than Spring; 6. The Passenger's Always Right; 7.
Useful Phrases; 8. You're a Long, Long Way from
America; 9. The Customer's Always Right; 10.
Something Very Strange; 11. Go Slow, Johnny; 12.
The Little Ones' ABC; 13. Don't Turn Away from
Love; 14. When You Want Me; 15. Why Do the
Wrong People Travel?.

Cpte E. Strich, Orig Broadway Cast, P. Matz (r1961)
　　　　　　　(11/93) (EMI) ① **ZDM7 64759-2**

COWELL, Henry (Dixon)
(1897–1965) USA

SECTION I: ORCHESTRAL

Air and Scherzo—alto saxophone and
orchestra (1963)
Manhattan CO, R.A. Clark (r1994) *Concert*
　　　　　　　(7/95) (KOCH) ① **37282-2**
Concerto Grosso—flute, oboe, clarinet,
cello, harp & strings (1963)
Manhattan CO, R.A. Clark (r1994) *Concert*
　　　　　　　(7/95) (KOCH) ① **37282-2**
Fanfare to the Forces of the Latin American
Allies—brass ensemble (1942)
LPO, J. Mester *Concert* (7/95) (KOCH) ① **37012-2**
LSO Brass Ens, E. Crees *Concert*
　　　　　　　(1/92) (COLL) ① **Coll1288-2**
Fiddler's Jig—violin and orchestra (1952)
Manhattan CO, R.A. Clark (r1994) *Concert*
　　　　　　　(7/95) (KOCH) ① **37282-2**
Hymn and Fuguing tune No. 10—oboe and
strings (1955)
C. Nicklin, ASMF, N. Marriner *Concert*
　　　　　　　(11/87) (ARGO) ① **417 818-2ZH**
Manhattan CO, R.A. Clark (r1994) *Concert*
　　　　　　　(7/95) (KOCH) ① **37282-2**

SECTION II: CHAMBER

Cleistogamy—violin and cello (1941-63)
K. Goldsmith, T. King *Concert*
　　　　　　　(11/91) (MUSI) ① **MACD-635**
4 Combinations—piano trio (1924)
Mirecourt Trio *Concert*
　　　　　　　(11/91) (MUSI) ① **MACD-635**
Grinnell Fanfare—brass and organ (1948)
London Gabrieli Brass Ens, C. Larkin *Concert*
　　　　　　　(5/92) (HYPE) ① **CDA66517**
Hymn and Fuguing Tune No. 12—three
horns (1958)
London Gabrieli Brass Ens, C. Larkin *Concert*
　　　　　　　(5/92) (HYPE) ① **CDA66517**
Pulse for 5 percussion players (1939)
Kroumata Perc Ens (pp1983) *Concert*
　　　　　　　(1/84) (BIS) ① **BIS-CD232**
Quartet Euphometric (1916-19)
Kronos Qt (r1992) *Concert*
　　　　　　　(8/93) (NONE) ① **7559-79310-2**
Rondo for Brass—3 trumpets, 2 horns & 2 2
trombones (1958)
London Gabrieli Brass Ens, C. Larkin *Concert*
　　　　　　　(5/92) (HYPE) ① **CDA66517**
Tall Tale—brass sextet (1947)
London Gabrieli Brass Ens, C. Larkin *Concert*
　　　　　　　(5/92) (HYPE) ① **CDA66517**
Trio—four combinations of three
instruments (1924)
Hartley Trio *Concert* (6/94) (GAMU) ① **GAMCD536**

SECTION III: INSTRUMENTAL

2 Woofs—piano (1928)
A. Feinberg (r1994) *Concert*
　　　　　　　(11/95) (ARGO) ① **444 457-2ZH**

COWEN, Sir Frederic (1852–1935)
England

SECTION I: ORCHESTRAL

The Butterfly's Ball—concert overture
(1901)
Košice St PO, A. Leaper *Concert*
　　　　　　　(2/91) (MARC) ① **8 223273**
Indian Rhapsody—orchestra (1903)
Košice St PO, A. Leaper *Concert*
　　　　　　　(2/91) (MARC) ① **8 223273**
Symphony No. 3 in C minor, 'Scandinavian'
(1880)
Košice St PO, A. Leaper *Concert*
　　　　　　　(2/91) (MARC) ① **8 223273**

SECTION IV: VOCAL AND CHORAL

The Swallows—song
L. Tetrazzini, orch (r1912) *Concert*
　　　　　　　(9/92) (PEAR) ① **GEMMCD9224**

CRAMER, Johann Baptist
(1771–1858) Germany/England

SECTION III: INSTRUMENTAL

Piano Studies (Studio per il pianoforte)
(1804)
1. C; 16. F minor; 19. D; 21. G; 29. C; 30. B flat
minor.
1, 16, 19, 21, 29, 30. I. Hobson *Concert*
　　　　　　　(3/89) (ARAB) ① **Z6596**
Sonata for Piano in F minor, Op. 27/1 (1802)
I. Hobson *Concert* (3/89) (ARAB) ① **Z6595**

CRANE, Laurence (b 1961)
England

SECTION IV: VOCAL AND CHORAL

Balanescu—soprano, clarinet & piano (1994)
(adapted cpsr from song cycle 'Weirdi')
Tapestry (r1994) *Concert*
　　　　　　　(12/95) (BRIT) ① **BML012**

CRAWFORD, Ruth (Porter)
(1901–1953) USA

née Seeger

SECTION II: CHAMBER

String Quartet (1931)
Arditti Qt *Concert* (11/90) (GVIS) ① **GV79440-2**

CREAMER, Henry (1879–1930)
USA

composed in collaboration with Turner Layton

SECTION IV: VOCAL AND CHORAL

After you've gone—song
Jeremy Taylor, London Sinfonietta, S. Rattle *Concert*
　　　　　　　(12/87) (EMI) ① **CDC7 47991-2**

CRECQUILLON, Thomas
(c1480–c1557) Franco/Flemish

SECTION IV: VOCAL AND CHORAL

Oncques amour ne fut sans grand
languer—chanson: 5vv (1553)
B. Dickey, Tragicomedia *Concert*
　　　　　　　(6/92) (ACCE) ① **ACC9173D**
Petite fleur coincte et jolye—chanson: 4vv
(1549)
B. Dickey, Tragicomedia *Concert*
　　　　　　　(6/92) (ACCE) ① **ACC9173D**

CREMA, Giovanni Maria da (fl
1540–1550) Italy

SECTION III: INSTRUMENTAL

Entre mes bras—chanson (pub. 1546) (arr
lute)
J. Lindberg *Concert* (10/89) (BIS) ① **BIS-CD399**
Mon amy—chanson (pub. 1546) (arr lute, from
melody by Gascongne)
J. Lindberg (arr lte from tune by Gascongne) *Concert*
　　　　　　　(10/89) (BIS) ① **BIS-CD399**

Recercar decimoquinto—lute (pub. 1546)
J. Lindberg *Concert* (10/89) (BIS) ① **BIS-CD399**
Recercar quinto—lute (pub. 1546)
J. Lindberg *Concert* (10/89) (BIS) ① **BIS-CD399**
Recercar sexto—lute (pub. 1546)
J. Lindberg *Concert* (10/89) (BIS) ① **BIS-CD399**
Saltarello ditto el giorgio—lute (pub. 1546)
J. Lindberg *Concert* (10/89) (BIS) ① **BIS-CD399**
Saltarello ditto la bertoncina—lute (pub. 1546)
J. Lindberg *Concert* (10/89) (BIS) ① **BIS-CD399**

CRESCENZO, Vincenzo di (1875–?) Italy

SECTION IV: VOCAL AND CHORAL

Guardanno 'a luna—song (Wds. G. Camerlingo)
E. Caruso, orch (r1913) *Concert*
(7/91) (RCA) ① [12] **GD60495(4)**
E. Caruso, orch (r1913) *Concert*
(10/91) (PEAR) ① [3] **EVC3(1)**
Première caresse—song (wds. P. Marinier)
E. Caruso, orch, J. Pasternack (r1919) *Concert*
(7/91) (RCA) ① [12] **GD60495(6)**
E. Caruso, orch, J. Pasternack (r1919) *Concert*
(10/91) (PEAR) ① [3] **EVC4(2)**
Quanno a femmena vo'—song
B. Gigli, orch, N. Shilkret (r1925) *Concert*
(9/88) (PEAR) ① **GEMMCD9316**
Rondine al nido—song (Wds. Sica)
L. Pavarotti, MMF Orch, Rome Op Orch, Z. Mehta (pp1990) *Concert* (10/90) (DECC) ① **430 433-2DH**
L. Pavarotti, NYPO, L. Magiera (pp1993) *Concert*
(2/95) (DECC) ① **444 450-2DH**
Tarantella sincera—song (Wds. E. Migliaccio)
E. Caruso, orch, W.B. Rogers (r1912) *Concert*
(12/90) (NIMB) ① **NI7809**
E. Caruso, orch, W.B. Rogers (r1912) *Concert*
(7/91) (RCA) ① [12] **GD60495(4)**
E. Caruso, orch, W.B. Rogers (r1912) *Concert*
(10/91) (PEAR) ① [3] **EVC3(1)**
Uocchie celeste—song (wds. A. Gill)
E. Caruso, orch, J. Pasternack (r1917) *Concert*
(7/91) (RCA) ① [12] **GD60495(6)**
E. Caruso, orch, J. Pasternack (r1917) *Concert*
(10/91) (PEAR) ① [3] **EVC4(1)**

CRESPO, Jorge Gomes (1900–1971) Argentina

SECTION III: INSTRUMENTAL

Norteña
J. Williams *Concert* (8/89) (SONY) ① **SK44898**

CRESSWELL, Lyell (b 1944) New Zealand/Scotland

SECTION I: ORCHESTRAL

Concerto for Cello and Orchestra (1984)
R. Jabłoński, Bratislava RSO, R. Bernas *Modern Ecstasy.* (12/92) (CNTI) ① **CCD1033**
O!—orchestra (1983)
NZ SO, W. Southgate *Concert*
(12/92) (CNTI) ① **CCD1034**
Salm—orchestra (1977)
NZ SO, W. Southgate *Concert*
(12/92) (CNTI) ① **CCD1034**
Speak for us, great sea—orchestra (1985)
NZ SO, W. Southgate *Concert*
(12/92) (CNTI) ① **CCD1034**

SECTION IV: VOCAL AND CHORAL

A Modern Ecstasy—mezzo-soprano, baritone and orchestra (1986) (Wds. cpsr)
P. Boylan, N. Leeson-Williams, Bratislava RSO, R. Bernas *Cello Concerto.*
(12/92) (CNTI) ① **CCD1033**

CRESTON, Paul (1906–1985) USA

SECTION I: ORCHESTRAL

Choreografic Suite—orchestra, Op. 86a (1965)
NY Chbr SO, G. Schwarz (r1991) *Concert*
(10/94) (DELO) ① **DE3127**
Corinthians: XIII—orchestra, Op. 82 (1963)
Louisville Orch, R. Whitney *Concert*
(6/90) (ALBA) ① **TROY021-2**
Cracow PO, D. Amos *Concert*
(4/92) (KOCH) ① **37036-2**

Fanfare for Paratroopers—brass ensemble (1942)
LPO, J. Mester *Concert* (7/91) (KOCH) ① **37012-2**
Fantasy for Trombone and Orchestra, Op. 42 (1947)
C. Lindberg, Malmö SO, J. DePreist (r1993) *Concert*
(9/94) (BIS) ① **BIS-CD628**
Invocation and Dance—orchestra, Op. 58 (1953)
Seattle SO, G. Schwarz *Concert*
(12/92) (DELO) ① **DE3114**
Out of the Cradle—orchestra
Seattle SO, G. Schwarz *Concert*
(12/92) (DELO) ① **DE3114**
Partita—flute, violin and string orchestra, Op. 12 (1937)
S. Goff, I. Talvi, Seattle SO, G. Schwarz *Concert*
(12/92) (DELO) ① **DE3114**
A Rumor—strings (1941)
ASMF, N. Marriner *Concert*
(11/87) (ARGO) ① **417 818-2ZH**
Symphony No. 2, Op. 35 (1944)
Cracow PO, D. Amos *Concert*
(4/92) (KOCH) ① **37036-2**
Detroit SO, N. Järvi (r1995) *Ives: Symphony 2.*
(11/95) (CHAN) ① **CHAN9390**
Symphony No. 3, 'Three Mysteries', Op. 48 (1950)
1. The Nativity; 2. The Crucifixion; 3. The Resurrection.
Seattle SO, G. Schwarz *Concert*
(12/92) (DELO) ① **DE3114**
Symphony No. 5, Op. 64 (1956)
Seattle SO, G. Schwarz (r1992) *Concert*
(10/94) (DELO) ① **DE3127**
Toccata—orchestra, Op. 68 (1957)
Seattle SO, G. Schwarz (r1992) *Concert*
(10/94) (DELO) ① **DE3127**
Walt Whitman—orchestra, Op. 53 (1952)
Cracow PO, D. Amos *Concert*
(4/92) (KOCH) ① **37036-2**

SECTION II: CHAMBER

String Quartet, Op. 8 (1936)
Hollywood Qt (r1953) *Concert*
(3/95) (TEST) ① **SBT1053**

CRISTO, Pedro de (c1550–1618) Portugal

SECTION IV: VOCAL AND CHORAL

Ave Maria—motet: 8vv
Tavener Ch, O. Rees (r1992) *Concert*
(1/94) (HERA) ① **HAVPCD155**
Ave maris stella—hymn
A Capella Portvgvesa, O. Rees (r1994) *Concert*
(11/94) (HYPE) ① **CDA66735**
Ave Regina caelorum—motet: 8vv
Tavener Ch, O. Rees (r1992) *Concert*
(1/94) (HERA) ① **HAVPCD155**
Beate martir—motet
A Capella Portvgvesa, O. Rees (r1994) *Concert*
(11/94) (HYPE) ① **CDA66735**
De profundis—motet
Tavener Ch, O. Rees (r1992) *Concert*
(1/94) (HERA) ① **HAVPCD155**
In manus tuas—compline responsory
A Capella Portvgvesa, O. Rees (r1994) *Concert*
(11/94) (HYPE) ① **CDA66735**
Lachrimans sitivit anima mea—motet
Tavener Ch, O. Rees (r1992) *Concert*
(1/94) (HERA) ① **HAVPCD155**
Magnificat—8vv
Tavener Ch, O. Rees (r1992) *Concert*
(1/94) (HERA) ① **HAVPCD155**
Osanna filio David—antiphon: 5vv
A Capella Portvgvesa, O. Rees (r1994) *Concert*
(11/94) (HYPE) ① **CDA66735**
Salva nos Domine—antiphon
A Capella Portvgvesa, O. Rees (r1994) *Concert*
(11/94) (HYPE) ① **CDA66735**
Sanctissimi quinque martires—motet
Tavener Ch, O. Rees (r1992) *Concert*
(1/94) (HERA) ① **HAVPCD155**
Sanctorum meritis—hymn
A Capella Portvgvesa, O. Rees (r1994) *Concert*
(11/94) (HYPE) ① **CDA66735**

CROFT, William (1678–1727) England

SECTION II: CHAMBER

Twin Rivals—Suite—trumpet, strings and continuo (1701) (written for G. Farquhar's play)
Parley of Instr, R. Goodman, P. Holman (reconstr Parley of Instr) *Concert*
(11/88) (HYPE) ① **CDA66108**

SECTION III: INSTRUMENTAL

Suite No. 3 in C minor—keyboard (Ground also attrib Purcell)
EXCERPTS: 1. Ground in C minor, Z D221; 2. Sarabande.
T. Pinnock *Concert* (11/90) (CRD) ① **CRD3307**
Voluntary in A minor—organ
T. Morris (r1992) *Concert*
(8/95) (CRD) ① **CRD3491**
Voluntary in D—keyboard
J. Bate *Concert* (7/91) (UNIC) ① **DKPCD9105**
R. Woolley (r1993) *Concert*
(9/94) (CHAN) ① **CHAN0553**
T. Morris (r1992) *Concert*
(8/95) (CRD) ① **CRD3491**
Voluntary in G—organ
R. Woolley (r1993) *Concert*
(9/94) (CHAN) ① **CHAN0553**
Voluntary in G minor—organ
R. Woolley (r1993) *Concert*
(9/94) (CHAN) ① **CHAN0553**

SECTION IV: VOCAL AND CHORAL

God is gone up with a merry noise—full anthem
Magdalen Oxford Coll Ch, J. Harper *Concert*
(11/91) (ABBE) ① **CDCA912**
New College Ch, E. Higginbottom, T. Morris (r1992) *Concert* (8/95) (CRD) ① **CRD3491**
Morning Service in D—soloists, choir and orchestra (1709) (thanksgiving for victories)
1. Te Deum; 2. Jubilate.
St Paul's Cath Ch, Parley of Instr, John Scott *Musica sacra.* (4/93) (HYPE) ① **CDA66606**
Musica sacra—anthems and Burial Service (pub 1724)
1. Blessed are all they; 2. Hear my prayer, O Lord (2vv); 3. Hear my prayer, O Lord (8vv); 4. I cryed unto the Lord with my voice; 5. I will alway give thanks (1708); 6. I will sing unto the Lord; 7. Laudate Dominum; 8. Lord, what love have I; 9. O be joyful; 10. O give thanks unto the Lord; 11. O Lord God of my salvation (3vv); 12. O Lord God of my slavation (4/6vv); 13. O Lord, grant the king a long life; 14. O Lord, I will praise Thee; 15. O Lord, rebuke me not; 16. O Lord, Thou has searched me out; 17. O praise the Lord, ye that fear Him (1709); 18. Out of the deep; 19. Praise the Lord, o my soul; 20. Rejoice in the Lord (1706); 21. Sing praises unto the Lord; 22. Sing unto God, O ye kingdoms; 23. Sing unto the Lord and praise His name (1708); 24. The earth is the Lord's; 25. The heavens declare the Glory of God; 26. The Lord is King; 27. The Lord is my strength (1711); 28. This is the day which the Lord hath made (1713); 29. Thou, O God, art praised in Sion (1723); 30. We wait for Thy loving kindness; 31. We will rejoice in Thy salvation; 32. Burial Service (incorporating Purcell's 'Thou knowest, Lord').
2, 6, 11, 14, 15, 30, 31. New College Ch, E. Higginbottom, T. Morris (r1992) *Concert*
(8/95) (CRD) ① **CRD3491**
20, 32. St Paul's Cath Ch, Parley of Instr, John Scott *Morning Service in D.* (4/93) (HYPE) ① **CDA66606**
O God, our help—hymn (Wds. I. Watts)
Chor, LSO, E. Elgar (r1928) *Concert*
(2/93) (EMI) ① [3] **CDS7 54564-2**
O worship the King—hymn tune (Hanover) (Wds. R. Grant)
St Paul's Cath Ch, C. Dearnley, John Scott *Concert*
(7/90) (HYPE) ① **CDH88036**

CROSSE, Gordon (b 1937) England

SECTION III: INSTRUMENTAL

5 Caprices on 'BREAM'—guitar (1970)
A. Gifford (r1990) *Concert*
(12/92) (NATI) ① **NTCD001**

CROTCH, William (1775–1847) England

SECTION I: ORCHESTRAL

Concerto for Organ and Orchestra No. 2 in A (c1805)
A. Lumsden, Milton Keynes CO, H.D. Wetton *Concert*
(1/93) (UNIC) ① **DKPCD9126**
Overture in G (1815)
Milton Keynes CO, H.D. Wetton *Concert*
(1/93) (UNIC) ① **DKPCD9126**
Sinfonia in E flat (1808 rev 1817) (unfinished)
Milton Keynes CO, H.D. Wetton *Concert*
(1/93) (UNIC) ① **DKPCD9126**
Sinfonia in F (1814)
Milton Keynes CO, H.D. Wetton *Concert*
(1/93) (UNIC) ① **DKPCD9126**

SECTION IV: VOCAL AND CHORAL

How dear are Thy counsels—anthem (1796)
Oxford Christ Church Cath Ch, S. Darlington *Concert*
(10/92) (NIMB) ① **NI5328**

CROUCH, Frederick Nicholls (1808–1896) England/USA

SECTION IV: VOCAL AND CHORAL

Kathleen Mavourneen—song (pub. 1836)
(Wds. J. M. Crawford)
A. Patti, A. Barili (r1906) *Concert*
(4/90) (PEAR) ① **GEMMCD9312**
J. McCormack, E. Schneider (r1927) *Concert*
(5/93) (MMOI) ① **CDMOIR418**

CRÜGER, Johannes (1598–1662) Germany

SECTION IV: VOCAL AND CHORAL

Nun danket alle Gott (Now thank we all our God)—hymn
St Paul's Cath Ch, C. Dearnley, English Brass Ens, John Scott (Eng) *Concert*
(7/90) (HYPE) ① **CDH88036**
Glasgow CWS Band, H. Snell (arr Snell) *Concert*
(9/92) (DOYE) ① **DOYCD005**

CRUMB, George (Henry) (b 1929) USA

SECTION I: ORCHESTRAL

A Haunted Landscape—orchestra (1984)
P. Myers, NYPO, A. Weisberg *Schuman: Colloquies.*
(2/88) (NEW) ① **NW326-2**

SECTION II: CHAMBER

Black Angels: 13 Images from the Dark Lands (Images I)—electric string quartet (1970)
Kronos Qt *Concert* (4/91) (NONE) ① **7559-79242-2**
Brodsky Qt (r1992) *Schubert: String Quartet, D810.*
(9/93) (TELD) ⑨ **9031-76260-2**
Cikada Qt (r1994) *Concert*
(12/95) (CALA) ① **CACD77001**
An Idyll for the Misbegotten—flute and percussion (1985)
Z. Mueller, G. Gottlieb, B. Herman, S. Paysen *Concert* (9/88) (NEW) ① **NW357-2**
Vox balaenae—amplified flute, cello and piano (1971)
1. Vocalise: Variations on Sea-Time; 2. Sea Theme; 3. Archeozoic; 4. Proterozoic; 5. Paleozoic; 6. Mesozoic; 7. Cenozoic; 8. Sea Nocturne.
Z. Mueller, F. Sherry, J. Gemmell *Concert*
(9/88) (NEW) ① **NW357-2**

SECTION III: INSTRUMENTAL

Gnomic Variations—piano (1981)
J. Jacob *Concert* (4/91) (CENT) ① **CRC2050**
Little Suite for Christmas, AD1979—piano
L. Orkis *Wernick: Piano Sonata (1982).*
(3/87) (BRID) ① **BCD9003**
Makrokosmos I—12 fanatasy-pieces after the Zodiac:amp pf (1972)
J. Jacob *Concert* (4/91) (CENT) ① **CRC2050**
5 Pieces—piano (1962)
J. Jacob *Concert* (4/91) (CENT) ① **CRC2050**
Sonata—cello (1955)
M. Haimovitz *Concert* (1/92) (DG) ① **431 813-2GH**
P. Wispelwey (r1992) *Concert*
(12/94) (GLOB) ① **GLO5089**

SECTION IV: VOCAL AND CHORAL

Madrigals—4 Books (1968-69)
Musica Varia, B. Dahlman, I. Lindgren, S. Asikainen, R. Kuisma *Music for a Summer Evening.*
(10/87) (BIS) ① **BIS-CD261**
J. de Gaetani, Pennsylvania Univ Chbr Players, R. Wernick *Concert* (9/88) (NEW) ① **NW357-2**
Music for a Summer Evening—Makrokosmos III (1974)
Musica Varia, B. Dahlman, I. Lindgren, S. Asikainen, R. Kuisma *Madrigals.* (10/87) (BIS) ① **BIS-CD261**

CRUSELL, Bernhard Henrik (1775–1838) Finland/Sweden

SECTION I: ORCHESTRAL

Concerto for Clarinet and Orchestra No. 1 in E flat, Op. 1 (1803)
K. Leister, Lahti SO, O. Vänskä *Concert*
(9/87) (BIS) ① **BIS-CD345**
E. Johnson, RPO, G. Herbig *Concert*
(9/91) (ASV) ① **CDDCA763**
A. Pay (cl/dir), OAE (r1990) *Concert*
(12/93) (VIRG) ① **VC7 59287-2**
Concerto for Clarinet and Orchestra No. 2 in F minor, Op. 5 (1808)
T. King, LSO, A. Francis *Weber: Clarinet Concerto 2.*
(8/85) (HYPE) ① **CDA66088**
E. Johnson, ECO, C. Groves *Concert*
(11/86) (ASV) ① **CDDCA559**
K. Leister, Lahti SO, O. Vänskä *Concert*
(9/87) (BIS) ① **BIS-CD345**
A. Pay (cl/dir), OAE (r1990) *Concert*
(12/93) (VIRG) ① **VC7 59287-2**
Concerto for Clarinet and Orchestra No. 3 in B flat, Op. 11 (1812)
K. Leister, Lahti SO, O. Vänskä *Concert*
(9/87) (BIS) ① **BIS-CD345**
E. Johnson, ECO, G. Schwarz *Concert*
(11/89) (ASV) ① **CDDCA659**
A. Pay (cl/dir), OAE (r1990) *Concert*
(12/93) (VIRG) ① **VC7 59287-2**
Introduction, Theme and Variations on a Swedish Air—clarinet and orchestra, Op. 12 (1804)
E. Johnson, ECO, Y.P. Tortelier *Concert*
(9/87) (ASV) ① **CDDCA585**
T. King, LSO, A. Francis *Concert*
(1/88) (HYPE) ① **CDA66022**

SECTION II: CHAMBER

Clarinet Quartet No. 1 in E flat, Op. 2 (c1803)
T. King, Allegri Qt *Concert*
(6/89) (HYPE) ① **CDA66077**
K. Kriikku, Avanti Qt *Concert*
(12/89) (ONDI) ① **ODE727-2**
Clarinet Quartet No. 2 in C minor, Op.4 (c1804)
T. King, Allegri Qt *Concert*
(6/89) (HYPE) ① **CDA66077**
K. Kriikku, Avanti Qt *Concert*
(12/89) (ONDI) ① **ODE727-2**
Clarinet Quartet No. 3 in D, Op. 7 (c1820)
T. King, Allegri Qt *Concert*
(6/89) (HYPE) ① **CDA66077**
K. Kriikku, Avanti Qt *Concert*
(12/89) (ONDI) ① **ODE727-2**
Quintet for Clarinet and Strings, Op. 4
K. Leister, Pražák Qt *Mozart: Clarinet Quintet, K581.*
(7/87) (ORFE) ① **C141861A**

CRUZ, Zulema de la (b 1954) Spain

SECTION III: INSTRUMENTAL

Quasar—piano (1974)
S. Marin *Concert* (4/93) (RNE) ① **M3/03**

CRUZ DE CASTRO, Carlos (b 1941) Spain

SECTION I: ORCHESTRAL

Concerto for Guitar and String Orchestra (1991)
W. Weigel, European Master Orch, P. Schmelzer (r1992) *Concert* (5/95) (SCHW) ① **312362**

CUI, César (1835–1918) Russia

SECTION I: ORCHESTRAL

Suite concertante—violin and orchestra, Op. 25 (1884)
T. Nishizaki, Hong Kong PO, K. Schermerhorn *Concert* (10/86) (MARC) ① **8 220308**
Suite Miniature No. 1, Op. 20 (1882)
Hong Kong PO, K. Schermerhorn *Concert*
(10/86) (MARC) ① **8 220308**
Berceuse C. Hansen, B. Zakharoff (arr vn,pf; r1924) *Concert* (12/91) (APR) ① [2] **APR7015**
Suite No. 3, 'in modo populari', Op. 43 (1890)
Hong Kong PO, K. Schermerhorn *Concert*
(10/86) (MARC) ① **8 220308**

SECTION II: CHAMBER

Kaleidoscope—24 pieces: violin and piano, Op. 50 (1893)
9. Orientale.
P. Sheppard, A. Shorr (r1994) *Violin Sonata in D.*
(12/95) (OLYM) ① **OCD456**
9. E. Feuermann, G. Moore (arr vc/pf; r1939) *Concert* (10/91) (PEAR) ① **GEMMCD9443**
9. Midori, R. McDonald (r1992) *Concert*
(9/93) (SONY) ① **SK52568**
9. T. Seidel, orch (r c1924) *Concert*
(7/93) (APR) ① [2] **APR7016**
9. E. Zimbalist, S. Chotzinoff (r1911) *Concert*
(7/93) (APR) ① [2] **APR7016**
Sonata for Violin and Piano in D, Op. 86 (1879)
P. Sheppard, A. Shorr (r1995) *Kaleidoscope.*
(12/95) (OLYM) ① **OCD456**

SECTION III: INSTRUMENTAL

25 Preludes—piano, Op. 64 (1903)
2, 8-10. M. Fingerhut *Concert*
(6/87) (CHAN) ① **CHAN8439**

SECTION IV: VOCAL AND CHORAL

Aeolian harps—song
N. Shevelev, anon (r1901) *Concert*
(6/93) (PEAR) ① [3] **GEMMCDS9007/9(2)**
Bolero, 'O my dear, charming one'—song
A. Nezhdanova, anon (r1907) *Concert*
(6/93) (PEAR) ① [3] **GEMMCDS9007/9(1)**
I remember the evening—song
N. Figner, anon (r1901) *Concert*
(6/93) (PEAR) ① [3] **GEMMCDS9997/9(1)**
O. Borodina, L. Gergieva (1994) *Concert*
(8/95) (PHIL) ① **442 780-2PH**
It's over—1v & piano (Wds. Pushkin)
O. Borodina, L. Gergieva (1994) *Concert*
(8/95) (PHIL) ① **442 780-2PH**
Oh, if Mother Volga—song
L. Sibiriakov, anon (r1910) *Concert*
(6/93) (PEAR) ① [3] **GEMMCDS9007/9(2)**
7 Songs—1v & piano, Op. 49 (1889-92)
1. I touched the bloom lightly (Wds. Nemirovich-Danchenko).
1. O. Borodina, L. Gergieva (1994) *Concert*
(8/95) (PHIL) ① **442 780-2PH**
5 Songs (c1890)
5. Ici-bas (wds. Sully-Prudhomme).
5. O. Borodina, L. Gergieva (1994) *Concert*
(8/95) (PHIL) ① **442 780-2PH**
25 Songs, Op. 57 (1899) (Wds. Pushkin)
11. Your wish and 'Thou'; 17. The statue of Tsarskoïe Selo; 25. Desire.
11, 17, 25. O. Borodina, L. Gergieva (1994) *Concert*
(8/95) (PHIL) ① **442 780-2PH**
17. N. Ghiaurov, P. Dokovska (r1993) *Concert*
(1/95) (RCA) ① **09026 62501-2**
17. P. Frijsh, D. Bucktrout (r1932) *Concert*
(4/95) (PEAR) ① [2] **GEMMCDS9095(2)**

SECTION V: STAGE WORKS

Angelo—opera: 4 acts (1876—St Petersburg)
(Libr. V Burenin, after V Hugo)
I live only for you L. Sobinov, anon (r1901) *Concert*
(6/93) (PEAR) ① [3] **GEMMCDS9997/9(1)**
A feast in time of plague—opera: 1 act (1900—Moscow) (Libr. Pushkin)
When powerful winter N. Shevelev, anon (r1901) *Concert*
(6/93) (PEAR) ① [3] **GEMMCDS9007/9(2)**
A Prisoner in the Caucasus—opera: 3 acts (1883—St Petersburg) (Lib. V. Krilov, after Pushkin)
Aria N. Shevelev, anon (r1901) *Concert*
(6/93) (PEAR) ① [3] **GEMMCDS9007/9(2)**

CURNOW, James E. (20th Cent) England

SECTION I: ORCHESTRAL

Legend in Brass—brass band
Sellers Engin Band, P. McCann (r1993) Concert
(11/95) (CHAN) ① CHAN4531
Rhapsody—euphonium and brass band
N. Childs, Britannia Building Soc Band, H. Snell
Concert (2/91) (DOYE) ① DOYCD002

CURZON, (Ernest) Frederic (1899–1973) England

SECTION I: ORCHESTRAL

The Boulevardier—characteristic intermezzo (1941)
Bratislava RSO, A. Leaper (r1991) Concert
(6/93) (MARC) ① 8 223425
Bravada—paso doble (1938)
Bratislava RSO, A. Leaper (r1991) Concert
(6/93) (MARC) ① 8 223425
Capricante—Spanish caprice (1949)
Bratislava RSO, A. Leaper (r1991) Concert
(6/93) (MARC) ① 8 223425
Cascade—waltz (1946)
Bratislava RSO, A. Leaper (r1991) Concert
(6/93) (MARC) ① 8 223425
Dance of an Ostracised Imp (1940)
Bratislava RSO, A. Leaper (r1991) Concert
(6/93) (MARC) ① 8 223425
Galavant (1949-50)
Bratislava RSO, A. Leaper (r1991) Concert
(6/93) (MARC) ① 8 223425
In Malaga—Spanish suite (pub 1935)
1. Spanish Ladies (Tango); 2. Serenade to Eulalie; 3.
Cachucha.
Bratislava RSO, A. Leaper (r1991) Concert
(6/93) (MARC) ① 8 223425
Pasquinade (1943)
Bratislava RSO, A. Leaper (r1991) Concert
(6/93) (MARC) ① 8 223425
La Peinata—orchestra
Bratislava RSO, A. Leaper (r1991) Concert
(6/93) (MARC) ① 8 223425
Punchinello—overture (1948)
Bratislava RSO, A. Leaper (r1991) Concert
(6/93) (MARC) ① 8 223425
Robin Hood—suite (1937)
1. In Sherwood; 2. Maid Marian; 3. March of the
Bowmen.
Bratislava RSO, A. Leaper (r1991) Concert
(6/93) (MARC) ① 8 223425
Saltarello—piano and orchestra (1951)
S. Cápová, Bratislava RSO, A. Leaper (r1991)
Concert (6/93) (MARC) ① 8 223425
Simonetta—serenade (1933)
Bratislava RSO, A. Leaper (r1991) Concert
(6/93) (MARC) ① 8 223425

CUTTING, Francis (fl 1583–c1603) England

SECTION III: INSTRUMENTAL

Almain—lute
C. Wilson Concert (11/91) (VIRG) ① VC7 59034-2
J. Bream (r1960) Concert
(8/93) (RCA) ① [28] 09026 61583-2(1)
J. Bream (r1960) Concert
(8/93) (RCA) ① 09026 61584-2
Galliard—lute
C. Wilson Concert (11/91) (VIRG) ① VC7 59034-2
Packington's Pound—lute
J. Bream (r1972) Concert
(8/93) (RCA) ① [28] 09026 61583-2(2)
J. Bream (r1972) Concert
(6/94) (RCA) ① 09026 61587-2
Variations on 'Greensleeves'—lute
J. Bream (r1972) Concert
(8/93) (RCA) ① [28] 09026 61583-2(2)
J. Bream (r1960) Concert
(8/93) (RCA) ① [28] 09026 61583-2(1)
J. Bream (r1972) Concert
(8/93) (RCA) ① 09026 61584-2
J. Bream (r1960) Concert
(6/94) (RCA) ① 09026 61587-2
Variations on 'Walsingham'—lute
J. Bream (r1960) Concert
(8/93) (RCA) ① [28] 09026 61583-2(1)
J. Bream (r1960) Concert
(8/93) (RCA) ① 09026 61584-2

CUVELIER, Johannes (fl 1372–1387) France

SECTION IV: VOCAL AND CHORAL

Se Galaas et le puissant Artus—ballade: 3vv
(in honour of Gaston Febus)
Organum Ens, M. Pérès Concert
(11/87) (HARM) ① HMC90 1252
Huelgas Ens, P. van Nevel Concert
(2/93) (SONY) ① SK48195

CUVILLIER, Charles (19th–20th Cent) Belgium

SECTION V: STAGE WORKS

The Lilac Domino—operetta (1914—New York) (English lyrics Harry B Smith)
EXCERPTS: 1. The Lilac Domino.
1. E. Painter, Orig Broadway Cast (r1915) Concert
(5/94) (PEAR) ① [3] GEMMCDS9056/8

CZERNY, Carl (1791–1857) Austria

SECTION II: CHAMBER

Andante and Polacca—horn and piano (1848)
B. Tuckwell, D. Blumenthal Schubert Fantasies, Op.
339. (9/92) (ETCE) ① KTC1121
3 Brilliant Fantasies on favourite themes from Schubert's works—horn and piano, Op. 339 (c1836)
B. Tuckwell, D. Blumenthal Andante and Polacca.
(9/92) (ETCE) ① KTC1121
Variations on 'Gott erhalte Franz den Kaiser—piano and string quartet, Op. 73
Maureen Jones, Zurich Chmbr Ens Hänsel: String
Quintet in G. (8/87) (JECK) ① JD608-2

SECTION III: INSTRUMENTAL

Fantaisie brillante sur divers motifs de Figaro—piano, Op. 493
C. Katsaris (r1992) Concert
(6/93) (SONY) ① SK52551
5 Variations on a theme of Rode—piano, Op.33
R. Burnett Concert (5/88) (AMON) ① CD-SAR7
V. Horowitz (r1944) Concert
(11/91) (RCA) ① GD60451

CZIBULKA, Alphons (1842–1894) Hungary

SECTION III: INSTRUMENTAL

Stephanie-Gavotte—piano, Op. 312
A. Etherden Concert
(7/93) (HUNT) ① HMPCD0589

DADMUN, John William (1819–1890) USA

SECTION IV: VOCAL AND CHORAL

The Babe of Bethlehem—song (1866)
Harmoneion Sngrs, N. Bruce, L. Skrobacs (r1977)
Concert (2/94) (NEW) ① 80220-2

DAHL, Adrian (1864–1935) Sweden

SECTION IV: VOCAL AND CHORAL

Bacchanal (Jag vill leva, jag vill älska)—song (Wds. F. Nycander)
J. Björling, orch, N. Grevillius (r1933) Concert
(8/92) (BLUE) ① ABCD016

DAHL, Ingolf (1912–1970) Switzerland/USA

SECTION I: ORCHESTRAL

Concerto for Alto Saxophone and Orchestra (1949 rev 1953)
J. Harle, New World Sym, M. Tilson Thomas (r1994)
Concert (9/95) (ARGO) ① 444 459-2ZH
The Tower of St Barbara—symphonic legend (1953-54 rev 1960) (planned as ballet: never choreographed)
1. Barbara; 2. The King; 3. The Tower; 4. The
Martyrdom.

New World Sym, M. Tilson Thomas (r1994) Concert
(9/95) (ARGO) ① 444 459-2ZH

SECTION II: CHAMBER

Music for Brass Instruments (1944)
1. Choral Fantasy, 'Christ lay in the Bonds of Death';
2. Intermezzo; 3. Fugue.
New World Brass (r1994) Concert
(9/95) (ARGO) ① 444 459-2ZH

SECTION III: INSTRUMENTAL

Hymn—piano (1947)
New World Sym, M. Tilson Thomas (r1994: orch L
Morton) Concert (9/95) (ARGO) ① 444 459-2ZH

DALE, Benjamin (James) (1885–1943) England

SECTION III: INSTRUMENTAL

Night Fancies—piano (1907)
Peter Jacobs Concert (5/93) (CNTI) ① CCD1044
Prunella—piano (1916)
Peter Jacobs Concert (5/93) (CNTI) ① CCD1044
Sonata for Piano in D minor (1902)
Peter Jacobs Concert (5/93) (CNTI) ① CCD1044

DALLA, Luciano (20th Cent) Italy

SECTION IV: VOCAL AND CHORAL

Caruso—song
L. Pavarotti, orch Concert
(7/90) (DECC) ① [2] 425 681-2DM2

DALLA CASA, Girolamo (1543–c1601) Italy

SECTION IV: VOCAL AND CHORAL

Vero modo di diminuir, libro I et II (1584) (treatise on ornamentation)
1. Petite fleur (Crecquillon).
1. B. Dickey, Tragicomedia Concert
(6/92) (ACCE) ① ACC9173D

DALLAPICCOLA, Luigi (1904–1975) Italy

SECTION I: ORCHESTRAL

Piccolo Concerto per Muriel Couvreux—piano and chamber orchestra (1939-41)
B. Canino, Dallapiccola Ens, L. Suvini (r1991)
Concert (3/94) (NUOV) ① 7109
Tartiniana seconda—violin and piano/orchestra (1955-56)
M. Rizzi, Dallapiccola Ens, L. Suvini (r1991) Concert
(3/94) (NUOV) ① 7109

SECTION IV: VOCAL AND CHORAL

Carmina Alcaei (Liriche Greche II)—soprano and 11 instruments (1943) (Wds Alcaeus, trans Quasimodo)
A. Morrison, Dallapiccola Ens. L. Suvini (r1991)
Concert (3/94) (NUOV) ① 7109
5 frammenti di Saffo (Liriche Greche I)—1v and 15 instruments (1942) (Wds. Sappho, trans Quasimodo)
1. Vespro, tuuto riporti; 2. O mia Gongila, ti prego; 3.
Muore il tenero Adone, o cietra; 4. Piena splendora la
luna; 5. Io lungamente ho parlato.
A. Morrison, Dallapiccola Ens, L. Suvini (r1991)
Concert (3/94) (NUOV) ① 7109
2 Liriche di Anacreonte (Liriche Greche III)—soprano and four instruments (1944-45)
1. Eros languido desidero cantare; 2. Eros come
tagliatore d'alberi.
A. Morrison, Dallapiccola Ens, L. Suvini (r1991)
Concert (3/94) (NUOV) ① 7109

DALL'AQUILA, Marco (c1480–after 1538) Italy

SECTION III: INSTRUMENTAL

La Battaglia—lute intabulation (after Jannequin)
P. O'Dette (r1990-2) Concert
(10/95) (HARM) ① HMU90 7043
Il est bon—lute intabulation (after Passereau)
P. O'Dette (r1990-2) Concert
(10/95) (HARM) ① HMU90 7043

Nous bergiers—lute intabulation (after
    Jannequin)
  P. O'Dette (r1990-2) *Concert*
                        (10/95) (HARM) ① **HMU90 7043**
Ricercar Lautre jour No. 101—lute
  P. O'Dette (r1990-2) *Concert*
                        (10/95) (HARM) ① **HMU90 7043**
Ricercars—lute
  EXCERPTS: 1. No. 1; 2. No. 2; 3. No. 3; 16. No. 16;
    33. No. 33.
  16, 33. P. O'Dette (r1990-2) *Concert*
                        (10/95) (HARM) ① **HMU90 7043**
La Traditora No. 2—lute
  P. O'Dette (r1990-2) *Concert*
                        (10/95) (HARM) ① **HMU90 7043**
La Traditora No. 3—lute
  P. O'Dette (r1990-2) *Concert*
                        (10/95) (HARM) ① **HMU90 7043**
Unidentified Ricercar—lute
  P. O'Dette (r1990-2) *Concert*
                        (10/95) (HARM) ① **HMU90 7043**

DALZA, Joan Ambrosio *(fl 1508)*
Italy

SECTION III: INSTRUMENTAL

Alla ferrarese—suite: lute (pub. 1508) (from
    'Intabulature di Lauto, Libro Quarto')
  1. Tastar de corde; 2. Recercar dietro; 3. Pavana alla
    ferrarese; 5. Saltarello; 6. Piva.
  J. Lindberg *Concert*   (10/89) (BIS) ① **BIS-CD399**
Alla venetiana—Suite—lute (pub. 1508) (from
    'Intabulatura de Lauto, Libro Quarto')
  J. Lindberg *Concert*   (10/89) (BIS) ① **BIS-CD399**
Calata ala Spagnola (pub 1508) (from
    'Intabalatura de Lauto, libro quarto')
  K. Ragossnig (ed. Petrucci) *Concert*
                        (2/86) (ARCH) ① **415 294-2AH**

DAMASE, Jean-Michel *(b 1928)*
France

SECTION II: CHAMBER

Quintet—flute, violin, viola, cello and harp
    (1948)
  A. Noakes, G. Tingay, R. Friedman, J. Atkins, F.
    Szucs *Concert*   (10/94) (ASV) ① **CDDCA898**
Sonata—flute and harp
  J. Stinton, A. Brewer *Concert*
                        (4/92) (COLL) ① **Coll1297-2**
  A. Noakes, G. Tingay *Concert*
                        (10/94) (ASV) ① **CDDCA898**
Trio—flute, cello and harp (1946)
  A. Noakes, G. Tingay, F. Szucs *Concert*
                        (10/94) (ASV) ① **CDDCA898**
Variations, 'Early Morning'—flute and harp
  J. Stinton, A. Brewer *Concert*
                        (4/92) (COLL) ① **Coll1297-2**
  A. Noakes, G. Tingay *Concert*
                        (10/94) (ASV) ① **CDDCA898**
Variations for Wind Quintet, Op. 22 (1951)
  Reykjavik Wind Qnt (r1993) *Concert*
                        (10/95) (CHAN) ① **CHAN9362**

DAMES, José *(20th Cent)*
Argentina

SECTION IV: VOCAL AND CHORAL

Fuimos—tango (Wds. H. Manzi)
  Buenos Aires Qnt, RPO, E. Stratta (arr J. Calandrelli)
    Concert   (1/93) (TELD) ① **9031-76997-2**

DANA, Mary Stanley Bruce
(1810–1883) USA

SECTION IV: VOCAL AND CHORAL

Flee as a bird—song (pub 1842) (in 'The
    Northern Harp')
  R. Taylor, L. Skrobacs (r1977) *Concert*
                        (2/94) (NEW) ① **80220-2**

DANDRIEU, Jean-François
(c1682–1738) France

SECTION III: INSTRUMENTAL

Noëls—organ/harpsichord (pub ?1721-33)
  1. Allons voir ce divin Gage; 2. A minuit fut fait un
    reveil; 3. Noël de Saintogne; 4. Si c'est pour être la
    vie; 5. Joseph est bien marié; 6. Chantons de voix
    hautaine; 7. Duo en cor de chasse; 8. Muzéte; 9.
    Noël sur les flûtes; 10. Une bergère jolie; 11.
    Chantons je vous prie; 12. Or nous dites Marie; 13.

Quand le Sauveur Jésus Christ; 14. Mais on San es
    allé nau; 15. Le Roy des Cieux.
  1. C. Herrick *Concert*   (3/89) (MERI) ① **CDE84148**
  3. M. Neary *Concert*   (12/88) (ASV) ① **CDQS6011**
  4. P. Hurford, M. Laird Brass Ens (r1990: arr Hurford)
    Concert   (9/92) (ARGO) ① **433 451-2ZH**
  4, 11, 15. P. Hurford (r1989) *Concert*
                        (4/91) (REGE) ① **REGCD105**
  4-9. A. Isoir *Concert*   (6/90) (CALL) ① **CAL9916**
  6, 14, 15. S. Standage (r1993) *Concert*
                        (12/93) (CONI) ① **CDCF517**
  10, 12. German Baroque sols, R. Ewerhart (org/dir)
    Concert   (12/91) (FSM) ① **FCD91220**
  13. G. Weir *Concert*   (12/92) (KOSS) ① **KC1013**
Premier livre d'orgue (pub 1739)
  EXCERPTS: 1. Suite in D; 2. Suite in G; 3. Suite in
    A; 4. Suite in D minor; 5. Suite in G minor; 6. Suite in
    A minor; 7. MASS FOR EASTER SUNDAY: 7a. Kyrie
    (Fugue); 7b. Kyrie (Récit de Nazard); 7c. Graduel;
    7d. Offertorie sur les grands jeux (O filii et filiae); 7e.
    Sanctus and Benedictus; 7f. Agnus Dei; 8. VESPERS
    FOR EASTER SUNDAY: 8a. Ave maris stella
    (Fugue); 8b. Magnificat.
  7b, 7d, 8a P. Bardon *Concert*
                        (3/87) (PIER) ① [2] **PV785051/2**
  7d P. Bardon *Concert*   (5/84) (PIER) ① **PV784011**
  7, 8. J-P. Brosse (r1993; interpolated with Gregorian
    Chant Services) *Concert*
                        (6/95) (PIER) ① **PV794034**

DANIEL-LESUR, (Jan Yves) *(b*
1908) France

SECTION III: INSTRUMENTAL

In paradisum—organ (1933)
  J. Filsell (r1993) *Concert*
                        (1/95) (ASV) ① **CDDCA900**
La vie intérieure—organ (1934)
  J. Filsell (r1993) *Concert*
                        (1/95) (ASV) ① **CDDCA900**

SECTION IV: VOCAL AND CHORAL

Le Cantique des Cantiques, 'Song of
    Songs'—choir (1952)
  EXCERPTS: 1. Dialogue; 2. La voix du bien-aimé; 3.
    Le songe; 4. Le roi Solomon; 5. Le jardin clos; 6. La
    Sulamite; 7. Epithalame.
  BBC Sym Chor, S. Jackson (r1993) *Concert*
                        (1/95) (ASV) ① **CDDCA900**
Messe du Jubilé—choir and organ (1959-
    60)
  BBC Sym Chor, S. Jackson, J. Filsell (r1993) *Concert*
                        (1/95) (ASV) ① **CDDCA900**

DANIELPOUR, Richard *(b 1956)*
USA

SECTION I: ORCHESTRAL

Metamorphosis—piano and orchestra (1989-
    90 rev 1993)
  M. Boriskin, Utah SO, J. Silverstein (r1993) *Concert*
                        (5/95) (HARM) ① **HMU90 7124**

DANKOWSKI, Adalbert (Wojciech)
(c1760–after 1800) Poland

SECTION I: ORCHESTRAL

Symphony in E flat
  Warsaw CO, M. Sewen *Concert*
                        (8/94) (OLYM) ① **OCD380**

DANKS, Hart Pease *(1834–1903)*
USA

SECTION IV: VOCAL AND CHORAL

Silver threads among the gold—song (pub
    1873) (Wds. E. E. Rexford)
  A. Galli-Curci, orch. R. Bourdon (r1923) *Concert*
                        (8/94) (ROMO) ① [2] **81004-2**

DANKWORTH, John (Philip
William) *(b 1927) England*

SECTION IV: VOCAL AND CHORAL

Bread and Butter—song (Wds. J. Thackery)
  Sarah Walker, R. Vignoles (pp1982) *Concert*
                        (3/89) (MERI) ① **CDE84167**
English Teeth—song (Wds. S. Milligan)
  Sarah Walker, R. Vignoles (pp1982) *Concert*
                        (3/89) (MERI) ① **CDE84167**

Lines to Ralph Hodgson, Esq—song (Wds. T.
    S. Eliot)
  Sarah Walker, R. Vignoles (pp1982) *Concert*
                        (3/89) (MERI) ① **CDE84167**

DANYEL, John *(1564–c1626)*
England

SECTION III: INSTRUMENTAL

Rosa—lute
  C. Wilson *Concert*   (11/91) (VIRG) ① **VC7 59034-2**

SECTION IV: VOCAL AND CHORAL

Songs for the Lute, Viol and Voice (pub
    1606)
  1. Can doleful notes: 1a. Can doleful notes; 1b. No,
    let chromatic tunes; 1c. Uncertain turns of thought; 2.
    Coy Daphne fled; 3. Dost thou withdraw thy grace?;
    4. Eyes, look no more; 5. Mrs. M E her funeral tears
    for the death of her husband: 5a. Grief kept withing;
    5b. Drop not mine eyes; 5c. Have all our passions?;
    6. He whose desires are still abroad; 7. I die whenas I
    do not see; 8. If I could shut the gate; 9. Let not
    Chloris think; 10. Like as the lute delights; 11. Now
    the earth, the skies, the air; 12. Stay, cruel, stay!; 13.
    Thou pretty bird; 14. Time, cruel Time; 15. What
    delight can they enjoy; 16. Why canst thou not?.
  4, 13. J. Bowman, D. Miller, King's Consort *Concert*
                        (10/91) (HYPE) ① **CDA66447**
  5, 5b, 5c M. Chance, C. Wilson (r1992) *Concert*
                        (10/94) (CHAN) ① **CHAN0538**
  6, 14. E. Kirkby, A. Rooley (pp1985) *Concert*
                        (6/87) (HYPE) ① **CDA66186**
  7. J. Bowman, D. Miller *Concert*
                        (10/91) (HYPE) ① **CDA66447**
  10. E. Kirkby, A. Rooley *Concert*
                        (8/91) (L'OI) ① **425 892-2OH**

DANZI, Franz (Ignaz) *(1763–1826)*
Germany

SECTION I: ORCHESTRAL

Concertante for Flute, Clarinet and
    Orchestra in B, Op. 41 (c1814)
  J. Galway, S. Meyer, Württemberg CO, J. Faerber
    (r1993) *Concert*   (2/95) (RCA) ① **09026 61976-2**
Concerto for Flute and Orchestra No. 1 in G,
    Op. 30 (c1806)
  A. Adorján, Munich CO, H. Stadlmair *Concert*
                        (8/88) (ORFE) ① **C003812H**
Concerto for Flute and Orchestra No. 2 in D
    minor, Op. 31 (c1806)
  A. Adorján, Munich CO, H. Stadlmair *Concert*
                        (8/88) (ORFE) ① **C003812H**
  J. Galway, Württemberg CO, J. Faerber (r1993)
    Concert   (2/95) (RCA) ① **09026 61976-2**
Concerto for Flute and Orchestra No. 3 in D
    minor, Op. 42 (1814)
  A. Adorján, Munich CO, H. Stadlmair *Concert*
                        (8/88) (ORFE) ① **C003812H**
Concerto for Flute and Orchestra No. 4 in D,
    Op. 43 (1814)
  A. Adorján, Munich CO, H. Stadlmair *Concert*
                        (8/88) (ORFE) ① **C003812H**
Fantasia on 'La ci darem la mano' from
    Mozart's 'Don Giovanni'—clarinet and
    orchestra
  S. Meyer, Württemberg CO, J. Faerber (r1993)
    Concert   (2/95) (RCA) ① **09026 61976-2**
Introduction, Theme and Variations in B
    flat—clarinet and orchestra, Op. 45 (1814)
  D. Klöcker, Berlin RSO, J. López-Cobos *Concert*
                        (11/88) (SCHW) ① **311045**

SECTION II: CHAMBER

Bassoon Quartet in B flat, Op. 40/3 (c1814)
  Daniel Smith, Coull Qt *Concert*
                        (10/88) (ASV) ① **CDDCA613**
Quintet in D minor—piano and wind, Op. 41
    (pub 1810)
  L. Derwinger, Berlin Phil Wind Qnt (r1991) *Wind*
    Quintets, Op.56.   (5/93) (BIS) ① **BIS-CD552**
Sextet in E flat, Op. 10 (c1800)
  R. Hill, J. Bradburg, J. Price, P. Tarlton, M.
    Thompson, R. Berry (r1994; arr cpsr wind instr) *Wind*
    Quintets, Op. 56.   (11/95) (NAXO) ① **8 553076**
Sonata for Basset-horn and Piano (or Cello),
    Op. 62 (pub 1823)
  K. Puddy, M. Martineau (r1992) *Concert*
                        (10/93) (CLRI) ① **CC0004**
Sonata for Clarinet and Piano in B flat
    (c1818)
  C. Neidich, R. Levin (r1993) *Concert*
                        (9/95) (SONY) ① **SK64302**

3 Wind Quintets—flute, oboe, clarinet, horn and bassoon, Op. 56 (1821)
1. B flat; 2. G minor; 3. F.
Berlin Phil Wind Qnt (r1991) *Wind Quintet, Op.41.*
(5/93) (BIS) ① **BIS-CD552**
1, 2, 3. M. Thompson Wind Qnt (r1994) *Sextet.*
(11/95) (NAXO) ① **8 553076**
Wind Quintets—cl, fl, ob, hn and bn, Op. 67 (pub 1824)
1. G; 2. E minor; 3. E flat.
2. Aulos Wind Qnt *Concert*
(10/89) (SCHW) ① **310011**

DAQUIN, Louis-Claude (1694–1772) France

SECTION II: CHAMBER

Air de Mr de Luly—flute and continuo
S. Preston, L. Carolan *Concert*
(3/87) (AMON) ① **CD-SAR19**

SECTION III: INSTRUMENTAL

Nouveau livre de noëls—organ/hpd, Op. 2 (pub c1740)
1. Noël sur les jeux d'anches, A la venue de Noël; 2. Noël en dialogue, Or dites-nous Marie; 3. Noël en musette, en dialogue et en duo; 4. Noël en duo sur les jeux d'anches, Noël, cette journée; 5. Noël en duo, Je me suis levé par un matinet; 6. Noël sur les jeux d'anches, Adam fut un pauvre homme; 7. Noël en trio et en dialogue; 8. Noël étranger, sur les jeux d'anches sans tremblant et en duo; 9. Noël sur les flûtes, Noël, pour l'amour de Marie; 10. Noël grand-jeu et duo, Quand Dieu naquit à Noël; 11. Noël en récit, en taille, Une jeune pucelle; 12. Noël suisse, O Dieu de clémence.
P. Bardon (3/86) (PIER) ① **PV783122**
C. Herrick (r1995) (12/95) (HYPE) ① **CDA66816**
6, 12. German Baroque sols, R. Ewerhart (org/dir) *Concert* (12/91) (FSM) ① **FCD91220**
8. M. Neary *Concert* (12/88) (ASV) ① **CDQS6011**
8, 10. M. Petri, National PO, M. Neary (arr. D. Overton) *Concert* (12/91) (RCA) ① **RD60060**
10. D. Sanger (r1983) *Concert*
(12/93) (MERI) ① **CDE84068**
10. M. Dupré (r c1926) *Concert*
(9/94) (BEUL) ① **1PD5**
12. C. Herrick *Concert* (3/89) (MERI) ① **CDE84148**
Premier livre de pièces de clavecin (pub 1735)
PREMIER SUITE—; 1. Allemande; 2. Rigaudons 1 and 2; 3. Musette en Rondeau/Tambourin en Rondeau; 4. La Guittare: Rondeau; 5. Les Vents en couroux; 6. Les Bergères; 7. La Ronde Bachique; 8. Les Trois Cadences. DEUXIÈME SUITE—; 9. Allemande; 10. Courante; 11. La Favorite, Le Double de la Favorite; 12. Les enchaînements Harmonieux; 13. Le Dépit Généreux; 14. Le Double du Dépit Généreux; 14. L'Hirondelle. TROISIÈME SUITE—; 15. Le Coucou; 16. La Joyeuse; 17. L'Amusante; 18. La Tendre Silvie. QUARTRIÈME SUITE—; 19. La Mélodieuse; 20. Menuets 1 and 2.
14. W. Landowska (r1934) *Concert*
(10/92) (MSCM) ① **MM30444**
14, 15. G. Cziffra (r1980-81) *Concert*
(3/95) (EMI) ① **CDM5 65253-2**
15. T. Pinnock *Concert*
(11/84) (ARCH) ① **413 591-2AH**
15. S. Preston, L. Carolan (arr Hotteterre) *Concert*
(3/87) (AMON) ① **CD-SAR19**
15. L. Rév *Concert* (7/87) (HYPE) ① **CDA66185**
15. R. Aldwinckle *Concert*
(7/87) (CARL) ① **PCD850**
15. V. Black *Concert* (5/91) (COLL) ① **Coll5024-2**
15. M. Lympany *Concert* (1/92) (EMIL) ① **CDZ111**
15. W. Landowska (r1928) *Concert*
(10/92) (MSCM) ① **MM30444**
15. S. Rachmaninov (1920) *Concert*
(3/93) (RCA) ① **[10] 09026 61265-2(3)**
15. G. Malcolm (r1962) *Concert*
(11/95) (DECC) ① **444 390-2DWO**

DAREWSKI, Hermann E. (1883–1947) England

SECTION IV: VOCAL AND CHORAL

Sister Susie's sewing shirts for soldiers—song for the show 'Dancing Around' (1914) (Wds. R. P. Weston)
A. Jolson, Orig Broadway Cast (r1914) *Concert*
(5/94) (PEAR) ① **[3] GEMMCDS9056/8**

DARGOMÏZHSKY, Alexander Sergeyevich (1813–1869) Russia

SECTION IV: VOCAL AND CHORAL

Bolero—song
F. Chaliapin, P. Coppola (r1933) *Concert*
(6/93) (PREI) ① **[2] 89207**
Elegy, 'She is coming'—song: 1v, viola/cello & piano (1843 arr 1861) (Wds. anon)
M. Shirai, T. Zimmermann, H. Höll (r1993-4) *Concert*
(9/95) (CAPR) ① **10 462**
The Garden—song (Wds. A. Pushkin)
A. Orda, J. Lee (bp1958) *Concert*
(12/89) (SYMP) ① **SYMCD1067**
The Miller—song (1850-51) (Wds. Pushkin)
A. Orda, J. Lee (bp1958) *Concert*
(12/89) (SYMP) ① **SYMCD1067**
The Old Corporal—song (1857-58) (Wds. Béranger trans Kurochkin)
F. Chaliapin, orch, G.W. Byng (r1929) *Concert*
(6/93) (PREI) ① **[2] 89207**
N. Ghiaurov, P. Dokovska (r1993) *Concert*
(1/95) (RCA) ① **09026 62501-2**
Sierre Nevada was covered with mist—song (1839-40) (Wds. Shirkov)
A. Orda, J. Lee (bp1958) *Concert*
(12/89) (SYMP) ① **SYMCD1067**
Spanish Romance—song (pub 1856) (Wds Pushkin, from The Stone Guest)
N. Ghiaurov, P. Dokovska (r1993) *Concert*
(1/95) (RCA) ① **09026 62501-2**
The Titular Councillor—song (pub 1859) (Wds Weinberg)
N. Ghiaurov, P. Dokovska (r1993) *Concert*
(1/95) (RCA) ① **09026 62501-2**
The Worm—song (after 1856) (Wds. Béranger trans Kurochkin)
N. Ghiaurov, P. Dokovska (r1993) *Concert*
(1/95) (RCA) ① **09026 62501-2**

SECTION V: STAGE WORKS

Rusalka—opera: 4 acts (1856—St Petersburg) (Lib. cpsr after Pushkin)
EXCERPTS: ACT 1: 1. Ah! you young girls are all the same (Miller's aria). ACT 2: 2. Slavonic Dance; 3. Gypsy Dance. ACT 3: 4. Once a husband asked his wife (Olga's aria); 5. Some unknown power (Prince's cavatina); 6. What does this mean? (Mad Scene and Death of Miller). ACT 4: 7. Natasha's aria; 8. Dance.
Hark, the trumpets are sounding...Days of past enjoyment E. Zbrueva, orch (r1910) *Concert*
(6/93) (PEAR) ① **[3] GEMMCDS9004/6(2)**
Scene of the Miller and the Prince M. Reizen, G. Nelepp, Bolshoi Th Orch, V. Nebolsin (r1950) *Concert* (2/95) (PREI) ① **89080**
1. A. Kipnis, Victor SO, N. Berezowski (r1945) *Concert* (9/92) (RCA) ① **GD60522**
1. M. Reizen, Bolshoi Th Orch, V. Nebolsin (r1948) *Concert* (12/92) (PREI) ① **89059**
1. L. Sibiriakov, orch (r1908) *Concert*
(6/93) (PEAR) ① **[3] GEMMCDS9001/3(2)**
1, 6. F. Chaliapin, G. Pozemkovsky, LSO, M. Steinmann (r1931) *Concert*
(6/88) (EMI) ① **CDH7 61009-2**
5. L. Sobinov, anon (r1901: 2 vers) *Concert*
(6/93) (PEAR) ① **[3] GEMMCDS9997/9(1)**
5. D. Smirnov, orch (r1913) *Concert*
(6/93) (PEAR) ① **[3] GEMMCDS9004/6(1)**
5. A. Bogdanovich, anon (r1903) *Concert*
(6/93) (PEAR) ① **[3] GEMMCDS9007/9(1)**

DARKE, Harold (Edwin) (1888–1976) England

SECTION III: INSTRUMENTAL

Andantino—organ (1918) (from A Little Organ Book in memory of Hubert Parry)
J. Rennert (r1991) *Concert*
(1/95) (PRIO) ① **PRCD374**
Bridal Procession in C—organ (1965)
J. Rennert (r1991) *Concert*
(1/95) (PRIO) ① **PRCD374**
3 Chorale Preludes—organ, Op. 20 (1919)
EXCERPTS: 1. On theme of St Peter, 'How sweet the name of Jesus sounds'; 2. Chorale-Fantasia on Darwall's 148th, 'Ye holy angels bright'; 3. On a theme of Tallis, 'Lord teach us how to pray aright'.
J. Rennert (r1991) *Concert*
(1/95) (PRIO) ① **PRCD374**

Chorale-Prelude on Heinlein, 'Forty days and forty nights'—organ
J. Rennert (r1991) *Concert*
(1/95) (PRIO) ① **PRCD374**
Elegy in E flat—organ (1949) (from A Book of Simple Voluntaries)
J. Rennert (r1991) *Concert*
(1/95) (PRIO) ① **PRCD374**
Fantasy in E—organ, Op. 39 (1930)
J. Rennert (r1991) *Concert*
(1/95) (PRIO) ① **PRCD374**
In Green Pastures in F—organ (1956) (from An Easy Album for Organ)
J. Rennert (r1991) *Concert*
(1/95) (PRIO) ① **PRCD374**
An Interlude in D—organ (1974) (from The Hovingham Sketches)
J. Rennert (r1991) *Concert*
(1/95) (PRIO) ① **PRCD374**
Meditation on 'Brother James' Air' in D—organ (1947)
J. Bielby *Concert* (5/91) (PRIO) ① **PRCD298**
J. Rennert (r1991) *Concert*
(1/95) (PRIO) ① **PRCD374**
Retrospection—organ (from Retrospection: organ music of the 1950s)
J. Rennert (r1991) *Concert*
(1/95) (PRIO) ① **PRCD374**
Rhapsody—organ, Op. 4
J. Rennert (r1991) *Concert*
(1/95) (PRIO) ① **PRCD374**

SECTION IV: VOCAL AND CHORAL

Evening Service in F (1910-13)
1. Magnificat; 2. Nunc dimittis.
1, 2. St Paul's Cath Ch, C. Dearnley, John Scott *Concert* (1/89) (HYPE) ① **CDA66305**
Morning Service in F
1. Te Deum; 2. Jubilate.
1, 2. Hereford Cath Ch, R. Massey, G. Bowen (r1994) *Concert* (2/95) (PRIO) ① **PRCD507**

DARZINS, Emil (1875–1910) Russia/Latvia

SECTION I: ORCHESTRAL

Valse mélancolique—orchestra (1904)
Detroit SO, N. Järvi (r1992) *Concert*
(8/94) (CHAN) ① **CHAN9227**

DAUGHERTY, Michael (b 1954) USA

SECTION I: ORCHESTRAL

Desi—orchestra (1990)
Baltimore SO, D. Zinman (r1994) *Concert*
(7/95) (ARGO) ① **444 454-2ZH**

DAUPRAT, Louis François (1781–1868) France

SECTION II: CHAMBER

Solo in E flat—horn and piano, Op. 11/3
B. Tuckwell, D. Blumenthal *Concert*
(11/92) (ETCE) ① **KTC1135**

DAUVERGNE, Antoine (1713–1797) France

SECTION II: CHAMBER

2 Concerts de simphonies—two violins, viola and continuo, Op. 3 (pub 1751)
2. F.
2. Cappella Coloniensis, W. Christie (1992) *Troqueurs.* (8/94) (HARM) ① **HMC90 1454**

SECTION V: STAGE WORKS

Les Troqueurs—intermède: 1 act and ballet (1753—Paris) (Lib. J-J Vade, after La Fontaine)
Cpte M. Saint-Palais, S. Marin-Degor, N. Rivenq, J-M. Salzmann, Cappella Coloniensis, W. Christie (r1992) *Concerts de Simphonies, Op. 3.*
(8/94) (HARM) ① **HMC90 1454**

DAVID, Félicien(-César) (1810–1876) France

SECTION II: CHAMBER

Nonet No.2 in C minor—brass ensemble (1839)
London Gabrieli Brass Ens, C. Larkin Concert
(4/92) (HYPE) ① CDA66470
3 Piano Trios (1857)
1. E flat; 2. D minor; 3. C minor.
2, 3. E. Perényi, T. Párkányi, I. Prunyi (r1991)
(5/94) (MARC) ① 8 223492

SECTION IV: VOCAL AND CHORAL

Le Désert—symphonic ode (1844)
O. Pascalin, B. Lazzaretti, Berlin St Hedwig's Cath
Ch, Berlin RSO, G.M. Guida Szymanowski: Songs,
Op.42.
(5/92) (CAPR) ① 10 379

SECTION V: STAGE WORKS

La Perle du Brésil—opéra-comique: 1 act
(c1857) (Lib. ?A. de Leuven)
EXCERPTS: 1. Charmant oiseau.
1. A. Galli-Curci, orch (r1912) Concert
(2/89) (PEAR) ① GEMMCD9308
1. L. Tetrazzini, orch (r1911) Concert
(9/92) (EMI) ① [3] CHS7 63802-2(1)
1. L. Tetrazzini, orch (r1911) Concert
(9/92) (PEAR) ① GEMMCD9222
1. L. Tetrazzini, orch (r1911) Concert
(9/92) (PEAR) ① GEMMCD9224
1. A. Nezhdanova, anon (r1907: Russ) Concert
(6/93) (PEAR) ① [3] GEMMCDS9007/9(1)
1. A. Galli-Curci, orch, J. Pasternack (r1917) Concert
(3/94) (ROMO) ① [2] 81003-2
1. A. Galli-Curci, orch (r1917) Concert
(8/94) (NIMB) ① NI7852
1. S. Jo, ECO, R. Bonynge (r1993) Concert
(9/94) (DECC) ① 440 679-2DH

DAVID, Johann Nepomuk (1895–1977) Austria

SECTION IV: VOCAL AND CHORAL

Wir zogen in das Feld—2 choruses
Orphei Drängar Ch, E. Ericson Concert
(7/88) (BIS) ① BIS-CD383

DAVIDOV, A.D (1838–1911) Russia

SECTION IV: VOCAL AND CHORAL

Leave me!—gypsy song
L. Sibiriakov, anon (r1906) Concert
(6/93) (PEAR) ① [3] GEMMCDS9001/3(2)
A. Davidov, anon (r1901) Concert
(6/93) (PEAR) ① [3] GEMMCDS9007/9(1)
Night, love and the moon—song
M. Mei-Figner, anon (r1901) Concert
(6/93) (PEAR) ① [3] GEMMCDS9997/9(1)
What happiness!—song
A. Bogdanovich, anon (r1905) Concert
(6/93) (PEAR) ① [3] GEMMCDS9007/9(1)

DAVIES, Evan Thomas (1879–?) Wales

SECTION IV: VOCAL AND CHORAL

Ynys y Plant, 'Children's Island'—song
(Wds. Elfed)
S. Bullock, A. Bryn Parri (r1994) Concert
(11/95) (SAIN) ① SCDC2070

DAVIES, Sir (Henry) Walford (1869–1941) England

SECTION I: ORCHESTRAL

Solemn Melody—organ and string orchestra
(1908)
J. Lloyd Webber, J. Birch, ASMF, N. Marriner (r1994)
Concert (12/94) (PHIL) ① 442 530-2PH

SECTION IV: VOCAL AND CHORAL

Blessed be the pure in heart—anthem (Wds.
J Keble)
St Paul's Cath Ch, John Scott, Andrew Lucas (r1994)
Concert (5/95) (HYPE) ① CDA66758
God be in my head—hymn
Huddersfield Choral Soc, W. Morris (r1964) Concert
(6/93) (DECC) ① 436 402-2DWO

Trinity Coll Ch, Cambridge, R. Marlow (r1993)
Concert (2/94) (CONI) ① CDCF219

DAVIES, William (1859–1907) Wales

SECTION IV: VOCAL AND CHORAL

O! Na byddai'n haf o hyd—song (Wds.
Buddug)
A. Davies, A. Bryn Parri (r1994) Concert
(11/95) (SAIN) ① SCDC2085

DAVIS, Anthony (b 1951) USA

SECTION V: STAGE WORKS

X: The Life and Times of Malcolm X—opera
(1985—Philadelphia) (Lib. cpsr)
Cpte E. Perry, T.J. Young, P. Baskerville, H. Harris,
H. Perry, C. Aaronson, T.D. Price, R. Bazemore, J.
Daniecki, R. Edwards, R. Byrne, Episteme, St. Luke's
Orch, W.H. Curry (r1992)
(4/93) (GVIS) ① [2] R2-79470

DAVIS, Carl (b 1936) USA/England

SECTION I: ORCHESTRAL

Philharmonic Fanfare—orchestra (1987)
LPO, Carl Davis Concert
(12/91) (VIRG) ① VJ7 59654-2

DAVY, Richard (c1465–c1507) England

SECTION IV: VOCAL AND CHORAL

A blessid Jhesu—carol (3vv)
The Sixteen, H. Christophers Concert
(7/93) (COLL) ① Coll1342-2
A myn hart remembir the well—3vv (from
'Eton Choirbook')
The Sixteen, H. Christophers Concert
(7/93) (COLL) ① Coll1342-2
O Domine caeli terraeque—5vv (from 'Eton
Choirbook')
The Sixteen, H. Christophers Concert
(7/93) (COLL) ① Coll1342-2
The Passion according to St.
Matthew—choir a cappella (from 'Eton
Choirbook')
Eton Coll Chapel Ch, R. Allwood (r1994) Concert
(5/95) (FUTU) ① FCM1004
Stabat mater—motet (5vv)
The Sixteen, H. Christophers Concert
(11/89) (MERI) ① CDE84175
The Sixteen, H. Christophers Concert
(4/92) (COLL) ① Coll1316-2

DAWES, Charles Gates (1865–1951) USA

SECTION II: CHAMBER

Melody in A—violin and piano (1912)
F. Kreisler, C. Lamson (r1924) Concert
(9/92) (BIDD) ① [2] LAB068/9
F. Kreisler, C. Lamson (r1921) Concert
(9/92) (BIDD) ① [2] LAB068/9

DAWSON, William Levi (1899–1990) USA

SECTION I: ORCHESTRAL

Negro Folk Symphony (1934)
Detroit SO, N. Järvi (r1992) Concert
(3/94) (CHAN) ① CHAN9226

DE BOECK, August (1865–1937) Belgium

SECTION I: ORCHESTRAL

Dahomeyan rhapsody—orchestra (1893)
Belgian Rad & TV Orch, A. Rahbari (r1992) Concert
(8/94) (DINT) ① DICD920101

DE BUSSY (?c1500–?c1550)

SECTION IV: VOCAL AND CHORAL

Las il n'a nul mal—chanson (16th cent)
C. Janequin Ens, D. Visse (r1994) Concert
(5/95) (HARM) ① HMC90 1453

DE CURTIS, Ernesto (1875–1937) Italy

SECTION IV: VOCAL AND CHORAL

Canta pe'me—song (Wds. L. Bovio)
E. Caruso, orch, W.B. Rogers (r1911) Concert
(7/90) (CLUB) ① CL99-060
E. Caruso, orch (r1911) Concert
(3/91) (PEAR) ① [3] EVC2
E. Caruso, orch (r1911) Concert
(7/91) (RCA) ① [12] GD60495(4)
Carmela—song (Wds. cpsr)
J. McCormack, F. Kreisler, Victor Orch, W.B. Rogers
(r1915) Concert (9/89) (PEAR) ① GEMMCD9315
R. Ponselle, orch, R. Bourdon (r1924) Concert
(10/89) (NIMB) ① NI7805
B. Gigli, orch, R. Bourdon (r1930) Concert
(5/90) (PEAR) ① GEMMCD9367
B. Gigli, orch (r1930) Concert
(6/93) (MMOI) ① CDMOIR417
Non ti scordar di me—song (1935) (Wds. D.
Furnò)
F. Araiza, Munich RSO, R. Weikert (arr Mattes)
Concert (3/93) (RCA) ① 09026 61163-2
P. Domingo, LSO, K-H. Loges Concert
(5/93) (DG) ① 431 104-2GB
L. Pavarotti, Los Angeles PO, Z. Mehta (pp1994)
Concert (12/94) (TELD) ① 4509-96200-2
L. Pavarotti, NYPO, L. Magiera (pp1993) Concert
(2/95) (DECC) ① 444 450-2DH
Senza nisciuno—song (Wds. A. Barbiere)
E. Caruso, orch, J. Pasternack (r1919) Concert
(7/91) (RCA) ① [12] GD60495(6)
E. Caruso, orch, J. Pasternack (r1919) Concert
(10/91) (PEAR) ① [3] EVC4(2)
B. Gigli, La Scala Orch, D. Olivieri (r1934) Concert
(5/92) (MMOI) ① CDMOIR409
So 'nnammurato 'e te!—Neapolitan song
(Wds. G. B. de Curtis)
L. Tetrazzini, T. Amici (r1922) Concert
(9/92) (EMI) ① [3] CHS7 63802-2(2)
L. Tetrazzini, orch (r1922) Concert
(9/92) (PEAR) ① GEMMCD9225
Torna a Surriento—song (1902) (Wds. G. B.
de Curtis)
L. Pavarotti, National PO, G. Chiaramello Concert
(8/83) (DECC) ① 410 015-2DH
L. Pavarotti, National PO, G. Chiaramello Concert
(7/86) (DECC) ① [2] 417 011-2DH2
L. Pavarotti, MMF Orch, Rome Op Orch, Z. Mehta
(pp1990) Concert (10/90) (DECC) ① 430 433-2DH
L. Pavarotti, RPO, K.H. Adler (pp1982) Concert
(5/92) (DECC) ① 430 716-2DM
P. Dvorský, Bratislava RSO, O. Lenárd Concert
(5/92) (NAXO) ① 8 550343
B. Gigli, La Scala Orch, D. Olivieri (r1935) Concert
(9/92) (MMOI) ① CDMOIR409
T. Ruffo, orch (r1929) Concert
(2/93) (PREI) ① [3] 89303(2)
Tu, ca nun chiagne!—song (1915) (Wds. L.
Bovio)
L. Pavarotti, Teatro Communale Orch, A. Guadagno
Concert (8/83) (DECC) ① 410 015-2DH
E. Caruso, orch, J. Pasternack (r1919) Concert
(7/91) (RCA) ① [12] GD60495(6)
E. Caruso, orch, J. Pasternack (r1919) Concert
(10/91) (PEAR) ① [3] EVC4(2)
J. Carreras, Los Angeles PO, Z. Mehta (pp1994)
Concert (12/94) (TELD) ① 4509-96200-2
Tu parte—song
A. Giorgini, orch (r1928) Concert
(4/95) (RECO) ① TRC3
Tu sola—song
B. Gigli, orch (r1921) Concert
(5/90) (NIMB) ① NI7807
Voce 'e notte!—song (1904) (Wds. E.
Nicolardi)
B. Gigli, orch, R. Bourdon (r1927) Concert
(5/90) (PEAR) ① GEMMCD9367

DE CURTIS, Giovanni Battista (1860–1926) Italy

SECTION IV: VOCAL AND CHORAL

Carmé, 'Canto Sorrentino'—song
R. Ponselle, orch, R. Bourdon (r1924) Concert
(11/94) (ROMO) ① [2] 81006-2

DE JONG, Marinus (1891–1984)
The Netherlands

SECTION I: ORCHESTRAL

Flemish rhapsody—orchestra (1935)
Belgian Rad & TV Orch, A. Rahbari (r1992) *Concert*
(8/94) (DINT) ① DICD920101

DE KOVEN, (Henry Louis) Reginald (1859–1920) USA

SECTION IV: VOCAL AND CHORAL

Rhapsody and Serenata Inutile—song
L. Tetrazzini, orch (r1913) *Concert*
(9/92) (PEAR) ① GEMMCD9224

SECTION V: STAGE WORKS

Rob Roy—musical show (1894—New York)
(Lyrics Smith)
EXCERPTS: 1. Who Can Tell Me Where She Dwells?.
1. F. Pollock, Orig Broadway Cast (r1913) *Concert*
(5/94) (PEAR) ① [3] GEMMCDS9056/8
Robin Hood—operetta (1890—Chicago) (Lib. Harry B. Smith)
EXCERPTS: 1. Song of Brown October Ale; 2. O Promise Me; 3. The Armorer's Song.
1. Cincinnati Uni Sngrs, Cincinnati Uni Th Orch, E. Rivers (r1978) *Concert*   (4/94) (NEW) ① 80221-2
2. J. B. Davis, Broadway Cast (r1898) *Concert*
(5/94) (PEAR) ① [3] GEMMCDS9050/2(1)
3. E. Cowles, Broadway Cast (r1906) *Concert*
(5/94) (PEAR) ① [3] GEMMCDS9050/2(1)

DE LA FOSSE ?France

SECTION IV: VOCAL AND CHORAL

Retour du printemps—song
P. Frijsh, C. Dougherty (r1942) *Concert*
(4/95) (PEAR) ① [2] GEMMCDS9095(1)

DE LARA, Isidore (1858–1935) England

SECTION IV: VOCAL AND CHORAL

Le champs de pavots—song
P. Aramis, anon (r1905) *Concert*
(12/94) (SYMP) ① SYMCD1172
Rondel de l'adieu—song
V. Maurel, anon (r1904) *Concert*
(9/91) (SYMP) ① SYMCD1089
V. Maurel, anon (r1903) *Concert*
(10/92) (SYMP) ① SYMCD1101
V. Maurel, anon (r1905) *Concert*
(12/94) (SYMP) ① SYMCD1128

SECTION V: STAGE WORKS

Méssaline—opera (1899—Monte Carlo)
Del del patrio suol F. Tamagno, anon (r1904) *Concert*   (4/94) (EMI) ① [3] CHS7 64860-2(2)
Elle m'avait pris A. Scotti, anon (r1902) *Concert*
(8/92) (IRCC) ① IRCC-CD802
O nuit d'amour A. Endrèze, orch, H. Defosse (r c1931) *Concert*   (11/92) (MSCM) ① MM30451
O nuit d'amour A. Scotti, anon (r1902) *Concert*
(3/93) (SYMP) ① SYMCD1100
Viens aimer A. Ghasne, orch (r1912) *Concert*
(9/91) (SYMP) ① SYMCD1089
Viens aimer A. Ghasne, anon (r1907) *Concert*
(8/92) (IRCC) ① IRCC-CD802

DE PORTA, J. (14th–15th Cent) France

SECTION IV: VOCAL AND CHORAL

Alma polis religio/Axe poli cum artica/Tenor/Contratenor—motet: 4 parts (14th Cent)
Gothic Voices, C. Page *Concert*
(3/92) (HYPE) ① CDA66463

DE SILVA, Andreas (c1475–80–c1530) Spain?

SECTION IV: VOCAL AND CHORAL

Nigra sum sed formosa—motet: 5vv (pub. 1539)
Tallis Scholars, P. Phillips *Concert*
(8/87) (GIME) ① CDGIM003

DE TEJADA ?Spain or Argentina

SECTION IV: VOCAL AND CHORAL

Perjura!—song
T. Ruffo, orch (r1922) *Concert*
(2/93) (PREI) ① [3] 89303(2)

DEBLASIO, Chris (1959–1993) USA

SECTION II: CHAMBER

God is our righteousness—guitar and organ (1992)
N. Goluses, H. Huff (r1993) *Concert*
(7/94) (CATA) ① 09026 61979-2

DEBUSSY, (Achille-)Claude (1862–1918) France

SECTION I: ORCHESTRAL

Berceuse héroïque—orchestra (1914) (after piano work)
FRNO, J. Martinon *Concert*
(3/89) (EMI) ① CDM7 69587-2
Belgian Rad & TV Orch, A. Rahbari (r1992) *Concert*
(11/93) (NAXO) ① 8 550505
Concertgebouw, E. van Beinum (r1957) *Concert*
(3/94) (PHIL) ① [2] 438 742-2PM2
Danse sacrée et danse profane—two pieces: harp and strings (1904)
O. Ellis, ASMF, N. Marriner *Concert*
(2/85) (ASV) ① CDDCA517
F. Fietov, St. Louis SO, L. Slatkin *Concert*
(9/85) (TELA) ① CD80071
V. Badings, Concertgebouw, B. Haitink *Concert*
(6/86) (PHIL) ① 416 437-2PH
G. Oppenheimer, M. Robles, COE, J. Galway (fl/dir) (ed. Robles) *Concert*   (5/87) (RCA) ① RD87173
S. Kanga, ASMF Chbr Ens *Concert*
(12/88) (CHAN) ① CHAN8621
M-C. Jamet, FRNO, J. Martinon *Concert*
(10/89) (EMI) ① CDM7 69589-2
Prometheus Ens *Concert*
(11/89) (ASV) ① CDDCA664
L. Laskine, SO, P. Coppola (r c1930) *Concert*
(6/90) (PEAR) ① GEMMCD9348
R. Masters, Ulster Orch, Y.P. Tortelier *Concert*
(9/92) (CHAN) ① CHAN8972
M. Klinko, Paris Opéra-Bastille Orch (r1993) *Concert*
(2/94) (EMI) ① CDC7 54884-2
V. Badings, Concertgebouw, B. Haitink (r1977) *Concert*   (3/94) (PHIL) ① [2] 438 742-2PM2
A.M. Stockton, Concert Arts Stgs, F. Slatkin (r1951) *Concert*   (3/95) (TEST) ① SBT1053
E. Phillips, Philadelphia, L. Stokowski (r1931) *Concert*   (8/95) (BIDD) ① WHL013
Fantaisie—piano and orchestra (1889-90)
A. Queffélec, Ulster Orch, Y.P. Tortelier *Concert*
(9/92) (CHAN) ① CHAN8972
W. Gieseking, Concertgebouw, W. Mengelberg (pp1938) *Concert*   (7/94) (MUSI) ① [4] MACD-780
Images (1905-12)
1. Gigues; 2. Ibéria; 2a. Par les rues et par les chemins; 2b. Les parfums de la nuit; 2c. Le matin d'un jour de fête; 3. Rondes de printemps.
Czech PO, S. Baudo *Concert*
(12/87) (SUPR) ① 2SUP0023
F. Thinat, J. Bernier (trans 2 pfs Caplet) *La Mer.*
(2/88) (ARIO) ① ARN68021
CBSO, S. Rattle *Concert*
(3/90) (EMI) ① CDC7 49947-2
Montreal SO, C. Dutoit *Nocturnes.*
(6/90) (DECC) ① 425 502-2DH
Ulster Orch, Y.P. Tortelier *Concert*
(10/90) (CHAN) ① CHAN8850
Santa Cecilia Academy Orch, L. Bernstein (pp1989) *Concert*   (1/91) (DG) ① 429 728-2GH
Czech PO, L. Pešek *La Mer.*
(2/92) (SUPR) ① 11 0396-2
Cleveland Orch, P. Boulez *Concert*
(9/92) (DG) ① 435 766-2GH
NYPO, L. Bernstein *Concert*
(5/93) (SONY) ① SMK47545
Belgian Rad & TV Orch, A. Rahbari (r1992) *Concert*
(11/93) (NAXO) ① 8 550505
Concertgebouw, B. Haitink (r1977) *Concert*
(3/94) (PHIL) ① [2] 438 742-2PM2
San Francisco SO, P. Monteux (r1951) *Concert*
(4/94) (RCA) ① [15] 09026 61893-2
Boston SO, C. Munch (r1957) *Concert*
(12/94) (RCA) ① 09026 61956-2
LSO, P. Monteux (r1963) *Concert*
(12/94) (PHIL) ① [5] 442 544-2PM5

BPO, James Levine (r1992) *Elgar: Enigma Variations.*   (2/95) (SONY) ① SK53284
SRO, A. Argenta (r1957) *Concert*
(5/95) (DECC) ① 443 580-2DCS
2. LSO, C. Abbado *Concert*
(3/88) (DG) ① 423 103-2GH
2. Chicago SO, F. Reiner *Concert*
(1/90) (RCA) ① GD60179
2. Philadelphia, A. Toscanini (r1941) *Concert*
(6/91) (RCA) ① [4] GD60328
2. NBC SO, A. Toscanini (r1950) *Concert*
(2/92) (RCA) ① GD60265
2. NYPSO, J. Barbirolli (r1938) *Concert*
(4/92) (PEAR) ① [3] GEMMCDS9922
2. SRO, A. Argenta (r1957) *Concert*
(6/93) (DECC) ① [2] 433 911-2DM2
2. FRNO, L. Stokowski (bp1958) *Concert*
(2/94) (MUSI) ① MACD-778
2. Detroit SO, P. Paray (r1955) *Concert*
(6/95) (MERC) ① 434 343-2MM
La Mer—three symphonic sketches (1903-05)
1. De l'aube à midi sur la mer; 2. Jeux de vagues; 3. Dialogue du vent et de la mer.
St. Louis SO, L. Slatkin *Concert*
(9/85) (TELA) ① CD80071
Crommelynck Duo (arr cpsr: pno duet) *Concert*
(8/86) (CLAV) ① CD50-8508
LPO, S. Baudo *Concert*
(10/87) (EMIN) ① CD-EMX9502
F. Thinat, J. Bernier (trans 2 pfs Caplet) *Images.*
(2/88) (ARIO) ① ARN68021
Boston SO, C. Munch *Concert*
(7/88) (RCA) ① GD86719
FNO, D-E. Inghelbrecht (r1962) *Concert*
(10/88) (MONT) ① [2] TCE8790
FRNO, J. Martinon *Concert*
(3/89) (EMI) ① CDM7 69587-2
LSO, R. Frühbeck de Burgos *Concert*
(6/89) (CARL) ① PCD915
BPO, H. von Karajan (r1964) *Concert*
(7/89) (DG) ① 427 250-2GGA
Los Angeles PO, C.M. Giulini *Concert*
(10/89) (DG) ① 427 213-2GH
Toulouse Capitole Orch, M. Plasson *Concert*
(1/90) (EMI) ① CDC7 49472-2
Philh, G. Sinopoli *Concert*
(7/90) (DG) ① 427 644-2GH
Santa Cecilia Academy Orch, L. Bernstein (pp1989) *Concert*   (1/91) (DG) ① 429 728-2GH
J. Campbell, Philh *Concert*
(5/91) (CALA) ① CACD1001
Paris Orch, J. Barbirolli *Concert*
(5/91) (EMI) ① [2] CZS7 62669-2
Philadelphia, A. Toscanini (r1942) *Concert*
(6/91) (RCA) ① [4] GD60328
Cleveland Orch, Vladimir Ashkenazy *Concert*
(8/91) (DECC) ① 430 732-2DM
SRO, A. Jordan *Concert*
(11/91) (ERAT) ① 2292-45605-2
NBC SO, A. Toscanini (r1950) *Concert*
(2/92) (RCA) ① GD60265
Czech PO, L. Pešek *Images.*
(2/92) (SUPR) ① 11 0396-2
Chicago SO, G. Solti *Concert*
(10/92) (DECC) ① 436 468-2DH
Philh, G. Cantelli (1954) *Concert*
(10/92) (TEST) ① SBT1011
BPO, H. von Karajan *Concert*
(11/92) (EMI) ① CDM7 64357-2
Detroit SO, N. Järvi *Concert*
(12/92) (CHAN) ① CHAN9072
Ulster Orch, Y. P. Tortelier *Concert*
(3/93) (CHAN) ① CHAN9114
Boston SO, C. Munch (r1956) *Concert*
(4/93) (RCA) ① 09026 61500-2
NYPO, L. Bernstein *Concert*
(5/93) (SONY) ① SMK47546
Strasbourg PO, A. Lombard (1981) *Concert*
(12/93) (ERAT) ① 4509-92867-2
Paris Orch, D. Barenboim (1978) *Concert*
(1/94) (DG) ① 439 407-2GCL
Concertgebouw, B. Haitink (r1976) *Concert*
(3/94) (PHIL) ① [2] 438 742-2PM2
Philadelphia, E. Ormandy (r1959) *Concert*
(3/94) (SONY) ① SBK53256
Concertgebouw, E. Inbal (r1969) *Concert*
(5/94) (BELA) ① 450 145-2
Philadelphia, R. Muti (r1993) *Concert*
(7/94) (EMI) ① CDC5 55120-2
Boston SO, P. Monteux (r1954) *Concert*
(9/94) (RCA) ① [15] 09026 61893-2
Cleveland Orch, P. Boulez *Concert*
(3/95) (DG) ① 439 896-2GH
Detroit SO, P. Paray (r1955) *Concert*
(6/95) (MERC) ① 434 343-2MM

Chicago SO, F. Reiner (r1960) *Concert*
  (9/95) (RCA) ① **09026 68079-2**
Concertgebouw, C. M. Giulini (r1995) *Concert*
  (11/95) (SONY) ① **SK66832**
BPO, H. von Karajan (r1964) *Concert*
  (12/95) (DG) ① **447 426-2GOR**
**Marche écossaise sur un thème
  populaire—orchestra (1894-96)** (after piano
  work)
FNO, D-E. Inghelbrecht (r1958) *Concert*
  (10/88) (MONT) ① [2] **TCE8790**
FRNO, J. Martinon *Concert*
  (3/89) (EMI) ① **CDM7 69587-2**
NBC SO, A. Toscanini (bp1940) *Concert*
  (6/90) (DELL) ① **CDDA9021**
Ulster Orch, Y.P. Tortelier (r1992) *Concert*
  (5/93) (CHAN) ① **CHAN9129**
Belgian Rad & TV Orch, A. Rahbari (r1992) *Concert*
  (11/93) (NAXO) ① **8 550505**
Concertgebouw, B. Haitink (r1976) *Concert*
  (3/94) (PHIL) ① [2] **438 742-2PM2**
**Le Martyre de Saint Sébastien—symphonic
  fragments from mystère (1911)** (arr A
  Caplet)
1. La Cour de Lys; 2. Danse extatique; 3. La
  Chambre magique; 4. La Passion; 5. Le Laurier
  blessé; 6. Le Bon Pasteur.
Belgian Rad & TV Orch, A. Rahbari (r1992) *Concert*
  (11/93) (NAXO) ① **8 550505**
1. Paris Orch, D. Barenboim *Concert*
  (11/91) (DG) ① **435 069-2GGA**
1, 2, 4, 6. Philh, G. Cantelli (r1954) *Concert*
  (10/92) (TEST) ① **SBT1011**
1, 2, 4, 6. Los Angeles PO, E-P. Salonen (r1993)
  Concert (12/94) (SONY) ① **SK58952**
Nocturnes (1900)
1. Nuages; 2. Fêtes; 3. Sirènes (with women's choir).
FRN Chor, FNO, D-E. Inghelbrecht (bp1963) *Pelléas
  et Mélisande.* (8/88) (MONT) ① [3] **TCE8710**
ORTF Chor, FRNO, J. Martinon *Concert*
  (3/89) (EMI) ① **CDM7 69587-2**
LSC, LSO, R. Frühbeck de Burgos *Concert*
  (6/89) (CARL) ① **PCD915**
Toulouse Mid-Pyrénées Chor, Toulouse Capitole
  Orch, M. Plasson *Concert*
  (1/90) (EMI) ① **CDC7 49472-2**
S. Coombs, Christopher Scott (trans. 2 pfs: Ravel)
  Concert (1/90) (HYPE) ① **CDA66468**
Montreal Sym Chor, Montreal SO, C. Dutoit *Images.*
  (6/90) (DECC) ① **425 502-2DH**
Philh Chor, Philh, G. Simon *Concert*
  (5/91) (CALA) ① **CACD1002**
French Rad Maîtrise, Paris Orch, J. Barbirolli *Concert*
  (5/91) (EMI) ① [2] **CZS7 62669-2**
Cleveland Orch Chor, Cleveland Orch, Vladimir
  Ashkenazy *Concert*
  (8/91) (DECC) ① **430 732-2DM**
Renaissance Sngrs, Grosvenor High Sch Ch (Female
  Voices), Ulster Orch, Y.P. Tortelier *Concert*
  (10/91) (CHAN) ① **CHAN8914**
Suisse Romande Chbr Ch, SRO, A. Jordan *Concert*
  (11/91) (ERAT) ① **2292-45605-2**
Paris Orch Chor, Paris Orch, D. Barenboim *Concert*
  (11/91) (DG) ① **435 069-2GGA**
Chicago Sym Chor, Chicago SO, G. Solti *Concert*
  (10/92) (DECC) ① **436 468-2DH**
Rhine Op Chor, Strasbourg PO, A. Lombard (r1981)
  Concert (12/93) (ERAT) ① **4509-92867-2**
Paris Orch Chor, Paris Orch, D. Barenboim (r1978)
  Concert (1/94) (DG) ① **439 407-2GCL**
Concertgebouw, B. Haitink (r1979) *Concert*
  (3/94) (PHIL) ① [2] **438 742-2PM2**
Temple Univ Women's Ch, Philadelphia, E. Ormandy
  (r1964) *Concert* (3/94) (SONY) ① **SBK53256**
Concertgebouw, Netherlands Rad Women's Ch, E.
  Inbal (r1969) *Concert* (5/94) (BELA) ① **450 145-2**
Berkshire Fest Chor, Boston SO, P. Monteux (r1955)
  Concert (9/94) (RCA) ① [15] **09026 61893-2**
Los Angeles Master Chorale, Los Angeles PO, E-P.
  Salonen (r1993) *Concert*
  (12/94) (SONY) ① **SK58952**
Cleveland Orch Chor, Cleveland Orch, P. Boulez
  Concert (3/95) (DG) ① **439 896-2GH**
Philadelphia, L. Stokowski (r1937/9) *Concert*
  (8/95) (BIDD) ① **WHL013**
1. NBC SO, A. Toscanini (bp1952) *Concert*
  (2/92) (RCA) ① **GD60265**
1, 2. Boston SO, C. Munch *Concert*
  (7/88) (RCA) ① **GD86719**
1, 2. Berlin St Op Orch, O. Klemperer (r1926)
  Concert (2/89) (SYMP) ① **SYMCD1042**
1, 2. NYPSO, F. Reiner (r1938) *Concert*
  (4/92) (PEAR) ① [3] **GEMMCDS9922**
1, 2. Philh, G. Cantelli (r1955) *Concert*
  (10/92) (TEST) ① **SBT1011**

1, 2. NYPO, L. Bernstein *Concert*
  (5/93) (SONY) ① **SMK47546**
2. NBC SO, A. Toscanini (bp1948) *Concert*
  (2/92) (RCA) ① **GD60265**
Petite Suite (orch Büsser from piano duet,
  1886-89)
1. En bateau; 2. Cortège; 3. Menuet; 4. Ballet.
FRNO, J. Martinon *Concert*
  (10/89) (EMI) ① **CDM7 69589-2**
Philh, G. Simon *Concert*
  (5/91) (CALA) ① **CACD1001**
Northern Sinfonia, J-B. Pommier *Concert*
  (12/91) (VIRG) ① **VJ7 59655-2**
1. ECO, P. Tortelier (arr Mouton) *Concert*
  (7/88) (VIRG) ① **VC7 59668-2**
1. J. Bálint, N. Mercz (r1992: arr fl/hp: Mercz) *Concert*
  (12/94) (NAXO) ① **8 550741**
1, 4. SO, T. Beecham (r1918) *Concert*
  (11/91) (SYMP) ① [2] **SYMCD1096/7**
4. G. Oppenheimer, M. Robles, COE, J. Galway
  (fl/dir) (ed. Galway) *Concert*
  (5/87) (RCA) ① **RD87173**
La Plus que lente—orchestra (pub 1912)
  (orch cpsr from piano work)
Ulster Orch, Y.P. Tortelier (r1991) *Concert*
  (5/93) (CHAN) ① **CHAN9129**
Montreal SO, C. Dutoit (r1994) *Concert*
  (8/95) (DECC) ① **444 386-2DH**
Prélude à l'après-midi d'un faune (1892-4)
St. Louis SO, L. Slatkin *Concert*
  (9/85) (TELA) ① **CD80071**
LSO, G. Simon *Concert*
  (3/87) (CALA) ① [2] **CACD0101**
LPO, S. Baudo *Concert*
  (10/87) (EMIN) ① **CD-EMX9502**
Czech PO, S. Baudo *Concert*
  (12/87) (SUPR) ① **2SUP0023**
LSO, C. Abbado *Concert*
  (3/88) (DG) ① **423 103-2GH**
ECO, P. Tortelier *Concert*
  (7/88) (VIRG) ① **VC7 59668-2**
Boston SO, C. Munch *Concert*
  (7/88) (RCA) ① **GD86719**
FNO, D-E. Inghelbrecht (r1962) *Concert*
  (10/88) (MONT) ① [2] **TCE8790**
FRNO, J. Martinon *Concert*
  (3/89) (EMI) ① **CDM7 69587-2**
LSO, R. Frühbeck de Burgos *Concert*
  (6/89) (CARL) ① **PCD915**
BPO, H. von Karajan (r1964) *Concert*
  (7/89) (DG) ① **427 250-2GGA**
Boston SO, M. Tilson Thomas *Concert*
  (10/89) (DG) ① **427 213-2GR**
Toulouse Capitole Orch, M. Plasson *Concert*
  (1/90) (EMI) ① **CDC7 49472-2**
M. Vengerov, I. Vinogradova (arr Heifetz) *Concert*
  (4/90) (BIDD) ① **LAW001**
RPO, T. Beecham *Concert*
  (7/90) (EMI) ① **CDM7 63379-2**
Santa Cecilia Academy Orch, L. Bernstein (pp1989)
  Concert (1/91) (DG) ① **429 728-2GH**
Ulster Orch, Y. P. Tortelier *Ravel: Daphnis et Chloé.*
  (7/91) (CHAN) ① **CHAN8893**
Cleveland Orch, Vladimir Ashkenazy *Concert*
  (8/91) (DECC) ① **430 732-2DM**
SRO, A. Jordan *Concert*
  (11/91) (ERAT) ① **2292-45605-2**
Concertgebouw, W. Mengelberg (r1938) *Concert*
  (12/91) (ARHI) ① **ADCD107**
Bergen PO, D. Kitaienko *Concert*
  (12/91) (VIRG) ① **VJ7 59659-2**
NBC SO, A. Toscanini (bp1953) *Concert*
  (2/92) (RCA) ① **GD60265**
Cleveland Orch, P. Boulez *Concert*
  (9/92) (DG) ① **435 766-2GH**
Chicago SO, G. Solti *Concert*
  (10/92) (DECC) ① **436 468-2DH**
Philh, G. Cantelli (r1954) *Concert*
  (10/92) (TEST) ① **SBT1011**
BPO, H. von Karajan (r1964) *Concert*
  (11/92) (EMI) ① **CDM7 64357-2**
LSO, M. Tilson Thomas *Concert*
  (11/92) (SONY) ① **SK48231**
NYPO, L. Bernstein *Concert*
  (5/93) (SONY) ① **SMK47546**
LPO, T. Beecham (r1939) *Concert*
  (10/93) (DUTT) ① **CDLX7002**
Strasbourg PO, A. Lombard (r1975) *Concert*
  (12/93) (ERAT) ① **4509-92867-2**
Paris Orch, D. Barenboim (r1981) *Concert*
  (1/94) (DG) ① **439 407-2GCL**
Hessian RO, L. Stokowski (bp1955) *Concert*
  (3/94) (MUSI) ① **MACD-778**
Concertgebouw, B. Haitink (r1976) *Concert*
  (3/94) (PHIL) ① [2] **438 742-2PM2**

Philadelphia, E. Ormandy (r1959) *Concert*
  (3/94) (SONY) ① **SBK53256**
Finnish RSO, J-P. Saraste (r1991) *Concert*
  (4/94) (VIRG) ① **VC5 45018-2**
Concertgebouw, J. Fournet (r1959) *Concert*
  (5/94) (BELA) ① **450 145-2**
LPO, T. Beecham (r1939) *Concert*
  (7/94) (PEAR) ① **GEMMCD9065**
Detroit SO, P. Paray (r1955) *Concert*
  (6/95) (MERC) ① **434 343-2MM**
Hallé, J. Barbirolli (r1953) *Concert*
  (7/95) (DUTT) ① **CDSJB1002**
Philadelphia, L. Stokowski (r1940) *Concert*
  (8/95) (BIDD) ① **WHL013**
Concertgebouw, C. M. Giulini (r1995) *Concert*
  (11/95) (SONY) ① **SK66832**
**Première rapsodie—clarinet and orchestra
  (1911)** (arr cpsr from chamber work)
E. Johnson, ECO, Y.P. Tortelier *Concert*
  (9/87) (ASV) ① **CDDCA585**
A. Boutard, Czech PO, S. Baudo *Concert*
  (12/87) (SUPR) ① **2SUP0023**
J. Campbell, Philh, G. Simon *Concert*
  (5/91) (CALA) ① **CACD1001**
C. King, Ulster Orch, Y.P. Tortelier *Concert*
  (9/92) (CHAN) ① **CHAN8972**
K. Kriikku, Finnish RSO, J-P. Saraste *Concert*
  (10/92) (ONDI) ① **ODE778-2**
S. Drucker, NYPO, L. Bernstein *Concert*
  (5/93) (SONY) ① **SMK47545**
Monte Carlo Op Orch, A. Jordan (r1981) *Concert*
  (12/93) (ERAT) ① **4509-92867-2**
G. Hamelin, orch, P. Coppola (r1931) *Concert*
  (2/94) (CLRI) ① **CC0005**
G. Pieterson, Concertgebouw, B. Haitink (r1976)
  Concert (3/94) (PHIL) ① [2] **438 742-2PM2**
F. Cohen, Cleveland Orch, P. Boulez *Concert*
  (3/95) (DG) ① **439 896-2GH**
Printemps—symphonic suite (1887)
Boston SO, C. Munch *Concert*
  (7/88) (RCA) ① **GD86719**
Toulouse Capitole Orch, M. Plasson *Concert*
  (1/90) (EMI) ① **CDC7 49472-2**
Paris Orch, D. Barenboim *Concert*
  (11/91) (DG) ① **435 069-2GGA**
Cleveland Orch, P. Boulez *Concert*
  (9/92) (DG) ① **435 766-2GH**
Ulster Orch, Y. P. Tortelier *Concert*
  (3/93) (CHAN) ① **CHAN9114**
Finnish RSO, J-P. Saraste (r1991) *Concert*
  (4/94) (VIRG) ① **VC5 45018-2**
Montreal SO, C. Dutoit (r1994) *Concert*
  (8/95) (DECC) ① **444 386-2DH**
**Rapsodie—saxophone and orchestra (1901-
  08)** (orch cpted Roger-Ducasse)
M. Viard, orch, P. Coppola (r c1930) *Concert*
  (9/90) (PEAR) ① **GEMMCD9348**
J. Harle, ASMF, N. Marriner *Concert*
  (1/92) (EMI) ① **CDC7 54301-2**
G. McChrystal, Ulster Orch, Y.P. Tortelier (r1992)
  Concert (5/93) (CHAN) ① **CHAN9129**

SECTION II: CHAMBER

**Danse sacrée et danse profane—two pianos
  (1904)** (arr cpsr)
S. Coombs, Christopher Scott *Concert*
  (1/90) (HYPE) ① **CDA66468**
En blanc et noir—two pianos (1915)
S. Coombs, Christopher Scott *Concert*
  (1/90) (HYPE) ① **CDA66468**
W. Haas, N. Lee (r1970) *Concert*
  (4/94) (PHIL) ① [2] **438 721-2PM2**
6 Epigraphes antiques—piano duet (1914)
  (Based on Chansons de Bilitis - 1901 version)
Crommelynck Duo *Concert*
  (8/86) (CLAV) ① **CD50-8508**
W. Haas, N. Lee (r1970) *Concert*
  (4/94) (PHIL) ① [2] **438 721-2PM2**
Lindaraja—two pianos (1901)
S. Coombs, Christopher Scott *Concert*
  (1/90) (HYPE) ① **CDA66468**
W. Haas, N. Lee (r1970) *Concert*
  (4/94) (PHIL) ① [2] **438 721-2PM2**
**Marche écossaise sur un thème
  populaire—two pianos (1891)**
Crommelynck Duo *Concert*
  (8/86) (CLAV) ① **CD50-8508**
W. Haas, N. Lee (r1970) *Concert*
  (4/94) (PHIL) ① [2] **438 721-2PM2**
Petite pièce—piano duet (1886-89)
Athena Ens *Concert* (5/87) (CHAN) ① **CHAN8385**
J. Campbell, J. York (r1994) *Concert*
  (2/95) (CALA) ① [2] **CACD1017**
Petite pièce—clarinet and piano (1909-10)
P. Meyer, E. Le Sage *Concert*
  (9/92) (DENO) ① **CO-79282**

Petite suite—piano duet (1886-89)
1. En bateau; 2. Cortège; 3. Menuet; 4. Ballet.
Crommelynck Duo *Concert*
(8/86) (CLAV) ① **CD50-8508**
Selandia Ens *Concert* (6/90) (KONT) ① **32032**
C. Cann, A. Cann (r1992) *Concert*
(5/93) (PP) ① **PP10393**
W. Haas, N. Lee (r1970) *Concert*
(4/94) (PHIL) ① [2] **438 721-2PM2**
1. F. Kreisler, C. Lamson (arr Kreisler: r1928)
Concert (1/90) (PEARL) ① **GEMMCD9324**
1. F. Kreisler, A. Sándor (arr Choisnel: r1926)
Concert (9/92) (BIDD) ① [2] **LAB049/50**
1. F. Kreisler, C. Lamson (r1928: arr Choisnel)
Concert (12/93) (BIDD) ① **LAB080**
1. B. Fromanger, M. Klinko (r1993: arr fl/hp:
Mildonian) *Concert* (2/94) (EMI) ① **CDC7 54884-2**
3. J. Szigeti, K. Ruhrseitz (arr Dushkin: r1927)
Concert (1/90) (BIDD) ① [2] **LAB005/6**
3. P. Casals, N. Mednikoff (arr Choisnel: r1926)
Concert (10/91) (BIDD) ① **LAB017**
3. J. Starker, G. Moore (r1958: arr vc/pf: Gurt)
Concert (12/95) (EMI) ① [6] **CZS5 68485-2**
3, 4. B. Eden, A. Tamir *Concert*
(6/90) (CARL) ① **PWK1134**
La Plus que lente—violin and piano (1910)
(arr Léon Roques with approval of Debussy)
J. Heifetz, E. Bay (r1946) *Concert*
(11/94) (RCA) ① [65] **09026 61778-2(40)**
J. Heifetz, I. Achron (r1925) *Concert*
(11/94) (RCA) ① [65] **09026 61778-2(02)**
J. Heifetz, B. Smith (r1972) *Concert*
(11/94) (RCA) ① [65] **09026 61778-2(46)**
**Prélude à l'après-midi d'un faune—two
pianos (1895)** (arr cpsr from orchestral
version)
S. Coombs, Christopher Scott *Concert*
(1/90) (HYPE) ① **CDA66468**
K. Jones, C. Edwards (r1993: arr fl/pf) *Concert*
(10/94) (CONI) ① [2] **CDCF905**
Premier trio in G—piano trio (c.1879)
(unpublished)
Parnassus Trio *Ravel: Piano Trio.*
(12/87) (MDG) ① **L3272**
J-J. Kantorow, P. Muller, J. Rouvier *Concert*
(2/89) (DENO) ① **CO-72508**
Trio di Milano *Concert* (5/89) (DYNA) ① **CDS49**
Solomon Trio *Concert* (7/92) (CARL) ① **MCD41**
Borodin Trio *Concert* (7/92) (CHAN) ① **CHAN9016**
Fontenay Trio *Concert*
(7/92) (TELD) ① **2292-44937-2**
Golub Kaplan Carr Trio *Concert*
(7/95) (ARAB) ① **Z6643**
Joachim Trio (r1993) *Concert*
(8/95) (NAXO) ① **8 550934**
A. Previn, J. Rosenfeld, G. Hoffman (r1992) *Ravel:
Piano Trio.* (11/95) (RCA) ① **09026 68062-2**
**Première rapsodie—clarinet and piano
(1909-10)**
Athena Ens *Concert* (5/87) (CHAN) ① **CHAN8385**
P. Meyer, E. Le Sage *Concert*
(9/92) (DENO) ① **CO-79282**
M. Collins, K. Stott *Concert*
(9/92) (EMI) ① **CDC7 54419-2**
J. Campbell, J. York (r1994) *Concert*
(2/95) (CALA) ① [2] **CACD1017**
**Rapsodie—clarinet/cor anglais and piano
(1901-08)**
S. Haram, J. York (r1994) *Concert*
(2/95) (CALA) ① [2] **CACD1017**
N. Daniel, J. Drake (r1994: arr cor ang) *Concert*
(2/95) (CALA) ① [2] **CACD1017**
Sonata for Cello and Piano (1915)
Athena Ens *Concert* (5/87) (CHAN) ① **CHAN8385**
Y. Turovsky, L. Edlina *Concert*
(5/87) (CHAN) ① **CHAN8458**
M. Rostropovich, B. Britten (r1961) *Concert*
(9/87) (DECC) ① **417 833-2DH**
M. Maréchal, R. Casadesus (r1930) *Concert*
(9/90) (PEAR) ① **GEMMCD9348**
M. Maisky, M. Argerich *Concert*
(2/91) (EMI) ① **CDM7 63577-2**
C. van Kampen, I. Brown *Concert*
(4/91) (VIRG) ① **VC7 59604-2**
N. Fischer, J.K. Fischer *Concert*
(9/91) (NORT) ① **NR238-CD**
W. Conway, Peter Evans *Concert*
(11/91) (LINN) ① **CKD002**
B. Gregor-Smith, Y. Wrigley *Concert*
(9/92) (ASV) ① **CDDCA796**
P. Tortelier, G. Moore (r1948) *Concert*
(12/95) (EMI) ① **CDH5 65502-2**
L. Harrell, Vladimir Ashkenazy (r1994) *Concert*
(12/95) (DECC) ① **444 318-2DH**
Sonata for Flute, Viola and Harp (1915)
Athena Ens *Concert* (5/87) (CHAN) ① **CHAN8385**

G. Oppenheimer, M. Robles, COE, J. Galway (fl/dir)
(ed. Galway/Robles) *Concert*
(5/87) (RCA) ① **RD87173**
S. Kanga, ASMF Chbr Ens *Concert*
(12/88) (CHAN) ① **CHAN8621**
O. Ellis, Melos Ens *Concert*
(1/89) (DECC) ① **421 154-2DM**
Netherlands Harp Ens *Concert*
(5/89) (ETCE) ① **KTC1021**
M. Jurkovič, M. Telecký, K. Nováková *Concert*
(9/89) (OPUS) ① **9351 1894**
Prometheus Ens *Concert*
(11/89) (ASV) ① **CDDCA664**
E. Talmi, G. Levertov, A. Giles *Concert*
(6/90) (CARL) ① **PWK1141**
M. Moyse, E. Ginot, L. Laskine (r c1927) *Concert*
(9/90) (PEAR) ① **GEMMCD9348**
W. Schulz, W. Christ, M-A. Süss *Concert*
(3/91) (DG) ① **429 738-2GH**
Philippa Davies, R. Chase, M. Robles *Concert*
(4/91) (VIRG) ① **VC7 59604-2**
M. Debost, Y. Menuhin, L. Laskine *Concert*
(4/91) (EMI) ① **CDM7 63986-2**
Auréole (r1991) *Concert* (7/93) (KOCH) ① **37102-2**
B. Fromanger, P. Lénert, M. Klinko (r1993) *Concert*
(2/94) (EMI) ① **CDC7 54884-2**
A. Nicolet, N. Imai, N. Yoshino (r1993) *Concert*
(12/94) (PHIL) ① **442 012-2PH**
W. Bennett, R. Tapping, I. Jones (r1994) *Concert*
(2/95) (CALA) ① [2] **CACD1017**
Sonata for Violin and Piano (1916-17)
Athena Ens *Concert* (5/87) (CHAN) ① **CHAN8385**
R. Dubinsky, L. Edlina *Concert*
(5/87) (CHAN) ① **CHAN8458**
K-W. Chung, R. Lupu *Concert*
(1/89) (DECC) ① **421 154-2DM**
J. Thibaud, A. Cortot (r1929) *Concert*
(7/89) (EMI) ① **CDH7 63032-2**
J-J. Kantorow, J. Rouvier *Concert*
(8/89) (DENO) ① **CO-72718**
D. Sitkovetsky, P. Gililov *Concert*
(9/89) (VIRG) ① **VC5 45002-2**
M. Rostal, C. Horsley (r1950s) *Concert*
(6/90) (SYMP) ① **SYMCD1076**
G. Neveu, J. Neveu (r1948) *Concert*
(8/90) (EMI) ① **CDH7 63493-2**
J. Thibaud, A. Cortot (r1929) *Concert*
(9/90) (PEAR) ① **GEMMCD9348**
J. Heifetz, E. Bay (r1950) *Concert*
(9/90) (RCA) ① **GD87871**
D-S. Kang, P. Devoyon *Concert*
(11/90) (NAXO) ① **8 550276**
M. Crayford, I. Brown *Concert*
(4/91) (VIRG) ① **VC7 59604-2**
Y. Menuhin, J. Février *Concert*
(4/91) (EMI) ① **CDM7 63986-2**
J. Thibaud, A. Cortot (r1929) *Concert*
(10/91) (MSCM) ① **MM30321**
F.P. Zimmermann, A. Lonquich *Concert*
(6/92) (EMI) ① **CDC7 54305-2**
J. Thibaud, A. Cortot (r1929) *Concert*
(6/92) (BIDD) ① **LHW006**
A. Grumiaux, R. Castagnone (r1955) *Concert*
(11/93) (PHIL) ① [3] **438 516-2PM3**
Chee-Yun, A. Eguchi (r1993) *Concert*
(1/94) (DENO) ① **CO-75625**
K. Takezawa, R. de Silva (r1992) *Concert*
(3/94) (RCA) ① **09026 61386-2**
J. Szigeti, A. Foldes (r1941) *Concert*
(7/94) (BIDD) ① [2] **LAB070/1**
G. Poulet, N. Lee (r1993) *Concert*
(9/94) (ARIO) ① **ARN68228**
J. Heifetz, E. Bay (r1950) *Concert*
(11/94) (RCA) ① [65] **09026 61778-2(44)**
P. Zukerman, M. Neikrug (r1993) *Concert*
(5/95) (RCA) ① **09026 62697-2**
I. van Keulen, R. Brautigam (r1994) *Concert*
(10/95) (SCHW) ① **315272**
A. Dumay, M-J. Pires (r1993) *Concert*
(10/95) (DG) ① **445 880-2GH**
C. Tetzlaff, L. O. Andsnes (r1994) *Concert*
(11/95) (VIRG) ① **VC5 45122-2**
I. Perlman, Vladimir Ashkenazy (r1994) *Concert*
(12/95) (DECC) ① **444 318-2DH**
T. Little, P. Lane (r1995) *Concert*
(12/95) (EMIN) ① **CD-EMX2244**
String Quartet in G minor, Op. 10 (1893)
Alban Berg Qt (r1984) *Ravel: String Quartet.*
(8/86) (EMI) ① **CDC7 47347-2**
Cleveland Qt (r1985) *Ravel: String Quartet.*
(3/87) (TELA) ① **CD80111**
Viotti Qt *Concert* (3/87) (PIER) ① **PV786102**
Quartetto Italiano (r1965) *Ravel: String Quartet.*
(10/88) (PHIL) ① **420 894-2PSL**
Talich Qt *Concert* (11/89) (CALL) ① **CAL9893**

Budapest Qt *Ravel: string quartet.*
(10/90) (SONY) ① **MPK44843**
New World Qt *Concert* (1/91) (CARL) ① **MCD17**
Talich Qt *Ravel: String Quartet.*
(4/91) (SUPR) ① **10 4110-2**
Danish Qt *Ravel: String Quartet.*
(8/92) (AUVI) ① **V4409**
LaSalle Qt *Ravel: String Quartet.*
(9/92) (DG) ① **435 589-2GGA**
Carmina Qt *Ravel: String Quartet.*
(3/93) (DENO) ① **CO-75164**
Juilliard Qt (r1989) *Concert*
(3/94) (SONY) ① **SK52554**
Hagen Qt (r1992-3) *Concert*
(6/94) (DG) ① **437 836-2GH**
Vogler Qt (r1993) *Concert*
(7/94) (RCA) ① **09026 61816-2**
Emerson Qt (r1984) *Ravel: String Quartet.*
(12/94) (DG) ① **445 509-2GMA**
Keller Qt (r1993) *Ravel: String Quartet.*
(2/95) (ERAT) ① **4509-96361-2**
Tokyo Qt (r1992/4) *Concert*
(4/95) (RCA) ① **09026 62552-2**
Parisii Qt (r1994) *Concert* (10/95) (AUVI) ① **V4730**
Lindsay Qt (r1994) *Concert*
(12/95) (ASV) ① **CDDCA930**

SECTION III: INSTRUMENTAL

---

2 Arabesques (1888-91)
EXCERPTS: 1. No 1; 2. No 2.
J. Rouvier *Concert* (5/86) (DENO) ① **C37-7734**
C. Ortiz *Concert* (6/87) (CARL) ① **PCD846**
K. Stott *Concert* (9/87) (CONI) ① **CDCF148**
T. Paraskivesco *Concert*
(8/88) (CALL) ① [4] **CAL9831/4**
Martin Jones *Concert* (7/89) (NIMB) ① **NI5160**
P. Rogé *Concert* (2/90) (DECC) ① **417 792-2DM**
Z. Kocsis *Concert* (2/90) (PHIL) ① **422 404-2PH**
G. Fergus-Thompson *Concert*
(10/90) (ASV) ① **CDDCA720**
N. Lee *Concert* (11/90) (AUVI) ① [4] **V4440**
Philh, G. Simon (orch Mouton) *Concert*
(5/91) (CALA) ① **CACD1001**
L. Rév *Concert* (4/92) (SAGA) ① **EC3376-2**
A. Ciccolini *Concert* (6/92) (EMI) ① **CDC7 54451-2**
M. Long (r c1930) *Concert*
(1/93) (PEAR) ① **GEMMCD9927**
W. Haas (r1961-3) *Concert*
(4/94) (PHIL) ① [2] **438 718-2PM2**
P. Crossley (r1993) *Concert*
(6/94) (SONY) ① **SK53973**
M. Lympany (r1993) *Concert*
(10/94) (CFP) ① **CD-CFP4653**
P. Rogé (r1977) *Concert*
(12/94) (DECC) ① [2] **443 021-2DF2**
1. G. Fergus-Thompson *Concert*
(9/92) (ASV) ① **CDWHL2066**
1. S. Cherkassky (bp1988) *Concert*
(6/93) (DECC) ① **433 651-2DH**
1. M. Klinko (arr hp) *Concert*
(8/93) (EMI) ① **CDC7 54467-2**
2. I. Scharrer (r1926) *Concert*
(7/94) (PEAR) ① **GEMMCD9978**
Ballade—piano solo (1890) (orig pub as
Ballade slave)
J. Rouvier *Concert* (5/86) (DENO) ① **C37-7734**
K. Stott *Concert* (9/87) (CONI) ① **CDCF148**
Martin Jones *Concert* (7/89) (NIMB) ① **NI5160**
G. Fergus-Thompson *Concert*
(9/90) (ASV) ① **CDDCA711**
N. Lee *Concert* (11/90) (AUVI) ① [4] **V4440**
L. Rév *Concert* (4/92) (SAGA) ① **EC3383-2**
A. Ciccolini *Concert* (6/92) (EMI) ① **CDC7 54447-2**
W. Haas (r1970) *Concert*
(4/94) (PHIL) ① [2] **438 721-2PM2**
P. Crossley (r1993) *Concert*
(6/94) (SONY) ① **SK53973**
Berceuse héroïque (1914)
J. Rouvier *Concert* (7/85) (DENO) ① **C37-7372**
T. Paraskivesco *Concert*
(8/88) (CALL) ① [4] **CAL9831/4**
Martin Jones *Concert* (2/90) (NIMB) ① **NI5164**
Z. Kocsis *Concert* (2/90) (PHIL) ① **422 404-2PH**
G. Fergus-Thompson *Concert*
(9/90) (ASV) ① **CDDCA711**
N. Lee *Concert* (11/90) (AUVI) ① [4] **V4440**
L. Rév *Concert* (4/92) (SAGA) ① **EC3383-2**
A. Ciccolini *Concert* (6/92) (EMI) ① **CDC7 54451-2**
P. Crossley (r1992) *Concert*
(2/94) (SONY) ① **SK53281**
W. Haas (r1970) *Concert*
(4/94) (PHIL) ① [2] **438 721-2PM2**
La Boîte à joujoux—piano (1913)
N. Lee *Concert* (11/90) (AUVI) ① [4] **V4440**
A. Ciccolini *Préludes.*
(6/92) (EMI) ① **CDC7 54448-2**

Montreal SO, C. Dutoit (r1992: orch Caplet) *Concert*
(8/95) (DECC) ① **444 386-2DH**

Children's Corner—suite (1906-8)
1. Doctor Gradus ad Parnassum; 2. Jimbo's lullaby;
3. Serenade for a doll; 4. The snow is dancing; 5. The
little shepherd; 6. Golliwog's cakewalk.
J. Rouvier *Concert*   (7/85) (DENO) ① **C37-7372**
A.B. Michelangeli (r1971) *Images*.
(7/86) (DG) ① **415 372-2GH**
T. Paraskivesco *Concert*
(8/88) (CALL) ① [4] **CAL9831/4**
Martin Jones *Concert*   (7/89) (NIMB) ① **NI5161**
FRNO, J. Martinon (orch Caplet) *Concert*
(10/89) (EMI) ① **CDM7 69589-2**
P. Rogé *Concert*   (2/90) (DECC) ① **417 792-2DM**
G. Fergus-Thompson *Concert*
(5/90) (ASV) ① **CDDCA695**
A. Vardi *Concert*   (6/90) (CARL) ① **PWK1132**
N. Lee *Concert*   (11/90) (AUVI) ① [4] **V4440**
Philh, G. Simon (orch Caplet) *Concert*
(5/91) (CALA) ① **CACD1002**
M. Horszowski (pp1986) *Concert*
(4/92) (LYRN) ① **LYRCD070**
L. Rév *Concert*   (4/92) (SAGA) ① **EC3377-2**
A. Cortot (r1928) *Concert*   (6/92) (BIDD) ① **LHW006**
A. Ciccolini *Concert*   (6/92) (EMI) ① **CDC7 54450-2**
P. Katin (r1990) *Concert*   (7/93) (SIMA) ① **PSC1067**
P. Crossley (r1992) *Concert*
(9/93) (SONY) ① **SK53111**
M. Horszowski (r1980s) *Concert*
(12/93) (NONE) ① [3] **7559-79261-2**
W. Haas (r1960s) *Concert*
(4/94) (PHIL) ① [2] **438 718-2PM2**
I. Biret (r1993) *Concert*
(10/94) (NAXO) ① **8 550885**
M. Lympany (r1993) *Concert*
(10/94) (CFP) ① **CD-CFP4653**
P. Cassard (r1993) *Concert*
(10/94) (ASTR) ① **E8531**
W. Kapell (bp c1951) *Concert*
(11/94) (VAI) ① **VAIA1048**
P. Rogé (r1979) *Concert*
(12/94) (DECC) ① [2] **443 021-2DF2**
L. Rév (r1991) *Concert*
(6/95) (HYPE) ① [3] **CDS44061/3**
Montreal SO, C. Dutoit (r1994: orch Caplet) *Concert*
(8/95) (DECC) ① **444 386-2DH**
Rhineland-Pfalz State PO, L. Segerstam (r1987:orch
Caplet) *Concert*   (9/95) (MARC) ① **8 223751**
1, 5. L. Rév *Concert*   (7/87) (HYPE) ① **CDA66185**
1, 6. S. Rachmaninov (r1921) *Concert*
(3/93) (RCA) ① [10] **09026 61265-2(3)**
3. V. Horowitz (bp1933) *Concert*
(8/92) (DANA) ① **DACOCD303**
3. V. Horowitz (r1928) *Concert*
(1/93) (APR) ① [2] **APR7014**
3. V. Horowitz (pp1953) *Concert*
(1/93) (RCA) ① **GD60463**
3. V. Horowitz (r1928) *Concert*
(1/93) (RCA) ① **GD60526**
3. V. Horowitz (pp1965) *Concert*
(7/94) (SONY) ① [3] **S3K53461**
3. A. Brailowsky (r1934) *Concert*
(11/95) (DANA) ① [2] **DACOCD338/9**
4, 5. O. De Spiegeleir (r1994) *Concert*
(10/95) (PAVA) ① **ADW7332**
5. G. Oppenheimer, M. Robles, COE, J. Galway
(fl/dir) *Concert*   (5/87) (RCA) ① **RD87173**
6. J. Lloyd Webber, ECO, N. Cleobury (arr C Palmer)
Concert   (3/85) (PHIL) ① **412 231-2PH**
6. C. Ortiz *Concert*   (6/87) (CARL) ① **PCD846**
6. M. Lympany *Concert*   (1/89) (EMIL) ① **CDZ110**
6. L. Godowsky (1925) *Concert*
(4/89) (APR) ① [2] **APR7011**
6. I. Perlman, S. Sanders (trans. Heifetz) *Concert*
(12/89) (EMI) ① **CDC7 49604-2**
6. Brodsky Qt (arr M. Thomas) *Concert*
(4/92) (TELD) ① **2292-46015-2**
6. J. Bream, J. Williams (1978; arr Bream) *Concert*
(11/93) (RCA) ① **09026 61452-2**
6. J. Heifetz, E. Bay (r1945) *Concert*
(11/94) (RCA) ① [65] **09026 61778-2(19)**
6. J. Heifetz, B. Smith (r1970) *Concert*
(11/94) (RCA) ① [65] **09026 61778-2(45)**
Danse bohémienne (1880)
J. Rouvier *Concert*   (7/85) (DENO) ① **C37-7372**
J. Rouvier *Concert*   (5/86) (DENO) ① **C37-7734**
Martin Jones *Concert*   (7/89) (NIMB) ① **NI5160**
G. Fergus-Thompson *Concert*
(9/90) (ASV) ① **CDDCA711**
N. Lee *Concert*   (11/90) (AUVI) ① [4] **V4440**
L. Rév *Concert*   (4/92) (SAGA) ① **EC3376-2**
A. Ciccolini *Concert*   (6/92) (EMI) ① **CDC7 54449-2**
Philadelphia, E. Ormandy (r1959: orch Ravel)
Concert   (3/94) (SONY) ① **SBK53256**

W. Haas (r1970) *Concert*
(4/94) (PHIL) ① [2] **438 721-2PM2**
P. Crossley (r1993) *Concert*
(6/94) (SONY) ① **SK53973**
P. Cassard (r1993) *Concert*
(10/94) (ASTR) ① **E8531**
D'un cahier d'esquisses (Equisse) (1903)
J. Rouvier *Concert*   (7/85) (DENO) ① **C37-7372**
Martin Jones *Concert*   (7/89) (NIMB) ① **NI5161**
Z. Kocsis *Concert*   (2/90) (PHIL) ① **422 404-2PH**
G. Fergus-Thompson *Concert*
(9/90) (ASV) ① **CDDCA711**
N. Lee *Concert*   (11/90) (AUVI) ① [4] **V4440**
L. Rév *Concert*   (4/92) (SAGA) ① **EC3383-2**
A. Ciccolini *Concert*   (6/92) (EMI) ① **CDC7 54451-2**
P. Crossley (r1992) *Concert*
(2/94) (SONY) ① **SK53281**
W. Haas (r1960s) *Concert*
(4/94) (PHIL) ① [2] **438 721-2PM2**
Elégie—piano (1915)
Martin Jones *Concert*   (2/90) (NIMB) ① **NI5164**
G. Fergus-Thompson *Concert*
(9/90) (ASV) ① **CDDCA711**
L. Rév *Concert*   (4/92) (SAGA) ① **EC3377-2**
A. Ciccolini *Concert*   (6/92) (EMI) ① **CDC7 54451-2**
P. Crossley (r1992) *Concert*
(2/94) (SONY) ① **SK53281**
6 Epigraphes antiques—piano solo (1914)
(arr cpsr from piano duet version)
T. Paraskivesco *Concert*
(8/88) (CALL) ① [4] **CAL9831/4**
Martin Jones *Concert*   (2/90) (NIMB) ① **NI5164**
A. Ciccolini *Concert*   (6/92) (EMI) ① **CDC7 54449-2**
Estampes (1903)
1. Pagodes; 2. Soirée dans Grenade; 3. Jardins sous
la pluie.
Z. Kocsis *Concert*   (4/85) (PHIL) ① **412 118-2PH**
J. Rouvier *Concert*   (7/87) (DENO) ① **CO-1411**
T. Paraskivesco *Concert*
(8/88) (CALL) ① [4] **CAL9831/4**
S. Richter (pp1962) *Concert*
(9/88) (DG) ① **423 573-2GDO**
Martin Jones *Concert*   (7/89) (NIMB) ① **NI5161**
G. Fergus-Thompson *Concert*
(5/90) (ASV) ① **CDDCA695**
N. Lee *Concert*   (11/90) (AUVI) ① [4] **V4440**
F. Ts'ong *Concert*   (6/91) (COLL) ① **Coll1052-2**
C. Arrau *Concert*
(2/92) (PHIL) ① [4] **432 304-2PM2**
A. Ciccolini *Concert*   (6/92) (EMI) ① **CDC7 54447-2**
P. Crossley (r1992) *Concert*
(9/93) (SONY) ① **SK53111**
W. Haas (r1960s) *Concert*
(4/94) (PHIL) ① [2] **438 718-2PM2**
P. Rogé (r1977) *Concert*
(12/94) (DECC) ① [2] **443 021-2DF2**
L. Zilberstein *Concert*   (2/95) (DG) ① **439 927-2GH**
G. Pludermacher (r1993) *Concert*
(3/95) (HARM) ① **HMC90 1503**
L. Rév (r1991) *Concert*
(6/95) (HYPE) ① [3] **CDS44061/3**
S. Richter (pp1962) *Concert*
(12/95) (DG) ① [2] **447 355-2GDB2**
P. Badura-Skoda *Concert*
(4/91) (HRMO) ① **H/CD8505**
1. Philh, G. Simon (orch Grainger) *Concert*
(5/91) (CALA) ① **CACD1001**
1. Rhineland-Pfalz State PO, L. Segerstam
(r1987:orch Caplet) *Concert*
(9/95) (MARC) ① **8 223751**
1, 3. W. Gieseking (r1930s) *Concert*
(4/91) (PEAR) ① **GEMMCD9449**
2. Philh, G. Simon (orch Stokowski) *Concert*
(5/91) (CALA) ① **CACD1002**
2. Philadelphia, L. Stokowski (r1940: orch Stokowski)
(5/95) (BIDD) ① **WHL013**
2, 3. V. Cliburn *Concert*   (5/91) (RCA) ① **GD60415**
2, 3. A. Rubinstein (r1945) *Concert*
(10/93) (RCA) ① **09026 61446-2**
3. C. Rosenberger *Concert*
(6/86) (DELO) ① **DE3006**
3. B. Moiseiwitsch (r1938) *Concert*
(9/90) (APR) ① [2] **APR7005**
3. C. Arrau (r1939) *Concert*
(9/92) (PEAR) ① **GEMMCD9928**
3. M. Long (r c1930) *Concert*
(1/93) (PEAR) ① **GEMMCD9927**
3. O. De Spiegeleir (r1994) *Concert*
(10/95) (PAVA) ① **ADW7332**
12 Etudes—piano (1915)
1. Pour les cinq doigts; 2. Pour les tierce; 3. Pour les
quartes; 4. Pour les sixtes; 5. Pour les octaves; 6.
Pour les huits doigts; 7. Pour les degrés
chromatiques; 8. Pour les agréments; 9. Pour les
notes répétés; 10. Pour les sonorités opposées; 11.
Pour les arpèges composés; 12. Pour les accords.

T. Paraskivesco *Concert*
(8/88) (CALL) ① [4] **CAL9831/4**
J. Rouvier   (8/88) (DENO) ① **CO-2200**
G. Ohlsson *Suite bergamasque*.
(2/90) (ARAB) ① **Z6601**
Martin Jones *Concert*   (2/90) (NIMB) ① **NI5164**
M. Uchida   (7/90) (PHIL) ① **422 412-2PH**
G. Fergus-Thompson *Pour le piano*.
(7/90) (ASV) ① **CDDCA703**
J. Swann *Fauré: Préludes*.
(9/90) (MUSI) ① **MACD-608**
N. Lee *Concert*   (11/90) (AUVI) ① [4] **V4440**
L. Rév *Concert*   (4/92) (SAGA) ① **EC3383-2**
A. Ciccolini *Concert*   (6/92) (EMI) ① **CDC7 54450-2**
P. Crossley (r1992) *Concert*
(2/94) (SONY) ① **SK53281**
M. Pollini (r1992) *Berg: Piano Sonata*.
(3/94) (DG) ① **423 678-2GH**
W. Haas (r1960s) *Concert*
(4/94) (PHIL) ① [2] **438 721-2PM2**
1, 11. M. Lympany (r1993) *Concert*
(10/94) (CFP) ① **CD-CFP4653**
1, 3, 5, 7, 9, 11. J. MacGregor (r1993) *Concert*
(8/94) (COLL) ① **Coll1404-2**
5. V. Cliburn *Concert*   (5/91) (RCA) ① **GD60415**
11. V. Horowitz (r1934) *Concert*
(3/90) (EMI) ① [3] **CHS7 63538-2**
11. A. Ciccolini (early vers) *Concert*
(6/92) (EMI) ① **CDC7 54450-2**
11. V. Horowitz (pp1965) *Concert*
(7/94) (SONY) ① **SK53471**
Hommage à Haydn (1909)
J. Rouvier *Concert*   (5/86) (DENO) ① **C37-7734**
M. Fingerhut *Concert*   (9/88) (CHAN) ① **CHAN8578**
Martin Jones *Concert*   (2/90) (NIMB) ① **NI5164**
Z. Kocsis *Concert*   (2/90) (PHIL) ① **422 404-2PH**
G. Fergus-Thompson *Concert*
(9/90) (ASV) ① **CDDCA711**
N. Lee *Concert*   (11/90) (AUVI) ① [4] **V4440**
L. Rév *Concert*   (4/92) (SAGA) ① **EC3377-2**
A. Ciccolini *Concert*   (6/92) (EMI) ① **CDC7 54449-2**
P. Crossley (r1992) *Concert*
(2/94) (SONY) ① **SK53281**
W. Haas (r1960s) *Concert*
(4/94) (PHIL) ① [2] **438 721-2PM2**
Images (1905 & 1908)
SET 1; 1. Reflets dans l'eau; 2. Hommage à
Rameau; 3. Mouvement; SET 2; 4. Cloches à travers
les fenilles; 5. Et la lune descend sur le temple qui
fût; 6. Poissons d'or.
A.B. Michelangeli (r1971) *Children's Corner*.
(7/86) (DG) ① **415 372-2GH**
J. Rouvier *Concert*   (7/87) (DENO) ① **CO-1411**
T. Paraskivesco *Concert*
(8/88) (CALL) ① [4] **CAL9831/4**
Martin Jones *Concert*   (7/89) (NIMB) ① **NI5161**
P. Rogé *Concert*   (2/90) (DECC) ① **417 792-2DM**
Z. Kocsis *Concert*   (2/90) (PHIL) ① **422 404-2PH**
G. Fergus-Thompson *Concert*
(5/90) (ASV) ① **CDDCA695**
N. Lee *Concert*   (11/90) (AUVI) ① [4] **V4440**
F. Ts'ong *Concert*   (6/91) (COLL) ① **Coll1052-2**
C. Arrau *Concert*
(2/92) (PHIL) ① [4] **432 304-2PM2**
L. Rév *Concert*   (4/92) (SAGA) ① **EC3376-2**
A. Ciccolini *Concert*   (6/92) (EMI) ① **CDC7 54447-2**
P. Crossley *Préludes*.   (4/93) (SONY) ① **SK52583**
W. Haas (r1960s) *Concert*
(4/94) (PHIL) ① [2] **438 718-2PM2**
P. Rogé (r1979) *Concert*
(12/94) (DECC) ① [2] **443 021-2DF2**
G. Pludermacher (r1993) *Concert*
(3/95) (HARM) ① **HMC90 1503**
L. Rév (r1990-1) *Concert*
(6/95) (HYPE) ① [3] **CDS44061/3**
A.B. Michelangeli (pp1987) *Concert*
(10/95) (MEMR) ① [4] **999001**
1. C. Ortiz *Concert*   (6/87) (CARL) ① **PCD846**
1. W. Gieseking (bp1944) *Concert*
(11/90) (MUSI) ① **MACD-612**
1. V. Cliburn *Concert*   (5/91) (RCA) ① **GD60415**
1. M. Lympany *Concert*   (1/92) (EMIL) ① **CDZ110**
1. M. Rosenthal (r1929) *Concert*
(9/93) (PEAR) ① **GEMMCD9963**
1. O. De Spiegeleir (r1994) *Concert*
(10/95) (PAVA) ① **ADW7332**
1, 2, 6. A. Rubinstein (r1945) *Concert*
(10/93) (RCA) ① **09026 61446-2**
1-3. K. Stott *Concert*   (9/87) (CONI) ① **CDCF148**
1-3. Y. Nagai *Préludes*.   (5/88) (BIS) ① **BIS-CD371**
1-3. L. Rév *Concert*   (1/91) (HYPE) ① **CDA66116**
1, 6. C. Rosenberger *Concert*
(6/86) (DELO) ① **DE3006**
2, 6. A. Rubinstein (r1945) *Concert*
(10/93) (RCA) ① **09026 61445-2**
4-6. Y. Nagai *Préludes*.   (3/89) (BIS) ① **BIS-CD405**

Pantomime—song (1882) (Wds. Verlaine)
M. Mesplé, D. Baldwin *Concert*
(5/92) (EMI) ① [3] **CMS7 64095-2**
J. Kaufmann, I. Gage (r1992) *Concert*
(2/94) (ORFE) ① **C305931A**
Paysage sentimental—song (1883) (Wds. P. Bourget)
M. Mesplé, D. Baldwin *Concert*
(5/92) (EMI) ① [3] **CMS7 64095-2**
Pierrot—song (1881) (Wds. Banville)
M. Mesplé, D. Baldwin *Concert*
(5/92) (EMI) ① [3] **CMS7 64095-2**
J. Kaufmann, I. Gage (r1992) *Concert*
(2/94) (ORFE) ① **C305931A**
7 Poèmes de Banville (1880-82)
1. Rêverie; 2. Souhait; 3. Le Lilas; 4. Sérénade; 5. Il dort encore; 6. Les Roses; 7. Fête Galante.
Cpte A-M. Rodde, N. Lee *Concert*
(4/88) (ETCE) ① **KTC1048**
5 Poèmes de Charles Baudelaire—songs (1887-89) (Wds. Baudelaire)
1. Le balcon; 2. Harmonie du soir; 3. Le jet d'eau; 4. Receillement; 5. La mort des amants.
H. Cuénod, M. Isepp (r1972) *Concert*
(6/90) (NIMB) ① **NI5231**
M. Command, D. Baldwin *Concert*
(5/92) (EMI) ① [3] **CMS7 64095-2**
N. Stutzmann, C. Collard *Concert*
(7/92) (RCA) ① **RD60899**
3. M. Teyte, G. Moore (r1940) *Concert*
(10/94) (EMI) ① [2] **CHS5 65198-2**
3. M. Teyte, G. Moore (r1940) *Concert*
(11/95) (PEAR) ① **GEMMCD9134**
3 Poèmes de Stéphane Mallarmé (1913)
1. Soupir; 2. Placet futile; 3. Eventail.
Cpte A-M. Rodde, N. Lee *Concert*
(4/88) (ETCE) ① **KTC1048**
H. Cuénod, M. Isepp (r1972) *Concert*
(6/90) (NIMB) ① **NI5231**
E. Ameling, D. Baldwin *Concert*
(5/92) (EMI) ① [3] **CMS7 64095-2**
Printemps—cantata (1884) (Wds. J Barbier)
B. Desnoues, Paris Sorbonne Chor, Paris Sorbonne Orch, J. Grimbert (r1993/4) *Concert*
(10/95) (MARC) ① **8 223755**
Le **Promenoir des deux amants—song cycle (1904-10)** (Wds. Lhermite)
1. La grotte; 2. Crois mon consil, chère Climène; 3. Je tremble en voyant ton visage.
Cpte M. Teyte, A. Cortot (r1936) *Concert*
(8/88) (EMI) ① [3] **CHS7 61038-2**
G. Souzay, D. Baldwin *Concert*
(5/92) (EMI) ① [3] **CMS7 64095-2**
M. Teyte, A. Cortot (r1936) *Concert*
(11/95) (PEAR) ① **GEMMCD9134**
3. G. Lubin, anon (r1954) *Concert*
(5/91) (EPM) ① **150 052**
Proses lyriques—songs (1892-93) (Wds. cpsr)
1. De rêve; 2. De grève; 3. De fleurs; 4. De Soir.
Cpte A-M. Rodde, N. Lee *Concert*
(4/88) (ETCE) ① **KTC1048**
M. Atger, Monte Carlo PO, M. Constant (orch Roger-Ducasse) *Concert*
(4/92) (AUVI) ① **V4644**
E. Ameling, D. Baldwin *Concert*
(5/92) (EMI) ① [3] **CMS7 64095-2**
C. Leblanc, V. Tryon *Concert*
(4/93) (UNIC) ① **DKPCD9133**
D. Jones, M. Martineau (r1992) *Concert*
(6/93) (CHAN) ① **CHAN9147**
1, 3, 4. M. Teyte, G. Moore (r1940) *Concert*
(10/94) (EMI) ① [2] **CHS5 65198-2**
1, 3, 4. M. Teyte, G. Moore (r1940) *Concert*
(11/95) (PEAR) ① **GEMMCD9134**
2. Sarah Walker, R. Vignoles *Concert*
(11/87) (HYPE) ① **CDA66165**
2. M. Teyte, A. Cortot (r1936) *Concert*
(8/88) (EMI) ① [3] **CHS7 61038-2**
2. M. Teyte, A. Cortot (r1936) *Concert*
(11/95) (PEAR) ① **GEMMCD9134**
Romance: Silence ineffrable—song: 1v and piano (1883 rev 1884) (Wds. P. Bourget)
N. Melba, G. Lapierre (r1913) *Concert*
(5/95) (ROMO) ① **81011-2(2)**
E. Clément, anon (r1910s) *Concert*
(8/95) (PEAR) ① **GEMMCD9161**
Rondeau (Fut-il jamais)—song (1882) (Wds. A. de Musset)
A-M. Rodde, N. Lee *Concert*
(4/88) (ETCE) ① **KTC1048**
M. Mesplé, D. Baldwin *Concert*
(5/92) (EMI) ① [3] **CMS7 64095-2**
Rondel chinois—song (c1881) (Wds. anon)
M. Mesplé, D. Baldwin *Concert*
(5/92) (EMI) ① [3] **CMS7 64095-2**

Voici que le printemps—song (1884) (Wds. Bourget)
M. Mesplé, D. Baldwin *Concert*
(5/92) (EMI) ① [3] **CMS7 64095-2**
P. Frijsh, C. Dougherty (r1940) *Concert*
(4/95) (PEAR) ① [2] **GEMMCDS9095(1)**
Zéphyr, 'Triolet à Philis'—song (1881) (Wds. T. de Banville)
M. Mesplé, D. Baldwin *Concert*
(5/92) (EMI) ① [3] **CMS7 64095-2**

SECTION V: STAGE WORKS

La **Boîte à joujoux—ballet for children (1919—Paris)** (orch. cpsr and Caplet from piano original)
G. Oppenheimer, M. Robles, COE, J. Galway (fl/dir) *Concert*
(5/87) (RCA) ① **RD87173**
Ulster Orch, Y.P. Tortelier *Ravel: Ma mère l'oye.*
(8/89) (CHAN) ① **CHAN8711**
FRNO, J. Martinon *Concert*
(10/89) (EMI) ① **CDM7 69589-2**
Martin Jones *Concert*
(2/90) (NIMB) ① **NI5163**
LSO, M. Tilson Thomas *Concert*
(11/92) (SONY) ① **SK48231**
Lyon Op Orch, K. Nagano (r1992) *Prokofiev: Peter and the Wolf.*
(8/95) (ERAT) ① **4509-97418-2**
La **Chûte de la maison Usher—opéra: 2 scènes (incomplete) (1908-17)** (Lib. cpsr after Poe)
Cpte C. Barbaux, F. Le Roux, P-Y. Le Maigat, J-P. Lafont, Monte Carlo PO, G. Prêtre (r1983: cpted Allende-Blin) *Concert*
(9/93) (EMI) ① **CDM7 64687-2**
L'**Enfant prodigue—scène lyrique (1884)** (Wds. Rossetti)
L'**année en vain chasse** S. Danco, SRO, I. Karr (bp1953) *Concert*
(1/93) (CASC) ① **VEL2010**
Prélude J. Martinez, A. Sándor (r1934) *Concert*
(11/94) (RCA) ① [65] **09026 61778-2(02)**
Jeux—ballet (1912)
Cpte LPO, S. Baudo *Concert*
(10/87) (EMIN) ① **CD-EMX9502**
Cpte Czech PO, S. Baudo (r1967) *Concert*
(12/87) (SUPR) ① **2SUP0023**
Cpte Martin Jones *Concert*
(2/90) (NIMB) ① **NI5163**
Cpte CBSO, S. Rattle *Concert*
(3/90) (EMI) ① **CDC7 49947-2**
Cpte Ulster Orch, Y. P. Tortelier *Concert*
(10/91) (CHAN) ① **CHAN8903**
Cpte NYPO, L. Bernstein (1960) *Concert*
(5/93) (SONY) ① **SMK47546**
LSO, M. Tilson Thomas *Concert*
(11/92) (SONY) ① **SK48231**
Concertgebouw, B. Haitink (r1979) *Concert*
(3/94) (PHIL) ① [2] **438 742-2PM2**
Finnish RSO, J-P. Saraste (r1992) *Concert*
(4/94) (VIRG) ① **VC5 45018-2**
Paris Cons, A. Cluytens (1963) *Concert*
(11/94) (EMI) ① [2] **CZS5 68220-2**
Cleveland Orch, P. Boulez *Concert*
(3/95) (DG) ① **439 896-2GH**
Khamma—ballet (1947—Paris) (cpted Koechlin)
Martin Jones (arr pf) *Concert*
(2/90) (NIMB) ① **NI5163**
Ulster Orch, Y. P. Tortelier *Concert*
(10/91) (CHAN) ① **CHAN8903**
Finnish RSO, J-P. Saraste (r1991) *Concert*
(4/94) (VIRG) ① **VC5 45018-2**
Concertgebouw, R. Chailly (r1994) *Ravel: Daphnis et Chloé.*
(10/95) (DECC) ① **443 934-2DH**
Le **Martyre de St. Sébastien—mystère: 5 acts (1911)** (Wds. G D'Annunzio)
EXCERPTS: ACT 1—La Cour des lys: 1. Prélude; 2. Sébastien!; 3. Danse extatique de Sébastien. ACT 2: La Chambre magique: 4. Prélude; 5. Je fauchais l'épi de froment; 6. Qui plane mon enfant si doux. ACT 3: Le Concile des faux dieux: 7. Prélude; 8. Païan, Lyre d'or, Arc d'argent!; 9. Avez-vous vu celui que j'aime?; 10. Ne pleurez plus!; 11. Io! Io! Adoniastes!; 12. Il est mort, le bel Adonis. ACT 4: Le Laurier blessé: 13. Prélude; 14. Il est là, la Pasteur. Regardez; 15. Hélas!. ACT 5: Le Paradis: 16. Interlude; 17. Gloire!.
Cpte E. Bannau, C. Gayraud, S. Michel, A. Falcon, ORTF Chor, FNO, D-E. Inglehbrecht (pp1960) *Concert*
(10/88) (MONT) ① **TCE8790**
Cpte S. McNair, N. Waugh, Murray, A. Murray, L. Caron, LSC, LSO, M. Tilson Thomas (r1991)
(3/93) (SONY) ① **SK48240**
Cpte S. Danco, N. Waugh, M-L. de Montmollin, Peilz Chor Union, SRO, E. Ansermet (r1954) *Concert*
(6/93) (DECC) ① [2] **433 400-2DM2**
LSO, P. Monteux (r1963) *Concert*
(12/94) (PHIL) ① [5] **442 544-2PM5**

Pelléas et Mélisande—opera: 5 acts (1902—Paris) (Lib. Maeterlinck, abridged cpsr)
EXCERPTS: ACT 1 SCENE 1: 1. Je ne pourrai plus sortir de cette forêt; 2. Pourquoi pleures-tu?; 3. Je suis perdu aussi. SCENE 2: 4. Voici ce qu'il écrit à son frère Pelléas; 5. Qu'en dites-vous?; 6. Interlude. SCENE 3: 7. Il fait sombre dans les jardins; 8. Hoé! Hisse Hoé. ACT 2 SCENE 1: 9. Vous ne savez pas où je vous ai menée?; 10. C'est au bord d'une fontaine; 11. Interlude: SCENE 2: 12. Ah! Ah! Tout va bien; 13. Voyons, donne-moi ta main; 14. Interlude. SCENE 3: 15. Oui, c'est ici nous y sommes. ACT 3 SCENE 1: 16. Mes longs cheveux; 17. Je les tiens dans les mains; 18. Que faites-vous ici?. SCENE 2: 19. Prenez garde: par ici. SCENE 3: 20. Ah! je respire enfin; 21. Interlude; 22. Viens, nous allons nous asseoir ici; 23. Qu'ils s'embrassent, petit père? ACT 4 SCENE 1: 24. Où va-tu? SCENE 2: 25. Maintenant que le père de Pelléas; 26. Pelléas part ce soir; 27. Ne mettez pas ainsi votre main à la gorge; 28. Interlude. SCENE 3: 29. Oh! Cette pierre est lourde. SCENE 4: 30. C'est le dernier soir; 31. Nous sommes venus ici il y a bien longtemps; 32. In dirait que ta voix; 33. Quel est ce bruit? ACT 5: 34. Ce n'est pas de cette petite blessure; 35. Attention; je crois qu'elle s'éveille; 36. Mélisande, as-tu pitié de moi; 37. Non, non n'avons pas été coupables; 38. Qu'avez-vous fait?; 39. Qu'y a-t-il?; 40. Attention...attention.
Cpte R. Stilwell, F. von Stade, J. Van Dam, R. Raimondi, N. Denize, C. Barbaux, P. Thomas, Berlin Deutsche Op Chor, BPO, H. von Karajan
(2/88) (EMI) ① [3] **CDS7 49350-2**
Cpte J. Jansen, M. Grancher, M. Roux, A. Vessières, S. Michel, F. Ogéas, M. Vigneron, FRN Chor, FNO, D-E. Inglehbrecht (pp1962) *Nocturnes.*
(8/88) (MONT) ① **TCE8710**
Cpte J. Jansen, I. Joachim, H. Etcheverry, P. Cabanel, G. Cernay, L.B. Sedira, A. Narçon, E. Rousseau, Y. Gouverné Ch, SO, R. Desormière (r1941) *Concert*
(8/88) (EMI) ① [3] **CHS7 61038-2**
Cpte M. Walker, E. Manchet, V. Le Texier, P. Meven, C. Yahr, Anon (treb), P. Le Hémonet, Nice Op Chor, Nice PO, J. Carewe
(8/89) (PIER) ① [2] **PV788093/4**
Cpte D. Henry, C. Alliot-Lugaz, G. Cachemaille, P. Thau, C. Carlson, F. Golfier, P. Ens, Montreal Sym Chor, Montreal SO, C. Dutoit (r1990)
(3/91) (DECC) ① [2] **430 502-2DH2**
Cpte E. Tappy, R. Yakar, P. Huttenlocher, F. Loup, J. Taillon, C. Alliot-Lugaz, M. Brodard, Monte Carlo Op Chor, Monte Carlo Nat Op Orch, A. Jordan
(12/91) (ERAT) ① [2] **2292-45684-2**
Cpte F. Le Roux, M. Ewing, J. Van Dam, J-P. Courtis, C. Ludwig, P. Pace, R. Mazzola, Vienna St Op Chor, VPO, C. Abbado
(3/92) (DG) ① [2] **435 344-2GH2**
Cpte J. Jansen, V. de los Angeles, G. Souzay, P. Froumenty, J. Collard, F. Ogéas, J. Vieuille, Raymond St Paul Chor, FRNO, A. Cluytens (r1956)
(6/95) (TEST) ① [3] **SBT3051**
4. S. Danco, A. Vessières, P. Mollet, SRO, E. Ansermet pp1963) *Concert*
(1/93) (CASC) ① **VEL2010**
15. M. Garden, C. Debussy (r1904) *Concert*
(8/88) (EMI) ① [3] **CHS7 61038-2**
15 (pt) C. Panzéra, Y. Brothier, SO, P. Coppola (r1927) *Concert* (3/93) (DANT) ① [2] **LYS003/4**
16. M. Garden, C. Debussy (r1904) *Concert*
(10/92) (SYMP) ① **SYMCD1093**
25 (pt) Vanni-Marcoux, orch, P. Coppola (r1927) *Concert* (7/92) (PEAR) ① [3] **GEMMCDS9924(2)**
Rodrigue et Chimène—opera: 3 acts (1890-92) (Lib. C Mendès, after G de Castro & Corneille)
Cpte L. Dale, D. Brown, H. Jossoud, G. Ragon, J-P. Fouchécourt, J. van Dam, J. Bastin, V. le Texier, J-L. Meunier, J. Deslescluse, Lyon Op Chor, Lyon Op Orch, K. Nagano (r1993/4: recons R Langham Smith: orch E Denisov)
(10/95) (ERAT) ① [2] **4509-98508-2**
Roi Lear—incidental music (1904)
FRNO, J. Martinon *Concert*
(3/89) (EMI) ① **CDM7 69587-2**
CBSO, S. Rattle *Concert*
(3/90) (EMI) ① **CDC7 49947-2**

DEL RIEGO, Teresa (c1876–1968) England

SECTION IV: VOCAL AND CHORAL

Homing—song (Wds. Salmon)
E. Turner, anon, anon (r1933) *Concert*
(9/89) (EMI) ① **CDH7 69791-2**

O dry those tears—song (Wds. cpsr)
E. Mason, orch (r1925) *Concert*
(8/93) (SYMP) ① **SYMCD1136**
E. Mason, orch, F. Black (r1925) *Concert*
(8/94) (ROMO) ① **81009-2**
Slave Song (1899) (Wds E. Nesbit)
A. Rolfe Johnson, G. Johnson (r1991/3) *Concert*
(8/94) (HYPE) ① **CDA66709**

DEL TREDICI, David (Walter) *(b 1937) USA*

SECTION I: ORCHESTRAL

Tattoo—orchestra
NYPO, L. Bernstein (pp1988) *Concert*
(1/92) (DG) ① **429 231-2GH**

SECTION IV: VOCAL AND CHORAL

Acrostic song—chorus a capella (from 'The Final Alice')
The Sixteen, H. Christophers *Concert*
(4/92) (COLL) ① **Coll1287-2**

DEL TURCO, Giovanni *(1577–1647) Italy*

SECTION IV: VOCAL AND CHORAL

Occhi belli e sia ver che in lungo pianto—madrigal: 1v and continuo (pub 1617) (Wds. anon)
N. Rogers, C. Tilney, A. Bailes, J. Savall, P. Ros (r1975) *Concert* (1/93) (ARCH) ① **437 075-2AT**

DELAGE, Maurice (Charles) *(1879–1961) France*

SECTION IV: VOCAL AND CHORAL

À Roussel—mezzo-soprano, flute and piano (1928) (Wds. R. Chalupt)
M. Cable, M. Fingerhut, W. Bennett *Concert*
(9/88) (CHAN) ① **CHAN8578**
4 Poèmes hindous—voice, 2 fl, ob, 2 cl, 2 vns, va, vc and hp (1912)
1. Une belle (Madras); 2. Un sapin isolé (Lahore); 3. Naissance de Bouddha (Bénarès); 4. Si vous pensez à elle (Jeyper).
D. Upshaw, Inst Ens *Concert*
(11/91) (NONE) ① **7559-79262-2**

DELALANDE, Michel-Richard *(1657–1726) France*

SECTION I: ORCHESTRAL

Sinfonies pour les soupers du Roi—strings, wind and continuo (c1690-1700)
1. Concert de trompettes; 2. Suite I; 3. Suite III; 3a. Chaconne de Villers-Cotterêt; 4. Suite III; 5. Suite IV; 6. Suite V; 6a. 2ème Fantaisie ou Caprice que le Roi demandoit souvent; 7. Suite VI: Airs du Ballet de Flore ou de Trianon; 8. Suite VII; 8a. 1er Caprice ou Caprice de Villers-Cotterêts; 9. Suite VIII; 10. Suite IX: Airs du Ballet de Mélicerte; 11. Suite X: Air du Ballet des Fées; 12. Suite XI: Airs du Ballet de la Paix; 13. Suite XII: dont les Airs formant la troisième Caprice.
Simphonie du Marais, H. Reyne
(7/91) (HARM) ① [4] **HMC90 1337/40**

SECTION II: CHAMBER

Symphonies des Noëls
1, 2, 6. German Baroque sols, R. Ewerhart (org/dir) *Concert* (12/91) (FSM) ① **FCD91220**

SECTION IV: VOCAL AND CHORAL

Cantate Domino—grand motet: soloists, 5vv and orchestra, S72 (1707)
Ex Cathedra Chbr Ch, Ex Cathedra Baroque Orch, J. Skidmore (r1994) *Concert*
(7/95) (ASV) ① **CDGAU141**
Cantique quatrième—canticle: 2 trebles and continuo (pub 1695) ('sur le bonheur des justes…')
V. Gens, N. Rime, Arts Florissants Chor, Arts Florissants Orch, W. Christie *Concert*
(4/93) (HARM) ① **HMC90 1416**
Confitebor tibi Domine—grand motet: soloists, 5vv and orchestra, S56 (1699)
V. Gens, S. Piau, A. Steyer, J-P. Fouchécourt, F. Piolino, J. Corréas, Arts Florissants Chor, Arts Florissants Orch, W. Christie *Concert*
(7/91) (HARM) ① **HMC90 1351**

De Profundis—grand motet: soloists, 5vv and orchestra, S23 (c1688)
Ex Cathedra Chbr Ch, Ex Cathedra Baroque Orch, J. Skidmore (r1994) *Concert*
(7/95) (ASV) ① **CDGAU141**
Dies irae—grand motet, S31 (1690)
L. Perillo, P. Kwella, H. Crook, H. Lamy, P. Harvey, Chapelle Royale Ch, Chapelle Royale Orch, P. Herreweghe *Miserere mei Deus secundum, S27.*
(12/91) (HARM) ① **HMC90 1352**
Miserator et misericors—petit motet (reduction of grand motet)
N. Rime, Arts Florissants Chor, Arts Florissants Orch, W. Christie *Concert* (4/93) (HARM) ① **HMC90 1416**
Miserere à voix seule—solo voice and choir (1687)
V. Gens, S. Piau, A. Steyer, Arts Florissants Chor, W. Christie *Concert* (4/93) (HARM) ① **HMC90 1416**
Miserere mei Deus secundum—grand motet, S27 (1687)
L. Perillo, P. Kwella, H. Crook, H. Lamy, P. Harvey, Chapelle Royale Ch, Chapelle Royale Orch, P. Herreweghe *Dies irae, S31.*
(12/91) (HARM) ① **HMC90 1352**
Regina Coeli—grand motet: soloists, 5vv and orchestra, S53 (1698)
Ex Cathedra Chbr Ch, Ex Cathedra Baroque Orch, J. Skidmore (r1994) *Concert*
(7/95) (ASV) ① **CDGAU141**
Super flumina—motet (1687)
V. Gens, S. Piau, A. Steyer, J-P. Fouchécourt, F. Piolino, J. Corréas, Arts Florissants Chor, Arts Florissants Orch, W. Christie *Concert*
(7/91) (HARM) ① **HMC90 1351**
Te Deum—grand motet, S32 (1684)
V. Gens, S. Piau, A. Steyer, J-P. Fouchécourt, F. Piolino, J. Corréas, Arts Florissants Chor, Arts Florissants Orch, W. Christie *Concert*
(7/91) (HARM) ① **HMC90 1351**
Vanum est vobis ante lucem—petit motet (reduction of grand motet)
V. Gens, Arts Florissants Chor, Arts Florissants Orch, W. Christie *Concert* (4/93) (HARM) ① **HMC90 1416**

DELANNOY, Marcel *(1898–1962) France*

SECTION III: INSTRUMENTAL

Diner sur l'eau—piano
B. Lerner *Concert* (1/89) (ETCE) ① **KTC1061**

DELAVIGNE, Philibert *(18th Cent) France*

SECTION II: CHAMBER

Sonata for Recorder and Continuo in C, '(La) Barssan' (from 'Sonates pour la Musette etc')
F. Brüggen, A. Bylsma, G. Leonhardt (r1970) *Concert*
(10/95) (TELD) ① **4509-97469-2**

DELDEN, Lex van *(b 1919) The Netherlands*

SECTION I: ORCHESTRAL

Concerto for Two String Orchestras, Op. 71 (1961)
Concertgebouw, E. Jochum (pp1966) *Concert*
(3/94) (ETCE) ① **KTC1156**
Musica sinfonica—orchestra, Op. 93 (1967)
Concertgebouw, B. Haitink (pp1969) *Concert*
(3/94) (ETCE) ① **KTC1156**
Piccolo Concerto—12 winds, percussion and piano, Op. 67 (1960)
Concertgebouw, E. Jochum (pp1964; mono) *Concert*
(3/94) (ETCE) ① **KTC1156**
Sinfonia No. 3, 'Facets'—orchestra, Op. 45 (1955)
Concertgebouw, G. Szell (pp1957; mono) *Concert*
(3/94) (ETCE) ① **KTC1156**

DELERUE, Georges *(1925–1992) France*

SECTION III: INSTRUMENTAL

Mosaïque—guitar (1978)
E. Kotzia *Concert* (6/89) (PEAR) ① **SHECD9609**

SECTION V: STAGE WORKS

Anne of the Thousand Days—film score (1969)
Overture National PO, C. Gerhardt *Concert*
(6/90) (VARE) ① **VSD5207**

Beaches—film score (1988)
EXCERPTS: 1. Friendship.
1. Orch, F. Fitzpatrick (r1989) *Concert*
(10/90) (VARE) ① **VSD5241**
Biloxi Blues—film score (1988)
EXCERPTS: 1. Main Title.
1. Orch, G. Delerue (r1989) *Concert*
(10/90) (VARE) ① **VSD5241**
Crimes of the Heart—film score (1986)
Suite Orch, G. Delerue (r1989) *Concert*
(10/90) (VARE) ① **VSD5241**
Exposed—film score (1983)
Suite Orch, G. Delerue (r1989) *Concert*
(10/90) (VARE) ① **VSD5241**
Her Alibi—film score (1989)
EXCERPTS: 1. Between You and Me (Wds F. Fitzpatrick); 2. End Title.
1, 2. Orch, G. Delerue (r1989) *Concert*
(10/90) (VARE) ① **VSD5241**
A Little Romance—film score (1979)
EXCERPTS: 1. Main Title; 2. Love's Not Like That; 3. Paris Montage; 4. Julius Edmond Santorin; 5. The Young Lovers; 6. Off to Italy; 7. Birthday Party; 8. Outdoor Cafe/Moving On; 9. A Little Romance; 10. The Bicycle Race; 11. The Lovers' Decision; 12. Venice; 13. Hiding in the Movies; 14. No Turning Back; 15. The Gondola; 16. Farewell...For Now/End Title.
Suite Orch, G. Delerue (r1989) *Concert*
(10/90) (VARE) ① **VSD5241**
Platoon—film score (1986) (largely replaced by Barber's Adagio for Strings)
EXCERPTS: 1. Main Title; 2. Bunker to Village; 3. Sorrow; 4. Barnes Shoots Elias/The Turning Point; 5. The Soul of an Innocent; 6. Killing Barnes/Aftermath; 7. Finale.
1. Orch, G. Delerue (r1989) *Concert*
(10/90) (VARE) ① **VSD5241**
Rich and Famous—film score (1981)
Suite Orch, G. Delerue (r1989) *Concert*
(10/90) (VARE) ① **VSD5241**
A Summer Story—film score (1988)
OST, G. Delerue (r1988) (4/89) (VIR2) ① **CDV2562**

DELIBES, (Clément Philibert) Léo *(1836–1891) France*

SECTION IV: VOCAL AND CHORAL

Bonjour, Suzon!—song (1861) (Wds. A. de Musset)
S. Varcoe, G. Johnson *Concert*
(6/88) (HYPE) ① **CDA66248**
C. Muzio, orch, L. Molajoli (r1935) *Concert*
(4/91) (NIMB) ① **NI7814**
C. Supervia, orch, A. Capdevila (r1930) *Concert*
(3/93) (NIMB) ① [2] **NI7836/7**
C. Muzio, orch (r1918: Eng) *Concert*
(1/95) (ROMO) ① [2] **81010-2**
Églogue—song
F. Lott, G. Johnson (r1984) *Concert*
(5/87) (HARM) ① **HMA190 1138**
C. Supervia, orch, M. Romero (r1930) *Concert*
(3/93) (NIMB) ① [2] **NI7836/7**
Les Filles de Cadiz—chanson espagnole (Wds. de Musset)
V. de los Angeles, Sinfonia of London, R. Frühbeck de Burgos (orch Gamley) *Concert*
(10/88) (EMI) ① **CDM7 69502-2**
A. Galli-Curci, orch (r1919) *Concert*
(2/89) (PEAR) ① **GEMMCD9308**
L. Pons, orch, A. Kostelanetz (r1947) *Concert*
(7/90) (SONY) ① **MPK45694**
C. Muzio, orch, L. Molajoli (r1935) *Concert*
(4/91) (NIMB) ① **NI7814**
L. Pons, F. La Forge (r1938) *Concert*
(4/92) (MSOU) ① **DFCDI-111**
P. McCann, Black Dyke Mills Band, P. Parkes (r1984: arr G Langford) *Concert*
(11/92) (CHAN) ① **CHAN4501**
A. Galli-Curci, orch, J. Pasternack (r1919) *Concert*
(3/94) (ROMO) ① [2] **81003-2**
J. Gomez, J. Constable (r1994) *Concert*
(9/94) (CONI) ① **CDCF243**
L. Garrett, RPO, P. Robinson (r1994) *Concert*
(4/95) (SILV) ① **SILKD6004**
O mer, ouvre-toi, Linceul du monde—song
M. Jeritza, orch (r1925) *Concert*
(4/94) (PREI) ① **89079**
Les Trois oiseaux—duet (Wds. F. Coppée)
F. Lott, A. Murray, G. Johnson (r1991) *Concert*
(7/92) (EMI) ① **CDC7 54411-2**

225

SECTION V: STAGE WORKS

Coppélia—ballet: 2 acts (1870—Paris)
O. ACT 1: 1. Prélude et mazurka; 2. Valse lente; 3.
Scène; 4. Mazurka; 5. Scène; 6. Ballade de l'épi; 7.
Thème slave varié; 8. Czárdás (Danse hongroise); 9.
Final. ACT 2: 10. Entr'acte et valse; 11. Scène; 12.
Scène; 13. Musique des automates; 14. Scène; 15.
Chanson à boire; 16. Scène et valse de la poupée;
17. Scène; 18. Boléro; 19. Gigue; 20. Scène; 21.
Marche de la cloche; 22a. Fête de la cloche-
Divertissement Introduction; 22b. Valse des heures;
22c. L'Aurore; 22d. La Prière; 22e. Le Travail (La
Fileuse); 22f. L'Hymen (Noce villageoise); 22g. La
Discorde et la guerre; 22h. La Paix; 22i. Danse de
fête; 22j. Galop final.
Cpte National PO, R. Bonynge
(12/86) (DECC) ① [2] 414 502-2DH2
Cpte SRO, R. Bonynge (r1969) *Massenet: Carillon.*
(1/90) (DECC) ① [2] 425 472-2DM2
Cpte Minneapolis SO, A. Dorati *Sylvia.*
(3/93) (MERC) ① [3] 434 313-2MM3
Cpte Lyon Op Orch, K. Nagano
(5/94) (ERAT) ① [2] 4509-91730-2
Excs ROHO, M. Ermler (7/93) (ROH) ① ROH006
Suite Berlin RSO, H. Fricke *Chopin: Sylphides.*
(12/86) (CAPR) ① 10 073
Suite Berlin RSO, H. Fricke
(5/90) (LASE) ① 15 616
Suite Boston SO, P. Monteux (r1953) *Concert*
(9/94) (RCA) ① [15] 09026 61893-2
Suite BPO, H. von Karajan (r1961) *Concert*
(10/94) (DG) ① [2] 437 404-2GX2
Waltz A. Galli-Curci, orch, R. Bourdon (r1924)
Concert (8/94) (ROMO) ① [2] 81004-2
1, 8, 16. BPO, H. von Karajan *Concert*
(5/90) (DG) ① 429 163-2GR

Lakmé—opera: 3 acts (1883—Paris) (Lib.
Gondinet and Gille)
ACT 1: 1. Prelude; 2a. A l'heure accoutumée; 2b.
Soyez trois fois bénis; 2c. Blanche Dourga; 3. Lakmé,
c'est toi qui nous protèges!; 4a. Viens Mallika; 4b.
Sous le dôme épais (Flower duet); 5. Ah! beaux
faiseurs de systèmes; 6a. Prendre le dessin; 6b.
Fantaisie aux divins mensonges; 7. O toi qui nous
protèges; 8a. Les fleurs me paraissent plus belles;
8b. Pourquoi dans les grands bois; 9a. D'où viens-
tu?; 9b. C'est le dieu de la jeunesse. ACT 2: 10.
Danses; 11a. C'est un pauvre qui mendie; 11b.
Lakmé, ton doux regard se voile; 12a. Par les dieux
inspirée; 12b. Où va la jeune indoue (Bell Song); 12c.
Là-bas dans la forêt plus sombre; 13a. Lakmé! c'est
toi; 13b. Ah! c'est l'amour endormi; 14. Dans la forêt
près de nous; 15. C'est pour admirer la déesse. ACT
3: 16. Lakmé! 17. Sous le ciel tout étoilé; 18.
Lakmé! Ah! viens dans la forêt profonde: 19. Tu m'as
donné le plus doux rêve.
Cpte M. Mesplé, C. Burles, R. Soyer, D. Millet, J-C.
Benoit, B. Antoine, M. Linval, A. Disney, J. Peyron,
Paris Opéra-Comique Chor, Paris Opéra-Comique
Orch, A. Lombard (r1970)
(7/88) (EMI) ① [2] CDS7 49430-2
Cpte J. Sutherland, A. Vanzo, G. Bacquier, J. Berbié,
C. Calès, G. Annear, J. Clément, M. Sinclair, E.
Belcourt, Monte Carlo Op Chor, Monte Carlo Op
Orch, R. Bonynge
(12/89) (DECC) ① [2] 425 485-2DM2
2c, 12b L. Tetrazzini, chor, orch (Ital: r1911) *Concert*
(9/92) (EMI) ① [3] CHS7 63802-2(1)
2c, 12b L. Tetrazzini, orch (Ital: r1911) *Concert*
(9/92) (PEAR) ① GEMMCD9222
2c, 12b M. Korjus, Berlin St Op Orch, B. Seidler-
Winkler (Ital: r1936) *Concert*
(10/93) (PREI) ① 89054
4a, 4b E. Eames, L. Homer, orch (r1908) *Concert*
(11/93) (ROMO) ① [2] 81001-2
4a, 4b A. Nezhdanova, E. Popello-Davidova, orch
(r1910; Russ) *Concert* (3/95) (NIMB) ① NI7865
**4a, 4b, 5, 6a, 6b, 8a, 8b, 9a, 9b, 11a, 12b, 12c, 13a,
13b, 14, 17, 18, 19.** J. Sutherland, A. Vanzo, G.
Bacquier, J. Berbié, C. Calès, G. Annear, J. Clément,
M. Sinclair, E. Belcourt, Monte Carlo Op Chor, Monte
Carlo Op Orch, R. Bonynge (r1967)
(10/93) (DECC) ① 436 305-2DA
4b V. Masterson, C. Powell, RPO, R. Stapleton
Concert (10/90) (CARL) ① MCD15
4b L. Garrett, Philh, A. Greenwood (r1990-1) *Concert*
(11/91) (SILV) ① SONGCD903
4b A. Panina, M. Michailova, orch (r1911: Russ)
Concert
(6/93) (PEAR) ① [3] GEMMCDS9001/3(2)
4b L. Garrett, L. Christian, Philh, A. Greenwood
Concert (10/93) (SILV) ① FILMCD127
6a, 6b Alfredo Kraus, WNO Orch, C. Rizzi (r1994)
Concert (8/95) (PHIL) ① 442 785-2PH

6a, 6b, 9a, 9b, 19. P. Alarie, L. Simoneau,
Lamoureux Orch, P. Dervaux (r1953) *Concert*
(11/94) (PHIL) ① [2] 438 953-2PM2
6b T. Schipa, orch (r1926) *Concert*
(2/89) (PEAR) ① GEMMCD9322
6b E. Clément, orch (r c1911) *Concert*
(8/95) (PEAR) ① GEMMCD9161
8b, 12b, 17. P. Alarie, Lamoureux Orch, A. Jouve
(r1953) *Concert*
(11/94) (PHIL) ① [2] 438 953-2PM2
9a, 9b J. Anderson, Alfredo Kraus, Paris Op Orch, M.
Veltri (pp1987) *Concert*
(12/88) (EMI) ① CDC7 49067-2
11b T. Ruffo, orch (r1923) *Concert*
(2/93) (PREI) ① [3] 89303(2)
11b L. Sibiriakov, anon (r1905: Russ) *Concert*
(6/93) (PEAR) ① [3] GEMMCDS9001/3(2)
12b M. André, Toulouse Capitole Orch, M. Plasson
(arr tpt) *Concert* (1/89) (EMI) ① CDC7 49219-2
12b L. Tetrazzini, orch (Ital: r1911) *Concert*
(10/90) (NIMB) ① NI7808
12b Dilbèr, Estonia Op Orch, E. Klas *Concert*
(9/92) (ONDI) ① ODE768-2
12b L. Tetrazzini, orch, P. Pitt (Ital: r1907) *Concert*
(9/92) (EMI) ① [3] CHS7 63802-2(1)
12b L. Tetrazzini, orch (Ital: r1911) *Concert*
(9/92) (PEAR) ① GEMMCD9224
12b L. Tetrazzini, orch, P. Pitt (Ital: r1907) *Concert*
(9/92) (PEAR) ① GEMMCD9221
12b A. Galli-Curci, orch, J. Pasternack (r1917)
Concert (3/94) (ROMO) ① [2] 81003-2
12b A. Galli-Curci, orch (r1917) *Concert*
(8/94) (NIMB) ① NI7852
12b A. Nezhdanova, orch (r1912: Russ) *Concert*
(3/95) (NIMB) ① NI7865
12b, 12c M. Callas, Philh, T. Serafin (r1954) *Concert*
(11/86) (EMI) ① CDC7 47282-2
12b, 12c J. Sutherland, ROHO, F. Molinari-Pradelli
Concert (1/90) (DECC) ① [2] 425 493-2DM2
12b, 12c L. Pons, orch, P. Cimara (r1944) *Concert*
(7/90) (SONY) ① MPK45694
12b, 12c L. Pons, orch, R. Bourdon (r1930) *Concert*
(4/92) (MSOU) ① DFCDI-111
12b, 12c M. Devia, Svizzera Italiana Orch, M. Rota
(pp1992) *Concert* (10/94) (BONG) ① GB2513-2
12b, 12c T. Dahl, Calgary PO, M. Bernardi (r1992)
Concert (12/94) (CBC) ① SMCD5125
12b, 12c S. Jo, Monte Carlo PO, P. Olmi (r1994)
Concert (6/95) (ERAT) ① 4509-97239-2
18. J. McCormack, orch (r1910) *Concert*
(7/92) (PEAR) ① [3] GEMMCDS9924(2)
**L' Omelette à la Follembuche—opérette
bouffe: 1 act (1859—Paris)** (Lib. E. Labiche &
M. Michel)
Excs L. Dachary, C. Jacquin, J. Mollien, R. Lenoty,
M. Pieri, ORTF Lyric Orch, J. Brebion (bp1973)
Concert (11/93) (MUSD) ① [2] 20239-2
**Le roi l'a dit—opéra-comique: 3 acts
(1873—Paris)** (Lib. E. Gondinet)
EXCERPTS: 1. Portons toujours des robes sombres.
Cpte J. Micheau, M. Sénéchal, A. Martineau, G.
Wion, R. Lenoty, G. Aurel, G. Donnarieix, A.
Lequenne, G. Parat, M. Le Breton, P. Saugey, J.
Scellier, J. Peyron, M. Hamel, French Rad Lyric
Chor, French Rad Lyric Orch, A. Girard (bp1958)
(11/93) (MUSD) ① [2] 20239-2
1. S. Jo, ECO, R. Bonynge (r1993) *Concert*
(4/94) (DECC) ① 440 679-2DH
**Le Roi s'amuse—comédie française—Suite
of 6 dances (1882—Paris)**
Ballet music RPO, T. Beecham *Concert*
(7/90) (EMI) ① CDM7 63379-2
**Les serpent à plumes—farce: 1 act
(1864—Paris)** (Lib. P. Gille & Cham)
Excs C. Harbell, M. Stiot, J. Peyron, R. Lenoty, B.
Plantey, ORTF Lyric Orch, J. Brebion (bp1973)
Concert (11/93) (MUSD) ① [2] 20239-2
Sylvia—ballet: 3 acts (1876—Paris)
ACT 1: 1. Prélude; 2. Faunes et Dryads (Scherzo);
3. Le Berger (Fantasie); 4. Les Chasseresses
(Fanfare); 5. Intermezzo; 6. Valse lente; 7. Scène; 8.
Cortège rustique; 9. Scène; 10. Entrée du sorcier.
ACT 2: 11. Entr'acte; 12. La Grotte d'Orion (Scène);
13. Pas de Éthopiens; 14. Chant bachique; 15.
Scène et danse de la bacchante; 16. Scène finale.
ACT 3: 17. Marche et cortège de Bacchus; 18.
Scène; 19. Barcarolle; 20. Pizzicati; 21. Andante; 22.
Pas des esclaves; 23. Variation-Valse; 24. Strette-
Galop; 25. Le Temple de Diane; 26. Apparition
d'Endymion (Apothéose).
Cpte New Philh, R. Bonynge *Massenet: Cid.*
(1/90) (DECC) ① [2] 425 475-2DM2
Cpte LSO, A. Fistoulari *Coppélia.*
(3/93) (MERC) ① [3] 434 313-2MM3
Suite Berlin RSO, H. Fricke *Concert*
(5/90) (LASE) ① 15 616

DELIUS, Frederick (Theodore Albert) (1862–1934) England

RT—denotes Robert Threlfall's catalogue (1977)

SECTION I: ORCHESTRAL

**Air and Dance—string orchestra, RTVI/21
(1915)**
LPO, V. Handley *Concert*
(1/85) (CHAN) ① CHAN8330
ASMF, N. Marriner *Concert*
(8/89) (LOND) ① 421 390-2LM
Martin Jones (trans pf: Grainger) *Concert*
(2/91) (NIMB) ① NI5255
ASMF, N. Marriner (r1977) *Concert*
(4/94) (DECC) ① 440 323-2DWO
Northern Sinfonia, R. Hickox (r1985) *Concert*
(7/94) (EMI) ① CDM5 65067-2
**2 Aquarelles—strings (orch. Fenby, 1936:
Orig. To be sung of a summer night on the
water)**
EXCERPTS: 1. No 1; 2. No 2.
Bournemouth Sinfonietta, Mar *Concert*
(1/91) (CHAN) ① CHAN6502
WNO Orch, C. Mackerras *Concert*
(7/92) (ARGO) ① 433 704-2ZH
ECO, D. Barenboim (1974) *Concert*
(4/94) (DG) ① 439 529-2GGA
Oxford Orch da Camera, G. Vass (r1993) *Concert*
(9/94) (MEDI) ① MQCD4002
Bournemouth Sinfonietta, R. Studt (vn/dir) (r1993)
Concert (10/94) (NAXO) ① 8 550823
**Brigg Fair (An English Rhapsody), RTVI/16
(1907)**
RPO, T. Beecham (r1956/7) *Concert*
(6/87) (EMI) ① [2] CDS7 47509-8
Philh, O.A. Hughes (1988) *Concert*
(12/88) (ASV) ① CDDCA627
Hallé, V. Handley *Concert*
(8/89) (CFP) ① CD-CFP4568
SO, T. Beecham (r1928/9) *Concert*
(11/90) (BEEC) ① BEECHAM3
Bratislava RSO, A. Leaper *Concert*
(1/91) (NAXO) ① 8 550229
LSO, B. Wordsworth *Concert*
(9/92) (COLL) ① Coll1336-2
BBC SO, A. Davis (r1992) *Concert*
(1/94) (TELD) ① 4509-90845-2
LSO, G. Toye (r1928) *Concert*
(3/94) (DUTT) ① CDAX8006
LSO, A. Collins (r1953) *Concert*
(8/95) (DUTT) ① CDLXT2503
RPO, C. Seaman (1994) *Concert*
(9/95) (TRIN) ① TRP036
Hallé, J. Barbirolli (1970) *Concert*
(10/95) (EMI) ① CMS5 65119-2
NZ SO, M. Fredman (r1994) *Concert*
(10/95) (NAXO) ① 8 553001
**Caprice and Elegy—cello and chamber
orchestra, RTVI/7 (1930)**
B. Harrison, CO, E. Fenby (r1930) *Concert*
(5/93) (TEST) ① SBT1014
J. Lloyd Webber, ASMF, N. Marriner (1994) *Concert*
(12/94) (PHIL) ① 442 530-2PH
**Concerto for Cello and Orchestra, RTVII/7
(1920-21)**
J. Lloyd Webber, Philh, V. Handley *Concert*
(7/87) (RCA) ① RD70800
R. Wallfisch, RLPO, C. Mackerras *Concert*
(3/92) (EMIN) ① CD-EMX2185
J. Du Pré, RPO, M. Sargent (r1965) *Concert*
(8/94) (EMI) ① [6] CZS5 68132-2
J. Du Pré, RPO, M. Sargent (r1965) *Concert*
(11/95) (EMI) ① CDC5 55529-2
**Concerto for Piano and Orchestra in C
minor, RTVII/4 (1897-1904 rev 1906-07 &
1909)**
P. Fowke, RPO, N. del Mar *Concert*
(3/92) (UNIC) ① DKPCD9108
B. Moiseiwitsch, Philh, C. Lambert (r1946) *Concert*
(5/93) (TEST) ① SBT1014
P. Fowke, RPO, N. del Mar (r1990) *Concert*
(8/95) (UNIC) ① UKCD2072
P. Lane, RLPO, V. Handley (r1994) *Concert*
(11/95) (EMIN) ① CD-EMX2239
**Concerto for Violin and Orchestra, RTVII/6
(1916)**
R. Holmes, RPO, V. Handley *Concert*
(9/85) (UNIC) ① DKPCD9040
May Harrison, Bournemouth Municipal Orch, R.
Austin (bp1937: incomplete) *Concert*
(12/90) (SYMP) ① SYMCD1075

T. Little, WNO Orch, C. Mackerras (ed Beecham)
Concert   (7/92) (ARGO) ① **433 704-2ZH**
A. Sammons, RLPO, M. Sargent (r1944) Concert
                   (5/93) (TEST) ① **SBT1014**
Y. Menuhin, RPO, M. Davies (r1976) Elgar: Violin
Concerto.   (2/94) (EMI) ① **CDM7 64725-2**
R. Holmes, RPO, V. Handley (r1984) Concert
                   (8/95) (UNIC) ① **UKCD2072**

**Concerto for Violin, Cello and Orchestra,
RTVI/5 (1915)**
R. Wallfisch, T. Little, RLPO, C. Mackerras Concert
                   (3/92) (EMI) ① **CD-EMX2185**

**A Dance Rhapsody No. 1—orchestra,
RTVI/18 (1908)**
RPO, N. del Mar Concert
                   (3/92) (UNIC) ① **DKPCD9108**
WNO Orch, C. Mackerras (ed Beecham) Concert
                   (7/92) (ARGO) ① **433 704-2ZH**
Queen's Hall Orch, Henry Wood (r1923) Concert
                   (1/94) (BEUL) ① **1PD3**
P. Thwaites, J. Lavender (r1989-91: arr 2 pfs:
Grainger) Concert   (1/94) (PEAR) ① **SHECD9631**
RPO, N. del Mar (r1990) Concert
                   (8/95) (UNIC) ① **UKCD2071**
Bournemouth SO, R. Hickox (r1994) Concert
                   (9/95) (CHAN) ① **CHAN9355**

**A Dance Rhapsody No. 2—orchestra,
RTVI/22 (1916)**
RPO, T. Beecham (r1956) Concert
                   (6/87) (EMI) ① [2] **CDS7 47509-8**
RPO, E. Fenby Concert
                   (1/88) (UNIC) ① **DKPCD9063**
WNO Orch, C. Mackerras (ed Beecham) Concert
                   (7/92) (ARGO) ① **433 704-2ZH**
RPO, E. Fenby (r1986) Concert
                   (8/95) (UNIC) ① **UKCD2071**
Bournemouth SO, R. Hickox (r1994) Concert
                   (9/95) (CHAN) ① **CHAN9355**

**Eventyr (Once upon a time)—orchestra,
RTVI/23 (1917)** (after Asbjörnsen's folklore)
LPO, T. Beecham (r1934) Concert
                   (6/89) (BEEC) ① **BEECHAM2**
Hallé, V. Handley Concert
                   (8/90) (CFP) ① **CD-CFP4568**
RPO, T. Beecham (r1951) Concert
                   (11/94) (SONY) ① **SMK58934**
NZ SO, M. Fredman (r1994) Concert
                   (10/95) (NAXO) ① **8 553001**

Fantastic Dance—orchestra, RTVI/28 (1931)
RPO, E. Fenby (r1981) Concert
                   (8/95) (UNIC) ① **UKCD2071**

**Fennimore and Gerda Intermezzo—small
orchestra (1938)** (Interludes to Scenes 10 &
11: arr Fenby)
RPO, T. Beecham (r1956) Concert
                   (6/87) (EMI) ① [2] **CDS7 47509-8**
RPO, E. Fenby Concert
                   (1/88) (UNIC) ① **DKPCD9063**
LPO, V. Handley Concert
                   (2/89) (CFP) ① **CD-CFP4304**
LPO, T. Beecham (r1936) Concert
                   (6/89) (BEEC) ① **BEECHAM2**
ASMF, N. Marriner Concert
                   (8/89) (LOND) ① **421 390-2LM**
Bournemouth Sinfonietta, N. del Mar Concert
                   (1/91) (CHAN) ① **CHAN6502**
WNO Orch, C. Mackerras Concert
                   (7/92) (ARGO) ① **433 704-2ZH**
ECO, D. Barenboim (r1974) Concert
                   (4/94) (DG) ① **439 529-2GGA**
ASMF, N. Marriner (r1977) Concert
                   (4/94) (DECC) ① **440 323-2DWO**
Northern Sinfonia, R. Hickox (r1985) Concert
                   (7/94) (EMI) ① **CDM5 65067-2**
Oxford Orch da Camera, G. Vass (r1993) Concert
                   (9/94) (MEDI) ① **MQCD4002**
Hallé, J. Barbirolli (r1956) Concert
                   (10/95) (EMI) ① [2] **CMS5 65119-2**

**Florida—suite for orchestra, RTVI/1 (1887 rev
1889)**
1. Daybreak—Dance; 2. By the River; 3.
Sunset—Near the Plantation; 4. At Night.
Ulster Orch, V. Handley North Country Sketches.
                   (12/86) (CHAN) ① **CHAN8413**
RPO, T. Beecham (r1956) Concert
                   (6/87) (EMI) ① [2] **CDS7 47509-8**
English SO, W. Boughton Concert
                   (2/90) (NIMB) ① **NI5208**

**In a Summer Garden—rhapsody, RTVI/17
(1908 rev 1909)** (all recordings use revised
version unless otherwise stated)
Philh, O.A. Hughes (r1988) Concert
                   (12/88) (ASV) ① **CDDCA627**
Hallé, V. Handley Concert
                   (8/90) (CFP) ① **CD-CFP4568**

LPO, T. Beecham (r1936) Concert
                   (11/90) (BEEC) ① **BEECHAM3**
Bratislava RSO, A. Leaper Concert
                   (1/91) (NAXO) ① **8 550229**
LSO, B. Wordsworth Concert
                   (9/92) (COLL) ① **Coll1336-2**
BBC SO, A. Davis (r1992) Concert
                   (1/94) (TELD) ① **4509-90845-2**
LSO, G. Toye (r1928) Concert
                   (3/94) (DUTT) ① **CDAX8006**
LSO, A. Collins (r1953) Concert
                   (8/95) (DUTT) ① **CDLXT2503**
Bournemouth SO, R. Hickox (r1994) Concert
                   (9/95) (CHAN) ① **CHAN9355**
Hallé, J. Barbirolli (r1968) Concert
                   (10/95) (EMI) ① [2] **CMS5 65119-2**

**Irmelin Prelude—small orchestra, RTVI/27
(1931)**
RPO, T. Beecham (r1956) Concert
                   (6/87) (EMI) ① [2] **CDS7 47509-8**
LPO, V. Handley Concert
                   (2/89) (CFP) ① **CD-CFP4304**
LPO, T. Beecham (r1938) Concert
                   (6/89) (BEEC) ① **BEECHAM2**
Bournemouth Sinfonietta, N. del Mar Concert
                   (1/91) (CHAN) ① **CHAN6502**
WNO Orch, C. Mackerras Concert
                   (7/92) (ARGO) ① **433 704-2ZH**
Northern Sinfonia, R. Hickox (r1985) Concert
                   (7/94) (EMI) ① **CDM5 65067-2**
National SO, Sidney Beer (r1944) Concert
                   (5/95) (DUTT) ① **CDK1200**
RPO, E. Fenby (r1981) Concert
                   (8/95) (UNIC) ① **UKCD2072**
RPO, C. Seaman (r1994) Concert
                   (9/95) (TRIN) ① **TRP036**
LSO, J. Barbirolli (r1966) Concert
                   (10/95) (EMI) ① [2] **CMS5 65119-2**
NZ SO, M. Fredman (r1994) Concert
                   (10/95) (NAXO) ① **8 553001**

**Late Swallows—string orchestra (arr Fenby
from Stg Qt slow movt)**
Hallé, J. Barbirolli Concert
                   (3/93) (EMIN) ① **CD-EMX2198**
Hallé, J. Barbirolli (r1968) Concert
                   (10/95) (EMI) ① [2] **CMS5 65119-2**

**Lebenstanz (Life's Dance)—tone poem:
orchestra, RTVI/15 (1899 rev 1901 and 1912)**
RPO, N. del Mar Concert
                   (3/92) (UNIC) ① **DKPCD9108**

**Légende—violin and orchestra, RTVII/3
(1895)**
R. Holmes, RPO, V. Handley Concert
                   (9/85) (UNIC) ① **DKPCD9040**

Marche-caprice, RTVI/6 (1889 rev 1890)
RPO, T. Beecham (r1956) Concert
                   (6/87) (EMI) ① [2] **CDS7 47509-8**
Black Dyke Mills Band, P. Parkes (arr brass band: G
Langford) (r1993) (CHAN) ① **CHAN4507**

North Country Sketches, RTVI/20 (1913-14)
1. Autumn; 2. Winter Landscape; 3. Dance; 4. The
March of Spring.
Ulster Orch, V. Handley Florida Suite.
                   (12/86) (CHAN) ① **CHAN8413**
RPO, T. Beecham (r1949) Concert
                   (11/94) (SONY) ① **SMK58934**
Bournemouth SO, R. Hickox (r1994) Concert
                   (9/95) (CHAN) ① **CHAN9355**

**On hearing the first cuckoo in Spring—small
orchestra, RTVI/19 (1912)** (No. 1 of 'Two
Pieces for Small Orchestra')
LPO, V. Handley Concert
                   (1/85) (CHAN) ① **CHAN8330**
RPO, T. Beecham (r1956) Concert
                   (6/87) (EMI) ① [2] **CDS7 47509-8**
LPO, V. Handley Concert
                   (2/89) (CFP) ① **CD-CFP4304**
ASMF, N. Marriner Concert
                   (5/89) (DECC) ① **417 778-2DM**
ASMF, N. Marriner Concert
                   (8/89) (LOND) ① **421 390-2LM**
RPS Orch, T. Beecham (r1927) Concert
                   (11/90) (BEEC) ① **BEECHAM3**
Bournemouth Sinfonietta, N. del Mar Concert
                   (1/91) (CHAN) ① **CHAN6502**
WNO Orch, C. Mackerras (ed Beecham) Concert
                   (7/92) (ARGO) ① **433 704-2ZH**
LSO, B. Wordsworth Concert
                   (9/92) (COLL) ① **Coll1336-2**
RLPO, M. Sargent (r1947) Concert
                   (5/93) (TEST) ① **SBT1014**
BBC SO, A. Davis (r1992) Concert
                   (1/94) (TELD) ① **4509-90845-2**
LSO, G. Toye (r1928) Concert
                   (3/94) (DUTT) ① **CDAX8006**

ECO, D. Barenboim (r1974) Concert
                   (4/94) (DG) ① **439 529-2GGA**
ASMF, N. Marriner (r1977) Concert
                   (4/94) (DECC) ① **440 323-2DWO**
Northern Sinfonia, R. Hickox (r1985) Concert
                   (7/94) (EMI) ① **CDM5 65067-2**
Oxford Orch da Camera, G. Vass (r1993) Concert
                   (9/94) (MEDI) ① **MQCD4002**
RPS Orch, T. Beecham (r1927) Concert
                   (10/94) (DUTT) ① **CDLX7011**
LSO, A. Collins (r1953) Concert
                   (8/95) (DUTT) ① **CDLXT2503**
RPO, C. Seaman (r1994) Concert
                   (9/95) (TRIN) ① **TRP036**
Hallé, J. Barbirolli (r1968) Concert
                   (10/95) (EMI) ① [2] **CMS5 65119-2**
English Sinfonia, C. Groves (r1988) Concert
                   (10/95) (CARL) ① **PCD2017**

**Over the hills and far away—fantasy
overture, RTVI/11 (1897)**
RPO, T. Beecham (r1957) Concert
                   (6/87) (EMI) ① [2] **CDS7 47509-8**
LPO, T. Beecham (r1936) Concert
                   (6/89) (BEEC) ① **BEECHAM2**
RPO, T. Beecham (r1950) Concert
                   (11/94) (SONY) ① **SMK58934**
RPO, C. Seaman (r1994) Concert
                   (9/95) (TRIN) ① **TRP036**

**Paris (The Song of a Great City)—orchestra,
RTVI/14 (1899-1900)**
LPO, T. Beecham (r1934) Concert
                   (6/89) (BEEC) ① **BEECHAM2**
RPO, N. del Mar Concert
                   (3/92) (UNIC) ① **DKPCD9108**
RLPO, C. Mackerras Concert
                   (3/92) (EMIN) ① **CD-EMX2185**
BBC SO, A. Davis (r1992) Concert
                   (1/94) (TELD) ① **4509-90845-2**
RPO, T. Beecham (r1955) Concert
                   (11/94) (SONY) ① **SMK46683**
LSO, A. Collins (r1953) Concert
                   (8/95) (DUTT) ① **CDLXT2503**
NZ SO, M. Fredman (r1994) Concert
                   (10/95) (NAXO) ① **8 553001**

Sleigh ride (Winter night), RTVI/7 (1889)
RPO, T. Beecham (r1956) Concert
                   (6/87) (EMI) ① [2] **CDS7 47509-8**
LPO, V. Handley Concert
                   (2/89) (CFP) ① **CD-CFP4304**
Northern Sinfonia, R. Hickox (r1985) Concert
                   (7/94) (EMI) ① **CDM5 65067-2**

Sonata for strings (1916 arr 1963 and 1977)
(trans Fenby from String Quartet (1916-19)
3. Late swallows.
New Zealand CO, N. Braithwaite Concert
                   (11/92) (KOCH) ① **37139-2**
3. Bournemouth Sinfonietta, N. del Mar Concert
                   (1/91) (CHAN) ① **CHAN6502**

**A Song before sunrise—small orchestra,
RTVI/24 (1918)**
RPO, T. Beecham (r1956) Concert
                   (6/87) (EMI) ① [2] **CDS7 47509-8**
Philh, O.A. Hughes (r1988) Concert
                   (12/88) (ASV) ① **CDDCA627**
LPO, V. Handley Concert
                   (2/89) (CFP) ① **CD-CFP4304**
ASMF, N. Marriner Concert
                   (8/89) (LOND) ① **421 390-2LM**
Bournemouth Sinfonietta, N. del Mar Concert
                   (1/91) (CHAN) ① **CHAN6502**
LSO, B. Wordsworth Concert
                   (9/92) (COLL) ① **Coll1336-2**
RPO, M. Sargent (r1993) Concert
                   (3/93) (EMIN) ① **CD-EMX2198**
ASMF, N. Marriner (r1977) Concert
                   (4/94) (DECC) ① **440 323-2DWO**
Northern Sinfonia, R. Hickox (r1985) Concert
                   (7/94) (EMI) ① **CDM5 65067-2**
Oxford Orch da Camera, G. Vass (r1993) Concert
                   (9/94) (MEDI) ① **MQCD4002**
RPO, C. Seaman (r1994) Concert
                   (9/95) (TRIN) ① **TRP036**
Hallé, J. Barbirolli (r1968) Concert
                   (10/95) (EMI) ① [2] **CMS5 65119-2**

**A Song of Summer—orchestra, RTVI/25
(1929-30)** (adapted from unpublished 'A Poem
of Life and Love')
Philh, O.A. Hughes (r1988) Concert
                   (12/88) (ASV) ① **CDDCA627**
Hallé, V. Handley Concert
                   (8/90) (CFP) ① **CD-CFP4568**
LSO, A. Collins (r1953) Concert
                   (8/95) (DUTT) ① **CDLXT2503**
RPO, E. Fenby (r1981) Concert
                   (8/95) (UNIC) ① **UKCD2072**

LSO, J. Barbirolli (r1966) *Concert*
(10/95) (EMI) ① [2] **CMS5 65119-2**
Suite—violin and orchestra, RTVII/1 (1890-91)
1. Pastorale; 2. Intermezzo; 3. (Elégie); 4. (Finale).
R. Holmes, RPO, V. Handley *Concert*
(9/85) (UNIC) ① **DKPCD9040**
Summer Evening, RTVI/7 (1890) (No. 1 of
'Three Small Tone Poems')
LPO, V. Handley *Concert*
(1/85) (CHAN) ① **CHAN8330**
RPO, T. Beecham (r1956) *Concert*
(6/87) (EMI) ① [2] **CDS7 47509-8**
English SO, W. Boughton *Concert*
(2/90) (NIMB) ① **NI5208**
LSO, B. Wordsworth *Concert*
(9/92) (COLL) ① **Coll1336-2**
Northern Sinfonia, R. Hickox (r1985) *Concert*
(7/94) (EMI) ① **CDM5 65067-2**
Summer Night on the River, RTVI/19 (1911)
(No. 2 of 'Two Pieces for Small Orchestra')
LPO, V. Handley *Concert*
(1/85) (CHAN) ① **CHAN8330**
RPO, T. Beecham (r1957) *Concert*
(6/87) (EMI) ① [2] **CDS7 47509-8**
Philh, O.A. Hughes (r1988) *Concert*
(12/88) (ASV) ① **CDDCA627**
LPO, V. Handley *Concert*
(2/89) (CFP) ① **CD-CFP4304**
ASMF, N. Marriner *Concert*
(8/89) (LOND) ① **421 390-2LM**
LPO, T. Beecham (r1935) *Concert*
(11/90) (BEEC) ① **BEECHAM3**
Bournemouth Sinfonietta, N. del Mar *Concert*
(1/91) (CHAN) ① **CHAN6502**
WNO Orch, C. Mackerras (ed Beecham) *Concert*
(7/92) (ARGO) ① **433 704-2ZH**
LSO, B. Wordsworth *Concert*
(9/92) (COLL) ① **Coll1336-2**
BBC SO, A. Davis (r1992) *Concert*
(1/94) (TELD) ① **4509-90845-2**
New SO, G. Toye (r1929) *Concert*
(3/94) (DUTT) ① **CDAX8006**
ECO, D. Barenboim (r1974) *Concert*
(4/94) (DG) ① **439 529-2GGA**
ASMF, N. Marriner (r1977) *Concert*
(4/94) (DECC) ① **440 323-2DWO**
Northern Sinfonia, R. Hickox (r1985) *Concert*
(7/94) (EMI) ① **CDM5 65067-2**
Oxford Orch da Camera, G. Vass (r1993) *Concert*
(9/94) (MEDI) ① **MQCD4002**
RPS Orch, T. Beecham (r1928) *Concert*
(10/94) (DUTT) ① **CDLX7011**
LSO, A. Collins (r1953) *Concert*
(8/95) (DUTT) ① **CDLXT2503**
Hallé, J. Barbirolli (r1968) *Concert*
(10/95) (EMI) ① [2] **CMS5 65119-2**

SECTION II: CHAMBER

2 Interludes from 'Fennimore and Gerda'—oboe and piano (1930s) (arr E Fenby from opera 'Fennimore and Gerda')
L. Jones, Malcolm Miller (r1994) *Concert*
(8/95) (MERI) ① [2] **CDE84298/9**
Légende—violin and piano (1895)
H. Holst, G. Moore (r1942) *Concert*
(5/93) (TEST) ① **SBT1014**
L. Jones, Malcolm Miller (r1994) *Concert*
(8/95) (MERI) ① [2] **CDE84298/9**
Lullaby—for a modern baby—violin and piano (pub 1929) (arr from 5 Piano Pieces—No 4)
L. Jones, Malcolm Miller (r1994) *Concert*
(8/95) (MERI) ① [2] **CDE84298/9**
Romance—violin and piano (1892)
L. Jones, Malcolm Miller (r1994) *Concert*
(8/95) (MERI) ① [2] **CDE84298/9**
Sonata for Cello and Piano, RTVIII/7 (1916)
R. Wallfisch, P. Wallfisch (r1986) *Concert*
(4/87) (CHAN) ① **CHAN8499**
B. Harrison, H. Craxton (r1926) *Concert*
(3/93) (CLAR) ① **CDGSE78-50-47**
B. Harrison, H. Craxton (r1926) *Concert*
(3/93) (SYMP) ① **SYMCD1140**
M. Welsh, I. Margalit (r1994) *Concert*
(8/95) (MERI) ① [2] **CDC5 55399-2**
J. Lloyd Webber, E. Fenby (r1972) *Concert*
(8/95) (UNIC) ① **UKCD2074**
Sonata for Violin and Piano in B (1892)
L. Jones, Malcolm Miller (r1994) *Concert*
(8/95) (MERI) ① [2] **CDE84298/9**
Sonata for Violin and Piano No. 1, RTVIII/9 (1914)
May Harrison, A. Bax (r1929) *Concert*
(3/93) (CLAR) ① **CDGSE78-50-47**

May Harrison, A. Bax (r1929) *Concert*
(3/93) (SYMP) ① **SYMCD1140**
L. Jones, Malcolm Miller (r1994) *Concert*
(8/95) (MERI) ① [2] **CDE84298/9**
R. Holmes, E. Fenby (r1972) *Concert*
(8/95) (UNIC) ① **UKCD2074**
J. Graham, I. Margalit (r1994) *Concert*
(8/95) (EMI) ① **CDC5 55399-2**
Sonata for Violin and Piano No. 2, RTVIII/9 (1923)
L. Jones, Malcolm Miller (r1994) *Concert*
(8/95) (MERI) ① [2] **CDE84298/9**
J. Graham, I. Margalit (r1994) *Concert*
(8/95) (EMI) ① **CDC5 55399-2**
R. Holmes, E. Fenby (r1972) *Concert*
(8/95) (UNIC) ① **UKCD2074**
Sonata for Violin and Piano No. 3, RTVIII/10 (c1918-1930)
May Harrison, A. Bax (r1937) *Concert*
(12/90) (SYMP) ① **SYMCD1075**
L. Jones, Malcolm Miller (r1994) *Concert*
(8/95) (MERI) ① [2] **CDE84298/9**
R. Holmes, E. Fenby (r1972) *Concert*
(8/95) (UNIC) ① **UKCD2074**
A. Barantschik, I. Margalit (r1994) *Concert*
(8/95) (EMI) ① **CDC5 55399-2**
A. Sammons, K. Long (r1944) *Concert*
(8/95) (DUTT) ① **CDAX8014**
String Quartet, RTVIII/8 (1916)
Brodsky Qt *Elgar: String Quartet.*
(7/89) (ASV) ① **CDDCA526**

SECTION III: INSTRUMENTAL

Dance—harpsichord, RTIX/6 (1919)
E. Howard Jones (r1929) *Concert*
(3/94) (DUTT) ① **CDAX8006**
5 Pieces for Piano (1921)
1. Mazurka for a little girl; 2. Waltz for a little girl; 3. Waltz; 4. Lullaby for a modern baby; 5. Toccata.
1, 2, 4, 5. E. Howard Jones (r1929) *Concert*
(3/94) (DUTT) ① **CDAX8006**
3 Preludes—piano, RTIX/8 (1922-23)
1. Scherzando; 2. Quick; 3. Con moto.
C. Headington *Concert*
(11/90) (KING) ① **KCLCD2017**
E. Howard Jones (r1929) *Concert*
(3/94) (DUTT) ① **CDAX8006**
E. Parkin (r1982) *Concert*
(8/95) (UNIC) ① **UKCD2071**
Zum Carnival—polka: piano, RTIX/1 (pub 1885)
E. Parkin (r1982) *Concert*
(8/95) (UNIC) ① **UKCD2071**

SECTION IV: VOCAL AND CHORAL

Appalachia—Variations on an old slave song—baritone, chorus and orchestra, RTII/2 (1902) (Wds. trad.)
EXCERPTS: 1. Oh, Honey, I am going down the river.
BBC Chor, LPO, T. Beecham (r1938) *Concert*
(10/94) (DUTT) ① **CDLX7011**
Ambrosian Sngrs, Hallé, J. Barbirolli (r1970: includes rehearsal) *Concert*
(10/95) (EMI) ① [2] **CMS5 65119-2**
Arabesque—baritone, chorus and orchestra, RTII/7 (1911) (Wds. J. P. Jacobsen)
T. Allen, Ambrosian Sngrs, RPO, E. Fenby (Eng) *Concert*
(1/88) (UNIC) ① **DKPCD9063**
J. Shirley-Quirk, Liverpool Phil Ch, RLPO, C. Groves (1968) *Concert* (6/93) (EMI) ① [2] **CMS7 64218-2**
Chanson d'automne—song, RTV/27 (1911) (Wds. P. Verlaine)
R. Golden, S. Sulich *Concert*
(10/91) (KOCH) ① **37043-2**
Cynara—baritone and orchestra, RTIII/5 (1907-1929) (Wds. E. Dowson)
J. Shirley-Quirk, RLPO, C. Groves *Concert*
(3/93) (EMIN) ① **CD-EMX2198**
7 Danish Songs—1v and orchestra/piano, RTIII/4 (1897) (Wds. various)
1. Summer Nights (wds. H. Drachmann); 2. Thro' long, long year (wds. J. P. Jacobsen); 3. Wine Roses (wds. J. P. Jacobsen); 4. Let Springtime Come (wds. J. P. Jacobsen); 5. Irmelin Rose (wds. J. P. Jacobsen); 6. In the Seraglio Garden (wds. J. P. Jacobsen); 7. Silken Shoes (wds. J. P. Jacobsen).
1. R. Golden, S. Sulich *Concert*
(10/91) (KOCH) ① **37043-2**
Idyll: Once I passed through a populous city—S, B and orchestra, RTIII/10 (1930-32) (Wds. W. WHitman, adapted R. Nicholls)
F. Lott, T. Allen, RPO, E. Fenby (r1981) *Concert*
(8/95) (UNIC) ① **UKCD2073**

A Late Lark—tenor and small orchestra, TIII/6 (1924-29) (Wds. W.E. Henley)
A. Rolfe Johnson, RPO, E. Fenby (r1981) *Concert*
(8/95) (UNIC) ① **UKCD2072**
La Lune blanche—song, RTV/26 (1910) (Wds. P. Verlaine)
R. Golden, S. Sulich *Concert*
(10/91) (KOCH) ① **37043-2**
Eine Messe des Lebens—SATB, chorus and orchestra, RTII/4 (1898, 1904-05) (Wds. F. Nietzsche. Eng: A Mass of Life)
H. Harper, H. Watts, R. Tear, B. Luxon, LP Ch, LPO, C. Groves (r1971) *Concert*
(6/93) (EMI) ① [2] **CMS7 64218-2**
Sea Drift—baritone, chorus and orchestra, RTII/3 (1903-04) (Wds. W. Whitman)
J. Brownlee, London Select Ch, LPO, T. Beecham (r1936) *Concert* (11/90) (BEEC) ① **BEECHAM3**
G. Clinton, Chor, RPO, T. Beecham (r1951) *Village Romeo and Juliet.*
(11/92) (EMI) ① [2] **CMS7 64386-2**
B. Terfel, Waynflete Sngrs, Southern Voices, Bournemouth Sym Chor, Bournemouth SO, R. Hickox (r1993) *Concert*
(11/93) (CHAN) ① **CHAN9214**
J. Shirley-Quirk, LSC, RPO, R. Hickox (1980) *Concert* (4/94) (DECC) ① **440 323-2DWO**
The Song of the High Hills—orchestra with wordless ST and chorus, RTII/6 (1911)
M. Midgley, V. Midgley, Ambrosian Sngrs, RPO, E. Fenby (r1986) *Concert*
(8/95) (UNIC) ① **UKCD2071**
3 Songs, RTV/12 (1891) (Wds. P. B. Shelley)
1. Indian Love Song; 2. Love's Philosophy; 3. To the Queen of my Heart.
R. Golden, S. Sulich *Concert*
(10/91) (KOCH) ① **37043-2**
2, 3. H. Nash, G. Moore (r1934) *Concert*
(11/95) (PEAR) ① **GEMMCD9175**
2 Songs—1v and piano, RTV/16 (1895) (Wds. P. Verlaine)
1. Il pleure dans mon coeur; 2. Le ciel est pardessus le toit.
1, 2. R. Golden, S. Sulich *Concert*
(10/91) (KOCH) ① **37043-2**
5 Songs from the Norwegian—1v and piano, RTV/5 (1888) (Wds. various)
1. Slumber song (wds. B. Bjørnson); 2. The Nightingale (wds. J. S. C. Welhaven); 3. Summer Eve (wds. J. Paulsen); 4. Longing (wds. T. Kjerulf); 5. Sunset (wds. A. Munch).
1. I. Partridge, J. Partridge *Concert*
(12/89) (ETCE) ① **KTC1063**
2. D. Labbette, T. Beecham (r1929) *Concert*
(10/94) (DUTT) ① **CDLX7011**
2-5. R. Golden, S. Sulich *Concert*
(10/91) (KOCH) ① **37043-2**
7 Songs from the Norwegian—1v and piano, RTV/9 (1889-90) (Wds. various)
1. Cradle Song (wds. H. Ibsen); 2. The Homeward Journey (wds. A. O. Vinje); 3. Evening Voices, or Twilight Fancies (wds. B. Bjørnson); 4. Sweet Venevil (wds. B. Bjørnson); 5. The Minstrel (wds. H. Ibsen); 6. Love concealed (wds. B. Bjørnson); 7. The Bird's Story (wds. H. Ibsen).
1, 3. D. Labbette, T. Beecham (r1929) *Concert*
(10/94) (DUTT) ① **CDLX7011**
1-4, 6, 7. R. Golden, S. Sulich *Concert*
(10/91) (KOCH) ① **37043-2**
2. I. Partridge, J. Partridge *Concert*
(12/89) (ETCE) ① **KTC1063**
2, 4, 6, 7. I. Partridge, J. Partridge *Concert*
(12/89) (ETCE) ① **KTC1063**
3. Sarah Walker, R. Vignoles *Concert*
(10/92) (CRD) ① **CRD3473**
Songs of Farewell—chorus and orchestra, RTII/9 (1930) (Wds. W. Whitman)
1. How sweet the silent backward tracings; 2. I stand as on some might eagle's beak; 3. Passage to you; 4. Joy, shipmate, joy!; 5. Now finalè to the shore.
RCS, RPO, M. Sargent *Concert*
(3/93) (EMIN) ① **CD-EMX2198**
Waynflete Sngrs, Southern Voices, Bournemouth Sym Chor, Bournemouth SO, R. Hickox (r1993) *Concert* (11/93) (CHAN) ① **CHAN9214**
Songs of Sunset—A, B, chorus and orchestra, RTII/5 (1906-07) (Wds. E. Dowson)
1. A Song of the Setting Sun; 2. Cease smiling, Dearl; 3. Pale amber moonlight; 4. Exceeding sorrow; 5. By the sad waters of separation; 6. See how the trees; 7. I was not sorrowful; 8. They are not long, the weeping and the laughter.
M. Forrester, J. Cameron, Beecham Choral Soc, RPO, T. Beecham (r1957) *Concert*
(6/87) (EMI) ① [2] **CDS7 47509-8**

3 Pieces—cello and piano (1967)
1. Lento I; 2. Allegro; 3. Lento II.
A. Zagorinsky, A. Shmitov (r1993) *Concert*
(12/94) (ETCE) ① **KTC1179**

4 Pieces—flute and piano (1977)
M. Wiesler, R. Pöntinen *Concert*
(6/90) (BIS) ① **BIS-CD419**

Sonata for Cello and Piano (1971)
A. Zagorinsky, A. Shmitov (r1993) *Concert*
(12/94) (ETCE) ① **KTC1179**

Sonata for Flute and Piano (1960)
M. Wiesler, R. Pöntinen *Concert*
(6/90) (BIS) ① **BIS-CD419**

Suite for Cello and Piano (1961)
A. Zagorinsky, A. Shmitov (r1993) *Concert*
(12/94) (ETCE) ① **KTC1179**

Variations on Schubert's theme—cello and piano (1986)
A. Zagorinsky, A. Shmitov (r1993) *Concert*
(12/94) (ETCE) ① **KTC1179**

Variations on the theme of 'Es ist genug' (Bach)—viola and chamber ensemble (1984-86) (arr cpsr from va/pf version)
N. Imai, Amsterdam Nieuw Sinfonietta, L. Markiz
Concert (9/92) (BIS) ① **BIS-CD518**

SECTION III: INSTRUMENTAL

Pour Daniel—piano (1989)
A. Shmitov (r1993) *Concert*
(12/94) (ETCE) ① **KTC1179**

Variations—piano (1961)
A. Shmitov (r1993) *Concert*
(12/94) (ETCE) ① **KTC1179**

SECTION IV: VOCAL AND CHORAL

The Bonfire of Snow—song-cycle: soprano and piano (1981) (Wds. A. Blok)
1. Solitude; 2. Elegy; 3. Night; 4. The snowy road; 5. My fate; 6. Bonfire of snow; 7. Confusion; 8. A warning; 9. Snow flowers; 10. Little lights; 11. Anticipation; 12. Twilight; 13. At your feet; 14. The second baptism; 15. The conventional sign; 16. The jolly wanderer; 17. In the desert; 18. The last meeting; 19. I also loved; 20. Year after year has flowed by; 21. Before sunset; 22. On the cross; 23. And again snows; 24. The final journey.
E. Vassilieva, J. Schab *Concert*
(4/90) (CHNT) ① **LDC278 951**

2 Poems—soprano and piano (1970) (Wds. I. Bunin)
1. Twilight; 2. Autumn.
E. Vassilieva, J. Schab *Concert*
(4/90) (CHNT) ① **LDC278 951**

To Flora—3 songs: soprano & piano (1980) (Wds. A. Josef)
E. Vassilieva, J. Schab *Concert*
(4/90) (CHNT) ① **LDC278 951**

DENSMORE, Gardenia

SECTION IV: VOCAL AND CHORAL

A Spring Fancy—song
E. Rethberg, F. Persson (r1928-9) *Concert*
(2/95) (ROMO) ① [2] **81012-2**

DENZA, Luigi *(1846–1922)* Italy/England

SECTION IV: VOCAL AND CHORAL

Funiculì-Funiculà—song (Wds. Turco)
L. Pavarotti, Teatro Communale Orch, A. Guadagno
Concert (8/83) (DECC) ① **410 015-2DH**
L. Pavarotti, Bologna Teatro Comunale Orch, A. Guadagno
(7/86) (DECC) ① [2] **417 011-2DH2**
B. Gigli, orch (r1924) *Concert*
(5/90) (NIMB) ① **NI7807**
F. Wunderlich, R. Lamy Sngrs, Graunke SO, H. Carste *Concert* (5/93) (DG) ① **431 110-2GB**

In questa sera—song
F. Marconi, anon (r1908) *Concert*
(6/90) (SYMP) ① **SYMCD1073**

Non t'amo più—song (Wds. L. De Giorgi)
E. Caruso, S. Cottone (r1902) *Concert*
(5/89) (EMI) ① **CDH7 61046-2**
E. Caruso, S. Cottone (r1902) *Concert*
(12/90) (PEAR) ① [3] **EVC1(1)**
E. Caruso, S. Cottone (r1902) *Concert*
(10/91) (RCA) ① [12] **GD60495(1)**

Occhi di fata—song (Wds. Tremacoldo)
O. Kamionsky, anon (r1908: Russ) *Concert*
(6/93) (PEAR) ① [3] **GEMMCDS9001/3(1)**
B. Gigli, orch, W. Goehr (r1938) *Concert*
(6/93) (MMOI) ① **CDMOIR417**

T. Gobbi, Orch, A. Erede (r1948) *Concert*
(8/93) (TEST) ① **SBT1019**
L. Pavarotti, NYPO, L. Magiera (pp1993) *Concert*
(2/95) (DECC) ① **444 450-2DH**

Se—song
B. Gigli, orch, R. Bourdon (r1929) *Concert*
(5/90) (PEAR) ① **GEMMCD9367**

Si vous l'aviez compris—song (Wds. L. S. Bordése)
E. Caruso, M. Elman, G. Scognamiglio (r1915)
Concert (7/91) (RCA) ① [12] **GD60495(5)**
E. Caruso, M. Elman, G. Scognamiglio (r1915)
Concert (10/91) (PEAR) ① [3] **EVC3(2)**
E. Caruso, M. Elman, G. Scognamiglio (r1915)
Concert (10/91) (BIDD) ① **LAB039**

Vieni a me—song
O. Kamionsky, A. Zaniboni, anon (r1905: Russ) *Concert*
(6/93) (PEAR) ① [3] **GEMMCDS9001/3(1)**
G. Zenatello, anon (r1907) *Concert*
(5/95) (PEAR) ① [4] **GEMMCDS9073(1)**
G. Zenatello, anon (r1907) *Concert*
(5/94) (SYMP) ① **SYMCD1168**

DERING, Richard *(c1580–1630)* England

SECTION IV: VOCAL AND CHORAL

Ave virgo gratiosa—5vv (pub 1617)
Cambridge Sngrs, J. Rutter *Concert*
(4/92) (CLLE) ① **COLCD116**

Cantica sacra—6vv and continuo (pub 1618) (alphabetical list)
1. Adjuro vos filiae; 2. Ardens est cor meum; 3. Cantate Domino; 4. Congratulamini mihi; 5. Factum est silentium; 6. Heu mihi Domine; 7. Jesu decus angelicum; 8. Jubilate Deo; 9. O crux ave; 10. O vos omnes; 11. Panis angelicus; 12. Paratum cor meum; 13. Quae est ista quae ascendit quasi aurora; 14. Quam pulchra es; 15. Quam vidistis; 16. Sancta et immaculata virginitas; 17. Surge amica mea; 18. Te laudamus; 19. Veni Jesu; 20. Virgo prudentissima; 21. Vulnerasti cor meum.
5. Oxford Christ Church Cath Ch, S. Preston *Concert*
(2/90) (GAMU) ① **GOUPCD153**
5. Cambridge Sngrs, J. Rutter *Concert*
(4/92) (CLLE) ① **COLCD113**
5. Oxford Christ Church Cath Ch, S. Darlington
Concert (10/92) (NIMB) ① **NI5328**
5. Jesus College Ch, D. Phillips, T. Horton *Concert*
(7/93) (CNTO) ① **CRCD2367**

T'amo, mia vita—madrigal: 3vv
Consort of Musicke, A. Rooley (lte/dir) *Concert*
(2/89) (BIS) ① **BIS-CD392**

DESPLANES, Jean Antoine *(1678–1704)* Italy

also known as Giovanni Antonio Piani

SECTION II: CHAMBER

Intrada (Adagio)—cello and continuo
J. Thibaud, T. Janopoulo (r1933: arr vn/pf: Nachez)
Concert (10/91) (MSCM) ① **MM30321**
J. Thibaud, T. Janopoulo (r1933: arr vn/pf: Nachez)
Concert (12/94) (APR) ① [2] **APR7028**

DESPOND, Luc *(16th–17th Cent)* France

SECTION III: INSTRUMENTAL

Variations on 'Filou'—lute (in Lord Herbert of Cherbury's Lute Book)
P. O'Dette *Concert* (4/93) (HARM) ① **HMU90 7068**

DESPORTES, Emile *(b 1909)* France

SECTION II: CHAMBER

Pastorale joyeuse
V. Taylor, T. Kain (arr Almeida) *Concert*
(9/92) (TALL) ① **TP003**

Pastorale mélancolique
V. Taylor, T. Kain (arr Almeida) *Concert*
(9/92) (TALL) ① **TP003**

Pastourelle
V. Taylor, T. Kain (arr Almeida) *Concert*
(9/92) (TALL) ① **TP003**

Ronde
V. Taylor, T. Kain (arr Almeida) *Concert*
(9/92) (TALL) ① **TP003**

DESPORTES, Yvonne (Berthe Melitta) *(b 1907)* France

SECTION I: ORCHESTRAL

Suite française—orchestra (1934-38)
1. Prélude; 2. Sarabande; 3. Gavotte; 4. Menuet; 5. Bourrée; 6. Gigue.
Thurston Cl Qt (arr cl qt) *Concert*
(10/93) (ASV) ① **CDWHL2076**

DESSAU, Paul *(1894–1979)* Germany

SECTION II: CHAMBER

String Quartet No. 1 (1932)
New Leipzig Qt (r1994) *Concert*
(5/95) (CPO) ① [2] **CPO999 002-2**

String Quartet No. 2 (1942-43)
New Leipzig Qt (r1994) *Concert*
(5/95) (CPO) ① [2] **CPO999 002-2**

String Quartet No. 3 (1943-46)
New Leipzig Qt (r1994) *Concert*
(5/95) (CPO) ① [2] **CPO999 002-2**

String Quartet No. 4 (1948)
New Leipzig Qt (r1994) *Concert*
(5/95) (CPO) ① [2] **CPO999 002-2**

String Quartet No. 5 (1955)
New Leipzig Qt (r1994) *Concert*
(5/95) (CPO) ① [2] **CPO999 002-2**

String Quartet No. 6 (1971-74)
New Leipzig Qt (r1994) *Concert*
(5/95) (CPO) ① [2] **CPO999 002-2**

String Quartet No. 7 (1975)
New Leipzig Qt (r1994) *Concert*
(5/95) (CPO) ① [2] **CPO999 002-2**

SECTION IV: VOCAL AND CHORAL

Hagadah shel Pessach—oratorio: 3 parts (1934-36) (Wds. M Brod, based on Jewish liturgical texts for Passover)
PART 1: 1a. Introduction; 1b. Moses slays the Egyptian; 1c. The Girls at the Well; 1d. The Mission. PART 2: 2a. Procession of the Pharoah; 2b. The Plagues; 2c. The Slaying of the First-born; 2d. Midnight Hymn. PART 3: 3. Israel's departure into freedom.
S. Ritterbusch, R. Spingler, Y. Jänicke, P. Galliard, G. Sadé, J. Schmeckenbecher, B. Weikl, J. Tilli, A. Muff, M. Hölle, N German Rad Chor, Weber Men's Ch, Hamburg PO, G. Albrecht (pp1994)
(10/95) (CAPR) ① [2] **10 590/1**

DESTINN, Emmy *(1878–1930)* Czecholsovakia

Ema Destinnová

SECTION IV: VOCAL AND CHORAL

Last tears—song (Wds. Wenig)
E. Destinn, orch, J. Pasternack (r1919) *Concert*
(11/93) (ROMO) ① [2] **81002-2**
E. Destinn, orch, J. Pasternack (r1919) *Concert*
(12/94) (SUPR) ① [12] **11 2136-2(5)**

Maiden's song—song (Wds. Bierbaum)
E. Destinn, orch, J. Pasternack (r1919) *Concert*
(11/93) (ROMO) ① [2] **81002-2**
E. Destinn, orch, J. Pasternack (r1919) *Concert*
(12/94) (SUPR) ① [12] **11 2136-2(5)**

Romance—song
E. Destinn, orch, J. Pasternack (r1920) *Concert*
(11/93) (ROMO) ① [2] **81002-2**
E. Destinn, orch, J. Pasternack (r1920) *Concert*
(12/94) (SUPR) ① [12] **11 2136-2(5)**

Wooing—song (Wds. Wenig)
E. Destinn, orch, J. Pasternack (r1919) *Concert*
(11/93) (ROMO) ① [2] **81002-2**
E. Destinn, orch, J. Pasternack (r1919) *Concert*
(12/94) (SUPR) ① [12] **11 2136-2(5)**

DETT, Nathaniel *(1882–1943)* USA

SECTION III: INSTRUMENTAL

8 Bible Vignettes—piano (1941-43)
D. Oldham *Concert* (9/89) (NEW) ① **NW367-2**

In the Bottoms—suite: piano (1913)
1. Prelude: Night; 2. His Song; 3. Honey; 4. Barcarolle: Morning; 5. Juba Dance.
D. Oldham *Concert* (9/89) (NEW) ① **NW367-2**

Magnolia Suite—piano (1911)
D. Oldham *Concert* (9/89) (NEW) ① **NW367-2**

DEVIENNE, François (1759–1803) France

SECTION II: CHAMBER

3 Bassoon Quartets—bassoon, violin, viola and cello, Op. 73 (pub c1800)
K. Thunemann, T. Zehetmair, T. Zimmermann, C. Henckel *Duos concertants, Op.34.*
(7/88) (CLAV) ① **CD50-8714**
6 Duos—flute and viola, Op. 5 (1784)
No.1. Auréole (r1991) *Concert*
(7/93) (KOCH) ① **37102-2**
Duos concertants—bassoon and cello, Op. 34
1, 4. K. Thunemann, C. Henckel *Bassoon Quartets, Op.73.*
(7/88) (CLAV) ① **CD50-8714**
Première Sonata for Clarinet and Fortepiano in B flat
R. Samuels, F. Renzi (r1993) *Concert*
(7/95) (KOCH) ① **37186-2**
Sonata for Flute and Harpsichord in E minor
S. Preston, L. Carolan *Concert*
(3/87) (AMON) ① **CD-SAR19**
3 Sonatas—oboe and continuo, Op. 71 (1798-99) (transcribed from flute sonatas)
1. C; 2. G; 3. D minor.
P. Bree, Roderick Shaw *Sonatas, Op. 23.*
(12/91) (ETCE) ① **KTC1106**
3 Sonatas—harpsichord/fortepiano and flute obbligato, Op. 23 (c1788)
3. G minor.
3. P. Bree, Roderick Shaw (trans ob) *Oboe Sonatas, Op. 71.*
(12/91) (ETCE) ① **KTC1106**
6 Sonatas for Bassoon and Continuo, Op. 24 (?1785)
1. C; 2. G; 3. F; 4. C; 5. G minor; 6. C.
D. Bond, R. van der Meer, R. Kohnen (r1992)
(11/94) (ACCE) ① **ACC9290D**

DEVREESE, Frédéric (b 1929) The Netherlands

SECTION I: ORCHESTRAL

Concerto for Piano and Orchestra No. 2 (1952)
D. Blumenthal, Belgian Rad & TV Orch, F. Devreese (r1991) *Concert* (11/93) (MARC) ① **8 223505**
Concerto for Piano and Orchestra No. 3 (1956)
D. Blumenthal, Belgian Rad & TV Orch, F. Devreese (r1991) *Concert* (11/93) (MARC) ① **8 223505**
Concerto for Piano and Orchestra No. 4 (1983)
D. Blumenthal, Belgian Rad & TV Orch, F. Devreese (r1991) *Concert* (11/93) (MARC) ① **8 223505**

SECTION III: INSTRUMENTAL

Soundtrack—dances, divertimenti and preludes for piano (arr cpsr from various film scores)
EXCERPTS: 1. Country Dance; 2. Chorale; 3. Butterfly (from Ciné-Romance); 4. Waltz I; 5. Moviola; 6. Waltz (from Rendez-vous à Bray); 7. The Other Waltz (from Het Sacrament); 8. Concertina Waltz (form Les noces barbares); 9. Danza Mobile (for L'oeuvre au noir, but not used in film); 10. Ballade for Damien (on a theme of Toots Thielemans); 11. Danse Sacrée (from L'oeuvre au noir); 12. Four a.m. 13. The Third Waltz (from Een man die zijn haar kort liet klippen); 14. Children's Portraits; 15. Children's Games; 16. Nocturne; 17. Divertimento I; 18. Divertimento II (both from Onze Lieve Vrouwe der Vissen); 19. March; 20. Rotations; 21. Intermezzo (both from Een vreemde reis); 22. Prélude (from Belle); 23. French Can-Can.
A. de Groote (r1993) (1/95) (MARC) ① **8 223651**

SECTION V: STAGE WORKS

Belle—film score
EXCERPTS: 1. Prélude; 2. Fagnes du Nord.
1, 2. Belgian Rad & TV Orch, F. Devreese (r1991) *Concert* (11/94) (MARC) ① **8 223681**
Benvenuta—concert suite from film score (1986)
EXCERPTS: 1. Dream; 2. Habanera; 3. Waltz; 4. Tango.
Belgian Rad & TV Orch, F. Devreese (r1991) *Concert* (11/94) (MARC) ① **8 223681**
L' Oeuvre au Noir—concert suite from film score (1988)
EXCERPTS: 1. Zénon; 2. Fête à Dranoutre; 3. Henri-Maximilien part pour l'Italie; 4. Enfance et Voyages de Zénon; 5. Les Ponts de Bruges; 6.

Cauchemar de Zénon; 7. Choral: Lamento du Prieur; 8. La Danse à l'Auberge.
Belgian Rad & TV Orch, F. Devreese (r1991) *Concert* (11/94) (MARC) ① **8 223681**
Un Soir, un Train—film score (1968)
EXCERPTS: 1. Thème; 2. Danse de l'Auberge.
1, 2. Belgian Rad & TV Orch, F. Devreese (r1991) *Concert* (11/94) (MARC) ① **8 223681**

DEVREESE, Godfried (1893–1972) Belgium

SECTION I: ORCHESTRAL

Concertino for Cello and Orchestra (1930 rev 1940)
V. Spanoghe, Belgian Rad & TV Orch, F. Devreese (r1993) *Concert* (11/94) (MARC) ① **8 223680**
Concerto for Violin and Orchestra No. 1 (1936)
G. de Neve, Belgian Rad & TV Orch, F. Devreese (r1993) *Concert* (11/94) (MARC) ① **8 223680**
Tombelène—choreographic suite (?1931)
1. Prelude; 2. Interlude.
Belgian Rad & TV Orch, F. Devreese (r1993) *Concert* (11/94) (MARC) ① **8 223680**

DEXTER, Harry (1910–1973) England

SECTION I: ORCHESTRAL

Siciliano—orchestra
RTE Concert Orch, E. Tomlinson (r1993) *Concert* (12/95) (MARC) ① **8 223522**

DI CAPUA, Eduardo (1865–1917) Italy

SECTION IV: VOCAL AND CHORAL

Maria, marì—song (1899) (Wds. V. Russo)
L. Pavarotti, Teatro Communale Orch, A. Guadagno *Concert* (8/83) (DECC) ① **410 015-2DH**
B. Gigli, orch, N. Shilkret (r1925) *Concert* (9/88) (PEAR) ① **GEMMCD9316**
R. Ponselle, orch, R. Bourdon (1924) *Concert* (10/89) (NIMB) ① **NI7805**
R. Ponselle, orch, R. Bourdon (1924) *Concert* (11/94) (ROMO) ① [2] **81006-2**
B. Gigli, orch, N. Shilkret (r1925) *Concert* (12/94) (MMOI) ① **CDMOIR425**
'O sole mio—song (1898) (Wds. G. Capurro)
L. Pavarotti, National PO, G. Chiaramello *Concert* (8/83) (DECC) ① **410 015-2DH**
E. Caruso, orch (r1916) *Concert* (5/89) (PEAR) ① **GEMMCD9309**
R. Stracciari, orch (r1925) *Concert* (2/90) (PREI) ① **89003**
J. Schmidt, orch (r1933) *Concert* (4/90) (EMI) ① **CDM7 69478-2**
L. Pavarotti, National PO, G. Chiaramello (arr Chiarmello) *Concert* (7/90) (DECC) ① [2] **425 681-2DM2**
J. Carreras, P. Domingo, L. Pavarotti, MMF Orch, Rome Op Orch, Z. Mehta (pp1990) *Concert* (10/90) (DECC) ① **430 433-2DH**
E. Caruso, orch, W.B. Rogers (r1916) *Concert* (12/90) (NIMB) ① **NI7809**
E. Caruso, orch, W.B. Rogers (r1916) *Concert* (7/91) (RCA) ① [12] **GD60495(5)**
E. Caruso, orch, W.B. Rogers (r1916) *Concert* (10/91) (PEAR) ① [3] **EVC3(2)**
G. Lugo, orch, F. Weiss (r1934) *Concert* (2/92) (PREI) ① **89034**
P. Dvorský, Bratislava RSO, O. Lenárd *Concert* (5/92) (NAXO) ① **8 550343**
J. Björling, Stockholm Royal Op Orch, N. Grevillius (r1937) *Concert* (9/92) (MMOI) ① **CDMOIR409**
F. Araiza, Munich RSO, R. Weikert (arr Friebe) *Concert* (3/93) (RCA) ① **09026 61163-2**
D. Giannini, orch, G.W. Byng (r1928) *Concert* (4/93) (PREI) ① **89044**
T. Gobbi, LSO, A. La Rosa Parodi (r1952) *Concert* (8/93) (TEST) ① **SBT1019**
J. Björling, orch, N. Grevillius (r1937) *Concert* (9/94) (CARL) ① **GLRS103**
L. Pavarotti, NYPO, L. Magiera (pp1993) *Concert* (2/95) (DECC) ① **444 450-2DH**
P. Bertin, A. Scholl, D. Visse, Camargue PO, Reinhardt Wagner (r1995: arr R Wagner) *Concert* (8/95) (HARM) ① **HMC90 1552**

DI CHIARA, Vincenzo (1860–1937) Italy

SECTION IV: VOCAL AND CHORAL

La Spagnola—song (Wds. cpsr)
B. Gigli, orch, L. Collingwood (r1939) *Concert* (6/93) (MMOI) ① **CDMOIR417**
R. Ponselle, orch, J. Pasternack (r1925) *Concert* (11/94) (ROMO) ① [2] **81006-2**

DI LAZZARO (20th Cent) Italy

SECTION IV: VOCAL AND CHORAL

Chitarra romana—song (Wds. Bruno)
L. Pavarotti, NYPO, L. Magiera (pp1993) *Concert* (2/95) (DECC) ① **444 450-2DH**

DIABELLI, Anton (1781–1858) Austria

SECTION III: INSTRUMENTAL

Sonata for Guitar in A
J. Bream (r1967-8; ed Bream) *Concert* (8/93) (RCA) ① [28] **09026 61583-2(4)**
J. Bream (r1967-8; ed Bream) *Concert* (6/94) (RCA) ① **09026 61593-2**
3 Sonatas for Guitar, Op. 29
1. F; 2. A; 3. C.
A. Glise (r1992) (7/95) (DORI) ① **DIS80113**
4 Sonatinas—piano, Op. 151 (1820s)
1. G; 2. C; 3. F; 4. C.
D. Blumenthal (r1991) *Concert* (10/93) (ETCE) ① [2] **KTC2018**

SECTION IV: VOCAL AND CHORAL

Pastoral Mass in F—soloists, choir and orchestra, Op. 147 (1830)
C. Degler, S. Linden, S. Rauschkolb, D. Clayton, Hartmut Müller, Munich St. Michael Ch, Munich St. Michael Orch, E. Ehret (5/90) (SCHW) ① **313015**

DIAMOND, David (Leo) (b 1915) USA

SECTION I: ORCHESTRAL

Concerto for small orchestra (1940)
NY Chbr SO, G. Schwarz *Concert* (4/91) (DELO) ① **DE3093**
Concerto for Violin and Orchestra No. 2 (1947)
I. Talvi, Seattle SO, G. Schwarz (r1991) *Concert* (1/94) (DELO) ① **DE3119**
Elegy in memory of Maurice Ravel—strings and percussion (1938 rev 1939) (orig version: brass, harp and percussion)
St Luke's Orch, J. Adams *Concert* (7/91) (NONE) ① **7559-79249-2**
The Enormous Room (1948) (after e e cummings)
Seattle SO, G. Schwarz (r1992) *Concert* (1/94) (DELO) ① **DE3119**
Kaddish—cello and orchestra (1987-88)
J. Starker, Seattle SO, G. Schwarz *Concert* (4/93) (DELO) ① **DE3103**
Psalm—orchestra (1936)
Seattle SO, G. Schwarz *Concert* (4/93) (DELO) ① **DE3103**
Symphony No. 1 (1940-41)
Seattle SO, G. Schwarz (r1992) *Concert* (1/94) (DELO) ① **DE3119**
Symphony No. 2 (1942)
Seattle SO, G. Schwarz *Concert* (4/91) (DELO) ① **DE3093**
Symphony No. 3 (1945)
Seattle SO, G. Schwarz *Concert* (4/93) (DELO) ① **DE3103**
Symphony No. 4 (1945)
Seattle SO, G. Schwarz *Concert* (4/91) (DELO) ① **DE3093**
Symphony No. 5 (1951 rev 1964)
Juilliard Orch, C. Keene *Concert* (7/91) (NEW) ① **80396-2**
Symphony No. 8 (1958-60)
Seattle SO, G. Schwarz (r1993) *Concert* (4/93) (DELO) ① **DE3141**
TOM—suite from the unproduced ballet (1936)
EXCERPTS: 1. Fanfare; 2. Prelude to Episode 1; 3. Introduction and Dance of the Benevolent Master & Mistress; 4. Eliza's Supplication; 5. The Mortgage; 6. Dance of the Slavetraders & Human Bloodhounds; 7. Dance of Thankfulness for Freedom; 8. Dance of

New England & New Orleans; 9. Entrance of Eva; 10.
Tom's Dance of Revelation through the Eternal Word;
11. Eva's Departure & Ascent Into Heaven
Accompanied by Angels; 12. Choral
Spiritual—Conclusion.
Seattle SO, G. Schwarz (r1992) *Concert*
(4/95) (DELO) ① **DE3141**

SECTION IV: VOCAL AND CHORAL

**This Sacred Ground—bar, chor & orch
(1962)** (setting of Lincoln's Gettysburg
Address)
E. Parce, Seattle Girls' Ch, Northwest Boychoir,
Seattle Sym Chorale, Seattle SO, G. Schwarz
(r1994) *Concert* (4/95) (DELO) ① **DE3141**

SECTION V: STAGE WORKS

**Romeo and Juliet—incidental music to
Shakespeare's play (1947 rev 1950)**
EXCERPTS: 1. Overture; 2. Balcony Scene; 3.
Romeo and Friar Laurence; 4. Juliet and her Nurse;
5. The Death of Romeo and Juliet.
NY Chbr SO, G. Schwarz *Concert*
(4/93) (DELO) ① **DE3103**

DIAZ DE LA PEÑA, Eugeno
(1837–1901) France

SECTION V: STAGE WORKS

Benvenuto Cellini—opera
De l'art splendeur immortelle G. De Luca, orch
(r1924) *Concert* (1/92) (PREI) ① **89036**

DIBDIN, Charles (1745–1814)
England

SECTION IV: VOCAL AND CHORAL

Tom Bowling—song (1789) (from 'The
Oddities')
Sarah Walker, R. Vignoles *Concert*
(11/87) (HYPE) ① **CDA66165**
J. Potter, Broadside Band, J. Barlow (r1992; arr J.
Barlow) *Concert* (6/93) (SAYD) ① **CD-SDL400**

SECTION V: STAGE WORKS

**The Brickdust Man—musical dialogue
(1772—London)** (Text I. Bickerstaffe)
Cpte Y. Barclay, K. West, Opera Restor'd, P. Holman
(orch Fiske & Holman) *Concert*
(5/93) (HYPE) ① **CDA66608**
**The Ephesian Matron; or The Widow's
Tears—comic serenata (1769—London)**
(Wds. I. Bickerstaffe)
Cpte B. Mills, J. Streeton, M. Padmore, A. Knight,
Opera Restor'd, P. Holman (orch Fiske & Holman)
Concert (5/93) (HYPE) ① **CDA66608**
**The Grenadier—musical dialogue
(1773—London)** (Text ?D. Garrick)
Cpte S. Bisatt, K. West, A. Mayor, Opera Restor'd, P.
Holman (orch Holman) *Concert*
(5/93) (HYPE) ① **CDA66608**

DICKINSON, Peter (b 1934)
England

SECTION IV: VOCAL AND CHORAL

**Mass of the Apocalypse—spkr, soloists,
choir, perc and pf (1984)**
D. Reeves, J. Maggs, M. Dickinson, St James's
Sngrs, J. Holland, D. Johnson, J. Alley, I. Bolton
Concert (5/89) (CONI) ① **CDCF167**
**Outcry—mezzo-soprano, choir and
orchestra (1968-69)** (Wds. various)
M. Dickinson, London Concert Ch, CLS, N. Cleobury
Concert (5/89) (CONI) ① **CDCF167**
The Unicorns—soprano and brass (Wds.
Heath Stubbs)
E. Söderström, Solna Brass, U. Björklund *Concert*
(5/89) (CONI) ① **CDCF167**

DIEPENBROCK, Alphons
(1862–1921) The Netherlands

SECTION I: ORCHESTRAL

Hymne—violin and orchestra (1917)
E. Verhey, Hague PO, H. Vonk *Concert*
(8/90) (CHAN) ① **CHAN8821**
Marsyas—concert suite: orchestra (1910) (arr
from incidental music to Verhangen's play)
Hague PO, H. Vonk *Concert*
(8/90) (CHAN) ① **CHAN8821**

Overture, '(The) Birds'—orchestra (1917)
(from incidental music to Aristophanes's play)
Hague PO, H. Vonk *Concert*
(8/90) (CHAN) ① **CHAN8821**

SECTION IV: VOCAL AND CHORAL

**2 Hymne an die Nacht—symphonic songs
(1899)** (wds. Novalis)
1. Gehoben ist der Stein; 2. Muss immer der Morgen
wiederkommen.
2. L. Finnie, Hague PO, H. Vonk *Concert*
(4/91) (CHAN) ① **CHAN8878**
**Im grossen Schweigen—baritone and
orchestra (1906)** (wds. F. Nietzsche)
R. Holl, Hague PO, H. Vonk *Concert*
(4/91) (CHAN) ① **CHAN8878**
H. Hagegård, Concertgebouw, R. Chailly *Mahler:
Symphony 7.* (5/95) (DECC) ① [2] **444 446-2DH2**
Die Nacht—contralto and orchestra (1911)
L. Finnie, Hague PO, H. Vonk *Concert*
(4/91) (CHAN) ① **CHAN8878**
**Wenige wissen das Geheimnis der
Liebe—hymn (1898)** (wds. Novalis)
C. Homberger, Hague PO, H. Vonk *Concert*
(5/93) (CHAN) ① **CHAN8878**

SECTION V: STAGE WORKS

**Elektra—concert suite from incidental music
(1919-20)**
Hague PO, H. Vonk *Concert*
(8/90) (CHAN) ① **CHAN8821**

DIESSENER, Gerhard (17th Cent)
Germany

SECTION II: CHAMBER

Sonata à 6 (Kassel MS)
Musica Fiata, R. Wilson (r1991) *Concert*
(8/93) (DHM) ① **05472 77183-2**

DIEUPART, Charles (?after
1667–c1740) France

SECTION II: CHAMBER

**6 Suittes divisées—flute/recorder & continuo
(pub 1701)** (chamber music version of Suittes
de clavecin)
EXCERPTS: 1. No ? in A; 5. No 5 in G; 5a.
Ouverture; 5b. Allemande; 5c. Courante; 5d.
Sarabande; 5e. Gavotte; 5f. Menuet en rondeau; 5g.
Gigue; 6. No 6 in F minor.
1. F. Brüggen, A. Bylsma, G. Leonhardt (r1971)
Concert (10/95) (TELD) ④ **4509-97468-2**
5. F. Brüggen, N. Harnoncourt, G. Leonhardt (r1965)
Concert (10/95) (TELD) ④ **4509-97468-2**
5d-f D. Munrow, R. Spencer (r1973) *Concert*
(10/95) (DECC) ① **440 079-2DM**

DIEZ, Consuelo (b 1958) Spain

SECTION III: INSTRUMENTAL

Sad—piano (1983)
S. Marin *Concert* (4/93) (RNE) ① **M3/03**

DILLON, James (b 1950)
Scotland

SECTION I: ORCHESTRAL

**La Femme invisible—2 fl, 2 ob, 2 cl, 2 sax,
perc and pf (1989)** (part of 'Nine Rivers'
cycle)
Music Projects London, R. Bernas *Concert*
(9/92) (NMC) ① **NMCD004**
German Triptych—orchestra
1. Überschreiten (1985-86); 2. helle Nacht (1986-87);
3. Blitzschlag (1990-95).
2. BBC SO, A. Tamayo (r1994) *Ignis noster.*
(8/95) (AUVI) ① **MO782038**
Ignis noster—orchestra (1991-92)
BBC SO, A. Tamayo (r1994) *German Triptych.*
(8/95) (AUVI) ① **MO782038**
**Windows and Canoples—2 fl, 2 ob, 2 hn,
perc and stgs (1985)**
Music Projects London, R. Bernas *Concert*
(9/92) (NMC) ① **NMCD004**

SECTION II: CHAMBER

**East 11th St NY10003—six percussionists
(1982)** (part of 'Nine Rivers' cycle)
Music Projects London, R. Bernas *Concert*
(9/92) (NMC) ① **NMCD004**

DIMITRIEV, Nikolai Dimitrievich
(1829–1893) Russia

SECTION IV: VOCAL AND CHORAL

In the wild north—song
A. Davidov, M. Michailova, V. Kastorsky, anon
(r1909) *Concert*
(6/93) (PEAR) ① [3] **GEMMCDS9007/9(1)**
Night—folksong setting
L. Sibiriakov, anon (r1908) *Concert*
(6/93) (PEAR) ① [3] **GEMMCDS9007/9(2)**

DINICU, Grigoraş (1889–1949)
Romania

SECTION II: CHAMBER

Hora Staccato—violin and piano (1906)
X. Wei, Pam Nicholson *Concert*
(9/90) (ASV) ① **CDDCA698**
S. Nakarjakov, A. Markovich (arr tpt/pf) *Concert*
(9/93) (NIMB) ① **NI5358**
K. Daeshik Kang, M. Rahkonen (r1992; arr Heifetz)
Concert (9/93) (NIMB) ① **NI5358**
J. Heifetz, E. Bay (r1950) *Concert*
(11/94) (RCA) ① [65] **09026 61778-2(40)**
J. Heifetz, E. Bay (r1937) *Concert*
(11/94) (RCA) ① [65] **09026 61778-2(03)**

DISCEPOLO, Enrique (20th Cent)
Argentina

SECTION IV: VOCAL AND CHORAL

Cafetin de Buenos Aires—tango (Wds.
Mores)
Buenos Aires Qnt, RPO, E. Stratta (arr J. Calandrelli)
Concert (1/93) (TELD) ① **9031-76997-2**
Uno—tango (Wds. Mores)
Buenos Aires Qnt, RPO, E. Stratta (arr J. Calandrelli)
Concert (1/93) (TELD) ① **9031-76997-2**

DITTERSDORF, Carl Ditters von
(1739–1799) Austria

SECTION I: ORCHESTRAL

Concerto for Harp and Orchestra (1779)
(trans K H Pilley from unfinished Hpd Conc)
M. Robles, ASMF, I. Brown *Concert*
(12/90) (DECC) ① **425 723-2DM**
**Sinfonia Concertante for Viola, Double-bass
and Orchestra**
Prague Virtuosi, R. Krečmer (r1994) *Concert*
(12/95) (DINT) ① **DICD920274**
**6 Symphonies after Ovid's Metamorphoses
(?1785)**
1. C; 2. D; 3. G; 4. F; 5. D; 6. A.
Cantilena, A. Shepherd
(5/88) (CHAN) ① [2] **CHAN8564/5**
Vienna Sinfonietta, K. Rapf
(5/90) (CALI) ① [2] **CAL50885/6**

SECTION II: CHAMBER

Sonata for Viola and Keyboard in E flat
A. B. Duetschler, U. Duetschler (r1994) *Concert*
(11/95) (CLAV) ① **CD50-9502**
6 String Quartets (pub 1788)
EXCERPTS: 1. D; 2. B flat; 3. G; 3b. Menuetto:
Moderato; 4. C; 5. E flat; 5c. Finale: Allegro; 6. A.
2, 6. Schubert Qt (r1991) *String Quintets (1789).*
(10/93) (CPO) ① **CPO999 122-2**
3b, 5c Elman Qt (r1917) *Concert*
(10/91) (BIDD) ① **LAB039**
**6 String Quintets—two violins, viola and two
cellos (pub 1789)**
3. C; 6. G.
3, 6. Schubert Qt, J. Berger (r1991) *String Quartets.*
(10/93) (CPO) ① **CPO999 122-2**

DIXON, Willie (1915–1992) USA

SECTION II: CHAMBER

Spoonful—string quartet (1960)
Kronos Qt (r1992; arr Mackey) *Concert*
(8/93) (NONE) ① **7559-79310-2**

DLUGORAJ, Wojciech (1557/8–? after c1619) Poland

SECTION III: INSTRUMENTAL
Fantasia—lute
J. Bream (r1966) *Concert*
    (8/93) (RCA) ① [28] **09026 61583-2(1)**
J. Bream (r1966) *Concert*
    (6/94) (RCA) ① **09026 61585-2**
2 Finales—lute
J. Bream (r1966) *Concert*
    (8/93) (RCA) ① [28] **09026 61583-2(1)**
J. Bream (r1966) *Concert*
    (6/94) (RCA) ① **09026 61585-2**
2 Villanellas—lute
J. Bream (r1966) *Concert*
    (8/93) (RCA) ① [28] **09026 61583-2(1)**
J. Bream (r1966) *Concert*
    (6/94) (RCA) ① **09026 61585-2**

DOBROVEN, Issay Alexandrovich (1894–1953) Norway

SECTION II: CHAMBER
Melody hebraïque—violin and piano
C. Flesch, I. Strasfogel (r1929) *Concert*
    (12/91) (BIDD) ① **LAB045**

DOCKER, Robert (1919–1992) England

SECTION I: ORCHESTRAL
Tabarinage—orchestra (1961)
RTE Concert Orch, E. Tomlinson (r1993) *Concert*
    (12/95) (MARC) ① **8 223522**

DODGSON, Stephen (b 1924) England

SECTION I: ORCHESTRAL
Concerto for Flute and Strings (1990-91)
R. Stallman, Northern Sinfonia, R. Zollman (r1992)
  Concert   (7/94) (BIDD) ① **LAW013**
Duo Concerto—violin, guitar and strings (1991)
J-J. Kantorow, A. Gifford, Northern Sinfonia, R.
  Zollman (r1992) *Concert* (7/94) (BIDD) ① **LAW013**

SECTION IV: VOCAL AND CHORAL
Last of the Leaves—bass, clarinet and strings (1975)
1. The rose and the garden (wds. A Dobson); 2. The
leaf burners (wds. E Rhys); 3. The donkey (wds. G K
Chesterton); 4. At a country dance in Provence (wds.
H Monro).
M. George, J. Bradbury, Northern Sinfonia, R.
  Zollman (r1992) *Concert* (7/94) (BIDD) ① **LAW013**

DOHNÁNYI, Ernö (1877–1960) Hungary

SECTION I: ORCHESTRAL
Concerto for Piano and Orchestra No. 1 in E minor, Op. 5 (1897-98)
M. Roscoe, BBC Scottish SO, F. Glushchenko *Piano*
  Concerto 2. (5/94) (HYPE) ① **CDA66684**
Concerto for Piano and Orchestra No. 2 in B minor, Op. 42 (1946-47)
M. Roscoe, BBC Scottish SO, F. Glushchenko *Piano*
  Concerto 1. (5/94) (HYPE) ① **CDA66684**
Konzertstück in D—cello and orchestra, Op. 12 (1903-04)
R. Wallfisch, LSO, C. Mackerras *Dvořák: Cello*
  Concerto. (5/89) (CHAN) ① **CHAN8662**
J. Starker, Philh, W. Susskind (r1956) *Concert*
  (12/95) (EMI) ① [6] **CZS5 68485-2**
Suite in F sharp minor—orchestra, Op. 19 (1908-09)
Chicago SO, F. Stock (1928) *Concert*
  (2/95) (BIDD) ① [2] **WHL021/2**
Symphonic Minuets (Szimfonikus percek), Op. 34 (1933)
Queen's Hall Orch, Henry Wood *Concert*
  (1/94) (BEUL) ① **1PD3**
Variations on a Nursery Theme—piano and orchestra, Op. 25 (1914)
E. Dohnányi, LSO, L. Collingwood (r1931) *Concert*
  (1/92) (SCHW) ① **311136**
E. Dohnányi, LSO, L. Collingwood (r1931) *Concert*
  (5/94) (EMI) ① **CDC5 55031-2**

M. Anderson, Hungarian St SO, A. Fischer (r1994)
  Brahms: Piano Concerto 1.
    (3/95) (NIMB) ① **NI5349**

SECTION II: CHAMBER
Quintet for Piano and Strings No. 1 in C minor, Op. 1 (1895)
W. Manz, Gabrieli Qt *String Quartet 2.*
  (5/89) (CHAN) ① **CHAN8718**
Vanbrugh Qt, M. Roscoe (r c1994) *Concert*
  (5/95) (ASV) ① **CDDCA915**
Quintet for Piano and Strings No.2 in E flat minor, Op. 26 (1914)
Vanbrugh Qt, M. Roscoe (r c1994) *Concert*
  (5/95) (ASV) ① **CDDCA915**
3 Ruralia Hungarica—violin and piano, Op. 32c (1914)
No 2. O. Shumsky, S. Lipkin (r1993) *Concert*
  (6/95) (BIDD) ① **LAW015**
Serenade in C—two violins and viola, Op. 10 (1902)
S. Lautenbacher, U. Koch, M. Ostertag *Concert*
  (11/91) (BAYE) ① **BR100058**
J. Heifetz, W. Primrose, E. Feuermann (r1941)
  Concert (11/94) (RCA) ① [65] **09026 61778-2(32)**
Sonata for Violin and Piano in C sharp minor, Op. 21 (1912)
O. Shumsky, S. Lipkin (r1993) *Concert*
  (6/95) (BIDD) ① **LAW015**
Sonata in B flat minor for Cello and Piano, Op. 8 (1899)
B. Gregor-Smith, Y. Wrigley *Concert*
  (9/92) (ASV) ① **CDDCA796**
String Quartet No. 2 in D flat, Op. 15 (1906)
Gabrieli Qt *Piano Quintet 1.*
  (5/89) (CHAN) ① **CHAN8718**

SECTION III: INSTRUMENTAL
6 Concert Etudes—piano, Op. 28 (1916)
1. A minor; 2. D flat; 3. E flat minor; 4. B flat minor; 5.
E; 6. F minor (Capriccio).
4. M. Hallman *Concert* (9/89) (CENT) ① **CRC2025**
6. S. Hough (r1987) *Concert*
  (1/89) (VIRG) ① **VC7 59509-2**
6. L. Godowsky (r1922) *Concert*
  (4/89) (APR) ① [2] **APR7011**
6. V. Horowitz (r1928) *Concert*
  (1/93) (APR) ① [2] **APR7014**
6. S. Rachmaninov (r1921) *Concert*
  (3/93) (RCA) ① [10] **09026 61265-2(3)**
6. V. Horowitz (r1928) *Concert*
  (7/94) (RCA) ① **09026 60986-2**
6. G. Cziffra (r1974) *Concert*
  (3/95) (EMI) ① **CDM5 65255-2**
Coppélia Waltz—piano (1925) (arr from Delibes ballet)
M. Hallman *Concert* (9/89) (CENT) ① **CRC2025**
G. Anda (r1954) *Concert* (9/89) (TEST) ① **SBT1067**
Gavotte and Musette—piano (1898)
P. Frankl (r?1992) *Concert*
  (6/93) (ASV) ① **CDDCA860**
5 Humoresques in the form of a Suite—piano, Op. 17 (1907)
March M. Hallman *Concert*
  (9/89) (CENT) ① **CRC2025**
Passacaglia in E flat minor—piano, Op. 6 (1899)
A. Servadei (r1994) *Concert*
  (5/95) (CNTI) ① **CCD1064**
Pastorale—piano (1920)
M. Roscoe *Concert* (10/93) (ASV) ① **CDDCA863**
4 Pieces—piano, Op. 2 (1896-97)
1. Scherzo in C sharp minor; 2. Intermezzo in A
minor; 3. Intermezzo in F minor; 4. Capriccio in B
minor.
M. Roscoe *Concert* (10/93) (ASV) ① **CDDCA863**
A. Servadei (r1994) *Concert*
  (5/95) (CNTI) ① **CCD1064**
4. M. Hallman *Concert* (9/89) (CENT) ① **CRC2025**
3 Pieces—piano, Op. 23 (1912)
1. Aria; 2. Valse impromptu; 3. Capriccio.
M. Roscoe *Concert* (10/93) (ASV) ① **CDDCA863**
1. M. Hallman *Concert* (9/89) (CENT) ① **CRC2025**
6 Pieces—piano, Op. 41 (1945)
1. Impromptu; 2. Scherzino; 3. Canzonetta; 4.
Cascade; 5. Ländler; 6. Cloches.
3. M. Hallman *Concert* (9/89) (CENT) ① **CRC2025**
4 Rhapsodies—piano, Op. 11 (1902-03)
1. G minor; 2. F sharp minor; 3. C; 4. E flat minor.
M. Roscoe *Concert* (10/93) (ASV) ① **CDDCA863**
1. M. Hallman *Concert* (9/89) (CENT) ① **CRC2025**
Ruralia hungarica—seven pieces: piano, Op. 32a (1923)
EXCERPTS: 1. Allegretto, molto tenero; 2. Presto,
ma non tanto; 3. Andante poco moto, rubato; 4.

Vivace; 5. Allegretto grazioso; 6. Adagio non troppo
(Gypsy Andante); 7. Molto vivace.
F. Kreisler, C. Lamson (r1928: arr Kreisler) *Concert*
  (12/93) (BIDD) ① **LAB080**
1, 5, 7. M. Hallman *Concert*
  (9/89) (CENT) ① **CRC2025**
2. LSO, E. Dohnányi (r1931) *Concert*
  (1/92) (SCHW) ① **311136**
6. J. Heifetz, A. Sándor (r1934) *Concert*
  (11/94) (RCA) ① [65] **09026 61778-2(02)**
7. T. Varga, M. Schwalb (r1938: arr vn/pf: Kreisler)
  Concert (11/93) (CLAV) ① [4] **CD50-9300/4**
7. T. Varga, M. Schwalb (r1938: arr vn/pf: Kreisler)
  Concert (11/93) (CLAV) ① **CD50-9314**
Suite in the Old Style—piano, Op. 24 (1913)
M. Roscoe (r c1994) *Concert*
  (5/95) (ASV) ① **CDDCA915**
Variations and Fugue on a theme by E. G.—piano, Op. 4 (1897)
A. Servadei (r1994) *Concert*
  (5/95) (CNTI) ① **CCD1064**
10 Winterreigen—bagatelles for piano, Op. 13 (1905)
1. Widmung; 2. Marsch der lustige Brüder; 3. An Ada;
4. Freund Viktor's Mazurka; 5. Sphrärenmusik; 6.
Valse aimable; 7. Um Mitternacht; 8. Tolle
Gesellschaft; 9. Morgengrauen; 10. Postludium.
5. M. Hallman *Concert* (9/89) (CENT) ① **CRC2025**

DOLAR, Johann Baptist (1620–1673) Bohemia

SECTION IV: VOCAL AND CHORAL
Salve regina—motet
Niederaltaicher Scholaren, K. Ruhland (r1992)
  Concert (10/93) (SONY) ① **SK53117**

DOLDINGER, Klaus (20th Cent) Germany

SECTION V: STAGE WORKS
Das Boot, '(The) Boat'—television score (1982)
EXCERPTS: 1. Main Theme.
1. M. Ayres (r1994; arr Ayres) *Concert*
  (11/94) (SILV) ① **FILMCD151**

DOMAŽLICKÝ, František (b 1913) Czechoslovakia

SECTION IV: VOCAL AND CHORAL
Czech Songs—children's chorus and string quartet, Op. 17 (1955)
1. I was waiting, I did not sleep; 2. You look beautiful
to me; 3. Don't even think of it, my parents; 4. What's
with you?; 5. Oh mountain, how tall you are; 6. You
art not what you pretend to be; 7. Lads, don't stand
under the window; 8. Black wool on the white lamb.
Disman Rad Children's Ch, J. Mráček, Z. Jiroušek, O.
Smola, P. Mišejka, J. Karas (1992) *Krása:*
  Brundibár. (3/93) (CHNN) ① **CCS5193**

DONALDSON, Walter (1893–1947) USA

SECTION IV: VOCAL AND CHORAL
My Blue Heaven—song (wds. G. Whiting)
Harvey and the Wallbangers, London Sinfonietta, S.
  Rattle *Concert* (12/87) (EMI) ① **CDC7 47991-2**

SECTION V: STAGE WORKS
Makin' Whoopee—musical (1928—New York)
(Lyrics Gus Kahn)
EXCERPTS: 1. Makin' Whoopee.
1. Harvey and the Wallbangers, London Sinfonietta,
  S. Rattle *Concert* (12/87) (EMI) ① **CDC7 47991-2**

DONATONI, Franco (b 1927) Italy

SECTION II: CHAMBER
Etwas ruhiger im Ausdruck—5 instruments (1967)
Nieuw Ens, E. Spanjaard *Concert*
  (7/88) (ETCE) ① **KTC1053**
Fili—flute and piano (1981)
Nieuw Ens, E. Spanjaard *Concert*
  (7/88) (ETCE) ① **KTC1053**
Refrain—8 instruments (1986)
Nieuw Ens, E. Spanjaard *Concert*
  (7/88) (ETCE) ① **KTC1053**

Spiri—10 instruments (1977)
Nieuw Ens, E. Spanjaard *Concert*
(7/88) (ETCE) ① **KTC1053**

Algo—two pieces for guitar (1977)
T. Korhonen *Concert* (8/90) (ONDI) ① **ODE730-2**

De Près—voice and 5 instruments (1978)
D. Dorow, Nieuw Ens, E. Spanjaard *Concert*
(7/88) (ETCE) ① **KTC1053**

DONAUDY, Stefano (1879–1925)
Italy

O bel nidi d'amore—song
B. Gigli, orch. R. Bourdon (r1927) *Concert*
(9/88) (PEAR) ① **GEMMCD9316**
B. Gigli, orch. R. Bourdon (r1927) *Concert*
(12/94) (MMOI) ① **CDMOIR425**
O del mio amato ben—song
C. Muzio, orch. L. Molajoli (r1935) *Concert*
(10/89) (NIMB) ① **NI7802**
D. Borgioli, I. Newton (r1930s) *Concert*
(12/90) (CLUB) ① **CL99-014**
C. Muzio, orch (r1922) *Concert*
(1/95) (ROMO) ① [2] **81010-2**
Vaghissima sembianza—song
E. Caruso, orch. J. Pasternack (r1920) *Concert*
(7/91) (RCA) ① [12] **GD60495(6)**
E. Caruso, orch. J. Pasternack (r1920) *Concert*
(10/91) (PEAR) ① [3] **EVC4(2)**

DONIZETTI, (Domenico) Gaetano
(Maria) (1797–1848) Italy

Concertino in B flat—clarinet and orchestra
Budapest Camerata, L. Kovács (r1994, recons R.
Meylan) *Concert* (10/95) (MARC) ① **8 223701**
Concerto for Cor Anglais and Orchestra in
G
Budapest Camerata, L. Kovács (r1994) *Concert*
(10/95) (MARC) ① **8 223701**
Concerto for Violin, Cello and Orchestra
Budapest Camerata, L. Kovács (r1994, recons J.
Wojciechowski) *Concert*
(10/95) (MARC) ① **8 223701**
Sinfonia in C—strings (1816)
Budapest Rossini Ens *Concert: Sonate a quattro.*
(5/93) (NAXO) ① **8 550621**
Sinfonia in D minor—string orchestra (1818)
(on the death of A Capuzzi)
Budapest Camerata, L. Kovács (r1994, recons M.
Andreae) *Concert* (10/95) (MARC) ① **8 223701**
Sinfonia in G minor—wind instruments
(1817)
Budapest Camerata, L. Kovács (r1994, recons B.
Päuler) *Concert* (10/95) (MARC) ① **8 223701**

Sonata for Flute and Harp
E. Talmi, Y. Talmi (fl/pf) *Concert*
(6/90) (CARL) ① **PWK1133**
Sonata for Oboe and Piano in F
Budapest Camerata, L. Kovács (r1994, orch W.
Hoffman) *Concert* (10/95) (MARC) ① **8 223701**
Sonata in C minor—flute and piano (1819)
Budapest Camerata, L. Kovács (r1994, orch W.
Hoffman) *Concert* (10/95) (MARC) ① **8 223701**
String Quartet in D (1828)
ASMF, N. Marriner (r1968) *Concert*
(7/95) (DECC) ① [2] **443 838-2DF2**
String Quartet No. 3 in C minor
Solisti Italiani (arr. stg orch) *Concert*
(5/88) (DENO) ① [2] **CO-1846/7**
String Quartet No. 5 in E minor
Solisti Italiani (arr. stg orch) *Concert*
(5/88) (DENO) ① [2] **CO-1846/7**
String Quartet No. 7 in F minor (1819)
Revolutionary Drawing Room (r1994) *Concert*
(10/95) (CPO) ① **CPO999 170-2**
String Quartet No. 8 in B flat (1819)
Revolutionary Drawing Room (r1994) *Concert*
(10/95) (CPO) ① **CPO999 170-2**
String Quartet No. 9 in D minor (1821)
Revolutionary Drawing Room (r1994) *Concert*
(10/95) (CPO) ① **CPO999 170-2**
String Quartet No. 13 in E minor (1836)
Alberni Qt *Concert* (5/89) (CRD) ① **CRD3366**

Studio No. 1 in B flat—clarinet (1821)
C. Bradbury *Concert* (6/90) (ASV) ① **CDDCA701**

L' Amor funesto—song:soprano, horn and
piano (Wds. F. Varesi)
D. Fischer-Dieskau, K. Wallendorf, H. Höll *Concert*
(4/88) (ORFE) ① **C153861A**
I. Caddy, S. Comberti, M. Tan *Concert*
(4/90) (MERI) ① **CDE84183**
J. Carreras, Martin Katz *Concert*
(9/90) (SONY) ① **SK45863**
Amor marinaro—Neapolitan song
J. Carreras, Martin Katz *Concert*
(9/90) (SONY) ① **SK45863**
Canto d'Ugolino—cantata (1828) (Wds.
Dante, from 'La Divina commedia')
I. Caddy, M. Tan *Concert*
(4/90) (MERI) ① **CDE84183**
Un Coeur pour abri—song (Wds. A.
Richomme)
I. Caddy, M. Tan *Concert*
(4/90) (MERI) ① **CDE84183**
Le Crépuscule—song (Wds. V. Hugo)
J. Carreras, Martin Katz *Concert*
(9/90) (SONY) ① **SK45863**
Le Départ pour la chasse—song with horn
obbligato (Wds. P. Lacroix)
I. Caddy, A. Halstead, M. Tan *Concert*
(4/90) (MERI) ① **CDE84183**
La Hart—song (Wds. P. Lacroix)
I. Caddy, M. Tan *Concert*
(4/90) (MERI) ① **CDE84183**
Una Lacrima—song
J. Carreras, Martin Katz *Concert*
(9/90) (SONY) ① **SK45863**
Messa da Requiem—soloists, chorus and
orchestra
C. Studer, H. Müller-Molinari, A. Baldin, J-H.
Rootering, J.P. Bogart, Bamberg Sym Chor,
Bamberg SO, M.A. Gómez-Martínez (r1984)
(8/89) (ORFE) ① **C172881A**
Judex ergo; Domine Jesu Christe; Ingemisco G.
Sabbatini, R. Bruson, Berlin RSO, R. Paternostro
Concert (10/89) (CAPR) ① **10 247**
Messa di Gloria e Credo—soloists, chorus
and orchestra (mid 1830s)
H. Mané, G. Vighi, P. Maus, M. Machi, K-B. Sebon,
A. Labko, Berlin St Hedwig's Cath Ch, Berlin RSO, R.
Bader (9/90) (SCHW) ① **313031**
Noé—scène du Déluge—song (1839) (Wds.
M. J. de Bouteiller)
I. Caddy, M. Tan *Concert*
(4/90) (MERI) ① **CDE84183**
Renégat—song (pub 1835) (Wds. E. Pacini)
I. Caddy, M. Tan *Concert*
(4/90) (MERI) ① **CDE84183**
Soirées d'automne à l'Infrascata—four
songs and one duet (pub 1837 & 1839)
1. La lontananza—Or ch'io sono a te rapita (1v: wds.
F. Romani); 2. L'amante spagnuolo—Corri destrier
(1v); 3. Amore e morte—Odi d'un uom che muore
(1v: wds. Redaelli); 4. Amor marinaro—Me voglio fa'
na casa (1v); 5. Il fiore (2vv).
4. R. Tebaldi, R. Bonynge (r1972) *Concert*
(9/94) (DECC) ① **436 202-2DM**
Il Sospiro—song (Wds. Guaita)
J. Carreras, Martin Katz *Concert*
(9/90) (SONY) ① **SK45863**
Spirto di Dio benefico—song
I. Caddy, M. Tan *Concert*
(4/90) (MERI) ① **CDE84183**
Te voglio bene assaje—Neapolitan song
J. Carreras, ECO, V. Sutej (r1992; arr Agostinelli)
Concert (6/93) (PHIL) ① **434 926-2PH**
Il Trovatore in caricatura—song (1837) (Wds.
L. Borsini)
I. Caddy, M. Tan *Concert*
(4/90) (MERI) ① **CDE84183**
Viva il matrimonio—cavatina buffa (pub
1843) (Wds. L. Tarantini)
I. Caddy, M. Tan *Concert*
(4/90) (MERI) ① **CDE84183**

L' Ajo nell'imbarazzo—opera: 2 acts
(1824—Rome) (Lib. J Ferretti; rev as 'Don
Gregorio'. 1826)
Cpte A. Corbelli, P. Barbacini, L. Serra, V. Gobbi, E.
Dara, A. Haengel, D. Menicucci, Turin Teatro Regio
Orch, B. Campanella (pp1984)
(12/95) (FONI) ① [2] **CDC81**

Alfredo di grande—dramma: 2 acts
(1823—Naples) (Lib. A L Tottola)
Che potrei dirti, o caro? L. Kitchen, T. Goble, D.
Jones, B. McBride, D. Ashman, I. Platt, G. Mitchell
Ch, D. Parry, D. Parry *Concert*
(8/95) (OPRA) ① [3] **ORCH104**
Anna Bolena—opera: 2 acts (1830—Milan)
(Lib. F. Romani)
EXCERPTS: 1. Overture. ACT 1: 2. Nè venne il re;
3. Ella di me, sollecita; 4a. Si taciturna e mesta; 4b.
Deh! non voler costringere; 4c. Come, innocente
giovane; 4d. Non v'ha sguardo; 5a. Oh! qual parlar fu
il suo!; 5b. Ecco il re; 5c. Tremate voi?; 6a. Chi
veggo?; 6b. Qua quel dì che, nei perduta; 6c. Ah! così
nei di ridenti; 7a. Desta sì tosto; 7b. Voi Regina; 7c.
Io senti sulla mia mano; 8a. È sgombra il loco; 8b.
Ah! parea che per istanti; 9a. Odo rumor; 9b. Basta,
tropp'oltre vai; 9c. S'ei t'abborre; 9d. Ah! per pietà del
mio spavento; 10a. Alcun potrai; 10b. In separato
carcere. ACT 2: 11. Dove mai ne andarono; 12a. Dio,
che mi vedi in core; 12b. Sul suo capo aggravi un
Dio; 13a. Ebben? dinanzi ai Giudici; 13b. Arresta
Enrico; 14a. Sposa a Percy; 14b. Vieni, Seymour, tu
sei Regina. SCENE 3: 15a. Tu pur dannato a morte;
15b. Vivi tu, ne la scongiuro; 16. Chi può vederla;
17a. Piangete voi?; 17b. Al dolce guidami; 17c. Qual
mesto suon?; 17d. Cielo, a' miei lunghi spasimi; 17e.
Coppia iniqua, l'estrema vendetta.
Cpte M. Callas, N. Rossi-Lemeni, G. Simionato, G.
Raimondi, P. Clabassi, G. Carturan, L. Rumbo, La
Scala Chor, La Scala Orch, G. Gavazzeni (pp1957)
(1/94) (EMI) ① [2] **CMS7 64941-2**
12a, 12b M. Caballé, S. Verrett, New Philh, A.
Guadagno *Concert* (5/92) (RCA) ① **GD60818**
15b R. Vargas, ECO, M. Viotti *Concert*
(11/92) (CLAV) ① **CD50-9202**
17a-e M. Callas, M. Sinclair, J. Lanigan, D.
Robertson, J. Rouleau, Philh Chor, Philh, N.
Rescigno *Concert* (6/86) (EMI) ① **CDC7 47283-2**
17e-e M. Callas, M. Sinclair, J. Lanigan, D.
Robertson, J. Rouleau, Philh, N. Rescigno *Concert*
(2/90) (EMI) ① [4] **CMS7 63244-2**
L' Assedio di Calais—opera: 3 acts
(1836—Naples) (Lib. Cammarano)
Cpte C. du Plessis, D. Jones, R. Smythe, E. Harrhy,
J. Treleaven, N. Bailey, N. Focile, G. Mitchell Ch,
Philh, D. Parry (7/89) (OPRA) ① [2] **ORC009**
Belisario—opera seria: 3 acts (1836—Venice)
(Lib. S. Cammarano, after Marmontel)
Liberi siete. Addio! J. Hadley, T. Hampson, WNO
Orch, C. Rizzi (r1992) *Concert*
(11/93) (TELD) ① **9031-73283-2**
Plauso! Voci di gioia...Sin la tromba M. Caballé, E.
Mauro, LSO, C.F. Cillario *Concert*
(11/92) (RCA) ① [2] **GD60941**
Il Campanello di notte—opera: 1 act
(1836—Naples) (Lib. cpsr, after Brunswick,
Troin and Lhérie)
Cpte A. Baltsa, E. Dara, C. Gaifa, B. Casoni, A.
Romero, Vienna St Op Chor, Vienna SO, G. Bertini
(8/88) (SONY) ① **MK38450**
Caterina Cornaro—opera seria: prologue, 4
acts (1844—Naples) (Lib. Sacchero)
Da che sposa Caterina; Non turbati a questi
accenti R. Bruson, Berlin RSO, R. Paternostro
Concert (10/89) (CAPR) ① **10 247**
Io tradir non voglio C. Merritt, Munich RSO, J. Fiore
(r1993) *Concert* (9/94) (PHIL) ① **434 102-2PH**
Chiara e Serafina, ossia i
pirati—melodramma semiserio: 2 acts
(1822—Milan) (Lib. F Romani)
Tremante, smarrito Y. Kenny, L. Davies, Philh, D.
Parry *Concert* (8/95) (OPRA) ① [3] **ORCH104**
Il diluvio universale—opera: 3 acts
(1830—Naples) (Lib. D Gilardoni, after Byron)
Non mi tradir speranza...Ah, non tacermi in core
M. Elkins, Philh, J. Judd (r1979) *Concert*
(9/94) (OPRA) ① **ORC004**
Dom Sébastien—opera: 5 acts (1843—Paris)
(Lib. Scribe)
EXCERPTS: 1. Seul sur la terre (Deserto in terra); 2.
O Lisbone, o ma patrie; 3. Ballet Music; 4. Que faire
où cacher ma tristesse.
1. E. Caruso, orch (r1908: Ital) *Concert*
(10/89) (NIMB) ① **NI7803**
1. E. Caruso, orch (r1908) *Concert*
(7/90) (CLUB) ① **CL99-060**
1 (2 vers) E. Caruso, orch (r1908) *Concert*
(12/90) (PEAR) ① [3] **EVC1(2)**
1. E. Caruso, orch (r1908: Ital) *Concert*
(7/91) (RCA) ① [12] **GD60495(2)**
1. A. Piccaver, orch (r1914: Ital) *Concert*
(8/93) (PREI) ① **89060**
1. C. Merritt, Munich RSO, J. Fiore (r1993; Ital)
Concert (9/94) (PHIL) ① **434 102-2PH**

1. Alfredo Kraus, WNO Orch, C. Rizzi (r1994; sung in
Italian) *Concert*   (8/95) (PHIL) ① 442 785-2PH
2. R. Bruson, Berlin RSO, R. Paternostro (Ital)
Concert   (10/89) (CAPR) ① 10 247
2. M. Battistini, orch (r1906: Ital) *Concert*
  (2/92) (PREI) ① 89045
2. M. Battistini, orch, C. Sabajno (Ital: r1906) *Concert*
  (10/92) (NIMB) ① NI7831
2. D. Hvorostovsky, Philh, I. Marin (r1992) *Concert*
  (9/94) (PHIL) ① 434 912-2PH
4. M. Elkins, Philh, J. Judd (r1979) *Concert*
  (9/94) (OPRA) ① ORC004

Don Pasquale—opera: 3 acts (1843—Paris)
(Lib. Ruffini and composer, after Anelli)
ACT 1: 1. Overture; 2. Son nov'ore; 3a. E'
permesso?; 3b. Bella siccome un angelo; 4. Ah!...Un
foco insolito; 5. Prender moglie?; 6. Sogno soave e
casto; 7a. Quel guardo il cavaliere; 7b. So anch'io la
virtù magica; 8a. Buone nuove, Norina; 8b. Pronto io
son; 8c. Vado, corro; ACT 2: 9a. Povero Ernesto!; 9b.
Cercherò lontana terra; 9c. E se fia; 10a. Quando
avrete; 10b. Via, da bravo; 11. Fra da un parte
etcetera; 12. Pria di partir, signore. 13. Siete marito e
moglie. ACT 3: 14. I diamanti, presto; 15a. Vediamo:
alla modista; 15b. Signorina, in tanta fretta; 15c. E'
finita, Don Pasquale; 16. Che interminabile (Servants'
Chorus); 17a. Siamo intesi; 17b. Don
Pasquale...Cognato; 18a. Cheti, cheti immantinente;
18b. Aspetta, aspetta cara sposina; 19. Com' è gentil;
20. Tornami a dir (Notturno); 21a. Eccoli: attenti
bene; 21b. Eccomi...A voi.
Cpte S. Bruscantini, M. Freni, G. Winbergh, L. Nucci,
G. Fabbris, Ambrosian Op Chor, Philh, R. Muti
(r1982)   (8/88) (EMI) ① [2] CDS7 47068-2
Cpte E. Dara, L. Serra, A. Bertolo, A. Corbelli, G.
Pasella, Turin Teatro Regio Chor, Turin Teatro Regio
Orch, B. Campanella (pp1988)
  (5/89) (NUOV) ① [2] 6715/6
Cpte E. Badini, A. Saraceni, T. Schipa, A. Poli, G.
Callegari, La Scala Chor, La Scala Orch, C. Sabajno
(r1932) *Concert*   (10/90) (MSCM) ① [2] MM30231
Cpte G. Bacquier, B. Hendricks, L. Canonici, G.
Quilico, R. Schirrer, Lyon Op Chor, Lyon Op Orch, G.
Ferro   (11/90) (ERAT) ① 2292-45487-2
Cpte F. Corena, G. Sciutti, J. Oncina, T. Krause, A.
Mercuriali, Vienna St Op Chor, Vienna St Op Orch, I.
Kertész *Cimarosa: Maestro di cappella.*
  (10/92) (DECC) ① [2] 433 036-2DM2
Cpte R. Capecchi, B. Rizzoli, P. Munteanu, G.
Valdengo, C. Adomi, Naples San Carlo Op Chor,
Naples San Carlo Op Orch, F. Molinari-Pradelli
(r1955)   (10/94) (PHIL) ① [2] 442 090-2PM2
Cpte R. Bruson, E. Mei, F. Lopardo, T. Allen, A.
Giacomotti, Bavarian Rad Chor, Munich RO, R.
Abbado (r1993)
  (12/94) (RCA) ① [2] 09026 61924-2
1. La Scala Orch, A. Toscanini (r1921) *Concert*
  (11/92) (RCA) ① GD60315
3b G. De Luca, anon (r1902) *Concert*
  (8/93) (SYMP) ① SYMCD1111
3b D. Hvorostovsky, Philh, I. Marin (r1992) *Concert*
  (9/94) (PHIL) ① 434 912-2PH
4. M. Ivogün, orch (r1924) *Concert*
  (8/92) (NIMB) ① NI7832
4. A. Pini-Corsi, E. Badini, orch (r1906) *Concert*
  (4/94) (EMI) ① [3] CHS7 64860-2(2)
6. D. Borgioli, orch (r1928) *Concert*
  (12/90) (CLUB) ① CL99-014
6. D. Borgioli, orch (r1928) *Concert*
  (4/94) (EMI) ① [3] CHS7 64864-2(1)
6. A. Giorgini, orch (r1905) *Concert*
  (4/95) (RECO) ① TRC3
6. G. Anselmi, anon (r1907) *Concert*
  (7/95) (SYMP) ① SYMCD1170
7a M. André, Toulouse Capitole Orch, M. Plasson
(arr rptr) *Concert*   (1/89) (EMI) ① CDC7 49219-2
7a A. Galli-Curci, R. Bourdon (r1919) *Concert*
  (5/90) (NIMB) ① NI7806
7a G. Pareto, orch (r1920) *Concert*
  (7/92) (PEAR) ① GEMMCDS9925(1)
7a A. Galli-Curci, J. Pasternack (r1919) *Concert*
  (3/94) (ROMO) ① [2] 81003-2
7a, 7b L. Aliberti, Munich RO, L. Gardelli *Concert*
  (11/86) (ORFE) ① C119814A
7a, 7b A. Galli-Curci, orch (r1919) *Concert*
  (2/89) (PEAR) ① GEMMCD9308
7a, 7b K. Battle, LPO, B. Campanella (r1991)
Concert   (12/93) (DG) ① 435 866-2GH
8b, 8c G. De Luca, L. Bori, orch (r1921) *Concert*
  (1/92) (PREI) ① 89036
9a-c R. Vargas, ECO, M. Viotti *Concert*
  (11/92) (CLAV) ① CD50-9202
9a-c R. Alagna, LPO, R. Armstrong *Concert*
  (12/95) (ERAT) ① CDC5 55540-2
9a-c, 19. R. Giménez, Scottish Phil Sngrs, Scottish
CO, M. Veltri *Concert*   (5/90) (NIMB) ① NI5224

9a, 9b L. Sobinov, orch (r1911: Russ) *Concert*
  (4/94) (EMI) ① [3] CHS7 64860-2(2)
15c(pt) E. Corsi, A. Pini-Corsi, orch (r1906) *Concert*
  (11/92) (MEMO) ① [2] HR4408/9(1)
19. L. Pavarotti, Ambrosian Sngrs, New Philh, L.
Magiera *Concert*
  (7/90) (DECC) ① [2] 425 681-2DM2
19. E. Caruso, anon (r1905) *Concert*
  (12/90) (PEAR) ① [3] EVC1(1)
19. D. Borgioli, orch (r c1923) *Concert*
  (12/90) (CLUB) ① CL99-014
19. E. Caruso, anon (r1905) *Concert*
  (7/91) (RCA) ① [12] GD60495(1)
19. E. Caruso, anon (r1905) *Concert*
  (7/95) (NIMB) ① NI7866
20. L. Aliberti, G. Sabbatini, Berlin RSO, R.
Paternostro *Concert*   (10/89) (CAPR) ① 10 247
20. T. Dal Monte, T. Schipa, La Scala Orch, F.
Ghione (r1933) *Concert*
  (4/90) (EMI) ① CDH7 63200-2
20. D. Borgioli, E. Surinach, orch (r c1923) *Concert*
  (12/90) (CLUB) ① CL99-014
20. E. Berger, G. Sinimberghi, Berlin Staatskapelle
(r1939: Ger) *Concert*   (10/93) (NIMB) ① NI7848
20. A. Galli-Curci, T. Schipa, orch, R. Bourdon
(r1928) *Concert*   (3/94) (CONI) ① CDHD201
20. A. Galli-Curci, T. Schipa, orch, R. Bourdon
(r1924) *Concert*   (8/94) (ROMO) ① [2] 81004-2
21b L. Aliberti, Berlin RSO, R. Paternostro *Concert*
  (10/89) (CAPR) ① 10 247

Il Duca d'Alba—opera: 4 acts (1882—Rome)
(Lib. Scribe & Duveyrier: score cpted Salvi etc)
EXCERPTS: 1a. Inosservato, penetrava; 1b. Angelo
casto e bel; 2. Nei miei superbi gaudi.
1a, 1b G. Morino, Warmia Nat PO, B. Amaducci
Concert   (10/90) (NUOV) ① 6851
1a, 1b R. Vargas, ECO, M. Viotti *Concert*
  (11/92) (CLAV) ① CD50-9202
1b E. Caruso, orch (r1915) *Concert*
  (10/89) (NIMB) ① NI7803
1b E. Caruso, orch, W.B. Rogers (r1915) *Concert*
  (7/91) (RCA) ① [12] GD60495(5)
1b E. Caruso, orch, W.B. Rogers (r1915) *Concert*
  (12/90) (PEAR) ① [3] EVC3(2)
1b C. Merritt, Munich RSO, J. Fiore (r1993) *Concert*
  (9/94) (PHIL) ① 434 102-2PH
1b G. Anselmi, orch (r1909) *Concert*
  (7/95) (SYMP) ① SYMCD1170
2. D. Hvorostovsky, Philh, I. Marin (r1992) *Concert*
  (9/94) (PHIL) ① 434 912-2PH

**L' Elisir d'amore, 'Elixir of Love'—opera: 2
acts (1832—Milan)** (Lib. Romani, after Scribe)
EXCERPTS: 1a. Prelude. ACT 1: 1. Bel conforto; 2.
Quanto è bella; 3. Della crudele Isotta; 4. March; 5a.
Come Paride vezzoso; 5b. Or se m'ami; 5c. Intanto,
mia ragazza; 6a. Una parola, Adina; 6b. Chiedi
all'aura lusinghiera; 7. Che vuoi dire codesta
suonata?; 8a. Udite, o rustici; 8b. Io farmi i paralitici;
9a. Ardir! Ha forse il cielo; 9b. Obbligato; 9c. Va,
mortale fortunato; 10a. Caro elisir!; 10b. Chi è mai;
10c. Esulti pur la barbara; 10d. Tran, tran, tran, tran;
11a. Signor sargente; 11b. Adina, credimi. ACT 2: 12.
Cantiamo, cantiam; 13a. Poiché cantar; 13b. La Nina
Gondoliera; 13c. Io son ricco e tu sei bella; 14a.
Cantiamo, cantiam; 14b. Le feste nuziali; 15a. Una
donna è un animale; 15b. Venti scudi; 16. Saria
possibile?; 17. Dell'elisir mirabile; 18a. Come sen va
contento!; 18b. Bella Adina; 19a. Quanto amore!; 19
Una furtiva lagrima; 20a. Eccola; 20b. Prendi...prendi,
per me sei libero; 21. Alto! *Concert*; 22. Ei corregge
ogni difetto; ADDITIONAL ARIA: 23. Nel dolce
incanto.
Cpte J. Sutherland, L. Pavarotti, D. Cossa, S. Malas,
M. Casula, Ambrosian Sngrs, ECO, R. Bonynge
  (6/86) (DECC) ① [2] 414 461-2DH2
Cpte K. Ricciarelli, J. Carreras, L. Nucci, D.
Trimarchi, S. Rigacci, Turin RAI Chor, Turin RAI
Orch, C. Scimone (1984)
  (6/86) (PHIL) ① [2] 412 714-2PH2
Cpte I. Cotrubas, P. Domingo, I. Wixell, G. Evans, L.
Watson, ROH Chor, ROHO, J. Pritchard
  (3/90) (SONY) ① [2] M2K79210
Cpte K. Battle, L. Pavarotti, L. Nucci, E. Dara, D.
Upshaw, NY Met Op Chor, NY Met Op Orch, James
Levine (1989)   (2/91) (DG) ① [2] 429 744-2GH2
Cpte M. Devia, R. Alagna, P. Spagnoli, B. Praticò, F.
Provvisionato, Tallis Chbr Ch, ECO, M. Viotti (r1992)
  (6/93) (ERAT) ① [2] 4509-91701-2
Cpte R. Carteri, L. Alva, R. Panerai, G. Taddei, A.
Vercelli, La Scala Chor, La Scala Orch, T. Serafin (r
c1958)   (5/94) (DECC) ① [2] CD-CFPD4733
Cpte H. Gueden, G. di Stefano, R. Capecchi, F.
Corena, L. Mandelli, MMF Chor, MMF Orch, F.
Molinari-Pradelli (r1955)
  (7/95) (DECC) ① [2] 443 542-2LF2

2. B. Gigli, orch (r1925) *Concert*
  (5/90) (PEAR) ① GEMMCD9367
2. B. Gigli, orch, R. Bourdon (r1925) *Concert*
  (10/90) (RCA) ① GD87811
2, 19. L. Pavarotti, Rome SO, N. Bonavolontà
(pp1967) *Concert*   (10/95) (RCA) ① 09026 62541-2
5a T. Gobbi, Philh, A. Erede (r1963) *Concert*
  (10/89) (EMI) ① CDM7 63109-2
5a A. Scotti, anon (r1905) *Concert*
  (4/94) (RCA) ① [6] 09026 61580-2(1)
5a D. Hvorostovsky, Philh, I. Marin (r1992) *Concert*
  (9/94) (PHIL) ① 434 912-2PH
6a G. Aragall, E. Tumagian, Bratislava RSO, A.
Rahbari (r1992) *Concert*
  (12/94) (NAXO) ① 8 550684
6a, 6b M. Freni, L. Pavarotti, Ater Orch, L. Magiera
(pp) *Concert*   (5/94) (DECC) ① [2] 443 018-2DF2
8a A. Didur, orch (r c1919) *Concert*
  (1/94) (CLUB) ① CL99-089
8a S. Baccaloni, orch (r1930) *Concert*
  (4/94) (EMI) ① [3] CHS7 64864-2(1)
8a F. Corradetti, anon, anon (r1907) *Concert*
  (12/94) (BONG) ① GB1043-2
8a, 8b F. Corena, MMF Chor, MMF Orch, F. Molinari-
Pradelli (r1955) *Concert*
  (10/93) (DECC) ① 436 464-2DM
9b F. de Lucia, E. Badini, anon (r1907) *Concert*
  (1/95) (SYMP) ① SYMCD1149
10a, 10b, 10c, 10d I. Mula-Tchako, P. Domingo,
Paris Opéra-Bastille Orch, E. Kohn (pp1992) *Concert*
  (6/94) (SONY) ① SK46691
11b T. Schipa, orch (r1928) *Concert*
  (2/89) (PEAR) ① GEMMCD9322
11b T. Schipa, orch, R. Bourdon (r1928) *Concert*
  (10/90) (MSCM) ① [2] MM30231
11b T. Schipa, orch, R. Bourdon (r1928) *Concert*
  (4/94) (RCA) ① [6] 09026 61580-2(4)
15a, 15b T. Gobbi, N. Monti, Rome Op Orch, G.
Santini (r1953) *Concert*
  (10/89) (EMI) ① CDM7 63109-2
15b E. Caruso, G. De Luca, orch, J. Pasternack
(r1919) *Concert*   (7/91) (RCA) ① [12] GD60495(6)
15b E. Caruso, G. De Luca, orch, J. Pasternack
(r1919) *Concert*   (10/91) (PEAR) ① [3] EVC4(2)
15b J. Hadley, T. Hampson, WNO Orch, C. Rizzi
(r1992) *Concert*   (11/93) (TELD) ① 9031-73283-2
19. L. Pavarotti, ECO, R. Bonynge *Concert*
  (7/86) (DECC) ① [2] 417 011-2DH2
19. P. Domingo, Los Angeles PO, C.M. Giulini
Concert   (7/86) (DG) ① 415 366-2GH
19. B. Gigli, orch, J. Barbirolli (1933) *Concert*
  (9/88) (EMI) ① CDH7 61051-2
19. J. Björling, Stockholm Royal Op Orch, N.
Grevillius (r1945) *Concert*
  (10/88) (EMI) ① CDH7 61053-2
19. Alfredo Kraus, Paris Op Orch, M. Veltri (pp1987)
Concert   (12/88) (EMI) ① CDC7 49067-2
19. M. André, Toulouse Capitole Orch, M. Plasson
(arr trpt) *Concert*   (1/89) (EMI) ① CDC7 49219-2
19. T. Schipa, La Scala Orch, C. Sabajno (r1931)
Concert   (2/89) (PEAR) ① GEMMCD9322
19. E. Caruso, S. Cottone (r1902) *Concert*
  (5/89) (EMI) ① CDH7 61046-2
19. H. Nash, orch (Eng: r1926) *Concert*
  (8/89) (PEAR) ① GEMMCD9319
19. K. Walker, J. Drake (arr bn) *Concert*
  (10/89) (REGE) ① REGCD104
19. E. Caruso, anon (r1904) *Concert*
  (10/89) (NIMB) ① NI7803
19. T. Schipa, orch, R. Bourdon (1925) *Concert*
  (12/89) (RCA) ① GD87803
19. J. Patzak, Berlin St Op Orch (r1932) *Concert*
  (3/90) (PEAR) ① GEMMCD9383
19. J. Schmidt, orch (r1934) *Concert*
  (4/90) (EMI) ① CDM7 69478-2
19. T. Schipa, La Scala Orch, C. Sabajno (r1929)
Concert   (4/90) (EMI) ① CDH7 63200-2
19. B. Gigli, orch, R. Bourdon (r1929) *Concert*
  (5/90) (RCA) ① GEMMCD9367
19. R. Giménez, Scottish CO, M. Veltri *Concert*
  (5/90) (NIMB) ① NI5224
19. L. Pavarotti, ECO, R. Bonynge *Concert*
  (7/90) (DECC) ① [2] 425 681-2DM2
19. E. Caruso, anon (r1904) *Concert*
  (7/90) (CLUB) ① CL99-060
19. D. Smirnov, orch (r1912) *Concert*
  (7/90) (CLUB) ① CL99-031
19. T. Schipa, orch, R. Bourdon (r1925) *Concert*
  (10/90) (MSCM) ① [2] MM30231
19. G. Morino, Warmia Nat PO, B. Amaducci *Concert*
  (10/90) (NUOV) ① 6851
19. B. Gigli, orch, R. Bourdon (r1929) *Concert*
  (10/90) (RCA) ① GD87811
19. E. Caruso, anon (r1904) *Concert*
  (12/90) (PEAR) ① [3] EVC1(1)

21. G. Morino, Warmia Nat PO, B. Amaducci *Concert* (10/90) (NUOV) Ⓓ **6851**

Gabriella di Vergy—opera: 3 acts (1869—Naples) (Lib. A L Tottola, after Du Belloy)

Cpte L. Andrew, C. du Plessis, M. Arthur, J. Tomlinson, J. Davies, J. Winfield, G. Mitchell Ch, RPO, A. Francis (r1978) *Concert* (9/94) (OPRA) Ⓓ [2] **ORC003**

Gabriella di Vergy—opera: 2 acts (1826) (Lib. A L Tottola, after Du Belloy)

EXCERPTS: 1a. Respiro alfin; 1b. A te sola; 1c. Ah, she fra palpiti; 2a. Minacciosa perchè me sgridi; 2b. Un padre severo; 2c. Che abisso d'orror!; 3a. Ah fermate!; 3b. Perchè non chiusi al dì.

1a-c D. Jones, RPO, A. Francis (r1978) *Concert* (9/94) (OPRA) Ⓓ [2] **ORC003**

2a-c E. Harrhy, D. Jones, RPO, A. Francis (r1978) *Concert* (9/94) (OPRA) Ⓓ [2] **ORC003**

3a, 3b E. Harrhy, RPO, A. Francis (r1978) *Concert* (9/94) (OPRA) Ⓓ [2] **ORC003**

Gemma di Vergy—opera seria: 2 acts (1834—Milan) (Lib. E. Bidera, after Dumas)

Lascia, Guido...Una voce al cor...Egli riede M. Caballé, Ambrosian Op Chor, LSO, C.F. Cillario *Concert* (11/92) (RCA) Ⓓ [2] **GD60941**

Qui pagnale!...Ah! nel cuor; Ecco il pegno...Questa soave immagine R. Bruson, Berlin RSO, R. Paternostro *Concert* (10/89) (CAPR) Ⓓ **10 247**

Gianni di Parigi—opera: 2 acts (1839—Milan) (Lib. F. Romani, after Saint-Just)

Cpte L. Serra, A. Romero, G. Morino, E. Zilio, E. Fissore, S. Manga, Milan RAI Chor, Milan RAI SO, C.F. Cillario (pp1988) (10/91) (NUOV) Ⓓ [2] **6752/3**

Mira o bella il trovatore M. Elkins, Philh, J. Judd (r1979) *Concert* (9/94) (OPRA) Ⓓ **ORC004**

Imelda de' Lambertazzi—opera seria: 2 acts (1830—Naples) (Lib. L. A. Tottola)

Vincesti alfin...Amarti e nel martoro M. Elkins, Philh, J. Judd (r1979) *Concert* (9/94) (OPRA) Ⓓ **ORC004**

Linda di Chamounix—opera: 3 acts (1842—Vienna) (Lib. Rossi, after D'Ennery and Lemoine)

ACT 1: 1. Overture; 2. Ambo nati in questa valle; 3a. Ah! tardai troppo; 3b. O luce di quest' anima; 4a. Cari luoghi ov'io passai; 4b. Per sua madre andò una figlia; 5a. Linda! Linda!; 5b. Da quel dì che t'incontrai. ACT 2: 6a. Già scorsero tre mesi; 6b. Al bel destin; 7. Se tanto in ira agli uomini; 8. Un buon servo del Visconte; 9a. Linda!...A che pensate?; 9b. A consolarmi affrettati.

Cpte E. Gruberová, D. Bernardini, A. Melander, E. Kim, M. Groop, S. Palatchi, U. Precht, K. Hedlund, Mikaeli Chbr Ch, Swedish RSO, F. Haider (r1993) (9/94) (NIGH) Ⓓ [3] **NC070561-2**

Cpte A. Stella, C. Valletti, R. Capecchi, G. Taddei, F. Barbieri, G. Modesti, R. Corsi, P. de Palma, Naples San Carlo Op Chor, Naples San Carlo Op Orch, T. Serafin (r1956) (9/94) (PHIL) Ⓓ [2] **442 093-2PM2**

2. M. Battistini, orch, C. Sabajno (r1912) *Concert* (10/92) (NIMB) Ⓓ **NI7831**

3a, 3b L. Aliberti, Munich RO, L. Gardelli *Concert* (11/86) (ORFE) Ⓓ **C119841A**

3a, 3b A. Galli-Curci, orch (r1922) *Concert* (2/89) (PEAR) Ⓓ **GEMMCD9308**

3a, 3b K. Battle, LPO, B. Campanella (r1991) *Concert* (12/93) (DG) Ⓓ **435 866-2GH**

3b T. dal Monte, La Scala Orch, C. Sabajno (r1929) *Concert* (2/90) (PREI) Ⓓ **89001**

3b A. Galli-Curci, orch, R. Bourdon (r1922) *Concert* (5/90) (NIMB) Ⓓ **NI7806**

3b L. Tetrazzini, orch (r1911) *Concert* (9/92) (EMI) Ⓓ [3] **CHS7 63802-2(1)**

3b L. Tetrazzini, orch, P. Pitt (r1910) *Concert* (9/92) (EMI) Ⓓ [3] **CHS7 63802-2(1)**

3b L. Tetrazzini, orch, P. Pitt (r1910) *Concert* (9/92) (PEAR) Ⓓ **GEMMCD9222**

3b L. Tetrazzini, orch (r1911) *Concert* (9/92) (PEAR) Ⓓ **GEMMCD9222**

3b L. Tetrazzini, orch (r1914) *Concert* (9/92) (PEAR) Ⓓ **GEMMCD9225**

3b L. Orgonášová, Bratislava RSO, W. Humburg *Concert* (2/93) (NAXO) Ⓓ **8 550605**

3b A. Galli-Curci, orch, J. Pasternack (r1922) *Concert* (8/94) (ROMO) Ⓓ [2] **81004-2**

4b E. Stignani, EIAR Orch, U. Tansini (r1937) *Concert* (1/91) (PREI) Ⓓ **89014**

4b J. Kowalski, Berlin RSO, H. Fricke *Concert* (10/92) (CAPR) Ⓓ **10 416**

4b E. Bruno, anon (r1902) *Concert* (4/94) (EMI) Ⓓ [3] **CHS7 64860-2(2)**

5a, 7. R. Vargas, ECO, M. Viotti *Concert* (11/92) (CLAV) Ⓓ **CD50-9202**

Lucia di Lammermoor, '(The) Bride of Lammermoor'—opera: 3 acts (1835—Naples) (Lib. Cammarano, after Scott)

ACT 1: 1a. Percorrete le spiagge vicine; 1b. Tu sei turbato; 1c. Cruda, funesta smania; 1d. La pietade in suo favore; 2a. Ancor non giunse?; 2b. Regnava nel silenzio; 2c. Quando rapito in estasi; 3a. Egli s'avanza; 3b. Lucia perdona; 3c. Sulla tomba; 3d. Ah! Verrano a te; ACT 2: 4. Lucia fra poco a te verrà; 5a. Appressati, Lucia; 5b. Il pallor funesto; 5c. Soffriva nel pianto; 5d. Se tradirmi; 6. Ebben?...Di tua speranza; 7a. Per te d'immenso giubilo; 7b. Per poco fra le tenebre; 7c. Dov'è Lucia?; 8. Chi mi frena (Sextet); 9. T'allontana, sciagurato. ACT 3: 10. Orrida è questa notte (Wolf's Crag Scene); 11. D'immenso giubilo; 12. Dalle stanze; 13a. Il dolce suono; 13b. Ardon gl'incensi; 13c. Alfin son tua; 13d. Spargi d'amaro pianto (Mad Scene); 14. Si tragga altrove; 15a. Tombe degl'avi miei; 15b. Fra poco a me ricovero; 15c. Giusto ciel, rispondete; 15d. Tu che a Dio. ALTERNATIVE ARIA FOR EXCERPT 2: 16a. Ancor non giunse?; 16b. Perchè non ho del vento.

Cpte J. Sutherland, L. Pavarotti, S. Milnes, N. Ghiaurov, H. Tourangeau, R. Davies, P.F. Poli, ROH Chor, ROHO, R. Bonynge (11/85) (DECC) Ⓓ [3] **410 193-2DH3**

Cpte M. Callas, Ferruccio Tagliavini, P. Cappuccilli, B. Ladysz, M. Elkins, L. del Ferro, R. Casellato, Philh Chor, Philh, T. Serafin (1/87) (EMI) Ⓓ [2] **CDS7 47440-8**

Cpte A. Moffo, C. Bergonzi, M. Sereni, E. Flagello, C. Vozza, P. Duval, V. Pandano, RCA Italiana Op Chor, RCA Italiana Op Orch, G. Prêtre (r1966) (9/88) (RCA) Ⓓ [2] **GD86504**

Cpte M. Callas, G. di Stefano, T. Gobbi, R. Arié, A.M. Canali, V. Natali, G. Sarri, MMF Chor, MMF Orch, T. Serafin (r1953) (10/89) (EMI) Ⓓ [2] **CMS7 69980-2**

Cpte J. Sutherland, R. Cioni, R. Merrill, C. Siepi, A.R. Satre, K. Macdonald, R. Pelizzoni, Santa Cecilia Academy Chor, Santa Cecilia Academy Orch, J. Pritchard (12/89) (DECC) Ⓓ [2] **411 622-2DM2**

Cpte M. Callas, G. di Stefano, R. Panerai, N. Zaccaria, L. Villa, G. Zampieri, Mario Carlin, La Scala Chor, Berlin RIAS Orch, H. von Karajan (pp1955) (2/91) (EMI) Ⓓ [2] **CMS7 63631-2**

Cpte E. Gruberová, N. Shicoff, A. Agache, A. Miles, D. Montague, B. Lombardo, F. Piccoli, Ambrosian Sngrs, LSO, R. Bonynge (11/92) (TELD) Ⓓ [2] **9031-72306-2**

Cpte E. Gruberová, Alfredo Kraus, R. Bruson, R. Lloyd, K. Kuhlmann, B. Bottone, B. Lazzaretti, Ambrosian Op Chor, RPO, N. Rescigno (r1983) (3/93) (EMI) Ⓓ [2] **CMS7 64622-2**

Cpte C. Studer, P. Domingo, J. Pons, S. Ramey, J. Larmore, F. de la Mora, A. Laciura, Ambrosian Op Chor, LSO, I. Marin (r1990) (4/93) (DG) Ⓓ [2] **435 309-2GH2**

1c R. Stracciari, orch (r1925) *Concert* (2/90) (PREI) Ⓓ **89003**

1c D. Hvorostovsky, Philh, I. Marin (r1992) *Concert* (9/94) (PHIL) Ⓓ **434 912-2PH**

2a E. Gruberová, V. Walterová, Czech PO, F. Haider *Concert* (5/90) (SONY) Ⓓ **SK45633**

2b L. Tetrazzini, orch (r1909) *Concert* (10/90) (NIMB) Ⓓ **NI7808**

2b T. dal Monte, orch (r1926) *Concert* (7/92) (PEAR) Ⓓ [3] **GEMMCDS9925(2)**

2b T. Dal Monte, orch, J. Pasternack (r1926) *Concert* (4/94) (RCA) Ⓓ [6] **09026 61580-2(3)**

2b, 2c L. Aliberti, Munich RO, L. Gardelli *Concert* (11/86) (ORFE) Ⓓ **C119841A**

2b, 2c M. Callas, M. Elkins, Philh, T. Serafin *Concert* (2/90) (EMI) Ⓓ **CDM7 63182-2**

2b, 2c L. Tetrazzini, orch, P. Pitt (r1909) *Concert* (9/92) (EMI) Ⓓ [3] **CHS7 63802-2(1)**

2b, 2c L. Tetrazzini, orch, P. Pitt (r1909) *Concert* (9/92) (PEAR) Ⓓ **GEMMCD9221**

2b, 13c, 13d T. dal Monte, Orch, J. Pasternack (r1926) *Concert* (2/90) (PREI) Ⓓ **89001**

2c F. Toresella, anon (r1900) *Concert* (12/89) (SYMP) Ⓓ **SYMCD1065**

3b-d Alfredo Kraus, Paris Op Orch, M. Veltri (pp1987) *Concert* (12/88) (EMI) Ⓓ **CDC7 49067-2**

3c F. Hempel, H. Jadlowker, orch (Ger: r1900s) *Concert* (12/91) (CLUB) Ⓓ **CL99-042**

3c G. Zenatello, M. Barrientos, anon (r1906) *Concert* (5/94) (SYMP) Ⓓ **SYMCD1168**

3c G. Zenatello, M. Barrientos, anon (r1906) *Concert* (5/94) (PEAR) Ⓓ [4] **GEMMCDS9073(1)**

3c, 3d M. Talley, B. Gigli, Vitaphone Orch, H. Heller (r1927) *Concert* (5/90) (PEAR) Ⓓ **GEMMCD9367**

3c, 3d A. Pertile, A. Rozsa, La Scala Orch, C. Sabajno, G. Nastrucci (r1930) *Concert* (9/90) (PREI) Ⓓ **89007**

3d A. Galli-Curci, T. Schipa, orch, R. Bourdon (r1928) *Concert* (12/89) (RCA) Ⓓ **GD87969**

3d A. Galli-Curci, T. Schipa, orch, R. Bourdon (r1924) *Concert* (5/90) (NIMB) Ⓓ **NI7806**

3d T. Schipa, A. Galli-Curci, orch, R. Bourdon (r1924) *Concert* (10/90) (MSCM) Ⓓ [2] **MM30231**

3d A. Galli-Curci, T. Schipa, orch (r1924) *Concert* (3/94) (CONI) Ⓓ **CDHD201**

3d A. Galli-Curci, T. Schipa, orch, R. Bourdon (r1924) *Concert* (8/94) (ROMO) Ⓓ [2] **81004-2**

7a, 11. ROH Chor, ROHO, B. Haitink *Concert* (12/89) (EMI) Ⓓ **CDC7 49849-2**

8. A. Galli-Curci, L. Homer, B. Gigli, A. Bada, G. De Luca, E. Pinza, NY Met Op Orch, G. Setti (r1927) *Concert* (9/88) (EMI) Ⓓ **CDH7 61051-2**

8. A. Galli-Curci, L. Homer, B. Gigli, A. Bada, G. De Luca, E. Pinza, NY Met Op Orch, G. Setti (r1927) *Concert* (5/90) (PEAR) Ⓓ **GEMMCD9367**

8. M. Sembrich, G. Severina, E. Caruso, F. Daddi, A. Scotti, M. Journet, orch, W.B. Rogers (r1908) *Concert* (12/90) (PEAR) Ⓓ [3] **EVC1(2)**

8. L. Tetrazzini, J. Jacoby, E. Caruso, A. Bada, P. Amato, M. Journet, orch, W.B. Rogers (r1912) *Concert* (7/91) (RCA) Ⓓ [12] **GD60495(4)**

8. M. Sembrich, G. Severina, E. Caruso, F. Daddi, A. Scotti, M. Journet, orch, W.B. Rogers (r1908) *Concert* (7/91) (RCA) Ⓓ [12] **GD60495(2)**

8. A. Galli-Curci, M. Egener, E. Caruso, A. Bada, G. De Luca, M. Journet, orch, J. Pasternack (2 vers: r1917) *Concert* (7/91) (RCA) Ⓓ [12] **GD60495(6)**

8. A. Galli-Curci, M. Egener, E. Caruso, A. Bada, G. De Luca, M. Journet, orch (r1917) *Concert* (7/91) (MSCM) Ⓓ **MM30352**

8. L. Tetrazzini, J. Jacoby, E. Caruso, A. Bada, P. Amato, M. Journet, orch, W.B. Rogers (r1912) *Concert* (10/91) (PEAR) Ⓓ [3] **EVC3(1)**

8. A. Galli-Curci, M. Egener, E. Caruso, A. Bada, G. De Luca, M. Journet, orch, J. Pasternack (2 vers: r1917) *Concert* (10/91) (PEAR) Ⓓ [3] **EVC4(1)**

8. L. Tetrazzini, J. Jacoby, E. Caruso, A. Bada, P. Amato, M. Journet, orch (r1912) *Concert* (9/92) (PEAR) Ⓓ **GEMMCD9224**

8. A. Galli-Curci, M. Egener, E. Caruso, A. Bada, G. De Luca, M. Journet, orch, J. Pasternack (r1917: two vers) *Concert* (3/94) (ROMO) Ⓓ [2] **81003-2**

8. M. Rappold, M. Matzenauer, G. Zenatello, A. Middleton, T. Chalmers, E. Baroni, orch (r1916) *Concert* (5/94) (PEAR) Ⓓ [4] **GEMMCDS9074(2)**

8. A. Galli-Curci, L. Homer, B. Gigli, A. Bada, G. De Luca, E. Pinza, NY Met Op Orch, G. Setti (r1927) *Concert* (8/94) (NIMB) Ⓓ **NI7852**

10. J. Hadley, T. Hampson, WNO Orch, C. Rizzi (r1992) *Concert* (11/93) (TELD) Ⓓ **9031-73283-2**

10. J. Lotrič, I. Morozov, Slovak RSO, J. Wildner (r1994) *Concert* (2/95) (NAXO) Ⓓ **8 553030**

12. E. Pinza, Chor, orch, C. Sabajno (r1923) *Concert* (2/89) (PEAR) Ⓓ **GEMMCD9306**

12. M. Journet, orch (r1916) *Concert* (7/92) (PEAR) Ⓓ [3] **GEMMCDS9924(2)**

12. E. Pinza, chor, orch, C. Sabajno (r1923) *Concert* (4/94) (EMI) Ⓓ [3] **CHS7 64864-2(1)**

13a M. Korjus, Berlin St Op Orch, B. Seidler-Winkler (r1936) *Concert* (10/93) (PREI) Ⓓ **89054**

13a A. Galli-Curci, orch, J. Pasternack (r1917) *Concert* (3/94) (ROMO) Ⓓ [2] **81003-2**

13a A. Galli-Curci, orch (r1917) *Concert* (8/94) (NIMB) Ⓓ **NI7852**

13a-d M. Callas, G. Sarri, R. Arié, MMF Chor, MMF Orch, T. Serafin (r1953) *Concert* (2/90) (EMI) Ⓓ [4] **CMS7 63244-2**

13a-d L. Orgonášová, Bratislava RSO, W. Humburg *Concert* (2/93) (NAXO) Ⓓ **8 550605**

13a-d J. Sutherland, Paris Op Chor, Paris Cons, N. Santi (r1959) *Concert* (10/93) (DECC) Ⓓ **436 461-2DM**

13a-d S. Jo, Monte Carlo PO, P. Olmi (r1994) *Concert* (6/95) (ERAT) Ⓓ **4509-97239-2**

13a, 13b Dilbèr, Estonia Op Orch, E. Klas *Concert* (9/92) (ONDI) Ⓓ **ODE768-2**

13a, 13b, 13c, 13d M. Devia, Svizzera Italiana Orch, M. Rota (pp1992) *Concert* (10/94) (BONG) Ⓓ **GB2513-2**

13b N. Melba, J. Lemmoné, orch, W.B. Rogers (r1910) *Concert* (3/89) (LARR) Ⓓ **CDLRH221**

13b L. Tetrazzini, orch (r1911) *Concert* (10/90) (NIMB) Ⓓ **NI7808**

13b M. Ivogün, orch (r1917) *Concert* (8/92) (NIMB) Ⓓ **NI7832**

13b L. Tetrazzini, orch, P. Pitt (r1907) *Concert* (9/92) (EMI) Ⓓ [3] **CHS7 63802-2(1)**

13b L. Tetrazzini, orch, P. Pitt (r1907) *Concert* (9/92) (PEAR) Ⓓ **GEMMCD9221**

13b L. Tetrazzini, orch (r1911) *Concert* (9/92) (PEAR) Ⓓ **GEMMCD9223**

13b N. Melba, orch (r1910) *Concert* (7/93) (NIMB) Ⓓ [2] **NI7840/1**

Ugo, Conte di Parigi—opera: 2 acts
(1832—Milan) (Lib. F. Romani)
Cpte M. Arthur, D. Jones, E. Harrhy, J. Price, Y.
Kenny, C. du Plessis, G. Mitchell Ch, New Philh, A.
Francis   (12/90) (OPRA) ① [3] ORC001
La Zingara—opera: 2 acts (1822—Naples)
(Lib. A. L. Tottola)
A te nell'appressarmi B. Ford, I. Platt, J. Rawnsley
Concert   (8/95) (OPRA) ① [3] ORCH104
Fra l'erbe cosparse E. Orel, anon (Russ: r c1902)
Concert   (7/93) (SYMP) ① SYMCD1105
Fra l'erbe cosparse M. Korjus, Berlin St Op Orch, B.
Seidler-Winkler (Ger: r1936) Concert
               (10/93) (PREI) ① 89054

DOPPLER, (Albert) Franz
(1821–1883) Poland

SECTION II: CHAMBER

Casilda fantaisie—flute and harp (comp with
Antonio Zamara)
K. Jones, A. Brewer (r1993) Concert
               (10/94) (CONI) ① [2] CDCF905
Fantaisie pastorale hongroises—flute and
piano, Op. 26
W. Bennett, ECO, S. Bedford Concert
               (10/89) (ASV) ① CDDCA652
Mazurka—flute and piano
Philippa Davies, T. Owen Concert
               (3/87) (CARL) ① PCD835

DORATI, Antál (1906–1988)
Hungary/USA

SECTION I: ORCHESTRAL

Symphony No. 1 (1957)
Stockholm PO, A. Dorati (pp1972) Symphony 2.
               (7/89) (BIS) ① BIS-CD408
Symphony No. 2, 'Querela Pacis' (1985)
Stockholm PO, A. Dorati (r1988) Symphony 1.
               (7/89) (BIS) ① BIS-CD408

DORNEL, Louis-Antoine
(c1680–1756) France

SECTION II: CHAMBER

Sonata for oboe and continuo (1713)
P. Dombrecht, W. Kuijken, R. Kohnen Concert
               (9/90) (ACCE) ① ACC8537D
Sonata for Three Recorders in B flat
F. Brüggen, K. Boeke, W. van Hauwe (r1978)
Concert   (10/95) (TELD) ① 4509-97469-2

DOSTAL, Nico (1891–1981)
Austria

SECTION V: STAGE WORKS

Die Ungarische Hochzeit—operetta:
prologue, 3 acts (1939—Stuttgart) (Lib. H
Hermecke, after K Mikszáth)
EXCERPTS: 1. Heimat, deine Lieder; 2.
Märchentraum der Liebe; 3a. Am alten Brunnen; 3b.
Spiel das Lied von Glück und Treu; 4. Hungarian
March.
3b L. Popp, ASMF, N. Marriner Concert
               (6/88) (EMI) ① CDC7 49700-2

DOTZAUER, (Justus Johann)
Friedrich (1783–1860) Germany

SECTION II: CHAMBER

Canon in G—two violins
J. Gatwood, L. Rautenberg (r1994) Concert
               (3/95) (SONY) ① SK64307
6 Pieces—three cellos, Op. 104
1. Andante, B flat; 2. Adagio—Allegro, A; 3. Scherzo:
Allegro non troppo—Trio in C; 4. Andante maestoso,
A flat; 5. Pastorale, F; 6. Larghetto—Allegro, G.
A. Bylsma, K. Slowik, S. Doane (r1994) Concert
               (3/95) (SONY) ① SK64307
Quartet for Cello obbligato, Two Violins and
Viola, Op. 64
V. Beths, J. Gatwood, L. Rautenberg, A. Bylsma
(r1994) Concert   (3/95) (SONY) ① SK64307
Quintet in D minor—2 violins, viola and 2
cellos, Op. 134
V. Beths, J. Gatwood, L. Rautenberg, A. Bylsma, K.
Slowik (r1994) Concert (3/95) (SONY) ① SK64307

SECTION III: INSTRUMENTAL

Allegro in A minor—cello, Op. 155/2
A. Bylsma (r1994) Concert
               (3/95) (SONY) ① SK64307
Allegro non troppo in B flat—cello, Op. 54/2
A. Bylsma (r1994) Concert
               (3/95) (SONY) ① SK64307
Presto in D—cello, Op. 158/2
A. Bylsma (r1994) Concert
               (3/95) (SONY) ① SK64307

DOWLAND, John (?1563–1626)
England

P—Numbers used in D. Poulton and B. Lam,
Collected Lute Music of John Dowland (1974)

SECTION II: CHAMBER

Captaine Digorie Piper his pavan—consort
(Kassel MS)
Parley of Instr, P. Holman (r1992) Concert
               (8/93) (HYPE) ① CDA66637
Frog Galliard—consort (pub 1599) (arr
Morley)
J. Bream, J. Bream Consort (r1987) Concert
               (8/93) (RCA) ① [28] 09026 61583-2(3)
J. Bream Consort (r1987) Concert
               (9/94) (RCA) ① 09026 61590-2
Lachrimae, or Seaven Teares—consort: 5
viols/violins and lute (pub 1604)
1. Lachrimae Antiquae; 2. Lachrimae Antiquae
Novae; 3. Lachrimae Gementes; 4. Lachrimae
Tristes; 5. Lachrimae Coactae; 6. Lachrimae
Amantis; 7. Lachrimae Verae; 8. Semper Dowland
Semper Dolens; 9. Sir Henry Umptons Funerall; 10.
M. John Langtons Pavan; 11. The King of Denmarks
Galiard; 12. The Earle of Essex Galiard; 13. Sir John
Souch his Galiard; 14. M. Henry Noell his Galiard; 15.
M. Giles Hobies Galiard; 16. M. Nicho. Gryffith his
Galiard; 17. M. Thomas Collier his Galiard with two
trebles; 18. Captaine Digorie Piper his Galiard; 19. M.
Buctons Galiard (Susanna Galliard); 20. Mistresse
Nichols Almand; 21. M. George Whitehead his
Almand.
Hespérion XX, J. Savall   (9/88) (ASTR) ① E8701
Rose Consort Concert
               (1/93) (AMON) ① CD-SAR55
Parley of Instr, P. Holman (r1992) Concert
               (8/93) (HYPE) ① CDA66637
C. Wilson, Fretwork (r1987/9)
               (7/94) (VIRG) ① VC5 45005-2
Dowland Consort, J. Lindberg (lte/dir)
               (12/86) (BIS) ① BIS-CD315
1. Tragicomedia, S. Stubbs Concert
               (1/90) (HYPE) ① CDA66307
1-7. C. Wilson, Fretwork Concert
               (11/89) (VIRG) ① VC7 59539-2
1, 7. J. Bream (r1967) Concert
               (8/93) (RCA) ① [28] 09026 61583-2(2)
1, 7. J. Bream (r1967) Concert
               (6/94) (RCA) ① 09026 61586-2
8-21. Fretwork Concert
               (3/91) (VIRG) ① VC7 59586-2
10, 13. J. Bream (r1976) Concert
               (8/93) (RCA) ① [28] 09026 61583-2(2)
10, 13. J. Bream (r1976) Concert
               (6/94) (RCA) ① 09026 61586-2
11. A. Dalton, Y. Imamura Concert
               (7/89) (ETCE) ① KTC1030

SECTION III: INSTRUMENTAL

Almains—lute, P47-54
1. Sir John Smith his Almain, P47; 1a. Smythes
Allmayne, P47a; 2. Dowlands Allmande, P48; 2a. The
Lady Laitones Almone, P48a; 3. Almain, P49; 4.
Mistris Whittes thinge, P50; 5. Almain, P51; 6. Mrs
Nichols Almand, P52; 7. Mrs Cliftons Allmaine, P53;
8. My Lady Hunsdons Allmande (Puffe), P54.
POSSIBLY SPURIOUS: 9. An Almand, P96
(Margaret Board Lute Book)
1, 3, 8. J. Bream (r1967) Concert
               (8/93) (RCA) ① [28] 09026 61583-2(2)
1, 3, 8. J. Bream (r1967) Concert
               (6/94) (RCA) ① 09026 61586-2
1-9. J. Lindberg (r1994) Concert
               (11/95) (BIS) ① [4] BIS-CD722/4
2a, 3-5. P. O'Dette (r1994) Concert
               (11/95) (HARM) ① HMU90 7160
4. P. O'Dette (r1983) Concert
               (11/88) (ASTR) ① E7715
4. Y. Imamura Concert   (7/89) (ETCE) ① KTC1030
8. C. Wilson Concert
               (11/91) (VIRG) ① VC7 59034-2

---

8. J. Bream (r1988; with Poetry recital by Dame P.
Ashcroft) Concert
               (8/93) (RCA) ① [28] 09026 61583-2(5)
Come away—song arrangement: lute, P60
(based on 'Come againe sweet loue')
J. Lindberg (r1994) Concert
               (11/95) (BIS) ① [4] BIS-CD722/4
Fantasies and Other Contrapuntal
Pieces—lute, P1-7
1. Fantasie, P1; 1a. A Fantasie, P1a; 2. Forlorne
Hope Fancye, P2; 3. Farwell, P3; 4. Farwell (on the
'In Nomine' theme), P4; 5. Fantasie, P5; 6. Fantasie
in G minor, P6; 7. Fantasie, P7. POSSIBLY
SPURIOUS: 8. A Fantasia, P71 (Jane Pickering's
MS); 9. A Chromatic Fancy, P72; 10. A Fancy, P73;
11. A Fancy, P74; 12. Fantasia, P101 (Hainhofer
MS).
1. J. Lindberg Concert   (2/89) (BIS) ① BIS-CD390
1a, 2-10. J. Lindberg (r1994) Concert
               (11/95) (BIS) ① [4] BIS-CD722/4
1, 10. D. Miller Concert
               (10/91) (HYPE) ① CDA66447
1, 3, 6. P. O'Dette (r1983) Concert
               (11/88) (ASTR) ① E7715
2. J. Bream (r1976) Concert
               (8/93) (RCA) ① [28] 09026 61583-2(1)
2. J. Bream (r1976) Concert
               (6/94) (RCA) ① 09026 61585-2
3, 10. J. Bream (r1976) Concert
               (8/93) (RCA) ① [28] 09026 61583-2(2)
3, 10. J. Bream (r1976) Concert
               (6/94) (RCA) ① 09026 61587-2
3, 5. P. O'Dette (r1994) Concert
               (11/95) (HARM) ① HMU90 7160
5. J. Bream, J. Bream Consort (r1962) Concert
               (8/93) (RCA) ① [28] 09026 61583-2(3)
5. J. Bream Consort (r1962; arr consort) Concert
               (9/94) (RCA) ① 09026 61589-2
10. C. Wilson Concert
               (11/91) (VIRG) ① VC7 59034-2
10. J. Bream (r1966) Concert
               (8/93) (RCA) ① [28] 09026 61583-2(1)
10. J. Bream (r1988; with Poetry recital by Dame P.
Ashcroft) Concert
               (8/93) (RCA) ① [28] 09026 61583-2(5)
10. J. Bream (r1966) Concert
               (6/94) (RCA) ① 09026 61585-2
Galliards—lute, P19-45
1. Captaine Digorie his Galiard, P19; 2. Dowlands
Galliard, P20; 3. John Dowlands Galliard (Captain
Candishe his Galyard), P21; 4. Dowlands First
Galliard, P22; 5. Frog Galliard, P23; 5a. Frogg
Galliard, P23a; 6. fr. Dac. Galliard, P24; 7.
Melancholy Galliard, P25; 8. Sir John Souch his
Galiard, P26; 9. Galliard, P27; 10. Galliard (upon a
galliard by Dan Bacheler), P28; 11. M. Giles Hobies
Galiard, P29; 12. Galliard in G minor, P30; 13.
Galliard (upon 'Walsingham'), P31; 14. Mrs Vaux
Galliarde, P32; 15. Mr Langtons Galliard, P33; 16.
Mignarda (Mignarde), P34; 17. Galliard, P35; 18. Mr
Knights Galliard, P36; 19. My Lord Chamberlaine his
Galliard, P37 (two upon one lute); 20. The Lord
Viscount Lisle (Sir Robert Sidney) his Galliard, P38;
20a. Susanna Galliard, P38a; 21. Doulands rounde
battell galyarde, P39; 22. The Battle Galliard (The
King of Denmarke his Galliard), P40; 23. K. Darceys
Galliard, P41; 23a. The most sacred Queene
Elizabeth her Galliard, P41a; 24. Can she excuse,
P42; 24a. The Earl of Essex his Galliard, P42a; 25.
My Ladie Riches Galyerd, P43a; 26. The Right
Hon Ferdinando Earle of Darby, his Galliard, P44;
26a. The Right Hon Ferdinando Earle of Derby, his
Galliard, P44a; 27. The Right Honourable the Lady
Cliftons Spirit, P45; 28. Galliard to Lachrimae, P46.
POSSIBLY SPURIOUS: 29. Galliard, P76; 30. The
Queenes Galliard, P97 (Margaret Board Lute Book);
31. Gagliarda, P103 (Hainhofer MS); 32. Galliard,
P104 (Matthew Otley's Cittern Book); 33. Galliard
(Galliarda Douland Cantus), P105.
1, 19, 28. J. Bream (r1976) Concert
               (8/93) (RCA) ① [28] 09026 61583-2(2)
1, 19, 28. J. Bream (r1976) Concert
               (6/94) (RCA) ① 09026 61586-2
1, 23a, 27. J. Bream (r1963) Concert
               (8/93) (RCA) ① [28] 09026 61583-2(1)
1, 23a, 27. J. Bream (r1963) Concert
               (8/93) (RCA) ① 09026 61584-2
1-4, 5a, 6-18, 20-24, 24a, 25a, 26a, 27-31. J.
Lindberg (r1994) Concert
               (11/95) (BIS) ① [4] BIS-CD722/4
4, 5, 20, 24a, 25, 26. J. Bream (r1967) Concert
               (6/94) (RCA) ① 09026 61586-2
4, 5, 20, 25, 26. J. Bream (r1967) Concert
               (8/93) (RCA) ① [28] 09026 61583-2(2)

5, 23a D. Miller *Concert*
(10/91) (HYPE) ① **CDA66447**
5, 5a, 7, 9, 11, 12, 17, 18, 25a, 32. P. O'Dette (r1994)
Concert   (11/95) (HARM) ① **HMU90 7160**
7, 16, 22, 23a, 26. J. Bream (r1988; with Poetry
recital by Dame P. Ashcroft) *Concert*
(8/93) (RCA) ① [28] **09026 61583-2(5)**
10, 16, 22. J. Bream (r1960) *Concert*
(8/93) (RCA) ① [28] **09026 61583-2(1)**
10, 16, 22. J. Bream (r1960) *Concert*
(8/93) (RCA) ① **09026 61584-2**
13, 23a, 25, 27, 28. P. O'Dette (r1983) *Concert*
(11/88) (ASTR) ① **E7715**
22. P. O'Dette (r1992) *Concert*
(8/93) (HYPE) ① **CDA66637**
23a K. Ragossnig *Concert*
(2/86) (ARCH) ① **415 294-2AH**
23a K. Heindel (lute-hpd) *Concert*
(2/91) (KING) ① **KCLCD2020**
23a J. Bream (r1966) *Concert*
(8/93) (RCA) ① [28] **09026 61583-2(1)**
23a J. Bream (r1966) *Concert*
(6/94) (RCA) ① **09026 61585-2**
24. J. Bream, J. Bream Consort (r1962) *Concert*
(8/93) (RCA) ① [28] **09026 61583-2(3)**
24. J. Bream, J. Bream Consort (r1987; ed Beck)
Concert   (8/93) (RCA) ① [28] **09026 61583-2(3)**
24. J. Bream Consort (r1962; arr consort) *Concert*
(9/94) (RCA) ① **09026 61589-2**
24. J. Bream Consort (r1987; ed Beck) *Concert*
(9/94) (RCA) ① **09026 61590-2**
24a J. Bream (r1967) *Concert*
(8/93) (RCA) ① [28] **09026 61583-2(2)**
26. A. Rooley *Concert*
(4/90) (VIRG) ① **VC7 59521-2**
28. Composers Ens, D. Muldowney (arr J. Woolrich)
Concert   (4/92) (NMC) ① **NMCD003**

Jigs, Corantos, Toys, etc—lute, P55-59
1. Mistris Winters Jumpe, P55; 2. Mrs Whites
Nothing, P56; 3. Mrs Vauxes Gigge, P57; 4. The
Shomakers Wife a Toy, P58; 5. Tarletones
Riserrections, P59. POSSIBLY SPURIOUS: 6. Mistris
Norrishis Delight, P77; 7. Jig, P78; 8. A Coye Joye,
P80; 9. Tarleton's Jigge, P81; 10. Mr Dowland's
Midnight, P99 (Margaret Board Lute Book); 11.
Coranto, P100 (Margaret Board Lute Book).
1. K. Ragossnig *Concert*
(2/86) (ARCH) ① **415 294-2AH**
1, 10. A. Rooley *Concert*
(4/90) (VIRG) ① **VC7 59521-2**
1-11. J. Lindberg (r1994) *Concert*
(11/95) (BIS) ① [4] **BIS-CD722/4**
1, 2. P. O'Dette (r1994) *Concert*
(11/95) (HARM) ① **HMU90 7160**
1, 2, 4. P. O'Dette (r1983) *Concert*
(11/88) (ASTR) ① **E7715**
1, 3, 4. Y. Imamura *Concert*
(7/89) (ETCE) ① **KTC1030**
3, 4. J. Bream (r1967) *Concert*
(8/93) (RCA) ① [28] **09026 61583-2(2)**
3, 4. J. Bream (r1967) *Concert*
(6/94) (RCA) ① **09026 61586-2**
4. L. Kirchhof *Concert*   (11/92) (SONY) ① **SK48068**
5. J. Bream (r1963) *Concert*
(8/93) (RCA) ① [28] **09026 61583-2(1)**
5. J. Bream, J. Bream Consort (r1962) *Concert*
(8/93) (RCA) ① [28] **09026 61583-2(3)**
5. J. Bream (r1988; with Poetry recital by Dame P.
Ashcroft) *Concert*
(8/93) (RCA) ① [28] **09026 61583-2(5)**
5. J. Bream (r1963) *Concert*
(8/93) (RCA) ① **09026 61584-2**
5. D. Tayler *Concert*   (9/93) (ARAB) ① **Z6622**
5. J. Bream Consort (r1962; arr consort) *Concert*
(9/94) (RCA) ① **09026 61589-2**
10. J. Lindberg   (2/89) (BIS) ① **BIS-CD390**

Mounsier's Almain—lute (not in Poulton's
catalogue)
J. Lindberg (r1994) *Concert*
(11/95) (BIS) ① [4] **BIS-CD722/4**

Pavans—lute, P8-18
1. Piper's Pavan, P8; 2. Semper Dowland Semper
Dolens, P9; 3. Solus cum sola, P10; 4. Mrs Bridge
Fleetswood pauen als Solus sine sola, P11; 5. Dr
Cases Pauen, P12; 6. Resoulcon (Dowland's adew
for Master Oliuer Cromwell), P13; 7. Sir John
Langton his Pauin, P14; 7a. Sir John Langton's
Pavan, P14a; 8. Lachrimae, P15; 9. Pavan, P16; 10.
The Lady Russell's Pavan, P17; 11. Pavan, P18.
POSSIBLY SPURIOUS: 12. A Dream, P75; 13.
Pauana Johan Douland, Pavan 94 (Schele MS); 14. La
mia Barbara, P95 (Schele MS).
1. Y. Imamura *Concert*   (7/89) (ETCE) ① **KTC1030**
1, 6. J. Bream (r1976) *Concert*
(8/93) (RCA) ① [28] **09026 61583-2(1)**

1, 6. J. Bream (r1976) *Concert*
(6/94) (RCA) ① **09026 61586-2**
1-6, 7a, 8-10, 13, 14. J. Lindberg (r1994) *Concert*
(11/95) (BIS) ① [4] **BIS-CD722/4**
2. A. Rooley *Concert*
(4/90) (VIRG) ① **VC7 59521-2**
2. C. Wilson *Concert*
(11/91) (VIRG) ① **VC7 59034-2**
2. J. Bream (r1967) *Concert*
(8/93) (RCA) ① [28] **09026 61583-2(2)**
2. J. Bream (r1967) *Concert*
(6/94) (RCA) ① **09026 61586-2**
2, 7, 8, 14. P. O'Dette (r1983) *Concert*
(11/88) (ASTR) ① **E7715**
2, 8. J. Bream (r1988; with Poetry recital by Dame P.
Ashcroft) *Concert*
(8/93) (RCA) ① [28] **09026 61583-2(5)**
5, 11, 12. P. O'Dette (r1994) *Concert*
(11/95) (HARM) ① **HMU90 7160**
6, 8. J. Bream, J. Bream Consort (r1962) *Concert*
(8/93) (RCA) ① [28] **09026 61583-2(3)**
6, 8. J. Bream Consort (r1962; arr consort) *Concert*
(9/94) (RCA) ① **09026 61589-2**
7. K. Heindel (lute-hpd) *Concert*
(2/91) (KING) ① **KCLCD2020**
7. J. Bream (r1963) *Concert*
(8/93) (RCA) ① [28] **09026 61583-2(1)**
7. J. Bream (r1963) *Concert*
(8/93) (RCA) ① **09026 61584-2**
8. S. Stubbs *Concert*   (12/90) (HYPE) ① **CDA66335**
8. Composers Ens, D. Muldowney (arr J. Woolrich)
Concert   (4/92) (NMC) ① **NMCD003**
8. J. Bream, J. Bream Consort (r1987; ed Beck)
Concert   (8/93) (RCA) ① [28] **09026 61583-2(3)**
8. D. Tayler *Concert*   (9/93) (ARAB) ① **Z6622**
8. J. Bream Consort (r1987; ed Beck) *Concert*
(9/94) (RCA) ① **09026 61590-2**
12. L. Kirchhof *Concert*
(11/92) (SONY) ① **SK48068**

2 Pavans—lute (1622) (recently rediscovered
in Mylius MS)
J. Lindberg (r1994) *Concert*
(11/95) (BIS) ① [4] **BIS-CD722/4**
P. O'Dette (r1994) *Concert*
(11/95) (HARM) ① **HMU90 7160**

Prelude—lute, P102 (N Hainhofer MS.
Probably spurious)
J. Lindberg (r1994) *Concert*   (2/89) (BIS) ① **BIS-CD390**
D. Miller *Concert*   (10/91) (HYPE) ① **CDA66447**
J. Lindberg (r1994) *Concert*
(11/95) (BIS) ① [4] **BIS-CD722/4**

Preludium—lute, P98 (from Margaret Board
lute book, ?possibly spurious)
J. Lindberg (r1994) *Concert*
(11/95) (BIS) ① [4] **BIS-CD722/4**

**Settings of Ballads and Other Popular
Tunes—lute, P61-70**
1. Orlando Sleepeth, P61; 2. Fortune my foe, P62; 3.
Complaint, P63; 4. Go from my Window, P64; 5. Lord
Strangs March, P65; 6. Lord Willoughby (Lord
Willoughby's Welcome Home), P66; 6a. My Lord
Willoughby's Welcome Home, P66a; 7. Walsingham,
P67; 8. The George Aloe, P68; 9. Loth to departe,
P69; 10. Robin (Sweet Robin, Jolly Robin etc), P70.
POSSIBLY SPURIOUS: 11. What is a day, P79.
1, 4, 6, 11. P. O'Dette (r1994) *Concert*
(11/95) (HARM) ① **HMU90 7160**
1-5, 6a, 7-11. J. Lindberg (r1994) *Concert*
(11/95) (BIS) ① [4] **BIS-CD722/4**
1, 9. J. Bream (r1988; with Poetry recital by Dame P.
Ashcroft) *Concert*
(8/93) (RCA) ① [28] **09026 61583-2(5)**
2. D. Tayler (r1992) *Concert*
(7/93) (KOCH) ① **37170-2**
3. Composers Ens, D. Muldowney (arr J. Woolrich)
Concert   (4/92) (NMC) ① **NMCD003**
4, 7, 9, 10. J. Bream (r1972) *Concert*
(8/93) (RCA) ① [28] **09026 61583-2(2)**
4, 7, 9, 10. J. Bream (r1972) *Concert*
(6/94) (RCA) ① **09026 61587-2**
6. T. Kropat, T. Krumeich (arr 2 gtrs) *Concert*
(7/93) (CHNN) ① **CG9103**
6. J. Bream (r1976) *Concert*
(8/93) (RCA) ① [28] **09026 61583-2(1)**
6. J. Bream (r1976) *Concert*
(6/94) (RCA) ① **09026 61585-2**
7, 8. P. O'Dette (r1983) *Concert*
(11/88) (ASTR) ① **E7715**

Sir Henry Guilforde's Almaine—lute (not in
Poulton's catalogue)
J. Bream (r1967) *Concert*
(8/93) (RCA) ① [28] **09026 61583-2(2)**
J. Bream (r1967) *Concert*
(6/94) (RCA) ① **09026 61586-2**
J. Lindberg (r1994) *Concert*
(11/95) (BIS) ① [4] **BIS-CD722/4**

1, 6. J. Bream (r1976) *Concert*
(6/94) (RCA) ① **09026 61586-2**
1-6, 7a, 8-10, 13, 14. J. Lindberg (r1994) *Concert*
(11/95) (BIS) ① [4] **BIS-CD722/4**

**Farre from triumphing court—lute song: 1v
(pub 1610)** (part of R. Dowland's 'A Musicall
Banquet')
E. Kirkby, A. Rooley (pp1985) *Concert*
(6/87) (HYPE) ① **CDA66186**

**The First Book of Songs or Ayres—4vv (pub
1597)**
1. Vnquiet thoughts; 2. Who euer thinks or hopes of
loue for loue; 3. My thoughts are wingd with hopes; 4.
If my complaints could passions moue; 5. Can she
excuse my wrongs with vertues cloake; 6. Now, O
now I needs must part; 7. Deare if you change ile
neuer chuse againe; 8. Burst forth my teares; 9. Go
Cristall teares; 10. Thinkst thou then by thy fainting;
11. Come away, come sweet loue; 12. Rest awhile
you cruell cares; 13. Sleepe wayward thoughts; 14.
All ye whom loue or fortune hath betraide; 15. Wilt
though vnkind thus reaue me me of my hart; 16.
Would my conceit that first enforst my woe; 17. Come
againe: sweet loue doyj now enuite; 18. His goulden
locks time hath to siluer turnd; 19. Awake sweet loue
thou art returnd; 20. Come heauy sleepe; 21. Awaie
with these selfe louing lads.
Cpte R. Covey-Crump, J. Lindberg
(3/91) (BIS) ① **BIS-CD430**
Cpte R. Müller, C. Wilson
(10/93) (ASV) ① **CDGAU135**
Cpte J. Elwes, M. Spaeter (r1994)
(3/95) (PIER) ① **PV794091**
1-18, 20, 21. Consort of Musicke, A. Rooley
(10/89) (L'OI) ① **421 653-2OH**
4, 6, 10, 14, 17-19, 21. J. Baird, D. Tayler, R.
DeCormier Sngrs, R. DeCormier *Concert*
(9/93) (ARAB) ① **Z6622**
5. M. Chance, C. Wilson (r1992) *Concert*
(10/94) (CHAN) ① **CHAN0538**
5, 6, 19. J. Bowman, D. Miller *Concert*
(10/91) (HYPE) ① **CDA66447**
5, 7, 14, 19. E. Kirkby, A. Rooley *Concert*
(4/90) (VIRG) ① **VC7 59521-2**
5, 7, 20. P. Pears, J. Bream (r1969) *Concert*
(8/93) (RCA) ① [28] **09026 61583-2(5)**
5, 7, 20. P. Pears, J. Bream (r1969) *Concert*
(8/93) (RCA) ① **09026 61602-2**
6. Martin Jones (1989: trans pf: Grainger) *Concert*
(7/90) (NIMB) ① **NI5232**
6. P. Thwaites (arr Grainger) *Concert*
(3/93) (UNIC) ① **DKPCD9127**
6, 10, 11, 20, 21. Echos Muse (r1992) *Concert*
(7/93) (KOCH) ① **37170-2**
9, 11, 17. A. Dalton, Y. Imamura *Concert*
(7/89) (ETCE) ① **KTC1030**
9, 20. C. Trevor, J. Heringman *Concert*
(1/93) (AMON) ① **CD-SAR55**
15. P. Pears, J. Bream (r1963) *Concert*
(8/93) (RCA) ① [28] **09026 61583-2(5)**
15. P. Pears, J. Bream (r1963) *Concert*
(8/93) (RCA) ① **09026 61602-2**
17. J. Bream, J. Bream Consort (r1987; arr consort)
Concert   (8/93) (RCA) ① [28] **09026 61583-2(3)**
17. J. Bream Consort (r1987; arr consort) *Concert*
(9/94) (RCA) ① **09026 61590-2**
18. E. Kirkby, A. Rooley (pp1985) *Concert*
(6/87) (HYPE) ① **CDA66186**
20. C. Hampe, M. Seiffge *Concert*
(11/90) (BAYE) ① **BR100095**

**In darknesse let mee dwell—lute song: 1v
(pub 1610)** (part of R. Dowland's 'A Musicall
Banquet')
A. Dalton, Y. Imamura *Concert*
(7/89) (ETCE) ① **KTC1030**
C. Trevor, J. Heringman *Concert*
(1/93) (AMON) ① **CD-SAR55**
Echos Muse (r1992) *Concert*
(7/93) (KOCH) ① **37170-2**
P. Pears, J. Bream (r1963) *Concert*
(8/93) (RCA) ① [28] **09026 61583-2(5)**
P. Pears, J. Bream (r1963) *Concert*
(8/93) (RCA) ① **09026 61602-2**
J. Baird, D. Tayler *Concert*   (9/93) (ARAB) ① **Z6622**

**Lady if you so spight me—lute song (pub
1610)** (pub in R. Dowland's 'A Musicall
Banquet')
Echos Muse (r1992) *Concert*
(7/93) (KOCH) ① **37170-2**

A Pilgrimes Solace—3-5vv (pub 1612)
1. Disdaine me still, that I may euer loue; 2. Sweete
stay a while, why will you?; 3. To aske for all thy loue;
4. Loue those beames that breede; 5. Shall I striue
with wordes to moue; 6. Were euery thought an eye;
7. Stay time a while thy flying; 8. Tell me true Loue; 9.
Goe nightly, cares the enemy to rest; 10. From silent
night, true register of moanes; 11. Lasso vita mia, mi
fa morire; 12. In this trembling shadow; 13. If that

Sinners sighes be Angels food; 14. Thou mighty God; 15. When 'Dauids' life by 'Saul'; 16. When the poore Criple; 17. Where Sinne sore wounding; 18. My heart and tongue were twinnes; 19. Vp merry Mates, to 'Neptunes' praise; 20. Welcome blacke night; 21. Cease these false sports.

2, 10. Echos Muse (r1992) *Concert*
(7/93) (KOCH) ① **37170-2**
2, 18. A. Dalton, Y. Imamura *Concert*
(7/89) (ETCE) ① **KTC1030**
2, 7. P. Pears, J. Bream (r1969) *Concert*
(8/93) (RCA) ① [28] **09026 61583-2(5)**
2, 7. P. Pears, J. Bream (r1969) *Concert*
(8/93) (RCA) ① **09026 61602-2**
7, 14. E. Kirkby, A. Rooley *Concert*
(4/90) (VIRG) ① **VC7 59521-2**
8. J. Baird, D. Tayler *Concert*
(9/93) (ARAB) ① **Z6622**
8, 9. J. Bowman, D. Miller, King's Consort *Concert*
(10/91) (HYPE) ① **CDA66447**
9. R. Tear, J. Bream Consort (r1987) *Concert*
(8/93) (RCA) ① [28] **09026 61583-2(3)**
9. R. Tear, J. Bream Consort (r1987) *Concert*
(9/94) (RCA) ① **09026 61590-2**
9, 11. M. Chance, C. Wilson, Fretwork *Concert*
(3/91) (VIRG) ① **VC7 59586-2**
10. C. Trevor, J. Heringman *Concert*
(1/93) (AMON) ① **CD-SAR55**
12. E. Kirkby, A. Rooley *Concert*
(8/91) (L'OI) ① **425 892-2OH**
The Second Booke of Songs or Ayres—2vv (nos 1-8); 4vv (nos 9-20); 5vv (nos 22-22) (pub 1600)
1. I saw my Lady weepe; 2. Flow my teares fall from your springs; 3. Sorrow sorrow stay, lend true repentant teares; 4. Dye not before thy day; 5. Mourne, mourne, daye is with darknesse fled; 6. Tymes eldest sonne, old age the heire of ease (first part); 7. Then sit thee downe, and say thy 'Nunc demittis' (second part); 8. When others sings 'Venite exultemus' (third part); 9. Praise blindnesse eies, for seeing is deceipt; 10. O sweet woods, the delight of solitarienesse; 11. If fluds of tears could clense my follies past; 12. Fine knacks for Ladies, cheap, choise, braue and new; 13. Now cease my wandring eyes; 14. Come ye heavie states of night; 15. White as Lillies was hir face; 16. Wofull heart with griefe opressed; 17. A Sheperd in a shade his plaining made; 18. Faction that euer dwells in court; 19. Shall I sue, shall I seeke for grace; 20. Finding in fields my 'Siluia' all alone (Toss not my soule); 21. Cleare or Cloudie sweet as 'April' showring; 22. Humor say what i makest thou heere.
Cpte Consort of Musicke, A. Rooley
(8/91) (L'OI) ① **425 889-2OH**
1. E. Kirkby, A. Rooley *Concert*
(8/91) (L'OI) ① **425 892-2OH**
1, 12, 17. A. Dalton, Y. Imamura *Concert*
(7/89) (ETCE) ① **KTC1030**
1, 19. P. Pears, J. Bream (r1969) *Concert*
(8/93) (RCA) ① [28] **09026 61583-2(5)**
1, 19. P. Pears, J. Bream (r1969) *Concert*
(8/93) (RCA) ① **09026 61602-2**
1-3. C. Trevor, J. Heringman *Concert*
(1/93) (AMON) ① **CD-SAR55**
1-3, 13, 17. Echos Muse (r1992) *Concert*
(7/93) (KOCH) ① **37170-2**
1-3, 17, 21. R. Covey-Crump, J. Lindberg *Concert*
(2/89) (BIS) ① **BIS-CD391**
1, 3, 19. M. Chance, C. Wilson (r1992) *Concert*
(10/94) (CHAN) ① **CHAN0538**
1, 5, 10, 12, 20. J. Baird, D. Tayler, R. DeCormier Sngrs, R. DeCormier *Concert*
(9/93) (ARAB) ① **Z6622**
2. D. Cordier, E. Headley, S. Stubbs *Concert*
(12/90) (HYPE) ① **CDA66335**
2. A. Schiøtz, J.G. Schmidt (r1941) *Concert*
(4/92) (EMI) ① [7] **CHS7 69741-2(5)**
2, 3. J. Bowman, D. Miller, King's Consort *Concert*
(10/91) (HYPE) ① **CDA66447**
3-5, 13, 16, 19. E. Kirkby, A. Rooley *Concert*
(4/90) (VIRG) ① **VC7 59521-2**
3, 6. P. Pears, J. Bream (r1963) *Concert*
(8/93) (RCA) ① [28] **09026 61583-2(5)**
12. Red Byrd, Circa 1500, N. Hadden (r1991) *Concert*
(8/93) (CRD) ① **CRD3487**
The Third and Last Book of Songs or Aires—5vv (pub 1603)
1. Farewell too faire; 2. Time stands still; 3. Behold a wonder heere; 4. Daphne was not so chaste as she was changing; 5. Me and me and none but me; 6. When Phoebus first did Daphne loue; 7. Say loue if euer thou didst finde; 8. Flow not so fast ye fountaines; 9. What if I neuer speede; 10. Loue stood amaz'd at sweet beautyes paine; 11. Lend your eares to my sorrow good people; 12. By a fountaine where I lay;

13. Oh what hath ouerwrought my all amazed thought; 14. Farewell vnkind farewell; 15. Weepe you no more sad fountaines; 16. Fie on this faining, is loue without desire; 17. I must complaine, yet doe enjoy; 18. It was a time when silly Bees could speake; 19. The lowest trees haue tops; 20. What poor Astronomers are they; 21. Come when I call, or tarrie till I come.

1, 3, 5, 19. E. Kirkby, A. Rooley *Concert*
(4/90) (VIRG) ① **VC7 59521-2**
1-9, 11-21. Consort of Musicke, A. Rooley
(11/91) (L'OI) ① **430 284-2OH**
2, 8. E. Kirkby, A. Rooley *Concert*
(9/87) (HYPE) ① **CDA66227**
2, 8, 18. E. Kirkby, A. Rooley (pp1985) *Concert*
(11/91) (HYPE) ① **CDA66186**
2, 9, 15, 19. J. Baird, D. Tayler, R. DeCormier Sngrs, R. DeCormier *Concert* (9/93) (ARAB) ① **Z6622**
4, 9, 15. A. Dalton, Y. Imamura *Concert*
(7/89) (ETCE) ① **KTC1030**
7. J. Bowman, D. Miller, King's Consort *Concert*
(10/91) (HYPE) ① **CDA66447**
7, 19. P. Pears, J. Bream (r1963) *Concert*
(8/93) (RCA) ① [28] **09026 61583-2(5)**
7, 19. P. Pears, J. Bream (r1963) *Concert*
(8/93) (RCA) ① **09026 61602-2**
7, 8, 15, 19. Echos Muse (r1992) *Concert*
(7/93) (KOCH) ① **37170-2**
15. P. Pears, J. Bream (r1969) *Concert*
(8/93) (RCA) ① [28] **09026 61583-2(5)**
15. P. Pears, J. Bream (r1969) *Concert*
(8/93) (RCA) ① **09026 61602-2**
The Whole Booke of Psalmes—4vv (pub 1592) (six contributions by Dowland)
1. Psalm 38: Put me not to rebuke, O Lord; 2. Psalm 100: All people that on earth do dwell; 3. Psalm 104: My soul praise the Lord; 4. Psalm 130: Lord to thee I make my moan; 5. Psalm 134: Behold and have regard; 6. A Prayer for the Queens most excellent Maiestie.
2. London Musica Antiqua, M. Uridge (r1980-83) *Concert* (12/93) (SYMP) ① **SYMCD1157**

DOWNEY, John (b 1927) USA

SECTION I: ORCHESTRAL

Edge of Space—fantasy for bassoon and orchestra (1978)
R. Thompson, LSO, G. Simon (r1981) *Concert*
(10/94) (CHAN) ① **CHAN9278**

DOYLE, Patrick (b 1953) Scotland

SECTION V: STAGE WORKS

Henry V—film score (1989)
EXCERPTS: 1. Opening title—'O! for a muse of fire'; 2. Henry V—The Boar's Head; 3. The Three Traitors; 4. 'Now, Lords, for France!'; 5. The Death of Falstaff; 6. 'Once more unto the breach'; 7. Threat to Governor of Harfleur/Katherine of France/March to Calais; 8. The Death of Bardolph; 9. 'Upon the King'; 10. St Crispin's Day—The Battle of Agincourt; 11. 'The day is come'; 12. 'Non nobis, Domine' (song); 13. The Wooing of Katherine; 14. 'Let this acceptance take'; 15. End Title.
1-15. OST, CBSO, S. Rattle (1989)
(2/90) (EMI) ① **CDC7 49919-2**
Needful Things—film score (1993)
EXCERPTS: 1. The Arrival; 2. To My Good Friend Brian; 3. Needful Things; 4. Brian's Deeds; 5. More Deeds; 6. Art & The Minister; 7. Gaunt's Web; 8. Racing Towards Apple Throwing Time; 9. Nettie Finds Her Dog; 10. Go Upstairs; 11. The Turning Point; 12. They Broke the Law; 13. The Devil's Here; 14. Just Blow Them Away; 15. End Titles; 16. Ave Maria (Schubert); 17. Peer Gynt—Hall of the Mountain King (Grieg).
1-17. OST, D. Snell (1993)
(8/94) (VARE) ① **VSD5438**

DRAGHI, Giovanni Battista (c1640–1708) Italy

SECTION III: INSTRUMENTAL

Ground, 'Scacca pur'—harpsichord (pub 1687) (attrib in 'Musick's Hand-Maid', pt 2)
T. Pinnock (1978) *Concert*
(4/89) (CRD) ① **CRD3347**
Suite in A—keyboard
D. Moroney (r1995) *Concert*
(5/95) (VIRG) ① **VC5 45166-2**

Suite in C minor—keyboard
D. Moroney (r1995) *Concert*
(5/95) (VIRG) ① **VC5 45166-2**
Suite in G—keyboard
D. Moroney (r1995) *Concert*
(5/95) (VIRG) ① **VC5 45166-2**
Suite in G minor—keyboard
D. Moroney (r1995) *Concert*
(5/95) (VIRG) ① **VC5 45166-2**

DRDLA, František Alois (1869–1944) Moravia

SECTION II: CHAMBER

Berceuse—violin and piano, Op. 56
J. Kubelík, anon (r1910) *Concert*
(6/91) (BIDD) ① [2] **LAB033/4**
Serenade No. 1 in A—violin and piano (1901)
J. Kubelík, anon (r1905) *Concert*
(6/91) (BIDD) ① [2] **LAB033/4**
J. Kubelík, anon (r1902) *Concert*
(6/91) (BIDD) ① [2] **LAB033/4**
Souvenir—violin and piano (1904)
J. Kubelík, anon (r1912) *Concert*
(6/91) (BIDD) ① [2] **LAB033/4**
J. Kubelík, anon (r1907) *Concert*
(6/91) (BIDD) ① [2] **LAB033/4**
F. Kreisler, C. Lamson (1921) *Concert*
(9/93) (BIDD) ① **LAB068/9**
F. Kreisler, C. Lamson (1928) *Concert*
(12/93) (BIDD) ① **LAB080**
Visione—violin and piano, Op. 28
J. Kubelík, anon (r1907) *Concert*
(6/91) (BIDD) ① [2] **LAB033/4**

DREGNAU DE LILLE, Marie de (?13th Cent) France

SECTION IV: VOCAL AND CHORAL

Mout m'abelist quant le voi—chanson de femme
Sinfonye, S. Wishart (r1992) *Concert*
(8/93) (HYPE) ① **CDA66625**

DRESHER, Paul (b 1951) USA

SECTION II: CHAMBER

Double Ikat—violin, piano and percussion (1988-90)
EXCERPTS: 1. Part One; 2. Part Two.
2. M. Bachmann, J. Klibonoff, J. Saporito (r1994) *Concert* (5/95) (CATA) ① **09026 62668-2**

DRESSER, Paul (1857–1906) USA

SECTION IV: VOCAL AND CHORAL

On the Banks of the Wabash—song
J. Björling, Inst Ens (r1920) *Concert*
(8/92) (BLUE) ① **ABCD016**

DRIGO, Riccardo (1846–1930) Italy

SECTION I: ORCHESTRAL

2 Airs de ballet—orchestra
2. Valse bluette.
2. I. Perlman, S. Sanders (trans. Heifetz) *Concert*
(12/89) (EMI) ① **CDC7 49604-2**
2. J. Heifetz, A. Benoist (r1917: arr Auer) *Concert*
(1/91) (BIDD) ① **LAB015**
2. J. Heifetz, A. Benoist (r1917) *Concert*
(11/94) (RCA) ① [65] **09026 61778-2(01)**
2. J. Heifetz, I. Achron (r1928) *Concert*
(11/94) (RCA) ① [65] **09026 61778-2(02)**
2. J. Heifetz, E. Bay (r1946) *Concert*
(11/94) (RCA) ① [65] **09026 61778-2(40)**

SECTION V: STAGE WORKS

Arlekinda, 'Harlequin's Millions'—ballet (1900—St Petersburg)
EXCERPTS: 1. Sérénade (Notturno d'amore).
1. B. Gigli, orch (r1922) *Concert*
(5/90) (NIMB) ① **NI7807**
1. H. Kreisler, F. Kreisler (arr vc/pf: r1921) *Concert*
(7/90) (BIDD) ① [2] **LAB009/10**
1. E. Feuermann, G. Moore (arr vc/pf: r1939) *Concert* (10/91) (PEAR) ① **GEMMCD9443**
1. M. Elman, P. Kahn (arr Auer: r1908) *Concert*
(12/91) (APR) ① [2] **APR7015**

1. M. Elman, P. Kahn (arr Auer; r1910) Concert
(12/91) (APR) ① [2] APR7015
1. L. Tetrazzini, orch, P. Pitt (Ital: r1922) Concert
(9/92) (EMI) ① [3] CHS7 63802-2(2)
1. L. Tetrazzini, orch (r1920) Concert
(9/92) (PEAR) ① GEMMCD9225
Le Corsaire—ballet (1899—St Petersburg)
(comp with Adam, Minkus & Pugni)
1. Pas de deux (written for 1899 revival).
1. English Concert Orch, R. Bonynge (arr Lanchbery)
Concert (11/90) (DECC) ① [2] 421 818-2DH2

DRING, Madeleine (1923–1977) England

SECTION II: CHAMBER

Danza Gaya—wind ens & gtr/ob & pf/2 pfs
(1964)
J. Polmear, D. Ambache Concert
(9/92) (UNIC) ① DKPCD9121

SECTION IV: VOCAL AND CHORAL

Crabbed age and youth—song (Wds
Shakespeare)
A. Rolfe Johnson, G. Johnson (r1991/3) Concert
(8/94) (HYPE) ① CDA66709
Dedications—songs (1967) (Wds. Herrick)
1. To daffodils; 2. To the Virgins; 3. To the willow
tree; 4. To Music; 5. To Phillis.
2. A. Rolfe Johnson, G. Johnson (r1991/3) Concert
(8/94) (HYPE) ① CDA66709

DRUCKMAN, Jacob (b 1928) USA

SECTION I: ORCHESTRAL

Nor Spell nor Charm—chamber orchestra
(1990)
Orpheus CO (r1990) Concert
(7/93) (DG) ① 435 389-2GH
Prism—3 pieces for large orchestra (1980)
NYPO, Z. Mehta Rochberg: Oboe Concerto.
(9/87) (NEW) ① NW335-2

DRUSCHETZKY, Georg (1745–1819) Bohemia

SECTION I: ORCHESTRAL

Concerto for Oboe, 8 Timpani, Wind and
Strings
J. Haas, G. Hunt, Bournemouth Sinfonietta, H.
Farberman Concert (10/89) (CRD) ① CRD3449
Partita in C—six timpani and orchestra
J. Haas, Bournemouth Sinfonietta, H. Farberman
Concert (10/89) (CRD) ① CRD3449

DU BUISSON III (d before 1688) France

SECTION III: INSTRUMENTAL

Troisième Suite in A minor—viola da
gamba
P. Pierlot (r1992) Concert
(2/94) (RICE) ① RIC118100

DU CAURROY, Eustache (1549–1609) France

SECTION II: CHAMBER

42 Fantasies—3-6 parts (pub 1610)
1, 6, 8, 9, 11, 12, 14, 17-20, 25, 26, 28, 34, 37, 40-42.
Hespèrion XX, J. Savall (11/88) (ASTR) ① E7749

SECTION III: INSTRUMENTAL

Dixiesme Fantaisie sur Requiem Aeternam (A
Quatre)—organ
J. van Oortmerssen Concert
(11/87) (BIS) ① BIS-CD316
Toulouse Sacqueboutiers, J. Bernfeld, B. Fabre-
Garrus (r1993) Concert (3/95) (ASTR) ① E8521

SECTION IV: VOCAL AND CHORAL

Une jeune fillette—chanson (pub 1610)
Baltimore Consort (r1992; arr Baltimore Consort)
Concert (4/95) (DORI) ① DOR90177

DU MONT, Henri (1610–1684) France

SECTION II: CHAMBER

Allemanda in G minor—two violins and
continuo (pub 1652) (Cantica Sacra)
Talens Lyriques (r1992) Concert
(9/93) (FNAC) ① 592098
Pavane in D minor—two violins and
continuo (pub 1657) (Mélanges)
Talens Lyriques (r1992) Concert
(9/93) (FNAC) ① 592098
Sarabande in D minor—two violins and
continuo (pub 1657) (Mélanges)
Talens Lyriques (r1992) Concert
(9/93) (FNAC) ① 592098
Symphonia in G minor—two violins and
continuo (pub 1652) (Cantica Sacra)
Talens Lyriques (r1992) Concert
(9/93) (FNAC) ① 592098

SECTION III: INSTRUMENTAL

Allemande—organ
J. Payne (r1994) Concert
(10/95) (NAXO) ① 8 553215
Allemande en tablature in A minor—organ
(pub 1668)
C. Rousset (r1992) Concert
(9/93) (FNAC) ① 592098
Allemande grave in D minor—organ (pub
1657) (Mélanges)
C. Rousset (r1992) Concert
(9/93) (FNAC) ① 592098
Allemande sur les Anches—organ
C. Rousset (r1992) Concert
(9/93) (FNAC) ① 592098
Pavane in D minor—organ
C. Rousset (r1992) Concert
(9/93) (FNAC) ① 592098

SECTION IV: VOCAL AND CHORAL

Dialogus angeli et peccatoris—2vv and
continuo (pub 1652) (Cantica Sacra)
Talens Lyriques (r1992) Concert
(9/93) (FNAC) ① 592098
Dialogus de anima—oratorio (pub 1657)
Paris Chapelle Royale Chor, P. Herreweghe Concert
(3/91) (HARM) ① HMA190 1077
Talens Lyriques (r1992) Concert
(9/93) (FNAC) ① 592098
Echo in lectulo meo—1v and continuo (pub
1681)
Talens Lyriques (r1992) Concert
(9/93) (FNAC) ① 592098
In Te Domine—dialogue: 3vv and continuo
(pub 1657) (Mélanges)
Talens Lyriques (r1992) Concert
(9/93) (FNAC) ① 592098
Litanies de la vierge—5vv and continuo (pub
1657) (Mélanges)
Talens Lyriques (r1992) Concert
(9/93) (FNAC) ① 592098
Magnificat—grand motet (pub 1684)
Paris Chapelle Royale Chor, P. Herreweghe Concert
(3/91) (HARM) ① HMA190 1077
Memorare—grand motet (pub 1684)
H. Ledroit, U. Studer, Paris Chapelle Royale Chor,
Paris Chapelle Royale Orch, P. Herreweghe Concert
(5/86) (HARM) ① HMC90 1167
Paris Chapelle Royale Chor, P. Herreweghe Concert
(3/91) (HARM) ① HMA190 1077
Super flumina Babylonis—grand motet (pub
1684)
Paris Chapelle Royale Chor, P. Herreweghe Concert
(3/91) (HARM) ① HMA190 1077

DU TERTRE, Estienne (16th Cent) France

SECTION II: CHAMBER

Première Pavane et Galliarde—consort
London Musica Antiqua, M. Uridge (r1980-83)
Concert (12/93) (SYMP) ① SYMCD1157

DUARTE, John W (b 1919) England

SECTION III: INSTRUMENTAL

English Suite—guitar, Op. 31
1. Prelude; 2. Folk Song; 3. Round Dance.
2. S. Isbin (r c1992) Concert
(7/94) (VIRG) ① VC5 45024-2

Nuages passantes—guitar, Op. 102 (1986)
S-E. Olsen Concert (9/88) (SIMA) ① PSC1031

DUBENSKY, Arcady (1890–1966) USA

SECTION IV: VOCAL AND CHORAL

The Raven—narrator and orchestra (1931)
(Wds. E. A. Poe)
B. de Loache, Philadelphia, L. Stokowski (r1932)
Concert (10/93) (STOK) ① LSCD20

DUBOIS, Théodore (François Clement) (1837–1924) France

SECTION III: INSTRUMENTAL

Grand choeur in B flat—organ
C. Herrick Concert (9/91) (HYPE) ① CDA66457
12 Pièces nouvelles—organ (pub 1886)
1. Noël; 2. Chant pastoral; 3. Toccata in G minor; 4.
Toccata in G.
1. C. Herrick Concert (3/89) (MERI) ① CDE84148
2. M. Harris Concert (12/90) (YORK) ① CD109
3. Andrew Lucas (r1994) Concert
(11/94) (NAXO) ① 8 550955

SECTION IV: VOCAL AND CHORAL

Jeunes fillettes—song
E. Clément, anon (r1910s) Concert
(8/95) (PEAR) ① GEMMCD9161

SECTION V: STAGE WORKS

Aben-Hamet—opera: prologue & 4 acts
(1884—Paris) (Lib. L. Detroyat, after
Chateaubriand)
Reine! toi qu'Hamet salue M. Imbert, orch (r1900s)
Concert (8/92) (IRCC) ① IRCC-CD802

DUFAULT, François (c1600–?1670) France

SECTION III: INSTRUMENTAL

Pavane in E minor—lute
P. Monteilhet (r1993) Concert
(3/94) (FNAC) ① 592267
Suite in C—pièces pour luth
1. Prélude (95); 2. Allemande (100); 3. Courante
(117); 4. Sarabande (137); 5. Gigue (148).
P. Monteilhet (r1993) Concert
(3/94) (FNAC) ① 592267
Suite in C—pièces pour luth
1. Pavane; 2. Courante (129); 3. Sarabande (65); 4.
Sauterelle (78).
P. Monteilhet (r1993) Concert
(3/94) (FNAC) ① 592267
Suite in C minor—pièces pour luth
1. Prélude (4); 2. Allemande (16); 3. Courante (37);
Sarabande (57); 5. Gigue (75).
P. Monteilhet (r1993) Concert
(3/94) (FNAC) ① 592267
Suite in D—pièces pour luth
1. Allemande: La Superbe (85); 2. Courante; 3.
Sarabande (146); 4. Sauterelle (160).
P. Monteilhet (r1993) Concert
(3/94) (FNAC) ① 592267
Suite in G minor—pièces pour luth
1. Pavane (161); 2. Gigue (147); 3. Courante (43); 4.
Courante (116); 5. Sarabande and doubles (66); 6.
Gigue (76).
P. Monteilhet (r1993) Concert
(3/94) (FNAC) ① 592267
Suite in G minor—pièces pour luth
P. Monteilhet (r1993) Concert
(3/94) (FNAC) ① 592267
Suite in G minor—pièces pour luth
1. Prélude; 2. Tombeau de Mr Blancrocher (22); 3.
Courante (39); 4. Sarabande (58); 5. Gigue (72).
P. Monteilhet (r1993) Concert
(3/94) (FNAC) ① 592267

DUFAY, Guillaume (c1400–1474) France

SECTION IV: VOCAL AND CHORAL

Adieu ces bons vins de Lannoys—rondeau
(3vv)
Gothic Voices, I. Barford, C. Page Concert
(12/86) (HYPE) ① CDA66144
Ave maris stella—motet
J. Garbarek, Hilliard Ens (r1993) Concert
(10/94) (ECM) ① 445 369-2
Ave regina celorum
G. Binchois Ens, D. Vellard Concert
(3/92) (VIRG) ① VC7 59043-2

New London Chmbr Ch, J. Wood *Concert*
　　　(3/93) (AMON) ① **CD-SAR56**
Balsamus et munda cera/Isti sunt agni
novelli—isorhythmic motet: 4vv (1431)
Orlando Consort (bp1994) *Concert*
　　　(11/95) (METR) ① **METCD1008**
Ecclesie militantis—isorhythmic motet
(5vv)
Orlando Consort (bp1994) *Concert*
　　　(11/95) (METR) ① **METCD1008**
Gloria ad modem tubae—4vv (doubtful)
Hilliard Ens *Concert*　　(6/91) (HYPE) ① **CDA66370**
J'atendray tant qu'il vous—rondeau (3vv)
Gothic Voices, I. Barford, C. Page *Concert*
　　　(12/86) (HYPE) ① **CDA66144**
Je me complains pitieusement—ballade
(3vv)
G. Binchois Ens, D. Vellard *Concert*
　　　(3/92) (VIRG) ① **VC7 59043-2**
Je requier a tous amoureux—rondeau: 3vv
Gothic Voices, C. Page *Concert*
　　　(11/95) (HYPE) ① **CDA66463**
Las, que feray? Ne que je
devenray?—rondeau: 3vv
Gothic Voices, C. Page *Concert*
　　　(3/92) (HYPE) ① **CDA66463**
Missa, 'Ecce ancilla Domini'
G. Binchois Ens, D. Vellard (r1992)
　　　(11/94) (VIRG) ① **VC5 45050-2**
Missa, '(L')homme armé'—4vv
Oxford Camerata, J. Summerly (r1994) *Concert*
　　　(10/95) (NAXO) ① **8 553087**
Mon cuer me fait tous dis penser—rondeau
(4vv)
Gothic Voices, I. Barford, C. Page *Concert*
　　　(12/86) (HYPE) ① **CDA66144**
Quel fronte signorille—rondeau (3vv)
Gothic Voices, C. Page *Concert*
　　　(12/88) (HYPE) ① **CDA66286**
Supremum est mortalibus
bonum—isorhythmic motet: 4vv (1433)
(written for peace treaty of Viterbo)
Oxford Camerata, J. Summerly (r1994) *Concert*
　　　(10/95) (NAXO) ① **8 553087**
Orlando Consort (bp1994) *Concert*
　　　(11/95) (METR) ① **METCD1008**
Vergene bella—strofa: 3vv (wds. Petrach)
Hilliard Ens *Concert*　　(6/91) (HYPE) ① **CDA66370**

DUFFERIN, Helen Selina,
Countess of Gifford *(1807–1867)*
Ireland

SECTION IV: VOCAL AND CHORAL

Terence's farewell to Kathleen—song
J. McCormack, E. Schneider (r1934) *Concert*
　　　(5/93) (MMOI) ① **CDMOIR418**

DUKAS, Paul (Abraham)
(1865–1935) France

SECTION I: ORCHESTRAL

L' Apprenti sorcier, '(The) Sorcerer's
Apprentice'—scherzo on a ballad by Goethe
(1897)
Dallas SO, E. Mata *Concert*
　　　(6/83) (RCA) ① **RCD14439**
Cincinnati Pops, E. Kunzel *Concert*
　　　(9/86) (TELA) ① **CD80115**
BPO, James Levine *Saint-Saëns: Symphony 3.*
　　　(8/87) (DG) ① **419 617-2GH**
Hallé, J. Loughran *Concert*
　　　(3/88) (CFP) ① **CD-CFP9011**
Montreal SO, C. Dutoit *Concert*
　　　(6/89) (DECC) ① **421 527-2DH**
NYO, C. Seaman *Stravinsky: Firebird.*
　　　(10/89) (CARL) ① **PCD921**
Philh, I. Markevitch *Concert*
　　　(1/90) (EMI) ① **CDM7 63160-2**
NYPSO, A. Toscanini (r1929) *Concert*
　　　(3/90) (PEAR) ① [3] **GEMMCDS9373**
Oslo PO, M. Jansons *Concert*
　　　(4/90) (EMI) ① **CDC7 49964-2**
Ulster Orch, Y.P. Tortelier *Concert*
　　　(2/91) (CHAN) ① **CHAN8852**
SNO, A. Gibson (r1972) *Concert*
　　　(3/91) (CHAN) ① **CHAN6503**
Philadelphia, E. Ormandy *Concert*
　　　(3/91) (SONY) ① **SBK46329**
Bergen PO, D. Kitaienko *Concert*
　　　(12/91) (VIRG) ① **VJ7 59659-2**
Philadelphia, L. Stokowski (r1937) *Concert*
　　　(2/92) (PEAR) ① **GEMMCD9488**

VPO, C. Krauss (pp1953) *Concert*
　　　(2/92) (DG) ① [12] **435 321-2GWP12**
NYPSO, A. Toscanini (r1929) *Concert*
　　　(11/92) (RCA) ① **GD60317**
NBC SO, A. Toscanini (r1950) *Concert*
　　　(11/92) (RCA) ① **GD60322**
Netherlands Rad PO, J. Fournet (r1992) *Concert*
　　　(6/93) (DENO) ① **CO-75284**
Philh, G. Cantelli (r1954) *Concert*
　　　(7/93) (TEST) ① **SBT1017**
Philadelphia, L. Stokowski (r1937) *Concert*
　　　(8/95) (BIDD) ① **WHL011**
Polyeucte—overture (1891)
BBC PO, Y. P. Tortelier (r1993) *Symphony.*
　　　(6/94) (CHAN) ① **CHAN9225**
Symphony in C (1896)
FRNO, J. Martinon *Concert*
　　　(1/90) (EMI) ① **CDM7 63160-2**
Netherlands Rad PO, J. Fournet (r1991) *Concert*
　　　(6/93) (DENO) ① **CO-75284**
BBC PO, Y. P. Tortelier (r1993) *Polyeucte.*
　　　(6/94) (CHAN) ① **CHAN9225**

SECTION II: CHAMBER

Villanelle—horn and piano (1906)
M. Thompson, P. Fowke *Concert*
　　　(9/92) (EMI) ① **CDC7 54420-2**
B. Tuckwell, D. Blumenthal *Concert*
　　　(11/92) (ETCE) ① **KTC1135**
D. Brain, G. Moore (r1952) *Concert*
　　　(12/93) (TEST) ① **SBT1022**

SECTION III: INSTRUMENTAL

La Plainte, au loin, du faune—piano (1920)
M. Fingerhut *Concert* (1/90) (CHAN) ① **CHAN8765**
Prélude élégiaque—piano (1908)
M. Fingerhut *Concert* (9/88) (CHAN) ① **CHAN8578**
M. Fingerhut *Concert* (1/90) (CHAN) ① **CHAN8765**
Sonata for Piano in E flat minor (1899-1901)
M. Fingerhut *Concert* (1/90) (CHAN) ① **CHAN8765**
Variations, interlude and final sur un thème de
Rameau—piano (?1899-1902)
M. Fingerhut *Concert* (1/90) (CHAN) ① **CHAN8765**

SECTION V: STAGE WORKS

Ariane et Barbe-bleue—opera: 3 acts, Paris
(1907) (Wds. Maeterlinck)
Cpte Katherine Ciesinski, G. Bacquier, M. Paunova,
H. Schaer, A-M. Blanzat, J. Chamonin, M. Command,
French Rad Chor, New PO, A. Jordan
　　　(9/91) (ERAT) ① [2] **2292-45663-2**
Prelude, Act 3. FRNO, J. Martinon *Concert*
　　　(1/90) (EMI) ① **CDM7 63160-2**
La Péri—ballet (1912—Paris)
1. Fanfare; 2. Poème dansé en un tableau.
Cpte Paris Op Orch, P. Dervaux *Concert*
　　　(1/90) (EMI) ① **CDM7 63160-2**
Cpte Ulster Orch, Y.P. Tortelier *Concert*
　　　(2/91) (CHAN) ① **CHAN8852**
Cpte Netherlands Rad PO, J. Fournet (r1990)
Concert　　　(6/93) (DENO) ① **CO-75284**

DUKE, Vernon *(1903–1969)*
Russia/USA

born Vladimir Dukelsky

SECTION IV: VOCAL AND CHORAL

Ages ago—song
Sarah Walker, R. Vignoles (pp1982) *Concert*
　　　(3/89) (MERI) ① **CDE84167**
Paris in New York—song (Wds. cpsr)
Sarah Walker, R. Vignoles (pp1982) *Concert*
　　　(3/89) (MERI) ① **CDE84167**

DUNHILL, Thomas Frederick
(1877–1946) England

SECTION II: CHAMBER

Cornucopia—A sheaf of Miniatures—horn
and piano, Op. 95
M. Thompson, P. Fowke *Concert*
　　　(9/92) (EMI) ① **CDC7 54420-2**
Lyric Suite for Bassoon and Piano (1940)
Daniel Smith, R. Vignoles *Concert*
　　　(9/89) (ASV) ① **CDDCA535**
Phantasy Suite, Op. 91 (pub 1941)
N. Carpenter, D. McArthur *Concert*
　　　(10/92) (HERA) ① **HAVPCD152**
E. Jóhannesson, P. Jenkins *Concert*
　　　(1/93) (CHAN) ① **CHAN9079**
Suite—flute and piano
K. Smith, P. Rhodes *Concert*
　　　(1/91) (ASV) ① **CDDCA739**

SECTION IV: VOCAL AND CHORAL

The **Cloths of Heaven—song, Op. 30/3** (Wds.
W. B. Yeats)
F. Lott, G. Johnson *Concert*
　　　(7/90) (CHAN) ① **CHAN8722**
Sarah Walker, R. Vignoles *Concert*
　　　(10/92) (CRD) ① **CRD3473**

DUNSTABLE, John *(c1390–1453)*
England

SECTION IV: VOCAL AND CHORAL

Quam pulchra es—motet: 3vv
Wellington College Chs, T. Byram-Wigfield, S.
Anderson *Concert* (10/92) (HERA) ① **HAVPCD153**
Speciosa facta es—motet: 3vv
Gothic Voices, C. Page *Concert*
　　　(11/87) (HYPE) ① **CDA66238**
Veni, Sancte spiritus—isorhythmic motet:
4vv (for Whitsunday)
Schola Gregoriana, M. Berry (r1992) *Concert*
　　　(11/93) (HERA) ① **HAVPCD161**

DUPARC, (Marie Eugène) Henri
(1848–1933) France

SECTION I: ORCHESTRAL

Aux étoiles—orchestra (1874 rev 1911)
Nancy SO, J. Kaltenbach (r1993) *Concert*
　　　(4/95) (ACCO) ① **20283-2**
Danse lente—orchestra (1911)
Nancy SO, J. Kaltenbach (r1993) *Concert*
　　　(4/95) (ACCO) ① **20283-2**
Lénore—symphonic poem (1875)
Nancy SO, J. Kaltenbach (r1993) *Concert*
　　　(4/95) (ACCO) ① **20283-2**

SECTION IV: VOCAL AND CHORAL

Au pays où se fait la guerre—song (?1869-70
orch c1876 rev ?c1911-13) (Wds. J. Gautier)
B. Hendricks, Lyon Op Orch, J.E. Gardiner *Concert*
　　　(4/89) (EMI) ① **CDC7 49689-2**
D. Borst, J. Cohen *Concert*
　　　(9/89) (REM) ① **REM311049**
Sarah Walker, R. Vignoles *Concert*
　　　(9/89) (HYPE) ① **CDA66323**
J. Van Dam, M. Pikulski (1993) *Concert*
　　　(1/94) (FORL) ① **UCD16692**
F. Pollet, Nancy SO, J. Kaltenbach (r1993) *Concert*
　　　(4/95) (ACCO) ① **20283-2**
Chanson triste—song (1868 rev 1902 orch
1912) (Wds. H. Cazalis)
J. Norman, D. Baldwin *Concert*
　　　(12/86) (PHIL) ① **416 445-2PH**
N. Melba, G. Lapierre (r1913) *Concert*
　　　(3/89) (LARR) ① **CDLRH221**
B. Hendricks, Lyon Op Orch, J.E. Gardiner *Concert*
　　　(4/89) (EMI) ① **CDC7 49689-2**
F. Le Roux, J. Cohen *Concert*
　　　(9/89) (REM) ① **REM311049**
Sarah Walker, R. Vignoles *Concert*
　　　(9/89) (HYPE) ① **CDA66323**
B. Greevy, Ulster Orch, Y.P. Tortelier *Concert*
　　　(1/90) (CHAN) ① **CHAN8735**
N. Miricioiu, D. Harper (pp1985) *Concert*
　　　(5/90) (ETCE) ① **KTC1041**
C. Panzéra, M. Panzéra-Baillot (r1931) *Concert*
　　　(3/93) (PEAR) ① **GEMMCD9919**
C. Panzéra, M. Panzéra-Baillot (r1935) *Concert*
　　　(3/93) (CDH) ① **CDH7 64254-2**
C. Panzéra, M. Panzéra-Baillot (r1935) *Concert*
　　　(3/93) (DANT) ① [2] **LYS003/4**
J. Van Dam, M. Pikulski (1993) *Concert*
　　　(1/94) (FORL) ① **UCD16692**
G. Souzay, D. Baldwin (r1971) *Concert*
　　　(9/94) (EMI) ① **CDM5 65161-2**
M. Teyte, G. Moore (r1941) *Concert*
　　　(10/94) (EMI) ① [2] **CHS5 65198-2**
A. Roocroft, LPO, F. Welser-Möst *Concert*
　　　(10/94) (EMI) ① **CDC5 55090-2**
G. Souzay, D. Baldwin (r1962) *Concert*
　　　(3/95) (PHIL) ① [4] **438 964-2PM4(2)**
F. Pollet, Nancy SO, J. Kaltenbach (r1993) *Concert*
　　　(4/95) (ACCO) ① **20283-2**
C. Maurane, L. Bienvenu (r1954) *Concert*
　　　(12/95) (PHIL) ① [2] **438 970-2PM2**
Élégie (1874 rev 1902) (Wds. T. Moore
trans ?E. MacSwiney)
F. Le Roux, J. Cohen *Concert*
　　　(9/89) (REM) ① **REM311049**
Sarah Walker, R. Vignoles *Concert*
　　　(9/89) (HYPE) ① **CDA66323**
C. Panzéra, M. Panzéra-Baillot (r1937) *Concert*
　　　(3/93) (EMI) ① **CDH7 64254-2**

B. Hendricks, Lyon Op Orch, J.E. Gardiner *Concert*
(4/89) (EMI) ① **CDC7 49689-2**
F. Le Roux, J. Cohen *Concert*
(9/89) (REM) ① **REM311049**
Sarah Walker, R. Vignoles *Concert*
(9/89) (HYPE) ① **CDA66323**
B. Greevy, Ulster Orch, Y.P. Tortelier *Concert*
(1/90) (CHAN) ① **CHAN8735**
C. Panzéra, M. Panzéra-Baillot (r1935) *Concert*
(3/93) (PEAR) ① **GEMMCD9919**
C. Panzéra, orch, P. Coppola (r c1926) *Concert*
(3/93) (PEAR) ① **GEMMCD9919**
C. Panzéra, M. Panzéra-Baillot (r1935) *Concert*
(3/93) (EMI) ① **CDH7 64254-2**
C. Panzéra, M. Panzéra-Baillot (r1935) *Concert*
(3/93) (DANT) ① [2] **LYS003/4**
D. Jones, M. Martineau (r1992) *Concert*
(6/93) (CHAN) ① **CHAN9147**
J. Van Dam, M. Pikulski (r1993) *Concert*
(1/94) (FORL) ① **UCD16692**
G. Souzay, D. Baldwin (r1971) *Concert*
(9/94) (EMI) ① **CDM5 65161-2**
G. Souzay, D. Baldwin (r1962) *Concert*
(3/95) (PHIL) ① [4] **438 964-2PM4(2)**
F. Pollet, Nancy SO, J. Kaltenbach *Concert*
(4/95) (ACCO) ① **20283-2**
C. Maurane, L. Bienvenu (r1954) *Concert*
(12/95) (PHIL) ① [2] **438 970-2PM2**

DUPHLY, Jacques *(1715–1789) France*

SECTION III: INSTRUMENTAL

Pièces de clavecin (1744-68) (some pieces in Livre 3 with vn accomp)
LIVRE 1 (1744); 1. Allemande; 2. Courante; 3. La Vanlo; 4. Rondeau; 5. La Tribolet; 6. Rondeau; 7. La Damanzy; 8. La Cazamajor; 9. Allemande; 10. La Boucon; 11. La Lazare; 12. Menuets; 13. Rondeau; 14. La Millettina; 15. Légèrement. LIVRE 2 (1748); 16. La Victoire; 17. La de Villeroy; 18. La Félix; 19. La de Vatre; 20. La Lanza; 21. Les Colombes; 22. La Damanzy; 23. La de Beuzeville; 24. La d'Héricourt; 25. Gavottes; 26. Menuets; 27. La de Redemption. La de Caze; 29. La de Brissac. LIVRE 3 (1758); 30. La Forqueray; 31. Chaconne; 32. Medée; 33. Les Grâces; 34. La de Belombre; 35. Menuets; 36. La de La Tour; 37. La de Guyon; 38. Menuets; 39. La de Chamlay; 40. La de Villeneuve. LIVRE 4 (1768); 41. La de Juigné; 42. La de Sartine; 43. La de Drummond; 44. La de Vaucanson; 45. La Porthouin; 46. La du Buq; 47. Ouverture; 48. La de May; 49. La Madin; 50. La de Casaubon; 51. La du Tailly; 52. La de Valmalette.
1, 2, 7, 9, 10, 13, 18, 20, 24, 30, 32, 33, 44, 45.
M. Raskin (r1992) (3/94) (PIER) ① **PV793021**
2, 26, 44-46. G. Leonhardt *Concert*
(5/92) (DHM) ① **RD77924**
2-4, 6, 10, 12, 15, 16, 18, 24, 30, 33, 40. M.
Meyerson (6/93) (ASV) ① **CDGAU108**
7. K. Heindel (lute-hpd) *Concert*
(2/91) (KING) ① **KCLCD2020**
27, 46. L.U. Mortensen (r1992) *Concert*
(6/93) (CHAN) ① **CHAN0531**
30. V. Black *Concert* (5/91) (COLL) ① **Coll5024-2**
30. G. Leonhardt *Concert*
(10/92) (SONY) ① **SK48080**
31, 33. J. Henry *Concert*
(10/92) (VICT) ① **VCD19013**
43. S. Preston, L. Carolan *Concert*
(3/87) (AMON) ① **CD-SAR19**

DUPONT, Gabriel Edouard Xavier *(1878–1914) France*

SECTION IV: VOCAL AND CHORAL

Mandoline—song (Wds. P Verlaine)
P. Frijsh, C. Dougherty (r1940) *Concert*
(4/95) (PEAR) ① [2] **GEMMCDS9095(1)**
La Rosita—song
R. Ponselle, orch, J. Pasternack (r1925) *Concert*
(11/94) (ROMO) ① [2] **81006-2**

DUPRÉ, Marcel *(1886–1971) France*

SECTION I: ORCHESTRAL

Symphony for Organ and Orchestra in G minor, Op. 25 (1928)
M. Murray, RPO, J. Ling (r1986) *Rheinberger: Organ Concerto 1.*
(6/87) (TELA) ① **CD80136**

SECTION III: INSTRUMENTAL

6 Antiennes pour le temps de Noël—organ (1952)
6. Lumen ad relevationem.
J. Filsell *Concert* (5/92) (GAMU) ① **GAMCD530**
Choral and Fugue—organ, Op. 57 (1957)
J. Filsell *Concert* (5/92) (GAMU) ① **GAMCD530**
79 Chorales—organ, Op. 28 (1931)
In dulci jubilo R. Noehren *Concert*
(7/91) (FACE) ① **FE8001**
In dulci jubilo R. Noehren *Concert*
(7/91) (DELO) ① **DE1028**
Cortège et Litanie—organ, Op. 19/2 (1921)
M. Murray *Concert* (3/89) (TELA) ① **CD80169**
J. Watts *Concert* (10/89) (PRIO) ① **PRCD237**
R. Noehren *Concert* (7/91) (DELO) ① **DE1028**
C. Herrick *Concert* (9/91) (HYPE) ① **CDA66457**
A. Fletcher *Concert* (11/91) (MIRA) ① **MRCD903**
R. Noehren *Concert* (7/91) (FACE) ① **FE8001**
Evocation—organ, Op. 37 (1941)
J. Filsell *Concert* (5/92) (GAMU) ① **GAMCD530**
Y. Castagnet (r1991) *Symphonie-Passion.*
(11/94) (SONY) ① **SK57485**
24 Inventions—organ, Op. 50 (1956)
13, 18, 19. D. Roth *Concert* (7/89) (MOTE) ① **CD10981**
Lamento—organ, Op. 24 (1926)
D. Roth *Concert* (7/89) (MOTE) ① **CD10981**
Offrande á la Vierge—organ, Op. 40 (1944)
1. D. Roth *Concert* (7/89) (MOTE) ① **CD10981**
Paraphrase sur le Te Deum—organ, Op. 43 (1946)
D. Roth *Concert* (7/89) (MOTE) ① **CD10981**
7 Pieces—organ, Op. 27 (1931)
1. Souvenir; 2. Thème; 3. Canon; 4. Carillon; 5. Pastoral; 6. Légende; 7. Final.
4. R. Noehren *Concert* (7/91) (FACE) ① **FE8001**
4. R. Noehren *Concert* (7/91) (DELO) ① **DE1028**
7. M. Murray *Concert* (3/89) (TELA) ① **CD80169**
7. J. Watts *Concert* (10/89) (PRIO) ① **PRCD237**
Poème symphonique—Psalm XVIII—organ, Op. 50 (1950)
J. Filsell *Concert* (5/92) (GAMU) ① **GAMCD530**
3 Preludes and Fugues—organ, Op. 7 (1912)
1. B; 2. F minor; 3. G minor.
J. Watts *Concert* (9/90) (PRIO) ① **PRCD286**
R. Noehren *Concert* (7/91) (DELO) ① **DE1028**
R. Noehren *Concert* (7/91) (FACE) ① **FE8001**
1. M. Keiser *Concert* (7/91) (GOTH) ① **G49037**
2. D. Roth *Concert* (7/89) (MOTE) ① **CD10981**
3. J.S. Whiteley *Concert* (7/87) (YORK) ① **CD101**
3. M. Dupré (r1926) *Concert*
(5/94) (EMI) ① **CDC5 55037-2**
3 Preludes and Fugues—organ, Op. 36 (1938)
1. E flat minor; 2. A flat; 3. C.
J. Watts *Concert* (8/94) (PRIO) ① **PRCD377**
2. D. Roth *Concert* (7/89) (MOTE) ① **CD10981**
2. J. Filsell *Concert* (5/92) (GAMU) ① **GAMCD530**
Scherzo—organ, Op. 16 (1918)
M-B. Dufourcet (r1992) *Concert*
(6/95) (PRIO) ① **PRCD422**
Suite bretonne—organ, Op. 21 (1923)
1. Berceuse; 2. Fileuse; 3. Les cloches de Perros-Guirec.
M. Harris *Concert* (3/92) (YORK) ① **CD112**
1. M. Dupré (r1929) *Concert*
(5/94) (EMI) ① **CDC5 55037-2**
2. R. Noehren *Concert* (7/91) (FACE) ① **FE8001**
2. R. Noehren *Concert* (7/91) (DELO) ① **DE1028**
Symphonie-Passion—organ, Op. 23 (1924)
1. Le monde dans l'attente du Sauveur; 2. Nativité; 3. Crucifixion; 4. Résurrection.
Y. Castagnet (r1991) *Evocation, Op. 37.*
(11/94) (SONY) ① **SK57485**
D. Briggs *Concert* (9/90) (PRIO) ① **PRCD284**
1. D. Roth *Concert* (7/89) (MOTE) ① **CD10981**
4. M.H. Long *Concert* (4/91) (KOCH) ① **37008-2**
Symphony No. 2 in C sharp minor—organ, Op. 26 (1929)
Intermezzo D. Roth *Concert*
(7/89) (MOTE) ① **CD10981**
Le Tombeau de Titelouze—organ, Op. 38 (1943)
EXCERPTS: 1. Creator alme siderum; 2. Jesu redemptor omnium; 3. A solis ortus cardine; 4. Audi benigne conditor; 5. Te lucis ante terminum; 6. Coelestis urbs Jerusalem; 7. Ad regias agni dapes; 8. Veni creator spiritus; 9. Vexilla regis; 10. Pange lingua; 11. Ave maris stella; 12. Iste confessor; 13. Lucis creator optime; 14. Ut queant laxis; 15. Te splendor et virtus; 16. Placare Christe servulis.
P. Wright (r1992) *Concert*
(10/94) (PRIO) ① **PRCD406**

Variations sur un vieux Noël—organ, Op. 20 (1922)
J. Watts *Concert* (10/89) (PRIO) ① **PRCD237**
M.H. Long *Concert* (4/91) (KOCH) ① **37008-2**
J. Jones *Concert* (8/91) (MOTE) ① **CD11491**
15 Versets sur les Vêpres de la Vierge—organ, Op. 18 (1919)
1. Dum esset rex; 2. Laeva eius; 3. Nigra sum; 4. Jam hiems transiit; 5. Speciosa fact es; 6. Ave Maris stella; 7. Ave Maris stella; 8. Ave Maris stella; 9. Ave Maris stella; 10. Magnificat; 11. Magnificat; 12. Magnificat; 13. Magnificat; 14. Magnificat; 15. Finale. P. Lefebvre Anon: *Divine Office: Vespers.*
(4/95) (HERA) ① **HAVPCD170**
6. D. Roth *Concert* (7/89) (MOTE) ① **CD10981**

DUPUIS, Thomas Sanders *(1733–1796) England*

SECTION III: INSTRUMENTAL

Voluntary in B flat—keyboard
J. Bate *Concert* (7/91) (UNIC) ① **DKPCD9104**

DURAND, Marie Auguste *(1830–1909) France*

SECTION III: INSTRUMENTAL

Chaconne in A minor—piano, Op. 62
E. Brown, J. Bonime (r c1924: arr Brown) *Concert*
(7/93) (APR) ① [2] **APR7016**
J. Bálint, N. Mercz (r1992: arr fl/hp) *Concert*
(12/94) (NAXO) ① **8 550741**
Waltz No. 1 in E flat—piano, Op. 83
A. Etherden *Concert*
(7/93) (HUNT) ① **HMPCD0589**
H. Bauer (r1925) *Concert* (9/93) (BIDD) ① **LHW007**
J. Bálint, N. Mercz (r1992: arr fl/hp) *Concert*
(12/94) (NAXO) ① **8 550741**

DURANTE, Francesco *(1684–1755) Italy*

SECTION I: ORCHESTRAL

8 Concerti per quartetto
1. F minor; 2. G minor; 3. E flat; 4. E minor; 5. A; 6. A; 7. C; 8. A.
2. Giardino Armonico Ens, G. Antonini (rec/dir) (r1993) *Concert* (11/94) (TELD) ① **4509-93157-2**
6, 7. Cologne Concerto (r1992) *Concert*
(1/94) (CAPR) ① **10 378**
Concerto for Harpsichord and Strings in B flat
G. Hambitzer, Cologne Concerto (r1992) *Concert*
(1/94) (CAPR) ① **10 378**

SECTION III: INSTRUMENTAL

Carillon—lute
L. Kirchhof *Concert* (11/92) (SONY) ① **SK48068**

SECTION IV: VOCAL AND CHORAL

Danza, danza, fanciulla
J. Baker, ASMF, N. Marriner *Concert*
(1/93) (PHIL) ① **434 173-2PM**
J. Carreras, ECO, V. Sutej (r1992; arr Agostinelli) *Concert* (6/93) (PHIL) ① **434 926-2PH**
Vergin, tutto amor—song (words added 19th Cent)
G. Lubin, anon (r1954) *Concert*
(5/91) (EPM) ① **150 052**

DUREY, Louis *(1888–1979) France*

SECTION II: CHAMBER

Neige—piano duet (1918: orch 1919)
P. Corre, E. Exerjean *Concert*
(5/94) (PIER) ① **PV786091**

SECTION IV: VOCAL AND CHORAL

Le Bestiaire—song (1919) (Wds. G. Apollinaire)
S. Varcoe, G. Johnson *Concert*
(6/88) (HYPE) ① **CDA66248**

DURKÓ, Zsolt *(b 1934) Hungary*

SECTION I: ORCHESTRAL

Sinfonietta—brass ensemble (1985)
PJBE *Concert* (2/88) (CHAN) ① **CHAN8490**

Petersen Qt (r1989/91) *Concert*
(2/95) (CAPR) ① **10 511**
Sine Nomine Qt (r1991) *Concert*
(5/95) (ERAT) ① **4509-91721-2**
Les citations—diptych: ob, hpd, db & perc (1985)
1. For Aldeburgh 85; 2. From Janequin to Jehan Alain.
M. Bourgue, H. Dreyfus, B. Cazauran, B. Balet (r1991) *Concert*   (5/95) (ERAT) ① **4509-91721-2**
2 figures de résonnances—two pianos (1970)
G. Joy, H. Dutilleux (r1991) *Concert*
(5/95) (ERAT) ① **4509-91721-2**
Sonata for Oboe and Piano (1947)
N. Daniel, J. Drake (r1990) *Concert*
(11/94) (VIRG) ① **CUV5 61141-2**
Sonatine—flute and piano
P. E. Davies, J. Alley *Concert*
(7/94) (EMI) ① **CDC5 55085-2**
K. Jones, C. Edwards (r1993) *Concert*
(10/94) (CONI) ① [2] **CDCF905**

SECTION III: INSTRUMENTAL
---

3 Preludes—piano
1. D'ombre et de silence (1973); 2. Sur un même accord (1977); 3. Le jeu des contraires (1988).
G. Joy (r1991) *Concert*
(5/95) (ERAT) ① **4509-91721-2**
Sonata for Piano (1947)
D. Amato Balakirev: *Piano Sonata (1900-05).*
(9/87) (ARHD) ① **DARC2**
G. Joy (r1988) *Concert*
(5/95) (ERAT) ① **4509-91721-2**
3 Strophes sur le nom de Sacher—cello
D. Geringas (r1991) *Concert*
(5/95) (ERAT) ① **4509-91721-2**
P. Demenga (r1993) *Concert*
(8/95) (ECM) ① [2] **445 234-2**

SECTION IV: VOCAL AND CHORAL
---

3 Sonnets de Jean Cassou—baritone and piano (1954)
1. Il n'y avait que des troncs déclinés; 2. J'ai rêve que je vous portais entre mes bras.
G. Cachemaille, H. Dutilleux (r1991) *Concert*
(5/95) (ERAT) ① **4509-91721-2**

SECTION V: STAGE WORKS

Le Loup—ballet (1953—Paris)
Symphonic fragments Paris Cons, G. Prêtre *Concert*   (3/92) (EMI) ① **CDM7 63945-2**

DUVERNOY, Charles (1766–1845) France

SECTION I: ORCHESTRAL

Concerto for Clarinet and Orchestra No. 3 in E flat (c1818)
R. Samuels, Collaborative Arts CO, J. Meena (r1993) *Concert*   (7/95) (KOCH) ① **37186-2**

DUVERNOY, Victor Alphonse (1842–1907) France

SECTION V: STAGE WORKS

Hellé—opera: 4 acts (1896—Paris) (Lib. C. DuLocle & C. Nuitter)
Voici le soir, la nuit s'avance R. Caron, anon (r1904) *Concert*   (8/92) (IRCC) ① **IRCC-CD802**
Voici le soir, la nuit s'avance R. Caron, anon (r1904) *Concert*   (12/94) (SYMP) ① **SYMCD1172**

DVOŘÁK, Antonín (1841–1904) Bohemia

B–Numbers from Burghauser's chronological catalogue of Dvořák's complete works

---
SECTION I: ORCHESTRAL

American Suite in A, B190 (Op. 98b) (1895)
RLPO, L. Pešek *Symphony 9.*
(12/88) (VIRG) ① **VC7 59505-2**
RPO, A. Dorati *Symphony 9.*
(8/91) (DECC) ① **430 702-2DM**
Carnival—concert overture, B169 (Op. 92) (1891)
Ulster Orch, V. Handley *Concert*
(7/86) (CHAN) ① **CHAN8453**
LPO, E. Bátiz *Symphony 8.*
(5/88) (ASV) ① **CDQS6006**
SNO, N. Järvi *Concert*
(5/88) (CHAN) ① **CHAN8575**
BRSO, R. Kubelík *Concert*
(10/88) (DG) ① [6] **423 120-2GX6**

Czech PO, V. Neumann *Concert*
(5/89) (PHIL) ① **422 387-2PH**
NYPO, Z. Mehta *Concert*
(11/89) (SONY) ① **SK44923**
RLPO, L. Pešek *Concert*
(1/90) (VIRG) ① **VC7 59257-2**
Hungarian St. Orch, T. Pál *Concert*
(3/91) (LASE) ① **15 517**
Los Angeles PO, A. Previn *Symphony 9.*
(4/91) (TELA) ① **CD80238**
Czech PO, B. Gregor *Concert*
(10/91) (SUPR) ① [2] **11 0526-2**
BRSO, R. Kubelík *Concert*
(11/91) (DG) ① [2] **435 074-2GGA2**
Czech PO, V. Neumann *Concert*
(12/91) (SUPR) ① **11 0714-2**
Czech PO, J. Bělohlávek *Symphony 9.*
(2/92) (SUPR) ① **11 0960-2**
LSO, I. Kertész *Concert*
(4/92) (DECC) ① [6] **430 046-2DC6**
Czech PO, V. Talich (r1935) *Slavonic Dances.*
(6/92) (MUSI) ① **MACD-658**
Danish RSO, F. Busch (bp1933) *Concert*
(8/92) (DANA) ① **DACOCD303**
RPO, J. Farrer *Concert*   (9/92) (ASV) ① **CDDCA794**
LSO, A. Coates (r1929) *Concert*
(4/93) (KOCH) ① [2] **37704-2**
NYPO, L. Bernstein *Concert*
(5/93) (SONY) ① **SMK47547**
Czech PO, G. Albrecht (pp1992) *Concert*
(6/93) (SUPR) ① **11 1830-2**
BBC PO, S. Gunzenhauser (r1992) *Concert*
(10/93) (NAXO) ① **8 550600**
RPO, P. Järvi (r1993) *Concert*
(3/95) (TRIN) ① **TRP010**
Chicago SO, F. Reiner (r1956) *Concert*
(8/95) (RCA) ① **09026 62587-2**
Concerto for Cello and Orchestra in B minor, B191 (Op. 104) (1894-95)
1. Allegro; 2. Adagio ma non troppo; 3. Allegro moderato.
F. Helmerson, Gothenburg SO, N. Järvi *Silent woods.*
(2/86) (BIS) ① **BIS-CD245**
M. Rostropovich, Boston SO, S. Ozawa *Tchaikovsky: Rococo Variations.*
(12/86) (ERAT) ① **2292-45252-2**
Y-Y. Ma, BPO, L. Maazel *Concert*
(1/87) (SONY) ① **SK42206**
L. Harrell, LSO, James Levine *Schubert: Arpeggione Sonata, D821.*   (11/87) (RCA) ① **GD86531**
J. Du Pré, Chicago SO, D. Barenboim (r1970) *Haydn: Cello Concerto in C.* (2/88) (EMI) ① **CDC7 47614-2**
P. Fournier, BPO, G. Szell *Elgar: Cello Concerto.*
(11/88) (DG) ① **423 881-2GGA**
M. Rostropovich, LPO, C.M. Giulini *Saint-Saëns: Cello Concerto 1.*   (2/89) (EMI) ① **CDC7 49306-2**
J. Lloyd Webber, Czech PO, V. Neumann *Concert*
(5/89) (PHIL) ① **422 387-2PH**
R. Wallfisch, LSO, C. Mackerras *Dohnányi: Konzertstück, Op.12.* (5/89) (CHAN) ① **CHAN8662**
P. Casals, Czech PO, G. Szell (r1937) *Concert*
(5/89) (PEAR) ① **GEMMCD9349**
M. Maisky, Israel PO, L. Bernstein (pp1988) *Bloch: Schelomo.*   (1/90) (DG) ① **427 347-2GH**
P. Fournier, BPO, G. Szell *Concert*
(5/90) (DG) ① **429 155-2GR**
P. Casals, Czech PO, G. Szell (r1937) *Concert*
(8/90) (EMI) ① **CDH7 63498-2**
J. Starker, LSO, A. Dorati *Concert*
(3/91) (MERC) ① **432 001-2MM**
L. Rose, Philadelphia, E. Ormandy *Concert*
(3/91) (SONY) ① **SBK46337**
N. Gutman, Philadelphia, W. Sawallisch *Symphonic Variations.* (3/92) (EMI) ① **CDC7 54320-2**
L. Harrell, Philh, Vladimir Ashkenazy *Schumann: Cello Concerto.* (8/92) (DECC) ① **430 743-2DM**
M. Kliegel, RPO, M. Halász *Elgar: Cello Concerto.*
(9/92) (NAXO) ① **8 550503**
G. Piatigorsky, Boston SO, C. Munch (r1960) *Walton: Cello Concerto.*   (4/93) (RCA) ① **09026 61498-2**
P. Fournier, Philh, R. Kubelík (r1948) *Concert*
(7/93) (TEST) ① **SBT1016**
H. Schiff, VPO, A. Previn (r1992) *Concert*
(9/93) (PHIL) ① **434 914-2PH**
G. Cassadó, Vienna Pro Musica Orch, J. Perlea (r1950s) *Concert* (11/93) (VOX) ① [2] **CDX2 5502**
T. Mørk, Oslo PO, M. Jansons (r1992) *Tchaikovsky: Rococo Variations.*   (1/94) (VIRG) ① **VC7 59325-2**
M. Rostropovich, Czech PO, V. Talich (r1952) *Piano Concerto.* (3/94) (SUPR) ① **11 1901-2**
J. Du Pré, Chicago SO, D. Barenboim (r1970) *Concert*   (8/94) (EMI) ① [6] **CZS5 68132-2**
N. Gutman, Philadelphia, W. Sawallisch (r1991) *Concert*   (10/94) (EMI) ① [2] **CMS7 64812-2**

M. Rostropovich, BPO, H. von Karajan (r1968) *Tchaikovsky: Rococo Variations.*
(5/95) (DG) ① **447 413-2GOR**
A. Noras, Finnish RSO, S. Oramo (r1994) *Schumann: Cello Concerto.*
(10/95) (FINL) ① **4509-98886-2**
J. Du Pré, Chicago SO, D. Barenboim (r1970) *Elgar: Cello Concerto.* (11/95) (EMI) ① **CDC5 55527-2**
J. Starker, Philh, W. Susskind (r1956) *Concert*
(12/95) (EMI) ① [6] **CZS5 68485-2**
1. G. Piatigorsky, Danish RSO, N. Malko (bp1932) *Concert*   (8/92) (DANA) ① **DACOCD303**
Concerto for Piano and Orchestra in G minor, B63 (Op. 33) (1876)
S. Richter, Bavarian St Orch, C. Kleiber *Schubert: Fantasy, D760.*   (11/87) (EMI) ① **CDC7 47967-2**
J. Frantz, N German PO, H. Müller-Brühl
(10/88) (SCHW) ① **316003**
I. Moravec, Czech PO, J. Bělohlávek (r1982) *Symphony 7.*   (8/93) (SUPR) ① **11 0675-2**
F. Maxián, Czech PO, V. Talich (r1951) *Cello Concerto.* (3/94) (SUPR) ① **11 1901-2**
J. Jandó, Polish Nat RSO, A. Wit (r1993) *Water Goblin.*   (12/94) (NAXO) ① **8 550896**
Concerto for Violin and Orchestra in A minor, B108 (Op. 53) (1880 rev 1882)
S. Mintz, BPO, James Levine *Sibelius: Violin Concerto.*   (8/87) (DG) ① **419 618-2GH**
I. Perlman, LPO, D. Barenboim (r1974) *Romance, Op. 11.*   (1/88) (EMI) ① **CDC7 47168-2**
S. Accardo, Concertgebouw, Colin Davis (r1979) *Sibelius: Violin Concerto.*
(10/88) (PHIL) ① **420 895-2PSL**
K-W. Chung, Philadelphia, R. Muti (r1988) *Romance, Op.11.*   (11/89) (EMI) ① **CDC7 49858-2**
Midori, NYPO, Z. Mehta *Concert*
(11/89) (SONY) ① **SK44923**
J. Suk, Czech PO, K. Ančerl *Suk: Fantasy.*
(12/89) (SUPR) ① **11 0601-2**
J. Suk, Czech PO, V. Neumann *Suk: Fantasy.*
(5/90) (SUPR) ① **11 0283-2**
T. Little, RLPO, V. Handley (r1989) *Bruch: Violin Concerto 1.*   (7/90) (CFP) ① **CD-CFP4566**
I. Stern, Philadelphia, E. Ormandy *Cello Concerto.*
(3/91) (SONY) ① **SBK46337**
U. Ughi, Philh, L. Slatkin *Concert*
(7/91) (RCA) ① **RD60431**
E. Peinemann, Czech PO, P. Maag *Concert*
(12/91) (DG) ① [2] **413 844-2GW2**
T. Zehetmair, Philh, E. Inbal (r1989) *Concert*
(7/93) (TELD) ① **4509-91444-2**
F.P. Zimmermann, LPO, F. Welser-Möst (r1993) *Glazunov: Violin Concerto.*
(3/94) (EMI) ① **CDC7 54872-2**
N. Milstein, Pittsburgh SO, W. Steinberg (r1957) *Concert*   (5/94) (EMI) ① [6] **ZDMF7 64830-2**
M. Neuss, Concertgebouw, W. Mengelberg (pp1943) *Concert*   (7/94) (MUSI) ① [4] **MACD-780**
C. Tetzlaff, Czech PO, L. Pešek (r1992) *Lalo: Symphonie Espagnole.*
(7/94) (VIRG) ① **VC5 45022 2**
I. Kaler, Polish Nat RSO, C. Kolchinsky (r1994) *Concert*   (4/95) (NAXO) ① **8 550758**
I. Perlman, LPO, D. Barenboim (r1974) *Concert*
(6/95) (EMI) ① [20] **CZS4 83177-2(1)**
Czech Suite, B93 (Op. 39) (1879)
Czech PO, L. Pešek *Symphony 5.*
(7/90) (VIRG) ① **VC7 59522-2**
N German RSO, J.E. Gardiner (r1992) *Concert*
(6/93) (DG) ① **437 506-2GH**
Polish Nat RSO, A. Wit (r1994) *Concert*
(8/95) (NAXO) ① **8 553005**
Fanfares—brass ensemble, B167 (1891)
London Gabrieli Brass Ens, C. Larkin *Concert*
(4/92) (HYPE) ① **CDA66470**
Festival March—orchestra, B88 (Op. 54) (1879)
Czech PO, V. Neumann *Concert*
(9/90) (ORFE) ① **C180891A**
Polish Nat RSO, A. Wit (r1994) *Concert*
(8/95) (NAXO) ① **8 553005**
The Golden Spinning-Wheel—symphonic poem, B197 (Op. 109) (1896)
SNO, N. Järvi *Symphony 7.*
(3/87) (CHAN) ① **CHAN8501**
Slovak PO, Z. Košler *Concert*
(11/89) (OPUS) ① [2] **9150 1996/7**
SNO, N. Järvi *Concert*
(4/90) (CHAN) ① [2] **CHAN8798/9**
Czech PO, B. Gregor *Concert*
(10/91) (SUPR) ① [2] **11 0526-2**
BRSO, R. Kubelík *Concert*
(11/91) (DG) ① [2] **435 074-2GGA2**
Czech PO, J. Bělohlávek *Symphony 8.*
(11/92) (CHAN) ① **CHAN9048**

LPO, A. Rahbari (r1993) *Symphony 8*.
(3/94) (DINT) ① **DICD920112**
Polish Nat RSO, S. Gunzenhauser (r1992) *Concert*
(5/94) (NAXO) ① **8 550598**
Heroic Song—symphonic poem, B199 (Op. 111) (1897)
SNO, N. Järvi *Symphony 1*.
(4/89) (CHAN) ① **CHAN8597**
Slovak PO, Z. Košler *Concert*
(11/89) (OPUS) ① [2] **9150 1996/7**
SNO, N. Järvi *Concert*
(4/90) (CHAN) ① [2] **CHAN8798/9**
Czech PO, B. Gregor *Concert*
(12/91) (SUPR) ① [2] **11 0378-2**
Polish Nat RSO, A. Wit (r1993) *Concert*
(8/95) (NAXO) ① **8 553005**
Hussite—concert overture, B132 (Op. 67) (1883)
BRSO, R. Kubelík *Concert*
(11/91) (DG) ① [2] **435 074-2GGA2**
RLPO, L. Pešek (r1990) *Concert*
(11/94) (VIRG) ① **VC7 59285-2**
Polish Nat RSO, A. Wit (r1994) *Concert*
(8/95) (NAXO) ① **8 553005**
In Nature's Realm—concert overture, B168 (Op. 91) (1891)
Ulster Orch, V. Handley *Concert*
(7/86) (CHAN) ① **CHAN8453**
Czech PO, L. Pešek *Symphony 6*.
(9/89) (VIRG) ① **VC7 59536-2**
Czech PO, B. Gregor *Concert*
(10/91) (SUPR) ① [2] **11 0526-2**
BRSO, R. Kubelík *Concert*
(11/91) (DG) ① [2] **435 074-2GGA2**
Czech PO, V. Neumann *Concert*
(12/91) (SUPR) ① **11 0714-2**
LSO, I. Kertész *Concert*
(4/92) (DECC) ① [6] **430 046-2DC6**
RPO, J. Farrer *Concert* (9/92) (ASV) ① **CDDCA794**
Czech PO, G. Albrecht (pp1992) *Concert*
(6/93) (SUPR) ① **11 1830-2**
BBC PO, S. Gunzenhauser (r1992) *Concert*
(10/93) (NAXO) ① **8 550600**
10 Legends—orchestra, B122 (Op. 59) (1881)
(arr cpsr from pf works, B117)
1. D minor; 2. G; 3. G minor; 4. C; 5. A flat; 6. C sharp minor; 7. A; 8. F; 9. D; 10. B flat minor.
Bamberg SO, N. Järvi *Janáček: Sinfonietta*.
(8/89) (BIS) ① **BIS-CD436**
ECO, R. Kubelík *Stabat Mater*.
(9/90) (DG) ① [2] **423 919-2GGA2**
ECO, C. Mackerras (r1994) *Concert*
(3/95) (EMIN) ① **CD-EMX2232**
1-5. Czech RSO, S. Gunzenhauser *Symphony 1*.
(6/92) (NAXO) ① **8 550266**
3. LPO, T. Beecham (r1935) *Concert*
(6/94) (DUTT) ① **CDLX7003**
4, 6, 7. Hallé, J. Barbirolli (r1958) *Concert*
(6/92) (EMI) ① **CDM7 64193-2**
6-10. Czech RSO, S. Gunzenhauser *Symphony 2*.
(6/92) (NAXO) ① **8 550267**
My Home—overture, B125a (Op. 62) (1882)
(arr cpsr from Josef Kajetán incid music)
SNO, N. Järvi *Symphony 9*.
(5/87) (CHAN) ① **CHAN8510**
Los Angeles PO, A. Previn (r1968) *Symphony 7*.
(4/90) (TELA) ① **CD80173**
SNO, N. Järvi *Concert*
(4/90) (CHAN) ① [2] **CHAN8798/9**
BRSO, R. Kubelík *Concert*
(11/91) (DG) ① [2] **435 074-2GGA2**
Czech PO, B. Gregor *Concert*
(12/91) (SUPR) ① [2] **11 0378-2**
LSO, I. Kertész *Concert*
(4/92) (DECC) ① [6] **430 046-2DC6**
BBC PO, S. Gunzenhauser (r1992) *Concert*
(10/93) (NAXO) ① **8 550600**
Nocturne in B—string orchestra, B47 (Op. 40) (?1875)
LPO, V. Handley *Symphony 8*.
(1/85) (CHAN) ① **CHAN8323**
Los Angeles PO, A. Previn *Concert*
(1/90) (TELA) ① **CD80206**
Serenata of London, B. Wilde (r1994) *Concert*
(2/95) (CARL) ① **PCD1108**
ECO, C. Mackerras (r1994) *Concert*
(3/95) (EMIN) ① **CD-EMX2232**
The Noon Witch—symphonic poem, B196 (Op. 108) (1896)
SNO, N. Järvi *Symphony 6*.
(11/87) (CHAN) ① **CHAN8530**
Slovak PO, Z. Košler *Concert*
(11/89) (OPUS) ① [2] **9150 1996/7**
SNO, N. Järvi *Concert*
(4/90) (CHAN) ① [2] **CHAN8798/9**

Czech PO, B. Gregor *Concert*
(10/91) (SUPR) ① [2] **11 0526-2**
BRSO, R. Kubelík *Concert*
(11/91) (DG) ① [2] **435 074-2GGA2**
Polish Nat RSO, S. Gunzenhauser (r1992) *Concert*
(5/94) (NAXO) ① **8 550598**
BPO, C. Abbado (pp1993) *Symphony 8*.
(2/95) (SONY) ① **SK64303**
Othello—concert overture, B174 (Op. 93) (1891-92)
Ulster Orch, V. Handley *Concert*
(7/86) (CHAN) ① **CHAN8453**
Oslo PO, M. Jansons *Concert*
(7/90) (EMI) ① **CDC7 49995-2**
Czech PO, B. Gregor *Concert*
(10/91) (SUPR) ① [2] **11 0526-2**
BRSO, R. Kubelík *Concert*
(11/91) (DG) ① [2] **435 074-2GGA2**
Czech PO, L. Pešek *Symphony 4*.
(3/92) (VIRG) ① **VC7 59016-2**
RPO, J. Farrer *Concert* (9/92) (ASV) ① **CDDCA794**
Czech PO, G. Albrecht (pp1992) *Concert*
(6/93) (SUPR) ① **11 1830-2**
BBC PO, S. Gunzenhauser (r1992) *Concert*
(10/93) (NAXO) ① **8 550600**
Polonaise in E flat—orchestra, B100 (1879)
Czech PO, V. Neumann *Concert*
(9/90) (ORFE) ① **C180891A**
Romance in F minor—violin and orchestra, B39 (Op. 11) (1873-79) (arr cpsr from String Qt No 5)
St. Paul CO, P.Zukerman (vn/dir) *Concert*
(11/87) (PHIL) ① **420 168-2PH**
I. Perlman, LPO, D. Barenboim (r1974) *Violin Concerto*.
(1/88) (EMI) ① **CDC7 47168-2**
K-W. Chung, Philadelphia, R. Muti (r1988) *Violin Concerto*.
(11/89) (EMI) ① **CDC7 49858-2**
Midori, NYPO, Z. Mehta *Concert*
(11/89) (SONY) ① **SK44923**
M. Szenthelyi, Hungarian St. Orch, T. Pál *Concert*
(3/91) (LASE) ① **15 517**
U. Ughi, Philh, L. Slatkin *Concert*
(7/91) (RCA) ① **RD60431**
T. Zehetmair, Philh, E. Inbal (1989) *Concert*
(7/93) (TELD) ① **4509-91444-2**
A.A. Meyers, Philh, A. Litton (1993) *Concert*
(2/94) (RCA) ① **09026 61700-2**
M. Stewart, RLPO, L. Pešek (r1990) *Concert*
(11/94) (VIRG) ① **VC7 59285-2**
S. Gonley, ECO, C. Mackerras (r1994) *Concert*
(3/95) (EMIN) ① **CD-EMX2232**
I. Kaler, Polish Nat RSO, C. Kolchinsky (r1994) *Concert*
(4/95) (NAXO) ① **8 550758**
Rondo in G minor—cello and orchestra, B181 (Op. 94) (1893)
Y.-Y. Ma, BPO, L. Maazel *Concert*
(1/87) (SONY) ① **SK42206**
G. Cassadó, Vienna Pro Musica Orch, J. Perlea (r1950s) *Concert* (11/93) (VOX) ① [2] **CDX2 5502**
Scherzo capriccioso—orchestra, B131 (Op. 66) (1883)
Ulster Orch, V. Handley *Concert*
(7/86) (CHAN) ① **CHAN8453**
BRSO, R. Kubelík *Concert*
(10/88) (DG) ① [6] **423 120-2GX6**
Philadelphia, W. Sawallisch *Symphony 9*.
(2/89) (EMI) ① **CDC7 49114-2**
BRSO, R. Kubelík *Symphony 9*.
(10/89) (DG) ① **427 202-2GR**
Los Angeles PO, A. Previn *Concert*
(1/90) (TELA) ① **CD80206**
RLPO, L. Pešek *Concert*
(1/90) (VIRG) ① **VC7 59257-2**
Oslo PO, M. Jansons *Concert*
(7/90) (EMI) ① **CDC7 49995-2**
Czech PO, B. Gregor *Concert*
(12/91) (SUPR) ① [2] **11 0378-2**
LSO, I. Kertész *Concert*
(4/92) (DECC) ① [6] **430 046-2DC6**
Hallé, J. Barbirolli (r1957) *Concert*
(6/92) (EMI) ① **CDM7 64193-2**
RPO, J. Farrer *Concert* (9/92) (ASV) ① **CDDCA794**
RPO, P. Järvi (r1993) *Concert*
(3/95) (TRIN) ① **TRP010**
Serenade in D minor—2 ob, 2 cl, 2 bn, dbn, 3 hn, vc, db, B77 (Op. 44) (1878)
ASMF, N. Marriner *Serenade, Op. 22*.
(4/83) (PHIL) ① **400 020-2PH**
Munich Wind Academy, A. Brezina *Gounod: Petite symphonie*.
(5/85) (ORFE) ① **C051831A**
COE, A. Schneider *Serenade, Op. 22*.
(11/86) (ASV) ① **CDCOE801**
Nash Ens *Concert* (7/89) (CRD) ① **CRD3410**
Bonn Beethovenhalle Orch, D.R. Davies *Concert*
(4/90) (SCHW) ① **311116**

NY Harmonie Ens, S. Richman (pp1990) *Concert*
(8/92) (MUSI) ① **MACD-691**
Lincoln Center Chbr Music Soc, D. Shifrin (r1992) *String Quintet, Op. 77*. (8/95) (DELO) ① **DE3152**
Serenade in E—string orchestra, B52 (Op. 22) (1875)
BPO, H. von Karajan *Tchaikovsky: Serenade, Op. 48*.
(3/83) (DG) ① **400 038-2GH**
ASMF, N. Marriner *Serenade, Op. 44*.
(4/83) (PHIL) ① **400 020-2PH**
COE, A. Schneider *Serenade, Op. 44*.
(11/86) (ASV) ① **CDCOE801**
Berne Camerata, T. Füri (vn/dir) *String Sextet*.
(9/87) (NOVA) ① **150 011-2**
Slovak CO, B. Warchal *Suk: Serenade, Op.6*.
(4/90) (OPUS) ① **9150 1501**
Orpheus CO *Concert*
(5/90) (DG) ① **429 488-2GDC**
Berlin CO, P. Wohlert *Slavonic Dances*.
(10/90) (LASE) ① **15 605**
RPO, C.P. Flor *Symphony 8*.
(4/91) (RCA) ① **RD60234**
London CO, C. Warren-Green (r1989) *Suk: Serenade, Op. 6*. (11/94) (VIRG) ① **CUV5 61144-2**
BRSO, Colin Davis *Tchaikovsky: Serenade, Op. 48*.
(12/94) (PHIL) ① **442 402-2PH**
Prague CO, B. Novotný (r1994) *Concert*
(7/95) (DENO) ① **CO-78919**
Silent woods—cello and orchestra, B182 (Op. 68/5) (1893) (arr cpsr from B173)
F. Helmerson, Gothenburg SO, N. Järvi *Cello Concerto*. (2/86) (BIS) ① **BIS-CD245**
Y.-Y. Ma, BPO, L. Maazel *Concert*
(1/87) (SONY) ① **SK42206**
M. Maisky, Paris Orch, S. Bychkov *Concert*
(10/92) (DG) ① **435 781-2GH**
G. Cassadó, Vienna Pro Musica Orch, J. Perlea (r1950s) *Concert* (11/93) (VOX) ① [2] **CDX2 5502**
J. Du Pré, Chicago SO, D. Barenboim (r1970) *Concert*
(8/94) (EMI) ① [6] **CZS5 68132-2**
T. Walden, RLPO, L. Pešek (r1990) *Concert*
(11/94) (VIRG) ① **VC7 59285-2**
Slavonic Dances—orchestra, B83 & B147 (Opp. 46 & 72) (1878 & 1886)
B83: (Op. 46): 1. C; 2. E minor; 3. A flat; 4. F; 5. A; 6. D; 7. C minor; 8. G minor. B147 (Op. 72): 9. B; 10. E minor; 11. F; 12. D flat; 13. B flat minor; 14. B flat; 15. C; 16. A flat.
SNO, N. Järvi (5/86) (CHAN) ① **CHAN8406**
BPO, L. Maazel (3/89) (EMI) ① **CDC7 49547-2**
Rhineland-Pfalz State PO, L. Segerstam (r1988)
(7/89) (BIS) ① **BIS-CD425**
Cleveland Orch, C. von Dohnányi
(12/90) (DECC) ① **430 171-2DH**
RPO, J. Farrer (3/91) (ASV) ① **CDDCA730**
RPO, A. Dorati (8/91) (DECC) ① **430 735-2DM**
Czech PO, V. Talich (r1935) *Carnival*.
(6/92) (MUSI) ① **MACD-658**
Cleveland Orch, G. Szell (r1963-65)
(11/92) (SONY) ① **SBK48161**
Czech PO, V. Talich (r1950)
(6/94) (SUPR) ① **11 1897-2**
VPO, A. Previn (r1993)
(10/94) (PHIL) ① **442 125-2PH**
Berlin RSO, K. Ančerl (r1960)
(11/95) (TAHR) ① **TAH118**
Russian Nat Orch, M. Pletnev (r1994)
(11/95) (DG) ① **447 056-2GH**
1. NYPO, B. Walter (r1941) *Concert*
(8/95) (SONY) ① **SMK64466**
1, 3. NYPO, L. Bernstein *Concert*
(5/93) (SONY) ① **SMK47547**
1, 3, 7, 10, 16. BPO, H. von Karajan *Symphony 9*.
(9/92) (DG) ① **435 590-2GGA**
1, 3, 8. Israel PO, L. Bernstein (pp1988) *Symphony 9*.
(10/89) (DG) ① **427 346-2GH**
1, 5, 6, 8, 9, 10. LSO, W. Boskovsky (r1974) *Brahms: Hungarian Dances*. (5/94) (BELA) ① **450 061-2**
1, 8. Black Dyke Mills Band, J. Watson (r1994) (arr Hanmer) *Concert* (3/94) (POLY) ① **QPRL053D**
1, 8, 10, 15. Slovak Radio New PO, A. Rahbari (r1993) *Symphony 7*. (3/94) (DINT) ① **DICD920109**
2. Y. Menuhin, M. Gazelle (arr Kreisler) (r1936) *Concert* (9/91) (TEST) ① **SBT1003**
3. BPO, W. Furtwängler (r1950) *Concert*
(3/95) (TAHR) ① [4] **FURT1008/11**
6, 8, 10. NYPO, K. Masur *Symphony 9*.
(6/92) (TELD) ① **9031-73244-2**
9-16. Berlin CO, P. Wohlert *Serenade, Op. 22*.
(10/90) (LASE) ① **15 605**
10. L. Mordkovitch, M. Gusak-Grin (arr Kreisler) *Concert* (11/90) (CHAN) ① **CHAN8748**
13. NY Harmonie Ens, S. Richman (arr Clements: pp1990) *Concert* (8/92) (MUSI) ① **MACD-691**

16. J. Heifetz, S. Chotzinoff (r1922) *Concert*
    (11/94) (RCA) ① [65] 09026 61778-2(01)
Sonata for Violin and Piano in F, B106 (Op. 57) (1880)
J. Suk, A. Holeček *Concert*
    (5/90) (SUPR) ① 11 0703-2
Sonatina for Violin and Piano in G, B183 (Op. 100) (1893)
I. Perlman, S. Sanders *Concert*
    (10/86) (EMI) ① CDC7 47399-2
J. Suk, A. Holeček *Concert*
    (5/90) (SUPR) ① 11 0703-2
V. Vaidman, E. Krasovsky *Concert*
    (6/90) (CARL) ① PWK1137
Movt 2. F. Kreisler, C. Lamson (arr Kreisler: r1928)
Concert (1/90) (PEAR) ① GEMMCD9324
Movt 2. F. Kreisler, C. Lamson (r1928: arr Kreisler)
Concert (12/93) (BIDD) ① LAB080
String Quartet Movement in F, B120 (1881)
Prague Qt *Concert*
    (8/90) (DG) ① [9] 429 193-2GCM9
Chilingirian Qt *Concert*
    (4/92) (CHAN) ① CHAN8874
String Quartet No. 1 in A, B8 (Op. 2) (1862)
Prague Qt *Concert*
    (8/90) (DG) ① [9] 429 193-2GCM9
String Quartet No. 2 in B flat, B17 (?1869-70)
Prague Qt *Concert*
    (8/90) (DG) ① [9] 429 193-2GCM9
String Quartet No. 3 in D, B18 (?1869-70)
Prague Qt *Concert*
    (8/90) (DG) ① [9] 429 193-2GCM9
String Quartet No. 4 in E minor, B19 (1870)
Prague Qt *Concert*
    (8/90) (DG) ① [9] 429 193-2GCM9
String Quartet No. 5 in F minor, B37 (Op. 9) (1873)
Prague Qt *Concert*
    (8/90) (DG) ① [9] 429 193-2GCM9
String Quartet No. 6 in A minor, B40 (Op. 12) (1873)
Prague Qt *Concert*
    (8/90) (DG) ① [9] 429 193-2GCM9
String Quartet No. 7 in A minor, B45 (Op. 16) (1874)
Prague Qt *Concert*
    (8/90) (DG) ① [9] 429 193-2GCM9
Chilingirian Qt *Cypresses.*
    (10/91) (CHAN) ① CHAN8826
String Quartet No. 8 in E, B57 (Op. 80) (1876)
Chilingirian Qt *String Quartet 9.*
    (5/90) (CHAN) ① CHAN8755
Prague Qt *Concert*
    (8/90) (DG) ① [9] 429 193-2GCM9
String Quartet No. 9 in D minor, B75 (Op. 34) (1877)
Chilingirian Qt *String Quartet 8.*
    (5/90) (CHAN) ① CHAN8755
Prague Qt *Concert*
    (8/90) (DG) ① [9] 429 193-2GCM9
Vermeer Qt (pp1993) *Messiaen: Quatuor.*
    (4/95) (NAIM) ① NAIMCD008
String Quartet No. 10 in E flat, B92 (Op. 51) (1878-79)
Kocian Qt (r1979) *String Quartet 14.*
    (6/85) (DENO) ① C37-7235
Prague Qt *Concert*
    (8/90) (DG) ① [9] 429 193-2GCM9
Chilingirian Qt *String Quartet 11.*
    (11/90) (CHAN) ① CHAN8837
Vanbrugh Qt (r1993) *Concert*
    (4/94) (COLL) ① Coll1381-2
Coull Qt (r1993) *Concert*
    (10/94) (HYPE) ① CDA66679
String Quartet No. 11 in C, B121 (Op. 61) (1881)
Talich Qt *String Quartet 12.*
    (7/87) (CALL) ① CAL9617
Prague Qt *Concert*
    (8/90) (DG) ① [9] 429 193-2GCM9
Chilingirian Qt *String Quartet 10.*
    (11/90) (CHAN) ① CHAN8837
String Quartet No. 12 in F, 'American', B179 (Op. 96) (1893)
Hagen Qt *Concert* (5/87) (DG) ① 419 601-2GH
Talich Qt *String Quartet 11.*
    (7/87) (CALL) ① CAL9617
Delmé Qt *Brahms: Clarinet Quintet.*
    (3/88) (CARL) ① PCD883
Quartetto Italiano (r1968) *Concert*
    (3/89) (PHIL) ① 420 876-2PSL
Prague Qt *Concert*
    (8/90) (DG) ① [9] 429 193-2GCM9

Moyzes Qt *String Quartet 14.*
    (10/90) (NAXO) ① 8 550251
Chilingirian Qt (r1990) *String Quartet 14.*
    (11/91) (CHAN) ① CHAN8919
Orlando Qt *Smetana: String Quartet 1.*
    (3/92) (OTTA) ① OTRC69028
Alban Berg Qt (pp1989) *Smetana: String Quartet 1.*
    (3/92) (EMI) ① CDC7 54215-2
Cleveland Qt *String Quartet 14.*
    (3/92) (TELA) ① CD80283
Medici Qt (r1992) *Schubert: String Quartet, D810.*
    (10/93) (MEDI) ① MQCD9001
Duke Qt (r1993) *Concert*
    (1/94) (COLL) ① Coll1386-2
Travníček Qt (r1994) *String Quartet 13.*
    (9/95) (DINT) ① DICD920248
String Quartet No. 13 in G, B192 (Op. 106) (1895)
Prague Qt *Concert*
    (8/90) (DG) ① [9] 429 193-2GCM9
Chilingirian Qt *Concert*
    (4/92) (CHAN) ① CHAN8874
Alban Berg Qt (r1975) *Concert*
    (2/95) (TELD) ① 4509-95503-2
Travníček Qt (r1994) *String Quartet 12.*
    (9/95) (DINT) ① DICD920248
String Quartet No. 14 in A flat, B193 (Op. 105) (1895)
Kocian Qt (r1979) *String Quartet 10.*
    (6/85) (DENO) ① C37-7235
Prague Qt *Concert*
    (8/90) (DG) ① [9] 429 193-2GCM9
Moyzes Qt *String Quartet 12.*
    (10/90) (NAXO) ① 8 550251
Chilingirian Qt (r1990) *String Quartet 12.*
    (11/91) (CHAN) ① CHAN8919
Cleveland Qt *String Quartet 12.*
    (3/92) (TELA) ① CD80283
String Quintet in E flat, 'American'—2 violins, 2 violas and cello, B180 (Op. 97) (1893)
Raphael Ens (r1988) *String Sextet.*
    (8/89) (HYPE) ① CDA66308
Chilingirian Qt, S. Rowland-Jones *Concert*
    (11/92) (CHAN) ① CHAN9046
J. Suk, Smetana Qt (r1986) *String Sextet.*
    (9/93) (SUPR) ① 11 1469-2
Lindsay Qt, P. Ireland *Concert*
    (9/93) (ASV) ① CDDCA806
Vienna Stg Sextet (1991) *String Sextet.*
    (10/94) (EMI) ① CDC7 54543-2
String Quintet in G—2 violins, viola, cello and double-bass, B49 (Op. 77) (1875)
S. Accardo, M. Batjer, T. Hoffman, P. Wiley, F. Petracchi *Terzetto, Op.74.*
    (10/89) (DYNA) ① CDS45
Chilingirian Qt, D. McTier *Concert*
    (11/92) (CHAN) ① CHAN9046
P. Nejtek, Panocha Qt (r1992) *Concert*
    (5/94) (SUPR) ① 11 1461-2
Coull Qt, P. Buckoke (r1993) *Concert*
    (10/94) (HYPE) ① CDA66679
Lincoln Center Chbr Music Soc, D. Shifrin (r1993)
    Serenade, Op. 44. (8/95) (DELO) ① DE3152
String Sextet in A, B80 (Op. 48) (1878)
Berne Camerata, T. Füri (vn/dir) *Serenade, Op. 22.*
    (9/87) (NOVA) ① 150 011-2
Raphael Ens (r1988) *String Quintet, Op. 97.*
    (8/89) (HYPE) ① CDA66308
Talich Qt, J. Najnar, V. Bernašek (r1989)
    Schoenberg: Verklärte Nacht.
    (1/90) (CALL) ① CAL9217
ASMF Chbr Ens *Concert*
    (5/90) (CHAN) ① CHAN8771
J. Suk, J. Chuchro, Smetana Qt (r1988) *String Quintet, Op. 97.* (9/93) (SUPR) ① 11 1469-2
J. Klusoň, M. Kaňka, Panocha Qt (r1992) *Concert*
    (5/94) (SUPR) ① 11 1461-2
Vienna Stg Sextet (1991) *String Quintet, Op.97.*
    (10/94) (EMI) ① CDC7 54543-2
Terzetto in C—two violins and viola, B148 (Op. 74) (1887)
S. Accardo, M. Batjer, T. Hoffman *String Quintet, Op.77.* (10/89) (DYNA) ① CDS45
D. Cummings, C. Callow, L. Iorio *Cypresses.*
    (12/90) (UNIC) ① DKPCD9079
H. Davis, P. Pople, R. Best *Concert*
    (10/92) (CRD) ① CRD3457
Lindsay Qt *Concert* (9/93) (ASV) ① CDDCA806
Chilingirian Qt (r1992) *Concert*
    (10/93) (CHAN) ① CHAN9173

2 Waltzes—string quartet (double-bass ad lib), B105 (Op. 54) (1880) (arr. cpsr from pf pieces - Nos 1 and 4)
1. A; 2. D flat minor.
Prague Qt *Concert*
    (8/90) (DG) ① [9] 429 193-2GCM9
Chilingirian Qt, D. McTier *Concert*
    (4/92) (CHAN) ① CHAN8874
Alberni Qt *Concert* (10/92) (CRD) ① CRD3457

SECTION III: INSTRUMENTAL

Dumka in C minor—piano, B136 (Op. 12/1) (1884)
W. Howard *Concert* (9/92) (CHAN) ① CHAN9044
Furiant in G minor—piano, B137 (Op. 12/2) (1884)
W. Howard *Concert* (9/92) (CHAN) ① CHAN9044
8 Humoresques—piano, B187 (Op. 101) (1894)
1. E flat minor; 2. B; 3. A flat; 4. F; 5. A minor; 6. B; 7. G flat; 8. B flat minor.
7. M. Lympany *Concert* (1/89) (EMIL) ① CDZ110
7. I. Stern, Columbia SO, M. Katims (arr Harris)
Concert (7/90) (SONY) ① SK45816
7. J. Kubelík, anon (arr Kreisler: r1912) *Concert*
    (6/91) (BIDD) ① [2] LAB033/4
7. J. Heifetz, Anon (pf) *Concert*
    (12/91) (APR) ① [2] APR7015
7. J. Hassid, G. Moore (arr Kreisler: r1940) *Concert*
    (10/92) (PEAR) ① GEMMCD9939
7. J. Hassid, G. Moore (arr Kreisler: r1940) *Concert*
    (10/92) (TEST) ① SBT1010
7. J. Novotná, orch, A. von Zemlinsky (wds Taus: r1935) *Concert* (4/93) (SUPR) ① 11 1491-2
7. F. Kreisler, F. Rupp (r1938: arr Kreisler) *Concert*
    (12/93) (EMI) ① CDH7 64701-2
7. F. Kreisler, C. Lamson (r1927: arr Kreisler)
Concert (12/93) (BIDD) ① LAB075
7. Detroit SO, N. Järvi (r1991: orch N Shilkret)
Concert (8/94) (CHAN) ① CHAN9227
7. J. Heifetz, M. Kaye (r1944) *Concert*
    (11/94) (RCA) ① [65] 09026 61778-2(19)
7. Serenata of London, B. Wilde (r1994:orch) *Concert*
    (2/95) (CARL) ① PCD1108
Poetic tone pictures—piano, B161 (Op. 85) (1889)
1. Nocturnal route; 2. Toying; 3. At the old castle; 4. Spring song; 5. Peasant ballad; 6. Reverie; 7. Furiant; 8. Goblins' dance; 9. Serenade; 10. Bakchanale; 11. Tittle-tattle; 12. By the tumulus; 13. On the holy mountain.
W. Howard *Concert* (9/92) (CHAN) ① CHAN9044
R. Kvapil (r1992) *Theme with Variations.*
    (8/93) (UNIC) ① DKPCD9137
Theme with Variations in A flat—piano, B65 (Op. 36) (pub 1879)
W. Howard *Concert* (9/92) (CHAN) ① CHAN9044
R. Kvapil (r1992) *Poetic Tone Pictures.*
    (8/93) (UNIC) ① DKPCD9137
8 Waltzes—piano, B101 (Op. 54) (1880)
1. A; 2. A minor; 3. E; 4. D flat; 5. G minor; 6. F; 7. D minor; 8. E flat.
W. Howard *Concert* (9/92) (CHAN) ① CHAN9044

SECTION IV: VOCAL AND CHORAL

10 Bibical Songs—song collection, B185 (Op. 99) (1894) (Wds. Bible)
1. Clouds and darkness; 2. Thou art my hiding-place; 3. Give ear to my prayer; 4. The Lord is my shepherd; 5. I will sing a new song; 6. Hear my cry; 7. By the rivers of Babylon; 8. Turn thee unto me; 9. I will lift up mine eyes; 10. O sing unto the Lord.
Cpte B. Rayner Cook, SNO, N. Järvi *Symphony 4.*
    (12/88) (CHAN) ① CHAN8608
1, 3, 4, 7, 8, 10. D. Fischer-Dieskau, J. Demus
(r1960: Ger) *Requiem.*
    (5/95) (DG) ① [2] 437 377-2GX2
5, 7, 10. G. Beňačková, R. Firkušný (1991) *Concert*
    (1/94) (RCA) ① 09026 60823-2
7 Gipsy Melodies, 'Zigeunerlieder'—song collection, B104 (Op. 55) (1880) (Wds. anon)
1. My song of love; 2. Hey! ring out my triangle; 3. All round about the woods are still; 4. Songs my mother taught me; 5. Tune thy strings; 6. Wide the sleeves; 7. Give a hawk a fine cage.
Cpte M. Horne, Martin Katz (r1992: Ger) *Concert*
    (3/94) (RCA) ① 09026 61681-2
G. Beňačková, R. Firkušný (1991) *Concert*
    (1/94) (RCA) ① 09026 60823-2
Sarah Walker, R. Vignoles *Concert*
    (4/94) (MERI) ① CDE84232
1, 6, 7. P. Frijsh, C. Dougherty (r1940: Ger) *Concert*
    (4/95) (PEAR) ① [2] GEMMCDS9095(1)
4. V. de los Angeles, Sinfonia of London, R. Frühbeck de Burgos (orch Gamley) *Concert*
    (10/88) (EMI) ① CDM7 69502-2

4. N. Melba, orch, W.B. Rogers (r1916) *Concert*
(3/89) (LARR) ① **CDLRH221**
4. F. Kreisler, C. Lamson (arr Kreisler: vn/pf; r1928)
Concert (1/90) (PEAR) ① **GEMMCD9324**
4. P. McCann, Black Dyke Mills Band, P. Parkes
(r1984: arr G Langford) *Concert*
(11/92) (CHAN) ① **CHAN4501**
4. B. Harrison (with nightingales: r1927) *Concert*
(3/93) (CLAR) ① **CDGSE78-50-47**
4. J. Novotná, RCA Victor Orch, F. Weissmann
(r1945) *Concert* (4/93) (SUPR) ① **11 1491-2**
4. N. Melba, F. St Leger (r1916) *Concert*
(9/93) (RCA) ① **09026 61412-2**
4. J. Lloyd Webber, J. Lenehan (r1992: arr vc/pf)
Concert (10/93) (PHIL) ① **434 917-2PH**
4. F. Kreisler, C. Lamson (r1928: arr Kreisler)
Concert (12/93) (BIDD) ① **LAB080**
4. R. Ponselle, orch, R. Bourdon (r1928: Eng)
Concert (11/94) (ROMO) ① [2] **81007-2**
4. N. Melba, orch, W.B. Rogers (r1916: Eng) *Concert*
(5/95) (ROMO) ① [3] **81011-2(2)**
4. N. Melba, F. St Leger (r1916: Eng) *Concert*
(5/95) (ROMO) ① [3] **81011-2(2)**
4. I. Perlman, S. Sanders (r1985: arr Kreisler)
Concert (6/95) (EMI) ① [20] **CZS4 83177-2(2)**
4. K. Flagstad, E. McArthur (r1936: Eng) *Concert*
(12/95) (PEAR) ① **GEMMCD9092**
4. K. Flagstad, E. McArthur (r1936: Eng) *Concert*
(12/95) (NIMB) ① **NI7871**
5, 7. H. Spani, orch, G. Nastrucci (r1929) *Concert*
(9/90) (CLUB) ① [2] **CL99-509/10**

**The Heirs of the White Mountain—hymn:
chorus and orchestra, B27 (Op. 30) (1872)**
(Wds. Hálek)
Prague Phil Chor, Czech PO, V. Neumann *Concert*
(11/85) (SUPR) ① **C37-7230**

**In Folk Tone—folksongs, B146 (Op. 73)
(1886)**
1. Good night, my darling; 2. When a maiden was a-
mowing; 3. Nothing can change for me; 4. I have a
faithful mare.
G. Beňačková, R. Firkušný (r1991) *Concert*
(1/94) (RCA) ① **09026 60823-2**
Sarah Walker, R. Vignoles *Concert*
(4/94) (MERI) ① **CDE84232**
L. Popp, G. Parsons (pp1981) *Concert*
(6/95) (ORFE) ① **C363941B**
2. E. Destinn, orch, J. Pasternack (r1921) *Concert*
(11/93) (ROMO) ① [2] **81002-2**
2. E. Destinn, orch, J. Pasternack (r1921) *Concert*
(12/94) (SUPR) ① [12] **11 2136-2(5)**

8 Love Songs, B160 (Op. 83) (1888) (Wds.
Pfleger-Moravský: rev of Cypresses, B11)
1. When thy sweet glances; 2. Death reigns; 3. Thou
only dear one; 4. I know that on my love; 5. Never will
love lead us; 6. I wander oft; 7. In deepest forest
glade; 8. Nature lies peaceful.
1, 2, 4, 5. G. Beňačková, R. Firkušný (r1991) *Concert*
(1/94) (RCA) ① **09026 60823-2**

Mass in D, B153 (Op. 86) (1887)
Bristol Cath Ch, A. Pinel, M. Archer *Concert*
(4/90) (MERI) ① **CDE84188**
N. Ritchie, A. Giles, A. Byers, R. Morton, Oxford
Christ Church Cath Ch, N. Cleobury, S. Preston *Liszt:
Missa choralis*, S10.
(9/91) (DECC) ① **430 364-2DM**
C. Ashton, E. Stirling, A. Murgatroyd, S. Birchall,
Dyfed Ch, P. Dyke, C. Barton (r1993) *Concert*
(7/94) (ABBE) ① **CDCA1954**

4 Moravian Duets, B50 (1875)
1. Destined; 2. The parting; 3. Poverty, or The silken
band; 4. The last wish.
Cpte Kühn Chor, S. Bogunia, P. Kühn *Concert*
(1/90) (SUPR) ① **CO-72646**

5 Moravian Duets, B60 (Op. 29) (1876) (Wds.
Trad)
1. From thee now; 2. Fly sweet songster; 3. The
slighted heart; 4. Parting without sorrow; 5. The
pledge of love.
Cpte E. Schwarzkopf, I. Seefried, G. Moore (r1955:
Ger) *Concert* (3/89) (EMI) ① **CDH7 69793-2**
Cpte Kühn Chor, S. Bogunia, P. Kühn *Concert*
(1/90) (SUPR) ① **CO-72646**
J. Banse, B. Fassbaender, C. Garben (r1993)
Concert (8/95) (SCHW) ① **312592**

9 Moravian Duets, B62 (Op. 32) (1876) (Wds.
Trad)
1. Forsaken; 2. Sad of heart; 3. The modest maid; 4.
The ring; 5. Omens; 6. The maid imprisoned; 7.
Comfort; 8. The wild rose; 9. The soldier's farewell.
Cpte Kühn Chor, S. Bogunia, P. Kühn *Concert*
(1/90) (SUPR) ① **CO-72646**
J. Banse, B. Fassbaender, C. Garben (r1993)
Concert (8/95) (SCHW) ① **312592**

Prague Chbr Ch, J. Pancik (r1994) *Concert*
(12/95) (CHAN) ① **CHAN9257**
1, 3, 5, 6. E. Söderström, K. Meyer, J. Eyron (r1974)
Concert (9/93) (BIS) ① **BIS-CD017**
1-8. E. Schwarzkopf, I. Seefried, G. Moore (r1955:
Ger) *Concert* (3/89) (EMI) ① **CDH7 69793-2**

4 Moravian Duets, B69 (Op. 38) (1877) (Wds.
Trad)
1. Hoping in vain; 2. Greeting from afar; 3. The
crown; 4. The smart.
Cpte Kühn Chor, S. Bogunia, P. Kühn *Concert*
(1/90) (SUPR) ① **CO-72646**
1, 2. V. de los Angeles, D. Fischer-Dieskau, G.
(r1960: Ger) *Concert*
(4/94) (EMI) ① [4] **CMS5 65061-2(2)**

**Psalm 149—male vv and orchestra, B91 (Op.
79) (1879)** (Wds. Bible)
Prague Phil Chor, Czech PO, V. Neumann *Concert*
(11/85) (SUPR) ① **C37-7230**
Prague Phil Chor, Czech PO, J. Bělohlávek *Stabat
Mater.* (2/92) (CHAN) ① [2] **CHAN8985/6**

**Requiem Mass—soloists, chorus and
orchestra, B165 (Op. 89) (1890)**
P. Lorengar, E. Komlóssy, R. Ilosfalvy, T. Krause,
Ambrosian Sngrs, LSO, I. Kertész *Concert*
(5/89) (DECC) ① **421 810-2DM2**
M. Stader, S. Wagner, E. Haefliger, K. Borg, Czech
Phil Chor, Czech PO, K. Ančerl (r1950s) *Biblical
Songs.* (5/95) (DG) ① [2] **437 377-2GX2**

**The Spectre's Bride—dramatic cantata:
STB, chorus and orchestra, B135 (Op. 69)
(1884)** (Wds. Erben)
L. Aghova, J. Protschka, I. Kusnjer, Prague Phil
Chor, Hamburg PO, G. Albrecht (pp1991)
(7/93) (ORFE) ① **C259921A**

**St. Ludmilla—oratorio: soloists, chorus and
orchestra, B144 (Op. 71) (1885-86)** (Wds. J.
Vrchlický)
Cpte D. Šounová-Brouková, D. Drobková, L.M.
Vodička, L. Vraspir, A. Švorc, Prague Children's Ch,
Prague Rad Chor, Prague RSO, V. Smetáček
(pp1984) (7/95) (PRAG) ① **PR250 059/60**

**Stabat mater—soloists, chorus and
orchestra, B71 (Op. 58) (1876-77)**
A.P. Jerič, E.N. Houška, J. Reja, F. Petrusanec,
Ljubljana Rad Chor, Ljubljana RSO, M. Munih
(3/88) (CAVA) ① [2] **CAVCD008/9**
E. Mathis, A. Reynolds, W. Ochman, J. Shirley-Quirk,
Bavarian Rad Chor, BRSO, R. Kubelík *Legends.*
(9/90) (DG) ① [2] **423 919-2GGA2**
L. Aghova, M. Schiml, A. Baldin, L. Vele, Prague
Children's Ch, Prague Phil Chor, Czech PO, J.
Bělohlávek *Psalm 149.*
(2/92) (CHAN) ① [2] **CHAN8985/6**
D. Tikalová, M. Krásová, B. Blachut, K. Kalaš, Czech
Phil Chor, Czech PO, V. Talich (r1952) *Suk: Asrael.*
(12/93) (SUPR) ① [2] **11 1902-2**
M. Gauci, N. Boschkowa, M. Dvorský, P. Mikuláš,
Slovak Phil Chor, Slovak Radio New PO, A. Rahbari
(r1992) *Te Deum.* (12/93) (DINT) ① **DICD920102/3**
S. Woytowicz, V. Soukupová, I. Žídek, K. Borg,
Czech Sngrs Chor, Czech PO, V. Smetáček (r1960s)
Janáček: Glagolitic Mass.
(12/94) (DG) ① [2] **437 937-2GX2**

**Te Deum—soprano, bass, chorus and
orchestra, B176 (Op. 103) (1892)**
1. Te Deum laudamus.
G. Beňačková, J. Souček, Prague Phil Chor, Czech
PO, V. Neumann *Concert*
(11/85) (SUPR) ① **C37-7230**
C. Brewer, R. Roloff, Atlanta Sym Chor, Atlanta SO,
Robert Shaw *Janáček: Glagolitic Mass.*
(7/91) (TELA) ① **CD80287**
M. Gauci, P. Mikuláš, Slovak Phil Chor, Slovak Radio
New PO, A. Rahbari (r1992) *Stabat mater.*
(12/93) (DINT) ① **DICD920102/3**

**There on our roof a swallow
carries—Moravian duet, B118 (1881)**
Kühn Chor, S. Bogunia, P. Kühn *Concert*
(1/90) (SUPR) ① **CO-72646**

SECTION V: STAGE WORKS

**Armida—opera: 4 acts, B206 (Op. 115)
(1904—Prague)** (Lib. J. Vrchlický)
At dawn, as I merrily pursued a slender gazelle L.
Popp, Munich RO, S. Soltesz (r1987) *Concert*
(4/89) (EMI) ① **CDC7 49319-2**

**Dimitrij—opera: 4 acts, B127 (Op. 64), rev as
B186 (1882—Prague)** (Lib. M. Červinková-
Riegrová)
Cpte L.M. Vodička, D. Drobková, M. Hajóssyová, L.
Aghova, P. Mikuláš, I. Kusnjer, L. Vele, Czech Phil
Chor, Prague Rad Chor, Czech PO, G. Albrecht
(3/93) (SUPR) ① [3] **11 1259-2**

**The Jacobin—opera: 3 acts, B159 (Op. 84):
rev as B200 (1889—Prague)** (Lib. M
Červinková-Riegrová)
Cpte V. Zítek, V. Přibyl, D. Šounová-Brouková, K.
Průša, R. Tuček, M. Machotková, K. Berman, B.
Blachut, I. Mixová, Kantiléna Children's Chor, Kühn
Chor, Brno St PO, J. Pinkas (r1977)
(12/94) (SUPR) ① [2] **11 2190-2**

**Kate and the Devil—opera: 3 acts, B201 (Op.
112) (1899—Prague)** (Lib. A. Wenig)
Cpte A. Barová, R. Novák, M. Ježil, D. Suryová, J.
Horáček, J. Hladík, A. Šťava, B. Šulcová, N.
Romanová, P. Kamas, O. Polášek, Brno Janáček Op
Chor, Brno Janáček Op Orch, J. Pinkas (r1979)
(9/94) (SUPR) ① [2] **11 1800-2**

Overture Czech PO, V. Neumann *Concert*
(9/90) (ORFE) ① **C180891A**

**Rusalka—opera: 3 acts, B203 (Op. 114)
(1901—Prague)** (Lib. Kvapil)
EXCERPTS: 1. Overture. ACT 1: 2. Ho, ho, ho!; 3.
Watersprite, my father dear; 4. He comes here
frequently; 5. O, moon high up in the deep, deep sky
(O silver moon); 6. Your ancient wisdom knows
everything; 7. Abracadabra; 8. Here she appeared; 9.
The hunt is over, return home at once; 10. I know
you're but magic that will pass. ACT 2: 11. Well them,
well then; 12. A week now do you dwell with me; 13.
Festival music: Ballet (Polonaise); 14. No one this
world can give; 15. White blossom all along the road;
16. Rusalka, daughter, I am here; 17. O, useless it is;
18. Strange fire in your eyes is burning. ACT 3: 19.
Insensible water power (God of the lake); 20. Ah, ah!
Already you have come back?; 21. Only human blood
can cleanse you; 22. I'll rather suffer; 23. Uprooted
and banished; 24. That you're afraid? Don't be silly;
25. Who is noisy?; 26. Hair, golden hair have I; 27.
Where are you, my white dove?; 28. Do you still love
me, lover?.
5. Czech PO, V. Neumann *Concert*
(5/89) (PHIL) ① **422 387-2PH**
5. L. Garrett, Philh, A. Greenwood (r1990-1) *Concert*
(11/91) (SILV) ① **SONGCD903**
5. P. McCann, Black Dyke Mills Band, P. Parkes
(r1984: arr P Parkes) *Concert*
(11/92) (CHAN) ① **CHAN4501**
5. L. Price, New Philh, N. Santi (r1977) *Concert*
(12/92) (RCA) ① [4] **09026 61236-2**
5. J. Hammond, Philh, V. Tausky (r1952) *Concert*
(12/92) (TEST) ① **SBT1013**
5. J. Novotná, G. King (r1956) *Concert*
(4/93) (SUPR) ① **11 1491-2**
5. Black Dyke Mills Band, J. Watson (r1992: arr
Langford) *Concert* (9/93) (POLY) ① **QPRL053D**
5. E. Destinn, orch, W.B. Rogers (r1915: Ger)
Concert (11/93) (ROMO) ① [2] **81002-2**
5. A. Roocroft, LPO, F. Welser-Möst *Concert*
(10/94) (EMI) ① **CDC5 55090-2**
5. E. Destinn, orch, W.B Rogers (r1915: Ger) *Concert*
(12/94) (SUPR) ① [12] **11 2136-2(5)**
5. L. Popp, G. Parsons (pp1981) *Concert*
(6/95) (ORFE) ① **C363941B**
5. S. Bullock, A. Bryn Parri (r1994) *Concert*
(11/95) (SAIN) ① **SCDC2070**
5, 23. L. Popp, Munich RO, S. Soltesz (r1987)
Concert (4/89) (EMI) ① **CDC7 49319-2**
26. J. Novotná, A. Sándor (r1931) *Concert*
(4/93) (SUPR) ① **11 1491-2**

**Vanda—opera: 5 acts, B55 (Op. 25)
(1876—Prague)** (Lib. V. B. Šumavský, after J.
Surzycki)
Overture BBC PO, S. Gunzenhauser (r1992)
Concert (10/93) (NAXO) ① **8 550600**

DYENS, Roland (b 1955) Tunisia

SECTION III: INSTRUMENTAL

Hommage à Villa-Lobos
R. Dyens *Concert* (9/88) (AUVI) ① **AV6114**

DYER, Susan (1880-1922) USA

SECTION II: CHAMBER

Outlandish Suite—violin and piano (1924)
EXCERPTS: 2. Florida Night Song.
2. J. Heifetz, E. Bay (r1945) *Concert*
(11/94) (RCA) ① [65] **09026 61778-2(19)**

DYKES, John Bacchus (1823–1876) England

SECTION IV: VOCAL AND CHORAL

Holy! Holy! Holy! Lord God Almighty (tune: Nicaea)—hymn (Wds. R. Heber)
King's College Ch, D. Willcocks, I. Hare, PJBE (arr. Willcocks) *Concert*   (1/91) (CFP) ① **CD-CFP4570**
Lead, kindly light—hymn (Wds. Newman)
A. Galli-Curci, orch, R. Bourdon (r1923) *Concert*
  (8/94) (ROMO) ① [2] **81004-2**

DYSON, Sir George (1883–1964) England

SECTION I: ORCHESTRAL

Children's Suite, 'Won't you look out of your window?'—small orchestra (1920)
CLS, R. Hickox (r1994) *Violin Concerto.*
  (9/95) (CHAN) ① **CHAN9369**
Concerto da camera—string orchestra (1949)
CLS, R. Hickox *Concert*
  (8/93) (CHAN) ① **CHAN9076**
Concerto da chiesa—string orchestra (1949)
CLS, R. Hickox *Concert*
  (8/93) (CHAN) ① **CHAN9076**
Concerto for Violin and Orchestra in E flat (1942)
L. Mordkovitch, CLS, R. Hickox (r1994) *Children's Suite.*
  (9/95) (CHAN) ① **CHAN9369**
Concerto leggiero—piano and strings
E. Parkin, CLS, R. Hickox *Concert*
  (8/93) (CHAN) ① **CHAN9076**
Prelude, Fantasy and Chaconne—cello and orchestra (1936)
EXCERPTS: 2. Fantasy.
2. J. Lloyd Webber, ASMF, N. Marriner (r1994) *Concert*   (12/94) (PHIL) ① **442 530-2PH**
Symphony in G (1937)
CLS, R. Hickox (r1993)
  (6/94) (CHAN) ① **CHAN9200**

SECTION II: CHAMBER

3 Rhapsodies—string quartet (1905-12)
Divertimenti (r1984) Howells: *String Quartet (1923).*
  (6/89) (HYPE) ① **CDA66139**

SECTION III: INSTRUMENTAL

Voluntary of Praise—organ
J. Bielby *Concert*   (5/91) (PRIO) ① **PRCD298**

SECTION IV: VOCAL AND CHORAL

Be strong and of good courage, 'Confortare'—choir, organ and brass (1953)
Westminster Abbey Ch, M. Baker, London Brass, M. Neary (r1993/4) *Concert*
  (9/94) (CNTO) ① **CSACD3050**
Evening Service in D (1924)
1. Magnificat; 2. Nunc Dimittis.
St Paul's Cath Ch, C. Dearnley, John Scott *Concert*
  (1/89) (HYPE) ① **CDA66305**
Lichfield Cath Ch, A. Lumsden, M. Shepherd (r1994) *Concert*   (10/95) (PRIO) ① **PRCD505**
2. Wellington College Chs, T. Byram-Wigfield, S. Anderson *Concert* (10/92) (HERA) ① **HAVPCD153**
Ye that do your Master's will—anthem (Wds. C. Wesley)
Wellington College Chs, T. Byram-Wigfield, S. Anderson *Concert* (10/92) (HERA) ① **HAVPCD153**

EARLE, William (Benson) (1740–1796) England

SECTION IV: VOCAL AND CHORAL

3 Old English Songs—4vv (pub 1786) (arrs of songs by other cpsrs)
EXCERPTS: 1. Go, rose! my Chloe's bosom grace (Greene).
1. Invocation (r1993) *Concert*
  (11/94) (HYPE) ① **CDA66698**

EASDALE, Brian (b 1909) England

SECTION V: STAGE WORKS

The Red Shoes—film score (1948)
1. Red Shoes Ballet.
1. Philh, K. Alwyn *Concert*
  (2/91) (SILV) ① **FILMCD713**

EAST, Michael (c1580–1648) England

SECTION IV: VOCAL AND CHORAL

Poor is the life that misses—Neapolitan (6vv) (pub 1606)
Amaryllis Consort, C. Brett *Concert*
  (3/88) (CARL) ① **PCD873**
Quicke, quicke, away dispatch—madrigal (6vv) (pub 1618)
Cambridge Sngrs, J. Rutter *Concert*
  (11/87) (CLLE) ① **COLCD105**
You meaner beauties of the night—song (1v and chorus) (pub 1624)
E. Kirkby, Consort of Musicke, A. Rooley *Concert*
  (9/87) (HYPE) ① **CDA66227**

EBELING, Johann Georg (1637–1676) Germany

SECTION IV: VOCAL AND CHORAL

All my heart this night rejoices—hymn (Wds. P. Gerhardt trans C. Winkworth)
Cambridge Sngrs, J. Rutter *Concert*
  (12/87) (CLLE) ① **COLCD106**

EBEN, Petr (b 1929) Czechoslovakia

SECTION II: CHAMBER

Chagall Windows—trumpet and organ (1976)
G. Touvron, E. Krapp (r1992) *Concert*
  (9/93) (RCA) ① **09026 61186-2**
J. Wallace, S. Wright (r1993) *Concert*
  (11/94) (EMI) ① **CDC5 55086-2**

SECTION III: INSTRUMENTAL

Sunday Music (Nedělní Hudba)—organ (1958)
1. Fantasia I; 2. Fantasia II; 3. Moto ostinato; 4. Finale.
3. D. Flood *Concert*   (4/91) (YORK) ① **CD108**

SECTION IV: VOCAL AND CHORAL

9 Folk Songs, 'About Swallows and Girls'—female chorus (1961) (Wds. Czech trad)
1. My lass, my lass, little Swallow; 2. Were you not at home; 3. The Dawn; 7. The Cuckoo is calling; 9. A little swallow is flying.
1-3, 7, 9. Prague Chbr Ch, J. Pancik (r1994) *Concert*
  (12/95) (CHAN) ① **CHAN9257**

EBERL, Anton (1765–1807) Austria

SECTION III: INSTRUMENTAL

Theme, Variations and Rondo Pastorale—harp (attrib. Mozart)
M. Robles *Concert*
  (2/93) (DECC) ① **433 869-2DWO**

EBERLIN, Johann Ernst (1702–1762) Germany

SECTION II: CHAMBER

10 Piezas a Psalterio
Pastorale Pantaleon Ens, K-H. Schickhaus (dulcimer/dir) (r1991) *Concert*
  (12/93) (TUDO) ① **Tudor 767**

ECCARD, Johannes (1553–1611) Germany

SECTION IV: VOCAL AND CHORAL

Fröhlich will ich singen—Lied: 1v
A. Köhler, Lautten Compagney (r1990/1) *Concert*
  (6/93) (CAPR) ① **10 431**
Unser lieben Hühnerchen—Lied: 1v
A. Köhler, Lautten Compagney (r1990/1) *Concert*
  (6/93) (CAPR) ① **10 431**
When to the temple Mary went—motet
Kings College Ch, D. Willcocks *Concert*
  (12/91) (EMI) ① **CDM7 64130-2**
Truro Cath Ch, D. Briggs, S. Morley (r1992) *Concert*
  (7/94) (PRIO) ① **PRCD429**

ECCLES, Henry (?1675/85–?1735/45) England

SECTION II: CHAMBER

Sonata—violin and continuo
J. Thibaud, T. Janopoulo (r1930: arr Salmon) *Concert*
  (12/94) (APR) ① [2] **APR7028**
Movt 1. S. Koussevitzky, B. Zighera (r1928: arr db/pf: Koussevitzky) *Concert*   (9/94) (BIDD) ① **WHL019**
Movt 1. S. Koussevitzky, P. Luboshutz (r1929: arr db/pf: Koussevitzky) *Concert*
  (9/94) (BIDD) ① **WHL019**

ECCLES, John (c1668–1735) England

SECTION IV: VOCAL AND CHORAL

Ah, how lovely, sweet and dear—dialogue between Acis and Galatea
E. Kirkby, E. Tubb, A. Rooley (r1994) *Concert*
  (10/95) (MOSC) ① **070979**
Ye gentle gales—song: 1v
E. Tubb, F. Kelly (r1992) *Concert*
  (9/94) (MOSC) ① **070987**

SECTION V: STAGE WORKS

The Comical History of Don Quixote—incidental music (1694—London) (collab with Purcell. Wds. D'Urfey)
EXCERPTS: 1. I burn, my brain consumes to ashes.
1. C. Bott, D. Roblou, M. Levy (r1990) *Concert*
  (2/93) (L'OI) ① **433 187-2OH**
Cyrus the Great, or The Tragedy of Love—incidental music (1695—London) (Wds. J. Banks)
EXCERPTS: 1. Oh! Take him gently from the pile.
1. C. Bott, D. Roblou, Á. Pleeth (r1990) *Concert*
  (2/93) (L'OI) ① **433 187-2OH**
1. E. Tubb, F. Kelly (r1992) *Concert*
  (9/94) (MOSC) ① **070987**
The Judgment of Paris—masque (1701—London) (Wds. Congreve)
EXCERPTS: 1. Symphony for Mercury (Trumpet Sonata); 2. Awake, awake, thy Spirits Raise.
1. Parley of Instr, R. Goodman, P. Holman *Concert*
  (11/88) (HYPE) ① **CDA66108**
2. E. Kirkby, English Tpt Virtuosi, A. Hoskins (tpt/dir), M. Hoskins (tpt/dir) (r1994) *Concert*
  (10/95) (MOSC) ① **070979**
The Mad Lover—incidental music (1700—London) (Wds. Motteux, after Fletcher)
EXCERPTS: 1. Must then a faithful lover go?; 2. Let all be gay; 3. Cease of Cupid to complain.
1-3. C. Bott, D. Roblou, M. Levy, A. Pleeth, P. Chateauneuf, T. Finucane (r1990) *Concert*
  (2/93) (L'OI) ① **433 187-2OH**
She Ventures, and He Wins—incidental music (1695—London)
EXCERPTS: 1. Restless in thought.
1. C. Bott, D. Roblou, M. Levy (r1990) *Concert*
  (2/93) (L'OI) ① **433 187-2OH**
1. E. Tubb, F. Kelly (r1992) *Concert*
  (9/94) (MOSC) ① **070987**
The Villain—incidental music (1698) (Wds T. Porter)
EXCERPTS: 1. Find me a lonely cave.
1. E. Tubb, F. Kelly (r1992) *Concert*
  (9/94) (MOSC) ① **070987**
The Way of the World—incidental music (1700—London) (Wds. Congreve)
EXCERPTS: 1. Love's but the fraility of man.
1. C. Bott, D. Roblou, M. Levy (r1990) *Concert*
  (2/93) (L'OI) ① **433 187-2OH**

ECKERT, Carl Anton Florian (1820–1879) Germany

SECTION IV: VOCAL AND CHORAL

L' Eco—song
L. Tetrazzini, orch (r1911) *Concert*
  (10/90) (NIMB) ① **NI7808**
L. Tetrazzini, orch (r1911) *Concert*
  (9/92) (PEAR) ① **GEMMCD9224**

ECKHARDT-GRAMATTÉ, Sophie-Carmen (1899–1974) Russia

SECTION III: INSTRUMENTAL

Sonata for Piano No. 1, E45 (1923)
M-A. Hamelin *Concert*
  (5/92) (ALTA) ① [2] **AIR-CD-9052**

Sonata for Piano No. 2, E46 (1923) (Die
Biscaya Sonate)
M-A. Hamelin *Concert*
(5/92) (ALTA) ① [2] **AIR-CD-9052**
Sonata for Piano No. 3, E52 (1924)
M-A. Hamelin *Concert*
(5/92) (ALTA) ① [2] **AIR-CD-9052**
Sonata for Piano No. 4, E68 (1927-31) (Die
Befreite Sonate)
M-A. Hamelin *Concert*
(5/92) (ALTA) ① [2] **AIR-CD-9052**
Sonata for Piano No. 5, E126 (1950)
(Klavierstük)
M-A. Hamelin *Concert*
(5/92) (ALTA) ① [2] **AIR-CD-9052**
Sonata for Piano No. 6, E130 (1952) (Drei
Klavierstücke)
M-A. Hamelin *Concert*
(5/92) (ALTA) ① [2] **AIR-CD-9052**

EDER, Helmut (b 1916) Austria

SECTION II: CHAMBER

Wind Quintet No. 3, 'Begagnung', Op. 91
(1989)
Vienna/Berlin Ens *Concert*
(11/92) (SONY) ① **SK48052**

EDMUNDSON, Garth (1900–1971) USA

SECTION III: INSTRUMENTAL

Toccata-Prelude: Vom Himmel
hoch—organ
Andrew Lucas (r1991) *Concert*
(2/94) (MIRA) ① **MRCD905**

EDWARDS, Gus (1879–1945) USA

SECTION IV: VOCAL AND CHORAL

In Zanzibar—song for the show 'The Medal
and the Maid' (1904) (Lyrics Will D Cobb)
E. Carus, Broadway Cast (r1904) *Concert*
(5/94) (PEAR) ① [3] **GEMMCDS9050/2(1)**

EDWARDS, Julian (1855–1910) England/USA

SECTION V: STAGE WORKS

Love's Lottery—musical show (1904—New
York) (Lyrics Stanislaus Stange)
EXCERPTS: 1. Sweet Thoughts of Home.
1. E. Schumann-Heink, Broadway Cast (r1906)
Concert
(5/94) (PEAR) ① [3] **GEMMCDS9050/2(2)**
Molly May—musical show (1910—New York)
(Lyrics Browne)
EXCERPTS: 1. Does Anybody Here Know Nancy?.
1. G. LaRue, Orig Broadway Cast (r1910) *Concert*
(5/94) (PEAR) ① [3] **GEMMCDS9053/5**
When Johnny Comes Marching
Home—musical show (1902—New York)
(Book & Lyrics Stanislaus Stange)
EXCERPTS: 1. Suwanee River; 2. Katie, My
Southern Rose; 3. My Own United States.
1-3. W. H. Thompson, Broadway Cast (r1903-4)
Concert
(5/94) (PEAR) ① [3] **GEMMCDS9050/2(1)**

EDWARDS, Richard (1524–1566) England

SECTION IV: VOCAL AND CHORAL

In goinge to my naked bedde—song
Theatre Of Voices, P. Hillier (r1992) *Concert*
(9/94) (ECM) ① **439 172-2**
When grypinge griefes—song
E. Kirkby, A. Rooley *Concert*
(8/91) (L'OI) ① **425 892-2OH**

EDWARDS, Ross (b 1943) Australia

SECTION III: INSTRUMENTAL

Marimba Dances (1982)
E. Glennie *Concert* (1/92) (RCA) ① **RD60557**

EESPERE, René (b 1953) Estonia

SECTION II: CHAMBER

Trivium—flute, violin and guitar (1991)
Tallinn Camerata (r1993) *Concert*
(5/95) (FINL) ① **4509-95705-2**

EGIDIUS (14th–15 cents) France/Italy

name refers to several musicians

SECTION IV: VOCAL AND CHORAL

Courtois et sages—ballade
Orlando Consort (bp1994) *Concert*
(11/95) (METR) ① **METCD1008**

EGK, Werner (1901–1983) Germany

SECTION I: ORCHESTRAL

Divertissement—11 wind instruments
(1973)
Mainz Wind Ens, K.R. Schöll *Concert*
(9/91) (WERG) ① **WER60179-50**
French Suite (after Rameau)—orchestra
(1949)
Berlin RIAS Orch, F. Fricsay (r1955) *Concert*
(11/94) (DG) ① **445 404-2GDO**
Berlin RIAS Orch, F. Fricsay (r1955) *Concert*
(11/94) (DG) ① [11] **445 400-2GDO10**
Die Zaubergeige Overture—11 wind
instruments and double-bass (1980) (arr cpsr
from opera)
Mainz Wind Ens, K.R. Schöll *Concert*
(9/91) (WERG) ① **WER60179-50**

SECTION V: STAGE WORKS

Peer Gynt—opera: 3 acts (1938—Berlin) (Lib.
cpsr, after Ibsen)
Cpte R. Hermann, N. Sharp, C. Wulkopf, J. Perry, H.
Hopfner, H. Hopf, K. Lövaas, H. Weber, P. Hansen,
P. Lika, W. Wild, F. Lenz, Bavarian Rad Chor,
Munich RO, H. Wallberg (r1981)
(10/89) (ORFE) ① [2] **C005822H**
Die Verlobung in San Domingo—opera: 2
acts (1963—Munich) (Lib. cpsr, after H von
Kleist)
Cpte E. Lear, M. Bence, H.G. Nöcker, H. Nasseri, F.
Wunderlich, M. Yahia, Richard Holm, K.C. Kohn,
Bavarian St Orch, W. Egk (bp1963)
(9/94) (ORFE) ① [2] **C343932I**

EICHHEIM, Henry (1870–1942) USA

SECTION I: ORCHESTRAL

Bali—Gamelan ensemble and orchestra
(1933)
Philadelphia, L. Stokowski (r1934) *Concert*
(10/93) (STOK) ① **LSCD20**
Oriental Impressions—oriental percussion
ensemble & orchestra (1919-22)
Japanese Nocturne Philadelphia, L. Stokowski
(r1929) *Concert* (10/93) (STOK) ① **LSCD20**

EIDELMAN, Cliff (20th Cent) USA

SECTION V: STAGE WORKS

To Die For—film score (1989)
Suite OST, C. Eidelman (r1989) *Concert*
(10/93) (SILV) ① **FILMCD127**

EINEM, Gottfried von (b 1918) Austria

SECTION I: ORCHESTRAL

Ballade—orchestra, Op. 23 (1957)
Berlin RSO, F. Fricsay (pp1961) *Concert*
(11/94) (DG) ① **445 404-2GDO**
Capriccio—orchestra, Op. 2 (1942-43)
BRSO, E. Ormandy (pp1959) *Concert*
(8/90) (ORFE) ① **C199891A**
Concerto for Piano and Orchestra, Op. 20
(1955)
G. Herzog, Berlin RSO, F. Fricsay (1961) *Concert*
(11/94) (DG) ① **445 404-2GDO**
G. Herzog, Berlin RSO, F. Fricsay (1961) *Concert*
(11/94) (DG) ① [11] **445 400-2GDO10**

SECTION V: STAGE WORKS

Dantons Tod—opera: 2 parts
(1947—Salzburg) (Lib. cpsr and B. Blacher,
after G. Büchner)
Cpte T. Adam, W. Hollweg, W. Gahmlich, H.
Hiestermann, K. Laki, H. Berger-Tuna, K. Rydl, F.
Wyzner, C. Doig, K. Terkal, A. Muff, I. Mayr, G. Sima,
M. Lipovšek, Austrian Rad Chor, Austrian RSO, L.
Zagrosek (pp1983)
(1/90) (ORFE) ① [2] **C102842H**

EISLER, Hanns (1898–1962) Germany

SECTION II: CHAMBER

Duo for Violin and Cello, Op. 7 (1924)
Zurich Chmbr Ens, C. Keller *Concert*
(11/87) (ACCO) ① **149158**
Nonet No. 1—flute, clarinet, bassoon, horn,
string quartet and double-bass (1939)
Zurich Chmbr Ens, C. Keller *Concert*
(11/87) (ACCO) ① **149158**
Nonet No. 2—flute, clarinet, bassoon,
trumpet, percussion, 3 violins and double-
bass (1941)
Zurich Chmbr Ens, C. Keller *Concert*
(11/87) (ACCO) ① **149158**
Sonata for Violin and Piano, 'Reisesonate'
(1937)
Zurich Chmbr Ens, C. Keller *Concert*
(11/87) (ACCO) ① **149158**
Variations—14 Arten für flute, clarinet,
violin/viola, cello and piano, Op. 70 (1940)
Zurich Chmbr Ens, C. Keller *Concert*
(11/87) (ACCO) ① **149158**

SECTION IV: VOCAL AND CHORAL

An den kleinen Radioapparat—voice and
piano (Wds. B. Brecht)
D. Fischer-Dieskau, A. Reimann (r1987) *Concert*
(12/95) (TELD) ① **4509-97459-2**
An den Schlaf—voice and piano (Wds. E.
Mörike)
D. Fischer-Dieskau, A. Reimann (r1987) *Concert*
(12/95) (TELD) ① **4509-97459-2**
Ändere die Welt, sie braucht es—lied: 1v
and piano (1930) (Wds. B. Brecht)
W. Sharp, S. Blier (r1991) *Concert*
(7/93) (KOCH) ① **37086-2**
Auf der Flucht—voice and piano (Wds. B.
Brecht)
D. Fischer-Dieskau, A. Reimann (r1987) *Concert*
(12/95) (TELD) ① **4509-97459-2**
Aus der Heimat hinter den Blitzen rot—voice
and piano (Wds. J. Eichendorff)
D. Fischer-Dieskau, A. Reimann (r1987) *Concert*
(12/95) (TELD) ① **4509-97459-2**
Deutsche Sinfonie—solo vv, chorus &
orchestra, Op. 50 (1935-39) (Wds. B Brecht)
H. Wangemann, A. Markert, M. Görne, P. Lika, G.
Gütschow, V. Schwarz, Ernst Senff Chor, Leipzig
Gewandhaus, L. Zagrosek (r1995)
(12/95) (DECC) ① **448 389-2DH**
Elegie 1939—voice and piano (Wds. B.
Brecht)
D. Fischer-Dieskau, A. Reimann (r1987) *Concert*
(12/95) (TELD) ① **4509-97459-2**
2 Elegien—voice and piano (1937) (Wds. B.
Brecht)
1. In die Städte kam ich; 2. An die Überlebenden.
D. Fischer-Dieskau, A. Reimann (r1987) *Concert*
(12/95) (TELD) ① **4509-97459-2**
Frühling—voice and piano (Wds. B. Brecht)
D. Fischer-Dieskau, A. Reimann (r1987) *Concert*
(12/95) (TELD) ① **4509-97459-2**
Gedenktafel für 4000 Soldaten die im Krieg
gegen Norwegen versenkt wurden—voice
and piano (Wds. B. Brecht)
D. Fischer-Dieskau, A. Reimann (r1987) *Concert*
(12/95) (TELD) ① **4509-97459-2**
6 Hölderlin-Fragmente—voice and piano
(1943)
EXCERPTS: 1. An die Hoffnung; 2. Andenken; 3.
Elegie 1943; 4. Die Heimat; 5. An eine Stadt
(Heidelberg); 6. Erinnerung.
M. Shirai, H. Höll *Concert*
(12/94) (CAPR) ① **10 534**
1-3. D. Fischer-Dieskau, A. Reimann (r1987) *Concert*
(12/95) (TELD) ① **4509-97459-2**
8 Die Hollywood-Elegien—voice and piano
(1942) (Wds. cpsr and B. Brecht)
1. Unter den grünen Pfefferbäumen; 2. Die Stadt ist
mach den Engein gemannt; 3. Jeden Morgen, mein
Brot zu verdienen; 4. Diese Stadt hat mich belehrt; 5.

In den Hügeln wird Gold gefunden.
D. Fischer-Dieskau, A. Reimann (r1987) *Concert*
(12/95) (TELD) ① **4509-97459-2**
Horatios Monolog—voice and piano (1956)
(Wds. Shakespeare)
D. Fischer-Dieskau, A. Reimann (r1987) *Concert*
(12/95) (TELD) ① **4509-97459-2**
Hotelzimmer 1942—voice and piano (Wds. B.
Brecht)
D. Fischer-Dieskau, A. Reimann (r1987) *Concert*
(12/95) (TELD) ① **4509-97459-2**
In den Weiden—voice and piano (Wds. B.
Brecht)
D. Fischer-Dieskau, A. Reimann (r1987) *Concert*
(12/95) (TELD) ① **4509-97459-2**
In der Frühe—voice and piano (Wds.
Anakreon)
D. Fischer-Dieskau, A. Reimann (r1987) *Concert*
(12/95) (TELD) ① **4509-97459-2**
Die Landschaft des Exils—voice and piano
(Wds. B. Brecht)
D. Fischer-Dieskau, A. Reimann (r1987) *Concert*
(12/95) (TELD) ① **4509-97459-2**
Die Letzte Elegie—voice and piano (Wds. B.
Brecht)
D. Fischer-Dieskau, A. Reimann (r1987) *Concert*
(12/95) (TELD) ① **4509-97459-2**
2 Lieder (after Pascal)—voice and piano
1. Despite these miseries; 2. The only thing.
D. Fischer-Dieskau, A. Reimann (r1987) *Concert*
(12/95) (TELD) ① **4509-97459-2**
Die Maske des Bösen—voice and piano
(Wds. B. Brecht)
D. Fischer-Dieskau, A. Reimann (r1987) *Concert*
(12/95) (TELD) ① **4509-97459-2**
Spruch—voice and piano (Wds. B. Brecht)
D. Fischer-Dieskau, A. Reimann (r1987) *Concert*
(12/95) (TELD) ① **4509-97459-2**
Spruch 1939—voice and piano (Wds. B.
Brecht)
D. Fischer-Dieskau, A. Reimann (r1987) *Concert*
(12/95) (TELD) ① **4509-97459-2**
Über den Selbstmord—voice and piano
(Wds. B. Brecht)
D. Fischer-Dieskau, A. Reimann (r1987) *Concert*
(12/95) (TELD) ① **4509-97459-2**
Über die Dauer des Exils—voice and piano
(1939) (Wds. B. Brecht)
D. Fischer-Dieskau, A. Reimann (r1987) *Concert*
(12/95) (TELD) ① **4509-97459-2**
Verfehlte Liebe—voice and piano (Wds.
Heine)
D. Fischer-Dieskau, A. Reimann (r1987) *Concert*
(12/95) (TELD) ① **4509-97459-2**
Vom Sprengen des Gartens—Lied: 1v and
piano (1942) (Wds. B. Brecht)
W. Sharp, S. Blier (r1991) *Concert*
(7/93) (KOCH) ① **37086-2**
Woodburry-Liederbüchlein—six female vv
(1941)
1. Evening talk; 2. I had a little nut-tree; 3. Ah hear
the wind blow; 4. The sick kitten; 5. Nach einem
Sprichwort; 6. Children rhyme; 7. Little Miss Muffat; 8.
Four and twenty tailors; 9. Kanon; 10. Hector
Protector; 11. The five toes; 12. Pussy cat; 13. The
old woman from France; 14. I had a little Doggie; 15.
The old woman; 16. An den Schlaf (wds. E. Mörike);
17. Für Lou; 18. Ode an die Langweile; 19. Sommer
adieu; 20. On New Year's Day in the morning.
Bel Canto Ens, S. Spohr (r1993) *Concert*
(3/95) (SCHW) ① **314322**
Zeitungsausschnitte—Lieder: 1v & piano,
Op. 11
Kriegslied eines Kindes C. Sieden, S. Blier (r1991)
Concert (7/93) (KOCH) ① **37086-2**
Zufluchtsstätte—voice and piano (Wds. B.
Brecht)
D. Fischer-Dieskau, A. Reimann (r1987) *Concert*
(12/95) (TELD) ① **4509-97459-2**

EKIMOVSKI, Victor *(b 1947)*
USSR

SECTION II: CHAMBER
Cantabile Quartet, composition 22 (1977)
Moscow Contemp Music Ens, A. Vinogradov (r1992)
Concert (9/93) (CDM) ① **LDC288 062**
Chamber Variations, composition 15 (1975)
Moscow Contemp Music Ens, A. Vinogradov (r1992)
Concert (9/93) (CDM) ① **LDC288 062**
Double Chamber Variations—12
instruments, composition 51
Moscow Contemp Music Ens, A. Vinogradov (r1992)
Concert (9/93) (CDM) ① **LDC288 062**

Mandala, composition 39 (1983)
Moscow Contemp Music Ens, A. Vinogradov (r1992)
Concert (9/93) (CDM) ① **LDC288 062**
Up in the hunting dogs—3 flutes,
composition 44 (1986)
Moscow Contemp Music Ens, A. Vinogradov (r1992)
Concert (9/93) (CDM) ① **LDC288 062**

SECTION III: INSTRUMENTAL
Prelude and Fugue—organ, composition 42
(1985)
L. Golub (r1992) *Concert*
(9/93) (CDM) ① **LDC288 062**

EKLÖF, Joel Ejnar *(1886–1954)*
Sweden

SECTION IV: VOCAL AND CHORAL
Morning—song (Wds. Ossiannilsson)
J. Björling, H. Ebert (r1940) *Concert*
(10/93) (NIMB) ① **NI7842**

EL DIN, Hamza *(b 1929)* Sudan

SECTION II: CHAMBER
Escalay (Waterwheel)—tar and string quartet
(1989)
Kronos Qt, H. El Din *Concert*
(11/92) (NONE) ① **7559-79275-2**

ELFMAN, Danny *(20th Cent)*
USA

SECTION V: STAGE WORKS
Batman—film score (1989)
EXCERPTS: 1. Batman Theme (March); 2. Roof
Fight; 3. First Confrontation; 4. Kitchen, Surgery,
Face-Off; 5. Flowers; 6. Clown Attack; 7. Batman to
the Rescue; 8. Roasted Dude; 9. Photos/Beautiful
Dreamer (comp Steven Foster); 10. Descent Into
Mystery; 11. The Bat Cave; 12. The Joker's Poem;
13. Childhood Remembered; 14. Love Theme; 15.
Charge of the Batmobile; 16. Attack of the Batwing;
17. Up the Cathedral; 18. Waltz to the Death; 19. The
Final Confrontation; 20. Finale; 21. Batman Theme
Reprise.
1. Prague City PO, W. Motzing (r1993) *Concert*
(8/94) (SILV) ① **FILMCD146**

ELGAR, Sir Edward (William)
(1857–1934) England

SECTION I: ORCHESTRAL
3 Bavarian Dances—orchestra, Op. 27 (1897)
(Nos. 1, 3 and 6 from 'Scenes from the
Bavarian Highlands')
1. The dance (Allegretto giocoso); 2. Lullaby
(Moderato); 3. The marksman (Allegro vivace).
Bournemouth Sinfonietta, N. del Mar (r1976) *Concert*
(2/92) (CHAN) ① **CHAN6544**
SO, E. Elgar (r1917) *Concert*
(9/92) (PEAR) ① [5] **GEMMCDS9951/5**
Black Dyke Mills Band, P. Parkes (arr brass band:
Parkes) *Concert* (9/93) (CHAN) ① **CHAN4507**
1, 2. LSO, E. Elgar (r1927) *Concert*
(2/93) (EMI) ① [3] **CDS7 54564-2**
3. LSO, E. Elgar (r1932) *Concert*
(2/93) (EMI) ① [3] **CDS7 54564-2**
Carissima—small orchestra (1913)
Northern Sinfonia, R. Hickox (r1985) *Concert*
(1/91) (EMI) ① **CDC7 47672-2**
SO, E. Elgar (r1914) *Concert*
(9/92) (PEAR) ① [5] **GEMMCDS9951/5**
New SO, E. Elgar (r1929) *Concert*
(8/93) (EMI) ① **CDS7 54568-2**
Chanson de matin, Op. 15/2 (1901) (arr from
vn & pf work: 1899)
ECO, Y. Menuhin (arr Fraser) *Concert*
(6/87) (ARAB) ① **Z6563**
Northern Sinfonia, R. Hickox (r1985) *Concert*
(1/91) (EMI) ① **CDC7 47672-2**
Bournemouth Sinfonietta, N. del Mar (r1976) *Concert*
(2/92) (CHAN) ① **CHAN6544**
C. Curley (r1991; arr org: Brewer) *Concert*
(4/92) (ARGO) ① **433 450-2ZH**
Brodsky Qt (arr P. Cassidy) *Concert*
(4/92) (TELD) ① **2292-46015-2**
LSO, E. Elgar (r1927) *Concert*
(2/93) (EMI) ① [3] **CDS7 54564-2**
BBC SO, A. Davis (r1993) *Concert*
(2/95) (TELD) ① **4509-92374-2**
English Sinfonia, C. Groves (r1988) *Concert*
(10/95) (CARL) ① **PCD2017**

Chanson de nuit, Op. 15/1 (1901) (arr from vn
& pf work: 1899)
ECO, Y. Menuhin (arr. Fraser) *Concert*
(6/87) (ARAB) ① **Z6563**
Northern Sinfonia, R. Hickox (r1985) *Concert*
(1/91) (EMI) ① **CDC7 47672-2**
Bournemouth Sinfonietta, N. del Mar (r1976) *Concert*
(2/92) (CHAN) ① **CHAN6544**
C. Curley (r1991; arr org: Brewer) *Concert*
(4/92) (ARGO) ① **433 450-2ZH**
SO, E. Elgar (r1919) *Concert*
(9/92) (PEAR) ① [5] **GEMMCDS9951/5**
RAHO, E. Elgar (r1926) *Concert*
(2/93) (EMI) ① [3] **CDS7 54564-2**
BBC SO, A. Davis (r1993) *Concert*
(2/95) (TELD) ① **4509-92374-2**
English Sinfonia, C. Groves (r1988) *Concert*
(10/95) (CARL) ① **PCD2017**
Civic Fanfare—brass ensemble (1927)
LSO, E. Elgar (pp1927) *Concert*
(6/92) (EMI) ① [3] **CDS7 54560-2**
Cockaigne, 'In London Town'—overture, Op.
40 (1900-01)
SNO, A. Gibson *Concert*
(3/84) (CHAN) ① **CHAN8309**
SNO, A. Gibson *Concert*
(6/87) (CHAN) ① **CHAN8429**
LPO, G. Solti *Concert*
(7/87) (DECC) ① **417 719-2DM**
Philh, J. Barbirolli *Concert*
(12/88) (EMI) ① **CDM7 69563-2**
LPO, L. Slatkin (r1988) *Concert*
(8/89) (RCA) ① **09026 60073-2**
English SO, W. Boughton *Concert*
(12/89) (NIMB) ① **NI5206**
Baltimore SO, D. Zinman *Concert*
(10/90) (TELA) ① **CD80192**
BBC SO, A. Davis *Concert*
(3/92) (TELD) ① **9031-73279-2**
Polish Nat RSO, A. Leaper *Violin Concerto.*
(4/92) (NAXO) ① **8 550489**
LSO, J. Tate *Symphony 1.*
(1/93) (EMI) ① **CDC7 54414-2**
Philh, O.A. Hughes *Symphony 1.*
(2/93) (ASV) ① **CDQS6082**
Philh, J. Barbirolli (r1962) *Symphony 1.*
(6/93) (EMI) ① **CDM7 64511-2**
LPO, V. Handley (r1978) *Concert*
(6/93) (CFP) ① **CD-CFP4617**
RAHO, E. Elgar (r1926) *Concert*
(8/93) (EMI) ① [3] **CDS7 54568-2**
BBC SO, E. Elgar (r1933) *Concert*
(8/93) (EMI) ① [3] **CDS7 54568-2**
LPO, G. Solti (r1977) *Concert*
(4/94) (DECC) ① **440 317-2DWO**
SNO, A. Gibson (r1978) *Walton: Symphony 1.*
(5/94) (CHAN) ① **CHAN6570**
English SO, W. Boughton (r1989) *Concert*
(7/94) (NIMB) ① **NI7015**
LSO, A. Previn (r1993) *Symphony 2.*
(3/95) (PHIL) ① **442 152-2PH**
LPO, G. Solti (r1988) *Concert*
(7/95) (DECC) ① [2] **443 856-2DF2**
Abridged SO, E. Elgar (r1917) *Concert*
(9/92) (PEAR) ① **GEMMCDS9951/5**
Concerto for Cello and Orchestra in E minor,
Op. 85 (1919)
1. Adagio—Moderato; 2. Allegro molto; 3. Adagio; 4.
Allegro.
Y-Y. Ma, LSO, A. Previn *Walton: Cello Concerto.*
(8/85) (SONY) ① **SK39541**
J. Du Pré, LSO, J. Barbirolli (r1965) *Sea Pictures.*
(5/86) (EMI) ① **CDC7 47329-2**
J. Lloyd Webber, RPO, Y. Menuhin *Enigma
Variations.* (6/86) (PHIL) ① **416 354-2PH**
R. Cohen, LPO, N. del Mar *Concert*
(11/87) (CFP) ① **CD-CFP9003**
J. Du Pré, Philadelphia, D. Barenboim (pp1970)
Enigma Variations. (4/88) (SONY) ① **SK76529**
P. Fournier, BPO, A. Wallenstein *Dvořák: Cello
Concerto.* (11/88) (DG) ① **423 881-2GGA**
J. Du Pré, LSO, J. Barbirolli *Concert*
(3/89) (EMI) ① [2] **CMS7 69707-2**
R. Golani, RPO, V. Handley (arr L.Tertis: va/orch)
Concert (4/89) (CONI) ① **CDCF171**
B. Harrison, New SO, E. Elgar (r1928) *Violin
Concerto.* (11/89) (EMI) ① **CDH7 69786-2**
B. Harrison, New SO, E. Elgar (r1928) *Violin
Concerto.* (11/89) (CLAR) ① **CDGSE78-50-31**
F. Schmidt, LSO, R. Frühbeck de Burgos *Concert*
(1/90) (CARL) ① **PCD930**
P. Casals, BBC SO, A. Boult (r1945) *Concert*
(8/90) (EMI) ① **CDH7 63498-2**
M. Maisky, Philh, G. Sinopoli *Tchaikovsky: Rococo
Variations.* (7/91) (DG) ① **431 685-2GH**

M. Braunstein, London Academy, R. Stamp (arr L.
Tertis: va/orch) *Enigma Variations.*
(12/91) (VIRG) ① **VJ7 59643-2**
T. Thedéen, Malmö SO, L. Markiz *Schumann: Cello
Concerto.* (8/92) (BIS) ① **BIS-CD486**
M. Kliegel, RPO, M. Halász *Dvořák: Cello Concerto.*
(9/92) (NAXO) ① **8 550503**
A. Baillie, BBC PO, E. Downes *Enigma Variations.*
(4/93) (CONI) ① **CDCF507**
R. Cohen, RPO, C. Mackerras (r1992) *Concert*
(6/93) (ARGO) ① **436 545-2ZH**
B. Harrison, New SO, E. Elgar (r1928) *Concert*
(8/93) (EMI) ① [3] **CDS7 54568-2**
P. Tortelier, BBC SO, M. Sargent (r1953) *Dream of
Gerontius.* (2/94) (TEST) ① [2] **SBT2025**
L. Harrell, Cleveland Orch, L. Maazel (r1979) *Violin
Concerto.* (4/94) (DECC) ① **440 319-2DWO**
M. Rostropovich, Moscow PO, G. Rozhdestvensky
(pp1964) *Concert* (7/94) (RUSS) ① **RDCD11104**
J. Du Pré, LSO, J. Barbirolli (r1965) *Concert*
(8/94) (EMI) ① [6] **CZS5 68132-2**
S. Isserlis, LSO, R. Hickox (r1988) *Bloch: Schelomo.*
(11/94) (VIRG) ① **CUV5 61125-2**
A. Noras, Finnish RSO, J-P. Saraste (r1993) *Lalo:
Cello Concerto.* (12/94) (FINL) ① **4509-95768-2**
M. Maisky, Philh, G. Sinopoli (r1990) *Concert*
(12/94) (DG) ① **445 511-2GMA**
Z. Nelsova, BBC SO, C. Groves (pp1969) *Concert*
(5/95) (BBCR) ① **BBCRD9111**
J. Du Pré, LSO, J. Barbirolli (r1965) *Dvořák: Cello
Concerto.* (11/95) (EMI) ① **CDC5 55527-2**
Abridged B. Harrison, SO, E. Elgar (r1919/20)
Concert (9/92) (PEAR) ① [5] **GEMMCDS9951/5**
3. B. Harrison, Princess Victoria (r1928: arr vc/pf)
Concert (3/93) (CLAR) ① **CDGSE78-50-47**
**Concerto for Violin and Orchestra in B
minor, Op. 61 (1909-10)**
K-W. Chung, LPO, G. Solti *Concert*
(8/89) (LOND) ① **421 388-2LM**
Y. Menuhin, LSO, E. Elgar (r1932) *Cello Concerto.*
(11/89) (EMI) ① **CDH7 69786-2**
Y. Menuhin, LSO, E. Elgar (r1932) *Concert*
(11/89) (CLAR) ① **CDGSE78-50-31**
D. Suk-Kang, Polish Nat RSO, A. Leaper *Cockaigne.*
(4/92) (NAXO) ① **8 550489**
S. Accardo, LSO, R. Hickox *Walton: Violin Concerto.*
(7/92) (COLL) ① **Coll1338-2**
Y. Menuhin, LSO, E. Elgar (r1932) *Concert*
(2/93) (EMI) ① [3] **CDS7 54564-2**
H. Bean, RLPO, C. Groves (r1972) *Violin Sonata.*
(9/93) (CFP) ① **CD-CFP4632**
P. Zukerman, St Louis SO, L. Slatkin (r1992) *Concert
d'amour.* (1/94) (RCA) ① **09026 61672-2**
P. Zukerman, LPO, D. Barenboim (r1976) *In the
South.* (1/94) (SONY) ① **SMK58927**
Y. Menuhin, New Philh, A. Boult (r1965) *Delius: Violin
Concerto.* (2/94) (EMI) ① **CDM7 64725-2**
K. Takezawa, BRSO, Colin Davis (r1993)
Introduction and Allegro.
(3/94) (RCA) ① **09026 61612-2**
K-W. Chung, LPO, G. Solti (r1977) *Cello Concerto.*
(4/94) (DECC) ① **440 319-2DWO**
A. Campoli, LPO, A. Boult (r1954) *Mendelssohn:
Violin Concerto, Op. 64.* (10/94) (BEUL) ① **1PD10**
J. Heifetz, LSO, M. Sargent (r1949) *Concert*
(11/94) (RCA) ① [65] **09026 61778-2(07)**
L. Chen, Arnhem PO, Y. Menuhin (r1994) *Bruch:
Violin Concerto 1.* (11/95) (UPBE) ① **URCD115**
Abridged M. Hall, SO, E. Elgar (r1916) *Concert*
(9/92) (PEAR) ① [5] **GEMMCDS9951/5**
Contrasts, Op. 10/3 (1899) (No. 3 of 'Three
Characteristic Pieces')
RPO, V. Handley *Concert*
(4/89) (CONI) ① **CDCF171**
Northern Sinfonia, R. Hickox (r1985) *Concert*
(1/91) (EMI) ① **CDC7 47672-2**
Bournemouth Sinfonietta, N. del Mar (r1976) *Concert*
(2/92) (CHAN) ① **CHAN6544**
LPO, E. Elgar (r1933) *Concert*
(8/93) (EMI) ① [3] **CDS7 54564-2**
Coronation March, Op. 65 (1911)
RPO, Y. Butt (r1988) *Concert*
(11/88) (ASV) ① **CDDCA619**
LPO, L. Ronald (r1935) *Concert*
(8/93) (EMI) ① [3] **CDS7 54568-2**
**Dream children—two pieces for small
orchestra, Op. 43 (1902)**
1. Andante; 2. Allegretto.
Northern Sinfonia, R. Hickox (r1985) *Concert*
(1/91) (EMI) ① **CDC7 47672-2**
Bournemouth Sinfonietta, N. del Mar (r1976) *Concert*
(2/92) (CHAN) ① **CHAN6544**
WNO Orch, C. Mackerras *Concert*
(10/92) (ARGO) ① **433 214-2ZH**
BBC SO, A. Davis (r1993) *Concert*
(2/95) (TELD) ① **4509-92374-2**

**Elegy—string orchestra with harp, Op. 58
(1909)**
New Philh, J. Barbirolli *Concert*
(2/87) (EMI) ① **CDC7 47537-2**
ECO, Y. Menuhin *Concert* (6/87) (ARAB) ① **Z6563**
LPO, N. del Mar *Concert*
(11/87) (CFP) ① **CD-CFP9003**
LPO, E. Elgar (r1933) *Concert*
(8/93) (EMI) ① [3] **CDS7 54568-2**
New Philh, J. Barbirolli (r1966) *Concert*
(2/94) (EMI) ① **CDM7 64724-2**
ASMF, N. Marriner (r1968) *Concert*
(4/94) (DECC) ① **440 317-2DWO**
English SO, W. Boughton (r1983) *Concert*
(7/94) (NIMB) ① **NI7015**
BBC SO, A. Davis (r1993) *Concert*
(2/95) (TELD) ① **4509-92374-2**
Smithsonian Chbr Plyrs, K. Slowik (r1994) *Concert*
(9/95) (DHM) ① **05472 77343-2**
Orpheus CO (r1985) *Concert*
(12/95) (DG) ① **445 561-2GMA**
Falstaff—symphonic study, Op. 68 (1913)
1. Interlude I - Jack Falstaff, Page to the Duke of
Norfolk; 2. Interlude II - Gloucestershire, Shallow's
orchard.
SNO, A. Gibson *Enigma Variations.*
(9/87) (CHAN) ① **CHAN8431**
Hallé, J. Barbirolli (r1964) *Enigma Variations.*
(11/88) (EMI) ① **CDM7 69185-2**
LSO, E. Elgar (r1931/2) *Concert*
(6/92) (EMI) ① [3] **CDS7 54560-2**
LPO, V. Handley (r1978) *Concert*
(6/93) (CFP) ① **CD-CFP4617**
CBSO, S. Rattle *Concert*
(3/95) (EMI) ① **CDC5 55001-2**
1, 2. Northern Sinfonia, R. Hickox (r1985) *Concert*
(1/91) (EMI) ① **CDC7 47672-2**
1, 2. Bournemouth Sinfonietta, N. del Mar (r1976)
Concert (2/92) (CHAN) ① **CHAN6544**
1, 2. New SO, E. Elgar (r1929) *Concert*
(8/93) (EMI) ① [3] **CDS7 54568-2**
**Froissart—concert overture, Op. 19 (1890 rev
1901)**
SNO, A. Gibson *Concert*
(3/84) (CHAN) ① **CHAN8309**
RPO, Y. Butt (r1988) *Concert*
(11/88) (ASV) ① **CDDCA619**
New Philh, J. Barbirolli *Concert*
(12/88) (EMI) ① **CDM7 69563-2**
LPO, L. Slatkin (r1988) *Concert*
(8/89) (RCA) ① **09026 60073-2**
English SO, W. Boughton *Concert*
(12/89) (NIMB) ① **NI5206**
BBC PO, E. Downes *Concert*
(1/91) (CONI) ① **CDCF187**
English Northern Philh, D. Lloyd-Jones *Concert*
(1/92) (HYPE) ① **CDA66515**
RPO, C. Mackerras (r1992) *Concert*
(6/93) (ARGO) ① **436 545-2ZH**
LPO, E. Elgar (r1933) *Concert*
(8/93) (EMI) ① [3] **CDS7 54568-2**
Imperial March, Op. 32 (1896-97)
M. Archer (arr org: Martin) *Concert*
(10/89) (MERI) ① **CDE84168**
A. Lumsden (arr Martin) *Concert*
(4/91) (GUIL) ① **GRCD7025**
S. Preston (trans org: arr. G C Martin) *Concert*
(8/91) (DECC) ① **430 091-2DWO**
C. Curley (r1991; arr org: Martin) *Concert*
(4/92) (ARGO) ① **433 450-2ZH**
C. Curley (r1991: arr Martin) *Concert*
(6/93) (DECC) ① **436 403-2DWO**
BBC PO, A. Hurst (r1992) *Symphony 1.*
(2/94) (NAXO) ① **8 550634**
**In the South, 'Alassio'—concert overture,
Op. 50 (1903)**
SNO, A. Gibson *Concert*
(3/84) (CHAN) ① **CHAN8309**
LPO, N. del Mar *Concert*
(11/87) (CFP) ① **CD-CFP9003**
RPO, Y. Butt (r1988) *Concert*
(11/88) (ASV) ① **CDDCA619**
LPO, G. Aykal Saygun *Viola Concerto.*
(4/90) (SCHW) ① **311002**
BBC PO, E. Downes *Concert*
(1/91) (CONI) ① **CDCF187**
LPO, L. Slatkin *Symphony 1.*
(6/91) (RCA) ① **RD60380**
ASMF, N. Marriner *Symphony 1.*
(12/91) (COLL) ① **Coll1269-2**
BBC SO, A. Davis *Symphony 1.*
(11/92) (TELD) ① **9031-74888-2**
LSO, E. Elgar (r1930) *Concert*
(8/93) (EMI) ① [3] **CDS7 54568-2**
LPO, D. Barenboim (r1976) *Violin Concerto.*
(1/94) (SONY) ① **SMK58927**

LPO, G. Solti (r1969) *Concert*
(4/94) (DECC) ① **440 317-2DWO**
Bournemouth SO, C. Silvestri (r1967) *Concert*
(11/94) (EMI) ① [2] **CZS5 68229-2**
Milan La Scala PO, R. Muti (r1993) *Brahms:
Serenade 1.* (1/95) (SONY) ① **SK57973**
LPO, G. Solti (r1979) *Concert*
(7/95) (DECC) ① [2] **443 856-2DF2**
abridged RAHO, E. Elgar (r1921/3) *Concert*
(9/92) (PEAR) ① [5] **GEMMCDS9951/5**
**Introduction and Allegro for string quartet
and string orchestra, Op. 47 (1904-05)**
Allegri Qt, Sinfonia of London, J. Barbirolli *Concert*
(2/87) (EMI) ① **CDC7 47537-2**
ECO, Y. Menuhin *Concert* (6/87) (ARAB) ① **Z6563**
LPO, V. Handley *Concert*
(10/87) (EMIN) ① **CD-EMX9503**
ECO, B. Britten *Concert*
(6/91) (DECC) ① **430 094-2DWO**
Polish CO, J. Stanienda (vn/dir) (pp1990) *Concert*
(12/91) (LINN) ① **CKD001**
BBC SO, A. Davis *Concert*
(3/92) (TELD) ① **9031-73279-2**
Britannia CO, D. Falkowski *Concert*
(6/92) (ENGL) ① **ERC5001**
LPO, V. Handley (r1983) *Concert*
(6/93) (CFP) ① **CD-CFP4617**
Boston SO, C. Munch (r1957) *Concert*
(9/93) (RCA) ① **09026 61424-2**
CLS, R. Hickox (r1991) *Concert*
(12/93) (EMI) ① **CDC7 54407-2**
BPO, S. Bychkov *Concert*
(3/94) (PHIL) ① **434 108-2PH**
BRSO, Colin Davis (r1993) *Violin Concerto.*
(3/94) (RCA) ① **09026 61612-2**
English SO, W. Boughton (r1983) *Concert*
(7/94) (NIMB) ① **NI7015**
Medici Qt, Oxford Orch da Camera, G. Vass (r1993)
Concert (9/94) (MEDI) ① **MQCD4002**
London CO, C. Warren-Green (vn/dir) (r1988)
Concert (11/94) (VIRG) ① **CUV5 61126-2**
Orpheus CO (r1985) *Concert*
(12/95) (DG) ① **445 561-2GMA**
May Song (orch 1928) (arr. of pno work)
Northern Sinfonia, R. Hickox (r1985) *Concert*
(1/91) (EMI) ① **CDC7 47672-2**
New SO, E. Elgar (r1929) *Concert*
(8/93) (EMI) ① [3] **CDS7 54568-2**
Mazurka—small orchestra, Op.10/1 (1899)
(No. 1 of 'Three Characteristic Pieces')
ECO, Y. Menuhin *Concert* (6/87) (ARAB) ① **Z6563**
RPO, V. Handley *Concert*
(4/89) (CONI) ① **CDCF171**
Northern Sinfonia, R. Hickox (r1985) *Concert*
(1/91) (EMI) ① **CDC7 47672-2**
New SO, E. Elgar (r1929) *Concert*
(2/93) (EMI) ① [3] **CDS7 54564-2**
Mina—small orchestra (1933)
Northern Sinfonia, R. Hickox (r1985) *Concert*
(1/91) (EMI) ① **CDC7 47672-2**
Light SO, Haydn Wood (r1935) *Concert*
(8/93) (EMI) ① [3] **CDS7 54568-2**
New Light SO, J. Ainslie Murray (r1934) *Concert*
(8/93) (EMI) ① [3] **CDS7 54568-2**
Minuet—orchestra, Op. 21 (1897) (orch
version of piano work)
New SO, E. Elgar (r1929) *Concert*
(8/93) (EMI) ① [3] **CDS7 54568-2**
Nursery Suite—orchestra (1931)
1. Aubade; 2. The Serious Doll; 3. Busy-ness; 4. The
Sad Doll; 5. The Wagon (passes); 6. The Merry Doll;
7. Dreaming Envoy.
Ulster Orch, B. Thomson (r1982) *Concert*
(10/84) (CHAN) ① **CHAN8318**
LSO, E. Elgar (r1931: orch version) *Concert*
(8/93) (EMI) ① [3] **CDS7 54564-2**
2. K. Smith, P. Rhodes (arr Smith) *Concert*
(1/91) (ASV) ① **CDDCA739**
Polonia—symphonic prelude, Op. 76 (1915)
Rutland Sinfonia, B. Collett *Concert*
(5/88) (PEAR) ① **SHECD9602**
SO, E. Elgar (r1919) *Concert*
(9/92) (PEAR) ① [5] **GEMMCDS9951/5**
**Pomp and Circumstance—military marches,
Op. 39 (1901-1930)**
1. D (1901); 2. A minor (1901); 3. C minor (1904); 4.
G (1907); 5. C (1930).
SNO, A. Gibson *Concert*
(6/87) (CHAN) ① **CHAN8429**
LPO, G. Solti *Concert*
(7/87) (DECC) ① **417 719-2DM**
RPO, A. Previn *Enigma Variations.*
(8/87) (PHIL) ① **416 813-2PH**
LPO, V. Handley *Sea Pictures.*
(11/87) (CFP) ① **CD-CFP9004**

LPO, D. Barenboim *Cello Concerto.*
(4/88) (SONY) ① **SK76529**
Philh, J. Barbirolli (r1962) *Falstaff.*
(11/88) (EMI) ① **CDM7 69185-2**
LPO, B. Thomson (r1988) *Concert*
(5/89) (CHAN) ① **CHAN8610**
LPO, L. Slatkin (1988) *Concert*
(8/89) (RCA) ① **09026 60073-2**
English SO, W. Boughton *Concert*
(12/89) (NIMB) ① **NI5206**
RPO, N. del Mar (r1975) *Pomp and Circumstance Marches.*
(9/90) (DG) ① **429 713-2GGA**
Baltimore SO, D. Zinman *Concert*
(10/90) (TELA) ① **CD80192**
Bratislava RSO, A. Leaper *Concert*
(1/91) (NAXO) ① **8 550229**
SNO, A. Gibson *Pomp and Circumstance Marches.*
(1/91) (CHAN) ① **CHAN6504**
BBC PO, E. Downes *Concert*
(1/91) (CONI) ① **CDCF187**
RPO, A. Litton *Cello Concerto.*
(12/91) (VIRG) ① **VJ7 59643-2**
NBC SO, A. Toscanini (r1951) *Mussorgsky: Pictures.*
(2/92) (RCA) ① **GD60287**
BBC SO, A. Davis *Concert*
(3/92) (TELD) ① **9031-73279-2**
LSO, A. Boult *Pomp and Circumstance Marches.*
(4/92) (EMI) ① **CDM7 64015-2**
RAHO, E. Elgar (r1920/1) *Concert*
(9/92) (PEAR) ① [5] **GEMMCDS9951/5**
RAHO, E. Elgar (r1926) *Concert*
(2/93) (EMI) ① [3] **CDS7 54564-2**
BBC PO, E. Downes *Cello Concerto.*
(4/93) (CONI) ① **CDCF507**
RPO, C. Mackerras (r1992) *Concert*
(6/93) (ARGO) ① **436 545-2ZH**
RAHO, E. Elgar (r1926) *Holst: Planets.*
(10/93) (EMI) ① **CDC7 54837-2**
English SO, W. Boughton (r1989) *Concert*
(7/94) (NIMB) ① **NI7015**
NYO, C. Seaman (r1993) *R. Strauss: Sinfonia domestica.*
(8/94) (CARL) ① **PCD1080**
Philh, A. Davis (r1981) *Pomp and Circumstance Marches.*
(9/94) (SONY) ① **SMK46684**
Philh, G. Sinopoli (r1987) *Concert*
(12/94) (DG) ① **445 511-2GMA**
BPO, James Levine (r1992) *Debussy: Images.*
(2/95) (SONY) ① **SK53284**
ASMF, N. Marriner (r1993) *Concert*
(2/95) (CAPR) ① **10 501**
LSO, E. Jochum (r1975) *Holst: Planets.*
(3/95) (DG) ① **439 446-2GCL**
CBSO, S. Rattle *Concert*
(3/95) (EMI) ① **CDC5 55001-2**
BBC SO, M. Sargent (pp1966) *Holst: Planets.*
(3/95) (BBCR) ① **BBCRD9104**
9. Martin Jones (r1989: trans pf: Grainger) *Concert*
(7/90) (NIMB) ① **NI5232**
9. LSO, P. Monteux *Concert*
(6/91) (DECC) ① **430 094-2DWO**
9. C. Curley (r1991; arr org: W H Harris) *Concert*
(4/92) (ARGO) ① **433 450-2ZH**
The Wand of Youth - Suite No. 1, Op. 1a (1907)
1. Overture; 2. Serenade; 3. Minuet; 4. Sun Dance; 5. Fairy Pipers; 6. Slumber Scene; 7. Fairies and Giants.
Ulster Orch, B. Thomson (r1982) *Concert*
(10/84) (CHAN) ① **CHAN8318**
WNO Orch, C. Mackerras (r1990) *Concert*
(10/92) (ARGO) ① **433 214-2ZH**
LSO, E. Elgar (r1928) *Concert*
(2/93) (EMI) ① [3] **CDS7 54564-2**
ASMF, N. Marriner (r1993) *Concert*
(2/95) (CAPR) ① **10 501**
1, 2, 4, 5, 7. SO, E. Elgar (with variant takes: r1917) *Concert* (9/92) (PEAR) ① [5] **GEMMCDS9951/5**
1-3, 7. Black Dyke Mills Band, P. Parkes (arr brass band: G Langford) *Concert*
(9/93) (CHAN) ① **CHAN4507**
The Wand of Youth - Suite No. 2, Op. 1b (1908)
1. March; 2. The Little Bells; 3. Moths and Butterflies; 4. Fountain Dance; 5. The Tame Bear; 6. Wild Bears.
Ulster Orch, B. Thomson (r1982) *Concert*
(10/84) (CHAN) ① **CHAN8318**
WNO Orch, C. Mackerras (r1990) *Concert*
(10/92) (ARGO) ① **433 214-2ZH**
LSO, E. Elgar (r1928) *Concert*
(2/93) (EMI) ① [3] **CDS7 54564-2**
ASMF, N. Marriner (r1993) *Concert*
(2/95) (CAPR) ① **10 501**
1-3, 5, 6. SO, E. Elgar (with variant takes: r1917/9) *Concert* (9/92) (PEAR) ① [5] **GEMMCDS9951/5**

1, 5, 6. Black Dyke Mills Band, P. Parkes (arr brass band: G Langford) *Concert*
(9/93) (CHAN) ① **CHAN4507**

SECTION II: CHAMBER

Adagio cantabile, 'Mrs Winslow's soothing syrup'—wind quintet (1879)
Athena Ens *Concert* (6/92) (CHAN) ① **CHAN6553**
Allegretto in C on G-E-D-G-E—violin and piano (1885)
W. Bouton, L. Hall (r1991) *Concert*
(10/93) (CARL) ① [2] **DPCD1039**
Andante con variazione (Evesham andante)—wind quintet (1879)
Athena Ens *Concert* (6/92) (CHAN) ① **CHAN6553**
Bizarrerie in G minor—violin and piano, Op. 13/1 (1889)
W. Bouton, L. Hall (r1991) *Concert*
(10/93) (CARL) ① [2] **DPCD1039**
Canto popolare—violin/viola and piano (extract from 'In the South')
N. Kennedy, P. Pettinger *Concert*
(8/85) (CHAN) ① **CHAN8380**
W. Bouton, L. Hall (r1991) *Concert*
(10/93) (CARL) ① [2] **DPCD1039**
P. Lane, J. Boyd (r1994) *Concert*
(3/95) (EMIN) ① **CD-EMX2229**
La Capricieuse—violin and piano, Op. 17 (1891)
K-W. Chung, P. Moll *Concert*
(9/87) (DECC) ① **417 289-2DH**
K-W. Chung, P. Moll *Concert*
(8/89) (LOND) ① **421 388-2LM**
I. Perlman, S. Sanders (arr. Heifetz) *Concert*
(12/89) (EMI) ① **CDC7 49604-2**
X. Wei, Pam Nicholson *Concert*
(9/90) (ASV) ① **CDDCA698**
J. Heifetz, A. Benoist (r1917) *Concert*
(1/91) (BIDD) ① **LAB015**
J. Heifetz, A. Benoist (r1917) *Concert*
(12/91) (APR) ① [2] **APR7015**
K-W. Chung, P. Moll (r1985) *Concert*
(5/92) (DECC) ① **433 220-2DWO**
J. Hassid, G. Moore (r1940) *Concert*
(10/92) (PEAR) ① **GEMMCD9939**
J. Hassid, G. Moore (r1940) *Concert*
(10/92) (TEST) ① **SBT1010**
J. Hassid, I. Newton (r1939) *Concert*
(10/92) (TEST) ① **SBT1010**
S. Chang, S. Rivers (ed.Heifetz) *Concert*
(1/93) (EMI) ① **CDC7 54352-2**
K. Daeshik Kang, M. Rahkonen (r1992) *Concert*
(9/93) (NIMB) ① **NI5358**
W. Bouton, L. Hall (r1991) *Concert*
(10/93) (CARL) ① [2] **DPCD1039**
Chee-Yun, A. Eguchi *Concert*
(12/93) (DENO) ① **CO-75118**
J. Hassid, G. Moore (r1940) *Concert*
(1/94) (DUTT) ① **CDLX7004**
B. Huberman, P. Frenkel (r1921) *Concert*
(3/94) (BIDD) ① [2] **LAB077/8**
B. Huberman, S. Schultze (r1930) *Concert*
(9/94) (BIDD) ① [2] **LAB081/2**
J. Heifetz, A. Benoist (r1917) *Concert*
(11/94) (RCA) ① [65] **09026 61778-2(01)**
J. Heifetz, A. Sándor (r1934) *Concert*
(11/94) (RCA) ① [65] **09026 61778-2(02)**
V. Spivakov, S. Bezrodny (r1991-2) *Concert*
(5/95) (RCA) ① **09026 62524-2**
I. Perlman, S. Sanders (r1988: arr Heifetz) *Concert*
(6/95) (EMI) ① [20] **CZS4 83177-2(3)**
Carissima—violin and piano (1914)
W. Bouton, L. Hall (r1991) *Concert*
(10/93) (CARL) ① [2] **DPCD1039**
Chanson de matin—violin and piano, Op. 15/2 (1897)
N. Kennedy, P. Pettinger *Concert*
(8/85) (CHAN) ① **CHAN8380**
Midori, R. McDonald (r1992) *Concert*
(6/93) (SONY) ① **SK52568**
W. Bouton, L. Hall (r1991) *Concert*
(10/93) (CARL) ① [2] **DPCD1039**
T. Trotter (r1992: arr org: H Brewer) *Concert*
(4/94) (DECC) ① **436 656-2DH**
Chanson de nuit—violin and piano, Op. 15/1 (1897)
N. Kennedy, P. Pettinger *Concert*
(8/85) (CHAN) ① **CHAN8380**
W. Bouton, L. Hall (r1991) *Concert*
(10/93) (CARL) ① [2] **DPCD1039**
4 Dances—wind quintet (1879)
1. Menuetto-allegretto; 2. Gavotte (The Alphonsa); 3. Sarabande-Largo (later re-used in 'The Spanish Lady', 1933); 4. Gigue-allegretto.
Athena Ens *Concert* (6/92) (CHAN) ① **CHAN6554**

Gavotte in A—violin and piano (1885)
W. Bouton, L. Hall (r1991) *Concert*
(10/93) (CARL) ① [2] **DPCD1039**
Harmony Music—four pieces for wind quintet (1878)
1, 5. Athena Ens *Concert*
(6/92) (CHAN) ① **CHAN6553**
2-4. Athena Ens *Concert*
(6/92) (CHAN) ① **CHAN6554**
Une Idylle in G—violin and piano, Op. 4/1 (1883)
W. Bouton, L. Hall (r1991) *Concert*
(10/93) (CARL) ① [2] **DPCD1039**
J. Lloyd Webber, J. Birch (r1994) *Concert*
(12/94) (PHIL) ① **442 530-2PH**
5 Intermezzos—wind quintet (1879)
1. Allegro molto (The Farmyard); 2. Adagio solenne; 3. Allegretto (Nancy); 4. Andante con moto; 5. Allegretto.
Athena Ens *Concert* (6/92) (CHAN) ① **CHAN6553**
May song—violin and piano (1901)
W. Bouton, L. Hall (r1991) *Concert*
(10/93) (CARL) ① [2] **DPCD1039**
Mazurka in C minor—violin and piano, Op. 10/1 (1888)
W. Bouton, L. Hall (r1991) *Concert*
(10/93) (CARL) ① [2] **DPCD1039**
Mot d'amour, 'Liebesahnung'—Bizarrerie: violin and piano (1889)
N. Kennedy, P. Pettinger *Concert*
(8/85) (CHAN) ① **CHAN8380**
W. Bouton, L. Hall (r1991) *Concert*
(10/93) (CARL) ① [2] **DPCD1039**
Offertoire (andante religioso)—violin and piano (pub 1903)
W. Bouton, L. Hall (r1991) *Concert*
(10/93) (CARL) ① [2] **DPCD1039**
Pastourelle in B flat—violin and piano, Op. 4/2 (1883)
W. Bouton, L. Hall (r1991) *Concert*
(10/93) (CARL) ① [2] **DPCD1039**
6 Promenades—wind quintet (1878)
1. Moderato e molto maestoso; 2. Moderato (Madame Taussard's); 3. Presto; 4. Andante (Somniferous); 5. Allegro molto; 6. Allegro maestoso (Hell and Tommy).
Athena Ens *Concert* (6/92) (CHAN) ① **CHAN6554**
Quintet for Piano and Strings in A minor, Op. 84 (1918-19)
J. Bingham, Medici Qt *String Quartet.*
(6/86) (MERI) ① **ECD84082**
Medici Qt, J. Bingham *String Quartet.*
(11/92) (MEDI) ① **MQCD7002**
Nash Ens (r1992) *Violin Sonata.*
(8/93) (HYPE) ① **CDA66645**
H. Cohen, Stratton Qt (r1933) *Concert*
(1/94) (DUTT) ① **CDLX7004**
B. Roberts, Chilingirian Qt (r1985) *String Quartet.*
(10/94) (EMI) ① **CDM5 65099-2**
P. Lane, Vellinger Qt (r1994) *Concert*
(3/95) (EMIN) ① **CD-EMX2229**
Reminiscence in D—violin and piano (1877)
W. Bouton, L. Hall (r1991) *Concert*
(10/93) (CARL) ① [2] **DPCD1039**
Romance for Bassoon and Piano, Op. 62 (c1909-10) (arr cpsr from orch work)
Daniel Smith, R. Vignoles *Concert*
(9/89) (ASV) ① **CDDCA535**
K. Walker, J. Drake *Concert*
(10/89) (REGE) ① **REGCD104**
J. Lloyd Webber, J. Lenehan (r1992) *Concert*
(10/93) (PHIL) ① **434 917-2PH**
Romance in C minor—violin and piano, Op. 1 (1878)
W. Bouton, L. Hall (r1991) *Concert*
(10/93) (CARL) ① [2] **DPCD1039**
Rosemary—violin, cello and piano (1882) (org 'Danse pensée')
W. Bouton, L. Hall (r1991) *Concert*
(10/93) (CARL) ① [2] **DPCD1039**
Salut d'amour, 'Liebesgrüss'—violin and piano, Op. 12
N. Kennedy, P. Pettinger *Concert*
(8/85) (CHAN) ① **CHAN8380**
K-W. Chung, P. Moll *Concert*
(9/87) (DECC) ① **417 289-2DH**
K-W. Chung, P. Moll *Concert*
(8/89) (LOND) ① **421 388-2LM**
K-W. Chung, P. Moll *Concert*
(6/91) (DECC) ① **430 094-2DWO**
K-W. Chung, P. Moll (r1985) *Concert*
(5/92) (DECC) ① **433 220-2DWO**
S. Chang, S. Rivers *Concert*
(1/93) (EMI) ① **CDC7 54352-2**
Margaret Harrison, B. Harrison, Princess Victoria (r1928) *Concert* (3/93) (CLAR) ① **CDGSE78-50-47**

Midori, R. McDonald (r1992) *Concert*
(6/93) (SONY) ① **SK52568**
W. Bouton, L. Hall (r1991) *Concert*
(10/93) (CARL) ① [2] **DPCD1039**
Chee-Yun, A. Eguchi *Concert*
(12/93) (DENO) ① **CO-75118**
A. A. Meyers, S. Rivers (r1993) *Concert*
(4/95) (RCA) ① **09026 62546-2**
V. Spivakov, S. Bezrodny (r1991-2) *Concert*
(5/95) (RCA) ① **09026 62524-2**
Soliloquy—oboe and piano (1930s) (from unfinished Suite: orch G Jacob)
L. Goossens, Bournemouth Sinfonietta, N. del Mar (orch G Jacob: r1976) *Concert*
(2/92) (CHAN) ① **CHAN6544**
Sonata for Violin and Piano in E minor, Op. 82 (1918)
N. Kennedy, P. Pettinger *Concert*
(8/85) (CHAN) ① **CHAN8380**
Medici Qt *Elgar/Binyon: Wood magic.*
(11/92) (MEDI) ① **MQCD7001**
Nash Ens (r1992) *Piano Quintet.*
(8/93) (HYPE) ① **CDA66645**
H. Bean, D. Parkhouse (r1971) *Violin Concerto.*
(9/93) (CFP) ① **CD-CFP4632**
W. Bouton, L. Hall (r1991) *Concert*
(10/93) (CARL) ① [2] **DPCD1039**
Sospiri—violin and piano, Op. 70 (1914)
N. Kennedy, P. Pettinger *Concert*
(8/85) (CHAN) ① **CHAN8380**
W. Bouton, L. Hall (r1991) *Concert*
(10/93) (CARL) ① [2] **DPCD1039**
String Quartet in E minor, Op. 83 (1918)
Medici Qt *Piano Quintet.*
(6/86) (MERI) ① **ECD84082**
Gabrieli Qt *Walton: String Quartet.*
(10/87) (CHAN) ① **CHAN8474**
Brodsky Qt *Delius: String Quartet (1916).*
(7/89) (ASV) ① **CDDCA526**
Britten Qt (r1991) *Walton: String Quartet.*
(7/92) (COLL) ① **Coll1280-2**
Medici Qt *Piano Quintet.*
(11/92) (MEDI) ① **MQCD7002**
Stratton Qt (r1933) *Concert*
(1/94) (DUTT) ① **CDLX7004**
Chilingirian Qt (r1985) *Piano Quintet.*
(10/94) (EMI) ① **CDM5 65099-2**
Coull Qt (r1993) *Concert*
(10/94) (HYPE) ① **CDA66718**
Vellinger Qt (r1994) *Concert*
(3/95) (EMIN) ① **CD-EMX2229**
Very easy melodious exercises in the first position—violin and piano, Op. 22 (1892)
N. Kennedy, P. Pettinger *Concert*
(8/85) (CHAN) ① **CHAN8380**
W. Bouton, L. Hall (r1991) *Concert*
(10/93) (CARL) ① [2] **DPCD1039**
Virelai—violin and piano, Op. 4/3 (1883)
W. Bouton, L. Hall (r1991) *Concert*
(10/93) (CARL) ① [2] **DPCD1039**

SECTION III: INSTRUMENTAL

Adieu—piano (pub. 1932)
P. Pettinger *Concert* (6/87) (CHAN) ① **CHAN8438**
Bournemouth Sinfonietta, G. Hurst (arr/orch H. Geehl) *Concert* (6/87) (CHAN) ① **CHAN8432**
J. Szigeti, N. Magaloff (arr vn/pf: Szigeti: r1934) *Concert* (1/90) (BIDD) ① [2] **LAB007/8**
C. Headington *Concert*
(11/90) (KING) ① **KCLCD2017**
A. Gravill *Concert* (3/91) (GAMU) ① **GAMCD516**
Bournemouth Sinfonietta, G. Hurst (arr/orch H Geehl: r1975) *Concert* (2/92) (CHAN) ① **CHAN6544**
J. Szigeti, N. Magaloff (r1934: arr vn/pf: Szigeti) *Concert* (1/94) (DUTT) ① **CDLX7004**
Carissima—piano (1913)
P. Pettinger *Concert* (6/87) (CHAN) ① **CHAN8438**
Chantant—piano (c1872)
P. Pettinger *Concert* (6/87) (CHAN) ① **CHAN8438**
Concert Allegro—piano (1901)
P. Pettinger *Concert* (6/87) (CHAN) ① **CHAN8438**
A. Gravill *Concert* (3/91) (GAMU) ① **GAMCD516**
Danse pensée—piano (1882) (orch 1915 and pub as 'Rosemary')
P. Pettinger *Concert* (6/87) (CHAN) ① **CHAN8438**
Dream Children—piano, Op. 43 (1902)
P. Pettinger *Concert* (6/87) (CHAN) ① **CHAN8438**
Griffinesque—piano (1884)
P. Pettinger *Concert* (6/87) (CHAN) ① **CHAN8438**
5 Improvisations—piano (1929)
E. Elgar (r1929) *Concert*
(8/93) (EMI) ① [3] **CDS7 54568-2**
In Smyrna—piano (1905) (ed J.N. Moore)
P. Pettinger *Concert* (6/87) (CHAN) ① **CHAN8438**
C. Headington *Concert*
(11/90) (KING) ① **KCLCD2017**

A. Gravill *Concert* (3/91) (GAMU) ① **GAMCD516**
May Song—piano (1901)
P. Pettinger *Concert* (6/87) (CHAN) ① **CHAN8438**
Minuet—piano (1897)
P. Pettinger *Concert* (6/87) (CHAN) ① **CHAN8438**
Pastourelle (Air de Ballet)—piano (1881)
P. Pettinger *Concert* (6/87) (CHAN) ① **CHAN8438**
Presto—piano (1889)
P. Pettinger *Concert* (6/87) (CHAN) ① **CHAN8438**
Salut d'amour—piano, Op. 12
A. Etherden *Concert*
(7/93) (HUNT) ① **HMPCD0589**
P. Zukerman, St Louis SO, L. Slatkin (r1992: arr vn/orch) *Violin Concerto.*
(1/94) (RCA) ① **09026 61672-2**
Serenade—piano (pub 1932)
P. Pettinger *Concert* (6/87) (CHAN) ① **CHAN8438**
J. Szigeti, N. Magaloff (arr vn/pf: Szigeti: r1934) *Concert* (1/90) (BIDD) ① [2] **LAB007/8**
C. Headington *Concert*
(11/90) (KING) ① **KCLCD2017**
J. Szigeti, N. Magaloff (r1934: arr vn/pf: Szigeti) *Concert* (1/94) (DUTT) ① **CDLX7004**
Skizze—piano (1903) (ed J.N. Moore)
P. Pettinger *Concert* (6/87) (CHAN) ① **CHAN8438**
A. Gravill *Concert* (3/91) (GAMU) ① **GAMCD516**
Sonata for Organ No. 1 in G, Op. 28 (1895)
C. Curley (r1991) *Concert*
(4/92) (ARGO) ① **433 450-2ZH**
G. Green *Concert* (3/93) (NAXO) ① **8 550582**
RLPO, V. Handley (r1989: orch G Jacob) *Dream of Gerontius.* (10/93) (EMIN) ① [2] **CD-EMXD2500**
John Scott (r1992) *Concert*
(8/94) (PRIO) ① **PRCD401**
Movt 1. S. Cleobury (pp1991 with Choral Evensong) *Concert* (10/92) (EMI) ① **CDC7 54412-2**
Movt 1. G.D. Cunningham (r c1930) *Concert*
(9/94) (BEUL) ① **1PD5**
Sonatina—piano (1889 rev 1931)
P. Pettinger (1889 & 1931 versions) *Concert*
(6/87) (CHAN) ① **CHAN8438**

SECTION IV: VOCAL AND CHORAL

Angelus—4vv, Op. 56 (1909) (Wds. Tuscan)
Worcester Cath Ch, A. Partington, David Hunt *Concert* (1/89) (HYPE) ① **CDA66313**
The Apostles—oratorio: soloists, chorus and orchestra, Op. 49 (1902-03) (Wds. cpsr, after Bible)
PROLOGUE: 1. The Spirit of the Lord.
Cpte A. Hargan, A. Hodgson, D. Rendall, B. Terfel, S. Roberts, R. Lloyd, LSC, LSO, R. Hickox
(12/90) (CHAN) ① [2] **CHAN8875/6**
1. Bristol Cath Ch, A. Pinel, M. Archer *Concert*
(10/89) (MERI) ① **CDE84168**
1. Southwark Cath Ch, P. Wright, S. Layton (r1992) *Concert* (7/94) (PRIO) ① **PRCD435**
As torrents fly—partsong: 4vv (1894-96) (from cantata 'King Olaf')
PCA, M. Brown *Concert* (3/87) (CONI) ① **CDCF145**
Ave Maria—choir, Op. 2/2 (1887)
Worcester Cath Ch, A. Partington, David Hunt *Concert* (1/89) (HYPE) ① **CDA66313**
Wellington College Chs, T. Byram-Wigfield, S. Anderson *Concert* (10/92) (HERA) ① **HAVPCD153**
Trinity Coll Ch, Cambridge, R. Marlow, S. Standage (r1992) *Concert* (6/93) (CONI) ① **CDCF214**
Ave maris—choir, Op. 2/3 (1887)
Worcester Cath Ch, A. Partington, David Hunt *Concert* (1/89) (HYPE) ① **CDA66313**
Trinity Coll Ch, Cambridge, R. Marlow, S. Standage (r1992) *Concert* (6/93) (CONI) ① **CDCF214**
Ave verum corpus—choir, Op. 2/1 (1887)
Worcester Cath Ch, A. Partington, David Hunt *Concert* (1/89) (HYPE) ① **CDA66313**
Bristol Cath Ch, A. Pinel, M. Archer *Concert*
(10/89) (MERI) ① **CDE84168**
Wellington College Chs, T. Byram-Wigfield, S. Anderson *Concert* (10/92) (HERA) ① **HAVPCD153**
Trinity Coll Ch, Cambridge, R. Marlow, P. Rushforth (r1992) *Concert* (6/93) (CONI) ① **CDCF214**
Westminster Cath Ch, J. O'Donnell, I. Simcock (r1993) *Concert* (3/94) (HYPE) ① **CDA66669**
Lincoln Cath Ch, J. Vivian, C. Walsh (r1993) *Concert* (7/94) (PRIO) ① **PRCD454**
P. Dyke, K. Beaumont, C. Barton (r1993) *Concert*
(7/94) (ABBE) ① **CDCA954**
The Banner of St George—ballad, Op. 33 (1896-97) (Wds. Wensley)
It comes from the misty ages Chor, LSO, E. Elgar (1928) *Concert* (2/93) (CHAN) ① [3] **CDS7 54564-2**
Caractacus—cantata: STB, chorus and orchestra, Op. 35 (1898) (Wds. H. C. Acworth)
1. Leap, leap to light (Sword Song); 2. Woodland Interlude; 3. O my warriors (Caractacus's Lament); 4.

Triumphal March.
Cpte J. Howarth, A. Davies, D. Wilson-Johnson, S. Roberts, A. Miles, LSC, LSO, R. Hickox *Severn Suite.* (2/93) (CHAN) ① [2] **CHAN9156/7**
2. Northern Sinfonia, R. Hickox (r1985) *Concert*
(1/91) (EMI) ① **CDC7 47672-2**
2. Bournemouth Sinfonietta, N. del Mar (r1976) *Concert* (2/92) (CHAN) ① **CHAN6544**
2, 4. LSO, L. Collingwood (r1934) *Concert*
(8/93) (EMI) ① [3] **CDS7 54568-2**
Carillon—reciter and orchestra, Op. 75 (1914) (Wds. E.Cammaerts: text rev 1942 Binyon)
R. Pasco, Rutland Sinfonia, B. Collett *Concert*
(5/88) (PEAR) ① **SHECD9602**
Abridged H. Ainley, SO, E. Elgar (r1915) *Concert*
(9/92) (PEAR) ① [5] **GEMMCDS9951/5**
4 Choral Songs, Op. 53 (1907) (Wds. various)
1. There is sweet music (Tennyson); 2. Deep in my soul (Bryon); 3. Old Wild West Wind (Shelley); 4. Owls (Elgar).
Worcester Cath Ch, K. Swallow, Don Hunt *Concert*
(4/88) (HYPE) ① [2] **CDA66271/2**
Finzi Sngrs, P. Spicer (r1993) *Concert*
(1/95) (CHAN) ① **CHAN9269**
1. Cambridge Sngrs, J. Rutter *Concert*
(4/87) (CLLE) ① **COLCD104**
2. King's Sngrs *Concert*
(6/88) (EMI) ① **CDC7 49765-2**
2 Choral Songs—unaccompanied chorus, Op. 71 (1913-14) (Wds. Vaughan)
1. The shower; 2. The fountain.
D. Hunt Sngrs, Don Hunt *Concert*
(4/88) (HYPE) ① [2] **CDA66271/2**
Finzi Sngrs, P. Spicer (r1993) *Concert*
(1/95) (CHAN) ① **CHAN9269**
2 Choral Songs—unacccompanied chorus, Op. 73 (1914) (Wds. Maykov trans R. Newmarch)
1. Love's Tempest; 2. Serenade.
Finzi Sngrs, P. Spicer (r1993) *Concert*
(1/95) (CHAN) ① **CHAN9269**
A Christmas greeting—boys' voices, 2 violins and piano, Op. 52 (1907) (Wds. C. A. Elgar)
Worcester Cath Ch, J. Ballard, R. Thurlby, K. Swallow, Don Hunt *Concert*
(4/88) (HYPE) ① [2] **CDA66271/2**
Coronation Ode—SATB, chorus and orchestra, Op. 44 (1902 rev 1911) (Wds. A. C. Benson)
1. Crown the King; 2a. The Queen; 2b. Daughter of Ancient Kings; 3. Braitain, ask of thyself; 4a. Hark, upon the hallowed air; 4b. Only let the heart be pure; 5. Peace, gentle peace; 6. Land of hope and glory.
Cpte T. Cahill, A. Collins, A. Hodgson, R. Gunson, S. Howell, Scottish Nat Chor, SNO, A. Gibson *Spirit of England.* (11/92) (CHAN) ① **CHAN6574**
Cpte F. Lott, A. Hodgson, R. Morton, S. Roberts, CUMS, King's College Ch, New Philh, P. Ledger (r1977) *Kingdom.*
(6/93) (EMI) ① [2] **CMS7 64209-2**
6. King's College Ch, P. Ledger, New Philh, F. Lott, A. Hodgson, R. Morton, S. Roberts, CUMS, Kneller Hall Band (r1977) (4/91) (CFP) ① **CD-CFP4570**
Credo in E minor—unaccompanied chorus (1880) (orig Op. 3: later withdrawn)
Philharmonic Chbr Ch, D. Temple *Concert*
(12/89) (MERI) ① **CDE84173**
Death on the hills—unaccompanied partsong: 8vv, Op. 72 (1914) (Wds. Maikov trans R. Newmarch)
D. Hunt Sngrs, Don Hunt *Concert*
(4/88) (HYPE) ① [2] **CDA66271/2**
Philharmonic Chbr Ch, D. Temple *Concert*
(12/89) (MERI) ① **CDE84173**
Finzi Sngrs, P. Spicer (r1993) *Concert*
(1/95) (CHAN) ① **CHAN9269**
Le Drapeau Belge—reciter and orchestra, Op. 79 (1917) (Wds. Cammaerts)
R. Pasco, Rutland Sinfonia, B. Collett *Concert*
(5/88) (PEAR) ① **SHECD9602**
The Dream of Gerontius—oratorio: ATB, chorus and orchestra, Op. 38 (1900) (wds. Cardinal Newman)
PART 1: 1. Prelude; 2. Jesu Maria, I am near to death; 3. Kyrie eleison; 4. Rouse thee, my fainting soul; 5. Sanctus fortis; 6. I can no more; 7. Rescue him, O Lord; 8. Proficiscere, anima Christiana; 9. Go in the name of Angels. PART 2: 10. I went to sleep; 11. It is a member of that family; 12a. Low-born clods of brute earth (Demons' Chorus); 12b. Dispossessed, aside thrust; 13. I see not those false spirits; 14. Praise to the Holiest (semi-chorus); 15a. But hark! a grand mysterious harmony; 15b. Praise to the Holiest

(double chorus); 16. Thy judgement now is near; 17. Jesu! by that shuddering dread; 18. Take me away; 19. Lord, Thou hast been our refuge; 20. Softly and gently (Angel's farewell).

Cpte A. Hodgson, R. Tear, B. Luxon, Scottish Nat Chor, SNO, A. Gibson (r1976)
(1/87) (CRD) ① [2] **CRD3326/7**

Cpte J. Baker, J. Mitchinson, J. Shirley-Quirk, CBSO Chor, CBSO, S. Rattle (r1986)
(1/88) (EMI) ① [2] **CDS7 49549-2**

Cpte F. Palmer, A. Davies, G. Howell, LSC, LSO, R. Hickox (r1988) Concert
(2/89) (CHAN) ① [2] **CHAN8641/2**

Cpte Y. Minton, P. Pears, J. Shirley-Quirk, Kings College Ch, LSC, LSO, B. Britten (r1971) Holst: Hymn of Jesus.
(5/89) (DECC) ① [2] **421 381-2LM2**

Cpte J. Baker, Richard Lewis, K. Borg, Hallé Ch, Sheffield Phil Chor, Ambrosian Sngrs, Hallé, J. Barbirolli (r1964) Sea Pictures.
(12/89) (EMI) ① [2] **CMS7 63185-2**

Cpte A. Rolfe Johnson, C. Wyn-Rogers, M. George, Liverpool Phil Ch, Huddersfield Choral Soc, RLPO, V. Handley (r1993) Organ Sonata 1.
(10/93) (EMIN) ① [2] **CD-EMXD2500**

Cpte G. Ripley, H. Nash, D. Noble, N. Walker, Huddersfield Choral Soc, Liverpool PO, M. Sargent (r1945) Cello Concerto.
(2/94) (TEST) ① [2] **SBT2025**

1, 20 (abridged) SO, E. Elgar (r1917) Concert
(9/92) (PEAR) ① [5] **GEMMCDS9951/5**

1, 3, 7, 9, 14, 15a, 15b, 17-20. M. Balfour, S. Wilson, H. Heyner, RCS, RAHO, E. Elgar (pp1927) Concert
(6/92) (EMI) ① [3] **CDS7 54560-2**

3, 6(pt), 7, 17, 18. M. Balfour, T. Davies, H. Stevens, Three Choirs Fest Chor, LSO, E. Elgar (pp1927) Concert
(6/92) (EMI) ① [3] **CDS7 54560-2**

15a, 15b P. Pears, Y. Minton, LSC, King's College Ch, LSO, B. Britten Concert
(6/91) (DECC) ① **430 094-2DWO**

Ecce sacerdos magnus—choir, organ (1888)
Worcester Cath Ch, A. Partington, David Hunt Concert
(1/89) (HYPE) ① **CDA66313**
P. Dyke, K. Beaumont, C. Barton (r1993) Concert
(7/94) (ABBE) ① **CDCA954**
Worcester Cath Ch, H. Bramma, C. Robinson (r1974) Concert
(9/94) (CHAN) ① **CHAN6601**

Evening scene—unaccompanied partsong: 4vv (1906) (Wds. C. Patmore)
Worcester Cath Ch, Don Hunt Concert
(4/88) (HYPE) ① [2] **CDA66271/2**
Philharmonic Chbr Ch, D. Temple Concert
(12/89) (MERI) ① **CDE84173**
Finzi Sngrs, P. Spicer (r1993) Concert
(1/95) (CHAN) ① **CHAN9269**

Fear not, O Land—anthem (4vv,organ) (1914)
Worcester Cath Ch, A. Partington, David Hunt Concert
(1/89) (HYPE) ① **CDA66313**

Fly, singing bird—female voices, 2 violins and piano, Op. 26/2 (1894 orch 1903) (Wds. C.A. Elgar)
Worcester Cath Ch, J. Ballard, R. Thurlby, K. Swallow, Don Hunt Concert
(4/88) (HYPE) ① [2] **CDA66271/2**

Fringes of the Fleet—4 baritones and orchestra (1917) (Wds. Kipling)
P. Kenyon, S. Godward, S. Theobold, R. Watson, Rutland Sinfonia, B. Collett Concert
(5/88) (PEAR) ① **SHECD9602**
C. Mott, F. Henry, F. Stewart, H. Barratt, H. Ainley, SO, E. Elgar (r1917) Concert
(9/92) (PEAR) ① [5] **GEMMCDS9951/5**

Give unto the Lord—anthem, Op. 74 (1914)
Worcester Cath Ch, A. Partington, David Hunt Concert
(1/89) (HYPE) ① **CDA66313**
Guildford Cath Ch, A. Millington, P. Wright Concert
(5/89) (PRIO) ① **PRCD257**
Bristol Cath Ch, A. Pinel, M. Archer Concert
(10/89) (MERI) ① **CDE84168**
Canterbury Cath Ch, D. Flood, A. Wicks Concert
(6/91) (DECC) ① **430 094-2DWO**
Winchester Cath Ch, Waynflete Sngrs, T. Byram-Wigfield, Bournemouth SO, D. Hill Concert
(4/92) (ARGO) ① **430 836-2ZH**
St Paul's Cath Ch, John Scott, Adrian Lucas (r1991) Concert
(8/93) (HYPE) ① **CDA66618**

Go, song of mine—choral song: 6vv, Op. 57 (1909) (Wds. Calvacanti trans D.G. Rossetti)
D. Hunt Sngrs, Worcester Cath Ch, Don Hunt Concert
(4/88) (HYPE) ① [2] **CDA66271/2**
Finzi Sngrs, P. Spicer (r1993) Concert
(1/95) (CHAN) ① **CHAN9269**

God be merciful unto us, and bless us (Psalm 67)—double chant (1907) (Wds. Bible)
Bristol Cath Ch, A. Pinel, M. Archer Concert
(10/89) (MERI) ① **CDE84168**

Goodmorrow—unaccompanied partsongs: 4vv (1929) (Wds. G. Gascoigne)
Worcester Cath Ch, Don Hunt Concert
(4/88) (HYPE) ① [2] **CDA66271/2**
Philharmonic Chbr Ch, D. Temple Concert
(12/89) (MERI) ① **CDE84173**

Great is the Lord—anthem: 4vv, Op. 67 (1912 orch 1913)
Worcester Cath Ch, A. Partington, David Hunt Concert
(1/89) (HYPE) ① **CDA66313**
S. Foulkes, Bristol Cath Special Ch, M. Archer Concert
(10/89) (MERI) ① **CDE84168**
D. Sweeney, Winchester Cath Ch, Waynflete Sngrs, T. Byram-Wigfield, Bournemouth SO, D. Hill Concert
(4/92) (ARGO) ① **430 836-2ZH**
Trinity Coll Ch, Cambridge, R. Marlow, P. Rushforth (r1992) Concert
(6/93) (CONI) ① **CDCF214**
St Paul's Cath Ch, John Scott, Andrew Lucas (r1994) Concert
(5/95) (HYPE) ① **CDA66758**

Hear thy children, gentle Jesus—hymn tune (1878) (tune: Drake's Boughton)
Bristol Cath Ch, A. Pinel, M. Archer Concert
(10/89) (MERI) ① **CDE84168**

A Herald—unaccompanied male voices: 4vv (1925) (Wds. A. Smith)
D. Hunt Sngrs, Don Hunt Concert
(4/88) (HYPE) ① [2] **CDA66271/2**

How calmly the evening—unaccompanied partsong: 4vv (1907) (Wds. T. Lynch)
Worcester Cath Ch, Don Hunt Concert
(4/88) (HYPE) ① [2] **CDA66271/2**
Philharmonic Chbr Ch, D. Temple Concert
(12/89) (MERI) ① **CDE84173**
Finzi Sngrs, P. Spicer (r1993) Concert
(1/95) (CHAN) ① **CHAN9269**

I sing the birth—carol (4vv) (1928) (Wds. B. Jonson)
Worcester Cath Ch, A. Partington, David Hunt Concert
(1/89) (HYPE) ① **CDA66313**
RCS, M. Sargent (pp1928) Concert
(7/95) (BEUL) ① **1PD13**

Is he not passing fair?—song (1886) (Wds. d'Orleans trans Costello)
J. Brecknock, V. Morris Concert
(12/89) (MERI) ① **CDE84173**
P. Jeffes, J. Constable Concert
(4/92) (GAMU) ① **GAMD506**

The Kingdom—oratorio, Op. 51 (1901-6) (Wds. cpsr after Bible)
Cpte M. Marshall, F. Palmer, A. Davies, D. Wilson-Johnson, LSC, LSO, R. Hickox Concert
(2/90) (CHAN) ① [2] **CHAN8788/9**
Cpte M. Price, Y. Minton, A. Young, J. Shirley-Quirk, LP Ch, LPO, A. Boult (r1968) Coronation Ode.
(6/93) (EMI) ① [2] **CMS7 64209-2**
Prelude BBC SO, E. Elgar (r1933) Concert
(8/93) (EMI) ① [3] **CDS7 54568-2**

Land of Hope and Glory—chorus and orchestra (arr Fagge: 1914)
M. Balfour, Chor, LSO, E. Elgar (r1928) Concert
(2/93) (EMI) ① [3] **CDS7 54564-2**

The Light of Life, 'Lux Christi'—short oratorio, Op. 29 (1896) (Wds. E. Capel-Cure, after Bible)
1. Meditation; 2. Seek Him that maketh the seven stars; 3. As Jesus passed by; 4. Be not extreme, O Lord; 5. Neither hath this man sinned; 6. Light out of darkness; 7. And when he had thus spoken; 8. Doubt not thy Father's care!; 9. He went his way therefore; 10. As a spirit didst Thou pass before mine eyes; 11. They brought him to the Pharisees; 12. Thou only hast the words of life; 13. But the Jews did not believe; 14. Woe to the shepherds of the flock; 15. I am the Good Shepherd; 16. Light of the World, we know Thy praise.
Cpte M. Marshall, H. Watts, R. Leggate, J. Shirley-Quirk, Liverpool Phil Ch, RLPO, C. Groves (1980)
(5/93) (EMI) ① **CDM7 64732-2**
Cpte J. Howarth, L. Finnie, A. Davies, J. Shirley-Quirk, LSC, LSO, R. Hickox (1993)
(5/94) (CHAN) ① **CHAN9208**
1. RPO, Y. Butt (r1988) Concert
(11/88) (ASV) ① **CDDCA619**
1. RAHO, E. Elgar (1925) Concert
(9/92) (PEAR) ① [5] **GEMMCDS9951/5**
1. RAHO, E. Elgar (1926) Concert
(2/93) (EMI) ① [3] **CDS7 54564-2**
2. Lincoln Cath Ch, J. Vivian, C. Walsh (r1993) Concert
(7/94) (PRIO) ① **PRCD454**
8, 16. Worcester Cath Ch, H. Bramma, C. Robinson (r1974) Concert
(9/94) (CHAN) ① **CHAN6601**

Lo! Christ the Lord is born—carol (4vv) (1897) (Wds. Wensley)
Worcester Cath Ch, A. Partington, David Hunt Concert
(1/89) (HYPE) ① **CDA66313**
Philharmonic Chbr Ch, D. Temple Concert
(12/89) (MERI) ① **CDE84173**

Love—unaccompanied partsong: 4vv, Op. 18/2 (1907) (Wds. A. Macquire)
D. Hunt Sngrs, Don Hunt Concert
(4/88) (HYPE) ① [2] **CDA66271/2**
Philharmonic Chbr Ch, D. Temple Concert
(12/89) (MERI) ① **CDE84173**
Finzi Sngrs, P. Spicer (r1993) Concert
(1/95) (CHAN) ① **CHAN9269**

Love's tempest—unaccompanied male voices: 4vv, Op. 73/1 (1914) (Wds. Maikov trans R. Newmarch)
D. Hunt Sngrs, Don Hunt Concert
(4/88) (HYPE) ① [2] **CDA66271/2**

The Music Makers—ode, Op. 69 (1912) (Wds. O'Shaughnessy)
1. Introduction; 2. We are the music makers; 3. With wonderful deathless ditties; 4. We, in the ages lying; 5. A breath of our inspiration; 6. They had no vision amazing; 7. And therefore today is thrilling; 8. But we, with our dreaming and singing; 9. For we afar with the dawning; 10. Great hail! We cry to the comers.
L. Finnie, LP Ch, LPO, B. Thomson (r1991) Sea Pictures.
(3/92) (CHAN) ① **CHAN9022**
J. Rigby, BBC Sym Chor, BBC SO, A. Davis (r1993) Concert
(2/95) (TELD) ① **4509-92374-2**
2, 5, 9. Three Choirs Fest Chor, LSO, E. Elgar (pp1927) Concert
(6/92) (EMI) ① [3] **CDS7 54560-2**

My love dwelt in a northern land—choral song, Op. 18/3 (1889) (Wds. A. Lang)
Cambridge Sngrs, J. Rutter Concert
(4/87) (CLLE) ① **COLCD104**
D. Hunt Sngrs, Don Hunt Concert
(4/88) (HYPE) ① [2] **CDA66271/2**
Finzi Sngrs, P. Spicer (r1993) Concert
(1/95) (CHAN) ① **CHAN9269**

O happy eyes—unaccompanied partsong: 4vv, Op. 18/1 (1876) (Wds. C. A. Elgar)
D. Hunt Sngrs, Don Hunt Concert
(4/88) (HYPE) ① [2] **CDA66271/2**
Philharmonic Chbr Ch, D. Temple Concert
(12/89) (MERI) ① **CDE84173**
Finzi Sngrs, P. Spicer (r1993) Concert
(1/95) (CHAN) ① **CHAN9269**

O hearken thou—Coronation Anthem (choir, organ/orchestra), Op. 64 (1911)
Worcester Cath Ch, A. Partington, David Hunt Concert
(1/89) (HYPE) ① **CDA66313**
Winchester Cath Ch, Waynflete Sngrs, T. Byram-Wigfield, Bournemouth SO, D. Hill Concert
(4/92) (ARGO) ① **430 836-2ZH**
Trinity Coll Ch, Cambridge, R. Marlow, P. Rushforth (r1992) Concert
(6/93) (CONI) ① **CDCF214**

O mightiest of the mighty—hymn (1901) (Wds. S. Childs Clarke)
Philharmonic Chbr Ch, D. Temple Concert
(12/89) (MERI) ① **CDE84173**

O salutaris hostia—unaccompanied vv (c1872) (recons. T. Hooke)
Worcester Cath Ch, A. Partington, David Hunt (ed Hunt) Concert
(1/89) (HYPE) ① **CDA66313**
Worcester Cath Ch, C. Robinson (r1974) Concert
(9/94) (CHAN) ① **CHAN6601**

O salutaris hostia—unaccompanied vv (1898) (recons. T. Hooke)
Worcester Cath Ch, A. Partington, David Hunt Concert
(1/89) (HYPE) ① **CDA66313**
Worcester Cath Ch, H. Bramma, C. Robinson (r1974) Concert
(9/94) (CHAN) ① **CHAN6601**

O salutaris hostia—unaccompanied vv (1880) (recons. T. Hooke)
Worcester Cath Ch, A. Partington, David Hunt (ed Hunt) Concert
(1/89) (HYPE) ① **CDA66313**
Worcester Cath Ch, H. Bramma, C. Robinson (r1974) Concert
(9/94) (CHAN) ① **CHAN6601**

Oh, soft was the song—song, Op. 59/3 (1909-10) (Wds. G. Parker)
R. Tear, CBSO, V. Handley (r1979) Concert
(3/94) (EMI) ① **CDM7 64731-2**

4 Partsongs—chorus a capella, Op. 53 (1907)
1. There is sweeet music (wds. Tennyson); 2. Deep in my soul (wds. Byron); 3. O wild west wind (wds. Shelley); 4. Owls (wds. cpsr).
1. L. Halsey Sngrs, L. Halsey Concert
(6/91) (DECC) ① **430 094-2DWO**

5 Partsongs from the Greek Anthology—male 4vv, Op. 45 (1902) (Wds. Anon)
1. Yea, cast me from the heights; 2. Whether I find thee; 3. After many a dusty mile; 4. It's oh to be a wild wind; 5. Feasting I watch.
D. Hunt Sngrs, Don Hunt *Concert*
(4/88) (HYPE) ① [2] CDA66271/2
Finzi Sngrs, P. Spicer (r1993) *Concert*
(1/95) (CHAN) ① CHAN9269
Pleading—song, Op. 48/1 (1908) (Wds. A. Salmon)
S. Varcoe, CLS, R. Hickox *Concert*
(1/90) (CHAN) ① CHAN8743
R. Tear, CBSO, V. Handley (r1979) *Concert*
(3/94) (EMI) ① CDM7 64731-2
A Poet's Life—song (1892) (Wds. E. Burroughs)
J. Brecknock, V. Morris *Concert*
(12/89) (MERI) ① CDE84173
The Prince of Sleep—unaccompanied chorus: 4vv (1925) (Wds. De la Mare)
Worcester Cath Ch, Don Hunt *Concert*
(4/88) (HYPE) ① [2] CDA66271/2
Finzi Sngrs, P. Spicer (r1993) *Concert*
(1/95) (CHAN) ① CHAN9269
Queen Mary's song (lute song)—song (1887) (Wds. Anon)
F. Lott, G. Johnson *Concert*
(7/90) (CHAN) ① CHAN8722
The Rapid stream—boys' vv and piano (1922) (Wds. C. MacKay)
Worcester Cath Ch, K. Swallow, Don Hunt *Concert*
(4/88) (HYPE) ① [2] CDA66271/2
Reveille—unaccompanied male voices: 4vv, Op. 54 (1908) (Wds. B. Harte)
D. Hunt Sngrs, Don Hunt *Concert*
(4/88) (HYPE) ① [2] CDA66271/2
The River—song, Op. 60/2 (1909-10 orch 1912) (Wds. Pietro d'Alba (pseudonym of Elgar))
J. Brecknock, V. Morris *Concert*
(12/89) (MERI) ① CDE84173
R. Tear, CBSO, V. Handley (r1979) *Concert*
(3/94) (EMI) ① CDM7 64731-2
Scenes from the Bavarian Highlands—chorus and piano, Op. 27 (1895 orch 1895) (Wds. trad. arr Elgar)
1. The dance; 2. False love; 3. Lullaby; 4. Aspiration; 5. On the alm; 6. The marksman.
Worcester Cath Ch, F. Wibaut, C. Robinson (r1974) *Concert*
(9/94) (CHAN) ① CHAN6601
Bournemouth Sym Chor, Bournemouth Sinfonietta, N. del Mar (r1980) *Stanford: Symphony 3.*
(7/95) (EMI) ① CDM5 65129-2
Scenes from The Saga of King Olaf—cantata, Op. 30 (1894-96) (Wds. Longworth and Acworth)
A little bird in the air RAHO, E. Elgar (arr cpsr: r1921) *Concert*
(9/92) (PEAR) ① [5] GEMMCDS9951/5
Sea Pictures—contralto and orchestra, Op. 37 (1899)
1. Sea Slumber Song (wds. R. Noel); 2. In Haven (wds. C. A. Elgar); 3. Sabbath morning at sea (wds. E. B. Browning); 4. Where corals lie (wds. R. Garnett); 5. The swimmer (wds. A. L. Gordon).
J. Baker, LSO, J. Barbirolli (1965) *Cello Concerto.*
(5/86) (EMI) ① CDC7 47329-2
B. Greevy, LPO, V. Handley *Pomp and Circumstance Marches.*
(11/87) (CFP) ① CD-CFP9004
J. Baker, LSO, J. Barbirolli (1965) *Dream of Gerontius.*
(12/89) (EMI) ① [2] CMS7 63185-2
L. Finnie, LPO, B. Thomson (r1991) *Music Makers.*
(3/92) (CHAN) ① CHAN9022
L. Megane, SO, E. Elgar (r1922/3) *Concert*
(9/92) (PEAR) ① [5] GEMMCDS9951/5
D. Jones, RPO, C. Mackerras *Symphony 2.*
(12/94) (ARGO) ① 443 321-2ZH
4. G. Ripley, Philh, G. Weldon (r1946) *Concert*
(4/92) (EMI) ① [7] CHS7 69741-2(1)
Serenade—unaccompanied partsong: 4vv, Op. 73/2 (1914) (Wds. Minski (N. M. Vilenkin): adapted R. Newmarch)
D. Hunt Sngrs, Don Hunt *Concert*
(4/88) (HYPE) ① [2] CDA66271/2
Philharmonic Chbr Ch, D. Temple *Concert*
(12/89) (MERI) ① CDE84173
Shepherd's Song—song, Op. 16/1 (1892) (Wds. B. Pain)
J. Brecknock, V. Morris *Concert*
(12/89) (MERI) ① CDE84173

The Snow—female voices, 2 violins and piano, Op. 26/1 (1894 orch 1903) (Wds. C.A. Elgar)
Worcester Cath Ch, J. Ballard, R. Thurlby, K. Swallow, Don Hunt *Concert*
(4/88) (HYPE) ① [2] CDA66271/2
A Song of Autumn—song (1892) (Wds. A. L. Gordon)
J. Brecknock, V. Morris *Concert*
(12/89) (MERI) ① CDE84173
Spanish Serenade, 'Stars of the Summer Night'—partsong, Op. 23 (1892 orch 1893) (Wds. Longfellow)
Worcester Cath Ch, J. Ballard, R. Thurlby, K. Swallow, Don Hunt *Concert*
(4/88) (HYPE) ① [2] CDA66271/2
Speak music—song, Op. 41/2 (1902) (Wds. Benson)
J. Brecknock, V. Morris *Concert*
(12/89) (MERI) ① CDE84173
The Spirit of England—soprano/tenor, chorus and orchestra, Op. 80 (1915-17) (Wds. Binyon)
1. The Fourth of August; 2. To Women; 3. For the fallen.
T. Cahill, Scottish Nat Chor, SNO, A. Gibson (r1976) *Coronation Ode.*
(11/92) (EMI) ① CDM6574
Tantum ergo—choir and organ (1878) (orig Op. 2)
Worcester Cath Ch, H. Bramma, C. Robinson (r1974) *Concert*
(9/94) (CHAN) ① CHAN6601
Te Deum and Benedictus—chorus and organ/orchestra, Op. 34 (1897)
Bristol Cath Ch, A. Pinel, M. Archer *Concert*
(10/89) (MERI) ① CDE84168
P. Dyke, K. Beaumont, C. Barton (1993) *Concert*
(7/94) (ABBE) ① CDCA954
Benedictus Trinity Coll Ch, Cambridge, R. Marlow, S. Standage (r1992) *Concert*
(6/93) (CONI) ① CDCF214
Te Deum Norwich Cath Ch, M. Nicholas, N. Taylor (r1993) *Concert*
(10/94) (PRIO) ① PRCD470
They are at rest—unaccompanied partsong: 4vv (1909) (Wds. H. Newman)
D. Hunt Sngrs, Don Hunt *Concert*
(4/88) (HYPE) ① [2] CDA66271/2
Cambridge Sngrs, J. Rutter *Concert*
(4/92) (CLLE) ① COLCD113
To her beloved whose steadfast star—unaccompanied chorus (1899) (Wds. F.W.H. Myers)
Philharmonic Chbr Ch, D. Temple *Concert*
(12/89) (MERI) ① CDE84173
The Torch—song, Op. 60/1 (1909-10 orch 1912) (Wds. cpsr)
R. Tear, CBSO, V. Handley *Concert*
(3/94) (EMI) ① CDM7 64731-2
Twilight—song, Op. 59/6 (1909-10) (Wds. G. Parker)
S. Varcoe, CLS, R. Hickox *Concert*
(1/90) (CHAN) ① CHAN8743
R. Tear, CBSO, V. Handley (1979) *Concert*
(3/94) (EMI) ① CDM7 64731-2
Une Voix dans le désert—reciter and orchestra, Op. 77 (1915) (Wds. Cammaerts)
R. Pasco, T. Cahill, Rutland Sinfonia, B. Collett *Concert*
(5/88) (PEAR) ① SHECD9602
The Wanderer—unaccompanied male voices: 4vv (1923) (Wds. Anon: adapted cpsr)
D. Hunt Sngrs, Don Hunt *Concert*
(4/88) (HYPE) ① [2] CDA66271/2
Was it some Golden Star?—song, Op. 59/5 (1909-10) (Wds. G. Parker)
J. Brecknock, V. Morris *Concert*
(12/89) (MERI) ① CDE84173
R. Tear, CBSO, V. Handley (1979) *Concert*
(3/94) (EMI) ① CDM7 64731-2
Weary Wind of the West—unaccompanied chorus: 4vv (1902) (Wds. T.E. Brown)
Worcester Cath Ch, Don Hunt *Concert*
(4/88) (HYPE) ① [2] CDA66271/2
Philharmonic Chbr Ch, D. Temple *Concert*
(12/89) (MERI) ① CDE84173
Finzi Sngrs, P. Spicer (r1993) *Concert*
(1/95) (CHAN) ① CHAN9269
When swallows fly—unaccompanied boys' voices (1922) (Wds. C. MacKay)
Worcester Cath Ch, K. Swallow, J. Ballard *Concert*
(4/88) (HYPE) ① [2] CDA66271/2
The Windlass song—unaccompanied chorus (Wds. W. Allingham)
Philharmonic Chbr Ch, D. Temple *Concert*
(12/89) (MERI) ① CDE84173

The Woodland stream—boys' vv and piano (1922) (Wds. C. MacKay)
Worcester Cath Ch, K. Swallow, Don Hunt *Concert*
(4/88) (HYPE) ① [2] CDA66271/2
Zut! Zut! Zut!—unaccompanied male voices: 4vv (?1923) (Wds R. Mardon (Elgar))
D. Hunt Sngrs, Don Hunt *Concert*
(4/88) (HYPE) ① [2] CDA66271/2

SECTION V: STAGE WORKS

Beau Brummel—incidental music to B. Matthews's play (1928—Birmingham)
EXCERPTS: 1. Minuet.
Minuet Bournemouth Sinfonietta, G. Hurst *Concert*
(8/87) (CHAN) ① CHAN8432
1. Bournemouth Sinfonietta, G. Hurst (r1975) *Concert*
(2/92) (CHAN) ① CHAN6544
1. LSO, E. Elgar (r1928) *Concert*
(8/93) (EMI) ① [3] CDS7 54568-2
1. New SO, E. Elgar (r1929) *Concert*
(8/93) (EMI) ① [3] CDS7 54568-2
1. RTE Concert Orch, E. Tomlinson (r1993) *Concert*
(12/95) (MARC) ① 8 223522
Crown of India—Imperial masque, Op. 66 (1911-12—London) (Wds. H. Hamilton)
1a. Introduction; 1b. Dance of Nautch Girls; 2. Menuetto; 3. Warriors' Dance; 4. Intermezzo; 5. March of the Mogul Emperors.
Cpte SNO, A. Gibson *Concert*
(6/87) (CHAN) ① CHAN8429
Cpte LSO, E. Elgar (r1930) *Concert*
(2/93) (EMI) ① [3] CDS7 54564-2
5. BBC SO, L. Bernstein (r1982) *Concert*
(11/84) (DG) ① 413 490-2GH
Grania and Diarmid—incidental music to Yeats's play, Op. 42 (1901—Dublin)
EXCERPTS: 1. Incidental Music; 2. Funeral March; 3. There are seven that pull the thread.
1, 2. CBSO, S. Rattle *Concert*
(3/95) (EMI) ① CDC5 55001-2
1-3. J. Miller, LPO, B. Thomson (r1988) *Concert*
(5/89) (CHAN) ① CHAN8610
King Arthur—incidental music to Binyon's play (1923—London)
Suite C. Glover, J. Lawrenson, Bournemouth Sinfonietta, G. Hurst (r1973) *Starlight Express.*
(11/93) (CHAN) ① CHAN6582
The Sanguine Fan—ballet, Op. 81 (1917—London)
Cpte LPO, B. Thomson (r1988) *Concert*
(5/89) (CHAN) ① CHAN8610
abridged SO, E. Elgar (r1920) *Concert*
(9/92) (PEAR) ① [5] GEMMCDS9951/5
The Spanish Lady—opera (sketches only), Op. 89 (Lib. B. Jackson, from B. Jonson's 'The Devil is an Ass')
Sketches ed J Young: 1955-56; 1. Country Dance: Allegretto e leggiero; 2. Burlesco: Allegro; 3. Adagio; 4. Sarabande: Maestoso; 5. Bourrée: Vivace. SONGS: 6. Modest and Fair; 7. Still to be Neat.
2. Bournemouth Sinfonietta, G. Hurst *Concert*
(8/87) (CHAN) ① CHAN8432
2. Bournemouth Sinfonietta, G. Hurst (r1975) *Concert*
(2/92) (CHAN) ① CHAN6544
The Starlight Express—incidental music to Blackwood's play, Op. 78 (1915—London)
EXCERPTS: 1. Overture: ACT 1: 2. O children, open your arms to me (Organ-Grinder); 3. Scene 1; 4a. Interlude; 4b. Scene 2; 5. There is a fairy hides in the beautiful eyes (Organ-Grinder). ACT 2: 6. Interlude; 7. The sun has gone (Curfew Song); 8. I'm everywhere (Laughter); 9a. Wake up you little Night Winds; 9b. Entr'acte (Sun Dance from 'The Wand of Youth'); 10a. Oh stars, shine brightly (Laughter); 10b. They'll listen to my song (Laughter); 11. We shall meet the morning spiders (Jane Anne's Dawn Song); 12. My Old Tunes (Organ-Grinder). ACT 3: 13. Dandelions, daffodils (Jane Anne); 14. Waltz; 15. Laugh a little ev'ry day (Laughter); 16. They're all soft-shiny now (Organ-Grinder); 17. Oh, think beauty (Jane Anne); 18. Dustman, Laughter, Tramp and busy Sweep (Finale).
2. Bournemouth Sinfonietta, G. Hurst (orch) *Concert*
(8/87) (CHAN) ① CHAN8432
2, 5, 7, 8, 9a, 9b, 10a, 10b, 11, 12, 18. A. Nicholls, C. Mott, SO, E. Elgar (r1916) *Concert*
(9/92) (PEAR) ① [5] GEMMCDS9951/5
2, 5, 8, 10a, 11-13, 18. C. Glover, J. Lawrenson, Bournemouth Sinfonietta, G. Hurst (r1973) *King Arthur.*
(11/93) (CHAN) ① CHAN6582
2, 5, 8, 9a, 10a, 11, 12, 17, 18. A. Hagley, B. Terfel, WNO Orch, C. Mackerras (r1990) *Concert*
(10/92) (ARGO) ① 433 214-2ZH
15. Bournemouth Sinfonietta, G. Hurst (orch: r1975) *Concert*
(2/92) (CHAN) ① CHAN6544

ELGAR & BINYON

SECTION II: CHAMBER

Wood Magic—Readings of documents relating to the Piano Quintet and its composition
B. Leigh-Hunt, R. Pasco, Medici Qt, J. Bingham (includes various musical excerpts) Elgar: Violin Sonata. (11/92) (MEDI) ① MQCD7001

ELIAS, Jonathan (20th cent) USA

SECTION V: STAGE WORKS

Vamp—film score (1986)
EXCERPTS: 1. The Vampire Coven's Prayer.
1. OST, J. Elias (r1986) Concert
(10/93) (SILV) ① FILMCD127

ELIAS, Manuel de Santo (18th Cent) Spain

SECTION IV: VOCAL AND CHORAL

Peroration—soprano (1973) (Wds. R Browning)
J. Manning (r1993) Concert
(10/95) (NMC) ① NMCD025

ELIASSON, Anders (b 1947) Sweden

SECTION III: INSTRUMENTAL

Disegno—trombone (1985)
C. Lindberg Concert (10/89) (BIS) ① BIS-CD388

ELLER, Heino (1887–1970) Estonia

SECTION I: ORCHESTRAL

Dawn—symphonic poem (1918)
SNO, N. Järvi Concert
(11/89) (CHAN) ① CHAN8525
Elegia—harp and strings orchestra (1931)
E. Pierce, SNO, N. Järvi Concert
(11/89) (CHAN) ① CHAN8525
5 Pieces—string orchestra (1953)
SNO, N. Järvi Concert
(11/89) (CHAN) ① CHAN8525
Twilight—symphonic poem (1917)
SNO, N. Järvi Concert
(11/89) (CHAN) ① CHAN8656

ELLINGTON, Duke (Edward Kennedy) (1899–1974) USA

SECTION I: ORCHESTRAL

Harlem—jazz band and orchestra (1950)
(orch L Henderson: 1959)
Detroit SO, N. Järvi (1993) Concert
(3/94) (CHAN) ① CHAN9226
Solitude—orchestra (1934)
Detroit SO, N. Järvi (r1992: trans stgs: M Gould) Concert (8/94) (CHAN) ① CHAN9227
A. Feinberg (r1994; trans Mark Tucker) Concert
(11/95) (ARGO) ① 444 457-2ZH

SECTION II: CHAMBER

Mainly Black, 'Black, brown and beige'—suite (1933-43)
N. Kennedy, A. Dankworth Bartók: Solo Violin Sonata. (5/87) (EMI) ① CDC7 47621-2

SECTION IV: VOCAL AND CHORAL

It don't mean a thing if it ain't got that swing—song (1932) (wds. Mills)
Harlem Boys Ch, W. J. Turnbull (pp1993) Concert
(2/95) (DECC) ① 444 450-2DH

SECTION V: STAGE WORKS

The River—concert suite from ballet (1971)
(orch R. Collier)
1. Spring; 2. Meander; 3. Giggling rapids; 4. Lake; 5. Vortex; 6. Riba; 7. Village virgins.
Detroit SO, N. Järvi (1,2,3,4,5,6,7) W. G. Still: Symphony 1. (4/93) (CHAN) ① CHAN9154

ELLIS, John Tilstone (b 1929) England

SECTION IV: VOCAL AND CHORAL

Sunset Song
R. A. Morgan Concert (12/87) (ETCE) ① KTC1049

ELLIS, Vivian (b 1903) England

SECTION I: ORCHESTRAL

Coronation Scot—orchestra (1937) (used as signature tune for BBC Radio series 'Paul Temple')
RTE Concert Orch, E. Tomlinson (r1993) Concert
(12/95) (MARC) ① 8 223522

ELMORE, Robert Hall (b 1913) USA

SECTION III: INSTRUMENTAL

Chorale Prelude on 'Seelenbrautigam'—organ
J. Jones Concert (8/91) (MOTE) ① CD11491

ELWYN-EDWARDS, Dilys (20th Cent) Wales

SECTION IV: VOCAL AND CHORAL

Mae hiraeth yn y môr—song (Wds. R. Williams, Parry)
A. Davies, A. Bryn Parri (r1994) Concert
(11/95) (SAIN) ① SCDC2085

EMMANUEL, (Marie François) Maurice (1862–1938) France

SECTION I: ORCHESTRAL

Le poème du Rhône—symphonic poem after F. Mistral (1938) (orch Béclard d'Harcourt)
Rhenish PO, G. Nopre (r1992) Concert
(3/94) (MARC) ① 8 223507
Symphony No. 1 in A, Op. 18 (1919)
Rhenish PO, J. Lockhart (r1990) Concert
(3/94) (MARC) ① 8 223507
Symphony No. 2 in A, 'Bretonne', Op. 25 (1930-31)
Rhenish PO, J. Lockhart (r1991) Concert
(3/94) (MARC) ① 8 223507

SECTION III: INSTRUMENTAL

6 Sonatines—piano
1. Sonatine Bourgignone (1893); 2. Sonatine Pastorale (1897); 3. (1920); 4. En divers Modes Hindous (1920); 5. Alla Francese (1926); 6. (1926).
Peter Jacobs (10/92) (CNTI) ① CCD1048

EMMET, Joseph Kline (19th Cent) USA

SECTION IV: VOCAL AND CHORAL

Lullaby—song from 'Fritz, Our Cousin German' (Gayler) (1870)
Cincinnati Uni Sngrs, Cincinnati Uni Th Orch, E. Rivers (r1978) Concert (4/94) (NEW) ① 80221-2

EMMETT, Dan(iel Decatur) (1815–1904) USA

SECTION I: ORCHESTRAL

Dixie—march (1859) (adopted by Confederate forces in US Civil War)
E. Eames, anon (r1905) Concert
(11/93) (ROMO) ① [2] 81001-2
Boston Pops, A. Fiedler (r1958; arr Black) Concert
(1/94) (RCA) ① 09026 61249-2

ENCINA, Juan del (1468–1529) Spain

SECTION IV: VOCAL AND CHORAL

A tal perdida tan triste—villancico: 4vv (1497)
Hespèrion XX, J. Savall Concert
(2/92) (ASTR) ① E8707
Amor con fortuna—villancico: 4vv (1492)
Hespèrion XX, J. Savall Concert
(2/92) (ASTR) ① E8707

Ay triste, que vengo—villancico: 3vv (1492)
Hespèrion XX, J. Savall Concert
(2/92) (ASTR) ① E8707
C. Bott, New London Consort, P. Pickett Concert
(7/92) (LINN) ① CKD007
Cucú, cucú, cucú—villancico: 4vv (1492)
Hespèrion XX, J. Savall Concert
(2/92) (ASTR) ① E8707
Despierta, despierta, tus fuerças, Pegaso—tragédie (1497)
Hespèrion XX, J. Savall Concert
(2/92) (ASTR) ① E8707
El que rige y el regido—villancico: 3vv (1497)
Hespèrion XX, J. Savall Concert
(2/92) (ASTR) ① E8707
Fata la parte—villancico: 4vv (1492)
Hespèrion XX, J. Savall Concert
(2/92) (ASTR) ① E8707
Levenata Pascual, levanta—villancico: 3vv (1492)
Hespèrion XX, J. Savall Concert
(2/92) (ASTR) ① E8707
Los sospiros no sosiegan—canción on the foliáa: 4vv
Gothic Voices, C. Page (r1993) Concert
(2/94) (HYPE) ① CDA66653
Mas vale trocar—villancico: 4vv (1497)
Hespèrion XX, J. Savall Concert
(2/92) (ASTR) ① E8707
C. Bott, New London Consort, P. Pickett Concert
(7/92) (LINN) ① CKD007
Mi libertad en sosiego—romance: 4vv
Gothic Voices, C. Page (r1993) Concert
(2/94) (HYPE) ① CDA66653
Mortal tristura me dieron—canción: 4vv (1492)
Hespèrion XX, J. Savall (instr) Concert
(2/92) (ASTR) ① E8707
C. Bott, New London Consort, P. Pickett Concert
(7/92) (LINN) ① CKD007
Oy comamos y bebamos—villancico: 4vv (1497)
Hespèrion XX, J. Savall Concert
(2/92) (ASTR) ① E8707
Pues que jamas olvidaros—4vv (from the Palacio Song Book)
Hespèrion XX, J. Savall Concert
(7/92) (ASTR) ① E8762
Quedate, carillo, adios—villancico: 4vv (1497)
Hespèrion XX, J. Savall (instr) Concert
(2/92) (ASTR) ① E8707
C. Bott, New London Consort, P. Pickett Concert
(7/92) (LINN) ① CKD007
Qu'es de ti, desconsolado?—romance: 3vv (1492)
Hespèrion XX, J. Savall Concert
(2/92) (ASTR) ① E8707
Romerico, tú que vienes—villancico: 3vv (from Segovia MS)
T. Berganza, N. Yepes Concert
(12/92) (DG) ① [2] 435 848-2GX2
Daedalus Ens Concert
(12/92) (ACCE) ① ACC9176D
Una Sañosa porfía—romance: 1v (1492)
Hespèrion XX, J. Savall Concert
(2/92) (ASTR) ① E8707
Si abrá en este baldres!—irregular villancico: 4vv
Hespèrion XX, J. Savall Concert
(2/92) (ASTR) ① E8707
Todos los bienes del mundo—villancico: 4vv (from Palacio songbook)
Daedalus Ens Concert
(12/92) (ACCE) ① ACC9176D
Triste España sin ventural—romance (4vv) (1497)
Hespèrion XX, J. Savall Concert
(2/92) (ASTR) ① E8707
C. Bott, New London Consort, P. Pickett Concert
(7/92) (LINN) ① CKD007
Ya no quiero tener fe—villancico: 3vv (from Segovia MS)
Daedalus Ens Concert
(12/92) (ACCE) ① ACC9176D

ENDERS, Georg (1898–1954) Sweden

SECTION IV: VOCAL AND CHORAL

Little princess—song (Wds. N. Perne & G. Eliasson)
J. Björling, orch, S. Waldimir (r1935) Concert
(8/92) (BLUE) ① ABCD016

ENDRES, Caspar (?–1674)
Germany

SECTION IV: VOCAL AND CHORAL

O alma virgo Maria—motet
Niederaltaicher Scholaren, K. Ruhland (r1992)
Concert
(10/93) (SONY) ① **SK53117**

ENESCU, George (1881–1955)
Romania

SECTION I: ORCHESTRAL

Andantino (1896) (from incomplete orchestral suite)
Romanian Nat Rad Orch, H. Andreescu (1995)
Concert
(11/95) (OLYM) ① **OCD495**
2 Intermezzi—string orchestra, Op. 12 (1902-03)
Lausanne CO, L. Foster Concert
(10/88) (CLAV) ① **CD50-8803**
Romanian Nat Rad Orch, H. Andreescu (r1994)
Concert
(6/95) (OLYM) ① **OCD444**
Overture on popular Romanian themes in A, Op. 32 (1948)
Romanian Nat Rad Orch, H. Andreescu (r1993)
Concert
(11/94) (OLYM) ① **OCD441**
Poème roumain—Orchestra and wordless chorus, Op. 1 (1897)
Romanian Nat Rad Orch, Romanian Rad Chor, H. Andreescu (r1993) Symphony 3.
(11/94) (OLYM) ① **OCD443**
2 Romanian Rhapsodies—orchestra, Op. 11 (1901)
1. A; 2. D.
SNO, N. Järvi Bartók: Concerto for orchestra.
(2/92) (CHAN) ① **CHAN8947**
Romanian Nat Rad Orch, H. Andreescu (r1993) Symphony 2.
(11/94) (OLYM) ① **OCD442**
1. Dallas SO, E. Mata Concert
(6/83) (RCA) ① **RCD14439**
1. Cincinnati Pops, E. Kunzel Concert
(10/89) (TELA) ① **CD80170**
1. LSO, A. Dorati Liszt: Hungarian Rhapsodies, S359. (11/91) (MERC) ① **432 015-2MM**
1. NYPO, L. Bernstein Concert
(5/93) (SONY) ① **SMK47572**
1. Empire Brass (r1992; R. Smedvig) Concert
(1/94) (TELA) ① **CD80305**
1. RCA Victor SO, L. Stokowski (r1960) Concert
(3/94) (RCA) ① **09026 61503-2**
2. LSO, A. Dorati (r1960) Concert
(8/93) (MERC) ① **434 326-2MM**
Study Symphony No. 4 in E flat (1898)
Romanian Nat Rad Orch, H. Andreescu (r1993)
Concert
(11/94) (OLYM) ① **OCD441**
Suite No. 1 in C—orchestra, Op. 9 (1903)
Romanian Nat Rad Orch, H. Andreescu (r1994)
Concert
(6/95) (OLYM) ① **OCD444**
Suite No. 2 in C—orchestra, Op. 20 (1915)
Romanian Nat Rad Orch, H. Andreescu (1995)
Concert
(11/95) (OLYM) ① **OCD495**
Suite No. 3 in D, 'Villageoise'—orchestra, Op. 27 (1937-38)
Romanian Nat Rad Orch, H. Andreescu (1995)
Concert
(11/95) (OLYM) ① **OCD495**
Symphonie concertante—cello and orchestra, Op. 8 (1901)
M. Cazacu, Romanian Nat Rad Orch, H. Andreescu (r1994) Concert
(6/95) (OLYM) ① **OCD444**
Symphony No. 1 in E flat, Op. 13 (1905)
Monte Carlo PO, L. Foster (r1990) Symphony 2.
(9/93) (EMI) ① **CDC7 54763-2**
Romanian Nat Rad Orch, H. Andreescu (r1993)
Concert
(11/94) (OLYM) ① **OCD441**
Symphony No. 2 in A, Op. 17 (1912-14)
Monte Carlo PO, L. Foster (r1992) Symphony 1.
(9/93) (EMI) ① **CDC7 54763-2**
Romanian Nat Rad Orch, H. Andreescu (r1993)
Romanian Rhapsodies, Op. 11.
(11/94) (OLYM) ① **OCD442**
Symphony No. 3 in C, Op. 71 (1918)
Romanian Nat Rad Orch, H. Andreescu (r1993)
Poème roumain, Op. 1.
(11/94) (OLYM) ① **OCD443**

SECTION II: CHAMBER

Cantabile e presto—flute and piano (1903-06)
S. Milan, I. Brown Concert
(11/88) (CHAN) ① **CHAN8609**

Chamber Symphony—12 Instruments, Op. 33 (1954)
Lausanne CO, L. Foster Concert
(10/88) (CLAV) ① **CD50-8803**
Konzertstück—viola and piano
Y. Bashmet, M. Muntain Concert
(12/90) (RCA) ① **RD60112**
Legend—trumpet and piano (c1905)
W. Marsalis, J.L. Stillman (r1992) Concert
(5/94) (SONY) ① **SK47193**
J. Wallace, S. Wright (r1993) Concert
(11/94) (EMI) ① **CDC5 55086-2**
Sonata for Violin and Piano No. 2 in F minor, Op. 6 (1899)
A. Oprean, J. Oprean Concert
(2/92) (HYPE) ① **CDA66484**
Sonata for Violin and Piano No. 3 in A minor, 'dans le caractère populaire roumain', Op. 25 (1926)
A. Oprean, J. Oprean Concert
(2/92) (HYPE) ① **CDA66484**
Y. Menuhin, H. Menuhin (r1936) Concert
(6/93) (BIDD) ① **LAB066**
2 Sonatas for Cello and Piano, Op. 26
1. (1898); 2. (1935).
1. R. Rust, D. Apter Concert
(10/90) (MARC) ① **8 223298**
String Octet in C, Op. 7 (1900)
ASMF Chbr Ens (r1992) Concert
(5/93) (CHAN) ① **CHAN9131**
R.C. Popescu, L. Moma, M. Moroianu, A. Winkler, G. Bâlă, F. Matei, M. Cazacu, D. Joitoiu, H. Andreescu (r1995) Wind Decet, Op. 14.
(11/95) (OLYM) ① **OCD445**
String Quartet No. 1 in E flat, Op. 22/1 (1916-20)
Voces Qt String Quartet 2.
(6/92) (OLYM) ① **OCD413**
String Quartet No. 2 in G, Op. 22/2 (1950-53)
Voces Qt String Quartet 1.
(6/92) (OLYM) ① **OCD413**
Violin Sonata, 'Torso' (1911) (incomplete)
A. Oprean, J. Oprean Concert
(2/92) (HYPE) ① **CDA66484**
Wind Decet, Op. 14 (1906)
Lausanne CO, L. Foster Concert
(10/88) (CLAV) ① **CD50-8803**
V. Frâncu, N. Maxim, A. Petrescu, F. Ionoaia, V. Bărbuceanu, L. Boantă, G. Orban, V. Feher, S. Jebeleanu, D. Cinca, H. Andreescu (r1995) String Octet. (11/95) (OLYM) ① **OCD445**

SECTION III: INSTRUMENTAL

Hommage à Gabriel Fauré—piano
M. Fingerhut Concert (9/88) (CHAN) ① **CHAN8578**
Sonata for Piano No. 1 in F sharp minor, Op. 24/1 (1924)
Movt 2. D. Lipatti (r1936) Concert
(10/95) (ARCI) ① [2] **ARC112/3**
Sonata for Piano No. 3 in D, Op. 24 (1933-35)
D. Lipatti (bp1943) Concert
(11/89) (EMI) ① **CDH7 63038-2**

ENGEL, Jan (fl 1770) Poland

SECTION I: ORCHESTRAL

Symphony in E flat
Warsaw CO, M. Sewen Concert
(8/94) (OLYM) ① **CD0380**
Symphony in F
Warsaw CO, M. Sewen Concert
(8/94) (OLYM) ① **OCD380**

ENGLANDER, Ludwig (1859–1914) Austria/USA

SECTION V: STAGE WORKS

The Passing Show—revue (1894—New York) (Lyrics S. Rosenfeld)
EXCERPTS: 1. Sex against Sex.
1. Cincinnati Uni Sngrs, Cincinnati Uni Th Orch, E. Rivers (r1978) Concert (4/94) (NEW) ① **80221-2**
The Rounders—musical show (1899—New York) (Lyrics Harry B Smith)
EXCERPTS: 1. Only a Hundred Girls in the World for Me.
1. T. Q. Seabrooke, Broadway Cast (1904) Concert
(5/94) (PEAR) ① [3] **GEMMCDS9050/2(1)**

ENGLUND, (Sven) Einar (b 1916)
Finland

SECTION I: ORCHESTRAL

Ciacona (1990)
Helsinki PO, S. Comissiona Concert
(4/92) (ONDI) ① **ODE767-2**
Symphony No. 1, 'War Symphony' (1946)
Estonian SO, P. Lilje Symphony 2.
(8/92) (ONDI) ① **ODE751-2**
Symphony No. 2 (1947)
Estonian SO, P. Lilje Symphony 1.
(8/92) (ONDI) ① **ODE751-2**

ENRIQUE (fl late 15th Cent)
Spain

SECTION IV: VOCAL AND CHORAL

Mi querer tanto vos quiere—canción: 4vv (from the Colombina Song Book)
Hespèrion XX, J. Savall Concert
(7/92) (ASTR) ① **E8763**
Gothic Voices, C. Page (r1993) Concert
(2/94) (HYPE) ① **CDA66653**
Pues con sobra de tristura (from the Colombina Song Book)
Hespèrion XX, J. Savall Concert
(7/92) (ASTR) ① **E8763**

ERBACH, Christian (1570/73–1635) Germany

SECTION II: CHAMBER

La Paglia—canzon: 5 parts
His Majesties Sagbutts and Cornetts, T. Roberts (r1993) Concert (6/94) (HYPE) ① **CDA66688**

SECTION III: INSTRUMENTAL

Canzona secundi toni—organ
T. Roberts (r1993) Concert
(6/94) (HYPE) ① **CDA66688**
Fantasia sub Elevatione—organ
T. Roberts (r1993) Concert
(6/94) (HYPE) ① **CDA66688**
Toccata octavi toni—organ (fragment)
I. Simcock (r1993) Concert
(6/94) (HYPE) ① **CDA66688**

SECTION IV: VOCAL AND CHORAL

Hic est sacerdos—alleluia: 5vv
Westminster Cath Ch, J. O'Donnell, T. Roberts, I. Simcock (r1993) Concert
(6/94) (HYPE) ① **CDA66688**
Posuisti Domine—communion: 5vv
Westminster Cath Ch, J. O'Donnell, T. Roberts, I. Simcock (r1993) Concert
(6/94) (HYPE) ① **CDA66688**
Sacerdotes Dei—introit: 5vv
Westminster Cath Ch, J. O'Donnell, T. Roberts, I. Simcock (r1993) Concert
(6/94) (HYPE) ① **CDA66688**

ERKEL, Ferenc (1810–1893)
Hungary

SECTION V: STAGE WORKS

Hunyadi László—opera (1844—Budapest) (Lib. Egressy, after L. Tóth)
Ah rebéges L. Nordica, anon (r1907) Concert
(7/93) (NIMB) ① [2] **NI7840/1**

ERLANGER, Camille (1863–1919)
France

SECTION IV: VOCAL AND CHORAL

Fédia—song
V. Maurel, anon (r1903) Concert
(10/92) (SYMP) ① **SYMCD1101**

ERNOUL (fl late 13th cent)
France

SECTION IV: VOCAL AND CHORAL

Por conforter mon corage—pastourelle: 1v
Gothic Voices, C. Page (r1994) Concert
(8/95) (HYPE) ① **CDA66773**

ERNST, Heinrich Wilhelm (1814–1865) Moravia

SECTION II: CHAMBER

Adagio sentimentale—violin and piano, Op. 13/1 (1841)
S. Lupu, P. Pettinger *Concert*
(7/90) (CNTI) ① CCD1017
Hungarian Airs—violin and piano, Op. 22 (c1850)
S. Lupu, P. Pettinger *Concert*
(7/90) (CNTI) ① CCD1017
O. Renardy, W. Robert (r1941) *Concert*
(12/92) (BIDD) ① [2] LAB061/2
Nocturne in E—violin and piano, Op. 8
H. Heermann, orch, F. Kark (r c1909: arr Heermann) *Concert*
(8/90) (SYMP) ① SYMCD1071
Polonaise in D—violin and piano, Op. 17 (1842)
S. Lupu, P. Pettinger *Concert*
(7/90) (CNTI) ① CCD1017
Rondo Papageno—violin and piano, Op. 20 (or Op. 21) (1846)
S. Lupu, P. Pettinger *Concert*
(7/90) (CNTI) ① CCD1017

SECTION III: INSTRUMENTAL

Der Erlkönig (Schubert)—song transcription: violin, Op. 26 (1854)
G. Kremer (r1993) *Concert*
(10/95) (DG) ① 445 820-2GH
Variations on 'The Last Rose of Summer'—violin
M. Vengerov *Concert* (4/90) (BIDD) ① LAW001
J. Kang (r1994) *Concert*
(8/95) (DINT) ① DICD920241

ERTL, Dominik (1857–1911) Germany

SECTION I: ORCHESTRAL

Hoch- und Deutschmeister—march
Berlin Phil Wind Qnt, H. von Karajan (r1973) *Concert*
(5/94) (DG) ① 439 346-2GX2

ESCHER, Rudolf (George) (1912–1980) The Netherlands

SECTION III: INSTRUMENTAL

Sonata—cello (1945-48)
P. Wispelwey (r1992) *Concert*
(12/94) (GLOB) ① GLO5089

ESCOBAR, Pedro de (c1465–1535) Portugal

SECTION IV: VOCAL AND CHORAL

Asperges me—motet
Quodlibet *Concert* (4/90) (CRD) ① CRD3450
Ave maris stella—hymn (4vv)
Quodlibet *Concert* (4/90) (CRD) ① CRD3450
Beatus es—motet
Quodlibet *Concert* (4/90) (CRD) ① CRD3450
Clamabat autem mulier—motet (4vv)
Quodlibet *Concert* (4/90) (CRD) ① CRD3450
G. Lesne, Circa 1500, N. Hadden *Concert*
(9/92) (VIRG) ① VC7 59071-2
Deus tuorum militum—hymn (4vv)
Quodlibet *Concert* (4/90) (CRD) ① CRD3450
Gran plaser siento yo ya—villancico
Circa 1500, N. Hadden *Concert*
(9/92) (VIRG) ① VC7 59071-2
Hostis Herodes—hymn (4vv)
Quodlibet *Concert* (4/90) (CRD) ① CRD3450
Missa Pro defunctis—4vv
Quodlibet *Concert* (4/90) (CRD) ① CRD3450
Pásame por Dios barquero—villancico (3vv)
G. Lesne, Circa 1500, N. Hadden *Concert*
(9/92) (VIRG) ① VC7 59071-2
Salve regina—antiphon (5vv)
Quodlibet *Concert* (4/90) (CRD) ① CRD3450
Secaronme los pesares—villancico
Circa 1500, N. Hadden *Concert*
(9/92) (VIRG) ① VC7 59071-2
Stabat mater—motet
Quodlibet *Concert* (4/90) (CRD) ① CRD3450

ESCRIBANO SANCHEZ, Maria (b 1954) Spain

SECTION III: INSTRUMENTAL

Quejío—piano (1982)
S. Marin *Concert* (4/93) (RNE) ① M3/03

ESPLÁ (Y TRIAY), Oscar (1886–1976) Spain

SECTION IV: VOCAL AND CHORAL

5 Canciones playeras—1v and piano/orchestra (1929) (Wds. R. Alberti)
1. Rutas; 2. Pregon; 3. Las doce; 4. El pescador; 5. Coplilla.
Y. Pappas, Israel SO, G. Stern *Concert*
(2/88) (MERI) ① CDE84134
V. de los Angeles, Paris Cons, R. Frühbeck de Burgos (r1962) *Concert*
(4/94) (EMI) ① [4] CMS5 65061-2(1)

ESTEVE, Pablo (d 1794) Spain

also known as Esteve y Grimau

SECTION IV: VOCAL AND CHORAL

Alma, sintamos—song
T. Berganza, F. Lavilla *Concert*
(12/92) (DG) ① [2] 435 848-2GX2

ESTEVES, João Rodrigues (c1700–1751) Portugal

SECTION IV: VOCAL AND CHORAL

Mass—8vv: double choir (1721)
Currende Voc Ens, Currende Instr Ens, E. van Nevel
D. Scarlatti: *Stabat mater*.
(5/92) (ACCE) ① ACC9069D

ESTÉVEZ, Antonio (1916–1988) Venezuela

SECTION IV: VOCAL AND CHORAL

4 Cantata Criolla, 'Florentino, el que canto' con el diablo'—2vv, chorusand orchestra (1954) (Wds. A. A. Torreálba)
I. Alvarez, W. Alvarado, Caracas Schola Cantorum, S. Bolívar Orfeón Universitario, S. Bolívar SO, E. Mata Villa-Lobos: *Chôros* 10.
(4/93) (DORI) ① DIS80101

EXAUDET, André-Joseph (c1710–1763) France

SECTION II: CHAMBER

Minuet (unidentified)
J. Szigeti, K. Ruhrseitz (r1927) *Concert*
(1/90) (BIDD) ① [2] LAB005/6

EYCK, Jacob van (1589/90–1657) The Netherlands

SECTION II: CHAMBER

Der Fluyten Lust-hof—variations for 1-2 recorders (pub 1649 and 1646) (Vol 1 is a reprint of 'Euterpe', pub 1644)
1. The English Nightingale (Engels Nachtegaeltje); 2. Prince Robert's Masque (Prins Robberts Masco); 3. Preludium Ofte Voorspel; 4. La Bergere; 5. Under the green Linden Tree (Onder de Linde Groene); 6. De Zoete Zoomer Tyden; 7. More Paltino; 8. Buffoons (Boffons); 9. Amarili mia bella; 10. Psalm 116; 11. Fantasia En Echo; 12. Philis Schoon Herderinne; 13. Courant II 'Little thief of my heart' (Of Harte Deifje); 14. Tweede Carilleen; 15. Lost Queen (Verwaelde Konighin); 16. Bravade; 17. A Child to us is born; 18. Puer nobis nascitur; 19. What shall we do this evening? (Wat zal men op de Avond doen); 20. Stil, stil zeen stys; 21. When Daphne, the most beautiful maiden (Doen Daphne d'over schoone Maeght); 22. Wei Jan; 23. Simon the Mad (Malle Symen); 24. Goat-foot (Boeckxvoetje); 25. Questa dolce sirena; 26. O sleep, sweet sleep (O slaep, o zoete slaep); 27. Lachrymae Pavan; 28. My friend Cella (L'Amie Cillae); 29. Get up, I'm going hunting (Wel op, wel op, ick gae ter jaght); 30. A little Scottish Song (Een Schots Lietjen); 31. English Song (Engels Lied).
1. Circa 1500, N. Hadden (r1991) *Concert*
(8/93) (CRD) ① CRD3487

1, 21, 27. F. Brüggen (r1960s) *Concert*
(10/95) (TELD) ① 4509-97466-2
1, 2, 5, 7-9, 13, 15, 16, 19, 21, 23-31. M. Verbruggen (r1991) (8/93) (HARM) ① HMU90 7072
17, 18. M. Petri, National PO, M. Neary (orch anon) *Concert* (12/91) (RCA) ① RD60060
19. B. Kol, A. Brodo, D. Shemer *Concert*
(6/90) (CARL) ① PWK1138

EYSLER, Edmund (1874–1949) Austria

SECTION V: STAGE WORKS

Bruder Straubinger—operetta (3 acts) (1903—Vienna) (Lib. M. West and I. Schnitzer)
Küssen ist keine Sünd P. Morrison, Chandos Concert Orch, S. Barry (Eng) *Concert*
(2/90) (CHAN) ① CHAN8759

FACCIO, Franco (1840–1891) Italy

SECTION V: STAGE WORKS

Amleto—opera: 4 acts (1865—Genoa) (Lib. A Boito)
Principe Amleto C. Owen, anon (r1950/60s) *Concert*
(6/94) (IRCC) ① IRCC-CD808

FACOLI, Marco (16th cent) Italy

SECTION III: INSTRUMENTAL

Pass'e mezzo Moderno—keyboard (pub 1588)
R. Alessandrini (r1994) *Concert*
(4/95) (O111) ① OPS30-118

FAHRBACH I, Philipp (1815–1885) Austria

SECTION I: ORCHESTRAL

Locomotiv—galop, Op. 31 (1838)
Košice St PO, M. Eichenholz (r1992) *Concert*
(2/94) (MARC) ① 8 223471

FAHRBACH II, Philipp (1843–1894) Austria

SECTION I: ORCHESTRAL

Storchschnäbel—galopp, Op. 149 (1880) (Eng: Storks' bills)
London Viennese Orch, J. Rothstein *Concert*
(5/93) (CHAN) ① CHAN9127

FAIN, Sammy (1902–1989) USA

SECTION V: STAGE WORKS

Flahooley—musical show (1951)
Cpte B. Cook, Y. Sumac, Orig Broadway Cast
(11/93) (EMI) ① ZDM7 64764-2
Peter Pan—musical film (1953) (Lyrics Sammy Cahn; additional songs by other cpsrs)
EXCERPTS: 1. Main Title; 2. Second Star to the Right; 3. You Can Fly! You Can Fly!; 4. A Pirate's Life (music & lyrics Penner); 5. Following the Leader (Hibler/Sears/Morey); 6. What Makes the Red Man Red?; 7. Your Mother and Mine; 8. The Elegant Captain Hook; 9. Never Smile at a Crocodile (Churchill/Lawrence); 10. Finale: You Can Fly!.
2. Voices of Ascension, D. Keene (r1994-5; arr Fraser) *Concert* (12/95) (DELO) ① DE3186

FALCONIERI, Andrea (1586–1656) Italy/England

SECTION II: CHAMBER

Il Primo libro di canzone—1-3 vns, va or other instr & continuo (pub 1650)
EXCERPTS: 1. Riñen y pelean entre Berzebillo con Satanasillo; 2. Bayle de dos dichos diabolos; 3. Fantasia detta la Portia; 4. L'Eroica a tre and Ciaccona; 5. Battaglia de Barabaso yerno de Satanas; 6. Folias echa para mi Señora Doña; 7. Fantasia echa para el muy reverendo Padre Falla; 8. Passacalle; 9. Corriente dicha la cuella; 10. Sinfonia la buon'hora; 11. Corriente dicha l'avellina; 12. Gioiosa fantasia; 13. La suave melodia y su corriente; 14. Corriente dicha la mota; 15. Il Rosso Brando; 16. Sinfonia quarta; 17. La Borga.

1-4. Newbery Consort, M. Springfels Concert
(7/92) (HARM) ① **HMU90 7022**

SECTION IV: VOCAL AND CHORAL

O bellissimi capelli—song
E. Pinza, F. Kitzinger (r1940) Concert
(9/93) (RCA) ① **09026 61245-2**

FALKENHAGEN, Adam
(1697-1761) Germany

SECTION III: INSTRUMENTAL

Variations on 'Wer nur den lieben Gott lässt walten'—lute
L. Kirchhof Concert   (11/92) (SONY) ① **SK48068**

FALL, Leo (1873-1925) Austria

SECTION V: STAGE WORKS

Der Fidele Bauer—operetta (3 acts)
(1907—Mannheim) (Lib. Leon)
O, frag' mich nicht P. Domingo, ECO, J. Rudel
Concert   (2/87) (EMI) ① **CDC7 47398-2**
Die Rose von Stambul—operetta (3 acts)
(1916—Vienna) (Lib. Brammer and Grünwald)
Excs E. Köth, R. Schock, Günther Arndt Ch, Berlin
SO, F. Fox Millöcker: Dubarry.
(2/91) (EURO) ① **GD69023**
Ihr stillen, süssen Frau'n P. Domingo, Ambrosian
Sngrs, ECO, J. Rudel Concert
(2/87) (EMI) ① **CDC7 47398-2**
Ihr stillen, süsser Frauen H.E. Groh, orch (r1932)
Concert   (9/92) (PEAR) ① **GEMMCD9419**

FALLA (Y MATHEU), Manuel de
(1876-1946) Spain

SECTION I: ORCHESTRAL

Concerto for Harpsichord, Flute, Oboe, Clarinet, Violin and Cello (1923-26)
T. Millan, J. Martin, M. Angulo, J-E. Lluna, S. Juan, J.
Pozas Sombrero de tres picos.
(9/92) (AUVI) ① **V4642**
J. Constable, London Sinfonietta, S. Rattle Concert
(9/92) (DECC) ① [2] **433 908-2DM2**
Teatre lliure CO, J. Pons (r1992) Concert
(5/93) (HARM) ① **HMC90 1432**
M. de Falla, Inst Ens (r1930) Concert
(11/93) (EMI) ① **CDC7 54836-2**
Homenajes—orchestra (1920-38)
1. Fanfare sobre el nombre de E.F. Arbós (1933); 2.
à Claude Debussy (after guitar piece of 1920); 3.
Rappel de la Fanfare (1941); 4. à Paul Dukas (after
piano piece of 1935); 5. Pedrelliana (1924-39).
Cincinnati SO, J. López-Cobos Concert
(11/87) (TELA) ① **CD80149**
SRO, E. Ansermet (pp1966) Atlántida.
(11/92) (CASC) ① **VEL2005**
1, 2, 3, 4, 5. S. Bolívar SO, E. Mata (r1994) Concert
(11/95) (DORI) ① **DOR90210**
Noches en los jardines de España, 'Nights in the Gardens of Spain'—symphonic impressions for piano and orchestra (1907-16)
1. En la Generalife; 2. Danza lejana; 3. En los
jardines de la Sierra de Córdoba.
A. de Larrocha, LPO, R. Frühbeck de Burgos Concert
(10/84) (DECC) ① **410 289-2DH**
M. Fingerhut, LSO, G. Simon Concert
(10/86) (CHAN) ① **CHAN8457**
A. Rubinstein, Philadelphia, E. Ormandy Concert
(10/87) (RCA) ① **RD85666**
A. de Larrocha, SRO, S. Comissiona Concert
(4/89) (DECC) ① **417 771-2DM**
A. de Larrocha, LPO, R. Frühbeck de Burgos Concert
(8/91) (DECC) ① **430 703-2DM**
G. Gonzalez, Tenerife SO, V.P. Pérez Concert
(4/91) (ETCE) ① **KTC1095**
G. Soriano, Paris Cons, R. Frühbeck de Burgos
Concert   (7/92) (EMI) ① [2] **CZS7 67474-2**
A. de Larrocha, LPO, R. Frühbeck de Burgos Concert
(9/92) (DECC) ① [2] **433 908-2DM2**
R. Casadesus, SRO, E. Ansermet (pp1957) Concert
(11/92) (CASC) ① **VEL2008**
A. Rubinstein, St Louis SO, V. Golschmann (r1949)
Concert   (9/93) (RCA) ① **09026 61261-2**
T. Barto, ASMF, N. Marriner Sombrero de tres picos.
(5/94) (EMI) ① **CDC5 55049-2**
A. Rubinstein, Philadelphia, E. Ormandy (r1969)
Concert   (8/94) (RCA) ① **09026 61863-2**
Polish Nat RSO, A. Wit (r1993) Concert
(3/95) (NAXO) ① **8 550753**
R. Orozco, Spanish Nat Youth Orch, E. Colomer
(r1994) Concert   (7/95) (AUVI) ① **V4724**

C. Haskil, Lamoureux Concerts Orch, I. Markevitch
(r1960) Concert
(11/95) (PHIL) ① [12] **442 685-2PM12**
C. Haskil, Lamoureux Concerts Orch, I. Markevitch
(r1960) Concert
(11/95) (PHIL) ① [4] **442 631-2PM4**

SECTION II: CHAMBER

Suite populaire espagnole—violin & piano
(arr Kochanski from 'Canciones populares
españoles')
1. El paño moruno; 2. Nana (berceuse); 3. Canción;
4. Polo; 5. Asturiana; 6. Jota.
J. Du Pré, E. Lush (arr Maréchal vc/pf: bp1961)
Concert   (9/89) (EMI) ① **CDM7 63165-2**
I. Perlman, S. Sanders Concert
(10/89) (EMI) ① **CDM7 63533-2**
K. Takezawa, P. Moll Concert
(2/93) (RCA) ① **09026 60704-2**
A. A. Meyers, S. Rivers (r1993) Concert
(4/95) (RCA) ① **09026 62546-2**
6. J. Du Pré, J. Williams (r1962: arr vc/gtr: Maréchal)
Concert   (11/95) (EMI) ① **CDC5 55529-2**

SECTION III: INSTRUMENTAL

El Amor brujo—piano transcription from the ballet (Eng: Love the Magician)
1. Pantomime; 2. Scene; 3. Song of the Will o' the
Wisp; 4. The Apparition; 5. Dance of the Game of
Love; 6. The Magic Circle (The Fisherman's Story); 7.
Midnight (Witchcraft); 8. Ritual Fire Dance; 9. Dance
of terror.
J-F. Heisser Concert
(7/90) (ERAT) ① **2292-45481-2**
A. de Larrocha Concert
(9/92) (DECC) ① [2] **433 929-2DM2**
8. R. Pöntinen Concert   (11/85) (BIS) ① **BIS-CD300**
8. M. Lympany Concert   (1/89) (EMIL) ① **CDZ110**
8. M. Hess (r1929) Concert
(3/95) (BIDD) ① **LHW024**
8. A. Brailowsky (r1928) Concert
(11/95) (DANA) ① [2] **DACOCD338/9**
8, 9. A. de Larrocha (r1973) Concert
(7/90) (DECC) ① **417 795-2DM**
8, 9. A. Rubinstein (r1947) Concert
(9/93) (RCA) ① **09026 61261-2**
9. A. de Larrocha (r1950s) Concert
(12/92) (EMI) ① **CDM7 64527-2**
Fantasía bética—piano (1919)
J-F. Heisser Concert
(7/90) (ERAT) ① **2292-45481-2**
A. de Larrocha Concert
(9/92) (DECC) ① [2] **433 926-2DM2**
A. de Larrocha (r1950s) Concert
(12/92) (EMI) ① **CDM7 64527-2**
A. Petchersky Concert
(12/92) (ASV) ① **CDQS6079**
A. de Larrocha (r1992) Concert
(9/94) (RCA) ① **09026 61389-2**
M. Hambourg (r1923) Concert
(6/95) (PEAR) ① **GEMMCD9147**
R. Orozco (r1994) Concert   (7/95) (AUVI) ① **V4724**
Homenaje, 'Pour le tombeau de Paul Dukas'—piano (1935)
J-F. Heisser Concert
(7/90) (ERAT) ① **2292-45481-2**
R. Orozco (r1994) Concert   (7/95) (AUVI) ① **V4724**
Homenaje, '(Le) tombeau de Claude Debussy'—guitar (1920)
J-F. Heisser (arr pf) Concert
(7/90) (ERAT) ① **2292-45481-2**
J. Bream (r1962) Concert
(8/93) (RCA) ① [28] **09026 61583-2(4)**
J. Bream (r1983) Concert
(8/93) (RCA) ① [28] **09026 61583-2(3)**
J. Bream (r1983; trans Bream) Concert
(8/93) (RCA) ① **09026 61591-2**
P. Romero (r1993) Concert
(4/95) (PHIL) ① **442 150-2PH**
R. Orozco (r1994) Concert   (7/95) (AUVI) ① **V4724**
1, 2, 3. J. Bream (r1962) Concert
(6/94) (RCA) ① **09026 61594-2**
Nocturno—piano (1899)
J-F. Heisser Concert
(7/90) (ERAT) ① **2292-45481-2**
4 Pièces espagnoles—piano (1902-08)
1. Aragonesa; 2. Cubana; 3. Montanesa; 4.
Andaluza.
J-F. Heisser Concert
(7/90) (ERAT) ① **2292-45481-2**
A. de Larrocha Concert
(9/92) (DECC) ① [2] **433 926-2DM2**
A. de Larrocha (r1950s) Concert
(12/92) (EMI) ① **CDM7 64527-2**
A. de Larrocha (r1992) Concert
(9/94) (RCA) ① **09026 61389-2**

R. Orozco (r1994) Concert   (7/95) (AUVI) ① **V4724**
4. A. Rubinstein (r1949) Concert
(9/93) (RCA) ① **09026 61261-2**
Serenata—piano (1901)
M.R. Bodini Concert   (5/90) (NUOV) ① **6809**
Serenata andaluza—piano (1899)
M.R. Bodini Concert   (5/90) (NUOV) ① **6809**
J-F. Heisser Concert
(7/90) (ERAT) ① **2292-45481-2**
A. de Larrocha (r1992) Concert
(9/94) (RCA) ① **09026 61389-2**
El Sombrero de tres picos—piano transcription from the ballet (Eng: Three-cornered hat)
1. Danza de los vecinos; 2. Danza del molinero; 3.
Danza de la molinera.
J-F. Heisser Concert
(7/90) (ERAT) ① **2292-45481-2**
A. de Larrocha Concert
(9/92) (DECC) ① [2] **433 929-2DM2**
1, 3. A. de Larrocha (r1950s) Concert
(12/92) (EMI) ① **CDM7 64527-2**
2. A. de Larrocha Concert
(7/90) (DECC) ① **417 795-2DM**
2. A. Rubinstein (r1954) Concert
(9/93) (RCA) ① **09026 61261-2**
Vals-capricho—piano (1900)
J-F. Heisser Concert
(7/90) (ERAT) ① **2292-45481-2**

SECTION IV: VOCAL AND CHORAL

7 Canciones populares españolas (1914-15)
(Wds. trad)
1. El paño moruno; 2. Seguidilla murciana; 3.
Asturiana; 4. Jota; 5. Nana; 6. Cancíon; 7. Polo.
M. Senn, M.R. Bodini Concert
(5/90) (NUOV) ① **6809**
A. Gjevang, E.S. Nökleberg Concert
(11/91) (VICT) ① **VCD19007**
V. de los Angeles, G. Moore (r1951) Concert
(4/92) (EMI) ① **CDH7 64028-2**
T. Berganza, N. Yepes Concert
(12/92) (DG) ① [2] **435 848-2GX2**
P. Rozario, M. Troop Concert
(12/92) (COLL) ① **Coll3052-2**
S. Danco, SRO, E. Ansermet (bp1953) Concert
(1/93) (CASC) ① **VEL2010**
C. Supervia, F. Marshall (r1930) Concert
(3/93) (NIMB) ① [2] **NI7836/7**
V. de los Angeles, Teatre lliure CO, J. Pons (r1992;
arr Halffter) Concert
(5/93) (HARM) ① **HMC90 1432**
A. Nafé, Lausanne CO, J. López-Cobos (r1992; orch
Berio) Amor Brujo.   (11/93) (DENO) ① **CO-75038**
M. Barrientos, M. de Falla (r1928/30) Concert
(11/93) (EMI) ① **CDC7 54836-2**
V. de los Angeles, G. Soriano (r1961/2) Concert
(9/94) (EMI) ① [4] **CMS5 65061-2(1)**
D. Jones, M. Martineau (r1993) Concert
(9/94) (CHAN) ① **CHAN9277**
M. Senn, S. Bolívar SO, A. Almeida (arr vn/orch: L.
Berio) Concert   (11/95) (DORI) ① **DOR90210**
3. N. Milstein, L. Mittman (1937: arr vn/pf:
Kochanski) Concert   (9/95) (BIDD) ① **LAB096**
4. C. Flesch, I. Strasfogel (arr Kochanski: r1929)
Concert   (4/91) (BIDD) ① **LAB045**
4. N. Milstein, L. Pommers (1957: arr Kochánski)
Concert   (5/94) (EMI) ① [6] **ZDMF7 64830-2**
4. J. Heifetz, E. Bay (1946) Concert
(11/94) (RCA) ① [65] **09026 61778-2(06)**
4. J. Heifetz, I. Achron (1928) Concert
(11/94) (RCA) ① [65] **09026 61778-2(2)**
4. J. Thibaud, T. Janopoulo (r1930: arr vn/pf:
Kochanski) Concert   (11/94) (APR) ① [2] **APR7028**
4, 5. J. Heifetz, B. Smith (1967) Concert
(11/94) (RCA) ① [65] **09026 61778-2(31)**
5. M. Maisky, P. Gililov (arr vc/pf) Concert
(7/91) (DG) ① **431 544-2GH**
5. J. Heifetz, B. Smith (1972) Concert
(11/94) (RCA) ① [65] **09026 61778-2(46)**
6. F. Kreisler, C. Lamson (1927: arr Kochánski)
Concert   (12/93) (BIDD) ① **LAB075**
Psyché—1v, fl, vn, va, vc and hp (1924)
(Wds. G. Jean-Aubry)
D. Upshaw, Inst Ens Concert
(11/91) (NONE) ① **7559-79262-2**
J. Smith, London Sinfonietta, S. Rattle Concert
(9/92) (DECC) ① [2] **433 908-2DM2**
V. de los Angeles, Teatre lliure CO, J. Pons (r1992)
Concert   (5/93) (HARM) ① **HMC90 1432**
V. de los Angeles, J-C. Gérard, A. Challan, French
Stg Trio (1969) Concert
(4/94) (EMI) ① [4] **CMS5 65061-2(2)**

Soneto a Córdoba—song: 1v and piano/harp (1927) (Wds. L. de Góngora)
M. Barrientos, M. de Falla (r1930) *Concert*
(11/93) (EMI) Ⓘ **CDC7 54836-2**
V. de los Angeles, A. Challan (r1969) *Concert*
(4/94) (EMI) Ⓘ [4] **CMS5 65061-2(2)**
Tus ojillos negros—song (1902-04) (Wds. C. de Castro)
M. Bayo, J.A. Alvarez-Parejo (r1992) *Concert*
(6/93) (CLAV) Ⓘ **CD50-9205**

SECTION V: STAGE WORKS

El Amor Brujo—ballet: 1 act (1915—Madrid)
(Eng: Love the Magician)
1. Introduction and Scene; 2. In the Cave (Night-time); 3. Song of Love's Sorrow; 4. The Apparition; 5. Dance of Terror; 6. The Magic Circle (The Fisherman's Story); 7. Midnight (Witchcraft); 8. Ritual Fire Dance; 9. Scene; 10. Song of the Will o' the Wisp; 11. Pantomime; 12. Dance of the Game of Love; 13. Finale (The Bells of Morning).
Cpte H. Tourangeau, Montreal SO, C. Dutoit *Sombrero de tres picos.*
(8/83) (DECC) Ⓘ **410 008-2DH**
Cpte Sarah Walker, LSO, G. Simon *Concert*
(10/86) (CHAN) Ⓘ **CHAN8457**
Cpte N. Mistral, New Philh, R. Frühbeck de Burgos *Concert*
(10/89) (DECC) Ⓘ **417 786-2DM**
Cpte M. Senn, Carme, L. Izquierdo (orig vers) *Concert*
(5/90) (NUOV) Ⓘ **6809**
Cpte G. Ortega, Teatre Lliure CO, J. Pons (r1990) *Retablo de Maese Pedro.*
(5/92) (HARM) Ⓘ **HMC90 5213**
Cpte O. Dominguez, Philh, A. Vandernoot *Concert*
(7/92) (EMI) Ⓘ [2] **CZS7 67474-2**
Cpte M. de Gabarain, SRO, E. Ansermet *Concert*
(9/92) (DECC) Ⓘ [2] **433 908-2DM2**
Cpte A. Nafé, S. Aguilar, A.B. Egea, Lausanne CO, J. López-Cobos (r1992) *Canciones populares españolas.*
(10/93) (DENO) Ⓘ **CO-75339**
Cpte J. Gomez, C. Powell, Aquarius, N. Cleobury (r1988) *Corregidor y la Molinera.*
(11/94) (VIRG) Ⓘ **CUV5 61138-2**
G. Bumbry, Berlin RSO, L. Maazel (r1965) *Concert*
(10/95) (DG) Ⓘ **447 414-2GOR**
M. Senn, S. Bolívar SO, E. Mata (r1994) *Concert*
(11/95) (DORI) Ⓘ **DOR90210**
1, 2, 7. Warsaw Nat PO, J. Semkow *Concert*
(5/94) (BELA) Ⓘ **450 129-2**
5, 6, 8, 10, 11. A. de Larrocha, Montreal SO, C. Dutoit *Concert*
(8/91) (DECC) Ⓘ **430 703-2DM**
5, 6, 8, 11. Mexico City PO, E. Bátiz *Concert*
(9/91) (ASV) Ⓘ **CDDCA735**
8. A. Rubinstein (arr.Rubinstein) *Concert*
(10/87) (RCA) Ⓘ **RD85666**
8. Cincinnati Pops, E. Kunzel *Concert*
(10/89) (TELA) Ⓘ **CD80170**
8. Brodsky Qt (arr M. Thomas) *Concert*
(4/92) (TELD) Ⓘ **2292-46015-2**
8. A. Rubinstein (r1961; arr pf) *Concert*
(8/94) (RCA) Ⓘ **09026 61863-2**
8. K. Labèque, M. Labèque (r1993; trans Bragiotti: 2 pfs) *Concert*
(9/94) (PHIL) Ⓘ **438 938-2PH**
8. M. Kliegel, B. Glemser (r1993: arr vc/pf:G Piatigorsky) *Concert*
(1/95) (NAXO) Ⓘ **8 550785**
8, 11. LSO, R. Frühbeck de Burgos *Concert*
(11/89) (CARL) Ⓘ **PCD924**
10. M. Barrientos, M. de Falla (r1930) *Concert*
(11/93) (EMI) Ⓘ **CDC7 54836-2**
11. J. Heifetz, E. Bay (r1946) *Concert*
(11/94) (RCA) Ⓘ [65] **09026 61778-2(06)**
Atlántida—scenic cantata: prologue and 3 parts (1962—Milan) (cpted E Halffter: wds. cpsr, after J Verdaguer)
Cpte M. Bayo, T. Berganza, S. Estes, Illes Balears Uni Chor, Laguna Uni Polyphonic Chor, Orfeon Navarro Reverter, Orfeon Uni Chor, Valencia Pequeños Cantores, Spanish Nat Youth Orch, E. Colomer (r1992)
(7/93) (AUVI) Ⓘ [2] **V4685**
M. Caballé, H. Rehfuss, Lausanne Youth Ch, Suisse Romande Rad Chor, Villamont Coll Little Ch, SRO, E. Ansermet (Ital: pp1963) *Homenajes.*
(11/92) (CASC) Ⓘ **VEL2005**
El Corregidor y la molinera—farsa mimica (2 scenes) (1917—Madrid)
Cpte J. Gomez, C. Powell, Aquarius, N. Cleobury (r1988) *Amor brujo.*
(11/94) (VIRG) Ⓘ **CUV5 61138-2**
Teatre Lliure CO, J. Pons (r1994) *Lorca: Canciones españolas antiguas.*
(7/95) (HARM) Ⓘ **HMC90 1520**
El gran teatro del mundo—incidental music (1928)
EXCERPTS: 1. Para empezar al auto; 2. Lento; 3. Alaben al Señor (Cantigo de Alfonso X); 4. Ama el otro como a ti; 5. Rey de este caduco; 6. Toda la

---

hermosura (Canto de montañas); 7. Finale—Tantum ergo (Victoria).
V. de los Angeles, Cor Lieder Camera, Teatre lliure CO, J. Pons (r1992) *Concert*
(5/93) (HARM) Ⓘ **HMC90 1432**
El Retablo de maese Pedro—puppet opera (1923—Paris) (Lib. cpsr, after Cervantes)
Cpte S. Linay, Adrian Thompson, M. Best, Matrix Ens, R. Ziegler *Concert*
(7/91) (ASV) Ⓘ **CDDCA758**
Cpte J. Martin, J. Cabero, I. Fresán, Teatre Lliure CO, J. Pons (r1990) *Amor brujo.*
(5/92) (HARM) Ⓘ **HMC90 5213**
Cpte J. Smith, A. Oliver, P. Knapp, London Sinfonietta, S. Rattle *Concert*
(9/92) (DECC) Ⓘ [2] **433 908-2DM2**
Sinfonia A. de Larrocha (r1992; trans pf) *Concert*
(9/94) (RCA) Ⓘ **09026 61389-2**
El Sombrero de tres picos—orchestral suites from the ballet
EXCERPTS: 1. Scences and Dances: 1a. Introduction—Afternoon; 1b. Dance of the Miller's Wife; 1c. The Corregidor; 1d. The Grapes. 2. Three Dances: 2a. The Neighbours; 2b. The Miller's Dance; 2c. Final Dance.
1b, 1c, 2b, 2c Berlin RSO, L. Maazel (r1965) *Concert*
(10/95) (DG) Ⓘ **447 414-2GOR**
2a J. Bream (r1983: trans gtr: Bream) *Concert*
(8/93) (RCA) Ⓘ [28] **09026 61583-2(3)**
2a J. Bream (r1983: trans gtr: Bream) *Concert*
(8/93) (RCA) Ⓘ **09026 61591-2**
2a-c LSO, R. Frühbeck de Burgos *Concert*
(11/89) (CARL) Ⓘ **PCD924**
2a-c Philh, G. Cantelli (r1954) *Concert*
(7/93) (TEST) Ⓘ **SBT1017**
2a, 2b, 2c M. Senn, S. Bolívar SO, E. Mata (r1994) *Concert*
(11/95) (DORI) Ⓘ **DOR90210**
2b B. Janis (r1962) *Concert*
(9/91) (MERC) Ⓘ **432 002-2MM**
2b T. Kropat, T. Krumeich (arr 2 gtrs) *Concert*
(7/93) (CHNN) Ⓘ **CG9103**
2b Empire Brass, E. Flower (r1991) *Concert*
(11/93) (TELA) Ⓘ **CD80301**
2b J. Szigeti, A. Foldes (r1940: arr vn/pf: Szigeti)
(7/94) (BIDD) Ⓘ [2] **LAB070/1**
El Sombrero de tres picos, 'Three-cornered Hat'—ballet: 2 scenes (1919—London)
1. Introduction - Afternoon; 2. Procession; 3. Dance of the Miller's Wife (Fandango); 4. Corregidor; 5. Miller's Wife; 6. The Grapes; 7. Neighbours' Dance (Seguidillas); 8. Miller's Dance (Farruca); 9. The Miller's Arrest; 10. Dance of the Corregidor; 11. Final Dance (Jota).
Cpte C. Boky, Montreal SO, C. Dutoit *Amor brujo.*
(8/83) (DECC) Ⓘ **410 008-2DH**
Cpte F. Quivar, M. May Fest Chor, Cincinnati SO, J. López-Cobos *Concert* (11/87) (TELA) Ⓘ **CD80149**
Cpte T. Berganza, SRO, E. Ansermet *Concert*
(4/89) (DECC) Ⓘ **417 771-2DM**
Cpte J. Gomez, Philh, Y.P. Tortelier *Albéniz: Iberia.*
(4/91) (CHAN) Ⓘ **CHAN8904**
Cpte M.L. Muntada, Spanish Nat Youth Orch, E. Colomer *Harpsichord Concerto.*
(9/92) (AUVI) Ⓘ **V4642**
Cpte L. Ambriz, Dallas SO, E. Mata *Albéniz: Iberia.*
(9/92) (PRO) Ⓘ **CDS581**
Cpte T. Berganza, SRO, E. Ansermet *Concert*
(9/92) (DECC) Ⓘ [2] **433 908-2DM2**
Cpte A. Murray, ASMF, N. Marriner *Nights in the Gardens of Spain.* (5/94) (EMI) Ⓘ **CDC5 55049-2**
Cpte B. Howitt, LSO, E. Jorda (r1960) *Bartók: Dance Suite.*
(4/95) (EVER) Ⓘ **EVC9000**
1a, 1b, 2a-c Philh, C.M. Giulini (r1957) *Concert*
(7/92) (EMI) Ⓘ [2] **CZS7 67474-2**
10. M. Robles (trans hp: cpsr) *Concert*
(4/93) (DECC) Ⓘ **433 869-2DWO**
La Vida breve—opera: 2 acts - 4 scenes (1913—Nice) (Lib. C. Fernández Shaw)
1. Prelude, Act 1; 2. Danse espagnole No.1; 3. Danse espagnole No.2; 4. Vivan los que rien!; 5. Allí está! Riyendo.
Cpte T. Berganza, P.P. Iñigo, A. Nafé, J. Carreras, J. Pons, M. Mairena, R. Contreras, M. Cid, Ambrosian Op Chor, LSO, G. Navarro
(10/92) (DG) Ⓘ **435 851-2GH**
1, 2. Cincinnati SO, J. López-Cobos *Concert*
(11/87) (TELA) Ⓘ **CD80149**
1, 2. SRO, E. Ansermet *Concert*
(4/89) (DECC) Ⓘ **417 771-2DM**
1, 2. SRO, E. Ansermet *Concert*
(9/92) (DECC) Ⓘ [2] **433 908-2DM2**
2. LSO, G. Simon *Concert*
(10/86) (CHAN) Ⓘ **CHAN8457**
2. F. Kreisler, C. Lamson (r1928: arr Kreisler) *Concert*
(1/90) (PEAR) Ⓘ **GEMMCD9324**

---

2. J. Szigeti, N. Magaloff (r1932) *Concert*
(1/90) (BIDD) Ⓘ [2] **LAB007/8**
2. Mexico City PO, E. Bátiz *Concert*
(9/91) (ASV) Ⓘ **CDDCA735**
2. Y. Menuhin, A. Balsam (arr Kreisler: r1932)
Concert
(9/91) (TEST) Ⓘ **SBT1003**
2. J. Thibaud, G. de Launay (r1929: arr vn/pf: Kreisler) *Concert* (10/91) (MSCM) Ⓘ **MM30321**
2. Y. Menuhin, A. Balsam (arr Kreisler: r1932)
Concert
(12/91) (BIDD) Ⓘ **LAB046**
2. Brodsky Qt (arr M. Thomas) *Concert*
(4/92) (TELD) Ⓘ **2292-46015-2**
2. N. Hall (arr gtr) *Concert*
(5/92) (DECC) Ⓘ **430 839-2DH**
2. R. Holmes, J. Walker (r1974: arr Kreisler) *Concert*
(5/92) (DECC) Ⓘ **433 220-2DWO**
2. Paris Cons, R. Frühbeck de Burgos *Concert*
(7/92) (EMI) Ⓘ [2] **CZS7 67474-2**
2. F. Kreisler, M. Raucheisen (arr Kreisler: r1926)
Concert
(9/92) (BIDD) Ⓘ [2] **LAB049/50**
2. F. Kreisler, A. Sándor (arr Kreisler: r1926) *Concert*
(9/92) (BIDD) Ⓘ [2] **LAB049/50**
2. I. Haendel, A. Kotowska (arr Kreisler: r1942)
Concert
(10/92) (PEAR) Ⓘ **GEMMCD9939**
2. T. Kropat, T. Krumeich (arr 2 gtrs) *Concert*
(7/93) (CHNN) Ⓘ **CG9103**
2. T. Varga, G. Moore (r1947: arr vn/pf: Kreisler)
Concert
(11/93) (CLAV) Ⓘ [4] **CD50-9300/4**
2. T. Varga, G. Moore (r1947: arr vn/pf: Kreisler)
Concert
(11/93) (CLAV) Ⓘ **CD50-9314**
2. J. Bream, J. Williams (r1971; arr Pujol, rev Bream)
Concert
(11/93) (RCA) Ⓘ **09026 61450-2**
2. F. Kreisler, F. Rupp (r1938: arr Kreisler) *Concert*
(12/93) (EMI) Ⓘ **CDH7 64701-2**
2. F. Kreisler, C. Lamson (r1928: arr Kreisler)
Concert
(12/93) (BIDD) Ⓘ **LAB080**
2. A. de Larrocha (1992; trans pf) *Concert*
(9/94) (RCA) Ⓘ **09026 61389-2**
2. J. Heifetz, E. Bay (r1935) *Concert*
(11/94) (RCA) Ⓘ [65] **09026 61778-2(03)**
2. J. Thibaud, G. de Launay (r1929: arr Kreisler)
Concert (12/94) (APR) Ⓘ [2] **APR7028**
2. M. Kliegel, B. Glemser (r1993: arr vc/pf: G Pekkera) *Concert* (1/95) (NAXO) Ⓘ **8 550785**
2. S. Nakarjakov, A. Markovich (r1994: arr tpt/pf)
Concert
(6/95) (TELD) Ⓘ **4509-94554-2**
2, 3. K. Labèque, M. Labèque (r1993; trans Samazeuilh: 2 pfs) *Concert*
(9/94) (PHIL) Ⓘ **438 938-2PH**
3. A. de Larrocha (r1950s: arr pf) *Concert*
(12/92) (EMI) Ⓘ **CDM7 64527-2**
4, 5. V. de los Angeles, Philh, S. Robinson (r1948)
Concert
(4/92) (EMI) Ⓘ **CDH7 64028-2**

FALTERMEYER, Harold (20th Cent) USA

SECTION V: STAGE WORKS

The Running Man—film score (1987)
EXCERPTS: 1. Main Theme.
1. Hollywood Sound Orch *Concert*
(5/93) (SILV) Ⓘ **SILVAD3001**

FALVO, Rodolfo (1874–1936) Italy

SECTION IV: VOCAL AND CHORAL

Dicitencello vuie—song (1930) (Wds. E. Fusco)
L. Infantino, RPO, A. Erede (r1948) *Concert*
(4/92) (EMI) Ⓘ [7] **CHS7 69741-2(7)**
T. Gobbi, Orch, A. Erede (r1948) *Concert*
(8/93) (TEST) Ⓘ **SBT1019**

FAMPAS, Dmitri (b 1921) Greece

SECTION III: INSTRUMENTAL

Greek Dance No. 1, 'Karaguana'—guitar
E. Kotzia *Concert* (6/89) (PEAR) Ⓘ **SHECD9609**
Greek Dance No. 3, 'Susta'—guitar
E. Kotzia *Concert* (6/89) (PEAR) Ⓘ **SHECD9609**

FANTINI, Girolamo (17th Cent) Italy

SECTION II: CHAMBER

Fanfara a 2—Intermedio 5, La Pellegrina (c1589) (attrib)
Taverner Plyrs, A. Parrott *Concert*
(8/88) (EMI) Ⓘ **CDC7 47998-2**

Modo per Imparare a sonare di Tromba—trumpet tutor (pub 1638)
1. Balletto detto il Lunati; 2. Balletto detti la Squilletti; 3. Brando detto l'Albizi; 4. Corrente delle Staccioli; 5. Sonata Imperiale I—Intrada and Toccata; 6. Sonata Imperiale II—Intrada; 7. Sonata a due detta del Gucciardini; 8. Saltarello detto del Naldi.
2, 3, 7, 8. S. Keavy, C. Steele-Perkins, Parley of Instr *Concert* (1/89) (HYPE) ① **CDA66255**
8 Sonatas—trumpet and continuo (pub 1638)
1. detta del Colloreto; 2. detta del Gonzaga; 3. detta del Niccolini; 4. detta del Saracinelli; 5. detta dell'Adimari; 6. detta del Morone; 7. detta del Vitelli; 8. detta del Nero.
1, 3, 8. J. Wallace, M. Alexander, S. Wright (r1993) *Concert* (11/94) (EMI) ① **CDC5 55086-2**

FARBERMAN, Harold (b 1929) USA

SECTION I: ORCHESTRAL

Concerto for Jazz Drummer and Orchestra (1985-86)
L. Bellson, Bournemouth SO, H. Farberman (r1986) *Shchedrin: Carmen Ballet.* (3/89) (BIS) ① **BIS-CD382**

FARINA, Carlo (c1600–c1640) Italy

SECTION I: ORCHESTRAL

Capriccio stravagante—instrumental ensemble (pub 1626)
Capriccio Stravagante, S. Sempé (hpd/dir) *Concert* (2/94) (DHM) ① **05472 77190-2**

FARINEL, Michel (1649–?) France/Italy

SECTION II: CHAMBER

Faronell's Ground—violin and continuo (pub 1685) (in Playford's 'The Division Viol')
Sonnerie Trio, S. Stubbs (r1992) *Concert* (5/94) (TELD) ① **4509-90841-2**

FARKAS, Ferenc (b 1905) Hungary

SECTION II: CHAMBER

Old Hungarian Dances of the 17th Century—wind quintet
Introduction; Sad; Shoulder Blade Dance;
Acrobats Thurston Cl Qt (arr cl qt) *Concert* (10/93) (ASV) ① **CDWHL2076**

FARMER, John (b c1570; fl 1591–1601) England

SECTION IV: VOCAL AND CHORAL

Fair Phyllis I saw sitting all alone—madrigal (4vv) (pub 1599)
Amaryllis Consort, C. Brett *Concert* (3/88) (CARL) ① **PCD873**
A Little pretty bonny lass—madrigal (4vv) (pub 1599)
Cambridge Sngrs, J. Rutter *Concert* (11/87) (CLLE) ① **COLCD105**
The Lord's Prayer
Magdalen Oxford Coll Ch, J. Harper *Concert* (11/91) (ABBE) ① **CDCA901**

FARNABY, Giles (c1563–1640) England

SECTION III: INSTRUMENTAL

Fain would I wed—keyboard
R. Aldwinckle *Concert* (3/88) (CARL) ① **PCD873**
Farnaby's Conceit—keyboard
A. Lawrence-King *Concert* (12/90) (HYPE) ① **CDA66335**
Giles Farnaby - His Dreame
A. Lawrence-King *Concert* (12/90) (HYPE) ① **CDA66335**
His humour
A. Lawrence-King *Concert* (12/90) (HYPE) ① **CDA66335**
His Rest
A. Lawrence-King *Concert* (12/90) (HYPE) ① **CDA66335**

Rosa Solis—keyboard
I. Watson (arr Walton) *Concert* (4/91) (CHAN) ① **CHAN8892**

FARNABY, Richard (b c1594) England

SECTION III: INSTRUMENTAL

Nobody's Jig—keyboard
Z. Růžičková *Concert* (10/89) (ORFE) ① **C139861A**

FARNON, Robert (b 1917) Canada/England

SECTION I: ORCHESTRAL

A la claire fontaine—orchestra (1940s)
Bratislava RSO, A. Leaper *Concert* (9/92) (MARC) ① **8 223401**
RPO, R. Farnon *Concert* (9/92) (REFE) ① **RRCD-47**
Derby Day (1950s)
Bratislava RSO, A. Leaper *Concert* (9/92) (MARC) ① **8 223401**
Gateway to the West (1956)
Bratislava RSO, A. Leaper *Concert* (9/92) (MARC) ① **8 223401**
How Beautiful is Night
Bratislava RSO, A. Leaper *Concert* (9/92) (MARC) ① **8 223401**
In a calm—No. 2 of 'Three Impressions for Orchestra' (1940s)
Bratislava RSO, A. Leaper *Concert* (9/92) (MARC) ① **8 223401**
Intermezzo—harp and strings (1951)
A. Brewer, RPO, R. Farnon *Concert* (9/92) (REFE) ① **RRCD-47**
Jumping Bean (1947)
Bratislava RSO, A. Leaper *Concert* (9/92) (MARC) ① **8 223401**
Lake of the Woods—tone poem (1940s)
Bratislava RSO, A. Leaper *Concert* (9/92) (MARC) ① **8 223401**
RPO, D. Gamley *Concert* (9/92) (REFE) ① **RRCD-47**
Little Miss Molly (1950s)
Bratislava RSO, A. Leaper *Concert* (9/92) (MARC) ① **8 223401**
Manhattan Playboy—No. 3 of 'Three Impressions for Orchestra' (1948)
Bratislava RSO, A. Leaper *Concert* (9/92) (MARC) ① **8 223401**
Melody Fair—orchestra
Bratislava RSO, A. Leaper *Concert* (9/92) (MARC) ① **8 223401**
The Peanut Vendor (1951)
Bratislava RSO, A. Leaper *Concert* (9/92) (MARC) ① **8 223401**
Pictures in the Fire (c1947)
Bratislava RSO, A. Leaper *Concert* (9/92) (MARC) ① **8 223401**
Portrait of a Flirt (1947)
Bratislava RSO, A. Leaper *Concert* (9/92) (MARC) ① **8 223401**
Prelude and Dance—harmonica and orchestra (1966)
T. Reilly, orch. R. Farnon (r1968) *Concert* (5/94) (CHAN) ① **CHAN9248**
A Promise of Spring—orchestra (1950s)
RPO, R. Farnon *Concert* (9/92) (REFE) ① **RRCD-47**
Rhapsody—violin and orchestra (1958)
R. Cohen, RPO, R. Farnon *Concert* (9/92) (REFE) ① **RRCD-47**
A Star is born (1947)
Bratislava RSO, A. Leaper *Concert* (9/92) (MARC) ① **8 223401**
State Occasion—orchestra (1953)
Bratislava RSO, A. Leaper *Concert* (9/92) (MARC) ① **8 223401**
RPO, R. Farnon *Concert* (9/92) (REFE) ① **RRCD-47**
Un Vie de Matelot—brass band (1975)
Black Dyke Mills Band, P. Parkes *Concert* (9/93) (RSR) ① **RSRD1002**
The Westminster Waltz (1956)
Bratislava RSO, A. Leaper *Concert* (9/92) (MARC) ① **8 223401**

SECTION V: STAGE WORKS

Captain Horatio Hornblower RN—concert suite from film score (1951)
1. Introduction; 2. The Wind; 3. Pohlwheal; 4. Lady Barbara; 5. Nativitad.

1-5. RPO, R. Farnon *Concert* (9/92) (REFE) ① **RRCD-47**
Colditz—television score (1972)
March Bratislava RSO, A. Leaper *Concert* (9/92) (MARC) ① **8 223401**

FARRANT, Richard (?c1525/30–1580) England

SECTION IV: VOCAL AND CHORAL

Ah, alas, you salt-sea gods—consort song: 1v and viol consort
J. Budd, Fretwork (r1990) *Concert* (7/94) (VIRG) ① **VC5 45007-2**
Hide not thou thy face—anthem (4vv)
Cambridge Sngrs, J. Rutter *Concert* (6/88) (CLLE) ① **COLCD107**
Magdalen Oxford Coll Ch, J. Harper *Concert* (11/91) (ABBE) ① **CDCA901**

FARRAR, Ernest (1885–1918) England

SECTION IV: VOCAL AND CHORAL

Brittany—song, Op. 21/1 (1914) (Wds. E. V. Lucas)
S. Varcoe, C. Benson *Concert* (6/88) (HYPE) ① [2] **CDA66261/2**
Come you, Mary—song, Op. 21/2 (1914) (Wds. N. Gale)
S. Varcoe, C. Benson *Concert* (6/88) (HYPE) ① [2] **CDA66261/2**
O mistress mine—song (Wds. Shakespeare)
I. Partridge, C. Benson *Concert* (9/91) (HYPE) ① **CDA66015**
3 Vagabond Songs, Op. 11 (1908-11) (Wds. various)
1. The Wanderer's Song (wds. A. Symons); 2. Silent noon (wds. D. G. Rossetti); 3. The Roadside Fire (wds. R. L. Stevenson).
S. Varcoe, C. Benson *Concert* (6/88) (HYPE) ① [2] **CDA66261/2**
Who would shepherd pipes—song, Op. 21/3 (1914) (Wds. N. Gale)
S. Varcoe, C. Benson *Concert* (6/88) (HYPE) ① [2] **CDA66261/2**

FASCH, Carl Friedrich Christian (1736–1800) Germany

SECTION I: ORCHESTRAL

Concerto for Trumpet, Oboe d'amore, Violin and Strings in E (attrib: possibly by J. F. Fasch)
J. Wallace, J. Anderson, P. Thomas, Philh, S. Wright *Concert* (4/89) (NIMB) ① **NI5121**
J. Wallace, J. Anderson, P. Thomas, Philh, S. Wright (r1988) *Concert* (2/95) (NIMB) ① **NI7016**

SECTION III: INSTRUMENTAL

Andantino con VII Variazioni—keyboard
C. Schornsheim (r1991) *Concert* (4/95) (CAPR) ① **10 424**

FASCH, Johann Friedrich (1688–1758) Germany

SECTION I: ORCHESTRAL

Concerto for Trumpet and Strings in D
J. Freeman-Attwood, I. Simcock (r1993; arr tpt/org) *Concert* (5/94) (PROU) ① **PROUCD135**
Concerto in D—trumpet, 2 oboes and strings
W. Marsalis, ECO, R. Leppard *Concert* (1/86) (SONY) ① **MK39061**
W. Marsalis, ECO, R. Leppard (r1993) *Concert* (5/95) (SONY) ① **SK57497**

SECTION II: CHAMBER

Quartet in G—flute, 2 recorders & continuo
F. Brüggen, J. van Wingerden, F. Vester, B. Pollard, A. Bylsma, G. Leonhardt (r1963) *Concert* (10/95) (TELD) ① **4509-97467-2**

FASOLO, Giovanni Battista (c1600–after 1659) Italy

SECTION III: INSTRUMENTAL

Intonazione—organ (pub 1645) (from 'Annuala')
T. Roberts (r1990; ed Roberts) *Concert* (4/93) (ARCH) ① [2] **437 552-2AH2**

J. Hubeau, R. Gallois-Montbrun, C. Lequien, A.
Navarra (r1969/70) *Concert*
(3/95) (ERAT) ① [3] 4509-96953-2
**Quintet for Piano and Strings No. 1 in D
minor, Op. 89 (1887-95, 1903-05)**
Rome Fauré Qnt *Piano Quintet 2.*
(3/87) (CLAV) ① CD50-8603
Parrenin Qt, J-P. Collard *Concert*
(5/89) (EMI) ① [2] CMS7 62548-2
J. Hubeau, Via Nova Qt (r1969/70) *Concert*
(3/95) (ERAT) ① [3] 4509-96953-2
Domus, A. Marwood (r1994) *Piano Quintet 2.*
(7/95) (HYPE) ① CDA66766
**Quintet for Piano and Strings No. 2 in C
minor, Op. 115 (1919-21)**
Rome Fauré Qnt *Piano Quintet 1.*
(3/87) (CLAV) ① CD50-8603
Parrenin Qt, J-P. Collard *Concert*
(5/89) (EMI) ① [2] CMS7 62548-2
J. Hubeau, Via Nova Qt (r1969/70) *Concert*
(3/95) (ERAT) ① [3] 4509-96953-2
Domus, A. Marwood (r1994) *Piano Quintet 1.*
(7/95) (HYPE) ① CDA66766
Romance in A—cello and piano, Op. 69
S. Isserlis, P. Devoyon *Concert*
(8/88) (HYPE) ① CDA66235
L. Blake, C. Palmer (r1992) *Concert*
(6/94) (ETCE) ① KTC1153
S. Isserlis, P. Devoyon (r1994) *Concert*
(8/95) (RCA) ① 09026 68049-2
**Romance in B flat—violin and piano, Op. 28
(1877)**
T. Reilly, ASMF Chbr Ens (arr. Moody) *Concert*
(12/86) (CHAN) ① CHAN8486
P. Amoyal, P. Rogé (r1992) *Concert*
(2/95) (DECC) ① 436 866-2DH
Sérénade—cello and piano, Op. 98 (1908)
S. Isserlis, P. Devoyon (r1994) *Concert*
(8/95) (RCA) ① 09026 68049-2
**Sicilienne—cello/violin and piano, Op. 78
(1898)**
T. Igloi, C. Benson *Concert*
(9/87) (CRD) ① CRD3316
S. Isserlis, P. Devoyon *Concert*
(8/88) (HYPE) ① CDA66235
V. Taylor, T. Kain (fl/gtr) *Concert*
(9/92) (TALL) ① TP003
L. Blake, C. Palmer (r1992) *Concert*
(6/94) (ETCE) ① KTC1153
K. Smietana, J.J. Blakely *Concert*
(10/94) (MERI) ① CDE84259
S. Isserlis, P. Devoyon (r1994) *Concert*
(8/95) (RCA) ① 09026 68049-2
**Sonata for Cello and Piano No. 1 in D minor,
Op. 109 (1917)**
T. Igloi, C. Benson *Concert*
(9/87) (CRD) ① CRD3316
L. Blake, C. Palmer (r1992) *Concert*
(6/94) (ETCE) ① KTC1153
S. Isserlis, P. Devoyon (r1994) *Concert*
(8/95) (RCA) ① 09026 68049-2
**Sonata for Cello and Piano No. 2 in G minor,
Op. 117 (1921)**
T. Igloi, C. Benson *Concert*
(9/87) (CRD) ① CRD3316
S. Isserlis, P. Devoyon *Concert*
(8/88) (HYPE) ① CDA66235
L. Blake, C. Palmer (r1992) *Concert*
(6/94) (ETCE) ① KTC1153
S. Isserlis, P. Devoyon (r1994) *Concert*
(8/95) (RCA) ① 09026 68049-2
**Sonata for Violin and Piano No. 1 in A, Op.
13 (1875-76)**
L. Mordkovitch, G. Oppitz *R. Strauss: Violin Sonata.*
(2/87) (CHAN) ① CHAN8417
K. Osostowicz, S. Tomes (r1987) *Violin Sonata 2.*
(11/88) (HYPE) ① CDA66277
J. Thibaud, A. Cortot (r1927) *Concert*
(7/89) (EMI) ① CDH7 63032-2
A. Grumiaux, P. Crossley *Concert*
(7/90) (PHIL) ① 426 384-2PC
M. Fujikawa, J.F. Osorio *Concert*
(7/90) (ASV) ① CDDCA705
M-A. Nicolas, B. Petrov *Franck: Violin Sonata.*
(10/92) (AUVI) ① V4656
Chee-Yun, A. Eguchi (r1993) *Concert*
(1/94) (DENO) ① CO-75625
K. Smietana, J.J. Blakely *Concert*
(10/94) (MERI) ① CDE84259
J. Heifetz, B. Smith (r1955) *Concert*
(11/94) (RCA) ① [65] 09026 61778-2(45)
J. Heifetz, E. Bay (r1936) *Concert*
(11/94) (RCA) ① [65] 09026 61778-2(04)
P. Amoyal, P. Rogé (r1992) *Concert*
(2/95) (DECC) ① 436 866-2DH

P. Zukerman, M. Neikrug (r1993) *Concert*
(5/90) (DECC) ① 425 606-2DH
I. van Keulen, R. Brautigam (r1994) *Concert*
(10/95) (SCHW) ① 315272
**Sonata for Violin and Piano No. 2 in E minor,
Op. 108 (1916-17)**
K. Osostowicz, S. Tomes (r1987) *Violin Sonata 1.*
(11/88) (HYPE) ① CDA66277
A. Grumiaux, P. Crossley *Concert*
(7/90) (PHIL) ① 426 384-2PC
M. Fujikawa, J.F. Osorio *Concert*
(7/90) (ASV) ① CDDCA705
J. Suk, J. Hála *Chausson: Concert, Op 21.*
(1/91) (SUPR) ① 11 0269-2
K. Smietana, J.J. Blakely *Concert*
(10/94) (MERI) ① CDE84259
P. Amoyal, P. Rogé (r1992) *Concert*
(2/95) (DECC) ① 436 866-2DH
J. Suk, J. Hála (r1994) *Concert*
(11/95) (DINT) ① DICD920306
**Souvenir de Bayreuth—fantasia on themes
from Wagner's 'Ring'—piano duet (?1888)**
(comp with Messager)
J-P. Collard, B. Rigutto *Concert*
(3/92) (EMI) ① [2] CZS7 62687-2
K. Stott, M. Roscoe (r1994) *Concert*
(5/95) (HYPE) ① [4] CDA66911/4
String Quartet in E minor, Op. 121 (1923-24)
Viotti Qt (r1989) (3/87) (PIER) ① PV786102
Parrenin Qt *Concert*
(5/89) (EMI) ① [2] CMS7 62548-2
Via Nova Qt (r1969/70) *Concert*
(3/95) (ERAT) ① [3] 4509-96953-2

SECTION III: INSTRUMENTAL

Ballade in F sharp—piano, Op. 19 (1877-79)
P. Crossley *Concert* (2/88) (CRD) ① CRD3426
K. Stott (r1994) *Concert*
(5/95) (HYPE) ① [4] CDA66911/4
13 Barcarolles—piano
1. A minor, Op. 26 (c1880); 2. G, Op. 41 (1885); 3. G
flat, Op. 42 (1885); 4. A flat, Op. 44 (1886); 5. F
sharp minor, Op. 66 (1894); 6. E flat, Op. 70 (1896);
7. D minor, Op. 90 (1905); 8. D flat, Op. 96 (1906); 9.
A minor, Op. 101 (1909); 10. A minor, Op. 104:2
(1913); 11. G minor, Op. 105 (1913); 12. E flat, Op.
106a (1915); 13. C, Op. 116 (1921).
P. Crossley (6/88) (CRD) ① CRD3422
J-P. Collard *Concert*
(3/92) (EMI) ① [2] CZS7 62687-2
K. Stott (r1994) *Concert*
(5/95) (HYPE) ① [4] CDA66911/4
1, 2, 4. P. Rogé *Concert*
(5/90) (DECC) ① 425 606-2DH
1, 4-6. K. Stott (r1986) *Concert*
(5/95) (CONI) ① [2] 75605 51751-2
2. A. Ferber (r1979) *Concert*
(3/94) (SAGA) ① EC3397-2
2, 7, 11, 12. K. Stott (r1988) *Concert*
(5/95) (CONI) ① [2] 75605 51751-2
3-5, 7, 9. Peter Jacobs *Concert*
(11/92) (CNTI) ① CCD1047
5. V. Perlemuter *Concert* (5/89) (NIMB) ① NI5165
9-13. J. Röling *Concert*
(9/92) (OTTA) ① OTRC109033
**Une Châtelaine en sa tour—harp, Op. 110
(1918)**
S. Drake (r1988) *Concert*
(2/90) (HYPE) ① CDA66340
M. Klinko *Concert* (8/93) (EMI) ① CDC7 54467-2
Impromptu—harp, Op. 86 (1904)
T. Owen *Concert* (3/87) (CARL) ① PCD835
S. Drake (r1988) *Concert*
(2/90) (HYPE) ① CDA66340
M-A. Süss *Concert* (12/91) (DENO) ① CO-76611
M. Robles *Concert*
(2/93) (DECC) ① 433 869-2DWO
M. Klinko *Concert* (8/93) (EMI) ① CDC7 54467-2
L. Laskine (r1963) *Concert*
(12/93) (ERAT) ① 4509-92131-2
K. Stott (r1994; arr pf) *Concert*
(5/95) (HYPE) ① [4] CDA66911/4
K. Stott (r1988) *Concert*
(5/95) (CONI) ① [2] 75605 51751-2
5 Impromptus—piano
1. E flat, Op. 25 (1881); 2. F minor, Op. 31 (1883); 3.
A flat, Op. 34 (?1883); 4. D flat, Op. 91 (1905-06); 5.
F sharp minor, Op. 102 (1909).
P. Crossley *Concert* (1/88) (CRD) ① CRD3423
J-P. Collard *Concert*
(3/92) (EMI) ① [2] CZS7 62687-2
K. Stott (r1994) *Concert*
(5/95) (HYPE) ① [4] CDA66911/4
1-3. K. Stott (r1986) *Concert*
(5/95) (CONI) ① [2] 75605 51751-2

2, 3. P. Rogé *Concert*
(5/90) (DECC) ① 425 606-2DH
2, 5. V. Perlemuter *Concert*
(5/89) (NIMB) ① NI5165
2, 5. M. Long (r1933) *Concert*
(1/93) (PEAR) ① GEMMCD9927
3. C. Ortiz *Concert* (6/87) (CARL) ① PCD846
5. J. Röling *Concert*
(9/92) (OTTA) ① OTRC109033
5. V. Horowitz *Concert* (4/93) (RCA) ① GD60463
Mazurka in B flat—piano, Op. 32 (c1878)
P. Crossley *Concert* (2/88) (CRD) ① CRD3426
J-P. Collard *Concert*
(3/92) (EMI) ① [2] CZS7 62687-2
K. Stott (r1988) *Concert*
(5/95) (CONI) ① [2] 75605 51751-2
K. Stott (r1994) *Concert*
(5/95) (HYPE) ① [4] CDA66911/4
13 Nocturnes—piano
1. E flat minor, Op. 33:1 (c1875); 2. B, Op. 33:2
(c1880); 3. A flat, Op. 33:3 (?1882); 4. E flat, Op. 36
(?1884); 5. B flat, Op. 37 (?1884); 6. D flat, Op. 63
(1894); 7. C sharp minor, Op. 74 (1898); 8. D flat, Op.
84:8 (1902); 9. B minor, Op. 97 (1908); 10. E minor,
Op. 99 (1909); 11. F sharp minor, Op. 104:1 (1913);
12. E minor, Op. 107 (1915); 13. B minor, Op. 119
(1921).
D. Lively (r1989) (9/90) (ETCE) ① KTC1082
K. Stott (r1994) *Concert*
(5/95) (HYPE) ① [4] CDA66911/4
1, 4, 6. K. Stott (r1986) *Concert*
(5/95) (CONI) ① [2] 75605 51751-2
1-5. P. Rogé *Concert*
(5/90) (DECC) ① 425 606-2DH
1-6. J. Martin (r1993) *Thème et Variations, Op. 73.*
(7/94) (NAXO) ① 8 550794
1, 6, 7, 12, 13. V. Perlemuter *Concert*
(5/89) (NIMB) ① NI5165
1-7. P. Crossley (6/88) (CRD) ① CRD3406
3. A. Rubinstein (r1963) *Concert*
(10/93) (RCA) ① 09026 61446-2
4. M. Long (r1937) *Concert*
(1/93) (PEAR) ① GEMMCD9927
6. Peter Jacobs *Concert* (11/92) (CNTI) ① CCD1047
7-13. J. Martin (r1993) *Concert*
(7/94) (NAXO) ① 8 550795
8-11. K. Stott (r1988) *Concert*
(5/95) (CONI) ① [2] 75605 51751-2
8-13. P. Crossley *Pièces brèves, Op.84.*
(6/88) (CRD) ① CRD3407
10-13. J. Röling *Concert*
(9/92) (OTTA) ① OTRC109033
13. V. Horowitz (pp1977) *Concert*
(6/92) (RCA) ① GD60377
8 Pièces brèves—piano, Op. 84 (1869-1902)
(for No. 8, see under Nocturnes)
1. Capriccio; 2. Fantaisie; 3. Fugue; 4. Adagietto; 5.
Improvisation; 6. Fugue; 7. Allegresse.
P. Crossley *Nocturnes.* (6/88) (CRD) ① CRD3407
J-P. Collard *Concert*
(3/92) (EMI) ① [2] CZS7 62687-2
K. Stott (r1994) *Concert*
(5/95) (HYPE) ① [4] CDA66911/4
1, 4, 5. A. Ferber (r1979) *Concert*
(3/94) (SAGA) ① EC3397-2
9 Préludes—piano, Op. 103 (1909-10)
1. D flat; 2. C sharp minor; 3. G minor; 4. F; 5. D
minor; 6. E flat minor; 7. A; 8. C minor; 9. E minor.
P. Crossley *Concert* (1/88) (CRD) ① CRD3423
J. Swann *Debussy: Etudes.*
(9/90) (MUSI) ① MACD-608
J. Röling *Concert* (9/92) (OTTA) ① OTRC109033
Peter Jacobs *Concert* (11/92) (CNTI) ① CCD1047
A. Ferber (r1979) *Concert*
(3/94) (SAGA) ① EC3397-2
K. Stott (r1994) *Concert*
(5/95) (HYPE) ① [4] CDA66911/4
3, 9. J. Martin (r1993) *Concert*
(7/94) (NAXO) ① 8 550795
**3 Romances sans paroles—piano, Op. 17
(?1863)**
1. Andante, quasi allegretto; 2. Allegro molto; 3.
Andante moderato.
P. Crossley *Concert* (2/88) (CRD) ① CRD3426
P. Rogé *Concert* (5/90) (DECC) ① 425 606-2DH
J-P. Collard *Concert*
(3/92) (EMI) ① [2] CZS7 62687-2
J. Martin (r1993) *Concert*
(7/94) (NAXO) ① 8 550795
K. Stott (r1986) *Concert*
(5/95) (CONI) ① [2] 75605 51751-2
K. Stott (r1994) *Concert*
(5/95) (HYPE) ① [4] CDA66911/4
3. A. Cortot (r1922) *Concert*
(10/94) (BIDD) ① [2] LHW014/5

1, 2. G. Souzay, D. Baldwin *Concert*
(4/92) (EMI) ① [4] **CMS7 64079-2(2)**
2. Sarah Walker, M. Martineau (r1991) *Concert*
(5/93) (CRD) ① **CRD3476**
Tantum ergo—motet, Op. 65/2 (1894)
Westminster Cath Ch, O. Hill *Concert*
(10/88) (CARL) ① **PCD896**
P. Stow, C. McCaldin, Z. Mundye, Cambridge Clare
College Ch, N. White, T. Brown *Concert*
(12/88) (MERI) ① **CDE84153**
Cambridge Sngrs, John Scott, J. Rutter *Concert*
(1/89) (CLLE) ① **COLCD109**
J. Coxwell, C. Jackson, J. Youde, Corydon Sngrs,
John Scott, M. Best *Concert*
(10/89) (HYPE) ① **CDA66292**
**Tarentelle—two sopranos and piano, Op.
10/2 (c1873)** (Wds. Monnier)
F. Lott, A. Murray, G. Johnson *Concert*
(11/90) (EMI) ① **CDC7 49930-2**
C. Alliot-Lugaz, F. Le Roux, J. Cohen (sop & bar)
Concert (4/91) (REM) ① **REM311086**
E. Ameling, D. Baldwin *Concert*
(4/92) (EMI) ① [4] **CMS7 64079-2(1)**
Sarah Walker, M. Martineau (r1991) *Concert*
(8/93) (CRD) ① **CRD3477**
Vocalise-étude—wordless song (1907)
E. Ameling, D. Baldwin *Concert*
(4/92) (EMI) ① [4] **CMS7 64079-2(2)**
Sarah Walker, M. Martineau (r1991) *Concert*
(8/93) (CRD) ① **CRD3477**

SECTION V: STAGE WORKS

**Caligula—incidental music, Op. 52
(1888—Paris)** (Wds. A. Dumas père)
Alix Bourbon Voc Ens, Toulouse Capitole Orch, M.
Plasson *Concert* (6/88) (EMI) ① **CDC7 47939-2**
**Pelléas et Mélisande—concert suite from
incidental music, Op. 80 (1898)** (play by
Maeterlinck. Orch Koechlin)
1. Prélude; 2. Fileuse; 3. Sicilienne; 4. La mort de
Mélisande; 5. Chanson de Mélisande.
L. Hunt, Boston SO, S. Ozawa *Concert*
(1/88) (DG) ① **423 089-2GH**
L. Finnie, Renaissance Sngrs, Ulster Orch, Y. P.
Tortelier *Concert* (12/91) (CHAN) ① **CHAN8952**
SRO, E. Ansermet (r1961) *Concert*
(5/94) (BELA) ① **450 131-2**
Loire PO, M. Soustrot (r1992) *Concert*
(6/94) (PIER) ① **PV792051**
1-4. ASMF, N. Marriner *Concert*
(11/83) (ARGO) ① **410 552-2ZH**
1-4. Atlanta SO, Robert Shaw (r1985) *Berlioz: Nuits
d'été.* (10/85) (TELA) ① **CD80084**
1-4. FNO, C. Munch (pp1966) *Concert*
(11/88) (MONT) ① **MUN2031**
1-4. Montreal SO, C. Dutoit *Concert*
(1/89) (DECC) ① **421 440-2DH**
1-4. Mexico City PO, E. Bátiz *Concert*
(3/90) (ASV) ① **CDDCA686**
1-4. Netherlands Rad PO, J. Fournet (r1988)
Chausson: Symphony, Op. 20.
(9/90) (DENO) ① **CO-73675**
1-4. Paris Orch, S. Baudo *Concert*
(5/91) (EMI) ① [2] **CZS7 62669-2**
1-4. SRO, A. Jordan (r1991) *Requiem.*
(6/93) (ERAT) ① **2292-45813-2**
1-4. Hallé, J. Barbirolli (r1954) *Concert*
(7/95) (DUTT) ① **CDSJB1002**
5. E. Ameling, D. Baldwin *Concert*
(4/92) (EMI) ① [4] **CMS7 64079-2(2)**
5. Sarah Walker, M. Martineau (r1991) *Concert*
(8/93) (CRD) ① **CRD3477**
**Pénélope—drame lyrique: 3 acts
(1913—Monte Carlo)** (Lib. R. Fauchois)
Cpte J. Norman, A. Vanzo, P. Huttenlocher, J. Van
Dam, J. Taillon, C. Alliot-Lugaz, C. Barbaux, D. Borst,
M. Command, N. Lerer, P. Guigue, G. Friedmann, F.
Le Roux, J. Laforge Choral Ens, Monte Carlo PO, C.
Dutoit (4/92) (ERAT) ① [2] **2292-45405-2**
Overture Loire PO, M. Soustrot (r1992) *Concert*
(6/94) (PIER) ① **PV792051**
**Shylock—concert suite from incidental
music, Op. 57 (1897)** (Wds. E. Haraucourt,
after Shakespeare)
1. Chanson; 2. Entr'acte; 3. Madrigal; 4. Ephithalame;
5. Nocturne; 6. Final.
1, 3. G. Souzay, D. Baldwin *Concert*
(4/92) (EMI) ① [4] **CMS7 64079-2(2)**
3. G. Souzay, D. Baldwin (r1964) *Concert*
(3/95) (PHIL) ① [4] **438 964-2PM4(1)**
5. Mexico City PO, E. Bátiz *Concert*
(3/90) (ASV) ① **CDDCA686**

FAURE, Jean-Baptiste (1830–1914) France

SECTION IV: VOCAL AND CHORAL

Credo—song
P. Plançon, anon (r1905) *Concert*
(12/94) (ROMO) ① [2] **82001-2**
Crucifix—sacred song
E. Caruso, M. Journet, orch, W.B. Rogers (r1912)
Concert (7/91) (RCA) ① [12] **GD60495(4)**
E. Caruso, M. Journet, orch, W.B. Rogers (r1912)
Concert (10/91) (PEAR) ① [3] **EVC3(1)**
E. Caruso, M. Journet, orch, W.B. Rogers (r1912)
Concert (1/93) (MMOI) ① **CDMOIR411**
E. Eames, E. de Gogorza, orch (r1906/7/9: three
vers) *Concert* (11/93) (ROMO) ① [2] **81001-2**
Les Rameaux—song
E. Caruso, orch, W.B. Rogers (2 vers: r1913/4)
Concert (7/91) (RCA) ① [12] **GD60495(4)**
P. Plançon, orch (r1906) *Concert*
(9/91) (PEAR) ① **GEMMCD9497**
E. Caruso, orch, W.B. Rogers (2 vers: r1913/4)
Concert (10/91) (PEAR) ① [3] **EVC3(1)**
P. Plançon, anon (r1902) *Concert*
(3/93) (SYMP) ① **SYMCD1100**
P. Plançon, orch (r1906) *Concert*
(12/94) (ROMO) ① [2] **82001-2**
P. Plançon, anon (r1903/5: 2 vers) *Concert*
(12/94) (ROMO) ① [2] **82001-2**
E. Clément, orch, R. Bourdon (r1913) *Concert*
(8/95) (ROMO) ① **82002-2**
Sancta Maria—song (Wds. J. G. Bertrand)
E. Caruso, orch, W.B. Rogers (r1916) *Concert*
(7/91) (RCA) ① [12] **GD60495(5)**
E. Caruso, orch, W.B. Rogers (r1916) *Concert*
(10/91) (PEAR) ① [3] **EVC4(1)**

FAYRFAX, Robert (1464–1521) England

SECTION IV: VOCAL AND CHORAL

Aeternae laudis lilium—motet: 5vv (?1502)
The Sixteen, H. Christophers (r1982) *Missa Albanus.*
(12/89) (HYPE) ① **CDA66073**
Ave Dei patris filia—votive antiphon: 5vv
Cardinall's Musick, A. Carwood (r1994) *Concert*
(6/95) (ASV) ① **CDGAU142**
Magnificat regale—5vv
The Sixteen, H. Christophers *Concert*
(4/92) (COLL) ① **Coll1314-2**
Missa Albanus—5vv
The Sixteen, H. Christophers (r1982) *Aeternae laudis
lilium.* (12/89) (HYPE) ① **CDA66073**
Missa, 'O Quam Glorifica'—5vv (1504)
Cardinall's Musick, A. Carwood (r1994) *Concert*
(6/95) (ASV) ① **CDGAU142**
Most clere of colour—song: 3vv
Hilliard Ens *Concert* (6/91) (HYPE) ① **CDA66370**
The Sixteen, H. Christophers (r1993) *Concert*
(2/94) (COLL) ① **Coll1395-2**
Somewhat musing—song
Cardinall's Musick, A. Carwood (r1994) *Concert*
(6/95) (ASV) ① **CDGAU142**
To complayne me, alas—song: 3vv
Cardinall's Musick, A. Carwood (r1994) *Concert*
(6/95) (ASV) ① **CDGAU142**

FELDMAN, Morton (1926–1987) USA

SECTION I: ORCHESTRAL

**Madame Press died last week at 90—12
instruments (1970)**
St Luke's Orch, J. Adams *Concert*
(7/91) (NONE) ① **7559-79249-2**

SECTION II: CHAMBER

Five Pianos (1972)
S. Schleiermacher, I. Mundry, M. Persson, K. Scholz,
N. Vigeland (r1993) *Concert*
(12/95) (HATH) ① **ARTCD6143**
**For Christian Wolff—flute, piano and celesta
(1986)**
E. Blum, N. Vigeland (r1992)
(7/94) (HATH) ① [3] **ARTCD3-6120**
**For Philip Guston—piccolo, flute, piano,
celeste & percussion (1984)**
E. Blum, N. Vigeland, J. Williams (r1991)
(4/94) (HATH) ① [4] **ARTCD4-6104**
Piano Quintet (1985)
Kronos Qt, A. Takahashi (r1991)
(2/94) (NONE) ① **7559-79320-2**

**Spring of Chosroes—violin and piano
(1977)**
P. Zukofsky, U. Oppens *Schnabel: Violin Sonata
(1935).* (4/92) (MOBS) ① **CP2102**
String Quartet (1979)
Group for Contemporary Music (r1993)
(8/94) (KOCH) ① **37251-2**
Structures—string quartet (1951)
Arditti Qt (r1991-92) *Concert*
(12/93) (MONT) ① **782010**
**Why Patterns (Instruments IV)—violin/flute,
piano and percussion (1978)**
D. Stone, G. Mowrey, California EAR Unit *Rothko
Chapel.* (10/92) (NALB) ① **NA039CD**

SECTION III: INSTRUMENTAL

Intermission 1—piano (1950)
S. Schleiermacher (r1993) *Concert*
(12/95) (HATH) ① **ARTCD6143**
Intermission 2—piano (1950)
S. Schleiermacher (r1993) *Concert*
(12/95) (HATH) ① **ARTCD6143**
Intermission 5—piano (1952)
S. Schleiermacher (r1993) *Concert*
(12/95) (HATH) ① **ARTCD6143**
Intermission 6—piano (1953)
S. Schleiermacher (r1993) *Concert*
(12/95) (HATH) ① **ARTCD6143**
4 Last Pieces—piano (1959)
S. Schleiermacher (r1993) *Concert*
(12/95) (HATH) ① **ARTCD6143**
Piano Piece (1952)
S. Schleiermacher (r1993) *Concert*
(12/95) (HATH) ① **ARTCD6143**
Principal Sound—organ (1980)
H-O. Ericsson *Concert* (4/93) (BIS) ① **BIS-CD510**

SECTION IV: VOCAL AND CHORAL

**Rothko Chapel—sop, mez, chor, va, perc
and cel (1971)**
D. Abel, K. Rosenak, W. Winant, Berkeley Univ Chbr
Chor, P. Brett *Why Patterns.*
(10/92) (NALB) ① **NA039CD**
**3 Voices—solo voice and two loudspeakers
(1982)** (Wds. F. O'Hara)
J. La Barbara (12/90) (NALB) ① **NA018CD**

FELIX, H. (19th–20th Cent) USA

SECTION V: STAGE WORKS

Pom-Pom—musical show (1916—New York)
(Lyrics Caldwell)
EXCERPTS: 1. Evelyn; 2. In the Dark.
1, 2. M. Hajos, Orig Broadway Cast (r1916) *Concert*
(5/94) (PEAR) ① [3] **GEMMCDS9056/8**

FELLNER (19th–20th cents) Austria

SECTION IV: VOCAL AND CHORAL

Ewiges Wien—Viennese song
E. Kunz, Kemmeter-Falti Schrammel Ens (r1949)
Concert (9/95) (TEST) ① **SBT1059**

FÉNELON, Philippe (b 1952) France

SECTION V: STAGE WORKS

**Le Chevalier Imaginaire—opera: prologue, 2
acts (1984-86)** (Lib. cpsr, after Cervantes &
Kafka)
Cpte L. Villanueva, A. Tomicich, M. Armitstead, M.
Davies, P. Doghan, L. Masson, Paris
InterContemporain Ens, P. Eötvös (pp1992)
(11/95) (ERAT) ① **4509-96394-2**

FENTON, George (b 1949) England

SECTION II: CHAMBER

**5 Parts of the dance—trumpet and
percussion (1992)**
G. Ashton, G. Knowles (r1992) *Concert*
(4/94) (VIRG) ① **VC5 45003-2**

SECTION V: STAGE WORKS

Dangerous Liaisons—film score (1989)
EXCERPTS: 1. Main Theme (Vivaldi, arr Fenton).
1. OST (r1989) *Concert* (9/91) (VIR2) ① **CDV2774**
Shadowlands—film score (1993)
EXCERPTS: 1. Front Titles—Veni Sancte Spiritus; 2.
The Golden Valley; 3. Quartet in D, 'The Randolph';
4. The Wardrobe; 5. 'The Plot Thickens'; 6. The

Lake; 7. O Little Town of Bethlehem (trad arr Fenton);
8. Once in Royal David's City (H.J. Gauntlett, arr A.H.
Mann); 9. The Friendship; 10. The Wedding; 11.
Sumer is Icumen In (Anon 13th Century); 12. The
Drive to the Hotel; 13. The Golden Valley, Part Two;
14. Mr C.S. Lewis; 15. Joy Goes Home; 16. 'I'll Be
Here Too'; 17. The Silence; 18. 'As a Boy and as a
Man'; 19. Sanctis Solemnis; 20. Joy and Douglas; 21.
Shadowlands—End Credits.
1. OST (r1993) *Concert*   (9/95) (VIR2) ① **CDV2774**
1-21. OST, Magdalen Oxford Coll Ch, G. Ives, LSO,
G. Fenton (r1993)   (8/94) (EMI) ① **CDQ5 55093-2**

FEO, Francesco (1691–1761) Italy

SECTION IV: VOCAL AND CHORAL

Salve Regina in C minor—sop, strings & continuo
L. Åkerlund, Accademia Bizantina, C. Chiarappa
(r1992) *Concert*   (2/95) (DENO) ① **CO-78904**

FERGUSON, Howard (b 1908) Northern Ireland

SECTION I: ORCHESTRAL

Overture for an Occasion—orchestra, Op. 16 (1952-53)
LSO, R. Hickox *Concert*
   (4/93) (CHAN) ① **CHAN9082**
Partita—orchestra, Op. 5a (1935-36)
LSO, R. Hickox *Concert*
   (4/93) (CHAN) ① **CHAN9082**

SECTION II: CHAMBER

Octet—cl, bn, hn, stg qt and db, Op. 4 (1933)
Nash Ens *Concert*   (7/91) (HYPE) ① **CDA66192**
P. Juler, D. Brain, C. James, J.E. Merrett, Griller Qt
(r1943) *Concert*   (12/95) (DUTT) ① **CDAX8014**
Partita—two pianos, Op. 5b (1935-36)
H. Shelley, H. Macnamara *Piano Music, Op. 8.*
   (1/91) (HYPE) ① **CDA66130**
4 Short Pieces—clarinet/viola and piano, Op. 6 (1932-36)
1. Prelude; 2. Scherzo; 3. Pastoral; 4. Burlesque.
T. King, C. Benson *Concert*
   (7/89) (HYPE) ① **CDA66014**
E. Jóhannesson, P. Jenkins *Concert*
   (1/93) (CHAN) ① **CHAN9079**
Sonata for Violin and Piano No. 1, Op. 2 (1931)
J. Heifetz, L. Steuber *Concert*
   (9/90) (RCA) ① **GD87872**
J. Heifetz, L. Steuber (r1966) *Concert*
   (11/94) (RCA) ① [65] **09026 61778-2(43)**
Sonata for Violin and Piano No. 2, Op. 10 (1946)
L. Chilingirian, C. Benson *Concert*
   (7/91) (HYPE) ① **CDA66192**

SECTION III: INSTRUMENTAL

5 Bagatelles—piano, Op. 9 (1944)
C. Benson *Concert*   (7/91) (HYPE) ① **CDA66192**
Piano Sonata in F minor, Op. 8 (1938-40)
H. Shelley *Partita, Op. 5b.*
   (1/91) (HYPE) ① **CDA66130**

SECTION IV: VOCAL AND CHORAL

2 Ballads—baritone and orchestra, Op. 1 (1928-32) (Wds. medieval anon)
1. The Twa Corbies; 2. A Lyke Wake Dirge.
B. Rayner Cook, LSC, LSO, R. Hickox *Concert*
   (4/93) (CHAN) ① **CHAN9082**
Discovery—song cycle: 1v and piano, Op. 13 (1951) (Wds. D Welch)
1. The Freedom of the City; 2. Babylon; 3. Jane
Allen; 4. Discovery; 5. Dreams melting.
K. Ferrier, E. Lush (bp1953) *Concert*
   (7/91) (LOND) ① **430 061-2LM**
The Dream of the Rood—S/T, chorus and orchestra, Op. 19 (1958-59) (Wds. anon Anglo-Saxon)
Anne Dawson, LSC, LSO, R. Hickox *Concert*
   (4/93) (CHAN) ① **CHAN9082**

FERNANDES, Gaspar (c1570–1629) Mexico

SECTION IV: VOCAL AND CHORAL

Elegit eum Dominus—secular motet: 5vv (1612) (for the entry of the Mexican viceroy into Puebla)
Compañía musical, La Fenice, J. Cabré (r1992)
Concert   (9/93) (K617) ① **K617024**

FERNANDEZ, Aires (16th Cent) Portugal

SECTION IV: VOCAL AND CHORAL

Alma redemptoris mater—motet
Taverner Ch, O. Rees (r1992) *Concert*
   (1/94) (HERA) ① **HAVPCD155**
Benedicamus Domino—Compline motet
A Capella Portvgvesa, O. Rees (r1994) *Concert*
   (11/94) (HYPE) ① **CDA66735**
Circumdederunt me—motet
A Capella Portvgvesa, O. Rees (r1994) *Concert*
   (11/94) (HYPE) ① **CDA66735**
Libera me Domine—requiem responsory
Taverner Ch, O. Rees (r1992) *Concert*
   (1/94) (HERA) ① **HAVPCD155**
Nunc dimittis—Compline canticle
A Capella Portvgvesa, O. Rees (r1994) *Concert*
   (11/94) (HYPE) ① **CDA66735**
Posuerunt super caput eius—motet (possibly by Rodrigo de Ceballos)
A Capella Portvgvesa, O. Rees (r1994) *Concert*
   (11/94) (HYPE) ① **CDA66735**
Te lucis ante terminum—Compline hymn
A Capella Portvgvesa, O. Rees (r1994) *Concert*
   (11/94) (HYPE) ① **CDA66735**

FERNANDEZ, Charles

SECTION II: CHAMBER

Muskrat Sousa—four clarinets (arr of Dixieland Jazz numbers)
1. 12th Street Rag; 2. South Rampart Street Parade.
Thurston Cl Qt *Concert*
   (10/93) (ASV) ① **CDWHL2076**

FERNEYHOUGH, Brian (b 1943) England

SECTION II: CHAMBER

La Chûte d'Icare—obbligato clarinet and small ensemble (1988)
A. Angster, Nieuw Ens, E. Spanjaard *Concert*
   (5/90) (ETCE) ① **KTC1070**
Mnemosyne—bass flute and pre-recorded tape (1986)
H. Starreveld *Concert*   (5/90) (ETCE) ① **KTC1070**

SECTION III: INSTRUMENTAL

Intermedio alla ciaccona—violin (1986)
I. Arditti *Concert*   (5/90) (ETCE) ① **KTC1070**
Superscriptio—piccolo (1981)
H. Starreveld *Concert*   (5/90) (ETCE) ① **KTC1070**

SECTION IV: VOCAL AND CHORAL

9 Etudes transcendantales—flute, oboe, soprano, harpsichord and cello (1982-85)
(Wds. E. Meister & A. Moll)
B. Mitchell, Nieuw Ens, E. Spanjaard *Concert*
   (5/90) (ETCE) ① **KTC1070**

FERNSTRÖM, John (Axel) (1897–1961) Sweden

SECTION I: ORCHESTRAL

Intimate Miniatures—string orchestra, Op. 2 (c1922)
1. Praeludium; 2. Intermezzo; 3. Lamento; 4. Rondino.
Musica Vitae CO, W. Rajski *Concert*
   (6/90) (BIS) ① **BIS-CD461**

SECTION II: CHAMBER

Wind Quintet—flute, oboe, clarinet, horn and bassoon, Op. 59 (1943)
Oslo Wind Qnt (r1993) *Concert*
   (3/95) (NAXO) ① **8 553050**

FERRABOSCO, Alfonso I (1543–1588) Italy

SECTION III: INSTRUMENTAL

Fantasia—lute
C. Wilson *Concert*   (11/91) (VIRG) ① **VC7 59034-2**
Galliard—lute
C. Wilson *Concert*   (11/91) (VIRG) ① **VC7 59034-2**
Pavan—lute
A. Rooley (pp1985) *Concert*
   (6/87) (HYPE) ① **CDA66186**
D. Miller *Concert*   (10/91) (HYPE) ① **CDA66447**
C. Wilson *Concert*   (11/91) (VIRG) ① **VC7 59034-2**
J. Bream (r1966) *Concert*
   (8/93) (RCA) ① [28] **09026 61583-2(1)**
J. Bream (r1966) *Concert*
   (6/94) (RCA) ① **09026 61585-2**

FERRABOSCO, Alfonso II (before 1578–1628) England

SECTION II: CHAMBER

Fantasia a 4—consort: 4 parts
C. Wilson, Fretwork *Concert*
   (3/88) (AMON) ① **CD-SAR29**
SCB, A. Wenzinger (r1956) *Concert*
   (4/95) (VANG) ① **08.5068.71**
Fantasia a 6—consort: 6 parts
SCB, A. Wenzinger (r1956) *Concert*
   (4/95) (VANG) ① **08.5068.71**
In Nomine a 5—consort: 5 parts
Fretwork *Concert*   (3/88) (AMON) ① **CD-SAR29**
Pavan—3 viols
Circa 1500, N. Hadden (r1991) *Concert*
   (8/93) (CRD) ① **CRD3487**
Pavan and Alman—5-part viol consort
Fretwork (r1990) *Concert*
   (7/94) (VIRG) ① **VC5 45007-2**

SECTION III: INSTRUMENTAL

Almayne a 5—consort: 5 parts
Fretwork (r1990) *Concert*
   (7/94) (VIRG) ① **VC5 45007-2**
Fantasia No. 5—lute
C. Wilson *Concert*   (3/88) (AMON) ① **CD-SAR29**

FERRADINI, Mario (1863–1907) Italy

SECTION IV: VOCAL AND CHORAL

Non penso a lei—song
T. Ruffo, orch (r1912) *Concert*
   (11/90) (NIMB) ① **NI7810**
T. Ruffo, orch (r1912) *Concert*
   (2/93) (PREI) ① [3] **89303(1)**

FERRANTI, Marco Aureliano de (1801–1878) Italy

SECTION III: INSTRUMENTAL

Exercise—guitar, Op. 50/14
S. Wynberg *Concert*   (7/87) (CHAN) ① **CHAN8512**
Fantasie variée sur la Romance d'Otello 'Assia à pie'—guitar, Op. 7
S. Wynberg *Concert*   (7/87) (CHAN) ① **CHAN8512**
6 Mélodies nocturnes originales—guitar, Op. 41a
1. Le souvenir; 2. La mélancolie; 3. Le désir; 4. La joie.
1-4. S. Wynberg *Concert*
   (7/87) (CHAN) ① **CHAN8512**
Nocturne sur la dernière pensée de Weber—guitar, Op. 40
S. Wynberg *Concert*   (7/87) (CHAN) ① **CHAN8512**
Ronde des fées—guitar, Op. 2
S. Wynberg *Concert*   (7/87) (CHAN) ① **CHAN8512**

FERRARA, Franco (b 1911) Italy

SECTION II: CHAMBER

Burleska—violin and piano
T. Varga, M. Schwalb (r1938) *Concert*
   (11/93) (CLAV) ① **CD50-9314**
T. Varga, M. Schwalb (r1938) *Concert*
   (11/93) (CLAV) ① [4] **CD50-9300/4**

FERRARI, Benedetto *(prob 1603/4–1681) Italy*

SECTION IV: VOCAL AND CHORAL

Averto ò cor
R. Jacobs, K. Junghänel (r1985) *Concert*
(5/87) (HARM) ① **HMA190 1183**
Le **Lazzarone**—song
P. Plançon, anon (r1905) *Concert*
(12/94) (ROMO) ① [2] **82001-2**
M'amo tanto costei
R. Jacobs, K. Junghänel (r1985) *Concert*
(5/87) (HARM) ① **HMA190 1183**

FERRER, José *(1835–1916) Spain*

SECTION III: INSTRUMENTAL

Belle—guitar
S. Wynberg *Concert* (7/87) (CHAN) ① **CHAN8512**
La **Danse de Naïdes**—guitar
S. Wynberg *Concert* (7/87) (CHAN) ① **CHAN8512**
L' **Étudiant de Salamanque**—guitar
S. Wynberg *Concert* (7/87) (CHAN) ① **CHAN8512**
Vals—guitar
S. Wynberg *Concert* (7/87) (CHAN) ① **CHAN8512**

FERRETTI, Giovanni *(c1540–after 1609) Italy*

SECTION IV: VOCAL AND CHORAL

Basciami vita mia—madrigal: 5vv
M. Arruabarrena, K. van Laethem, M. Valenta, J.
Benet, M. van Altena, J. Cabré, T. de Zwart, A. Pols,
R. Van Der Meer, K. Junghänel (lte/dir) *Concert*
(1/92) (ACCE) ① **ACC8864D**
Mirate che m'ha fatto—madrigal: 5vv
M. Arruabarrena, K. van Laethem, M. Valenta, J.
Benet, M. van Altena, J. Cabré, T. de Zwart, A. Pols,
R. Van Der Meer, K. Junghänel (lte/dir) *Concert*
(1/92) (ACCE) ① **ACC8864D**
Occhi, non occhi—madrigal: 5vv
M. Arruabarrena, K. van Laethem, M. Valenta, J.
Benet, M. van Altena, J. Cabré, T. de Zwart, A. Pols,
R. Van Der Meer, K. Junghänel (lte/dir) *Concert*
(1/92) (ACCE) ① **ACC8864D**
Un **Tempo sospirava**—madrigal: 5vv
M. Arruabarrena, K. van Laethem, M. Valenta, J.
Benet, M. van Altena, J. Cabré, T. de Zwart, A. Pols,
R. Van Der Meer, K. Junghänel (lte/dir) *Concert*
(1/92) (ACCE) ① **ACC8864D**

FERROUD, Pierre-Octave *(1900–1936) France*

SECTION III: INSTRUMENTAL

3 Pièces—flute (1921)
1. Bergère captive; 2. Jade; 3. Toan-Yan, la fete du
double cinq.
R. Aitken *Concert* (9/89) (BIS) ① **BIS-CD184**
P. Lloyd *Concert* (9/92) (CARL) ① **PCD991**

FESTA, Costanzo *(c1490–1545) Italy*

SECTION IV: VOCAL AND CHORAL

Chi vuol veder—madrigal: 4vv (pub 1549)
Huelgas Ens, P. van Nevel (r1993) *Concert*
(11/94) (SONY) ① **SK53116**
Constantia'l vo' pur dire—madrigal: 5vv (pub
1540)
Huelgas Ens, P. van Nevel (r1993) *Concert*
(11/94) (SONY) ① **SK53116**
E morta la speranza—madrigal: 4vv (pub
1537)
Huelgas Ens, P. van Nevel (r1993) *Concert*
(11/94) (SONY) ① **SK53116**
Madonna oymè—madrigal: 4vv (pub 1544)
Huelgas Ens, P. van Nevel (r1993) *Concert*
(11/94) (SONY) ① **SK53116**
Magnificat septimi toni—4vv
Huelgas Ens, P. van Nevel (r1993) *Concert*
(11/94) (SONY) ① **SK53116**
Missa, 'Se congie pris'—motet: 5vv
Huelgas Ens, P. van Nevel (r1993) *Concert*
(11/94) (SONY) ① **SK53116**
Quando ritrovo la mia pastorella—madrigal:
4vv (pub 1541)
Huelgas Ens, P. van Nevel (r1993) *Concert*
(11/94) (SONY) ① **SK53116**

Quis dabit oculis—motet: 4vv (pub 1538)
Huelgas Ens, P. van Nevel (r1993) *Concert*
(11/94) (SONY) ① **SK53116**
Super flumina Babylonis—motet: 5vv
Huelgas Ens, P. van Nevel (r1993) *Concert*
(11/94) (SONY) ① **SK53116**
Tribus miraculis—motet: 6vv (pub 1519)
Huelgas Ens, P. van Nevel (r1993) *Concert*
(11/94) (SONY) ① **SK53116**

FETRÁS, Oscar *(1854–1931) Germany*

pseudonym for Oscar Faster

SECTION I: ORCHESTRAL

Die **Mondnacht auf der Alster**—waltz (1890)
(Eng: Moonlight over the Alster)
Berlin Ens *Concert* (5/91) (ORFE) ① **C126901A**

FÉVRIER, Henry *(1875–1957) France*

SECTION IV: VOCAL AND CHORAL

L' **Intruse**—song (Wds. Maeterlinck)
P. Frijsh, C. Dougherty (r1942) *Concert*
(4/95) (PEAR) ① [2] **GEMMCDS9095(1)**

SECTION V: STAGE WORKS

Gismonda—opéra-comique: 4 acts
(1919—Chicago) (Lib. H Cain & L Payen, after
Sardou)
Toute blanche, les deux seins nus M. Namara,
anon (r1930s) *Concert*
(8/92) (IRCC) ① **IRCC-CD802**
Monna Vanna—opera (1909—Paris) (Lib. after
M. Maeterlinck)
Ce n'est pas un vieillard Vanni-Marcoux, orch
(r1924) *Concert* (1/94) (CLUB) ① **CL99-101**
C'est étrange; Elle est à moi F. Ansseau, orch, P.
Coppola (r1929) *Concert* (1/91) (PREI) ① **89022**
C'est étrange que l'homme; Ah! j'aurais mieux
aimé. F. Ansseau, orch, P. Coppola (r1929) *Concert*
(8/92) (IRCC) ① **IRCC-CD802**

FIALA, Josef *(1754–1816) Bohemia*

SECTION I: ORCHESTRAL

Concerto for Oboe and Orchestra in B flat
I. Goritzki, Polish Chmbr PO, W. Rajski *Concert*
(9/91) (CLAV) ① **CD50-9018**
Concerto for Two Horns and Orchestra in E
flat
Z. Tylšar, B. Tylšar, Capella Istropolitana, F. Vajnar
Concert (3/93) (NAXO) ① **8 550459**

FIBICH, Zdeněk *(Antonín Václav) (1850–1900) Bohemia*

SECTION I: ORCHESTRAL

At twilight—idyll for orchestra, Op. 39
(1893)
Poem J. Novotná, orch, A. von Zemlinsky (wds
Balling (r1935) *Concert* (4/93) (SUPR) ① **11 1491-2**
Poem S. Nakarjakov, A. Markovich (arr tpt/pf)
Concert (5/93) (TELD) ① **9031-77705-2**
Poème Czech PO, V. Neumann *Concert*
(9/90) (ORFE) ① **C180891A**
Symphony No. 1 in F, Op. 117 (1877-83)
Detroit SO, N. Järvi *Smetana: Má Vlast.*
(12/93) (CHAN) ① **CHAN9230**
Symphony No. 2 in E flat, Op. 38 (1892-3)
Brno St PO, J. Waldhans *Symphony 3.*
(2/88) (SUPR) ① **CO-1256**
Detroit SO, N. Järvi (r1994) *Symphony 3.*
(12/94) (CHAN) ① **CHAN9328**
Symphony No. 3 in E minor, Op. 53 (1898)
Brno St PO, J. Bělohlávek *Symphony 2.*
(2/88) (SUPR) ① **CO-1256**
Detroit SO, N. Järvi (r1994) *Symphony 2.*
(12/94) (CHAN) ① **CHAN9328**

SECTION II: CHAMBER

Sonata in B flat—piano duet, Op. 28 (1886)
A. Goldstone, C. Clemmow *Concert*
(7/93) (MERI) ① **CDE84237**

SECTION III: INSTRUMENTAL

Moods, Impressions and
Reminiscences—piano, Op. 44 (pub 1895)
EXCERPTS: 1. No. 183, Anežčin portrét.
1. R. Kvapil (r1993) *Concert*
(10/94) (UNIC) ① **DKPCD9149**

Moods, Impressions and
Reminiscences—piano, Op. 47 (pub 1896)
EXCERPTS: 1. No. 281, D minor; 2. No. 282, F
sharp minor.
1, 2. R. Kvapil (r1993) *Concert*
(10/94) (UNIC) ① **DKPCD9149**
Moods, Impressions and
Reminiscences—piano, Op. 57 (pub 1902)
EXCERPTS: 1. No. 355, A; 2. No. 358, Tema con
variazione, E minor/major; 3. No. 368, D minor.
1-3. R. Kvapil (r1993) *Concert*
(10/94) (UNIC) ① **DKPCD9149**
Moods, Impressions and Reminiscences,
Nos. 1-99—piano, Op. 41 (1892-93)
EXCERPTS: 4. G minor; 8. E flat; 13. A flat; 14. D
minor; 15. C; 19. E minor; 20. Žárlivosti, G minor; 21.
Fantastická soirée, B flat minor; 24. Sny, kdyby se ze
žárlivosti zabil, G minor; 25. Jak udelal Anežce
bolest, F minor; 28. Jak jsme spolu rozmlouvali, C;
35. A minor; 36. B flat; 44. B flat; 49. A sharp minor;
50. A flat; 51. F minor; 52. F; 54. A flat; 67.
Znaménka krku, C; 74. E; 78. G; 81. B
flat minor; 85. G minor; 87. B flat; 88. A flat; 94. Č, A
flat; 98. B flat; 99. A flat.
4, 8, 13-15, 19, 21, 24, 25, 36, 44, 49, 50-52, 54, 74,
78, 85, 88, 94, 98, 99. W. Howard (r1993) *Moods,
Op. 41, Part 2.* (9/95) (CHAN) ① **CHAN9381**
19-21, 24, 25, 35, 67, 81, 87, 94. R. Kvapil (r1993)
Concert (10/94) (UNIC) ① **DKPCD9149**
Moods, Impressions and Reminiscences,
Nos. 100-171—piano, Op. 41 (1892-93)
EXCERPTS: 4. No. 103, A minor; 7. No. 106, A flat;
9. No. 108, C; 10. No. 109, C; 23. No. 122, F minor;
24. No. 123, G minor; 25. No. 124, G; 28. No. 127,
Jak jsme spolu rozmlouvali, C; 35. No. 134, A minor;
36. No. 135, A; 40. No. 139, Večery na Žofíne, D flat;
44. No. 143, B flat minor; 47. No. 146, G; 50. No.
149, D; 55. No. 154, G; 59. No. 158, C minor; 62. No.
161, B flat; 72. No. 171, Poème (unidentified).
4, 28, 40. R. Kvapil (r1993) *Concert*
(10/94) (UNIC) ① **DKPCD9149**
4, 7, 9, 10, 23-25, 28, 35, 36, 40, 44, 47, 50, 55, 59,
62. W. Howard (r1993) *Moods, Op. 41, Part 1.*
(9/95) (CHAN) ① **CHAN9381**
72. J. Kubelík, anon (r1914: arr J Kubelík) *Concert*
(6/91) (BIDD) ① [2] **LAB033/4**
72. A. Etherden *Concert*
(7/93) (HUNT) ① **HMPCD0589**
Studies of Paintings—piano, Op. 56 (1898-
9)
EXCERPTS: 1. Forest Solitude (Lesní samota), F; 2.
The Quarrel between Shrovetide and Lent (Spor
masopustu s postem), C; 3. The Dance of the
Blessed Ones (Rej blažených), C; 4. Io and Jupiter
(Jo a Jupiter), E minor; 5. The Garden Party
(Zahradní slavnost), C.
R. Kvapil (r1993) *Concert*
(10/94) (UNIC) ① **DKPCD9149**

SECTION V: STAGE WORKS

The **Bride of Messina**—opera: 3 acts, Op. 18
(1884—Prague) (Lib. O Hostinský, after
Schiller)
Cpte L. Márová, V. Zítek, I. Žídek, G. Beňačková, K.
Hanuš, J. Horáček, M. Švejda, N. Šormová, Prague
Rad Chor, Prague Nat Th Chor, Prague Nat Th Orch,
F. Jílek (r1975) (12/94) (SUPR) ① [2] **11 1492-2**
Šárka—opera: 3 acts, Op. 51 (1897) (Lib. A.
Schulzová)
Cpte V. Zítek, V. Přibyl, J. Klán, E. Děpoltová, E.
Randová, J. Janská, B. Effenberková, J. Pavlová, A.
Barová, V. Bakalová, D. Suryová, Brno Janáček Op
Chor, Brno St PO, J. Štych
(10/88) (SUPR) ① [3] **CO-1746/8**

FIEDEL, Brad *(b 1951) USA*

SECTION V: STAGE WORKS

Fright Night—film score (1985)
EXCERPTS: 1. Come to Me.
1. OST, B. Fiedel (r1985) *Concert*
(10/93) (SILV) ① **FILMCD127**
The **Terminator**—film score (1984)
EXCERPTS: 1. Theme.
1. Prague City PO, W. Motzing (r1993) *Concert*
(8/94) (SILV) ① **FILMCD146**

FIELD, John *(1782–1837)*
Ireland

H—Numbers used in C. Hopkinson's Thematic
Catalogue, 1961

SECTION I: ORCHESTRAL

**Concerto for Piano and Orchestra No. 1 in E
flat, H27 (1799)**
M. O'Rourke, LMP, M. Bamert (r1994) *Piano
Concerto 2.*　　　(9/95) (CHAN) ① **CHAN9368**
**Concerto for Piano and Orchestra No. 2 in A
flat, H31 (-1811)**
J. O'Conor, Scottish CO, C. Mackerras (r1993) *Piano
Concerto 3.*　　　(8/94) (TELA) ① **CD80370**
M. O'Rourke, LMP, M. Bamert (r1994) *Piano
Concerto 1.*　　　(9/95) (CHAN) ① **CHAN9368**
**Concerto for Piano and Orchestra No. 3 in E
flat, H32 (?1805)**
J. O'Conor, Scottish CO, C. Mackerras (r1993) *Piano
Concerto 2.*　　　(8/94) (TELA) ① **CD80370**

SECTION II: CHAMBER

**Andante in C minor—piano: four hands, H11
(1811)**
R. Burnett, L. Fulford *Concert*
　　　　　　　　(11/92) (AMON) ① **CD-SAR48**
**The Bear Dance in E flat—piano: four hands,
H12 (1811)**
R. Burnett, L. Fulford *Concert*
　　　　　　　　(11/92) (AMON) ① **CD-SAR48**
**Variations on a Russian Air in A
minor—piano: four hands, H10 (1808)**
R. Burnett, L. Fulford *Concert*
　　　　　　　　(11/92) (AMON) ① **CD-SAR48**

SECTION III: INSTRUMENTAL

Air du bon roi Henri IV—piano, H20 (1814)
M. O'Rourke (r1991) *Concert*
　　　　　　　　(3/95) (CHAN) ① **CHAN9315**
2 Album Leaves in C minor—piano
1. Preludio; 2. Largo.
M. O'Rourke (r1991) *Concert*
　　　　　　　　(3/95) (CHAN) ① **CHAN9315**
Andante inédit in E flat—piano, H64 (c1837)
(pub posth)
M. O'Rourke (r1991) *Concert*
　　　　　　　　(3/95) (CHAN) ① **CHAN9315**
**Fantaisie sur l'air de Martini—piano, H15
(c1811)** (based on a aria from a comic opera by
Martin y Soler)
M. O'Rourke (r1991) *Concert*
　　　　　　　　(3/95) (CHAN) ① **CHAN9315**
**Fantaisie sur un air russe, 'In the
Garden'—piano (c1823)**
M. O'Rourke (r1991) *Concert*
　　　　　　　　(3/95) (CHAN) ① **CHAN9315**
Grand Pastorale in E—piano, H54A (1832)
R. Burnett *Concert*　(11/92) (AMON) ① **CD-SAR48**
**Irish Dance, 'Go to the Devil'—keyboard, H3
(pub c1797)** (possibly spurious)
M. O'Rourke (r1991) *Concert*
　　　　　　　　(3/95) (CHAN) ① **CHAN9315**
Marche triomphale—piano, H16 (1812-13)
M. O'Rourke (r1991) *Concert*
　　　　　　　　(3/95) (CHAN) ① **CHAN9315**
Nocturne in B flat—piano, H63 (1829) (pub
1991)
M. O'Rourke (r1991) *Concert*
　　　　　　　　(3/95) (CHAN) ① **CHAN9315**
Nocturnes—keyboard (Numbers used relate to
Breitkopf & Härtel and Peters edns.)
1. E flat, H24 (1812); 2. C minor, H25 (c1812); 3. A
flat, H26 (c1812); 4. A, H36 (1817); 5. B flat, H37
(1817); 6. F, H40 (1817); 7. C, H45 (c1821); 8. A,
H14E (1815); 9. E flat, H30 (1816); 10. E minor,
H46B (1827); 11. E flat, H56A (1833); 12. G, H58D
(1834); 13. D minor, H59 (1834); 14. C (1835); 15. C,
H61 (1836); 16. F, H62A (1836); 17. E, H54A (1832);
(18) E, H13K (1832).
M. O'Rourke　　(9/89) (CHAN) ① [2] **CHAN8719/20**
1-15. R. Mamou　　(8/93) (PAVA) ① **ADW7110**
1-16. J. Leach　　(10/93) (ATHN) ① **ATHCD1**
1, 2, 3, 4, 5, 6, 11, 12, 14. R. Burnett *Concert*
　　　　　　　　(11/92) (AMON) ① **CD-SAR48**
1, 2, 4, 5, 6, 8, 9, 10, 11, 12, 13, 14, 15, 16, 18. J.
O'Conor (r1989)　　(5/90) (TELA) ① **CD80199**
3, 7, 17. J. O'Conor *Concert*
　　　　　　　　(11/92) (TELA) ① **CD80290**
Nouvelle fantaisie in G—piano, H35 (c1815)
M. O'Rourke (r1991) *Concert*
　　　　　　　　(3/95) (CHAN) ① **CHAN9315**
Polonaise en rondeau—piano, H21 (1814)
M. O'Rourke (r1991) *Concert*
　　　　　　　　(3/95) (CHAN) ① **CHAN9315**

Rondeau écossois—piano, H23 (1814) (based
on a tune by J Moorehead)
M. O'Rourke (r1991) *Concert*
　　　　　　　　(3/95) (CHAN) ① **CHAN9315**
Rondo in A flat—piano, H18 (c1817)
M. O'Rourke (r1991) *Concert*
　　　　　　　　(3/95) (CHAN) ① **CHAN9315**
Sehnsuchtswalzer—piano, H51 (pub posth)
M. O'Rourke (r1991) *Concert*
　　　　　　　　(3/95) (CHAN) ① **CHAN9315**
Sonata in B—keyboard, H17 (pub 1813)
M. O'Rourke *Sonatas, H8.*
　　　　　　　　(11/90) (CHAN) ① **CHAN8787**
J. O'Conor *Concert*　(11/92) (TELA) ① **CD80290**
3 Sonatas for Piano, H8 (Op. 1) (1801)
1. E flat; 2. A; 3. C minor.
M. O'Rourke *Piano Sonata, H17.*
　　　　　　　　(11/90) (CHAN) ① **CHAN8787**
J. O'Conor *Concert*　(11/92) (TELA) ① **CD80290**
1. I. Hobson *Concert*　　(3/89) (ARAB) ① **Z6595**
1. R. Burnett *Concert*
　　　　　　　　(11/92) (AMON) ① **CD-SAR48**
1. G. Cziffra (r1955) *Concert*
　　　　　　　　(11/93) (APR) ① [2] **APR7021**
**Variations in B flat on a Russian Air,
'Kamarinskaya'—piano, H22 (1809)**
R. Burnett *Concert*　(11/92) (AMON) ① **CD-SAR48**
M. O'Rourke (r1991) *Concert*
　　　　　　　　(3/95) (CHAN) ① **CHAN9315**
**Variations in D minor on a Russian song,
'My dear bosom friend'—piano, H41
(c1818)**
R. Burnett *Concert*　(11/92) (AMON) ① **CD-SAR48**
M. O'Rourke (r1991) *Concert*
　　　　　　　　(3/95) (CHAN) ① **CHAN9315**

FILIBERTO, Juan de Dios

SECTION IV: VOCAL AND CHORAL

Caminito—song (Wds. Covia; cpsd with G.
Coria Peñazola)
J. Carreras, P. Domingo, L. Pavarotti, MMF Orch,
Rome Op Orch, Z. Mehta (pp1990) *Concert*
　　　　　　　　(10/90) (DECC) ① **430 433-2DH**
Buenos Aires Qnt, RPO, E. Stratta (arr J. Calandrelli)
Concert　　(1/93) (TELD) ① **9031-76997-2**

FILITZ, F. *(1804–1876)* **Germany**

SECTION IV: VOCAL AND CHORAL

**Lead us, heavenly Father—hymn:
tune—Mannheim** (Wds. J. Edmeston)
St John's College Ch, B. Runnett, G. Guest (r1963)
Concert　　(6/93) (DECC) ① **436 402-2DWO**

FILLIMARINO, Fabrizio *(fl 1594)*
Italy

SECTION III: INSTRUMENTAL

Canzon cromatica—harp/lute
A. Lawrence-King *Concert*
　　　　　　　　(9/87) (HYPE) ① **CDA66229**

FINCK, Herman *(1872–1939)*
England

SECTION III: INSTRUMENTAL

In the Shadows—dance (1910)
Southern Fest Orch, R. White (arr orch) *Concert*
　　　　　　　　(5/93) (CHAN) ① **CHAN9110**
A. Etherden *Concert*
　　　　　　　　(7/93) (HUNT) ① **HMPCD0589**

FINE, Irving (Gifford) *(1914–1962)*
USA

SECTION I: ORCHESTRAL

Blue Towers—orchestra (1959)
Moscow RSO, J. Spiegelman (r1993) *Concert*
　　　　　　　　(7/94) (DELO) ① **DE3139**
Diversions for Orchestra (1959-60)
Moscow RSO, J. Spiegelman (r1993) *Concert*
　　　　　　　　(7/94) (DELO) ① **DE3139**
Symphony (1952)
Moscow RSO, J. Spiegelman (r1993) *Concert*
　　　　　　　　(7/94) (DELO) ① **DE3139**
Toccata concertante—orchestra (1947)
Moscow RSO, J. Spiegelman (r1993) *Concert*
　　　　　　　　(7/94) (DELO) ① **DE3139**

SECTION II: CHAMBER

Partita—wind quintet (1949)
Reykjavik Wind Qnt (r1992) *Concert*
　　　　　　　　(11/93) (CHAN) ① **CHAN9174**

SECTION III: INSTRUMENTAL

Music for Piano (1947)
1. Prelude; 2. Waltz-Gavotte; 3. Variations; 4.
Interlude—Finale.
Moscow RSO, J. Spiegelman (r1993; orch:
Spiegelman) *Concert*　　(7/94) (DELO) ① **DE3139**

SECTION IV: VOCAL AND CHORAL

The Hour Glass—SATB a capella (1949)
(Wds. B. Jonson)
1. O know to end as to begin; 2. Have you senen the
white lily grow?; 3. O do not wanton with those eyes;
4. Against jealousy; 5. Lament; 6. The Hour Glass.
The Sixteen, H. Christophers *Concert*
　　　　　　　　(4/92) (COLL) ① **Coll1287-2**

FINE, Sylvia *(20th Cent)* **USA**

SECTION V: STAGE WORKS

The Court Jester—musical film (1956) (Lyrics
Sammy Cahn)
EXCERPTS: 1. Overture; 2. Life Could Not Be
Better; 3. Outfox the Fox; 4. I'll Take You Dreaming;
5. My Heart Knows A Lovely Song; 6. L Live to Love
(not in film); 7. Willow, Willow, Waley; 8. Pass the
Basket (not in film); 9. The Maladjusted Jester; 10.
Where Walks My True Love (not in film); 11. Life
Could Not Better Be (reprise).
1-11. D. Kaye, OST, V. Shoen (r1956) *F. Loesser:
Hans Christian Anderson.*
　　　　　　　　(11/94) (VARE) ① **VSD5498**

FINETTI, Giacomo *(fl 1605–1631)*
Italy

SECTION IV: VOCAL AND CHORAL

**O Maria, quae rapis corda hominum—motet:
2vv (pub 1621)** (from 'Concerti ecclesiastici')
Gabrieli Consort, Gabrieli Players, P. McCreesh
(r1990; ed Roche) *Concert*
　　　　　　　　(4/93) (ARCH) ① [2] **437 552-2AH2**

FINGER, Gottfried *(c1660–1730)*
Moravia

SECTION I: ORCHESTRAL

**Suite in G minor, 'Farewell' (for the death of
Purcell) (1696)**
Parley of Instr, R. Goodman *Concert*
　　　　　　　　(3/93) (HYPE) ① **CDA66578**

SECTION II: CHAMBER

Sonata for Oboe, Violin and Continuo
English Tpt Virtuosi, A. Hoskins (tpt/dir), M. Hoskins
(tpt/dir) (r1994) *Concert* (11/94) (MOSC) ① **070979**

SECTION IV: VOCAL AND CHORAL

While I with wounding grief—song (1694)
(Wds. D'Urfey)
C. Bott, P. Chateauneuf (r1990) *Concert*
　　　　　　　　(2/93) (L'OI) ① **433 187-2OH**

FINK, Michael *(b 1939)* **USA**

SECTION IV: VOCAL AND CHORAL

What sweeter music—chorus (Wds. R.
Herrick)
St John's Episcopal Cath Ch, D. Pearson *Concert*
　　　　　　　　(10/92) (DELO) ① **DE3125**

FINNISSY, Michael (Peter) *(b 1946)*
England

SECTION II: CHAMBER

Câtana—nine instruments (1984)
Uroboros Ens, M. Finnissy (bp1986) *Concert*
　　　　　　　　(2/92) (ETCE) ① **KTC1096**
Contretänze—six instruments (1985)
Exposé Ens (bp1987) *Concert*
　　　　　　　　(2/92) (ETCE) ① **KTC1096**
String Trio (1986)
Gagliano Trio (bp1987) *Concert*
　　　　　　　　(2/92) (ETCE) ① **KTC1096**

SECTION III: INSTRUMENTAL

English Country-Tunes—piano (1977)
1. Green Meadows; 2. Midsummer Morn; 3. I'll give
my Love a Garland; 4. May and December; 5. Lies
and Marvels; 6. The seeds of Love; 7. My bonny boy;
8. Come beat the Drums and sound the Fifes.
M. Finnissy (12/90) (ETCE) ① **KTC1091**

SECTION IV: VOCAL AND CHORAL

**Beuk o' Newcasasel Sangs—soprano,
clarinet & piano (1989)** (Wds. adapted from
Joseph Crawhall)
EXCERPTS: 1. Up the Raw, maw bonny; 2. I
thought to marry a parson; 3. Buy broom buzzems; 4.
A' the neet ower an' ower; 5. As me an' me marra
was gannin' ta wark; 6. There's Quayside for sailors;
7. It's O but aw ken weel.
Tapestry (r1994) *Concert*

(12/95) (BRIT) ① **BML012**

FINZI, Gerald (Raphael)
(1901–1956) England

SECTION I: ORCHESTRAL

**Concerto for Cello and Orchestra in A minor,
Op. 40 (1951-52, 1954-55)**
R. Wallfisch, RLPO, V. Handley *Leighton: Veris
gratia.* (10/86) (CHAN) ① **CHAN8471**
**Concerto for Clarinet and Strings in C minor,
Op. 31 (1948-49)**
T. King, Philh, A. Francis (r1979) *Stanford: Clarinet
Concerto.* (6/87) (HYPE) ① **CDA66001**
G. Macdonald, Northern Sinfonia, S. Bedford *Concert*
(2/88) (ASV) ① **CDDCA568**
A. Hacker, English Stg Orch, W. Boughton *Concert*
(12/88) (NIMB) ① **NI5101**
R. Stoltzman, Guildhall Str Ens *Concert*
(9/91) (RCA) ① **RD60437**
E. Johnson, RPO, C. Groves *Concert*
(6/92) (ASV) ① **CDDCA787**
**Eclogue—piano and orchestra, Op. 10 (late
1920s, rev late 1940s)** (from an incomplete
piano concerto)
Martin Jones, English Stg Orch, W. Boughton (r1992)
Concert (8/93) (NIMB) ① **NI5366**
P. Lane, RLPO, V. Handley (r1994) *Concert*
(11/95) (EMIN) ① **CD-EMX2239**
**The Fall of the Leaf—elegy in D minor, Op.
20 (1929 rev 1939-41)** (orch cpted H.
Ferguson)
Northern Sinfonia, R. Hickox (r1988) *Concert*
(8/94) (EMI) ① **CDM7 64721-2**
**Grand Fantasia and Toccata in D
minor—piano and orchestra, Op. 38 (c1928
and 1953)** (Fantasia added 1953)
P. Fowke, RLPO, R. Hickox (r1988) *Intimations of
Immortality.* (10/93) (EMI) ① **CDM7 64720-2**
**New Year Music—nocturne for orchestra,
Op. 7 (1926, rev 1940s)**
Northern Sinfonia, R. Hickox (r1988) *Concert*
(8/94) (EMI) ① **CDM7 64721-2**
**Prelude in F minor—string orchestra, Op. 25
(1920s)** (pub posth)
English Stg Orch, W. Boughton *Concert*
(12/88) (NIMB) ① **NI5101**
**Romance in E flat—string orchestra, Op. 11
(1928)**
English Stg Orch, W. Boughton *Concert*
(12/88) (NIMB) ① **NI5101**

SECTION II: CHAMBER

**5 Bagatelles—clarinet and piano, Op. 23
(1938-43)**
1. Prelude; 2. Romance; 3. Carol; 4. Forlana; 5.
Fughetta.
G. de Peyer, G. Pryor *Concert*
(11/87) (CHAN) ① **CHAN8549**
T. King, C. Benson *Concert*
(7/89) (HYPE) ① **CDA66014**
R. Stoltzman, Guildhall Str Ens (arr Ashmore)
Concert (9/91) (RCA) ① **RD60437**
M. Khouri, P. Pettinger *Concert*
(6/92) (CNTI) ① **CCD1038**
E. Johnson, M. Martineau *Concert*
(6/92) (ASV) ① **CDDCA787**
N. Carpenter, D. McArthur *Concert*
(10/92) (HERA) ① **HAVPCD152**
Elegy in F—violin and piano, Op. 22 (1940)
L. Chilingirian, C. Benson *Concert*
(7/91) (HYPE) ① **CDA66192**
**Interlude in A minor—oboe and string
quartet, Op. 21 (1932-36)**
N. Daniel, J. Drake (arr Ferguson) *Concert*
(10/93) (LEMA) ① **LC44801**

SECTION IV: VOCAL AND CHORAL

**All this night—4vv chorus a cappella, Op. 33
(1951)** (Wds. W. Austin)
Finzi Sngrs, P. Spicer *Concert*
(9/91) (CHAN) ① **CHAN8936**
**Before and after Summer—ten songs:
baritone and piano, Op. 16 (1932-49)** (Wds. T
Hardy)
S. Varcoe, C. Benson *Concert*
(3/90) (HYPE) ① [2] **CDA66161/2**
**Earth and Air and Rain—ten songs: baritone
and piano, Op. 16 (1928-32)** (Wds. Hardy)
S. Varcoe, C. Benson *Concert*
(3/90) (HYPE) ① [2] **CDA66161/2**
**God is gone up—chorus, organ and strings,
Op. 27/2 (1951)** (Wds. E Taylor)
St Paul's Cath Ch, Andrew Lucas, John Scott
Concert (9/91) (HYPE) ① **CDA66374**
Salisbury Cath Ch, R. Seal *Concert*
(11/90) (MERI) ① **CDE84180**
Finzi Sngrs, H. Bicket, P. Spicer *Concert*
(9/91) (CHAN) ① **CHAN8936**
Norwich Cath Ch, M. Nicholas, N. Taylor *Concert*
(3/92) (PRIO) ① **PRCD351**
**I said to Love—six songs: baritone and
piano, Op. 19 (1928-56)** (Wds. T Hardy)
S. Varcoe, C. Benson *Concert*
(3/90) (HYPE) ① [2] **CDA66161/2**
**Intimations of Immortality—ode: tenor,
chorus and orchestra, Op. 29 (1936-38 and
1949-50)** (Wds. W. Wordsworth)
P. Langridge, Liverpool Phil Ch, RLPO, R. Hickox
(r1988) *Grand Fantasia.*
(10/93) (EMI) ① **CDM7 64720-2**
**Let us garlands bring—tenor and
strings/piano, Op. 18 (1940)** (Wds.
Shakespeare)
1. Come away, come away, death; 2. Who is Silvia?;
3. Fear no more the heat o' the sun; 4. O mistress
mine; 5. It was a lover and his lass.
Cpte S. Varcoe, CLS, R. Hickox *Concert*
(10/94) (CHAN) ① **CHAN8743**
B. Terfel, M. Martineau (r1994) *Concert*
(8/95) (DG) ① **445 946-2GH**
5. C. Robbin, M. McMahon (r1985) *Concert*
(7/94) (MARQ) ① **ERAD113**
**Lo, the full, final sacrifice—festival anthem:
chorus and organ/orchestra, Op. 26 (1946
orch 1947)** (Wds R Crashaw)
Worcester Cath Ch, A. Partington *Concert*
(3/90) (HYPE) ① **CDA66078**
Finzi Sngrs, H. Bicket, P. Spicer *Concert*
(9/91) (CHAN) ① **CHAN8936**
St Paul's Cath Ch, John Scott *Concert*
(4/92) (HYPE) ① **CDA66519**
**Magnificat—soloists (ad lib), chorus and
organ/orchestra, Op. 36 (1952 orch 1956)**
Finzi Sngrs, H. Bicket, P. Spicer *Concert*
(9/91) (CHAN) ① **CHAN8936**
**My lovely one—anthem: chorus and organ,
Op. 27/1 (1948)** (Wds. E Taylor)
Finzi Sngrs, H. Bicket, P. Spicer *Concert*
(9/91) (CHAN) ① **CHAN8936**
**Oh fair to see—seven songs: high voice and
piano, Op. 13 (1929-56)** (Wds. various)
1. I'll seek her (wds T Hardy); 2. Oh fair to see (wds
C Rossetti); 3. As I lay in the early sun (wds E
Shanks); 4. Only the wanderer (wds I Gurney); 5. To
Joy (wds E Blunden); 6. Harvest (wds E Blunden); 7.
Since we loved (wds R Bridges).
I. Partridge, C. Benson *Concert*
(9/91) (HYPE) ① **CDA66015**
Only a man harrowing clods—song (1923)
(Wds. T. Hardy)
S. Varcoe, C. Benson *Concert*
(6/88) (HYPE) ① [2] **CDA66261/2**
**7 Partsongs—4vv chorus a cappella, Op. 17
(1934-37)** (Wds. R Bridges)
1. I praise the tender flower; 2. I have loved the
flowers that fade; 3. My spirit sang all day; 4. Clear
and gentle stream; 5. Nightingales; 6. Haste on, my
joys!; 7. Wherfore tonight so full of care.
Finzi Sngrs, P. Spicer *Concert*
(9/91) (CHAN) ① **CHAN8936**
2, 3. King's Sngrs *Concert*
(6/88) (EMI) ① **CDC7 49765-2**
**Requiem da Camera—baritone, chorus and
orchestra (1924)** (Wds various)
Britten Sngrs, CLS, R. Hickox *Concert*
(3/92) (CHAN) ① **CHAN8997**
**3 Short Elegies—chorus a cappella, Op. 5
(1926)** (Wds. W Drummond)
1. Life a right shadow is; 2. This world a hunting is; 3.
This life, which seems so fair.

Finzi Sngrs, P. Spicer *Concert*
(9/91) (CHAN) ① **CHAN8936**
**Thou didst delight my eyes—3vv male
chorus a cappella, Op. 32 (1952)** (Wds. R.
Bridges)
Finzi Sngrs, P. Spicer *Concert*
(9/91) (CHAN) ① **CHAN8936**
**Till Earth outwears—seven songs: high
voice and piano, Op. 19 (1927-56)** (Wds. T
Hardy)
M. Hill, C. Benson *Concert*
(3/90) (HYPE) ① [2] **CDA66161/2**
**To a Poet—six songs: low voice and piano,
Op. 13 (1920s-1956)** (Wds. various: pub
posth)
1. To a poet a thousand years hence (wds. J. Elroy
Flecker); 2. On parent knees (wds. attrib W. Jones,
from the Persian); 3. Intrada (wds. T. Traherne); 4.
The Birthnight (wds W. de la Mare); 5. June on
Castle Hill (wds. F. L. Lucas); 6. Ode on rejection of
St Cecilia (wds. G. Barker).
S. Roberts, C. Benson *Concert*
(9/91) (HYPE) ① **CDA66015**
**Welcome sweet and sacred feast—anthem:
chorus and organ, Op. 27/3 (1953)** (Wds. H
Vaughan)
Finzi Sngrs, H. Bicket, P. Spicer *Concert*
(9/91) (CHAN) ① **CHAN8936**
Magdalen Oxford Coll Ch, G. Webber *Concert*
(11/91) (ABBE) ① **CDCA914**
**White-flowering days—4vv chorus a
cappella, Op. 37 (1953)** (Wds. E. Blunden)
Finzi Sngrs, P. Spicer *Concert*
(9/91) (CHAN) ① **CHAN8936**
Cambridge Univ Chbr Ch, T. Brown *Concert*
(4/92) (GAMU) ① **GAMCD529**
**A Young Man's Exhortation—ten songs:
tenor and piano, Op. 14 (1926-29)** (Wds. T
Hardy)
M. Hill, C. Benson *Concert*
(3/90) (HYPE) ① [2] **CDA66161/2**

SECTION V: STAGE WORKS

**Loves Labour's Lost—concert suite from
incidental music, Op. 28 (1946-55)**
1. Introduction; 2. Moth; 3. Nocturne: 4. The Hunt; 5.
Dance; 6. Quodlibet (Clowns); 7. Soliloquy I; 8.
Soliloquy II; 9. Soliloquy III; 10. Finale.
English Stg Orch, W. Boughton *Concert*
(12/88) (NIMB) ① **NI5101**

FIOCCO, Joseph-Hector
(1703–1741) Italy/South
Netherlands

SECTION III: INSTRUMENTAL

Pièces de clavecin, Op. 1 (pub 1730)
1. Suite No. 1 in G major/minor; 1a. Adagio; 1b.
Allegro; 2. Suite No. 2 in D minor.
T. Koopman (3/90) (ASTR) ① [2] **E7731**
1. I. Tracey (arr Tracey) *Concert*
(1/90) (CFP) ① **CD-CFP4558**
1a T. Pinnock *Concert*
(11/84) (ARCH) ① **413 591-2AH**
1a A. Stringer, N. Rawsthorne (1974) *Concert*
(11/87) (CRD) ① **CRD3308**
1b Y. Menuhin, L. Persinger (arr Bent/O'Neill: r1928)
Concert (4/91) (BIDD) ① **LAB031**

FIORILLO, Federico (1755–1825)
Italy

SECTION III: INSTRUMENTAL

36 Etude-caprices—violin, Op. 3
EXCERPTS: 28. No 28.
28. J. Kubelík, anon (r1913; arr Randegger) *Concert*
(6/91) (BIDD) ① [2] **LAB033/4**

FIRSOVA, Elena (b 1950) USSR

SECTION I: ORCHESTRAL

Cassandra—orchestra, Op. 60 (1992-3)
BBC Nat Orch of Wales, T. Otaka (r1994)
Gubaidulina: Pro et contra.
(11/94) (BIS) ① **BIS-CD668**

FISCHER, Edwin (1886–1960) Switzerland

SECTION III: INSTRUMENTAL

Das **Donnerwetter**—piano (1916) (after
Mozart's Contredanse, K534)
C. Katsaris (r1992) Concert
(6/93) (SONY) ① **SK52551**

FISCHER, Johann Caspar Ferdinand (?c1670–1746) Germany

SECTION II: CHAMBER

La **Journal du Printems** (pub 1695)
EXCERPTS: 7. Ouverture a 5 in G minor.
7. Parley of Instr, R. Goodman, P. Holman Concert
(9/91) (HYPE) ① **CDA66074**

SECTION III: INSTRUMENTAL

Musicalischer Parnassus—keyboard (pub
1738) (9 Suites on the Muses)
1. Uranie, D minor; 2. Eciterpe, F; 3. Clio, C; 4. Erato,
E minor.
1, 2. W. Christie (r1979) Pièces de clavessin.
(4/88) (HARM) ① **HMA190 1026**
Passacaglia in D minor (1738) (From
Musicalischer Parnassus)
T. Pinnock Concert
(11/84) (ARCH) ① **413 591-2AH**
Les **Pièces de clavessin, Op. 2** (pub 1696)
1, 2, 3. W. Christie (r1979) Parnasse Musical.
(4/88) (HARM) ① **HMA190 1026**
**Praeludium and Chaconne
VIII**—harpsichord
M. Märkl (1994) Concert
(5/95) (HARM) ① **HMC90 1505**

FISCHER, (Johann Ignaz) Ludwig (1745–1825) Germany

SECTION I: ORCHESTRAL

Symphony for 8 Timpani and Orchestra
J. Haas, Bournemouth Sinfonietta, H. Farberman
Concert (10/89) (CRD) ① **CRD3449**

SECTION IV: VOCAL AND CHORAL

Der **Kritikaster und der Trinker**—bass and
piano (pub 1802)
1. In kühlen Kellar sitz (In cellar cool/Drinking).
1. O. Natzke, H. Greenslade (Eng: r1940) Concert
(12/92) (ODE) ① **CDODE1365**

FISCHER, William G. (1835–1912) USA

SECTION IV: VOCAL AND CHORAL

I love to tell the story—song (pub 1869)
(Wds. K. Hankey)
R. Taylor, R. Murcell, Harmoneion Sngrs, N. Bruce,
L. Skrobacs (r1977) Concert
(2/94) (NEW) ① **80220-2**

FISHER, Aidan (b 1959) England

SECTION IV: VOCAL AND CHORAL

Leviathan—soprano, clarinet & piano (1990)
(Wds. B C Leale)
Tapestry (r1994) Concert
(12/95) (BRIT) ① **BML012**

FITKIN, Chris (20th Cent) England

SECTION II: CHAMBER

Sextet—3 vibraphones, 3 marimbas/pianos
(1989)
Piano Circus Concert
(7/92) (ARGO) ① **433 522-2ZH**

FITKIN, Graham (b 1963) England

SECTION I: ORCHESTRAL

Cud—band (1987-88)
J. Harle Band, G. Fitkin (r1992) Concert
(10/93) (ARGO) ① **440 216-2ZH**

SECTION II: CHAMBER

Hook—marimba quartet and drums (1991-
92)
Bash Ens (r1992) Concert
(10/93) (ARGO) ① **440 216-2ZH**
Icebreaker—wind instruments, guitars and
keyboards (1991-92)
Icebreaker (r1992) Concert
(10/93) (ARGO) ① **440 216-2ZH**
Line—pianos
Piano Circus Concert
(1/93) (ARGO) ① **436 100-2ZH**
Log—pianos
Piano Circus Concert
(1/93) (ARGO) ① **436 100-2ZH**
Loud—pianos
Piano Circus Concert
(1/93) (ARGO) ① **436 100-2ZH**
Stub—saxophone quartet (1991-92)
Icebreaker (r1992) Concert
(10/93) (ARGO) ① **440 216-2ZH**

FLAHERTY, Stephen (20th Cent) ?USA

SECTION V: STAGE WORKS

Once On This Island—musical show
(1990—New York) (Book & Lyrics Lynn Ahrens,
after Rosa Guy)
EXCERPTS: 1. Prologue/We Dance; 2. One Small
Girl; 3. Waiting For Life; 4. And the Gods Heard Her
Prayer; 5. Rain; 6. Discovering Daniel; 7. Pray; 8.
Forever Yours; 9. The Sad Tale of the
Beauxhommes; 10. Ti Moune; 11. Mama Will
Provide; 12. Some Say; 13. The Human Heart; 14.
Pray (reprise); 15. Some Girls; 16. The Ball; 17. Ti
Moune's Dance; 18. When We Are Wed; 19.
Promises/Forever Yours (reprise); 20. Wedding
Sequence; 21. A Part of Us; 22. Why We Tell the
Story.
Cpte Orig London Cast, R. Balcombe (r1994)
(6/95) (TER) ① **CDTER1224**

FLECHA, Mateo (1481–1553) Spain

SECTION IV: VOCAL AND CHORAL

El Jubilate—ensaladas: 5vv
Hilliard Ens Concert (6/91) (HYPE) ① **CDA66370**
El Fuego—ensalada (5vv)
Huelgas Ens, P. van Nevel Concert
(9/92) (SONY) ① **SK46699**
La **Justa**—ensalada (5vv)
Huelgas Ens, P. van Nevel Concert
(9/92) (SONY) ① **SK46699**
Colombina Ens (r1994) Concert
(11/95) (ACCE) ① **ACC94103D**
La **Negrina**—ensalada (5vv)
Huelgas Ens, P. van Nevel Concert
(9/92) (SONY) ① **SK46699**
Colombina Ens (r1994) Concert
(11/95) (ACCE) ① **ACC94103D**

FLÉGIER, Ange (1846–1927) France

SECTION IV: VOCAL AND CHORAL

Le **Cor**—song
P. Plançon, anon (r1905) Concert
(9/91) (PEAR) ① **GEMMCD9497**
F. Chaliapin, orch, G.W. Byng (r1929) Concert
(6/93) (PREI) ① [2] **89207**
P. Plançon, anon (r1905) Concert
(12/94) (ROMO) ① [2] **82001-2**
Stances—song
L. Escalais, anon (r1905) Concert
(12/93) (SYMP) ① **SYMCD1126**

FLETCHER, Percy (Eastman) (1879–1932) England

SECTION I: ORCHESTRAL

An **Epic Symphony**—brass band (1926)
Black Dyke Mills Band, R. Newsome Concert
(7/93) (CHAN) ① **CHAN4508**
Labour and Love—tone poem for brass band
(1913)
Black Dyke Mills Band, P. Parkes Concert
(9/93) (CHAN) ① **CHAN4506**

Two **Parisian Sketches**—orchestral suite
(1914)
Southern Fest Orch, R. White Concert
(5/93) (CHAN) ① **CHAN9110**

FLEURY, André (Edouard Antoine Marie) (b 1903) France

SECTION III: INSTRUMENTAL

Prelude, Andante and Toccata—organ
(1932)
J. Parker-Smith Concert
(9/90) (ASV) ① **CDDCA702**
G. Barber Concert (7/91) (PRIO) ① **PRCD314**

FLIES, Bernhard (1770–?) Austria

SECTION IV: VOCAL AND CHORAL

Wiegenlied—song (Previously attrib. Mozart)
E. Schumann, orch, L. Collingwood (r1930) Concert
(6/91) (PREI) ① **89031**
E. Destinn, orch, W.B. Rogers (1916) Concert
(11/93) (ROMO) ① [2] **81002-2**
I. Seefried, H. von Nordberg (r1947) Concert
(4/94) (TEST) ① **SBT1026**
E. Destinn, orch, W.B Rogers (1916) Concert
(12/94) (SUPR) ① [12] **11 2136-2(5)**
E. Rethberg, anon (r1925) Concert
(2/95) (ROMO) ① [2] **81012-2**

FLOTOW, Friedrich (Adolf Ferdinand) von (1812–1883) Germany

SECTION V: STAGE WORKS

Alessandro Stradella—opera: 3 acts
(1844—Hamburg) (Lib. Riese)
Wie freundlich strahlt W. Ludwig, Berlin City Op
Orch, W. Ladwig (r1932) Concert
(7/95) (PREI) ① **89088**
Martha—opera: 4 acts (1847—Vienna) (Lib.
Riese)
ACT 1: 1. Overture; 2. Darf mit nächtig; 3a. Teure
Lady!; 3b. Von den edlen Kavalieren (Duet); 4a.
Gnaden Tristan Mickleford; 4b. Schöne Lady (Trio);
5. Wohlgemut junges Blut; 6. Mädchen, brav und
treu; 7. Wie das schnattert (Duet)...Ja! Seit früher
Kindheit Tagen; 8a. Der Markt beginnt; 8b. Sieh nur
(Quartet); 9. Hier! Da nehmt die Abstandssumme.
ACT 2: 10. Nur näher, schöne Mädchen; 11a.
Mädels, dort is eure Kammer; 11b. Was soll ich dazu
sagen? (Quartet); 12a. Nancy! Julia!; 12b. Blickt sein
Auge (Duet); 12c. Letzte Rose (Ballad); 12d. Martha -
Herr!; 12e. Martha, nimme zum frommen Bunde
(Duet); 13a. Warte nur!; 13b. Mitternacht! (Nottumo);
14. Nancy! Lady! Was nun weiter? (Finale). ACT 3:
15a. Entr'acte; 15b. Lasst mich euch fragen (Porter
Song); 16. Jägerin, schlau im Sinn; 17a. Blitz! Die
wilde Jagd!; 17b. An dem Frechen; 18a. Schau
pflück' ich; 18b. Ach so fromm (M'appari tutt'amor);
19a. Die Herrin rastet dort; 19b. Hier in den stillen
Schattengründen; 20. Mag der Himmel (Quintet).
ACT 4: 21a. Entr'acte; 21b. Zum treuen Freunde;
21c. Den Teuren zu versöhnen; 22. Der Lenz ist
gekommen; 23a. Fasst Euch, Lady!; 23b. Ja! Was
Nun? (Duet); 24. Hier die Buden (Finale).
ADDITIONAL ITEM FOR ITALIAN VERSION—; 25a.
Povero Lionello; 25b. Il mio Lionel.
Cpte L. Popp, D. Soffel, S. Jerusalem, K.
Ridderbusch, S. Nimsgern, P. Lika, Bavarian Rad
Chor, Munich RO, H. Wallberg
(2/89) (EURO) ① [2] **352 878**
Cpte A. Rothenberger, B. Fassbaender, N. Gedda,
H. Prey, D. Weller, H.G. Knoblich, Bavarian St Op
Chor, Bavarian St Orch, R. Heger
(5/89) (EMI) ① [2] **CMS7 69339-2**
7. E. Caruso, M. Journet, orch (Ital: r1910) Concert
(3/91) (PEAR) ① [3] **EVC2**
7. E. Caruso, M. Journet, orch, W.B. Rogers (r1910:
Ital) Concert (7/91) (RCA) ① [12] **GD60495(3)**
9. L. Pavarotti, National PO, O. de Fabritiis (Ital)
Concert (7/90) (DECC) ① [2] **425 681-2DM2**
10, 11a, 11b, 13a F. Alda, J. Jacoby, E. Caruso, M.
Journet, orch (Ital: r1912) Concert
(3/91) (PEAR) ① [3] **EVC2**
10, 11a, 11b, 13a F. Alda, J. Jacoby, E. Caruso, M.
Journet, orch, W.B Rogers (Ital: r1912) Concert
(7/91) (RCA) ① [12] **GD60495(4)**
12b, 12c F. Marconi, B. Mililotti, C. Sabajno (r1907:
Ital) Concert (9/92) (SYMP) ① **SYMCD1069**
12c F. Saville, anon (r c1902) Concert
(10/92) (SYMP) ① **SYMCD1093**

12c L. Price, LSO, E. Downes (Eng) *Concert*
(12/92) (RCA) ① [4] 09026 61236-2
12c E. Mason, orch (r1924) *Concert*
(8/93) (SYMP) ① SYMCD1136
12c A. Galli-Curci, orch, J. Pasternack (r1917: Eng)
Concert (3/94) (ROMO) ① [2] 81003-2
12c A. Galli-Curci, orch, J. Pasternack (r1921: Eng)
Concert (8/94) (ROMO) ① [2] 81004-2
12c E. Mason, orch, F. Black (r1925) *Concert*
(8/94) (ROMO) ① 81009-2
12c E. Mason, orch, F. Black (r1924) *Concert*
(8/94) (ROMO) ① 81009-2
12c E. Steber, orch, H. Barlow (bp1946) *Concert*
(11/95) (VAI) ① VAIA1072
12c, 18b H. Roswaenge, orch (r1935: Ger) *Concert*
(4/95) (PREI) ① [2] 89209
15b A. Kipnis, Berlin St Op Orch, C. Schmalstich
(r1930) *Concert* (12/90) (PREI) ① 89019
15b P. Plançon, orch (Fr: r1907) *Concert*
(9/91) (PEAR) ① GEMMCD9497
15b E. de Reszke, anon (Ital: r1903) *Concert*
(7/92) (PEAR) ① [3] GEMMCDS9923(1)
15b T. Ruffo, orch (Ital: r1922) *Concert*
(2/93) (PREI) ① [3] 89303(2)
15b E. de Reszke, anon (Ital: r1903: Ital) *Concert*
(7/93) (NIMB) ① [2] NI7840/1
15b A. Didur, orch (r c1918: Ital) *Concert*
(1/94) (CLUB) ① CL99-089
15b P. Plançon, orch (r1907: Ital) *Concert*
(12/94) (ROMO) ① [2] 82001-2
16. D. Soffel, Swedish CO, M. Liljefors (pp1984)
Concert (4/93) (CPRI) ① CAP21428
18b P. Domingo, Los Angeles PO, C.M. Giulini
Concert (7/86) (DG) ① 415 366-2GH
18b J. Björling, orch, N. Grevillius (r1939: Ital)
Concert (10/88) (EMI) ① CDH7 61053-2
18b T. Schipa, orch (Ital: r1927) *Concert*
(2/89) (PEAR) ① GEMMCD9322
18b J. Patzak, Berlin St Op Orch, A. Melichar (r1932)
Concert (3/90) (PREI) ① GEMMCD9383
18b J. Schmidt, Berlin St Op Orch, C. Schmalstich
(r1929) *Concert* (4/90) (EMI) ① CDM7 69478-2
18b B. Gigli, orch, R. Bourdon (Ital: r1923) *Concert*
(5/90) (NIMB) ① NI7807
18b E. Caruso, orch (Ital: r1906) *Concert*
(7/90) (CLUB) ① CL99-060
18b E. Caruso, orch (Ital: r1906) *Concert*
(12/90) (PEAR) ① [3] EVC1(2)
18b E. Caruso, orch, J. Pasternack (Ital: r1917)
Concert (7/91) (RCA) ① [12] GD60495(6)
18b E. Caruso, orch (r1906: Ital) *Concert*
(7/91) (RCA) ① [12] GD60495(2)
18b E. Caruso, orch, J. Pasternack (Ital: r1917)
Concert (10/91) (PEAR) ① [3] EVC4(1)
18b R. Tauber, orch (r1930) *Concert*
(9/92) (MMOI) ① CDMOIR409
18b L. Sobinov, anon (r1904: Russ) *Concert*
(6/93) (PEAR) ① [3] GEMMCDS9997/9(2)
18b B. Gigli, orch, R. Bourdon (Ital: r1929) *Concert*
(6/93) (MMOI) ① CDMOIR417
18b P. Anders, Berlin St Op Orch, J. Schüler
(bp1944) *Concert* (8/93) (ACAN) ① 43 268
18b J. Björling, orch, N. Grevillius (r1939: Ital)
Concert (10/93) (NIMB) ① NI7842
18b E. Caruso, orch (r1917/32: Ital) *Concert*
(5/94) (CLAR) ① CDGSE78-50-52
18b J. Björling, orch, N. Grevillius (r1939: Ital)
Concert (9/94) (CARL) ① GLRS103
18b J. Björling, orch, N. Grevillius (r1939: Ital)
Concert (9/94) (CONI) ① CDHD214
18b H. Roswaenge, orch (r1935) *Concert*
(9/94) (NIMB) ① NI7856
18b A. Pertile, La Scala Orch, C. Sabajno (r1930:
Ital) *Concert* (10/94) (PREI) ① 89072
18b E. Caruso, orch (r1906: Ital) *Concert*
(7/95) (NIMB) ① NI7866
18b R. Alagna, LPO, R. Armstrong (Ital) *Concert*
(12/95) (EMI) ① CDC5 55540-2
20. H. von Debička, E. Leisner, H. Roswaenge, R.
Watzke, orch (r1928) *Concert*
(2/92) (PREI) ① [2] 89201
25a, 25b M. Battistini, orch, C. Sabajno (r1906)
Concert (10/92) (NIMB) ① NI7831
25a, 25b M. Battistini, orch, C. Sabajno (r1906)
Concert (10/92) (PEAR) ① GEMMCD9936
25b M. Battistini, orch (r1906: Ital) *Concert*
(2/92) (PREI) ① 89045
L' Ombre—opera (3 acts) (1870—Paris) (Lib.
Saint-Georges and de Leuven)
Quand je monte cocotte; Midi, minuit L. Fugère,
orch (r c1929) *Concert*
(6/93) (SYMP) ① SYMCD1125

FLOYD, Carlisle (b 1926) USA

SECTION V: STAGE WORKS

Susannah—music drama: 2 acts
(1954—Tallahassee) (Lib. cpsr)
Cpte C. Studer, J. Hadley, S. Ramey, K. Chester, M.
Druiett, S. Cole, S. Kale, D. Pittsinger, A. Howells, S.
Jones, J. Glennon, E. Laurence, Lyon Op Chor, Lyon
Op Orch, K. Nagano
(10/94) (VIRG) ① [2] VCD5 45039-2
Hear me, O Lord S. Ramey, NY Met Op Orch, J.
Conlon (pp1991) *Concert*
(6/93) (RCA) ① 09026 61509-2

FLYNN, John H. (19th–20th Cent) USA

SECTION IV: VOCAL AND CHORAL

Yip-I-Addy-I-Ay!—song for the show 'The
Merry Widow Burlesque' (1909) (Lyrics Will D.
Cobb)
B. Ring, Orig Broadway Cast (r1909) *Concert*
(5/94) (PEAR) ① [3] GEMMCDS9053/5

FOERSTER, Josef Bohuslav (1859–1951) Bohemia

SECTION I: ORCHESTRAL

Cyrano de Bergerac—orchestral suite, Op.
55 (1903)
Czech PO, V. Smetáček *From Shakespeare.*
(11/93) (CAMP) ① RRCD1319
From Shakespeare—orchestral suite, Op. 76
(1908-09)
Prague SO, V. Smetáček *Cyrano, Op. 55.*
(11/93) (CAMP) ① RRCD1319

SECTION II: CHAMBER

Sonata quasi fantasia—violin and piano, Op.
77 (1943)
J. Suk, J. Panenka *Concert*
(5/90) (SUPR) ① 11 0705-2
Wind Quintet in D, Op. 95 (1909)
Aulos Wind Qnt (r1988) *Concert*
(6/93) (SCHW) ① 310051

SECTION IV: VOCAL AND CHORAL

An die Laute—Lied: 1v and piano (Wds.
Rochlitz)
H. Hagegård, T. Schuback (r1976) *Concert*
(5/94) (BIS) ① BIS-CD054

FOLQUET DE MARSEILLE (c1150–60–1231) France

SECTION IV: VOCAL AND CHORAL

En chantan m'aven a membrar—chanson
(c1187)
E. Lamandier *Concert* (2/88) (ALIE) ① AL1019

FOMENKO, Mykola (1894–1961) Russia/USA

SECTION IV: VOCAL AND CHORAL

The Mighty Knieper—song (Wds. anon)
P. Plishka, T. Hrynkiv *Concert*
(11/92) (FORL) ① UCD16645

FONTAINE, Pierre (?1390–95–c1450) France

SECTION IV: VOCAL AND CHORAL

Pour vous tenir
G. Binchois Ens, D. Vellard *Concert*
(3/92) (VIRG) ① VC7 59043-2

FONTANA, Giovanni Battista (1571–c1630) Italy

SECTION II: CHAMBER

Sonate a 1,2,3 per il Violono o Cornetto,
Chitarrone, Violincino o simile altri
instromento (1641)
2. Sonata seconda (1 instrument); 3. Sonata terza (1
instrument); 6. Sonata sesta (1 instrument); 16.
Sonata seidici (3 instruments).
Prima E. Haupt, S. Pank *Concert*
(2/90) (CAPR) ① 10 234

---

2. M. Verbruggen, Sonnerie Trio *Concert*
(2/90) (ASV) ① CDGAU113
2. B. Dickey, Tragicomedia *Concert*
(6/92) (ACCE) ① ACC9173D
3. B. Kol, A. Brodo, D. Shemer (recorder) *Concert*
(6/90) (CARL) ① PWK1138
16. J. Holloway, S. Ritchie, A. Manze, N. North, M.
Springfels, J. Toll (r1993) *Concert*
(2/94) (HARM) ① HMU90 7091

FONTEI, Nicolò (c1600–1647 or later) Italy

SECTION IV: VOCAL AND CHORAL

Auree stelle—Gondoglianza notturna
(Bizzarie pretiche) (1639)
T. Berganza, Ens, J.E. Dähler (hpd/dir) *Concert*
(3/84) (CLAV) ① CD50-8206

FONTENAILLES, Nicholas de (19th Cent) France

SECTION IV: VOCAL AND CHORAL

À l'aimé—song (Wds. Dortzal)
R. Ponselle, R. Romani (r1939) *Concert*
(1/90) (RCA) ① GD87810
Les Deux coeurs—song
J. Lassalle, anon (r1905) *Concert*
(9/91) (SYMP) ① SYMCD1089
Obstination—song
C. Formichi, orch (r1927) *Concert*
(11/94) (PREI) ① 89055

FONTEYNS (14th Cent) England

SECTION IV: VOCAL AND CHORAL

Regali ex progenie—3vv
Gothic Voices, C. Page (lte/dir) *Concert*
(9/92) (HYPE) ① CDA66588

FOOTE, Arthur (1853–1937) USA

SECTION I: ORCHESTRAL

Suite in E—strings, Op. 63 (1907 rev 1908)
Boston SO, S. Koussevitzky (r1940) *Concert*
(12/91) (PEAR) ① GEMMCD9492

SECTION II: CHAMBER

At dusk—flute, harp and cello (1920)
F. Smith, C. Yeats, Ronald Thomas *Concert*
(9/90) (NORT) ① NR227-CD
3 Character Pieces—violin and piano, Op. 9
(1885)
1. Morgengesang; 2. Menuetto serioso; 3. Romanza.
J. Silverstein, V. Eskin *Concert*
(7/90) (NORT) ① NR206-CD
Nocturne and Scherzo—flute and string
quartet (1918)
F. Smith, L. Chang, V. Uritsky, K. Murdoch, B.
Coppock *Concert* (9/90) (NORT) ① NR227-CD
Piano Trio No. 2 in B flat, Op. 65 (1907-08)
J. Silverstein, J. Eskin, V. Eskin *Concert*
(7/90) (NORT) ① NR206-CD
3 Pieces—cello and piano, Op. 1 (1881)
J. Eskin, V. Eskin *Concert*
(7/90) (NORT) ① NR206-CD
3 Pieces—oboe/flute and piano, Op. 31 (pub
1931)
F. Smith, R. Hodgkinson *Concert*
(9/90) (NORT) ① NR227-CD
Sarabande and Rigaudon—oboe/flute,
viola/violin, piano, Op. 21 (1921)
F. Smith, M. Thompson, R. Hodgkinson *Concert*
(9/90) (NORT) ① NR227-CD

FORD, Thomas (c1580–1648) England

SECTION II: CHAMBER

Cate of Bardy—two viols (pub 1607)
Circa 1500, N. Hadden (r1991) *Concert*
(8/93) (CRD) ① CRD3487
Musicke of Sundrie Kindes, Part II—two bass
viols (pub 1607)
1. The baggepipes: Sir Charles Howard's delight; 2.
Snatch and away: Sir John Pawlet's toy; 3. M.
Southcote's Paven and Galliard; 4. Pavan (M.
Maine's choice) and Galliard; 5. Forget me not; 6.
The Wild Goose Chase; 7. Why not here? M. Crosse,
his Choice; 8. Untitled Pavan and Gallaird.

1, 4, 7. W. Kuijken, S. Kuijken, R. Kohnen *Concert*
(1/87) (ACCE) ① **ACC68014D**

Come, Phyllis—1v and lute
P. Pears, J. Bream (r1969) *Concert*
(8/93) (RCA) ① [28] **09026 61583-2(5)**
P. Pears, J. Bream (r1969) *Concert*
(8/93) (RCA) ① **09026 61602-2**
Musicke of Sundrie Kindes, Part I—4vv and instruments (pub 1607)
1. Faire sweet cruell; 2. Go passions to the cruel fair; 3. Since first I saw your face; 4. There is a ladie, sweet and kind; 5. What then is love, sings Coridon; 6. How shall I then describe my love?.
1. P. Pears, J. Bream (r1969) *Concert*
(8/93) (RCA) ① [28] **09026 61583-2(5)**
1. P. Pears, J. Bream (r1969) *Concert*
(8/93) (RCA) ① **09026 61602-2**
1, 3, 5. M. Chance, C. Wilson (r1992) *Concert*
(10/94) (CHAN) ① **CHAN0538**
2. E. Kirkby, A. Rooley (pp1985) *Concert*
(6/87) (HYPE) ① **CDA66186**
2, 6. Magdalen (Oxford) Coll Ch, G. Ives *Concert*
(11/92) (CNTO) ① **CRCD2366**
3. J. Bowman, D. Miller *Concert*
(10/91) (HYPE) ① **CDA66447**
4. Amaryllis Consort, C. Brett *Concert*
(3/88) (CARL) ① **PCD873**

FORQUERAY, Antoine (1671/2–1745) France

Pièces de viole—viola da gamba and continuo (pub 1747) (arr/ed J-B Forqueray: with hpd trans & 3 orig wks)
EXCERPTS: SUITE 1 IN D MINOR: 1a. Allemande, La Laborde; 1b. La Forqueray; 1c. La Cottin; 1d. La Bellemont; 1e. La Portugaise; 1f. La Couperin. SUITE 2 IN G: 2a. La Bouron; 2b. La Mandoline; 2c. La Du Breüil; 2d. La Leclair; 2e. Chaconne, La Buisson. SUITE 3 IN D: 3a. La Ferrand; 3b. La Régente; 3c. La Tronchin; 3d. La Angrave; 3e. La Du Vaucel; 3f. La Eynaud; 3g. Chaconne, La Morangis ou La Plissay. SUITE 4 IN G MINOR: 4a. La Marella; 4b. La Clément; 4c. Sarabande; 4d. La Carillon de Passy—La Latour. SUITE 5 IN C MINOR: 5a. La Rameau; 5b. La Guignon; 5c. La Léon, Sarabande; 5d. La Boisson; 5e. La Montigni; 5f. La Sylva; 5g. Jupiter.
1a-f, 2b, 2d, 2e, 3a, 3b, 3f, 4b, 4d, 5a, 5d, 5f, 5g M. Raskin (r1993) (2/95) (PIER) ① **PV794051**
1a, 1e, 2e, 3a, 3b, 5g J. Bernfeld, S. Sempé *Pièces de viole.* (5/92) (DHM) ① **RD77262**
1b, 1c, 1f, 2d, 4a, 4c, 5a S. Sempé (trans hpd) *Pièces de viole.* (5/92) (DHM) ① **RD77262**
1, 2. J. Savall, T. Koopman, C. Coin
(10/89) (ASTR) ① **E7762**
3b-d, 3f, 3g, 4a-d G. Leonhardt *Concert*
(10/92) (SONY) ① **SK48080**
3g S. Standage, L.U. Mortensen (r1992: trans hpd) *Concert* (6/93) (CHAN) ① **CHAN0531**
3, 5. M. Meyerson (r1989: trans hpd)
(5/94) (VIRG) ① **VC7 59310-2**
5a, 5d, 5f, 5g S. Yates (r1993) *Concert*
(11/93) (CHAN) ① **CHAN0545**

FORREST, George (b 1915) USA
in association with Robert Wright (b 1914)

Grand Hotel—musical show (1992—New York) (Lyrics Forrest & Wright; Book L. Davis; additional songs by M. Yeston)
EXCERPTS: 1a. The Grand Parade (comp Yeston); 1b. Some Have, Some Have Not; 1c. As It Should Be; 2a. At the Grand Hotel (Yeston); 2b. Table With a View; 3a. Maybe My Baby Loves Me; 4a. Fire and Ice; 4b. Twenty-Two Years (Yeston); 4c. Villa on a Hill; 5. I Want to Go to Hollywood (Yeston); 6a. The Crooked Path; 6b. Some Have, Some Have Not (reprise); 6c. As It Should Be (reprise); 7. Who Couldn't Dance With You?; 8. Love Can't Happen (Yeston); 9. What You Need; 10. Bonjour Amour (Yeston); 11a. H.A.P.P.Y; 11b. We'll Take a Glass Together; 12. I Waltz Alone; 13. Roses at the Station (Yeston); 14. Bolero; 15. How Can I Tell Her?; 16. Final Scene; 17. The Grand Waltz.
Cpte Orig Broadway Cast, J. Lee (r1992)
(1/93) (RCA) ① **09026 61327-2**

Kismet—musical show based on Borodin's music (1953—New York) (Lyrics Forrest & Wright, after E. Knoblock)
EXCERPTS: 1. Overture. ACT 1: 2. Sands of time; 3. Rhymes have I; 4. Fate; 5. The hand of fate; 6. Bazaar of the caravans; 7. Entrance of Lalume; 8a. Not since Nineveh; 8b. Not since Nineveh Dance; 9. Stolen Oranges; 10. Baubles, bangles and beads; 11. Paradise garden; 12. Stranger in Paradise; 13. He's in love; 14. Gesticulate; 15. Act One Finale: Fate (reprise). ACT 2: 16. Entr'acte; 17. Nights of my nights; 18. Stranger in Paradise (reprise); 19. Was I Wazir?; 20a. Rahadlakum; 20b. Rahadlakum Dance; 21. And this is my beloved; 22. The poets meet; 23. The Olive Tree; 24. Zubbediya; 25. Samaris' Dance; 26. Act Two Finale: Night of my nights/Sands of time (reprise); 27. Bored (additional item for 1955 film version).
Cpte V. Masterson, D. Maxwell, D. Rendall, R. van Allan, R. Ashe, E. Barham, B. Bottone, B. Hubbard, J. Kaye, Ambrosian Chor, Philh, J.O. Edwards (r1989) *Timbuktu.*
(7/90) (TER) ① [2] **CDTER2 1170**
Cpte Rodne Brown, J. Bassi, D. Egan, M. Hume, S. Ramey, R.A. Swenson, J. Migenes, D. DeLuise, J. Hadley, J. Neal, J. Bingham, J. Long, B. Myers, G. Limansky, M. Patinkin, Ambrosian Sngrs, NY Concert Chorale, LSO, P. Gemignani
(3/92) (SONY) ① **SK46438**
21. I. Garrett, Philh, A. Greenwood (r1990-1)
Concert (11/91) (SILV) ① **SONGCD903**
Song of Norway—musical show based on music of Grieg (1944—New York) (Book M. Lazarus; Lyrics Forrest & Wright)
EXCERPTS: 1a. Prelude. ACT 1: 1b. The Legend; 2a. Nina appears; 2b. Hill of dreams; 3. Entr'acte; 4a. Pillow dance; 4b. Halling; 5. Freddy and his fiddle; 6a. Louisa's entrance; 6b. Now; 7. Strange music; 8. Louisa discovers Grieg; 9. Midsummer's Eve; 10. A song for Nina; 11. March of the Trollds; 12a. Edvard announces bethrothal; 12b. Hymn of betrothal; 13. Louisa changes her mind; 14. Act One Finale. ACT 2: 15. Opening; 16. Bon vivant; 17. Three loves; 18a. Finaletto; 18b. Rikaard's Farewell; 18c. Conclusion; 19. Entr'acte No. 3; 20. Waltz Eternal; 21. Peer Gynt Ballet; 22. Exit of Louisa; 23. I love you; 24. At Christmas time; 25. Christmas postlude; 26. Act Two Finale: Piano Concerto.
Cpte V. Masterson, D. Maxwell, D. Montague, D. Rendall, E. Bainbridge, J. Howard, R. van Allan, Y. Seow, Ambrosian Chor, Philh, J.O. Edwards (r1990)
(1/93) (TER) ① [2] **CDTER2 1173**
Timbuktu—musical show (1978—New York) (reworking of 'Kismet')
EXCERPTS: 1. In the beginning woman; 2. Golden land, golden life; 3. My magic lamp; 4. Power.
1-4. V. Masterson, R. Ashe, E. Barham, B. Bottone, B. Hubbard, Ambrosian Chor, Philh, J.O. Edwards (r1989) *Kismet.* (7/90) (TER) ① [2] **CDTER2 1170**

FÖRSTER, Christoph (Heinrich) (1693–1745) Germany

Sonata à 3—two violins, viol and continuo (Uppsala MS)
Musica Fiata, R. Wilson (r1991) *Concert*
(8/93) (DHM) ① **05472 77183-2**
Sonata à 7—2 cornets, 2 vns, dulcian, va, viol & continuo (Uppsala MS)
Musica Fiata, R. Wilson (r1991) *Concert*
(8/93) (DHM) ① **05472 77183-2**

FORSTER, Emanuel (1748–1823) Germany

Sonata for Oboe and Continuo in C minor (attrib)
P. Dombrecht, W. Kuijken, R. Kohnen *Concert*
(9/86) (ACCE) ① **ACC57804D**

FORTNER, Wolfgang (1907–1987) Germany

Zum Spielen für dem 70 Geburtstag—theme and variations: cello (1975)
P. Demenga (r1993) *Concert*
(8/95) (ECM) ① [2] **445 234-2**

Geh unter, schöne Sonne—Lied (1934) (Wds Hölderlin)
M. Shirai, H. Höll *Concert*
(12/94) (CAPR) ① **10 534**

Die Bluthochzeit—opera: 2 acts (1957) (Lib. after Lorca)
Interlude N German RSO, G. Wand (pp1985)
Concert (1/92) (RCA) ① **RD60827**

FOSS, Lukas (b 1922) USA

Orpheus and Euridice—2 violins and orchestra (1972, rev 1984)
Y. Menuhin, E. Michell, Brooklyn PO, L. Foss *Concert*
(10/89) (NEW) ① **NW375-2**
Renaissance Concerto for Flute and Orchestra
C. Wincene, Brooklyn PO, L. Foss *Concert*
(10/89) (NEW) ① **NW375-2**
Salomon Rossi Suite—orchestra (1975)
Brooklyn PO, L. Foss *Concert*
(10/89) (NEW) ① **NW375-2**

3 American Pieces—violin & piano (1944)
1. Early Song (Andante); 2. Dedication (Lento); 3. Composer's Holiday (Allegro).
I. Perlman, Boston SO, S. Ozawa (orch anon)
Concert (6/95) (EMI) ① **CDC5 55360-2**
Capriccio—cello and piano (1948)
Y. Hanani, M. Levin (r1990) *Concert*
(10/93) (KOCH) ① **37070-2**

Curriculum vitae Tango—accordion (1977)
U. Oppens (arr pf) *Concert*
(5/90) (MUSI) ① **MACD-604**

Song of Songs—soprano and orchestra (1946) (Wds. Bible)
J. Tourel, NYPO, L. Bernstein (r1958) *Concert*
(11/92) (SONY) ① [2] **SM2K47533**

FOSSA, François de (1775–1849) France

3 Trios—guitar, violin and cello, Op. 18 (pub c1826)
1. A; 2. G; 3. F.
1, 2, 3. S. Wynberg, M. Beaver, B. Epperson (r1993)
(3/95) (NAXO) ① **8 550760**

FOSTER, Stephen Collins (1826–1864) USA

Ah! May the red rose live alway—song (pub 1850) (Wds cpsr)
R. Crooks, F. la Forge (r1937) *Concert*
(9/93) (CLAR) ① **CDGSE78-50-50**
2. K. Holvik, NY Met Op Orch, J. Conlon (pp1991)
Concert (6/93) (RCA) ① **09026 61509-2**
Beautiful dreamer—song (pub 1864) (Wds. cpsr)
Glasgow CWS Band, H. Snell (arr Snell) *Concert*
(9/92) (DOYE) ① **DOYCD005**
Come, where my love lies dreaming—4vv a cappella (pub 1855) (Wds. cpsr)
R. Crooks, F. la Forge (r1937) *Concert*
(9/93) (CLAR) ① **CDGSE78-50-50**
If you've only got a moustache—song (pub 1894) (Wds. cpsr)
M. Horne, Martin Katz (pp1994) *Concert*
(1/95) (RCA) ① **09026 62547-2**
Jeanie with the light brown hair—song (1854) (Wds. cpsr)
I. Stern, Columbia SO, M. Katims (arr Harris) *Concert*
(7/90) (SONY) ① **SK45816**
J. Björling, Stockholm Royal Op Orch, N. Grevillius
(r1948) *Concert* (8/92) (BLUE) ① **ABCD016**
J. McCormack, E. Schneider (r1934) *Concert*
(5/93) (MMOI) ① **CDMOIR418**
J. Heifetz, M. Kaye (r1944) *Concert*
(11/94) (RCA) ① [65] **09026 61778-2(19)**

My old Kentucky home, good night!—song
(pub 1853) (Wds. cpsr)
Welbeck Light Qt *Concert*
(10/91) (PEAR) ① **PASTCD9744**
E. Mason, Male Trio, orch, F. Black (r1928) *Concert*
(8/94) (ROMO) ① **81009-2**
R. Ponselle, Male Qt, orch, J. Pasternack (r1925)
Concert (11/94) (ROMO) ① [2] **81006-2**
Old folks at home—song (pub 1851) (Wds.
cpsr)
N. Melba, orch, W.B. Rogers (r1913) *Concert*
(3/89) (LARR) ① **CDLRH221**
I. Perlman, S. Sanders (trans. Heifetz) *Concert*
(12/89) (EMI) ① **CDC7 49604-2**
A. Patti, L. Ronald (r1905) *Concert*
(4/90) (PEAR) ① **GEMMCD9312**
I. Perlman, S. Sanders (r1988: arr Heifetz) *Concert*
(5/93) (EMI) ① [4] **CMS7 64617-2**
F. Kreisler, C. Lamson (r1928: arr Kreisler) *Concert*
(12/93) (BIDD) ① **LAB080**
A. Galli-Curci, orch, J. Pasternack (r1922) *Concert*
(3/89) (LARR) ① [2] **81004-2**
R. Ponselle, orch, J. Pasternack (r1925: 2 vers)
Concert (11/94) (ROMO) ① [2] **81006-2**
J. Heifetz, M. Kaye (r1944) *Concert*
(11/94) (RCA) ① [65] **09026 61778-2(19)**
N. Melba, orch, W.B. Rogers (r1913) *Concert*
(5/95) (ROMO) ① [3] **81011-2(2)**
I. Perlman, S. Sanders (r1988: arr vn/pf: Heifetz)
Concert (6/95) (EMI) ① [20] **CZS4 83177-2(3)**

FOUCART, Jacques *(d 1640)*
France/Denmark

SECTION II: CHAMBER

3 Courentes
Dowland Consort, J. Lindberg (lte/dir) *Concert*
(2/89) (BIS) ① **BIS-CD390**

FOULDS, John *(1880–1939)*
England

SECTION I: ORCHESTRAL

April - England—orchestra, Op. 48/1 (1926
orch 1932)
LPO, B. Wordsworth *Concert*
(5/93) (LYRI) ① **SRCD212**
Le Cabaret—overture to a French comedy,
Op. 72a (1921)
LPO, B. Wordsworth *Concert*
(5/93) (LYRI) ① **SRCD212**
Dynamic Triptych—piano and orchestra, Op.
88 (1929)
H. Shelley, RPO, V. Handley *Vaughan Williams:*
Piano Concerto. (3/93) (LYRI) ① **SRCD211**
Hellas, a suite of ancient Greece—orchestra,
Op. 45 (1932)
LPO, B. Wordsworth *Concert*
(5/93) (LYRI) ① **SRCD212**
3 Mantras—orchestra, Op. 61b
1. Mantra of activity; 2. Mantra of bliss; 3. Mantra of
will.
LPO, B. Wordsworth *Concert*
(5/93) (LYRI) ① **SRCD212**
Pasquinade Symphonique No. 2—orchestra,
Op. 98 (1935)
LPO, B. Wordsworth *Concert*
(5/93) (LYRI) ① **SRCD212**

SECTION II: CHAMBER

Aquarelles (Music Pictures group 2)—string
quartet, Op. 32 (1914)
Endellion Qt *Concert*
(1/88) (PEAR) ① **SHECD9564**
String Quartet No. 9 (Quartetto intimo), Op.
89 (1931)
Endellion Qt *Concert*
(1/88) (PEAR) ① **SHECD9564**
String Quartet No. 10, 'Quartetto geniale',
Op. 97 (1931)
Lento quieto Endellion Qt *Concert*
(1/88) (PEAR) ① **SHECD9564**

FRACKENPOHL, Arthur R. *(b*
1924) USA

SECTION II: CHAMBER

Pop Suite—tuba quartet
Finale British Tuba Qt (pp1991) *Concert*
(8/92) (POLY) ① **QPRL049D**

FRANÇAIX, Jean *(b 1912)*
France

SECTION I: ORCHESTRAL

Concerto for Two Pianos and Orchestra
(1965)
J. Françaix, C. Françaix, South-West German RSO,
P. Stoll *Concert* (1/92) (WERG) ① **WER6087-2**
L' Horloge de flore—suite: oboe and
orchestra (1961)
J. de Lancie, LSO, A. Previn (r1966) *Concert*
(12/91) (RCA) ① **GD87989**
J. Anderson, Philh, S. Wright *Concert*
(12/92) (NIMB) ① **NI5330**
Piano Concertino (1932)
I. Hobson, Illinois Sinfonia da Camera *Concert*
(1/88) (ARAB) ① **Z6541**
Piano Concerto (1936)
I. Hobson, Illinois Sinfonia da Camera *Concert*
(1/88) (ARAB) ① **Z6541**
Variations sur un thème plaisant (1976)
J. Françaix, Mainz Wind Ens, K.R. Schöll *Concert*
(1/92) (WERG) ① **WER6087-2**

SECTION II: CHAMBER

Canon à l'octave—horn and piano (1953)
B. Tuckwell, D. Blumenthal *Concert*
(11/92) (ETCE) ① **KTC1135**
Danses exotiques—wind instruments and
percussion (1982)
Mainz Wind Ens *Concert*
(9/89) (WERG) ① **WER60143-50**
Divertissement—oboe, clarinet and bassoon
(1947)
Aulos Wind Qnt *Concert*
(10/89) (SCHW) ① **310022**
Hommage à l'ami Papageno—piano and 10
wind instruments (1984)
J. Françaix, Mainz Wind Ens *Concert*
(9/89) (WERG) ① **WER60143-50**
Mozart new-look (fantasy after Don
Giovanni's Serenade)—wind instruments
and double-bass (1984)
Mainz Wind Ens *Concert*
(9/89) (WERG) ① **WER60143-50**
Musique pour une faire plaisir—piano and
wind instruments (1984)
J. Françaix, Mainz Wind Ens *Concert*
(9/89) (WERG) ① **WER60143-50**
Piano Trio—violin, cello and piano (1986)
J. Heifetz, J. de Pasquale, G. Piatigorsky (r1964)
Concert (11/94) (RCA) ① [65] **09026 61778-2(43)**
Quartet—cor anglais, violin, viola, cello
(1970)
Marwood Ens (r1994) *Concert*
(4/95) (COLL) ① **Coll1438-2**
Quartet for wind instruments—flute, oboe,
clarinet and bassoon (1933)
Aulos Wind Qnt *Concert*
(10/89) (SCHW) ① **310022**
Selandia Ens *Concert* (9/90) (KONT) ① **32032**
Quasi improvvisando—11 wind instruments
(1975)
Mainz Wind Ens *Concert*
(9/89) (WERG) ① **WER60143-50**
Quintette—flute, oboe, clarinet, horn &
bassoon (1948)
Reykjavik Wind Qnt (r1993) *Concert*
(10/95) (CHAN) ① **CHAN9362**
Sonatine—trumpet and piano (1950)
H. Hardenberger, R. Pöntinen *Concert*
(11/85) (BIS) ① **BIS-CD287**
J. Wallace, S. Wright (r1991) *Concert*
(11/94) (EMI) ① **CDC5 55086-2**
Sonatine for violin and piano (1934)
F.P. Zimmermann, A. Lonquich (r1991) *Concert*
(1/95) (EMI) ① **CDC7 54541-2**
String Trio—violin, viola, cello (1933)
Marwood Ens (r1994) *Concert*
(4/95) (COLL) ① **Coll1438-2**
Tema con variazioni—clarinet and piano
J. Cohler, J. Gordon (r1993) *Concert*
(5/95) (CRYS) ① **Crystal CD733**
R. Samuels, F. Renzi (r1993) *Concert*
(7/95) (KOCH) ① **37186-2**
Trio in C—violin, viola and cello (1933)
J. Heifetz, J. de Pasquale, G. Piatigorsky *Concert*
(9/90) (RCA) ① **GD87872**
11 Variations sur un thème de Haydn—wind
instruments and double-bass (1984)
Mainz Wind Ens *Concert*
(9/89) (WERG) ① **WER60143-50**

Wind Quintet No. 1—flute, oboe, clarinet,
horn and bassoon (1948)
Aulos Wind Qnt *Concert*
(10/89) (SCHW) ① **310022**
Vienna/Berlin Ens *Concert*
(11/92) (SONY) ① **SK48052**
Pro Arte Wind Quintet *Concert*
(1/93) (NIMB) ① **NI5327**
Berlin Phil Wind Qnt *Concert*
(4/93) (BIS) ① **BIS-CD536**
London Haffner Wnd Ens (r1994) *Concert*
(4/95) (COLL) ① **Coll1438-2**
Wind Quintet No. 2—flute, oboe, clarinet,
horn and bassoon (1987)
Aulos Wind Qnt *Concert*
(10/89) (SCHW) ① **310022**
London Haffner Wnd Ens (r1994) *Concert*
(4/95) (COLL) ① **Coll1438-2**

SECTION III: INSTRUMENTAL

5 Portraits de jeunes filles (1936)
J. Françaix *Concert* (1/92) (WERG) ① **WER6087-2**

FRANCÉS DE IRIBARREN, Juan
(1698–1767) Spain

SECTION IV: VOCAL AND CHORAL

Quién nos dirá de una flor—carol to the
Blessed Sacrament: 4vv & violins (1740)
Al Ayre Español, E. L. Banzo (r1994) *Concert*
(8/95) (DHM) ① **05472 77325-2**
Viendo que Jil, hizo raya—Christmas ballad:
6vv & instruments (1745)
Al Ayre Español, E. L. Banzo (r1994) *Concert*
(8/95) (DHM) ① **05472 77325-2**

FRANCESCHINI, Petronio
(c1650–1680) Italy

SECTION I: ORCHESTRAL

Sonata for Two Trumpets, Strings and
Continuo in D
S. Keavy, C. Steele-Perkins, Parley of Instr *Concert*
(1/89) (HYPE) ① **CDA66255**
H. Läubin, W. Läubin, ECO, S. Preston (hpd/dir)
Concert (12/91) (DG) ① **431 817-2GH**
St James's Baroque Plyrs, I. Bolton (r1988) *Concert*
(9/93) (TELD) ① **4509-91192-2**
H. Hardenberger, I Musici (r1993) *Concert*
(5/95) (PHIL) ① **442 131-2PH**

FRANCHETTI, (Baron) Alberto
(1860–1942) Italy

SECTION V: STAGE WORKS

Cristoforo Colombo—opera: 3 acts and
epilogue (1892—Genoa) (Lib. L. Illica)
EXCERPTS: 1. Aman lassù le stelle; 2. Dunque ho
sognato?.
Cpte R. Bruson, R. Scandiuzzi, R. Ragatzu, M. Berti,
G. Pasino, V. Ombuena, A. Ulbrich, E. Turco, P.
Lefebvre, F. Previati, D. Jenis, Hungarian Rad Chor,
Frankfurt RSO, M. Viotti (pp1991)
(7/92) (SCHW) ① [3] **310302**
1. T. Ruffo, orch (r1914) *Concert*
(2/93) (PREI) ① [3] **89303(1)**
2. T. Ruffo, orch (r1921) *Concert*
(2/93) (PREI) ① [3] **89303(2)**
3. E. Giraldoni, anon (r1902) *Concert*
(6/90) (SYMP) ① **SYMCD1073**
La figlia di Iorio—opera (1906—Milan) (Lib.
after d'Annunzio)
Che c'è egli? G. Zenatello, E. Giraldoni, anon
(r1906) *Concert*
(4/94) (EMI) ① [3] **CHS7 64860-2(2)**
Che c'è egli?; Rinverdisca per noi G. Zenatello, E.
Giraldoni, anon (r1906) *Concert*
(5/94) (PEAR) ① [4] **GEMMCDS9073(1)**
Che c'è egli?; Rinverdisca per noi G. Zenatello, E.
Giraldoni, anon (r1906) *Concert*
(5/94) (SYMP) ① **SYMCD1168**
Germania—opera: prologue, 2 scenes and
epilogue (1902—Milan) (Lib. Illica)
EXCERPTS: PROLOGUE: 1. Studenti udite. ACT 1:
2. Non, non chiuder gli occhi vaghi.
1, 2. E. Caruso, S. Cottone (r1902) *Concert*
(5/89) (EMI) ① **CDH7 61046-2**
1, 2. E. Caruso, S. Cottone (r1902) *Concert*
(12/90) (PEAR) ① [3] **EVC1(1)**
1, 2. E. Caruso, orch (r1910) *Concert*
(3/91) (PEAR) ① [3] **EVC2**
1, 2. E. Caruso, S. Cottone (r1902) *Concert*
(7/91) (RCA) ① [12] **GD60495(1)**

1, 2. E. Caruso, orch (r1910) *Concert*
(7/91) (RCA) ① [12] **GD60495(3)**
1, 2. G. Zenatello, orch (r1910) *Concert*
(5/94) (PEAR) ① [4] **GEMMCDS9073(2)**
1, 2. G. Zenatello, orch (r1910) *Concert*
(5/94) (SYMP) ① **SYMCD1168**
2. E. Caruso, anon (r1903) *Concert*
(12/90) (PEAR) ① [3] **EVC1(1)**
2. E. Caruso, anon (r1903) *Concert*
(7/91) (RCA) ① [12] **GD60495(1)**
2. E. Caruso, S. Cottone (r1902) *Concert*
(4/94) (EMI) ① [3] **CHS7 64860-2(2)**
3. A. Pinto, S. Cottone (r1902) *Concert*
(4/94) (EMI) ① [3] **CHS7 64860-2(2)**
4. M. Sammarco, anon (r1902) *Concert*
(7/92) (PEAR) ① [3] **GEMMCDS9924(2)**
4. M. Sammarco, anon (r1902) *Concert*
(4/94) (EMI) ① [3] **CHS7 64860-2(2)**
5. A. Pinto, anon (r1902) *Concert*
(8/93) (SYMP) ① **SYMCD1111**

FRANCHOMME, Auguste (Joseph) (1808–1884) France

SECTION II: CHAMBER

Air auvergnat varié in A minor—cello and piano, Op. 26
A. Bylsma, Archibudelli, Smithsonian Chbr Plyrs
(r1993) *Concert* (4/95) (SONY) ① **SK53980**
Air russe varié No. 2 in D minor—cello and strings, Op. 32
A. Bylsma, Archibudelli, Smithsonian Chbr Plyrs
(r1993) *Concert* (4/95) (SONY) ① **SK53980**
12 Caprices—two cellos, Op. 7
2. E minor; 4. A minor; 7. C.
2, 4, 7. A. Bylsma, K. Slowik (r1993) *Concert*
(4/95) (SONY) ① **SK53980**
Grande valse—morceau de concert: cello and strings, Op.34
A. Bylsma, Archibudelli, Smithsonian Chbr Plyrs
(r1993) *Concert* (4/95) (SONY) ① **SK53980**
Nocturne—cello and piano (trans of Chopin
Nocturnes Op 15/1 & Op 37/1)
A. Bylsma, L. Orkis (r1993) *Concert*
(4/95) (SONY) ① **SK53980**
3 Nocturnes—cello and piano, Op. 15
3. A flat minor.
A. Bylsma, L. Orkis (r1993) *Concert*
(4/95) (SONY) ① **SK53980**

FRANCISQUE, Anthoine (c1575–1605) France

SECTION III: INSTRUMENTAL

Treasure of Orpheus—lute (1600)
1. Courante; 2. Pavane and Bransles.
S. McDonald (hp) *Concert*
(10/84) (DELO) ① **DE3005**

FRANCK, César (-Auguste-Jean-Guillaume-Hubert) (1822–1890) Belgium/France

SECTION I: ORCHESTRAL

Ce qu'on entend sur la montagne—symphonic poem (c1845–47)
RTBF SO, B. Priestman *Organiste I.*
(2/89) (SCHW) ① **311105**
Le Chasseur maudit, '(The) Accursed Huntsman'—symphonic poem based on ballad by Burger (1882)
Cincinnati SO, J. López-Cobos *Symphony.*
(3/91) (TELA) ① **CD80247**
Paris Orch, D. Barenboim *Concert*
(1/93) (DG) ① [2] **437 244-2GGA2**
Philadelphia, R. Muti (r1981) *Concert*
(9/93) (EMI) ① **CDM7 64747-2**
Belgian Nat Orch, A. Cluytens (r1962) *Concert*
(11/94) (EMI) ① [2] **CZS5 68220-2**
BBC Nat Orch of Wales, T. Otaka (r1994) *Psyché.*
(6/95) (CHAN) ① **CHAN9342**
Concerto for Piano and Orchestra No. 2 in B minor, Op. 11 (first series) (c1835)
J-C. Vanden Eynden, RTBF New SO, E. Doneux
Auber Variations. (3/90) (SCHW) ① **311111**
Les Djinns—symphonic poem: piano and orchestra (1884)
L. Parham, RPO, J-C. Casadesus (r1993) *Concert*
(7/94) (RPO) ① **CDRPO7023**
Les Eolides—symphonic poem (1875–76)
NYPO, K. Masur *Symphony.*
(5/93) (TELD) ① **9031-74863-2**

Psyché—symphonic poem with chorus (1887–88)
1. Sommeil de Psyché; 2. Psyché enlevée par les
zéphirs; 3. Le jardin d'Éros; 4. Psyché et Éros.
Lyon Nat Orch, E. Krivine (r1992) *Symphony.*
(7/93) (DENO) ① **CO-75199**
Belgian Rad & TV Chor, Liège Orch, P. Strauss
(r1974) (5/95) (EMI) ① **CDM5 65162-2**
BBC Welsh Chor, BBC Nat Orch of Wales, T. Otaka
(r1994) *Chasseur maudit.*
(6/95) (CHAN) ① **CHAN9342**
4. Concertgebouw, W. Mengelberg (r1937/8) *Concert*
(12/91) (ARHI) ① **ADCD107**
4. NBC SO, A. Toscanini (r1952) *Concert*
(11/92) (RCA) ① **GD60322**
4. Philh, C.M. Giulini (r1958) *Concert*
(9/93) (EMI) ① [2] **CZS7 67723-2**
4. BPO, C.M. Giulini (1986) *Symphony.*
(8/94) (DG) ① **439 523-2GGA**
Symphonic Variations—piano and orchestra (1885)
A. Rubinstein, Sym of the Air, A. Wallenstein *Concert*
(10/87) (RCA) ① **RD85666**
R. Firkušný, RPO, C.P. Flor (r1989) *Symphony.*
(8/90) (RCA) ① **RD60146**
P. Rogé, London Fest Orch, R. Pople *Concert*
(11/91) (ASV) ① **CDDCA769**
C. Curzon, LPO, A. Boult *Concert*
(1/92) (DECC) ① **433 628-2DSP**
A. Rubinstein, Sym of the Air, A. Wallenstein (r1958)
Concert (4/93) (RCA) ① **09026 61496-2**
M. Dalberto, Philh, J-B. Pommier (1992) *Concert*
(6/93) (DENO) ① **CO-75258**
A. Weissenberg, BPO, H. von Karajan (1972)
Concert (9/93) (EMI) ① **CDM7 64747-2**
M. Hess, CBO, B. Cameron (r1941) *Concert*
(2/94) (DUTT) ① **CDLX7005**
L. Parham, RPO, J-C. Casadesus (r1993) *Concert*
(7/94) (RPO) ① **CDRPO7023**
P. Entremont, FRNO, J. Martinon *Concert*
(8/94) (ERAT) ① **4509-92871-2**
A. Rubinstein, Sym of the Air, A. Wallenstein (r1958)
Concert (8/94) (RCA) ① **09026 61863-2**
F-J. Thiollier, Ireland National SO, A. de Almeida
(r1993) *Concert* (1/95) (NAXO) ① **8 550754**
P. Crossley, VPO, C. M. Giulini (r1993) *Symphony.*
(3/95) (SONY) ① **SK58958**
C. Curzon, LPO, A. Boult (r1955) *Concert*
(4/95) (DECC) ① **425 082-2DCS**
Symphony in D minor (1886–8)
FNO, C. Munch (pp1967) *Concert*
(11/88) (MONT) ① **MUN2031**
Chicago SO, P. Monteux *Concert*
(3/89) (RCA) ① **GD86805**
NBC SO, A. Toscanini (bp1946) *Concert*
(6/90) (DELL) ① **CDDA9021**
RPO, C.P. Flor (r1988) *Symphonic Variations.*
(8/90) (RCA) ① **RD60146**
Philh, F. d'Avalos *Chausson: Symphony, Op. 20.*
(8/90) (ASV) ① **CDDCA708**
Cincinnati SO, J. López-Cobos *Chasseur maudit.*
(3/91) (TELA) ① **CD80247**
Montreal SO, C. Dutoit *Indy: Symphonie, Op. 25.*
(1/92) (DECC) ① **430 278-2DH**
FRNO, T. Beecham *Lalo: Symphony in G minor.*
(9/92) (EMI) ① **CDM7 63396-2**
NBC SO, A. Toscanini (bp1940/46) *Saint-Saëns:
Symphony 3.* (11/92) (RCA) ① **GD60320**
NYPO, L. Bernstein *Concert*
(5/93) (SONY) ① **SMK47548**
NYPO, K. Masur *Eolides.*
(5/93) (TELD) ① **9031-74863-2**
Lyon Nat Orch, E. Krivine (r1992) *Psyché.*
(7/93) (DENO) ① **CO-75199**
Paris Orch, H. von Karajan (r1969) *Concert*
(9/93) (EMI) ① **CDM7 64747-2**
Philh, C.M. Giulini (r1957) *Concert*
(9/93) (EMI) ① [2] **CZS7 67723-2**
LPO, T. Beecham (r1940) *Concert*
(7/94) (PEAR) ① **GEMMCD9065**
Boston SO, S. Ozawa *Poulenc: Organ Concerto.*
(7/94) (DG) ① **437 827-2GH**
FRNO, J. Martinon *Concert*
(8/94) (ERAT) ① **4509-92871-2**
BPO, C.M. Giulini (1986) *Psyché.*
(8/94) (DG) ① **439 523-2GGA**
Chicago SO, P. Monteux (r1961) *Concert*
(9/94) (RCA) ① [15] **09026 61893-2**
NBC SO, G. Cantelli (r1954) *Concert*
(11/94) (EMI) ① **CZS5 68217-2**
LPO, T. Beecham (r1940) *Concert*
(3/95) (DUTT) ① [2] **2CDAX2003**
VPO, C. M. Giulini (pp1993) *Symphonic Variations.*
(3/95) (SONY) ① **SK58958**
Philadelphia, L. Stokowski (r1935) *Concert*
(8/95) (BIDD) ① **WHL011**

FNO, L. Bernstein (pp1981) *Roussel: Symphony 3.*
(10/95) (DG) ① **445 512-2GMA**
Variations Brillantes sur la Ronde Favorite de Gustave III (Auber)—piano and orchestra, Op. 8 (first version) (1834–45)
J-C. Vanden Eynden, RTBF New SO, E. Doneux
Piano Concerto. (3/90) (SCHW) ① **311111**

SECTION II: CHAMBER

Andantino quietoso in E flat—violin and piano, Op. 6 (1843)
M. Sarbu, M. Sirbu *Concert*
(9/92) (DYNA) ① [2] **CDS21/2**
Duo in B flat on motives from Dalayrac's 'Gulistan'—violin and piano, Op. 14 (1844)
M. Sarbu, M. Sirbu *Concert*
(9/92) (DYNA) ① [2] **CDS21/2**
Duo sur 'God Save the King'—piano duet, Op. 4 (1842)
A. Goldstone, C. Clemmow (1988) *Concert*
(4/89) (SYMP) ① **SYMCD1037**
Piano Quintet in F minor (1878-79)
A. Cortot, International Qt (r1927) *Concert*
(11/91) (BIDD) ① **LAB029**
P. Rogé, R. Friedman, S. Smith, C. Wellington, R.
Pople *Concert* (11/91) (ASV) ① **CDDCA769**
G. Tacchino, Athenaeum-Enescu Qt *Chausson:
String Quartet, Op. 35.*
(12/92) (PIER) ① **PV792032**
J. Heifetz, I. Baker, W. Primrose, G. Piatigorsky, L.
Pennario (r1961) *Concert*
(9/86) (ETCE) ① **KTC1038**
Sonata for Violin and Piano in A (1886)
1. Allegretto ben moderato; 2. Allegro; 3.
Recitativo—Fantasia; 4. Allegretto poco mosso.
R. Ricci, M. Argerich *Concert*
(9/86) (ETCE) ① **KTC1038**
K-W. Chung, R. Lupu *Concert*
(1/89) (DECC) ① **421 154-2DM**
J. Thibaud, A. Cortot (r1929) *Concert*
(7/89) (EMI) ① **CDH7 63032-2**
C. Boulier, M. Dedieu-Vidal *Lekeu: Violin Sonata in
G.* (8/89) (REM) ① **REM311059**
J. Suk, J. Panenka *Concert*
(5/90) (SUPR) ① **11 0710-2**
J. Du Pré, D. Barenboim (r1971/2: trans vc/pf)
Chopin: Cello Sonata.
(6/90) (EMI) ① **CDM7 63184-2**
A. Grumiaux, G. Sebok *Concert*
(7/90) (PHIL) ① **426 384-2PC**
J. Heifetz, A. Rubinstein (r1937) *Concert*
(1/91) (BIDD) ① **LAB031**
M. Maisky, M. Argerich (arr vc/pf) *Concert*
(2/91) (EMI) ① **CDM7 63577-2**
K. Danczowska, K. Zimerman (r1980) *Concert*
(8/91) (DG) ① **431 469-2GGA**
R. Pople, P. Rogé (trans vc/pf) *Concert*
(11/91) (ASV) ① **CDDCA769**
R. Cohen, R. Vignoles (trans vc/pf) *Concert*
(1/92) (CRD) ① **CRD3391**
M. Sarbu, M. Sirbu *Concert*
(9/92) (DYNA) ① [2] **CDS21/2**
I. Perlman, Vladimir Ashkenazy *Concert*
(9/92) (DECC) ① **433 695-2DM**
N. Imai, R. Vignoles (r1992: trans vc/pf) *Concert*
(9/92) (CHAN) ① **CHAN8873**
M-A. Nicolas, B. Petrov *Fauré: Violin Sonata 1.*
(10/92) (AUVI) ① **V4656**
L. Mordkovitch, M. Gusak-Grin *Concert*
(4/93) (CHAN) ① **CHAN9109**
J. Du Pré, D. Barenboim (r1971: trans vc/pf) *Concert*
(8/94) (EMI) ① **CZS5 68132-2**
O. Harnoy, C. Katsaris (r1992: trans vc/pf) *Chopin:
Cello Sonata.* (10/94) (RCA) ① **09026 61818-2**
J. Heifetz, B. Smith (r1972) *Concert*
(11/94) (RCA) ① [65] **09026 61778-2(46)**
J. Heifetz, A. Rubinstein (r1937) *Concert*
(11/94) (RCA) ① [65] **09026 61778-2(18)**
P. Zukerman, M. Neikrug (1993) *Concert*
(5/95) (RCA) ① **09026 62697-2**
A. Dumay, M-J. Pires (1993) *Concert*
(10/95) (DG) ① **445 880-2GH**
J. Suk, J. Hála (r1994) *Concert*
(9/95) (DINT) ① **DICD920306**
Trio concertant No. 4 in B minor—violin, cello and piano, Op. 42 (1842) (original finale
to Trio, Op 1/3)
M. Sarbu, R. Colan, M. Dancila *Concert*
(9/92) (DYNA) ① [2] **CDS21/2**
3 Trios Concertants—violin, cello and piano, Op. 1 (1839-42)
1. F sharp minor; 2. B flat (Trio de Salon); 3. B minor.
M. Sarbu, M. Sirbu, M. Dancila *Concert*
(9/92) (DYNA) ① [2] **CDS21/2**

SECTION III: INSTRUMENTAL

Andantino in G minor—organ (?1858)
C. Walsh *Concert* (3/90) (PRIO) ① PRCD281
Chorales—organ (1890)
1. E; 2. B minor; 3. A minor.
F-H. Houbart (r1984) *Concert*
(3/87) (PIER) ① PV785031
M. Murray *Concert* (7/90) (TELA) ① [2] CD80234
W. Rübsam *Concert*
(7/91) (BAYE) ① [3] BR100091/3
J-P. Lecaudey (7/91) (SCHW) ① 315018
P. Hurford (r1983) *Concert*
(10/95) (DECC) ① 444 568-2DM
1. M. Howard *Concert*
(6/90) (HERA) ① HAVPCD125
1. N. Hakim *Concert* (7/91) (PRIO) ① PRCD327
2. J. Bate *Concert* (4/85) (UNIC) ① DKPCD9014
2. John Scott *Concert* (12/87) (CIRR) ① CICD1007
2. M. Murray *Concert* (3/89) (TELA) ① CD80169
2. J.V. Michalko *Concert*
(6/90) (OPUS) ① 9351 2130
2, 3. P. Kee *Concert* (9/91) (CHAN) ① CHAN8891
3. J. Bate *Concert* (9/85) (UNIC) ① DKPCD9030
3. D. Hill *Concert* (9/86) (CARL) ① PCD823
3. C. Walsh *Concert* (3/90) (PRIO) ① PRCD281
3. H. Musch *Concert* (7/91) (CHRI) ① CD74606
3. J-G. Proulx *Concert*
(8/91) (REM) ① REM311078
3. P. Hurford *Concert*
(8/91) (DECC) ① 430 710-2DM
3. Andrew Lucas (r1994) *Concert*
(11/94) (NAXO) ① 8 550955
3. P. Crossley (r1993: trans pf: P Crossley) *Concert*
(2/95) (SONY) ① SK58914
Cinq Pièces—harmonium (c1858)
1. Offertoire; 2. Petit Offertoire; 3. Verset I in F minor;
4. Verset II in F minor; 5. Communion.
A. Sacchetti *Concert* (3/92) (EURM) ① [4] 350224
Danse lente—piano (1885)
R. Silverman *Concert* (6/94) (CBC) ① MVCD1061
P. Crossley (r1993)
(2/95) (SONY) ① SK58914
Fantaisie idylle—organ (1878)
F-H. Houbart (r1984) *Concert*
(3/87) (PIER) ① PV785031
Fantaisie in A—organ (1884)
M. Murray *Concert* (3/85) (TELA) ① CD80096
J. Bate *Concert* (4/85) (UNIC) ① DKPCD9014
M. Howard *Concert* (6/90) (HERA) ① HAVPCD125
M. Murray *Concert* (7/90) (TELA) ① [2] CD80234
J. Watts *Concert* (9/90) (PRIO) ① PRCD286
W. Rübsam *Concert*
(7/91) (BAYE) ① [3] BR100091/3
P. Kee *Concert* (10/93) (CHAN) ① CHAN9188
Fantaisie in C—organ, Op. 16 (1860-62)
M. Howard *Concert* (6/90) (HERA) ① HAVPCD125
M. Murray *Concert* (7/90) (TELA) ① [2] CD80234
W. Rübsam *Concert*
(7/91) (BAYE) ① [3] BR100091/3
Final in B flat—organ, Op. 21 (1860-62)
J. Bate *Concert* (9/85) (UNIC) ① DKPCD9030
M. Murray *Concert* (7/90) (TELA) ① [2] CD80234
W. Rübsam *Concert*
(7/91) (BAYE) ① [3] BR100091/3
**Grande pièce symphonique in F sharp
minor—organ, Op. 17 (1860-62)**
J. Bate *Concert* (4/85) (UNIC) ① DKPCD9014
M. Murray *Concert* (7/90) (TELA) ① [2] CD80234
W. Rübsam *Concert*
(7/91) (BAYE) ① [3] BR100091/3
Andante Philadelphia, L. Stokowski (r1937: arr orch:
O'Connell) *Concert* (8/95) (BIDD) ① WHL011
**Offertoire sur un air bréton—harmonium
(1871)**
A. Sacchetti *Concert* (3/92) (EURM) ① [4] 350224
**L' Organiste, Volume 1—63 pieces for organ
or harmonium (1889)**
1. Poco allegretto; 2. Andantino; 3. Poco lento; 4.
Maestoso; 5. Poco lento; 6. Poco allegro - Amen
moderato; 7. Offertoire in C; 8. Andante; 9.
Andantino; 10. Poco andantino; 11. Poco allegro; 12.
Lento; 13. Andantino poco mosso - Amen; 14.
Andante; 15. Quasi allegro; 16. Chant de la Creuse;
17. Quasi andante; 18. Vieux Noël; Andantino; 19.
Maestoso; 20. Vieux Noël: Maestoso; 21. Sortie or
Offertoire in D - Amen; 22. Andantino poco allegretto;
23. Quasi lento; 24. Molto moderato; 25. Allegretto;
26. Poco allegro; 27. Andantino - Amen; 28.
Offertoire in E flat; 29. Andante quasi allegretto; 30.
Moderato; 31. Prière; 32. Non troppo lento; 33.
Allegretto; 34. Poco allegro - Amen; 35. Offertoire
or Communion in E minor; 36. Allegretto; 37.
Andantino; 38. Lento - Amen; 42. Sortie in F; 43. Air
béarnais; 44. Chant béarnais; 45. Andantino; 46.

Poco lento; 47. Poco allegro; 48. Poco allegretto -
Amen; 49. Offertoire funèbre in F minor; 50. Poco
allegretto; 51. Vieux Noël: Poco lento; 52. Noël
angévin: Allegretto; 53. Quasi lento; 54. Noël
angévin: Quasi allegro; 55. Allegretto vivo - Amen;
56. Sortie in G; 57. Poco maestoso; 58. Allegretto
amabile; 59. Andantino; 60. Andantino; 61. Lento; 62.
Andantino quasi allegretto; 63. Poco maestoso.
A. Sacchetti *Concert* (3/92) (EURM) ① [4] 350224
5, 8, 16, 18, 19, 22, 24, 31, 43, 52. RTBF SO, A.
Walter (orch Büsser) *Ce qu'on entend sur la
montagne.* (2/89) (SCHW) ① 311105
16, 18, 20, 39, 43, 44, 51, 52, 54. R. Silverman (pf)
Concert (6/94) (CBC) ① MVCD1061
**L' Organiste, Volume 2—44 pieces for organ
or harmonium (1858-63)**
1. Offertoire I in F minor; 2. Offertoire in C minor; 3.
Elevation in A; 4. Magnificat in D; 5. Grand Choeur I
in D; 6. Andantino in D; 7. Quasi marcia in D minor;
8. Allegretto I in D; 9. Grand Choeur II in D; 10. Amen
in D; 11. Gloria Patri in D; 12. Offertoire in A; 13.
Quasi lento in F; 14. Allegretto in C minor; 15.
Andantino in C; 16. Allegretto in D minor; 17.
Allegretto II in D; 18. Magnificat I in E flat; 19.
Magnificat II in E flat; 20. Grand Choeur in E flat; 21.
Moderato in E flat; 22. Andantino I in E flat; 23.
Allegretto in E flat; 24. Gloria Patri I in E flat; 25.
Gloria Patri II in E flat; 26. Amen in E flat; 27. Gloria
Patri III in E flat; 28. Prélude pour l'Ave Maris Stella I
in D minor; 29. Prélude pour l'Ave Maris Stella in D;
30. Prélude pour l'Ave Maris Stella II in D minor; 31.
Benedicamus in C; 32. Lento in D minor; 33.
Andantino II in E flat; 34. Kyrie de la Messe de Noël
in C minor; 35. Moderato I in C minor; 36. Moderato II
in C minor; 37. Grand Choeur in C minor; 38. Grand
Choeur in C; 39. Offertoire pour la Messe de minuit in
D minor; 40. Offertoire in G minor; 41. Sortie in D; 42.
Offertoire II in F minor; 43. Allegro moderato in E flat;
44. Offertoire in B.
A. Sacchetti *Concert* (3/92) (EURM) ① [4] 350224
39. M. Howard *Concert*
(6/90) (HERA) ① HAVPCD125
Pastorale in E—organ, Op. 19 (1860-62)
M. Murray *Concert* (3/85) (TELA) ① CD80096
J. Bate *Concert* (9/85) (UNIC) ① DKPCD9030
M. Howard *Concert* (6/90) (HERA) ① HAVPCD125
M. Murray *Concert* (7/90) (TELA) ① [2] CD80234
W. Rübsam *Concert*
(7/91) (BAYE) ① [3] BR100091/3
P. Hurford *Concert*
(10/95) (DECC) ① 444 568-2DM
J.V. Michalko *Concert*
(6/90) (OPUS) ① 9351 2130
Petit Offertoire in E—harmonium (c1858)
P. Kee (arr Vierne) *Concert*
(9/91) (CHAN) ① CHAN8891
3 Pièces—organ (1878)
1. Fantaisie in C; 2. Cantabile in B; 3. Pièce héroïque in B
minor.
2. H. Musch *Concert* (7/91) (CHRI) ① CD74606
2, 3. M. Murray *Concert*
(7/90) (TELA) ① [2] CD80234
2, 3. W. Rübsam *Concert*
(7/91) (BAYE) ① [3] BR100091/3
2, 3. P. Kee *Concert* (9/91) (CHAN) ① CHAN8891
3. F-H. Houbart (r1984) *Concert*
(3/87) (PIER) ① PV785031
3. J.V. Michalko *Concert*
(6/90) (OPUS) ① 9351 2130
3. D. Flood *Concert* (4/91) (YORK) ① CD108
3. San Francisco SO, P. Monteux (r1941: orch
O'Connell) *Concert*
(9/94) (RCA) ① [15] 09026 61893-2
3. P. Hurford *Concert* (1982) *Concert*
(10/95) (DECC) ① 444 568-2DM
Les plaintes d'une poupée—piano (1865)
R. Silverman *Concert* (6/94) (CBC) ① MVCD1061
Prélude, aria et final—piano (1886-87)
R. Silverman *Concert* (6/94) (CBC) ① MVCD1061
P. Crossley (r1993) *Concert*
(2/95) (SONY) ① SK58914
Prélude, choral et fugue—piano (1884)
C. Smith, P. Sellick (arr Odom) *Concert*
(9/89) (NIMB) ① NI5178
M. Perahia *Concert* (10/91) (SONY) ① SK47180
J. Bolet (1988) *Concert*
(4/94) (DECC) ① 436 648-2DH
R. Silverman *Concert* (6/94) (CBC) ① MVCD1061
P. Devoyon *Concert*
(8/94) (ERAT) ① 4509-92871-2
P. Crossley (r1993) *Concert*
(2/95) (SONY) ① SK58914
G. Cziffra (r1964) *Concert*
(3/95) (EMI) ① CDM5 65255-2
S. Cherkassky (r1987) *Concert*
(3/95) (NIMB) ① NI7705

A. Rubinstein (r1970) *Concert*
(7/95) (RCA) ① 09026 62590-2
E. Petri (r1940) *Concert*
(8/95) (APR) ① [2] APR7027
**Prélude, fugue et variation in B
minor—organ, Op. 18 (1860-62)**
J. Parker-Smith *Concert*
(3/89) (ASV) ① CDDCA610
M. Murray *Concert* (7/90) (TELA) ① [2] CD80234
J. Watts *Concert* (9/90) (PRIO) ① PRCD286
W. Rübsam *Concert*
(7/91) (BAYE) ① [3] BR100091/3
P. Kee *Concert* (9/91) (CHAN) ① CHAN8891
R. Silverman (pf) *Concert*.
(6/94) (CBC) ① MVCD1061
M. Dupré (r c1930) *Concert* (9/94) (BEUL) ① 1PD5
P. Crossley (r1993: trans pf: H Bauer) *Concert*
(2/95) (SONY) ① SK58914
P. Hurford (r1983) *Concert*
(10/95) (DECC) ① 444 568-2DM
J.V. Michalko *Concert*
(6/90) (OPUS) ① 9351 2130
**Prière in C sharp minor—organ, Op. 20
(1860-62)**
J. Bate *Concert* (9/85) (UNIC) ① DKPCD9030
M. Murray *Concert* (7/90) (TELA) ① [2] CD80234
W. Rübsam *Concert*
(7/91) (BAYE) ① [3] BR100091/3
N. Hakim *Concert* (7/91) (PRIO) ① PRCD327
Quasi marcia—harmonium, Op. 22 (1862)
A. Sacchetti *Concert* (3/92) (EURM) ① [4] 350224

SECTION IV: VOCAL AND CHORAL

Les Béatitudes—oratorio, Op. 53 (1869-79)
(Wds. Bible)
Cpte D. Montague, I. Danz, C. Kallisch, K. Lewis, S.
Weir, G. Cachemaille, J. Cheek, J. Vasle, R. Hagen,
Stuttgart Gächinger Kantorei, Stuttgart RSO, H.
Rilling (7/91) (HANS) ① [2] 98 964
Le Mariage des roses—song (1871) (Wds. E.
David)
D. Fischer-Dieskau, H. Höll (r c1987) *Concert*
(12/95) (TELD) ① 4509-97457-2
Nocturne—song (1884) (Wds. L. de
Fourcard)
C. Ludwig, Paris Orch, D. Barenboim *Concert*
(1/93) (DG) ① [2] 437 244-2GGA2
G. Souzay, D. Baldwin (1963) *Concert*
(3/95) (PHIL) ① [4] 438 964-2PM4(2)
D. Fischer-Dieskau, H. Höll (r c1987) *Concert*
(12/95) (TELD) ① 4509-97457-2
Panis angelicus—sacred song (1872) (interpolated
into the Messe à 3)
J. Norman, Ambrosian Sngrs, RPO, A. Gibson (arr.
Hope) *Concert* (4/83) (PHIL) ① 400 019-2PH
K. Te Kanawa, St Paul's Cath Ch, ECO, Barry Rose
Concert (5/85) (PHIL) ① 412 629-2PH
L. Pavarotti, National PO, K.H. Adler *Concert*
(7/86) (DECC) ① [2] 417 011-2DH2
E. Schwarzkopf, Ambrosian Sngrs, D. Vaughan,
Philh, C. Mackerras (arr Mackerras) *Concert*
(12/90) (EMI) ① CDM7 63574-2
B. Hendricks, Stockholm CO, E. Ericson *Concert*
(4/91) (EMI) ① CDC7 54098-2
L. Pavarotti, Wandsworth Sch Boys' Ch, National PO,
K.H. Adler (arr Gamley) *Concert*
(12/91) (DECC) ① 433 710-2DH
B. Gigli, Berlin St Op Chor, Berlin St Op Orch, B.
Seidler-Winkler (r1936) *Concert*
(1/93) (MMOI) ① CDMOIR411
R. Scotto, St Patrick's Cath Ch, St Patrick's Cath
Orch, L. Anselmi (r1981) *Concert*
(12/93) (VAI) ① VAIA1013
L. Quilico, G. Quilico, Toronto SO, J.A. Bartle (r1992:
arr Cable) *Concert* (12/93) (CBC) ① SMCD5119
Trinity Coll Ch, Cambridge, R. Marlow (r1993)
Concert (3/94) (CONI) ① CDCF219
Westminster Cath Ch, J. O'Donnell, I. Simcock
(r1993: arr Guest) *Concert*
(3/94) (HYPE) ① CDA66669
BBC PO, M. Bamert (r1994: orch Stokowski) *Concert*
(6/95) (CHAN) ① CHAN9349
Philadelphia, L. Stokowski (r1936: arr orch:
Stokowski) *Concert* (8/95) (BIDD) ① WHL011
I. Galante, Latvian Nat SO, A. Vilumanis (r1994: arr
Brinums) (11/95) (CAMP) ① RRCD1335
**La Procession—song: 1v and orchestra
(1888)** (Wds. C. Brizeux)
S. Varcoe, G. Johnson *Concert*
(3/88) (HYPE) ① CDA66248
E. Caruso, F. Lapitino, orch, W.B. Rogers (r1916)
Concert (7/91) (RCA) ① [12] GD60495(5)
E. Caruso, orch, W.B. Rogers (r1916) *Concert*
(10/91) (PEAR) ① [3] EVC3(2)

Rédemption—symphonic poem (1v, female
vv, speaker and orchestra) (1871-72 rev
1874) (Wds. E. Blau)
5. Morceau symphonique.
L. Wilson, B. Uria-Monzon, Orléon Donostiarra,
Toulouse Capitole Orch, M. Plasson (r1993/4)
(5/95) (EMI) ① **CDC5 55056-2**
5. Paris Orch, D. Barenboim Concert
(1/93) (DG) ① [2] **437 244-2GGA2**
Roses et papillons—song (1872) (Wds. V.
Hugo)
D. Fischer-Dieskau, H. Höll (r c1987) Concert
(12/95) (TELD) ① **4509-97457-2**
S'il est un charmant gazon—song (two
settings) (pub 1922) (Wds. V. Hugo)
F. Lott, G. Johnson (r1984) Concert
(5/87) (HARM) ① **HMA190 1138**

FRANCK, Johann Wolfgang (1644–c1710) Germany

SECTION IV: VOCAL AND CHORAL

Weil, Jesus ich in meinem Sinn—cantata
J. Bowman, King's Consort, R. King Concert
(3/87) (MERI) ① **CDE84126**

FRANCO, Hernando (1532–1585) Spain

SECTION IV: VOCAL AND CHORAL

Slave Regina a 5—chorus a capella
Westminster Cath Ch, J. O'Donnell Concert
(12/90) (HYPE) ① **CDA66330**

FRANCOEUR, François (1698–1787) France

SECTION II: CHAMBER

Sonata for Cello and Continuo in E
Largo & Allegro vivo G. Piatigorsky, I. Newton (arr
Trowell: r1934) Concert
(10/91) (MUSI) ① **MACD-644**

FRANÇOIS, Claude (20th Cent) France

SECTION IV: VOCAL AND CHORAL

My Way—song (1969) (comp with J Revaux &
G Thibaut)
P. Bertin, F. Couturier (r1995: arr R Wagner) Concert
(8/95) (HARM) ① **HMC90 1552**

FRANCUS DE INSULA (fl 1420–25) Flanders

SECTION IV: VOCAL AND CHORAL

Amours mont cure
Gothic Voices, I. Barford, C. Page Concert
(12/86) (HYPE) ① **CDA66144**

FRANK, Alan (1910–1993) England

SECTION II: CHAMBER

Suite for Two Clarinets
F. Thurston, R. Clarke (r1936) Concert
(2/94) (CLRI) ① **CC0005**

FRANKEL, Benjamin (1906–1973) England

SECTION I: ORCHESTRAL

Carriage and Pair (1950) (concert arrangement
from film 'So long at the Fair')
RTE Concert Orch, E. Tomlinson (r1993) Concert
(12/95) (MARC) ① **8 223522**
Concertante Lirico—string orchestra, Op. 27
(1952)
Seattle NW CO, A. Francis (r1993) Concert
(2/95) (CPO) ① **CPO999 221-2**
May Day—concert overture, Op. 22 (1948)
Queensland SO, W. A. Albert (r1993) Concert
(7/94) (CPO) ① **CPO999 240-2**
3 Sketches—string orchestra, Op. 2 (early
1930s)
1. Presto; 2. Andante cantabile ed espressivo; 3.
Allegro, molto-ritmico e giocoso.
Seattle NW CO, A. Francis (r1993) Concert
(2/95) (CPO) ① **CPO999 221-2**

Solemn Speech and Discussion—string
orchestra, Op. 11 (1941)
Seattle NW CO, A. Francis (r1993) Concert
(2/95) (CPO) ① **CPO999 221-2**
Symphony No. 1, Op. 33 (1958)
Queensland SO, W. A. Albert (r1993) Concert
(7/94) (CPO) ① **CPO999 240-2**
Symphony No. 2, Op. 38 (1962)
Queensland SO, W. A. Albert (r1994) Symphony 3.
(8/95) (CPO) ① **CPO999 241-2**
Symphony No. 3, Op. 40 (1964)
Queensland SO, W. A. Albert (r1994) Symphony 2.
(8/95) (CPO) ① **CPO999 241-2**
Symphony No. 5, Op. 67 (1867)
Queensland SO, W. A. Albert (r1993) Concert
(7/94) (CPO) ① **CPO999 240-2**
Youth Music—string orchestra, Op. 12
(1942)
1. On the march; 2. Playful moment; 3. Pause for
thought (we remember the fallen); 4. Forward ...
March.
Seattle NW CO, A. Francis (r1993) Concert
(2/95) (CPO) ① **CPO999 221-2**

SECTION IV: VOCAL AND CHORAL

The Aftermath—song cycle: tenor, strings,
trumpet and timpani, Op. 17 (1947) (Wds. R.
Nichols)
R. Dan, Seattle NW CO, A. Francis (r1993) Concert
(2/95) (CPO) ① **CPO999 221-2**

SECTION V: STAGE WORKS

The Battle of the Bulge—film score (1965)
EXCERPTS: 1. Prelude.
1. Prague City PO, P. Bateman (r1994) Concert
(11/94) (SILV) ① **FILMCD151**
A Kid for Two Farthings—film score (1955)
EXCERPTS: 1. Theme.
1. Orch, G. Melachrino (r1955) Concert
(9/94) (EMI) ① **CDGO 2059**

FRANZ, Oscar Germany

SECTION I: ORCHESTRAL

Konzertstück in F—two horns and orchestra,
Op. 4
M. Rimon (hn/dir), Israel PO Concert
(2/92) (CARL) ① **MCD31**

FRANZ, Robert (1815–1892) Germany

SECTION IV: VOCAL AND CHORAL

Aus Osten—six Lieder: 1v and piano, Op. 42
(c1872)
1. Wozu?; 2. Die helle Sonne leuchtet (wds. Mirza-
Schaffy); 3. Selige Nacht (wds. Petöfi); 4. Weisst du
noch, wds. Hafis); 5. Es hat die Rose sich beklagt
(wds. Mirza-Schaffy); 6. Wenn der Frühling auf die
Berge steigt (wds. Mirza-Schaffy).
5. H. Hotter, H. Dokoupil (r1968-9) Concert
(8/89) (PREI) ① **93390**
12 Lieder—1v and piano, Op. 1 (1843)
BOOK 1: 1. Ihr Auge (wds. Burns); 2. Nachtlied
(wds. Hahn-Hahn); 3. Die Lotosblume (wds. Geibel);
4. Nun holt mir eine Kanne Wein (wds. Burns); 5. O
säh' ich auf der Heide (wds. Burns); 6. Tanzlied im
Mai (wds. Hoffmann von Fallersleben). BOOK 2: 7.
Sonntag (wds. Eichendorff); 8. Für Einen (wds.
Burns); 9. Jagdlied (wds. Tieck); 11. Vöglein, wohin so
schnell (wds. Geibel); 12. In meinem Garten (wds.
Geibel).
1, 4. T. Hampson, G. Parsons (pp1993) Concert
(1/95) (EMI) ① **CDC5 55147-2**
12 Lieder—1v and piano, Op. 4 (1845) (Wds.
various)
BOOK 1: 1. Mein Hochlandskind (wds. R Burns); 2.
Die süsse Dirn' von Inverness (wds. R Burns); 3.
Liebliche Maid (wds. R Burns); 4. Ihr Hügel dort am
schönen Doon; 5. Montgomery Gretchen; 6. Du hast
mich verlassen. BOOK 2: 7. Er ist gekommen (wds. F
Rückert); 8. Kurzes Wiedersehen (wds. Osterwald); 9.
Durch säuselnde Bäumel (wds. Osterwald); 10.
Ach, dass du kamst (wds. Osterwald); 11.
Wanderlied (wds. Osterwald); 12. Ach, dass du
kamst (wds. Osterwald).
2. T. Hampson, G. Parsons (pp1993) Concert
(1/95) (EMI) ① **CDC5 55147-2**
12 Lieder—1v and piano, Op. 5 (1846)
BOOK 1: 1. Aus meinen grossen Schmerzen (wds.
Heine); 2. Liebchen ist da (wds. Schröer); 3. Auf dem
Meere (wds. Heine); 4. Will über Nacht wohl übers
Tal (wds. Osterwald); 5. Mädchen mit dem roten
Mündchen (wds. Heine); 6. Ich hab' in deinem Auge

(wds. Rückert). BOOK 2: 7. Gute Nacht (wds.
Eichendorff); 8. Ich lobe mir die Vögelein (wds.
Osterwald); 9. Stiller Abend (wds. Schröer); 10.
Erinnerung (wds. Osterwald); 11. Hör ich das
Liedchen klingen (wds. Heine); 12. Genesung (wds.
Schröer).
1. H. Hotter, H. Dokoupil (r1968-9) Concert
(8/89) (PREI) ① **93390**
6 Lieder—1v and piano, Op. 10 (1860)
1. Für Musik (wds. Geibel); 2. Stille Sicherheit (wds.
Lenau); 3. Mutter, o sing' mich zur Ruh' (wds.
Hemans); 4. Der vielschönen Fraue (wds.
Eichendorff); 5. Und die Rosen, sie prangen (wds.
Osterwald); 6. Gewitternacht (wds. Osterwald).
1. H. Hotter, H. Dokoupil (r1968-9) Concert
(8/89) (PREI) ① **93390**
6 Lieder—1v and piano, Op. 17 (pub c1860)
1. Ave Maria (wds. Geibel); 2. Ständchen (wds.
Osterwald); 3. Lieb' Liebchen (wds H Heine); 4. Die
Trauernde (folksong); 5. Im Frühling (wds.
Osterwald); 6. Im Herbst (wds. Müller).
6. K. Flagstad, E. McArthur (r1937) Concert
(12/95) (SIMA) ① [3] **PSC1821(2)**
6 Lieder—1v and piano, Op. 20 (c1865)
1. Die blauen Frühlingsgaugen (wds. Heine); 2. Die
letzte Rose (wds. Gottschall); 3. Verfehlte Liebe
(wds. Heine); 4. Abends (wds. Osterwald); 5. Das
macht das dunkelgrüne Land (wds. Roquette); 6. Im
Herbst (wds. Geibel).
5. H. Hotter, H. Dokoupil (r1968-9) Concert
(8/89) (PREI) ① **93390**

FRASER-SIMSON, Harold (1878–1944) England

SECTION V: STAGE WORKS

The Maid of the Mountains—musical
comedy: 3 acts (1916—Manchester) (Lyrics
Harris and Valentine)
1. Friends have to part; 2. Live for today; 3. My life is
love (composed James W. Tate); 4. Teresa's
Farewell; 5. Though curs may quail. ACT 2: 6. Love
will find a way; 7. Save us; 8. What fortune?; 9. Dirty
work; 10. Paradise for two (composed J. W. Tate);
11. A Bachelor gay am I (composed J. W. Tate). ACT
3: 12. When each day; 13. Good people, gather
round; 14. When you're in love (composed J. W.
Tate); 15. Over here and over there; 16. Finale.
10. M. Hill Smith, P. Morrison, Chandos Concert
Orch, S. Barry Concert
(2/90) (CHAN) ① **CHAN8759**

FREDERICK II, King of Prussia (1712–1786) Germany

known as Frederick the Great

SECTION I: ORCHESTRAL

4 Concerti for Flute, Strings and Continuo
1. G; 2. G; 3. C; 4. D.
3. P. Gallois, CPE Bach CO, P. Schreier (r1993)
Concert
(2/95) (DG) ① **439 895-2GH**
Hohenfriedberg—march (attrib)
Berlin Phil Wind Qnt, H. von Karajan (r1973) Concert
(5/94) (DG) ① **439 346-2GX2**

SECTION II: CHAMBER

Sonata in C—flute and harpsichord
R. Brown, J. Coe, L.U. Mortensen Concert
(5/94) (CHAN) ① **CHAN0541**
Sonata in G—flute and harpsichord
M. Petri, H. Petri (trans rec) Concert
(10/88) (RCA) ① **RD87749**

SECTION V: STAGE WORKS

Il Ré pastore—serenata (1747—Berlin)
Sulle più belle piante J. Kowalski, Berlin CO, M.
Pommer Concert
(9/88) (CAPR) ① **10 113**

FREIRE, Osman Perez (1878–1930) Chile/Spain

SECTION IV: VOCAL AND CHORAL

Ay, Ay, Ay—Creole song
T. Schipa, orch, R. Bourdon (r1926) Concert
(12/89) (RCA) ① **GD87969**
P. Domingo, LSO, K-H. Loges Concert
(5/93) (DG) ① **431 104-2GB**

FRENCH, William Percy (?–1920) Ireland

SECTION IV: VOCAL AND CHORAL

Ach, I dunno—song (Wds. M. Helen French)
A. Murray, G. Johnson (r1992) *Concert*
(8/93) (HYPE) ① CDA66627
Gortnamona—song (Wds. Green)
A. Murray, G. Johnson (r1992) *Concert*
(8/93) (HYPE) ① CDA66627
Phil the Fluter's Ball—song (1912) (Wds. cpsr)
A. Campoli, Orch, W. Goehr *Concert*
(10/91) (PEAR) ① PASTCD9744
A. Murray, G. Johnson (r1992) *Concert*
(8/93) (HYPE) ① CDA66627
1. Black Dyke Mills Band, R. Newsome (r1977; arr brass band: G. Langford) *Concert*
(1/94) (CHAN) ① CHAN4528

FRESCOBALDI, Girolamo (1583–1643) Italy

SECTION II: CHAMBER

Canzona in A minor—recorder and continuo
B. Kol, A. Brodo, D. Shemer *Concert*
(6/90) (CARL) ① PWK1138
5 Canzoni per canto solo—recorder and continuo (c1615)
E. Haupt, C. Schornsheim, S. Pank, A. Beyer *Concert*
(2/90) (CAPR) ① 10 234
Il Primo libro delle canzoni—Canzoni with titles (pub 1628 rev 1634) (2 editions: 1628 & 1634, contents varying in each)
EXCERPTS: 2. La Bernadina; 3. La Lucchesina; 4. La Donatina; 5. La Tomboncina; 6. L'Altera; 7. La Tucchina o La Superba; 8. L'Ambitiosa; 9. La Gualterina; 10. L'Henricuccia (a due canti); 11. La Plettenberger; 12. La Todeschina; 13. La Bianchina; 15. La Lievoratta (a due bassi); 16. La Samminiata (a due bassi); 17. La Diodata (a due bassi); 19. La Capriola (canto e bassi); 20. La Lipparella; 24. La Nobile (a due bassi e canto); 25. La Garzoncina (a due bassi e canto); 26. La Moricona (a due bassi e canto); 27. La Lanciona (a due canti e basso); 28. La Lanberta (a due canti e basso); 29. La Boccellina (a due canti e basso); 30. La Cittadellia (a due canti e due bassi); 31. L'Arnolfinia (a due canti a due bassi); 32. L'Altogradina (a due canti e basso); 34. La Sandoninia (a due canti e basso).
2. F. Brüggen, A. Bylsma, G. Leonhardt (r1978) *Concert*
(10/95) (TELD) ① 4509-97466-2
2, 13, 28. Capella Sancti Michaelis Instr Ens, E. van Nevel *Concert*
(11/89) (RICE) ① RIC062026
2, 16, 19. B. Dickey, Tragicomedia *Concert*
(6/92) (ACCE) ① ACC9173D
2, 3. J. Freeman-Attwood, I. Simcock (r1993; arr tpt/org) *Concert*
(5/94) (PROU) ① PROUCD135
13. Gabrieli Players, P. McCreesh (r1992-3) *Concert*
(1/94) (ARCH) ① 437 833-2AH
30. Wallace Collection, S. Wright *Concert*
(11/90) (TELA) ① CD80204

SECTION III: INSTRUMENTAL

Canzoni alla francese in partitura—Libro quarto—keyboard (pub 1645)
1. prima, detta la Rovetta; 2. seconda, detta la Sabbatina; 3. terza, detta la Crivelli; 4. quarta, detta la Scacchi; 5. quinta, detta la Bellerofonte; 6. sesta, detta la Pesenti; 7. settima, detta la Tarditi; 8. ottava, detta la Vincenti; 9. nona, detta la Querina; 10. decima, detta la Paulini; 11. undecima, detta la Guardana.
1. P. Hurford, M. Laird Brass Ens (r1990: ed Leonhardt) *Concert* (9/92) (ARGO) ① 433 451-2ZH
Fiori musicali—organ, Op. 12 (pub 1635) (recordings may include Gregorian chant)
Messa della Domenica: 1a. Toccata avanti la Messa; 1b. Kyrie della Domenica; 1c. Kyrie; 1d. Christe; 1e. 3 Christes alio modi; 1f. 3 Kyries alio modo; 1g. Kyrie ultimo; 1h. 2 Kyries alio modi; 1i. Canzon dopo l'Epistola; 1j. Recercar dopo il Credo; 1k. Toccata cromatica per l'Elevatione; 1l. Canzon post il Comune. Messa degli Apostoli: 2a. Toccata avanti la Messa; 2b. Kyrie degli Apostoli; 2c. 2 Kyries; 2d. 2 Christes; 2e. 3 Kyries; 2f. Canzon dopo l'Epistola; 2g. Toccata avanti il Recercar; 2h. Recercar cromatico post il Credo; 2i. Altro Recercar; 2j. Toccata per l'Elevatione; 2k. Canzon con obligo del basso come appare; 2l. Canznon quarti toni dpo il Postcommunio. Messa della Madonna: 3a. Toccata avanti la Messa; 3b. Kyrie della Madonna; 3c. Kyrie;
3d. Christe; 3e. 2 Kyries; 3f. Christe alio modo; 3g. Canzon dopo l'Epistola; 3h. Recercar dopo il Credo; 3i. Toccata avanti il Recercar; 3j. Toccata per l'Elevatione; 3k. Recercar con obligo di cantare la quinta parte senze tocarla; 3l. Toccata per l'Elevatione; 4. Bergamasca; 5. Capriccio sopra la Girolmeta.
Cpte R. Alessandrini, E. Onofri, Chant Sch, J. Cabré (with chant) (1/91) (ASTR) ① [2] E8714
1k, 2j L. Cummings (r1992) *Concert*
(10/93) (COLL) ① Coll1360-2
2g, 2j T. Roberts (r1992-3) *Concert*
(1/94) (ARCH) ① 437 833-2AH
3a J. Laleman *Concert*
(11/89) (RICE) ① RIC062026
Il Primo libro di Capricci fatti sopra diversa soggetti et arie in partitura—keyboard (pub 1624 rev 1626)
1. Bassa fiammenga; 2. Cromatico di ligature al contrario; 3. Il Cucho; 4. Di durezze; 5. La sol fa mi re ut; 6. La sol fa re mi; 7. Obligo di cantare la quinta parte, senza toccarlo; 8. Or che noi rimena; 9. Ruggiero; 10. Spagnoletta; 11. Un soggetto; 12. Ut re mi fa sol la.
1. Amsterdam Loeki Stardust Qt *Concert*
(10/94) (L'OI) ① 440 207-2OM
1, 3-12. G. Leonhardt, H. van der Kamp (1/91) (DHM) ① GD77071
Il Primo libro di Ricercari et Canzoni francese sopra diverse oblighi in partitura—keyboard/1-4 instruments (pub 1615)
1. primo; 1b. secondo; 1c. terzo; 1d. quarto, sopra mi re fa mi; 1e. quinto; 1f. sesto, sopra fa fa sol la fa; 1g. sttimo, sopra sol mi fa la sol; 1h. ottavo, obligo di non sucir di grado; 1i. non, con quattro soggetti; 1j. decimo, sopra la fa sol la re; 2. Canzoni alla francese; 2a. prima; 2b. seconda; 2c. terza, detta la Crivelli; 2d. quarta; 2e. quinta.
1a Amsterdam Loeki Stardust Qt *Concert*
(10/94) (L'OI) ① 440 207-2OM
Il Primo libro di Toccate, Partite, Correnti, Balletti, Ciaccone, Passacagli—keyboard (pub 1637)
1. Toccate: 1a. prima; 1b. seconda; 1c. terza; 1d. quarta; 1e. quinta; 1f. sesta; 1g. septima; 1h. ottava; 1i. nona; 1j. decima; 1k. undecima; 1l. duodecima; 2. Partite: 2a. XIV, sopra l'aria della Romanesca; 2b. II, sopra l'aria della Monica; 2c. XII, sopra l'aria di Ruggiero; 2d. VI, sopra l'aria di Follia; 2e. Cento Partite, sopra passacagli; 2f. Sopra l'aria detta la Frescobalda; 3. Correnti: 3a. corrente quatro; 3b. corrente e ciaccona; 4. Balletti: 4a. primo, Corrente, Passacagli; 4b. secondo, Corrente; 4c. terzo, Corrente, Passacagli; 4d. Balletto e Ciaccona; 5. Capricci: 5a. Fra Jacopino, sopra l'aria di Ruggiero; 5b. sopra la Battaglia; 5c. pastorale.
1e, 1l, 1j, 4d A. Lawrence-King *Concert*
(6/92) (HYPE) ① CDA66518
Il Secondo libro di Toccate, Canzone, Versi d'hinni, Magnificat, Gagliarde, Correnti...—keyboard (pub 1627)
1. Toccate: 1a. prima; 1b. seconda; 1c. terza, alla elevatione; 1d. quarta, alla elevatione; 1e. quinta, sopra i pedali, e senza; 1f. sesta, sopra i pedali, e senza; 1g. settima; 1h. ottava, di durezze e ligature; 1i. nona, non senza fatiga si giunge al fine; 1j. decima; 1k. undecima; 2. Canzone: 2a. prima; 2b. seconda; 2c. terza; 2d. quarta; 2f. sesta; 3. Hinni: 3a. della Domenica; 3b. Iste Confessor; 3c. Ave maris stella; 4. Magnificat: 4a. primi toni; 4b. secundi toni; 4c. sesti toni; 5. Gagliarde: 5a. prima; 5b. seconda; 5c. terza; 5d. quarta; 5e. quinta; 6. Correnti: 6a. primo; 6b. secondo; 6c. terzo; 6d. quarto; 6e. quinto; 6f. sesto; 7. Madrigal on Archadelt's 'Ancidetemi pur'; 8. Arie: 8a. detta Balletto; 8b. detta la Frescobalda.
1a, 1k, 2d, 2e C. Farr *Concert*
(1/90) (ETCE) ① KTC1056
1c J. Laleman *Concert*
(11/89) (RICE) ① RIC062026
1i S. Sempé (hpd/dir) *Concert*
(10/91) (DHM) ① RD77220
1k S. Sempé (hpd/dir) *Concert*
(10/91) (DHM) ① RD77220
3a K. Gilbert *Concert* (6/88) (NOVA) ① 150 018-2
8a, 8b A. Lawrence-King *Concert*
(6/92) (HYPE) ① CDA66518
8b J. Bream (r1959; arr Segovia) *Concert*
(8/93) (RCA) ① [28] 09026 61583-2(4)
8b J. Bream (r1959; arr Segovia) *Concert*
(6/94) (RCA) ① 09026 61592-2
Toccata—keyboard (unidentified)
R. Alessandrini (r1994) *Concert*
(4/95) (O111) ① OPS30-118

SECTION IV: VOCAL AND CHORAL

Arie musicali per cantarsi, primo libro—1-3vv, theorbo and harpsichord (pub 1630)
1. A pie della gran croce (1v); 2. Ardo, e taccio il mio mal (1v); 3. Begli occhi (2vv); 4. Con dolcezza e pietate (3vv); 5. Corilla danzando (3vv); 6. Così me disprezzate (1v); 7. Deganti, O gran Fernando (1v); 8. Di licori un guardo (3vv); 9. Donna, siam rei di morte (1v); 10. Dopò si lungo error (1v); 11. Dove, dove ne'vai (2vv); 12. Dove, dove, Signor (1v); 13. Dunque dovrò, 'Aria di Romanesca' (1v); 14. Eri già tutta mia (2vv); 15. Intro nave dorata (1v); 16. Non mi negate, ohimè (1v); 17. Occhi che sete (2vv); 18. Se l'aura spira (1v); 19. Se l'onde, ohimè (1v); 20. Se m'amate io v'adoro (2vv); 21. Signor, c'ora fra gli-ostri (1v); 22. Troppo sotto due stelle (3vv); 23. Voi partite mio sole (1v).
1. M. van Egmond, Ricercar Consort *Concert*
(1/90) (RICE) ① RIC054032
6, 18. J. Bowman, S. Sempé, J. Bernfeld *Concert*
(9/89) (ARIO) ① ARN68046
6, 18. M. van Egmond, C. Farr *Concert*
(1/90) (ETCE) ① KTC1056
Arie musicali per cantarsi, secondo libro—1-3vv, theorbo and harpsichord (pub 1630)
1. A miei pianti al fine (1v); 2. Bella tiranna infida (2vv); 3. Ben veggio donna (1v); 4. Deh, vien da me pastorella (2vv); 5. Deh, volate o miei voci (3vv); 6. Doloroso mio core (3vv); 7. Dove, dove sparir (1v); 8. Gioite, O selve, O venti (2vv); 9. La mia pallida faccia (1v); 10. Non vi partite (2vv); 11. O dolore, O ferita (3vv); 12. Ohimè, che pur, che seno (1v); 13. O mio cor, dolce mia vita (1v); 14. Oscure selve (1v); 15. Quanto piu sorda sete (3vv); 16. Soffrir non posso (2vv); 17. Son ferito, son morto (1v); 18. Ti lascio, anima mia (1v); 19. Vanne, O carta amorosa (1v); 20. Voi partite mio sole (1v).
19. J. Bowman, S. Sempé, J. Bernfeld *Concert*
(9/89) (ARIO) ① ARN68046
19. M. van Egmond, C. Farr *Concert*
(1/90) (ETCE) ① KTC1056
Messa sopra l'aria della Monica—8vv and continuo
King's College Ch, S. Cleobury *Concert*
(5/85) (EMI) ① CDC7 47065-2
Capella Sancti Michaelis Voc Ens, Capela Sancti Michaelis Instr Ens, E. van Nevel *Concert*
(11/89) (RICE) ① RIC062026
O Iesu mel dulcissime—motet: 1v and continuo (pub 1627)
Gabrieli Consort, Gabrieli Players, P. McCreesh, T. Roberts (r1992-3) *Concert*
(1/94) (ARCH) ① 437 833-2AH

FRESNEAU, Henry (?c1500–c1550) France

SECTION IV: VOCAL AND CHORAL

La Fricassée—chanson: 4vv (1538)
C. Janequin Ens, D. Visse (r1994) *Concert*
(5/95) (HARM) ① HMC90 1453
Souspir d'amours—chanson: 4vv (1539)
C. Janequin Ens, D. Visse (r1994) *Concert*
(5/95) (HARM) ① HMC90 1453

FRICKER, Peter Racine (1920–1990) England

SECTION IV: VOCAL AND CHORAL

O Mistress Mine—song: tenor and guitar (1961) (Wds. Shakespeare)
P. Pears, J. Bream (r1963-4) *Concert*
(8/93) (RCA) ① [28] 09026 61583-2(5)
P. Pears, J. Bream (r1964) *Concert*
(9/94) (RCA) ① 09026 61601-2

FRIED, Gerald (b 1928) USA

SECTION V: STAGE WORKS

The Return of Dracula—film score (1958)
EXCERPTS: 1. Overture.
1. OST, G. Fried (r1958) *Concert*
(10/93) (SILV) ① FILMCD127

FRIEDBERG, Carl (1872–1955) Germany

SECTION II: CHAMBER

Old French Gavotte—violin and piano
F. Kreisler, C. Lamson (r1924) *Concert*
(9/93) (BIDD) ① [2] LAB068/9

FRIEDHOFER, Hugo (1902–1981) USA

SECTION V: STAGE WORKS

The **Best Years of Our Lives**—film score (1946)
EXCERPTS: 1. Main Title; 2. The Homecoming; 3. The Elevator; 4. Boone City; 5. Peggy; 6. Fred & Peggy; 7. The Nightmare; 8. Fred Asleep; 9. Neighbours; 10. Homer Goes Upstairs; 11. The Citation; 12. Exit Music.
2. LPO, F. Collura *Concert*
(5/93) (SILV) ① **SILVAD3002**
Lifeboat—film score (1942)
EXCERPTS: 1. Disaster.
1. Prague City PO, P. Bateman (recons & orch Philip Lane) *Concert* (9/95) (SILV) ① **FILMCD159**
Private Parts—film score (1971)
Suite Graunke SO, K. Graunke *Richthofen and Brown.* (2/91) (FACE) ① **FE8105**
Richthofen and Brown—film score (1971)
Suite Graunke SO, K. Graunke *Private Parts.*
(2/91) (FACE) ① **FE8105**
The **Sun Also Rises**—film score (1957)
EXCERPTS: 1. Prologue (Solennelle); 2. The Lights of Paris.
1, 2. National PO, C. Gerhardt *Concert*
(11/91) (RCA) ① **GD80912**
This **Earth is Mine**—film score (1959)
OST, H. Friedhofer (r1959) *Young Lions.*
(10/93) (VARE) ① [2] **VSD2-5403**
The **Young Lions**—film score (1958)
OST, H. Friedhofer (r1958) *This Earth is Mine.*
(10/93) (VARE) ① [2] **VSD2-5403**

FRIEDMAN, Ignacy (1882–1948) Poland

SECTION III: INSTRUMENTAL

Music Box—piano, Op. 33/3
S. Hough (r1987) *Concert*
(1/89) (VIRG) ① **VC7 59509-2**
Study on a Theme of Paganini—piano, Op. 47b (1914)
M. Raekallio *Concert* (8/92) (ONDI) ① **ODE777-2**

FRIEDMAN, Leo (1869–1927) USA

SECTION IV: VOCAL AND CHORAL

Meet me tonight in dreamland—song (Wds. B. Slater Whitsun)
L. Melchior, Orch (Danish: r1913) *Concert*
(8/88) (DANA) ① [2] **DACOCD311/2**

FRIEDMANN, Carl Berthold Ulrich (1862–1952) Germany/USA

SECTION I: ORCHESTRAL

Slavonic Rhapsody No. 2—orchestra
Glasgow CWS Band, H. Snell (arr Wright) *Concert*
(9/92) (DOYE) ① **DOYCD005**

FRIML, (Charles) Rudolf (1879–1972) Czechoslovakia/USA

SECTION III: INSTRUMENTAL

Dance of the maidens—piano, Op. 48
F. Kreisler, C. Lamson (r1927: arr Kreisler) *Concert*
(12/93) (BIDD) ① **LAB075**

SECTION V: STAGE WORKS

The **Firefly**—operetta (1912—New York) (Lib. Harbach)
EXCERPTS: 1. The Donkey Serenade; 2. A Woman's Smile.
1. J. Hadley, American Th Orch, P. Gemignani (r1993; orch W. D. Brohn) *Concert*
(12/95) (RCA) ① **09026 62681-2**
2. C. Campbell, Orig Broadway Cast (r1913) *Concert*
(5/94) (PEAR) ① [3] **GEMMCDS9053/5**
Katinka—musical show (1915—New York) (Lyrics Harbach)
EXCERPTS: 1. Rackety Coo.
1. S. Ash, M. Naudain, Orig Broadway Cast (r1916) *Concert* (5/94) (PEAR) ① [3] **GEMMCDS9056/8**

Rose Marie—operetta (1924—New York) (Lib. Hammerstein and Harbach)
EXCERPTS: 1. Indian Love Call; 2. Rose Marie.
1. F. Kreisler, C. Lamson (r1926: arr Kreisler) *Concert* (12/93) (BIDD) ① **LAB075**
1. V. Masterson, T. Allen, Philh, J.O. Edwards (r1990) *Concert* (5/94) (TER) ① **CDVIR8317**
1. B. Hendricks, G. Quilico, Lyon Op Orch, L. Foster (r1993) *Concert* (6/95) (EMI) ① **CDC5 55151-2**
The **Vagabond King**—operetta (1925—New York) (Lib. Hooker & Post, after E M Royle)
EXCERPTS: 1. Overture; 2. Some day; 3. The Vagabond King Waltz; 4. The Scotch Archer's Song; 5. Only a rose; 6. Love me tonight; 7. Drinking Song; 8. This same heart; 9. Song of the Vagabonds; 10. Tomorrow; 11. Nocturne; 12. Finale.
5. J. Björling, Stockholm Royal Op Orch, N. Grevillius (r1937) *Concert* (12/94) (MMOI) ① **CDMOIR425**
9. J. Hadley, Harvard Glee Club, American Th Orch, P. Gemignani (r1993; orch W. D. Brohn) *Concert*
(12/95) (RCA) ① **09026 62681-2**

FROBERGER, Johann Jacob (1616–1667) Germany

SECTION III: INSTRUMENTAL

Keyboard Works, Book 2 (1649)
Prima Parte—; 1. Toccata I in A min; 2. Toccata II in D min; 3. Toccata III in G; 4. Toccata IV in C; 5. Toccata V alla Levatione in D min; 6. Toccata VI alla Levatione in G min. Parte Seconda—; 7. Fantasia I sopra Ut, Re, Mi, Fa, Sol, La in C; 8. Fantasia II in A min/ E min; 9. Fantasia III in F/C; 10. Fantasia IV sopra Sol, La, Re in G; 11. Fantasia V in A min; 12. Fantasia VI in A min. Terza Parte—; 13. Canzon I in D min; 14. Canzon II in G min; 15. Canzon III in F/C; 16. Canzon IV in G; 17. Canzon V in C/G; 18. Canzon VI in A min. Quarta Parte—; 19. Suite I in A min; 20. Suite II in D min; 21. Suite III in G; 22. Suite IV in F; 23. Suite V in C; 24. Suite 'Auff Die Mayerin'.
2. C. Rousset *Concert*
(5/92) (HARM) ① **HMC90 1372**
8. Gradus ad Parnassum, K. Junghänel (r1994) *Concert* (7/95) (DHM) ① **05472 77326-2**
Keyboard Works, Book 4 (1656)
Prima Parte—; 1. Toccata VII in G; 2. Toccata VIII in E min; 3. Toccata IX in C; 4. Toccata X in F; 5. Toccata XI in E min; 6. Toccata XII in A min. Seconda Parte—; 7. Ricercar I in D min; 8. Ricercar II in G min; 9. Ricercar III in G min; 10. Ricercar IV in G; 11. Ricercar V in D min; 12. Ricercar VI in F sharp minor. Terza Parte—; 13. Capriccio I in G; 14. Capriccio II in G min; 15. Capriccio III in E min; 16. Capriccio IV in F; 17. Capriccio V in A min; 18. Capriccio VI in E min/ A min. Quarta Parte—; 19. Suite VII in E min; 20. Suite VIII in A; 21. Suite IX in G min; 22. Suite X in A min; 23. Suite XI in D; 24. Suite XII in C.
3. C. Rousset *Concert*
(5/92) (HARM) ① **HMC90 1372**
Keyboard Works from various sources—transcriptions by various hands (c1670–c1705)
1. Suite XXI in F (Grimm, 1699); 2. Suite XXII in E min (Grimm, 1699); 3. Suite XXIII in E min (Grimm, 1699); 4. Suite XXIV in D (Grimm, 1699); 5. Suite XXIVa in D (Grimm, 1699); 6. Suite XXV in D min (Grimm, 1699); 7. Suite XXVI in B min (Grimm, 1699); 8. Suite XXVII in E min (Tappert, c1670); 9. Suite XXIX-Nova in E flat (Möller, c1705); 10. Toccata XIII in E min (Diverse..., 1693); 11. Toccata XIV in G (Diverse..., 1693); 12. Capriccio XIII in G (Divese Curiose..., 1696); 13. Capriccio XIV in D min (Divese Curiose..., 1696); 14. Capriccio XV in F (Divese Curiose..., 1696); 15. Suite XIII in D min (10 Suittes..., 1698); 16. Suite XIV in G min (10 Suittes..., 1698); 17. Suite XV in A min (10 Suittes..., 1698); 18. Suite XVI in G (10 Suittes..., 1698); 19. Suite XVII in F (10 Suittes..., 1698); 20. Suite XIX in C min (10 Suittes..., 1698); 21. Suite XX in D, 'Méditation faite' (10 Suites..., 1698).
11, 20, 21. C. Rousset *Concert*
(5/92) (HARM) ① **HMC90 1372**
Keyboard Works from various sources—transcriptions by various hands (c1680–c1740)
1. Toccata XIX in D min (Muffat, c1740); 2. Toccata XX in A min (Muffat, c1740); 3. Capriccio XVI in E min (Muffat, c1740); 4. Suite XVIII in G min (Bauyn Ms, c1608); 5. Suite XXVIII in A min (Bauyn Ms, c1680); 6. Suite XV in G min (Bauyn Ms, c1680); 7. Toccata XVI in C (Bauyn MS, c1680); 8. Toccata XVII in D (Bauyn Ms, c1680); 9. Toccata XVIII in F (Bauyn Ms, c1680); 10. Suite XXX in A min (Minoriten Ms, c1730); 11. Tombeau faict à Paris (Minoriten Ms, c1730); 12. Lamentation in F min

(Minoriten Ms, c1730); 13. Capriccio XVII in C (Eckelt,; 14. Fantasia VII in G(Eckelt, 1692); 15. Ricercar XIII in C (Kimberger, c1760); 16. Ricercar XIV in D min (Kimberger, c1760).
4, 9-12. C. Rousset *Concert*
(5/92) (HARM) ① **HMC90 1372**
11. K. Gilbert *Concert* (6/88) (NOVA) ① **150 018-2**
Unidentified Gigue—keyboard
A. Segovia (gtr; r1939) *Concert*
(5/89) (EMI) ① [2] **CHS7 61047-2**

FRÖHLICH, Friedrich Theodor (1803–1836) Switzerland

SECTION IV: VOCAL AND CHORAL

Rückkehr in die Heimat—Lied (1830) (Wds Hölderlin)
M. Shirai, H. Höll *Concert*
(12/94) (CAPR) ① **10 534**

FRUMERIE, Gunnar (1908–1987) Sweden

SECTION IV: VOCAL AND CHORAL

Songs of the Heart, Op. 27 (1942) (Wds. Lagerkvist)
1. When you close my eyes; 2. Beauty grows where you walk; 3. Blessed the wait; 4. From the depths of ny soul; 5. You are my Afrodite; 6. Like a wave.
1, 6. B. Nilsson, G. Parsons (pp1974) *Concert*
(6/92) (BLUE) ① **ABCD009**

FRYE, Walter (fl c1450–75) England

SECTION IV: VOCAL AND CHORAL

Alas, alas is my chief song—ballade: 3vv
Hilliard Ens (r1992) *Concert*
(6/93) (ECM) ① **437 684-2**
Ave regina celorum—motet: 3vv (1450s) (three later anon settings: 4vv)
G. Binchois Ens, D. Vellard *Concert*
(3/92) (VIRG) ① **VC7 59043-2**
Hilliard Ens (r1992; with one 4vv setting) *Concert*
(6/93) (ECM) ① **437 684-2**
Missa, 'Flos Regalis'—4vv (Ordinary, without Kyrie)
Hilliard Ens (r1992) *Concert*
(6/93) (ECM) ① **437 684-2**
Myn hertis lust—ballade: 3vv (attrib. Bedyngham)
Hilliard Ens (r1992) *Concert*
(6/93) (ECM) ① **437 684-2**
O florens rosa—motet: 3vv
Hilliard Ens (r1992) *Concert*
(6/93) (ECM) ① **437 684-2**
Salve virgo mater pya—motet: 3vv
Hilliard Ens (r1992) *Concert*
(6/93) (ECM) ① **437 684-2**
So ys emprentid—ballade: 3vv (attrib Bedyngham)
Hilliard Ens (r1992) *Concert*
(6/93) (ECM) ① **437 684-2**
Sospitati dedit—motet: 3vv
Hilliard Ens (r1992) *Concert*
(6/93) (ECM) ① **437 684-2**
Tout a par moy—rondeau: 3vv (attrib Binchois)
Hilliard Ens (r1992) *Concert*
(6/93) (ECM) ① **437 684-2**
Trinitatis dies—motet: 3vv
Hilliard Ens (r1992) *Concert*
(6/93) (ECM) ① **437 684-2**

FUCHS, Robert (1847–1927) Germany

SECTION I: ORCHESTRAL

Serenade for Strings in E minor, Op. 21 (pub 1878)
Berne Camerata *Concert*
(1/89) (NOVA) ① **150 022-2**

SECTION II: CHAMBER

20 Duos—two violins, Op. 55 (pub 1896)
1. Ziemlich ruhig, G; 2. Langsam, wehmüthig, B minor; 3. Lebhaft und lustig, G; 4. Mässig bewegt, E minor; 5. Anmuthig, C; 6. Einfach, lieblich, G; 7. Etwas bewegt, B minor; 8. Langsam, sehr innig, D; 9. Kräftig, D minor; 10. Heiter bewegt, G; 11. Sehr ruhig, G minor; 12. Leicht bewegt, E flat; 13. Kräftig, gemessen, G minor; 14. Sehr innig, B flat; 15. Anmuthig, D; 16. Schnell und flüchtig, G minor; 17.

Heiter bewegt, B; 18. Leicht bewegt, D minor; 19.
Etwas bewegt, gemüthvoll, F; 20. Etwas steif, C.
E. Drucker, P. Setzer (r1993) *Bartók: Duos, Sz98.*
(3/95) (BIDD) ① **LAW007**

**Fantasiestücke—cello and piano, Op. 78
(1905)**
N. Green, C. Palmer *Concert*
(4/93) (BIDD) ① **LAW005**
M. Drobinsky, D. Blumenthal (r1992) *Concert*
(11/93) (MARC) ① **8 223423**

**10 Fantasy Pieces—violin and piano, Op. 74
(1904)**
A. Steinhardt, V. Steinhardt (r1993) *Concert*
(1/95) (BIDD) ① [2] **LAW012**

**6 Fantasy Pieces—viola and piano, Op. 117
(1920)**
A. Steinhardt, V. Steinhardt (r1993) *Concert*
(1/95) (BIDD) ① [2] **LAW012**

**Quintet for Clarinet and Strings in E flat, Op.
102 (1914)**
T. King, Britten Qt *Concert*
(7/92) (HYPE) ① **CDA66479**

**Sonata for Cello and Piano No. 1 in D minor,
Op. 29 (1881)**
N. Green, C. Palmer *Concert*
(4/93) (BIDD) ① **LAW005**
M. Drobinsky, D. Blumenthal (r1992) *Concert*
(11/93) (MARC) ① **8 223423**

**Sonata for Cello and Piano No. 2 in E flat
minor, Op. 83 (1908)**
N. Green, C. Palmer *Concert*
(4/93) (BIDD) ① **LAW005**
M. Drobinsky, D. Blumenthal (r1992) *Concert*
(11/93) (MARC) ① **8 223423**

**Sonata for Violin and Piano No. 6 in G minor,
Op. 103 (1915)**
A. Steinhardt, V. Steinhardt (r1993) *Concert*
(1/95) (BIDD) ① [2] **LAW012**

SECTION III: INSTRUMENTAL

Jugendklänge—piano, Op. 32
D. Blumenthal (r1992) *Concert*
(2/94) (MARC) ① **8 223474**

**Sonata for Piano No. 1 in G flat, Op. 19
(?1877)**
D. Blumenthal (r1991) *Piano Sonata 2.*
(6/93) (MARC) ① **8 223377**

**Sonata for Piano No. 2 in G minor, Op. 88
(c1910)**
D. Blumenthal (r1991) *Piano Sonata 1.*
(6/93) (MARC) ① **8 223377**

**Sonata for Piano No. 3 in D flat, Op. 109
(c1919)**
D. Blumenthal (r1992) *Concert*
(2/94) (MARC) ① **8 223474**

12 Waltzes—piano, Op. 110
D. Blumenthal (r1992) *Concert*
(2/94) (MARC) ① **8 223474**

**FUČÍK, Julius Arnošt Vilém
(1872–1916) Bohemia**

SECTION I: ORCHESTRAL

Attila—Hungarian March
Czech PO, V. Neumann *Concert*
(9/87) (ORFE) ① **C147861A**

**Der alte Brummbär—comic polka:bassoon
and orchestra, Op. 210** (Eng: The bear with
the sore head)
A. Pendlebury, RLPO, L. Pešek (r1990) *Concert*
(11/94) (VIRG) ① **VC7 59285-2**

Donausagen—waltz, Op. 233
Czech PO, V. Neumann *Concert*
(9/87) (ORFE) ① **C147861A**

**Einzug der Gladiatoren—triumphal march,
Op. 68** (Eng: The entry of the gladiators)
Czech PO, V. Neumann *Concert*
(9/87) (ORFE) ① **C147861A**
Britannia Building Soc Band, H. Snell (1990; arr
Snell: brass band) *Concert*
(8/92) (DOYE) ① **DOYCD004**
RLPO, L. Pešek (r1990) *Concert*
(11/94) (VIRG) ① **VC7 59285-2**

Florentiner—march, Op. 214 (1908)
Cleveland Winds, F. Fennell *Concert*
(10/84) (TELA) ① **CD80099**
Czech PO, V. Neumann *Concert*
(6/87) (ORFE) ① **C107201A**
Berlin Ens *Concert*
(5/91) (DG) ① **C126901A**
Berlin Phil Wind Qnt, H. von Karajan (r1973) *Concert*
(5/94) (DG) ① **439 346-2GX2**

Liebesflammen—waltz
Czech PO, V. Neumann *Concert*
(6/87) (ORFE) ① **C107201A**

Die lustige Dorfschmiede—march, Op. 218
(Eng: The merry blacksmiths)
Czech PO, V. Neumann *Concert*
(6/87) (ORFE) ① **C107201A**
RLPO, L. Pešek (r1990) *Concert*
(11/94) (VIRG) ① **VC7 59285-2**

Marinarella—concert overture, Op. 215
Czech PO, V. Neumann *Concert*
(9/87) (ORFE) ① **C147861A**

Miramare—concert overture
Czech PO, V. Neumann *Concert*
(6/87) (ORFE) ① **C107201A**

Mississippi River—march
Czech PO, V. Neumann *Concert*
(9/87) (ORFE) ① **C147861A**

Die Regimentskinder—march, Op. 169 (Eng:
Children of the Regiment)
Berlin Phil Wind Qnt, H. von Karajan (r1973: arr
Blaha) *Concert* (5/94) (DG) ① **439 346-2GX2**

Sempre avanti—march
Czech PO, V. Neumann *Concert*
(6/87) (ORFE) ① **C107201A**

Traumideale—concert waltz (1906)
Czech PO, V. Neumann *Concert*
(9/87) (ORFE) ① **C147861A**

Triglav—Slovak march, Op. 72
Czech PO, V. Neumann *Concert*
(9/87) (ORFE) ① **C147861A**

Winterstürme—concert waltz, Op. 184
Czech PO, V. Neumann *Concert*
(9/87) (ORFE) ① **C147861A**

FUCITO, Salvatore (?1875–1929)

SECTION IV: VOCAL AND CHORAL

Scordame—song (Wds. S. Manente)
E. Caruso, orch. J. Pasternack (r1919) *Concert*
(7/91) (RCA) ① [12] **GD60495(6)**
E. Caruso, orch. J. Pasternack (r1919) *Concert*
(10/91) (PEAR) ① [3] **EVC4(2)**

Sultano a Tte—song (Wds. R. Cordiferro)
E. Caruso, orch. J. Pasternack (r1919) *Concert*
(12/90) (NIMB) ① **NI7809**
E. Caruso, orch. J. Pasternack (r1919) *Concert*
(7/91) (RCA) ① [12] **GD60495(6)**
E. Caruso, orch. J. Pasternack (r1919) *Concert*
(10/91) (PEAR) ① [3] **EVC4(2)**

**FUENLLANA, Miguel de (early
16th Cent–after 1568) Spain**

SECTION III: INSTRUMENTAL

**Orphenica lyra—vihuela intabulations &
original pieces (pub 1554)** (includes texts &
voice parts)
EXCERPTS: 1. De los alamos (Vásquez); 2.
Morenica dame (Vásquez); 3. Teresica hermana
(Flecha); 4. Duélete de mí, Señora; 5. Con que la
lavare (Vásquez); 6. Duo de Josquin; 7. Glosa sobre
Tan que vivray (Sermisy); 8. De Antequera sale el
moro (Morales); 9. Fantasia; 10. Fantasia de redoble
galanos; 11. Pérdida de Antequera; 12. Vos me
matastes.
1, 4. J. Gomez, J. Constable (r1994; arr Tarragó)
Concert (9/94) (CONI) ① **CDCF243**
9. P. Chateauneuf *Concert*
(9/92) (VIRG) ① **VC7 59071-2**
11. T. Berganza, N. Yepes *Concert*
(12/92) (DG) ① [2] **435 848-2GX2**

**FUMET, Dyam Victor (1867–1949)
France**

SECTION I: ORCHESTRAL

La Nuit—symphonic poem (1914)
P. Dechorgnat, J. Ferrandis, H. Noël, J-J. Wiederker,
J-J. Wiederker CO, F. Bouaniche (r1992) *Concert*
(6/95) (SCHW) ① **310652**

**FUNCK, David (c1630–after 1690)
Germany**
---

also known as Funccius

SECTION II: CHAMBER

**Stricturae viola da gamba—four suites for
four viola da gambas (pub 1677)**
1. D minor; 2. F; 3. Adagio; 4. Allemande; 5.
Sarabande and Variations; 6. Gavotte; 7. Sarabande;
8. Gigue.
2. Ricercar Consort, P. Pierlot (va da gamba/dir)
(r1992) *Concert* (8/94) (RICE) ① **RIC098112**

**FÜRSTENAU, Anton Bernhard
(1792–1852) Germany**

SECTION II: CHAMBER

**Adagio and Variations, '(The) Illusion'—flute
and piano, Op. 133** (on themes from Bellini's
'Norma')
K. Jones, C. Edwards (r1993) *Concert*
(10/94) (CONI) ① [2] **CDCF905**

**FURTWÄNGLER, Wilhelm
(1886–1954) Germany**

SECTION I: ORCHESTRAL

Overture in E flat, Op. 3 (1899)
Košice St PO, A. Walter (r1993) *Concert*
(7/95) (MARC) ① **8 223645**

**Symphonic Concerto in B minor—piano and
orchestra (1924-36)**
D. Lively, Košice St PO, A. Walter
(12/91) (MARC) ① **8 223333**
Movt 2. Edwin Fischer, BPO, W. Furtwängler (r1939)
Concert (7/94) (BIDD) ① [2] **WHL006/7**

Symphony in B minor (1908)
1. Largo.
1. Košice St PO, A. Walter (r1993) *Concert*
(7/95) (MARC) ① **8 223645**

Symphony in D (1903)
1. Allegro.
1. Košice St PO, A. Walter (r1993) *Concert*
(7/95) (MARC) ① **8 223645**

Symphony No. 1 in B minor (1938-41)
Košice St PO, A. Walter
(7/91) (MARC) ① **8 223295**

Symphony No. 2 in E minor (1944-45)
BBC SO, A. Walter (r1992)
(8/93) (MARC) ① **8 223436**
VPO, W. Furtwängler (pp1953)
(4/95) (ORFE) ① **C375941B**

Symphony No. 3 in C sharp minor (1947-53)
RTBF SO, A. Walter (r1987)
(2/89) (MARC) ① **8 223105**

SECTION IV: VOCAL AND CHORAL

Auf dem See—1v & piano (1900) (Wds. J W
Goethe)
G. Pikal, A. Walter (r1993) *Concert*
(12/95) (MARC) ① **8 223546**

**Du sendest, Freund, mir Lieder—1v & piano
(1895)** (Wds. L Uhland)
G. Pikal, A. Walter (r1993) *Concert*
(12/95) (MARC) ① **8 223546**

**Erinnerung, 'Schweigend in des Abends
Stille'—1v & piano** (Wds. T Körner)
G. Pikal, A. Walter (r1993) *Concert*
(12/95) (MARC) ① **8 223546**

**Erinnerung, 'Willst du immer weiter
schweifen'—1v & piano (1897)** (Wds. J W
Goethe)
G. Pikal, A. Walter (r1993) *Concert*
(12/95) (MARC) ① **8 223546**

Geduld—1v and piano (1897) (Wds. P
Heyse)
G. Pikal, A. Walter (r1993) *Concert*
(12/95) (MARC) ① **8 223546**

**Lied, 'Wenn die Engel Harfe spielen'—1v &
piano (c1899)** (Wds. C Sylva)
G. Pikal, A. Walter (r1993) *Concert*
(12/95) (MARC) ① **8 223546**

Möwenflug—1v and piano (1900) (Wds. C F
Meyer)
G. Pikal, A. Walter (r1993) *Concert*
(12/95) (MARC) ① **8 223546**

**Religious Hymns—sop, ten, chorus & orch
(1903)** (Wds from Goethe's 'Faust', pt 2)
Frankfurt Singakademie (Oder), Frankfurt PO (Oder),
A. Walter (r1993) *Concert*
(12/95) (MARC) ① **8 223546**

Der Schatzgräber—1v & piano (c1899) (Wds.
J von Eichendorff)
G. Pikal, A. Walter (r1993) *Concert*
(12/95) (MARC) ① **8 223546**

**Schwindet, ihr dunklen Wölbungen—chorus
(1902)** (Wds. after Goethe)
Frankfurt Singakademie (Oder), Frankfurt PO (Oder),
A. Walter (r1993) *Concert*
(12/95) (MARC) ① **8 223546**

Der Soldat—1v & piano (1899) (Wds. A von
Chamisso)
G. Pikal, A. Walter (r1993) *Concert*
(12/95) (MARC) ① **8 223546**

Te Deum—soloists, chorus & orchestra (1902-10 rev 1915)
Frankfurt Singakademie (Oder), Frankfurt PO (Oder), A. Walter (r1993) *Concert*
(12/95) (MARC) ① 8 223546
Der traurige Jäger—1v & piano (c1899) (Wds. J von Eichendorff)
G. Pikal, A. Walter (r1993) *Concert*
(12/95) (MARC) ① 8 223546
Das Vaterland—1v & piano (1896) (Wds. L Uhland)
G. Pikal, A. Walter (r1993) *Concert*
(12/95) (MARC) ① 8 223546

FUX, Johann Joseph (1660–1741) Austria

SECTION IV: VOCAL AND CHORAL

La **Fede sacrilega nella morte del Precursor S Giovanni Battista—oratorio (1714)** (Wds. Pariati)
Cpte M. Lins, J. Koslowsky, H. Helling, J. Calaminus, G. Schwarz, Neuss Capella Piccola, T. Reuber
(10/91) (THOR) ① [2] DCTH2071/2
Justorum animae—motet
Niederaltaicher Scholaren, K. Ruhland (r1992)
Concert (10/93) (SONY) ① SK53117
Litaniae Beatae Mariae Virginis—motet
Niederaltaicher Scholaren, K. Ruhland (r1992)
Concert (10/93) (SONY) ① SK53117

FUZZY (b 1939) Denmark

SECTION II: CHAMBER

Fireplay—electronics and percussion (1991)
Safri Duo (r1994) *Concert*
(4/95) (CHAN) ① CHAN9330

GABRIEL, (Mary Ann) Virginia (1825–1877) England

SECTION IV: VOCAL AND CHORAL

Orpheus—song (Wds Shakespeared)
A. Rolfe Johnson, G. Johnson (r1991/3) *Concert*
(8/94) (HYPE) ① CDA66709

GABRIELI, Andrea (c1510–1586) Italy

SECTION II: CHAMBER

Ricercar del duodecimo tuono a 4—brass (pub 1589) (Madrigali et Ricercari, VII)
Wallace Collection, S. Wright *Concert*
(11/90) (TELA) ① CD80204

SECTION III: INSTRUMENTAL

Intonationi—organ (pub 1593)
1. del primo tono; 2. del secondo tono; 3. del terzo tono; 4. del quarto tono; 5. del quinto tono; 6. del sesto tono; 7. del settimo tono; 8. del ottavo tono; 9. Toccata del primo tono; 10. Toccata del sesto tono; 11. Toccata del ottavo tono; 12. Toccata del nono tono.
1, 7. J. O'Donnell, T. Roberts *Concert*
(5/90) (VIRG) ① VC7 59006-2
Toccata decimo tuono—keyboard
R. Micconi *Concert* (3/90) (MOTE) ① CD10561

SECTION IV: VOCAL AND CHORAL

Benedictus Dominus Deus—motet: 8vv (pub 1587)
J. O'Donnell, T. Roberts (trans orgs) *Concert*
(5/90) (VIRG) ① VC7 59006-2
Cinto m'havea tra belle e nude braccia—madrigal: 6vv (1580)
M. Arruabarrena, K. van Laethem, M. Valenta, J. Benet, M. van Altena, J. Cabré, T. de Zwart, A. Pols, R. Van Der Meer, K. Junghänel (lte/dir) *Concert*
(1/92) (ACCE) ① ACC8864D
Ciori à Damon dicea—madrigal: 6vv (1580)
M. Arruabarrena, K. van Laethem, M. Valenta, J. Benet, M. van Altena, J. Cabré, T. de Zwart, A. Pols, R. Van Der Meer, K. Junghänel (lte/dir) *Concert*
(1/92) (ACCE) ① ACC8864D
Come vuoi tu ch'io viva—madrigal: 6vv (1580)
M. Arruabarrena, K. van Laethem, M. Valenta, J. Benet, M. van Altena, J. Cabré, T. de Zwart, A. Pols, R. Van Der Meer, K. Junghänel (lte/dir) *Concert*
(1/92) (ACCE) ① ACC8864D

De profundis clamavi—motet: 6vv (pub 1583)
The Sixteen, H. Christophers (r1992) *Concert*
(10/93) (COLL) ① Coll1360-2
Duo rose fresche
Amaryllis Consort *Concert*
(6/86) (CARL) ① PCD822
In nobil sangue—madrigal (pub 1587) (Wds. Petrarch)
Consort of Musicke, A. Rooley (lte/dir) *Concert*
(2/89) (BIS) ① BIS-CD392
Jubilate Deo—motet
Gentlemen of the Chappell, His Majesties Sagbutts and Cornetts, P. Bassano (r1990) *Concert*
(5/91) (ASV) ① CDGAU122
Laudate Dominum in sanctis eius—10vv & instruments (pub 1588)
Wren Orch, J. Iveson, S. Saunders, R. Gowman, R. Gowman, Bernard Rose (r1977) *Concert*
(7/91) (DECC) ① 430 359-2DM
Missa—12-16vv (pub 1587) (Kyrie, Gloria, Sanctus and Benedictus only)
Gabrieli Consort, Gabrieli Players, P. McCreesh
Concert (5/90) (VIRG) ① VC7 59006-2
O sacrum convivium—motet: 5vv (pub 1565)
Gabrieli Consort, Gabrieli Players, P. McCreesh
Concert (5/90) (VIRG) ① VC7 59006-2
Lincoln Cath Ch, C. Walsh (r1993) *Concert*
(7/94) (PRIO) ① PRCD454
Quem vidistis pastores?—motet: 8vv (pub 1587)
Chanticleer (r1990) *Concert*
(12/94) (CHTI) ① CR-8803
Sonno diletto e caro—madrigal: 6vv (1580)
M. Arruabarrena, K. van Laethem, M. Valenta, J. Benet, M. van Altena, J. Cabré, T. de Zwart, A. Pols, R. Van Der Meer, K. Junghänel (lte/dir) *Concert*
(1/92) (ACCE) ① ACC8864D

GABRIELI, Giovanni (c1553/6–1612) Italy

SECTION II: CHAMBER

Canzon duodecimi toni a 10 (No. 2)—brass (pub 1597) (Sacrae Symphoniae, IX)
Wallace Collection, S. Wright *Concert*
(11/90) (TELA) ① CD80204
His Majesties Sagbutts and Cornetts, P. Bassano (r1990) *Concert* (5/91) (ASV) ① CDGAU122
ASMF, N. Marriner (r1964) *Concert*
(9/93) (DECC) ① 436 224-2DM
6 Canzoni—brass (pub 1608)
1. Canzon la spiritata; 2. Canzon seconda a 4; 3. Canzon terza; 4. Canzon quarta; 5. Canzon 'Fa sol la re'; 6. Canzon 'Sol sol la sol fa mi'.
1. Wallace Collection, S. Wright *Concert*
(11/90) (TELA) ① CD80204
4. PJBE, S. Cleobury (1986) *Concert*
(2/88) (ARGO) ① 417 468-2ZH
Canzoni et Sonate—3-22 instruments and organ continuo (pub 1615)
1. Canzon I, a 5; 2. Canzon II, a 6; 3. Canzon III, a 6; 4. Canzon IV, a 6; 5. Canzon V, a 7; 6. Canzon VI, a 7; 7. Canzon VII, a 7; 8. Canzon VIII, a 8; 9. Canzon IX, a 8; 10. Canzon X, a 8; 11. Canzon XI, a 8; 12. Canzon XII, a 8; 13. Sonata XIII, a 8; 14. Canzon XIV, a 10; 15. Canzon XV, a 10; 16. Canzon XVI, a 12; 17. Canzon XVII, a 12; 18. Sonata XVIII, a 14; 19. Sonata XIX, a 15; 20. Sonata XX, a 22; 21. Sonata per tre violini.
1, 4, 7, 8, 18, 19, 21. London Cornett and Sackbutt Ens, A. Parrott (r1978) *Sacrae symphoniae (1597).*
(1/93) (ARCH) ① 437 073-2AT
4, 12. PJBE, S. Cleobury (1986) *Concert*
(2/88) (ARGO) ① 417 468-2ZH
7. His Majesties Sagbutts and Cornetts, P. Bassano (r1990) *Concert* (5/91) (ASV) ① CDGAU122
7, 10, 12, 15, 16, 18, 19, 20. Wallace Collection, S. Wright *Concert* (11/90) (TELA) ① CD80204
8. Taverner Plyrs, A. Parrott *Concert*
(8/91) (EMI) ① CDC7 54117-2
17, 18, 20, 21. Taverner Plyrs, A. Parrott (r1990) *Concert* (2/92) (EMI) ① CDC7 54265-2
21. J. Holloway, S. Ritchie, A. Manze, N. North, M. Springfels, J. Toll (r1993) *Concert*
(2/94) (HARM) ① HMU90 7091
Sacrae symphoniae—8, 10 and 12 instruments (pub 1597)
1. Canzon primi toni, a 8; 2. Canzon primi toni, a 10; 3. Canzon quarti toni, a 15; 4. Canzon septimi toni, a 8; 5. Canzon septimi toni, a 8; 6. Canzon septimi e octavi toni, a 12; 7. Canzon noni toni, a 12; 8. Canzon noni toni, a 8; 9. Canzon duodecimi toni, a 8; 10. Canzon duodecimi toni, a 10; 11. Canzon

duodecimi toni, a 10; 12. Canzon duodecima toni, a 10; 13. Canzon in echo duodecimi toni, a 10; 14. Canzon sudetta accomodata per concertar con l'organo, a 10; 15. Sonata octavi toni, a 12; 16. Sonata pian e forte alla quarta bassa, a 8.
1, 6, 7, 16. Wallace Collection, S. Wright *Concert*
(11/90) (TELA) ① CD80204
3, 6, 16. Gabrieli Players, P. McCreesh *Concert*
(5/90) (VIRG) ① VC7 59006-2
4-6, 15, 16. London Cornett and Sackbutt Ens, A. Parrott (r1978) *Canzoni et Sonate (1615).*
(1/93) (ARCH) ① 437 073-2AT
5. Musica Fiata, R. Wilson (r1991) *Concert*
(8/93) (DHM) ① 05472 77183-2
13, 16. Taverner Plyrs, A. Parrott (r1990) *Concert*
(2/92) (EMI) ① CDC7 54265-2
16. E. van Evera, S. Hemington-Jones, S. Berridge, Angus Smith, Gentlemen of the Chappell, His Majesties Sagbutts and Cornetts, P. Bassano (r1990) *Concert* (5/91) (ASV) ① CDGAU122
16. BBC PO, M. Bamert (r1994: orch Stokowski)
Concert (6/95) (CHAN) ① CHAN9349

SECTION III: INSTRUMENTAL

Fantasia IV toni—organ
R. Micconi *Concert* (3/90) (MOTE) ① CD10561
Fuga IX toni—keyboard
R. Micconi *Concert* (3/90) (MOTE) ① CD10561
Taverner Plyrs, A. Parrott *Concert*
(8/91) (EMI) ① CDC7 54117-2
Intonationi—organ (pub 1593)
1. del primo tono; 2. del primo tono transportado alla quarta alta; 3. del secondo tono; 4. del secondo tono transportado alla quinta alta; 5. del terzo et quarto tono; 6. del terzo et quarto tono transportado alla quarta alta; 7. del quinto tono; 8. del quinto tono transportado alla quarta alta; 9. del sesto tono; 10. del sesto tono transportado alla quarta alta; 11. del settimo tono; 12. del settimo tono transportado alla quinta bassa; 13. del ottavo tono; 14. del ottavo tono transportado alla quarta bassa; 15. del nono tono; 16. del nono nono transportado alla quinta bassa; 17. del decimo tono; 18. del decimo tono trasportado alla quarta alta; 19. del undicesimo tono; 20. del undicesimo transportado alla quarta bassa; 21. duodecimo tono; 22. duodecimo tono transportado alla quinta bassa.
Intonazione T. Roberts (r1990; ed Roberts) *Concert*
(4/93) (ARCH) ① [2] 437 552-2AH2
8, 13. J. O'Donnell *Concert*
(5/90) (VIRG) ① VC7 59006-2
15. Taverner Plyrs, A. Parrott *Concert*
(8/91) (EMI) ① CDC7 54117-2
Ricercar ottavo tono—organ (1595)
R. Micconi *Concert* (3/90) (MOTE) ① CD10561
Ricercari del libro secundo—organ (1595)
1. Terzo tuono; 2. VII tuono; 3. VIII tuono.
Terza tuono R. Micconi *Concert*
(3/90) (MOTE) ① CD10561

SECTION IV: VOCAL AND CHORAL

Audite principes—motet (16vv) (pub 1615)
King's Consort Ch, King's Consort, R. King *Concert*
(12/90) (HYPE) ① CDA66398
Taverner Consort, Taverner Ch, Taverner Plyrs, A. Parrott (r1990) *Concert*
(2/92) (EMI) ① CDC7 54265-2
Dulcis Jesu patris imago—motet (20vv)
Taverner Consort, Taverner Ch, Taverner Plyrs, A. Parrott (r1990) *Concert*
(2/92) (EMI) ① CDC7 54265-2
Hic est filius Deus—motet (18vv) (Kassel Ms)
Taverner Consort, Taverner Ch, Taverner Plyrs, A. Parrott (r1990) *Concert*
(2/92) (EMI) ① CDC7 54265-2
Hodie Christus natus est—8vv (pub. 1603)
Wren Orch, J. Iveson, S. Saunders, R. Gowman, R. Gowman, Bernard Rose (r1977) *Concert*
(7/91) (DECC) ① 430 359-2DM
In nobil sanguine/Amor s'è in lei—6vv (pub 1587) (composed in collaboration with A. Gabrieli)
Consort of Musicke, A. Rooley (lte/dir) *Concert*
(2/89) (BIS) ① BIS-CD392
Jubilate Deo I—motet (8vv) (pub 1613)
A. Wright, Westminster Cath Ch, S. Cleobury *Concert* (7/83) (ARGO) ① 410 005-2ZH
C. Brett, W. Kendall, P. Hall, I. Caddy, R. Farnes, S. Layton, King's College Ch, PJBE, S. Cleobury (1986) *Concert* (2/88) (ARGO) ① 417 468-2ZH
Jubilate Deo II—motet (8vv) (Gumpelzhaimer Ms)
Taverner Consort, Taverner Ch, Taverner Plyrs, A. Parrott (r1990) *Concert*
(2/92) (EMI) ① CDC7 54265-2

Lieto godea—madrigal (8vv) (pub 1587)
Schütz Academy, H. Arman (r1991) *Concert*
    (5/93) (CAPR) ① 10 409
Miserere mei, Deus II—motet (4vv)
  (Gumpelzhaimer Ms)
Taverner Ch, Taverner Plyrs, A. Parrott (r1990)
  Concert   (2/92) (EMI) ① CDC7 54265-2
O Jesu mi dulcissime II—motet 8vv)
  (Gumpelzhaimer Ms)
Taverner Consort, Taverner Ch, Taverner Plyrs, A.
Parrott (r1990) *Concert*
    (2/92) (EMI) ① CDC7 54265-2
O magnum mysterium—motet (8vv) (pub
  1587)
C. Brett, W. Kendall, P. Hall, I. Caddy, R. Fames, S.
Layton, King's College Ch, PJBE, S. Cleobury
(r1986) *Concert*   (2/88) (ARGO) ① 417 468-2ZH
King's Consort Ch, King's Consort, R. King *Concert*
    (12/90) (HYPE) ① CDA66398
S. Berridge, His Majesties Sagbutts and Cornetts, P.
Bassano (r1990) *Concert*
    (5/91) (ASV) ① CDGAU122
Symphoniae sacrae—6–8, 10, 12, 14–16vv
  and instruments (pub 1597)
1. Kyrie, 12vv; 2. Gloria, 12vv; 3. Sanctus, 12vv; 4.
Benedictus, 12vv; 5. Angelus Domini descendit, 8vv;
6. Beata es, virgo Maria, 6vv; 7. Beati immaculati,
8vv; 8. Beati omnes, 8vv; 9. Benedicam Dominum,
10vv; 10. Benedixisti Domine, 7vv; 11. Cantate
Domine, 6vv; 12. Deus qui beatum Marcum, 10vv;
13. Diligam te, Domine, 8vv; 14. Domine, Dominus
noster, 8vv; 15. Domine, exaudi orationem, 8vv; 16.
Domine, exaudi orationem, 10vv; 17. Ego sum qui
sum, 8vv; 18. Exaudi Deus, 7vv; 19. Exaudi Domine,
6vv; 20. Exultate justi in Domino, 8vv; 21. Hoc tegitir,
8vv; 22. Hodie Christus natus est, 10vv; 23. In te
Domine speravi, 8vv; 24. Jam non dicam vos servos,
8vv; 25. Jubilate Deo, 8vv; 26. Jubilate Deo, 15vv;
27. Laudate nomen Domini, 8vv; 28. Magnificat, 8vv;
29. Magnificat, 12vv; 30. Magnificat, 14vv; 31.
Miserere mei, Deus, 6vv; 32. Misericordias Domini,
8vv; 33. Nunc dimittis, 14vv; 34. O Domine Jesu
Christe, 8vv; 35. O Jesu mi dulcissime, 8vv; 36.
Omnes gentes plaudite manibus, 16vv; 37. O quam
suavis, 7vv; 38. Plaudite omnis terra, 12vv; 39. Quis
est iste qui venit, 10vv; 40. Regina coeli, 12vv; 41.
Sancta et immaculata, 8vv; 42. Sancta
maria succurre miseris, 7vv; 43. Surrexit pastor
bonus, 10vv; 44. Virtute magna, 12vv.
12, 36. Gabrieli Consort, Gabrieli Players, P.
McCreesh *Concert* (5/90) (VIRG) ① VC7 59006-2
34, 36. Gentlemen of the Chappell, His Majesties
Sagbutts and Cornetts, P. Bassano (r1990) *Concert*
    (5/91) (ASV) ① CDGAU122
35. C. Brett, W. Kendall, P. Hall, I. Caddy, R. Fames,
S. Layton, King's College Ch, PJBE, S. Cleobury
(r1986) *Concert*   (2/88) (ARGO) ① 417 468-2ZH
38. Wren Orch, J. Iveson, S. Saunders, R. Gowman,
R. Gowman, Bernard Rose (r1977) *Concert*
    (7/91) (DECC) ① 430 359-2DM
Symphoniae sacrae, liber secundus—7, 8,
  10–17, 19vv and instruments (pub 1615)
1. Kyrie, 12vv; 2. Sanctus, 12vv; 3. Benedictus, 12vv;
4. Attendite popule meus, 8vv; 5. Benedictus es,
Dominus, 8vv; 6. Buccinate in neomenia tuba, 19vv;
7. Cantate Domino, 8vv; 8. Confiteibor tibi, Domine,
13vv; 9. Congratulamini mihi, 6vv; 10. Deus in
nomine tuo, 8vv; 11. Exaudi Deus, 12vv; 12. Exaudi
me Domine, 16vv; 13. Exultavit cor meum, 6vv; 14.
Hodie completi sunt, 8vv; 15. In ecclesiis, 14vv; 16.
Jubilate Deo, 10vv; 17. Litaniae BVM (Kyrie), 8vv; 18.
Magnificat, 12vv; 19. Magnificat, 14vv; 20. Magnificat,
17vv; 21. Misericordia tua Domine, 12vv; 22. O
gloriosa virgo (O gloriose Jesu), 12vv; 23. O Jesu mi
dulcissime, 8vv; 24. O quam gloriosa, 16vv; 25. O
quam suavis, 8vv; 26. Quem vidistis pastores, 14vv;
27. Salvator noster, 15vv; 28. Sancta et immaculata,
7vv; 29. Surrexit christus, 1vv; 30. Suscipe
clementissime, 12vv; 31. Vox Domini, 10vv.
14. The Sixteen, H. Christophers, L. Cummings, R.
Jeffrey (r1992) *Concert*
    (10/93) (COLL) ① Coll1360-2
15. E. Futral, J. Malafronte, F. Urrey, W. Pauley,
Musica Sacra, R. Westenburg *Concert*
    (1/93) (RCA) ① 09026 60970-2
15, 19. Taverner Ch, Taverner Consort, Taverner
Plyrs, A. Parrott *Concert*
    (8/91) (EMI) ① CDC7 54117-2
15, 26. C. Brett, W. Kendall, P. Hall, I. Caddy, R.
Fames, S. Layton, King's College Ch, PJBE, S.
Cleobury (r1986) *Concert*
    (2/88) (ARGO) ① 417 468-2ZH
19. Schütz Academy, H. Arman (r1991) *Concert*
    (5/93) (CAPR) ① 10 409
26, 27. King's Consort, King's Consort, R. King
Concert   (12/90) (HYPE) ① CDA66398

Timor et tremor—motet (6vv) (pub 1615)
C. Brett, W. Kendall, P. Hall, I. Caddy, R. Fames, S.
Layton, King's College Ch, PJBE, S. Cleobury
(r1986) *Concert*   (2/88) (ARGO) ① 417 468-2ZH

GABRIELLI, Domenico (1651–1690) Italy

SECTION I: ORCHESTRAL

Sonata à con tromba in D, D XI 8
St James's Baroque Plyrs, I. Bolton (1988) *Concert*
    (9/93) (TELD) ① 4509-91192-2

GABRILOVICH, Ossip (1878–1936) Russia/USA

SECTION III: INSTRUMENTAL

Caprice-Burlesque—piano
S. Hough (r1986) *Concert*
    (1/89) (VIRG) ① VC7 59509-2
Melodie in E—piano
S. Hough (r1986) *Concert*
    (1/89) (VIRG) ① VC7 59509-2

GACE BRULÉ (c1160–after 1213) France

SECTION IV: VOCAL AND CHORAL

A la douçour de la bele seson—chanson (1v)
  (before 1186)
Gothic Voices, C. Page *Concert*
    (10/89) (HYPE) ① CDA66336
Cil qui d'amours—grand chant: 1v
Gothic Voices, C. Page (r1994) *Concert*
    (8/95) (HYPE) ① CDA66773
De bien amer grant joie atent—grand chant:
  1v
Gothic Voices, C. Page (r1994) *Concert*
    (8/95) (HYPE) ① CDA66773
Desconfortez, plains de dolor—grand chant:
  1v
Gothic Voices, C. Page (r1994) *Concert*
    (8/95) (HYPE) ① CDA66773
Quant define fueille et flor—grand chant: 1v
Gothic Voices, C. Page (r1994) *Concert*
    (8/95) (HYPE) ① CDA66773

GADE, Niels (Wilhelm) (1817–1890) Denmark

SECTION I: ORCHESTRAL

Concerto for Violin and Orchestra in D
  minor, Op. 56 (1880)
A. Kontra, Malmö SO, P. Järvi (r1994)
  Schmidt/Jansson: Öresund Symphony.
    (6/95) (BIS) ① BIS-CD672
Echoes from Ossian (Ekterlange af
  Ossian)—overture, Op. 1 (1840)
Danish Nat RSO, D. Kitaienko *Concert*
    (11/92) (CHAN) ① CHAN9075
Aarhus RAM Orch, O. Schmidt (r1993) *Concert*
    (7/95) (KONT) ① 32194
Symphony No. 1 in C minor, Op. 5 (1840)
Stockholm Sinfonietta, N. Järvi *Symphony 8.*
    (11/87) (BIS) ① BIS-CD339
Copenhagen Collegium Musicum, M. Schønwandt
Symphony 2. (5/94) (MARC) ① DCCD9201
Symphony No. 2 in E, Op. 10 (1843)
Stockholm Sinfonietta, N. Järvi *Symphony 7.*
    (12/87) (BIS) ① BIS-CD355
Copenhagen Collegium Musicum, M. Schønwandt
Symphony 1. (5/94) (MARC) ① DCCD9201
Symphony No. 3 in A minor—1847, Op. 15
Stockholm Sinfonietta, N. Järvi *Symphony 4.*
    (7/87) (BIS) ① BIS-CD338
Symphony No. 4 in B flat, Op. 20 (1850)
Stockholm Sinfonietta, N. Järvi *Symphony 3.*
    (7/87) (BIS) ① BIS-CD338
Copenhagen Collegium Musicum, M. Schønwandt
Symphony 6. (5/94) (MARC) ① DCCD9202
Symphony No. 5 in D minor, Op. 25 (1852)
R. Pöntinen, Stockholm Sinfonietta, N. Järvi
Symphony 5. (12/87) (BIS) ① BIS-CD356
Symphony No. 6 in G minor, Op. 32 (1857)
Stockholm Sinfonietta, N. Järvi *Symphony 5.*
    (12/87) (BIS) ① BIS-CD356
Copenhagen Collegium Musicum, M. Schønwandt
Symphony 4. (5/94) (MARC) ① DCCD9202
Symphony No. 7 in F, Op. 45 (1865)
Stockholm Sinfonietta, N. Järvi *Symphony 2.*
    (12/87) (BIS) ① BIS-CD355

Symphony No. 8 in B minor, Op. 47 (1871)
Stockholm Sinfonietta, N. Järvi *Symphony 1.*
    (11/87) (BIS) ① BIS-CD339

SECTION II: CHAMBER

Capriccio in A minor—violin and piano
  (1878)
S. Elbaek, E. Westenholz (r1993) *Concert*
    (12/94) (KONT) ① 32164
3 Fantasiestücke—clarinet/violin and piano,
  Op. 43 (pub 1864)
1. Andantino con moto; 2. Allegro vivace; 3. Allegro
molto vivace.
S. Elbaek, E. Westenholz (r1993) *Concert*
    (12/94) (KONT) ① 32164
Octet in F—strings, Op. 17 (pub 1848)
Archibudelli, Smithsonian Chbr Plyrs *Mendelssohn:
Octet, Op. 20.* (3/93) (SONY) ① SK48307
Sextet in E flat—two violins, two violas and
  two cellos, Op. 44 (1863)
Johannes Ens *String Quintet 1.*
    (2/93) (KONT) ① 32121
Sonata for Violin and Piano in A (1839)
4th mvt S. Elbaek, E. Westenholz (r1993) *Concert*
    (12/94) (KONT) ① 32164
Sonata for Violin and Piano No. 1 in A, Op. 6
  (1842)
S. Elbaek, E. Westenholz *Concert*
    (3/93) (KONT) ① 32098
Sonata for Violin and Piano No. 2 in D minor,
  Op. 21 (1849)
S. Elbaek, E. Westenholz *Concert*
    (3/93) (KONT) ① 32098
Sonata for Violin and Piano No. 3 in B flat,
  Op. 59 (1885)
S. Elbaek, E. Westenholz *Concert*
    (3/93) (KONT) ① 32098
String Quartet in D, Op. 63 (1888)
Kontra Qt *Concert* (10/92) (BIS) ① BIS-CD516
String Quartet in E minor (1877)
Kontra Qt *Concert* (10/92) (BIS) ① BIS-CD516
String Quartet in F minor (1851)
Kontra Qt *Concert* (10/92) (BIS) ① BIS-CD516
String Quintet in E minor, Op. 8 (1845)
Johannes Ens *Sextet, Op. 44.*
    (2/93) (KONT) ① 32121
Volkstänze in nordischen Charakter—violin
  and piano, Op. 62 (pub 1886)
S. Elbaek, E. Westenholz (r1993) *Concert*
    (12/94) (KONT) ① 32164

SECTION III: INSTRUMENTAL

Aquarelles—piano, Op. 19 (pub 1850)
VOL. 1: 1. Elegie; 2. Scherzo; 3. Canzonette; 4.
Humoreske; 5. Barcarolle. VOL. 2: 6. Capriccio; 7.
Romance; 8. Intermezzo; 9. Novellette; 10. Scherzo.
1, 2, 3. S. Elbaek, E. Westenholz (r1993; arr vn/pf N.
Hansen) *Concert* (12/94) (KONT) ① 32164
Arabeske—piano, Op. 27 (1854)
E. Westenholz *Concert* (5/93) (KONT) ① 32124
4 Fantasy Pieces—piano, Op. 41 (1861)
E. Westenholz *Concert* (5/93) (KONT) ① 32124
Folkdance and Romance—piano
E. Westenholz *Concert* (5/93) (KONT) ① 32124
Folkdances—piano, Op. 31 (1855)
E. Westenholz *Concert* (5/93) (KONT) ① 32124
From the sketchbook—piano (1857)
E. Westenholz *Concert* (5/93) (KONT) ① 32124
Idylls—piano, Op. 34 (1857)
1. Blomsterhaven; 3. Traekfugle; 4.
Abenddämmerung.
E. Westenholz *Concert* (5/93) (KONT) ① 32124
4. S. Elbaek, E. Westenholz (r1993; arr vn/pf N.
Hansen) *Concert* (12/94) (KONT) ① 32164

SECTION IV: VOCAL AND CHORAL

Comala (after Ossian)—cantata: soloists,
  chorus and orchestra, Op. 12 (pub 1846)
A.M. Dahl, E. Halling, H. Katagiri, J. Mannov,
Canzone Ch, Sønderjylland SO, F. Rasmussen
(r1993)   (11/94) (CHAN) ① CHAN9180
Elf-king's daughter (Elverskud)—soloists,
  chorus and orchestra, Op. 30 (pub 1853)
E. Johansson, A. Gjevang, P. Elming, Danish Nat
Rad Ch, Danish Nat RSO, D. Kitaienko *Concert*
    (11/92) (CHAN) ① CHAN9075
Oft when I ride—song (Wds. K. F. Molbech)
L. Melchior, Orch (r1913) *Concert*
    (8/88) (DANA) ① [2] DACOCD311/2
5 Songs—chorus a capella, Op. 13 (pub
  1846) (Wds. various)
1. Ritter Frühling (wds. E. Geibel); 2. Die Wasserrose
(wds. E. Geibel); 3. Morgenwanderung (wds. E.
Geibel); 4. Herbstlied (wds. L. Tieck); 5. Im Wald
(wds. E. Geibel).

Danish Nat Rad Chbr Ch, S. Parkman *Concert*
(11/92) (CHAN) ① **CHAN9075**

GAERTNER, Eduard *(1862–1918)* Austria

SECTION III: INSTRUMENTAL

Viennese Dances—piano
EXCERPTS: 1. No 1; 2. No 2.
2. L. Howard (arr. Friedman) *Concert*
(12/86) (HYPE) ① **CDA66090**

GAGLIANO, Marco Da *(1582–1643)* Italy

SECTION IV: VOCAL AND CHORAL

Valli profonde, al sol memiche
rupi—madrigal: 1v and continuo (pub 1615)
(Wds. L. Tansillo)
N. Rogers, C. Tilney, A. Bailes, J. Savall, P. Ros
(r1975) *Concert*   (1/93) (ARCH) ① **437 075-2AT**

GÁL, Hans *(1890–1987)* Austria

SECTION II: CHAMBER

Sonata for Clarinet and Piano, Op. 84 (1964)
M. Khouri, J. McCabe (r1990) *Concert*
(8/93) (CNTI) ① **CCD1027**

GALÁN, Cristóbal *(c1630–1684)* Spain

SECTION IV: VOCAL AND CHORAL

Al espejo que retrata—villancico: 9vv & instruments
Al Ayre Español, E. L. Banzo (r1994) *Concert*
(8/95) (DHM) ① **05472 77325-2**
Humano ardor—sacred duet
Al Ayre Español, E. L. Banzo (r1994) *Concert*
(8/95) (DHM) ① **05472 77325-2**

GALILEI, Vincenzo *(late 1520s–1591)* Italy

SECTION III: INSTRUMENTAL

Fronimo—instrumental treatise (pub 1568)
1. Duo tutti di fantasia; 2. Ricercare (Lorenzini).
1, 2. J. Lindberg (r1991) *Concert*
(11/93) (BIS) ① **BIS-CD599**
Polymnia—lute (1584)
P. O'Dette *Concert*   (4/88) (HYPE) ① **CDA66228**

GALINDO DIMAS, Blas *(b 1910)* Mexico

SECTION I: ORCHESTRAL

Sones de Mariachi—1953
Xalapa SO, H. de la Fuente *Concert*
(12/93) (CARL) ① **MCD63**

GALL, Jan Karol *(1856–1912)* Poland

SECTION IV: VOCAL AND CHORAL

The enchanted princess—song
A. Didur, anon (r1901) *Concert*
(6/93) (PEAR) ① [3] **GEMMCDS9997/9(2)**
Hidden love—song
A. Didur, anon (r1900) *Concert*
(6/93) (PEAR) ① [3] **GEMMCDS9997/9(2)**
A. Didur, anon (r1901) *Concert*
(6/93) (PEAR) ① [3] **GEMMCDS9997/9(2)**
I love men—song
I. Bohuss, anon (r1902) *Concert*
(6/93) (PEAR) ① [3] **GEMMCDS9004/6(1)**

GALLIERA, Arnaldo *(1871–1934)* Italy

SECTION III: INSTRUMENTAL

Venerdi Santo dal 'Trittico'—organ
L. Benedetti (r1992) *Concert*
(4/95) (PRIO) ① **PRCD427**

GALLO, Domenico *(1730–?)* Italy

SECTION II: CHAMBER

12 Trio Sonatas—two violins and continuo (pub 1771) (incorrectly attrib Pergolesi)
1. G; 1a. Moderato; 2. B flat; 2a. Presto; 7. G minor;
7a. Allegro; 12. E.
1, 2. Europa Galante, F. Biondi (vn/dir) (r1993)
Concert   (4/94) (O111) ① **OPS30-88**
12. N. Milstein, L. Mittman (r1937; arr Longo) *Concert*
(10/92) (BIDD) ① **LAB055**

GALLOT, Jacques *(c1600–c1690)* France

SECTION III: INSTRUMENTAL

Pieces in A minor—lute
1. Prélude; 2. Allemande le bout de l'an de Mr
Gautier; 3. Courante la Cigogne; 4. Canaries les
Castagnettes; 5. Gavotte la Jalousée; 6. Volte la
Brugeloise; 7. Folies d'Espagne.
1-7. H. Smith (r1994) *Concert*
(8/95) (ASTR) ① **E8528**
Pieces in C—lute
1. Chaconne la Comète.
1. H. Smith (r1994) *Concert*
(8/95) (ASTR) ① **E8528**
Pieces in D minor—lute
1. Pavane Tombeau de la Reyne; 2. Courante la
Bonne Aventure; 3. Sarabande la Mignarde.
1-3. H. Smith (r1994) *Concert*
(8/95) (ASTR) ① **E8528**
Pieces in F—lute
1. Allemande la Belle Voilée, Duchesse de la
Valliere; 2. Courante le Tonnerre.
1, 2. H. Smith (r1994) *Concert*
(8/95) (ASTR) ① **E8528**
Pieces in F sharp minor—lute
1. Prélude; 2. Tombeau de muses françoises, le
chefdoeuvre de Mr Gallot V; 3. Courante l'Eternelle;
4. Sarabande la Divine; 5. Gigue la Grande Virago; 6.
Chaconne le Doge de Venise; 7. Sarabande la Sans
Pareille.
1-7. H. Smith (r1994) *Concert*
(8/95) (ASTR) ① **E8528**

GALOS, C. *(19th Cent)*

SECTION III: INSTRUMENTAL

Chant du Berger—piano
A. Etherden *Concert*
(7/93) (HUNT) ① **HMPCD0589**

GALUPPI, Baldassare *(1706–1785)* Italy

SECTION I: ORCHESTRAL

Concerto for Flute and Strings in D
J. Galway, Solisti Veneti, C. Scimone (r1991) *Concert*
(4/94) (RCA) ① **09026 61164-2**
Concerto for Harpsichord and Strings in G
Solisti Italiani *Concert*
(10/89) (DENO) ① **CO-73335**

SECTION II: CHAMBER

Sonata for Flute, Oboe and Harpsichord
R. Micconi (arr org) *Concert*
(3/90) (MOTE) ① **CD10561**

SECTION III: INSTRUMENTAL

Andantino—keyboard
R. Veyron-Lacroix (r1989) *Concert*
(12/93) (ERAT) ① **4509-92135-2**
Largo in F—keyboard
R. Micconi *Concert*   (3/90) (MOTE) ① **CD10561**
Sonata in D minor—keyboard
R. Micconi *Concert*   (3/90) (MOTE) ① **CD10561**

SECTION IV: VOCAL AND CHORAL

Arripe alpestri ad vallem—alto and strings
G. Lesne, Seminario musicale (r1992) *Confitebor tibi,
Domini.*   (10/94) (VIRG) ① **VC5 45030-2**
**Confitebor tibi, Domini—motet: soprano,
alto, bass, flutes and strings (1733)**
V. Gens, G. Lesne, P. Harvey, Seminario musicale
(r1992) *Arripe alpestri ad vallem.*
(10/94) (VIRG) ① **VC5 45030-2**

Magnificat in G—soprano, chorus and orchestra
A.-M. Miranda, R. Bollen, Berne Chbr Ch, South-West
German CO, J.E. Dähler *Vivaldi: Gloria, RV589.*
(10/86) (CLAV) ① **CD50-0801**

GAMBARDELLA, Salvatore *(19th/20th Cent)* Italy

SECTION IV: VOCAL AND CHORAL

O marenariello—Song (1893) (Wds.
Ottaviano)
L. Pavarotti, Teatro Communale Orch, A. Guadagno
(8/83) (DECC) ① **410 015-2DH**

GANDOLFI, Martin *(b 1956)* USA

SECTION I: ORCHESTRAL

Points of Departure—chamber orchestra (1988)
1. Spirale; 2. Strati; 3. Visione; 4. Ritorno.
Orpheus CO (r1990) *Concert*
(7/93) (DG) ① **435 389-2GH**

GANNE, (Gustave) Louis *(1862–1923)* France

SECTION II: CHAMBER

Andante et Scherzo—flute and piano
S. Milan, I. Brown *Concert*
(11/88) (CHAN) ① **CHAN8609**

SECTION V: STAGE WORKS

**Hans, le Jouer de Flûte—operetta: 3 acts
(1906—Monte Carlo)** (Lib. M. Vaucaire & G.
Mitchell)
Cpte M. Dens, N. Broissin, J. Peyron, A. Balbon, G.
Parat, R. Lenoty, M. Sansonnetti, G. Rey, Génio, P.
Roi, M. Enot, R. Liot, J. Levasseur, J. Mollien, A.
Caurat, M. Rossignol, French Rad Chor, French Rad
Lyric Orch, J. Gressier (bp1957) *Saltimbanques.*
(3/92) (MUSD) ① [2] **20151-2**
**Les Saltimbanques—opéra-comique (3 acts)
(1899—Paris)** (Lib. M. Ordonneau)
C'est l'amour M. Hill Smith, P. Morrison, Chandos
Sngrs, Chandos Concert Orch, S. Barry (Eng)
Concert   (2/90) (CHAN) ① **CHAN8759**
Excs J. Micheau, R. Massard, G. Moizan, R. Amade,
M. Roux, chor, orch, P. Dervaux (bp1958) *Hans.*
(3/92) (MUSD) ① [2] **20151-2**

GANNON, Lee *(b 1960)* USA

SECTION II: CHAMBER

**Triad-O-Rama—2 oboes, 2 clarinets, 2 horns
and 2 bassoons (1993)**
Aspen wind Qnt, R. Dallessio, D. Gilbert, D. Grabois,
S. Dibner (r1993) *Concert*
(7/94) (CATA) ① **09026 61979-2**

GANZ, Rudolph *(1877–1972)* USA

SECTION III: INSTRUMENTAL

St. Louis Symphony March (1923)
St Louis SO, L. Slatkin (orch R.Hayman) *Concert*
(6/89) (RCA) ① **RD87716**

GARCÍA, Manuel *(1775–1832)* Spain

SECTION V: STAGE WORKS

**Il Califfo di Bagdad—opera (2 acts)
(1813—Naples)** (Lib. Tottola)
Ogni piacere è grato M. Moreno, K. John, Philh, D.
Parry *Concert*   (10/96) (OPRA) ① [3] **ORCH103**

GARCÍA LORCA, Federico *(1898–1936)* Spain

SECTION IV: VOCAL AND CHORAL

13 Canciones españolas antiguas
1. Anda, jaleo; 2. Los cuatro muleros; 3. Las tres
hojas; 4. Los mozos de Monleón; 5. Las morillas de
Jaén; 6. Sevillanas del siglo XVIII; 7. El café de
Chinitas; 8. Nana de Sevilla; 9. Los pelegrinitos; 10.
Zorongo; 11. Romance de Don Boyso; 12. Los reyes
de la baraja; 13. La Tarara.
T. Berganza, N. Yepes *Concert*
(12/92) (DG) ① [2] **435 848-2GX2**

GARÇIMUÑOZ (15th–16th Cent)
Spain

SECTION IV: VOCAL AND CHORAL

Pues bien, para ésta (from the Palacio Song
Book)
Hespérion XX, J. Savall *Concert*
(7/92) (ASTR) ① **E8762**

GARDANE, Antonio (1509–1569)
France

SECTION II: CHAMBER

**Intabolatura Nova de Varie Sorte de
Balli—dance collection** (pub 1551)
1. Gagliarda Moneghina; 2. Gagliarda la Canella.
1, 2. Broadside Band, J. Barlow *Concert*
(3/88) (HYPE) ① **CDA66244**

GARDANO, Angelo (1540–1611)
Italy

SECTION IV: VOCAL AND CHORAL

Stava a pie de la croce—lauda (pub 1588)
(Primo libro delle laudi. Wds Giustiniani)
Daedalus Ens (r1992) *Concert*
(11/93) (ACCE) ① **ACC9289D**

GARDEL, Carlos (c1887–1935)
Argentina

SECTION IV: VOCAL AND CHORAL

El Día que me quieras—tango (Wds. A. Le
Pera)
Buenos Aires Qnt, RPO, E. Stratta (arr J. Calandrelli)
Concert (1/93) (TELD) ① **9031-76997-2**

GARDINER, Henry Balfour
(1877–1950) England

SECTION I: ORCHESTRAL

**Shepherd Fennell's Dance—orchestra
(c1911)**
Liverpool PO, M. Sargent (r1947) *Concert*
(5/95) (DUTT) ① **CDAX8012**

SECTION III: INSTRUMENTAL

Humoresque—piano (pub 1906)
Peter Jacobs *Concert* (10/92) (CNTI) ① **CCD1049**
The **Joyful Homecoming—quick march:
piano** (1919) (original orchestral version lost)
Peter Jacobs *Concert* (10/92) (CNTI) ① **CCD1049**
Mere—piano (pub 1905)
Peter Jacobs *Concert* (10/92) (CNTI) ① **CCD1049**
Michaelchurch—piano (1920-25)
Peter Jacobs *Concert* (10/92) (CNTI) ① **CCD1049**
Noël—piano (pub 1908) (also for 2 pfs—pub
1935; and orch)
Peter Jacobs *Concert* (10/92) (CNTI) ① **CCD1049**
5 Pieces—piano (pub 1911)
1. Molto allegro; 2. Adagio non troppo; 3. London
Bridge—Allegretto; 4. Andante con moto assai; 5.
Gavotte—Allegro assai.
Peter Jacobs *Concert* (10/92) (CNTI) ① **CCD1049**
Prelude No. 2—piano (pub 1920)
Peter Jacobs *Concert* (10/92) (CNTI) ① **CCD1049**
Salamanca—piano (1920)
Peter Jacobs *Concert* (10/92) (CNTI) ① **CCD1049**
Shenadoah, and other pieces—piano (pub
1922)
1. Con brio; 2. Allegretto; 3. Molto allegro e vivace; 4.
Shenadoah—Andante; 5. Allegro giusto.
Peter Jacobs *Concert* (10/92) (CNTI) ① **CCD1049**

SECTION IV: VOCAL AND CHORAL

**Evening Hymn, 'Te lucis ante
terminum'—anthem** (1903) (Wds. 8th Cent
Anon)
St Paul's Cath Ch, Andrew Lucas, John Scott
Concert (9/90) (HYPE) ① **CDA66374**
Norwich Cath Ch, M. Nicholas, N. Taylor *Concert*
(3/92) (PRIO) ① **PRCD351**
Trinity Coll Ch, Cambridge, R. Marlow (r1993)
Concert (2/94) (CONI) ① **CDCF219**
**Winter, 'When the icicles hang by the
wall'—song** (1908) (Wds. Shakespeare)
A. Rolfe Johnson, G. Johnson *Concert*
(5/92) (HYPE) ① **CDA66480**

GARDNER, Clarence G.
(19th–20th Cent) USA

SECTION IV: VOCAL AND CHORAL

Love is mine—song (Wds. E. Teschemacher)
E. Caruso, orch (r1911) *Concert*
(3/91) (PEAR) ① [3] **EVC2**
E. Caruso, orch, W.B. Rogers (r1911) *Concert*
(7/91) (RCA) ① [12] **GD60495(4)**
Trusting Eyes—song (wds. E.
Teschemacher)
E. Caruso, orch, W.B. Rogers (r1914) *Concert*
(7/91) (RCA) ① [12] **GD60495(5)**
E. Caruso, orch, W.B. Rogers (r1914) *Concert*
(10/91) (PEAR) ① [3] **EVC3(1)**

GARDNER, Johann von (b 1898)
Russia

SECTION IV: VOCAL AND CHORAL

The **Cross, exalted, invites all
creation—Russian liturgical chant**
N. Gedda, Paris Russian Orthodox Cath Ch, E. Evetz
Concert (1/93) (PHIL) ① **434 174-2PM**

GARDNER, Samuel (1891–1984)
Ukraine/USA

SECTION II: CHAMBER

2 Pieces—violin and piano, Op. 5 (1918)
EXCERPTS: 1. From the Canebrake.
1. J. Heifetz, M. Kaye (r1944) *Concert*
(11/94) (RCA) ① [65] **09026 61778-2(19)**

GARNER, Erroll (Louis)
(1921–1977) USA

SECTION III: INSTRUMENTAL

Erroll's Blues—piano
J. MacGregor (trans MacGregor) *Concert*
(8/89) (COLL) ① **Coll1299-2**
Erroll's Bounce—piano
J. MacGregor (trans MacGregor) *Concert*
(8/89) (COLL) ① **Coll1299-2**
Misty—piano (used in the film 'Play Misty For
Me')
Thurston Cl Qt (arr cl qt: Bland) *Concert*
(10/93) (ASV) ① **CDWHL2076**

GARTH, John (1722–1810)
England

SECTION I: ORCHESTRAL

**Concerto for Cello and Orchestra in B flat,
Op. 1/2** (pub 1760)
A. Baillie, ECCO, D. Demetriades *Concert*
(8/88) (HYPE) ① **CDH88015**

GASTALDON, Stanislaus
(1861–1939) Italy

SECTION IV: VOCAL AND CHORAL

Musica proibita—song, Op. 5 (1881) (Wds. N.
Malpadi)
P. Domingo, NYPO, Z. Mehta (pp1988) *Concert*
(9/89) (SONY) ① **MK44942**
E. Caruso, orch, J. Pasternack (r1917) *Concert*
(7/91) (RCA) ① [12] **GD60495(6)**
E. Caruso, orch, J. Pasternack (r1917) *Concert*
(10/91) (PEAR) ① [3] **EVC4(1)**
T. Parvis, orch (r c1910) *Concert*
(12/94) (BONG) ① **GB1043-2**
Ti vorrei rapire—song
T. Parvis, orch (r c1910) *Concert*
(12/94) (BONG) ① **GB1043-2**

GASTOLDI, Giovanni Giacomo
(c1550–1622) Italy

SECTION II: CHAMBER

Balletti a cinque voci—dance collection (pub
1591)
1. Balletto La Sirena.
1. Broadside Band, J. Barlow *Concert*
(3/88) (HYPE) ① **CDA66244**

SECTION IV: VOCAL AND CHORAL

Un **Novo cacciator—madrigal: 5vv**
M. Arruabarrena, K. van Laethem, M. Valenta, J.
Benet, M. van Altena, J. Cabré, T. de Zwart, A. Pols,
R. Van Der Meer, K. Junghänel (lte/dir) *Concert*
(1/92) (ACCE) ① **ACC8864D**
Viver lieto voglio
Amaryllis Consort *Concert*
(6/86) (CARL) ① **PCD822**

GAUBERT, Philippe (1879–1941)
France

SECTION II: CHAMBER

Ballade—flute and piano (1927)
S. Milan, I. Brown *Concert*
(11/91) (CHAN) ① [2] **CHAN8981/2**
Berceuse—flute and piano (1907)
S. Milan, I. Brown *Concert*
(11/91) (CHAN) ① [2] **CHAN8981/2**
2 Esquisses—flute and piano (1914)
1. Soir sur la plaine; 2. Orientale.
S. Milan, I. Brown *Concert*
(11/91) (CHAN) ① [2] **CHAN8981/2**
Fantaisie—flute and piano (1912)
S. Milan, I. Brown *Concert*
(11/88) (CHAN) ① **CHAN8609**
S. Milan, I. Brown *Concert*
(11/91) (CHAN) ① [2] **CHAN8981/2**
Madrigal—flute and piano (1908)
S. Milan, I. Brown *Concert*
(11/91) (CHAN) ① [2] **CHAN8981/2**
Morceau symphonique
C. Lindberg, R. Pöntinen *Concert*
(9/85) (BIS) ① **BIS-CD298**
**Nocturne et Allegro Scherzando—flute and
piano** (1906)
S. Milan, I. Brown *Concert*
(11/88) (CHAN) ① **CHAN8609**
W. Bennett, ECO, S. Bedford *Concert*
(10/89) (ASV) ① **CDDCA652**
S. Milan, I. Brown *Concert*
(11/91) (CHAN) ① [2] **CHAN8981/2**
Romance—flute and piano (1905)
S. Milan, I. Brown *Concert*
(11/91) (CHAN) ① [2] **CHAN8981/2**
Sicilienne—flute and piano (1914)
S. Milan, I. Brown *Concert*
(11/91) (CHAN) ① [2] **CHAN8981/2**
Sonata No. 1—flute and piano (1917)
S. Milan, I. Brown *Concert*
(11/91) (CHAN) ① [2] **CHAN8981/2**
P. Lloyd, R. Holt *Concert* (9/92) (CARL) ① **PCD991**
Sonata No. 2—flute and piano (1924)
S. Milan, I. Brown *Concert*
(11/91) (CHAN) ① [2] **CHAN8981/2**
Sonata No. 3—flute and piano (1933)
S. Milan, I. Brown *Concert*
(11/91) (CHAN) ① [2] **CHAN8981/2**
Sonatine—flute and piano (1937)
S. Milan, I. Brown *Concert*
(11/91) (CHAN) ① [2] **CHAN8981/2**
Suite—flute and piano (1921)
1. Invocation (danse de prêtresses); 2. Berceuse
orientale; 3. Barcarolle; 4. Scherzo-Valse.
S. Milan, I. Brown *Concert*
(11/91) (CHAN) ① [2] **CHAN8981/2**
Sur l'eau—flute and piano (1910)
S. Milan, I. Brown *Concert*
(11/91) (CHAN) ① [2] **CHAN8981/2**

GAULTIER, Denis (1603–1672)
France

SECTION III: INSTRUMENTAL

Gigue—lute
L. Kirchhof *Concert* (11/92) (SONY) ① **SK48068**
Rhétorique des Dieux—lute suites (c1652)
(compiled from various individual movts)
1. SUITE IN D: 1a. Pavane: La Dedicasse; 1b.
Allemande: Phaeton Foudroye; 1c. Gigue: La
Panegirique; 1d. Courante: Minerve; 1e. Courante et
Double: Ulysse; 1f. Sarabande; 2. SUITE IN A: 2a.
Prélude; 2b. Allemande: Le Tombeau de M.
Blancrocher (Andromede); 2c. Courante: Diane; 2d.
Courante: La Coquette Virtuosa; 2e. Gigue; 2f.
Gigue: Atalante; 2g. Chaconne en rondeaux; 3.
SUITE IN F SHARP MINOR: 3a. Allemande; 3b.
Rondeau; 3c. Gaillarde: Mars Superbe; 3d. Courante
et Double: Cleopatre amante; 3e. Sarabande; 4.
SUITE IN F SHARP MINOR: 4a. Courante ou Volte:
Artemise ou l'Oraison Funèbre; 4b. Courante: Le
Triomphe; 4c. Volte; 4d. Gigue; 4e. Gigue; 5. SUITE

IN G: 5a. Allemande; 5b. Courante et Double; 5c.
Courante et Double; 5d. Courante et Double; 5e.
Sarabande; 6. SUITE IN F: 6a. Allemande: Appolon
Orateur; 6b. Courante; 6c. Courante et Double; 6d.
Sarabande; 7. SUITE IN F: 7a. Allemande; 7b.
Courante: La Caressante; 7c. Canarie: 8. SUITE IN
G MINOR: 8a. Pavane: Circe; 8b. Courante:
Cephale; 8c. Sarabande; 9. SUITE IN G MINOR: 9a.
Allemande: L'Héroïque; 9b. Courante; 10. SUITE IN
A MINOR: 10a. Prélude; 10b. Allemande: Orphée;
10c. Gigue: Echos; 10d. Courante; 10e. Courante: La
Belle Homicide (L'Homicide); 10f. Sarabande; 10g.
Gaillarde: La Gaillarde; 10h. Courante et Double: La
Champre; 11. SUITE IN A MINOR: 11a. Pavane;
11b. Gigue: La Pastorale; 11c. Courante: La Belle
Ténébreuse (Narcisse); 11d. Courante: Junon ou La
Jalouse; 11e. Volte; 12. SUITE IN A MINOR: 12a.
Allemande: Tombeau de M. de Lenclos; 12b. Volte:
La Consolation aux Amis du Sr. Lenclos; 12c.
Sarabande: La Resolution des Amis du Sr. Lenclos
sur sa Mort.
  L. Pernot   (6/90) (ACCO) ① [2] 20070-2

GAULTIER, Ennemond (1575–1651) France

SECTION III: INSTRUMENTAL

Chaconne—lute
  L. Kirchhof Concert   (11/92) (SONY) ① SK48068

GAUNT, Percy (1852–1896) USA

SECTION V: STAGE WORKS

A Trip to Chinatown—musical show
(1891—New York) (Book & Lyrics Charles H
Hoyt)
  EXCERPTS: 1. Reuben and Cynthia; 2. The Bowery.
  1, 2. Cincinnati Uni Sngrs, Cincinnati Uni Th Orch, E.
  Rivers (r1978) Concert   (4/94) (NEW) ① 80221-2

GAUSSIN, Allain (b 1943) France

SECTION II: CHAMBER

Chakra—string quartet (1984)
  Arditti Qt Concert   (9/92) (MONT) ① 782002

GAUTHIER DE COINCY (1177/8–1236) France

SECTION IV: VOCAL AND CHORAL

Le Cycle de Sainte Leochade—song cycle
  EXERPTS: 1. Que de mémoyre; 2. Las, las, las; 3.
  Quatre jours plains; 4. Sour cest rivage; 5. N'est pas
  merveille; 6. De sainte Leochade.
  A. Azéma, C. A. Fulton, S. Kammen, J. Lepkoff
  (r1993) Concert   (11/94) (ERAT) ① 4509-94830-2

GAUTIER D'ANGLETERRE, Jaques (c1595–after 1652) France/England

SECTION III: INSTRUMENTAL

3 Courantes—lute (in Lord Herbert of
Cherbury's Lute Book)
  1. Courante; 2. 'Son adieu'; 3. Courante sur 'J'avois
  brisé mesfers'.
  P. O'Dette Concert   (4/93) (HARM) ① HMU90 7068

GAUTIER DE DARGIES (c1165–after 1236) France

SECTION IV: VOCAL AND CHORAL

Autre que je ne seuill fas—isorhythmic poem
(13th cent)
  Gothic Voices, C. Page Concert
                           (12/90) (HYPE) ① CDA66423
La Doce pensee—descort: 1v
  Gothic Voices, C. Page (r1994) Concert
                           (8/95) (HYPE) ① CDA66773

GAWTHROP, Daniel (20th Cent) USA

SECTION III: INSTRUMENTAL

Exultate—organ, Op. 3/3 (1984)
  J. Rees-Williams Concert
                           (4/91) (ABBE) ① CDCA902

GAY, John (1685–1732) England

SECTION V: STAGE WORKS

The Beggar's Opera (1728—London) (Lib.
cpsr: composed in association with Pepusch)
  EXCERPTS: 1. Overture. ACT 1: 2. Through all the
  employments of life; 3. 'Tis woman that seduces all
  mankind; 4. If any wench Venus' girdle wear; 5. If
  love the virgin's heart invade; 6. A maiden is like the
  golden ore; 7. Virgins are like the fair flower in its
  lustre; 8. Our Polly is like a ship; 9. Can love be
  control'd by advice?; 10. O Polly, you might have
  toy'd and kissed; 11. I like a ship in storms was
  tossed; 12. A fox may steal your hens, sir; 13. Oh,
  ponder well!; 14. The turtle thus with plaintive crying;
  15. Pretty Polly say; 16. My heart was so free; 17.
  When I laid on Greenland's coast; 18. O what pain it
  is to part!; 19. The miser thus a shilling sees. ACT 2:
  20. Fill ev'ry glass, for wine inspires us; 21. Let us
  take the road; 22. If the heart of a man is deprest; 23.
  Youth's the season made for joys; 24. Before the
  barn door crowing; 25. The gamesters and lawyers
  are jugglers alike; 26. At the Tree I shall suffer with
  pleasure; 27. Man may escape from rope and gun;
  28. Thus when a good huswife sees a rat; 29. How
  cruel are the traitors; 30. The first time at the looking-
  glass; 31. When you censure the age; 32. Is then his
  fate decreed, sir?; 33. You'll think e'er many ways
  ensure; 34. If you at an office solicit your due; 35.
  This when the swallow seeking prey; 36. How happy
  could I be with either; 37. I'm bubbled; 38. Cease
  your fuming; 39. How now, Madame Flirt?; 40.
  No power on earth can e'er divide; 41. I like the fox
  shall grieve. ACT 3: 42. When young at the bar; 43.
  My love is all madness and folly; 44. Thus gamesters
  united in friendship are found; 45. The modes of court
  so common are grown; 46. What gudgeons are we
  men!; 47. In the days of my youth; 48. I'm like a skiff
  on the ocean tossed; 49. When a wife's in her pout;
  50. A curse attends that woman's love; 51. Among
  the men, coquets we find; 52. Come, sweet lass; 53.
  Hither, dear husband; 54. Which way shall I turn
  me?; 55. When my hero in court appears; 56. When
  he holds up his hand; 57. Ourselves, like the great;
  58. The charge is prepar'd; 59. O cruel, cruel, cruel
  case!; 60. Of all the friends in time of grief; 61. Since I
  must swing; 62. But now again my spirits sink; 63.
  But valour the stronger grows; 64. If thus a man must
  die; 65. So I drink off this bumper; 66. But can I leave
  my pretty hussies; 67. Their days, their lips, their
  busses; 68. Since laws were made for ev'ry degree;
  69. Would I might be hung'd; 70. Thus I stand like a
  Turk.
  Cpte K. Te Kanawa, J. Morris, J. Sutherland, S.
    Dean, A. Marks, A. Lansbury, R. Resnik, A. Rolfe
    Johnson, G. Clark, A. Murray, A. Wilkens, J. Gibbs,
    W. Mitchell, M. Hordern, London Voices, National
    PO, R. Bonynge (arr Bonynge/Gamley)
                         (5/91) (DECC) ① [2] 430 066-2DH2
  Cpte B. Mills, Adrian Thompson, Anne Dawson, R.
    Jackson, C. Daniels, Sarah Walker, Sarah Walker, I.
    Honeyman, R. Bryson, C. Wyn-Rogers, B. Hoskins, I.
    Caddy, Broadside Band, J. Barlow
                         (1/92) (HYPE) ① [2] CDA66591/2
  Cpte A. Murray, P. Langridge, Y. Kenny, J.
    Rawnsley, R. Lloyd, A. Collins, N. Willis, C. Gillett, D.
    Mulholland, Aldeburgh Fest Ch, Aldeburgh Fest
    Orch, S. Bedford (ed/arr Britten)
                         (9/93) (ARGO) ① [2] 436 850-2ZHO2
  Cpte J. Waters, P. Gilmore, F. Cuka, J. Carter, J.
    Cossins, H. Hazell, P. Kenton, D. Calder, A.
    Richards, R. Durden, London Cast, N. Rhoden
    (r1968; ed Turner, orch Pearce-Higgins; without
    dialogue)   (10/94) (SONY) ① SMK66171
  7, 38. K. Te Kanawa, National PO, R. Bonynge
    Concert   (11/87) (DECC) ① 417 645-2DH
  10, 16, 17. C. Willis, A. Mildmay, Roy Henderson, M.
    Redgrave, orch, M. Mudie (r1940) Concert
                         (6/94) (EMI) ① CDH5 65072-2
  45. Broadside Band (Tune: Lilliburlero) Concert
                         (3/88) (AMON) ① CD-SAR28

GAZTAMBIDE, Joaquín (1822–1870) Spain

SECTION V: STAGE WORKS

Una Vieja—zarzuela: 1 act (1860—Madrid)
(Lib. D. F. Camprodon)
  Un español que vien A. Cortis, orch (r1925) Concert
                         (3/94) (NIMB) ① NI7850

GAZZANIGA, Giuseppe (1743–1818) Italy

SECTION IV: VOCAL AND CHORAL

Gloria—3vv, chorus and orchestra
  L. Viviani, G. Chiarini, M. Scardoni, Verona Cath
  Cappella Musicale, A. Turco (pp1992) Stabat Mater.
                         (5/94) (BONG) ① GB5518-2
Stabat Mater—4vv, chorus and orchestra
  L. Viviani, M.T. Toso, G. Chiarini, M. Scardoni,
  Verona Cath Cappella Musicale, A. Turco (pp1992)
  Gloria.   (5/94) (BONG) ① GB5518-2

SECTION V: STAGE WORKS

Don Giovanni Tenorio o sia Il convitato di
pietra—opera: 1 act (1787—Venice) (Lib.
Bertati)
  Cpte J. Aler, E. Steinsky, P. Coburn, M. Kinzel, G.
    von Kannen, R. Swensen, J. Kaufman, J-L.
    Chaignaud, A. Scharinger, A. Rosner, Bavarian Rad
    Chor, Munich RO, S. Soltesz
                         (4/91) (ORFE) ① [2] C214902H
  Cpte D. Johnson, E. Szmytka, L. Serra, E. Schmid, J.
    Tilli, C. Allemano, E. Szmytka, F. Furlanetto, A.
    Scharinger, H. Wildhaber, Stuttgart Chbr Ch,
    Tafelmusik, B. Weil (omits recits)
                         (1/92) (SONY) ① SK46693

GEEHL, Henry Ernest (1881–1961) England

SECTION IV: VOCAL AND CHORAL

For you alone—song (Wds. P. J. O'Reilly)
  E. Caruso, orch (r1910) Concert
                         (12/90) (NIMB) ① NI7809
  E. Caruso, orch (r1910) Concert
                         (3/91) (PEAR) ① [3] EVC2
  E. Caruso, orch (r1910) Concert
                         (7/91) (RCA) ① [12] GD60495(3)
  R. Tauber, Dajos Bela Orch (r1920s: Ger) Concert
                         (9/92) (MMOI) ① CDMOIR409
  R. Crooks, orch (r1931) Concert
                         (9/93) (CLAR) ① CDGSE78-50-50

GEIJER, Erik Gustaf (1783–1847) Sweden

SECTION IV: VOCAL AND CHORAL

The Dance (Dansen)—duet
  E. Söderström, K. Meyer, J. Eyron (r1974) Concert
                         (9/93) (BIS) ① BIS-CD017

GELDARD, William (20th Cent) England

SECTION I: ORCHESTRAL

Tribute to Ted Heath—brass band
  Desford Colliery Caterpillar Band, J. Watson
  (pp1991) Concert   (8/92) (POLY) ① QPRL049D

GELINEK, Josef (1758–1825) Austria

SECTION III: INSTRUMENTAL

Air de mystères d'Isis—piano (pub 1805)
(after Mozart's 'Die Zauberflöte')
  C. Katsaris (r1992) Concert
                         (6/93) (SONY) ① SK52551

GEMINIANI, Francesco (Xaverio) (1687–1762) Italy

SECTION I: ORCHESTRAL

12 Concerti Grossi (pub 1726-27)
(arrangements of Corelli's Sonatas, Op. 5)
  1. D; 2. B flat; 3. C; 4. F; 5. G minor; 6. A; 7. D minor;
  8. E minor; 9. A; 10. F; 11. E; 12. D minor (La folia).
  3, 5. Tafelmusik, J. Lamon Concerti grossi, Op. 2.
                         (11/92) (SONY) ① SK48043
  5, 12. Petite Bande, S. Kuijken Concert
                         (11/90) (DHM) ① GD77010
  12. Purcell Band Concert
                         (11/88) (HYPE) ① CDA66264
  12. Solisti Italiani Concert
                         (10/89) (DENO) ① CO-73335
  12. English Concert, T. Pinnock (hpd/dir) (r1979)
  Concert   (1/93) (ARCH) ① 437 088-2AT

6 Concerti Grossi, Op. 2 (pub 1732 rev 1755)
1. C minor; 2. C minor; 3. D minor; 4. D; 5. D minor; 6. A.
Tafelmusik, J. Lamon Concerti grossi (Corelli Op. 5).
(11/92) (SONY) ① SK48043
2. Capella Istropolitana, J. Krechek (r1993) Concert
(3/95) (NAXO) ① 8 550877
5, 6. Petite Bande, S. Kuijken Concert
(11/90) (DHM) ① GD77010

6 Concerti Grossi, Op. 3 (pub 1733 rev c1755)
1. D; 2. G minor; 3. E minor; 4. D minor; 5. B flat; 6. E minor.
Berne Camerata, T. Füri (r1991; revised version)
(1/93) (NOVA) ① 150 083-2
3. Berlin Ancient Music Academy Concert
(7/87) (CAPR) ① 10 134
3. Petite Bande, S. Kuijken Concert
(11/90) (DHM) ① GD77010
3. ASMF, N. Marriner (r1964) Concert
(9/93) (DECC) ① 436 224-2DM

6 Concerti Grossi, Op. 7 (pub 1746)
1. D; 2. D minor; 3. C; 4. D minor; 5. C minor; 6. B flat.
ASMF, I. Brown (edit Eckersley)
(11/90) (ASV) ① CDDCA724
2. Purcell Band Concert
(11/88) (HYPE) ① CDA66264
2. Petite Bande, S. Kuijken Concert
(11/90) (DHM) ① GD77010

SECTION II: CHAMBER

5 Scots Airs—solo instrument and continuo (pub 1749) (from 'A Treatise of Good Taste...')
1. Auld Bob Morrice; 2. Lady Ann Bothwells' Lament; 3. Sleepy body.
1-3. Palladian Ens (r1992) Concert
(7/93) (LINN) ① CKD010
Sonata for Oboe and Continuo No. 1 in E minor
P. Dombrecht, W. Kuijken, R. Kohnen Concert
(9/86) (ACCE) ① ACC57804D
12 Sonatas for Violin and Continuo, Op. 1 (1716 rev 1729)
1. A; 2. D minor; 3. E minor; 4. D; 5. B flat; 6. G minor; 7. C minor; 8. B minor; 9. F; 10. E; 11. B minor; 12. A.
1. Locatelli Trio Concert
(5/93) (HYPE) ① CDA66583
3. Purcell Qt Concert (11/88) (HYPE) ① CDA66264
10. Barthold Kuijken, W. Kuijken, R. Kohnen (arr. flute) Concert (5/92) (ACCE) ① ACC9177D
12 Sonatas for Violin and Continuo, Op. 4 (pub 1739)
1. D; 2. E minor; 3. C; 4. D minor; 5. A minor; 6. D; 7. A; 8. D minor; 9. C minor; 10. A; 11. B minor; 12. A.
12. Purcell Qt Concert
(11/88) (HYPE) ① CDA66264
6 Sonatas for 2 Violins and Continuo (c1757) (arr from Violin Sonatas, Op. 1/7-12)
1. C minor; 2. B minor; 3. F; 4. E; 5. A minor; 6. D minor.
3, 5, 6. Purcell Qt Concert
(11/88) (HYPE) ① CDA66264

GENERALI, Pietro (1773–1832)
Italy

SECTION V: STAGE WORKS

Adelina—opera (1 act), Lib. Rossi (1810—Venice)
Giusto cielo! correte, andate M. Hill Smith, P. Guy-Bromley, R. Smythe, Philh, D. Parry Concert
(10/90) (OPRA) ① [3] ORCH103

GENZMER, Harald (b 1909)
Germany

SECTION II: CHAMBER

Sonata for Trumpet and Organ in C (mid 1960s)
G. Touvron, E. Krapp (r1992) Concert
(9/93) (RCA) ① 09026 61186-2

GEORGES, Alexandre (1850–1938) France

SECTION IV: VOCAL AND CHORAL

Le Filibustier—song
P. Plançon, anon (r1905) Concert
(12/94) (ROMO) ① [2] 82001-2

La pluie—song (Wds. J Richepin)
P. Frijsh, E. Nielsen (r1933) Concert
(4/95) (PEAR) ① [2] GEMMCDS9095(2)

GERHARD, Roberto (1896–1970)
Spain/Britain

SECTION I: ORCHESTRAL

Albada—interludi i dansa—interludi i dansa (1936)
Tenerife SO, V.P. Pérez Concert
(10/92) (AUVI) ① V4660
Pedrelliana—orchestra (1941) (final movt of Symphony 'Homenaje a Pedrell')
Tenerife SO, V.P. Pérez Concert
(10/92) (AUVI) ① V4660
Symphony No. 1 (1952-53)
Tenerife SO, V. P. Pérez (r1994) Symphony 3.
(9/95) (AUVI) ① V4728
Symphony No. 3, 'Collages'—orchestra and tape (1960)
Tenerife SO, V. P. Pérez (r1994) Symphony 1.
(9/95) (AUVI) ① V4728

SECTION III: INSTRUMENTAL

Fantasia—guitar (1957)
J. Bream (r1983) Concert
(8/93) (RCA) ① [28] 09026 61583-2(4)
J. Bream (r1983) Concert
(6/94) (RCA) ① 09026 61596-2

SECTION IV: VOCAL AND CHORAL

Cancionero de Pedrell—song cycle: 1v and piano/orchestra (1941)
EXCERPTS: 1. Sa ximbomba; 2. La mal maridada; 3. Laieta; 4. Soledad; 5. Muera yo... 6. Farruquiño; 7. Alatá; 8. Corrandes.
Cpte J. Benet, Teatre Lliure CO, J. Pons (r1993) Concert (11/94) (HARM) ① HMC90 1500
B. Valente, T. Crone Shahrazada.
(2/89) (ETCE) ① KTC1060
2, 5, 6. J. Gomez, J. Constable (r1994) Concert
(9/94) (CONI) ① CDCF243
7 Haiku—song cycle (1922, rev 1958) (Wds Junoy)
EXCERPTS: 1. Au milieu de la prairie verte; 2. J'ai caressé ta flottante; 3. Sous les lucioles; 4. Douce voix; 5. Pensée; 6. Sous la pluie d'été; 7. Mais en exil.
Cpte J. Benet, Teatre Lliure CO, J. Pons (r1993) Concert (11/94) (HARM) ① HMC90 1500
L' Infantament Meravellos de Shahrazade—song cycle: 1v and piano, Op. 1 (1917) (Wds. J. M. López-Picó)
B. Valente, T. Crone Cancionero de Pedrell.
(2/89) (ETCE) ① KTC1060

SECTION V: STAGE WORKS

Alegrías—divertissement flamenco: two pianos/orchestra (1943—Birmingham)
1. Preámbub; 2. Jácaro (Danza del Abánico); 3. Farruca; 4. Jaleo.
Teatre Lliure CO, J. Pons (r1993) Concert
(11/94) (HARM) ① HMC90 1500
Alegrías—concert suite from ballet (1942)
Tenerife SO, V.P. Pérez Concert
(7/92) (ETCE) ① KTC1095
Don Quixote—ballet: 1 act (1940 rev 1950—London)
Tenerife SO, V.P. Pérez Concert
(10/92) (AUVI) ① V4660
Pandora—concert suite from ballet (1942-3, rev 1950)
EXCERPTS: 1. The Quest; 2. Psyché and the Youth; 3. Pandora's Carnival; 4. The Monsters' Drill; 5. Death and the Mothers.
Teatre Lliure CO, J. Pons (r1993) Concert
(11/94) (HARM) ① HMC90 1500

GERMAN, Sir Edward (1862–1936) England

SECTION I: ORCHESTRAL

Gipsy Suite—four characteristic pieces (1892)
1. Valse melancolique; 2. Allegro di bravura; 3. Menuetto; 4. Tarantella.
Bratislava RSO, A. Leaper (r1991) Concert
(6/93) (MARC) ① 8 223419
Merrie England—dances (arr cpsr from operetta)
1. Hornpipe; 2. Minuet; 3. Rustic Dance; 4. Jig.
1-4. Bratislava RSO, A. Leaper (r1991) Concert
(6/93) (MARC) ① 8 223419

Nell Gwyn—suite (1900) (arr from incidental music to A. Hope's play)
1. Pastoral Dance; 2. Country Dance; 3. Merrymaker's Dance.
Southern Fest Orch, R. White Concert
(5/93) (CHAN) ① CHAN9110
1-3. Bratislava RSO, A. Leaper (r1991) Concert
(6/93) (MARC) ① 8 223419
Nell Gwyn—overture (1900) (arr from incidental music to A. Hope's play)
Bratislava RSO, A. Leaper (r1991) Concert
(6/93) (MARC) ① 8 223419
Richard III—concert overture (1889) (expanded from Overture to incidental music)
EXCERPTS: 1. Overture.
RTE Concert Orch, A. Penny (r1994) Concert
(11/95) (MARC) ① 8 223695
The Seasons—symphonic suite (1899)
1. Spring; 2. Summer (Harvest Dance); 3. Autumn; 4. Winter (Christmastide).
RTE Concert Orch, A. Penny (r1994) Concert
(11/95) (MARC) ① 8 223695
Theme and Six Diversions—orchestra (1919)
RTE Concert Orch, A. Penny (r1994) Concert
(11/95) (MARC) ① 8 223695

SECTION V: STAGE WORKS

The Conqueror—incidental music to Fyffe's play (1905—London)
EXCERPTS: 1. Berceuse.
1. Bratislava RSO, A. Leaper (r1991) Concert
(6/93) (MARC) ① 8 223419
Henry VIII—incidental music (1892)
EXCERPTS: 1. Overture; 2. Shepherd's Dance (Act 1); 3. Torch Dance (Act 1); 4. Morris Dance (Act 4).
2-4. Bratislava RSO, A. Leaper (r1991) Concert
(6/93) (MARC) ① 8 223419
Merrie England—operetta: 2 acts (1902—London) (Lib. B. Hood)
EXCERPTS: 1. Overture. ACT 1: 2. Opening chorus; 3. Oh! where the deer do lie; 5. I do counsel that your playtime; 6. That every Jack should have a Jill; 7. Love is meant to make us glad; 8. She had a letter from her love; 9. When true love hath found a man; 10. When a man is a lover; 11. The Yeomen of England; 12a. Entrance of Queen Elizabeth...God save Elizabeth; 12b. O peaceful England; 13. King Neptune sat on his lonely throne; 14. Finale. ACT 2: 15. The month of May has come today; 16. In England, Merrie England; 17. The big brass band; 18. It is the merry month of May; 19a. The Queen of May is crowned today; 19b. Rustic dance; 20. Dan Cupid hath a garden (The English Rose); 21. Two merry men a-drinking; 22. Who shall say that love is cruel?; 23. When Cupid first this old world trod; 24. Oh! here's a to-do to die today; 25. Finale.
11. P. Morrison, Ambrosian Sngrs, Chandos Concert Orch, S. Barry Concert
(7/88) (CHAN) ① CHAN8561
20. R. Tauber, orch (r1938) Concert
(2/92) (LYRC) ① [2] SRO830
20. J. Johnston, Philh, J. Robertson (r1950) Concert
(4/95) (TEST) ① SBT1058
22. M. Hill Smith, Southern Fest Orch, R. White Concert (5/93) (CHAN) ① CHAN9110
Romeo and Juliet—incidental music to Shakepeare's play (1895—London)
EXCERPTS: 1. Pavane; 2. Nocturne; 3. Pastorale.
1-3. Bratislava RSO, A. Leaper (r1991) Concert
(6/93) (MARC) ① 8 223419
Tom Jones—comic opera: 3 acts (1907—Manchester) (Lib. Courtneidge, Thomson & Taylor, after Fielding)
EXCERPTS—ACT 1: 1. Dont' you find the weather charming?; 2. On a January night in Zummersetsheer; 3. West Country lad; 4. Today my spinet; 5. Wisdon says 'Festina lente'; 6. The Barley Mow; 7. Here's a paradox for lovers; 8. For Aye, My Love. ACT 2: 9. Hurry, Bustle!; 10. A Person of Parts; 11. Dream o'Day Jill; 12. Gurt Uncle Jan Tappit; 13. My Lady's coach has been attacked; 14. As all the Maises; 15. You have a pretty wit; 16. A soldier's scarlet coat; 17. Hey Dewy Down; 18. Where be my daughter?; 19. Love maketh a garden fair. ACT 3: 20a. Morris Dance; 20b. Gavotte; 20c. Jig; 21. The Green Ribbon; 22. If lov'es content; 23a. Which is my own truer self; 23b. For tonight (Waltz Song); 24. Wise Old Saws; 25. Hark! the merry marriage bells. ADDITIONAL ITEM: 26. We Redcoat Soldiers serve the King.
23b Bratislava RSO, A. Leaper (r1991; arr Tomlinson) Concert (6/93) (MARC) ① 8 223419

GERMANI, Fernando (1906–?)
Italy

SECTION III: INSTRUMENTAL
Toccata—organ, Op. 12
N. Kynaston Concert (4/89) (HYPE) ① CDA66265

GERSHWIN, George (1898–1937)
USA

SECTION I: ORCHESTRAL
An American in Paris (1928)
Cincinnati SO, E. Kunzel (r1981) Rhapsody in Blue.
(1/84) (TELA) ① CD80058
K. Labèque, M. Labèque (original 2-pno version)
Grainger: Porgy and Bess fantasy.
(12/84) (EMI) ① CDC7 47044-2
Pittsburgh SO, A. Previn Concert
(11/85) (PHIL) ① 412 611-2PH
LSO, A. Previn Concert
(9/86) (EMI) ① CDC7 47161-2
Boston Pops, A. Fiedler Concert
(11/87) (RCA) ① GD86519
D. Blumenthal, ECO, S. Bedford Concert
(3/88) (CFP) ① CD-CFP9012
San Francisco SO, S. Ozawa Concert
(10/89) (DG) ① 427 203-2GR
Seattle SO, G. Schwarz (orig full vers) Concert
(9/90) (DELO) ① DE3078
Budapest PO, J. Sándor Concert
(11/90) (LASE) ① 15 606
NYPO, L. Bernstein Rhapsody in Blue.
(11/90) (SONY) ① MK42619
G. Gershwin, Victor SO, N. Shilkret (r1929) Concert
(9/91) (HALC) ① DHDL101
LSO, Carl Davis Concert
(11/91) (COLL) ① Coll1139-2
San Francisco SO, S. Ozawa Concert
(12/91) (DG) ① [2] 413 851-2GW2
London Fest Orch, Carl Davis Concert
(1/92) (DECC) ① 433 616-2DSP
NYPO, L. Bernstein (r1958) Concert
(11/92) (SONY) ① SMK47529
NBC SO, A. Toscanini (r1945) Concert
(11/92) (RCA) ① GD60307
Minneapolis SO, A. Dorati (r1957) Concert
(7/93) (MERC) ① 434 329-2MM
J. Gibbons (cpsr's pf improvisation, trans Daly, arr
Gibbons) Concert (8/93) (ASV) ① CDWHL2077
Chicago SO, James Levine (r1990) Concert
(9/93) (DG) ① 431 625-2GH
F. Milne (r1933: trans 2 pfs: Milne: plays both parts)
Concert (4/94) (NONE) ① 7559-79287-2
RCA Victor Orch, L. Bernstein (r1947) Concert
(7/94) (RCA) ① 09026 61650-2
BBC PO, Y. P. Tortelier (r1994) Concert
(4/95) (CHAN) ① CHAN9325
Pittsburgh SO, W. Steinberg (r c1960) Concert
(4/95) (EVER) ① EVC9003
Catfish Row—symphonic suite from 'Porgy
and Bess' (1936)
Cincinnati Pops, E. Kunzel (r1983) Grofé: Grand
Canyon Suite. (10/87) (TELA) ① CD80086
Chicago SO, James Levine (r1990) Concert
(9/93) (DG) ① 431 625-2GH
J. Gibbons (r1992-3; trans Gibbons: pf) Concert
(3/95) (ASV) ① CDWHL2082
BBC PO, Y. P. Tortelier (r1994) Concert
(4/95) (CHAN) ① CHAN9325
Concerto for Piano and Orchestra in F
(1925)
1. Allegro; 2. Adagio; 3. Finale: Allegro agitato.
A. Previn (pf/dir), Pittsburgh SO Concert
(11/85) (PHIL) ① 412 611-2PH
A. Previn (pf/dir), LSO Concert
(9/86) (EMI) ① CDC7 47161-2
E. Wild, Boston Pops, A. Fiedler Concert
(11/87) (RCA) ① GD86519
D. Blumenthal, ECO, S. Bedford Concert
(3/88) (CFP) ① CD-CFP9012
W. Tritt, Cincinnati Pops, E. Kunzel Concert
(9/88) (TELA) ① CD80166
R. Szidon, LPO, E. Downes Concert
(10/89) (DG) ① 427 203-2GR
S. Knor, Prague SO, V. Neumann Concert
(11/90) (SUPR) ① 11 1105-2
P. Jablonski, RPO, Vladimir Ashkenazy Concert
(7/91) (DECC) ① 430 542-2DH
J. MacGregor, LSO, Carl Davis Concert
(11/91) (COLL) ① Coll1139-2
R. Szidon, LPO, E. Downes Concert
(12/91) (DG) ① [2] 413 851-2GW2

H. Shelley, Philh, Y. P. Tortelier Concert
(3/93) (CHAN) ① CHAN9092
E. List, Berlin SO, S. Adler Barber: Piano Concerto.
(5/93) (VOX) ① 115719-2
L. Stifelman, Concordia, M. Alsop (r1992/3: arr Grofé)
Concert (1/94) (EMI) ① CDC7 54851-2
Cuban Overture (1932)
Prague SO, V. Neumann Concert
(11/90) (SUPR) ① 11 1105-2
Cleveland Orch, L. Maazel Concert
(1/92) (DECC) ① 433 616-2DSP
Chicago SO, James Levine (r1990) Concert
(9/93) (DG) ① 431 625-2GH
J. Gibbons (r1992-3; trans Gibbons: pf) Concert
(3/95) (ASV) ① CDWHL2082
Promenade—orchestra (1937) (orig 'Walking
the Dog' in 'Shall we Dance')
Detroit SO, N. Järvi (r1993) Concert
(8/94) (CHAN) ① CHAN9227
Rhapsody in Blue—piano and jazz band
(later orchestra) (1924) (orch Grofé: 1926 rev
1942)
L. Bernstein (pf/dir), Los Angeles PO (pp1982)
Concert (8/83) (DG) ① 410 025-2GH
E. List, Cincinnati SO, E. Kunzel (r1981) American in
Paris. (1/84) (TELA) ① CD80058
M. Dichter, Philh, N. Marriner Concert
(8/84) (PHIL) ① 411 123-2PH
A. Previn (pf/dir), Pittsburgh SO Concert
(11/85) (PHIL) ① 412 611-2PH
M. Tilson Thomas (pf/dir), Los Angeles PO Concert
(1/86) (SONY) ① MK39699
A. Previn (pf/dir), LSO Concert
(9/86) (EMI) ① CDC7 47161-2
J. Tocco, LSO, G. Simon Concert
(3/87) (CALA) ① [2] CACD0101
E. Wild, Boston Pops, A. Fiedler Concert
(11/87) (RCA) ① GD86519
P. Donohoe, London Sinfonietta, S. Rattle (orig
version) Concert (12/87) (EMI) ① CDC7 47991-2
D. Blumenthal, ECO, S. Bedford Concert
(3/88) (CFP) ① CD-CFP9012
W. Tritt, Cincinnati Jazz Orch, E. Kunzel (orig
version) Concert (9/88) (TELA) ① CD80166
T. Barto, LPO, A. Davis Concert
(1/89) (EMI) ① CDC7 49495-2
S. Stöckigt, Leipzig Gewandhaus, K. Masur Concert
(10/89) (DG) ① 427 203-2GR
W. Marshall, CLS, R. Hickox (orig version) Concert
(11/89) (VIRG) ① VC7 59520-2
J. Jandó, Budapest PO, J. Sándor Concert
(11/90) (LASE) ① 15 606
NYPO, L. Bernstein (pf/dir) American in Paris.
(11/90) (SONY) ① MK42619
G. Gershwin, Orch, P. Whiteman (r1927) Concert
(9/91) (HALC) ① DHDL101
J. MacGregor, LSO, Carl Davis Concert
(11/91) (COLL) ① Coll1139-2
K. Labèque, M. Labèque, Cleveland Orch, R. Chailly
Concert (12/91) (DECC) ① 430 726-2DM
S. Stöckigt, Leipzig Gewandhaus, K. Masur Concert
(12/91) (DG) ① [2] 413 851-2GW2
S. Black (pf/dir), London Fest Orch Concert
(1/92) (DECC) ① 433 616-2DSP
L. Bernstein (pf/dir), NYPO (r1958) Concert
(11/92) (SONY) ① SMK47529
H. Shelley, Philh, Y. P. Tortelier (orch Grofé) Concert
(3/93) (CHAN) ① CHAN9092
S. Nakarjakov, A. Markovich (arr Dokshitser) Concert
(5/93) (TELD) ① 9031-77705-2
James Levine (pf/dir), Chicago SO (r1990) Concert
(9/93) (DG) ① 431 625-2GH
L. Lortie, Netherlands Wind Ens, R. Dufallo (r1993:
orig vers) Concert (3/94) (CHAN) ① CHAN9210
Andante G. Gershwin (r1928) Concert
(9/91) (HALC) ① DHDL101
Second Rhapsody for piano and orchestra
(1931)
M. Tilson Thomas (pf/dir), Los Angeles PO Concert
(1/86) (SONY) ① MK39699
H. Shelley, Philh, Y. P. Tortelier Concert
(3/93) (CHAN) ① CHAN9092
Variations on 'I Got Rhythm'—piano and
orchestra (1934)
E. Wild, Boston Pops, A. Fiedler Concert
(11/87) (RCA) ① GD86519
W. Tritt, Cincinnati Pops, E. Kunzel Concert
(9/88) (TELA) ① CD80166
D. Parkhouse, London Fest Rec Ens, B. Herrmann
Concert (1/92) (DECC) ① 433 616-2DSP
J. Gibbons (r1992-3; trans Gibbons: pf) Concert
(3/95) (ASV) ① CDWHL2082
H. Shelley, BBC PO, Y. P. Tortelier (r1994) Concert
(4/95) (CHAN) ① CHAN9325

SECTION II: CHAMBER
Concerto in F—two pianos
K. Labèque, M. Labèque Rhapsody in Blue.
(3/86) (PHIL) ① 400 022-2PH
Slow movt J. Gibbons (arr Gibbons: solo pf) Concert
(8/93) (ASV) ① CDWHL2074
Lullaby—string quartet (1919)
Moscow PO, D. Kitaienko (orch. vers.) Concert
(2/88) (SHEF) ① CD27
Rhapsody in Blue—two pianos (1924)
K. Labèque, M. Labèque Concert
(3/86) (PHIL) ① 400 022-2PH
Second Rhapsody—2 pianos (arr cpsr from
pf/orch version)
J. Gibbons (r1992-3; trans Gibbons: pf) Concert
(3/95) (ASV) ① CDWHL2082

SECTION III: INSTRUMENTAL
For Lily Pons—Melody No. 79 (1933)
M. Tilson Thomas (recons. Tilson Thomas) Concert
(1/86) (SONY) ① MK39699
Gershwin Songbook—piano (1932) (transc
cpsr)
1. Swanee; 2. Nobody but you; 3. Please do it again;
4. I'll build a stairway to paradise; 5. Fascinating
rhythm; 6. Oh, lady be good; 7. The man I love;
Somebody loves me; 9. That certain feeling; 10.
Sweet and low-down; 11. Clap yo' hands; 12. Do, do
do; 13. My one and only; 14. 's Wonderful; 15. Strike
up the band; 16. Liza (All the clouds'll roll away); 17.
Who cares (so long as you care for me)?; 18. I got
rhythm.
D. Achatz Concert (10/89) (BIS) ① BIS-CD404
A. Brownridge Concert
(1/91) (HYPE) ① CDH88045
1. G. Gershwin (r1920: pf roll) Concert
(4/94) (NONE) ① 7559-79287-2
Impromptu in two keys—piano (c1924)
D. Achatz Concert (10/89) (BIS) ① BIS-CD404
A. Brownridge Concert
(1/91) (HYPE) ① CDH88045
Jazzbo Brown Blues—piano (1935)
A. Brownridge Concert
(1/91) (HYPE) ① CDH88045
Merry Andrew—piano
D. Achatz Concert (10/89) (BIS) ① BIS-CD404
A. Brownridge Concert
(1/91) (HYPE) ① CDH88045
Novelette in Fourths—piano
G. Gershwin (r1919: pf roll) Concert
(4/94) (NONE) ① 7559-79287-2
Promenade, 'Walking the Dog'—piano (orig
in 'Shall We Dance')
L. Howard Concert (12/86) (HYPE) ① CDA66090
A. Brownridge Concert
(1/91) (HYPE) ① CDH88045
Rhapsody in Blue—piano
L. Lortie Concert (9/89) (CHAN) ① CHAN8733
J. Gibbons Concert (8/93) (ASV) ① CDWHL2074
G. Gershwin (r1925/6: pf roll) Concert
(4/94) (NONE) ① 7559-79287-2
Rialto Ripples—piano rag (1917) (with
W.Donaldson)
W. Tritt Concert (9/88) (TELA) ① CD80166
D. Achatz Concert (10/89) (BIS) ① BIS-CD404
A. Brownridge Concert
(1/91) (HYPE) ① CDH88045
Short Story (1925)
M. Tilson Thomas (recons. Tilson Thomas) Concert
(1/86) (SONY) ① MK39699
M. Kliegel, R. Havenith (arr vc/pf) Concert
(9/92) (MARC) ① 8 223403
R. Stoltzman, LSO, E. Stern (r1993; arr Sebesky)
Concert (12/93) (RCA) ① 09026 61790-2
Sleepless Night—Melody No. 17 (1936)
M. Tilson Thomas Concert
(1/86) (SONY) ① MK39699
Three Preludes for piano (1926)
1. B flat; 2. C sharp minor; 3. E flat minor.
M. Tilson Thomas Concert
(1/86) (SONY) ① MK39699
E. Parkin Concert (1/89) (PREA) ① PRCD1776
D. Achatz Concert (10/89) (BIS) ① BIS-CD404
I. Perlman, S. Sanders (trans. Heifetz) Concert
(12/89) (EMI) ① CDC7 49604-2
A. Brownridge Concert
(1/91) (HYPE) ① CDH88045
P. Jablonski Concert
(7/91) (DECC) ① 430 542-2DH
G. Gershwin (r1928) Concert
(9/91) (HALC) ① DHDL101
J. Gibbons (cpsr's pf improvisation, trans Gibbons)
Concert (8/93) (ASV) ① CDWHL2077
R. Stoltzman, LSO, E. Stern (r1993; arr Sebesky)
Concert (12/93) (RCA) ① 09026 61790-2

Y-Y. Ma, J. Kahane (r1992: trans vc/pf: Ma) *Concert*
 (4/94) (SONY) ① **SK53126**
S. Isbin (r c1992: arr gtr: Barbosa-Lima) *Concert*
 (7/94) (VIRG) ① **VC5 45024-2**
J. Heifetz, E. Bay (r1945) *Concert*
 (11/94) (RCA) ① [65] **09026 61778-2(19)**
J. Heifetz, B. Smith (r1965) *Concert*
 (11/94) (RCA) ① [65] **09026 61778-2(40)**
M. Legrand (r1994) *Concert*
 (7/95) (ERAT) ① **4509-96386-2**
2. L. Bernstein (pp1982) *Concert*
 (8/83) (DG) ① **410 025-2GH**
Three-quarter blues—piano
D. Achatz *Concert* (10/89) (BIS) ① **BIS-CD404**
A. Brownridge *Concert*
 (1/91) (HYPE) ① **CDH88045**
Irish waltz J. Gibbons (cpsr's pf improvisation, trans
Gibbons) *Concert* (8/93) (ASV) ① **CDWHL2077**
Violin Pieces—Melody No. 40
M. Tilson Thomas (recons. Tilson Thomas) *Concert*
 (1/86) (SONY) ① **MK39699**
2 Waltzes in C—piano (1933)
A. Brownridge *Concert*
 (1/91) (HYPE) ① **CDH88045**
**When you want'em, you can't get'em, when
you've got'em, you don't want'em—piano
transcription (1916)** (trans cpsr from song)
G. Gershwin (r1916: pf roll) *Concert*
 (4/94) (NONE) ① **7559-79287-2**

SECTION IV: VOCAL AND CHORAL

By Strauss—song (1936) (written for 'The
Show is On')
K. Te Kanawa, New Princess Th Orch, J. McGlinn
(orch. R.Warner) *Concert*
 (10/87) (EMI) ① **CDC7 47454-2**
Sarah Walker, R. Vignoles (pp1982) *Concert*
 (3/89) (MERI) ① **CDE84167**
E. Parkin (arr Parkin) *Concert*
 (10/89) (CLOU) ① **ACN6002**
Hi-Ho!—duet (comp for 'Shall we dance': wds I
Gershwin)
W. Sharp, S. Blier *Concert*
 (7/91) (KOCH) ① **37028-2**
**I was so young (you were so
beautiful—song for 'Good Morning, Judge'
(1919)** (Wds. Bryan & Caesar)
J. Gibbons (cpsr's pf improvisation, trans Gibbons)
Concert (8/93) (ASV) ① **CDWHL2074**
The Jolly Jack Tar—song (Wds. I.
Gershwin)
Sarah Walker, R. Vignoles (pp1988) *Concert*
 (3/89) (MERI) ① **CDE84167**
**Limehouse nights—song for 'Morris Gest
Midnight Whirl' (1919)** (Wds. De Sylva and
Mears)
J. Gibbons (cpsr's pf improvisation, trans Gibbons)
Concert (8/93) (ASV) ① **CDWHL2074**
Till then—song (1933) (Wds. I. Gershwin)
W. Sharp, S. Blier *Concert*
 (7/91) (KOCH) ① **37028-2**
**Tra-la-la—interpolation song for Daly's 'For
Goodness Sake' (1922)** (Wds. Francis)
E. Parkin (arr Parkin) *Concert*
 (10/89) (CLOU) ① **ACN6002**

SECTION V: STAGE WORKS

**Blue Monday Blues—opera: 1 act
(1925—New York)** (Lib. De Sylva)
Cpte A. Burton, G. Hopkins, W. Sharp, A. Woodley,
J.J. Offenbach, Concordia, M. Alsop (r1992/3)
Concert (1/94) (EMI) ① **CDC7 54851-2**
Has anyone seen Joe? B. Hendricks, K. Labèque,
M. Labèque (arr. Jeanneau) *Concert*
 (1/87) (PHIL) ① **416 460-2PH**
Capitol Revue (1919—New York) (music by
various cpsrs)
EXCERPTS: 1. Come to the moon (wds. Paly & N.
Wayburn); 2. Swanee (wds. I. Caesar).
1, 2. J. Gibbons (cpsr's pf improvisation, trans
Gibbons) *Concert* (8/93) (ASV) ① **CDWHL2074**
2. K. Criswell, B. Barrett, Ambrosian Sngrs, London
Sinfonietta, J. McGlinn *Concert*
 (8/93) (EMI) ① **CDC7 54586-2**
**Crazy for You—pastiche after 'Girl Crazy'
(1993—London)** (arr Ludwig & Ockrent)
EXCERPTS: (original sources where known in
parentheses) 1. Overture (Girl Crazy); 2. K-ra-zy For
You (Treasure Girl); 3. I Can't Be Bothered Now (A
Damsel in Distress); 4. Bidin' My Time (Girl Crazy); 5.
Things Are Looking Up (A Damsel in Distress); 6.
Someone To Watch Over Me (Oh, Kay!); 7. Could
Use Me? (Girl Crazy); 8. Shall We Dance? (Shal
We Dance); 9. Entrance to Nevada (Scandals 1922;
Treasure Girl); 10. Slap That Bass (Shal We Dance);
11. Embraceable You (Girl Crazy); 12. Tonight's The

Night; 13. I Got Rhythm (Girl Crazy); 14. The Real
American Folk Song - Is A Rag (Ladies First); 15.
What Causes That?; 16. Naughty Baby (Primrose);
17. Stiff Upper Lip (A Damsel in Distress); 18. They
Can't Take That Away From Me (Shall We Dance);
19. But Not For Me (Girl Crazy); 20. New York
Interlude (Piano Concerto); 21. Nice Work If You Can
Get It (A Damsel in Distress); 22. Bidin' My Time
(reprise); 23. Finale.
Cpte Orig Broadway Cast (r1992)
 (7/93) (EMI) ① **CDC7 54618-2**
A **Damsel in Distress—songs for the film
(1937)** (Lyrics I. Gershwin)
EXCERPTS: 1. Overture; 2. A Foggy Day; 3. I can't
be bothered now; 4. The jolly tar and the milk maid;
5. Nice work if you can get it; 6. Stiff Upper lip; 7.
Things are looking up.
2. J. MacGregor (arr Finnissy) *Concert*
 (8/89) (COLL) ① **Coll1299-2**
2. E. Parkin (arr Parkin) *Concert*
 (10/89) (CLOU) ① **ACN6002**
5. B. Hendricks, K. Labèque, M. Labèque (arr.
Jeanneau) *Concert* (1/87) (PHIL) ① **416 460-2PH**
5. J. Kaye, S. Blier *Concert*
 (7/91) (KOCH) ① **37028-2**
5, 7. K. Te Kanawa, NY Choral Artists, New Princess
Th Orch, J. McGlinn (orch. R.R.Bennett) *Concert*
 (10/87) (EMI) ① **CDC7 47454-2**
**Funny Face—musical comedy (1927—New
York)** (Lyrics I. Gershwin)
EXCERPTS: 1. Overture; 2. The babbit and the
bromide; 3. Dance along with you; 4. Funny face; 5.
He loves and she loves; 6. High hat; 7. Let's kiss and
make up; 8. My one and only; 9. 'S wonderful; 10.
The world is mine.
4, 5, 8, 9. J. Gibbons (cpsr's pf improvisation, trans
Gibbons) *Concert* (8/93) (ASV) ① **CDWHL2077**
5. J. Kaye, S. Blier *Concert*
 (7/91) (KOCH) ① **37028-2**
5, 9. E. Parkin (arr Parkin) *Concert*
 (10/89) (CLOU) ① **ACN6002**
8, 9. G. Gershwin (trans pf: cpsr; r1928) *Concert*
 (9/91) (HALC) ① **DHDL101**
**George White's Scandals of 1920—revue
(1920—New York)** (Book A Ride & G White:
lyrics A J Jackson)
EXCERPTS: 1. Idle dreams; 2. My lady; 3. On my
mind the whole night long; 4. Scandal walk; 5. The
songs of long ago; 6. Turn on and tiss me.
1, 2, 4. G. Gershwin (r1920: pf roll) *Concert*
 (4/94) (NONE) ① **7559-79287-2**
**George White's Scandals of 1921—revue
(1921—New York)** (Book A Baer & White.
Lyrics Jackson)
EXCERPTS: 1. Drifting along with the tide; 2. I love
you; 3. She's just my baby; 4. South sea isles; 5.
Where East meets West.
1. J. Gibbons (cpsr's pf improvisation, trans Gibbons)
Concert (8/93) (ASV) ① **CDWHL2074**
**George White's Scandals of 1924—revue
(1924—New York)** (Wds. Wells and White)
EXCERPTS: 1. Overture; 2. I need a garden; 3.
Kongo Kate; 4. Mah-jongg; 5. Night time in Araby; 6.
Rose of Madrid; 7. Somebody loves me; 8. Tune in;
9. Year after year.
7. K. Te Kanawa, New Princess Th Orch, J. McGlinn
(orch.M.de Packh) *Concert*
 (10/87) (EMI) ① **CDC7 47454-2**
Girl Crazy—musical show (1930—New York)
(Book Bolton and J. McGowan; lyrics I.
Gershwin)
EXCERPTS: 1. Overture; 2. Bidin' my time; 3. Boy!
What love has done to me; 4. But not for me; 5.
Could you use me?; 6. Embraceable you; 7. I got
rhythm; 8. Sam and Delilah; 9. Treat me rough.
Cpte L. Luft, David Carroll, J. Blazer, F. Gorshin, D.
Garrison, V. Lewis, Chor, Orch, J. Mauceri
 (2/91) (NONE) ① **7559-79250-2**
1. A. Brownridge (arr pf) *Concert*
 (1/91) (HYPE) ① **CDH88045**
1. BBC PO, Y. P. Tortelier (r1994) *Concert*
 (4/95) (CHAN) ① **CHAN9325**
4. J. MacGregor (arr Finnissy) *Concert*
 (4/92) (PHIL) ① **422 401-2PH**
4. J. Norman, J.T. Williams (r1987) *Concert*
 (8/89) (COLL) ① **Coll1299-2**
4, 6, 7. K. Te Kanawa, Foursome, New Princess Th
Orch, J. McGlinn (orch. R.R.Bennett) *Concert*
 (10/87) (EMI) ① **CDC7 47454-2**
4, 7. B. Hendricks, K. Labèque, M. Labèque (arr.
Jeanneau) *Concert* (1/87) (PHIL) ① **416 460-2PH**
5. Britannia Building Soc Band, H. Snell (arr Howarth)
Concert (7/93) (DOYE) ① **DOYCD011**
6. P. Thwaites, J. Lavender (r1989-91: arr 2 pfs)
Grainger) *Concert* (1/94) (PEAR) ① **SHECD9631**

6, 7. E. Parkin (arr Parkin) *Concert*
 (10/89) (CLOU) ① **ACN6002**
6, 7. J. Gibbons (cpsr's pf improvisation, trans & arr
Gibbons) *Concert* (8/93) (ASV) ① **CDWHL2077**
7. K. Criswell, London Sinfonietta, J. McGlinn (r1992)
Concert (8/93) (EMI) ① **CDC7 54802-2**
Goldwyn Follies—songs for the film (1938)
(Book B. Hecht; lyrics Ira Gershwin)
EXCERPTS: 1. Overture; 2. I love to rhyme; 3. I was
doing all right; 4. Love is here to stay; 5. Love walked
in.
2, 4. Sarah Walker, R. Vignoles (pp1988) *Concert*
 (3/89) (MERI) ① **CDE84167**
4. B. Hendricks, K. Labèque, M. Labèque (arr.
Jeanneau) *Concert* (1/87) (PHIL) ① **416 460-2PH**
4. G. Saba (trans Grainger) *Concert*
 (10/87) (CARL) ① **PCD858**
4. J. Gibbons (r1992-3; trans Gibbons: pf) *Concert*
 (3/95) (ASV) ① **CDWHL2082**
4, 5. K. Te Kanawa, New Princess Th Orch, J.
McGlinn (orch. E.Powell) *Concert*
 (10/87) (EMI) ① **CDC7 47454-2**
4, 5. E. Parkin (arr Parkin) *Concert*
 (10/89) (CLOU) ① **ACN6002**
5. Martin Jones (r1989: trans pf: Grainger) *Concert*
 (7/90) (NIMB) ① **NI5232**
**La La Lucille—musical comedy (1919—New
York)** (Book F Jackson: Lyrics various)
EXCERPTS: 1. The best of everything; 2. From now
on; 3. Nobody but you; 4. Somehow it seldom comes
true; 5. Tee-oodle-um-bum-bo; 6. There more to the
kiss than the x-x-x.
3, 5. J. Gibbons (cpsr's pf improvisation, trans
Gibbons) *Concert* (8/93) (ASV) ① **CDWHL2074**
**Lady, Be Good!—musical comedy
(1924—New York)** (Lyrics I. Gershwin)
EXCERPTS: 1. Overture; 2. Hang on to me; 3. A
wonderful party; 4. End of a string; 5. We're here
because; 6. Fascinating rhythm; 7. So am I; 8. Oh,
Lady be good; 9. Finale (Act 1); 10. Linger in the
lobby; 11. The half of it, dearie, blues; 12. Juanita;
13. I'd rather Charleston (for London production,
1926); 14. Reprises; 15. Little jazz bird; 16. Carnival
time; 17. Swiss miss; 18. Finale ultimo. ADDITIONAL
ITEM: 19. The Man I love.
Cpte L. Teeter, A. Morrison, Jason Alexander, M.
Maguire, J. Pizzarelli, I. Austin, M. Nicastro, R.
Langford, C. Swarbrick, Chor, Orch, E. Stern (r1992;
restored by T. Krasker)
 (7/93) (TELD) ① **7559-79308-2**
1. A. Brownridge (arr pf) *Concert*
 (1/91) (HYPE) ① **CDH88045**
2-4, 6-9. J. Gibbons (cpsr's pf improvisation, trans
Gibbons) *Concert* (8/93) (ASV) ① **CDWHL2074**
4. E. Parkin (arr pf: Parkin) *Concert*
 (10/89) (CLOU) ① **ACN6002**
6. A. Feinberg (r1994: arr Earl Wild) *Concert*
 (11/95) (ARGO) ① **444 457-2ZH**
6, 8, 11, 15. J. Kaye, W. Sharp, S. Blier *Concert*
 (7/91) (KOCH) ① **37028-2**
7. G. Gershwin (r1925: pf roll) *Concert*
 (4/94) (NONE) ① **7559-79287-2**
11. Sarah Walker, R. Vignoles (pp1988) *Concert*
 (3/89) (MERI) ① **CDE84167**
19. A. Feinberg (r1991: arr Percy Grainger) *Concert*
 (11/95) (ARGO) ① **444 457-2ZH**
**Of Thee I Sing—musical comedy (1931—New
York)** (Book Kaufman & Ryskind; Lyrics I.
Gershwin)
EXCERPTS: 1. Prelude. ACT ONE: 2. Wintergreen
for President; 3. Who Is The Lucky Girl to Be?; 4. The
Dimple On My Knee; 5. Because, Because; 6. Never
Was There a Girl So Fair; 7. Some Girls Can Bake a
Pie; 8. Love Is Sweeping the Country; 9. Of Thee I
Sing; 10. Finaletto: 10a. The Supreme Court Judge;
10b. Here's a Kiss for Cinderella; 10c. I Was the Most
Beautiful Blossom; 10e. Of Thee I Sing (reprise).
ACT TWO: 11. Hello, Good Morning; 12. Mine; 13.
Who Cares?; 14. Garçon, s'il vous plait; 15. The
Illegitimate Daughter; 16. Because, Because
(reprise); 17. Who Cares? (reprise); 18. The Senate
Roll Call: Impeachment; 19. Jilted; 20. I'm About to
Be a Mother; 21. Trumpeter Blow Your Horn; 22.
Finale.
Cpte J. Carson, P. Hartman, Broadway Cast, M.
Levine (r1952: revival cast)
 (1/95) (EMI) ① **ZDM5 65025-2**
1, 19. J. Gibbons (r1992-3: trans Gibbons: pf)
Concert (3/95) (ASV) ① **CDWHL2082**
13. S. Blier (arr cpsr) *Concert*
 (7/91) (KOCH) ① **37028-2**
**Oh, Kay!—musical comedy (1926—New
York)** (Lyrics I. Gershwin)
EXCERPTS: 1. Overture; 2. Clap yo' hands; 3. Dear
little girl; 4. Do, do, do; 5. Fidgety Feet; 6. Heaven on
earth; 7. Maybe; 8. Oh, Kay!; 9. Someone to watch

over me.
Cpte D. Upshaw, K. Ollmann, A. Arkin, chor, St
Luke's Orch, E. Stern (r c1994)
(8/95) (NONE) ① **7559-79361-2**
2. A. Feinberg (r1991; trans Artis Wodehouse)
Concert (11/95) (ARGO) ① **444 457-2ZH**
2, 4, 7, 9. G. Gershwin (trans pf: cpsr; r1926) *Concert*
(9/91) (HALC) ① **DHDL101**
2, 4, 7, 9. J. Gibbons (cpsr's pf improvisation, trans
Gibbons) *Concert* (8/93) (ASV) ① **CDWHL2077**
2, 7, 9. E. Parkin (arr Parkin) *Concert*
(10/89) (CLOU) ① **ACN6002**
5. J. MacGregor (arr Finnissy) *Concert*
(8/89) (COLL) ① **Coll1299-2**
9. K. Te Kanawa, New Princess Th Orch, J. McGlinn
(orch. H.Anderson) *Concert*
(10/87) (EMI) ① **CDC7 47454-2**
9. Sarah Walker, R. Vignoles (pp1982) *Concert*
(3/89) (MERI) ① **CDE84167**

Our Nell—musical comedy (1922—New York)
(Lyrics B. Hooker & A. E. Thomas)
EXCERPTS: 1. Overture; 2. By and by; 3. Innocent
ingenue baby; 4. My old New England baby; 5.
Walking home with Angeline.
3. W. Sharp, S. Blier *Concert*
(7/91) (KOCH) ① **37028-2**

**Pardon My English—musical comedy
(1933—New York)** (Lyrics I. Gershwin; Book H.
Fields & M. Ryskind)
EXCERPTS: 1. Overture; 2. Fatherland, Mother of
the Band; 3. The Lorelei; 4. In Three-Quarter Time; 5.
Dancing in the Streets; 6. So What?; 7. Isn't It a
Pity?; 8. Freud and Jung and Adler/He's Oversexed;
9. Watch Your Head; 10. My Cousin in Milwaukee;
11. Luckiest Man in the World; 12. Hail the Happy
Couple; 13. Dresden Northwest Mounted; 14.
Tonight; 15. Act II Opening; 16. Where You Go, I Go;
17. I've Got to Be There; 18. Reprises; 19. Finale:
He's Not Himself.
Cpte W. Katt, J. Cullum, A. Walker, M. Nicastro, P. A.
Chaffin, P. Tiffany, R. Wall, P. Kevoian, D. Engel,
Chor, Orch, E. Stern (r1993)
(11/94) (NONE) ① **7559-79338-2**
3. K. Criswell, Ambrosian Sngrs, London Sinfonietta,
J. McGlinn (r1992) *Concert*
(4/94) (EMI) ① **CDC7 54802-2**
3, 7. Sarah Walker, R. Vignoles (pp1988) *Concert*
(3/89) (MERI) ① **CDE84167**
7. J. Gibbons (r1992-3; trans Gibbons: pf) *Concert*
(3/95) (ASV) ① **CDWHL2082**
7, 10. E. Parkin (arr Parkin) *Concert*
(10/89) (CLOU) ① **ACN6002**
10. J. Kaye, S. Blier *Concert*
(7/91) (KOCH) ① **37028-2**

**Porgy and Bess—opera: 3 acts
(1935—Boston)** (Lib. Heyward and I.
Gershwin)
EXCERPTS: ACT ONE: 1. Introduction...Jasbo
Brown Blues; 2. Summertime; 3. A woman is a
sometime thing; 4. Here come de honey man; 5.
Don't you ever let a woman; 6. Oh, little stars; 7.
Wake up an' hit it out; 8. Gone, gone, gone; 9.
Overflow; 10. Um! A saucer-burial; 11. My man's
gone now; 12. Headin' for the Promis' Lan'. ACT 2:
13. It takes a long pull; 14. I got plenty o' nuttin'; 15. I
hates yo' struttin' style; 16. Buzzard Song; 17. Bess,
you is my woman now; 18. Oh, I can't sit down; 19. I
ain' got no shame; 20. It ain't necessarily so; 21.
What you want wid Bess?; 22. Honey, dat's all de
breakfast; 23. Oh, doctor Jesus; 24. Oh dey's so
fresh an' fine; 25a. Now de time; 25b. Porgy, dat you
there; 26. I loves you, Porgy; 27. Why you been out
on that wharf; 28. Oh, Doctor Jesus; 29. Oh, de Lawd
shake de Heavens; 30. Oh, dere's somebody; 31. A
red-headed woman. ACT 3: 32. Clara, don't you be
downhearted; 33. Interlude; 34a. Introduction; 34b.
Wait for us at the corner, Al; 35. You've got to go,
Porgy; 36. There's a boat dat's leavin'; 37a.
Introduction; 37b. Good mornin', sistuh!; 38. Dem
white folks; 39. Oh, Bess; 40. Bess is gone; 41. Oh
Lawd, I'm on my way.
Cpte W. White, L. Mitchell, B. Hendricks, F. Quivar,
F. Clemmons, B. Conrad, M. Boatwright, Arthur
Thompson, J.V. Pickens, S. Hagan, William Brown,
C. Deane, A. Ford, I. Jones, J. Buck, R. Snook, R.
Nealley, A. Leatherman, D. Zucca, J. Jones,
Cleveland Orch Children's Chor, Cleveland Orch
Chor, Cleveland Orch, L. Maazel
(2/86) (DECC) ① [3] **414 559-2DH3**
Cpte D.R. Albert, C. Dale, B. Lane, W. Shakesnider,
L. Marshall, C. Brice, Andrew Smith, A.B. Smalls,
Houston Grand Op Chor, Houston Grand Op Orch, J.
DeMain (9/86) (RCA) ① [3] **RD82109**

Cpte W. White, C. Haymon, H. Blackwell, C. Clarey,
D. Evans, M. Simpson, Gregg Baker, B. Hubbard, B.
Coleman, J. Worthy, Curtis Watson, M. Wallace, M.
Brathwaite, A. Paige, W. Johnson, P. Ingram, L.
Thompson, Colenton Freeman, C. Johnson, A.
Tilvern, B.J. Mitchell, T. Maynard, R. Travis, W.
Marshall, Glyndebourne Fest Chor, LPO, S. Rattle
(r1988) (6/89) (EMI) ① [3] **CDS7 49568-2**
Fantasy E. Wild (trans Wild) *Concert*
(10/90) (CHES) ① **Chesky CD32**
1-3, 8, 14, 17, 20, 21, 26, 36, 39, 41. L. Price, W.
Warfield, J.W. Bubbles, R. Henson, B. Webb, M.
Burton, Alonzo Jones, B. Hall, RCA Victor Chor, RCA
Victor Orch, S. Henderson (r1963)
(4/89) (RCA) ① **GD85234**
1-3, 8, 9, 11, 12, 14, 17, 18, 20, 21, 36, 39, 41. D.R.
Albert, C. Dale, Andrew Smith, W. Shakesnider, B.
Lane, C. Brice, A.B. Smalls, L. Marshall, Houston
Grand Op. Chor, Houston Grand Op Orch, J. DeMain
(2/86) (RCA) ① **RD84680**
2. K. Te Kanawa, NY Choral Artists, New Princess Th
Orch, J. McGlinn
(10/87) (EMI) ① **CDC7 47454-2**
2. C. Berberian, B. Canino *Concert*
(7/89) (WERG) ① **WER60054-50**
2. K. Battle, M. Garrett (pp1991) *Concert*
(7/92) (DG) ① **435 440-2GH**
2. Thurston Cl Qt (arr cl qt: Bland) *Concert*
(3/93) (ASV) ① **CDWHL2076**
2, 14, 17, 20, 26. Budapest Stgs (arr anon) *Concert*
(11/90) (LASE) ① **15 606**
2, 17. Brodsky Qt (arr M. Thomas) *Concert*
(4/92) (TELD) ① **2292-46015-2**
2, 17, 20. X. Wei, Pam Nicholson (arr Heifetz)
Concert (9/90) (ASV) ① **CDDCA698**
2, 26. B. Hendricks, K. Labèque, M. Labèque (arr.
Jeanneau) *Concert* (1/87) (PHIL) ① **416 460-2PH**
2, 3, 11, 17, 20, 36. J. Heifetz, B. Smith (r1965)
Concert (11/94) (RCA) ① [65] **09026 61778-2(40)**
2, 3, 11, 17, 20, 36. J. Heifetz, E. Bay (r1945)
Concert (11/94) (RCA) ① [65] **09026 61778-2(19)**
12. D. Woods, Collegiate Chorale, NY Met Op Orch,
J. Conlon (pp1991) *Concert*
(6/93) (RCA) ① **09026 61509-2**
12, 29. J. Kaye, W. Sharp, S. Blier *Concert*
(7/91) (KOCH) ① **37028-2**
14, 17, 22, 27, 32, 37b, 41. J. Gibbons (r1992-3;
trans Gibbons: pf) *Concert*
(3/95) (ASV) ① **CDWHL2082**
14, 39. L. Tibbett, Orch, A. Smallens (r1935) *Concert*
(3/90) (RCA) ① **GD87808**
17. J. Lloyd Webber, RPO, N. Cleobury (arr vc)
Concert (3/89) (PHIL) ① **416 698-2PH**
17. E. Parkin (arr Parkin) *Concert*
(10/89) (CLOU) ① **ACN6002**
17. I. Stern, Columbia SO, M. Katims (arr Harris)
Concert (7/90) (SONY) ① **SK45816**
17. R. Stoltzman, LSO, E. Stern (r1993; arr
Silverman) *Concert*
(12/93) (RCA) ① **09026 61790-2**
17. W. White, C. Haymon, LPO, S. Rattle (r1988)
Concert (6/94) (EMI) ① **CDH5 65072-2**
20. S. Chang, S. Rivers (trans Heifetz) *Concert*
(1/93) (EMI) ① **CDC7 54352-2**
20. J. Heifetz, B. Smith (r1970) *Concert*
(11/94) (RCA) ① [65] **09026 61778-2(35)**
20. A. A. Meyers, S. Rivers (r1993; trans Heifetz:
vn/pf) *Concert* (4/95) (RCA) ① **09026 62546-2**
Porgy and Bess—concert suite from opera
Detroit SO, A. Dorati Grofé: *Grand Canyon Suite*.
(8/91) (DECC) ① **430 712-2DM**
Bournemouth SO, J. Farrer (r1993; arr Russell
Bennett) *Concert* (8/94) (CARL) ① **MCD75**
Primrose—musical comedy (1924—London)
(Book C. Bolton and G. Grossmith: lyrics D.
Carter and I Gershwin)
EXCERPTS: 1. Overture; 2. Boy wanted; 3. Isn't it
wonderful?; 4. Naughty baby; 5. Some far-away
someone.
Ballet A. Brownridge (arr pf) *Concert*
(1/91) (HYPE) ① **CDH88045**
2. K. Te Kanawa, New Princess Th Orch, J. McGlinn
(orch. F.Saddler) *Concert*
(10/87) (EMI) ① **CDC7 47454-2**
3. J. Kaye, S. Blier *Concert*
(7/91) (KOCH) ① **37028-2**
Rosalie—musical comedy (1928—New York)
(Lyrics I. Gershwin)
EXCERPTS: 1. Overture; 2. Ev'ry body knows I love
somebody; 3. How long has this been going on?; 4.
Oh gee! Oh joy!; 5. Say so!.
3. E. Parkin (arr Parkin) *Concert*
(10/89) (CLOU) ① **ACN6002**
3. W. Sharp, S. Blier *Concert*
(7/91) (KOCH) ① **37028-2**

Shall we dance?—songs for the film (1936)
(Lyrics I. Gershwin)
EXCERPTS: 1. Overture; 2. Beginner's luck; 3. Let's
call the whole thing off; 4. Shall we dance?; 5. Slap
that bass; 6. They all laughed; 7. They can't take that
away from me; 8. Promenade.
3, 7. J. Gibbons (r1992-3; trans Gibbons: pf) *Concert*
(3/95) (ASV) ① **CDWHL2082**
4. E. Parkin (arr Parkin) *Concert*
(10/89) (CLOU) ① **ACN6002**
7. B. Hendricks, K. Labèque, M. Labèque (arr.
Jeanneau) *Concert* (1/87) (PHIL) ① **416 460-2PH**
8. M. Tilson Thomas (pf/dir), Los Angeles PO
Concert (1/86) (SONY) ① **MK39699**
8. R. Stoltzman, LSO, E. Stern (r1993; arr Silverman)
Concert (12/93) (RCA) ① **09026 61790-2**

**The Shocking Miss Pilgrim—songs for the
film (1946)** (Lyrics I. Gershwin)
EXCERPTS: 1. Overture; 2. Aren't you kind of glad
we did?; 3. The Back Bay Polka; 4. Changing my
tune; 5. For you, for me, for evermore; 6. One, two,
three.
2, 4. E. Parkin (arr Parkin) *Concert*
(10/89) (CLOU) ① **ACN6002**
5. J. Gibbons (r1992-3; trans Gibbons: pf) *Concert*
(3/95) (ASV) ① **CDWHL2082**

**Show Girl—musical comedy (1929—New
York)** (Lyrics W. A. McGuire & J. P. McEvoy)
EXCERPTS: 1. Overture; 2. Do what you do!; 3.
Harlem Serenade; 4. I must be home by twelve
o'clock; 5. Liza; 6. So are you!; 7. Home Blues
(unpub).
5. E. Parkin (arr Parkin) *Concert*
(10/89) (CLOU) ① **ACN6002**
5. J. Kaye, S. Blier *Concert*
(7/91) (KOCH) ① **37028-2**
5. J. Gibbons (arr Gershwin/Gibbons) *Concert*
(8/93) (ASV) ① **CDWHL2077**

**Strike Up the Band (1st version)—musical
comedy (1927—Philadelphia)** (Lyrics I.
Gershwin)
EXCERPTS: 1. Overture; 2. Military dancing drill; 3.
The man I love; 4. Seventeen and twenty-one; 5.
Strike up the band; 6. Yankee doodle rhythm; 7.
Meadow Serenade (unpub).
Cpte B. Barrett, D. Chastain, R. Luker, J. Graae, B.
Fowler, C. Goff, J. Lambert, J. Lyons, D. Sandish, J.
Rocco, Chor, Orch, J. Mauceri *Strike Up the Band II*.
(1/92) (NONE) ① [2] **7559-79273-2**
3. B. Hendricks, K. Labèque, M. Labèque (arr.
Jeanneau) *Concert* (1/87) (PHIL) ① **416 460-2PH**
3. G. Saba (trans Grainger) *Concert*
(10/87) (CARL) ① **PCD858**
3. K. Te Kanawa, New Princess Th Orch, J. McGlinn
(orch. W.Daly) *Concert*
(10/87) (EMI) ① **CDC7 47454-2**
3. Sarah Walker, R. Vignoles (pp1988) *Concert*
(3/89) (MERI) ① **CDE84167**
3. E. Parkin (arr Parkin) *Concert*
(10/89) (CLOU) ① **ACN6002**
3. Martin Jones (r1989: trans pf: Grainger) *Concert*
(7/90) (NIMB) ① **NI5232**
3. A. Murphy, Glasgow CWS Band, H. Snell (arr
Snell) *Concert* (9/92) (DOYE) ① **DOYCD005**
3, 6. J. Kaye, W. Sharp, S. Blier *Concert*
(7/91) (KOCH) ① **37028-2**
7. K. Te Kanawa, New Princess Th Orch, J. McGlinn
(orch. M.Peress & L.Moore) *Concert*
(10/87) (EMI) ① **CDC7 47454-2**
7. J. Gibbons (cpsr's pf improvisation, trans Gibbons)
Concert (8/93) (ASV) ① **CDWHL2077**

**Strike Up The Band (2nd version)—musical
comedy (1930—New York)** (Lyrics I.
Gershwin)
EXCERPTS: 1. Overture; 2. Hangin' around with
you; 3. I mean to say; 4. I want to be a war bride; 5.
I've got a crush on you; 6. Mademoiselle in New
Rochelle; 7. Soon; 8. Strike up the band.
Cpte B. Barrett, D. Chastain, R. Luker, J. Graae, B.
Fowler, C. Goff, J. Lambert, J. Lyons, D. Sandish, J.
Rocco, Chor, Orch, J. Mauceri (appendix to vers I)
Strike Up the Band I.
(1/92) (NONE) ① [2] **7559-79273-2**
1. J. Gibbons (cpsr's pf improvisation, trans Gibbons)
Concert (8/93) (ASV) ① **CDWHL2077**
1. BBC PO, Y. P. Tortelier (r1994) *Concert*
(4/95) (CHAN) ① **CHAN9325**
2. J. Kaye, S. Blier *Concert*
(7/91) (KOCH) ① **37028-2**
7. K. Te Kanawa, New Princess Th Orch, J. McGlinn
(orch. S.Berkowitz) *Concert*
(10/87) (EMI) ① **CDC7 47454-2**
8. Boston Pops, A. Fiedler (r1958) *Concert*
(1/94) (RCA) ① **09026 61249-2**

Tell me more—musical comedy (1925—New York) (lyrics De Sylva and I. Gershwin)
EXCERPTS: 1. Baby; 2. Kickin' the clouds away; 3. My fair lady; 4. Tell me more; 5. Three times a day; 6. Why do I love you.
2. J. Gibbons (cpsr's pf improvisation, trans Gibbons) *Concert*
(8/93) (ASV) ① **CDWHL2074**
4. G. Gershwin (r1925: pf roll) *Concert*
(4/94) (NONE) ① **7559-79287-2**

Tip-Toes—musical comedy (1925—New York) (Book Bolton and Thompson: lyrics I. Gershwin)
EXCERPTS: 1. Overture; 2. Looking for a boy; 3. Nice baby!; 4. Nightie-night; 5. Sweet and low-down; 6. That certain feeling; 7. These charming people; 8. When do we dance?.
2, 5, 6, 8. G. Gershwin (trans pf: cpsr; r1926) *Concert*
(9/91) (HALC) ① **DHDL101**
2, 5, 6, 8. J. Gibbons (cpsr's pf improvisation, trans Gibbons) *Concert* (8/93) (ASV) ① **CDWHL2077**
5, 6. G. Gershwin (r1926: pf roll) *Concert*
(4/94) (NONE) ① **7559-79287-2**
6. A. Feinberg (r1994; trans Artis Wodehouse) *Concert* (11/95) (ARGO) ① **444 457-2ZH**

Treasure Girl—musical comedy (1928—New York) (Lyrics I. Gershwin)
EXCERPTS: 1. Feeling I'm falling; 3. Got a rainbow; 4. I don't think I'll fall in love today; 5. I've got a crush on you; 6. K-ra-zy for you; 7. Oh, so nice; 8. What are we here for?; 9. Where's the boy? here's the girl!.
2, 7. J. Kaye, W. Sharp, S. Blier *Concert*
(7/91) (KOCH) ① **37028-2**
7. E. Parkin (arr Parkin) *Concert*
(10/89) (CLOU) ① **ACN6002**

GERVAISE, Claude (fl 1540–60) France

SECTION II: CHAMBER

Branle de Bourgogne
Ulsamer Collegium, J. Ulsamer *Concert*
(2/86) (ARCH) ① **415 294-2AH**
Branle de Champage
Ulsamer Collegium, J. Ulsamer *Concert*
(2/86) (ARCH) ① **415 294-2AH**
Pavane et Galliarde, 'Est il conclud'—consort
London Musica Antiqua, M. Uridge (r1980-83) *Concert* (12/93) (SYMP) ① **SYMCD1157**

GESUALDO, Carlo (Prince of Venosa, Count of Conza) (c1561–1613) Italy

SECTION II: CHAMBER

Gagliarda del Principe di Venosa
Ulsamer Collegium, J. Ulsamer *Concert*
(2/86) (ARCH) ① **415 294-2AH**

SECTION III: INSTRUMENTAL

Canzon francese a 4—keyboard
Arts Florissants Instr Ens *Concert*
(10/88) (HARM) ① **HMC90 1268**

SECTION IV: VOCAL AND CHORAL

Ahi, disperata vita—madrigal (5vv) (pub 1595)
Arts Florissants Voc Ens, Arts Florissants Instr Ens, W. Christie *Concert*
(10/88) (HARM) ① **HMC90 1268**
Arde il mio cor, ed è si dolce il foco—madrigal (5vv) (pub 1596)
Arts Florissants Voc Ens, Arts Florissants Instr Ens, W. Christie *Concert*
(10/88) (HARM) ① **HMC90 1268**
Arditi Zanzaretta—madrigal (5vv), pub 1611
Arts Florissants Voc Ens, Arts Florissants Instr Ens, W. Christie *Concert*
(10/88) (HARM) ① **HMC90 1268**
Ardo per te, mio bene—madrigal (5vv) (pub 1611)
Arts Florissants Voc Ens, Arts Florissants Instr Ens, W. Christie *Concert*
(10/88) (HARM) ① **HMC90 1268**
Asciugate i begli occhi—madrigal (5vv) (pub 1611)
Arts Florissants Voc Ens, Arts Florissants Instr Ens, W. Christie *Concert*
(10/88) (HARM) ① **HMC90 1268**
Assumpta est Maria—6vv (1603) (cpted Stravinsky: pub 1960)
New London Chmbr Ch (compl Stravinsky) *Concert*
(2/92) (HYPE) ① **CDA66410**

Trinity Coll Ch, Cambridge, R. Marlow (r1994) *Concert*
(6/95) (CONI) ① **75605 51232-2**
Corret, amanti, a prova—madrigal (5vv) (pub 1611)
Arts Florissants Voc Ens, Arts Florissants Instr Ens, W. Christie *Concert*
(10/88) (HARM) ① **HMC90 1268**
Da pacem, Domine—6vv (1603) (cpted Stravinsky: pub 1960)
New London Chmbr Ch (compl Stravinsky) *Concert*
(2/92) (HYPE) ① **CDA66410**
Trinity Coll Ch, Cambridge, R. Marlow (r1994) *Concert*
(6/95) (CONI) ① **75605 51232-2**
Dolcissima mia vita—madrigal (5vv) (pub 1611)
Monteverdi Ch, J. E. Gardiner (r1969) *Concert*
(2/94) (DECC) ① **440 032-2DM**
Ecco, morirò dunque—motet: 5vv (1596)
Monteverdi Ch, J. E. Gardiner (r1969) *Concert*
(2/94) (DECC) ① **440 032-2DM**
Illumina nos misericordiarum—7vv (1603) (cpted Stravinsky: Tres sacrae cantiones, 1960)
New London Chmbr Ch (compl Stravinsky) *Concert*
(2/92) (HYPE) ① **CDA66410**
Trinity Coll Ch, Cambridge, R. Marlow (r1994) *Concert*
(6/95) (CONI) ① **75605 51232-2**
Invan dunque—madrigal (5vv)
Arts Florissants Voc Ens, Arts Florissants Instr Ens, W. Christie *Concert*
(10/88) (HARM) ① **HMC90 1268**
Io parto, e non più dissi—madrigal (5vv) (1610)
Arts Florissants Voc Ens, Arts Florissants Instr Ens, W. Christie *Concert*
(10/88) (HARM) ① **HMC90 1268**
Io tacerò, ma nel silenzio mio—madrigal (5vv) (pub 1596)
Arts Florissants Voc Ens, Arts Florissants Instr Ens, W. Christie *Concert*
(10/88) (HARM) ① **HMC90 1268**
Luci serene e chiare—madrigal (5vv) (pub. 1596) (Wds. Arlotti)
Amaryllis Consort *Concert*
(6/86) (CARL) ① **PCD822**
Arts Florissants Voc Ens, Arts Florissants Instr Ens, W. Christie *Concert*
(10/88) (HARM) ① **HMC90 1268**
Mercè grido piangendo—madrigal (5vv) (pub 1611)
Arts Florissants Voc Ens, Arts Florissants Instr Ens, W. Christie *Concert*
(10/88) (HARM) ① **HMC90 1268**
Moro, lasso, al mio duolo—madrigal (5vv) (pub 1611)
Amaryllis Consort *Concert*
(6/86) (CARL) ① **PCD822**
Monteverdi Ch, J. E. Gardiner (r1969) *Concert*
(2/94) (DECC) ① **440 032-2DM**
Non t'amo, o voce ingrata—madrigal (5vv) (pub 1595)
Arts Florissants Voc Ens, Arts Florissants Instr Ens, W. Christie *Concert*
(10/88) (HARM) ① **HMC90 1268**
O mainati messagi—madrigal (5vv)
Arts Florissants Voc Ens, Arts Florissants Instr Ens, W. Christie *Concert*
(10/88) (HARM) ① **HMC90 1268**
O vos omnes—motet (6vv) (pub 1611)
Monteverdi Ch, J. E. Gardiner (r1969) *Concert*
(2/94) (DECC) ① **440 032-2DM**
Occhi del mio cor vita—madrigal (5vv) (pub 1611)
Arts Florissants Voc Ens, Arts Florissants Instr Ens, W. Christie *Concert*
(10/88) (HARM) ① **HMC90 1268**
Responsoria et alia ad Officum Hebdonadae Sanctae spectantia—6vv (1611)
1. Feria V; 1a. Im monte Oliveti; 1b. Tritis est anima mea; 1c. Ecce vidimus eum; 1d. Amicus meus; 1e. Judas mercator pessimus; 1f. Unus ex discipulis meis; 1g. Eram quasi agnus innocens; 1h. Una hora non potuitis; 1i. Seniores populi; 2. Feria VI; 2a. Omnes amici mei; 2b. Velum templi; 2c. Vinea mea electa; 2d. Tamquam ad latronem; 2e. Tenebrae factae sunt; 2f. Animam meam dilectam; 2g. Tradiderunt me; 2h. Jesum tradidit impius; 2i. Caligaverunt oculi mei; 3. Sabbato Sancto; 3a. Sicut ovis; 3b. Jerusalem, surge; 3c. Plange quasi virgo; 3d. Recessit pastor noster; 3e. O vos omnes; 3f. Ecce quomodo moritur justus; 3g. Astiterunt reges terrae; 3h. Aestimatus sum; 3i. Sepulto Domino; 4. Benedictus Dominus Deus Israel; 5. Miserere mei, Deus.
Cpte Hilliard Ens (3/92) (ECM) ① [2] **843 867-2**

3a-I Tallis Scholars, P. Phillips *Sacrarum cantionum (5vv).* (12/87) (GIME) ① **CDGIM015**
3a-I Paris Chapelle Royale European Ens, P. Herreweghe *Concert*
(12/90) (HARM) ① **HMC90 1320**
3a-I Trinity Coll Ch, Cambridge, R. Marlow (r1994) *Concert* (6/95) (CONI) ① **75605 51232-2**
Sacrarum cantionum—motets: 5vv (pub 1603)
1. Ave, dulcissima Maria; 2. Ave, regina coelorum; 3. Deus refugium; 4. Dignare me, laudare te; 5. Domine, ne despicias; 6. Exaudi, Deus, deprecationem meam; 7. Hei mihi, Domine; 8. Illumina faciem tuam; 9. Laboravi in gemitu meo; 10. Maria, mater gratiae; 11. O crux benedicta; 12. O vos omnes; 13. Peccantem me quotidie; 14. Precibus et meritis beatae Mariae; 15. Reminiscere miserationum tuarum; 16. Sancti Spiritus, Domine, corda nostra; 17. Tribularer si nescirem; 18. Tribulationem et dolorem inveni; 19. Venit lumen tuum.
1. Monteverdi Ch, EBS, J.E. Gardiner *Concert*
(7/85) (ERAT) ① **2292-45219-2**
1, 13, 17, 18. Paris Chapelle Royale European Ens, P. Herreweghe *Concert*
(12/90) (HARM) ① **HMC90 1320**
1, 2, 10, 14. Tallis Scholars, P. Phillips *Concert*
(12/87) (GIME) ① **CDGIM015**
1, 7. Monteverdi Ch, J. E. Gardiner (r1969) *Concert*
(2/94) (DECC) ① **440 032-2DM**
Se la mia morte brami—madrigal (5vv), pub 1611
Arts Florissants Voc Ens, Arts Florissants Instr Ens, W. Christie *Concert*
(10/88) (HARM) ① **HMC90 1268**
Sospriravra il mio core—madrigal (5vv) (pub 1595)
Arts Florissants Voc Ens, Arts Florissants Instr Ens, W. Christie *Concert*
(10/88) (HARM) ① **HMC90 1268**
Sparge la morte al mio Signor nel viso—madrigal (5vv) (pub 1596)
Arts Florissants Voc Ens, Arts Florissants Instr Ens, W. Christie *Concert*
(10/88) (HARM) ① **HMC90 1268**

GESZLER, György (b 1912) Hungary

SECTION II: CHAMBER

The Humming Top—violin and piano
T. Varga, G. Moore (r1947) *Concert*
(11/93) (CLAV) ① [4] **CD50-9300/4**
T. Varga, G. Moore (r1947) *Concert*
(11/93) (CLAV) ① **CD50-9314**

GETTY, Gordon (b 1947) USA

SECTION IV: VOCAL AND CHORAL

The White Election—song cycle (Wds. E. Dickinson)
K. Erickson, A. Guzelimian
(12/89) (DELO) ① **DE3057**

GHEDINI, Giorgio Federico (1892–1965) Italy

SECTION I: ORCHESTRAL

Concerto for Violin and Strings, '(Il Belprato' (1947)
Accademia Bizantina, C. Chiarappa (vn/dir) (r1993) *Concert* (3/95) (DENO) ① **CO-78916**

GHERARDELLO DA FIRENZE (c1320/25–1362/63) Florence

SECTION IV: VOCAL AND CHORAL

I' vo' bene—ballata
E. Lamandier *Concert* (2/88) (ALIE) ① **AL1019**

GIAMPIERI, Alamiro (1893–1963) Italy

SECTION II: CHAMBER

Il Carnevale di Venezia—variations: clarinet and piano
E. Johnson, G. Back *Concert*
(5/91) (ASV) ① **CDDCA732**

1, 9, 13. A. Tysall, Rose Consort *Concert*
(10/93) (WOOD) ① **WOODM002-2**
2, 3, 6a-d, 11. T. Bonner, Rose Consort (r1992)
Concert (2/95) (NAXO) ① **8 550603**
Now in the Lord my heart doth pleasure take
(Hymnes and Songs of the Church, 4)
Clerkes of Oxenford, D. Wulstan *Concert*
(12/89) (CALL) ① **CAL9611**
Now shall the praises of the Lord (Hymnes
and Songs of the Church, 1)
Clerkes of Oxenford, D. Wulstan *Concert*
(12/89) (CALL) ① **CAL9611**
King's College Ch, S. Preston, D. Willcocks
Concert (10/92) (DECC) ① **433 677-2DM**
O all true faithful hearts—verse anthem
Trinity Coll Ch, Cambridge, Fretwork, R. Marlow
(r1994) *Concert* (8/95) (CONI) ① **75605 51231-2**
O clap your hands—full anthem: 8vv
Cambridge Sngrs, J. Rutter *Concert*
(6/88) (CLLE) ① **COLCD107**
New College Ch, E. Higginbottom *Concert*
(12/88) (CRD) ① **CRD3451**
Clerkes of Oxenford, D. Wulstan *Concert*
(12/89) (CALL) ① **CAL9611**
New College Ch, E. Higginbottom *Concert*
(3/90) (PROU) ① **PROUCD125**
Worcester Cath Ch, Don Hunt *Concert*
(9/90) (CARL) ① **PCD937**
King's College Ch, H. McLean, B. Ord (r1955)
Concert (10/92) (DECC) ① **433 677-2DM**
St John's College Ch, C. Robinson (r1993) *Concert*
(11/94) (CHAN) ① **CHAN0559**
Worcester Cath Ch, Don Hunt, R. Johnston (r1993)
Concert (2/95) (ABBE) ① **CDCA957**
Trinity Coll Ch, Cambridge, Fretwork, R. Marlow
(r1994) *Concert* (8/95) (CONI) ① **75605 51231-2**
O God, the king of glory—verse anthem:
4/5vv
New College Ch, D. Burchell, E. Higginbottom
Concert (12/88) (CRD) ① **CRD3451**
St John's College Ch, C. Robinson (r1993) *Concert*
(11/94) (CHAN) ① **CHAN0559**
O Lord, how do my woes increase—full
anthem: 4vv (pub 1614)
Clerkes of Oxenford, D. Wulstan *Concert*
(12/89) (CALL) ① **CAL9611**
Trinity Coll Ch, Cambridge, Fretwork, R. Marlow
(r1994) *Concert* (8/95) (CONI) ① **75605 51231-2**
O Lord, I lift my heart to thee—full anthem:
5vv
Clerkes of Oxenford, D. Wulstan *Concert*
(12/89) (CALL) ① **CAL9611**
Magdalen Oxford Coll Ch, J. Harper *Concert*
(11/91) (ABBE) ① **CDCA912**
Trinity Coll Ch, Cambridge, Fretwork, R. Marlow
(r1994) *Concert* (8/95) (CONI) ① **75605 51231-2**
O Lord, in thee is all my trust—full anthem:
5vv
Trinity Coll Ch, Cambridge, Fretwork, R. Marlow
(r1994) *Concert* (8/95) (CONI) ① **75605 51231-2**
O Lord, in thy wrath rebuke me not—full
anthem: 6vv
New College Ch, E. Higginbottom *Concert*
(12/88) (CRD) ① **CRD3451**
Clerkes of Oxenford, D. Wulstan *Concert*
(12/89) (CALL) ① **CAL9611**
Oxford Christ Church Cath Ch, S. Preston *Concert*
(2/90) (GAMU) ① **GOUPCD153**
Magdalen Oxford Coll Ch, J. Harper *Concert*
(11/91) (ABBE) ① **CDCA912**
King's College Ch, H. McLean, B. Ord (r1955)
Concert (10/92) (DECC) ① **433 677-2DM**
R. Johnston, Worcester Cath Ch, Don Hunt *Concert*
(5/93) (ABBE) ① **CDCA943**
St John's College Ch, C. Robinson (r1993) *Concert*
(11/94) (CHAN) ① **CHAN0559**
Trinity Coll Ch, Cambridge, Fretwork, R. Marlow
(r1994) *Concert* (8/95) (CONI) ① **75605 51231-2**
O Lord of Hosts and God of Israel (Hymnes
and Songs of the Church, 22)
Clerkes of Oxenford, D. Wulstan *Concert*
(12/89) (CALL) ① **CAL9611**
O my love, how comely now (Hymnes and
Songs of the Church, 13)
Clerkes of Oxenford, D. Wulstan *Concert*
(12/89) (CALL) ① **CAL9611**
Out of the deep—full anthem: 6vv (also attrib.
W Byrd)
Trinity Coll Ch, Cambridge, Fretwork, R. Marlow
(r1994) *Concert* (8/95) (CONI) ① **75605 51231-2**
Praise the Lord, O my soul—verse anthem:
7/6vv
Clerkes of Oxenford, D. Wulstan *Concert*
(12/89) (CALL) ① **CAL9611**
Trinity Coll Ch, Cambridge, Fretwork, R. Marlow
(r1994) *Concert* (8/95) (CONI) ① **75605 51231-2**

Preces and Psalm 145—verse reponses (pub
1641)
1. Preces; 2. Psalm 145—The eyes of all wait upon
thee.
Clerkes of Oxenford, D. Wulstan *Concert*
(12/89) (CALL) ① **CAL9611**
King's College Ch, D. Willcocks (r1958) *Concert*
(10/92) (DECC) ① **433 677-2DM**
Second (Verse) Service—5vv (pub 1641)
1. Te Deum; 2. Jubilate; 3. Magnificat; 4. Nunc
dimittis.
New College Ch, D. Burchell, E. Higginbottom (ed
Higginbottom) *Concert* (12/88) (CRD) ① **CRD3451**
1, 2. King's College Ch, S. Preston, D. Willcocks
(r1958) *Concert* (10/92) (DECC) ① **433 677-2DM**
See, see, the word is incarnate—verse
anthem: 6/6vv (1616)
New College Ch, D. Burchell, E. Higginbottom
Concert (12/88) (CRD) ① **CRD3451**
Clerkes of Oxenford, D. Wulstan *Concert*
(12/89) (CALL) ① **CAL9611**
Red Byrd, Rose Consort *Concert*
(12/91) (AMON) ① **CD-SAR46**
King's College Ch, Jacobean Consort of Viols, D.
Willcocks (r1958) *Concert*
(10/92) (DECC) ① **433 677-2DM**
Trinity Coll Ch, Cambridge, Fretwork, R. Marlow
(r1994) *Concert* (8/95) (CONI) ① **75605 51231-2**
The Silver swan—madrigal: 5vv (pub 1612)
Cambridge Sngrs, J. Rutter *Concert*
(11/87) (CLLE) ① **COLCD105**
Amaryllis Consort, C. Brett *Concert*
(3/88) (CARL) ① **PCD873**
Hilliard Ens, P. Hillier *Concert*
(2/89) (EMI) ① **CDC7 49197-2**
J. Budd, Fretwork (r1990) *Concert*
(7/94) (VIRG) ① **VC5 45007-2**
Sing praises Is'rel to the Lord (Hymnes and
Songs of the Church, 3)
Clerkes of Oxenford, D. Wulstan *Concert*
(12/89) (CALL) ① **CAL9611**
Sing unto the Lord, o ye saints—verse
anthem: 4/5vv
New College Ch, D. Burchell, E. Higginbottom
Concert (12/88) (CRD) ① **CRD3451**
Clerkes of Oxenford, D. Wulstan *Concert*
(12/89) (CALL) ① **CAL9611**
So God loved the world—verse anthem
St John's College Ch, C. Robinson (r1993) *Concert*
(11/94) (CHAN) ① **CHAN0559**
Song of joy unto the Lord we sing (Hymnes
and Songs of the Church, 47)
Clerkes of Oxenford, D. Wulstan *Concert*
(12/89) (CALL) ① **CAL9611**
This is the record of John—verse anthem:
1/5vv
Red Byrd, Rose Consort *Concert*
(12/91) (AMON) ① **CD-SAR46**
King's College Ch, Jacobean Consort of Viols, D.
Willcocks (r1958) *Concert*
(10/92) (DECC) ① **433 677-2DM**
Wellington College Chs, T. Byram-Wigfield, S.
Anderson *Concert* (10/92) (HERA) ① **HAVPCD153**
R. Johnston, Worcester Cath Ch, Don Hunt *Concert*
(5/93) (ABBE) ① **CDCA943**
Trinity Coll Ch, Cambridge, P. Rushforth, R. Marlow
(r1993) *Concert* (12/93) (CONI) ① **CDCF517**
Trinity Coll Ch, Cambridge, Fretwork, R. Marlow
(r1994) *Concert* (8/95) (CONI) ① **75605 51231-2**
Thy beauty, Israel, is gone (Hymnes and
Songs of the Church, 5)
Clerkes of Oxenford, D. Wulstan *Concert*
(12/89) (CALL) ① **CAL9611**
We praise Thee, O Father—verse anthem
St John's College Ch, C. Robinson (r1993) *Concert*
(11/94) (CHAN) ① **CHAN0559**
What is our life—madrigal: 5vv (pub 1612)
(Wds. W. Raleigh)
Amaryllis Consort, C. Brett *Concert*
(3/88) (CARL) ① **PCD873**
J. Budd, M. Chance, Fretwork (r1990) *Concert*
(7/94) (VIRG) ① **VC5 45007-2**
When one among the Twelve there was
(Hymnes and Songs of the Church, 67)
Clerkes of Oxenford, D. Wulstan *Concert*
(12/89) (CALL) ① **CAL9611**
Who's this, that leaning on her friend
(Hymnes and Songs of the Church, 18)
Clerkes of Oxenford, D. Wulstan *Concert*
(12/89) (CALL) ① **CAL9611**

GIBBS, Cecil Armstrong
(1889–1960) England

SECTION I: ORCHESTRAL

Fancy dress—dance suite: orchestra, Op.
82/1
1. Hurly burly; 3. Dusk.
3. RTE Concert Orch, E. Tomlinson (r1993) *Concert*
(12/95) (MARC) ① **8 223522**
Symphony No. 1 in E, Op. 70 (1931-32)
Ireland National SO, A. Penny (r1993) *Symphony 3.*
(5/95) (MARC) ① **8 223553**
Symphony No. 3 in B flat, 'Westmorland',
Op. 104 (1944)
Ireland National SO, A. Penny (r1993) *Symphony 1.*
(5/95) (MARC) ① **8 223553**

SECTION IV: VOCAL AND CHORAL

The Ballad of Semmerwater—song (1930)
(Wds. W. Watson)
N. Hancock-Child, R. Hancock-Child (r1991) *Concert*
(11/93) (MARC) ① **8 223458**
A Ballad-maker—song (1935) (Wds. P.
Colum)
N. Hancock-Child, R. Hancock-Child (r1991) *Concert*
(11/93) (MARC) ① **8 223458**
The Cherry Tree—song (1949) (Wds. M.
Rose)
P. Jeffes, J. Constable *Concert*
(4/92) (GAMU) ① **GAMD506**
N. Hancock-Child, R. Hancock-Child (r1991) *Concert*
(11/93) (MARC) ① **8 223458**
Dream Song (1932) (Wds. W. de la Mare)
N. Hancock-Child, R. Hancock-Child (r1991) *Concert*
(11/93) (MARC) ① **8 223458**
Hypochondriacus—song, Wds. C. Lamb
(1949)
N. Hancock-Child, R. Hancock-Child (r1991) *Concert*
(11/93) (MARC) ① **8 223458**
Jenny Jones—song (1927) (Wds. D. Rowley)
N. Hancock-Child, R. Hancock-Child (r1991) *Concert*
(11/93) (MARC) ① **8 223458**
Midnight—song (1934) (Wds. J. Lang)
N. Hancock-Child, R. Hancock-Child (r1991) *Concert*
(11/93) (MARC) ① **8 223458**
Nightfall—song (1949) (Wds. H. Dawson)
N. Hancock-Child, R. Hancock-Child (r1991) *Concert*
(11/93) (MARC) ① **8 223458**
Padraic the Fidiler—song (1931) (Wds. P.
Gregory)
N. Hancock-Child, R. Hancock-Child (r1991) *Concert*
(11/93) (MARC) ① **8 223458**
Proud Maisie—song (1926) (Wds. W. Scott)
N. Hancock-Child, R. Hancock-Child (r1991) *Concert*
(11/93) (MARC) ① **8 223458**
The Sleeping Beauty—song (1922) (Wds. W.
de la Mare)
N. Hancock-Child, R. Hancock-Child (r1991) *Concert*
(11/93) (MARC) ① **8 223458**
2 Songs, Op. 14 (1918) (Wds. W. de la Mare)
1. Music unheard (Sweet Sounds begone); 2. The
Bells.
2. N. Hancock-Child, R. Hancock-Child (r1991)
Concert (11/93) (MARC) ① **8 223458**
3 Songs—soprano and piano/string quartet,
Op. 15 (orig Op. 9) (Wds. W. de la Mare)
1. The little green orchard; 2. Five eyes; 3. A song of
shadows.
2. Sarah Walker, R. Vignoles *Concert*
(10/92) (CRD) ① **CRD3473**
2. N. Hancock-Ccild, R. Hancock-Child (r1991)
Concert (11/93) (MARC) ① **8 223458**
2 Songs, Op. 30 (1920) (Wds. W. de la Mare)
1. John Mouldy; 2. Silver.
2. F. Lott, G. Johnson *Concert*
(7/90) (CHAN) ① **CHAN8722**
2. Sarah Walker, R. Vignoles *Concert*
(10/92) (CRD) ① **CRD3473**
2. N. Hancock-Child, R. Hancock-Child (r1991)
Concert (11/93) (MARC) ① **8 223458**
3 Songs (1920) (Wds. E. Shanks)
1. As I lay in the early sun; 2. The fields are full; 3.
For remembrance.
1. N. Hancock-Child, R. Hancock-Child (r1991)
Concert (11/93) (MARC) ① **8 223458**
2 Songs (1932) (Wds. Trad)
1. Down in Yonder Meadow; 2. Lily-bright and Shine-
a.
1. N. Hancock-Child, R. Hancock-Child (r1991)
Concert (11/93) (MARC) ① **8 223458**
4 Songs from 'Crossings', Op. 20 (1924)
(Wds. W. de la Mare)
1. Ann's Cradle Song; 2. Araby; 3. Beggar's Song; 4.
Candlestick Maker's Song.

Cpte N. Hancock-Child, R. Hancock-Child (r1991)
Concert   (11/93) (MARC) ① **8 223458**
The **Splendour Falls—song (1943)** (Wds. A.E.
Tennyson)
N. Hancock-Child, R. Hancock-Child (r1991) *Concert*
                    (11/93) (MARC) ① **8 223458**
Take Heed, Young Heart—song (1925) (Wds.
W. de la Mare)
N. Hancock-Child, R. Hancock-Child (r1991) *Concert*
                    (11/93) (MARC) ① **8 223458**
The **Tiger-lily—song (1921)** (Wds. D.P.
Bouverie)
N. Hancock-Child, R. Hancock-Child (r1991) *Concert*
                    (11/93) (MARC) ① **8 223458**
The **Wanderer—song (1926)** (Wds. W. de la
Mare)
N. Hancock-Child, R. Hancock-Child (r1991) *Concert*
                    (11/93) (MARC) ① **8 223458**
The **Witch—song (1938)** (Wds. M. Currie)
N. Hancock-Child, R. Hancock-Child (r1991) *Concert*
                    (11/93) (MARC) ① **8 223458**

GIBBS, Joseph (1699–1788) England

SECTION II: CHAMBER

**8 Solos for a Violin with a Thorough Bass,
Op. 1 (pub c1746)**
1. D minor; 2. A; 3. G; 4. B flat; 5. E; 6. F; 7. A minor;
8. E flat.
S. Bezkorvany, J. Dawson
                    (12/88) (CLAU) ① [2] **CR3606/7-2**
1. Locatelli Trio *Concert*
                    (5/93) (HYPE) ① **CDA66583**

GIBSON, Jon (b 1940) USA

SECTION II: CHAMBER

**Extensions II—saxophones and various
other sounds (1981-82)**
J. Gibson, M. Riesman, B. Ruyle, J. Snyder (r1992)
Concert   (6/93) (PNT) ① **434 873-2PTH**
Waltz—saxophone and piano (1982)
J. Gibson, M. Goldray (r1992) *Concert*
                    (6/93) (PNT) ① **434 873-2PTH**

SECTION III: INSTRUMENTAL

Song 3—saxophone (1976)
J. Gibson (r1992) *Concert*
                    (6/93) (PNT) ① **434 873-2PTH**

GIELEN, Michael (b 1927) Germany

SECTION II: CHAMBER

Variations for string quartet (1949)
Artis Qt *Concert*   (7/92) (SONY) ① **SK48059**

GIESEKING, Walter (Wilhelm) (1895–1956) Germany

SECTION IV: VOCAL AND CHORAL

21 Kinderlieder
1. Geht leise; 2. Witte woll schlafen; 3. Seereise; 4.
Mein Wagen; 5. Heilsprüchel; 6. Wenn Rumpumpel
brummig ist; 7. Der Pudding; 8. Zwei Mäulchen; 9.
Mückebold; 10. Das Scherchen; 11. Tintenheinz und
Plätscherlottchen; 12. Es regnet; 13. Trösterchen; 14.
Drei Bäumchen; 15. Schabernack; 16. Hänsel und
Gretel; 17. Kinderküche; 18. Der Reitersmann; 19.
Käferlied; 20. Puhstemuhme; 21. Gutenachtliedchen.
Cpte E. Schwarzkopf, W. Gieseking (r1955) *Concert*
                    (12/90) (EMI) ① **CDM7 63655-2**

GIGAULT, Nicolas (c1627–1707) France

SECTION III: INSTRUMENTAL

Fugue grave—organ
J. Payne (r1994) *Concert*
                    (10/95) (NAXO) ① **8 553215**
Kyrie double à 5 parties—organ
J. Payne (r1994) *Concert*
                    (10/95) (NAXO) ① **8 553215**

GIGER, Paul (b 1951) Switzerland

SECTION III: INSTRUMENTAL

Chatres—violin
P. Giger   (8/89) (ECM) ① **837 752-2**

GIGOUT, Eugène (1844–1925) France

SECTION III: INSTRUMENTAL

10 Pièces—organ
4. Toccata; 5. Andante religioso; 6. Grand choeur
dialogué; 8. Scherzo.
4. J. Parker-Smith *Concert*
                    (4/86) (ASV) ① **CDDCA539**
4, 6. C. Walsh *Concert*   (3/90) (PRIO) ① **PRCD281**
6. John Scott *Concert*   (4/89) (GUIL) ① **GRCD7022**
8. John Scott *Concert*   (12/87) (CIRR) ① **CICD1007**
8. G. Weir *Concert*   (12/92) (KOSS) ① **KC1013**
8. Andrew Lucas (r1994) *Concert*
                    (11/94) (NAXO) ① **8 550955**
Rapsodie sur des Noëls—organ
P. Rushforth (r1993) *Concert*
                    (12/93) (CONI) ① **CDCF517**

GILBERT prob Scotland

SECTION IV: VOCAL AND CHORAL

Bonnie Sweet Bessie—song
L. Tetrazzini, orch (r1913) *Concert*
                    (9/92) (PEAR) ① **GEMMCD9224**

GILBERT, Anthony (b 1934) England

SECTION IV: VOCAL AND CHORAL

**Beastly Jingles—songs: soprano & instr ens
(1984)** (Wds. various)
1. Those belonging to the Emperor (wds. C G
Leland); 2. Those which are tame or domesticated
(wds. W MacGonagall); 3. Etc (wds. anon); 4.
Uncountable ones (wds. anon).
J. Manning, Jane's Minstrels, R. Montgomery (1993)
Concert   (10/95) (NMC) ① **NMCD025**

GILBERT, Jean (1872–1942) Germany

SECTION V: STAGE WORKS

Puppchen—revue
Puppchen, du bist mein Augenstern Berlin Ens
Concert   (5/91) (ORFE) ① **C126901A**

GILL, Harry (b 1897) England

SECTION IV: VOCAL AND CHORAL

In Memoriam—song (Wds. H. P. Dixon)
S. Roberts, C. Benson *Concert*
                    (9/91) (HYPE) ① **CDA66015**

GILLES, Jean (1668–1705) France

SECTION IV: VOCAL AND CHORAL

**3 Lamentations—soloists, chorus and
instruments (?1692)**
A. Azéma, W. Hite, C. Kale, D. McCabe, Boston
Schola Cantorum, Boston Camerata, J. Cohen
(r1994) *Concert*   (11/95) (ERAT) ① **4509-98480-2**
**Messe des morts—5vv, strings and continuo
(pub 1764)** (carillon added by M. Corrette)
A-M. Rodde, J. Nirouët, M. Hill, U. Studer, P. Kooy,
Ghent Collegium Vocale, Cologne Musica Antiqua, P.
Herreweghe (r1981)
                    (1/83) (ARCH) ① **437 087-2AT**

GIMÉNEZ (Y BELLIDO), Jerónimo (1854–1923) Spain

SECTION V: STAGE WORKS

**El barbero de Sevilla—zarzuela
(1901—Madrid)** (Lib. Perrín & Palacios)
Me llaman la primorosa I. Rey, ECO, E. Ricci
(r1994) *Concert*   (2/95) (ERAT) ① **4509-95789-2**
La Tempranica—zarzuela (1900—Madrid)
(Lib. J. Romea)
Canción de la Tempranica P. Perez Inigo, Madrid
SO, E. G. Asensio (pp1991) *Concert*
                    (11/92) (CARL) ① **MCD45**

GINASTERA, Alberto (Evaristo) (1916–1983) Argentina

SECTION I: ORCHESTRAL

**Concerto for Harp and Orchestra, Op. 25
(1956)**
N. Allen, Mexico City PO, E. Bátiz *Concert*
                    (8/89) (ASV) ① **CDDCA654**
R. Masters, CLS, R. Hickox *Concert*
                    (2/93) (CHAN) ① **CHAN9094**
A. H. Pilot, ECO, I. Jackson (r1993) *Mathias: Harp
Concerto, Op. 50.*   (12/94) (KOCH) ① **37261-2**
**Concerto for Piano and Orchestra No. 1, Op.
28 (1961)**
O. Tarrago, Mexico City PO, E. Bátiz *Concert*
                    (8/89) (ASV) ① **CDDCA654**
Popol Vuh—orchestra, Op. 44 (1982-83)
(unfinished)
St Louis SO, L. Slatkin (r1990) *Concert*
                    (5/93) (RCA) ① **09026 60993-2**

SECTION II: CHAMBER

Duo—flute and oboe, Op. 13 (1945)
A. Noakes, M. Argiros *Concert*
                    (12/92) (KING) ① **KCLCD2027**
**Impresiones de la Puna—flute and string
quartet (pub 1942)**
A. Noakes, M. Denman, R. Friedman, K. Musker, J.
Pearson *Concert*   (12/92) (KING) ① **KCLCD2027**
C. Barile, Camerata Bariloche (r1994) *Concert*
                    (11/95) (DORI) ① **DOR90202**
**Pampeana No. 1—violin and piano, Op. 16
(1947)**
S. Lupu, A. Portugheis *Concert*
                    (3/95) (ASV) ① **CDDCA902**
**Pampeana No. 2—cello and piano, Op. 21
(1950)**
A. Natola-Ginastera, A. Portugheis *Concert*
                    (10/93) (ASV) ① **CDDCA865**
Quintet for Piano and Strings, Op. 29 (1963)
A. Portugheis, Bingham Qt *Concert*
                    (3/95) (ASV) ① **CDDCA902**
Sonata for Cello and Piano, Op. 49 (1979)
A. Natola-Ginastera, A. Portugheis *Concert*
                    (10/93) (ASV) ① **CDDCA865**

SECTION III: INSTRUMENTAL

**12 American Preludes—piano, Op. 12
(1944)**
A. Portugheis *Concert*   (10/93) (ASV) ① **CDDCA865**
3 Danzas argentinas—piano, Op. 2 (1937)
1. Danza del viejo boyero; 2. Danza de la moza
donosa; 3. Danza del gaucho matrero.
A. Portugheis *Concert*
                    (10/93) (ASV) ① **CDDCA865**
3 Danzas from Estancia—piano
1. Pequena danza; 2. Danza del trigo; 3. Los
trabajadores agricolas.
1. A. Portugheis *Concert*
                    (10/93) (ASV) ① **CDDCA865**
Malambo, Op. 7 (1940)
A. Portugheis *Concert*   (3/94) (ASV) ① **CDDCA880**
Milonga—piano
A. Portugheis *Concert*   (3/94) (ASV) ① **CDDCA880**
3 Piezas—piano, Op. 6 (1940)
A. Portugheis *Concert*   (3/94) (ASV) ① **CDDCA880**
Piezas Infantiles—piano (1934)
1. Preludio; 2. Osito bailando; 3. Arrullo; 4.
Soldaditos; 5. Anton Pirulero; 6. Arrorró; 7.
Chacareta; 8. Arroz con leche.
1-8. A. Portugheis *Concert*
                    (3/94) (ASV) ① **CDDCA880**
Puneña No 2—cello, Op. 45 (1976)
P. Demenga (r1993) *Concert*
                    (8/95) (ECM) ① [2] **445 234-2**
**Rondo sobre temas infantiles
argentinos—piano, Op. 19 (1947)**
A. Portugheis *Concert*   (3/94) (ASV) ① **CDDCA865**
Sonata for Guitar, Op. 47 (1976)
T. Korhonen *Concert*   (8/90) (ONDI) ① **ODE730-2**
J. Freire *Concert*   (7/92) (LEMA) ① **LC42601**
A-S. Ramírez (r1993) *Concert*
                    (12/95) (DENO) ① **CO-78931**
Sonata for Piano No. 1, Op. 22 (1952)
A. Portugheis *Concert*
                    (10/93) (ASV) ① **CDDCA865**
Sonata for Piano No. 2, Op. 53 (1981)
A. Portugheis *Concert*   (3/94) (ASV) ① **CDDCA880**
Sonata for Piano No. 3, Op. 55 (1982)
A. Portugheis *Concert*   (3/94) (ASV) ① **CDDCA880**
Suite de danzas criollas—piano (1946)
A. Portugheis *Concert*   (3/94) (ASV) ① **CDDCA880**

Toccata—piano (1970)
A. Portugheis *Concert* (3/94) (ASV) ① **CDDCA880**

SECTION IV: VOCAL AND CHORAL

Canción a la luna lunanca—song, Op. 3/1
(1938) (Wds. Silva y Valdés)
O. Blackburn, Bingham Qt *Concert*
(3/95) (ASV) ① **CDDCA902**
Canción al arbol del olvido—song, Op. 3/2
(1938) (Wds. Silva y Valdés)
O. Blackburn, Bingham Qt *Concert*
(3/95) (ASV) ① **CDDCA902**
5 Canciones populares argentinas, Op. 10
(1943)
O. Blackburn, Bingham Qt *Concert*
(3/95) (ASV) ① **CDDCA902**
Triste A. Natola-Ginastera, A. Portugheis (trans
vc/pf: P Fournier) *Concert*
(10/93) (ASV) ① **CDDCA865**
Las Horas de una estancia—1v and piano,
Op. 11 (1943)
O. Blackburn, Bingham Qt *Concert*
(3/95) (ASV) ① **CDDCA902**

SECTION V: STAGE WORKS

Estancia—concert suite from ballet, Op. 8a
(1943)
Mexico City PO, E. Bátiz *Concert*
(8/89) (ASV) ① **CDDCA654**
New World Sym, M. Tilson Thomas (r1992) *Concert*
(6/93) (ARGO) ① **436 737-2ZH**
LSO, E. Goossens (r1958) *Concert*
(4/95) (EVER) ① **EVC9007**
S. Bolívar SO, E. Mata (r1994) *Concert*
(8/95) (DORI) ① **DOR90211**
Panambi—concert suite from ballet, Op. 1a
(1937)
LSO, E. Goossens (r1958) *Concert*
(4/95) (EVER) ① **EVC9007**

GIOÈ, Joseph Giuseppe
(1890–1957) USA

SECTION IV: VOCAL AND CHORAL

I' m'arricordo 'e Napule—song (Wds. P. L.
Esposito)
E. Caruso, orch, J. Pasternack (r1920) *Concert*
(7/91) (RCA) ① **[12] GD60495(6)**
E. Caruso, orch, J. Pasternack (r1920) *Concert*
(10/91) (PEAR) ① **[3] EVC4(2)**

GIORDANI, Tommaso
(c1733–1806) Italy

SECTION IV: VOCAL AND CHORAL

Caro mio ben—arietta (possibly spurious: ? by
Giuseppe Giordani)
H. Jadlowker, orch (r1927) *Concert*
(12/91) (CLUB) ① **CL99-042**
C. Bartoli, G. Fischer *Concert*
(12/92) (DECC) ① **436 267-2DH**
J. Baker, ASMF, N. Marriner *Concert*
(1/93) (PHIL) ① **434 173-2PM**
J. Carreras, ECO, V. Sutej (r1992; arr Agostinelli)
Concert (6/93) (PHIL) ① **434 926-2PH**
E. Pinza, F. Kitzinger (r1940) *Concert*
(9/93) (RCA) ① **09026 61245-2**
H. Schlusnus, F. Rupp (r1930) *Concert*
(1/94) (PREI) ① **[2] 89205**
A. Galli-Curci, orch, J. Pasternack (r1917) *Concert*
(3/94) (ROMO) ① **[2] 81003-2**

GIORDANO, Umberto
(1867–1948) Italy

SECTION IV: VOCAL AND CHORAL

Canzone guerresca—song
C. Muzio, orch (r1917) *Concert*
(1/95) (ROMO) ① **[2] 81010-2**

SECTION V: STAGE WORKS

Andrea Chénier—opera: 4 acts (1896—Milan)
(Lib. Illica)
ACT 1: 1a. Questo azzurro sofà; 1b. Son
sessant'anni; 2. T'odio, casa dorata!; 3. Per stasera
pazienza!; 4. O Pastorelle; 5. Signor Chénier; 6a.
Colpito qui m'avete; 6b. Un di all'azzurro spazio
(Improvviso); 7. Perdonatemi!. ACT 2: 8. Per l'ex
inferno!; 9a. Credo a una possanza; 9b. Io non ho
amato ancor; 10a. Ecco l'altare; 10b. Udite! Son
solal; 10c. Ora soave. ACT 3: 11. Dumouriez
traditore; 12. Prendi! e un ricordo; 13a. Nemico della
Patria?; 13b. Un di m'era di gioia; 14. Sta bene! Ove
trovarti; 15a. Come sa amare!; 15b. La mamma

morta; 16. E l'angelo si accosta; 17a. Gravier de
Vergennes; 17b. Sì, fui soldato; 18. Udiamo i
testimoni!; ACT 4: 19a. Cittadino, men duol; 19b.
Come un bel di di maggio; 20. Viene a costei
concesso; 21a. Benedico il destino!; 21b. Vicino a te
s'acqueta; 21c. La nostra morte.
Cpte L. Pavarotti, M. Caballé, L. Nucci, P. de Palma,
A. Varnay, K. Kuhlmann, T. Krause, H. Cuénod, N.
Howlett., G. Morresi, R. Hamer, F. Andreolli, C.
Ludwig, G. Tadeo, WNO Chor, National PO, R.
Chailly (2/85) (DECC) ① **[2] 410 117-2DH2**
Cpte J. Carreras, E. Marton, G. Zancanaro, T. Pane,
T. Takács, K. Takács, F. Federici, G. Vághelyi, T.
Bátor, J. Tóth, K. Sárkány, I. Rozsos, J. Moldvay, E.
Farkas, J. Gregor, Hungarian Rad & TV Chor,
Hungarian St Orch, G. Patané
(11/87) (SONY) ① **[2] M2K42369**
Cpte P. Domingo, R. Scotto, S. Milnes, M. Sénéchal,
J. Kraft, M. Ewing, A. Monk, T. Sharpe, S. Harling, I.
Bushkin, M. King, P. de Palma, N. Beavan, G.
Killebrew, E. Dara, John Alldis Ch, National PO,
James Levine (r1976)
(9/89) (RCA) ① **[2] GD82046**
Cpte F. Corelli, A. Stella, M. Sereni, P. De Palma, L.
Moneta, S. Malagù, G. Modesti, D. Mantovani, P.
Pedani, A. di Stasio, P. Montarsolo, Rome Op Chor,
Rome Op Orch, G. Santini (r1963)
(7/95) (EMI) ① **[2] CMS5 65287-2**
1b, 13a T. Ruffo, orch (r1920) *Concert*
(2/93) (PREI) ① **[3] 89303(2)**
4. ROH Chor, ROHO, B. Haitink *Concert*
(12/89) (EMI) ① **CDC7 49849-2**
6a, 6b A. Pertile, orch (r1925) *Concert*
(4/94) (EMI) ① **[3] CHS7 64864-2(1)**
6a, 6b G. Zenatello, anon (r1905/6: 2 vers) *Concert*
(5/94) (PEAR) ① **[4] GEMMCDS9073(1)**
6a, 6b G. Zenatello, anon (r1905) *Concert*
(5/94) (SYMP) ① **SYMCD1168**
6a, 6b, 17b G. Zenatello, orch (r1908) *Concert*
(5/94) (SYMP) ① **SYMCD1168**
6a, 6b, 17b G. Zenatello, orch (r1908) *Concert*
(5/94) (PEAR) ① **[4] GEMMCDS9073(1)**
6a, 6b, 19b B. Heppner, Munich RO, R. Abbado
(r1993/4) *Concert* (11/95) (RCA) ① **09026 62504-2**
6b G. Martinelli, orch, J. Pasternack (r1926) *Concert*
(10/89) (NIMB) ① **NI7804**
6b B. Gigli, La Scala Orch, U. Berrettoni (r1941)
Concert (5/90) (EMI) ① **CDH7 61052-2**
6b G. Zenatello, anon (r1903) *Concert*
(11/91) (CLUB) ① **CL99-025**
6b G. Lauri-Volpi, La Scala Orch, F. Ghione (r1934)
Concert (9/90) (PREI) ① **89012**
6b B. Gigli, orch, J. Pasternack (r1922) *Concert*
(10/90) (RCA) ① **GD87811**
6b J. Carreras, MMF Orch, Rome Op Orch, Z. Mehta
(pp1990) *Concert* (10/90) (DECC) ① **430 433-2DH**
6b E. Caruso, orch (r1907) *Concert*
(12/90) (PEAR) ① **[3] EVC1(2)**
6b E. Caruso, orch (r1907) *Concert*
(7/91) (RCA) ① **[12] GD60495(2)**
6b G. Zenatello, orch (r c1916) *Concert*
(11/91) (CLUB) ① **CL99-025**
6b F. Tamagno, Anon (pf) (r1903-04) *Concert*
(2/92) (OPAL) ① **OPALCD9846**
6b B. Gigli, La Scala Orch, U. Berrettoni (r1941)
Concert (7/92) (PEAR) ① **[3] GEMMCDS9926(2)**
6b G. Lauri-Volpi, La Scala Orch, F. Ghione (r1934)
Concert (7/92) (PEAR) ① **[3] GEMMCDS9925(2)**
6b G. Martinelli, orch, J. Pasternack (r1926) *Concert*
(3/93) (PREI) ① **89062**
6b B. Gigli, orch, J. Pasternack (r1922) *Concert*
(6/93) (MMOI) ① **CDMOIR417**
6b G. Lauri-Volpi, La Scala Orch, F. Ghione (r1934)
Concert (7/93) (NIMB) ① **NI7845**
6b G. Zenatello, anon (r1903) *Concert*
(5/94) (PEAR) ① **[4] GEMMCDS9073(1)**
6b G. Zenatello, orch (r1916) *Concert*
(5/94) (PEAR) ① **[4] GEMMCDS9074(1)**
6b R. Zanelli, La Scala Orch, C. Sabajno (r1929)
Concert (9/94) (NIMB) ① **NI7856**
6b A. Pertile, La Scala Orch, C. Sabajno (r1927)
Concert (10/94) (PREI) ① **89072**
6b B. Gigli, La Scala Orch, O. de Fabritiis (r1941)
Concert (12/94) (MMOI) ① **CDMOIR425**
6b E. Caruso, orch (r1907) *Concert*
(7/95) (NIMB) ① **NI7866**
6b, 19b B. Gigli, orch (r1922) *Concert*
(5/90) (NIMB) ① **NI7807**
6b, 17b F. Merli, orch, L. Molajoli (r1928) *Concert*
(1/91) (PREI) ① **89026**
9a G. Zenatello, orch (r1909) *Concert*
(5/94) (SYMP) ① **SYMCD1168**
9a G. Zenatello, orch (r1910) *Concert*
(5/94) (PEAR) ① **[4] GEMMCDS9073(2)**
9b A. Cortis, La Scala Orch, C. Sabajno (r1930)
Concert (10/91) (PREI) ① **89043**

13a T. Gobbi, Rome Op Orch, O. de Fabritiis (r1955)
Concert (10/89) (EMI) ① **CDM7 63109-2**
13a L. Tibbett, orch (pp1935) *Concert*
(3/91) (PEAR) ① **[2] GEMMCDS9452**
13a C. Galeffi, La Scala Orch, L. Molajoli (r1930)
Concert (2/92) (PREI) ① **89040**
13a T. Ruffo, orch (r1929) *Concert*
(2/93) (PREI) ① **[3] 89303(2)**
13a G. Hüsch, Berlin St Op Orch, H.U. Müller (r1937:
Ger) *Concert* (3/94) (PREI) ① **89071**
13a C. Formichi, orch, H. Harty (r1927) *Concert*
(11/94) (PREI) ① **89055**
13a J.C. Thomas, Victor SO, F. Tours (r1939)
Concert (10/95) (NIMB) ① **NI7867**
13a, 13b T. Gobbi, Rome Op Orch, O. de Fabritiis
(r1955) *Concert*
(4/92) (EMI) ① **[7] CHS7 69741-2(7)**
13a, 13b J. Van Dam, Loire PO, M. Soustrot (r1992)
Concert (8/93) (FORL) ① **UCD16681**
13b M. Sammarco, orch (r1908) *Concert*
(7/92) (PEAR) ① **[3] GEMMCDS9924(1)**
13b E. Giraldoni, orch (r1909) *Concert*
(11/92) (MEMO) ① **[2] HR4408/9(2)**
13b M. Sammarco, orch (r1908) *Concert*
(4/94) (EMI) ① **[3] CHS7 64860-2(1)**
15b A. Tomowa-Sintow, Munich RO, P. Sommer
Concert (11/86) (ORFE) ① **C106841A**
15b M. Callas, Philh, T. Serafin (r1954) *Concert*
(11/86) (EMI) ① **CDC7 47282-2**
15b C. Muzio, orch (r1920) *Concert*
(5/90) (BOGR) ① **[2] BIM705-2**
15b G. Cigna, orch, L. Molajoli (r1931) *Concert*
(11/90) (LYRC) ① **SRO805**
15b M. Seinemeyer, Berlin St Op Orch, F.
Weissmann (r1928) *Concert*
(11/90) (PREI) ① **89029**
15b K. Te Kanawa, LSO, Myung-Whun Chung
Concert (11/90) (EMI) ① **CDC7 54062-2**
15b C. Muzio, orch, L. Molajoli (r1935) *Concert*
(4/91) (NIMB) ① **NI7814**
15b R. Tebaldi, Santa Cecilia Academy Orch, G.
Gavazzeni *Concert*
(8/91) (DECC) ① **[2] 430 481-2DX2**
15b M. Freni, Venice La Fenice Orch, R. Abbado
(9/92) (DECC) ① **433 316-2DH**
15b L. Price, RCA Italiana Op Orch, F. Molinari-
Pradelli *Concert*
(12/92) (RCA) ① **[4] 09026 61236-2**
15b J. Hammond, Philh, L. Collingwood (r1947)
Concert (12/92) (TEST) ① **SBT1013**
15b R. Pampanini, orch, L. Molajoli (r1927) *Concert*
(8/93) (PREI) ① **89063**
15b E. Carelli, S. Cottone (r1904) *Concert*
(8/93) (SYMP) ① **SYMCD1111**
15b R. Raisa, orch (r1933) *Concert*
(1/94) (CLUB) ① **CL99-052**
15b C. Muzio, orch (r1920) *Concert*
(1/94) (ROMO) ① **[2] 81005-2**
15b Z. Milanov, RCA SO, A. Basile (r1958) *Concert*
(4/94) (RCA) ① **[6] 09026 61580-2(5)**
15b E. Rethberg, orch (r1925) *Concert*
(7/94) (PREI) ① **89051**
15b M. Reining, Vienna St Op Orch, R. Moralt
(r1942: Ger) *Concert* (9/94) (PREI) ① **89065**
15b E. Rethberg, orch (r1924) *Concert*
(2/95) (ROMO) ① **[2] 81012-2**
15b(pt) Lotte Lehmann, Vienna St Op Orch, R.
Heger (pp1933: Ger) *Concert*
(11/95) (SCHW) ① **[2] 314622**
17b B. Gigli, La Scala Orch, C. Sabajno (r1933)
Concert (9/88) (EMI) ① **CDH7 61051-2**
17b B. Gigli, La Scala Orch, O. de Fabritiis (r1941)
Concert (9/88) (EMI) ① **CDH7 61051-2**
17b G. Zenatello, orch, R. Bourdon (r1929) *Concert*
(11/91) (CLUB) ① **CL99-025**
17b G. Zenatello, orch (r1908) *Concert*
(11/91) (PREI) ① **89038**
17b G. Zenatello, orch (r1908) *Concert*
(7/92) (PEAR) ① **[3] GEMMCDS9924(1)**
17b B. Gigli, La Scala Orch, C. Sabajno (r1933)
Concert (4/94) (EMI) ① **[3] CHS7 64864-2(2)**
17b G. Zenatello, orch, R. Bourdon (r1929) *Concert*
(5/94) (PEAR) ① **[4] GEMMCDS9074(2)**
19b G. Martinelli, orch, R. Bourdon (r1927) *Concert*
(10/89) (NIMB) ① **NI7804**
19b F. Giraud, S. Cottone (r1904) *Concert*
(6/90) (SYMP) ① **SYMCD1073**
19b E. Caruso, orch, J. Pasternack (r1916) *Concert*
(7/91) (RCA) ① **[12] GD60495(5)**
19b E. Caruso, orch, J. Pasternack (r1916) *Concert*
(10/91) (PEAR) ① **[3] EVC4(1)**
19b G. Martinelli, orch, R. Bourdon (r1927) *Concert*
(3/93) (PREI) ① **89062**
19b J. Björling, orch, N. Grevillius (r1944) *Concert*
(10/93) (EMI) ① **CDH7 64707-2**

19b A. Pertile, La Scala Orch, C. Sabajno (r1929)
Concert (10/94) (PREI) ① **89072**
19b E. Caruso, orch (r1916) *Concert*
(7/95) (NIMB) ① **NI7866**
21b, 21c A. Pertile, M. Sheridan, La Scala Orch, C.
Sabajno (r1928) *Concert* (10/94) (PREI) ① **89072**
La Cena delle Beffe—opera (1924—Milan)
(Lib. Benelli)
Ah, che tormento; Mi svesti A. Cortis, orch (r1927)
Concert (3/94) (NIMB) ① **NI7850**
Ed io non ne godevo...Sempre così. F. Alda, orch,
R. Bourdon (r1925) *Concert*
(4/94) (RCA) ① [6] **09026 61580-2(2)**
Fedora—opera: 3 acts (1898—Milan) (Lib.
Colautti, after Sardou)
ACT 1: 1a. Ed ecco il suo ritratto; 1b. O grandi gli
occhi lucenti; 2a. Continuate; 2b. Su questa santa
croce. ACT 2: 3a. Signori, vi presento Lazinski; 3b. Io
sono lo sbadiglio molesto; 4. La donna russa; 5.
Amor ti vieta; 6. Appena giunta; 7. Intermezzo; 8a.
Loris, Ipanoff, oggi to Zar; 8b. Mia madre, la mia
vecchia madre; 9. La fante mi svela; 10a. Ma chi
m'accusa; 10b. Vedi, io piango; 11a. Lascia che
pianga sola; 11b. Dove ten vai?. ACT 3: 12. Dice la
capinera; 13. E voi più non tubate?; 14. Quel truce
sgherro; 15. Son pronta; 16. La montanina mia; 17.
Dio di giustizia; 18a. O bianca madre; 18b. Jariskin
recò all'Imperatore; 18c. Morti per me; 19a. Se quella
sciagurata; 19b. Forse con te; 19c. Se quell'infelice;
20. Tutto tramonta.
Cpte M. Olivero, M. del Monaco, T. Gobbi, S.
Maionica, L. Cappellino, R. Cassinelli, P. Binder, K.
Te Kanawa, L. Monreale, V. Carbonari, A. Cesarini,
L. Monreale, A. Bokatti, S. Caspari, P. Rogers, P. de
Palma, Monte Carlo Op Chor, Monte Carlo Nat Op
Orch, L. Gardelli *Zandonai: Francesca da Rimini.*
(3/92) (DECC) ① [2] **433 033-2DM2**
1b G. Bellinicioni, S. Cottone (r1903) *Concert*
(6/90) (SYMP) ① **SYMCD1073**
1b, 17. M. Jeritza, orch (r1923) *Concert*
(4/94) (PREI) ① **89079**
4. T. Gobbi, Philh, A. Erede (r1963) *Concert*
(10/89) (EMI) ① **CDM7 63109-2**
4. T. Gobbi, Philh, A. Erede (r1963) *Concert*
(4/94) (EMI) ① [3] **CHS7 64864-2(2)**
5. J. Björling, orch, N. Grevillius (r1944) *Concert*
(10/88) (EMI) ① **CDH7 61053-2**
5. E. Caruso, U. Giordano (r1902) *Concert*
(5/89) (EMI) ① **CDH7 61046-2**
5. P. Domingo, NYPO, Z. Mehta (pp1988) *Concert*
(9/89) (SONY) ① **MK44942**
5. G. Martinelli, orch, J. Pasternack (r1926) *Concert*
(10/89) (NIMB) ① **NI7804**
5. B. Gigli, orch, U. Berrettoni (r1940) *Concert*
(10/90) (EMI) ① **CDH7 61052-2**
5. L. Pavarotti, National PO, O. de Fabritiis *Concert*
(7/90) (DECC) ① [2] **425 681-2DM2**
5. E. Caruso, U. Giordano (r1902) *Concert*
(12/90) (PEAR) ① [3] **EVC1(1)**
5. D. Borgioli, orch (r c1923) *Concert*
(12/90) (CLUB) ① **CL99-014**
5. E. Caruso, U. Giordano (r1902) *Concert*
(7/91) (RCA) ① [12] **GD60495(1)**
5. M. del Monaco, New SO, A. Erede (r1956) *Concert*
(10/93) (DECC) ① **436 463-2DM**
5. G. Anselmi, orch (r1907) *Concert*
(7/95) (SYMP) ① **SYMCD1170**
5. J. Björling, MMF Orch, A. Erede (r1959) *Concert*
(10/95) (DECC) ① **443 930-2DM**
5. A. Davies, A. Bryn Parri (r1994) *Concert*
(11/95) (SAIN) ① **SCDC2085**
5, 8b G. Martinelli, orch, J. Pasternack (r1926)
Concert (3/93) (PREI) ① **89062**
5, 8b A. Giorgini, anon (r1904) *Concert*
(4/95) (RECO) ① **TRC3**
7. BPO, H. von Karajan *Concert*
(10/87) (DG) ① [3] **419 257-2GH3**
7. Gothenburg SO, N. Järvi *Concert*
(6/90) (DG) ① **429 494-2GDC**
10b E. Garbin, G. Russ, orch (r1908) *Concert*
(7/92) (PEAR) ① [3] **GEMMCDS9924(2)**
10b F. de Lucia, anon (r1904) *Concert*
(1/95) (SYMP) ① **SYMCD1149**
20. E. Carelli, E. Ventura, anon (r1904) *Concert*
(11/92) (MEMO) ① [2] **HR4408/9(2)**
20. E. Carelli, E. Ventura, S. Cottone (r1904) *Concert*
(8/93) (SYMP) ① **SYMCD1111**
**Madame Sans-Gêne—opera: 3 acts
(1915—New York)**
Che me ne faccio del vostro castello C. Muzio,
orch (r1922) *Concert*
(5/90) (BOGR) ① [2] **BIM705-2**
Che me ne faccio del vostro castello C. Muzio,
orch (r1922) *Concert*
(1/94) (ROMO) ① [2] **81005-2**

Che me ne faccio del vostro castello C. Muzio,
orch (r1917) *Concert*
(1/95) (ROMO) ① [2] **81010-2**
Marcella—opera: 3 acts (1907—Milan) (Lib. L.
Stecchetti, after H. Cain, J. Adonis)
No, non pensarci più. E. Perea, orch (r1910)
Concert (11/92) (MEMO) ① [2] **HR4408/9(2)**
Siberia—opera: 3 acts (1927—Milan) (Lib.
Illica)
EXCERPTS: 1a. Glèby!... 1b. Quest'orgoglio; 2a.
No! se unpensier; 2b. Nel suo amor rianimata. ACT
2: 3. Intermezzo; 4. O bella mia; 5. È qui con te; 6.
Oride steppe. ACT 3: 7a. No, mio onore; 7b.
T'incontrai per la via!; 8. Qual vergogna; 9. Cena di
Pasqua.
1a, 1b R. Storchio, G. De Luca, R. Delle Ponti
(r1903) *Concert*
(4/94) (EMI) ① [3] **CHS7 64860-2(2)**
2a, 2b R. Storchio, R. Delle Ponti (r1903) *Concert*
(4/94) (EMI) ① [3] **CHS7 64860-2(2)**
5. G. Zenatello, R. Storchio, R. Delle Ponti (r1903)
Concert (5/94) (PEAR) ① [4] **GEMMCDS9073(1)**
6. G. Zenatello, R. Delle Ponti (r1903) *Concert*
(4/94) (EMI) ① [3] **CHS7 64860-2(2)**
6, 7a, 7b G. Zenatello, R. Delle Ponti (r1903) *Concert*
(5/94) (PEAR) ① [4] **GEMMCDS9073(1)**
7b G. Zenatello, orch (r1911) *Concert*
(5/94) (PEAR) ① [4] **GEMMCDS9073(2)**

GIORDIGIANI, Luigi (1806–1860) Italy

SECTION IV: VOCAL AND CHORAL

Ogni Sabato—song
E. Bendazzi-Garulli, anon (r1902) *Concert*
(5/91) (SYMP) ① **SYMCD1077**

GIORGINAKIS, Kiriakos (b 1950) Greece

SECTION III: INSTRUMENTAL

4 Greek images—guitar
1. Sea song; 2. Field song; 3. Mountain song; 4.
Village song.
E. Kotzia *Concert* (6/89) (PEAR) ① **SHECD9609**

GIOVANNELLI, Ruggiero (c1560–1625) Italy

SECTION IV: VOCAL AND CHORAL

Jubilate Deo
Westminster Abbey Ch, S. Preston *Concert*
(5/86) (ARCH) ① **415 517-2AH**

GIOVANNI DA CASCIA (fl 1340–1350) Italy

also known as Johannes de Florentia

SECTION IV: VOCAL AND CHORAL

Quando la stella—trecentro madrigal (2vv)
Gothic Voices, C. Page *Concert*
(12/88) (HYPE) ① **CDA66286**

GIRAMO, Pietro Antonio (fl 1619–after 1630) Italy

SECTION IV: VOCAL AND CHORAL

Festa, riso
King's Sngrs, Tragicomedia *Concert*
(9/92) (EMI) ① **CDC7 54191-2**

GIRAUT DE BORNELH (c1140–c1200) France

SECTION IV: VOCAL AND CHORAL

Reis glorios—chanson
P. Hillier, S. Stubbs, A. Lawrence-King, E. Headley
Concert (7/89) (ECM) ① **837 360-2**

GISTOU, Nicolas (d 1609) Denmark

SECTION III: INSTRUMENTAL

Paduana and Galliard—lute (pub 1609)
J. Lindberg *Concert* (2/89) (BIS) ① **BIS-CD390**

SECTION IV: VOCAL AND CHORAL

**Quel Augellin che canta—madrigal: 5vv (pub
1606)**
Consort of Musicke, A. Rooley (lte/dir) *Concert*
(2/89) (BIS) ① **BIS-CD392**

GITECK, Janice (b 1946) USA

SECTION II: CHAMBER

**Breathing Songs from a Turning Sky—fl, cl,
bn, vc, pf, perc and lights (1980)**
New Perf Group *Concert*
(9/89) (MODE) ① **Mode 14**

SECTION IV: VOCAL AND CHORAL

**Callin' Home Coyote—burlesque—tenor,
steel drums and double-bass (1978)** (Wds.
MacAdams)
New Perf Group *Concert*
(9/89) (MODE) ① **Mode 14**
**Thunder like a White Bear Dancing: ritual
based on the Mide Picture Songs of the
Ojibwa Indian—sop, fl, pf, perc, slide
projector (1977)**
New Perf Group *Concert*
(9/89) (MODE) ① **Mode 14**

GIULIANI, Mauro (Giuseppe Sergio Pantaleo) (1781–1829) Italy

SECTION I: ORCHESTRAL

**Concerto for Guitar and Strings in A, Op. 30
(1808)**
J. Bream, Melos Ens (r1959) *Concert*
(8/93) (RCA) ① [28] **09026 61583-2(4)**
2. J. Bream, Melos Ens (r1959) *Concert*
(7/94) (RCA) ① **09026 61599-2**

SECTION II: CHAMBER

**Divertimenti Notturni—flute and guitar, Op.
86**
M. Helasvuo, J. Savijoki *Concert*
(1/91) (BIS) ① **BIS-CD412**
**Duettino facile—flute and guitar, Op. 77 (pub
1817)**
M. Helasvuo, J. Savijoki *Concert*
(1/91) (BIS) ① **BIS-CD411**
Duo—flute and guitar, WoO (pub 1810-11)
M. Helasvuo, J. Savijoki *Concert*
(1/91) (BIS) ① **BIS-CD411**
**Duo concertant in E minor, 'Grand
Sonata'—violin/flute and guitar, Op. 25**
J. Swensen, K. Yamashita *Concert*
(12/92) (RCA) ① **09026 60237-2**
M. Huggett, R. Savino (r1993) *Concert*
(5/95) (HARM) ① **HMU90 7116**
**Gran duetto concertante in A—flute/violin
and guitar, Op. 52**
M. Helasvuo, J. Savijoki *Concert*
(1/91) (BIS) ① **BIS-CD411**
J. Galway, K. Yamashita *Concert*
(12/92) (RCA) ① **09026 60237-2**
**Gran Quintetto—guitar and string quartet,
Op. 65**
R. Savino, Artaria Qt (r1991) *Boccherini: Guitar
Quintets, G445-453.*
(2/94) (HARM) ① **HMU90 7069**
**Grand Potpourri—flute and guitar, Op. 53
(pub 1816)**
M. Helasvuo, J. Savijoki *Concert*
(1/91) (BIS) ① **BIS-CD413**
**Grand Sonata in A—flute/violin and guitar,
Op. 85 (pub 1817)**
M. Helasvuo, J. Savijoki *Concert*
(1/91) (BIS) ① **BIS-CD411**
Grande Sérénade—flute and guitar, Op. 82
M. Helasvuo, J. Savijoki *Concert*
(1/91) (BIS) ① **BIS-CD412**
**Gran-Potpourri—flute and guitar, Op. 126
(pub 1827)**
M. Helasvuo, J. Savijoki *Concert*
(1/91) (BIS) ① **BIS-CD413**
**12 Ländler samt Coda—flute and guitar, Op.
75 (pub 1817)**
M. Helasvuo, J. Savijoki *Concert*
(1/91) (BIS) ① **BIS-CD411**
**Pièces faciles et agréables—flute and guitar,
Op. 74 (pub 1816)**
M. Helasvuo, J. Savijoki *Concert*
(1/91) (BIS) ① **BIS-CD413**

Potpourri tiré de l'opéra 'Tancredi'—flute
and guitar, Op. 76 (pub 1817)
M. Helasvuo, J. Savijoki *Concert*
(1/91) (BIS) ① **BIS-CD413**
Serenade—flute and guitar, Op. 127
M. Helasvuo, J. Savijoki *Concert*
(1/91) (BIS) ① **BIS-CD412**
Serenade in A—violin, cello and guitar, Op.
19
J. Swensen, K. Yamashita, E. Anderson *Concert*
(12/92) (RCA) ① **09026 60237-2**
Sonata for Violin and Guitar
J. Williams, I. Perlman *Concert*
(7/87) (SONY) ① **MK34508**
6 Variations—flute and guitar, Op. 81 (pub
1817)
M. Helasvuo, J. Savijoki *Concert*
(1/91) (BIS) ① **BIS-CD413**
Variations—flute and guitar, Op. 84
M. Helasvuo, J. Savijoki *Concert*
(1/91) (BIS) ① **BIS-CD412**
Variazioni Concertanti—two guitars, Op.
130
J. Bream, J. Williams (r1973) *Concert*
(11/93) (RCA) ① **09026 61452-2**

| SECTION III: INSTRUMENTAL |

Bagatelles—guitar, Op. 73 (pub 1819)
9. Minuetto.
9. D. Starobin *Concert*   (3/92) (BRID) ① **BCD9029**
Choix des mes Fleurs chéries (ou Le
Bouquet Emblématique)—guitar, Op. 46
2. La pensée; 4. Le Jasmin; 5. Le Rosmarin; 9. La
Rose.
4, 5, 9. D. Starobin *Concert*
(3/92) (BRID) ① **BCD9029**
Etude in E minor—guitar, Op. 100/13 (pub
1819)
D. Starobin *Concert*   (3/92) (BRID) ① **BCD9029**
Grande Ouverture, Op. 61 (1814)
N. North *Concert*   (6/87) (AMON) ① **CD-SAR18**
D. Starobin *Concert*   (3/92) (BRID) ① **BCD9029**
J. Bream (r1967-8) *Concert*
(8/93) (RCA) ① [28] **09026 61583-2(4)**
J. Bream (r1967-8) *Concert*
(6/94) (RCA) ① **09026 61593-2**
18 Leçons Progressives—guitar, Op. 51
(1814)
3, 7, 14. D. Starobin *Concert*
(3/92) (BRID) ① **BCD9029**
Préludes—guitar, Op. 83 (orig for 5-stg gtr by
Antoine de l'Hoyer)
5, 6. D. Starobin *Concert*
(3/92) (BRID) ① **BCD9029**
6 Rondeaux Progressives—guitar, Op. 14
1, 5. D. Starobin *Concert*
(3/92) (BRID) ① **BCD9029**
Rossiniana No. 1—guitar, Op. 119
J. Bream (r1974) *Concert*
(8/93) (RCA) ① [28] **09026 61583-2(3)**
J. Bream (r1974) *Concert*
(8/93) (RCA) ① **09026 61591-2**
Rossiniana No. 3—guitar, Op. 121
J. Bream (r1974; rev Bream) *Concert*
(8/93) (RCA) ① [28] **09026 61583-2(4)**
J. Bream (r1974; rev Bream) *Concert*
(6/94) (RCA) ① **09026 61593-2**
Sonata for Guitar in C, Op. 15
J. Bream (r1967-8) *Concert*
(8/93) (RCA) ① [28] **09026 61583-2(3)**
J. Bream (r1967-8) *Concert*
(8/93) (RCA) ① **09026 61591-2**
6 Variations on an Original Theme—guitar,
Op. 20 (1809)
D. Starobin *Concert*   (3/92) (BRID) ① **BCD9029**
Variazioni sulla Cavatina favorita, 'De calma
oh ciel'—guitar, Op. 101 (pub 1819)
D. Starobin *Concert*   (3/92) (BRID) ① **BCD9029**

| SECTION IV: VOCAL AND CHORAL |

6 Ariette—voice & guitar/piano, Op. 95 (pub
1818) (Wds. Metastasio)
1. Ombre amene; 2. Fra tutte le pene; 3. Quando
sarà quella di; 4. Le dimore; 5. Ad alto laccio; 6. Di due
bell'anime.
1-4. E. Parcells, F. Justen *Concert*
(5/92) (SCHW) ① **314063**
6 Lieder, Op. 89 (pub c1817)
1. Abschied (wds. Goethe); 2. Lied aus der Ferne
(wds. Matthisson); 3. Abschied II (wds. ?Schiller); 4.
Lied (wds. Steigentesch); 5. Ständchen (wds.
Tiedge); 6. An das Schicksal (wds. Reissig).
Cpte I. Partridge, J. Lindberg *Concert*
(10/89) (PEAR) ① **SHECD9608**

GLADSTONE, Francis Edward
(19th Cent) England

| SECTION IV: VOCAL AND CHORAL |

Te Deum in F (from Morning, Evening and
Communion Service)
Norwich Cath Ch, M. Nicholas, N. Taylor (r1993)
Concert   (10/94) (PRIO) ① **PRCD470**

GLASS, Philip (b 1937) USA

| SECTION I: ORCHESTRAL |

The Canyon—orchestra (1988)
Atlanta SO, Robert Shaw *Itaipu*.
(11/93) (SONY) ① **SK46352**
Concerto for Violin and Orchestra (1987)
G. Kremer, VPO, C. von Dohnányi (pp1992)
Schnittke: Concerto Grosso 5.
(10/93) (DG) ① **437 091-2GH**
Façades—two saxophones and strings
Philip Glass *Concert*
(1/94) (SONY) ① **SK64133**
A Gentleman's Honor—orchestra
Philip Glass *Concert*
(1/94) (SONY) ① **SK64133**
'Low' Symphony—orchestra (from music by
D Bowie & B Eno)
Brooklyn PO, D.R. Davies (r1992)
(5/93) (PNT) ① **438 150-2PTH**

| SECTION II: CHAMBER |

Brass Sextet
London Gabrieli Brass Ens, C. Larkin *Concert*
(5/92) (HYPE) ① **CDA66517**
Closing—instrumental ensemble
Philip Glass Ens *Concert*
(1/94) (SONY) ① **SK64133**
Dance Nos. 1-5 (1975-76)
Philip Glass Ens, M. Riesman (arr cpsr)
(9/89) (SONY) ① [2] **M2K44765**
Dance 8—instrumental ensemble
Philip Glass Ens *Concert*
(1/94) (SONY) ① **SK64133**
String Quartet No. 1 (1966)
Duke Qt (r1993) *Concert*
(1/94) (COLL) ① **Coll1386-2**

| SECTION III: INSTRUMENTAL |

Contrary Motion—organ (1969)
D. Joyce (r1993) *Concert*
(1/94) (CATA) ① **09026 61825-2**
Dance II—organ (1979)
D. Joyce (r1993) *Concert*
(1/94) (CATA) ① **09026 61825-2**
Dance IV—organ
D. Joyce (r1993) *Concert*
(1/94) (CATA) ① **09026 61825-2**
Mad rush—piano (1981)
P. Glass *Concert*   (3/90) (SONY) ① **MK45576**
D. Joyce (r1993) *Concert*
(1/94) (CATA) ① **09026 61825-2**
Metamorphosis—piano (1988)
P. Glass *Concert*   (3/90) (SONY) ① **MK45576**
Metamorphosis Four—piano
P. Glass *Concert*   (1/94) (SONY) ① **SK64133**
Wichita Vortex Sutra—piano (1988)
P. Glass *Concert*   (3/90) (SONY) ① **MK45576**

| SECTION IV: VOCAL AND CHORAL |

Changing Opinion—vocals, flute and piano
B. Fowler, P. Dunkel, M. Riesman *Concert*
(1/94) (SONY) ① **SK64133**
Itaipu—chorus and orchestra (1988) (Wds.
trad Guarnaní Indian, trans D. Thomas)
1. Mato Grosso; 2. The Lake; 3. The Dam; 4. To the
Sea.
Atlanta Sym Chor, Atlanta SO, Robert Shaw *Canyon*.
(11/93) (SONY) ① **SK46352**
Lightning—vocals and instrumental
ensemble
Philip Glass Ens, J. Pendarvis *Concert*
(1/94) (SONY) ① **SK64133**

| SECTION V: STAGE WORKS |

Akhnaten—opera: 3 acts (1984—Stuttgart)
(Lib. cpsr)
EXCERPTS: ACT 1: 1. Year 1 of Akhnaten's
Reign—Thebes; 2. Prelude—Refrain and Three
Verses; 3. Scene 1: Funeral of Amenhotep III; 4.
Scene 2: The Coronation of Akhnaten; 5. Scene 3:
The Window of Appearances. ACT 2: 6. Years 5 to
15—Thebes and Akhnaten; 7. Scene 1: The Temple;
8. Scene 2: Akhnaten and Nefertiti; 9. Scene 3: The
City. Dance; 10. Scene 4: Hymn. ACT 3: 11. Year 17

and the Present—Akhnaten; 12. Scene 1: The
Family; 13. Scene 2: Attack and Fall; 14. Scene 3:
The Ruins; 15. Scene 4: Epilogue.
Cpte P. Esswood, M. Vargas, M. Liebermann, T.
Hannula, H. Holzapfel, C. Hauptmann, D. Warrilow,
Stuttgart Op Chor, Stuttgart Op Orch, D.R. Davies
(2/88) (SONY) ① [2] **M2K42457**
1c, 2d P. Esswood, Stuttgart St Orch, Stuttgart State
Chor *Concert*   (1/94) (SONY) ① **SK64133**
Einstein on the Beach—opera (4 acts)
(1975—Paris) (Lib. Wilson)
Cpte L. Childs, S. Johnson, P. Mann, S. Sutton, P.
Zukofsky, Philip Glass Ens, M. Riesman
(9/86) (SONY) ① [4] **M4K38875**
Cpte L. Childs, G. Dolbashian, J. McGruder, S.
Sutton, G. Fulkerson, chor, Philip Glass Ens, M.
Riesman (r1993)
(1/94) (NONE) ① [3] **7559-79323-2**
Bed J. Gibson (r1992; arr sax) *Concert*
(6/93) (PNT) ① **434 873-2PTH**
Bed J. Pendarvis *Concert*
(1/94) (SONY) ① **SK64133**
Hydrogen Jukebox—theatrical piece
(1990—Philadelphia) (Lib. A. Ginsberg)
EXCERPTS: 1. from Iron Horse; 2. Jaweh and Allah
Battle; 3. from Iron Horse; 4. To P. O. 5. from
Crossing Nation; 6. From Wichita Vortex Sutra; 7.
from Howl Part II; 8. from Cabin in the Rockies; 9.
from Nagasaki Days; 10. Aunt Rose; 11. from The
Green Automobile; 12. from N. S. A. Dope Calypso;
13. from Nagasaki Days; 14. Ayers Rock/Uluru Song;
15. Father Death Blues.
Cpte M. Goldray, C. Wincene, A. Sterman, F.
Cassara, J. Pugliese, R. Peck, E. Futral, M.A. Eaton,
M.A. Hart, R. Fracker, G. Purnhagen, N. Watson, A.
Ginsberg, P. Glass, M. Goldray (r1992-3)
(1/94) (NONE) ① **7559-79286-2**
Satyagraha: opera: 3 acts
(1980—Rotterdam)
EXCERPTS: 1. ACT 1: Tolstoy—; 1a. Scene 1: The
Kuru Field of Justice; 1b. Scene 2: Tolstoy Farm
(1910); 1c. Scene 3: The Vow (1906); 2. ACT 2:
Tagore—; 2a. Scene 1: Confrontation and Rescue
(1896); 2b. Scene 2: Indian Opinion; 2c. Scene 3:
Protest. ACT 3: 3. King—Newcastle March (1913).
Cpte D. Perry, C. Cummings, R. Liss, R. McFarland,
S. Reeve, S. Woods, NYC Op Chor, NYC Op Orch,
C. Keene   (9/86) (SONY) ① [3] **M3K39672**
Act III Conclusion D. Joyce (r1993; arr Riesman:
org) *Concert*   (1/94) (CATA) ① **09026 61825-2**
1a, 2c D. Perry, NYC Op Orch, NYC Op Chor
Concert   (1/94) (SONY) ① **SK64133**

GLAZUNOV, Alexander
Konstantinovich (1865–1936)
Russia/USSR

| SECTION I: ORCHESTRAL |

Ballade in F—orchestra, Op. 78 (1902)
USSR RSO, O. Dimitriedi *Concert*
(8/88) (OLYM) ① **OCD130**
USSR RSO, O. Dimitriedi *Concert*
(11/90) (OLYM) ① [6] **OCD5001**
Chant du ménéstrel—cello and orchestra,
Op. 71 (1900)
R. Wallfisch, LPO, B. Thomson *Concert*
(6/88) (CHAN) ① **CHAN8579**
M. Rostropovich, Boston Sym, S. Ozawa *Concert*
(8/91) (DG) ① **431 475-2GGA**
M. Maisky, Paris Orch, S. Bychkov *Concert*
(10/92) (DG) ① **435 781-2GH**
M. Rostropovich, Boston Sym, S. Ozawa *Concert*
(10/94) (DG) ① [2] **437 952-2GX2**
Concert Waltz No. 1 in D, Op. 47 (1893)
Moscow PO, L. Leighton Smith *Concert*
(2/88) (SHEF) ① **CD27**
Bamberg SO, N. Järvi (r1984) *Symphony 2.*
(11/90) (ORFE) ① **C148101A**
Concert Waltz No.2 in F, Op. 51 (1894)
Bamberg SO, N. Järvi *Symphony 3.*
(11/90) (ORFE) ① **C157101A**
Concerto for Piano and Orchestra No. 2 in B,
Op. 100 (1917)
D. Alexeev, USSR RSO, Y. Nikolaevsky *Concert*
(2/90) (OLYM) ① **OCD165**
Concerto for saxophone and strings in E flat,
Op. 109 (1934)
L. Mikhailov, USSR RSO Sols Ens, A. Korneiev
Concert   (2/90) (OLYM) ① **OCD165**
J. Harle, ASMF, N. Marriner *Concert*
(1/92) (EMI) ① **CDC7 54301-2**
Concerto for Violin and Orchestra in A
minor, Op. 82 (1904)
O. Shumsky, SNO, N. Järvi *Seasons.*
(3/89) (CHAN) ① **CHAN8596**

1. M. Fingerhut (r1992) *Concert*
(4/94) (CHAN) ① **CHAN9218**
Suite on the name 'Sacha'—piano, Op. 2 (1883)
T. Fránova (r1990) *Concert*
(7/93) (MARC) ① **8 223151**
Waltzes on the Theme 'Sabela'—piano, Op. 23 (1890)
T. Fránova (r1990) *Concert*
(7/93) (MARC) ① **8 223151**

SECTION V: STAGE WORKS

Raymonda—ballet: 3 acts, Op. 57 (1896-97)
EXCERPTS: ACT 1: 1a. Introduction
(moderato—poco più mosso); 1b. Scène (lento
maestoso); 1c. La Traditrice (moderato—allegretto);
1d. Scène (moderato—allegro agitato); 1e. Entrée de
Raymonda (allegro); 2a. Grande Valse (allegro più
sostenuto); 2b. Pizzicato (allegretto); 3. Scène
(andante marcile); 4. Reprise de la Valse; 5a. Scène
mimique (moderato—allegro); 5b. Entrée des
vasseux et des paysans (andante marciale); 5c.
Scène: Pas de deux (andantino—animato); 6.
Prélude et La Romanesca (moderato); 7. Prélude et
Variation (allegretto); 8a. Scène mimique (andante);
8b. Scène: Apparition de la Dame blanche; 8c. Grand
Adagio; 9. Valse fantastique
(allegro—animato—allegro); 10. Variation I
(allegretto); 11. Variation II (allegretto); 12. Variation
pour Raymonda (tempo di valse); 13. Coda (presto);
14a. Scène (moderato—con
moto—animando—appassionato); 14b. Scène
(andante). ACT 2: 15a. Marche (allegro moderato);
15b. Entrée d'Abérame (moderato pesante—più
tranquillo); 15c. Grand pas d'action
(andante—grandioso); 16a. Variation I (moderato);
16b. Variation II (allegretto); 17. Variation pour
Raymonda (allegretto); 18. Grand Coda (allegro
moderato—poco più mosso—allegro—poco più
mosso); 19a. Scène (moderato); 20a. Danse des
garçons Arabes (vivace); 20b. Entrée des Sarrazins
(presto); 21. Grand pas espangol (andante—allegro);
22a. Danse orientale (andante); 22b. Bacchanal
(allegro—animando); 22c. Scène (moderato
maestoso—agitato—sostenuto); 22d. La combat
(allegro assai—moderato); 22e. Hymne. ACT 3: 23a.
Entr'acte (allegro moderato—moderato); 23b. Le
cortège hongrois (moderato maestoso); 24. Grand
pas hongrois (moderato maestoso—molto
pesante—presto); 25. Entrée (allegretto—poco meno
mosso); 26. Pas classique hongroise(adagio); 27.
Variation (prestissimo); 28. Variation
(moderato—allegro); 29. Variation (adagio); 30.
Variation (allegro moderato); 31. Coda
(allegro—vivo); 32. Galop (allegro assai—vivo); 33.
Apothéose (andante).
1a-e, 2a, 2b, 4, 6, 7, 8a, 8c, 9, 13, 15c, 16a, 16b, 17,
18, 21, 23a SNO, N. Järvi
(7/86) (CHAN) ① **CHAN8447**
1a, 1b, 2a, 2b, 4, 6, 7, 15a, 21, 23a Leningrad PO, E.
Mravinsky (pp1969) *Concert*
(6/92) (ERAT) ① [11] **2292-45763-2**
1a, 1b, 2a, 2b, 4, 6, 7, 15a, 21, 23a Leningrad PO, E.
Mravinsky (pp1969) *Concert*
(6/92) (ERAT) ① **2292-45757-2**
2a L. Mordkovitch, M. Gusak-Grin (trans Zimbalist)
Concert (3/87) (CHAN) ① **CHAN8500**
2a J. Heifetz, S. Chotzinoff (r1920) *Concert*
(11/94) (RCA) ① [65] **09026 61778-2(01)**
8c J. Heifetz, S. Chotzinoff (r1922) *Concert*
(11/94) (RCA) ① [65] **09026 61778-2(01)**
Les Ruses d'amour—ballet: 1 act, Op. 61 (1900—St. Petersburg)
EXCERPTS: 1. Introduction; 2. Valse; 3. Ballabile.
1, 2. Chicago SO, F. Stock (r1929) *Concert*
(2/95) (BIDD) ① [2] **WHL021/2**
The Seasons—ballet: 1 act, Op. 67 (1899—St Petersburg)
Cpte RPO, Vladimir Ashkenazy *Tchaikovsky:
Nutcracker.* (4/92) (DECC) ① [2] **433 000-2DH2**
SNO, N. Järvi *Violin Concerto.*
(3/89) (CHAN) ① **CHAN8596**
Bratislava RSO, O. Lenárd *Tchaikovsky: Sleeping
Beauty.* (10/90) (NAXO) ① **8 550079**
Minnesota Orch, E. de Waart (r1993) *Scènes de
Ballet.* (12/93) (TELA) ① **CD80347**
orch, A. Glazunov (r1929) *Concert*
(5/95) (EMI) ① **CDC5 55223-2**

GLEBOV, Yevgeni (b 1929) USSR

SECTION I: ORCHESTRAL

5 Fantastic Dances
Belorussian St Rad & TV Orch, B. Raisky *Concert*
(10/92) (OLYM) ① **OCD552**
Symphony No. 5
Belorussian St Rad & TV Orch, B. Raisky *Concert*
(10/92) (OLYM) ① **OCD552**

SECTION V: STAGE WORKS

The Little Prince—concert suite from ballet
Belorussian St Rad & TV Orch, B. Raisky *Concert*
(10/92) (OLYM) ① **OCD552**

GLENNIE, Evelyn (b 1965) Scotland

SECTION III: INSTRUMENTAL

Light in Darkness—marimba
E. Glennie *Concert* (1/92) (RCA) ① **RD60557**

GLIÈRE, Reinhold (1875–1956) Ukraine/USSR

SECTION I: ORCHESTRAL

Concerto for Harp and Orchestra, Op. 74 (1938)
R. Masters, CLS, R. Hickox *Concert*
(2/93) (CHAN) ① **CHAN9094**
Concerto for Horn and Orchestra in B flat, Op. 91 (1950)
R. Watkins, BBC PO, E. Downes (r1994) *Bronze
Horseman Suite.* (12/95) (CHAN) ① **CHAN9379**
The Sirens—symphonic poem, Op. 33 (1908)
Slovak PO, S. Gunzenhauser (r1985) *Symphony 1.*
(9/86) (MARC) ① **8 220349**
Slovak PO, S. Gunzenhauser (r1985) *Symphony 1.*
(10/95) (NAXO) ① **8 550898**
Symphony No. 1 in E flat, Op. 8 (1899-1900)
Slovak PO, S. Gunzenhauser (r1985) *Sirens, Op. 33.*
(9/86) (MARC) ① **8 220349**
BBC PO, E. Downes (r1992) *Red Poppy Suite.*
(7/93) (CHAN) ① **CHAN9160**
Slovak PO, S. Gunzenhauser (r1985) *Sirens, Op. 33.*
(10/95) (NAXO) ① **8 550898**
Symphony No. 2 in C minor, Op. 25 (1907-08)
BBC PO, E. Downes (r1991) *Zaporozhy Cossacks.*
(7/92) (CHAN) ① **CHAN9071**
Bratislava RSO, K. Clark (r1987) *Zaporozhy
Cossacks.* (10/95) (NAXO) ① **8 550899**
Symphony No. 3, 'Il'ya Mouromets', Op. 42 (1909-11)
RPO, H. Farberman
(3/89) (UNIC) ① [2] **UKCD2014/5**
BBC PO, E. Downes (5/92) (CHAN) ① **CHAN9041**
San Diego SO, Y. Talmi (9/92) (PRO) ① **CDS589**
Czech RSO, D. Johanos (r1991)
(2/94) (NAXO) ① **8 550858**
Philadelphia, L. Stokowski (r1940) *Concert*
(7/94) (BIDD) ① **WHL005**
Houston SO, L. Stokowski (r1957) *Loeffler: Pagan
Poem.* (7/94) (EMI) ① **CDM5 65074-2**
The Zaporozhy Cossacks—orchestra, Op. 64 (1921)
BBC PO, E. Downes (r1991) *Symphony 2.*
(7/92) (CHAN) ① **CHAN9071**
Bratislava RSO, K. Clark (r1987) *Symphony 2.*
(10/95) (NAXO) ① **8 550899**

SECTION II: CHAMBER

Intermezzo and Tarantelle—double-bass and piano, Op. 9
Tarantelle M. Hanskov, T. Lønskov *Concert*
(3/92) (DANA) ① **DACOCD378**
8 Pieces—violin and cello, Op. 39 (1909)
EXCERPTS: 1. Prelude.
E. Turovsky, Y. Turovsky *Concert*
(7/89) (CHAN) ① **CHAN8652**
1. J. Heifetz, G. Piatigorsky (r1964) *Concert*
(11/94) (RCA) ① [65] **09026 61778-2(31)**
Waltz in A—cello and piano, Op. 48/2
S. Nakarjakov, A. Markovich (arr tpt/pf) *Concert*
(5/93) (TELD) ① **9031-77705-2**

SECTION IV: VOCAL AND CHORAL

The Blacksmith—song, Op. 22
A. Orda, J. Lee (bp1959) *Concert*
(12/89) (SYMP) ① **SYMCD1067**

Concerto for Coloratura Soprano and Orchestra, Op. 82 (1943)
B. Hoch, Hong Kong PO, K. Schermerhorn *Concert*
(11/86) (CARL) ① **PCD827**
E. Hulse, CLS, R. Hickox *Concert*
(2/93) (CHAN) ① **CHAN9094**
The Lark—song
K. Vayne, C. Tilney (r1966) *Concert*
(6/95) (PREI) ① **89996**
Merry I'll be—song, Op. 52/12 (Wds. S. Skitalets)
A. Orda, J. Lee (bp1959) *Concert*
(12/89) (SYMP) ① **SYMCD1067**

SECTION V: STAGE WORKS

Bronze Horseman—concert suite from the ballet (1948-9)
BBC PO, E. Downes (r1994) *Horn Concerto, Op. 91.*
(12/95) (CHAN) ① **CHAN9379**
Khrizis—ballet-pantomime (1912)
Suite Bolshoi Th Orch, R. Glière (r1947) *Sheep's
Spring.* (11/95) (COCE) ① **813000**
The Red Poppy—ballet, Op. 70 (1927—Moscow)
EXCERPTS.
6. Empire Brass (r1992; arr. E. Smedvig) *Concert*
(1/94) (TELA) ① **CD80305**
The Red Poppy—concert suite from ballet, Op. 70 (1927)
1. Heroic Coolie Dance; 2. Scene and Dance; 3.
Chinese Dance; 4. Phoenix; 5. Valse; 6. Russian
Sailors' Dance.
BBC PO, E. Downes (r1992) *Symphony 1.*
(7/93) (CHAN) ① **CHAN9160**
6. St. Louis SO, L. Slatkin *Concert*
(12/83) (TELA) ① **CD80072**
6. Philadelphia, L. Stokowski (r1934) *Concert*
(7/94) (BIDD) ① **WHL005**
6. National SO, A. Fistoulari (r1944) *Concert*
(5/95) (DUTT) ① **CDK1200**
Sheep's Spring—ballet (1922) (rev as 'The Comedians': 1930)
Suite Moscow All-Union RSO, R. Glière (r1947)
Khrizis. (11/95) (COCE) ① **813000**

GLINKA, Mikhail Ivanovich (1804–1857) Russia

SECTION I: ORCHESTRAL

Jota aragonesa—Spanish overture No. 1 (1845)
NBC SO, A. Toscanini (bp1940) *Concert*
(1/91) (RCA) ① **GD60308**
SRO, E. Ansermet (r1964) *Concert*
(6/93) (DECC) ① [2] **433 911-2DM2**
Philh, P. Kletzki (r1958) *Concert*
(9/93) (EMI) ① [2] **CZS7 67726-2**
LSO, C. Mackerras (r1961) *Concert*
(12/95) (MERC) ① **434 352-2MM**
Kamarinskaya—orchestra (1848)
NBC SO, A. Toscanini (bp1940) *Concert*
(11/92) (RCA) ① **GD60323**
LSO, A. Coates (r1930) *Concert*
(12/92) (KOCH) ① **37700-2**
Detroit SO, N. Järvi (r1992) *Concert*
(8/94) (CHAN) ① **CHAN9227**
Valse-fantaisie—orchestra (1856) (arr cpsr from piano work)
Detroit SO, N. Järvi (r1992) *Concert*
(8/94) (CHAN) ① **CHAN9227**

SECTION II: CHAMBER

Divertimento brillants on themes from Bellini's 'La sonnambula'—piano, string quartet and double-bass (1832)
L. Ogrinchuk, Russian Nat Orch Sols Ens (r1993)
Concert (7/94) (OLYM) ① **OCD529**
Septet in E flat—ob, bn, hn, 2 vns, vc, db (c1823)
Russian Nat Orch Sols Ens (r1993) *Concert*
(7/94) (OLYM) ① **OCD529**
Serenata on themes from Donizetti's 'Anna Bolena' in E flat—pf, hp, bn, hn, va, vc, db (1832)
L. Ogrinchuk, Russian Nat Orch Sols Ens (r1993)
Concert (7/94) (OLYM) ① **OCD529**
Sextet in E flat, 'Gran sestetto originale'—string quartet, piano and double-bass (1832)
Capricorn *Rimsky-Korsakov: Piano and Wind
Quintet.* (5/86) (HYPE) ① **CDA66163**
Shostakovich Qt, A. Nasyedkin, R. Gabdullin *Concert*
(7/93) (OLYM) ① **OCD523**
M. Pletnev, Russian Nat Orch Sols Ens (r1993)
Concert (7/94) (OLYM) ① **OCD529**

Sonata for Viola and Piano (1825-28) (cpted
V. Borisovsky)
N. Imai, R. Pöntinen *Concert*
(2/88) (BIS) ① **BIS-CD358**
Y. Bashmet, M. Muntian *Concert*
(3/93) (RCA) ① **09026 61273-2**

SECTION III: INSTRUMENTAL

Contredanse in G—piano (unidentified)
V. Kamishov *Concert* (6/89) (OLYM) ① **OCD124**
Cotillon in B flat—piano (by 1828)
V. Kamishov *Concert* (6/89) (OLYM) ① **OCD124**
Farewell Waltz in G—piano (1831)
V. Kamishov *Concert* (6/89) (OLYM) ① **OCD124**
Galopade—piano (1838 or 1839)
V. Kamishov *Concert* (6/89) (OLYM) ① **OCD124**
Grand Waltz in G—piano (1839)
V. Kamishov *Concert* (6/89) (OLYM) ① **OCD124**
**A Greeting to my Native Land—piano
(1847)**
1. Souvenir d'une mazurka, B flat; 2. Barcarolle, G; 3.
Prière, A; 4. Thème écossais varié.
1, 2, 4. V. Kamishov *Concert*
(6/89) (OLYM) ① **OCD124**
Mazurka in F—piano
V. Kamishov *Concert* (6/89) (OLYM) ① **OCD124**
Las Mollares—piano (?1855)
V. Kamishov *Concert* (6/89) (OLYM) ① **OCD124**
Monastryka (new contredanse)—piano
(unidentified)
V. Kamishov *Concert* (6/89) (OLYM) ① **OCD124**
4 New Contredanses—piano (by 1828)
V. Kamishov *Concert* (6/89) (OLYM) ① **OCD124**
Nocturne in E flat—harp
S. Drake (r1988) *Concert*
(2/90) (HYPE) ① **CDA66340**
Polonaise in E—piano (1839)
V. Kamishov *Concert* (6/89) (OLYM) ① **OCD124**
**Rondo brillante on a theme from 'Montecchi
e Capuletti' (Bellini)—piano (1831)**
V. Kamishov *Concert* (6/89) (OLYM) ① **OCD124**
Tarantella in A minor—piano (1843)
V. Kamishov *Concert* (6/89) (OLYM) ① **OCD124**
**Variations on a theme from 'Montecchi e
Capuletti' (Bellini)—piano (1832)**
V. Kamishov *Concert* (6/89) (OLYM) ① **OCD124**
**Variations on a theme of Mozart in E
flat—harp (1822)**
S. Drake *Concert* (9/86) (HYPE) ① **CDA66038**
**Variations on 'The Nightingale'
(Alabiev)—piano (1833)**
V. Kamishov *Concert* (6/89) (OLYM) ① **OCD124**
**Variations on 2 themes from the ballet
'Chao-Kang'—piano (1831)**
V. Kamishov *Concert* (6/89) (OLYM) ① **OCD124**

SECTION IV: VOCAL AND CHORAL

Declaration—song: 1v and piano (1839)
(Wds. Pushkin)
N. Storozhev, Montreal I Musici, Y. Turovsky (r1992:
orch V. Milman) *Concert*
(9/93) (CHAN) ① **CHAN9149**
Doubt—song (1838) (Wds. Kulol'nik)
F. Chaliapin, C. Sharpe, I. Newton (r1931) *Concert*
(6/93) (PREI) ① **[3] 89207**
E. Zbrueva, R.O. Von Beke, anon (r1909) *Concert*
(6/93) (PEAR) ① **[3] GEMMCDS9004/6(2)**
N. Storozhev, Montreal I Musici, Y. Turovsky (r1992:
orch V. Milman) *Concert*
(9/93) (CHAN) ① **CHAN9149**
N. Ghiaurov, P. Dokovska (r1993) *Concert*
(1/95) (RCA) ① **09026 62501-2**
Elegy, 'When my soul'—duet (Wds.
Jakovlev)
L. Sibiriakov, A. Aleksandrovich, anon (r1912)
Concert
(6/93) (PEAR) ① **[3] GEMMCDS9007/9(2)**
A farewell to St Petersburg—songs (1840)
(Wds. Kukol'nik)
1. Romance; 2. Hebrew Song; 3. Bolero; 4. Cavatina;
5. Cradle Song; 6. Travelling Song; 7. Fantasia; 8.
Barcarolle; 9. Virtus antiqua; 10. The lark; 11. To
Molly; 12. Song of farewell.
1. V. Bogachev, Montreal I Musici, Y. Turovsky
(r1992: orch V. Milman) *Concert*
(9/93) (CHAN) ① **CHAN9149**
10. P. Fowke (arr Balakirev: pf) *Concert*
(8/89) (CRD) ① **CRD3396**
10. G. Fergus-Thompson (arr Balakirev) *Concert*
(10/92) (ASV) ① **CDWHL2066**
10. E. Zimbalist, F. Moore (r1918: arr Auer) *Concert*
(7/93) (APR) ① **[2] APR7016**
11. N. Storozhev, Montreal I Musici, Y. Turovsky
(r1992: orch V. Milman) *Concert*
(9/93) (CHAN) ① **CHAN9149**

**The Fire of longing burns in my heart—song
(1838)** (Wds. Pushkin)
A. Labinsky, anon (r1901) *Concert*
(6/93) (PEAR) ① **[3] GEMMCDS9001/3(1)**
N. Storozhev, Montreal I Musici, Y. Turovsky (r1992:
orch V. Milman) *Concert*
(9/93) (CHAN) ① **CHAN9149**
How sweet it is to be with you—song (1840)
(Wds. P. Rindin)
N. Storozhev, Montreal I Musici, Y. Turovsky (r1992:
orch V. Milman) *Concert*
(9/93) (CHAN) ① **CHAN9149**
I am here, Inezilla—song (1834) (Wds.
Pushkin after B. Cornwall)
V. Bogachev, Montreal I Musici, Y. Turovsky (r1992:
orch V. Milman) *Concert*
(9/93) (CHAN) ① **CHAN9149**
I recall a wonderful moment—song (1840)
(Wds. Pushkin)
V. Bogachev, Montreal I Musici, Y. Turovsky (r1992:
orch V. Milman) *Concert*
(9/93) (CHAN) ① **CHAN9149**
The night review—song (1836) (Wds.
Zhukovsky)
F. Chaliapin, orch. E. Goossens (r1926) *Concert*
(6/93) (PREI) ① **[2] 89207**
L. Sibiriakov, orch (r1912) *Concert*
(6/93) (PEAR) ① **[3] GEMMCDS9007/9(2)**
**Say not that it grieves the heart—song
(1856)** (Wds. Pavlov)
N. Storozhev, Montreal I Musici, Y. Turovsky (r1992:
orch V. Milman) *Concert*
(9/93) (CHAN) ① **CHAN9149**
Venetian Night—song (1832) (Wds. Kozlov)
A. Rolfe Johnson, G. Johnson *Concert*
(3/88) (HYPE) ① **CDA66112**
**Wedding Song, '(The) North Star'—1v and
piano (1839)** (Wds. E. Rostopchina)
V. Bogachev, Montreal I Musici, Y. Turovsky (r1992:
orch V. Milman) *Concert*
(9/93) (CHAN) ① **CHAN9149**

SECTION V: STAGE WORKS

**A Life for the Tsar—opera: 4 acts (1836—St
Petersburg)** (Lib. G. Rosen)
Cpte B. Martinovich, A. Pendachanska, C. Merritt, S.
Toczyska, S. Georgiev, M. Popov, K. Videv, Sofia
National Op Chor, Sofia Fest Orch, E. Tchakarov
(9/91) (SONY) ① **[3] S3K46487**
Ballet Music Philh, E. Kurtz (r1961) *Concert*
(9/93) (EMI) ① **[2] CZS7 67729-2**
Brothers, follow me H. Roswaenge, Berlin St Op
Orch, B. Seidler-Winkler (r1940: Ger) *Concert*
(5/90) (PREI) ① **89018**
I do not grieve for that E. Bronskaya, orch (r1913)
Concert
(3/95) (NIMB) ① **NI7865**
Introduction; Polonaise; Final Chorus Bolshoi Th
Chor, Bolshoi SO, A. Lazarev (r1993) *Concert*
(5/94) (ERAT) ① **4509-91723-2**
It is not for that that I grieve M. Kuznetsova, orch
(r1904) *Concert*
(6/93) (PEAR) ① **[3] GEMMCDS9004/6(1)**
It is not for that that I grieve A. Nezhdanova, anon
(r1907) *Concert*
(6/93) (PEAR) ① **[3] GEMMCDS9007/9(1)**
It is not for that I grieve E. Orel, anon (r c1904)
Concert (7/93) (SYMP) ① **SYMCD1105**
My dawn will come F. Chaliapin, anon (r1902)
Concert (7/93) (SYMP) ① **SYMCD1105**
My poor horse fell in the field E. Zbrueva, anon
(r1903) *Concert*
(6/93) (PEAR) ① **[3] GEMMCDS9004/6(2)**
**My poor horse fell...Open up!; Light the
fires!...Saddle your horses** E. Zbrueva, chor, orch
(r1913) *Concert*
(6/93) (PEAR) ① **[3] GEMMCDS9004/6(2)**
The rose that blooms L. Sibiriakov, M. Michailova,
G. Nikitina, A. Labinsky, orch (r1908) *Concert*
(6/93) (PEAR) ① **[3] GEMMCDS9007/9(2)**
They guess the truth F. Chaliapin, anon (r1914)
Concert (6/88) (EMI) ① **CDH7 61009-2**
They guess the truth N. Rossi-Lemeni, Philh, T.
Benintende-Neglia (r1952) *Concert*
(4/92) (EMI) ① **[7] CHS7 69741-2(7)**
They guess the truth M. Reizen, Bolshoi Th Orch,
V. Nebolsin (r1955) *Concert*
(12/92) (PREI) ① **89059**
They guess the truth L. Sibiriakov, anon (r1908)
Concert
(6/93) (PEAR) ① **[3] GEMMCDS9001/3(2)**
They guess the truth D. Bukhtoyarov, anon (r1902)
Concert
(6/93) (PEAR) ① **[3] GEMMCDS9001/3(1)**
What about a wedding? L. Sibiriakov, chor, orch
(r1910) *Concert*
(6/93) (PEAR) ① **[3] GEMMCDS9007/9(2)**

**Ruslan and Lyudmila—opera: 5 acts
(1842—St. Petersburg)** (Lib. V F Shirkov, after
S Pushkin)
EXCERPTS: 1. Overture. ACT 1: 2. There is a
desert country (The Bard's song); 3. Soon I must
leave thee (Lyudmila's cavatina). ACT 2: 5.
Introduction (entr'acte); 8. The happy day is gone
(Farlaf's rondo); 9. O say, ye fields! (Ruslan's aria).
ACT 3: 11. The evening shadows (Persian song); 12.
O my Ratmir! (Gorislava's romance and cavatina);
13. The wondrous dream of love (Ratmir's aria); 14.
Dances. ACT 4: 19. Chernomor's march; 20. Oriental
dances.
Ah, thou my fate A. Nezhdanova, anon, anon
(r1907) *Concert*
(6/93) (PEAR) ① **[3] GEMMCDS9007/9(1)**
1. St. Louis SO, L. Slatkin *Concert*
(12/83) (TELA) ① **CD80072**
1. LPO, C. Mackerras *Concert*
(11/87) (CFP) ① **CD-CFP9000**
1. Moscow PO, L. Leighton Smith *Concert*
(2/88) (SHEF) ① **CD25**
1. Chicago SO, F. Reiner *Concert*
(1/90) (RCA) ① **GD60176**
1. Berlin SO, C.P. Flor (pp1988) *Concert*
(4/90) (RCA) ① **RD60119**
1. Leningrad PO, E. Mravinsky *Concert*
(6/92) (ERAT) ① **2292-45757-2**
1. Leningrad PO, E. Mravinsky *Concert*
(6/92) (ERAT) ① **[11] 2292-45763-2**
1. LSO, A. Coates (r1928) *Concert*
(12/92) (KOCH) ① **37700-2**
1. Malmö SO, J. DePreist *Concert*
(1/93) (BIS) ① **BIS-CD570**
1. Queen's Hall Orch, Henry Wood (r1937) *Concert*
(1/94) (BEUL) ① **1PD3**
1. Kirov Th Orch, V. Gergiev (r1993) *Concert*
(4/94) (PHIL) ① **442 011-2PH**
1. Chicago SO, F. Reiner (r1959) *Concert*
(8/94) (RCA) ① **09026 61958-2**
1. Philh, C. Silvestri (r1959) *Concert*
(11/94) (EMI) ① **[2] CZS5 68229-2**
1. Russian Nat Orch, M. Pletnev *Concert*
(12/94) (DG) ① **439 892-2GH**
1. Baltimore SO, D. Zinman (r1989) *Concert*
(12/95) (TELA) ① **CD80378**
2. D. Smirnov, orch (r1913) *Concert*
(6/93) (PEAR) ① **[3] GEMMCDS9004/6(1)**
2. A. Bogdanovich, anon (r1903) *Concert*
(6/93) (PEAR) ① **[3] GEMMCDS9007/9(1)**
3. E. Orel, anon (r c1902) *Concert*
(7/93) (SYMP) ① **SYMCD1105**
8. F. Chaliapin, LSO, M. Steinmann (r1931) *Concert*
(6/88) (EMI) ① **CDH7 61009-2**
8. F. Chaliapin, LSO, M. Steinmann (r1931) *Concert*
(12/89) (PEAR) ① **GEMMCD9314**
8. M. Reizen, Bolshoi Th Orch, A. Melik-Pashayev
(r1948) *Concert* (12/92) (PREI) ① **89059**
8. V. Kastorsky, orch (r1908) *Concert*
(6/93) (PEAR) ① **[3] GEMMCDS9001/3(1)**
9. F. Chaliapin, orch (r1908) *Concert*
(6/88) (EMI) ① **CDH7 61009-2**
9. M. Reizen, Bolshoi Th Orch, S. Samosud (r1948)
Concert (12/92) (PREI) ① **89059**
9. P. Orlov, anon (r1902) *Concert*
(6/93) (PEAR) ① **[3] GEMMCDS9001/3(1)**
11. E. Zimbalist, E. Bay (r1925: arr Zimbalist) *Concert*
(7/93) (APR) ① **[2] APR7016**
12. M. Kuznetsova, orch (r1904) *Concert*
(6/93) (PEAR) ① **[3] GEMMCDS9004/6(1)**
12. M. Kuznetsova, orch (r1905) *Concert*
(7/93) (SYMP) ① **SYMCD1105**
13, And blazing heat, She is my life E. Zbrueva,
orch (r1907) *Concert*
(6/93) (PEAR) ① **[3] GEMMCDS9004/6(2)**

GLINSKY, Albert (b 1952) USA

SECTION II: CHAMBER

Toccata-Scherzo—violin and piano
M. Bachmann, J. Klibonoff (r1993) *Concert*
(12/93) (CATA) ① **09026 61824-2**

**GLOBOKAR, Vinko (b 1934)
France/Yugoslavia**

SECTION II: CHAMBER

Discours III—five oboes (1969)
H. Holliger *Concert* (7/93) (SCHW) ① **310632**
Discours VI—string quartet (1983)
Domus *Concert* (7/93) (SCHW) ① **310632**

SECTION III: INSTRUMENTAL

Toucher—percussion (1973)
J-P. Drouet *Concert* (7/93) (SCHW) ① **310632**

Voix instrumentalisée—bass clarinet (1973)
M. Riessler *Concert*   (7/93) (SCHW) ① 310632

Accord—soprano and five soloists (1966)
(Wds. cpsr)
M. Vilotijevič, M. Siracusa, S. Viola, M. Chiapperino,
V. Lambiase, D. Sabatini *Concert*
          (7/93) (SCHW) ① 310632

Les Émigrés—music theatre
Ljubljana Voc Qnt, Musique Vivante Ens, D. Masson,
V. Globokar (pp1990)
          (9/92) (HARM) ① HMC90 5212

Concerto for Flute and Orchestra in G
(doubtful: arr H. Scherchen)
P-L. Graf, Zurich Camerata, R. Tschupp *Concert*
          (11/87) (JECK) ① JD506-2

Allegretto—string quartet (unidentified)
Rasumovsky Qt *Concert*
          (12/92) (IMPE) ① RAZCD901
**8 Trio Sonatas—two violins and continuo
(pub 1746)**
1. C; 2. G minor; 3. A; 4. B flat; 5. E flat; 6. F; 7. E; 8.
F.
V. Šimčisko, A. Plaskurová, J. Alexander, M.
Dobiášová   (10/91) (OPUS) ① 9351 2034

Alceste—opera: 3 acts (1776—Paris) (Lib.
Calzabigi)
EXCERPTS—; 1. Overture. ACT 1 2. Grands Dieux,
du destin qui m'accable; 3a. Où suis-je? O
malheureuse Alceste!; 3b. Non, ce n'est point un
sacrifice; 4. Tes destins sont remplis; 5. Divinités du
Styx. ACT 2: 6a. O moment délicieux!; 6b. Bannis la
crainte et les alarmes; 7a. Ciel!...Tu pleurs? Je
tremble!; 7b. Je n'ai jamais chéri la vie; 8a. Tu
m'aimes, je t'adore; 8b. Barbare! Non, sans toi, je ne
puis vivre; 9a. Grands Dieux! Pour mon époux
j'implore; 9b. Ah, malgré moi, mon faible coeur. ACT
3: 10. Nous ne pouvons trop trop répandre des
larmes; 11. Après de longs travaux; 12a. Grands
Dieux, soutenez mon courage!; 12b. Ah, divinités
implacables; 13. Reçois, Dieu bienfaisant; 14. O mes
amis!...O mes enfants!.
Cpte J. Norman, N. Gedda, T. Krause, R. Gambill, P.
Lika, S. Nimsgern, B. Weikl, R. Bracht, K. Rydl,
Bavarian Rad Chor, BRSO, S. Baudo (r1982)
          (6/87) (ORFE) ① [3] C027823F
Gavotte E. Petri (pp1959: arr pf: Brahms) *Concert*
          (3/94) (MUSI) ① [4] MACD-772
1. Concertgebouw, W. Mengelberg (r1935) *Concert*
          (7/90) (SYMP) ① SYMCD1078
1. Concertgebouw, W. Mengelberg (arr Mottl: r1935)
Concert   (1/91) (KOCH) ① 37011-2
5. G. Bumbry, Stuttgart RSO, S. Soltesz *Concert*
          (11/86) (ORFE) ① C081841A
5. M. Callas, FRNO, G. Prêtre *Concert*
          (2/88) (EMI) ① CDC7 49059-2
5. M. Callas, FRNO, G. Prêtre *Concert*
          (2/90) (EMIN) ① CD-EMX2123
5. E. Stignani, EIAR Orch, U. Tansini (Ital: r1941)
Concert   (1/91) (PREI) ① 89014
5. L. Price, LSO, E. Downes *Concert*
          (12/92) (RCA) ① [4] 09026 61236-2
5. M. Klose, Berlin St Op Orch, B. Seidler-Winkler
(r1938: Ger) *Concert*   (7/95) (PREI) ① 89082
6b G. Thill, Orch, E. Bigot (r1930) *Concert*
          (1/89) (EMI) ① CDM7 69548-2
6b G. Thill, orch, E. Bigot (r1930) *Concert*
          (8/95) (FORL) ① UCD16727
9b R. Bampton, Victor SO, W. Pelletier (r1941)
Concert   (4/92) (EMI) ① [7] CHS7 69741-2(1)
9b R. Bampton, RCA SO, W. Pelletier (r1941)
Concert   (4/94) (RCA) ① [6] 09026 61580-2(4)
**Alessandro, '(The) Love of Alexander and
Roxane'—ballet (1764—Vienna)**
Cologne Musica Antiqua, R. Goebel (r1994) *Concert*
          (12/95) (ARCH) ① 445 824-2AH
Armide—opera: 5 acts (1777—Paris) (Lib. P.
Quinnault)
Ah! si la liberté. F. Leider, orch, J. Barbirolli (r1928)
Concert   (2/90) (PREI) ① 89004
Ah! si la liberté. F. Leider, orch, J. Barbirolli (r1928)
Concert (7/92) (PEAR) ① [3] GEMMCDS9926(1)

**Le Cinesi—opera-serenade: 1 act
(1754—Vienna)** (Wds. Metastasio)
Cpte K. Erickson, A. Milcheva, M. Schiml, T. Moser,
Munich RO, L. Gardelli (r1983)
          (1/90) (ORFE) ① C178891A
**La Corona—opera: 1 act (composed 1765 -
not performed)** (Wds. Metastasio)
Cpte A. Słowakiewicz, H. Górzyńska, L. Juranek, B.
Nowicka, Bavarian Rad Chor, Warsaw Chbr Op
Orch, T. Bugaj (r1983) *Danza*.
          (3/88) (ORFE) ① [2] C135872H
La Danza—opera: 1 act (1755—Vienna)
(Wds. Metastasio)
Cpte E. Ignatowicz, K. Myrlak, Warsaw Chbr Op
Orch, T. Bugaj (r1983) *Corona*.
          (3/88) (ORFE) ① [2] C135872H
Don Juan—pantomime (1761—Vienna)
Cpte Stuttgart Arcata Ens, P. Strub
          (5/90) (BAYE) ① BR100016
Cpte Tafelmusik, B. Weil (r1992) *Semiramis*.
          (10/93) (SONY) ① SK53119
**Iphigénie en Aulide—tragedy: 3 acts
(1774—Paris)** (Lib. du Roullet, after Racine)
Cpte L. Dawson, J. Van Dam, A.S. von Otter, J. Aler,
B. Delétré, G. Cachemaille, R. Schirrer, G. Laurens,
A. Monoyios, I. Eschenbrenner, Monteverdi Ch, Lyon
Op Orch, J.E. Gardiner
          (6/90) (ERAT) ① [2] 2292-45003-2
Gavotte M. Levitzki (arr Brahms: r1927) *Concert*
          (6/92) (APR) ① [2] APR7020
Gavotte I. Biret (r1993: trans pf: Brahms) *Concert*
          (5/95) (NAXO) ① 8 550958
Overture Philh, O. Klemperer *Concert*
          (8/92) (EMI) ① CDM7 64143-2
**Iphigénie en Tauride—opera: 4 acts
(1779—Paris)** (Lib. Guillard and Du Roullet)
EXCERPTS: ACT 1: 1. Grands Dieux! soyez-nous
secourables; 2a. Iphigénie, ô ciel!; 2b. Ô songe
affreux!; 3a. Ô race de Pélops; 3b. Ô toi qui
prolongeas mes jours; 3c. Quand verrons-nous tarir
nos pleurs?; 4. Ballet; 5. Il nous fallait du sang. ACT
2: 6a. Quel silence effrayant!; 6b. Dieux qui me
poursuivez; 7a. Quel langage accablant; 7b. Unis dès
la plus tendre enfance; 8a. Dieux! la malheur en tous
lieux suit mes pas; 8b. De noirs pressentiments; 9a.
Les Dieux apaisent leur courroux; 9b. Dieux! étouffez
en moi; 10a. Et vous, à vos Dieux tutélaires; 10b. Il
nous fallait du sang; 11. Etrangers malheureux; 12a.
Dieux protecteurs; 12b. Le calme rentre dans mon
coeur; 13. Vengeons et la nature et le silence; 14. Je
vois toute l'horreur; 15a. Patrie infortunée; 15b. Ô
malheureuse Iphigénie!; 15c. Honorez avec moi ce
héros; 15d. Contemplez ces tristes apprêts; 15e. Ô
mon frère. ACT 3: 16a. Je cède à mon effroi;
D'une image, hélas! trop chérie; 17. Voici ces captifs
malheureux; 18a. Ô joie inattendue!; 18b. Je pourrais
du tyran tromper la barbarie; 19a. Ô moment trop
heureux!; 19b. Et tu prétends encore que tu m'aimes;
19c. Quoi! je ne vaincrai pas; 19d. Ah! mon ami,
j'implore ta pitié!; 19e. Pylade!...Ah! mon ami,
j'implore ta pitié!; 20a. Malgré toi, je saurai t'arracher
au trépas!; 20b. Quoi? toujours à mes voeux; 21a.
Puisque le ciel à vos jours s'intéresse; 21b. Divinité
des grandes âmes; 22a. Non. Cet affreux devoir; 22b.
Je t'implore et je tremble; 23a. Ô Diane, sois-nous
propice; 23b. La force m'abandonne; 23c. Chaste fille
de Latone; 23d. Quel moment! Dieux puissants; 24.
Tremblez! tremblez!; 25. De tes forfaits la trame est
découverte; 26. Qu'oses-tu proposer, barbare?; 27.
C'est à toi de mourir!; 28. Arrêtez! écoutez mes
decrets éternels; 29a. Ta soeur qu'ai-je entendu?;
29b. Dans cet objet touchant; 29c. Les Dieux,
longtemps en courroux.
Cpte D. Montague, J. Aler, T. Allen, N. Argenta, S.
Boulton, C. Alliot-Lugaz, R. Massis, Monteverdi Ch,
Lyon Op Orch, J.E. Gardiner (r1985)
          (6/86) (PHIL) ① [2] 416 148-2PH2
Cpte P. Lorengar, F. Bonisolli, W. Grönroos, A.J.
Smith, S. Klare, A. Nowski, D. Fischer-Dieskau,
Bavarian Rad Chor, BRSO, L. Gardelli (r1982)
          (12/87) (ORFE) ① [2] C052832H
Cpte C. Vaness, G. Winbergh, T. Allen, A. Zoroberto,
M. Remor, S. Brunet, G. Surian, A. Veccia, E. Turco,
S. Krasteva, La Scala Chor, La Scala Orch, R. Muti
(pp1992)   (10/93) (SONY) ① [2] S2K52492
3b K. Te Kanawa, ROHO, J. Tate *Concert*
          (2/90) (EMI) ① CDC7 49863-2
8b V. Maurel, anon (r1903) *Concert*
          (10/92) (SYMP) ① SYMCD1101
15b M. Callas, Paris Cons, G. Prêtre *Concert*
          (2/88) (EMI) ① CDC7 49059-2
15b M. Callas, Paris Cons, G. Prêtre *Concert*
          (2/90) (EMI) ① [4] CMS7 63244-2

**Orfeo ed Euridice—opera: 3 acts
(1762—Vienna)** (Lib. Calzabigi. Italian version
of Orphée et Eurydice)
EXCERPTS: ACT 1: 1a. Overture; 1b.
Introduction...Ah! se intorno; 2. Amici, quel lamento;
3. Pantomime; 4. Ah! se intorno; 5. Restar vogl'io; 6.
Ritornello; 7. Chiamo il mio ben; 8. Euridice, Euridice;
9. Cerco il mio ben; 10. Euridice! Euridice!; 11.
Piango il mio ben; 12. O Numi, barbari Numi; 13. Se il
dolce suon; 14. Ciel! rivederla potrò!; 15. Gli sguardi
trattieni; 16. Che disse!; 17. Addio, addio. ACT 2: 18.
Danza in E flat; 19. Chi mai dell'Erebo; 20. Ballo in C
minor; 21. Chi mai dell'Erebo; 22. Deh! placetevi; 23.
Misero giovine!; 24. Mille pene; 25. Ah! quale
incognito affetto; 26. Men tiranno; 27. Ah! quale
incognito affetto; 28. Dance of the Furies; 29. Ballet
in F; 30. Ballet in D minor (Dance of the Blessed
Spirits): (flute solo); 31. Ballet in C; 32. Questo asilo;
33. Che puro ciel!; 34. Vieni ai regni; 35. Dance of
heroes; 36. Oh voi, eternal felici; 37. Torna, o bella. ACT
3: 38. Vieni! segui i miei passi; 39. Vieni appaga il tuo
consorte; 40. Qual vita; 41. Che fiero momento; 42.
Ecco novel tormento; 43. Che farò senza Euridice;
44. Ah! finisca e per sempre; 45. Trionfi Amore; 46.
Grazioso; 47. Gavotte; 48. Ballet; 49. Minuet; 50.
Divo Amore; 51. Ballet in A; 52. Ballet in D; 53.
Ciaccona in D.
Cpte M. Horne, P. Lorengar, H. Donath, ROH Chor,
ROHO, G. Solti
          (8/89) (DECC) ① [2] 417 410-2DM2
Cpte R. Jacobs, M. Kweksilber, M. Falewicz, Ghent
Collegium Vocale, Petite Bande, S. Kuijken (Ed.
Andriessen & S. Kuijken)
          (1/90) (ACCE) ① [2] ACC48223/4D
Cpte J. Kowalski, D. Schellenberger, C. Fliegner,
Berlin Rad Chor, CPE Bach Orch, Hans Haenchen
          (1/90) (CAPR) ① [2] 60 008-2
Cpte S. Verrett, A. Moffo, J. Raskin, Rome
Polyphonic Chor, Virtuosi di Roma, R. Fasano
          (1/91) (RCA) ① [2] GD87896
Cpte A. Baltsa, M. Marshall, E. Gruberová,
Ambrosian Op Chor, Philh, R. Muti
          (3/91) (EMI) ① [2] CMS7 63637-2
Cpte M. Chance, N. Argenta, S. Beckerbauer,
Stuttgart Chbr Ch, Tafelmusik, F. Bernius
          (8/92) (SONY) ① [2] SX2K48040
Cpte M. Forrester, T. Stich-Randall, H. Steffek,
Vienna Academy Ch, Vienna St Op Orch, C.
Mackerras   (12/92) (VANG) ① [2] 08.4040.72
Cpte J. Baker, E. Speiser, E. Gale, Glyndebourne
Fest Chor, LPO, R. Leppard
          (5/93) (ERAT) ① [2] 2292-45864-2
Cpte G. Simionato, S. Jurinac, G. Sciutti, Vienna St
Op Chor, VPO, H. von Karajan (pp1959)
          (11/93) (DG) ① [2] 439 101-2GX2
Cpte D.L. Ragin, S. McNair, C. Sieden, Monteverdi
Ch, EBS, J.E. Gardiner (r1991)
          (2/94) (PHIL) ① [2] 434 093-2PH2
Cpte J. Bowman, L. Dawson, C. McFadden, Namur
Chbr Ch, Grande Ecurie, J-C. Malgoire (pp1994)
          (1/95) (ASTR) ① [2] E8538
Cpte D. Fischer-Dieskau, M. Stader, R. Streich,
Berlin RIAS Chbr Ch, Berlin Motet Ch, Berlin RSO, F.
Fricsay (r1956: Ger)
          (2/95) (DG) ① [2] 439 711-2GX2
4, 8, 11, 15, 16, 19, 22, 23, 33, 34, 38, 39, 41, 43-45.
K. Ferrier, A. Ayars, Z. Vlachopoulos, Glyndebourne
Fest Chor, Southern PO, F. Stiedry (r1947)
          (6/92) (DECC) ① 433 468-2DM
7, 22, 33, 43. K. Ferrier, Netherlands Op Chor,
Netherlands Op Orch, C. Bruck (r1951) *Concert*
          (6/88) (EMI) ① CDH7 61003-2
11, 43. M. Klose, Berlin St Op Orch, B. Seidler-
Winkler (r1938: Ger) *Concert*
          (7/95) (PREI) ① 89082
16, 17. J. Baker, LPO, R. Leppard (pp1982) *Concert*
          (10/95) (BBCR) ① [2] DMCD98
16, 17, 31, 33, 43. C. Watkinson, Amsterdam Bach
Sols, J.W. de Vriend *Concert*
          (3/89) (ETCE) ① KTC1064
28, 30. S. Preston, AAM, C. Hogwood *Concert*
          (12/83) (L'OI) ① 410 553-2OH
28, 30. I. Biret (trans Kempff) *Concert*
          (5/93) (MARC) ① 8 223452
28, 30. Calgary PO, M. Bernardi (1992) *Concert*
          (12/94) (CBC) ① SMCD5125
30. P-L. Graf, Zurich Camerata, R. Tschupp *Concert*
          (11/87) (JECK) ① JD506-2
30. RLPO, C. Groves *Concert*
          (1/89) (EMIL) ① CDZ114
30. M. Hambourg (r1929: arr pf: Sgambati) *Concert*
          (4/89) (OPAL) ① OPALCD9839
30. ASMF, N. Marriner *Concert*
          (11/89) (CFP) ① CD-CFP4557
30. NYPSO, A. Toscanini (r1929) *Concert*
          (3/90) (PEAR) ① [3] GEMMCDS9373

GODARD, Robert (c1536–c1560) France

SECTION III: INSTRUMENTAL

Ce mois de May—lute (intabulation P. Phalese)
L. Kirchhof *Concert*   (11/92) (SONY) ① **SK48068**

GODEFROID, Félix (1818–1897) Belgium

SECTION III: INSTRUMENTAL

Bois solitaire, 'Romance sans paroles'—harp
S. Drake *Concert*   (9/86) (HYPE) ① **CDA66038**
Etude de concert in E flat minor—harp, Op. 193
S. Drake *Concert*   (9/86) (HYPE) ① **CDA66038**
T. Owen *Concert*   (3/87) (CARL) ① **PCD835**

GODEFROY DE ST VICTOIRE (fl 1170–1190)

SECTION IV: VOCAL AND CHORAL

Planctus ante nescia—complaint
Hilliard Ens *Concert*   (6/91) (HYPE) ① **CDA66370**

GODOLIN, Pierre (c1610) France

SECTION IV: VOCAL AND CHORAL

Sur l'arbre de la Crotz
A. Azéma (r1994) *Concert*
     (11/95) (ERAT) ① **4509-98480-2**

GODOWSKY, Leopold (1870–1938) Poland/USA

SECTION II: CHAMBER

The Hunter's Call, 'Woodland Mood'—piano duet
L. Godowsky, L. Godowsky II (r1921) *Concert*
     (4/89) (APR) ① [2] **APR7011**

SECTION III: INSTRUMENTAL

Humoresque—piano
L. Godowsky (r1920) *Concert*
     (4/89) (APR) ① [2] **APR7011**
12 Impressions—piano (1916)
1. Légende; 2. Poème (Andante cantabile); 3. Perpetuum mobile; 4. Élégie; 5. Valse; 6. Oriental; 7. Tyrolean (Schuhplatter); 8. Larghetto lamentoso; 9. Profile (Chopin); 10. Saga; 11. Viennese (Wienerisch); 12. Valse macabre.
G. Schneider, C. Garben
     (8/89) (ETCE) ① **KTC1067**
5. J. Heifetz, S. Chotzinoff (r1920) *Concert*
     (11/94) (RCA) ① [65] **09026 61778-2(01)**
11. J. Heifetz, M. Kaye (r1944) *Concert*
     (11/94) (RCA) ① [65] **09026 61778-2(19)**
12. F. Kreisler, C. Lamson (arr Kreisler: vn/pf; r1916)
Concert   (1/90) (PEAR) ① **GEMMCD9324**
Java Suite—piano
The Gardens of Buitenzorg S. Hough (r1986)
Concert   (1/89) (VIRG) ① **VC7 59509-2**
The Gardens of Buitenzorg L. Godowsky (r1935/6)
Concert   (4/89) (APR) ① [2] **APR7011**
Paraphrase on Johann Strauss's 'Künstlerleben'—piano
E. Wild *Concert*   (8/92) (VANG) ① **08.4033.71**
Passacaglia—44 variations, cadenza and fugue on the opening of Schubert's 'Unfinished' S—piano (1927)
R. de Waal *Concert*   (3/92) (HYPE) ① **CDA66496**
Potpourri on Johann Strauss's 'Die Fledermaus'—piano
B. Moiseiwitsch (r1928) *Concert*
     (10/91) (KOCH) ① **37035-2**
Renaissance—piano
6. Tambourin, E minor (Rameau); 8. Pastorale, G (Corelli); 12. Gigue, E (Loeillet).
6, 12. S. Barere (r1934) *Concert*
     (5/91) (APR) ① [2] **APR7001**
6, 8, 12. S. Barere (pp1947) *Concert*
     (11/89) (APR) ① [2] **APR7008**
53 Studies on Chopin Etudes—piano (1900-14)
EXCERPTS: 1. Op 10/1 in C (diatonic); 2. Op 10/1 in D flat (left hand); 3. Op 10/2 in A minor (left hand); 4. Op 10/2 in A minor ('Ignis fatuus'); 5. Op 10/3 in D flat (left hand); 6. Op 10/4 in C sharp minor (left hand); 7. Op 10/5 in G flat; 8. Op 10/5 in C; 9. Op

10/5 in A minor ('Tarantella'); 10. Op 10/5 in A ('Capriccio'); 11. Op 10/5 in G flat; 12. Op 10/5 in G flat; 12a. Op 10/5 in G flat (left hand); 13. Op 10/6 in E flat minor; 14. Op 10/7 in C; 15. Op 10/7 in G flat; 15a. Op 10/7 in E flat (left hand); 16. Op 10/8 in F; 16a. Op 10/8 in G flat (left hand); 17. Op 10/9 in C sharp minor; 18. Op 10/9 in F minor (imitation of Op 25/2); 18a. Op 10/9 in F sharp minor (left hand); 19. Op 10/10 in D; 20. Op 10/10 in A flat (left hand); 22. Op 10/12 in C sharp minor (left hand); 25. Op 25/1 in A flat; 27. Op 25/2 in C minor ('Waltz'); 32. Op 25/4 in F minor ('Polonaise'); 34. Op 25/5 in C sharp minor ('Mazurka'); 36. Op 25/6 in G sharp minor ('Study in Thirds'); 38. Op 25/8 in D flat ('Study in Sixths'); 42. Op 25/11 in A minor; 45. Nouvelle Etude 2 in E; 46. Nouvelle Etude 3 in G ('Menuetto'); 47. Op 10/5 in G flat ('Badinage'); 48. Op 10/11 & Op 25/3 in F.
1, 4, 5, 13, 15, 17, 22, 25, 27, 32, 34, 36, 38, 42, 45, 46, 47, 48. I. Hobson   (2/88) (ARAB) ① **Z6537**
Triakontameron—30 moods and scenes in triple time: piano (1920)
BOOK 1: 1. Nacht in Tanger (Night in Tangiers); 2. Wald in Tirol (Forest in the Tyrol); 3. Paradoxe Stimmungen (Paradoxical Moods); 4. Rendezvous; 5. Dämmerungerscheinungen (Twilight). BOOK 2 : 6. Der flehende Troubadour (The Imploring Troubadour); 7. Vergangene Jahre... (Lost Years...); 8. Eine Watteau-Landschaft (A Watteau Landscape); 9. Das verzauberte Tal (The Enchanted Glen); 10. Resignation. BOOK 3: 11. Alt Wien (Old Vienna); 12. Äthopische Serenade (Ethopian Serenade); 13. Vindobona tanzt (Vindobona Dances); 14. Schaumwellen (Foaming Waves); 15. Die Verführerin (The Seductress). BOOK 4: 16. Eine alte Ballade (An Old Ballad); 17. Ein amerikanisches Idyll (An American Idyll); 18. Anachronismus (Anachronism); 19. Ein kleiner Tangotanz (A Little Tango Dance); 20. Tanzende Derwische (Whirling Dervishes). BOOK 5: 21. In Salon (In the Salon); 22. Ein Gedicht (A Poem); 23. Spieldose (Music box); 24. Wiegenlied (Lullaby); 25. Erinnerungen (Memories). BOOK 6: 26. Die Kuckucksuhr (The Cuckoo Clock); 27. Klage (Lament); 28. Don Quixote Irrfahrten (The Wanderings of Don Quixote); 29. Totengedicht (Death Poem); 30. Requiem (1914-18: Epilog).
11. J. Heifetz, E. Bay (arr Heifetz; r1932) *Concert*
     (12/91) (APR) ① [2] **APR7015**
11. R. de Waal *Concert*
     (3/92) (HYPE) ① **CDA66496**
11. G. Fergus-Thompson *Concert*
     (10/92) (ASV) ① **CDWHL2066**
11. J. Heifetz, E. Bay (r1946) *Concert*
     (11/94) (RCA) ① [65] **09026 61778-2(40)**
11. J. Heifetz, A. Sándor (r1934) *Concert*
     (11/94) (RCA) ① [65] **09026 61778-2(02)**
11. V. Spivakov, S. Bezrodny (r1991-2; arr Heifetz)
Concert   (5/95) (RCA) ① **09026 62524-2**

GOEDICKE, Alexandr (1877–1957) Russia

SECTION II: CHAMBER

Concert Etude—trumpet and piano, Op. 49 (originally for trumpet and orchestra)
J. Wallace, S. Wright (r1993) *Concert*
     (11/94) (EMI) ① **CDC5 55086-2**

GOEHR, (Peter) Alexander (b 1932) England

SECTION I: ORCHESTRAL

... a musical offering (J.S.B. 1985) ..., Op. 46 (1985)
London Sinfonietta, O. Knussen *Concert*
     (11/91) (UNIC) ① **DKPCD9102**
Concerto for Piano and Orchestra, Op. 33 (1972)
P. Serkin, London Sinfonietta, O. Knussen (pp1993)
Symphony No. 29.   (8/95) (NMC) ① **NMCD023**
Lyric Pieces—wind quintet, trumpet, trombone and double bass, Op. 35 (1974)
London Sinfonietta, O. Knussen *Concert*
     (11/91) (UNIC) ① **DKPCD9102**
Metamorphosis Dance—cello and orchestra, Op. 36 (1973-74)
RLPO, D. Atherton *Romanza, Op.24.*
     (7/91) (UNIC) ① **UKCD2039**
Romanza—cello and orchestra, Op. 24 (1968)
M. Welsh, RLPO, D. Atherton *Metamorphosis, Op.36.*
     (7/91) (UNIC) ① **UKCD2039**
Sinfonia, Op. 42 (1980)
London Sinfonietta, O. Knussen *Concert*
     (11/91) (UNIC) ① **DKPCD9102**

Symphony in One Movement, Op. 29 (1969 rev 1981)
BBC Scottish SO, R. Bernas (r1992) *Piano Concerto.*
     (8/95) (NMC) ① **NMCD023**

SECTION IV: VOCAL AND CHORAL

Behold the Sun—concert aria: soprano and vibraphone obbligato, Op. 44a (1981) (Wds. J. McGrath)
J. Thames, J. Holland, London Sinfonietta, O. Knussen *Concert*   (11/91) (UNIC) ① **DKPCD9102**
The Death of Moses—5vv, chorus and 13 instruments, Op. 51 (1991-92) (Wds. J. Hollander)
M. Chance, S. Leonard, G. Rangarajan, S. Richardson, P. Robinson, Sawston Village College Chbr Ch, Cambs Children's Ch, CUMS, Ens, S. Cleobury (1993)   (12/93) (UNIC) ① **DKPCD9146**
The Mouse Metemorphosed into a Maid—unaccompanied voice, Op. 54 (1991) (Wds. M. Moore, after La Fontaine)
L. Shelton *Sing. Ariel, Op. 51.*
     (9/93) (UNIC) ① **DKPCD9129**
Sing, Ariel—principal soprano, 2 sops and 5 instruments, Op. 51 (1989-90) (Wds. F. Kermode)
L. Shelton, E. Hulse, S. Leonard, D. White, J. Wallace, M. Crayford, C-C. Nwanoku, O. Knussen *Mouse Metamorphosed, Op. 54.*
     (9/93) (UNIC) ① **DKPCD9129**

GOETZ, Hermann (Gustav) (1840–1876) Germany

SECTION I: ORCHESTRAL

Concerto for Piano and Orchestra No. 2 in B flat, Op. 18 (1867)
M. Ponti, Luxembourg RSO, P. Cao *Sinding: Piano Concerto.*   (5/93) (VOX) ① **115715-2**

SECTION II: CHAMBER

Sonata for Piano Duet in G minor, Op. 17 (1867)
A. Goldstone, C. Clemmow *Concert*
     (7/93) (MERI) ① **CDE84237**

SECTION V: STAGE WORKS

Widerspenstigen Zähmung—opera: 4 acts (1874—Mannheim) (Lib. J. V. Widmann, after Shakespeare)
Es schweige die Klage Lotte Lehmann, orch (r1919)
Concert   (6/92) (PREI) ① [3] **89302**

GOFFIN, John Dean (b 1909) New Zealand

SECTION I: ORCHESTRAL

Rhapsody in Brass—brass band (1942)
Britannia Building Soc Band, H. Snell (r1990) *Concert*
     (8/92) (DOYE) ① **DOYCD004**

GOLDEN, John L. (19th–20th Cent) USA

SECTION IV: VOCAL AND CHORAL

You Can't Play Every Instrument in the Band—song from the show 'Sunshine Girl' (1913) (Lyrics Joseph Cawthorn)
J. Cawthorn, Orig Broadway Cast (r1913) *Concert*
     (5/94) (PEAR) ① [3] **GEMMCDS9056/8**

SECTION V: STAGE WORKS

Sybil—musical show (1916—New York) (Lyrics Joseph Cawthorn)
EXCERPTS: 1. I Can Dance with Everybody But My Wife.
1. J. Cawthorn, Orig Broadway Cast (r1916) *Concert*
     (5/94) (PEAR) ① [3] **GEMMCDS9056/8**

GOLDENTHAL, Elliot B. (b 1954) USA

SECTION V: STAGE WORKS

Demolition Man—film score (1993)
EXCERPTS: 1. Dies Irae; 2. Fire Fight; 3. Guilty As Charged; 4. Action, Guns, Fun; 5. Machine Waltz; 6. Defrosting; 7. Tracking the Chief; 8. Museum Dis Duel; 9. Subterranean Slugfest; 10. Meeting Cocteau; 11. Tracking Simon Phoenix; 12. Obligatory Car Chase; 13. Flawless Pearl; 14. Final Confrontation; 15. Code; 16. Silver Screen Kiss.
1-16. OST, J. Sheffer, A. Kane (1993)
     (8/94) (VARE) ① **VSD5447**

Golden Gate—film score (1993)
EXCERPTS: 1. Golden Gate; 2. The Woman Cries;
3. Between Bridge and Water; 4. Tender Deception;
5. Bopathonix Hex; 6. The Woman Warrior; 7. The
Softest Heart; 8. The Moon Watches; 9. Whisper
Dance; 10. Kwan Ying; 11. Motel Street Meltdown;
12. Judgment On Mason Street; 13. Write It As Time;
14. Between Bridge and Sky.
1-14. OST, PAO, J. Sheffer (r1993)
(8/94) (VARE) ① **VSD5470**

**GOLDENWEISER, Alexander
Borisovich *(1875–1961) Russia***

SECTION III: INSTRUMENTAL

**Kabardino-Balkarsky Songs and
Dance—piano**
A. Goldenweiser (r1949) *Concert*
(8/95) (MELO) ① **74321 25173-2**
A. Goldenweiser (r1949) *Concert*
(8/95) (MELO) ① **[11] 74321 25172-1(1)**

**GOLDMARK, Károly *(1830–1915)
Austro-Hungary***

SECTION I: ORCHESTRAL

**Concerto for Violin and Orchestra No. 1 in A
minor, Op. 28 (pub 1877)**
I. Perlman, Pittsburgh SO, A. Previn *Korngold: Violin
Concerto.* (2/88) (EMI) ① **CDC7 47846-2**
N. Milstein, Philh, H. Blech (r1957: includes reh
takes) *Lalo: Symphonie espagnole.*
(11/95) (TEST) ① **SBT1047**
N-Y. Hu, Seattle SO, G. Schwarz (r1993/4) *Bruch:
Violin Concerto 2.* (12/95) (DELO) ① **DE3156**
Movt 2. J. Heifetz, orch, J. Pasternack (r1920)
Concert (11/94) (RCA) ① **[65] 09026 61778-2(01)**
**Der Gefesselte Prometheus—Symphonic
poem, Op. 38 (1889)**
Philh, Y. Butt (r1994) *Concert*
(11/95) (ASV) ① **CDDCA934**
**Im Frühling—Symphonic poem, Op. 36
(1888)**
Chicago SO, F. Stock (r1925) *Concert*
(2/95) (BIDD) ① **[2] WHL021/2**
Ireland National SO, S. Gunzenhauser (r1993)
Concert (12/95) (NAXO) ① **8 550745**
In Italien—Symphonic poem, Op. 49 (1904)
Philh, Y. Butt (r1994) *Concert*
(11/95) (ASV) ① **CDDCA934**
Ireland National SO, S. Gunzenhauser (r1993)
Concert (12/95) (NAXO) ① **8 550745**
**Ländliche Hochzeit (Rustic
Wedding)—symphonic poem, Op. 26 (1877)**
RPO, Y. Butt *Sakuntala.*
(5/92) (ASV) ① **CDDCA791**
Utah SO, M. Abravanel (r1964)
(4/93) (VANG) ① **08.9051.71**
Ireland National SO, S. Gunzenhauser (r1993)
Concert (12/95) (NAXO) ① **8 550745**
Penthisilea Overture, Op. 31 (1879)
Rhenish PO, M. Halász (r1985) *Symphony 2.*
(8/87) (MARC) ① **8 220417**
Sakuntala Overture, Op. 13 (1865)
RPO, Y. Butt *Rustic wedding.*
(5/92) (ASV) ① **CDDCA791**
Symphony No. 2 in E flat, Op. 35 (1887)
Rhenish PO, M. Halász (r1985) *Penthisilea Ov.*
(8/87) (MARC) ① **8 220417**
Philh, Y. Butt (r1994) *Concert*
(11/95) (ASV) ① **CDDCA934**

SECTION V: STAGE WORKS

**Das Heimchen am Herd—opera: 3 acts
(1896—Vienna)** (Lib. A M Willner, after
Dickens)
EXCERPTS: 1. Ein Geheimnis wundersüss; 2. Ach,
das ist herrlich.
1, 2. M. Jeritza, orch (r1914) *Concert*
(4/94) (PREI) ① **89079**
**Die Königin von Saba—opera: 4 acts, Op. 27
(1879—Vienna)** (Lib. Mosenthal)
EXCERPTS—ACT 1: 1. Dein Freund ist dein
(Sulamith & Chorus); 2a. Am Fuss des Libanon
(Assad); 2b. Da plätschert eine Silberquelle; 3.
March; 4. Ballet Music. ACT 2: 5. Aus dem Jubels
Festgepränge (Queen); 6. Magische Töne (Assad); 7.
Blick empor zu jenen Räumen! (Solomon). ACT 3: 8.
Ballet Music; 9a. Dieser Augenblick, die ihn mir geraubt
(Sulamith); 9b. Doch eh! ich in des Todes Tal
(Sulamith). ACT4: 10a. Komm, Tod, geendet sind
die Qualen (Assad); 10b. Du Ew'ger, der mein Aug'
gelichtet (Assad).

2b L. Slezak, orch (r1905) *Concert*
(2/91) (PREI) ① **89020**
6. E. Caruso, orch (r1909: Ital) *Concert*
(10/89) (NIMB) ① **NI7803**
6. E. Caruso, orch (Ital: r1909) *Concert*
(3/91) (PEAR) ① **[3] EVC2**
6. E. Caruso, orch, W.B. Rogers (r1909: Ital) *Concert*
(7/91) (RCA) ① **[12] GD60495(3)**
6. L. Slezak, orch (r1909) *Concert*
(9/94) (NIMB) ① **NI7856**
10b L. Slezak, orch (r1908) *Concert*
(2/91) (PREI) ① **89020**

**GOLDSCHMIDT, Berthold *(b 1903)
Germany/England***

SECTION I: ORCHESTRAL

Ciaconna sinfonica—orchestra (1930s)
Magdeburg PO, M. Husmann (r1994) *Concert*
(7/95) (CPO) ① **CPO999 277-2**
Concerto for Cello and Orchestra (1953)
D. Geringas, Magdeburg PO, M. Husmann (r1994)
Concert (7/95) (CPO) ① **CPO999 277-2**

SECTION II: CHAMBER

Encore—violin & piano (1993)
H. Schneeberger, K. Lessing (r1994) *Concert*
(3/95) (LARG) ① **Largo 5128**
**Quartet—clarinet, violin, viola and cello
(1982-83)**
I. Hausmann, Mandelring Qt *Concert*
(11/92) (LARG) ① **Largo 5117**
Retrospectrum—string trio (1992)
Gaede Trio (pp1993) *Concert*
(3/95) (LARG) ① **Largo 5128**
String Quartet No. 1, Op. 8 (1925)
Mandelring Qt *Concert*
(11/92) (LARG) ① **Largo 5117**
String Quartet No. 2 (1936)
Mandelring Qt *Concert*
(11/91) (LARG) ① **Largo 5115**
String Quartet No. 3 (1989)
Mandelring Qt *Concert*
(11/91) (LARG) ① **Largo 5115**
String Quartet No. 4 (1992)
Mandelring Qt (r1994) *Concert*
(3/95) (LARG) ① **Largo 5128**

SECTION III: INSTRUMENTAL

Capriccio—piano Op. 11 (1927)
K. Lessing (r1994) *Concert*
(3/95) (LARG) ① **Largo 5128**
Capriccio—violin (1991-2)
K. Lessing (r1994) *Concert*
(3/95) (LARG) ① **Largo 5128**
From the Ballet—piano (1957) (arr cpsr from
ballet Chronica, 1938)
K. Lessing (r1994) *Concert*
(3/95) (LARG) ① **Largo 5128**
Little Legend—piano (1957) (arr cpsr from
Suite for Orchestra, 1928)
K. Lessing (r1994) *Concert*
(3/95) (LARG) ① **Largo 5128**
Scherzo—piano (1922, rev 1958)
K. Lessing (r1994) *Concert*
(3/95) (LARG) ① **Largo 5128**
Sonata—piano, Op. 10 (1926)
K. Lessing (r1994) (11/92) (LARG) ① **Largo 5117**
**Variations on a Palestinian Shepherd's
Song—piano, Op. 32 (1934)**
K. Lessing (r1994) *Concert*
(3/95) (LARG) ① **Largo 5128**

SECTION IV: VOCAL AND CHORAL

Belsatzar—chorus a capella (1985) (Wds.
Heine)
Berlin Ars-Nova Ens, P. Schwarz *Concert*
(11/91) (LARG) ① **Largo 5115**
Clouds—song: 1v and piano
I. Vermillion, B. Goldschmidt (r1994) *Concert*
(7/95) (SONY) ① **[2] S2K66836**
**Letzte Kapitel, 'Final Chapters'—narr, chbr
ch, pf & perc (1931)** (Wds. Kästner)
1. A masked ball in the mountains; 2. The final
chapter.
Berlin Ars-Nova Ens, A. Marks, P. Schwarz *Concert*
(11/91) (LARG) ① **Largo 5115**
**Mediterranean Songs—1v and orchestra
(1958)** (Wds. various)
Cpte J. M. Ainsley, Leipzig Gewandhaus, L.
Zagrosek (r1992) *Gewaltige Hahnrei.*
(3/94) (DECC) ① **[2] 440 850-2DHO2**
Nebelweben—Lied: 1v and piano
I. Vermillion, B. Goldschmidt (r1994) *Concert*
(7/95) (SONY) ① **[2] S2K66836**

2 Psalmen—tenor & strings (1935)
1. Psalm 120, 'Ich rufe zu dem Herrn'; 2. Psalm 124,
'Wo der Herr nicht bei uns wäre'.
E. Wottrich, Berlin RSO, B. Goldschmidt (r1994)
Concert (7/95) (LARG) ① **[2] Largo5130**
Ein Rosenzweig—Lied: 1v and piano
I. Vermillion, B. Goldschmidt (r1994) *Concert*
(7/95) (SONY) ① **[2] S2K66836**
Time—song: 1v and piano
I. Vermillion, B. Goldschmidt (r1994) *Concert*
(7/95) (SONY) ① **[2] S2K66836**

SECTION V: STAGE WORKS

**Beatrice Cenci—opera: 3 acts
(1988—London)** (Lib. M Esslin, after P B
Shelley)
Cpte S. Estes, D. Jones, R. Alexander, F. Kimm, P.
Rose, E. Wottrich, S. Lorenz, R. Beyer, S. Stoll, J. D.
de Haan, I. Bostridge, Berlin Rad Chor, Berlin
Deutsches SO, L. Zagrosek (r1994) *Concert*
(7/95) (SONY) ① **[2] S2K66836**
Chronica—concert suite from ballet (1950s)
EXCERPTS: 1. Prologue: Intrada—Marche militaire
(1932); 2. Passacaglia (Prison yard); 3. Rondine
(Ballroom scene); 4. Cantilena; 5. Scherzo
(Propaganda); 6. Intermedio; 7. Canone; 8. Capriccio
(Finale).
Magdeburg PO, M. Husmann (r1994) *Concert*
(7/95) (CPO) ① **CPO999 277-2**
**Der gewaltige Hahnrei—Musikalische
Tragikomodie: 3 acts, Op. 14
(1932—Mannheim)** (Lib. after F.
Crommelynck)
Cpte R. Alexander, R. Wörle, M. Kraus, C. Otelli, H.
Lawrence, M. Petzold, E. Wottrich, M. Posselt, C.
Berggold, F-J. Kapellmann, Berlin Rad Chor, Berlin
Deutsches SO, L. Zagrosek (r1992) *Mediterranean
Songs.* (3/94) (DECC) ① **[2] 440 850-2DHO2**

**GOLDSCHMIDT, Otto (Moritz
David) *(1829–1907) Germany***

SECTION IV: VOCAL AND CHORAL

A Tender shoot—carol (Wds. W
Bartholomew, after cpsr)
Canterbury Cath Ch, M. Harris, A. Wicks *Concert*
(12/87) (CONI) ① **CDCF160**

GOLDSMITH, Jerry *(b 1929) USA*

SECTION V: STAGE WORKS

Alien—film score (1979)
EXCERPTS: 1. Main Title; 2. Face Hugger; 3.
Breakaway; 4. Acid Test; 5. The Landing; 6. The
Droid; 7. The Recovery; 8. The Alien Planet; 9. The
Shaft; 10. End Title.
Cpte National PO, W. Motzing (r1993) *Concert*
(8/94) (SILV) ① **FILMCD146**
Angie—film score (1994)
EXCERPTS: 1. Angie's Theme; 2. Shopping; 3.
Family Life; 4. The Museum; 5. Two Bells; 6. We're
Having A Baby; 7. The Prognosis; 8. The Journey
Begins; 9. Something Better; 10. Is It Ain't Easy; 11.
He's Alive; 12. Angie's Theme (Reprise); 13. Thais
(Massenet).
1-13. OST, J. Goldsmith (r1994)
(8/94) (VARE) ① **VSD5469**
The Blue Max—film score (1966)
EXCERPTS: 1. The Blue Max (Main Title); 2. The
New Arrival; 3. A Toast to Bruno; 4. First Blood; 5.
First Victory; 6. The Captive; 7. The Victim; 8. The
Cobra; 9. The Attack; 10. A Small Favor; 11. Love
Theme; 12. The Rivals; 13. Finale to Part 1; 14.
Prelude to Part 2; 15. Love Theme; 16. The Bridge;
17. Love Theme; 18. Retreat; 19. Stachel to Berlin;
20. Nothing Needed; 21. Kaeti has a Plan; 22.
Stachel's Last Flight; 23. End Title. SOURCE MUSIC:
24. Pour le Merite (Traditional); 25. Presentiar March
(Traditional); 26. Student Song Medley (Traditional);
27. Artist's Life (J. Strauss II); 28. Gloria March (G.
Piefke); 29. Deutschland über Alles (after Haydn); 30.
Watch on the Rhine (K. Wilhelm).
1-30. OST, National PO, J. Goldsmith (r1966)
(9/95) (COLU) ① **JK57890**
The Chairman—film score (1969)
OST, J. Goldsmith (r1969) *Ransom.*
(4/92) (SILV) ① **FILMCD081**
Explorers—film score (1985)
EXCERPTS: 1. The Construction.
1. Prague City PO, W. Motzing (r1993) *Concert*
(8/94) (SILV) ① **FILMCD146**

Gremlins 2: The New Batch—film score (1990)
EXCERPTS: 1. End Title.
1. Prague City PO, W. Motzing (r1993) *Concert*
(8/94) (SILV) ① **FILMCD146**

The Illustrated Man—film score (1968)
EXCERPTS: 1. Main Title; 2. Frightened Willie.
1, 2. Prague City PO, W. Motzing (r1993) *Concert*
(8/94) (SILV) ① **FILMCD146**

In Harm's Way—film score (1965)
EXCERPTS: 1. Prelude: The Rock; 2. Intermezzo: The Rock and His Lady/Love Theme; 3. Finale: First Victory.
1, 3. Prague City PO, P. Bateman (r1994; arr J. Bell) *Concert*
(11/94) (SILV) ① **FILMCD151**
1-3. Prague City PO, P. Bateman (r1994; arr Bell) *Concert*
(11/94) (SILV) ① **FILMCD153**

King Solomon's Mines—film score (1985)
EXCERPTS: 1. Main Title; 2. Welcoming Committee; 3. No Sale; 4. The Mummy; 5. Have a Cigar; 6. Good Morning; 7. Under the Train; 8. Dancing Shots; 9. Pain; 10. Forced Flight; 11. The Chieftain; 12. Pot Luck; 13. Upside Down People; 14. The Crocodiles; 15. The Mines; 16. The Ritual/Low Bridge; 17. Falling Rocks/No Diamonds.
1-17. OST, Hungarian St Op Orch, J. Goldsmith (r1985) (5/93) (SILV) ① **FILMCD045**

Legend—film score (1985) (partially used in European release only)
EXCERPTS: 1a. Main Title; 1b. The Goblins; 2a. My True Love's Eyes (Wds. J. Bettis); 2b. The Cottage; 3. The Unicorns; 4a. Living River (Wds. Bettis); 4b. Bumps and Hollows (Wds. Bettis); 4c. The Freeze; 5a. The Faeries; 5b. The Riddle; 6. Sing the Wee (Wds. Bettis); 7. Forgive Me; 8. Faerie Dance; 9. The Armour; 10a. Oona; 10b. The Jewels; 11. The Dress Waltz; 12. Darkness Fails; 13. The Ring; 14. Re-United (Wds. Bettis).
1a, 1b, 2a, 2b, 3, 4a-c, 5a, 5b, 6-9, 10a, 10b, 11-14. OST, National PO, J. Goldsmith (r1985)
(5/93) (SILV) ① **FILMCD045**

Lionheart—film score (1987)
EXCERPTS: 1. The Ceremony; 2. Failed Knight; 3. The Circus; 4. Robert and Blanche; 5. Children in Bondage; 6. The Road from Paris; 7. The Lake; 8. The Banner; 9. The Castle; 10. Mathilda; 11. The Wrong Flag; 12. The Dress; 13. Forest Hunt; 14. Final Fight; 15. King Richard.
1-15. OST, J. Goldsmith (r1987)
(11/94) (VARE) ① **VSD5484**

Macarthur: The Rebel General—film score (1977)
EXCERPTS: 1. March.
1. Prague City PO, P. Bateman (r1994) *Concert*
(11/94) (SILV) ① **FILMCD151**

The Omen—film score (1976)
EXCERPTS: 1. Ave Satani (Main Title); 2. The New Ambassador; 3. Killer's Storm; 4. A Sad Message; 5. The Demise of Mrs Baylock; 6. Don't Let Him; 7. The Piper Dreams (Lyrics Carol Heather); 8. The Fall; 9. Safari Park; 10. The Dog's Attack; 11. The Homecoming; 12. The Altar.
1. Los Angeles Master Chorale, Hollywood Bowl SO, J. Mauceri (r1993) *Concert*
(1/95) (PHIL) ① **442 425-2PH**

Papillon—film score (1973)
EXCERPTS: 1. Papillon Theme; 2. The Camp; 3. Reunion; 4. New Friend; 5. Freedom; 6. Gift From the Sea; 7. Antonio's Death; 8. Cruel Sea; 9. Hospital; 10. Survival.
1-10. OST, J. Goldsmith (r1973)
(12/88) (SILV) ① **FILMCD029**

Patton: Lust for Glory—film score (1969)
EXCERPTS: 1. Main Theme; 2. Battleground; 3. First Battle; 4. Attack; 5. Funeral; 6. Winter March; 7. Patton March; 8. No Assignment; 9. German Advice; 10. Hospital; 11. Payoff; 12. End Title; 13. Patton's Speech.
7. Prague City PO, P. Bateman (r1994) *Concert*
(11/94) (SILV) ① **FILMCD151**

The Planet of the Apes—film score (1968)
EXCERPTS: 1. Main Title; 2. The Revelation; 3. The Clothes Snatchers; 4. The Hunt; 5. New Identity; 6. The Forbidden Zone; 7. The Search; 8. The Cave; 9. A Bid for Freedom; 10. A New Mate; 11. No Escape.
1-11. OST, J. Goldsmith (r1968)
(5/93) (INTD) ① **FMT8006D**

Ransom—film score (1975)
OST, J. Goldsmith (r1975) *Chairman.*
(4/92) (SILV) ① **FILMCD081**

Rudy—film score (1993)
EXCERPTS: 1. Main Title; 2. A Start; 3. Waiting; 4. Back on the Field; 5. To Notre Dame; 6. Tryouts; 7. The Key; 8. Take Us Out; 9. The Plaque; 10. The Final Game.

1-10. OST, J. Goldsmith (r1993)
(8/94) (VARE) ① **VSD5446**

Seconds—film score (1966)
EXCERPTS: 1. Main Title; 2. Hamilton's Train Journey; 3. Wilson's Visit to His Wife; 4. Finale.
1-4. Prague City PO, W. Motzing (r1993) *Concert*
(8/94) (SILV) ① **FILMCD146**

Star Trek V, '(The) Final Frontier'—film score (1989)
EXCERPTS: 1. The Mountain; 2. The Barrier; 3. Without Help; 4. A Busy Man; 5. Open the Gates; 6. The Moon's a Window to Heaven (Song); 7. An Angry God; 8. Let's Get Out of Here; 9. Free Minds; 10. Life is a Dream.
1-10. OST, J. Goldsmith (r1989)
(3/90) (EPIC) ① **465925-2**

Supergirl—film score (1984)
EXCERPTS: 1. Overture; 2. Main Title & Argo City; 3. Argo City; 4. The Butterfly; 5. The Journey Begins; 6. Arrival on Earth/Flying Ballet; 7. Chicago Lights/Street Attack; 8. The Superman; 9. A New School; 10. The Map; 11. Spellbound; 12. The Monster Tractor; 13. Flying Ballet (alternative version); 14. The Map (alternate version); 15. The Bracelet; 16. First Kiss/The Monster Storm; 17. 'Where is She?'/The Monster Bumper Cars; 18. The Flying Bumper Car; 19. 'Where's Linda?'; 20. Black Magic; 21. The Phantom Zone; 22. The Vortex/The End of Zaltar; 23. The Final Showdown & Victory/End Title.
1-23. OST, National Phil Chor, National PO, J. Goldsmith (r1984) (10/93) (SILV) ① **FILMCD132**

Total Recall—film score (1990)
EXCERPTS: 1. The Dream (Main Title); 2. The Hologram; 3. The Big Jump; 4. The Mutant; 5. Clever Girl; 6. First Meeting; 7. The Treatment; 8. Where Am I?; 9. End of a Dream; 10. A New Life.
1. Prague City PO, W. Motzing (r1993) *Concert*
(8/94) (SILV) ① **FILMCD146**

Warlock—film score (1989)
EXCERPTS: 1. The Sentence; 2. III Wind; 3. The Ring; 4. The Trance; 5. Old Age; 6. Growing Pains; 7. The Weather Vane; 8. Nails; 9. The Uninvited; 10. Salt Water Attack; 11. Salt Flats.
1-11. OST, Melbourne SO, J. Goldsmith (r1989)
(11/89) (SILV) ① **FILMCD038**

GOLDSMITH, Joel *(20th Cent)* USA

SECTION V: STAGE WORKS

Moon 44—film score (1989)
EXCERPTS: 1. First Training Flight.
1. OST *Concert*
(5/93) (SILV) ① **SILVAD3003**

GOLLAND, John *(b 1942)* England

SECTION I: ORCHESTRAL

Concerto for Euphonium and Brass Band No. 1, Op. 64 (1981)
R. Childs, Britannia Building Soc Band, H. Snell *Concert*
(2/91) (DOYE) ① **DOYCD002**

GOMBERT, Nicolas *(c1495–c1560)* Flanders

SECTION IV: VOCAL AND CHORAL

Ave Maria—motet: 5vv (pub 1539)
Ars Nova, B. Holten *Concert*
(10/90) (KONT) ① **32038**

Ave salus mundi—motet: 6vv
Ars Nova, B. Holten *Concert*
(10/90) (KONT) ① **32038**

Chansons
1. Aime qui vouldra; 2. Quand je suis aupres; 3. Mille regres; 4. Puisqu'ainsi est; 5. Je prens congies; 6. A bien grant tort.
Scholars (r1993) *Concert*
(2/95) (NAXO) ① **8 550880**
3-6. C. Janequin Ens, D. Visse (r1994) *Concert*
(5/95) (HARM) ① **HMC90 1453**

Credo—8vv (pub 1564)
Ars Nova, B. Holten *Concert*
(10/90) (KONT) ① **32038**

In te Domini speravi—motet: 6vv (pub 1549)
Huelgas Ens, P. van Nevel *Concert*
(4/93) (SONY) ① **SK48249**

Je prens congie—chanson: 8vv
Huelgas Ens, P. van Nevel *Concert*
(4/93) (SONY) ① **SK48249**

Lugebat David Absalon—motet: 4vv (also attrib Josquin Desprez)
Ars Nova, B. Holten *Concert*
(5/89) (KONT) ① **32008**

Magnificat I (Primi Toni)—4vv
Ars Nova, B. Holten *Concert*
(10/90) (KONT) ① **32038**

Magnificat II (Secundi Tuni)—2-5vv
Huelgas Ens, P. van Nevel *Concert*
(4/93) (SONY) ① **SK48249**

Magnificat VIII (Octavi Toni)—4vv
Ars Nova, B. Holten *Concert*
(10/90) (KONT) ① **32038**

Media vita—motet: 6vv (pub 1539)
Huelgas Ens, P. van Nevel *Concert*
(4/93) (SONY) ① **SK48249**

Missa Tempore paschali—6vv
Huelgas Ens, P. van Nevel *Concert*
(4/93) (SONY) ① **SK48249**

Musae Jovis—motet: 6vv
Ars Nova, B. Holten *Concert*
(5/89) (KONT) ① **32008**

Regina coeli—Marian antiphon: 12vv (pub 1534)
Huelgas Ens, P. van Nevel *Concert*
(4/93) (SONY) ① **SK48249**

Si ignoras te o pulchra—motet: 4vv (pub 1541)
Ars Nova, B. Holten *Concert*
(10/90) (KONT) ① **32038**

Tous les regretz—chanson: 6vv (pub 1544)
Huelgas Ens, P. van Nevel *Concert*
(4/93) (SONY) ① **SK48249**

GOMES, (Antonio) Carlos *(1836–1896) Brazil*

SECTION V: STAGE WORKS

Il Guarany—opera: 4 acts (1870—Milan) (Lib. Scalvini and d'Ormeville)
EXCERPTS: 1. Prelude. ACT 1: 2. Ave Maria; 3. Gentile di cuore; 4. Sento una forza indomita. ACT 2: 5. Vanto io pur superba cuna; 6. Sena tetto, senza cuna. ACT 3: 7. Regina della tribù; 8. Perchè di mesti.
Il torvo sguardo A. Amadi, orch (r1910s) *Concert*
(6/94) (IRCC) ① **IRCC-CD808**
3. B. Sayão, orch (r1930) *Concert*
(6/94) (IRCC) ① **IRCC-CD808**
4. F. Marconi, B. Millotti, C. Sabajno (r1907) *Concert*
(10/90) (SYMP) ① **SYMCD1069**
4. G. Zenatello, E. Mazzoleni, orch (r1911) *Concert*
(5/94) (SYMP) ① **SYMCD1168**
4. G. Zenatello, E. Mazzoleni, orch (r1911) *Concert*
(5/94) (PEAR) ① **[4] GEMMCDS9074(1)**
4. E. Mazzoleni, G. Zenatello, orch (r1910) *Concert*
(6/94) (IRCC) ① **IRCC-CD808**
5. B. Gigli, orch, E. Sivieri (r1951) *Concert*
(10/90) (RCA) ① **GD87811**
6. E. Destinn, E. Caruso, orch, W.B. Rogers (r1914) *Concert*
(7/91) (RCA) ① **[12] GD60495(5)**
6. E. Caruso, E. Destinn, orch, W.B Rogers (r1914) *Concert*
(10/91) (PEAR) ① **[3] EVC3(1)**
6. M. Battistini, orch (r1924) *Concert*
(7/93) (NIMB) ① **[2] NI7840/1**
6. E. Destinn, E. Caruso, orch (r1914) *Concert*
(11/93) (ROMO) ① **[2] 81002-2**
6. P. Amato, orch (r1912) *Concert*
(6/94) (IRCC) ① **IRCC-CD808**
6. E. Destinn, E. Caruso, orch, W.B Rogers (r1914) *Concert*
(12/94) (SUPR) ① **[12] 11 2136-2(5)**
6. G. Zenatello, M. Pereira, anon (r1912) *Concert*
(5/94) (PEAR) ① **[4] GEMMCDS9074(1)**

Salvator Rosa—opera: 4 acts (1874—Genoa) (Lib. Ghislanzoni)
EXCERPTS: 1. Mia picciriella; 2. Di sposa, di padre; 3. È quanto.
1. C. Muzio, orch (r1920) *Concert*
(5/90) (BOGR) ① **[2] BIM705-2**
1. E. Caruso, orch, J. Pasternack (r1919) *Concert*
(7/91) (RCA) ① **[12] GD60495(4)**
1. E. Caruso, orch, J. Pasternack (r1919) *Concert*
(10/91) (PEAR) ① **[3] EVC4(2)**
1. C. Muzio, orch (r1920) *Concert*
(1/94) (ROMO) ① **[2] 81005-2**
2. A. Didur, orch (r c1918) *Concert*
(1/94) (CLUB) ① **CL99-089**

Lo Schiavo—opera: 4 acts (1889—Rio de Janeiro) (Lib. R. Paravicini, after Taunay)
EXCERPTS: 1. Prelude; 2a. L'importuna insistenza; 2b. Quando nascesti tu; 3. Sogni d'amore; 4. Ciel di Parahyba.
2a, 2b E. Caruso, orch (r1911) *Concert*
(10/89) (NIMB) ① **NI7803**

2a, 2b B. Gigli, orch. E. Sivieri (r1951) *Concert*
(10/90) (RCA) ① **GD87811**
2a, 2b E. Caruso, orch (r1911) *Concert*
(3/91) (PEAR) ① [3] **EVC2**
2a, 2b E. Caruso, orch (r1911) *Concert*
(7/91) (RCA) ① [12] **GD60495(4)**
2a, 2b E. Caruso, orch (r1911) *Concert*
(7/91) (MSCM) ① **MM30352**
2a, 2b E. Caruso, orch (r1911) *Concert*
(12/93) (NIMB) ① **NI7851**
2b G. Lauri-Volpi, orch, R. Bourdon (1928) *Concert*
(9/90) (PREI) ① **89012**
2b G. Lauri-Volpi, orch, R. Bourdon (1929) *Concert*
(7/93) (NIMB) ① **NI7845**

GONTIER (fl before 1220) Netherlands

SECTION IV: VOCAL AND CHORAL

Dolerousement commence—grand chant:
1v
Gothic Voices, C. Page (r1994) *Concert*
(8/95) (HYPE) ① **CDA66773**

GOODWIN, Ron (b 1925) England

SECTION V: STAGE WORKS

Battle of Britain—film score (1969)
EXCERPTS: 1. Main Theme; 2. Luftwaffe March
(later reworked as concert piece 'Aces High').
2. Prague City PO, P. Bateman (r1994) *Concert*
(11/94) (SILV) ① **FILMCD151**
Force 10 from Navarone—film score (1978)
EXCERPTS: 1. Main Theme (March).
1. Prague City PO, P. Bateman (r1994) *Concert*
(11/94) (SILV) ① **FILMCD151**
Frenzy—film score (1972)
EXCERPTS: 1. The London Theme.
1. Prague City PO, P. Bateman (r1993) *Concert*
(3/94) (SILV) ① **FILMCD137**
Where Eagles Dare—film score (1969)
EXCERPTS: 1. Main Title.
1. Prague City PO, P. Bateman (r1994) *Concert*
(11/94) (SILV) ① **FILMCD151**
633 Squadron—film score (1963)
EXCERPTS: 1. Main Theme.
1. Prague City PO, P. Bateman (r1994) *Concert*
(11/94) (SILV) ① **FILMCD151**

GORDON, Ricky Ian (b 1956) USA

SECTION IV: VOCAL AND CHORAL

Water Music: A Requiem—chorus a cappella (1992)
Musica Sacra, R. Westenburg (r1993) *Concert*
(12/93) (CATA) ① **09026 61822-2**

GORE, Michael (20th Cent) USA

SECTION V: STAGE WORKS

Defending Your Life—film score (1991)
EXCERPTS: 1. Finale.
1. Hollywood Bowl SO, J. Mauceri (r1991) *Concert*
(9/91) (PHIL) ① **432 109-2PH**

GÓRECKI, Henryk (Mikolaj) (b 1933) Poland

SECTION I: ORCHESTRAL

Chorus I—string orchestra, Op. 20 (1964)
Cracow PO, R. Bader (r1990) *Concert*
(11/93) (SCHW) ① **310412**
Concerto for Harpsichord and String Orchestra, Op. 40 (1980)
E. Chojnacka, London Sinfonietta, M. Stenz (r c1994)
Concert (9/95) (NONE) ① **7559-79362-2**
Genesis II: Canti strumentali—instrumental ensemble, Op. 19/2 (1961)
Polish St PO, J. Krenz (r1967) *Concert*
(4/93) (OLYM) ① **OCD385**
Kleines Requiem für eine Polka—piano and orchestra, Op. 66 (1993)
J. Constable, London Sinfonietta, D. Zinman (r
c1994) *Concert* (9/95) (NONE) ① **7559-79362-2**
Old Polish Music—brass and strings, Op. 24 (1969)
Warsaw Nat PO, A. Markowski (r1967) *Concert*
(4/93) (OLYM) ① **OCD385**
Czech PO, J. Nelson (r1992) *Concert*
(4/93) (ARGO) ① **436 835-2ZH**

3 Pieces in Old Style—string orchestra (1963)
Warsaw Nat PCO, K. Teutsch (r1970) *Concert*
(4/93) (OLYM) ① **OCD313**
Warsaw CO, K. Teutsch *Symphony 3.*
(4/93) (SCHW) ① **311041**
Cracow PO, R. Bader (r1990) *Concert*
(11/93) (SCHW) ① **310412**
Katowice RSO, A. Wit (r1993) *Symphony 3.*
(10/94) (NAXO) ① **8 550822**
Refrain—orchestra, Op. 21 (1965)
Polish St PO, J. Krenz (r1967) *Concert*
(4/93) (OLYM) ① **OCD385**
Scontri, 'Collisions'—orchestra, Op. 17 (1960)
Polish St PO, J. Krenz (r1967) *Concert*
(4/93) (OLYM) ① **OCD385**
Symphony No. 1, '1959'—pf, hpd, perc and stg orch, Op. 14 (1959)
Cracow PO, R. Bader (r1990) *Concert*
(11/93) (SCHW) ① **310412**
Symphony No. 2, 'Copernican'—soprano, baritone, chorus and orchestra, Op. 31 (1972) (Wds. N Copernicus & Psalm 37)
E. Soós, T. Altorjay, Bartók Chor, Fricsay SO, T. Pál
(r1993) *Beatus vir, Op. 38.*
(7/94) (STDV) ① **STR33324**
Symphony No. 3, 'Symphony of Sorrowful Songs'—soprano and large orchestra, Op. 36 (1976)
S. Woytowicz, Polish Nat RSO, J. Katlewicz (r1987)
Concert (4/93) (OLYM) ① **OCD313**
D. Upshaw, London Sinfonietta, D. Zinman
(4/93) (NONE) ① **7559-79282-2**
S. Woytowicz, Berlin RSO, W. Kamirski *Olden Style Pieces.*
(4/93) (SCHW) ① **311041**
Z. Kilanowicz, Katowice RSO, A. Wit (r1993) *Olden Style Pieces.*
(10/94) (NAXO) ① **8 550822**
J. Kozlowska, Warsaw PO, K. Kord (r1990s)
(1/95) (PHIL) ① **442 411-2PM**

SECTION II: CHAMBER

Already it is Dusk (String Quartet No. 1), Op. 62 (1988)
Kronos Qt *Lerchenmusik.*
(9/91) (NONE) ① **7559-79257-2**
Quartet No. 1 (Already it is dusk)—strings, Op. 62 (1988)
Kronos Qt (r1990) *String Quartet 2.*
(4/93) (NONE) ① **7559-79319-2**
Quartet No. 2 (Quasi una fantasia)—strings, Op. 64 (1990-91)
1. Largo sostenuto—Mesto; 2. Deciso—Energico;
Furioso—Tranquillo—Mesto; 3. Arioso: Andante
cantabile; 4. Allegro—Sempre con grande passione e
molto marcato; Lento—Tranquillissimo.
Kronos Qt (r1990) *String Quartet 1.*
(4/93) (NONE) ① **7559-79319-2**
Recitatives and Ariosos: Lerchenmusik—clarinet, cello and piano, Op. 53 (1984-85)
M. Collins, C. van Kampen, J. Constable *Already it is Dusk.*
(9/91) (NONE) ① **7559-79257-2**
Camerata Vistula *Concert*
(11/91) (OLYM) ① **OCD343**

SECTION IV: VOCAL AND CHORAL

Amen—choir a capella, Op. 34 (1975)
Poznan Boys' Ch, J. Kurczewski (r1976) *Concert*
(4/93) (OLYM) ① **OCD313**
Oxford Pro Musica Sngrs, M. Smedley (r1993)
Concert (12/94) (PROU) ① **PROUCD136**
Kings College Ch, S. Cleobury (r1994) *Concert*
(12/94) (EMI) ① **CDC5 55096-2**
Chicago Sym Chor, Chicago Lyric Op Chor, J.
Nelson (r1994) *Concert*
(3/95) (NONE) ① **7559-79348-2**
Beatus vir—baritone, chorus and orchestra, Op. 38 (1979)
N. Storozhev, Prague Philharmonic Ch, Czech PO, J.
Nelson (r1992) *Concert*
(4/93) (ARGO) ① **436 835-2ZH**
T. Altorjay, Bartók Chor, Fricsay SO, T. Pál (r1993)
Symphony 2. (7/94) (STDV) ① **STR33324**
Epitafium—mixed choir and instrumental ensemble, Op. 12 (1958)
Polish St Phil Chor, Polish St PO, J. Krenz (r1967)
Concert (4/93) (OLYM) ① **OCD385**
Euntes ibant et flebant—choir, Op. 32 (1972)
(Wds Psalms 126/v7 & 95/v6)
Oxford Pro Musica Sngrs, M. Smedley (r1993)
Concert (12/94) (PROU) ① **PROUCD136**
Chicago Sym Chor, Chicago Lyric Op Chor, J.
Nelson (r1994) *Concert*
(3/95) (NONE) ① **7559-79348-2**

Good Night, 'In Memoriam Michael Vyner'—soprano, alto flute, 3 tam-tams & piano, Op. 63 (1990)
D. Upshaw, S. Bell, D. Hockings, J. Constable (r
c1994) *Concert* (9/95) (NONE) ① **7559-79362-2**
Miserere—choir a cappella, Op. 41 (1981)
Chicago Sym Chor, Chicago Lyric Op Chor, J.
Nelson (r1994) *Concert*
(3/95) (NONE) ① **7559-79348-2**
O Domina nostra—soprano and organ, Op. 55 (1982, rev 1985 & 1990)
S. Leonard, C. Bowers-Broadbent (r1992) *Concert*
(5/93) (ECM) ① **437 956-2**
Szeroka Woda, 'Oh, Our River Narew'—choir a cappella, Op. 39 (1979)
Lira Chbr Chor, L. Ding (r1994) *Concert*
(3/95) (NONE) ① **7559-79348-2**
Totus tuus—chorus a cappella, Op. 60 (1987)
(Wds. M. Boguslawska)
Oxford Schola Cantorum, J. Summerly *Concert*
(4/92) (PREL) ① **PROUCD129**
Prague Philharmonic Ch (r1992) *Concert*
(4/93) (ARGO) ① **436 835-2ZH**
Oxford Pro Musica Sngrs, M. Smedley (r1993)
Concert (12/94) (PROU) ① **PROUCD136**
Kings College Ch, S. Cleobury (r1994) *Concert*
(12/94) (EMI) ① **CDC5 55096-2**
Wisło moja, 'My Vistula'—choir a cappella, Op. 46 (1981)
Lira Chbr Chor, L. Ding (r1994) *Concert*
(3/95) (NONE) ① **7559-79348-2**

GORLI, Sandro (b 1948) Italy

SECTION IV: VOCAL AND CHORAL

Requiem—chorus
Paris Chapelle Royale European Ens, P.
Herreweghe *Concert*
(12/90) (HARM) ① **HMC90 1320**

GÖRNER, Johann Valentin (1702-1762) Germany

SECTION IV: VOCAL AND CHORAL

An den Schlaf—Lied (Wds F von Hagedorn)
A. Scholl, A. Verzier, K. E. Schröder, M. Märkl
(r1994) *Concert* (5/95) (HARM) ① **HMC90 1505**
Die Nacht—Lied (Wds F von Hagedorn)
A. Scholl, A. Verzier, K. E. Schröder, M. Märkl
(r1994) *Concert* (5/95) (HARM) ① **HMC90 1505**

GORZANIS, Giacomo (c1520-c1575/9) Italy

SECTION III: INSTRUMENTAL

Suite on the 'Passamezzo antico'—lute
1. Recercar; 2. Pass'e mezo anticho; 3. Padoana; 4.
Saltarello.
J. Lindberg (r1991) *Concert*
(11/93) (BIS) ① **BIS-CD599**

GOSCALCH (fl ?1385-1395) France

SECTION IV: VOCAL AND CHORAL

En nul estat—ballade (3vv)
Organum Ens, M. Pérès *Concert*
(11/87) (HARM) ① **HMC90 1252**

GOSS, Sir John (1800-1880) England

SECTION IV: VOCAL AND CHORAL

List! for the breeze—part song (trans from the Spanish)
PCA, M. Brown *Concert* (3/87) (CONI) ① **CDCF145**
Hilliard Ens, L-L. Kiesel *Concert*
(12/91) (MERI) ① **DUOCD89009**
Praise my soul, the King of Heaven—hymn
(Wds. Psalm 103, adpated H F Lyte)
St Paul's Cath Ch, C. Dearnley, English Brass Ens,
John Scott *Concert* (7/90) (HYPE) ① **CDH88036**
King's College Ch, S. Cleobury, C. Hughes (pp1991
with Choral Evensong) *Concert*
(10/92) (EMI) ① **CDC7 54412-2**
King's College Ch, Wren Orch, S. Cleobury (1985)
Concert (6/93) (DECC) ① **436 402-2DWO**
These are they which follow the Lamb—anthem: 4vv (1859) (Wds. Bible)
Cambridge Sngrs, J. Rutter *Concert*
(4/92) (CLLE) ① **COLCD113**

GOSSEC, François-Joseph (1734–1829) Belgium/France

SECTION I: ORCHESTRAL

Marche lugubre
Wallace Collection, J. Wallace *Concert*
(7/89) (NIMB) ① **NI5175**
Symphonie militaire—wind instruments (1793-94)
Wallace Collection, J. Wallace (orch J. Humphries) *Concert*
(7/89) (NIMB) ① **NI5175**

SECTION II: CHAMBER

Tambourin—flute and drum
V. Taylor, T. Kain (fl/gtr) *Concert*
(9/92) (TALL) ① **TP003**

SECTION V: STAGE WORKS

Le Camp du Grand pré—opera (1793)
Tambourin Welbeck Light Qt *Concert*
(10/91) (PEAR) ① **PASTCD9744**
Rosine, ou L'épouse abandonnée—opera: 3 acts (1786—Paris) (Lib. N. Gersin)
Gavotte
K-W. Chung, P. Moll (arr Meyer) *Concert*
(9/87) (DECC) ① **417 289-2DH**
A. Busch, B. Seidler-Winkler (arr Burmester: r1921) *Concert*
(6/93) (SYMP) ① **SYMCD1109**

GOSTENA, Giovanni Battista della (c1540–1598) Italy

SECTION III: INSTRUMENTAL

Fantasia—lute (pub 1599) (in Molinaro's 'Intavolatura di liuto')
J. Lindberg (r1991) *Concert*
(11/93) (BIS) ① **BIS-CD599**

GOTHÓNI, Ralf (b 1946) Finland

SECTION IV: VOCAL AND CHORAL

Der Ochs und sein Hirte—cantata: sop, bar & chbr ens
S. Isokoski, J. Hynninen, Chbr Ens, R. Gothóni (r1994)
(9/95) (ONDI) ① **ODE832-2**

GOTTSCHALK, Louis Moreau (1829–1869) USA

RO-Numbers from Offergeld's catalogue.

SECTION I: ORCHESTRAL

Grande tarantelle—piano and orchestra, RO259 (1858-64)
R. Nibley, Utah SO, M. Abravanel *Concert*
(5/93) (VANG) ① **08.4051.71**
Symphony No. 1, 'La nuit des tropiques'—orchestra, RO255 (1858-59)
Utah SO, M. Abravanel *Concert*
(5/93) (VANG) ① **08.4051.71**

SECTION II: CHAMBER

L' étincelle—mazurka sentimentale—piano: four hands, RO80 (Op. 21) (1848-53) (arr cpsr from Op. 20)
E. List, J. Werner *Concert*
(5/93) (VANG) ① **08.4051.71**
La gallina: danse cubaine—piano: four hands, RO100 (Op. 53) (1859-63)
E. List, J. Werner *Concert*
(5/93) (VANG) ① **08.4051.71**
La jota aragonesa: caprice espagnol—piano: four hands, RO130 (Op. 14) (1853) (arr cpsr)
E. List, C. Lewis (arr Savant) *Concert*
(5/93) (VANG) ① **08.4051.71**
P. Martin (r1993) *Concert*
(10/94) (HYPE) ① **CDA66697**
Marche de nuit—piano: four hands, RO151 (Op. 17) (1855) (arr cpsr: 1873)
E. List, J. Werner *Concert*
(5/93) (VANG) ① **08.4051.71**
P. Martin (r1993) *Concert*
(10/94) (HYPE) ① **CDA66697**
Orfa: grande polka—piano: four hands, RO186 (Op. 71) (1863-64) (arr cpsr: 1876)
E. List, C. Lewis *Concert*
(5/93) (VANG) ① **08.4051.71**
Printemps d'amour: mazurka, caprice de concert—piano: four hands, RO214 (Op. 40) (1855) (arr cpsr: 1873)
E. List, C. Lewis *Concert*
(5/93) (VANG) ① **08.4051.71**

Radieuse: grande valse de concert—piano: four hands, RO217 (Op. 72) (1863-64)
E. List, J. Werner *Concert*
(5/93) (VANG) ① **08.4051.71**
Réponds-moi: danse cubaine, caprice brillant—piano: four hands, RO225 (Op. 50) (1859)
E. List, C. Lewis *Concert*
(5/93) (VANG) ① **08.4051.71**
Ses yeux: polka de concert—piano: four hands, RO234 (Op. 66) (1865)
E. List, J. Werner *Concert*
(5/93) (VANG) ① **08.4051.71**
Tremolo: grand étude de concert—piano: four hands, RO265 (Op. 58) (1868)
E. List, C. Lewis *Concert*
(5/93) (VANG) ① **08.4051.71**

SECTION III: INSTRUMENTAL

Apothéose—grande marche solennelle, RO8 (Op. 29) (1855-56)
G. Rabol *Concert* (4/92) (O111) ① **OPS50-9114**
Ballade—piano, RO271 (1853)
P. Martin (r1993) *Concert*
(10/94) (HYPE) ① **CDA66697**
Ballade No. 6—piano, RO14 (Op. 83) (after 1869)
R. Burnett *Concert* (5/89) (AMON) ① **CD-SAR32**
P. Martin (r1993) (HYPE) ① **CDA66459**
Bamboula - danza des nègres—piano, RO20 (Op. 2) (1844-45)
K. Kaufmann *Concert* (8/90) (SCHW) ① **310035**
E. List *Concert* (5/93) (VANG) ① **08.4050.71**
A. Feinberg (r1994) *Concert*
(11/95) (ARGO) ① **444 457-2ZH**
Le Bananier—Chanson nègre, piano solo, RO21 (Op. 5) (1846)
R. Burnett *Concert* (5/89) (AMON) ① **CD-SAR32**
K. Kaufmann *Concert* (8/90) (SCHW) ① **310035**
P. Martin *Concert* (9/91) (HYPE) ① **CDA66459**
E. List *Concert* (5/93) (VANG) ① **08.4050.71**
Le Banjo—esquisse américaine, RO22 (Op. 15) (1854/55)
K. Kaufmann *Concert* (8/90) (SCHW) ① **310035**
P. Martin *Concert* (9/91) (HYPE) ① **CDA66459**
E. List *Concert* (5/93) (VANG) ① **08.4050.71**
M. Legrand (r1994) *Concert*
(7/95) (ERAT) ① **4509-96386-2**
Berceuse, RO27 (Op. 47) (1860)
R. Burnett *Concert* (5/89) (AMON) ① **CD-SAR32**
G. Rabol *Concert* (4/92) (O111) ① **OPS50-9114**
P. Martin (r1993) *Concert*
(10/94) (HYPE) ① **CDA66697**
Canto del Gitano—piano, RO35 (1852)
R. Burnett *Concert* (5/89) (AMON) ① **CD-SAR32**
P. Martin *Concert* (9/91) (HYPE) ① **CDA66459**
Caprice—piano, RO44 (Op. 79) (1856) (pub posth)
P. Martin (r1993; ed Espadero) *Concert*
(10/94) (HYPE) ① **CDA66697**
Columbia: caprice américain—piano, RO61 (Op. 34) (1859)
P. Martin *Concert* (9/91) (HYPE) ① **CDA66459**
A. Feinberg (r1994) *Concert*
(11/95) (ARGO) ① **444 457-2ZH**
Danse Ossianique—piano, RO64 (Op. 12) (1850-51) (revision of Polka de Salon, Op. 1)
G. Rabol *Concert* (4/92) (O111) ① **OPS50-9114**
Danza—piano, RO66 (Op. 33) (1857)
P. Martin *Concert* (9/91) (HYPE) ① **CDA66459**
Le Deuxième Banjo—piano, RO24 (Op. 82) (1852-53)
G. Rabol *Concert* (4/92) (O111) ① **OPS50-9114**
The Dying Poet—meditation, RO75 (1863/64)
R. Burnett *Concert* (5/89) (AMON) ① **CD-SAR32**
E. List *Concert* (5/93) (VANG) ① **08.4050.71**
El cocoyé—grand caprice cubain di bravura, RO57 (Op. 80) (1853-54)
G. Rabol *Concert* (4/92) (O111) ① **OPS50-9114**
La Gallina—Danse cubaine, piano, RO101 (pub c1868) (arr Wachtmann from 4-hand version)
R. Burnett *Concert* (5/89) (AMON) ① **CD-SAR32**
K. Kaufmann *Concert* (8/90) (SCHW) ① **310035**
La Gitanella—caprice caracteristique, RO103 (Op. 35) (1857)
G. Rabol *Concert* (4/92) (O111) ① **OPS50-9114**
Grand scherzo, RO114 (Op. 57) (1869)
G. Rabol *Concert* (4/92) (O111) ① **OPS50-9114**
P. Martin (r1993) *Concert*
(10/94) (HYPE) ① **CDA66697**
Grande fantaisie triumphal sur l'hymne national bréslien, RO108 (Op. 69) (1869)
C. Ortiz, RPO, M. Atzmon (orch Hazell) *Concert*
(9/86) (DECC) ① **414 348-2DH**

C. Ortiz, RPO, M. Atzmon (orch Hazell) *Concert*
(12/91) (DECC) ① **430 726-2DM**
The Last hope—religious meditation, RO133 (Op. 16) (1854)
K. Kaufmann *Concert* (8/90) (SCHW) ① **310035**
E. List *Concert* (5/93) (VANG) ① **08.4050.71**
The maiden's blush—piano: grand valse de concert, RO141 (1863-64)
E. List *Concert* (5/93) (VANG) ① **08.4050.71**
Le Mancenillier—Sérénade, RO142 (Op. 11) (1848/49)
R. Burnett *Concert* (5/89) (AMON) ① **CD-SAR32**
P. Martin *Concert* (9/91) (HYPE) ① **CDA66459**
G. Rabol *Concert* (4/92) (O111) ① **OPS50-9114**
Manchega—Piano Concert Study, RO143 (Op. 38) (1856)
R. Burnett *Concert* (5/89) (AMON) ① **CD-SAR32**
G. Rabol *Concert* (4/92) (O111) ① **OPS50-9114**
P. Martin (r1993) *Concert*
(10/94) (HYPE) ① **CDA66697**
M. Legrand (r1994) *Concert*
(7/95) (ERAT) ① **4509-96386-2**
Mazurka
R. Burnett *Concert* (5/89) (AMON) ① **CD-SAR32**
P. Martin *Concert* (9/91) (HYPE) ① **CDA66459**
G. Rabol *Concert* (4/92) (O111) ① **OPS50-9114**
Minuit à Seville—caprice: piano, RO170 (Op. 30) (1852-56)
R. Burnett *Concert* (5/89) (AMON) ① **CD-SAR32**
P. Martin *Concert* (9/91) (HYPE) ① **CDA66459**
G. Rabol *Concert* (4/92) (O111) ① **OPS50-9114**
Miserere du Trovatore—Paraphrase de concert, RO171 (Op. 52) (1856)
P. Martin (r1993) *Concert*
(10/94) (HYPE) ① **CDA66697**
O ma charmante, épargnez-moi—caprice: piano, RO182 (Op. 44) (1861)
G. Rabol *Concert* (4/92) (O111) ① **OPS50-9114**
Ojos Criollos (Danse Cubaine)—piano, RO185 (1860) (arr cpsr from piano duet version)
K. Kaufmann *Concert* (8/90) (SCHW) ① **310035**
P. Martin *Concert* (9/91) (HYPE) ① **CDA66459**
E. List *Concert* (5/93) (VANG) ① **08.4050.71**
Pasquinade—caprice, RO189 (Op. 59) (1869)
K. Kaufmann *Concert* (8/90) (SCHW) ① **310035**
E. List *Concert* (5/93) (VANG) ① **08.4050.71**
P. Martin (r1993) *Concert*
(10/94) (HYPE) ① **CDA66697**
Polka in A flat—piano, RO275 (1859)
R. Burnett *Concert* (5/89) (AMON) ① **CD-SAR32**
P. Martin (r1993) *Concert*
(10/94) (HYPE) ① **CDA66697**
Polka in B flat—piano, RO273
R. Burnett *Concert* (5/89) (AMON) ① **CD-SAR32**
P. Martin (r1993) *Concert*
(10/94) (HYPE) ① **CDA66697**
Ricordati—piano, RO227 (Op. 26) (?1856)
K. Kaufmann *Concert* (8/90) (SCHW) ① **310035**
Romance—piano
R. Burnett *Concert* (5/89) (AMON) ① **CD-SAR32**
P. Martin *Concert* (9/91) (HYPE) ① **CDA66459**
La Savane—ballad créole: piano, RO232 (Op. 2) (1845-46)
R. Burnett *Concert* (5/89) (AMON) ① **CD-SAR32**
K. Kaufmann *Concert* (8/90) (SCHW) ① **310035**
E. List *Concert* (5/93) (VANG) ① **08.4050.71**
P. Martin (r1993) *Concert*
(10/94) (HYPE) ① **CDA66697**
Scherzo-romantique, RO233 (Op. 73) (1851)
K. Kaufmann *Concert* (8/90) (SCHW) ① **310035**
P. Martin (r1993; ed Espadero) *Concert*
(10/94) (HYPE) ① **CDA66697**
Souvenir d'Andalousie—Caprice de concert, RO242 (Op. 22) (1851)
R. Burnett *Concert* (5/89) (AMON) ① **CD-SAR32**
E. List, J. Werner (arr pf 4 hands) *Concert*
(5/93) (VANG) ① **08.4051.71**
(10/94) (HYPE) ① **CDA66697**
Souvenir de la Havane: grand caprice de concert—piano, RO246 (Op. 39) (1860)
P. Martin *Concert* (9/91) (HYPE) ① **CDA66459**
G. Rabol *Concert* (4/92) (O111) ① **OPS50-9114**
Souvenir de Lima—mazurka, RO247 (Op. 74) (1865)
P. Martin (r1993) *Concert*
(10/94) (HYPE) ① **CDA66697**
Souvenir de Porto Rico—Marche des Gibaros, for piano, RO250 (Op. 31) (1857)
R. Burnett *Concert* (5/89) (AMON) ① **CD-SAR32**
K. Kaufmann *Concert* (8/90) (SCHW) ① **310035**
P. Martin *Concert* (9/91) (HYPE) ① **CDA66459**
E. List *Concert* (5/93) (VANG) ① **08.4050.71**

Suis-moi! caprice—Piano solo, RO253 (Op. 45) (1861)
R. Burnett *Concert*   (5/89) (AMON) ① **CD-SAR32**
G. Rabol *Concert*   (4/92) (O111) ① **OPS50-9114**
E. List *Concert*   (5/93) (VANG) ① **08.4050.71**
P. Martin (r1993) *Concert*
          (10/94) (HYPE) ① **CDA66697**
Tournament Galop, RO264 (1854)
E. List *Concert*   (5/93) (VANG) ① **08.4050.71**
Union—Paraphrase de concert, RO269 (Op. 48) (1862)
K. Kaufmann *Concert*   (8/90) (SCHW) ① **310035**
P. Martin *Concert*   (9/91) (HYPE) ① **CDA66459**
E. List, C. Lewis (arr E. List) *Concert*
          (5/93) (VANG) ① **08.4051.71**
Ynés—piano, RO277 (1860)
P. Martin (r1993) *Concert*
          (10/94) (HYPE) ① **CDA66697**

SECTION V: STAGE WORKS

Cakewalk—ballet (1951) (arr/orch H. Kay from various piano works)
Cpte Louisville Orch, H. Kay. A. Endo *Piston: Incredible Flutist.*
          (3/90) (ALBA) ① **TROY016-2**

GOUBLIER, Henri (1888–1951) France

SECTION IV: VOCAL AND CHORAL

Le credo du paysan—song
T. Ruffo, orch (r1923) *Concert*
          (2/93) (PREI) ① [3] **89303(2)**

GOUDIMEL, Claude (1514/20–1572) France

SECTION IV: VOCAL AND CHORAL

Bonjour mon coeur—chanson
Hilliard Ens *Concert*   (6/91) (HYPE) ① **CDA66370**
Cantique de Siméon—4vv (c1565) (Wds. Bible, trans C Marot)
C. Goudimel Ens, C. Morel (r1994) *Concert*
          (6/95) (NAXO) ① **8 553025**
Par le désert des mes peines—chanson spirituelle (Wds. A de la Roche Chandieu)
C. Goudimel Ens, C. Morel (r1994) *Concert*
          (6/95) (NAXO) ① **8 553025**
Psalm 104—4vv (c1565) (Wds. Bible, trans C Marot)
C. Goudimel Ens, C. Morel (r1994) *Concert*
          (6/95) (NAXO) ① **8 553025**
Psalm 137—Estans assis aux rives aquatiques (pub 1571)
Baltimore Consort (r1992; arr Baltimore Consort) *Concert*   (4/95) (DORI) ① **DOR90177**
Psalms—3-5vv (1551-66) (Wds. Bible, trans C Marot)
1. Psalm 13; 2. Psalm 104; 3. Psalm 114; 4. Psalm 115; 5. Psalm 128 (first setting); 6. Psalm 128 (second setting); 7. Psalm 130; 8. Psalm 137; 9. Psalm 160.
C. Goudimel Ens, C. Morel (r1994) *Concert*
          (6/95) (NAXO) ① **8 553025**

GOULD, Glenn (1932–1982) Canada

SECTION II: CHAMBER

Sonata—bassoon and piano
C. Marchese, E. Naoumoff *Concert*
          (11/92) (SONY) ① **SK47184**
String Quartet, Op. 1
B. Monsaigeon, G. Apap, G. Caussé, A. Meunier *Concert*   (11/92) (SONY) ① **SK47184**

SECTION III: INSTRUMENTAL

2 Pieces—piano
E. Naoumoff *Concert*   (11/92) (SONY) ① **SK47184**
Sonata—piano (incomplete: unfinished)
E. Naoumoff *Concert*   (11/92) (SONY) ① **SK47184**

SECTION IV: VOCAL AND CHORAL

Lieberson Madrigal—4vv and piano (Wds. cpsr)
C. McFadden, M-T. Keller, J-P. Fouchécourt, H. van der Kamp, E. Naoumoff, N. Rivenq *Concert*
          (11/92) (SONY) ① **SK47184**
So you want to write a Fugue?—4vv and string quartet (1963) (Wds. cpsr)
C. McFadden, M-T. Keller, J-P. Fouchécourt, H. van der Kamp, B. Monsaigeon, G. Apap, G. Caussé, A. Meunier, N. Rivenq *Concert*
          (11/92) (SONY) ① **SK47184**

GOULD, Morton (b 1913) USA

SECTION I: ORCHESTRAL

American Salute, 'When Johnny comes marching home' (1943)
Boston Pops, A. Fiedler (r1958) *Concert*
          (1/94) (RCA) ① **09026 61249-2**
American Symphonette No. 2—orchestra (1938)
Louisville Orch, J. Mester *Concert*
          (10/89) (ALBA) ① [2] **TROY013/4-2**
Columbia—Broadsides for orchestra on Columbian themes—orchestra (1967)
Louisville Orch, M. Gould *Concert*
          (10/89) (ALBA) ① [2] **TROY013/4-2**
Columbian Fanfares—brass ensemble (1967)
LPO, J. Mester *Concert*   (7/91) (KOCH) ① **37012-2**
Concerto for Viola and Orchestra (1945)
R. Glazer, Louisville Orch, L.L. Smith *Concert*
          (10/89) (ALBA) ① [2] **TROY013/4-2**
Dance Variations—two pianos and orchestra (1953)
J. Pierce, D. Jonas, RPO, D. Amos (r1989) *Concert*
          (10/90) (KOCH) ① **37002-2**
Derivations—clarinet and jazz band (1956)
B. Goodman, Columbia Jazz Combo, M. Gould *Concert*   (5/87) (SONY) ① **MK42227**
Fanfare for Freedon—brass ensemble (1942)
LPO, J. Mester *Concert*   (7/91) (KOCH) ① **37012-2**
Flourishes and Galop—orchestra (1983)
Louisville Orch, L.L. Smith *Concert*
          (10/89) (ALBA) ① [2] **TROY013/4-2**
Housewarming—orchestra (1982)
Louisville Orch, L.L. Smith *Concert*
          (10/89) (ALBA) ① [2] **TROY013/4-2**
Soundings—orchestra (1976)
Louisville Orch, M. Gould *Concert*
          (10/89) (ALBA) ① [2] **TROY013/4-2**
Spirituals—string choir and orchestra (1941)
LSO, W. Susskind (r c1958) *Concert*
          (4/95) (EVER) ① **EVC9003**
Symphony of Spirituals—orchestra (1976)
Louisville Orch, L.L. Smith *Concert*
          (10/89) (ALBA) ① [2] **TROY013/4-2**

SECTION III: INSTRUMENTAL

Boogie Woogie Etude—piano (1943)
S. Cherkassky (pp1991) *Concert*
          (1/93) (DECC) ① **433 654-2DH**
M. Legrand (r1994) *Concert*
          (7/95) (ERAT) ① **4509-96386-2**

SECTION IV: VOCAL AND CHORAL

A capella—chorus a capella
1. Tolling; 2. Solfegging.
G. Smith Sngrs, G. Smith *Concert*
          (4/91) (KOCH) ① **37026-2**
Of Time and the River—chorus a capella (1946) (wds. T. Wolfe)
1. Prologue; 2. Play was a Tune; 3. Soliloquy; 4. Spring song; 5. Epilogue: The Sills of Evening.
G. Smith Sngrs, G. Smith *Concert*
          (4/91) (KOCH) ① **37026-2**
Quotations—two choruses and orchestra (1984)
1. Preface; 2. Hallelujah Amen; 3. Hosanna Amen; 4. Interlude; 5. The Early Bird; 6. A Bird in Hand. Ballads: 7. The lass of Richmond Hill; 8. Women and Roses; 10. We'll go no more a-roving; 11. Gather, ye rosebuds; 12. Music, when soft voices die; 13. Song; 14. Sermon; 15. Interlude; 16. Postscript.
NY Choral Soc, NY Choral Soc Orch, J.D. Goodwin *Concert*   (4/91) (KOCH) ① **37026-2**

SECTION V: STAGE WORKS

Fall River Legend—ballet (1947)
B. Peters, National PO, M. Rosenstock
          (4/92) (ALBA) ① **TROY035-2**

GOUNOD, Charles (François) (1818–1893) France

SECTION I: ORCHESTRAL

Marche funèbre d'une marionette—orchestra (1872 orch 1879) (orig piano)
St Louis SO, L. Slatkin *Concert*
          (6/89) (RCA) ① **RD87716**
Detroit SO, P. Paray (r1959) *Concert*
          (11/93) (MERC) ① **434 332-2MM**
Prague City PO, P. Bateman (r1993) *Concert*
          (3/94) (SILV) ① **FILMCD137**

T. Trotter (r1992: trans W T Best) *Concert*
          (4/94) (DECC) ① **436 656-2DH**
LPO, Henry Wood (r1940) *Concert*
          (9/94) (DUTT) ① **CDAX8008**
Boston Pops, A. Fiedler (r1963) *Concert*
          (12/95) (RCA) ① **09026 68131-2**
Symphony No. 1 in D (1855)
Toulouse Capitole Orch, M. Plasson *Symphony 2.*
          (3/92) (EMI) ① **CDM7 63949-2**
Symphony No. 2 in E flat (1856)
Toulouse Capitole Orch, M. Plasson *Symphony 1.*
          (3/92) (EMI) ① **CDM7 63949-2**

SECTION II: CHAMBER

6 Mélodies—horn and piano (c1840-48)
1. G minor; 2. E flat; 3. B flat; 4. C minor/major; 5. F; 6. B flat.
B. Tuckwell, D. Blumenthal *Concert*
          (11/92) (ETCE) ① **KTC1135**
Petite symphonie—2 fl, 2 ob, 2 cl, 2 hn & 2 bn (1885)
Munich Wind Academy, A. Brezina *Dvořák: Serenade, Op. 44.*   (5/85) (ORFE) ① **C051831A**
String Quartet No. 3 in A minor (1895)
Daniel Qt (r1991) *Concert*
          (12/94) (DINT) ① **DICD920159**

SECTION IV: VOCAL AND CHORAL

À la brise, 'Aura gentil che mormori'—song: 1v and piano (pub 1875) (Wds. anon, trans Barbier)
R. Doria, J. Boguet (Ital) *Concert*
          (12/91) (MSCM) ① **MM30373**
À toi mon coeur—song: 1v and piano (?1872) (Wds. Barbier)
H. Hagegård, T. Schuback (r1976) *Concert*
          (5/94) (BIS) ① **BIS-CD054**
L' Absent—song: 1v and piano (1876) (Wds. cpsr)
R. Doria, J. Boguet *Concert*
          (12/91) (MSCM) ① **MM30373**
F. Lott, G. Johnson (r1993) *Concert*
          (3/94) (HYPE) ① [2] **CDA66801/2**
G. Souzay, D. Baldwin (r1963) *Concert*
          (3/95) (PHIL) ① [4] **438 964-2PM4(2)**
L' Arithmétique—song: 1v and song (?1853-55) (Wds. Marzials)
F. Lott, A. Murray, G. Johnson *Concert*
          (11/90) (EMI) ① **CDC7 49930-2**
The Arrow and the Song—song: 1v and piano (1885) (Wds. H. Longfellow)
A. Murray, G. Johnson (r1993) *Concert*
          (3/94) (HYPE) ① [2] **CDA66801/2**
Au printemps—song: 1v and piano (pub 1868) (Wds. Barbier)
E. Rethberg, orch (r1924) *Concert*
          (2/95) (ROMO) ① [2] **81012-2**
Au rossignol—song: 1v and piano (1867) (Wds. Lamartine)
R. Doria, J. Boguet *Concert*
          (12/91) (MSCM) ① **MM30373**
A. Murray, G. Johnson (r1993) *Concert*
          (3/94) (HYPE) ① [2] **CDA66801/2**
M. de Reszke, J. de Reszke (r1905) *Concert*
          (12/94) (SYMP) ① **SYMCD1172**
Ave maria—religious song: 1v and piano/orchestra (1853 cpted 1859) (Adapted from Bach's 'Wohltemperirte Klavier' BWV846)
J. Lloyd Webber, ECO, N. Cleobury (arr C Palmer) *Concert*   (3/85) (PHIL) ① **412 231-2PH**
J. McCormack, F. Kreisler, V. O'Brien (r1914) *Concert*   (9/89) (PEAR) ① **GEMMCD9315**
R. Ponselle, orch, R. Bourdon (r1926) *Concert*
          (1/90) (RCA) ① **GD87810**
A. Patti, L. Ronald (r1905) *Concert*
          (4/90) (PEAR) ① **GEMMCD9312**
E. Burzio, orch (r1913) *Concert*
          (1/91) (CLUB) ① [2] **CL99-587/8**
B. Hendricks, Stockholm CO, E. Ericson *Concert*
          (4/91) (EMI) ① **CDC7 54098-2**
M. Maisky, P. Gililov (arr cvlc) *Concert*
          (7/91) (DG) ① **431 544-2GH**
E. Feuermann, M. Taube (arr vc/pf: r1930) *Concert*
          (10/91) (PEAR) ① **GEMMCD9443**
F. Alda, M. Elman, F. La Forge (r1915) *Concert*
          (10/91) (BIDD) ① **LAB039**
J. Galway *Concert*   (12/91) (RCA) ① **RD60736**
L. Pavarotti, Wandsworth Sch Boys' Ch, National PO, K.H. Adler (arr Gamley) *Concert*
          (12/91) (DECC) ① **433 710-2DH**
T. Hampson, St Paul CO, H. Wolff (arr Pasatieri) *Concert*   (12/91) (TELD) ① **9031-73135-2**
L. Price, VPO, H. von Karajan (arr Sabatini) *Concert*
          (12/91) (DECC) ① **433 010-2DM**

Reine du matin R. Doria, J. Boguet *Concert*
(12/91) (MSCM) ① **MM30373**
**Roméo et Juliette, 'Romeo and
Juliet'—opéra: 5 acts (1867—Paris)** (Lib.
Barbier and Carré, after Shakespeare)
EXCERPTS. ACT 1: 1. L'heure s'envoie; 2. Écoutez!
écoutez!; 3. Allons! jeunes gens!; 4a. Enfin la place
est libre; 4b. Mab, la reine des mensonges; 4c. Eh
bien! que l'avertissment; 5. Je veux vivre (Waltz); 6a.
Le nom de cette belle enfant?; 6b. Ange adorable;
7a. Quelqu'un!; 7b. Le voici. ACT 2: 8a. O nuit! sous
tes ailes; 8b. L'amour, l'amour; 8c. Ah! lève-toi, soleil!;
9. Hélas! moi, le haïr!; 10a. O nuit divine; 10b. Ah! ne
fuis pas encore. ACT 3: 11. Mon père! Dieu vous
gardel; 12. Dieu qui fit l'homme; 13a. Depuis hier je
cherche en vain mon maître!; 13b. Que faites-tu,
blanche tourterelle; 14. Ah! voici nos gens!; 15. Eh
quoi? toujours du sang?. ACT 4: 16a. Va! Je t'ai
pardonné; 16b. Nuit d'hymenée!; 16c. Non, ce n'est
pas le jour; 17a. Quoi! ma fille; 17b. Que l'hymne
nuptiale; 18a. Mon père! tout m'accable; 18b. Buvez
donc ce breuvage; 19. Dieu! quel frisson court dans
mes veines!; 20. Cortège nuptial; 21. Ma fille, cède
aux voeux (Finale). ACT 5: 22. Le sommeil de
Juliette; 23. Salut! tombeau sombre.
Cpte Alfredo Kraus, C. Malfitano, J. Van Dam, G.
Quilico, A. Murray, G. Bacquier, J. Taillon, C. Burles,
K. Ollmann, J-M. Frémeau, Midi-Pyrenees Regional
Ch, Toulouse Capitole Chor, Toulouse Capitole Orch,
M. Plasson (3/87) (EMI) ① **CDS7 47365-8**
Cpte R. Jobin, J. Micheau, O. Ricquier, H. Rehfuss,
C. Cambon, L. Rialland, P. Mollet, A. Philippe, C.
Collart, C. Roquetty, Paris Op Chor, Paris Op Orch,
A. Erede (r1953)
(6/95) (DECC) ① **[2] 443 539-2LF2**
March SO, T. Beecham (r1917) *Concert*
(11/91) (SYMP) ① **[2] SYMCD1096/7**
3. L. Melchissédec, anon (r1907) *Concert*
(9/91) (SYMP) ① **SYMCD1089**
3. P. Plançon, anon (r1904) *Concert*
(9/91) (PEAR) ① **GEMMCD9497**
3. P. Plançon, anon (r1904) *Concert*
(7/92) (PEAR) ① **[3] GEMMCDS9923(2)**
3. P. Plançon, anon (r1902) *Concert*
(3/93) (SYMP) ① **SYMCD1100**
3. P. Plançon, anon (r1904) *Concert*
(12/94) (ROMO) ① **82001-2**
3. P. Plançon, anon (r1904) *Concert*
(1/95) (NIMB) ① **NI7860**
5. M. Callas, FRNO, G. Prêtre *Concert*
(2/88) (EMI) ① **CDC7 49059-2**
5. E. Norena, orch (r1928) *Concert*
(10/89) (NIMB) ① **NI7802**
5. J. Sutherland, ROHO, F. Molinari-Pradelli *Concert*
(1/90) (DECC) ① **[2] 425 493-2DM2**
5. M. Callas, FRNO, G. Prêtre *Concert*
(2/90) (EMI) ① **CDM7 63182-2**
5. A. Galli-Curci, orch, R. Bourdon (r1917) *Concert*
(5/90) (NIMB) ① **NI7806**
5. R. Pinkert, anon (r1906) *Concert*
(7/92) (PEAR) ① **[3] GEMMCDS9923(1)**
5. L. Tetrazzini, orch, P. Pitt (r1908) *Concert*
(9/92) (EMI) ① **[3] CHS7 63802-2(1)**
5. L. Tetrazzini, orch, P. Pitt (r1908) *Concert*
(9/92) (PEAR) ① **GEMMCD9221**
5. L. Tetrazzini, anon (r c1904) *Concert*
(9/92) (PEAR) ① **GEMMCD9225**
5(pt) R. Pinkert, anon (r1906) *Concert*
(11/92) (MEMO) ① **[2] HR4408/9(1)**
5. S. Adams, anon (r1902) *Concert*
(3/93) (SYMP) ① **SYMCD1100**
5. M. Caballé, New Philh, R. Giovaninetti (r1970)
Concert (5/93) (DG) ① **431 103-2GB**
5. A. Nezhdanova, U. Masetti (r1906: Russ) *Concert*
(6/93) (PEAR) ① **GEMMCDS9007/9(1)**
5. E. Eames, anon (r1905) *Concert*
(11/93) (ROMO) ① **[2] 81001-2**
5. E. Eames, orch (r1906) *Concert*
(11/93) (ROMO) ① **[2] 81001-2**
5. A. Galli-Curci, orch, J. Pasternack (r1917) *Concert*
(3/94) (ROMO) ① **[2] 81003-2**
5. M. Devia, Svizzera Italiana Orch, M. Rota (pp1992)
Concert (10/94) (BONG) ① **GB2513-2**
5. P. Alarie, Lamoureux Orch, P. Dervaux (r1953)
Concert (11/94) (PHIL) ① **[2] 438 953-2PM2**
5. E. Eames, orch (r1906) *Concert*
(1/95) (NIMB) ① **NI7860**
5. L. Garrett, RPO, P. Robinson (r1994) *Concert*
(4/95) (SILV) ① **SILKD6004**
5. I. Galante, Latvian Nat SO, A. Vilumanis (r1994)
Concert (11/95) (CAMP) ① **RRCD1335**
5. A. Pendachanska, Sofia SO, M. Angelov (r1994)
Concert (12/95) (CAPR) ① **10 706**

6a, 6b, 8b, 8c, 10b, 16a, 16b, 23. H. Schymberg, J.
Björling, Stockholm Royal Op Orch, N. Grevillius
(Swedish; pp1940) *Puccini: Bohème.*
(3/92) (BLUE) ① **ABCD013**
6b F. Marconi, B. Militotti, C. Sabajno (r1907: Ital)
Concert (10/90) (SYMP) ① **SYMCD1069**
6b L. Bori, B. Gigli, orch, R. Bourdon (r1923) *Concert*
(10/90) (RCA) ① **GD87811**
6b E. Scaramberg, G. Bréjean-Silver, anon (r1905)
Concert (7/92) (PEAR) ① **[3] GEMMCDS9923(2)**
6b J. Björling, A-L. Björling, Stockholm Concert Soc
Orch, N. Grevillius (r1949) *Concert*
(8/92) (BLUE) ① **ABCD016**
6b E. Clément, G. Farrar, orch, R. Bourdon (r1913)
Concert (8/95) (ROMO) ① **82002-2**
6b E. Clément, G. Farrar, orch, R. Bourdon (r1913)
Concert (8/95) (PEAR) ① **GEMMCD9161**
8b, 8c G. Thill, Orch, P. Gaubert (r1927) *Concert*
(1/89) (EMI) ① **CDM7 69548-2**
8b, 8c Alfredo Kraus, Toulouse Capitole Orch, M.
Plasson *Concert* (10/89) (EMI) ① **CDM7 63104-2**
8c G. Morino, Warmia Nat PO, B. Amaducci *Concert*
(10/90) (NUOV) ① **6851**
8c L. Slezak, orch (Ger: r1907) *Concert*
(2/91) (PREI) ① **89020**
8c J. Björling, Stockholm Royal Op Orch, N.
Grevillius (r1946) *Concert*
(4/92) (EMI) ① **[7] CHS7 69741-2(5)**
8c J. Björling, orch, N. Grevillius (r1945) *Concert*
(8/92) (BLUE) ① **ABCD016**
8c I. Alchevsky, anon (r1900s) *Concert*
(7/93) (SYMP) ① **SYMCD1105**
8c A. Piccaver, orch (r1912: Ger) *Concert*
(8/93) (PREI) ① **89060**
8c J. Björling, Stockholm Royal Op Orch, N.
Grevillius (r1945) *Concert*
(10/93) (EMI) ① **CDH7 64707-2**
8c E. Clément, anon (r1905) *Concert*
(8/95) (ROMO) ① **82002-2**
8c G. Thill, orch, P. Gaubert (r1927) *Concert*
(8/95) (FORL) ① **UCD16727**
8c A. Davies, A. Bryn Parri (r1994) *Concert*
(11/95) (SAIN) ① **SCDC2085**
8c, 22. F. Ansseau, orch (r1926) *Concert*
(1/91) (PREI) ① **89022**
10a, 16b F. Hempel, H. Jadlowker, orch (Ger:
r1900s) *Concert* (12/91) (CLUB) ① **CL99-042**
13a, 13b G. Swarthout, RCA SO, W. Pelletier (r1942)
Concert (4/94) (RCA) ① **[6] 09026 61580-2(4)**
23. G. Thill, G. Féraldy, Orch, J. Szyfer (r1929)
Concert (1/89) (EMI) ① **CDM7 69548-2**
23. R. Alagna, LPO, R. Armstrong *Concert*
(12/95) (EMI) ① **CDC5 55540-2**
Sapho—opéra: 3 acts (1851—Paris) (Lib.
Augier)
EXCERPTS: 1a. Introduction and March; 1b. O
Jupiter; 2a. Tu ne suis pas la multitude; 2b. Puis-je
oublier; 3. Violà Sapho; 4a. Quel entretien si doux;
4b. Quand de cloître elle me presse; 5a. Salut Alcée;
5b. Les entrailles des victimes; 5c. Les Dieux d'un
oeil clément; 6. O Liberté, déesse austère; 7a. Meure
le tyrannie; 7b. Sapho! Sapho! Sapho!; 8. Héros sur
la tour solitaire; 9. Fête d'Apollon. ACT 2: 10a. Gloire
à Bacchus; 10b. Assez chanté! Phaon, fais sortir; 11.
Oui, jourons tous; 12a. Reste là! Pythéas; 12b.
Comprends-moi bien, ma bonne Phèdre; 13. Ma vie
en se séjour; 14. Glycère ici! Que cherche-t-elle; 15a.
Je viens sauver ta tête; 15b. O Douleur qui
m'oppresse. ACT 3: 15c. Prelude; 16a. J'arrive le
premier; 16b. O jours heureux; 17a. Adieu Patrie;
17b. La mer et le vaisseau; 17c. Sois béni; 17d.
Adieu, adieu Patrie; 18. Broutez le thym; 19a. Où
suis-je; 19b. O ma lyre immortelle.
Cpte M. Command, S. Coste, C. Papis, E. Faury, L.
Sarrazin, P. Georges, S. Martinez, Saint-Etienne
Lyric Chor, Saint-Etienne Nouvel Orch, P. Fournillier
(1992) (7/94) (SCHW) ① **[2] 313112**
19b G. Bumbry, Stuttgart RSO, S. Soltesz *Concert*
(11/86) (ORFE) ① **C081841A**
19b F. Litvinne, anon (r1903) *Concert*
(10/92) (SYMP) ① **SYMCD1101**
**Le Tribut de Zamora—opéra: 4 acts
(1881—Paris)** (Lib. d'Ennery & Brésil)
Garde la couronne des reines Z. de Lussan, anon
(r1906) *Concert* (8/92) (IRCC) ① **IRCC-CD802**

GOUVY, Louis Théodore *(1819–1898) France*

SECTION II: CHAMBER

Aubade—piano duet, Op. 77/2
Y. Tal, A. Groethuysen (r1992) *Concert*
(10/93) (SONY) ① **SK53110**
Ghiribizzi—piano duet, Op. 83
5. Impromptu.
5. Y. Tal, A. Groethuysen (r1992) *Concert*
(10/93) (SONY) ① **SK53110**
6 Morceaux—piano duet, Op. 59
1. Prelude (Allegro di molto); 2. Caprice (Allegretto).
1, 2. Y. Tal, A. Groethuysen (r1992) *Concert*
(10/93) (SONY) ① **SK53110**
Scherzo—piano duet, Op. 77/1
Y. Tal, A. Groethuysen (r1992) *Concert*
(10/93) (SONY) ① **SK53110**
Sonata for Piano Duet in C minor, Op. 49
Y. Tal, A. Groethuysen (r1992) *Concert*
(10/93) (SONY) ① **SK53110**
Sonata for Piano Duet in D minor, Op. 36
Y. Tal, A. Groethuysen (r1992) *Concert*
(10/93) (SONY) ① **SK53110**
Sonata for Piano Duet in F, Op. 51
Y. Tal, A. Groethuysen (r1992) *Concert*
(10/93) (SONY) ① **SK53110**

GOW, Niel *(1727–1807) Scotland*

SECTION III: INSTRUMENTAL

**A Collection of Strathspey Reels (pub 1784,
rev 1801)**
EXCERPTS: 1. Niel Gow's Lamentation for
Abercairney; 2. Tulloch Gorum (Traditional).
1, 2. Scottish Early Music Consort (r1987) *Concert*
(10/95) (CHAN) ① **CHAN0581**
**A Second Collection of Strathspey Reels
(pub 1788, rev 1803)**
EXCERPTS: 1. Loch Erroch Side.
1. Scottish Early Music Consort (r1987) *Concert*
(10/95) (CHAN) ① **CHAN0581**

GOWERS, Patrick *(b 1936) England*

SECTION IV: VOCAL AND CHORAL

Viri Galilaei—song
St Paul's Cath Ch, John Scott *Concert*
(4/92) (HYPE) ① **CDA66519**

GRABERT, Martin *(1868–1951) Germany*

SECTION II: CHAMBER

**Sonata for Oboe and Piano in G minor, Op.
52**
P. Bree, P. Komen *Concert*
(2/90) (ETCE) ① **KTC1074**

GRABU, Louis *(fl 1665–1694) France/England*

SECTION V: STAGE WORKS

Albion and Albanius—opera (1685—London)
(Lib. J Dryden)
EXCERPTS: 1. Concert of Venus.
1. Parley of Instr, P. Holman (r1993) *Concert*
(6/94) (HYPE) ① **CDA66667**
**Valentinian—incidental music for
Rochester's play (1684—London)**
EXCERPTS: 1. Air pour les hautbois; 2. Air pour les
flutes; 3. Air pour les suivans de Jupiter; 4. Air pour
les songes affreux; 5. Air pour les satires; 6. Menuet.
1-6. Parley of Instr, P. Holman (r1993) *Concert*
(6/94) (HYPE) ① **CDA66667**

GRAENER, Paul *(1872–1944) Germany*

SECTION I: ORCHESTRAL

Die Flöte von Sanssouci—orchestra (1930s)
(Op. 88)
1. Introduction and Sarabande; 2. Gavotte; 3. Air; 4.
Rigaudon.
NBC SO, A. Toscanini (bp1938) *Concert*
(10/95) (DELL) ① **CDDA9024**

SECTION IV: VOCAL AND CHORAL

Lieder, Op. 71 (Wds. Löns)
3. Der König; 6. Männertreu; 7. Der Kuckuck; 9.
Verspruch; 10. Winter.
3, 10. H. Schlusnus, F. Rupp (r1933) *Concert*
(1/94) (PREI) ① [2] **89205**
3, 7. W. Ludwig, F. Leitner (r1935) *Concert*
(7/95) (PREI) ① **89088**
Vale carissima—Lied (Wds. Stieler)
H. Schlusnus, F. Rupp (r1933) *Concert*
(1/94) (PREI) ① [2] **89205**

SECTION V: STAGE WORKS

Friedemann Bach—opera: 3 acts, Op. 90
(1931—Schwerin) (Lib. R Lothar, after A E
Brachvogel)
Preis dir und Dank; Kein Hälmlein wächst auf
Erden W. Ludwig, Berlin City Op Orch, W. Ludwig
(r1932) *Concert* (7/95) (PREI) ① **89088**

GRÄFE, Johann Friedrich
(1711–1787) Germany

SECTION IV: VOCAL AND CHORAL

Aria di Giovannini
Willst du dein Herz mir schenken R. Jacobs, K.
Junghänel (r1985) *Concert*
(5/87) (HARM) ① **HMA190 1183**

GRAHAM, Peter (20th Cent)
Scotland

SECTION I: ORCHESTRAL

Brilliante—two euphoniums and brass band
(1987)
R. Childs, N. Childs, Besses o' the Barn Band, R.
Newsome (pp1987: arr brass band: Sargent) *Concert*
(11/93) (CHAN) ① **CHAN4513**
Prelude to a New Age—brass band
Glasgow CWS Band, H. Snell *Concert*
(9/92) (DOYE) ① **DOYCD005**

GRAHL, Traugott (Carl Gottfried)
(1802–1884) Germany/Sweden

SECTION I: ORCHESTRAL

Greetings from Sweden to Norway—waltz
(1871)
Košice St PO, M. Eichenholz (r1992) *Concert*
(2/94) (MARC) ① **8 223470**

GRAINER, Ron (1924–1981)
Australia/England

SECTION V: STAGE WORKS

Robert and Elizabeth—musical
(1964—London) (Lyrics Millar)
1. Overture; 2. Wimpole Street song; 3. The Family
Moulton-Barrett; 4. The world outside; 5. Moon in my
pocket; 6. I said love; 7. The real thing; 8. You only to
love me; 9. In a simple way; 10. I know now; 11.
Soliloquy; 12. Pass the Eau de Cologne; 13. I'm the
master here; 14. Escape me never; 15. Hate me,
please; 16. The girls that boys dream about; 17.
Woman and man; 18. Frustration; 19. Finale: I know
now.
10, 17. M. Hill Smith, National SO, J.O. Edwards
(r1989-91) *Concert* (10/91) (TER) ① **CDVIR8314**

GRAINGER, (George) Percy
(Aldridge) (1882–1961)
Australia/USA

Key: AFMS—American Folk-music settings;
BFMS—British Folk-music settings; OEPM—Settings
of Songs and Tunes from William Chappell's Old
English Popular Music; RMTB—Room-music Tit-bits;
S—sentimentals.

SECTION I: ORCHESTRAL

Blithe bells—Ramble on Bach's 'Sheep may
safely graze' (Cantata No. 208)
Martin Jones (r1989) *Concert*
(7/90) (NIMB) ① **NI5232**
Bournemouth Sinfonietta, K. Montgomery (r1978)
Concert (2/92) (CHAN) ① **CHAN6542**
Colonial Song, S1 (1911 orch 1918)
Eastman-Rochester Orch, F. Fennell (r1959) *Concert*
(11/93) (MERC) ① **434 330-2MM**

Country gardens, BFMS22 (1908/18)
Bournemouth Sinfonietta, K. Montgomery (orch
Schmid) *Concert* (2/92) (CHAN) ① **CHAN6542**
Eastman-Rochester Orch, F. Fennell (r1959) *Concert*
(11/93) (MERC) ① **434 330-2MM**
Danish Folk-Music Suite—orchestra (1928
rev 1941)
1. The Power of Love; 2. Lord Peter's Stable Boy; 3.
The Nightingale and the Two Sisters; 4. Jutish
Medley.
Melbourne SO, G. Simon (r1989) *Concert*
(11/90) (KOCH) ① **37003-2**
Duke of Marlborough's Fanfare—brass choir
and cymbal, BFMS36 (1905, 1939)
ECO, B. Britten (r1968) *Concert*
(1/90) (LOND) ① **425 159-2LM**
Green bushes—room music: 22 solo
instruments/orchestra, BFMS12 (1909-21)
ECO, S. Bedford (r1972) *Concert*
(1/90) (LOND) ① **425 159-2LM**
Bournemouth Sinfonietta, K. Montgomery (r1978)
Concert (2/92) (CHAN) ① **CHAN6542**
Handel in the Strand, RMTB2 (1932)
Bournemouth Sinfonietta, K. Montgomery *Concert*
(2/92) (CHAN) ① **CHAN6542**
Eastman-Rochester Orch, F. Fennell (r1959) *Concert*
(11/93) (MERC) ① **434 330-2MM**
Queen's Hall Orch, Henry Wood (r1935: orch Wood)
Concert (9/94) (DUTT) ① **CDAX8008**
Hill Song No. 1—orchestra (1901-02 rev
1923)
Melbourne SO, G. Simon (r1989) *Concert*
(11/90) (KOCH) ① **37003-2**
Hill Song No. 2—wind orchestra (1907)
Melbourne SO, G. Simon (r1989) *Concert*
(11/90) (KOCH) ① **37003-2**
The Immovable Do (or the Ciphering C)
(c1939)
Eastman-Rochester Orch, F. Fennell (r1959) *Concert*
(11/93) (MERC) ① **434 330-2MM**
Irish Tune from County Derry (Londonderry
Air), BFMS15 (1913)
St Louis SO, L. Slatkin *Concert*
(12/83) (TELA) ① **CD80059**
J. Lloyd Webber, ECO, N. Cleobury (arr C Palmer)
Concert (3/85) (PHIL) ① **412 231-2PH**
ECO, S. Bedford (r1972) *Concert*
(1/90) (LOND) ① **425 159-2LM**
Melbourne SO, G. Simon (r1989) *Concert*
(11/90) (KOCH) ① **37003-2**
London Wind Orch, D. Wick *Concert*
(11/92) (ASV) ① **CDWHL2067**
Eastman-Rochester Orch, F. Fennell (r1959) *Concert*
(11/93) (MERC) ① **434 330-2MM**
Lincolnshire Posy—large wind ensemble,
BFMS34 (1940)
Cleveland Winds, F. Fennell *Concert*
(10/84) (TELA) ① **CD80099**
London Wind Orch, D. Wick *Concert*
(11/92) (ASV) ① **CDWHL2067**
Mock morris, RMTB1 (1910)
Bournemouth Sinfonietta, K. Montgomery *Concert*
(2/92) (CHAN) ① **CHAN6542**
Eastman-Rochester Orch, F. Fennell (r1959) *Concert*
(11/93) (MERC) ① **434 330-2MM**
British SO, Henry Wood (r1932) *Concert*
(9/94) (DUTT) ① **CDAX8008**
Molly on the shore, BFMS1 (1907 rev c1911)
ECO, B. Britten (r1972) *Concert*
(1/90) (LOND) ① **425 159-2LM**
Welbeck Light Qt *Concert*
(10/91) (PEAR) ① **PASTCD9744**
Bournemouth Sinfonietta, K. Montgomery *Concert*
(2/92) (CHAN) ① **CHAN6542**
Eastman-Rochester Orch, F. Fennell (r1959) *Concert*
(11/93) (MERC) ① **434 330-2MM**
British SO, Henry Wood (r1932) *Concert*
(9/94) (DUTT) ① **CDAX8008**
Molly on the shore—concert band, BFMS23
London Wind Orch, D. Wick *Concert*
(11/92) (ASV) ① **CDWHL2067**
My Robin is to the greenwood gone, OEPM2
(1912)
ECO, B. Britten (r1968) *Concert*
(1/90) (LOND) ① **425 159-2LM**
Bournemouth Sinfonietta, K. Montgomery (r1978)
Concert (2/92) (CHAN) ① **CHAN6542**
Eastman-Rochester Orch, F. Fennell (r1959) *Concert*
(11/93) (MERC) ① **434 330-2MM**
Over the hills and far away—children's
march, RMTB4:I:4 (1919)
Eastman-Rochester Orch, F. Fennell (r1959) *Concert*
(11/93) (MERC) ① **434 330-2MM**
Shepherd's Hey—full orchestra, BFMS16
ECO, B. Britten (r1968) *Concert*
(1/90) (LOND) ① **425 159-2LM**

Bournemouth Sinfonietta, K. Montgomery *Concert*
(2/92) (CHAN) ① **CHAN6542**
Shepherd's Hey—large wind ensemble,
BFMS31 (1918)
Cleveland Winds, F. Fennell *Concert*
(10/84) (TELA) ① **CD80099**
London Wind Orch, D. Wick *Concert*
(11/92) (ASV) ① **CDWHL2067**
Eastman-Rochester Orch, F. Fennell (r1959) *Concert*
(11/93) (MERC) ① **434 330-2MM**
Spoon river, AFMS2 (1920)
Bournemouth Sinfonietta, K. Montgomery (r1978)
Concert (2/92) (CHAN) ① **CHAN6542**
Eastman-Rochester Orch, F. Fennell (r1959) *Concert*
(11/93) (MERC) ① **434 330-2MM**
Walking tune, RMTB3 (1900/05)
Bournemouth Sinfonietta, K. Montgomery *Concert*
(2/92) (CHAN) ① **CHAN6542**
The Warriors—music for an imaginary ballet
(1913-16)
Melbourne SO, G. Simon (r1989) *Concert*
(11/90) (KOCH) ① **37003-2**
Philh, J. E. Gardiner (r1994) *Holst: Planets*.
(8/95) (DG) ① **445 860-2GH**
Youthful rapture—cello with room-music
(1901)
M. Welsh, Bournemouth Sinfonietta, K. Montgomery
Concert (2/92) (CHAN) ① **CHAN6542**
J. Lloyd Webber, ASMF, N. Marriner (r1994) *Concert*
(12/94) (PHIL) ① **442 530-2PH**
Youthful Suite
1. Northern March (1899, 1942 rev 1943-5); 2. Rustic
Dance (1899, rev 1943-5); 3. Norse Dirge (1899,
1945); 4. Eastern Intermezzo (1899, 1945); 5.
English Waltz (1899-1901, rev 1940-3).
2, 4. Bournemouth Sinfonietta, K. Montgomery
(r1978) *Concert* (2/92) (CHAN) ① **CHAN6542**

SECTION II: CHAMBER

Always Merry and Bright—two pianos
P. Thwaites, J. Lavender *Concert*
(10/89) (PEAR) ① **SHECD9611**
Blithe bells—Ramble on Bach's 'Sheep may
safely graze' (Cantata No. 208)—two pianos
(1930-31)
P. Thwaites, J. Lavender (r1989-91) *Concert*
(1/94) (PEAR) ① **SHECD9623**
Children's March: Over the Hills and Far
Away—two pianos: four hands, RMTB4
(1916-18)
P. Thwaites, J. Lavender (r1989-91) *Concert*
(1/94) (PEAR) ① **SHECD9623**
Colonial Song—violin, cello and piano, S1
(1911)
J. Smirnoff, J. Moerschel, S. Drury *Concert*
(3/90) (NORT) ① **NR228-CD**
Country gardens—piano—four hands,
BFMS22 (1936)
P. Thwaites, J. Lavender *Concert*
(10/89) (PEAR) ① **SHECD9611**
Crew of the Long Dragon—piano duet
(1940)
P. Thwaites, J. Lavender (r1989-91) *Concert*
(1/94) (PEAR) ① **SHECD9631**
Duke of Marlborough's Fanfare—two
pianos
P. Thwaites, J. Lavender *Concert*
(10/89) (PEAR) ① **SHECD9611**
Eastern Intermezzo—two pianos, RMTB5
(1922)
P. Thwaites, J. Lavender *Concert*
(10/89) (PEAR) ① **SHECD9611**
English Waltz—two pianos (1947)
P. Thwaites, J. Lavender *Concert*
(10/89) (PEAR) ① **SHECD9611**
Fantasy on George Gershwin's 'Porgy and
Bess'
K. Labèque, M. Labèque *Gershwin: American in*
Paris. (12/84) (EMI) ① **CDC7 47044-2**
P. Thwaites, J. Lavender (r1989-91) *Concert*
(1/94) (PEAR) ① **SHECD9631**
Handel in the Strand—violin, cello and
piano, RMTB2 (1912)
J. Smirnoff, J. Moerschel, S. Drury *Concert*
(3/90) (NORT) ① **NR228-CD**
Handel in the Strand—two pianos: four
hands, RMTB2 (1947)
P. Thwaites, J. Lavender (r1989-91) *Concert*
(1/94) (PEAR) ① **SHECD9623**
Harvest Hymn—violin, cello and piano
(1932)
J. Smirnoff, J. Moerschel, S. Drury *Concert*
(3/90) (NORT) ① **NR228-CD**

SECTION III: INSTRUMENTAL

Ramble on themes from Richard Strauss's 'Der Rosenkavalier'—piano
G. Saba *Concert* (10/87) (CARL) ① **PCD858**
Martin Jones (r1989) *Concert*
(7/90) (NIMB) ① **NI5232**
Rimmer and Goldcastle—piano, DFMS3 (pub 1951)
Martin Jones *Concert* (10/90) (NIMB) ① **NI5244**
The Rival Brother—piano (pub 1951) (Faeroe Island setting)
Martin Jones *Concert* (10/90) (NIMB) ① **NI5244**
Sailor's Song—piano (1954)
Martin Jones *Concert* (4/90) (NIMB) ① **NI5220**
Saxon Twi-play—piano (1897-99)
Martin Jones *Concert* (4/90) (NIMB) ① **NI5220**
3 Scotch Folksongs—piano transcriptions (1954)
1. Leezie Lindsay (8); 2. O Gin I were where Gourie rins (13); 3. Ni Nighean Dhu (14).
R. Stevenson *Concert*
(9/95) (ALTA) ① **AIR-CD-9040**
Scotch Strathspey and Reel—piano, BFMS37 (1937-39)
Martin Jones *Concert* (10/90) (NIMB) ① **NI5244**
R. Stevenson *Concert*
(9/95) (ALTA) ① **AIR-CD-9040**
Shepherd's Hey—piano, BFMS4 (1911) (English Morris dance tune)
Martin Jones *Concert* (10/90) (NIMB) ① **NI5244**
P. Thwaites *Concert* (3/93) (UNIC) ① **DKPCD9127**
14 Songs of the North—folksong transcriptions: piano (1954)
1. Willie's gane to Melville Castle; 2. Weaving song; 3. Skye boat song; 4. This is not my plaid; 5. Turn ye to me; 6. Drowned; 7. Fair young Mary; 8. Lizzie Lindsay; 9. The women are a'gane wud; 10. My faithful ged one; 11. Bonnie George Campbell; 12. O'er the moor; 13. O gin I were where Gowrie rins; 14. Mo Ninghean Dhu.
R. Stevenson *Concert*
(9/95) (ALTA) ① **AIR-CD-9040**
Spoon River—piano, AFMS1 (1919-22)
Martin Jones *Concert* (10/90) (NIMB) ① **NI5244**
Stalt Vesselil, 'Proud Vesselil'—piano, DFMS (unnumbered) (pub 1951)
Martin Jones *Concert* (10/90) (NIMB) ① **NI5244**
The Sussex Mummers' Christmas Carol—piano, BFMS52 (1905-11) (English traditional song)
Martin Jones *Concert* (10/90) (NIMB) ① **NI5244**
P. Thwaites *Concert* (3/93) (UNIC) ① **DKPCD9127**
Tiger-tiger—piano, KS4/JBC9 (1939) (after R. Kipling)
Martin Jones *Concert* (2/91) (NIMB) ① **NI5255**
To a Nordic Princess—piano (1927-28)
Martin Jones *Concert* (4/90) (NIMB) ① **NI5220**
P. Thwaites *Concert* (3/93) (UNIC) ① **DKPCD9127**
Walking Tune—piano, RMTB3 (1911)
Martin Jones *Concert* (10/90) (NIMB) ① **NI5220**
The Widow's Party—piano, KS7 (pub 1954)
Martin Jones *Concert* (10/90) (NIMB) ① **NI5244**
Will ye gang to the Hielands—piano transcription
Martin Jones *Concert* (10/90) (NIMB) ① **NI5244**

SECTION IV: VOCAL AND CHORAL

Bold William Taylor—voice and ensemble, BFMS43 (1908)
J. Shirley-Quirk, ECO, B. Britten (r1968) *Concert*
(1/90) (LOND) ① **425 159-2LM**
Brigg Fair—Lincolnshire folksong setting: tenor solo with mixed chorus, BFMS7
P. Sheffield, Cambridge Sngrs, J. Rutter *Concert*
(4/87) (CLLE) ① **COLCD104**
King's Sngrs *Concert*
(6/88) (EMI) ① **CDC7 49765-2**
P. Pears, Ambrosian Sngrs, S. Bedford (r1972) *Concert* (1/90) (LOND) ① **425 159-2LM**
N. Stone, Oriana Madrigal Soc, C. Kennedy Scott (r1927) *Concert* (3/94) (DUTT) ① **CDAX8006**
J. Lloyd Webber, ASMF, N. Marriner (r1994; arr C. Palmer: vc) *Concert* (12/94) (PHIL) ① **442 530-2PH**
I'm seventeen come Sunday—chorus and brass ensemble, BFMS8 (1905-12)
Ambrosian Sngrs, ECO, B. Britten (r1968) *Concert*
(1/90) (LOND) ① **425 159-2LM**
Irish Tune from County Derry—folksong setting, BFMS5 (1902)
Cambridge Sngrs, J. Rutter *Concert*
(4/87) (CLLE) ① **COLCD104**
Lord Maxwell's Goodnight—baritone and strings, BFMS14 (1904-12)
P. Pears, ECO, B. Britten (r1968) *Concert*
(1/90) (LOND) ① **425 159-2LM**

The Lost lady found—choral folksong, BFMS33 (1905-10)
Ambrosian Sngrs, ECO, B. Britten (r1968) *Concert*
(1/90) (LOND) ① **425 159-2LM**
Love at first sight—chorus (1946) (arr of Ella Grainger's song)
P. Thwaites (trans Stevenson) *Concert*
(3/93) (UNIC) ① **DKPCD9127**
Pretty maid milking her cow—voice and piano, BFMS27 (1920)
P. Pears, B. Britten (r1968) *Concert*
(1/90) (LOND) ① **425 159-2LM**
Scotch Strathspey and Reel—2 tenors, 2 baritones, 16 instruments, BFMS28 (1901-11)
ECO, B. Britten (r1968) *Concert*
(1/90) (LOND) ① **425 159-2LM**
Shallow Brown—choral folksong, SCS3 (1923-25)
J. Shirley-Quirk, ECO, B. Britten (r1968) *Concert*
(1/90) (LOND) ① **425 159-2LM**
Shenandoah—unaccompanied voices, SCS (unnumbered) (1907)
J. Shirley-Quirk, Linden Sngrs, Wandsworth Sch Boys' Ch, S. Bedford (r1972) *Concert*
(1/90) (LOND) ① **425 159-2LM**
The Sprig of Thyme—voice and piano, BFMS24 (1907, 1920)
P. Pears, B. Britten (r1968) *Concert*
(1/90) (LOND) ① **425 159-2LM**
F. Lott, G. Johnson *Concert*
(7/90) (CHAN) ① **CHAN8722**
There was a pig went out to dig—female voices, BFMS18 (1905 rev 1910)
Ambrosian Sngrs (r1968) *Concert*
(1/90) (LOND) ① **425 159-2LM**
Willow, willow—song, OEPM1 (1902-11)
P. Pears, ECO, B. Britten (r1972) *Concert*
(1/90) (LOND) ① **425 159-2LM**

GRANADOS (Y CAMPIÑA), Enrique *(1867-1916) Spain*

SECTION III: INSTRUMENTAL

Allegro de concierto—piano (1904)
T. Rajna *Concert* (11/88) (CRD) ① **CRD3323**
A. de Larrocha *Concert*
(7/90) (DECC) ① **417 795-2DM**
A. de Larrocha *Concert* (2/91) (RCA) ① **RD60408**
A. de Larrocha *Concert*
(9/92) (DECC) ① [2] **433 923-2DM2**
A. Petchersky *Concert*
(12/92) (ASV) ① **CDQS6079**
Capricho español—piano (1879)
J. Horreaux, J-M. Tréhard (trs. gtr duo) *Concert*
(9/88) (CALL) ① **CAL9204**
T. Rajna *Concert* (11/88) (CRD) ① **CRD3323**
Carezza (Vals)—piano, Op. 38
T. Rajna *Concert* (11/88) (CRD) ① **CRD3322**
Cuentos de la juventud—piano, Op. 1 (1902-06)
1. Dedicatoria; 2. La Mendiga; 3. Cancion de Mayo; 4. Cuento Viejo; 5. Viniendo de la fuente; 7. Recuerdos de la infancia; 8. El Fantasma; 9. La huérfana; 10. Marcha.
1. J. Bream (r1982; trans Bream) *Concert*
(8/93) (RCA) ① [28] **09026 61583-2(6)**
1. J. Bream (r1982; trans Bream) *Concert*
(6/94) (RCA) ① **09026 61608-2**
Danza lenta—piano
T. Rajna *Concert* (5/88) (CRD) ① **CRD3322**
A. de Larrocha *Concert* (2/91) (RCA) ① **RD60408**
2 Danzas caraterisica—piano, Op. posth
1. Danza gitana; 2. Danza aragonesa.
J. Horreaux, J-M. Tréhard (trs. gtr duo) *Concert*
(9/88) (CALL) ① **CAL9204**
12 Danzas españolas—piano, Op. 37 (1892-1900)
1. Galante (Minuetto); 2. Oriental; 3. Fandango (Zarabando); 4. Villanesca; 5. Andaluza (Playera); 6. Jota (Rondella aragonesa); 7. Valenciana (Calasera); 8. Sardana (Asturiana); 9. Romantica (Mazurca); 10. Melancolica (Danza triste); 11. Arabaesca; 12. Bolero (Zambra).
T. Rajna (r1975) (12/90) (CRD) ① **CRD3321**
A. Romero, Celedonio Romero (arr 2 gtrs)
(6/91) (TELA) ① **CD80216**
A. de Larrocha *Concert*
(9/92) (DECC) ① [2] **433 923-2DM2**
J-F. Heisser *Escenas románticas.*
(11/92) (ERAT) ① **2292-45803-2**
A. Hewitt *Goyescas.* (11/94) (CBC) ① **MVCD1074**
2. Empire Brass, E. Flower (r1991) *Concert*
(11/93) (TELA) ① **CD80301**

2. J. Bream, J. Williams (r1978; arr Bream) *Concert*
(11/93) (RCA) ① **09026 61450-2**
2, 4, 11, 12. J. Horreaux, J-M. Tréhard (trs. gtr duo) *Concert* (9/88) (CALL) ① **CAL9204**
2, 5, 6. Mexico City PO, E. Bátiz (orch de Grignon) *Concert* (9/91) (ASV) ① **CDDCA735**
4, 5. J. Bream (r1982; trans Bream) *Concert*
(8/93) (RCA) ① [28] **09026 61583-2(6)**
4, 5. J. Bream (r1982; trans Bream) *Concert*
(6/94) (RCA) ① **09026 61608-2**
5. I. Perlman, S. Sanders (arr Kreisler) *Concert*
(11/90) (EMI) ① **CDM7 63533-2**
5. J. Thibaud, T. Janopoulo (r1930: arr vn/pf: Kreisler) *Concert* (10/91) (MSCM) ① **MM30321**
5. M. Hanskov, T. Lønskov (arr db) *Concert*
(3/92) (DANA) ① **DACOCD378**
5. A.B. Michelangeli (r1939) *Concert*
(8/93) (EMI) ① **CDH7 64490-2**
5. A. Rubinstein (r1954) *Concert*
(9/93) (RCA) ① **09026 61261-2**
5. J. Heifetz, S. Chotzinoff (r1922) *Concert*
(11/94) (RCA) ① [65] **09026 61778-2(01)**
5. J. Thibaud, T. Janopoulo (r1930: arr vn/pf: Thibaud) *Concert* (12/94) (APR) ① [2] **APR7028**
5. LSO, A. Argenta (r1957: orch ?) *Concert*
(5/95) (DECC) ① **443 580-2DCS**
5. I. Perlman, S. Sanders (r1978: arr vn/pf: Kreisler) *Concert* (6/95) (EMI) ① [20] **CZS4 83177-2(2)**
5, 10. A. Segovia (gtr; r1939) *Concert*
(5/89) (EMI) ① [2] **CHS7 61047-2**
6. P. Casals, N. Mednikoff (arr Casals: r1928) *Concert* (10/91) (BIDD) ① **LAB017**
6, 11. J. Bream, J. Williams (r1973; trans Llobet) *Concert* (11/93) (RCA) ① **09026 61452-2**
7, 10. E. Granados (r c1912) *Concert*
(11/93) (RCA) ① **CDC7 54836-2**
6 Escenas románticas—piano
1. Mazurca; 2. Recitativo y berceuse; 3. El poeta y el ruisenor; 4. Allegro: Pequenia Lanza; 5. Allegro appasionato; 6. Epilogo: Andantino spianato.
T. Rajna *Concert* (5/88) (CRD) ① **CRD3322**
A. de Larrocha *Concert*
(9/92) (DECC) ① [2] **433 920-2DM2**
J-F. Heisser *Danzas españolas.*
(11/92) (ERAT) ① **2292-45803-2**
Goyescas—suite for piano (1911)
Book 1: 1. Los requiebros; 2. Coloquio en la reja; 3. El fandango de Candil; 4. Quejas o la maja y el ruiseñor. Book 2: 5. El amor y la muerte (Balada); 6. Epilogo: La serenada del espectro; 7. El pelele.
A. de Larrocha (3/89) (DECC) ① **411 958-2DH**
T. Rajna (3/89) (CRD) ① **CRD3301**
A. de Larrocha *Concert* (2/91) (RCA) ① **RD60408**
A. Ciccolini *Albéniz: Iberia.*
(3/92) (EMI) ① **CZS7 62889-2**
A. de Larrocha *Concert*
(9/92) (DECC) ① [2] **433 920-2DM2**
A. de Larrocha *Concert*
(12/92) (EMI) ① [2] **CMS7 64524-2**
1-6. J-M. Luisada (12/92) (DG) ① **435 787-2GH**
4. M. Lympany *Concert* (1/89) (EMIL) ① **CDZ110**
4. A. Rubinstein (r1949) *Concert*
(9/93) (RCA) ① **09026 61261-2**
4, 7. A. de Larrocha *Concert*
(7/90) (DECC) ① **417 795-2DM**
4, 7. A. Hewitt *Danzas españolas.*
(11/94) (CBC) ① **MVCD1074**
6. J. Horreaux, J-M. Tréhard (trs. gtr duo) *Concert*
(9/88) (CALL) ① **CAL9204**
7. E. Granados (r c1912) *Concert*
(11/93) (RCA) ① **CDC7 54836-2**
2 Impromptus—piano, Op. 39
T. Rajna *Concert* (11/88) (CRD) ① **CRD3323**
Moresque—piano
J. Horreaux, J-M. Tréhard (trs. gtr duo) *Concert*
(9/88) (CALL) ① **CAL9204**
Oriental—Cancion variada, Intermedio y Final—piano
T. Rajna *Concert* (11/88) (CRD) ① **CRD3323**
6 Piezas sobre cantos populares españoles—piano
1. Preludio; 2. Anoranza; 3. Ecos de la Parranda; 4. Vascongada; 5. Marcha Oriental; 6. Zambra; 7. Zapateado.
T. Rajna *Concert* (5/88) (CRD) ① **CRD3322**
A. de Larrocha *Concert*
(9/92) (DECC) ① [2] **433 920-2DM2**
A. de Larrocha *Concert*
(12/92) (EMI) ① [2] **CMS7 64524-2**
6. A. de Larrocha *Concert*
(7/90) (DECC) ① **417 795-2DM**
Rapsodia aragonesa—piano
J. Horreaux, J-M. Tréhard (trs. gtr duo) *Concert*
(9/88) (CALL) ① **CAL9204**

T. Rajna *Concert*   (11/88) (CRD) ① **CRD3323**

7 Valses poéticos—piano (1887)
1. Melodioso; 2. Valse noble; 3. Valse lente; 4.
Allegro umoristico; 5. Allegretto; 6. Quasi ad libitum;
7. Viro.
J. Horreaux, J-M. Tréhard (trs. gtr duo) *Concert*
          (9/88) (CALL) ① **CAL9204**
T. Rajna *Concert*   (11/88) (CRD) ① **CRD3323**
J. Williams (r1991) *Concert*
          (7/92) (SONY) ① **SK48480**
A. de Larrocha *Concert*
          (12/92) (EMI) ① [2] **CMS7 64524-2**
J. Bream (r1982; trans Bream) *Concert*
          (8/93) (RCA) ① [28] **09026 61583-2(6)**
J. Bream (r1982; trans Bream) *Concert*
          (6/94) (RCA) ① **09026 61608-2**

SECTION IV: VOCAL AND CHORAL

7 Canciones amatorias—songs
1. Mira que soy niña; 2. Llorad, corazón, que tenéis
razón; 3. No lloréis, ojuelos; 4. Iban al pinar; 5.
Descúbrase el pensamiento de mi secreto cuidado;
6. Mañanica era; 7. Gracia mía.
Cpte M. Bayo, J.A. Alvarez-Parejo (r1992) *Concert*
          (6/93) (CLAV) ① **CD50-9205**
1, 2, 4, 6. Y. Pappas, Israel SO, G. Stern *Concert*
          (2/88) (MERI) ① **CDE84134**
2, 4. V. de los Angeles, Paris Cons, R. Frühbeck de
Burgos (r1962) *Concert*
          (4/94) (EMI) ① [4] **CMS5 65061-2(1)**

15 Tonadillas al estilo antiguo—songs (Wds.
F. Periquet y Zuaznabar)
1. Amor y odio; 2. Callejo; 3. La maja dolorosa; 3a.
Oh! Muerte cruel; 3b. Ay! Majo de mi vida; 3c. De
aquel majo amante; 4. El majo discreto; 5. El majo
Olvidado; 6. El majo timido; 7. La maja de Goya; 8. El
mirar de la Maja; 9. Las Currutacas modestas; 10.
Playera; 11. El tra la la y el punteado; 12. Elegia
eterna; 13. La maja a el el ruisenor; 14. Cano d'amor;
15. L'oceli profeta.
1, 3, 4. N. Miricioiu, D. Harper (pp1985) *Concert*
          (5/90) (ETCE) ① **KTC1041**
1, 3, 4, 8, 11. P. Rozario, M. Troop *Concert*
          (12/92) (COLL) ① **Coll3052-2**
3. J. Gomez, J. Constable (r1994) *Concert*
          (9/94) (CONI) ① **CDCF243**
3, 4, 11. D. Jones, M. Martineau (r1993) *Concert*
          (9/94) (CHAN) ① **CHAN9277**
3, 4, 6, 11. T. Berganza, F. Lavilla *Concert*
          (12/92) (DG) ① [2] **435 848-2GX2**
3, 4, 8, 11. V. de los Angeles, G. Parsons (pp1990)
Concert   (12/91) (COLL) ① **Coll1247-2**
4. H. Spani, orch, G. Nastrucci (r1930) *Concert*
          (9/90) (CLUB) ① [2] **CL99-509/10**
7. M. Kayath (arr Kayaths) *Concert*
          (5/88) (CARL) ① **PCD876**
7. J. Horreaux, J-M. Tréhard (trs. gtr duo) *Concert*
          (9/88) (CALL) ① **CAL9204**
7. J. Bream (r1982; trans Bream) *Concert*
          (8/93) (RCA) ① [28] **09026 61583-2(6)**
7. J. Bream (r1982; trans Bream) *Concert*
          (6/94) (RCA) ① **09026 61608-2**
7. P. Romero (r1993; trans P. Romero) *Concert*
          (4/95) (PHIL) ① **442 150-2PH**

SECTION V: STAGE WORKS

Goyescas—opera: 1 act (1916—New York)
(Lib. F. Periquet y Zuaznabar)
EXCERPTS: 1. Intermezzo; 2. La maja y el ruiseñor
(Lover and the nightingale); 3. Elegia eterna.
1. New Philh, R. Frühbeck de Burgos *Concert*
          (10/89) (DECC) ① **417 786-2DM**
1. LSO, R. Frühbeck de Burgos *Concert*
          (11/89) (CARL) ① **PCD924**
1. Mexico City PO, E. Bátiz *Concert*
          (9/91) (ASV) ① **CDDCA735**
1. P. Casals, N. Mednikoff (arr Cassadó: r1927)
Concert   (10/91) (BIDD) ① **LAB017**
1. M. Hanskov, T. Lønskov (arr db/pf) *Concert*
          (3/92) (DANA) ① **DACOCD378**
1. M. Kliegel, R. Havenith (arr vc/pf) *Concert*
          (9/92) (MARC) ① **8 223403**
1. T. Kropat, T. Krumeich (arr gtr duet) *Concert*
          (7/93) (CHNN) ① **CG9103**
1. J. Bream, J. Williams (r1971; arr Pujol) *Concert*
          (11/93) (RCA) ① **09026 61450-2**
2. V. de los Angeles, Philh, A. Fistoulari (r1950)
Concert   (4/92) (EMI) ① **CDH7 64028-2**
2. M. Caballé, M. Burgueras (pp1994) *Concert*
          (1/95) (RCA) ① **09026 62547-2**

GRANDI, Alessandro
(?1575/80–1630) Italy

SECTION IV: VOCAL AND CHORAL

18 Motets—1v and continuo (pub 1621)
1. Audite populi; 2. Columna es; 3. Deus canticum
novum; 4. Dixi iniqui; 5. Ecce sacerdos magnus; 6.
Fasciculus mirrhae; 7. Gaudeamus omnes in
Domino; 8. Hodie virgo; 9. In lectulo meo; 10. O dulce
nomen Jesus; 11. O intemerata; 12. O lampas
ecclesiae; 13. Osculetor me; 14. Quam pulchra es;
15. Respice Domine; 16. Sancti Aloysi; 17. Tota
pulchra es; 18. Virgo prudentissima.
11. Gabrieli Consort, Gabrieli Players, P. McCreesh
(r1990; ed McCreesh) *Concert*
          (4/93) (ARCH) ① [2] **437 552-2AH2**

Motets, Book 1—2-5 or 8vv and continuo:
with a Mass (pub 1610)
1. Ad te de luce viglio (2vv); 2. Audivit Dominus (2vv);
3. Benedictus Dominus (4vv); 4. Cantabo Domino
(4vv); 5. Caro mea (4vv); 6. Congratulamini omnes
(4vv); 7. Deus, meus (3vv); 8. Exaudi, Domine (2vv);
9. Hic est vere martyr (4vv); 10. Hodie nobis de caelo
(2vv); 11. In semita judiciorum (2vv); 12. In te speravi
(3vv); 13. Missus est (5vv); 14. Nativitas tua (8vv);
15. Obaudite me (4vv); 16. O quam tu pulchra es
(3vv); 17. Quam dilecta (3vv); 18. Quam dives es
(2vv); 19. Sicut oculi sevorum (3vv); 20. Vidi
speciosam (4vv); 21. Messa sexti toni (4vv,
continuo).
16. Jeffrey Thomas, Taverner Ch, Taverner Consort,
Taverner Plyrs, A. Parrott *Concert*
          (8/91) (EMI) ① **CDC7 54117-2**

O quam tu pulchra es—motet: 1v (pub
1625)
J. Bowman, S. Sempé, J. Bernfeld *Concert*
          (9/89) (ARIO) ① **ARN68046**
Gabrieli Consort, Gabrieli Players, P. McCreesh
(r1990; ed McCreesh) *Concert*
          (4/93) (ARCH) ① [2] **437 552-2AH2**

GRANDJANY, Marcel (1891–1975)
France/USA

SECTION III: INSTRUMENTAL

Automne—harp
L. Laskine (r1975) *Concert*
          (12/93) (ERAT) ① **4509-92131-2**

Siciliana—harp
S. McDonald *Concert*   (10/84) (DELO) ① **DE3005**

GRANIER, Jean (19th Cent)

SECTION IV: VOCAL AND CHORAL

Hosanna—religious song (Wds J. J. Didiée)
E. Caruso, orch (r1912) *Concert*
          (7/91) (RCA) ① [12] **GD60495(4)**
E. Caruso, orch (r1912) *Concert*
          (10/91) (PEAR) ① [3] **EVC3(1)**
L. Escalais, anon (r1905) *Concert*
          (12/93) (SYMP) ① **SYMCD1126**

SECTION V: STAGE WORKS

Pierre l'ermite—opera
Scène pour ténor L. Escalais, anon (r1906) *Concert*
          (12/93) (SYMP) ① **SYMCD1126**

GRANT, Bert (19th–20th Cent)
USA

SECTION V: STAGE WORKS

Step This Way—musical show (1916—New
York)
EXCERPTS: 1. If I Knock the 'L' Out of Kelly (Lyrics
Young/Lewis); 2. By the Sad Luana Shore (Lyrics
Goetz).
1, 2. M. Farrell, Orig Broadway Cast (r1916) *Concert*
          (5/94) (PEAR) ① [3] **GEMMCDS9056/8**

GRANT, David (1833–1893)
Scotland

SECTION IV: VOCAL AND CHORAL

Psalm 23, '(The) Lord's my Shepherd' (tune:
Crimond)
Westminster Abbey Ch, M. Neary *Concert*
          (10/89) (CARL) ① **PCD919**

GRASSE, Edwin (1884–1954)
USA

SECTION II: CHAMBER

Wellenspiel—violin and piano
J. Heifetz, E. Bay (r1945) *Concert*
          (11/94) (RCA) ① [65] **09026 61778-2(19)**

GRAUN, Carl Heinrich
(1703/4–1759) Germany

SECTION III: INSTRUMENTAL

Sonata for Keyboard in D minor
C. Schornsheim (r1991) *Concert*
          (4/95) (CAPR) ① **10 424**

SECTION V: STAGE WORKS

Artaserse—opera (1743—Berlin) (Lib.
Metastasio)
Sulle sponde del torbido lete J. Kowalski, Berlin
CO, M. Pommer *Concert*   (9/88) (CAPR) ① **10 113**
Cleopatra e Cesare—opera (1742—Berlin)
(Lib. Botarelli, after Corneille)
Cortese il cielo non può donare J. Kowalski, Berlin
CO, M. Pommer *Concert*   (9/88) (CAPR) ① **10 113**
Montezuma—opera (1775—Berlin) (Lib.
Frederick II, trans Tagliazucchi)
Cpte E. Vazquez, D. Wirtz, C. Julian, L. Ambriz, A.U.
Sanchez, M.L. Tamez, A.C. Acosta, Cantica Nova
Chbr Ch, Neuss German Chbr Acad, J. Goritzki
(r1992)   (7/93) (CAPR) ① [2] **60 032**
Rodelinda—opera (1741—Berlin) (Lib.
Botarelli, after Salvi)
Pompe vane di morte...Se a questa vita J.
Kowalski, Berlin CO, M. Pommer *Concert*
          (9/88) (CAPR) ① **10 113**

GRAUN, Johann Gottlieb
(1704–1759) Germany

SECTION II: CHAMBER

Trio for Violin, Viola and Continuo in G
minor
M. Comberti, J. Coe, L.U. Mortensen, S. Standage
(vn/dir) *Concert*   (5/94) (CHAN) ① **CHAN0541**

GRAUPNER, (Johann) Christoph
(1683–1760) Germany

SECTION I: ORCHESTRAL

Overture-Suite for Chalumeau, Strings and
Continuo in B flat (c1743)
J-C. Veilhan, Mensa Sonora Ens, J. Maillet (vn/dir)
(r1994) *Concert*   (4/95) (PIER) ① **PV794114**
Overture-Suite for 2 Chalumeaux, Strings
and Continuo in F (c1735-7)
J-C. Veilhan, Y. Tetsu, Mensa Sonora Ens, J. Maillet
(vn/dir) (r1994) *Concert*   (4/95) (PIER) ① **PV794114**
Overture-Suite for 3 Chalumeaux, Strings
and Continuo in D minor (c1741)
J-C. Veilhan, Y. Tetsu, F. Jacquemart, Mensa Sonora
Ens, J. Maillet (vn/dir) *Concert*
          (4/95) (PIER) ① **PV794114**

SECTION II: CHAMBER

Suite for 3 Chalumeaux (1741)
K. Puddy, G. Brodie, P. Price (r1992) *Concert*
          (10/93) (CLRI) ① **CC0004**

GRAY, Alan (1855–1931)
England

SECTION IV: VOCAL AND CHORAL

What are these that glow from
afar?—anthem
Worcester Cath Ch, A. Partington, Don Hunt *Concert*
          (9/90) (CARL) ① **PCD937**
Truro Cath Ch, D. Briggs, S. Morley (1992) *Concert*
          (7/94) (PRIO) ① **PRCD429**

GRAY, Allan (1902–1973) Poland
or Austria

SECTION V: STAGE WORKS

A Matter of Life and Death—film score
(1946)
EXCERPTS: 1. Prelude.
1. QHLO, C. Williams (1946) *Concert*
          (9/94) (EMI) ① **CDGO 2059**

GRAZIOLI, Alessandro (1770–1834) Italy

SECTION III: INSTRUMENTAL

Sinfonia strumentale in F—keyboard
R. Micconi (arr org) Concert
(3/90) (MOTE) ① CD10561

GREAVES, Thomas (fl 1604) England

SECTION IV: VOCAL AND CHORAL

Come away, sweet love—madrigal
Amaryllis Consort, C. Brett Concert
(3/88) (CARL) ① PCD873

GRECHANINOV, Alexandr Tikhonovich (1864–1956) Russia/USA

SECTION I: ORCHESTRAL

Symphony No. 1 in B minor, Op. 6 (1895)
Russian St SO, V. Polyansky Concert
(12/95) (CHAN) ① CHAN9397

SECTION II: CHAMBER

Piano Trio No. 1 in C minor, Op. 38 (1906)
V. Šimčisko, J. Alexander, D. Rusó Piano Trio 2.
(6/93) (MARC) ① 8 223416
Piano Trio No. 2 in G, Op. 128 (1930)
V. Šimčisko, J. Alexander, D. Rusó Piano Trio 1.
(6/93) (MARC) ① 8 223416
String Quartet No. 1 in G, Op. 2 (1892-93)
Shostakovich Qt Concert
(10/94) (OLYM) ① OCD522
String Quartet No. 2 in D minor, Op. 70 (1913)
Moyzes Qt (r1993) String Quartet 4.
(10/94) (MARC) ① 8 223646
String Quartet No. 4 in F, Op. 124 (1929)
Moyzes Qt (r1990) String Quartet 2.
(10/94) (MARC) ① 8 223646

SECTION IV: VOCAL AND CHORAL

Epicedium—song
K. Vayne, C. Tilney (r1966) Concert
(6/95) (PREI) ① 89996
I wish I were with you—song
D. Smirnov, anon (r1913) Concert
(6/93) (PEAR) ① [3] GEMMCDS9004/6(2)
Liturgy of St John Chrysostom No. 1—chorus a capella, Op. 13 (1897)
Cantus Sacred Music Ens, L. Arshavskaya (r1993)
(6/95) (OLYM) ① OCD447
Liturgy of St John Chrysostom No. 3—soloists, chorus and orchestra, Op. 79 (1917)
Cpte V. Radkevich, A. Obraztsova, L. Golub, Russian St Sym Cappella, Russian St SO, V. Polyansky
(pp1989) (8/95) (CHAN) ① CHAN9365
Litany F. Chaliapin, Paris Russian Met Church Ch, N. Afonsky (r1932) Concert
(1/93) (MMOI) ① CDMOIR411
Litany F. Chaliapin, Paris Russian Met Church Ch, N. Afonsky (r1932) Concert
(6/93) (PREI) ① [2] 89207
Liturgy of St John Chrysostom No. 4—chorus a capella, Op. 177 (1943)
Cantus Sacred Music Ens, L. Arshavskaya (r1994)
(9/95) (OLYM) ① OCD480
Lullaby—song, Op. 1/5
A. Kipnis, C. Dougherty (r1939) Concert
(9/92) (RCA) ① GD60522
D. Smirnov, anon (r1912) Concert
(6/93) (PEAR) ① [3] GEMMCDS9004/6(2)
Missa Sancti Spiritus—choir & organ, Op. 169 (1943)
Cpte T. Jeranje, Russian St Sym Cappella, V. Polyansky (r1995) Concert
(12/95) (CHAN) ① CHAN9397
My native land—song (Wds. K. Schindler)
A. Kipnis, C. Dougherty (r1939) Concert
(9/92) (RCA) ① GD60522
Over the Steppe—song
V. Sharonov, anon (r1903) Concert
(7/93) (SYMP) ① SYMCD1105
M. Garden, J. Dansereau (1926) Concert
(8/93) (SYMP) ① SYMCD1136
M. Garden, J. Dansereau (1929) Concert
(8/94) (ROMO) ① 81008-2

The seven days of the Passion—chorus a cappella (1911)
1. Behold the bridegroom; 2. I see Thy bridal chamber; 3. In Thy kingdo; 4. O gladsome light; 5. Let my prayer be set forth; 6. Now the powers of heaven; 7. At Thy mystical supper; 8. O Lord, this very day; 9. O Lord, in a single hair; 10a. The Lord is God; 10b. Noble Joseph; 11. Weep not for me, O Mother; 12a. As many of you; 12b. Arise, O God; 13. Let all mortal flesh.
Cpte Russian St Sym Cappella, V. Polyansky (r1990s) (1/95) (CHAN) ① CHAN9303
She was yours—song
D. Smirnov, anon (r1912) Concert
(6/93) (PEAR) ① [3] GEMMCDS9004/6(2)
A. Bogdanovich, anon (r1903) Concert
(6/93) (PEAR) ① [3] GEMMCDS9007/9(1)
Snowflakes—Songs from the World of Childhood—song cycle: 1v/choir & piano/orchestra, Op. 47 (1909, orch 1910)
EXCERPTS: 1. Snowflakes (Wds. V Bryusov); 2. Little Willows (Wds. A Blok); 3. About the calf (Wds. I Novikov); 4. In the Forest (Wds. S Gorodetskiy); 5. Tom Thumb (Wds. V Zhukovskiy); 6. Gnomes (Wds. K Balmont); 7. Night; 8. Frost (Wds. N N); 9. The Snowdrop; 10. Fairy's Song (Wds. K Balmont).
Cpte L. Kuznetsova, Russian St Sym Cappella, V. Polyansky (r1995) Concert
(12/95) (CHAN) ① CHAN9397

SECTION V: STAGE WORKS

Dobrinya Nikitich—opera, Op. 22 (1903—Moscow) (Lib. cpsr)
Flowers were blooming in the fields L. Sobinov, anon (r1901) Concert
(6/93) (PEAR) ① [3] GEMMCDS9997/9(1)
Flowers were blooming in the fields D. Smirnov, orch, P. Pitt (r1921) Concert
(6/93) (PEAR) ① [3] GEMMCDS9004/6(2)
Zabava's aria A. Nezhdanova, U. Masetti (r1906) Concert
(6/93) (PEAR) ① [3] GEMMCDS9007/9(1)

GREEBE, Benedict (d 1619) Denmark

SECTION III: INSTRUMENTAL

Paduana and Galliard—lute (pub 1609)
J. Lindberg Concert (2/89) (BIS) ① BIS-CD390

GREEN, Philip (1911–1982) England

SECTION V: STAGE WORKS

Ha'penny Breeze—film score (1950)
EXCERPTS: 1. Theme.
1. Orch, P. Green (r1950) Concert
(9/94) (EMI) ① CDGO 2059

GREENE, Maurice (1696–1755) England

SECTION III: INSTRUMENTAL

A Collection of Lessons—harpsichord (pub 1750)
EXCERPTS: 1. Allegro in A minor; 2. Vivace in A minor; 3. Molto allegro in A minor; 4. Aria con Variazioni in A.
1-4. L. U. Mortensen (r1994) Concert
(8/95) (MOSC) ① 070978
6 Overtures in seven parts—harpsichord/spinet (pub 1745) (arr of orch works)
2. D.
No 1. T. Pinnock (r1978) Concert
(4/89) (CRD) ① CRD3347
Voluntary—organ (unidentified)
T. Dart (r1957) Concert (5/95) (JMS) ① JMSCD1
12 Voluntaries—organ/harpsichord (pub 1779)
EXCERPTS: 1. B minor; 2. C minor; 3. G; 7. No 7 in E flat.
1. J. Bate Concert (5/91) (UNIC) ① DKPCD9101
1, 3. G. Cooper Concert (9/92) (CRD) ① CRD3484
2. J. Bate Concert (5/91) (UNIC) ① DKPCD9099
7. J. Bate Concert (7/91) (UNIC) ① DKPCD9104
7. L. U. Mortensen (r1994) Concert
(8/95) (MOSC) ① 070978

SECTION IV: VOCAL AND CHORAL

Battilio siediti—Anacreontic Ode (Wds. Rolli)
E. Kirkby, H. Gough, L. U. Mortensen (r1994) Concert
(8/95) (MOSC) ① 070978

Bel mirar—Anacreontic Ode (Wds. Rolli)
E. Kirkby, H. Gough, L. U. Mortensen (r1994) Concert
(8/95) (MOSC) ① 070978
A Cantata and Four English Songs, Book 1 (pub 1745)
EXCERPTS: 1. Orpheus with his Lute (Wds. Shakespeare).
1. E. Kirkby, L. U. Mortensen (r1994) Concert
(8/95) (MOSC) ① 070978
A Cantata and Four English Songs, Book 2 (pub 1746)
EXCERPTS: 1. Beauty, an Ode (Wds. John Hughes).
1. E. Kirkby, U. Weiss, I. Davies, M. Kelly, H. Gough, L. U. Mortensen (r1994) Concert
(8/95) (MOSC) ① 070978
The Chaplet—a Collection of 12 English Songs (pub 1738)
EXCERPTS: 1. Ye purple-blooming Roses; 2. Sweet Annie fra the sea beach came; 3. Fair Sally (aka The Bonny Seaman).
1-3. E. Kirkby, L. U. Mortensen (r1994) Concert
(8/95) (MOSC) ① 070978
Farfalietta festosetta—aria: 1v, vn & continuo (Wds. Anon)
E. Kirkby, U. Weiss, H. Gough, L. U. Mortensen (r1994) Concert (8/95) (MOSC) ① 070978
God is our hope and strength—anthem: 4 soloists, 4-part chorus and organ (1743)
New College Ch, D. Burchell, E. Higginbottom Concert (10/89) (MERI) ① CDE84151
New College Ch, E. Higginbottom Concert
(9/92) (CRD) ① CRD3484
Have mercy upon me, o God—verse anthem (1743)
New College Ch, E. Higginbottom Concert
(9/92) (CRD) ① CRD3484
How long wilt thou forget me, O Lord, for ever—anthem: 8vv (1743)
New College Ch, D. Burchell, E. Higginbottom Concert (10/89) (MERI) ① CDE84151
New College Ch, E. Higginbottom Concert
(9/92) (CRD) ① CRD3484
The King shall rejoice—verse anthem (1743)
New College Ch, E. Higginbottom Concert
(9/92) (CRD) ① CRD3484
Let God arise—verse anthem (1721)
New College Ch, E. Higginbottom Concert
(9/92) (CRD) ① CRD3484
Lord let me know mine end—anthem (2 sops, 4vv)
New College Ch, D. Burchell, E. Higginbottom Concert (10/89) (MERI) ① CDE84151
Magdalen Oxford Coll Ch, J. Harper Concert
(11/91) (ABBE) ① CDCA912
New College Ch, E. Higginbottom Concert
(9/92) (CRD) ① CRD3484
Oxford Christ Church Cath Ch, S. Darlington Concert (10/92) (NIMB) ① NI5328
Lincoln Cath Ch, J. Vivian, C. Walsh (r1993) Concert (7/94) (PRIO) ① PRCD454
Nell'orror—aria: 1v, vn & continuo (Wds. Anon)
E. Kirkby, U. Weiss, H. Gough, L. U. Mortensen (r1994) Concert (8/95) (MOSC) ① 070978
O clap your hands together—anthem: 5vv (1743)
New College Ch, E. Higginbottom Concert
(9/92) (CRD) ① CRD3484
O God of my righteousness—anthem (1743)
I will lay me down in peace K. Ferrier, G. Moore (r1944) Concert (6/88) (EMI) ① CDH7 61003-2
Praise the Lord, O my soul—anthem
O praise the Lord K. Ferrier, G. Moore (r1944) Concert (6/88) (EMI) ① CDH7 61003-2
Quanto contenta godi—aria: 1v, vn & continuo (Wds. Anon)
E. Kirkby, U. Weiss, L. U. Mortensen (r1994) Concert (8/95) (MOSC) ① 070978
Spenser's Amoretti—song collection: 1v & continuo (pub 1739) (Wds. Spenser)
EXCERPTS: 1. The rolling wheele (Sonnet V); 2. How long shall this (Sonnet VII); 3. Sweet smile (Sonnet XII); 4. The love which me (Sonnet XIV); 5. Faire ye be sure (SOnnet XVII); 6. Like as the Culver (Sonnet XXV).
1-6. E. Kirkby, L. U. Mortensen (r1994) Concert
(8/95) (MOSC) ① 070978
Thou, O God, art praised in Zion—verse anthem (1743)
Thou visitest the earth New College Ch, E. Higginbottom Concert (9/92) (CRD) ① CRD3484

GREENWOOD, John (1889–1975) England

SECTION V: STAGE WORKS

Hungry Hill—film score (1946)
EXCERPTS: 1. Waltz into Jig.
1. LSO, M. Mathieson (r1946) *Concert*
(9/94) (EMI) ① **CDGO 2059**

GREGORY, Will (20th cent)

SECTION II: CHAMBER

Hoe down—saxophone, percussion & keyboards
Apollo Sax Qt, J. Harle, W. Gregory, M. Hamnett
(r1993) *Concert*   (8/95) (ARGO) ① **443 903-2ZH**

GREGSON, Edward (b 1945) England

SECTION I: ORCHESTRAL

Concerto for French Horn and Brass Band (1971)
F. Lloyd, Desford Colliery Caterpillar Band, E.
Gregson *Concert*   (9/93) (DOYE) ① **DOYCD017**
Connotations—brass band (1977)
Desford Colliery Caterpillar Band, E. Gregson
Concert   (9/93) (DOYE) ① **DOYCD017**
Black Dyke Mills Band, P. Parkes (pp1978) *Concert*
(3/94) (CHAN) ① **CHAN4522**
Dances and Arias—brass band (1984)
Desford Colliery Caterpillar Band, E. Gregson
Concert   (9/93) (DOYE) ① **DOYCD017**
Of Men and Mountains—brass band (1990)
Desford Colliery Caterpillar Band, E. Gregson
Concert   (9/93) (DOYE) ① **DOYCD017**
The Planagenets—symphonic study: brass band (1971)
Black Dyke Mills Band, G. Brand *Concert*
(10/91) (CHAN) ① **CHAN6539**

GRENON, Nicolas (c1380–1486) France

SECTION II: CHAMBER

Je ne requier de ma dame—ballade
G. Binchois Ens, D. Vellard *Concert*
(3/92) (VIRG) ① **VC7 59043-2**

GRÉTRY, André-Ernest-Modeste (1741–1813) Belgium

SECTION I: ORCHESTRAL

Concerto for Flute and Orchestra in C
(doubtful)
M. Grauwels, ECCO, D. Demetriades *Concert*
(8/88) (HYPE) ① **CDH88015**

SECTION V: STAGE WORKS

Les Fausses apparences ou L'amant jaloux—opéra-comique: 3 acts (1778—Paris)
(Lib. d'Hèle, after S. Centlivre)
EXCERPTS: 1. Je romps la chaîne qui m'engage.
1. S. Jo, ECO, R. Bonynge (r1993) *Concert*
(9/94) (DECC) ① **440 679-2DH**
Richard Coeur-de-Lion—opéra-comique: 3 acts (1784—Paris) (Lib. Sedaine)
O Richard, o mon roi G. Soulacroix, anon (r1904)
(9/91) (SYMP) ① **SYMCD1089**
Zémire et Azor—opéra-comique: 4 acts (1771—Fontainebleau) (Lib. Marmontel)
Ballet music RPO, T. Beecham (r1956) *Concert*
(9/92) (EMI) ① **CDM7 63401-2**

GREVER, Maria (1894–1951) Mexico

SECTION IV: VOCAL AND CHORAL

Jurame—Song
F. Araiza, Munich RSO, R. Weikert (arr Figyes)
Concert   (3/93) (RCA) ① **09026 61163-2**

GRIEG, Edvard (Hagerup) (1843–1907) Norway

CW denotes work without Op. number

SECTION I: ORCHESTRAL

Concerto for Piano and Orchestra in A minor, Op. 16 (1868)
G. Anda, BPO, R. Kubelík *Schumann: Piano
Concerto.*   (8/87) (DG) ① **415 850-2GGA**
R. Lupu, LSO, A. Previn *Schumann: Piano Concerto.*
(12/87) (DECC) ① **417 728-2DM**
S. Richter, Monte Carlo Nat Op Orch, L. von Matačić
Schumann: Piano Concerto.
(12/88) (EMI) ① **CDC7 47164-2**
M. Perahia, BRSO, Colin Davis (pp1988) *Schumann:
Piano Concerto.*   (5/89) (SONY) ① **SK44899**
V. Cliburn, Philadelphia, E. Ormandy *Concert*
(8/89) (RCA) ① **GD87834**
D. Alexeev, RPO, Y. Temirkanov (r1988) *Schumann:
Piano Concerto.*   (12/89) (EMIN) ① **CD-EMX2195**
M. Fingerhut, Ulster Orch, V. Handley *Concert*
(9/90) (CHAN) ① **CHAN8723**
L. Fleisher, Cleveland Orch, G. Szell *Schumann:
piano concerto.*   (10/90) (SONY) ① **MPK44849**
J. Jandó, Budapest PO, J. Sandor *Concert*
(11/90) (LASE) ① **15 617**
P. Devoyon, LPO, J. Maksymiuk (r1990) *Schumann:
Piano Concerto.*   (2/91) (CFP) ① **CD-CFP4574**
L.O. Andsnes, Bergen PO, D. Kitaienko *Concert*
(4/91) (VIRG) ① **VC7 59613-2**
G. Anda, BPO, R. Kubelík *Concert*
(12/91) (DG) ① [2] **413 158-2GW2**
C. Curzon, LSO, Ø. Fjeldstad *Concert*
(1/92) (DECC) ① **433 628-2DSP**
E. Wild, RPO, R. Leibowitz *Concert*
(11/92) (CHES) ① **Chesky CD50**
L. Vogt, CBSO, S. Rattle *Schumann: Piano Concerto.*
(1/93) (EMI) ① **CDC7 54746-2**
S. Eisenberger, Cincinatti Cons, A. von Kreisler
(bp1938) *Concert*   (6/93) (PEAR) ① **GEMMCD9933**
M. Dalberto, Philh, J-B. Pommier (r1992) *Concert*
(6/93) (DENO) ① **CO-75258**
L. Zilberstein, Gothenburg SO, N. Järvi (r1993)
Concert   (7/93) (DG) ① **437 524-2GH**
S. Kovacevich, BBC SO, Colin Davis (r1971) *Concert*
(8/93) (PHIL) ① [2] **438 380-2PM2**
Solomon, Philh, H. Menges (1956) *Concert*
(9/93) (EMI) ① [2] **CZS7 67735-2**
L. Derwinger, Norrköping SO, J. Hirokami (r1993;
orig vers) *Concert*   (9/93) (BIS) ① **BIS-CD619**
G. Cziffra, Hungarian St Orch, Z. Rozsnyai (r1956)
Concert   (11/93) (APR) ① [2] **APR7021**
F-R. Duchâble, Strasbourg PO, T. Guschlbauer
Rachmaninov: Piano Concerto 2.
(12/93) (ERAT) ① **4509-92872-2**
A. Rubinstein, Philadelphia, E. Ormandy (r1942)
Concert   (4/94) (RCA) ① [3] **09026 61879-2**
P. Jablonski, Philh, P. Maag *Tchaikovsky: Piano
Concerto.*   (10/94) (DECC) ① **443 174-2DH**
J-M. Luisada, LSO, M. Tilson Thomas (r1993)
Schumann: Concerto.
(12/94) (DG) ① **439 913-2GH**
R. O'Hora, RPO, J. Judd (r1994) *Concert*
(6/95) (TRIN) ① **TRP024**
E. Pobłocka, Polish RSO, T. Wojciechowski (r1994)
Concert   (8/95) (CONI) ① [2] **75605 51750-2**
O. Mustonen, San Francisco SO, H. Blomstedt
(r1994) *Chopin: Piano Concerto 1.*
(11/95) (DECC) ① **444 518-2DH**
Cadenza I. Johnsen (r1940) *Concert*
(6/93) (SIMA) ① [3] **PSC1809(2)**
Cadenza A. de Greef (r1921) *Concert*
(6/93) (SIMA) ① [3] **PSC1809(1)**
Cadenza P. Grainger (bp1957) *Concert*
(6/93) (SIMA) ① [3] **PSC1809(1)**
Cadenza A.B. Michelangeli (r1941) *Concert*
(6/93) (SIMA) ① [3] **PSC1809(2)**
Cadenza P. Grainger (r1908) *Concert*
(6/93) (SIMA) ① [3] **PSC1809(1)**
Movt 1. Martin Jones (arr pf: Grainger) *Concert*
(2/91) (NIMB) ① **NI5255**
Movt 1 cadenza P. Grainger (r1908) *Concert*
(6/93) (PEAR) ① **GEMMCD9933**
2 Elegiac Melodies—string orchestra, Op. 34 (1881)
1. The wounded heart; 2. Last spring.
Norwegian CO, T. Tønnesen *Concert*
(1/87) (BIS) ① **BIS-CD147**
Ulster Orch, V. Handley *Concert*
(8/87) (CHAN) ① **CHAN8524**
Orpheus CO *Concert*   (2/88) (DG) ① **423 060-2GH**
Musica Vitae CO, W. Rajski *Concert*
(6/90) (BIS) ① **BIS-CD461**

Trondheim Sols, B. Fiskum *Concert*
(3/93) (VICT) ① **VCD19066**
Gothenburg SO, N. Järvi (r1992) *Concert*
(6/93) (DG) ① **437 520-2GH**
Swiss CO, A. Duczmal *Concert*
(3/94) (ASV) ① **CDQS6094**
ASMF, N. Marriner (r1994) *Concert*
(1/95) (HANS) ① **98 995**
Serenata of London, B. Wilde (r1994) *Concert*
(2/95) (CARL) ① **PCD1108**
Polish RSO, T. Wojciechowski (r1994) *Concert*
(8/95) (CONI) ① [2] **75605 51750-2**
**2. Besses o' the Barn Band, Black Dyke Mills Band,
Yorkshire Imperial Band, H. Mortimer (pp1987: arr
Ryan) *Concert*   (11/93) (CHAN) ① **CHAN4513**
**2. Boston SO, S. Koussevitzky (r1950) *Concert*
(4/94) (RCA) ① [3] **09026 61879-2**
**2. Philadelphia, E. Ormandy (r1967) *Concert*
(7/94) (SONY) ① **SBK53257**
**2. O.E. Antonsen, W. Marshall (r1992: arr tpt/org:
Antonsen/Marshall) *Concert*
(10/94) (EMI) ① **CDC5 55048-2**
**Funeral March for Rikard Nordraak—military
band, CW117 (1866, rev 1867 and 1899)**
London Brass Virtuosi, D. Honeyball *Concert*
(7/87) (HYPE) ① **CDA66189**
Gothenburg SO, N. Järvi *Concert*
(6/89) (DG) ① **427 321-2GH**
Trondheim SO, O.K. Ruud (r1993) *Concert*
(4/95) (VIRG) ① **VC5 45051-2**
Holberg Suite—string orchestra, Op. 40 (1884 orch 1885)
1. Preludium; 2. Sarabande; 3. Gavotte; 4. Air; 5.
Rigaudon.
ASMF, N. Marriner *Concert*
(1/86) (PHIL) ① **412 727-2PH**
Norwegian CO, T. Tønnesen *Concert*
(1/87) (BIS) ① **BIS-CD147**
Scottish Baroque Ens, Lionel Friedman *Concert*
(10/87) (CRD) ① **CRD3342**
Serenata of London *Concert*
(11/87) (CARL) ① **PCD861**
Orpheus CO *Concert*   (2/88) (DG) ① **423 060-2GH**
Israel CO, Y. Talmi *Concert*
(8/88) (CHAN) ① **CHAN8593**
BPO, H. von Karajan *Concert*
(7/89) (DG) ① **419 474-2GGA**
Oslo PO, M. Jansons *Concert*
(12/89) (NKF) ① **NKFCD50002-2**
Moscow Sols Ens, Y. Bashmet *Concert*
(3/91) (RCA) ① **RD60368**
London Little Orch, L. Jones *Concert*
(9/92) (UNIC) ① **UKCD2047**
Gothenburg SO, N. Järvi (r1992) *Concert*
(6/93) (DG) ① **437 520-2GH**
ECO, R. Leppard (r1979) *Concert*
(8/93) (PHIL) ① [2] **438 380-2PM2**
Trondheim Sols, B. Fiskum (r1993) *Concert*
(11/93) (VICT) ① **VCD19071**
Swiss CO, A. Duczmal *Concert*
(3/94) (ASV) ① **CDQS6094**
ASMF, N. Marriner (r1994) *Concert*
(1/95) (HANS) ① **98 995**
Polish RSO, T. Wojciechowski (r1994) *Concert*
(8/95) (CONI) ① [2] **75605 51750-2**
**In Autumn—concert overture, Op. 11 (1866
rev/arr 1887)** (orch cpsr from pf 4 hands)
Gothenburg SO, N. Järvi *Concert*
(6/89) (DG) ① **427 321-2GH**
Iceland SO, P. Sakari *Concert*
(8/92) (CHAN) ① **CHAN9028**
Gothenburg SO, N. Järvi (r1988) *Concert*
(7/93) (DG) ① **437 524-2GH**
2 Lyric Pieces—string orchestra (1898) (from
Op. 68/4-5: orch cpsr)
1. Evening in the mountains; 2. At the Cradle.
Moscow Sols Ens, Y. Bashmet *Concert*
(3/91) (RCA) ① **RD60368**
Gothenburg SO, N. Järvi (r1991) *Concert*
(6/93) (DG) ① **437 520-2GH**
ASMF, N. Marriner (r1994) *Concert*
(1/95) (HANS) ① **98 995**
Polish RSO, T. Wojciechowski (r1994) *Concert*
(8/95) (CONI) ① [2] **75605 51750-2**
1, 2. BBC Scottish SO, J. Maksymiuk (r1993) *Concert*
(10/94) (NAXO) ① **8 550864**
2. Norwegian CO, T. Tønnesen *Concert*
(1/87) (BIS) ① **BIS-CD147**
Lyric Suite—orchestra, Op. 54 (orch 1904)
1. Shepherd's Boy; 2. Gangar (Norwegian March); 3.
Nocturne; 4. March of the Dwarfs; 5. Bell Ringing.
ECO, R. Leppard (r1979) *Concert*
(8/93) (PHIL) ① [2] **438 380-2PM2**
Polish RSO, T. Wojciechowski (r1994) *Concert*
(8/95) (CONI) ① [2] **75605 51750-2**

1. R. Fleming, NY Met Op Orch, J. Conlon (pp1991)
Concert   (6/93) (RCA) ① 09026 61509-2
4 Impressions—songs (1912-16) (Wds.
Wilde)
1. Le jardin; 2. Impression du matin; 3. La mer; 4. Le
réveillon.
O. Stapp, D. Richardson Concert
          (11/88) (NEW) ① NW273-2
Meeres Stille—song (c1903-11) (Wds.
Goethe)
S. Milnes, J. Spong Concert
          (11/88) (NEW) ① NW273-2
T. Hampson, A. Guzelimian Concert
          (4/92) (TELD) ① 9031-72168-2
**Mein Herz ist wie die dunkle Nacht—song
(c1903-11)** (Wds. Geibel)
T. Hampson, A. Guzelimian Concert
          (4/92) (TELD) ① 9031-72168-2
Mit schwarzen Segeln—song (c1903-11)
(Wds. Heine)
T. Hampson, A. Guzelimian Concert
          (4/92) (TELD) ① 9031-72168-2
Des Müden Abendlied—song (c1903-11)
(Wds. Geibel)
T. Hampson, A. Guzelimian Concert
          (4/92) (TELD) ① 9031-72168-2
Nachtlied—song (1912) (Wds. Geibel)
T. Hampson, A. Guzelimian Concert
          (4/92) (TELD) ① 9031-72168-2
**So halt' ich endlich umfangen—song (c1903-
11)** (Wds. Geibel)
T. Hampson, A. Guzelimian Concert
          (4/92) (TELD) ① 9031-72168-2
Song of the dagger—song (1916) (Wds.
Roman traditional)
S. Milnes, J. Spong Concert
          (11/88) (NEW) ① NW273-2
Das Sterbende Kind—song (c1903-11) (Wds.
Geibel)
T. Hampson, A. Guzelimian Concert
          (4/92) (TELD) ① 9031-72168-2
Der Träumende See—song (c1903-09) (Wds.
Mosen)
T. Hampson, A. Guzelimian Concert
          (4/92) (TELD) ① 9031-72168-2
**Wo ich bin, mich rings umdunkelt—song
(c1903-11)** (Wds. Heine)
T. Hampson, A. Guzelimian Concert
          (4/92) (TELD) ① 9031-72168-2
**Wohl lag ich einst in Gram und Herz—Lied
(c1903-09)** (Wds. Geibel)
T. Hampson, A. Guzelimian Concert
          (4/92) (TELD) ① 9031-72168-2
**Zwei Könige sassen auf Orkadal—song
(c1910)** (Wds. Geibel)
T. Hampson, A. Guzelimian Concert
          (4/92) (TELD) ① 9031-72168-2

**GRIGNY, Nicolas de (1672–1703)
France**

SECTION III: INSTRUMENTAL

Fugue à 5—organ
J. Payne (r1994) Concert
          (10/95) (NAXO) ① 8 553214
**Organ Works—Book 1 (Premier livre
d'orgue)—Mass and Hymns of the Christian
Year (pub 1699)** (some performances may
include plainchant)
Organ Mass: 1a. Kyrie (5 versets); 1b. Et in terra pax
(9 versets); 1c. Offertoire; 1d. Sanctus (3 versets);
1e. Elévation; 1f. Agnus Dei (2 versets); 1h.
Communion. Hymns: 2a. Veni Creator (5 versets);
2b. Pange lingua (5 versets); 2c. Verbum supernum
(4 versets); 2d. Ave maris stella (4 versets); 2e. A
soiis ortus (3 versets); 2f. Point d'orgue.
Sagittarius Ens, A. Isoir (r1992; with plainchant)
Concert   (10/93) (ERAT) ① [2] 4509-91722-2
1. A. Isoir (r1972)   (11/87) (CALL) ① CAL6911
2. R. Saorgin   (3/92) (REM) ① REM311077
2d, 2e J. Payne (r1994) Concert
          (10/95) (NAXO) ① 8 553214

**GROFÉ, Ferde (1892–1972)
USA**

SECTION I: ORCHESTRAL

Grand Canyon Suite (1931)
1. Sunrise; 2. Painted Desert; 3. On the Trail; 4.
Sunset; 5. Cloudburst.
Cincinnati Pops, E. Kunzel (1985) Gershwin: Catfish
Row.   (10/87) (TELA) ① CD80086
Detroit SO, A. Dorati (Gershwin: Porgy and Bess
Suite.   (8/91) (DECC) ① 430 712-2DM

NBC SO, A. Toscanini (r1945) Concert
          (11/92) (RCA) ① GD60307
NYPO, L. Bernstein (r1963) Concert
          (5/93) (SONY) ① SMK47544
Morton Gould Orch, M. Gould (r1960) Concert
          (2/94) (RCA) ① 09026 61667-2

**GRØNDAHL, Agathe (Ursula)
(1847–1907) Norway**

née Backer

SECTION IV: VOCAL AND CHORAL

Endnu et streif kun af sol—song
K. Flagstad, orch (r1914) Concert
          (12/95) (SIMA) ① [3] PSC1821(1)
Eventide—song, Op. 42/7
K. Flagstad, E. McArthur (r1937) Concert
          (12/95) (PEAR) ① GEMMCD9092
K. Flagstad, orch (r1923) Concert
          (12/95) (SIMA) ① [3] PSC1821(1)
The Linden—song (Wds. V Bergsøe)
P. Frijsh, E. Nielsen (bp1938) Concert
          (4/95) (PEAR) ① [2] GEMMCDS9095(2)
Songs, Op. 13
5. You meet me in the dance.
5. P. Frijsh, C. Dougherty (r1939) Concert
          (4/95) (PEAR) ① [2] GEMMCDS9095(2)

**GROS, Joseph Arnold (18th Cent)
Germany**

SECTION I: ORCHESTRAL

Concerto for Trumpet and Strings in D
W. Basch, Orpheus CO Concert
          (3/89) (SCHW) ① 311071

**GROSSIN, Estienne (fl c1420)
France**

SECTION IV: VOCAL AND CHORAL

Va t'ent souspier—rondeau (3vv)
Gothic Voices, C. Page Concert
          (12/88) (HYPE) ① CDA66286

**GROVEN, Eivind (b 1901)
Norway**

SECTION I: ORCHESTRAL

Concerto for Piano and Orchestra (1947-49)
W. Plagge, Trondheim SO, O. K. Ruud (r1991)
Symphony 2.   (12/94) (SIMA) ① PSC3111
**Symphony No. 2, 'The midnight hour' (1939-
43)**
Trondheim SO, O. K. Ruud (r1992) Piano Concerto.
          (12/94) (SIMA) ① PSC3111

**GROVLEZ, Gabriel (1879–1944)
France**

SECTION II: CHAMBER

Romance et Scherzo—flute and piano
S. Milan, I. Brown Concert
          (11/88) (CHAN) ① CHAN8609

SECTION III: INSTRUMENTAL

L' Almanach aux Images—piano
1. Les Marionettes; 2. Berceuse de la Poupée; 3. La
Sarabande; 4. Chanson du Chasseur; 5. Les Anes; 6.
Le Pastour; 7. Chanson de l'Escarpolette; 8. Petites
Litanies de Jésus.
P. Katin (r1990) Concert   (7/93) (SIMA) ① PSC1067

**GRUBER, Heinz Karl 'Nali' (b
1943) Austria**

SECTION I: ORCHESTRAL

**Concerto for Violin and Orchestra No. 1
(1978)**
E. Kovacic, London Sinfonietta, H. K. Gruber (r1993)
Concert   (9/94) (LARG) ① Largo 5124
**Der rote Teppich wird ausgerollt—chamber
ensemble (1968)** (Eng: The Red Carpet. Orig
from Revue, Op. 22)
London Sinfonietta, H. K. Gruber (r1993) Concert
          (9/94) (LARG) ① Largo 5124

SECTION II: CHAMBER

**Bossa Nova—violin and piano, Op. 21e
(1968, arr/pub 1973)**
E. Kovacic, P. Crossley (r1993) Concert
          (9/94) (LARG) ① Largo 5124

SECTION III: INSTRUMENTAL

**6 Episoden (aus einer unterbrochenen
Chronik)—piano, Op. 20 (1966-7)** (Eng:
Episodes from a discontinued chronicle)
P. Crossley (r1993) Concert
          (9/94) (LARG) ① Largo 5124
4 Pieces—violin, Op. 11 (1966)
E. Kovacic (r1993) Concert
          (9/94) (LARG) ① Largo 5124

**GRUBER, Ludwig (1874–1964)
Austria**

SECTION IV: VOCAL AND CHORAL

**Mei Muaterl war a Weanerin—Viennese
song**
E. Kunz, Kemmeter-Faltl Schrammel Ens (r1949)
Concert   (9/95) (TEST) ① SBT1059

**GRUENBERG, Louis (1884–1964)
USA**

SECTION I: ORCHESTRAL

Concerto for Violin and Orchestra, Op. 47
J. Heifetz, San Francisco SO, P. Monteux (r1945)
Walton: Violin Concerto.
          (11/94) (RCA) ① [65] 09026 61778-2(23)

SECTION V: STAGE WORKS

**The Emperor Jones—opera: 2 acts, Op. 36
(1931)** (Lib. cpsr and K. de Jaffa, after O'Neill)
Standin' in the need of prayer L. Tibbett, NY Met
Op Orch, W. Pelletier (r1934) Concert
          (3/90) (RCA) ① GD87808
Standin' in the need of prayer L. Tibbett, orch
(pp1934) Concert
          (3/91) (PEAR) ① [2] GEMMCDS9452

GUAGNI-BENVENUTI

SECTION IV: VOCAL AND CHORAL

Guardami!—song
C. Muzio, orch (r1924) Concert
          (5/90) (BOGR) ① [2] BIM705-2
C. Muzio, orch (r1924) Concert
          (1/94) (ROMO) ① [2] 81005-2

**GUARNIERI, Mozart Camargo
(1907–1993) Brazil**

SECTION I: ORCHESTRAL

Dansa brasileira—orchestra (1928)
NYPO, L. Bernstein (r1963) Concert
          (5/93) (SONY) ① SMK47544

SECTION III: INSTRUMENTAL

**Ponteios No. 24—Tranquillo—piano (1954-
55)**
M. Verzoni Concert   (4/90) (SCHW) ① 310019
**Ponteios No. 42—Dengoso—piano (1958-
59)**
M. Verzoni Concert   (4/90) (SCHW) ① 310019
**Ponteios No. 44—Descensolado—piano
(1958-59)**
M. Verzoni Concert   (4/90) (SCHW) ① 310019
**Ponteios No. 45—Com alegria—piano (1958-
59)**
M. Verzoni Concert   (4/90) (SCHW) ① 310019
**Ponteios No. 49—Torturando—piano (1958-
59)**
M. Verzoni Concert   (4/90) (SCHW) ① 310019
**Ponteios No. 50—Lentamente—piano (1958-
59)**
M. Verzoni Concert   (4/90) (SCHW) ① 310019

**GUASTAVINO, Carlos (b 1912)
Argentina**

SECTION II: CHAMBER

Bailecito in C sharp minor—two pianos
H. Moreno, N. Capelli (r1992) Concert
          (5/94) (MARC) ① 8 223462
Gato—two pianos
H. Moreno, N. Capelli (r1992) Concert
          (5/94) (MARC) ① 8 223462
Romance del Plata—sonatina: piano duet
H. Moreno, N. Capelli (r1992) Concert
          (5/94) (MARC) ① 8 223462

3 Romances—two pianos (pub 1951)
1. Las Niñas; 2. Muchacho Jujeña; 3. Baile.
H. Moreno, N. Capelli (r1992) Concert
(5/94) (MARC) ① **8 223462**
Se equivicó la paloma—two pianos (arr cpsr from song)
H. Moreno, N. Capelli (r1992) Concert
(5/94) (MARC) ① **8 223462**

SECTION III: INSTRUMENTAL

10 Cantilenas argentinas y final—piano (1956-58)
1. Santa Fe para llorar; 2. Adolescencia; 3. Jaracandá; 4. El ceibo; 5. Abelarda Olmos; 6. Juanita; 7. Herbert; 8. Santa Fe antiguo; 9. Trébol; 10. La casa; 11. Final: Romance en Colastiné.
4, 6, 10, 11. Camerata Bariloche r1994; arr chbr orch) Concert (11/95) (DORI) ① **DOR90202**
Presencias—piano/guitar
EXCERPTS: 1. Loduvina (1959); 2. Horacio Lavalle (1961); 3. Jeromita Linares (1965).
N. Capelli (r1992) Concert
(5/94) (MARC) ① **8 223462**
3. P. Cohen, Camerata Bariloche r1994; arr chbr orch/gtr) Concert (11/95) (DORI) ① **DOR90202**
La Siesta—piano (pub 1955)
1. El Patio; 2. El Sauce; 3. Gorriones.
H. Moreno (r1992) Concert
(5/94) (MARC) ① **8 223462**

SECTION IV: VOCAL AND CHORAL

Canción de Navidad—carol
Quink Concert (12/89) (TELA) ① **CD80202**
7 Canciones (Wds. R. Alberti)
1. Jardín de amores; 2. A volarí; 3. Nana del niño malo; 4. La novia; 5. Geografía física; 6. Al puente de la golondrina!; 7. Elegía.
U. Espaillat, P. Zinger (r1992) Concert
(1/94) (NALB) ① **NA058CD**
4 Canciones Argentinas
1. Desde que te conocí; 2. Viniendo de Chilecito; 3. En los surcos del amor; 4. Mi garganta.
U. Espaillat, P. Zinger (r1992) Concert
(1/94) (NALB) ① **NA058CD**
4 Canciones Coloniales (Wds. L. Benerós)
1. Cuando acaba de llover; 2. Préstame tu pañuelito; 3. Ya me voy a retirar; 4. Las puertas de la mañana.
U. Espaillat, P. Zinger (r1992) Concert
(1/94) (NALB) ① **NA058CD**
Cita—song (Wds. L. Varela)
U. Espaillat, P. Zinger (r1992) Concert
(1/94) (NALB) ① **NA058CD**
Piececitos—song (Wds. Mistral)
U. Espaillat, P. Zinger (r1992) Concert
(1/94) (NALB) ① **NA058CD**
Pueblito, mi pueblo—song (Wds. F. Silva)
U. Espaillat, P. Zinger (r1992) Concert
(1/94) (NALB) ① **NA058CD**
La rosa y el sauce—song (Wds. F. Silva)
U. Espaillat, P. Zinger (r1992) Concert
(1/94) (NALB) ① **NA058CD**
Se equivicó la paloma—song (Wds. R. Alberti)
U. Espaillat, P. Zinger (r1992) Concert
(1/94) (NALB) ① **NA058CD**

GUBAIDULINA, Sofia (b 1931) USSR/Russia

SECTION I: ORCHESTRAL

Concerto for Bassoon and Low Strings (1975)
H. Ahrnas, Lahti Chbr Ens, O. Vänskä (r1993) Concert (6/94) (BIS) ① **BIS-CD636**
Concordanza—chamber ensemble (1971)
Lahti Chbr Ens, O. Vänskä (r1993) Concert
(6/94) (BIS) ① **BIS-CD636**
Detto II—cello and chamber ensemble (1972)
I. Pälli, Lahti Chbr Ens, O. Vänskä (r1993) Concert (6/94) (BIS) ① **BIS-CD636**
Introitus: Concerto for Piano and Chamber Orchestra (1978)
A. Haefliger, N German Rad PO, B. Klee (r1993) Concert (5/95) (SONY) ① **SK53960**
Offertorium—concerto for violin and orchestra (1980)
G. Kremer, Boston SO, C. Dutoit (1988) Hommage.
(9/89) (DG) ① **427 336-2GH**
O. Krysa, Stockholm PO, J. DePreist (r1992) Rejoice!. (7/93) (BIS) ① **BIS-CD566**
Pro et Contra—large orchestra (1989)
BBC Nat Orch of Wales, T. Otaka (1994) Firsova: Cassandra, Op. 60. (11/94) (BIS) ① **BIS-CD668**

Symphony, 'Stimmen Verstummen'—12 movements (1986)
Stockholm PO, G. Rozhdestvensky Stufen.
(8/93) (CHAN) ① **CHAN9183**

SECTION II: CHAMBER

2 Ballads—two trumpets and piano (1976)
R. Friedrich, W. Bauer, T. Duis (r1992) Concert
(6/93) (CAPR) ① **10 439**
In croce—cello and organ (1983)
M. Beiser, D. Papadakos (r c1994) Concert
(11/95) (KOCH) ① **37258-2**
In Erwartung—saxophone quartet & six percussionists (1994)
Raschèr Sax Qt, Kroumata Perc Ens (r1994) Concert
(11/95) (BIS) ① **BIS-CD710**
5 Pieces, 'Silenzio'—classical accordion, violin & cello (1991)
G. Draugsvoll, A. B. Møller, H. Brendstrup (r1994) Concert (11/95) (BIS) ① **BIS-CD710**
Rejoice!—violin and cello (1981)
O. Krysa, T. Thedéen (r1992) Offertorium.
(7/93) (BIS) ① **BIS-CD566**
Seven Last Words—cello, accordion and strings (1982)
F. Lips, M. Milman, Moscow Virtuosi, V. Spivakov (r1990) Concert (5/93) (RCA) ① **09026 60466-2**
Song without words—trumpet and piano (1977)
R. Friedrich, T. Duis (r1992) Concert
(6/93) (CAPR) ① **10 439**
String Quartet No. 2 (1987)
Arditti Qt Concert (4/92) (MONT) ① **789007**
Kronos Qt (r1992) Concert
(8/93) (NONE) ① **7559-79310-2**
String Quartet No. 3 (1987)
Arditti Qt Concert (7/91) (GVIS) ① **GV79439-2**
Trio—three trumpets (1976)
R. Friedrich, W. Bauer, M. Mester (r1992) Concert
(6/93) (CAPR) ① **10 439**

SECTION III: INSTRUMENTAL

Chaconne—piano (1962)
N. Demidenko (pp1993) Concert
(1/94) (HYPE) ① [2] **CDA66781/2**
A. Haefliger (r1994) Concert
(5/95) (SONY) ① **SK53960**
De profundis—classical accordion (1978)
G. Draugsvoll (r1994) Concert
(11/95) (BIS) ① **BIS-CD710**
Musical Toys—piano (1969)
A. Haefliger (r1994) Concert
(5/95) (SONY) ① **SK53960**
10 Preludes (Studies)—cello (1974)
M. Beiser (r c1994) Concert
(11/95) (KOCH) ① **37258-2**
Sonata for Classical Accordion, 'Et expecto' (1985)
G. Draugsvoll (r1994) Concert
(11/95) (BIS) ① **BIS-CD710**
Sonata for Piano (1965)
A. Haefliger (r1993) Concert
(5/95) (SONY) ① **SK53960**

SECTION IV: VOCAL AND CHORAL

Hommage à T. S. Eliot—octet and soprano (1987) (Wds. T. S. Eliot)
C. Whittlesey, G. Kremer, I. Van Keulen, T. Zimmermann, D. Geringas, A. Posch, E. Brunner, K. Thunemann, R. Vlatković (1987) Offertorium.
(9/89) (DG) ① **427 336-2GH**
Jetzt immer Schnee—chamber choir & ensemble (1993) (Wds. Gennadi Aigi)
S. Kleindienst, Netherlands Chbr Ch, Schoenberg Ens, R. de Leeuw (r1992) Perception.
(4/95) (PHIL) ① **442 531-2PH**
Perception—soprano, baritone & strings (1981-3) (Wds. Francisco Tanzer)
S. Lorenz, L. Stasov, Schoenberg Ens, R. de Leeuw (r1992) Jetzt immer Schnee.
(4/95) (PHIL) ① **442 531-2PH**
Stufen/Steps—orchestra with speaking choir (1972) (Wds. Rilke)
Stockholm PO, G. Rozhdestvensky Symphony (1986). (8/93) (CHAN) ① **CHAN9183**

GUDMUNDSEN-HOLMGREEN, Pelle (b 1932) Denmark

SECTION I: ORCHESTRAL

Triptykon—percussion and orchestra (composed in association with Gert Mortensen)
G. Mortensen, Danish RSO, J. Panula Concert
(4/89) (BIS) ① **BIS-CD256**

GUERAU, Francisco (mid 17th Cent–early 18th Cent) Spain

SECTION III: INSTRUMENTAL

Poema harmónico—baroque guitar (1694)
1. Canario; 2. Pasacalles de 7o tono; 3. Marionas; 4. Villano; 5. Pasacalles de 1o tono; 6. Jacaras de la Costa; 7. Mariazapalos; 8. Pasacalles de Patilla 8o punto alto; 9. Jacaras; 10. Pabana; 11. Folias; 12. Matachin.
1. P. Romero (r1993; trans P. Romero) Concert
(4/95) (PHIL) ① **442 150-2PH**
1, 3. J. M. Moreno (r1992) Concert
(8/95) (GLOS) ① **GCD920103**
1, 4. J. Bream (r1983-4) Concert
(8/93) (RCA) ① [28] **09026 61583-2(4)**
1, 4. J. Bream (r1983-4) Concert
(6/94) (RCA) ① **09026 61592-2**
3. Romanesca (r1991-2) Concert
(11/94) (GLOS) ① **GCD920201**
10, 11, 12. M.D.M. Fernández Doval, Extempore Stg Ens Concert (7/92) (HYPE) ① **CDA66327**

GUERRERO, Francisco (1528–1599) Spain

SECTION IV: VOCAL AND CHORAL

Alma Redemptoris Mater—motet: 4vv
Capella Reial Voc Ens, Hespèrion XX (r1992) Concert (10/93) (ASTR) ① **E8766**
Ave Maria—motet: 4vv
Capella Reial Voc Ens, Hespèrion XX (r1992) Concert (10/93) (ASTR) ① **E8766**
Ave Maria—motet: 8vv
Capella Reial Voc Ens, Hespèrion XX (r1992) Concert (10/93) (ASTR) ① **E8766**
Ave virgo sanctissima—motet: 5vv (pub 1566)
Westminster Cath Ch, D. Hill Concert
(3/87) (HYPE) ① **CDA66168**
Cambridge Sngrs, J. Rutter Concert
(4/92) (CLLE) ① **COLCD115**
Capella Reial Voc Ens, Hespèrion XX (r1992) Concert (10/93) (ASTR) ① **E8766**
A Capella Portvgvesa, O. Rees (r1994) Concert
(11/94) (HYPE) ① **CDA66725**
Beata Dei genitrix, Maria—motet: 6vv
Capella Reial Voc Ens, Hespèrion XX (r1992) Concert (10/93) (ASTR) ① **E8766**
Dexó la venda, el arco—song
Hespèrion XX, J. Savall (r1991-92) Concert
(6/93) (ASTR) ① **E8764**
Duo Seraphim—motet: 12vv
Capella Reial Voc Ens, Hespèrion XX (r1992) Concert (10/93) (ASTR) ① **E8766**
Gabriel archangelus—motet: 4vv
Capella Reial Voc Ens, Hespèrion XX (r1992) Concert (10/93) (ASTR) ① **E8766**
Laudate Dominum—motet: 8vv (pub 1597)
Capella Reial Voc Ens, Hespèrion XX (r1992) Concert (10/93) (ASTR) ① **E8766**
La luz de vuestros ojos—villanesca (pub 1589)
A Capella Portvgvesa, O. Rees (r1994) Concert
(11/94) (HYPE) ① **CDA66725**
O altitudo—motet: 8vv (pub 1597)
Westminster Cath Ch, D. Hill Concert
(3/87) (HYPE) ① **CDA66168**
Capella Reial Voc Ens, Hespèrion XX (r1992) Concert (10/93) (ASTR) ① **E8766**
O celestial medicina (pub 1589) (from 'Canciones y villancicos espirituales')
Compañia musical, La Fenice, J. Cabré (r1992) Concert (9/93) (K617) ① **K617024**
O Domine Jesu—motet: 4vv (pub 1570)
Westminster Cath Ch, D. Hill Concert
(3/87) (HYPE) ① **CDA66168**
Capella Reial Voc Ens, Hespèrion XX (r1992; voc & instr vers) Concert (10/93) (ASTR) ① **E8766**
O sacrum convivium—motet: 5vv (pub 1570)
Westminster Cath Ch, D. Hill Concert
(3/87) (HYPE) ① **CDA66168**
Capella Reial Voc Ens, Hespèrion XX (r1992) Concert (10/93) (ASTR) ① **E8766**
Ojos claros—song
Hespèrion XX, J. Savall (r1991-92) Concert
(6/93) (ASTR) ① **E8764**
Pan divino, gracioso
Compañia musical, La Fenice, J. Cabré (r1992) Concert (9/93) (K617) ① **K617024**

Pater Noster—motet: 8vv
Capella Reial Voc Ens, Hespèrion XX (r1992)
Concert (10/93) (ASTR) ① E8766
Prado verde y florido—song
Hespèrion XX, J. Savall (r1991-92) Concert
(6/93) (ASTR) ① E8764
Regina coeli—motet: 8vv
Westminster Cath Ch, D. Hill Concert
(3/87) (HYPE) ① CDA66168
Capella Reial Voc Ens, Hespèrion XX (r1992)
Concert (10/93) (ASTR) ① E8766
Salve Regina—motet: 4vv (pub 1555)
Capella Reial Voc Ens, Hespèrion XX (r1992)
Concert (10/93) (ASTR) ① E8766
Si tus penas no pruevo (pub 1589) (Wds.
Lope de Vega)
M. Figueras, Hespèrion XX, J. Savall Concert
(2/92) (ASTR) ① E8729
Surge propera—motet (pub 1570)
Westminster Cath Ch, D. Hill Concert
(3/87) (HYPE) ① CDA66168
Trahe me post te
Compañia musical, La Fenice, J. Cabré (r1992)
Concert (9/93) (K617) ① K617024
Trahe me post te, Virgo Maria—motet: 5vv
Capella Reial Voc Ens, Hespèrion XX (r1992)
Concert (10/93) (ASTR) ① E8766
Virgen sancta—motet
King's College Sngrs, E.H. Warrell Concert
(12/91) (REGE) ① REGCD106
Chanticleer (r1990) Concert
(12/94) (CHTI) ① CR-8803

> ### GUERRERO (Y TORRES), Jacinto
> *(1895–1951) Spain*

SECTION V: STAGE WORKS

Los Gavilanes—zarzuela (1923—Madrid)
(Lib. J R Martín)
Marcha de la Amistad G. Sanchez, T. Verdera, P.
Perez Inigo, P. Domingo, Madrid SO, E. G. Asensio
(pp1991) Concert (11/92) (CARL) ① MCD45
Mi aldea!; Flor roja P. Domingo, Madrid SO, M.
Moreno-Buendia (r1987) Concert
(1/89) (EMI) ① CDC7 49148-2
El Huésped del Sevillano—zarzuela (Madrid)
(Lib. E. Reoyo and J. I. Luca de Tena)
Canto a la espada P. Domingo, Madrid SO, E. G.
Asensio (pp1991) Concert
(11/92) (CARL) ① MCD45
Canto a la espada J. Carreras, ECO, E. Ricci
(r1994) Concert (2/95) (ERAT) ① 4509-95789-2
Mujer de los negros ojos P. Domingo, Madrid SO,
M. Moreno-Buendia (r1987) Concert
(1/89) (EMI) ① CDC7 49148-2
La Rosa del azafrán—zarzuela (1930) (Lib. F
Romero & G Fernández-Shaw)
Cuando siembro voy cantando P. Domingo, Madrid
Zarzuela Chor, Madrid SO, M. Moreno-Buendia
(r1987) Concert (1/89) (EMI) ① CDC7 49148-2

> ### GUERRERO, Pedro *(b c1520)*
> *Spain*

SECTION IV: VOCAL AND CHORAL

Di, perra mora—song (attrib)
Hespèrion XX, J. Savall (r1991-92) Concert
(6/93) (ASTR) ① E8764

> ### GUEST, Douglas *(b 1916)*
> *England*

SECTION IV: VOCAL AND CHORAL

For the Fallen (1971) (Wds. L Binyon)
Westminster Abbey Ch, M. Neary, M. Baker (r1994)
Concert (12/95) (SONY) ① SK66614

> ### GUI IV, 'Li Chastelain de Couci' *(fl
> 1180–1200) France*

SECTION IV: VOCAL AND CHORAL

Li nouviaz tanz—chanson (1v) (1190)
Gothic Voices, C. Page Concert
(10/89) (HYPE) ① CDA66336

> ### GUIARD *(16th cent) France*

SECTION IV: VOCAL AND CHORAL

Or oiez les introites—chanson
C. Janequin Ens, D. Visse (r1994) Concert
(5/95) (HARM) ① HMC90 1453

> ### GUIDO *(fl 1372–4) France*

SECTION IV: VOCAL AND CHORAL

**Dieux gart qui bien le chantera—rondeau
(3vv)**
Organum Ens, M. Pérès Concert
(11/87) (HARM) ① HMC90 1252
Or voit tout en aventure—ballade (3vv)
Organum Ens, M. Pérès Concert
(11/87) (HARM) ① HMC90 1252

> ### GUILAIN, Jean-Adam *(fl 1702–39)
> France*

SECTION III: INSTRUMENTAL

**Pièces d'orgue pour le Magnificat (pub
1706)**
1. SUITE DU 1er TON: 1a. Plein d'orgue; 1b. Trio;
1c. Duo; 1d. Basse de trompette; 1e. Récit; 1f.
Dialogue; 1g. Petit Plein Jeu; 2. SUITE DU 2ème
TON: 2a. Prélude; 2b. Tierce en taille; 2c. Duo; 2d.
Basse de trompette; 2e. Trio de flûtes; 2f. Dialogue;
2g. Petit Plein Jeu; 3. SUITE DU 3ème TON: 3a.
Plein Jeu; 3b. Quatuor; 3c. Dialogue de Voix
humaine; 3d. Basse de trompette; 3e. Duo; 3f. Grand
Jeu; 3g. Petit Plein Jeu; 4. SUITE DU 4ème TON:
Suite du deuxième ton P. Bardon Concert
(3/87) (PIER) ① [2] PV785051/2
1-3, 4a F. Espinasse (r1991) Marchand: Pièces
choisies pour l'orgue. (7/94) (SONY) ① SK57489
2. J. van Oortmerssen Concert
(11/87) (BIS) ① BIS-CD316
2. P. Hurford (r1989) Concert
(4/91) (REGE) ① REGCD105
2, 3. A. Isoir Concert (6/90) (CALL) ① CAL9916

> ### GUILLAUME IX, Duke of
> Aquitaine, Count of Poitiers
> *(1071–1127) France*

SECTION IV: VOCAL AND CHORAL

Farai un vers—chanson
P. Hillier, S. Stubbs, A. Lawrence-King, E. Headley
Concert (7/89) (ECM) ① 837 360-2

> ### GUILLEMAIN, Louis-Gabriel
> *(1705–1770) France*

SECTION II: CHAMBER

**Premier livre de (12) Sonates—violin and
continuo, Op. 1 (pub 1734)**
4. A.
4. S. Standage, L.U. Mortensen (r1992) Concert
(6/93) (CHAN) ① CHAN0531

> ### GUILMANT, (Felix) Alexandre
> *(1837–1911) France*

SECTION I: ORCHESTRAL

**Marche élégiaque in C minor—organ and
orchestra, Op. 74/1 (1887)**
P. Wisskirchen, Cologne Gürzenich Orch, V.
Hempfling (pp1988) Concert
(9/90) (MOTE) ① CD40101
**Symphony No. 1 in D minor—organ and
orchestra, Op. 42 (1874)** (reworking of Organ
Sonata No. 1)
P. Wisskirchen, Cologne Gürzenich Orch, V.
Hempfling (pp1988) Concert
(9/90) (MOTE) ① CD40101
I. Tracey, BBC PO, Y. P. Tortelier (r1993) Concert
(11/94) (CHAN) ① CHAN9271
**Symphony No. 2 in A—organ and orchestra,
Op. 91 (1906)** (reworking of Organ Sonata No.
8)
P. Wisskirchen, Cologne Gürzenich Orch, V.
Hempfling (pp1988) Concert
(9/90) (MOTE) ① CD40101

SECTION III: INSTRUMENTAL

Allegro in F sharp minor
N. Kynaston Concert (4/89) (HYPE) ① CDA66265
J. Watts (r1992) Concert
(8/94) (PRIO) ① PRCD414
**Cantilène pastorale (Souvenir)—organ, Op.
19**
S. Lindley Concert (3/93) (NAXO) ① 8 550581
C. Walsh Concert (3/90) (PRIO) ① PRCD281
**Fantaisie sur deux mélodies
anglaises—organ, Op. 43**
C. Herrick Concert (5/89) (HYPE) ① CDA66258

Fughetta de concert—organ, Op. 29b
M. Keiser Concert (7/91) (GOTH) ① G49037
**Grand Choeur in D, 'alla Handel'—organ,
Op. 18 (1866)**
J. Parker-Smith Concert
(3/89) (ASV) ① CDDCA610
A. Lumsden Concert (4/91) (GUIL) ① GRCD7025
S. Lindley Concert (3/93) (NAXO) ① 8 550581
Grand choeur triomphale—organ, Op. 47/2
C. Herrick Concert (7/86) (HYPE) ① CDA66121
C. Walsh Concert (3/90) (PRIO) ① PRCD281
**Introduction et Variations sur un ancien noël
polonais—organ**
C. Herrick Concert (3/89) (MERI) ① CDE84148
**March upon Handel's 'Lift up your
heads'—organ, Op. 15**
C. Herrick Concert (7/86) (HYPE) ① CDA66121
D. Hill Concert (9/86) (CARL) ① PCD823
John Scott Concert (4/89) (GUIL) ① GRCD7022
J. Watts Concert (10/89) (PRIO) ① PRCD237
C. Curley Concert (2/91) (ARGO) ① 430 200-2ZH
S. Preston Concert
(6/91) (DECC) ① 430 091-2DWO
Noël Brabançon—organ
C. Herrick Concert (3/89) (MERI) ① CDE84148
Offertoire sur deux Noëls—organ
C. Herrick Concert (3/89) (MERI) ① CDE84148
**Paraphrase (on a chorus from Handel's
'Judas Maccabaeus')—organ, Op. 90/16**
C. Herrick Concert (10/92) (HYPE) ① CDA66605
Scherzo, Op. 80
J. Parker-Smith Concert
(4/86) (ASV) ① CDDCA539
**Scherzo symphonique in C—organ, Op.
55/2**
G. Weir Concert (12/92) (KOSS) ① KC1013
**Sonata No. 1 in D minor—organ, Op. 42 (pub
1898)**
J. Watts Concert (10/89) (PRIO) ① PRCD237
Final C. Herrick Concert
(3/89) (MERI) ① CDE84148
Sonata No. 4 in D minor—organ, Op. 61
D.M. Patrick Concert (5/93) (PRIO) ① PRCD371
Sonata No. 5 in C minor—organ, Op. 80
J. Parker-Smith Concert
(9/90) (ASV) ① CDDCA702
J. Watts (r1992) Concert
(8/94) (PRIO) ① PRCD414

> ### GUION, David (Wendel Fentress)
> *(1892–1981) USA*

SECTION III: INSTRUMENTAL

The Harmonica player—piano
B. Janis (r1962) Concert
(9/91) (MERC) ① 432 002-2MM

> ### GUMBERT, Ferdinand
> *(1818–1896) Germany*

SECTION IV: VOCAL AND CHORAL

**An des Rheines grünen Ufern—insertion aria
for Lortzing's 'Undine'**
G. Hüsch, Berlin St Op Orch, H.U. Müller (r1935)
Concert (3/94) (PREI) ① 89071

> ### GUNGL, Joseph *(1809–1889)
> Hungary*

SECTION I: ORCHESTRAL

Eisenbahn-Dampf—galop, Op. 5 (1838)
Košice St PO, M. Eichenholz (r1992) Concert
(2/94) (MARC) ① 8 223471

> ### GURIDI (BIDAOLA), Jesús
> *(1886–1961) Spain*

SECTION III: INSTRUMENTAL

Triptico del Buen Pastor—organ (c1953)
1. El rebano; 2. La oveja perdida; 3. El Buen Pastor.
J. Rees-Williams Concert
(4/91) (ABBE) ① CDCA902

SECTION IV: VOCAL AND CHORAL

6 Canciones castellanas
3. Llámale con el pañuelo; 4. No quiero tus
avellanas; 5. Cómo quieres que adivine; 6. Mañanita
de San Juan.
D. Jones, M. Martineau (r1993) Concert
(9/94) (CHAN) ① CHAN9277
3-5. T. Berganza, F. Lavilla Concert
(12/92) (DG) ① [2] 435 848-2GX2

6. J. Gomez, J. Constable (r1994) *Concert*
(9/94) (CONI) ① **CDCF243**

GURILYOV, Alexander L'vovich (1803–1858) Russia

SECTION IV: VOCAL AND CHORAL
A little bird flew away—song (Wds Sel'skii)
N. Ghiaurov, P. Dokovska (r1993) *Concert*
(1/95) (RCA) ① **OS026 62501-2**

GURLITT, Manfred (1890–1972) Germnay

SECTION V: STAGE WORKS
Wozzeck—opera: 18 scenes & epilogue, Op. 16 (1926—Bremen) (Lib. after G Büchner)
EXCERPTS: SCENE 1: 1. Langsam, Wozzeck, langsam. SCENE 2: 2. Du, der Platz ist verflucht! SCENE 3A: 3. He Bub! Sasa! Rarara! Da kommen sie! SCENE 3B: 4. Mädel, was fängst du jetzt an? SCENE 3C: 5. Wer da? Bist du's Franz? Komm herein! SCENE 4: 6. Marie! Geh einmal vor dich hin. SCENE 5A: 7. Wie die Steine glänzen! SCENE 5B: 8. Unter dein ein Fingern glänzts ja. SCENE 6: 9. Wohin so elig, geehrtester Herr Sargnagel? SCENE 7: 10. Guten Tag, Franz. SCENE 8: 11. Frau Wirtin hat eine brave Magd. SCENE 9: 12. Ein Jäger aus dem Pfalz ritt einst durch einen Grünen Wald. SCENE 10: 13. Immerzu! Still! Musik! SCENE 11: 14. Andres! Ich kann nicht schlafen! SCENE 12: 15. Ich bin ein Mann! Ich hab' ein Weibsbild. SCENE 13: 16. Und ist kein Betrug in seinem Munde erfunden worden. SCENE 14: 17. Das Pistölchen ist zu teuer. SCENE 15A: 18. Wie heute schön die Sonne scheint. SCENE 15B: 19. Es war einmal ein arm Kind. SCENE 16: 20. Das Kamisölchen, Andres, gehört mit zur Montur. SCENE 17: 21. Dort links gehts in die Stadt. SCENE 17: 22. Das Messer! Wo ist das Messer! Wo ist das Messer! EPILOGUE: 23. Lament for Wozzeck.
Cpte R. Hermann, C. Lindsley, A. Scharinger, J. Gottschick, R. Wörle, E. Wottrich, C. Berggold, R. Ginzel, R. Schudel, G. Schreckenbach, Berlin RIAS Chbr Ch, Berlin Rad Children's Ch, Berlin Deutsches SO, G. Albrecht (r1993) (11/95) (CAPR) ① **60 052**

GURNEY, Ivor (Bertie) (1890–1937) England

SECTION III: INSTRUMENTAL
Nocturne in A flat—piano (1908) (unpublished)
A. Gravill *Concert*   (3/91) (GAMU) ① **GAMCD516**
Nocturne in B—piano (1909) (unpublished)
A. Gravill *Concert*   (3/91) (GAMU) ① **GAMCD516**
A Picture—piano (?1909) (unpublished)
A. Gravill *Concert*   (3/91) (GAMU) ① **GAMCD516**
Prelude in C—piano (?1920) (unpublished)
A. Gravill *Concert*   (3/91) (GAMU) ① **GAMCD516**
Prelude in C minor—piano (?1920) (unpublished)
A. Gravill *Concert*   (3/91) (GAMU) ① **GAMCD516**
Prelude in D flat—piano (1919) (unpublished)
A. Gravill *Concert*   (3/91) (GAMU) ① **GAMCD516**
Prelude in F sharp—piano (?1919) (unpublished)
A. Gravill *Concert*   (3/91) (GAMU) ① **GAMCD516**
5 Preludes—piano (1919-20)
1. F sharp (1919); 2. A minor; 3. D flat; 4. F sharp (1920); 5. D.
A. Gravill *Concert*   (3/91) (GAMU) ① **GAMCD516**
Revery—piano (1909) (ynpublished)
A. Gravill *Concert*   (3/91) (GAMU) ① **GAMCD516**
To E. H. M.—a birthday present from Ivor—piano (unpublished)
A. Gravill *Concert*   (3/91) (GAMU) ① **GAMCD516**

SECTION IV: VOCAL AND CHORAL
All night under the moon—song (1918) (Wds. W. Gibson)
I. Partridge, J. Partridge *Concert*
(12/89) (ETCE) ① **KTC1063**
The Apple Orchard—song (1919) (Wds. B. Carmen)
B. Luxon, D. Willison *Concert*
(11/90) (CHAN) ① **CHAN8831**
Black Stitchel—song (1920) (Wds. W. Gibson)
M. George, C. Benson *Concert*
(6/88) (HYPE) ① [2] **CDA66261/2**
B. Luxon, D. Willison *Concert*
(11/90) (CHAN) ① **CHAN8831**

Blaweary—song (1921) (Wds. W. Gibson)
M. George, C. Benson *Concert*
(6/88) (HYPE) ① [2] **CDA66261/2**
The Boat is chafing—song (1920) (Wds. J. Davidson)
M. George, C. Benson *Concert*
(6/88) (HYPE) ① [2] **CDA66261/2**
Bread and cherries—song (?1921) (Wds. W. de la Mare)
I. Partridge, J. Partridge *Concert*
(12/89) (ETCE) ① **KTC1063**
Brown is my love—song (1920) (Wds. anon)
I. Partridge, J. Partridge *Concert*
(12/89) (ETCE) ① **KTC1063**
By a bierside—song (1917) (Wds. J. Masefield)
M. George, C. Benson *Concert*
(6/88) (HYPE) ① [2] **CDA66261/2**
B. Luxon, D. Willison *Concert*
(11/90) (CHAN) ① **CHAN8831**
The Carol of the Skiddaw Yowes—song (1919) (Wds. E. Casson)
B. Luxon, D. Willison *Concert*
(11/90) (CHAN) ① **CHAN8831**
Cathleen ni Houlihan—song (1919) (Wds. W. B. Yeats)
M. George, C. Benson *Concert*
(6/88) (HYPE) ① [2] **CDA66261/2**
The Cloths of heaven—song (?1919-20) (Wds. W. B. Yeats)
I. Partridge, J. Partridge *Concert*
(12/89) (ETCE) ① **KTC1063**
Cranham Woods—song (1918-19) (Wds. F. W. Harvey)
B. Luxon, D. Willison *Concert*
(11/90) (CHAN) ① **CHAN8831**
Desire in Spring—song (Wds F. Ledwidge)
I. Partridge, J. Partridge *Concert*
(12/89) (ETCE) ① **KTC1063**
B. Luxon, D. Willison *Concert*
(11/90) (CHAN) ① **CHAN8831**
Down by the Salley Gardens—song (1921) (Wds. W. B. Yeats)
I. Partridge, J. Partridge *Concert*
(12/89) (ETCE) ① **KTC1063**
B. Luxon, D. Willison *Concert*
(11/90) (CHAN) ① **CHAN8831**
S. Roberts, C. Benson *Concert*
(9/91) (HYPE) ① **CDA66015**
Edward, Edward—ballad (1914) (Wds. 'Percy's Reliques' (1765))
M. George, C. Benson *Concert*
(6/88) (HYPE) ① [2] **CDA66261/2**
An Epitaph—song (1920) (Wds. W. de la Mare)
I. Partridge, J. Partridge *Concert*
(12/89) (ETCE) ① **KTC1063**
B. Luxon, D. Willison *Concert*
(11/90) (CHAN) ① **CHAN8831**
Epitaph in old mode—song (1920) (Wds J. C. Squire)
S. Varcoe, C. Benson *Concert*
(6/88) (HYPE) ① [2] **CDA66261/2**
Even such is time—song (1917) (Wds. W. Raleigh)
M. George, C. Benson *Concert*
(6/88) (HYPE) ① [2] **CDA66261/2**
The Fiddler of Dooney—song (1917) (Wds, W. B. Yeats)
M. George, C. Benson *Concert*
(6/88) (HYPE) ① [2] **CDA66261/2**
B. Luxon, D. Willison *Concert*
(11/90) (CHAN) ① **CHAN8831**
The Fields are full—song (1919) (Wds. E. Shanks)
I. Partridge, J. Partridge *Concert*
(12/89) (ETCE) ① **KTC1063**
B. Luxon, D. Willison *Concert*
(11/90) (CHAN) ① **CHAN8831**
J. Baker, G. Moore (r1967) *Concert*
(11/94) (EMI) ① **CDM5 65009-2**
The Folly of being comforted—song (1917) (Wds. W. B. Yeats)
I. Partridge, J. Partridge *Concert*
(12/89) (ETCE) ① **KTC1063**
B. Luxon, D. Willison *Concert*
(11/90) (CHAN) ① **CHAN8831**
Goodnight to the meadows—song (1920) (Wds. R. Graves)
M. George, C. Benson *Concert*
(6/88) (HYPE) ① [2] **CDA66261/2**
Ha'nacker Mill—song (1920) (Wds. H. Belloc)
M. George, C. Benson *Concert*
(6/88) (HYPE) ① [2] **CDA66261/2**
B. Luxon, D. Willison *Concert*
(11/90) (CHAN) ① **CHAN8831**

Hawk and buckle—song (1920) (Wds. John Doyle (R. Graves))
M. George, C. Benson *Concert*
(6/88) (HYPE) ① [2] **CDA66261/2**
B. Luxon, D. Willison *Concert*
(11/90) (CHAN) ① **CHAN8831**
S. Roberts, C. Benson *Concert*
(9/91) (HYPE) ① **CDA66015**
I praise the tender flower—song (1912) (Wds. R. Bridges)
B. Luxon, D. Willison *Concert*
(11/90) (CHAN) ① **CHAN8831**
In Flanders—song (1917) (Wds. F. W. Harvey)
S. Varcoe, C. Benson *Concert*
(6/88) (HYPE) ① [2] **CDA66261/2**
B. Luxon, D. Willison *Concert*
(11/90) (CHAN) ① **CHAN8831**
Last hours—song (1919) (Wds. J. Freeman)
S. Varcoe, C. Benson *Concert*
(6/88) (HYPE) ① [2] **CDA66261/2**
Ludlow and Teme—song cycle: tenor, piano and string quartet (1920) (Wds. Housman)
1. When smoke stood up from Ludlow; 2. Far in a western brookland; 3. 'Tis time, I think, by Ludlow town; 4. Ludlow Fair; 5. On the idle hill of summer; 6. When I was one-and-twenty; 7. The Lent Lily.
Adrian Thompson, Delmé Qt, I. Burnside *Concert*
(9/90) (HYPE) ① **CDA66385**
Most holy night—song (1920) (Wds. H. Belloc)
M. George, C. Benson *Concert*
(6/88) (HYPE) ① [2] **CDA66261/2**
The Night of Trafalgar—song (1913) (Wds. T. Hardy)
M. George, C. Benson *Concert*
(6/88) (HYPE) ① [2] **CDA66261/2**
Nine of the clock—song (1920) (Wds. John Doyle (R. Graves))
S. Varcoe, C. Benson *Concert*
(6/88) (HYPE) ① [2] **CDA66261/2**
On the Downs—song (1918) (Wds. J. Masefield)
B. Luxon, D. Willison *Concert*
(11/90) (CHAN) ① **CHAN8831**
Orpheus—song (1912) (Wds. Shakespeare)
M. Hill, C. Benson *Concert*
(6/88) (HYPE) ① [2] **CDA66261/2**
The Scribe—song (1918) (Wds. W. de la Mare)
B. Luxon, D. Willison *Concert*
(11/90) (CHAN) ① **CHAN8831**
Severn meadows—song (1917) (Wds. cpsr)
M. George, C. Benson *Concert*
(6/88) (HYPE) ① [2] **CDA66261/2**
I. Partridge, J. Partridge *Concert*
(12/89) (ETCE) ① **KTC1063**
The Ship—song (1920) (Wds. J. C. Squire)
M. George, C. Benson *Concert*
(6/88) (HYPE) ① [2] **CDA66261/2**
The Singer—song (1919) (Wds. E. Shanks)
I. Partridge, J. Partridge *Concert*
(12/89) (ETCE) ① **KTC1063**
Sleep—song (Wds. J. Fletcher)
M. Hill, C. Benson *Concert*
(6/88) (HYPE) ① [2] **CDA66261/2**
B. Luxon, D. Willison *Concert*
(11/90) (CHAN) ① **CHAN8831**
S. Roberts, C. Benson *Concert*
(9/91) (HYPE) ① **CDA66015**
Sarah Walker, R. Vignoles *Concert*
(10/92) (CRD) ① **CRD3473**
Snow—song (1921) (Wds. E. Thomas)
I. Partridge, J. Partridge *Concert*
(12/89) (ETCE) ① **KTC1063**
Spring—song (1912) (Wds. T. Nashe)
M. Hill, C. Benson *Concert*
(6/88) (HYPE) ① [2] **CDA66261/2**
Tears—song (1912) (Wds J. Fletcher)
M. Hill, C. Benson *Concert*
(6/88) (HYPE) ① [2] **CDA66261/2**
Thou didst delight my eyes—song (1921) (Wds. R. Bridges)
M. George, C. Benson *Concert*
(6/88) (HYPE) ① [2] **CDA66261/2**
To violets—song (1920) (Wds. R. Herrick)
S. Varcoe, C. Benson *Concert*
(6/88) (HYPE) ① [2] **CDA66261/2**
Twa corbies—song (1914) (Wds. from 'Border Ballads')
M. George, C. Benson *Concert*
(6/88) (HYPE) ① [2] **CDA66261/2**
B. Luxon, D. Willison *Concert*
(11/90) (CHAN) ① **CHAN8831**

Under the greenwood tree—song (1912)
(Wds. Shakespeare)
M. Hill, C. Benson *Concert*
(6/88) (HYPE) ① [2] **CDA66261/2**
The Western Playland—song cycle (1926)
(Wds. A. E. Housman)
1. Reveille; 2. Loveliest of trees; 3. Golden friends
(With rue my heart is laden); 4. Twice a week; 5. The
Aspens (Along the field); 6. Is my team ploughing?; 7.
The far country (into my heart an air that kills); 8.
March (The sun at noon in higher air).
Cpte G. Trew, R. Vignoles, Coull Qt *Concert*
(11/90) (MERI) ① **CDE84185**
S. Varcoe, Delmé Qt, I. Burnside *Concert*
(9/90) (HYPE) ① **CDA66385**
You are my sky—song (1920) (Wds. J. C.
Squire)
S. Varcoe, C. Benson *Concert*
(6/88) (HYPE) ① [2] **CDA66261/2**

GWYNN WILLIAMS, W. S. *Wales*

SECTION IV: VOCAL AND CHORAL

The Flower maiden—song
R. A. Morgan *Concert* (12/87) (ETCE) ① **KTC1049**
Morning Light—song
R. A. Morgan *Concert* (12/87) (ETCE) ① **KTC1049**
My little Welsh home—song
S. Burrows, J. Constable *Concert*
(4/92) (GAMU) ① **GAMD506**

HAAS, Pavel *(1899–1944)*
Czechoslovakia

SECTION II: CHAMBER

**String Quartet No. 2, 'Z opičích hor', Op. 7
(1925)**
Hawthorne Qt (r1993) *Concert*
(3/94) (DECC) ① **440 853-2DH**
String Quartet No. 3, Op. 15 (1938)
Hawthorne Qt (r1993) *Concert*
(3/94) (DECC) ① **440 853-2DH**
Wind Quintet, Op. 10 (1929)
Aulos Wind Qnt (r1988) *Concert*
(6/93) (SCHW) ① **310051**

SECTION IV: VOCAL AND CHORAL

**4 Songs on Chinese Poetry—bass and piano
(1944)** (Wds. trans B. Mathesius)
1. I heard wild geese; 2. In the bamboo frove; 3. The
moon is far from home; 4. Sleepless night.
K. Průša, J. Pokorný *Concert*
(8/92) (ROMA) ① [2] **RR1941**

HÁBA, Alois *(1893–1973)*
Czechoslovakia

SECTION V: STAGE WORKS

The Mother—quarter-tone opera (1927-29)
(Lib. cpsr)
Cpte V. Urbanová, O. Spisar, M. Lemariová, M.
Sandtnerová, J. Polívková, L. Havlák, M. Borský, V.
Jedenáctik, E. Zikmundová, P. Kočí, J. Janoušek,
Prague Nat Th Chor, Prague Nat Th Orch, J. Jirouš
(r1964) (1/94) (SUPR) ① [2] **10 8258-2**

HACQUART, Carolus
(c1640–?1701) The Netherlands

SECTION II: CHAMBER

**Harmonia parnassia: 10 sonatas—3 and 4vv
(pub 1686)**
10. J. Holloway, S. Ritchie, A. Manze, N. North, M.
Springfels, J. Toll (r1993) *Concert*
(2/94) (HARM) ① **HMU90 7091**

HADJIDAKIS, Manos *(b 1925)*
Greece

SECTION IV: VOCAL AND CHORAL

A Carnation behind your ear—song (Wds. A.
Sakellarios)
A. Baltsa, K. Papadopoulos, Athens Exp Orch, S.
Xarhakos (arr. Xarhakos) *Concert*
(2/87) (DG) ① **419 236-2GH**
Dream of urban children—song (Wds. cpsr)
A. Baltsa, K. Papadopoulos, Athens Exp Orch, S.
Xarhakos (arr. Xarhakos) *Concert*
(2/87) (DG) ① **419 236-2GH**

The Postman—song (Wds. cpsr)
A. Baltsa, K. Papadopoulos, Athens Exp Orch, S.
Xarhakos (arr. Xarhakos) *Concert*
(2/87) (DG) ① **419 236-2GH**

SECTION V: STAGE WORKS

America, America—film score (1963)
EXCERPTS: 1. Main Title.
1. OST (r1963) *Concert* (11/91) (STAN) ① **STZ112**

HADLEY, Patrick (Arthur Sheldon)
(1899–1973) England

SECTION IV: VOCAL AND CHORAL

The Cup of Blessing—anthem (unpub)
Gonville & Caius College Ch, R. Hill, G. Webber
Concert (3/94) (ASV) ① **CDDCA881**
**Lenten Cantata—tenor, bass, chorus and
organ (1962)** (Wds. C Cudworth)
J.M. Ainsley, D. Sweeney, Gonville & Caius College
Ch, R. Hill, G. Webber *Concert*
(3/94) (ASV) ① **CDDCA881**
My beloved spake—anthem (1938)
St Paul's Cath Ch, Andrew Lucas, John Scott
Concert (9/90) (HYPE) ① **CDA66374**
Winchester Cath Ch, Waynflete Sngrs, T. Byram-
Wigfield, Bournemouth SO, D. Hill *Concert*
(4/92) (ARGO) ① **430 836-2ZH**
Dundee Cath Ch, R. Lightband (org/dir) *Concert*
(8/92) (ABBE) ① **CDCA926**
Gonville & Caius College Ch, Michael Phillips, G.
Webber *Concert* (3/94) (ASV) ① **CDDCA881**
Southwark Cath Ch, P. Wright, S. Layton (r1992)
Concert (7/94) (PRIO) ① **PRCD435**
A Song for Easter—chorus and organ (1936)
(Wds. G Herbert)
Gonville & Caius College Ch, R. Hill, G. Webber
Concert (3/94) (ASV) ① **CDDCA881**
**The Trees so high—symphonic ballad in A
minor—baritone, chorus and orchestra
(1931)**
D. Wilson-Johnson, Philh Chor, Philh, M. Bamert
(r1992) *Sainton: Island.*
(10/93) (CHAN) ① **CHAN9181**

HAEFFNER, Johann Christian
Friedrich *(1759–1833)*
Germany/Sweden

SECTION V: STAGE WORKS

Electra—tragic opera: 3 acts
(1787—Stockholm) (Lib Guillard, after
Sophocles)
Cpte H. Martinpelto, P. Mattei, H. Hinz, M.
Samuelson, K. Hedlund, S. Tysklind, A. Häggstam,
C. Högman, L. Wedin, S-E. Alexandersson,
Stockholm Rad Chor, Drottningholm Baroque Ens, T.
Schuback (r1992) (7/94) (CPRI) ① [2] **CAP22030**

HAENSEL, A.

SECTION I: ORCHESTRAL

**Concerto for 2 Horns and String Orchestra,
Op. 80**
M. Rimon (hn/dir), Israel PO *Concert*
(2/92) (CARL) ① **MCD31**

HAENTZSCHEL, Georg
(1907–1992) Germany

SECTION V: STAGE WORKS

Annelie—film score (1941)
EXCERPTS: 1. Wiegenlied; 2. Intermezzo.
1, 2. Cologne RSO, E. Smola (r1992) *Concert*
(8/94) (CAPR) ① **10 400**
Münchhausen—film score (1943)
EXCERPTS: 1. Münchhausen's narrative; 2. Dance
at the folk festival; 3. Rococo scene; 4. Abduction of
the Princess; 5. On the Moon; 6. Münchhausen's
farewell to Adventures.
1-6. Cologne RSO, E. Smola (r1992) *Concert*
(8/94) (CAPR) ① **10 400**
**Musical Film Festival—concert suite from
film scores**
1. Emil und die Detektive; 2. Meine Kinder und ich; 3.
Hotel Adlon.
Cologne RSO, E. Smola (r1992) *Concert*
(8/94) (CAPR) ① **10 400**
Robinson soll nicht sterben—film score
EXCERPTS: 1. Robinson's island and prologue; 2.
Children playing and musicians; 3. Thoughts of a
young girl; 4. Revolt of youth; 5. Dance in the prison
yard; 6. In the royal palace; 7. Departure from

Robinson's island.
1-7. Cologne RSO, E. Smola (r1992) *Concert*
(8/94) (CAPR) ① **10 400**
Via mala—film score (1948)
EXCERPTS: 1. Sommer auf der Lauretz-Mühle; 2.
Erwachende Liebe; 3. Zwischenspiel; 4. Ausklang.
1-4. Cologne RSO, E. Smola (r1992) *Concert*
(8/94) (CAPR) ① **10 400**

HAGEMAN, Richard *(1882–1966)*
The Netherlands/USA

SECTION IV: VOCAL AND CHORAL

Do not go, my love—song
L. Melchior, orch (r1926) *Concert*
(8/88) (DANA) ① [2] **DACOCD313/4**
D. Borgioli, I. Newton (r1930s) *Concert*
(12/90) (CLUB) ① **CL99-014**
R. Herincx, J. Constable *Concert*
(4/92) (GAMU) ① **GAMD506**

SECTION V: STAGE WORKS

**Caponsacchi—opera (1932—Freiburg)
I know you better...This very vivid morn** H.
Jepson, RCA SO, A. Smallens (r1936) *Concert*
(4/94) (RCA) ① [6] **09026 61580-2(4)**
**She Wore a Yellow Ribbon—film score
(1949)**
1. Prague City PO, P. Bateman (r1994; arr Snell)
Concert (11/94) (SILV) ① **FILMCD153**
Stagecoach—film score (1939) (trad themes
adapted by Hageman, Harling, Leopold, Shuken
& Gruenberg)
Suite: Narrative for orchestra Prague City PO, P.
Bateman (r1994; arr Townend) *Concert*
(11/94) (SILV) ① **FILMCD153**

HAGEN, Bernhard Joachim *(18th
Cent) Germany*

SECTION III: INSTRUMENTAL

Menuetto con variazioni di Locatelli—lute
K. E. Schröder (r1994) *Concert*
(5/95) (HARM) ① **HMC90 1505**

HAGUE, Albert *(b 1920) USA*

SECTION V: STAGE WORKS

**Plain and Fancy—musical show (1955—New
York)** (Lyrics A B Horwitt)
Cpte B. Cook, S. Conway, Orig Broadway Cast
(11/93) (EMI) ① **ZDM7 64762-2**

HAHN, Reynaldo *(1875–1947)*
Venezuela/France

SECTION III: INSTRUMENTAL

Premières Valses—piano (1898)
C. Joly *Rossignol éperdu.*
(5/90) (ACCO) ① **20054-2**
Le Rossignol éperdu—piano (1898-1910)
C. Joly *Premières Valses.*
(5/90) (ACCO) ① **20054-2**
Thème varié—piano
M. Fingerhut *Concert* (9/88) (CHAN) ① **CHAN8578**

SECTION IV: VOCAL AND CHORAL

À Chloris—mélodie (1916) (Wds. T. de Viau)
M. Hill, G. Johnson *Concert*
(8/88) (HYPE) ① **CDA66045**
F. le Roux, J. Cohen *Concert*
(11/91) (REM) ① **REM311069**
H. Hagegård, T. Schuback (r1976) *Concert*
(5/94) (BIS) ① **BIS-CD054**
L' Air—song (Wds. de Banville)
M. Hill, G. Johnson *Concert*
(8/88) (HYPE) ① **CDA66045**
Automne—mélodie (Wds. de Banville)
M. Hill, G. Johnson *Concert*
(8/88) (HYPE) ① **CDA66045**
Chansons grises—song cycle (pub 1893)
(Wds. Verlaine)
1. Chanson d'automne; 2. Tous deux; 3. L'allée est
sans fin; 4. En sourdine; 5. L'heure exquise; 6.
Paysage triste; 7. La bonne chanson.
M. Hill, G. Johnson *Concert*
(8/88) (HYPE) ① **CDA66045**
F. le Roux, J. Cohen *Concert*
(11/91) (REM) ① **REM311069**
5. D. Fischer-Dieskau, H. Höll (r c1987) *Concert*
(12/95) (TELD) ① **4509-97457-2**

La **Chère blessure—mélodie** (Wds. Mme
Blanchecotte)
M. Hill, G. Johnson *Concert*
(8/88) (HYPE) ① **CDA66045**
Le **cimetière de campagne—song** (Wds.
Vicaire)
C. Panzéra, M. Panzéra-Baillot (r1923) *Concert*
(3/93) (EMI) ① **CDH7 64254-2**
Les **Cygnes—mélodie (1893-94)** (Wds. A.
Renaud)
F. le Roux, J. Cohen *Concert*
(11/91) (REM) ① **REM311069**
Dans la nuit—mélodie (wds. J. Moréas)
F. le Roux, J. Cohen *Concert*
(11/91) (REM) ① **REM311069**
D'une prison—mélodie (1892) (Wds. P.
Verlaine)
M. Hill, G. Johnson *Concert*
(8/88) (HYPE) ① **CDA66045**
F. le Roux, J. Cohen *Concert*
(11/91) (REM) ① **REM311069**
C. Panzéra, M. Panzéra-Baillot (r1923) *Concert*
(3/93) (EMI) ① **CDH7 64254-2**
N. Melba (r1909) *Concert*
(9/93) (RCA) ① **09026 61412-2**
C. Formichi, orch (r1927) *Concert*
(11/94) (PREI) ① **89055**
N. Melba, anon (r1909) *Concert*
(5/95) (ROMO) ① [3] **81011-2(1)**
En sourdine—mélodie (1894) (Wds. P.
Verlaine)
S. Varcoe, G. Johnson *Concert*
(6/88) (HYPE) ① **CDA66248**
M. Teyte, G. Moore (r1941) *Concert*
(10/94) (EMI) ① [2] **CHS5 65198-2**
L' **Enamourée—mélodie** (Wds. de Banville)
M. Hill, G. Johnson *Concert*
(8/88) (HYPE) ① **CDA66045**
V. de los Angeles, Sinfonia of London, R. Frühbeck
de Burgos (orch Gamley) *Concert*
(10/88) (EMI) ① **CDM7 69502-2**
Étoiles—mélodie (Wds. de Banville)
M. Hill, G. Johnson *Concert*
(8/88) (HYPE) ① **CDA66045**
Études latines—mélodies (1900)
4. Belle lune d'argent (wds. J. Moréas).
4. M. Teyte, G. Moore (r1944) *Concert*
(4/92) (EMI) ① [7] **CHS7 69741-2(1)**
4. M. Teyte, G. Moore (r1944) *Concert*
(10/94) (EMI) ① [2] **CHS5 65198-2**
Fêtes galantes—mélodie (1892) (Wds.
Verlaine)
M. Hill, G. Johnson *Concert*
(8/88) (HYPE) ① **CDA66045**
F. le Roux, J. Cohen *Concert*
(11/91) (REM) ① **REM311069**
Les **Fontaines—mélodie** (Wds. H. de
Régnier)
M. Hill, G. Johnson *Concert*
(8/88) (HYPE) ① **CDA66045**
F. le Roux, J. Cohen *Concert*
(11/91) (REM) ① **REM311069**
Fumée—mélodie (Wds. J. Moréas)
F. le Roux, J. Cohen *Concert*
(11/91) (REM) ① **REM311069**
L' **Heure exquise—mélodie** (Wds. Verlaine)
V. Maurel, anon (r1903) *Concert*
(10/92) (SYMP) ① **SYMCD1101**
M. Teyte, G. Moore (r1941) *Concert*
(10/94) (EMI) ① [2] **CHS5 65198-2**
G. Souzay, D. Baldwin (r1963) *Concert*
(3/95) (PHIL) ① [4] **438 964-2PM4(2)**
L' **Incrédule—mélodie (1893)** (Wds. P.
Verlaine)
M. Hill, G. Johnson *Concert*
(8/88) (HYPE) ① **CDA66045**
F. le Roux, J. Cohen *Concert*
(11/91) (REM) ① **REM311069**
E. Eames, anon (r1905) *Concert*
(11/93) (ROMO) ① [2] **81001-2**
Infidélité—mélodie (1891) (Wds. T. Gautier)
M. Hill, G. Johnson *Concert*
(8/88) (HYPE) ① **CDA66045**
F. le Roux, J. Cohen *Concert*
(11/91) (REM) ① **REM311069**
P. Frijsh, C. Dougherty (r1940) *Concert*
(4/95) (PEAR) ① [2] **GEMMCDS9095(1)**
Je me metz en vostre mercy—mélodie (Wds.
C. d'Orléans)
Vanni-Marcoux, anon (r1931) *Concert*
(1/94) (CLUB) ① **CL99-101**
Mai—mélodie (Wds. F. Coppée)
F. le Roux, J. Cohen *Concert*
(11/91) (REM) ① **REM311069**
My Ships—song: 1v and piano
M. Garden, J. Dansereau (r1926: Eng) *Concert*
(8/94) (ROMO) ① **81008-2**

Nocturne—mélodie (1893) (Wds. J. Lahor)
F. le Roux, J. Cohen *Concert*
(11/91) (REM) ① **REM311069**
La **Nuit—mélodie**
F. le Roux, J. Cohen *Concert*
(11/91) (REM) ① **REM311069**
Offrande—mélodie (1891) (Wds. P. Verlaine)
M. Hill, G. Johnson *Concert*
(8/88) (HYPE) ① **CDA66045**
F. le Roux, J. Cohen *Concert*
(11/91) (REM) ① **REM311069**
Vanni-Marcoux, anon, anon (r1931) *Concert*
(1/94) (CLUB) ① **CL99-101**
M. Teyte, G. Moore (r1941) *Concert*
(10/94) (EMI) ① [2] **CHS5 65198-2**
Paysage—mélodie (1890) (Wds. A. Theuriet)
F. le Roux, J. Cohen *Concert*
(11/91) (REM) ① **REM311069**
Le **Printemps—mélodie (pub 1899)** (Wds. T.
de Banville)
F. le Roux, J. Cohen *Concert*
(11/91) (REM) ① **REM311069**
Quand je fus pris au pavillon—mélodie (Wds.
Duc Charles d'Orléans)
M. Hill, G. Johnson *Concert*
(8/88) (HYPE) ① **CDA66045**
F. le Roux, J. Cohen *Concert*
(11/91) (REM) ① **REM311069**
Quand la nuit n'est pas étoilée—mélodie
(Wds. V. Hugo)
F. le Roux, J. Cohen *Concert*
(11/91) (REM) ① **REM311069**
Rêverie—mélodie (1893) (Wds. V. Hugo)
F. Lott, G. Johnson (r1984) *Concert*
(5/87) (HARM) ① **HMA190 1138**
F. le Roux, J. Cohen *Concert*
(11/91) (REM) ① **REM311069**
Le **Rossignol des lilas—mélodie** (Wds. L.
Dauphin)
G. Boué, A. Collard (r c1942) *Concert*
(4/92) (EMI) ① [7] **CHS7 69741-2(3)**
V. de los Angeles, G. Soriano (r1966) *Concert*
(4/94) (EMI) ① [4] **CMS5 65061-2(1)**
Séraphine—mélodie (1892) (Wds. Heine)
F. le Roux, J. Cohen *Concert*
(11/91) (REM) ① **REM311069**
Seule—mélodie (1892) (Wds. T. Gautier)
F. le Roux, J. Cohen *Concert*
(11/91) (REM) ① **REM311069**
Si mes vers avaient des ailes—mélodie (pub
1895) (Wds. V. Hugo)
F. Lott, G. Johnson (r1984) *Concert*
(5/87) (HARM) ① **HMA190 1138**
M. Hill, G. Johnson *Concert*
(8/88) (HYPE) ① **CDA66045**
E. Schwarzkopf, G. Moore (r1956) *Concert*
(12/90) (EMI) ① **CDM7 63654-2**
F. le Roux, J. Cohen *Concert*
(11/91) (REM) ① **REM311069**
N. Melba, A. Sassoli (r1907) *Concert*
(9/93) (RCA) ① **09026 61412-2**
M. Teyte, G. Moore (r1941) *Concert*
(10/94) (EMI) ① [2] **CHS5 65198-2**
N. Melba, A. Sassoli (r1907) *Concert*
(5/95) (ROMO) ① [3] **81011-2(1)**
D. Fischer-Dieskau, H. Höll (r c1987) *Concert*
(12/95) (TELD) ① **4509-97457-2**
Sur l'eau—mélodie (Wds. S. Prudhomme)
F. le Roux, J. Cohen *Concert*
(11/91) (REM) ① **REM311069**
The **Swing—song: 1v and piano**
M. Garden, J. Dansereau (r1926: Eng) *Concert*
(8/94) (ROMO) ① **81008-2**
Trois jours de vendage—mélodie (wds. A.
Daudet)
F. le Roux, J. Cohen *Concert*
(11/91) (REM) ① **REM311069**
V. de los Angeles, G. Soriano (r1966) *Concert*
(4/94) (EMI) ① [4] **CMS5 65061-2(1)**
Tyndaris—mélodie (Wds. Leconte de Lisle)
M. Hill, G. Johnson *Concert*
(8/88) (HYPE) ① **CDA66045**
**Venezia - Chansons en dialecte
Vénetian—song cycle (1901)**
1. Sopra l'acqua indormenzada; 2. La barcheta; 3.
L'Avertimento; 4. La Biondina in gondoleta; 5. Che
pecal; 6. La Primavera.
1-6. F. Lott, A. Rolfe Johnson, R. Jackson, G.
Johnson *Concert* (8/98) (HYPE) ① **CDA66112**

Le **Bal de Béatrice d'Este—concert suite
from ballet (1909)**
New London Orch, R. Corp *Concert*
(10/89) (HYPE) ① **CDA66347**

NY Harmonie Ens, S. Richman *Concert*
(7/92) (MUSI) ① **MACD-649**
Ciboulette—operetta (1923—Paris) (Lib. De
Flers and De Croisset)
EXCERPTS: ACT 1: 1. Nous sommes six hussards;
2. Est-ce monsieur Thiers?; 3. Bien des jeunes gens;
4. Toi! Vous!; 5. Après cette nuit d'orgie; 6. Nous
sommes les bons maraîchers; 7a. La voilà! La voilà!;
7b. C'est le printemps qui m'a surprise; 8a. Y a des
femm's qui font la folie; 8b. Moi m'appelle Ciboulette;
9. Oh! mon Dieu!; 10. Les parents, quand on est
bébé; 11. Mettons nos tabliers coquets. ACT 2: 12a.
Prelude; 12b. C'est le doux silence des champs; 13.
Nous avons fait un beau voyage; 14. Y a des
arbes...C'est sa banlieue; 15. C'est nous; 16. Ah! si
vous étiez Nicolas; 17. Qu'il est doux de fair
campagne; 18. Moi j'aime (Mélodrame); 19. C'est
tout ce qui me reste d'elle; 20. Nous somm's les bons
villageois. ACT 3: 21. Ah! Monsieur Métral; 22. J'ai
vingt-huit ans; 23. Mon amour, daigne me permettre;
24. C'est le moment inévitable de la chanson.
13. B. Hendricks, G. Quilico, Lyon Op Orch, L. Foster
(r1993) *Concert* (6/95) (EMI) ① **CDC5 55151-2**
**Mozart—musical comedy: 3 acts
(1925—Paris)** (Lib. S. Guitry)
EXCERPTS: 1. Overture. ACT 1: 2. Je me suis
longtemps souvenu (Grimm); 3. Comme c'est facile
(Mozart); 4a. Tiens, c'est drôle que vous me parliez
de cela; 4b. Etre adore. ACT 2: 5. Quand on pense
que des gens (Mozart); 6. Madame n'est pas là?
(Grimaud, Louise, Mozart); 7a. Ballet; 7b. Gavotte;
7c. Comme elle danse (Mozart); 8. Depuis ton
départ, mon amant (Mozart). ACT 3: 9. Je t'y prendrai
douc toujours (Grimaud, Louise); 10. La vérité, vous
savez bien; 11. Melodrame (Grimaud, Mozart, La
Guimard); 12. Alors, adieu donc, mon amour
(Mozart).
Cpte G. Boué, R. Bourdin, M. Alicia, B. Dheran, F.
Marette, M. Delavaivre, H. Hennetier, J. Pruvost,
French Rad Lyric Orch, P-M. LeConte (with dialogue:
bp1959) (3/92) (MUSD) ① **20137-2**
**O mon bel inconnu!—musical comedy: 3
acts (1933—Paris)** (Lib. S. Guitry)
Cpte L. Dachary, C. Château, M. Stiot, D. Tirmont,
M. Hamel, A. Doniat, P. Gaudin, J. Peyron, J.
Provins, French Rad Lyric Orch, J. Brebion (bp1971)
(4/94) (MUSD) ① [2] **202562**

HAJDU, André *(b 1932)*
Hungary/Israel

The **Milky Way—piano**
Excs A. Vardi *Concert* (6/90) (CARL) ① **PWK1132**

HAKIM, Naji *(b 1955)*
Lebanon/France

The **Embrace of Fire—organ (1986)**
N. Hakim *Concert* (10/89) (MOTE) ① **CD40081**
Hommage à Igor Stravinsky—organ (1987)
N. Hakim *Concert* (7/91) (PRIO) ① **PRCD327**
Memor—organ (1989)
N. Hakim *Concert* (7/91) (PRIO) ① **PRCD327**

HAKMOUN, Hassan *(b 1963)*
Morocco

**Saade (I'm happy)—vocals, percussion and
string quartet (1991)**
Kronos Qt, H. Hakmoun, R. Laktib, S. Hakmoun
Concert (11/92) (NONE) ① **7559-79275-2**

**HALÉVY, (Jacques-François-
)Fromental(-Elie)** *(1799–1862)*
France

Charles VI—opera: 5 acts (1843—Paris) (Lib.
C and G. Delavigne)
Avec la douce chansonnette J. Noté, anon (r1903)
Concert (9/91) (SYMP) ① **SYMCD1089**
La **Juive—opera: 5 acts (1835—Paris)** (Lib.
Scribe)
ACT 1: 1. Overture; 2. Introduction; 3. Si la rigueur.
ACT 2: 4. Dieu que ma main tremblante; 5. Dieu! que ma voix tremblante; 6. Il va
venir; 7. Lorsqu'à toi (Passover Music); 8. Mon doux seigneur et
maître (Boléro); 9. Vous qui du Dieu vivant. ACT 4:
10. Ah, que ma voix plaintive; 11a. Va prononcer ma

mort; 11b. Rachel, quand du Seigneur. ACT 5: 12.
Dieu m'éclaire; 13. Il est temps! (Finale).
Cpte J. Carreras, J. Varady, J. Anderson, F.
Furlanetto, D. Gonzalez, R. Massis, R. Schirrer,
Ambrosian Op Chor, Philh, A. de Almeida
　　　(11/89) (PHIL) ① [3] **420 190-2PH3**
Ah, j'implore en tremblant L. Slezak, W. Hesch,
orch (Ger: r1908) *Concert*　　(2/91) (PREI) ① **89020**
Ah, j'implore en tremblant A. Didur, T. Leliwa, orch
(r c1911: Ital) *Concert*　(1/94) (CLUB) ① **CL99-089**
Pour lui, pour moi, mon père J. Korolewicz-Wayda,
anon (r1900s: Pol) *Concert*
　　　　　　　(6/93) (PEAR) ① [3] **GEMMCDS9004/6(1)**
3. E. Pinza, orch, C. Sabajno (Ital: r1923) *Concert*
　　　　　　　　(2/89) (PEAR) ① **GEMMCD9306**
3. E. Pinza, NY Met Op Orch, F. Cleva (r1946: Ital)
Concert　　　　(4/90) (SONY) ① **MPK45693**
3. I. Andrésen, orch (Ger: r1929) *Concert*
　　　　　　　　　(10/90) (PREI) ① **89028**
3. A. Kipnis, Berlin Charlottenburg Op Orch, J.
Heidenreich (r1923) *Concert*
　　　　　　　　　(10/91) (PEAR) ① **GEMMCD9451**
3. L. Sibiriakov, anon (r1906: Russ) *Concert*
　　　　　　　(6/93) (PEAR) ① [3] **GEMMCDS9001/3(2)**
3, 9. E. Pinza, orch, R. Bourdon (r1927) *Concert*
　　　　　　　　　(3/92) (PREI) ① **89050**
4. F. Völker, chor, Berlin Staatskapelle, A. Melichar
(r1933: Ger) *Concert*　　(8/94) (PREI) ① **89070**
5. L. Slezak, orch (Ger: r1907) *Concert*
　　　　　　　　　(2/91) (PREI) ① **89020**
6. Lotte Lehmann, orch (Ger: r1921) *Concert*
　　　　　　　　(6/92) (PREI) ① [3] **89302**
6. R. Ponselle, orch, R. Romani (r1924) *Concert*
　　　　　　　　　(10/93) (NIMB) ① **NI7846**
6. E. Destinn, orch (r1911: Ger) *Concert*
　　　　　　　(12/94) (SUPR) ① [12] **11 2136-2(4)**
9. E. Pinza, orch (Ital: r1924) *Concert*
　　　　　　　　(2/89) (PEAR) ① **GEMMCD9306**
9. N. de Angelis, orch, L. Molajoli (Ital: r1928)
Concert　　　　(7/92) (PREI) ① **89042**
9. F. Navarini, anon (Ital: r1906) *Concert*
　　　　　　　(11/92) (MEMO) ① [2] **HR4408/9(1)**
9. A. Didur, S. Cottone (r1903: Ital) *Concert*
　　　　　　　(6/93) (PEAR) ① [3] **GEMMCDS9997/9(2)**
9. L. Sibiriakov, orch (r1908: Russ) *Concert*
　　　　　　　(6/93) (PEAR) ① [3] **GEMMCDS9001/3(2)**
9. F. Navarini, anon (Ital: r1907: Ital) *Concert*
　　　　　　　(4/94) (EMI) ① [3] **CHS7 64860-2(1)**
11a, 11b, 12. L. Escalais, anon (2 vers, Fr/Ital:
r1905/6) *Concert*　(12/93) (SYMP) ① **SYMCD1126**
11b E. Caruso, orch, J. Pasternack (r1920) *Concert*
　　　　　　　　(10/89) (NIMB) ① **NI7803**
11b F. Völker, Berlin St Op Orch, A. Melichar (r1933:
Ger) *Concert*　　　(2/90) (PREI) ① **89005**
11b B. Gigli, ROHO, R. Zamboni (r1946) *Concert*
　　　　　　　　(5/90) (EMI) ① **CDH7 61052-2**
11b E. Caruso, orch, J. Pasternack (r1920) *Concert*
　　　　　　　(7/91) (RCA) ① [12] **GD60495(6)**
11b E. Caruso, orch, J. Pasternack (r1920) *Concert*
　　　　　　　　(10/91) (PEAR) ① [3] **EVC4(2)**
11b A. Davidov, anon (r1901: Russ) *Concert*
　　　　　　　(6/93) (PEAR) ① [3] **GEMMCDS9007/9(1)**
11b E. Caruso, orch, J. Pasternack (r1920) *Concert*
　　　　　　　(4/94) (RCA) ① [6] **09026 61580-2(1)**
11b G. Thill, orch, E. Bigot (r1931) *Concert*
　　　　　　　　(8/95) (FORL) ① **UCD16727**
12. L. Escalais, anon (r1905: Ital) *Concert*
　　　　　　　(4/94) (EMI) ① [3] **CHS7 64860-2(1)**
Le Val d'Andorre—opéra-comique: 3 acts
(1848—Paris) (Lib. J H Vernoy de Saint-
Georges)
Chanson du chevrier L. Fugère, orch (r1930)
Concert　　　(6/93) (SYMP) ① **SYMCD1125**

HALFFTER, Cristóbal (b 1930)
Spain

SECTION II: CHAMBER

String Quartet No. 3
Arditti Qt *Concert*　(12/91) (MONT) ① **789006**

SECTION III: INSTRUMENTAL

Variations on the theme eSACHERe—cello
(1975)
T. Demenga (r1993) *Concert*
　　　　　　　(8/95) (ECM) ① [2] **445 234-2**

HALFFTER (ESCRICHE), Ernesto
(1905–1989) Spain/Mexico

SECTION I: ORCHESTRAL

Rapsodia Portuguesa—piano and orchestra
(1940 rev 1951)
G. Gonzalez, Tenerife SO, V.P. Pérez *Concert*
　　　　　　　(7/92) (ETCE) ① **KTC1095**

SECTION III: INSTRUMENTAL

2 Danzas—piano (1931)
1. La pastora; 2. La gitana.
A. de Larrocha *Concert*
　　　　　　　(9/92) (DECC) ① [2] **433 929-2DM2**
2. I. Perlman, S. Sanders (arr Heifetz) *Concert*
　　　　　　　(11/90) (EMI) ① **CDM7 63533-2**
2. J. Heifetz, E. Bay (r1946) *Concert*
　　　　　(11/94) (RCA) ① [65] **09026 61778-2(06)**
Espagnolade—piano (1937)
B. Lerner *Concert*　　(1/89) (ETCE) ① **KTC1061**

HALFFTER, Rodolfo (1900–1987)
Spain

SECTION V: STAGE WORKS

Don Lindo de Almeria—concert suite from
ballet
Minería SO, H. de la Fuente (pp) *Concert*
　　　　　　　(12/93) (CARL) ① **MCD63**

HALL, Henry (c1656–1707)
England

SECTION IV: VOCAL AND CHORAL

Yes, my Aminta, 'tis too true—ode on the
death of Purcell (1695-96)
R. Holton, S. Birchall, Parley of Instr, P. Holman
Concert　　　(3/93) (HYPE) ① **CDA66578**

HALL, William (d 1700) England

SECTION IV: VOCAL AND CHORAL

These full two hours now—song (Wds
Cowley)
Consort of Musicke, A. Rooley (lte/dir) (r1993)
Concert　　　(1/95) (MOSC) ① **070986**

HALLGRIMSSON, Haflidi (b 1941)
Iceland

SECTION IV: VOCAL AND CHORAL

Syrpa—Icelandic songs: sop, cl & pf (1993)
EXCERPTS: 1. Lullaby (Icelandic folksong); 2.
Nonsense rhyme for children; 3. Text by Magnus
Asgeirsson.
Tapestry (r1994) *Concert*
　　　　　　　(12/95) (BRIT) ① **BML012**

HALLGRÍMSSON, Halfidhi (b 1941)
Iceland

SECTION I: ORCHESTRAL

Poemi—violin and orchestra (1983)
T. Tønnesen, T. Tønnesen (vn/dir), C. Eggen *Concert*
　　　　　　　(10/91) (VICT) ① **VCD19014**

HALLOCK, Peter (20th Cent)
USA

SECTION IV: VOCAL AND CHORAL

The Lord is my light—chorus (Wds. from
Psalms 27, 139 & 63)
St John's Episcopal Cath Ch, D. Pearson *Concert*
　　　　　　　(10/92) (DELO) ① **DE3125**

HALVORSEN, Johan (1864–1935)
Norway

SECTION I: ORCHESTRAL

3 Danses norvégiennes—violin and
orchestra (1915)
Danse norvegienne K. Parlow, Anon (pf) (arr vn,pf;
r1909) *Concert*　(12/91) (APR) ① [2] **APR7015**
Entry March of the Boyars—orchestra
(1895)
Cincinnati Pops, E. Kunzel *Concert*
　　　　　　　(10/89) (TELA) ① **CD80170**

L. Derwinger (r1993; arr Grieg: pf) *Concert*
　　　　　　　(10/93) (BIS) ① **BIS-CD620**

SECTION II: CHAMBER

4 Mosaïques—suite des morceaux
caractéristiques
4. Chant de Veslemøy.
4. K. Parlow, Anon (pf) (r1909) *Concert*
　　　　　　　(12/91) (APR) ① [2] **APR7015**

HAMMERSCHMIDT, Andreas
(1611/12–1675)
Bohemia/Germany

SECTION IV: VOCAL AND CHORAL

Die Kunst des Küssens—voice and
continuo
R. Jacobs, K. Junghänel (r1985) *Concert*
　　　　　　　(5/87) (HARM) ① **HMA190 1183**
A. Scholl, A. Verzier, K. E. Schröder, M. Märkl
(r1994) *Concert*　　(5/95) (HARM) ① **HMC90 1505**
Sonata super 'Nun lob, mein Seel, den
Herren'—cantata (1v and instruments)
G. de Reyghere, Ricercar Consort (r1989) *Concert*
　　　　　　　(5/90) (RICE) ① **RIC060048**
Wo ist der neugeborne König—oratorio
G. de Reyghere, A. Mellon, D. Visse, G. de Mey, V.
Demaiffe, Ricercar Consort (r1989) *Concert*
　　　　　　　(5/90) (RICE) ① **RIC060048**

HAMMERSTEIN II, Oscar (Greely
Clendenning) (1895–1960) USA

SECTION V: STAGE WORKS

Carmen Jones—musical: 4 acts (1943—New
York) (based on Bizet's 'Carmen')
EXCERPTS: 1. Overture ACT 1: 2. Cain't let you go;
3a. Honey gal o' mine; 3b. Good luck Mr flyin' man; 4.
Dat's love; 5. You talk jus' like my maw; 6. Dere's a
Cafe on de corner ACT 2: 7. Beat out dat rhythm on a
drum; 8. Stan' up and fight; 9. Whizzin' away along
de track; 10. Dis flower; 11. If you would only come
away ACT 3: 12a. De cards don't lie; 12b. Dat ol' boy;
13. Poncho de Panther from Brazil; 14. My Joe ACT
4: 15. Git yer program for de big fight; 16. Dat's our
man!; 17. Finale.
Cpte M. Horne, L. Hutcherson, M. Hayes, O. James,
Brock Peters, J. Crawford, P. Bailey, B. Peterson,
Orig Film Cast, H. B. Gilbert (r1954; film version)
　　　　　　　(11/91) (RCA) ① **GD81881**
Cpte W. Fernandez, S. Benson, D. Evans, M. Austin,
Gregg Baker, K. Parks, J. Garcia, C. Rowe, D.J.
Jules, C. Sebron, W. Brown, orch, H. Lewis
　　　　　　　(11/91) (EMI) ① **CDC7 54351-2**
4. L. Garrett, Philh, A. Greenwood (r1990-1) *Concert*
　　　　　　　(11/91) (SILV) ① **SONGCD903**

HAMPTON, Calvin (1938–1984)
USA

SECTION II: CHAMBER

Variations on 'Amazing Grace'—cor anglais
and organ (1983)
T. Stacy, H. Huff (r1993) *Concert*
　　　　　　　(7/94) (CATA) ① **09026 61979-2**

HANCOCK, Gerre (b 1934) USA

SECTION IV: VOCAL AND CHORAL

Introit for a Feast Day—chorus, orchestra
and organ
E. Futral, J. Malafronte, F. Urrey, W. Pauley, Musica
Sacra, R. Westenburg *Concert*
　　　　　　　(1/93) (RCA) ① **09026 60970-2**

HANDEL, George Frideric
(1685–1759) Germany/England

HWV—Numbers used in B. Baselt (comp), Versirnis
der Werke G.F. Händels (1979)

SECTION I: ORCHESTRAL

Airs from Vauxhall Gardens—trumpet and
orchestra (compiled/arr/ed C Steele-Perkins)
1. Serse—Caro voi siete all'alma (Andante); 2.
Admeto—Se l'arcovessi (Allegro); 3.
Scipione—March; 4. Judas Maccabaeus—See, the
conqu'ring hero comes; 5. Atlanta—Overture.
C. Steele-Perkins, Tafelmusik, J. Lamon (vn/dir)
(r1993) *Concert*　　(4/95) (SONY) ① **SK53365**

Philh Baroque Orch, N. McGegan
(2/89) (HARM) ① HMU90 7010
ASMF, N. Marriner (3/90) (EMI) ① CDC7 49810-2
Concertgebouw CO, S. Preston *Fireworks Music.*
(8/91) (DECC) ① 430 717-2DM
St. Luke's Orch, C. Mackerras
(1/92) (TELA) ① CD80279
Orpheus CO *Fireworks Music.*
(11/92) (DG) ① 435 390-2GH
ASMF, N. Marriner *Concerto grosso: Alexander's Feast.*
(1/93) (PHIL) ① 434 729-2PM
EBS, J.E. Gardiner (r1991)
(5/93) (PHIL) ① 434 122-2PH
Amsterdam Baroque Orch, T. Koopman (r1992)
(10/94) (ERAT) ① 4509-91716-2
ECO, G. Malcolm (6/95) (ASV) ① CDQS6152
exc I. Tracey (arr Tracey) *Concert*
(1/90) (CFP) ① CD-CFP4558
1. AAM, C. Hogwood *Fireworks Music.*
(3/83) (L'OI) ① 400 059-2OH
1a Solisti Italiani *Concert*
(10/89) (DENO) ① CO-73335
1a, 1b, 1d, 1f, 1i, 2b, 3f H. Snell Brass, H. Snell
(r1991 arr Snell:brass ens) *Concert*
(8/92) (POLY) ① QPRL007D
1f, 1i AAM, C. Hogwood *Concert*
(2/91) (NIMB) ① NI5255
1i Martin Jones (trans pf: Grainger) *Concert*
(3/92) (ACOU) ① CDACS014
1, 2. Concert des Nations, J. Savall (r1993) *Fireworks Music.*
(3/94) (ASTR) ① E8512
2, 3. K. John (transc John) *Concert*
(5/89) (PRIO) ① PRCD235

Water Music—suite transcribed for symphony orchestra (transc Harty 1923)
1. Allegro; 2. Air; 3. Bourrée; 4. Hornpipe; 5. Andante espressivo; 6. Allegro deciso.
RPO, G. Weldon *Concert* (1/89) (EMIL) ① CDZ114
Ulster Orch, B. Thomson (r1979) *Concert*
(1/93) (CHAN) ① CHAN6583
LPO, H. Harty (r1933) *Concert*
(9/95) (DUTT) ① CDLX7016
1, 2, 6. LSO, G. Szell *Concert*
(10/91) (DECC) ① 430 500-2DWO

SECTION II: CHAMBER

Movement for Violin and Continuo in A minor, HWV408
1, 2, 4. Ecole d'Orphée *Concert*
(10/92) (CRD) ① CRD3374
Movement for Violin and Continuo in C minor, HWV412
1, 2, 4. Ecole d'Orphée *Concert*
(10/92) (CRD) ① CRD3374
Overture (Suite) in D—two clarinets and horn, HWV424 (c1742)
K. Puddy, G. Brodie, S. Dent (1992) *Concert*
(10/93) (CLRI) ① CC0004
Sinfonia in B flat—trio sonata for 2 violins and continuo, HWV338 (1704-6)
Ecole d'Orphée *Concert*
(10/92) (CRD) ① CRD3377
Sonata for Harmonica and Strings (transc Moody from Sonatas, Op. 1)
T. Reilly, ASMF Chbr Ens *Concert*
(12/86) (CHAN) ① CHAN8486
Sonata in G—oboe, 2 violins and continuo, HWV404 (c1718-20)
S. Francis (ob/dir), London Hpd Ens (r1994) *Concert*
(8/95) (UNIC) ① DKPCD9153
Sonatas for Flute and Continuo
EXCERPTS: 1. E minor, HWV359b (Op.1:1b); 2. G, HWV363b (Op.1:5); 3. B minor, HWV367b (Op.1:9); 3a. Largo; 3f. Andante; 4. A minor, HWV374 (Halle); 5. E minor, HWV375 (Halle); 6. B minor, HWV376 (Halle); 7. D, HWV378; 8. E minor, HWV379 (Op.1:1a); 9. D (spurious).
1, 2, 3. R. Stallman, E. Swanborn, K. Bennion (r1993) *Recorder Sonatas.* (7/95) (VAI) ① VAIA1091
1-8. Ecole d'Orphée (10/92) (CRD) ① CRD3373
1-8. Barthold Kuijken, W. Kuijken, R. Kohnen (r1991)
(11/93) (ACCE) ① ACC9180D
2. E. Talmi, Y. Talmi *Concert*
(6/90) (CARL) ① PWK1133
3. M. André, ECO, C. Mackerras (arr Thilde) *Concert*
(11/90) (EMI) ① CDM7 63528-2
3a H. Temianka, J. Graudan (arr Hubay: r1936)
Concert (2/93) (BIDD) ① [2] LAB059/60
3a N. Milstein, L. Pommers (r1960: arr Hubay)
Concert (5/94) (EMI) ① [6] ZDMF7 64830-2
3f J. Hubay, Budapest Cons Orch, Mr Zsolt (arr Hubay as 'Larghetto': r1929) *Concert*
(12/91) (BIDD) ① LAB045

3f A. Rosand, H. Sung (r1992; ed Chrysander) *Violin Sonatas.* (1/94) (BIDD) ① LAW004
Sonatas for Oboe and Continuo
1. B flat, HWV357 (Fitzwilliam); 2. F, HWV363a; 3. G minor, HWV364a (Op.1:6 - also violin version); 4. C minor, HWV366 (Op.1:8).
M. Zupnik, M. Shuman, R. Leppard *Concert*
(9/89) (ASV) ① CDDCA663
1, 2, 3, 4. S. Francis (ob/dir), London Hpd Ens
(r1994) *Concert* (8/95) (UNIC) ① DKPCD9153
1, 2, 4. Ecole d'Orphée *Concert*
(10/92) (CRD) ① CRD3374
2. P. Dombrecht, W. Kuijken, R. Kohnen *Concert*
(9/86) (ACCE) ① ACC57804D
2, 4. Cologne Divitia Ens *Concert*
(2/92) (CHNN) ① CCS0890
Sonatas for Recorder and Continuo
1. G minor, HWV360 (Op.1:2); 2. A minor, HWV362 (Op.1:4); 3. C, HWV365 (Op.1:7); 4. D minor, HWV367a (Fitzwilliam); 5. F, HWV369 (Op.1:11); 6. B flat, HWV377 (Fitzwilliam).
M. Petri, K. Jarrett (9/91) (RCA) ① RD60441
H. Reyne, J. Hantaï, P. Monteilhet, M. Hantaï *Violin Sonatas.* (9/92) (HARM) ① HMC90 5211
Ecole d'Orphée *Concert*
(10/92) (CRD) ① CRD3378
F. Brüggen, A. Bylsma, G. Leonhardt (r1961) *Trio Sonatas, Op. 2.* (10/95) (TELD) ① 4509-97471-2
1, 2, 3, 5. R. Stallman, E. Swanborn, K. Bennion
(r1993) *Flute Sonatas.* (7/95) (VAI) ① VAIA1091
5. B. Kol, A. Brodo, D. Shemer *Concert*
(6/90) (CARL) ① PWK1138
5. D. Munrow, O. Brookes, C. Hogwood (r1973)
Concert (10/95) (DECC) ① 440 079-2DM
Sonatas for Violin and Continuo
EXCERPTS: 1. G, HWV358; 2. D minor, HWV359a; 3. A, HWV361 (Op.1:3); 4. G minor, HWV364a (Op.1:6 - also oboe version); 5. G minor, HWV368 (Op.1:10); 6. F, HWV370 (Op.1:12); 6a. Adagio; 7. D, HWV371 (Sonata XIII); 7c. Larghetto; 8. A, HWV372 (Sonata XIV); 9. E, HWV373 (Sonata XV).
1. H. Reyne, J. Hantaï, P. Monteilhet, M. Hantaï (arr rec/ens) *Recorder Sonatas.*
(9/92) (HARM) ① HMC90 5211
1. Ecole d'Orphée (rec/hpd) *Concert*
(10/92) (CRD) ① CRD3378
1-4, 7, 8. R. Terakado, H. Suzuki, K. Uemura (r1993)
(12/94) (DENO) ① CO-75858
2-4, 7. Ecole d'Orphée *Concert*
(10/92) (CRD) ① CRD3374
3. N. Milstein, G. Pludermacher (pf1986) *Concert*
(5/95) (TELD) ① 4509-95998-2
3f A. Rosand, H. Sung (r1992; ed Chrysander)
Flute Sonatas. (1/94) (BIDD) ① LAW004
4. J. Dornenburg, M. Proud *Concert*
(12/91) (MERI) ① CDE84189
7. J. Szigeti, N. Magaloff (r1937) *Concert*
(1/90) (BIDD) ① [2] LAB007/8
7. J. Szigeti, N. Magaloff (r1937) *Concert*
(10/91) (MSCM) ① MM30320
7. G. Enescu, S. Schlüssel (r1929) *Concert*
(12/91) (MSCM) ① MM30322
7. G. Enescu, S. Schlüssel (r1929) *Concert*
(6/93) (BIDD) ① LAB066
7. N. Milstein, A. Balsam (r1955) *Concert*
(5/94) (EMI) ① [6] ZDMF7 64830-2
7. J. Heifetz, E. Bay (r1953) *Concert*
(11/94) (RCA) ① [65] 09026 61778-2(08)
7c M. Maisky, P. Gililov (arr vc/pf) *Concert*
(7/91) (DG) ① 431 544-2GH
9. J. Heifetz, E. Bay (r1953) *Concert*
(11/94) (RCA) ① [65] 09026 61778-2(09)
Trio Sonata in C—2 violins and continuo, HWV403 (c1738)
Ecole d'Orphée *Concert*
(10/92) (CRD) ① CRD3377
Trio Sonata in F—2 recorders and continuo, HWV405 (c1707-09)
Ecole d'Orphée *Concert*
(10/92) (CRD) ① CRD3378
Trio Sonatas—2 violins, oboes or flutes and continuo, Op. 2 (HWV386-91) (c1718)
1a. C minor; 1b. B minor; 2. G minor; 3. B flat; 4. F; 5. G minor; 6. G minor.
la Quattro Temperamenti *Concert*
(8/89) (BIS) ① BIS-CD403
1a Ecole d'Orphée *Concert*
(10/92) (CRD) ① CRD3377
1b F. Brüggen, A. Harnoncourt, N. Harnoncourt, H.
Tachezi (r1969) *Concert*
(10/95) (TELD) ① 4509-97474-2
1b, 2, 3, 4, 5, 6. London Baroque
(4/93) (HARM) ① HMC90 1379
1b, 4. Ecole d'Orphée *Trio Sonatas, Op. 2.*
(10/92) (CRD) ① CRD3375

2, 3, 5, 6. Ecole d'Orphée *Trio Sonatas, Op. 2.*
(10/92) (CRD) ① CRD3375
4. F. Brüggen, A. Harnoncourt, N. Harnoncourt, H.
Tachezi (r1969) *Recorder Sonatas.*
(10/95) (TELD) ① 4509-97471-2
Trio Sonatas—2 violins or flutes and continuo, Op. 5 (HWV396-402) (c1737-8)
1. A; 2. D; 3. E minor; 4. G; 5. G minor; 6. F; 7. B flat.
Ecole d'Orphée (10/92) (CRD) ① CRD3376
London Baroque (4/93) (HARM) ① HMC90 1389
4. G. Lesne, Seminario Musicale *Concert*
(12/91) (VIRG) ① VC7 59059-2
Trio Sonatas, 'Dresden'—2 violins and continuo
EXCERPTS: 1. F, HWV392 (Op.2:III, c1706-9); 2. G minor, HWV393 (Op.2:VIII, c1720); 3. E, HWV394 (Op.2:IX, c1730); 3a. Adagio.
Ecole d'Orphée *Concert*
(10/92) (CRD) ① CRD3377
1. London Baroque *Concert*
(4/87) (AMON) ① CD-SAR14
3a A. Spalding, W. Primrose, A. Benoist (r1941)
Concert (9/94) (BIDD) ① LAB088

SECTION III: INSTRUMENTAL

Capriccio in F—keyboard, HWV481 (pub c1733)
A. Cuckston *Concert* (2/92) (NAXO) ① 8 550416
Fugue in E—keyboard, HWV612 (attrib)
T. Koopman *Concert* (5/91) (CAPR) ① 10 254
P. Nicholson (r1994) *Concert*
(6/95) (HYPE) ① [2] CDA66931/2
Fugue in F—keyboard, HWV611
T. Dart (r1957) *Concert* (5/95) (JMS) ① JMSCD1
P. Nicholson (r1994) *Concert*
(6/95) (HYPE) ① [2] CDA66931/2
12 Fugues and Voluntaries—organ/keyboard (pub c1780) (not individually attrib)
1. C; 4. G minor; 8. C.
1. J. Bate *Concert* (11/91) (UNIC) ① DKPCD9106
4. J. Bate *Concert* (7/91) (UNIC) ① DKPCD9105
8. J. Bate *Concert* (7/91) (UNIC) ① DKPCD9104
6 Fugues or Voluntaries—keyboard, HWV605-10 (1735 or earlier)
1. G minor, HWV605; 2. G, HWV606; 3. B flat, HWV607; 4. B minor, HWV608; 5. A minor, HWV609; 6. C minor, HWV610.
T. Koopman *Concert* (5/91) (CAPR) ① 10 254
P. Nicholson (r1994) *Concert*
(6/95) (HYPE) ① [2] CDA66931/2
1. J. Bate *Concert* (7/91) (UNIC) ① DKPCD9104
2. J. Bate *Concert* (11/91) (UNIC) ① DKPCD9106
3. J. Bate *Concert* (2/91) (UNIC) ① DKPCD9096
4. J. Bate *Concert* (5/91) (UNIC) ① DKPCD9101
5. J. Bate *Concert* (5/91) (UNIC) ① DKPCD9099
6. J. Bate *Concert* (7/91) (UNIC) ① DKPCD9105
3 Lessons—keyboard
1. Prelude, Air and Variations in B flat; 2. Menuet in G minor; 3. Chaconne and 21 variations in G.
2. I. Biret (trans Kempff) *Concert*
(5/93) (MARC) ① 8 223452
3. Edwin Fischer (r1931) *Concert*
(12/94) (APR) ① APR5502
Sonata in G minor—keyboard
A. Cuckston *Concert* (2/92) (NAXO) ① 8 550416
Sonatina in D minor—keyboard
A. Cuckston *Concert* (2/92) (NAXO) ① 8 550416
8 Suites for Keyboard, Set I, HWV426-33 (pub 1720)
1. Suite No 1 in A, HWV426; 2. Suite No 2 in F, HWV427; 3. Suite No 3 in D minor, HWV428; 4. Suite No 4 in E minor, HWV429; 4a. Sarabande; 5. Suite No 5 in E, HWV430; 5a. Air and Variations, '(The) Harmonious Blacksmith'; 6. Suite No 6 in F sharp minor, HWV431; 7. Suite No 7 in G minor, HWV432; 7f. Passacaille; 8. Suite No 8 in F minor, HWV433.
S. Ross (2/90) (ERAT) ① [2] 2292-45452-2
P. Nicholson (r1994) *Concert*
(6/95) (HYPE) ① [2] CDA66931/2
K. Gilbert (r1976)
(12/95) (HARM) ① [2] HMA190 447/8
1, 2, 3, 4, 5. M. Souter (r1992)
(7/93) (ISIS) ① ISISCD003
1-5. A. Cuckston (2/92) (NAXO) ① 8 550415
2, 5, 7. W. Landowska (r1935) *Concert*
(1/93) (MSCM) ① MM30445
3(Movts 1, 5, 6) Edwin Fischer (r1934) *Concert*
(12/94) (APR) ① APR5502
5. R. Aldwinckle *Concert* (7/87) (CARL) ① PCD850
5. T. Pinnock *Concert* (11/90) (CRD) ① CRD3307
5a T. Pinnock *Concert*
(11/84) (ARCH) ① 413 591-2AH
5a K. Gilbert *Concert* (6/88) (NOVA) ① 150 018-2
5a M. Lympany *Concert* (1/92) (EMIL) ① CDZ111
5a W. Landowska (r1926) *Concert*
(1/93) (MSCM) ① MM30445

5a S. Rachmaninov (r1936) *Concert*
(3/93) (RCA) ① [10] 09026 61265-2(1)
5a H. Bauer (r1939) *Concert*
(4/94) (BIDD) ① LHW009
5a A. Cortot (r1926) *Concert*
(5/95) (BIDD) ① LHW020
5a, 7. V. Black *Concert*
(5/91) (COLL) ① Coll5024-2
5c E. Wild (r1995) *Concert*
(12/95) (SONY) ① SK62036
5, 7. M. Souter D. *Scarlatti: Keyboard Sonatas.*
(3/93) (ISIS) ① ISISCD001
6-8. A. Cuckston *Concert*
(2/92) (NAXO) ① 8 550416
7(Passacaglia) T. Tønnesen, L.A. Tomter (arr
Halvorsen) *Concert* (10/91) (VICT) ① VCD19006
7(Passacaglia) E. Brown, M. Katims (r c1940: arr
Halvorsen) *Concert* (7/93) (APR) ① [2] APR7016
7(Passacaglia) J. Heifetz, G. Piatigorsky (r1963)
Concert (11/94) (RCA) ① [65] 09026 61778-2(30)
7(Passacaglia) J. Heifetz, W. Primrose (r1941)
Concert (11/94) (RCA) ① [65] 09026 61778-2(09)
8. M. Proud *Concert* (12/91) (MERI) ① CDE84189
8(Prelude & Fugue) R. Veyron-Lacroix (r1978)
Concert (12/95) (ERAT) ① 4509-92135-2
7 Suites for Keyboard, Set II, HWV434, 436-
41 (pub 1733) (for No. 2, see Chaconne,
HWV435)
1. B flat; 1a. Air and Variations; 3. D minor; 3a.
Sarabande; 4. D minor; 5. E minor; 6. G minor; 7. B
flat; 8. G.
1. A. Schiff (pp1994) *Concert*
(11/95) (TELD) ① 4509-99051-2
1a W. Landowska (r1937) *Concert*
(1/93) (MSCM) ① MM30445
1a, 4. A. Cuckston (r1990) *Concert*
(2/92) (NAXO) ① 8 550416
1, 1a J. Henry *Concert*
(10/92) (VICT) ① VCD19013
2(Sarabande) T. Tønnesen, L.A. Tomter (arr
Halvorsen) *Concert* (10/91) (VICT) ① VCD19006
3, 8. W. Landowska (r1935) *Concert*
(1/93) (MSCM) ① MM30445
4. M. Souter (r1994-5) *Concert*
(12/95) (ISIS) ① ISISCD010
Theme and Variations in G minor—harp
(attrib)
M. Robles *Concert*
(12/90) (DECC) ① 425 723-2DM
Toccata in G minor—keyboard
A. Cuckston *Concert* (2/92) (NAXO) ① 8 550416
Unidentified Suite—keyboard (possibly
spurious)
T. Dart (r1957) *Concert* (5/95) (JMS) ① JMSCD1
Voluntary in C minor—keyboard (attrib)
J. Bate *Concert* (5/91) (UNIC) ① DKPCD9101

SECTION IV: VOCAL AND CHORAL

A miravi io son intento—duet, HWV178 (by
1710/11)
G. Fisher, J. Bowman, King's Consort, R. King
(hpd/dir) *Concert* (4/91) (HYPE) ① CDA66440
Aci, Galatea e Polifemo, 'Sorge il
di'—dramatic cantata, HWV72 (1708)
Qui l'augel di pianta N. Stutzmann, Hanover Band,
R. Goodman *Concert*
(3/93) (RCA) ① 09026 61205-2
Acis and Galatea—oratorio, HWV49b (1718)
(Wds. Gay and others)
1. Sinfonia; 2. Oh, the pleasure of the plains!; 3. Ye
verdant plains; 4. Hush, ye pretty warbling quire!; 5.
Where shall I seek the charming fair?; 6. Stay,
shepherd, stay!; 7a. Lo! here my love!; 7b. Love in
her eyes sits playing; 8a. Oh! didst thou know; 8b. As
when the dove; 9. Happy we! What joys I feel; 10.
Wretched lovers!; 11. I rage, I melt, I burn!; 12. O
ruddier than the cherry; 13a. Whither, fairest; 13b.
Cease to beauty to be suing; 14. Would you gain the
tender creature; 15a. His hideous love provokes my
rage; 15b. Love sounds th'alarm; 16. Consider, fond
shepherd; 17a. Cease, oh cease, thou gentle youth;
17b. The flocks shall leave the mountain; 18. Help,
Galatea! help; 19. Mourn, all ye muses!; 20. Must I
my Acis still bemoan; 21a. 'Tis done; 21b. Heart, the
seat of soft delight; 22. Galatea, dry thy tears.
Cpte N. Burrowes, A. Rolfe Johnson, M. Hill, W.
White, EBS, J.E. Gardiner
(8/88) (ARCH) ① [2] 423 406-2AH2
Cpte C. McFadden, J.M. Ainsley, R. Covey-Crump,
M. George, R. Harre-Jones, Kings' Consort, R. King
Look down, harmonious saint.
(6/90) (HYPE) ① [2] CDA66361/2
4. C. Högman, Quattro Temperamenti, M. Bergman
Concert (8/89) (BIS) ① BIS-CD403
8a, 8b K. Battle, ASMF, N. Marriner *Concert*
(7/90) (EMI) ① CDC7 49179-2

---

12. M. George, King's Consort, R. King *Concert*
(8/88) (CARL) ① PCD894
12. D. Thomas, Philh Baroque Orch, N. McGegan
(Ital) *Concert* (8/90) (HARM) ① HMU90 7016
14, 15b R. White, City of London Baroque Sinfonia, I.
Bolton *Concert* (12/91) (VIRG) ① VJ7 59644-2
Acis und Galatea—Mozart's arrangement,
K566 (1788) (added insts: 2 fl, 2 cl, rev tpt
parts)
Cpte B. Schlick, C. Prégardien, M. Bach, W.
Jochens, M. Schäfer, K. Mertens, P. Lika, Cologne
Chorus Musicus, Neue Orch, C. Spering (r1991) *Ode*
for St. Cecilia's Day.
(6/92) (Olll) ① [2] OPS45-9109/10
Agrippina condotta a morire, 'Dunque sarà
pur vero'—cantata: 1v & strings, HWV110
(c1708)
A. Mackay, ECCO, E. Aadland *Concert*
(12/91) (ASV) ① CDDCA766
Ah, che troppo ineguali—sacred cantata:
sop and strings, HWV230
A.S. von Otter, Cologne Musica Antiqua, R. Goebel
Concert (7/94) (ARCH) ① 439 866-2AH
E. Ameling, Collegium Aureum (r1966) *Concert*
(12/91) (ERAT) ① [4] 74321 26617-2(1)
Alexander's Feast—ode for St Cecilia's Day,
HWV75 (1736) (Wds. J. Dryden)
1. Overture; 1a. Andante. PART ONE: 2. 'Twas at the
Royal Feast; 3. Happy pair!; 4. Timotheus, plac'd on
high; 5. The song began from Jove; 6. The list'ning
crowd; 7. With ravish'd ears; 8. The praise of
Bacchus; 9. Bacchus, ever fair and young; 10.
Sooth'd with the sound; 11. He chose a mournful
Muse; 12. He sung Darius, great and good; 13. With
downcast looks; 14. Behold Darius, great and good;
15. The mighty master smil'd; 16. Softly sweet, in
Lydian measures; 17. War, he sung, is toil and
trouble; 18. The many rend the skies; 19. The Prince,
unable to conceal his pain; 20. The many rend the
skies 9da capo). PART TWO: 21. Now strike the
golden Lyre again!; 22. Revenge, revenge,
Timotheus cries; 23. Give the vengeance due; 24.
The princes applaud; 25. Thais led the way; 26.
Thus, long ago; 27. At last divine Cecilia came; 28a.
Let old Timotheus yield the prize (recit); 28b. Let old
Timotheus yield the prize (chorus); 29. Your voices
tune.
Cpte D. Brown, C. Watkinson, A. Stafford, N.
Robson, S. Varcoe, Monteverdi Ch, EBS, J.E.
Gardiner *Concerto grosso: Alexander's Feast.*
(11/88) (PHIL) ① [2] 422 053-2PH2
Cpte N. Argenta, I. Partridge, M. George, The
Sixteen, The Sixteen Orch, H. Christophers *Concert*
(10/91) (COLL) ① [2] Coll7016-2
1. EBS, J.E. Gardiner *Concert*
(7/92) (PHIL) ① 434 154-2PM
16, 19. A. Auger, Mostly Mozart Orch, G. Schwarz
Concert (11/86) (DELO) ① DE3026
17. E. Kirkby, AAM, C. Hogwood (r1991) *Concert*
(7/93) (L'OI) ① 436 132-2OH
22. M. George, King's Consort, R. King *Concert*
(8/88) (CARL) ① PCD894
L' Allegro, il penseroso ed il
moderato—oratorio, HWV55 (1740) (Wds. C.
Jennens, after Milton)
EXCERPTS: PART 1: 1. Hence loathed melancholy;
2. Hence vain deluding joys; 3. Come, thou Goddess;
4. Come, rather, Goddess; 5. Haste thee, nymph; 6.
Haste thee, nymph (chorus); 7. Come, and trip it; 8.
Come, pensive nun; 9a. Come, but keep thy wonted
state; 9b. Join with thee; 10a. Hence loathed
Melancholy; 10b. And if I give the honour due; 11a.
First, and chief, on golden wing; 11b. Sweet bird; 12.
If I give thee honour due; 13. Oft on a plat of rising
ground; 14. Far from all resort of Mirth; 15a. If I give
thee honour due; 15b. Let me wander, not unseen;
16. Straight mine eyes; 17a. Or let merry bells; 17b.
And young and old come. PART 2: 18. Hence, vain
deluding joys; 19. Thus night oft see me; 20.
Populous cities; 21. There let Hymen oft appear; 22.
Me, when sun begins to fling; 23. I'll to the well-trod
stage anon; 24. And ever against eating cares; 25.
Orpheus 'self may heave his head'; 26a. These
delights if thou canst give; 26b. These delights
(chorus); 27. But let my due feet never fail; 28a.
There let the pealing organ blow; 28b. And let their
sweetness; 29a. May at last my weary age; 29b.
These pleasures, Melancholy, give; 29c. These
pleasures (chorus). PART 3: 30a. Hence, boast not;
30b. All this company serve; 31. Come, with gentle
hand restrain; 32. No more short life; 33. As steals
the morn; 34. Thy pleasures, Moderation, give.
Cpte M. Ginn, P. Kwella, M. McLaughlin, J. Smith, M.
Davies, M. Hill, S. Varcoe, Monteverdi Ch, EBS, J.E.
Gardiner (r1980)
(7/85) (ERAT) ① [2] 2292-45377-2

Sweet bird K. Battle, ASMF, N. Marriner *Concert*
(7/90) (EMI) ① CDC7 49179-2
Sweet bird E. Schwarzkopf, VPO, J. Krips (r1946)
Concert (7/90) (EMI) ① CDH7 63201-2
4. K. Battle, J-P. Rampal, M. Lutzke, Anthony
Newman (pp1991) *Concert*
(9/94) (SONY) ① SK53106
11b B. Hoch, Hong Kong PO, K. Schermerhorn
Concert (11/86) (CARL) ① PCD827
11b M. Ivogün, orch (r1925: Ital) *Concert*
(8/92) (NIMB) ① NI7832
11b E. Kirkby, AAM, C. Hogwood (r1991) *Concert*
(7/93) (L'OI) ① 436 132-2OH
11b M. Ivogün, orch (r1925) *Concert*
(1/94) (CLUB) ① CL99-020
11b N. Melba, orch, W.B. Rogers (r1907) *Concert*
(5/95) (ROMO) ① [3] 81011-2(1)
11b N. Melba, orch, W.B. Rogers (r1910) *Concert*
(5/95) (ROMO) ① [3] 81011-2(2)
29a J. Kowalski, ASMF, N. Marriner (r1993) *Concert*
(8/94) (CAPR) ① 10 532
Alpestre monte—cantata (1v, 2 violins and
continuo), HWV81
E. Kirkby, AAM, C. Hogwood *Concert*
(7/90) (L'OI) ① 414 473-2OH
Amarilli vezzosa, '(II) duello
amoroso'—cantata: 2vv, 2 vns & continuo,
HWV82 (1708)
N. Argenta, M. Chance, Freiburg Baroque Orch, G.
von der Goltz (r1993) *Concert*
(10/94) (DHM) ① 05472 77295-2
Aminta e Fillide, 'Arresta il passo'—cantata:
2vv & strings, HWV83 (1708)
G. Fisher, P. Kwella, London Handel Orch, D. Darlow
(7/85) (HYPE) ① CDA66118
Apollo e Dafne, '(La) terra è
liberata'—dramatic cantata, HWV122
(c1708)
EXCERPTS: 1. Overture; 2a. Recit: La terra e
liberata; 2b. Aria: Pende il ben; 3a. Recit: Ch'il
superbetto Amore; 3b. Aria: Spezza l'arco; 4. Aria:
Felicissima quest'alma; 5. Recit: Che voce! Che
beltà!; 6. Aria: Ardi, adori; 7a. Recit: Che crudeli; 7b.
Duo: Una guerra ho dentro il seno; 8a. Recit: Placati
al fin, o cara; 8b. Aria: Come rosa in su la spina; 9a.
Recit: Ah! ch'un Dio; 9b. Aria: Come in ciel benigna
stella; 10a. Recit: Odi la mia ragion; 10b. Duo: Deh!
lascia corrente; 11a. Recit: Sempre t'adorero; 11b.
Aria: Mie piante soltanto; 12. Aria: Cara pianta, co'
miei pianti.
J. Nelson, D. Thomas, San Francisco Philh Baroque
Orch, N. McGegan *Oboe Concertos.*
(6/86) (HARM) ① HMU90 5157
Aria in C minor (unidentified)
M. Maisky, D. Hovora (r1993: arr vc/pf) *Concert*
(9/94) (DG) ① 439 863-2GH
Armida abbandonata, 'Dietro l'orme
fugaci'—cantata: 1v, 2 vns & continuo (1707)
(Wds. after Tasso)
M. C. Kiehr, Teatro Armonico, A. de Marchi (hpd/dir)
(r1993) *Concert* (9/94) (ADES) ① 20271-2
Athalia—oratorio, HWV52 (1733) (Wds.
Humphreys, after Racine)
1a. Sinfonia. ACT 1: 1b. Blooming virgins, spotless
train; 1c. The rising world Jehovah crown'd; 1d.
Tyrants would in impious throngs; 1e. When he is in
his wrath releav'd; 2. Your sacred songs awhile
forbear; 3a. What scenes of horrors; 3b. The gods,
whose chosen blessings shed; 3c. Cheer her; O
Baal; 3d. Gentle airs, melodious strains!; 3e. Softest
sounds no more can ease me; 3f. The traitor if you
there descry; 4a. My Josabeth!; 4b. Faithful cares in
vain extended; 4c. Gloomy tyrants, we disdain. ACT
2: 5a. The mighty pow'r; 5b. Ah, canst thou but prove
me!; 6a. Confusion to my thoughts; 6b. Will Good,
whose mercies ever flow; 6c. My vengeance awakes
me; 6d. My spirits fail; 7a. Dear Josabeth; 7b. Cease
thy anguish; 7c. The clouded scene. ACT 3: 8a. What
sacred horrors; 8b. Unfold, great seer; 8c. Let
harmony breathe soft around; 8d. With firm united
hearts; 9a. O princess, I approach thee; 9b. Soothing
tyrant, falsely smiling!; 10. Apostate priest!; 11a. O
bold seducer; 11b. Around let acclamations ring; 11c.
Oppression, no longer I dread thee; 11d. Hark! Hark!
thunders round me roll; 11e. To darkness eternall;
12a. Now, Josabeth, thy fears are o'er; 12b. Give
glory to his awful name.
Cpte J. Sutherland, E. Kirkby, A. Jones, J. Bowman,
A. Rolfe Johnson, D. Thomas, New College Ch,
AAM, C. Hogwood
(2/87) (L'OI) ① [2] 417 126-2OH2
3d R. White, City of London Baroque Sinfonia, I.
Bolton *Concert* (12/91) (VIRG) ① VJ7 59644-2
5b D. Thomas, Philh Baroque Orch, N. McGegan
Concert (8/90) (HARM) ① HMU90 7016

Belshazzar—oratorio, HWV61 (1745) (Wds. Jennens)

1. Overture. ACT 1: 2a. Vain, fluctuating state; 2b. Thou, God most high; 2c. The fate of Babylon; 2d. Lament not thus, oh Queen; 3a. Behold, by Persia's hero made; 3b. Well may they laugh!; 3c. Oh memory!; 3d. Oppress with never-ceasing grief; 3e. Dry those unavailing tears; 3f. Be comforted; 3g. Methought, as on the bank of deep Euphrates; 3h. Now, tell me, Gobrias; 3i. Behold the monstrous human beast; 3j. Can you then think it strange; 3k. Great God! who, yet but darkly known; 3l. My friends, be confident; 3m. All empires upon God depend; 4a. On sacred oracles of Truth!; 4b. Rejoice, my countrymen; 4c. Thus saith the Lord to Cryus; 4d. Sing, oh ye heav'ns; 5a. Let festal joy triumphant reign!; 5b. For you, my friends; 5c. The leafy honours of the field; 5d. It is the custom; 5e. Recall, oh king! thy rash command; 5f. They tell you true; 5g. Oh dearer than my life, forbear!; 5h. By slow degrees the wrath of God. ACT 2: 6a. See, from post Euphrates flies!; 6b. You see, my friends, a path; 6c. Amaz'd to find the foe so near; 6d. To arms, to arms!; 7a. Ye tutelat gods of our empire; 7b. Let the deep bowl thy praise confes; 7c. Where is the God of Judah's boasted pow'r?; 7d. Call all my Wise Men; 8. A Symphony (Allegro Postillions); 9a. Ye sages!; 9b. Alas! too hard a task; 9c. Oh misery!; 9d. Oh king, live for ever!; 9e. No! to thyself thy trifles be; 9f. Yet, to obey his dread command; 9g. Oh sentence too severe!; 9h. Regard, oh son, my flowing tears; 10a. Oh God of Truth!; 10b. You, Gobrias, lead directly to the palace; 10c. Oh glorious prince! ACT 3: 11a. Alternate hopes and fears; 11b. Fain would I hope; 11c. Can the black Aethiop change his skin?; 11d. My hopes revive; 11e. Bel boweth down!; 12a. I thank thee, Sesach; 12b. A Martial Symphony; 13a. To pow'r immortal my first thanks; 13b. Be it thy care, good Gobrias; 13c. Destructive War, thy limits know; 13d. Great victor, at your feet I bow; 13e. Say, venerable prophet; 13f. Tell it out among the heathen; 13g. Yes, I will build thy city; 13h. I will magnify thee.

Cpte A. Auger, J. Gooding, C. Robbin, J. Bowman, N. Short, A. Rolfe Johnson, N. Robertson, D. Wilson-Johnson, R. Wistreich, English Concert Ch, English Concert, T. Pinnock (10/91) (ARCH) ① [3] **431 793-2AH3**

4a J. Kowalski, ASMF, N. Marriner (r1993) *Concert* (8/94) (CAPR) ① **10 532**

Blessed are they that considereth the poor—anthem for the Foundling Hospital, HWV268 (1749)

1. Blessed are they that considereth the poor and needy; 2. Blessed are they ...They deliver the poor that crieth; 3. O God, who from the suckling's mouth; 4. The Charitable shall be had in everlasting remembrance; 5. Comfort them, O Lord, when they are sick; 6. The people will tell of their wisdom; 7. Hallelujah!.

J. Nelson, E. Kirkby, S. Minty, J. Bowman, M. Hill, D. Thomas, Oxford Christ Church Cath Ch, AAM, S. Preston *Concert* (8/89) (L'OI) ① **421 654-2OH**

G. Fisher, L. Crabtree, C. Brett, J. Elwes, Winchester Cath Ch, Brandenburg Consort, D. Hill (r1993) *Coronation Anthems.* (2/95) (ARGO) ① **440 946-2ZH**

Carco sempre di Gloria—cantata, HWV87 (1739)

G. Lesne, Seminario Musicale *Concert* (12/91) (VIRG) ① **VC7 59059-2**

D.L. Ragin, Cologne Divitia Ens *Concert* (2/92) (CHNN) ① **CCS0890**

Chandos Anthem No. 2, 'In the Lord will I put my trust', HWV247 (1717-18)

1. Overture.

1. BBC PO, M. Bamert (r1994: orch Stokowski) *Concert* (6/95) (CHAN) ① **CHAN9349**

Chandos Anthem No. 4a, 'O sing unto the Lord', HWV249a (c1717)

L. Dawson, I. Partridge, The Sixteen, The Sixteen Orch, H. Christophers *Concert* (8/89) (CHAN) ① **CHAN0504**

Chandos Anthem No. 5b, 'I will magnify thee', HWV250b (1717-18)

L. Dawson, I. Partridge, The Sixteen, The Sixteen Orch, H. Christophers *Concert* (8/89) (CHAN) ① **CHAN0504**

Chandos Anthem No. 6, 'As pants the hart', HWV251 (1717-18)

L. Dawson, I. Partridge, The Sixteen, The Sixteen Orch, H. Christophers *Concert* (8/89) (CHAN) ① **CHAN0504**

W. Missin, P. Cave, New College Ch, Fiori Musicali, E. Higginbottom *Concert* (3/90) (PROU) ① **PROUCD125**

Chandos Anthem No. 7, 'My song shall be alway', HWV252 (1717-18)

P. Kwella, J. Bowman, I. Partridge, M. George, The Sixteen, The Sixteen Orch, H. Christophers *Concert* (2/90) (CHAN) ① **CHAN0505**

Chandos Anthem No. 8, 'O come, let us sing unto the Lord', HWV253 (1717-18)

P. Kwella, J. Bowman, I. Partridge, The Sixteen, The Sixteen Orch, H. Christophers *Concert* (2/90) (CHAN) ① **CHAN0505**

Chandos Anthem No. 9, 'O praise the Lord with one consent', HWV254 (1717-18)

P. Kwella, J. Bowman, I. Partridge, M. George, The Sixteen, The Sixteen Orch, H. Christophers *Concert* (2/90) (CHAN) ① **CHAN0505**

Chandos Anthem No. 10, '(The) Lord is my light', HWV255 (1717-18)

L. Dawson, I. Partridge, The Sixteen, The Sixteen Orch, H. Christophers *Chandos Anthem 11.* (7/90) (CHAN) ① **CHAN0509**

Chandos Anthem No. 11, 'Let God arise', HWV256 (c1717-20)

L. Dawson, I. Partridge, The Sixteen, The Sixteen Orch, H. Christophers *Chandos Anthem 10.* (7/90) (CHAN) ① **CHAN0509**

The **Choice of Hercules—oratorio, HWV69 (1743)** (Wds. R. Lowth)

EXCERPTS: 1. There the brisk sparkling Nectar; 2. Yet can I hear that dulcet lay.

1. C. Flesch, I. Strasfogel (arr Flesch as 'March'; r1929) *Concert* (12/91) (BIDD) ① **LAB045**

1. R. White, City of London Baroque Sinfonia, I. Bolton *Concert* (12/91) (VIRG) ① **VJ7 59644-2**

Clori, Tirsi e Fileno, 'Cor fedele'—dramatic cantata, HWV96 (1707)

Cpte L. Hunt, J. Feldman, D. Minter, P. O'Dette, Philh Baroque Orch, N. McGegan (2/93) (HARM) ① **HMU90 7045**

Conservate, raddioppiate—duet, HWV185 (by 1710/11)

G. Fisher, J. Bowman, King's Consort, R. King (hpd/dir) *Concert* (4/91) (HYPE) ① **CDA66440**

Il consigno, 'Tra le fiamme'—soprano, HWV170 (1707-8)

E. Kirkby, AAM, C. Hogwood *Concert* (3/86) (L'OI) ① **414 473-2OH**

Coronation Anthems, HWV258-61 (1727)

1. Zadok the Priest; 2. Let thy hand be strengthened; 3. The king shall rejoice; 4. My heart is inditing.

J. Rodgers, C. Denley, A. Rolfe Johnson, ASMF Chor, ASMF Chor, ASMF, N. Marriner *Judas Maccabaeus.* (1/86) (PHIL) ① **412 733-2PH**

New College Ch, King's Consort, R. King (r1989) *Fireworks Music.* (12/89) (HYPE) ① **CDA66350**

King's College Ch, ECO, D. Willcocks (r1963) *Concert* (8/93) (DECC) ① **436 256-2DM**

Winchester Cath Ch, Brandenburg Consort, D. Hill (r1993) *Blessed are they that considereth the poor.* (2/95) (ARGO) ① **440 946-2ZH**

Westminster Abbey Ch, English Concert, S. Preston (r1981) *Concerti a due cori.* (6/95) (ARCH) ① **447 280-2AMA**

1. King's College Ch, ECO, D. Willcocks *Concert* (10/91) (DECC) ① **430 500-2DWO**

1. King's College Ch, ECO, D. Willcocks (r1963) *Concert* (6/93) (DECC) ① **436 403-2DWO**

1. Winchester Quiristers, King's Consort Ch, Orch, R. King *Concert* (12/93) (UNIT) ① **88002-2**

1. Westminster Abbey Ch, ECO, M. Neary (r1993/4) *Concert* (9/94) (CNTO) ① **CSACD3050**

1. Westminster Abbey Ch, ECO, M. Neary, M. Baker (r1994) *Concert* (12/95) (SONY) ① **SK66614**

1, 3. Monteverdi Ch, EBS, J. E. Gardiner (r1993) *Israel in Egypt.* (11/95) (PHIL) ① [2] **432 110-2PH2**

Deborah—oratorio (1733) (Wds. Humphreys, after Judges V)

Cpte Y. Kenny, S. Gritton, C. Denley, J. Bowman, M. George, New College Ch, Salisbury Cath Ch, King's Consort, R. King (r1993) (2/94) (HYPE) ① [2] **CDA66841/2**

Barak, my son;Awake the ardour; Thy ardours warm;Swift inundation; Tears, such as tender fathers shed D. Thomas, Philh Baroque Orch, N. McGegan *Concert* (8/90) (HARM) ① **HMU90 7016**

Dettingen Anthem, '(The) King shall rejoice', HWV265 (1743)

C. Tipping, M. Pearce, Westminster Abbey Ch, English Concert, S. Preston *Dettingen Te Deum.* (9/84) (ARCH) ① **410 647-2AH**

Dixit Dominus, HWV232 (1707) (Wds. Psalm 50)

H. Martinpelto, A.S. von Otter, Stockholm Bach Ch, Drottningholm Baroque Ens, A. Öhrwall *Concerti grossi, Op. 6.* (11/86) (BIS) ① **BIS-CD322**

A. Auger, L. Dawson, D. Montague, L. Nixon, S. Birchall, Westminster Abbey Ch, Westminster Abbey Orch, S. Preston *Concert* (2/89) (ARCH) ① **423 594-2AH**

J. Feldman, E. Van Evera, M. Cable, J. Cornwell, D. Thomas, Taverner Ch, Taverner Plyrs, A. Parrott *Concert* (6/89) (EMI) ① [2] **CDS7 49749-2**

L. Dawson, Lynda Russell, C. Brett, I. Partridge, M. George, The Sixteen, The Sixteen Orch, H. Christophers *Concert* (3/92) (CHAN) ① **CHAN0517**

Donna che in ciel—sacred cantata: sop, chor and strings, HWV233

A.S. von Otter, chor, Cologne Musica Antiqua, R. Goebel *Concert* (7/94) (ARCH) ① **439 866-2AH**

Esther—oratorio, HWV50 (1718) (Wds. Pope and Arbuthnot)

1. Overture; 2a. Pluck root and branch; 2b. Shall we the God of Israel fear?; 3a. Tune your harps to cheerful strains; 3b. Shall we of servitude complain; 3c. Praise the Lord with cheerful voice; 3d. Sing songs of praise; 4a. Ye sons of Israel mourn; 4b. O Jordan, sacred tide; 5a. Dread not, righteous Queen; 5b. Tears assist me; 5c. Save us, O Lord; 6a. Who calls my parting soul from death?; 6b. O beauteous Queen; 6c. How can I stay; 6d. Virtue, truth and innocence; 6e. Jehovah, crown'd with glory bright; 6f. He comes to end our woes; 7a. Turn not, O Queen; 7b. Fall'ring tongue; 7c. How art thou fall'n; 8a. The Lord our enemy has slain; 8b. For ever blessed Thy Holy Name; 8c. Let Israel songs of joy repeat; 8d. The Lord his people shall restore; 8e. Mount Lebanon his firs resigns; 8f. For ever blessed be Thy Holy Name.

Cpte E. Kirkby, P. Kwella, D. Minter, A. Rolfe Johnson, D. Thomas, I. Partridge, P. Elliott, A. King, Westminster Cath Boys' Ch, AAM Chor, AAM, C. Hogwood (12/85) (L'OI) ① [2] **414 423-2OH2**

2a, 7a, 7c D. Thomas, Philh Baroque Orch, N. McGegan *Concert* (8/90) (HARM) ① **HMU90 7016**

3a, 3b R. White, City of London Baroque Sinfonia, I. Bolton *Concert* (12/91) (VIRG) ① **VJ7 59644-2**

Fronda leggiera e mobile—duet, HWV186 (c1704-5)

G. Fisher, J. Bowman, King's Consort, R. King (hpd/dir) *Concert* (4/91) (HYPE) ① **CDA66440**

German Arias, HWV202-10 (1724-27) (Wds. adpated from Irdisches Vergnügen)

1. Künft'ger Zeiten eitler Kummer; 2. Das zitternde Glänzen; 3. Süsser Blumen Ambraflocken; 4. Süsse Stille, sanfte Quelle; 5. Singe, Seele, Gott zum Preise; 6. Meine Seele hört im Sehen; 7. Die ihr aus dunklen Grüften; 8. In den angenehmen; 9. Flammende Rose, Zierde der Erden.

E. Speiser, J. Schröder, K. Gohl, J. Sonnleitner (9/87) (JECK) ① **JD589-2**

C. Högman, Quattro Temperamenti *Concert* (8/89) (BIS) ① **BIS-CD403**

Haec est regina virginum—soprano and strings, HWV235 (1707)

E. Kirkby, Taverner Plyrs, A. Parrott *Concert* (6/89) (EMI) ① [2] **CDS7 49749-2**

A.S. von Otter, Cologne Musica Antiqua, R. Goebel *Concert* (7/94) (ARCH) ① **439 866-2AH**

Hercules—oratorio, HWV60 (1745) (Wds. T. Boughton, after Sophocles)

1. Overture; 1a. Minuet. ACT 1: 2. See with what grand dejection; 3. No longer, Fate, relentless frown; 4. O Hercules! why art thou absent?; 5. The world, when day's career is run; 6. Princess! be comforted; 7. I feel the god; 8. Then I am lost!; 9. There in myrtle shades reclined; 10. Despair not! but let rising hope suspend; 11. Where congealed the northern streams; 12. O filial piety!; 13. Banish your fears!; 14. Begone, my fears; 15. A train of captives, red with honest wounds; 16. March; 17. Thanks to the powers above; 18. My father! Ah! methinks I see; 19. Now farewell, arms!; 20. The god of battle quits the bloody field; 21. Crown with festal pomp the day. ACT 2: 22. How blest the maid ordained to dwell; 23. It must be so!; 24. When beauty's sorrows livery wears; 25. Whence this unjust suspicion?; 26. Ah! think what ills the jealous prove; 27. It is too sure that Hercules is false; 28. Jealousy! Infernal pest; 29. She knows my passion; 30. From celestial seats descending; 31. Wanton god of amorous fires; 32. Yes, I congratulate your titles, swelled; 33. Alcides' name in latest story; 34. O glorious pattern of heroic deeds!; 35. Resign thy club and lion's spoils; 36. You are deceived!; 37. Cease, ruler of the day, to rise; 38. Some kinder power inspire me; 39. Joys of freedom, joys of power; 40. Father of Hercules, great Jove, O help; 41. Love and Hymen, hand in hand. ACT 3: 42. Sinfonia; 43. Ye sons of Trachin; 44. O scene of unexampled woe; 45. Tyrants now no more shall dread; 46. O Jove! what land is this; 47. Great Jove! relieve his pains; 48. Let not thy fame the tidings spread; 49. Where

shall I fly?; 50. Lo! the fair fatal cause of all this ruin!; 51. My breast with tender pity swells; 52. Princess, rejoice!; 53. Words are too faint; 54. Prince, whose virtue all admire; 55. Ye sons of freedom; 56. To him your grateful notes of priase belong.

Cpte J. Smith, Sarah Walker, C. Denley, A. Rolfe Johnson, J. Tomlinson, P. Savidge, Monteverdi Ch, EBS, J.E. Gardiner (1/88) (ARCH) ① [3] **423 137-2AH3**

4, 5, 49. M. Forrester, Vienna RSO, B. Priestman *Concert* (12/92) (CBC) ① **PSCD2002**

49. C. Watkinson, Amsterdam Bach Sols, J.W. de Vriend *Concert* (3/89) (ETCE) ① **KTC1064**

49. A.S. von Otter, Drottningholm Baroque Ens, A. Öhrwall *Concert* (10/91) (PROP) ① **PRCD9008**

49. J. Larmore, Lausanne CO, J. López-Cobos (r1994) *Concert* (12/95) (TELD) ① **4509-96800-2**

Israel in Egypt—oratorio, HWV54 (1739 rev 1756) (Part 1 in 1739 vers only)

PART 1—Lamentation of the Israelites: 1. Overture; 2a. The sons of Israel do mourn; 2b. How is the mighty fall'n!; 2c. He put on righteousness; 2d. When the ear heard Him; 3a. How is the mighty fall'n!; 3b. He deliver'd the poor that cried; 3c. How is the mighty fall'n!; 4a. Their bodies are buried in peace; 4b. The people will tell; 4c. They shall receive; 5. The merciful goodness of the Lord. PART 2—Exodus: 6a. Now there arose a new king; 6b. And the children of Israel; 7a. Then sent he Moses; 7b. They loathed to drink; 8. Their land brought forth frogs; 9. He spake the word; 10. He gave them hailstones; 11. He sent a thick darkness; 12. He smote all the first-born; 13. But as for His people; 14. Egypt was glad; 15a. He rebuked the Red Sea; 15b. He led them through the deep; 15c. But the waters overwhelmed; 16a. And Israel saw; 16b. And believed the Lord. PART 3—Moses' Song: 17a. Moses and the children of Israel; 17b. I will sing unto the Lord; 18. The Lord is my strength; 19a. He is my God; 19b. And I will exalt; 20. The Lord is a man of war; 21. The depths have covered them; 22a. Thy right hand O Lord; 22b. And in the greatness; 22c. Thou sentest forth Thy wrath; 23. And with the blast; 24. The enemy said; 25. Thou didst blow; 26a. Who is like unto Thee; 26b. The earth swallowed Them; 27. Thou in Thy mercy; 28. The people shall hear; 29. Thou shalt bring them in; 31. For the horse of Pharoah; 32. The Lord shall reign; 33a. And Miriam the prophetess; 33b. Sing ye to the Lord.

Cpte H. Harper, P. Clark, P. Esswood, A. Young, M. Rippon, C. Keyte, Leeds Fest Chor, ECO, C. Mackerras (9/90) (ARCH) ① [2] **429 530-2AGA2**

Cpte N. Argenta, E. van Evera, T. Wilson, A. Rolfe Johnson, D. Thomas, J. White, Taverner Ch, Taverner Plyrs, A. Parrott (r1989) (2/91) (EMI) ① [2] **CDS7 54018-2**

Cpte The Sixteen, The Sixteen Orch, H. Christophers (r1993) *Organ Concertos.* (1/94) (COLL) ① [2] **Coll7035-2**

Cpte R. Holton, E. Priday, D. Deam, A. Stafford, M. Chance, P. Collin, J. P. Kenny, N. Robertson, P. Salmon, P. Tindall, A. Tusa, J. Clarkson, C. Purves, Monteverdi Ch, EBS, J. E. Gardiner (pp1990) *Coronation Anthems.* (11/95) (PHIL) ① [2] **432 110-2PH2**

8. J. Kowalski, ASMF, N. Marriner (r1993) *Concert* (8/94) (CAPR) ① **10 532**

10. Handel Op Chor, RPO, C. Farncombe *Concert* (10/91) (DECC) ① **430 500-2DWO**

13, 17a, 20. Leeds Fest Chor, LPO, T. Beecham (r1934) *Concert* (6/94) (VAI) ① **VAIA1045**

Jephtha—oratorio, HWV70 (1752) (Wds. Bible)

1. Overture. PART 1: 2. Pour forth no more (Zebul); 3. No more to Ammon's god and king (chorus); 4. Virtue my soul shall still embrace (Jephtha); 5. In gentle murmurs will I mourn (Storgè); 6. Dull delay, in piercing anguish (Hamor); 7. Take the heart you fondly gave (Iphis); 8. These labour past (Iphis & Hamor); 9. If, Lord, sustain'd by Thy Almighty pow'r (Jephtha); 10. O God, behold our sore distress (chorus); 11. Scenes of horror, scenes of woe (Storgè); 12. The smiling dawn of happy days (Iphis); 13. When his loud voice in thunder spoke (chorus). PART 2: 14. Cherub and Seraphim (chorus); 15. Up the dreadful steep ascending (Hamor); 16. Tune the soft melodious lute (Iphis); 17. Freedom now once more possessing (Zebul); 18. His mighty arm, with sudden blow (Jephtha); 19. In glory high, in might serene (chorus); 20. Sinfonia; 21. Welcome, as the cheerful light (Iphis); 22. Open thy marble jaws, O tomb (Jephtha); 23. Let other creatures die (Storgè); 24. On me let blind mistaken zeal (Hamor); 25. Happy they! this vital vital breath (Iphis); 26. Deeper, and deeper still (Jephtha); 27. How dark, O Lord, are Thy decrees (chorus). PART 3: 28. Waft her, angels, through the skies (Jephtha); 29. Farewell, ye limpid springs and floods (Iphis); 30. Doubtful fear and reverent awe (chorus); 31. Happy, Iphia, shalt thou live (Angel); 32. Theme sublime of endless praise (chorus); 33. Laud her, all ye virgin train (Zebul); 34. Sweet as sight to the blind (Storgè); 35. 'Tis Heaven's all-ruling pow'r (Hamor); 36. Freely I to Heaven resign (Iphis); 37. Ye house of Gilead, with one voice (chorus).

Cpte L. Dawson, R. Holton, A.S. von Otter, M. Chance, N. Robson, S. Varcoe, Monteverdi Ch, EBS, J.E. Gardiner (r1988) (6/89) (PHIL) ① [3] **422 351-2PH3**

1, 20. EBS, J.E. Gardiner *Concert* (7/92) (PHIL) ① **434 154-2PM**

6, 35. M. Forrester, ECO, J. Somary *Concert* (12/92) (CBC) ① **PSCD2002**

11. M. Forrester, Zagreb Sols, A. Janigro *Concert* (12/92) (CBC) ① **PSCD2002**

26, 28. H. Nash, orch (r1931) *Concert* (8/89) (PEAR) ① **GEMMCD9319**

26, 28. W. Widdop, Orch, J. Harrison (r1925) *Concert* (11/92) (CLAR) ① **CDGSE78-50-46**

28. J.M. Ainsley, King's Consort, R. King *Concert* (8/88) (CARL) ① **PCD894**

35. A. Deller, Handel Fest Orch, A. Lewis (r1960) *Concert* (1/95) (VANG) ① **08.5069.71**

Joshua—oratorio, HWV64 (1748) (Wds. ? Morell)

1. Introduction; 2. Ye sons of Israel, ev'ry tribe attend; 3. Behold, my friends; 4. O first in wisdom, first in pow'r; 5. Matrons and virgins, with unwearied pray'r; 6. Oh! who can tell, oh! who can hear; 7. Caleb, attend to all I now prescribe; 8. To long posterity we here record; 9. So long the memory shall last; 10. While Kedron's brook to Jordan's stream; 11. But, who is he?; 12. Awful, pleasing being, say; 13. Joshua, I come commisioned; 14. Haste, Israel, haste; 15. The Lord commands, and Joshua leads; 16. In these blest scenes; 17. Hark! 'tis the linnet and the thrush; 18. O Achsah, form'd for ev'ry chaste delight; 19. Our limpid streams with freedom flow; 20. The trumpet calls; 21. May all the host of heav'n attend him round; 22. 'Tis well; six times the Lord hath been obey'd; 23. A Solemn March; 24. Glory to God!; 25. The walls are levell'd, pour the chosen bands; 26. See, the raging flames arise; 27. To Vanity and earthly Pride; 28. Let all the seed of Abrah'm now prepare; 29. Almighty ruler of the skies; 30. Joshua, the men dispatch'd by thee; 31. How soon our tow'ring hopes are cross'd!; 32. Whence this dejection?; 33. With redoubled rage return; 34. Now give the army breath; 35. Heroes when with glory burning; 36. Indulgent heav'n hath heard my virgin pray't; 37. As cheers the sun the tender flow'r; 38. Sure I'm deceived, with sorrow I behold; 39. Nations, who in future story; 40. Brethen and friends. ACT 3: 41. Oh! thou bright orb, great ruler of the day!; 42. Hail! mighty Joshua, hail!; 43. Happy, Oh, trice happy we; 44. Caleb, for holy Eleazer send; 45. Shall I in Mamre's fertile plain; 46. O Caleb, fer'd by foes, by friends ador'd; 47. Place danger around me; 48. Father of Mercy; 49. In bloom of youth; 50. See the conqu'ring hero comes!; 51. Welcome! my son, my Othniel; 52. O had I Jubal's lyre; 53. While life shall last; 54. O peerless maid, with beauty blest; 55. While lawless tyrants, with ambitions blind; 56. The great Jehovah is our awful theme.

Cpte E. Kirkby, J. Bowman, A. Oliver, J.M. Ainsley, M. George, New College Ch, King's Consort, R. King (7/91) (HYPE) ① [2] **CDA66461/2**

Cpte J. Baird, D. Fortunato, J. Aler, J. Ostendorf, Palmer Sngrs, Brewer CO, R. Palmer (7/91) (NEWP) ① [2] **NPD85515**

10. R. White, City of London Baroque Sinfonia, I. Bolton *Concert* (12/91) (VIRG) ① **VJ7 59644-2**

35. J. Bowman, King's Consort, R. King *Concert* (8/88) (CARL) ① **PCD894**

52. L. Popp, ECO, G. Fischer (r1967) *Concert* (10/88) (EMI) ① **CDM7 69546-2**

52. K. Battle, ASMF, N. Marriner *Concert* (7/90) (EMI) ① **CDC7 49179-2**

52. E. Schumann, Vienna St Op Orch, K. Alwin (Ger: r1928) *Concert* (6/91) (PREI) ① **89031**

52. V. de los Angeles, G. Moore (r1960) *Concert* (4/94) (EMI) ① [4] **CMS5 65061-2(2)**

52. I. Baillie, orch, C. Prentice (r1928) *Concert* (7/95) (DUTT) ① **CDLX7013**

Judas Maccabaeus—oratorio, HWV63 (1747) (Wds. Morell, after Bible)

EXCERPTS: 1. Overture. PART 1: 2. Mourn, ye afflicted children; 3. Well, may your sorrows; 4. From this dread scene; 5. For Sion lamentation make; 6. Not vain is all this storm of grief; 7. Pious orgies, pious airs; 8. O Father, whose almighty power; 9. I feel the Deity within; 10. Arm, arm, ye brave!; 11. We come, in bright array; 12. 'Tis well, my friends; 13. Call forth thy pow'rs; 14. To Heav'n's almighty King we knell; 15. Oh liberty, thou choicest treasure; 16. Come, ever-smiling liberty (Aria); 17. Oh Judas, may these noble views inspire; 19. Come, ever-smiling liberty (Duet). PART 2: 20. Lead on, lead on!; 21. So will'd my father; 22. Disdainful of danger; 23. Ambition! If e'er honour was thine arm; 24. No unhallow'd desire; 25. Haste we, my brethen; 26. Hear us, oh Lord; 27. Fall'n is the foe; 28. Victorious hero!; 29. So rapid thy course is; 30. Well may we hope; 31. Sion now her head shall raise (Duet); 32. Sion now her head shall raise (Chorus); 33. O let eternal honours; 34. From mighty kings; 35. Hail, Judaea, happy land! (Duet); 36. Hail, Judaea, happy land! (Chorus); 37. Thanks to my brethren; 38. How vain is man; 39. Oh Judas, oh my brethen!; 40. Ah! wretched Israel! (Air); 41. Ah! wretched Israel! (Chorus); 42. Be comforted; 43. The Lord worketh wonders; 44. My arms, against this Gorgias will I go; 45. Sound an alarm!. PART 3: 46. We hear the pleasing dreadful call; 47. Enough! To heav'n we leave the rest; 48. With pious hearts; 49a. Ye worshippers of God; 49b. No more in Sion; 50. Wise men, flatt'ring, may deceive us; 51. Oh! never bow we down; 52. We never will bow down; 53. Father of Heaven!; 54. See, yon flames; 55. Oh grant it, Heav'n; 56. So shall the lute and harp awake; 57a. From Capharsalama on eagle wings; 57b. But lo! the conqueror comes; 58. See, the conqu'ring hero comes! (Chorus); 59. March; 60. Sing unto God; 61. Sweet flow the strains; 62. With honour let desert be crown'd; 63. Peace to my countrymen; 64. To our great God; 65. Again to earth let gratitude descend; 66. O lovely peace; 67. Rejoice, oh Judah; 68. Hallelujah! Amen.

Cpte E. Kirkby, C. Denley, J. Bowman, J. MacDougall, M. George, S. Birchall, New College Ch, King's Consort, R. King (12/92) (HYPE) ① [2] **CDA66641/2**

Cpte H. Harper, H. Watts, A. Young, J. Shirley-Quirk, Amor Artis Chorale, Wandsworth Sch Boys' Ch, ECO, J. Somary (r1971) (7/93) (VANG) ① [2] **08.4072.72**

Cpte L. Saffer, P. Spence, B. Asawa, G. de Mey, L. Kromm, D. Thomas, Berkeley Univ Chbr Chor, Philh Baroque Orch, N. McGegan (r1992) (1/94) (HARM) ① [2] **HMU90 7077/8**

10. N. Walker, orch, L. Collingwood (r1954) *Concert* (4/92) (EMI) ① [7] **CHS7 69741-2(2)**

45. Richard Lewis, LSO, M. Sargent *Concert* (8/89) (CFP) ① **CD-CFP4532**

45. W. Widdop, Orch, J. Barbirolli (r1929) *Concert* (11/92) (CLAR) ① **CDGSE78-50-46**

53. K. Ferrier, LPO, A. Boult (r1952) *Concert* (6/92) (DECC) ① **433 474-2DM**

56. R. White, City of London Baroque Sinfonia, I. Bolton *Concert* (12/91) (VIRG) ① **VJ7 59644-2**

58. ASMF Chor, ASMF, N. Marriner *Coronation Anthems.* (1/86) (PHIL) ① **412 733-2PH**

58. Handel Op Chor, RPO, C. Farncombe *Concert* (10/91) (DECC) ① **430 500-2DWO**

Langue, geme e sospira—duet, HWV188 (c1722-4)

G. Fisher, J. Bowman, King's Consort, R. King (hpd/dir) *Concert* (4/91) (HYPE) ① **CDA66440**

Laudate pueri Dominum—soprano and strings, HWV236/7 (1st version: c1703-06; 2nd version: 1707) (Wds. Psalm 112)

E. Kirkby, Taverner Ch, Taverner Plyrs, A. Parrott *Concert* (6/89) (EMI) ① [2] **CDS7 49749-2**

S. McNair, Monteverdi Ch, EBS, J.E. Gardiner (r1992) *Concert* (2/94) (PHIL) ① **434 920-2PH**

Look down, harmonious saint (The Praise of Harmony)—cantata: 1v, strings & continuo, HWV124 (?1736) (Wds. N. Hamilton)

J.M. Ainsley, Kings' Consort, R. King *Acis and Galatea.* (6/90) (HYPE) ① [2] **CDA66361/2**

La **Lucrezia—cantata (c1709)**

G. Lesne, Seminario Musicale *Concert* (12/91) (VIRG) ① **VC7 59059-2**

Lungi da me pensier tiranno—cantata (1v and continuo), HWV125

D.L. Ragin, Cologne Divitia Ens *Concert* (2/92) (CHNN) ① **CCS0890**

Mentre il tutto è in furore—cantata: soprano and continuo (1708)

M. C. Kiehr, Teatro Armonico, A. de Marchi (hpd/dir) (r1993) *Concert* (9/94) (ADES) ① **20271-2**

Messiah—oratorio: soloists, chorus and orchestra, HWV56 (1742) (Wds. Bible: selected C. Jennes)

EXCERPTS: 1. Overture (PART 1): 2. Comfort ye my people; 3. Every valley shall be exalted; 4. And the glory of the Lord; 5. Thus saith the Lord; 6. But who may abide?; 7. And he shall purify; 8. Behold, a

The Occasional Oratorio—oratorio, HWV62 (1746) (Wds. Hamilton, after various)
EXCERPTS: 1. Overture; 1d. March. ACT ONE: 2. Why do the gentiles tumult; 3. Let us break off; 4. O Lord, how many are my foes!; 5. Him or his God we not fear!; 6. Jehovah, to my words give ear; 7. Him or his God we scorn to fear!; 8. The Highest who in Heaven doth dwell; 9. O, who shall pour into my swollen eyes; 10. Fly from the threat'ning vengeance; 11. Humbled with fear and awful reverence; 12. His sceptre is the rod of righteousness; 13. Be wise at length, ye kings averse (Aria); 14. Be wise at length (Chorus); 15. Of many millions the populous rout; 16. Jehovah is my shield; 17. Fools or madmen stand not within thy sight; 18. God found them guilty. ACT TWO: 19. O liberty, thou choicest treasure; 20. Who trusts in God should ne'er despair; 21. Prophetic visions strike my eye; 22. May God, from whom all mercies spring; 23. The Lord hath heard my pray'r; 24. Then will I Jehovah's praise; 25. All his mercies shall endure; 26. How great and many perils do enfold; 27. After long storms and tempests overblown; 28. To God, our strength, sing loud and clear; 29. He has his mansion fix'd on high; 30. Hallelujah, your voices raise. ACT THREE: 31. Symphony (A tempo giusto); 32. Musette; 33. I will sing unto the Lord; 34. Thou shalt bring them in; 35. Who is like unto thee; 36. When warlike ensigns wave on high; 37. The enemy said; 38. The sword that's drawn in virtue's cause; 39. Millions unborn shall bless the hand; 40. When Israel, like the bounteous Nile; 41. Tyrants, whom no cov'nants bind; 42. May balmy peace; 43. Blessed are all they that fear the Lord.
Cpte S. Gritton, L. Milne, J. Bowman, J. M. Ainsley, M. George, New College Ch, King's Consort Choristers, King's Consort Ch, King's Consort, R. King (r1994) (6/95) (HYPE) ① [2] **CDA66961/2**

Occhi miei, che faceste?—cantata: 1v and continuo, HWV146
J. Baird, M. Proud, J. Dornenburg *Concert* (12/91) (MERI) ① **CDE84189**

Ode for St Cecilia's Day, HWV76 (1739) (Wds. J. Dryden)
1. Overture; 2a. From harmony; 2b. When nature underneath a heap; 3. From harmony, from heav'nly harmony (chorus); 4. What passion cannot music raise and quell; 5. The trumpet's loud clangour; 6. March; 7. The soft complaining flute; 8. Sharp violins proclaim; 9. But oh! what art can teach; 10. Orpheus could lead the savage race; 11. But bright Cecilia; 12. As from pow'r of sacred lays.
Cpte B. Schlick, C. Prégardien, M. Bach, W. Jochens, M. Schäfer, K. Mertens, P. Lika, Cologne Chorus Musicus, Neue Orch, C. Spering (r1991; Ger: arr Mozart) *Acis und Galatea, K566.* (6/92) (O111) ① [2] **OPS45-9109/10**
Cpte A. Cantelo, I. Partridge, King's College Ch, ASMF, D. Willcocks (r1967) *Concert* (8/93) (DECC) ① **436 259-2DM**
5. J.M. Ainsley, King's Consort, R. King *Concert* (8/88) (CARL) ① **PCD894**
8. R. White, City of London Baroque Sinfonia, I. Bolton *Concert* (12/91) (VIRG) ① **VJ7 59644-2**

Ode for the Birthday of Queen Anne, 'Eternal source of light divine', HWV74 (1713) (Wds. A. Philips)
1. Eternal source of light divine; 2. Let all the winged race with joy; 3. Let flocks and herds their fear forget; 4. Let rolling streams their gladness show; 5. Kind Health descend on downy wings; 6. Let Envy then conceal her head; 7. United nations shall combine.
Cpte G. Fisher, J. Bowman, M. George, New College Ch, King's Consort, R. King *Concert* (7/89) (HYPE) ① **CDA66315**
Cpte J. Nelson, E. Kirkby, S. Minty, J. Bowman, M. Hill, D. Thomas, Oxford Christ Church Cath Ch, AAM, S. Preston *Concert* (8/89) (L'OI) ① **421 654-2OH**
1. E. Gruberová, W. Marsalis, ECO, R. Leppard *Concert* (1/86) (SONY) ① **MK39061**
1. J. Bowman, King's Consort, R. King *Concert* (3/87) (MERI) ① **CDE84126**
1. K. Battle, W. Marsalis, St Luke's Orch, J. Nelson *Concert* (8/92) (SONY) ① **SK46672**

Pensieri notturni di Filli, 'Nel dolce dell'oblio'—cantata: soprano, recorder and continuo, HWV134 (c1707)
C. Högman, Quattro Temperamenti *Concert* (8/89) (BIS) ① **BIS-CD403**
K. Battle, J-P. Rampal, M. Lutzke, Anthony Newman (pp1991) *Concert* (9/94) (SONY) ① **SK53106**
M. C. Kiehr, Teatro Armonico, A. de Marchi (hpd/dir) (r1993) *Concert* (9/94) (ADES) ① **20271-2**
1. E. Ameling, H-M. Linde, Collegium Aureum (r1966) *Concert* (12/95) (DHM) ① [4] **74321 26617-2(1)**

Il pianto di Maria, 'Giunta l'ora fatal'—sacred cantata: 1v & strings, HWV234 (attrib Handel; actually comp G. B. Ferrandini)
A.S. von Otter, Cologne Musica Antiqua, R. Goebel *Concert* (7/94) (ARCH) ① **439 866-2AH**

Qual fior che all'alba ride (Duetto XV)—2 sopranos and continuo (?1708)
J. Baird, M. Proud, J. Dornenburg *Concert* (12/91) (MERI) ① **CDE84189**

La Resurrezione di Nostro Signor Gesù Cristo—oratorio (1708) (wds. C. S. Capece)
PART 1: 1. Sonata; 2a. Disserratevi, o porte d'Averno; 2b. Qual'insolita luce; 2c. Ma che veggio?; 2d. D'amor fu consiglio; 2e. O voi, dell'Erebo; 3a. Notte, notte funesta; 3b. Piangete, sì, piangete; 3c. Dolci chiodi; 3d. Quando è parto dell'affetto; 3e. Naufragando va per l'onde; 3f. Così la tortorella; 3g. Ho un so che nel cor; 4. Nume vincitor. PART 2: 5. Introduction; 6. Ecco il sol; 7a. Risorga il mondo; 7b. Di rabbia indarno freme; 7c. Per celare il nuovo scorno; 7d. Impedirlo saprò; 8. Per me già di morire; 9a. Vedo il Ciel che più sereno; 9b. Se per colpa di donna infelice; 9c. Del ciglio dolente; 9d. Augelletti, ruscelletti; 10a. Caro Figlio!; 10b. Se impassibile, immortale; 10c. Diasi lode in Cielo, in terra.
Cpte N. Argenta, B. Schlick, G. Laurens, G. de Mey, K. Mertens, Amsterdam Baroque Orch, T. Koopman (7/91) (ERAT) ① [2] **2292-45617-2**
Cpte L. Saffer, J. Nelson, P. Spence, Jeffrey Thomas, M. George, Philh Baroque Orch, N. McGegan (7/91) (HARM) ① [2] **HMU90 7027/8**

Saeviat tellus—soprano and strings, HWV240 (1707-08)
J. Feldman, Taverner Plyrs, A. Parrott *Concert* (6/89) (EMI) ① [2] **CDS7 49749-2**

Salve Regina—soprano and strings, HWV241 (1707)
A. Auger, Westminster Abbey Orch, S. Preston *Concert* (2/89) (ARCH) ① **423 594-2AH**
E. Van Evera, Taverner Plyrs, A. Parrott *Concert* (6/89) (EMI) ① [2] **CDS7 49749-2**

Samson—oratorio, HWV57 (1743) (Wds. Hamilton, after Milton)
1. Overture (Sinfonie); 1a. Minuetto. ACT 1: 3. Awake the trumpet's lofty sound; 4. Ye men of Gaza; 6. Loud as the thunder's awful voice; 7. Then free from sorrow; 10. Torments, alas! are not confin'd; 12. Oh mirror of our fickle state; 14. Total eclipse; 15. Since light so necessary; 16. Oh first created beam; 19. God of our fathers; 21. Thy glorious deeds inspir'd; 23. My griefs for this; 24. Why does the God of Israel sleep?; 26. Then shall they know; 28. Then long eternity shall greet your bliss; 29. Joys that are pure; 30. Then round about the starry throne. ACT 2: 32. Just are the ways of God to man; 34. Return, O God of host; 35. To dust his glory they would tread; 36b. My wife? my traitress!; 36c. She stands, and eyes thee fix'd; 36d. With doubtful feet; 36e. Out thou hyaena!; 36f. I would not lessen my offense; 37. With plaintive notes; 38. Did love constrain thee; 39. Your charms to ruin led the way; 41. My/her faith and truth; 42. Her faith and truth; 43. To fleeting pleasure pleasures make your court; 44. Her faith and truth (reprise); 45. How charming is domestic ease; 46. Her faith and truth (reprise); 49. Traitor/Traitress to love! I'll sue no more; 51. It is not virtue; 52. To man God's universal law; 55. Honour and arms scorn such a foe; 57a. Put on your arms; 57b. My strength is from the living God; 59. Go, baffled coward, go; 61. Hear, Jacob's God; 63. To song and dance we give the day; 64. To song and dance; 65. Fix'd in his everlasting seat. ACT 3: 69. With thunder arm'd; 71. Thus when the sun from's wat'ry bed; 73a. The Holy One of Israel by thy guide; 73b. To fame immortal go; 75. Great Dagon has subdued our foe; 77. How willing my paternal love; 78c. Hear us, Our God; 80. Ye sons of Israel, now lament; 81a. Weep, Israel, weep; 82. Dead March; 84. Glorious hero; 86. Let the bright Seraphim; 87. Let their celestial concerts all unite.
Cpte R. Alexander, A.M. Blasi, M. Venuti, J. Kowalski, A. Rolfe Johnson, C. Prégardien, A. Scharinger, A. Miles, A. Schoenberg Ch, VCM, N. Harnoncourt (pp1992) (2/94) (TELD) ① [2] **9031-74871-2**
1. E. Gruberová, W. Marsalis, ECO, R. Leppard *Concert* (1/86) (SONY) ① **MK39061**
1. Queen's Hall Orch, Henry Wood (r1935) *Concert* (1/94) (BEUL) ① **1PD3**
14. R. White, City of London Baroque Sinfonia, I. Bolton *Concert* (12/91) (VIRG) ① **VJ7 59644-2**
34. K. Ferrier, LPO, A. Boult (r1952) *Concert* (6/92) (DECC) ① **433 474-2DM**
34. M. Forrester, Zagreb Sols, A. Janigro *Concert* (12/92) (CBC) ① **PSCD2002**
55. O. Natzke, orch, H. Geehl (r1938) *Concert* (12/92) (ODE) ① **CDODE1365**
77. M. George, King's Consort, R. King *Concert* (8/88) (CARL) ① **PCD894**
86. A. Auger, Mostly Mozart Orch, G. Schwarz *Concert* (11/86) (DELO) ① **DE3026**
86. J. Sutherland, ROHO, F. Molinari-Pradelli *Concert* (1/90) (DECC) ① [2] **425 493-2DM2**
86. J. Sutherland, ROHO, F. Molinari-Pradelli *Concert* (10/91) (DECC) ① **430 500-2DWO**
86. Vienna Boys' Ch, U.C. Harrer *Concert* (12/91) (PHIL) ① **426 307-2PH**
86. K. Battle, W. Marsalis, St Luke's Orch, J. Nelson *Concert* (8/92) (SONY) ① **SK46672**
86. J. Sutherland, ROHO, F. Molinari-Pradelli (r1960) *Concert* (6/93) (DECC) ① **436 402-2DWO**
86. A. Roocroft, LPO, F. Welser-Möst *Concert* (10/94) (EMI) ① **CDC5 55090-2**
86. I. Baillie, Hallé, W. Braithwaite (r1943) *Concert* (7/95) (DUTT) ① **CDLX7013**
86, 87. K. Te Kanawa, St Paul's Cath Ch, ECO, Barry Rose *Concert* (5/85) (PHIL) ① **412 629-2PH**

Saul—oratorio, HWV53 (1738) (Wds. C. Jennens)
EXCERPTS: 1a. Overture. PART 1: 1b. How excellent Thy name; 2. Infernal spirits; 3. Along the monster atheist strode; 4. The youth inspir'd by Thee; 5. How excellent Thy name; 6. He comes, he comes!; 7. Oh god-like youth!; 8. Behold, o king; 9. O king, your favours; 10. O early piety!; 11. What abject thoughts; 12. Yet think, on whom this honour; 13. Birth and fortune I despise!; 14. Go on, illustrious pair!; 15. While yet thy tide of blood; 16. Thou, Merab, first in birth; 17. My soul rejects the thought; 18. See, with what a scornful air; 19. Ah! lovely youth!; 20. Sinfonia; 21. Already see the daughters of the land; 22. Welcome, welcome, mighty king!; 23. What do I hear?; 24. David his ten thousands slew; 25. To him ten thousands; 26. With rage I shall burst; 27. Imprudent women!; 28. Fell rage and black despair; 29. This but the smallest part; 30. By thee this universal frame; 31. Rack'dwith infernal pains; 32. O Lord, whose mercies; 33. Sinfonia; 34. 'T is all in vain; 35. A serpent, in my bosom warm'd; 36. Has he escap'd my rage?; 37. Capricious man, in humour lost; 38. O filial piety! o sacred friendship; 39. No, cruel father, no!; 40. O Lord, whose providence; 41. Preserve him. PART 2: 42. Envy! eldest born of Hell!; 43. Ah! dearest friend; 44. But sooner Jordan's stream; 45. O strange vicissitude!; 46. Such haughty beauties; 47. My father comes; 48. Hast thou ob'yed my orders?; 49. Sin not, o king; 50. As great Jehovah lives; 51. From cities storm'd; 52. Appear, my friend; 53. Your words, o king; 54. Yes, he shall wed; 55. A father's will; 56. O fairest of ten thousand fair; 57. Is there a man; 58. Sinfonia; 58a. Allegro; 59. Thy father is as cruel; 60. At persecution I can laugh; 61. Whom dost thou seek?; 62. No, no, let the guilty tremble; 63. Mean as he was; 64. Author of peace; 65. Symphony; 66. The time at length is come; 67. Where is the son of Jesse?; 68. O fatal consequence. PART 3: 69. Wretch that I am!; 70. 'T is said, here lives a woman; 71. With me what woulds't thou?; 72. Infernal spirits; 73. Why hast thou forc'd me; 74. Sinfonia; 75. Whence comest thou?; 76. Impious wretch; 77. Dead March; 78. Mourn, Israel, mourn; 79. O let it not in Gath; 80. From this unhappy day; 81. Brave Jonathan; 82. Eagles were not so swift; 83. In sweetest harmony; 84. O fatal day!; 85. Ye men of Judah; 86. Gird on thy sword.
Cpte L. Dawson, D. Brown, D.L. Ragin, J.M. Ainsley, N. Mackie, A. Miles, P. Salmon, P. Slane, R. Savage, S. Oberst, Monteverdi Ch, EBS, J.E. Gardiner (pp1989) (8/91) (PHIL) ① [3] **426 265-2PH3**
37. E. Kirkby, AAM, C. Hogwood (r1991) *Concert* (7/93) (L'OI) ① **436 132-2OH**
77. S. Preston (trans org: Cunningham Woods) *Concert* (6/91) (DECC) ① **430 091-2DWO**

Se tu non lasci amore—duet, HWV193 (c1720-24)
G. Fisher, J. Bowman, King's Consort, R. King (hpd/dir) *Concert* (4/91) (HYPE) ① **CDA66440**

Semele—oratorio, HWV58 (1744) (Wds. Congreve)
1. Overture. ACT 1: 2a. Behold! auspicious flashes rise!; 2b. Lucky omens bless our rites; 2c. Daughter, obey, hear and obey!; 2d. Ah me! What refuge now is left me!; 2e. O Jove! in pity teach me; 2f. The morning lark; 2g. Hymen, haste, thy torch prepare; 2h. Why dost thou thus untimely grieve; 2i. Avert these omens; 2j. Again auspicious flashes rise; 2k. Cease, cease your vows; 3a. Turn, hopeless lover; 3b. Your tuneful voice; 3c. Ypu've undone me; 4. Ah, wretched prince; 5a. Hail Cadmus, hail!; 5b. Endless pleasure, endless love. ACT 2: 6. Sinfonia; 7a. There from mortal cares retiring; 7b. Hence, Iris, hence

away; 8. O sleep, why dost thou leave me?; 9a. Lay your doubts and fears aside; 9b. With food desiring; 9c. How engaging, how endearing; 9d. I must with speed amuse her; 9e. Now Love that everlasting boy invites; 9f. Where'er you walk; 10a. But hark! the heav'nly sphere; 10c. Prepare then, ye immortal choir; 10d. Bless the glad earth. ACT 3: 11a. Symphony; 11b. Leave me, loathsome light; 11c. More sweet is that name; 11d. Obey my will; 12. My racking thoughts; 13a. Behold in this mirror; 13b. Myself I shall adore; 13d. Thus ley my thanks be paid; 14a. Come to my arms; 14b. O Semele!; 14c. I ever am granting; 14d. Ah, take heed what you press; 14e. No, no! I'll take no less; 15. Ah! whither is she gone; 16. Above measure is the pleasure; 17. Ah me! too late I now repent; 18a. Oh, terror and astonishment!; 18b. Despair no more shall wound me; 19a. Sinfonia; 19b. Happy, happy shall we be.

Cpte N. Burrowes, D. Jones, A. Rolfe Johnson, T. Penrose, R. Lloyd, M. Davies, P. Kwella, C. Denley, D. Thomas, E. Priday, Monteverdi Ch, EBS, J.E. Gardiner (r1981) (6/93) (ERAT) ① [2] **2292-45982-2**

Cpte K. Battle, M. Horne, S. McNair, M. Chance, J. Aler, N. Mackie, S. Ramey, M.S. Doss, Ambrosian Op Chor, ECO, J. Nelson (6/93) (DG) ① [3] **435 782-2GH3**

7b J. Larmore, Lausanne CO, J. López-Cobos (r1994) *Concert* (12/95) (TELD) ① **4509-96800-2**

8. J. McCormack, orch, J. Pasternack (r1920) *Concert* (5/93) (MMOI) ① **CDMOIR418**

8, 9f R. White, City of London Baroque Sinfonia, I. Bolton *Concert* (12/91) (VIRG) ① **VJ7 59644-2**

9f J.M. Ainsley, King's Consort, R. King *Concert* (8/88) (CARL) ① **PCD894**

9f A.S. von Otter, Drottningholm Baroque Ens, A. Öhrwall *Concert* (10/91) (PROP) ① **PRCD9008**

9f K. McKellar, ROHO, A. Boult (r1961) *Concert* (10/91) (DECC) ① **430 500-2DWO**

9f L. Price, Philh, H. Lewis (r1979) *Concert* (12/92) (RCA) ① [4] **09026 61236-2**

Siete rose rugiadose—cantata (1v and continuo), HWV162

D.L. Ragin, Cologne Divitia Ens *Concert* (2/92) (CHNN) ① **CCS0890**

Silete venti—motet for soprano and strings, HWV242 (c1724)

A. Mackay, ECCO, E. Aadland *Concert* (12/91) (ASV) ① **CDDCA766**

L. Dawson, The Sixteen Orch, H. Christophers *Concert* (3/92) (CHAN) ① **CHAN0517**

S. McNair, EBS, J.E. Gardiner (r1992) *Concert* (2/94) (PHIL) ① **434 920-2PH**

Sing unto God—wedding anthem, HWV263 (1736)

G. Fisher, J. Bowman, J.M. Ainsley, M. George, New College Ch, King's Consort, R. King *Concert* (7/89) (HYPE) ① **CDA66315**

Solitudini care, amata libertà—cantata: 1v and continuo, HWV163

J. Baird, M. Proud, J. Dornenburg *Concert* (12/91) (MERI) ① **CDE84189**

Solomon—oratorio, HWV67 (1749) (Wds. Bible)

EXCERPTS: 1a. Overture; 1b. Your harps and cymbals sound; 2a. Almighty power; 2b. With pious heart and holy tongue; 3a. Imperial Solomon, thy prayers are heard; 3b. Sacred raptures cheer my breast; 4a. Blest be the Lord; 4b. What tho' I trace each herb and flower; 5. Blest the day; 6a. Thou fair inhabitant of Nile; 6b. Welcome as the dawn; 7a. When thou art absent from my heart; 7b. With thee th' unsheltered moor; 8a. My blooming fair come; 8b. May no rash intruder; 8c. Sinfonia (Arrival of Queen of Sheba); 9a. From Arabia's spicy shores; 9b. Every sight these eyes; 10a. Sweep, sweep the string; 10b. Music, spread thy voice; 11. Now a different measure try; 12. Then at once from rage; 13a. Next the tortured soul release; 13b. Thus rolling surges; 14a. Thy harmony's divine; 14b. From the censer curling rise; 15. From the East unto the West; 16a. Thrice happy king; 16b. Golden columns bright and fair; 17. Beneath the vine; 18a. Gold now is common; 18b. How green our fertile pastures; 19. Swell the full chorus; 20a. May peace in Salem ever dwell; 20b. Will the sun forget to streak; 21a. Adieu, fair Queen; 21b. Praise the Lord.

Cpte C. Watkinson, N. Argenta, B. Hendricks, J. Rodgers, D. Jones, A. Rolfe Johnson, S. Varcoe, Monteverdi Ch, EBS, J.E. Gardiner (12/85) (PHIL) ① [2] **412 612-2PH2**

1a ASMF, K. Sillito (r1993) *Concert* (8/94) (CAPR) ① **10 420**

1a, 8c EBS, J.E. Gardiner *Concert* (7/92) (PHIL) ① **434 154-2PM**

8c Cantilena, A. Shepherd *Concert* (7/83) (CHAN) ① **CHAN8301**

8c AAM, C. Hogwood *Concert* (12/83) (L'OI) ① **410 553-2OH**

8c Cantilena, A. Shepherd *Concert* (9/84) (CHAN) ① **CHAN8319**

8c English Concert, T. Pinnock (hpd/dir) *Concert* (1/86) (ARCH) ① **415 518-2AH**

8c Taverner Plyrs, A. Parrott *Concert* (12/88) (EMI) ① **CDM7 69853-2**

8c Y. Menuhin (vn/dir), C. Ferras *Concert* (1/89) (EMIL) ① **CDZ114**

8c ASMF, N. Marriner *Concert* (10/91) (DECC) ① **430 500-2DWO**

8c S. Mayor (arr Mayor: mandolin ens) *Concert* (3/92) (ACOU) ① **CDACS012**

8c Cologne Stravaganza *Concert* (3/93) (DENO) ① **CO-79943**

8c LPO, T. Beecham (r1933) *Concert* (6/94) (DUTT) ① **CDLX7003**

8c LPO, T. Beecham (r1933) *Concert* (6/94) (VAI) ① **VAIA1045**

9b, 20a, 20b K. Battle, ASMF, N. Marriner *Concert* (7/90) (EMI) ① **CDC7 49179-2**

21b R. White, City of London Baroque Sinfonia, I. Bolton *Concert* (12/91) (VIRG) ① **VJ7 59644-2**

Sono liete, fortunate—duet, HWV194 (1706-12)

G. Fisher, J. Bowman, King's Consort, R. King (hpd/dir) *Concert* (4/91) (HYPE) ① **CDA66440**

Splenda l'alba in Oriente—cantata

G. Lesne, Seminario Musicale *Concert* (12/91) (VIRG) ① **VC7 59059-2**

St John Passion (?1704, spurious) (Wds. Bible, adapted Postel)

Cpte M. Klietmann, J. Moldvay, C. Brett, M. Zádori, I. Verebics, J. Németh, G. Kállay, I. Gáti, Capella Savaria, P. Németh (7/88) (HUNG) ① **HCD12908**

Susanna—oratorio (1749) (Wds. after Apocrypha)

1. Overture. PART 1: 2a. How long, oh Lord, shall Israel groan; 2b. Clouds o'ertake the brightest day; 2c. When thou art nigh; 2d. Who fears the Lord; 2e. When first I saw my lovely maid; 2f. Would custom bid; 2g. Peace crown'd with roses; 2h. Without the swain's assiduous care; 2i. The parent bird in search of food; 3a. On Joacim may every joy attend; 3b. Bending to the throne of glory; 4a. Tyrannic love; 4b. Ye verdant hills, ye balmy vales; 5a. Say, is it fit that age?; 5b. The oak that for a thousand years; 5c. When the trumpet sounds to arms; 5d. Righteous heav'n beholds their guile. PART 2: 6a. Frost nips the flowers; 6b. On fair Euphrates' verdant side; 7a. Lead me to some cool retreat; 7b. Crystal streams in murmurs flowing; 7c. Ask if yon damask rose; 7d. Beneath the cypress' gloomy shade; 8a. But hark, what sudden noise?; 8b. Blooming as the face of spring; 8c. The torrent that sweeps in its course; 8d. Away, ye tempt me both in vain; 9a. I caught the fair delinquent; 9b. If guiltless blood be your intent; 9c. Let justice reign; 10a. Is fair Susanna false?; 10b. On the rapid whirlwind's wing; 10c. On Joacim, thy wedded truth? PART 3: 11a. The cause is decided; 11b. Faith displays her rosy winf; 11c. Round thy urn my tears shall flow; 11d. 'Tis not age's sullen face; 11e. Impartial heav'n!; 11f. Chastity, thou cherub bright; 12a. Gold within the furnace try'd; 12b. Raise your voice to sounds of joy; 12c. Bless'd be the day that gave Susanna birth!; 12d. Guilt trembling spoke my doom; 12e. To my chaste Susanna's praise; 12f. A virtuous wife shall soften Fortune's frown.

Cpte L. Hunt, J. Feldman, D. Minter, Jeffrey Thomas, W. Parker, D. Thomas, Berkeley Univ Chbr Chor, Philh Baroque Orch, N. McGegan (pp1989) (10/90) (HARM) ① [3] **HMU90 7030/2**

Tanti strali al sen mi scocchi—duet, HWV197 (1710-12)

G. Fisher, J. Bowman, King's Consort, R. King (hpd/dir) *Concert* (4/91) (HYPE) ① **CDA66440**

Te decus virgineum—alto and strings, HWV243 (1707-08)

M. Nichols, Taverner Plyrs, A. Parrott (ed Burrows) *Concert* (6/89) (EMI) ① [2] **CDS7 49749-2**

Te Deum in D, 'Dettingen', HWV283 (1743)

C. Tipping, H. Christophers, S. Varcoe, M. Pearce, Westminster Abbey Ch, English Concert, S. Preston *King shall rejoice (Dettingen).* (9/84) (ARCH) ① **410 647-2AH**

Verlich uns Herr Y. Menuhin, L. Persinger (arr Flesch: r1929) *Concert* (4/91) (BIDD) ① **LAB031**

Verlich uns Herr C. Flesch, I. Strasfogel (arr Flesch as 'Prayer'; r1929) *Concert* (12/91) (BIDD) ① **LAB045**

Te Deum in D, 'Queen Caroline', HWV280 (1714)

J. Bowman, J.M. Ainsley, M. George, New College Ch, King's Consort, R. King *Concert* (7/89) (HYPE) ① **CDA66315**

M. van der Sluis, G. Pushee, H. van Berne, H. van der Kamp, Alsfeld Voc Ens, Bremen Baroque Orch, W. Helbich (r1993) *Ways of Zion do mourn.* (10/95) (CPO) ① **CPO999 244-2**

Theodora—oratorio, HWV68 (1750) (Wds. T. Morell)

1. Overture. ACT 1: 2a. 'Tis Dioclesian's natal Day; 2b. Go my faithful Soldier, go; 2c. And draw a blessing down; 2d. Vouchsafe, dread Sir, a gracious Ear; 2e. Rachs, Gibbets, Sword, and Fire; 2f. For ever thus stands fix'd the Doom; 3a. Most cruel Edict!; 3b. The raptur'd Soul defies the Sword; 3c. I know the Virtues; 3d. Descend, kind Pity, heavenly Guest; 4a. Tho' hard my Friends; 4b. Fond, flatt'ring World; adieu!; 4c. O bright Example of all Goodness; 4d. Bane of Virtue; 4e. Come mighty Father; 5a. Fly, fly, my Brethen; 5b. As with rosy steps the Morn advancing; 5c. All Pow'r in Heav'n above; 6a. Mistaken wretches!; 6b. Dread the Fruits of Christian Folly; 6c. Deluded Mortal!; 6d. Angels, ever bright and fair; 7a. Unhappy, happy Crew!; 7b. Kind Heav'n, if Virtue be thy care; 8. O Love; how great thy Power!; 8a. O lOve; how great thy Pow'r!. ACT 2: 9a. Ye Men of Antioch; 9b. Queen of Summer, Queen of Love; 9c. Wide spread his Name; 9d. Return, Septimus; 9e. Venus laughing from the skies; 10. Interlude; 11a. O Thou bright Sun!; 11b. With Darkness, deep as is my wo; 11c. Symphony of Soft Musick; 11d. But why art Thou disquieted, my Soul?; 11e. Oh! that I on wings could rise; 12a. Long have I known; 12b. Tho' the Honours; 12c. O save her then; 12d. To the sincerity of Pray'r; 13a. The Clouds begin to veil the Hemisphere; 13b. Defend her, Heav'n; 14a. Or lull'd with Grief; 14b. Sweet Rose, and Lilly, flow'ry Form; 14c. O save me, Heav'n; 14d. The Pilgrim's Home; 14e. Forbid it, Heav'n!; 14f. To Thee, Thou glorious Son of Worth (Duet); 15a. 'Tis night; 15b. He saw the lovely Youth. ACT 3: 16a. Lord, to Thee each Night and Day; 16b. But see! the good, the Virtuous Didymus!; 16c. When sunk in Anguish and Despair; 16d. Blest be the Hand; 17a. Undaunted in the Court; 17b. Ah! Theodora; 17c. Whither, Princess, do you fly (Duet); 17d. She's gone, disdaining Liberty and Life; 17e. New scenes of Joy come crowding on; 18a. Is is a Christian Virtue then; 18b. Such my Religion; 19a. Be That my Doom; 19b. From Virtue springs each gen'rous deed; 19c. Cease, ye Slaves, your fruitless Pray'r; 19d. 'Tis kind, my Friends; 19e. How strange their Ends; 19f. On me your Frowns; 19g. Ye Ministers of Justice; 20a. And must such BEauty suffer?; 20b. Streams of Pleasure ever flowing; 21a. E'er This, their Doom; 21b. O Love Divine, Thou Source of Fame.

Cpte R. Alexander, J. Kowalski, J. van Nes, H-P. Blochwitz, A. Scharinger, A. Schoenberg Ch, VCM, N. Harnoncourt (8/91) (TELD) ① [2] **2292-46447-2**

Cpte L. Hunt, J. Lane, D. Minter, Jeffrey Thomas, N. Rogers, D. Thomas, Berkeley Univ Chbr Chor, Philh Baroque Orch, N. McGegan (10/92) (HARM) ① [3] **HMU90 7060/2**

Cpte H. Harper, M. Forrester, M. Lehane, A. Young, E. Fleet, J. Lawrenson, Amor Artis Chorale, ECO, J. Somary (r1968) (7/93) (VANG) ① [2] **08.4075.72**

5c J. Bowman, Orch, R. King *Concert* (12/93) (UNIT) ① **88002-2**

6d E. Albani, anon (r1904) *Concert* (10/92) (SYMP) ① **SYMCD1093**

6d I. Baillie, orch (r1928) *Concert* (7/95) (DUTT) ① **CDLX7013**

7b, 14a, 14b M. Forrester, ECO, J. Somary *Concert* (12/92) (CBC) ① **PSCD2002**

7b, 14b A. Deller, Handel Fest Orch, A. Lewis (r1960) *Concert* (1/95) (VANG) ① **08.5069.71**

The **Triumph of Time and Truth—oratorio, HWV71 (1757)** (Wds. Morell, after Pamphili. Extensive rev of 'Il Trionfo del Tempo e della Verità')

1. Overture. ACT 1: 2. Time is supreme; 3. Faithful mirror; 4. Pensive sorrow; 5. Come, come live with Pleasure; 6. The Beauty smiling; 7. Ever-flowing tides of pleasure; 8. Loathsome urns; 9. Strengthen us O Lord; 10. Happy, if still they reign; 11. Like the shadow. ACT 2: 12. Pleasure submits to pain; 13. Oh how great the glory; 14. Dryads, Sylvans; 15. Lo! We all attend; 16. Come, O Time; 17. Mortals think that Time is sleeping; 18. False destructive ways of Pleasure; 19. Lovely Beauty; 20. Melancholy; 21. Fain would I; 22. On the valleys; 23. Ere to dust is changed thy beauty. ACT 3: 24. Sinfonia; 25. Sharp thorns despising; 26. My former ways resigning; 27. Thus to ground; 28. From the heart; 29. Like clouds;

30. Guardian angels, oh protect me; 31. Alleluja!.
Cpte G. Fisher, E. Kirkby, C. Brett, I. Partridge, S. Varcoe, London Handel Ch, London Handel Orch, D. Darlow (2/87) (HYPE) Ⓓ [2] **CDA66071/2**
25. E. Kirkby, London Handel Orch, D. Darlow *Concert* (9/87) (HYPE) Ⓓ **CDA66227**

Troppo cruda, troppo fiera—duet, HWV198 (c1706)
G. Fisher, J. Bowman, King's Consort, R. King (hpd/dir) *Concert* (4/91) (HYPE) Ⓓ **CDA66440**

Tu fedel? tu costante?—cantata, HWV171 (1706-07)
E. Kirkby, AAM, C. Hogwood *Concert* (3/86) (L'OI) Ⓓ **414 473-2OH**
M. C. Kiehr, Teatro Armonico, A. de Marchi (hpd/dir) (r1993) *Concert* (9/94) (ADES) Ⓓ **20271-2**

Udite il mio consiglio—cantata: 1v and continuo, HWV172
J. Baird, M. Proud, J. Dornenburg *Concert* (12/91) (MERI) Ⓓ **CDE84189**
D.L. Ragin, Cologne Divitia Ens *Concert* (2/92) (CHNN) Ⓓ **CCS0890**

Vedendo amor—cantata (1v and continuo), HWV175 (1708)
J. Bowman, S. Sempé, J. Bernfeld *Concert* (9/89) (ARIO) Ⓓ **ARN68046**

The **Ways of Zion do mourn—anthem for the funeral of Queen Caroline, HWV264 (1737)**
N. Burrowes, C. Brett, M. Hill, S. Varcoe, Monteverdi Ch, Monteverdi Orch, J. E. Gardiner (r1979) (2/95) (ERAT) Ⓓ **4509-96954-2**
M. van der Sluis, G. Pushee, H. van Berne, H. van der Kamp, Alsfeld Voc Ens, Bremen Baroque Orch, W. Helbich (r1993) *Queen Caroline Te Deum.* (10/95) (CPO) Ⓓ **CPO999 244-2**

SECTION V: STAGE WORKS

Admeto, re di Tessaglia—opera: 3 acts, HWV22 (1727—London) (Lib. cpsr)
1. Overture; 2. Introduction; 3. Admeto's Aria: 3a. Orride larve; 3b. Chiudetevi, miei lumi; 4. Se l'arco avessi (Trazimede's Aria); 5. Cangio d'aspetto; 6. Sinfonia.
1, 2, 3a, 3b, 6. A. Köhler, Halle Op House Handel Fest Orch, H. Arman (r1994) *Concert* (6/95) (CAPR) Ⓓ **10 547**
5. K. Ferrier, P. Spurr (bp1949; Eng) *Concert* (6/92) (DECC) Ⓓ **433 473-2DM**
6. AAM, C. Hogwood *Concert* (8/94) (PHIL) Ⓓ **434 992-2PH**

Agrippina—opera: 3 acts (1709—Venice) (Lib. Grimani)
EXCERPTS: 1. Sinfonia. ACT 1: 2. Nerone amato figlio; 3. Con saggio tuo consiglio; 4. Per così grand'impresa; 5. La mia sorte fortunata; 6. Or che Pallante è vinto; 7a. Volo pronto; 7b. Quanto fa; 8. L'alma mia; 9a. Qual piacer; 9b. Amici al sen; 11. Alle tue piante; 12a. Tù ben degno; 12b. L'ultima del gioir; 13. Lusinghiera; 14. Vaghe perle; 15. Otton, Claudio, Nerone; 16. E' un foco quel d'amore; 17. Mà qui Agrippina viene; 18a. Hò un non sò; 18b. Cieli, quai strani; 19a. Fà quanto vuoi; 19b. Non veggo alcun; 20a. Pur ritorno; 21a. Vieni, o cara; 21b. Che mai farò; 22. E quando mai?; 23. Pur al fin; 24a. Non hò cor; 24b. Se Ottone m'inganno; 25. Se giunge un dispetto. ACT 2: 26. Dunque noi siam traditi?; 27a. Coronato il crin; 27b. Roma, piu ch'il trionfo; 28. Ecco il superbo!; 29a. Di timpani, e trombe; 29b. Bella Brittania; 30. Cade il Mondo; 31. Signor, quanto il mio core; 32a. Nulla sperar da me; 32b. Tuo ben è'l Trono; 33a. Sotto il lauro; 33b. Scherzo son; 34. Otton, Otton, qual portentoso; 35. Voi, che udite; 37a. Bella pur nel mio diletto; 37b. Il tormento d'Ottone; 38. Vaghe fonti; 39. Mà quì che veggo!; 40a. Ti vo' giusta; 40b. Da quali ordite; 41. Ingannata una sol; 43a. Col peso del tuo amor; 43b. Qual bramato; 44. Quando invita; 45a. Pensieri; 45b. Quel ch'oprai; 46. Se ben nemica; 47. Col raggio placido; 48. Di giunger non dispero; 49a. Spererò; 49b. Per dar la pace; 50a. Vagheggiar de tuoi; 50b. Vorrei della bellezza; 51a. Basta, che sol tù chieda; 51b. Favorevol; 52. Ogni vento. ACT 3: 53. Il caro Otton; 54a. Tacerò; 54b. Attendo qui Nerone; 55. Anelante ti reco; 57. Amico Ciel; 58. Io di Roma il Giove sono; 59. Pur al fin se n'andò; 60. Pur ch'io ti stringa; 61a. Piega pur del mio cor; 61b. Bel piacere; 62. Contantò osò Poppea?; 63. Come nube; 64. Evvi donna più empia?; 65. Adorato mio sposo; 66. Se vuol pace; 67. Ecco la mia rivale; 68. D'Ottone e di Poppea; 69. V'accendano le Tede; 70. Lieto il Tebro increspi l'onda.
Cpte S. Bradshaw, W. Hill, L. Saffer, N. Isherwood, D. Minter, M. Dean, R. Popken, B. Szilágyi, G. Banditelli, Capella Savaria, N. McGegan (3/93) (HARM) Ⓓ [3] **HMU90 7063/5**
1. ASMF, K. Sillito (r1993) *Concert* (8/94) (CAPR) Ⓓ **10 420**
45a, 52. L. Hunt, Philh Baroque Orch, N. McGegan *Concert* (3/93) (HARM) Ⓓ **HMU90 7056**
61b K. te Kanawa, AAM, C. Hogwood *Concert* (8/94) (PHIL) Ⓓ **434 992-2PH**

Alceste—incidental music, HWV45 (1749) (Lib. T. Smollett. Music used in 'The Choice of Hercules')
EXCERPTS: 1. Overture; 2. Grand entrée; 3. Ye happy people; 4. Triumph, Hymen, in the pair; 5. Still caressing, and caress'd; 6. Ye swift minutes as ye fly; 7. O bless, ye powers above; 8. Gentle Morpheus, son of night; 9. Ye fleeting shades, I come; 10. Thrice happy who in life excel; 11. Enjoy the sweet Elsian grove; 12. Thrice happy; 13. Come, fancy, empress of the brain; 14. Symphony; 15. He comes, he rises from below; 16. All hail, thou mighty son of Jove!; 17. Symphony; 18. From high Olympus' top; 19. Tune your harp, all ye Nine; 20. First dance; 21. The last dance; 22. Triumph, thou glorious son of Jove.
Cpte E. Kirkby, J. Nelson, M. Cable, P. Elliott, D. Thomas, AAM, C. Hogwood (r1979) *Comus.* (11/94) (L'OI) Ⓓ **443 183-2OM**

Alcina—opera: 3 acts, HWV34 (1735—London) (Lib. after Ariosto)
EXCERPTS: 1. Overture. ACT 1: 2a. Oh Dei! quivi non scorgo; 2b. O s'apre al riso; 3a. Questo è il cielo; 3b. Ballet; 3c. Ecco l'infido; 3d. Di', cor mio, quanto t'amai; 4a. Generosi guerrier; 4b. Chi m'insegna il caro padre?; 5a. Mi ravvisi, Ruggier, dimmi; 5b. Di te mi rido; 6. Qua dunque ne veniste; 7. È gelosia; 8. Io dunque; 9a. La cerco in vano; 9b. Semplicetto!; 10. Ah, infedele; 11a. Regina: il tuo soggiorno; 11b. Sì, son quella!; 12. Se nemico mi fossi; 13a. Bradamente favella?; 13b. La bocca vaga; 14. A quai strani perigli; 15a. Tornami a vagheggiar; 15b. Gavotte - Sarabande - Menuet - Gavotte. ACT 2: 16a. Musette—Menuet; 16b. Col celarvi; 16c. Qual portento; 16d. Pensa a chi geme; 17a. Qual odio ingiusto; 17b. Vorrei vendicarmi; 18a. Chi scopre al mio pensiero; 18b. Mi lusinga il dolce affetto; 19. S'acquieti il rio; 20. Ama, sospira; 21a. Non scorgo nel tuo viso; 21b. Mio bel tesoro; 22a. Reina: io cerco in vano; 22b. Tra speme e timore; 23a. Reina, sei tradita; 23b. Ah! mio cor! schernito sei!; 24. Or, che dici; 25. È un folle; 26. Ed è ver che mi narri?; 27. Verdi prati, selve amene; 28a. Ah! Ruggiero crudel; 28b. Ombre pallide; 29. Ballet (Dream Music). ACT 3: 30. Sinfonia; 31a. Voglio amar; 31b. Credete al mio dolore; 31c. M'inganna, me n'avveggo; 31d. Un momento di contento; 32a. Molestissimo incontro!; 32b. Ma quando tornerai; 33a. Tutta d'armate squadre; 33b. Sta nell'Ircana; 34a. Vanne tu seco ancora; 34b. All'alma fedel; 35a. Niuna forza lo arresta; 35b. Mi restano le lagrime; 36a. Sin per le vie del sole; 36b. Già vicino è il momento; 36c. Barbara! Io ben lo so; 37a. Le lusinghe; 37b. Non è amor; 38. Prendi e vivi; 39a. Dall'orror di notte cieca; 39b. Ballet; 39c. Dopo tante amare pene.
Cpte A. Auger, D. Jones, K. Kuhlmann, E. Harrhy, P. Kwella, M. Davies, J. Tomlinson, Op Stage Chor, City of London Baroque Sinfonia, R. Hickox (r1985) (11/88) (EMI) Ⓓ [3] **CDS7 49771-2**
1. ASMF, N. Marriner *Concert* (2/92) (DECC) Ⓓ **430 261-2DM**
1. ASMF, K. Sillito (r1993) *Concert* (8/94) (CAPR) Ⓓ **10 420**
1, 28a, 28b, 29. K. te Kanawa, AAM, C. Hogwood *Concert* (8/94) (PHIL) Ⓓ **434 992-2PH**
15. K. Battle, ASMF, N. Marriner *Concert* (7/90) (EMI) Ⓓ **CDC7 49179-2**
15a, 31b E. Kirkby, AAM, C. Hogwood (r1991) *Concert* (7/93) (L'OI) Ⓓ **436 132-2OH**
15b Halle Op House Handel Fest Orch, H. Arman (r1994) *Concert* (6/95) (CAPR) Ⓓ **10 547**
18b, 27, 33b A. Murray, OAE, C. Mackerras (r1994) *Concert* (8/95) (FORL) Ⓓ **UCD16738**
27. J. Kowalski, CPE Bach Orch, Hartmut Haenchen *Concert* (3/88) (CAPR) Ⓓ **10 213**
27. J. Bowman, King's Consort, R. King *Concert* (12/91) (HYPE) Ⓓ **CDA66483**

Alessandro—opera: 3 acts (1726—London) (Lib. Rolli)
EXCERPTS: 1. Overture; 2a. ACT 1: E tanto ancor s'indugia; 2b. Sinfonia; 3a. Grazie all'eterno Giove; 3b. Fra la stragi; 4. Che vidi!; 5a. Ecco Tassile; 5b. Quanto dolce amor saria; 5c. Ne'trofei d'Alessandro; 5d. Lusinghe più care; 5e. Sventurato ch'io sono!; 5f. Vibra, cortese Amor, un'altro strale; 6a. Fra le guerre; 6b. Apprestasti, oh Cleone; 7a. Dalla vittoria; 7b. No, più soffrir; 8a. Vilipese bellezze; 8b. Men fedele; 8c. Si, lusingando; 8d. Un lusinghiero; 9a. Tu, che Rossane adori; 9b. Pregi son; 9c. Sempre sel suo valor; 9d. A sprone, a fren leggiero; 14a. Sinfonia; 14b. Al magnanimo; 14c. Primo motor; 14d. Figlio del Re; 14e. Placa l'alma; 14f. Fra gli uomini; 14g. Da un breve riposo. ACT 2: 15a. Solitudini amate; 15b. Aure, fonti; 16a. Eccola in preda al sonno; 16b. Vano amore; 17a. Tiranna passion; 17b. Sempre fido e disprezzato; 17c. Pur troppo veggio; 17d. Che tiranna d'Amor; 18a. Qui aspetto l'inconstante; 18b. Alla sua gabbia; 19a. Vincitor generoso; 19b. Risolvo abbandonar; 19c. Finto sereno; 19d. La cervetta nei lacci avvolta; 20. Dopo il sublime onor; 21. Oh Dei!; 22a. Sire, il popol già vento; 22b. Il cor mio; 22c. Svanisci, oh reo; 22d. Dica il falso. ACT 3: 23a. Sfortunato è il mio valore; 23b. L'adulador s'appressa; 24a. Rendetti, o muori; 24b. Saro qual vento; 25a. La resa liberta; 25b. Si, m'e caro imitar; 25c. Sento un'inferno; 25d. Brilla nell'alma; 26a. Qual tormento crudel; 26b. L'amor, che per te sento; 27a. E qual fisso pensier; 27b. Pupille amati; 27c. Numi eterni; 27d. Tempesta e calma; 28a. D'uom fiero nel soglio; 28b. Chi osera traditore; 28c. Prove sono di grandezza; 29a. Spegni o supremo; 29b. Si festeggi il bel giorno; 29c. In generoso onor.
Cpte R. Jacobs, S. Boulin, I. Poulenard, J. Nirouët, S. Varcoe, G. de Mey, R. Bollen, Petite Bande, S. Kuijken (2/91) (DHM) Ⓓ [3] **GD77110**
26b L. Saffer, Philh Baroque Orch, N. McGegan *Concert* (12/91) (HARM) Ⓓ **HMU90 7036**

Almira—opera: 3 acts (1705—Hamburg) (Lib. F. C Feustking, after G Pamcieri)
Rigaudon Queen's Hall Orch, Henry Wood (r1937) *Concert* (1/94) (BEUL) Ⓓ **1PD3**

Amadigi di Gaula—opera: 3 acts (1715—London) (Lib. Haym)
EXCERPTS: 1. Overture. ACT 1: 2a. Or che di negro ammanto; 2b. Pugnero contro del fato; 3a. Oh notte! oh cara notte; 3b. Notte amica dei riposi; 3c. Che miro; 4a. Et tu cerchi fuggir?; 4b. Non sa temere; 5a. Il crudel m'abbandona; 5b. Ah! spietato!; 6a. Risveglian queste fiamme; 6b. Vado, corro al mio tesoro; 7a. Deh! ferma, oh Dio!; 7b. Agitato il cor mi sento; 7c. Sinfonia; 8a. Cieli, che fia?; 8b. Gioie, venite in sen; 8c. In questo istante; 8d. E si dolce il mio contento; 8e. Andiamo ora, mio ben; 8f. Oh caro mio tesor; 9a. Cieli! Numi!; 9b. Io godo, scherzo, e rido; 10a. Ferma, deh!; 10b. O rendetemi il mio bene; 11a. Io ramingo men vado; 11b. Sussurrate, onde vezzose; 11c. Numi! che veggio?; 12. Svenne Amadigi; 13a. Cieli! che sara mai?; 13b. S'estinto e l'idol mio; 13c. Ma, qual scampo; 13d. T'amai, quant'il mio cor; 13e. Che mai creduto havria; 13f. Ti pentirai, crudel!; 14a. Dunque! colei; 14b. Crudel, tu non farai; 15a. D'un sventurato amante; 15b. Pena tiranna; 16a. Arresta, oh Prence!; 16b. Se tu brami di godere; 17. Ma, se questo no basta; 18a. Amadigi, mio bene!; 18b. Tu mia speranza; 18c. Ma qui il rival!; 19a. Cieli! Numi! soccorso; 19b. Afannami, torementami; 20a. Mi dreide l'amante; 20b. Destero dall'empia Dite. ACT 3: 21a. Dove mi guida; 21b. Dolve vita del mio petto; 22a. Sento, ne so che sia; 22b. Vanne lungi dal mio petto; 23a. Se t'offese Oriana; 23b. Cangia al fine; 24. Han'penetrato; 25a. Cieli! ingiusti, e inclementi; 25b. Addio, crudo Amadigi!; 25c. Che orrore!; 25d. Sinfonia; 26a. Son finiti i tormenti; 26b. Sento la gioia; 26c. Godete omai felici; 26d. Godete, oh cori amanti; 27. Ballo.
Cpte N. Stutzmann, J. Smith, E. Harrhy, B. Fink, P. Bertin, Musiciens du Louvre, M. Minkowski (9/91) (ERAT) Ⓓ [2] **2292-45490-2**
5b R. White, City of London Baroque Sinfonia, I. Bolton *Concert* (12/91) (VIRG) Ⓓ **VJ7 59644-2**
15b J. Bowman, King's Consort, R. King *Concert* (12/91) (HYPE) Ⓓ **CDA66483**

Arianna in Creta—opera (1734—London) (Lib. cpsr)
Mirami; Qual leon L. Hunt, Philh Baroque Orch, N. McGegan *Concert* (3/93) (HARM) Ⓓ **HMU90 7056**

Ariodante—opera: 3 acts (1735—London) (Lib. adapted from Salvi)
EXCERPTS: 1. Overture. ACT ONE: 2a. Vezzi, lusinghe, e brio; 2b. Ami dunque, o signora?; 3a. Ginevra?; 3b. Orrida agli occhi miei; 4a. Orgogliosa beltade!; 4b. Apri le luci, e mira; 5a. Mie speranze, che fate?; 5b. Coperta la frode; 6a. Qui d'amor; 6b. T'amerò dunque sempre; 6c. Prendi da questa mano; 7a. Non vi turbate; 7b. Volate, amori; 8a. Vanne pronto, Odoardo; 8b. Voli colla sua tromba; 9a. Oh! felice mio core!; 9b. Con l'ali di costanza; 10a. Conosco il merto tuo; 10b. Spero per voi; 11a. Dalinda, in occidente; 11b. Del mio sol vezzosi rai; 12a. Ah! che quest'alma amante; 12b. Il primo ardor; 13a. Pare, ovunque m'aggiri; 13b. E qual propizia stella; 13c. Sinfonai pastorale (Il ballo); 13d. Se rinasce nel mio cor; 13e. Si godete al vostro amor; 13f. Ballet. ACT TWO: 14a. Preludio (Notte con lume di luna); 14b. Di Dalinda l'amore; 15a. Tu preparati a morire; 15b. Ginevra?; 15c. Tu vivi, e punito; 16a. E vivo ancora?; 16b. Scherza infida in grembo al drudo; 17a. Lo stral ferì nel segno; 17b. Se tanto piace al cor; 18a. Felice fu il mio inganno; 18b. Se l'inganno

sortisce felice; 19a. Andiam, fidi, al consiglio; 19b. Invida sorte avara; 20a. Mi palpita il core; 20b. Sta' lieta, o principessa!; 21a. Mio Re!; 21b. Il tuo sangue; 22. Quante sventure un giorno sol ne porta!; 23a. A me impudica?; 23b. Il mio crudel martoro; 23c. Ballet; 23d. Che vidi? Oh Dei! ACT THREE: 24a. Numi! Lasciarmi vivere; 24b. Perfidi! io son tradita!; 24c. Cieca notte, infidi sguardi; 25a. Ingrato Polinesso!; 25b. Neghittosi, or voi che fate?; 26a. Sire, deh, non negare; 26b. Dover, giustizia, amor; 27. Or venga a me la figlia; 28a. Io ti bacio; 28b. Figlia, da dubbia sorte; 28c. Al sen ti stringo; 29a. Così mi lascia il padre?; 29b. Si, morrò, ma l'onor mio; 30. Arrida il cielo alla giustizia; 31. Dopo notte, atra e funesta; 32a. Dalinda! ecco risorge; 32b. Dite spera, e son contento; 33a. Da dubbia infausta sorte; 33b. Manca, oh Dei!; 34a. Fuglia! innocente figlia!; 34b. Bramo aver mille vite... 35a. Ognuno acclami bella virtute; 35b. Ballet; 35c. Sa trionfar ognor.

Cpte J. Baker, E. Mathis, N. Burrowes, J. Bowman, D. Rendall, S. Ramey, A. Oliver, London Voices, ECO, R. Leppard (r1978) (12/94) (PHIL) ① [3] **442 096-2PM3**

1. ASMF, N. Marriner *Concert* (2/92) (DECC) ① **430 261-2DM**

1. ASMF, K. Sillito (r1993) *Concert* (8/94) (CAPR) ① **10 420**

13c AAM, C. Hogwood *Concert* (8/94) (PHIL) ① **434 992-2PH**

16b J. Bowman, King's Consort, R. King *Concert* (12/91) (HYPE) ① **CDA66483**

16b, 31. A. Murray, OAE, C. Mackerras (r1994) *Concert* (8/95) (FORL) ① **UCD16738**

25b E. Kirkby, AAM, C. Hogwood (r1991) *Concert* (7/93) (L'OI) ① **436 132-2OH**

31. C. Watkinson, Amsterdam Bach Sols, J.W. de Vriend *Concert* (3/89) (ETCE) ① **KTC1064**

31. J. Larmore, Lausanne CO, J. López-Cobos (r1994) *Concert* (12/95) (TELD) ① **4509-96800-2**

Atalanta—opera: 3 acts (1736—London) (Lib. adapted from Valeriano)

EXCERPTS: 1. Overture. ACT 1: 2. Care selve, ombre beate; 3. Sempre ti lagni; 4a. Ecco Aminta!; 4b. Lascia ch'io parta solo; 5a. Ch'io rimanga con te?; 5b. S'è tuo piacer; 6a. Perchè sospesa; 6b. Impara, ingrata; 7a. Ah! Che purtroppo adoro; 7b. Come alla tortorella langue; 8a. Al varco, oh pastori!; 8b. Oh Tirsi, e tu; 9a. Cerchi in vano la morte; 9b. Sinfonia; 9c. Trattenetelo, og fidi; 9d. Riportai gloriosa palma; 10a. Ah! che tu sei la fera; 10b. Non sarà poco. ACT 2: 11. Oggi rimbombano di feste; 12a. Sei pur sola una volta; 12b. Lassa! ch'io t'ho perduta; 13. Amarilli?; 14a. Ah! ch'io ancora; 14b. Si, sì, mel raccorderò; 15a. Il mio caro pastore; 15b. Soffri in pace il tuo dolore; 16a. E non moro d'affanno?; 16b. Di ad Irene, tiranna; 17a. Ma giunge il caro mio; 17b. M'allontano, sdegnose pupille; 18a. Poveri affetti miei!; 18b. Se nasce un rivoletto. ACT 3: 19. Sinfonia; 20a. E dalla man di Tirsi; 20b. Bench'io non sappia ancor; 21a. Sono Irene?; 21b. Diedi il core ad altra Ninfa; 22a. Ohimè! che pene!; 22b. Ben'io sento l'ingrata; 23. Oh! del crudo mio bene; 24a. Io vo morir; 24b. Custodite, o dolci sogni; 24c. Io vo morir; 25a. Re Meleagro; 25b. Oh, forza del destin!; 25c. Carol/Cara!; 25d. Sinfonia; 26a. Del supremo Tonante; 26b. Sol prova contenti; 26c. Dalla stirpe degli Eroi; 26d. Con voce giuliva; 26e. Gridiam tutti!; 26f. Sonifonia; 26g. Viva la face, viva l'amor; 26h. Gavotta; 26i. Con voce giuliva.

2. A. Auger, Mostly Mozart Orch, G. Schwarz *Concert* (11/86) (DELO) ① **DE3026**

2. E. Norena, orch, J. Messner (r1938) *Concert* (3/91) (PREI) ① **89041**

2. F. Quartararo, RCA Victor Orch, J-P. Morel (r1947) *Concert* (4/92) (EMI) ① [7] **CHS7 69741-2(1)**

2. L. Price, RCA Italiana Op Orch, F. Molinari-Pradelli *Concert* (12/92) (RCA) ① [4] **09026 61236-2**

2. J. McCormack, E. Schneider (r1924: Eng) *Concert* (5/93) (MMOI) ① **CDMOIR418**

7b K. Ferrier, P. Spurr (bp1949: Eng) *Concert* (6/92) (DECC) ① **433 473-2DM**

Berenice—opera: 3 acts, HWV38 (1737—London)

EXCERPTS: 1. Overture; 1a. Minuet.

1. AAM, C. Hogwood *Concert* (12/83) (L'OI) ① **410 553-2OH**

1. Y. Menuhin (vn/dir), C. Ferras *Concert* (1/89) (EMIL) ① **CDZ114**

1. ASMF, K. Sillito (r1993) *Concert* (8/94) (CAPR) ① **10 420**

1a ASMF, N. Marriner *Concert* (10/91) (DECC) ① **430 500-2DWO**

Comus—incidental music (1745—Exton, Leicestershire) (Lib. Milton)

EXCERPTS; 1. There in blissful shades and bow'rs; 2. Happy, happy, happy plains!; 3. There sweetest flowers of mingled hue; 4. Happy, happy, happy plains!; 5. There youthful Cupid, high advanc'd; 6. Happy, happy, happy plains!.

P. Kwella, M. Cable, D. Thomas, AAM, C. Hogwood (r1980) *Alceste.* (11/94) (L'OI) ① **443 183-2OM**

Ezio—opera: 3 acts (1732—London) (Lib adapted from Metastasio)

Perchè tanto tormento? Se un bell'ardire; Follè colui; Nasce al bosco; Che indegno! Già risonar D. Thomas, Philh Baroque Orch, N. McGegan *Concert* (8/90) (HARM) ① **HMU90 7016**

Tergi l'ingiuste lagrime P. Domingo, National PO, E. Kohn *Concert* (11/90) (EMI) ① **CDC7 54053-2**

Flavio, Rè di Longobardi—opera: 3 acts (1723—London) (Lib. Haym)

Cpte J. Gall, D.L. Ragin, L. Lootens, B. Fink, C. Högman, G. Fagotto, U. Messthaler, Ens 415, R. Jacobs (r1989) (7/90) (HARM) ① [2] **HMC90 1312/3**

Amor, nel mio penar D. Minter, Philh Baroque Orch, N. McGegan *Concert* (4/88) (HARM) ① **HMC90 5183**

Amor nel mio penar; Rompo i lacci A. Köhler, Halle Op House Handel Fest Orch, H. Arman (r1994) *Concert* (6/95) (CAPR) ① **10 547**

Chi mai l'intende ... Amante stravagante L. Saffer, Philh Baroque Orch, N. McGegan *Concert* (12/91) (HARM) ① **HMU90 7036**

Overture ECCO, E. Aadland *Concert* (12/91) (ASV) ① **CDDCA766**

Floridante—opera: 3 acts (1721—London) (Lib. Rolli, after Silvani)

Cpte D. Minter, M. Zádori, I. Gáti, J. Moldvay, A. Markert, K. Farkas, Capella Savaria, N. McGegan (pp1990) (1/93) (HUNG) ① [3] **HCD31304/6**

Alma mia E. Pinza, F. Kitzinger (r1940) *Concert* (9/93) (RCA) ① **09026 61245-2**

Bramo te sola; Se dolce m'era gia N. Stutzmann, Hanover Band, R. Goodman *Concert* (3/93) (RCA) ① **09026 61205-2**

Excs N. Argenta, I. Attrot, C. Robbin, L. Maguire, M. Braun, Tafelmusik, A. Curtis (hpd/dir) (1/93) (CBC) ① **SMCD5110**

Giulio Cesare, 'Julius Caesar'—opera: 3 acts, HWV17 (1724—London) (Lib. Haym)

EXCERPTS: 1a. Overture. ACT 1: 1b. Viva, il nosto Alcide; 2. Presto omai l'Egizia terra; 3. Empio, dirò, tu sei; 4. Priva son d'ogni conforto; 5. Svegliatevi nel core; 6. Non disperar, chi sa?; 7. L'empio sleale, indegno; 8. Alma del gran Pompeo; 9. Non è si vago e bello; 10. Tutto può donna vezzosa; 11. Nel tu seno; 12. Cara speme, questo core; 13. Tu la mia stella sei; 14. Va tacito e nascosto; 15. Tu sei il cor di questo core; 16. Son nata a lagrimar. ACT 2: 17. V'adoro, pupille; 18. Se in fiorito ameno prato; 19. Deh piangete, oh mesti lumi; 20. Se a me non sei crudele; 21. Sì spietata, il tuo rigore; 22. Cessa omai di sospirare!; 23. L'angue offeso mai riposa; 24. Venere bella, per un istante; 25. Al lampo dell'armi; 26. Che sento? oh Dio!; 27. Se pietà di me non senti; 28. Belle dea di questo core; 29. L'aure che spira. ACT 3: 30. Dal fulgor di questa spada; 31a. Sinfonia; 31b. Domerò la tua fierezza; 32. Piangerò, la sorte mia; 33. Dall' ondoso periglio; 34. Quel torrente, che cade dal monte; 35. La giustizia; 36. Voi, che mie fide ancelle; 37. Da tempeste il legno infranto; 38. Non ha più che temere; 39a. Sinfonia and March; 39b. Caro! Più amabile beltà; 40. Ritorni omai.

Cpte J. Baker, V. Masterson, Sarah Walker, D. Jones, J. Bowman, J. Tomlinson, C. Booth-Jones, D. James, ENO Chor, ENO Orch, C. Mackerras (Eng: ed. Mackerras) (5/89) (EMI) ① [3] **CMS7 69760-2**

Cpte J. Larmore, B. Schlick, B. Fink, M. Rørholm, D.L. Ragin, F. Zanasi, O. Lallouette, D. Visse, Cologne Concerto, R. Jacobs (Appendix; Qui perde un momento - 1725 vers) (4/92) (HARM) ① [4] **HMC90 1385/7**

Cpte W. Berry, L. Popp, C. Ludwig, F. Wunderlich, K.C. Kohn, H.G. Nöcker, H.B. Ernst, M. Proebstl, Stuttgart Rad Chor, Munich PO, F. Leitner (bp1965: Ger) (3/95) (ORFE) ① [3] **C351943D**

5. P. Domingo, National PO, E. Kohn *Concert* (11/90) (EMI) ① **CDC7 54053-2**

5. P. Domingo, National PO, E. Kohn (r1989) *Concert* (6/94) (EMI) ① **CDC5 55017-2**

5, 12, 23, 29, 35. L. Hunt, Philh Baroque Orch, N. McGegan *Concert* (3/93) (HARM) ① **HMU90 7056**

6, 13, 17, 31a, 32. K. te Kanawa, AAM, C. Hogwood *Concert* (8/94) (PHIL) ① **434 992-2PH**

9. B. Fassbaender, Stuttgart RSO, H. Graf *Concert* (11/86) (ORFE) ① **C096841A**

9, 14. D. Minter, Philh Baroque Orch, N. McGegan *Concert* (4/88) (HARM) ① **HMC90 5183**

13, 39b I. Seefried, D. Fischer-Dieskau, Berlin RSO, K. Böhm (r1960) *Concert* (9/93) (DG) ① [2] **437 677-2GDO2**

14. J. Kowalski, CPE Bach Orch, Hartmut Haenchen *Concert* (3/88) (CAPR) ① **10 213**

14. A. Köhler, Halle Op House Handel Fest Orch, H. Arman (r1994) *Concert* (6/95) (CAPR) ① **10 547**

14, 18. N. Stutzmann, Hanover Band, R. Goodman *Concert* (3/93) (RCA) ① **09026 61205-2**

14, 18, 32, 33. A. Murray, OAE, C. Mackerras (r1994) *Concert* (8/95) (FORL) ① **UCD16738**

14, 25. J. Bowman, King's Consort, R. King *Concert* (12/91) (HYPE) ① **CDA66483**

17. C. Ludwig, Berlin SO, H. Stein (Ger) *Concert* (9/92) (EMI) ① [4] **CMS7 64074-2(2)**

26, 27, 32, 37. L. Saffer, Philh Baroque Orch, N. McGegan *Concert* (12/91) (HARM) ① **HMU90 7036**

32. A. Auger, Mostly Mozart Orch, G. Schwarz *Concert* (11/86) (DELO) ① **DE3026**

32. L. Popp, ECO, G. Fischer (r1967) *Concert* (10/88) (EMI) ① **CDM7 69546-2**

32. K. Battle, ASMF, N. Marriner *Concert* (7/90) (EMI) ① **CDC7 49179-2**

32. A.S. von Otter, Drottningholm Baroque Ens, A. Öhrwall *Concert* (10/91) (PROP) ① **PRCD9008**

32. K. Battle, M. Garrett (pp1991) *Concert* (7/92) (DG) ① **435 440-2GH**

32. M. Forrester, Vienna St Op Orch, R. Zeller *Concert* (12/92) (CBC) ① **PSCD2002**

32. A. Roocroft, LPO, F. Welser-Möst *Concert* (10/94) (EMI) ① **CDC5 55090-2**

Giustino—opera: 3 acts (1737—London) (Wds. after N. Beregani)

EXCERPTS: 1. Overture. ACT ONE: 1a. Tema il nemico; 1b. Viva Augusto eterno impero; 1c. Ah! mio Sovrano Augusto; 2a. Vitaliano, il di cui Nome; 2b. Un vostro sguardo; 3a. Arianna, che pensi?; 3b. Da tuoi begl'occhi impara; 4a. Può ben nascer tra li Boschi; 4b. Ah! perché non poss'io; 4c. Bel ristoro de'mortali; 5a. Corri, vola, a'tuoi Trofei; 5b. Chi mi chiama alla gloria?; 5c. Se parla nel mio cor; 6a. Cieli! Numi soccorso!; 6b. Sinfonia; 6c. Oh! eterni Numi!; 6d. Nacque al Bosco, nacque al Prato; 7a. Amanzio!; 7b. È Virtute insin la frode; 8a. Leggo nel tuo sembiante; 8b. Allor, ch'io forte avrò; 9a. Sia fausta ognor la sorte; 9b. Non si vanti un'alma audace; 10a. All'armi, o Guerrieri; 10b. Signor, ti arrise il Fato; 11. Vanne sì, superba và; 12a. Dunque si poco temi; 12b. Mio dolce amato Sposo. ACT TWO: 13. Sinfonia; 14. A Dispetto dell'Onde; 15a. Questa è la cruda Spiaggia; 15b. Ritrosa belezza; 16a. Numi! che'l Ciel reggete; 16b. Sinfonia; 16c. Respiro: e'tutto deggio; 17a. Mio bel tesoro!; 17b. Ma quale orrido Mostro; 18. Per Voi soave e bella; 19. Troppo fosti, o mio core; 20a. Ah! quai crudeli pene; 20b. Sventurata Navicella; 21a. Verdi Lauri; 21b. Vieni, barbaro, altero; 21c. Sull'Altar di questo Nume; 22a. Già il valor di Giustino; 22b. Quel Torrente che s'innalza. ACT THREE: 23. Sinfonia; 24a. Amici, tutto devo; 24b. Il piacer della vendetta; 24c. Signor', a'tuoi Trionfi; 24d. O fiero e rio sospetto; 25a. Generoso Giustino, oh! quanto ammiro; 25b. Zeffiretto, che scorre nel prato; 26a. E fia ver, che infedele; 26b. Di Re sdegnato l'ira tremenda; 27a. Qual'infernal veleno; 27b. Il mio cor già piu non sà; 28a. Giustino, anima mia!; 28b. Augelletti garruletti; 29a. Riusci il bel disegno; 29b. Dall'occaso in oriente; 30. Fortuna, m'hai tradito!; 31a. Prima che splenda in oriente il sole; 31b. Trattien l'acciar; 31c. Qual voce ascolto; 31d. Sollevar'il mondo oppresso; 32. Or che cinto ho il crin d'alloro; 33a. Qual marzial fragor?; 33b. Olà? Renditi a me!; 33c. Ti rendo questo cor; 33d. Signor, se vile intercessor non sono; 33e. In braccio a te la calma.

Cpte M. Chance, D. Röschmann, D. Kotoski, J. Gondek, D. Ely, J. Lane, M. Padmore, D. Minter, Halle Cantamus Chbr Ch, Freiburg Baroque Orch, N. McGegan (r1994) (12/95) (HARM) ① [3] **HMU90 7130/2**

Adagio AAM, C. Hogwood *Concert* (8/94) (PHIL) ① **434 992-2PH**

5b, 5c J. Kowalski, CPE Bach Orch, Hartmut Haenchen *Concert* (3/88) (CAPR) ① **10 213**

5c, 25b J. Bowman, King's Consort, R. King *Concert* (12/91) (HYPE) ① **CDA66483**

The **Gods Go a'Begging—ballet (1928—London)** (music taken from various stage works: ed/arr Beecham)

1. Introduction (Admeto, Act 2—Overture); 2. First Dance (Teseo—Overture); 3. Minuet (Alcina—ballet music); 4. Hornpipe (Concerto grosso, Op. 6/7—mvt 5); 5. Musette (Il Pastor Fido, Act 2); 6. Second Dance (Alcina, Act 1—Questo e il cielo); 7. Larghetto (Alcina, Act 2—Dream music); 8. Tambourine (Alcina, Act 3—Final Dance); 9. Gavotte (Alcina—Overture; Il Pastor Fido, Act 2—Dance); 10. Sarabande (Terpsichore).

3, 4. LPO, T. Beecham (r1937) *Concert* (6/94) (VAI) ① **VAIA1045**

5. LPO, T. Beecham (r1934) *Concert* (6/94) (VAI) ① **VAIA1045**
8, 10. LPO, T. Beecham (r1933) *Concert* (6/94) (VAI) ① **VAIA1045**

Imeneo—opera: 3 acts (1740—London) (Lib. adapted from Stampiglia)
Cpte J. Ostendorf, J. Baird, D. Fortunato, B. Hoch, J. Opalach, Brewer Chbr Chor, Brewer CO, R. Palmer (8/93) (VOX) ① [2] **115451-2**

Muzio Scevola (Act 3)—opera: 3 acts (1721—London) (Lib Rolli. Act 1, Amadei; Act 2, Bononcini)
EXCERPTS: 1. Overture. ACT 3: 2a. Doppo l'arrivi degl'illustri; 2b. Lungo pensar e dubitar; 3a. Eccessi di virtu; 3b. Soave affetti miei; 4a. Pensoso a passo lento; 4b. Pupille sdegnose!; 4c. Io altro regno; 4d. Dimmi, crudele Amore; 4e. Chi mai più giusto sdegno; 4f. Volate più dei venti; 5a. Mio cor, pria ti ricorda; 5b. Il confine della vita; 6a. Patria della bellezza; 6b. Non ti fidar; 7b. Come, se ti vedro; 7c. Oh come passi al coer; 7d. Con lui volate; 8a. Gia m'udiste; 8b. Spera che tra le care; 9a. Ahi che pur troppo; 9b. Ah, dolce nome; 10a. Lasciate d'inseguir; 10b. Vivo senza alma; 11a. Piene di lor contento; 11b. Ma come amar e come mai fidar; 11c. Dono d'alta fortuna; 11d. Romani, udite!; 11e. Unica erede; 12. Si sara più dolce amore.
Cpte J. Ostendorf, D. Fortunato, J. Baird, E. Mills, J. Lane, A. Matthews, F. Urrey, Brewer CO, R. Palmer *Concert* (3/93) (NEWP) ① [2] **NPD85540**
4c, 4d L. Hunt, Philh Baroque Orch, N. McGegan *Concert* (3/93) (HARM) ① **HMU90 7056**

The **Origin of Design—ballet (1932—London)** (music taken from various stage works: arr/orch Beecham)
EXCERPTS: 1. Bourrée (Ariodante); 2. Rondeau (Ariodante); 3. Gigue (Terpsichore); 4. Minuet (Il pastor fido); 5. Musette (Ariodante); 6. Battle and Finale.
1-3, 5, 6. LPO, T. Beecham (r1933) *Concert* (6/94) (VAI) ① **VAIA1045**
4. LPO, T. Beecham (r1934) *Concert* (6/94) (VAI) ① **VAIA1045**

Orlando—opera: 3 acts, HWV31 (1733—London) (Lib. adapted from Capece, after L. Arioso)
EXCERPTS: 1. Overture. ACT 1: 2. Giergliofici eterni; 3a. Stimulato dalla gloria; 3b. Purgalo ormai da effeminati sensi; 3c. Sinfonia; 3d. Lascia Amor; 4a. Imagini funeste; 4b. Non fu già men forte Alcide; 5a. Quanto diletto avea; 5b. Io non so; 5c. Itene pur tremendo; 5d. Ho un certu rossore; 6a. M'hai vinto al fin; 6b. Ritornava al suo bel viso; 6c. Spera, mio ben; 6d. Chi possessore; 7a. Ecco Dorinda; 7b. Se il cor mai ti dirà; 8a. Povera me!; 8b. O care parolette; 9a. Noti a me sono; 9b. Se fedel vuoi; 10a. T'ubbirdirò, crudele; 10b. Fammi combattere; 11. Angelica,deh lascia; 12a. O Angelica, o Medoro; 12b. Consolati o bella. ACT 2: 13. Quando spieghi i tuoi tormenti; 14a. Perchè, gentil Dorinda; 14b. Se mi rivolgo al prato; 15a. E' questa la mercede; 15b. Cielo! Se tu il consenti; 16a. A qual rischio vi espone; 16b. Tra caligini profonde; 17a. Da queste amiche piante; 17b. Verdi allori sempre unito; 18a. Dopo tanti perigli; 18b. Non potrà dirmi ingrata; 19a. Dove, dove giudate, Furi; 19b. Verdi piante; 20a. Tutto a poter partire; 20b. Ah perfida, qui sei!; 21. Ohime! Che miro!; 22. Amor, caro amore; 23a. Ah Stigie larve!; 23b. Già latra Cerbero; 23c. Ma la Furia; 23d. Vaghe pupille, non piangete. ACT 3: 24. Sinfonia; 25a. Di Dorinda alle mura; 25b. Vorrei poterti amar; 26. Più obbligata gli sono; 27a. Pur ti trovo, o mio bene; 27b. Unisca amor in noi; 27c. Già lo stringo, gia l'abbraccio; 28a. Di Dorinda all'albergo; 28b. Così giusta è questa speme; 29a. S'è corrisposto un core; 29b. Amor è qual vento; 30a. Impari ognum da Orlando; 30b. O voi del mio poter; 30c. Sorge infausta una procella; 31. Dorinda, e perchè piangi?; 32a. Più non fuggir petrai; 32b. Finchè prendi ancora il sangue; 32c. Vieni—Vanne precipitando; 32d. Già per la man d'Orlando; 32e. Già l'ebro mio ciglio; 33a. Ecco il tempo prefisso!; 33b. Tu che del gran tonante; 33c. Sinfonia; 33d. Ah! non che fate signor?; 33e. Dormo ancora, o son desto?; 33f. Per fa mia diletta; 34a. Che vedo, oh dei!; 34b. Vinse incanti; 34c. Trionfa oggi'l mio cor.
Cpte J. Bowman, A. Auger, C. Robbin, E. Kirkby, D. Thomas, AAM, C. Hogwood (8/91) (L'OI) ① [3] **430 845-2OH3**
3d, 30a-c D. Thomas, Philh Baroque Orch, N. McGegan *Concert* (8/90) (HARM) ① **HMU90 7016**
10a, 10b, 15a, 15b, 23a-d, 32d, 32e D. Minter, Philh Baroque Orch, N. McGegan *Concert* (4/88) (HARM) ① **HMC90 5183**
10b, 15b A. Köhler, Halle Op House Handel Fest Orch, H. Arman (r1994) *Concert* (6/95) (CAPR) ① **10 547**
10b, 23a-c N. Stutzmann, Hanover Band, R. Goodman *Concert* (3/93) (RCA) ① **09026 61205-2**
23a A. Deller, Handel Fest Orch, A. Lewis (r1960) *Concert* (1/95) (VANG) ① **08.5069.71**

Ottone—opera: 3 acts (1723—London) (Lib. N. Haym)
EXCERPTS: 1. Overture. ACT 1: 2. Pur che regni; 3a. Chi più lento è di me?; 3b. La speranza è giunta in porto; 4a. Vien di Romano inclita figlia; 4b. Bel labbro formato; 5a. È tale Otton?; 5b. Falsa immagine; 6. Concerto; 7a. Te, che assalir le nostre navi osati; 7b. Del minacciar del vento; 8a. Tutto a più leite cure; 8b. Ritorna, o dolce amore; 9a. Anch'io sperai; 9b. Diresti poi così?; 10a. Tu la madre d'Otton; 10b. Pensa ad amare; 11a. Adelaide, di cui con tanta lode; 11b. Indietro, indietro; 12a. Giunge Otton?; 12b. Affanni del pensier; 13. Sinfonia; 14a. Cedi il ferro, o la vita; 14b. Tu puoi straziarmi; 15a. È di più mio rival?; 15b. Dell'onda ai fiero moti. ACT 2: 16. Sinfonia; 17a. Per berve spazio a me colui; 17b. Lascia, nel suo viso; 18a. (Ah! che più non resisto); 18b. Ah! tu non sai; 19a. Ah, Matilda, Matilda; 19b. Vieni, o figlio; 20. Spera sì; 21a. (Quegli, è certo il mio sposo); 21b. All'orror d'un duolo eterno; 22a. O illustre Teofane; 22b. Alla fama; 23a. Con gelosi sospetti; 23b. Dopo l'orrore; 24a. O grati orrori; 24b. S'io dir potessi; 25a. Dal gran sasso; 25b. Le profonde vie dell'onde; 26a. (Ode gente); 26b. Deh! non dir; 27. Già d'ogni interno; 28a. Odo il suono; 28b. Notte cara. ACT 3: 29. Dove sei; 30a. Già t'invola; 30b. Trema, tiranno; 31a. Io son tradito; 31b. Tanti affanni; 32. Sinfonia; 33a. Empi, al vostro attentato; 33b. D'innalzar i flutti; 34. Perchè in vita tornai?; 35a. Si, mi traete alme; 35b. Benchè mi sia crudele; 36a. Deh! ti trattiene; 36b. No, non temere, o bella; 37a. Pur cangiasti alla fin; 37b. Gode l'alma consolata; 38a. Uno de'servi miei; 38b. Nel suo sangue; 39. Matilda, arresta il piede; 40a. Frena, crudel; 40b. A'teneri affetti; 41a. Ma qual caso; 41b. Faccia ritorno l'antica pace.
Cpte D. Minter, L. Saffer, M. Dean, J. Gondek, R. Popken, P. Spence, Freiburg Baroque Orch, N. McGegan (3/93) (HARM) ① [3] **HMU90 7073/5**
Cpte J. Bowman, C. McFadden, M. George, J. Smith, D. Visse, C. Denley, King's Consort, R. King (r1993) (7/93) (HYPE) ① [3] **CDA66751/3**
Vinto è d'amor L. Popp, ECO, G. Fischer (r1967) *Concert* (10/88) (EMI) ① **CDM7 69546-2**
3b M. Forrester, Vienna St Op Orch, R. Zeller *Concert* (12/92) (CBC) ① **PSCD2002**
3b, 19b K. Ferrier, G. Moore (r1945: Eng) *Concert* (6/88) (EMI) ① **CDH7 61003-2**
5a, 5b, 12a, 12b L. Saffer, Philh Baroque Orch, N. McGegan *Concert* (12/91) (HARM) ① **HMU90 7036**
19b L. Hunt, Philh Baroque Orch, N. McGegan *Concert* (3/93) (HARM) ① **HMU90 7056**
31b J. Bowman, King's Consort, R. King *Concert* (12/91) (HYPE) ① **CDA66483**

Partenope—opera: 3 acts (1730—London) (Lib. adapted from Stampiglia)
EXCERPTS: 1. Overture. ACT 1: 2a. Tu dell'eccelse mura; 2b. Viva, viva, Partenope viva; 2c. Miei fidi arride il cielo; 3. Arsace—Armindo; 4a. Regina, in folte schiere; 4b. L'amor ed il destin; 4c. O Eurimene; 5a. Cavalier, se gli Dei; 5b. Se non ti sai spiegar; 5c. Armindo ardisci e prova; 5d. Voglio dire al mio tesoro; 6a. Ah! ch'un volto fatal; 6b. Un altra volta ancor; 6c. Rosmira, oh! Dio!; 6d. Sento amor con novi dardi; 7a. Stan pronit i miei guerrieri; 7b. T'appresta forse amore; 8. Signora—Armindo; 9. E di che reo son io?; 10a. E se giunge Eurimene?; 10b. Sei mia gioia; 10c. I novelli amor tuoi; 10d. Dimmi pietoso ciel; 11a. Ecco Emilio; 11b. Anch'io pugnar saprò; 12a. Arsace, tu sarai; 12b. Io ti levo l'impero dell'armi; 13a. Lascai deh!; 13b. E' figlio il mio timore; 14a. Prence, di te mi lagno; 14b. Io seguo sol fiero. ACT 2: 15a. Sinfonia; 15b. Forti mie schiere; 15c. Marcia; 15d. Ma le nemiche squadre; 15e. Con valorosa mano—Battaglia I; 15f. Soccorso—Battaglia II; 15g. Renditi, o pure estinto; 15h. Vi circondi la gloria; 16a. Contro un pudico amor; 16b. Barbaro fato si; 17a. Care mura in sei bel giorno; 17b. Emilio!—Alta Regina; 17c. Voglio amare infin ch'io moro; 18a. Ti bramo amico; 18b. E vuoi con dure tempre; 19a. Non più darsi in un petto; 19b. Furie son dell'alma mia; 20a. A prò di chi t'offese; 20b. Poterti dir vorrei; 21a. Regina—Arminda, ancora; 21b. Non chiedo o luci vaghe; 21c. Più d'ogn'altro; 21d. Qual farfalletta; 22. Quanto godo Eurimene; 23a. Rosmira mia; 23b. Furibondo spira il vento. ACT 3: 24a. Sinfonia; 24b. Regina ti compiace; 24c. Non è incauto mio consiglio; 25a. Partenope, Eurimene; 25b. Arscae, oh Dio!; 25c. Chi m'apre i lumi; 25d. Spera e godi o mio tesoro; 26a. Prencipe ardir; 26b. La speme ti consoli; 27a. Rosmira, dove ti guida; 27b. Ch'io parta; 27c. Oh Dio!; 27d. Quel volto mi piace; 28a. Ormonte, ti destino giudice; 28b. Nobil core, che ben ama; 29a. Non chiedo, o miei tromenti!; 29b. Ma quai note di mesti lamenti; 30. Cieli che miro; 31a. Ma Partenope vien; 31b. Un cor infedele si deve punir; 31c. Passo di duolo in duolo; 31d. Fatto è Amor un Dio d'inferno; 32a. Di bel desire avvampo; 32b. La gloria in nobil alma; 33a. Sinfonia; 33b. Regina, in queste arene; 33c. Si scherza sì; 33d. Arminda sia mio sposo; 33e. D'Imeneo le belle.
Cpte K. Laki, R. Jacobs, J.Y. Skinner, S. Varcoe, H. Müller-Molinari, M. Hill, Petite Bande, S. Kuijken (2/91) (DHM) ① [3] **GD77109**
23b N. Stutzmann, Hanover Band, R. Goodman *Concert* (3/93) (RCA) ① **09026 61205-2**

Il **Pastor Fido—opera: 3 acts (1712 rev 1734)** (Lib. Rossi)
EXCERPTS: 1. Overture. ACT 1: 2. Ah! infelice mia patria!; 3. D'amor a fier contrasti; 4. Lontan del mio tesoro; 5. Frode, sol a te rivolta; 6. Finchè un Zeffiro soave; 7. Quanto mai felici siete; 8. Non vo' mai seguitar; 9. Ballets: 9a. March; 9b. Pour les Chasseurs; 9c. Hunters' dance; 10. Oh! quanto bella gloria. ACT 2: 11. Caro amor; 13. Ho un non sò che nel cor; 14. Torni pure un bel splendore; 15. Finte labbra; 16. Sol nel mezzo risona del core; 17. Se in ombre nascosto; 18. Sì, rivedrò; 19. Scherza in mar la navicella; 20a. Accorrete, voi pastori; 21. Ballets: 21a. Shepherds' dance; 21b. Musette; 21c. Menuets I and II. ACT 3: 22. Sinfonia; 23. Oh! quanto bella gloria; 24. Sento nel sen; 25. Secondaste al fine; 26a. Oh! Mirtillo, Mirtillo; 26b. Ah! non son io che parlo; 27a. Sciogliete quelle mani; 27b. Per te, mio dolce bene; 27c. Si unisce al tuo martir; 28a. Dell'empia frode il velo; 28b. Caro/Cara; 28c. Sciolga dunque al ballo; 29. Ballets: 29a. General dance; 29b. Gavotte; 29c. Ballet; 29d. Chorus and General Dance: Replicati al ballo.
9a-c, 21a-c, 29a-c Cologne Stravaganza *Concert* (12/92) (DENO) ① **CO-79250**

Poro, re dell'Indie—opera: 3 acts (1731—London) (Lib after Metastasio)
Cpte G. Banditelli, R. Bertini, B. Fink, G. Lesne, S. Naglia, R. Abbondanza, Europa Galante, F. Biondi (r1994) (11/94) (O111) ① [3] **OPS30-113/5**

Radamisto—opera: 3 acts, HWV12a (1720—London) (Lib. Haym)
EXCERPTS: 1. Overture. ACT ONE: 2. Sommi Dei; 3a. Reina, infausto avviso; 3b. Deh! fuggi un traditore; 4a. Seguirem dunque la crudele impresa; 4b. L'ingrato non amar; 5a. Ecco l'infido sposo; 5b. Tu vuoi ch'io parta; 6a. Il crudel odio tuo; 6b. Con la strage; 7a. Ove seguirmi vuoi; 7b. Cara sposa, amato bene; 8a. Ver le nemiche mura; 8b. Son contenta di morire; 9a. Seguila, o figlio!; 9b. Perfido, di a quell'empio tiranno; 10a. Fraarte, omai quel ferro; 10b. Son lievi le catene; 11a. Coraggio, amici!; 11b. Sinfonia (Battle Symphony); 12a. Già vint'è il nemico; 12b. Segni di crudeltà; 13a. Pur troppo è vero; 13b. Dopo l'orride procelle. ACT TWO: 14a. Sposo, vien meno il piè; 14b. Quando mai, spietata sorte; 15a. Oh crudo ciel!; 15b. Vuol ch'io serva; 16a. Prencipe generoso; 16b. Ombra cara di mia sposa; 17a. Mitiga il grave affanno; 17b. lascia pur amica spene; 18a. Oh senza esempio dispietata sorte!; 18b. Già che morir non posso; 19a. Signor...E che mi rechi?; 19b. Si che ti renderai; 20a. Nulla già di speranza; 20b. Fatemi, o cieli, almen; 21a. Questo vago giardin; 21b. La sorte, il ciel, amor; 22a. Adorato german, quanto più lieta; 22b. Vanne, sorella ingrata; 23a. Trà il german, trà lo sposo; 23b. Che farà quest'alma mia; 24. Troppo sofferse; 25a. Due seggi, olà!; 25b. Empio, perverso cor!; 26a. Ascolta, Ismen; 26b. Se teco vive il cor. ACT THREE: 27a. Stanco di più soffrir; 27b. S'adopri il braccio armato; 28. So ben che nel mio amore; 28a. So ben che nel mio maore; 28b. So ch'è vana la speranza; 29a. Non temo, idolo mio; 29b. Dolce bene di quest'alma; 30a. O della Tracia, o dell'Armenia; 30b. Vieni, d'empietà mostro; 30c. Vile! se mi dai vita; 31a. Mio Rè, mio Tiridate, ascolta; 31b. Barbaro! partirò; 32a. Farasmane la segua; 32b. Alzo al volo; 33a. Di Radamisto il capo?; 33b. Deggio dunque, oh Dio; 34a. Oh Dio! parte Zenobia; 34b. Qual nave smarrita; 35a. In questo tempio; 35b. O cedere o perir; 36a. Arrestatevi, o fidi; 36b. non ho più affanni; 37a. Festeggi omai la reggia; 37b. Un dì più felice.
Cpte R. Popken, J. Gondek, L. Saffer, D. Hanchard, M. Frimmer, M. Dean, N. Cavallier, Freiburg Baroque Orch, N. McGegan (hpd/dir) (r1993: 1720 ver) (6/94) (HARM) ① [3] **HMU90 7111/3**
Passacaille; Giga Halle Op House Handel Fest Orch, H. Arman (r1994) *Concert* (6/95) (CAPR) ① **10 547**

Così dunque sospiran; 6d. La turba adulatrice; 7a. Amici, troppo oscuro; 7b. Alla stragge, alla morte (reprise); 7c. Mà chi ritorna in vita; 7d. Oh Diva Hecate; 7e. Dite pace. ACT TWO: 8a. Padre, germano, e sposo; 8b. E ben dall'alta torre; 8c. Se m'ascolti; 9a. Mio Rè, l'ultimo sforzo; 9b. Se discordia ci disciolse; 10a. E così tu disprezzi; 10b. Sò ch'il Ciel ben spesso gode; 10c. Quanto più Melo ha sdegno; 10d. Sento il cor che lieto gode; 11a. Grazie al Cielo; 11b. Per le porte del tormento; 11c. Signor, tuo regio sangue; 11d. Alle sfere della gloria; 11e. Viva! viva e regni fortunato; 12a. Son tuo congiunto; 12b. Vado al campo; 12c. Mio sposo, ahi qual orror; 12d. In mille dolci modi; 12e. Parmi ch'un dolce; 12f. Vola l'augello. ACT THREE: 13. Sinfonia; 14a. Mi siegue la Regina; 14b. S'io cadrò per tuo consiglio; 15a. Melo, dov'è il tuo zelo?; 15b. Cuor di madre e cuor di moglia; 15c. A deluder le frodi; 15d. Sincero affetto; 16a. Per la segreta porta; 16b. Altomaro, si renda libera lo steccato!; 16c. Tiene Giove; 16d. Signor, qui giunge Argone; 16e. Tu caro, caro sei; 16f. Fugga da questo; 16g. Dopo l'ire si funeste.
Cpte D. Fortunato, J. Aler, J. Baird, D. Minter, N. Watson, J. Lane, R. Pellerin, Taghkanic Chorale, Amor Artis Orch, J. Somary (r1993)
(12/94) (NEWP) ① [2] NPD85575
3b E. Rethberg, orch (r1928) Concert
(2/95) (ROMO) ① [2] 81012-2
5a, 5b, 10c, 10d, 16b, 16c D. Thomas, Philh Baroque Orch, N. McGegan Concert
(8/90) (HARM) ① HMU90 7016
Tamerlano—opera: 3 acts (1724—London) (Lib. Haym)
Serav Asteria ... Se non mi vuol amar L. Saffer, Philh Baroque Orch, N. McGegan Concert
(12/91) (HARM) ① HMU90 7036
Teseo—opera: 5 acts (1713—London) (Lib. Haym, after Quinault)
EXCERPTS: 1. Overture. ACT 1: 2. Sia qual'vuole il mio fato; 3a. Clizia, son'gli Ateniesi; 3b. E pur' bello, in' nobil core; 4a. Ora svelaci Arcane; 4b. Deh' serbatè ò giusti Dei; 5a. Parte Agilea; 5b. Ti credo, si ben' mio; 5c. Commanda dunque ò bella; 5d. Ah! cruda gelosia!; 5e. Dunque all'affetto mio; 5f. Addio! mio caro mio; 6a. Serenatevi, oh luci belle!; 6b. Or'ch'affermito o il soglio; 6c. Ricordati, oh bella; 6d. Ah, che sol'er Teseo; 6e. M'adora l'idol mio. ACT 2: 7a. Dolce riposo, ed innocente pace!; 7b. L'infelice Medea; 7c. Quell'amor, ch'è nato à forza; 8a. Delle armi nostre; 8b. Si ti lascio; 9. Sire, tutto è periglio; 10a. Ogn'un acclami il nostro Alcide!; 10b. Amici, à bastanza nostrate il vostro affretto; 11a. Teseo, dove ten'vai!; 11b. Quanto che à mè siam' care; 11c. Ai vostri amori; 11d. Non so più che bramar; 12a. Ira, sdegno, e furore; 12b. O stringerò nel' sen. ACT 3: 13a. Risplendete, amiche stelle; 13b. Perdona, omai perdona; 13c. Più non cerca liberta; 14a. Quivi sarà frà poco; 14b. Vieni, torna, idolo mio; 14c. Teseo qui giunge; 15a. Pur ti riveggio al'fine; 15b. S'armi il fato, s'armi amore!; 16. Egeo di qui venir m'impose; 17a. Tu ben'sai Principessa; 17b. Numi, chi ci soccorre!; 17c. Deh'dammi aita Arcane; 17d. Ombre, sortite dall' eterna nottel; 17e. O ciel, che mai saral; 17f. Sibillando, ululando, fulminate, la rival. ACT 4: 18a. Sire, come imponesti; 18b. Voglio stragi; 18c. Amor per Agilea; 18d. Benchè tuoni e l'etra avvampi; 19a. Cruda, ed'ancor'non vuoi; 19b. E che mai veggio oh Dio!; 20b. E ancor su'gli occhi miei; 20c. Dal cupo baratro; 20d. S'arma contro di me tutto l'inferno?; 21a. Chi ritorna alla mia mente; 21b. Non so più che prendol; 22a. Agilea più non m'ama; 22b. Qual' tigre o qual' megera t'impresse; 22c. Tu piangi! e à me, l'ascondi!; 22d. Amarti si vorrei; 23a. Troppo un rè che t'adora; 23b. Chi di non più beato?; 24. Cara/caro, ti dono in pegno il cor. ACT 5: 25a. Dunque per vendicarmi; 25b. Morirò, ma vendicata; 25c. Scopria, mà non veduta; 26a. Questo vaso he miri; 26b. Non è da Rè quel cor; 26c. Ma del Popolo l'odio; 27a. Giuro per questo acciaro; 27b. Che miro oh Ciel!; 28a. Ami! perfida Medea!; 28b. Tegno in pugno; 28c. Signore in questo giorno; 28d. Unito à un puro affetto; 29. Essenti del mio sdegno; 30a. Soccorretici o Numi!; 30b. Il ciel gia si compiace; 30c. Goda ogn'alma in sel bel giorno.
Cpte E. James, J. Gooding, D. Jones, D.L. Ragin, C. Napoli, J. Gall, F. Bazola-Minori, Musiciens du Louvre, M. Minkowski
(3/93) (ERAT) ① [2] 2292-45806-2
Tolomeo, Rè di Egitto—opera: 3 acts (1728—London) (Lib. Haym)
EXCERPTS: 1. Overture; 2. Non lo dirò col labbro ('Silent worship'); 3a. Che più si tarda si trada omai; 3b. Stille amare; 4. Piangi pur.
1. G. Gifford (trans hpd) Concert
(5/90) (LIBR) ① LRCD156

2. T. Allen, J. Constable (Eng) Concert
(4/92) (GAMU) ① GAMD506
3a, 3b D. Minter, Philh Baroque Orch, N. McGegan Concert
(4/88) (HARM) ① HMC90 5183
4. D. Thomas, Philh Baroque Orch, N. McGegan Concert
(8/90) (HARM) ① HMU90 7016

HANDFORD, George (1582/85–1647) England

SECTION IV: VOCAL AND CHORAL
Now each creature—ayre (compiled 1609)
E. Kirkby, A. Rooley (pp1985) Concert
(6/87) (HYPE) ① CDA66186

HANDL, Jacob (1550–1591) Slovenia

SECTION IV: VOCAL AND CHORAL
O magnum mysterium—motet (4vv)
The Sixteen, H. Christophers Concert
(12/88) (HYPE) ① CDA66263
Pueri concinite—motet (4vv)
The Sixteen, H. Christophers Concert
(12/88) (HYPE) ① CDA66263
Resonet in laudibus—motet (4vv)
The Sixteen, H. Christophers Concert
(12/88) (HYPE) ① CDA66263
Trinity Coll Ch, Cambridge, R. Marlow Concert
(12/90) (CONI) ① CDCF501

HANFF, Johann Nicolaus (1665–1711/12) Germany

SECTION III: INSTRUMENTAL
Ach Gott, von Himmel sieh darein—chorale prelude
B. Coudurier Concert (10/89) (BNL) ① BNL112754
Auf meinen lieben Gott—chorale prelude
B. Coudurier Concert (10/89) (BNL) ① BNL112754
Ein feste Burg ist unser Gott—chorale prelude
B. Coudurier Concert (10/89) (BNL) ① BNL112754
Erbarm dich mein, o Herre Gott I—chorale prelude
B. Coudurier Concert (10/89) (BNL) ① BNL112754
Erbarm dich mein, o Herre Gott II—chorale prelude
B. Coudurier Concert (10/89) (BNL) ① BNL112754
Helft mir Gott's Güte preisen—chorale prelude
B. Coudurier Concert (10/89) (BNL) ① BNL112754
Wär Gott nicht mit uns diese Zeit—chorale prelude
B. Coudurier Concert (10/89) (BNL) ① BNL112754

HÄNSEL, Peter (1770–1831) Germany

SECTION II: CHAMBER
String Quintet in G
Zurich Chmbr Ens Czerny: Variations, Op.73.
(8/87) (JECK) ① JD608-2

HANSON, Howard (1896–1981) USA

SECTION I: ORCHESTRAL
Chorale and Fanfare—brass ensemble
LPO, J. Mester Concert (7/91) (KOCH) ① 37012-2
Concerto for Piano and Orchestra, Op. 36 (1948)
C. Rosenberger, Seattle SO, G. Schwarz Concert
(3/93) (DELO) ① DE3130
Dies Natalis I—orchestra (1967) (trans wind band, 1972)
Seattle SO, G. Schwarz (r1994) Concert
(5/95) (DELO) ① DE3160
Elegy in memory of Srge Koussevitzky (1956)
Seattle SO, G. Schwarz Concert
(3/90) (DELO) ① DE3073
Fanfare for the Signal Corps—brass ensemble (1942)
LPO, J. Mester Concert (7/91) (KOCH) ① 37012-2
Fantasy Variations on a Theme of Youth—piano and orchestra (1951)
C. Rosenberger, Seattle SO, G. Schwarz Concert
(2/91) (DELO) ① DE3092

Lux aeterna—symphonic poem, with viola obbligato, Op. 24 (1923)
Seattle SO, G. Schwarz (r1994) Concert
(5/95) (DELO) ① DE3160
Mosaics (1958)
Seattle SO, G. Schwarz Concert
(3/93) (DELO) ① DE3130
Pastorale—oboe, harp and strings, Op. 38 (1949) (arr cpsr from ob & pf work)
NY Chbr SO, G. Schwarz Concert
(7/92) (DELO) ① DE3105
Serenade—flute, harp and strings, Op. 36 (1945)
NY Chbr SO, G. Schwarz Concert
(7/92) (DELO) ① DE3105
Symphony No. 1 in E minor, 'Nordic', Op. 21 (1922)
Seattle SO, G. Schwarz Concert
(3/90) (DELO) ① DE3073
Eastman-Rochester Orch, H. Hanson Concert
(2/91) (MERC) ① 432 008-2MM
Symphony No. 2, 'Romantic', Op. 30 (1930)
Seattle SO, G. Schwarz Concert
(3/90) (DELO) ① DE3073
Eastman-Rochester Orch, H. Hanson Concert
(2/91) (MERC) ① 432 008-2MM
Symphony No. 3 (1936-38)
NY CO, G. Schwarz Concert
(2/91) (DELO) ① DE3092
Symphony No. 4, '(The) Requiem', Op. 34 (1943)
Seattle SO, G. Schwarz Concert
(7/92) (DELO) ① DE3105
Symphony No. 5, 'Sinfonia sacra', Op. 43 (1954)
Seattle SO, G. Schwarz Concert
(3/93) (DELO) ① DE3130
Symphony No. 6 (1967-68)
NY CO, G. Schwarz Concert
(2/91) (DELO) ① DE3092
Symphony No. 7, '(A) Sea Symphony'—chorus and orchestra (1977) (Wds. W. Whitman)
Seattle Sym Chorale, Seattle SO, G. Schwarz Concert
(3/93) (DELO) ① DE3130

SECTION IV: VOCAL AND CHORAL
Lament for Beowulf—chorus and orchestra, Op. 25 (1925)
Seattle Sym Chorale, Seattle SO, G. Schwarz Concert
(7/92) (DELO) ① DE3105
Lumen in Christo—chorus & orchestra (1974) (Wds. Bible)
Seattle Sym Chorale, Seattle SO, G. Schwarz
(r1994) Concert (5/95) (DELO) ① DE3160
The Mystic Trumpeter—narr, chorus & orch (1970) (Wds. Whitman)
J. E. Jones, Seattle Sym Chorale, Seattle SO, G. Schwarz (r1994) Concert (5/95) (DELO) ① DE3160
A Prayer of the Middle Ages—motet: chorus a capella (1976) (Wds. Anon 8th Cent)
Roberts Wesleyan Coll Chorale, R. Shewan Concert
(6/90) (BAY) ① BCD-1011
Psalm 8, 'How excellent Thy name'—female chorus and piano, Op. 41 (1952)
Roberts Wesleyan Coll Chorale, B. Harbach, R. Shewan Concert (6/90) (BAY) ① BCD-1011
Psalm 121, 'I will lift up mine eyes'—baritone, chorus and orchestra (1963)
T. Sipes, Roberts Wesleyan Coll Chorale, B. Harbach, R. Shewan Concert
(6/90) (BAY) ① BCD-1011
Psalm 150, 'Praise ye the Lord'—mens' chorus (1965)
Roberts Wesleyan Coll Chorale, B. Harbach, R. Shewan Concert (6/90) (BAY) ① BCD-1011
Song of Democracy—chorus and orchestra (1957)
Eastman Music Sch Chor, Eastman-Rochester Orch, H. Hanson Concert
(2/91) (MERC) ① 432 008-2MM

SECTION V: STAGE WORKS
Merry Mount—opera: 3 acts, Op. 31 (1933—New York) (Lib. R. L. Stokes, after Hawthorne)
Suite Seattle SO, G. Schwarz Concert
(7/92) (DELO) ① DE3105
'Tis an earth defiled L. Tibbett, NY Met Op Orch, W. Pelletier (r1934) Concert (3/90) (RCA) ① GD87808

HARBISON, John H. (b 1938) USA

SECTION I: ORCHESTRAL

Concerto for Oboe and Orchestra (1990-91)
W. Bennett, San Francisco SO, H. Blomstedt (r1993)
Concert   (7/94) (DECC) ① **443 376-2DH**

Remembering Gatsby—overture to a projected opera (1990)
Baltimore SO, D. Zinman (r1994) *Concert*
(7/95) (ARGO) ① **444 454-2ZH**

Symphony No. 2 (1987)
San Francisco SO, H. Blomstedt (r1993) *Concert*
(7/94) (DECC) ① **443 376-2DH**

SECTION II: CHAMBER

String Quartet No. 2 (1987)
Emerson Qt (r1992) *Concert*
(11/93) (DG) ① **437 537-2GH**

Twilight Music—horn, violin and piano (1984)
American Chbr Players *Concert*
(7/91) (KOCH) ① **37027-2**

Variations—clarinet, violin and piano (1982)
American Chbr Players *Concert*
(7/91) (KOCH) ① **37027-2**

Wind Quintet (1978)
Reykjavik Wind Qnt (r1992) *Concert*
(11/93) (CHAN) ① **CHAN9174**

HARDELOT, Guy d' (1858–1936) France/England

nom de plume of Helen Rhodes

SECTION IV: VOCAL AND CHORAL

Because—song (1902) (Wds. F. E. Weatherly)
E. Turner, orch (r1926) *Concert*
(9/89) (EMI) ① **CDH7 69791-2**
E. Caruso, orch (r1912) *Concert*
(12/90) (NIMB) ① **NI7809**
E. Caruso, orch (r1912) *Concert*
(7/91) (RCA) ① [12] **GD60495(4)**
E. Caruso, orch (r1912) *Concert*
(10/91) (PEAR) ① [3] **EVC3(1)**
J. Björling, Stockholm Royal Op Orch, N. Grevillius
(r1948) *Concert*   (8/92) (BLUE) ① **ABCD016**
R. Crooks, orch (r1931) *Concert*
(9/93) (CLAR) ① **CDGSE78-50-50**
A. Davies, A. Bryan Parri (r1994; sung in Welsh as 'Dim Ond') *Concert*   (11/95) (SAIN) ① **SCDC2085**

Sometimes in my dreams—song (Wds. Glanville)
E. Turner, orch (r1926) *Concert*
(9/89) (EMI) ① **CDH7 69791-2**

A Year ago—song: 1v and piano
V. Maurel, anon (r1907) *Concert*
(12/94) (SYMP) ① **SYMCD1128**

HARDING, James (d 1626) England

SECTION III: INSTRUMENTAL

A Fancy—keyboard
Amsterdam Loeki Stardust Qt (r1991) *Concert*
(2/94) (L'OI) ① **436 155-2OH**

HARINGTON, Henry (1727–1816) England

SECTION IV: VOCAL AND CHORAL

Damon and Clora—2vv
Invocation (r1993) *Concert*
(11/94) (HYPE) ① **CDA66698**

Enchanting harmonist—2vv
Invocation (r1993) *Concert*
(11/94) (HYPE) ① **CDA66698**

The lyre—1v
Invocation (r1993) *Concert*
(11/94) (HYPE) ① **CDA66698**

Ode to the memory of Italian virtuosi—4vv
Invocation (r1993) *Concert*
(11/94) (HYPE) ① **CDA66698**

HARLINE, Leigh (1907–1969) USA

SECTION V: STAGE WORKS

Pinocchio—musical film (1940) (Lyrics Ned Washington; underscore Paul J Smith)
EXCERPTS: 1. When You Wish Upon a Star; 2. Hi-diddle-dee-dee; 3. Give a Little Whistle; 4. I've Got No Strings.
1. ECO, D. Fraser (r1994-5; arr Fraser) *Concert*
(12/95) (DELO) ① **DE3186**

HARNELL, Joe (b 1924) USA

SECTION V: STAGE WORKS

V for Victory—film score (1988)
EXCERPTS: 1. Main Title.
1. Prague City PO, W. Motzing (r1993) *Concert*
(8/94) (SILV) ① **FILMCD146**

HARPER, Edward (James) (b 1941) England

SECTION IV: VOCAL AND CHORAL

The Universe—carol (Wds. Chester MS and W. de la Mare)
Oxford Christ Church Cath Ch, S. Darlington *Concert*
(10/92) (NIMB) ① **NI5328**

HARPER, John (20th Cent) England

SECTION IV: VOCAL AND CHORAL

Salve regina—choir and organ
Magdalen Oxford Coll Ch, J. Harper *Concert*
(11/91) (ABBE) ① **CDCA915**

Ubi caritas—choir and organ
Magdalen Oxford Coll Ch, J. Harper *Concert*
(11/91) (ABBE) ① **CDCA915**

HARRIS, Clement (1871–1897) England

SECTION I: ORCHESTRAL

Festival March (1892)
Thüringian SO, K. Bach (r1993/4) *Concert*
(2/95) (MARC) ① **8 223660**

Paradise Lost—symphonic poem after Milton (1892-95)
Thüringian SO, K. Bach (r1993/4) *Concert*
(2/95) (MARC) ① **8 223660**

HARRIS, Richard (20th Cent)

SECTION II: CHAMBER

Hexada—six pianos (1990s)
Piano Circus (r1992-93) *Concert*
(2/95) (ARGO) ① **443 527-2ZH**

Swive—six pianos (1990s)
Piano Circus (r1992-93) *Concert*
(2/95) (ARGO) ① **443 527-2ZH**

HARRIS, Roy (1898–1979) USA

SECTION I: ORCHESTRAL

American Creed—orchestra (1940)
Seattle SO, G. Schwarz (r1992) *Concert*
(5/93) (DELO) ① **DE3140**

Chorale for Organ and Brass (1943)
London Gabrieli Brass Ens, C. Larkin *Concert*
(5/92) (HYPE) ① **CDA66517**

Concerto for Violin and Orchestra (1949)
G. Fulkerson, Louisville Orch, L.L. Smith *Concert*
(6/89) (ALBA) ① **AR012**

Fanfare for the Forces—brass ensemble (1942)
LPO, J. Mester *Concert*   (7/91) (KOCH) ① **37012-2**

Symphony No. 1, 'Symphony 1933' (1933)
Louisville Orch, J. Mester *Concert*
(6/89) (ALBA) ① **AR012**
Boston SO, S. Koussevitzky (pp1934) *Concert*
(12/91) (PEAR) ① **GEMMCD9492**

Symphony No. 3 (1937)
NBC SO, A. Toscanini (bp1940) *Concert*
(1/90) (DELL) ① **CDDA9020**
Boston SO, S. Koussevitzky (r1939) *Concert*
(12/91) (PEAR) ① **GEMMCD9492**

Symphony No. 5 (1943 rev 1945)
Louisville Orch, R. Whitney *Concert*
(6/89) (ALBA) ① **AR012**

When Johnny comes Marching Home—an American Overture (1934)
Seattle SO, G. Schwarz (r1992) *Concert*
(5/93) (DELO) ① **DE3140**

SECTION II: CHAMBER

Lyric Study—flute and piano (1950)
P. Robison, T. Hester *Concert*
(11/90) (MMAS) ① **MMD 60195A**

SECTION III: INSTRUMENTAL

6 American Ballads—piano (1942-45)
1. Streets of Laredo; 2. Wayfaring Stranger; 3. The Bird; 4. Black is the color of My True Love's Hair; 5. When Johnny comes Marching Home.
B. Lerner *Concert*   (12/89) (ETCE) ① **KTC1036**

SECTION IV: VOCAL AND CHORAL

Symphony for Voices—chorus a capella (1935) (Wds. W. Whitman)
L. Hendrix, Roberts Wesleyan Coll Chorale, R. Shewan *Concert*   (6/90) (BAY) ① **BCD-1011**

When Johnny comes Marching Home—chorus a capella (1937)
Roberts Wesleyan Coll Chorale, R. Shewan *Concert*
(6/90) (BAY) ① **BCD-1011**

Whitman Triptych—sols, chorus, pf/org (ad lib) (1939-41)
1. Psalm III (doubtful); 2. A Red-bird in a Green Tree (wds. Trad); 3. To thee, Old Comrade (wds. Whitman); 4. Year that trembles (wds. Whitman); Freedom's Land (wds. MacLeish).
3-5. J. Vaverka, Roberts Wesleyan Coll Chorale, R. Shewan *Concert*   (6/90) (BAY) ① **BCD-1011**

HARRIS, Sir William H(enry) (1883–1973) England

SECTION III: INSTRUMENTAL

Flourish for an Occasion—organ
J. Bielby *Concert*   (5/91) (PRIO) ① **PRCD298**

Organ Sonata in A minor (pub 1938)
John Scott (r1992) *Concert*
(8/94) (PRIO) ① **PRCD401**

SECTION IV: VOCAL AND CHORAL

Bring us, O Lord God—anthem (Wds. J Donne)
Worcester Cath Ch, Don Hunt *Concert*
(9/90) (CARL) ① **PCD937**
Salisbury Cath Ch, R. Seal *Concert*
(11/90) (MERI) ① **CDE84180**
St Bride's Ch, Fleet St, R. Jones *Concert*
(2/91) (REGE) ① **REGSB701CD**
Magdalen Oxford Coll Ch, G. Webber *Concert*
(11/91) (ABBE) ① **CDCA914**
Norwich Cath Ch, M. Nicholas, N. Taylor *Concert*
(3/92) (PRIO) ① **PRCD351**
Cambridge Sngrs, J. Rutter *Concert*
(4/92) (CLLE) ① **COLCD113**
St Paul's Cath Ch, John Scott, Andrew Lucas (r1993)
Concert   (6/94) (HYPE) ① **CDA66678**

Faire is the Heaven—motet: double choir (1925) (Wds. E. Spenser)
Cambridge Sngrs, J. Rutter *Concert*
(6/88) (CLLE) ① **COLCD107**
Salisbury Cath Ch, R. Seal *Concert*
(11/90) (MERI) ① **CDE84180**
King's College Ch, D. Willcocks *Concert*
(1/91) (CFP) ① **CD-CFP4570**
New College Ch, E. Higginbottom *Concert*
(9/92) (MERI) ① **CDE84123**
King's College Ch, S. Cleobury (r1991) *Concert*
(6/93) (EMI) ① **CDC7 54418-2**
St Paul's Cath Ch, John Scott, Adrian Lucas (r1991)
Concert   (9/93) (HYPE) ① **CDA66618**
Westminster Cath Ch, J. O'Donnell (r1993) *Concert*
(7/94) (HYPE) ① **CDA66669**
Southwark Cath Ch, P. Wright, S. Layton (r1992)
Concert   (7/94) (PRIO) ① **PRCD435**

Let my prayer come up—choir and organ (1953)
Westminster Abbey Ch, M. Baker, M. Neary (r1993/4)
Concert   (9/94) (CNTO) ① **CSACD3050**

Love of love, light of light—anthem: double chorus (Wds. R. Bridges)
Oxford Christ Church Cath Ch, S. Darlington *Concert*
(10/92) (NIMB) ① **NI5328**

O what their joy and their glory must be—anthem (1931) (Wds. P. Abelard trans J. M. Neale)
Wellington College Chs, T. Byram-Wigfield, S. Anderson *Concert*   (10/92) (HERA) ① **HAVPCD153**
St Paul's Cath Ch, John Scott, Andrew Lucas (r1994)
Concert   (5/95) (HYPE) ① **CDA66758**

Strengthen ye the weak hands—anthem
Jesus College Ch, D. Phillips, T. Horton *Concert*
(7/93) (CNTO) ① **CRCD2367**
Llandaff Cath Ch, M. Smith, M. Hoeg (r1994) *Concert*
(10/95) (PRIO) ① **PRCD510**
Te Deum
Hereford Cath Ch, R. Massey, G. Bowen (r1994)
Concert (2/95) (PRIO) ① **PRCD507**

HARRISON, Annie Fortescue (1851–1944) England

pseudonym of Lady Arthur Hill

SECTION IV: VOCAL AND CHORAL

In the gloaming—song (1877) (Wds. Meta Orred)
M. Garden, A. Russell (r1929: 3 vers) *Concert*
(8/94) (ROMO) ① **81008-2**
A. Rolfe Johnson, G. Johnson (r1991/3) *Concert*
(8/94) (HYPE) ① **CDA66709**

HARRISON, Lou (b 1917) USA

SECTION I: ORCHESTRAL

Concerto for Flute and Percussion No. 1 (1939)
M. Wiesler, R. Pilat, Kroumata Perc Ens *Concert*
(2/86) (BIS) ① **BIS-CD272**
Suite for Violin and American Gamelan (or Strings) (1973)
D. Abel, American Gamelan, J. Bergamo *Concert*
(11/90) (NALB) ① **NA015CD**
Symphony No. 2, 'Elegiac' (1975)
American Cpsrs Orch, D.R. Davies *Concert*
(5/93) (MUSM) ① **7021-2**
Symphony No. 3 (1982)
Cabrillo Music Fest Orch, D.R. Davies *Grand Duo.*
(5/95) (MUSM) ① **7073-2**

SECTION II: CHAMBER

Canticle No. 3—flute/ocarina, guitar and percussion (1941)
J. Schneider, J. Tipton, Cal Arts Perc Ens, J.
Bergamo *Concert* (9/91) (ETCE) ① **KTC1071**
Double Concerto for Violin, Cello and Gamelan (1981-82)
K. Goldsmith, T. King, Mills College Gamelan Ens
Concert (11/91) (MUSI) ① **MACD-635**
Fugue—percussion ensemble (1941)
Perc Ens (r1993) *Concert*
(2/94) (NALB) ① **NA055CD**
Grand Duo—violin and piano (1985)
R. Tecco, D.R. Davies *Symphony 3.*
(5/95) (MUSM) ① **7073-2**
Harp Suite—guitar and percussion (various pieces trans cpsr)
1. Serenade for Frank Wigglesworth (1952); 2. Avalokiteshvara (1964); 3. Music for Bill and Me (1966-67); 4. Jahla (1972); 5. Sonata in Ishartum; 6. Beverly's Troubadour Piece (1967); 7. A Waltz for Evelyn Hinrichsen.
D. Tanenbaum, W. Winant (r1993) *Concert*
(2/94) (NALB) ① **NA055CD**
Perilous Chapel—flute, cello, drums and harp (1948)
San Francisco Contemp Music Plyrs, S. Mosko
(r1993) *Concert* (2/94) (NALB) ① **NA055CD**
Serenade—guitar with percussion (1978)
J. Schneider, G. Strimling *Concert*
(9/91) (ETCE) ① **KTC1071**
D. Tanenbaum, W. Winant (r1993) *Concert*
(2/94) (NALB) ① **NA055CD**
Song of Quetzalcoatl—percussion ensemble (1941)
Perc Ens (r1993) *Concert*
(2/94) (NALB) ① **NA055CD**
Suite No. 1—guitar and percussion (1976)
1. Avalokiteshvara; 2. Music for Bill and Me; 3. Sonata in Ishartum.
J. Schneider, D. Ross, G. Strimling *Concert*
(9/91) (ETCE) ① **KTC1071**
Varied Trio—violin, percussion and piano (1986)
D. Abel, W. Winant, J. Steinberg *Concert*
(11/90) (NALB) ① **NA015CD**

SECTION III: INSTRUMENTAL

Plaint and Variations on 'Song of Palestine'—guitar (1978)
J. Schneider *Concert* (9/91) (ETCE) ① **KTC1071**
Serenado por Gitaro—guitar (1952)
J. Schneider *Concert* (9/91) (ETCE) ① **KTC1071**
Waltz for Evelyn Hinrichsen—piano (1977)
J. Schneider (arr: gtr) *Concert*
(9/91) (ETCE) ① **KTC1071**

SECTION IV: VOCAL AND CHORAL

La Koro Sutro (The Heart Sutro)—100-voices chorus, hp, org and American Gamelan (1971) (Wds. 1st Cent, trans B. N. Kennedy into Esperanto)
Berkeley Univ Chor, Berkeley Univ Chbr Chor, K. Gottlieb, A. Sauerbeck, American Gamelan, P. Brett *Concert* (11/90) (NALB) ① **NA015CD**
Mass to St Anthony—chorus, trumpet, harp and strings (1939-54)
L. DenBeste, L. Crockett, Oregon Repertory Sngrs, G. Seeley (r1992) *Pärt: Berliner Messe.*
(4/94) (KOCH) ① **37177-2**
May Rain—1v, piano and percussion (1941) (Wds. E. Gidlow)
J. Duykers, J. Steinberg, W. Winant (r1993) *Concert*
(2/94) (NALB) ① **NA055CD**

HARRISON, May (1891–1959) England

SECTION IV: VOCAL AND CHORAL

The May Song—song
P. Allanson, S. Betteridge (r1989) *Concert*
(12/90) (SYMP) ① **SYMCD1075**

HARRISON, Michael (20th Cent) USA

SECTION III: INSTRUMENTAL

From Ancient Worlds—harmonic piano (?1990)
M. Harrison (10/92) (NALB) ① **NA042CD**

HARRISON, Sadie (b 1965) Australia

SECTION IV: VOCAL AND CHORAL

Nani ka itou—soprano, clarinet & piano (1993) (Wds. 'From the 36 Immortal Japanese Women Poets')
Tapestry (r1994) *Concert*
(12/95) (BRIT) ① **BML012**

HARSÁNYI, Tibor (1898–1954) Hungary/France

SECTION III: INSTRUMENTAL

Le Tourbillon mécanique—piano
B. Lerner *Concert* (1/89) (ETCE) ① **KTC1061**

HARTLEY, Fred (1905–1991) England

SECTION III: INSTRUMENTAL

Twentieth-Century Nocturne—piano
Welbeck Light Qt *Concert*
(10/91) (PEAR) ① **PASTCD9744**

HARTMANN, Johan Peter Emilius (1805–1900) Denmark

SECTION III: INSTRUMENTAL

Arbucklenian Polka—piano
S. Nakarjakov, A. Markovich (arr Hoch) *Concert*
(5/93) (TELD) ⑨ **9031-77705-2**

SECTION V: STAGE WORKS

Little Christine—opera (1 act), Op. 44 (1846—Copenhagen) (Wds. H. C. Anderson)
Now, my young swain L. Melchior, A. Neumann, Orch (r1913) *Concert*
(8/88) (DANA) ① [2] **DACOCD311/2**
Sverkel's Romance L. Melchior, Orch (Danish: r c1920) *Concert*
(8/88) (DANA) ① [2] **DACOCD311/2**

HARTMANN, John (18th Cent) England

SECTION II: CHAMBER

Fantasia brillante on the air 'Rule Britannia'
H. Hardenberger, R. Pöntinen *Concert*
(11/85) (BIS) ① **BIS-CD287**

HARTMANN, Karl Amadeus (1905–1963) Germany

SECTION I: ORCHESTRAL

Concerto funèbre—violin and string orchestra (1939)
C. Edinger, Katowice RSO, K. Penderecki
Szymanowski: Violin Concerto 1.
(9/90) (THOR) ① **CTH2057**
Moscow Virtuosi, V. Spivakov (vn/dir) *Concert*
(10/90) (RCA) ① **RD60370**
Deutsche Kammerphilharmonie, T. Zehetmair (vn/dir)
(r1991) *Concert* (6/95) (TELD) ① **4509-97449-2**
Sinfonia Tragica (1940)
Bamberg SO, K. A. Rickenbacher *Concert*
(5/94) (SCHW) ① **312952**
Symphony No. 1—contralto and orchestra (1936) (Wds. W. Whitman)
D. Soffel, BRSO, F. Rieger *Concert*
(5/90) (WERG) ① [4] **WER60187-50**
Symphony No. 2—Adagio (1946)
BRSO, R. Kubelík *Concert*
(5/90) (WERG) ① [4] **WER60187-50**
Bamberg SO, K. A. Rickenbacher (r1992) *Concert*
(5/94) (SCHW) ① **312952**
Symphony No. 3 (1948-49)
BRSO, F. Leitner *Concert*
(5/90) (WERG) ① [4] **WER60187-50**
Bamberg SO, I. Metzmacher (r1994) *Ives: Robert Browning Overture.*
(10/95) (EMI) ① **CDC5 55254-2**
Symphony No. 4—string orchestra (1947)
BRSO, R. Kubelík *Concert*
(5/90) (WERG) ① [4] **WER60187-50**
Symphony No. 5, 'Symphonie concertante' (1950)
BRSO, R. Kubelík *Concert*
(5/90) (WERG) ① [4] **WER60187-50**
Symphony No. 6 (1951-53)
BRSO, R. Kubelík *Concert*
(5/90) (WERG) ① [4] **WER60187-50**
Symphony No. 7 (1957-58)
BRSO, Z. Macal *Concert*
(5/90) (WERG) ① [4] **WER60187-50**
Symphony No. 8 (1960-62)
BRSO, R. Kubelík *Concert*
(5/90) (WERG) ① [4] **WER60187-50**

SECTION II: CHAMBER

String Quartet No. 1, 'Carillon' (1933)
Pellegrini Qt (r1992) *String Quartet 2.*
(8/94) (CPO) ① **CPO999 219-2**
String Quartet No. 2 (1945-6)
Pellegrini Qt (r1993) *String Quartet 1.*
(8/94) (CPO) ① **CPO999 219-2**

SECTION III: INSTRUMENTAL

Jazz-Toccata und Fugue—piano (1928)
S. Mauser (8/91) (VIRG) ① **VC7 59017-2**
2 Kleine Suiten—piano (1924-26)
S. Mauser *Concert* (8/91) (VIRG) ① **VC7 59017-2**
Sonata: 27 April 1945—piano (1945)
S. Mauser *Concert* (8/91) (VIRG) ① **VC7 59017-2**
Sonatine—piano (1931)
S. Mauser *Concert* (8/91) (VIRG) ① **VC7 59017-2**

SECTION IV: VOCAL AND CHORAL

Gesangsszene zu Giraudoux' 'Sodom und Gomorrha'—baritone and orchestra (1961-3) (Wds. J. Giraudoux)
D. Fischer-Dieskau, BRSO, R. Kubelík *Concert*
(5/90) (WERG) ① [4] **WER60187-50**
S. Nimsgern, Bamberg SO, K. A. Rickenbacher
(r1992) *Concert* (5/94) (SCHW) ① **312952**

SECTION V: STAGE WORKS

Simplicius Simplicissimus—three scenes from his youth—chamber opera (1948—Munich)
Cpte H. Donath, E. Büchner, K. König, B. Brinkmann, R. Scholze, H. Berger-Tuna, W. Euba, Munich Concert Ch, BRSO, H. Fricke (r1985)
(11/95) (WERG) ① [2] **WER6259-2**

HARTY, Sir (Herbert) Hamilton (1879–1941) Ireland

SECTION I: ORCHESTRAL

The Children of Lir—poem for orchestra with soprano (1938)
H. Harper, Ulster Orch, B. Thomson *Ode to a Nightingale.* (10/87) (CHAN) ① **CHAN8387**

A Comedy Overture (1906)
Ulster Orch, B. Thomson (r1980) *Irish Symphony.*
(9/84) (CHAN) ① **CHAN8314**
Concerto for Piano and Orchestra in B minor (1922)
M. Binns, Ulster Orch, B. Thomson (r1983) *Concert*
(4/85) (CHAN) ① **CHAN8321**
Concerto for Violin and Orchestra in D minor (1908)
R. Holmes, Ulster Orch, B. Thomson *Variations on a Dublin Air.*
(1/87) (CHAN) ① **CHAN8386**
In Ireland—Fantasy for flute, harp and orchestra (1915)
C. Fleming, D. Kelly, Ulster Orch, B. Thomson
(r1983) *Concert* (4/85) (CHAN) ① **CHAN8321**
Ulster Orch, B. Thomson (r1983) *Concert*
(11/93) (CHAN) ① **CHAN6583**
An Irish Symphony (1904)
1. On the Shores of Lough Neagh; 2. The Fair Day;
3. In the Antrim Hills; 4. The Twelfth of July.
Ulster Orch, B. Thomson (r1980) *Comedy overture.*
(9/84) (CHAN) ① **CHAN8314**
3. Ulster Orch, B. Thomson *Concert*
(7/83) (CHAN) ① **CHAN8301**
A John Field Suite—orchestra (1939) (from pf wks by Field)
1. Polka; 2. Nocturne (No. 5); 3. Slow Waltz; 4. Rondo.
Ulster Orch, B. Thomson (r1979) *Concert*
(11/93) (CHAN) ① **CHAN6583**
Liverpool PO, M. Sargent (r1943) *Concert*
(5/95) (DUTT) ① **CDAX8012**
Variations on a Dublin Air—violin and orchestra (1912)
R. Holmes, Ulster Orch, B. Thomson *Violin Concerto.*
(1/87) (CHAN) ① **CHAN8386**
With the Wild Geese—poem for orchestra (1910)
Ulster Orch, B. Thomson (r1983) *Concert*
(4/85) (CHAN) ① **CHAN8321**

SECTION IV: VOCAL AND CHORAL

Ode to a Nightingale—soprano and orchestra, Wds. Keats (1907)
H. Harper, Ulster Orch, B. Thomson *Children of Lir.*
(10/87) (CHAN) ① **CHAN8387**

HARUT'UNYAN, Alexander Grigori (b 1920) Armenia

may be spelt Arutiunian

SECTION I: ORCHESTRAL

Concerto for Trumpet and Orchestra (1950)
B. Soustrot, Loire PO, M. Soustrot *Concert*
(1/89) (PIER) ① **PV788011**

HARVEY, Jonathan Dean (b 1939) England

SECTION I: ORCHESTRAL

Concerto for Cello and Orchestra (1990)
F-M. Uitti, Toscanini SO, J. R. Encinar (pp1991)
Concert (7/93) (ETCE) ① **KTC1148**

SECTION II: CHAMBER

Bhakti—chamber ensemble (1982)
Spectrum, G. Protheroe (bp1984)
(9/89) (NMC) ① **NMCD001**
Natajara—flute (doubling piccolo) and piano (1983)
H. Starreveld, R. Eckhardt *Concert*
(11/92) (BRID) ① **BCD9031**
Philia's Dream—cello and synthesizer (1992)
F-M. Uitti, J. Harvey (r1992) *Concert*
(7/93) (ETCE) ① **KTC1148**
Ricercare una melodia—cello and tape delay (1985)
F-M. Uitti, J. Harvey (r1992) *Concert*
(7/93) (ETCE) ① **KTC1148**
String Quartet No. 1 (1977)
Group for Contemporary Music (r1991) *Concert*
(11/92) (KOCH) ① **37121-2**

SECTION III: INSTRUMENTAL

Curve with Plateaux—cello (1982)
F-M. Uitti (r1992) *Concert*
(7/93) (ETCE) ① **KTC1148**
Ritual Melodies—quadrophonic tape (1990)
D. Atherton, B. Koeppel, K. Malsky, P. Sohn *Concert*
(11/92) (BRID) ① **BCD9031**
3 Sketches—cello (1989)
F-M. Uitti (r1992) *Concert*
(7/93) (ETCE) ① **KTC1148**

SECTION IV: VOCAL AND CHORAL

The Angels—chorus a capella (1994)
Joyful Company of Sngrs, P. Broadbent (r1994)
Concert (7/95) (ASV) ① **CDDCA917**
Carol—chorus a capella (1968)
Joyful Company of Sngrs, P. Broadbent (r1994)
Concert (7/95) (ASV) ① **CDDCA917**
Come, Holy Ghost—chorus (1984) (Wds. trans. J. Cosin)
J. Budd, St Paul's Cath Ch, John Scott *Concert*
(10/91) (HYPE) ① **CDA66439**
Magdalen Oxford Coll Ch, J. Harper *Concert*
(11/91) (ABBE) ① **CDCA915**
Joyful Company of Sngrs, P. Broadbent (r1994)
Concert (7/95) (ASV) ① **CDDCA917**
Forms of Emptiness—chorus a capella (1986) (Wds. e e cummings)
Joyful Company of Sngrs, P. Broadbent (r1994)
Concert (7/95) (ASV) ① **CDDCA917**
2 Fragments—chorus a capella (1966)
1. Audivi vocem (All night by the rose); 2. Round: Virgo viginium (This morning in the sweet month of May).
Joyful Company of Sngrs, P. Broadbent (r1994)
Concert (7/95) (ASV) ① **CDDCA917**
From Silence—sop, vn, va, perc, elec kybds, computer & tape (1988)
K. Bennett, L.C. Stoltzman, M. Thompson, D. Anderson, K. Supové, J. MacDonald, D. Dabby, D. Atherton, B. Koeppel, K. Malsky, P. Sohn, B. Vercoe
Concert (11/92) (BRID) ① **BCD9031**
I love the Lord—hymn (Wds. Psalm 116)
New College Ch, E. Higginbottom *Concert*
(3/87) (PROU) ① **PROUCD114**
New College Ch, E. Higginbottom *Concert*
(9/92) (MERI) ① **CDE84123**
King's College Ch, S. Cleobury (r1991) *Concert*
(6/93) (EMI) ① **CDC7 54418-2**
St Paul's Cath Ch, John Scott, Andrew Lucas (r1993)
Concert (6/94) (HYPE) ① **CDA66678**
Joyful Company of Sngrs, P. Broadbent (r1994)
Concert (7/95) (ASV) ① **CDDCA917**
Lauds—chorus a capella and cello (1987no) (Wds. J V Taylor)
Joyful Company of Sngrs, P. Broadbent, P. Watkins
(r1994) *Concert* (7/95) (ASV) ① **CDDCA917**
O Jesu, nomen dulce—chorus a capella (1979)
Joyful Company of Sngrs, P. Broadbent (r1994)
Concert (7/95) (ASV) ① **CDDCA917**
Sobre un éxtasis alte contemplación—chorus a capella (1975) (Wds. San Juan de la Cruz)
Joyful Company of Sngrs, P. Broadbent (r1994)
Concert (7/95) (ASV) ① **CDDCA917**
Song Offerings—soprano and orchestra (1985) (Wds. R. Tagore)
P. Walmsley-Clark, London Sinfonietta, G. Benjamin
Concert (10/89) (NIMB) ① **NI5167**
The Tree—choir and organ (1981) (Wds. Job XIV vv7-9)
Magdalen Oxford Coll Ch, J. Harper *Concert*
(11/91) (ABBE) ① **CDCA915**
Norwich Cath Ch, M. Nicholas, N. Taylor *Concert*
(3/92) (PRIO) ① **PRCD351**

HARVEY, Paul Milton (b 1935) England

SECTION III: INSTRUMENTAL

Suite on Themes of Gershwin—clarinet solo (1975)
G. de Peyer *Concert*
(11/87) (CHAN) ① **CHAN8549**

HARWOOD, Basil (1859–1949) England

SECTION III: INSTRUMENTAL

Sonata for Organ No. 1 in C sharp minor, Op. 5 (1886)
A. Partington (r1991) *Concert*
(8/94) (PRIO) ① **PRCD384**

SECTION IV: VOCAL AND CHORAL

Evening Service, Op. 6 (1890s)
1. Magnificat; 2. Nunc dimittis.
1, 2. St Paul's Cath Ch, C. Dearnley, John Scott
Concert (1/89) (HYPE) ① **CDA66305**
Morning Service in A flat
1. Te Deum.
1. Hereford Cath Ch, R. Massey, G. Bowen (r1994)
Concert (2/95) (PRIO) ① **PRCD507**

O how glorious is the kingdom—anthem (1894)
Wellington College Chs, T. Byram-Wigfield, S. Anderson *Concert* (10/92) (HERA) ① **HAVPCD153**
St Paul's Cath Ch, John Scott, Adrian Lucas (r1991)
Concert (8/93) (HYPE) ① **CDA66618**

HAŠLER, Karel (1879–1941) Bohemia

SECTION I: ORCHESTRAL

Die Funfunddreissiger
Czech PO, V. Neumann *Concert*
(6/87) (ORFE) ① **C107101A**

HASSE, Johann (Adolph) (1699–1783) Germany

SECTION I: ORCHESTRAL

Concerto for Flute and Strings in G
I. Spranger, Concerto Copenhagen, A. Manze
(r1992) *Concert* (6/93) (CHAN) ① **CHAN0535**

SECTION II: CHAMBER

Trio Sonatas (Sonate a tre)—2 fl/vn, vc & continuo, Op. 2 (pub 1740)
EXCERPTS: **6.**
6. N. Hadden, E. Headley, M. Proud (r1991) *Concert*
(11/94) (CRD) ① **CRD3488**

SECTION III: INSTRUMENTAL

6 Keyboard Sonatas, Op. 7 (pub 1758)
EXCERPTS: 1. B flat; 2. G; 3. B flat; 4. E flat; 5. D minor; 6. C minor.
6. M. Proud (r1991) *Concert*
(11/94) (CRD) ① **CRD3488**
Sonata for Keyboard in E flat
C. Schornsheim (r1991) *Concert*
(4/95) (CAPR) ① **10 424**

SECTION IV: VOCAL AND CHORAL

Alta nubes illustrata—motet: 1v
M. Zanetti, Parlement de Musique, M. Gester (org/dir)
(r1993) *Concert* (1/95) (O111) ① **OPS30-100**
La Conversione di Sant' Agostino—oratorio: 2 parts (1750) (Wds. M. A. Walpurgis)
EXCERPTS: 1. Aria: Ah Dio, ritornate.
Cpte M. Georg, A. Köhler, R. Popken, R. Wörle, G. Schwarz, Berlin RIAS Chbr Ch, Berlin Ancient Music Academy, M. Creed (r1991)
(7/93) (CAPR) ① [2] **10 389/90**
1. J. Baird, N. Hadden, E. Headley, M. Proud (r1991)
Concert (11/94) (CRD) ① **CRD3488**
Fille, dolce mio bene—cantata: 1v, fl/vn & continuo
J. Baird, N. Hadden, E. Headley, M. Proud (r1991)
Concert (11/94) (CRD) ① **CRD3488**
Gentes barbarae, Tartarae turbae—motet: 1v (c1733-40)
J. Lane, Parlement de Musique, M. Gester (org/dir)
(r1993) *Concert* (1/95) (O111) ① **OPS30-100**
Miserere in E minor—soprano, alto, bass, chorus & orchestra
G. de Reyghere, S. Moncayo von Hase, D. Snellings, Fondamento Ch, Fondamento Orch (r1992) *Requiem in C.* (11/93) (O111) ① **OPS30-80**
Quel vago seno, o Fille—cantata: 1v, fl & continuo
J. Baird, N. Hadden, E. Headley, M. Proud (r1991)
Concert (11/94) (CRD) ① **CRD3488**
Requiem in C (1763)
G. de Reyghere, S. Moncayo von Hase, I. Honeyman, D. Snellings, Fondamento Ch, Fondamento Orch (r1992) *Miserere in E minor.*
(11/93) (O111) ① **OPS30-80**
Salve Regina in A—antiphon: 1v
J. Lane, Parlement de Musique, M. Gester (org/dir)
(r1993) *Concert* (1/95) (O111) ① **OPS30-100**
Salve Regina in G—antiphon: 1v
M. Zanetti, Parlement de Musique, M. Gester (org/dir)
(r1993) *Concert* (1/95) (O111) ① **OPS30-100**
4 Venetian Ballads—1v, fl, vn & hpd
EXCERPTS: 1. Grazie agli inganni tuoi; 2. No ste' a condanarme; 3. Cosa e' sta Cossa?; 4. Si', la gondola avere', non crie'.
J. Baird, N. Hadden, E. Headley, M. Proud (r1991)
Concert (11/94) (CRD) ① **CRD3488**

SECTION V: STAGE WORKS

Artaserse—opera: 3 acts (1730—Venice) (Lib. Lalli, after Metastasio)
Palido il sole J. Kowalski, Berlin RSO, H. Fricke
Concert (10/92) (CAPR) ① **10 416**

La **Clemenza di Tito—opera (3 acts)**
(1735—Dresden) (Lib. Metastasio)
Tardi s'avvedde d'un tradimento J. Kowalski,
Berlin CO, M. Pommer *Concert*
(9/88) (CAPR) ① **10 113**
Cleofide (Alessandro nell'Indie)—opera (3
acts) (1731—Leipzig) (Wds. Boccardi, after
Metastasio)
Cpte E. Kirkby, A. Mellon, D.L. Ragin, D. Visse, R.
Wong, D. Cordier, Cappella Coloniensis, W. Christie
(2/88) (CAPR) ① **[4] 10 193/6**
Lucio Papirio—opera (3 acts)
(1742—Dresden) (Lib. Zeno)
All'onor mio rifletti J. Kowalski, Berlin CO, M.
Pommer *Concert* (9/88) (CAPR) ① **10 113**
Piramo e Tisbe—intermezzo tragico (2 acts)
(1768—Vienna) (Lib. M. Coltellini)
Cpte B. Schlick, S. Gari, M. Lecocq, Capella
Clementina, H. Müller-Brühl (r1984)
(4/94) (SCHW) ② **310882**

HASSELMANS, Alphonse (Jean) (1845–1912) Belgium/France

SECTION III: INSTRUMENTAL

Chanson de mai—harp, Op. 40
S. Drake *Concert* (9/86) (HYPE) ① **CDA66038**
Feuilles d'automne—harp
T. Owen *Concert* (3/87) (CARL) ① **PCD835**
Follets, 'Will-o'-the-wisp'—harp
L. Laskine (r1975) *Concert*
(12/93) (ERAT) ① **4509-92131-2**
Mazurka—harp, Op. 31
S. Drake (r1988) *Concert*
(2/90) (HYPE) ① **CDA66340**
Nocturne—harp, Op. 43
S. Drake (r1988) *Concert*
(2/90) (HYPE) ① **CDA66340**
Prelude—harp, Op. 52
S. Drake *Concert* (9/86) (HYPE) ① **CDA66038**
La Source—étude: harp, Op. 44
S. Drake *Concert* (9/86) (HYPE) ① **CDA66038**
T. Owen *Concert* (3/87) (CARL) ① **PCD835**
M. Robles *Concert*
(2/93) (DECC) ① **433 869-2DWO**
M. Klinko *Concert* (8/93) (EMI) ① **CDC7 54467-2**
L. Laskine (r1975) *Concert*
(12/93) (ERAT) ① **4509-92131-2**

HASSLER, Hans (Johann) Leo (1564–1612) Germany

SECTION II: CHAMBER

Canzon duodecimi toni—8 parts (pub 1601)
(from Sacri concentus)
His Majesties Sagbutts and Cornetts, T. Roberts, I.
Simcock (r1993) *Concert*
(6/94) (HYPE) ① **CDA66688**
Canzon noni toni—8 parts (pub 1601) (from
Sacri concentus)
His Majesties Sagbutts and Cornetts, T. Roberts, I.
Simcock (r1993) *Concert*
(6/94) (HYPE) ① **CDA66688**

SECTION III: INSTRUMENTAL

Canzon—lute
L. Kirchhof *Concert* (11/92) (SONY) ⑤ **SK48068**
Toccata in G—organ (pub 1601) (from Sacri
concentus)
I. Simcock (r1993) *Concert*
(6/94) (HYPE) ① **CDA66688**

SECTION IV: VOCAL AND CHORAL

Ad Dominum cum tribularer—motet
Paris Chapelle Royale European Ens, P. Herreweghe
(r1991) *Concert* (10/93) (HARM) ① **HMC90 1401**
Cantate Domino canticum novum—motet
(pub 1601) (from Sacri concentus)
His Majesties Sagbutts and Cornetts, I. Schöllhorn
(r1993) *Concert* (6/94) (HYPE) ① **CDA66688**
Domine Deus, Israel—motet
Paris Chapelle Royale European Ens, P. Herreweghe
(r1991) *Concert* (10/93) (HARM) ① **HMC90 1401**
Domine Dominus noster—motet (pub 1601)
(from Sacri concentus)
His Majesties Sagbutts and Cornetts, I. Schöllhorn
(r1993) *Concert* (6/94) (HYPE) ① **CDA66688**
Entrust all your doings—song (Wds. P.
Gerhardt)
L. Melchior, Anon (org) (Danish: r1915) *Concert*
(8/88) (DANA) ① **[2] DACOCD311/2**
Missa I super Dixit Maria
Paris Chapelle Royale European Ens, P. Herreweghe
(r1991) *Concert* (10/93) (HARM) ① **HMC90 1401**

O admirabile commercium—motet
Paris Chapelle Royale European Ens, P. Herreweghe
(r1991) *Concert* (10/93) (HARM) ① **HMC90 1401**
O sacrum convivium—motet (pub 1601)
(from Sacri concentus)
Westminster Cath Ch, J. O'Donnell, T. Roberts, I.
Simcock (r1993) *Concert*
(6/94) (HYPE) ① **CDA66688**
Tanzen und Springen—madrigal
Magdalen (Oxford) Coll Ch, G. Ives *Concert*
(11/92) (CNTO) ① **CRCD2366**
Usquequo, Domine—motet
Paris Chapelle Royale European Ens, P. Herreweghe
(r1991) *Concert* (10/93) (HARM) ① **HMC90 1401**
Vater unser in Himmelreich—chorale (pub
1607) (from Psalmen und Christliche
Gesänge)
Paris Chapelle Royale European Ens, P. Herreweghe
(r1991) *Concert* (10/93) (HARM) ① **HMC90 1401**

HATTON, John Liptrot (1808–1886) England

SECTION IV: VOCAL AND CHORAL

Simon the Cellarer—song
C. Santley, anon (r1913) *Concert*
(7/93) (NIMB) ① **[2] NI7840/1**
When ev'ning's twilight—partsong (Wds.
unknown)
PCA, M. Brown *Concert* (3/87) (CONI) ① **CDCF145**
Hilliard Ens, L-L. Kiesel *Concert*
(12/91) (MERI) ① **DUOCD89009**
Magdalen (Oxford) Coll Ch, G. Ives *Concert*
(11/92) (CNTO) ① **CRCD2366**

HAUCOURT, Johannes (fl 1390–1410) France

SECTION IV: VOCAL AND CHORAL

Je demande ma bienvenue—rondeau (3vv)
Gothic Voices, A. Lawrence-King, C. Page, C. Page
Concert (12/88) (HYPE) ① **CDA66286**

HAUER, Josef Matthias (1883–1959) Austria

SECTION IV: VOCAL AND CHORAL

3 Hölderlin-Lieder, Op. 12 (1914-15) (Wds
Hölderlin)
Ehmals und jetzt M. Shirai, H. Höll *Concert*
(12/94) (CAPR) ① **10 534**

HAUG, Halvor (b 1952) Norway

SECTION I: ORCHESTRAL

Silence for Strings (1977)
LSO, P. Dreier *Concert*
(3/88) (AURO) ① **ARCD1910**
Sinfonietta (1983)
LSO, P. Dreier *Concert*
(3/88) (AURO) ① **ARCD1910**
Symphony No. 1 (1981-82)
LSO, P. Dreier *Concert*
(3/88) (AURO) ① **ARCD1910**

HAUSSMANN, Valentin (1565/70–1613/14) Germany

SECTION II: CHAMBER

Catkanei
Ulsamer Collegium, J. Ulsamer *Concert*
(2/86) (ARCH) ① **415 294-2AH**
Galliard
Ulsamer Collegium, J. Ulsamer *Concert*
(2/86) (ARCH) ① **415 294-2AH**
Paduan
Ulsamer Collegium, J. Ulsamer *Concert*
(2/86) (ARCH) ① **415 294-2AH**
Tantz
Ulsamer Collegium, J. Ulsamer *Concert*
(2/86) (ARCH) ① **415 294-2AH**

HAWES, Jack (b 1916) England

SECTION IV: VOCAL AND CHORAL

Evening Service in D—choir and organ
(1983)
Chichester Cath Ch, A. Thurlow, J. Thomas (r1994)
Concert (5/95) (PRIO) ① **PRCD511**

HAWLEY, Charles Beach (1858–1915) USA

SECTION IV: VOCAL AND CHORAL

The Sweetest flower that blows—song
E. Palliser, anon (r1902) *Concert*
(10/92) (SYMP) ① **SYMCD1093**

HAYDN, Franz Joseph (1732–1809) Austria

Hob—Numbers from Hoboken's Thematic Catalogue
of Haydn's works (1957-71)

SECTION I: ORCHESTRAL

Concerto for Cello and Orchestra No. 1 in C,
HobVIIb/1 (?c1761-65)
C. Coin, AAM, C. Hogwood (hpd/dir) *Cello Concerto*
in D. (12/85) (L'OI) ① **414 615-2OH**
J. Du Pré, ECO, D. Barenboim (r1967) *Dvořák: Cello*
Concerto. (2/88) (EMI) ① **CDC7 47614-2**
J. Starker, Scottish CO, G. Schwarz *Concert*
(9/88) (DELO) ① **DE3062**
M. Rostropovich (vc/dir), ASMF (r1975) *Cello*
Concerto in D. (11/88) (EMI) ① **CDC7 49305-2**
H. Schiff, ASMF, N. Marriner *Cello Concerto in D.*
(11/88) (PHIL) ① **420 923-2PH**
J. Du Pré, ECO, D. Barenboim *Concert*
(3/89) (EMI) ① **[2] CMS7 69707-2**
L. Claret, ECO, G. Malcolm *Boccherini: Cello*
Concerto, G480. (10/89) (HARM) ① **HMP390 5204**
M. Haimovitz, ECO, A. Davis *Concert*
(4/90) (DG) ① **429 219-2GH**
W. Conway, Goldberg Ens, M. Layfield *Concert*
(11/90) (MERI) ① **CDE84177**
A. Bylsma, Tafelmusik, J. Lamon *Concert*
(9/91) (DHM) ① **RD77757**
M. Rostropovich, ECO, B. Britten *Concert*
(2/92) (DECC) ① **430 633-2DM**
T. Mørk, Norwegian CO, I. Brown *Cello Concerto in*
D. (8/92) (SIMA) ① **PSC1078**
L. Harrell, ASMF, N. Marriner *Concert*
(11/92) (EMI) ① **CDM7 64326-2**
C. Walevska, ECO, E. de Waart (r1972) *Concert*
(4/94) (PHIL) ① **[2] 438 797-2PM2**
T. Mørk, Norwegian CO, I. Brown (r1991) *Cello*
Concerto in D. (6/94) (VIRG) ① **VC5 45014-2**
J. Du Pré, ECO, D. Barenboim (r1967) *Concert*
(8/94) (EMI) ① **[6] CZS5 68132-2**
A. Lamasse, Instr Ens of France, J-P. Wallez (r1990)
Cello Concerto in D. (11/94) (FORL) ① **FF040**
P. Wispelwey, Florilegium Ens (r1994) *Concert*
(7/95) (CHNN) ① **CCS7395**
Concerto for Cello and Orchestra No. 2 in D,
HobVIIb/2 (1783)
C. Coin, AAM, C. Hogwood (hpd/dir) *Cello Concerto*
in C. (12/85) (L'OI) ① **414 615-2OH**
Y-Y. Ma, ECO, J-L. Garcia *Concert*
(1/86) (SONY) ① **MK39310**
J. Du Pré, LSO, J. Barbirolli (r1967) *Boccherini: Cello*
Concerto, G482. (12/87) (EMI) ① **CDC7 47840-2**
M. Rostropovich (vc/dir), ASMF (r1975) *Cello*
Concerto in C. (11/88) (EMI) ① **CDC7 49305-2**
H. Schiff, ASMF, N. Marriner *Cello Concerto in C.*
(11/88) (PHIL) ① **420 923-2PH**
A. Bylsma, Tafelmusik, J. Lamon *Concert*
(9/91) (DHM) ① **RD77757**
T. Mørk, Norwegian CO, I. Brown *Cello Concerto in*
C. (8/92) (SIMA) ① **PSC1078**
J. Starker, Scottish CO, G. Schwarz *Concert*
(10/92) (DELO) ① **DE3063**
L. Harrell, ASMF, N. Marriner *Concert*
(11/92) (EMI) ① **CDM7 64326-2**
C. Walevska, ECO, E. de Waart (r1972) *Concert*
(4/94) (PHIL) ① **[2] 438 797-2PM2**
T. Mørk, Norwegian CO, I. Brown (r1991) *Cello*
Concerto in C. (6/94) (VIRG) ① **VC5 45014-2**
J. Du Pré, LSO, J. Barbirolli (r1967) *Concert*
(8/94) (EMI) ① **[6] CZS5 68132-2**
A. Lamasse, Instr Ens of France, J-P. Wallez (r1990)
Cello Concerto in C. (11/94) (FORL) ① **FF040**
P. Wispelwey, Florilegium Ens (r1994) *Concert*
(7/95) (CHNN) ① **CCS7395**
J. Starker, Philh, C.M. Giulini (r1958) *Concert*
(12/95) (EMI) ① **[6] CZS5 68485-2**
Concerto for Horn and Orchestra No. 1 in D,
HobVIId/3 (1762)
D. Bourgue, Versailles Camerata, A. du Closel
Concert (2/89) (FORL) ① **UCD16567**
A. Halstead, Hanover Band, R. Goodman *Concert*
(11/89) (NIMB) ① **NI5190**
B. Tuckwell, ASMF, N. Marriner *Concert*
(2/92) (DECC) ① **430 633-2DM**

Philh Hungarica, A. Dorati *Concert*
 (6/91) (DECC) ① [32] **430 100-2DM32(1)**
VCM, N. Harnoncourt *Concert*
 (7/91) (TELD) ① **2292-46018-2**
Hanover Band, R. Goodman *Concert*
 (12/91) (HYPE) ① **CDA66523**
Lausanne CO, J. López-Cobos *Concert*
 (6/92) (DENO) ① **CO-77612**
AAM, C. Hogwood *Concert*
 (6/93) (L'OI) ① [3] **433 661-2OH3**
Northern CO, N. Ward (r1993) *Concert*
 (11/94) (NAXO) ① **8 550722**

Symphony No. 8 in G, 'Le soir' (?1761)
English Concert, T. Pinnock *Concert*
 (1/88) (ARCH) ① **423 098-2AH**
Austro-Hungarian Haydn Orch, A. Fischer *Concert*
 (9/90) (NIMB) ① **NI5240**
Philh Hungarica, A. Dorati *Concert*
 (6/91) (DECC) ① [32] **430 100-2DM32(1)**
VCM, N. Harnoncourt *Concert*
 (7/91) (TELD) ① **2292-46018-2**
Hanover Band, R. Goodman *Concert*
 (12/91) (HYPE) ① **CDA66523**
Lausanne CO, J. López-Cobos *Concert*
 (6/92) (DENO) ① **CO-77612**
AAM, C. Hogwood *Concert*
 (6/93) (L'OI) ① [3] **433 661-2OH3**
Northern CO, N. Ward (r1993) *Concert*
 (11/94) (NAXO) ① **8 550722**

Symphony No. 9 in C (?1762)
Philh Hungarica, A. Dorati *Concert*
 (6/91) (DECC) ① [32] **430 100-2DM32(1)**
Cantilena, A. Shepherd *Concert*
 (10/91) (CHAN) ① **CHAN8813**
Hanover Band, R. Goodman (hpd/dir) *Concert*
 (12/92) (HYPE) ① **CDA66529**
AAM, C. Hogwood *Concert*
 (6/93) (L'OI) ① [3] **433 661-2OH3**

Symphony No. 10 in D (-1766 (?1761)
Philh Hungarica, A. Dorati *Concert*
 (6/91) (DECC) ① [32] **430 100-2DM32(1)**
Cantilena, A. Shepherd *Concert*
 (10/91) (CHAN) ① **CHAN8813**
Hanover Band, R. Goodman (hpd/dir) *Concert*
 (12/92) (HYPE) ① **CDA66529**
AAM, C. Hogwood (r1991) *Concert*
 (4/94) (L'OI) ① [3] **436 428-2OH3**

Symphony No. 11 in E flat (-1769: -?1760)
Philh Hungarica, A. Dorati *Concert*
 (6/91) (DECC) ① [32] **430 100-2DM32(1)**
Cantilena, A. Shepherd *Concert*
 (10/91) (CHAN) ① **CHAN8813**
Hanover Band, R. Goodman (hpd/dir) *Concert*
 (12/92) (HYPE) ① **CDA66529**
AAM, C. Hogwood (r1991) *Concert*
 (4/94) (L'OI) ① [3] **436 428-2OH3**

Symphony No. 12 in E (1763)
Philh Hungarica, A. Dorati *Concert*
 (6/91) (DECC) ① [32] **430 100-2DM32(1)**
Cantilena, A. Shepherd *Concert*
 (10/91) (CHAN) ① **CHAN8813**
Hanover Band, R. Goodman (hpd/dir) *Concert*
 (12/92) (HYPE) ① **CDA66529**
AAM, C. Hogwood *Concert*
 (6/93) (L'OI) ① [3] **433 661-2OH3**

Symphony No. 13 in D (1763)
Philh Hungarica, A. Dorati *Concert*
 (6/91) (DECC) ① [32] **430 100-2DM32(1)**
AAM, C. Hogwood *Concert*
 (6/93) (L'OI) ① [3] **433 661-2OH3**
Hanover Band, R. Goodman (r1993) *Concert*
 (3/94) (HYPE) ① **CDA66534**

Symphony No. 14 in A (-1764)
Philh Hungarica, A. Dorati *Concert*
 (6/91) (DECC) ① [32] **430 100-2DM32(1)**
Austro-Hungarian Haydn Orch, A. Fischer *Concert*
 (11/92) (NIMB) ① **NI5331**
Hanover Band, R. Goodman (r1993) *Concert*
 (3/94) (HYPE) ① **CDA66534**

Symphony No. 15 in D (-1766)
Philh Hungarica, A. Dorati *Concert*
 (6/91) (DECC) ① [32] **430 100-2DM32(1)**
Austro-Hungarian Haydn Orch, A. Fischer *Concert*
 (11/92) (NIMB) ① **NI5331**
Hanover Band, R. Goodman (r1993) *Concert*
 (3/94) (HYPE) ① **CDA66534**

Symphony No. 16 in B flat (-1766)
Philh Hungarica, A. Dorati *Concert*
 (6/91) (DECC) ① [32] **430 100-2DM32(1)**
Austro-Hungarian Haydn Orch, A. Fischer *Concert*
 (11/92) (NIMB) ① **NI5331**
AAM, C. Hogwood *Concert*
 (6/93) (L'OI) ① [3] **433 661-2OH3**
Hanover Band, R. Goodman (r1993) *Concert*
 (3/94) (HYPE) ① **CDA66534**

Symphony No. 17 in F (-1766)
Philh Hungarica, A. Dorati *Concert*
 (6/91) (DECC) ① [32] **430 100-2DM32(1)**
Austro-Hungarian Haydn Orch, A. Fischer *Concert*
 (11/92) (NIMB) ① **NI5331**
Hanover Band, R. Goodman *Concert*
 (12/93) (HYPE) ① **CDA66533**

Symphony No. 18 in G (-1766)
Philh Hungarica, A. Dorati *Concert*
 (6/91) (DECC) ① [32] **430 100-2DM32(1)**
Hanover Band, R. Goodman *Concert*
 (12/93) (HYPE) ① **CDA66533**
AAM, C. Hogwood (r1991) *Concert*
 (4/94) (L'OI) ① [3] **436 428-2OH3**

Symphony No. 19 in D (-1766)
Philh Hungarica, A. Dorati *Concert*
 (6/91) (DECC) ① [32] **430 100-2DM32(1)**
Hanover Band, R. Goodman *Concert*
 (12/93) (HYPE) ① **CDA66533**

Symphony No. 20 in C (-1766)
Philh Hungarica, A. Dorati *Concert*
 (6/91) (DECC) ① [32] **430 100-2DM32(1)**
Hanover Band, R. Goodman *Concert*
 (12/93) (HYPE) ① **CDA66533**

Symphony No. 21 in A (1764)
Scottish CO, G. Schwarz *Concert*
 (9/88) (DELO) ① **DE3062**
AAM, C. Hogwood *Concert*
 (12/90) (L'OI) ① [3] **430 082-2OH3**
Philh Hungarica, A. Dorati *Concert*
 (6/91) (DECC) ① [32] **430 100-2DM32(1)**
Hanover Band, R. Goodman *Concert*
 (12/93) (HYPE) ① **CDA66533**

Symphony No. 22 in E flat, 'Philosopher' (1764)
Scottish CO, G. Schwarz *Concert*
 (9/88) (DELO) ① **DE3061**
Orpheus CO *Concert* (7/89) (DG) ① **427 337-2GH**
Austro-Hungarian Haydn Orch, A. Fischer *Concert*
 (12/89) (NIMB) ① **NI5179**
AAM, C. Hogwood *Concert*
 (12/90) (L'OI) ① [3] **430 082-2OH3**
Philh Hungarica, A. Dorati *Concert*
 (6/91) (DECC) ① [32] **430 100-2DM32(1)**
Austro-Hungarian Haydn Orch, A. Fischer (r1989)
Concert (8/93) (NIMB) ① **NI5392**
Hanover Band, R. Goodman (r1994) *Concert*
 (6/95) (HYPE) ① **CDA66536**
Northern CO, N. Ward (r1992) *Concert*
 (6/95) (NAXO) ① **8 550724**

Symphony No. 23 in G (1764)
AAM, C. Hogwood *Concert*
 (12/90) (L'OI) ① [3] **430 082-2OH3**
Philh Hungarica, A. Dorati *Concert*
 (6/91) (DECC) ① [32] **430 100-2DM32(1)**
Hanover Band, R. Goodman (r1994) *Concert*
 (6/95) (HYPE) ① **CDA66536**

Symphony No. 24 in D (1764)
Austro-Hungarian Haydn Orch, A. Fischer *Concert*
 (12/89) (NIMB) ① **NI5179**
AAM, C. Hogwood *Concert*
 (12/90) (L'OI) ① [3] **430 082-2OH3**
Philh Hungarica, A. Dorati *Concert*
 (6/91) (DECC) ① [32] **430 100-2DM32(1)**
Hanover Band, R. Goodman (r1994) *Concert*
 (6/95) (HYPE) ① **CDA66536**

Symphony No. 25 in C (-1766)
Philh Hungarica, A. Dorati *Concert*
 (6/91) (DECC) ① [32] **430 100-2DM32(1)**
Hanover Band, R. Goodman (r1994) *Concert*
 (6/95) (HYPE) ① **CDA66536**

Symphony No. 26 in D minor, 'Lamentatione' (-1770)
Northern CO, N. Ward (r1992) *Concert*
 (1/94) (NAXO) ① **8 550721**
AAM, C. Hogwood (r1989) *Concert*
 (11/94) (L'OI) ① [3] **440 222-2OH3**
Estro Armonico, D. Solomons (r1983) *Concert*
 (11/95) (SONY) ① **SMK66929**

Symphony No. 27 in G (-1766)
Philh Hungarica, A. Dorati *Concert*
 (6/91) (DECC) ① [32] **430 100-2DM32(1)**
AAM, C. Hogwood *Concert*
 (4/94) (L'OI) ① [3] **436 428-2OH3**

Symphony No. 28 in A (1765)
AAM, C. Hogwood *Concert*
 (12/90) (L'OI) ① [3] **430 082-2OH3**
Philh Hungarica, A. Dorati *Concert*
 (6/91) (DECC) ① [32] **430 100-2DM32(1)**
ECCO, E. Aadland *Concert*
 (9/92) (CARL) ① **PCD978**

Symphony No. 29 in E (1765)
AAM, C. Hogwood *Concert*
 (12/90) (L'OI) ① [3] **430 082-2OH3**

Philh Hungarica, A. Dorati *Concert*
 (6/91) (DECC) ① [32] **430 100-2DM32(1)**
Northern CO, N. Ward (r1994) *Concert*
 (6/95) (NAXO) ① **8 550724**

Symphony No. 30 in C, 'Alleluja' (1765)
Vienna Academy Orch, M. Haselböck (r1989)
Concert (4/90) (NOVA) ① **150 045-2**
AAM, C. Hogwood *Concert*
 (12/90) (L'OI) ① [3] **430 082-2OH3**
Philh Hungarica, A. Dorati *Concert*
 (6/91) (DECC) ① [32] **430 100-2DM32(1)**
VCM, N. Harnoncourt *Concert*
 (6/93) (TELD) ① **9031-76460-2**
Northern CO, N. Ward (r1992) *Concert*
 (5/95) (NAXO) ① **8 550757**

Symphony No. 31 in D, 'Hornsignal' (1765)
Hanover Band, R. Goodman *Concert*
 (11/89) (NIMB) ① **NI5190**
St Luke's Orch, C. Mackerras (r1988) *Symphony 45.*
 (3/90) (TELA) ① **CD80156**
AAM, C. Hogwood *Concert*
 (12/90) (L'OI) ① [3] **430 082-2OH3**
Philh Hungarica, A. Dorati *Concert*
 (6/91) (DECC) ① [32] **430 100-2DM32(1)**
VCM, N. Harnoncourt *Concert*
 (4/95) (TELD) ① **4509-90843-2**

Symphony No. 32 in C (-1766)
Philh Hungarica, A. Dorati *Concert*
 (6/91) (DECC) ① [32] **430 100-2DM32(1)**
AAM, C. Hogwood (r1991) *Concert*
 (4/94) (L'OI) ① [3] **436 428-2OH3**

Symphony No. 33 in C (-1769)
Philh Hungarica, A. Dorati *Concert*
 (6/91) (DECC) ① [32] **430 100-2DM32(1)**

Symphony No. 34 in D minor (1767)
AAM, C. Hogwood *Concert*
 (12/90) (L'OI) ① [3] **430 082-2OH3**
Philh Hungarica, A. Dorati *Concert*
 (6/91) (DECC) ① [32] **430 100-2DM32(1)**
ECCO, E. Aadland *Concert*
 (9/92) (CARL) ① **PCD978**

Symphony No. 35 in B flat (1767)
Philh Hungarica, A. Dorati *Concert*
 (6/91) (DECC) ① [32] **430 100-2DM32(1)**
AAM, C. Hogwood *Concert*
 (4/92) (L'OI) ① [3] **433 012-2OH3**
Northern CO, N. Ward (r1992) *Concert*
 (1/94) (NAXO) ① **8 550721**

Symphony No. 36 in E flat (-1769)
Philh Hungarica, A. Dorati *Concert*
 (6/91) (DECC) ① [32] **430 100-2DM32(1)**

Symphony No. 37 in C (-?1758)
Philh Hungarica, A. Dorati *Concert*
 (6/91) (DECC) ① [32] **430 100-2DM32(1)**
AAM, C. Hogwood (r1991) *Concert*
 (4/94) (L'OI) ① [3] **436 428-2OH3**

Symphony No. 38 in C (-1769)
Philh Hungarica, A. Dorati *Concert*
 (6/91) (DECC) ① [32] **430 100-2DM32(1)**
AAM, C. Hogwood *Concert*
 (4/92) (L'OI) ① [3] **433 012-2OH3**

Symphony No. 39 in G minor (?1765-1770)
Philh Hungarica, A. Dorati *Concert*
 (6/91) (DECC) ① [32] **430 100-2DM32(1)**
AAM, C. Hogwood *Concert*
 (4/92) (L'OI) ① [3] **433 012-2OH3**

Symphony No. 40 in F (1763)
Philh Hungarica, A. Dorati *Concert*
 (6/91) (DECC) ① [32] **430 100-2DM32(1)**
AAM, C. Hogwood *Concert*
 (6/93) (L'OI) ① [3] **433 661-2OH3**

Symphony No. 41 in C (-1770)
Philh Hungarica, A. Dorati *Concert*
 (6/91) (DECC) ① [32] **430 100-2DM32(1)**
AAM, C. Hogwood *Concert*
 (4/92) (L'OI) ① [3] **433 012-2OH3**
Tafelmusik, B. Weil *Concert*
 (4/93) (SONY) ① **SK48370**

Symphony No. 42 in D (1771)
English Concert, T. Pinnock (hpd/dir) *Concert*
 (9/90) (ARCH) ① **429 756-2AH**
Philh Hungarica, A. Dorati *Concert*
 (6/91) (DECC) ① [32] **430 100-2DM32(1)**
Hanover Band, R. Goodman *Concert*
 (2/93) (HYPE) ① **CDA66530**
Tafelmusik, B. Weil *Concert*
 (4/93) (SONY) ① **SK48370**
AAM, C. Hogwood (r1992) *Concert*
 (11/94) (L'OI) ① [3] **440 222-2OH3**
English Concert, T. Pinnock (r1989) *Concert*
 (7/95) (ARCH) ① **447 281-2AMA**

Symphony No. 43 in E flat, 'Mercury' (-1772)
English Concert, T. Pinnock *Concert*
 (7/90) (ARCH) ① **429 400-2AH**

Philh Hungarica, A. Dorati *Concert*
    (6/91) (DECC) ① [32] **430 100-2DM32(1)**
ECCO, E. Aadland *Concert*
    (9/92) (CARL) ① **PCD978**
Hanover Band, R. Goodman *Concert*
    (2/93) (HYPE) ① **CDA66530**
Tafelmusik, B. Weil *Concert*
    (4/93) (SONY) ① **SK48370**
AAM, C. Hogwood (r1992) *Concert*
    (11/94) (L'OI) ① [3] **440 222-2OH3**
**Symphony No. 44 in E minor,
'Trauersinfonie' (1772)**
St John's Smith Square Orch, J. Lubbock *Mozart:
    Symphony 40.*   (8/86) (CARL) ① **PCD820**
English Concert, T. Pinnock (hpd/dir) *Concert*
    (9/90) (ARCH) ① **429 756-2AH**
Philh Hungarica, A. Dorati *Concert*
    (6/91) (DECC) ① [32] **430 100-2DM32(1)**
Hanover Band, R. Goodman *Concert*
    (2/93) (HYPE) ① **CDA66530**
Tafelmusik, B. Weil *Concert*
    (4/93) (SONY) ① **SK48371**
AAM, C. Hogwood (r1992) *Concert*
    (11/94) (L'OI) ① [3] **440 222-2OH3**
**Symphony No. 45 in F sharp minor,
'Farewell' (1772)**
Austro-Hungarian Haydn Orch, A. Fischer *Concert*
    (12/89) (NIMB) ① **NI5179**
St Luke's Orch, C. Mackerras (r1988) *Symphony 31.*
    (3/90) (TELA) ① **CD80156**
Philh Hungarica, A. Dorati *Concert*
    (6/91) (DECC) ① [32] **430 100-2DM32(1)**
Capella Istropolitana, B. Wordsworth *Concert*
    (9/91) (NAXO) ① **8 550382**
Hanover Band, R. Goodman *Concert*
    (10/91) (HYPE) ① **CDA66522**
LSO, Henry Wood (r1934) *Concert*
    (9/94) (DUTT) ① [2] **2CDAX2002**
Tafelmusik, B. Weil (r1993) *Concert*
    (11/94) (SONY) ① **SK53986**
English Concert, T. Pinnock (r1989) *Concert*
    (7/95) (ARCH) ① **447 281-2AMA**
Symphony No. 46 in B (1772)
English Concert, T. Pinnock (hpd/dir) *Concert*
    (9/90) (ARCH) ① **429 756-2AH**
Philh Hungarica, A. Dorati *Concert*
    (6/91) (DECC) ① [32] **430 100-2DM32(1)**
Hanover Band, R. Goodman *Concert*
    (10/91) (HYPE) ① **CDA66522**
Tafelmusik, B. Weil (r1993) *Concert*
    (11/94) (SONY) ① **SK53986**
English Concert, T. Pinnock (r1989) *Concert*
    (7/95) (ARCH) ① **447 281-2AMA**
Symphony No. 47 in G (1772)
Philh Hungarica, A. Dorati *Concert*
    (6/91) (DECC) ① [32] **430 100-2DM32(1)**
Hanover Band, R. Goodman *Concert*
    (10/91) (HYPE) ① **CDA66522**
Tafelmusik, B. Weil (r1993) *Concert*
    (11/94) (SONY) ① **SK53986**
**Symphony No. 48 in C, 'Maria Theresia'
(?1769)**
Philh Hungarica, A. Dorati *Concert*
    (6/91) (DECC) ① [32] **430 100-2DM32(1)**
Capella Istropolitana, B. Wordsworth *Concert*
    (9/91) (NAXO) ① **8 550382**
Hanover Band, R. Goodman *Concert*
    (7/93) (HYPE) ① **CDA66531**
AAM, C. Hogwood (r1992) *Concert*
    (11/94) (L'OI) ① [3] **440 222-2OH3**
Estro Armonico, D. Solomons (r1983) *Concert*
    (11/95) (SONY) ① **SMK66929**
**Symphony No. 49 in F minor, 'La Passione'
(1768)**
St John's Smith Square Orch, J. Lubbock *Schubert:
    Symphony 5.*   (8/86) (CARL) ① **PCD819**
Philh Hungarica, A. Dorati *Concert*
    (6/91) (DECC) ① [32] **430 100-2DM32(1)**
Hanover Band, R. Goodman *Concert*
    (7/93) (HYPE) ① **CDA66531**
Northern CO, N. Ward (r1992) *Concert*
    (1/94) (NAXO) ① **8 550721**
AAM, C. Hogwood (r1992) *Concert*
    (11/94) (L'OI) ① [3] **440 222-2OH3**
Estro Armonico, D. Solomons (r1981) *Concert*
    (11/95) (SONY) ① **SMK66929**
Symphony No. 50 in C (1773)
Philh Hungarica, A. Dorati *Concert*
    (6/91) (DECC) ① [32] **430 100-2DM32(1)**
Hanover Band, R. Goodman *Concert*
    (7/93) (HYPE) ① **CDA66531**
Tafelmusik, B. Weil (r1993) *Concert*
    (11/94) (SONY) ① **SK53985**
Symphony No. 51 in B flat (-1774)
Scottish CO, G. Schwarz *Concert*
    (5/90) (DELO) ① **DE3064**

English Concert, T. Pinnock *Concert*
    (7/90) (ARCH) ① **429 400-2AH**
Philh Hungarica, A. Dorati *Concert*
    (6/91) (DECC) ① [32] **430 100-2DM32(1)**
Tafelmusik, B. Weil *Concert*
    (4/93) (SONY) ① **SK48371**
Symphony No. 52 in C minor (-1774)
English Concert, T. Pinnock *Concert*
    (7/90) (ARCH) ① **429 400-2AH**
Philh Hungarica, A. Dorati *Concert*
    (6/91) (DECC) ① [32] **430 100-2DM32(1)**
Tafelmusik, B. Weil *Concert*
    (4/93) (SONY) ① **SK48371**
**Symphony No. 53 in D, 'Imperial' (?1778-
79)**
Philh Hungarica, A. Dorati *Concert*
    (6/91) (DECC) ① [32] **430 100-2DM32(1)**
VCM, N. Harnoncourt *Concert*
    (6/93) (TELD) ① **9031-76460-2**
Orpheus CO *Concert*   (9/94) (DG) ① **439 779-2GH**
N. Esterházy Sinfonia, B. Drahos (r1993) *Concert*
    (11/94) (NAXO) ① **8 550768**
Symphony No. 54 in G (1774)
Philh Hungarica, A. Dorati *Concert*
    (6/91) (DECC) ① [32] **430 100-2DM32(1)**
**Symphony No. 55 in E flat, 'Schoolmaster'
(1774)**
Philh Hungarica, A. Dorati *Concert*
    (6/91) (DECC) ① [32] **430 100-2DM32(1)**
Northern CO, N. Ward (r1992) *Concert*
    (5/95) (NAXO) ① **8 550757**
Symphony No. 56 in C (1774)
Philh Hungarica, A. Dorati *Concert*
    (6/91) (DECC) ① [32] **430 100-2DM32(1)**
Symphony No. 57 in D (1774)
Philh Hungarica, A. Dorati *Concert*
    (6/91) (DECC) ① [32] **430 100-2DM32(1)**
Symphony No. 58 in F (-1775)
Philh Hungarica, A. Dorati *Concert*
    (6/91) (DECC) ① [32] **430 100-2DM32(1)**
AAM, C. Hogwood *Concert*
    (4/92) (L'OI) ① [3] **433 012-2OH3**
Symphony No. 59 in A, 'Fire' (-1769)
Philh Hungarica, A. Dorati *Concert*
    (6/91) (DECC) ① [32] **430 100-2DM32(1)**
AAM, C. Hogwood *Concert*
    (4/92) (L'OI) ① [3] **433 012-2OH3**
VCM, N. Harnoncourt (r1993) *Concert*
    (4/95) (TELD) ① **4509-90843-2**
Symphony No. 60 in C, 'Il distratto' (-1774)
Philh Hungarica, A. Dorati *Concert*
    (6/91) (DECC) ① [32] **430 100-2DM32(2)**
Philh Hungarica, A. Dorati *Concert*
    (6/91) (DECC) ① [4] **425 920-2DM4**
CBSO, S. Rattle *Concert*
    (4/92) (EMI) ① **CDC7 54297-2**
Orpheus CO (r1992) *Concert*
    (12/93) (DG) ① **437 783-2GH**
Northern CO, N. Ward (r1993) *Concert*
    (6/95) (NAXO) ① **8 550724**
Symphony No. 61 in D (1776)
Philh Hungarica, A. Dorati *Concert*
    (6/91) (DECC) ① [32] **430 100-2DM32(2)**
Philh Hungarica, A. Dorati *Concert*
    (6/91) (DECC) ① [4] **425 920-2DM4**
Scottish CO, G. Schwarz *Concert*
    (10/92) (DELO) ① **DE3063**
Symphony No. 62 in D (-1781)
Philh Hungarica, A. Dorati *Concert*
    (6/91) (DECC) ① [32] **430 100-2DM32(2)**
Philh Hungarica, A. Dorati *Concert*
    (6/91) (DECC) ① [4] **425 920-2DM4**
**Symphony No. 63 in C, 'La Roxelane' (-1781
?1779)**
Orpheus CO (2nd vers) *Concert*
    (7/89) (DG) ① **427 337-2GH**
Philh Hungarica, A. Dorati *Concert*
    (6/91) (DECC) ① [4] **425 920-2DM4**
Philh Hungarica, A. Dorati *Concert*
    (6/91) (DECC) ① [32] **430 100-2DM32(2)**
Northern CO, N. Ward (r1993) *Concert*
    (5/95) (NAXO) ① **8 550757**
**Symphony No. 64 in A, 'Tempora mutantus'
(-1778 (?1773)**
Philh Hungarica, A. Dorati *Concert*
    (6/91) (DECC) ① [32] **430 100-2DM32(2)**
Philh Hungarica, A. Dorati *Concert*
    (6/91) (DECC) ① [4] **425 920-2DM4**
Tafelmusik, B. Weil (r1993) *Concert*
    (11/94) (SONY) ① **SK53985**
N. Esterházy Sinfonia, B. Drahos (r1993) *Concert*
    (3/95) (NAXO) ① **8 550770**
Symphony No. 65 in A (-1778 (?1771-73)
Philh Hungarica, A. Dorati *Concert*
    (6/91) (DECC) ① [32] **430 100-2DM32(2)**

Philh Hungarica, A. Dorati *Concert*
    (6/91) (DECC) ① [4] **425 920-2DM4**
AAM, C. Hogwood *Concert*
    (4/92) (L'OI) ① [3] **433 012-2OH3**
Tafelmusik, B. Weil (r1993) *Concert*
    (11/94) (SONY) ① **SK53985**
Symphony No. 66 in B flat (-1779)
Philh Hungarica, A. Dorati *Concert*
    (6/91) (DECC) ① [32] **430 100-2DM32(2)**
Philh Hungarica, A. Dorati *Concert*
    (6/91) (DECC) ① [4] **425 920-2DM4**
Symphony No. 67 in F (-1779 (?1775-76)
Philh Hungarica, A. Dorati *Concert*
    (6/91) (DECC) ① [32] **430 100-2DM32(2)**
Philh Hungarica, A. Dorati *Concert*
    (6/91) (DECC) ① [4] **425 920-2DM4**
Symphony No. 68 in B flat (-1779 (?1774-75)
Philh Hungarica, A. Dorati *Concert*
    (6/91) (DECC) ① [4] **425 920-2DM4**
Philh Hungarica, A. Dorati *Concert*
    (6/91) (DECC) ① [32] **430 100-2DM32(2)**
Concertgebouw, N. Harnoncourt (r1986/7) *Concert*
    (8/93) (TELD) ① **9031-74859-2**
Concertgebouw, N. Harnoncourt (r1986-7) *Concert*
    (4/94) (TELD) ① [6] **4509-92628-2**
**Symphony No. 69 in C, 'Loudon' (-1779
(?1775/-76)**
Philh Hungarica, A. Dorati *Concert*
    (6/91) (DECC) ① [32] **430 100-2DM32(2)**
Philh Hungarica, A. Dorati *Concert*
    (6/91) (DECC) ① [4] **425 920-2DM4**
VCM, N. Harnoncourt *Concert*
    (6/93) (TELD) ① **9031-76460-2**
Symphony No. 70 in D (1779)
Philh Hungarica, A. Dorati *Concert*
    (6/91) (DECC) ① [32] **430 100-2DM32(2)**
Philh Hungarica, A. Dorati *Concert*
    (6/91) (DECC) ① [4] **425 920-2DM4**
CBSO, S. Rattle *Concert*
    (4/92) (EMI) ① **CDC7 54297-2**
Hanover Band, R. Goodman *Concert*
    (9/92) (HYPE) ① **CDA66526**
Symphony No. 71 in B flat (-1780)
Philh Hungarica, A. Dorati *Concert*
    (6/91) (DECC) ① [4] **425 920-2DM4**
Philh Hungarica, A. Dorati *Concert*
    (6/91) (DECC) ① [32] **430 100-2DM32(2)**
Hanover Band, R. Goodman *Concert*
    (9/92) (HYPE) ① **CDA66526**
Symphony No. 72 in D (-1781 (?1763-65)
Philh Hungarica, A. Dorati *Concert*
    (6/91) (DECC) ① [32] **430 100-2DM32(2)**
Hanover Band, R. Goodman *Concert*
    (9/92) (HYPE) ① **CDA66526**
AAM, C. Hogwood *Concert*
    (6/93) (L'OI) ① [3] **433 661-2OH3**
N. Esterházy Sinfonia, B. Drahos (r1994) *Concert*
    (12/95) (NAXO) ① **8 550797**
**Symphony No. 73 in D, 'La chasse' (-1782
(?1781)**
Vienna Academy Orch, M. Haselböck (r1989)
    Concert   (4/90) (NOVA) ① **150 045-2**
Hanover Band, R. Goodman *Concert*
    (3/91) (HYPE) ① **CDA66520**
Philh Hungarica, A. Dorati *Concert*
    (6/91) (DECC) ① [32] **430 100-2DM32(2)**
Orpheus CO *Concert*   (9/94) (DG) ① **439 779-2GH**
VCM, N. Harnoncourt (r1992) *Concert*
    (4/95) (TELD) ① **4509-90843-2**
Symphony No. 74 in E flat (1781)
Hanover Band, R. Goodman *Concert*
    (3/91) (HYPE) ① **CDA66520**
Philh Hungarica, A. Dorati *Concert*
    (6/91) (DECC) ① [32] **430 100-2DM32(2)**
Symphony No. 75 in D (-1781)
Hanover Band, R. Goodman *Concert*
    (3/91) (HYPE) ① **CDA66520**
Philh Hungarica, A. Dorati *Concert*
    (6/91) (DECC) ① [32] **430 100-2DM32(2)**
Symphony No.76 in E flat (?1782)
Philh Hungarica, A. Dorati *Concert*
    (6/91) (DECC) ① [32] **430 100-2DM32(2)**
Hanover Band, R. Goodman *Concert*
    (5/92) (HYPE) ① **CDA66525**
Symphony No. 77 in B flat (?1782)
Philh Hungarica, A. Dorati *Concert*
    (6/91) (DECC) ① [32] **430 100-2DM32(2)**
Hanover Band, R. Goodman *Concert*
    (5/92) (HYPE) ① **CDA66525**
Symphony No. 78 in C minor (?1782)
Philh Hungarica, A. Dorati *Concert*
    (6/91) (DECC) ① [32] **430 100-2DM32(2)**
Hanover Band, R. Goodman *Concert*
    (5/92) (HYPE) ① **CDA66525**

Symphony No. 79 in F (1784)
Philh Hungarica, A. Dorati *Concert*
(6/91) (DECC) ① [32] 430 100-2DM32(2)
Orpheus CO *Concert* (9/94) (DG) ① 439 779-2GH
Symphony No. 80 in D minor (-1784)
Australian CO, C. Mackerras *Symphony 81.*
(12/88) (CONI) ① CDCF165
Orpheus CO *Concert* (7/89) (DG) ① 427 337-2GH
Philh Hungarica, A. Dorati *Concert*
(6/91) (DECC) ① [32] 430 100-2DM32(2)
Symphony No. 81 in G (-1784)
Australian CO, C. Mackerras *Symphony 80.*
(12/88) (CONI) ① CDCF165
Philh Hungarica, A. Dorati *Concert*
(6/91) (DECC) ① [32] 430 100-2DM32(2)
Symphony No. 82 in C, 'L'ours' (1786) (Eng: The Bear)
OAE, S. Kuijken *Concert*
(2/90) (VIRG) ① VC7 59537-2
Philh Hungarica, A. Dorati *Concert*
(6/91) (DECC) ① [32] 430 100-2DM32(2)
Hanover Band, R. Goodman (hpd/dir) *Concert*
(10/92) (HYPE) ① CDA66527
St Paul CO, H. Wolff *Symphony 84.*
(4/93) (TELD) ① 9031-74005-2
NYPO, L. Bernstein *Concert*
(5/93) (SONY) ① [2] SM2K47550
BPO, H. von Karajan (r1980) *Concert*
(1/95) (DG) ① [2] 445 532-2GMA2
Austro-Hungarian Haydn Orch, A. Fischer (r1992)
Concert (3/95) (NIMB) ① [2] NI5419/20
Tafelmusik, B. Weil (r1994) *Concert*
(7/95) (SONY) ① SK66295
Symphony No. 83 in G minor, 'La poule' (1785)
OAE, S. Kuijken *Concert*
(2/90) (VIRG) ① VC7 59537-2
Philh Hungarica, A. Dorati *Concert*
(6/91) (DECC) ① [32] 430 100-2DM32(2)
Hanover Band, R. Goodman (hpd/dir) *Concert*
(10/92) (HYPE) ① CDA66527
St Paul CO, H. Wolff *Symphony 87.*
(10/92) (TELD) ① 9031-73133-2
Amsterdam Baroque Orch, T. Koopman *Concert*
(12/92) (ERAT) ① 2292-45807-2
NYPO, L. Bernstein *Concert*
(5/93) (SONY) ① [2] SM2K47550
BPO, H. von Karajan (r1980) *Concert*
(1/95) (DG) ① [2] 445 532-2GMA2
Austro-Hungarian Haydn Orch, A. Fischer (r1991)
Concert (3/95) (NIMB) ① [2] NI5419/20
Tafelmusik, B. Weil (r1994) *Concert*
(7/95) (SONY) ① SK66295
Symphony No. 84 in E flat (-1786)
OAE, S. Kuijken *Concert*
(2/90) (VIRG) ① VC7 59537-2
Philh Hungarica, A. Dorati *Concert*
(6/91) (DECC) ① [4] 425 930-2DM4
Philh Hungarica, A. Dorati *Concert*
(6/91) (DECC) ① [32] 430 100-2DM32(2)
Hanover Band, R. Goodman (hpd/dir) *Concert*
(10/92) (HYPE) ① CDA66527
Amsterdam Baroque Orch, T. Koopman *Concert*
(12/92) (ERAT) ① 2292-45807-2
St Paul CO, H. Wolff *Symphony 82.*
(4/93) (TELD) ① 9031-74005-2
NYPO, L. Bernstein *Concert*
(5/93) (SONY) ① [2] SM2K47550
BPO, H. von Karajan (r1980) *Concert*
(1/95) (DG) ① [2] 445 532-2GMA2
N. Esterházy Sinfonia, B. Drahos (r1993) *Concert*
(3/95) (NAXO) ① 8 550770
Austro-Hungarian Haydn Orch, A. Fischer (r1994)
Concert (3/95) (NIMB) ① [2] NI5419/20
Tafelmusik, B. Weil (r1994) *Concert*
(7/95) (SONY) ① SK66295
Symphony No. 85 in B flat, 'La reine' (?1785)
OAE, S. Kuijken *Concert*
(5/90) (VIRG) ① VC7 59557-2
Philh Hungarica, A. Dorati *Concert*
(6/91) (DECC) ① [32] 430 100-2DM32(2)
Philh Hungarica, A. Dorati *Concert*
(6/91) (DECC) ① [4] 425 930-2DM4
St Paul CO, A. Wolff *Symphony 86.*
(9/91) (TELD) ① 2292-46313-2
Amsterdam Baroque Orch, T. Koopman *Concert*
(12/92) (ERAT) ① 2292-45807-2
NYPO, L. Bernstein *Concert*
(5/93) (SONY) ① [2] SM2K47550
Hanover Band, R. Goodman (r1993) *Concert*
(11/94) (HYPE) ① CDA66535
BPO, H. von Karajan (r1980) *Concert*
(1/95) (DG) ① [2] 445 532-2GMA2
Austro-Hungarian Haydn Orch, A. Fischer (r1991)
Concert (3/95) (NIMB) ① [2] NI5419/20

Tafelmusik, B. Weil (r1994) *Concert*
(7/95) (SONY) ① SK66296
Symphony No. 86 in D (1786)
OAE, S. Kuijken *Concert*
(5/90) (VIRG) ① VC7 59557-2
Philh Hungarica, A. Dorati *Concert*
(6/91) (DECC) ① [32] 430 100-2DM32(2)
Philh Hungarica, A. Dorati *Concert*
(6/91) (DECC) ① [4] 425 930-2DM4
St Paul CO, A. Wolff *Symphony 85.*
(9/91) (TELD) ① 2292-46313-2
NYPO, L. Bernstein *Concert*
(5/93) (SONY) ① [2] SM2K47550
LSO, B. Walter (r1938) *Concert*
(8/94) (DUTT) ① CDLX7008
N. Esterházy Sinfonia, B. Drahos (r1993) *Concert*
(11/94) (NAXO) ① 8 550768
Hanover Band, R. Goodman (r1993) *Concert*
(11/94) (HYPE) ① CDA66535
BPO, H. von Karajan (r1980) *Concert*
(1/95) (DG) ① [2] 445 532-2GMA2
Austro-Hungarian Haydn Orch, A. Fischer (r1994)
Concert (3/95) (NIMB) ① [2] NI5419/20
Tafelmusik, B. Weil (r1994) *Concert*
(7/95) (SONY) ① SK66296
Symphony No. 87 in A (1785)
Bournemouth Sinfonietta, R. Thomas *Symphony 103.*
(11/89) (CRD) ① CRD3400
OAE, S. Kuijken *Concert*
(5/90) (VIRG) ① VC7 59557-2
Philh Hungarica, A. Dorati *Concert*
(6/91) (DECC) ① [32] 430 100-2DM32(2)
Philh Hungarica, A. Dorati *Concert*
(6/91) (DECC) ① [4] 425 930-2DM4
St Paul CO, H. Wolff *Symphony 83.*
(10/92) (TELD) ① 9031-73133-2
NYPO, L. Bernstein *Concert*
(5/93) (SONY) ① [2] SM2K47550
N. Esterházy Sinfonia, B. Drahos (r1993) *Concert*
(11/94) (NAXO) ① 8 550768
Hanover Band, R. Goodman (r1993) *Concert*
(11/94) (HYPE) ① CDA66535
BPO, H. von Karajan (r1980) *Concert*
(1/95) (DG) ① [2] 445 532-2GMA2
Austro-Hungarian Haydn Orch, A. Fischer (r1994)
Concert (3/95) (NIMB) ① [2] NI5419/20
Tafelmusik, B. Weil (r1994) *Concert*
(7/95) (SONY) ① SK66296
Symphony No. 88 in G, 'Letter V' (?1787)
Bournemouth Sinfonietta, R. Thomas *Symphony 104.*
(8/87) (CRD) ① CRD3370
BRSO, C. Krauss (pp1953) *Concert*
(8/90) (ORFE) ① C196891A
VPO, C. Krauss (r1929) *Concert*
(1/91) (KOCH) ① 37011-2
Philh Hungarica, A. Dorati *Concert*
(6/91) (DECC) ① [32] 430 100-2DM32(2)
Philh Hungarica, A. Dorati *Concert*
(6/91) (DECC) ① [4] 425 930-2DM4
VPO, C. Krauss (r1929) *Concert*
(11/92) (PREI) ① 90112
NYPO, L. Bernstein (r1963) *Concert*
(5/93) (SONY) ① [2] SM2K47563
Chicago SO, F. Reiner (r1960) *Concert*
(7/93) (RCA) ① 09026 60729-2
Leipzig Gewandhaus, H. Abendroth (bp1944)
Concert (9/94) (TAHR) ① [2] TAH106/7
Tafelmusik, B. Weil (r1994) *Concert*
(10/95) (SONY) ① SK66253
VPO, L. Bernstein (pp1983) *Concert*
(12/95) (DG) ① 445 554-2GMA
BPO, W. Furtwängler (r1951) *Schubert: Symphony 9.*
(12/95) (DG) ① 447 439-2GOR
Symphony No. 89 in F (1787)
Philh Hungarica, A. Dorati *Concert*
(6/91) (DECC) ① [32] 430 100-2DM32(2)
Philh Hungarica, A. Dorati *Concert*
(6/91) (DECC) ① [4] 425 930-2DM4
Austro-Hungarian Haydn Orch, A. Fischer (r1991)
Concert (1/94) (NIMB) ① NI5341
Tafelmusik, B. Weil (r1994) *Concert*
(10/95) (SONY) ① SK66253
Symphony No. 90 in C (1788)
Philh Hungarica, A. Dorati *Concert*
(6/91) (DECC) ① [32] 430 100-2DM32(2)
Philh Hungarica, A. Dorati *Concert*
(6/91) (DECC) ① [4] 425 930-2DM4
Hanover Band, R. Goodman *Concert*
(6/91) (HYPE) ① CDA66521
CBSO, S. Rattle *Concert*
(4/92) (EMI) ① CDC7 54297-2
N. Esterházy Sinfonia, B. Drahos (r1993) *Concert*
(3/95) (NAXO) ① 8 550770
Petite Bande, S. Kuijken (r1989) *Symphony 91.*
(10/95) (VIRG) ① VC5 45068-2

Tafelmusik, B. Weil (r1994) *Concert*
(10/95) (SONY) ① SK66253
Symphony No. 91 in E flat (1788)
Philh Hungarica, A. Dorati *Concert*
(6/91) (DECC) ① [32] 430 100-2DM32(2)
Hanover Band, R. Goodman *Concert*
(6/91) (HYPE) ① CDA66521
Philh Hungarica, A. Dorati *Concert*
(6/91) (DECC) ① [4] 425 930-2DM4
Orpheus CO (r1992) *Concert*
(12/93) (DG) ① 437 783-2GH
Austro-Hungarian Haydn Orch, A. Fischer (r1991)
Concert (1/94) (NIMB) ① NI5341
Petite Bande, S. Kuijken (r1989) *Symphony 90.*
(10/95) (VIRG) ① VC5 45068-2
Symphony No. 92 in G, 'Oxford' (1789)
1. Adagio—Allegro spiritoso; 2. Adagio; 3. Menuet; 4. Presto.
English Sinfonia, C. Groves (r1988) *Symphony 104.*
(6/89) (CARL) ① PCD916
Cleveland Orch, G. Szell *Concert*
(3/91) (SONY) ① SBK46332
Philh Hungarica, A. Dorati *Concert*
(6/91) (DECC) ① [32] 430 100-2DM32(2)
Hanover Band, R. Goodman *Concert*
(6/91) (HYPE) ① CDA66521
VPO, L. Bernstein (pp1984) *Concert*
(12/95) (DG) ① 445 554-2GMA
Symphony No. 93 in D (1791)
LPO, G. Solti *Symphony 99.*
(11/87) (DECC) ① 417 620-2DH
Prague CO *Concert* (12/87) (SUPR) ① 2SUP0016
Austro-Hungarian Haydn Orch, A. Fischer *Concert*
(12/89) (NIMB) ① [5] NI5200/4
COE, C. Abbado *Symphony 101.*
(5/91) (DG) ① 429 776-2GH
Philh Hungarica, A. Dorati *Concert*
(6/91) (DECC) ① [32] 430 100-2DM32(2)
Philh Hungarica, A. Dorati *Concert*
(6/91) (DECC) ① [4] 425 930-2DM4
LPO, G. Solti *Concert*
(3/93) (DECC) ① [6] 436 290-2DM6
NYPO, L. Bernstein *Concert*
(5/93) (SONY) ① [3] SM3K47553
Hanover Band, R. Goodman *Concert*
(8/93) (HYPE) ① CDA66532
Concertgebouw, N. Harnoncourt (r1992) *Concert*
(8/93) (TELD) ① 9031-74859-2
RPO, T. Beecham (r1957) *Concert*
(9/93) (EMI) ① [2] CMS7 64389-2
Petite Bande, S. Kuijken (r1992) *Concert*
(10/93) (DHM) ① 05472 77275-2
Concertgebouw, N. Harnoncourt (r1992) *Concert*
(4/94) (TELD) ① [6] 4509-92628-2
LPO, T. Beecham (r1936) *Concert*
(3/95) (DUTT) ① [2] 2CDAX2003
Berlin RSO, K. Ančerl (r1937) *Schubert: Symphony 9.*
(11/95) (TAHR) ① TAH117
N. Esterházy Sinfonia, B. Drahos (r1994) *Concert*
(12/95) (NAXO) ① 8 550797
Symphony No. 94 in G, 'Surprise' (1791)
1. Adagio—Vivace assai; 2. Andante; 3. Menuet; 4. Allegro di molto.
Philh Hungarica, A. Dorati *Concert*
(7/87) (DECC) ① 417 718-2DM
Prague CO *Concert* (12/87) (SUPR) ① 2SUP0016
LPO, E. Jochum *Symphony 101.*
(11/88) (DG) ① 423 883-2GGA
Austro-Hungarian Haydn Orch, A. Fischer *Concert*
(12/89) (NIMB) ① [5] NI5200/4
Vienna Academy Orch, M. Haselböck (1989)
Concert (4/90) (NOVA) ① 150 045-2
Cleveland Orch, G. Szell *Concert*
(3/91) (SONY) ① SBK46332
Philh Hungarica, A. Dorati *Concert*
(6/91) (DECC) ① [4] 425 930-2DM4
Philh Hungarica, A. Dorati *Concert*
(6/91) (DECC) ① [32] 430 100-2DM32(2)
LPO, G. Solti *Concert*
(3/93) (DECC) ① [6] 436 290-2DM6
NYPO, L. Bernstein *Concert*
(5/93) (SONY) ① [3] SM3K47553
Hanover Band, R. Goodman *Concert*
(8/93) (HYPE) ① CDA66532
RPO, T. Beecham (r1957/8) *Concert*
(9/93) (EMI) ① [2] CMS7 64389-2
Petite Bande, S. Kuijken (r1992) *Concert*
(10/93) (DHM) ① 05472 77275-2
Concertgebouw, N. Harnoncourt (r1990) *Concert*
(4/94) (TELD) ① [6] 4509-92628-2
BPO, H. Knappertsbusch (r1941) *Brahms: Symphony 3.*
(5/94) (PREI) ① 90121
Philh, L. Slatkin (r1993) *Concert*
(2/95) (RCA) ① 09026 62549-2

VPO, L. Bernstein (pp1985) *Concert*
(12/95) (DG) ① **445 554-2GMA**
Symphony No. 95 in C minor (1791)
Prague CO *Concert*   (12/87) (SUPR) ① **2SUP0016**
Austro-Hungarian Haydn Orch, A. Fischer *Concert*
(12/89) (NIMB) ① [5] **NI5200/4**
Philh Hungarica, A. Dorati *Concert*
(6/91) (DECC) ① [32] **430 100-2DM32(2)**
Philh Hungarica, A. Dorati *Concert*
(6/91) (DECC) ① [4] **425 930-2DM4**
LPO, G. Solti *Concert*
(3/93) (DECC) ① [6] **436 290-2DM6**
NYPO, L. Bernstein *Concert*
(5/93) (SONY) ① [3] **SM3K47553**
SO, F. Reiner (r1963) *Concert*
(7/93) (RCA) ① **09026 60729-2**
Hanover Band, R. Goodman *Concert*
(8/93) (HYPE) ① **CDA66532**
RPO, T. Beecham (r1957) *Concert*
(9/93) (EMI) ① [2] **CMS7 64389-2**
Petite Bande, S. Kuijken (r1992) *Concert*
(10/94) (DHM) ① **05472 77275-2**
Concertgebouw, N. Harnoncourt (r1990) *Concert*
(4/94) (TELD) ① [6] **4509-92628-2**
N. Esterházy Sinfonia, B. Drahos (r1994) *Concert*
(12/95) (NAXO) ① **8 550797**
Symphony No. 96 in D, 'Miracle' (1791)
1. Adagio—Allegro; 2. Andante; 3. Menuetto; 4.
Vivace (assai).
Philh Hungarica, A. Dorati *Concert*
(7/87) (DECC) ① **417 718-2DM**
Scottish CO, G. Schwarz *Concert*
(9/88) (DELO) ① **DE3062**
Prague CO *Concert*   (2/89) (SUPR) ① **2SUP0034**
Austro-Hungarian Haydn Orch, A. Fischer *Concert*
(12/89) (NIMB) ① [5] **NI5200/4**
Cleveland Orch, G. Szell *Concert*
(3/91) (SONY) ① **SBK46332**
Philh Hungarica, A. Dorati *Concert*
(6/91) (DECC) ① [32] **430 100-2DM32(2)**
Philh Hungarica, A. Dorati *Concert*
(6/91) (DECC) ① [4] **425 935-2DM4**
VPO, B. Walter (r1937) *Concert*
(11/92) (PREI) ① **90114**
LPO, G. Solti *Concert*
(3/93) (DECC) ① [6] **436 290-2DM6**
NYPO, L. Bernstein *Concert*
(5/93) (SONY) ① [3] **SM3K47553**
RPO, T. Beecham (r1957) *Concert*
(9/93) (EMI) ① [2] **CMS7 64389-2**
Concertgebouw, N. Harnoncourt (r1992) *Concert*
(4/94) (TELD) ① [6] **4509-92628-2**
Leipzig Gewandhaus, H. Abendroth (bp1945)
Concert   (9/94) (TAHR) ① [2] **TAH106/7**
Petite Bande, S. Kuijken (r1993) *Concert*
(10/94) (DHM) ① **05472 77294-2**
3. F. Kreisler, C. Lamson (r1924: arr Friedberg)
Concert   (9/93) (BIDD) ① [2] **LAB068/9**
Symphony No. 97 in C (1792)
Prague CO *Concert*   (2/89) (SUPR) ① **2SUP0034**
Austro-Hungarian Haydn Orch, A. Fischer *Concert*
(12/89) (NIMB) ① [5] **NI5200/4**
Philh Hungarica, A. Dorati *Concert*
(6/91) (DECC) ① [32] **430 100-2DM32(2)**
Philh Hungarica, A. Dorati *Concert*
(6/91) (DECC) ① [4] **425 935-2DM4**
LPO, G. Solti *Concert*
(3/93) (DECC) ① [6] **436 290-2DM6**
NYPO, L. Bernstein *Concert*
(5/93) (SONY) ① [3] **SM3K47553**
RPO, T. Beecham (r1957/8) *Concert*
(9/93) (EMI) ① [2] **CMS7 64389-2**
Concertgebouw, N. Harnoncourt (r1992) *Concert*
(4/94) (TELD) ① [6] **4509-92628-2**
Eighteenth Century Orch, F. Brüggen (pp1992)
Symphony 98.   (9/94) (PHIL) ① **434 921-2PH**
Petite Bande, S. Kuijken (r1993) *Concert*
(10/94) (DHM) ① **05472 77294-2**
N. Esterházy Sinfonia, B. Drahos (r1994) *Symphony
98.*   (3/95) (NAXO) ① **8 550780**
Symphony No. 98 in B flat (1792)
Prague CO *Concert*   (2/89) (SUPR) ① **2SUP0034**
Austro-Hungarian Haydn Orch, A. Fischer *Concert*
(12/89) (NIMB) ① [5] **NI5200/4**
Philh Hungarica, A. Dorati *Concert*
(6/91) (DECC) ① [32] **430 100-2DM32(2)**
Philh Hungarica, A. Dorati *Concert*
(6/91) (DECC) ① [4] **425 935-2DM4**
LPO, G. Solti *Concert*
(3/93) (DECC) ① [6] **436 290-2DM6**
NYPO, L. Bernstein *Concert*
(5/93) (SONY) ① [3] **SM3K47553**
RPO, T. Beecham (r1957/8) *Concert*
(9/93) (EMI) ① [2] **CMS7 64389-2**
Concertgebouw, N. Harnoncourt (r1990) *Concert*
(4/94) (TELD) ① [6] **4509-92628-2**

Eighteenth Century Orch, F. Brüggen (pp1992)
Symphony 97.   (9/94) (PHIL) ① **434 921-2PH**
Petite Bande, S. Kuijken (r1993) *Concert*
(10/94) (DHM) ① **05472 77294-2**
Philh, L. Slatkin (r1993) *Concert*
(2/95) (RCA) ① **09026 62549-2**
N. Esterházy Sinfonia, B. Drahos (r1994) *Symphony
97.*   (3/95) (NAXO) ① **8 550780**
COE, C. Abbado (pp1993) *Concert*
(10/95) (DG) ① **439 932-2GH**
Symphony No. 99 in E flat (1793)
LPO, G. Solti *Symphony 93.*
(11/87) (DECC) ① **417 620-2DH**
Austro-Hungarian Haydn Orch, A. Fischer *Concert*
(12/89) (NIMB) ① [5] **NI5200/4**
Philh Hungarica, A. Dorati *Concert*
(6/91) (DECC) ① [32] **430 100-2DM32(2)**
Philh Hungarica, A. Dorati *Concert*
(6/91) (DECC) ① [4] **425 935-2DM4**
RPO, T. Beecham (r1958/9) *Concert*
(9/92) (EMI) ① [2] **CMS7 64066-2**
NBC SO, A. Toscanini (bp1949) *Concert*
(11/92) (RCA) ① **GD60282**
LPO, G. Solti *Concert*
(3/93) (DECC) ① [6] **436 290-2DM6**
NYPO, L. Bernstein *Concert*
(5/93) (SONY) ① [3] **SM3K47553**
Concertgebouw, N. Harnoncourt (r1990) *Concert*
(4/94) (TELD) ① [6] **4509-92628-2**
LCP, R. Norrington (r1993) *Concert*
(12/94) (EMI) ① **CDC5 55192-2**
LPO, T. Beecham (r1935/6) *Concert*
(3/95) (DUTT) ① [2] **2CDAX2003**
Symphony No. 100 in G, 'Military' (1793-94)
Philh Hungarica, A. Dorati *Concert*
(7/87) (DECC) ① **417 718-2DM**
Austro-Hungarian Haydn Orch, A. Fischer *Concert*
(12/89) (NIMB) ① [5] **NI5200/4**
Scottish CO, G. Schwarz *Concert*
(5/90) (DELO) ① **DE3064**
Philh Hungarica, A. Dorati *Concert*
(6/91) (DECC) ① [4] **425 935-2DM4**
Philh Hungarica, A. Dorati *Concert*
(6/91) (DECC) ① [32] **430 100-2DM32(2)**
RPO, T. Beecham (r1958/9) *Concert*
(9/92) (EMI) ① [2] **CMS7 64066-2**
LPO, G. Solti *Concert*
(3/93) (DECC) ① [6] **436 290-2DM6**
NYPO, L. Bernstein *Concert*
(5/93) (SONY) ① [2] **SM2K47557**
Concertgebouw, N. Harnoncourt (r1986/7) *Concert*
(8/93) (TELD) ① **9031-74859-2**
VPO, B. Walter (r1938) *Concert*
(3/94) (PREI) ① **90141**
Concertgebouw, N. Harnoncourt (r1986-7) *Concert*
(4/94) (TELD) ① [6] **4509-92628-2**
LCP, R. Norrington (r1993) *Concert*
(12/94) (EMI) ① **CDC5 55192-2**
COE, C. Abbado (r1992) *Concert*
(10/95) (DG) ① **439 932-2GH**
Symphony No. 101 in D, 'Clock' (1793-94)
1. Adagio—Presto; 2. Andante; 3. Menuet; 4. Vivace.
LPO, E. Jochum *Symphony 94.*
(11/88) (DG) ① **423 883-2GGA**
Prague CO *Symphony 104.*
(2/89) (SUPR) ① **2SUP0032**
Austro-Hungarian Haydn Orch, A. Fischer *Concert*
(12/89) (NIMB) ① [5] **NI5200/4**
NYPSO, A. Toscanini (r1929) *Concert*
(3/90) (PEAR) ① [3] **GEMMCDS9373**
COE, C. Abbado *Symphony 93.*
(5/91) (DG) ① **429 776-2GH**
Philh Hungarica, A. Dorati *Concert*
(6/91) (DECC) ① [4] **425 935-2DM4**
Philh Hungarica, A. Dorati *Concert*
(6/91) (DECC) ① [32] **430 100-2DM32(2)**
RPO, T. Beecham (r1958/9) *Concert*
(9/92) (EMI) ① [2] **CMS7 64066-2**
NBC SO, A. Toscanini (r1946/7) *Concert*
(11/92) (RCA) ① **GD60282**
NYPSO, A. Toscanini (r1929) *Concert*
(11/92) (RCA) ① **GD60316**
Hanover Band, R. Goodman *Concert*
(12/92) (HYPE) ① **CDA66528**
St Luke's Orch, C. Mackerras *Symphony 104.*
(2/93) (TELA) ① **CD80311**
LPO, G. Solti *Concert*
(3/93) (DECC) ① [6] **436 290-2DM6**
NYPO, L. Bernstein *Concert*
(5/93) (SONY) ① [2] **SM2K47557**
SO, F. Reiner (r1963) *Concert*
(7/93) (RCA) ① **09026 60729-2**
Concertgebouw, N. Harnoncourt (r1988) *Concert*
(4/94) (TELD) ① [6] **4509-92628-2**
LCP, R. Norrington (r1993) *Symphony 102.*
(12/94) (EMI) ① **CDC5 55111-2**

Symphony No. 102 in B flat (1794)
1. Largo—Vivace; 2. Adagio; 3. Menuet; 4. Presto.
Austro-Hungarian Haydn Orch, A. Fischer *Concert*
(12/89) (NIMB) ① [5] **NI5200/4**
Philh Hungarica, A. Dorati *Concert*
(6/91) (DECC) ① [32] **430 100-2DM32(2)**
Philh Hungarica, A. Dorati *Concert*
(6/91) (DECC) ① [4] **425 935-2DM4**
Capella Istropolitana, B. Wordsworth *Concert*
(9/91) (NAXO) ① **8 550382**
VPO, L. Bernstein (pp1971) *Concert*
(2/92) (DG) ① [12] **435 321-2GWP12**
RPO, T. Beecham (r1958) *Concert*
(9/92) (EMI) ① [2] **CMS7 64066-2**
Hanover Band, R. Goodman *Concert*
(12/92) (HYPE) ① **CDA66528**
LPO, G. Solti *Concert*
(3/93) (DECC) ① [6] **436 290-2DM6**
NYPO, L. Bernstein *Concert*
(5/93) (SONY) ① [2] **SM2K47557**
Concertgebouw, N. Harnoncourt (r1988) *Concert*
(4/94) (TELD) ① [6] **4509-92628-2**
VPO, A. Previn (r1993) *Symphony 104.*
(12/94) (PHIL) ① **438 934-2PH**
LCP, R. Norrington (r1993) *Symphony 104.*
(12/94) (EMI) ① **CDC5 55111-2**
Symphony No. 103 in E flat, 'Drumroll' (1795)
Bournemouth Sinfonietta, R. Thomas *Symphony 87.*
(11/89) (CRD) ① **CRD3400**
Austro-Hungarian Haydn Orch, A. Fischer *Concert*
(12/89) (NIMB) ① [5] **NI5200/4**
Philh Hungarica, A. Dorati *Concert*
(6/91) (DECC) ① [4] **425 935-2DM4**
Philh Hungarica, A. Dorati *Concert*
(6/91) (DECC) ① [32] **430 100-2DM32(2)**
RPO, T. Beecham (r1958/9) *Concert*
(9/92) (EMI) ① [2] **CMS7 64066-2**
Scottish CO, G. Schwarz *Concert*
(10/92) (DELO) ① **DE3063**
LPO, G. Solti *Concert*
(3/93) (DECC) ① [6] **436 290-2DM6**
NYPO, L. Bernstein *Concert*
(5/93) (SONY) ① [2] **SM2K47557**
Concertgebouw, N. Harnoncourt (r1987) *Concert*
(4/94) (TELD) ① [6] **4509-92628-2**
LCP, R. Norrington (r1992) *Symphony 104.*
(7/94) (EMI) ① **CDC5 55002-2**
Symphony No. 104 in D, 'London' (1795)
1. Adagio—Allegro; 2. Andante; 3. Menuet; 4.
Spiritoso.
Bournemouth Sinfonietta, R. Thomas *Symphony 88.*
(8/87) (CRD) ① **CRD3370**
Scottish CO, G. Schwarz *Concert*
(9/88) (DELO) ① **DE3061**
Prague CO *Symphony 101.*
(2/89) (SUPR) ① **2SUP0032**
English Sinfonia, C. Groves (r1988) *Symphony 92.*
(6/89) (CARL) ① **PCD916**
Austro-Hungarian Haydn Orch, A. Fischer *Concert*
(12/89) (NIMB) ① [5] **NI5200/4**
Philh Hungarica, A. Dorati *Concert*
(6/91) (DECC) ① [4] **425 935-2DM4**
Philh Hungarica, A. Dorati *Concert*
(6/91) (DECC) ① [32] **430 100-2DM32(2)**
Barbirolli CO, J. Barbirolli (r1928) *Concert*
(3/92) (KOCH) ① **37077-2**
RPO, T. Beecham (r1958/9) *Concert*
(9/92) (EMI) ① [2] **CMS7 64066-2**
St Luke's Orch, C. Mackerras *Symphony 101.*
(2/93) (TELA) ① **CD80311**
LPO, G. Solti *Concert*
(3/93) (DECC) ① [6] **436 290-2DM6**
NYPO, L. Bernstein *Concert*
(5/93) (SONY) ① [2] **SM2K47557**
Concertgebouw, N. Harnoncourt (r1987) *Concert*
(4/94) (TELD) ① [6] **4509-92628-2**
LCP, R. Norrington (r1992) *Symphony 103.*
(7/94) (EMI) ① **CDC5 55002-2**
VPO, A. Previn (r1993) *Symphony 102.*
(12/94) (PHIL) ① **438 934-2PH**
Philh, L. Slatkin (1993) *Concert*
(2/95) (RCA) ① **09026 62549-2**
LPO, T. Beecham (r1935) *Concert*
(3/95) (DUTT) ① [2] **2CDAX2003**
Florilegium Ens (r1994: trans fl, 2 vns, va, vc & fp)
Concert   (7/95) (CHNN) ① **CCS7395**
4. S. Mayor (arr Mayor: Mandolin ens) *Concert*
(3/92) (ACOU) ① **CDACS014**
Symphony No. 107 (Partita) in B flat (c1757-60)
AAM, C. Hogwood (r1990) *Concert*
(4/94) (L'OI) ① [3] **436 428-2OH3**

6 String Quartets, 'Tost III', Op. 64 (HobIII/63-68) (1790)
EXCERPTS: 1. C; 2. B minor; 3. B flat; 4. G; 5. D, 'Lark'; 6. E flat.
Amadeus Qt *String Quartet, Op. 51.*
(10/91) (DG) ① [3] **431 145-2GCM3**
Festetics Qt (r1991)
(12/95) (HARM) ① [2] **HMA190 3040/1**
1-3. Kodály Qt (r1992) (1/94) (NAXO) ① **8 550673**
3. Pro Arte Qt (r1937) *Concert*
(6/95) (TEST) ① [3] **SBT3055**
4. Pro Arte Qt (r1936) *Concert*
(6/95) (TEST) ① [3] **SBT3055**
4-6. Kodály Qt (r1992) (1/94) (NAXO) ① **8 550674**
5. Gabrieli Qt *String Quartets, Op. 54.*
(11/87) (CHAN) ① **CHAN8531**
5. Hagen Qt *Concert* (7/89) (DG) ① **423 622-2GH**
5. Quartetto Italiano *Concert*
(6/90) (PHIL) ① **426 097-2PC**
5(Vivace) J. Heifetz, S. Chotzinoff (r1922) *Concert*
(11/94) (RCA) ① [65] **09026 61778-2(01)**
5. Lindsay Qt (pp1987) *Concert*
(5/95) (ASV) ① **CDQS6145**
5. Flonzaley Qt (r1928) *Concert*
(10/95) (BIDD) ① [2] **LAB089/90**
5. Capet Qt (r1927-8) *Concert*
(12/95) (BIDD) ① **LAB097**
6. Pro Arte Qt (r1933) *Concert*
(6/95) (TEST) ① [4] **SBT4056**

SECTION III: INSTRUMENTAL

Adagio in F, HobXVII/9 (1786) (attrib Haydn)
A. Brendel *Concert* (11/85) (PHIL) ① **412 228-2PH**
J. Cload *Concert* (9/86) (MERI) ① **ECD84083**
A. Brendel *Concert*
(3/87) (PHIL) ① [4] **416 643-2PH4**
J. McCabe (r1974-77) *Concert*
(12/95) (LOND) ① [12] **443 785-2LC12(2)**
Capriccio in G—keyboard, HobXVII/1 (1765)
J. McCabe (r1974-77) *Concert*
(12/95) (LOND) ① [12] **443 785-2LC12(2)**
Fantasia (Capriccio) in C—keyboard, HobXVII/4 (1789)
A. Brendel *Concert* (11/85) (PHIL) ① **412 228-2PH**
A. Brendel *Concert*
(3/87) (PHIL) ① [4] **416 643-2PH4**
J. McCabe (r1974-77) *Concert*
(12/95) (LOND) ① [12] **443 785-2LC12(2)**
32 Flute-clock Pieces, HobXIX (c1789-96)
1. F; 2. F; 3. F; 4. C; 5. F; 6. F; 7. C; 8. C; 9. Menuet, C; 10. Andante, C; 11. C; 12. Andante, C; 13. C; 14. C; 15. C; 16. Fuga, C; 17. C; 18. Presto, C; 19. C; 20. C; 21. G; 22. C; 23. C; 24. Presto, C; 25. Marche, D; 26. Andante, Allegro, E; 27. Allegretto, G; 28. Allegro, C; 29. C; 30. Presto, G; 31. Presto, C; 32. Allegro, F.
Excs I. Tracey (r1990; arr Tracey) *Concert*
(4/91) (MIRA) ① **MRCD901**
6, 9, 15, 20, 32. I. Hare *Concert*
(2/90) (MERI) ① **DUOCD89003**
Keyboard Sonata in C
G. Gifford *Concert* (5/90) (LIBR) ① **LRCD156**
5 Menuets from 'Kleine Tänze für die Jugend'—keyboard, HobIX/8 (—1785)
J. McCabe (r1974-77) *Concert*
(12/95) (LOND) ① [12] **443 785-2LC12(1)**
The Seven Last Words of Jesus Christ—piano (1787) (arr of string quartet version)
Y. Le Gaillard (12/87) (CHNT) ① **LDC278 842**
J. van Immerseel (r1994)
(8/95) (CHNN) ① **CCS6894**
J. McCabe (r1974-77) *Concert*
(12/95) (LOND) ① [12] **443 785-2LC12(2)**
Sonata for Keyboard in B flat, HobXVI/17 (spurious: probably by Schwanenberger)
J. McCabe (r1974-77) *Concert*
(12/95) (LOND) ① [12] **443 785-2LC12(1)**
Sonata for Keyboard in E flat (Divertimento), HobXVI/6 (doubtful)
J. McCabe (r1974-77) *Concert*
(12/95) (LOND) ① [12] **443 785-2LC12(1)**
Sonata for Keyboard No. 1 in G (Parthia), HobXVI/8 (before 1766) (numbering based on Christa Landon Edition)
J. McCabe (r1974-6) *Concert*
(12/95) (LOND) ① [12] **443 785-2LC12(1)**
Sonata for Keyboard No. 2 in C (Parthia), HobXVI/7 (before 1766) (numbering based on Christa Landon Edition)
J. McCabe (r1974-7) *Concert*
(12/95) (LOND) ① [12] **443 785-2LC12(1)**
Sonata for Keyboard No. 3 in F (Divertimento), HobXVI/9 (?1760) (numbering based on Christa Landon Edition)
J. McCabe (r1974-7) *Concert*
(12/95) (LOND) ① [12] **443 785-2LC12(1)**

Sonata for Keyboard No. 4 in G (Divertimento), HobXVI/G.1 (?1760) (numbering based on Christa Landon Edition)
J. McCabe (r1974-6) *Concert*
(12/95) (LOND) ① [12] **443 785-2LC12(1)**
Sonata for Keyboard No. 5 in G (Divertimento), HobXVI/11 (?) (numbering based on Christa Landon Edition)
J. McCabe (r1974-7) *Concert*
(12/95) (LOND) ① [12] **443 785-2LC12(1)**
Sonata for Keyboard No. 6 in C (Divertimento), HobXVI/10 (before 1767) (numbering based on Christa Landon Edition)
J. McCabe (r1974-5) *Concert*
(12/95) (LOND) ① [12] **443 785-2LC12(1)**
Sonata for Keyboard No. 7 in D (Divertimento), HobXVI/D.1 (?) (numbering based on Christa Landon Edition)
J. McCabe (r1974-7) *Concert*
(12/95) (LOND) ① [12] **443 785-2LC12(1)**
Sonata for Keyboard No. 8 in A (Divertimento), HobXVI/5 (before 1763) (numbering based on Christa Landon Edition)
C. Faron *Concert* (9/92) (SCHW) ① **310094**
J. McCabe (r1974-7) *Concert*
(12/95) (LOND) ① [12] **443 785-2LC12(1)**
Sonata for Keyboard No. 9 in D (Divertimento), HobXVI/4 (1766) (numbering based on Christa Landon Edition)
C. Faron *Concert* (9/92) (SCHW) ① **310094**
J. McCabe (r1974-6) *Concert*
(12/95) (LOND) ① [12] **443 785-2LC12(1)**
Sonata for Keyboard No. 10 in C (Parthia), HobXVI/1 (? c1750-55) (numbering based on Christa Landon Edition)
J. McCabe (r1974-7) *Concert*
(12/95) (LOND) ① [12] **443 785-2LC12(1)**
Sonata for Keyboard No. 11 in B (Parthia), HobXVI/2 (before ?1767) (numbering based on Christa Landon Edition)
C. Faron *Concert* (9/92) (SCHW) ① **310094**
S. Richter *Concert* (3/93) (DECC) ① **436 455-2DH**
J. McCabe (r1974-77) *Concert*
(12/95) (LOND) ① [12] **443 785-2LC12(1)**
Sonata for Keyboard No. 12 in A, HobXVI/12 (before 1767) (numbering based on Christa Landon Edition)
J. McCabe (r1974-7) *Concert*
(12/95) (LOND) ① [12] **443 785-2LC12(1)**
Sonata for Keyboard No. 13 in G (Parthia), HobXVI/6 (1767) (numbering based on Christa Landon Edition)
C. Faron *Concert* (9/92) (SCHW) ① **310094**
J. McCabe (r1974-77) *Concert*
(12/95) (LOND) ① [12] **443 785-2LC12(1)**
Sonata for Keyboard No. 14 in C (Parthia), HobXVI/3 (1767) (numbering based on Christa Landon Edition)
J. McCabe (r1974-77) *Concert*
(12/95) (LOND) ① [12] **443 785-2LC12(1)**
Sonata for Keyboard No. 15 in E, HobXVI/13 (before 1767) (numbering based on Christa Landon Edition)
J. McCabe (r1974-77) *Concert*
(12/95) (LOND) ① [12] **443 785-2LC12(1)**
Sonata for Keyboard No. 16 in D (Parthia), HobXVI/14 (1767) (numbering based on Christa Landon Edition)
C. Faron *Concert* (9/92) (SCHW) ① **310094**
J. McCabe (r1974-77) *Concert*
(12/95) (LOND) ① [12] **443 785-2LC12(1)**
Sonata for Keyboard No. 17 in E flat (? c1755) (numbering based on Christa Landon Edition)
J. McCabe (r1974-77) *Concert*
(12/95) (LOND) ① [12] **443 785-2LC12(1)**
Sonata for Keyboard No. 18 in E flat (1788) (numbering based on Christa Landon Edition)
J. McCabe (r1974-77) *Concert*
(12/95) (LOND) ① [12] **443 785-2LC12(1)**
Sonata for Keyboard No. 19 in E minor, Vgl/Cf. HobXVI/47 (?1765) (numbering based on Christa Landon Edition)
J. McCabe (r1974-77) *Concert*
(12/95) (LOND) ① [12] **443 785-2LC12(1)**
Sonata for Keyboard No. 20 in B flat, HobXVI/18 (1788) (numbering based on Christa Landon Edition)
J. McCabe (r1974-77) *Concert*
(12/95) (LOND) ① [12] **443 785-2LC12(1)**
Sonata for Keyboard No. 28 in D (Divertimento), HobXIV/5 (fragment only: Menuet & Trio)
J. McCabe (r1974-77; completed McCabe) *Concert*
(12/95) (LOND) ① [12] **443 785-2LC12(1)**

Sonata for Keyboard No. 29 in E flat, HobXVI/45 (1766) (numbering based on Christa Landon Edition)
J. McCabe (r1974-77) *Concert*
(12/95) (LOND) ① [12] **443 785-2LC12(1)**
Sonata for Keyboard No. 30 in D, HobXVI/19 (1767) (numbering based on Christa Landon Edition)
I. Pogorelich *Keyboard Sonata 31.*
(5/92) (DG) ① **435 618-2GH**
J. McCabe (r1974-77) *Concert*
(12/95) (LOND) ① [12] **443 785-2LC12(1)**
Sonata for Keyboard No. 31 in A flat, HobXVI/46 (1778) (numbering based on Christa Landon Edition)
Y.E. Mei (r1989) *Concert*
(5/90) (LDR) ① **LDRCD1010**
I. Pogorelich *Keyboard Sonata 30.*
(5/92) (DG) ① **435 618-2GH**
S. Richter *Concert* (3/93) (DECC) ① **436 455-2DH**
J. McCabe (r1974-77) *Concert*
(12/95) (LOND) ① [12] **443 785-2LC12(1)**
Sonata for Keyboard No. 32 in G minor, HobXVI/44 (1778) (numbering based on Christa Landon Edition)
A. Wilde *Concert* (11/92) (COLL) ① **Coll3017-2**
S. Richter *Concert* (3/93) (DECC) ① **436 454-2DH**
E. Ax (r1993) *Concert* (7/95) (SONY) ① **SK53635**
J. McCabe (r1974-77) *Concert*
(12/95) (LOND) ① [12] **443 785-2LC12(1)**
S. Richter (r1961) *Concert*
(12/95) (DG) ① [2] **447 355-2GDB2**
Sonata for Keyboard No. 33 in C minor, HobXVI/20 (1771) (numbering based on Christa Landon Edition)
A. Brendel *Concert*
(3/87) (PHIL) ① [4] **416 643-2PH4**
M. Pletnev (r1988) *Concert*
(11/89) (VIRG) ① **VC7 59258-2**
Y.E. Mei (r1989) *Concert*
(5/90) (LDR) ① **LDRCD1010**
A. Wilde *Concert* (11/92) (COLL) ① **Coll3017-2**
J. McCabe (r1974-77) *Concert*
(12/95) (LOND) ① [12] **443 785-2LC12(1)**
Sonata for Keyboard No. 34 in D, HobXVI/33 (1778) (numbering based on Christa Landon Edition)
A. Staier (r1992) *Concert*
(2/94) (DHM) ① **05472 77285-2**
J. McCabe (r1974-77) *Concert*
(12/95) (LOND) ① [12] **443 785-2LC12(1)**
Sonata for Keyboard No. 35 in A flat, HobXVI/43 (1783) (numbering based on Christa Landon Edition)
J. McCabe (r1974-77) *Concert*
(12/95) (LOND) ① [12] **443 785-2LC12(1)**
Sonata for Keyboard No. 36 in C, HobXVI/21 (1773) (numbering based on Christa Landon Edition)
J. Jandó (r1993) *Concert*
(6/95) (NAXO) ① **8 553127**
J. McCabe (r1974-77) *Concert*
(12/95) (LOND) ① [12] **443 785-2LC12(1)**
Sonata for Keyboard No. 37 in E, HobXVI/22 (1773) (numbering based on Christa Landon Edition)
J. Jandó (r1993) *Concert*
(6/95) (NAXO) ① **8 553127**
J. McCabe (r1974-77) *Concert*
(12/95) (LOND) ① [12] **443 785-2LC12(1)**
Sonata for Keyboard No. 38 in F, HobXVI/23 (1773) (numbering based on Christa Landon Edition)
J. Cload *Concert* (5/90) (MERI) ① **CDE84210**
V. Horowitz (pp1966) *Concert*
(7/94) (SONY) ① [3] **S3K53461**
J. Jandó (r1993) *Concert*
(6/95) (NAXO) ① **8 553127**
J. McCabe (r1974-77) *Concert*
(12/95) (LOND) ① [12] **443 785-2LC12(1)**
Sonata for Keyboard No. 39 in D, HobXVI/24 (?1773) (numbering based on Christa Landon Edition)
J. Cload *Concert* (3/93) (MERI) ① **CDE84210**
S. Richter *Concert* (3/93) (DECC) ① **436 455-2DH**
S. Richter *Concert*
(8/94) (PHIL) ① [2] **438 617-2PH2**
J. Jandó (r1993) *Concert*
(6/95) (NAXO) ① **8 553127**
J. McCabe (r1974-77) *Concert*
(12/95) (LOND) ① [12] **443 785-2LC12(1)**
Sonata for Keyboard No. 40 in E flat, HobXVI/25 (?1763) (numbering based on Christa Landon Edition)
J. Jandó (r1993) *Concert*
(6/95) (NAXO) ① **8 553127**

SECTION IV: VOCAL AND CHORAL

Ah tu non senti...Qual destra omicida—insertion recitative and aria (1786) (for Traetta's 'Ifigenia in Tauride')
C.H. Ahnsjö, Lausanne CO, A. Dorati (r1980)
Concert   (6/93) (PHIL) ① [3] 432 416-2PH3
All through the night, '(The) Widow's Lament'—Welsh folksong arrangement, HobXXXIb/9 (1803)
A. Pearce, S. Drake Concert
(10/91) (HYPE) ① CDA66104
An der Mond—song (attrib Haydn. Wds. anon)
P. Schreier, K. Ragossnig Concert
(10/89) (NOVA) ① 150 039-2
Applausus—cantata: soloists, chorus and orchestra, HobXXIVa:6 (1768) (Wds. Latin anon)
Cpte R. Musoleno, K. Dolberg, D. Johnson, D. Byrne, J-P. Courtis, Haydn Voc Ens, Picardy Regional Orch, P. Foumillier   (4/93) (O111) ① [2] OPS61-9207/8
Arianna a Naxos—cantata, HobXXVIb/2 (1790)
C. Bott, M. Tan Concert
(1/86) (MERI) ① ECD84080
T. Berganza, ECO, M. Viotti Concert
(3/91) (CLAV) ① CD50-9016
J. Nelson, E. Thornburgh Concert
(11/91) (KOCH) ① 37044-2
C. Bartoli, A. Schiff (r1992) Concert
(11/93) (DECC) ① 440 297-2DH
The Ash Grove, 'Sir Watkyn's Dream'—Welsh folksong arrangement, HobXXXIb/7 (1804)
A. Pearce, S. Drake Concert
(10/91) (HYPE) ① CDA66104
M. Lawson, R. Podger, O. Kogan, O. Tverskaya (r1994) Concert   (5/95) (O111) ① OPS30-121
Auld Rob Morris—Scottish folksong arrangement, HobXXXIa/192 (1801) (Wds. Burns)
Scottish Early Music Consort (r1987) Concert
(10/95) (CHAN) ① CHAN0581
Ave Regina in A—soprano, chorus amd strings, HobXXIIIb/3 (-1763)
M-C. Vallin, Tolz Boys' Ch, Archibudelli, B. Weil (r1992-93) Concert   (9/94) (SONY) ① SK53368
Away, my herd, under the green oak—Welsh folksong arrangement, HobXXXIb/11 (1803)
A. Pearce, S. Drake Concert
(10/91) (HYPE) ① CDA66104
Berenice che fai—cantata, HobXXIVa/10 (1795)
A. Roocroft, ASMF, N. Marriner Concert
(12/95) (EMI) ① CDC5 55396-2
The Bonny bruckey lassie—song (before 1792)
L. Beznosiuk, F. Kelly (instr vers) Concert
(1/86) (MERI) ① ECD84080
The Break of Day—Welsh folksong arrangementd, HobXXXIb/3 (1803)
A. Pearce, S. Drake Concert
(10/91) (HYPE) ① CDA66104
Che vive amnate—insertion aria, HobXXIVb/13 (1787) (for Bianchi's 'Alessandro nell'Indie')
E. Mathis, Lausanne CO, A. Jordan (r1980) Concert
(6/93) (PHIL) ① [3] 432 420-2PH3
The Creation—oratorio: English text version of Die Schöpfung, HobXXI/2 (1796-8)
EXCERPTS: PART 1: 1. The Representation of Chaos; 2a. In the beginning; 2b. Now vanish before the holy beams; 3. And God made the firmament; 4. The marv'lous work beholds amazed; 5. And God said; 6. Rolling in foaming billows; 7. And God said; 8. With verdure clad; 9. And the heavenly hosts; 10. Awake the harp; 11. And God said; 12. In splendour bright; 13. The heavens are telling. PART 2: 14. And God said; 15. On mighty pens uplifted; 16. And God created great whales; 17. And the angels struck; 18. Most beautiful appear; 19. The Lord is great; 20. And God said; 21. Straight opening her fertile womb; 22. Now heaven in fullest glory shone; 23. And God created man in His own image; 24. In native worth; 25. And God saw everything; 26. Achieved is the glorious work; 27. On Thee each living soul awaits; 28. Achieved is the glorious work. PART 3: In rosy mantle appears; 30. By Thee with bliss, o bounteous Lord; 31. Our duty we performed now; 32. Graceful consort!; 33. O happy pair; 34. Sing the Lord ye voices all.
Cpte E. Kirkby, A. Rolfe Johnson, M. George, New College Ch, AAM Chor, AAM, C. Hogwood (r1990: ed Brown)   (3/91) (L'OI) ① [2] 430 397-2OH2

Cpte A. Auger, P. Langridge, D. Thomas, CBSO Chor, CBSO, S. Rattle (ed Temperley)
(4/91) (EMI) ① [2] CDS7 54159-2
Cpte D. Upshaw, H. Grant-Murphy, J. Humphrey, J.M. McGuire, J. Cheek, Atlanta Sym Chbr Chor, Atlanta SO, Robert Shaw (r1992: ed Shaw)
(12/92) (TELA) ① [2] CD80298
Cpte J. Raskin, A. Young, J. Reardon, Westminster Ch, NYPO, L. Bernstein (r1966) Mass 14.
(5/93) (SONY) ① [2] SM2K47560
7, 8. C. Bott, M. Tan Concert
(1/86) (MERI) ① ECD84080
8. I. Baillie, Hallé, L. Heward (r1941) Concert
(1/93) (MMOI) ① CDMOIR411
8. I. Baillie, Hallé, L. Heward (r1941) Concert
(7/95) (DUTT) ① CDLX7013
13. King's College Ch, ASMF, D. Willcocks Concert
(1/91) (CFP) ① CD-CFP4570
23. J. Shirley-Quirk, ASMF, D. Willcocks Concert
(8/89) (CFP) ① CD-CFP4532
The Crystal Ground—Welsh folksong arrangement, HobXXXIb/1 (1803)
A. Pearce, S. Drake Concert
(10/91) (HYPE) ① CDA66104
David of the White Rock—Welsh folksong arrangement, HobXXXIb/4 (1804)
A. Pearce, S. Drake Concert
(10/91) (HYPE) ① CDA66104
The Despairing Bard—Welsh folksong arrangement, HobXXXIb/19 (1804)
A. Pearce, S. Drake Concert
(10/91) (HYPE) ① CDA66104
The Dimpled Cheek—Welsh folksong arrangement, HobXXXIb/10 (1803)
A. Pearce, S. Drake Concert
(10/91) (HYPE) ① CDA66104
2 Duetti of Nisa and Tirsi—soprano, tenor and keyboard, HobXXVa/1-2 (1796) (Wds. C. F. Badini)
1. Saper vorrei se m'ami; 2. Guarda qui che io vedrai.
K. Livingstone, N. Mackie, J.J. Blakely Concert
(2/89) (UNIC) ① UKCD2009
D'una sposa meschinella—insertion aria, HobXXIVb/2 (c1777) (for Paisiello's 'La Frascatana')
E. Mathis, Lausanne CO, A. Jordan (r1980) Concert
(6/93) (PHIL) ① [3] 432 420-2PH3
Infelice sventurata—insertion aria, HobXXIVb/15 (1789) (for Cimarosa's 'I due supposti conti')
E. Mathis, Lausanne CO, A. Jordan (r1980) Concert
(6/93) (PHIL) ① [3] 432 420-2PH3
Insanae et vanae curae—motet (pub 1809) (spurious)
Norwich Cath Ch, M. Nicholas, N. Taylor Concert
(3/92) (PRIO) ① PRCD351
Die Jahreszeiten—oratorio: German text version of The Seasons, HobXXI/3 (1799-1801) (Wds. van Swieten, after Thomson)
EXCERPTS: SPRING: 1a. Introduction; 1b. Seht, wie der strenge Winter; 2. Komm, holder Lenz!; 3. Vom Widder strahlet jetzt; 4. Schon eilet froh; 5. Der Landmann hat sein Werk vollbracht; 6. Sei nun gnädig, milder Himmel!; 7. Erhört ist unser Flehn; 8. O wie lieblich; 9. Ewiger, mächter, gütiger Gott!. SUMMER: 10. In grauem Schleier; 11a. Der munt're Hirt versammelt nun; 11b. Die Morgenröte bricht hervor; 12a. Sie steigt herauf, die Sonne; 13. Nun regt und bewegt sich; 14. Die Mittagssonne brennt jetzt; 15. Dem Druck erlieget die Natur; 16. Willkommen jetzt, o dunkler Hain!; 17a. Welche Labung für die Sinne!; 18. O seht!; 19. Ach, das Ungewitter naht!; 20. Die düstren Wolken trennen sich. AUTUMN: 21a. Introduction; 21b. Was durch seine Blüte; 22. Den reichen Vorrat; 23. Seht an die Natur; 24. Seht, wie zum Haselbusche; 25. Ihn Schönen aus der Stadt; 26. Nun zeiget das entblösste Feld; 27. Seht auf die breiten Wiesen hin!; 28. Hier treibt ein dichter Kreis; 29. Hört, hört, das laute Getön; 30. Am Rebenstocke blinket jetzt; 31. Juchhe! Der Wein ist da. WINTER: 32. Introduction; 33. Nun senket sich; 34. Licht und Leben sind geschwächt; 35. Gefesselt steht der breite See; 36. Hier steht der Wand'rer nun; 37. So wie er naht; 38. Knurre, schnurre, knurre; 39. Abgesponnen ist der Flachs; 40. Ein Mädchen, das auf Ehre; 41. Vom dürren Osten dringt; 42. Erblicke hier, betörter Mensch; 43. Die bleibt allein; 44. Dann bricht der grosse Morgen an.
Cpte G. Janowitz, W. Hollweg, W. Berry, Berlin Deutsche Op Chor, BPO, H. von Karajan
(7/88) (EMI) ① [2] CMS7 69224-2
Cpte T. Eipperle, J. Patzak, G. Hann, Vienna St Op Chor, VPO, C. Krauss (bp1942)
(6/90) (PREI) ① [2] 93053

Cpte A. Auger, J. Aler, H. Hagegård, Minnesota Chorale, St Paul CO, J. Revzen
(1/92) (KOCH) ① [2] 37065-2
Cpte B. Bonney, A. Rolfe Johnson, A. Schmidt, Monteverdi Ch, EBS, J.E. Gardiner (r1990)
(5/92) (ARCH) ① [2] 431 818-2AH2
Cpte R. Ziesak, U. Heilmann, R. Pape, Chicago Sym Chor, Chicago SO, G. Solti (pp1992)
(2/94) (DECC) ① [2] 436 840-2DH2
Cpte A. Stumphius, A. Stevenson, W. Schöne, Stuttgart Gächinger Kantorei, Stuttgart Bach Collegium, H. Rilling (r1992)
(2/94) (HANS) ① [2] 98 982
Cpte E. Mathis, S. Jerusalem, D. Fischer-Dieskau, ASMF Chor, ASMF, N. Marriner (r1980)
(6/94) (PHIL) ① [2] 438 715-2PM2
Cpte G. Janowitz, P. Schreier, M. Talvela, Vienna Singverein, Vienna SO, K. Böhm (r1967)
(5/95) (DG) ① [2] 437 940-2GX2
2-5, 9, 17-20, 27-29, 33, 36, 39-41. G. Janowitz, W. Hollweg, W. Berry, Berlin Deutsche Op Chor, BPO, H. von Karajan   (9/87) (EMI) ① CDM7 69010-2
4. F. Schorr, LSO, J. Barbirolli (r1931) Concert
(9/91) (PEAR) ① GEMMCD9398
4. P. Plançon, anon (r1905: Fr) Concert
(9/91) (PEAR) ① GEMMCD9497
4. P. Plançon, anon (r1905: Fr) Concert
(12/94) (ROMO) ① [2] 82001-2
14, 15, 35, 36. U. Heilmann, Leipzig Gewandhaus, P. Schreier (r1993) Concert
(3/95) (DECC) ① 440 680-2DH
Jenny's Mantle—Welsh folksong arrangement, HobXXXIb/5 (1803)
A. Pearce, S. Drake Concert
(10/91) (HYPE) ① CDA66104
John Anderson—Scottish folksong arrangement (1792) (HobXXXIa/2)
M. Lawson, R. Podger, O. Kogan, O. Tverskaya (r1994) Concert   (5/95) (O111) ① OPS30-121
Lambs' Fold Vale—Welsh folksong arrangement, HobXXXIb/22 (1804)
A. Pearce, S. Drake Concert
(10/91) (HYPE) ① CDA66104
Logie of Buchan—British folksong arrangement, HobXXXIa/73 (c1792)
C. Bott, L. Beznosiuk, A. Pleeth, F. Kelly Concert
(1/86) (MERI) ① ECD84080
The Looking glass—Scottish folksong arrangement, HobXXXIa/158 (1801)
M. Lawson, R. Podger, O. Kogan, O. Tverskaya (r1994) Concert   (5/95) (O111) ① OPS30-121
The March of the Men of Harlech—Welsh folksong arrangement, HobXXXIb/2 (1803)
A. Pearce, S. Drake Concert
(10/91) (HYPE) ① CDA66104
Mass No. 1a in G, 'Rorate coeli desuper', HobXXII/3
Oxford Christ Church Cath Ch, AAM, S. Preston Concert   (6/89) (L'OI) ① 421 478-2OH
Mass No. 1b—chorus and strings, HobXXII/2
Tolz Boys' Ch, Archibudelli, B. Weil (r1992-93) Concert   (9/94) (SONY) ① SK53368
Mass No. 2 in F, 'Missa brevis'—2 sopranos, chorus and strings, HobXXII/7 (?1749)
J. Nelson, E. Kirkby, Oxford Christ Church Cath Ch, AAM, S. Preston Concert
(8/89) (L'OI) ① 421 654-2OH
Mass No. 3 in C, 'Missa Cellensis in honorem BVM'—soloists, chorus and orchestra, HobXXII/5 (1766) (Caeciliaemesse)
J. Nelson, M. Cable, M. Hill, D. Thomas, Oxford Christ Church Cath Ch, AAM, S. Preston
(12/86) (L'OI) ① 417 125-2OH
Mass No. 5 in E flat, 'Missa in honorem BVM'—soloists, 4vv chorus and orchestra, HobXXII/4 (1774) (Great Organ Mass)
J. Nelson, C. Watkinson, M. Hill, D. Thomas, Oxford Christ Church Cath Ch, AAM, S. Preston Concert   (8/89) (L'OI) ① 421 478-2OH
Mass No. 6 in G, 'Missa Sancti Nicolai'—soloists, chorus and orchestra, HobXXII/6 (1772) (Nikolaimesse)
J. Nelson, S. Minty, R. Covey-Crump, D. Thomas, Oxford Christ Church Cath Ch, AAM, S. Preston Concert   (8/89) (L'OI) ① 421 478-2OH
Mass No. 7 in B flat, 'Missa brevis Sancti Joannis de Deo'—soprano, chorus and orchestra, HobXXII/7 (1779) (Little Organ Mass)
L. Kitchen, Haydn Soc Chor, Haydn Soc Orch, D. McCaldin Concert   (2/90) (MERI) ① DUOCD89003
B. Hendricks, Leipzig Rad Chor, Staatskapelle Dresden, N. Marriner Mass 13.
(8/90) (EMI) ① CDC7 54002-2

1, 2, 6, 8-10, 13, 15, 18, 22, 24, 28, 30. N. Burrowes,
S. Greenberg, R. Wohlers, J. Morris, S. Nimsgern,
Chicago Sym Chor, Chicago SO, G. Solti
(8/92) (DECC) ① **430 739-2DH**
15. E. Norena, orch, J. Messner (r1938) *Concert*
(3/91) (PREI) ① **89041**
23, 24. U. Heilmann, Leipzig Gewandhaus, P.
Schreier (r1993) *Concert*
(3/95) (DECC) ① **440 680-2DH**
Se tu mi sprezzi—insertion aria,
HobXXIVb/14 (1788) (for Sarti's 'I finti eredi')
A. Baldin, Lausanne CO, A. Dorati (r1980) *Concert*
(6/93) (PHIL) ① [3] **432 416-2PH3**
The **Seven Last Words—oratorio, HobXX/2**
(1795-6) (Wds. Friebert, rev van Swieten)
I. Nielsen, R. Burtscher, M. Hintermeier, A. Rolfe
Johnson, R. Holl, A. Schoenberg Ch, VCM, N.
Harnoncourt (5/92) (TELD) ① **2292-46458-2**
The **Shepherd's wife—Scottish folksong**
arrangement, HobXXXIa/128 (1795)
M. Lawson, R. Podger, O. Kogan, O. Tverskaya
(r1994) *Concert* (5/95) (O111) ① **OPS30-121**
The **Sleeping Beauty—Welsh folksong**
arrangement, HobXXXIb/17 (1804)
A. Pearce, S. Drake *Concert*
(10/91) (HYPE) ① **CDA66104**
Sleepy Bodie—British folksong
arrangement, HobXXXIa/31 (c1792)
C. Bott, A. Bury, A. Pleeth, M. Tan *Concert*
(1/86) (MERI) ① **ECD84080**
Solo e pensoso—aria, HobXXIVb/20 (1798)
(sonetto from Petrach's Canzoniere)
E. Mathis, Lausanne CO, A. Jordan (r1980) *Concert*
(6/93) (PHIL) ① [3] **432 420-2PH3**
Son pietosa, son bonina—aria, HobXXXII/1b
(1789) (for 'Circe': pasticcio by Naumann,
Haydn etc)
E. Mathis, Lausanne CO, A. Dorati (r1980) *Concert*
(6/93) (PHIL) ① [3] **432 420-2PH3**
Sono Alcina e sono ancora—insertion
cavatina, HobXXIVb/9 (1786) (for Gazzaniga's
'L'isola di Alcina')
E. Mathis, Lausanne CO, A. Jordan (r1980) *Concert*
(6/93) (PHIL) ① [3] **432 420-2PH3**
The **Spirit's Song—canzonetta, HobXXVIa/41**
(1800) (Wds. Hunter)
J. Nelson, E. Thornburgh *Concert*
(11/91) (KOCH) ① **37044-2**
Invocation (r1994) *Concert*
(3/95) (HYPE) ① **CDA66740**
Stabat Mater—soloists, chorus and
orchestra, HobXXbis (1767)
P. Rozario, C. Robbin, A. Rolfe Johnson, C.
Hauptmann, English Concert Ch, English Concert, T.
Pinnock (9/90) (ARCH) ① **429 733-2AH**
A. Auger, A. Hodgson, A. Rolfe Johnson, G. Howell,
London Chbr Ch, Argo CO, L. Heltay
(5/92) (DECC) ① **433 172-2DM**
B. Bonney, E. von Magnus, H. Lippert, A. Miles, A.
Schoenberg Ch, VCM, N. Harnoncourt (r1994)
(8/95) (TELD) ① **4509-95085-2**
Te Deum in C for Prince Nicolaus
Esterházy—soloists, chorus and orchestra,
HobXXIIIc/1 (-1765)
Vienna Boys' Ch, Chorus Viennensis, Vienna CO, H.
Gillesberger *Concert* (11/87) (RCA) ① **GD86535**
Te Deum in C for the Empress Marie
Therese—SATB, orchestra & organ,
HobXXIIIc/2 (c1800)
English Concert Ch, English Concert, T. Pinnock
Mass 11. (2/88) (ARCH) ① **423 097-2AH**
Vada adagio, signorina—insertion aria,
HobXXIVb/12 (1787) (for Guglielmi's 'La
quacquara spiritosa')
E. Mathis, Lausanne CO, A. Jordan (r1980) *Concert*
(6/93) (PHIL) ① [3] **432 420-2PH3**
What can a young lassie do—Scottish
folksong arrangement, HobXXXIa/134bis
(1801) (Wds. Burns)
Scottish Early Music Consort (1987) *Concert*
(10/95) (CHAN) ① **CHAN0581**
The **White Cockade—Scottish folksong**
arrangement, HobXXXIa/22 (c1792)
C. Bott, A. Bury, L. Beznosiuk, A. Pleeth, F. Kelly
Concert (1/86) (MERI) ① **ECD84080**
M. Lawson, R. Podger, O. Kogan, O. Tverskaya
(r1994) *Concert* (5/95) (O111) ① **OPS30-121**

SECTION V: STAGE WORKS

Acide e Galatea—festa teatrale: 1 act,
HobXXVIII/1 (1763—Einsenstadt) (Lib.
Migliavacca)
EXCERPTS: 1. Overture (pub 1959).
Tergi i vezzosi rai M. Devlin, Lausanne CO, A.
Dorati (r1980) *Concert*
(6/93) (PHIL) ① [3] **432 416-2PH3**

L' **Anima del filosofo, ossia Orfeo ed**
Euridice—dramma per music: 4 acts (1791)
(Lib. Badini: probably unfinished)
Cpte R. Swensen, H. Donath, S. Greenberg, T.
Quasthoff, P. Hansen, A. Suzuki, Bavarian Rad Chor,
Munich RO, L. Hager (r1992)
(9/95) (ORFE) ① [2] **C262932H**
Armida—opera: 3 acts, HobXXVIII/12
(1783—Eszterháza) (Lib. cpsr)
1. Sinfonia; 2. March; 3. Parti Rinaldo; 4. Se pietade
avete; 5. Caro sarò fedele; 6. Barbaro! E ardici ancor;
7. Odio, furor, dispetto; 8. Ah, non ferir.
Cpte J. Norman, C.H. Ahnsjö, N. Burrowes, S.
Ramey, R. Leggate, A. Rolfe Johnson, Lausanne
CO, A. Dorati (r1978)
(6/93) (PHIL) ① [2] **432 438-2PH2**
1. Orpheus CO (r1992) *Concert*
(12/93) (DG) ① **437 783-2GH**
La **Circe, ossia L'isola incantata—pasticcio**
(1789) (attrib Haydn)
EXCERPTS: 1. Terzetto: Lavatevi presto.
1. C.H. Ahnsjö, A. Baldin, M. Devlin, Lausanne CO,
A. Dorati (r1980) *Concert*
(6/93) (PHIL) ① [3] **432 416-2PH3**
La **Fedeltà premiata—opera: 3 acts,**
HobXXVIII/10 (1780—Eszterháza) (Lib. after
Lorenzi)
Cpte L.V. Terrani, T. Landy, F. von Stade, A. Titus, I.
Cotrubas, L. Alva, M. Mazzieri, K. Lövaas, Suisse
Romande Rad Chor, Lausanne CO, A. Dorati (r1975)
(6/93) (PHIL) ① [3] **432 430-2PH3**
Overture Versailles Camerata, A. du Closel *Concert*
(2/89) (FORL) ① **UCD16567**
L' **Incontro improvviso—opera: 3 acts,**
HobXXVIII/6 (1775—Eszterháza) (Lib.
Friebert)
Cpte C.H. Ahnsjö, L. Zoghby, M. Marshall, D. Jones,
D. Trimarchi, B. Luxon, J. Prescott, J. Hooper, N.
Scarpinati, Lausanne CO, A. Dorati (r1979) *Concert*
(6/93) (PHIL) ① [3] **432 416-2PH3**
L' **Infedeltà delusa—opera: 2 acts,**
HobXXVIII/5 (1773—Eszterháza) (Lib.
Cotellini)
1. Overture; 2. Intermezzo.
Cpte E. Mathis, B. Hendricks, C.H. Ahnsjö, A. Baldin,
M. Devlin, Lausanne CO, A. Dorati (r1980)
(6/93) (PHIL) ① [2] **432 413-2PH2**
L' **isola disabitata—opera: 2 acts,**
HobXXVIII/9 (1779—Eszterháza) (Lib.
Metastasio)
Cpte N. Lerer, L. Zoghby, L. Alva, R. Bruson,
Lausanne CO, A. Dorati (r1977)
(6/93) (PHIL) ① [2] **432 427-2PH2**
Il **Mondo della luna—opera: 3 acts,**
HobXXVIII/7 (1777—Eszterháza) (Lib.
Goldoni)
1. Overture; (ACT 2) 12. Sinfonia; 13. Ballet music;
14. Ballet music; 17. March; 23. Ballet music.
Cpte D. Trimarchi, L. Alva, F. von Stade, A. Auger, E.
Mathis, L.V. Terrani, A. Rolfe Johnson, Suisse
Romande Rad Chor, Lausanne CO, A. Dorati (r1977)
Concert (6/93) (PHIL) ① [3] **432 420-2PH3**
1. COE, C. Abbado (pp1993) *Concert*
(10/95) (DG) ① **439 932-2GH**
Orlando Paladino—opera: 3 acts,
HobXXVIII/11 (1782—Eszterháza) (Lib. Badini
and Porta)
Cpte A. Auger, E. Ameling, G. Killebrew, G. Shirley,
C.H. Ahnsjö, B. Luxon, D. Trimarchi, M. Mazzieri, G.
Carelli, Lausanne CO, A. Dorati (r1976)
(6/93) (PHIL) ① [3] **432 434-2PH3**
Lo **Speziale—opera: 3 acts, HobXXVIII/3**
(1768—Eszterháza) (Lib. Goldoni)
Overture Versailles Camerata, A. du Closel *Concert*
(2/89) (FORL) ① **UCD16567**
La **Vera costanza—opera: 3 acts,**
HobXXVIII/8 (1779—Eszterháza) (Lib. Puttini)
1. Sinfonia; 2. Con un tenero sospiro; 3a. Misera, chi
m'aiuta; 3b. Dove fuggo; 4a. Eccomi giuta al colmo;
4b. care spiagge; 5. Caro figlio, partiamo; 6. Rosina
vezzosina.
Cpte J. Norman, H. Donath, C.H. Ahnsjö, W.
Ganzarolli, D. Trimarchi, K. Lövaas, A. Rolfe
Johnson, Lausanne CO, A. Dorati (r1991)
Concert (1/94) (NIMB) ① **NI5341**
1. Austro-Hungarian Haydn Orch, A. Fischer (r1991)
Concert (2/89) (FORL) ① **UCD16567**

P—Nos. from Perger (1907); MH—Nos. from
Sherman/Thomas (1993)

SECTION I: ORCHESTRAL

Coburg March (spurious)
Berlin Phil Wind Qnt, H. von Karajan (r1973) *Concert*
(5/94) (DG) ① **439 346-2GX2**
Concerto for Flute and Orchestra in D, MH81
(P54) (1766)
A.O. Popa (cl/dir), Quodlibet Musicum CO (arr cl)
Concert (10/90) (OLYM) ① **OCD406**
I-Z. Nagy, Austro-Hungarian Haydn Orch, A. Fischer
(r1992) *Concert* (8/93) (NIMB) ① **NI5392**
Concerto for Flute and Orchestra in D,
MH105 (P56) (1765-68)
I-Z. Nagy, Austro-Hungarian Haydn Orch, A. Fischer
(r1992) *Concert* (8/93) (NIMB) ① **NI5392**
Concerto for Horn and Strings in D, MH53
(Hob VIId:3) (c1760-1762)
A. Halstead, Hanover Band, R. Goodman *Concert*
(11/89) (NIMB) ① **NI5190**
Concerto for Organ/Harpsichord, Viola and
Orchestra in C, MH41 (P55) (?1761)
E. Botár, A.I. Thurzo, Oradea PO, E. Acél *Concert*
(10/90) (OLYM) ① **OCD406**
Concerto for Trumpet and Orchestra in C,
MH60 (P34) (before 1763) (movts 1 & 2 of
incomplete Concerto)
C. Steele-Perkins, ECO, A. Halstead *Concert*
(6/86) (CARL) ① **PCD821**
J. Wallace, Philh, S. Wright *Concert*
(4/89) (NIMB) ① **NI5121**
H. Hardenberger, LPO, E. Howarth *Concert*
(3/91) (PHIL) ① **426 311-2PH**
R. Friedrich, ASMF, N. Marriner *Concert*
(6/93) (CAPR) ① **10 436**
Concerto for Trumpet and Orchestra in D,
MH104 (c1765-1768)
W. Marsalis, ECO, R. Leppard *Concert*
(6/88) (SONY) ① **SK42478**
R. Friedrich, ASMF, N. Marriner *Concert*
(6/93) (CAPR) ① **10 436**
Concerto for Violin and Strings in B flat,
MH36 (P53) (1760)
G. Ille, Oradea PO, E. Acél *Concert*
(10/90) (OLYM) ① **OCD406**
Pappenheim March (spurious)
Berlin Phil Wind Qnt, H. von Karajan (r1973) *Concert*
(5/94) (DG) ① **439 346-2GX2**
Pastorello in C—2 cls, 2 tbns, 2 vns, va,
timp, continuo, MH63 (P91) (1766)
Oradea PO, E. Acél *Concert*
(10/90) (OLYM) ① **OCD404**
Symphony in A, MH63 (P3) (1763)
Slovak CO, B. Warchal (r1991) *Concert*
(8/93) (CPO) ① **CPO999 152-2**
Symphony in B flat, MH62 (P51) (1763)
Slovak CO, B. Warchal (r1991) *Concert*
(8/93) (CPO) ① **CPO999 152-2**
Symphony in B flat, MH133 (P52) (c1768-
1770)
Oradea PO, E. Acél *Concert*
(10/90) (OLYM) ① **OCD404**
Symphony in B flat, MH475 (P28) (1788)
Oradea PO, E. Acél *Concert*
(10/90) (OLYM) ① **OCD404**
Symphony in C, MH23 (P35) (c1758-1760)
Slovak CO, B. Warchal (r1991) *Concert*
(8/93) (CPO) ① **CPO999 101-2**
Symphony in C, MH37 (P2) (1761)
Slovak CO, B. Warchal (r1991) *Concert*
(8/93) (CPO) ① **CPO999 101-2**
Symphony in C, MH64 (P4) (1764)
Slovak CO, B. Warchal (r1991) *Concert*
(8/93) (CPO) ① **CPO999 152-2**
Symphony in C, MH188 (P10) (1773)
Oradea PO, E. Acél *Concert*
(10/90) (OLYM) ① **OCD407**
Symphony in C, MH252 (P12) (after 1777)
Oradea PO, R. Rîmbu (r1993) *Concert*
(8/93) (CPO) ① **CPO999 152-2**
Symphony in D, MH50 (P36) (c1760-1762)
Slovak CO, B. Warchal (r1991) *Concert*
(8/93) (CPO) ① **CPO999 153-2**
Symphony in D, MH69 (P38) (1764)
Slovak CO, B. Warchal (r1991) *Concert*
(8/93) (CPO) ① **CPO999 153-2**
Symphony in D, MH198 (P11) (1774)
Oradea PO, E. Acél *Concert*
(10/90) (OLYM) ① **OCD407**

Symphony in D, MH272 (P42) (c1778)
Oradea PO, E. Acél *Concert*
(10/90) (OLYM) ① **OCD404**
Symphony in D, MH287 (P43) (c1778-1780)
Oradea PO, R. Rîmbu (r1993) *Concert*
(4/94) (OLYM) ① **OCD435**
Symphony in D, MH476 (P29) (1788)
Oradea PO, E. Acél *Concert*
(10/90) (OLYM) ① **OCD404**
Symphony in D minor, MH393 (P20) (1784)
Oradea PO, M. Raţiu *Concert*
(10/90) (OLYM) ① **OCD407**
Symphony in E, MH65 (P5) (1764)
Slovak CO, B. Warchal (r1992) *Concert*
(8/93) (CPO) ① **CPO999 153-2**
Symphony in E, MH151 (P44) (after 1771)
Oradea PO, R. Rîmbu (r1993) *Concert*
(4/94) (OLYM) ① **OCD435**
Symphony in E flat, MH473 (P26) (1788)
Oradea PO, E. Acél *Concert*
(10/90) (OLYM) ① **OCD404**
Symphony in F (?1770) (unidentified)
Austro-Hungarian Haydn Orch, A. Fischer (r1992)
Concert (8/93) (NiMB) ① **NI5392**
Symphony in F, MH51 (P45) (c1760-1762)
Slovak CO, B. Warchal (r1992) *Concert*
(8/93) (CPO) ① **CPO999 153-2**
Symphony in F, MH507 (P32) (1789)
Oradea PO, R. Rîmbu (r1993) *Concert*
(4/94) (OLYM) ① **OCD435**
Symphony in G, MH26 (c1758-1760)
Slovak CO, B. Warchal (r1991) *Concert*
(8/93) (CPO) ① **CPO999 101-2**

SECTION II: CHAMBER

Divertimento for 2 Oboes, 2 Bassoons and 2 Horns in D, MH418 (P95) (1786)
Consortium Classicum *Concert*
(9/90) (SCHW) ① **310002**
Divertimento for 2 Violins, 2 Violas and Cello in B flat, MH412 (P105) (c1786)
Archibudelli (r1993) *Concert*
(8/94) (SONY) ① **SK53987**
Notturno for 2 Violins, 2 Violas and Continuo in C, MH187 (P108) (1773)
Archibudelli (r1993) *Concert*
(8/94) (SONY) ① **SK53987**
Notturno for 2 Violins, 2 Violas and Continuo in G, MH189 (P109) (1773)
Archibudelli (r1993) *Concert*
(8/94) (SONY) ① **SK53987**

SECTION IV: VOCAL AND CHORAL

Ave Regina (unidentified)
St John's College Ch, G. Guest *Concert*
(6/91) (DECC) ① **430 159-2DM**
Missa Sancti Aloysii—3vv, chorus, 2 vns and continuo, MH257 (KI I/12) (1777)
S. Standage, M. Comberti, D. Yeadon, A. Halstead,
C. Rutherford, S. Standage, P. Rushforth, Trinity Coll
Ch, Cambridge, R. Marlow (r1993) *Concert*
(2/94) (CONI) ① **CDCF220**
Missa sub titulo Sancti Leopoldi—3vv, chorus and orchestra, MH837 (KI I/24) (1805)
S. Standage, M. Comberti, D. Yeadon, A. Halstead,
C. Rutherford, S. Standage, P. Rushforth, Trinity Coll
Ch, Cambridge, R. Marlow (r1993) *Concert*
(2/94) (CONI) ① **CDCF220**
Vesperae pro festo Sanctissimae innocentium—3vv, chorus and orchestra, MH548 (KI IV/5) (1793)
S. Standage, M. Comberti, D. Yeadon, A. Halstead,
C. Rutherford, S. Standage, P. Rushforth, Trinity Coll
Ch, Cambridge, R. Marlow (r1993) *Concert*
(2/94) (CONI) ① **CDCF220**

HAYES, Nick (b 1963) England

SECTION IV: VOCAL AND CHORAL

The Basket—soprano, clarinet & piano (1993) (Wds. C Nankivell)
Tapestry (r1994) *Concert*
(12/95) (BRIT) ① **BML012**

HAYES, Philip (1738–1797) England

SECTION I: ORCHESTRAL
---

6 Concertos for the Organ, Harpsichord or Forte-Piano (pub 1769)
EXCERPTS: 4. A.
4. P. Nicholson (kybds/dir), Parley of Instr, P. Holman
(r1993) *Concert* (8/94) (HYPE) ① **CDA66700**

HAYES, William (1708–1777) England

SECTION IV: VOCAL AND CHORAL

O worship the Lord—anthem
New College Ch, D. Burchell, E. Higginbottom
Concert (10/89) (MERI) ① **CDE84151**

HAYMAN, Richard (b 1920) USA

SECTION I: ORCHESTRAL

Kid Stuff—orchestral suite
1. Children's Marching Song (Malcolm Arnold); 2.
March of the Siamese Children (Richard Rodgers); 3.
Mickey Mouse March (Dodd); 4. All around the
Mulberry Bush; 5. Mary had a Little Lamb; 6.
Alouette.
Boston Pops, A. Fiedler (1959) *Concert*
(12/95) (RCA) ① **09026 68131-2**

HAYNE VAN GHIZEGHEM (c1445–between 1472 and 1497) Netherlands
---

SECTION IV: VOCAL AND CHORAL

De tous biens plaine—chanson: 3vv
Daedalus Ens *Concert*
(12/92) (ACCE) ① **ACC9176D**

HAYNES, Battison (1859–1900) England

SECTION IV: VOCAL AND CHORAL

Off to Philadelphia—Irish folksong arrangement (Wds. ed S Temple)
J. McCormack, G. Moore (r1941) *Concert*
(5/93) (MMOI) ① **CDMOIR418**

HAZELL, Chris (b 1948) England

SECTION I: ORCHESTRAL

Mr Jums—brass ensemble
Glasgow CWS Band, H. Snell (arr Catherall) *Concert*
(9/92) (DOYE) ① **DOYCD005**

HEAD, Michael (Dewar) (1900–1976) England

SECTION IV: VOCAL AND CHORAL

Bird-song—song: 1v, flute and piano (Wds M Rayment)
K. Battle, J-P. Rampal, M. Garrett (pp1991) *Concert*
(4/94) (SONY) ① **SK53106**
Sweet chance, that led my steps abroad—song (1929) (Wds. W. H. Davies)
F. Lott, G. Johnson *Concert*
(7/90) (CHAN) ① **CHAN8722**

HEADINGTON, Christopher (b 1930) England

SECTION I: ORCHESTRAL

Concerto for Violin and Orchestra (1959)
X. Wei, LPO, J. Glover R. Strauss: Violin Concerto.
(12/91) (ASV) ① **CDDCA780**

SECTION III: INSTRUMENTAL

Ballade-Image—piano (1982)
C. Headington *Concert*
(11/90) (KING) ① **KCLCD2017**
Cinquanta—piano (1987)
C. Headington *Concert*
(11/90) (KING) ① **KCLCD2017**

HEAP, Charles Swinnerton (1847–1900) England

SECTION III: INSTRUMENTAL

Study No. 3 in A minor—organ
Margaret Phillips *Concert*
(7/91) (GAMU) ① **GAMCD522**

HEATH, David (b 1956) England

SECTION I: ORCHESTRAL

Out of the Cool—saxophone and orchestra (1989)
J. Harle, ASMF, N. Marriner *Concert*
(1/92) (EMI) ① **CDC7 54301-2**

HEATH, Reginald (19th–20th cent) England

SECTION I: ORCHESTRAL

Frolic for Trombones—3 trombones and brass band
B. Deans, M. Stenhouse, D. Platt, Glasgow CWS
Band, H. Snell *Concert*
(9/92) (DOYE) ① **DOYCD005**

HEBDEN, John (1712–1765) England

SECTION I: ORCHESTRAL

Concerti for Strings (c1745-1748)
1. A; 2. C; 3. C minor; 4. E flat; 5. C minor; 6. D
minor.
Cantilena, A. Shepherd
(4/85) (CHAN) ① **CHAN8339**

HEBERLE, Anton (18th–19th Cent) Germany

SECTION III: INSTRUMENTAL

Fantasia for Descant Recorder
M. Petri *Concert* (10/88) (RCA) ① **RD87749**

HEDUS, Petrus (15th–16th Cent) Italy

SECTION IV: VOCAL AND CHORAL

O Vergene gentile—lauda (Paris Bibliothèque Nationale MS)
Daedalus Ens (r1992) *Concert*
(11/93) (ACCE) ① **ACC9289D**

HEIFETZ, Jascha (1901–1988) Lithuania/USA

SECTION IV: VOCAL AND CHORAL

Heifetz on Music—talk given by the violinist (1970)
J. Heifetz (1970) *Concert*
(11/94) (RCA) ① [65] **09026 61778-2(35)**

HEIN, Silvio (19th–20th Cent) USA

SECTION IV: VOCAL AND CHORAL

When You're All Dressed Up and No Place to Go—song for the show 'The Beauty Shop' (1914) (Lyrics B H Burt)
R. Hitchcock (r1916) *Concert*
(5/94) (PEAR) ① [3] **GEMMCDS9056/8**

HEINICHEN, Johann David (1683–1729) Germany

S—Nos from Siebel

SECTION I: ORCHESTRAL

Concerto in C—multiple instruments, S211
Cologne Musica Antiqua, R. Goebel (1992) *Concert*
(5/93) (ARCH) ① [2] **437 549-2AH2**
Amsterdam Loeki Stardust Qt, AAM, C. Hogwood
(r1992) *Concert* (7/94) (L'OI) ① **436 905-2OH**
Concerto in F—multiple instruments, S226
Cologne Musica Antiqua, R. Goebel (1992) *Concert*
(5/93) (ARCH) ① [2] **437 549-2AH2**
Concerto in F—multiple instruments, S231
Cologne Musica Antiqua, R. Goebel (1992) *Concert*
(5/93) (ARCH) ① [2] **437 549-2AH2**
Concerto in F—multiple instruments, S232
Cologne Musica Antiqua, R. Goebel (1992) *Concert*
(5/93) (ARCH) ① [2] **437 549-2AH2**
Concerto in F—multiple instruments, S233
Cologne Musica Antiqua, R. Goebel (1992) *Concert*
(5/93) (ARCH) ① [2] **437 549-2AH2**
Concerto in F—multiple instruments, S234
Cologne Musica Antiqua, R. Goebel (1992) *Concert*
(5/93) (ARCH) ① [2] **437 549-2AH2**

Concerto in F—multiple instruments, S235
 Cologne Musica Antiqua, R. Goebel (r1992) *Concert*
  (5/93) (ARCH) ① [2] **437 549-2AH2**
Concerto in G—multiple instruments, S213
 Cologne Musica Antiqua, R. Goebel (r1992) *Concert*
  (5/93) (ARCH) ① [2] **437 549-2AH2**
Concerto in G—multiple instruments, S215
 Cologne Musica Antiqua, R. Goebel (r1992) *Concert*
  (5/93) (ARCH) ① [2] **437 549-2AH2**
Concerto in G—multiple instruments, S217
 Cologne Musica Antiqua, R. Goebel (r1992) *Concert*
  (5/93) (ARCH) ① [2] **437 549-2AH2**
Concerto in G—multiple instruments, S214
 (1715) (Darmstadt MS)
 Cologne Musica Antiqua, R. Goebel (r1992) *Concert*
  (5/93) (ARCH) ① [2] **437 549-2AH2**
Concerto in G—multiple instruments, S214
 (1715) (Venezia MS)
 Cologne Musica Antiqua, R. Goebel (r1992) *Concert*
  (5/93) (ARCH) ① [2] **437 549-2AH2**
Concerto Movement in C minor—oboe, violin
 and strings, S240
 Cologne Musica Antiqua, R. Goebel (r1992) *Concert*
  (5/93) (ARCH) ① [2] **437 549-2AH2**
Pastorale in A, 'Per la notte della Nativitate
 Christi'—two oboes and orchestra
 Virtuosi Saxoniae, L. Güttler *Concert*
  (12/89) (CAPR) ① **10 225**
Serenata di Moritzburg in F—2 flutes, 2
 oboes, 2 horns and strings, S204
 Cologne Musica Antiqua, R. Goebel (r1992) *Concert*
  (5/93) (ARCH) ① [2] **437 549-2AH2**
Sonata in A—2 flutes, 2 oboes and strings,
 S208
 Cologne Musica Antiqua, R. Goebel (r1992) *Concert*
  (5/93) (ARCH) ① [2] **437 549-2AH2**

**HEINZE, Gustav Adolf
(1820–1904) The Netherlands**

SECTION I: ORCHESTRAL

Konzertstück in F—clarinet and orchestra
 T. King, ECO, J. Judd *Concert*
  (4/90) (HYPE) ① **CDA66300**

**HEISE, Peter (Arnold)
(1830–1879) Denmark**

SECTION IV: VOCAL AND CHORAL

The Eagle ascends with mighty
 strokes—song (1859) (Wds. B. Bjørnson)
 L. Melchior, Orch (r1913: Odeon) *Concert*
  (8/88) (DANA) ① [2] **DACOCD311/2**
 L. Melchior, Orch (r1913: HMV) *Concert*
  (8/88) (DANA) ① [2] **DACOCD311/2**
Fair is the gentle spring—song (Wds. E. von
 der Recke)
 L. Melchior, Orch (r1913) *Concert*
  (8/88) (DANA) ① [2] **DACOCD311/2**
My Lord and King, stay with me—song (Wds.
 E. von der Recke)
 L. Melchior, A. Neumann, Orch (r1913) *Concert*
  (8/88) (DANA) ① [2] **DACOCD311/2**
Though the tide turns against you—song
 (Wds. S. S. Blicher)
 L. Melchior, Orch (r1913) *Concert*
  (8/88) (DANA) ① [2] **DACOCD311/2**
When that I was and a little tiny boy—song
 (Wds. Shakespeare, trans E. Lembcke)
 L. Melchior, Anon (pf) (r c1921) *Concert*
  (8/88) (DANA) ① [2] **DACOCD311/2**

SECTION V: STAGE WORKS

Drot og Marsk, 'King and Marshall'—opera:
 4 acts (1878—Copenhagen) (Lib. C.
 Richardt)
 Cpte P. Elming, B. Norup, E. Johansson, K. Westi, C.
 Christiansen, A. Haugland, O. Hedegaard, I. Nielsen,
 R. Johansen, Danish Nat Rad Ch, Danish Nat RSO,
 M. Schønwandt (r1992)
  (6/93) (CHAN) ① [3] **CHAN9143/5**

**HELFER, Charles d' (d after 1664)
France**

SECTION IV: VOCAL AND CHORAL

Missa pro defunctis—4vv (pub 1656)
 Sagittarius Ens, La Fenice, M. Laplénie, A. Pumir
 (pp1993) *Colin: Missa pro defunctis.*
  (3/95) (CALL) ① **CAL9891**
 A Sei Voci, Lorraine Psallette, Toulouse
 Sacqueboutiers, J. Bernfeld, B. Fabre-Garrus (r1993)
 Concert
  (3/95) (ASTR) ① **E8521**

**HELLENDAAL, Pieter
(1721–1799) The Netherlands**

SECTION I: ORCHESTRAL

6 Grand Concertos—strings and continuo,
 Op. 3 (pub c1758)
 EXCERPTS: 1. G minor; 2. D minor; 3. F; 4. E flat; 5.
 D; 6. F.
 4. English Concert, T. Pinnock (hpd/dir) (r1979)
 Concert
  (1/93) (ARCH) ① **437 088-2AT**

SECTION II: CHAMBER

Hellendaal's Celebrated Rondo—violin and
 continuo (c1790)
 Locatelli Trio *Concert*   (5/93) (HYPE) ① **CDA66583**

**HELLER, Stephen (István)
(1813–1888) Hungary/France**

SECTION III: INSTRUMENTAL

Études d'expression et de rhythme—piano,
 Op. 125
 L. Laskine (r1975; trans Hasselmans: hp) *Concert*
  (12/93) (ERAT) ① **4509-92131-2**

**HELY, Cuthbert (fl 1620–1648)
England**

SECTION III: INSTRUMENTAL

3 Fantasias—lute (in Lord Herbert of
 Cherbury's Lute Book)
 P. O'Dette *Concert* (4/93) (HARM) ① **HMU90 7068**
Sarabrand—lute (in Lord Herbert of Cherbury's
 Lute Book)
 P. O'Dette *Concert* (4/93) (HARM) ① **HMU90 7068**

**HELY-HUTCHINSON, (Christian)
Victor (1901–1947) South
Africa/England**

SECTION I: ORCHESTRAL

Carol Symphony—orchestra (1920s)
 PAO, Barry Rose (r1966) *Concert*
  (12/91) (EMI) ① **CDM7 64131-2**

HEMPHILL, Julius (b 1940) USA

SECTION III: INSTRUMENTAL

Parchment—piano
 U. Oppens *Concert*   (5/90) (MUSI) ① **MACD-604**

HENRI, Jacques

SECTION II: CHAMBER

Légende amoureuse, 'Méodie
 sentimentale'—violin and piano
 F. Macmillen, anon (r1910) *Concert*
  (7/93) (APR) ① [2] **APR7016**

**HENRION, Paul (1819–1940)
France**

SECTION IV: VOCAL AND CHORAL

Le vieux ruban—song
 L. Fugère, anon (r1928) *Concert*
  (6/93) (SYMP) ① **SYMCD1125**

**HENRION, Richard (1854–1940)
Germany**

SECTION I: ORCHESTRAL

Fehrbelliner Reitermarsch
 Berlin Phil Wind Qnt, H. von Karajan (r1973: arr
 Berlin Phil Wind Qnt *Concert* (5/94) (DG) ① **439 346-2GX2**
Kreuzritter-Fanfare—march (1890s)
 Berlin Phil Wind Qnt, H. von Karajan (r1973) *Concert*
  (5/94) (DG) ① **439 346-2GX2**

**HENRIQUES, Fini Valdemar
(1867–1940) Denmark**

SECTION IV: VOCAL AND CHORAL

Maiden, do not sleep—song (Wds. E
 Lembcke)
 P. Frijsh, E. Nielsen (bp1938) *Concert*
  (4/95) (PEAR) ① [2] **GEMMCDS9095(2)**

HENRY, John Wales

SECTION IV: VOCAL AND CHORAL

Galwad y Tywysog—song (Wds. Mynydogg)
 A. Davies, A. Bryn Parri (r1994) *Concert*
  (11/95) (SAIN) ① **SCDC2085**

HENRY, Mike (1963) England

SECTION II: CHAMBER

Jazz Song—clarinet and piano
 N. Carpenter, D. McArthur *Concert*
  (10/92) (HERA) ① **HAVPCD152**

**HENRY VIII, King of England
(1491–1547) England**

SECTION IV: VOCAL AND CHORAL

En vray amoure—chanson: 4 parts
 (from Henry VIII Ms)
 Amsterdam Loeki Stardust Qt (r1991; arr recorder
 consort) *Concert*   (2/94) (L'OI) ① **436 155-2OH**
Pastyme with good companye—song (3vv)
 Oxford Christ Church Cath Ch, S. Darlington *Concert*
  (10/92) (NIMB) ① **NI5328**
 London Musica Antiqua, M. Uridge (r1980-83)
 Concert   (12/93) (SYMP) ① **SYMCD1157**

**HENSCHEL, George (1850–1934)
England**

SECTION IV: VOCAL AND CHORAL

Spring—song
 E. Eames, anon (r1908) *Concert*
  (11/93) (ROMO) ① [2] **81001-2**

**HENSELT, (George Martin) Adolf
(von) (1814–1889) Germany**

SECTION I: ORCHESTRAL

Concerto for Piano and Orchestra in F
 minor, Op. 16
 M. Ponti, Philh Hungarica, O. Maga *Concert*
  (5/93) (VOX) ① **115717-2**
 M-A. Hamelin, BBC Scottish So, M. Brabbins (r1993)
 Concert   (8/94) (HYPE) ① **CDA66717**
Variations de concert on 'Quand je quittai la
 Normandie' from Meyerbeer's 'Robert le
 Diable'—piano and orchestra, Op. 11 (1840)
 M-A. Hamelin, BBC Scottish So, M. Brabbins (r1993)
 Concert   (8/94) (HYPE) ① **CDA66717**

SECTION III: INSTRUMENTAL

12 Etudes—piano, Op. 2
 6. Si oiseau j'étais.
 6. S. Rachmaninov (r1923) *Concert*
  (3/93) (RCA) ① [10] **09026 61265-2(3)**
Wiegenlied in G flat—piano, Op. 45
 L. Godowsky (r1916) *Concert*
  (4/89) (APR) ① [2] **APR7011**
 L. Godowsky (r1924) *Concert*
  (4/89) (APR) ① [2] **APR7011**

**HENTZSCHEL, Johann (fl 1649)
Germany**

SECTION II: CHAMBER

Canzon a 8—viola da gambas or trumpets
 (1649)
 Ricercar Consort, P. Pierlot (va da gamba/dir) (r1992)
 Concert   (8/94) (RICE) ① **RIC098112**

**HENZE, Hans Werner (b 1926)
Germany**

SECTION I: ORCHESTRAL

Barcarola—orchestra (1979)
 CBSO, S. Rattle *Symphony 7*
  (11/93) (EMI) ① **CDC7 54762-2**
Requiem—Nine Sacred Concertos: pf, tpt &
 chbr orch (1990)
 U. Wiget, H. Hardenberger, Modern Ens, I.
 Metzmacher (pp1993) (11/94) (SONY) ① **SK58972**
Symphony No. 1—chamber orchestra (1947
 rev 1963)
 BPO, H.W. Henze *Concert*
  (12/90) (DG) ① [2] **429 854-2GC2**
Symphony No. 2—orchestra (1949)
 BPO, H.W. Henze *Concert*
  (12/90) (DG) ① [2] **429 854-2GC2**

Symphony No. 3—orchestra (1949-50)
BPO, H.W. Henze *Concert*
(12/90) (DG) ① [2] **429 854-2GC2**
Symphony No. 4—orchestra (1955)
BPO, H.W. Henze *Concert*
(12/90) (DG) ① [2] **429 854-2GC2**
Symphony No. 5—orchestra (1962)
BPO, H.W. Henze *Concert*
(12/90) (DG) ① [2] **429 854-2GC2**
Symphony No. 6—two chamber orchestras (1969)
LSO, H.W. Henze *Concert*
(12/90) (DG) ① [2] **429 854-2GC2**
Symphony No. 7
CBSO, S. Rattle *Barcarola.*
(11/93) (EMI) ① **CDC7 54762-2**

--- SECTION II: CHAMBER ---

String Quartet No. 1 (1947)
Arditti Qt *Concert*
(3/90) (WERG) ① [2] **WER60114/5-50**
String Quartet No. 2 (1952)
Arditti Qt *Concert*
(3/90) (WERG) ① [2] **WER60114/5-50**
String Quartet No. 3 (1975-76)
Arditti Qt *Concert*
(3/90) (WERG) ① [2] **WER60114/5-50**
String Quartet No. 4 (1976)
Arditti Qt *Concert*
(3/90) (WERG) ① [2] **WER60114/5-50**
String Quartet No. 5 (1976-77)
Arditti Qt *Concert*
(3/90) (WERG) ① [2] **WER60114/5-50**

--- SECTION III: INSTRUMENTAL ---

Capriccio—cello (1979-81)
P. Demenga (r1993) *Concert*
(8/95) (ECM) ① [2] **445 234-2**
M. Haimovitz (r1994) *Concert*
(12/95) (DG) ① **445 834-2GH**
Royal Winter Music—sonata on Shakespearean characters: guitar (1975-76)
J. Bream (r1981-2) *Concert*
(8/93) (RCA) ① [28] **09026 61583-2(4)**
J. Bream (r1981-2) *Concert*
(9/94) (RCA) ① **09026 61597-2**
Sonatina—trumpet (1976)
R. Friedrich (r1992) *Concert*
(6/93) (CAPR) ① **10 439**
G. Ashton (r1991) *Concert*
(4/94) (VIRG) ① **VC5 45003-2**

--- SECTION IV: VOCAL AND CHORAL ---

El Cimarrón—baritone, flute, guitar and percussion (1969-70) (Wds. Barnet, trans Enzensberger)
P. Yoder, M. Faust, R. Evers, M. Ardeleanu
(1/92) (SCHW) ① **314030**
Kammermusik—tenor, gtr/hp, cl, hn, bn, stg qnt (1958)
EXCERPTS: 1. Drei Tientos (solo guitar).
Drei Tientos J. Bream (r1966) *Concert*
(6/94) (RCA) ① **09026 61595-2**
1. J. Bream (r1966) *Concert*
(8/93) (RCA) ① [28] **09026 61583-2(4)**
Orpheus behind the wire—T, chorus a capella (1981-83) (Wds. E. Bond)
Danish Nat Rad Chbr Ch, S. Parkman *Concert*
(12/91) (CHAN) ① **CHAN8963**
Voices—song cycle (1973) (Wds. various)
1. Los poetas cubanos (wds. H. Padilla); 2. Prison song (wds. Ho Chi Minh); 3. Keiner oder alle (wds. B. Brecht); 4. The electric cop (wds. V. H. Cruz); 5. The distant drum (wds. C. C. Hernton); 6. 42 Schulkinder (wds. E. Fried); 7. Caino (wds. G. de Sanctis); 8. Il Pasi (wds. M. Tobino); 9. Heimkehr (wds. H. Heine); 10. Grecia 1970 (wds. G. Ungaretti); 11. Legende von der Entstehung des Buches Taoteking (wds. B. Brecht); 12. Gedanken eines Revuemädchens (wds. B. Brecht); 13. Das wirkliche Messer (wds.H. M. Enzensberger); 14. Recht und billig (wds. E. Fried); 15. Patria (wds. M. Barnet); 16. Screams (wds. M. Smith); 17. The worker (wds. R. W. Thomas); 18. Para aconsejar a una dama (wds. H. Padilla); 19. Roses and revolution (wds. D. Randall); 20. Vermutung über Hessen (wds. F. C. Delius); 21. Schluss (wds. M. Katsaros); 22. Das Blumenfest (wds. H. M. Enzensberger).
Cpte R. Trexler, J. Vogt, Leipzig SO, H. Neumann
(r1978-9) (12/95) (BERL) ① [2] **0021 802BC**
1-3, 5-7, 9-13, 15, 16, 18-20. G. Pelker, F. Lang, Musikfabrik NRW, J. Kalitzke (r1992)
(12/95) (CPO) ① **CPO999 192-2**

--- SECTION V: STAGE WORKS ---

Die Bassariden—opera: 1 act (1956-66—Salzburg) (Lib. W H Auden & C Kallman, after Euripides)
Cpte K. Riegel, A. Schmidt, M. Burt, R. Tear, W. Murray, K. Armstrong, C. Lindsley, O. Wenkel, Berlin Rad Chbr Ch, South German Rad Chor, Berlin RSO, G. Albrecht
(10/91) (SCHW) ① [2] **314006**
Boulevard Solitude—opera: 7 scenes (1952—Hanover) (Lib. W. Jokisch, after G. Weil)
Cpte E. Vassilieva, J. Pruett, C-J. Falkman, J-M. Salzmann, B. Brewer, D. Ottevaere, Children's Chor, Lausanne Op Chor, Rencontres Musicales Orch, I. Anguelov (pp1987)
(12/92) (CASC) ① [2] **VEL1006**
The English Cat—opera (1983—Stuttgart) (Lib. E. Bond)
Cpte R. Berkeley-Steele, M. Coles, A. Watt, I. Platt, J. Pike, L. Kennedy, G. Nilsson, D. Bennett, C. Court, J. Bremar, R. Hallawell, G. Davenport, Parnassus Orch, M. Stenz
(12/92) (WERG) ① [2] **WER6204-2**
Der junge Lord—opera: 2 acts (1965—Berlin) (Lib. I Bachmann, after W Hauff)
Cpte B. McDaniel, L. Driscoll, V. Little, M. Röhrl, I. Sardi, E. Krukowski, H. Krebs, P. Johnson, R. Hesse, L. Otto, E. Mathis, B. Jasper, M. Türke, D. Grobe, G. Treptow, F. Hoppe, Schöneberg Boys' Ch, Berlin Deutsche Op Chor, Berlin Deutsche Op Orch, C. von Dohnányi (r1960s)
(9/94) (DG) ① [2] **445 248-2GC2**

HERBECK, Johann Ritter Von (1831–1877) Austria

--- SECTION IV: VOCAL AND CHORAL ---

Pueri concinite—motet
Vienna Boys' Ch, U.C. Harrer *Concert*
(12/91) (PHIL) ① **426 307-2PH**

HERBERT, Victor August (1859–1924) USA

--- SECTION II: CHAMBER ---

A la valse—violin and piano
K. Daeshik Kang, M. Rahkonen (r1992) *Concert*
(9/93) (NIMB) ① **NI5358**
J. Heifetz, M. Kaye (r1944) *Concert*
(11/94) (RCA) ① [65] **09026 61778-2(19)**

--- SECTION IV: VOCAL AND CHORAL ---

Indian Summer—song based on film theme (1919) (Lyrics Al Dubin, added 1940)
J. Hadley, American Th Orch, P. Gemignani (r1993; orch W. D. Brohn)
(12/95) (RCA) ① **09026 62681-2**

--- SECTION V: STAGE WORKS ---

Angel Face—operetta (1919—Chicago) (Book & Lyrics H B Smith & R B Smith)
EXCERPTS: 1. I Might Be Your 'Once-in-a-While'.
1. J. Hadley, American Th Orch, P. Gemignani (r1993; orch W. D. Brohn) *Concert*
(12/95) (RCA) ① **09026 62681-2**
Babes in Toyland—operetta (1903—Chicago) (Lib. MacDonough)
EXCERPTS: 1. March of the Toys; 2. Toyland; 3. Floretta; 4. The moon will help you out; 5. Jane; 6. Eccentric Dance; 7. Never mind, Bo-Peep; 8. Children's Theme; 9. Before and After; 10. I can't do the sum.
1. St Louis SO, L. Slatkin *Concert*
(6/89) (RCA) ① **RD87716**
1. Boston Pops, A. Fiedler (r1958) *Concert*
(1/94) (RCA) ① **09026 61249-2**
10. Cincinnati Uni Sngrs, Cincinnati Uni Th Orch, E. Rivers (r1978) *Concert* (4/94) (NEW) ① **80221-2**
Eileen—operetta (1917—Cleveland) (Lib. Blossom. Orig. title Hearts of Erin)
EXCERPTS: 1. The Irish Have a Great Night Tonight; 2. Thine Alone; 3. Ireland, My Sireland; 4. Free Trade and a Misty Moon.
1, 3, 4. G. Evans, V. Stiles, S. Welsh, Orig Broadway Cast, V. Herbert (r1917) *Concert*
(5/94) (PEAR) ① [3] **GEMMCDS9059/61**
The Fortune Teller—operetta (1898—Toronto) (Lib. H. B. Smith)
EXCERPTS: 1. Gypsy Love Song; 2. Romany Life; 3. Opening Chorus of Schoolgirls; 4. Always Do as People Say You Should; 5. 2nd Act Finale: Chorus of Trumpets and Drums.

1. E. Cowles, Broadway Cast (r1906) *Concert*
(5/94) (PEAR) ① [3] **GEMMCDS9050/2(1)**
1. J. Hadley, American Th Orch, P. Gemignani (r1993; orch W. D. Brohn) *Concert*
(12/95) (RCA) ① **09026 62681-2**
2. M. Hill Smith, Chandos Sngrs, Chandos Concert Orch, S. Barry *Concert*
(2/90) (CHAN) ① **CHAN8759**
3-5. A. Nielsen, Broadway Cast (r1898) *Concert*
(5/94) (PEAR) ① [3] **GEMMCDS9050/2(1)**
Mademoiselle Modiste—operetta: 2 acts (1905—Trenton, New Jersey) (Lib. H. Blossom)
EXCERPTS: 1. Kiss me again.
1. R. Ponselle, orch, R. Romani (r1920) *Concert*
(10/93) (NIMB) ① **NI7846**
1. R. Ponselle, orch, R. Romani (r1920) *Concert*
(12/93) (NIMB) ① **NI7851**
1. A. Galli-Curci, orch, R. Bourdon (r1923) *Concert*
(8/94) (ROMO) ① [2] **81004-2**
Naughty Marietta—operetta (1910—New York) (Lib. Young)
EXCERPTS: 1. Tramp! Tramp! Tramp; 2. Ah! sweet mystery of life (Song of the fountain); 3. It can never, never can be love; 4. If I were anybody else but me; 5. 'Neath a Southern moon; 6. Zing, Zing (Italian Street Song); 7. Turna like dat-a, Pierrette (Dance of the marionettes); 8. You may a marionette; 9. New Orleans, jeunesse Dorée; 10. The loves of New Orleans; 11. The sweet by-and-by; 12. Live for today; 13. It's pretty soft for Simon; 14. I'm falling in with some one.
I'm falling in love with someone R. Crooks, orch (r1929) *Concert* (9/93) (CLAR) ① **CDGSE78-50-50**
1. P. Morrison, Chandos Concert Orch, S. Barry *Concert*
(6/85) (CHAN) ① **CHAN8362**
2. J. Peerce, Philh, A. Fistoulari (r1950) *Concert*
(4/92) (EMI) ① [7] **CHS7 69741-2(2)**
2, 6. B. Hendricks, Ambrosian Sngrs, Philh, L. Foster (r1992) *Concert* (8/93) (EMI) ① **CDC7 54626-2**
14. J. Hadley, American Th Orch, P. Gemignani (r1993; orch W. D. Brohn) *Concert*
(12/95) (RCA) ① **09026 62681-2**
The Only Girl—operetta (1914) (Lib. H. Blossom, arr. G. Trinkhaus)
EXCERPTS—; 1. When you're away.
1. J. Hadley, American Th Orch, P. Gemignani (r1993; orch W. D. Brohn) *Concert*
(12/95) (RCA) ① **09026 62681-2**
Orange Blossoms—operetta (1922)
A kiss in the dark C. Muzio, orch (r1924) *Concert*
(5/90) (BOGR) ① [2] **BIM705-2**
A kiss in the dark F. Kreisler, C. Lamson (r1924: arr Kreisler) *Concert* (9/93) (BIDD) ① [2] **LAB068/9**
A kiss in the dark C. Muzio, orch (r1924) *Concert*
(1/94) (ROMO) ① [2] **81005-2**
A kiss in the dark A. Galli-Curci, orch, R. Bourdon (r1923) *Concert* (8/94) (ROMO) ① [2] **81004-2**
The Princess Pat—operetta (1915—Atlantic City) (Lib. Blossom)
EXCERPTS: 1. Neapolitan Love Song; 2. Love is the Best of All.
1. J. Hadley, American Th Orch, P. Gemignani (r1993; orch W. D. Brohn) *Concert*
(12/95) (RCA) ① **09026 62681-2**
2. E. Painter, Orig Broadway Cast (r1915) *Concert*
(5/94) (PEAR) ① [3] **GEMMCDS9056/8**
The Red Mill—operetta (1906—Buffalo) (Lib. Blossom)
EXCERPTS—; 1. For every day is Ladies' Day for me; 2. In the isle of our dreams; 3. Whistle it; 4. Dance I want you to marry me; 5. You can never tell about a woman; 6. The Legend of the Mill; 7. Because you're you; 8. The streets of New York.
1, 8. J. Hadley, Harvard Glee Club, American Th Orch, P. Gemignani (r1993; orch W. D. Brohn) *Concert* (12/95) (RCA) ① **09026 62681-2**
The Serenade—operetta (1897—New York) (Lyrics H B Smith)
EXCERPTS: 1. Don Jose of Sevilla; 2. Dreaming, Dreaming.
1, 2. H. C. Barnabee, J. B. Davis, H. Fredricks, G. Frothingham, W. H. MacDonald, Broadway Cast (r1898) *Concert*
(5/94) (PEAR) ① [3] **GEMMCDS9050/2(1)**
Sweethearts—operetta (1913—Baltimore) (Lib. H.B. & R.B. Smith, De Gresac)
EXCERPTS—; 1. On Parade; 2. Every lover must meet his fate; 3. Sweethearts; 4. In the convent they never taught me that; 5. The fame of love; 6. Mother Goose; 7. Angelus; 8. Pretty as a picture; 9. The cricket on the hearth; 10. Jeanette's wooden shoes.
3, 7, 9. C. McDonald, Orig Broadway Cast (r1913) *Concert* (5/94) (PEAR) ① [3] **GEMMCDS9056/8**

HERBERT OF CHERBURY, Lord Edward *(1582–1648) England*

SECTION III: INSTRUMENTAL

Pavan of the composition of mee Herbert of Cherbury and Castle Island—lute (1640) (in Lord Herbert of Cherbury's Lute Book)
P. O'Dette *Concert*   (4/93) (HARM) ① **HMU90 7068**

HERMAN, Jerry (Gerald) *(b 1932) USA*

SECTION V: STAGE WORKS

La Cage aux folles—musical show (1983—New York) (Lyrics cpsr; Book H. Fierstein, after J. Poiret)
EXCERPTS: 1. Prelude; 2. We Are What We Are; 3. A Little More Mascara; 4. With Anne On My Arm; 5. With You On My Arm; 6. Song on the Sand (La Da Da Da); 7. La Cage aux Folles; 8. I Am What I Am; 9. Song on the Sand (reprise); 10. Masculinity; 11. Look Over There; 12. Cocktail Counterpoint; 13. The Best of Times; 14. Look Over There (reprise); 15. Finale.
Cpte Orig Broadway Cast, D. Pippin (r1983)
(3/87) (RCA) ① **BD84824**
Jerry's Girls—musical revue (1985—New York) (Lyrics cpsr)
EXCERPTS: 1. Overture. ACT ONE: 2. Jerry's Girls (It's Today/Mame); 3. It Takes a Woman (Hello, Dolly!); 4. Put On Your Sunday Clothes (Hello, Dolly!); 5. Wherever We Ain't (Mack and Mabel); 6. We Need a Little Christmas (Mame); 7. I Won't Send Roses (Mack and Mabel); 8. Tap Your Troubles Away (Mack and Mabel); 9. Vaudeville Medley: 9a. Two-a-Day (Parade); 9b. Bosom Buddies (Mame); 9c. The Man in the Moon (Mame); 9d. So Long Dearie (Hello, Dolly!); 9e. Take It All Off; 9f. Two-a-Day (reprise); 10. Shalom (Milk and Honey); 11. Milk and Honey; 12. Showtune (Nightcap); 13. If He Walked Into My Life (Mame); 14. Hello, Dolly! ACT TWO: 15. Entr'acte; 16. Movie Medley: 16a. Just Go to the Movies (A Day In Hollywood); 16b. Movies Were Movies (Mack and Mabel); 16c. Look What Happened to Mabel (Mack and Mabel); 16d. Nelson (A Day In Hollywood); 16e. Just Go to the Movies (reprise); 17. Time Heals Everything; 18. It's Today; 19. Mame; 20. Kiss Her Now (Dear World); 21. That's How Young I Feel (Mame); 22. Gooch's Song (Mame); 23. Before the Parade Passes By (Hello, Dolly!); 24. I Don't Want to Know (Dear World); 25. La Cage Aux Folles Medley (cont'd A Tyler): 25a. Jerry's New Girl; 25b. La Cage Aux Folles; 25c. Song On the Sand; 25d. I Am What I Am; 25e. The Best of Times; 26. Jerry's Turn; 27. Jerry's Girls (reprise).
Cpte C. Channing, L. Uggams, A. McArdle, Orig Cast, J. Glazener (r1984; pre-Broadway cast)
(3/87) (TER) ① [2] **CDTER2 1093**

HERMANN, Hans *(1870–1931) Germany*

SECTION IV: VOCAL AND CHORAL

Drei Wandrer—Lied (Wds. Busse)
H. Schlusnus, Berlin St Op Orch, A. Melichar (r1932) *Concert*   (1/94) (PREI) ① [2] **89205**
Mahnung—Lied
H. Schlusnus, Berlin St Op Orch, A. Melichar (r1932) *Concert*   (1/94) (PREI) ① [2] **89205**

HERMANNUS CONTRACTUS *(1013–1054) Germany*

SECTION IV: VOCAL AND CHORAL

Salve regina—Marian antiphon
Hilliard Ens *Concert*   (6/91) (HYPE) ① **CDA66370**

HÉROLD, (Louis Joseph) Ferdinand *(1791–1833) France*

SECTION V: STAGE WORKS

La Fille mal gardée—ballet: 2 acts (1828—Paris) (Current musical score ed/arr Lanchbery)
O. ACT 1: EXCERPTS - ACT 1: 1. Introduction; 2. Danse du coq et des poules; 3. Lise et le ruban; 4a. Colas; 4b. Colas' Solo; 5. Colas and Simone; 6. Villageois; 7. Simone and Lise; 8. Lise and Colas; 9. Jeunes villageoises; 10. Thomas and Alain; 11. Départ pour la moisson; 12. Colas; 13. Pique-nique; 14. Danse à la flûte; 15. Querelle; 16. Pas de deux de Fanny Elssier; 17a. Simone; 17b. Danse des

sabots; 18. Danse du mai; 19. Orage et final. ACT 2: 20. Ouverture; 21. Lise and Simone; 22. Fileuse; 23. Danse au tambour de basque; 24. Moissonneurs; 25. Quand je serai mariée; 26. Retour de Simone; 27. Thomas, Alain et les notaires; 28. Consternation et pardon; 29. Pas de deux; 30. Finale.
Cpte ROHO, J. Lanchbery (arr Lanchbery) *Lecocq: Mam'zelle Angot Ballet.*
(12/91) (DECC) ① [2] **430 849-2DM2**
Excs ROHO, J. Lanchbery (r1962: arr Lanchbery)
(1/94) (DECC) ① **430 196-2DM**
Le Pré aux Clercs—opera: 3 acts (1832—Paris) (Lib. Planard, after Mérimée)
EXCERPTS: 1. Jours de mon enfance; 2. Souvenir de jeune age.
Jours de mon enfance S. Jo, ECO, R. Bonynge (r1993) *Concert*   (9/94) (DECC) ① **440 679-2DH**
Zampa—opera: 3 acts (1831—Paris) (Lib. Mélesville)
Pourquoi tremblez-vous? M. Battistini, orch (r1906: Ital) *Concert*   (2/92) (PREI) ① **89045**
Pourquoi tremblez-vous? M. Battistini, orch, C. Sabajno (Ital: r1906) *Concert*
(10/92) (NIMB) ① **NI7831**
Pourquoi tremblez-vous? M. Battistini, orch, C. Sabajno (Ital: r1906) *Concert*
(10/92) (PEAR) ① **GEMMCD9936**

HERON, Henry *(1730–1795) England*

SECTION III: INSTRUMENTAL

10 Voluntaries—organ (pub 1760)
1. G minor; 8. G.
1. Margaret Phillips *Concert*   (5/91) (GAMU) ① **GAMCD514**
8. J. Bate *Concert*   (11/91) (UNIC) ① **DKPCD9106**

HERRMANN, Bernard *(1911–1975) USA*

SECTION I: ORCHESTRAL

Currier and Ives Suite (1935)
1. The Whirlwind Skater; 2. Waltz; 3. Gallop—The Whip; 4. The Fat Man; 5. Torchlight Finale.
NZ SO, J. Sedares (r1993) *Concert*   (6/94) (KOCH) ① **37224-2**
For the Fallen—orchestra (1943)
NZ SO, J. Sedares (r1993) *Concert*   (6/94) (KOCH) ① **37224-2**
Silent noon—idyll: orchestra (1975) (rev of 'Aubade' (1933): ed C Husted)
NZ SO, J. Sedares (r1993) *Concert*   (6/94) (KOCH) ① **37224-2**
Sinfonietta—string orchestra (1936, rev 1975)
Berlin SO, I. Jackson (r1992) *Concert*   (7/93) (KOCH) ① **37152-2**
Symphony No. 1 (1937-40)
Phoenix SO, J. Sedares *Schuman: New England Triptych.*   (9/92) (KOCH) ① **37135-2**
National PO, B. Herrmann (r1974) *Fantasticks.*   (1/94) (UNIC) ① **UKCD2063**
Welles Raises Kane—suite (1942) (arr from film scores 'Citizen Kane' & 'The Magnificent Ambersons')
EXCERPTS: 1. Overture; 2. Theme and Variations; 3. Ragtime—The Saturday Night Band Concert; 4. Meditation—Antimacassar; 5. Finale—Pursuit and Happiness.
LPO, B. Herrmann (r1967) *Concert*   (11/94) (UNIC) ① **UKCD2065**

SECTION II: CHAMBER

Echoes—string quartet (1965) (performed in 1971 as the ballet 'Ante Room')
Amici Qt (r1966) *Souvenirs de voyage.*   (5/95) (UNIC) ① **UKCD2069**
Souvenirs de voyage—clarinet quintet (1967)
J.C. Lerner, Lyric Art Qt *Concert*   (10/90) (BAY) ① **BCD-1014**
R. Hill, Ariel Qt (r1974) *Echoes.*   (5/95) (UNIC) ① **UKCD2069**

SECTION IV: VOCAL AND CHORAL

Bernard Herrmann on Film Music—talk by the composer (1970s)
B. Herrmann *Concert*   (3/94) (MILA) ① **74321 14081-2**

The Fantasticks—song cycle (1942) (Wds. N. Breton)
1. January; 2. February; 3. March; 4. April; 5. May.
G. Humphreys, M. Dickinson, J. Amis, M. Rippon, Thames Chbr Ch, National PO, B. Herrmann (r1975) *Symphony 1.*   (1/94) (UNIC) ① **UKCD2063**

SECTION V: STAGE WORKS

Beneath the 12-Mile Reef—film score (1953)
EXCERPTS: 1. The Sea: The Lagoon; 2. Descending; 3. The Octopus: Homecoming.
Suite National PO, C. Gerhardt *Concert*   (11/91) (RCA) ① **GD80707**
The Bride Wore Black—film score (1967)
Suite RPO, E. Bernstein (r1992: arr Palmer) *Concert*   (3/94) (MILA) ① **74321 14081-2**
Citizen Kane—film score (1941)
EXCERPTS: 1. Prelude; 2. Susan in Night Club (Rain Sequence); 3a. Thatcher's Library (Litany); 3b. MS Reading and Snow Picture; 3c. Walter's Sacrifice; 3d. Charlie meets; 4. Galop; 5a. Dissolve to Thatcher; 5b. Second MS; 5c. Bernstein's Narration; 6a. Kane's News Office (Inquirer Polka); 6b. Carter's Exit; 6c. Chronicle Scherzo; 7. Bernstein's Presto; 8. Kane's Return; 9. Sunset Narrative; 10. Theme and Variations (Breakfast Montage); 11a. Kane meets Susan; 11b. Susan's Room; 11c. Mother Memory; 12a. The Trip to Susan's; 12b. Getty's Departure; 12c. Kane marries; 13. Salaambo's Aria; 14. Lelands's Dismissal; 15. Susan in Night Club (New Dawn Sequence); 16. Opera Montage; 17a. Xanadu; 17b. Jigsaw Puzzles (Perpetual Motion); 17c. Second Xanadu; 18a. Kane's Picnic; 18b. Susan leaves; 19. El Rancho (Seond Dawn Sequence); 20. Finale; 21. End Titles.
Suite K. Te Kanawa, National PO, C. Gerhardt *Concert*   (11/91) (RCA) ① **GD80707**
1, 6c, 21. RPO, E. Bernstein (r1992) *Concert*   (3/94) (MILA) ① **74321 14081-2**
13. K. Te Kanawa, National PO, C. Gerhardt *Concert*   (10/92) (RCA) ① **GD82792**
The Day the Earth Stood Still—film score (1951)
EXCERPTS: 1a. Prelude; 1b. Outer Space; 1c. Radar; 2. Danger; 3. Klaatu; 4a. Gort; 4b. The Visor; 4c. The Telescope; 5. Escape; 6. Solar Diamonds; 7. Arlington; 8. Lincoln Memorial; 9a. Nocturne; 9b. The Flashlight; 9c. The Robot; 9d. Space Control; 10a. The Elevator; 10b. Magnetic Pull; 10c. The Study; 10d. The Conference; 10e. The Jewelry Store; 11. Panic; 12a. The Glowing; 12b. Alone; 12c. Gort's Rage; 12d. Nikto; 12e. The Captive; 12f. Terror; 13. The Prison; 14. Rebirth; 15. Departure; 16. Farewell; 17. Finale.
1a-c, 2, 3, 4a-c, 5-8, 9a-d, 10a-e, 11, 12a-e, 13-17. OST, B. Herrmann, L. Newman, Alfred Newman (r1951) *Alf Newman: 20th Century Fox Fanfare.*   (11/94) (FOX) ① **07822 11010-2**
The Devil and Daniel Webster—film score (1941)
EXCERPTS: 1. The Devil's Concerto; 2. Sleigh-ride; 3. Swing, your partners.
1-3. RPO, E. Bernstein (r1992) *Concert*   (3/94) (MILA) ① **74321 14081-2**
The Devil and Daniel Webster—concert suite from film score (1942)
EXCERPTS: 1. Mr Scratch; 2. Ballad of Springfield Mountain; 3. Sleighride; 4. The Miser's Waltz; 5. Swing Your Partners.
NZ SO, J. Sedares (r1993) *Concert*   (6/94) (KOCH) ① **37224-2**
LPO, B. Herrmann (r1967) *Concert*   (11/94) (UNIC) ① **UKCD2065**
Fahrenheit 451—film score (1966)
EXCERPTS: 1. Prelude; 2. Fire Engine; 3. The Bedroom; 4. The Reading; 5. The Garden; 6. The Nightmare; 7. Flowers of Fire; 8. Flamethrower; 9. Captain's Death; 10. The Road (Finale).
10. RPO, E. Bernstein (r1992) *Concert*   (3/94) (MILA) ① **74321 14081-2**
Hangover Square—film score (1945)
EXCERPTS: 1. Concerto Macabre (piano and orchestra).
1. J. Achucarro, National PO, C. Gerhardt *Concert*   (11/91) (RCA) ① **GD80707**
It's Alive 2—film score (1978) (posthumously arr by L. Johnson)
EXCERPTS: 1. Main Title; 2. Birth Traumas; 3. Evil Evolving; 4. Savage Trilogy; 5. Nightmares; 6. Beautiful and Bizarre; 7. Revulsion; 8. Basement Nursery; 9. Lamentation; 10. Living with Fear; 11. Stalking the Infants; 12. Climax.
1. OST *Concert*   (5/93) (SILV) ① **SILVAD3003**
1-12. OST, L. Johnson (r1978)   (11/91) (SILV) ① **FILMCD074**

Jane Eyre—film score (1943)
EXCERPTS: 1. Prelude; 2. Jane's Departure; 3. Jane alone; 4. Dreaming—Vanity; 5. Elgy—Jane's sorrow; 6. Time passage—The letter; 7. Thornfield Hall—Valse bluette; 8. Rochester; 9. The piano—Promenade; 10. Rochester's past—The fire; 11. Duo—The door; 12. Springtime; 13. Mr. Mason; 14. The room—The rattle; 15. The garden; 16. 'Farewell'; 17. Song (Jane's confession)—The storm; 18. The wedding—The wife; 19. Jane's farewell (Rochester's confession); 20. Jane's return; 21. Finale.
1, 2, 5, 7, 9, 10, 13, 15, 17-21. OST, B. Herrmann (r1943) *Concert* (11/94) (FOX) ① **07822 11006-2**

Jason and the Argonauts—film score (1963)
EXCERPTS: 1. Prelude; 2a. The Skeletons; 2b. The Battle with the Skeletons; 2c. Finale.
1, 2a-c OST, B. Herrmann (r1963) *Concert* (11/88) (CLOU) ① **ACN7014**

The Man Who Knew Too Much—film score (1956)
EXCERPTS: 1. The Storm Clouds (re-orch of A Benjamin's Cantata); 2. Prelude.
1. C. Henry, Ambrosian Sngrs, RPO, E. Bernstein (r1992) *Concert* (3/94) (MILA) ① **74321 14081-2**

Marnie—film score (1964)
EXCERPTS: 1. Prelude; 2. Theme.
Suite San Diego SO, L. Schifrin (r1990) *Concert* (11/91) (PRO) ① **CDS524**
1. Prague City PO, P. Bateman (r1993) *Concert* (7/94) (SILV) ① **FILMCD137**

Mysterious Island—film score (1961)
EXCERPTS: 1. Fanfare; 2. Prelude; 3. Civil War; 4. Escape to the Clouds; 4a. Escape/The Balloon; 5. The Island; 6. The Giant Crab; 7. The Granite House; 7a. The Cave; 8. The Phorarhacos; 8a. The Giant Bird; 9. Pirates/The Doomed Ship; 10. Nemo/The Grotto; 11. The Cephalopod; 11a. Pipeline/The Ship Raising; 12. Escape from the Island.
1-12. OST, B. Herrmann (r1961; stereo soundtrack) (10/93) (CLOU) ① **ACN7017**
2, 4a, 6, 7a, 8a, 9, 11a OST, B. Herrmann (r1961) *Concert* (11/88) (CLOU) ① **ACN7014**

North by Northwest—film score (1959)
EXCERPTS: 1. Main Titles; 2. Abduction of George Kaplan; 3. The Elevator; 4. Murder at the United Nations; 5. Conversation Piece; 6. Crash of the Cropduster; 7. The Auction and the Airport; 8. Cafeteria Shooting; 9. Duo; 10. Stalking Vandamm's House; 11. The Matchbox; 12a. The Aeroplane; 12b. Mount Rushmore; 12c. Finale.
1. San Diego SO, L. Schifrin (r1990) *Concert* (11/91) (PRO) ① **CDS524**
1. Prague City PO, P. Bateman (r1993) *Concert* (3/94) (SILV) ① **FILMCD137**
1. RPO, E. Bernstein (r1992) *Concert* (3/94) (MILA) ① **74321 14081-2**
1-11, 12a-c London Studio SO, L. Johnson (r1979) (5/91) (UNIC) ① **UKCD2040**
5. Prague City PO, P. Bateman (orch Mike Townend) *Concert* (7/94) (SILV) ① **FILMCD159**

Obsession—film score (1975)
EXCERPTS: 1a. Main Title; 1b. Valse Lente; 1c. Kidnap; 2a. Newsboy; 2b. The Tape; 2c. The Ferry; 3a. The Tomb; 3b. Sandra; 4a. The Church; 4b. Court's Confession; 4c. Bryn Mawr; 5a. New Orleans; 5b. Wedding; 5c. Court, The Morning After; 6a. The Plane; 6b. Court and La Salle's Struggle; 6c. Airport.
1a-c, 2a-c, 3a, 3b, 4a-c, 5a-c, 6a-c OST, National PO, B. Herrmann (r1975) *Concert* (11/91) (UNIC) ① **UKCD2065**

On Dangerous Ground—film score (1951)
EXCERPTS: 1. Prelude; 2. Blindness; 3. The Silence; 4. The Hunt; 5. Finale.
4. National PO, C. Gerhardt *Concert* (11/91) (RCA) ① **GD80707**

Psycho—film score (1960)
EXCERPTS: 1. Prelude; 2a. The City; 2b. Marion; 2c. Marion and Sam; 3. Temptation; 4a. Flight; 4b. The Patrol Car; 4c. The Car Lot; 4d. The Package; 4e. The Rainstorm; 5a. Hotel Room; 5b. The Window; 5c. The Parlour; 6. The Madhouse; 7. The Peephole; 8a. The Bathroom; 8b. The Murder; 8c. The Body; 8d. The Office; 9a. The Office; 9b. The Curtain; 9c. The Water; 9d. The Car; 9e. The Swamp; 10a. The Search; 10b. The Shadow; 10c. Phone Booth; 11a. The Porch; 11b. The Stairs; 11c. The Knife; 12a. The Search; 12b. The First Floor; 12c. Cabin 10; 12d. Cabin 1; 13a. The Hill; 13b. The Bedroom; 13c. The Toys; 13d. The Cellar; 13e. Discovery; 14. Finale.
National PO, B. Herrmann (r1975) (11/89) (UNIC) ① **UKCD2021**
1, 2a, 4e, 8b, 14. Prague City PO, P. Bateman (r1993) *Concert* (3/94) (SILV) ① **FILMCD137**

1, 2a, 8b, 14. San Diego SO, L. Schifrin (r1990) *Concert* (11/91) (PRO) ① **CDS524**
1, 8b, 14. San Diego SO, L. Schifrin *Concert* (5/93) (SILV) ① **SILVAD3003**
1, 8b, 14. RPO, E. Bernstein (r1992) *Concert* (3/94) (MILA) ① **74321 14081-2**

The Seventh Voyage of Sinbad—film score (1958)
EXCERPTS: 1a. Overture; 1b. Baghdad; 2a. The Cyclops' Fury; 2b. The Capture; 3. The Fight; 4a. The Shell; 4b. The Genie's Home; 5a. Fight with the Cyclops; 5b. Cyclops' Death; 6. The Egg; 7. The Dragon; 8. Duel with the Skeleton; 9a. The Dragon and the Second Cyclops; 9b. Death of the Second Cyclops; 9c. The Crossbow; 9d. Death of the Dragon; 10. Finale.
1a, 1b, 2a, 2b, 3, 4a, 4b, 5a, 5b, 6-8, 9a-d, 10. OST, B. Herrmann (r1958) *Concert* (11/88) (CLOU) ① **ACN7014**

The Snows of Kilimanjaro—film score (1952)
EXCERPTS: 1. Memory Waltz; 2. Interlude.
1. Hollywood Bowl SO, J. Mauceri (r1993; restored Husted) *Concert* (6/94) (PHIL) ① **438 685-2PH**

Taxi Driver—film score (1975)
EXCERPTS: 1. A Night Piece for Saxophone & Orchestra (arr C. Palmer).
1. D. Roach, RPO, E. Bernstein (r1992) *Concert* (3/94) (MILA) ① **74321 14081-2**

The Three Worlds of Gulliver—film score (1960)
EXCERPTS: 1. Overture; 2. Wapping Market; 3. Gulliver and Elizabeth; 4. The Storm; 5. The Lilliputians; 6. The Stakes/The Emperor's March; 7. Clouds; 8. A Hatful of Fish (Hornpipe); 9. Trees; 10. Wonderful Gulliver (Duning/Washington); 11. The Tightrope; 12. Gentle Love (Duning/Washington); 13. War March/The Naval Battle; 14. The Banquet/The Fire/Escape; 15. The Ocean/Glumdalclitch; 16. Reunion/Nocturne; 17. The Wedding/Woodland; 18. The Giant Squirrel; 19. The Chess Game; 20. Alchemy; 21. The Cage/The Giant Crocodile; 22. Pursued by Giants; 23. Finale.
1, 4-6, 8, 9, 11, 13, 16, 21-23. OST, B. Herrmann (r1960) *Concert* (11/88) (CLOU) ① **ACN7014**

Vertigo—film score (1958)
EXCERPTS: 1. Vertigo Prelude and Rooftop; 2. Madeleine and Carlotta's Portrait; 3. The Beach; 4. Farewell and The Tower; 5. The Nightmare and Dawn; 6. Scene d'Amour (Love Scene); 7. The Necklace and The Return and Finale.
Suite San Diego SO, L. Schifrin (r1990) *Concert* (11/91) (PRO) ① **CDS524**
1, 5. Prague City PO, P. Bateman (r1993) *Concert* (9/95) (SILV) ① **FILMCD159**
1, 5, 6. San Diego SO, L. Schifrin *Concert* (5/93) (SILV) ① **SILVAD3002**
1, 6. Hollywood Bowl SO, J. Mauceri (r1993) *Concert* (1/95) (PHIL) ① **442 425-2PH**
6. RPO, E. Bernstein (r1992) *Concert* (3/94) (MILA) ① **74321 14081-2**
6. Prague City PO, P. Bateman (r1993) *Concert* (3/94) (SILV) ① **FILMCD137**

White-Witch Doctor—film score (1953)
EXCERPTS: 1a. Talking Drums; 1b. Prelude; 1c. The Riverboat; 1d. Petticoatd Dance; 1e. The Safari; 2a. Tarantuka; 2b. The Lion; 3. Nocturne; 4a. Abduction of the Bakuba Boy; 4b. The Skulls; 5a. Lonni bound by ropes; 5b. Departure.
Suite National PO, C. Gerhardt *Concert* (11/91) (RCA) ① **GD80707**

Wrong Man—film score (1957)
EXCERPTS: 1. Prelude.
1. RPO, E. Bernstein (r1992) *Concert* (3/94) (MILA) ① **74321 14081-2**

Wuthering Heights—opera: 4 acts (1982—Portland, Oregon) (Lib. L. Fletcher, after Brontë)
Cpte M. Beaton, D. Bell, J. Kitchiner, P. Bowden, J. Ward, E. Bainbridge, M. Rippon, D. Kelly, M. Snashall, Elizabethan Sngrs, PAO, B. Herrmann (r1966) (8/93) (UNIC) ① [3] **UKCD2050/2**

HERRMANN, Gottfried (1808–1878) Germany

SECTION IV: VOCAL AND CHORAL

Du bist wie eine Blume—Lied (1843) (Wds. Heine)
D. Fischer-Dieskau, D. Klöcker, H. Höll *Concert* (4/88) (ORFE) ① **C153861A**
Erfüllung—Lied (1843) (Wds. Glaser)
D. Fischer-Dieskau, D. Klöcker, H. Höll *Concert* (4/88) (ORFE) ① **C153861A**

Ich denke dein—Lied (1843) (Wds. Kraft)
D. Fischer-Dieskau, D. Klöcker, H. Höll *Concert* (4/88) (ORFE) ① **C153861A**

HERSCH, Fred (b 1955) USA

SECTION II: CHAMBER

Tango Bittersweet—cello and piano
E. Friedlander, F. Hersch (r1993) *Concert* (7/94) (CATA) ① **09026 61979-2**

HERSCHEL, William (1738–1822) Germany/England

SECTION II: CHAMBER

6 Sonatas for Harpsichord with Violin and Cello, Op. 4 (pub 1769)
EXCERPTS: 4. D.
1. Invocation (r1993) *Concert* (11/94) (HYPE) ① **CDA66698**

HERTEL, Johann Wilhelm (1727–1789) Germany

SECTION I: ORCHESTRAL

Concerto a cinque in D—tpt, 2 ob, 2 bn and strings
W. Basch, K. Kärcher, G. Vetter, K. Ventulett, M. Roscher, Orpheus CO *Concert* (3/89) (SCHW) ① **311071**
Concerto for Trumpet and Orchestra in E flat
M. André, ECO, C. Mackerras *Concert* (11/90) (EMI) ① **CDM7 63528-2**
H. Hardenberger, LPO, E. Howarth *Concert* (3/91) (PHIL) ① **426 311-2PH**
M. André, F. Liszt CO, J. Rolla (r1994) *Concert* (7/95) (EMI) ① **CDC5 55231-2**
Concerto for Trumpet and Strings in D
H. Hardenberger, ASMF, N. Marriner (r1986) *Concert* (12/87) (PHIL) ① **420 203-2PH**
W. Basch, Orpheus CO *Concert* (3/89) (SCHW) ① **311071**
Concerto for 8 Timpani, Wind and Strings
N. Bardach, Berlin RSO, V. Handley *Concert* (10/88) (SCHW) ① **311052**

HERTZ, M. (1844–?)

SECTION IV: VOCAL AND CHORAL

The Old King—song
A. Didur, anon (r1901) *Concert* (6/93) (PEAR) ① [3] **GEMMCDS9997/9(2)**

HERZ, Henri (Heinrich) (1803–1888) Germany

SECTION III: INSTRUMENTAL

Variations on 'Non più mesta' from Rossini's 'La Cenerentola'—piano
E. Wild *Concert* (8/92) (VANG) ① **08.4033.71**

HERZOGENBERG, (Leopold) Heinrich (1843–1900) Austria

SECTION II: CHAMBER

Piano Trio in D—piano, oboe and horn, Op. 61 (1889)
R. Requejo, I. Goritzki, B. Tuckwell *Reinecke: Piano Trio, Op. 188.* (6/87) (CLAV) ① **CD50-0803**
Variations on a theme of Brahms—piano duet, Op. 23 (pub 1876)
A. Goldstone, C. Clemmow (r1988) *Concert* (4/89) (SYMP) ① **SYMCD1037**

HESDIN, Nicolle des Celliers de (?–1538) France

SECTION IV: VOCAL AND CHORAL

Ramonez moy ma cheminée—chanson (1536)
C. Janequin Ens, D. Visse (r1994) *Concert* (5/95) (HARM) ① **HMC90 1453**

HESPE, George (b 1900) England

SECTION I: ORCHESTRAL

The **Three Musketeers—suite for brass band** (1953)
Black Dyke Mills Band, D. Broadbent *Concert*
(9/93) (CHAN) ① **CHAN4506**

HESS Czechoslovakia

SECTION IV: VOCAL AND CHORAL

Home—song
E. Destinn, orch, J. Pasternack (r1919) *Concert*
(11/93) (ROMO) ① [2] **81002-2**
E. Destinn, orch, J. Pasternack (r1919) *Concert*
(12/94) (SUPR) ① [12] **11 2136-2(5)**

HESS, Nigel (20th Cent) England

SECTION I: ORCHESTRAL

East Coast Pictures—wind band (1985)
1. Shelter Island; 2. The Catskills; 3. New York.
London Symphonic Wind Orch, N. Hess *Concert*
(3/94) (FLY) ① **FLYCD105**
Global Variations—wind band (1990)
London Symphonic Wind Orch, N. Hess *Concert*
(3/94) (FLY) ① **FLYCD105**
Stephenson's Rocket—wind band (1991)
London Symphonic Wind Orch, N. Hess *Concert*
(3/94) (FLY) ① **FLYCD105**
Thames Journey—wind band (1991)
London Symphonic Wind Orch, N. Hess *Concert*
(3/94) (FLY) ① **FLYCD105**

HESSE, Johann Heinrich (c1712–1778) Germany

SECTION III: INSTRUMENTAL

Fantasia in C minor
H. Fagius, D. Sanger *Concert*
(10/85) (BIS) ① **BIS-CD273**

HÉTU, Jacques (b 1938) France

SECTION III: INSTRUMENTAL

Variations—piano
G. Gould *Concert*
(3/93) (SONY) ① **SMK52677**

HEUBERGER, Richard (Franz Joseph) (1850–1914) Austria

SECTION I: ORCHESTRAL

Variations on a theme by Schubert—orchestra, Op. 11
Berlin RSO, M. Bamert *Concert*
(9/90) (SCHW) ① **311135**

SECTION V: STAGE WORKS

Der **Opernball, 'Opera Ball'—opera** (1898—Vienna)
EXCERPTS: 1. Overture; 2. Im chambre separée.
Midnight Bells X. Wei, Pam Nicholson (arr Kreisler)
Concert (9/90) (ASV) ① **CDDCA698**
1. BPO, E. Kleiber (r1932) *Concert*
(5/94) (ARCI) ① **ARC102**
2. E. Schwarzkopf, Philh, O. Ackermann *Concert*
(1/86) (EMI) ① **CDC7 47284-2**
2. R. Tauber, Odeon Künstlerorchester, F. Weissmann (r1931) *Concert*
(12/89) (EMI) ① **CDH7 69787-2**
2. Raphaele Concert Orch, P. Walden (arr Waldenmaier) *Concert*
(5/91) (MOZA) ① **MECD1002**
2. H.E. Groh, orch (r1936) *Concert*
(3/92) (PEAR) ① **GEMMCD9419**
2. F. Kreisler, C. Lamson (r1923: arr Kreisler)
Concert (9/93) (BIDD) ① [2] **LAB068/9**
2. F. Kreisler, M. Raucheisen (r1930: arr Kreisler)
Concert (12/93) (EMI) ① **CDH7 64701-2**
2. J. Migenes, Vienna Volksoper Orch, L. Schifrin
(r1993) *Concert* (1/94) (ERAT) ① **4509-92875-2**
2. B. Hendricks, G. Quilico, Lyon Op Orch, L. Foster
(r1993) *Concert* (6/95) (EMI) ① **CDC5 55151-2**

HEWITT, James (1770–1827) USA

SECTION III: INSTRUMENTAL

Mark, My Alford: a favourite air with variations—piano (1808)
W. Naboré (r1992) *Concert*
(8/94) (DORO) ① **DRC3001**

HEWITT, John Hill (1801–1890) USA

SECTION IV: VOCAL AND CHORAL

The **little old garden—song**
R. Ponselle, orch, J. Pasternack (r1925) *Concert*
(11/94) (ROMO) ① [2] **81006-2**
Out where the big ships go—song
O. Natzke, chor, orch (r1943) *Concert*
(12/92) (ODE) ① **CDODE1365**

HEYKENS, Jonny (1884–?) Holland

SECTION I: ORCHESTRAL

Serenade No. 1 (1920)
A. Campoli, Orch *Concert*
(10/91) (PEAR) ① **PASTCD9744**

HICKS, J.W. (19th Cent) USA

SECTION IV: VOCAL AND CHORAL

The **Last Hymn—song (pub 1877)** (Wds. M. Farningham)
R. Taylor, R. Murcell, Harmoneion Sngrs, N. Bruce, L. Skrobacs (r1977) *Concert*
(2/94) (NEW) ① **80220-2**

HIDALGO, Juan (1612/16–1685) Spain

SECTION II: CHAMBER

Pasacalle—consort
Extempore Stg Ens *Concert*
(7/92) (HYPE) ① **CDA66327**

SECTION IV: VOCAL AND CHORAL

Ay amor, ay ausencia—lament
Newberry Consort, M. Springfels *Concert*
(7/92) (HARM) ① **HMU90 7022**
Ay, que me río de Amor—tono humano
Romanesca (r1991-2) *Concert*
(11/94) (GLOS) ① **GCD920201**
Crédito es di mi decorso!—lament from L de Ulloa's play 'Pico y Canente' (1656)
Newberry Consort, M. Springfels *Concert*
(7/92) (HARM) ① **HMU90 7022**
Cuydado pastor—tono humano
Romanesca (r1991-2) *Concert*
(11/94) (GLOS) ① **GCD920201**
En los floridos páramos—tono
Newberry Consort, M. Springfels *Concert*
(7/92) (HARM) ① **HMU90 7022**

SECTION V: STAGE WORKS

Celos aun del aire matan—opera: 3 acts (1660—Madrid) (Lib. Calderón)
EXCERPTS: 1. Noble en Tinacria naciste (jácara); 2. A to dos miro (recit).
1, 2. Newberry Consort, M. Springfels *Concert*
(7/92) (HARM) ① **HMU90 7022**
La **Estatua de Prometeo—zarzuela** (1672—Madrid) (Lib. Calderón)
1. Tonante Dios!.
1. Romanesca (r1991-2) *Concert*
(11/94) (GLOS) ① **GCD920201**
Los celos hacen estrellas—zarzuela (1672—Madrid) (performed for the birthday of Queen Mariana)
EXCERPTS: 1. De los ceños del diciembre; 2. Como ha de saber Belilla?; 3. De los luces que en el mar; 4. La noche tenebrosa; 5. Trompi cábalas amor; 6. Trom picávalas amor; 7. Peynándose estaba un olmo.
1-5. Newberry Consort, M. Springfels *Concert*
(7/92) (HARM) ① **HMU90 7022**
3, 7. Romanesca (r1991-2) *Concert*
(11/94) (GLOS) ① **GCD920201**

El **templo de Palas—zarzuela** (1675—Madrid) (Lib Avellaneda)
EXCERPTS: 1. Ay que si, ay que no.
1. Newberry Consort, M. Springfels *Concert*
(7/92) (HARM) ① **HMU90 7022**
1. Romanesca (r1991-2) *Concert*
(11/94) (GLOS) ① **GCD920201**

HILDACH, Eugen (1849–1924) Germany

SECTION IV: VOCAL AND CHORAL

Der **Spielmann—Lied, Op. 15/1**
Lotte Lehmann, orch (r1921) *Concert*
(6/92) (PREI) ① [3] **89302**
E. Rethberg, orch (r1924-5) *Concert*
(2/95) (ROMO) ① [2] **81012-2**

HILDEGARD OF BINGEN, Abbess (1098–1179) Germany

SECTION IV: VOCAL AND CHORAL

Ave generosa—hymn (Wds. cpsr)
E. Kirkby, Gothic Voices, D. Muskett, R. White, C. Page *Concert* (7/85) (HYPE) ① **CDA66039**
Augsburg Early Music Ens *Concert*
(3/93) (CHRI) ① **CHR74584**
Oxford Camerata, J. Summerly (r1993) *Concert*
(9/95) (NAXO) ① **8 550998**
Ave Maria, o auctrix vitae—responsory
Augsburg Early Music Ens (arr consort) *Concert*
(3/93) (CHRI) ① **CHR74584**
Sequentia (r1993) *Concert*
(5/95) (DHM) ① **05472 77320-2**
Caritas abundat in omnia—antiphon
Sequentia (r1993) *Concert*
(5/95) (DHM) ① **05472 77320-2**
Columba aspexit per cancellos—sequence (Wds. cpsr)
E. Kirkby, Gothic Voices, D. Muskett, R. White, C. Page *Concert* (7/85) (HYPE) ① **CDA66039**
E. Kirkby, Gothic Voices, C. Page *Concert*
(9/87) (HYPE) ① **CDA66227**
Cum processit factura—antiphon
Sequentia (r1993) *Concert*
(5/95) (DHM) ① **05472 77320-2**
Kyrie eleison
Oxford Camerata, J. Summerly (r1993) *Concert*
(9/95) (NAXO) ① **8 550998**
Laus Trinitati—antiphon
Oxford Camerata, J. Summerly (r1993) *Concert*
(9/95) (NAXO) ① **8 550998**
Nunc aperuit nobis—antiphon
Sequentia (r1993) *Concert*
(5/95) (DHM) ① **05472 77320-2**
O aeterne Deus—antiphon
Augsburg Early Music Ens *Concert*
(3/93) (CHRI) ① **CHR74584**
O choruscans stellarum—antiphon
Sequentia (r1993) *Concert*
(5/95) (DHM) ① **05472 77320-2**
O ecclesia oculi tui—sequence (Wds. cpsr)
E. Kirkby, Gothic Voices, R. White, C. Page *Concert* (7/85) (HYPE) ① **CDA66039**
O Euchari, in leta vita—sequence (Wds. cpsr)
E. Kirkby, Gothic Voices, D. Muskett, R. White, C. Page *Concert* (7/85) (HYPE) ① **CDA66039**
Oxford Camerata, J. Summerly (r1993) *Concert*
(9/95) (NAXO) ① **8 550998**
O felix anima—responsory
Augsburg Early Music Ens *Concert*
(3/93) (CHRI) ① **CHR74584**
O frondens virga—antiphon
Augsburg Early Music Ens (arr consort) *Concert*
(3/93) (CHRI) ① **CHR74584**
O ignis Spiritus Paracliti—sequence
E. Kirkby, Gothic Voices, D. Muskett, R. White, C. Page *Concert* (7/85) (HYPE) ① **CDA66039**
Sequentia (r1993) *Concert*
(5/95) (DHM) ① **05472 77320-2**
Oxford Camerata, J. Summerly (r1993) *Concert*
(9/95) (NAXO) ① **8 550998**
O Jerusalem aure civitas—sequence (Wds. cpsr)
E. Kirkby, Gothic Voices, D. Muskett, R. White, C. Page *Concert* (7/85) (HYPE) ① **CDA66039**
O magne Pater—antiphon
Augsburg Early Music Ens *Concert*
(3/93) (CHRI) ① **CHR74584**
O nobilissima viriditas—responsory
Sequentia (r1993) *Concert*
(5/95) (DHM) ① **05472 77320-2**

O pastor animarum—antiphon
Sequentia (r1993) Concert
(5/95) (DHM) ① 05472 77320-2
Oxford Camerata, J. Summerly (r1993) Concert
(9/95) (NAXO) ① 8 550998
O presul vere civitatis—sequence (Wds.
cpsr)
E. Kirkby, Gothic Voices, D. Muskett, R. White, C.
Page Concert (7/85) (HYPE) ① CDA66039
Oxford Camerata, J. Summerly (r1993) Concert
(9/95) (NAXO) ① 8 550998
O quam mirabilis—antiphon
Augsburg Early Music Ens Concert
(3/93) (CHRI) ① CHR74584
O tu suavissima virga—responsory
Sequentia (r1993) Concert
(5/95) (DHM) ① 05472 77320-2
O virga ac diadema—sequence
Oxford Camerata, J. Summerly (r1993) Concert
(9/95) (NAXO) ① 8 550998
O virga mediatrix—Alleluia-antiphon
Sequentia (r1993) Concert
(5/95) (DHM) ① 05472 77320-2
Oxford Camerata, J. Summerly (r1993) Concert
(9/95) (NAXO) ① 8 550998
O viridissima virga—sequence
E. Kirkby, Gothic Voices, D. Muskett, R. White, C.
Page Concert (7/85) (HYPE) ① CDA66039
Sequentia (r1993) Concert
(5/95) (DHM) ① 05472 77320-2
Oxford Camerata, J. Summerly (r1993) Concert
(9/95) (NAXO) ① 8 550998
O virtus sapientae—antiphon
Augsburg Early Music Ens Concert
(3/93) (CHRI) ① CHR74584
O vis aeternitatis—responsory
Augsburg Early Music Ens Concert
(3/93) (CHRI) ① CHR74584
Sequentia (r1993) Concert
(5/95) (DHM) ① 05472 77320-2
Quia ergo femina—antiphon
Sequentia (r1993) Concert
(5/95) (DHM) ① 05472 77320-2
Spiritus Sanctus vivificans vita—antiphon
Sequentia (r1993) Concert
(5/95) (DHM) ① 05472 77320-2

SECTION V: STAGE WORKS

Ordo Virtutum—morality play
1. Procession.
1. Oxford Camerata, J. Summerly (r1993) Concert
(9/95) (NAXO) ① 8 550998

HILL, Alfred (Francis)
(1870–1960) Australia

SECTION I: ORCHESTRAL

The Sacred Mountain
Melbourne SO, W. Lehmann Concert
(3/86) (MARC) ① 8 220345
Symphony No. 4 in C minor, 'Pursuit of
Happiness' (1955)
Melbourne SO, W. Lehmann Concert
(3/86) (MARC) ① 8 220345
Symphony No. 6 in B flat, 'Celtic' (1956)
Melbourne SO, W. Lehmann Concert
(3/86) (MARC) ① 8 220345

HILLEMACHER, Paul Joseph
Guillaume (1852–1933) France

SECTION II: CHAMBER

Gavotte tendre—cello and piano
P. Casals, N. Mednikoff (r1926) Concert
(10/91) (BIDD) ① LAB017

HILLER, Ferdinand (1811–1885)
Germany

SECTION I: ORCHESTRAL

Concerto for Piano and Orchestra in F sharp
minor, Op. 69 (1861)
M. Ponti, Luxembourg RSO, L. de Froment Concert
(5/93) (VOX) ① 115712-2
Konzertstück—piano and orchestra, Op. 113
(c1865)
J. Rose, Luxembourg RSO, P. Cao Concert
(5/93) (VOX) ① 115717-2

SECTION II: CHAMBER

Piano Trio No. 4, Op. 64 (?1855)
Göbel Trio, Berlin Concert
(7/88) (THOR) ① CTH2002

HILMAR, František Matěj
(1803–1881) Bohemia

SECTION I: ORCHESTRAL

Alböhmisch-Polka
Czech PO, V. Neumann Concert
(6/87) (ORFE) ① C107101A
Esmerelada Polka
Czech PO, V. Neumann Concert
(6/87) (ORFE) ① C107101A

HINDEMITH, Paul (1895–1963)
Germany

SECTION I: ORCHESTRAL

Concert Music—viola and large chamber
orchestra, Op. 48 (1930)
G. Schmidt, BRSO, R. Heger Concert
(6/88) (SCHW) ① 310045
P. Cortese, Philh, M. Brabbins (1995) Concert
(9/95) (ASV) ① CDDCA931
Concert Music—piano, brass and 2 harps,
Op. 49 (1930)
R. Kvapil, J. Wallace, Wallace Collection, S. Wright
Concert (7/89) (NIMB) ① NI5103
Concert Music—brass and strings, Op. 50
(1930)
Israel PO, L. Bernstein Concert
(5/91) (DG) ① 429 404-2GH
Melbourne SO, W.A. Albert Concert
(12/91) (CPO) ① CPO999 006-2
San Francisco SO, H. Blomstedt Concert
(4/93) (DECC) ① 433 809-2DH
NYPO, L. Bernstein Concert
(5/93) (SONY) ① SMK47566
Philh, P. Hindemith (1956) Concert
(5/94) (EMI) ① [2] CDS5 55032-2
Concerto for Cello and Orchestra (1940)
T. de Machula, Concertgebouw, K. Kondrashin
(bp1973) Clarinet Concerto.
(6/88) (ETCE) ① KTC1006
R. Wallfisch, BBC PO, Y. P. Tortelier Four
Temperaments. (3/93) (CHAN) ① CHAN9124
J. Starker, Bamberg SO, D. R. Davies (1994)
Schumann: Cello Concerto.
(10/95) (RCA) ① 09026 68027-2
Concerto for Clarinet and Orchestra (1947)
G. Pieterson, Concertgebouw, K. Kondrashin
(bp1979) Cello Concerto.
(6/88) (ETCE) ① KTC1006
L. Cahuzac, Philh, P. Hindemith (r1956) Concert
(5/94) (EMI) ① [2] CDS5 55032-2
U. Mehlhart, Frankfurt RSO, W. A. Albert (r1993)
Concert (11/95) (CPO) ① CPO999 142-2
Concerto for Flute, Oboe, Clarinet, Bassoon,
Harp and Orchestra (1949)
U. Mehlhart, C. Wilkening, W. Büchsel, L. Varcol, C.
Cassedanne, Frankfurt RSO, W. A. Albert (1994)
Concert (11/95) (CPO) ① CPO999 142-2
Concerto for Horn and Orchestra (1949)
D. Brain, Philh, P. Hindemith (r1956) Concert
(10/87) (EMI) ① CDC7 47834-2
D. Brain, Philh, P. Hindemith (r1956) Concert
(5/94) (EMI) ① [2] CDS5 55032-2
M. L. Neunecker, Frankfurt RSO, W. A. Albert (r1993)
Concert (11/95) (CPO) ① CPO999 142-2
Concerto for Orchestra (1925)
Chicago SO, N. Järvi (pp1991) Schmidt: Symphony
3. (3/92) (CHAN) ① CHAN9000
Concerto for Piano and Orchestra (1945)
S. Mauser, Frankfurt RSO, W.A. Albert Four
Temperaments. (12/91) (CPO) ① CPO999 078-2
Concerto for Trumpet, Bassoon and
Orchestra (1949)
R. Friedrich, C. Wilkening, Frankfurt RSO, W. A.
Albert (r1990) Concert
(11/95) (CPO) ① CPO999 142-2
Concerto for Violin and Orchestra (1939)
D. Oistrakh, LSO, P. Hindemith Concert
(9/92) (DECC) ① 433 081-2DM
I. Stern, NYPO, L. Bernstein (r1964) Concert
(7/93) (SONY) ① SMK47599
F. Helmann, Concertgebouw, W. Mengelberg
(pp1940) Concert (12/93) (ARHI) ① ADCD110
J. Fuchs, LSO, E. Goossens (r1959) Symphony in E
flat. (4/95) (EVER) ① EVC9009
Cupid and Psyche—ballet overture (1943)
Queensland SO, W.A. Albert Concert
(12/91) (CPO) ① CPO999 004-2
The Four Temperaments—theme and
variations: piano and orchestra (1940)
C. Rosenberger, RPO, J. DePreist Nobilissima
visione. (7/87) (DELO) ① DE1006

C. Haskil, BRSO, P. Hindemith (pp1961) Concert
(8/90) (ORFE) ① C197891A
S. Mauser, Frankfurt RSO, W.A. Albert Piano
Concerto. (12/91) (CPO) ① CPO999 078-2
H. Shelley, BBC PO, Y. P. Tortelier Cello Concerto.
(3/93) (CHAN) ① CHAN9124
Kammermusik No. 1—12 instruments, Op.
24/1 (1922)
Concertgebouw, R. Chailly Concert
(11/92) (DECC) ① [2] 433 816-2DH2
Kammermusik No. 2—piano and 12
instruments (1924)
R. Brautigam, Concertgebouw, R. Chailly Concert
(11/92) (DECC) ① [2] 433 816-2DH2
Kammermusik No. 3—cello and 10
instruments, Op. 36/2 (1925)
L. Harrell, Concertgebouw, R. Chailly Concert
(11/92) (DECC) ① [2] 433 816-2DH2
Kammermusik No. 4—violin and orchestra,
Op. 36/3 (1925)
K. Kulka, Concertgebouw, R. Chailly Concert
(11/92) (DECC) ① [2] 433 816-2DH2
Kammermusik No. 5—viola and large
chamber orchestra, Op. 36/4 (1927)
G. Schmidt, BRSO, R. Kubelík Concert
(6/88) (SCHW) ① 310045
K. Kashkashian, Concertgebouw, R. Chailly Concert
(11/92) (DECC) ① [2] 433 816-2DH2
P. Cortese, Philh, M. Brabbins (r1995) Concert
(9/95) (ASV) ① CDDCA931
Kammermusik No. 6—viola da gamba and
chamber orchestra, Op. 46/1 (1927)
N. Blume, Concertgebouw, R. Chailly Concert
(11/92) (DECC) ① [2] 433 816-2DH2
Kammermusik No. 7—organ and chamber
orchestra, Op. 46/2 (1927)
L. Van Doeselaar, Concertgebouw, R. Chailly
Concert (11/92) (DECC) ① [2] 433 816-2DH2
Lustige Sinfonietta—small orchestra, Op. 4
(1916)
Berlin RSO, G. Albrecht Rag Time.
(9/89) (WERG) ① WER60150-50
Queensland SO, W.A. Albert Concert
(12/91) (CPO) ① CPO999 005-2
Mathis der Maler—symphony (1934)
BPO, H. von Karajan (r1957) Bartók: Music for
Strings, Percussion and Celesta.
(4/88) (EMI) ① CDM7 69242-2
San Francisco SO, H. Blomstedt Concert
(10/88) (DECC) ① 421 523-2DH
Atlanta SO, Y. Levi Concert
(7/90) (TELA) ① CD80195
BRSO, E. Ormandy (pp1950) Concert
(8/90) (ORFE) ① C199891A
Israel PO, L. Bernstein Concert
(5/91) (DG) ① 429 404-2GH
SRO, P. Kletzki Concert
(9/92) (DECC) ① 433 081-2DM
Philadelphia, E. Ormandy (r1962) Concert
(4/94) (SONY) ① SBK53258
BPO, P. Hindemith (r1934) Concert
(5/94) (SCHW) ① 311342
Sydney SO, W.A. Albert (r1992) Concert
(11/94) (CPO) ① CPO999 008-2
NZ SO, F-P. Decker (r1994) Concert
(6/95) (NAXO) ① 8 553078
Philadelphia, W. Sawallisch (r1994) Concert
(6/95) (EMI) ① CDC5 55230-2
BPO, C. Abbado (r1994) Concert
(9/95) (DG) ① 447 389-2GH
Nobilissima Visione—dance legend (1938)
RPO, J. DePreist Four Temperaments.
(7/87) (DELO) ① DE1006
Atlanta SO, Y. Levi Concert
(7/90) (TELA) ① CD80195
Philh, O. Klemperer (r1954) Concert
(10/91) (EMI) ① [2] CMS7 63835-2
Queensland SO, W.A. Albert Concert
(12/91) (CPO) ① CPO999 004-2
BBC PO, Y. P. Tortelier Concert
(10/92) (CHAN) ① CHAN9060
San Francisco SO, H. Blomstedt Concert
(4/93) (DECC) ① 433 809-2DH
Philh, P. Hindemith (r1954) Concert
(5/94) (EMI) ① [2] CDS5 55032-2
NZ SO, F-P. Decker (r1994) Concert
(6/95) (NAXO) ① 8 553078
Philadelphia, W. Sawallisch (r1994) Concert
(6/95) (EMI) ① CDC5 55230-2
BPO, C. Abbado (r1994) Concert
(9/95) (DG) ① 447 389-2GH
Das Nusch-Nuschi—dance suite, Op. 21
(1921) (from music to play for marionettes)
Melbourne SO, W.A. Albert Concert
(12/91) (CPO) ① CPO999 006-2

Des Morgens—Lied (1935) (Wds. Hölderlin)
D. Fischer-Dieskau, A. Reimann *Concert*
(2/88) (ORFE) ① **C156861A**
Ehmals und jetzt—Lied (1935) (Wds.
Hölderlin)
D. Fischer-Dieskau, A. Reimann *Concert*
(2/88) (ORFE) ① **C156861A**
Fragment—Lied (1933) (Wds. Hölderlin)
D. Fischer-Dieskau, A. Reimann *Concert*
(2/88) (ORFE) ① **C156861A**
Das Ganze, nicht das Einzelne—Lied (1933)
(Wds. Rückert)
D. Fischer-Dieskau, A. Reimann *Concert*
(2/88) (ORFE) ① **C156861A**
3 Gesänge—soprano and orchestra, Op. 9
(1917) (Wds. various)
1. Meine Nächte sind heiser zerschrien (wds. Lotz);
2. Weltende (wds. Lasker-Schüler); 3. Aufbruch der
Jugend (wds. Lotz).
J. Martin, Berlin RSO, G. Albrecht (r1984) *Sancta
Susanna.* (2/89) (WERG) ① **WER60106-50**
Hymne—Lied (1933) (Wds. Novalis)
D. Fischer-Dieskau, A. Reimann *Concert*
(2/88) (ORFE) ① **C156861A**
Ich will nicht klagen mehr—Lied (1933) (Wds.
Novalis)
D. Fischer-Dieskau, A. Reimann *Concert*
(2/88) (ORFE) ① **C156861A**
Die Junge Magd—contralto, flute, clarinet
and string quartet, Op. 23/2 (1922) (Wds.
Trakl)
1. Oft am Brunnen; 2. Stille schafft sie in der
Kammer; 3. Nächtens übern kahlen Auger; 4. In der
Schmiede dröght der Hammer; 5. Schmächtig
hingestreckt im Bette; 6. Abends schweben blutige
Linnen.
G. Schnaut, Berlin RSO, G. Albrecht *Todes Tod.*
(2/89) (WERG) ① **WER60117-50**
Das Marienleben—15 lieder for soprano, Op.
27 (1922-23 rev 1948) (Wds. R.M. Rilke)
1. Geburt Mariä; 2. Die Darstellung Mariä im Tempel;
3. Mariä Verkündigung; 4. Mariä Heimsuchung; 5.
Argwohn Josephs; 6. Verkündigung über den Hirten;
7. Geburt Christi; 8. Rast auf der Flucht in Ägypten;
9. Von der Hochzeit zu Kana; 10. Vor der Passion;
11. Pietà; 12. Stillung Mariä mit dem Auferstandenen;
13. Vom Tode Mariä I; 14. Vom Tode Mariä II
(Thema mit Variationen); 15. Vom Tode Mariä III.
Cpte G. Janowitz, I. Gage (1948 vers)
(6/88) (JECK) ① **JD574-2**
The Moon—song (1942) (Wds. Shelley)
D. Fischer-Dieskau, A. Reimann *Concert*
(2/88) (ORFE) ① **C156861A**
O, nun heb du an, dort in deinem Moor—Lied
(1919) (Wds. W. Whitman)
D. Fischer-Dieskau, A. Reimann *Concert*
(2/88) (ORFE) ① **C156861A**
On hearing 'The Last Rose of
Summer'—song (1942) (Wds. C. Wolfe)
D. Fischer-Dieskau, A. Reimann *Concert*
(2/88) (ORFE) ① **C156861A**
Sing on there in the Swamp—song (1943)
(Wds. W. Whitman)
D. Fischer-Dieskau, A. Reimann *Concert*
(2/88) (ORFE) ① **C156861A**
Singet leise—Lied (1936) (Wds. C. Brentano)
D. Fischer-Dieskau, A. Reimann *Concert*
(2/88) (ORFE) ① **C156861A**
Die Sonne sinkt—Lied (1939) (Wds.
Nietzsche)
D. Fischer-Dieskau, A. Reimann *Concert*
(2/88) (ORFE) ① **C156861A**
Sonnenuntergang—Lied (1935) (Wds.
Hölderlin)
D. Fischer-Dieskau, A. Reimann *Concert*
(2/88) (ORFE) ① **C156861A**
Der Tod—Lied (1933) (Wds. Claudius)
D. Fischer-Dieskau, A. Reimann *Concert*
(2/88) (ORFE) ① **C156861A**
Des Todes Tod—soprano/mez, 2 violas and
2 cellos, Op. 23a (1922) (Wds. E. Reinacher)
1. Gesicht von Tod und Eland; 2. Gottes Tod; 3. Des
Todes Tod.
G. Schreckenbach, Berlin RSO, G. Albrecht *Junge
Magd.* (2/89) (WERG) ① **WER60117-50**
Vor dir schein' ich aufgewacht—Lied (1920)
(Wds. Morgenstern)
D. Fischer-Dieskau, A. Reimann *Concert*
(2/88) (ORFE) ① **C156861A**
When lilacs last in the door-yard bloom'd
(Requiem for those we love)—mezzo-
soprano, baritone chorus and orchestra
(1946) (Wds. Whitman)
J. de Gaetani, W. Stone, Atlanta Sym Chor, Atlanta
SO, Robert Shaw (7/87) (TELA) ① **CD80132**

B. Fassbaender, D. Fischer-Dieskau, Vienna St Op
Chor, Vienna SO, W. Sawallisch
(12/87) (ORFE) ① **C112851A**
Overture Sydney SO, W.A. Albert (r1992) *Concert*
(11/94) (CPO) ① **CPO999 008-2**
The Wild Flower's Song (1942) (Wds. Blake)
D. Fischer-Dieskau, A. Reimann *Concert*
(2/88) (ORFE) ① **C156861A**

SECTION V: STAGE WORKS

Cardillac—opera: 3 acts, Op. 39 (1926) (Lib.
F. Lion, after Hoffmann)
Cpte S. Nimsgern, V. Schweizer, R. Schunk, H.
Stamm, J. Protschka, G. Schnaut, A. Schmidt, Berlin
Rad Chbr Chor, Berlin RSO, G. Albrecht
(7/89) (WERG) ① [2] **WER60148/9-50**
Cpte S. Nimsgern, L. Kirschstein, D. Grobe,
K.C. Kohn, E. Katz, E. Söderström, W. Nett, Cologne
Rad Chor, Cologne RSO, J. Keilberth (1926 vers)
Mathis der Maler.
(12/91) (DG) ① [2] **431 741-2GC2**
Der Dämon—dance-pantomime: 2 scenes,
Op. 28 (1922)
Cpte Berlin RSO, G. Albrecht *Mörder, Hoffnung der
Frauen.* (2/89) (WERG) ① **WER60132-50**
Cpte Leipzig Gewandhaus, L. Zagrosek (r1994)
Concert (5/95) (DECC) ① **444 182-2DH**
Hérodiade—ballet (1944) (orchestral recitation
after Mallarmé)
Atlantic Sinfonietta, A. Schenck (r1990) *Concert*
(4/92) (KOCH) ① **37051-2**
Mathis der Maler—opera: 7 scenes
(1938—Zurich) (Lib. cpsr)
Cpte R. Hermann, J. Protschka, V. von Halem, H.
Winkler, H. Stamm, H. Kruse, U. Hielscher, U. Ress,
S. Hass, G. Rossmanith, M. Schmiege, N German
Rad Chor, Cologne Rad Chor, Cologne RSO, G.
Albrecht (r1990)
(9/94) (WERG) ① [3] **WER6255-2**
Cpte D. Fischer-Dieskau, J. King, G. Feldhoff, M.
Schmidt, P. Meven, W. Cochran, A. Malta, D. Grobe,
R. Wagemann, U. Koszut, T. Schmidt, Bavarian Rad
Chor, BRSO, R. Kubelik (r1977)
(7/95) (EMI) ① [3] **CDS5 55237-2**
Excs D. Fischer-Dieskau, P. Lorengar, D. Grobe,
Berlin RSO, L. Ludwig *Cardillac.*
(12/91) (DG) ① [2] **431 741-2GC2**
Mörder, Hoffnung der Frauen—opera: 1 act,
Op. 12 (1919) (Lib. O. Kokoschka)
Cpte F. Grundheber, G. Schnaut, W. Gahmlich, V.
von Halem, B-O. Magnusson, L. Peacock, G.
Schreckenbach, B. Haldas, Berlin RIAS Chbr Ch,
Berlin RSO, G. Albrecht *Dämon.*
(2/89) (WERG) ① **WER60132-50**
Neues vom Tage—opera: 3 parts
(1929—Berlin) (Lib. M. Schiffer)
EXCERPTS: 1a. Overture; 1b. Overture (concert
version: 1930).
1b BBC PO, Y. P. Tortelier *Concert*
(10/92) (CHAN) ① **CHAN9060**
Das Nusch-Nuschi—play for Burmese
marionettes: 1 act, Op. 20 (1920) (Lib. F.
Blei)
Cpte H. Stamm, M. Schumacher, V. von Halem, J.
Becker, D. Knutson, W. Gahmlich, P. Maus, A.
Ramirez, V. Schweizer, C. Lindsley, G.
Schreckenbach, G. Sieber, G. Resick, G. Pohl, W.
Marschall, M. Kleber, Berlin RSO, G. Albrecht
(7/89) (WERG) ① **WER60146-50**
Sancta Susanna—opera: 1 act, Op. 21 (1921)
(Lib. Stramm)
Cpte H. Donath, G. Schnaut, G. Schreckenbach,
Berlin RIAS Chbr Ch, Berlin RSO, G. Albrecht
(r1984) *Gesänge, Op. 9.*
(2/89) (WERG) ① **WER60106-50**

HIROSE, Ryohei (b 1930) Japan

SECTION III: INSTRUMENTAL

Hymn—recorder (1979-82)
D. Laurin (r1993) *Concert*
(8/94) (BIS) ① **BIS-CD655**
Meditation—recorder
D. Laurin (r1993) *Concert*
(8/94) (BIS) ① **BIS-CD655**

HIRSCH, Louis Achille (1881-1924) USA

SECTION IV: VOCAL AND CHORAL

That Wasn't All—song for the show 'The
Soul Kiss' (1908) (Lyrics Burkhardt &
Woodward)
R. C. Herz, Broadway Cast (r1908) *Concert*
(5/94) (PEAR) ① [3] **GEMMCDS9050/2(2)**

HODDINOTT, Alun (b 1929) Wales

SECTION I: ORCHESTRAL

Doubles—concertante for oboe, harpsichord
and strings, Op. 106 (1982)
D. Cowley, R. Armstrong, BBC Welsh SO, T. Otaka
(r1992) *Concert* (7/93) (NIMB) ① **NI5357**
The Heaventree of Stars—poem for violin
and orchestra, Op. 102 (1980)
H. Kun, BBC Welsh SO, T. Otaka (r1992) *Concert*
(7/93) (NIMB) ① **NI5357**
Passaggio, Op. 94 (1977)
BBC Welsh SO, T. Otaka (r1992) *Concert*
(7/93) (NIMB) ① **NI5357**
Star Children, Op. 135 (1989)
BBC Welsh SO, T. Otaka (r1992) *Concert*
(7/93) (NIMB) ① **NI5357**

SECTION III: INSTRUMENTAL

Sonata for Piano No. 1, Op. 17 (1959)
Martin Jones (r1992) *Concert*
(12/93) (NIMB) ① **NI5369**
Sonata for Piano No. 2, Op. 27 (1962)
Martin Jones (r1992) *Concert*
(12/93) (NIMB) ① **NI5369**
Sonata for Piano No. 3, Op. 40 (1965)
Martin Jones (r1992) *Concert*
(12/93) (NIMB) ① **NI5369**
Sonata for Piano No. 4, Op. 49 (1966)
Martin Jones (r1992) *Concert*
(12/93) (NIMB) ① **NI5369**
Sonata for Piano No. 5, Op. 57 (1968)
Martin Jones (r1992) *Concert*
(12/93) (NIMB) ① **NI5369**
Sonata for Piano No. 6, Op. 78/3 (1972)
Martin Jones (r1992) *Concert*
(5/95) (NIMB) ① **NI5370**
Sonata for Piano No. 7, Op. 114 (1984)
Martin Jones (r1992) *Concert*
(5/95) (NIMB) ① **NI5370**
Sonata for Piano No. 8, Op. 125 (1986)
Martin Jones (r1992) *Concert*
(5/95) (NIMB) ① **NI5370**
Sonata for Piano No. 9, Op. 134 (1989)
Martin Jones (r1992) *Concert*
(5/95) (NIMB) ① **NI5370**
Sonata for Piano No. 10, Op. 136 (1989)
Martin Jones (r1992) *Concert*
(5/95) (NIMB) ① **NI5370**

HOÉRÉE, Arthur (1897-1986) Belgium

SECTION III: INSTRUMENTAL

Fanfare pour Albert Roussel—piano (1928-
29)
M. Fingerhut *Concert* (9/88) (CHAN) ① **CHAN8578**

HOFER, Andreas (1629-1659) Austria

SECTION IV: VOCAL AND CHORAL

Laudate pueri Dominum—motet
Niederaltaicher Scholaren, K. Ruhland (r1992)
Concert (10/93) (SONY) ① **SK53117**

HØFFDING, (Niels) Finn (b 1899) Denmark

SECTION II: CHAMBER

5 Dialogues—oboe and clarinet
N. Eje, B. Sand *Concert* (6/90) (KONT) ① **32032**

HOFFMAN, Al (1902-1960) USA

SECTION V: STAGE WORKS

Cinderella—musical film (1949) (Lyrics Mack
David; music collab with Jerry Livingston)
EXCERPTS: 1. Cinderella; 2. A Dream is a Wish
Your Heart Makes; 3. Oh Sing Sweet Nightingale; 4.
The Work Song; 5. Bibbidi-Bobbidi-Boo; 6. So This is
Love.
2. ECO, D. Fraser (r1994-5; arr Fraser) *Concert*
(12/95) (DELO) ① **DE3186**

HOFFMANN, Ernst Theodor Amadeus *(1776–1822) Germany*

SECTION V: STAGE WORKS

Undine—opera: 3 acts (1816—Berlin) (Lib. F. Fouqué)
Cpte K. Laki, R. Hermann, H. Franzen, E. Glauser, M. Mekler, K. Ridderbusch, U. Ress, D. Koschak, H. Orama, Berlin St. Hedwig's Cath Ch, Berlin RSO, R. Bader (r1982)   (10/93) (SCHW) ① [3] 310922

HOFFMEISTER, Franz Anton *(1754–1812) Austria*

SECTION II: CHAMBER

Quartet in A—fl, vn, va and vc (after Mozart's Alla Turca Sonata, K331)
Israel Fl Ens *Concert*   (6/90) (CARL) ① PWK1139

HOFFSTETTER, Roman *(1742–1815) Germany*

SECTION II: CHAMBER

6 String Quartets, Op. 3 (-1777) (attrib previously to Haydn)
1. E; 2. C; 3. G; 4. B flat; 5. F; 5a. Serenade; 5b. Andante cantabile; 6. A.
1(Movt 3) Flonzaley Qt (r1928) *Concert*
     (10/95) (BIDD) ① [2] LAB089/90
4. Pro Arte Qt (r1937) *Concert*
     (6/95) (TEST) ① [4] SBT4056
5. Quartetto Italiano *Concert*
     (6/90) (PHIL) ① 426 097-2PC
5. Busch Qt (r1922) *Concert*
     (6/93) (SYMP) ① SYMCD1109
5. Pro Arte Qt (r1933) *Concert*
     (6/95) (TEST) ① [4] SBT4056
5a I Musici *Concert*   (12/83) (PHIL) ① 410 606-2PH
5a Rasumovsky Qt *Concert*
     (12/92) (IMPE) ① RAZCD901
5a Guildhall Str Ens, R. Salter (vn/dir) (r1992) *Concert*   (2/94) (ASV) ① 09026 61275-2
5b Flonzaley Qt (r1925) *Concert*
     (10/95) (BIDD) ① [2] LAB089/90

HOFMANN, Josef (Casimir) *(1876–1957) Poland/USA*

SECTION I: ORCHESTRAL

Chromaticon—piano and orchestra
J. Hofmann, Curtis Inst Student Orch, I. Hilsberg (pp1937) *Concert*   (5/93) (VAI) ① [2] VAIA1020
J. Hofmann, Curtis Inst Student Orch, F. Reiner (pp1937) *Concert*   (5/93) (VAI) ① [2] VAIA1020

SECTION III: INSTRUMENTAL

Kaleidoskop, Op. 40
S. Cherkassky (pp1991) *Concert*
     (1/93) (DECC) ① 433 654-2DH

HOFMANN, Leopold *(1738–1793) Austria*

SECTION I: ORCHESTRAL

Concerto for Flute and Strings in D (—1771) (attrib Haydn—HobVIIf:D1)
Barthold Kuijken, Tafelmusik, J. Lamon (r1991) *Concert*   (7/93) (SONY) ① SK48045

HOGBEN, Dorothy *(19th–20th Cents) England*

SECTION IV: VOCAL AND CHORAL

The Shawl—song (pub 1926)
F. Lott, G. Johnson *Concert*
     (7/90) (CHAN) ① CHAN8722

HÖHNE, Carl

SECTION II: CHAMBER

Slavonic Fantasy—cornet and piano
J. Wallace, S. Wright (r1993) *Concert*
     (11/94) (EMI) ① CDC5 55086-2

HOIBY, Lee *(b 1926) USA*

SECTION IV: VOCAL AND CHORAL

Jabberwocky—song (1986) (Wds. L. Carroll)
Sarah Walker, R. Vignoles *Concert*
     (10/92) (CRD) ① CRD3473

HOLBORNE, Antony *(fl ?1584–1602) England*

SECTION II: CHAMBER

Almain, '(The) Choise' (pub 1599)
Dowland Consort, J. Lindberg (lte/dir) *Concert*
     (4/92) (BIS) ① BIS-CD469
Almain, '(The) Honiesuckle'—consort
Dowland Consort, J. Lindberg (lte/dir) *Concert*
     (4/92) (BIS) ① BIS-CD469
Toulon Musica Antiqua, C. Mendoze *Concert*
     (9/93) (PIER) ① PV787092
F. Brüggen, Brüggen Consort (r1967/79) *Concert*
     (10/95) (TELD) ① 4509-97465-2
As it fell on a Holy Eve—dance
Dowland Consort, J. Lindberg (lte/dir) *Concert*
     (4/92) (BIS) ① BIS-CD469
Coranto, '(The) Fairie Round'—consort
Dowland Consort, J. Lindberg (lte/dir) *Concert*
     (4/92) (BIS) ① BIS-CD469
L. Kenny *Concert*   (11/92) (CNTO) ① CRCD2366
J. Bream (r1972) *Concert*
     (8/93) (RCA) ① [28] 09026 61583-2(2)
Rose Consort *Concert*
     (10/93) (WOOD) ① WOODM002-2
J. Bream (r1972) *Concert*
     (6/94) (RCA) ① 09026 61587-2
Coranto, 'Heigh ho Holiday'—consort
K. Ragossnig, Ulsamer Collegium, J. Ulsamer *Concert*   (2/86) (ARCH) ① 415 294-2AH
Dowland Consort, J. Lindberg (lte/dir) *Concert*
     (4/92) (BIS) ① BIS-CD469
J. Bream (r1972) *Concert*
     (8/93) (RCA) ① [28] 09026 61583-2(2)
Toulon Musica Antiqua, C. Mendoze *Concert*
     (9/93) (PIER) ① PV787092
J. Bream (r1972) *Concert*
     (6/94) (RCA) ① 09026 61587-2
Ecce quam bonum—consort
Rose Consort *Concert*
     (10/93) (WOOD) ① WOODM002-2
The Fruit of Love—dance
Rose Consort *Concert*
     (10/93) (WOOD) ① WOODM002-2
Galliard, 'Lullaby'—consort: 5 viols
Rose Consort *Concert*
     (12/91) (AMON) ① CD-SAR46
J. Lindberg *Concert*   (4/92) (BIS) ① BIS-CD469
Heres paternus—consort
Dowland Consort, J. Lindberg (lte/dir) *Concert*
     (4/92) (BIS) ① BIS-CD469
M. Chance, C. Wilson (r1992) *Concert*
     (10/94) (CHAN) ① CHAN0538
The Image of Melancholy—consort piece
Rose Consort *Concert*
     (10/93) (WOOD) ① WOODM002-2
Infernum—consort
Dowland Consort, J. Lindberg (lte/dir) *Concert*
     (4/92) (BIS) ① BIS-CD469
Fretwork (r1990) *Concert*
     (7/94) (VIRG) ① VC5 45007-2
Last will and testament—consort (pub 1599)
Dowland Consort, J. Lindberg (lte/dir) *Concert*
     (4/92) (BIS) ① BIS-CD469
Muy linda—consort
Dowland Consort, J. Lindberg (lte/dir) *Concert*
     (4/92) (BIS) ① BIS-CD469
M. Chance, C. Wilson (r1992) *Concert*
     (10/94) (CHAN) ① CHAN0538
The Night watch—consort
Dowland Consort, J. Lindberg (lte/dir) *Concert*
     (4/92) (BIS) ① BIS-CD469
Toulon Musica Antiqua, C. Mendoze *Concert*
     (9/93) (PIER) ① PV787092
M. Chance, C. Wilson (r1992) *Concert*
     (10/94) (CHAN) ① CHAN0538
F. Brüggen, Brüggen Consort (r1967/79) *Concert*
     (10/95) (TELD) ① 4509-97465-2
Noels' Galliard
Ulsamer Collegium, J. Ulsamer *Concert*
     (2/86) (ARCH) ① 415 294-2AH
R. Aldwinckle *Concert*   (7/87) (CARL) ① PCD850
Old almaine—consort (arr Queen's almaine)
Circa 1500, N. Hadden (r1991) *Concert*
     (8/93) (CRD) ① CRD3487

Pavan and Galliard—viol consort, LPM37/38
Fretwork (r1990) *Concert*
     (7/94) (VIRG) ① VC5 45007-2
Pavan and Galliard—viol consort, LPM39/40
Fretwork (r1990) *Concert*
     (7/94) (VIRG) ① VC5 45007-2
Pavan and Galliard—viol consort, LPM41/42
Fretwork (r1990) *Concert*
     (7/94) (VIRG) ① VC5 45007-2
Pavan, '(The) Cradle'—consort: 5 viols
Rose Consort *Concert*
     (12/91) (AMON) ① CD-SAR46
Pavan, '(The) Funerals'—consort
Ulsamer Collegium, J. Ulsamer *Concert*
     (2/86) (ARCH) ① 415 294-2AH
Rose Consort *Concert*
     (10/93) (WOOD) ① WOODM002-2
Reade's Almain—consort
New London Consort, P. Pickett (r1992) *Concert*
     (4/94) (LINN) ① CKD011
The Sighes—consort
Dowland Consort, J. Lindberg (lte/dir) *Concert*
     (4/92) (BIS) ① BIS-CD469
F. Brüggen, Brüggen Consort (r1967/79) *Concert*
     (10/95) (TELD) ① 4509-97465-2
Spero—consort
Dowland Consort, J. Lindberg (lte/dir) *Concert*
     (4/92) (BIS) ① BIS-CD469
Various consort pieces—unidentified
Pavans, Galliards etc (some may be arr. for solo instruments)
Almain Rose Consort *Concert*
     (10/93) (WOOD) ① WOODM002-2
Lute Galliard No.17. L. Kenny *Concert*
     (11/92) (CNTO) ① CRCD2366
Pavan & Galliard F. Brüggen, Brüggen Consort (r1967/79) *Concert*
     (10/95) (TELD) ① 4509-97465-2
Pavan; 2 Galliards Toulon Musica Antiqua, C. Mendoze *Concert*   (9/93) (PIER) ① PV787092
3 Pavans; 7 Galliards; Almain; Fantasia; Jig Dowland Consort, J. Lindberg (lte/dir) *Concert*   (4/92) (BIS) ① BIS-CD469
Widow's Myte
Dowland Consort, J. Lindberg (lte/dir) *Concert*
     (4/92) (BIS) ① BIS-CD469

SECTION III: INSTRUMENTAL

As it fell on a Holy Eve—lute
C. Wilson *Concert*   (11/91) (VIRG) ① VC7 59034-2
The Countess of Pembroke's Funeral—lute
C. Wilson *Concert*   (11/91) (VIRG) ① VC7 59034-2
The Countess of Pembroke's Paradise—lute
C. Wilson *Concert*   (11/91) (VIRG) ① VC7 59034-2
Fantasia No. 3—lute
M. Chance, C. Wilson (r1992) *Concert*
     (10/94) (CHAN) ① CHAN0538
Heart's Ease—lute
J. Bream (r1972) *Concert*
     (8/93) (RCA) ① [28] 09026 61583-2(2)
J. Bream (r1972) *Concert*
     (6/94) (RCA) ① 09026 61587-2
Heigh Ho Holiday—lute galliard (pub 1599)
F. Brüggen, Brüggen Consort (r1967/79) *Concert*
     (10/95) (TELD) ① 4509-97465-2
Maydens of the Countrey—instrumental solo
J. Lindberg *Concert*   (4/92) (BIS) ① BIS-CD469
Passion—lute
C. Wilson *Concert*   (11/91) (VIRG) ① VC7 59034-2
Pavan and Galliard—lute
J. Bream (r1960) *Concert*
     (8/93) (RCA) ① [28] 09026 61583-2(1)
J. Bream (r1960) *Concert*
     (8/93) (RCA) ① 09026 61584-2
Prelude/Quadro Pavan—instrumental solo
J. Lindberg *Concert*   (4/92) (BIS) ① BIS-CD469
The Spanish Pavan—keyboard
J. Lindberg *Concert*   (4/92) (BIS) ① BIS-CD469
The voyce of the ghost
Circa 1500 (r1991) *Concert*
     (8/93) (CRD) ① CRD3487
Walsingham—lute
P. O'Dette *Concert*   (2/88) (HARM) ① HMC90 5192

HOLBROOKE, Joseph (1878–1958) England

SECTION I: ORCHESTRAL

The Birds of Rhiannon—symphonic poem, Op. 87 (1925)
Ukraine National SO, A. Penny (r1994) Concert
(12/95) (MARC) ① 8 223721
The Raven—symphonic poem, Op. 25 (1900)
Bratislava RSO, A. Leaper (r1992) Concert
(11/93) (MARC) ① 8 223446
Symphony No. 3 in E minor, 'Ships', Op. 90 (1925)
Finale orch, C. Raybould (r1937) Concert
(4/93) (SYMP) ① SYMCD1130
Ulalume—poem for orchestra No 4, Op. 35 (1901-03)
Bratislava RSO, A. Leaper (r1992) Concert
(11/93) (MARC) ① 8 223446
Variations on 'Three Blind Mice'—symphonic variations, Op. 37/1 (1900)
Queen's Hall Orch, Henry Wood (r1916) Concert
(1/94) (BEUL) ① 1PD3

SECTION II: CHAMBER

Piano Quartet No. 1 in G minor, Op. 21 (1902)
Movts 1, 2. J. Holbrooke, Phil Qt (r1919) Concert
(4/93) (SYMP) ① SYMCD1130
Quintet for Clarinet and Strings No. 1 in G, Op. 27/1 (c1903)
R. Kell, Willoughby Qt (r1939) Concert
(6/91) (TEST) ① SBT1002

SECTION III: INSTRUMENTAL

Pieces—piano, Op. 101
3. Rangoon rice carriers.
3. J. Holbrooke (r1930) Concert
(4/93) (SYMP) ① SYMCD1130
Pieces—piano, Op. 105
2, 4. J. Holbrooke (r1930) Concert
(4/93) (SYMP) ① SYMCD1130

SECTION IV: VOCAL AND CHORAL

The Bells—chorus and orchestra, Op. 50 (Wds. E. A. Poe)
1. Prelude.
Prelude Bratislava RSO, A. Leaper (r1992) Concert
(11/93) (MARC) ① 8 223446
Byron—chorus and orchestra (1904) (Wds. J. Jeats)
Slovak Phil Chor, Bratislava RSO, A. Leaper (r1992) Concert
(11/93) (MARC) ① 8 223446

SECTION V: STAGE WORKS

Bronwen—opera, Op. 75 (1929—Huddersfield) (Lib. H. de Walden)
EXCERPTS: 1. Overture. ACT 1: 2. Bran's answer; 3. The Bard's song. ACT 2: 4. Cradle song. ACT 3: 5. Taliessin's song; 6. Funeral march.
1. Bratislava RSO, A. Leaper (r1992) Concert
(11/93) (MARC) ① 8 223446
1-6. D. Vane, J. Coates, SO, C. Powell (r1929) Concert
(4/93) (SYMP) ① SYMCD1130
The Children of Don—drama, Op. 56 (1911—London) (Lib H. de Walden)
EXCERPTS: 1. Overture; 2. Noden's song.
1. orch, A. Hammond (r1937) Concert
(4/93) (SYMP) ① SYMCD1130
1. Ukraine National SO, A. Penny (r1994) Concert
(12/95) (MARC) ① 8 223721
2. N. Walker, orch, C. Raybould (r1937) Concert
(4/93) (SYMP) ① SYMCD1130
Dylan—drama, Op. 53 (1914—London) (Lib. H. de Walden)
EXCERPTS: 1. Overture; 2. The Sea King's song; 3. Prelude.
1. orch, C. Raybould (r1937) Concert
(4/93) (SYMP) ① SYMCD1130
2. N. Walker, orch, J. Holbrooke (r1937) Concert
(4/93) (SYMP) ① SYMCD1130
3. Ukraine National SO, A. Penny (r1994) Concert
(12/95) (MARC) ① 8 223721
The Enchanter—opera, Op. 70 (1915)
EXCERPTS: 2. Dance.
2. J. Holbrooke (trans pf: cpsr: r1930) Concert
(4/93) (SYMP) ① SYMCD1130

HOLD, Trevor (b 1939) England

SECTION III: INSTRUMENTAL

Kaleidoscopes—piano (1989)
Peter Jacobs (r1992) Concert
(10/93) (CNTI) ① CCD1066
Kemp's Nine Daies Wonder—piano suite (1970)
Peter Jacobs (r1987) Concert
(10/93) (CNTI) ① CCD1066
The Lilford Owl—folk-tune preludes: piano (1977)
Peter Jacobs (r1987) Concert
(10/93) (CNTI) ① CCD1066

HOLDRIDGE, Lee (b 1944) USA

SECTION I: ORCHESTRAL

Elegy—harp and strings (1976) (arr cpsr from TV film score 'Gemini Man')
Nuremberg SO, R. Kaufman (r1991) Concert
(10/92) (COLO) ① CST34 8048
Scenes of Summer (1973)
EXCERPTS: 1. Festival; 2. Countryside; 3. Dance.
Nuremberg SO, R. Kaufman (r1991) Concert
(10/92) (COLO) ① CST34 8048

SECTION V: STAGE WORKS

Film Themes Suite (arr cpsr from various films)
EXCERPTS: 1. East of Eden—Main Theme (1981); 2. Beauty and the Beast—Main Theme (1987 - TV score); 3. El Pueblo del Sol—Waltz (1982); 4. 16 Days of Glory—Main Title (1984).
Nuremberg SO, R. Kaufman (r1991) Concert
(10/92) (COLO) ① CST34 8048
Old Gringo—film score (1989)
EXCERPTS: 1. Ride to the Hacienda; 2. The Battle; 3. Harriet's Theme; 4. Bitter's Last Ride; 5. The Mirrors; 6. Nightime; 7. The Bell Tower; 8. The Sigh; 9. The Battle (Resolution); 10. Bitter's Destiny; 11. Finale.
1-11. OST, L. Holdridge (r1989)
(3/90) (GNP) ① GNPD8017
El Pueblo del Sol—film score (1981)
OST, LSO, L. Holdridge (r1981)
(10/92) (BAY) ① BCD-1031
Transylvania 6-5000—film score (1985)
Suite OST, L. Holdridge (r1985) Concert
(10/93) (SILV) ① FILMCD127

HOLLANDER, Frederick (Friedrich) (1896–1976) Germany/USA

SECTION V: STAGE WORKS

Sabrina—film score (1954)
EXCERPTS: 1. Main Title; 2. The Larrabee Estate.
1, 2. National PO, C. Gerhardt Concert
(10/90) (RCA) ① GD80422

HOLLIGER, Heinz (b 1939) Switzerland

SECTION I: ORCHESTRAL

Ostinato funebre—small orchestra (1991)
Modern Ens, H. Holliger (r1991) Concert
(7/93) (ECM) ① [2] 437 441-2
Siebengesang—oboe, vv, loudspeaker & orchestra (1966-67) (Wds. G Trakl)
H. Holliger, Stuttgart Schola Cantorum, Basle SO, F. Travis (r1970) Magische Tänzer.
(10/94) (DG) ① 445 251-2GC
Turm-Musik—flute, small orchestra and tape (1984)
Excs A. Nicolet, Modern Ens, H. Holliger (r1991) Concert
(7/93) (ECM) ① [2] 437 441-2
Übungen zu Scardanelli—small and tape (1975-85) (part of Scardanelli-Zyklus)
Modern Ens, H. Holliger (r1991) Concert
(7/93) (ECM) ① [2] 437 441-2

SECTION III: INSTRUMENTAL

'(t)air(e)'—flute (1980-83) (part of Scardanelli-Zyklus)
A. Nicolet (r1991) Concert
(7/93) (ECM) ① [2] 437 441-2
Chaconne—cello solo (1975)
T. Demenga (r1993) Concert
(8/95) (ECM) ① 445 234-2

SECTION IV: VOCAL AND CHORAL

Alb-Chehr—speaker & alpine music ensemble (1991) (Wds. Swiss folk tale)
O. Bumann, F. Abgottspon, E. Schmid, K. Schmid, P. Locher, M. Volken, M. Tenisch, S. Gertschen, E. Volken (r1992-3) Beiseit.
(8/95) (ECM) ① 447 391-2
Beiseit—12 Lieder on texts by Robert Walser (1990-1)
1. Beiseit; 2. Schnee; 3. Bangen; 4. Wie immer; 5. Trug; 6. Zu philosophisch; 7. Abend; 8. Weiter; 9. Angst; 10. Und gang; 11. Drückendes Licht; 12. Im Mondschein (Epilog).
D. James, E. Schmid, T. Anzellotti, J. Nied, H. Holliger (r1994) Alb-Chehr.
(8/95) (ECM) ① 447 391-2
Die Jahreszeiten—3 sets of 4 songs for choir (1975, 1977 and 1978) (Wds. Scardanelli & Hölderin)
London Voices, T. Edwards (r1991) Concert
(7/93) (ECM) ① [2] 437 441-2

SECTION V: STAGE WORKS

Der magische Tänzer—1963-65 (Lib. N Sachs)
Cpte E. Gilhofer, H. Riediker, D. Dorow, P. Langridge, Stuttgart Schola Cantorum, Basle Th Ch, Basle SO, H. Zender (r1970) Siebengesang.
(10/94) (DG) ① 445 251-2GC

HOLLMAN, Joseph (1852–1927) The Netherlands/France

SECTION IV: VOCAL AND CHORAL

Chanson d'amour—song
F. Alda, M. Elman, F. La Forge (r1915) Concert
(10/91) (BIDD) ① LAB039
E. Eames, J. Hollman, anon (r1906) Concert
(11/93) (ROMO) ① [2] 81001-2

HOLLOWAY, Robin (Greville) (b 1943) England

SECTION I: ORCHESTRAL

Romanza—violin and small orchestra, Op. 31 (1976)
E. Gruenberg, CLS, R. Hickox (r1981) Sea-Surface Full of Clouds.
(9/94) (CHAN) ① CHAN9228
Second Concerto—orchestra, Op. 40 (1979)
BBC SO, O. Knussen (r1993)
(5/94) (NMC) ① NMCD015

SECTION IV: VOCAL AND CHORAL

Lord, what is man?—song
St Paul's Cath Ch, John Scott Concert
(4/92) (HYPE) ① CDA66519
Sea-Surface Full of Clouds—sop, cond-alto, ten, chorus & orch, Op. 28 (1975-76)
P. Walmsley-Clark, M. Cable, C. Brett, M. Hill, Richard Hickox Sngrs, CLS, R. Hickox (r1981)
Romanza, Op. 31. (9/94) (CHAN) ① CHAN9228
Since I believe in God the Father Almighty—anthem: chorus a capella (1982) (Wds. R. Bridges)
W. Kendall, G. Webber, R. Hill Wood: St Mark Passion. (5/93) (ASV) ① CDDCA854

HOLMBOE, Vagn (b 1909) Denmark

SECTION I: ORCHESTRAL

Concerto for Cello and Orchestra, Op. 120 (1974)
E.B. Bengtsson, Danish Nat RSO, J. Ferencsik (r1975) Concert (7/93) (BIS) ① BIS-CD078
Symphony No. 1—chamber orchestra, Op. 4 (1935)
Aarhus SO, O. A. Hughes (r1993) Concert
(11/94) (BIS) ① BIS-CD605
Symphony No. 3, 'Sinfonia rustica', Op. 25 (1941)
Aarhus SO, O. A. Hughes (r1993) Concert
(11/94) (BIS) ① BIS-CD605
Symphony No. 4, 'Sinfonia sacra' and orchestra, Op. 29 (1941 rev 1945) (Wds. cpsr, trans P. J. Jensen)
Jutland Op Ch, Aarhus SO, O.A. Hughes Symphony 5. (6/93) (BIS) ① BIS-CD572
Symphony No. 5, Op. 35 (1944)
Aarhus SO, O.A. Hughes Symphony 4.
(6/93) (BIS) ① BIS-CD572

Symphony No. 6, Op. 43 (1947)
Aarhus SO, O.A. Hughes Symphony 7.
(6/93) (BIS) ① **BIS-CD573**
Symphony No. 7 in one movement, Op. 50 (1950)
Aarhus SO, O.A. Hughes Symphony 6.
(6/93) (BIS) ① **BIS-CD573**
Symphony No. 8, 'Sinfonia boreale', Op. 56 (1951)
Aarhus SO, O. A. Hughes (r1993) Symphony 9.
(8/95) (BIS) ① **BIS-CD618**
Symphony No. 9, Op. 95 (1967-8, rev 1969)
Aarhus SO, O. A. Hughes (r1993) Symphony 8.
(8/95) (BIS) ① **BIS-CD618**
Symphony No. 10, Op. 105 (1970-71)
Aarhus SO, O. A. Hughes (r1993) Concert
(11/94) (BIS) ① **BIS-CD605**

SECTION II: CHAMBER

Quintet—two trumpets, horn, trombone & tuba, Op. 79 (1961)
Swedish Brass Qnt (r1983) Concert
(7/93) (BIS) ① **BIS-CD078**
String Quartet No. 1, Op. 46 (1949)
Kontra Qt (r1992) Concert
(6/94) (MARC) ① **DCCD9203**
String Quartet No. 3, Op. 48 (1949)
Kontra Qt (r1992) Concert
(6/94) (MARC) ① **DCCD9203**
String Quartet No. 4, Op. 63 (1954)
Kontra Qt (r1992) Concert
(6/94) (MARC) ① **DCCD9203**
Triade—trumpet and organ, Op. 123 (c1974)
E. Tarr, E. Westenholz (r1979) Concert
(7/93) (BIS) ① **BIS-CD078**

SECTION IV: VOCAL AND CHORAL

Benedic Domino—chorus a capella, Op. 59 (1952) (Wds. Psalm 103)
1. Benedic, anima mea; 2. Hominis dies; 3. Benedicite Domino.
Camerata Chbr Ch, P. Enevold (r1977) Concert
(7/93) (BIS) ① **BIS-CD078**

HOLMÈS, Augusta (1847–1903) France

SECTION I: ORCHESTRAL

Andromède—symphonic poem (1901)
Rhineland-Pfalz State PO, S. Friedmann (r1991) Concert
(10/94) (MARC) ① **8 223449**
Irlande—symphonic poem (1882)
Rhineland-Pfalz State PO, S. Friedmann (r1990) Concert
(10/94) (MARC) ① **8 223449**
Ouverture pour une comédie (c1871-75)
Rhineland-Pfalz State PO, S. Friedmann (r1990) Concert
(10/94) (MARC) ① **8 223449**
Pologne—symphonic poem (1883)
Rhineland-Pfalz State PO, S. Friedmann (r1990) Concert
(10/94) (MARC) ① **8 223449**

SECTION IV: VOCAL AND CHORAL

Le chemin du ciel—song
M. Renaud, anon (r1902) Concert
(3/93) (SYMP) ① **SYMCD1100**
Ludus pro Patria—symphonic ode: chorus and orchestra (1888) (Wds. Puvis de Chavannes)
1. Interlude: La nuit et l'amour.
1. Rhineland-Pfalz State PO, P. Davin (r1992) Concert
(10/94) (MARC) ① **8 223449**

HOLST, Gustav(us Theodore von) (1874–1934) England

H—numbers used in I. Holst Thematic Catalogue (1972)

SECTION I: ORCHESTRAL

Beni Mora—oriental suite, H107 (Op. 29/1) (1909-10)
1. First Dance; 2. Second Dance; 3. Finale: In the street of the Ouled Naïls.
LSO, G. Holst (r1923) Concert
(4/91) (PEAR) ① **GEMMCD9417**
LPO, A. Boult Concert (7/92) (LYRI) ① **SRCD222**
Brook Green Suite—strings with flute, oboe and bassoon ad lib, H190 (1933)
1. Prelude; 2. Air; 3. Dance.
New Zealand CO, N. Braithwaite Concert
(4/92) (KOCH) ① **37058-2**
C. Aronowitz, ECO, I. Holst Concert
(4/93) (LYRI) ① **SRCD223**
CLS, R. Hickox (r1993) Concert
(7/94) (CHAN) ① **CHAN9270**

Oxford Orch da Camera, G. Vass (r1993) Concert
(9/94) (MEDI) ① **MQCD4002**
ECO, Y. Menuhin (r1993) Concert
(12/94) (EMIN) ① **CD-EMX2227**
Capriccio for orchestra, H185 (1932) (rev ver ed I Holst)
ECO, I. Holst Concert (4/93) (LYRI) ① **SRCD223**
First Choral Symphony—soprano, chorus and orchestra, H155 (Op. 41) (1925) (Wds. Keats)
1. Prelude: Invocation to Pan; 2. Song and Bacchanale: 'Beneath my palm trees'; 3. Ode to a Grecian Urn; 4a. Scherzo: 'Ever let the Fancy roam'; 4b. Folly's Song: 'When wedding fiddles are a-playing'; 5. Finale: 'Spirit here that reignest'.
L. Dawson, Guildford Choral Soc, RPO, H.D. Wetton (r1993) Choral Fantasia.
(3/94) (HYPE) ① **CDA66660**
Concerto for 2 Violins and Orchestra, H175 (Op. 49) (1930)
E. Hurwitz, K. Sillito, ECO, I. Holst Concert
(4/93) (LYRI) ① **SRCD223**
N. Ward, A. Watkinson, CLS, R. Hickox (r1993) Concert (7/94) (CHAN) ① **CHAN9270**
The Cotswold Symphony, H47 (1900)
1. Allegro con brio; 2. Elegy in memoriam William Morris; 3. Scherzo; 4. Finale.
2. LSO, D. Atherton Concert
(6/93) (LYRI) ① **SRCD209**
Egdon Heath, 'Homage to Thomas Hardy'—orchestra, H172 (Op. 47) (1927)
LPO, G. Solti (r1961) Concert
(4/94) (DECC) ① **440 318-2DWO**
BBC SO, A. Davis (r1993) Planets.
(12/94) (TELD) ① **4509-94541-2**
A Fugal Concerto—flute, oboe and strings, H152 (Op. 40/2) (1923)
A. Still, S. Popperwell, New Zealand CO, N. Braithwaite Concert (4/92) (KOCH) ① **37058-2**
W. Bennett, P. Graeme, ECO, I. Holst Concert
(4/93) (LYRI) ① **SRCD223**
D. Dobing, C. Hooker, CLS, R. Hickox (r1993) Concert (7/94) (CHAN) ① **CHAN9270**
J. Snowden, D. Theodore, ECO, Y. Menuhin (r1993) Concert (12/94) (EMIN) ① **CD-EMX2227**
A Fugal Overture, H151 (Op. 40/1) (1922) (originally used as overture to opera 'The Perfect Fool')
LPO, A. Boult Concert (7/92) (LYRI) ① **SRCD222**
London Fest Orch, R. Pople Concert
(9/92) (ASV) ① **CDDCA782**
The Golden Goose—choral ballet after Grimm, H163 (Op. 45/1) (1926)
Ballet Music ECO, I. Holst Concert
(4/93) (LYRI) ① **SRCD223**
Hammersmith—military band/orchestra, H178 (Op. 52) (1930 orch 1931)
1. Prelude; 2. Scherzo.
London Wind Orch, D.Wick Concert
(7/88) (ASV) ① **CDQS5021**
Eastman Wind Ens, F. Fennell Concert
(12/91) (MERC) ① **432 009-2MM**
LPO, A. Boult Concert (7/92) (LYRI) ① **SRCD222**
Stockholm Sym Wind Orch, O. Vänskä Concert
(3/93) (CPRI) ① **CAP21415**
Indra—symphonic poem, H66 (1903)
LSO, D. Atherton Concert
(6/93) (LYRI) ① **SRCD209**
Invocation—cello and orchestra, H75 (Op. 19/2) (1911)
J. Lloyd Webber, Philh, V. Handley Concert
(7/87) (RCA) ① **RD70800**
A. Baillie, LSO, D. Atherton Concert
(6/93) (LYRI) ① **SRCD209**
J. Lloyd Webber, ASMF, N. Marriner (1994) Concert
(12/94) (PHIL) ① **442 530-2PH**
Japanese Suite, H126 (Op. 33) (1915)
1. Prelude: Song of the Fisherman; 2. Ceremonial Dance; 3. Dance of the Fisherman; 4. Interlude: Song of the Fisherman; 5. Dance of the Cherry Tree; 6. Finale: Dance of the Wolves.
LSO, A. Boult Concert (7/92) (LYRI) ① **SRCD222**
Lyric Movement—viola and chamber orchestra, H191 (1933)
V. Yendoll, New Zealand CO, N. Braithwaite Concert
(4/92) (KOCH) ① **37058-2**
C. Aronowitz, ECO, I. Holst Concert
(4/93) (LYRI) ① **SRCD223**
S. Tees, CLS, R. Hickox (r1993) Concert
(7/94) (CHAN) ① **CHAN9270**
A Moorside Suite—brass band, H173 (1928)
1. Scherzo; 2. Nocturne; 3. March.
London Collegiate Brass, J. Stobart Concert
(9/86) (CRD) ① **CRD3434**

London Brass Virtuosi, D. Honeyball Concert
(7/87) (HYPE) ① **CDA66189**
City of London Wind Ens, G. Brand (arr. Wright) Concert (3/90) (LDR) ① **LDRCD1012**
Black Dyke Mills Band, W. Halliwell (r1928) Concert
(11/93) (BEUL) ① **1PD2**
Nocturne W. Bennett, P. Graeme, ECO, I. Holst (arr stgs: I Holst) Concert (4/93) (LYRI) ① **SRCD223**
Morris Dance Tunes—orchestra (1910)
1. SET 1: 1a. Bean Setting (Stick Dance); 1b. LaudnumBunches (Corner Dance); 1c. Country Garden (Handkerchief Dance); 1d. Constant Billy (Stick Dance); 1e. Trunkles; 1f. Morris Off; 2. SET 2: 2a. Rigs O'Marlow (Stick Dance); 2b. Bluff King Hal; 2c. How D'ye Do, Sir (Corner Dance); 2d. Shepherd's Hey (Stick or Hand-clapping Dance); 2e. The Blue-eyed Stranger; 2f. Morris Off.
New Zealand CO, N. Braithwaite Concert
(4/92) (KOCH) ① **37058-2**
The Planets—suite: orchestra, H125 (Op. 32) (1916)
1. Mars, the Bringer of War; 2. Venus, the Bringer of Peace; 3. Mercury, the Winged Messenger; 4. Jupiter, the Bringer of Jollity; 5. Saturn, the Bringer of Old Age; 6. Uranus, the Magician; 7. Neptune, the Mystic.
SNO, A. Gibson (r1979)
(1/84) (CHAN) ① **CHAN8302**
Ambrosian Sngrs, LSO, A. Previn
(12/85) (EMI) ① **CDC7 47160-2**
Brighton Fest Chor, RPO, A. Previn (r1986)
(12/86) (TELA) ① **CD80133**
Montreal Sym Chor, Montreal SO, C. Dutoit
(4/87) (DECC) ① **417 553-2DH**
Ambrosian Sngrs, Philh, S. Rattle (r1980)
(3/88) (EMIN) ① **CD-EMX9513**
London Voices, LSO, R. Hickox (r1987)
(5/88) (CARL) ① **PCD890**
Hallé Ch, Hallé, J. Loughran
(1/90) (CFP) ① **CD-CFP4243**
Bratislava RSO, A. Leaper Suite de ballet.
(1/91) (NAXO) ① **8 550193**
Chicago SO, Chicago Sym Chor, James Levine
(1/91) (DG) ① **429 730-2GH**
LSO, G. Holst (r1926) Vaughan Williams: Symphony 4. (4/91) (KOCH) ① **37018-2**
LSO, G. Holst (r1923) Concert
(4/91) (PEAR) ① **GEMMCD9417**
LPO, G. Solti Elgar: Pomp and Circumstance Marches. (5/91) (DECC) ① **430 447-2DM**
London Fest Orch, R. Pople Concert
(9/92) (ASV) ① **CDDCA782**
The Sixteen, Philh, E. Svetlanov Rimsky-Korsakov: Mlada. (9/92) (COLL) ① **Coll1348-2**
King's College Ch, RPO, J. Judd
(3/93) (DENO) ① **CO-75076**
NYPO, L. Bernstein Concert
(5/93) (SONY) ① **SMK47567**
LSO, G. Holst (r1926) Elgar: Enigma Variations.
(10/93) (EMI) ① **CDC7 54837-2**
LP Ch, LPO, G. Solti (r1978) Concert
(4/94) (DECC) ① **440 318-2DWO**
N. Marriner, Toronto SO, A. Davis Concert
(7/94) (EMI) ① **CDM7 64300-2**
Ambrosian Sngrs, RPO, V. Handley (r1993) St Paul's Suite. (7/94) (TRIN) ① **TRP007**
BBC Sym Chor (Women's Voices), BBC SO, A. Davis (r1993) Egdon Heath.
(12/94) (TELD) ① **4509-94541-2**
Ambrosian Sngrs, Philh, S. Rattle Janáček: Sinfonietta. (3/95) (EMI) ① **CDM7 64740-2**
New England Cons Chor, Boston SO, W. Steinberg (r1970) Elgar: Enigma Variations.
(3/95) (DG) ① **439 446-2GCL**
BBC SO, M. Sargent (pp1965) Elgar: Enigma Variations. (3/95) (BBCR) ① **BBCRD9104**
Monteverdi Ch, Philh, J. E. Gardiner (r1994)
Grainger: Warriors. (8/95) (DG) ① **445 860-2GH**
1, 3, 4, 6. LSO, A. Coates (r1926) Concert
(4/93) (KOCH) ① [2] **37704-2**
4. SNO, A. Gibson Concert
(7/83) (CHAN) ① **CHAN8301**
Scherzo—orchestra, H192 (1933-34)
LPO, A. Boult Concert (7/92) (LYRI) ① **SRCD222**
A Somerset Rhapsody—orchestra, H87 (Op. 21/1) (1906-07)
LPO, A. Boult Concert (7/92) (LYRI) ① **SRCD222**
ECO, Y. Menuhin (r1993) Concert
(12/94) (EMIN) ① **CD-EMX2227**
A Song of the Night—violin and orchestra, H74 (1905)
L. McAslan, LSO, D. Atherton Concert
(6/93) (LYRI) ① **SRCD209**

Songs of the West—orchestra, H86 (Op. 21/1) (1905-07)
City of London Wind Ens, G. Brand (r1988: arr concert band: Curnow) *Concert*
(7/89) (LDR) ① **LDRCD1001**

2 Songs without words for orchestra, H88 (Op. 22) (1906)
1. Country song; 2. Marching song.
LSO, G. Holst (r1923) *Concert*
(4/91) (PEAR) ① **GEMMCD9417**
CLS, R. Hickox (r1993) *Concert*
(7/94) (CHAN) ① **CHAN9270**
2. ECO, I. Holst *Concert* (4/93) (LYRI) ① **SRCD223**

St Paul's Suite—string orchestra, H118 (Op. 29) (1912-13)
1. Jig; 2. Ostinate; 3. Intermezzo; 4. Finale: The Dargason.
Bournemouth Sinfonietta, G. Hurst *Concert*
(8/85) (CHAN) ① **CHAN8375**
orch, G. Holst (r1923) *Concert*
(4/91) (PEAR) ① **GEMMCD9417**
ASMF, K. Sillito *Concert*
(10/91) (COLL) ① **Coll1234-2**
New Zealand CO, N. Braithwaite *Concert*
(4/92) (KOCH) ① **37058-2**
Britannia CO, D. Falkowski *Concert*
(6/92) (ENGL) ① **ERC5001**
London Fest Orch, R. Pople *Concert*
(9/92) (ASV) ① **CDDCA782**
CLS, R. Hickox (r1993) *Concert*
(7/94) (CHAN) ① **CHAN9270**
RPO, V. Handley (r1993) *Planets.*
(7/94) (TRIN) ① **TRP007**
Bournemouth Sinfonietta, R. Studt (vn/dir) (r1993) *Concert*
(10/94) (NAXO) ① **8 550823**
ECO, Y. Menuhin (r1993) *Concert*
(12/94) (EMIN) ① **CD-EMX2227**

Suite de ballet in E flat—orchestra, H43 (Op. 10) (1899 rev 1912)
1. Danse rustique; 2. Valse; 3. Scène de nuit; 4. Carnival.
Bratislava RSO, A. Leaper *Planets.*
(1/91) (NAXO) ① **8 550193**

Suite No. 1 in E flat—military band, H105 (Op. 28/1) (1909)
1. Chaconne; 2. Intermezzo; 3. March.
Cleveland Winds, F. Fennell *Concert*
(12/83) (TELA) ① **CD80038**
Coldstream Guards Band, R.A. Ridings (arr. Ridings) *Concert* (4/87) (BAND) ① **BNA5002**
London Wind Orch, D.Wick *Concert*
(7/88) (ASV) ① **CDQS6021**

Suite No. 2 in F—military band, H106 (Op. 28/2) (1911)
1. March; 2. Song without words: 'I'll love my love'; 3. Song of the Blacksmith.
Cleveland Winds, F. Fennell *Concert*
(12/83) (TELA) ① **CD80038**
Coldstream Guards Band, R.A. Ridings (arr. Ridings) *Concert* (4/87) (BAND) ① **BNA5002**
London Wind Orch, D.Wick *Concert*
(7/88) (ASV) ① **CDQS6021**
3. Black Dyke Mills Band, R. Newsome (r1977; arr brass band: S. Herbert) *Concert*
(1/94) (CHAN) ① **CHAN4528**

A Winter Idyll—orchestra, H31 (1897)
LSO, D. Atherton *Concert*
(6/93) (LYRI) ① **SRCD209**

SECTION II: CHAMBER

Air and Variations—oboe and string quartet, H8 (Op. 2/1) (1896 rev 1910)
S. Francis, English Qt *Concert*
(7/87) (CHAN) ① **CHAN8392**

Dances—piano duet (1895)
A. Goldstone, C. Clemmow (r1990) *Concert*
(10/95) (CHAN) ① **CHAN9382**

3 Pieces—oboe and string quartet, H8a (Op. 2) (1896 rev 1910)
1. March; 2. Minuet; 3. Scherzo.
S. Francis, English Qt *Concert*
(7/87) (CHAN) ① **CHAN8392**

The Planets—2 pianos, H125 (Op. 32) (1916) (arr cpsr)
Richard Rodney Bennett, S. Bradshaw
(10/90) (FACE) ① **FE8002**

Quintet in A minor—piano, oboe, clarinet, horn & double bass, H11 (Op. 3) (1896)
A. Goldstone, Elysian Wind Qnt *Concert*
(10/92) (CHAN) ① **CHAN9077**

Short Piano Trio in E (1894)
Pirasti Trio (r1994) *Concert*
(9/95) (ASV) ① **CDDCA925**

Wind Quintet in A flat—flute, oboe, clarinet, horn, bassoon, H67 (Op. 14) (1903)
Elysian Wind Qnt *Concert*
(10/92) (CHAN) ① **CHAN9077**

SECTION III: INSTRUMENTAL

Arpeggio Study—piano (1892)
A. Goldstone (r1990) *Concert*
(10/95) (CHAN) ① **CHAN9382**

Chrissemas Day in the Morning, on a tune from, 'North Country Ballads'—piano, Op. 46/1 (1926)
A. Goldstone (r1990) *Concert*
(10/95) (CHAN) ① **CHAN9382**

2 Folk Song Arrangements—piano, Op. 46/2 (1927)
A. Goldstone (r1990) *Concert*
(10/95) (CHAN) ① **CHAN9382**

Jig—piano (1932)
A. Goldstone (r1990) *Concert*
(10/95) (CHAN) ① **CHAN9382**

Nocturne—piano (1930)
A. Goldstone (r1990) *Concert*
(10/95) (CHAN) ① **CHAN9382**

A Piece for Yvonne—piano (1924)
A. Goldstone (r1990) *Concert*
(10/95) (CHAN) ① **CHAN9382**

2 Pièces—piano (1895)
1. Fancine; 2. Lucille.
A. Goldstone (r1990) *Concert*
(10/95) (CHAN) ① **CHAN9382**

Toccata on the Northumbrian Pipe Tune, 'Newburn Lads'—piano (1924)
A. Goldstone (r1990) *Concert*
(10/95) (CHAN) ① **CHAN9382**

SECTION IV: VOCAL AND CHORAL

Ave Maria—8vv female choir, H49 (Op. 9b) (1900)
Cambridge Sngrs, J. Rutter *Concert*
(4/92) (CLLE) ① **COLCD116**
Westminster Cath Ch, J. O'Donnell (r1993) *Concert*
(3/94) (HYPE) ① **CDA66669**
Holst Sngrs, S. Layton (r1993) *Concert*
(6/94) (HYPE) ① **CDA66705**

Bring us in good ale—carol, H131 (Op. 34/4) (1916) (Wds. 15th cent anon)
King's Sngrs *Concert*
(6/88) (EMI) ① **CDC7 49765-2**
Holst Sngrs, S. Layton (r1993) *Concert*
(6/94) (HYPE) ① **CDA66705**

3 Carols—unison chorus and orchestra, H133 (1916-17) (see also Christmas Index)
1. I saw three ships (wds. trad); 2. Christmas song, 'Personent hodie' (wds. trans J Joseph); 3. Masters in this Hall (wds. W. Morris).
2. Trinity Coll Ch, Cambridge, G. Jackson, R. Marlow *Concert* (12/90) (CONI) ① **CDCF501**

A Choral Fantasia—soprano, chorus, organ and orchestra, H177 (Op. 51) (1930) (Wds. R. Bridges)
L. Dawson, Guildford Choral Soc, RPO, H.D. Wetton, J. Birch (r1993) *Choral Symphony.*
(3/94) (HYPE) ① **CDA66660**

6 Choral Folk Songs—folksong arrangements—chorus, Op. 36b) (1916) (Wds Traditional)
EXCERPTS: 1. I sowed the seeds of love; 2. There was a tree; 3. Matthew, Mark, Luke and John; 4. The Song of the Blacksmith; 5. I love my love; 6. Swansea Town.
1-6. Holst Sngrs, S. Layton (r1993) *Concert*
(6/94) (HYPE) ① **CDA66705**
4. King's Sngrs *Concert*
(6/88) (EMI) ① **CDC7 49765-2**

The Cloud Messenger—mezzo soprano, chorus and orchestra, H111 (Op. 30) (1909-10 rev 1912) (Wds. Kalidasa trans cpsr)
D. Jones, LSC, LSO, R. Hickox *Hymn of Jesus.*
(5/91) (CHAN) ① **CHAN8901**

Diverus and Lazarus—folksong arrangement, H137 (c1917) (Wds. trad)
Holst Sngrs, S. Layton (r1993) *Concert*
(6/94) (HYPE) ① **CDA66705**

2 Eastern Pictures—female chorus and harp, H112 (1911) (Wds. Kalidasa trans cpsr)
1. Spring; 2. Summer.
RCM Chbr Ch, RPO, D. Willcocks *Concert*
(3/86) (UNIC) ① **DKPCD9046**
Holst Sngrs, S. Williams, S. Layton (r1993) *Concert*
(6/94) (HYPE) ① **CDA66705**

The Evening watch—chorus a cappella, H159 (Op. 43/1) (1924) (Wds. H. Vaughan)
Holst Sngrs, H.D. Wetton *Concert*
(1/90) (HYPE) ① **CDA66329**

Magdalen Oxford Coll Ch, G. Webber *Concert*
(11/91) (ABBE) ① **CDCA914**

3 Festival Choruses—chorus and orchestra, H134 (Op. 36a) (1916)
1. Let all mortal flesh (wds. trans Moultrie); 2. Turn back, o man (wds. C. Bax); 3. A Festival Chime.
2. St Paul's Cath Ch, John Scott, Adrian Lucas (r1991) *Concert* (8/93) (HYPE) ① **CDA66618**

The Hymn of Jesus—chorus and orchestra, H140 (Op. 37) (1917)
BBC Chor, BBC SO, A. Boult (r1961) *Elgar: Dream of Gerontius.* (5/89) (DECC) ① [2] **421 381-2LM2**
LSC, LSO, R. Hickox *Cloud Messenger.*
(5/91) (CHAN) ① **CHAN8901**
Huddersfield Choral Soc, Liverpool PO, M. Sargent (r1944) *Concert* (5/95) (DUTT) ① **CDAX8012**

Hymn to Dionysus—female chorus and orchestra, H116 (Op. 31/2) (1913) (Wds. Euripides trans Murray)
RCM Chbr Ch, RPO, D. Willcocks *Concert*
(3/86) (UNIC) ① **DKPCD9046**

Hymns from the Rig Veda—voice and piano, H90 (Op. 24) (1907-08) (Wds. trans cpsr)
1. Ushas; 2. Varuna I; 3. Maruts; 4. Indra; 5. Varuna II; 6. Song of the Frogs; 7. Vac; 8. Creation; 9. Faith.
1, 5. L. Finnie, A. Legge *Concert*
(4/90) (CHAN) ① **CHAN8749**

In Youth is Pleasure—chorus, H76 (c1907) (Wds R. Wever)
Holst Sngrs, S. Layton (r1993) *Concert*
(6/94) (HYPE) ① **CDA66705**

Light Leaves Whisper—chorus, H20 (1896) (Wds Hart)
Holst Sngrs, S. Layton (r1993) *Concert*
(6/94) (HYPE) ① **CDA66705**

Lullay my liking—soprano and chorus, H129 (Op. 34/2) (1916) (Wds. anon)
Lichfield Cath Ch, J. Rees-Williams *Concert*
(12/90) (ABBE) ① **CDCA903**
Holst Sngrs, S. Layton (r1993) *Concert*
(6/94) (HYPE) ① **CDA66705**

6 Male Choruses, H186 (Op. 53) (1931-32)
1. Intercession; 2. Good Friday; 3. Drinking song; 4. A love song; 5. How mighty are the Sabbaths; 6. Before sleep.
Holst Sngrs, Holst Orch, H.D. Wetton *Concert*
(1/90) (HYPE) ① **CDA66329**

Nunc dimittis—8vv a cappella, H127 (1915) (Wds. Roman Catholic liturgy)
Holst Sngrs, H.D. Wetton *Concert*
(1/90) (HYPE) ① **CDA66329**
Westminster Cath Ch, J. O'Donnell (r1993) *Concert*
(3/94) (HYPE) ① **CDA66669**
Chichester Cath Ch, A. Thurlow, J. Thomas (r1994) *Concert* (5/95) (PRIO) ① **PRCD511**

O Spiritual Pilgrim—partsong, H188 (1933) (Wds J.E. Flecker)
Holst Sngrs, S. Layton (r1993) *Concert*
(6/94) (HYPE) ① **CDA66705**

Of one that is so fair—carol, H130 (Op. 34/3) (c1916) (Wds Anon)
Holst Sngrs, S. Layton (r1993) *Concert*
(6/94) (HYPE) ① **CDA66705**

7 Partsongs—female chorus and strings, H162 (Op. 44) (1925-26) (Wds. R. Bridges)
1. Say who is this?; 2. O Love, I complain; 3. Angel spirits of sleep; 4. When first we met; 5. Sorrow and joy; 6. Love on my heart; 7. Assemble, all ye maidens.
Holst Sngrs, Holst Orch, H.D. Wetton *Concert*
(1/90) (HYPE) ① **CDA66329**

2 Psalms (1912)
1. Psalm 86 (tenor, chorus, strings and organ: wds Bible & J Bryan); 2. Psalm 148 (chorus, strings and organ: wds F R Gray).
Holst Sngrs, Holst Orch, H.D. Wetton *Concert*
(1/90) (HYPE) ① **CDA66329**
Britten Sngrs, CLS, R. Hickox *Concert*
(3/92) (CHAN) ① **CHAN8997**

Rig Veda - Group 1—chorus and orchestra, H97 (Op. 26/1) (1908-10) (Wds. trans cpsr)
1. Battle Hymn; 2. To the Unknown God; 3. Funeral Hymn.
1, 2. RCM Chbr Ch, RPO, D. Willcocks *Concert*
(3/86) (UNIC) ① **DKPCD9046**

Rig Veda - Group 2—female chorus and orchestra, H98 (Op. 26/2) (1909) (Wds. trans cpsr)
1. To Varuna; 2. To Agni; 3. Funeral Chant.
1-3. RCM Chbr Ch, RPO, D. Willcocks *Concert*
(3/86) (UNIC) ① **DKPCD9046**

Rig Veda - Group 3—female chorus, harp and orchestra, H99 (Op. 26/3) (1910) (Wds. trans cpsr)
1. Hymn to the Dawn; 2. Hymn to the Waters; 3. Hymn to Vena; 4. Hymn of the Travellers.

RCM Chbr Ch, O. Ellis, D. Willcocks *Concert*
(3/86) (UNIC) ① DKPCD9046
S. Minty, M. Hill, J. Pearce, T. Owen, Holst Sngrs,
Holst Orch, H.D. Wetton *Concert*
(11/88) (HYPE) ① CDA66175
**Rig Veda - Group 4—male chorus, strings,
brass and percussion, H100 (Op. 26/4) (1912)**
(Wds. trans cpsr)
1. Hymn to Agni; 2. Hymn to Soma; 3. Hymn to
Manas; 4. Hymn to Indra.
2, 3. RCM Chbr Ch, RPO, D. Willcocks *Concert*
(3/86) (UNIC) ① DKPCD9046
12 Songs, H174 (Op. 48) (1929) (Wds. H.
Wolfe)
1. Persephone; 2. Things lovelier; 3. Now in these
fairylands; 4. A Little Music; 5. The Thought; 6. The
Floral Bandit; 7. Envoi; 8. The Dream-city; 9.
Journey's End; 10. In the Street of Lost Time; 11.
Rhyme; 12. Betelgeuse.
P. Kwella, CLS, R. Hickox (r1983) *Sávitri*.
(2/88) (HYPE) ① CDA66099
1, 3, 4, 6, 8, 9. S. Leonard, M. Martineau (r1993)
(3/95) (UNIT) ① 88016-2
**Songs from The Princess—3-8 female vv,
H80-1 (Op. 20a) (1905)** (Wds Tennyson)
EXCERPTS: 1. Sweet and low; 2. The splendour
falls; 3. Tears, idle tears; 4. O Swallow, Swallow; 5.
Now sleeps the crimson petal. ADDITIONAL
SETTING: 6. Home they brought her warrior dead,
H81.
1-6. Holst Sngrs, S. Layton (r1993) *Concert*
(6/94) (HYPE) ① CDA66705
**This have I done for my true love—chorus a
capella, H128 (Op. 34/1) (1916)** (wds. trad)
Holst Sngrs, S. Layton (r1993) *Concert*
(6/94) (HYPE) ① CDA66705
**12 Welsh Folk Songs—chorus a cappella,
H183 (1930-31)** (Wds. trans S Wilson)
1. Lisa Lan; 2. Green Grass; 3. The Dove; 4. Awake,
awake; 5. The Nightingale and Linnet; 6. The mother-
in-law; 7. The first love; 8. O 'twas on a Monday
morning; 9. My sweetheart's like Venus; 10. White
Summer Rose; 11. The Lively Pair; 12. The lover's
complaint.
9. Cambridge Sngrs, J. Rutter *Concert*
(4/87) (CLLE) ① COLCD104
9. Holst Sngrs, S. Layton (r1993) *Concert*
(6/94) (HYPE) ① CDA66705

| SECTION V: STAGE WORKS |

The Lure—ballet, H149 (1921)
LPO, D. Atherton (ed I Holst/C Matthews) *Concert*
(6/93) (LYRI) ① SRCD209
**The Morning of the Year—choral ballet,
H164 (Op. 25/2) (1926-27)** (Wds. S Wilson)
Dances LPO, D. Atherton (ed I Holst/C Matthews)
Concert (6/93) (LYRI) ① SRCD209
**The Perfect Fool—opera: 1 act, H150 (Op.
39) (1923—London)** (Wds. cpsr, after
Shakespeare)
EXCERPTS: 1. Ballet Music.
1. Black Dyke Mills Band, P. Parkes (arr brass band:
Parkes) *Concert* (9/93) (CHAN) ① CHAN4507
1. LPO, A. Boult (r1961) *Concert*
(4/94) (DECC) ① 440 318-2DWO
1. ECO, Y. Menuhin (r1993) *Concert*
(12/94) (EMIN) ① CD-EMX2227
1. LPO, M. Sargent (r1946) *Concert*
(7/95) (BEUL) ① 1PD13
**Sávitri—opera da camera: 1 act, H96 (Op. 25)
(1916—London)** (Lib. cpsr)
Cpte F. Palmer, P. Langridge, S. Varcoe, Richard
Hickox Sngrs, CLS, R. Hickox (r1983) *Songs, H174.*
(2/88) (HYPE) ① CDA66099
Sita—opera: 3 acts, H89 (Op. 23) (1900-06)
(Lib. cpsr)
EXCERPTS: ACT 3: 1. Interlude; 2. Closing scene.
1. L. McAslan, A. Baillie, LPO, LSO, D. Atherton (ed
C Matthews) *Concert* (6/93) (LYRI) ① SRCD209

**HOLST, Imogen (1907–1984)
England**

| SECTION II: CHAMBER |

String Quartet No. 1 (1946)
Brindisi Qt *Concert* (5/91) (CONI) ① CDCF196

**HOLT, Simon (b 1958) Great
Britain**

| SECTION I: ORCHESTRAL |

**Sparrow Night—ob, fl, cl, hn, vn, va, vc, db,
pf & hp (1989)**
Nash Ens (r1991) *Concert*
(5/93) (NMC) ① NMCD008

| SECTION II: CHAMBER |

**...era madrugada—flute, clarinet, horn, viola
cello, bass and piano (1984)**
Nash Ens (r1991) *Concert*
(5/93) (NMC) ① NMCD008
**Shadow Realm—clarinet, cello and harp
(1983)**
Nash Ens (r1991) *Concert*
(5/93) (NMC) ① NMCD008

| SECTION IV: VOCAL AND CHORAL |

**Canciones—voice, flute, oboe, horn, harp &
string quintet (1986)**
1. Ojos, a la sombra (wds. anon); 2. Canción de
Jinete (wds. Lorca); 3. La muerte dentro del Rosal
(wds. anon).
F. Kimm, Nash Ens (r1991) *Concert*
(5/93) (NMC) ① NMCD008

HOLTEN, Bo (b 1948) Denmark

| SECTION I: ORCHESTRAL |

Concerto for Clarinet and Orchestra (1987)
J. Schou, Danish Nat RSO, J. Panula (r1990)
Sinfonia concertante. (7/94) (CHAN) ① CHAN9272
**Sinfonia Concertante—cello and orchestra
(1985-86)**
M. Zeuthen, Danish Nat RSO, H. Graf (1987)
Clarinet Concerto. (7/94) (CHAN) ① CHAN9272

**HOLTER, Iver (1850–1941)
Norway**

| SECTION II: CHAMBER |

String Quartet No. 1 in E flat, Op. 1 (c1875)
Norwegian Qt (r1992) *String Quartet 2.*
(11/93) (NKF) ① NKFCD50027-2
String Quartet No. 2 in G, Op. 18 (1910)
Norwegian Qt (r1991) *String Quartet 1.*
(11/93) (NKF) ① NKFCD50027-2

**HOLZBAUER, Ignaz (Jakob)
(1711–1783) Austria**

| SECTION II: CHAMBER |

**Quintet for Flute, Violin, Viola, Cello and
Keyboard in B flat**
VCM, N. Harnoncourt (r1963) *Concert*
(7/93) (TELD) ① 4509-91002-2

**HOMILIUS, Gottfried August
(1714–1785) Germany**

| SECTION IV: VOCAL AND CHORAL |

Pater noster—4vv
Lower Rhine Choral Soc, H. Schmitt *Concert*
(2/90) (SCHW) ① 313001

**HONEGGER, Arthur (1892–1955)
France/Switzerland**

H—Numbers from Halbreich's chronological
catalogue

| SECTION I: ORCHESTRAL |

**Le Chant de Nigamon—orchestra, H16
(1917)**
FNO, C. Munch (pp1962) *Concert*
(10/89) (MONT) ① MUN2051
Monte Carlo PO, M. Constant *Concert*
(2/94) (ERAT) ① 2292-45862-2
Pasdeloup Orch, Rhené-Baton (r c1929) *Concert*
(4/94) (MUSI) ① MACD-767
**Concertino for Piano and Orchestra, H55
(1925)**
T. Vásáry (pf/dir), Bournemouth Sinfonietta *Concert*
(12/91) (CHAN) ① CHAN8993
**Concerto da camera for Flute, Cor anglais
and Strings, H196 (1949)**
T. Hutchins, P-V. Plante, Montreal i Musici, Y.
Turovsky *Concert* (12/88) (CHAN) ① CHAN8632

J. Stinton, G. Browne, Scottish CO, S. Bedford
Concert (8/91) (COLL) ① Coll1210-2
A. Nicolet, H. Holliger, ASMF, N. Marriner (r1991)
Concert (9/93) (PHIL) ① 434 105-2PH
**Concerto for Cello and Orchestra, H72
(1929)**
J. Lloyd Webber, ECO, Y.P. Tortelier *Concert*
(6/91) (PHIL) ① 432 084-2PH
M. Maréchal, Paris Cons, A. Honegger (r1943)
Concert (6/94) (EMI) ① CDC5 55036-2
Monopartita—orchestra (1951)
Monte Carlo PO, M. Constant *Concert*
(2/94) (ERAT) ① 2292-45862-2
Pastorale d'été, H31 (1920)
BRSO, C. Dutoit *Concert*
(12/86) (ERAT) ① 2292-45242-2
FNO, C. Munch (pp1962) *Concert*
(10/89) (MONT) ① MUN2051
Bournemouth Sinfonietta, T. Vásáry *Concert*
(12/91) (CHAN) ① CHAN8993
ORTF Nat Orch, J. Martinon *Concert*
(3/92) (EMI) ① CDM7 63944-2
Toulouse Capitole Orch, M. Plasson (r1991) *Concert*
(9/93) (DG) ① 435 438-2GH
SO, A. Honegger (r1930) *Concert*
(4/94) (MUSI) ① MACD-767
SO, A. Honegger (r1931) *Concert*
(6/94) (EMI) ① CDC5 55036-2
**Prélude, arioso et fugue on
BACH—orchestra (1936)**
Montreal i Musici, Y. Turovsky *Concert*
(12/88) (CHAN) ① CHAN8632
Bournemouth Sinfonietta, T. Vásáry *Concert*
(12/91) (CHAN) ① CHAN8993
Prélude, fugue et postlude—orchestra (1948)
(from ballet 'Amphion')
Monte Carlo PO, M. Constant *Concert*
(2/94) (ERAT) ① 2292-45862-2
**3 Symphonic Movements, H53, H67, H83
(1923, 1928 & 1932-3)**
1. Pacific 231; 2. Rugby; 3. No. 3.
BRSO, C. Dutoit *Concert*
(12/86) (ERAT) ① 2292-45242-2
1. Danish Nat RSO, N. Järvi (r1992) *Concert*
(9/93) (CHAN) ① CHAN9176
1. SO, P. Coppola (r1927) *Concert*
(9/93) (KOCH) ① 37702-2
1. Paris Orch, S. Bychkov *Concert*
(3/94) (PHIL) ① 432 993-2PH
1. Oslo PO, M. Jansons *Concert*
(7/94) (EMI) ① CDC5 55122-2
1, 2. ORTF Nat Orch, J. Martinon *Concert*
(3/92) (EMI) ① CDM7 63944-2
1, 2. Toulouse Capitole Orch, M. Plasson (r1991)
Concert (9/93) (DG) ① 435 438-2GH
1, 2. SO, A. Honegger (r1929) *Concert*
(4/94) (MUSI) ① MACD-767
Symphony No. 1 in C, H75 (1930)
BRSO, C. Dutoit *Concert*
(12/86) (ERAT) ① 2292-45242-2
**Symphony No. 2—strings with trumpet
obbligato, H153 (1941)**
BPO, H. von Karajan (r1969) *Concert*
(6/88) (DG) ① 423 242-2GC
USSR Ministry of Culture SO, G. Rozhdestvensky
Concert (10/88) (OLYM) ① OCD212
Montreal i Musici, Y. Turovsky *Concert*
(12/88) (CHAN) ① CHAN8632
FNO, C. Munch (pp1964) *Concert*
(10/89) (MONT) ① MUN2051
Seattle Sym Stgs, G. Schwarz, S. Gulkis, R. Davis,
C. Butler (r1992) *Concert* (4/94) (DELO) ① DE3121
Oslo PO, M. Jansons *Concert*
(7/94) (EMI) ① CDC5 55122-2
BPO, H. von Karajan (r1969) *Concert*
(12/95) (DG) ① 447 435-2GOR
Symphony No. 3, 'Liturgique', H186 (1945)
BPO, H. von Karajan (r1969) *Symphony 2.*
(6/88) (DG) ① 423 242-2GC
BRSO, E. Ansermet (pp1964) *Brahms: Symphony 3.*
(8/90) (ORFE) ① C202891A
Danish Nat RSO, N. Järvi (r1992) *Concert*
(9/93) (CHAN) ① CHAN9176
Stuttgart RSO, N. Marriner (r1980) *Concert*
(1/94) (CAPR) ① 10 428
SO, A. Honegger (r c1949) *Concert*
(4/94) (MUSI) ① MACD-767
Oslo PO, M. Jansons *Concert*
(7/94) (EMI) ① CDC5 55122-2
BPO, H. von Karajan (r1969) *Concert*
(12/95) (DG) ① 447 435-2GOR
**Symphony No. 4 in A, 'Deliciae basiliensis',
H191 (1946)**
T. Carey, Bournemouth Sinfonietta, T. Vásáry
Concert (12/91) (CHAN) ① CHAN8993

Symphony No. 5 in D, 'Di tre re', H202 (1951)
FNO, C. Munch (pp1964) *Concert*
(10/89) (MONT) ① **MUN2051**
Danish Nat RSO, N. Järvi (r1992) *Concert*
(9/93) (CHAN) ① **CHAN9176**
La Tempête—prelude (1923) (after Shakespeare)
Toulouse Capitole Orch, M. Plasson (r1991) *Concert*
(9/93) (DG) ① **435 438-2GH**
Monte Carlo PO, M. Constant *Concert*
(2/94) (ERAT) ① **2292-45862-2**
SO, A. Honegger (r1929) *Concert*
(4/94) (MUSI) ① **MACD-767**
La Traversée des Andes—suite (1943)
Bratislava RSO, Adriano *Concert*
(4/89) (MARC) ① **8 223134**
Toulouse Capitole Orch, M. Plasson (r1991) *Concert*
(9/93) (DG) ① **435 438-2GH**
Le Vol sur l'Atlantique—suite (1943)
Bratislava RSO, Adriano *Concert*
(4/89) (MARC) ① **8 223134**
Toulouse Capitole Orch, M. Plasson (r1991) *Concert*
(9/93) (DG) ① **435 438-2GH**

SECTION II: CHAMBER

Arioso—violin and piano, H214 (c1927-29)
D-S. Kang, P. Devoyon (r1991) *Concert*
(9/93) (TIMP) ① [4] **4C1012**
D-S. Kang, P. Devoyon (r1991) *Concert*
(9/93) (TIMP) ① **1C1008**
Colloque—flute, celesta, violin and viola, H216 (unknown)
A. Marion, P. Devoyon, D-S. Kang, P-H. Xuereb (r1991) *Concert*
(9/93) (TIMP) ① [4] **4C1012**
A. Marion, P. Devoyon, D-S. Kang, P-H. Xuereb (r1991) *Concert*
(9/93) (TIMP) ① **1C1010**
3 Contrepoints—piccolo, oboe/cor anglais, violin & cello, H22 (1922)
1. Prélude; 2. Choral; 3. Canon sur basse obstinée.
A. Marion, C. Moreaux, D-S. Kang, R. Wallfisch (r1991) *Concert*
(9/93) (TIMP) ① [4] **4C1012**
A. Marion, C. Moreaux, D-S. Kang, R. Wallfisch (r1991) *Concert*
(9/93) (TIMP) ① **1C1010**
P. Corre, E. Exerjean (arr pf duet) *Concert*
(5/94) (PIER) ① **PV786091**
Hommage du Trombone exprimant la tristesse de l'auteur absent—trombone and piano, H59 (1925)
M. Becquet, P. Devoyon (r1991) *Concert*
(9/93) (TIMP) ① [4] **4C1012**
M. Becquet, P. Devoyon (r1991) *Concert*
(9/93) (TIMP) ① **1C1010**
Intrada—trumpet and piano, H193 (1947)
H. Hardenberger, R. Pöntinen *Concert*
(11/85) (BIS) ① **BIS-CD287**
R. Friedrich, T. Duis (r1992) *Concert*
(6/93) (CAPR) ① **10 439**
T. Caens, P. Devoyon (r1991) *Concert*
(9/93) (TIMP) ① [4] **4C1012**
T. Caens, P. Devoyon (r1991) *Concert*
(9/93) (TIMP) ① **1C1010**
W. Marsalis, J.L. Stillman (r1992) *Concert*
(5/94) (SONY) ① **SK47193**
Introduction et Danse—flute, harp, violin, viola and cello, H217 (unknown)
A. Marion, P. Zanlonghi, D-S. Kang, P-H. Xuereb, R. Wallfisch (r1991) *Concert*
(9/93) (TIMP) ① [4] **4C1012**
A. Marion, P. Zanlonghi, D-S. Kang, P-H. Xuereb, R. Wallfisch (r1991) *Concert*
(9/93) (TIMP) ① **1C1010**
J'avais un fidèle amant—string quartet, H74 (1929)
Ludwig Qt (r1991) *Concert*
(9/93) (TIMP) ① [4] **4C1012**
Ludwig Qt (r1991) *Concert*
(9/93) (TIMP) ① **1C1010**
Morceau de concours—violin and piano, H179 (1945)
D-S. Kang, P. Devoyon (r1991) *Concert*
(9/93) (TIMP) ① [4] **4C1012**
D-S. Kang, P. Devoyon (r1991) *Concert*
(9/93) (TIMP) ① **1C1008**
Petite Suite—two flutes and piano, H89 (1934)
A. Marion, A. Haraldsdottir, P. Devoyon (r1991) *Concert*
(9/93) (TIMP) ① [4] **4C1012**
A. Marion, A. Haraldsdottir, P. Devoyon (r1991) *Concert*
(9/93) (TIMP) ① **1C1010**
A. Nicolet, H. Holliger, J. Constable (r1991) *Concert*
(9/93) (PHIL) ① **434 105-2PH**
A. Nicolet, N. Imai, N. Yoshino (r1993; arr fl, va & hp) *Concert*
(12/94) (PHIL) ① **442 012-2PH**
Piano Trio in F minor, H6 (1914)
D-S. Kang, R. Wallfisch, P. Devoyon (r1991) *Concert*
(9/93) (TIMP) ① [4] **4C1012**

D-S. Kang, R. Wallfisch, P. Devoyon (r1991) *Concert*
(9/93) (TIMP) ① **1C1009**
Prélude for Double Bass and Piano, H79 (1932)
J. Rossi, P. Devoyon (r1991) *Concert*
(9/93) (TIMP) ① [4] **4C1012**
J. Rossi, P. Devoyon (r1991) *Concert*
(9/93) (TIMP) ① **1C1009**
Rapsodie—two flutes, clarinet and piano, H13 (1917)
A. Marion, A. Haraldsdottir, M. Arrignon, P. Devoyon (r1991) *Concert*
(9/93) (TIMP) ① [4] **4C1012**
A. Marion, A. Haraldsdottir, M. Arrignon, P. Devoyon (r1991) *Concert*
(9/93) (TIMP) ① **1C1010**
Romance—flute and piano, H211 (1953)
A. Marion, P. Devoyon (r1991) *Concert*
(9/93) (TIMP) ① [4] **4C1012**
A. Marion, P. Devoyon (r1991) *Concert*
(9/93) (TIMP) ① **1C1010**
Sonata for Cello and Piano, H32 (1920)
R. Wallfisch, P. Devoyon (r1991) *Concert*
(9/93) (TIMP) ① [4] **4C1012**
R. Wallfisch, P. Devoyon (r1991) *Concert*
(9/93) (TIMP) ① **1C1009**
Sonata for Viola and Piano, H28 (1920)
P-H. Xuereb, P. Devoyon (r1991) *Concert*
(9/93) (TIMP) ① [4] **4C1012**
P-H. Xuereb, P. Devoyon (r1991) *Concert*
(9/93) (TIMP) ① **1C1009**
Sonata for Violin and Piano in D minor (No. 0), H3 (1912)
D-S. Kang, P. Devoyon (r1991) *Concert*
(9/93) (TIMP) ① [4] **4C1012**
D-S. Kang, P. Devoyon (r1991) *Concert*
(9/93) (TIMP) ① **1C1008**
Sonata for Violin and Piano No. 1, H17 (1916-18)
D-S. Kang, P. Devoyon (r1991) *Concert*
(9/93) (TIMP) ① [4] **4C1012**
D-S. Kang, P. Devoyon (r1991) *Concert*
(9/93) (TIMP) ① **1C1008**
Sonata for Violin and Piano No. 2, H24 (1919)
D-S. Kang, P. Devoyon (r1991) *Concert*
(9/93) (TIMP) ① [4] **4C1012**
D-S. Kang, P. Devoyon (r1991) *Concert*
(9/93) (TIMP) ① **1C1008**
Sonatina for Clarinet and Piano, H42 (1921-22)
V. Soames, J. Drake *Concert*
(9/92) (CLRI) ① **CC0001**
P. Meyer, E. Le Sage *Concert*
(9/92) (DENO) ① **CO-79282**
M. Arrignon, P. Devoyon (r1991) *Concert*
(9/93) (TIMP) ① [4] **4C1012**
M. Arrignon, P. Devoyon (r1991) *Concert*
(9/93) (TIMP) ① **1C1010**
J. Cohler, J. Gordon (r1993) *Concert*
(5/95) (CRYS) ① **Crystal CD733**
Sonatina for Two Violins, H29 (1920)
D-S. Kang, J-P. Audoli (r1991) *Concert*
(9/93) (TIMP) ① [4] **4C1012**
D-S. Kang, J-P. Audoli (r1991) *Concert*
(9/93) (TIMP) ① **1C1009**
Sonatina for Violin and Cello, H80 (1932)
E. Turovsky, Y. Turovsky *Concert*
(7/85) (CHAN) ① **CHAN8358**
D-S. Kang, R. Wallfisch (r1991) *Concert*
(9/93) (TIMP) ① [4] **4C1012**
D-S. Kang, R. Wallfisch (r1991) *Concert*
(9/93) (TIMP) ① **1C1009**
String Quartet No. 1, H15 (1916-7)
Ludwig Qt (r1991) *Concert*
(9/93) (TIMP) ① [4] **4C1012**
Ludwig Qt (r1991) *Concert*
(9/93) (TIMP) ① **1C1011**
String Quartet No. 2, H103 (1934-6)
Ludwig Qt (r1991) *Concert*
(9/93) (TIMP) ① [4] **4C1012**
Ludwig Qt (r1991) *Concert*
(9/93) (TIMP) ① **1C1011**
String Quartet No. 3, H114 (1936-37)
Ludwig Qt (r1991) *Concert*
(9/93) (TIMP) ① [4] **4C1012**
Ludwig Qt (r1991) *Concert*
(9/93) (TIMP) ① **1C1011**

SECTION III: INSTRUMENTAL

Danse de la Chèvre—flute, H39 (1921)
M. Cox *Concert*
(3/90) (KING) ① **KCLCD2013**
V. Taylor *Concert*
(9/92) (TALL) ① **TP003**
Pro Arte Wind Quintet *Concert*
(1/93) (NIMB) ① **NI5327**
A. Marion (r1991) *Concert*
(9/93) (TIMP) ① [4] **4C1012**
A. Marion (r1991) *Concert*
(9/93) (TIMP) ① **1C1010**

Fugue and Chorale—organ (1917)
M-B. Dufourcet (r1992) *Concert*
(6/95) (PRIO) ① **PRCD422**
Hommage à Albert Roussel—piano (1928)
M. Fingerhut *Concert*
(9/88) (CHAN) ① **CHAN8578**
Paduana—cello, H181 (1945)
R. Wallfisch (r1991) *Concert*
(9/93) (TIMP) ① [4] **4C1012**
R. Wallfisch (r1991) *Concert*
(9/93) (TIMP) ① **1C1009**
Prélude, arioso et fughetta sur le nom de BACH—piano (1932)
M. Kazakevich (r1993) *Concert*
(9/94) (CONI) ① **CDCF235**
Scenic Railway—piano (1937)
B. Lerner *Concert*
(1/89) (ETCE) ① **KTC1061**
Sonata for Solo Violin, H143 (1940)
D-S. Kang (r1991) *Concert*
(9/93) (TIMP) ① [4] **4C1012**
D-S. Kang (r1991) *Concert*
(9/93) (TIMP) ① **1C1008**

SECTION IV: VOCAL AND CHORAL

Une Cantate de Noël—baritone, chorus and organ, H212 (1953)
J. Jindrák, Kühn Children's Chor, Czech Phil Chor, J. Tvrzský, Prague SO, S. Baudo *Jeanne d'Arc*.
(2/92) (SUPR) ① [2] **11 0557-2**
C. Maurane, ORTF Chor, ORTF Nat Orch, J. Martinon *Concert*
(3/92) (EMI) ① **CDM7 63944-2**
Chanson de Ronsard—1v, flute and string quartet, H54 (1924)
F. Kondo, A. Haraldsdottir, Ludwig Qt (r1991) *Concert*
(9/93) (TIMP) ① [4] **4C1012**
F. Kondo, A. Haraldsdottir, Ludwig Qt (r1991) *Concert*
(9/93) (TIMP) ① **1C1010**
3 Chansons de la Petite Sirène d'Anderson—voice, flute and strings, H63 (1924) (Wds. Morax)
1. Chanson des sirènes; 2. Berceuse de la Sirène; 3. Chanson de la poire.
F. Kondo, A. Haraldsdottir, Ludwig Qt (r1991) *Concert*
(9/93) (TIMP) ① [4] **4C1012**
F. Kondo, A. Haraldsdottir, Ludwig Qt (r1991) *Concert*
(9/93) (TIMP) ① **1C1010**
Jeanne d'Arc au bûcher—stage oratorio, H99 (1934-35) (Wds. Claudel)
Cpte M. Keller, G. Wilson, P-M. Escourrou, F. Pollet, M. Command, N. Stutzmann, French Rad Chor, FNO, S. Ozawa (pp1989)
(4/91) (DG) ① **429 412-2GH**
Cpte C. Château, A-M. Rodde, H. Brachet, P. di Proenza, Z. Jankovský, F. Loup, Kühn Children's Chor, Czech Phil Chor, Czech PO, S. Baudo *Cantate de Noël*. (2/92) (SUPR) ① [2] **11 0557-2**
Cpte J. Claus, B. Zintl, B. Remmert, J. Hammar, C. Hees, K. Paul, S. Altschul, H. Seezen, O. Schröder, T. Otto, R.F. Voss, Frankfurt Neeber-Schuler Chor, Hersfeld Children's Chor, Hersfeld Fest Chor, Cracow RSO, S. Heinrich (pp1991; Ger)
(12/93) (SCHW) ① **312922**
Pâques à New York—song fragments, H30 (1920) (Wds. B. Cendrars)
1. C'est à cette heure; 2. Faites, Seigneur; 3. Dic nobis Maria.
F. Kondo, Ludwig Qt (r1991) *Concert*
(9/93) (TIMP) ① [4] **4C1012**
F. Kondo, Ludwig Qt (r1991) *Concert*
(9/93) (TIMP) ① **1C1011**
3 Poèmes de Paul Fort—songs, H9 (1916)
1. Le chasseur perdu en forêt; 2. Cloche du soir; 3. Chanson de Fol.
3. S. Varcoe, G. Johnson *Concert*
(6/88) (HYPE) ① **CDA66248**
Le Roi David—dramatic psalm, H37 (1921) (Wds. Morax)
Cpte C. Eda-Pierre, M. Senn, T. Raffalli, D. Mesguich, A. Gaillard, Kühn Children's Chor, Czech Phil Chor, Czech PO, S. Baudo
(6/88) (SUPR) ① **11 0132-2**
Cpte H. Doublier, J. Brumaire, D. Scharley, J. Potier, E. Brasseur Chorale, Paris Op Orch, S. Baudo
(5/90) (ACCO) ① **20082-2**
Cpte A. Marc, S. Sullé, L. Dale, D. Mesguich, Saint-Denis Fest Chor, Lille Nat Orch, J-C. Casadesus (r1992)
(7/93) (EMI) ① **CDC7 54793-2**
Saluste du Bartas—6 Villanelles, H152 (1941)
1. Le château du Bartas; 2. Tout le long de la Baïse; 3. Le départ; 4. La promenade; 5. Nérac en fête; 6. Duo.
C. Robbin, M. McMahon (r1985) *Concert*
(7/94) (MARQ) ① **ERAD113**

SECTION V: STAGE WORKS

Antigone—incidental music for Cocteau's play (1922)
H. Holliger, H. Holliger, U. Holliger (r1991) *Concert*
(9/93) (PHIL) ① **434 105-2PH**

Les aventures du roi Pausole—operetta: 3 acts (1930—Paris) (Lib. A. Willemetz, after Louÿs)
Cpte G. Bacquier, M. Sénéchal, C. Barbaux, R. Macias, B. Antoine, R. Yakar, M. Barscha, C. Ossola, B. Fournier, Basle Madrigalists, Swiss Workshop PO, M. Venzago (r1992) (9/94) (MGB) ① [2] **CD6115**
Overture; Ballet Odeon Grand Orch, A. Honegger (r1930) *Concert* (4/94) (MUSI) ① **MACD-767**

Crime et Châtiment—concert suite from film score (1934)
1. Généric; 2. Raskolnikov—Sonion; 3. Départ pour le crime; 4. Meutre d'Elisabeth; 5. Visite nocturne—Final.
J. Tchamkerten, Bratislava RSO, Adriano (r1992) *Concert* (6/94) (MARC) ① **8 223466**

Le Déserteur ou Je t'attendrai—fragment symphonique from film score (1939)
J. Tchamkerten, Adriano (r1993) *Concert* (6/94) (MARC) ① **8 223466**

Le Dit des Jeux du Monde—concert suite (1918)
P. Dechorgnat, J. Ferrandis, H. Noël, J-J. Wiederker, J-J. Wiederker CO, F. Bouaniche (r1992) *Concert* (6/95) (SCHW) ① **310652**

Farinet ou L'Or dans la Montagne—concert suite from film score (1938)
1. Générique; 2. Brume du matin; 3. Fuite et mort de Farinet; 4. Final.
J. Tchamkerten, Adriano (r1992) *Concert* (6/94) (MARC) ① **8 223466**

Le Grand Barrage—image musicale from film score (1942)
J. Tchamkerten, Adriano (r1992) *Concert* (6/94) (MARC) ① **8 223466**

Horace victorieux—mimed symphony: ballet (1920)
Toulouse Capitole Orch, M. Plasson (r1991) *Concert* (9/93) (DG) ① **435 438-2GH**

L' Idée—film score (1934)
J. Tchamkerten, Bratislava RSO, Adriano (r1992) *Concert* (6/94) (MARC) ① **8 223466**

Les Misérables—film score, H88a (1934)
EXCERPTS: 1. Générique; 2. Jean Valjean sur la route; 3. Evocation des forçats; 4. Une tempête sous un crâne; 5. Fantine; 6. Fuite de Jean Valjean; 7. Cosette et Marius; 8. La foire à Montfermeil; 9. Le Luxembourg; 10. Le jardin de la rue Plumet—Le convoi nocturne (orch Adriano); 11. L'Emeute; 12. Mort d'Eponine; 13. L'Assaut; 14. Dans les égouts; 15. Musique chez Gillenormand; 16. Solitude; 17. Mort de Jean Valjean.
Cpte Bratislava RSO, Adriano (3/91) (MARC) ① **8 223181**
1, 11, 14, 15, 17. Bratislava RSO, Adriano *Concert* (4/89) (MARC) ① **8 223134**

Napoléon—film score, H64 (1927)
Suite d'orchestre; 1. Calme; 2. La romance de violine; 3. Danse des enfants; 4. Interlude et final; 5. Chaconne de l'Imperatrice; 6. Napoléon; 7. Les ombres; 8. Les mendiants de la gloire.
Bratislava RSO, Adriano *Concert* (4/89) (MARC) ① **8 223134**
3, 5, 6. USSR Ministry of Culture Chbr Ch, USSR Ministry of Culture SO, G. Rozhdestvensky (ed. Rozhdestvensky) (10/88) (OLYM) ① **OCD212**
7. Monte Carlo PO, M. Constant *Concert* (2/94) (ERAT) ① **2292-45862-2**

Phoedre—incidental music (1926) (Text D'Annunzio)
EXCERPTS: 1. Prélude; 2. Imprécation de Thésée; 3. Mort de Phaedre.
USSR Ministry of Culture Chbr Ch, USSR Ministry of Culture SO, G. Rozhdestvensky (ed. Rozhdestvensky) *Concert* (10/88) (OLYM) ① **OCD212**
1-3. Monte Carlo PO, M. Constant *Concert* (2/94) (ERAT) ① **2292-45862-2**

La Roue—Overture from the film score, H44 (1923) (Overture only survives)
Bratislava RSO, Adriano *Concert* (4/89) (MARC) ① **8 223134**

HOOK, James (1746–1827) England

SECTION I: ORCHESTRAL

6 Concertos for the Harpsichord or Forte-Piano, Op. 1
EXCERPTS: 5. D.
5. P. Nicholson (kybds/dir), Parley of Instr, P. Holman (r1993; arr Holman) *Concert* (8/94) (HYPE) ① **CDA66700**

SECTION III: INSTRUMENTAL

Voluntary in C minor—organ (c1815)
J. Bate *Concert* (11/91) (UNIC) ① **DKPCD9106**

SECTION IV: VOCAL AND CHORAL

The Emigrant—song (c1790s) (Wds. Amelia Opie)
R. Müller, F. Kelly *Concert* (12/91) (HYPE) ① **CDA66497**

Hours of Love—collection of sonnets (pub 1792)
M. Ritchie, Philh, L. Collingwood (r1948; arr Frankel) *Concert* (4/92) (EMI) ① [7] **CHS7 69741-2(1)**

The Lass of Richmond Hill—song (1789) (Wds. cpsr)
J. Potter, Broadside Band, J. Barlow (r1992; arr J. Barlow) *Concert* (6/93) (SAYD) ① **CD-SDL400**

'Twas within a mile—song
A. Patti, L. Ronald (r1906) *Concert* (4/90) (PEAR) ① **GEMMCD9312**
A. Patti, A. Barili (r1906) *Concert* (7/93) (NIMB) ① [2] **NI7840/1**

HOPKINS, Edward John (1818–1901) England

SECTION III: INSTRUMENTAL

Andante grazioso—organ
Margaret Phillips *Concert* (7/91) (GAMU) ① **GAMCD522**

HORDER, Mervyn (b 1910)

SECTION IV: VOCAL AND CHORAL

5 Songs (Wds. A. E. Housman)
1. Loveliest of trees; 2. Goldcups; 3. The Lent Lily; 4. When I was one and twenty; 5. White in the Moon.
5. A. Rolfe Johnson, G. Johnson (r c1994) *Concert* (8/95) (HYPE) ① [2] **CDA66471/2**

7 Songs (Wds. Shakespeare)
1. Blow! Blow!; 2. Under the Greenwood Tree; 3. It was a lover and his lass; 4. O Mistress Mine; 5. The Wind and the Rain; 6. Sigh no more, ladies; 7. Who is Silvia?
7. A. Rolfe Johnson, G. Johnson *Concert* (5/92) (HYPE) ① **CDA66480**

HORENSTEIN, Jascha (1898–1973) Russia

SECTION IV: VOCAL AND CHORAL

Interview between Jascha Horenstein and Alan Blyth (early 1970s) (recorded by the BBC)
J. Horenstein, A. Blyth *Brahms: Symphony 2.* (9/91) (UNIC) ① **UKCD2036**

HORNEMAN, (Christian Drederick) Emil (1840–1906) Denmark

SECTION V: STAGE WORKS

Gurre Suite—orchestral suite after incidental music (1902)
Aarhus RAM Orch, S.K. Hansen (r1994) *Concert* (7/95) (KONT) ① **32194**

HORNER, James (b 1953) USA

SECTION IV: VOCAL AND CHORAL

If we hold on together—song from the film 'The Land Before Time' (1988) (Wds. W. Jennings)
D. Ross, Gumpoldskirchner Kinderchor, Vienna SO, V. Sutej (pp1992; arr Schifrin) *Concert* (12/93) (SONY) ① **SK53358**

SECTION V: STAGE WORKS

Krull—film score (1983)
EXCERPTS: 1. Main Title & Colwyn's Arrival; 2. Riding the Fire Mares; 3. Slayer's Attack; 4. Widow's Web; 5. Widow's Lulaby; 6. Destruction of the Black Fortress; 7. Epilogue.
1. OST *Concert* (5/93) (SILV) ① **SILVAD3003**

Red Heat—film score (1988)
OST, J. Horner (r1988) (4/89) (VIR2) ① **CDV2558**

Thunderheart—film score (1992)
EXCERPTS: 1. Main Title; 2. The Oglala Sioux; 3. Jimmy's Escape; 4. Proud Nation; 5. Evidence; 6. First Vision; 7. Ghost Dance; 8. The Goons; 9. Medicine Man; 10. My People, Wounded Knee; 11. Thunder Heart; 12. Run for the Stronghold; 13. This Land is Not for Sale & End Titles.
1-13. OST, J. Horner (r1992) (5/93) (INTD) ① **MAF7027D**

Willow—film score (1988)
EXCERPTS: 1. Elora Danan; 2. Escape from the Tavern; 3. Willow's Journey Begins; 4. Canyon of Mazes; 5. Tir Asleen; 6. Willow's Theme; 7. Bavmorda's Spell is Cast; 8. Willow the Sorcerer.
1-8. OST, Wimbledon King's Coll Sch Boys' Ch, LSO, J. Horner (r1988) (4/89) (VIR2) ① **CDV2538**

HOROVITZ, Joseph (b 1926) Austria/Britain

SECTION I: ORCHESTRAL

Concerto for Euphonium and Brass Band (1972)
R. Childs, Black Dyke Mills Band, P. Parkes (r1989) *Concert* (10/94) (CHAN) ① **CHAN4523**

SECTION II: CHAMBER

Sonatina for clarinet and piano (1981)
G. de Peyer, G. Pryor *Concert* (11/87) (CHAN) ① **CHAN8549**
M. Khouri, P. Pettinger *Concert* (6/92) (CNTI) ① **CCD1038**

Variations on a theme of Paganini—brass quartet (1980s)
City of London Brass Qt *Concert* (3/90) (LDR) ① **LDRCD1012**

HOROWITZ, Vladimir (1904–1989) Ukraine/USA

SECTION III: INSTRUMENTAL

Moment exotique (Danse excentrique)—piano
V. Horowitz (r1930) *Concert* (1/93) (APR) ① [2] **APR7014**
V. Horowitz (r1930) *Concert* (1/93) (RCA) ① **GD60526**
V. Horowitz (r1925: pf roll) *Concert* (7/93) (COND) ① **690.07.009**

Variations on a Theme from Bizet's 'Carmen'—piano
V. Horowitz (r1928) *Concert* (1/93) (APR) ① [2] **APR7014**
V. Horowitz (r1928) *Concert* (1/93) (RCA) ① **GD60526**
V. Horowitz (r1928: pf roll) *Concert* (7/93) (COND) ① **690.07.009**
V. Horowitz (pp1968) *Concert* (7/94) (SONY) ① **SK53465**

Waltz in F minor—piano
V. Horowitz (r1929: pf roll) *Concert* (7/93) (COND) ① **690.07.009**

HORSLEY, William (1774–1858) England

SECTION IV: VOCAL AND CHORAL

Come gentle zephyr—partsong (Wds. Raunie)
PCA, M. Brown *Concert* (3/87) (CONI) ① **CDCF145**
Hilliard Ens, L-L. Kiesel *Concert* (12/91) (MERI) ① **DUOCD89009**

There is a green hill far away—hymn (Wds. Alexander)
St Paul's Cath Ch, C. Dearnley, John Scott *Concert* (7/90) (HYPE) ① **CDH88036**

HORTIZ, Joseph (19th–20th Cent) USA

SECTION IV: VOCAL AND CHORAL

Sing Me a Song, Fritz—song for the show 'Our Friend Fritz' (1908)
J. Hortiz, Broadway Cast (r1908) *Concert* (5/94) (PEAR) ① [3] **GEMMCDS9050/2(2)**

HOSCHNA, Karl (1877–1911) USA

SECTION V: STAGE WORKS

Madame Sherry—operetta (1910—New York)
(Lib. Hauerbach)
Ev'ry little movement L. Tetrazzini, T. Amici (Fr: r1922) *Concert*
(9/92) (EMI) ① [3] **CHS7 63802-2(2)**
Je ne sais comment L. Tetrazzini, orch (r1922)
Concert (9/92) (PEAR) ① **GEMMCD9225**
Three Twins—musical show (1908—New York) (Lyrics Otto Harbach)
EXCERPTS: 1. Gunga Din (Rudyard Kipling).
1. C. Crawford, Orig Broadway Cast (r1910) *Concert*
(5/94) (PEAR) ① [3] **GEMMCDS9053/5**

HOTTETERRE, Jacques(-Martin) (1674–1763) France

SECTION II: CHAMBER

Airs and Brunettes—flute, viol and continuo
R. Brown, M Caudle, J. Johnstone *Concert*
(2/94) (CHAN) ① **CHAN0544**
Deuxième livres de pièces—flûte (other instruments) and continuo (1715)
Nos 1, 2. P. Dombrecht, W. Kuijken, R. Kohnen
Concert (9/90) (ACCE) ① **ACC8537D**
Première livre de pièces—flûte (other instruments) and continuo, Op. 2 (1708)
1. F. Brüggen, K. Boeke (r1970) *Concert*
(10/95) (TELD) ① **4509-97468-2**
Troisième suitte de pièces—2 fls/recs/obs/musettes, Op. 8 (pub 1722)
2. Prélude in G minor.
Royal Trio (r1991) *Concert*
(8/93) (DHM) ① **05472 77176-2**

SECTION III: INSTRUMENTAL

Rochers, vous etes sourds in G minor—air et double: flute (after Lully)
W. Hazelzet (r1991) *Concert*
(8/93) (DHM) ① **05472 77176-2**

HOUBART, François-Henri (b 1952) France

SECTION III: INSTRUMENTAL

Improvisation on Gaudens, gaudebo and Laetare Jerusalem—organ
F-H. Houbart *Concert* (3/86) (PIER) ① **PV784041**

HOVALT, Lauritz (1885–1953) Denmark

SECTION IV: VOCAL AND CHORAL

Christiansborg—song (Wds. H. Carlsen & K. Nathansen)
L. Melchior, Orch (r c1921) *Concert*
(8/88) (DANA) ① [2] **DACOCD311/2**

HOVHANESS, Alan (b 1911) USA

SECTION I: ORCHESTRAL

Alleluia and Fugue—strings, Op. 40b (1941)
Seattle SO, G. Schwarz (r1994) *Concert*
(7/94) (DELO) ① **DE3157**
Philh, D. Amos (r1988) *Concert*
(4/95) (CRYS) ① **Crystal CD810**
Anahid—chamber orchestra, Op. 57 (1944)
Philh, D. Amos (r1988) *Concert*
(4/95) (CRYS) ① **Crystal CD810**
And God Created Great Whales—taped whale song and orchestra, Op. 229/1 (1970)
Seattle SO, G. Schwarz (r1993) *Concert*
(7/94) (DELO) ① **DE3157**
Philh, D. Amos (r1988) *Concert*
(4/95) (CRYS) ① **Crystal CD810**
Celestial Fantasy—strings, Op. 44 (1935, orch 1944)
Seattle SO, G. Schwarz (r1993) *Concert*
(7/94) (DELO) ① **DE3157**
Concerto No. 8—orchestra, Op. 117 (1957)
Philh, D. Amos (r1988) *Concert*
(4/95) (CRYS) ① **Crystal CD810**
Elibris—flute & string orchestra, Op. 50 (1944)
C. Messiter, Philh, D. Amos (r1988) *Concert*
(4/95) (CRYS) ① **Crystal CD810**

Fantasy on Japanese Woodprints—marimba and orchestra, Op. 211 (1965)
R. van Sice, RTE SO, C. Pearce *Concert*
(6/90) (ETCE) ① **KTC1085**
R. Johnson, Seattle SO, G. Schwarz (r1994) *Concert*
(7/95) (DELO) ① **DE3168**
Haroutiun—trumpet and strings, Op. 71 (1948)
1. Aria; 2. Fugue.
1. C. Gekker, Manhattan CO, R. A. Clark (r1993)
Concert (7/94) (KOCH) ① **37221-2**
Lousadzak—piano and string orchestra, Op. 48 (1944)
K. Jarrett, American Cpsrs Orch, D.R. Davies
Concert (5/93) (MUSM) ① **7021-2**
Meditation on Orpheus—orchestra, Op. 155 (1957)
Seattle SO, G. Schwarz (r1994) *Concert*
(7/95) (DELO) ① **DE3168**
Prayer of St Gregory—trumpet & strings, Op. 62b (1946)
C. Gekker, Manhattan CO, R. A. Clark (r1993)
Concert (7/94) (KOCH) ① **37221-2**
Seattle SO, G. Schwarz (r1993) *Concert*
(7/94) (DELO) ① **DE3157**
Prelude and Quadruple Fugue, Op. 128 (1936, orch 1954)
Seattle SO, G. Schwarz (r1993) *Concert*
(7/94) (DELO) ① **DE3157**
Requiem and Resurrection—brass choir & percussion, Op. 224 (1967)
N. Jersey Wind SO, A. Hovhaness (r1970s)
Symphony 19. (4/95) (CRYS) ① **Crystal CD805**
Return and Rebuild the Desolate Places—trumpet and wind orchestra, Op. 213 (1944 rev 1965)
C. Gekker, Manhattan CO, R. A. Clark (r1993)
Concert (7/94) (KOCH) ① **37221-2**
Symphony No. 1, 'Exile', Op. 17/2 (1936)
Seattle SO, G. Schwarz (r1994) *Concert*
(7/95) (DELO) ① **DE3168**
Symphony No. 2, 'Mysterious mountain', Op. 132 (1955)
American Cpsrs Orch, D.R. Davies *Concert*
(5/93) (MUSM) ① **7021-2**
Seattle SO, G. Schwarz (r1994) *Concert*
(7/94) (DELO) ① **DE3157**
Chicago SO, F. Reiner (r1958) *Concert*
(9/95) (RCA) ① **09026 61957-2**
Symphony No. 6, '(The) Celestial Gate'—chamber orchestra, Op. 173 (1959 rev 1960)
Manhattan CO, R. A. Clark (r1993) *Concert*
(7/94) (KOCH) ① **37221-2**
Symphony No. 19, 'Vishnu', Op. 217 (1967)
Sevan PO, A. Hovhaness (r1970s) *Requiem and Resurrection, Op. 224.*
(4/95) (CRYS) ① **Crystal CD805**
Symphony No. 22, 'City of Light', Op. 236 (1971)
Seattle SO, A. Hovhaness (r1992) *Symphony 50.*
(12/93) (DELO) ① **DE3137**
Symphony No. 39—guitar and orchestra, Op. 321 (1978)
M. Long, KBS SO, V. Jordania (r1993) *Concert*
(7/94) (KOCH) ① **37208-2**
Symphony No. 46, 'To the Green Mountains', Op. 347 (1980)
KBS SO, V. Jordania (r1993) *Concert*
(7/94) (KOCH) ① **37208-2**
Symphony No. 50, 'Mount St Helens', Op. 360 (1983)
Seattle SO, G. Schwarz (r1992) *Symphony 22.*
(12/93) (DELO) ① **DE3137**

SECTION II: CHAMBER

4 Bagatelles—string quartet, Op. 30 (1964)
Shanghai Qt (r1994) *Concert*
(3/95) (DELO) ① **DE3162**
Mountains and Rivers without End—chamber symphony: 10 instruments, Op. 225 (1968)
Manhattan CO, R. A. Clark (r1993) *Concert*
(7/94) (KOCH) ① **37221-2**
String Quartet No. 1, 'Jupiter', Op. 8 (1936)
Shanghai Qt (r1994) *Concert*
(3/95) (DELO) ① **DE3162**
String Quartet No. 2, Op. 147 (1951)
EXCERPTS: 1. Spirit Murmurs; 5. Gamelan in Sosi Style; 7. Hymn.
1, 5, 7. Shanghai Qt (r1994) *Concert*
(3/95) (DELO) ① **DE3162**

String Quartet No. 3, 'Reflections on my Childhood', Op. 208/1 (1964) (Childhood Fantasia in New England)
Shanghai Qt (r1994) *Concert*
(3/95) (DELO) ① **DE3162**
String Quartet No. 4, 'The Ancient Tree', Op. 208/2 (1964) (Under the Ancient Maple Tree)
Shanghai Qt (r1994) *Concert*
(3/95) (DELO) ① **DE3162**

SECTION III: INSTRUMENTAL

Achtamar—piano, Op. 64/1 (1948)
M. Rosen *Concert* (6/93) (KOCH) ① **37195-2**
Fantasy on an Ossetin Tune—piano, Op. 85 (1951)
M. Rosen *Concert* (6/93) (KOCH) ① **37195-2**
2 Ghazals—piano, Op. 36a-b (1963)
Op. 36a M. Rosen *Concert*
(6/93) (KOCH) ① **37195-2**
2 Macedonia Mountain Dances—piano, Op. 144 (1962)
M. Rosen *Concert* (6/93) (KOCH) ① **37195-2**
Orbit No. 2—piano, Op. 102 (1952)
M. Rosen *Concert* (6/93) (KOCH) ① **37195-2**
Slumber Song—piano, Op. 52/2 (1938)
M. Rosen *Concert* (6/93) (KOCH) ① **37195-2**
Sonata for Piano, 'Fred the cat', Op. 301 (1977)
M. Rosen *Concert* (6/93) (KOCH) ① **37195-2**
Sonata for Piano, 'Mount Chocorua', Op. 335 (1979)
M. Rosen *Concert* (6/93) (KOCH) ① **37195-2**
Sonata for Piano, 'Prospect Hill', Op. 346 (1981)
M. Rosen *Concert* (6/93) (KOCH) ① **37195-2**
3 Sonatas for Piano, Op. 299 (1977)
2. Mount Ossipee.
2. M. Rosen *Concert* (6/93) (KOCH) ① **37195-2**

SECTION IV: VOCAL AND CHORAL

The Rubaiyat of Omar Khayyam—narrator and orchestra, Op. 282 (1975)
M. York, D. Schmidt, Seattle SO, G. Schwarz (r1994)
Concert (7/95) (DELO) ① **DE3168**

HØVLAND, Egil (b 1924) Norway

SECTION III: INSTRUMENTAL

Toccata - Now thank we all our God—organ (1973)
C. Herrick *Concert* (7/86) (HYPE) ① **CDA66121**

HOWARD, Brian (b 1951) Australia

SECTION I: ORCHESTRAL

Sun and steel—12 solo instruments (1986)
Soloists of Australia, R.Thomas (vn/dir) (pp1986)
Concert (4/87) (CHAN) ① **CHAN8498**

HOWARTH, Elgar (b 1935) England

SECTION I: ORCHESTRAL

American Dream—brass band (1976)
Britannia Building Soc Band, H. Snell *Concert*
(7/93) (DOYE) ① **DOYCD011**
The Bandsman's Tale—brass band (1983)
Britannia Building Soc Band, H. Snell *Concert*
(7/93) (DOYE) ① **DOYCD011**
Cantabile for John Fletcher—two euphoniums and brass band
R. Childs, N. Childs, Britannia Building Soc Band, H. Snell *Concert* (2/91) (DOYE) ① **DOYCD002**
Concerto for Trombone and Orchestra (1958)
C. Lindberg, BBC Nat Orch of Wales, G. Llewellyn
(r1993) *Concert* (10/95) (BIS) ① **BIS-CD658**
In Memoriam R. K.—brass band (1976)
Britannia Building Soc Band, H. Snell *Concert*
(7/93) (DOYE) ① **DOYCD011**
Legends—four cornets and brass band (1987)
W. Lang, M. Murphy, J. Shepherd, P. McCann, Black Dyke Mills Band, P. Parkes (pp1987) *Concert*
(11/93) (CHAN) ① **CHAN4513**

HOWELLS, Herbert (Norman) (1892–1983) England

SECTION I: ORCHESTRAL

Concerto for Piano and Orchestra No. 2 in C minor (1924)
K. Stott, RLPO, V. Handley *Concert*
(3/93) (HYPE) ① **CDA66610**

Concerto for Strings (1939)
RLPO, V. Handley *Concert*
(3/93) (HYPE) ① **CDA66610**
CLS, R. Hickox (r1991) *Concert*
(7/93) (CHAN) ① **CHAN9161**

3 Dances—violin and orchestra (1915)
M. Stewart, RLPO, V. Handley *Concert*
(3/93) (HYPE) ① **CDA66610**

Elegy for Viola, String Quartet and String Orchestra (1917)
CLS, R. Hickox (r1991) *Concert*
(7/93) (CHAN) ① **CHAN9161**

Pageantry—suite: brass band (1937)
Black Dyke Mills Band, G. Brand *Concert*
(9/93) (RSR) ① **RSRD1002**

Serenade for String Orchestra (1917)
CLS, R. Hickox (r1991) *Concert*
(7/93) (CHAN) ① **CHAN9161**

Suite for String Orchestra (1942)
CLS, R. Hickox (r1991) *Concert*
(7/93) (CHAN) ① **CHAN9161**

SECTION II: CHAMBER

Cradle Song—violin and piano, Op. 9/1 (1918)
P. Barritt, C. Edwards (r1993) *Concert*
(3/94) (HYPE) ① **CDA66665**

Fantasy Quartet—strings, Op. 25 (1917)
Lyric Qt (r1992) *Concert*
(10/93) (METI) ① **MSVCD92003**

Piano Quartet in A minor, Op. 21 (1916)
Lyric Qt, A. West (r1992) *Concert*
(10/93) (METI) ① **MSVCD92003**

3 Pieces—violin and piano, Op. 28 (1917)
P. Barritt, C. Edwards (r1993) *Concert*
(3/94) (HYPE) ① **CDA66665**

Rhapsodic Quintet—clarinet, 2 violins, viola, cello, Op. 31 (1919)
M. Collins, Lyric Qt (r1992) *Concert*
(10/93) (METI) ① **MSVCD92003**

Sonata for Clarinet and Piano (1949)
T. King, C. Benson *Concert*
(11/89) (HYPE) ① **CDA66044**

Sonata for Oboe and Piano (1943)
N. Daniel, J. Drake *Concert*
(10/93) (LEMA) ① **LC44801**

Sonata for Violin and Piano No. 1, Op. 18 (1917-19)
P. Barritt, C. Edwards (r1993) *Concert*
(3/94) (HYPE) ① **CDA66665**

Sonata for Violin and Piano No. 2, Op. 26 (1917)
P. Barritt, C. Edwards (r1993) *Concert*
(3/94) (HYPE) ① **CDA66665**

Sonata for Violin and Piano No. 3, Op. 38 (1923)
P. Barritt, C. Edwards (r1993) *Concert*
(3/94) (HYPE) ① **CDA66665**

String Quartet, 'in Gloucestershire', 1923
Divertimenti (r1984) Dyson: *Rhapsodies.*
(6/89) (HYPE) ① **CDA66139**

SECTION III: INSTRUMENTAL

Chosen Tune—piano (1920)
M. Fingerhut (r1993) *Concert*
(9/94) (CHAN) ① **CHAN9273**

Cobler's Hornpipe—piano (1926) (founded on tunes from Playford's 'English Dancing Master')
M. Fingerhut (r1993) *Concert*
(9/94) (CHAN) ① **CHAN9273**

Flourish for a bidding—organ (1969)
P. Kenyon (ed Wells) *Concert*
(4/89) (HERA) ① **HAVPCD115**
E. Higginbottom *Concert*
(3/90) (CRD) ① **CRD3454**

Gadabout—piano (pub 1928)
M. Fingerhut (r1993) *Concert*
(9/94) (CHAN) ① **CHAN9273**

Howells' Clavichord—20 pieces for clavichord or piano (Bk.1 1941; Bk.2 1961)
EXCERPTS: BOOK ONE: 1. Goff's Fireside; 2. Patrick's Siciliano; 3. Jacob's Brawl; 4. Dart's Sarabande; 5. Arnold's Antic; 6. Andrews' Air; 7. Boult's Brangill; 8. Rubbra's Soliloquy; 9. Newman's Flight; 10. Dyson's Delight. BOOK TWO: 11. E.B.'s

Fanfarando; 12. Ralph's Pavane; 13. Ralph's Galliard; 14. Finzi's Rest; 15. Berkeley's Hunt; 16. Malcolm's Vision; 17. Bliss's Ballet; 18. Julian's Dream; 19. Jacques's Mask; 20. Walton' Toye.
J. McCabe (r1993) *Lambert's Clavichord.*
(8/94) (HYPE) ① **CDA66689**
3, 20. E. Higginbottom *Concert*
(3/90) (CRD) ① **CRD3454**

Intrata in D—organ (1941)
P. Kenyon (ed Wells) *Concert*
(4/89) (HERA) ① **HAVPCD115**

Lambert's Clavichord—12 pieces for clavichord, Op. 41 (1927)
EXCERPTS: 1. Lambert's Fireside; 2. Fellowes's Delight; 3. Hughes's Ballet; 4. Wortham's Grounde; 5. Sargent's Fantastic Sprite; 6. Foss's Dump; 7. My Lord Sandwich's Dreame; 8. Samuel's Air; 9. De la Mare's Pavane; 10. Sir Hugh's Galliard; 11. H. H. His Fancy; 12. Sir Richard's Toye.
J. McCabe (r1993) *Howells' Clavichord.*
(8/94) (HYPE) ① **CDA66689**
1, 3, 9, 10. M. Fingerhut (r1993) *Concert*
(9/94) (CHAN) ① **CHAN9273**
9. E. Higginbottom *Concert*
(3/90) (CRD) ① **CRD3454**

Musica sine Nomine—piano (1959)
M. Fingerhut (r1993) *Concert*
(9/94) (CHAN) ① **CHAN9273**

6 Pieces—organ (1940)
1. Preludio, 'Sine nomine'; 2. Saraband for the Morning of Easter; 3. Master Tallis's Testament; 4. Fugue, Chorale and Epilogue; 5. Saraband in modo elegiaco; 6. Paean.
R.B. Dobey *Organ Sonata 2.*
(4/89) (PROR) ① **CD7005**
1. E. Higginbottom *Concert*
(12/91) (CRD) ① **CRD3455**
3. C. Dearnley *Concert*
(9/88) (HYPE) ① **CDA66260**
3. A. Lumsden *Concert*
(4/91) (GUIL) ① **GRCD7025**
6. E. Higginbottom *Concert*
(12/91) (CRD) ① **CRD3455**

3 Pieces—piano, Op. 14 (1918-20)
1. Rhapsody; 2. Jackanapes; 3. Procession.
M. Fingerhut (r1993) *Concert*
(9/94) (CHAN) ① **CHAN9273**

3 Psalm-Preludes (Set 1)—organ, Op. 32 (1915-16)
1. Psalm 34 v6; 2. Psalm37 v11; 3. Psalm 23 v4.
C. Dearnley *Concert* (9/90) (HYPE) ① **CDA66394**
G. Green *Concert* (3/93) (NAXO) ① **8 550582**
S. Cleobury (r1993) *Concert*
(6/95) (PRIO) ① **PRCD480**
1. E. Higginbottom *Concert*
(12/91) (CRD) ① **CRD3455**
1. C. Hughes (pp1991 with Choral Evensong) *Concert* (10/92) (EMI) ① **CDC7 54412-2**
2. S. Cleobury *Concert*
(7/92) (ARGO) ① **430 205-2ZH**
3. J. Lancelot *Concert* (8/88) (PRIO) ① **PRCD228**

3 Psalm-Preludes (Set 2)—organ (1938-39)
1. De profundis clamavi ad te, Domine (Psalm 130 v1); 2. Yea the darkness is no darkness (Pslam 139 v11); 3. Sing unto Him a new song (Psalm 33 v3).
C. Dearnley *Concert* (9/90) (HYPE) ① **CDA66394**
S. Cleobury (r1993) *Concert*
(6/95) (PRIO) ① **PRCD480**
1. C. Dearnley *Concert*
(9/88) (HYPE) ① **CDA66260**

3 Rhapsodies, Op. 17 (1915-18)
1. No 1; 2. No 2; 3. No 3; 4. No 4.
C. Dearnley *Concert* (9/90) (HYPE) ① **CDA66394**
S. Cleobury (r1993) *Concert*
(6/95) (PRIO) ① **PRCD480**
3. A. Partington *Concert* (9/90) (CARL) ① **PCD937**
3. S. Cleobury *Concert*
(7/92) (ARGO) ① **430 205-2ZH**

Rhapsody No. 4 in C—organ (1958)
S. Cleobury (r1993) *Concert*
(6/95) (PRIO) ① **PRCD480**

Sarum sketches—piano (1943)
1. Ooce March; 2. The Drudge talks to himself; 3. The Drudge forgotten; 4. Ooce reads 'Arabian Nights'; 5. Ooce at leisure; 6. Charades.
M. Fingerhut (r1993) *Concert*
(9/94) (CHAN) ① **CHAN9273**

6 Short Pieces—organ
1. Tranquillo, ma con moto; 2. Allegro Scherzando; 3. Aria; 4. Allegro impetuoso; 5. Chorale; 6. Quasi Lento.
P. Kenyon (ed Wells) *Concert*
(4/89) (HERA) ① **HAVPCD115**

Siciliano for a High Ceremony—organ (1953)
A. Fletcher *Concert* (11/91) (MIRA) ① **MRCD903**

2 Slow airs—organ
P. Kenyon (arr Wells) *Concert*
(4/89) (HERA) ① **HAVPCD115**

Slow Dance, 'Double the Cape'—piano (1926) (founded on tunes from Palyford's 'English Dancing Master')
M. Fingerhut (r1993) *Concert*
(9/94) (CHAN) ① **CHAN9273**

Snapshots—piano, Op. 30 (1916-18)
1. The Street Dances; 2. The Polar Bear; 3. Wee Willie Winkee.
M. Fingerhut (r1993) *Concert*
(9/94) (CHAN) ① **CHAN9273**

Sonata No. 2—organ (1933)
R.B. Dobey *Pieces.* (4/89) (PROR) ① **CD7005**

Sonatina—piano (1971)
1-4. M. Fingerhut (r1993) *Concert*
(9/94) (CHAN) ① **CHAN9273**

St Louis comes to Clifton—organ (1977)
P. Kenyon (ed Wells) *Concert*
(4/89) (HERA) ① **HAVPCD115**
E. Higginbottom *Concert*
(3/90) (CRD) ① **CRD3454**

SECTION IV: VOCAL AND CHORAL

All my hope on God is founded—hymn
Cambridge Sngrs, J. Rutter, W. Marshall *Concert*
(12/92) (CLLE) ① **COLCD118**

Behold, O God our defender—choir and orchestra/organ (1953)
St Paul's Cath Ch, C. Dearnley, John Scott *Concert*
(9/88) (HYPE) ① **CDA66260**
New College Ch, E. Higginbottom *Concert*
(12/91) (CRD) ① **CRD3455**
Westminster Abbey Ch, ECO, M. Neary (r1993/4) *Concert* (9/94) (CNTO) ① **CSACD3050**

Blaweary—song: 1v and piano (Wds. W W Gibson)
C. Pierard, J. Drake (r1992) *Concert*
(8/94) (CHAN) ① [2] **CHAN9185/6**

By the Hearth-Stone—song: 1v and piano (Wds. H Newbolt)
C. Pierard, J. Drake (r1992) *Concert*
(8/94) (CHAN) ① [2] **CHAN9185/6**

3 Children's Songs—1v and piano (Wds. C Rossetti)
1. Eight o'clock, the postman's knock; 2. The days are clear; 3. Mother, shake the cherry-tree.
L. Dawson, J. Drake (r1992) *Concert*
(8/94) (CHAN) ① [2] **CHAN9185/6**

Come, my soul—anthem: SATB (1977) (Wds. J. Newton)
Magdalen Oxford Coll Ch, J. Harper *Concert*
(11/91) (ABBE) ① **CDCA915**
Finzi Sngrs, P. Spicer *Concert*
(12/92) (CHAN) ① **CHAN9021**

Come sing and Dance—song (1928)
F. Lott, G. Johnson *Concert*
(7/90) (CHAN) ① **CHAN8722**
Sarah Walker, R. Vignoles *Concert*
(10/92) (CRD) ① **CRD3473**
C. Pierard, J. Drake (r1992) *Concert*
(8/94) (CHAN) ① [2] **CHAN9185/6**
S. Leonard, M. Martineau (r1993) *Concert*
(3/95) (UNIT) ① **88016-2**

Coventry Antiphon, 'My house shall be called'—anthem (1961) (Wds. from an inscription in Coventry Cathedral)
Llandaff Cath Ch, M. Smith, M. Hoeg (r1994) *Concert*
(10/95) (PRIO) ① **PRCD510**

An English Mass—4vv (1956)
Liverpool Phil Ch, RLPO, V. Handley *Hymnus Paradisi.* (5/92) (HYPE) ① **CDA66488**

Evening Service, 'Chichester Service'—4vv & organ
1. Magnificat; 2. Nunc Dimittis.
Oxford Queen's Coll Ch, M. Owens, D. Went *Concert*
(5/93) (ASV) ① **CDDCA851**

Evening Service, 'Gloucester Service'—4vv & organ (1946)
1. Magnificat; 2. Nunc Dimittis.
Gloucester Cath Ch, J. Sanders, M. Lee (r1994) *Concert* (4/95) (PRIO) ① **PRCD494**
1. Cambridge Sngrs, J. Rutter, W. Marshall *Concert*
(12/92) (CLLE) ① **COLCD118**
1, 2. St Paul's Cath Ch, C. Dearnley, John Scott *Concert* (1/89) (HYPE) ① **CDA66305**
1, 2. King's College Ch, S. Cleobury, C. Hughes (pp1991 with Choral Evensong) *Concert*
(10/92) (EMI) ① **CDC7 54412-2**

Evening Service in G—4vv & organ
1. Magnificat; 2. Nunc dimittis.
Lichfield Cath Ch, A. Lumsden, M. Shepherd (r1994) *Concert* (10/95) (PRIO) ① **PRCD505**

Evening Service, 'New College Service'—4vv & organ (1953)
New College Ch, D. Burchell, E. Higginbottom
Concert (3/90) (CRD) ① **CRD3454**
Evening Service, 'St Paul's Service'—4vv & organ (1954)
St Paul's Cath Ch, C. Dearnley, John Scott Concert
(9/88) (HYPE) ① **CDA66260**
Evening Service, 'Worcester Service'—4vv & organ
1. Magnificat; 2. Nunc Dimittis.
1, 2. Worcester Cath Ch, A. Partington, Don Hunt
Concert (9/90) (CARL) ① **PCD937**
The Fear of the Lord—anthem: 4vv and organ (1976)
Cambridge Sngrs, J. Rutter, W. Marshall Concert
(12/92) (CLLE) ① **COLCD118**
Flood—song: 1v and piano (1933) (Wds. from 'The Joyce Book')
J. M. Ainsley, J. Drake (r1992) Concert
(8/94) (CHAN) ① [2] **CHAN9185/6**
3 Folksongs—1v and piano (Wds. anon)
1. I will give my love an apple; 2. The brisk young Widow; 3. Cendrillon.
L. Dawson, J. M. Ainsley, J. Drake (r1992) Concert
(8/94) (CHAN) ① [2] **CHAN9185/6**
4 French Chansons—1v and piano, Op. 29 (1918)
1. Sainte Catherine; 2. C'est le grand duc du Maine; 3. Angèle au Couvent; 4. Le petit couturier.
L. Dawson, J. Drake (r1992) Concert
(8/94) (CHAN) ① [2] **CHAN9185/6**
A Garland for de la Mare—songs: 1v and piano (Wds. W de la Mare)
1. Wanderers; 2. The Lady Caroline; 3. Before dawn; 4. The old stone house; 5. The three cherry trees; 6. The old soldier; 7. The song of the secret; 8. Some one; 9. A queer story; 10. The old house; 11. Andy Battle.
C. Pierard, J. M. Ainsley, B. Luxon, J. Drake (r1992) Concert (8/94) (CHAN) ① [2] **CHAN9185/6**
Gavotte—song (1919) (Wds. H. Newbolt)
F. Lott, G. Johnson Concert
(7/90) (CHAN) ① **CHAN8722**
Sarah Walker, R. Vignoles Concert
(10/92) (CRD) ① **CRD3473**
J. M. Ainsley, J. Drake (r1992) Concert
(8/94) (CHAN) ① [2] **CHAN9185/6**
S. Leonard, M. Martineau (r1993) Concert
(3/95) (UNIT) ① **88016-2**
Goddess of the Night—song: 1v and piano (Wds. F W Harvey)
J. M. Ainsley, J. Drake (r1992) Concert
(8/94) (CHAN) ① [2] **CHAN9185/6**
Here she lies—song: 1v and piano (1917) (Wds. R. Herrick)
J. M. Ainsley, J. Drake (r1992) Concert
(8/94) (CHAN) ① [2] **CHAN9185/6**
Holy spirit, ever dwelling—hymn (Wds. T. Rees)
Lincoln Cath Ch, J. Vivian, C. Walsh (r1993) Concert
(7/94) (PRIO) ① **PRCD454**
House of the Mind—motet (1949-58) (Wds. J. Beaumont)
New College Ch, D. Burchell, E. Higginbottom
Concert (3/90) (CRD) ① **CRD3454**
Finzi Sngrs, P. Spicer Concert
(5/92) (CHAN) ① **CHAN9019**
A Hymn for St Cecilia—anthem (1961) (Wds. U. Vaughan Williams)
New College Ch, D. Burchell, E. Higginbottom
Concert (3/90) (CRD) ① **CRD3454**
Oxford Queen's Coll Ch, M. Owens, D. Went Concert
(5/93) (ASV) ① **CDDCA851**
St Paul's Cath Ch, John Scott, Andrew Lucas (r1993) Concert (6/94) (HYPE) ① **CDA66678**
Lincoln Cath Ch, J. Vivian, C. Walsh (r1993) Concert
(7/94) (PRIO) ① **PRCD454**
Hymnus Paradisi—soprano, tenor, choir and orchestra (1938)
J. Kennard, J.M. Ainsley, Liverpool Phil Ch, RLPO, V. Handley English Mass.
(5/92) (HYPE) ① **CDA66488**
In Green Ways—song cycle (pub 1928)
1. Under the Greenwood tree (wds. Shakespeare); 2. The goat paths (wds. J Stephens); 3. Merry Margaret (wds. J Skelton); 4. Wanderer's night song (wds. J W Goethe); 5. On the merry first of May (wds. H Burkitt Parker & C Aveling).
L. Dawson, J. Drake (r1992) Concert
(8/94) (CHAN) ① [2] **CHAN9185/6**
1. A. Rolfe Johnson, G. Johnson Concert
(5/92) (HYPE) ① **CDA66480**
Inheritance—partsong (1953)
D. Hunt Sngrs, Don Hunt Concert
(3/90) (HYPE) ① **CDA66078**

Cambridge Univ Chbr Ch, T. Brown Concert
(4/92) (GAMU) ① **GAMCD529**
King David—song (1921) (Wds. de la Mare)
Sarah Walker, R. Vignoles Concert
(10/92) (CRD) ① **CRD3473**
B. Luxon, J. Drake (r1992) Concert
(8/94) (CHAN) ① [2] **CHAN9185/6**
S. Leonard, M. Martineau (r1993) Concert
(3/95) (UNIT) ① **88016-2**
King of Glory—motet (1949) (Wds. G. Herbert)
New College Ch, D. Burchell, E. Higginbottom
Concert (3/90) (CRD) ① **CRD3454**
Let all the world in every corner sing—antiphon: SATB (1977) (Wds. G. Herbert)
Finzi Sngrs, P. Spicer Concert
(12/92) (CHAN) ① **CHAN9021**
Like as the hart—anthem (1941) (Wds. Psalm 42)
St Paul's Cath Ch, C. Dearnley, John Scott Concert
(9/88) (HYPE) ① **CDA66260**
Magdalen Oxford Coll Ch, G. Webber Concert
(11/91) (ABBE) ① **CDCA914**
Cambridge Sngrs, J. Rutter, W. Marshall Concert
(12/92) (CLLE) ① **COLCD118**
Oxford Queen's Coll Ch, M. Owens, D. Went Concert
(5/93) (ASV) ① **CDDCA851**
King's College Ch, S. Cleobury, C. Hughes (r1991) Concert (6/93) (EMI) ① **CDC7 54418-2**
Lincoln Cath Ch, J. Vivian, C. Walsh (r1993) Concert
(7/94) (PRIO) ① **PRCD454**
The little boy lost—song: 1v and song (Wds. W Blake)
B. Luxon, J. Drake (r1992) Concert
(8/94) (CHAN) ① [2] **CHAN9185/6**
Long, long ago—sacred partsong
Cambridge Sngrs, J. Rutter, W. Marshall Concert
(12/92) (CLLE) ① **COLCD118**
Finzi Sngrs, P. Spicer (r1991) Concert
(6/93) (CHAN) ① **CHAN9139**
Lost love—song: 1v and piano (1934) (Wds. Chinese, trans C Bax)
C. Pierard, J. Drake (r1992) Concert
(8/94) (CHAN) ① [2] **CHAN9185/6**
2 Madrigals—chorus a capella
1. In youth is pleasure (1915); 2. Before me, careless lying (1918).
Finzi Sngrs, P. Spicer (r1991) Concert
(6/93) (CHAN) ① **CHAN9139**
Mally O!—song: 1v and piano (Wds. 17th cent anon)
B. Luxon, J. Drake (r1992) Concert
(8/94) (CHAN) ① [2] **CHAN9185/6**
Mass in the Dorian Mode—4vv a capella (1912)
Finzi Sngrs, P. Spicer Concert
(12/92) (CHAN) ① **CHAN9021**
Missa Aedis Christi—4vv a capella (1958)
1. Kyrie; 2. Credo; 3. Sanctus; 4. Benedictus; 5. Agnus Dei; 6. Gloria.
New College Ch, E. Higginbottom Concert
(12/91) (CRD) ① **CRD3455**
Missa Sabrinensis—soloists, chorus and orchestra (1954)
Cpte J. Watson, D. Jones, M. Hill, D. Maxwell, LSC, LSO, G. Rozhdestvensky (r1994)
(6/95) (CHAN) ① **CHAN9348**
A Muggers's Song—song: 1v and piano (1919) (Wds. W W Gibson)
B. Luxon, J. Drake (r1992) Concert
(8/94) (CHAN) ① [2] **CHAN9185/6**
My eyes for beauty pine—SATB and organ (Wds. R. Bridges)
Oxford Queen's Coll Ch, M. Owens, D. Went Concert
(5/93) (ASV) ① **CDDCA851**
Nunc dimittis—double choir (1914)
Cambridge Sngrs, J. Rutter Concert
(4/92) (CLLE) ① **COLCD113**
Finzi Sngrs, P. Spicer Concert
(12/92) (CHAN) ① **CHAN9021**
O Garlands, hanging by the door—song: 1v and piano (1920) (Wds. trans from Greek)
J. M. Ainsley, J. Drake (r1992) Concert
(8/94) (CHAN) ① [2] **CHAN9185/6**
O my deir hert—song (1923) (Wds. anon)
J. Bowman, Downshire Players, P. Ash (orch A.Ridout) Concert (3/89) (MERI) ① **CDE84158**
C. Pierard, J. Drake (r1992) Concert
(8/94) (CHAN) ① [2] **CHAN9185/6**
O pray for the peace of Jerusalem—anthem (1941)
New College Ch, D. Burchell, E. Higginbottom
Concert (3/90) (CRD) ① **CRD3454**
Southwark Cath Ch, P. Wright, S. Layton (r1992)
Concert (7/94) (PRIO) ① **PRCD435**

O salutaris Hostia—4vv a capella (1913)
Finzi Sngrs, P. Spicer Concert
(12/92) (CHAN) ① **CHAN9021**
Oxford Queen's Coll Ch, M. Owens Concert
(5/93) (ASV) ① **CDDCA851**
an Old Man's Lullaby—song: 1v and piano (1917) (Wds. T Dekker)
J. M. Ainsley, J. Drake (r1992) Concert
(8/94) (CHAN) ① [2] **CHAN9185/6**
Old Meg—song: 1v and piano (1923) (Wds. W W Gibson)
L. Dawson, J. Drake (r1992) Concert
(8/94) (CHAN) ① [2] **CHAN9185/6**
Old Skinflint—song: 1v and piano (1918) (Wds. W W Gibson)
B. Luxon, J. Drake (r1992) Concert
(8/94) (CHAN) ① [2] **CHAN9185/6**
Peacock Pie—song cycle (1919) (Wds. W. de la Mare)
1. Tires Tim; 2. Alas, alack!; 3. Mrs MacQueen; 4. The dunce; 5. Full moon; 6. Miss T.
B. Luxon, J. Drake (r1992) Concert
(8/94) (CHAN) ① [2] **CHAN9185/6**
5. J. Bowman, Downshire Players, P. Ash (orch A.Ridout) Concert (3/89) (MERI) ① **CDE84158**
Preces and Responses
1. O Lord, open Thou our lips; 2. The Lord be with you.
1, 2. King's College Ch, P. Barley, S. Cleobury
Concert (7/92) (ARGO) ① **430 205-2ZH**
Regina caeli—double choir
Cambridge Sngrs, J. Rutter Concert
(4/92) (CLLE) ① **COLCD116**
Finzi Sngrs, P. Spicer Concert
(12/92) (CHAN) ① **CHAN9021**
Requiem—STB, mixed chorus (1936 reassembled 1980)
1. I: Salvator mundi.
J. Coxwell, M. Chance, P. Salmon, J. Best, Corydon Sngrs, M. Best Concert
(10/87) (HYPE) ① **CDA66076**
Finzi Sngrs, P. Spicer Concert
(5/92) (CHAN) ① **CHAN9019**
Cambridge Sngrs, J. Rutter, W. Marshall Concert
(12/92) (CLLE) ① **COLCD118**
S. Barber, J. Field, M. Johnstone, A. Angus, Vasari, J. Backhouse (r1994) Concert
(12/94) (UNIT) ① **88033-2**
The Restful branches—song: 1v and piano (Wds. W A Bryne)
B. Luxon, J. Drake (r1992) Concert
(8/94) (CHAN) ① [2] **CHAN9185/6**
Salve Regina—double choir (1915)
Finzi Sngrs, P. Spicer Concert
(12/92) (CHAN) ① **CHAN9021**
Oxford Queen's Coll Ch, M. Owens Concert
(5/93) (ASV) ① **CDDCA851**
The Scribe—partsong (1957) (Wds. W. de la Mare)
D. Hunt Sngrs, Don Hunt Concert
(3/90) (HYPE) ① **CDA66078**
A Sequence for St Michael—motet (1961) (Wds. Alcuin of York)
New College Ch, D. Burchell, E. Higginbottom
Concert (3/90) (CRD) ① **CRD3454**
Finzi Sngrs, P. Spicer Concert
(5/92) (CHAN) ① **CHAN9019**
Services, 'Collegium Regale'—canticles (1944)
1. COMMUNION SERVICE—; 1a. Kyrie; 1b. Credo; 1c. Surcum corda; 1d. Sanctus; 1e. Benedictus; 1f. Agnus Dei; 1g. Gloria; 2. MATTINS—; 2a. Te Deum; 2b. Jubilate; 3. EVENSONG—; 3a. Magnificat; 3b. Nunc dimittis.
1a, 1b, 1d, 1e, 1f, 1g, 2, 3. King's College Ch, P. Barley, S. Cleobury Concert
(7/92) (ARGO) ① **430 205-2ZH**
2. St Paul's Cath Ch, John Scott Concert
(9/88) (HYPE) ① **CDA66260**
2a, 2b Norwich Cath Ch, M. Nicholas, N. Taylor (r1993) Concert (10/94) (PRIO) ① **PRCD470**
3. St Bride's Ch, Fleet St, C. Etherington, R. Jones Concert (2/91) (REGE) ① **REGSB701CD**
4 Songs—1v and piano, Op. 26
1. There was a maiden (wds W L Courtney); 2. A Madrigal (wds A Dobson); 3. The Widow Bird (wds P B Shelley); 4. Girl's Song (wds W W Gibson).
C. Pierard, J. Drake (r1992) Concert
(8/94) (CHAN) ① [2] **CHAN9185/6**
4. S. Leonard, M. Martineau (r1993) Concert
(3/95) (UNIT) ① **88016-2**
2 South African Settings—1v and piano (c1921) (Wds. J F E Celliers)
1. Einsaamlied (Loneliness); 2. Vrijheidsgess (Spirit of Freedom).

C. Pierard, J. Drake (r1992) *Concert*
(8/94) (CHAN) ① [2] **CHAN9185/6**
Stabat mater—tenor, chorus and orchestra (1963)
1. Stabat mater dolorosa; 2. Cuius animam gementem; 3. Quis est homo?; 4. Eia mater; 5. Sancta mater; 6. Fac ut portem; 7. Christe cum sit hinc exire.
N. Archer, LSC, LSO, S. Rozhdestvensky (r1994)
(1/95) (CHAN) ① **CHAN9314**
The summer is coming—chorus a capella (1965) (Wds. B. Guiness)
Finzi Sngrs, P. Spicer (r1991) *Concert*
(8/93) (CHAN) ① **CHAN9139**
Sweet Content—song: 1v and piano (Wds. R Greene)
L. Dawson, J. Drake (r1992) *Concert*
(8/94) (CHAN) ① [2] **CHAN9185/6**
Sweetest of sweets—anthem: SSAATB (1977) (Wds. G. Herbert)
Finzi Sngrs, P. Spicer *Concert*
(12/92) (CHAN) ① **CHAN9021**
Take him, earth, for cherishing—unaccompanied motet (1963) (Wds. Prudentius, trans. H. Wadell)
Corydon Sngrs, M. Best *Concert*
(10/87) (HYPE) ① **CDA66076**
St Paul's Cath Ch, C. Dearnley, John Scott *Concert*
(9/88) (HYPE) ① **CDA66260**
King's College Ch, P. Barley, S. Cleobury *Concert*
(7/92) (ARGO) ① **430 205-2ZH**
New College Ch, E. Higginbottom *Concert*
(9/92) (MERI) ① **CDE84123**
Finzi Sngrs, P. Spicer (r1991) *Concert*
(6/93) (CHAN) ① **CHAN9139**
Truro Cath Ch, D. Briggs, S. Morley (r1992) *Concert*
(7/94) (PRIO) ① **PRCD429**
Vasari, J. Backhouse (r1994) *Concert*
(12/94) (UNIT) ① **88033-2**
Thee will I love—choir and organ (1970)
Magdalen Oxford Coll Ch, J. Harper *Concert*
(11/91) (ABBE) ① **CDCA915**
Upon a Summer's Day—song: 1v and piano (Wds. M Baring)
C. Pierard, J. Drake (r1992) *Concert*
(8/94) (CHAN) ① [2] **CHAN9185/6**
Westminster Service—SATB & organ (1957)
EXCERPTS: 1. Magnificat; 2. Nunc Dimittis.
Westminster Abbey Ch, M. Neary, M. Baker (r1994) *Concert*
(12/95) (SONY) ① **SK66614**
Where wast thou?—motet (1948)
New College Ch, E. Higginbottom *Concert*
(12/91) (CRD) ① **CRD3455**

HOYER, Frans (19th Cent) ?Finland

Jernban—galop (1862)
Košice St PO, M. Eichenholz (r1992: orch Sandberg) *Concert*
(2/94) (MARC) ① **8 223470**

HOYER, Karl (1891–1936) Germany

Introduction, Variations and Fugue on the chorale 'Jerusalem, du hochgebaute Stadt'—organ (pub 1913)
G. Barber *Concert*
(5/91) (PRIO) ① **PRCD297**

HUBAY, Jenö (1858–1937) Hungary

Berceuse—violin and piano, Op. 79/9
J. Hubay, O. Herz (r1928) *Concert*
(12/91) (BIDD) ① **LAB045**
6 Blumenleben—violin and piano, Op. 30
5. Der Zephir.
5. J. Szigeti, K. Ruhrseitz (r1926) *Concert*
(1/90) (BIDD) ① [2] **LAB005/6**
5. J. Kubelík, anon (r1906) *Concert*
(6/91) (BIDD) ① [2] **LAB033/4**
5. I. Menges, E. Beattie (r1930) *Concert*
(12/91) (APR) ① [2] **APR7015**
5. K. Daeshik Kang, M. Rahkonen (r1992) *Concert*
(9/93) (NIMB) ① **NI5358**
5. T. Varga, I. Pongracz (r1935) *Concert*
(11/93) (CLAV) ① [4] **CD50-9300/4**
5. T. Varga, I. Pongracz (r1935) *Concert*
(11/93) (CLAV) ① **CD50-9314**

14 Scènes de la Csárda—violin and piano
3. Maros vize (Op. 18); 4. Hejre Kati (op. 32); 5. Hullámzó balaton (Op. 33); 12. Little dove (Op. 83).
Anon (pf) (r1925) *Concert*
(12/91) (APR) ① [2] **APR7015**
3. J. Szigeti, N. Magaloff (r1932) *Concert*
(1/90) (BIDD) ① [2] **LAB007/8**
3. J. Szigeti, A. Foldes (r1941) *Concert*
(7/94) (BIDD) ① [2] **LAB070/1**
4. A. Campoli, S. Crooke *Concert*
(10/91) (PEAR) ① **PASTCD9744**
4. C. Hansen, B. Zakharoff (r1925) *Concert*
(12/91) (APR) ① [2] **APR7015**
5. J. Hubay, O. Herz (r1928) *Concert*
(12/91) (BIDD) ① **LAB045**
12. J. Hubay, Budapest Cons Orch, Mr Zsolt (r1929) *Concert*
(8/90) (SYMP) ① **SYMCD1071**
12. J. Hubay, Budapest Cons Orch, Mr Zsolt (r1929) *Concert*
(12/91) (BIDD) ① **LAB045**

Ugy-e jani?—song (Eng: Clever Jack)
M. Basilides, J. Hubay, O. Herz (r1929) *Concert*
(12/91) (BIDD) ① **LAB045**

The Cremona lutenist—opera: 2 acts, Op. 40 (1894—Budapest) (Lib. F. Coppée & H. Beauclair)
Intermezzo J. Hubay, O. Herz (r1928) *Concert*
(12/91) (BIDD) ① **LAB070/1**

HUBBELL, Raymond (1879–1954) USA

The Ladder of Roses—song for the show 'Hip-Hip Hooray' (1915) (Lyrics Burnside)
Orig Broadway Cast (r1916) *Concert*
(5/94) (PEAR) ① [3] **GEMMCDS9056/8**

The Jolly Bachelors—musical show (1910—New York) (Lyrics Glen MacDonough; see also under Norworth)
EXCERPTS: 1. Savannah; 2. Rosa Rosetta.
1, 2. S. Mayhew, Orig Broadway Cast (r1910) *Concert*
(5/94) (PEAR) ① [3] **GEMMCDS9053/5**

HUBER, Klaus (b 1924) Switzerland

Transpositio ad infinitum—cello (1976)
T. Demenga (r1993) *Concert*
(8/95) (ECM) ① [2] **445 234-2**

HUBER, Paul (b 1918) Switzerland

Symphonic Music—brass band (1979)
Black Dyke Mills Band, P. Parkes (pp1979) *Concert*
(3/94) (CHAN) ① **CHAN4522**

HÜBLER, Heinrich Germany

Concerto for 4 Horns and Orchestra in F (1854)
M. Rimon (hn/dir), Israel PO *Concert*
(2/92) (CARL) ① **MCD31**

HÜE, Georges (Adolphe) (1858–1948) France

Fantasia for Flute and Piano
W. Bennett, ECO, S. Bedford *Concert*
(10/89) (ASV) ① **CDDCA652**

HUET, Gregorio (c1550–1616) The Netherlands

Fantasia Graegorii—lute
J. Lindberg *Concert*
(2/89) (BIS) ① **BIS-CD390**
J. Bream (r1966) *Concert*
(8/93) (RCA) ① [28] **09026 61583-2(1)**
J. Bream (r1966) *Concert*
(6/94) (RCA) ① **09026 61585-2**

HUGHES, Herbert (1882–1937) Ireland

The Bard of Armagh—Irish folksong arrangement (Wds. traditional)
A. Murray, G. Johnson (r1992) *Concert*
(8/93) (HYPE) ① **CDA66627**
The Cork Leg—Irish folksong arrangement (Wds. traditional)
A. Murray, G. Johnson (r1992) *Concert*
(8/93) (HYPE) ① **CDA66627**
Down by the Salley Gardens—Irish folksong arrangement (Wds. traditional)
K. Ferrier, P. Spurr (r1949) *Concert*
(6/92) (DECC) ① **433 475-2DM**
Cambridge Sngrs, CLS, J. Rutter (r1992; arr Rutter) *Concert*
(11/93) (CLLE) ① **COLCD120**
I have a bonnet with blue—Irish folksong arrangement (Wds. traditional)
A. Murray, G. Johnson (r1992) *Concert*
(8/93) (HYPE) ① **CDA66627**
I will walk with my love—Irish folksong arrangement (Wds. traditional)
A. Murray, G. Johnson (r1992) *Concert*
(8/93) (HYPE) ① **CDA66627**
The Lepreuchan—Irish folksong arrangement (Wds. P. W. Joyce)
A. Murray, G. Johnson (r1992) *Concert*
(8/93) (HYPE) ① **CDA66627**
Monday, Tuesday—Irish folksong arrangement (Wds. traditional)
A. Murray, G. Johnson (r1992) *Concert*
(8/93) (HYPE) ① **CDA66627**
The Next Market Day—Irish folksong arrangement (Wds. traditional)
A. Murray, G. Johnson (r1992) *Concert*
(8/93) (HYPE) ① **CDA66627**
She moved through the fair—Irish folksong arrangement
Magdalen (Oxford) Coll Ch, G. Ives *Concert*
(11/92) (CNTO) ① **CRCD2366**
A. Murray (r1992) *Concert*
(8/93) (HYPE) ① **CDA66627**
Cambridge Sngrs, CLS, J. Rutter (r1992; arr Runswick) *Concert*
(11/93) (CLLE) ① **COLCD120**
E. Costello, Brodsky Qt (r1994; arr Cassidy) *Concert*
(10/94) (SILV) ① **SILKD6001**
The Stuttering Lovers—Irish folksong arrangement (Wds. traditional)
A. Murray, G. Johnson (r1992) *Concert*
(8/93) (HYPE) ① **CDA66627**
A young maid stood in her father's garden—Irish folksong arrangement (Wds. traditional)
A. Murray, G. Johnson (r1992) *Concert*
(8/93) (HYPE) ① **CDA66627**

HUGHES, Richard Samuel (1855–1893) Wales

Arafa Don—song (Wds. Tudno Jones)
A. Davies, A. Bryn Parri (r1994) *Concert*
(11/95) (SAIN) ① **SCDC2085**

HUGO DE LANTINS (fl 1420–1430) France/Low Countries

Plaindre m'estuet de ma damme joly—rondeau (3vv)
Gothic Voices, C. Page *Concert*
(12/88) (HYPE) ① **CDA66286**

HUME, Alexander (1811–1859) Scotland

Afton Water—song: 1v and piano
M. Garden, J. Dansereau (r1927/9: 2 vers) *Concert*
(8/94) (ROMO) ① **81008-2**

HUME, James Ord (1864–1925) Scotland

SECTION I: ORCHESTRAL

BB & CF (British Bandsman & Contest Field)—march
Besses o' the Barn Band, Black Dyke Mills Band, Yorkshire Imperial Band, H. Mortimer (pp1987)
Concert (11/93) (CHAN) ① **CHAN4513**

HUME, Tobias (?c1569–1645) England

SECTION II: CHAMBER

Captaine Humes Poeticall Musicke—concert pieces and airs (pub 1607)
1. The Lady of Sussex delight; 2. The King of Denmarks delight; 3. A French Almain—The Duke of Lenox delight; 4. A mery conceit—The Queens delight; 5. What greater grief (song); 6. Sweet Musicke—The Earl of Salisburies favoret; 7. Sweet Ayre—The Earl of Arundels favoret; 8. The Earle of Pembrokes Galiard; 9. An Almaine—The Lady Canes delight; 10. The Pashion of Musicke—Sir C. Hattons choice; 11. An Almaine—The Duke of Holstones delight; 12. A masque; 13. Hark! Hark!; 14. A Spanish Humour—Lord Hayes favoret.
1, 2, 3, 4, 5, 6, 7, 8, 9, 10, 11, 12. M. Figueras, P. Hillier, Hespèrion XX, J. Savall *First Part of Ayres.*
(4/92) (DHM) ① **RD77165**
2, 14. E. Headley, A. Lawrence-King, S. Stubbs *Concert* (12/90) (HYPE) ① **CDA66335**
13. E. Headley *Concert*
(12/90) (HYPE) ① **CDA66335**

The Virgin's Muse—consort
D. Cordier, Tragicomedia, S. Stubbs *Concert*
(1/90) (HYPE) ① **CDA66307**

SECTION IV: VOCAL AND CHORAL

The First Part of Ayres, French, Pollish and other together—ayres, pavans, galliard and almaines (pub 1605) (vocal and instrumental works)
EXCERPTS: 1. Fain would I change that note (song); 2. The Souldiers song; 3. Alas poore men (song); 4. Tabacco (song); 5. A Jigg for ladies (consort); 6. My mistresse hath a pritty thing (lyra viol); 7. Touch me lightly (lyra viol).
1-5. M. Figueras, P. Hillier, Hespèrion XX, J. Savall *Captaine Humes Poeticall Musicke.*
(4/92) (DHM) ① **RD77165**

HUMFREY, Pelham (1647–1674) England

SECTION IV: VOCAL AND CHORAL

By the waters of Babylon—verse anthem: 4vv, choir, strings and organ
D. Minter, R. Covey-Crump, J. Potter, D. Thomas, Cambridge Clare College Ch, Romanesca, N. McGegan *Concert* (3/93) (HARM) ① **HMU90 7053**

Have mercy upon me, O God—verse anthem: 3vv, choir and organ
D. Minter, R. Covey-Crump, D. Thomas, Cambridge Clare College Ch, Romanesca, N. McGegan *Concert* (3/93) (HARM) ① **HMU90 7053**

Hear my crying, O God—verse anthem: 5vv, choir, strings and organ
D. Dean, D. Minter, R. Covey-Crump, J. Potter, D. Thomas, Cambridge Clare College Ch, Romanesca, N. McGegan *Concert* (3/93) (HARM) ① **HMU90 7053**

Hear my prayer, O God—verse anthem: 4vv, choir, strings and organ
D. Dean, D. Minter, R. Covey-Crump, D. Thomas, Cambridge Clare College Ch, Romanesca, N. McGegan *Concert* (3/93) (HARM) ① **HMU90 7053**

Hear, O Heav'ns—verse anthem: 3vv, choir and strings
D. Minter, J. Potter, D. Thomas, Cambridge Clare College Ch, Romanesca, N. McGegan *Concert* (3/93) (HARM) ① **HMU90 7053**

A Hymne to God the Father, 'Wilt thou forgive that sin'—sacred song (1688)
J. Bowman, Orch, R. King *Concert*
(12/93) (UNIT) ① **88002-2**

Lift up your heads—verse anthem: 2vv, choir, strings and organ
D. Minter, R. Covey-Crump, Cambridge Clare College Ch, Romanesca, N. McGegan *Concert* (3/93) (HARM) ① **HMU90 7053**

Like as the hart—verse anthem: 4vv, choir, strings and organ
D. Dean, D. Minter, J. Potter, D. Thomas, Cambridge Clare College Ch, Romanesca, N. McGegan *Concert* (3/93) (HARM) ① **HMU90 7053**

O give thanks unto the Lord—verse anthem: 4vv, choir, strings and organ
D. Minter, R. Covey-Crump, J. Potter, D. Thomas, Cambridge Clare College Ch, Romanesca, N. McGegan *Concert* (3/93) (HARM) ① **HMU90 7053**

O Lord my God—verse anthem: 3vv, choir, strings and organ
D. Minter, R. Covey-Crump, D. Thomas, Cambridge Clare College Ch, Romanesca, N. McGegan *Concert* (3/93) (HARM) ① **HMU90 7053**

HUMMEL, Johann Nepomuk (1778–1837) Austria

SECTION I: ORCHESTRAL

Concerto for Bassoon and Orchestra in F
K. Walker, LMP, J. Glover *Concert*
(8/89) (GALL) ① **CD-499**
K. Thunemann, ASMF, N. Marriner *Concert*
(5/91) (PHIL) ① **432 081-2PH**

Concerto for Piano and Orchestra in A minor, Op. 85 (c1816)
S. Hough, ECO, B. Thomson *Piano Concerto in B minor.* (6/87) (CHAN) ① **CHAN8507**

Concerto for Piano and Orchestra in B minor, Op. 89 (1819)
S. Hough, ECO, B. Thomson *Piano Concerto in A minor.* (6/87) (CHAN) ① **CHAN8507**

Concerto for Piano and Orchestra in E, Op. 110 (1814)
H. Kann, Hamburg SO, H. Beissel *Kalkbrenner: Piano Concerto 1.* (5/93) (VOX) ① **115716-2**

Concerto for Trumpet and Orchestra in E (1803) (also played in E flat)
G. Schwarz (tpt/dir), NY Y CO *Haydn: Trumpet Concerto.* (10/84) (DELO) ① **DE3001**
W. Marsalis, National PO, R. Leppard *Concert* (5/85) (SONY) ① **SK37846**
H. Hardenberger, ASMF, N. Marriner (1986; played in E) *Concert* (12/87) (PHIL) ① **420 203-2PH**
B. Soustrot, Loire PO, M. Soustrot *Concert* (1/89) (PIER) ① **PV788011**
M. André, BPO, H. von Karajan (trans. ed. Oubradous) *Concert* (2/89) (EMI) ① **CDC7 49237-2**
W. Basch, Orpheus CO *Concert* (3/89) (SCHW) ① **311071**
R. Friedrich, ASMF, N. Marriner *Concert* (6/93) (CAPR) ① **10 436**
S. Nakarjakov, Lausanne CO, J. López-Cobos (r1993) *Concert* (10/93) (TELD) ① **4509-90846-2**
O.E. Antonsen, ECO, J. Tate (r1993) *Concert* (2/94) (EMI) ① **CDC7 54897-2**
A. Sandoval, LSO, L. Haza (r1993) *Concert* (1/95) (GRP) ① **GRK75002**
J. Wallace, Philh, C. Warren-Green (r1986) *Concert* (2/95) (NIMB) ① **NI7016**
W. Marsalis, ECO, R. Leppard (r1993) *Concert* (5/95) (SONY) ① **SK57497**
M. André, F. Liszt CO, J. Rolla (r1994) *Concert* (7/95) (EMI) ① **CDC5 55231-2**

Introduction, Theme and Variations in F—oboe and orchestra, Op. 102
L. Lencses, Stuttgart RSO, N. Marriner *Concert* (6/93) (CAPR) ① **10 308**
M. André, Zurich CO, E. de Stoutz (trans tpt) *Concert* (9/91) (EMI) ① **CDC7 54086-2**
E. Rombout, Concertgebouw CO (r1993) *Concert* (12/94) (DECC) ① **440 605-2DH**

SECTION II: CHAMBER

Grand Sonata in C—keyboard and mandolin/violin, Op. 37a (1810)
1. Allegro con spirito; 2. Andante moderato siziliano; 3. Rondo.
A. Stephens, R. Burnett *Concert*
(3/92) (AMON) ① **CD-SAR53**

Nocturne in F—piano: 4 hands, Op. 99 (1822)
R. Holmes, R. Burnett (trans. Eichler) *Concert* (7/87) (AMON) ① **CD-SAR12**

Octet-Partita in E flat—wind ensemble (1803)
COE Wind Sols *Concert*
(4/90) (ASV) ① **CDCOE812**

Piano Quintet—piano and strings, Op. 87 (1802)
Schubert Ens of London *Schubert: Trout Quintet, D667.* (6/90) (HYPE) ① **CDH88010**

Piano Trio in E, Op. 83 (pub 1819)
Parnassus Trio (r1987-8) *Concert*
(6/93) (MDG) ① [2] **L3307/8**

Piano Trio in E flat, Op. 12 (pub c1803)
Parnassus Trio (r1987-8) *Concert*
(6/93) (MDG) ① [2] **L3307/8**

Piano Trio in E flat, Op. 93 (1821)
Parnassus Trio (r1987-8) *Concert*
(6/93) (MDG) ① [2] **L3307/8**

Piano Trio in E flat, Op. 96 (pub c1822)
Parnassus Trio (r1987-8) *Concert*
(6/93) (MDG) ① [2] **L3307/8**

Piano Trio in F, Op. 22 (1799: pub c1807)
Parnassus Trio (r1987-8) *Concert*
(6/93) (MDG) ① [2] **L3307/8**

Piano Trio in G, Op. 35 (pub 1811)
Parnassus Trio (r1987-8) *Concert*
(6/93) (MDG) ① [2] **L3307/8**

Piano Trio in G, Op. 65 (pub c1814-15)
Parnassus Trio (r1987-8) *Concert*
(6/93) (MDG) ① [2] **L3307/8**

Quintet for Clarinet and Strings in E flat
C. Neidich, Archibudelli (r1993) *Concert*
(9/95) (SONY) ① **SK57968**

Septet in C, 'Septet Militaire'—fl, cl, tpt, vn, vc, db and pf, Op. 114 (1829)
Capricorn *Septet, Op.74.*
(5/91) (HYPE) ① **CDA66396**

Septet in D minor—pf, fl, ob, hn, va, vc, db, Op. 74 (c1816)
Nash Ens *F. Berwald: Septet.*
(6/89) (CRD) ① **CRD3344**
Capricorn *Septet, Op.114.*
(5/91) (HYPE) ① **CDA66396**

Sonata for Cello and Piano in A, Op. 104 (1827)
J. Alexander, A. Cattarino *Viola Sonata, Op.5/3.*
(6/89) (OPUS) ① **9351 1895**

Sonata for Piano and Flute/Violin in A, Op. 64 (c1814-15)
C. Croshaw, C. Conway *Concert*
(6/93) (MERI) ① **CDE84236**

Sonata for Piano and Viola in E flat, Op. 5/3 (c1798)
R. Holmes, R. Burnett (trans. Eichler) *Concert* (7/87) (AMON) ① **CD-SAR12**
M. Telecký, H. Gáfforová *Cello Sonata, Op.104.*
(6/89) (OPUS) ① **9351 1895**
C. Croshaw, N. Blume *Concert*
(6/93) (MERI) ① **CDE84236**
A. B. Duetschler, U. Duetschler (r1994) *Concert* (11/95) (CLAV) ① **CD50-9502**

Sonata for Piano and Violin/Flute in D, Op. 50 (c1810-14)
R. Holmes, R. Burnett *Concert*
(7/87) (AMON) ① **CD-SAR12**
C. Croshaw, C. Conway *Concert*
(6/93) (MERI) ① **CDE84236**

3 String Quartets, Op. 30 (before 1804)
1. C; 2. G; 3. E flat.
Delmé Qt (9/92) (HYPE) ① **CDA66568**

SECTION III: INSTRUMENTAL

La bella capricciosa in B flat—polonaise: piano, Op. 55 (c1811-15)
C. Croshaw *Concert* (6/93) (MERI) ① **CDE84236**

Piano Sonata No. 3 in F minor, Op. 20 (pub. c1807)
I. Hobson *Piano Sonata 4.* (6/87) (ARAB) ① **Z6566**

Piano Sonata No. 4 in C, Op. 38 (pub. c1808)
I. Hobson *Piano Sonata 3.* (6/87) (ARAB) ① **Z6566**

Rondo in E flat, 'Rondo favori'—piano, Op. 11 (c1803)
E. Wild *Concert* (8/92) (VANG) ① **08.4033.71**
J. Heifetz, A. Sándor (r1934) *Concert*
(11/94) (RCA) ① [65] **09026 61778-2(02)**

Rondo quasi una fantasia in E—piano, Op. 19 (c1806)
C. Croshaw *Concert* (6/93) (MERI) ① **CDE84236**

Variations on theme from Gluck's 'Armide'—piano, Op.57 (c1811-15)
R. Burnett *Concert* (5/88) (AMON) ① **CD-SAR7**

SECTION IV: VOCAL AND CHORAL

Hallelujah (unidentified)
R. Anday, H. Dawson (r1929) *Concert*
(5/92) (PREI) ① **89046**
E. Destinn, orch. B. Seidler-Winkler (r1908) *Concert* (12/94) (SUPR) ① [12] **11 2136-2(2)**
E. Destinn, orch (r1911) *Concert*
(12/94) (SUPR) ① [12] **11 2136-2(4)**

A **Select Collection of Original Scottish Airs—folksong arrangements (pub 1826)** (collected by George Thomson)
EXCERPTS: 1. I saw thee weep; 2. For the sake o' Somebody.
2. Scottish Early Music Consort (r1987) *Concert*
(10/95) (CHAN) ① **CHAN0581**

HUMPERDINCK, Engelbert (1854–1921) Germany

SECTION I: ORCHESTRAL

Humoresque in E—orchestra (1878–89)
Bamberg SO, K.A. Rickenbacher (r1993) *Concert*
(4/95) (SCHW) ① **311972**
Königskinder—concert overture (based on Introduction, Act 1: 'Der Königsohn')
Bamberg SO, K.A. Rickenbacher (r1990) *Concert*
(11/94) (VIRG) ① **CUV5 61128-2**
Overture No. 2 to 'Die Heirat wider Willen'—orchestra (1906)
Bamberg SO, K.A. Rickenbacher (r1993) *Concert*
(4/95) (SCHW) ① **311972**
Shakespeare Suite No. 1—orchestra (1905-08)
Bamberg SO, K.A. Rickenbacher (r1993) *Concert*
(4/95) (SCHW) ① **311972**
Shakespeare Suite No. 2—orchestra (1905-08)
Bamberg SO, K.A. Rickenbacher (r1993) *Concert*
(4/95) (SCHW) ① **311972**

SECTION IV: VOCAL AND CHORAL

Weihnachten—Lied (1898) (Wds. Wette)
E. Schwarzkopf, Ambrosian Sngrs, Philh, C. Mackerras (orch Mackerras) *Concert*
(12/90) (EMI) ① **CDM7 63574-2**
Winterlied—Lied (1887 orch 1920) (Wds. A. von Platen)
E. Schwarzkopf, M. Raucheisen (bp1944) *Concert*
(5/93) (ACAN) ① **43 128**

SECTION V: STAGE WORKS

Der Blaue Vogel—incidental music to Maeterlinck's play (1912)
EXCERPTS—; 1. Vorspiel: Der Weinachstraum; 2. Sternenreigen.
1, 2. Bamberg SO, K.A. Rickenbacher (r1990) *Concert* (11/94) (VIRG) ① **CUV5 61128-2**
Dornröschen—opera: 3 acts (1902—Frankfurt am Main) (Lib. E. Ebeling & B. Filhès, after Perrault)
EXCERPTS—; 1. Introduction; 2. Ballade; 3. Irrfahrten; 4. Das Dornenschloss; 5. Festklänge.
1-5. Bamberg SO, K.A. Rickenbacher (r1990) *Concert* (11/94) (VIRG) ① **CUV5 61128-2**
Hänsel und Gretel—opera: 3 acts (1893—Weimar) (Lib. Wette)
EXCERPTS: ACT 1: 1. Prelude; 2a. Suse, liebe, Suse; 2b. Brüderchen, komm, tanz' mit mir (Dance Duet); 3. Hallo! Himmel, die Mutter; 4a. Rallalala, rallalala; 4b. Ach, wir armen, armen Leute. ACT 2: 5. Hexenritt (Witch's Ride); 6. Ein Männlein steht im Walde; 7a. Der kleine Sandmann bin ich; 7b. Abends will ich schlafen gehn (Evening Hymn); 8. Dream Pantomime. ACT 3: 9. Prelude; 10a. Der kleine Taumann heiss ich; 10b. Wo bin ich? Wach ich? Ist es ein Traum?; 11. Bleib' stehn! Bleib' stehn!; 12. Knusper, knusper Knäuschen; 13. Erlöst, befreit!; 14a. Vater! Mutter!; 14b. Kinder schaut das Wunder an.
Cpte E. Grümmer, E. Schwarzkopf, M. von Ilosvay, J. Metternich, A. Felbermayer, E. Schürhoff, Loughton High School for Girls Ch, Bancroft's School Choir, Philh, H. von Karajan (r1953)
(4/88) (EMI) ① [2] **CMS7 69293-2**
Cpte F. von Stade, I. Cotrubas, C. Ludwig, S. Nimsgern, K. Te Kanawa, R. Welting, E. Söderström, Cologne Op Children's Ch, Cologne Gürzenich Orch, J. Pritchard (11/88) (SONY) ① [2] **M2K79217**
Cpte A.S. von Otter, B. Bonney, H. Schwarz, A. Schmidt, B. Hendricks, E. Lind, M. Lipovšek, Tolz Boys' Ch, BRSO, J. Tate
(11/90) (EMI) ① [2] **CDS7 54022-2**
Cpte A. Murray, E. Gruberová, G. Jones, F. Grundheber, B. Bonney, C. Oelze, C. Ludwig, Staatskapelle Dresden, Colin Davis (r1992)
(10/93) (PHIL) ① [2] **438 013-2PH2**
Cpte J. Larmore, R. Ziesak, H. Behrens, B. Weikl, R. Joshua, C. Schäfer, H. Schwarz, Tolz Boys' Ch, BRSO, D. Runnicles (r1994)
(1/95) (TELD) ① [2] **4509-94549-2**
1. LSO, A. Coates (r1926) *Concert*
(4/93) (KOCH) ① [2] **37704-2**

---

1. Bamberg SO, K.A. Rickenbacher (r1990) *Concert* (11/94) (VIRG) ① **CUV5 61128-2**
1. BBC SO, A. Boult (r1932) *Concert* (2/95) (BEUL) ① **1PD12**
2a, 2b E. Schwarzkopf, I. Seefried, Philh, J. Krips (r1947) *Concert* (3/89) (EMI) ① **CDH7 69793-2**
2a, 2b C. Supervia, I.M. Ferraris, orch, A. Albergoni (r1928: Ital) *Concert* (9/90) (CLUB) ① **CL99-074**
2a, 2b C. Supervia, I.M. Ferraris, orch, A. Albergoni (Ital: r1928) *Concert* (9/90) (PREI) ① **89023**
2b C. Supervia, I.M. Ferraris, orch, A. Albergoni (r1928: Ital) *Concert*
(4/94) (EMI) ① [3] **CHS7 64864-2(1)**
4a G. Hüsch, Berlin St Op Orch, H.U. Müller (r1937) *Concert* (10/93) (NIMB) ① **NI7848**
4a G. Hüsch, Berlin St Op Orch, H.U. Müller (r1936) *Concert* (3/94) (PREI) ① **89071**
7b K. Battle, F. von Stade, Orch, A. Previn (pp1991) *Concert* (12/92) (SONY) ① **SK48235**
7b Fine Arts Brass Ens, M. Shepherd, P. Spicer (r1992; arr Roberts) *Concert*
(12/93) (BIRM) ① **BBCCD2**
8. RCA Victor Orch, F. Reiner (r1950) *Concert* (8/94) (RCA) ① **09026 61792-2**
10b E. Schwarzkopf, E. Grümmer, Philh, H. von Karajan (r1953) *Concert*
(12/90) (EMI) ① **CDM7 63657-2**
Die Königskinder—melodrama: 3 acts (1897—Munich) (Lib. E. Rosmer)
EXCERPTS—; 1. Hellafest, Kinderreigen; 2. Introduction, Act 3.
Cpte A. Dallapozza, H. Donath, H. Prey, H. Schwarz, K. Ridderbusch, G. Unger, B. Lindner, G. Wewel, H. Ankersen, F. Lenz, O. Wenkel, T. Nicolai, Tolz Boys' Ch, Bavarian Rad Chor, Munich RO, H. Wallberg
(8/89) (EMI) ① [3] **CMS7 69936-2**
Verdorben, gestorben G. Hüsch, Berlin St Op Orch, H.U. Müller (r1936) *Concert* (3/94) (PREI) ① **89071**
Verdorben! Gestorben! T. Hampson, Pestalozzi Children's Ch, Munich RO, F. Luisi (r1994) *Concert*
(9/95) (EMI) ① **CDC5 55233-2**
1, 2. Bamberg SO, K.A. Rickenbacher (r1990) *Concert* (11/94) (VIRG) ① **CUV5 61128-2**

HUMPHRIES, John (c1707–before c1740) England

SECTION I: ORCHESTRAL

Concerto for Trumpet and Strings, pub. 1740 (pub. 1740)
C. Steele-Perkins, ECO, A. Halstead *Concert*
(6/86) (CARL) ① **PCD821**

HUNNIS, William (d 1597) England

SECTION IV: VOCAL AND CHORAL

In terror trapp'd—song
J. Bowman, King's Consort *Concert*
(10/91) (HYPE) ① **CDA66447**

HUPFELD, Herman (1894–1951) USA

SECTION IV: VOCAL AND CHORAL

As time goes by—song from the revue 'Everybody's Welcome' (1931) (also used in the film 'Casablanca'—see under Steiner)
M. Patinkin, Orch, E. Stern (r1993; orch Troob, arr Ford) *Concert* (11/94) (NONE) ① **7559-79330-2**

HURFORD, Peter (John) (b 1930) England

SECTION IV: VOCAL AND CHORAL

Litany to the Holy Spirit—chorale
Westminster Abbey Ch, M. Neary, M. Baker (r1994) *Concert* (12/95) (SONY) ① **SK66614**

HURLSTONE, William (Yeates) (1876–1906) England

SECTION I: ORCHESTRAL

The Magic Mirror Suite—orchestra (1900)
LPO, N. Braithwaite *Concert*
(4/93) (LYRI) ① **SRCD208**
Variations on a Hungarian air—orchestra (by 1899)
LPO, N. Braithwaite *Concert*
(4/93) (LYRI) ① **SRCD208**

Variations on an Original Theme—orchestra (1896)
LPO, N. Braithwaite *Concert*
(4/93) (LYRI) ① **SRCD208**

SECTION II: CHAMBER

4 Characteristic pieces—clarinet and piano
1. Ballade; 2. Croon Song; 3. Intermezzo; 4. Scherzo.
T. King, C. Benson *Concert*
(7/89) (HYPE) ① **CDA66014**
E. Jóhannesson, P. Jenkins *Concert*
(1/93) (CHAN) ① **CHAN9079**
Sonata for Bassoon and Piano in F (pub 1904)
Daniel Smith, R. Vignoles *Concert*
(9/89) (ASV) ① **CDDCA535**

HURTADO DE XERES (fl 1500) Spain

SECTION IV: VOCAL AND CHORAL

No tenga madie sperança (from the Colombina Song Book)
Hespèrion XX, J. Savall *Concert*
(7/92) (ASTR) ① **E8763**

HURUM, Alf (1882–1972) Norway

SECTION IV: VOCAL AND CHORAL

Pale nights—song (Wds. Krag)
K. Flagstad, E. McArthur (r1937) *Concert*
(12/95) (PEAR) ① **GEMMCD9092**
K. Flagstad, E. McArthur (r1937) *Concert*
(12/95) (SIMA) ① [3] **PSC1821(2)**

HUSA, Karel (b 1921) Czechoslovakia/USA

SECTION I: ORCHESTRAL

Fresque—orchestra (1949 rev 1963)
Slovak RSO, B. Kolman (r1993) *Concert*
(5/95) (MARC) ① **8 223640**
Music for Prague—wind orchestra/orchestra (1968 orch 1970)
1. Introduction and Fanfare; 2. Aria; 3. Interlude; 4. Toccata and Chorale.
Slovak RSO, B. Kolman (r1993/4) *Concert*
(5/95) (MARC) ① **8 223640**
Reflections, 'Symphony No. 2'—orchestra (1982-83)
Slovak RSO, B. Kolman (r1993) *Concert*
(5/95) (MARC) ① **8 223640**

HVOSLEF, Ketil (b 1939) Norway

formerly Ketil Saeverud

SECTION I: ORCHESTRAL

Antigone—symphonic variations for orchestra (1982)
Bergen PO, D. Kitaienko *Violin Concerto.*
(4/93) (AURO) ① **ACD4969**
Concerto for Violin and Orchestra (1988-89)
T. Saeverud, Bergen PO, C. Eggen *Antigone.*
(4/93) (AURO) ① **ACD4969**

HYGONS, Richard (c1435–c1509) England

SECTION IV: VOCAL AND CHORAL

Salve Regina
The Sixteen, H. Christophers *Concert*
(4/92) (COLL) ① **Coll1314-2**

IBERT, Jacques (François Antoine) (1890–1962) France

SECTION I: ORCHESTRAL

Bacchanale—scherzo for orchestra (1956)
Montreal SO, C. Dutoit *Concert*
(6/94) (DECC) ① **440 332-2DH**
Bostoniana—derived from 2nd Symphony (lost) (1955-61)
Montreal SO, C. Dutoit *Concert*
(6/94) (DECC) ① **440 332-2DH**
Concertino da camera—alto saxophone and 11 instruments (1935)
J. Harle, ASMF, N. Marriner *Concert*
(7/88) (EMI) ① **CDC7 54301-2**
M. Whitcombe, San Diego CO, D. Barra *Concert*
(4/92) (KOCH) ① **37094-2**

Concerto for Cello and Wind Instruments (1925)
J. Kreger, NY Harmonie Ens, S. Richman *Concert*
(7/92) (MUSI) ① **MACD-649**
Concerto for Flute and Orchestra (1934)
S. Milan, CLS, R. Hickox *Concert*
(10/90) (CHAN) ① **CHAN8840**
J. Stinton, Scottish CO, S. Bedford *Concert*
(8/91) (COLL) ① **Coll1210-2**
P. Alanko, Finnish RSO, J-P. Saraste (r1993)
Concert (11/93) (ONDI) ① **ODE802-2**
T. Hutchins, Montreal SO, C. Dutoit (r1992) *Concert*
(12/94) (DECC) ① **440 332-2DH**
M. Faust, Cologne RSO, S. Baudo (r1991) *Concert*
(12/94) (CAPR) ① **10 495**
Divertissement—chamber orchestra (1930)
ASMF, N. Marriner *Concert*
(2/85) (ASV) ① **CDDCA517**
Montreal SO, C. Dutoit *Concert*
(6/89) (DECC) ① **421 527-2DH**
San Diego CO, D. Barra *Concert*
(4/92) (KOCH) ① **37094-2**
Ulster Orch, Y. P. Tortelier *Concert*
(9/92) (CHAN) ① **CHAN9023**
Cincinnati Pops, E. Kunzel *Concert*
(11/92) (TELA) ① **CD80294**
Boston Pops, A. Fiedler (r1956) *Concert*
(1/94) (RCA) ① **09026 61429-2**
Tapiola Sinfonietta, P. Järvi (r1993) *Concert*
(6/94) (BIS) ① **BIS-CD630**
Hallé, J. Barbirolli (r1954) *Concert*
(7/95) (DUTT) ① **CDSJB1002**
Escales—symphonic poem (1922)
1. Rome-Palermo; 2. Tunis-Nefia; 3. Valencia.
Detroit SO, P. Paray *Concert*
(4/91) (MERC) ① **432 003-2MM**
Boston SO, C. Munch (r1956) *Concert*
(4/93) (RCA) ① **09026 61500-2**
FRNO, L. Stokowski (bp1958) *Concert*
(2/94) (MUSI) ① **MACD-778**
Montreal SO, C. Dutoit (r1992) *Concert*
(6/94) (DECC) ① **440 332-2DH**
San Francisco SO, P. Monteux (r1946) *Concert*
(9/94) (RCA) ① **[15] 09026 61893-2**
Hommage à Mozart—rondo: orchestra (1956)
Montreal SO, C. Dutoit (r1992) *Concert*
(6/94) (DECC) ① **440 332-2DH**
Louisville Concerto (1953)
Montreal SO, C. Dutoit (r1992) *Concert*
(6/94) (DECC) ① **440 332-2DH**
Suite Symphonique, 'Paris'—perc, pf, cel, harm, xylophone, 5 winds & stgs (1930)
1. Le métro; 2. Faubourgs; 3. La mosquée de Paris; 4. Restaurant au Bois de Boulogne; 5. La Paquebot 'Ile de France'; 6. Parade Foraine.
NY Harmonie Ens, S. Richman *Concert*
(7/92) (MUSI) ① **MACD-649**
Montreal SO, C. Dutoit (r1992) *Concert*
(6/94) (DECC) ① **440 332-2DH**
Symphonie concertante—oboe and strings (1949)
J. de Lancie, LSO, A. Previn (r1966) *Concert*
(12/91) (RCA) ① **GD87989**

SECTION II: CHAMBER

Aria—fl, vn & pf or fl/ob, cl & pf (1930)
T. L. Christiansen, Collegium Musicum Sols (r1994)
Concert (12/95) (KONT) ① **32202**
Carignane—bassoon and piano (1953)
K. Walker, J. Drake *Concert*
(10/89) (REGE) ① **REGCD104**
Entr'acte—flute and harp/violin and guitar (1937)
H. Schellenberger, M-A. Süss *Concert*
(12/91) (DENO) ① **CO-76611**
V. Taylor, T. Kain *Concert* (9/92) (TALL) ① **TP003**
B. Fromanger, M. Klinko (r1993) *Concert*
(2/94) (EMI) ① **CDC7 54884-2**
T. L. Christiansen, Collegium Musicum Sols (r1994)
Concert (12/95) (KONT) ① **32202**
Histoires—flute & piano (1933) (Nos. 1,2,5 & 8-10 of pf work)
1. La meneuse de tortues d'or; 2. Le petit âne blanc; 3. Dans la maison triste; 4. La cage de cristal; 5. La marchande d'eau fraîche; 6. Le cortège de Balkis.
T. L. Christiansen, Collegium Musicum Sols (r1994)
Concert (12/95) (KONT) ① **32202**
2 Interludes from 'Le burlador'—flute, violin and harpsichord/harp (1946)
Auréole (r1991) *Concert* (7/93) (KOCH) ① **37102-2**
T. L. Christiansen, Collegium Musicum Sols (r1994)
Concert (12/95) (KONT) ① **32202**
Jeux—flute/violin and piano (1923)
T. L. Christiansen, Collegium Musicum Sols (r1994)
Concert (12/95) (KONT) ① **32202**

2 Mouvements—2 fls, cl & bn or fl, ob, cl & bn (1922)
1. Allant; 2. Assez vif et rhythmé.
T. L. Christiansen, Collegium Musicum Sols (r1994)
Concert (12/95) (KONT) ① **32202**
3 Pièces brèves—wind quintet (1930)
Pro Arte Wind Quintet *Concert*
(1/93) (NIMB) ① **NI5327**
Berlin Phil Wind Qnt *Concert*
(4/93) (BIS) ① **BIS-CD536**
Reykjavik Wind Qnt (r1993) *Concert*
(10/95) (CHAN) ① **CHAN9362**
T. L. Christiansen, Collegium Musicum Sols (r1994)
Concert (12/95) (KONT) ① **32202**
5 Pièces en trio—oboe, clarinet and bassoon (1935)
London Wind Trio *Concert*
(9/92) (CARL) ① **MCD38**

SECTION III: INSTRUMENTAL

L' Espiègle au village de Lilliput—piano (1937)
B. Lerner *Concert* (1/89) (ETCE) ① **KTC1061**
10 Histoires—piano (1931)
1. La meneuse de tortues d'or; 2. Le petite âne blanc; 3. Le vieux mendiant; 4. A giddy girl; 5. Dans la maison triste; 6. Le palais abandonné; 7. Bajo la mesa; 8. La cage de cristal; 9. La marchande d'eau fraîche; 10. Le Cortège de Balkis.
P. Katin (r1990) *Concert* (7/93) (SIMA) ① **PSC1067**
2. C. Ortiz *Concert* (6/87) (CARL) ① **PCD846**
2. J. Heifetz, B. Smith (r1965) *Concert*
(11/94) (RCA) ① **[65] 09026 61778-2(45)**
Pièce pour flûte seule (1936)
T. L. Christiansen (r1994) *Concert*
(12/95) (KONT) ① **32202**
6 Pièces—harp (1917)
2. Scherzetto.
2. M. Klinko *Concert* (8/93) (EMI) ① **CDC7 54467-2**
2. L. Laskine (r1975) *Concert*
(12/93) (ERAT) ① **4509-92131-2**
Toccata sur le nom d'Albert Roussel—piano (1929)
M. Fingerhut *Concert* (9/88) (CHAN) ① **CHAN8578**

SECTION IV: VOCAL AND CHORAL

4 Chansons de Don Quichotte (1932)
1. Chanson du départ de Don Quichotte (wds. Ronsard); 2. Chanson à Dulcinée (wds. Arnoux); 3. Chanson du Duc (wds. Arnoux); 4. Chanson de la mort de Don Quichotte (wds. Arnoux).
J. Van Dam, J-P. Collard *Concert*
(1/90) (EMI) ① **CDC7 49288-2**
H. Kiichli, Bratislava RSO, Adriano *Concert*
(3/91) (MARC) ① **8 223287**
J. van Dam, Lyon Op Orch, K. Nagano *Concert*
(2/93) (VIRG) ① **VC7 59236-2**
F. Chaliapin, orch, J. Ibert (r1933) *Concert*
(6/93) (PREI) ① **[2] 89207**

SECTION V: STAGE WORKS

Don Quichotte—film (1933)
1. Chanson de Sancho (orch Adriano).
H. Kiichli, Bratislava RSO, Adriano *Concert*
(3/91) (MARC) ① **8 223287**
Golgotha—concert suite from film score (1935)
EXCERPTS: 1. La fête de Pâques; 2. Les vendeurs au Temple; 3. Le Calvaire; 4. La crucifixion; 5. L'agonie—La mise au tombeau.
Bratislava RSO, Adriano *Concert*
(3/91) (MARC) ① **8 223287**
Le Jardinier de Samos—concert suite from incidental music (1925)
1. Ouverture; 2. Air de danse; 3. Prélude, Act 2; 4. Prélude, Act 4; 5. Finale (animé).
T. L. Christiansen, Collegium Musicum Sols (r1994)
Concert (12/95) (KONT) ① **32202**
Macbeth—concert suite from film score (1948)
EXCERPTS: 1. Overture; 2. Murder of King Duncan; 3. Macbeth after the murder; 4. The ghost of Banquo; 5. Death of Lady Macbeth; 6. Triumph of Macduff's armies.
Bratislava RSO, Adriano *Concert*
(3/91) (MARC) ① **8 223287**

IL VERSO, Antonio (?c1560–1621) Italy

SECTION IV: VOCAL AND CHORAL

Lasciatemi morire—madrigal: 5vv (1619)
(Wds. Rinuccini)
Capriccio Stravagante, S. Sempé (hpd/dir) *Concert*
(2/94) (DHM) ① **05472 77190-2**

ILES, John Henry (1871–1951) England

SECTION I: ORCHESTRAL

Championship Medley No. 3—brass band (1935)
Massed Brass Bands, J. H. Iles (r1935) *Concert*
(11/93) (BEUL) ① **1PD2**
Homeland Melodies—medley: brass bands (1936)
Massed Brass Bands, J. H. Iles (r1936) *Concert*
(11/93) (BEUL) ① **1PD2**
Sing a song—medley: brass band (1935)
Massed Brass Bands, J. H. Iles (r1935) *Concert*
(11/93) (BEUL) ① **1PD2**

INDIA, Sigismondo d' (c1582–1629) Italy

SECTION IV: VOCAL AND CHORAL

Le musiche I—secular song collection: 1-2vv & continuo (pub 1609) (1v unless indicated)
1. Andate a mitigar; 2. Apertamente dice la gente (wds. Chiabrera; 3. Belissima Dori; 4. Ben'è ver ch'ei pargoleggia; 5. Cara mia cetra andianne; 6. Che fai, Tirsi gentile (2vv: wds. Chiabrera); 7. Che farai, Meliseo?; 8. Crud'Amarilli, che col nome ancora (wds. Guarini); 9. Da l'onde del mio pianto; 10. Donna i' vorrei dir molto (wds. Guarini); 11. Donna, mentr'io vi miro (wds. Guarini); 12. Dove potro mai gir (2vv); 13. Ecco la luce (wds. Chiabrera); 14. E diceva piangendo (wds. Tasso); 15. Ferma, ascolta, Licori; 16. Ferma, Dorinda mia; 17. Forse averra (wds. Tasso); 18. Forsennata grivada (wds. Tasso); 19. Forse vien fuor l'aurora; 20. Fresch'herbette novelle (2vv); 21. Intenerite voi, lagrime mie (wds. Rinuccini); 22. Io son del duol vi vinto; 23. Io viddi in terra (wds. Petrarch); 24. La tra le selve; 25. La tra 'l sangue (wds. Tasso); 26. Ma che? squallid'è oscuro (wds. Tasso); 27. Ma se le mie speranz' (wds. Guarini); 28. Mirate dal gran tronco; 29. Misera non credea (wds. Tasso); 30. Nelle guancie di rose; 31. Occhi begli et amorosi; 32. O dolcezz' amarissime d'Amore (wds. Guarini); 33. O quanto in suia beltà; 34. O lungamente sospirato (wds. Guarini); 35. O primavera, gioventù dell'anno (wds. Guarini); 36. O se torna io mio sol; 37. Piange madonna; 38. Pianget', occhi miei lassi; 39. Piangono al pianger mio (wds. Rinuccini); 40. Qual fiera si crudel; 41. Quella vermiglia rosa (wds. Rinuccini); 42. Qui pur vedrolla (wds. Guarini); 43. Riede la primavera (wds. Marino); 44. Se bel rio (wds. Chiabrera); 45. Se'n me donna movete; 46. Son gli accenti ch'ascolto; 47. Sovente all'hor (wds. Tasso); 48. Tu parti, ahi lasso (wds. Marino); 49. Una placid'auretta; 50. Un di soletto (wds. Chiabrera); 51. Vaghe faville; 52. Vorrei baciarti, o Filli (wds. Marino); 53. Vostro fui, vostro son (wds. B. Tasso).
N. Rogers, C. Tilney, A. Bailes, J. Savall, P. Ros (r1975) *Concert* (1/93) (ARCH) ① **437 075-2AT**
8, 21, 35, 37, 39, 41. N. Rogers, P. O'Dette, A. Lawrence-King *Concert*
(4/93) (VIRG) ① **VC7 59231-2**
39. E. Kirkby, A. Rooley *Concert*
(2/87) (HYPE) ① **CDA66106**
39. E. Kirkby, A. Rooley *Concert*
(9/87) (HYPE) ① **CDA66227**
Le musiche III—secular song collection: 1-2vv & continuo (pub 1618) (1v unless indicated)
1. Ahi! che fia; 2. Arditi baci; 3. Com'è soave cosa (wds. Guarini); 4. Della nascente aurora (2vv); 5. Donna, siam rei di morte; 6. E tu parti (wds. Castellano); 7. Giunto a la tomba (wds. Tasso); 8. Hor che'l ciel (wds. Petrarch); 9. Io veggio our pietade ancora (wds. Guarini); 10. Lagrimat'occhi miei; 12. O bella destra (wds. Tasso); 13. O ben mio, dove sei?; 14. Occhi, convien morire; 15. Questa mia Aurora (2vv); 16. Schemiscimi, crudele; 17. Soccors'ohime, ben mio; 18. Tutto il di piango (wds. Petrarch); 19. Voi ch'ascoltate (wds. Petrarch).
1, 18. N. Rogers, P. O'Dette, A. Lawrence-King *Concert* (4/93) (VIRG) ① **VC7 59231-2**
Le musiche IV—secular song collection: 1-2vv & continuo (pub 1621) (1v unless indicated)
1. Amico, hai vinto (wds. Tasso); 2. Che stringo? ah' dove sono? (wds. cpsr); 3. Che veggio, ohimè che miro?—Lamneto d'Orfeo (wds. cpsr); 4. Di quel rosignuolo; 5. Mentre che'l cor (wds. Petrarch); 6. Occhi della mia vita (2vv); 7. Pallidetta qual viola è (wds. Ferranti); 8. Piansi e cantai (wds. Bembo); 9. Quell'infedele (wds. Queiroli); 10. Sprezzami, bionda

(wds. Ferranti); 11. Torna, dunque, deh torna (wds. Marino); 12. Tu mi lasci, o cruda (wds. Bonardo); 13. Vogli il mio duol scoprir (wds. Ferranti).
1. E. Kirkby, A. Rooley *Concert*
(2/87) (HYPE) ① **CDA66106**
3, 5, 7, 9, 10, 12. N. Rogers, P. O'Dette, A. Lawrence-King *Concert*
(4/93) (VIRG) ① **VC7 59231-2**
5. J. Bowman, S. Sempé, J. Bernfeld *Concert*
(9/89) (ARIO) ① **ARN68046**
Le musiche V—secular song collection: 1v & continuo (pub 1623)
1. Ancidetemi pur—Lamento di Giasone (wds. cpsr); 2. Infelice Didone (wds. cpsr); 3. Io che dal ciel; 4. Misera me sia vero (wds. cpsr); 5. O che gradita; 6. O del cielo d'amor unico sole; 7. O gioia de mortali; 8. Questo dardo, quest'arco; 9. Sfere fermate; 10. Su, destati, Clori; 11. Torna il sereno zefiro.
1, 7, 9, 10, 11. N. Rogers, P. O'Dette, A. Lawrence-King *Concert* (4/93) (VIRG) ① **VC7 59231-2**
4. E. Kirkby, A. Rooley *Concert*
(2/87) (HYPE) ① **CDA66106**
6. J. Bowman, S. Sempé, J. Bernfeld *Concert*
(9/89) (ARIO) ① **ARN68046**
8. E. Kirkby, A. Rooley *Concert*
(9/87) (HYPE) ① **CDA66227**
8, 9, 11, E. Kirkby, A. Rooley *Concert*
(2/87) (HYPE) ① **CDA66106**

INDY, (Paul Marie Théodore) Vincent d' (1851–1931) France

SECTION I: ORCHESTRAL

Concerto for piano, flute, cello and strings, Op. 89 (1926)
P. Dechorgnat, J. Ferrandis, H. Noël, J-J. Wiederker, J-J. Wiederker CO, F. Bouaniche (r1992) *Concert*
(6/95) (SCHW) ① **310652**
Diptyque méditerranéen—symphonic poem, Op. 87 (1925-6)
Monte Carlo PO, G. Prêtre *Poème des rivages.*
(3/92) (EMI) ① **CDM7 63954-2**
Fantaisie sur des thèmes populaires français—oboe and orchestra, Op. 31 (1888)
P. Cousu, Württemberg PO, J-M. Burfin (r1992) *Concert* (1/95) (MARC) ① **8 223659**
La Forêt enchantée—symphonic legend, Op. 8 (1878)
Loire PO, P. Dervaux *Concert*
(3/92) (EMI) ① **CDM7 63953-2**
Istar—symphonic variations, Op. 42 (1896)
Loire PO, P. Dervaux *Concert*
(3/92) (EMI) ① **CDM7 63953-2**
San Francisco SO, P. Monteux (r1945) *Concert*
(9/94) (RCA) ① [15] **09026 61893-2**
Jour d'été à la montagne—symphonic triptych, Op. 61 (1905)
1. Aurore; 2. Jour (après-midi sous les pins); 3. Soir.
French Rad PO, M. Janowski (r1991) *Symphonie, Op. 25.* (7/93) (ERAT) ① **2292-45821-2**
Karadec—suite: orchestra, Op. 34 (1890)
1. Prélude; 2. Chanson; 3. Noce bretonne.
Württemberg PO, G. Nopre (r1992) *Concert*
(7/95) (MARC) ① **8 223654**
Lied—cello/viola and orchestra, Op. 19 (1884)
J. Lloyd Webber, ECO, Y.P. Tortelier *Concert*
(6/91) (PHIL) ① **432 084-2PH**
Médée—suite: orchestra, Op. 47 (1898)
1. Prélude; 2. Pantomime; 3. L'attente de Médée; 4. Médée et Jason; 5. Le triomphe aurole.
Württemberg PO, G. Nopre (r1992) *Concert*
(7/95) (MARC) ① **8 223654**
Poème des rivages—symphonic suite, Op. 77 (1919-21)
Monte Carlo PO, G. Prêtre *Diptyque méditerranéen.*
(3/92) (EMI) ① **CDM7 63954-2**
Saugefleurie—legend after de Bonnières, Op. 21 (1884)
Strasbourg PO, T. Guschlbauer (r1992) *Concert*
(9/93) (AUVI) ① **V4686**
Württemberg PO, G. Nopre (r1992) *Concert*
(1/95) (MARC) ① **8 223654**
Souvenirs—poem, Op. 62 (1906)
Strasbourg PO, T. Guschlbauer (r1992) *Concert*
(9/93) (AUVI) ① **V4686**
Württemberg PO, G. Nopre (r1992) *Concert*
(7/95) (MARC) ① **8 223654**
Symphonie sur un chant montagnard français in G—piano and orchestra, Op. 25 (1886)
N. Henriot-Schweitzer, Boston SO, C. Munch *Concert*
(3/89) (RCA) ① **GD86805**

J-Y. Thibaudet, Montreal SO, C. Dutoit *Franck: Symphony.* (1/92) (DECC) ① **430 278-2DH**
A. Ciccolini, Paris Orch, S. Baudo *Symphony 2.*
(3/92) (EMI) ① **CDM7 63952-2**
C. Collard, French Rad PO, M. Janowski (r1991) *Jour d'été, Op. 61.* (7/93) (ERAT) ① **2292-45821-2**
V. Traficante, RPO, J. Serebrier (r1993) *Concert*
(6/94) (CARL) ① **MCD71**
M. Shapiro, San Francisco SO, P. Monteux (r1941) *Concert* (9/94) (RCA) ① [15] **09026 61893-2**
F-J. Thiollier, Ireland National SO, A. de Almeida (r1993) *Concert* (1/95) (NAXO) ① **8 550754**
N. Henriot-Schweitzer, Boston SO, C. Munch (r1958) *Berlioz: Harold in Italy.*
(5/95) (RCA) ① **09026 62582-2**
Symphony No. 2 in B flat, Op. 57 (1902-03)
Toulouse Capitole Orch, M. Plasson *Symphonie, Op. 25.* (3/92) (EMI) ① **CDM7 63952-2**
San Francisco SO, P. Monteux (r1942) *Concert*
(9/94) (RCA) ① [15] **09026 61893-2**
Symphony No. 3, 'de bello gallico', Op. 70 (1916-18)
Strasbourg PO, T. Guschlbauer (r1992) *Concert*
(9/93) (AUVI) ① **V4686**
6 Tableaux de voyage—orchestra, Op. 36 (1888 orch 1891-92) (after pf works Op 33/1-2,4-6 & 13)
1. Préamble; 2. En marche; 3. Le glas; 4. Lac vert; 5. La poste; 6. Rêve.
Württemberg PO, G. Nopre (r1992) *Concert*
(1/95) (MARC) ① **8 223659**
Wallenstein—three symphonic overtures after Schiller, Op. 12 (1873, rev 1879-81)
1. Le camp; 2. Les piccolomini (1873), Max et Thécla (1881); 3. Le mort de Wallenstein.
Loire PO, P. Dervaux *Concert*
(3/92) (EMI) ① **CDM7 63953-2**

SECTION II: CHAMBER

String Quartet No. 1 in D, Op. 35 (1890)
Kodály Qt *String Quartet 2.*
(10/91) (MARC) ① **8 223140**
String Quartet No. 2 in E, Op. 45 (1897)
Kodály Qt *String Quartet 1.*
(10/91) (MARC) ① **8 223140**

SECTION III: INSTRUMENTAL

Menuet sur le nom d'Haydn—piano, Op. 65 (1909)
M. Fingerhut *Concert* (9/88) (CHAN) ① **CHAN8578**
Prélude in B minor—organ, Op. 66 (1911)
M-B. Dufourcet (r1992) *Concert*
(6/95) (PRIO) ① **PRCD422**

SECTION IV: VOCAL AND CHORAL

Lied maritime—song, Op. 43 (Wds. cpsr)
D. Fischer-Dieskau, H. Höll (r c1987) *Concert*
(12/95) (TELD) ① **4509-97457-2**
Madrigal—song, Op. 4 (cpted 1872) (Wds. de Bonnières)
D. Fischer-Dieskau, H. Höll (r c1987) *Concert*
(12/95) (TELD) ① **4509-97457-2**

SECTION V: STAGE WORKS

L' Etranger—action musicale: 2 acts, Op. 53 (1903—Brussels) (Lib. cpsr)
EXCERPTS: 1. Act 2, Prélude.
1. Württemberg PO, G. Nopre (r1992) *Concert*
(1/95) (MARC) ① **8 223659**
Fervaal—action musicale: prologue; 3 acts, Op. 40 (1897—Brussels)
EXCERPTS: 1. Prélude.
1. San Francisco SO, P. Monteux (r1945) *Concert*
(9/94) (RCA) ① [15] **09026 61893-2**
1. Württemberg PO, G. Nopre (r1992) *Concert*
(1/95) (MARC) ① **8 223659**

INFANTE, Manuel (1883–1958) Spain

SECTION II: CHAMBER

Danses Andalouses—piano: four hands (1921)
1. Ritmo; 2. Sentimiento; 3. Gracia.
K. Labèque, M. Labèque (r1993) *Concert*
(9/94) (PHIL) ① **438 938-2PH**

IPPOLITOV-IVANOV, Mikhail Mikhailovich (1859–1935) Russia/USSR

SECTION I: ORCHESTRAL

Armenian Rhapsody on National Themes—orchestra, Op. 48 (1895)
V. Šimčisko, Bratislava RSO, D. Johanos (r1993) *Concert* (10/94) (MARC) ① **8 223629**
Caucasian Sketches, Op. 10 (1894)
1. In a mountain pass; 2. In a village; 3. In a mosque; 4. Procession of the Sardar.
Armenian PO, L. Tjeknavorian *Concert*
(4/92) (ASV) ① **CDDCA773**
BBC PO, F. Glushchenko (pp1993) *Concert*
(5/95) (CHAN) ① **CHAN9321**
Baltimore SO, D. Zinman (r1994) *Concert*
(12/95) (TELA) ① **CD80378**
2. Philadelphia, L. Stokowski (r1925) *Concert*
(7/94) (BIDD) ① **WHL005**
4. St Louis SO, L. Slatkin *Concert*
(6/89) (RCA) ① **RD87716**
4. National PO, L. Stokowski *Concert*
(4/92) (EMI) ① **CDM7 64140-2**
4. Black Dyke Mills Band, J. Watson (r1992: arr Sparke) *Concert* (4/93) (POLY) ① **QPRL053D**
4. Empire Brass (r1992; arr. R. Smedvig) *Concert*
(1/94) (TELA) ① **CD80305**
4. Boston Pops, A. Fiedler (r1958) *Concert*
(1/94) (RCA) ① **09026 61249-2**
4. Philadelphia, L. Stokowski (r1927) *Concert*
(7/94) (BIDD) ① **WHL005**
From Ossian's songs—three musical tableaux, Op. 56 (1925)
1. Lake Lyano; 2. Kolyma's lament; 3. Ossian's monologue on contemporary heroes.
Bratislava RSO, D. Johanos (r1993) *Concert*
(10/94) (MARC) ① **8 223629**
Jubilee March—orchestra
Bratislava RSO, D. Johanos (r1993) *Concert*
(10/94) (MARC) ① **8 223629**
Symphonic Scherzo, Op. 2 (1882)
Bratislava RSO, D. Johanos (r1993) *Concert*
(10/94) (MARC) ① **8 223629**
Yar-khmel', 'Spring Overture', Op. 1 (1882)
Bratislava RSO, D. Johanos (r1993) *Concert*
(10/94) (MARC) ① **8 223629**

SECTION IV: VOCAL AND CHORAL

An Episode from the Life of Schubert—tenor and orchestra, Op. 61 (1920)
M. Dvorský, Bratislava RSO, D. Johanos (r1993) *Concert* (10/94) (MARC) ① **8 223629**
In the long grey twilight—song
I. Tartakov, anon (r1901) *Concert*
(6/93) (PEAR) ① [3] **GEMMCDS9997/9(1)**
In the Manger (attrib)
BBC PO, M. Bamert (r1994: orch Stokowski) *Concert*
(6/95) (CHAN) ① **CHAN9349**

IRELAND, John (Nicholson) (1879–1962) England

SECTION I: ORCHESTRAL

A Comedy Overture—brass band (1934) (later orch version as 'A London Overture')
London Collegiate Brass, J. Stobart *Concert*
(9/86) (CRD) ① **CRD3434**
City of London Wind Ens, G. Brand (arr. Steadman-Allen) *Concert* (3/90) (LDR) ① **LDRCD1012**
GUS Band, G. Brand (r1976) *Concert*
(2/94) (EMI) ① **CDM7 64716-2**
Concertino pastorale—string orchesttra (1939)
Bournemouth Sinfonietta, G. Hurst *Concert*
(8/85) (CHAN) ① **CHAN8375**
CLS, R. Hickox (r1994) *Concert*
(11/95) (CHAN) ① **CHAN9376**
Concerto for Piano and Orchestra in E flat (1930)
E. Parkin, LPO, B. Thomson *Concert*
(1/87) (CHAN) ① **CHAN8461**
G. Tozer, Melbourne SO, D. Measham *Rubbra: Violin Concerto.* (1/87) (UNIC) ① **DKPCD9056**
K. Stott, RPO, V. Handley *Concert*
(1/90) (CONI) ① **CDCF175**
E. Joyce, Hallé, L. Heward (r1942) *Moeran: Symphony.* (5/93) (DUTT) ① **CDAX8001**
C. Horsley, RPO, B. Cameron (r1957) *Concert*
(2/94) (EMI) ① **CDM7 64716-2**

The **Land of Lost Content**—song cycle: 1v
and piano (1921) (Wds. A E Housman)
1. The Lent Lily; 2. Lads love; 3. Goal and Wicket; 4.
The Vain Desire; 5. The Encounter; 6. Epilogue.
1, 3-6. A. Rolfe Johnson, G. Johnson (r c1994)
Concert (8/95) (HYPE) ① [2] **CDA66471/2**
My true love hath my heart—song: 1v and
piano (Wds. P Sidney)
S. Leonard, M. Martineau (r1993) *Concert*
(3/95) (UNIT) ① **88016-2**
Sea Fever—song (1913) (Wds. Masefield)
T. Allen, R. Vignoles *Concert*
(11/87) (HYPE) ① **CDA66165**
R. Herincx, J. Constable *Concert*
(4/92) (GAMU) ① **GAMD506**
R. Lloyd, N. Walker (r1977) *Concert*
(2/94) (EMI) ① **CDM7 64716-2**
B. Terfel, M. Martineau (r1994) *Concert*
(8/95) (DG) ① **445 946-2GH**
Songs of the Wayfarer (c1903) (Wds.
various)
1. Memory (wds. W. Blake); 2. When daffodils begin
to peer (wds. Shakespeare); 3. English May (wds. D.
G. Rossetti); 4. I was not sorrowful (wds. E. Dowson).
2. A. Rolfe Johnson, G. Johnson *Concert*
(5/92) (HYPE) ① **CDA66480**
Songs Sacred and Profane—song cycle
(1929-31)
1. The advent (wds. A. Meynell); 2. Hymn for a child
(wds. S. T. Warner); 3. My fair (wds. A. Meynell); 4.
The salley gardens (wds. W. B. Yeats); 5. The
soldier's return (wds. S. T. Warner); 6. The
scapegoat (wds. S. T. Warner).
4. J. Baker, G. Moore (r1967) *Concert*
(2/94) (EMI) ① **CDM7 64716-2**
4. J. Baker, G. Moore (r1967) *Concert*
(11/94) (EMI) ① **CDM5 65009-2**
4. S. Leonard, M. Martineau (r1993) *Concert*
(3/95) (UNIT) ① **88016-2**
3 Songs to Poems by Thomas Hardy (1925)
1. Summer schemes; 2. Her song; 3. Weathers.
2. S. Leonard, M. Martineau (r1993) *Concert*
(3/95) (UNIT) ① **88016-2**
The **Trellis**—song: 1v and piano (Wds. A
Huxley)
S. Leonard, M. Martineau (r1993) *Concert*
(3/95) (UNIT) ① **88016-2**
The **Vagabond**—song: 1v & piano (Wds. J
Masefield)
B. Terfel, M. Martineau (r1994) *Concert*
(8/95) (DG) ① **445 946-2GH**

IRVINE, J. Seymour *(1836–1887)*
Scotland

SECTION IV: VOCAL AND CHORAL

The **Lord's my shepherd (Psalm 23)**—hymn
tune: Crimond (Wds. Scottish Psalter, 1650)
Huddersfield Choral Soc, W. Morris (r1964) *Concert*
(6/93) (DECC) ① **436 402-2DWO**

IRWIN, May *(1862–1938)*
Canada/USA

SECTION IV: VOCAL AND CHORAL

The **Bully Song**—song from 'The Widow
Jones' (1893) (arr from negro folksong)
Cincinnati Uni Sngrs, Cincinnati Uni Th Orch, E.
Rivers (r1978) *Concert* (4/94) (NEW) ① **80221-2**
M. Irwin, Broadway Cast (r1907) *Concert*
(5/94) (PEAR) ① [3] **GEMMCDS9050/2(1)**
The **Frog Song**—song from the show 'The
Swell Miss Fitzwell' (1897)
M. Irwin, Broadway Cast (r1907) *Concert*
(5/94) (PEAR) ① [3] **GEMMCDS9050/2(1)**

ISAAC, Heinrich *(c1450–1517)*
Flanders

may also be known as Henricus Yzac

SECTION IV: VOCAL AND CHORAL

A la battaglia—4vv
London Pro Musica, B. Thomas *Concert*
(2/87) (CARL) ① **PCD825**
London Pro Musica, B. Thomas (arr. instr) *Concert*
(2/87) (CARL) ① **PCD825**
Angeli, Archangeli
Clerk's Group, E. Wickham (r1994) *Concert*
(3/95) (ASV) ① **CDGAU139**
De tous biens playne—quodlibet: 2vv (from
Segovia MS)
Daedalus Ens *Concert*
(12/92) (ACCE) ① **ACC9176D**

Donna di dentro dalla tua casa—4vv
London Pro Musica, B. Thomas *Concert*
(2/87) (CARL) ① **PCD825**
Fortuna disperata—litany of All Saints: 5vv
(from Segovia MS)
Daedalus Ens *Concert*
(12/92) (ACCE) ① **ACC9176D**
La morra—4vv
London Pro Musica, B. Thomas *Concert*
(2/87) (CARL) ① **PCD825**
Missa de apostolis—6vv
Tallis Scholars, P. Phillips *Concert*
(10/91) (GIME) ① **CDGIM023**
Morte que fay—chanson: 4vv (from Segovia
MS)
Daedalus Ens *Concert*
(12/92) (ACCE) ① **ACC9176D**
Ne più bella di queste—madrigal (4vv)
London Pro Musica, B. Thomas *Concert*
(2/87) (CARL) ① **PCD825**
Optime pastor—motet (6vv)
Tallis Scholars, P. Phillips *Concert*
(10/91) (GIME) ① **CDGIM023**
Palle, palle—4vv
London Pro Musica, B. Thomas *Concert*
(2/87) (CARL) ① **PCD825**
Quis dabit capiti meo aquam—motet (4vv)
London Pro Musica, B. Thomas *Concert*
(2/87) (CARL) ① **PCD825**
Regine caeli laetare—motet: 5vv
Tallis Scholars, P. Phillips *Concert*
(10/91) (GIME) ① **CDGIM023**
Resurrexi et adhuc tecum sum—introitus
Tallis Scholars, P. Phillips *Concert*
(10/91) (GIME) ① **CDGIM023**
Tota pulchra es—motet: 4vv
Hilliard Ens *Concert* (6/91) (HYPE) ① **CDA66370**
(10/91) (GIME) ① **CDGIM023**
Virgo prudentissima—motet: 6vv
Tallis Scholars, P. Phillips *Concert*
(10/91) (GIME) ① **CDGIM023**

ISAACS, Mark *(b 1958) Australia*

SECTION II: CHAMBER

So it does—chamber ensemble (1985)
Australia Ens *Concert* (7/92) (TALL) ① **TP002**

ISHAM, Mark *(20th Cent) USA*

SECTION V: STAGE WORKS

The **Hitcher**—film score (1986)
EXCERPTS: 1. Headlights—Main Title; 2. The
Chosen; 3. Keys; 4. Dust & Gasoline; 5. Dream; 6.
Dogs; 7. Suicide; 8. Gun; 9. Cars & Helicopters; 10.
Motel; 11. Transfer; 12. Endgame; 13. Guards &
Cards; 14. The Hitcher—End Credits.
1. OST *Concert* (5/93) (SILV) ① **SILVAD3001**

ISHII, Maki *(b 1936) Japan*

SECTION III: INSTRUMENTAL

Black Intention—recorder (1975)
D. Laurin (r1993) *Concert*
(8/94) (BIS) ① **BIS-CD655**
east.green.spring—recorder, Op. 94 (1991)
D. Laurin (r1993) *Concert*
(8/94) (BIS) ① **BIS-CD655**

ÍSÓLFSSON, Páll *(1893–1974)*
Iceland

SECTION I: ORCHESTRAL

Festival March (c1950)
Iceland SO, P. Sakari (r1993) *Concert*
(10/93) (CHAN) ① **CHAN9180**
Festival Overture (c1950)
Iceland SO, P. Sakari (r1993) *Concert*
(10/93) (CHAN) ① **CHAN9180**

ISOUARD, Nicolas *(1775–1818)*
France

SECTION V: STAGE WORKS

Joconde—opera: 3 acts (1814—Paris) (Lib.
Etienne)
Dans un délire extrême M-N. Bouvet, anon (r1903)
Concert (9/91) (SYMP) ① **SYMCD1089**

IVAN IV, Tsar *(1530–1584)*
Russia

known as Ivan the Terrible

SECTION IV: VOCAL AND CHORAL

Kuimi pokhvalienui mi—chorus a capella
Tallis Scholars, P. Phillips *Concert*
(6/91) (GIME) ① **CDGIM002**

IVANOV, Mikhail Mikhaylovich
(1849–1927) Russia

SECTION IV: VOCAL AND CHORAL

The **Lord's Prayer**—Russian liturgical
chant
N. Gedda, Paris Russian Orthodox Cath Ch, E. Evetz
Concert (1/93) (PHIL) ① **434 174-2PM**

SECTION V: STAGE WORKS

Zabava Putyatishna—opera
Solovej Budomirovich's serenade L. Sobinov,
anon (r1901) *Concert*
(6/93) (PEAR) ① [3] **GEMMCDS9997/9(1)**

IVES, Charles E(dward)
(1874–1954) USA

SECTION I: ORCHESTRAL

Central Park in the Dark—small orchestra
(1906)
Boston SO, S. Ozawa *Concert*
(10/88) (DG) ① **423 243-2GC**
Chicago SO, M. Tilson Thomas *Concert*
(10/88) (SONY) ① **SK42381**
NYPO, L. Bernstein (pp1988) *Concert*
(8/90) (DG) ① **429 220-2GH**
St Louis SO, L. Slatkin *Concert*
(4/93) (RCA) ① **09026 61222-2**
NYPO, L. Bernstein, S. Ozawa, M. Peress *Concert*
(5/93) (SONY) ① **SMK47568**
Country Band March—small orchestra
(1903)
New England Orch, J. Sinclair *Concert*
(2/91) (KOCH) ① **37025-2**
**Fugue in 4 Keys, on 'The Shining
Shore'**—flute, cornet and strings (1897)
St Louis SO, L. Slatkin *Concert*
(4/93) (RCA) ① **09026 61222-2**
The **Gong on the Hook and Ladder,
'Firemen's Parade on Main Street'**—small
orchestra (?1911)
NYPO, L. Bernstein (pp1988) *Concert*
(8/90) (DG) ① **429 220-2GH**
Modern Ens, I. Metzmacher *Concert*
(6/93) (EMI) ① **CDC7 54552-2**
Holidays—symphony (compiled from various
sources)
1. Washington's Birthday (1909); 2. Decoration Day
(1912); 3. The Fourth of July (1911-13); 4.
Thanksgiving Day (1912).
Chicago Sym Chor, Chicago SO, M. Tilson Thomas
Concert (10/88) (SONY) ① **SK42381**
**March No. 3, with 'My Old Kentucky
Home'**—orchestra (1892)
St Louis SO, L. Slatkin *Concert*
(4/93) (RCA) ① **09026 61222-2**
**Orchestral Set No. 1, 'A New England
Symphony'**—Three Places in New England
(1908 rev 1929: ed Sinclair large orch 1976)
1. The Saint-Gaudens in Boston Common; 2.
Putnam's Camp, Redding, Connecticut; 3. The
Housatonic at Stockbridge.
Boston SO, M. Tilson Thomas *Concert*
(10/88) (DG) ① **423 243-2GC**
New England Orch, J. Sinclair *Concert*
(2/91) (KOCH) ① **37025-2**
St Louis SO, L. Slatkin *Concert*
(4/93) (RCA) ① **09026 61222-2**
Orpheus CO *Concert* (10/94) (DG) ① **439 869-2GH**
Cleveland Orch, C. von Dohnányi (r1993) *Concert*
(12/95) (DECC) ① **443 776-2DH**
Orchestral Set No. 2 (1909)
1. An Elegy to our Forefathers; 2. The Rockstrewn
Hills Join in the People's Outdoor Meeting; 3. From
Hanover Square North ...
Cincinnati Philh, G. Samuel, CCM Perc Ens, CCM
Chbr Ch (r1994) *Concert*
(5/95) (CENT) ① **CRC2205**
Cleveland Orch Chor, Cleveland Orch, C. von
Dohnányi (r1994) *Concert*
(12/95) (DECC) ① **443 776-2DH**

The **Pond**—small orchestra (1906)
Modern Ens, I. Metzmacher *Concert*
(6/93) (EMI) ① **CDC7 54552-2**
Postlude in F (1895)
New England Orch, J. Sinclair *Concert*
(2/91) (KOCH) ① **37025-2**
4 Ragtime Dances—small orchestra (1902-4)
New England Orch, J. Sinclair *Concert*
(2/91) (KOCH) ① **37025-2**
The **Rainbow, 'So may it be'**—small orchestra (1914)
Modern Ens, I. Metzmacher (ed Porter) *Concert*
(6/93) (EMI) ① **CDC7 54552-2**
Robert Browning Overture—orchestra (1908-12)
American SO, L. Stokowski (r1966) *Concert*
(12/91) (SONY) ① **MPK46726**
Bamberg SO, I. Metzmacher (r1994) K. A. Hartmann:
Symphony 3. (10/95) (EMI) ① **CDC5 55254-2**
Set for Theatre or Chamber Orchestra (1906-11)
1. In the Cage; 2. In the Inn; 3. In the Night.
New England Orch, J. Sinclair *Concert*
(2/91) (KOCH) ① **37025-2**
Modern Ens, I. Metzmacher *Concert*
(6/93) (EMI) ① **CDC7 54552-2**
Orpheus CO *Concert* (10/94) (DG) ① **439 869-2GH**
Set No. 1—small orchestra (1907-11)
1. The See'r; 2. A lecture; 3. The ruined river; 4. Like
a sick eagle; 5. Calcium light night; 6. When the
moon, or Allegretto sombreoso.
Modern Ens, I. Metzmacher (ed Porter) *Concert*
(6/93) (EMI) ① **CDC7 54552-2**
G. Kalish, Orpheus CO *Concert*
(10/94) (DG) ① **439 869-2GH**
5. New England Orch, J. Sinclair *Concert*
(2/91) (KOCH) ① **37025-2**
Set No. 2—small orchestra (1911-12)
1. Largo 'The indians'; 2. 'Gyp the blood' or Hearst!?
Which is Worst?!; 3. Andante 'The last reader'.
1, 2. Modern Ens, I. Metzmacher (ed Porter) *Concert*
(6/93) (EMI) ① **CDC7 54552-2**
Set No. 3—small orchestra (?1918)
1. Adagio sostenuto 'At sea'; 2. Luck and work; 3.
Premonitions.
1. Modern Ens, I. Metzmacher (ed Porter) *Concert*
(6/93) (EMI) ① **CDC7 54552-2**
Symphony No. 1 (1895-98)
Chicago SO, M. Tilson Thomas *Symphony 4.*
(2/91) (SONY) ① **SK44939**
Detroit SO, N. Järvi *Concert* (3/92) (CHAN) ① **CHAN9053**
Symphony No. 2 (1902-02)
NYPO, L. Bernstein (pp1987) *Concert*
(8/90) (DG) ① **429 220-2GH**
Concertgebouw, M. Tilson Thomas *Symphony 3.*
(5/91) (SONY) ① **MPK46440**
NYPO, L. Bernstein
(5/93) (SONY) ① **SMK47568**
Detroit SO, N. Järvi (r1995) *Creston: Symphony 2.*
(11/95) (CHAN) ① **CHAN9390**
Symphony No. 3, 'The Camp Meeting' (1904)
ASMF, N. Marriner *Concert*
(11/87) (ARGO) ① **417 818-2ZH**
Concertgebouw, M. Tilson Thomas *Symphony 2.*
(5/91) (SONY) ① **MPK46440**
St Louis SO, L. Slatkin *Concert*
(4/93) (RCA) ① **09026 61222-2**
NYPO, L. Bernstein
(5/93) (SONY) ① **SMK47568**
Orpheus CO *Concert* (10/94) (DG) ① **439 869-2GH**
Symphony No. 4 (1910-18)
Tanglewood Fest Chor, Boston SO, S. Ozawa
Concert (10/88) (DG) ① **423 243-2GC**
Chicago SO, M. Tilson Thomas *Symphony 1.*
(2/91) (SONY) ① **SK44939**
NY Schola Cantorum, American SO, L. Stokowski, D.
Katz, J. Serebrier (r1965) *Concert*
(12/91) (SONY) ① **MPK46726**
Cleveland Orch, C. von Dohnányi *Concert*
(11/94) (DECC) ① **443 172-2DH**
Tone Roads et al—orchestra (?1915)
1. Fast 'All Roads Lead to the Centre'; 2. Slow; 3.
Slow and fast 'Rondo rapid transit'.
1. NYPO, L. Bernstein (pp1988) *Concert*
(8/90) (DG) ① **429 220-2GH**
1, 3. Modern Ens, I. Metzmacher *Concert*
(6/93) (EMI) ① **CDC7 54552-2**
The **Unanswered Question** (1906)
Moscow PO, D. Kitaienko *Concert*
(2/88) (SHEF) ① **CD27**
A. Herseth, Chicago SO, M. Tilson Thomas (orig &
rev versions) *Concert* (10/88) (SONY) ① **SK42381**

NYPO, L. Bernstein (pp1988) *Concert*
(8/90) (DG) ① **429 220-2GH**
St Luke's Orch, J. Adams *Concert*
(7/91) (NONE) ① **7559-79249-2**
St Louis SO, L. Slatkin *Concert*
(4/93) (RCA) ① **09026 61222-2**
Czech PO, A. Copland (pp1973) *Concert*
(6/93) (ROMA) ① **RR1973**
Orpheus CO *Concert* (10/94) (DG) ① **439 869-2GH**
Cleveland Orch, C. von Dohnányi *Concert*
(11/94) (DECC) ① **443 172-2DH**
Cincinnati Philh, G. Samuel, CCM Perc Ens, CCM
Chbr Ch (r1994) *Concert*
(5/95) (CENT) ① **CRC2205**
Universe Symphony—multiple orchestra
(1911-51)
Cincinnati Philh, G. Samuel, CCM Perc Ens, CCM
Chbr Ch (r1994) *Concert*
(5/95) (CENT) ① **CRC2205**
Yale-Princeton Football Game (?1898)
New England Orch, J. Sinclair (ed Sinclair) *Concert*
(2/91) (KOCH) ① **37025-2**

SECTION II: CHAMBER

All the way around and back—clarinet,
bugle, violin, bells & piano duet (1906)
Modern Ens, I. Metzmacher *Concert*
(6/93) (EMI) ① **CDC7 54552-2**
**From the Steeples and the
Mountains**—trumpet, trombone & 4 sets of
bells (1901-?02)
London Gabrieli Brass Ens, C. Larkin *Concert*
(5/92) (HYPE) ① **CDA66517**
Modern Ens, I. Metzmacher *Concert*
(6/93) (EMI) ① **CDC7 54552-2**
Halloween—string quartet and piano (1906)
NYPO, L. Bernstein (pp1988) *Concert*
(8/90) (DG) ① **429 220-2GH**
F. Oldenburg, Mondriaan Qt (r1992) *Concert*
(3/94) (ETCE) ① **KTC1169**
In re con moto et al—string quartet and
piano, Op. 20 (1913)
F. Oldenburg (r1992) *Concert*
(3/94) (ETCE) ① **KTC1169**
Intermezzo—string quartet (1898)
Mondriaan Qt (r1992) *Concert*
(3/94) (ETCE) ① **KTC1169**
Largo—violin, clarinet and piano (?1902)
L.C. Stoltzman, R. Stoltzman, R. Goode *Concert*
(11/90) (RCA) ① **RD60170**
Largo Risoluto—piano quintet (1906)
1. Prelude and Statement (of the law of diminishing
returns); 2. A Shadow made a Silouette.
F. Oldenburg, Mondriaan Qt (r1992) *Concert*
(3/94) (ETCE) ① **KTC1169**
3 Quarter-tone pieces—two pianos (1921)
Pianoduo *Concert* (3/93) (CHNN) ① **CCS4592**
A **Set of Three Short Pieces**—string quartet
(1903-14)
1. Largo cantabile: Hymn; 2. Scherzo: Holding Your
Own; 3. Andante cantabile: The Innate.
F. Oldenburg, Q. Van Regteren Altena, Mondriaan Qt
(r1992) *Concert* (3/94) (ETCE) ① **KTC1169**
1. NYPO, L. Bernstein (pp1988) *Concert*
(8/90) (DG) ① **429 220-2GH**
1. New England Orch, J. Sinclair *Concert*
(2/91) (KOCH) ① **37025-2**
2. Emerson Qt (r1991) *Concert*
(4/93) (DG) ① **435 864-2GH**
2. Arditti Qt (r1991-92) *Concert*
(12/93) (MONT) ① **782010**
**Sonata for Violin and Piano No. 4,
'Children's Day at the Camp Meeting'** (1905-16)
J. Szigeti, A. Foldes (r1941) *Concert*
(7/94) (BIDD) ① [2] **LAB070/1**
**String Quartet No. 1, 'From the Salvation
Army'** (1896)
Emerson Qt (r1990) *Concert*
(4/93) (DG) ① **435 864-2GH**
String Quartet No. 2 (1907-13)
Emerson Qt (r1990) *Concert*
(4/93) (DG) ① **435 864-2GH**
Mondriaan Qt (r1988) *Concert*
(3/94) (ETCE) ① **KTC1169**
Trio for Violin, Clarinet and Piano (1904-05)
Pacific Art Trio *Korngold: Piano Trio, Op. 1.*
(9/90) (DELO) ① **DE1009**
R. Lefkowitz, Y-Y. Ma, G. Kalish (r1992: ed J
Kirkpatrick) *Concert* (4/94) (SONY) ① **SK53126**
Hartley Trio *Concert* (6/94) (GAMU) ① **GAMCD536**

SECTION III: INSTRUMENTAL

Adeste fidelis: in an organ prelude (1897)
H-O. Ericsson *Concert* (4/93) (BIS) ① **BIS-CD510**

The **Anti-Abolitionist Riots**—piano (1908)
J. MacGregor *Concert* (8/89) (COLL) ① **Coll1299-2**
Sonata for Piano No. 1 (1909)
J. Jensen *Concord Sonata.*
(11/90) (MUSI) ① **MACD-630**
J. MacGregor *Concert* (3/92) (COLL) ① **Coll1107-2**
P. Lawson *Concert* (r1991)
(2/94) (VIRG) ① **VC7 59316-2**
**Sonata for Piano No. 2, 'Concord, Mass.':
1840-60'** (1910-15)
1. Emerson; 2. Hawthorne; 3. The Alcotts; 4.
Thoreau.
M-A. Hamelin *M. Wright: Piano Sonata (1982).*
(9/89) (NEW) ① **NW378-2**
D. Coleman *Concert* (11/90) (ETCE) ① **KTC1079**
J. Jensen *Piano Sonata 1.*
(11/90) (MUSI) ① **MACD-630**
P. Salo (2/91) (KONT) ① **32046**
3. J. MacGregor *Concert* (8/89) (COLL) ① **Coll1299-2**
**Study No. 21, 'Some Southpaw
Pitching'**—piano (?1909)
J. MacGregor *Concert* (8/89) (COLL) ① **Coll1299-2**
Three Page Sonata—piano (1905)
J. MacGregor *Concert* (8/89) (COLL) ① **Coll1299-2**
D. Coleman *Concert* (11/90) (ETCE) ① **KTC1079**
P. Lawson *Concert* (5/91) (VIRG) ① **VC7 59008-2**
S. Cherkassky (pp1991) *Concert*
(1/93) (TELD) ① **9031-74007-2**
4 Transcriptions from Emerson—piano
(?1917-22)
D. Coleman *Concert* (11/90) (ETCE) ① **KTC1079**
Variations on 'America'—organ (?1891)
J. Jones *Concert* (8/91) (MOTE) ① **CD11491**
LSO Brass Ens, E. Crees (arr Crees) *Concert*
(1/92) (COLL) ① **Coll1288-2**
NYPO, K. Masur (arr Schuman: pp1991) *Concert*
(12/92) (TELD) ① **9031-74007-2**
H-O. Ericsson *Concert* (4/93) (BIS) ① **BIS-CD510**
St Louis SO, L. Slatkin (r1991; orch Schuman)
Concert (4/93) (RCA) ① **09026 61282-2**
Seattle SO, G. Schwarz (orch Schuman) *Concert*
(7/93) (DELO) ① **DE3115**
Varied Air and Variations—piano (?1923)
J. MacGregor *Concert* (8/89) (COLL) ① **Coll1299-2**

SECTION IV: VOCAL AND CHORAL

Aeschylus and Sophocles—song (1922)
(Wds. Landor)
H. Herford, Modern Ens, I. Metzmacher *Concert*
(6/93) (EMI) ① **CDC7 54552-2**
Afterglow—song (1919) (Wds. Cooper)
H. Herford, R. Bowman *Concert*
(3/92) (UNIC) ① **DKPCD9112**
Die **alte Mutter**—song (1900) (Wds.
Lobedanz, after Vinje)
R. Alexander, T. Crone *Concert*
(8/89) (ETCE) ① **KTC1068**
Ann Street—song (1921) (Wds. Morris)
R. Alexander, T. Crone *Concert*
(8/89) (ETCE) ① **KTC1068**
R. Stoltzman, R. Goode *Concert*
(11/90) (RCA) ① **RD60170**
H. Herford, R. Bowman *Concert*
(9/91) (UNIC) ① **DKPCD9111**
At sea—song (1921) (Wds. Johnson)
R. Alexander, T. Crone *Concert*
(8/89) (ETCE) ① **KTC1068**
H. Herford, R. Bowman *Concert*
(3/92) (UNIC) ① **DKPCD9112**
At the river—song (?1916) (Wds. Lowry)
R. Alexander, T. Crone *Concert*
(8/89) (ETCE) ① **KTC1068**
D. Upshaw, St Luke's Orch, J. Adams (orch Adams)
Concert (7/91) (NONE) ① **7559-79249-2**
August—song (1920) (Wds. C. Rosetti, after
Folgore)
H. Herford, R. Bowman *Concert*
(3/92) (UNIC) ① **DKPCD9112**
Autumn—song (1907) (Wds. Twichell)
H. Herford, R. Bowman *Concert*
(3/92) (UNIC) ① **DKPCD9112**
The **Bells of Yale, 'Chapel
chimes'**—baritone and male chorus (1897)
(Wds. Mason)
H. Herford, Modern Ens, I. Metzmacher *Concert*
(6/93) (EMI) ① **CDC7 54552-2**
Berceuse—song (?1903) (Wds. cpsr)
H. Herford, R. Bowman *Concert*
(9/91) (UNIC) ① **DKPCD9111**
The **Cage**—song (1906) (Wds. cpsr)
R. Stoltzman, R. Goode *Concert*
(11/90) (RCA) ① **RD60170**
H. Herford, R. Bowman *Concert*
(3/92) (UNIC) ① **DKPCD9112**

Tarrant Moss—song (?1898) (Wds. R. Kipling)
H. Herford, R. Bowman *Concert*
(3/92) (UNIC) ① **DKPCD9112**

There is a certain garden—song (1893) (Wds. Anon)
H. Herford, R. Bowman *Concert*
(9/91) (UNIC) ① **DKPCD9111**

There is a lane—song (1902) (Wds. cpsr)
R. Alexander, T. Crone *Concert*
(8/89) (ETCE) ① **KTC1068**

They are there!—song (1942) (Wds. cpsr)
R. Alexander, T. Crone *Concert*
(8/89) (ETCE) ① **KTC1068**
Kronos Qt (arr Kronos Qt/Geist) *Concert*
(4/91) (NONE) ① **7559-79242-2**
H. Herford, R. Bowman *Concert*
(9/91) (UNIC) ① **DKPCD9111**
G. Smith Sngrs, Ithaca Coll Concert Ch, American SO, L. Stokowski *Concert*
(12/91) (SONY) ① **MPK46726**

The Things our fathers loved—song (1917) (Wds. cpsr)
R. Stoltzman, R. Goode *Concert*
(11/90) (RCA) ① **RD60170**
H. Herford, R. Bowman *Concert*
(9/91) (UNIC) ① **DKPCD9111**

Thoreau—song (1915) (Wds. cpsr, after Thoreau)
D. Upshaw, St Luke's Orch, J. Adams (orch Adams) *Concert*
(7/91) (NONE) ① **7559-79249-2**
H. Herford, R. Bowman *Concert*
(3/92) (UNIC) ① **DKPCD9112**

Tom sails away—song (1917) (Wds. cpsr)
H. Herford, R. Bowman *Concert*
(9/91) (UNIC) ① **DKPCD9111**

Ein Ton—song (?1895) (Wds. Cornelius)
T. Hampson, A. Guzelimian *Concert*
(4/92) (TELD) ① **9031-72168-2**

Two little flowers—song (1921) (Wds. cpsr)
H. Herford, R. Bowman *Concert*
(9/91) (UNIC) ① **DKPCD9111**

Two Slants, or Christian and Pagan—songs (1921)
1. Duty (wds. Emerson); 2. Vita (wds. Manlius).
1. H. Herford, R. Bowman *Concert*
(3/92) (UNIC) ① **DKPCD9112**

Walking—song (1902) (Wds. cpsr)
R. Stoltzman, R. Goode *Concert*
(11/90) (RCA) ① **RD60170**
H. Herford, R. Bowman *Concert*
(3/92) (UNIC) ① **DKPCD9112**

Walt Whitman—song (1921) (Wds. W. Whitman)
H. Herford, R. Bowman *Concert*
(3/92) (UNIC) ① **DKPCD9112**

Waltz—song (?1894) (Wds. cpsr)
H. Herford, R. Bowman *Concert*
(3/92) (UNIC) ① **DKPCD9112**

Watchman—song (1913) (Wds. Bowring)
R. Alexander, T. Crone *Concert*
(8/89) (ETCE) ① **KTC1068**

Weil' auf mir—song (?1901) (Wds. Lenau)
R. Alexander, T. Crone *Concert*
(8/89) (ETCE) ① **KTC1068**
T. Hampson, A. Guzelimian *Concert*
(4/92) (TELD) ① **9031-72168-2**

West London—song (1921) (Wds. Arnold)
H. Herford, R. Bowman *Concert*
(9/91) (UNIC) ① **DKPCD9111**

Where the eagle—song (1906) (Wds. M.P. Turnbull)
H. Herford, R. Bowman *Concert*
(9/91) (UNIC) ① **DKPCD9111**

The White Gulls—song (1921) (Wds. Morris)
H. Herford, R. Bowman *Concert*
(9/91) (UNIC) ① **DKPCD9111**

Widmung—song (?1897) (Wds. Müller)
T. Hampson, A. Guzelimian *Concert*
(4/92) (TELD) ① **9031-72168-2**

Wiegenlied—song (?1900) (Wds. from 'Des Knaben Wunderhorn')
T. Hampson, A. Guzelimian *Concert*
(4/92) (TELD) ① **9031-72168-2**

Yellow Leaves—song (1923) (Wds. H. Bellamann)
H. Herford, R. Bowman *Concert*
(9/91) (UNIC) ① **DKPCD9111**

IVES, (Charles) Grayston (b 1948) England

SECTION IV: VOCAL AND CHORAL

Edington Service—choir and organ (1973)
Lichfield Cath Ch, A. Lumsden, M. Shepherd (r1994) *Concert*
(10/95) (PRIO) ① **PRCD505**

JACCHINI, Giuseppe Maria (C1663–1727) Italy

SECTION II: CHAMBER

Trattenimenti per camera—3-6 insts, some with 1 or 2 tpts, Op. 5
1. D.
1. St James's Baroque Plyrs, I. Bolton (r1988) *Concert*
(9/93) (TELD) ① **4509-91192-2**

JACKSON, Francis (Alan) (b 1917) England

SECTION III: INSTRUMENTAL

5 Preludes on English Hymn Tunes—organ, Op. 60
G. Barber *Concert*
(7/91) (PRIO) ① **PRCD314**
Sonata No. 3—organ, Op. 50 (1979)
G. Barber *Concert*
(3/92) (PRIO) ① **PRCD373**
Sonata No. 4—organ, Op. 68 (1985)
G. Barber *Concert*
(1/93) (PRIO) ① **PRCD391**

SECTION IV: VOCAL AND CHORAL

Alleluia, laudate pueri Dominum—anthem (1971) (Wds. Psalm 113)
St Paul's Cath Ch, John Scott, Andrew Lucas (r1993) *Concert*
(6/94) (HYPE) ① **CDA66678**
Benedicite in G—chorus and organ (1949)
Ely Cath Ch, P. Trepte *Concert*
(2/92) (GAMU) ① **GAMCD527**

JACKSON, Gabriel (1962) Bermuda

SECTION IV: VOCAL AND CHORAL

French Song—soprano, clarinet & piano (1991) (Wds. Richard George Elliott)
Tapestry (r1994) *Concert*
(12/95) (BRIT) ① **BML012**

JACKSON, William (1730–1803) England

SECTION II: CHAMBER

6 Sonatas for Harpsichord with Violin obbligato, Op. 2 (pub 1760)
EXCERPTS: 3. A minor.
3. Invocation (r1993) *Concert*
(11/94) (HYPE) ① **CDA66698**

SECTION IV: VOCAL AND CHORAL

The Day saw that saw thy beauty rise—canzonet
R. Müller, T. Roberts *Concert*
(12/91) (HYPE) ① **CDA66497**
Invocation and Six Elegies—4vv and continuo, Op. 3 (pub c1760)
EXCERPTS: 4. Elegy III: Could he whom my dissembled rigour grieves.
4. Invocation (r1993) *Concert*
(11/94) (HYPE) ① **CDA66698**
6 Quartets—4vv and continuo, Op. 11 (arrs of songs by other cpsrs)
EXCERPTS: 6. Where the bee sucks (Arne).
6. Invocation (r1993) *Concert*
(11/94) (HYPE) ① **CDA66698**
A Second Set of Twelve Canzonets—2vv and continuo, Op. 13 (pub c1782)
EXCERPTS: 7. Love in thine eyes for ever plays.
7. Invocation (r1993) *Concert*
(11/94) (HYPE) ① **CDA66698**
Time has not thinn'd my flowing hair
E. Kirkby, R. Müller, F. Kelly *Concert*
(12/91) (HYPE) ① **CDA66497**

JACOB, Gordon (Percival Septimus) (1895–1984) England

SECTION I: ORCHESTRAL

Concerto for Bassoon, Strings and Percussion (1935)
R. Thompson, ECO, G. Simon (r1981) *Concert*
(10/94) (CHAN) ① **CHAN9278**
Concerto for Timpani and Band (1984)
T. Fry, City of London Wind Ens, G. Brand (r1991) *Concert*
(7/89) (LDR) ① **LDRCD1001**
Concerto for Trombone and Orchestra (1955)
C. Lindberg, BBC Nat Orch of Wales, G. Llewellyn (r1993) *Concert*
(10/95) (BIS) ① **BIS-CD658**
5 Pieces for Harmonica and Orchestra
1. Caprice; 2. Cradle Song; 3. Country Dance; 4. Threnody; 5. Russian Dance.
T. Reilly, ASMF, N. Marriner *Concert*
(10/88) (CHAN) ① **CHAN8617**
2. RTE Concert Orch, E. Tomlinson (r1993; arr ob/stgs) *Concert*
(12/95) (MARC) ① **8 223522**
William Byrd Suite—wind orchestra (1923)
1. The Earle of Oxford's March; 2. Pavana; 3. John come kisse me now; 4. The Mayden's Song; 5. Wolsey's Wilde; 6. The Bells.
Eastman Wind Ens, F. Fennell *Concert*
(12/91) (MERC) ① **432 009-2MM**

SECTION II: CHAMBER

Divertimento—harmonica and string quartet (1956)
T. Reilly, Hindar Qt *Concert*
(10/90) (CHAN) ① **CHAN8802**
Quartet for oboe and strings (1938)
S. Francis, English Qt *Concert*
(7/87) (CHAN) ① **CHAN8392**
Sextet—wind quintet and piano, Op. 3 (1962)
A. Goldstone, Elysian Wind Qnt *Concert*
(10/92) (CHAN) ① **CHAN9077**
4 Sketches for Bassoon and Piano (1976)
Daniel Smith, R. Vignoles *Concert*
(9/89) (ASV) ① **CDDCA535**
Suite for Bassoon and String Quartet (1969)
Daniel Smith, Coull Qt *Concert*
(10/88) (ASV) ① **CDDCA613**

SECTION III: INSTRUMENTAL

7 Bagatelles—oboe/cor anglais
1. March; 2. Elegy; 3. Waltz; 4. Slow Air; 5. Limerick; 6. Chinese Tune; 7. Galop.
H. Schellenberger *Concert*
(12/91) (DENO) ① **CO-76611**

JACOB DE SENLECHES (fl 1378–95) France

SECTION IV: VOCAL AND CHORAL

En ce gracieux tamps joli—virelai
Gothic Voices, C. Page *Concert*
(3/92) (HYPE) ① **CDA66463**
La Harpe de melodie—virelai (3vv)
Organum Ens, M. Pérès *Concert*
(11/87) (HARM) ① **HMC90 1252**

JACOBI, Victor (1883–1921) Hungary

SECTION V: STAGE WORKS

Apple Blossoms—songs for Fritz Kreisler's musical (1919—New York) (Lyrics Le Baron)
EXCERPTS: 1. You Are Free; 2. Little Girls.
1, 2. J. C. Thomas, Orig Broadway Cast (r1920) *Concert*
(5/94) (PEAR) ① [3] **GEMMCDS9059/61**
Sybil—operetta (1914—Budapest) (Lib. Bródy and Martos)
The Colonel of the Crimson Hussars M. Hill Smith, Ambrosian Sngrs, Chandos Concert Orch, S. Barry *Concert*
(7/88) (CHAN) ① **CHAN8561**

JACOPO DA BOLOGNA (fl 1340–c1360) Italy

SECTION IV: VOCAL AND CHORAL

Non al suo amante—ballata
Newberry Consort, M. Springfels (r1990) *Concert*
(7/93) (HARM) ① **HMU90 7038**

JADIN, Hyacinthe (1769–1802)
France

SECTION I: ORCHESTRAL
Ouverture in F—wind orchestra (1795)
Wallace Collection, J. Wallace *Concert*
(7/89) (NIMB) ① NI5175

SECTION III: INSTRUMENTAL
3 Sonatas for Piano, Op. 4 (pub 1795)
EXCERPTS: 1. B flat; 2. F sharp minor; 3. C sharp minor.
2. C. Wang (r1990) *Piano Sonatas, Op. 6.*
(1/95) (DINT) ① DICD920192
3 Sonatas for Piano, Op. 6 (pub 1804)
EXCERPTS: 1. C minor; 3. F.
1, 3. C. Wang (r1990) *Piano Sonatas, Op. 4.*
(1/95) (DINT) ① DICD920192

JADIN, Jean Baptiste (d c1789)
France

SECTION II: CHAMBER
6 Quartets, Op. 1 (1777-82) (Nos 1-3 stg quartet; Nos 4-6 fl quartet)
3 (Polonaise) Rasumovsky Qt *Concert*
(12/92) (IMPE) ① RAZCD901

JAELL, Alfred (19th Cent)

SECTION III: INSTRUMENTAL
Chant romantique—piano
A. Etherden *Concert*
(7/93) (HUNT) ① HMPCD0589

JAGGARD, David (20th Cent)
USA

SECTION III: INSTRUMENTAL
Tango—piano
U. Oppens *Concert* (5/90) (MUSI) ① MACD-604

JAMES, John (d 1745) England

SECTION III: INSTRUMENTAL
Voluntary—keyboard
Margaret Phillips *Concert*
(5/91) (GAMU) ① GAMCD514

JANÁČEK, Leoš (1854–1928)
Moravia

SECTION I: ORCHESTRAL
Adagio—orchestra (1891)
Gonville & Caius College Ch, G. Webber (r1994, 2 vers ed Reinberger) *Concert*
(6/95) (ASV) ① CDDCA914
Capriccio—piano left hand, and chamber ensemble (1926) (Vzdor (Defiance)
R. Kvapil, Wallace Collection, J. Wallace *Concert*
(7/89) (NIMB) ① NI5103
P. Crossley, London Sinfonietta, D. Atherton *Concert*
(10/89) (DECC) ① [2] 421 852-2DH2
M. Papadopoulos (pf/dir), RPO *Concert*
(11/89) (HYPE) ① CDA66167
J. Páleníček, Czech Phil Chbr Ens *Concert*
(3/92) (SUPR) ① 11 0768-2
Cleveland Orch, C. von Dohnányi (r1993) *Concert*
(4/95) (DECC) ① 443 173-2DH
Concerto for Violin and Orchestra, 'Pilgrimage of the Soul' (1927-28)
J. Suk, Czech PO, V. Neumann *Concert*
(6/91) (SUPR) ① 11 0717-2
C. Tetzlaff, Philh, L. Pešek *Concert*
(6/92) (VIRG) ① VC7 59076-2
I. Ženatý, Brno St PO, F. Jílek (r1992) *Concert*
(9/93) (SUPR) ① 11 1522-2
T. Zehetmair, Philh, H. Holliger (r1991) *Concert*
(6/95) (TELD) ① 4509-97449-2
The Danube—symphonic poem (1923-28) (cpted O. Chlubna. 'Dunaj')
K. Dvořáková, Brno St PO, F. Jílek (r1992) *Concert*
(9/93) (SUPR) ① 11 1522-2
The Fiddler's Child—ballad (symphonic poem) after S. Čech (1912)
Czech PO, J. Bělohlávek *Concert*
(11/92) (CHAN) ① CHAN9080

Jealousy—orchestra (1894) (original prelude to Jenufa)
Czech PO, J. Bělohlávek *Concert*
(11/92) (CHAN) ① CHAN9080
R. Firkušný, I. Ardašev (r1993: arr pf duet) *Concert*
(3/95) (SUPR) ① 11 1878-2
Lachian dances—orchestra, 1925
1. Starodávný I; 2. Požehnany (The Blessed One); 3. Dymák; 4. Starodávný II; 5. Čeladenský (Čeladná Dance); 6. Pilky (The Saws).
Brno St PO, F. Jílek *Concert*
(8/90) (SUPR) ① 11 0282-2
LPO, F. Huybrechts (r1970) *Makropulos Affair.*
(10/91) (DECC) ① [2] 430 372-2DH2
Bratislava RSO, O. Lenárd *Concert*
(3/92) (NAXO) ① 8 550411
The blessed one; Pilky Czech PO, V. Neumann *Concert* (9/90) (ORFE) ① C180891A
Sinfonietta—Military Sinfonietta (1926)
Czech PO, V. Neumann *Taras Bulba.*
(11/85) (SUPR) ① 10 3400-2
Philh, S. Rattle (r1982) *Glagolitic Mass.*
(10/88) (EMI) ① CDC7 47504-2
Los Angeles PO, A. Previn (r1988) *Bartók: Concerto for orchestra.* (3/89) (TELA) ① CD80174
BPO, C. Abbado *Diary of One who Disappeared.*
(5/89) (DG) ① 427 313-2GH
Slovak PO, D. Nazareth *Taras Bulba.*
(8/89) (NAXO) ① 9350 2013
Bamberg SO, N. Järvi *Dvořák: Legends.*
(8/89) (BIS) ① BIS-CD436
Czech PO, K. Ančerl *Bartók: Concerto for Orchestra.*
(12/89) (SUPR) ① 11 0604-2
Brno St PO, F. Jílek *Concert*
(8/90) (SUPR) ① 11 0282-2
Czech PO, J. Bělohlávek *Concert*
(1/91) (CHAN) ① CHAN8897
Czech PO, V. Neumann *Concert*
(6/91) (SUPR) ① 11 0717-2
VPO, C. Mackerras *Concert*
(12/91) (DECC) ① 430 727-2DM
Bratislava RSO, O. Lenárd *Concert*
(3/92) (NAXO) ① 8 550411
Philh, L. Pešek *Concert*
(6/92) (VIRG) ① VC7 59076-2
BRSO, R. Kubelík *Concert*
(1/93) (DG) ① 437 254-2GGA
Brno St PO, F. Jílek (r1986) *Concert*
(9/93) (SUPR) ① 11 1522-2
Montreal SO, C. Dutoit (r1991) *Glagolitic Mass.*
(4/94) (DECC) ① 436 211-2DH
NYPO, K. Masur (pp1993) *Dvořák: Symphony 8.*
(12/94) (TELD) ① 4509-90847-2
BPO, C. Abbado (r1987) *Concert*
(12/94) (DG) ① 445 501-2GMA
Philh, S. Rattle *Holst: Planets.*
(3/95) (EMI) ① CDM7 64740-2
BBC SO, R. Kempe (pp1974) *Concert*
(10/95) (BBCR) ① [2] DMCD98
Allegretto London Brass Virtuosi, D. Honeyball *Concert* (7/87) (HYPE) ① CDA66189
Allegretto Empire Brass (r1992; arr. R. Smedvig) *Concert* (1/94) (TELA) ① CD80305
Suite—string orchestra (1877)
Slovak CO, B. Warchal *Concert*
(10/89) (OPUS) ① 9350 1773
Prague CO, B. Novotný (r1994) *Concert*
(7/95) (DENO) ① CO-78919
Prague Virtuosi, O. Vlček (r1993-4) *Concert*
(9/95) (DINT) ① DICD920234
Taras Bulba—Rhapsody for Orchestra, after Gogol (1915-18)
Czech PO, V. Neumann *Sinfonietta.*
(11/85) (SUPR) ① 10 3400-2
Slovak PO, D. Nazareth *Sinfonietta.*
(8/89) (OPUS) ① 9350 2013
Czech PO, K. Ančerl *Glagolitic Mass.*
(12/89) (SUPR) ① 11 0609-2
BRSO, R. Kubelík (r1970) *Glagolitic Mass.*
(4/90) (DG) ① 429 182-2GGA
Brno St PO, F. Jílek *Concert*
(8/90) (SUPR) ① 11 0282-2
Czech PO, V. Neumann *Concert*
(6/91) (SUPR) ① 11 0717-2
VPO, C. Mackerras *Concert*
(12/91) (DECC) ① 430 727-2DM
Bratislava RSO, O. Lenárd *Concert*
(3/92) (NAXO) ① 8 550411
Philh, S. Rattle *Cunning Little Vixen.*
(3/92) (EMI) ① [2] CDS7 54212-2
Philh, L. Pešek *Concert*
(6/92) (VIRG) ① VC7 59076-2
Czech PO, J. Bělohlávek *Concert*
(11/92) (CHAN) ① CHAN9080
Czech PO, V. Talich (r1954) *Concert*
(1/94) (SUPR) ① 11 1905-2

RPO, R. Kubelík (r1958) *Concert*
(11/94) (EMI) ① [2] CZS5 68223-2
Orig opening Brno St PO, L. Svárovský (r1994) *Concert* (3/95) (SUPR) ① 11 1878-2

SECTION II: CHAMBER
Allegro—violin and piano (1916) (discarded fifth movt of Violin Sonata)
U. Wallin, R. Pöntinen (r1993) *Concert*
(4/95) (BIS) ① [2] BIS-CD663/4
Concertino—piano and chamber ensemble (1925)
P. Crossley, London Sinfonietta, D. Atherton *Concert*
(10/89) (DECC) ① [2] 421 852-2DH2
J. Páleníček, Czech Phil Wind Ens *Concert*
(3/92) (SUPR) ① 11 0768-2
Dumka—violin and piano (1875)
R. Zimansky, C. Keller *Concert*
(9/92) (ACCO) ① 20093-2
U. Wallin, R. Pöntinen (r1993) *Concert*
(4/95) (BIS) ① [2] BIS-CD663/4
Fanfare in A—four violins (1875)
M. Gajdošová, L. Zavadilík, A. Formáček, D. Kellerová (r1994) *Concert*
(3/95) (SUPR) ① 11 1878-2
Fanfare in D minor—four violins (1875)
M. Gajdošová, L. Zavadilík, A. Formáček, D. Kellerová (r1994) *Concert*
(3/95) (SUPR) ① 11 1878-2
From a Fairy Tale—cello and piano (1910 rev 1923)
A. Gastinel, P.-L. Aimard (r1995) *Concert*
(9/95) (AUVI) ① V4748
March of the Blue Boys—instrumental ensemble (1924)
P. Šumpík, E. Podafilová, F. Kantor, M. Opršal (r1994) *Concert* (3/95) (SUPR) ① 11 1878-2
Mládí (Youth)—fl, ob, cl. hn, bn, bass cl (1924)
COE Wind Sols *Concert*
(4/90) (ASV) ① CDCOE812
London Sinfonietta, D. Atherton *Concert*
(10/91) (DECC) ① [2] 430 375-2DH2
K. Berger, Aulos Wind Qnt (r1988) *Concert*
(6/93) (SCHW) ① 310051
Pohádka (Fairy Tale)—cello and piano (1910)
P. Demenga, C. Keller *Concert*
(9/92) (ACCO) ① 20093-2
A. Shulman, I. Brown *Concert*
(12/93) (EMI) ① CDC7 54787-2
M. Rondin, R. Pöntinen (r1994) *Concert*
(4/95) (BIS) ① [2] BIS-CD663/4
Presto—cello and piano (?1910)
P. Demenga, C. Keller *Concert*
(9/92) (ACCO) ① 20093-2
M. Rondin, R. Pöntinen (r1994) *Concert*
(4/95) (BIS) ① [2] BIS-CD663/4
Romance—violin and piano (1879) (originally No.4 of Seven Romances)
R. Zimansky, C. Keller *Concert*
(9/92) (ACCO) ① 20093-2
U. Wallin, R. Pöntinen (r1993) *Concert*
(4/95) (BIS) ① [2] BIS-CD663/4
Sonata for Violin and Piano (1914 rev 1921)
D. Sitkovetsky, P. Gililov *Concert*
(8/89) (VIRG) ① VC5 45202-2
J. Suk, J. Panenka *Concert*
(5/90) (SUPR) ① 11 0705-2
G. Kremer, M. Argerich *Concert*
(1/91) (DG) ① 427 351-2GH
F.P. Zimmermann, A. Lonquich *Concert*
(6/92) (EMI) ① CDC7 54305-2
A. Hardy, L. Devos *Concert*
(6/92) (OLYM) ① OCD355
R. Zimansky, C. Keller *Concert*
(9/92) (ACCO) ① 20093-2
P. Manning, I. Brown *Concert*
(12/93) (EMI) ① CDC7 54787-2
U. Wallin, R. Pöntinen (r1993) *Concert*
(4/95) (BIS) ① [2] BIS-CD663/4
C. Tetzlaff, L. O. Andsnes (r1994) *Concert*
(11/95) (VIRG) ① VC5 45122-2
String Quartet No. 1, 'The Kreutzer Sonata' (1923)
Talich Qt *Concert* (4/89) (CALL) ① CAL9699
Hagen Qt *Concert* (1/90) (DG) ① 427 669-2GH
Doležal Qt *Diary of one who disappeared.*
(4/90) (ACCO) ① 22031-2
Lindsay Qt *Concert* (11/91) (ASV) ① CDDCA749
Gabrieli Qt *Concert* (8/92) (DECC) ① 430 295-2DM
Melos Qt *String Quartet 2.*
(8/92) (HARM) ① HMC90 1380
Britten Qt *Concert* (12/93) (EMI) ① CDC7 54787-2
Vanbrugh Qt (r1992) *Concert*
(4/94) (COLL) ① Coll1381-2

Vogler Qt (r1993) *Concert*
(7/94) (RCA) ① **09026 61816-2**
Alban Berg Qt (pp1993) *String Quartet 2.*
(12/95) (EMI) ① **CDC5 55457-2**
String Quartet No. 2, 'Intimate Letters'
(1928)
Talich Qt *Concert* (4/89) (CALL) ① **CAL9699**
Hagen Qt *Concert* (1/90) (DG) ① **427 669-2GH**
Lindsay Qt *Concert* (11/91) (ASV) ① **CDDCA749**
Gabrieli Qt *Concert* (8/92) (DECC) ① **430 295-2DM**
Melos Qt *String Quartet 1.*
(8/92) (HARM) ① **HMC90 1380**
Britten Qt *Concert* (12/93) (EMI) ① **CDC7 54787-2**
Vanbrugh Qt (r1992) *Concert*
(4/94) (COLL) ① **Coll1381-2**
Petersen Qt (r1989/91) *Concert*
(2/95) (CAPR) ① **10 511**
Alban Berg Qt (pp1994) *String Quartet 1.*
(12/95) (EMI) ① **CDC5 55457-2**

SECTION III: INSTRUMENTAL

Along an Overgrown Path—15 pieces: piano
(1901-08)
BOOK 1: 1. Our evenings; 2. A blown-away leaf; 3.
Come with us!; 4. The Madonna of Frýdek; 5. They
chattered like swallows; 6. Words fail!; 7. Good night!;
8. Unútterable anguish!; 9. In tears; 10. Thhe barn
owl has not flown away. BOOK 2: 11. Andante; 12.
Allegretto—Presto; 13. Paralipomena: 13a. Più
mosso; 13b. Allegro—Adagio; 13c. Vivo.
J. Röling *In the mists.*
(8/88) (OTTA) ① **OTRC38607**
R. Firkušný *Concert* (3/91) (DG) ① **429 857-2GC**
R. Firkušný *Concert* (3/91) (RCA) ① **RD60147**
M. Rudy *Concert* (3/91) (EMI) ① **CDC7 54094-2**
R. Pöntinen (r1993) *Concert*
(4/95) (BIS) ① [2] **BIS-CD663/4**
R. Kvapil (r1994) *Concert*
(11/95) (UNIC) ① **DKPCD9156**
1-10. R. Kvapil *Concert* (8/88) (CALL) ① **CAL9206**
1-10. R. Kvapil *Concert* (4/89) (CALL) ① **CAL9699**
1-10. L.O. Andsnes *Concert*
(10/91) (VIRG) ① **VC7 59639-2**
1-10. J. Páleníček *Concert*
(3/92) (SUPR) ① **10 1481-2**
1, 2, 4, 7, 10. A. Bárta (1994: harm) *Concert*
(3/95) (SUPR) ① **11 1878-2**
I'm waiting for you—keyboard (1928)
A. Bárta (r1994) *Concert*
(3/95) (SUPR) ① **11 1878-2**
R. Firkušný (r1993: pf) *Concert*
(3/95) (SUPR) ① **11 1878-2**
In the mists—piano (1912)
J. Röling *Along an Overgrown Path.*
(8/88) (OTTA) ① **OTRC38607**
R. Firkušný *Concert* (3/91) (DG) ① **429 857-2GC**
R. Firkušný *Concert* (3/91) (RCA) ① **RD60147**
M. Rudy *Concert* (3/91) (EMI) ① **CDC7 54094-2**
L.O. Andsnes *Concert*
(10/91) (VIRG) ① **VC7 59639-2**
J. Páleníček *Concert* (3/92) (SUPR) ① **10 1481-2**
R. Pöntinen (r1993) *Concert*
(4/95) (BIS) ① [2] **BIS-CD663/4**
R. Kvapil (r1994) *Concert*
(11/95) (UNIC) ① **DKPCD9156**
3 Moravian Dances—piano (c1892)
M. Rudy *Concert* (3/91) (EMI) ① **CDC7 54094-2**
R. Pöntinen (r1993) *Concert*
(4/95) (BIS) ① [2] **BIS-CD663/4**
Reminiscence—piano (1928)
R. Firkušný *Concert* (3/91) (RCA) ① **RD60147**
M. Rudy *Concert* (3/91) (EMI) ① **CDC7 54094-2**
R. Pöntinen (r1993) *Concert*
(4/95) (BIS) ① [2] **BIS-CD663/4**
Sonata 1.X.1905, 'From the street'—piano
(1905) (Movt. 3 lost)
M. Papadopoulos *Concert*
(11/89) (HYPE) ① **CDA66167**
R. Firkušný *Concert* (3/91) (DG) ① **429 857-2GC**
R. Firkušný *Concert* (3/91) (RCA) ① **RD60147**
M. Rudy *Concert* (3/91) (EMI) ① **CDC7 54094-2**
L.O. Andsnes *Concert*
(10/91) (VIRG) ① **VC7 59639-2**
J. Páleníček *Concert* (3/92) (SUPR) ① **10 1481-2**
C. Keller *Concert* (9/92) (ACCO) ① **20093-2**
R. Pöntinen (r1993) *Concert*
(4/95) (BIS) ① [2] **BIS-CD663/4**
R. Kvapil (r1994) *Concert*
(11/95) (UNIC) ① **DKPCD9156**
Thema con variazione (Ždenka)—piano, Op.
1 (1880)
R. Firkušný *Concert* (3/91) (DG) ① **429 857-2GC**
R. Pöntinen (r1993) *Concert*
(4/95) (BIS) ① [2] **BIS-CD663/4**

SECTION IV: VOCAL AND CHORAL

Amarus—cantata (1897 rev 1901, 1906) (Wds.
J. Vrchlický)
K. Němečková, L.M. Vodička, Czech Phil Chor,
Czech PO, C. Mackerras *Martinů: Field Mass.*
(4/86) (SUPR) ① **C37-7735**
4 Ballads—1v & piano (1908-12)
D. Pecková, I. Kusnjer, M. Lapšanský (r1994)
Concert (11/95) (SUPR) ① **11 2225-2**
Detvan brigand songs, 'Písně
detvanské'—1v & piano (1916)
D. Pecková, I. Kusnjer, M. Lapšanský (r1994)
Concert (11/95) (SUPR) ① **11 2225-2**
Diary of one who disappeared—song cycle
(1917-9) (Wds. anon)
G. Hirst, S. Love, Columbia Pro Cantare, A. Kubalek
(3/88) (ARAB) ① **Z6513**
P. Langridge, B. Balleys, Berlin RIAS Chbr Ch, BPO,
C. Abbado *Sinfonietta.* (5/89) (DG) ① **427 313-2GH**
C. Wirz, P. Keller, Lucerne Sngrs, M. Venzago (pf/dir)
String Quartet 1. (11/94) (ACCO) ① **22031-2**
Elegy on the death of his daughter Olga
(Elegie ma smrt dcery Olgy)—tenor, male vv
& piano (1903 rev 1904) (Wds. M N Vevritsa)
H. Vels, M. Bon, Netherlands Chbr Ch, R. de Leeuw
(r1993) *Concert* (12/95) (PHIL) ① **442 534-2PH**
Exaudi Deus—choir and organ (1875 rev
1877)
Gonville & Caius College Ch, G. Webber (r1994)
Concert (6/95) (ASV) ① **CDDCA914**
Festival Chorus—bar, choruses and piano
(1877 rev 1878)
J. Bělor, Prague Phil Chor, J. Holeňa (1994: third
vers) *Concert* (3/95) (SUPR) ① **11 1878-2**
7 Folk nocturnes, 'Lidová nokturna'—two
female vv & piano (1906)
D. Pecková, I. Kusnjer, M. Lapšanský (r1994)
Concert (11/95) (SUPR) ① **11 2225-2**
5 Folksongs—1v & piano (1916-17)
(preserved in sketch form)
D. Pecková, I. Kusnjer, M. Lapšanský (r1994)
Concert (11/95) (SUPR) ① **11 2225-2**
6 Folksongs which Eva Gabel sang,
'Náarodních písní jež zpívala Gabel Fra'—1v
& piano (1909)
D. Pecková, I. Kusnjer, M. Lapšanský (r1994)
Concert (11/95) (SUPR) ① **11 2225-2**
Glagolitic Mass—SATB, organ, chorus and
orchestra (1926 rev 1929)
1. Prelude (Urod); 2. Kyrie (Gospodi pomiluy); 3.
Gloria (Slava); 4. Credo (Věruju); 5. Sanctus (Svet);
6. Agnus Dei (Agneôe Božij); 7. organ solo; 8.
Postlude (Intrada).
Cpte E. Söderström, D. Drobková, F. Livora, R.
Novák, Czech Phil Chor, Czech PO, C. Mackerras
(10/86) (SUPR) ① **C37-7448**
Cpte F. Palmer, A. Gunson, J. Mitchinson, M. King,
J. Parker-Smith, CBSO Chor, CBSO, S. Rattle
(r1981) *Sinfonietta.* (10/88) (EMI) ① **CDC7 47504-2**
Cpte L. Domanínská, V. Soukupová, B. Blachut, E.
Haken, Czech Phil Chor, Czech PO, K. Ančerl *Taras*
Bulba. (12/89) (SUPR) ① **11 0609-2**
Cpte E. Lear, H. Rössl-Majdan, E. Haefliger, F.
Crass, Bavarian Rad Chor, BRSO, R. Kubelík (1964)
Taras Bulba. (4/90) (DG) ① **429 182-2GGA**
Cpte M. Hajóssyová, V. Stracenská, V. Přibyl, R.
Novák, I. Sokol, Slovak Phil Chor, Bratislava Nat Op
Chor, Slovak PO, L. Slovák
(7/91) (OPUS) ① **9152 0700**
Cpte C. Brewer, M. Simpson, K. Dent, R. Roloff,
Atlanta Sym Chor, Atlanta SO, Robert Shaw *Dvořák:*
Te Deum. (7/91) (TELA) ① **CD80287**
Cpte H. Pilarczyk, J. Martin, N. Gedda, G. Gaynes,
Westminster Ch, NYPO, L. Bernstein (1963)
Poulenc: Gloria. (5/93) (SONY) ① **SMK47569**
Cpte N. Troitskaya, E. Randová, K. Kaludov, S.
Leiferkus, T. Trotter, Montreal Sym Chor, Montreal
SO, C. Dutoit (r1991) *Sinfonietta.*
(4/94) (DECC) ① **436 211-2DH**
Cpte E. Lear, H. Rössl-Majdan, E. Haefliger, F.
Crass, Bavarian Rad Chor, BRSO, R.
Kubelík (1960s) *Dvořák: Stabat Mater.*
(12/94) (DG) ① [2] **437 937-2GX2**
Cpte L. Domanínská, V. Soukupová, B. Blachut, E.
Haken, J. Vodrážka, Czech Phil Chor, Czech PO, K.
Ančerl (1963) *Concert*
(12/94) (SUPR) ① **11 1930-2**
Cpte T. Kiberg, R. Stene, P. Svensson, U. Cold, P.
Salo, Danish Nat Rad Ch, Danish Nat RSO, C.
Mackerras (1994: orig vers) *Kodály: Psalmus*
Hungaricus. (12/94) (CHAN) ① **CHAN9310**
Gradule in festo purificationis (Suscepimus
Deus)—choir a capella (1870 rev 1887)
Gonville & Caius College Ch, G. Webber (r1994)
Concert (6/95) (ASV) ① **CDDCA914**

Hail Mary—tenor, choir and organ (1904)
Gonville & Caius College Ch, G. Webber (r1994)
Concert (6/95) (ASV) ① **CDDCA914**
13 Hukvaldy folk poetry in songs, 'Ukvalská
lidová poesie v písních'—1v & piano (1898)
1. Andrew, Andrew (Ondraš, Ondraš); 2. Hukvaldy
Church (Ty ukvalsky kostelíčku); 3. Sweet Mother of
Mine (Ma mila mamulko); 4. The Wealthy Farmer's
Meadows (Na tych fojtovych łukach); 5. Why are you
sad? (Proč kalindo smutna stojíš?); 6. Farmer's Annie
(Fojtova Hanka); 7. Little Cowherd Lassie (Pasavala
kravarečka); 8. What are these shadows? (Co su to
sa tiné?); 9. There's an oak in our yard (V našim
dvoře dub); 10. As I walked through the dark forest
(Dyž semja šel přes); 11. Hukvaldy Church (Ty
ukvalsky kostelíčku!); 12. God bless you (Pan Buh
vam zaplat'); 13. As I passed by the Backyard (Dyž
sem ja šel kolem dvorka).
D. Pecková, I. Kusnjer, M. Lapšanský (r1994)
Concert (11/95) (SUPR) ① [2] **11 2214-2**
In Nomine Jesu—choir
Gonville & Caius College Ch, G. Webber (r1994)
Concert (6/95) (ASV) ① **CDDCA914**
The Lord's Prayer—tenor, choir, harp and
organ (1901 rev 1906)
Gonville & Caius College Ch, G. Webber (r1994)
Concert (6/95) (ASV) ① **CDDCA914**
9 Male-voice choruses (1885-1922)
1. Ah, Soldier, Soldier; 2. Our Birch Tree; 3. The
Evening Witch; 4. Parting; 5. The Czech Legion; 6.
The Wandering Madman; 7. Schoolmaster Halfar; 8.
Maryčka Magdonova; 9. The Seventy Thousand.
2, 6, 7. T. Willemstijn, B. Borden, H. Vels, J. Bremer,
D. Barrick, Netherlands Chbr Ch, R. de Leeuw
(r1993) *Concert* (12/95) (PHIL) ① **442 534-2PH**
3 Male-voice choruses (1888)
1. Parting; 2. The dove; 3. The jealous one.
2. Netherlands Chbr Ch, R. de Leeuw (r1993) *Concert*
(12/95) (PHIL) ① **442 534-2PH**
Mass in E flat—choir and organ (1907-08)
(cpted V. Petrželka)
Gonville & Caius College Ch, G. Webber (r1994; ed
Wingfield) *Concert* (6/95) (ASV) ① **CDDCA914**
Moravian folk poetry in songs—53 folksong
arrangements (pub 1908)
1. Love (Láska); 2. Charm (Kouzlo); 3. Tender little
tune (Zpěvulenka); 4. Bright lover's light (Záře od
milého); 5. Lover's likeness (Zahrádečka); 7. Blossom sweet and
tender (Kvítí milodějné); 8. Honeysuckle (Polajka); 9.
Corn cockle (Koukol); 10. Carnatio (Karafiát); 11.
Apple tree (Jabloňka); 12. Sweet apple (Jablúčko);
13. Red apples (Červená jablúčka); 14. Hazel nut
(Oříšek léskový); 15. Faithfulness (Věrnost'); 16.
Steadiness (Stálost'); 17. For whom the flower (Komu
kytha); 18. My lover's horses (Koníčky milého); 19.
Light feather (Péročko); 20. Desire (Tužba); 21.
Burden (Tíha); 22. Mementos (Památky); 23.
Message (Vzkázáni); 24. Wakening (Budíček); 25.
Promise (Slib); 26. Alderman's Daughter (Šáfárova
céra); 27. Forester (Hájný); 28. Uncertainty
(Nejistota); 29. Love letter (Psaníčko); 30. Rosemary
(Rozmarýn); 31. Good hunt (Dobrý lov); 32. Cuckoo
(Kukačka); 33. Calumny (Pomluva); 34. Orphan
(Sirota); 35. Woe (Stesk); 36. Then and now (Jindy a
nyní); 37. Bench (Lavečka); 38. Parting (Loučení); 39.
Lonely (Osamělý); 40. What sky is that (Co je to za
nebe); 41. Tears of solace (Slzy útěchy); 42.
Guelderrose (Kalina); 43. Fate (Osud); 44. Farewell
to Sweetheart (Loučení s milenky); 45. Cologna
(Kolín); 46. Belgrade (Belegrad); 47. Headache
(Bolavá hlava); 48. Good advice (Dobrá rada); 49.
The Flies' Wedding (Svatba komáří); 50. Lover who
killer (Milenec vrah); 51. Musicians (Muzikanti); 52.
Burial (Pohřeb zbojníkův); 53. Wed far away (Dalek
provdaná).
D. Pecková, I. Kusnjer, M. Lapšanský (r1994)
Concert (11/95) (SUPR) ① [2] **11 2214-2**
Excs Z. Kloubová, L.M. Vodička, R. Kvapil (r1994)
Concert (4/95) (UNIC) ① **DKPCD9154**
19, 27, 29, 47. L. Beňačková, R. Firkušný (r1991)
Concert (1/94) (RCA) ① **09026 60823-2**
Nursery Rhymes—introduction & 18 pieces:
choir & instr ens (1927)
1. Introduction (Úpod); 2. The Sugar Beet's Wedding
(Řípa se vdávala); 3. Nothing better that Springtime
(Není lepší jako z jary); 4. Mole comes crawling (Leze
krtek); 5. Charlie went on a ride to Hell (Karel do
pekla zajel); 6. Trousers in rags (Roztrhané kalhoty);
7. Frank the Knacker's son (Franta rasů); 8. That dog
of ours (Náš pes, náš pes); 9. I preach, I preach you
this sermon (Délám, délám kázání); 10. There was an
old woman (Stará bába čarovala); 11. Lee bui gwa,
t'cows do cum (Hó, hó, krávy dó); 12. Little wee wife
of mine (Moje žena malučičká); 13. Granny's gone off
to the lilac bush (Bába leze do bezu); 14. The white

goat picks up the pears (Koza bílá hrušky sbírá); 15.
Grumpy German smashed the pots (Němec brouk,
hrnce tlouk); 16. Nanny goat's lying in the hay (Koza
leží na sené); 17. Ted, Fred, Drummer Boy (Vašek,
pašek, bubeník); 18. Little Frank, little Frank
(Frantíku, Frantíku); 19. Bruin sat upon a log (Seděl
medvíď na kolodi).
Cpte London Sinfonietta Chor, London Sinfonietta, D.
Atherton *Concert*
(10/91) (DECC) ① [2] 430 375-2DH2
Cpte Czech Phil Chor, Czech Phil Chbr Ens, J.
Veselka *Concert*　(3/92) (SUPR) ① 11 0768-2
R. Coupe, Netherlands Chbr Ch, Schoenberg Ens, R.
de Leeuw (r1993) *Concert*
(12/95) (PHIL) ① 442 534-2PH
Regnum mundi—choir a capella (c1878)
Gonville & Caius College Ch, G. Webber (r1994)
Concert　(6/95) (ASV) ① CDDCA914
**10 Silesian songs from Helena Salichová's
Collection—1v & piano (1918)**
1. And there's me (A choť sem ja); 2. As I went (Dyž
sem šel); 3. Though I may be a young lass (A choť
sem děvucha); 4. Our own house (To naše stavení);
5. Hey, what's that rustle (Aj, co to tan šusti); 6.
There's water in the track (V kolaji voda); 7. And
what a charming Nightingale (Aj, co to je za slaviček);
8. There's a fair daughter you have (Panimamo,
švarnu cerku matě); 9. If you harness the horses (A
dybysté zapřihli); 10. In a dark wood (V černym lese).
D. Pecková, I. Kusnjer, M. Lapšanský (r1994)
Concert　(11/95) (SUPR) ① [2] 11 2214-2
**Songs of Hradčany (Hradčanske
písničky)—soprano & female vv (1916)** (Wds.
F S Procházka)
1. The golden alley; 2. The weeping fountain; 3.
Belveder (with harp).
A. Gold, E. Pameijer, E. Stoop, Netherlands Chbr Ch,
R. de Leeuw (r1993) *Concert*
(12/95) (PHIL) ① 442 534-2PH
**War Song (first version)—male vv a capella
(1873)**
Prague Phil Chor (r1994) *Concert*
(3/95) (SUPR) ① 11 1878-2
**War Song (second version), 'Blessing the
flag'—male chorus, trumpet, 3 trombones &
piano (1873)**
Prague Phil Chor, L. Kozderka, K. Kohout, K. Kučera,
M. Brázda, J. Holeňa (r1994) *Concert*
(3/95) (SUPR) ① 11 1878-2
**The Wild duck (Kacena divoká)—chorus
(c1885)** (Wds. anon)
Netherlands Chbr Ch, R. de Leeuw (r1993) *Concert*
(12/95) (PHIL) ① 442 534-2PH
**The Wolf's trail (Vlčí stopa)—soprano,
female vv & piano (1916)** (Wds. J Vrchlický)
B. Sellers, M. Bon, Netherlands Chbr Ch, R. de
Leeuw (r1993) *Concert*
(12/95) (PHIL) ① 442 534-2PH

SECTION V: STAGE WORKS

**The Cunning Little Vixen—opera: 3 acts
(1924—Brno)** (Lib. cpsr, after R. Těsnohlídek)
Cpte L. Popp, E. Randová, L. Márová, G. Jahn, I.
Mixová, R. Novák, E. Zikmundová, D. Jedlička, V.
Krejčík, B. Blachut, V. Zítek, Bratislava Children's Ch,
Vienna St Op Chor, VPO, C. MacKerras *Cunning
Little Vixen Suite*.
(11/86) (DECC) ① [2] 417 129-2DH2
Cpte L. Watson, D. Montague, K. Shelby, M. King, G.
Groves, G. Howell, G. Knight, P. Purcell, T. Allen, R.
Tear, J. Dobson, E. Bainbridge, N. Folwell, ROH
Chor, ROHO, S. Rattle (Eng) *Taras Bulba*.
(3/92) (EMI) ① [2] CDS7 54212-2
Cpte M. Hajóssyová, G. Beňačková, I. Mixová, L.
Domanínská, B. Effenberková, K. Průša, H. Buldrová,
M. Mrázová, R. Novák, M. Frydlewicz, K. Hanuš, D.
Tikalová, J. Souček, Kühn Children's Chor, Czech
Phil Chor, Czech PO, V. Neumann (r1979/80)
(4/93) (SUPR) ① [2] 10 3471-2
Suite Czech PO, F. Jílek *Concert*
(11/85) (SUPR) ① C37-7303
Suite Czech PO, J. Bělohlávek *Concert*
(11/92) (CHAN) ① CHAN9080
Suite Czech PO, V. Talich (r1954; arr Talich) *Concert*
(1/94) (SUPR) ① 11 1905-2
**Cunning Little Vixen—concert suite from
opera**
VPO, C. MacKerras (arr. Talich) *Cunning Little Vixen*.
(11/86) (DECC) ① [2] 417 129-2DH2

**The Excursions of Mr Brouček to the Moon
and to the 15th Century—opera: 4 acts
(1920—Prague)** (Lib. V Dyk & F S Procházka)
Cpte L. Fehenberger, F. Wunderlich, K. Böhme, W.
Lipp, K. Engen, A. Fahberg, L. Benningsen, P. Kuen,
K. Ostertag, Bavarian St Orch, Bavarian St Op Chor,
J. Keilberth (pp1959)
(2/95) (ORFE) ① [2] C354942I
Cpte V. Přibyl, M. Švejda, Bohumil Maršík, J.
Jonášová, R. Novák, J. Marková, L. Márová, V.
Krejčík, J. Souček, J. Olejníček, R. Tuček, K. Hanuš,
Czech Phil Chor, Czech PO, F. Jílek (r1980)
(2/95) (SUPR) ① [2] 11 2153-2
Postlude to Part 1. M. Kopp, A. Barová, J. Janská,
V. Doležal, Y. Tannenbergerova, M. Ungrová, Brno
St PO, L. Svárovský (r1994) *Concert*
(3/95) (SUPR) ① 11 1878-2
**Fate (Osud)—opera: 3 acts, Brno Radio
(1934)** (Lib. F. Bartošová and cpsr)
Cpte H. Field, P. Langridge, K. Harries, P. Bronder,
S. Kale, C. Teare, E. Gaskell, D. Hood, Mary Davies,
G. Keeble, B. Mora, M. Hoiland, C. Bell, R. Moseley-
Morgan, G. Rhys-Davies, P. Lloyd-Evans, R. Mason,
T. German, F. Manning, C. Edwards, S. Linay, Y.
Jones, M. Preston-Roberts, WNO Chor, WNO Orch,
C. Mackerras (Eng)　(9/90) (EMI) ① CDC7 49993-2
Suite Czech PO, F. Jílek *Concert*
(11/85) (SUPR) ① C37-7303
**From the House of the Dead—opera: 3 acts,
Brno (1930)** (Lib. cpsr, after F. Dostoyevsky)
Cpte D. Jedlička, J. Janská, J. Zahradníček, V.
Krejčík, R. Novák, A. Švorc, B. Blachut, I. Žídek, J.
Souček, E. Zikmundová, Z. Soušek, V. Zítek, Z.
Švehla, Vienna St Op Chor, VPO, C. MacKerras
Concert　(10/91) (DECC) ① [2] 430 375-2DH2
Cpte R. Novák, M. Jirglová, V. Přibyl, J. Stříška, K.
Berman, J. Horáček, B. Blachut, I. Žídek, J. Jindrák,
K. Průša, A. Míková, M. Karpíšek, J. Souček, V. Kočí,
M. Švejda, Czech Phil Chor, Czech PO, V. Neumann
(r1979)　(9/94) (SUPR) ① [2] 10 2941-2
Prelude Philh, L. Pešek *Concert*
(6/92) (VIRG) ① VC7 59076-2
Suite Czech PO, F. Jílek *Concert*
(11/85) (SUPR) ① C37-7303
Jenůfa—opera: 3 acts (1904—Brno) (Lib.
cpsr, after G. Preissová)
Cpte E. Söderström, W. Ochman, E. Randová, P.
Dvorský, L. Popp, M. Mrázová, V. Zítek, D. Jedlička,
I. Mixová, V. Soukupová, J. Pokorná, J. Jonášová,
Vienna St Op Chor, VPO, C. MacKerras (r1982)
(12/85) (DECC) ① [2] 414 483-2DH2
Cpte G. Beňačková, V. Přibyl, N. Kniplová, V.
Krejčík, J. Pokorná, A. Barová, K. Berman, V. Halíř,
K. Belanová, D. Suryová, C. Strádalová, J. Janská,
Brno Janáček Op Chor, Brno Janáček Op Orch, F.
Jílek (r1977/8)　(4/93) (SUPR) ① [2] 10 2751-2
Cpte L. Domanínská, V. Přibyl, N. Kniplová, I. Žídek,
M. Boháčová, M. Mrázová, J. Jindrák, Z. Kroupa, J.
Procházková, E. Hlobilová, B. Effenberková, A.
Rousková, Prague Nat Th Chor, Prague Nat Th Orch,
B. Gregor (r1969)
(12/95) (EMI) ① CMS5 65476-2
**And that's how we would go...Ah, he was so
strong** J. Pavlová, Y. Tannenbergerova, Brno St PO,
L. Svárovský (r1994) *Concert*
(3/95) (SUPR) ① 11 1878-2
This is my mother's room L. Popp, Munich RO, S.
Soltesz (r1987) *Concert*
(4/89) (EMI) ① CDC7 49319-2
**Káťa Kabanová—opera: 3 acts
(1921—Prague)** (Wds. cpsr, aster A.N.
Ostrovosky)
Cpte E. Söderström, P. Dvorský, N. Kniplová, D.
Jedlička, V. Krejčík, Z. Švehla, L. Márová, J. Souček,
J. Pavlová, G. Jahn, Vienna St Op Chor, VPO, C.
Mackerras *Concert*
(10/89) (DECC) ① [2] 421 852-2DH2
Cpte D. Tikalová, B. Blachut, L. Komancová, Z.
Kroupa, B. Vích, V. Kočí, I. Mixová, R. Jedlička, E.
Hlobilová, M. Lemariová, Prague Nat Th Chor,
Prague Nat Th Orch, J. Krombholc (r1959)
(11/93) (SUPR) ① [2] 10 8016-2
The Living Corpse—opera fragment (1916)
(Lib. cpsr, after Tolstoy)
Y. Tannenbergerova, J. Janská, J. Jiskrová, Brno St
PO, L. Svárovský (r1994) *Concert*
(3/95) (SUPR) ① 11 1878-2
**The Makropulos Affair—opera: 3 acts
(1926—Prague)** (Wds. cpsr, after K. Čapek)
Cpte E. Söderström, P. Dvorský, V. Krejčík, A.
Czaková, V. Zítek, Z. Švehla, D. Jedlička, J. Joran, I.
Mixová, B. Blachut, B. Vítková, Vienna St Op Chor,
VPO, C. Mackerras (r1978) *Lachian Dances*.
(10/91) (DECC) ① [2] 430 372-2DH2

Cpte L. Prylová, I. Žídek, R. Vonásek, H.
Tattermuschová, P. Kočí, V. Kočí, K. Berman, J.
Joran, J. Procházková, M. Karpíšek, M. Musilová,
Prague Nat Th Chor, Prague Nat Th Orch, B. Gregor
(r1965/6)　(5/95) (SUPR) ① [2] 10 8351-2
Šárka—opera: 3 acts (1925—Brno) (Lib. J.
Zeyer (work written 1887-88, rev 1918-19 &
1924-25)
Cpte A. Nováková, A. Jurečka, F. Kunc, J. Válka,
Brno Rad Chor, Brno RSO, B. Bakala (r1953)
(6/94) (MULT) ① 310154-2
**Schluk und Jau—incidental music to G.
Hauptmann's play (1928)**
Brno St PO, F. Jílek (r1992) *Concert*
(9/93) (SUPR) ① 11 1522-2

JANEQUIN, Clément
(c1485–1558) France

M—Nos from A.T. Merritt & F. Lesure

SECTION IV: VOCAL AND CHORAL

A ce joly moys—chanson, M iii/97
C. Janequin Ens *Concert*
(8/85) (HARM) ① HMC90 1099
Assouvy suis—chanson, M i/8
C. Janequin Ens *Concert*
(8/85) (HARM) ① HMC90 1099
Au joly jeu—chanson, M i/12
Magdalen (Oxford) Coll Ch, G. Ives *Concert*
(11/92) (CNTO) ① CRCD2366
**L' Aveuglé dieu qui partout vole—chanson,
M v/209**
C. Janequin Ens (arr Albert de Rippe) *Concert*
(8/85) (HARM) ① HMC90 1099
Le Chant des oiseaux—chanson, M i/2
C. Janequin Ens *Concert*
(8/85) (HARM) ① HMC90 1099
Hilliard Ens *Concert*　(6/91) (HYPE) ① CDA66370
Scholars (r1993) *Concert*
(2/95) (NAXO) ① 8 550880
Le Chant du rossignol—chanson, M ii/68
C. Janequin Ens *Concert*
(8/85) (HARM) ① HMC90 1099
**La Guerre, '(La) bataille de
Marignan'—chanson: 5vv, M vi/234**
K. Marshall (arr Marshall) *Concert*
(7/92) (AUVI) ① V4645
Hélas mon Dieu, y a il—chanson, M iv/135
C. Janequin Ens *Concert*
(8/85) (HARM) ① HMC90 1099
Herbes et fleurs—chanson, M vi/237
C. Janequin Ens *Concert*
(8/85) (HARM) ① HMC90 1099
Il estoit une fillette—chanson, M iii/77
C. Janequin Ens *Concert*
(8/85) (HARM) ① HMC90 1099
J'atens le temps—chanson, M iii/89
C. Janequin Ens *Concert*
(8/85) (HARM) ① HMC90 1099
Las on peult juger—chanson, M iii/107
C. Janequin Ens (arr. Morlaye) *Concert*
(8/85) (HARM) ① HMC90 1099
**Ma peine n'est pas grande—chanson, M
iii/110**
C. Janequin Ens *Concert*
(8/85) (HARM) ① HMC90 1099
Me fault il tant de mal—chanson, M iii/84
C. Janequin Ens *Concert*
(8/85) (HARM) ① HMC90 1099
M'amye a eu de die—chanson, M iii/124
C. Janequin Ens *Concert*
(8/85) (HARM) ① HMC90 1099
M'y levay par ung matin—chanson, M i/9
C. Janequin Ens *Concert*
(8/85) (HARM) ① HMC90 1099
**O doulx regard, o parler—chanson, M
iv/138**
C. Janequin Ens *Concert*
(8/85) (HARM) ① HMC90 1099
O mal d'aymer—chanson, M iii/104
C. Janequin Ens *Concert*
(8/85) (HARM) ① HMC90 1099
Or sus vous dormés trop—chanson, M i/5
C. Janequin Ens *Concert*
(8/85) (HARM) ① HMC90 1099
Or vien ça, vien, m'amye—chanson, M ii/41
Scholars (r1993) *Concert*
(2/95) (NAXO) ① 8 550880
**Quand contremont verras—chanson, M
iv/148**
C. Janequin Ens *Concert*
(8/85) (HARM) ① HMC90 1099
**Quelqu'un me disoit l'aultre jour—chanson,
M v/201**
C. Janequin Ens *Concert*
(8/85) (HARM) ① HMC90 1099

21 Fantasias in three parts—two violins and
   bass viol
  1. Scaramouche (r1992) *Concert*
            (5/94) (CHNN) ① **CCS4792**
8 Fantasia-Suites in four parts—two violins,
   two bass viols and organ
  EXCERPTS: 2. A minor; 6. F; 8. D.
  2, 6, 8. Parley of Instr, P. Holman *Concert*
         (12/92) (HYPE) ① **CDA66604**
10 Fantasia-Suites in four parts—three
   violins, bass viol and organ
  EXCERPTS: 6. F; 8. C; 10. E minor.
  6, 8, 10. Parley of Instr, P. Holman *Concert*
         (12/92) (HYPE) ① **CDA66604**
2 Fantasia-Suites in two parts (fantasia-air-
   corant)—violin, bass viol and organ
  EXCERPTS: 1. A minor.
  1. Rose Consort (r1992) *Concert*
         (8/94) (NAXO) ① **8 550687**
2 In Nomines in six parts—two treble, two
   tenor, two bass viols and organ
  EXCERPTS: 1. G minor.
  Hespèrion XX, M. Behringer (r1990) *Concert*
         (2/92) (ASTR) ① **E8724**
  1. Rose Consort (r1992) *Concert*
         (8/94) (NAXO) ① **8 550687**
Pavan and Galliard, 'Newarke Seidge'—viol
   consort
  Rose Consort (r1992) *Concert*
         (8/94) (NAXO) ① **8 550687**
2 Pavans in six parts—two treble, two tenor,
   two bass viols and organ
  EXCERPTS: 1. Bell Pavan.
  Hespèrion XX, M. Behringer (r1990) *Concert*
         (2/92) (ASTR) ① **E8724**
Pavan in F Rose Consort (r1992) *Concert*
         (8/94) (NAXO) ① **8 550687**

SECTION IV: VOCAL AND CHORAL

Why sigh'st thou, shepherd—song
  C. Bott, M. George, New London Consort, P. Pickett
  (r1992) *Concert*   (4/94) (LINN) ① **CKD011**

JENNINGS, Terry (b 1940) USA

SECTION II: CHAMBER

Terry's G Dorian 12-Bar Blues (9x5) &
   3—saxophone and keyboards (1962)
  J. Gibson, M. Riesman, L.M. Young, B. Ruyle (r1992)
  Concert   (6/93) (PNT) ① **434 873-2PTH**

JENSEN, Adolf (1837–1879)
Germany

SECTION IV: VOCAL AND CHORAL

Altar—song
  K. Ferrier, P. Spurr (bp1949) *Concert*
         (6/92) (DECC) ① **433 473-2DM**
Leis' rudern hier, mein Gondolier—Lied, Op.
   50/4 (1876) (Wds. Moore)
  A. Rolfe Johnson, G. Johnson *Concert*
         (3/88) (HYPE) ① **CDA66112**
Murmelndes Lüftchen—Lied, Op. 21/4 (Wds.
   Heyse)
  E. Rethberg, anon, stg qt (r1928-9) *Concert*
         (2/95) (ROMO) ① [2] **81012-2**
Wenn durch die Piazzetta—Lied, Op. 50/3
   (1876) (Wds. Moore)
  A. Rolfe Johnson, G. Johnson *Concert*
         (3/88) (HYPE) ① **CDA66112**

JENSEN, Ludwig Irgens
(1894–1969) Norway

SECTION I: ORCHESTRAL

Sinfonia in D—orchestra (1941)
  Oslo PO, Ø. Fjeldstad (r1972) *Concert*
         (12/94) (SIMA) ① **PSC3118**
Tema con variazioni—orchestra (1925)
  Oslo PO, O. Grüner-Hegge (r1972) *Concert*
         (12/94) (SIMA) ① **PSC3118**

SECTION IV: VOCAL AND CHORAL

Japanese Spring—1v and piano (1920)
  1. Today; 2. The Flowering Twig; 3. The willow in the
  Wind; 4. To a Friend; 5. The Sound of Love; 6.
  Reflection; 7. A simple Game; 8. Solitude; 9. The
  constant in the Fleeting.
  K. Langebo, Oslo PO, Ø. Fjeldstad (r1972) *Concert*
         (12/94) (SIMA) ① **PSC3118**

JERAL, Wilhelm (1861–1935)
Czechoslovakia

SECTION II: CHAMBER

Sérénade viennois—violin and piano, Op.
  18
  F. Kreisler, H. Kreisler, C. Keith (r1921: arr. Kreisler)
  Concert   (7/90) (BIDD) ① [2] **LAB009/10**

JERSILD, Jørgen (b 1913)
Denmark
---

3 Romantiske korsange—chorus a cappella
  (1971 rev 1984, 1989)
  1. My favourite valley (Min yndlingsdal: wds S S
  Blicher); 2. Rain in the night (Natteregn: wds N
  Petersen); 3. The evening glow (Aftenrøden: wds S
  Staffeldt).
  Danish Nat Rad Ch, S. Parkman (r1993) *Concert*
         (4/95) (CHAN) ① **CHAN9264**

JERÚSALEM, Ignacio de
(c1710–1769) Italy/Mexico

SECTION IV: VOCAL AND CHORAL

Dixit Dominus
  Chanticleer, Chanticleer Sinfonia, J. Jennings (r1993)
  Concert   (12/94) (TELD) ① **4509-93333-2**
Polychoral Mass in D—double choir (attrib)
  Chanticleer, Chanticleer Sinfonia, J. Jennings (r1993)
  Concert   (12/94) (TELD) ① **4509-93333-2**
Responsorio Segundo de S. S. José:
  'Esuriente terra Aegypti'—2nd repsonsory
  for St Jospeh
  Chanticleer, Chanticleer Sinfonia, J. Jennings (r1993)
  Concert   (12/94) (TELD) ① **4509-93333-2**

JESSEL, Leon (1871–1942)
Germany

SECTION IV: VOCAL AND CHORAL

Der Rose Hochzeitsung—Lied (1911) (Eng:
  The Wedding of the Rose)
  A. Campoli, Orch, W. Goehr *Concert*
         (10/91) (PEAR) ① **PASTCD9744**

SECTION V: STAGE WORKS

Schwarzwaldmädel—operetta (3 acts)
  (1917—Berlin) (Lib. A. Neidhart)
  Excs M. Schramm, A. Herrfurth, L. Schädle, U.
  Schirmacher, R. Schock, K-E. Mercker, F.
  Ollendorff, W. Reichert, Berlin RIAS Chbr Ch, Berlin
  SO, W. Schmidt-Boelcke
         (2/91) (EURO) ① **GD69027**

JINDŘICH, Jindřich (1876–1967)
Czechoslovakia

SECTION IV: VOCAL AND CHORAL

Je teskno dnes—song (Wds. Hájck)
  E. Destinn, anon (r1909) *Concert*
         (12/94) (SUPR) ① [12] **11 2136-2(2)**
Jen kdybych věděl—song (Wds. Vrchlický)
  E. Destinn, anon (r1909) *Concert*
         (12/94) (SUPR) ① [12] **11 2136-2(2)**
My sweetheart—song
  E. Destinn, orch, J. Pasternack (r1919) *Concert*
         (11/93) (ROMO) ① [2] **81002-2**
  E. Destinn, orch, J. Pasternack (r1919) *Concert*
         (12/94) (SUPR) ① [12] **11 2136-2(5)**
O Mountains—folksong arrangement
  E. Destinn, orch, J. Pasternack (r1919) *Concert*
         (12/94) (SUPR) ① [12] **11 2136-2(5)**
The Ostroh Castle—song
  E. Destinn, orch, J. Pasternack (r1919) *Concert*
         (11/93) (ROMO) ① [2] **81002-2**
  E. Destinn, orch, J. Pasternack (r1919) *Concert*
         (12/94) (SUPR) ① [12] **11 2136-2(5)**

JOACHIM, Joseph (1831–1907)
Austro-Hungary

SECTION I: ORCHESTRAL

Concerto for Violin and Orchestra in
  Hungarian style, Op. 11 (pub 1861)
  E. Oliveira, LPO, L. Botstein *Concert*
         (8/91) (CARL) ① **MCD27**
Hamlet—overture, Op. 4 (pub c1855)
  LPO, L. Botstein *Concert*   (8/91) (CARL) ① **MCD27**

Heinrich IV—overture, Op. 7 (pub c1855)
  LPO, L. Botstein *Concert*   (8/91) (CARL) ① **MCD27**

SECTION II: CHAMBER

Romance in B flat—violin and piano
  A. Rosand, H. Sung *Brahms: Hungarian Dances.*
         (3/93) (BIDD) ① **LAW003**
Variations on an original theme in F—viola
  and piano, Op. 10 (pub 1860)
  R. Golani, K. Bogino *Concert*
         (9/92) (CONI) ① **CDCF199**

JOÃO IV, King of Portugal
(1604–1645) Portugal

SECTION IV: VOCAL AND CHORAL

Crux fidelis—motet
  Oxford Camerata, J. Summerly (r1993) *Concert*
         (3/95) (NAXO) ① **8 550843**

JOBIM, Antonio Carlos (b 1927)
Brazil

SECTION IV: VOCAL AND CHORAL

Estrada do Sol—song (late 1950s) (Wds.
  Durán)
  S. Isbin (arr Barbosa-Lima) *Concert*
         (10/90) (VIRG) ① **VC7 59591-2**
Garota de Ipanema, '(The) Girl from
  Ipanema'—song (1964) (Wds. N Gimbel & V
  de Moraes)
  Thurston Cl Qt (arr cl qt: Blezard) *Concert*
         (10/93) (ASV) ① **CDWHL2076**

JOEL, Billy (b 1949) USA

SECTION IV: VOCAL AND CHORAL

Just the way you are—song (1977) (Wds.
  cpsr)
  J. Norman, J.T. Williams (r1989) *Concert*
         (4/92) (PHIL) ① **422 401-2PH**

JOHANNES DE LYMBURGIA (fl.
1400–14) France

SECTION IV: VOCAL AND CHORAL

Tota pulchra es, amica mea—motet: 4vv
  (Songs of Songs)
  Gothic Voices, C. Page *Concert*
         (3/92) (HYPE) ① **CDA66463**

JOHANSEN, David Monrad
(1888–1974) Norway

SECTION II: CHAMBER

String Quartet, Op. 35 (1969)
  Oslo Qt (r1993) *Concert*
         (10/94) (NAXO) ① **8 550879**

JOHN, Elton (b 1947) England
---

pseudonym of Reginald Kenneth Dwight

SECTION V: STAGE WORKS

The Lion King—songs for film (1994) (Lyrics
  Tim Rice; underscore by Hans Zimmer)
  EXCERPTS: 1. Can You Feel the Love Tonight.
  1. P. Barritt, ECO, D. Fraser (r1994-5; arr Fraser)
  Concert   (12/95) (DELO) ① **DE3186**

JOHNSON, David N. (b 1922)
USA

SECTION III: INSTRUMENTAL

Trumpet Tune in A—organ
  C. Herrick *Concert*   (10/92) (HYPE) ① **CDA66605**
Trumpet tune in D—organ (pub. 1962)
  C. Herrick *Concert*   (7/86) (HYPE) ① **CDA66121**

JOHNSON, Edward (1545–1602)
England

SECTION IV: VOCAL AND CHORAL

Come again—consort song: 1v and viol
  consort
  J. Budd, M. Chance, Fretwork (r1990) *Concert*
         (7/94) (VIRG) ① **VC5 45007-2**

Eliza is the fayrest quene—song for voice
and 4 viols (1591) (written for the Elvetham
entertainment)
J. Bowman, King's Consort *Concert*
(10/91) (HYPE) ① **CDA66447**
J. Budd, Fretwork (r1990) *Concert*
(7/94) (VIRG) ① **VC5 45007-2**

JOHNSON, James (Price)
(1894–1955) USA

SECTION III: INSTRUMENTAL
The **Mule Walk**—piano (c1914-17)
A. Feinberg (r1994; trans Riccardo Scivales) *Concert*
(11/95) (ARGO) ① **444 457-2ZH**

JOHNSON, James Weldon
(1871–1938) USA

SECTION IV: VOCAL AND CHORAL
Since you went away—song
J. McCormack, F. Kreisler, E. Schneider (r1920)
Concert (9/89) (PEAR) ① **GEMMCD9315**
Under the Bamboo Tree—song used in the
revue 'Sally In Our Alley' (1902) (Lyrics Bob
Cole & J. Rosamond Johnson)
M. Cahill, Broadway Cast (r1917) *Concert*
(5/94) (PEAR) ① [3] **GEMMCDS9050/2(1)**

JOHNSON, John (c1541–c1594)
England

SECTION II: CHAMBER
Delight Pavan—consort
Musicians of Swanne Alley *Concert*
(2/88) (HARM) ① **HMC90 5192**
Go merely wheele—two lutes (attrib)
P. O'Dette, L. Nordstrom *Concert*
(2/88) (HARM) ① **HMC90 5192**
Green garters—consort
Musicians of Swanne Alley *Concert*
(11/89) (VIRG) ① **VC7 59534-2**
Greensleeves—two lutes/consort (attrib)
Musicians of Swanne Alley *Concert*
(11/89) (VIRG) ① **VC7 59534-2**
Passamezzo moderno—two lutes
Musicians of Swanne Alley *Concert*
(11/89) (VIRG) ① **VC7 59534-2**
Pavan and Galliard—two guitars (trans
Bream)
J. Bream, J. Williams (r1978) *Concert*
(11/93) (RCA) ① **09026 61452-2**
Short Almain—two lutes
Musicians of Swanne Alley *Concert*
(11/89) (VIRG) ① **VC7 59534-2**

SECTION III: INSTRUMENTAL
The **carmans whistle**—lute (probably
authentic)
L. Sayce *Concert* (4/93) (DERV) ① **DRVCD101**
J. Bream (r1960) *Concert*
(8/93) (RCA) ① [28] **09026 61583-2(1)**
J. Bream (r1960) *Concert*
(8/93) (RCA) ① **09026 61584-2**
Delight pavan—lute
L. Sayce *Concert* (4/93) (DERV) ① **DRVCD101**
Flat pavan—lute
L. Sayce *Concert* (4/93) (DERV) ① **DRVCD101**
J. Bream, J. Bream Consort (r1962) *Concert*
(8/93) (RCA) ① [28] **09026 61583-2(2)**
J. Bream Consort (r1962; arr consort) *Concert*
(9/94) (RCA) ① **09026 61589-2**
Galliard to Delight pavan—lute
C. Wilson *Concert* (11/91) (VIRG) ① **VC7 59034-2**
L. Sayce *Concert* (4/93) (DERV) ① **DRVCD101**
Galliard to the Flat pavan—lute
L. Sayce *Concert* (4/93) (DERV) ① **DRVCD101**
Galliard to the Passemeasures pavan—lute
(doubtful: probably anon)
L. Sayce *Concert* (4/93) (DERV) ① **DRVCD101**
6 Galliards—lute (untitled)
1. F; 2. C.
1, 2. L. Sayce *Concert*
(4/93) (DERV) ① **DRVCD101**
The **gathering of Peascods**—lute
L. Sayce *Concert* (4/93) (DERV) ① **DRVCD101**
**Johnsons Jewell, 'My Lord Barnayes
Galliard'**—lute
L. Sayce *Concert* (4/93) (DERV) ① **DRVCD101**
Passemeasures pavan in F minor—lute
L. Sayce *Concert* (4/93) (DERV) ① **DRVCD101**
Passemeasures pavan in G minor—lute
L. Sayce *Concert* (4/93) (DERV) ① **DRVCD101**

3 Pavans—lute (untitled)
1. F minor.
1. L. Sayce *Concert* (4/93) (DERV) ① **DRVCD101**
Walsingham—lute
P. O'Dette *Concert* (2/88) (HARM) ① **HMC90 5192**
L. Sayce *Concert* (4/93) (DERV) ① **DRVCD101**

JOHNSON, Laurie (b 1927)
England

SECTION V: STAGE WORKS
The **First Men in the Moon**—film score
(1964)
EXCERPTS: 1. Prelude; 2. Modern Moon Landing;
3. Newscasters/Union Jack/Journy to Dymchurch; 4.
Cherry Cottage/Kate & Bedford; 5. Arguments; 6.
Cavor's Experiments; 7. The Sphere; 8. Love Theme;
9. To the Moon; 10. Lunar
Landing/Moonscape/Weightlessness/Planting the
Union Jack; 11. Lens Pit/Shadows; 12. Battle with the
Selenites; 13. Search for the Sphere/Kate in Peril; 14.
Lens Complex/Dismantling the Sphere/Coccooning
Selenites/The Eclipse; 15. End of the Eclipse/The
Grand Lunar; 16. Bedford Shoots at the Grand Lunar;
17. Pursuit & Escape from the Moon/End Title.
1-17. OST, L. Johnson (r1964) *Concert*
(11/91) (CLOU) ① **ACN7015**

JOHNSON, Scott (b 1952) USA

SECTION II: CHAMBER
**How it Happens (The Voice of I. F.
Stone)**—string quartet (1991-93)
1. Soliloquy; 2. It raged.
1. Kronos Qt (r1992) *Concert*
(8/93) (NONE) ① **7559-79310-2**

JOHNSON I, Robert
(c1500–c1560) Scotland

SECTION II: CHAMBER
In Nomine a 5—consort: 5 parts
Fretwork *Concert* (3/88) (AMON) ① **CD-SAR29**

SECTION III: INSTRUMENTAL
**Miscellaneous pices in Lord Herbert of
Cherbury's Lute Book**—lute
1. Pavin; 2. Almaine; 3. Fantasie.
P. O'Dette *Concert* (8/93) (HARM) ① **HMU90 7068**

JOHNSON II, Robert
(c1583–1633) England

SECTION II: CHAMBER
**Dances from Ben Johnson's 'Masque of
Oberon' (1611)** (doubtful)
1. Three almans (Main dances); 2. Fairies' Dance; 3.
Satyr's Dance.
1, 2. L. Sayce *Concert* (4/93) (DERV) ① **DRVCD101**
1, 2. A. Rooley (r1991) *Concert*
(4/94) (VIRG) ① **VC7 59321-2**
**Dances from Chapman's 'Masque of the
Middle Temple and Lincoln's Inn'**—consort
(1613) (Nos 1-3 & 6 also for lute)
1. First of the Temple; 2. Second of the Temple; 3.
Third of the Temple; 4. Baboon's Dance (doubtful); 5.
Torch-bearers Dance (doubtful); 6. Three dances.
6. L. Sayce *Concert* (4/93) (DERV) ① **DRVCD101**
3 Masque Dances—lutes
J. Lindberg, R. Meunier, N. North, P. O'Dette, Ens, R.
Goodman *Concert* (12/86) (BIS) ① **BIS-CD341**
Naglein Blumen—consort (unidentified)
Toulon Musica Antiqua, C. Mendoze *Concert*
(9/93) (PIER) ① **PV787092**
The **Temporiser a 4**
Amsterdam Loeki Stardust Qt *Concert*
(10/94) (L'OI) ① **440 207-2OM**

SECTION III: INSTRUMENTAL
Almans—lute
1. 'Hit and take it'; 2. 'Lady Strang's'; 3. 'The
Princes'; 4. F; 5. C minor; 6. C.
J. Bream (r1960) *Concert*
(8/93) (RCA) ① **09026 61584-2**
Almand Toulon Musica Antiqua, C. Mendoze (arr
consort) *Concert* (9/93) (PIER) ① **PV787092**
unidentified Almans J. Bream (r1960) *Concert*
(8/93) (RCA) ① [28] **09026 61583-2(1)**
1. A. Rooley (r1991) *Concert*
(4/94) (VIRG) ① **VC7 59321-2**
1, 2, 4, 5, 6. L. Sayce *Concert*
(4/93) (DERV) ① **DRVCD101**

Corant—lute
A. Rooley (r1991) *Concert*
(4/94) (VIRG) ① **VC7 59321-2**
Fantasia—lute
L. Sayce *Concert* (4/93) (DERV) ① **DRVCD101**
J. Bream (r1960) *Concert*
(8/93) (RCA) ① [28] **09026 61583-2(1)**
J. Bream (r1960) *Concert*
(8/93) (RCA) ① **09026 61584-2**
A. Rooley (r1991) *Concert*
(4/94) (VIRG) ① **VC7 59321-2**
Galliards—lute
1. 'My Lady Mildemays Delight; 2. D.
1. A. Rooley (r1991) *Concert*
(4/94) (VIRG) ① **VC7 59321-2**
1, 2. L. Sayce *Concert*
(4/93) (DERV) ① **DRVCD101**
Pavans—lute
1. F minor; 2. C minor (x 2).
1, 2. L. Sayce *Concert*
(4/93) (DERV) ① **DRVCD101**
2. A. Rooley (r1991) *Concert*
(4/94) (VIRG) ① **VC7 59321-2**

SECTION IV: VOCAL AND CHORAL
Adieu, fond love—song from 'The Lover's
Progress': 1v and lute (Wds. Beaumont &
Fletcher)
D. Thomas, A. Rooley (r1991) *Concert*
(4/94) (VIRG) ① **VC7 59321-2**
Arm, arm!—secular song: 1v (c1616) (Wds.
Beaumont & Fletcher from 'The Mad Lover')
D. Thomas, A. Rooley (r1991) *Concert*
(4/94) (VIRG) ① **VC7 59321-2**
As I walked forth—secular song: 1v (Wds.
anon)
E. Kirkby, A. Rooley (r1991) *Concert*
(4/94) (VIRG) ① **VC7 59321-2**
Away delights—song (c1612) (Wds.
Beaumont and Fletcher)
E. Van Evera, Musicians of Swanne Alley *Concert*
(11/89) (VIRG) ① **VC7 59534-2**
E. Kirkby, A. Rooley (r1991) *Concert*
(4/94) (VIRG) ① **VC7 59321-2**
Care-charming sleep—song (c1614) (Wds.
Beaumont and Fletcher)
R. Jacobs, K. Junghänel (r1985) *Concert*
(5/87) (HARM) ① **HMA190 1183**
E. Van Evera, Musicians of Swanne Alley *Concert*
(11/89) (VIRG) ① **VC7 59534-2**
E. Kirkby, A. Rooley (r1991) *Concert*
(4/94) (VIRG) ① **VC7 59321-2**
Charon, oh Charon—secular song: 2vv (Wds.
anon)
E. Kirkby, A. Rooley (r1991) *Concert*
(4/94) (VIRG) ① **VC7 59321-2**
Come away, Hecate—song from 'The Witch':
1v and lute (Wds. Middleton)
E. Kirkby, D. Thomas, A. Rooley (r1991) *Concert*
(4/94) (VIRG) ① **VC7 59321-2**
Come away, thou lady gay—song from 'The
Chances': 2vv and lute (Wds. Beaumont &
Fletcher)
E. Kirkby, D. Thomas, A. Rooley (r1991) *Concert*
(4/94) (VIRG) ① **VC7 59321-2**
Come, heavy sleep—song: 1v and lute (Wds.
anon)
E. Kirkby, A. Rooley (r1991) *Concert*
(4/94) (VIRG) ① **VC7 59321-2**
Come hither, you that love—song from 'The
Captain': 1v and lute (Wds. Beaumont &
Fletcher)
E. Kirkby, A. Rooley (r1991) *Concert*
(4/94) (VIRG) ① **VC7 59321-2**
Full fathom five—secular song (1611) (Wds.
Shakespeare)
D. Thomas, A. Rooley (r1991) *Concert*
(4/94) (VIRG) ① **VC7 59321-2**
Hark, hark! the lark—song from 'Cymbeline':
1v and lute (Wds. Shakespeare)
E. Kirkby, A. Rooley (r1991) *Concert*
(4/94) (VIRG) ① **VC7 59321-2**
Have you seen the bright lily grow?—secular
song: 1v (1616) (Wds. B. Johnson from 'The
Devil is an Ass')
D. Thomas, A. Rooley (r1991) *Concert*
(4/94) (VIRG) ① **VC7 59321-2**
O let us howl—song from 'The Duchess of
Malfi': 1v and lute (Wds. Webster)
D. Thomas, A. Rooley (r1991) *Concert*
(4/94) (VIRG) ① **VC7 59321-2**
Tell me dearest—song from 'The Captain':
2vv and lute (Wds. Beaumont & Fletcher)
E. Kirkby, D. Thomas, A. Rooley (r1991) *Concert*
(4/94) (VIRG) ① **VC7 59321-2**

'Tis late and cold—secular song: 1v (Wds. from 'The Lover's Progress')
D. Thomas, A. Rooley (r1991) *Concert*
(4/94) (VIRG) ① **VC7 59321-2**
Where the bee sucks—secular song (1600) (Wds. Shakespeare)
E. Kirkby, D. Thomas, A. Rooley (r1991) *Concert*
(4/94) (VIRG) ① **VC7 59321-2**
Woods, rocks and mountains—song: 1v and lute (Wds. anon)
E. Kirkby, A. Rooley (r1991) *Concert*
(4/94) (VIRG) ① **VC7 59321-2**

JOLIVET, Andre (1905–1974) France

SECTION I: ORCHESTRAL

Concertino for Trumpet, Piano and Strings (1948)
S. Nakarjakov, A. Markovich, Lausanne CO, J. López-Cobos (r1993) *Concert*
(10/93) (TELD) ① **4509-90846-2**
Concerto for Flute and Strings (1949)
S. Milan, CLS, R. Hickox *Concert*
(10/90) (CHAN) ① **CHAN8840**
P. Alanko, Avanti CO, J-P. Saraste (r1993) *Concert*
(11/93) (ONDI) ① **ODE802-2**
M. Wiesler, Tapiola Sinfonietta, P. Järvi (r1993) *Concert*
(6/94) (BIS) ① **BIS-CD630**
Concerto for Trumpet and Orchestra (1954)
B. Soustrot, Loire PO, M. Soustrot *Concert*
(1/89) (PIER) ① **PV788011**

SECTION II: CHAMBER

Alla Rustica (Divertissement)—flute and harp (1963)
J. Stinton, A. Brewer *Concert*
(4/92) (COLL) ① **Coll1297-2**
Arioso barocco—trumpet and organ (1968)
G. Touvron, E. Krapp (r1992) *Concert*
(9/93) (RCA) ① **09026 61186-2**
Chant de Linos—flute & piano/flute, string trio & harp (1944)
R. Aitken, R. McCabe *Concert*
(9/89) (BIS) ① **BIS-CD184**
P. Racine, R. Zimansky, M. Clemann, C. Coray, X. Schindler *Concert* (10/90) (CLAV) ① **CD50-9003**
K. Jones, Britten-Pears Ens (r1994) *Concert*
(8/95) (ASV) ① **CDDCA918**
Heptade—trumpet and piano (1971)
G. Ashton, G. Knowles (r1992) *Concert*
(4/94) (VIRG) ① **VC5 45003-2**
Pastorales de Noël—fl/vn, bn/va/vc, hp (1943)
1. L'Etoile; 2. Les Mages; 3. La Vierge et l'Enfant; 4. Entrée et Danse des Bergers.
Britten-Pears Ens (r1994) *Concert*
(8/95) (ASV) ① **CDDCA918**
Sérénade—oboe, piano and wind quintet (1945)
Bergen Wind Qnt *Concert*
(9/86) (BIS) ① **BIS-CD291**
Sonata for Flute and Piano (1958)
P. Racine, D. Cholette *Concert*
(10/90) (CLAV) ① **CD50-9003**
Suite en concert—flute and four percussion (1965)
M. Wiesler, R. Pilat, Kroumata Perc Ens *Concert*
(2/86) (BIS) ① **BIS-CD272**
P. Alanko, T. Ferchen, A. Takalo, O-P. Martikainen, M. Sandström, T. Pulakka (r1993) *Concert*
(11/93) (ONDI) ① **ODE802-2**

SECTION III: INSTRUMENTAL

Ascèses—flute (1967)
1. Pour que demeure le secret. Nous tairons jusqu'au silence; 2. Tu surgis de l'absence; 3. Matière, triste abîme des étoiles, des atomes et des générations; 4. Le Dieu a créé les rêves pour indiquer la route au dormeur ... 5. O femme qui ne sais que tu portais en toi la monde.
P. Meyer (r1993) *Concert*
(7/95) (DENO) ① **CO-78917**
Chansons naïves—6 pieces for piano (1951)
Nos 1, 3. L. Rév *Concert*
(7/87) (HYPE) ① **CDA66185**
Hymne à l'univers—organ (1962)
C. Herrick *Concert* (9/91) (HYPE) ① **CDA66457**
5 Incantations—flute (1936)
1. Pour accueillir les négociations, et que l'entrevie soit pacifique; 2. Pour que l'enfant qui va naître soit un fils; 3. Pourque la moisson soit riche qui naîtra des sillons; 4. Pour communication sereine de l'être avec le monde; 5. Aux funérailles du chef, pour

obtenir la protection de l'âme.
R. Aitken *Concert* (9/89) (BIS) ① **BIS-CD184**

SECTION IV: VOCAL AND CHORAL

Poèmes pour l'enfant—mezzo-soprano and chamber orchestra (1937)
1. Naissance; 2. Adoration; 3. Eveil; 4. Berceuse; 5. Jeux.
B. Rearick, Britten-Pears Ens (r1994) *Concert*
(8/95) (ASV) ① **CDDCA918**
Suite liturgique—sop/ten, ob, cor ang, vc & hp (1942)
1. Prélude; 2. Salve Regina; 3. Alleluia; 4. Magnificat; 5. Musette; 6. Benedictus; 7. Interlude; 8. Final.
B. Rearick, Britten-Pears Ens (r1994) *Concert*
(8/95) (ASV) ① **CDDCA918**

JOLSON, Al (1886–1950) USA

SECTION V: STAGE WORKS

Robinson Crusoe, Jr.—Al Jolson's songs from the musical (1916—New York) (Original show by Sigmund Romberg & Harold Atteridge)
EXCERPTS: 1. Yaaka Hoola, Hickey Doola (Wendling/Goetz/Young); 2. You're a Dangerous Girl (Monaco/Clarke); 3. Where Did Robinson Crusoe Go with Friday (Meyer/Lewis/Young); 4. Tillie Titwillow (Schwartz/Atteridge); 5. Down Where the Swanee River Flows (Von Tilzer/McCarron/Alberte); 6. Now He's Got a Beautiful Girl (Snyder).
1-6. A. Jolson, Orig Broadway Cast (r1916-17) *Concert* (5/94) (PEAR) ① [3] **GEMMCDS9056/8**
Sinbad—Al Jolson's songs for Romberg's show (1918—New York)
EXCERPTS: 1. Rock-a-bye Your Baby (Schwartz/Young/Lewis); 2. Some Beautiful Morning (Jolson/Friend); 3. On the Road to Calais (Jolson/Bryan); 4. Swanee (Gershwin - see also Capitol Revue, 1919); 5. Chloe (Jolson/De Sylva); 6. There's a Lump of Sugar Down in Dixie (Gumble/Bryan/Yellen); 7. Tell That to the Marines (Atteridge/Schwartz/Jolson); 8. I'll Say She Does (Jolson/Kahn/De Sylva); 9. Hello Central, Give Me No Man's Land (Schwartz/Lewis/Young); 10. I Gave Her That (Jolson/De Sylva); 11. I Wonder Why She Kept On Saying 'Si-Si-Si-Senor' (Snyder/Lewis/Young); 12. Avalon (Jolson/De Sylva/Rose); 13. 'N Everything (Jolson/Kahn/De Sylva); 14. You Ain't Heard Nothing Yet (Jolson/Kahn/De Sylva).
1-14. A. Jolson, Orig Broadway Cast (r1917-19) *Concert* (5/94) (PEAR) ① [3] **GEMMCDS9059/61**

JOMMELLI, Nicolò (1714–1774) Italy

SECTION IV: VOCAL AND CHORAL

La Calandrina—song (Wds. cpsr)
K. Ott, C. Keller *Concert*
(12/90) (CPO) ① **CPO999 044-2**

SECTION V: STAGE WORKS

Armida abbandonata—opera: 3 acts (1770—Naples) (Lib. Saverio de' Rogati, after Tasso)
Cpte E. Malas-Godlewska, C. Brua, G. Ragon, V. Gens, L. Polverelli, P. Petibon, C. Perrin, Talens Lyriques, C. Rousset (r1994)
(4/95) (FNAC) ① [3] **592326**

JONES, Daniel (1912–1993) Wales

SECTION III: INSTRUMENTAL

Prelude, '(A) Refusal to Mourn'—organ (1978)
J. Watts (r1994) *Concert*
(10/95) (PRIO) ① **PRCD491**

JONES, Edward (1752–1824) Wales

Bardd y Brenin

SECTION III: INSTRUMENTAL

Ground and Variations—harp
F. Kelly (r1992) *Concert* (9/94) (MOSC) ① **070987**

JONES, Joyce Gilstrap (b 1930) USA

SECTION III: INSTRUMENTAL

Improvisation on 'Aka tombo' (The Red Dragonfly)—organ
J. Jones *Concert* (8/91) (MOTE) ① **CD11491**

JONES, Richard (late 17th Cent–1744) England

SECTION II: CHAMBER

Chamber Air's for a Violin (and Thorough Bass), Op. 2 (pub c1736)
1. Suite in A minor.
1. Locatelli Trio *Concert*
(5/93) (HYPE) ① **CDA66583**

SECTION IV: VOCAL AND CHORAL

And is it night? Are they thine eyes that shine?—song
D. Cordier, Tragicomedia, S. Stubbs *Concert*
(12/90) (HYPE) ① **CDA66335**
Farewell, fond youth—song
M. Chance, D. Cordier, Tragicomedia, S. Stubbs
Concert (12/90) (HYPE) ① **CDA66335**
Grief of my best love's absenting—song
M. Chance, Tragicomedia, S. Stubbs *Concert*
(12/90) (HYPE) ① **CDA66335**
Hark! Wot ye what?—song
M. Chance, D. Cordier, Tragicomedia, S. Stubbs
Concert (12/90) (HYPE) ① **CDA66335**
Ite caldi sospiri—song
M. Chance, Tragicomedia, S. Stubbs *Concert*
(12/90) (HYPE) ① **CDA66335**
My complaining is but feigning—song
M. Chance, D. Cordier, Tragicomedia, S. Stubbs
Concert (12/90) (HYPE) ① **CDA66335**
On a time in summer season—song
M. Chance, D. Cordier, Tragicomedia, S. Stubbs
Concert (12/90) (HYPE) ① **CDA66335**
Once did I serve a cruel heart—song
M. Chance, D. Cordier, Tragicomedia, S. Stubbs
Concert (12/90) (HYPE) ① **CDA66335**
Sweet Kate—secular song
M. Chance, D. Cordier, Tragicomedia, S. Stubbs
Concert (12/90) (HYPE) ① **CDA66335**
Through your strangeness frets my heart—song
M. Chance, D. Cordier, Tragicomedia, S. Stubbs
Concert (12/90) (HYPE) ① **CDA66335**
Will said to his mammy—song
M. Chance, D. Cordier, Tragicomedia, S. Stubbs
Concert (12/90) (HYPE) ① **CDA66335**

JONES, Robert (fl 1597–1615) England

SECTION IV: VOCAL AND CHORAL

A Musicall Dreame or the Fourth Booke of Ayres (pub 1609)
1. Ite caldi sospiri; 2. If in this flesh; 3. O thred of life; 4. When I sit reading; 5. Will said to his Mammy.
2. E. Kirkby, A. Rooley *Concert*
(8/91) (L'OI) ① **425 892-2OH**

JONES, Sidney (James) (1861–1946) England

SECTION V: STAGE WORKS

An Artist's Model—musical show (1895—London) (Lyrics Harry Greenbank; Book Owen Hall)
EXCERPTS: 1. Laughing Song (Le fou rire); 2. Queen of the Sea and Earth; 3. Daisy With the Dimple on Her Chin; 4. Give Me Love; 5. Music and Laughter; 6. On y revient toujours.
1. M. Farkoa (r1905) *Concert*
(5/94) (PEAR) ① [3] **GEMMCDS9050/2(1)**
The Geisha—musical play: 2 acts (1896—London) (Lyrics H. Greenbank and O. Hall)
EXCERPTS: 1. Act 1 Opening Chorus; 2. Jack's the Boy; 3. The Amorous Goldfish; 4. Chin-Chin Chinaman; 5. Chon-Kina; 6. We're going to Call on the Marquis; 7. The Interfering Parrot; 8. A Geisha's Life; 9. Act 2 Opening Chorus; 10. Toy Monkey; 11. What Will They Do With Molly?; 12. Star of My Soul; 13. Mimosa; 14. Jolly Young Jacks; 15. The Jewel of Asia; 16. Love! Love!; 17. The Message in the Violet; 18. I Can't Refrain from Laughing; 19. The Kissing Duet; 20. Act 3 Opening Chorus.

4. J. T. Powers, Broadway Cast (r1898) *Concert*
(5/94) (PEAR) ① [3] **GEMMCDS9050/2(1)**
12. P. Morrison, Chandos Concert Orch, S. Barry
(2/90) (CHAN) ① **CHAN8759**
13. F. Marconi, B. Mililotti, C. Sabajno (r1907)
Concert (6/90) (SYMP) ① **SYMCD1073**

JONGEN, Joseph (Marie Alphonse Nicholas) (1873–1953) Belgian

<u>SECTION I: ORCHESTRAL</u>

Allegro appassionato—viola and orchestra, Op. 79 (1925-28)
T-M. Gilissen, French Rad & TV SO, B. Priestman
Concert (8/92) (SCHW) ① **315012**
Suite—viola and orchestra, Op. 48 (1915-19)
T-M. Gilissen, French Rad & TV SO, B. Priestman
Concert (8/92) (SCHW) ① **315012**
Symphonie Concertante for organ and orchestra, Op. 81 (1926)
M. Murray, San Francisco SO, E. de Waart *Concert*
(3/85) (TELA) ① **CD80096**
H. Schoonbroodt, Liège SO, R. Defossez *Concert*
(8/92) (SCHW) ① **315012**

<u>SECTION II: CHAMBER</u>

Aria et Polonaise, Op. 128 (1943)
C. Lindberg, R. Pöntinen *Concert*
(9/85) (BIS) ① **BIS-CD298**
Jeux d'enfants—piano: four hands, Op. 120 (1941)
I. Beyer, H. Dagul *Concert*
(10/92) (FOUR) ① **FHMD9212**

<u>SECTION III: INSTRUMENTAL</u>

Cantilène—organ (1908)
J.S. Whiteley (r1989-91) *Concert*
(7/93) (PRIO) ① **PRCD324**
Elégie—organ (1891)
J.S. Whiteley (r1989-91) *Concert*
(7/93) (PRIO) ① **PRCD324**
Petit Prélude—organ (1937)
J.S. Whiteley (r1989-91) *Concert*
(7/93) (PRIO) ① **PRCD324**
Petite Pièce—organ (1936)
J.S. Whiteley (r1989-91) *Concert*
(7/93) (PRIO) ① **PRCD324**
Pièce pour Grand Orgue—organ (1892)
J.S. Whiteley (r1989-91) *Concert*
(7/93) (PRIO) ① **PRCD324**
5 Pièces—organ, Op. 5 (1893-96)
1. Andante cantabile; 2. Pastorale; 3. Offertoire
(Grand Choeur); 4. Offertoire; 5. Communion.
1-3, 5. J.S. Whiteley (r1989-91) *Concert*
(7/93) (PRIO) ① **PRCD324**
2 Pièces—organ, Op. 47 (1914-15)
1. Prélude Eléiaque; 2. Pensée d'Automne.
J.S. Whiteley (r1989-91) *Concert*
(7/93) (PRIO) ① **PRCD324**
2 Pièces—organ, Op. 53 (1917)
1. Chant de May; 2. Menuet-Scherzo.
J.S. Whiteley (r1989-91) *Concert*
(7/93) (PRIO) ① **PRCD324**
2. J.S. Whiteley *Concert* (7/87) (YORK) ① **CD101**
2. D. Flood *Concert* (4/91) (YORK) ① **CD108**
2. G. Weir *Concert* (12/92) (KOSS) ① **KC1013**
4 Pièces—organ, Op. 37 (1910)
1. Cantabile; 2. Improvisation-caprice; 3. Prière; 4.
Choral in E.
2. N. Kynaston *Concert*
(4/89) (HYPE) ① **CDA66265**
2. J. Parker-Smith *Concert*
(9/90) (ASV) ① **CDDCA702**
4. C. Curley *Concert*
(2/91) (ARGO) ① **430 200-2ZH**
Prélude et Fugue—organ, Op. 121 (1941-43)
J.S. Whiteley (r1989-91) *Concert*
(7/93) (PRIO) ① **PRCD324**
13 Préludes—piano, Op. 69 (1922)
11. Papillons noirs.
11. J.S. Whiteley (r1989-91; arr Whitely: org) *Concert*
(7/93) (PRIO) ① **PRCD324**
Toccata—organ, Op. 104 (1935)
J.S. Whiteley (r1989-91) *Concert*
(7/93) (PRIO) ① **PRCD324**
Toccata in D flat—organ, Op. 14 (pub 1937)
N. Kynaston *Concert* (4/89) (HYPE) ① **CDA66265**
M.H. Long *Concert* (4/91) (KOCH) ① **37008-2**

JOPLIN, Scott (1868–1917) USA

<u>SECTION III: INSTRUMENTAL</u>

Bethena—concert waltz: piano (1908)
I. Perlman, A. Previn (arr. Perlman) *Concert*
(9/86) (EMI) ① **CDC7 47170-2**
The Easy winners—rag: piano (1901)
I. Perlman, A. Previn (arr. Perlman) *Concert*
(9/86) (EMI) ① **CDC7 47170-2**
Elite Syncopations—rag: piano (1902)
I. Perlman, A. Previn (arr. Perlman) *Concert*
(9/86) (EMI) ① **CDC7 47170-2**
I. Perlman, A. Previn *Concert*
(6/95) (EMI) ① [20] **CZS4 83177-2(3)**
The Entertainer—ragtime two-step: piano (1902)
I. Perlman, A. Previn (arr. Perlman) *Concert*
(9/86) (EMI) ① **CDC7 47170-2**
I. Perlman, A. Previn *Concert*
(6/95) (EMI) ① [20] **CZS4 83177-2(3)**
M. Legrand (r1994) *Concert*
(7/95) (ERAT) ① **4509-96386-2**
Magnetic Rag—syncopations classiques: piano (1914)
I. Perlman, A. Previn (arr. Perlman) *Concert*
(9/86) (EMI) ① **CDC7 47170-2**
A. Feinberg (r1994) *Concert*
(11/95) (ARGO) ① **444 457-2ZH**
Maple leaf Rag—piano (1899)
M. Legrand (r1994) *Concert*
(7/95) (ERAT) ① **4509-96386-2**
Pine Apple Rag—piano (1908)
I. Perlman, A. Previn (arr. Perlman) *Concert*
(9/86) (EMI) ① **CDC7 47170-2**
I. Perlman, A. Previn (r1974: arr Perlman) *Concert*
(5/93) (EMI) ① [4] **CMS7 64617-2**
I. Perlman, A. Previn *Concert*
(6/95) (EMI) ① [20] **CZS4 83177-2(3)**
The Ragtime dance—piano (1906)
I. Perlman, A. Previn (arr. Perlman) *Concert*
(9/86) (EMI) ① **CDC7 47170-2**
I. Perlman, A. Previn (r1974: arr Perlman) *Concert*
(5/93) (EMI) ① [4] **CMS7 64617-2**
I. Perlman, A. Previn *Concert*
(6/95) (EMI) ① [20] **CZS4 83177-2(3)**
Solace—a Mexican serenade: piano (1909)
I. Perlman, A. Previn (arr. Perlman) *Concert*
(9/86) (EMI) ① **CDC7 47170-2**
The Strenuous Life—a Ragtime Two-step (1902)
I. Perlman, A. Previn (arr. Perlman) *Concert*
(9/86) (EMI) ① **CDC7 47170-2**
Sugar Cane—rag: piano (1908)
I. Perlman, A. Previn (arr. Perlman) *Concert*
(9/86) (EMI) ① **CDC7 47170-2**

<u>SECTION V: STAGE WORKS</u>

Treemonisha—opera: 3 acts (1915—New York) (Lib. cpsr)
Cpte C. Balthrop, B. Allen, C. Rayam, W. White, B.
Harney, C. Johnson, K. Hicks, D. Duckens, D.
Ransom, R. Bazemore, E. Pierson, Houston Grand
Op Chor, Houston Grand Op Orch, G. Schuller
(8/92) (DG) ① [2] **435 709-2GX2**

JORDAN, Sverre (1889–1972) Norway

<u>SECTION IV: VOCAL AND CHORAL</u>

Lullaby—song (Wds. H Meidell)
P. Frijsh, E. Nielsen (r1926) *Concert*
(9/95) (PEAR) ① [2] **GEMMCDS9095(2)**

JOSÉ DE TORRES (c1670–1738) Spain

<u>SECTION IV: VOCAL AND CHORAL</u>

Al clamor—miserere villancico
Al Ayre Español, E. L. Banzo (r1994) *Concert*
(8/95) (DHM) ① **05472 77325-2**
Más no puede ser—cantata on the Nativity: 8vv & instruments
Al Ayre Español, E. L. Banzo (r1994) *Concert*
(8/95) (DHM) ① **05472 77325-2**

JOSEPHS, Wilfred (b 1927) England

<u>SECTION I: ORCHESTRAL</u>

In the North (1990)
Helsinki PO, S. Comissiona *Concert*
(4/92) (ONDI) ① **ODE767-2**

JOSQUIN DESPREZ (c1440–1521) Northern France

<u>SECTION IV: VOCAL AND CHORAL</u>

Absalon fili mi—motet: 4vv
Hilliard Ens, P. Hillier *Concert*
(3/89) (EMI) ① **CDC7 49209-2**
MCA, K. Ruhland *Concert*
(10/90) (RCA) ① **GD71966**
Adieu mes amours—chanson: 4vv
A. Lawrence-King (r1992: arr hp) *Concert*
(5/93) (EMI) ① **CDC7 54659-2**
Alma redemptoris mater/Ave regina celorum—motet: 4vv
A Sei Voci (r1993) *Concert* (2/94) (ASTR) ① **E8507**
Ave Maria, gratia plena...virgo serena—motet: 4vv
Hilliard Ens, P. Hillier *Concert*
(3/89) (EMI) ① **CDC7 49209-2**
Ave Maria...virgo serena—motet: 4vv
Tallis Scholars, P. Phillips *Concert*
(12/86) (GIME) ① **CDGIM010**
Paris Chapelle Royale Chor, P. Herreweghe *Concert*
(4/87) (HARM) ① **HMC90 1243**
Ave nobilissima creatura/Benedicta tu—motet: 6vv
Paris Chapelle Royale Chor, P. Herreweghe *Concert*
(4/87) (HARM) ① **HMC90 1243**
Benedicta es, celorum regina—motet: 6vv
Tallis Scholars, P. Phillips *Concert*
(7/90) (GIME) ① **CDGIM001**
Tallis Scholars, P. Phillips (r1981) *Concert*
(1/94) (GIME) ① [4] **CDGIMB400**
Bergerette savoyenne—chanson: 4vv
Chanticleer (1987) *Concert*
(7/94) (CHTI) ① **CR-8805**
Credo, 'De tous biens playne'—mass movement: 4vv
Capella Alamire, P. Urquhart (1993) *Concert*
(11/95) (DORI) ① **DIS80131**
De profundis clamavi—motet: 4vv
Hilliard Ens, P. Hillier *Concert*
(3/89) (EMI) ① **CDC7 49209-2**
Domine, non secundum peccata nostra—motet: 4vv
Chanticleer (1990) *Concert*
(7/94) (CHTI) ① **CR-8808**
En l'ombre d'un buissonet au matinet—chanson: 4vv
Hilliard Ens, P. Hillier *Concert*
(3/89) (EMI) ① **CDC7 49209-2**
Faute d'argent—chanson
Scholars (r1993) *Concert*
(2/95) (NAXO) ① **8 550880**
Gaude Virgo, Mater Christi—motet: 4vv
Taverner Consort, Taverner Ch, A. Parrott (1992)
Concert (5/93) (EMI) ① **CDC7 54659-2**
A Sei Voci (r1993) *Concert* (2/94) (ASTR) ① **E8507**
El grillo—chanson: 4vv
Hilliard Ens, P. Hillier *Concert*
(3/89) (EMI) ① **CDC7 49209-2**
Illibata Dei Virgo nutrix/La mia la—motet: 5vv
Taverner Consort, Taverner Ch, A. Parrott (1992)
Concert (5/93) (EMI) ① **CDC7 54659-2**
In te Domine speravi, per trovar pietà—chanson: 4vv
Hilliard Ens, P. Hillier *Concert*
(3/89) (EMI) ① **CDC7 49209-2**
A. Lawrence-King (r1992: arr hp) *Concert*
(5/93) (EMI) ① **CDC7 54659-2**
Inviolata integra et castra es, Maria—motet: 5vv
New College Ch, E. Higginbottom *Concert*
(8/86) (MERI) ① **ECD84093**
Je me complains—chanson: 5vv
Hilliard Ens, P. Hillier *Concert*
(3/89) (EMI) ① **CDC7 49209-2**
Je ne me puis tenir d'aimer—chanson: 5vv
Hilliard Ens, P. Hillier *Concert*
(3/89) (EMI) ① **CDC7 49209-2**
Je n'ose plus—chanson: 3vv
A. Lawrence-King (r1992: arr hp) *Concert*
(5/93) (EMI) ① **CDC7 54659-2**
Magnificat—4vv (doubtful: Segovia MS)
Capella Alamire, P. Urquhart (r1993) *Concert*
(11/95) (DORI) ① **DIS80131**
Memor esto verbi tui—motet: 4vv
A Sei Voci (r1993) *Concert* (8/86) (FORL) ① **UCD16552**
Mille regretz—chanson: 4vv
Hilliard Ens, P. Hillier *Concert*
(3/89) (EMI) ① **CDC7 49209-2**
Scholars (r1993) *Concert*
(2/95) (NAXO) ① **8 550880**

Miserere mei, Deus—motet: 5vv
Paris Chapelle Royale Chor, P. Herreweghe *Concert*
(4/87) (HARM) ① **HMC90 1243**
MCA, K. Ruhland *Concert*
(10/90) (RCA) ① **GD71966**
Missa, '(L')Ami Baudichon'—4vv (based on popular song)
Capella Alamire, P. Urquhart (r1992) *Concert*
(11/95) (DORI) ① **DIS80131**
Missa, 'Ave maris stella'—4vv
Taverner Consort, Taverner Ch, A. Parrott (r1992)
Concert (5/93) (EMI) ① **CDC7 54659-2**
A Sei Voci (r1993) *Concert* (2/94) (ASTR) ① **E8507**
Missa, 'De beata virgine'—4-5vv
A Sei Voci *Concert* (8/86) (FORL) ① **UCD16552**
Theatre of Voices, P. Hillier (r1993) *Concert*
(11/95) (HARM) ① **HMU90 7136**
Missa, 'Hercules Dux Ferrarie'—4vv
New London Chmbr Ch, J. Wood *Concert*
(3/87) (AMON) ① **CD-SAR24**
Missa, '(L')homme armé' sexti toni—4vv (pub 1502)
Tallis Scholars, P. Phillips *Concert*
(7/89) (GIME) ① **CDGIM019**
Agnus Dei III Tallis Scholars, P. Phillips *Concert*
(1/91) (GIME) ① **CDGIM999**
Missa, '(L')homme armé' super voces musicales—4vv (pub 1502)
PCA, B. Turner *Ockeghem: Missa Pro Defunctis*.
(4/86) (ARCH) ① **415 293-2AH**
Tallis Scholars, P. Phillips *Concert*
(7/89) (GIME) ① **CDGIM019**
Missa, 'La sol fa re mi'—4vv
Tallis Scholars, P. Phillips *Missa Pange lingua*.
(3/87) (GIME) ① **CDGIM009**
MCA, K. Ruhland *Concert*
(10/90) (RCA) ① **GD71966**
Missa, 'Mater Patris'—4vv (on Brumel's motet)
Chanticleer (r1990) *Concert*
(7/94) (CHTI) ① **CR-8808**
Missa, 'Pange lingua'—4vv
C. Janequin Ens, Organum Ens, M. Pérès
(2/87) (HARM) ① **HMC90 1239**
Tallis Scholars, P. Phillips *Missa La sol fa re mi*.
(3/87) (GIME) ① **CDGIM009**
Westminster Cath Ch, J. O'Donnell *Concert*
(4/93) (HYPE) ① **CDA66614**
Missa sine nomine—canonic mass: 4vv
1. Kyrie; 2. Gloria; 3. Credo; 4. Sanctus & Benedictus; 5. Agnus Dei.
3. Capella Alamire, P. Urquhart (r1994) *Concert*
(11/95) (DORI) ① **DIS80131**
Monstra te esse matrem (Ave maris stella)—motet: 4vv (verses 4, 6 & 7 of hymn)
A Sei Voci (r1993) *Concert* (2/94) (ASTR) ① **E8507**
Nymphes des bois/Requiem, 'La déploration de Johannes Ockeghem'—chanson: 5vv
A Sei Voci *Concert* (8/86) (FORL) ① **UCD16552**
New London Chmbr Ch, J. Wood *Concert*
(3/87) (AMON) ① **CD-SAR24**
Hilliard Ens, P. Hillier *Concert*
(3/89) (EMI) ① **CDC7 49209-2**
Clerks' Group, E. Wickham (r1993) *Concert*
(10/93) (PROU) ① **PROUCD133**
O bone et dulcissime Jesu—motet: 4vv
Paris Chapelle Royale Chor, P. Herreweghe *Concert*
(4/87) (HARM) ① **HMC90 1243**
Pater noster, qui es in celis—motet: 6vv
Taverner Consort, A. Parrott *Concert*
(8/87) (EMI) ① **CDC7 47699-2**
Petite camusette—chanson: 6vv
Hilliard Ens, P. Hillier *Concert*
(3/89) (EMI) ① **CDC7 49209-2**
Plaine de dueil—chanson: 5vv
Taverner Consort, Taverner Ch, A. Parrott (r1992)
Concert (5/93) (EMI) ① **CDC7 54659-2**
Planxit autem David—motet: 4vv
A Sei Voci *Concert* (8/86) (FORL) ① **UCD16552**
MCA, K. Ruhland *Concert*
(10/90) (RCA) ① **GD71966**
Westminster Cath Ch, J. O'Donnell *Concert*
(4/93) (HYPE) ① **CDA66614**
Praeter rerum seriem—motet: 6vv
New College Ch, E. Higginbottom *Concert*
(8/86) (MERI) ① **ECD84093**
New London Chmbr Ch, J. Wood *Concert*
(3/93) (AMON) ① **CD-SAR56**
Gabrieli Consort, Gabrieli Players, P. McCreesh, T. Roberts (r1992-3) *Concert*
(1/94) (ARCH) ① **437 833-2AH**
Tallis Scholars, P. Phillips *Concert*
(6/94) (GIME) ① **CDGIM029**

Que vous madame/In pace in idipsum—chanson: 3vv
Taverner Consort, Taverner Ch, A. Parrott (r1992)
Concert (5/93) (EMI) ① **CDC7 54659-2**
Qui velatus facie fuisti—motet: 4vv
1. Qui velatus facie fuisti; 2. Horia qui ductis tertia; 3. In flagellis potum felis; 4. In amaris crucis ara; 5. Qui jacuisti mortuus; 6. Christum ducem.
1-5. MCA, K. Ruhland *Concert*
(10/90) (RCA) ① **GD71966**
6. A Sei Voci *Concert* (8/86) (FORL) ① **UCD16552**
Regretz sans fin—chanson: 6vv
Taverner Consort, Taverner Ch, A. Parrott (r1992)
Concert (5/93) (EMI) ① **CDC7 54659-2**
Salve regina—motet: 4vv
New College Ch, E. Higginbottom *Concert*
(8/86) (MERI) ① **ECD84093**
Paris Chapelle Royale Chor, P. Herreweghe *Concert*
(4/87) (HARM) ① **HMC90 1243**
A Sei Voci (r1993) *Concert* (2/94) (ASTR) ① **E8507**
Salve regina—motet: 5vv
Taverner Consort, Taverner Ch, A. Parrott (r1992)
Concert (5/93) (EMI) ① **CDC7 54659-2**
Sanctus de Passione—mass movement: 4vv
MCA, K. Ruhland *Concert*
(10/90) (RCA) ① **GD71966**
Scaramella va alla guerra—chanson: 4vv
Hilliard Ens, P. Hillier *Concert*
(3/89) (EMI) ① **CDC7 49209-2**
C. Janequin Ens, D. Visse (r1994) *Concert*
(5/95) (HARM) ① **HMC 1453**
Stabat mater dolorosa/Comme femme desconfortée—motet: 5vv
New College Ch, E. Higginbottom *Concert*
(8/86) (MERI) ① **ECD84093**
Paris Chapelle Royale Chor, P. Herreweghe *Concert*
(4/87) (HARM) ① **HMC90 1243**
Tu solus qui facis mirabilia—motet: 4vv
MCA, K. Ruhland *Concert*
(10/90) (RCA) ① **GD71966**
Usquequo, Domine, obivisceris me in finem—motet: 4vv
Paris Chapelle Royale Chor, P. Herreweghe *Concert*
(4/87) (HARM) ① **HMC90 1243**
Veni, Sancte Spiritus—motet: 6vv
New College Ch, E. Higginbottom *Concert*
(8/86) (MERI) ① **ECD84093**
Hilliard Ens, P. Hillier *Concert*
(3/89) (EMI) ① **CDC7 49209-2**
Virgo prudentissima—motet: 4vv
New College Ch, E. Higginbottom *Concert*
(8/86) (MERI) ① **ECD84093**
Virgo salutiferi/Ave Maria—motet: 5vv
New College Ch, E. Higginbottom *Concert*
(8/86) (MERI) ① **ECD84093**
Vultum tuum deprecabuntur—motet: 4vv
1. Vultum tuum; 2. Sancta Dei; 3. Internerata virgo; 4. O Maria; 5. Mente tota; 6. Ora pro nobis; 7. Christe, Fili Dei.
Westminster Cath Ch, J. O'Donnell *Concert*
(4/93) (HYPE) ① **CDA66614**
A Sei Voci (r1993) *Concert* (2/94) (ASTR) ① **E8507**

JOUBERT, John (Pierre Herman) (b 1927) South Africa/England

SECTION IV: VOCAL AND CHORAL

The Brechin Service—canticles (1986) (for the Brechin Diocesan Festival)
1. Magnificat; 2. Nunc dimittis.
Dundee Cath Ch, R. Lightband (org/dir) *Concert*
(8/92) (ABBE) ① **CDCA926**
O Lorde, the maker of al thing—anthem, Op. 7b (1952)
Magdalen Oxford Coll Ch, G. Webber *Concert*
(11/91) (ABBE) ① **CDCA914**
St Paul's Cath Ch, John Scott *Concert*
(4/92) (HYPE) ① **CDA66519**

JULLIEN, Gilles (c1650/53–1703) France

SECTION III: INSTRUMENTAL

Premier livre d'orgue (pub 1690)
1. Prélude à cinq parties; 2. Cromone en taille; 3. Dialogue; 4. Dessus de voix humaine; 5. Basse de Trompette.
Excs P. Bardon *Concert*
(3/87) (PIER) ① [2] **PV785051/2**
Excs A. Isoir *Concert* (6/90) (CALL) ① **CAL9907**
4, 5. J. Payne (r1994) *Concert*
(10/95) (NAXO) ① **8 553215**

JUON, Paul (1872–1940) Russia/Germany

SECTION II: CHAMBER

4 Pieces—violin and piano, Op. 28
3. Berceuse.
3. J. Heifetz, S. Chotzinoff (r1920) *Concert*
(11/94) (RCA) ① [65] **09026 61778-2(01)**

JUOZAPAITIS, Jurgis (b 1942) USSR/Lithuania

SECTION I: ORCHESTRAL

Perpetuum mobile—strings (1988)
Ostrobothnian CO, J. Kangas (r1994) *Concert*
(11/95) (FINL) ① **4509-97893-2**

KABALEVSKY, Dmitry Borisovich (1904–1987) USSR

SECTION I: ORCHESTRAL

The Comedians—suite for small orchestra, Op. 26 (1940)
Philh, E. Kurtz (r1961) *Concert*
(9/93) (EMI) ① [2] **CZS7 67729-2**
Galop Britannia Building Soc Band, H. Snell (1990; arr Snell:brass band) *Concert*
(8/92) (DOYE) ① **DOYCD004**
Concerto for Cello and Orchestra No. 1 in G minor, Op. 49 (1948-49)
M. Tarasova, Russia SO, V. Dudarova (1993)
Concert (6/94) (OLYM) ① **OCD292**
Concerto for Cello and Orchestra No. 2 in G, Op. 77 (1964)
R. Wallfisch, LPO, B. Thomson *Concert*
(6/88) (CHAN) ① **CHAN8579**
M. Tarasova, Russia SO, V. Dudarova (1993)
Concert (6/94) (OLYM) ① **OCD292**
Concerto for Piano and Orchestra No. 2 in G minor, Op. 23 (1935)
N. Petrov, Moscow PO, D. Kitaienko (bp1984)
Concert (12/92) (OLYM) ① **OCD269**
Concerto for Piano and Orchestra No. 3 in D, Op. 50 (1952)
Emil Gilels, USSR TV & Rad Orch, D. Kabalevsky
(r1954) *Concert* (12/92) (OLYM) ① **OCD269**
Concerto for Piano and Orchestra No. 4, 'Prague' (1979)
Y. Popov, Moscow PO, D. Kabalevsky (r1981)
Concert (12/92) (OLYM) ① **OCD269**
Concerto for Violin and Orchestra in C, Op. 48 (1948)
L. Mordkovitch, SNO, N. Järvi *Khachaturian: Violin Concerto*.
(3/91) (CHAN) ① **CHAN8918**
Symphony No. 1 in C sharp minor, Op. 18 (1932)
Szeged PO, E. Acél *Symphony 2*.
(10/92) (OLYM) ① **OCD268**
Symphony No. 2 in C minor, Op. 19 (1934)
Szeged PO, E. Acél *Symphony 1*.
(10/92) (OLYM) ① **OCD268**
New Philh, D. Measham (r1973) *Concert*
(2/95) (UNIC) ① **UKCD2066**
Symphony No. 4 in C minor, Op. 54 (1956)
Leningrad PO, D. Kabalevsky (r1956) *Requiem*.
(1/93) (OLYM) ① [2] **OCD290**

SECTION II: CHAMBER

Improvisation—violin and piano, Op. 21 (1934)
1. Irato.
1. N. Likhopoi, L. Kuritskaya (r1993) *Concert*
(6/94) (OLYM) ① **OCD292**
Rondo—violin and piano, Op. 69 (1961)
N. Likhopoi, L. Kuritskaya (r1993) *Concert*
(6/94) (OLYM) ① **OCD292**
String Quartet No. 1 in A minor, Op. 8 (1928)
Glazunov Qt (r1993) *String Quartet 2*.
(7/94) (OLYM) ① **OCD293**
String Quartet No. 2 in G minor, Op. 44 (1945)
Glazunov Qt (r1993) *String Quartet 1*.
(7/94) (OLYM) ① **OCD293**

SECTION III: INSTRUMENTAL

4 Preludes—piano, Op. 5 (1920s)
1. A minor; 2. C; 3. B minor; 4. A.
M. McLachlan *Concert* (5/93) (OLYM) ① **OCD267**
A. Pizarro (r1994) *Concert*
(12/94) (COLL) ① **Coll1418-2**

24 Preludes—piano (1943-44)
1. C; 2. A minor; 3. G; 4. E minor; 5. D; 6. B minor; 7.
A; 8. F sharp minor; 9. E; 10. C sharp minor; 11. B;
12. G sharp minor; 13. F sharp; 14. E flat minor; 15.
D flat; 16. B flat minor; 17. A flat; 18. F minor; 19. E
flat; 20. C minor; 21. B flat; 22. G minor; 23. F; 24. D
minor.
M. McLachlan *Concert*   (4/93) (OLYM) ① **OCD266**
Recitative and Rondo—piano, Op. 84 (1967)
A. Pizarro (r1994) *Concert*
                        (12/94) (COLL) ① **Coll1418-2**
Rondo in A minor—piano, Op. 59 (1958)
M. McLachlan *Concert*   (5/93) (OLYM) ① **OCD267**
Sonata for Piano No. 1 in F, Op. 6 (1927)
M. McLachlan *Concert*   (5/93) (OLYM) ① **OCD267**
A. Pizarro (r1994) *Concert*
                        (12/94) (COLL) ① **Coll1418-2**
**Sonata for Piano No. 2 in E flat, Op. 45
(1945)**
M. McLachlan *Concert*   (5/93) (OLYM) ① **OCD267**
A. Pizarro (r1994) *Concert*
                        (12/94) (COLL) ① **Coll1418-2**
Sonata for Piano No. 3 in F, Op. 46 (1946)
V. Horowitz (r1947) *Concert*
                        (6/92) (RCA) ① **GD60377**
M. McLachlan *Concert*   (4/93) (OLYM) ① **OCD266**
A. Pizarro (r1994) *Concert*
                        (12/94) (COLL) ① **Coll1418-2**
**Sonatina for Piano No. 1 in C, Op. 13/1
(1930)**
M. McLachlan *Concert*   (4/93) (OLYM) ① **OCD266**
**Sonatina for Piano No. 2 in G minor, Op. 13/2
(1930)**
M. McLachlan *Concert*   (5/93) (OLYM) ① **OCD267**

SECTION IV: VOCAL AND CHORAL

Requiem, Op. 71 (1962) (Wds. R.
Rozhdestvensky)
V. Levko, V. Valaitis, Moscow Artistic Ed Inst Ch,
Moscow SO, D. Kabalevsky (r1964) *Symphony 4.*
                        (1/93) (OLYM) ① [2] **OCD290**

SECTION V: STAGE WORKS

**Colas Breugnon—opera: 3 acts, Op. 24
(1938—Leningrad)** (Lib. Bragin, after Rolland)
EXCERPTS: 1. Overture.
Cpte L. Boldin, N. Isakova, V. Kayevchenko, E.
Masimenko, G. Dudarev, N. Gutorovich, A.
Mishchevski, A. Shitkova, L. Yeliseev, M.
Syromyatnikov, V. Zamberg, Moscow Stanislavsky
Th Chor, Moscow Stanislavsky Th Orch, G.
Zhemchuzhin (r1973)
                        (5/93) (OLYM) ① [2] **OCD291**
1. NBC SO, A. Toscanini (bp1943) *Concert*
                        (1/90) (DELL) ① **CDDA9020**
1. Chicago SO, F. Reiner (r1959) *Concert*
                        (8/94) (RCA) ① **09026 61958-2**
1. Russian Nat Orch, M. Pletnev *Concert*
                        (12/94) (DG) ① **439 892-2GH**

**KABELÁČ, Miloslav (1908–1979)
Czechoslovakia**

SECTION I: ORCHESTRAL

**Hamlet Improvisation—large orchestra, Op.
46 (1963)**
Czech PO, K. Ančerl (r1966) *Concert*
                        (12/94) (SUPR) ① **11 1930-2**
**Mystery of Time—passacaglia: orchestra,
Op. 31 (1953-56)**
Czech PO, K. Ančerl (r1960) *Concert*
                        (12/94) (SUPR) ① **11 1930-2**

**KAGEL, Mauricio (b 1931)
Argentina**

SECTION II: CHAMBER

**Atem—1 wind instrument and tape machine
(1970)**
C. Lindberg *Concert*   (10/89) (BIS) ① **BIS-CD388**
**Exotica—non-European instruments (1970-
71)**
Inst Ens, M. Kagel (r1972) *Tactil.*
                        (10/94) (DG) ① **445 252-2GC**
Tactil—guitar, harmonica and piano (1970)
Inst Ens (r1972) *Exotica.*
                        (10/94) (DG) ① **445 252-2GC**

KAHN, Gus (1886–1941) USA

SECTION IV: VOCAL AND CHORAL

Nobody's Sweetheart—song (1924) (cpsd
with E.Erdman, B.Meyers & E.Schoebel)
London Sinfonietta, S. Rattle *Concert*
                        (12/87) (EMI) ① **CDC7 47991-2**

**KAHN, Percy (Benedict)
(1880–1966) England**

SECTION IV: VOCAL AND CHORAL

Ave Maria—sacred song
E. Caruso, M. Elman, P. Kahn (r1913) *Concert*
                        (7/91) (RCA) ① [12] **GD60495(4)**
E. Caruso, M. Elman, P. Kahn (r1913) *Concert*
                        (10/91) (PEAR) ① [3] **EVC3(1)**
E. Caruso, M. Elman, P. Kahn (r1913) *Concert*
                        (10/91) (BIDD) ① **LAB039**
R. Ponselle, orch. R. Bourdon (r1927) *Concert*
                        (11/94) (ROMO) ① [2] **81007-2**

**KAIPAINEN, Jouni (Ilari) (b 1956)
Finland**

SECTION I: ORCHESTRAL

**Concerto for Clarinet and Orchestra, 'Carpe
diem!', Op. 38 (1990)**
K. Kriikku, Avanti CO, J-P. Saraste *Concert*
                        (10/92) (ONDI) ① **ODE778-2**

SECTION IV: VOCAL AND CHORAL

**Starlit Night (Stärnenatten)—soprano, low
strings, percussion and piano, Op. 35 (1989)**
(Wds. E. Södergran)
1. Evening (Kväll); 2. The Moon's Secret (Månens
hemlighet); 3. Starlit Night (Stärnenatten); 4. The
Moon (Månen); 5. Early Dawn (Tidig gryning); 6.
Dawn (Gryningen).
K. Mattila, Lahti Chbr Ens, O. Vänskä *Concert*
                        (8/93) (ONDI) ① **ODE792-2**

**KALINNIKOV, Vasily Sergeyevich
(1866–1901) Russia**

SECTION I: ORCHESTRAL

The Cedar and the Palm—orchestra
SNO, N. Järvi *Concert*
                        (6/90) (CHAN) ① **CHAN8805**
**Intermezzo No. 1 in F sharp
minor—orchestra (1896)**
LSO, N. Järvi *Concert*
                        (5/90) (CHAN) ① **CHAN8614**
Intermezzo No. 2 in G—orchestra (1897)
LSO, N. Järvi *Concert*
                        (5/90) (CHAN) ① **CHAN8614**
Symphony No. 1 in G minor (1894-95)
SNO, N. Järvi *Concert*
                        (10/88) (CHAN) ① **CHAN8611**
Russia SO, V. Dudarova (r1992) *Symphony 2.*
                        (5/91) (OLYM) ① **OCD511**
Symphony No. 2 in A (1895-97)
SNO, N. Järvi *Concert*
                        (6/90) (CHAN) ① **CHAN8805**
Russia SO, V. Dudarova (r1992) *Symphony 1.*
                        (5/91) (OLYM) ① **OCD511**

SECTION V: STAGE WORKS

**Tsar Boris—incidental music to Tolstoy's
play (1899)**
EXCERPTS: 1. Overture; 2. Act 2—Entr'acte; 3. Act
3—Entr'acte; 4. Act 4—Entr'acte; 5. Act 5—Entr'acte.
1. SNO, N. Järvi *Concert*
                        (6/90) (CHAN) ① **CHAN8805**

**KALKBRENNER, Frédéric
(Friedrich Wilhelm Michael)
(1785–1849) France**

SECTION I: ORCHESTRAL

**Concerto No. 1 in D minor—piano and
orchestra, Op. 61 (pub 1823)**
H. Kann, Hamburg SO, H. Beissel *Hummel: Piano
Concerto, Op. 110.*   (5/93) (VOX) ① **115716-2**

SECTION III: INSTRUMENTAL

**Nocturne in A flat, '(Les) soupirs de la harpe
Eolienne'—piano, Op. 129**
N. Demidenko (pp1993) *Concert*
                        (1/94) (HYPE) ① [2] **CDA66781/2**

**KALLIWODA, Johannes
Wenceslaus (1801–1866)
Bohemia**

SECTION I: ORCHESTRAL

**Concertino in F—oboe and orchestra, Op.
110**
B. Glaetzner, Berlin SO, C.P. Flor *Concert*
                        (5/90) (CAPR) ① **10 281**
I. Goritzki, Polish Chmbr PO, W. Rajski *Concert*
                        (9/91) (CLAV) ① **CD50-9018**
**Introduction, Theme and Variations in B
flat—clarinet and orchestra, Op. 128**
D. Klöcker, Berlin RSO, J. López-Cobos *Concert*
                        (11/88) (SCHW) ① **311045**

SECTION II: CHAMBER

Le Morceau de salon—oboe and keyboard
R. Canter, R. Burnett *Concert*
                        (4/87) (AMON) ① **CD-SAR22**
C. Bradbury, O. Davies *Concert*
                        (6/90) (ASV) ① **CDDCA701**

**KALLSTENIUS, Edvin
(1881–1967) Sweden**

SECTION I: ORCHESTRAL

**En serenade i sommarnatten—tone poem,
Op. 10 (1918)** (Eng: A summer night's
serenade)
Stockholm PO, S. Westerberg *Concert*
                        (8/92) (MSVE) ① **MSCD620**

**KÁLMÁN, Imre (Emmerich)
(1882–1953) Hungary/USA**

SECTION V: STAGE WORKS

**Die Csárdásfürstin, '(The) Gypsy
Princess'—operetta: 3 acts (1915—Vienna)**
(Lib. Stein & Jenbach)
EXCERPTS—; 1. Introduction. ACT 1: 2. Heia, heia,
in den Bergen ist mein Heimatland; 3a. Alle sind wir
Sünder; 3b. Die Mädis von Chantant; 4a. Sylva, ich
will nur dich; 4b. Ja, Mädchen gibt es wunderfeine;
5a. Aus ist's mit der Liebe; 5b. Ganz ohne Weiber
geht die Chose nicht; 6. O jag' dem Glück nicht nach;
7a. Ich, Edwin Ronald; 7b. Jetzt, gerade jetzt!; 7c.
Heissa, so verliebt zu sein. ACT 2: 8. Entr'acte; 9.
Erstrahlen die Lichter (Tanzwalzer); 10a. Ich warte
auf das grosse wunder; 10b. Machen wir's den
Schwalben nach; 11. Mädel, guck; 12a. Liebchen, mich
reisst es; 12b. Dance with dialogue; 12c. Weisst du
es noch?; 13a. Mädel, guck; 13b. Das ist die Liebe;
14a. Tanzen möcht' ich; 14b. Tausend kleine Engel
singen; 15a. Verzeih', Papa; 15b. Lieben sich zwei
Menschenkinder. ACT 3: 16a. Intermezzo; 16b.
Nimm, Zigeuner, deine Geige; 16c. Jaj, Mamán,
Bruderherz, ich kauf mir die Welt; 17. Mädel, guck ...
Das list die Liebe (reprise); 18. Tausend kleine Engel
singen (finale).
2. M. Hill Smith, Philh, J.O. Edwards (1989-91; Eng)
Concert   (10/91) (TER) ① **CDVIR8314**
12c P. Domingo, I. Perlman, NY Studio Orch, J.
Tunick (r1990) *Concert*
                        (3/92) (EMI) ① **CDC7 54266-2**
14a, 14b M. Hill Smith, P. Morrison, Chandos
Concert Orch, S. Barry (Eng) *Concert*
                        (6/85) (CHAN) ① **CHAN8362**
Die Faschingsfee—operetta (1917—Vienna)
(Lib. Willner & Oesterreicher)
Lieber Himmelvater M. Hill Smith, Chandos Concert
Orch, S. Barry *Concert*
                        (10/91) (CHAN) ① **CHAN8978**
**Gräfin Mariza, 'Countess Maritza'—operetta:
3 acts (1924—Vienna)** (Lib. Brammer and
Grünwald)
EXCERPTS—; 1. Overture. ACT 1: 2. Glück ist ein
schöner Traum; 4a. Wenn es Abend wird; 4b. Grüss
mir die süssen (Grüss mir mein Wien); 5a. Höre ich
Zigeunergeigen; 5b. Wo wohnt die Liebe; 6a.
Sonnenschein, hüll' dich ein; 6b. O schöne
Kinderzeit; 7a. Ich bitte, nicht lachen; 7b. Komm mit
nach Varasdin; 8a. Zigeunermusik; 8b. Auch war
einst feiner Csárdáskavalier; 8c. Komm, Zigány; 8d.
Ei bravo, Herr Verwalter; 8e. Bitte sehr, das ist noch
gar nix, nein!; 8f. Geigen schallen, Lichter blitzen; 8g.
Eh' ein kurzer Mond ins Land mag entfliehen; 8h.
Komm, Zigány. ACT 2: 9. Schwesterlein,
Schwesterlein; 10a. Wenn ich abends schlafen geh';
10b. Ich möchte trämen vor dir; 11a. mein Pickikám!; 11.
Genung, genug, ich will mit Geschäften; 12a.
Herrgott, was ist denn heut' los; 12b. Einmal möcht'

ich wieder tanzen; 13a. Junger Mann ein Mädchen liebt; 13b. Behüt' dich Gott, komm nach Haus; 14a. Geigen schallen, Lichter blitzen; 14b. Ja!, Heut' um Zehn sind wir in Tabarin; 15a. Mein lieber Schatz; 15b. Sag' ja, mein Lieb, sag' ja; 16a. Hei, Mariza, hei; 16b. Hab' mich einmal toll verliebt; 16c. Eh' ein Kurzer Mond im Land mag entfliehen. ACT 3: 17. Zigeunermusik; 18a. Ungarmädel, Haut wie Rosen; 18b. Braunes Mädel von der Puszta; 18c. Fein könnt' auf der Welt es sein; 18d. Wer hat euch erdacht, ihr süssen Frau'n; 19. Komm mit nach Varasdin; 20a. Ich trag' mit starker Hand; 20b. Sag' ja, die Stunde des Glücks ist da.
4a, 4b R. Tauber, Odeon Künstlerorchester, F. Weissmann (r1932) *Concert*
(12/89) (EMI) ① **CDH7 69787-2**
4b R. Tauber, Vienna Th an der Wien Orch, A. Paulik (r1924) *Concert* (12/92) (NIMB) ① **NI7833**
4, 8b, 8c P. Domingo, Ambrosian Sngrs, ECO, J. Rudel *Concert* (2/87) (EMI) ① **CDC7 47398-2**
5a J. Migenes, Vienna Volksoper Orch, L. Schifrin (r1993) *Concert* (1/94) (ERAT) ① **4509-92875-2**
15b M. Hill Smith, New Sadler's Wells Op Orch, B. Wordsworth (r1989-91; Eng) *Concert*
(10/91) (TER) ① **CDVIR8314**
Die **Herzogin von Chicago**—operetta (1928—Vienna) (Lib. Brammer & Grünwald)
Ein kleiner Slowfix mit Mary M. Hill Smith, Chandos Concert Orch, S. Barry *Concert*
(10/91) (CHAN) ① **CHAN8978**
Hollandweibchen—operetta (1920—Vienna) (Lib. Stein & Jenbach)
O du holde Zeit M. Hill Smith, Chandos Concert Orch, S. Barry *Concert*
(10/91) (CHAN) ① **CHAN8978**
Kaiserin Josephine—operetta (1936—Zurich) (Lib. Knepler & Herczeg)
Mein Traum; Schöne Marquise M. Hill Smith, Chandos Concert Orch, S. Barry *Concert*
(10/91) (CHAN) ① **CHAN8978**
Das **Veilchen vom Montmartre**—operetta (1930—Vienna) (Lib. Brammer & Grünwald)
Das Veilchen vom Montmartre M. Hill Smith, Chandos Concert Orch, S. Barry *Concert*
(10/91) (CHAN) ① **CHAN8978**
Die **Zirkusprinzessin, 'Circus Princess'**—operetta: 3 acts (1926—Vienna) (Lib. Brammer & Grünwald)
EXCERPTS—ACT 1: 1. Bravo, bravo, Herr Direktor!; 2a. Was in der Welt geschieht; 2b. Ja, ist denn die Liebe wirklich gar so schön; 3a. Wenn ein einsames Wienerkind; 3b. Wo ist der Himmel so blau wie in Wien; 4. Es ist noch Zeit!; 5a. Weider hinaus ins strahlende Licht; 5b. Zwei Märchenaugen; 6a. Wenn ich in den Zirkus gehe; 6b. Die kleine Mäderln im Trikot; 7a. Manchal treibt das Schicksal; 7b. Wer wind denn gleich weinen, mein Kind; 8. Hoheit hat uns eingelanden heute zum Souper!; 9a. Heissa, die Nacht erwacht; 9b. Juppla, Josefinchen. ACT 2: 10. Freut euch des Lebens; 11a. Der Husar; 11b. Mädel, gib acht!, Schleis dein Fenster; 12a. Wollen sie mir nicht gestehen; 12b. Mein Darling!, muss so sein wie Du!; 13a. Wieder blüht die Primel; 13b. Leise, leise, komm mit mir auf die Wesse; 14a. Süsseste von allen Frauen; 14b. Ich und Du - Du und ich!; 15a. Iwan Peter Petrowitsch; 15b. Mein heissgeliebter, süssen Iwan; 16. Ein Hochzeitsfest, welche Pracht! (finale). ACT 3: 17a. Nimmt man Abschied von dieser Stadt; 17b. Wo ist der Himmel so blau in Wien!; 18. Glaubst Du denn, ich werd' dich kränken; 18b. Wenn Du mich sitzen lässt; 19. Der alte Herrgott, der weiss er tut; 20. Mein darling muss lieb sein wie du.
2a M. Hill Smith, Chandos Concert Orch, S. Barry *Concert* (10/91) (CHAN) ① **CHAN8978**
5b R. Tauber, Berlin Künstlertheater Orch, E. Hauke (r1927) *Concert* (12/89) (EMI) ① **CDH7 69787-2**
5b R. Tauber, Berlin Künstlertheater Orch, E. Hauke (r1927) *Concert* (12/92) (NIMB) ① **NI7833**

KALOMIRIS, Manolis *(1883–1962) Greece*

SECTION I: ORCHESTRAL

Symphony No. 1, 'Levendia', Op. 21 (1918-20)
Vienna Singverein, Vienna RSO, M. Caridis (pp1986) *Skalkottas: Odyssey Symphony.*
(10/90) (SCHW) ① **311110**

KAMEN, Michael *(b 1948) USA*

SECTION V: STAGE WORKS

The **Dead Zone**—film score (1983)
EXCERPTS: 1. Opening Titles; 2. Coma; 3. Hospital Visit; 4. First Vision—Second Sight; 5. Lost Love; 6.

Drowning Vision—Through the Ice; 7. School Days; 8. In the Snow—Hope; 9. Alone; 10. Political Death; 11. Rally—Meet Your Local Candidate; 12. Realisation—Destiny; 13. Death of a Visionary; 14. Civic Duty & Sacrifice; 15. The Dead Zone; 16. Coda to a Coma—The Balcony.
1. Prague City PO, W. Motzing (r1993) *Concert*
(8/94) (SILV) ① **FILMCD146**

KANCHELI, Giya Alexandrovich *(b 1935) USSR*

SECTION I: ORCHESTRAL

Abii ne viderem—viola & string orchestra (1992-4)
K. Kashkashian, Stuttgart CO, D. R. Davies (r1994) *Concert* (4/95) (ECM) ① **445 941-2**
Mourned by the Wind—liturgy: viola and orchestra (1988)
S. Belonogov, Moscow SO, F. Glushchenko *Concert*
(4/93) (OLYM) ① **OCD424**
Symphony No. 1 (1967)
Moscow SO, F. Glushchenko *Concert*
(4/93) (OLYM) ① **OCD424**
Symphony No. 2, 'Songs' (1970)
Berlin RSO, M. Jurowski (r1994) *Symphony 7.*
(8/95) (CPO) ① **CPO999 263-2**
Symphony No. 3—tenor and orchestra (1973)
G. Gonashvili, Georgia St SO, D. Kakhidze (r1979) *Symphony 6.* (9/90) (OLYM) ① **OCD401**
Symphony No. 4, 'In Commemoration of Michaelangelo' (1975)
Georgia St SO, D. Kakhidze *Symphony 5.*
(4/91) (OLYM) ① **OCD403**
Symphony No. 5 (1976)
Georgia St SO, D. Kakhidze *Symphony 4.*
(4/91) (OLYM) ① **OCD403**
Symphony No. 6—two violas and orchestra (1981)
A. Kharadze, G. Chaduneli, Georgia St SO, D. Kakhidze (r1981) *Symphony 3.*
(9/90) (OLYM) ① **OCD401**
Tbilisi SO, J. Kakhidze (r1994) *Symphony 7.*
(5/95) (SONY) ① **SMK66590**
Symphony No. 7, 'Epilogue' (1986)
Moscow SO, F. Glushchenko *Concert*
(4/93) (OLYM) ① **OCD424**
Tbilisi SO, J. Kakhidze (r1994) *Symphony 2.*
(5/95) (SONY) ① **SMK66590**
Berlin RSO, M. Jurowski (r1994) *Symphony 2.*
(8/95) (CPO) ① **CPO999 263-2**
Vom Winde beweint—liturgy for large orchestra & solo viola (1990)
K. Kashkashian, Bonn Beethovenhalle Orch, D.R. Davies *Schnittke: Viola Concerto.*
(4/93) (ECM) ① **437 199-2**

SECTION IV: VOCAL AND CHORAL

Evening Prayers—voices & chamber orchestra (1991)
Hilliard Ens, Stuttgart CO, D. R. Davies (r1994) *Concert* (4/95) (ECM) ① **445 941-2**
Exil—song-cycle: soprano & instruments (1994)
EXCERPTS: 1. Psalm 23; 2. Einmal (Wds. Paul Celan); 3. Zähle die Mandeln (Wds. Celan); 4. Psalm (Wds. Celan); 5. Exil (Wds. Hans Sahl).
M. Deubner, N. Pschenitschnikova, C. Demenga, R. Killius, R. Firth, C. Sutter, W. Jurowski (r1994) *Concert* (4/95) (ECM) ① **447 808-2**
Morning Prayers—voice, alto flute & chamber orchestra (1990)
V. Tevdorashvili, N. Pschenitschnikova, Stuttgart CO, D. R. Davies (r1994) *Concert*
(4/95) (ECM) ① **445 941-2**

KANDER, John Harold *(b 1927) USA*

SECTION IV: VOCAL AND CHORAL

A **Letter from Sullivan Ballou**—song: 1v & piano (Text: letter written during the American Civil War)
R. Fleming, W. Jones (pp1994) *Concert*
(1/95) (RCA) ① **09026 62547-2**

SECTION V: STAGE WORKS

Zorba—musical show (1968—New York) (Lyrics Fred Ebb, after Kazantzakis)
EXCERPTS: 1. Life Is; 2. The First Time; 3. The Top of the Hill; 4. No Boom Boom; 5. The Butterfly; 6. Goodbye, Canavaro; 7. Grandpapa—Zorba's Dance; 8. Only Love; 9. The Bend of the Road; 10. Entr'acte; 11. Y'Assou; 12. Why Can't I Speak?; 13. The Crow;

---

14. Happy Birthday; 15. I Am Free; 16. Life Is (reprise).
Cpte H. Bernardi, M. Harnilova, Orig Broadway Cast, H. Hastings (r1968)
(11/93) (EMI) ① **ZDM7 64665-2**

KANGRO, Raimo *(b 1949) Estonia*

SECTION II: CHAMBER

Idioms, Op. 43a (1992)
Tallinn Camerata (r1993) *Concert*
(5/95) (FINL) ① **4509-95705-2**

SECTION III: INSTRUMENTAL

Suite for Piano, Op. 1 (1968)
L. Väinmaa (r1993) *Concert*
(7/95) (FINL) ① **4509-95704-2**

KAPER, Bronislaw *(1902–1983) Poland/USA*

SECTION V: STAGE WORKS

Auntie Mame—film score (1958)
Theme B. Kaper (arr cpsr: pf) *Concert*
(2/91) (FACE) ① **FE8101**
The **Brothers Karamazov**—film score
Theme B. Kaper (arr cpsr: pf) *Concert*
(2/91) (FACE) ① **FE8101**
Butterfield 8—film score (1961)
Theme B. Kaper (arr cpsr: pf) *Concert*
(2/91) (FACE) ① **FE8101**
The **Chocolate Soldier**—film score (1941)
Theme B. Kaper (arr cpsr: pf) *Concert*
(2/91) (FACE) ① **FE8101**
The **Glass Slipper**—film score (1955)
Theme B. Kaper (arr cpsr: pf) *Concert*
(2/91) (FACE) ① **FE8101**
Green Dolphin Street—film score (1947)
Theme B. Kaper (arr cpsr: pf) *Concert*
(2/91) (FACE) ① **FE8101**
Invitation—film score (1952)
Theme B. Kaper (arr cpsr: pf) *Concert*
(2/91) (FACE) ① **FE8101**
Lili—musical film (1953) (Lyrics H. Deutsch)
EXCERPTS: 1. Adoration (ballet); 2. Hi-Lili, Hi-Lo; 3. Lili and the Puppets (ballet).
Theme B. Kaper (arr cpsr: pf) *Concert*
(2/91) (FACE) ① **FE8101**
Lord Jim—film score (1964)
Theme B. Kaper (arr cpsr: pf) *Concert*
(2/91) (FACE) ① **FE8101**
Mutiny on the Bounty—film score (1962)
EXCERPTS: 1. Overture.
Theme B. Kaper (arr cpsr: pf) *Concert*
(2/91) (FACE) ① **FE8101**
San Francisco—film score (1936)
Theme B. Kaper (arr cpsr: pf) *Concert*
(2/91) (FACE) ① **FE8101**
The **Swan**—film score (1956)
Theme B. Kaper (arr cpsr: pf) *Concert*
(2/91) (FACE) ① **FE8101**

KÁPRÁLOVÁ, Vítěslava *(1915–1940) Czechoslovakia*

SECTION III: INSTRUMENTAL

Dubnova Preludia Suite—piano, Op. 13 (c1939)
V. Eskin *Concert* (5/93) (NORT) ① **NR248-CD**

KAPSPERGER, Johann Hieronymus (Giovanni Girolamo) *(c1580–1651) Germany/Italy*

SECTION III: INSTRUMENTAL

Libro I d'intavolatura di chitarrone (1604)
1. Aria di Firenze; 2. Ciachone; 3. Corrente 2a; 4. Gagliarda 11a; 5. Toccata prima arpeggiata; 6. Toccata prima arpeggiata; 7. Toccata seconda arpeggiata.
1, 3. L. Kirchhof *Concert*
(11/92) (SONY) ① **SK48068**
1-6. P. O'Dette *Concert*
(6/91) (HARM) ① **HMU90 7020**
7. R. Lislevand, E. Eguez, B. Feehan, G. Morini, L. Duftschmid, P. Estevan (r1993) *Chitarrone Book IV.*
(4/95) (ASTR) ① **E8515**
Libro I d'intavolatura di lauto (1611)
1. Corrente 1a; 2. Corrente 7a; 3. Corrente 11a; 4. Corrente 12a; 5. Gagliarda 1a; 6. Gagliarda 4a; 7. Gagliarda 10a; 8. Gagliarda 12a; 9. Toccata I; 10. Toccata III; 11. Toccata IV; 12. Toccata V; 13.

Toccata VI.
1-12. P. O'Dette *Concert*
(6/91) (HARM) ① **HMU90 7020**
5. L. Kirchhof *Concert* (11/92) (SONY) ① **SK48068**
Libro IV d'intavolatura di chitarrone (1640)
1. Ballo primo; 2. Battaglia; 3. Bergamasca; 4.
Canario; 5. Canzone prima; 6. Capona—Sferraina; 7.
Ciaconna; 8. Colasione; 9. Kapsperger; 10.
Passacaglia in A; 11. Passacaglia in D; 12.
Passacaglia in G; 13. Toccata 1a; 14. Toccata 2a;
15. Toccata 7a; 16. Toccata 9a; 17. Toccata 10a.
R. Lislevand, E. Eguez, B. Feehan, G. Morini, L.
Duftschmid, P. Estevan (r1993) *Chitarrone Book I.*
(4/95) (ASTR) ① **E8515**
3, 4, 5, 8, 13, 14. P. O'Dette *Concert*
(6/91) (HARM) ① **HMU90 7020**

KARATÏGIN, Vyacheslav (Gavrilovich) (1875–1925) Russia

SECTION IV: VOCAL AND CHORAL

Farewell to thee—song
F. Chaliapin, I. Newton (r1929) *Concert*
(6/93) (PREI) ① [2] **89207**

KARAYEV, Kara (1918–1982) USSR

SECTION V: STAGE WORKS

In the path of thunder—ballet (1957)
EXCERPTS: 1. General Dance; 2. Dance of the Girls
with Guitars; 3. Night in stille veld; 4. Scene and
Duet; 5. Lullaby; 6. In the path of thunder.
Moscow Radio & TV SO, R. Abdullayev (r1993)
Seven Beauties. (12/95) (OLYM) ① **OCD491**
Seven Beauties—ballet (1952)
EXCERPTS: 1. Waltz; 2. Adagio; 3. Dance of
Merriment; 4. Prelude; 5. Indian Dance; 6. Khorezm
Dance; 7. Slavonic Dance; 8. Magrib Dance; 9.
Chinese Dance; 10. The most beautiful of all
beauties; 11. Procession.
Moscow Radio & TV SO, R. Abdullayev (r1993) *In
the Path of Thunder.* (12/95) (OLYM) ① **OCD491**

KARETNIKOV, Nikolai (1930–1994) USSR

SECTION V: STAGE WORKS

Till Eulenspiegel—opera: 2 acts (1983) (Lib.
cpsr & Lounguin, after C de Coster)
Cpte B. Kudriavtsev, E. Mazo, A. Martynov, L.
Mkrtchian, A. Pruzhansky, A. Mochalov, P. Gluboky,
Chor, Soviet Cinema Orch, E. Khachaturian, V.
Polianski (r1988)
(7/92) (CDM) ① [2] **LDC288 029/30**

KARG-ELERT, Sigfrid (1877–1933) Germany

SECTION III: INSTRUMENTAL

**66 Choral-Improvisationen—organ, Op. 65
(1908-10)**
EXCERPTS: 1. Ach bleib mit deiner Gnade; 2. Aus
meinem Herzens Grunde; 5. Freu dich sehr, o meine
Seele; 9. Marche triomphale; 10. Jerusalem, du
hochgebaute Stadt; 16. Herzlich tut mich verlangen;
20. O Lamm Gottes; 21. O Welt, ich muss dich
lassen; 22. O Gott, du frommer Gott; 24. Dir, dir,
Jehova will sich singen; 25. Erscheinen ist der
Herrlich Tag; 28. Lobe den Herren, o meine Seele;
33. Wachet auf; 37. Ich dank dir, lieber Herre; 39.
Komm, heiliger Geist; 40. O dass ich tausend Zungen
hätte; 41. O Durchbrecher aller Bande; 44. Wie
schön leucht' uns der Morgenstern; 45. Aus tiefer
Not; 49. Meinen Jesum lass ich nicht; 50. O Gott, du
frommer Gott; 51. Nun danket alle Gott; 54. Werde
munter, mein Gemüte; 56. Jesu, geh' voran; 58. Lobe
den Herrn, den mächtigen König; 59. Nun danket alle
Gott; 61. Was Gott tut, das ist wohlgetan; 63. Wer nur
den lieben Gott lässt walten; 66. Wunderbarer König.
51. P. Hurford (r1982) *Concert*
(6/93) (DECC) ① **436 402-2DWO**
51. P. Hurford (r1982) *Concert*
(10/95) (DECC) ① **444 567-2DM**
59. S. Cleobury *Concert*
(3/87) (PRIO) ① **PRCD185**
59. C. Curley *Concert*
(2/91) (ARGO) ① **430 200-2ZH**
59. S. Preston *Concert*
(6/91) (DECC) ① **430 091-2DWO**

59. P. Hurford *Concert*
(8/91) (DECC) ① **430 710-2DM**
Diverse Pieces—organ, Op. 75 (1910)
1. Funerale; 2. In dulci jubilo; 3. Der Hölle Pforten
sind zerstört; 4. Gelobt sei Gott im höchsten Thron.
1-4. G. Barber (r1990) *Concert*
(11/93) (PRIO) ① **PRCD315**
2. D. Sanger (r1983) *Concert*
(12/93) (MERI) ① **CDE84068**
3 Impressions—organ, Op. 72 (1911)
1. Harmonies du soir; 2. Clair de lune.
1, 2. M.H. Long *Concert* (4/91) (KOCH) ① **37008-2**
3 Impressions—organ, Op. 108 (1922)
1. Sunset; 2. Starlight; 3. Elegiac Poem.
G. Barber *Concert* (7/91) (PRIO) ① **PRCD314**
Partita in D—harmonium, Op. 37 (1906)
H.C. Jacobs *Concert*
(7/91) (CPO) ① **CPO999 051-2**
Partita in E—organ, Op. 100 (1924)
G. Barber *Concert* (1/93) (PRIO) ① **PRCD391**
**Passacaglia in E flat minor (Variationen über
einen basso ostinato)—harmonium, Op. 25
(1905)**
H.C. Jacobs *Concert*
(7/91) (CPO) ① **CPO999 051-2**
**Passcaglia and Fugue on BACH—organ, Op.
150 (1933)**
J. Watts *Concert* (10/89) (PRIO) ① **PRCD237**
**7 Pastels from the Lake of
Constance—organ, Op. 96 (1919)**
1. J.S. Whiteley *Concert* (7/87) (YORK) ① **CD101**
10 Pieces—organ, Op. 142 (1932)
1. Stimmen der Nacht; 2. Valse mignonne in E; 7.
Ciacono with variations in C minor; 10. Noël.
1. G. Barber (r1990) *Concert*
(11/93) (PRIO) ① **PRCD315**
2. J. Parker-Smith *Concert*
(9/90) (ASV) ① **CDDCA702**
8 Short Pieces—organ, Op. 154
1. Introitus; 2. Gagliarda; 3. Melodia monastica; 4.
Aria semplice; 5. Appassionata; 6. Canzona solenne;
7. Toccatina; 8. Corale.
G. Barber *Concert* (5/91) (PRIO) ① **PRCD297**
**3 sinfonische Kanzonen—organ, Op. 85
(1910)**
1. E flat; 3. Fugue, Kanzone and Epilog (with violin
and female chorus).
3. R. Noehren, Detroit Mariner's Church Ch, M. Smith
Concert (11/87) (DELO) ① **DE3045**
**Sonata No. 1 in B minor—harmonium, Op. 36
(1905)**
H.C. Jacobs *Concert*
(7/91) (CPO) ① **CPO999 051-2**
**Symphony in F sharp minor—organ, Op. 130
(1930)**
G. Barber *Concert* (3/92) (PRIO) ① **PRCD373**

KASEMETS, Udo (b 1919) Estonia/Canada

SECTION I: ORCHESTRAL

**The Eight Houses of the I Ching—12 strings
(1993)**
L. Borealis Ens, P. Järvi (r1993) *Concert*
(4/95) (KOCH) ① **37165-2**
**Requiem Renga—15 strings and 2
percussion (1992)**
L. Borealis Ens, P. Järvi (r1993) *Concert*
(4/95) (KOCH) ① **37165-2**

SECTION IV: VOCAL AND CHORAL

**Palestrina on Devil's Staircase—2 sopranos,
3 violins and 3 cellos (1993)**
L. Borealis Ens, P. Järvi (r1993) *Concert*
(4/95) (KOCH) ① **37165-2**

KASHEVAROV, ? (19th/20th Cent) Russia

SECTION IV: VOCAL AND CHORAL

Tranquillity—song
D. Smirnov, anon (r1912) *Concert*
(6/93) (PEAR) ① [3] **GEMMCDS9004/6(2)**

KAŠPAR, J. (19th Cent) Bohemia

SECTION I: ORCHESTRAL

Elbewellen
Czech PO, V. Neumann *Concert*
(6/87) (ORFE) ① **C107201A**

KASPAROV, Yuri (b 1955) Armenia

SECTION I: ORCHESTRAL

Concerto for Oboe and Orchestra (1988)
S. Velikanov, USSR Cinema SO, V. Ponkin *Concert*
(9/93) (OLYM) ① **OCD296**
**Genesis—micro-symphony for orchestra
(1989)**
USSR Cinema SO, V. Ponkin *Concert*
(9/93) (OLYM) ① **OCD296**
Linkos—sequence for orchestra (1988)
USSR Cinema SO, E. Khachaturian *Concert*
(9/93) (OLYM) ① **OCD296**
Silencium—chamber orchestra (1990)
Moscow Contemp Music Ens, A. Vinogradov (r1992)
Concert (9/93) (CDM) ① **LDC288 060**

SECTION II: CHAMBER

Invention—string quartet (1989)
Moscow Contemp Music Ens
(9/93) (OLYM) ① **OCD296**
**Landscape fading into infinity—clarinet,
violin, cello and piano (1992)**
Moscow Contemp Music Ens, A. Vinogradov (r1992)
Concert (9/93) (CDM) ① **LDC288 060**
Variations for Clarinet and Piano (1990)
Moscow Contemp Music Ens, A. Vinogradov (r1992)
Concert (9/93) (CDM) ① **LDC288 060**

SECTION III: INSTRUMENTAL

Cantus firmus—violin (1990)
Moscow Contemp Music Ens, A. Vinogradov (r1992)
Concert (9/93) (CDM) ① **LDC288 060**
Credo—organ (1990)
Moscow Contemp Music Ens, A. Vinogradov (r1992)
Concert (9/93) (CDM) ① **LDC288 060**
Postlude—harp (1990)
Moscow Contemp Music Ens, A. Vinogradov (r1992)
Concert (9/93) (CDM) ① **LDC288 060**

SECTION IV: VOCAL AND CHORAL

**Ave Maria—12vv, violin, organ & vibraphone
(1989)**
Tamara Pilipchuk Voc Ens, Moscow Contemp Music
Ens *Concert* (9/93) (OLYM) ① **OCD296**
**Stabat Mater—soprano and string quartet
(1991)**
Anon (sop), Moscow Contemp Music Ens *Concert*
(9/93) (OLYM) ① **OCD296**

SECTION V: STAGE WORKS

**Nevermore—opera-monodrama: baritone
and chamber ensemble (1992)** (Wds. E. A.
Poe: 'The Ravens')
EXCERPTS: 1. Overture.
1. Moscow Contemp Music Ens, A. Vinogradov
(r1992) *Concert* (9/93) (CDM) ① **LDC288 060**

KASTAL'SKY, Alexandr Dmitriyevich (1856–1926) Russia/USSR

SECTION IV: VOCAL AND CHORAL

**Liturgy of St John Chrysostom—chorus a
capella**
Bolshoi Children's Ch, A. Zaboronok (r1994) *Concert*
(7/95) (COLL) ① **Coll1443-2**
**On this day the Virgin—Russian liturgical
chant**
N. Gedda, Paris Russian Orthodox Cath Ch, E. Evetz
Concert (1/93) (PHIL) ① **434 174-2PM**

KATSARIS, Cyprien (20th Cent) Greece

SECTION III: INSTRUMENTAL

In Memoriam Mozart—piano (1985)
C. Katsaris (r1992) *Concert*
(6/93) (SONY) ① **SK52551**
Mozartiana—piano (1991)
C. Katsaris (r1992) *Concert*
(6/93) (SONY) ① **SK52551**

KAUER, Ferdinand (1751–1831) Austria

SECTION III: INSTRUMENTAL

6 Viennese Sonatinas—piano (arr of Mozart's Divertimenti, KAnh229/439b)
1. C; 2. A; 3. B flat; 4. F; 5. C.
D. Blumenthal (r1991) Concert
(10/93) (ETCE) ① [2] KTC2018

KAUKESEL, Guibert (fl c1230–1255) France

SECTION IV: VOCAL AND CHORAL

Un Chant novel—ballade: 1v and percussion
Gothic Voices, C. Page (r1994) Concert
(8/95) (HYPE) ① CDA66773
Fins cuers enamourés—grand chant: 1v
Gothic Voices, C. Page (r1994) Concert
(8/95) (HYPE) ① CDA66773

KEEBLE, John (c1711–1786) England

SECTION III: INSTRUMENTAL

Select Piece No. 1 in G—organ (c1775)
J. Bate Concert (7/91) (UNIC) ① DKPCD9105
Voluntary in D minor—keyboard (pub 1777–78)
Margaret Phillips Concert
(5/91) (GAMU) ① GAMCD514

KEETMAN, Gunild (b 1904) Germany

SECTION IV: VOCAL AND CHORAL

Weihnachtslieder
Excs Tolz Boys' Ch, G. Schmidt-Gaden, Inst Ens, Salzburg Shepherd Boys, T. Reiser, Munich Chmbr Chor, F. Schieri, Cologne Children's Ch, H-G. Lenders Orff: Weihnachtsgeschichte.
(12/90) (DHM) ① RD77139

KEISER, Reinhard (1674–1739) Germany

SECTION IV: VOCAL AND CHORAL

St. Mark Passion (?1717)
B.Hirtreiter, T. d'Althann, P. Geitner, M. Paulsen, J. Elbert, H. Elbert, C. Brembeck, Parthenia Vocal, Parthenia Baroque (r1993)
(3/95) (CHRI) ① CHR77143

SECTION V: STAGE WORKS

Masagniello furioso, oder Die Neapolitanische Fischer-Empörung—opera: 3 acts (1706—Hamburg) (Lib. B. Feind)
Cpte M. Schopper, B. Schlick, D. Röschmann, D. Cordier, W. Jochens, H. van der Kamp, H. Meens, J. Dreyer, W. Mikus, Bremen Voc Ens, Fiori Musicali, T. Albert (pp1989)
(11/93) (CPO) ① [2] CPO999 110-2

KELLER, Gottfried (c1650–1704) Germany/England

SECTION II: CHAMBER

3 Trumpet Sonatas—trumpet/oboe/recorder, strings and continuo (pub 1700)
1. D.
1. Parley of Instr, R. Goodman, P. Holman Concert
(11/88) (HYPE) ① CDA66108

KELLER, Jens (b 1944) Denmark

SECTION II: CHAMBER

Pastorale—double-bass and organ (1990–91)
M. Hanskov, N.E. Aggesen Concert
(3/92) (DANA) ① DACOCD378

KELLNER, David (c1670–1748) Germany

SECTION III: INSTRUMENTAL

XVI Auserlesene Lauten-Stücke—lute (pub 1747) (actually 17 pieces)
1. Fantasia in C; 2. Fantasia in A minor; 3. Fantasia in A; 4. Fantasia in D minor; 5. Fantasia in D; 6. Fantasia in F; 7. Camapanella; 8. Aria; 9. Courante; 10. Sarabande; 11. Giga I; 12. Giga II; 13. Gavotte; 14. Rondeau; 15. Pastorel; 16. Passepied; 17. Chaconne.
S. Stubbs (r1982) (9/93) (CPO) ① CPO999 097-2
1, 2. J. Lindberg (r1986) Concert
(11/87) (BIS) ① BIS-CD327

KELLNER, Johann Christoph (1736–1803) Germany

SECTION III: INSTRUMENTAL

Quartetto in E flat (1789)
H. Fagius, D. Sanger Concert
(10/85) (BIS) ① BIS-CD273

KELLY, Bryan (George) (b 1934) England

SECTION IV: VOCAL AND CHORAL

Evening Service in C
Gloucester Cath Ch, J. Sanders, M. Lee (r1994) Concert (4/95) (PRIO) ① PRCD494

KELLY, Frederick Septimus (1881–1916) Australia

SECTION IV: VOCAL AND CHORAL

Shall I compare thee?—song, Op. 1 (1912) (Wds. Shakespeare)
S. Varcoe, C. Benson Concert
(6/88) (HYPE) ① [2] CDA66261/2

KELLY, Thomas Alexander Erskine, Earl of (1732–1781) Scotland

SECTION III: INSTRUMENTAL

Favourite Minuets—keyboard
1. Duchess of Gordon; 2. Lord Stanley.
G. Gifford Concert (5/90) (LIBR) ① LRCD156

KELLYK, Hugh (fl late 15th Cent) England

SECTION IV: VOCAL AND CHORAL

Gaude flore virginali—7vv (Eton Choirbook)
The Sixteen, H. Christophers (r1993) Concert
(2/94) (COLL) ① Coll1395-2

KELWAY, Thomas (c1695–1744) England

SECTION IV: VOCAL AND CHORAL

Evening Service in B minor—choir and organ
Chichester Cath Ch, A. Thurlow, J. Thomas (r1994) Concert (5/95) (PRIO) ① PRCD511

KEMPEL, Arthur (20th Cent) USA

SECTION V: STAGE WORKS

Double Impact—film score (1991)
EXCERPTS: 1. The Brothers' Revenge.
1. OST Concert (5/93) (SILV) ① SILVAD3001

KEMPFF, Wilhelm (1895–1991) Germany

SECTION III: INSTRUMENTAL

Italian Suite—piano, Op. 68 (pub 1953)
I. Biret Concert (5/93) (MARC) ① 8 223452
Pastorale variée—piano (trans from works by Mozart)
I. Biret Concert (5/93) (MARC) ① 8 223452
C. Katsaris (r1992) Concert
(6/93) (SONY) ① SK52551

Sonata—piano, Op. 47 (1947)
I. Biret Concert (5/93) (MARC) ① 8 223452

KEPPEL

SECTION IV: VOCAL AND CHORAL

Robin Adair—song
A. Patti, L. Ronald (r1905) Concert
(4/90) (PEAR) ① GEMMCD9312

KERKER, Gustave (1857–1923) Germany/USA

SECTION V: STAGE WORKS

The Belle of New York—musical show (1897—New York) (Lyrics C M S McLellan)
EXCERPTS: 1. They All Follow Me; 2. The Purity Brigade.
1, 2. E. May, Broadway Cast (r1900) Concert
(5/94) (PEAR) ① [3] GEMMCDS9050/2(1)
Castles in the Air—musical show (1890—New York) (Lyrics Charles Alfred Byrne)
EXCERPTS: 1. You Can Always Explain Things Away.
1. D. Hopper, Broadway Cast (r ?1890) Concert
(5/94) (PEAR) ① [3] GEMMCDS9050/2(1)
The White Hen—musical show (1907—New York) (Lyrics Paul West)
EXCERPTS: 1. Very Well, Then.
1. R. C. Herz, Broadway Cast (r1908) Concert
(5/94) (PEAR) ① [3] GEMMCDS9050/2(2)
Yankee Doodle Dandy—musical show (1898—New York) (Lyrics McLellan)
EXCERPTS: 1. O'Hoolihan Held the Fuse.
1. T. Q. Seabrooke, Broadway Cast (r1904) Concert
(5/94) (PEAR) ① [3] GEMMCDS9050/2(1)

KERLL, Johann Kaspar (1627–1693) Germany

SECTION II: CHAMBER

Batalla Imperial
Hespèrion XX, J. Savall Concert
(2/92) (ASTR) ① E8729

KERN, Jerome (David) (1885–1945) USA

SECTION IV: VOCAL AND CHORAL

How'd You Like to Spoon With Me?—song from Caryll's show 'The Earl and the Girl' (1905) (Lyrics Laska)
Cincinnati Uni Sngrs, Cincinnati Uni Th Orch, E. Rivers (r1978) Concert (4/94) (NEW) ① 80221-2
The Land Where the Good Songs Go—song (Lyrics P. G. Wodehouse)
S. McNair, A. Previn, D. Finck (r1993) Concert
(12/94) (PHIL) ① 442 129-2PH
The Last Time I Saw Paris—song for film of Gershwin's 'Lady Be Good' (1940) (Lyrics O. Hammerstein)
K. Te Kanawa, London Sinfonietta, J. Tunick (r1991: arr Tunick) Concert (7/93) (EMI) ① CDC7 54527-2
T. Hampson, London Sinfonietta, J. McGlinn (r1992) Concert (4/94) (EMI) ① CDC7 54883-2
Look in Her Eyes—song for the show 'Der Lieber Augustin' (1913—New York) (Lyrics Rourke)
G. MacFarlane, Orig Broadway Cast (r1914) Concert (5/94) (PEAR) ① [3] GEMMCDS9056/8
My Castle in the Air—song for Kalmán's operetta 'Miss Springtime' (1916) (Lyrics P G Wodehouse)
G. MacFarlane, Orig Broadway Cast (r1917) Concert (5/94) (PEAR) ① [3] GEMMCDS9056/8

SECTION V: STAGE WORKS

The Cabaret Girl—musical show (1922—London) (Book & Lyrics Grossmith & Wodehouse)
EXCERPTS: 1. Dancing Time; 2. Shimmy With Me; 3. Looking All Over For You; 4. Nerves; 5. Mr Grips and Mr Gravvins; 6. Journey's End; 7. First Rose of Summer; 8. Whoop-De-Oodle-Do.
1. E. Parkin (r1993; arr Parkin: pf) Concert
(3/95) (SILV) ① SILVAD3006
Can't Help Singing—songs for the film (1944) (Lyrics E. Y. Harburg)
EXCERPTS: 1. Can't Help Singing; 2. More and More; 3. Californ-i-ay; 4. Any Moment Now.
1. S. McNair, A. Previn, D. Finck (r1993) Concert
(12/94) (PHIL) ① 442 129-2PH

1. E. Parkin (r1993; arr Parkin: pf) *Concert*
(3/95) (SILV) ① **SILVAD3006**

The **Cat and the Fiddle**—musical show
(1931—New York) (Lyrics O. Harbach)
EXCERPTS: 1. Violà les livres; 2. The Night Was
Made for Love; 3. She Didn't say 'Yes'; 4. I Watch
the Love Parade; 5a. The Breeze Kissed Your Hair;
5b. One Moment Alone; 6. Try to Forget; 7. Poor
Pierrott; 8. A New Love is Old; 9. Ha! Cha! Cha!.
3. J. Lehman, London Sinfonietta, J. McGlinn (r1992)
Concert (4/94) (EMI) ① **CDC7 54883-2**
3. E. Parkin (r1993; arr Parkin: pf) *Concert*
(3/95) (SILV) ① **SILVAD3006**

Centennial Summer—songs for film (1946)
(Lyrics Robin, Hammerstein & Harburg)
EXCERPTS: 1. Overture: Centennial—Long Live
Our Free America; 2. Railroad Song; 3. The Right
Romance; 4. Up With the Lark; 5. In Love in Vain; 6.
All Through the Day; 7. Cinderella Sue; 8. Finale: Up
With the Lark (reprise).
6. K. Te Kanawa, London Sinfonietta, J. Tunick
(r1991: arr Tunick) *Concert*
(7/93) (EMI) ① **CDC7 54527-2**

Cover Girl—songs for the film (1944) (Lyrics
O. Harbach)
EXCERPTS: 1. Main Title; 2. The Show Must Go
On; 3. Who's Complaining; 4. Sure Thing; 5. Make
Way for Tomorrow; 6. Put Me to the Test; 7. Long
Ago (and Far Away); 8. Poor John!; 9. Cover Girl
(chorus); 10. Finale.
4. E. Parkin (r1993; arr Parkin: pf) *Concert*
(3/95) (SILV) ① **SILVAD3006**
4, 7. S. McNair, A. Previn, D. Finck (r1993) *Concert*
(12/94) (PHIL) ① **442 129-2PH**
7. K. Te Kanawa, London Sinfonietta, J. Tunick
(r1991: arr Tunick) *Concert*
(7/93) (EMI) ① **CDC7 54527-2**

Dear Sir—musical show (1924—New York)
(Lyrics E. Selwyn & H. Dietz)
EXCERPTS: 1. I Want to Be There; 2. Wishing Well
Scene.
1, 2. R. Luker, G. Dvorsky, London Sinfonietta, J.
McGlinn (r1992) *Concert*
(4/94) (EMI) ① **CDC7 54883-2**

The **Girl from Utah**—songs for the
Rubens/Jones show (1914—New York)
(Lyrics H. Reynolds)
EXCERPTS: 1. Overture; 2. They Didn't Believe Me;
3. I'd Like to Wander With Alice in Wonderland; 4.
Why Don't They Dance the Polka Anymore?.
2. S. McNair, A. Previn, D. Finck (r1993) *Concert*
(12/94) (PHIL) ① **442 129-2PH**
2. E. Parkin (r1993; arr Parkin: pf) *Concert*
(3/95) (SILV) ① **SILVAD3006**

Have a Heart—musical show (1917—New
York) (Book G. Bolton; Lyrics P. G.
Wodehouse)
EXCERPTS: 1. I'm So Busy; 2. Napoleon, Parts 1 &
2.
1. R. Luker, G. Dvorsky, London Sinfonietta, J.
McGlinn (r1992) *Concert*
(4/94) (EMI) ① **CDC7 54883-2**
2. B. B. Van, Orig Broadway Cast (1917) *Concert*
(5/94) (PEAR) ① [3] **GEMMCDS9056/8**

High, Wide and Handsome—songs for the
film (1937) (Lyrics O. Hammerstein II)
EXCERPTS: 1. The Folks Who Live On the Hill; 2.
Can I Forget You?.
1. K. Te Kanawa, London Sinfonietta, J. Tunick
(r1991: arr Tunick) *Concert*
(7/93) (EMI) ① **CDC7 54527-2**
1. T. Hampson, London Sinfonietta, J. McGlinn
(r1992) *Concert* (4/94) (EMI) ① **CDC7 54883-2**
1. E. Parkin (r1993; arr Parkin: pf) *Concert*
(3/95) (SILV) ① **SILVAD3006**
1, 2. S. McNair, A. Previn, D. Finck (r1993) *Concert*
(12/94) (PHIL) ① **442 129-2PH**

I Dream Too Much—songs for the film (1935)
(Lyrics D. Fields)
EXCERPTS: 1. I'm the Echo; 2. The Jockey on the
Carousel; 3. I Dream Too Much.
I dream too much L. Pons, orch, A. Kostelanetz
(r1935) *Concert* (4/92) (MSOU) ① **DFCDI-111**
3. E. Parkin (r1993; arr Parkin: pf) *Concert*
(3/95) (SILV) ① **SILVAD3006**

Joy of Living—songs for the film (1938)
(Lyrics D. Fields)
EXCERPTS: 1. You Couldn't Be Cuter.
1. S. McNair, A. Previn, D. Finck (r1993) *Concert*
(12/94) (PHIL) ① **442 129-2PH**

Leave it to Jane—musical show (1917—New
York) (Book G. Bolton; Lyrics P. G.
Wodehouse)
EXCERPTS: ACT 1: 1. Good old Atwater; 2. A
peach of a life; 3. Wait till tomorrow; 4. Just you
watch my step; 5. Leave it to Jane; 6. The siren's

song; 7. There it is again; 8. Cleopatterer; 9. The
crickets are calling. ACT 2: 10. Good old Atwater; 11.
Sir Galahad; 12. The sun shines brightly; 13. I'm
going to find a girl some day; 14. Poor Prune.
7. E. Parkin (r1993; arr Parkin: pf) *Concert*
(3/95) (SILV) ① **SILVAD3006**

Love o' Mike—musical show (1917—New
York) (Book T. Sidney; Lyrics H. B. Smith)
EXCERPTS: 1. Drift With Me.
1. J. Lehman, London Sinfonietta Chor, London
Sinfonietta, J. McGlinn (r1992) *Concert*
(4/94) (EMI) ① **CDC7 54883-2**

Men of the Sky—songs for the film (1931)
(Lyrics O. Harbach)
EXCERPTS: 1. Every little while.
1. J. Lehman, G. Dvorsky, London Sinfonietta, J.
McGlinn (r1992) *Concert*
(4/94) (EMI) ① **CDC7 54883-2**

Miss 1917—musical revue (1917—New York)
(collab with V. Herbert; Book Bolton; Lyrics
Wodehouse)
EXCERPTS: 1. Go Little Boat.
1. S. McNair, A. Previn, D. Finck (r1993) *Concert*
(12/94) (PHIL) ① **442 129-2PH**
1. E. Parkin (r1993; arr Parkin: pf) *Concert*
(3/95) (SILV) ① **SILVAD3006**

Music in the Air—musical show (1932—New
York) (Lyrics O. Hammerstein II)
EXCERPTS: ACT 1: 1. I've Told Every Little Star; 2.
One More Dance; 3. There's a Hill Beyond a Hill; 4.
And Love Was Born; 5. I'm Coming Home (Letter
Song); 6a. I'm Alone; 6b. I'm So Eager; 7. In Egern of
the Tegern See. ACT 2: 8. One More Dance; 9.
When Spring is in the Air; 10. The Song is You; 11.
We Belong Together.
Medley E. Parkin (r1993; arr Parkin: pf) *Concert*
(3/95) (SILV) ① **SILVAD3006**
3. K. Te Kanawa, London Sinfonietta, J. Tunick
(r1991: arr Tunick) *Concert*
(7/93) (EMI) ① **CDC7 54527-2**
7. J. Lehman, London Sinfonietta, J. McGlinn (r1992)
Concert (4/94) (EMI) ① **CDC7 54883-2**
10. T. Hampson, London Sinfonietta, J. McGlinn
(r1992) *Concert* (4/94) (EMI) ① **CDC7 54883-2**
10. S. McNair, A. Previn, D. Finck (r1993) *Concert*
(12/94) (PHIL) ① **442 129-2PH**

Night Boat—musical show (1920—New York)
(Lyrics A Caldwell, after A. Bisson)
EXCERPTS: 1. Whose Baby Are You?; 2. Left all
Alone Again Blues.
2. E. Parkin (r1993; arr Parkin: pf) *Concert*
(3/95) (SILV) ① **SILVAD3006**

O, Lady! Lady!—musical show (1918—New
York) (Book G. Bolton; Lyrics P. G.
Wodehouse)
EXCERPTS: 1. Bill (dropped from show—later used
in Showboat).
1. J. Lehman, London Sinfonietta, J. McGlinn *Concert*
(8/93) (EMI) ① **CDC7 54586-2**

Oh Boy!—musical show (1917—New York)
(Book G. Bolton; Lyrics P. G. Wodehouse)
EXCERPTS: 1. Till the Clouds Roll By; 2. You Never
Knew About Me; 3. Rolled Into One.
1. R. Luker, H. Panaro, London Sinfonietta, J.
McGlinn (r1992) *Concert*
(4/94) (EMI) ① **CDC7 54883-2**
1. S. McNair, A. Previn, D. Finck (r1993) *Concert*
(12/94) (PHIL) ① **442 129-2PH**
1. E. Parkin (r1993; arr Parkin: pf) *Concert*
(3/95) (SILV) ① **SILVAD3006**
1, 2. T. Powers (r1919) *Concert*
(5/94) (PEAR) ① [3] **GEMMCDS9059/61**
1, 3. A. Wheaton, Orig Broadway Cast (1917)
Concert (5/94) (PEAR) ① [3] **GEMMCDS9059/61**

One Night in the Tropics—songs for the film
(1940) (Lyrics D. Fields)
EXCERPTS: 1. Remind Me; 2. Your Dream.
1. S. McNair, A. Previn, D. Finck (r1993) *Concert*
(12/94) (PHIL) ① **442 129-2PH**

The **Red Petticoat**—musical show
(1912—New York) (Book R. J. Young; Lyrics P.
West)
EXCERPTS: 1. The Ragtime Restaurant.
1. R. Luker, H. Panaro, London Sinfonietta Chor,
London Sinfonietta, J. McGlinn (r1992) *Concert*
(4/94) (EMI) ① **CDC7 54883-2**

Roberta—musical show (1933—New York)
(Lyrics O. Harbach, after Miller)
EXCERPTS: 1. Overture; 2. You're Devastating; 3.
Yesterdays; 4. The Touch of Your Hand; 5. I'll Be
Hard to Handle; 6. Smoke Gets In Your Eyes; 7. Let's
Begin; 8. You're Devastating (reprise).
2, 6, 7, 9. E. Parkin (r1993; arr Parkin: pf) *Concert*
(3/95) (SILV) ① **SILVAD3006**

3, 6. K. Te Kanawa, London Sinfonietta, J. Tunick
(r1991: arr Tunick) *Concert*
(7/93) (EMI) ① **CDC7 54527-2**
6. J. Lehman, London Sinfonietta, J. McGlinn (r1992)
Concert (4/94) (EMI) ① **CDC7 54883-2**
6, 9. S. McNair, A. Previn, D. Finck (r1993) *Concert*
(12/94) (PHIL) ① **442 129-2PH**

Sally—musical show (1920—New York)
(Book G. Bolton; Lyrics C. Grey)
EXCERPTS: ACT ONE: 1. In the Night Time; 2. You
Can't Keep a Good Girl Down; 3. Look for the Silver
Lining; 4. Sally; 5. Finale. ACT TWO: 6. The Social
Game; 7. Wild Rose; 8. The Lorelei; 9. The Church
'round the Corner; 10. Sweet and Low Down.
3. K. Te Kanawa, London Sinfonietta, J. Tunick
(r1991: arr Tunick) *Concert*
(7/93) (EMI) ① **CDC7 54527-2**
3. S. McNair, A. Previn, D. Finck (r1993) *Concert*
(12/94) (PHIL) ① **442 129-2PH**

She's a Good Fellow—musical show
(1919—New York) (Lyrics A. Caldwell)
EXCERPTS: 1. The Bullfrog Patrol.
1. R. Luker, J. Lehman, London Sinfonietta Chor,
London Sinfonietta, J. McGlinn (r1992) *Concert*
(4/94) (EMI) ① **CDC7 54883-2**
1. Duncan Sisters (r1922) *Concert*
(5/94) (PEAR) ① [3] **GEMMCDS9059/61**

Show Boat—musical comedy: 2 acts
(1927—New York) (Lyrics O. Hammerstein II,
after Ferber)
EXCERPTS: 1. Overture. ACT 1: 2. Cotton
Blossom; 3a. Who cares if my boat goes upstream;
3b. Only make believe; 4. Ol' man river; 5. Can't help
lovin' dat man; 6a. Why do stage struck maidens
clamor; 6b. Life upon the wicked stage; 7a. The man
who ventures with chance; 7b. Till good luck comes
my way; 8a. Her face is fair to look upon; 8b. I would
like yo play a lover's part; 8c. Little girl, you are safe
with me; 8d. I might fall back on you; 9a. Is de theatre
fill' up, Cap'n Andy?; 9b. Queenie's Ballyhoo; 10a. I
can't stand it this way any longer; 10b. You are love;
11. Oh tell me, did you ever! (Finale). ACT 2: 12a.
When we tell them about it all; 12b. At the fair; 13a.
I'm walking on the air, dear; 13b. Why do I love you?;
13c. In Dahomey; 14. Bill (wds. P G Woodhouse);
15a. So you're going away; 15b. Goodbye, my lady
love; 16a. Ladies and gentlemen; 16b. After the ball;
17a. When you yere for a gent; 17b. Hey, feller; 18a.
Hello, Gay; 18b. Finale ultmio. DISCARDED
NUMBERS FOR 1927 PRODUCTION: 19. What cher
doin' all day resort, Miss Nola (Pantry Scene); 20.
Number four, black! (Waterfront Saloon Scene); 21a.
Bet your hat; 21b. Yes! Ma'am; 22. Why do I love
you? (Kim's Imitations); 23. One half is fair to my
fireside so weary (A Pack of Cards); 24a. That you,
Nola?; 24b. The Creole Love Song; 25. There was a
sun sinking slowly in the West. LONDON
PRODUCTION, 1928: 26a. Music in the air; 26b.
Dance away the night. ADDITIONAL ITEMS FOR
1936 FILM VERSION: 27. Liza Matilda Hill (Gallivant'
Aroun'); 28a. Seems to me I've seen that stocking
someplace; 28b. I have the room above her; 29a.
Joe! Dere you go again; 29b. Ah still suits me.
BROADWAY REVIVAL, 1946: 30a. I was a shy,
demure type; 30b. Nobody else but me.
Cpte F. von Stade, J. Hadley, T. Stratas, B. Hubbard,
K. Burns, D. Garrison, P. O'Hara, R. Nichols, N. Kulp,
F. von Stade, L. Gish, Ambrosian Chor, London
Sinfonietta, J. McGlinn (1987; contains additional
and discarded music)
(11/88) (EMI) ① [3] **CDS7 49108-2**
Cpte J. Kelly, J. Howard, S. Burgess, W. White, S.
Powell, S. Green, C. O'Connor, B. Greene, F.
Landesman, J. Buller, G. Snook, chor, National SO,
J. O. Edwards (r1993: 1946 vers)
(6/94) (TER) ① [2] **CDTER2 1199**
3b V. Masterson, T. Allen, Philh, J.O. Edwards
(r1990) *Concert* (5/94) (TER) ① **CDVIR8317**
4. S. Ramey, J. Levine (pp1994) *Concert*
(1/95) (RCA) ① **09026 62547-2**
5, 14. K. Te Kanawa, London Sinfonietta, J. Tunick
(r1991: arr Tunick) *Concert*
(7/93) (EMI) ① **CDC7 54527-2**
28b E. Parkin (r1993; arr Parkin: pf) *Concert*
(3/95) (SILV) ① **SILVAD3006**
30b S. McNair, A. Previn, D. Finck (r1993) *Concert*
(12/94) (PHIL) ① **442 129-2PH**

Sunny—musical show, later films (1925;
films 1930, 1941—New York) (Lyrics O
Harbach & O Hammerstein II)
EXCERPTS: 1. Who?; 2. D'ye Love Me?; 3. Sunny;
4. Two Little Bluebirds.
1. R. Luker, B. Barrett, London Sinfonietta, J.
McGlinn *Concert* (8/93) (EMI) ① **CDC7 54586-2**

Sweet Adeline—musical show, later film (1929; film 1935—New York) (Lyrics O. Hammerstein II)
EXCERPTS: 1. Overture; 2. Here Am I; 3. Some Girl Is On My Mind; 4. Why Was I Born?; 5. Don't Ever Leave Me; 6. Lonely Feet.
2-5. R. Luker, J. Kaye, G. Dvorsky, B. Barrett, C. Groenendaal, D. Gaines, Ambrosian Sngrs, London Sinfonietta, J. McGlinn *Concert*
(8/93) (EMI) ① CDC7 54586-2
4. S. McNair, A. Previn, D. Finck (r1993) *Concert*
(12/94) (PHIL) ① 442 129-2PH

Swing Time—songs for the film (1936) (Lyrics D. Fields)
EXCERPTS: 1a. Main Title; 1b. Pick Yourself Up; 2. The Way You Look Tonight; 3. Waltz in Swing Time; 4. Never Gonna Dance; 5. Bojangles of Harlem; 6. A Fine Romance.
1b, 2, 3. E. Parkin (r1993; arr Parkin: pf) *Concert*
(3/95) (SILV) ① SILVAD3006
1b, 6. S. McNair, A. Previn, D. Finck (r1993) *Concert*
(12/94) (PHIL) ① 442 129-2PH
2. K. Te Kanawa, London Sinfonietta, J. Tunick (r1991: arr Tunick) *Concert*
(7/93) (EMI) ① CDC7 54527-2

Very Good Eddie—musical show (1915—New York) (Book Bartholomai & Bolton; Lyrics Green)
EXCERPTS: 1. Babes in the Wood.
1. R. Luker, H. Panaro, London Sinfonietta, J. McGlinn (r1992) *Concert*
(4/94) (EMI) ① CDC7 54883-2

Very Warm for May—musical show (1939—New York) (Lyrics O. Hammerstein II)
EXCERPTS: 1. Overture; 2. All the Things You Are; 3. All in Fun; 4. In the Heart of the Dark; 5. Heaven In My Arms; 6. Harlem Boogie-Woogie.
2. K. Te Kanawa, London Sinfonietta, J. Tunick (r1991: arr Tunick) *Concert*
(7/93) (EMI) ① CDC7 54527-2
2. R. Luker, J. Lehman, G. Dvorsky, C. Groenendaal, Ambrosian Sngrs, London Sinfonietta, J. McGlinn *Concert* (8/93) (EMI) ① CDC7 54586-2
2. S. McNair, A. Previn, D. Finck (r1993) *Concert*
(12/94) (PHIL) ① 442 129-2PH
2, 4. E. Parkin (r1993; arr Parkin: pf) *Concert*
(3/95) (SILV) ① SILVAD3006
4. K. Criswell, Ambrosian Sngrs, London Sinfonietta, J. McGlinn (r1992) *Concert*
(4/94) (EMI) ① CDC7 54802-2
5. R. Luker, J. Lehman, L. Milá, H. Panaro, G. Dvorsky, London Sinfonietta Chor, London Sinfonietta, J. McGlinn (r1992) *Concert*
(4/94) (EMI) ① CDC7 54883-2
6. London Sinfonietta, J. McGlinn (r1992) *Concert*
(4/94) (EMI) ① CDC7 54883-2

You Were Never Lovelier—songs for the film (1942) (Lyrics J. Mercer)
EXCERPTS: 1. Dearly Beloved; 2. You Were Never Lovelier; 3. I'm Old Fashioned.
3. K. Te Kanawa, London Sinfonietta, J. Tunick (r1991: arr Tunick) *Concert*
(7/93) (EMI) ① CDC7 54527-2
3. M. Patinkin, Orch, E. Stern (r1993; orch Troob, arr Ford) *Concert* (11/94) (NONE) ① 7559-79330-2
3. S. McNair, A. Previn, D. Finck (r1993) *Concert*
(12/94) (PHIL) ① 442 129-2PH

Zip Goes a Millon—musical show (1919—Worcester) (Lyrics G. Bolton & De Sylva)
EXCERPTS: 1. Whip-Poor-Will.
1. J. Lehman, G. Dvorsky, London Sinfonietta, J. McGlinn (r1992) *Concert*
(4/94) (EMI) ① CDC7 54883-2

KERNIS, Aaron J. (b 1960) USA

SECTION I: ORCHESTRAL

New Era Dance—orchestra (1992)
Baltimore SO, D. Zinman (r1994) *Concert*
(7/95) (ARGO) ① 444 454-2ZH

Symphony in Waves (1989)
NY Chbr SO, G. Schwarz (r1991) *String Quartet (1990).*
(6/93) (ARGO) ① 436 287-2ZH

SECTION II: CHAMBER

String Quartet, 'Musica celestis' (1990)
Lark Qt (r1991) *Symphony in Waves.*
(6/93) (ARGO) ① 436 287-2ZH

KETE, Edmund (17th Cent) England

SECTION II: CHAMBER

Barrow Faustus dreame—consort
Musicians of Swanne Alley *Concert*
(11/89) (VIRG) ① VC7 59534-2

KETÈLBEY, Albert W(illiam) (1875–1959) England

SECTION I: ORCHESTRAL

The Adventurers—concert overture (pub 1954)
Bratislava RSO, A. Leaper (r1992) *Concert*
(4/94) (MARC) ① 8 223442

Bells across the meadows—orchestra (1927)
London Prom, A. Faris *Concert*
(4/83) (PHIL) ① 400 011-2PH
Philh, J. Lanchbery (r1977) *Concert*
(3/94) (CFP) ① CD-CFP4637
Bratislava RSO, A. Leaper (r1992) *Concert*
(4/94) (MARC) ① 8 223442

Caprice pianistique—piano and orchestra (pub 1947)
Bratislava RSO, A. Leaper (r1992) *Concert*
(4/94) (MARC) ① 8 223442

Chal Romano—descriptive overture (1924)
Philh, J. Lanchbery (r1977) *Concert*
(3/94) (CFP) ① CD-CFP4637
Bratislava RSO, A. Leaper (r1992) *Concert*
(4/94) (MARC) ① 8 223442

The Clock and the Dresden Figures—orchestra (1930)
M. Reeves, London Prom, A. Faris *Concert*
(4/83) (PHIL) ① 400 011-2PH
L. Pearson, Philh, J. Lanchbery (r1977) *Concert*
(3/94) (CFP) ① CD-CFP4637
Bratislava RSO, A. Leaper (r1922) *Concert*
(4/94) (MARC) ① 8 223442

Cockney Suite—orchestra (pub 1924)
1. A State Occasion; 2. Cockney Lover (Lambeth Walk); 3. At the Palais de Danse (Anywhere); 5. Bank Holiday ('Appy 'Ampstead).
3, 5. Bratislava RSO, A. Leaper (r1992) *Concert*
(4/94) (MARC) ① 8 223442
5. London Prom, A. Faris *Concert*
(4/83) (PHIL) ① 400 011-2PH

Dance of the Merry Mascots—orchestra (1932)
M. Reeves, London Prom, A. Faris *Concert*
(4/83) (PHIL) ① 400 011-2PH

In a Chinese Temple Garden—oriental phantasy (1925)
Ambrosian Sngrs, London Prom, A. Faris *Concert*
(4/83) (PHIL) ① 400 011-2PH
Ambrosian Sngrs, Philh, J. Lanchbery (r1977) *Concert* (3/94) (CFP) ① CD-CFP4637

In a Monastery Garden—characteristic intermezzo (1915)
Ambrosian Sngrs, London Prom, A. Faris *Concert*
(4/83) (PHIL) ① 400 011-2PH
O. Natzke, chor, orch, W. Braithwaite (r1939) *Concert*
(12/92) (ODE) ① CDODE1365
Ambrosian Sngrs, Philh, J. Lanchbery (r1977) *Concert* (3/94) (CFP) ① CD-CFP4637
Slovak Phil Male Chor, Bratislava RSO, A. Leaper (r1992) *Concert* (4/94) (MARC) ① 8 223442

In a Persian Market—intermezzo-scene (1920)
Ambrosian Sngrs, London Prom, A. Faris *Concert*
(4/83) (PHIL) ① 400 011-2PH
Berlin Ens *Concert* (5/91) (ORFE) ① C126901A
Ambrosian Sngrs, Philh, J. Lanchbery (r1977) *Concert* (3/94) (CFP) ① CD-CFP4637
Slovak Phil Male Chor, Bratislava RSO, A. Leaper (r1992) *Concert* (4/94) (MARC) ① 8 223442

In the Moonlight, 'Sous la lune'—poetic intermezzo (1919)
Philh, J. Lanchbery (r1977) *Concert*
(3/94) (CFP) ① CD-CFP4637
Bratislava RSO, A. Leaper (r1992) *Concert*
(4/94) (MARC) ① 8 223442

In the Mystic Land of Egypt (1931)
Ambrosian Sngrs, L. Dale, London Prom, A. Faris *Concert* (4/83) (PHIL) ① 400 011-2PH
V. Midgley, Ambrosian Sngrs, Philh, J. Lanchbery (r1977) *Concert* (3/94) (CFP) ① CD-CFP4637

Phantom melody (1912)
Bratislava RSO, A. Leaper (r1992) *Concert*
(4/94) (MARC) ① 8 223442

Sanctuary of the Heart—Méditation religieuse (1924)
London Prom, A. Faris *Concert*
(4/83) (PHIL) ① 400 011-2PH
O. Natzke, chor, orch, W. Braithwaite (r1939) *Concert*
(12/92) (ODE) ① CDODE1365
J. Temperley, Ambrosian Sngrs, Philh, J. Lanchbery (r1977) *Concert* (3/94) (CFP) ① CD-CFP4637

Suite romantique—orchestra (pub 1924)
1. Romance (Réveil d'amour); 2. Scherzo (Pensées troublées); 3. Valse dramatique (Querelle er Réconciliation).
Bratislava RSO, A. Leaper (r1992) *Concert*
(4/94) (MARC) ① 8 223442

Wedgewood blue—orchestra (pub 1930)
Bratislava RSO, A. Leaper (r1992) *Concert*
(4/94) (MARC) ① 8 223442

With Honour crowned
London Prom, A. Faris *Concert*
(4/83) (PHIL) ① 400 011-2PH

KETTERER, Eugène (1831–1870) France

SECTION III: INSTRUMENTAL

Gaëtana—piano
A. Etherden *Concert*
(7/93) (HUNT) ① HMPCD0589

KHACHATURIAN, Aram Il'yich (1903–1978) USSR

SECTION I: ORCHESTRAL

Armenian Folksong and Dance—wind orchestra (1932)
Stockholm Sym Wind Orch, B. Priestman *Concert*
(3/93) (CPRI) ① CAP21415

Concerto for Cello and Orchestra (1946)
R. Wallfisch, LPO, B. Thomson *Concert*
(6/88) (CHAN) ① CHAN8579

Concerto for Piano and Orchestra (1936)
C. Orbelian, SNO, N. Järvi *Concert*
(11/87) (CHAN) ① CHAN8542
A. Portugheis, LSO, L. Tjeknavorian *Concert*
(11/87) (ASV) ① CDDCA589
L. Oborin, Czech PO, E. Mravinsky (pp1946) *Violin Concerto.*
D. Atamian, Seattle SO, G. Schwarz (r1993) *Prokofiev: Piano Concerto 3.*
(12/94) (DELO) ① DE3155
W. Kapell, Boston SO, S. Koussevitzky (r1946) *Concert* (5/95) (RCA) ① GD60921

Concerto for Violin and Orchestra in D minor (1940)
I. Perlman, Israel PO, Z. Mehta *Tchaikovsky: Souvenir d'un lieu cher, Op. 42.*
(7/85) (EMI) ① CDC7 47087-2
V. Klimov, USSR Academy SO, E. Svetlanov (r1981) *Schoenberg: Violin Concerto.*
(10/89) (OLYM) ① OCD135
L. Mordkovitch, SNO, N. Järvi *Kabalevsky: Violin Concerto.* (3/91) (CHAN) ① CHAN8918
L. Kaufman, Santa Monica Orch, J. Rachmilovich (r c1946) *Concert* (8/92) (CAMB) ① CD-1063
P. Gallois, Philh, I. Marin (arr Gallois) *Rodrigo: Concierto pastoral.* (10/92) (DG) ① 435 767-2GH
H. Szeryng, LSO, A. Dorati *Brahms: Violin Concerto.*
(2/93) (MERC) ① 434 318-2MM
I. Perlman, Israel PO, Z. Mehta (r1983) *Concert*
(5/93) (EMI) ① [4] CMS7 64617-2
J. Stinton, Philh, S. Bedford (1992; arr Rampal: fl/orch) *Barber: Violin Concerto.*
(9/93) (COLL) ① Coll1383-2
D. Oistrakh, Prague RSO, R. Kubelík (pp1947) *Piano Concerto.* (4/94) (PRAG) ① PR250 017
D. Oistrakh, Philh, A. Khachaturian (r1954) *Concert*
(7/94) (EMI) ① CDC5 55035-2
I. Perlman, Israel PO, Z. Mehta (1983) *Concert*
(6/95) (EMI) ① [20] CZS4 83177-2(2)

Symphony No. 1 in E minor (1934)
Armenian PO, L. Tjeknavorian *Symphony 3.*
(6/93) (ASV) ① CDDCA858

Symphony No. 2 in E minor, '(The) Bell' (1943)
SNO, N. Järvi *Gayaneh.*
(10/91) (CHAN) ① CHAN8945
Armenian PO, L. Tjeknavorian *Battle for Stalingrad Suite.* (6/93) (ASV) ① CDDCA858

Symphony No. 3 in C, 'Simfoniya-poema' (1947)
Armenian PO, L. Tjeknavorian *Symphony 1.*
(6/93) (ASV) ① CDDCA858
BBC PO, F. Glushchenko (pp1993) *Concert*
(5/95) (CHAN) ① CHAN9321

Triumph Poem—orchestra
BBC PO, F. Glushchenko (pp1993) *Concert*
(5/95) (CHAN) ① **CHAN9321**
Uzbek March and Dancing Song—wind orchestra (1932)
Stockholm Sym Wind Orch, B. Priestman *Concert*
(3/93) (CPRI) ① **CAP21415**

SECTION II: CHAMBER

Trio for Clarinet, Violin and Piano (1932)
W. Boeykens Ens (r1992) *Concert*
(6/93) (HARM) ① **HMC90 1419**

SECTION III: INSTRUMENTAL

Sonatina—piano (1959)
A. Portugheis *Concert*
(11/87) (ASV) ① **CDDCA589**
Toccata (1932)
R. Pöntinen *Concert*   (9/85) (BIS) ① **BIS-CD276**
A. Portugheis *Concert*
(11/87) (ASV) ① **CDDCA589**

SECTION V: STAGE WORKS

The Battle for Stalingrad—concert suite from film score (1952)
1. City on the Volga; 2. Invasion; 3. Stalingrad on Fire; 4. Battle for the Motherland; 5. Forward in victory; 6. There is a crag on the Volga.
Armenian PO, L. Tjeknavorian *Symphony 2.*
(6/93) (ASV) ① **CDDCA859**
Gayaneh—ballet (1942 rev 1952 new version 1957)
1. Sabre Dance; 2. Ayesha's Dance; 3. Dance of the Rose Maidens; 4. Dance of the Kurds; 5. Lullaby; 6. Dance of the Young Kurds; 7. Armen's Variation; 8. Lezghinka; 9. Gopak; 10. Introduction (Andante); 11. Gayaneh's adagio; 12. Fire; 13. Lyrical duo; 14. Dance of the old people; 15. Dance of the Highlanders; 16. Nounes variation; 17. Russian Dance; 18. Dance of Welcome; 19. Dance of an Old Man and Carpet Weavers; 20. Embroidering of the Carpets; 21. Scene; 22. Gayaneh's Variation and Dance Finale; 23. Final Scene.
1. J. Lloyd Webber, ECO, N. Cleobury (arr C Palmer) *Concert*   (3/85) (PHIL) ① **412 231-2PH**
1. Cincinnati Pops, E. Kunzel *Concert*
(10/89) (TELA) ① **CD80170**
1. S. Chang, S. Rivers *Concert*
(1/93) (EMI) ① **CDC7 54352-2**
1. Empire Brass (r1992; arr. R. Smedvig) *Concert*
(1/94) (TELA) ① **CD80305**
1. Kirov Th Orch, V. Gergiev (r1993) *Concert*
(4/94) (PHIL) ① **442 011-2PH**
1. J. Heifetz, B. Smith (r1954) *Concert*
1. G. Cziffra (r1956; trans Cziffra: pf) *Concert*
(3/95) (EMI) ① **CDM5 65255-2**
1, 3, 5, 6, 8. Boston Pops, A. Fiedler (r1958) *Concert*
(12/95) (RCA) ① **09026 68132-2**
1, 3, 5, 8. SNO, N. Järvi *Concert*
(11/87) (CHAN) ① **CHAN8542**
1, 3, 5, 8. SNO, N. Järvi *Symphony 2.*
(10/91) (CHAN) ① **CHAN8945**
1, 3–5, 8. Armenian PO, L. Tjeknavorian *Concert*
(4/92) (ASV) ① **CDDCA773**
1-3, 5, 8, 11, 13, 14. Philh, A. Khachaturian (r1954) *Concert*   (7/94) (EMI) ① **CDC5 55035-2**
1-8. LSO, A. Dorati (r1960) *Shostakovich: Symphony 5.*   (8/93) (MERC) ① **434 323-2MM**
1-9. RPO, Y. Temirkanov *Concert*
(7/86) (EMI) ① **CDC7 47348-2**
7, 12, 13, 16-19. Armenian PO, L. Tjeknavorian *Concert*   (3/94) (ASV) ① **CDDCA884**
Masquerade—incidental music to Lermontov's play (1941)
SUITE: 1. Waltz; 2. Nocturne; 3. Mazurka; 4. Romance; 5. Galop.
1-3. Philh, A. Khachaturian (r1954) *Concert*
(7/94) (EMI) ① **CDC5 55035-2**
1-5. SNO, N. Järvi *Concert*
(11/87) (CHAN) ① **CHAN8542**
1-5. Armenian PO, L. Tjeknavorian *Concert*
(4/92) (ASV) ① **CDDCA773**
1, 5. Philh, E. Kurtz (r1961) *Concert*
(9/93) (EMI) ① [2] **CZS7 67729-2**
2. Chee-Yun, A. Eguchi *Concert*
(12/93) (DENO) ① **CO-75118**
5. Boston Pops, A. Fiedler (r1959) *Concert*
(12/95) (RCA) ① **09026 68132-2**
Spartacus—ballet: 3 acts (1954 rev 1968)
EXCERPTS—ACT 1: 1. Introduction; 1a. The Triumph of Rome; 1b. The Slaves brought before Crassus; 1c. Spartacus; 2a. The Slave Market; 2b. Spartacus and Phrygia parting; 2c. Phrygia alone; 3a. The orgy at Crassus' villa; 3b. Scene-dance; 3c. Variation of Aegina; 3d. Final Bacchanalia scene; 4.

The fight of the Gladiators; 5a. Death of a Gladiator; 5b. The Gladiators rise up. ACT 2: 6. Introduction; 6a. The Appian Way; 6b. The Shepherd's dance; 6c. Spartacus' call to arms - The uprising; 6d. Spartacus proclaimed leader; 6e. Spartacus seaches for Phrygia; 6f. Spartacus and Phrygia (Pas de deux); 7a. Crassus' villa - The Feast; 7b. Dance of Aegina; 7c. The Feast continues; 7d. Crassus and Aegina - adagio; 7e. Variation; 7f. Dance and coming of the rebels; 7g. Invasion of the villa; 7h. Spartacus and Crassus fight; 7i. Humiliation of Crassus. ACT 3: 8. Introduction; 8a. Conspiracy; 8b. Crassus swears revenge; 8c. Aegina schemes to help Crassus; 9a. Spartacus' encampment; 9b. Phrygia - adagio; 9c. Phrygia and Spartacus - adagio; 10a. Treason; 10b. Spartacus prepares for the battle; 10c. Spartacus' anguish at the doubt of some of his captains; 10d. Oath of Loyalty; 10e. Entry of the Merchants and Whores; 10f. Dance of the courtesan (Aegina); 10g. Wild Dance; 10h. Crassus plans his ultimate revenge; 11a. The Final Battle; 11b. Death of Spartacus; 11c. Lament of Phrygia and Requiem.
9c Kirov Th Orch, V. Gergiev (r1993) *Concert*
(4/94) (PHIL) ① **442 011-2PH**
Spartacus—Ballet Suite No. 1 (1943)
1. Introduction and Dance of Nymphs; 2. Introduction, Adagio of Aegina and Harmodius; 3. Variations of Aegina and Bacchanalia; 4. Scene and Dance with Crotalums; 5. Dance of the Gaditanian Maidens and Victory of Spartacus.
SNO, N. Järvi *Concert*
(5/91) (CHAN) ① **CHAN8927**
3-5. RPO, Y. Temirkanov *Concert*
(7/86) (EMI) ① **CDC7 47348-2**
3-5. Armenian PO, L. Tjeknavorian *Concert*
(4/92) (ASV) ① **CDDCA773**
Spartacus—Ballet Suite No. 2 (1943)
1. Adagio of Spartacus and Phrygia; 2. Entrance of the Merchants, Dance of a Roman Courtesan, General Dance; 3. Entrance of Spartacus, Quarrel, Harmondius' Treachery; 4. Dance of the Pirates.
SNO, N. Järvi *Concert*
(5/91) (CHAN) ① **CHAN8927**
1. RPO, Y. Temirkanov *Concert*
(7/86) (EMI) ① **CDC7 47348-2**
1. Armenian PO, L. Tjeknavorian *Concert*
(4/92) (ASV) ① **CDDCA773**
Spartacus—Ballet Suite No. 3 (1943)
1. The Market; 2. Dance of a Greek slave; 3. Dance of an Eygptian girl; 4. Dance of Phrygia and the Parting Scene; 5. Sword Dance of the young Thracians.
SNO, N. Järvi *Concert*
(5/91) (CHAN) ① **CHAN8927**
The Valencian Widow—incidental music (1940)
1. Introduction; 2. Serenade; 3. Song; 4. Comic Dance; 5. Intermezzo; 6. Dance.
Armenian PO, L. Tjeknavorian *Concert*
(3/94) (ASV) ① **CDDCA884**

KHACHATURIAN, Karen *(b 1920)* USSR

SECTION II: CHAMBER

Sonata for Violin and Piano, Op. 1 (1947)
J. Heifetz, L. Steuber *Concert*
(9/90) (RCA) ① **GD87872**
J. Heifetz, L. Steuber (r1966) *Concert*
(11/94) (RCA) ① [65] **09026 61778-2(43)**

KHRENNIKOV, Tikhon Nikolayevich *(b 1913)* USSR

SECTION IV: VOCAL AND CHORAL

The Drunkard's Song
N. Ghiaurov, P. Dokovska (r1993) *Concert*
(1/95) (RCA) ① **09026 62501-2**

KIALLMARK, George *(19th Cent)* USA

SECTION IV: VOCAL AND CHORAL

The Old Oaken Bucket—song (1843) (Wds. S Woodworth, 1817; music based on 'Araby's Daughter')
Old Homestead Double Qt, Broadway Cast (r1905; from 1904 production) *Concert*
(5/94) (PEAR) ① [3] **GEMMCDS9050/2(1)**

KIELLAND, Olav *(b 1901)* Norway

SECTION I: ORCHESTRAL

Symphony No. 1, Op. 3 (1935)
RPO, O. Kielland *Villarkorn, Op. 13.*
(12/94) (SIMA) ① **PSC3120**

SECTION III: INSTRUMENTAL

Villarkorn—piano, Op. 13
E. Knardahl *Symphony 1.*
(12/94) (SIMA) ① **PSC3120**

KIENZL, Wilhelm *(1857–1941)* Austria

SECTION V: STAGE WORKS

Der Evangelimann—musical play: 2 acts, Op. 45 (1894—Berlin) (Lib. cpsr, after Meissner)
EXCERPTS: ACT 2: 13. O schöne Jugendtage; 16a. Selig sind, die Verfolgung leiden; 16b. Lasset die Kleinen zu mir kommen!.
13. R. Anday, orch (r1926) *Concert*
(5/92) (PREI) ① **89046**
13. K. Branzell, orch (r1928) *Concert*
(8/92) (PREI) ① **89039**
16a P. Anders, South-West German RSO, O. Ackermann (bp1952) *Concert*
(8/93) (ACAN) ① **43 268**
16a, 16b R. Tauber, orch (r1919) *Concert*
(12/92) (NIMB) ① **NI7830**
16a, 16b W. Ludwig, Berlin St Op Orch, G. Steeger (r1940) *Concert*   (7/95) (PREI) ① **89088**
Der Kuhreigen—opera: 3 acts, Op. 85 (1911—Vienna) (Lib. R Batka, after R H Bartsch)
Lug, Dursel, lug ... Zu Strassburg auf der Schanz
F. Wunderlich, Stuttgart Rad Chor, Stuttgart RSO, A. Rischner (bp1959) *Concert*
(10/89) (ACAN) ① **43 267**
Zu Strassburg auf der Schanz W. Ludwig, Berlin St Op Orch, G. Steeger (r1940) *Concert*
(7/95) (PREI) ① **89088**

KILAR, Wojciech *(b 1932)* Poland

SECTION V: STAGE WORKS

Balance (Bilans Kwartalny)—film score (1975)
1. Suite.
1. OST, Polish SO, W. Kilar (r1973) *Concert*
(8/94) (OLYM) ① **OCD602**
Hypothesis (Hipoteza)—film score (1973)
1. Suite.
1. OST, Polish SO, W. Kilar (r1973) *Concert*
(8/94) (OLYM) ① **OCD602**
Jealousy and Medicine (Zazdrość i Medycyna)—film score (1973)
EXCERPTS: 1. SUITE: 1a. Barcarole; 1b. Scherzo.
1. OST, Polish SO, W. Kilar (r1973) *Concert*
(8/94) (OLYM) ① **OCD602**
Land of Promise (Ziemia Obiecana)—film score (1975)
1. SUITE: 1a. Scherzo; 1b. Valse romantique.
1. OST, Polish SO, W. Kilar (r1975) *Concert*
(8/94) (OLYM) ① **OCD602**
Leper (Tredowata)—film score (1976)
EXCERPTS: 1. SUITE: 1a. Theme and Variations; 1b. Waltz.
1. OST, Polish SO, W. Kilar (r1976) *Concert*
(8/94) (OLYM) ① **OCD602**
Pearl in the Crown (Perła w Koronie)—film score (1972)
1. OST, Polish SO, W. Kilar (r1972) *Concert*
(8/94) (OLYM) ① **OCD602**
Polaniecki Family (Rodzinka Polanieckich)—television score (1978)
1. Suite.
1. OST, Polish SO, W. Kilar (r1978) *Concert*
(8/94) (OLYM) ① **OCD602**
Salto—film score (1965)
1. Suite.
1. OST, Polish SO, W. Kilar (r1965) *Concert*
(8/94) (OLYM) ① **OCD602**
The Silence (Milczenie)—film score (1963)
1. Suite.
1. OST, Polish SO, W. Kilar (r1963) *Concert*
(8/94) (OLYM) ① **OCD602**

The **Taste of the Black Earth (Sól Ziemi Czarnej)**—film score (1972)
1. Suite.
1. OST, Polish SO, W. Kilar (r1972) *Concert*
(8/94) (OLYM) ① **OCD602**

KILLMAYER, Wilhelm (b 1927) Germany

SECTION I: ORCHESTRAL

The **Broken Farewell**—trumpet and small orchestra (1977)
R. Friedrich, Frankfurt RSO, D. Kitaienko (r1991-2) *Concert*
(6/93) (CAPR) ① **10 482**

SECTION II: CHAMBER

Brahms-Bildnis—piano trio (1976)
S. Mauser, C. Altenburger, J. Berger *Concert*
(10/89) (CPO) ① **CPO999 020-2**
Piano Quartet (1975)
S. Mauser, C. Altenburger, B. Westphal, J. Berger
Concert (10/89) (CPO) ① **CPO999 020-2**
3 Pieces—trumpet and piano (1968)
R. Friedrich, T. Duis (r1992) *Concert*
(6/93) (CAPR) ① **10 439**
String Quartet No. 1 (1969)
C. Altenburger, G. Weinmeister, B. Westphal, J. Berger *Concert* (10/89) (CPO) ① **CPO999 020-2**
String Trio—2 violins and cello (1984)
C. Altenburger, G. Weinmeister, J. Berger *Concert*
(10/89) (CPO) ① **CPO999 020-2**
Vanitas Vanitatum—5 romances for violin and piano (1987-88)
C. Altenburger, S. Mauser *Concert*
(10/89) (CPO) ① **CPO999 020-2**

SECTION V: STAGE WORKS

Yolimba oder Die Grenzen der Magie—musical farce: 1 act (1964—Wiesbaden) (Wds. Dorst & cpsr)
Cpte M. Venuti, A. Titus, C. Prégardien, U. Ress, H.J. Porcher, W. Euba, R. Herrmann, Anon (treb), Anon (treb), Anon (treb), M. Kinzel, C. Ulbrich, F. Subrata, R. Swensen, R.J. Kleinhenz, H. Farinelli, A. Kloose, I. Assenheimer, H. Weber, Bavarian Rad Chor, BRSO, P. Schneider
(5/93) (ORFE) ① **C257921A**

KILPINEN, Yryö (1892-1959) Finland

SECTION IV: VOCAL AND CHORAL

Lakeus—song cycle, Op. 22 (Wds. Koskenniemi)
1. Lakeus I; 2. Lakeus II; 3. Lakeus III; 4. Lakeus IV; 5. Lakeus V.
J. Hynninen, R. Gothóni *Concert*
(11/92) (ONDI) ① **ODE772-2**
7 Lieder, Op. 79 (Wds. H F von Zwehl)
1. Mancher Stunden Wehen; 2. Der Heimatlose; 3. Vorfrühling; 4. Venezianisches Intermezzo; 5. Lied der Renate; 6. Nachts auf Posten; 7. Marienkirche zu Danzig im Gerüst.
J. Hynninen, R. Gothóni *Concert*
(11/92) (ONDI) ① **ODE772-2**
Lieder um den Tod—song cycle, Op. 62 (1928) (Wds. Morgenstern)
1. Bird of sorrow; 2. In a dilapidated churchyard; 3. Death and the lonely drunkard; 4. Winter night; 5. The sower; 6. Unfailing surety.
J. Hynninen, R. Gothóni *Concert*
(11/92) (ONDI) ① **ODE772-2**
8 Minstrel's Songs, Op. 77 (1932-33) (wds. A. Sergel)
1. You eternal stars; 2. Silent snow-covered fields; 3. I play where there's dancing; 4. Choral dance; 5. Minstrel's longing; 6. In the dewy morn; 7. If there were no wine; 8. I sang my way though German land.
J. Hynninen, R. Gothóni *Concert*
(11/92) (ONDI) ① **ODE772-2**
Reflections—song cycle, Opp. 33-34 (1922) (Wds. P. Lagerkvist)
3. Like a blossoming almond tree (Som ett blommande mandelträd); 4. Your smile is lighter than mine; 7. In a thousand years (Om tiotusen år).
3, 7. K. Borg, E. Werba (r1959) *Concert*
(12/94) (FINL) ① [3] **4509-95606-2**

KIM, Earl (b 1920) USA

SECTION IV: VOCAL AND CHORAL

Where Grief Slumbers—seven songs: sop, hp and stg orchno (1982)
1. Listen to it rain; 2. from Drunken Boat; 3. It's raining; 4. Ophelia; 5. The Farewell; 6. The Departure; 7. The girl with orange lips.
D. Upshaw, Inst Ens *Concert*
(11/91) (NONE) ① **7559-79262-2**

KING, Charles (19th-20th Cent) USA

SECTION V: STAGE WORKS

The **Slim Princess**—songs for the show (1911) (Lyrics E Brice)
EXCERPTS: 1. Let Me Stay and Live in Dixieland; 2. That's Ever-Loving Love.
1, 2. E. Brice, C. King, Orig Broadway Cast (r1911) *Concert* (5/94) (PEAR) ① [3] **GEMMCDS9053/5**

KING, Karl L. (1891-1971) USA

SECTION I: ORCHESTRAL

Barnum and Bailey's Favorite
Cleveland Winds, F. Fennell *Concert*
(10/84) (TELA) ① **CD80099**

KING, Robert (fl 1676-1728) England

SECTION IV: VOCAL AND CHORAL

False, foolish Heart—song (pub c1695) (Wds Cowley)
Consort of Musicke, A. Rooley (lte/dir) (r1993)
Concert (1/95) (MOSC) ① **070986**
No, to what purpose—song (pub c1695) (Wds Cowley)
Consort of Musicke, A. Rooley (lte/dir) (r1993)
Concert (1/95) (MOSC) ① **070986**

KING, William (1624-1680) England

SECTION IV: VOCAL AND CHORAL

Go bid the Needle—song (pub 1668) (Wds Cowley)
Consort of Musicke, A. Rooley (lte/dir) (r1993)
Concert (1/95) (MOSC) ① **070986**
I wonder what those Lovers mean—song (pub 1668) (Wds Cowley)
Consort of Musicke, A. Rooley (lte/dir) (r1993)
Concert (1/95) (MOSC) ① **070986**
It gave a piteous groan—song (pub 1668) (Wds Cowley)
Consort of Musicke, A. Rooley (lte/dir) (r1993)
Concert (1/95) (MOSC) ① **070986**
What Mines of Sulphur—song (Wds Cowley)
Consort of Musicke, A. Rooley (lte/dir) (r1993)
Concert (1/95) (MOSC) ① **070986**

KINKEL, Charles (1832-?) USA

SECTION III: INSTRUMENTAL

The **Angel's Serenade**—piano
A. Etherden *Concert*
(7/93) (HUNT) ① **HMPCD0589**

KINSELLA, John (b 1932) Ireland

SECTION II: CHAMBER

String Quartet No. 3 (1977)
Vanbrugh Qt (r1993) *Concert*
(10/94) (CHAN) ① **CHAN9295**

KIRCHNER, Theodor (1823-1903) Germany

SECTION II: CHAMBER

Triptych—violin and cello (1988)
L. Chang, Y-Y. Ma (r1991) *Concert*
(4/94) (SONY) ① **SK53126**

KIRKMAN, Jan (c1750-1812) The Netherlands/England

SECTION III: INSTRUMENTAL

Voluntary in B flat—keyboard (pub 1790)
Margaret Phillips *Concert*
(5/91) (GAMU) ① **GAMCD514**

KISSIN, Evgeni (b 1971) USSR

SECTION III: INSTRUMENTAL

2 Inventions—piano
E. Kissin (pp1984) *Concert*
(8/95) (MELO) ① **74321 25182-2**
E. Kissin (pp1984) *Concert*
(8/95) (MELO) ① [11] **74321 25172-2(2)**

KJELLERUP, Christian (1889-1947) Denmark

SECTION IV: VOCAL AND CHORAL

Beloved mine, of youthful spring—song (Wds. A. W. Holm)
L. Melchior, Anon (pf) (r c1921) *Concert*
(8/88) (DANA) ① [2] **DACOCD311/2**

KJERULF, Halfdan (1815-1868) Norway

SECTION IV: VOCAL AND CHORAL

My heart and my lyre—song, Op. 16/2 (1867) (Wds. T. Moore)
L. Melchior, Orch (Danish: r1913) *Concert*
(8/88) (DANA) ① [2] **DACOCD311/2**

KLAMI, Uuno (Kalervo) (1900-1961) Finland

SECTION I: ORCHESTRAL

Kalevala sarja—suite, Op. 23 (1933 rev 1943)
Iceland SO, P. Sakari (r1993) *Concert*
(8/94) (CHAN) ① **CHAN9268**
Karelian Rhapsody (Karjalainen rapsodia)—orchestra (1927)
Iceland SO, P. Sakari (r1993) *Concert*
(8/94) (CHAN) ① **CHAN9268**
Lemminkäinen's Island Adventures (Lemminkäisen seikkailut saaressa) (1934) (originally intended as scherzo for Kalevala Suite)
Lahti SO, O. Vänskä (r1993) *Concert*
(12/94) (BIS) ① **BIS-CD656**
Sea Pictures—orchestra (1928-32)
1. The Foggy Morning; 2. Captain Scrapuchinat; 3. The Deserted Three-Master; 4. Song of the Watch; 5. Scène de ballet; 6. 3 Bf.
Iceland SO, P. Sakari (r1993) *Concert*
(8/94) (CHAN) ① **CHAN9268**

SECTION II: CHAMBER

Rag-Time and Blues—2 violins, clarinet, trumpet and piano (1931)
Lahti Chbr Ens *Concert*
(8/93) (ONDI) ① **ODE792-2**

SECTION IV: VOCAL AND CHORAL

Song of Lake Kuujärvi—ballad for male voice and orchestra (1956) (Wds Y. Jylhä)
E. Ruuttunen, Lahti SO, O. Vänskä (r1993) *Concert*
(12/94) (BIS) ① **BIS-CD656**

SECTION V: STAGE WORKS

Whirls (Pyörteitä)—ballet (1958-61) (unfinished. Cpsr's orchestration extant for 2nd act only)
EXCERPTS: 1. SUITE No. 1: 1a. Prelude; 1b. The Boy of the Day & the Maidens of the Day; 1c. Dances of a Summer Day; 1d. The Boy of the Moon; 2. SUITE No. 2: 2a. Dances of the Night; 2b. Finale: Farewell Dance of the North Star & the Boy of the Moon.
1, 2. Lahti SO, O. Vänskä (r1993) *Concert*
(12/94) (BIS) ① **BIS-CD656**

KLATZOW, Peter (b 1945) South Africa

SECTION I: ORCHESTRAL

Concerto for Marimba and String Orchestra (1985)
1. Moderato; 2. Elegy; 3. Toccata.
R. van Sice, Claremont Stg Orch, E. Garcia-Asensio
Concert   (6/90) (ETCE) ① **KTC1085**

KLEIN, Gideon (1919–1945) Czechoslovakia

SECTION II: CHAMBER

Duo—violin & cello (1939)
S-J. Huang, S. Knudsen *Concert*
(5/93) (NORT) ① **NR248-CD**
Fantasie a Fuga—string quartet (1942-43)
Hawthorne Qt *Concert*
(12/91) (CHNN) ① **CCS1691**
Group for New Music (r1992) *Concert*
(8/94) (KOCH) ① **37230-2**
String Quartet, Op. 2
Hawthorne Qt *Concert*
(12/91) (CHNN) ① **CCS1691**
Trio for Violin, Viola and Cello (1944)
Hawthorne Qt *Concert*
(12/91) (CHNN) ① **CCS1691**
Czech Stg Trio *Concert*
(8/92) (ROMA) ① [2] **RR1941**
Group for New Music (r1992) *Concert*
(8/94) (KOCH) ① **37230-2**

SECTION III: INSTRUMENTAL

Sonata for Piano (1943)
V. Eskin *Concert*   (12/91) (CHNN) ① **CCS1691**
V. Nishri *Concert*   (8/92) (ROMA) ① [2] **RR1941**
A. Sternfield (r1992) *Concert*
(8/94) (KOCH) ① **37230-2**

SECTION IV: VOCAL AND CHORAL

Czech and Russian Folksongs (1942)
1. They are taking out my horse; 2. Our God loved us; 3. On air meadows; 4. Walking fox; 5. Walking, walking; 6. Across the plain.
Prague Philharmonic Ch, P. Kühn (r1992) *Concert*
(8/94) (KOCH) ① **37230-2**
First Sin—Czech folk poem: tenor & male chorus (1942)
K. Kožušník (r1992) *Concert*
(8/94) (KOCH) ① **37230-2**
2 Madrigals (1942-43)
1. Das Angenehme Dieser Welt (wds. F. Hölderlin); 2. Mort j'appelle de ta rigeur (wds. F. Villon).
Prague Philharmonic Ch, P. Kühn (r1992) *Concert*
(8/94) (KOCH) ① **37230-2**

KLEIN, Manuel (1876–1919) England/USA

SECTION V: STAGE WORKS

Around the World—musical show (1911—New York) (Lyrics Penn)
EXCERPTS: 1. It's a Long Lan That Has No Turning; 2. My Old Town.
M. Sylva, Orig Broadway Cast (r1911) *Concert*
(5/94) (PEAR) ① [3] **GEMMCDS9053/5**
The Pied Piper—musical show (1908—New York) (Lyrics Strong & Burnside)
EXCERPTS: 1. Adam and Eve; 2. Whose Baby Girl Are You?.
1, 2. G. Cameron, Orig Broadway Cast (r1909) *Concert*
(5/94) (PEAR) ① [3] **GEMMCDS9053/5**

KLEMPERER, Otto (1885–1973) Germany

SECTION V: STAGE WORKS

Das Ziel—opera (1915 rev 1970)
1. Merry Waltz.
1. New Philh, L. Stokowski (pp1974) *Concert*
(3/95) (BBCR) ① **BBCRD9107**

KLENAU, Paul (August) von (1883–1946) Denmark

SECTION IV: VOCAL AND CHORAL

To my bride—song (Wds. Ross)
L. Melchior, orch (r1926) *Concert*
(8/88) (DANA) ① [2] **DACOCD313/4**

KLEYNJANS, Francis (b 1951) France

SECTION II: CHAMBER

3 Climats—guitar duet
T. Kropat, T. Krumeich (arr 2 gtrs) *Concert*
(7/93) (CHNN) ① **CG9103**

KMOCH, František (1848–1912) Bohemia

SECTION I: ORCHESTRAL

Am Motor—Galop
Czech PO, V. Neumann *Concert*
(6/87) (ORFE) ① **C107101A**
Auf der Weise—Mazurka
Czech PO, V. Neumann *Concert*
(6/87) (ORFE) ① **C107101A**
Böhmische Musik—March
Czech PO, V. Neumann *Concert*
(6/87) (ORFE) ① **C107101A**
Romance for Flügelhorn
Czech PO, V. Neumann *Concert*
(6/87) (ORFE) ① **C107101A**

KNIPPER, Lev Konstantinovich (1898–1974) Russia

SECTION I: ORCHESTRAL

Cossack Patrol
Black Dyke Mills Band, R. Newsome (arr G Langford) *Concert*   (10/91) (CHAN) ① **CHAN6539**

KNUSSEN, (Stuart) Oliver (b 1952) England

SECTION I: ORCHESTRAL

Coursing—chamber orchestra, Op. 17 (1979)
London Sinfonietta, O. Knussen *Concert*
(9/88) (UNIC) ① **UKCD2010**
Ophelia Dances, Book 1, Op. 13 (1975)
London Sinfonietta, O. Knussen *Concert*
(9/88) (UNIC) ① **UKCD2010**
Symphony No. 2—soprano and chamber orchestra, Op. 7 (1970-71)
E. Barry, London Sinfonietta, O. Knussen *Concert*
(9/88) (UNIC) ① **UKCD2010**
Symphony No. 3, Op. 18 (1973-79)
Philh, M. Tilson Thomas *Concert*
(9/88) (UNIC) ① **UKCD2010**
RPO, Vladimir Ashkenazy (pp1989) *Concert*
(1/91) (RPO) ① **CDRPO7015**

SECTION II: CHAMBER

Cantata—oboe and string trio, Op. 15 (1977)
Nash Ens *Concert*   (9/88) (UNIC) ① **UKCD2010**
Songs without Voices—eight instrumentalists, Op. 26 (1991-92)
1. Winter's Foil; 2. Prairie Sunset; 3. First Dandelion; 4. Elegiac Arabesques.
Lincoln Center Chbr Music Soc, O. Knussen (r1992) *Concert*   (10/93) (VIRG) ① **VC7 59308-2**

SECTION III: INSTRUMENTAL

Sonya's Lullaby—piano, Op. 16 (1977-78)
P. Serkin (r1992) *Concert*
(10/93) (VIRG) ① **VC7 59308-2**
Variations—piano, Op. 24 (1989)
P. Serkin (r1992) *Concert*
(10/93) (VIRG) ① **VC7 59308-2**

SECTION IV: VOCAL AND CHORAL

Hums and songs of Winnie-the-Pooh—soprano and five instrumentalists, Op. 6 (1970 rev 1983)
1. Aphorisms: 1a. Inscription; 1b. Hum; 1c. The Hundred Acre Wood; 1d. Piglet meets a Heffalump; 1e. Hum continued and Little Nonsense Song; 1f. Hum (instrumental); 1g. Vocalise: Climbing the tree; 1h. Codetta; 2. Bee Piece and Cadenza: The Fall of Pooh; 3. Cloud Piece.
L. Saffer, Lincoln Center Chbr Music Soc, O. Knussen (r1992) *Concert*
(10/93) (VIRG) ① **VC7 59308-2**
4 Late Poems and an Epigram of Rainer Maria Rilke—soprano, Op. 23 (1988)
1. Idol; 2. Gravity; 3. Imaginary Life; 4. Gong.
L. Saffer (r1992) *Concert*
(10/93) (VIRG) ① **VC7 59308-2**

Océan de terre—soprano and chamber ensemble, Op. 10 (1972-73 rev 1976)
L. Shelton, Lincoln Center Chbr Music Soc, O. Knussen (r1992) *Concert*
(10/93) (VIRG) ① **VC7 59308-2**
Trumpets—soprano and 3 clarinets, Op. 12 (1975)
L. Hirst, M. Collins, E. Pillinger, I. Mitchell, O. Knussen *Concert*   (9/88) (UNIC) ① **UKCD2010**
Whitman Settings—soprano and piano, Op. 25 (1991)
1. When I heard the Learn'd Astronomer; 2. A Noiseless, patient Spider; 3. The Dalliance of the Eagles; 4. The Voice of the Rain.
L. Shelton, P. Serkin (r1992) *Concert*
(10/93) (VIRG) ① **VC7 59308-2**

KNYVETT, William (1779–1856) England

SECTION IV: VOCAL AND CHORAL

Jessie—glee: 4vv (c1810) (Wds Burns)
Invocation (r1994) *Concert*
(3/95) (HYPE) ① **CDA66740**

KOBAYASHI, Kenichiro (b 1930) Japan

SECTION I: ORCHESTRAL

Concerto for Violin and Orchestra No. 1 (1978)
V. Šimčisko, Slovak RSO, O. Lenárd *Concert*
(9/92) (CAMP) ① **RRCD1317**

KOCH, (Sigurd Christian) Erland von (b 1910) Sweden

SECTION I: ORCHESTRAL

Concertino Pastorale—flute and strings (1947 rev 1963)
Musica Vitae CO, W. Rajski, M. Wiesler *Concert*
(6/90) (BIS) ① **BIS-CD461**

KODÁLY, Zoltán (1882–1967) Hungary

SECTION I: ORCHESTRAL

Dances from Galánta—orchestra (1933)
BPO, V. de Sabata (r1939) *Concert*
(11/92) (KOCH) ① **37126-2**
St Paul CO, H. Wolff (r1991) *Concert*
(5/94) (TELD) ⑨ **9031-73134-2**
Dances of Marosszék (1930) (orch cpsr from pf work)
St Paul CO, H. Wolff (r1991) *Concert*
(5/94) (TELD) ⑨ **9031-73134-2**
Berlin RIAS Orch, F. Fricsay (r1954) *Concert*
(11/94) (DG) ① **445 410-2GDO**
Berlin RIAS Orch, F. Fricsay (r1954) *Concert*
(11/94) (DG) ① [11] **445 400-2GDO10**
Summer Evening—orchestra (1906 rev 1929-30)
Philh, Y. Butt (r1994) *Concert*
(9/95) (ASV) ① **CDDCA924**
Symphony in C (1931-1960s)
Berlin RSO, F. Fricsay (bp1961) *Concert*
(11/94) (DG) ① [11] **445 400-2GDO10**
Berlin RSO, F. Fricsay (bp1961) *Concert*
(11/94) (DG) ① **445 410-2GDO**
Philh, Y. Butt (r1994) *Concert*
(9/95) (ASV) ① **CDDCA924**
Variations on a Hungarian folksong, '(The) Peacock'—orchestra (1938-39)
Hungarian St Orch, A. Dorati *Psalmus Hungaricus*.
(3/87) (HUNG) ① **HCD11392**
LPO, F. Welser-Möst (r1992/3) *Concert*
(11/94) (EMI) ① **CDC7 54858-2**
LSO, I. Kertész (r1970) *Concert*
(10/95) (DECC) ① [2] **443 488-2DF2**

SECTION II: CHAMBER

Adagio—violin (or viola or cello) and piano (1905)
K. Kashkashian, R. Levin *Concert*
(9/86) (ECM) ① **827 744-2**
Duo—violin and cello, Op. 7 (1914)
Y. Turovsky, E. Turovsky *Cello Sonata, Op. 8.*
(2/88) (CHAN) ① **CHAN8427**
J. Gingold, J. Starker *Concert*
(9/89) (DELO) ① **DE1015**
J. Heifetz, G. Piatigorsky (r1960) *Concert*
(11/94) (RCA) ① [65] **09026 61778-2(27)**

Gavotte (unidentified)
Kontra Qt *Concert* (1/95) (BIS) ① **BIS-CD564**
Magyar Rondo—cello and piano (1917)
C. Warren-Green, Philh, Y. Butt (r1994) *Concert* (9/95) (ASV) ① **CDDCA924**
Serenade—two violins and viola, Op. 12 (1919-20)
S. Lautenbacher, G. Egger, U. Koch *Concert* (11/91) (BAYE) ① **BR100058**
Sonata for Cello and Piano, Op. 4 (1909-10)
A. Gastinel, P-L. Aimard (r1995) *Concert* (9/95) (AUVI) ① **V4748**
String Quartet No. 1, Op. 2 (1908-9)
Kodály Qt *String Quartet 2.* (1/86) (HUNG) ① **HCD12362**
Kontra Qt *Concert* (1/95) (BIS) ① **BIS-CD564**
String Quartet No. 2, Op. 10 (1916-18)
Kodály Qt *String Quartet 1.* (1/86) (HUNG) ① **HCD12362**
Hagen Qt *Concert* (5/87) (DG) ① **419 601-2GH**
Kontra Qt *Concert* (1/95) (BIS) ① **BIS-CD564**

SECTION III: INSTRUMENTAL

7 Pieces—piano, Op. 11 (1910-18)
3. It is raining in the village.
P. Frankl (r?1992) *Concert* (6/93) (ASV) ① **CDDCA860**
3. N. Milstein, L. Mittman (r1938: arr vn/pf: Milstein) *Concert* (9/95) (BIDD) ① **LAB096**
Sonata for solo cello, Op. 8 (1915)
Y. Turovsky *Duo, Op. 7.* (2/88) (CHAN) ① **CHAN8427**
J. Starker *Concert* (1/89) (DELO) ① **DE1015**
P. Wispelwey (r1992) *Concert* (12/94) (GLOB) ① **GLO5089**
J. Starker (r1957) *Concert* (12/95) (EMI) ① [6] **CZS5 68485-2**
M. Haimovitz (r1993) *Concert* (12/95) (DG) ① **445 834-2GH**

SECTION IV: VOCAL AND CHORAL

Bicinia hungarica—180 progressive 2-part songs (1937-42)
58. Kiolvasó (Nursery Rhyme); 80. Csillagoknak teremtője (Creator of the stars).
58, 80. E. Söderström, K. Meyer, J. Eyron (r1974) *Concert* (9/93) (BIS) ① **BIS-CD017**
Budavári Te Deum—soloists, chorus, organ and orchestra (1936)
E. Andor, M. Szirmay, J. Réti, J. Gregor, Hungarian Rad Chor, Hungarian Radio & TV Orch, J. Ferencsik *Missa Brevis.* (6/87) (HUNG) ① **HCD11397**
Hungarian Folk Music—51 settings: 1v and piano
1. Mónár Anna (Annie Miller); 6. Három árva (The three orphans); 7. Kitrákotty mese (Cockricoo!); 8. A rosz feleség (The heartless wife); 9. Szomorú fűzfának (The weeping willow); 10. Egy nagyóru bóha (Long nose); 11. Elkiáltom magamat (Far across the village green); 12. Kocsi, szekér (Wheelcart, barrow); 13. Meghalok, meghalok (Woe is me); 14. Virágos kenderem (all the hemp); 15. Akkor szép az erdő (Lovely is the forest); 16. Asszony, asszony, ki az ágyból (Woman, woman, out of your bed); 18. Kádár Kata (Katie Kádár); 19. A nővérek (The sisters); 20. Tücsöklakodalom (The cricket's wedding); 21. Zöld erdőben (in the forest); 23. Most jöttem Erdélyből (I have but just arrived); 24. Cigánynóta (Gipsy song); 27. Ifjúság mint sólyommadár (A little sad song); 30. Szőlőhegyen keresztül (Kitty and Johnny); 32. Katona vagyok én (Called to serve my country); 33. Arról alúi (Over yonder); 37. Kádár István (Stephen Kádár); 39. Megégett Rácorszag (All our homes); 40. Labanc gúndyal a kurucra (Labantz mocking 'kurutz'); 41. Körtéfa (The pear tree of Gyöngyős); 42. Rákóczi keservője (Rákóczi's lament).
12, 15, 27. L. Popp, G. Parsons (pp1981) *Concert* (6/95) (ORFE) ① **C363941B**
Hymn of Zrínyi (1954) (Wds. Zríyni)
B. Luxon, Brighton Fest Chor, L. Heltay *Concert* (5/89) (DECC) ① [2] **421 810-2DM2**
Laudes organi—choir and organ (1966)
Regent Chbr Ch, John Scott, G. Cole *Concert* (5/89) (REGE) ① **REGCD103**
Netherlands Chbr Ch, U. Gronostay, E. Krapp (r1993) *Missa Brevis.* (1/95) (GLOB) ① **GLO5115**
Missa Brevis—chorus and organ (1944)
A. Ekert, K. Makkay, E. Mohácsi, M. Szirmay, J. Réti, J. Gregor, Hungarian Rad Chor, Hungarian Radio & TV Orch, J. Ferencsik *Budavári Te Deum.* (6/87) (HUNG) ① **HCD11397**
Regent Chbr Ch, John Scott, G. Cole *Concert* (5/89) (REGE) ① **REGCD103**
E. Gale, S. le Sage, H. Francis, A. Hodgson, I. Caley, M. Rippon, C. Bowers-Broadbent, Brighton Fest Chor, L. Heltay (r1975/6) *Concert* (8/92) (DECC) ① **433 080-2DM**
Netherlands Chbr Ch, U. Gronostay, E. Krapp (r1993) *Laudes Organi.* (1/95) (GLOB) ① **GLO5115**
Pange lingua—choir and organ (1929)
Regent Chbr Ch, John Scott, G. Cole *Concert* (5/89) (REGE) ① **REGCD103**
Brighton Fest Chor, C. Bowers-Broadbent, L. Heltay (r1975/6) *Concert* (8/92) (DECC) ① **433 080-2DM**
The **peacock—folksong: male vv a cappella (1937)** (Wds. Ady)
LSC, I. Kertész (r1969) *Concert* (10/95) (DECC) ① [2] **443 488-2DF2**
Psalm 114—chorus and organ (1952) (Wds. Bible)
Brighton Fest Chor, G. Weir, L. Heltay (r1977) *Concert* (8/92) (DECC) ① **433 080-2DM**
Psalmus Hungaricus—tenor, chorus and orchestra, Op. 13 (1923) (Wds. Kecskeméte Vég)
J. Simándy, Hungarian Rad & TV Children's Chor, Budapest Chor, Hungarian St Orch, A. Dorati *Peacock Variations.* (3/87) (HUNG) ① **HCD11392**
L. Kozma, Brighton Fest Chor, Wandsworth Sch Boys' Ch, LSO, I. Kertész *Concert* (5/89) (DECC) ① [2] **421 810-2DM2**
L. Kozma, Brighton Fest Chor, Wandsworth Sch Boys' Ch, LSO, I. Kertész (r1970) *Concert* (8/92) (DECC) ① **433 080-2DM**
E. Haefliger, Berlin St Hedwig's Cath Ch, Berlin RSO, F. Fricsay (bp1959) *Concert* (11/94) (DG) ① **445 410-2GDO**
E. Haefliger, Berlin St Hedwig's Cath Ch, Berlin RSO, F. Fricsay (bp1959) *Concert* (11/94) (DG) ① [11] **445 400-2GDO10**
P. Svensson, Copenhagen Boys' Ch, Danish Nat Rad Ch, Danish Nat RSO, C. Mackerras (r1994) *Janáček: Glagolitic Mass.* (12/94) (CHAN) ① **CHAN9310**
R. Nilsson, LP Ch, LPO, J. Ferencsik (r c1958) *Bartók: Concerto for Orchestra.* (4/95) (EVER) ① **EVC9008**
L. Kozma, Brighton Fest Chor, Wandsworth Sch Boys' Ch, LSO, I. Kertész (r1969) *Concert* (10/95) (DECC) ① [2] **443 488-2DF2**
Sadly rustle the leaves—song, Op. 6/5 (1912) (Wds. Kölcsey)
E. Koréh, H. von Nordberg (r1949) *Concert* (4/92) (EMI) ① [7] **CHS7 69741-2(6)**

SECTION V: STAGE WORKS

Háry János—Singspiel: 5 scenes, Op. 15 (1926—Budapest) (Lib. Paulini and Harsáyni)
Cpte E. Komlóssy, L. Palócz, G. Melis, Z. Bende, O. Szönyi, Margit László, P. Ustinov, Edinburgh Fest Chor, Wandsworth Sch Boys' Ch, LSO, I. Kertész (r1968) *Concert* (10/95) (DECC) ① [2] **443 488-2DF2**
Háry János—concert suite from opera, Op. 15 (1927)
1. Prelude; 2. Viennese Musical Clock; 3. Song; 4. Battle and Defeat of Napoleon; 5. Intermezzo; 6. Entrance of the Emperor and his court.
LSO, R. Frühbeck de Burgos *Tchaikovsky: Symphony 5.* (7/90) (NIMB) ① **NI5194**
NBC SO, A. Toscanini (bp1947) *Concert* (1/91) (RCA) ① **GD60279**
L. Kaptain, Chicago SO, G. Solti (pp1993) *Concert* (1/95) (DECC) ① **443 444-2DH**
5. J. Szigeti, A. Foldes (r1941: arr vn/pf: Szigeti) *Concert* (7/94) (BIDD) ① [2] **LAB070/1**

KOECHLIN, Charles (Louis Eugène) *(1867–1950) France*

SECTION I: ORCHESTRAL

Ballade—piano and orchestra, Op. 50 (1911-15, orch 1919)
B. Rigutto, Monte Carlo PO, A. Myrat *Seven Stars Symphony.* (3/93) (EMI) ① **CDM7 64369-2**
Bandar-Log—symphonic poem after Kipling, Op. 176 (1939-40)
BBC SO, A. Dorati *Concert* (3/92) (EMI) ① **CDM7 63948-2**
Rhineland-Pfalz State PO, L. Segerstam (r1985) *Concert* (6/94) (MARC) ① **8 223484**
Berlin RSO, D. Zinman (r1993) *Concert* (6/94) (RCA) ① [2] **09026 61955-2**
Le **Buisson ardent—symphonic poem, Op. 202/171 (1938-45)**
1. Part 1, Op. 203; 2. Part 2, Op. 171.
Rhineland-Pfalz State PO, L. Segerstam (r1985) *Concert* (8/95) (MARC) ① **8 223704**
La **course de printemps—symphonic poem after Kipling, Op. 95 (1908-25)**
Rhineland-Pfalz State PO, L. Segerstam (r1985) *Concert* (6/94) (MARC) ① **8 223484**
Berlin RSO, D. Zinman (r1993) *Concert* (6/94) (RCA) ① [2] **09026 61955-2**
Les **Heures Persanes—orchestral cycle, Op. 65 (1913 orch 1921)**
1. Sieste, avant le départ; 2. La caravane (rêve, pendant la sieste); 3. L'escalade obscure; 4. Matin frais, dans la haute vallée; 5. En vue da la ville; 6. A travers les rues; 7. Chant du soir; 8. Clair de lune sur les terrasses; 9. Aubade; 10. Roses au soleil de midi; 11. A l'ombre, près de la fontaine de marbre; 12. Arabesques; 13. Les collines, au coucher au soleil; 14. Le conteur; 15. La paix du soir, au cimetière; 16. Derviches dans la nuit—Clair de lune sur la place déserte.
Rhineland-Pfalz State PO, L. Segerstam (r1992) (7/94) (MARC) ① **8 223504**
La **loi de la Jungle—symphonic poem after Kipling, Op. 175 (1939)**
Rhineland-Pfalz State PO, L. Segerstam (r1985) *Concert* (6/94) (MARC) ① **8 223484**
Berlin RSO, D. Zinman (r1993) *Concert* (6/94) (RCA) ① [2] **09026 61955-2**
La **méditation de Purun Bhagat—symphonic poem after Kipling, Op. 159 (1936)**
Rhineland-Pfalz State PO, L. Segerstam (r1985) *Concert* (6/94) (MARC) ① **8 223484**
Berlin RSO, D. Zinman (r1993) *Concert* (6/94) (RCA) ① [2] **09026 61955-2**
Quelques chorals pour des fêtes populaires—concert band, Op. 153a (1935-36)
Gardiens de la Paix Orch, D. Dondeyne *Concert* (8/88) (CALL) ① **CAL9859**
The **Seven Stars Symphony—suite symphonique, Op. 132 (1933)**
1. Douglas Fairbanks (en souvenir du voleur de Bagdad); 2. Lilian Harvey (menuet fugue); 3. Greta Garbo (choral païen); 4. Clara Bow et la joyeuse Californie; 5. Marlène Dietrich (variations); 6. Emil Jannings (en souvenir de l'Abge Bleu); 7. Charlie Chaplin (variations).
F. Pellié, Monte Carlo PO, A. Myrat *Ballade.* (3/93) (EMI) ① **CDM7 64369-2**
Sur les flots lointains—symphonic poem, Op. 130 (1933)
Rhineland-Pfalz State PO, L. Segerstam (r1987) *Concert* (8/95) (MARC) ① **8 223704**
Sur les flots lointains—string orchestra, Op. 130 (1933)
Rhineland-Pfalz State PO, L. Segerstam (r1987) *Concert* (8/95) (MARC) ① **8 223704**
2 Symphonic Pieces, Op. 20 (1896; 1900)
1. En rève (1896); 2. Au loin (1900).
1. Rhineland-Pfalz State PO, L. Segerstam (r1987) *Concert* (8/95) (MARC) ① **8 223704**

SECTION II: CHAMBER

14 Chants—flute and piano, Op. 157b (1936)
1. Vieille chanson: Andante con moto; 2. Gai, assez animé; 3. Andante espressivo; 4. Moderato con moto; 5. Allegro moderato; 6. Andante quasi adagio; 7. Beau soir: Largo; 8. Andantino; 9. Allgretto con moto; 10. Allegretto quasi andantino; 11. Allegretto; 12. Danse printanière: Allegretto; 13. Marche funèbre: Andante; 14. Allegro moderato.
F. Smith, M. Amlin *Concert* (10/90) (HYPE) ① **CDA66414**
Morceau de lecture pour la flûte—flute and piano, Op. 218 (1948)
F. Smith, M. Amlin *Concert* (10/90) (HYPE) ① **CDA66414**
15 Pieces—horn(s) and piano, Op. 180 (1942)
B. Tuckwell, D. Blumenthal *Concert* (9/90) (ASV) ① **CDDCA716**
Quintet, 'Primavera'—flute, harp, violin, viola and cello, Op. 156 (1936)
P. Racine, R. Zimansky, M. Clemann, C. Coray, X. Schindler *Concert* (10/90) (CLAV) ① **CD50-9003**
Septet—fl, ob, cor ang, cl, alto sax, bn, hn (1937)
M. Preis, G. Stempnik, Berlin Phil Wind Qnt *Concert* (4/93) (BIS) ① **BIS-CD536**
Sonata for Horn and Piano, Op. 70 (1918-25)
B. Tuckwell, D. Blumenthal *Concert* (9/90) (ASV) ① **CDDCA716**
Sonata for Oboe and Piano, Op. 58 (1911-16)
N. Daniel, J. Drake (r1990) *Concert* (11/94) (VIRG) ① **CUV5 61141-2**

Sonata for Piano and Flute, Op. 52 (1911-13)
F. Smith, M. Amlin *Concert*
(10/90) (HYPE) ① **CDA66414**
P. Racine, D. Cholette *Concert*
(10/90) (CLAV) ① **CD50-9003**
Sonata for Two Flutes, Op. 75 (1918-20)
F. Smith, L. Buyse *Concert*
(10/90) (HYPE) ① **CDA66414**

SECTION III: INSTRUMENTAL

Hommage à Gabriel Fauré—piano
M. Fingerhut *Concert* (9/88) (CHAN) ① **CHAN8578**
11 Monodies—cl (1-9); ob d'amore/cl/sax (10); cor ang (11), Op. 216 (1947-48)
No 11. H. Schellenberger *Concert*
(12/91) (DENO) ① **CO-76611**
Morceau de lecture—horn
B. Tuckwell *Concert* (9/90) (ASV) ① **CDDCA716**
20 Sonneries—horn(s), Op. 123 (1932)
1, 3, 10, 13, 20. B. Tuckwell *Concert*
(9/90) (ASV) ① **CDDCA716**
20 Sonneries—horn, Op. 142 (1935)
2, 5. B. Tuckwell *Concert*
(9/90) (ASV) ① **CDDCA716**
10 Sonneries—horn(s), Op. 153/2 (1935)
2, 3, 5, 11. B. Tuckwell *Concert*
(9/90) (ASV) ① **CDDCA716**
Stéle funéraire—fl/picc/alto fl, Op. 224 (1950)
P. Racine *Concert* (5/92) (ACCO) ① **20123-2**
Vers le soleil—7 pieces: ondes martenot, Op. 174 (1939)
C. Simonin *Concert* (5/92) (ACCO) ① **20123-2**

SECTION IV: VOCAL AND CHORAL

3 Poèmes, Op. 18 (1899-1901, orch 1903-4) (Wds Kipling)
EXCERPTS: 1. Berceuse phoque (Seal Lullaby); 2. Chanson de nuit dans la jungle (Night-Song in the Jungle); 3. Chant de Kala Nag (Song of Kala Nag).
I. Vermillion, J. Botha, R. Lukas, Berlin Rad Chbr Ch, Berlin RSO, J. Conlon *Concert* (r1993)
(6/94) (RCA) ① [2] **09026 61955-2**
7 Rondels—songs, Op. 8 (1891-95 orch. 1896) (Wds. Banville)
1. La pêche; 2. L'hiver; 3. Les pierreries; 4. La lune; 5. L'air; 6. Le matin; 7. La paix.
2. P. Frijsh, E. Nielsen (r1933) *Concert*
(4/95) (PEAR) ① [2] **GEMMCDS9095(2)**
Si tu le veux—song, Op. 5/5 (1893-97) (Wds. de Marsan)
E. Eames, anon (r1908) *Concert*
(11/93) (ROMO) ① [2] **81001-2**
E. Clément, anon (r1910s) *Concert*
(8/95) (PEAR) ① **GEMMCD9161**

SECTION V: STAGE WORKS

Premier album de Lilian—9 pieces: sop, fl, cl (ad lib) and pf, Op. 139 (1934) (from film score)
1. Keep that schoolgirl complexion; 2. Fugue sans protocole; 3. Valse de la réconciliation; 4. Les yeux clairs; 5. Joie de plein air; 6. Skating-smiling; 7. En route vers ta bonheur; 8. Pleurs; 9. Tout va bien.
J. West, F. Smith, M. Amlin *Concert*
(10/90) (HYPE) ① **CDA66414**
K. Graf, P. Racine, D. Cholette *Concert*
(5/92) (ACCO) ① **20123-2**
Second album de Lilian—8 pieces: fl, ondes martenot, hpd and pf, Op. 149 (1935)
1. Sérénade à l'étoile errante; 2. Swimming; 3. Les jeux du clown; 4. Le voyage chimérique.
P. Racine, C. Simonin, D. Cholette *Concert*
(5/92) (ACCO) ① **20123-2**
1-4. F. Smith, M. Amlin *Concert*
(10/90) (HYPE) ① **CDA66414**

KOENEMANN, Feodor (1873–1937) Russia

SECTION IV: VOCAL AND CHORAL

The Song of the Volga Boatmen—song
F. Chaliapin, orch. A. Coates (r1927) *Concert*
(6/93) (PREI) ① [2] **89207**
When the King went forth to war—song, Op. 7/6
F. Chaliapin, orch. L. Collingwood (r1927) *Concert*
(6/93) (PREI) ① [2] **89207**
F. Chaliapin, anon (r1902) *Concert*
(7/93) (SYMP) ① **SYMCD1105**

KOHAUT, (Wenzel) Josef (Thomas) *(1738–?1793)* Bohemia

SECTION I: ORCHESTRAL

Concerto for Lute and Strings in F
J. Bream, Monteverdi Orch, J.E. Gardiner (r1974; ed Bream) *Concert*
(8/93) (RCA) ① [28] **09026 61583-2(2)**
J. Bream, Monteverdi Orch, J.E. Gardiner (r1974; ed Bream) *Concert* (8/93) (RCA) ① **09026 61588-2**

KÓKAI, Rezsö *(1906–1962)* Hungary

SECTION II: CHAMBER

Quartettino—clarinet and string trio (1952)
W. Boeykens Ens (r1992) *Concert*
(6/93) (HARM) ① **HMC90 1419**

KOKKONEN, Joonas *(b 1921)* Finland

SECTION I: ORCHESTRAL

Concerto for Cello and Orchestra (1969)
T. Thedéen, Lahti SO, O. Vänskä *Concert*
(12/91) (BIS) ① **BIS-CD468**
'... Durch einen Spiegel ... ' (1977)
Lahti SO, U. Söderblom *Concert*
(8/92) (BIS) ① **BIS-CD528**
Inauguratio (1971)
Lahti SO, O. Vänskä *Concert*
(8/92) (BIS) ① **BIS-CD498**
Music for Strings (1956-57)
Lahti SO, U. Söderblom *Concert*
(4/92) (BIS) ① **BIS-CD485**
Opus sonorum—piano and orchestra (1965)
I. Sivonen, Lahti SO, U. Söderblom *Concert*
(8/92) (BIS) ① **BIS-CD508**
Il Paesaggio—chamber orchestra (1987)
Lahti SO, O. Vänskä *Concert*
(8/92) (BIS) ① **BIS-CD528**
Sinfonia da camera (1962)
Lahti SO, O. Vänskä *Concert*
(12/91) (BIS) ① **BIS-CD468**
Symphonic Sketches—orchestra (1968)
Lahti SO, U. Söderblom *Concert*
(4/92) (BIS) ① **BIS-CD485**
Symphony No. 1 (1958-60)
Lahti SO, U. Söderblom *Concert*
(8/92) (BIS) ① **BIS-CD498**
Symphony No. 2 (1960-61)
Lahti SO, O. Vänskä *Concert*
(8/92) (BIS) ① **BIS-CD508**
Symphony No. 3 (1967)
Lahti SO, U. Söderblom *Concert*
(12/91) (BIS) ① **BIS-CD468**
Symphony No. 4 (1971)

SECTION II: CHAMBER

Piano Quintet
T. Valsta, Sibelius Academy Qt *Concert*
(8/92) (BIS) ① **BIS-CD458**
String Quartet No. 1 (1958-59)
Sibelius Academy Qt *Concert*
(8/92) (BIS) ① **BIS-CD458**
String Quartet No. 2 (1964-66)
Sibelius Academy Qt *Concert*
(8/92) (BIS) ① **BIS-CD458**
String Quartet No. 3 (1976)
Sibelius Academy Qt *Concert*
(8/92) (BIS) ① **BIS-CD458**
Wind Quintet (1973)
Lahti Sinfonia Wind Qnt *Concert*
(8/92) (BIS) ① **BIS-CD528**

SECTION IV: VOCAL AND CHORAL

Erekhtheion—cantata (1969)
1. Erekhtheion; 2. Hahmo; 3. Aikamiesten tanssi; 4. Tämä maa.
S. Vihavainen, W. Grönroos, Academic Choral Soc, Lahti SO, O. Vänskä *Concert*
(8/92) (BIS) ① **BIS-CD498**
The Hades of the Birds—song cycle (1958) (Wds. P. Mustapää)
1. In the world of perfection; 2. The Hades of the birds; 3. The rain.
M. Groop, Lahti SO, U. Söderblom *Concert*
(4/92) (BIS) ① **BIS-CD485**

Requiem—soprano, baritone, chorus and orchestra (1981)
S. Isokoski, W. Grönroos, Savonlinna Op Fest Chor, Lahti SO, U. Söderblom *Concert*
(8/92) (BIS) ① **BIS-CD508**

SECTION V: STAGE WORKS

The Last Temptations—opera: 2 acts (1975—Helsinki)
Interludes Lahti SO, O. Vänskä *Concert*
(8/92) (BIS) ① **BIS-CD498**

KOMAROVA, Tatiana *(b 1968)* USSR

SECTION III: INSTRUMENTAL

Sonata for Piano (1990)
L. Vogt (r1991) *Concert*
(11/93) (EMI) ① **CDC7 54548-2**

KOMMA, Karl Michael *(b 1913)* Germany

SECTION IV: VOCAL AND CHORAL

5 Hölderlin Fragments (pub 1976) (Wds Hölderlin)
EXCERPTS: 1. Warum, o schöne Sonne; 2. Wenn nämlich der Rebe Saft; 3. Wenn über dem Weinberg es flammt; 4. An meine Schwester; 5. Zu Rossen.
M. Shirai, H. Höll *Concert*
(12/94) (CAPR) ① **10 534**

KOMOROWSKI, I.M. *(1824–1857)*

SECTION IV: VOCAL AND CHORAL

The Guelder-rose—song
J. Korolewicz-Wayda, anon (r1908) *Concert*
(6/93) (PEAR) ① [3] **GEMMCDS9004/6(1)**

KOMPANYEISKY, N. *(1848–1910)* Russia

SECTION IV: VOCAL AND CHORAL

The Angel declared to Mary—Russian liturgical chant
N. Gedda, Paris Russian Orthodox Cath Ch, E. Evetz *Concert* (1/93) (PHIL) ① **434 174-2PM**

KOMZÁK, Karel II *(1850–1905)* Bohemia

SECTION I: ORCHESTRAL

Erzherzog Albrecht-Marsch, Op. 136
Czech PO, V. Neumann *Concert*
(6/87) (ORFE) ① **C107101A**
Berlin Phil Wind Qnt, H. von Karajan (r1973: arr Villinger) *Concert* (5/94) (DG) ① **439 346-2GX2**
Mein Baden, Op. 228
Czech PO, V. Neumann *Concert*
(6/87) (ORFE) ① **C107101A**
Vindobona—march
Berlin Phil Wind Qnt, H. von Karajan (r1973: arr Mader) *Concert* (5/94) (DG) ① **439 346-2GX2**

KOPPEL, Anders *(b 1947)* Denmark

SECTION II: CHAMBER

Toccata—vibraphone (1990)
Safri Duo (r1994) *Concert*
(4/95) (CHAN) ① **CHAN9330**

KOPYTMAN, Mark *(b 1929)* USSR/Israel

SECTION I: ORCHESTRAL

Cantus V—viola and orchestra (1990)
T. Zimmermann, Jerusalem SO, D. Shallon (r1993) *Concert* (8/94) (EMI) ① **CDC5 55107-2**

KORNGOLD, Erich Wolfgang (1897–1957) Austro-Hungary/USA

SECTION I: ORCHESTRAL

Concerto for Cello and Orchestra in C, 'Deception', Op. 37 (1946) (arr from the film Deception)
J. Berger, NW German PO, W.A. Albert *Concert*
(10/91) (CPO) ① CPO999 077-2
F. Gabarro, National PO, C. Gerhardt *Concert*
(11/91) (RCA) ① GD80185
Concerto for Violin and Orchestra, Op. 35 (1945)
I. Perlman, Pittsburgh SO, A. Previn *Goldmark: Violin Concerto 1.*
(2/88) (EMI) ① CDC7 47846-2
J. Heifetz, Los Angeles PO, A. Wallenstein (r1953) *Concert*
(4/89) (RCA) ① GD87963
I. Perlman, Pittsburgh SO, A. Previn (r1980) *Concert*
(5/93) (EMI) ① [4] CMS7 64617-2
G. Shaham, LSO, A. Previn (r1993) *Concert*
(9/94) (DG) ① 439 886-2GH
J. Heifetz, Los Angeles PO, A. Wallenstein (r1953) *Concert* (11/94) (RCA) ① [65] 09026 61778-2(21)
I. Perlman, Pittsburgh SO, A. Previn (r1980) *Concert*
(6/95) (EMI) ① [20] CZS4 83177-2(1)
Concerto in C sharp—piano left-hand and orchestra, Op. 17 (1923)
S. de Groote, NW German PO, W.A. Albert *Concert*
(10/91) (CPO) ① CPO999 046-2
Die Kleine Serenade—small orchestra, Op. 24 (1931-32)
NW German PO, W.A. Albert *Concert*
(10/91) (CPO) ① CPO999 077-2
Schauspiel—overture, Op. 4 (1911)
NW German PO, W.A. Albert *Concert*
(10/91) (CPO) ① CPO999 037-2
Sinfonietta, Op. 5 (1912)
Berlin RSO, G. Albrecht (r1983)
(10/91) (VARE) ① VSD5311
NW German PO, W.A. Albert *Concert*
(10/91) (CPO) ① CPO999 037-2
BBC PO, M. Bamert (r1994) *Sursum corda, Op. 13.*
(5/95) (CHAN) ① CHAN9317
Straussiana—orchestra (1953) (arr from various works of J. Strauss II)
NW German PO, W.A. Albert *Concert*
(10/91) (CPO) ① CPO999 146-2
Sursum corda—symphonic overture, Op. 13 (1921)
NW German PO, W.A. Albert *Concert*
(10/91) (CPO) ① CPO999 046-2
BBC PO, M. Bamert (r1994) *Sinfonietta.*
(5/95) (CHAN) ① CHAN9317
Symphonic Serenade in B—string orchestra, Op. 39 (1947-48)
NW German PO, W.A. Albert *Concert*
(10/91) (CPO) ① CPO999 077-2
Symphony in F sharp, Op. 40 (1951-52)
NW German PO, W.A. Albert *Concert*
(10/91) (CPO) ① CPO999 146-2
Munich PO, R. Kempe (r1972)
(6/92) (VARE) ① VSD5346
BBC PO, E. Downes (r1994) *Abschiedslieder, Op. 14.*
(9/93) (CHAN) ① CHAN9171
Theme and Variations—orchestra, Op. 42 (1953)
NW German PO, W.A. Albert *Concert*
(10/91) (CPO) ① CPO999 146-2
Austrian RSO, M. Schönherr (r1955) *Concert*
(3/93) (CAMB) ① CD-1066
Tomorrow—tone poem, Op. 33 (1943) (also exists as vocal work)
Austrian RSO, M. Schönherr (r1949) *Concert*
(3/93) (CAMB) ① CD-1066

SECTION II: CHAMBER

Piano Trio in D, Op. 1 (1909)
Pacific Art Trio *Ives: Piano Trio.*
(9/90) (DELO) ① DE1009
Beaux Arts Trio *Zemlinsky: Trio, Op. 3.*
(6/94) (PHIL) ① 434 072-2PH
G. Dicterow, A. Stepansky, I. Margalit (r1994) *Violin Sonata, Op.6.* (7/95) (EMI) ① CDC5 55401-2
Sextet for Strings in D, Op. 10 (1917)
Raphael Ens *Schoenberg: Verklärte Nacht.*
(1/91) (HYPE) ① CDA66425
Sonata for Violin and Piano in D, Op. 6 (1913)
G. Dicterow, I. Margalit (r1994) *Piano Trio, Op.1.*
(7/95) (EMI) ① CDC5 55401-2
String Quartet No. 2 in E, Op. 26 (1935)
Lyric Art Qt *Concert* (10/90) (BAY) ① BCD-1014

New World Qt (r1978) *Concert*
(10/93) (VOX) ① [2] 115775-2

SECTION III: INSTRUMENTAL

Potpourri aus 'Der Ring des Polykrates'—piano (arr cpsr)
S. Woolley (r1994) *Schneemann.*
(4/95) (KOCH) ① 37277-2
Sonata for Piano No. 1 in D minor (1908)
M. Verschoor *Concert* (7/87) (ETCE) ① KTC1042
Sonata for Piano No. 2 in E, Op. 2 (1910)
M. Verschoor *Concert* (7/87) (ETCE) ① KTC1042
Sonata for Piano No. 3 in C, Op. 25 (1931)
M. Verschoor *Concert* (7/87) (ETCE) ① KTC1042

SECTION IV: VOCAL AND CHORAL

Abschiedslieder—1v and piano/orchestra, Op. 14 (1909) (Wds. various)
1. Sterbelied (wds. Rosetti trans A. Kerr); 2. Dies eine kann mein Sehnen nimmer fassen (wds. E. Ronsperger); 3. Mond, so gehst du wieder auf (wds. E. Lothar); 4. Gefasster Abschied (wds. E. Lothar).
1-4. L. Finnie, BBC PO, E. Downes (r1992) *Symphony, Op. 40.* (9/93) (CHAN) ① CHAN9171
1, 4. A.S. von Otter, B. Forsberg (r1991/3) *Concert*
(6/94) (DG) ① 437 515-2GH
6 Einfache Lieder—voice and piano, Op. 9 (1911-16)
1. Schneeglöckchen (wds. J. von Eichendorff); 2. Nachtwander (wds. J. von Eichendorff); 3. Ständchen (wds. J. von Eichendorff); 4. Liebesbriefchen (wds. E. Honold); 5. Das Heldengrab am Pruth (wds. H. Kipper); 6. Sommer (wds. S. Trebitsch).
1-3. B. Skovhus, H. Deutsch (r1993) *Concert*
(1/95) (SONY) ① SK57969
4. A.S. von Otter, B. Forsberg (r1991) *Concert*
(6/94) (DG) ① 437 515-2GH
3 Lieder—voice and piano, Op. 18 (1924) (Wds. H. Kaltneker)
1. In meine innige Nacht; 2. Tu ab den Schmerz; 3. Du reine Frau.
A.S. von Otter, B. Forsberg (r1991) *Concert*
(6/94) (DG) ① 437 515-2GH
5 Lieder—1v and piano, Op. 38 (1947)
EXCERPTS: 1. Glückwunsch (wds R Dehmel); 2. Der Kranke (wds Eichendorff); 3. Alt-spanisch (wds H Koch).
1, 2. S. Kimbrough, D. Baldwin (r1990) *Concert*
(2/95) (SCHW) ① 310942
1, 3. A.S. von Otter, B. Forsberg (r1991/3) *Concert*
(6/94) (DG) ① 437 515-2GH
2. B. Skovhus, H. Deutsch (r1993) *Concert*
(1/95) (SONY) ① SK57969
Sonett für Wien, Op. 41 (1952) (Wds. Kaltneker)
A.S. von Otter, B. Forsberg (r1993) *Concert*
(6/94) (DG) ① 437 515-2GH
Unvergänglichkeit—five songs, Op. 27 (pub 1935) (Wds E. van der Straaten)
EXCERPTS: 1. Unvergänglichkeit; 2. Bächlein, Bächlein, wie du eilen kannst; 3. Wenn du schläfst; 4. Stärker als der Tod; 5. Unvergänglichkeit.
Cpte S. Kimbrough, D. Baldwin (r1990) *Concert*
(2/95) (SCHW) ① 310942

SECTION V: STAGE WORKS

The Adventures of Robin Hood—film score (1938)
EXCERPTS: 1. Prologue (Main Title); 2. Banquet at Nottingham Castle; 3. Robin enters the Great Hall; 4. Escape from the Castle; 5. Robin meets Little John; 6. The Oath and the Black Arrow; 7. Robin and Friar Tuck; 8. Ambush in Sherwood; 9. Feast in the Forest; 10. Robin and Marian; 11. The Archery Tournament; 12. Escape from the Gallows; 13. Love Scene; 14. Dagger Fight—King Richard in Sherwood; 15. Coronation Procession; 16. Duel, Victory and Epilogue.
1-16. Utah SO, V. Kojian (r1983)
(3/87) (TER) ① CDTER1066
1-3, 5, 7-9, 12, 13, 16. B. Rathbone, Warner Bros Studio Orch, E. Korngold (bp1938; disc includes 1968 interviews with Errol Flynn)
(2/91) (FACE) ① FE8104
1(pt), 8, 10, 16(pt) orch, L. Newman (r1961) *Concert*
(11/91) (STAN) ① STZ117
11-13, 15. National PO, C. Gerhardt *Concert*
(11/91) (RCA) ① GD80912
13, 16. Hollywood Bowl SO, J. Mauceri (r1991) *Concert* (9/91) (PHIL) ① 432 109-2PH
Another Dawn—film score (1937)
EXCERPTS -; 1. Main Title; 2. Night Scene.
2. National PO, C. Gerhardt *Concert*
(11/91) (RCA) ① GD80185

Anthony Adverse—film score (1936)
EXCERPTS -; 1. The Lovers: 1a. Main Title (No father, no mother, no name); 1b. The coast rise; 1c. The dinner; 1d. Maria and the Madonna; 1e. Rendez-vous in the forest (Love scene); 2. Anthony is born: 2a. The recuperation; 2b. Dennis visits Maria; 2c. Escape; 2d. Candles in the window; 2e. The death of Dennis; 3. Casa de Bonnyfeather: 3a. The trip through the snow; 3b. The birth of Anthony and the death of Maria; 3c. Leghorn and the House of Bonnyfeather; 4. Anthony and Angela: 4a. The convent; 4b. Young Angela; 5. From Leghorn to Cuba: 5a. The love of Anthony and Angela; 5b. The lottery and the march through Leghorn; 5c. Havana; 5d. Brother François; 6. Adventures in Africa: 6a. The embitted Anthony; 6b. The misery of the slave trade; 6c. The torrential rains; 6d. Anthony's illness; 6e. The death of Brother François; 7. Anthony returns to Europe: 7a. The snown Alps; 7b. Crossing the border in Napoleon's France; 7c. Paris; 7d. Angela spots Anthony; 7e. At the cottage; 7f. Anthony meet his son; 7g. The Madonna; 7h. Anthony and his son leave for America; 7i. End Title and Credits.
Berlin RSO, John Scott (r1990)
(11/91) (VARE) ① VSD5285
1e National PO, C. Gerhardt *Concert*
(11/91) (RCA) ① GD80185
1e, 3b, 7(pt) orch, L. Newman (r1961) *Concert*
(11/91) (STAN) ① STZ117
Between Two Worlds—film score (1944)
EXCERPTS: 1. Main Title; 2. Mother and Son; 3. Piano Rhapsody.
2, 3. National PO, C. Gerhardt *Concert*
(6/90) (VARE) ① VSD5207
Captain Blood—film score (1935)
EXCERPTS: 1. Main Title; 2. Ship in the Night; 3. Slaves; 4. Arabella and Blood; 5. Tortuga; 6. Port Royal, Island of Magra, English and Pirates' Ship; 7. Pirates' Flag; 8. Finale.
1. National PO, C. Gerhardt *Concert*
(10/92) (RCA) ① GD82792
2. National PO, C. Gerhardt *Concert*
(11/91) (RCA) ① GD80912
The Constant Nymph—film score (1942)
EXCERPTS: 1. Overture (Main Title); 2. Tomorrow (Farewell).
1. National PO, C. Gerhardt *Concert*
(6/90) (VARE) ① VSD5207
1, 2. orch, L. Newman (r1961) *Concert*
(11/91) (STAN) ① STZ117
Escape me never—film score (1946)
EXCERPTS: 1. Main Title; 2. Venice; 3. March; 4. Love Scene; 5. Love for Love; 6. Finale.
5. National PO, C. Gerhardt *Concert*
(6/90) (VARE) ① VSD5207
Juarez—film score (1939)
EXCERPTS: 1. Overture; 2. Carlotta.
2. National PO, C. Gerhardt *Concert*
(3/90) (RCA) ① GD80183
Die Kathrin—opera: 3 acts, Op. 28 (1939—Stockholm) (Lib. E. Decsey)
Ich bin ein Liedersänger G. Janowitz, R. Christ, Austrian St Rad Orch, W. Loibner (bp) *Concert*
(5/92) (CAMB) ① CD-1032
Letter scene I. Steingruber, Austrian St Rad Orch, G. Kassowitz (bp) *Concert*
(5/92) (CAMB) ① CD-1032
Malignac's aria A. Poell, Austrian St Rad Orch, J. Strobl (bp) *Concert* (5/92) (CAMB) ① CD-1032
Soldaten Marsch und Gebet I. Steingruber, Austrian St Rad Orch, G. Kassowitz (bp) *Concert*
(5/92) (CAMB) ① CD-1032
Szene in Nachtlokal R. Schwaiger, A. Dermota, Austrian St Rad Orch, G. Kassowitz (bp) *Concert*
(5/92) (CAMB) ① CD-1032
Wanderlied A. Dermota, Austrian St Rad Orch, E. Korngold (bp1949) *Concert*
(5/92) (CAMB) ① CD-1032
Kings Row—film score (1942)
EXCERPTS: 1. Main Title; 2. The Children (Parris and Cassie); 3. Parris and Grandmother; 4. Cassie's Party; 5. Icehouse Operation; 6. Cassie's Farewell; 7. Parris Goes to Dr Tower; 8. Winter; 9. Grandmother's Last Will; 10. Seduction; 11. All is Quiet; 12. Grandmother Dies; 13. Sunset; 14. Parris Leaves King's Row; 15. Flirtation; 16. Vienna and Happy New Year 1900; 17. Randy and Drake; 18. Financial Ruin; 19. Accident and Amputation; 20. Drake Awakens; 21. Vienna—Cable—Randy and Drake; 22. Letters Across the Ocean; 23. Parris Comes Back; 24. King's Row; 25. Elise; 26. Parris's Decision; 27. Finale.
1, 2, 12, 17. orch, L. Newman (r1961) *Concert*
(11/91) (STAN) ① STZ117

Much Ado About Nothing—concert suite from incidental music (1920)
EXCERPTS: 1. Overture; 2. Maiden in the Bridal Chamber; 3. Dogberry and Verges (March of the Sentinel); 4. Intermezzo (Garden Scene); 5. Hornpipe.
NW German PO, W.A. Albert *Concert*
    (10/91) (CPO) ① **CPO999 046-2**
Austrian RSO, M. Schönherr (r1949) *Concert*
    (3/93) (CAMB) ① **CD-1066**
2-5. G. Shaham, A. Previn (r1993) *Concert*
    (9/94) (DG) ① **439 886-2GH**
3. J. Heifetz, E. Bay (r1946) *Concert*
    (11/94) (RCA) ① **[65] 09026 61778-2(06)**
3. J. Heifetz, A. Sándor (r1934) *Concert*
    (11/94) (RCA) ① **[65] 09026 61778-2(02)**
4. J. Heifetz, E. Bay (r1947) *Concert*
    (11/94) (RCA) ① **[65] 09026 61778-2(06)**
4. J. Heifetz, B. Smith (r1970) *Concert*
    (11/94) (RCA) ① **[65] 09026 61778-2(40)**
Of Human Bondage—film score (1945)
EXCERPTS: 1. Main Title; 2. Christmas; 3. Sally; 4. Nora; 5. Lullaby; 6. Finale.
1-3, 5, 6. National PO, C. Gerhardt *Concert*
    (11/91) (RCA) ① **GD80185**
The Prince and the Pauper—film score (1937)
EXCERPTS: 1. Overture; 2. Flirtation; 3. The Boys Go to Play.
1. National PO, C. Gerhardt *Concert*
    (11/91) (RCA) ① **GD80185**
2. National PO, C. Gerhardt *Concert*
    (6/90) (VARE) ① **VSD5207**
2. Hollywood Bowl SO, J. Mauceri (r1993) *Concert*
    (6/94) (PHIL) ① **438 685-2PH**
3. orch, L. Newman (r1961) *Concert*
    (11/91) (STAN) ① **STZ117**
The Private Lives of Elizabeth and Essex—film score (1939)
EXCERPTS: 1. Main Title; 2. Narrative; 3. March; 4. Shadow and Parade; 5. The Throne Room; 6. After Elizabeth Slaps Essex; 7. Elizabeth and Essex; 8. The Courier; 9. The Chess Game; 10. Mirror Scene; 10a. Song: The Passionate Shepherd to His Love; 11. The Queen; 12. Messenger; 13. Poor Child; 14. The Hunting; 15. Raleigh and Essex; 16. Silver Armour; 17. Lady Penelope; 18. Darling; 19. Card Game; 20. Love Scene; 21. Council Dismissed; 22. Love and the Ring; 23. Ireland; 24. Shadow of Penelope; 25. Elizabeth Weeps; 26. The Battle; 27. The Truce; 28. The Palace; 29. Queen Elizabeth; 30. Essex Returns; 31. Love Scene; 32. Arrest; 33. The Tower; 34. Cecil; 35. Essex; 36. Love Scene; 37. Executioner; 38. End Cast (Finale).
1, 36-38. orch, L. Newman (r1961) *Concert*
    (11/91) (STAN) ① **STZ117**
11. National PO, C. Gerhardt *Concert*
    (3/90) (RCA) ① **GD80183**
11. National PO, C. Gerhardt *Concert*
    (10/92) (RCA) ① **GD82792**
The Private Lives of Elizabeth and Essex—concert overture (1939) (arr cpsr for film premiere)
National PO, C. Gerhardt *Concert*
    (11/91) (RCA) ① **GD80185**
Der Ring des Polykrates—opera: 1 act, Op. 7 (1916—Munich) (Lib. after H. Tewles)
Tagesbuch der Laura G. Janowitz, Austrian St Rad Orch, W. Loibner (bp) *Concert*
    (5/92) (CAMB) ① **CD-1032**
Der Schneemann—pantomime (1910—Vienna) (orch Zemlinsky from orig piano version)
EXCERPTS—; 1. Prelude; 2. Serenade; 3. Entr'acte.
S. Woolley (r1994; piano version) *Polykrates Potpourri* (4/95) (KOCH) ① **37277-2**
1, 2. Austrian RSO, M. Schönherr (r1949) *Concert*
    (3/93) (CAMB) ① **CD-1066**
1-3. L. Farkas, NW German PO, W.A. Albert *Concert*
    (10/91) (CPO) ① **CPO999 037-2**
The Sea Hawk—film score (1940)
EXCERPTS: 1. Main Title; 2a. The Spanish Galleas; 2b. Galley Slaves; 2c. The Albatross; 3. The Captain's Table; 4. Dona Maria & Capt Thorpe; 5a. Elizabeth's Throne Room; 5b. Entrance of the Sea Hawks; 6. Thorpe's Pet Monkey; 7. Map of Panama (The Orchid); 8. The Chess Game; 9a. Farewell (The Rose Garden); 9b. Panama; 10a. Jungle March (Panama March); 10b. Battle; 11. Return to the Albatross; 12a. Condemned to the Galley; 12b. Dona Maria's Song; 13a. Queen Elizabeth; 13b. Maria's Anguish; 14a. Escape from the Galley; 14b. Fight on Deck; 14c. Strike for the Shores of Dover; 15. Reunion; 16a. Thorpe Confronts Wolfingham; 16b. The Duel (Sword Fight); 17a. Fanfare (Rise, Sir Geoffrey Thorpe!); 17b. Finale (End Title).

1, 15. orch, L. Newman (r1961) *Concert*
    (11/91) (STAN) ① **STZ117**
2c, 5a, 5b, 7, 10a, 14c, 16b National PO, C. Gerhardt *Concert* (11/91) (RCA) ① **GD80912**
The Sea Wolf—film score (1941)
EXCERPTS: 1. Main Title; 2. Escape in the Fog; 3. Love Scene; 4. Finale.
1-4. National PO, C. Gerhardt *Concert*
    (11/91) (RCA) ① **GD80185**
Die Tote Stadt—opera: 3 acts, Op. 12 (1920—Hamburg and Cologne) (Lib. Schott, after Rodenbach)
EXCERPTS - ACT 1: 6a. Nun, zu der alten Laute; 6b. Glück, das mir verblieb (Mariettalied). ACT 2: 8. Prelude; 12. Mein Sehnen, mein Wähnen (Pierrotlied). ACT 3: 14. Prelude; 16. Und der Erste, der Lieb mich gelehrt (Marietta); 18. O Freund, ich werde sie nicht wiedersehen.
Cpte R. Kollo, C. Neblett, B. Luxon, R. Wageman, H. Prey, G. Fuchs, P. Clark, A. de Ridder, W. Brokmeier, Tolz Boys' Ch, Bavarian Rad Chor, Munich RO, E. Leinsdorf (r1975)
    (11/89) (RCA) ① **[2] GD87767**
6b J. Schmidt, orch (r1933) *Concert*
    (4/90) (EMI) ① **CDM7 69478-2**
6b J. Hammond, Philh, W. Susskind (r1953) *Concert*
    (4/92) (RCA) ① **[7] CHS7 69741-2(1)**
6b I. Steingruber, A. Dermota, Austrian St Rad Orch, E. Korngold (bp1949) *Concert*
    (5/92) (CAMB) ① **CD-1032**
6b L. Price, New Philh, N. Santi (r1977) *Concert*
    (12/92) (RCA) ① **[4] 09026 61236-2**
6b M. Németh, orch (r1930s) *Concert*
    (1/94) (CLUB) ① **CL99-007**
6b M. Jeritza, orch, J. Pasternack, F. Lapitino (r1922) *Concert* (4/94) (RCA) ① **[6] 09026 61580-2(3)**
6b M. Jeritza, orch (r1927) *Concert*
    (4/94) (PREI) ① **89079**
6b, 18. R. Tauber, Lotte Lehmann, orch, G. Szell (r1924) *Concert* (3/92) (EMI) ① **CDH7 64029-2**
6b, 18. R. Tauber, Lotte Lehmann, orch, G. Szell (r1924) *Concert* (12/92) (NIMB) ① **NI7830**
12. R. Schwaiger, A. Poell, Austrian St Rad Orch, E. Korngold (bp1949) *Concert*
    (5/92) (CAMB) ① **CD-1032**
12. F. Kreisler, C. Lamson (r1924: arr Kreisler) *Concert* (9/93) (BIDD) ① **[2] LAB068/9**
12. T. Hampson, Munich RO, F. Luisi (r1994) *Concert*
    (2/95) (EMI) ① **CDC5 55233-2**
16. Lotte Lehmann, Berlin St Op Orch, G. Szell (r1924) *Concert* (6/92) (PREI) ① **[3] 89302**
18. R. Tauber, orch, G. Szell (r1924) *Concert*
    (12/92) (TEST) ① **SBT1005**
Violanta—opera: 1 act, Op. 8 (1916—Munich) (Lib. H. Müller)
Cpte E. Marton, S. Jerusalem, W. Berry, H. Laubenthal, G. Stoklassa, R. Hesse, M. Schmidt, H. Weber, P. Hansen, K. Hautermann, R. Freyer, Bavarian Rad Chor, Munich RO, M. Janowski
    (9/89) (SONY) ① **MK79229**
Prelude; Carnival Austrian RSO, M. Schönherr (r1949) *Concert* (3/93) (CAMB) ① **CD-1066**
Wie schön seid ihr H. Hillebrecht, H. Hoppe, Austrian St Rad Orch, J. Strobl (bp) *Concert*
    (5/92) (CAMB) ① **CD-1032**
Das Wunder der Heliane—opera: 3 acts, Op. 20 (1927—Hamburg) (Lib. Muller, after H. Kaltneker)
Cpte A. Tomowa-Sintow, H. Welker, J.D. de Haan, R. Runkel, R. Rape, N. Gedda, M. Petzold, Berlin Rad Chor, Berlin RSO, J. Mauceri (r1992)
    (4/93) (DECC) ① **[3] 436 636-2DH3**
Ich ging zu ihm I. Steingruber, Austrian St Rad Orch, J. Strobl (bp) *Concert*
    (5/92) (CAMB) ① **CD-1032**

KORSCHAT

Verlassen—song
E. Rethberg, orch (r1924-5) *Concert*
    (2/95) (ROMO) ① **[2] 81012-2**

KORZYŃSKI, Andrzej (b 1940) Poland

The Birchwood (Brzezina)—film score (1970)
EXCERPTS: 1. The Birchwood (Landscape); 2. Leading Motif; 3. Song of Death.
1-3. OST, A. Korzyński (r1970) *Concert*
    (8/94) (OLYM) ① **OCD601**

Hunting Flies (Polowanie na Muchy)—film score (1969)
EXCERPTS: 1. Bossa Nova; 2. The Dziekanka Students' Hostel (rock group); 3. Leading Motif (rock group); 4. Dziekanka Students' Hostel II (Dance); 5. A Country Landscape; 6. The Wonderful House; 7. Trying to Catch a Fly.
1-8. OST, A. Korzyński (r1969) *Concert*
    (8/94) (OLYM) ① **OCD601**
Man of Iron (złowiek z Zelaza)—film score (1981)
EXCERPTS: 1. Hope; 2. Man's Destiny; 3. Janek Wiśniewski; 4. Gdańsk 80; 5. Poem by Miłosz; 6. Truncheon Man; 7. You are my hope; 8. Polish All Souls' Day (Funeral Music); 9. Ballad of Janek Wiśniewski.
1-9. OST, A. Korzyński (r1981) *Concert*
    (8/94) (OLYM) ① **OCD601**
Man of Marble (złowiek z Marmuru)—film score (1977)
EXCERPTS: 1. Leading Motif; 2. The Striptease (Kung Fu); 3. Saved from Oblivion; 4. Figures of Marble; 5. A Witness; 6. In the Shipyard; 7. The Katowice Ironworks.
1-8. OST, A. Korzyński (r1977) *Concert*
    (8/94) (OLYM) ① **OCD601**

KOSAKU, Yamada (1886–1965) Japan

Aka-Tonbo—song
A. A. Meyers, S. Rivers (r1993; arr Sigeaki: vn/pf) *Concert* (4/95) (RCA) ① **09026 62546-2**

KOSHKIN, Nikita (b 1956) USSR

Usher Waltz (after Edgar Allen Poe)—guitar, Op. 29
J. Williams (r1992) *Concert*
    (1/94) (SONY) ① **SK53359**

KOSKELIN, Olli (b 1955) ?Finland

Tutte le corde—guitar and pre-recorded tape (1988-89)
T. Korhonen *Concert* (8/90) (ONDI) ① **ODE730-2**

KOSUGI, Takehisa (b 1938) Japan

75 Letters and Improvisation (1987-1993)
T. kosugi (r1993) *Concert*
    (8/94) (KOCH) ① **[2] 37238-2**

KOUSSEVITZKY, Sergei (1874–1951) Russia/USA

Concerto for Double Bass and Orchestra, Op. 3 (1905)
Movt 2. S. Koussevitzky, P. Luboshutz (r1929) *Concert* (9/94) (BIDD) ① **WHL019**

Chanson triste—double-bass and piano, Op. 2
S. Koussevitzky, P. Luboshutz (r1929) *Concert*
    (9/94) (BIDD) ① **WHL019**
Valse miniature—double-bass and piano, Op. 1/2
S. Koussevitzky, P. Luboshutz (r1929) *Concert*
    (9/94) (BIDD) ① **WHL019**

KOVAŘOVIC, Karel (1862–1920) Czechoslovakia

The Miners' polka—orchestra (1894)
Czech PO, V. Neumann *Concert*
    (9/90) (ORFE) ① **C180891A**

SECTION V: STAGE WORKS

The **Dogs' Heads**—opera: 3 acts
(1898—Prague) (Lib. Šípek, after A Jirásek)
Belle cruelle E. Destinn, orch, B. Seidler-Winkler
(r1908) *Concert*
(12/94) (SUPR) ① [12] **11 2136-2(1)**
Zelení hájové. J. Novotná, orch (r1926) *Concert*
(4/93) (SUPR) ① **11 1491-2**
Nazarene—opera (unfinished)
Slovácká Pisen E. Destinn, orch, W.B. Rogers
(r1915) *Concert* (11/93) (ROMO) ① [2] **81002-2**
Slovácká píseň. E. Destinn, orch, W.B Rogers
(r1915) *Concert*
(12/94) (SUPR) ① [12] **11 2136-2(5)**

KOŽELUCH, Leopold (1747–1818) Bohemia/Austria

SECTION I: ORCHESTRAL

Concerto for Clarinet and Orchestra in E flat
(before 1970)
E. Johnson, RPO, G. Herbig *Concert*
(9/91) (ASV) ① **CDDCA763**

SECTION IV: VOCAL AND CHORAL

A **Select Collection of Original Scottish
Airs**—folksong arrangements: 1v, pf, vn, vc
(pub 1798) (Wds R. Burns unless indicated)
EXCERPTS: 1. No. 37: Nae gentle dames (Air: The
Deuks Dang O'er My Daddie); 2. No. 75: Here's a
health to ane I lo'e dear; 3. No. 43: Ye banks and
braes o' bonie Doon; 4. No. 61: Blythe and merry was
she (Air: Andrew wi' his Cutty Gun); 5. No. 38: Lord
Gregory—O mirk mirk (Air: Ancient Gallowegian
melody); 6. No. 99: My Nannie's Awa'—Now in her
green mantle (Air: Coolun); 7. No. 44: And ye shall
walk in silk attire (Wds anon; Air: Siller Crown); 8. No.
42: Turn again, thou fair Eliza (Air: The Bonny
Brucket Lassie); 9. No. 65: Contented wi' little (Air:
Lunmps O' Pudding); 10. No. 28: The day returns
(Air: The Seventh of November); 11. No. 88: On a
bank of flowers; 12. No. 34: Adieu, ye streams (Wds
anon); 13. No. 79: What numbers shall the muse
repeat! (Wds anon; Air: Allan Water); 14. No. 35: My
love she's but a lassie yet; 15. No. 46: True hearted
was she (Air: Bonnie Dundee); 16. No. 40: She's fair
and fause; 17. No. 56: O this is my aine lassie; 18.
No. 87: The Tears of Scotland—Mourn hapless
Caledonia (Wds anon); 19. Auld lang syne.
19. Scottish Early Music Consort (r1987) *Concert*
(10/95) (CHAN) ① **CHAN0581**

SECTION V: STAGE WORKS

La **Ritrovata Figlia di Ottone II**—ballet: 5
acts, Op. 39 (1794—Vienna)
Gavotte H. Bauer (r1926: arr Bauer) *Concert*
(9/93) (BIDD) ① **LHW007**
Gavotte F. Kreisler, C. Lamson (r1925: arr Kramer)
Concert (9/93) (BIDD) ① [2] **LAB068/9**

KRAFT, Anton (1749–1820) Bohemia

SECTION I: ORCHESTRAL

Concerto for Cello and Orchestra in C, Op. 4
(pub ?1792)
A. Bylsma, Tafelmusik, J. Lamon *Concert*
(9/91) (DHM) ① **RD77757**

KRAFT, William (b 1923) USA

SECTION I: ORCHESTRAL

Concerto for Piano and Orchestra (1972-73)
M. Golabek, Alabama SO, P. Polivnick (1990)
Concert (2/94) (HARM) ① **HMU90 7106**
Concerto for Timpani and Orchestra (1984)
T. Akins, Alabama SO, P. Polivnick (1988)
(2/94) (HARM) ① **HMU90 7106**
Veils and Variations—horn and orchestra
(1988)
J. von der Schmidt, Berkeley SO, K. Nagano (1992)
Concert (2/94) (HARM) ① **HMU90 7106**

SECTION III: INSTRUMENTAL

Evening Voluntaries—horn
J. von der Schmidt (r1992) *Concert*
(2/94) (HARM) ① **HMU90 7106**

KRÄHMER, Ernst (18th/19th Cent) ?Germany

SECTION II: CHAMBER

Variations brillantes—recorder and
harpsichord
M. Petri, H. Petri *Concert*
(10/88) (RCA) ① **RD87749**

KRAKAUER, Alexander (1866–1894) Austria

SECTION IV: VOCAL AND CHORAL

Du guater Himmelvater—Viennese song
E. Kunz, Kemmeter-Faltl Schrammel Ens (r1949)
Concert (9/95) (TEST) ① **SBT1059**

KRÁL, Jan Nepomuk (1839–1896) Bohemia

SECTION I: ORCHESTRAL

Emilie Mazurka
Czech PO, V. Neumann *Concert*
(6/87) (ORFE) ① **C107101A**
Für Kaiser und Vaterland—March
Czech PO, V. Neumann *Concert*
(6/87) (ORFE) ① **C107101A**

KRAMER, A. Walter (1890–1969) USA

SECTION II: CHAMBER

Entr'acte—violin and piano, Op. 46/2
F. Kreisler, C. Lamson (r1923) *Concert*
(9/93) (BIDD) ① [2] **LAB068/9**

SECTION IV: VOCAL AND CHORAL

The **Last Hour**—song, Op. 34/6
J. McCormack, F. Kreisler, V. O'Brien, L. Schwab, E.
Schneider, Victor Orch, W.B. Rogers (r1920) *Concert*
(9/89) (PEAR) ① **GEMMCD9315**

KRÁSA, Hans (1899–1944) Czechoslovakia

SECTION II: CHAMBER

String Quartet (1921)
Hawthorne Qt (r1993) *Concert*
(3/94) (DECC) ① **440 853-2DH**
Tanec—string trio
Czech Stg Trio *Concert*
(8/92) (ROMA) ① [2] **RR1941**

SECTION V: STAGE WORKS

Brundibár, '(The) Bumble Bee'—children's
opera: 2 acts (1938) (Lib. K. Hoffmeister)
Cpte P. Krištofová, V. Ondráčka, G. Přibilová, T.
Staněk, M. Alexandridis, K. Tichá, D. Horáčková, J.
Kratěnová, B. Drofová, J. Flegl, Disman Rad
Children's Ch, Disman Rad Children's Orch, J. Karas
(r1992) Domažlický: *Czech Songs.*
(8/93) (CHNN) ① **CCS5193**
Bambini di Praga, Prague FISYO, M. Klemens
(bp1990) *Concert* (8/92) (ROMA) ① [2] **RR1941**

KRATZL (19th–20th cents) Austria

SECTION IV: VOCAL AND CHORAL

Das Glück is' a Vogerl—Viennese song
E. Kunz, Kemmeter-Faltl Schrammel Ens (r1949)
Concert (9/95) (TEST) ① **SBT1059**

KRAUS, Joseph Martin (1756–1792) Sweden

SECTION I: ORCHESTRAL

**Concerto for Violin and Orchestra in C,
VB151** (1777 rev 1783)
E. Peinemann, Stuttgart CO, M. Sieghart *Concert*
(11/92) (ORFE) ① **C254921A**
Riksdagsmarsch, VB154 (1789)
OAE, A. Halstead *Concert*
(11/92) (MSVE) ① **MSCD419**
Sinfonia con fugato per la chiesa, VB146
(1789)
OAE, A. Halstead *Concert*
(11/92) (MSVE) ① **MSCD419**

Concerto Cologne (r1992) *Concert*
(9/93) (CAPR) ① **10 430**
Symphonie funèbre in C minor, VB148
(1792)
Stuttgart CO, M. Sieghart *Concert*
(11/92) (ORFE) ① **C254921A**
Concerto Cologne (r1992) *Concert*
(9/93) (CAPR) ① **10 430**
Symphony in C, VB139 (1781)
Cologne Concerto (r1991) *Concert*
(8/92) (CAPR) ① **10 396**
OAE, A. Halstead *Concert*
(11/92) (MSVE) ① **MSCD419**
**Symphony in C, 'con violino obligato',
VB138**
Concerto Cologne (r1992) *Concert*
(9/93) (CAPR) ① **10 430**
Symphony in C minor, VB142 (1783)
Cologne Concerto (r1991) *Concert*
(8/92) (CAPR) ① **10 396**
Stuttgart CO, M. Sieghart *Concert*
(11/92) (ORFE) ① **C254921A**
OAE, A. Halstead *Concert*
(11/92) (MSVE) ① **MSCD419**
Symphony in C sharp minor, VB140 (1781)
Concerto Cologne (r1992) *Concert*
(9/93) (CAPR) ① **10 430**
Symphony in D, VB143 (?1783)
Cologne Concerto (r1991) *Concert*
(8/92) (CAPR) ① **10 396**
Symphony in E flat, VB144 (c1784)
Cologne Concerto (r1991) *Concert*
(8/92) (CAPR) ① **10 396**

SECTION II: CHAMBER

Quintet in D—flute and string quartet, VB184
(1783)
L. Weman, J. Schröder, P. Sandklef, B. Sjögren, K.
Ottesen *Concert* (2/93) (MSVE) ① **MSCD415**
Sonata in C—violin and piano, VB164
J. Schröder, L. Negro *Concert*
(2/93) (MSVE) ① **MSCD415**
Sonata in D minor—violin, cello and piano,
VB158 (?1777)
N-E. Sparf, M. Wieslander, K. Ottesen *Concert*
(2/93) (MSVE) ① **MSCD415**
Trio in D—violin, cello and piano, VB172
(?1787)
L. Negro, J. Schröder, K. Ottesen *Concert*
(2/93) (MSVE) ① **MSCD415**

SECTION V: STAGE WORKS

Olympie—incidental music, VB29 (c1785)
1. Overture.
1. OAE, A. Halstead *Concert*
(11/92) (MSVE) ① **MSCD419**

KRAUSSOLD, Lorenz (1803–1881) Germany

SECTION IV: VOCAL AND CHORAL

Abschied im Herbst—Lied (Wds. Ludwig I)
D. Fischer-Dieskau, D. Klöcker, H. Höll *Concert*
(4/88) (ORFE) ① **C153861A**

KRAUZE, Zygmunt (b 1938) Poland

SECTION II: CHAMBER

Quatuor pour la Naissance—clarinet, violin,
cello and piano (1985)
J. MacGregor, M. Mitchell, C. Van Kampen, D.
Campbell (r1993) *Messiaen: Quatuor.*
(6/94) (COLL) ① **Coll1393-2**

KREBS, Johann Ludwig (1713–1780) Germany

SECTION II: CHAMBER

Es ist gewisslich an der Zeit—chorale
prelude: organ and instrumental ensemble
(c1743)
E. Swanborn, J. Tinsley *Concert*
(12/89) (NORT) ① **NR211-CD**
Fantasia a 4 in F—oboe and organ
E. Swanborn, T. Valentine *Concert*
(12/89) (NORT) ① **NR211-CD**
Fantasia in G minor—oboe and organ
E. Swanborn, T. Valentine *Concert*
(12/89) (NORT) ① **NR211-CD**
Gott der Vater wohn' uns bei—chorale
prelude: organ and instrumental ensemble
E. Swanborn, J. Tinsley *Concert*
(12/89) (NORT) ① **NR211-CD**

J. Weber (r1992: arr pf: Rachmaninov) *Concert*
(12/93) (CARL) ① **PCD1051**
F. Kreisler, C. Lamson (r1926: two vers) *Concert*
(12/93) (BIDD) ① **LAB075**
H. Shelley (r1991: arr pf: Rachmaninov) *Concert*
(3/94) (HYPE) ① [8] **CDS44041/8**
A. A. Meyers, S. Rivers (r1993) *Concert*
(4/95) (RCA) ① **09026 62546-2**
V. Spivakov, S. Bezrodny (r1991-2) *Concert*
(5/95) (RCA) ① **09026 62524-2**
I. Perlman, S. Sanders *Concert*
(6/95) (EMI) ① [20] **CZS4 83177-2(2)**
H. Szeryng, C. Reiner (r1963) *Concert*
(12/95) (MERC) ① **434 351-2MM**
E. Wild (r1995: trans pf: Rachmaninov) *Concert*
(12/95) (SONY) ① **SK62036**
Marche miniature viennoise—violin and piano
F. Kreisler, H. Kreisler, C. Keith (r1924) *Concert*
(7/90) (BIDD) ① [2] **LAB009/10**
F. Kreisler, H. Kreisler, M. Raucheisen (r1927) *Concert*
(9/92) (BIDD) ① [2] **LAB049/50**
Midori, R. McDonald (r1992) *Concert*
(6/93) (SONY) ① **SK52568**
Menuet in the style of Porpora
J. Heifetz, A. Benoist (r1918) *Concert*
(1/91) (BIDD) ① **LAB015**
J. Heifetz, A. Benoist (r1918) *Concert*
(11/94) (RCA) ① [65] **09026 61778-2(01)**
H. Szeryng, C. Reiner (r1963) *Concert*
(12/95) (MERC) ① **434 351-2MM**
Paraphrase on two Russian folksongs—violin and piano
F. Kreisler, C. Lamson (r1925) *Concert*
(9/93) (BIDD) ① [2] **LAB068/9**
Polichinelle—serenade: violin and piano
F. Kreisler, M. Raucheisen (r1930) *Concert*
(12/93) (EMI) ① **CDH7 64701-2**
Praeludium and Allegro in the style of Pugnani
K-W. Chung, P. Moll *Concert*
(9/87) (DECC) ① **417 289-2DH**
A. Busch, B. Seidler-Winkler (r1922) *Concert*
(6/93) (SYMP) ① **SYMCD1109**
Midori, R. McDonald (r1992) *Concert*
(6/93) (SONY) ① **SK52568**
N. Milstein, L. Pommers (r1959) *Concert*
(5/94) (EMI) ① [6] **ZDMF7 64830-2**
H. Szeryng, C. Reiner (r1963) *Concert*
(12/95) (MERC) ① **434 351-2MM**
Précieuse in the style of Couperin
F. Kreisler, H. Squire (r1911) *Concert*
(7/90) (BIDD) ① [2] **LAB009/10**
F. Kreisler, M. Raucheisen (r1930) *Concert*
(12/93) (EMI) ① **CDH7 64701-2**
Rondino on a Theme by Beethoven
F. Kreisler, C. Lamson (r1928) *Concert*
(1/90) (PEAR) ① **GEMMCD9324**
F. Kreisler, F. Rupp (r1938) *Concert*
(12/93) (EMI) ① **CDH7 64701-2**
F. Kreisler, C. Lamson (r1928) *Concert*
(12/93) (BIDD) ① **LAB080**
H. Szeryng, C. Reiner (r1963) *Concert*
(12/95) (MERC) ① **434 351-2MM**
Scherzo in the style of Dittersdorf
F. Kreisler, H. Squire (r1908) *Concert*
(1/90) (PEAR) ① **GEMMCD9324**
F. Kreisler, H. Squire (r1911) *Concert*
(7/90) (BIDD) ① [2] **LAB009/10**
A. Busch, B. Seidler-Winkler (r1922) *Concert*
(6/93) (SYMP) ① **SYMCD1109**
Kreisler Qt (r1935) *Concert*
(12/93) (EMI) ① **CDH7 64701-2**
Schön Rosmarin—violin and piano
V. Vaidman, E. Krasovsky *Concert*
(6/90) (CARL) ① **PWK1137**
R. Holmes, J. Walker (r1974) *Concert*
(5/92) (DECC) ① **433 220-2DWO**
A. Grumiaux, R. Castagnone (r1958) *Concert*
(11/93) (PHIL) ① [3] **438 516-2PM3**
F. Kreisler, F. Rupp (r1938) *Concert*
(12/93) (EMI) ① **CDH7 64701-2**
F. Kreisler, C. Lamson (r1927) *Concert*
(12/93) (BIDD) ① **LAB075**
M. Vengerov, I. Golan (r1993) *Concert*
(4/94) (TELD) ① **9031-77351-2**
V. Spivakov, S. Bezrodny (r1991-2) *Concert*
(5/95) (RCA) ① **09026 62524-2**
I. Perlman, S. Sanders (r1985) *Concert*
(6/95) (EMI) ① [20] **CZS4 83177-2(2)**
H. Szeryng, C. Reiner (r1963) *Concert*
(12/95) (MERC) ① **434 351-2MM**
Shepherd's Madrigal—violin and piano
F. Kreisler, C. Lamson (r1927) *Concert*
(12/93) (BIDD) ① **LAB075**

Siciliano and Rigaudon in the style of Francoeur—violin and piano
J. Szigeti, K. Ruhrseitz (r1926) *Concert*
(1/90) (BIDD) ① [2] **LAB005/6**
J. Heifetz, A. Benoist (r1918) *Concert*
(1/91) (BIDD) ① **LAB015**
A. Campoli, S. Crooke *Concert*
(10/91) (PEAR) ① **PASTCD9744**
Y. Menuhin, A. Balsam (r1932) *Concert*
(12/91) (BIDD) ① **LAB046**
T. Varga, M. Schwalb (r1938) *Concert*
(11/93) (CLAV) ① **CD50-9314**
T. Varga, M. Schwalb (r1938) *Concert*
(11/93) (CLAV) ① [4] **CD50-9300/4**
J. Heifetz, A. Benoist (r1918) *Concert*
(11/94) (RCA) ① [65] **09026 61778-2(01)**
I. Perlman, S. Sanders *Concert*
(6/95) (EMI) ① [20] **CZS4 83177-2(2)**
String Quartet in A minor (1919)
Portland Qt (r1984) *R.Strauss: String Quartet, Op. 2.*
(4/88) (ARAB) ① **Z6521**
Syncopation—violin and piano
F. Kreisler, H. Kreisler, C. Keith (r1924) *Concert*
(7/90) (BIDD) ① [2] **LAB009/10**
F. Kreisler, H. Kreisler, M. Raucheisen (r1927) *Concert*
(9/92) (BIDD) ① [2] **LAB049/50**
Midori, R. McDonald (r1992) *Concert*
(6/93) (SONY) ① **SK52568**
I. Perlman, S. Sanders *Concert*
(6/95) (EMI) ① [20] **CZS4 83177-2(2)**
Tambourin chinois—violin and piano
F. Kreisler, C. Lamson (r1928) *Concert*
(1/90) (PEAR) ① **GEMMCD9324**
J. Szigeti, K. Ruhrseitz (r1927) *Concert*
(1/90) (BIDD) ① [2] **LAB005/6**
F. Kreisler, H. Squire (r1911) *Concert*
(7/90) (BIDD) ① [2] **LAB009/10**
Y. Menuhin, M. Gazelle (r1935) *Concert*
(9/91) (TEST) ① **SBT1003**
A. Grumiaux, R. Castagnone (r1958) *Concert*
(11/93) (PHIL) ① [3] **438 516-2PM3**
F. Kreisler, F. Rupp (r1936) *Concert*
(12/93) (EMI) ① **CDH7 64701-2**
F. Kreisler, C. Lamson (r1928) *Concert*
(12/93) (BIDD) ① **LAB080**
M. Vengerov, I. Golan (r1993) *Concert*
(4/94) (TELD) ① **9031-77351-2**
I. Perlman, S. Sanders *Concert*
(6/95) (EMI) ① [20] **CZS4 83177-2(2)**
H. Szeryng, C. Reiner (r1963) *Concert*
(12/95) (MERC) ① **434 351-2MM**
Tempo di Menuetto in the style of Pugnani
G. Enescu, S. Schlüssel (r1929) *Concert*
(12/91) (MSCM) ① **MM30322**
S. Chang, S. Rivers *Concert*
(1/93) (EMI) ① **CDC7 54352-2**
G. Enescu, S. Schlüssel (r1929) *Concert*
(6/93) (BIDD) ① **LAB066**
I. Perlman, S. Sanders (r1985) *Concert*
(6/95) (EMI) ① [20] **CZS4 83177-2(2)**
H. Szeryng, C. Reiner (r1963) *Concert*
(12/95) (MERC) ① **434 351-2MM**
Toy Soldier's march—violin and piano
F. Kreisler, C. Lamson (r1921) *Concert*
(9/93) (BIDD) ① [2] **LAB068/9**
I. Perlman, S. Sanders *Concert*
(6/95) (EMI) ① [20] **CZS4 83177-2(2)**
Variations on a theme of Corelli in the style of Tartini—violin and piano (c1910)
A. Campoli, S. Crooke *Concert*
(10/91) (PEAR) ① **PASTCD9744**
G. Neveu, G. Beck (r1939) *Concert*
(10/92) (TEST) ① **SBT1010**

SECTION III: INSTRUMENTAL

Recitative and scherzo-caprice—violin, Op. 6
A. A. Meyers (r1993) *Concert*
(4/95) (RCA) ① **09026 62546-2**
I. Perlman *Concert*
(6/95) (EMI) ① [20] **CZS4 83177-2(2)**
H. Szeryng (r1963) *Concert*
(12/95) (MERC) ① **434 351-2MM**

SECTION IV: VOCAL AND CHORAL

The Old Refrain
P. Domingo, I. Perlman, NY Studio Orch, J. Tunick
(r1990) *Concert* (3/92) (EMI) ① **CDC7 54266-2**
H. Szeryng, C. Reiner (r1963) *Concert*
(12/95) (MERC) ① **434 351-2MM**

SECTION V: STAGE WORKS

Apple Blossoms—operetta (1919)
I'm in love; Letter song H. Kreisler, F. Kreisler
(r1921: arr. Kreisler) *Concert*
(7/90) (BIDD) ① [2] **LAB009/10**

KREISLER, Hugo (1884–1929)
Austria

SECTION II: CHAMBER

Viennese Folksong Fantasy—cello and piano
H. Kreisler, F. Kreisler (r1921) *Concert*
(7/90) (BIDD) ① [2] **LAB009/10**

KRENEK, Ernst (1900–1991)
Austria/USA

SECTION I: ORCHESTRAL

Potpourri—orchestra, Op. 54 (1927)
N German Rad PO, T. Ukigaya (r1993) *Symphony 3.*
(9/95) (CPO) ① **CPO999 236-2**
Symphony No. 3, Op. 16 (1922)
N German Rad PO, T. Ukigaya (r1993) *Potpourri, Op. 54.*
(9/95) (CPO) ① **CPO999 236-2**

SECTION II: CHAMBER

String Quartet No. 3, Op. 20 (1923)
Sonare Qt *String Quartet 7.* (1/89) (MDG) ① **L3281**
String Quartet No. 7, Op. 96 (1943-44)
Sonare Qt *String Quartet 3.* (1/89) (MDG) ① **L3281**

SECTION III: INSTRUMENTAL

Echoes from Austria—piano, Op. 166 (1958)
G.D. Madge *Concert*
(4/93) (CPO) ① **CPO999 099-2**
George Washington Variations—piano, Op. 120 (1950)
G.D. Madge *Concert*
(4/93) (CPO) ① **CPO999 099-2**
Little Suite—piano, Op. 13a (1922)
G.D. Madge *Concert*
(4/93) (CPO) ① **CPO999 099-2**
Piano Sonata No. 1 in E flat, Op. 2 (1919)
G.D. Madge *Concert* (6/92) (SCHW) ① **310047**
Piano Sonata No. 2, Op. 59 (1928)
G.D. Madge *Concert* (6/92) (SCHW) ① **310048**
M. Bratke (r1993) *Concert*
(4/94) (OLYM) ① **OCD431**
M. Yudina (r1961) *Concert*
(8/95) (MELO) ① **74321 25176-2**
M. Yudina (r1961) *Concert*
(8/95) (MELO) ① [11] **74321 25172-2(1)**
Piano Sonata No. 3, Op. 92/4 (1943)
G.D. Madge *Concert* (6/92) (SCHW) ① **310047**
M. Bratke (r1993) *Concert*
(4/94) (OLYM) ① **OCD431**
Piano Sonata No. 4 (1948)
G.D. Madge *Concert* (6/92) (SCHW) ① **310048**
Piano Sonata No. 5 (1950)
G.D. Madge *Concert* (6/92) (SCHW) ① **310047**
Piano Sonata No. 6 (1951)
G.D. Madge *Concert* (6/92) (SCHW) ① **310048**
Piano Sonata No. 7, Op. 240 (1988)
G.D. Madge *Concert* (6/92) (SCHW) ① **310048**
Toccata and Chaconne—piano, Op. 13
G.D. Madge *Concert*
(4/93) (CPO) ① **CPO999 099-2**
12 Variations in three movements—piano, Op. 79 (1937 rev 1940 and 1957)
G.D. Madge *Concert*
(4/93) (CPO) ① **CPO999 099-2**

SECTION IV: VOCAL AND CHORAL

Lamentatio Jeremiae prophetae—chorus a capella, Op. 93 (1941-42)
Netherlands Chbr Ch, U. Gronostay (r1992)
(10/92) (GLOB) ① **GLO5085**
Berlin RIAS Chbr Ch, M. Creed (r1992)
(7/95) (HARM) ① **HMC90 1551**
Reisbuch aus den österreichischen Alpen—song cycle, Op. 62 (1929) (Wds. cpsr)
1. Motiv; 2. Verkehr; 3. Kloster in den Alpen; 4. Wetter; 5. Traurige Stunde; 6. Friedhof im Gebirgsdorf; 7. Regentag; 8. Unser Wein; 9. Rückblick; 10. Auf und Ab; 11. Alpenbewohner; 12. Politik; 13. Gewitter; 14. Heimweh; 15. Heisser Tag am See; 16. Kleine Stadt in den südlichen Alpen; 17. Ausblick nach Süden; 18. Entscheidung; 19. Heimkehr; 20. Epilog.
Cpte M. Köhler, R. Schmiedel (r1992)
(10/93) (CPO) ① **CPO999 203-2**

SECTION V: STAGE WORKS

**Jonny spielt auf—opera: 2 acts, Op. 45
(1927—Leipzig)** (Lib. cpsr)
Cpte K. St. Hill, H. Kruse, A. Marc, M. Kraus, M.
Posselt, D. Scholz, M. Petzold, M. Weichert, E.
Noack, Leipzig Op Chor, Chinchilla, Leipzig
Gewandhaus, L. Zagrosek (r1991)
　　　　　(4/93) (DECC) ① [2] **436 631-2DH2**

KREUTZER, Conradin
(1780–1849) Germany

SECTION II: CHAMBER

**Grand Septet in E flat—cl, hn, bn, vn, va, vc
& db, Op. 62**
Charis Ens Witt: *Septet in F.*
　　　　　(11/87) (MDG) ① **L3232**

SECTION IV: VOCAL AND CHORAL

Das Mühlrad—Lied (Wds. Uhland)
D. Fischer-Dieskau, K. Wallendorf, H. Höll *Concert*
　　　　　(4/88) (ORFE) ① **C153861A**

SECTION V: STAGE WORKS

**Das Nachtlager in (von) Granada—romantic
opera (2 acts) (1834—Vienna)** (Lib. von Braun,
after Kind)
1. Overture. ACT ONE: 2. Da mir alles nun entrissen;
3a. Wie traurig und wie schön; 3b. Trauernd trieb ich
meine Herde; 4. Ach, könnt ich mit ihm gehn!; 5a.
Nun, Gott, sei Dank; 5b. Ein Schütz bin ich; 6. Welch
feurig Aug!; 7. Hinweg!; 8a. Vom Berg ziehn wir
hernieder; 8b. Zeigt dem Gast dass er wilkommen;
8c. Nun, liebes Mädchen; 8d. Wer klagt am
Gitterfenster; 8e. Schon die Abendglocken klangen.
ACT TWO: 9a. Wem mag das Ross wohl angehören;
9b. Nur froh vertraut der Hunde Laut; 10. Nun saget,
lieber Herr; 11. Die Nacht ist schön; 12a. Leise
wehet, leise wallet; 12b. Wacht auf, o Herr; 12c. Nicht
ohne Grund scheint ihr Verdacht!; 12d. Ist alles still?;
13a. Ha, Bube!; 13b. Was soll des Hornes Ruf
bedeuten?; 14a. Doch nun zu dir, du Holde; 14b.
Trenne nicht das Band der Liebe.
Cpte H. Prey, R. Klepper, M. Pabst, W.M. Friedrich,
C. Hauptmann, M. Blasius, Cologne Rad Chor,
Cologne RSO, H. Froschauer (r1992)
　　　　　(1/94) (CAPR) ① [2] **60 029**
11. T. Hampson, Munich RO, F. Luisi (r1994) *Concert*
　　　　　(9/95) (EMI) ① **CDC5 55233-2**

KŘIČKA, Jaroslav (1882–1969)
Czechoslovakia

SECTION IV: VOCAL AND CHORAL

L' Albatros—song, Op. 14/1 (Wds. K
Balmont)
P. Frijsh, D. Bucktrout (r1932) *Concert*
　　　　　(4/95) (PEAR) ① [2] **GEMMCDS9095(2)**

KRIEGER, Adam (1634–1666)
Germany

SECTION IV: VOCAL AND CHORAL

Ihr bleibet nicht Bestand verpflicht—Lied
A. Scholl, P. Valetti, S. Pfister, F. Heumann, J. M.
Quintana, A. Verzier, K. E. Schröder, M. Märkl
(r1994) *Concert*　　(5/95) (HARM) ① **HMC90 1505**
**Der Liebe Macht herrscht Tag und
Nacht—Lied**
A. Scholl, P. Valetti, S. Pfister, F. Heumann, J. M.
Quintana, A. Verzier, K. E. Schröder, M. Märkl
(r1994) *Concert*　　(5/95) (HARM) ① **HMC90 1505**
Die Liebesgluth verkehrt den Muth—Lied
A. Scholl, P. Valetti, S. Pfister, F. Heumann, J. M.
Quintana, A. Verzier, K. E. Schröder, M. Märkl
(r1994) *Concert*　　(5/95) (HARM) ① **HMC90 1505**
Der Rheinische Wein—Lied
A. Scholl, P. Valetti, S. Pfister, F. Heumann, J. M.
Quintana, A. Verzier, K. E. Schröder, M. Märkl
(r1994) *Concert*　　(5/95) (HARM) ① **HMC90 1505**

KRIEGER, Johann Philipp
(1649–1725) Germany

SECTION II: CHAMBER

**Sonata a doi—violin, viola da gamba &
continuo, Op. 2 (1693)**
P. Valetti, F. Heumann, M. Märkl (r1994) *Concert*
　　　　　(5/95) (HARM) ① **HMC90 1505**

SECTION IV: VOCAL AND CHORAL

**An die Einsamkeit—Lied from opera
'Procris' (pub 1690)**
R. Jacobs, K. Junghänel (r1985) *Concert*
　　　　　(5/87) (HARM) ① **HMA190 1183**
A. Scholl, A. Verzier, K. E. Schröder, M. Märkl
(r1994) *Concert*　　(5/95) (HARM) ① **HMC90 1505**
**Die Heissverliebte—Lied from opera 'Flora'
(pub 1690)**
A. Scholl, A. Verzier, K. E. Schröder, M. Märkl
(r1994) *Concert*　　(5/95) (HARM) ① **HMC90 1505**
**Die Holde Nacht—Lied from opera
'Cecrops' (pub 1690)**
A. Scholl, A. Verzier, K. E. Schröder, M. Märkl
(r1994) *Concert*　　(5/95) (HARM) ① **HMC90 1505**
**Schmilz, hartes Herz—Lied from opera
'Cecrops' (pub 1690)**
A. Scholl, P. Valetti, S. Pfister, F. Heumann, A.
Verzier, K. E. Schröder, M. Märkl (r1994) *Concert*
　　　　　(5/95) (HARM) ① **HMC90 1505**
**Verliebtes Weinen und Lachen—Lied from
opera 'Flora' (pub 1690)**
A. Scholl, A. Verzier, K. E. Schröder, M. Märkl
(r1994) *Concert*　　(5/95) (HARM) ① **HMC90 1505**

KROLL, William (1901–1980)
USA

SECTION II: CHAMBER

Banjo and Fiddle—violin and piano
L. Mordkovitch, M. Gusak-Grin *Concert*
　　　　　(11/90) (CHAN) ① **CHAN8748**
K. Daeshik Kang, M. Rahkonen (r1992) *Concert*
　　　　　(9/93) (NIMB) ① **NI5358**
J. Heifetz, E. Bay (r1947) *Concert*
　　　　　(11/94) (RCA) ① [65] **09026 61778-2(40)**

KROMMER, Franz (Vinzenz)
(1759–1831) Bohemia

born František Kramář Vincenc

SECTION I: ORCHESTRAL

**Concertino for Flute, Oboe and Orchestra in
C, Op. 65 (c1810)** (arr cpsr from String Quartet,
Op. 24)
P.-L. Graf, H. Holliger, ECO *Concert*
　　　　　(12/85) (CLAV) ① **CD50-8203**
Concerto for Clarinet and Orchestra, Op. 86
(orig. for flute)
T. Friedli, ECO, A. Pay *Concert*
　　　　　(2/87) (CLAV) ① **CD50-8602**
**Concerto for Clarinet and Orchestra in E flat,
Op. 36 (1803)**
T. Friedli, ECO, A. Pay *Concert*
　　　　　(2/87) (CLAV) ① **CD50-8602**
E. Johnson, RPO, G. Herbig *Concert*
　　　　　(9/91) (ASV) ① **CDDCA763**
A.O. Popa, Iaşi Moldova PO, P. Popescu *Concert*
　　　　　(9/92) (OLYM) ① **OCD418**
N. Esterházy Sinfonia, K. Berkes (cl/dir) (r1994)
Concert　　(8/95) (NAXO) ① 8 **553178**
**Concerto for Flute and Orchestra No. 1 in G,
Op. 30 (1802)**
P.-L. Graf, ECO, H. Holliger *Concert*
　　　　　(12/85) (CLAV) ① **CD50-8203**
**Concerto for Oboe and Orchestra in F, Op.
37 (1803)**
S. Francis, LMP, H. Shelley *Concert*
　　　　　(9/91) (HYPE) ① **CDA66411**
I. Goritzki, Polish Chmbr PO, W. Rajski *Concert*
　　　　　(9/91) (CLAV) ① **CD50-9018**
**Concerto for Oboe and Orchestra in F, Op.
52 (1805)**
H. Holliger, ECO, P.-L. Graf *Concert*
　　　　　(12/85) (CLAV) ① **CD50-8203**
S. Francis, LMP, H. Shelley *Concert*
　　　　　(4/91) (HYPE) ① **CDA66411**
**Concerto for Two Clarinets and Orchestra,
Op. 35 (?1802)**
T. Friedli, ECO, A. Pay (cl/dir) *Concert*
　　　　　(2/87) (CLAV) ① **CD50-8602**
K. Tsutsui, N. Esterházy Sinfonia, K. Berkes (cl/dir)
(r1994) *Concert*　　(8/95) (NAXO) ① 8 **553178**
**Concerto for Two Clarinets and Orchestra in
E flat, Op. 91 (1815)**
T. Takashima, N. Esterházy Sinfonia, K. Berkes
(cl/dir) (r1994) *Concert*　(8/95) (NAXO) ① 8 **553178**
**3 Partitas—wind ensemble, Op. 45 (pub
1803)**
1. B flat; 2. E flat; 3. B flat.
J. Triebensee Ens, J. Weierink *Partitas, Op. 45.*
　　　　　(11/92) (ETCE) ① **KTC1141**

---

2. C. Kavalovski, S. Brubaker, NY Harmonie Ens, S.
Richman (pp1990) *Concert*
　　　　　(8/92) (MUSI) ① **MACD-691**
2. J. Triebensee Ens, J. Weierink *Partitas, Op. 45.*
　　　　　(11/92) (ETCE) ① **KTC1141**
Symphony No. 2 in D, Op. 40 (pub 1803)
LMP, M. Bamert (r1993) *Symphony 4.*
　　　　　(7/94) (CHAN) ① **CHAN9275**
Symphony No. 4 in C minor, Op. 102
LMP, M. Bamert (r1993) *Symphony 2.*
　　　　　(7/94) (CHAN) ① **CHAN9275**

SECTION II: CHAMBER

**Octet-Partita in B flat—wind ensemble, Op.
67**
Nash Ens *Concert*　　(7/89) (CRD) ① **CRD3410**
**Octet-Partita in B flat—wind ensemble, Op.
78**
Meyer Wind Ens *Concert*
　　　　　(5/92) (EMI) ① **CDC7 54383-2**
Octet-Partita in C—wind ensemble, Op. 76
Meyer Wind Ens *Concert*
　　　　　(5/92) (EMI) ① **CDC7 54383-2**
**Octet-Partita in E flat—wind ensemble, Op.
71**
Meyer Wind Ens *Concert*
　　　　　(5/92) (EMI) ① **CDC7 54383-2**
Octet-Partita in E flat, Op. 79 (1807-10)
Nash Ens *Concert*　　(7/89) (CRD) ① **CRD3410**
Octet-Partita in F, Op. 57 (1807-10)
COE Wind Sols *Concert*
　　　　　(4/90) (ASV) ① **CDCOE812**
Meyer Wind Ens *Concert*
　　　　　(5/92) (EMI) ① **CDC7 54383-2**

KRUFFT, Nikolaus von
(1779–1818) Austria

SECTION II: CHAMBER

Sonata in F—horn and piano
L. Greer, S. Lubin *Concert*
　　　　　(9/92) (HARM) ① **HMU90 7037**

KUBELÍK, Rafael (b 1914)
Czechoslovakia/Switzerland

SECTION I: ORCHESTRAL

Orphikon—symphony in three movements
BRSO, R. Kubelík (pp1984) *Concert*
　　　　　(2/95) (PANT) ① **81 1264-2**

SECTION IV: VOCAL AND CHORAL

**Cantata without Words—chorus and
orchestra**
Bavarian Rad Chor, BRSO, R. Kubelík (pp1981)
Concert　　(2/95) (PANT) ① **81 1264-2**
**Inventions and Interludes—children's
chorus, 4 oboes and 4 trumpets (1946)**
Kühn Children's Chor, Inst Ens, R. Kubelík (1993)
Concert　　(2/95) (PANT) ① **81 1264-2**

KUCHYNSKA, Vojta (1871–1942)
Czechoslovakia

SECTION II: CHAMBER

Canzonette—double-bass and piano
M. Hanskov, N.E. Aggesen *Concert*
　　　　　(3/92) (DANA) ① **DACOCD378**

KÜFFNER, Joseph (1777–1856)
Germany

SECTION II: CHAMBER

**Introduction, Theme and Variations—clarinet
and strings, Op. 32** (Wrongly attrib. Weber)
H-R. Stalder, J. von Vintscher, Z. Sirokay, Zurich
Chbr Music *Concert*　　(11/87) (JECK) ① **JD536-2**

KUHLAU, (Daniel) Friedrich
(Rudolph) (1786–1832)
Germany/Denmark

SECTION I: ORCHESTRAL

**Concertino in F minor—two horns and
orchestra, Op. 45 (1821)**
I. Lazky-Otto, F.R. Werke, Odense SO, O. Maga
Concert　　(9/91) (UNIC) ① **DKPCD9110**
**Concerto for Piano and Orchestra in C, Op. 7
(1810)**
M. Ponti, Odense SO, O. Maga *Concert*
　　　　　(9/91) (UNIC) ① **DKPCD9110**

SECTION II: CHAMBER

3 Quintets—flute, violins, 2 violas and cello, Op. 51 (pub 1822)
1. D; 2. E; 3. A.
E. Rafn, K. Sjøgren, B.B. Rasmussen, G.S. Andersen, L.H. Johansen (r1985)
(10/95) (NAXO) ① **8 553303**

Sonata for Flute and Piano in A, 'Grande sonate concertante', Op. 85 (1827)
Scherzo E. Talmi, Y. Talmi Concert
(6/90) (CARL) ① **PWK1133**

SECTION III: INSTRUMENTAL

3 Sonatinas for Piano, Op. 20 (1819)
1. C; 2. G; 3. F.
D. Blumenthal (r1991) Concert
(10/93) (ETCE) ① [2] **KTC2018**

SECTION V: STAGE WORKS

The elf's hill (Elverhøj)—incidental music: 5 acts, Op. 100 (1828—Copenhagen) (Play by J.L. Heiberg)
1. Overture.
Suite Odense SO, O. Maga Concert
(5/93) (UNIC) ① **DKPCD9132**
1. Odense SO, O. Maga Concert
(9/91) (UNIC) ① **DKPCD9110**
Lulu—opera: 2 acts, Op. 65 (1824—Copenhagen) (Lib. C F Güntelberg)
EXCERPTS: 1. Overture.
1. Odense SO, E. Serov Concert
(5/93) (UNIC) ① **DKPCD9132**
The robber's castle (Røverborgen)—Singspiel (1814—Copenhagen) (Wds. A. Oehlenschlaeger)
EXCERPTS: 1. Overture.
1. Odense SO, E. Serov Concert
(5/93) (UNIC) ① **DKPCD9132**
The triplet brothers from Damascus (Trillingbrødrene fra Damask)—incidental music to Oehlenschlaeger's play, Op. 115 (1830—Copenhagen)
EXCERPTS: 1. Overture.
1. Odense SO, E. Serov Concert
(5/93) (UNIC) ① **DKPCD9132**
William Shakespeare—drama, Op. 74 (1826) (Wds. C. J. Boye)
EXCERPTS: 1. Overture.
1. Odense SO, E. Serov Concert
(5/93) (UNIC) ① **DKPCD9132**

KÜHNEL, August (1645–c1700) Germany

SECTION II: CHAMBER

14 Sonate ô Partite—va da gamba(s) and continuo (1698)
2. Sonata in E minor (2 va da gambas & bc); 11. Sonata in D minor (va da gamba solo).
2. Ricercar Consort, P. Pierlot (va da gamba/dir)
(r1992) Concert   (8/94) (RICE) ① **RIC098112**

KÜNNEKE, Eduard (1885–1953) Germany

SECTION V: STAGE WORKS

Die **Grosse Sündern—operetta: 3 acts (1935—Berlin)** (Lib. Stoll and Roemmer)
EXCERPTS: 1. Histörchen, Geschichten; 2. Das Lied vom Leben des Schrenk; 3. Immerzu singt dein Herz meinem Herzen zu; 4. Das Lied vom indischen Märchen.
1, 4. H. Roswaenge, Berlin St Op Orch, B. Seidler-Winkler (r1935) Concert
(4/95) (PREI) ① [2] **89209**
2, 3. H. Roswaenge, T. Lemnitz, Berlin St Op Orch, E. Künneke (r1935) Concert
(4/95) (PREI) ① [2] **89209**
Die **Vetter aus Dingsda—operetta: 3 acts (1921—Berlin)** (Lib Haller & Rideamus)
EXCERPTS: ACT 1: 1a. Noch ein Gläschen Bordeaux?; 1b. Onkel und Tante, ja das sind Verwandte; 2. Strahlender Mond, der am Himmelszelt thront; 3. O werter, verehrter, von Liebe Betörter...Überleg's Dir's; 4a. Hallo, hallo, hier rief's doch irgendwo; 4b. Ich hab' mich verlaufen; 4c. Sag' an, wer bist Du Holde, sag' an; 4d. Ich bin nur ein armer Wandergesell. ACT 2. Ganz unverhofft kommt oft das Glück; 5b. Wenn Du glaubst, dass ich weiss, wer das ist; 5d. Der Roderich, der Roderich; 6a. Weisst Du noch, wie wir als Kinder gespiel?; 6b. Kindchen, Du musst nicht so schrecklich viel denken; 7a. Ich hab' an sie nur stets gedacht; 7b. Mann, o Mann; 8. Sieben Jahre lebt' ich in Batavia; 9a. Nicht

wahr, hier ist's wie im Zauberreich; 9b. Und im Märchen, da wurden die beiden ein Paar; 9c. Ich bin nur ein armer Wandergesell; 10. Ach Heil'ger Nikolaus. ACT 3: 11a. Ganz unverhofft kommt oft das Glück; 11b. Dort ist er, dort steht er, der Lump, der Verräter; 11c. Er ist's, er ist's, der Augustin!.
1a, 1b, 2, 3, 4a-d, 5a-d, 6a, 6b, 7a, 7b, 8, 9a-c, 10, 11a-c R. Holm, U. Schirrmacher, E. Krukowski, B. Mira, K-E. Mercker, R. Schock, C. Nicolai, Berlin SO, W. Schmidt-Boelcke   (2/91) (EURO) ① **GD69025**

KUPFERMAN, Meyer (b 1926) USA

SECTION III: INSTRUMENTAL

Moonflower, Baby!—clarinet (1986)
J. Cohler (r1993) Concert
(5/95) (CRYS) ① **Crystal CD733**

KURTÁG, György (b 1926) Hungary

SECTION II: CHAMBER

Hommage à Mihály András—12 Microludes—string quartet, Op. 13 (1977-78)
Arditti Qt Concert   (4/92) (MONT) ① **789007**
Officium breve in memoriam Andreae Szervánszky—string quartet, Op. 28
Arditti Qt Concert   (4/92) (MONT) ① **789007**
Quartetto per archi, Op. 1 (1959)
Arditti Qt Concert   (4/92) (MONT) ① **789007**
...Quasi una Fantasia..—piano and groups of instruments, Op. 27 (1987)
C. Whittlesey, H. Kretzschmar, Modern Ens (r1990) Concert   (12/93) (SONY) ① **SK53290**

SECTION III: INSTRUMENTAL

Plays and Games, Books 1-4—piano (1973-76)
1. Book 1; 2. Book 2; 3. Book 3; 4. Book 4.
3 (excs) P. Frankl (r?1992) Concert
(6/93) (ASV) ① **CDDCA860**

SECTION IV: VOCAL AND CHORAL

Messages of the late Miss R. V. Troussova—soprano and chamber ensemble, Op. 17 (1976-80)
1. Loneliness; 2. A Little Erotic; 3. Bitter Experience—Delight and Grief.
R. Hardy, Modern Ens, P. Eötvös (r1990) Concert
(12/93) (SONY) ① **SK53290**
Scenes from a Novel—soprano: 1v, violin, double-bass and cimbalom, Op. 19 (1981-82) (Wds. R. Dalos)
1. Come; 2. From meeting to parting; 3. Supplication; 4. Allow me; 5. Counting-out rhyme; 6. Dream; 7. Rondo; 8. Nakedness; 9. Hardy-gurdy waltz; 10. Tale; 11. Again; 12. Sundays; 13. Visit; 14. True story; 15. Epilogue.
C. Whittlesey, Modern Ens, P. Eötvös (r1990) Concert   (12/93) (SONY) ① **SK53290**

KUTAVIČIUS, Bronius (b 1932) Lithuania/USSR

SECTION I: ORCHESTRAL

Northern Gates (1991)
Ostrobothnian CO, J. Kangas (r1994) Concert
(11/95) (FINL) ① **4509-97893-2**

KUZDO, Victor (1859–1966) Hungary

SECTION III: INSTRUMENTAL

2 Pieces—violin, Op. 25
EXCERPTS: 2. Witches' Dance.
2. E. Brown (r c1922) Concert
(7/93) (APR) ① [2] **APR7016**

KVANDAL, Johann (b 1919) Norway

SECTION II: CHAMBER

Nonet No. 1—eight wind instruments and double-bass, Op. 54 (1946 rev 1980)
Norwegian Wind Ens Concert
(7/89) (SIMA) ① **PSC1037**
Nonet No. 2—eight wind instruments and double-bass, Op. 57 (1981)
Norwegian Wind Ens Concert
(7/89) (SIMA) ① **PSC1037**

3 Sacred Folktunes—flute, oboe, clarinet, horn and bassoon, Op. 23b (1963)
Oslo Wind Qnt (r1993) Concert
(3/95) (NAXO) ① **8 553050**
Wind Quintet—flute, oboe, clarinet, horn & bassoon, Op. 34 (1971)
Oslo Wind Qnt (r1993) Concert
(3/95) (NAXO) ① **8 553050**

SECTION III: INSTRUMENTAL

Guitar Sonata, Op. 65 (1985-86)
S-E. Olsen Concert   (9/88) (SIMA) ① **PSC1031**

L. H. OF LIVERPOOL, Miss (18th–19th Cent) England

SECTION IV: VOCAL AND CHORAL

My Mother—song (Wds Ann Taylor)
A. Rolfe Johnson, G. Johnson (r1991/3) Concert
(8/94) (HYPE) ① **CDA66709**

LA BARRE, Michel de (c1675–1743/4) France

SECTION II: CHAMBER

Pièces pour la Flûte transversière, Book II—flute and continuo
9. G.
9. R. Brown, J. Johnstone Concert
(2/94) (CHAN) ① **CHAN0544**

LA CEPPEDE, Jean de (1548–1623) France

SECTION IV: VOCAL AND CHORAL

Mais qui vous meut
A. Azéma (r1994) Concert
(11/95) (ERAT) ① **4509-98480-2**

LA RUE, Pierre de (c1460–1518) Flanders

SECTION IV: VOCAL AND CHORAL

Autant en Emporte le Vent—chanson (from Chanson album of Marguerite)
C. Janequin Ens, D. Visse (r1994) Concert
(5/95) (HARM) ① **HMC90 1453**
Missa, '(L')homme armé'—4vv
Ars Nova, B. Holten Concert
(5/89) (KONT) ① **32008**
C. Janequin Ens Missa pro defunctis.
(9/89) (HARM) ① **HMC90 1296**
Missa pro defunctis—4vv
New London Chmbr Ch, J. Wood Concert
(3/87) (AMON) ① **CD-SAR24**
Ars Nova, B. Holten Concert
(11/87) (KONT) ① **32001**
C. Janequin Ens Missa L'homme armé.
(9/89) (HARM) ① **HMC90 1296**
O salutaris hostia—motet: 4vv (may replace 'Osanna' in 'Missa de S Anna')
J. Garbarek, Hilliard Ens (r1993) Concert
(10/94) (ECM) ① **445 369-2**

LABITZKY, Joseph (1802–1881) Bohemia

SECTION I: ORCHESTRAL

Sylvia—March
Czech PO, V. Neumann Concert
(6/87) (ORFE) ① **C107101A**

LABSKÝ, Jaroslav (1875–1949) Bohemia

SECTION I: ORCHESTRAL

Olympiade—March
Czech PO, V. Neumann Concert
(6/87) (ORFE) ① **C107201A**

LACALLE, Joseph M. (1859–1937) Spain/USA

SECTION IV: VOCAL AND CHORAL

Amapola—song (1941) (Wds. cpsr)
T. Schipa, orch, J. Pasternack (r1926) Concert
(12/89) (RCA) ① **GD87969**
J. Carreras, P. Domingo, L. Pavarotti, MMF Orch, Rome Op Orch, Z. Mehta (pp1990) Concert
(10/90) (DECC) ① **430 433-2DH**

LACHENMANN, Helmut Friedrich (b 1935) Germany

SECTION III: INSTRUMENTAL

5 Variations on a Theme of Franz Schubert—piano (1958)
L. Vogt *Concert* (5/92) (EMI) ① **CDC7 54446-2**

LACHNER, Franz Paul (1803–1890) Germany

SECTION I: ORCHESTRAL

Ball-Suite in D, Op. 170 (pub 1874)
Košice St PO, A. Walter (r1993) *Symphony 8.*
(3/95) (MARC) ① **8 223594**
Symphony No. 1 in E flat, Op. 32 (pub 1828)
Singapore SO, C. Huey (r1985) *Spohr: Symphony 2.*
(10/86) (MARC) ① **8 220360**
Symphony No. 5 in C minor, 'Preis-Symphonie', Op. 52 (1835)
Košice St PO, P. Robinson (r1992)
(5/94) (MARC) ① **8 223502**
Symphony No. 8 in G minor, Op. 100 (pub 1851)
Košice St PO, P. Robinson (r1992) *Ball-Suite, Op. 170.*
(3/95) (MARC) ① **8 223594**

SECTION II: CHAMBER

Andante in A flat—4 hns, 2 tpts & 3 tbns (1833)
London Gabrieli Brass Ens, C. Larkin *Concert*
(4/92) (HYPE) ① **CDA66470**

LADMIRAULT, Paul (Emile) (1877–1944) France

SECTION II: CHAMBER

Dan Lullaby—piano: four hands
I. Beyer, H. Dagul *Concert*
(10/92) (FOUR) ① **FHMD9212**

SECTION III: INSTRUMENTAL

Hommage à Gabriel Fauré—piano
M. Fingerhut *Concert* (9/88) (CHAN) ① **CHAN8578**

LAJTHA, László (1892–1963) Hungary

SECTION I: ORCHESTRAL

Suite No. 3, Op. 56 (1953)
Pécs SO, N. Pasquet (r1994) *Concert*
(4/95) (MARC) ① **8 223667**
2 Symphonic Pictures—concert suite from film 'Hortobágy', Op. 21 (1946)
1. The great Hungarian Plain (Andante); 2. Gallop in the Puszta (Presto).
Pécs SO, N. Pasquet (r1994) *Concert*
(4/95) (MARC) ① **8 223667**
Symphony No. 7, 'Revolution', Op. 63 (1957)
Pécs SO, N. Pasquet (r1994) *Concert*
(4/95) (MARC) ① **8 223667**

SECTION III: INSTRUMENTAL

3 Berceuses—piano (1955-57)
1. For Terry; 2. For Christopher; 3. For Kathryn and Adrian.
K. Körmendi *Concert* (4/93) (MARC) ① **8 223473**
Contes—piano, Op. 2 (1915)
K. Körmendi *Concert* (4/93) (MARC) ① **8 223473**
Des écrits d'un musicien—piano, Op. 1 (1913)
K. Körmendi *Concert* (4/93) (MARC) ① **8 223473**
6 Pieces—piano, Op. 14 (1930)
1. Ostinato; 2. Invention for two voices; 3. Invention for three voices; 4. Scherzo; 5. Fugue; 6. Toccata.
K. Körmendi *Concert* (4/93) (MARC) ① **8 223473**
Prélude—piano (1918)
K. Körmendi *Concert* (4/93) (MARC) ① **8 223473**

LALO, Edouard(-Victoire-Antoine) (1823–1892) France

SECTION I: ORCHESTRAL

Concerto for Cello and Orchestra in D minor (1877)
M. Haimovitz, Chicago SO, James Levine *Concert*
(6/89) (DG) ① **427 323-2GH**
H. Schiff, New Philh, C. Mackerras *Concert*
(8/91) (DG) ① **431 166-2GR**

J. Starker, LSO, S. Skrowaczewski *Concert*
(4/92) (MERC) ① **432 010-2MM**
L. Rose, Philadelphia, E. Ormandy (r1967) *Concert*
(5/93) (SONY) ① **SBK48278**
S. Rolland, BBC PO, G. Varga *Concert*
(12/93) (ASV) ① **CDDCA867**
L. Harrell, Berlin RSO, R. Chailly (r1984) *Concert*
(2/94) (DECC) ① **436 483-2DM**
A. Noras, Finnish RSO, J-P. Saraste (r1993) *Elgar:
Cello Concerto.* (12/94) (FINL) ① **4509-95768-2**
P. Fournier, Lamoureux Orch, J. Martinon (r c1960)
Concert (5/95) (DG) ① [2] **437 371-2GX2**
J. Du Pré, Cleveland Orch, D. Barenboim (pp1973)
R. Strauss: Don Quixote.
(11/95) (EMI) ① **CDC5 55528-2**
Concerto for Violin and Orchestra in F, Op. 20 (1873)
A. Dumay, Toulouse Capitole Orch, M. Plasson
Symphonie espagnole.
(2/90) (EMI) ① **CDC7 49833-2**
Fantaisie norvégienne—violin and orchestra (1878)
J. Thibaud, T. Janopoulo (r1930: arr vn/pf: 2 vers)
Concert (12/94) (APR) ① [2] **APR7028**
Rapsodie norvégienne—orchestra (1879)
RPO, Y. Butt *Concert* (10/90) (ASV) ① **CDDCA709**
FRNO, J. Martinon (r c1970) *Concert*
(5/95) (DG) ① [2] **437 371-2GX2**
Scherzo (1884)
RPO, Y. Butt *Concert* (10/90) (ASV) ① **CDDCA709**
Symphonie espagnole—violin and orchestra, Op. 21 (1873)
1. Allegro non troppo; 2. Scherzando (Allegro molto);
3. Intermezzo (Allegretto non troppo); 4. Andante; 5.
Rondo (Allegro).
A-S. Mutter, FNO, S. Ozawa *Sarasate:
Zigeunerweisen.* (1/86) (EMI) ① **CDC7 47318-2**
A. Dumay, Toulouse Capitole Orch, M. Plasson *Violin
Concerto.* (2/90) (EMI) ① **CDC7 49833-2**
B. Huberman, VPO, G. Szell (r1934) *Concert*
(10/91) (EPM) ① **150 032**
Y. Menuhin, Paris SO, G. Enescu (r1933) *Concert*
(12/91) (BIDD) ① **LAB046**
S. Mintz, Israel PO, Z. Mehta (pp1988) *Concert*
(3/92) (DG) ① **427 676-2GH**
A.A. Meyers, RPO, J. López-Cobos *Bruch: Scottish
Fantasy.* (9/92) (RCA) ① **RD60942**
R. Ricci, SRO, E. Ansermet (r1959) *Concert*
(6/93) (DECC) ① [2] **433 911-2DM2**
I. Perlman, LSO, A. Previn (r1968) *Concert*
(7/93) (RCA) ① **07863 56520-2**
L. Kogan, Philh, K. Kondrashin (r1959) *Concert*
(9/93) (EMI) ① **CZS7 67732-2**
M. Bisengaliev, Polish Nat RSO, J. Wildner (r1992)
Concert (12/93) (NAXO) ① **8 550494**
K-W. Chung, Montreal SO, C. Dutoit (r1980) *Concert*
(2/94) (DECC) ① **436 483-2DM**
C. Tetzlaff, Czech PO, L. Pešek (r1993) *Dvořák:
Violin Concerto.* (7/94) (VIRG) ① **VC5 45022 2**
J. Heifetz, RCA Victor SO, W. Steinberg (r1951)
Concert (11/94) (RCA) ① [65] **09026 61778-2(22)**
J. Thibaud, SRO, E. Ansermet (pp1941) *Concert*
(12/94) (APR) ① [2] **APR7028**
I. Perlman, Paris Orch, D. Barenboim (r1980)
Concert (3/95) (DG) ① **445 549-2GMA**
N. Milstein, St Louis SO, V. Golschmann (r1954)
Goldmark: Violin Concerto 1.
(11/95) (TEST) ① **SBT1047**
Intermezzo A. Dumay, Monte Carlo PO, A. Dumay
Concert (6/87) (EMI) ① **CDC7 47544-2**
2. F. Kreisler, C. Lamson (r1925) *Concert*
(9/93) (BIDD) ① [2] **LAB068/9**
4. J. Heifetz, orch. J. Pasternack (r1925) *Concert*
(11/94) (RCA) ① [65] **09026 61778-2(01)**
4, 5. B. Huberman, P. Frenkel (r1923) *Concert*
(3/94) (BIDD) ① [2] **LAB077/8**
Symphony in G minor (1886)
RPO, Y. Butt *Concert* (10/90) (ASV) ① **CDDCA709**
FRNO, T. Beecham *Franck: Symphony.*
(9/92) (EMI) ① **CDM7 63396-2**

SECTION II: CHAMBER

Piano Trio No. 1 in C minor, Op. 7 (c1850)
Parnassus Trio (r1992) *Concert*
(4/94) (MDG) ① **L3482**
Henry Trio (r1992) *Concert*
(8/94) (PIER) ① **PV794031**
Barbican Pf Trio *Concert*
(11/94) (ASV) ① **CDDCA899**
Piano Trio No. 2 in B minor (?1852)
Parnassus Trio (r1992) *Concert*
(4/94) (MDG) ① **L3482**
Henry Trio (r1992) *Concert*
(8/94) (PIER) ① **PV794031**
Barbican Pf Trio *Concert*
(11/94) (ASV) ① **CDDCA899**

Piano Trio No. 3 in A minor—violin, cello and piano, Op. 26 (1880)
Parnassus Trio (r1992) *Concert*
(4/94) (MDG) ① **L3482**
Henry Trio (r1992) *Concert*
(8/94) (PIER) ① **PV794031**
Barbican Pf Trio *Concert*
(11/94) (ASV) ① **CDDCA899**
String Quartet in E flat, Op. 45 (1880) (rev of Op. 19)
Daniel Qt (r1991) *Concert*
(12/94) (DINT) ① **DICD920159**

SECTION IV: VOCAL AND CHORAL

Au fond des halliers—soprano, tenor and piano (1887) (wds. Theuriet: arr from opera 'Fiesque')
C. Alliot-Lugaz, F. Le Roux, J. Cohen (sop & bar)
Concert (4/91) (REM) ① **REM311086**
Guitare—Song, Op. 17/1 (1856) (Wds. Hugo)
F. Lott, G. Johnson (r1984) *Concert*
(5/87) (HARM) ① **HMA190 1138**
Souvenir—song (1872) (Wds. V. Hugo)
S. Varcoe, G. Johnson *Concert*
(6/88) (HYPE) ① **CDA66248**

SECTION V: STAGE WORKS

Namouna—ballet: 2 acts (1882)
EXCERPTS: Prologue: 1. Prélude; 2. Scene du
Balcon. ACT 1: 3. Allegro vivace; 4. Pas des
Cymbales; 5. Valse de la Cigarette; 6. Tambourin; 7.
Danse Marocaine; 8. La Gitane; 9. Parades de Foire;
10. Danse de Namouna; 11. Fête Foraine. ACT 2:
12. La Sieste; 13. Mazurka; 14. Presto: Danse de
toutes les Esclaves; 15. Théme varié; 16.
Bacchanale.
Cpte Monte Carlo PO, D. Robertson (r1991)
(5/94) (AUVI) ① **V4677**
5. RPO, Y. Butt (r1993) *Concert*
(5/94) (ASV) ① **CDDCA878**
Namouna—concert suites from ballet (1882)
1. SUITE 1: 1a. Prélude; 1b. Sérénade; 1c. Thème
varié; 1d. Parade de foire; 1e. Fête foraine; 2. SUITE
2—; 2a. Danse marocaine; 2b. Mazurka; 2c. La
sieste; 2d. Pas de cymbales; 2e. Danse des
esclaves.
RPO, Y. Butt (r1993) *Concert*
(5/94) (ASV) ① **CDDCA878**
FRNO, J. Martinon (r c1970) *Concert*
(5/95) (DG) ① [2] **437 371-2GX2**
Le Roi d'Ys—opera: 3 acts (1888—Paris)
(Libr. E. Blau)
EXCERPTS: 1. Overture; 2. Noël!; 3. Margared, ô
ma soeur!; 4. Vainement j'ai parlé; 5. Désireux
d'accomplir. ACT 2: 6. Tous ces côtes j'aperçois; 7.
Hélas, pourrais-je en mes alarmes; 8. Tais-toi,
Margared!; 9. Victorie!; 10. Perdu! ACT 3: 11. Vous
qui venez ici; 12a. Puisqu'on ne peut fléchir; 12b.
Vainement, ma bien-aimée! (Aubade); 13. Voici
l'heure; 14. Salut á l'époux; 15. Ces rumeurs, ces cris
d'alarm; 16. Ô Puissance infinie!.
1. RPO, Y. Butt *Concert*
(10/90) (ASV) ① **CDDCA709**
1. San Francisco PO, P. Monteux (r1942) *Concert*
(9/94) (RCA) ① [15] **09026 61893-2**
1. Luxembourg Rad & TV SO, L. de Froment (r1992)
Concert (11/94) (FORL) ① **FF045**
6. S. Juyol, Paris Op Orch, L. Fourestier (r1947)
Concert (4/92) (EMI) ① [7] **CHS7 69741-2(3)**
12a, 12b B. Gigli, orch (r1922) *Concert*
(5/90) (NIMB) ① **NI7807**
12a, 12b B. Gigli, ROHO, R. Zamboni (r1946)
Concert (5/90) (CDH) ① **CDH7 61052-2**
12a, 12b B. Gigli, orch, J. Pasternack (r1922)
Concert (5/90) (RCA) ① **GD87811**
12a, 12b N. Melba, orch, W.B. Rogers (r1910)
Concert (5/95) (ROMO) ① [3] **81011-2(2)**
12a, 12b Alfredo Kraus, WNO Orch, C. Rizzi (r1994)
Concert (11/95) (PHIL) ① **442 785-2PH**
12b G. Morino, Warmia Nat PO, B. Amaducci
Concert (10/90) (NUOV) ① **6851**
12b J. Szigeti, A. Farkas (arr Szigeti: r1941) *Concert*
(5/93) (SONY) ① **MPK52569**
12b N. Melba, orch, W.B. Rogers (r1910) *Concert*
(9/93) (RCA) ① **09026 61412-2**
12b J. Szigeti, A. Foldes (r1941: arr vn/pf: Szigeti)
Concert (7/94) (BIDD) ① [2] **LAB070/1**
12b E. Clément, orch (r1911) *Concert*
(8/95) (ROMO) ① **82002-2**
12b E. Clément, orch (r1911) *Concert*
(8/95) (PEAR) ① **GEMMCD9161**

LAMA, Gaetano (1886–?) Italy

SECTION IV: VOCAL AND CHORAL

Cara piccina—song (Wds. Bovio)
L. Tetrazzini, T. Amici (r1922) *Concert*
(9/92) (EMI) ① [3] CHS7 63802-2(2)
Come le rose—song (Wds. Genise)
L. Tetrazzini, orch, P. Pitt (r1922) *Concert*
(9/92) (EMI) ① [3] CHS7 63802-2(2)
L. Tetrazzini, orch (r1920) *Concert*
(9/92) (PEAR) ① GEMMCD9225
Napule che canta—Neapolitan song
L. Tetrazzini, orch (r1922) *Concert*
(9/92) (PEAR) ① GEMMCD9225
'O mare canta!—Neapolitan song (Wds. Bovio)
L. Tetrazzini, T. Amici (r1922) *Concert*
(9/92) (EMI) ① [3] CHS7 63802-2(2)
Piccolo amore—song (Wds. Bovio)
L. Tetrazzini, A. Baggiore, T. Amici (r1922) *Concert*
(9/92) (EMI) ① [3] CHS7 63802-2(2)
L. Tetrazzini, A. Baggiore, orch (r1922) *Concert*
(9/92) (PEAR) ① GEMMCD9225

LAMB, Joseph Francis (1877–1960) USA

SECTION III: INSTRUMENTAL

American Beauty Rag—piano (1913)
J. Rifkin *Concert* (4/92) (DECC) ① 425 225-2DH
Bohemia Rag—piano (1919)
J. Rifkin *Concert* (4/92) (DECC) ① 425 225-2DH
Ragtime Nightingale—piano (1915)
J. Rifkin *Concert* (4/92) (DECC) ① 425 225-2DH
Top Liner Rag—piano (1916)
J. Rifkin *Concert* (4/92) (DECC) ① 425 225-2DH

LAMB, Peter (b 1925) England

SECTION II: CHAMBER

Sonata—flute and piano (1988)
K. Smith, P. Rhodes *Concert*
(1/91) (ASV) ① CDDCA739

LAMBARDI, Francesco (c1587–1642) Italy

SECTION III: INSTRUMENTAL

Gagliarda—keyboard
R. Alessandrini (r1994) *Concert*
(4/95) (O111) ① OPS30-118
Partite sopra Fidele—keyboard
R. Alessandrini (r1994) *Concert*
(4/95) (O111) ① OPS30-118
Toccata e gagliarda—Italian hp
Tragicomedia *Concert*
(9/92) (EMI) ① CDC7 54191-2

LAMBE, Walter (?1450/1–in or after 1499) England

SECTION IV: VOCAL AND CHORAL

Nesciens mater—motet (5vv)
The Sixteen, H. Christophers *Concert*
(12/88) (HYPE) ① CDA66263
The Sixteen, H. Christophers *Concert*
(11/89) (MERI) ① CDE84175
Eton Coll Chapel Ch, R. Allwood (r1994) *Concert*
(5/95) (FUTU) ① FCM1004
Stella caeli—motet (4vv)
The Sixteen, H. Christophers *Concert*
(11/89) (MERI) ① CDE84175
The Sixteen, H. Christophers *Concert*
(7/93) (COLL) ① Coll1342-2

LAMBERT, (Leonard) Constant (1905–1951) England

SECTION I: ORCHESTRAL

Aubade héroïque—orchestra (1942)
English Northern Philh, D. Lloyd-Jones *Concert*
(6/92) (HYPE) ① CDA66565
Concerto for Piano and Nine Players (1930-31)
I. Brown, Nash Ens, L. Friend (r1994) *Concert*
(7/95) (HYPE) ① CDA66754

SECTION III: INSTRUMENTAL

Elegiac Blues—piano (1927)
A. Goldstone (r1993) *Concert*
(10/95) (CHAN) ① CHAN9382
Elegy—piano (1938)
A. Goldstone (r1993) *Concert*
(10/95) (CHAN) ① CHAN9382
Sonata for Piano (1928-29)
I. Brown (r1994) *Concert*
(7/95) (HYPE) ① CDA66754
A. Goldstone (r1993) *Concert*
(10/95) (CHAN) ① CHAN9382

SECTION IV: VOCAL AND CHORAL

8 Poems—voice and piano/chamber ensemble (1926-29) (Wds. Li-Po)
1. A Summer Day; 2. Nocturne; 3. With a Man of Leisure; 4. Lines; 5. The Ruin of Ku-Su Palace; 6. The Intruder; 7. On the City Street; 8. The Long Departed Love.
Cpte P. Langridge, Nash Ens, L. Friend (r1994) *Concert*
(7/95) (HYPE) ① CDA66754
Rio Grande—piano, chorus and orchestra (1927) (Wds. S. Sitwell)
S. Burgess, J. Gibbons, Op North Chor, English Northern Philh, D. Lloyd-Jones *Concert*
(6/92) (HYPE) ① CDA66565
Summer's Last Will and Testament—baritone, chorus and orchestra (1932-35) (Wds. T. Nashe)
W. Shimell, Leeds Fest Chor, English Northern Philh, D. Lloyd-Jones *Concert*
(6/92) (HYPE) ① CDA66565

SECTION V: STAGE WORKS

Horoscope—ballet: 1 act (1938—London)
EXCERPTS—; 1. Dance of the followers of Virgo; 2. Saraband for the followers of Virgo; 3. Valse for the Gemini; 4. Bacchanale; 5. Invocation to the moon and finale.
1-5. English Northern Philh, D. Lloyd-Jones *Concert*
(3/91) (HYPE) ① CDA66436
Mr Bear Squash-you-all-flat—ballet: narrator & ensemble (1924) (text based on Russian children's tale)
N. Hawthorne, Nash Ens, L. Friend (r1994) *Concert*
(7/95) (HYPE) ① CDA66754
Rendez-vous—ballet: 1 act (1933—London)
(after Auber: L'enfant prodigue)
English Concert Orch, R. Bonynge *Concert*
(11/90) (DECC) ① [2] 421 818-2DH2

LAMORETTI, Pietro Maria (17th Cent) Italy

SECTION IV: VOCAL AND CHORAL

Bell' il vana tua beltade—First Book of Madrigals (1621)
T. Berganza, Ens, J.E. Dähler (hpd/dir) *Concert*
(3/84) (CLAV) ① CD50-8206

LAMPE, John Frederick (c1703–1751) England

SECTION I: ORCHESTRAL

Concerto for Flute and Orchestra in G, 'The' Cuckoo' (c1740)
R. Brown, Opera Restor'd, P. Holman (r1994) *Pyramus and Thisbe*
(12/95) (HYPE) ① CDA66759

SECTION V: STAGE WORKS

Britannia—opera (1732—London) (Lib. Lediard)
EXCERPTS: 1. Welcome Mars.
1. E. Kirkby, AAM, C. Hogwood (r1991) *Concert*
(7/93) (L'OI) ① 436 132-2OH
Dione—opera (1733—London) (Lib. Gay and others)
EXCERPTS: 1. Pretty warblers.
1. E. Kirkby, AAM, C. Hogwood (r1991) *Concert*
(7/93) (L'OI) ① 436 132-2OH
Pyramus and Thisbe—mock opera: 1 act (1745—London) (Lib. ?cspr, after Shakespeare)
EXCERPTS: 1. Overture; 2. The wretched sighs and groans (Wall air); 3. And thou, O wall; 4. O wicked wall; 5. Fly, swift good Time; 6. Not Shafulus (Whispering duetto); 7. I go without delay; 8. Ladies don't fright you; 9. The man in the moon I am, sir; 10. Where is my love, my Pyre dear; 11. Sweet moon, I thank thee; 12. Approach, ye furies fell; 13. Now I am dead; 14. These lily lips; 15. Dance; 16. Thus folding, beholding; 17. Now e'er you remove.

Cpte M. Padmore, S. Bisatt, M. Manderson, A. Trehame, A. Knight, P. Milne, A. McMahon, J. Edwards, P. Hyde, C. Baldy, Opera Restor'd, P. Holman (r1994) *Cuckoo Concerto.*
(12/95) (HYPE) ① CDA66759

LANCHBERY, John (b 1923) England

SECTION V: STAGE WORKS

Tales of Beatrix Potter—filmed ballet (1970)
(later re-created as stage ballet)
EXCERPTS: 1. The Tale of Two Bad Mice; 2. The Tale of Squirrel Nutkin; 3. Mrs Tiggy-Winkle's Laundry; 4. The Tale of Jemima Puddle-Duck; 5. The Tale of Jeremy Fisher; 6. The Tale of Pigling Bland; 7. The Mouse Waltz; 8. Finale.
ROHO, J. Lanchbery (r1970)
(11/94) (EMI) ① CDC7 54537-2

LANDENBURG

SECTION IV: VOCAL AND CHORAL

Too late tomorrow—song
R. Crooks, orch (r1933) *Concert*
(9/93) (CLAR) ① CDGSE78-50-50

LANDI, Stefano (1586 or 1587–1639) Italy

SECTION V: STAGE WORKS

La Mort d'Orfeo—tragicommedia pastorale: 5 acts (1619—?Rome)
1. Calliope's Aria (Act IV).
Cpte J. Elwes, J. Koslowsky, D. Cordier, M. Chance, M. Kroese, W. Jochens, N. van der Meel, H. van der Kamp, L. Deroo, Currende Voc Ens, Tragicomedia, S. Stubbs
(10/88) (ACCE) ① [2] ACC8746/7D

LANDINI, Francesco (c1325–1397) Italy

SECTION IV: VOCAL AND CHORAL

La bionda treçça—ballata: two violins (Codex Squarcialupi)
Newberry Consort, M. Springfels (r1990) *Concert*
(7/93) (HARM) ① HMU90 7038
Dolce signiore—ballatta
Newberry Consort, M. Springfels (r1990) *Concert*
(7/93) (HARM) ① HMU90 7038
Donna, s'i t'ò fallito—ballata
Newberry Consort, M. Springfels (r1990) *Concert*
(7/93) (HARM) ① HMU90 7038
Giunta vaga biltà—ballata (3vv)
Gothic Voices, I. Barford, C. Page *Concert*
(12/86) (HYPE) ① CDA66144
El gran disio—ballata
Newberry Consort, M. Springfels (r1990) *Concert*
(7/93) (HARM) ① HMU90 7038
Nessun ponga speranca—ballata (3vv)
Gothic Voices, I. Barford, C. Page *Concert*
(12/86) (HYPE) ① CDA66144
Ochi dolenti mie—ballata (2vv)
Gothic Voices, C. Page *Concert*
(12/88) (HYPE) ① CDA66286
Per seguir la speranca—ballata (3vv)
Gothic Voices, C. Page *Concert*
(12/88) (HYPE) ① CDA66286

LANDOWSKA, Wanda (1879–1959) Poland

SECTION III: INSTRUMENTAL

Bourrée d'Auvergne No. 2—harpsichord
W. Landowska (r1928) *Concert*
(10/92) (MSCM) ① MM30444

LANDRY, Jeanne (b 1922) France

SECTION III: INSTRUMENTAL

Orah—organ (1987)
J-G. Proulx *Concert* (8/91) (REM) ① REM311078

LANE, Burton (b 1912) USA

SECTION IV: VOCAL AND CHORAL

The **Lady's In Love With You—song from the film 'Some Like It Hot' (1939)** (Lyrics F. Loesser)
M. Feinstein, B. Lane Concert
(8/94) (NONE) ① **7559-79285-2**
Look who's here—baritone and piano (1932) (Wds. H Adamson)
M. Feinstein, B. Lane Concert
(8/94) (NONE) ① **7559-79285-2**
Where have I seen your face before—baritone and piano (1980) (Wds E Y Harburg)
M. Feinstein, B. Lane Concert
(8/94) (NONE) ① **7559-79285-2**

SECTION V: STAGE WORKS

Carmelina—musical show (1979) (Lyrics A J Lerner)
EXCERPTS: 1. Overture; 2. Prayer; 3. It's Time for a Love Song; 4. Why Him?; 5. I Must Have Her; 6. Someone in April; 7. Signora Campbell; 8. Love Before Breakfast; 9. Yankee Doodles Are Coming to Town; 10. One More Walk Around the Garden; 11. All That He Wants Me to Be; 12. Carmelina; 13. The Image of Me; 14. I'm a Woman; 15. Finale.
3. M. Feinstein, B. Lane Concert
(8/94) (NONE) ① **7559-79285-2**
Dancing Lady—songs for film (1933) (Wds. H Adamson)
EXCERPTS: 1. Everything I Have Is Yours; 2. Heigh-Ho the Gang's All Here; 3. Let's Go Bavarian.
1. M. Feinstein, B. Lane Concert
(8/94) (NONE) ① **7559-79285-2**
Dancing on a Dime—songs for film (1941) (Wds. F Loesser)
EXCERPTS: 1. I Hear Music.
1. M. Feinstein, B. Lane Concert
(8/94) (NONE) ① **7559-79285-2**
Finian's Rainbow—musical show (1947—New York) (Lyrics E Y Harburg)
EXCERPTS: 1. Overture; 2. This Time of the Year; 3. How Are Things in Glocca Morra?; 4. If This Isn't Love; 5. Look to the Rainbow; 6. Old Devil Moon; 7. Something Sort of Grandish; 8. Necessity; 9. When the Idle Poor Become the Idle Rich; 10. The Begat; 11. When I'm Not Near the Girl I Love; 12. That Great Come and Get It Day.
3. M. Patinkin, Orch, E. Stern (r1993; orch Troob, arr Ford) Concert (11/94) **7559-79330-2**
Give a Girl a Break—songs for film (1952) (Wds. I Gershwin)
EXCERPTS: 1. It Happens Every Time.
1. M. Feinstein, B. Lane Concert
(8/94) (NONE) ① **7559-79285-2**
Hold on to your Hats—songs for film (1940) (Wds. E Y Harburg)
EXCERPTS: 1. The World Is In My Arms; 2. Don't Let It Get You Down.
1, 2. M. Feinstein, B. Lane Concert
(8/94) (NONE) ① **7559-79285-2**
Kid Millions—songs for film (1934) (Wds. H Adamson)
EXCERPTS: 1. Your Head On My Shoulder; 2. I Want to Be a Minstrel.
1. M. Feinstein, B. Lane Concert
(8/94) (NONE) ① **7559-79285-2**
Love on Toast—songs for film (1937) (Wds. S Coslow)
EXCERPTS: 1. I Want a New Romance.
1. M. Feinstein, B. Lane Concert
(8/94) (NONE) ① **7559-79285-2**
On a Clear Day You Can See Forever—musical show, later film (1965—New York) (Lyrics A J Lerner)
EXCERPTS: 1. Overture; 2. Hurry! It's Lovely Up Here!; 3. Tosy and Cosh; 4. On a Clear Day; 5. On the S.S. Bernard Cohn; 6. Don't Tamper With My Sister; 7. She Wasn't You; 8. Melinda; 9. When I'm Being Born Again; 10. What Did I Have That I Don't Have?; 11. Wait Till We're Sixty-Five; 12. Come Back to Me; 13. Finale.
2-5, 7, 8, 10-12. M. Feinstein, B. Lane Concert
(8/94) (NONE) ① **7559-79285-2**
Royal Wedding—musical film (1951) (Lrics A J Lerner)
EXCERPTS: 1. Open Your Eyes; 2. The Happiest Day of My Life; 3. Too Late Now; 4. I Left My Heart in Haiti; 5. Sunday Jumps (orchestra); 6. You Are All the World to Me; 7. How Could You Believe Me When I Said I Love You...
1, 2. M. Feinstein, B. Lane Concert
(8/94) (NONE) ① **7559-79285-2**

Ship Ahoy—musical film (1942) (Lyrics E Y Harburg)
EXCERPTS: 1. Opening Music (Medley); 2. Last Call for Love; 3. I'll Take Tallulah; 4. Poor You; 5. Processional & Cape Dance (orchestra; comp W. Ruick); 6. On Moonlight Bay (comp P. Weinrich; lyrics E. Madden); 7. Last Call for Love (reprise); 8. Closing Music (Poor You—instrumental).
4. M. Feinstein, B. Lane Concert
(8/94) (NONE) ① **7559-79285-2**

LANE, Eastwood (1879–1951) USA

SECTION III: INSTRUMENTAL

The **Crapshooters—piano**
L. Godowsky (r1925) Concert
(4/89) (APR) ① [2] **APR7011**

LANG, Craig Sellar (1891–1971) England

SECTION III: INSTRUMENTAL

Tuba Tune—organ (1929)
J. Bielby Concert (5/91) (PRIO) ① **PRCD298**
G. Green Concert (3/93) (NAXO) ① **8 550582**

LANG, David (b 1957) USA

SECTION I: ORCHESTRAL

Under Orpheus—two pianos and orchestra (1989-94) (reworking of 'Orpheus Over and Under')
E. Corver, S. Grotenhuis, Netherlands Wind Ens, S. Mosko (r1993/4) Concert
(10/95) (CHAN) ① **CHAN9363**

SECTION II: CHAMBER

Face so pale—multiple pianos (1992) (based on Dufay's 'Se la face ay pale')
Piano Circus (r1992) Concert
(1/94) (ARGO) ① **440 294-2ZH**

SECTION IV: VOCAL AND CHORAL

Are you experienced?—narrator and chamber ensemble (1990) (Wds. cpsr)
D. Lang, Netherlands Wind Ens, S. Mosko (r1993/4) Concert
(10/95) (CHAN) ① **CHAN9363**

LANGE, Gustav (1830–1889)

SECTION III: INSTRUMENTAL

Spring's message—piano
A. Etherden Concert
(7/93) (HUNT) ① **HMPCD0589**

LANGE-MÜLLER, Peter Erasmus (1850–1926) Denmark

SECTION IV: VOCAL AND CHORAL

Florence, city of flowers—song (Wds. E. Christiansen)
L. Melchior, Anon (pf) (r c1920) Concert
(8/88) (DANA) ① [2] **DACOCD311/2**

LANGFORD, Gordon (b 1930) England

SECTION I: ORCHESTRAL

A **Scottish Lament—brass band** (arr from trad melodies)
1. Will ye no come back again; 2. Auld Lang Syne.
Black Dyke Mills Band, R. Newsome (r1977) Concert
(1/94) (CHAN) ① **CHAN4528**
A **Stephen Foster Fantasy—brass band**
Black Dyke Mills Band, R. Newsome (r1977) Concert
(1/94) (CHAN) ① **CHAN4528**

LANGGAARD, Rued (1893–1952) Denmark

BVN Nos. from Bendt Viinholdt Nielsen Catalogue, 1991

SECTION I: ORCHESTRAL

Drapa—orchestra (1907-09) (upon the death of Edvard Grieg)
Rubinstein PO, I. Stupel Concert
(12/94) (DANA) ① **DACOCD405**

Heltedød, 'Death of Hero'—tone poem (1907-8)
Rubinstein PO, I. Stupel Concert
(12/94) (DANA) ① **DACOCD406**
Interdikt—orchestra (1947-48) (At the grave of Christopher I in Ribe)
Rubinstein PO, I. Stupel Concert
(12/94) (DANA) ① **DACOCD406**
Sphinx—orchestra (1909)
Rubinstein PO, I. Stupel Concert
(12/94) (DANA) ① **DACOCD408**
Suite (Symphony No. 14), 'Morgenen'—orchestra (1947 rev 1951)
Rubinstein PO, I. Stupel Concert
(12/94) (DANA) ① **DACOCD409**
Symphony No. 1, 'Klippepastoraler' (1908 rev 1909-11)
Rubinstein PO, I. Stupel
(12/94) (DANA) ① **DACOCD404**
Symphony No. 2, 'Varrbrud'—soprano and orchestra (1912-14 rev 1933)
R. Owsinska, Rubinstein PO, I. Stupel Concert
(12/94) (DANA) ① **DACOCD405**
Symphony No. 3, 'Ungdomsbrus'—piano and orchestra (1915-16 rev 1933)
T. Chmielewski, Rubinstein PO, I. Stupel Concert
(12/94) (DANA) ① **DACOCD405**
Symphony No. 4, 'Løvfald' (1916)
Danish Nat RSO, N. Järvi Concert
(12/92) (CHAN) ① **CHAN9064**
Rubinstein PO, I. Stupel Concert
(12/94) (DANA) ① **DACOCD406**
Danish RSO, J. Frandsen (pp1981) Concert
(12/94) (DANA) ① [2] **DACOCD340/1**
Symphony No. 5, 'Steppennatur' (1931)
Danish Nat RSO, N. Järvi Concert
(12/92) (CHAN) ① **CHAN9064**
Rubinstein PO, I. Stupel Concert
(12/94) (DANA) ① **DACOCD407**
Symphony No. 6, 'Det himmelrivende' (1919-20)
Danish Nat RSO, N. Järvi Concert
(12/92) (CHAN) ① **CHAN9064**
Rubinstein PO, I. Stupel Concert
(12/94) (DANA) ① **DACOCD406**
Danish RSO, J. Frandsen (pp1977) Concert
(12/94) (DANA) ① [2] **DACOCD340/1**
Symphony No. 7, 'Ved Tordenskjold i Holmens kirke' (1925-26)
Rubinstein PO, I. Stupel Concert
(12/94) (DANA) ① **DACOCD407**
Symphony No. 8, 'Minder ved Amalienborg' (1926-28 rev 1929-34)
Rubinstein PO, I. Stupel Concert
(12/94) (DANA) ① **DACOCD409**
Symphony No. 9, 'Fra Dronning Dagmars By' (1942)
Rubinstein PO, I. Stupel Concert
(12/94) (DANA) ① **DACOCD407**
Symphony No. 10, 'Hin Torden-Bolig' (1944-45)
Rubinstein PO, I. Stupel Concert
(12/94) (DANA) ① **DACOCD408**
Symphony No. 11, 'Ixion' (1944)
Rubinstein PO, I. Stupel Concert
(12/94) (DANA) ① **DACOCD408**
Symphony No. 12, 'Hélsingeborg' (1946)
Rubinstein PO, I. Stupel Concert
(12/94) (DANA) ① **DACOCD408**
Symphony No. 13, 'Undertro' (1947)
Rubinstein PO, I. Stupel Concert
(12/94) (DANA) ① **DACOCD410**
Symphony No. 15, 'Sostormen' (1937 rev 1949)
Rubinstein PO, I. Stupel Concert
(12/94) (DANA) ① **DACOCD409**
Symphony No. 16, 'Syndflod af sol' (1951)
Rubinstein PO, I. Stupel Concert
(12/94) (DANA) ① **DACOCD410**

SECTION IV: VOCAL AND CHORAL

Music of the Spheres (Sfaernes Musick)—soprano, chorus and orchestra (1918)
E. Guillaume, Danish Rad Chor, Danish RSO, J. Frandsen (pp1980) Concert
(12/94) (DANA) ① [2] **DACOCD340/1**

SECTION V: STAGE WORKS

Antikrist—opera (1916-36) (Lib cpsr, after Book of Revelation)
EXCERPTS: 1. Prelude.
1. Rubinstein PO, I. Stupel Concert
(12/94) (DANA) ① **DACOCD410**

LANGLAIS, Jean (1907–1991) France

SECTION II: CHAMBER

7 Chorales—trumpet/oboe/flute, organ/piano (1973)
1. Andante; 2. Allegro; 3. Adagio; 4. Moderato; 5. Allegro; 6. Moderato maestoso; 7. Allegro vivo.
1, 2, 4, 7. G. Touvron, E. Krapp (r1992) *Concert*
(9/93) (RCA) ① 09026 61186-2

SECTION III: INSTRUMENTAL

Fantasy on Two Old Scottish Themes—organ (1987)
J. Watts (r1992) *Concert*
(8/94) (PRIO) ① PRCD414
Folkloric Suite—organ (1952)
1. Fugue on 'O Filii'; 2. Légende de St Nicolas (1937); 3. Cantique; 4. Canzona; 5. Rapsodie sur deux Noëls.
P. Cogen *Concert*
(3/91) (CYBE) ① CY867
Hommage à Frescobaldi—organ (1952)
G. Weir *Concert*
(12/92) (KOSS) ① KC1013
Incantation pour un jour saint—organ (1949)
C. Herrick *Concert*
(5/89) (HYPE) ① CDA66258
T. Horton *Concert*
(7/93) (CNTO) ① CRCD2367
3 Méditations—organ (1962)
1. Pater Noster; 2. Noel Nouvelet; 3. Veni Creator Spiritus.
S. Lindley *Concert*
(3/93) (NAXO) ① 8 550581
5 Méditations sur l'apocalypse—organ (1972-73)
1. Celui qui a des oreilles, qu'il écoute; 2. Il était, il est et il vient; 3. Visions prophétiques; 4. Oh, oui, viens Seigneur Jésus; 5. La cinquième trompette.
5. John Scott *Concert*
(4/89) (GUIL) ① GRCD7022
3 Paraphrases grégoriennes—organ, Op. 5 (1933-34)
1. Ave Maria, Ave maris stella; 2. Mors et Resurrectio; 3. Hymne d'actions de grâce (Te Deum).
C. Crozier (r1993) *Concert*
(2/95) (DELO) ① DE3147
J. Watts (r1994) *Concert*
(10/95) (PRIO) ① PRCD491
3. J. Lancelot *Concert*
(8/88) (PRIO) ① PRCD228
3. J. O'Donnell *Concert*
(9/88) (HYPE) ① CDA66270
3. J-G. Proulx *Concert*
(8/91) (REM) ① REM311078
3. Andrew Lucas (r1994) *Concert*
(11/94) (NAXO) ① 8 550955
3. P. Hurford (r1987) *Concert*
(10/95) (DECC) ① 444 567-2DM
Poem of Happiness—organ (1967)
K. Bowyer (r1992) *Concert* (1/95) (NIMB) ① NI5408
3 Poèmes évangéliques—organ, Op. 2 (1932)
1. L'Anonciation; 2. La Nativité; 3. Les Rameaux (Entrée de Jésus à Jérusalem.
J. O'Donnell *Concert*
(9/88) (HYPE) ① CDA66270
1. M. Keiser *Concert* (7/91) (GOTH) ① G49037
2. J-G. Proulx *Concert*
(8/91) (REM) ① REM311078
2. Andrew Lucas (r1994) *Concert*
(11/94) (NAXO) ① 8 550955
Prelude and Fugue—organ, Op. 1 (1927)
M-B. Dufourcet (r1992) *Concert*
(6/95) (PRIO) ① PRCD422
Suite brève—organ (1947)
EXCERPTS: 1. Grands jeux; 2. Cantilène; 3. Plainte; 4. Dialogue sur les mixtures.
K. Bowyer (r1992) *Concert* (1/95) (NIMB) ① NI5408
Suite française—organ (1948)
EXCERPTS: 1. Prélude ou les grands jeux; 2. Nazard; 4. Française; 6. Arabesque sur les flûtes; 10. Final rhapsodique.
1, 2, 4, 10. M. Harris *Concert*
(3/92) (YORK) ① CD112
2, 6. K. Bowyer (r1992) *Concert*
(1/95) (NIMB) ① NI5408
Suite médiévale en forme de messe basse—organ (1947)
1. Prelude; 2. Tiento; 3. Improvisation; 4. Méditation; 5. Acclamations.
1. I. Shaw *Concert* (7/91) (PRIO) ① PRCD296
Symphony No. 1—organ (1941-42)
P. Cogen *Concert* (3/91) (CYBE) ① CY867
K. Bowyer (r1992) *Concert* (1/95) (NIMB) ① NI5408
J. Watts (r1994) *Concert*
(10/95) (PRIO) ① PRCD491

Symphony No. 2, 'Alla Webern'—organ (1977)
K. Bowyer (r1992) *Concert* (1/95) (NIMB) ① NI5408
Triptyque—organ (1957)
P. Cogen *Concert* (3/91) (CYBE) ① CY867
Triptyque grégorien—organ (1978)
1. Rosa mystica; 2. In Paradisum; 3. Alléluia.
1. J. O'Donnell *Concert*
(9/88) (HYPE) ① CDA66270

SECTION IV: VOCAL AND CHORAL

Messe solonnelle—4vv, congregation, 2 organs/brass and organ, 1949
P. Bengtson, Täby Church Youth Ch, Orpheus Chbr Ens, K. Ek *Olsson: Te Deum*.
(8/86) (BIS) ① BIS-CD289
Westminster Cath Ch, J. O'Donnell, D. Hill *Concert*
(9/88) (HYPE) ① CDA66270
Regent Chbr Ch, Adrian Lucas, G. Cole *Concert*
(10/88) (REGE) ① REGCD101
Missa Salve Regina—chorus, brass and two organs/organ (1954)
Westminster Cath Ch, ECO Brass Ens, J. O'Donnell, A. Lumsden, D. Hill *Concert*
(9/88) (HYPE) ① CDA66270

LANGUETUIT, Marcel France

SECTION III: INSTRUMENTAL

Toccata in D—organ
D.M. Patrick *Concert* (5/93) (PRIO) ① PRCD371

LANNER, Joseph (Franz Karl) (1801–1843) Austria

SECTION I: ORCHESTRAL

Amalien—polka, Op. 14 (?1827)
Vienna Ens (arr H. Pek) *Concert*
(9/92) (SONY) ① SK47187
Ankunfts—waltz, Op. 34 (1829)
Košice St PO, M. Eichenholz (r1992) *Concert*
(2/94) (MARC) ① 8 223470
Die Bestürmung von Constantine—galop, Op. 127 (1838)
Vienna Ens (arr H. Pek) *Concert*
(9/92) (SONY) ① SK47187
Dampf—waltz, Op. 94 (1835)
Vienna Ens *Concert* (9/92) (SONY) ① SK47187
Košice St PO, M. Eichenholz (r1992) *Concert*
(2/94) (MARC) ① 8 223471
D'ersten Gedanken—waltz, Op. 1 (?1826)
Vienna Ens *Concert* (9/92) (SONY) ① SK47187
Dornbacher—Ländler, Op. 9 (?1826)
Vienna Biedermaier Ens (trans H. Puffler) *Concert*
(3/89) (DENO) ① CO-72587
Hans-Jörgel—polka, Op. 194
Vienna Biedermeier Ens (trans A. Weinmann) *Concert*
(3/89) (DENO) ① CO-72587
VPO, R. Muti (pp1993) *Concert*
(3/93) (PHIL) ① 438 493-2PH
Marien—Waltz, Op. 143 (1839)
A. Posch, Alban Berg Qt (r1992: arr Weinmann) *Concert*
(6/94) (EMI) ① CDC7 54881-2
Neue Wiener Ländler with Coda, Op. 1 (1825)
Vienna Biedermeier Ens (trans A. Weinmann/H. Puffler) *Concert* (3/89) (DENO) ① CO-72587
Die Romantiker—Waltz, Op. 167 (1841)
Vienna Biedermeier Ens (trans A. Weinmann/H. Puffler) *Concert* (3/89) (DENO) ① CO-72587
Die Schmetterlinge—Ländler, Op. 65 (1833)
Vienna Ens (arr H. Pek) *Concert*
(9/92) (SONY) ① SK47187
Die Schönbrunner—Waltz, Op. 200
VPO, L. Maazel (pp1994) *Concert*
(7/94) (SONY) ① SK46694
Steyrische-Tänze, Op. 165 (1841)
Vienna Biedermeier Ens (trans A. Weinmann) *Concert* (3/89) (DENO) ① CO-72587
VPO, R. Muti (pp1993) *Concert*
(3/93) (PHIL) ① 438 493-2PH
A. Posch, Alban Berg Qt (r1992: arr Weinmann) *Concert* (6/94) (EMI) ① CDC7 54881-2
Die Werber, Op. 103
Vienna Biedermeier Ens (trans A. Weinmann) *Concert* (3/89) (DENO) ① CO-72587
VPO, C. Abbado (pp1991) *Concert*
(4/91) (DG) ① 431 628-2GH
A. Posch, Alban Berg Qt (r1992: arr Weinmann) *Concert* (6/94) (EMI) ① CDC7 54881-2

LAPARRA, Raoul (1876–1943) France

SECTION V: STAGE WORKS

La Habanera—opera: 3 acts (1908)
Et c'est à moi que l'on dit 'Chantel'; Le sort m'a désigné. Vanni-Marcoux, orch (r1931) *Concert*
(1/94) (CLUB) ① CL99-101

LARA, Augustín (1900–1969) Mexico

SECTION IV: VOCAL AND CHORAL

Granada—song (1932) (Wds. cpsr)
P. Domingo, NYPO, Z. Mehta (orch Shifrin/Hayes) *Concert* (9/89) (SONY) ① MK44942
J. Carreras, MMF Orch, Rome Op Orch, Z. Mehta (pp1990) *Concert* (10/90) (DECC) ① 430 433-2DH
P. Dvorský, Bratislava RSO, O. Lenárd *Concert*
(5/92) (NAXO) ① 8 550343
F. Araiza, Munich RSO, R. Weikert (arr Sommerlatte) *Concert* (3/93) (RCA) ① 09026 61163-2
P. Domingo, LSO, M. Peeters *Concert*
(5/93) (DG) ① 431 104-2GB
P. Domingo, Los Angeles PO, Z. Mehta (pp1994) *Concert* (12/94) (TELD) ① 4509-96200-2

LARCHET, John F(rancis) (1884–1967) Ireland

SECTION IV: VOCAL AND CHORAL

Padriac the Fiddler—song
J. McCormack, F. Kreisler, E. Schneider (r1924) *Concert* (9/89) (PEAR) ① GEMMCD9315
J. McCormack, F. Kreisler, E. Schneider (r1924) *Concert* (9/93) (BIDD) ① [2] LAB068/9

LAROCCA, Nick (1889–1961) USA

SECTION II: CHAMBER

Tiger Rag (c1915)
A. Campoli, Raymonde Orch, W. Goehr *Concert*
(10/91) (PEAR) ① PASTCD9744

LARSEN, Libby (b 1950) USA

SECTION I: ORCHESTRAL

Collage: Boogie—orchestra (1988)
Baltimore SO, D. Zinman (r1994) *Concert*
(7/95) (ARGO) ① 444 454-2ZH

SECTION IV: VOCAL AND CHORAL

6 Sonnets from the Portuguese—1v and orchestra (1991) (Wds. E. Barrett Browning)
1. I thought once how Theocritus had sung; 2. My letters; 3. With the same heart, I said; 4. If I leave all for thee; 5. Oh, Yes!; 6. How do I love thee?.
A. Auger, St Paul CO, Minnesota Orch, J. Revzen (pp1991) *Concert* (4/94) (KOCH) ① 37248-2

LARSSON, Lars-Erik (1908–1986) Sweden

SECTION I: ORCHESTRAL

Concertino No. 7—trombone and strings, Op. 45/7 (1955)
C. Lindberg, New Stockholm CO, O. Kamu *Concert*
(8/88) (BIS) ① BIS-CD348
Concerto—violin and orchestra, Op. 42 (1952)
L. Kaufman, Swedish RSO, S. Frykberg (r1955) *Concert* (1/92) (MUSI) ① MACD-667
The Hours of the Day (Dagens stunder)—lyrical suite (1938) (incorporates Pastoral Suite, Op. 19)
Excs Malmö SO, J. DePreist *Concert*
(1/93) (BIS) ① BIS-CD570
Little Serenade—string orchestra, Op. 12 (1934)
Stockholm Sinfonietta, E-P. Salonen *Concert*
(4/85) (BIS) ① BIS-CD285
Musica Vitae CO, W. Rajski *Concert*
(6/90) (BIS) ① BIS-CD460

LASKA, Gustav (1847–1928)
Bohemia

SECTION IV: VOCAL AND CHORAL

Wiegenlied—song: 1v and piano
S. Koussevitzky, P. Luboshutz (r1929: arr db/pf)
Concert   (9/94) (BIDD) ① **WHL019**

LASSEN, Edward (1830–1904)
Belgium

SECTION IV: VOCAL AND CHORAL

Es war ein Traum—song
E. Rethberg, orch (r1928-9: Eng) *Concert*
                                 (2/95) (ROMO) ① [2] **81012-2**

LASSON, Mathieu (d 1595)
France

SECTION IV: VOCAL AND CHORAL

**In manibus tuis sortes meae,
Domine—motet**
A Sei Voci, Lorraine Psallette, Toulouse
Sacqueboutiers, J. Bernfeld, B. Fabre-Garrus (r1993)
Concert   (3/95) (ASTR) ① **E8521**

LASSUS, Orlande de (1532–1594)
Flanders/Germany

SECTION IV: VOCAL AND CHORAL

**Alleluja laus et gloria—motet: 4vv (pub
1604)**
Trinity Coll Ch, Cambridge, R. Marlow (r1994)
Concert   (11/94) (CONI) ① **CDCF230**
**Alma redemptoris mater—motet: 8vv (pub
1604)**
Tallis Scholars, P. Phillips *Concert*
                                 (7/89) (GIME) ① **CDGIM018**
Trinity Coll Ch, Cambridge, R. Marlow (r1994)
Concert   (11/94) (CONI) ① **CDCF230**
**Amour donne-moy pays—chanson: 5vv (pub
1571)** (Wds P. de Ronsard)
Cantus Cölln, K. Junghänel (lte/dir) (r1993) *Concert*
                                 (7/94) (DHM) ① **05472 77304-2**
**Angelus Domini locutus est—motet: 5vv
(pub 1571)**
Hanover Childrens' Ch, Collegium Vocale, P.
Herreweghe (r1979) *Concert*
                                 (12/93) (ASTR) ① **E7780**
Aurora lucis rutilat—motet: 10vv (pub 1604)
Trinity Coll Ch, Cambridge, R. Marlow (r1994)
Concert   (11/94) (CONI) ① **CDCF230**
**Ave regina caelorum—motet: 6vv (pub
1604)**
Tallis Scholars, P. Phillips *Concert*
                                 (7/89) (GIME) ① **CDGIM018**
PCA, Hamburg Early Music Wind Ens, B. Turner
(r1974) *Concert*   (1/93) (ARCH) ① **437 072-2AT**
Beau le cristal—chanson
Scholars (r1993) *Concert*
                                 (2/95) (NAXO) ① **8 550880**
**Benedictio et claritas—motet: 6vv (pub
1582)**
Trinity Coll Ch, Cambridge, R. Marlow (r1994)
Concert   (11/94) (CONI) ① **CDCF230**
**Bon jour mon coeur—chanson: 4vv (pub
1564)** (Wds. Ronsard)
Cantus Cölln, K. Junghänel (lte/dir) (r1993) *Concert*
                                 (7/94) (DHM) ① **05472 77304-2**
Scholars (r1993) *Concert*
                                 (2/95) (NAXO) ① **8 550880**
**Christus resurgens ex mortuis—motet: 5vv
(pub 1582)**
Trinity Coll Ch, Cambridge, R. Marlow (r1994)
Concert   (11/94) (CONI) ① **CDCF230**
**Comme un qui prend—chanson: 5vv (pub
1571)** (Wds P. de Ronsard)
Cantus Cölln, K. Junghänel (lte/dir) (r1993) *Concert*
                                 (7/94) (DHM) ① **05472 77304-2**
Crudele acerba—madrigal: 5vv (pub 1555)
(Wds Petrarch)
Cantus Cölln, K. Junghänel (lte/dir) (r1993) *Concert*
                                 (7/94) (DHM) ① **05472 77304-2**
**Elle s'en va de moy—chanson: 5vv (pub
1560)** (Wds. Marot)
C. Janequin Ens *Concert*
                                 (2/93) (HARM) ① **HMC90 1391**
**Emendemus in melius—motet: 5vv (pub
1571)**
Hanover Childrens' Ch, Collegium Vocale, P.
Herreweghe (r1979) *Concert*
                                 (12/93) (ASTR) ① **E7780**

**En un chasteau, madame—chanson: 4vv
(pub 1570)**
C. Janequin Ens *Concert*
                                 (2/93) (HARM) ① **HMC90 1391**
Exaltabo te Domine—motet: 4vv (pub 1582)
Oxford Christ Church Cath Ch, S. Darlington *Concert*
                                 (4/89) (NIMB) ① **NI5150**
Exultate justi—motet: 4vv (pub 1568)
Trinity Coll Ch, Cambridge, R. Marlow (r1994)
Concert   (11/94) (CONI) ① **CDCF230**
**Four Language Printing, '(6) Chansons
françaises nouvelles'—French chanons: 4vv
(pub 1573)**
1. Di moy mon cuer (Dialogue: 8vv); 2. Sces tu dir
l'Ave disoit il; 3. Si du mal'heur vous avies; 4. Qui
bien se mire bien se voit; 5. Quant un cordier
cordant; 6. Si je suis brun; 7. Un jeune moine est sorti
du convent.
3, 7. C. Janequin Ens *Concert*
                                 (2/93) (HARM) ① **HMC90 1391**
6, 7. Scholars (r1993) *Concert*
                                 (2/95) (NAXO) ① **8 550880**
**Fuyons tous d'amour—chanson: 5vv (pub
1564)**
C. Janequin Ens *Concert*
                                 (2/93) (HARM) ① **HMC90 1391**
**Hodie completi sunt—motet: 6vv (pub
1582)**
Tallis Scholars, P. Phillips *Concert*
                                 (7/89) (GIME) ① **CDGIM018**
Trinity Coll Ch, Cambridge, R. Marlow (r1994)
Concert   (11/94) (CONI) ① **CDCF230**
I' voi piangendo—madrigal: 5vv (pub 1567)
(Wds Petrarch)
Cantus Cölln, K. Junghänel (lte/dir) (r1993) *Concert*
                                 (7/94) (DHM) ① **05472 77304-2**
Infelix ego—motet: 5vv (pub 1566)
Oxford Schola Cantorum, J. Summerly (r1993)
Concert   (8/94) (NAXO) ① **8 550842**
Jam non dicam vos—motet: 6vv (pub 1573)
Trinity Coll Ch, Cambridge, R. Marlow (r1994)
Concert   (11/94) (CONI) ① **CDCF230**
J'ay de vous voir—chanson: 4vv (pub 1584)
(Wds Du Bellay)
Cantus Cölln, K. Junghänel (lte/dir) (r1993) *Concert*
                                 (7/94) (DHM) ① **05472 77304-2**
J'ay un mary—chanson
C. Janequin Ens (arr lte solo) *Concert*
                                 (2/93) (HARM) ① **HMC90 1391**
Je l'ayme bien—chanson: 4vv (pub 1555)
C. Janequin Ens *Concert*
                                 (2/93) (HARM) ① **HMC90 1391**
J'espère et crains—chanson: 5vv (pub 1571)
(Wds P. de Ronsard)
Cantus Cölln, K. Junghänel (lte/dir) (r1993) *Concert*
                                 (7/94) (DHM) ① **05472 77304-2**
**Jesu nostra redemptio—motet: 6vv (pub
1567)**
Trinity Coll Ch, Cambridge, R. Marlow (r1994)
Concert   (11/94) (CONI) ① **CDCF230**
Justorum animae—motet: 5vv (pub 1582)
Trinity Coll Ch, Cambridge, R. Marlow (r1994)
Concert   (11/94) (CONI) ① **CDCF230**
Laetentur coeli—motet: 4vv (pub 1569)
Trinity Coll Ch, Cambridge, R. Marlow (r1994)
Concert   (11/94) (CONI) ① **CDCF230**
**Lagrime di San Pietro ... con un mottetto nel
fine—sacred madrigals: 7vv (pub 1595)** (Wds
Tansillo)
EXCERPTS: 1. Il magnanimo Pietro; 2. Ma gli archi;
3. Tre volte haveva a l'incontro; 4. Qual a l'incontro
di quelli occhi santi; 5. Giovane donna il suo bel volto
in specchio; 6. Cosi talhór; 7. Ogni occhio del signór
lingua veloce; 8. Nessún fedél trovai; 9. Chi ad una
ad una raccontár potesse; 10. Come falda di neve;
11. E non fu il pianto suo rivo; 12. Quel volto, ch'era
poco inanzi stato; 13. Veduto il míser quanto
differente; 14. E vago d'incontrár chi giusta pena; 15.
Vàttene vita va; 16. O vita troppo rea; 17. A quanti
già felici in giovanezza; 18. Non trovara mia fé si duro
intoppo; 19. Queste opre e piü; 20. Negando il mio
signór; 21. Motet: Vide homo, quae pro te patior.
Cpte Européen Voc Ens, P. Herreweghe (r1993)
Concert   (8/94) (HARM) ① **HMC90 1483**
Huelgas Ens, P. Van Nevel (r1993)
                                 (8/94) (SONY) ① **SK53373**
**9 Lamentations of Jeremiah, 'Lamentationes
Hieremiae'—5vv (pub 1585)**
MAUNDY THURSDAY—Noctum I: 1. Incipit
Lamentatio Jeremiae; 2. Zain. Recordata est 3.
Lamed. O vos omnes. GOOD FRIDAY—Noctum I: 4.
De lamentatione Jeremiae; 5. Mem. Qui comparabo
te?; 6. Alpeh. Ego vir videns. HOLY
SATURDAY—Noctum I: 7. De Lamentatione
Jeremiae; 8. Aleph. Quomodo obscuratum; 9. Incipit
Oratio Jeremiae.

Paris Chapelle Royale European Ens, P. Herreweghe
                                 (12/89) (HARM) ① **HMC90 1299**
J-P. Gipon Voc Ens, J-P. Gipon (r1992) *Concert*
                                 (10/94) (JADE) ① [2] **JADC102**
1, 3. Oxford Camerata, J. Summerly *Concert*
                                 (4/93) (NAXO) ① **8 550572**
Las me fault-il—chanson: 5vv (pub 1560)
C. Janequin Ens *Concert*
                                 (2/93) (HARM) ① **HMC90 1391**
Lauda mater ecclesia—motet: 5vv (1597)
Oxford Camerata, J. Summerly (r1993) *Concert*
                                 (3/95) (NAXO) ① **8 550843**
**Libro de villanelle, moresche, et altre
canzoni—4-6, 8vv (pub 1581)**
1. Ad altre le voi dare (4vv); 2. Allala la pia calia
(4vv); 3. Canta Giorgia canta (6vv); 4. Cathalina apra
finestra (6vv); 5. Chi chilichi (6vv); 6. Ecco la
ninph'ebraica chiamata (4vv); 7. Hai Lucia buona
cosa (4vv); 8. Io ti vorria contar (4vv); 9. Lucia celu
hai biscamia (4vv); 10. Matona mia cara (4vv); 11. Mi
me chiamere (5vv); 12. O bella fusa (4vv); 13. Ogni
giorno m'han ditt' (4vv); 14. O la o che bon eccho
(8vv); 15. O occhi manza mia (4vv); 16. Parch'hai
lasciato (4vv); 17. S'io fusse siaul' (4vv); 18. S'io ti
vedess'una sol volt'il giorno (4vv); 19. S'io ve dico
(4vv); 20. Tutto 'l di mi dici (4vv); 21. Tutto' l di mi dici
(8vv); 22. Zanni piasi patro (8vv).
Cpte Concerto Italiano, R. Alessandrini (r1994)
                                 (10/95) (O111) ① **OPS30-94**
2-5, 7, 9. C. Janequin Ens *Concert*
                                 (2/93) (HARM) ① **HMC90 1391**
**Lucescit jam o socii—chanson: 4vv (pub
1578)**
C. Janequin Ens *Concert*
                                 (2/93) (HARM) ① **HMC90 1391**
**Madonna mia pietà—madrigal: 4vv (pub
1555)**
J. Lindberg, R. Meunier, N. North (instr vers) *Concert*
                                 (12/86) (BIS) ① **BIS-CD341**
Concerto Italiano, R. Alessandrini (r1994) *Concert*
                                 (10/95) (O111) ① **OPS30-94**
Mais qui pourroit—chanson: 6vv (pub 1584)
C. Janequin Ens *Concert*
                                 (2/93) (HARM) ① **HMC90 1391**
Matona mia cara—madrigal: 4vv (pub 1581)
Amaryllis Consort *Concert*
                                 (6/86) (CARL) ① **PCD822**
**Mia benigna fortun'e—madrigal: 5vv (pub
1555)** (Wds Petrarch)
Cantus Cölln, K. Junghänel (lte/dir) (r1993) *Concert*
                                 (7/94) (DHM) ① **05472 77304-2**
Missa Bell'Amfitrit'altera—8vv (pub 1610)
Oxford Christ Church Cath Ch, S. Preston *Psalmi
Davidis poenitentiales.*
                                 (10/92) (DECC) ① **433 679-2DM**
The Sixteen, H. Christophers (r1992) *Concert*
                                 (10/93) (COLL) ① **Coll1360-2**
Westminster Cath Ch, His Majesties Sagbutts and
Cornetts, J. O'Donnell, T. Roberts, I. Simcock (r1993)
Concert   (6/94) (HYPE) ① **CDA66688**
Oxford Schola Cantorum, J. Summerly (r1993)
Concert   (6/94) (NAXO) ① **8 550836**
Missa Entre vous filles—5vv (pub 1581)
Oxford Schola Cantorum, J. Summerly (r1993)
Concert   (8/94) (NAXO) ① **8 550842**
**Missa 'Jäger', 'Venatorum'—4vv (pub
1577)**
Oxford Christ Church Cath Ch, S. Darlington *Concert*
                                 (4/89) (NIMB) ① **NI5150**
Missa Osculetur me—8vv (after 1582)
Tallis Scholars, P. Phillips *Concert*
                                 (7/89) (GIME) ① **CDGIM018**
**Missa Qual donna attende à gloriosa
fama—5vv (pub 1589)**
Oxford Christ Church Cath Ch, S. Darlington *Concert*
                                 (4/89) (NIMB) ① **NI5150**
Missa Susanne un jour—5vv (pub 1577)
Oxford Schola Cantorum, J. Summerly (r1993)
Concert   (8/94) (NAXO) ① **8 550842**
**Multarum hic resonat—motet: 5vv (pub
1571)**
Hanover Childrens' Ch, Collegium Vocale, P.
Herreweghe (r1979) *Concert*
                                 (12/93) (ASTR) ① **E7780**
**La Nuict froide et sombre—chanson: 4vv
(pub 1576)** (Wds. Du Bellamy)
C. Janequin Ens *Concert*
                                 (2/93) (HARM) ① **HMC90 1391**
Cantus Cölln, K. Junghänel (lte/dir) (r1993) *Concert*
                                 (7/94) (DHM) ① **05472 77304-2**
Scholars (r1993) *Concert*
                                 (2/95) (NAXO) ① **8 550880**
O foible esprit—chanson: 5vv (pub 1571)
(Wds. Du Bellay)
C. Janequin Ens *Concert*
                                 (2/93) (HARM) ① **HMC90 1391**

Cantus Cölln, K. Junghänel (lte/dir) (r1993) *Concert*
(7/94) (DHM) ① **05472 77304-2**
O Lucia miau—moresca: 3vv (pub 1560)
C. Janequin Ens *Concert*
(2/93) (HARM) ① **HMC90 1391**
Concerto Italiano, R. Alessandrini (r1994) *Concert*
(10/95) (O111) ① **OPS30-94**
O mors, quam amara est—motet: 6vv (pub 1564)
PCA, B. Turner (r1974) *Concert*
(1/93) (ARCH) ① **437 072-2AT**
Omnes de Saba—motet: 8vv (pub 1604)
The Sixteen, H. Christophers *Concert*
(12/88) (HYPE) ① **CDA66263**
Trinity Coll Ch, Cambridge, R. Marlow (r1994)
Concert (11/94) (CONI) ① **CDCF230**
Osculetur me—motet: 8vv (pub 1582)
Tallis Scholars, P. Phillips *Concert*
(7/89) (GIME) ① **CDGIM018**
Pater Abraham miserere—motet: 5vv (pub 1571)
Hanover Childrens' Ch, Collegium Vocale, P.
Herreweghe (r1979) *Concert*
(12/93) (ASTR) ① **E7780**
Pater noster—motet: 6vv (pub 1585)
Hanover Childrens' Ch, Collegium Vocale, P.
Herreweghe (r1979) *Concert*
(12/93) (ASTR) ① **E7780**
Peccantem me quotidie—motet: 4vv (pub 1555)
Trinity Coll Ch, Cambridge, R. Marlow (r1994)
Concert (11/94) (CONI) ① **CDCF230**
Poichè'l mio largo pianto—lauda a Santa Maria del Pianto (pub 1588) (in Gardano's 'Primo libro delle laudi')
Daedalus Ens (r1992) *Concert*
(11/93) (ACCE) ① **ACC9289D**
Popule meus—motet: 5vv (pub 1582)
Trinity Coll Ch, Cambridge, R. Marlow (r1994)
Concert (11/94) (CONI) ① **CDCF230**
Prophetiae Sibyllarum—motet: 4vv (pub 1600)
1. Virgine matre; 2. Ecce dies venient; 3. Non tarde;
4. In veneris; 5. Ecce dies nigras; 6. Jam mea; 7.
Dum meditor; 8. Ipsa Deum; 9. Virginis aeternum; 10.
Verax ipse; 11. Cerno Dei; 12. Summus erit.
Cantus Cölln, K. Junghänel (lte/dir) (r1993) *Concert*
(7/94) (DHM) ① **05472 77304-2**
Psalmi Davidis poenitentiales—5vv (pub 1584)
1. Domine ne in furore tuo...miserere; 2. Beati
quorum remissae sunt; 3. Domine ne in furore
tuo...quoniam; 4. Miserere mei Deus; 5. Domine
exaudi...non avertas; 6. De profundis; 7. Domine
exaudi...auribus percipe.
1. PCA, B. Turner (r1974) *Concert*
(1/93) (ARCH) ① **437 072-2AT**
6. Oxford Christ Church Cath Ch, S. Darlington
Concert (4/89) (NIMB) ① **NI5150**
7. Oxford Christ Church Cath Ch, S. Preston *Missa
Bell'amfitrit'altera.* (10/92) (DECC) ① **433 679-2DM**
Une puce j'ay dedans l'oreill'—chanson: 5vv (pub 1571) (Wds. Baïf)
C. Janequin Ens *Concert*
(2/93) (HARM) ① **HMC90 1391**
Quand mon mary vient—chanson: 4vv (pub 1564)
C. Janequin Ens (arr lte solo) *Concert*
(2/93) (HARM) ① **HMC90 1391**
C. Janequin Ens *Concert*
(2/93) (HARM) ① **HMC90 1391**
Quem vidistis pastores—motet: 5vv (pub 1569)
Trinity Coll Ch, Cambridge, R. Marlow (r1994)
Concert (11/94) (CONI) ① **CDCF230**
Quid prodest homini—motet: 5vv (pub 1571)
Hanover Childrens' Ch, Collegium Vocale, P.
Herreweghe (r1979) *Concert*
(12/93) (ASTR) ① **E7780**
Regina Coeli—motet: 6vv (pub 1585)
Trinity Coll Ch, Cambridge, R. Marlow (r1994)
Concert (11/94) (CONI) ① **CDCF230**
Regina coeli laetare—motet: 4vv (pub 1604)
Trinity Coll Ch, Cambridge, R. Marlow (r1994)
Concert (11/94) (CONI) ① **CDCF230**
Regina coeli laetare—motet: 5vv (pub 1604) (two settings)
Trinity Coll Ch, Cambridge, R. Marlow (r1994)
Concert (11/94) (CONI) ① **CDCF230**
Regina coeli laetare—motet: 7vv (pub 1604)
Tallis Scholars, P. Phillips *Concert*
(7/89) (GIME) ① **CDGIM018**

Trinity Coll Ch, Cambridge, R. Marlow (r1994)
Concert (11/94) (CONI) ① **CDCF230**
Rends-moi mon coeur—chanson: 5vv (pub 1561) (Wds P. de Ronsard)
Cantus Cölln, K. Junghänel (lte/dir) (r1993) *Concert*
(7/94) (DHM) ① **05472 77304-2**
Resonet in laudibus—motet: 5vv (pub 1569)
Trinity Coll Ch, Cambridge, R. Marlow (r1994)
Concert (11/94) (CONI) ① **CDCF230**
Saccio 'na cosa—madrigal: 4vv (pub 1581)
Concerto Italiano, R. Alessandrini (r1994) *Concert*
(10/95) (O111) ① **OPS30-94**
Salve regina mater—motet: 8vv (pub 1604)
Tallis Scholars, P. Phillips *Concert*
(7/89) (GIME) ① **CDGIM018**
PCA, B. Turner (r1974) *Concert*
(1/93) (ARCH) ① **437 072-2AT**
Si bona suscepimus—motet: 5vv (pub 1571)
Hanover Childrens' Ch, Collegium Vocale, P.
Herreweghe (r1979) *Concert*
(12/93) (ASTR) ① **E7780**
S'io esca vivo—madrigal: 6vv (pub 1579) (Wds. Petrarch)
Amaryllis Consort *Concert*
(6/86) (CARL) ① **PCD822**
Sol'e pensoso i più deserti campi—madrigal: 5vv (pub 1555)
Concerto Italiano, R. Alessandrini (r1994) *Concert*
(10/95) (O111) ① **OPS30-94**
Soleasi nel mio cor—madrigal: 5vv (pub 1576) (Wds Petrarch)
Cantus Cölln, K. Junghänel (lte/dir) (r1993) *Concert*
(7/94) (DHM) ① **05472 77304-2**
St Matthew Passion, 'Passio Domini nostri Jesu Christi secundum Mattheum'—5vv (pub 1575)
Cpte Theatre of Voices, P. Hillier (r1993) *Concert*
(9/94) (HARM) ① **HMU90 7076**
Stabunt justi—motet: 5vv (pub 1571)
Hanover Childrens' Ch, Collegium Vocale, P.
Herreweghe (r1979) *Concert*
(12/93) (ASTR) ① **E7780**
Standomi un giorno—madrigal: 5vv (pub 1557) (Wds Petrarch)
Cantus Cölln, K. Junghänel (lte/dir) (r1993) *Concert*
(7/94) (DHM) ① **05472 77304-2**
Le Temps peut bien—chanson: 4vv (pub 1564)
C. Janequin Ens (arr lte solo) *Concert*
(2/93) (HARM) ① **HMC90 1391**
Tenebrae Responsories, 'Pro Triduo sacro in nocturno II et III'—4vv (c1580-85)
(Responsories for 2nd & 3rd Nocturns of Holy Week)
MAUNDY THURSDAY—Nocturn II: 1. Amicus meus;
2. Judas mercator pessimus; 3. Unus ex discipulis.
Nocturn III: 4. Eram quasi agnus; 5. Una hora; 6.
Seniores populi. GOOD FRIDAY—Nocturn II: 7.
Tamquam ad latronen; 8. Tenebrae factae sunt; 9.
Animam meam. Nocturn III: 10. Tradiderunt me; 11.
Jesum tradidit; 12. Caligaverunt oculi mei. HOLY
SATURDAY—Nocturn II: 13. Recessit pastor noster;
14. O vos omnes; 15. Ecc quomodo moritur. Nocturn
III: 16. Astiterunt reges terrae; 17. Aestimatus sum;
18. Sepulto Domino.
J-P. Gipon Voc Ens, J-P. Gipon (r1992) *Concert*
(10/94) (JADE) ① [2] **JADC102**
La terre les eaux va beuvant—chanson: 5vv (Wds P. de Ronsard)
Cantus Cölln, K. Junghänel (lte/dir) (r1993) *Concert*
(7/94) (DHM) ① **05472 77304-2**
Timor et tremor—motet: 6vv (pub 1564)
Tallis Scholars, P. Phillips *Concert*
(7/89) (GIME) ① **CDGIM018**
Trinity Coll Ch, Cambridge, R. Marlow (r1994)
Concert (11/94) (CONI) ① **CDCF230**
Un triste coeur rempli—chanson: 5vv (pub 1560)
C. Janequin Ens *Concert*
(2/93) (HARM) ① **HMC90 1391**
Tristis est anima mea—motet: 5vv (pub 1565)
Oxford Christ Church Cath Ch, S. Darlington *Concert*
(4/89) (NIMB) ① **NI5150**
Tui sunt coeli—motet: 8vv (pub 1604)
The Sixteen, H. Christophers (r1992) *Concert*
(10/93) (COLL) ① **Coll1360-2**
Trinity Coll Ch, Cambridge, R. Marlow (r1994)
Concert (11/94) (CONI) ① **CDCF230**
Tutto 'I di plango—madrigal: 5vv (pub 1567)
Concerto Italiano, R. Alessandrini (r1994) *Concert*
(10/95) (O111) ① **OPS30-94**

Trinity Coll Ch, Cambridge, R. Marlow (r1994)
Concert (11/94) (CONI) ① **CDCF230**
Veni dilecte mi—motet: 5vv (pub 1571)
Hanover Childrens' Ch, Collegium Vocale, P.
Herreweghe (r1979) *Concert*
(12/93) (ASTR) ① **E7780**
Verba mea auribus percipe—motet: 5vv (pub 1571)
Hanover Childrens' Ch, Collegium Vocale, P.
Herreweghe (r1979) *Concert*
(12/93) (ASTR) ① **E7780**
Vignon vignon vignette—chanson: 6vv (pub 1584)
C. Janequin Ens *Concert*
(2/93) (HARM) ① **HMC90 1391**
La vita fugge—madrigal: 5vv (pub 1563) (Wds Petrarch)
Cantus Cölln, K. Junghänel (lte/dir) (r1993) *Concert*
(7/94) (DHM) ① **05472 77304-2**

LAUDER, James (1535–1595) Scotland

SECTION II: CHAMBER

My Lord of Marche Paven—consort (1584)
New London Consort, P. Pickett (1992) *Concert*
(4/94) (LINN) ① **CKD011**

LAURO, Antonio (1917–1986) Venezuela

SECTION III: INSTRUMENTAL

El Niño—guitar
J. Williams *Concert* (8/89) (SONY) ① **SK44898**
Sonata for Guitar (1975)
1. Allegro; 2. Cancion; 3. Bolera.
J.C. Balbi *Concert* (11/91) (ETCE) ① **KTC1110**
Suite venezolana—guitar (1963)
1. Registro; 2. Danza negra; 3. Cancion; 4. Vals.
J.C. Balbi *Concert* (11/91) (ETCE) ① **KTC1110**
Triptíco—guitar (1984)
1. Armida; 2. Madrugada; 3. La Negra.
J.C. Balbi *Concert* (11/91) (ETCE) ① **KTC1110**
4 Valses Venezolanos—guitar (1963)
1. Tatiana (D major); 2. Andreina (E minor); 3.
Natalia/Criolla (E minor/E major); 4. Yacambú (A minor).
J.C. Balbi *Concert* (11/91) (ETCE) ① **KTC1110**
2. M. Kayath *Concert* (9/87) (CARL) ① **PCD853**
3. J. Williams *Concert* (8/89) (SONY) ① **SK44898**
6 Valses Venezolanos—guitar (1968)
1. El Marabino; 2. El negrito; 3. El Totumo de
Guarenas (Canonico); 4. Maria Luisa; 5. Carora; 6.
Angostura.
1, 2. M. Kayath *Concert* (9/87) (CARL) ① **PCD853**
1, 4, 5, 6. J.C. Balbi *Concert*
(11/91) (ETCE) ① **KTC1110**
4. J. Williams *Concert* (8/89) (SONY) ① **SK44898**
Variaciones sobre un Tema Infantil Venezolano—guitar (1969) (variations on a Venezuelan children's song)
J.C. Balbi *Concert* (11/91) (ETCE) ① **KTC1110**

LAVAGNINO, Angelo Francesco (b 1909) Italy

SECTION V: STAGE WORKS

Orson Welles' Othello—film score (1952) (collab with Alberto Bargeris)
EXCERPTS: 1a. Main Title; 1b. Chant; 2. There Was
Once In Venice a Moor; 3a. The Wrath of Brabantio;
3b. Iago's Theme; 3c. 'An Hour to Spend With Thee';
4. The Turks Retreat; 5a. The Proclamation; 5b.
Deceiving Rodrigo; 6. The Celebration & Antagonism
of Cassio; 7. 'My Reputation, Iago, My Reputation'; 8.
The Seed of Doubt; 9. The Handkerchief; 10. Othello
Eavesdrops; 11. 'Let Me See your Eyes'; 12. Who Is
Thy Lord'; 13. The Murder of Rodrigo (The Public
Thermae); 14. 'Put Out the Light, Then Put Out the
Light'; 15a. The Deceiver is Revealed; 15b. The
Death of Othello.
1a, 1b, 2, 3a-c, 4, 5a, 5b, 6-14, 15a, 15b Chicago
Lyric Op Chor, Chicago SO, M. Pendowski (r1993)
(8/94) (VARE) ① **VSD5420**

LAWES, Henry (1596–1662) England

SECTION IV: VOCAL AND CHORAL

Amintor's welladay—secular song
Consort of Musicke, A. Rooley *Concert*
(12/89) (HYPE) ① **CDA66135**
Come, sad turtle—secular song
Consort of Musicke, A. Rooley *Concert*
(12/89) (HYPE) ① **CDA66135**

Farewell. despairing hopes—secular song
Consort of Musicke, A. Rooley *Concert*
(12/89) (HYPE) ① **CDA66135**
Gather ye rosebuds while ye may—secular song (1648) (Wds. Henick)
E. Kirkby, A. Rooley (pp1985) *Concert*
(6/87) (HYPE) ① **CDA66186**
Hark, shepherd swains—secular song
Consort of Musicke, A. Rooley *Concert*
(12/89) (HYPE) ① **CDA66135**
I laid me down—secular song
Consort of Musicke, A. Rooley *Concert*
(12/89) (HYPE) ① **CDA66135**
I prithee send me—secular song
Consort of Musicke, A. Rooley *Concert*
(12/89) (HYPE) ① **CDA66135**
I rise and grieve—song: 1v
E. Tubb, F. Kelly (r1992) *Concert*
(9/94) (MOSC) ① **070987**
In quel gelato core—secular song
Consort of Musicke, A. Rooley *Concert*
(12/89) (HYPE) ① **CDA66135**
The Lark—secular song
E. Kirkby, Consort of Musicke, A. Rooley *Concert*
(9/87) (HYPE) ① **CDA66227**
Consort of Musicke, A. Rooley *Concert*
(12/89) (HYPE) ① **CDA66135**
Man's life is but vain—secular song
Consort of Musicke, A. Rooley *Concert*
(12/89) (HYPE) ① **CDA66135**
My soul the Great God's praises sing—secular song
Consort of Musicke, A. Rooley *Concert*
(12/89) (HYPE) ① **CDA66135**
Orpheus's Hymn—secular song
Consort of Musicke, A. Rooley *Concert*
(12/89) (HYPE) ① **CDA66135**
Sing fair Clorinda—secular song
Consort of Musicke, A. Rooley *Concert*
(12/89) (HYPE) ① **CDA66135**
Sitting by the streams—secular song
Consort of Musicke, A. Rooley *Concert*
(12/89) (HYPE) ① **CDA66135**
Slide soft you silver floods—secular song
Consort of Musicke, A. Rooley *Concert*
(12/89) (HYPE) ① **CDA66135**
Sweet, stay awhile—secular song
Consort of Musicke, A. Rooley *Concert*
(12/89) (HYPE) ① **CDA66135**
Thee and thy wondrous deeds—secular song
Consort of Musicke, A. Rooley *Concert*
(12/89) (HYPE) ① **CDA66135**
This mossy bank—secular song
Consort of Musicke, A. Rooley *Concert*
(12/89) (HYPE) ① **CDA66135**
Zadok the Priest—coronation anthem for King Charles II (1661) (Wds. Bible)
Westminster Abbey Ch, cond'r, S. Preston (1986)
Concert (7/95) (ARCH) ① **447 155-2AP**

LAWES, William *(1602–1645) England*

SECTION II: CHAMBER

Airs—three lyra viols
Fretwork, P. Nicholson *Concert*
(8/91) (VIRG) ① **VC7 59021-2**
Consort Sett a 5 in A minor—consort: 5 pts
Fretwork (r1991) *Concert*
(10/95) (VIRG) ① **VC5 45147-2**
Consort Sett a 5 in C minor—consort (5 pts)
Fretwork, P. Nicholson *Concert*
(8/91) (VIRG) ① **VC7 59021-2**
Consort Sett a 5 in F—consort (5 pts)
Fretwork, P. Nicholson *Concert*
(8/91) (VIRG) ① **VC7 59021-2**
Consort Sett a 5 in G minor—consort: 5 pts
Fretwork (r1991) *Concert*
(10/95) (VIRG) ① **VC5 45147-2**
Consort Sett a 6 in B flat—consort: 6 pts
Fretwork (r1991) *Concert*
(10/95) (VIRG) ① **VC5 45147-2**
Consort Sett a 6 in C—consort: 6 pts
Fretwork (r1991) *Concert*
(10/95) (VIRG) ① **VC5 45147-2**
Consort Sett a 6 in C minor—consort (6 pts)
Fretwork, P. Nicholson *Concert*
(8/91) (VIRG) ① **VC7 59021-2**
Consort Sett a 6 in F—consort (6 pts)
Fretwork, P. Nicholson *Concert*
(8/91) (VIRG) ① **VC7 59021-2**

Consort Sett a 6 in G minor—consort: 6 pts
Fretwork (r1991) *Concert*
(10/95) (VIRG) ① **VC5 45147-2**
Divisions in G minor—two bass viols and organ
Fretwork, P. Nicholson *Concert*
(8/91) (VIRG) ① **VC7 59021-2**
8 Fantasia-Suites—violin, bass viol and organ
1. G minor; 2. G; 3. A minor; 4. C; 5. D minor; 6. D; 7. D minor; 8. D.
8. Sonnerie Trio (r1992) *Concert*
(5/94) (TELD) ① **4509-90841-2**
8 Fantasia-Suites—2 violins, bass and organ
1. G minor; 2. G; 3. A minor; 4. C; 5. D minor; 6. D; 7. D minor; 8. D.
London Baroque (r1992)
(6/93) (HARM) ① **HMC90 1423**
Purcell Qt (r1993) (5/94) (CHAN) ① **CHAN0552**
7. Scaramouche (r1992) *Concert*
(5/94) (CHNN) ① **CCS4792**
Royall Consorts—10 suites: 2 vns, 2 bass viols, 2 theorbos (c1630)
EXCERPTS: 1. No 1 in D; 2. No 2 in D minor; 3. No 3 in D minor; 4. No 4 in D; 5. No 5 in D; 6. No 6 in D; 7. No 7 in A minor; 8. No 8 in C; 9. No 9 in F; 10. No 10 in B flat.
Purcell Qt, N. North, P. O'Dette (1994)
(11/95) (CHAN) ② **CHAN0584/5**
Suite in D—two lutes
J. Bream, J. Williams (r1971; trans Bream) *Concert*
(11/93) (RCA) ① **09026 61450-2**

SECTION III: INSTRUMENTAL

2 Aires—lyra viol, VdGS462-3
1. Aire, VdGS462; 2. Aire, VdGS463.
R. Boothby (r1991) *Concert*
(10/95) (VIRG) ① **VC5 45147-2**
2 Dances—lyra viol, VdGS421-2
1. Countrey Coll, VdGS421; 2. Jigg, VdGS422.
R. Boothby (r1991) *Concert*
(10/95) (VIRG) ① **VC5 45147-2**
3 Dances—lyra viol, VdGS430-2
1. Almaine, VdGS430; 2. Corant, VdGS431; 3. Saraband, VdGS432.
R. Boothby (r1991) *Concert*
(10/95) (VIRG) ① **VC5 45147-2**

SECTION IV: VOCAL AND CHORAL

Amarillis tear thy hair—song: 1v
E. Tubb, F. Kelly (r1992) *Concert*
(9/94) (MOSC) ① **070987**
Gather ye rosebuds while you may—secular song: 1vv (Wds. Herrick)
L. Skeaping, Broadside Band, J. Barlow (r1992; arr J. Barlow) *Concert* (6/93) (SAYD) ① **CD-SDL400**
C. Bott, R. Boothby, P. Nicholson (r1991) *Concert*
(10/95) (VIRG) ① **VC5 45147-2**
On the Lillyes, 'White though eye be'—secular song: 1v (Wds. R. Herrick from 'Hesprides')
C. Bott, R. Boothby, P. Nicholson (r1991) *Concert*
(10/95) (VIRG) ① **VC5 45147-2**
To Pansies, 'Ah cruel love'—secular song: 1v (Wds. R. Herrick from 'Heprides')
C. Bott, R. Boothby, P. Nicholson (r1991) *Concert*
(10/95) (VIRG) ① **VC5 45147-2**
To the sycamore, 'I'm sick of love'—secular song: 1v (Wds. Herrick from 'Hesprides')
C. Bott, R. Boothby, P. Nicholson (r1991) *Concert*
(10/95) (VIRG) ① **VC5 45147-2**

LE FLEM, Paul *(1881–1984) France*

SECTION I: ORCHESTRAL

7 Pièces enfantines—orchestra (1912 orch ?) (orch cpsr from pf work)
1. Prière; 2. Bastions de sable; 3. Après gronderie; 4. Chatterie; 5. La vieille mendiante; 6. La chapelle; 7. Bigoudens.
Rhenish PO, J. Lockhart (1987) *Concert*
(12/94) (MARC) ① **8 223655**
Symphony No. 4 (1971-72)
Rhenish PO, J. Lockhart (1987) *Concert*
(12/94) (MARC) ① **8 223655**
Tryptique symphonique—orchestra
1. Pour les morts (1912 orch 1920).
1. Rhenish PO, J. Lockhart (1987) *Concert*
(12/94) (MARC) ① **8 223655**

SECTION V: STAGE WORKS

Le Grand jardinier de France—film score (1942) (Eng: The Great Gardener of France)
Rhenish PO, G. Nopre (r1993) *Concert*
(12/94) (MARC) ① **8 223655**

LE JEUNE, Claude *(1528/30–1600) France*

SECTION IV: VOCAL AND CHORAL

La Bel'aronde—chanson
P. Thwaites, J. Lavender (1989-91: 2 vers: arr 2 pfs: Grainger) *Concert* (1/94) (PEAR) ① **SHEC9631**
Benedicite Dominum omnes angeli—motet: 3-7vv (pub 1612)
New College Ch, E. Higginbottom (org/dir) *Concert*
(10/91) (HYPE) ① **CDA66387**
Ce n'est que fiel—chanson
Scholars (r1993) *Concert*
(2/95) (NAXO) ① **8 550880**
Hélas! Seigneur, je te prie sauve-moi!—3vv (pub 1620-10) (Wds. Psalm 69)
Sagittarius Ens, M. Laplénie *Concert*
(4/93) (ERAT) ① **2292-45825-2**
Hélas! Seigneur, je te prie sauve-moi!—5vv (pub 1601) (Wds. Psalm 69)
Viol Ens, M. Laplénie *Concert*
(4/93) (ERAT) ① **2292-45825-2**
Magnificat—4-7vv (pub 1612)
New College Ch, E. Higginbottom (org/dir) *Concert*
(10/91) (HYPE) ① **CDA66387**
Messe du Manuscrit de Savoie—4-6vv
Sagittarius Ens, F. Eichelberger, M. Laplénie *Concert*
(4/93) (ERAT) ① **2292-45825-2**
Miséricorde au pauvre vicieux—5vv (pub 1601) (Wds. Psalm 51)
Sagittarius Ens, M. Laplénie *Concert*
(4/93) (ERAT) ① **2292-45825-2**
Missa ad Placitum—4-7vv (1607)
New College Ch, E. Higginbottom (org/dir) *Concert*
(10/91) (HYPE) ① **CDA66387**
Sagittarius Ens, E. Mandarin, M. Laplénie *Concert*
(4/93) (ERAT) ① **2292-45825-2**
Toutes gens loué le Seigneur—6vv (pub 1612) (Wds. Psalm 117)
Sagittarius Ens, M. Laplénie *Concert*
(4/93) (ERAT) ① **2292-45825-2**

LE ROUX, Gaspard *(2nd half of 17th Cent–1705/7) France*

SECTION III: INSTRUMENTAL

Pièces de clavessin—7 suites: keyboard (pub 1705)
1. D minor; 2. D; 3. A minor; 4. A; 5. F; 6. F sharp minor; 7. G minor.
C. Rousset (r1993) (7/95) (L'OI) ① **443 329-2OH**
5. G. Leonhardt *Concert* (5/92) (DHM) ① **RD77924**

LE ROY, Adrian *(c1520–1598) France*

SECTION IV: VOCAL AND CHORAL

Has tu point veu—chanson (pub 1573)
Baltimore Consort (r1992; arr Baltimore Consort) *Concert* (4/95) (DORI) ① **DOR90177**
J'ay le rebours—chanson (pub 1555)
Baltimore Consort (r1992; arr Baltimore Consort) *Concert* (4/95) (DORI) ① **DOR90177**
Une m'avois promis—chanson (pub 1555)
Baltimore Consort (r1992; arr Baltimore Consort) *Concert* (4/95) (DORI) ① **DOR90177**
Mes pas semez—chanson (pub 1555)
Baltimore Consort (r1992; arr Baltimore Consort) *Concert* (4/95) (DORI) ① **DOR90177**

LE ROY/BALLARD

SECTION III: INSTRUMENTAL

Branle de Poictou
N. North *Concert* (6/87) (AMON) ① **CD-SAR18**
Pimontoyse
N. North *Concert* (6/87) (AMON) ① **CD-SAR18**

LE SUER, Jean-François (1760–1837) France

SECTION IV: VOCAL AND CHORAL

3 Oratorios for the Coronation of Charles X at Reims (1825)
Chorus Musicus, Neue Orch, C. Spering (r1992)
(10/94) (O111) ① OPS30-89

LEBÈGUE, Nicolas-Antoine (c1631–1702) France

SECTION III: INSTRUMENTAL

Dessus de Cromhorne—organ
J. Payne (r1994) Concert
(10/95) (NAXO) ① 8 553215
Offertoire in C—organ
J. Payne (r1994) Concert
(10/95) (NAXO) ① 8 553215
Tierce en taille—organ
J. Payne (r1994) Concert
(10/95) (NAXO) ① 8 553215
Trio à trois claviers—organ
J. Payne (r1994) Concert
(10/95) (NAXO) ① 8 553215
Troisième livre d'orgue (pub ?1685)
Pour l'amour de Marie German Baroque sols, R. Ewerhart (org/dir) Concert
(12/91) (FSM) ① FCD91220
Puer nobis nascitur; Laissez paistre vos bêtes; Une jeune pucelle D. Ferran Concert
(4/88) (ARIO) ① ARN68015
Une Vierge pucelle—organ
J. Payne (r1994) Concert
(10/95) (NAXO) ① 8 553215

LEBERTOUL, Franchois (fl 1409–10) The Netherlands

SECTION IV: VOCAL AND CHORAL

Las, que me demanderoye—rondeau (3vv)
Gothic Voices, C. Page Concert
(11/87) (HYPE) ① CDA66238

LECHNER, Leonhard (c1553–1606) Austria/Germany

SECTION IV: VOCAL AND CHORAL

Ach herzigs Herz—villanella (Neue teutsche Lieder: 1576)
Cantus Cölln, K. Junghänel (lte/dir) Concert
(11/90) (DHM) ① RD77182
Ach Lieb, ich muss dich lassen—villanella (Neu teutscher Lieder: 1576)
Cantus Cölln, K. Junghänel (lte/dir) Concert
(11/90) (DHM) ① RD77182
Ach, wer wird mir mein' Geist—canzone (Neue teutsche Lieder: 1586)
Cantus Cölln, K. Junghänel (lte/dir) Concert
(11/90) (DHM) ① RD77182
Aus tiefer Not schrei ich zu dir—hymn (Wds. M. Luther)
Cantus Cölln, K. Junghänel (lte/dir) Concert
(11/90) (DHM) ① RD77182
Come nave ch'io mezzo—madrigal (Neue teutsche Lieder: 1579)
Cantus Cölln, K. Junghänel (lte/dir) Concert
(11/90) (DHM) ① RD77182
Deutsche Sprüche von Leben und Tod
Cantus Cölln, K. Junghänel (lte/dir) Concert
(11/90) (DHM) ① RD77182
Das Erst und ander Kapital—ty (Wds. Song of Songs: chapters 1-2)
Cantus Cölln, K. Junghänel (lte/dir) Concert
(11/90) (DHM) ① RD77182
Frau, ich bin euch von Herzen—villanella (Neu teutsche Lieder: 1576)
Cantus Cölln, K. Junghänel (lte/dir) Concert
(11/90) (DHM) ① RD77182
Freu dich heut und allezeit—song motet (Wds. P. Dulner)
Cantus Cölln, K. Junghänel (lte/dir) Concert
(11/90) (DHM) ① RD77182
Ganz sehr betrübt—villanella (Neu teutsche Lieder: 1576)
Cantus Cölln, K. Junghänel (lte/dir) Concert
(11/90) (DHM) ① RD77182
Gott bhüte dich—canzone (Neue teutsche Lieder: 1586)
Cantus Cölln, K. Junghänel (lte/dir) Concert
(11/90) (DHM) ① RD77182

Hört, was sich hat zutragen—canzone (Neue teutsche Lieder: 1586)
Cantus Cölln, K. Junghänel (lte/dir) Concert
(11/90) (DHM) ① RD77182
Ich ging einmal spazieren—madrigal (Wds. P. Dulner)
Cantus Cölln, K. Junghänel (lte/dir) Concert
(11/90) (DHM) ① RD77182
Der Mai viel schöner Blümlein—madrigal (Wds. P. Dulner)
Cantus Cölln, K. Junghänel (lte/dir) Concert
(11/90) (DHM) ① RD77182
Musicus wollt fröhlich sein—madrigal (Wds. P. Dulner)
Cantus Cölln, K. Junghänel (lte/dir) Concert
(11/90) (DHM) ① RD77182
Nach meiner Lieb—villanella (Neue teutsche Lieder: 1579)
Cantus Cölln, K. Junghänel (lte/dir) Concert
(11/90) (DHM) ① RD77182
Nackend bin ich—motet (Wds. Job I:21)
Cantus Cölln, K. Junghänel (lte/dir) Concert
(11/90) (DHM) ① RD77182
O Tod, du bist ein bittre Gallen—song motet (Wds. P. Dulner)
Cantus Cölln, K. Junghänel (lte/dir) Concert
(11/90) (DHM) ① RD77182
Si bona suscepimus—motet
Paris Chapelle Royale Baroque Ens, P. Herreweghe
(r1991) Concert (10/93) (HARM) ① HMC90 1401
Wie war mir nur in jungen Tagen—madrigal (Wds. P.Dulner)
Cantus Cölln, K. Junghänel (lte/dir) Concert
(11/90) (DHM) ① RD77182
Wohl dem, der den Herren—motet (Wds. Psalm 112)
Cantus Cölln, K. Junghänel (lte/dir) Concert
(11/90) (DHM) ① RD77182
Zart edles Gmüt—madrigal
Cantus Cölln, K. Junghänel (lte/dir) Concert
(11/90) (DHM) ① RD77182

LECLAIR, Jean-Marie (1697–1764) France

SECTION I: ORCHESTRAL

6 Concertos—violin, strings and continuo, Op. 7 (pub 1737)
1. D minor; 2. D; 3. C (for flute/oboe); 4. F; 5. A minor; 6. A.
1. Collegium Musicum 90, S. Standage (vn/dir) (r1995) Concertos, Op. 10.
(11/95) (CHAN) ① CHAN0589
2, 5. Collegium Musicum 90, S. Standage (vn/dir) Concertos, Op. 10. (8/94) (CHAN) ① CHAN0551
3. R. Brown, Collegium Musicum 90, S. Standage (r1994) Concert (2/95) (CHAN) ① CHAN0564
3, 5. Concerto Amsterdam, J. Schröder (vn/dir) (r1978) Concert (2/94) (TELD) ① 4509-92180-2
4, 6. S. Standage (vn/dir), Collegium Musicum 90 (r1994) Concert (2/95) (CHAN) ① CHAN0564
6 Concertos for Violin and Strings, Op. 10 (1745)
1. B flat; 2. A; 3. D; 4. F; 5. E minor; 6. G minor.
1, 5. Collegium Musicum 90, S. Standage (vn/dir) Concertos, Op. 7. (8/94) (CHAN) ① CHAN0551
2. S. Standage (vn/dir), Collegium Musicum 90 (r1994) Concert (2/95) (CHAN) ① CHAN0564
3, 4, 6. Collegium Musicum 90, S. Standage (vn/dir) (r1995) Concertos, Op. 7.
(11/95) (CHAN) ① CHAN0589
6. Concerto Amsterdam, J. Schröder (vn/dir) (r1978) Concert (2/94) (TELD) ① 4509-92180-2

SECTION II: CHAMBER

Ouvertures et Sonates en trio—two violins and continuo, Op. 13 (pub 1753)
1. Ouverture I in G; 2. Sonata I in D; 3. Ouverture II in D; 4. Sonata II in B minor; 5. Ouverture III in A; 6. Sonata III in G minor.
Talens Lyriques, C. Rousset (hpd/dir) (r1992)
(9/93) (FNAC) ① 592100
Purcell Qt (12/93) (CHAN) ① CHAN0542
3. Cologne Musica Antiqua, R. Goebel (r1978)
Concert (1/93) (ARCH) ① 437 086-2AT
5. Florilegium Ens (r1994) Concert
(12/95) (CHNN) ① CCS7595
Première Recréation de musique d'une exécution facile in D—2 violins and continuo, Op. 6 (pub 1736)
Nieces de Rameau (r1993) Recréation de musique II.
(9/94) (PIER) ① PV794011

Deuxième Recréation de musique d'une exécution facile in G minor—2 recorders/violins and continuo, Op. 8 (pub c1737)
Nieces de Rameau (r1993) Recréation de musique I.
(9/94) (PIER) ① PV794011
Florilegium Ens (r1994) Concert
(12/95) (CHNN) ① CCS7595
Music's Recreation Concert
(6/88) (MERI) ① CDE84114
6 Sonatas for Two Violins, Op. 3 (1730)
1. G; 2. A; 3. C; 4. F; 5. E minor; 6. D.
C. Banchini, J. Holloway
(4/91) (ERAT) ① 2292-45013-2
4. I. Perlman, P. Zukerman Concert
(12/91) (RCA) ① RD60735
12 Sonatas for Violin and Continuo, Premier livre, Op. 1 (pub c1723)
1. A minor; 2. C (fl also); 3. B flat; 4. D; 5. A; 6. E minor (fl also); 7. F; 8. G; 9. A; 10. D; 11. B flat; 12. B minor.
2. Barthold Kuijken, W. Kuijken, R. Kohnen Violin Sonatas, Op.2. (2/86) (ACCE) ① ACC58435D
6. Barthold Kuijken, W. Kuijken, R. Kohnen Concert (2/86) (ACCE) ① ACC58436D
12 Sonatas for Violin and Continuo, Quatrième livre, Op. 9 (pub 1743)
1. A; 2. E minor (fl also); 3. D; 4. A minor; 6. D; 7. G (fl also); 8. C; 9. E flat; 10. F minor; 11. G minor; 12. G.
2, 7. Barthold Kuijken, W. Kuijken, R. Kohnen Concert (2/86) (ACCE) ① ACC58436D
3 (Movts 1/3) Y. Menuhin, L. Persinger (arr Sarasate: r1929) Concert (4/91) (BIDD) ① LAB031
3. H. Szeryng, C. Reiner (r1963) Concert
(2/86) (MERC) ① 434 351-2MM
4. S. Standage, L.U. Mortensen (r1992) Concert (6/93) (CHAN) ① CHAN0531
7. R. Brown, J. Johnstone Concert
(2/94) (CHAN) ① CHAN0544
7, 9. Sonnerie Trio Violin Sonatas, Op. 5.
(1/87) (ASV) ① CDGAU106
12 Sonatas for Violin and Continuo, Second livre, Op. 2 (pub c1728)
1. E minor (fl also); 2. F; 3. C (fl also); 4. A; 5. G (fl also); 6. D; 7. B flat; 8. D (fl also); 9. E; 10. C minor; 11. B minor (fl also); 12. G minor.
1. R. Brown, J. Johnstone Concert
(2/94) (CHAN) ① CHAN0544
1, 3, 5. Barthold Kuijken, W. Kuijken, R. Kohnen Violin Sonatas, Op.1.
(2/86) (ACCE) ① ACC58435D
8, 11. Barthold Kuijken, W. Kuijken, R. Kohnen Concert (2/86) (ACCE) ① ACC58436D
12 Sonatas for Violin and Continuo, Troisième livre, Op. 5 (pub 1734)
1. A; 2. F. E minor; 4. B flat; 5. B minor; 6. C minor; 7. A minor; 8. D; 9. E; 10. C; 11. G minor; 12. G.
4, 6-10. R. Terakado, H. Suzuki, K. Uemura, C. Rousset (r1993) (11/94) (DENO) ① CO-75720
6. Sonnerie Trio Violin Sonatas, Op. 5.
(1/87) (ASV) ① CDGAU106
7. S. Standage, L.U. Mortensen (r1992) Concert
(6/93) (CHAN) ① CHAN0531
Sonates en trio—two violins and continuo, Op. 4 (pub c1731-33)
1. D minor; 2. B flat; 3. D minor; 4. F; 5. G minor; 6. A.
Purcell Qt (r1992) (7/93) (CHAN) ① CHAN0536
Trio in A—suite with overture: 2 vns & cont, Op. 14 (1766)
1. Overture.
1. Cologne Musica Antiqua, R. Goebel (r1978) Concert (1/93) (ARCH) ① 437 086-2AT

LECOCQ, (Alexandre) Charles (1832–1918) France

SECTION V: STAGE WORKS

Le Jour et la Nuit—operetta: 3 acts (1881—Paris) (Lib. E. Letterier & A. Vanloo)
Cpte L. Berton, L. Dachary, F. Betti, C. Manfredini, M. Siderer, G. Aurel, H. Bedex, G. Rey, M. Hamel, G. Moryn, P. Roi, French Rad Lyric Orch, R. Ellis (with dialogue: bp) Rose Mousse.
(3/92) (MUSD) ① [2] 20136-2
Mam'zelle Angot—ballet: 2 acts (1947—London) (music arr/ed G. Jacob)
EXCERPTS—; 1. Ouverture. ACT 1: 2. Allegro; 3. Allegretto; 4. Mazurka; 5. Andantine—Valse; 6. Tempo di marcia; 7. Allegro vivace; 8. Allegro. ACT 2: 9. Allegro—Gavotta; 10. Allegretto—Galop; 11. Allegro—Valse; 12. Allegro; 13. Adagio; 14. Allegro moderato; 15. Allegro molto—Donkey Polka.

Cpte National PO, R. Bonynge *Hérold: Fille mal
gardée.*　(12/91) (DECC) ① [2] **430 849-2DM2**
**Rose Mousse—musical comedy: 1 act
(1904—Paris)** (Lib. A. Alexandre & P. Carin)
Cpte L. Dachary, J. Maréchal, A. Doniat, J. Peyron,
R. Lenoty, G. Parat, R. Vallier, ORTF Lyric Orch, J-C.
Hartemann (with dialogue: bp) *Jour et la Nuit.*
　(3/92) (MUSD) ① [2] **20136-2**

LECUONA, Ernesto (1896–1963)
Cuba

SECTION IV: VOCAL AND CHORAL

Malagueña—song
K. Labèque, M. Labèque (r1993; arr Nash: 2 pfs)
Concert　(9/94) (PHIL) ① **438 938-2PH**

LEDERER, Deszö (1858–?)

SECTION II: CHAMBER

**2 Poèmes hongroise—violin and piano, Op.
16**
1. E minor; 2. D.
1. F. Macmillen, anon (r1910) *Concert*
　(7/93) (APR) ① [2] **APR7016**

LEEMANS, Pierre (1897–1980)
Belgium

SECTION I: ORCHESTRAL

Belgian Paratroopers—march
Cleveland Winds, F. Fennell *Concert*
　(10/84) (TELA) ① **CD80099**

LEFANU, Nicola (Frances) (b 1947)
England

SECTION II: CHAMBER

Lullaby—clarinet and piano (1988)
Mühlfeld Ens (r1993) *Concert*
　(10/94) (CLRI) ① **CC0007**
Nocturne—cello and piano (1988)
Mühlfeld Ens (r1993) *Concert*
　(10/94) (CLRI) ① **CC0007**

SECTION IV: VOCAL AND CHORAL

**The old woman of Beare—monodrama
(1981)** (Wds. trad Irish)
Lontano, O. de la Martinez *Concert*
　(9/92) (LORE) ① **LNT101**

LEFÉBURE-WÉLY, Louis Alfred
James (1817–1869) France

SECTION III: INSTRUMENTAL

March in C—organ
C. Herrick (r1993) *Concert*
　(8/94) (HYPE) ① **CDA66676**
Meditations religiosa—organ, Op. 122
1. Introduction; 2. Marche funèbre in C minor; 3.
Récit de Hautbois; 4. March in F; 6. Fugue; 7.
Andante.
4. C. Herrick *Concert*　(9/91) (HYPE) ① **CDA66457**
Sortie in B flat—organ
J. Parker-Smith *Concert*
　(4/86) (ASV) ① **CDDCA539**
G. Weir *Concert*　(12/92) (KOSS) ① **KC1013**
Sortie in B flat No. 2—organ
C. Herrick *Concert*　(5/89) (HYPE) ① **CDA66258**
Sortie in E flat—organ
C. Herrick *Concert*　(10/92) (HYPE) ① **CDA66605**

LEFEBVRE, Charles Edouard
(1843–1917) France

SECTION II: CHAMBER

Suite—wind quintet, Op. 57 (1884)
Aulos Wind Qnt *Concert*
　(10/91) (SCHW) ① **310087**

LEFÈVRE, (Jean) Xavier
(1763–1829) France

SECTION IV: VOCAL AND CHORAL

**Hymne à l'agriculture—chorus and orchestra
(1796)**
Leeds Fest Chor, Wallace Collection, J. Wallace
Concert　(7/89) (NIMB) ① **NI5175**

LEGRAND, Michel (b 1932)
France

SECTION V: STAGE WORKS

**Les Parapluies de Cherbourg—film score
(1964)**
EXCERPTS: 1. I Will Wait For You.
1. J. Norman, J.T. Williams (r1989) *Concert*
　(4/92) (PHIL) ① **422 401-2PH**
Yentl—film score (1983) (Lyrics A. & M.
Bergman)
EXCERPTS: 1. Where is it Written?; 2. Papa Can
You Hear Me?.
1, 2. J. Norman, J.T. Williams (r1987 & 1989)
Concert　(4/92) (PHIL) ① **422 401-2PH**

LEGRANT, Guillaume (fl
1418–1456) France

Real name Guillaume Lemacherier

SECTION III: INSTRUMENTAL

Wilhelmus Legrant—organ
G. Binchois Ens, D. Vellard *Concert*
　(3/92) (VIRG) ① **VC7 59043-2**

LEGRENZI, Giovanni (1626–1690)
Italy

SECTION II: CHAMBER

16 Sonatas da chiesa, Op. 8 (pub 1663)
8. La Bevilaqua.
8. Taverner Plyrs, A. Parrott *Concert*
　(8/91) (EMI) ① **CDC7 54117-2**

SECTION V: STAGE WORKS

Eteocle e Polinice—opera (1675—Venice)
Che fiero costume E. Pinza, F. Kitzinger (r1940)
Concert　(9/93) (RCA) ① **09026 61245-2**

LEGUERNEY, Jacques (Alfred
Georges Emile) (b 1906) France

SECTION IV: VOCAL AND CHORAL

A son page—mélodie (1949) (Wds. Ronsard)
G. Souzay, D. Baldwin (r1963) *Concert*
　(3/95) (PHIL) ① [4] **438 964-2PM4(2)**
Ma douce jouvence—song (1950) (Wds.
Ronsard)
G. Souzay, D. Baldwin (r1963) *Concert*
　(3/95) (PHIL) ① [4] **438 964-2PM4(2)**

LEHÁR, Franz (1870–1948)
Hungary/Austria

SECTION I: ORCHESTRAL

**Ballsirenen, 'Sirens of the Ball'—waltz on
themes from 'Die lustige Witwe'**
VJSO, W. Boskovsky *Concert*
　(8/84) (EMI) ① **CDC7 47020-2**
**Eva—waltz sequence (based on themes from
operetta)**
VJSO, W. Boskovsky *Concert*
　(8/84) (EMI) ① **CDC7 47020-2**
**Gold und Silber, 'Gold and Silver'—waltz,
Op. 79 (1902)**
VJSO, W. Boskovsky *Concert*
　(8/84) (EMI) ① **CDC7 47020-2**
**Die lustige Witwe, '(The) Merry
Widow'—concert overture (1940) (based on
themes from the operetta)**
17. VPO, F. Lehár (r1940) *Concert*
　(1/94) (PREI) ① **90150**
**Luxembourg—waltz sequence (based on
themes from 'Der Graf von Luxembourg')**
VJSO, W. Boskovsky *Concert*
　(8/84) (EMI) ① **CDC7 47020-2**
**Musikalische Memoiren—orchestral
potpourri (c1940)**
VPO, F. Lehár (r1940) *Concert*
　(1/94) (PREI) ① **90150**
Wilde Rosen—waltz
G. Eweler, orch, F. Lehár (r c1926) *Concert*
　(3/89) (PEAR) ① **GEMMCD9310**
**Wo die Lerche singt, 'Where the lark
sings'—waltz**
VJSO, W. Boskovsky *Concert*
　(8/84) (EMI) ① **CDC7 47020-2**
**Ziguenerliebe, 'Gipsy Love'—waltz
sequence (based on themes from operetta)**
VJSO, W. Boskovsky *Concert*
　(8/84) (EMI) ① **CDC7 47020-2**

SECTION IV: VOCAL AND CHORAL

Wien, du bist das Herz der Welt—Lied (Wds.
Welisch)
E. Réthy, Vienna SO, F. Lehár (r1942) *Concert*
　(1/94) (PREI) ① **90150**

SECTION V: STAGE WORKS

**Alone at Last—musical show (1915—New
York)** (English adaptation by Woodward;
additional songs by Hein)
EXCERPTS: 1. Thy Heart My Prize; 2. Some Little
Bug is Going to Find You (Hein/Burt/Atwell).
1, 2. R. Atwell, J. C. Thomas, Orig Broadway Cast
(r1915) *Concert*
　(5/94) (PEAR) ① [3] **GEMMCDS9056/8**
**Die Blaue Mazur, '(The) Blue
Mazurka'—operetta: 2 acts (1920—Vienna)**
(Lib. L. Stein & B. Jenbach)
Ich bin zum ersten Mal verliebt Berlin Ens *Concert*
　(5/91) (ORFE) ① **C126901A**
**Eva (Das Fabriksmädel)—operetta: 3 acts
(1911—Vienna)** (Lib. Willner, Bodanzky and E.
Spero)
EXCERPTS: 1. Overture. ACT 1: 2. Heissa, jucheia,
jetzt gibt's was zu seh'n; 3a. Im heimlichen Dämmer
der silbernen Ampel; 3b. Wär' es auch nichts als ein
Augenblick; 4. Bestimmung—Fatum—das ist alles!;
5. Glück und Glas, kingeling; 6a. Nur keine
Angst—hier kann uns nichts passieren; 6b. Pipsi,
holdes Pipsi; 7a. Um zwölf in der Nacht; 7b. Die
Geister von Montmartre; 8. Halt! Ein Augenblick, ihr
Leute (finale). ACT 2: 9. Retten Sie mich, Dagobert,
die Herren sind zu keck!; 10a. Hat man das erste
Stiefelpaar vetreten in Paris; 10b. O du Pariser
Pflaster; 11a. Rechts das Männchen meiner Wahl;
11b. Geschieden muss sein, so heisst es im Lied; 12.
Erschrecken Sie nicht—ich bin's!; 13a. Nur das eine
Wort—sprich es aus!; 13b. Schwül aus tiefen
Kelchen lockt dich ein Duft; 14. Octave, gesteh' dir's
ein—du bist verliebt!; 15a. Ziehe hin zu deinem
Vater; 15b. Sei nicht bös—nicht nervös; 16a. Mädel!
Mein süsses Aschenbrödel du; 16b. Wär' es auch
nichts als ein Augenblick; 17. Silentium! Silentium!
Ich bringe einen Toast! (finale). ACT 3: 18a. Wenn
die Pariserin spazieren fährt; 18b. Manches diskret
man zeigt; 19a. Gib acht, gib acht, mein schönes
Kind; 19b. Herrgott, lass mir doch meinen Leichtsinn
nur; 20. Pipse, holdes Pipsi (reprise); 21. Ein Mädel
wie Sie, so nett und so fein (finale).
1, 3a, 3b M. Reining, VPO, F. Lehár (r1942) *Concert*
　(1/94) (PREI) ① **90150**
1, 3a, 3b M. Reining, VPO, F. Lehár (r1942) *Concert*
　(1/94) (EMI) ① **CDC7 54838-2**
3a, 3b M. Reining, VPO, F. Lehár (r1942) *Concert*
　(4/92) (EMI) ① [7] **CHS7 69741-2(4)**
3a, 3b M. Reining, VPO, F. Lehár (r1942) *Concert*
　(9/94) (PREI) ① **89065**
3b M. Hill Smith, Chandos Concert Orch, S. Barry
Concert　(10/91) (CHAN) ① **CHAN8978**
Frasquita—operetta: 3 acts (1922—Vienna)
(Lib. A M Willner & H Reichert, after P Louys)
EXCERPTS: 1. Overture. ACT 1; 2a. Neun gegen
acht—das nenn ich Glück; 2b. Gib mit dem Fächer
ein Zeichen mir; 3. Weit war uns're Wand'rung heut;
4. Wer hat das gesagt?; 5a. Wie wird sie wohl sein?;
5b. Sag mir, sag' mir; 6a. Einem Kavalier, der so wie
dieser; 6b. Wenn ganz sacht über Nacht; 7. Fragst
mich, was Liebe ist?; 8. Meine Mutter hat eine Gans;
9a. Tanzen, das ist jetzt die grosse Mode; 9b. Darum
Mädel suchst du einem Mann; 10. Ich hab' meine
Jugend im Sonnenlicht (finale); 11a. Wenn nur eine
Rose ich schenke; 11b. Du siehst auf jedem kleinen Blatt.
ACT 2: 12a. Schwärmerisch sprach Don Rodrigo;
12b. Geh' mit mir in die Alhambra; 13a. Wüsst' ich,
wer morgen mein Liebster ist; 13b. Wüsst' ich wer
morgen mein Liebster ist; 14a. So weit sind wir noch
lange nicht; 14b. Weisst du nicht was ein Herz voller
Sehnsucht begehrt?; 15a. Amelie, die gute Tante gab
den Rat mir immer; 15b. Ich gäb' was drum; 16a.
Schatz, ich bitt' dich, komm heut' Nacht; 16b. Hab'
ein blaues Himmelbett; 17a. Kinder, heute fühl' ich
mich wie zwanzig Jahr; 17b. Jung ist jeder, der jung
sich noch fühlt; 18. Sehr viel verlangen Sie, mein
Freund! (finale); 18a. War in einem Städtchen einst
ein armes Mädchen; 19. Lasst den Tage seine
Sonne. ACT 3: 20. Durch die schwarze Maske; 21a.
Oh, glaub' mir, mein Freund; 21b. Wo du weisst, was
du immer tust; 22. Kinder! Kinder! Heut' ist Karneval!;
23a. Wenn zwei sich immer küssen; 23b. Da küss
mich immerzu; 24. Träumen möcht' ich für mich hin
(finale).
7. M. Hill Smith, Chandos Concert Orch, S. Barry
Concert　(10/91) (CHAN) ① **CHAN8978**
14b J. Migenes, Vienna Volksoper Orch, L. Schifrin
(r1993) *Concert*　(1/94) (ERAT) ① **4509-92875-2**

16b F. Kreisler, C. Lamson (arr Kreisler: vn/pf: r1926) *Concert* (1/90) (PEAR) ① **GEMMCD9324**
16b F. Kreisler, C. Lamson (r1926: arr Kreisler) *Concert* (12/93) (BIDD) ① **LAB075**
16b R. Tauber, Berlin Künstlertheater Orch, E. Hauke (r1927) *Concert* (12/94) (MMOI) ① **CDMOIR425**
16b I. Perlman, S. Sanders (arr vn/pf: Kreisler) *Concert* (6/95) (EMI) ① [20] **CZS4 83177-2(2)**

Friederike—play with music: 3 acts (1928—Berlin) (Lib. L. Herzer & F. Löhner)
EXCERPTS: 1. Overture. ACT 1: 2. Gott gab einen schönen Tag; 3. Kleine Blumen, kleine Blätter; 4. Mit Mädchen sich vertragen; 5. Mädchen sind nur zum Küssen Da!; 6. O, wie schön, wie wunderschön!; 7. Blicke ich auf deine Hände; 8. Lämmchen brav; 9. Sah ein Knab' ein Röslein stehn; 10a. Zu allen guten Stunden (finale); 10b. Ich weiss nur, dass ich ihn liebe. ACT 2: 11. Elsässer Kind; 12. Lieber Doktor, lieber Doktor!; 13. All mein Fühlen, all mein Sehnen; 14. O Mädchen, mein Mädchen; 15. Warum hast du mich wachgeküsst?; 16. Liebe, seliger Traum (finale). ACT 3: 17. Riekchen, komm mit uns zum Tanz; 18. Heute tanzen wir den Pfälzertanz; 19. Ein Herz, wie Gold so rein.
Cpte H. Donath, A. Dallapozza, M. Finke, G. Fuchs, H. Grabenhorst, E. Rüggeberg, G. Greindl-Rosner, H. Kalenberg, G. Datz, M. Stadler, C. Wolff, J. von Pawels, Bavarian Rad Chor, Munich RO, H. Wallberg (r1980: with dialogue) (2/95) (EMI) ① [2] **CMS5 65369-2**
Liebe, gold'ner Traum R. Tauber, Vienna St Op Orch, E. Hauke (r c1928) *Concert* (3/89) (PEAR) ① **GEMMCD9310**
1, 3, 6, 7, 13-15. R. Schock, M. Schramm, Berlin SO, W. Schmidt-Boelcke *Schön ist die Welt.* (2/91) (EURO) ① **GD69021**
6, 9, 14. J. Hislop, orch, J. Heuvel (r1930: Eng) *Concert* (1/93) (PEAR) ① **GEMMCD9956**
9. H. Nash, orch (r1930: Eng) *Concert* (11/95) (PEAR) ① **GEMMCD9175**
14. R. Tauber, Berlin Staatskapelle, E. Hauke (r1928) *Concert* (12/89) (EMI) ① **CDH7 69787-2**
14. H. Nash, orch (r1930: Eng) *Concert* (9/91) (PEAR) ① **GEMMCD9473**
14. R. Tauber, Berlin Staatskapelle, E. Hauke (r1928) *Concert* (12/94) (MMOI) ① **CDMOIR425**
15. L. Popp, ASMF, N. Marriner *Concert* (6/88) (EMI) ① **CDC7 49700-2**
15. M. Hill Smith, Chandos Concert Orch, S. Barry (Eng) *Concert* (2/90) (CHAN) ① **CHAN8759**
15. B. Hendricks, Philh, L. Foster (r1992) *Concert* (8/93) (EMI) ① **CDC7 54626-2**
15. M. Reining, VPO, F. Lehár (r1942) *Concert* (1/94) (PREI) ① **90150**
15. M. Reining, VPO, F. Lehár (r1942) *Concert* (1/94) (EMI) ① **CDC7 54838-2**
15. M. Reining, VPO, F. Lehár (r1942) *Concert* (9/94) (PREI) ① **89065**

Der **Fürst der Berge—operetta: 2 acts (1934—Berlin)**
Lange Jahre; Schweig, zogendes Herz R. Tauber, orch (r1932) *Concert* (3/89) (PEAR) ① **GEMMCD9310**

Giuditta—opera: 5 acts (1934—Vienna) (Lib. Knepler and Löhner)
ACT 1: 1a. Prelude; 1b. O mia cara Donna Emilia; 1c. Du lieber, alter Knabe; 2a. Unser Schiff geht Schlag acht Uhr; 2b. So, mein Kleines Vögelchen; 3a. Alle Tag' nichts, als Müh und Plag; 3b. Also hier ist die Osteria; 4a. Freund, das Leben ist lebenswert!; 4b. O Signora, o Signora!; 5a. Ah!...Wohin, wohin will es mich treiben; 5b. In einem Meer von Liebe; 5c. He Wirt, zahlen!; 5d. Schönste der Frau'n; 5e. 'Giuditta' hat ergesagt; 6a. Mein kleinger Vogel; 6b. Weit über's Meer; 6c. Giuditta! Giuditta!; 6d. Herr Kapitän, der Weg ist weit; 6e. Pierrino, ich habe mein Kätzchen vergessen!; 6f. Da, schau, Sebastiano!. ACT 2: 7a. Das ist das Haus, in dem Giuditta; 7b. Zwei, die sich lieben, vergessen die Welt; 7c. Schönste der Frau'n, dann soll das Glück; 8. Schön, wie die blaue Sommernacht; 9. Anita! Anita!. ACT 3: 10. Unsre Heimat ist die Wüste; 11a. Welch tiefes Rätsel ist die Liebe; 11b. Du bist meine Sonne; 12a. Giuditta! Was machst du hier!; 12b. Octavio, es ist Zeit!; 12c. Und das soll Liebe sein?; 12d. In die Stirne fällt die Locke; 12e. Mein Herz ruft Tag und Nacht mir zu; 12f. Entr'acte. ACT 4: 13a. In einem Meer von Liebe; 13b. Bravo!, Hoch, Giuditta; 14a. Ich bin nicht schön, dass weiss ich; 14b. Ja, die Liebe ist so wie ein Schaukelbrett; 14c. Wen sucht du kenn, Kleiner?; 15a. Ich hab'ich mich so gehr gesehnt; 15b. Schaut der Mond; 15c. Herr Direktor!; 16a. Ich weiss es selber nicht; 16b. Meine Lippen, sie küssen so heiss; 16c. Giuditta... 16d. Wollen der Herr hier Platz; 17a. So wie um den Sonnenball; 17b. Wo ist Giuditta?; 17c. Prelude. ACT 5: 18a. 'Schönste der Frau'n' begann das Lied; 18b. Ist alles in Ordnung?; 18c. Unser Lied!; 19. Octavio! Octavio! Du?; 20. Finale: Ich danke Ihnen.
Cpte E. Moser, N. Gedda, K. Hirte, L. Baumann, J. Jung, T. Wiedenhofer, J. von Pawels, G. Wewel, B. Lindner, M. Finke, F. Lenz, Munich Concert Chor, Munich RO, W. Boskovsky (r1983/4: with dialogue) (2/95) (EMI) ① [2] **CMS5 65378-2**
Serenade F. Kreisler, C. Lamson (arr Kreisler: r1926) *Concert* (1/90) (PEAR) ① **GEMMCD9324**
Serenade F. Kreisler, C. Lamson (r1926: arr Kreisler) *Concert* (12/93) (BIDD) ① **LAB075**
1. VJSO, W. Boskovsky *Concert* (8/84) (EMI) ① **CDC7 47020-2**
1a-c, 2a, 2b, 3a, 4a, 4b, 5a-e, 7a, 7b, 8, 11a, 12a-e, 13a, 13b, 14a, 15b, 16a, 16b, 18a, 19. H. Gueden, E. Loose, W. Kmentt, M. Dickie, E. Majkut, K. Equiluz, K. Dönch, H. Duhan, W. Berry, H. Pröglhöf, Vienna St Op Chor, Vienna St Op Orch, R. Moralt (r1957) (6/95) (LOND) ① **436 900-2LA**
4a P. Domingo, NYPO, Z. Mehta (Eng: pp1988) *Concert* (9/89) (SONY) ① **MK44942**
4a F. Araiza, Munich RSO, R. Weikert *Concert* (3/93) (RCA) ① **09026 61163-2**
4a, 5d, 8, 11b, 16b, 17a J. Novotná, R. Tauber, VPO, F. Lehár (r1934) *Concert* (3/89) (PEAR) ① **GEMMCD9310**
4a, 8, 11b, 18a R. Tauber, J. Novotná, VPO, F. Lehár (r1934) *Concert* (1/94) (PREI) ① **90150**
4a, 8, 11b, 16b, 17a, 18a J. Novotná, R. Tauber, VPO, F. Lehár (r1934) *Concert* (1/94) (EMI) ① **CDC7 54838-2**
5b M. Hill Smith, Chandos Concert Orch, S. Barry *Concert* (10/91) (CHAN) ① **CHAN8978**
5b, 16b L. Popp, Ambrosian Op. Chor, ASMF, N. Marriner *Concert* (6/88) (EMI) ① **CDC7 49700-2**
11b R. Tauber, VPO, F. Lehár (r1934) *Concert* (7/89) (EMI) ① **CDM7 69476-2**
11b R. Tauber, Vienna St Op Orch, F. Lehár (pp1935) *Concert* (7/94) (SCHW) ① [2] **314512**
16b M. Hill Smith, Chandos Concert Orch, S. Barry (Eng) *Concert* (6/85) (CHAN) ① **CHAN8362**
16b E. Schwarzkopf, Philh, O. Ackermann *Concert* (1/86) (EMI) ① **CDC7 47284-2**
16b B. Hendricks, Philh, L. Foster (r1992) *Concert* (8/93) (EMI) ① **CDC7 54626-2**
16b E. Réthy, VPO, F. Lehár (r1940) *Concert* (1/94) (PREI) ① **90150**
16b J. Novotná, Vienna St Op Orch, F. Lehár (pp1934) *Concert* (7/94) (SCHW) ① [2] **314512**
16b L. Garrett, RPO, P. Robinson (r1994; Eng) *Concert* (4/95) (SILV) ① **SILKD6004**

Der **Graf von Luxemburg, '(The) Count of Luxembourg'—operetta: 3 acts (1909—Vienna)** (Lib. Willner & Bodanzky)
ACT 1: 1. Karneval, ja, du allerschönste Zeit (Introduction); 2. Mein Anherr war der Luxemburg; 3. Ein Stübchen so klein; 4a. Pierre, der schreibt an kleine Fleurette; 4b. Denn doppelt schmekt's dem Bübchen; 5. So liri, liri, lari; 6. Ich bin verliebt; 7. Ein Scheck auf die englische Bank!; 8a. Heut' noch werd' ich Ehefrau; 8b. Unbekannt deshalb nich minder intressant; 9a. Frau Gräfin, Sie erlauben wohl!; 9b. Sie geht links, er geht rechts; 9c. Bist du's, lachendes Glück; 9d. Sah nur die kleine Hand; 9e. Leichsinn ist die Parole. ACT 2: 10a. Hoch, evöe, Angèle Didier; 10b. Ich danke, meine Herrn und meine Damen; 11a. Sind Sie von Sinnen, Herr Baron?; 11b. Lieber Freund, man greift nicht nach von Sternen; 12a. Schau'n Sie freundlichst mich an; 12b. Mädel klein, Mädel fein; 13. Ach seh'n Sie doch, er ist ganz blass; 14. Der Handshuch, wie pikant; 15. Es duftet nach Trèfle incarnat; 16. Ein Löwe war ich im Salon (Polkatänzer); 17. Kam ein Falter leicht geflattert; 18a. Bin jener Graf von Luxemburg; 18b. Adieuu, Angèle. ACT 3: 19. Introduction; 20. Alles mit Ruhe geniessen; 21. Mädel klein, Mädel fein; 22a. Packt die Liebe einem Alten; 22b. Liebe, ach, du Sonnenschein; 23. Es duftet nach Trèfle incarnat; 24. Wir bummeln durch's Leben (finale).
7, 8a, 8b, 9a, 9b, 9c, 23, 24. H. Gueden, W. Kmentt, Vienna Volksoper Chor, Vienna Volksoper Orch, M. Schönherr (r1965) *Zarewitsch.* (6/95) (LOND) ① **436 896-2LA**
8a, 10a E. Schwarzkopf, chor, Philh, O. Ackermann *Concert* (1/86) (EMI) ① **CDC7 47284-2**
18b M. Hill Smith, New Sadler's Wells Op Chor, New Sadler's Wells Op Orch, B. Wordsworth (r1989-91; Eng) *Concert* (10/91) (TER) ① **CDVIR8314**

Gypsy Love—musical show based on Zigeunerliebe (1911—New York) (English adaptation by A M Willner & R Bodansky)
EXCERPTS: 1. Melody of Love; 2. There is a Land of Fancy; 3. I Will Give You all for Love; 4. Love is Like the Rose.
1-4. A. Albro, C. Hayden, M. Sylva, Orig Broadway Cast (r1911) *Concert* (5/94) (PEAR) ① [3] **GEMMCDS9053/5**

Das **Land des Lächelns, 'Land of Smiles'—operetta: 3 acts (1929—Berlin)** (Lib. L Herzer & F Löhner)
EXCERPTS: 1a. Overture. ACT 1: 1b. Hoch soll sie leben; 1c. Ich danke fur die Huldigung; 1d. Heut! meine Herr'n was win Tag; 1e. Flirten, bisschen flirten; 1f. Gern, gern, wär'ich verliebt; 2. Es ist nicht das erstemal; 3a. Ich trete ins Zimmer, von Sehnsucht durchbebt; 3b. Immer nur lächeln und immer vergnügt; 3c. Ich kann es nicht sagen, ich sage es nie; 4a. Ach, trinken Sie vielleicht; 4b. Bei einem Tee en deux; 5. Von Apfelblüten einem Kranz; 6a. Wir sind allein; 6b. Ein Lied, es verfolget mich Tag und Nacht; 6c. Es wird schon so sein. ACT 2: 7a. Prelude; 7b. Dschinthien wuomen ju chon ma goa can; 7c. In Namen unseres Wen Sway Jeh; 8a. Dich sehe ich und nur dich sehe ich!; 8b. Wer hat die Liebe uns ins Herz; 9. Im Salon zur blau'n Pagode; 10a. Als Gott die Welt erschuf; 10b. Meine Liebe, deine Liebe; 11. Dein ist mein ganzes Herz! (You are my heart's delight); 12a. Alles vorbei!; 12b. Ich möcht' einmal die Heimat seh'n; 13a. Mit welchem Recht?!; 13b. Du hast mich vor allen gedemütigt; 13c. Ihr Götter, sagt, was ist mir gescheh'n? ACT 3: 14a. Liebe besiegt; 14b. Märchen von Glück; 15a. Wenn die Chyrsanthemen blüh'n; 15b. Du bist so zart; 15c. Wie rasch verwelkte doch das kleine Blümchen Glück!; 16a. Dieselbe Sonne, die über Europa scheint; 16b. Liebes Schwesterlein.
Cpte E. Schwarzkopf, E. Kunz, N. Gedda, E. Loose, O. Kraus, BBC Chor, Philh, O. Ackermann (r1953) (11/88) (EMI) ① [2] **CHS7 69523-2**
Cpte A. Rothenberger, H. Friedauer, N. Gedda, R. Holm, J. Moeller, Bavarian Rad Chor, Graunke SO, W. Mattes (r1967: with dialogue) (2/95) (EMI) ① [2] **CMS5 65372-2**
1a, 1b M. Hill Smith, Chandos Concert Orch, S. Barry (Eng) *Concert* (2/90) (CHAN) ① **CHAN8759**
1a, 1b, 3a, 4b, 5, 6a-c, 7a-c, 8a, 8b, 9, 10a, 10b, 11, 12a, 12b, 15a-c, 16a, 16b M. Schramm, F. Gruber, R. Schock, L. Schmidt, Günther Arndt Ch, Berlin SO, R. Stolz (4/88) (EURO) ① **258 373**
3b, 4b, 5, 11. R. Tauber, V. Schwarz, Berlin Staatskapelle, F. Lehár (r1929) *Concert* (12/89) (EMI) ① **CDH7 69787-2**
3b, 4b, 5, 6b, 8a, 8b, 11. R. Tauber, V. Schwarz, Berlin St Op Orch, F. Lehár (r1929) *Concert* (3/89) (PEAR) ① **GEMMCD9310**
3b, 4b, 5, 8b, 11, 12a, 12b, 13c V. Schwarz, R. Tauber, Berlin Staatskapelle, F. Lehár (r1929) *Concert* (1/94) (EMI) ① **CDC7 54838-2**
4a, 4b B. Hendricks, G. Quilico, Lyon Op Orch, L. Foster (r1993) *Concert* (6/95) (EMI) ① **CDC5 55151-2**
5. R. Tauber, Berlin Staatskapelle, F. Lehár (r1929) *Concert* (12/92) (NIMB) ① **NI7833**
5. A. Davies, S. Bullock, A. Bryn Parri (r1994; sung in English) *Concert* (11/95) (SAIN) ① **SCDC2085**
8a, 8b M. Hill Smith, Chandos Concert Orch, S. Barry *Concert* (10/91) (CHAN) ① **CHAN8978**
11. P. Domingo, ECO, J. Rudel *Concert* (2/87) (EMI) ① **CDC7 47398-2**
11. J. Lloyd Webber, RPO, N. Cleobury (arr vc/orch) *Concert* (3/87) (PHIL) ① **416 698-2PH**
11. R. Tauber, Berlin St Op Orch, F. Lehár (r1929) *Concert* (7/89) (EMI) ① **CDM7 69476-2**
11. P. Domingo, MMF Orch, Rome Op Orch, Z. Mehta (pp1990) *Concert* (10/90) (DECC) ① **430 433-2DH**
11. F. Araiza, Munich RSO, R. Weikert *Concert* (3/93) (RCA) ① **09026 61163-2**
11. J. Björling, orch, N. Grevillius (r1932: Swed) *Concert* (12/94) (MMOI) ① **CDMOIR425**
11. O. Bjarnason, W. Jones (pp1994) *Concert* (1/95) (RCA) ① **09026 62547-2**
11. J. Björling, Inst Ens (r1959) *Concert* (10/95) (DECC) ① **443 930-2DM**
12b L. Popp, ASMF, N. Marriner *Concert* (6/88) (EMI) ① **CDC7 49700-2**

Die **Lustige Witwe, '(The) Merry Widow'—operetta: 3 acts (1905—Vienna)** (Lib. Léon & Stein)
EXCERPTS—ACT 1: 1a. Verehrteste Damen und Herren (Introduction); 1b. Ballroom music; 2. So kommen Sie!...Ich bin eine anständ'ge Frau (Valencienne, Camille); 3a. Bitte, meine Herr'n (Entrance song: Hanna, ensemble); 3b. Ballroom music; 4. O Vaterland...Da geh' ich zu Maxim (Entrance song: Danilo); 5. Ja was? ein trautes Zimmerlein (Zauber der Häuslichkeit (Val, Cam); 6. Damenwahl!...O kommet doch, o kommt, Ihr Ballsiren). ACT 2: 7a. Ich bin, hier jetzt zu verweilen (Introduction and Dance); 7b. Es lebt eine Vilja, ein

Waldmägdelein (Vilja-Lied: Hanna, chorus); 8. Heia,
Mädel, aufgeschaut...Dummer, dummer Reitersmann
(Hanna, Danilo); 9. Wie die Weiber man behandelt?
(March-septet); 10. Play-scene and Dance duet
(Hanna, Danilo); 11. Mein Freund, Vernunft!...Wie
eine Rosenknospe (Valencienne, Camille); 12. Ha!
Ha! Wir fragen...Es waren zwei Königskinder (Finale).
ACT 3: 13a. Entr'acte (Vilja-song); 13b. Maxim's
music; 13c. Dance scene (Cake-walk); 14a. Ja, wir
sind es, die Grisetten (Valencienne, Grisettes); 14b.
Da geh' ich zu Maxim (Reminiscence: Danilo,
Grisettes); 15. Lippen schweigen (Hanna, Danilo);
16. Ja, das Stadium der Weiber ist schwerz (Finale).
ADDITIONAL NUMBERS: 17. Overture (composed
1940); 18. Butterflies (Grisettes: London, 1907); 19. I
was born, by cruel fate (Njegus: London, 1907).
Cpte E. Schwarzkopf, E. Waechter, J. Knapp, N.
  Gedda, H. Steffek, H. Strohbauer, K. Equiluz, F.
  Böheim, Philh Chor, Philh, L. von Matačić (omits
  5,13c)   (4/86) (EMI) ① [2] CDS7 47178-8
Cpte E. Schwarzkopf, E. Kunz, A. Niessner, N.
  Gedda, E. Loose, J. Schmidinger, O. Kraus, BBC
  Chor, Philh, O. Ackermann (omits
  5,10,13a,13b,13c,14b: r1953)
                        (11/88) (EMI) ① CDH7 69520-2
Cpte E. Harwood, R. Kollo, Z. Kélémen, W. Hollweg,
  T. Stratas, W. Krenn, D. Grobe, Berlin Deutsche Op
  Chor, BPO, H. von Karajan Concert
                        (8/92) (DG) ① [2] 435 712-2GX2
Cpte F. Lott, T. Hampson, R. Poulton, J. Aler, E.
  Szmytka, R. Schasching, K. Azesberger, D. Bogarde,
  Glyndebourne Fest Chor, LPO, F. Welser-Möst
  (pp1993: Eng narr)
                        (9/94) (EMI) ① [2] CDS5 55152-2
Cpte C. Studer, B. Skovhus, B. Terfel, R. Trost, B.
  Bonney, U. Peper, K-M. Fredriksson, H. Zednik, R.
  Savage, L. Alcantara, P. Salmon, C. Backes, J.
  Clarkson, A. Kazimierczuk, Wiener
  Tschaschenkapelle, VPO, J. E. Gardiner (r1994: with
  dialogue)   (2/95) (DG) ① 439 911-2GH
1a, 1b, 2, 3a, 4, 6, 7b, 8-10, 14a, 15, 16. E. Harwood,
  T. Stratas, R. Kollo, W. Hollweg, Z. Kélémen, D.
  Grobe, W. Krenn, Berlin Deutsche Op Chor, BPO, H.
  von Karajan (r1972)   (3/86) (DG) ① 415 524-2GH
1a, 2, 3a, 4-6, 7a, 7b, 8-12, 13a, 13b, 14a, 15, 16. H.
  Gueden, E. Loose, P. Grunden, W. Kmentt, P. Klein,
  K. Equiluz, K. Dönch, H. Duhan, M. Rus, L.
  Pantscheff, Vienna St Op Chor, Vienna St Op Orch,
  R. Stolz (r1958)   (6/95) (LOND) ① 436 899-2LA
1-4, 6-9, 11-16. E. Harrhy, H. Kucharek, J. Moyle, A.
  Oke, G. Winslade, P. Parfitt, M. Curtis, New Sadler's
  Wells Op. Chor, New Sadler's Wells Op. Orch. B.
  Wordsworth (Eng)   (12/86) (TER) ① CDTER1111
6(pt) R. Tauber, orch, D. Bela (French: r c1933)
  Concert   (3/89) (PEAR) ① GEMMCD9310
7a, 7b L. Popp, Ambrosian Op. Chor, ASMF, N.
  Marriner Concert   (6/88) (EMI) ① CDC7 49700-2
7a, 7b M. Hill Smith, Ambrosian Sngrs, Chandos
  Concert Orch, S. Barry (Eng) Concert
                          (7/88) (CHAN) ① CHAN8561
7b J. Lloyd Webber, ECO, N. Cleobury (arr C
  Palmer) Concert   (3/85) (PHIL) ① 412 231-2PH
7b R. Tauber, Orch (r1932) Concert
                          (12/89) (EMI) ① CDH7 69787-2
7b E. Schwarzkopf, O. Ackermann (r1953)
  Concert   (12/90) (EMI) ① CDM7 63657-2
7b B. Hendricks, Philh, L. Foster (r1992) Concert
                          (8/93) (EMI) ① CDC7 54626-2
7b J. Migenes, Vienna Volksoper Orch, L. Schifrin
  (r1993) Concert   (1/94) (ERAT) ① 4509-92875-2
7b H. Donath, K. Donath (pp1994) Concert
                          (1/95) (RCA) ① 09026 62547-2
7b L. Popp, G. Parsons (pp1981) Concert
                          (6/95) (ORFE) ① C363941B
14b P. Domingo, ECO, J. Rudel Concert
                          (2/87) (EMI) ① CDC7 47398-2
14b, 15. M. Hill Smith, P. Morrison, Chandos Concert
  Orch, S. Barry (Eng) Concert
                          (6/85) (CHAN) ① CHAN8362
15. R. Tauber, Orch, E. Korngold (r1931) Concert
                          (12/89) (EMI) ① CDH7 69787-2
15. R. Tauber, Odeon Künstlerorchester, E. Korngold
  (r1932) Concert   (12/92) (NIMB) ① NI7833
15. B. Hendricks, G. Quilico, Lyon Op Orch, L. Foster
  (r1993) Concert   (6/95) (EMI) ① CDC5 55151-2
17. VPO, F. Lehár (r1940) Concert
                          (1/94) (EMI) ① CDC7 54838-2
Paganini—operetta: 3 acts (1925—Berlin)
  (Lib. Knepler and Jenbach)
ACT 1: 1. Violin solo; 2. Mein lieber Freund; 3.
  Schönes Italien; 4. So jung noch; 5. Feuersglut
  Lodert; 6. Niemals habe ich mich interessiert; 7. Die
  Fürstin Anna Elisa. ACT 2: 8. Wenn keine Liebe wär';
  9. Gern hab' ich die Frau'n geküsst; 10. Einen
  süssen Rosenmund; 11. Launisch sind alle Frau'n;
  12a. Sag' mir, wieviel süsse; 12b. Niemand liebt dich

so wie; 13a. Ich kann es nicht fassen; 13b. Liebe du
Himmel auf Erden; 14. Was ist's, das unsern Sinn
erregt?. ACT 3: 15. Neapolitanisches Lied und Tanz;
16. Schnapslied; 17. Melodram und Reminiszenz; 18.
Jetzt beginnt ein neues Leben; 19. Wo meine Wiege
stand; 20. Du bist geflohen.
3, 9. R. Tauber, Berlin St Op Orch, H. Weigert
  (r1925) Concert   (12/92) (NIMB) ① NI7833
9. P. Domingo, ECO, J. Rudel Concert
                          (2/87) (EMI) ① CDC7 47398-2
9. M. Hill Smith, Chandos Concert Orch, S. Barry
  (Eng) Concert   (7/88) (CHAN) ① CHAN8561
9. R. Tauber, Berlin Künstlertheater Orch, E. Hauke
  (r1927) Concert   (12/89) (EMI) ① CDH7 69787-2
13b M. Reining, Berlin Deutsche Op Orch, W. Lutze
  (r1939) Concert   (9/92) (PREI) ① 90083
13b E. Réthy, VPO, F. Lehár (r1940) Concert
                          (1/94) (PREI) ① 90150
13b E. Réthy, VPO, F. Lehár (r1940) Concert
                          (1/94) (EMI) ① CDC7 54838-2
13b J. Migenes, Vienna Volksoper Orch, L. Schifrin
  (r1993) Concert   (1/94) (ERAT) ① 4509-92875-2
13b, 15. M. Hill Smith, Chandos Concert Orch, S.
  Barry Concert   (10/91) (CHAN) ① CHAN8978
**Der Rastelbinder—operetta: 2 acts
  (1902—Vienna)** (Lib. Léon)
Wenn zwei sich lieben R. Tauber, C. Vanconti, orch
  (r1928) Concert   (3/89) (PEAR) ① GEMMCD9310
The Rogue Song—film (1930) (music
  adapted/arr H. Stothart)
EXCERPTS: 1. The white dove; 2. The rogue song;
  3. When I'm looking at you; 4. Narrative.
1. L. Tibbett, orch, N. Shilkret (r1930) Concert
                          (3/91) (PEAR) ① [2] GEMMCDS9452
**Schön ist die Welt, 'Beautiful
  World'—operetta: 3 acts (1930—Berlin)** (Lib.
  F. Löhrer and L. Herzer)
EXCERPTS: 1. Overture. ACT 1: 2. Nichts zu seh'n,
  gar nichts zu seh'n; 3a. Wie süss muss die Liebe
  sein; 3b. Sag', armes Herzchen, sag; 4. Herzogin
  Marie; 5. Hier in an Viertelstündchen; 6a. Bruder
  Leichtsinn, so werd'ich genannt; 6b. Schön ist die
  Welt; 7a. Ein Ausflug mit Ihnen; 7b. Frei und jung
  dabei; 8a. Tropfenglut hat ihr Blut; 8b. Rio de Janeiro;
  9. Ja, was ist mir mir? (finale). ACT 2: 10. Jetzt mit
  der rechten Hand; 11. Es steht vom Lieben so oft
  geschrieben; 12. Liebste, glaub' an mich; 13. Was ist
  geschehen? Eine Lawine! (finale). ACT 3: 14. Herr
  Direktor, bitte sehr!; 15. Ja, die Liebe ist brutal; 16a.
  Dort in der kleinen Taschbar; 16b. In der kleinen Bar;
  17. Ich bin verliebt; 18a. Heimlich wie in der Nacht
  die Diebe; 18b. Schön sind lachende Frau'n; 19.
  Liebste, glaub' an mich (finale).
3b, 17. J. Migenes, Vienna Volksoper Orch, L.
  Schifrin (r1993) Concert
                          (1/94) (ERAT) ① 4509-92875-2
6b, 7b, 9 (pt), 11, 17, 19. R. Schock, S. Geszty,
  Berlin SO, W. Schmidt-Boelcke Friederike.
                          (2/91) (EURO) ① GD69021
17. M. Hill Smith, Chandos Concert Orch, S. Barry
  (Eng) Concert   (10/91) (CHAN) ① CHAN8978
17. E. Réthy, Vienna SO, F. Lehár (r1942) Concert
                          (1/94) (PREI) ① 90150
17. E. Réthy, Vienna SO, F. Lehár (r1942) Concert
                          (1/94) (EMI) ① CDC7 54838-2
**Wo die Lerche singt, 'Where the Lark
  sings'—operetta (1918—Vienna)** (Lib. Willner
  & Reichert, after F. Martos)
Durch die weiten singt M. Hill Smith, Chandos
  Concert Orch, S. Barry Concert
                          (10/91) (CHAN) ① CHAN8978
**Der Zarewitsch, '(The)
  Czarevich'—operetta: 3 acts (1927—Berlin)**
  (Wds. B. Jenbach & H. Reichart)
EXCERPTS: ACT 1: 1. Es steht ein Soldat am
  Wolgastrand; 2. Hell erklingt ein liebliches frohed
  Heimatlied (Melodram); 3a. War' ein echter
  Schwerenöter; 3b. Wo die Lerche singt; 4. Schaukle,
  Liebchen, schaulke; 5. Einer wird kommen; 6. Allein!
  Wieder allein (Wolgalied); 7a. Win Weib! Du ein
  Weib?; 7b. Geh' trinke deinen Tee; 7c. Trinkt man auf
  du und du. ACT 2: 8. Herz, warum schlägst du so
  bang?; 9. Ich Name war Amalie von Bresterheim; 10.
  Hab' nur dich allein; 11. Heute hab' ich (Napolitana);
  12. O Komm, es hat der Frühling ach nur einen Mai;
  13. Heute Abend komm' ich zu dir; 14. Das Leben
  ruft; 15a. Liebe mich, küsse mich; 15b. Setz' dich her!
  Denke du bist ein Märchenprinzl; 15c. Ich bin
  verliebt; 15d. Berauscht mich der mich heimatliche
  Tanz! (Finale). ACT 3: 16. Interessiert; 17. Kosende
  Wellen; 18. Warum hat jeder Frühling, ach, nur einen
  Mai?; 20. Ich bin bereit! zu jeder Zeit; 21a. Der in
  grossen Zar; 21b. Wir wollen dir dienen; 22. Warum
  hat jeder Frühling, ach, nur einen Mai? (reprise).

1, 2, 5, 7c, 10, 17. H. Gueden, W. Kmentt, Vienna
  Volksoper Chor, Vienna Volksoper Orch, M.
  Schönherr (r1965) Graf von Luxemburg.
                          (6/95) (LOND) ① 436 896-2LA
4. J. Migenes, Vienna Volksoper Orch, L. Schifrin
  (r1993) Concert   (1/94) (ERAT) ① 4509-92875-2
5. E. Schwarzkopf, Philh, O. Ackermann Concert
                          (1/86) (EMI) ① CDC7 47284-2
5. M. Reining, Berlin Deutsche Op Orch, W. Lutze
  (r1939) Concert   (9/92) (PREI) ① 90083
5. E. Réthy, Vienna SO, F. Lehár (r1942) Concert
                          (1/94) (PREI) ① 90150
5. E. Réthy, Vienna SO, F. Lehár (r1942) Concert
                          (1/94) (EMI) ① CDC7 54838-2
5, 17. M. Hill Smith, Chandos Concert Orch, S. Barry
  Concert   (10/91) (CHAN) ① CHAN8978
6. F. Araiza, Munich RSO, R. Weikert Concert
                          (3/93) (RCA) ① 09026 61163-2
**Zigeunerliebe, 'Gipsy Love'—operetta: 3
  acts (1910—Vienna)** (Lib. Willner and
  Bodanzky)
EXCERPTS—; 1. Introduction. ACT 1: 2. Heissa,
  heissa!; 3. So sprach noch niemals ein Mann zu mir!;
  4. Es liegt in blauen Fernen; 5. So treaska! Liebe
  Gäste!; 6. Trägst den Zweig in deinen Händchen
  rosig zart; 7. Will die Männer ich berücken; 8. Zuerst
  such man Gelegenheit; 9a. Da habt Ihr nun den
  Mond in voller Pracht; 9b. Lass' uns nach dem
  Garten ziehen; 9c. Glück hat als Gast - nie lange
  Rast!. ACT 2: 10. Kutyaláces, der Spaktakel; 11. Ich
  bin ein Zigeunerkind; 12. Endlich, Józsi, bist di hier!;
  13. Welsche von uns allen, würde Dir gefallen; 14a.
  War einst ein Mädel; 14b. Gib mir dort vom
  Himmelszelt; 15a. Ich weiss ein Rezept; 15b. Nur die
  Liebe macht uns jung; 16. Lieben Männchen, folge
  mir; 17. Ha, ha, das find'ich köstlich; 18a. Lass Dich
  bezaubern ach, durch mein Fleh'n; 18b. Zorika,
  Zorika, kehre zrück; 19. Vorwärts, Mädeln, rührt die
  Hände; 20. Ich bin ein Zigeunerkind. ACT 3: 21. Gib
  mir das Zweiglein; 22. Lieber Onkel, hör mich nur an;
  23. Hör' ich Cymbalklänge; 24. Ich bin ein
  Zigeunerkind (reprise); 25. Zorika, Zorika, nun bist du
  mein. LATER INTERPOLATIONS: 26. Wer nennt
  nicht die Liebe sein einziges Glück.
1. H.H. Bollman, Berlin SO, F. Lehár (r c1926)
  Concert   (3/89) (PEAR) ① GEMMCD9310
4. R. Tauber, W. Schwarz, orch (r1928) Concert
                          (3/89) (PEAR) ① GEMMCD9310
14b M. Hill Smith, Chandos Concert Orch, S. Barry
  Concert   (10/91) (CHAN) ① CHAN8978
20. J. Schmidt, orch (r1936) Concert
                          (4/90) (EMI) ① CDM7 69478-2
23. R. Tauber, Berlin Künstlertheater Orch, E. Hauke
  (r1927) Concert   (12/89) (EMI) ① CDH7 69787-2
23. M. Hill Smith, Philh, J.O. Edwards (r1989-91;
  Eng) Concert   (10/91) (TER) ① CDVIR8314
23. R. Tauber, Berlin Künstlertheater Orch, E. Hauke
  (r1927) Concert   (12/92) (NIMB) ① NI7833
23. E. Réthy, Vienna SO, F. Lehár (r1942) Concert
                          (1/94) (PREI) ① 90150
23. E. Réthy, Vienna SO, F. Lehár (r1942) Concert
                          (1/94) (EMI) ① CDC7 54838-2

LEHMANN, Liza (1862-1918)
England

SECTION IV: VOCAL AND CHORAL

**4 Cautionary Tales and a Moral—song cycle
  (1909)** (Wds. Belloc)
EXCERPTS: 1. Henry King; 5. Charles Augustus
  Fortesque.
1, 5. A. Rolfe Johnson, G. Johnson (r1991/3) Concert
                          (8/94) (HYPE) ① CDA66709
**In a Persian Garden—song cycle: 4vv and
  piano (pub 1895)** (Wds Omar Khayyám, trans
  E. Fitzgerald)
EXCERPTS: 1. Ah moon of my delight (tenor solo).
Myself when young O. Natzke, H. Greenslade
  (r1938) Concert   (12/92) (ODE) ① CDODE1365
1. A. Rolfe Johnson, G. Johnson (r1991/3) Concert
                          (8/94) (HYPE) ① CDA66709
The Lily of a Day—song (after 1916) (Wds
  Jonson)
A. Rolfe Johnson, G. Johnson (r1991/3) Concert
                          (8/94) (HYPE) ① CDA66709
Magdalen at Michael's gate—song (Wds. H.
  Kingsley)
N. Melba, G. Lapierre (r1913) Concert
                          (5/95) (ROMO) ① [3] 81011-2(2)
The Swing—song
F. Lott, G. Johnson Concert
                          (7/90) (CHAN) ① CHAN8722

Thoughts have wings—song (1909) (Wds Gostling)
A. Rolfe Johnson, G. Johnson (r1991/3) *Concert*
(8/94) (HYPE) ① **CDA66709**
Titania's Cradle—song: 1v and piano (Wds. Shakespeare)
S.J. Langton, K. Schmidt (r1991) *Concert*
(12/93) (KOCH) ① **37240-2**
A widow bird sate mourning—song (pub 1895) (Wds Shelley)
A. Rolfe Johnson, G. Johnson (r1991/3) *Concert*
(8/94) (HYPE) ① **CDA66709**

LEIDZEN, Erik (W(illiam) G(ustav) (1894–1962) Sweden/USA

SECTION I: ORCHESTRAL

Sinfonietta—brass band (1955)
Sellers Engin Band, P. McCann (r1993) *Concert*
(11/95) (CHAN) ① **CHAN4531**

LEIFS, Jón (1899–1968) Iceland

SECTION I: ORCHESTRAL

Galdra-Loftur—suite, Op. 6
1. Overture; 2. Funeral March.
1, 2. Iceland SO, P. Sakari (r1993) *Concert*
(10/93) (CHAN) ① **CHAN9180**

SECTION II: CHAMBER

String Quartet No. 1, 'Mors et vita', Op. 21 (1939)
Yggdrasil Qt (r1994) *Concert*
(7/95) (BIS) ① **BIS-CD691**
String Quartet No. 2, 'Vita et mors', Op. 36 (1948-51)
Yggdrasil Qt (r1994) *Concert*
(7/95) (BIS) ① **BIS-CD691**
String Quartet No. 3, 'El Greco', Op. 64 (1965)
Yggdrasil Qt (r1994) *Concert*
(7/95) (BIS) ① **BIS-CD691**

LEIGH, Walter (1905–1942) England

SECTION II: CHAMBER

Music for Three Pianos
P. Hewitt, R. Douglas, P. Mountford *Concert*
(9/92) (TREM) ① **TREM101-2**
3 Waltzes—two pianos
P. Hewitt, R. Douglas *Concert*
(9/92) (TREM) ① **TREM101-2**

SECTION III: INSTRUMENTAL

Eclogue—piano
P. Hewitt *Concert* (9/92) (TREM) ① **TREM101-2**
Klavieralbum—piano
1. Allegretto; 2. Allegro; 3. Moderato; 4. Alla marcia; 5. Scherzando; 6. Ritmo di Mazurka; 7. Andante lamenterole; 8. Allegro marcato; 9. Larghetto, molto tranquillo; 10. Vivace.
P. Hewitt *Concert* (9/92) (TREM) ① **TREM101-2**
Piano Album
P. Hewitt *Concert* (9/92) (TREM) ① **TREM101-2**
Playtime Pieces—piano
1. Nice monring; 2. Doll's house tea; 3. I love my teddy bear; 4. Pierrot reflects; 5. Grand toy dance.
P. Hewitt *Concert* (9/92) (TREM) ① **TREM101-2**
Polka—piano
P. Hewitt *Concert* (9/92) (TREM) ① **TREM101-2**

SECTION IV: VOCAL AND CHORAL

Bells—song (Wds. J. Bunyan)
E. Nash, S. Down *Concert*
(9/92) (TREM) ① **TREM101-2**
Come away, Death—song (Wds. W. Shakespeare)
E. Nash, S. Down *Concert*
(9/92) (TREM) ① **TREM101-2**
Cradle Song—song (Wds. P. Colum)
E. Nash, S. Down *Concert*
(9/92) (TREM) ① **TREM101-2**
Down by the Salley Gardens—song (Wds. W. B. Yeats)
E. Nash, S. Down *Concert*
(9/92) (TREM) ① **TREM101-2**
Echo's Lament for Narcissus—song (Wds. B. Jonson)
E. Nash, S. Down *Concert*
(9/92) (TREM) ① **TREM101-2**
How sweet I roamed—song (Wds. W. Blake)
E. Nash, S. Down *Concert*
(9/92) (TREM) ① **TREM101-2**

The Mocking Fairy—song (Wds. W. de la Mare)
E. Nash, S. Down *Concert*
(9/92) (TREM) ① **TREM101-2**
Violets—song (Wds. V. C. Clinton-Baddeley)
E. Nash, S. Down *Concert*
(9/92) (TREM) ① **TREM101-2**
We don't care—song (Wds. V. Vaughan)
E. Nash, S. Down *Concert*
(9/92) (TREM) ① **TREM101-2**

LEIGHTON, Kenneth (1929–1988) England

SECTION I: ORCHESTRAL

Concerto for Cello and Orchestra, Op. 31 (1956)
R. Wallfisch, SNO, B. Thomson *Symphony 3.*
(10/89) (CHAN) ① **CHAN8741**
Symphony No. 3—tenor and orchestra
N. Mackie, SNO, B. Thomson *Cello Concerto, Op. 31.*
(10/89) (CHAN) ① **CHAN8741**
Veris gratia—cello and strings, Op. 9 (1950)
R. Wallfisch, RLPO, V. Handley *Finzi: Cello Concerto.*
(10/86) (CHAN) ① **CHAN8471**

SECTION II: CHAMBER

Alleluia Pascha Nostrum—cello and piano, Op. 85 (1981)
R. Wallfisch, P. Wallfisch (r1992) *Concert*
(5/93) (CHAN) ① **CHAN9132**
Fantasy on an American Hymn Tune—clarinet, cello and piano, Op. 70 (1974)
J. Hilton, R. Wallfisch, P. Wallfisch (r1992) *Concert*
(5/93) (CHAN) ① **CHAN9132**
7 Variations—string quartet, Op. 43 (1964)
4. Rasumovsky Qt (r1992) (IMPE) ① **RAZCD901**

SECTION III: INSTRUMENTAL

Sonata for Piano, Op. 64 (1972)
P. Wallfisch (r1992) *Concert*
(5/93) (CHAN) ① **CHAN9132**
Variations—piano, Op. 30 (1955)
P. Wallfisch (r1992) *Concert*
(5/93) (CHAN) ① **CHAN9132**

SECTION IV: VOCAL AND CHORAL

Crucifixus pro nobis—cantata: T/S, chorus and organ, Op. 38 (1961)
1. Christ in the cradle; 2. Christ in the garden; 3. Christ in his passion; 4. Hymn—Drop, drop, slow tears.
N. Mackie, St Paul's Cath Ch, John Scott, Adrian Lucas *Concert* (12/92) (HYPE) ① **CDA66489**
Oxford Queen's Coll Ch, M. Owens, D. Went *Concert*
(5/93) (ASV) ① **CDDCA851**
4. Magdalen Oxford Coll Ch, J. Harper *Concert*
(11/91) (ABBE) ① **CDCA915**
An Evening Hymn—soprano and chorus a capella (1979)
St Paul's Cath Ch, John Scott *Concert*
(12/92) (HYPE) ① **CDA66489**
Give me wings of faith—choir and organ
Magdalen Oxford Coll Ch, J. Harper *Concert*
(11/91) (ABBE) ① **CDCA915**
Oxford Queen's Coll Ch, M. Owens, D. Went *Concert*
(5/93) (ASV) ① **CDDCA851**
Jesus College Ch, D. Phillips, T. Horton *Concert*
(7/93) (CNTO) ① **CRCD2367**
God's Grandeur—choir (1959) (Wds. G.M. Hopkins)
New College Ch, E. Higginbottom *Concert*
(9/92) (MERI) ① **CDE84123**
Let all the world in every corner sing—motet (1965) (Wds. G. Herbert)
St Paul's Cath Ch, John Scott, Adrian Lucas *Concert*
(12/92) (HYPE) ① **CDA66489**
King's College Ch, S. Cleobury, C. Hughes (r1991) *Concert* (6/93) (EMI) ① **CDC7 54418-2**
Magdalen Service—choir and organ (1960)
Lichfield Cath Ch, A. Lumsden, M. Shepherd (r1994) *Concert* (10/95) (PRIO) ① **PRCD505**
Missa brevis—choir and organ, Op. 50 (1968)
1. Kyrie; 2. Gloria; 3. Sanctus and Benedicite; 4. Agnus Dei.
St Paul's Cath Ch, John Scott, Adrian Lucas *Concert*
(12/92) (HYPE) ① **CDA66489**
O sacrum convivium—SS and organ
Oxford Queen's Coll Ch, M. Owens *Concert*
(5/93) (ASV) ① **CDDCA851**
Of a Rose is all my Song (1970)
Elysian Sngrs, M. Greenall *Concert*
(12/91) (CNTI) ① **CCD1043**

Sarum Mass—soloists, chorus and organ, Op. 66 (1972)
Gloria Salisbury Cath Ch, R. Seal *Concert*
(11/90) (MERI) ① **CDE84180**
Second Service, Op. 62
1. Magnificat; 2. Nunc Dimittis.
Durham Cath Ch, J. Lancelot, I. Shaw *Concert*
(7/91) (PRIO) ① **PRCD296**
St Paul's Cath Ch, John Scott, Adrian Lucas *Concert*
(12/92) (HYPE) ① **CDA66489**
Oxford Queen's Coll Ch, M. Owens, D. Went *Concert*
(5/93) (ASV) ① **CDDCA851**
Solus ad Victimam—SATB and organ
Oxford Queen's Coll Ch, M. Owens, D. Went *Concert*
(5/93) (ASV) ① **CDDCA851**
Te Deum laudamus—S, B, chorus and organ (1964 rev 1966) (Wds. Book of Common Prayer)
St Paul's Cath Ch, John Scott, Adrian Lucas *Concert*
(12/92) (HYPE) ① **CDA66489**

LEKEU, Guillaume (Jean Joseph Nicholas) (1870–1894) Belgium

SECTION I: ORCHESTRAL

Adagio—string quartet and string orchestra, Op. 3 (1891)
Musique Oblique Ens (r1994) *Concert*
(4/95) (HARM) ① **HMC90 1455**
Largthetto (Suite)—cello and orchestra (1892)
I. Veyrier, Musique Oblique Ens (r1994) *Concert*
(4/95) (HARM) ① **HMC90 1455**

SECTION II: CHAMBER

Molto adagio, 'Commentaire sur les paroles du Christ'—string quartet (1887)
Musique Oblique Ens (r1994) *Concert*
(4/95) (HARM) ① **HMC90 1455**
Piano Quartet (1893) (unfinished: movt 2 cpted d'Indy)
Musique Oblique Ens (r1994) *Concert*
(4/95) (HARM) ① **HMC90 1455**
Piano Trio in C minor (1890)
Monnaie Piano Trio (6/90) (SCHW) ① **310060**
Sonata for Violin and Piano in G (1891)
J-J. Kantorow, J. Rouvier *Concert*
(8/89) (DENO) ① **CO-72718**
C. Boulier, M. Dedieu-Vidal *Franck: Violin Sonata.*
(8/89) (REM) ① **REM311059**
A. Grumiaux, R. Castagnone (r1955) *Concert*
(11/93) (PHIL) ① [3] **438 516-2PM3**

SECTION IV: VOCAL AND CHORAL

Andromède—poème lyrique: solo vv, chorus & orch (1891) (Wds. J. Sauvenière)
D. Bryant, Z. Vandersteene, P. Huttenlocher, J. Bastin, Namur Sym Chor, Liège PO, P. Bartholomée *Burgraves.* (10/92) (RICE) ① **RIS099083**
3 Poèmes—soprano and piano (1892) (Wds cpsr)
EXCERPTS: 1. Sur une tombe; 2. Ronde; 3. Nocturne.
R. Yakar, Musique Oblique Ens (r1994) *Concert*
(4/95) (HARM) ① **HMC90 1455**

SECTION V: STAGE WORKS

Les Burgraves—drama lyrique (1887) (Wds. V. Hugo)
EXCERPTS: 1. Symphonic Introduction: Part 1 (1889); 2. Symphonic Introduction: Part 2 (1889).
Liège PO, P. Bartholomée *Andromède.*
(10/92) (RICE) ① **RIS099083**

LEMAIRE, Louis (1693/4–c1750) France

SECTION IV: VOCAL AND CHORAL

Assumpta est Maria—two equal voices (c1733)
V. Gens, N. Rime, Arts Florissants Chor, Arts Florissants Orch, W. Christie *Concert*
(4/93) (HARM) ① **HMC90 1416**
Vous dansez, Marquise (Gavotte des Mathurins)—song (Wds. Bazot)
L. Tetrazzini, T. Amici (r1922) *Concert*
(9/92) (EMI) ① [3] **CHS7 63802-2(2)**
L. Tetrazzini, orch (r1922) *Concert*
(9/92) (PEAR) ① **GEMMCD9225**

LEMARE, Edwin (Henry) (1865–1934) England/USA

SECTION III: INSTRUMENTAL

Andantino in D flat—organ (1888)
F. Kreisler, C. Lamson (r1926: arr Saenger) *Concert*
(12/93) (BIDD) ① **LAB075**
Concert Fantasia—organ, Op. 91
C. Herrick *Concert* (5/89) (HYPE) ① **CDA66258**
Concert Fantasia on 'Hanover'—organ, Op. 4
C. Herrick *Concert* (9/91) (HYPE) ① **CDA66457**
Marche Héroïque in D—organ, Op. 74
C. Herrick *Concert* (9/91) (HYPE) ① **CDA66457**
Rondo capriccioso—a study in accents—organ, Op. 64
C. Curley (r1991) *Concert*
(4/92) (ARGO) ① **433 450-2ZH**
Symphony in G minor—organ, Op. 35 (pub 1899)
1. Allegro moderato.
Scherzo C. Herrick *Concert*
(5/89) (HYPE) ① **CDA66258**
Toccata di Concerto—organ, Op. 59
C. Herrick *Concert* (10/92) (HYPE) ① **CDA66605**

LEMBA, Artur (1885–1963) Estonia

SECTION I: ORCHESTRAL

Symphony in C sharp minor (1908)
SNO, N. Järvi *Concert*
(11/89) (CHAN) ① **CHAN8656**

LENNON & McCARTNEY, John & Paul England

Beatles collaborations

SECTION IV: VOCAL AND CHORAL

Eleanor Rigby—Beatles song (1966) (from the album 'Revolver')
T. Reilly, ASMF Chbr Ens (arr. G. Martin) *Concert*
(12/86) (CHAN) ① **CHAN8486**
Michelle—Beatles song (1965) (from the album 'Rubber Soul')
T. Reilly, ASMF Chbr Ens (arr. G. Martin) *Concert*
(12/86) (CHAN) ① **CHAN8486**
Ticket to Ride—Beatles song (1965)
C. Berberian, B. Canino *Concert*
(7/89) (WERG) ① **WER60054-50**
When I'm 64—Beatles song (1966) (from the album 'Sgt Pepper's Lonely Hearts Club Band')
J. Lloyd Webber, RPO, N. Cleobury (arr vc) *Concert*
(3/87) (PHIL) ① **416 698-2PH**
Yesterday—Beatles song (1965) (from the album 'Help!')
F. Araiza, Munich RSO, R. Weikert (arr Fried)
Concert (3/93) (RCA) ① **09026 61163-2**

LEO, Leonardo (1694–1744) Italy

SECTION I: ORCHESTRAL

Concerto for 4 Violins and Strings in D
Cologne Musica Antiqua, R. Goebel *Concert*
(9/92) (ARCH) ① **435 393-2AH**
6 Concertos for Cello and Strings (1737-38)
1. D; 2. C minor; 3. A; 4. F minor; 5. A; 6. D minor.
6. W. Matzke, Cologne Concerto (r1992) *Concert*
(1/94) (CAPR) ① **10 378**

SECTION IV: VOCAL AND CHORAL

Salve regina in F—1v and strings
B. Schlick, Europa Galante, F. Biondi (vn/dir) (r1993)
Concert (4/94) (O111) ① **OPS30-88**

LÉONARD, Hubert (1819–1890) Belgium

SECTION II: CHAMBER

5 Scènes humoristiques—violin and piano, Op. 61
1. Coq et poules; 3. Chatte et souris; 4. L'âne et l'ânier; 5. Sérénade du lapin belliqueux.
5. E. Brown, M. Mischakoff, B. Rabinof, J. Zayde (r c1939) *Concert* (7/93) (APR) ① **[2] APR7016**

LEONCAVALLO, Ruggiero (1858–1919) Italy

SECTION IV: VOCAL AND CHORAL

Lasciati amar—song (pub 1913)
E. Caruso, orch (r1913) *Concert*
(7/91) (RCA) ① **[12] GD60495(4)**
E. Caruso, orch (r1913) *Concert*
(10/91) (PEAR) ① **[3] EVC3(1)**
Mattinata, '(L')aurora di bianco vestita'—song (1904) (Wds. cpsr)
L. Pavarotti, Philh, P. Gamba *Concert*
(7/86) (DECC) ① **[2] 417 011-2DH2**
E. Caruso, R. Leoncavallo (r1904) *Concert*
(5/89) (EMI) ① **CDH7 61046-2**
J. Schmidt, orch, O. Dobrindt (r1933) *Concert*
(4/90) (EMI) ① **CDM7 69478-2**
D. Smirnov, orch (r1912) *Concert*
(7/90) (CLUB) ① **CL99-031**
J. Carreras, P. Domingo, L. Pavarotti, MMF Orch, Rome Op Orch, Z. Mehta (pp1990) *Concert*
(10/90) (DECC) ① **430 433-2DH**
E. Caruso, R. Leoncavallo (r1904) *Concert*
(12/90) (PEAR) ① **[3] EVC1(1)**
Berlin Ens (arr anon: orch) *Concert*
(5/91) (ORFE) ① **C126901A**
E. Caruso, R. Leoncavallo (r1904) *Concert*
(7/91) (RCA) ① **[12] GD60495(1)**
G. Lugo, orch, F. Weiss (r1934) *Concert*
(2/92) (PREI) ① **89034**
B. Gigli, La Scala Orch, F. Ghione (r1935) *Concert*
(9/92) (MMOI) ① **CDMOIR409**
F. Araiza, Munich RSO, R. Weikert (arr Waldenmaier) *Concert*
(3/93) (RCA) ① **09026 61163-2**
P. Domingo, LSO, M. Peeters *Concert*
(5/93) (DG) ① **431 104-2GB**
J. Björling, orch, N. Grevillius (r1944) *Concert*
(10/93) (EMI) ① **CDH7 64707-2**
G. Zenatello, orch (r1910) *Concert*
(5/94) (PEAR) ① **[4] GEMMCDS9073(2)**
L. Pavarotti, NYPO, L. Magiera (pp1993) *Concert*
(2/95) (DECC) ① **444 450-2DH**
J. Johnston, orch, E. Robinson (r1949: Eng) *Concert*
(4/95) (TEST) ① **SBT1058**
Sérénade française—song (1904) (wds. E. Collet)
E. Caruso, M. Elman, G. Scognamiglio (r1915)
Concert (7/91) (RCA) ① **[12] GD60495(5)**
E. Caruso, M. Elman, G. Scognamiglio (r1915)
Concert (10/91) (PEAR) ① **[3] EVC3(2)**
E. Caruso, M. Elman, G. Scognamiglio (r1915)
Concert (10/91) (BIDD) ① **LAB039**

SECTION V: STAGE WORKS

La Bohème, 'Bohemian Life'—opera: 4 acts (1897—Venice) (Lib. cpsr)
EXCERPTS: ACT 1: 1. No, signor mio, così non può durare; 2. Bella dama; 3a. Musette svaria sulla bocca viva; 3b. Se insieme lo cercassimo; 4. Platonico è l'amante; 5. Mimì Pinson la biondinetta; 6. Vita mia!...O Musette; 7. Senti Marcello! ACT 2: 8. Auf! ce n'è ancora?; 9. Io non ho che una povera stanzetta; 10. L'immenso tesoro; 11a. Ed ora vengano; 11b. Qualcun... 12. Dei vent'anni fra l'ebbrezza (Inno della Bohème); 13. Domando la parola; 14. Da quel suon soavemente; 15. Brav! Bravissima!; 16. L'occhio celeste; 17. Ma quando smettete? ACT 3: 18. E che! Ti pur sei vedo?; 19. Addio!...È destin! Debbo andarmene...Coraggio!; 20. Tu qui! Perchè? Che vuoi?; 21. Sei proprio tu che hai scritto ciò?; 22. Va via, fantasma del passato!; 23a. Musette! o gioia della mia dimora; 23b. Testa adorata. ACT 4: 24. Scuoti, o vento, fra i sibili; 25. Brrr! Che freddo!; 26. Mimì, Buona sera!...V'incomodo; 27. Mimì Pinson la biondinetta; 28. No, morir non voglio.
Cpte L. Popp, B. Weikl, F. Bonisolli, A. Milcheva, A. Titus, R. Grumbach, A. Malta, N. Orth, S. Lis, J.W. Wilsing, F. Lenz, Bavarian Rad Chor, Munich RO, H. Wallberg (r1981) (8/88) (ORFE) ① **[2] C023822H**
5. R. Storchio, orch (r1910) *Concert*
(11/92) (MEMO) ① **[2] HR4408/9(1)**
9. G. Zenatello, orch (r1911) *Concert*
(5/94) (PEAR) ① **[4] GEMMCDS9073(2)**
9, 23b E. Caruso, orch (r1911) *Concert*
(3/91) (PEAR) ① **[3] EVC2**
9, 23b E. Caruso, orch (r1911) *Concert*
(7/91) (RCA) ① **[12] GD60495(4)**
9, 23b E. Caruso, orch (r1911) *Concert*
(7/95) (NIMB) ① **NI7866**
23a, 23b B. Heppner, Munich RO, R. Abbado
(r1993/4) *Concert* (11/95) (RCA) ① **09026 62504-2**
23b E. Caruso, orch (r1911) *Concert*
(5/89) (PEAR) ① **GEMMCD9309**

I Medici
Ascolta il canto mio G. Kaschmann, S. Cottone
(r1903) *Concert* (12/89) (SYMP) ① **SYMCD1065**
Ascolta il canto mio G. Kaschmann, S. Cottone
(r1903) *Concert*
(4/94) (EMI) ① **[3] CHS7 64860-2(1)**

I Pagliacci, '(The) Clowns'—opera: prologue and 2 acts (1892—Milan) (Lib. Cpsr)
1. Si può? (Prologue); ACT 1: 2. Son qua!; 3. Un grande spettacolo; 4. Un tal gioco; 5a. I zampognari!; 5b. Din, don (Bell Chorus); 6a. Qual fiamma avea nel guardo!; 6b. Oh! Che volo d'augelli; 6c. Stridono lassù; 7a. Sei là!; 7b. So ben che difforme; 8a. Silvio! A quest'ora; 8b. Decidi il mio destin; 8c. E allor perchè; 9a. Recitar!; 9b. Vesti la giubba; 10. Intermezzo. ACT 2: 11. Presto, affrettiamoci; 12a. Pagliaccio, mio marito; 12b. O Colombina (Serenade); 12c. È dessa!; 13a. Versa il filtro; 13b. No, Pagliaccio non son; 14a. Ebben, se mi giudichi; 14b. No, per mia madre!.
Cpte P. Domingo, T. Stratas, J. Pons, A. Rinaldi, F. Andreolli, La Scala Chor, La Scala Orch, G. Prêtre
(2/86) (PHIL) ① **411 484-2PH**
Cpte G. di Stefano, M. Callas, T. Gobbi, R. Panerai, N. Monti, La Scala Chor, La Scala Orch, T. Serafin (r1954) *Mascagni: Cavalleria Rusticana.*
(10/87) (EMI) ① **[3] CDS7 47981-8**
Cpte C. Bergonzi, J. Carlyle, G. Taddei, R. Panerai, U. Benelli, La Scala Chor, La Scala Orch, H. von Karajan *Concert*
(10/87) (DG) ① **[3] 419 257-2GH3**
Cpte L. Pavarotti, M. Freni, I. Wixell, L. Saccomani, V. Bello, London Voices, National PO, G. Patanè *Mascagni: Cavalleria Rusticana.*
(1/89) (DECC) ① **[2] 414 590-2DH2**
Cpte J. Björling, V. de los Angeles, L. Warren, R. Merrill, P. Franke, Columbus Boychoir, R. Shaw Chorale, RCA Victor Orch, R. Cellini (r1953)
(12/89) (EMI) ① **CDC7 49503-2**
Cpte J. Carreras, R. Scotto, K. Nurmela, T. Allen, U. Benelli, Ambrosian Op Chor, Philh, R. Muti (r1979) *Mascagni: Cavalleria rusticana.*
(3/91) (EMI) ① **[2] CMS7 63650-2**
Cpte F. Corelli, L. Amara, T. Gobbi, M. Zanasi, M. Spina, La Scala Chor, La Scala Orch, L. von Matačić (r1960) *Mascagni: Cavalleria Rusticana.*
(3/92) (EMI) ① **[2] CMS7 63967-2**
Cpte N. Martinucci, M. Gauci, E. Tumagian, B. Skovhus, M. Dvorský, Slovak Phil Chor, Bratislava RSO, A. Rahbari (4/93) (NAXO) ① **8 660021**
Cpte L. Pavarotti, D. Dessì, J. Pons, P. Coni, E. Gavazzi, Westminster Symphonic Ch, Philadelphia Boys' Ch, Philadelphia, R. Muti (pp1992)
(4/93) (PHIL) ① **434 131-2PH**
Excs T. Mazaroff, G. Monthy, A. Michalsky, Vienna St Op Chor, Vienna St Op Orch, W. Loibner (pp1938) *Concert* (12/94) (SCHW) ① **[2] 314542**
Excs J. Björling, M. Bokor, F. Ginrod, Vienna St Op Chor, Vienna St Op Orch, K. Alwin (pp1937: Ger/Swed) *Concert* (12/94) (SCHW) ① **[2] 314542**
1. G. Bechi, Santa Cecilia Academy Orch, V. Bellezza (r1946) *Concert* (2/90) (PREI) ① **89009**
1. R. Stracciari, orch (r1925) *Concert*
(2/90) (PREI) ① **89003**
1. L. Tibbett, Orch, R. Bourdon (r1926) *Concert*
(3/90) (RCA) ① **GD87808**
1. J. Hynninen, Estonian SO, E. Klas *Concert*
(4/90) (ONDI) ① **ODE731-2**
1. H. Schlusnus, Berlin St Op Orch, L. Blech (Ger: r1935) *Concert* (9/90) (PREI) ① **89006**
1. T. Ruffo, orch, C. Sabajno (r1912) *Concert*
(10/90) (NIMB) ① **NI7810**
1. C. Tagliabue, Turin EIAR Orch, U. Tansini (r1939) *Concert* (11/90) (PREI) ① **89015**
1. L. Tibbett, orch, R. Bourdon (r1926) *Concert*
(3/91) (PEAR) ① **GEMMCDS9452**
1. C. Galeffi, La Scala Orch, L. Molajoli (r1930) *Concert* (5/91) (PEAR) ① **89040**
1. L. Warren, RCA Orch, R. Cellini (r1953) *Concert*
(4/92) (EMI) ① **[7] CHS7 69741-2(2)**
1. D. Noble, Sadlers Wells Op Orch, W. Braithwaite (Eng: r1939) *Concert*
(7/92) (PEAR) ① **[3] GEMMCDS9925(1)**
1. M. Ancona, C. Sabajno (r1904) *Concert*
(7/92) (PEAR) ① **[3] GEMMCDS9923(1)**
1. M. Battistini, orch, C. Sabajno (r1911) *Concert*
(10/92) (PEAR) ① **GEMMCD9936**
1. P. Lisitsian, Bolshoi Th Orch, S. Samosud (r1955: Russ) *Concert* (8/93) (PREI) ① **89061**
1. L. Warren, orch, W. Pelletier (r1940) *Concert*
(8/93) (VAI) ① **VAIA1017**
1. T. Gobbi, RPO, A. Erede (r1948) *Concert*
(8/93) (TEST) ① **SBT1019**
1. J. Van Dam, Loire PO, M. Soustrot (r1992)
Concert (8/93) (FORL) ① **UCD16681**

1. E. Tumagian, Bratislava RSO, A. Rahbari (r1992)
Concert   (12/94) (NAXO) ① **8 550684**
4. G. Zenatello, orch, R. Bourdon (r1929) Concert
(11/91) (CLUB) ① **CL99-025**
4. G. Zenatello, orch, R. Bourdon (r1929) Concert
(11/91) (PREI) ① **89038**
4. F. de Lucia, orch (r1917) Concert
(7/92) (PEAR) ① **[3]** GEMMCDS9923(2)
4. G. Zenatello, anon (r1907) Concert
(5/94) (SYMP) ① **SYMCD1158**
4. G. Zenatello, orch (r1907) Concert
(5/94) (PEAR) ① **[4]** GEMMCDS9073(1)
4. G. Zenatello, orch, R. Bourdon (r1929) Concert
(5/94) (PEAR) ① **[4]** GEMMCDS9074(2)
4, 13b G. Zenatello, orch (r1909) Concert
(5/94) (SYMP) ① **SYMCD1158**
4, 13b G. Zenatello, orch (r1909) Concert
(5/94) (PEAR) ① **[4]** GEMMCDS9073(2)
4, 9a, 9b J. Björling, R. Moberg, Stockholm Royal Op
Orch, L. Gardelli (Swedish: pp1954) Concert
(3/92) (BLUE) ① **ABCD028**
6a C. Muzio, orch (r1917) Concert
(1/95) (ROMO) ① **[2]** 81010-2
6a I. Galante, Latvian Nat SO, A. Vilumanis (r1994)
Concert   (11/95) (CAMP) ① **RRCD1335**
6a-c K. Te Kanawa, LSO, Myung-Whun Chung
Concert   (11/90) (EMI) ① **CDC7 54062-2**
6a-c L. Price, Philh, H. Lewis (r1979) Concert
(12/92) (RCA) ① **[4]** 09026 61236-2
6a-c A. Gluck, orch (r1911) Concert
(4/94) (RCA) ① **[6]** 09026 61580-2(2)
6a, 6b, 8a C. Muzio, M. Laurenti, orch (r1921)
Concert   (5/90) (BOGR) ① **[2]** BIM705-2
6a, 8a C. Muzio, M. Laurenti, orch (r1921) Concert
(1/94) (ROMO) ① **[2]** 81005-2
6a, 8a, 8b X. Belmas, W. Domgraf-Fassbaender,
orch, A. Kitschin (r1929) Concert
(10/92) (PREI) ① **89047**
6c E. Destinn, orch (r1912) Concert
(5/94) (SUPR) ① **11 1337-2**
6c E. Destinn, orch, B. Seidler-Winkler (r1908: Ger)
Concert   (12/94) (SUPR) ① **[12]** 11 2136-2(2)
6c E. Destinn, orch (r1912: 2 vers) Concert
(12/94) (SUPR) ① **[12]** 11 2136-2(5)
6c, 9b, 13b(pt) A. Piccaver, G. Monthy, E.
Schumann, Vienna St Op Chor, Vienna St Op Orch,
K. Alwin (pp1937: Ger) Concert
(6/95) (SCHW) ① **[2]** 314632
7a, 7b A. Granforte, A. Saraceni, La Scala Orch, C.
Sabajno (r1929) Concert   (12/91) (PREI) ① **89048**
8a-c H. Spani, A. Granforte, La Scala Orch, C.
Sabajno (r1927) Concert
(9/90) (CLUB) ① **CL99-509/10**
8b H. Spani, A. Granforte, La Scala Orch, C. Sabajno
(r1927) Concert   (12/92) (PREI) ① **89037**
8b E. Steber, G. Cehanovsky, L. Warren, orch, W.
Pelletier (r1940) Concert
(11/95) (VAI) ① **VAIA1072**
9a, 9b L. Pavarotti, National PO, G. Patanè Concert
(7/86) (DECC) ① **[2]** 417 011-2DH2
9a, 9b L. Melchior, LSO, J. Barbirolli (r1930: Ger)
Concert   (8/88) (DANA) ① **[2]** DACOCD315/6
9a, 9b J. Björling, orch, N. Grevillius (r1944) Concert
(10/88) (EMI) ① **CDH7 61053-2**
9a, 9b E. Caruso, S. Cottone (r1902) Concert
(5/89) (EMI) ① **CDH7 61046-2**
9a, 9b E. Caruso, orch (r1907) Concert
(10/89) (NIMB) ① **NI7803**
9a, 9b G. Martinelli, orch, R. Bourdon (r1927)
Concert   (10/89) (NIMB) ① **NI7804**
9a, 9b M. Fleta, orch (r1927) Concert
(2/90) (PREI) ① **89002**
9a, 9b J. Schmidt, orch (r1933: Ger) Concert
(4/90) (EMI) ① **CDM7 69478-2**
9a, 9b L. Pavarotti, National PO, O. de Fabritiis
Concert   (7/90) (DECC) ① **[2]** 425 681-2DM2
9a, 9b E. Caruso, S. Cottone (r1902) Concert
(12/90) (PEAR) ① **[3]** EVC1(1)
9a, 9b E. Caruso, anon (r1904) Concert
(12/90) (PEAR) ① **[3]** EVC1(1)
9a, 9b E. Caruso, orch (r1907) Concert
(12/90) (PEAR) ① **[3]** EVC1(2)
9a, 9b E. Caruso, anon (r1904) Concert
(7/91) (RCA) ① **[12]** GD60495(1)
9a, 9b E. Caruso, orch (r1907) Concert
(7/91) (RCA) ① **[12]** GD60495(2)
9a, 9b E. Caruso, S. Cottone (r1902) Concert
(7/91) (RCA) ① **[12]** GD60495(1)
9a, 9b E. Caruso, orch, W.B. Rogers (r1907) Concert
(10/92) (TEST) ① **SBT1005**
9a, 9b M. del Monaco, Santa Cecilia Academy Orch,
F. Molinari-Pradelli (r1959) Concert
(10/93) (DECC) ① **436 463-2DM**
9a, 9b J. Vickers, Rome Op Orch, T. Serafin (r1961)
Concert   (4/94) (RCA) ① **[6]** 09026 61580-2(7)

9a, 9b G. Zenatello, anon (r1905/6: 2 vers) Concert
(5/94) (PEAR) ① **[4]** GEMMCDS9073(1)
9a, 9b G. Zenatello, orch (r1908) Concert
(5/94) (PEAR) ① **[4]** GEMMCDS9073(2)
9a, 9b G. Zenatello, orch (r1912) Concert
(5/94) (PEAR) ① **[4]** GEMMCDS9074(1)
9a, 9b G. Zenatello, orch (r1916) Concert
(5/94) (PEAR) ① **[4]** GEMMCDS9074(2)
9a, 9b A. Pertile, La Scala Orch, C. Sabajno (r1927)
Concert   (10/94) (PREI) ① **89072**
9a, 9b A. Giorgini, orch (r c1913) Concert
(4/95) (RECO) ① **TRC3**
9a, 9b G. Thill, orch, E. Bigot (r c1928: Fr) Concert
(8/95) (FORL) ① **UCD16727**
9a, 9b, 13b F. Ansseau, orch, P. Coppola (r1927)
Concert   (1/91) (PREI) ① **89022**
9b E. Caruso, orch (r1907) Concert
(5/89) (PEAR) ① **GEMMCD9309**
9b R. Tauber, orch, W. Goehr (Eng: r1936) Concert
(7/89) (EMI) ① **CDM7 69476-2**
9b F. Völker, Berlin St Op Orch, H. Weigert (r1930:
Ger) Concert   (2/90) (PREI) ① **89005**
9b B. Gigli, orch (r1922) Concert
(5/90) (NIMB) ① **NI7807**
9b E. Barham, RPO, R. Stapleton Concert
(10/90) (CARL) ① **MCD15**
9b A. Garulli, anon (r1902) Concert
(5/91) (SYMP) ① **SYMCD1077**
9b G. Zenatello, orch (r c1917) Concert
(11/91) (CLUB) ① **CL99-025**
9b G. Lugo, orch, F. Weiss (Fr: r1933) Concert
(2/92) (PREI) ① **89034**
9b H.E. Groh, orch (Ger: r1933) Concert
(3/92) (PEAR) ① **GEMMCD9419**
9b G. Martinelli, orch, R. Bourdon (r1927) Concert
(3/93) (PREI) ① **89062**
9b D. Yuzhin, anon (r1902: Russ) Concert
(6/93) (PEAR) ① **[3]** GEMMCDS9001/3(1)
9b G. Lauri-Volpi, orch (r1923) Concert
(7/93) (NIMB) ① **NI7845**
9b E. Caruso, orch (r1907/32) Concert
(5/94) (CLAR) ① **CDGSE78-50-52**
9b G. Zenatello, anon (r1906) Concert
(5/94) (SYMP) ① **SYMCD1158**
9b G. Zenatello, orch (r1908) Concert
(5/94) (SYMP) ① **SYMCD1158**
9b P. Domingo, Los Angeles PO, Z. Mehta (pp1994)
Concert   (12/94) (TELD) ① **4509-96200-2**
9b B. Gigli, La Scala Orch, F. Ghione (r1934)
Concert   (12/94) (MMOI) ① **CDMOIR425**
9b J. Johnston, orch, M. Mudie (r1948: Eng) Concert
(4/95) (TEST) ① **SBT1058**
9b(pt) H. Roswaenge, Vienna St Op Orch (pp1930s)
Concert   (6/95) (SCHW) ① **[2]** 314622
9b, 12b G. Anselmi, anon (r1907) Concert
(7/95) (SYMP) ① **SYMCD1170**
9b, 13b H. Roswaenge, Berlin St Op Orch, B.
Seidler-Winkler (r1939: Ger) Concert
(5/90) (PREI) ① **89018**
9b, 13b F. Merli, orch, L. Molajoli (r1929) Concert
(1/91) (PREI) ① **89026**
10. Gothenburg SO, N. Järvi Concert
(6/90) (DG) ① **429 494-2GDC**
12b T. Schipa, orch (r1926) Concert
(2/89) (PEAR) ① **GEMMCD9322**
12b H. Nash, M. Licette, BNOC Orch, E. Goossens
(Eng: r1927) Concert
(8/89) (PEAR) ① **GEMMCD9319**
12b T. Schipa, orch, R. Bourdon (r1926) Concert
(12/89) (RCA) ① **GD87969**
12b I. Pacetti, B. Gigli, La Scala Orch, F. Ghione
(r1934) Concert   (5/90) (EMI) ① **CDH7 61052-2**
12b T. Schipa, orch, R. Bourdon (r1925) Concert
(10/90) (MSCM) ① **[2]** MM30231
12b G. Zenatello, orch (r1911) Concert
(5/94) (SYMP) ① **SYMCD1158**
12b G. Zenatello, orch (r1911) Concert
(5/94) (PEAR) ① **[4]** GEMMCDS9073(2)
13b B. Gigli, orch, J. Barbirolli (r1933) Concert
(9/88) (EMI) ① **CDH7 61051-2**
13b E. Caruso, orch (r1910) Concert
(5/89) (PEAR) ① **GEMMCD9309**
13b G. Anthony, G. Martinelli, chor, orch, G. Setti
(r1927) Concert   (10/89) (NIMB) ① **NI7804**
13b E. Caruso, orch (r1910) Concert
(10/89) (NIMB) ① **NI7803**
13b E. Caruso, orch (r1910) Concert
(10/89) (NIMB) ① **NI7801**
13b E. Caruso, orch (r1910) Concert
(3/91) (PEAR) ① **[3]** EVC2
13b E. Caruso, orch (r1910) Concert
(7/91) (RCA) ① **[12]** GD60495(3)
13b G. Martinelli, G. Anthony, NY Met Op Chor, NY
Met Op Orch, G. Setti (r1927) Concert
(3/93) (PREI) ① **89062**

13b F. Völker, Berlin Staatskapelle, J. Schüler
(r1937: Ger) Concert   (8/94) (PREI) ① **89070**
13b B. Gigli, LSO, J. Barbirolli (r1933) Concert
(9/94) (NIMB) ① **NI7856**
13b, 14b F. Völker, W. Achsel, E. Schipper, K.
Hammes, Vienna St Op Chor, Vienna St Op Orch, K.
Alwin (pp1934: Ger) Concert
(9/95) (SCHW) ① **[2]** 314662

Der Roland von Berlin—opera: 4 acts
(1904—Berlin) (Lib. cpsr, after W Alexis)
Hennig darf ein Patrizierkind; Fahr wohl,
Trautgesell E. Destinn, R. Leoncavallo (r1905)
Concert   (12/94) (SUPR) ① **[12]** 11 2136-2(1)
Ratenow's Prayer F.M. Bonini, anon (r1905)
Concert   (12/94) (BONG) ① **GB1043-2**
Zazà—opera: 4 acts (1900—Milan) (Lib. cpsr,
after P. Berton & C. Simon)
EXCERPTS: ACT 1: 1. A voi, su presto; 2. Salute a
tutti; 3. Lo sai tu che vuol dire; 4. Augusto, buona
sera; 5. Ah, ah, là, là; 6. Signor, entrate. ACT 2: 7. È
deciso, tu parti? 8. Or lasciami andare!; 9. Ecco gli
stivaletti; 10. Toh, o che quadretto; 11. Buona Zazà
del mio buon tempo; 12. Hai ragione. ACT 3: 13. O
mio piccolo tavolo; 14. Eccomi pronta; 15a. Mama
usciva di casa; 15b. Dir che ci sono al mondo. ACT 4:
16. Dunque nessuna nuova; 17. Zazà, piccola
zingara; 18. Che non vorresti farlo; 19. Tu non
m'amavi più; 20. Ed ora io mi domando.
È un riso gentil G. Martinelli, orch, R. Bourdon
(r1927) Concert   (3/93) (PREI) ① **89062**
È un riso gentil G. Martinelli, orch (r1922) Concert
(9/94) (NIMB) ① **NI7856**
11, 17. T. Gobbi, La Scala Orch, U. Berrettoni (r1942)
Concert   (10/89) (EMI) ① **CDM7 63109-2**
11, 17. T. Ruffo, orch (r1912) Concert
(11/90) (NIMB) ① **NI7810**
11, 17. A. Granforte, La Scala Orch, C. Sabajno
(r1929) Concert   (12/91) (PREI) ① **89048**
11, 17. T. Ruffo, orch (r1912) Concert
(2/93) (PREI) ① **[3]** 89303(1)
15a, 15b C. Muzio, Anon (pf) (r1921) Concert
(5/90) (BOGR) ① **[2]** BIM705-2
15a, 15b C. Muzio, orch (r1921) Concert
(1/94) (ROMO) ① **[2]** 81005-2
17. P. Lisitsian, Bolshoi Th Orch, V. Piradov (r1948:
Russ) Concert   (8/93) (PREI) ① **89061**
17. R. Zanelli, orch (r1919) Concert
(10/95) (NIMB) ① **NI7867**

LEONI, Franco (1864–1949)
Italy

SECTION V: STAGE WORKS

L' Oracolo—opera: 1 act (1905—London)
Mio figlio A. Didur, orch (r c1919) Concert
(1/94) (CLUB) ① **CL99-089**

LÉONIN (fl c1163–90) France

SECTION IV: VOCAL AND CHORAL

Viderunt omnes—organum: 2vv (c1160-70)
(Gradual for Mass on Christmas Day)
London Early Music Consort, D. Munrow Concert
(8/85) (ARCH) ① **415 292-2AH**

LEOZ, Jesús García (1904–1953)
Spain

SECTION IV: VOCAL AND CHORAL

Tríptico de canciones
1. Por el aire van; 2. De Cádiz a Gibraltar; 3. A la flor,
a la pitiflor.
M. Bayo, J.A. Alvarez-Parejo (r1992) Concert
(6/93) (CLAV) ① **CD50-9205**

LEPKYI, L. Russia

SECTION IV: VOCAL AND CHORAL

Song of the Cranes (Wds. B. Lepkyi)
P. Plishka, T. Hrynkiv (arr Revutsky) Concert
(11/92) (FORL) ① **UCD16645**

LERDAHL, Fred (Alfred Whitford)
(b 1943) USA

SECTION I: ORCHESTRAL

Waves—chamber orchestra (1988)
Orpheus CO (r1990) Concert
(7/93) (DG) ① **435 389-2GH**

LEROUX, Xavier (1863–1919) France

SECTION IV: VOCAL AND CHORAL

Le Nil—song (Wds. Renaud)
J. McCormack, F. Kreisler, V. O'Brien (r1914)
Concert (8/89) (PEAR) ① GEMMCD9315

SECTION V: STAGE WORKS

La Reine Fiammette—opéra-comique: 4 acts
(1903—Paris) (Lib. C. Mendès)
Tu sais...Je ne suis plus reine M. Carré, X. Leroux
(r1904) Concert (8/92) (IRCC) ① IRCC-CD802

LESCHETIZKY, Theodore (1830–1915) Poland

SECTION III: INSTRUMENTAL

Andante finale: paraphrase on the opera
'Lucia di Lammermoor' by Donizetti—piano:
left hand, Op. 13
P. Ritzen (r1992) Concert
(7/94) (MARC) ① 8 223525
Arabesque in A flat—piano
B. Moiseiwitsch (r1922) Concert
(4/89) (OPAL) ① OPALCD9839
Aria—piano, Op. 36/1
P. Ritzen (r1992) Concert
(7/94) (MARC) ① 8 223525
Intermezzo en octaves—piano, Op. 44/4
P. Ritzen (r1992) Concert
(7/94) (MARC) ① 8 223525
Marche militaire—piano, Op. 17
P. Ritzen (r1992) Concert
(7/94) (MARC) ① 8 223525
6 Méditations—piano, Op. 19
BOOK 1: 1. La Mélusine; 2. Réponse; 3. L'approche
du printemps. BOOK 2: 4. Berceuse; 5.
Découragement; 6. Consolation.
P. Ritzen (r1992) Concert
(7/94) (MARC) ① 8 223525
2 Pieces—piano, Op. 35
1. Le bal d'hier; 2. Souvenir d'Ischl.
P. Ritzen (r1992) Concert
(7/94) (MARC) ① 8 223525
3 Pieces—piano, Op. 48
1. Prélude humoresque; 2. Intermezzo scherzando;
3. Etude héroïque.
P. Ritzen (r1992) Concert
(7/94) (MARC) ① 8 223525
Suite, 'A la campagne'—piano, Op. 40
1. Jeux des ondes; 2. Romance; 3. Primula veris; 4.
A la Mazurka; 5. Danse à la Russe.
P. Ritzen (r1992) Concert
(7/94) (MARC) ① 8 223525
Toccata—piano
M. Novello (r c1923) Concert
(4/89) (OPAL) ① OPALCD9839

LESLIE, Henry (David) (1822–1896) England

SECTION IV: VOCAL AND CHORAL

Annabelle Lee—song
S. Burrows, J. Constable Concert
(4/92) (GAMU) ① GAMD506
Charm me asleep—partsong (Wds. Herrick)
PCA, M. Brown Concert (3/87) (CONI) ① CDCF145

LESSEL, Franciszek (c1780–1838) Poland

SECTION I: ORCHESTRAL

Adagio et rondeau à la polonaise—piano and
orchestra, Op. 9 (pub 1810)
J. Sterczynski, Silesian PSO, J. Salwarowski (r1992)
Concert (10/93) (CHNT) ① LDC278 1092
Concerto for Piano and Orchestra in C, Op.
14 (1813)
J. Sterczynski, Silesian PSO, J. Salwarowski (r1992)
Concert (10/93) (CHNT) ① LDC278 1092

SECTION III: INSTRUMENTAL

Variations in A minor—piano, Op. 15/2 (pub
1934)
J. Sterczynski (r1992) Concert
(10/93) (CHNT) ① LDC278 1092
Variations on a Ukranian song, 'Jichaw
kozak zza Dunaju'—piano, Op. 15/1 (1810)
J. Sterczynski (r1992) Concert
(10/93) (CHNT) ① LDC278 1092

L'ESTOCART, Paschal de (cl539–cl584) France

SECTION I: ORCHESTRAL

Dun fond de ma pensée—symphonie
Toulouse Sacqueboutiers, J. Bernfeld, B. Fabre-
Garrus (r1993) Concert (3/95) (ASTR) ① E8521

SECTION IV: VOCAL AND CHORAL

Psalms—3-6vv (Wds. Bible, trans C Marot)
1. Psalm 25; 2. Psalm 33.
C. Goudimel Ens, C. Morel (r1994) Concert
(6/95) (NAXO) ① 8 553025

LEVADÉ, Charles (Gaston) (1869–1948) France

SECTION IV: VOCAL AND CHORAL

Les vieilles de chez-nous—song
L. Fugère, anon (r1928) Concert
(6/93) (SYMP) ① SYMCD1125

LEVANT, Oscar (1906–1972) USA

SECTION I: ORCHESTRAL

Caprice—orchestra (1940)
Concordia, M. Alsop (r1992/3) Concert
(1/94) (EMI) ① CDC7 54851-2

LEVERIDGE, Richard (1670–1758) England

SECTION IV: VOCAL AND CHORAL

Black and gloomy as the grave—song (Wds.
D'Urfey)
E. Tubb, English Tpt Virtuosi, A. Hoskins (tpt/dir), M.
Hoskins (tpt/dir) (r1994) Concert
(10/95) (MOSC) ① 070979
Old English Melodies
This Great World is a Trouble E. Schwarzkopf, M.
Raucheisen (Ger: bp1944) Concert
(6/87) (ACAN) ① 43 801
The Roast Beef of old England—song (1735)
(Wds. cpsr)
L. Skeaping, Broadside Band, J. Barlow (r1992; arr J.
Barlow) Concert (6/93) (SAYD) ① CD-SDL400

LEVIN, Todd USA

SECTION IV: VOCAL AND CHORAL

De Luxe—mezzo-soprano, vocalist &
orchestra (1994)
T. Levin, M. Nessinger, LSO, D.A. Miller (r1994)
(8/95) (DG) ① 445 847-2GH

LEVITZKI, Mischa (1898–1941) Russia

SECTION III: INSTRUMENTAL

Valse de concert—piano, Op. 1
M. Levitzki (r1924) Concert
(1/93) (APR) ① [2] APR7014
Waltz in A flat—piano, Op. 2
S. Hough (r1986) Concert
(1/89) (VIRG) ① VC7 59509-2
M. Levitzki (r1929) Concert
(6/92) (APR) ① APR7020
M. Levitzki (r1924) Concert
(1/93) (APR) ① [2] APR7014

LEVY, Jules (1838–1903) England

SECTION I: ORCHESTRAL

Grand Russian Fantasia—cornet and wind
orchestra (1994)
W. Marsalis, Eastman Wind Ens, D. Hunsberger (arr
D Hunsberger) Concert (9/87) (SONY) ① MK42137

LEVY, Marvin David (b 1932) USA

SECTION V: STAGE WORKS

Mourning Becomes Electra—opera (3 acts)
(1967—New York) (Lib. after O'Neill)
Too weak to kill the man I hate S. Milnes, NY Met
Op Orch, J. Conlon (pp1991) Concert
(6/93) (RCA) ① 09026 61509-2
Too weak to kill S. Milnes, New Philh, A. Guadagno
(r1968) Concert
(4/94) (RCA) ① [6] 09026 61580-2(8)

LEWIS, Idris Wales

SECTION IV: VOCAL AND CHORAL

Bugail Aberdyfi—song (Wds. Ceirog)
A. Davies, A. Bryn Parri (r1994) Concert
(11/95) (SAIN) ① SCDC2085

LEWIS, Michael J. (b 1939) England

SECTION V: STAGE WORKS

The Madwoman of Chaillot—film score
(1969)
End Title National PO, C. Gerhardt Concert
(6/90) (VARE) ① VSD5207

LEY, Henry George (1887–1962) England

SECTION IV: VOCAL AND CHORAL

Evening Hymn of Charles I—choir a
cappella
Lincoln Cath Ch, C. Walsh (r1993) Concert
(7/94) (PRIO) ① PRCD454
Morning Service in C minor
1. Te Deum; 2. Jubilate.
1, 2. Hereford Cath Ch, R. Massey, G. Bowen
(r1994) Concert (2/95) (PRIO) ① PRCD507
Prayer of King Henry VI
King's College Ch, S. Cleobury (pp1991 with Choral
Evensong) Concert
(10/92) (EMI) ① CDC7 54412-2
Oxford Christ Church Cath Ch, S. Darlington Concert
(10/92) (NIMB) ① NI5328

LHÉRITIER, Jean (c1480–after 1552) France

SECTION IV: VOCAL AND CHORAL

Nigra sum—motet
Tallis Scholars, P. Phillips Concert
(8/87) (GIME) ① CDGIM003
Tallis Scholars, P. Phillips (r1983) Concert
(1/94) (GIME) ① [4] CDGIMB400
Surrexit pastor bonus—motet
Oxford Camerata, J. Summerly (r1993) Concert
(3/95) (NAXO) ① 8 550843

LIADOV (LYADOV), Anatole Konstantinovich (1855–1914) Russia

SECTION I: ORCHESTRAL

About olden times—ballade in D minor, Op.
21b (1890 orch 1906)
Mexico City PO, E. Bátiz Concert
(9/89) (ASV) ① CDDCA657
Russia SO, V. Dudarova (1992) Concert
(9/89) (OLYM) ① OCD513
Baba-Yaga, Op. 56 (?1891-1904)
Mexico City PO, E. Bátiz Concert
(9/89) (ASV) ① CDDCA657
LSO, N. Järvi Concert
(2/90) (CHAN) ① CHAN8783
Russia SO, V. Dudarova (1992) Concert
(9/89) (OLYM) ① OCD513
RPO, E. Kurtz (r1957) Concert
(9/93) (EMI) ① [2] CZS7 67729-2
Kirov Th Orch, V. Gergiev (1993) Concert
(4/94) (PHIL) ① 442 011-2PH
Dance of the Amazon, Op. 65 (1910)
Russia SO, V. Dudarova (1992) Concert
(6/93) (OLYM) ① OCD513
The Enchanted Lake, Op. 62 (1909)
Mexico City PO, E. Bátiz Concert
(9/89) (ASV) ① CDDCA657

LSO, N. Järvi *Concert*
(2/90) (CHAN) ① **CHAN8783**
Russia SO, V. Dudarova (r1992) *Concert*
(6/93) (OLYM) ① **OCD513**
RPO, E. Kurtz (r1957) *Concert*
(9/93) (EMI) ① [2] **CZS7 67729-2**
Kirov Th Orch, V. Gergiev (r1993; includes bonus
sampler CD) *Concert* (7/95) (PHIL) ① **442 775-2PH**
3 Fanfares—orchestra
Mexico City PO, E. Bátiz *Concert*
(9/89) (ASV) ① **CDDCA657**
From the Apocalypse, Op. 66 (1909)
Russia SO, V. Dudarova (r1992) *Concert*
(6/93) (OLYM) ① **OCD513**
Kikimora, Op. 63 (1909)
Mexico City PO, E. Bátiz *Concert*
(9/89) (ASV) ① **CDDCA657**
LSO, N. Järvi *Concert*
(2/90) (CHAN) ① **CHAN8783**
NBC SO, A. Toscanini (r1952) *Concert*
(11/92) (RCA) ① **GD60323**
Russia SO, V. Dudarova (r1992) *Concert*
(6/93) (OLYM) ① **OCD513**
RPO, E. Kurtz (r1957) *Concert*
(9/93) (EMI) ① [2] **CZS7 67729-2**
Kirov Th Orch, V. Gergiev (r1993) *Concert*
(4/94) (PHIL) ① **442 011-2PH**
Hallé, A. Boult (r1942) *Concert*
(2/95) (DUTT) ① **CDAX8010**
**Musical snuffbox—orchestra, Op. 32 (pub
1893)** (orch. cpsr from piano work)
Mexico City PO, E. Bátiz *Concert*
(9/89) (ASV) ① **CDDCA657**
SNO, N. Järvi *Concert*
(10/90) (CHAN) ① **CHAN8804**
RPO, E. Kurtz (r1957) *Concert*
(9/93) (EMI) ① [2] **CZS7 67729-2**
Nénie, Op. 67 (1914)
Russia SO, V. Dudarova (r1992) *Concert*
(6/93) (OLYM) ① **OCD513**
**Polonaise in C, 'In Memory of A.S. Pushkin',
Op. 49 (1899)**
Mexico City PO, E. Bátiz *Concert*
(9/89) (ASV) ① **CDDCA657**
Russia SO, V. Dudarova (r1992) *Concert*
(6/93) (OLYM) ① **OCD513**
**Polonaise in D, 'for unveiling of statue of
A.S. Rubinstein', Op. 55 (1902)**
Mexico City PO, E. Bátiz *Concert*
(9/89) (ASV) ① **CDDCA657**
**8 Russian Folksongs—orchestra, Op. 58
(pub 1906)**
1. Religious chant; 2. Christmas carol; 3. Plaintive
song; 4. Humorous song; 5. Legend of the birds; 6.
Cradle song; 7. Round dance; 8. Village-dance song.
Mexico City PO, E. Bátiz *Concert*
(9/89) (ASV) ① **CDDCA657**
LSO, A. Coates (r1929) *Concert*
(12/92) (KOCH) ① **37700-2**
Russia SO, V. Dudarova (r1992) *Concert*
(6/93) (OLYM) ① **OCD513**
Scherzo No.1 in D, Op. 16 (1879-86)
Russia SO, V. Dudarova (r1992) *Concert*
(6/93) (OLYM) ① **OCD513**

SECTION III: INSTRUMENTAL
---

2 Bagatelles—piano, Op. 17 (1887)
1. Stradaniye, B flat minor; 2. Pastorale, B minor.
1. M. Fingerhut (r1992) *Concert*
(4/94) (CHAN) ① **CHAN9218**
**A Musical snuffbox—piano, Op. 32 (pub
1893)**
Vladimir Ashkenazy (r1983) *Concert*
(7/93) (DECC) ① **430 759-2DM**
M. Rosenthal (r1930) *Concert*
(9/93) (PEAR) ① **GEMMCD9963**
S. Cherkassky (r1956) *Concert*
(9/94) (TEST) ① **SBT1033**
3 Pieces—piano, Op. 11 (1885)
1. Prelude, B minor; 2. Mazurka in the Dorian mode,
A minor; 3. Mazurka, F sharp minor.
1. M. Fingerhut (r1992) *Concert*
(4/94) (CHAN) ① **CHAN9218**
4 Preludes—piano, Op. 39 (1895)
1. A flat; 2. C minor; 3. B; 4. F flat minor.
4. M. Fingerhut (r1992) *Concert*
(4/94) (CHAN) ① **CHAN9218**
4 Preludes—piano, Op. 46 (pub 1899)
1. B flat; 2. G minor; 3. G; 4. E minor.
1. M. Rosenthal (r1930) *Concert*
(9/93) (PEAR) ① **GEMMCD9963**

LICHT, Daniel (20th cent) USA

SECTION V: STAGE WORKS

Children of the Night—film score (1992)
EXCERPTS: 1. The Blood Sucker's Ball.
1. OST, D. Licht (r1992) *Concert*
(10/93) (SILV) ① **FILMCD127**

**LIDDLE, Samuel (?1867–1951)
England**

SECTION IV: VOCAL AND CHORAL

How lovely are thy dwellings—hymn
R. Crooks, orch (r1933) *Concert*
(9/93) (CLAR) ① **CDGSE78-50-50**

**LIDHOLM, Ingvar (Natanael) (b
1921) Sweden**

SECTION I: ORCHESTRAL

**Greetings from an Old World—orchestra
(1976)**
Stockholm PO, G. Rozhdestvensky (r1993) *Concert*
(3/94) (CHAN) ① **CHAN9231**
Kontakion—orchestra (1978)
Stockholm PO, G. Rozhdestvensky (r1993) *Concert*
(3/94) (CHAN) ① **CHAN9231**
Music for strings (1952)
A. Nilsson, Stockholm Sinfonietta, E-P. Salonen
Concert (4/85) (BIS) ① **BIS-CD285**
Ritornell—orchestra (1955)
Stockholm PO, G. Rozhdestvensky (r1993) *Concert*
(3/94) (CHAN) ① **CHAN9231**
Toccata e canto—chamber orchestra (1944)
Stockholm PO, G. Rozhdestvensky (r1993) *Concert*
(3/94) (CHAN) ① **CHAN9231**

SECTION IV: VOCAL AND CHORAL

**...a riveder le stelle—S, chorus a capella
(1971-73)** (Wds. Dante)
Danish Nat Rad Chbr Ch, S. Parkman *Concert*
(12/91) (CHAN) ① **CHAN8963**

SECTION V: STAGE WORKS

**A Dream Play—opera: prelude and 2 acts
(1992—Stockholm)** (Lib. cspr, after J.
Strindberg)
Cpte H. Martinpelto, H. Hagegård, I. Tobiasson, S.
Wahlund, C. Appelgren, L. Kullenbo, A. Helleland, A.
Bergström, S. Sandlund, H. Westberg, R. Cederlöf,
N. Stemme, C. Unander-Scharin, Stockholm Royal
Ch, Stockholm Royal Orch, K. Ingebretsen (r1992/3)
(9/93) (CPRI) ① [2] **CAP22029**

LIE, Sigurd (1871–1904) Norway

SECTION IV: VOCAL AND CHORAL

The Key—song (Wds. A Vaa)
K. Flagstad, LSO, Ø. Fjeldstad (r1959) *Concert*
(12/95) (LOND) ① **440 492-2LM**
K. Flagstad, LSO, Ø. Fjeldstad (r1959) *Concert*
(12/95) (LOND) ① [5] **440 490-2LM5(1)**
The Letter—song (Wds. A Vaa)
K. Flagstad, LSO, Ø. Fjeldstad (r1959) *Concert*
(12/95) (LOND) ① [5] **440 490-2LM5(1)**
K. Flagstad, LSO, Ø. Fjeldstad (r1959) *Concert*
(12/95) (LOND) ① **440 492-2LM**
Snow—Norwegian song
J. Szigeti, N. Magaloff (arr Szigeti: r1937) *Concert*
(1/90) (BIDD) ① [2] **LAB007/8**
K. Flagstad, E. Alnaes (r1929) *Concert*
(12/95) (SIMA) ① [3] **PSC1821(1)**

**LIEBERMANN, Rolf (b 1910)
Switzerland**

SECTION I: ORCHESTRAL

Furioso—orchestra (1947)
Berlin RIAS Orch, F. Fricsay (r1954) *Concert*
(11/94) (DG) ① **445 404-2GDO**
Berlin RIAS Orch, F. Fricsay (r1954) *Concert*
(11/94) (DG) ① [11] **445 400-2GDO10**

LIEBERSON, Peter (b 1946) USA

SECTION I: ORCHESTRAL

Piano Concerto
P. Serkin, Boston SO, S. Ozawa
(2/88) (NEW) ① **NW325-2**

SECTION III: INSTRUMENTAL
---

3 Bagatelles—piano (1985)
P. Serkin *Concert* (4/87) (NEW) ① **NW344-2**

**LIENAS, Juan de (fl c1620–1650)
?Spain/Mexico**

SECTION IV: VOCAL AND CHORAL

Mass—5vv
Ordinary Compañia musical, La Fenice, J. Cabré
(r1992) *Concert* (9/93) (K617) ① **K617024**

**LIEURANCE, Thurlow (Weed)
(1878–1963) USA**

SECTION IV: VOCAL AND CHORAL

**By the Waters of Minnetonka (Moon
Deer)—song (1917)** (Wds. Cavanass)
E. Schumann-Heink, orch (r1926) *Concert*
(2/91) (NIMB) ① **NI7811**

**LIGETI, Gyorgy (Sandor) (b 1923)
Hungary/Austria**

SECTION I: ORCHESTRAL

Atmosphères—orchestra (1961)
South-West German RSO, E. Bour *Concert*
(10/89) (WERG) ① **WER60162-50**
VPO, C. Abbado (pp1988) *Concert*
(4/90) (DG) ① **429 260-2GH**
**Chamber Concerto—13 instruments (1969-
70)**
Reihe Ens, F. Cerha *Concert*
(10/89) (WERG) ① **WER60162-50**
Modern Ens, P. Eötvös (r1990) *Concert*
(6/94) (SONY) ① **SK58945**
Concerto for Cello and Orchestra (1966)
M. Perényi, Modern Ens, P. Eötvös (r1990) *Concert*
(6/94) (SONY) ① **SK58945**
J-G. Queyras, Paris InterContemporain Ens, P.
Boulez (r1992) *Concert*
(1/95) (DG) ① **439 808-2GH**
Concerto for Flute, Oboe and Strings (1972)
G. von Bahr, T. Lännerholm, Swedish RSO, E.
Howarth (pp.1975) *Concert*
(6/88) (BIS) ① **BIS-CD053**
Concerto for Piano and Orchestra (1985-86)
M. Perényi, Modern Ens, P. Eötvös (r1990) *Concert*
(6/94) (SONY) ① **SK58945**
P-L. Aimard, Paris InterContemporain Ens, P. Boulez
(r1992) *Concert* (1/95) (DG) ① **439 808-2GH**
Concerto for Violin and Orchestra (1990-92)
S. Gawriloff, Paris InterContemporain Ens, P. Boulez
(r1993) *Concert* (1/95) (DG) ① **439 808-2GH**
Lontano—orchestra (1967)
VPO, C. Abbado (pp1988) *Concert*
(4/90) (DG) ① **429 260-2GH**
**Ramifications—12 strings/string orchestra
(1968-69)**
South-West German RSO, E. Bour *Concert*
(10/89) (WERG) ① **WER60162-50**
Saarbrücken Rad CO, A. Janigro *Concert*
(10/89) (WERG) ① **WER60162-50**
**San Francisco Polyphony—orchestra (1973-
74)**
Swedish RSO, E. Howarth (pp.1975) *Concert*
(6/88) (BIS) ① **BIS-CD053**

SECTION II: CHAMBER

Bagatelles—wind quintet (1953)
Vienna/Berlin Ens *Concert*
(11/92) (SONY) ① **SK48052**
3 Pieces—2 pianos (1976)
1. Monument; 2. Selbstporträt; 3. Bewegung.
B. Uriarte, K-H. Mrongovius *Concert*
(3/89) (WERG) ① **WER60131-50**
10 Pieces—wind quintet (1968)
South-West German Rad Wind Qnt *Concert*
(11/89) (WERG) ① **WER60161-50**
**String Quartet No. 1—Métamorphoses
nocturnes**
Voces Intimae Qt *Concert*
(6/88) (BIS) ① **BIS-CD053**
Arditti Qt *String Quartet 2.*
(8/89) (WERG) ① **WER60079-50**
Hagen Qt *String Quartet 2.*
(9/91) (DG) ① **431 686-2GH**
String Quartet No. 2 (1968)
Arditti Qt *String Quartet 1.*
(8/89) (WERG) ① **WER60079-50**
Trio—violin, horn and piano (1982)
A. Cazalet, G. Comentale, C. Huvé *Brahms: Horn
Trio.* (5/93) (MONT) ① **782006**

SECTION III: INSTRUMENTAL

Artikulation—4-track tape (1958)
G. Ligeti, G.M. Koenig, C. Cardew *Concert*
(11/89) (WERG) ① **WER60161-50**

Capriccio No. 1—piano (1947)
B. Uriarte *Concert*
(3/89) (WERG) ① **WER60131-50**

Capriccio No. 2—piano (1947)
K-H. Mrongovius *Concert*
(11/89) (WERG) ① **WER60131-50**

Continuum—harpsichord (1968)
E. Nordwall *Concert* (6/88) (BIS) ① **BIS-CD053**
A. Vischer *Concert*
(11/89) (WERG) ① **WER60161-50**

Glissandi—1-track tape (1957)
G. Ligeti *Concert*
(11/89) (WERG) ① **WER60161-50**

Invention—piano (1948)
B. Uriarte *Concert*
(3/89) (WERG) ① **WER60131-50**

Musica ricercata—11 pieces for piano (1951-53)
L. Pohjola *Concert* (6/88) (BIS) ① **BIS-CD053**
B. Uriarte, K-H. Mrongovius *Concert*
(3/89) (WERG) ① **WER60131-50**

Organ Study No. 1, 'Harmonies' (1967)
Z. Szathmáry *Concert*
(11/89) (WERG) ① **WER60161-50**

Organ Study No. 2, 'Coulère'—organ (1969)
Z. Szathmáry *Concert*
(11/89) (WERG) ① **WER60161-50**

Sonata for Cello (1948-53)
M. Haimovitz *Concert* (1/92) (DG) ① **431 813-2GH**
P. Wispelwey (r1993) *Concert*
(7/95) (CHNN) ① **CCS7495**

Volumina—organ (1961-62)
K-E. Welin *Concert*
(11/89) (WERG) ① **WER60161-50**

SECTION IV: VOCAL AND CHORAL

Hungarian Studies—16vv (1983) (Wds. S. Weöres)
France Groupe Vocal, G. Reibel *Concert*
(10/91) (EMI) ① **CDC7 54096-2**

Loneliness—3-pt chorus a capella (1946)
(Wds. S. Weöres)
France Groupe Vocal, G. Reibel *Concert*
(10/91) (EMI) ① **CDC7 54096-2**

Lux aeterna—16vv / chorus (1966)
Stuttgart Schola Cantorum, C. Gottwald *Concert*
(10/89) (WERG) ① **WER60162-50**
France Groupe Vocal, G. Reibel *Concert*
(10/91) (EMI) ① **CDC7 54096-2**
Musica Sacra, R. Westenburg (r1993) *Concert*
(12/93) (CATA) ① **09026 61822-2**

4 Mátraszentimre Songs—folksong arrangements (1955)
France Groupe Vocal, G. Reibel *Concert*
(10/91) (EMI) ① **CDC7 54096-2**

Night and Morning—8-pt chorus a capella (1955) (Wds. S. Weöres)
France Groupe Vocal, G. Reibel *Concert*
(10/91) (EMI) ① **CDC7 54096-2**

Pápainé—8vv a capella (1953) (Wds. Hungarian trad)
France Groupe Vocal, G. Reibel *Concert*
(10/91) (EMI) ① **CDC7 54096-2**

3 Phantasien—chorus a capella (1982) (Wds. Hölderlin)
France Groupe Vocal, G. Reibel *Concert*
(10/91) (EMI) ① **CDC7 54096-2**

SECTION V: STAGE WORKS

Le Grand Macabre—opera: 2 acts (1978—Stockholm) (Lib. Meschke & cpsr, after Ghelderode)
Cpte E. Davies, E. Davies, P. Walmsley-Clark, O. Fredricks, K. Smith, C. Puhlmann-Richter, P. Haage, D. Weller, U. Krekow, J. Leutgeb, E. Salzer, L. Modos, H. Prikopa, E.L. Strachwitz, Gumpoldskirchner Spatzen, Austrian Rad Chor, A. Schoenberg Ch, Austrian RSO, E. Howarth
(12/91) (WERG) ① [2] **WER6170-2**

LILBURN, Douglas (b 1915) New Zealand

SECTION I: ORCHESTRAL

Allegro—string orchestra (1942)
New Zealand CO (r1993) *Concert*
(9/95) (KOCH) ① **37260-2**

Diversions—string orchestra (1947)
New Zealand CO (r1993) *Concert*
(9/95) (KOCH) ① **37260-2**

Symphony No. 1 (1948)
NZ SO, J. Hopkins (r1982) *Concert*
(3/94) (KIWI) ① **CDSLD-90**
NZ SO, J. Hopkins (r1993) *Concert*
(8/94) (CNTI) ① **CCD1069**

Symphony No. 2 (1951)
NZ SO, A. Heenan (r1975) *Concert*
(3/94) (KIWI) ① **CDSLD-90**
NZ SO, J. Hopkins (r1992) *Concert*
(8/94) (CNTI) ① **CCD1069**

Symphony No. 3 (1961)
NZ SO, J. Hopkins (r1968) *Concert*
(3/94) (KIWI) ① **CDSLD-90**
NZ SO, J. Hopkins (r1993) *Concert*
(8/94) (CNTI) ① **CCD1069**

SECTION IV: VOCAL AND CHORAL

Landfall in Unknown Seas—narrator and string orchestra (1942) (Wds. A Curnow)
E. Hillary, New Zealand CO (r1993) *Concert*
(9/95) (KOCH) ① **37260-2**

LILIUOKALANI, Queen of Hawaii (1838–1917) Hawaii

SECTION IV: VOCAL AND CHORAL

Aloha Oe—song (1892)
F. Kreisler, C. Lamson (r1925: arr Kreisler) *Concert*
(9/93) (BIDD) ① [2] **LAB068/9**

LINCKE, (Carl Emile) Paul (1866–1946) Germany

SECTION I: ORCHESTRAL

Geburtstagsstädchen
Berlin Ens *Concert* (5/91) (ORFE) ① **C126901A**

SECTION V: STAGE WORKS

Frau Luna—operetta-revue: 1 act (1899—Berlin) (Lib. Bolten-Baeckers)
Castles in the Air R. Crooks, orch (r1933: Eng)
Concert (9/93) (CLAR) ① **CDGSE78-50-50**
Schlösser, die im Monde liegen L. Popp, ASMF, N.
Marriner *Concert* (6/88) (EMI) ① **CDC7 49700-2**
Im Reiche des Indra—operetta (1 act)
(1899—Berlin) (Lib. Bolten-Baeckers)
Es war einmal R. Tauber, orch (r1929) *Concert*
(7/88) (EMI) ① **CDM7 69476-2**

LINDBERG, Oskar (Fredrik) (1887–1955) Sweden

SECTION I: ORCHESTRAL

Från de stora skogarna—symphonic poem (1918) (Eng: From the great forests)
Stockholm PO, S. Westerberg *Concert*
(8/92) (MSVE) ① **MSCD620**

SECTION III: INSTRUMENTAL

Old Tune from Dalecarlia—organ (1936)
O.E. Antonsen, W. Marshall (r1992: arr tpt/org)
Concert (10/94) (EMI) ① **CDC5 55048-2**
Organ Sonata in G minor, Op. 23 (1925)
3. Alla Sarabanda; 4. Allegro con brio.
3, 4. C. Herrick (r1993) *Concert*
(8/94) (HYPE) ① **CDA66676**

LINDEMANN, Wilhelm (1882–1941) Germany

SECTION I: ORCHESTRAL

Unter dem Grillenbanner—march (after J. Strauss II)
Berlin Phil Wind Qnt, H. von Karajan (r1973: arr
Schmidt) *Concert* (5/94) (DG) ① **439 346-2GX2**

LINDPAINTNER, Peter Joseph von (1791–1856) Germany

SECTION I: ORCHESTRAL

Concertino for Clarinet and Orchestra in E flat (1815)
D. Klöcker, Berlin RSO, J. López-Cobos *Concert*
(11/88) (SCHW) ① **311045**

LINLEY, Thomas (1733–1795) England

aka Linley the Elder

SECTION IV: VOCAL AND CHORAL

Alas, from the day my poor heart—song (pub 1780) (from 12 Ballads)
Invocation (r1993) *Concert*
(11/94) (HYPE) ① **CDA66698**

Awake, my lyre—cantata: 1v and continuo (Wds. A. Cowley)
Invocation (r1993) *Concert*
(11/94) (HYPE) ① **CDA66698**

6 Elegies and an Invocation—3vv and continuo (pub 1770)
EXCERPTS: 1. Invocation: Fly to my aid, O mighty Love; 2. Elegy I: Ah! what avails the sprightly morn of life; 3. Elegy II: Ye sportive loves, that round me wait; 6. Elegy V: He who could first two gentle hearts unbind; 7. Elegy VI: In thousand thoughts of love and thee.
1-3, 6, 7. Invocation (r1993) *Concert*
(11/94) (HYPE) ① **CDA66698**

The Lark sings high in the cornfield—song (pub 1780) (from 12 Ballads)
E. Kirkby, T. Roberts *Concert*
(12/91) (HYPE) ① **CDA66497**

Think not, my love, when secret grief—song
E. Kirkby, F. Kelly *Concert*
(12/91) (HYPE) ① **CDA66497**

LINLEY, William (1771–1835) England

SECTION IV: VOCAL AND CHORAL

Down in the gleamy vale—elegy: 4vv (1799)
Invocation (r1994) *Concert*
(3/95) (HYPE) ① **CDA66740**

Lawn, as white as driven snow—song (pub 1816) (Wds. Shakespeare)
A. Rolfe Johnson, G. Johnson *Concert*
(5/92) (HYPE) ① **CDA66480**

LINLEY II, Thomas (1756–1778)

aka Linley the Younger

SECTION II: CHAMBER

Sonata in A—violin and continuo (c1768)
Locatelli Trio *Concert* (5/93) (HYPE) ① **CDA66583**

SECTION IV: VOCAL AND CHORAL

Ode on the Spirits of Shakespeare—3vv, chorus and orchestra (1776) (Wds. F. Laurence)
L. Anderson, J. Gooding, R. Wistreich, Parley of Instr
Ch, Parley of Instr, P. Nicholson
(5/93) (HYPE) ① **CDA66613**

To heal the wound a bee had made—song from Colman's pantomime 'Mother Shipton' (1770)
Invocation (r1993) *Concert*
(11/94) (HYPE) ① **CDA66698**

LIPAIEV Russia

SECTION IV: VOCAL AND CHORAL

Credo—Russian liturgical chant
N. Gedda, Paris Russian Orthodox Cath Ch, E. Evetz
Concert (1/93) (PHIL) ① **434 174-2PM**

LIPATTI, Dinu (1917–1950) Romania

SECTION I: ORCHESTRAL

Concertino in the Classical Style—piano and chamber orchestra, Op. 3 (1936)
D. Lipatti, orch (pp c1948) *Concert*
(10/95) (ARCI) ① [2] **ARC112/3**

Romanian Dances—piano and orchestra (1943 orch 1945)
D. Lipatti, SRO, E. Ansermet (pp1945) *Concert*
(10/95) (ARCI) ① [2] **ARC112/3**

Symphonie Concertante—two pianos and orchestra (1938)
M. Lipatti, B. Siki, SRO, E. Ansermet (pp1951)
Concert (10/95) (ARCI) ① [2] **ARC112/3**

Tziganes (Satraril)—suite: orchestra (1934)
SRO, E. Ansermet (pp c1951) *Concert*
(10/95) (ARCI) ① [2] **ARC112/3**

Orpheus—symphonic poem, S98 (1853-54)
Leipzig Gewandhaus, K. Masur (r1977/8) *Concert*
　　　　　　　　(10/94) (EMI) ① **CDM7 64850-2**
LPO, B. Haitink (r1968) *Concert*
　　　　　　　　(10/94) (PHIL) ① [2] **438 751-2PM2**
NBC SO, A. Toscanini (bp1938) *Concert*
　　　　　　　　(10/95) (DELL) ① **CDDA9024**
**Polonaise brillante (Weber)—piano and
orchestra, S367 (c1851)** (from Weber's
Polacca brillante, J268)
M. Dichter, Philh, N. Marriner *Concert*
　　　　　　　　(8/84) (PHIL) ① **411 123-2PH**
**Les Préludes—symphonic poem, S97 (1848
rev ?1853)**
Philadelphia, R. Muti *Concert*
　　　　　　　　(3/85) (EMI) ① **CDC7 47022-2**
Luxembourg Rad & TV SO, J-C. Casadesus *Concert*
　　　　　　　　(8/85) (FORL) ① **UCD16516**
Cincinnati Pops, E. Kunzel *Concert*
　　　　　　　　(9/86) (TELA) ① **CD80115**
BPO, H. von Karajan (r1967) *Concert*
　　　　　　　　(9/86) (DG) ① [2] **415 967-2GH2**
Berlin SO, C.P. Flor (pp1988) *Concert*
　　　　　　　　(4/90) (RCA) ① **RD60119**
Concertgebouw, W. Mengelberg (r1929) *Concert*
　　　　　　　　(12/91) (ARHI) ① **ADCD107**
BPO, O. Fried (r1928) *Concert*
　　　　　　　　(2/93) (KOCH) ① **37146-2**
NYPO, L. Bernstein *Concert*
　　　　　　　　(5/93) (SONY) ① **SMK47572**
Black Dyke Mills Band, J. Watson (r1992: arr
Rimmer) *Concert*　　　(9/93) (POLY) ① **QPRL053D**
BPO, H. Knappertsbusch (r1942) *Beethoven:
Symphony 3.*　　　　(5/94) (PREI) ① **90976**
Boston SO, P. Monteux (r1952) *Concert*
　　　　　　　　(9/94) (RCA) ① [15] **09026 61893-2**
Leipzig Gewandhaus, K. Masur (r1977/8) *Concert*
　　　　　　　　(10/94) (EMI) ① **CDM7 64850-2**
LPO, B. Haitink (r1968) *Concert*
　　　　　　　　(10/94) (PHIL) ① [2] **438 751-2PM2**
SRO, N. Järvi (r1994) *Concert*
　　　　　　　　(9/95) (CHAN) ① **CHAN9360**
**Prometheus—symphonic poem, S99 (1850
rev 1855)** (orch Raff)
LPO, B. Haitink (r1968) *Concert*
　　　　　　　　(10/94) (PHIL) ① [2] **438 751-2PM2**
BPO, C. Abbado (pp1992) *Concert*
　　　　　　　　(1/95) (SONY) ① **SK53978**
Rákóczy March, S117 (1865) (based on pf
works S242/13 and S244/15)
Philh Hungarica, W. Boskovsky *Concert*
　　　　　　　　(6/93) (EMI) ① **CDM7 64627-2**
**Tasso—symphonic poem after Byron, S96
(1849 rev 1850-51)**
BPO, H. von Karajan (r1967) *Concert*
　　　　　　　　(9/86) (DG) ① [2] **415 967-2GH2**
Leipzig Gewandhaus, K. Masur (r1977/8) *Concert*
　　　　　　　　(10/94) (EMI) ① **CDM7 64850-2**
LPO, B. Haitink (r1968) *Concert*
　　　　　　　　(10/94) (PHIL) ① [2] **438 751-2PM2**
**Totentanz—piano and orchestra, S126 (1849
rev 1853, 1859)**
F. Clidat, Luxembourg Rad & TV SO, J-C.
Casadesus *Concert*　　(8/85) (FORL) ① **UCD16516**
K. Zimerman, Boston SO, S. Ozawa *Concert*
　　　　　　　　(11/88) (DG) ① **423 571-2GH**
S. Mayer, LSO, T. Vásáry *Concert*
　　　　　　　　(10/91) (ASV) ① **CDDCA778**
B. Janis, Chicago SO, F. Reiner (1957) *Concert*
　　　　　　　　(4/93) (RCA) ① **09026 61250-2**
A.B. Michelangeli, Rome RAI Orch, G. Gavazzeni
(pp1962) *Concert*　　(10/95) (MEMR) ① [4] **999001**
Ungarischer Sturmmarsch, S119 (1875)
(based on pf work, S232)
Philh Hungarica, W. Boskovsky *Concert*
　　　　　　　　(6/93) (EMI) ① **CDM7 64627-2**
**Von der Wiege bis zum Grabe—symphonic
poem, S107 (1881-82)**
LPO, B. Haitink (r1971) *Concert*
　　　　　　　　(10/94) (PHIL) ① [2] **438 754-2PM2**
NBC SO, A. Toscanini (bp1941) *Concert*
　　　　　　　　(10/95) (DELL) ① **CDDA9024**
**Wandererfantasie (Schubert)—piano and
orchestra, S366 (before 1852)**
J. Bolet, LPO, G. Solti *Concert*
　　　　　　　　(2/90) (DECC) ① **425 689-2DX**

SECTION II: CHAMBER

**Concerto pathétique—two pianos, S258
(before 1857)**
M. Hambourg, Michal Hambourg (r1933) *Concert*
　　　　　　　　(6/95) (PEAR) ① **GEMMCD9147**
**Elegie No. 1—cello, piano and harp, S130
(1874)**
A. Gastinel, P-L. Aimard (r1995) *Concert*
　　　　　　　　(9/95) (AUVI) ① **V4748**

**Elegie No. 2—violin/cello and piano, S131
(1877)**
A. Gastinel, P-L. Aimard (r1995) *Concert*
　　　　　　　　(9/95) (AUVI) ① **V4748**
**Grand duo concertant on Lafont's Le
marin—violin & piano, S128 (c1837, rev
?1849)**
G. Kremer, O. Maisenberg (r1993) *Concert*
　　　　　　　　(10/95) (DG) ① **445 820-2GH**
**Harold in Italy (Berlioz)—viola and piano
transcription, S472 (c1836)**
B. Pasquier, J-F. Heisser *Schumann: Märchenbilder.*
　　　　　　　　(12/91) (HARM) ① **HMA190 1246**
P. Coletti, L. Howard *Concert*
　　　　　　　　(11/93) (HYPE) ① **CDA66683**
**La lugubre gondola—violin/cello and piano,
S134 (1882)**
A. Gastinel, P-L. Aimard (r1995) *Concert*
　　　　　　　　(9/95) (AUVI) ① **V4748**
G. Kremer, O. Maisenberg (r1993) *Concert*
　　　　　　　　(10/95) (DG) ① **445 820-2GH**
**Romance oubliée—violin/viola/cello and
piano, S132 (1880)**
K. Kashkashian, R. Levin *Concert*
　　　　　　　　(9/86) (ECM) ① **827 744-2**
P. Coletti, L. Howard *Concert*
　　　　　　　　(11/93) (HYPE) ① **CDA66683**
**Symphony No. 9 (Beethoven)—2 pianos
transcription, S657 (c1851)**
B. Canino, A. Ballista　　(8/88) (DYNA) ① **DC-U24**
A. Planès, G. Pludermacher
　　　　　　　　(8/88) (HARM) ① **HMC90 1198**

SECTION III: INSTRUMENTAL

À la Chappelle Sixtine—piano, S461 (1862)
1. Allegri: Miserere; 2. Mozart: Ave verum corpus.
L. Howard *Concert*　(5/92) (HYPE) ① **CDA66438**
2. C. Katsaris (r1992) *Concert*
　　　　　　　　(6/93) (SONY) ① **SK52551**
Adagio in C—piano (1841)
L. Howard *Concert*　　(1/90) (HYPE) ① **CDA66357**
**Adelaide (Beethoven)—piano transcription,
S466 (1839)**
L. Howard *Concert*
　　　　　　　　(4/92) (HYPE) ① [2] **CDA66481/2**
**Africaine illustrations (Meyerbeer)—piano
transcriptions, S415 (1865)**
1. Prière des matelots; 2. Marche indienne.
L. Howard *Concert*
　　　　　　　　(12/90) (HYPE) ① [2] **CDA66371/2**
**Aida (Verdi)—Danza sacra e duetto
final—piano transcription, S436 (pub 1879)**
L. Howard *Concert*
　　　　　　　　(12/90) (HYPE) ① [2] **CDA66371/2**
E. Ax (r1992) *Concert*　(11/93) (SONY) ① **SK48484**
**Albumblatt in Walzerform—piano, S166
(1842)**
L. Howard *Concert*　　(11/87) (HYPE) ① **CDA66201**
**Allegro di bravura—piano, S151 (Op. 4/1)
(1824)**
L. Howard *Concert*
　　　　　　　　(7/94) (HYPE) ① [2] **CDA66771/2**
**Alleluja and Ave Maria (Arcadelt)—piano,
S183 (1862)**
1. Alleluja; 2. Ave Maria.
L. Howard *Concert*
　　　　　　　　(9/91) (HYPE) ① [2] **CDA66421/2**
**Almira sarabande and chaconne
(Handel)—piano transcription, S181 (1879)**
L. Howard *Concert*
　　　　　　　　(12/90) (HYPE) ① [2] **CDA66371/2**
**Am Grabe Richard Wagners—piano, S202
(1883)**
M. Rudy *Concert*　　　(5/90) (CALL) ① **CAL9685**
G. Oppitz (r1993) *Concert*
　　　　　　　　(2/95) (RCA) ① **09026 61843-2**
**An die ferne Geliebte (Beethoven)—piano
transcription, S469 (1849)**
1. Auf dem Hügel sitz ich spähend; 2. Wo die Berge
so blau; 3. Leichte Segler in den Höhn; 4. Diese
Wolken in den Höhen; 5. Es kehret der Maien; 6.
Nimm sie hin dinn dieser Lieder.
L. Howard *Concert*
　　　　　　　　(4/92) (HYPE) ① [2] **CDA66481/2**
N. Demidenko (pp1993) *Concert*
　　　　　　　　(1/94) (HYPE) ① [2] **CDA66781/2**
**Dem Andenken Petöfis—piano, S195
(1877)**
J. Swann *Concert*　　(8/89) (MUSI) ① **MACD-245**
**Années de pèlerinage—année 1:
Suisse—piano, S160 (1848-54)**
1. La chapelle de Guillaume Tell; 2. Au lac de
Wallenstadt; 3. Pastorale; 4. Au bord d'une source; 5.
Orage; 6. Vallée d'Obermann; 7. Eglogue; 8. Le mal
du pays; 9. Les cloches de Genève.

J. Bolet　　　(12/84) (DECC) ① **410 160-2DH**
L. Berman (r1977) *Concert*
　　　　　　　　(11/93) (DG) ① [3] **437 206-2GX3**
G. Cziffra (r1970s) *Concert*
　　　　　　　　(3/95) (EMI) ① [4] **CMS7 64882-2**
2, 4. K.W. Paik *Concert*
　　　　　　　　(12/91) (VIRG) ① **VJ7 59646-2**
2, 4, 5, 7. O. De Spiegeleir (r1994) *Concert*
　　　　　　　　(10/95) (PAVA) ① **ADW7332**
4. J. Bolet *Concert*　(2/90) (DECC) ① **425 689-2DX**
4. M. Perahia *Concert*　(10/91) (SONY) ① **SK47180**
4. V. Horowitz (r1947) *Concert*
　　　　　　　　(7/92) (RCA) ① **GD60523**
4. A. Cortot (r1923) *Concert*
　　　　　　　　(10/94) (BIDD) ① [2] **LHW014/5**
5. B. Janis (r1961) *Concert*
　　　　　　　　(9/91) (MERC) ① **432 002-2MM**
6. E. Ax (r1992) *Concert*
　　　　　　　　(11/93) (SONY) ① **SK48484**
6. L. Berman (r1977) *Concert*
　　　　　　　　(1/94) (DG) ① **439 409-2GCL**
6. V. Horowitz (pp1966) *Concert*
　　　　　　　　(7/94) (SONY) ① [3] **S3K53461**
**Années de pèlerinage—année 2:
Italie—piano, S161 (1837-49)**
1. Sposalizio; 2. Il penseroso; 3. Canzonetta del
Salvatore Rosa; 4. Sonetto 47 del Petrarca; 5.
Sonetto 104 del Petrarca; 6. Sonetto 123 del
Petrarca; 7. Après une lecture du Dante—fantasia
quasi sonata.
J. Bolet　　　(7/85) (DECC) ① **410 161-2DH**
L. Lortie　　(9/91) (CHAN) ① **CHAN8900**
L. Berman (r1977) *Concert*
　　　　　　　　(11/93) (DG) ① [3] **437 206-2GX3**
M. Dalberto (r1992) *Funeral Odes.*
　　　　　　　　(2/94) (DENO) ① **CO-75500**
W. Stephenson (r1994) *Études d'exécution, S139.*
　　　　　　　　(11/94) (OLYM) ① **OCD277**
G. Cziffra (r1965 & 1970s) *Concert*
　　　　　　　　(3/95) (EMI) ① [4] **CMS7 64882-2**
4. J. Bolet *Concert*
　　　　　　　　(12/85) (DECC) ① **411 803-2DH**
4-6. T. Barto *Concert*
　　　　　　　　(6/89) (EMI) ① **CDC7 49566-2**
4-6. M. Rudy *Concert*
　　　　　　　　(5/90) (EMI) ① **CDC7 49842-2**
4-6. K. Stott *Concert*　(8/90) (CONI) ① **CDCF180**
4-6. D. Barenboim *Concert*
　　　　　　　　(9/92) (DG) ① **435 591-2GGA**
4-6. A. Pizarro *Concert*
　　　　　　　　(2/93) (COLL) ① **Coll1357-2**
4-7. J. Browning *Piano Sonata, S178.*
　　　　　　　　(4/86) (DELO) ① **DE3022**
4-7. E. Wild *Concert*
　　　　　　　　(6/88) (ETCE) ① [2] **KTC2012**
5. V. Horowitz (pp1985) *Concert*
　　　　　　　　(12/86) (DG) ① **419 499-2GH**
5. D. Lipatti (r1947) *Concert*
　　　　　　　　(11/89) (EMI) ① **CDH7 63038-2**
5. S. Barere (pp1947) *Concert*
　　　　　　　　(11/89) (APR) ① [2] **APR7007**
5. J. Bolet *Concert*　(2/90) (DECC) ① **425 689-2DX**
5. S. Barere (r1934) *Concert*
　　　　　　　　(5/91) (APR) ① [2] **APR7001**
5. M. Perahia *Concert*　(10/91) (SONY) ① **SK47180**
5. L. Berman *Concert*　(6/92) (AUDI) ① **CD72041**
5. V. Horowitz (r1951) *Concert*
　　　　　　　　(7/92) (RCA) ① **GD60523**
5, 6. L. Kuzmin (1992) *Concert*
　　　　　　　　(5/94) (RUSS) ① **RDCD10021**
6, 7. M. Langer (r1986) *Dante Symphony.*
　　　　　　　　(3/94) (PRAG) ① **PR250 036**
7. H. Grimaud *Concert*　(3/88) (DENO) ① **CO-1786**
7. P. Katin *Concert*　　(11/88) (OLYM) ① **OCD199**
7. L. Zilberstein *Concert*
　　　　　　　　(9/92) (DG) ① **435 385-2GH**
7. S. Hough *Concert*
　　　　　　　　(10/92) (VIRG) ① **VC7 59222-2**
7. D. Barenboim (r1993) *Dante Symphony.*
　　　　　　　　(7/94) (TELD) ① **9031-77340-2**
7. E. Nebolsin (r1993) *Concert*
　　　　　　　　(7/94) (DECC) ① **440 935-2DH**
7. M. Anderson (r1993) *Concert*
　　　　　　　　(7/95) (NIMB) ① **NI5422**
**Années de pèlerinage—année 3—piano,
S163 (1867-77)**
1. Angelus!; 2. Aux cyprès de la Villa d'Este (3-4); 3.
Aux cyprès de la Villa d'Este (4-4); 4. Les jeux d'eau
à la Villa d'Este; 5. Sunt lachrymae rerum; 6. Marche
funèbre; 7. Sursum corda.
L. Berman *Concert*
　　　　　　　　(11/93) (DG) ① [3] **437 206-2GX3**
G. Cziffra (r1970s) *Concert*
　　　　　　　　(3/95) (EMI) ① [4] **CMS7 64882-2**
2-4. S. Hough *Concert*
　　　　　　　　(10/92) (VIRG) ① **VC7 59222-2**

SECTION IV: VOCAL AND CHORAL

H. Schlusnus, Berlin St Op Orch, A. Melichar (r1932)
Concert   (1/94) (PREI) ① [2] **89205**
T. Hampson, G. Parsons (r1993) *Concert*
                (5/94) (EMI) ① **CDC5 55047-2**
K. Erb, W. Lutz, B. Seidler-Winkler (r1937) *Concert*
                (6/94) (PREI) ① [2] **89208**
M. Price, J. Lockhart (r1973) *Concert*
                (11/95) (CFP) ① **CD-CFP4669**
Es rauschen die Winde—Lied, S294 (?c1845)
(Wds. Rellstab)
T. Hampson, G. Parsons (r1993) *Concert*
                (5/94) (EMI) ① **CDC5 55047-2**
Es war ein König in Thule—Lied, S278 (1842)
(Wds. Goethe)
B. Fassbaender, J-Y. Thibaudet *Concert*
                (9/92) (DECC) ① **430 512-2DH**
**Ein Fichtenbaum steht einsam—Lied, S309
(c1855)** (Wds. Heine)
K. McMillan, M. McMahon (r1992) *Concert*
                (6/93) (CBC) ① **MVCD1052**
Freudvoll und leidvoll—Lied, S280 (1844)
(Wds. Goethe)
B. Fassbaender, J-Y. Thibaudet *Concert*
                (9/92) (DECC) ① **430 512-2DH**
M. Price, G. Johnson (r1993) *Concert*
                (2/95) (FORL) ① **UCD16728**
Go not, happy day—song, S335 (1879) (Wds.
A. E. Tennyson)
T. Hampson, G. Parsons (r1993) *Concert*
                (5/94) (EMI) ① **CDC5 55047-2**
Hohe Liebe—Lied, S307 (c1849) (Wds.
Uhland)
B. Fassbaender, J-Y. Thibaudet *Concert*
                (9/92) (DECC) ① **430 512-2DH**
**Hungarian Coronation Mass—soloists,
chorus and orchestra, S11 (1867)**
V. Kincses, K. Takács, D. Gulyás, L. Polgár,
Hungarian Rad & TV Chor, Budapest SO, G. Lehel
                (3/86) (HUNG) ① **HCD12148**
Ich möchte hingehn—Lied, S296 (1845)
(Wds. Herwegh)
B. Fassbaender, J-Y. Thibaudet *Concert*
                (9/92) (DECC) ① **430 512-2DH**
**Ihr Auge (Nimm einen Strahl der
Sonne)—Lied, S310 (?c1855)** (Wds. Rellstab)
B. Fassbaender, J-Y. Thibaudet *Concert*
                (9/92) (DECC) ① **430 512-2DH**
T. Hampson, G. Parsons (r1993) *Concert*
                (5/94) (EMI) ① **CDC5 55047-2**
Kling leise, mein Lied—Lied, S301 (1848)
(Wds. Nordmann)
M. Price, J. Lockhart (r1973) *Concert*
                (11/95) (CFP) ① **CD-CFP4669**
Lasst mich ruhen—Lied, S317 (?c1858)
(Wds. H. von Fallersleben)
B. Fassbaender, J-Y. Thibaudet *Concert*
                (9/92) (DECC) ① **430 512-2DH**
Die Loreley—Lied, S273 (1841) (Wds.
Heine)
M. Price, J. Lockhart (r1973) *Concert*
                (11/95) (CFP) ① **CD-CFP4669**
Mignons Lied, S275 (1842 rev 1860)
(Wds. Goethe)
B. Fassbaender, J-Y. Thibaudet *Concert*
                (9/92) (DECC) ① **430 512-2DH**
M. Price, G. Johnson (r1993) *Concert*
                (2/95) (FORL) ① **UCD16728**
**Missa choralis—chorus and organ, S10
(1865)**
L. Atkinson, M. Tinkler, C. Royall, W. Kendall, R.
Suart, St John's College Ch, S. Cleobury, G. Guest
Dvořák: Mass in d. (9/91) (DECC) ① **430 364-2DM**
BBC Northern Sngrs, F. Jackson, G. Thorne *Via
Crucis, S53.* (3/94) (SAGA) ① **EC3399-2**
**Missa solemnis zur Einweihung der Basilika
in Gran—soloists, chorus and orchestra, S9
(1855 rev 1857-58)**
I. Kassai, K. Körmendi (r1992: trans pf 4 hands:
Mosonyi) *Concert*   (12/94) (MARC) ① **8 223558**
**O lieb, so lang du lieben kannst—Lied, S298
(c1845)** (Wds. Freiligrath)
T. Schipa, orch (Ital: r1925) *Concert*
                (2/89) (PEAR) ① **GEMMCD9322**
B. Fassbaender, J-Y. Thibaudet *Concert*
                (9/92) (DECC) ① **430 512-2DH**
M. Price, J. Lockhart (r1973) *Concert*
                (11/95) (CFP) ① **CD-CFP4669**
O Meer im Abendstrahl—duet, S344 (c1880)
(Wds. Meissner)
H. Komatsu, K. Moll, C. Garben *Concert*
                (9/91) (HARM) ① **HMC90 5210**
Oh! quand je dors—song, S282 (1842) (Wds.
Hugo)
F. Lott, G. Johnson (r1984) *Concert*
                (5/87) (HARM) ① **HMA190 1138**

H. Prey, L. Hokanson (Ger) *Concert*
                (6/87) (DENO) ① **CO-1254**
S. Varcoe, G. Johnson *Concert*
                (6/88) (HYPE) ① **CDA66248**
K. Battle, M. Garrett (pp1991) *Concert*
                (7/92) (DG) ① **435 440-2GH**
E. Destinn, orch, W.B. Rogers (r1916) *Concert*
                (11/93) (ROMO) ① [2] **81002-2**
T. Hampson, G. Parsons (r1993) *Concert*
                (5/94) (EMI) ① **CDC5 55047-2**
E. Destinn, orch, W.B Rogers (r1916) *Concert*
                (12/94) (SUPR) ① [12] **11 2136-2(5)**
**S'il est un charmant gazon—Lied, S284
(c1844)** (Wds. Hugo)
A. Gjevang, E.S. Nökleberg *Concert*
                (11/91) (VICT) ① **VCD19007**
K. Battle, M. Garrett (pp1991) *Concert*
                (7/92) (DG) ① **435 440-2GH**
**3 Sonetti di Petrarca—songs, S270 (1838-39
rev 1861)** (Wds. Petrarch)
1. Pace non trovo; 2. Benedetto sia'l giorno; 3. I vidi
in terra angelici costumi.
R. Scotto, I. Davis (pp1983) *Concert*
                (10/86) (ETCE) ① **KTC2002**
M. Price, J. Lockhart (r1970) *Concert*
                (5/95) (RCA) ① [2] **09026 61635-2**
Die Stille Wasserrose—Lied, S321 (?1860)
(Wds. Geibel)
M. Price, J. Lockhart (r1973) *Concert*
                (11/95) (CFP) ① **CD-CFP4669**
La Tombe et la rose—song, S285 (1844)
(Wds. V. Hugo)
A. Gjevang, E.S. Nökleberg *Concert*
                (11/91) (VICT) ① **VCD19007**
T. Hampson, G. Parsons (r1993) *Concert*
                (5/94) (EMI) ① **CDC5 55047-2**
**Über allen Gipfeln ist Ruh—Lied, S306
(c1848)** (Wds. Goethe)
B. Fassbaender, J-Y. Thibaudet *Concert*
                (9/92) (DECC) ① **430 512-2DH**
T. Hampson, G. Parsons (r1993) *Concert*
                (5/94) (EMI) ① **CDC5 55047-2**
M. Price, G. Johnson (r1993) *Concert*
                (2/95) (FORL) ① **UCD16728**
**Und wir dachten der Toten—Lied, S338
(c1880)** (Wds. Freiligrath)
B. Fassbaender, J-Y. Thibaudet *Concert*
                (9/92) (DECC) ① **430 512-2DH**
Die Vätergruft—Lied, S281 (1844) (Wds.
Uhland)
T. Hampson, G. Parsons (r1993) *Concert*
                (5/94) (EMI) ① **CDC5 55047-2**
**Vergiftet sind meine Lieder—Lied, S289
(1842)** (Wds. Heine)
K. McMillan, M. McMahon (r1992) *Concert*
                (6/93) (CBC) ① **MVCD1052**
T. Hampson, G. Parsons (r1993) *Concert*
                (5/94) (EMI) ① **CDC5 55047-2**
**Via crucis—soloists, chorus, organ/piano,
S53 (1878-9)**
J-C. Guérinot Ch, L. Mallié *Mallié: Improvisation.*
                (10/89) (REM) ① **REM311033**
BBC Northern Sngrs, F. Jackson, G. Thorne *Missa
choralis, S10.*   (3/94) (SAGA) ① **EC3399-2**
**Was Liebe sei—Lied, S288 (1843, rev 1855 &
1878)** (Wds. von Hagen)
B. Fassbaender, J-Y. Thibaudet *Concert*
                (9/92) (DECC) ① **430 512-2DH**
**Wieder möcht ich dir begegnen—Lied, S332
(1860)** (Wds. Cornelius)
B. Fassbaender, J-Y. Thibaudet *Concert*
                (9/92) (DECC) ① **430 512-2DH**

LITAIZE, Gaston (Gilbert)
(1909–1991) France

SECTION II: CHAMBER

**Cortège—3 trumpets, 3 trombones and
organ (1951)**
O. Latry, Paris St Maur CNR Brass Ens *Concert*
                (10/90) (BNL) ① **BNL112768**
Pentecôte—triptyque (2 organs)
O. Latry, D. Comtet, Paris St Maur Brass Ens
Concert   (10/90) (BNL) ① **BNL112768**

SECTION III: INSTRUMENTAL

Epiphanie—organ
O. Latry *Concert*   (10/90) (BNL) ① **BNL112768**
Jeux de rhythmes—organ
O. Latry *Concert*   (10/90) (BNL) ① **BNL112768**
Lied—organ
O. Latry *Concert*   (10/90) (BNL) ① **BNL112768**
Prélude et Danse fuguée—organ (1964)
O. Latry *Concert*   (10/90) (BNL) ① **BNL112768**
M. Harris *Concert*   (3/92) (YORK) ① **CD112**

Prélude liturgique—organ
O. Latry *Concert*   (10/90) (BNL) ① **BNL112768**
Scherzo—organ
O. Latry *Concert*   (10/90) (BNL) ① **BNL112768**
**Variations sur un Noël angevin—organ
(1939)**
M. Harris *Concert*   (3/92) (YORK) ① **CD112**

LITERES (CARRIÓN), Antonio
(1673–1747) Spain

SECTION IV: VOCAL AND CHORAL

**Ah del rustico pastor—solo cantata for
Epiphany (1710)**
Al Ayre Español, E. L. Banzo (r1994) *Concert*
                (8/95) (DHM) ① **05472 77325-2**

LITOLFF, Henry (Charles)
(1818–1891) England/France

SECTION I: ORCHESTRAL

**Concerto symphonique No. 3 in E
flat—piano and orchestra, Op. 45 (c1846)**
M. Ponti, Berlin SO, V. Schmidt-Gertenbach *Concert*
                (5/93) (VOX) ① **115712-2**
**Concerto symphonique No. 4 in D
minor—piano and orchestra, Op. 102
(c1852)**
Scherzo
M. Dichter, Philh, N. Marriner *Concert*
                (8/84) (PHIL) ① **411 123-2PH**
C. Ortiz, RPO, M. Atzmon *Concert*
                (9/86) (DECC) ① **414 348-2DH**
C. Ortiz, RPO, M. Atzmon *Concert*
                (12/91) (DECC) ① **430 726-2DM**
I. Scharrer, LSO, Henry Wood (r1933) *Concert*
                (7/94) (PEAR) ① **GEMMCD9978**
I. Scharrer, LSO, Henry Wood (r1933) *Concert*
                (9/94) (DUTT) ① [2] **2CDAX2002**
C. Curzon, LPO, A. Boult (r1958) *Concert*
                (4/95) (DECC) ① **425 082-2DCS**

LLOBET, Miguel (1878–1938)
Spain

SECTION III: INSTRUMENTAL

Catalan Folksongs—guitar
1. La nit de Nadal; 2. Lo rossinyol; 3. El mestre; 4. La
filadora; 5. El testament d'Amelia; 6. Cançó del
lladre; 7. Plany; 8. El Noi de la Mare; 9. L'hereu
Riera; 10. La filla del marxant.
T. Kerstens *Concert*   (7/92) (CONI) ① **CDCF509**
J. Williams *Concert*   (7/92) (SONY) ① **SK48480**
1-9. J. Bream (r1983-90) *Concert*
                (8/93) (RCA) ① [28] **09026 61583-2(6)**
1-9. J. Bream (r1983-90) *Concert*
                (6/94) (RCA) ① **09026 61609-2**
5. J. Bream (r1962) *Concert*
                (8/93) (RCA) ① [28] **09026 61583-2(3)**
5. J. Bream (r1962) *Concert*
                (8/93) (RCA) ① **09026 61591-2**

LLOYD, Charles Harford
(1849–1919) England

SECTION IV: VOCAL AND CHORAL

Annette—song with clarinet obbligato (1886)
(Wds. W. L. Courtney)
D. Fischer-Dieskau, D. Klöcker, H. Höll *Concert*
                (4/88) (ORFE) ① **C153861A**
Evening Service in A
Gloucester Cath Ch, J. Sanders, M. Lee (r1994)
Concert   (4/95) (PRIO) ① **PRCD494**

LLOYD, George (b 1913)
England

SECTION I: ORCHESTRAL

**Concerto for Piano and Orchestra No. 3
(1968)**
K. Stott, BBC PO, G. Lloyd (r1988)
                (3/90) (ALBA) ① **TROY019-2**
**Concerto for Piano and Orchestra No. 4
(1970)**
K. Stott, LSO, G. Lloyd (r1984) *Concert*
                (8/89) (ALBA) ① **AR004**
**The Forest of Arden—symphonic sketch:
concert band (1987)**
City of London Wind Ens, G. Brand (r1991) *Concert*
                (7/89) (LDR) ① **LDRCD1001**

Symphony No. 1 in A (1932)
Albany SO, G. Lloyd (r1990) *Symphony 12.*
                              (2/91) (ALBA) ① TROY032-2
Symphony No. 2 (1933 rev 1982)
BBC PO, G. Lloyd (r1986) *Symphony 9.*
                              (6/87) (ALBA) ① TROY055-2
Symphony No. 4 in B, '(The) Arctic' (1946)
Albany SO, G. Lloyd (r1987)
                              (1/89) (ALBA) ① AR002
Symphony No. 5 in B flat (1948)
BBC PO, G. Lloyd (r1989)
                              (1/90) (ALBA) ① TROY022-2
Symphony No. 6 (1956)
BBC PO, G. Lloyd (r1988) *Concert*
                              (8/89) (ALBA) ① TROY015-2
Symphony No. 7 (1959)
BBC PO, G. Lloyd (r1986)
                              (6/87) (ALBA) ① TROY057-2
Symphony No. 9 (1969)
BBC PO, G. Lloyd (r1984) *Symphony 2.*
                              (6/87) (ALBA) ① TROY055-2
Symphony No. 10, 'Winter Journeys'—brass ensemble (1982)
BBC Phil Brass, G. Lloyd (r1988) *Concert*
                              (8/89) (ALBA) ① TROY015-2
Symphony No. 11 (1985)
Albany SO, G. Lloyd (r1986)
                              (6/87) (ALBA) ① TROY060-2
Symphony No. 12 (1989)
Albany SO, G. Lloyd (r1990) *Symphony 1.*
                              (2/91) (ALBA) ① TROY032-2

SECTION II: CHAMBER

Lament, Air and Dance—violin and piano (1975)
T. Little, M. Roscoe (r1989) *Violin Sonata.*
                              (9/90) (ALBA) ① TROY029-2
Sonata for Violin and Piano (1976)
T. Little, M. Roscoe (r1989) *Lament, Air and Dance.*
                              (9/90) (ALBA) ① TROY029-2

SECTION III: INSTRUMENTAL

An African Shrine—piano (1966)
M. Roscoe (r1987) *Concert*
                              (5/89) (ALBA) ① AR003
The Aggressive Fishes—piano (1972)
M. Roscoe (r1987) *Concert*
                              (5/89) (ALBA) ① AR003
Intercom Baby—violin (1977) (transc cpsr for piano)
M. Roscoe (r1987) *Concert*
                              (5/89) (ALBA) ① AR003
The Lily-leaf and the Grasshopper—piano (1972)
K. Stott (r1984) *Concert*   (8/89) (ALBA) ① AR004
The Road to Samarkand—piano (1972)
M. Roscoe (r1987) *Concert*
                              (5/89) (ALBA) ① AR003
St. Antony and the Bogside Beggar—piano (1972)
M. Roscoe (r1987) *Concert*
                              (5/89) (ALBA) ① AR003
The Transformation of the Naked Ape—piano (1972 rev 1987)
1. Her Hair; 2. Her Tongue; 3. Her Eyes; 4. Her Brain;
5. Her Mind; 6. Her Soul.
K. Stott (r1984) *Concert*   (8/89) (ALBA) ① AR004

SECTION IV: VOCAL AND CHORAL

A Symphonic Mass—chorus and orchestra (1993)
Brighton Fest Chor, Bournemouth SO, G. Lloyd
(r1993)   (12/93) (ALBA) ① TROY100-2

SECTION V: STAGE WORKS

Iernin—opera: 3 acts (1934—Penzance) (Lib. W. Lloyd)
M. Hill Smith, G. Pogson, H. Herford, M. Rivers, J.
Robarts, J. White, S. Jackson, C. Powell, BBC Sngrs,
BBC Concert Orch, G. Lloyd (r1985)
                              (9/94) (ALBA) ① [3] TROY121/3
John Socman—opera: 3 acts (1951—Bristol) (Lib. W. Lloyd)
EXCERPTS: 1. Overture. ACT 1; 2. Scene 1; 3.
Scene 2; 4. Scene 3. ACT 2: 5. Scene 1; 6. Scene 2;
7. ACT 3.
1. BBC PO, G. Lloyd (r1988) *Concert*
                              (8/89) (ALBA) ① TROY015-2
2, 3, 5, 7. D. Wilson-Johnson, T. Booth, J. Watson, D.
Montague, J. Winfield, M. George, M. Rivers, P.
Sheffield, S. Adler, London Voices, Trinity Boy's Ch,
Philh, G. Lloyd (r1994)
                              (1/95) (ALBA) ① TROY131-2

LLOYD, Richard *(b 1933)* England

SECTION IV: VOCAL AND CHORAL

Jubilate in D minor
Hereford Cath Ch, R. Massey, G. Bowen (r1994)
Concert   (2/95) (PRIO) ① PRCD507
The Windows (Wds. G. Herbert)
Durham Cath Ch, J. Lancelot, I. Shaw *Concert*
                        (7/91) (PRIO) ① PRCD296

LLOYD WEBBER, Sir Andrew *(b 1948) England*

SECTION I: ORCHESTRAL

Variations—cello and six-piece rock band (1977 orch 1985)
J. Lloyd Webber, LPO, L. Maazel (orch Cullen) *W.
Lloyd Webber: Aurora.*
                        (3/87) (PHIL) ① 420 342-2PH

SECTION IV: VOCAL AND CHORAL

Requiem—soprano, treble, tenor, chorus & orchestra (1984)
1. Requiem & Kyrie; 2. Dies irae...Rex tremendae; 3.
Recordare; 4. Ingemisco...Lacrymosa; 5. Offertorium;
6. Hosanna; 7. Pie Jesu; 8. Lux aeterna & Libera me.
Pie Jesu B. Hendricks, E. Ericson Chbr Ch, Swedish
RSO, E. Ericson *Concert*
                        (4/91) (EMI) ① CDC7 54098-2

SECTION V: STAGE WORKS

Cats—musical show (1981—London) (Lyrics
T S Eliot, with additions by T Nunn & R
Stilgoe)
EXCERPTS: 1. Overture—Prologue; 2. The Naming
of Cats; 3. The Invitation to the Jellicle Ball; 4. Old
Gumbie Cat; 5. Rum Tum Tugger; 6. Grizabella; 7.
Bustopher Jones; 8. Mungojerrie and Rumpleteazer;
9. Old Deuteronomy; 10. The Jellicle Ball; 11.
Memory; 12. Moments of Happiness; 13. Gus,
Theatre Cat; 14. Growltiger's Last Stand; 15. The
Ballad of Billy McCaw; 16. Skimbleshanks; 17.
Macavity; 18. Mr Mistoffolees; 19. Memory (reprise);
20. The Journey to the Heaviside Layer; 21. The Ad-
dressing of Cats.
11. J. Carreras, P. Domingo, L. Pavarotti, MMF Orch,
Rome Op Orch, Z. Mehta (pp1990) *Concert*
                        (10/90) (DECC) ① 430 433-2DH
**The Phantom of the Opera—musical play
(1986—London)** (Book cpsr & R. Stilgoe; Lyrics
C. Hart & others)
EXCERPTS: 1. Overture; 2. Think of Me; 3. Angel of
Music; 4. Little Lotte; 5. The Mirror; 6. The Phantom
of the Opera; 7. The Music of the Night; 8. I
Remember; 9. Stranger Than You Dreamt It; 10.
Magical Lasso; 11. Prima Donna; 12. Poor Fool, He
Makes Me Laugh; 13. All I Ask of You; 14. Entr'acte;
15. Masquerade/Why So Silent?; 16. Twisted Every
Way; 17. Wishing You Were Somehow Here Again;
18. Wandering Child; 19. The Point of No Return; 20.
Down Once More; 21. Finale.
13. V. Masterson, T. Allen, Philh, J.O. Edwards
(r1990) *Concert*   (5/94) (TER) ① CDVIR8317

LLOYD WEBBER, William S. *(1914–1982) England*

SECTION I: ORCHESTRAL

**Andante affettuoso (arr for vc and orch from
an unidentified cantata)**
J. Lloyd Webber, ECO, N. Cleobury (arr C Palmer)
Concert   (3/85) (PHIL) ① 412 231-2PH
Aurora—orchestra
LPO, L. Maazel *A. Lloyd Webber: Variations.*
                        (3/87) (PHIL) ① 420 342-2PH

SECTION II: CHAMBER

**Air varié—cello and piano (adapted from C.
Franck's 'Tantum Ergo')**
J. Lloyd Webber, J. Lill *Concert*
                        (11/87) (ASV) ① CDDCA584
**In the half-light—soliloquoy for cello and
piano (1951)**
J. Lloyd Webber, J. Lill *Concert*
                        (11/87) (ASV) ① CDDCA584

SECTION III: INSTRUMENTAL

Arabesque—piano
J. Lill *Concert*   (11/87) (ASV) ① CDDCA584
Badinage de Noël—piano
J. Lill *Concert*   (11/87) (ASV) ① CDDCA584

Presto for Perseus—piano
J. Lill *Concert*   (11/87) (ASV) ① CDDCA584
Romantic Evening—piano
J. Lill *Concert*   (11/87) (ASV) ① CDDCA584
Scherzo in G minor—piano
J. Lill *Concert*   (11/87) (ASV) ① CDDCA584
Song without words—piano
J. Lill *Concert*   (11/87) (ASV) ① CDDCA584

SECTION IV: VOCAL AND CHORAL

The Divine Compassion—cantata (1950s)
Thou art the King J. Graham-Hall, P. Ledger
Concert   (11/87) (ASV) ① CDDCA584
**Missa Sanctae Mariae
Magdalenae—unaccompanied mixed voices
(1979)**
Richard Hickox Sngrs, I. Watson, R. Hickox *Concert*
                        (11/87) (ASV) ① CDDCA584
**Over the bridge—1v and piano (Wds. J.
Thompson)**
J. Graham-Hall, P. Ledger *Concert*
                        (11/87) (ASV) ① CDDCA584
**The Pretty washer-maiden—1v and piano
(Wds. W.E. Henley)**
J. Graham-Hall, P. Ledger *Concert*
                        (11/87) (ASV) ① CDDCA584
**A Rent for love—1v and piano (Wds. I.
Morgan)**
J. Graham-Hall, P. Ledger *Concert*
                        (11/87) (ASV) ① CDDCA584
The Saviour—cantata (1950s)
The King of Love J. Graham-Hall, P. Ledger
Concert   (11/87) (ASV) ① CDDCA584
**So lovely the rose—1v and piano (Wds. J.
Murrells)**
J. Graham-Hall, P. Ledger *Concert*
                        (11/87) (ASV) ① CDDCA584
Utopia—1v and piano (Wds. F.T. Palgrave)
J. Graham-Hall, P. Ledger *Concert*
                        (11/87) (ASV) ① CDDCA584

LOBO, Alonso *(c1555–1617)* Spain

SECTION IV: VOCAL AND CHORAL

Ave Maria—motet (8vv) (pub 1602)
Westminster Cath Ch, D. Hill *Concert*
                        (3/87) (HYPE) ① CDA66168
**O quam suavis est, Domine—motet (6vv)
(pub 1602)**
Westminster Cath Ch, D. Hill *Concert*
                        (3/87) (HYPE) ① CDA66168
Versa est in luctum—motet (6vv) (pub 1602)
Westminster Cath Ch, D. Hill *Concert*
                        (3/87) (HYPE) ① CDA66168
Tallis Scholars, P. Phillips *Victoria: Officium
defunctorum (1605).*   (9/87) (GIME) ① CDGIM012

LÔBO, Duarte *(?1565–1646)* Portugal

SECTION IV: VOCAL AND CHORAL

**Audivi vocem de caelo—motet (6vv) (pub
1621)**
The Sixteen, H. Christophers (r1993) *Concert*
                        (8/94) (COLL) ① Coll1407-2
Missa pro defunctis—motet (6vv) (pub 1621)
Taverner Ch, O. Rees (r1992) *Concert*
                        (1/94) (HERA) ① HAVPCD155
The Sixteen, H. Christophers (r1993) *Concert*
                        (8/94) (COLL) ① Coll1407-2
Missa Vox clamantis—6vv (pub 1639)
Tallis Scholars, P. Phillips *Requiem (6vv).*
                        (3/93) (GIME) ① CDGIM028
Pater peccavi—motet (1621)
The Sixteen, H. Christophers (r1993) *Concert*
                        (8/94) (COLL) ① Coll1407-2
Requiem—6vv (pub 1639)
Tallis Scholars, P. Phillips *Missa Vox clamantis.*
                        (3/93) (GIME) ① CDGIM028

LOCATELLI, Pietro Antonio *(1695–1764) Italy*

SECTION I: ORCHESTRAL

12 Concerti grossi, Op. 1 (1721)
1. F; 2. C minor; 3. B flat; 4. E minor; 5. D; 6. C
minor; 7. F; 8. F minor (Christmas); 9. D; 10. C; 11. C
minor; 12. G minor.
3, 12. Cologne Concerto (r1994) *Concert*
                        (2/95) (TELD) ① 4509-94551-2
8. Solisti Italiani (r1993) *Concert*
                        (12/94) (DENO) ① CO-78912

9. ASMF, N. Marriner (r1961) *Concert*
(9/93) (DECC) ① **436 224-2DM**
11. Scottish Ens, J. Rees (r1991) *Concert*
(12/91) (VIRG) ① **VJ7 59652-2**
12. Capella Istropolitana, J. Krechek (r1993) *Concert*
(3/95) (NAXO) ① **8 550877**
6 Concerti grossi—strings, Op. 7 (pub 1741)
1. D; 2. B flat; 3. G; 4. F; 5. G; 6. E flat, 'Il pianto d'Arianna'.
4, 6. Cologne Concerto (r1994) *Concert*
(2/95) (TELD) ① **4509-94551-2**
12 Concertos—L'arte del violino, Op. 3 (pub. 1733)
1. D; 2. C minor; 3. F; 4. E; 5. C; 6. G minor; 7. B flat; 8. E minor. 9. G; 10. F; 11. A; 12. D.
Elizabeth Wallfisch, Raglan Baroque Players, N. Kraemer (r1992-3)
(1/95) (HYPE) ① [3] **CDA66721/3**
6 Introduttioni teatrali and 6 Concerti—strings, Op. 4 (pub 1735)
(Introduttioni 1-6; Concerti 7-12)
1. D; 2. F; 3. B flat. 4. G; 5. D; 6. C; 8. F minor; 10. E flat; 12. F.
10. Cologne Concerto (r1994) *Concert*
(2/95) (TELD) ① **4509-94551-2**
12. Cologne Musica Antiqua, R. Goebel *Concert*
(9/92) (ARCH) ① **435 393-2AH**

SECTION II: CHAMBER

12 Sonatas for Flute and Continuo, Op. 2 (pub. 1732)
No 1. Barthold Kuijken, W. Kuijken, R. Kohnen *Concert*
(5/92) (ACCE) ① **ACC9177D**
12 Sonate da camera—violin and continuo, Op. 6 (pub 1737)
2. F; 6. D; 11. E flat; 12. D minor.
1, 6, 11, 12. Locatelli Trio
(11/90) (HYPE) ① **CDA66363**

SECTION III: INSTRUMENTAL

24 Caprices—violin, Op. 3
23. D, 'Il laberinto armmonico'.
23. H. Szeryng, C. Reiner (r1963: arr vn/pf) *Concert*
(12/95) (MERC) ① **434 351-2MM**

LOCKE, Matthew *(1621/2–1677)* England

SECTION I: ORCHESTRAL

Curtain Tune in C (pub 1680s) (from unknown play)
Parley of Instr, P. Holman (r1993) *Concert*
(6/94) (HYPE) ① **CDA66667**
Curtain Tune in D (pub 1680s) (from unknown play)
Parley of Instr, P. Holman (r1993) *Concert*
(6/94) (HYPE) ① **CDA66667**
Suite in G minor—violin, two violas, bass violin and continuo
Parley of Instr, P. Holman (r1993) *Concert*
(6/94) (HYPE) ① **CDA66667**
Suite of Brawles in B flat—branles and other dances (pub 1680s)
Parley of Instr, P. Holman (r1993) *Concert*
(6/94) (HYPE) ① **CDA66667**

SECTION II: CHAMBER

Broken Consort in D (unidentified)
Palladian Ens (r1992) *Concert*
(7/93) (LINN) ① **CKD010**
The Broken Consort, Part I: 6 Suites—strings (1661)
1. G; 2. G; 3. C; 4. C; 5. D minor; 6. D.
3, 4. Scaramouche, K. Junghänel (r1992) *Concert*
(5/94) (CHNN) ① **CCS4792**
Duo in C—2 bass viols (1652)
W. Kuijken, S. Kuijken, R. Kohnen *Concert*
(1/87) (ACCE) ① **ACC68014D**
Duo in C minor—2 bass viols (1652)
W. Kuijken, S. Kuijken, R. Kohnen *Concert*
(1/87) (ACCE) ① **ACC68014D**

SECTION III: INSTRUMENTAL

Melothesia, or Certain General Rules for Playing upon a Continued Bass—six lessons: harpsichord/organ (pub 1673)
4. Suite No 4 D minor.
4. T. Pinnock (r1978) *Concert*
(4/89) (CRD) ① **CRD3347**
7 Voluntaries—organ (pub 1673) (Nos. 62-8 from Melothesia)
EXCERPTS: 1. A minor; 2. F; 3. A minor; 4. D minor; 5. G; 6. A minor; 7. D minor, 'For a Double Organ'.
J. Butt (r1992) *Concert*
(6/94) (HARM) ① **HMU90 7103**

J. Butt (r1992) *Concert*
(7/95) (HARM) ① [6] **HMX290 1528/33(2)**
Three voluntaries G. Leonhardt (r1994) *Concert*
(11/95) (SONY) ① **SK53981**
3, 6, 7. R. Woolley (r1993) *Concert*
(9/94) (CHAN) ① **CHAN0553**
7. T. Dart (r1957) *Concert* (5/95) (JMS) ① **JMSCD1**

SECTION IV: VOCAL AND CHORAL

Audi, Domine, clamantes ad te—verse motet (1-5/5vv and instruments)
New College Ch, Parley of Instr, E. Higginbottom *Concert*
(9/91) (HYPE) ① **CDA66373**
Be thou exalted—verse anthem (12vv and instruments) (1666)
New College Ch, Parley of Instr, E. Higginbottom *Concert*
(9/91) (HYPE) ① **CDA66373**
How doth the city sit solitary—verse anthem (1-4/5vv and continuo)
New College Ch, Parley of Instr, E. Higginbottom *Concert*
(9/91) (HYPE) ① **CDA66373**
Jesu auctor clementie—verse motet (1/3vv and instruments)
New College Ch, Parley of Instr, E. Higginbottom *Concert*
(9/91) (HYPE) ① **CDA66373**
Lord, let me know mine end—verse anthem (1-4/5vv and continuo)
New College Ch, Parley of Instr, E. Higginbottom *Concert*
(9/91) (HYPE) ① **CDA66373**
O be joyful—verse anthem (1-3/4vv and instruments)
New College Ch, Parley of Instr, E. Higginbottom *Concert*
(9/91) (HYPE) ① **CDA66373**
Oxford Act Song, 'Descende caelo cincta sororibus'—verse motet: 4/4vv & instruments (?1672)
New College Ch, Parley of Instr, E. Higginbottom *Concert*
(9/91) (HYPE) ① **CDA66373**
Super flumina Babylonis—verse motet (1-3/4vv and instruments)
New College Ch, Parley of Instr, E. Higginbottom *Concert*
(9/91) (HYPE) ① **CDA66373**

SECTION V: STAGE WORKS

The Tempest—incidental music to Shakespeare's play (1674—London) (adapted Davenant & Dryden)
EXCERPTS: (Song composers in brackets): 1a. Introduction; 1b. Galliard; 1c. Gavot. SECOND MUSICK: 2a. Saraband; 2b. Lilk; 3. Curtain Tune; 4. First Act Tune (Rustick Air); 5. Second Act Tune (Minoit); 6. Third Act Tune (Corant); 7. A Martial Jigge; 8. Conclusion (A Canon 4 in 2). SONGS: 9. Masque of the Three Devils (Pelham Humphrey); 10. Go thy way (John Banister); 11. Come unto these yellow sands (John Banister); 12. Full fathom five (John Banister); 13. Dry those eyes (John Banister); 14. Go thy way (John Banister); 15. The Masque of Neptune (Pelham Humfrey); 16. Where the bee sucks (Pelham Humfrey); 17. Adieu to the Pleasures (James Hart).
1a-c, 2a, 2b, 3-8. Parley of Instr, P. Holman (r1993) *Concert*
(6/94) (HYPE) ① **CDA66667**

LOCKHART, Charles *(1745–1815)* England

SECTION IV: VOCAL AND CHORAL

For all thy Saints, O Lord—hymn
Durham Cath Ch, J. Lancelot, I. Shaw *Concert*
(7/91) (PRIO) ① **PRCD296**

LODEWIJK, Lodewijk *(1868–1952)* Belgium

SECTION I: ORCHESTRAL

Spring day (Lenteday)—symphonic poem
Belgian Rad & TV Orch, A. Rahbari (r1992) *Concert*
(8/94) (DINT) ① **DICD920100**

LOEFFLER, Charles Martin *(1861–1935)* France/USA

SECTION I: ORCHESTRAL

La Mort de Tintagiles—tone-poem with viola d'amore obbligato, Op. 6 (1900)
J. Hansen, Indianapolis SO, J. Nelson *Irish Fantasies.*
(9/88) (NEW) ① **NW332-2**
A Pagan Poem—orchestra with cor anglais and piano, Op. 14 (1906) (after chbr work)
SO, L. Stokowski (r1957) *Glière: Symphony 3.*
(7/94) (EMI) ① **CDM5 65074-2**

SECTION II: CHAMBER

2 Rhapsodies—oboe, viola and piano (1901) (arr from songs)
Chbr Music NW (r1992) *Concert*
(12/93) (DELO) ① **DE3136**

SECTION IV: VOCAL AND CHORAL

5 Irish Fantasies—tone-poem with voice (1920) (Wds after W. B. Yeats)
N. Rosenshein, Indianapolis SO, J. Nelson *Mort de Tintagiles.*
(9/88) (NEW) ① **NW332-2**
4 Poèms—songs: 1v, viola & piano, Op. 5 (1904)
1. La cloche fêlée (wds. Baudelaire); 2. Dansons la gigue (wds. Verlaine); 3. Le son du cor (wds. Verlaine); 4. Sérénade (wds. Verlaine).
M. Shirai, T. Zimmermann, H. Höll (r1993-4) *Concert*
(9/95) (CAPR) ① **10 462**

LOEILLET DE GANT, Jean Baptiste *(1688–c1720)* Flanders

SECTION II: CHAMBER

12 Sonatas—recorder and continuo, Op. 3 (pub 1715)
1. C; 2. B flat. 3. G minor; 4. G; 5. C minor; 6. E minor; 7. E flat; 8. F; 9. B flat; 10. D minor; 11. A; 12. E minor.
12. M. André, H. Bilgram (arr tpt/org) *Concert*
(1/93) (EMI) ① **CDC7 54330-2**

LOEILLET OF LONDON, John *(1688–c1730)* Flanders/England

SECTION II: CHAMBER

Quintet in B minor—2 recorders, 2 flutes & continuo
F. Brüggen, J. van Wingerden, F. Vester, J. Tromp, B. Pollard, A. Bylsma, G. Leonhardt (r1963) *Concert*
(10/95) (TELD) ① **4509-97467-2**
12 Solos—flute/recorder and continuo, Op. 1
1. C; 2. D minor; 3. F; 4. A minor; 5. G minor; 6. D minor; 7. E minor; 8. G; 9. D; 10. B minor; 11. D; 12. G.
9. H. Hardenberger, S. Preston (arr tpt, org) *Concert*
(12/92) (PHIL) ① **434 074-2PH**
Sonata in C minor—recorder & continuo (Unidentified)
F. Brüggen, N. Harnoncourt, G. Leonhardt (r c1966) *Concert*
(10/95) (TELD) ① **4509-97474-2**
Sonata in G—recorder & continuo (Unidentified)
F. Brüggen, A. Bylsma, G. Leonhardt (r1969) *Concert*
(10/95) (TELD) ① **4509-97474-2**

LOESSER, Frank (Henry) *(1910–1969)* USA

SECTION V: STAGE WORKS

Guys and Dolls—musical show (1950—New York) (Lyrics cpsr, after Damon Runyon)
EXCERPTS: 1. Runyonland; 2. Fugue for Tinhorns; 3. Follow the Fold; 4. The Oldest Established; 5. I'll know; 6. A Bushel and a Peck; 7. Adelaide's Lament; 8. Guys and Dolls; 9. Havana; 10. If I were a Bell; 11. My Time of Day; 12. I've never been in love before; 13a. Entr'acte; 13b. Take Back Your Minks; 14. Adelaide's Lament (reprise); 15. More I cannot wish you; 16. The Crapshooters' Dance; 17. Luck be a Lady; 18. Sue me; 19. Sit down, you're rockin' the boat; 20. Marry the Man Today; 21. Guys and Dolls (reprise).
Cpte N. Lane, F. Prince, P. Gallagher, J. de Guzman, Broadway Cast, Orch, Edward Strauss (r1992)
(10/92) (RCA) ① **09026 61317-2**
11, 12. V. Masterson, T. Allen, Philh, J.O. Edwards
(1990) *Concert* (5/94) (TER) ① **CDVIR8317**
Hans Christian Andersen—musical film (1952) (Lyrics cpsr)
EXCERPTS: 1. I'm Hans Christian Anderson; 2. Anywhere I Wander; 3. The Ugly Duckling; 4. Inchworm; 5. Thumbelina; 6. No Two People; 7. The King's New Clothes; 8. Wonderful Copenhagen.
1, 2, 4, 5, 8. Boston Pops, A. Fiedler (r1960: arr R Hayman) *Concert* (12/95) (RCA) ① **09026 68131-2**
1-8. D. Kaye, OST, G. Jenkins (r1952) *S. Fine: Court Jester.* (11/94) (VARE) ① **VSD5498**
The Most Happy Fella—musical show (1956—New York) (Book S. Howard; Lyrics cpsr)
EXCERPTS: 1. Overture. ACT 1: 2. Ooh, my feet; 3. I know how it is; 4. Seven million crumbs; 5. The

letter; 6. Somebody somewhere; 7. The most happy fella; 8. Standing on the corner; 9. The letter song; 10. Joey, Joey, Joey; 11. Soon you gonna leave me; 12. Rosabella; 13. Abbondanza; 14. Plenty bambini; 15. Sposalizio; 16. Special delivery; 17. Benvenuta; 18. Aren't you glad?; 19. Don't cry; 20. Finale. ACT 2: 21. Prelude; 22. Fresno beauties; 23. Love and kindness; 24. Happy to make your acquaitance; 25. My heart is so full of you; 26. Big 'D'; 27. How beautiful the days; 28. Young people; 29. Warm all over; 30. Old people; 31. I like everybody; 32. I know how it is; 33. I love him; 34. Like a woman loves a man; 36. Hoedown; 37. Mama, Mama. ACT 3: 38. Prelude; 39. Abbondanza (reprise); 40. Goodbye, darlin'; 41. Song of the summer night; 42. Please let me tell you; 43. Tony's thoughts; 44. She gonne come home with me; 45. I made a fist; 46. Finale.
6. M. Hill Smith, National SO, J.O. Edwards (r1989-91) *Concert*   (10/91) (TER) ① **CDVIR8314**

LOEVENDIE, Theo (b 1930) The Netherlands

SECTION II: CHAMBER

Back Bay Bicinium—seven instruments (1986)
Nieuw Ens, E. Spanjaard *Concert*
          (12/91) (ETCE) ① **KTC1097**
Music for Flute and Piano (1979)
Nieuw Ens, E. Spanjaard *Concert*
          (12/91) (ETCE) ① **KTC1097**
Venus and Adonis—five instruments (1981)
1. Part 1; 2. Part 2.
Nieuw Ens, E. Spanjaard *Concert*
          (12/91) (ETCE) ① **KTC1097**

SECTION III: INSTRUMENTAL

Strides—piano (1976)
J. Snijders *Concert*   (12/91) (ETCE) ① **KTC1097**

SECTION IV: VOCAL AND CHORAL

2 Songs—mezzo-soprano and 8 instruments (1986) (extracted from opera 'Naima')
1. The Man of Life Upright (wds. T. Campion); 2. As Fast as Thou Shalt Wane (wds. Shakespeare).
J. van Nes, Nieuw Ens, E. Spanjaard *Concert*
          (12/91) (ETCE) ① **KTC1097**
6 Turkish Folk Poems—female voice and seven instruments (1977)
R. Hardy, Nieuw Ens, E. Spanjaard *Concert*
          (12/91) (ETCE) ① **KTC1097**

LOEWE, (Johann) Carl (Gottfried) (1796–1869) Germany

SECTION IV: VOCAL AND CHORAL

Archibald Douglas—ballad: contralto/bass and piano, Op. 128 (Wds. Fontane)
H. Hotter, H. Dokoupil (r1968-9) *Concert*
          (8/89) (PREI) ① **93390**
C. Hauptmann, K. Melber (r1989) *Concert*
          (5/90) (BAYE) ① **BR100038**
Der Asra—ballad, Op. 133 (1860) (Wds. Heine)
D. Fischer-Dieskau, H. Höll (r c1987) *Concert*
          (12/95) (TELD) ① **4509-97458-2**
3 Balladen, Op. 1 (1824)
1. Edward (Scots., trans. Herder); 2. Der Wirthin Töchterlein (wds. Uhland); 3. Erlkönig (wds. Goethe).
2. D. Fischer-Dieskau, H. Höll (r c1987) *Concert*
          (12/95) (TELD) ① **4509-97458-2**
3 Balladen, Op. 2 (1824)
1. Treueröschen (wds. Körner); 2. Herr Oluf (wds. Danish, trans. Herder); 3. Walpurgisnacht (wds. Alexis).
2. C. Hauptmann, K. Melber (r1989) *Concert*
          (5/90) (BAYE) ① **BR100038**
2. T. Hampson, G. Parsons *Concert*
          (10/90) (TELD) ① **2292-44923-2**
3 Balladen, Op. 20 (1832) (Wds. Goethe)
1. Hochzeitlied; 2. Der Zauberlehrling; 3. Die wandelnde Glocke.
1. K. Borg, M. Raucheisen (r1953) *Concert*
          (12/94) (FINL) ① [3] **4509-95606-2**
2 Balladen, Op. 94 (1843)
1. Die Überfahrt (wds. Uhland); 2. Die schwarzen Augen (wds. Vogl).
1. D. Fischer-Dieskau, H. Höll (r c1987) *Concert*
          (12/95) (TELD) ① **4509-97458-2**
2 Balladen, Op. 121 (1853)
1. Kaiser Ottos Weihnachtsfeier (A/Bar) (wds. Mühler); 2. Der Drachenfels (S/T) (wds. Lütze).
1. C. Hauptmann, K. Melber (r1989) *Concert*
          (5/90) (BAYE) ① **BR100038**

3 Balladen, Op. 129 (1857)
1. Der Teufel (wds. Siebel after The Koran); 2. Der Nöck (wds. Kopisch); 3. Die Schwanenjungfrau (wds. Vogl).
2. H. Hotter, H. Dokoupil (r1968-9) *Concert*
          (8/89) (PREI) ① **93390**
Canzonette—Lied (1835) (Wds. Goethe)
E. Rethberg, orch (r1924) *Concert*
          (2/95) (ROMO) ① [2] **81012-2**
Das Dunkle Auge—Lied (1839)
D. Fischer-Dieskau, H. Höll (r c1987) *Concert*
          (12/95) (TELD) ① **4509-97458-2**
Findlay—Lied: 1v and piano (c1837) (Wds. R Burns, trans Freiligrath)
T. Hampson, G. Parsons (pp1993) *Concert*
          (1/95) (EMI) ① **CDC5 55147-2**
2 Gedichte, Op. 61 (1837) (Wds. Alexis)
1. Fridericus Rex; 2. General Schwerin.
1. H. Hermann Nissen, B. Seidler-Winkler (r1939) *Concert*   (12/95) (PREI) ① **89090**
1. D. Fischer-Dieskau, H. Höll (r c1987) *Concert*
          (12/95) (TELD) ① **4509-97458-2**
Der Gefangene Admiral—ballad, Op. 115 (1848) (Wds. Strachwitz)
D. Fischer-Dieskau, H. Höll (r c1987) *Concert*
          (12/95) (TELD) ① **4509-97458-2**
54 Gesammelte Lieder, Gesänge, Romanzen und Balladen, Op. 9 (1818-39)
BOOK I: 1. Die Lotosblume (wds. Heine); 2. Der König auf dem Turme (wds. Uhland); 3. Über allen Gipfeln ist Ruh (wds. Goethe); 4. Auf dem vom Himmel wissen (wds. Goethe); 5. Geisterleben (wds. Uhland); 6. Die Elfenkönigin (wds. Matthisson). BOOK II: 7. Totengräberlied (wds. Shakespeare); 8. Lied der Desdemona (wds. Shakespeare); 9. Die Abgeschiedenen (wds. Uhland); 10. Das Ständchen (wds. Uhland); 11. Die Jungfrau und der Tod (wds. Kugler). BOOK III: 12. Ich denke dein (wds. Goethe); 13. Meine Ruh ist hin (wds. Goethe); 14. Wie der Tag mir schleichet (wds. Rousseau, trans. Gotter); 15. Der Treuergebene (wds. von Stretlingen); 16. Sehnsucht (wds. Goethe). BOOK IV: 17. Wenn du wärst mein eigen (wds. Kosegarten); 18. Abschied (wds. von Gerstenberg); 19. Frühlingserwachen (wds. Gamberg); 20. Ihr Spaziergang (wds. Talvj); 21. Graf Eberhards Weissdorn (wds. Uhland). BOOK V: 22. Minnelied (wds. Voss); 23. Hans und Grete (wds. Uhland); 24. Bauernregel (wds. Uhland); 25. Die Zufriedenen (wds. Uhland); 26. An die fleissige Spinnerin (wds. Krausenack). BOOK VI: 27. Wach auf (wds. Kurowsky-Eichen); 28. Liebesgedanken (wds. Müller); 29. Vogelgesang (wds. Tieck); 30. Mädchen sind wie der Wind; 31. Graf Eberstein (wds. Uhland). BOOK VII: 32. Der Pilgrim vor St Just (wds. von Platen); 33. Im Traum sah ich die Geliebte (wds. Heine); 34. Erste Liebe (wds. Heine); 35. Neuer Frühling (wds. Heine); 36. Du schönes Fischermädchen (wds. Heine); 37. Ich hab' im Traume geweinet (wds. Heine). BOOK VIII: 38. Turmwächter Lynceus du den Füssen der Helena (wds. Goethe); 39. Lynceus der Helena seine Schätze darbietend (wds. Goethe); 40. Lynceus auf Fausts Sternwarte singend (wds. Goethe); 41. Mädchenwünsche (wds. Goethe); 42. Gutmann und Gutweib (wds. Goethe). BOOK IX: 43. Szene aus Faust (wds. Goethe); 44. Der alte Goethe (wds. Förster); 45. Die verliebte Schäferin Scapine (wds. Goethe); 46. Ein Aphroditen (wds. Sappho, trans. Blankensee); 47. Eis tettiga (wds. Anacreon, trans. Blankensee); 48. Der Fernen (wds. von Gerstenberg). BOOK X: 49. Jugend und Alter (wds. von Fallersleben); 50. Die Sylphide (wds. Herder); 51. Der Bräutigam (wds. Gruppe); 52. Niemand hat's gesehen (wds. Gruppe); 53. Einrichtung (wds. Gruppe); 54. Der Apotheker als Nebenbuhler (wds. Gruppe).
24, 31, 44. D. Fischer-Dieskau, H. Höll (r c1987) *Concert*   (12/95) (TELD) ① **4509-97458-2**
31. H. Hotter, H. Dokoupil (r1968-9) *Concert*
          (8/89) (PREI) ① **93390**
3 Gesänge, Op. 123 (1853)
1. Sängers Gebet (wds. Redwitz); 2. Trommelständchen (wds. Moehrcke); 3. Die Uhr (wds. Seidl).
3. C. Hauptmann, K. Melber (r1989) *Concert*
          (5/90) (BAYE) ① **BR100038**
Gregor auf dem Stein—legend, Op. 38 (1834) (Wds. Kugler)
R. Hermann, G. Parsons *Kaiser Karl V, Op.99*.
          (4/82) (CLAV) ① **CD50-8106**
Der Grosse Christoph—legend, Op. 34 (1834) (Wds. Kind)
2. Der Räuber.
2. C. Hauptmann, K. Melber (r1989) *Concert*
          (5/90) (BAYE) ① **BR100038**

6 Hebraäische Gesänge, Book III, Op. 13 (1825)
1. Sanheribs Niederlage; 2. Belsazars Gesicht; 3. Die höh're Welt; 4. Jordans Ufer; 5. Wohin, O Seele?; 6. Die Sonne der Schlaflosen.
4, 6. D. Fischer-Dieskau, H. Höll (r c1987) *Concert*
          (12/95) (TELD) ① **4509-97458-2**
6 Hebräische Gesänge, Book II, Op. 5 (1824)
1. Sie geht in Schönheit; 2. Jephtas Tochter; 3. Die wilde Gazelle; 4. Weint um Israel; 5. Mein Geist ist trüb; 6. Saul vor seiner letzten Schlacht.
5. D. Fischer-Dieskau, H. Höll (r c1987) *Concert*
          (12/95) (TELD) ① **4509-97458-2**
Ich bin ein guter Hirte—Lied (1860) (Wds. Bible)
D. Fischer-Dieskau, H. Höll (r c1987) *Concert*
          (12/95) (TELD) ① **4509-97458-2**
Kaiser Karl V—ballads, Op. 99 (1844)
1. Das Wiegenfest zu Gent (wds. Grün); 2. Karl Kaiser V in Wittenberg (wds. Holfeld); 3. Der Pilgrim vor St Just (wds. Platen); 4. Der Leiche zu St Just (wds. Grün).
R. Hermann, G. Parsons *Gregor auf dem Stein, Op.38*.   (4/82) (CLAV) ① **CD50-8106**
3. C. Hauptmann, K. Melber (r1989) *Concert*
          (5/90) (BAYE) ① **BR100038**
Kleiner Haushalt—lyric fantasia, Op. 71 (1838) (Wds. Rückert)
E. Schwarzkopf, G. Parsons (r1968) *Concert*
          (12/90) (EMI) ① **CDM7 63654-2**
K. Borg, M. Raucheisen (r1953) *Concert*
          (12/94) (FINL) ① [3] **4509-95606-2**
3 Legenden—Lieder, Op. 33 (1834)
1. Jungfrau Lorenz (wds. F Kugler); 2. Das heilige Haus in Loretto (wds. L Giesebrecht); 3. Des fremden Kindes heil'ger Christ (wds. F. Rückert).
3. K. Erb, orch, B. Seidler-Winkler (r1937) *Concert*
          (6/94) (PREI) ① [2] **89208**
4 Legenden—contralto and piano, Op. 75 (1837)
1. Das Grab zu Ephessus (wds. Binder); 2. Der Weichdorn (wds. Rückert); 3. Der heilige Franziskus (wds. Wessenberg); 4. Das Wunder auf der Flucht (wds. Rückert).
2, 4. D. Fischer-Dieskau, H. Höll (r c1987) *Concert*
          (12/95) (TELD) ① **4509-97458-2**
3. C. Hauptmann, K. Melber (r1989) *Concert*
          (5/90) (BAYE) ① **BR100038**
3 Lieder, Op. 103 (1844)
1. Gruss vom Meere (wds. Schwarzenberg); 2. Menschenlose (wds. Frankl); 3. Deutsche Barkarole (wds. Prechtlau).
1. D. Fischer-Dieskau, H. Höll (r c1987) *Concert*
          (12/95) (TELD) ① **4509-97458-2**
5 Lieder—contralto/bass and piano, Op. 145 (c1859)
1. Meeresleuchten (wds. Siebel); 2. Der Feind (wds. Scherenberg); 3. Im Sturme (wds. Siebel); 4. Heimlichkeit (wds. Siebel); 5. Reiterlied (wds. Redwitz).
C. Hauptmann, K. Melber (r1989) *Concert*
          (5/90) (BAYE) ① **BR100038**
Liedergabe, Op. 130 (1859)
1. Die Waldkapelle (wds. Siebel); 2. Herzensrose (wds. Rückert, after Goethe); 3. Die Amsel flötet (wds. Rose); 4. Der Hirt auf der Brücke (wds. Ziegler); 5. Frühlingsankunft (wds. Ziegler).
3. E. Schwarzkopf, M. Raucheisen (bp1943) *Concert*
          (6/87) (ACAN) ① **43 801**
Der Mönch zu Pisa—ballad: baritone/bass and piano, Op. 114 (1846) (Wds. Vogl)
C. Hauptmann, K. Melber (r1989) *Concert*
          (5/90) (BAYE) ① **BR100038**
Odins Meeresritt, oder Der Schmied auf Helgoland—ballad, Op. 118 (1851) (Wds. Schreiber)
C. Hauptmann, K. Melber (r1989) *Concert*
          (5/90) (BAYE) ① **BR100038**
H. Hermann Nissen, B. Seidler-Winkler (r1939) *Concert*   (12/95) (PREI) ① **89090**
Der seltne Beter (Der alte Dessauer)—ballad: baritone/bass and piano, Op. 141 (pub 1868) (Wds. Fitzau)
D. Fischer-Dieskau, H. Höll (r c1987) *Concert*
          (12/95) (TELD) ① **4509-97458-2**
Tom der Reimer—Scottish ballad, Op. 135a (c1860) (Wds. trans. Fontane)
R. Tauber, Dajos Bela Orch (r1929) *Concert*
          (4/90) (PEAR) ① **GEMMCD9381**
Traumlicht—Lied (1842) (Wds. Rückert)
C. Hauptmann, K. Melber (r1989) *Concert*
          (5/90) (BAYE) ① **BR100038**
Wandrers Nachtlied—Lied
K. Livingstone, J.J. Blakely (Eng) *Concert*
          (1/90) (MERI) ① **DUOCD89002**

LOEWE, Frederick (1901–1988) Germany/USA

SECTION V: STAGE WORKS

Brigadoon—musical show: 2 acts (1947—New York) (Lyrics A. J. Lerner)
EXCERPTS. PROLOGUE: 1. Overture; 2. Once in the Highlands. ACT 1: 3a. Brigadoon; 3b. Vendor's Calls; 4a. Down on MacConnachy Square; 4b. Waitin' for my dearie; 4c. I'll go home with bonnie Jean; 4d. Dance; 4e. The heather on the hill; 5. The love of my life; 6a. Jeannie's packin' up; 6b. Come to me, bend to me; 6c. Dance; 6d. Almost like being in love; 7a. Entrance of the clans; 7b. Wedding ceremony; 7c. Wedding dance; 7d. Sword dance; 8. End of Act 1. ACT 2: 9. The chase; 10. There but for you I go; 11a. Glen scene opening; 11b. My mother's weddin' day; 11c. Dance; 11d. Funeral dance; 11e. From this day on; 11f. Farewell music; 12. Change of scene; 13. Reprises; 14. Finale.
Cpte London Cast, S. Calvert (r1988)
          (3/89) (FRST) ① **CASTCD16**
Cpte B. Barrett, R. Luker, J. Kaye, J.M. Ainsley, Ambrosian Chor, London Sinfonietta, J. McGlinn
          (1/93) (EMI) ① **CDC7 54481-2**
4e V. Masterson, T. Allen, Philh, J.O. Edwards
  (r1990) Concert   (5/94) (TER) ① **CDVIR8317**
Gigi—musical film (1958) (Book & Lyrics A. J. Lerner, after Colette)
EXCERPTS: 1. Overture; 2. Thank Heaven for Little Girls; 3. It's a Bore; 4. The Parisians; 5. Waltz at Maxim's: She Is Not Thinking of Me; 6. The Night They Invented Champagne; 7. I Remember It Well; 8. Say a Prayer for Me Tonight; 9. I'm Glad I'm Not Young Any More; 10. Gaston's Soliloquy: Gigi (Fountain Scene); 11. Finale: Thank Heaven for Little Girls.
1, 5, 10. Hollywood Bowl SO, J. Mauceri (r1993; arr Mauceri; restored Palmer) Concert
          (6/94) (PHIL) ① **438 685-2PH**
My Fair Lady—musical show (1956—New York) (Book & Lyrics A J Lerner)
EXCERPTS: 1. Overture; 2. Why Can't the English?; 3. Wouldn't It Be Lovely; 4. With a Little Bit of Luck; 5. I'm an Ordinary Man; 6. Just You Wait; 7. The Rain in Spain; 8. I Could Have Danced All Night; 9. Ascot Gavotte; 10. Embassy Waltz; 11. On the Street Where You Live; 12. You Did It; 13. Show Me; 14. Get Me to the Church On Time; 15. A Hymn to Him; 16. Without You; 17. I've Grown Accustomed to Her Face.
8. M. Hill Smith, Philh, J.O. Edwards (r1989-91) Concert   (10/91) (TER) ① **CDVIR8314**
8. B. Hendricks, C. Henry, S. Minty, L. Richardson, Philh, L. Foster (r1992) Concert
          (8/93) (EMI) ① **CDC7 54626-2**
13. J. Norman, J.T. Williams (r1989) Concert
          (4/92) (PHIL) ① **422 401-2PH**
My Fair Lady—musical film based on show (1964) (orch Courage, Franklyn, Woodbury & Tucker)
EXCERPTS: 1. Overture; 2. Why Can't the English?; 3. Wouldn't It Be Lovely?; 4. The Flower Market (orchestra); 5. I'm Just an Ordinary Man; 6. With a Little Bit of Luck; 7. Just You Wait; 8. Servants' Chorus; 9. The Rain in Spain; 10. I Could Have Danced All Night; 11. Ascot Gavotte; 12. On the Street Where You Live; 13. Intermission Music (orchestra); 14. The Transylvanian March; 15. The Embassy Waltz; 16. You Did it; 17. Show Me; 18. The Flower Market (ensemble); 19. Get Me to the Church On Time; 20. A Hymn to Him; 21. Without You; 22. I've Grown Accustomed to Her Face; 23. End Titles; 24. Exit Music.
Cpte A. Hepburn, M. Nixon, R. Harrison, W. Hyde-White, S. Holloway, G. Cooper, B. Shirley, Orig Film Cast, A. Previn (r1964; Eliza mostly sung by Marni Nixon)   (5/95) (SONY) ① **SK66711**

LOGAN, Frederick Knight (1871–1929) USA

SECTION IV: VOCAL AND CHORAL

Pale moon—song (1920)
F. Kreisler, C. Lamson (r1922: arr Kreisler) Concert
      (9/93) (BIDD) ① [2] **LAB068/9**

LÖHR, Hermann (1871–1943) England

SECTION IV: VOCAL AND CHORAL

Where my caravan has rested—song
B. Crosby, J. Heifetz, orch, V. Young (r1946) Concert
    (11/94) (RCA) ① [65] **09026 61778-2(19)**

LOLE, Simon (b 1957) England

SECTION IV: VOCAL AND CHORAL

Angels (1990) (Wds. K. Walker)
St Mary Collegiate Church Ch, K. Bowyer, S. Lole
  (r1992) Concert   (3/94) (REGE) ① **REGCD107**
An **Evening Hymn** (Wds. I. Watts)
St Mary Collegiate Church Ch, K. Bowyer, S. Lole
  (r1992) Concert   (3/94) (REGE) ① **REGCD107**
The **Father's Love—wedding anthem** (Wds. Bible)
St Mary Collegiate Church Ch, K. Bowyer, S. Lole
  (r1992) Concert   (3/94) (REGE) ① **REGCD107**
I **got me Flowers** (Wds. G. Herbert)
St Mary Collegiate Church Ch, K. Bowyer, S. Lole
  (r1992) Concert   (3/94) (REGE) ① **REGCD107**
I **will lift up mine eyes—wedding anthem** (Wds. Psalm 121)
St Mary Collegiate Church Ch, K. Bowyer, S. Lole
  (r1992) Concert   (3/94) (REGE) ① **REGCD107**
Love Eternal (Wds. G. Cole)
St Mary Collegiate Church Ch, K. Bowyer, S. Lole
  (r1992) Concert   (3/94) (REGE) ① **REGCD107**
O **God the Holy Spirit—Whitsun anthem** (E. Milner-White)
St Mary Collegiate Church Ch, K. Bowyer, S. Lole
  (r1992) Concert   (3/94) (REGE) ① **REGCD107**
Shall we not love thee, Mother dear?—anthem (Wds. H.W. Baker)
St Mary Collegiate Church Ch, K. Bowyer, S. Lole
  (r1992) Concert   (3/94) (REGE) ① **REGCD107**
The **St David's Service—treble voices (1991)**
1. Magnificat; 2. Nunc Dimittis.
St Mary Collegiate Church Ch, K. Bowyer, S. Lole
  (r1992) Concert   (3/94) (REGE) ① **REGCD107**
The **St Mary's Service** (Church of England Communion Service Rite B)
1. Gloria; 2. Sanctus; 3. Benedictus; 4. Agnus Dei.
St Mary Collegiate Church Ch, K. Bowyer, S. Lole
  (r1992) Concert   (3/94) (REGE) ① **REGCD107**
The **St Nicholas Service** (Church of England Communion Service Rite A)
1. Gloria; 2. Sanctus; 3. Benedictus; 4. Agnus Dei.
St Mary Collegiate Church Ch, K. Bowyer, S. Lole
  (r1992) Concert   (3/94) (REGE) ① **REGCD107**
This is the Day—choral fanfare
St Mary Collegiate Church Ch, K. Bowyer, S. Lole
  (r1992) Concert   (3/94) (REGE) ① **REGCD107**
Vesper Responsary
St Mary Collegiate Church Ch, K. Bowyer, S. Lole
  (r1992) Concert   (3/94) (REGE) ① **REGCD107**

LONG, Samuel (18th Cent) England

SECTION III: INSTRUMENTAL

Voluntary in D minor—keyboard
J. Bate Concert   (5/91) (UNIC) ① **DKPCD9099**

LONG, Zhou (20th Cent) China

SECTION II: CHAMBER

Song of the Ch'in—string quartet (1982)
Shanghai Qt (r1994) Concert
          (3/95) (DELO) ① **DE3162**

LOOSEMORE, Henry (d 1670) England

SECTION IV: VOCAL AND CHORAL

O **Lord, increase my faith—anthem: 4vv** (previously attrib Gibbons)
Dundee Cath Ch, R. Lightband (org/dir) Concert
      (8/92) (ABBE) ① **CDCA926**
King's College Ch, H. McLean, B. Ord (r1955) Concert   (10/92) (DECC) ① **433 677-2DM**

LOPE DE VEGA, Félix (1562–1635) Spain

SECTION IV: VOCAL AND CHORAL

Como retumban los remos
M. Figueras, Hespèrion XX, J. Savall Concert
      (2/92) (ASTR) ① **E8729**
De pechos sobre una torre (Lamento de Belisa)
M. Figueras, Hespèrion XX, J. Savall Concert
      (2/92) (ASTR) ① **E8729**

LÓPEZ (16th Cent) Spain

SECTION III: INSTRUMENTAL

Fantasia—vihuela (pub c1593) (from Ramillete de Flores)
J. M. Moreno (r1994) Concert
      (8/95) (GLOS) ① **GCD920103**

LOPEZ, Antonio (16–17th Cent) Portugal

SECTION IV: VOCAL AND CHORAL

Heu mihi, Domine—motet (Santa Cruz, Coimbra MS)
A Capella Portvgvesa, O. Rees (r1994) Concert
    (11/94) (HYPE) ① **CDA66735**

LÓPEZ BUCHARDO, Carlos (1881–1948) Argentina

SECTION IV: VOCAL AND CHORAL

Canción del carretero—song (Wds. Carabello)
H. Spani, orch, G. Nastrucci (r1930) Concert
      (9/90) (CLUB) ① [2] **CL99-509/10**
H. Spani, Inst Ens, G. Nastrucci (r1930) Concert
      (12/92) (PREI) ① **89037**

LÓPEZ CAPILLAS, Francisco (c1615–1673) Mexico

SECTION IV: VOCAL AND CHORAL

Alleluia—choir a capella
Westminster Cath Ch, J. O'Donnell Concert
    (12/90) (HYPE) ① **CDA66330**
Dic nobis, Maria—choir a capella
Westminster Cath Ch, A. Watts, A. Lawrence-King, J. O'Donnell Concert   (12/90) (HYPE) ① **CDA66330**
Magnificat quarti voci—4vv and organ
Westminster Cath Ch, I. Simcock, J. O'Donnell Concert   (12/90) (HYPE) ① **CDA66330**

LOPRESTI, Ronald (1933–1986) USA

SECTION I: ORCHESTRAL

The **Masks—orchestra (1955)**
Oregon SO, J. DePreist Concert
      (1/93) (KOCH) ① **37156-2**

LOQUEVILLE, Richard de (d 1418) France

SECTION III: INSTRUMENTAL

Je vous pri que j'aye un baysier—rondeau
A. Lawrence-King Concert
    (11/87) (HYPE) ① **CDA66238**

SECTION IV: VOCAL AND CHORAL

Pour mesdians—rondeau (3vv)
Gothic Voices, A. Lawrence-King, C. Page Concert
    (12/88) (HYPE) ① **CDA66286**
Puisque je suy amoureux—rondeau (3vv)
Gothic Voices, A. Lawrence-King, C. Page Concert
    (12/88) (HYPE) ① **CDA66286**
Qui ne veroit que vos deulx yeux—rondeau (3vv)
Gothic Voices, A. Lawrence-King, C. Page Concert
    (12/88) (HYPE) ① **CDA66286**

LORCA, Federico García (1899–1936) Spain

SECTION IV: VOCAL AND CHORAL

Canciones españolas antiguas—Spanish folksongs
1. Anda, jaleo (arr F. Gasull); 2. El Café de Chinitas (arr F. Gasull); 3. Las morillas de Jaén (arr J. Pons); 4. Las tres hojas (arr J. A. Amargós); 5. Romance de Don Boyso (arr J. Pons); 6. Los reyes de la baraja (arr L. Vidal); 7. Los pelegrinitos (arr F. Gasull); 8. Zorongo (arr L. Vidal); 9. Los cuatro muleros (arr J. A. Amargós); 10. Nana de Sevilla (arr L. Vidal); 11. Sevillanas del Siglo XVIII (arr J. A. Amargós).
G. Ortega, Teatre lliure CO, J. Pons (r1994) *Falla: Corregidor y la molinera.*
(7/95) (HARM) ① **HMC90 1520**

LORENTZ, Johann (c1580–1650) Germany

SECTION III: INSTRUMENTAL

Praeludium in D minor—organ
G. Leonhardt *Concert* (10/94) (SONY) ① **SK53371**

LORENZINI (fl c1570–71) Italy

SECTION III: INSTRUMENTAL

Fantasis—lute (in Lord Herbert of Cherbury's Lute Book)
P. O'Dette *Concert* (4/93) (HARM) ① **HMU90 7068**

LORENZO DA FIRENZE (d 1372/3) Italy

SECTION IV: VOCAL AND CHORAL

Non vedi tu, Amor—ballata (Wds. ?cpsr)
E. Lamandier *Concert* (2/88) (ALIE) ① **AL1019**

LORENZO FERNÁNDEZ, Oscar (1897–1948) Brazil

SECTION I: ORCHESTRAL

Reisado do pastoreio—symphonic poem (1930)
Bataque NYPO, L. Bernstein (r1963) *Concert* (5/93) (SONY) ① **SMK47544**

LORTZING, (Gustav) Albert (1801–1851) Germany

SECTION V: STAGE WORKS

Undine—opera: 4 acts (1845—Magdeburg) (Lib. after la de la Motte-Fouqué)
EXCERPTS: 1. Overture; 2. Da lieg, du altes Mordgewehr; 3. Ach, welche Freude, welche Wonne; 4. Ich ritt zum grossen Waffenspiele; 5. Zürchtig Bräutlein, darfst erscheinen; 6. Uns beiden ist die Hauptstadt wohlbekannt!; 7. Ihr seid nun vereint; 8. Viel schöne Gaben; 9. Doch halt, wo ist der Mann. ACT 2: 10. Introduction; 11. Was seh' ich! Ihr seid glücklich wieder da?; 12. So munter und so fröhlich; 2b. A, B, C, D, der Junggesellenstand tut weh; 2c. Ein Schreiben von Herrn Grafen; 3. Lass Er doch hören!; 4. Auf des Lebens rauschen Wogen; 5. Was meint Ihr, lieber Freund; 6. Sehr dort den muntern Jäger; 7a. Lasset und nach Hause gehen; 7b. Bin ich schlichtes Kind vom Lande. ACT 2: 8. Strahl der Sonne, schönstes Licht; 9. Bleiben soll ich und stets sie sehen; 10. Was seh' ich? Mir aus den Augen!; 11. Ihr Weib?...Mein teures Weib!; 12. Ich habe Numro Eins; 13. Fünftausend Taler!. ACT 3: 14a. Wie freundlich strahlt die helle Morgensonne; 14b. Heiterkeit und Fröhlichkeit; 15. Um die Laube zu schmücken; 16. Komm, liebes Gretchen; 17a. Was seh' ich?...Alle Teufel!; 17b. Kann ich im Erdenleben; 17c. Under Herr lebe hoch!; 17d. O du, der du die Tugend selber bist.
Cpte M. Krause, J. Protschka, C. Hampe, J. Janssen, K. Häger, I. Most, H. Kruse, A. Schmidt, G. Wewel, D. Schortemeier, Cologne Rad Chor, Cologne RSO, K. Eichhorn (3/91) (CAPR) ① [2] **60 017-2**
12. Lotte Lehmann, orch (r1919) *Concert* (6/92) (PREI) ① [3] **89302**
20. R. Tauber, orch (r1928) *Concert* (7/89) (PEAR) ① **GEMMCD9327**
20. F. Wunderlich, Stuttgart RSO, A. Rischner (bp1957) *Concert* (10/89) (ACAN) ① **43 267**
20. R. Schock, Berlin Deutsche Op Orch, W. Schüchter (r1952) *Concert* (4/92) (EMI) ① [7] **CHS7 69741-2(4)**

20. R. Tauber, Berlin Schauspielhaus Orch, E. Hauke (r1928) *Concert* (12/92) (NIMB) ① **NI7830**
20. P. Anders, Berlin RSO, A. Rother (bp1943) *Concert* (8/93) (ACAN) ① **43 268**
20. R. Tauber, orch (r1928) *Concert* (12/94) (MMOI) ① **CDMOIR425**
23. G. Hüsch, Berlin St Op Orch, H.U. Müller (r1935) *Concert* (3/94) (PREI) ① **89071**
Der Waffenschmied—opera: 3 acts (1846—Vienna) (Lib. after von Ziegler)
EXCERPTS: 1. Overture. ACT 1; 2a. Sprühe, Flamme! glühe, Eisen!; 2b. Bringt eilig Hut und Mantel mir; 2c. Horch! die Feierstunde schlägt; 3. Man wird ja einmal nur geboren; 4. Welt, du kannst mir nicht gefallen; 5a. Bei nächt'gem Dunkel; 5b. Der Meister!—Der Vater!; 5c. Er schläft! Wir alle sind in Angst und Not...Er ist so gut; 6. Interlude. ACT 2: 7. Ihr wisst, dass er Euch liebt?; 8. Der Mann scheint nicht bei Sinnen; 9. Du bist ein arbeitsamer Mensch; 10. Wie herrlich ist's im Grünen; 11. War einst ein junger Springinsfeld; 12. Zu Hilfe! Zu Hilfe! ACT 3: 13. Wir armen, armen Mädchen; 14. Gut, dass ich Euch noch treffe; 15. Auch ich war ein Jüngling mit lockigem Haar; 16. March with dialogue; 17. Gern gäb' ich Glanz und Reichtum hin.
3. F. Wunderlich, Munich RO, H. Moltkau *Concert* (9/93) (DG) ① **431 110-2GB**
3, 11. F. Wunderlich, Stuttgart Rad Chor, Stuttgart RSO, A. Rischner (bp1957) *Concert* (10/89) (ACAN) ① **43 267**
5c M. Teschemacher, Berlin City Op Orch, H.U. Müller (r1934) *Concert* (11/92) (PREI) ① **89049**
15. E. Kunz, Philh, O. Ackermann (r1953) *Concert* (9/95) (TEST) ① **SBT1059**
Der Wildschütz—opera: 3 acts (1842—Leipzig) (Wds. cpsr)
EXCERPTS: 1. Overture. ACT 1: 2a. Es lebe das Brautpaar!...So munter und so fröhlich; 2b. A, B, C, D, der Junggesellenstand tut weh; 2c. Ein Schreiben von Herrn Grafen; 3. Lass Er doch hören!; 4. Auf des Lebens rauschen Wogen; 5. Was meint Ihr, lieber Freund; 6. Sehr dort den muntern Jäger; 7a. Lasset und nach Hause gehen; 7b. Bin ich schlichtes Kind vom Lande. ACT 2: 8. Strahl der Sonne, schönstes Licht; 9. Bleiben soll ich und stets sie sehen; 10. Was seh' ich? Mir aus den Augen!; 11. Ihr Weib?...Mein teures Weib!; 12. Ich habe Numro Eins; 13. Fünftausend Taler!. ACT 3: 14a. Wie freundlich strahlt die helle Morgensonne; 14b. Heiterkeit und Fröhlichkeit; 15. Um die Laube zu schmücken; 16. Komm, liebes Gretchen; 17a. Was seh' ich?...Alle Teufel!; 17b. Kann ich im Erdenleben; 17c. Under Herr lebe hoch!; 17d. O du, der du die Tugend selber bist.
Cpte G. Hornik, D. Soffel, P. Schreier, E. Mathis, G. von Otthenthal, H. Sotin, G. Resick, R. Süss, B. Riedel, Berlin Rad Children's Ch, Berlin Rad Chor, Berlin Staatskapelle, B. Klee (r1980/2) (12/95) (BERL) ① [2] **0011 432BC**
4. F. Hempel, orch (r c1914/5) *Concert* (3/94) (NIMB) ① **NI7849**
4, 11. I. Seefried, E. Haefliger, Bamberg SO, C. Stepp (r1965) *Concert* (9/93) (DG) ① [2] **437 677-2GDO2**
13. A. Kipnis, Berlin St Op Orch, E. Orthmann (r1931) *Concert* (12/90) (PREI) ① **89019**
13. E. Kunz, Philh, O. Ackermann (r1953) *Concert* (9/95) (TEST) ① **SBT1059**
14a, 14b T. Hampson, Munich RO, F. Luisi (r1994) *Concert* (9/95) (EMI) ① **CDC5 55233-2**
14a, 14b G. Hüsch, Berlin St Op Orch, F. Weissmann (r1928) *Concert* (10/95) (NIMB) ① **NI7867**
Zar und Zimmermann—comic opera: 3 acts (1837—Leipzig) (Lib after C. C. Römers)
Lebe wohl, mein flandrisch Mädchen F. Wunderlich, I. Hallstein, Bavarian Rad Chor, Bamberg SO, H. Gierster *Concert* (5/93) (DG) ① **431 110-2GB**
O Sancta Justitia E. Kunz, Philh, O. Ackermann (r1953) *Concert* (9/95) (TEST) ① **SBT1059**
Sonst spielt ich H. Schlusnus, Berlin St Op Orch, J. Schüler (r1937) *Concert* (9/90) (PREI) ① **89006**
Sonst spielt ich G. Hüsch, Berlin St Op Orch, H.U. Müller (r1937) *Concert* (3/94) (PREI) ① **89071**
Verraten!...Die Macht des Szepters B. Weikl, Munich RO, H. Wallberg *Concert* (3/89) (ACAN) ① **43 266**
Verraten!...Die Macht des Zeptes T. Hampson, Munich RO, F. Luisi (r1994) *Concert* (9/95) (EMI) ① **CDC5 55233-2**

LOTTI, Antonio (c1667–1740) Italy

SECTION I: ORCHESTRAL

Concerto for Oboe d'amore and Strings in A
H. Holliger, I Musici *Concert* (4/88) (PHIL) ① **420 189-2PH**

SECTION IV: VOCAL AND CHORAL

Crucifixus—motet: 6vv
Taverner Ch, Taverner Consort, Taverner Plyrs, A. Parrott *Concert* (8/91) (EMI) ① **CDC7 54117-2**
Crucifixus—motet: 8vv
Westminster Cath Ch, S. Cleobury *Concert* (7/83) (ARGO) ① **410 005-2ZH**
The Sixteen, H. Christophers *Concert* (10/90) (COLL) ① **Coll5009-2**
St John's College Ch, G. Guest (r1977) *Concert* (7/95) (DECC) ① [2] **443 868-2DF2**
Crucifixus—motet: 10vv
Taverner Ch, Taverner Consort, Taverner Plyrs, A. Parrott *Concert* (8/91) (EMI) ① **CDC7 54117-2**

SECTION V: STAGE WORKS

Arminio—pasticcio (1714)
EXCERPTS: 1. Pur dicesti.
1. A. Patti, L. Ronald (r1905) *Concert* (4/90) (PEAR) ① **GEMMCD9312**
1. H. Jadlowker, arch (r1927) *Concert* (12/91) (CLUB) ① **CL99-042**
1. L. Tetrazzini, P. Pitt (r1910) *Concert* (9/92) (EMI) ① [3] **CHS7 63802-2(2)**
1. C. Bartoli, G. Fischer *Concert* (12/92) (DECC) ① **436 267-2DH**
1. J. Baker, ASMF, N. Marriner *Concert* (1/93) (PHIL) ① **434 173-2PM**

LOUIGUY, R.S. (1916–1991) France

pseudonym of Luis Guglielmi

SECTION IV: VOCAL AND CHORAL

La Vie en rose, 'Take me to your heart again'—song (1946) (French wds E. Piaf; Eng wds M. David)
J. Carreras, P. Domingo, L. Pavarotti, MMF Orch, Rome Op Orch, Z. Mehta (pp1990) *Concert* (1/93) (DECC) ① **430 433-2DH**

LOURIÉ, Arthur Vincent (1892–1966) Russia

SECTION I: ORCHESTRAL

a Little Chamber Music (1932)
T. Klug, Deutsche Kammerphilharmonie (r1992) *Concert* (2/94) (DG) ① **437 788-2GH**

SECTION II: CHAMBER

Concerto da Camera for Violin and String Orchestra (1947)
1. Intrata; 2. Aria; 3. Intermezzo; 4. Fantasia; 5. Serenata; 6. Epilogo.
G. Kremer, T. Klug, Deutsche Kammerphilharmonie (r1992) *Concert* (2/94) (DG) ① **437 788-2GH**

SECTION IV: VOCAL AND CHORAL

Little Gidding—tenor and instrumental ensmble (1952) (Wds. T S Eliot)
1. Prelude; 2. Ash on an old man's sleeve; 3. The dove descending breaks the air; 4. We shall not cease from exploration.
K. Riegel, Deutsche Kammerphilharmonie (r1992) *Concert* (2/94) (DG) ① **437 788-2GH**

LOUSSIER, Jacques (b 1936) France

SECTION I: ORCHESTRAL

Concerto for Trumpet and Chamber Orchestra (1987)
G. Touvron, Prague CO *Concert* (8/94) (DECC) ① **436 798-2DH**
Concerto for Violin and Percussion (1988)
J-P. Wallez, A. Arpino, Prague CO *Concert* (8/94) (DECC) ① **436 798-2DH**
Tableaux vénetiens—strings (1988)
Prague CO *Concert* (8/94) (DECC) ① **436 798-2DH**

LOVATT, Samuel Ernest (1877–1954) England

SECTION IV: VOCAL AND CHORAL

The **Little green lane—partsong** (Wds. Gaunt)
King's Sngrs *Concert*
(6/88) (EMI) ① **CDC7 49765-2**

LOVENSKJOLD, Hermann (1815–1870) Denmark

SECTION V: STAGE WORKS

La **Sylphide—ballet: 2 acts** (1836—Copenhagen)
Cpte Royal Danish Orch, D. Garforth
(4/92) (CHAN) ① **CHAN6546**

LOVREGLIO, Donato (1841–1907) Italy

SECTION II: CHAMBER

Fantasia on Verdi's 'La Traviata'—clarinet and piano, Op. 45
C. Bradbury, O. Davies *Concert*
(6/90) (ASV) ① **CDDCA701**
E. Johnson, G. Back *Concert*
(5/91) (ASV) ① **CDDCA732**
M. Collins, K. Stott *Concert*
(9/92) (EMI) ① **CDC7 54419-2**

LOWRY, Robert (1826–1899) USA

SECTION IV: VOCAL AND CHORAL

Shall we know each other there?—gospel song (pub 1868) (in 'Chapel Melodies')
Jacqueline Pierce, R. Taylor, Harmoneion Sngrs, N. Bruce, L. Skrobacs (r1977) *Concert*
(2/94) (NEW) ① **80220-2**

LUBBOCK, Mark (1898–1986) England

SECTION I: ORCHESTRAL

Polka Dots—orchestra
RTE Concert Orch, E. Tomlinson (r1993) *Concert*
(12/95) (MARC) ① **8 223522**

LÜBECK, Vincent (1654–1740) Germany

SECTION III: INSTRUMENTAL

Ich ruf zu dir, Herr Jesu Christ—chorale fantasia (incomplete)
B. Coudurier *Concert*   (10/89) (BNL) ① **BNL112753**
Nun lasst Gott, dem Herren—chorale partita
B. Coudurier *Concert*   (10/89) (BNL) ① **BNL112753**
Prelude and Fugue in C—organ
B. Coudurier *Concert*   (10/89) (BNL) ① **BNL112753**
Prelude and Fugue in C minor—organ
B. Coudurier *Concert*   (10/89) (BNL) ① **BNL112753**
Prelude and Fugue in D minor—organ
B. Coudurier *Concert*   (10/89) (BNL) ① **BNL112753**
Prelude and Fugue in E—organ
B. Coudurier *Concert*   (10/89) (BNL) ① **BNL112753**
Prelude and Fugue in F—organ
B. Coudurier *Concert*   (10/89) (BNL) ① **BNL112753**
Prelude and Fugue in G—organ
B. Coudurier *Concert*   (10/89) (BNL) ① **BNL112753**
Prelude and Fugue in G minor—organ
B. Coudurier *Concert*   (10/89) (BNL) ① **BNL112753**

SECTION IV: VOCAL AND CHORAL

Willkommen, süsser, Bräutigam—cantata (2vv, 2 violins and continuo)
G. de Reyghere, Ricercar Consort (r1989) *Concert*
(5/90) (RICE) ① **RIC060048**

LUCAS, Leighton (1903–1982) England

SECTION I: ORCHESTRAL

Chorale and Variations—brass band/orchestra (1960s)
Black Dyke Mills Band, R. Newsome *Concert*
(9/93) (RSR) ① **RSRD1002**

SECTION V: STAGE WORKS

Stage Fright—film score (1950)
EXCERPTS: 1. Rhapsody (orch Philip Lane).
1. Prague City PO, P. Bateman *Concert*
(9/95) (SILV) ① **FILMCD159**

LUCCHESI, Andrea (1741–1801) Italy

SECTION II: CHAMBER

6 Sonatas—violin and keyboard, Op. 1 (c1772)
1. F; 2. F; 3. C.
R. Micconi (arr org) *Concert*
(3/90) (MOTE) ① **CD10561**

LUCE, J.

SECTION IV: VOCAL AND CHORAL

Fin du rêve—song
M. Journet, anon (r1931) *Concert*
(1/94) (CLUB) ① **CL99-034**
Vos yeux—song
M. Journet, anon (r1931) *Concert*
(1/94) (CLUB) ① **CL99-034**

LUCIER, Alvin (Augustus Jr) (b 1931) USA

SECTION I: ORCHESTRAL

Fragments for Strings (1961)
Arditti Qt (r1991-92) *Concert*
(12/93) (MONT) ① **782010**

LUDERS, Gustav (Carl) (1865–1913) Germany/USA

SECTION V: STAGE WORKS

The **Prince of Pilsen—operetta** (1903—New York)
EXCERPTS: 1. The Heidelberg Stein Song.
1. Cincinnati Uni Sngrs, Cincinnati Uni Th Orch, E. Rivers (r1978) *Concert*   (4/94) (NEW) ① **80221-2**

LUDFORD, Nicholas (c1485–?1557) England

SECTION IV: VOCAL AND CHORAL

Ave cuius conceptio—votive antiphon: 5vv
Cardinall's Musick, A. Carwood (ed Skinner) *Missa Videte miraculum.*   (7/93) (ASV) ① **CDGAU131**
Ave Maria ancilla trinitatis—votive antiphon: 5vv
Cardinall's Musick, A. Carwood *Concert*
(1/95) (ASV) ① **CDGAU140**
Domine Jesu Christe—prayer-motet: 5vv
Cardinall's Musick, A. Carwood (ed Skinner) *Concert*
(7/94) (ASV) ① **CDGAU133**
Magnificat Benedicta—6vv
Cardinall's Musick, A. Carwood *Missa Benedicta.*
(12/93) (ASV) ① **CDGAU132**
Missa Benedicta—6vv
Cardinall's Musick, A. Carwood *Magnificat Benedicta.*
(12/93) (ASV) ① **CDGAU132**
Missa Christi virgo—5vv
Cardinall's Musick, A. Carwood (ed Skinner) *Concert*
(7/94) (ASV) ① **CDGAU133**
Missa Lapidaverunt Stephanum—5vv
Cardinall's Musick, A. Carwood *Concert*
(1/95) (ASV) ① **CDGAU140**
Missa Videte miraculum—6vv
Cardinall's Musick, A. Carwood *Ave cuius conceptio.*   (7/93) (ASV) ① **CDGAU131**

LUENING, Otto (b 1900) USA

SECTION I: ORCHESTRAL

Legend—oboe and strings (1951)
E. Larsen, Oslo PO, J. Serebrier (r1960s) *Concert*
(5/91) (ASV) ① **CDDCA741**
Lyric Scene—flute and strings (1958)
P. Oien, Oslo PO, J. Serebrier (r1960s) *Concert*
(5/91) (ASV) ① **CDDCA741**

LUIGINI, Alexandre (Clément Léon Joseph) (1850–1906) France

SECTION V: STAGE WORKS

Ballet égyptien, Op. 12 (1875—Lyons)
EXCERPTS: 1. Allegro non troppo; 2. Allegro; 3. Andante sostenuto; 8. Finale (Andante sostenuto).
1, 2, 3, 8. RPO, A. Fistoulari (r1958) *Concert*
(3/94) (CFP) ① **CD-CFP4637**

LULLY, Jean-Baptiste (1632–1687) Italy/France

SECTION I: ORCHESTRAL

Gavotte (unidentified)
M. Maisky, P. Gililov (arr vc/pf) *Concert*
(7/91) (DG) ① **431 544-2GH**
G. Cziffra (r1969; arr pf) *Concert*
(3/95) (EMI) ① **CDM5 65255-2**

SECTION III: INSTRUMENTAL

Gavotte en rondeau—keyboard (unidentified)
G. Cziffra (r1980-81) *Concert*
(3/95) (EMI) ① **CDM5 65253-2**
Les **Songes agréables d'Atys—harpsichord**
W. Landowska (r1934) *Concert*
(10/92) (MSCM) ① **MM30444**

SECTION IV: VOCAL AND CHORAL

Anima Christi—petit motet (3vv)
Arts Florissants Voc Ens, Arts Florissants Instr Ens, W. Christie *Concert*   (6/88) (HARM) ① **HMC90 1274**
Au clair de la lune—song
E. Clément, G. Farrar, anon (r1913) *Concert*
(8/95) (ROMO) ① **82002-2**
E. Clément, G. Farrar, anon (r1913) *Concert*
(8/95) (PEAR) ① **GEMMCD9161**
Ave coeli—petit motet (3vv)
Arts Florissants Voc Ens, Arts Florissants Instr Ens, W. Christie *Concert*   (6/88) (HARM) ① **HMC90 1274**
Dies Irae—grand motet (2 choirs) (?1674)
D. Brown, G. Laurens, H. Crook, H. Lamy, P. Kooy, Paris Chapelle Royale Chor, Paris Chapelle Royale Orch, P. Herreweghe *Concert*
(5/86) (HARM) ① **HMC90 1167**
Divertissement I—chamber suite (trans Sempé from various stage works)
1. Ouverture d'Amadis; 2. Répands charmante nuit; 3. Recit d'Orphée; 4. Entrée pour Bacchus et Ariadne; 5. Rochers vous êtes sourds; 6. Plainte de Vénus sur la Mort d'Adonis; 7. Dieu des enfers.
G. Laurens, Capriccio Stravagante, S. Sempé (hpd/dir) *Concert*   (1/91) (DHM) ① **RD77218**
Divertissement II—chamber suite (arr Sempé from various stage works)
1. Ouverture de Psyché; 2. Plainte italienne; 3. Chaconne d'Amadis.
G. Laurens, Capriccio Stravagante, S. Sempé (hpd/dir) *Concert*   (1/91) (DHM) ① **RD77218**
Divertissement III—chamber suite (arr Sempé from various stage works)
1. Entré d'Apollon; 2. Si l'amour vous soumet; 3. Enfin il es en ma puissance; 4. Air pour les démons et les monstres; 5. Passacaille d'Armide.
G. Laurens, Capriccio Stravagante, S. Sempé (hpd/dir) *Concert*   (1/91) (DHM) ① **RD77218**
Dixit Dominus—petit motet (3vv)
Arts Florissants Voc Ens, Arts Florissants Instr Ens, W. Christie *Concert*   (6/88) (HARM) ① **HMC90 1274**
Domine salvum—petit motet: 3vv
Arts Florissants Voc Ens, Arts Florissants Instr Ens, W. Christie *Concert*   (6/88) (HARM) ① **HMC90 1274**
D. Collot, E. Gall, F. Masset, S. Vatillon (r1993) *Concert*   (10/93) (ERAT) ① [2] **4509-91722-2**
Exaudi Deus—petit motet: 3vv
Arts Florissants Voc Ens, Arts Florissants Instr Ens, W. Christie *Concert*   (6/88) (HARM) ① **HMC90 1274**
Laudate pueri—petit motet: 3vv (?1686)
Arts Florissants Voc Ens, Arts Florissants Instr Ens, W. Christie *Concert*   (6/88) (HARM) ① **HMC90 1274**
Miserere—grand motet: two choirs (1664)
D. Brown, G. Laurens, H. Crook, H. Lamy, P. Kooy, Paris Chapelle Royale Chor, Paris Chapelle Royale Orch, P. Herreweghe *Concert*
(5/86) (HARM) ① **HMC90 1167**
I. Desrochers, D. Favat, R. Duguay, H. Lamy, P. Harvey, Concert Spirituel Orch, H. Niquet (r1993) *Concert*   (11/94) (FNAC) ① **592308**
O dulcissime—petit motet: 3vv
Arts Florissants Voc Ens, Arts Florissants Instr Ens, W. Christie *Concert*   (6/88) (HARM) ① **HMC90 1274**

O sapientia—petit motet: 3vv
Arts Florissants Voc Ens, Arts Florissants Instr Ens,
W. Christie *Concert* (6/88) (HARM) ① **HMC90 1274**
Omnes gentes—petit motet: 3vv
Arts Florissants Voc Ens, Arts Florissants Instr Ens,
W. Christie *Concert* (6/88) (HARM) ① **HMC90 1274**
Plaude laetare Gallia—grand motet: two choirs (1668)
I. Desrochers, D. Favat, R. Duguay, H. Lamy, P.
Harvey, Concert Spirituel Orch, H. Niquet (r1993)
Concert (11/94) (FNAC) ① **592308**
Regina coeli—petit motet: 3vv
Arts Florissants Voc Ens, Arts Florissants Instr Ens,
W. Christie *Concert* (6/88) (HARM) ① **HMC90 1274**
Salve regina—petit motet: 3vv
Arts Florissants Voc Ens, Arts Florissants Instr Ens,
W. Christie *Concert* (6/88) (HARM) ① **HMC90 1274**
Te Deum—grand motet: two choirs (1677)
I. Desrochers, D. Favat, R. Duguay, H. Lamy, P.
Harvey, Concert Spirituel Orch, H. Niquet (r1993)
Concert (11/94) (FNAC) ① **592308**

SECTION V: STAGE WORKS

Alceste (ou le triomphe d'Alcide)—tragédie lyrique: prologue and 5 acts (1674—Paris)
(Lib. Quinault)
Cpte C. Alliot-Lugaz, J-P. Lafont, H. Crook, S. Marin-
Degor, G. Ragon, J-F. Gardeil, F. Loup, G. Reinhart,
M. Dens, V. Gens, C. Le Coz, M. Ruggeri, O.
Lallouette, D. Nasrawi, Grande Ecurie, Sagittarius
Ens, Compagnie Barocco, J-C. Malgoire (pp1992)
(4/93) (ASTR) ① **[3] E8527**
Amadis—opera (prologue and 5 acts) (1686—Versailles) (Lib. Quinault)
Bois épais E. Caruso, orch, J. Pasternack (r1920)
Concert (7/91) (RCA) ① **[12] GD60495(6)**
Bois épais E. Caruso, orch, J. Pasternack (r1920)
Concert (10/91) (PEAR) ① **[3] EVC4(2)**
Les Amants magnifiques—comédie-ballet: 5 acts (1670—St Germain) (Lib. Molière and Benserade)
Minuet SO, T. Beecham (r1918) *Concert*
(11/91) (SYMP) ① **[2] SYMCD1096/7**
Armide—opera: prologue, 5 acts (1686—Paris) (Lib. Quinault)
G. Laurens, H. Crook, V. Gens, N. Rime, B. Delétré,
G. Ragon, J. Hancock, L. Coadou, Collegium Vocale,
Chapelle Royale Ch, Chapelle Royale Orch, P.
Herreweghe (r1992)
(8/93) (HARM) ① **[2] HMC901 1456/7**
Atys—opera (prologue and 5 acts) (1675—Saint-Germain) (Lib. Quinault)
Cpte B. Delétré, M. Zanetti, J-P. Fouchécourt, G.
Ragon, A. Steyer, A. Mellon, G. de Mey, J. Bona, F.
Semellaz, G. Laurens, N. Rime, J-F. Gardeil, M.
Laplénie, S. Maciejewski, I. Desrochers, V. Gens,
Arts Florissants Chor, Arts Florissants Orch, W.
Christie (7/87) (HARM) ① **[3] HMC90 1257/9**
Le Bourgeois gentilhomme—comédie-ballet (1670—Paris)
R. Yakar, D. Jungmann, R. Jacobs, K. Heider, M.
Lecoq, N. Lohmann, S. Nimsgern, D. Schortemeier,
F. Müller-Heuser, M. Friesenhausen, Tolz Boys' Ch,
Petite Bande, G. Leonhardt (r1973) *Campra: Europe
galante.* (2/91) (DHM) ① **[2] GD77059**
London Ob Band, M-A. Petit, P. Goodwin (r1994)
Concert (4/95) (HARM) ① **HMU90 7122**
Cadmus et Hermione—opera (1673—Paris)
London Ob Band, M-A. Petit, P. Goodwin (r1994)
Concert (4/95) (HARM) ① **HMU90 7122**
Les Nopces de Village, 'A Village Wedding'—ballet (1663—Vincennes)
London Ob Band, M-A. Petit, P. Goodwin (r1994)
Concert (4/95) (HARM) ① **HMU90 7122**
Phaëton—opera (prologue, 5 acts) (1683—Versailles) (Lib. Quinault)
Cpte H. Crook, R. Yakar, J. Smith, V. Gens, G.
Thervel, J-P. Fouchécourt, P. Huttenlocher, L.
Naouri, V. Pochon, J. Varnier, F. Couderc, Sagittarius
Ens, Musiciens du Louvre, M. Minkowski (r1993)
(8/94) (ERAT) ① **[2] 4509-91737-2**

LUMBYE, Hans Christian (1810–1874) Denmark

SECTION I: ORCHESTRAL

Amager—polka (1849)
Odense SO, P. Guth (vn/dir) (pp1989) *Concert*
(2/90) (UNIC) ① **DKPCD9089**
Amelie (Amélie vals)—waltz (1849)
Odense SO, P. Guth (vn/dir) (pp1989) *Concert*
(2/90) (UNIC) ① **DKPCD9089**
Danish Nat RSO, G. Rozhdestvensky (r1993)
Concert (2/94) (CHAN) ① **CHAN9209**

Britta—polka (1864)
Danish Nat RSO, G. Rozhdestvensky (r1993)
Concert (2/94) (CHAN) ① **CHAN9209**
Odense SO, P. Guth (pp) *Concert*
(2/94) (UNIC) ① **DKPCD9143**
Canon—galop
Odense SO, P. Guth (pp) *Concert*
(2/94) (UNIC) ① **DKPCD9143**
Cecilie—waltz
Odense SO, P. Guth (pp) *Concert*
(2/94) (UNIC) ① **DKPCD9143**
Champagne (Champagnegalop)—galop, Op. 14 (1845)
Odense SO, P. Guth (vn/dir) (pp1989) *Concert*
(2/90) (UNIC) ① **DKPCD9089**
Danish Nat RSO, G. Rozhdestvensky (r1993)
Concert (2/94) (CHAN) ① **CHAN9209**
Columbine—polka mazurka (1862)
Odense SO, P. Guth (vn/dir) (pp1989) *Concert*
(2/90) (UNIC) ① **DKPCD9089**
Danish Nat RSO, G. Rozhdestvensky (r1993)
Concert (2/94) (CHAN) ① **CHAN9209**
Concert—polka: two violins and orchestra (1863)
K. Sjøgren, A. Kontra, Danish Nat RSO, G.
Rozhdestvensky (r1993) *Concert*
(2/94) (CHAN) ① **CHAN9209**
Copenhagen Steam Railway Galop (Københavns Jernbane Damp Galop) (1847)
Odense SO, P. Guth (vn/dir) (pp1989) *Concert*
(2/90) (UNIC) ① **DKPCD9089**
Danish Nat RSO, G. Rozhdestvensky (r1993)
Concert (2/94) (UNIC) ① **CHAN9209**
Košice St PO, M. Eichenholz (r1992) *Concert*
(2/94) (MARC) ① **8 223470**
Helga—polka mazurka (1864)
Odense SO, P. Guth (vn/dir) (pp1989) *Concert*
(2/90) (UNIC) ① **DKPCD9089**
Hesperus (Hesperus vals)—waltz (1853)
Odense SO, P. Guth (vn/dir) (pp1989) *Concert*
(2/90) (UNIC) ① **DKPCD9089**
Indian War Dance
Odense SO, P. Guth (pp) *Concert*
(2/94) (UNIC) ① **DKPCD9143**
King Christian IX's March of Honour (1864)
Odense SO, P. Guth (pp) *Concert*
(2/94) (UNIC) ① **DKPCD9143**
King George I's March of Honour (1863)
Odense SO, P. Guth (pp) *Concert*
(2/94) (UNIC) ① **DKPCD9143**
Krolls ballklänge—waltz (1846)
Odense SO, P. Guth (pp) *Concert*
(2/94) (UNIC) ① **DKPCD9143**
The Lady of St Petersburg—polka (1850)
Danish Nat RSO, G. Rozhdestvensky (r1993)
Concert (2/94) (CHAN) ① **CHAN9209**
Lilie—polka (1847)
Odense SO, P. Guth (vn/dir) (pp1989) *Concert*
(2/90) (UNIC) ① **DKPCD9089**
Manoeuvre—galop
Odense SO, P. Guth (pp) *Concert*
(2/94) (UNIC) ① **DKPCD9143**
Memories from Vienna—waltz (1844)
Odense SO, P. Guth (pp) *Concert*
(2/94) (UNIC) ① **DKPCD9143**
Mon salut à Petersburg (1850)
Danish Nat RSO, G. Rozhdestvensky (r1993)
Concert (2/94) (CHAN) ① **CHAN9209**
Nordic Brotherhood—galop
(2/94) (UNIC) ① **DKPCD9143**
Pegasus—galop
Odense SO, P. Guth (pp) *Concert*
(2/94) (UNIC) ① **DKPCD9143**
Pictures from a Dream (Drómmebilleder)—fantasia (1846)
Odense SO, P. Guth (vn/dir) (pp1989) *Concert*
(2/90) (UNIC) ① **DKPCD9089**
Danish Nat RSO, G. Rozhdestvensky (r1993)
Concert (2/94) (CHAN) ① **CHAN9209**
Polonaise with cornet solo
C. Nilsson, Danish Nat RSO, G. Rozhdestvensky
(r1993) *Concert* (2/94) (CHAN) ① **CHAN9209**
Queen Louise's Waltz (Dronning Louise) (1869)
Odense SO, P. Guth (pp1989) *Concert*
(2/90) (UNIC) ① **DKPCD9089**
Danish Nat RSO, G. Rozhdestvensky (r1993)
Concert (2/94) (CHAN) ① **CHAN9209**
Salute to August Bournonville—galop (1869)
Odense SO, P. Guth (vn/dir) (pp1989) *Concert*
(2/90) (UNIC) ① **DKPCD9089**
K. Sjøgren, A. Kontra, C. Nilsson, Danish Nat RSO,
G. Rozhdestvensky (r1993) *Concert*
(2/94) (CHAN) ① **CHAN9209**

Salute to our Friends (1867)
Odense SO, P. Guth (vn/dir) (pp1989) *Concert*
(2/90) (UNIC) ① **DKPCD9089**
The Sandman (after H. C. Andersen)—galop fantastique (1851)
Odense SO, P. Guth (vn/dir) (pp1989) *Concert*
(2/90) (UNIC) ① **DKPCD9089**
Sophie—waltz
Odense SO, P. Guth (pp) *Concert*
(2/94) (UNIC) ① **DKPCD9143**
St Petersburg Champagne—galop (1850)
Danish Nat RSO, G. Rozhdestvensky (r1993)
Concert (2/94) (CHAN) ① **CHAN9209**
A Summernight at Møns Cliff—galop
Odense SO, P. Guth (pp) *Concert*
(2/94) (UNIC) ① **DKPCD9143**
Velocipedes—galop (1869)
Odense SO, P. Guth (pp) *Concert*
(2/94) (UNIC) ① **DKPCD9143**
Victoria—quadrille
Odense SO, P. Guth (pp) *Concert*
(2/94) (UNIC) ① **DKPCD9143**
Welcome—mazurka
Odense SO, P. Guth (pp) *Concert*
(2/94) (UNIC) ① **DKPCD9143**
Les Zouaves—galop (1859)
Odense SO, P. Guth (pp) *Concert*
(2/94) (UNIC) ① **DKPCD9143**

SECTION V: STAGE WORKS

The Guard of Amager (Livaegerne paa Amager)—ballet (1871—Copenhgen) (various composers: Finale by Lumbye)
Final Galop Odense SO, P. Guth (vn/dir) (pp1989)
Concert (2/90) (UNIC) ① **DKPCD9089**
Final Galop Danish Nat RSO, G. Rozhdestvensky
(r1993) *Concert* (2/94) (CHAN) ① **CHAN9209**
Napoli—ballet (1842—Copenhagen) (various composers: Finale by Lumbye)
Final Galop Odense SO, P. Guth (vn/dir) (pp1989)
Concert (2/90) (UNIC) ① **DKPCD9089**
Final Galop Danish Nat RSO, G. Rozhdestvensky
(r1993) *Concert* (2/94) (CHAN) ① **CHAN9209**

LUMSDAINE, David (b 1931) Australia

SECTION IV: VOCAL AND CHORAL

Aria for Edward John Eyre (1972)
J. Manning, J. Baddeley, J. Rye, B. Guy, Gemini, E.
Howarth *What shall I sing?*
(6/93) (NMC) ① **NMCD007**
What shall I sing?—soprano and two clarinets (1982) (short songs and nursery rhymes)
M. Wiegold, E. Pillinger, I. Mitchell *Aria.*
(6/93) (NMC) ① **NMCD007**

LUNA (Y CARNÉ), Pablo (1879–1942) Spain

SECTION V: STAGE WORKS

El Niño judío—zarzuela (1918—Madrid)
EXCERPTS—; 1. De España vengo; 2. Danza India;
3. Soy un rayito de luna.
1. V. de los Angeles, Sinfonia of London, R.
Frühbeck de Burgos (orch Gamley) *Concert*
(10/88) (EMI) ① **CDM7 69502-2**
Sangre de Reyes—zarzuela (1926—Pavón)
Adiós para siempre J. Carreras, ECO, E. Ricci
(r1994) *Concert* (2/95) (ERAT) ① **4509-95789-2**

LUNDQUIST, Torbjörn Iwan (b 1920) Finland

SECTION I: ORCHESTRAL

Arktis—symphonic band (1984)
Stockholm Sym Wind Orch, O. Vänskä *Concert*
(3/93) (CPRI) ① **CAP21415**

SECTION II: CHAMBER

Sisu for 6 percussions (1976)
Kroumata Perc Ens (pp1983) *Concert*
(1/84) (BIS) ① **BIS-CD232**

LUPI, Johannes (c1506–1539) Franco-Flemish

SECTION II: CHAMBER

Libro di gagliardo, tordiglione, Passo e mezzo, canario e passeggi—dance collection (pub 1607)
1. Balletto atta carretta.
1. Broadside Band, J. Barlow *Concert*
(3/88) (HYPE) ① CDA66244

SECTION IV: VOCAL AND CHORAL

Ergone conticuit—in Johannem Ockegi, Musicorum Principem, Naenia (Wds. Erasmus)
Cappella Nova, R. Taruskin *Ockeghem: Missa prolationum.* (2/87) (ASV) ① CDGAU103

LUPO, Thomas (c1598–1628) England

SECTION II: CHAMBER

Fantasies a 4—2 violins, 2 bass viols and organ
4, 9. Parley of Instr, P. Holman *Concert*
(9/91) (HYPE) ① CDA66395
Fantasy-airs a 3—2 violins, bass viol and organ
16, 17, 20. Parley of Instr, P. Holman *Concert*
(9/91) (HYPE) ① CDA66395
Fantasy-airs a 4—2 violins, bass viol and organ
5, 6, 7, 11, 12. Parley of Instr, P. Holman *Concert*
(9/91) (HYPE) ① CDA66395
Masque Music II and III—consort
(unidentified)
New London Consort, P. Pickett (r1992) *Concert*
(4/94) (LINN) ① CKD011

LURANO, Filippo de (c1475–1520) Italy

also known as Luprano

SECTION IV: VOCAL AND CHORAL

Ne le tue braze, O Vergene Maria—lauda (pub 1508) (in Petrucci's 'Lauda Libro secondo')
Daedalus Ens (r1992) *Concert*
(11/93) (ACCE) ① ACC9289D

LURIE, John (b 1952) USA

SECTION II: CHAMBER

Stranger then Paradise—string quartet
Balanescu Qt (r1992) *Concert*
(3/93) (ARGO) ① 436 565-2ZH

LUTOSŁAWSKI, Witold (1913–1994) Poland

SECTION I: ORCHESTRAL

Chain 1—chamber orchestra (1983)
Junge Deutsche Phil, H. Holliger *Concert*
(9/90) (POLS) ① PNCD044
Chain 2—violin and orchestra (1985)
A-S. Mutter, BBC SO, W. Lutosławski *Concert*
(2/89) (DG) ① 423 696-2GH
K. Jakowicz, Pomeranian PO, T. Ukigaya *Concert*
(11/89) (THOR) ① CTH2041
K. Jakowicz, Warsaw Nat PO, K. Kord *Concert*
(9/90) (POLS) ① PNCD044
A-S. Mutter, BBC SO, W. Lutosławski (1988)
Concert (12/94) (DG) ① [3] 445 487-2GX3
I. van Keulen, Philh, H. Schiff (r1995) *Schnittke: Viola Concerto.* (11/95) (SCHW) ① 315232
Chain 3—orchestra (1986)
Katowice RSO, W. Lutosławski *Concert*
(9/90) (POLS) ① PNCD044
BBC SO, W. Lutosławski *Concert*
(4/92) (DG) ① 431 664-2GH
Concerto for Cello and Orchestra (1970)
M. Rostropovich, Paris Orch, W. Lutosławski (1974)
Dutilleux: Cello Concerto.
(5/88) (EMI) ① CDC7 49304-2
R. Jabłoński, Katowice RSO, W. Lutosławski *Concert*
(9/90) (POLS) ① PNCD042
Concerto for Orchestra (1954)
Warsaw Nat PO, W. Rowicki *Concert*
(9/90) (POLS) ① PNCD040
Chicago SO, D. Barenboim (r1992) *Symphony 3.*
(8/93) (ERAT) ① 4509-91711-2

French Rad PO, M. Janowski (r1992) *Concert*
(11/93) (RCA) ① [2] 09026 61520-2
Polish Nat RSO, W. Lutosławski (r1976-7) *Concert*
(7/95) (EMI) ① CDM5 65305-2
Concerto for Piano and Orchestra
K. Zimerman, BBC SO, W. Lutosławski *Concert*
(4/92) (DG) ① 431 664-2GH
Dance Preludes—orchestra (1955)
T. King, ECO, A. Litton *Concert*
(1/88) (HYPE) ① CDA66215
J. Hilton, SNO, M. Bamert *Concert*
(10/88) (CHAN) ① CHAN8618
Camerata Vistula *Concert*
(11/91) (OLYM) ① OCD343
Double Concerto for oboe, harp and chamber orchestra (1980)
E. Brunner, M. Graf, Bamberg SO, L. Zagrosek (trans Brunner) *Concert* (4/90) (SCHW) ① 311065
Funeral music (1958)
Pomeranian PO, T. Ukigaya *Concert*
(11/89) (THOR) ① CTH2041
Warsaw Nat PO, W. Rowicki *Concert*
(9/90) (POLS) ① PNCD040
Polish Nat RSO, W. Lutosławski (r1976-7) *Concert*
(2/95) (EMI) ① CDM5 65076-2
Little Suite—orchestra (1951)
Pomeranian PO, T. Ukigaya *Concert*
(11/89) (THOR) ① CTH2041
Livre pour orchestre (1968)
Warsaw Nat PO, J. Krenz *Concert*
(9/90) (POLS) ① PNCD042
Polish Nat RSO, W. Lutosławski (r1976-7) *Concert*
(7/95) (EMI) ① CDM5 65305-2
Mi-parti—orchestra (1976)
Polish CO, W. Lutosławski *Concert*
(9/90) (POLS) ① PNCD043
Polish Nat RSO, W. Lutosławski (r1976-7) *Concert*
(7/95) (EMI) ① CDM5 65305-2
Novelette—orchestra (1978-79)
Junge Deutsche Phil, H. Holliger *Concert*
(9/90) (POLS) ① PNCD043
BBC SO, W. Lutosławski *Concert*
(4/92) (DG) ① 431 664-2GH
Paganini Variations—piano and orchestra (1978)
P. Jablonski, RPO, Vladimir Ashkenazy *Concert*
(12/92) (DECC) ① 436 239-2DH
Partita—violin and orchestra (1988) (rev of Partita for violin and piano)
A-S. Mutter, P. Moll, BBC SO, W. Lutosławski
Concert (2/89) (DG) ① 423 696-2GH
A-S. Mutter, P. Moll, BBC SO, W. Lutosławski
(r1988) *Concert* (12/94) (DG) ① [3] 445 487-2GX3
Postlude No. 1—orchestra (1958)
Katowice RSO, J. Krenz *Concert*
(9/90) (POLS) ① PNCD042
Preludes and Fugues—13 strings (1972)
Polish CO, W. Lutosławski *Concert*
(9/90) (POLS) ① PNCD043
Symphonic Variations—orchestra (1938)
Polish Nat RSO, W. Lutosławski (r1976-7) *Concert*
(2/95) (EMI) ① CDM5 65076-2
Symphony No. 1 (1947)
Katowice RSO, J. Krenz *Concert*
(9/90) (POLS) ① PNCD040
Polish Nat RSO, W. Lutosławski (r1976-7) *Concert*
(2/95) (EMI) ① CDM5 65076-2
Symphony No. 2 (1966-67)
Warsaw Nat PO, W. Lutosławski *Concert*
(9/90) (POLS) ① PNCD041
Polish Nat RSO, W. Lutosławski (r1976-7) *Concert*
(2/95) (EMI) ① CDM5 65076-2
Symphony No. 3 (1983)
BPO, W. Lutosławski (r1985) *Espaces du sommeil.*
(6/87) (PHIL) ① 416 387-2PH
Katowice RSO, A. Wit *Concert*
(9/90) (POLS) ① PNCD044
Chicago SO, D. Barenboim (r1992) *Concerto for Orchestra (1954).* (8/93) (ERAT) ① 4509-91711-2
Los Angeles PO, E-P. Salonen (r1985) *Concert*
(11/94) (SONY) ① SK66280
Symphony No. 4 (1993)
Los Angeles PO, E-P. Salonen (r1993) *Concert*
(11/94) (SONY) ① SK66280
Venetian games—orchestra (1961)
Pomeranian PO, T. Ukigaya *Concert*
(11/89) (THOR) ① CTH2041
Warsaw Nat PO, W. Rowicki *Concert*
(9/90) (POLS) ① PNCD041
Polish Nat RSO, W. Lutosławski (r1976-7) *Concert*
(7/95) (EMI) ① CDM5 65305-2

SECTION II: CHAMBER

Epitaph—oboe and piano (1979)
H. Holliger, S. Esztényi *Concert*
(9/90) (POLS) ① PNCD045

Grave—violin and piano (1981)
R. Jabłoński, S. Esztényi *Concert*
(9/90) (POLS) ① PNCD045
M. Wasiolka, M. Paderewski *Concert*
(10/91) (ACCO) ① 201142
W. Conway, Peter Evans (r1992) *Concert*
(10/93) (LINN) ① CKD009
Mini Overture—brass ensemble (1982)
PJBE *Concert* (2/88) (CHAN) ① CHAN8490
Mini Overture—brass quintet (1982)
Wallace Collection, J. Wallace *Concert*
(3/92) (COLL) ① Coll1229-2
Partita—violin and piano (1984)
K. Kulka, E. Knapnik *Concert*
(9/90) (POLS) ① PNCD045
T. Gadzina, M. Paderewski *Concert*
(10/91) (ACCO) ① 201142
String Quartet (1964)
LaSalle Qt *Concert* (8/88) (DG) ① 423 245-2GC
Varsovia Qt *Concert* (6/89) (OLYM) ① OCD328
LaSalle Qt *Concert* (9/90) (POLS) ① PNCD045
Hagen Qt *Concert* (9/91) (DG) ① 431 686-2GH
Wilanów Qt *Concert* (10/91) (ACCO) ① 201142
Cikada Qt (r1994) *Concert*
(12/95) (CALA) ① CACD77001
String Quartet (1965)
Arditti Qt *Concert* (4/92) (MONT) ① 789007
Subito—violin & piano (1992)
J. Kang, M. Chen (r1994) *Concert*
(8/95) (DINT) ① DICD920241
Variations on a Theme of Paganini (1941)
J. Łukaszczyk, M. Łukaszczyk *Concert*
(9/90) (POLS) ① PNCD045

SECTION III: INSTRUMENTAL

Bucolics—piano (1952)
E. Wiedner-Zając (r1993) *Concert*
(9/95) (DORI) ① DIS80121
12 Folk melodies—piano (1945)
1. Oh, my Johnny; 2. Hey, I come from Cracow; 3. There is a path; 4. The shepherd girl; 5. An apple hangs on the apple-tree; 6. A river flows from Sieradz; 7. Master Michael; 8. The lime-tree in the field; 9. Flirting; 10. The grove; 11. The gander; 12. The schoolmaster.
J. Bream (r1992: arr gtr: Bream) *Concert*
(4/94) (EMI) ① CDC7 54901-2
Sacher Variation—cello (1976)
T. Demenga (r1993) *Concert*
(8/95) (ECM) ① [2] 445 234-2
2 Studies—piano (1941)
M. Drewnowski *Concert*
(9/90) (POLS) ① PNCD045

SECTION IV: VOCAL AND CHORAL

Les Espaces du sommeil—baritone and orchestra
D. Fischer-Dieskau, BPO, W. Lutosławski (r1986) *Symphony 3.* (6/87) (PHIL) ① 416 387-2PH
J. Shirley-Quirk, Los Angeles PO, E-P. Salonen (r1985) *Concert* (11/94) (SONY) ① SK66280
Lacrimosa—soprano, choir and orchestra (1937)
S. Woytowicz, Silesian Phil Ch, Katowice RSO, W. Lutosławski *Concert* (9/90) (POLS) ① PNCD040
Paroles tissées—tenor and chamber orchestra (1965) (Wds. J. F. Chabrun)
L. Devos, Warsaw Nat PO, W. Lutosławski *Concert*
(9/90) (POLS) ① PNCD042
3 Poèmes d'Henri Michaux—20vv and orchestra (1963)
Polish Rad Chor, Katowice RSO, J. Krenz *Concert*
(9/90) (POLS) ① PNCD041
5 Songs—female voices and orchestra (1958)
H. Lukomska, Warsaw Nat PO, A. Markowski *Concert* (9/90) (POLS) ① PNCD045

LUTYENS, (Agnes) Elisabeth (1906–1983) England

SECTION I: ORCHESTRAL

6 Tempi—10 instruments, Op. 42 (1957)
Jane's Minstrels, R. Montgomery (r1992) *Concert*
(10/93) (NMC) ① NMCD011

SECTION II: CHAMBER

Chamber Concerto No. 1—nine instruments, Op. 8/1 (1939-40)
Jane's Minstrels, R. Montgomery (r1992) *Concert*
(10/93) (NMC) ① NMCD011
Driving out the Death—oboe quartet, Op. 81 (1971)
Redcliffe Ens *Concert* (11/92) (REDC) ① RR006

Trio—clarinet, cello and piano, Op. 135 (1979)
Mühlfeld Ens (r1993) *Concert*
(10/94) (CLRI) ① **CC0007**
Triolet I—clarinet/bass clarinet, cello and mandolin, Op. 160a (1982)
Jane's Minstrels (r1992) *Concert*
(10/93) (NMC) ① **NMCD011**
Triolet II—cello, marimba and harp, Op. 160b (1983)
Jane's Minstrels (r1992) *Concert*
(10/93) (NMC) ① **NMCD011**

SECTION IV: VOCAL AND CHORAL

As I walked out one evening—song (pub 1942) (Wds W.H. Auden)
A. Rolfe Johnson, G. Johnson (r1991/3) *Concert*
(8/94) (HYPE) ① **CDA66709**
Requiescat, 'in memoriam Igor Stravinsky'—soprano and string orchestra (1971)
J. Manning, Jane's Minstrels (r1992) *Concert*
(10/93) (NMC) ① **NMCD011**
The Valley of Hatsu-se—soprano, flute, clarinet, cello and piano, Op. 62 (1965)
1. Fuyu-Komori; 2. Uguisu no; 3. Koye tayezu; 4. Hana we ne ni; 5. Nake ya, nake; 6. Usu-zumi no; 7. Awa-yuki no; 8. Futuri-yukedo; 9. (Hatsu-se no ya).
J. Manning, Jane's Minstrels (r1992) *Concert*
(10/93) (NMC) ① **NMCD011**

SECTION V: STAGE WORKS

Isis and Osiris—lyric drama: 8vv and small orchestra, Op. 74 (1970)
Lament of Isis on the death of Osiris J. Manning
(r1992) *Concert* (10/93) (NMC) ① **NMCD011**

LUZZASCHI, Luzzasco (c1545–1607) Italy

SECTION IV: VOCAL AND CHORAL

Cor mio deh non languire—madrigal (2vv)
Consort of Musicke, A. Rooley *Concert*
(12/91) (DHM) ① **RD77154**
Non sa che sia dolore—madrigal (3vv)
Consort of Musicke, A. Rooley *Concert*
(12/91) (DHM) ① **RD77154**
O dolcezze amarissime—madrigal (4vv)
Consort of Musicke, A. Rooley *Concert*
(12/91) (DHM) ① **RD77154**
Occhi del pianto mio—madrigal (3vv)
Consort of Musicke, A. Rooley *Concert*
(12/91) (DHM) ① **RD77154**
T'amo mia vita—madrigal (3vv)
Consort of Musicke, A. Rooley (lte/dir) *Concert*
(2/89) (BIS) ① **BIS-CD392**
Consort of Musicke, A. Rooley *Concert*
(12/91) (DHM) ① **RD77154**

LVOV, Alexey Fyodorovich (1798–1870) Estonia

SECTION IV: VOCAL AND CHORAL

Standing by the Cross—Russian liturgical chant
N. Gedda, Paris Russian Orthodox Cath Ch, E. Evetz
Concert (1/93) (PHIL) ① **434 174-2PM**

LYAPUNOV, Sergey Mikhaylovich (1859–1924) Russia

SECTION I: ORCHESTRAL

Ballada in C sharp minor—overture, Op. 2 (1883 rev 1894-96)
Moscow St SO, F. Glushchenko (r1993) *Symphony 1.* (11/93) (OLYM) ① **OCD519**
Hashish—symphonic poem, Op. 53 (1913)
USSR Academy SO, E. Svetlanov *Concert*
(7/89) (OLYM) ① **OCD129**
Polonaise—orchestra, Op. 16 (1902)
USSR Academy SO, E. Svetlanov *Concert*
(7/89) (OLYM) ① **OCD129**
Rhapsody on Ukranian Themes in F sharp minor—piano and orchestra, Op. 28 (1907)
M. Ponti, Westphalian SO, S. Landau *Concert*
(5/93) (VOX) ① **115714-2**
Solemn Overture on Russian Theme, Op. 7 (1896)
USSR Academy SO, E. Svetlanov *Concert*
(7/89) (OLYM) ① **OCD129**
Symphony No. 1 in B minor—orchestra, Op. 12 (1887)
Moscow St SO, F. Glushchenko (r1993) *Ballada.*
(11/93) (OLYM) ① **OCD519**

Zhelyazova Volya—symphonic poem, Op. 37 (1909)
USSR Academy SO, E. Svetlanov *Concert*
(7/89) (OLYM) ① **OCD129**

SECTION III: INSTRUMENTAL

12 Studies, 'Études d'exécution transcendente'—piano, Op. 11 (pub 1900-05)
1. F sharp, 'Berceuse'; 2. D sharp, 'Ronde des fantômes'; 3. B, 'Carillon'; 4. G sharp minor, 'Terek'; 5. E, 'Nuite d'été'; 6. C sharp minor, 'Tempête'; 7. A, 'Idylle'; 8. F sharp minor, 'Chant épique'; 9. D, 'Harpes éoliennes'; 10. B minor, 'Lesghinka'; 11. G, 'Ronde des sylphes'; 12. E minor, 'Elégie en memoire de François Liszt'.
M. Binns (5/92) (PEAR) ① **SHECD9624**
K. Scherbakov (r1992) (4/94) (MARC) ① **8 223491**

LYATOSHYNSKY, Boris (Mykolayovich) (1895–1968) Ukraine

SECTION I: ORCHESTRAL

Fantastic March—orchestra, Op. 3 (1920)
Young Russia State SO, V. Baley (r1994) *Concert*
(1/95) (CDM) ① **RUS288 085**
Grazhyna—symphonic poem, Op. 58 (1955)
Ukrainian St SO, T. Kuchar (r1994) *Symphony 1.*
(4/95) (MARC) ① **8 223542**
Intermezzo—orchestra (1922, orch 1960s)
(orch cpsr from String Quartet No. 2)
Young Russia State SO, V. Baley (r1994) *Concert*
(1/95) (CDM) ① **RUS288 085**
Lyric Poem—orchestra, Op. 66 (1964)
Young Russia State SO, V. Baley (r1994) *Concert*
(1/95) (CDM) ① **RUS288 085**
Overture on four Ukrainian themes—orchestra, Op. 20 (1927)
Young Russia State SO, V. Baley (r1994) *Concert*
(1/95) (CDM) ① **RUS288 085**
Polish Suite—orchestra, Op. 60 (1961)
Young Russia State SO, V. Baley (r1994) *Concert*
(1/95) (CDM) ① **RUS288 085**
Symphony No. 1 in A, Op. 2 (1919)
Ukrainian St SO, T. Kuchar (r1994) *Grazhyna.*
(4/95) (MARC) ① **8 223542**
Symphony No. 2, Op. 26 (1935-36 rev 1940)
Ukrainian St SO, T. Kuchar (r1993) *Symphony 3.*
(11/94) (MARC) ① **8 223540**
Symphony No. 3 in B minor, Op. 50 (1951 rev 1954)
Ukrainian St SO, T. Kuchar (r1993) *Symphony 2.*
(11/94) (MARC) ① **8 223540**
Ukrainian St SO, V. Gnedash (r1976) *Romeo and Juliet Suite.* (7/95) (RUSS) ① **RDCD11060**
Symphony No. 4 in B flat minor, Op. 63 (1963)
Ukrainian St SO, T. Kuchar (r1993) *Symphony 5.*
(1/95) (MARC) ① **8 223541**
Cracow PO, R. Bader (r1994) *Symphony 5.*
(4/95) (CPO) ① **CPO999 183-2**
Symphony No. 5 in C, 'Slavonic', Op. 67 (1965-66)
Ukrainian St SO, T. Kuchar (r1993) *Symphony 4.*
(1/95) (MARC) ① **8 223541**
Cracow PO, R. Bader (r1994) *Symphony 4.*
(4/95) (CPO) ① **CPO999 183-2**

SECTION V: STAGE WORKS

Romeo and Juliet—concert suite from incidental music, Op. 56 (1955)
Ukrainian Rad & TV SO, V. Gnedash (r1976)
Symphony 3. (7/95) (RUSS) ① **RDCD11060**

LYSENKO, Mykola Vytal'yevych (1842–1912) Ukraine

SECTION IV: VOCAL AND CHORAL

The Boundless field—song (Wds. I. Franko)
P. Plishka, T. Hrynkiv *Concert*
(11/92) (FORL) ① **UCD16645**
Days pass—song (Wds. T. Shevchenko)
P. Plishka, T. Hrynkiv *Concert*
(11/92) (FORL) ① **UCD16645**
Oh, Dnieper!—song (Wds. T. Shevchenko)
P. Plishka, T. Hrynkiv *Concert*
(11/92) (FORL) ① **UCD16645**
Oh Hetmans!—song (Wds. T. Shevchenko)
P. Plishka, T. Hrynkiv *Concert*
(11/92) (FORL) ① **UCD16645**

MAC LOW, Jackson (b 1922) USA

comp with Anne Tardos, b 1943, France

SECTION IV: VOCAL AND CHORAL

First Four-Language Word Event in Memoriam John Cage—visual poem/performance score (1992)
J. Mac Low, A. Tardos (r1993) *Concert*
(8/94) (KOCH) ① [2] **37238-2**

MACAULAY, Tony (20th Cent) England

SECTION V: STAGE WORKS

Windy City—musical show (1982—London)
(Book & Lyrics Vosburgh, after Hecht & MacArthur)
EXCERPTS: 1. Overture; 2. Hey Hallelujah!; 3. Wait Till I Get You On Your Own; 4. Waltz for Mollie; 5. Saturday; 6. Long Night Again Tonight; 7. No One Walks Out On Me; 8. Saturday (reprise); 9. Windy City; 10. Round In Circles; 11. I Can Just Imagine It; 12. I Can Talk To You; 13. Perfect Casting; 14. Bensinger's Poem; 15. Water Under the Bridge; 16. Windy City (reprise).
Cpte D. Waterman, D. Langton, A. Rodgers, Orig London Cast, A. Bowles (r1982) *Windy City.*
(12/94) (EMI) ① **CDANGEL 8**
3, 9, 12. D. Waterman, D. Langton, Orig London Cast, A. Bowles (r1982; arr Ingman) *Windy City.*
(12/94) (EMI) ① **CDANGEL 8**

MCCABE, John (b 1939) England

SECTION II: CHAMBER

3 Pieces—clarinet and piano (1964)
1. Nocturne: Aria; 2. Improvisation: Bossa Nova; 3. Fantasy.
N. Carpenter, D. McArthur *Concert*
(10/92) (HERA) ① **HAVPCD152**

MACCOMBIE, Bruce (b 1943) USA

SECTION III: INSTRUMENTAL

Nightshade Rounds—guitar (1979)
S. Isbin (r 1992) *Concert*
(7/94) (VIRG) ① **VC5 45024-2**

MACCUNN, Hamish (1868–1916) Scotland

SECTION I: ORCHESTRAL

The Land of the mountain and the flood—overture, Op. 3 (1887)
SNO, A. Gibson *Concert*
(9/85) (CHAN) ① **CHAN8379**
RLPO, G. Llewellyn (r1992) *Concert*
(6/93) (ARGO) ① **436 401-2ZH**

MCDONALD, Harl (1899–1955) USA

SECTION I: ORCHESTRAL

Concerto for Two Pianos and Orchestra (1936)
J. Behrend, A. Kelberine, Philadelphia, L. Stokowski
(r1937) *Concert* (10/93) (STOK) ① **LSCD20**
Festival of the Workers—orchestra
Dance of the Workers Philadelphia, L. Stokowski
(r1935) *Concert* (10/93) (STOK) ① **LSCD20**
The Legend of the Arkansas Traveller—orchestra (1939)
Philadelphia, L. Stokowski (r1940) *Concert*
(10/93) (STOK) ① **LSCD20**
San Juan Capistrano—nocturnes for orchestra (1938)
1. The Mission; 2. Fiesta.
Boston SO, S. Koussevitzky (r1939) *Concert*
(12/91) (PEAR) ① **GEMMCD9492**
Symphony No. 2, '(The) Rhumba' (1934)
Rhumba Philadelphia, L. Stokowski (r1935) *Concert*
(10/93) (STOK) ① **LSCD20**

MACDOWELL, Edward (Alexander) (1860–1908) USA

SECTION I: ORCHESTRAL

Concerto for Piano and Orchestra No. 1 in A minor, Op. 15 (1882)
D. Amato, LPO, P. Freeman *Piano Concerto 2*.
(6/87) (ARHD) ① **DARC1**
T. Tirino, Bulgarian RSO, V. Kazandjiev (r1991)
Piano Concerto 2. (10/93) (CENT) ① **CRC2149**

Concerto for Piano and Orchestra No. 2 in D minor, Op. 23 (1884–86)
D. Amato, LPO, P. Freeman *Piano Concerto 1*.
(6/87) (ARHD) ① **DARC1**
E. List, Westphalian SO, S. Landau *Beach: Piano Concerto*. (5/93) (VOX) ① **115718-2**
T. Tirino, Bulgarian RSO, V. Kazandjiev (r1991)
Piano Concerto 1. (10/93) (CENT) ① **CRC2149**

SECTION II: CHAMBER

Sea Pieces—piano, Op. 55 (1898)
1. To the sea; 2. From the wandering iceberg; 3. AD1620; 4. Starlight; 5. Song; 6. From the depths; 7. Nautilaus; 7. In mid-ocean.
J. Barbagallo (r1993; arr pf) *Concert*
(4/95) (MARC) ① **8 223631**

SECTION III: INSTRUMENTAL

2 Fantasiestücke—piano, Op. 17 (1883)
1. Erzählung; 2. Hexentanz.
2. S. Hough (r1986) *Concert*
(1/89) (VIRG) ① **VC7 59509-2**
2. L. Godowsky (r1924) *Concert*
(4/89) (APR) ① [2] **APR7011**
2. C. Cann, A. Cann (r1992: arr Niemann) *Concert*
(5/93) (PP) ① **PP10393**

Fireside Tales—piano, Op. 61 (1901-02)
1. An old love story; 2. Ol Brier Rabbit; 3. From a German heart; 4. Of Salamanders; 5. A haunted house; 6. By smouldering timbers.
J. Barbagallo (r1993) *Concert*
(4/95) (MARC) ① **8 223631**

New England Idyls—piano, Op. 62 (1901-02)
1. An old garden; 2. Mid-summer; 3. Mid-winter; 4. With sweet lavender; 5. In deep woods; 6. Indian idyl; 7. To an old white pine; 8. From Puritan days; 9. From a log cabin; 10. The joy of autumn.
J. Barbagallo (r1993) *Concert*
(4/95) (MARC) ① **8 223631**
M. Legrand (r1994) *Concert*
(7/95) (ERAT) ① **4509-96386-2**

Sonata for Piano No. 1 in G minor, 'Tregian', Op. 45 (1891/2)
J. Tocco *Concert* (7/89) (KING) ① **KCLCD2009**

Sonata for Piano No. 2 in G minor, 'Eroica', Op. 50 (1894/5)
J. Tocco *Concert* (7/89) (KING) ① **KCLCD2009**
C. Fierro *Etudes, op 46*. (10/90) (DELO) ① **DE1019**

Sonata for Piano No. 3 in D minor, 'Norse', Op. 57 (1899)
J. Tocco *Concert* (7/89) (KING) ① **KCLCD2009**

Sonata for Piano No. 4 in E minor, 'Keltic', Op. 59
G. Landes *Concert* (7/89) (KOCH) ① **37045-2**

12 Virtuoso Etudes—piano, Op. 46 (1893-94)
1. Novelette; 2. Moto perpetuo; 3. Wilde Jagd; 4. Improvisation; 5. Elfentanz; 6. Valse triste; 7. Burleske; 8. Bluette; 9. Träumerei; 10. Märzwind; 11. Impromptu; 12. Polonaise.
C. Fierro *Piano Sonata 2*.
(10/90) (DELO) ① **DE1019**

Woodland Sketches—piano, Op. 51 (1896)
1. To a wild rose; 2. Will-o'-the-wisp; 3. At an old trysting place; 4. In Autumn; 5. From an Indian lodge; 6. To a water-lily; 7. From Uncle Remus; 8. A deserted farm; 9. By a meadow brook; 10. Told at sunset.
J. Barbagallo (r1993) *Concert*
(4/95) (MARC) ① **8 223631**
1. M. Lympany *Concert* (1/89) (EMIL) ① **CDZ110**
1. E. Brown, J. Zayde (r c1940: arr Hartmann) *Concert* (7/93) (APR) ① [2] **APR7016**
1. R. Goss-Custard (r c1930: arr org) *Concert*
(9/94) (BEUL) ① **1PD5**
1. Manhattan CO, R.A. Clark (r1994; arr A. Luck) *Concert* (7/95) (KOCH) ① **37282-2**

SECTION IV: VOCAL AND CHORAL

3 Lieder, Op. 11 (1881) (Wds. Heine)
1. Mein Liebchen; 2. Du liebst mich nicht; 3. Oben wo die Sterne.
Cpte T. Hampson, A. Guzelimian *Concert*
(4/92) (TELD) ① **9031-72168-2**

2 Lieder, Op. 12 (1880-81)
1. Nachtlied (wds. Geibel); 2. Das Rosenband (wds. Klopstock).
Cpte T. Hampson, A. Guzelimian *Concert*
(4/92) (TELD) ① **9031-72168-2**

MCEWEN, Sir John (Blackwood) (1868–1948) Scotland

SECTION I: ORCHESTRAL

3 Border Ballads—orchestra (1905-08)
1. Coronach; 2. Grey Galloway; 3. The Demon Lover.
LPO, A. Mitchell (r1993)
(3/94) (CHAN) ① **CHAN9241**

Hills O' Heather—retrospect for cello and orchestra (1918)
M. Welsh, LPO, A. Mitchell (r1994) *Concert*
(6/95) (CHAN) ① **CHAN9345**

Solway Symphony (1911)
LPO, A. Mitchell (r1994) *Concert*
(6/95) (CHAN) ① **CHAN9345**

Where the Wild Thyme blows—orchestra
LPO, A. Mitchell (r1994) *Concert*
(6/95) (CHAN) ① **CHAN9345**

MACFARREN, Sir George Alexander (1813–1887) England

SECTION I: ORCHESTRAL

Chevy Chace—overture (1836)
English Northern Philh, D. Lloyd-Jones *Concert*
(1/92) (HYPE) ① **CDA66515**

MACHADO, Manuel (c1590–1646) Portugal/Spain

SECTION IV: VOCAL AND CHORAL

Afuera, afuera que sale—song
M. Figueras, Hespèrion XX, J. Savall *Concert*
(2/92) (ASTR) ① **E8729**

Dos estrellas le siguen—song
G. Lesne, Circa 1500, N. Hadden *Concert*
(9/92) (VIRG) ① **VC7 59071-2**

Paso a paso, empeños mios—song
G. Lesne, Circa 1500, N. Hadden *Concert*
(9/92) (VIRG) ① **VC7 59071-2**

MACHAUT, Guillaume de (c1300–1377) France

SECTION II: CHAMBER

Danse balladée—2 vielles (arr Kammen/Mealy)
S. Kammen, R. Mealy (r1993) *Concert*
(10/94) (NALB) ① **NA068CD**

Hoquetus David—double hocket
London Early Music Consort, D. Munrow *Concert*
(8/85) (ARCH) ① **415 292-2AH**

SECTION IV: VOCAL AND CHORAL

Ay mi! dame de valour—3vv
Gothic Voices, C. Page (r1994) *Concert*
(2/95) (HYPE) ① **CDA66739**

C'est force, faire le weil—virelai: 1v
Gothic Voices, C. Page *Concert*
(3/92) (HYPE) ① **CDA66463**

Comment qu'a moy lonteinne—virelai: 1v
Gothic Voices, C. Page *Concert*
(3/92) (HYPE) ① **CDA66463**

Dame, a vous sans retollir—virelai: 1v (from the Remede de Fortune)
PAN Ens (r1993) *Concert*
(10/94) (NALB) ① **NA068CD**

Dame, de qui toute ma joie vient—ballade: 3vv (from the Remede de Fortune)
PAN Ens, R. Mealy (r1993) *Concert*
(10/94) (NALB) ① **NA068CD**

Dame, je sui cilz/Fins cuer doulz—isorhythmic motet: 3vv
Gothic Voices, C. Page, A. Lawrence-King *Concert*
(6/93) (HYPE) ① **CDA66619**

Dame, mon cuer en vous remaint—rondeau: 3vv (from the Remede de Fortune)
PAN Ens (r1993) *Concert*
(10/94) (NALB) ① **NA068CD**

Dame, vostre doulz viaire—ballade: 3vv
E. Lamandier *Concert* (2/88) (ALIE) ① **AL1019**

De toutes flours—ballade: 3vv
PAN Ens (r1993) *Concert*
(10/94) (NALB) ① **NA068CD**

Donnez, signeurs—ballade: 3vv
Gothic Voices, C. Page (lte/dir) *Concert*
(9/92) (HYPE) ① **CDA66588**

Dou mal qui m'a longuement—virelai: 1v
E. Lamandier *Concert* (2/88) (ALIE) ① **AL1019**

En amer a douce vie—ballade: 3vv (from the Remede de Fortune)
PAN Ens, R. Mealy (r1993) *Concert*
(10/94) (NALB) ① **NA068CD**

Foy porter, honneur garder—virelai: 1v
E. Kirkby *Concert* (9/87) (HYPE) ① **CDA66227**
E. Lamandier *Concert* (2/88) (ALIE) ① **AL1019**

J'aim la flour de valour—lai: 1v
E. Lamandier *Concert* (2/88) (ALIE) ① **AL1019**

Je ne cesse de prier (Le lai de la Fonteinne)—lai: 1v and 3vv
Hilliard Ens, P. Hillier *Concert*
(2/90) (HYPE) ① **CDA66358**

Joie, plaisence et douce norriture—chanson royal: 1v (from the Remede de Fortune)
PAN Ens (r1993) *Concert*
(10/94) (NALB) ① **NA068CD**

Lasse! comment oublieray/Se j'aim mon loyal/Pour quoy me bat mes maris?—isorhythmic motet: 3vv
London Early Music Consort, D. Munrow *Concert*
(8/85) (ARCH) ① **415 292-2AH**

Liement me deport—virelai: 1v
PAN Ens (r1993) *Concert*
(10/94) (NALB) ① **NA068CD**

Ma fin est mon commencement—rondeau: 3vv
Hilliard Ens, P. Hillier *Concert*
(2/90) (HYPE) ① **CDA66358**

Messe de Nostre Dame—4vv
Taverner Consort, A. Parrott *Anon: Festival of the Virgin Mary*. (8/88) (EMI) ① **CDC7 47949-2**
Hilliard Ens, P. Hillier *Concert*
(2/90) (HYPE) ① **CDA66358**

Pas de tor en thies païs—ballade: 3vv
Gothic Voices, C. Page (lte/dir) *Concert*
(9/92) (HYPE) ① **CDA66588**

Quand je ne voy ma dame—rondeau: 3vv
Gothic Voices, C. Page (lte/dir) *Concert*
(9/92) (HYPE) ① **CDA66588**

Quant je sui mis au retour—virelai: 1v
Hilliard Ens *Concert* (6/91) (HYPE) ① **CDA66370**

Qui es promesses de Fortune/Ha, Fortune! trop suis mis loing/ Et ne scet on adjuvet—isorhythmic motet: 3vv
London Early Music Consort, D. Munrow *Concert*
(8/85) (ARCH) ① **415 292-2AH**

Qui n'aroit autre deport—lai: 1v (from the Remede de Fortune)
PAN Ens (r1993) *Concert*
(10/94) (NALB) ① **NA068CD**

Riches d'amour et mendians—ballade: 2vv
Gothic Voices, C. Page (lte/dir) *Concert*
(9/92) (HYPE) ① **CDA66588**

Rose, liz, printemps, verdure—rondeau: 4vv
PAN Ens (r1993) *Concert*
(10/94) (NALB) ① **NA068CD**

Se mesdisans en acort—virelai: 1v
Gothic Voices, C. Page, A. Lawrence-King *Concert*
(6/93) (HYPE) ① **CDA66619**

Tant doucement me sens emprisonnes—rondeau: 4vv
Gothic Voices, C. Page *Concert*
(3/92) (HYPE) ① **CDA66463**

Tels rit au main qui au soir—complainte: 1v (from the Remede de Fortune)
PAN Ens (r1993) *Concert*
(10/94) (NALB) ① **NA068CD**

Tres bonne et belle, mi oueil—virelai: 3vv
Gothic Voices, C. Page, A. Lawrence-King *Concert*
(6/93) (HYPE) ① **CDA66619**

Trop plus est bele/Biaute paree/Je ne sui mie—isorhythmic motet: 3vv
Gothic Voices, C. Page, A. Lawrence-King *Concert*
(6/93) (HYPE) ① **CDA66619**
Second part: Biaute paree PAN Ens, R. Mealy
(r1993) *Concert* (10/94) (NALB) ① **NA068CD**

MÂCHE, François-Bernard (b 1935) France

SECTION II: CHAMBER

Eridan—string quartet, Op. 57 (1986)
Arditti Qt *Concert* (9/92) (MONT) ① **782002**

MCHUGH, Jimmy (1894–1969) USA

SECTION I: ORCHESTRAL

Universal Pictures Fanfare
National PO, C. Gerhardt *Concert*
(10/92) (RCA) ① GD82792

MACHY, 'Sieur' de (fl 1686–92) France

SECTION III: INSTRUMENTAL

Pièces de viole—viola da gamba (pub 1685)
(Nos 1-4 staff notation; 5-8 tabulature)
1. D minor; 2. D; 3. G minor; 4. G; 5. A minor; 6. A; 7. D minor; 8. D.
1, 3, 4. J. Savall (1/89) (ASTR) ① E7746
4, 7. P. Pierlot (r1992) *Concert*
(2/94) (RICE) ① RIC118100

MACKENZIE, Sir Alexander (Campbell) (1847–1935) Scotland

SECTION I: ORCHESTRAL

Benedictus—chamber orchestra (1888) (arr cpsr from vn & pf pieces, Op. 37)
BBC Scottish SO, M. Brabbins (r1994) *Concert*
(5/95) (HYPE) ① CDA66764
Britannia—nautical overture, Op. 52 (1894)
English Northern Philh, D. Lloyd-Jones *Concert*
(1/92) (HYPE) ① CDA66515
Scottish Rhapsody No. 2, 'Burns', Op. 24 (1880)
BBC Scottish SO, M. Brabbins (r1994) *Concert*
(5/95) (HYPE) ① CDA66764
Twelfth Night—concert overture, Op. 40 (1888)
BBC Scottish SO, M. Brabbins (r1994) *Concert*
(5/95) (HYPE) ① CDA66764

SECTION V: STAGE WORKS

Coriolanus—concert suite from incidental music, Op. 61 (pub 1906)
BBC Scottish SO, M. Brabbins (r1994) *Concert*
(5/95) (HYPE) ① CDA66764
The Cricket on the Hearth—opera: 3 acts, Op. 62 (1901; staged 1914—London) (Lib. J Sturgis, after Dickens)
EXCERPTS: 1. Overture.
1. BBC Scottish SO, M. Brabbins (r1994) *Concert*
(5/95) (HYPE) ① CDA66764

MCKENZIE, Mark (20th cent) USA

SECTION V: STAGE WORKS

Son of Darkness: To Die For II—film score (1991)
EXCERPTS: 1. Finale.
1. OST, M. McKenzie (r1991) *Concert*
(10/93) (SILV) ① FILMCD127

MACKEY, Steven (b 1956) USA

SECTION II: CHAMBER

Physical Property—guitar and string quartet (1992)
Kronos Qt, S. Mackey (r1992) *Concert*
(8/93) (NONE) ① 7559-79310-2

MCKIE, Sir William (Neil) (1901–1984) Australia

SECTION IV: VOCAL AND CHORAL

Psalm 121—I will lift up mine eyes (1960)
Westminster Abbey Ch, I. Simcock, M. Neary *Concert*
(10/89) (CARL) ① PCD919
We wait for thy loving kindness, O God—antiphon (1947) (for the wedding of Princess Elizabeth & Philip Mountbatten)
Westminster Abbey Ch, M. Neary, M. Baker (r1994) *Concert*
(12/95) (SONY) ① SK66614

MCKINLEY, William Thomas (b 1938) USA

SECTION IV: VOCAL AND CHORAL

4 Text Settings—choir a cappella (1979) (Wds. M M M McKinley)
J. Oliver Chorale, J. Oliver (r1992) *Concert*
(5/95) (KOCH) ① 37178-2

MCKUEN, Rod (b 1933) USA

SECTION V: STAGE WORKS

The Unknown War—film score (?1978)
EXCERPTS: 1. Barbarossa; 2. Kiev.
1, 2. USSR Cinema SO, S. Redwine (r1978) *Concert*
(11/91) (STAN) ① STZ112

MCLAUGHLIN, John (b 1942) England/USA

SECTION I: ORCHESTRAL

Concerto for Guitar and Orchestra, '(The) Mediterranean' (1984)
J. McLaughlin, LSO, M. Tilson Thomas *Concert*
(8/90) (SONY) ① MK45578

SECTION II: CHAMBER

Brise de coeur—guitar and piano
J. McLaughlin, K. Labèque *Concert*
(8/90) (SONY) ① MK45578
Montana—guitar and piano
J. McLaughlin, K. Labèque *Concert*
(8/90) (SONY) ① MK45578
2 Sisters—guitar and piano
J. McLaughlin, K. Labèque *Concert*
(8/90) (SONY) ① MK45578
Until such time—guitar and piano
J. McLaughlin, K. Labèque *Concert*
(8/90) (SONY) ① MK45578
Zakir—guitar and piano
J. McLaughlin, K. Labèque *Concert*
(8/90) (SONY) ① MK45578

MCLEOD, John (b 1934) Scotland

SECTION II: CHAMBER

The Song of Dionysius—percussion and piano (1989)
E. Glennie, Philip Smith *Concert*
(1/92) (RCA) ① RD60557

MACMILLAN, Sir Ernest (1893–1973) Canada

SECTION III: INSTRUMENTAL

Cortège académique—organ (1953)
J. Watts (r1992) *Concert*
(8/94) (PRIO) ① PRCD414

MACMILLAN, James (b 1959) Scotland

SECTION I: ORCHESTRAL

The Confession of Isobel Gowdie—orchestra (1990)
BBC Scottish SO, J. Maksymiuk *Tryst.*
(10/92) (SCHW) ① 310502
Tryst—orchestra (1989)
BBC Scottish SO, J. Maksymiuk *Confession of Isobel Gowdie.*
(10/92) (SCHW) ① 310502
Veni, veni, Emmanuel—concerto: percussion and orchestra (1992)
E. Glennie, Scottish CO, J-P. Saraste (r1993) *Concert*
(9/93) (CATA) ① 09026 61916-2

SECTION II: CHAMBER

After the tryst—violin and piano (1988)
R. Crouch, P. Evans (r1993) *Concert*
(9/93) (CATA) ① 09026 61916-2
3 Dawn Rituals—chamber ensemble (trans cpsr from 'The Piper at the Gates of Dawn')
Scottish CO, J. MacMillan (r1993) *Concert*
(9/93) (CATA) ① 09026 61916-2
Kiss on Wood—violin and piano (1994)
M. Bachmann, J. Klibonoff (r1994) *Concert*
(5/95) (CATA) ① 09026 62668-2
'...others see us...'—mixed ensemble (1990)
Scottish CO, J. MacMillan (r1993) *Concert*
(9/93) (CATA) ① 09026 61916-2

Untold—wind quintet (1987 rev 1991)
Scottish CO, J. MacMillan (r1993) *Concert*
(9/93) (CATA) ① 09026 61916-2

SECTION IV: VOCAL AND CHORAL

Cantos Sagrados, 'Sacred Songs'—choir & organ (1989)
Polyphony, C. Bowers-Broadbent, S. Layton, J. MacMillan (r1994) *Seven Last Words.*
(5/95) (CATA) ① 09026 68125-2
Seven Last Words from the Cross—choir & string orchestra (1993)
Polyphony, London CO, S. Layton, J. MacMillan (r1994) *Cantos Sagrados.*
(5/95) (CATA) ① 09026 68125-2

SECTION V: STAGE WORKS

Búsqueda—music-theatre piece (1988) (Texts trans. D G Markus)
Cpte J. Stevenson, Ruth Anderson, C. Spink, A. Bentley, Scottish CO, J. MacMillan (r1993) *Visitatio Sepulchri.*
(4/95) (CATA) ① 09026 62669-2
Visitatio Sepulchri—sacred opera: 3 scenes (1993—Glasgow) (Text 13th-Century Latin Easter play)
Cpte O. Blackburn, C. Bunning, T. Dives, R. O. Forbes, A. Oke, S. Richardson, R. Bryson, Scottish CO, I. Bolton (r1993) *Búsqueda.*
(4/95) (CATA) ① 09026 62669-2

MACMILLEN, Francis (1885–1973) USA

SECTION II: CHAMBER

Causerie (Prairy flowers)—violin and piano
F. Macmillen, anon (r1909) *Concert*
(7/93) (APR) ① [2] APR7016

MACMURROUGH, Dermot (1872–1943) Ireland

SECTION IV: VOCAL AND CHORAL

Macushla, your sweet voice is calling—song (pub 1910) (Wds. J. Rowe)
J. McCormack, orch (r1911) *Concert*
(5/93) (MMOI) ① CDMOIR418
R. Crooks, orch (r1933) *Concert*
(9/93) (CLAR) ① CDGSE78-50-50
H. Nash, G. Moore (r1931) *Concert*
(11/95) (PEAR) ① GEMMCD9175

MCNEELY, Joel (20th Cent) USA

SECTION V: STAGE WORKS

Iron Will—film score (1994)
EXCERPTS: 1. Main Title; 2. Jack's Death; 3. Leaving Birch Ridge; 4. The Race Begins; 5. Pushing Onward; 6. Gus Rescues Will; 7. Devil's Slide; 8. The Final Day; 9. Race to the Finish; 10. Crossing the Line; 11. End Credits.
1-11. OST, J. McNeely (r1994)
(8/94) (VARE) ① VSD5467

MACONCHY, Elizabeth (1907–1994) England

SECTION I: ORCHESTRAL

Concertino No. 1—clarinet and string orchestra (1945)
T. King, ECO, B. Wordsworth (r1992) *Concert*
(12/93) (HYPE) ① CDA66634
Concertino No. 2—clarinet and small orchestra (1984)
T. King, ECO, B. Wordsworth (r1992) *Concert*
(12/93) (HYPE) ① CDA66634

SECTION II: CHAMBER

5 Sketches—viola and piano (1984)
P. Dukes, S. Rahman (r1992) *Concert*
(4/94) (GAMU) ① GAMCD537
String Quartet No. 1 (1932-33)
Hanson Qt *Concert* (11/89) (UNIC) ① DKPCD9080
String Quartet No. 2 (1936)
Hanson Qt *Concert* (11/89) (UNIC) ① DKPCD9080
String Quartet No. 3 (1938)
Hanson Qt *Concert* (11/89) (UNIC) ① DKPCD9080
String Quartet No. 4 (1942-43)
Hanson Qt *Concert* (11/89) (UNIC) ① DKPCD9080
String Quartet No. 5 (1948)
Hanson Qt *Concert* (11/89) (UNIC) ① DKPCD9081
String Quartet No. 6 (1950)
Bingham Qt *Concert* (6/90) (UNIC) ① DKPCD9081

String Quartet No. 7 (1955-56)
Bingham Qt *Concert*   (6/90) (UNIC) ① **DKPCD9081**
String Quartet No. 8 (1966)
Bingham Qt *Concert*   (6/90) (UNIC) ① **DKPCD9081**
String Quartet No. 9 (1968)
Mistry Qt *Concert*   (2/91) (UNIC) ① **DKPCD9082**
String Quartet No. 10 (1972)
Mistry Qt *Concert*   (2/91) (UNIC) ① **DKPCD9082**
String Quartet No. 11 (1976)
Mistry Qt *Concert*   (2/91) (UNIC) ① **DKPCD9082**
String Quartet No. 12 (1979)
Mistry Qt *Concert*   (2/91) (UNIC) ① **DKPCD9082**
String Quartet No. 13, 'Quartetto Corto'
(1984)
Mistry Qt *Concert*   (2/91) (UNIC) ① **DKPCD9082**

SECTION IV: VOCAL AND CHORAL

**Have you seen but a bright lily grow—song
(pub 1930)** (Wds Jonson)
A. Rolfe Johnson, G. Johnson (r1991/3) *Concert*
(8/94) (HYPE) ① **CDA66709**
Meditation for his Mistress—song (pub 1930)
(Wds Herrick)
A. Rolfe Johnson, G. Johnson (r1991/3) *Concert*
(8/) (HYPE) ① **CDA66709**
**My dark heart—song (198 , Wds. Petrarch,
trans J M Synge)**
Lontano, O. de la Martinez *Concert*
(9/92) (LORE) ① **LNT101**

MCPHAIL, Lindsay (1895-1965) USA

composed in collaboration with Walter Michels (19t

SECTION I: ORCHESTRAL

San
London Sinfonietta, S. Rattle *Concert*
(12/87) (EMI) ① **CDC7 47991-2**

MCPHEE, Colin (1901-1964) Canada/USA

SECTION II: CHAMBER

**Balinese Ceremonial Music—piano duet: 4
hands**
1. Pwmúngkah (overture to Shadowplay); 2. Rébong
(love music from Shaowplay); 3. Gambangan
(intermezzo); 4. Lagú Delèm (music from
Shadowplay); 5. Tabú Telú (ceremonial music).
B. Britten, C. McPhee (r1941) *Concert*
(10/95) (PEAR) ① **GEMMCD9177**

MACPHERSON, (Charles) Stewart (1865-1941) England

SECTION III: INSTRUMENTAL

Andante in G—organ
D. Briggs *Concert*   (7/91) (PRIO) ① **PRCD322**

MACQUE, Giovanni de (?1548-50-1614) Flanders

SECTION II: CHAMBER

**Gagliarda seconda—fl, va da gamba, Italian
hp & vihuela**
Tragicomedia *Concert*
(9/92) (EMI) ① **CDC7 54191-2**

SECTION III: INSTRUMENTAL

Gagliarda prima (1617) (British Museum MS)
A. Lawrence-King *Concert*
(6/92) (HYPE) ① **CDA66518**
Prima stravaganza (1617) (British Museum
MS)
A. Lawrence-King *Concert*
(6/92) (HYPE) ① **CDA66518**
Toccata a modo di trombetta (1617) (British
Museum MS)
A. Lawrence-King *Concert*
(6/92) (HYPE) ① **CDA66518**

SECTION IV: VOCAL AND CHORAL

Bacciami vita mia—madrigal: 6vv
M. Arruabarrena, K. van Laethem, M. Valenta, J.
Benet, M. van Altena, J. Cabré, T. de Zwart, A. Pols,
R. Van Der Meer, K. Junghänel (lte/dir) *Concert*
(1/92) (ACCE) ① **ACC8864D**
Hor un laccio—madrigal: 5vv (stanza IV of a
6-stanza cycle by various comps)
M. Arruabarrena, K. van Laethem, M. Valenta, J.
Benet, M. van Altena, J. Cabré, T. de Zwart, A. Pols,
R. Van Der Meer, K. Junghänel (lte/dir) *Concert*
(1/92) (ACCE) ① **ACC8864D**

Io canterò—madrigal: 5vv
M. Arruabarrena, K. van Laethem, M. Valenta, J.
Benet, M. van Altena, J. Cabré, T. de Zwart, A. Pols,
R. Van Der Meer, K. Junghänel (lte/dir) *Concert*
(1/92) (ACCE) ① **ACC8864D**
Vorria saper da voi—madrigal: 6vv
M. Arruabarrena, K. van Laethem, M. Valenta, J.
Benet, M. van Altena, J. Cabré, T. de Zwart, A. Pols,
R. Van Der Meer, K. Junghänel (lte/dir) *Concert*
(1/92) (ACCE) ① **ACC8864D**

MADERNA, Bruno (1920-1973) Italy

SECTION I: ORCHESTRAL

**Concerto for Oboe and Orchestra No. 1
(1962, rev 1963)**
H. Holliger, Cologne RSO, G. Bertini (r1993) *Concert*
(9/94) (PHIL) ① **442 015-2PH**
**Concerto for Oboe and Orchestra No. 2
(1967)**
H. Holliger, Cologne RSO, G. Bertini (r1993) *Concert*
(9/94) (PHIL) ① **442 015-2PH**
**Concerto for Oboe and Orchestra No. 3
(1973)**
H. Holliger, Cologne RSO, G. Bertini (r1993) *Concert*
(9/94) (PHIL) ① **442 015-2PH**

SECTION V: STAGE WORKS

Hyperion—opera (1960-69) (Lib. after
Hölderlin)
Cpte P. Walmsley-Clark, B. Ganz, J. Zoon, Jeunes
Sols Voc Ens, Asko Ens, P. Eötvös (pp1992)
(9/93) (MONT) ① [2] **782014**
**Satyricon—opera: 1 act
(1973—Scheveningen)** (Lib. Maderna &
Strasfogel, after Petronius)
Cpte P. Sperry, A. Tomicich, L. Oliveri, M. Vargas,
Divertimento Ens, S. Gorli (r1991)
(9/93) (SALA) ① **SCD9101**

MADETOJA, Leevi (1897-1947) Finland

SECTION I: ORCHESTRAL

Comedy Overture—orchestra, Op. 53 (1928)
Iceland SO, P. Sakari *Concert*
(8/92) (CHAN) ① **CHAN9036**
**Okon Fuoko—ballet suite No. 1, Op. 58
(1930)**
Iceland SO, P. Sakari *Concert*
(8/92) (CHAN) ① **CHAN9036**
Finnish RSO, J-P. Saraste (r1994) *Concert*
(4/95) (FINL) ① **4509-96867-2**
Symphony No. 1 in F, Op. 29 (1915-16)
Iceland SO, P. Sakari *Symphony 2.*
(1/93) (CHAN) ① **CHAN9115**
Symphony No. 2 in E flat, Op. 35 (1917-18)
Iceland SO, P. Sakari *Symphony 1.*
(1/93) (CHAN) ① **CHAN9115**
Symphony No. 3 in A, Op. 55 (1926)
Iceland SO, P. Sakari *Concert*
(8/92) (CHAN) ① **CHAN9036**
Finnish RSO, J-P. Saraste (r1993) *Concert*
(4/95) (FINL) ① **4509-96867-2**

SECTION V: STAGE WORKS

**Juha—opera: 6 tableaux, Op. 74
(1935—Helsinki)** (Lib. cpsr & Ackté, after Aho)
Cpte J. Hynninen, M. Lokka, E. Erkkilä, A. Välkki, M.
Haverinen, T. Valtasaari, M. Wirkkala, M. Metsomäki,
K. Haartti, K. Airinen, K. Olli, Finnish Rad Youth Ch,
Finnish RSO, J. Jalas (r1977)
(11/92) (ONDI) ① [2] **ODE714-2**
**The Ostrobothnians—concert suite from
opera, Op. 52 (1922)**
Iceland SO, P. Sakari *Concert*
(8/92) (CHAN) ① **CHAN9036**
Finnish RSO, J-P. Saraste (r1993) *Concert*
(4/95) (FINL) ① **4509-96867-2**

MAES, Jef (b 1905) Netherlands

SECTION I: ORCHESTRAL

**Arabesque and Scherzo—flute & orchestra
(1960s)**
F. Vanhove, Royal Flanders PO, G. Oskamp (r1994)
Concert   (11/95) (MARC) ① **8 223741**
**Concertante Overture—concert overture
(1961)**
Royal Flanders PO, G. Oskamp (r1994) *Concert*
(11/95) (MARC) ① **8 223741**

Concerto for Viola and Orchestra (c1939)
L. DeNeve, Royal Flanders PO, G. Oskamp (r1994)
Concert   (11/95) (MARC) ① **8 223741**
Symphony No. 2 in A (1965)
Royal Flanders PO, G. Oskamp (r1994) *Concert*
(11/95) (MARC) ① **8 223741**

MAGALHAES, Filipe de (c1571-1652) Portugal

SECTION IV: VOCAL AND CHORAL

Asperges me—motet (4vv)
A Capella Portvgvesa, O. Rees (r1994) *Concert*
(11/94) (HYPE) ① **CDA66725**
**Commissa mea pavesco—motet (6vv) (pub
1636)**
A Capella Portvgvesa, O. Rees (r1994) *Concert*
(11/94) (HYPE) ① **CDA66725**
Missa O soberana luz—5vv
A Capella Portvgvesa, O. Rees (r1994) *Concert*
(11/94) (HYPE) ① **CDA66725**

MAGE, Pierre du (c1676-1751) France

SECTION III: INSTRUMENTAL

**Livre d'orgue contenant une suite du
permier ton—organ (pub 1708)**
G.C. Baker *Clérambault: Premier Livre d'orgue.*
(3/92) (FY) ① **FYCD043**

MÄGI, Ester (b 1922) Estonia

SECTION II: CHAMBER

**Cantus and Processus—cello and guitar
(1987-88)**
Tallinn Camerata (r1993) *Concert*
(5/95) (FINL) ① **4509-95705-2**

SECTION III: INSTRUMENTAL

The Ancient Kannel—piano (1985)
L. Väinmaa (r1993) *Concert*
(7/95) (FINL) ① **4509-95704-2**

MAGIN, Miloscz (b 1929) Poland

SECTION III: INSTRUMENTAL

**Three Pieces
Danse noble; Nostalgie du pays; Chant des
moissons** L. Rév *Concert*
(7/87) (HYPE) ① **CDA66185**

MAGNARD, (Lucien Denis Gabriel) Alberic (1865-1914) France

SECTION II: CHAMBER

Piano Trio in F minor, Op. 18 (1904)
A. Oprean, T. Demenga, C. Keller *Piano and Wind
Quintet.*   (3/90) (ACCO) ① **20010-2**
**Quintet for Piano and Wind in D minor, Op. 8
(1894)**
A-K. Graf, R. Schmid, E. Schmid, J. Flieger, C. Keller
Piano Trio.   (3/90) (ACCO) ① **20010-2**
String Quartet in E minor, Op. 16 (1903)
Artis Qt   (3/90) (ACCO) ① **22060-2**

MAHLER, Alma (1879-1964) Austria

SECTION IV: VOCAL AND CHORAL

5 Lieder (1910)
1. Die stille Stadt (wds. R. Dehmel); 2. In meiner
Vaters Garten (wds. O. E. Hartleben); 3. Laue
Sommernacht (wds. G. Falke); 4. Bei dir ist es traut
(wds. R. M. Rilke); 5. Ich wandle unter Blumen (wds.
H. Heine).
I. Lippitz, B. Heller-Reichenbach *Concert*
(3/89) (CPO) ① **CPO999 018-2**
3, 5. M. Hajóssyová, M. Lapšanský *Concert*
(8/90) (OPUS) ① **9352 1887**
4 Lieder (1915)
1. Licht in der Nacht (wds. O. J. Bierbaum); 2.
Waldeinsamkeit (wds. R. Dehmel); 3. Anstrum (wds.
R. Dehmel); 4. Emtelied (wds. G. Falke).
I. Lippitz, B. Heller-Reichenbach *Concert*
(3/89) (CPO) ① **CPO999 018-2**
3. M. Hajóssyová, M. Lapšanský *Concert*
(8/90) (OPUS) ① **9352 1887**
5 Lieder (1924)
1. Hymne (wds. Novalis); 2. Ekstase (wds. O. J.
Bierbaum); 3. Der Erkennende (wds. F. Werfel); 4.

Lobgesang (wds. R. Dehmel); 5. Hymne an die Nacht
(wds. Novalis).
I. Lippitz, B. Heller-Reichenbach *Concert*
(3/69) (CPO) ① **CPO999 018-2**
M. Hajóssyová, M. Lapšanský *Concert*
(8/90) (OPUS) ① **9352 1887**

MAHLER, Gustav (1860–1911)
Bohemia

SECTION I: ORCHESTRAL

Blumine—symphonic movement (1884) (in
original five-movement version of Symphony
No. 1 but later discarded)
Golders Orkest, Y. Talmi *Concert*
(7/87) (OTTA) ① **OTRC98402**
CBSO, S. Rattle (pp1991) *Symphony 1*.
(12/92) (EMI) ① **CDC7 54647-2**
Danish Nat RSO, L. Segerstam (r1993) *Symphony 1*.
(3/94) (CHAN) ① **CHAN9242**
Florida PO, J. Judd (r1993) *Symphony 1*.
(9/94) (HARM) ① **HMU90 7118**
Polish Nat RSO, M. Halász (r1993) *Symphony 1*.
(4/95) (NAXO) ① **8 550522**
SNO, N. Järvi (r1993) *Symphony 1*.
(5/95) (CHAN) ① **CHAN9308**
**Symphonisches Praeludium—orchestra
(?1870s)** (doubtful: pf trans H Tschuppik,
1876)
SNO, N. Järvi (r1992: orch A Gürsching) *Symphony
6*. (2/94) (CHAN) ① **CHAN9207**
**Symphony No. 1 in D (1888 rev 1893, 1896-
98)** (orig 5 movts but reduced to 4 in 1896)
EXCERPTS: 1. Langsam. Schleppend; 2. Kräftig
bewegt, doch nicht zu schnell (Ländler: Scherzo); 3.
Feierlich und gemessen, ohne zu schleppen; 4.
Stürmisch bewegt.
Frankfurt RSO, E. Inbal
(12/85) (DENO) ① **C37-7537**
BPO, B. Haitink (r1987)
(10/88) (PHIL) ① **420 936-2PH**
BRSO, Colin Davis (1/89) (NOVA) ① **150 033-2**
Concertgebouw, L. Bernstein (pp1987)
(3/89) (DG) ① **427 303-2GH**
LSO, J. Horenstein (4/89) (UNIC) ① **UKCD2012**
FNO, I. Markevitch (pp1967) *Stravinsky: Symphony
of Psalms*. (4/89) (MONT) ① **TCE8811**
Prague Fest Orch, P. Urbanek
(5/90) (LASE) ① **15 529**
BRSO, R. Kubelík *Concert*
(5/90) (DG) ① [10] **429 042-2GX10**
Philh, G. Sinopoli (7/90) (DG) ① **429 228-2GH**
BPO, C. Abbado (10/91) (DG) ① **431 769-2GH**
Chicago SO, K. Tennstedt (pp1990)
(11/91) (EMI) ① **CDC7 54217-2**
Concertgebouw, L. Bernstein (pp1987) *Concert*
(2/92) (DG) ① [13] **435 162-2GX13**
Chicago SO, G. Solti *Concert*
(4/92) (DECC) ① [10] **430 804-2DC10**
VPO, L. Maazel *Concert*
(11/92) (SONY) ① [14] **SX14K48198**
NYPO, K. Masur (pp1992) *Lieder eines fahrenden
gesellen*. (12/92) (TELD) ① **9031-74868-2**
CBSO, S. Rattle (pp1991) *Blumine*.
(12/92) (EMI) ① **CDC7 54647-2**
LPO, K. Tennstedt (r1977) *Concert*
(4/93) (EMI) ① [4] **CMS7 64471-2**
NYPO, L. Bernstein *Symphony 2*.
(5/93) (SONY) ① **SM2K47573**
Danish Nat RSO, L. Segerstam (r1993) *Blumine*.
(3/94) (CHAN) ① **CHAN9242**
Israel PO, Z. Mehta (r1974) *Symphony 3*.
(5/94) (DECC) ① [2] **443 030-2DF2**
Florida PO, J. Judd (r1993) *Blumine*.
(9/94) (HARM) ① **HMU90 7118**
Concertgebouw, B. Haitink (r1962) *Concert*
(11/94) (PHIL) ① [10] **442 050-2PB10**
Polish Nat RSO, M. Halász (r1993) *Blumine*.
(4/95) (NAXO) ① **8 550522**
SNO, N. Järvi (r1993) *Blumine*.
(5/95) (CHAN) ① **CHAN9308**
BPO, C. Abbado (pp1989) *Concert*
(12/95) (DG) ① [12] **447 023-2GX12**
2. M. Kazakevich (r1993: trans pf: Kazakevich)
Concert (7/94) (CONI) ① **CDCF227**
**Symphony No. 2 in C minor,
'Resurrection'—soprano, contralto, chorus
and orchestra (1884-1886 rev 1893-6)**
1. Allegro moderato (Totenfeier); 2. Andante
moderato; 3. In ruhig fliessender Bewegung; 4.
Urlicht; 5. In tempo des Scherzos.
K. Battle, M. Forrester, St. Louis Sym. Chor, St. Louis
SO, L. Slatkin (r1982)
(1/85) (TELA) ① **CD80081/2**

H. Donath, D. Soffel, N German Rad Chor, Dale
Warland Sngrs, Frankfurt RSO, E. Inbal
(3/86) (DENO) ① [2] **C37-7603/4**
A. Auger, J. Baker, CBSO Chor, CBSO, S. Rattle
(12/87) (EMI) ① [2] **CDS7 47962-8**
B. Hendricks, C. Ludwig, Westminster Ch, NYPO, L.
Bernstein (pp 1987)
(7/88) (DG) ① [2] **423 395-2GH2**
B. Valente, M. Forrester, LSC, Ardwyn Sngrs, Cardiff
Polyphonic Ch, Dyfed Ch, BBC Welsh Chor, LSO, G.
Kaplan (r1987) (1/89) (CARL) ① [2] **DPCD910**
S. Greenberg, F. Quivar, Israel Nat Ch, Tel Aviv Phil
Ch, Ihud Ch, Israel PO, Z. Mehta (pp1988)
(1/90) (CARL) ① **PWK1136**
E. Schwarzkopf, H. Rössl-Majdan, Philh Chor, Philh,
O. Klemperer (r1961/2)
(1/90) (EMI) ① **CDM7 69662-2**
E. Mathis, N. Procter, Bavarian Rad Chor, BRSO, R.
Kubelík *Concert*
(5/90) (DG) ① [10] **429 042-2GX10**
J. Vincent, K. Ferrier, Amsterdam Toonkunst Ch,
Concertgebouw, O. Klemperer (pp1951)
(7/91) (DECC) ① **425 970-2DM**
B. Hendricks, C. Ludwig, Westminster Ch, NYPO, L.
Bernstein (pp1987) *Concert*
(2/92) (DG) ① [13] **435 162-2GX13**
M. Zakai, Y. Minton, Chicago Sym Chor, Chicago
SO, G. Solti *Concert*
(4/92) (DECC) ① [10] **430 804-2DC10**
E. Marton, J. Norman, Vienna St Op Chor, VPO, L.
Maazel *Concert*
(11/92) (SONY) ① [14] **SX14K48198**
E. Mathis, D. Soffel, LP Ch, LPO, K. Tennstedt
(r1981) *Concert* (4/93) (EMI) ① [4] **CMS7 64471-2**
S. Armstrong, J. Baker, Edinburgh Fest Chor, LSO;
L. Bernstein *Symphony 1*.
(5/93) (SONY) ① [2] **SM2K47573**
H. Lisowska, J. Rappé, Cracow Rad & TV Chor,
Polish Nat RSO, A. Wit (r1993)
(3/94) (NAXO) ① [2] **8 550523/4**
I. Cotrubas, C. Ludwig, Vienna St Op Chor, VPO, Z.
Mehta (r1975) *Schmidt: Symphony 4*.
(5/94) (DECC) ① [2] **440 615-2DF2**
C. Studer, W. Meier, A. Schoenberg Ch, VPO, C.
Abbado (pp1992)
(5/94) (DG) ① [2] **439 953-2GH2**
E. Ameling, A. Heynis, Netherlands Rad Chor,
Concertgebouw, B. Haitink (r1968) *Concert*
(11/94) (PHIL) ① [10] **442 050-2PB10**
S. McNair, J. van Nes, Ernst Senff Chor, BPO, B.
Haitink (r1993)
(11/94) (PHIL) ① [2] **438 935-2PH2**
R. Ziesak, C. Hellekant, San Francisco Sym Chor,
San Francisco SO, H. Blomstedt (r1992)
(12/94) (DECC) ① [2] **443 350-2DX2**
N. Gustafson, F. Quivar, Prague Philharmonic Ch,
Israel PO, Z. Mehta (r1994)
(2/95) (TELD) ① **4509-94545-2**
T. Kilberg, K. Dolberg, Danish Nat Rad Chor, Danish
Nat RSO, L. Segerstam (r1992) *Beethoven: String
Quartet 11.* (10/95) (CHAN) ① [2] **CHAN9266/7**
C. Studer, W. Meier, A. Schoenberg Ch, VPO, C.
Abbado (pp1992) *Concert*
(12/95) (DG) ① [12] **447 023-2GX12**
1. Danish Nat RSO, L. Segerstam *Symphony 6*.
(12/91) (CHAN) ① [2] **CHAN8956/7**
**Symphony No. 3 in D minor—contralto,
boys' choir, female chorus & orchestra
(1893-96 rev 1906)** (Wds. Nietzsche)
EXCERPTS: 1. Kräftig; 2. Tempo di menuetto; 3.
Scherzando; 4. Sehr langsam: 'O Mensch! Gib acht';
5. Lustig im Tempo: 'Es sungen drei Engel'; 6.
Langsam.
D. Soffel, Limberg Cath Children's Ch, Frankfurt
Kantorei Women's Chor, Frankfurt RSO, E. Inbal
(8/86) (DENO) ① [2] **C37-7828/9**
H. Rössl-Majdan, Vienna Boys' Ch, Vienna St Op
Chor, Vienna Concert Orch, C. Adler (r1952)
(2/88) (HARM) ① [2] **HMA190 501/2**
J. Norman, Vienna Boys' Ch, Vienna St. Op. Concert
Ch, VPO, C. Abbado
(11/88) (DG) ① [2] **410 715-2GH2**
N. Procter, Wandsworth Sch Boys' Ch, Ambrosian
Sngrs, LSO, J. Horenstein (r1970)
(11/88) (UNIC) ① **UKCD2006/7**
J. Baker, LSC, Southend Boys' Ch, LSO, M. Tilson
Thomas *Rückert Lieder*.
(11/88) (SONY) ① [2] **M2K44553**
C. Ludwig, NY Choral Artists, Brooklyn Boys' Chor,
NYPO, L. Bernstein (pp1987)
(6/89) (DG) ① [2] **427 328-2GH2**
M. Thomas, Tolz Boys' Ch, Bavarian Rad Chor,
BRSO, R. Kubelík *Concert*
(5/90) (DG) ① [10] **429 042-2GX10**

C. Ludwig, NY Choral Artists, Brooklyn Boys' Chor,
NYPO, L. Bernstein (pp1987) *Concert*
(2/92) (DG) ① [13] **435 162-2GX13**
A. Gjevang, Copenhagen Boys' Ch, Danish Nat Rad
Chor, Danish Nat RSO, L. Segerstam
(3/92) (CHAN) ① [2] **CHAN8970/1**
H. Dernesch, Chicago Sym Chor, Glen Ellyn
Children's Chor, Chicago SO, G. Solti *Concert*
(4/92) (DECC) ① [10] **430 804-2DC10**
J. van Nes, BPO, B. Haitink
(4/92) (PHIL) ① [2] **432 162-2PH2**
A. Baltsa, Vienna Boys' Ch, Vienna St Op Chor,
VPO, L. Maazel *Concert*
(11/92) (SONY) ① [14] **SX14K48198**
L. Finnie, RSO Junior Chor, Scottish Nat Chor, SNO,
N. Järvi *Kindertotenlieder*.
(3/93) (CHAN) ① [2] **CHAN9117/8**
O. Wenkel, Southend Boys' Ch, LP Ch, LPO, K.
Tennstedt (r1979) *Concert*
(4/93) (EMI) ① [4] **CMS7 64471-2**
M. Forrester, California Boys' Ch, Los Angeles
Master Chorale, Los Angeles PO, Z. Mehta (r1978)
Symphony 1. (5/94) (DECC) ① [2] **443 030-2DF2**
M. Forrester, St Willibrord's Boys' Ch, Netherlands
Rad Chor, Concertgebouw, B. Haitink (r1966)
Concert (11/94) (PHIL) ① [10] **442 050-2PB10**
J. Norman, Tanglewood Fest Chor, American
Boychoir, Boston SO, S. Ozawa (pp1993) *Symphony
6.* (3/95) (PHIL) ① [3] **434 909-2PH3**
O. Alexandrova, Ostankino TV Russian Acad Ch,
Moscow Boys' Cappella, Russian St SO, E.
Svetlanov (r1994)
(11/95) (CDM) ① [2] **RUS288 111/2**
J. Norman, Vienna Boys' Ch, Vienna St Op Chor,
VPO, C. Abbado (r1980) *Concert*
(12/95) (DG) ① [12] **447 023-2GX12**
**Symphony No. 4 in G—soprano (movt 4) and
orchestra (1892, 1899-1900 rev 1901-10)**
(Wds. from 'Des Knaben Wunderhorn')
EXCERPTS: 1. Heiter, bedächtig; 2. In gemächlicher
Bewegung; 3. Ruhevoll; 4. Sehr behaglich.
K. Te Kanawa, Chicago SO, G. Solti
(8/84) (DECC) ① **410 188-2DH**
F. von Stade, VPO, C. Abbado
(11/84) (DG) ① **413 454-2GH**
H. Donath, Frankfurt RSO, E. Inbal
(2/87) (DENO) ① **C37-7952**
H. Wittek, Concertgebouw, L. Bernstein (pp1987)
(8/88) (DG) ① **423 607-2GH**
E. Schwarzkopf, Philh, O. Klemperer (r1961)
(4/89) (EMI) ① **CDM7 69667-2**
E. Morison, BRSO, R. Kubelík *Concert*
(5/90) (DG) ① [10] **429 042-2GX10**
E. Mathis, BPO, H. von Karajan
(1/91) (DG) ① **419 863-2GGA**
M. Shirai, Stuttgart RSO, N. Marriner
(7/91) (CAPR) ① **10 358**
E. Wiens, SRO, A. Jordan
(11/91) (ERAT) ① **2292-45628-2**
D. Halban, NYPO, B. Walter (r1945) *Lieder und
Gesänge.* (12/91) (SONY) ① **MPK46450**
H. Wittek, Concertgebouw, L. Bernstein (pp1987)
Concert (2/92) (DG) ① [13] **435 162-2GX13**
L. Finnie, SNO, N. Järvi *Lieder eines fahrenden
Gesellen.* (2/92) (CHAN) ① **CHAN8951**
H. Gueden, VPO, B. Walter (pp1955) *Concert*
(2/92) (DG) ① [2] **435 321-2GWP12**
H. Gueden, VPO, B. Walter (pp1955) *Mozart:
Symphony 38.* (4/92) (DG) ① [2] **435 334-2GWP**
K. Te Kanawa, Chicago SO, G. Solti *Concert*
(4/92) (DECC) ① [10] **430 804-2DC10**
B. Hendricks, Los Angeles PO, E-P. Salonen
(8/92) (SONY) ① **SK48380**
A. Hargan, Hallé, S. Skrowaczewski
(9/92) (CARL) ① **PCD972**
K. Battle, VPO, L. Maazel *Concert*
(11/92) (SONY) ① [14] **SX14K48198**
L. Popp, LPO, K. Tennstedt *Concert*
(4/93) (EMI) ① [4] **CMS7 64471-2**
R. Grist, NYPO, L. Bernstein
(5/93) (SONY) ① **SMK47579**
E. Gruberová, Philh, G. Sinopoli (r1991)
(6/93) (DG) ① **437 527-2GH**
E. Loose, Philh, P. Kletzki (r1957) *Concert*
(9/93) (EMI) ① [2] **CZS7 67726-2**
S. McNair, BPO, B. Haitink (r1992)
(11/93) (PHIL) ① **434 123-2PH**
E. Ameling, Concertgebouw, B. Haitink (r1967)
Concert (11/94) (PHIL) ① [10] **442 050-2PB10**
F. von Stade, VPO, C. Abbado (r1977) *Concert*
(12/95) (DG) ① [12] **447 023-2GX12**
4. Y. Kenny, G. Mahler (r1905/92: trans pf: cpsr)
Concert (12/93) (CARL) ① **GLRS101**
4. G. Mahler (r1905: trans pf: cpsr) *Concert*
(12/93) (CARL) ① **GLRS101**

NYPO, K. Masur (r1994)
(5/95) (TELD) ① **4509-90882-2**
VPO, C. Abbado (pp1987) *Concert*
(12/95) (DG) ① [12] **447 023-2GX12**
Symphony No. 10 in F sharp minor (1910)
(short score only)
1. Adagio; 2. Scherzo; 3. Purgatorio; 4. (Scherzo); 5. Finale.
Philadelphia, E. Ormandy (ed. Cooke)
(10/90) (SONY) ① **MPK45882**
Bournemouth SO, S. Rattle (r1980: ed Cooke)
(5/92) (EMI) ① **CDC7 54406-2**
Frankfurt RSO, E. Inbal (ed Cooke)
(4/93) (DENO) ① **CO-75129**
1. Frankfurt RSO, E. Inbal *Symphony 9.*
(1/88) (DENO) ① [2] **CO-1566/7**
1. VPO, C. Abbado (pp1985) *Symphony 9.*
(8/88) (DG) ① [2] **423 564-2GH2**
1. BRSO, R. Kubelík *Concert*
(5/90) (DG) ① [10] **429 042-2GX10**
1. VPO, L. Bernstein (pp1974) *Symphony 8.*
(10/91) (DG) ① [2] **435 102-2GH2**
1. VPO, L. Bernstein (pp1974) *Concert*
(2/92) (DG) ① [13] **435 162-2GX13**
1. VPO, L. Maazel *Concert*
(11/92) (SONY) ① [14] **SX14K48198**
1. LPO, K. Tennstedt *Concert*
(4/93) (EMI) ① [3] **CMS7 64481-2**
1. NYPO, L. Bernstein *Concert*
(5/93) (SONY) ① [3] **SM3K47585**
1. Concertgebouw, B. Haitink (r1971) *Concert*
(11/94) (PHIL) ① [10] **442 050-2PB10**
1. Danish Nat RSO, L. Segerstam (r1994) *Symphony 8.*
(5/95) (CHAN) ① [2] **CHAN9305/6**
1. BPO, B. Haitink (r1992) *Symphony 7.*
(5/95) (PHIL) ① [2] **434 997-2PH2**
1. VPO, C. Abbado (pp1985) *Concert*
(12/95) (DG) ① [12] **447 023-2GX12**

SECTION II: CHAMBER

Quartet in A minor—piano and string trio (1876)
Domus *Brahms: Piano Quartet 2.*
(1/89) (VIRG) ① **VC7 59144-2**
Villiers Pf Qt *Brahms: Piano Quartet 1.*
(11/89) (ETCE) ① **KTC1072**

SECTION IV: VOCAL AND CHORAL

Im Lenz—Lied (1880) (Wds. cpsr)
J. Baker, G. Parsons *Concert*
(4/87) (HYPE) ① **CDA66100**
T. Hampson, D. Lutz (r1992) *Concert*
(8/94) (TELD) ① **9031-74002-2**
Kindertotenlieder—song cycle (1901/4) (Wds. Rückert)
1. Nun will die Sonn' so hell aufgeh'n; 2. Nun seh' ich wohl, warum so dunkle Flammen; 3. Wenn dein Mütterlein; 4. Oft denk' ich, sie sind nur augesgangen; 5. In diesem Wetter, in diesem Braus.
C. Ludwig, BPO, H. von Karajan (r1974) *Symphony 5.*
(9/85) (DG) ① [2] **415 096-2GH2**
D. Fischer-Dieskau, BPO, K. Böhm *Concert*
(9/85) (DG) ① **415 191-2GH**
D. Fischer-Dieskau, BPO, R. Kempe (r1955) *Concert*
(6/87) (EMI) ① **CDC7 47657-2**
J. Baker, Hallé, J. Barbirolli *Concert*
(12/87) (EMI) ① **CDC7 47793-2**
K. Ferrier, VPO, B. Walter (r1949) *Concert*
(6/88) (EMI) ① **CDH7 61003-2**
C. Ludwig, Philh, A. Vandernoot *Concert*
(10/88) (EMI) ① **CDM7 69499-2**
T. Hampson, VPO, L. Bernstein (pp1988) *Symphony 6.*
(1/90) (DG) ① [2] **427 697-2GH2**
W. Meier, Paris Orch, D. Barenboim *Concert*
(4/90) (ERAT) ① **2292-45417-2**
T. Hampson, VPO, L. Bernstein *Concert*
(9/91) (DG) ① **431 682-2GH**
A. Schmidt, Cincinnati SO, J. López-Cobos *Concert*
(5/92) (TELA) ① **CD80269**
G. Schreckenbach, P. Moll *Concert*
(5/92) (CAPR) ① **10 332**
J. Baker, Hallé, J. Barbirolli *Concert*
(8/92) (EMI) ① [2] **CZS7 62707-2**
K. Ferrier, Concertgebouw, O. Klemperer (pp1951) *Concert*
(9/92) (DECC) ① **425 995-2DM**
A. Baltsa, VPO, L. Maazel *Concert*
(11/92) (SONY) ① [14] **SX14K48198**
L. Finnie, SNO, N. Järvi *Symphony 3.*
(3/93) (CHAN) ① **CHAN9117/8**
M. Lipovšek, BPO, C. Abbado (pp1992) *Concert*
(10/93) (SONY) ① **SK53360**
N. Foster, Bamberg SO, J. Horenstein (r1955) *Symphony 9.*
(11/93) (VOX) ① [2] **CDX2 5509**

B. Fassbaender, Berlin Deutsches SO, R. Chailly
(r1988/9) *Concert* (4/94) (DECC) ① **425 790-2DH**
J. van Nes, Schoenberg Ens, R. De Leeuw (r1991: arr De Leeuw) *Concert* (5/94) (SCHW) ① **312632**
B. Terfel, Philh, G. Sinopoli (r1992) *Symphony 7.*
(6/94) (DG) ① [2] **437 851-2GH2**
M. Anderson, San Francisco SO, P. Monteux (r1950) *Concert* (9/94) (RCA) ① [15] **09026 61893-2**
D. Soffel, Vienna SO, E. Inbal (r1992) *Concert*
(1/95) (DENO) ① **CO-75969**
C. Ludwig, BPO, H. von Karajan (r1974) *Concert*
(4/95) (DG) ① [2] **439 678-2GX2**
K. Flagstad, Vienna SO, A. Boult (r1957) *Concert*
(12/95) (LOND) ① **440 491-2LM**
K. Flagstad, VPO, A. Boult (r1957) *Concert*
(12/95) (LOND) ① [5] **440 490-2LM5(1)**
Das Klagende Lied—cantata (1880 rev 1892-93 and 1898-99) (Wds. cpsr)
1. Waldmärchen; 2. Der Spielmann; 3. Hochzeitstück.
Cpte J. Rodgers, L. Finnie, H-P. Blochwitz, R. Hayward, Bath Fest Chor, Waynflete Sngrs, Bournemouth SO, R. Hickox (r1993)
(5/94) (CHAN) ① **CHAN9247**
S. Dunn, B. Fassbaender, W. Hollweg, M. Baur, A. Schmidt, Berlin Rad Sym Chor, Berlin RSO, R. Chailly
(2/92) (DECC) ① **425 719-2DH**
C. Studer, W. Meier, R. Goldberg, T. Allen, Shin-Yuh Kai Chor, Philh, G. Sinopoli (pp1990)
(8/92) (DG) ① **435 382-2GH**
Das Lied von der Erde—'Song of the Earth'—symphony: contralto/baritone, tenor & orchestra (1908-9) (Wds. from Bethge's 'Die chinesische Flöte')
1. Das Trinklied vom Jammer der Erde (ten); 2. Der Einsame im Herbst (mez/bar); 3. Von der Jugend (ten); 4. Von der Schönheit (mez/bar); 5. Der Trunkene im Frühling (ten); 6. Der Abschied (mez/bar).
B. Fassbaender, F. Araiza, BPO, C.M. Giulini
(10/84) (DG) ① **413 459-2GH**
K. Ferrier, J. Patzak, VPO, B. Walter (r1952)
(1/85) (DECC) ① **414 194-2DH**
J. Norman, J. Vickers, LSO, Colin Davis
(4/85) (PHIL) ① **411 474-2PH**
C. Ludwig, F. Wunderlich, Philh, New Philh, O. Klemperer (r1964) (12/85) (EMI) ① **CDC7 47231-2**
C. Ludwig, R. Kollo, BPO, H. von Karajan (r1973)
(4/88) (DG) ① **419 058-2GGA**
J. van Nes, P. Schreier, Frankfurt RSO, E. Inbal (r1988)
(1/89) (DENO) ① **CO-72605**
M. Forrester, Richard Lewis, Chicago SO, F. Reiner (r1959)
(10/91) (RCA) ① **GD60178**
W. Meier, S. Jerusalem, Chicago SO, D. Barenboim (pp1991) (4/92) (ERAT) ① **2292-45624-2**
M. Dickie, D. Fischer-Dieskau, Philh, P. Kletzki *Concert* (8/92) (EMI) ① [2] **CZS7 62707-2**
A. Baltsa, K. König, LPO, K. Tennstedt (r1982/4)
(2/93) (EMI) ① **CDC7 54603-2**
K. Thorborg, C. Kullman, VPO, B. Walter (pp1936) *Concert* (12/93) (MUSI) ① **MACD-749**
R. Bemmert, H-P. Blochwitz, Musique Oblique Ens, P. Herreweghe (r1993: trans chbr orch Schoenberg & Riehn) (12/94) (HARM) ① **HMC90 1477**
J. Baker, J. Mitchinson, BBC Northern SO, R. Leppard (pp1977) (3/95) (BBCR) ① **BBCRD9120**
J. Rigby, R. Tear, Premiere Ens, M. Wigglesworth (r1993: arr Schoenberg: chamber ens)
(3/95) (RCA) ① **09026 68043-2**
M. Groop, J. Silvasti, Lahti Chbr Ens, O. Vänskä (r1994: arr Schoenberg/Riehn)
(7/95) (BIS) ① **BIS-CD681**
R. Donose, T. Harper, Ireland National SO, M. Halász (r1994) (11/95) (NAXO) ① **8 550933**
Lieder aus 'Des Knaben Wunderhorn'—voice(s) and orchestra (1888-89)
1. Der Schildwache Nachtlied; 2. Verlor'ne Müh; 3. Trost im Unglück; 4. Wer hat dies Liedlein erdacht?; 5. Das irdische Leben; 6. Des Antonius von Padua Fischpredigt; 7. Rheinlegendchen; 8. Lied des Verfolgten im Turm; 9. Wo die schönen Trompeten blasen; 10. Lob des hohen Verstandes; 11. Es sungen drei Engel; 12. Uricht; 13. Revelge; 14. Der Tambours'gesll; 15. Das himmlische Leben.
T. Hampson, G. Parsons (r1991-3)
(2/94) (TELD) ① **9031-74726-2**
1-10, 12-14. L. Popp, A. Schmidt, Concertgebouw, L. Bernstein (pp1987) (6/89) (DG) ① **427 302-2GH**
1-10, 12-14. C. Ludwig, W. Berry, L. Bernstein (pp1968)
(3/92) (SONY) ① [2] **SM2K47170**
1-10, 12-14. J. van Nes, J. Bröcheler, Arnhem PO, R. Benzi (1992) (2/94) (OTTA) ① **OTRC79238**
1-10, 13, 14. E. Schwarzkopf, D. Fischer-Dieskau, LSO, G. Szell (r1968)
(11/88) (EMI) ① **CDC7 47277-2**

1-10, 13, 14. D. Fischer-Dieskau, BPO, D. Barenboim *Lieder eines fahrenden Gesellen.*
(5/90) (SONY) ① **SK44935**
1-10, 13, 14. J. Baker, G. Evans, LPO, W. Morris (r1966) *Lieder eines fahrenden Gesellen.*
(5/93) (CARL) ① **PCD1035**
1, 4-7, 9, 10. C. Ludwig, G. Moore *Concert*
(9/92) (EMI) ① [4] **CMS7 64074-2(1)**
1, 4-9, 13, 14. D. Fischer-Dieskau, W. Sawallisch (pp1976) *Concert* (6/94) (ORFE) ① **C333931B**
2, 5-7, 9, 10. B. Fassbaender, J. Wustman *Concert*
(9/88) (ACAN) ① **43 579**
2, 7, 9, 10. A.S. von Otter, R. Gothóni *Concert*
(6/89) (DG) ① **423 666-2GH**
4. E. Schumann, G. Reeves (r1930) *Concert*
(6/91) (PREI) ① **89031**
4, 6, 9, 13, 14. L. Popp, B. Weikl, LPO, K. Tennstedt (8/92) (EMI) ① [2] **CZS7 62707-2**
5, 6, 12. B. Fassbaender, Berlin Deutsches SO, R. Chailly (r1988/9) *Concert*
(4/94) (DECC) ① **425 790-2DH**
5, 7. C. Ludwig, C. Spencer (pp1993) *Concert*
(10/93) (RCA) ① **09026 61547-2**
5, 9. C. Ludwig, Philh, O. Klemperer *Concert*
(10/88) (EMI) ① **CDM7 69499-2**
6. E. Schwarzkopf, G. Parsons (r1966) *Concert*
(12/90) (EMI) ① **CDM7 63654-2**
6, 7. C. Ludwig, E. Werba (pp1963) *Concert*
(7/94) (ORFE) ① **C331931A**
7, 14. H. Schlusnus, Berlin St Op Orch, H. Weigert (r1931) *Concert* (1/94) (PREI) ① [2] **89205**
10. M. Horne, Martin Katz (pp1994) *Concert*
(1/95) (RCA) ① **09026 62547-2**
12. C. Ludwig, E. Werba (pp1968) *Concert*
(7/94) (ORFE) ① **C331931A**
Lieder eines fahrenden Gesellen, 'Songs of a Wayfarer'—voice and orchestra/piano (1884 rev c1892, 1896: orch version pub 1912) (Wds. cpsr)
1. Wenn mein Schatz Hochzeit macht; 2. Ging heut' Morgen übers Feld; 3. Ich hab' ein glühend Messer; 4. Die zwei blauen Augen.
D. Fischer-Dieskau, BRSO, R. Kubelík *Concert*
(9/85) (DG) ① **415 191-2GH**
J. Baker, G. Parsons *Concert*
(4/87) (HYPE) ① **CDA66100**
D. Fischer-Dieskau, Philh, W. Furtwängler (r1953) *Concert* (6/87) (EMI) ① **CDC7 47657-2**
J. Baker, Hallé, J. Barbirolli *Concert*
(12/87) (EMI) ① **CDC7 47793-2**
A. Holroyd, Versailles Camerata, A. du Closel *Concert* (9/88) (AUVI) ① **AV6110**
C. Ludwig, Philh, A. Boult *Concert*
(10/88) (EMI) ① **CDM7 69499-2**
D. Fischer-Dieskau, BPO, D. Barenboim *Knaben Wunderhorn.* (5/90) (SONY) ① **SK44935**
J. Norman, BPO, L. Bernstein *Symphony 6.*
(4/91) (PHIL) ① [2] **426 257-2PH2**
T. Hampson, VPO, L. Bernstein *Concert*
(9/91) (DG) ① **431 682-2GH**
L. Finnie, SNO, N. Järvi *Symphony 4.*
(2/92) (CHAN) ① **CHAN8951**
D. Fischer-Dieskau, L. Bernstein *Concert*
(3/92) (SONY) ① [2] **SM2K47170**
A. Schmidt, Cincinnati SO, J. López-Cobos *Concert*
(5/92) (TELA) ① **CD80269**
G. Schreckenbach, P. Moll *Concert*
(5/92) (CAPR) ① **10 332**
C. Robbin, R. Armenian, Kitchener-Waterloo SO *Concert* (5/92) (CBC) ① **SMCD5098**
J. Baker, Hallé, J. Barbirolli *Concert*
(8/92) (EMI) ① [2] **CZS7 62707-2**
H. Hagegård, NYPO, K. Masur (pp1992) *Symphony 1.* (12/92) (TELD) ① **9031-74868-2**
R. Hermann, Symphonica of London, W. Morris *Knaben Wunderhorn.* (5/93) (CARL) ① **PCD1035**
B. Fassbaender, Berlin Deutsches SO, R. Chailly (r1988/9) *Concert* (4/94) (DECC) ① **425 790-2DH**
J. Bröcheler, Schoenberg Ens, R. De Leeuw (r1991: arr de Leeuw) *Concert* (5/94) (SCHW) ① **312632**
H. Schey, Concertgebouw, O. Klemperer (pp1948) *Concert* (8/94) (ARCI) ① **ARC109**
T. Hampson, D. Lutz (r1992) *Concert*
(8/94) (TELD) ① **9031-74002-2**
D. Soffel, Vienna SO, E. Inbal (r1992) *Concert*
(1/95) (DENO) ① **CO-75969**
K. Flagstad, Vienna SO, A. Boult (r1957) *Concert*
(12/95) (LOND) ① **440 491-2LM**
K. Flagstad, VPO, A. Boult (r1957) *Concert*
(12/95) (LOND) ① [5] **440 490-2LM5(1)**
2. C. Carlson, G. Mahler (r1915/92: trans pf: cpsr) *Concert* (12/93) (CARL) ① **GLRS101**
2. G. Mahler (r1905: trans pf: cpsr) *Concert*
(12/93) (CARL) ① **GLRS101**

Lieder und Gesänge—voice and piano (1880-90) (Wds. various)
1. Frühlingsmorgen (wds. Leander); 2. Erinnerung (wds. Leander); 3. Hans und Grethe (wds. cpsr); 4. Serenade aus Don Juan (wds. de Molina trans Braunfels); 5. Phantasie aus Don Juan (wds. de Molina trans Braunfels); 6. Um schlimme Kinder artig zu machen (wds. Des knaben Wunderhorn); 7. Ich ging mit Lust durch einen grünen Wald (wds. Des knaben Wunderhorn); 9. Starke Einbildungskraft (wds. Des knaben Wunderhorn); 10. Zu Strassburg auf der Schanz (wds. Des knaben Wunderhorn); 11. Ablösung im Sommer (wds. Des knaben Wunderhorn); 12. Scheiden und Meiden (wds. Des knaben Wunderhorn); 13. Nicht wiedersehen! (wds. Des knaben Wunderhorn); 14. Selbstgefühl (wds. Des knaben Wunderhorn).
J. Baker, G. Parsons *Concert*
(4/87) (HYPE) ① **CDA66100**
1, 2, 3, 5, 7, 12. T. Hampson, Philh, L. Berio (r1992; arr Berio: Sechs frühe Lieder) *Concert*
(8/94) (TELD) ① **9031-74002-2**
1, 2, 4, 5, 11, 12. M. Zakai, Yonathan Zak *Concert*
(5/91) (KOCH) ① **37021-2**
1, 2, 4, 5, 7, 8. A.S. von Otter, R. Gothóni *Concert*
(6/89) (DG) ① **423 666-2GH**
1, 2, 4-7, 10-14. D. Fischer-Dieskau, L. Bernstein *Concert* (3/92) (SONY) ① [2] **SM2K47170**
1, 2, 5, 9, 12, 14. M. Hajóssyová, M. Lapšanský *Concert* (8/90) (OPUS) ① **9352 1887**
1, 3, 6, 7. C. Ludwig, G. Moore *Concert*
(9/92) (EMI) ① [4] **CMS7 64074-2(1)**
1-3, 6, 7, 10-13. A. Schmidt, Berlin RSO, C. Garben (r1992; orch Berio) *Concert*
(8/94) (RCA) ① **09026 61184-2**
1-3, 7, 9, 11-13. D. Halban, B. Walter (r1952) *Symphony 4.* (12/91) (SONY) ① **MPK46450**
1, 5, 6, 10-14. D. Fischer-Dieskau, B. Walter (pp1976) *Concert* (6/94) (ORFE) ① **C333931B**
1, 5-7, 12. C. Ludwig, C. Spencer (pp1994) *Concert*
(3/95) (RCA) ① **09026 62652-2**
2, 6, 10, 11, 13. T. Hampson, Philh, L. Berio (r1992; arr Berio Fünf frühe Lieder) *Concert*
(8/94) (TELD) ① **9031-74002-2**
4, 8, 9, 14. T. Hampson, D. Lutz (r1992) *Concert*
(8/94) (TELD) ① **9031-74002-2**
6. E. Schwarzkopf, G. Parsons (r1968) *Concert*
(12/90) (EMI) ① **CDM7 63654-2**
6, 7, 10-13. T. Hampson, G. Parsons *Concert*
(10/90) (TELD) ① **2292-44923-2**
6, 7, 9, 11, 13. L. Popp, G. Parsons (pp1981) *Concert*
(6/95) (ORFE) ① **C363941B**
7. G. Mahler (r1905: trans pf: cpsr) *Concert*
(12/93) (CARL) ① **GLRS101**
7. C. Carlson, G. Mahler (r1905/92: trans pf: cpsr) *Concert* (12/93) (CARL) ① **GLRS101**
7. C. Ludwig, E. Werba (pp1963) *Concert*
(7/94) (ORFE) ① **C331931A**
Maitanz im Grünen—Lied: tenor and piano (1880) (Wds. cpsr)
T. Hampson, D. Lutz (r1992) *Concert*
(8/94) (TELD) ① **9031-74002-2**
5 Rückert-Lieder (1902)
1. Ich atmet' einem linden Duft; 2. Liebst du um Schönheit; 3. Blicke mir nicht in die Lieder; 4. Ich bin der Welt abhanden gekommen; 5. Um Mitternacht.
C. Ludwig, BPO, H. von Karajan (r1974) *Symphony 6.* (4/85) (DG) ① [2] **415 099-2GH2**
D. Fischer-Dieskau, D. Barenboim (r1978) *Concert*
(6/87) (EMI) ① **CDC7 47657-2**
J. van Nes, Golders Orkest, Y. Talmi *Concert*
(7/87) (OTTA) ① **OTRC98402**
J. Baker, New Philh, J. Barbirolli *Concert*
(12/87) (EMI) ① **CDC7 47793-2**
J. Baker, LSO, M. Tilson Thomas *Symphony 3.*
(11/88) (SONY) ① [2] **M2K44553**
H. Schwarz, Chicago SO, C. Abbado *Symphony 6.*
(3/89) (DG) ① [2] **423 928-2GGA2**
T. Hampson, VPO, L. Bernstein *Concert*
(9/91) (DG) ① **431 682-2GH**
G. Schreckenbach, P. Moll *Concert*
(5/92) (CAPR) ① **10 332**
A. Schmidt, Cincinnati SO, J. López-Cobos *Concert*
(5/92) (TELA) ① **CD80269**
C. Robbin, R. Armenian, Kitchener-Waterloo SO *Concert* (5/92) (CBC) ① **SMCD5098**
J. Baker, New Philh, J. Barbirolli *Concert*
(8/92) (EMI) ① [2] **CZS7 62707-2**
B. Fassbaender, Berlin Deutsches SO, R. Chailly (1988/9) *Concert* (4/94) (DECC) ① **425 790-2DH**
D. Soffel, Vienna SO, E. Inbal (r1992) *Concert*
(1/95) (DENO) ① **CO-75969**
C. Ludwig, BPO, H. von Karajan (r1974) *Concert*
(4/95) (DG) ① [2] **439 678-2GX2**

---

1. K. Livingstone, J.J. Blakely (Eng) *Concert*
(1/90) (MERI) ① **DUOCD89002**
1. E. Schwarzkopf, G. Parsons (r1966) *Concert*
(12/90) (EMI) ① **CDM7 63654-2**
1. C. Kullman, orch, M. Sargent (r1938: Eng) *Concert*
(12/93) (MUSI) ① **MACD-749**
1, 2, 4, 5. C. Ludwig, G. Moore *Concert*
(9/92) (EMI) ① [4] **CMS7 64074-2(1)**
1, 3. D. Fischer-Dieskau, W. Sawallisch (pp1976) *Concert* (6/94) (ORFE) ① **C333931B**
1, 3-5. D. Fischer-Dieskau, BPO, K. Böhm *Concert*
(9/85) (DG) ① **415 191-2GH**
1, 3-5. D. Fischer-Dieskau, L. Bernstein *Concert*
(3/92) (SONY) ① [2] **SM2K47170**
1, 4, 5. C. Ludwig, Philh, O. Klemperer *Concert*
(10/88) (EMI) ① **CDM7 69499-2**
1, 4, 5. K. Ferrier, VPO, B. Walter (r1952) *Concert*
(6/92) (DECC) ① **433 477-2DM**
2, 3, 5. M. Hajóssyová, M. Lapšanský *Concert*
(8/90) (OPUS) ① **9352 1887**
4. M. Lipovšek, BPO, C. Abbado (pp1992) *Concert*
(10/93) (SONY) ① **SK53360**
4. K. Thorborg, VPO, B. Walter (pp1936) *Concert*
(12/93) (MUSI) ① **MACD-749**
4. C. Ludwig, E. Werba (pp1963) *Concert*
(7/94) (ORFE) ① **C331931A**
4, 5. C. Ludwig, C. Spencer (pp1993) *Concert*
(10/93) (RCA) ① **09026 61547-2**
5. K. Ferrier, VPO, B. Walter (r1952) *Concert*
(6/91) (DECC) ① **430 096-2DWO**
Winterlied—Lied (1880) (Wds. cpsr)
J. Baker, G. Parsons *Concert*
(4/87) (HYPE) ① **CDA66100**
T. Hampson, D. Lutz (r1992) *Concert*
(8/94) (TELD) ① **9031-74002-2**

MAINERIO, Giorgio (c1535–1582) Italy

SECTION II: CHAMBER

Il Primo libro di Balli a Quattro Voci—dance collection (pub 1578)
EXCERPTS: 1. Schiarazula marazula; 2. Ballo tedesca; 4. Ballo ungareschia; 5. Pass e mezzo della Paganina; 6. La Parma; 7. Ballo anglese; 8. Putta nera ballo furlano; 9. Gagliarda, 'La Lavandara'; 10. L'Arboscello ballo furlano.
1, 2, 3, 4. Broadside Band, J. Barlow *Concert*
(3/88) (HYPE) ① **CDA66244**
1, 3, 4. Ulsamer Collegium, J. Ulsamer *Concert*
(2/86) (ARCH) ① **415 294-2AH**

SECTION IV: VOCAL AND CHORAL

Ballo furlano
Amaryllis Consort *Concert*
(6/86) (CARL) ① **PCD822**

MAJOR, John (19th Cent) England .

SECTION IV: VOCAL AND CHORAL

If love make me forsworn—song (pub 1864) (Wds. Shakespeare)
A. Rolfe Johnson, G. Johnson *Concert*
(5/92) (HYPE) ① **CDA66480**

MALASHKIN, Leonid Dimitrievitch (1842–1902) Russia

SECTION IV: VOCAL AND CHORAL

Oh could I but express in song—song
O. Natzke, H. Greenslade (Eng: r1947) *Concert*
(12/92) (ODE) ① **CDODE1365**
F. Chaliapin, orch, E. Goossens (r1928) *Concert*
(6/93) (PREI) ① **89207**

MALATS, Joaquín (1872–1912) Spain

SECTION III: INSTRUMENTAL

Serenata española
A. Segovia (r1930) *Concert*
(5/89) (EMI) ① [2] **CHS7 61047-2**
A. Gifford (r1990; trans Azpiazu) *Concert*
(12/92) (NATI) ① **NTCD001**
J. Bream (r1983-90) *Concert*
(8/93) (RCA) ① [28] **09026 61583-2(6)**
J. Bream (r1983-90) *Concert*
(6/94) (RCA) ① **09026 61609-2**

MALCOLM, George (John) (b 1917) England

SECTION III: INSTRUMENTAL

Bach Before the Mast—harpsichord (The Sailors' Hornpipe played in the style of Bach)
G. Malcolm (r1962) *Concert*
(11/95) (DECC) ① **444 390-2DWO**

MALDERE, Pierre van (1729–1768) Belgium

SECTION I: ORCHESTRAL

Symphony in G minor—pub 1764, Op. 4/1
ECCO, J. Faerber *Concert*
(10/86) (HYPE) ① **CDA66156**

MALENGREAU, Paul (Eugène) (1887–1959) Belgium

SECTION III: INSTRUMENTAL

Suite Mariale—organ
S. Lindley *Concert* (3/93) (NAXO) ① **8 550581**

MALIBRAN, Maria (1808–1836) Italy

SECTION IV: VOCAL AND CHORAL

Prendi, per me sei libero—song (interpolated into Donizetti's 'L'Elisir d'amore')
F. Toresella, anon (r1900) *Concert*
(12/89) (SYMP) ① **SYMCD1065**

MALIPIERO, Gian Francesco (1882–1973) Italy

SECTION I: ORCHESTRAL

7 Invenzioni—orchestra (1933)
Veneto PO, P. Maag (r1991) *Concert*
(9/93) (MARC) ① **8 223397**
Quattro Invenzioni, '(La) festa degli indolenti' (1933)
Veneto PO, P. Maag (r1991) *Concert*
(9/93) (MARC) ① **8 223397**
Sinfonia del mare (1906)
Moscow SO, A. de Almeida (1993) *Concert*
(4/94) (MARC) ① **8 223602**
Sinfonia del silenzio de la morte (1909-10)
Moscow SO, A. de Almeida (r1993) *Concert*
(4/94) (MARC) ① **8 223603**
Sinfonia dello Zodiaco—orchestra (1951)
1. Partita I, 'Spring'; 2. Partita II, 'Summer'; 3. Partita III, 'Autumn'; 4. Partita IV, 'Winter'.
Moscow SO, A. de Almeida (1993) *Concert*
(2/95) (MARC) ① **8 223697**
Sinfonia in un tempo (1950)
Moscow SO, A. de Almeida (1993) *Concert*
(4/94) (MARC) ① **8 223604**
Sinfonia per Antigenida (1962)
Moscow SO, A. de Almeida (1993) *Concert*
(4/94) (MARC) ① **8 223604**
Symphony No. 1, 'in quattro tempi, come le quattro stagioni' (1933)
Moscow SO, A. de Almeida (r1993) *Concert*
(4/94) (MARC) ① **8 223603**
Symphony No. 2, 'elegiaca' (d1936)
Moscow SO, A. de Almeida (r1993) *Concert*
(4/94) (MARC) ① **8 223603**
Symphony No. 3, 'delle campane' (1944-45)
Moscow SO, A. de Almeida (r1993) *Concert*
(4/94) (MARC) ① **8 223602**
Symphony No. 4, 'im memoriam' (1946)
Moscow SO, A. de Almeida (r1993) *Concert*
(4/94) (MARC) ① **8 223602**
Symphony No. 5, 'Concertante, in eco' (1947)
Moscow SO, A. de Almeida (1993) *Concert*
(2/95) (MARC) ① **8 223696**
Symphony No. 6, 'degli archi'—string orchestra (1947)
Moscow SO, A. de Almeida (1994) *Concert*
(2/95) (MARC) ① **8 223696**
Solisti Italiani (r1994) *Concert* (5/95) (DENO) ① **CO-78949**
Symphony No. 7, 'delle canzoni' (1948)
Moscow SO, A. de Almeida (1993) *Concert*
(4/94) (MARC) ① **8 223604**
Symphony No. 8, 'Symphonia brevis' (1964)
Moscow SO, A. de Almeida (1994) *Concert*
(2/95) (MARC) ① **8 223696**

Symphony No. 9, 'dell'ahime' (1966)
Moscow SO, A. de Almeida (r1994) *Concert*
(2/95) (MARC) ① **8 223697**
Symphony No. 10, 'atropo' (1967)
Moscow SO, A. de Almeida (r1994) *Concert*
(2/95) (MARC) ① **8 223697**
Symphony No. 11, 'delle cornamuse' (1969)
Moscow SO, A. de Almeida (r1994) *Concert*
(2/95) (MARC) ① **8 223696**
Vivaldiana—orchestra (1952) (based on works
by Vivaldi)
Veneto PO, P. Maag (r1991) *Concert*
(9/93) (MARC) ① **8 223397**

SECTION II: CHAMBER

String Quartet No. 1, 'Rispetti e strambotti'
(1920)
Orpheus Qt *Concert*
(2/92) (ASV) ① [2] **CDDCD457**
String Quartet No. 2, 'Stornelli e ballata'
(1923)
Orpheus Qt *Concert*
(2/92) (ASV) ① [2] **CDDCD457**
String Quartet No. 3, 'Cantari alla
Madrigalesca' (1931)
Orpheus Qt *Concert*
(2/92) (ASV) ① [2] **CDDCD457**
String Quartet No. 4 (1934)
Orpheus Qt *Concert*
(2/92) (ASV) ① [2] **CDDCD457**
String Quartet No. 5, 'dei capricci' (1950)
(from opera 'I capricci di Callot')
Orpheus Qt *Concert*
(2/92) (ASV) ① [2] **CDDCD457**
String Quartet No. 6, 'L'arca di Noè' (1947)
Orpheus Qt *Concert*
(2/92) (ASV) ① [2] **CDDCD457**
String Quartet No. 7 (1950)
Orpheus Qt *Concert*
(2/92) (ASV) ① [2] **CDDCD457**
String Quartet No. 8, 'per Elisabetta' (1963-
64)
Orpheus Qt *Concert*
(2/92) (ASV) ① [2] **CDDCD457**

SECTION III: INSTRUMENTAL

A Claude Debussy—piano (1920)
S. I. Bartoli (r1994) *Concert*
(9/95) (ASV) ① **CDDCA929**
Barlumi—piano (1917)
1. Non troppo lento, scorrevole; 2. Lento; 3. Vivace,
alquanto mosso; 4. Lento, misterioso; 5. Molto
mosso.
S. I. Bartoli (r1994) *Concert*
(9/95) (ASV) ① **CDDCA929**
Maschere che passano—piano (1918)
1. Allegro vivace. Molto capriccio; 2. Lento ma non
troppo. Con una certa goffaggine; 3. Mosso. Spirtato;
4. Un poco ritenuto. Con enfasi grottesca; 5.
Vivacissimo. Furiosamente.
S. I. Bartoli (r1994) *Concert*
(9/95) (ASV) ① **CDDCA929**
Omaggi—piano (1920)
1. A un pappagallo; 2. A un elefante; 3. A un idiota.
S. I. Bartoli (r1994) *Concert*
(9/95) (ASV) ① **CDDCA929**
Poemi asolani—piano (1916)
1. La notte dei morti; 2. Dittico; 3. I partenti.
S. I. Bartoli (r1994) *Concert*
(9/95) (ASV) ① **CDDCA929**
Preludi Autunnali—piano (1914)
1. Lento, ma carezzevole; 2. Ritenuto, ma spigliato;
3. Lento, triste; 4. Veloce.
S. I. Bartoli (r1994) *Concert*
(9/95) (ASV) ① **CDDCA929**

SECTION V: STAGE WORKS

Il Finto Arlecchino—opera (1925) (Lib. cpsr)
Symphonic fragments Veneto PO, P. Maag (r1991)
Concert (9/93) (MARC) ① **8 223397**

MALLIÉ, Loïc (b 1947) France

SECTION III: INSTRUMENTAL

Improvisation on themes by Liszt—organ
(1987)
L. Mallié *Liszt: Via crucis, S53.*
(10/89) (REM) ① **REM311033**

MALLORY, Margaret (20th Cent) USA

SECTION IV: VOCAL AND CHORAL

Indian Summer—song (Wds. D. Parker)
Sarah Walker, R. Vignoles (pp1982) *Concert*
(3/89) (MERI) ① **CDE84167**
Résumé... serenade to a gravedigger—song
(Wds. D. Parker)
Sarah Walker, R. Vignoles (pp1982) *Concert*
(3/89) (MERI) ① **CDE84167**
Unfortunate Coincidence—song (Wds. D.
Parker)
Sarah Walker, R. Vignoles (pp1982) *Concert*
(3/89) (MERI) ① **CDE84167**
Words of Comfort (to be scratched on a
mirror)—song (Wds. D. Parker)
Sarah Walker, R. Vignoles (pp1982) *Concert*
(3/89) (MERI) ① **CDE84167**

MALVEZZI, Cristofano (1547–1599) Italy

SECTION II: CHAMBER

Sinfonia—unidentified
Capriccio Stravagante, S. Sempé (hpd/dir) *Concert*
(10/91) (DHM) ① **RD77220**
Sinfonia a 6—Intermedio 1, La Pellegrina
(c1589)
Taverner Plyrs, A. Parrott *Concert*
(8/88) (EMI) ① **CDC7 47998-2**
Sinfonia II a 6—Intermedio 4, La Pellegrina
(c1589)
Taverner Plyrs, A. Parrott *Concert*
(8/88) (EMI) ① **CDC7 47998-2**
Sinfonia III a 6—Intermedio 5, La Pellegrina
(c1589)
Taverner Plyrs, A. Parrott *Concert*
(8/88) (EMI) ① **CDC7 47998-2**

SECTION IV: VOCAL AND CHORAL

A voi, reali Amanti—madrigal (6vv) -
Intermedio 1, La Pellegrina (c1589) (Wds.
Rinuccini)
Taverner Consort, Taverner Plyrs, A. Parrott *Concert*
(8/88) (EMI) ① **CDC7 47998-2**
Coppia gentil—madrigal (6vv) - Intermedio 1,
La Pellegrina (c1589) (Wds. Rinuccini)
Taverner Consort, Taverner Ch, Taverner Plyrs, A.
Parrott *Concert* (8/88) (EMI) ① **CDC7 47998-2**
Dal vago e bel sereno—madrigal (6vv) -
Intermedio 6, La Pellegrina (c1589) (Wds.
Anon)
Taverner Consort, Taverner Plyrs, A. Parrott *Concert*
(8/88) (EMI) ① **CDC7 47998-2**
Dolcissime sirene—madrigal (6vv) -
Intermedio 1, La Pellegrina (c1589) (Wds.
Rinuccini)
T. Bonner, Taverner Consort, Taverner Plyrs, A.
Parrott *Concert* (8/88) (EMI) ① **CDC7 47998-2**
E noi, con questa bella diva—madrigal (5vv)
- Intermedio 5, La Pellgrina (c1589) (Wds.
Rinuccini or Bardi)
Taverner Consort, Taverner Plyrs, A. Parrott *Concert*
(8/88) (EMI) ① **CDC7 47998-2**
Io, che l'onde raffreno—aria (1v) - Intermedio
5, La Pellegrina (c1589) (Wds. Rinuccini)
E. Kirkby, Taverner Plyrs, A. Parrott *Concert*
(8/88) (EMI) ① **CDC7 47998-2**
Lieti solcando il mare—madrigal (7vv) -
Intermedio 5, La Pellegrina (c1589) (Wds.
Rinuccini)
Taverner Consort, Taverner Plyrs, A. Parrott *Concert*
(8/88) (EMI) ① **CDC7 47998-2**
Noi, che cantando—madrigal (8vv) -
Intermedio 1, La Pellegrina (c1589) (Wds.
Rinuccini)
Taverner Consort, Taverner Plyrs, A. Parrott *Concert*
(8/88) (EMI) ① **CDC7 47998-2**
O fortunato giorno—madrigal (7vv) -
Intermedio 6, La Pellegrina (c1589) (Wds.
Rinuccini)
Taverner Consort, Taverner Ch, Taverner Plyrs, A.
Parrott *Concert* (8/88) (EMI) ① **CDC7 47998-2**
O quale, o qual risplende—madrigal (6vv) -
Intermedio 5, La Pellegrina (c1589) (Wds.
Rinuccini)
Taverner Consort, Taverner Plyrs, A. Parrott *Concert*
(8/88) (EMI) ① **CDC7 47998-2**

Or che le due grand'Alme—madrigal (6vv) -
Intermedio 4, La Pellegrina (c1589) (Wds.
Strozzi)
Taverner Consort, Taverner Plyrs, A. Parrott *Concert*
(8/88) (EMI) ① **CDC7 47998-2**

MANCINELLI, Luigi (1848–1921) Italy

SECTION I: ORCHESTRAL

Scene veneziane—suite for orchestra
(1888)
Il volo degli amanti NBC SO, A. Toscanini (bp1946)
Concert (5/94) (ATS) ① [2] **ATCD100**

MANCINI, Francesco (1672–1737) Italy

SECTION II: CHAMBER

Sonata for Recorder, Two Violins and
Continuo in D minor
Giardino Armonico Ens, G. Antonini (rec/dir) (r1993)
Concert (11/94) (TELD) ① **4509-93157-2**
Sonata in F minor—recorder and continuo
E. Haupt, C. Schornsheim *Concert*
(2/90) (CAPR) ① **10 234**

SECTION V: STAGE WORKS

Gl'Amanti Generosi—opera (1705—Naples)
Sinfonia C. Steele-Perkins, Parley of Instr *Concert*
(1/89) (HYPE) ① **CDA66255**

MANCINI, Henry (1924–1994) USA

SECTION V: STAGE WORKS

Fear—film score (1990)
EXCERPTS: 1. Casey's Theme.
1. Mancini Pops Orch, H. Mancini (r1990; arr
Mancini) *Concert* (5/91) (RCA) ① **RD60471**
Frenzy—film score (1972) (score rejected by
director A Hitchcock)
EXCERPTS: 1. Main Title.
1. Mancini Pops Orch, H. Mancini (r1990; arr
Mancini) *Concert* (5/91) (RCA) ① **RD60471**
The Great Waldo Pepper—film score (1975)
EXCERPTS: 1. Waldo Pepper March.
1. San Diego SO, L. Schifrin *Concert*
(5/93) (SILV) ① **SILVAD3001**
The Man Who Loved Women—film score
(1983)
EXCERPTS: 1. Little Boys.
1. Mancini Pops Orch, H. Mancini (r1990; arr
Mancini) *Concert* (5/91) (RCA) ① **RD60471**
Mommie Dearest—film score (1981)
EXCERPTS: 1. Theme.
1. Mancini Pops Orch, H. Mancini (r1990; arr
Mancini) *Concert* (5/91) (RCA) ① **RD60471**
Monster Movie Suite (arr cpsr from various
films)
1. The Monster gets Mark (Creature from the Black
Lagoon: 1954); 2a. The Thing strikes (It Came from
Outer Space: 1953); 2b. Desert Rendezvous (It
Came from Outer Space: 1953); 3. Terror Strikes
(Tarantula: 1955).
Mancini Pops Orch, H. Mancini (r1990) *Concert*
(5/91) (RCA) ① **RD60471**
Nightwing—film score (1979)
EXCERPTS: 1. Main Title.
1. Mancini Pops Orch, H. Mancini (r1990; arr
Mancini) *Concert* (5/91) (RCA) ① **RD60471**
The Prisoner of Zenda—film score (1979)
EXCERPTS: 1. Main Title; 2. Coronation Waltz; 3.
Croquette.
1-3. Mancini Pops Orch, H. Mancini (r1990; arr
Mancini) *Concert* (5/91) (RCA) ① **RD60471**
Sunset—film score (1987)
EXCERPTS: 1. Theme; 2. Cheryl's Theme; 3. The
Cowboys.
1-3. Mancini Pops Orch, H. Mancini (r1990; arr
Mancini) *Concert* (5/91) (RCA) ① **RD60471**
The White Dawn—film score (1974)
EXCERPTS: 1. Arctic Whale Hunt.
1. Mancini Pops Orch, H. Mancini (r1990; arr
Mancini) *Concert* (5/91) (RCA) ① **RD60471**
Without a Clue—film score (1987)
1. Super Sleuth; 2. Theme: End Title.
1, 2. Mancini Pops Orch, H. Mancini (r1990; arr
Mancini) *Concert* (5/91) (RCA) ① **RD60471**

MANCINUS, Thomas (1550–1611/12) Germany

SECTION IV: VOCAL AND CHORAL

Cantio Nova (c1590) (after Psalm 28)
Hilliard Ens, P. Hillier *Concert*
(2/89) (BIS) ① **BIS-CD389**

MANFREDINI, Francesco Onofrio (1684–1762) Italy

SECTION I: ORCHESTRAL

12 Sinfonie—strings, Op. 2 (pub 1709)
10. C minor.
10. Capella Istropolitana, J. Krechek (r1993) *Concert*
(3/95) (NAXO) ① **8 550877**
12 Concerti grossi, Op. 3
1. F; 2. A minor; 3. B flat; 4. D minor; 5. D minor; 6.
D; 7. G; 8. F; 9. D; 10. G minor; 11. C minor; 12. C,
'Christmas Concerto'.
10. ASMF, N. Marriner (r1962) *Concert*
(9/93) (DECC) ① **436 224-2DM**
12. BPO, H. von Karajan *Concert*
(8/87) (DG) ① **419 046-2GGA**
12. Virtuosi Saxoniae, L. Güttler *Concert*
(12/89) (CAPR) ① **10 225**
12. Giardino Armonico Ens *Concert*
(12/91) (TELD) ① **2292-46013-2**
12. Solisti Italiani (r1993) *Concert*
(12/94) (DENO) ① **CO-78912**

MANFROCE, Nicola Antonio (?–1813) Italy

SECTION V: STAGE WORKS

Ecuba—opera: 3 acts (1812—Naples) (Lib.
Schmidt, after Milcent)
Si tenero amatore M. Bovino, H. Nichol, Y. Kenny,
P. Nilon, Philh, D. Parry *Concert*
(10/90) (OPRA) ① [3] **ORCH103**

MANGEANT, Jacques (d ?1633) France

SECTION IV: VOCAL AND CHORAL

Jean de Nivelle—chanson (c1610)
Baltimore Consort (r1992; arr Baltimore Consort)
Concert (4/95) (DORI) ① **DOR90177**

MANGOLD, Carl Armand (1813–1889) Germany

SECTION IV: VOCAL AND CHORAL

Abraham—oratorio: 2 parts: sois, double
choir & orch (1859-60) (Wds. Bible)
M. Ruhr, M. Frimmer, M. Georg, B. Gärtner, G. Türk,
T. Essmann, G. Cachemaille, T. Sehrbrock,
Darmstadt Chor, Darmstadt PO, W. Seeliger (r1986)
(11/95) (CHRI) ① [2] **CHR77172**
Zweigesang—Lied
F. Hempel, B. Seidler-Winkler (r1935) *Concert*
(3/94) (NIMB) ① **NI7849**

MANSON (?19th Cent)

SECTION IV: VOCAL AND CHORAL

3 Songs of Love and Youth
2. A birthday; 3. Hence away, begone!.
2, 3. W. Widdop, anon (r1924) *Concert*
(11/92) (CLAR) ① **CDGSE78-50-46**

MANYKIN-NEVSTRUEV, Nikolai Alexander (1869–?) Russia

SECTION IV: VOCAL AND CHORAL

Song of the needy pilgrim
F. Chaliapin, Afonsky Ch, Balalaika Orch (r1934)
Concert (6/93) (PREI) ① [2] **89207**

MAQUE, Giovanni de (1550–1614) Italy

SECTION III: INSTRUMENTAL

Keyboard Works
1. Gagliarda prima; 2. Gagliarda seconda; 3.
Seconde Stravaganze; 4. Consonanze stravaganti.
R. Alessandrini (r1994) *Concert*
(4/95) (O111) ① **OPS30-118**

MARAIRE, Dumisani (b 1943) Rhodesia/Zimbabwe

SECTION II: CHAMBER

Mai Nozipo (Mother Nozipo)—ngoma, hosha
and string quartet (1990)
Kronos Qt, D. Maraire *Concert*
(11/92) (NONE) ① **7559-79275-2**

SECTION IV: VOCAL AND CHORAL

Kutambarra (Spreading)—vocal, mbira,
hosho, chorus & string quartet (1990)
D. Maraire, D. Pauli, T. Kelly, Kronos Qt, T. Kelly
Concert (11/92) (NONE) ① **7559-79275-2**

MARAIS, Marin (1656–1728) France

SECTION II: CHAMBER

La gamme et autres morceaux de
simphonies—violin, viola da gamba and
harpsichord (pub 1723) ('en forme de petit
opéra')
1. La gamme en forme d'un petit opéra; 2. Sonate à
la mariesienne; 3. Sonerie de Saint-Geneviève du
Mont.
1, 2, 3. Boston Museum Trio (r1990)
(2/94) (CENT) ① **CRC2129**
2. Royal Trio (r1991) *Concert*
(8/93) (DHM) ① **05472 77176-2**
2, 3. Cologne Musica Antiqua, R. Goebel (r1978)
Concert (1/93) (ARCH) ① **437 086-2AT**
3. Spectre de la Rose (r1993) *Concert*
(2/94) (NAXO) ① **8 550750**
3. Guildhall Str Ens, R. Salter (vn/dir) (r1992) *Concert*
(2/94) (RCA) ① **09026 61275-2**
Pièces de viole, Livre 1—Part 1—viola da
gamba and continuo (pub 1686 and 1689
(continuo)) (Suites 1-4)
(Suite in D minor): 1. Prélude; 2. Allemande; 3.
Courante; 4. Sarabande; 5. Gigue; 6. Gavotte; 7.
Menuet. (Suite in G): 8. Prélude; 9. Allemande; 10.
Courante; 11. Sarabande; 12. Gigue; 13. Gavotte en
rondeau; 14. Menuet; 15. Gavotte; 16. Fantasie en
écho; 17. Chaconne; 18. Le tombeau de M. Meliton.
1-18. Smithsonian Chbr Plyrs
(3/91) (DHM) ① **RD77146**
1, 2, 3, 4, 5, 6, 7. M. Muller, S. Abramowicz, E. Ferré,
P. Monteilhet (r1992) *Concert*
(2/94) (ADES) ① **20235-2**
8. Spectre de la Rose (r1993) *Concert*
(2/94) (NAXO) ① **8 550750**
Pièces de viole, Livre 2—Part 1—viola da
gamba and continuo (pub 1701) (Suites 1-4)
(Suite in A minor): 1. Prelude I; 2. Fantaisie; 3.
Prelude II; 4. Prelude III; 5. Bourasque; 6. Prelude IV;
7. Allemande; 8. La folette; 9. Courante; 10.
Sarabande I; 11. Sarabande II; 12. Gigue La
favourite; 13. Gigue; 14. Caprice; 15. Gavotte; 16.
Menuet I; 17. Menuet II; 18. Menuet III; 19. Ballet Le
rondeau; 20. Couplets de folies: Les folies
d'Espagne. (Suite in D minor): 21. Prelude; 22.
Prelude II; 23. Allemande I; 24. Allemande II; 25.
Courante I; 26. Courante II; 27. Sarabande grave; 28.
Sarabande; 29. Boutade; 30. Fantaisie luthée; 31.
Gigue I; 32. Gigue II; 33. Double; 34. Double en
rondeau; 35. Menuet I; 36. Menuet II; 37. Rondeau
champêtre; 38. Cloches ou carillon; 39. Paysanne;
40. La polonoise; 41. Menuet III. (Suite in B minor):
42. Prelude; 43. Fantaisie; 44. Prelude lentement; 45.
Allemande I; 46. Double; 47. Allemande la familiare;
48. Double; 49. Allemande III; 50. Double; 51.
Courante I; 52. Courante II; 53. Sarabande I; 54.
Sarabande II; 55. Gigue; 56. Gigue angloise; 57.
Gavotte; 58. Rondeau; 59. La vilageoise; 60. Menuet
I; 61. Menuet II; 62. Menuet III; 63. Les voix
humaines; 64. Chaconne.
19. Royal Trio (r1991) *Concert*
(8/93) (DHM) ① **05472 77176-2**
20. S. Cunningham, M. Meyerson, A. Maurette
Concert (5/89) (ASV) ① **CDGAU112**
20. M. Verbruggen, Sonnerie Trio *Concert*
(2/90) (ASV) ① **CDGAU113**
20. Purcell Qt *Concert* (4/90) (HYPE) ① **CDA66310**
Pièces de viole, Livre 2—Part 2—viola da
gamba and continuo (pub 1701) (Suites 5-8)
(Suite in B minor): 1. Prelude; 2. Petite fantaisie; 3.
Allemande I; 4. Allemande II; 5. Courante; 6.
Sarabande I; 7. Sarabande II; 8. Gigue I; 9. Gigue II;
10. Menuet I; 11. Gavotte; 12. Menuet II; 13.
Tombeau pour M. de Lully. Suite in E minor: 14.
Prelude; 15. Allemande; 16. Courante; 17.
Sarabande; 18. Gigue; 19. Rondeau champetre; 20.

Tombeau pour M. de Ste. Colombe.
13. S. Cunningham, M. Meyerson, A. Maurette
Concert (5/89) (ASV) ① **CDGAU112**
20. Royal Trio (r1991) *Concert*
(8/93) (DHM) ① **05472 77176-2**
20. P. Pierlot, S. Watillon, R. Lislevand (r1992)
Concert (2/94) (RICE) ① **RIC118100**
20. Spectre de la Rose (r1993) *Concert*
(2/94) (NAXO) ① **8 550750**
Pièces de viole, Livre 3—Part 1—viola da
gamba and continuo (pub 1711) (Suites 1-4)
(Suite in A minor): (A minor): 1. Prelude; 2.
Allemande; 3. Courante; 4. Sarabande; 5. Gigue; 6.
Double; 7. Gavotte; 8. Menuet; 9. Autre; 10.
Rondeau; 11. Prelude; 12. Gavotte La petite; 13.
Grand ballet. (Suite in A): (D major): 14. Prelude; 15.
Allemande; 16. Double; 17. Sarabande; 18.
Courante; 19. Gavotte; 20. Gigue L'inconstance; 21.
Fantaisie; 22. Menuet I; 23. Menuet II; 24. Rondeau;
25. Gigue La gotique (Suite in F): 26. Prelude; 27.
Fantaisie; 28. Allemande; 29. Double; 30. Courante;
31. Double; 32. Gavotte La badine; 33. Sarabande;
34. Gigue; 35. Menuet I; 36. Menuet II; 37. Rondeau;
38. Chaconne; 39. Boursaque. (Suite in D): 40.
Prelude; 41. Fantaisie; 42. Allemande; 43. Courante;
44. Sarabande; 45. La Folette; 46. Gigue; 47.
Courante; 48. Bourée paysanne; 49. Gavotte; 50.
Petit rondeau; 51. Menuet La chantarelle; 52. Menuet
La trompette; 53. Rondeau; 54. Boureau; 55. Plainte;
56. Chaconne; 57. La brillante; 58. Charivary.
11, 1, 2, 3, 4, 5, 6, 13, 40, 41, 54, 55, 57, 45. J.
Savall, H. Smith, T. Koopman *Pièces de viole, III/I.*
(12/92) (ASTR) ① **E8761**
13. M. Muller, S. Abramowicz, E. Ferré, P. Monteilhet
(r1992) *Concert* (2/94) (ADES) ① **20235-2**
13, 26-28, 30, 32-35. B. Re, R. Kohnen *Concert*
(9/88) (PIER) ① **PV788012**
40-42, 55, 58. Purcell Qt *Concert*
(4/90) (HYPE) ① **CDA66310**
Pièces de viole, Livre 3—Part 2—viola da
gamba and continuo (pub 1711) (Suites 5-9)
(Suite in B flat): 1. Prelude; 2. Fantaisie; 3.
Allemande I; 4. Allemande II; 5. Courante; 6. Double;
7. Sarabande; 8. Gigue I; 9. Gigue II; 10. Gavotte; 11.
Gavotte La sincope; 12. Gavotte du goust du
theorbe; 13. Rondeau; 14. Bourée paysanne; 15.
Double; 16. Menuet I; 17. Menuet II. (Suite in G
minor): (Suite in D): 18. Prelude; 19. Caprice; 20.
Allemande; 21. Courante; 22. Double de
L'Allemande; 23. Sarabande; 24. Gigue La chicane;
25. Gigue; 26. Rondeau louré; 27. Gavotte; 28.
Plainte; 29. Menuet; 30. Menuet fantasque; 31.
Double; 32. Fugue gaye; 33. Le moulinet. (Suite in
D): 34. Prelude; 35. Caprice; 36. Allemande; 37.
Double; 38. Allemande La mariagnole; 39. Double;
40. Courante; 41. Sarabande grave; 42. Gigue à
l'anglaise; 43. Gigue La petite; 44. Gavotte; 45.
Menuet; 46. Menuet La corde chasse; 47. La Muzette
I; 48. La Muzette II; 49. La guitarre. (Suite in C): 50.
Prelude; 51. Caprice; 52. Allemande; 53. Double; 54.
Sarabande; 55. Sarabande en rondeau; 56.
Courante; 57. Double; 58. Gigue; 59. Gigue en
rondeau; 60. Menuet I; 61. Menuet II; 62. Saillie du
caffé; 63. Rondeau; 64. Chaconne. (Suite in G minor):
65. Prelude; 66. Fantaisie; 67. Double; 68.
Allemande; 69. Courante; 70. Sarabande grave; 71.
Gigue; 72. Rondeau; 73. Gavotte; 74. Menuet I; 75.
Menuet II; 76. Contrefaiseurs.
18, 20, 21, 22, 23, 25, 28. M. Muller, S. Abramowicz,
E. Ferré, P. Monteilhet (r1992) *Concert*
(2/94) (ADES) ① **20235-2**
34, 35, 38-42. S. Cunningham, M. Meyerson, A.
Maurette *Concert* (5/89) (ASV) ① **CDGAU112**
34, 38, 39, 40, 41, 42, 45, 47, 48, 49. J. Savall, H.
Smith, T. Koopman *Pièces de viole, III/I.*
(12/92) (ASTR) ① **E8761**
65, 67, 68, 71. Spectre de la Rose (r1993) *Concert*
(2/94) (NAXO) ① **8 550750**
Pièces de viole, Livre 4—Parts 2 and 3—1/3
violas da gamba and continuo (pub 1717)
(Suites 7-9)
(Suite d'un goût étranger): 1. Marche tartate; 2.
Sarabande; 3. La tartarine; 4. Double; 5. Gavotte; 6.
Les fêtes champestres; 7. Gigue La fleselle; 8.
Rondeau Le bijou; 9. Le tourbillon; 10. L'uniforme;
11. Suitte; 12. Suitte; 13. L'ameriquane; 14.
Allemande pour le sujet; 15. Gigue pour la basse; 16.
Allemande L'asmatique; 17. La tourneuse; 18.
Muzette; 19. Caprice ou Sonate; 20. Le labyrinthe;
21. La sauterelle; 22. La fougade; 23. Allemande La
bizare; 24. La minaudiere; 25. Allemande La
singuliere; 26. L'arabesque; 27. Allemade La
superbe; 28. La reveuse; 29. Marche; 30. Gigue; 31.
Pièce luthée; 32. Gigue La caustique; 33. Le
badinage. (Suite in D): 34. Allemande; 35. Allemande;
36. Courante I; 37. Menuet I; 38. Courante II; 39.

Menuet II; 40. Sarabande; 41. Gigue; 42. Gavotte;
43. Petite paysanne; 44. Rondeau. (Suite in G): 45.
Caprice; 46. Allemande; 47. Courante; 48. Paysane
gracieuse; 49. Sarabande; 50. Gigue; 51. Gavotte;
52. Rondeau; 53. Muzette I; 54. Muzette II; 55.
Double; 56. Menuet mircette.
1, 3, 4, 6, 9, 20, 26-30, 33. J. Savall, T. Koopman, H.
Smith   (9/88) (ASTR) ① **E7727**
19. M. Muller, S. Abramowicz, E. Ferré, P. Monteilhet
(r1992) *Concert*   (2/94) (ADES) ① **20235-2**
20. S. Cunningham, M. Meyerson, A. Maurette
Concert   (5/89) (ASV) ① **CDGAU112**
20, 26, 28, 33. Spectre de la Rose (r1993) *Concert*
(2/94) (NAXO) ① **8 550750**
28, 33. Fitzwilliam Ens *Pièces en trio.*
(11/92) (AUVI) ① **V4638**
Pièces de viole, Livre 5—Part 2—viola da
gamba and continuo (pub 1725) (Suites 5-7)
(Suite in G minor): 1. Prelude; 2. Fantaisie; 4.
Sarabande; 5. Gigue La pagode; 6. Gavotte; 7.
Menuet; 8. Allemande La marianne; 9. Le Tombeau
pour Marais le Cadet; 10. Rondeau Le badin; 11. La
georgienne dite La maupertis. (Suite in A minor): 12.
Prelude Le soligni; 13. Petit caprice; 14. Allemande
Le facile; 15. Sarabande; 16. Grande gavotte; 17.
Menute mnariée; 18. La mariée; 19. Gigue La mutine;
20. La bagatelle; 21. Rondeau: Moitié pincé... (Suite
in G): 22. Chaconne; 23. Dialogue; 24. Le jeu du
volant; 25. La poitevine; 29. (Suite in E minor/major):
30. Prelude; 32. La simplicité paysanne; 33.
Allemande La Bailly Duchené; 36. Sarabande; 37.
Menuet I; 38. Menuet II; 40. Marche persane diet La
sauvigny; 42. Gigue La resolue; 46. Le tableau de
l'operation de la taille; 47. Les relavailles; 48. Suite.
1, 2, 4-11, 30, 32, 33, 36-38, 40, 42, 46-48. J. Savall,
T. Koopman, H. Smith   (2/88) (ASTR) ① **E7708**
1, 2, 4, 5, 8, 9, 12-25, 46. W. Kuijken, R. Kohnen, K.
Uemura   (2/88) (ACCE) ① **ACC78744D**
12, 13, 14, 15, 18, 19. M. Muller, S. Abramowicz, E.
Ferré, P. Monteilhet (r1992) *Concert*
(2/94) (ADES) ① **20235-2**
Pièces en trio—trio sonatas: two treble
instruments & continuo (pub 1692)
Suite in C (C major): 1. Prelude; 2. Sarabande I; 3.
Sarabande I. 4. Fantaisie; 5. Loure; 6. La bagatelle;
7. Gavotte; 8. Menuet; 9. Rondeau; 10. Autre; 11.
Chaconne (Suite in B flat): 12. Prelude; 13.
Sarabande; 14. Air; 15. Gigue; 16. Gavotte; 17.
Caprice; 18. Menuet I; 19. Menuet II; 20. La
marianne; 21. Autre; 22. Plainte. (Suite in G minor):
23. Prelude; 24. Fantaisie; 25. Sarabande I; 26.
Sarabande I; 27. Rondeau; 28. Gigue; 29. Gavotte;
30. Menuet I; 31. Menuet II; 32. Plainte; 33.
Passacaille; 34. Air. (Suite in F): 35. Prelude; 36.
Sarabande; 37. Fantaisie champestre; 38. Gavotte
en rondeau; 39. Double; 40. Gavotte; 41. Gigue; 42.
Bransle de village; 43. Rigaudon; 44. Menuet I; 45.
Menuet II; 46. Menuet III; 47. Menuet IV; 48.
Simphonie. (Suite in E minor): 49. Prelude; 50.
Sarabande; 51. Rondeau; 52. Caprice; 53. Gavotte;
54. Menuet; 55. Autre; 56. Fantaisie; 57. La desolée
ou La bacaille lente. (Suite in G minor): (Suite in G
minor): 58. Prelude: lentement; 59. Fantaisie; 60.
Gavotte; 61. Rondeau; 62. Sarabande en rondeau;
63. Menuet I; 64. Sarabande; 65. Menuet II; 66.
Caprice; 67. Passacaille.
Quadro Hotteterre
(7/93) (TELD) ① [2] **9031-77617-2**
1-4, 6, 7, 9, 11, 58, 61-63, 66, 67. Purcell Qt *Concert*
(4/90) (HYPE) ① **CDA66310**
12-22, 49-67. Fitzwilliam Ens *Pièces de viole IV/II.*
(11/92) (AUVI) ① **V4638**
Variations on 'Les folies d'Espagne'—32
variations on an old Spanish sarabande
R. Canter, A. Pleeth, M. Tan *Concert*
(4/87) (AMON) ① **CD-SAR22**
H. Schellenberger, R. Koenen, J. Fink (trans ob)
Bach: Flute Sonatas, BWV1030-5.
(8/88) (DENO) ① **CO-2142**

SECTION V: STAGE WORKS

Alcyone—tragédie lyrique: prologue and 5
acts (1706) (Lib. A. Houdar de la Motte)
Cpte J. Smith, G. Ragon, P. Huttenlocher, V. le
Texier, S. Boulin, B. Delétré, J-P. Fouchécourt, V.
Gens, Musiciens du Louvre, M. Minkowski
(4/92) (ERAT) ① [3] **2292-45522-2**
Suites Concert des Nations, J. Savall (r1993)
(8/93) (ASTR) ① **E8525**

Cantate ninfe leggiadrette e belle—madrigal (6vv) (pub 1581)
Consort of Musicke, A. Rooley *Concert*
(12/91) (DHM) ① **RD77154**
Care mie selve a Dio—madrigal (5vv) (pub 1595) (Wds. B. Guarini)
C. Janequin Ens *Concert*
(11/90) (HARM) ① **HMC90 1281**
Chi dal defino—madrigal (6vv) - Intermedio 2, La Pellegrina (c1589) (Wds. O. Rinucinni)
Taverner Consort, Taverner Plyrs, A. Parrott *Concert*
(8/88) (EMI) ① **CDC7 47998-2**
Cruda Amarilli che co 'l nom' ancora—madrigal (5vv) (pub 1595) (Wds. B. Guarini)
Amaryllis Consort *Concert*
(6/86) (CARL) ① **PCD822**
C. Janequin Ens *Concert*
(11/90) (HARM) ① **HMC90 1281**
Dissi a l'amata mia lucida stella—madrigal: 4vv (1585)
M. Arruabarrena, K. van Laethem, M. Valenta, J. Benet, M. van Altena, J. Cabré, T. de Zwart, A. Pols, R. Van Der Meer, K. Junghänel (lte/dir) *Concert*
(1/92) (ACCE) ① **ACC8864D**
Hor pien d'altro desio—madrigal: 5vv (1582) (stanza III of a 6-stanza cycle by various comps)
M. Arruabarrena, K. van Laethem, M. Valenta, J. Benet, M. van Altena, J. Cabré, T. de Zwart, A. Pols, R. Van Der Meer, K. Junghänel (lte/dir) *Concert*
(1/92) (ACCE) ① **ACC8864D**
Jubilate Deo—motet (8vv) (pub 1600)
Capella Sancti Michaelis Voc Ens, Capella Sancti Michaelis Instr Ens, E. van Nevel *Concert*
(11/89) (RICE) ① **RIC062026**
Lamentabatur Jacob—motet (12vv) (pub 1604)
Capella Sancti Michaelis Voc Ens, Capella Sancti Michaelis Instr Ens, E. van Nevel *Concert*
(11/89) (RICE) ① **RIC062026**
Laudate Dominum I—motet (8vv)
Capella Sancti Michaelis Voc Ens, Capella Sancti Michaelis Instr Ens, E. van Nevel *Concert*
(11/89) (RICE) ① **RIC062026**
Madonna mia gentil rigratio Amore—madrigal: 5vv (1580)
M. Arruabarrena, K. van Laethem, M. Valenta, J. Benet, M. van Altena, J. Cabré, T. de Zwart, A. Pols, R. Van Der Meer, K. Junghänel (lte/dir) *Concert*
(1/92) (ACCE) ① **ACC8864D**
Madrigals, Book 1 (Madrigali...libro primo)—4vv (pub 1585)
EXCERPTS: 1. Ahi dispietata morte, ahi crudel vita! (Wds. Petrarch); 2. Apollo, s'ancor vive il bel desio (Wds. Petrarch); 3. Chi vòl udire i miei sospiri in rime (Wds. Sannazaro); 4. Dissi a l'amata mia lucida stella (Wds. Moscaglia); 5. Dolci son le quadrella ond'Amor punge (Wds. della Casa); 6. Hor vedi, Amor, che giovinetta donna (Wds. Petrarch); 7. I lieti amanti e le fanciulle tenere (Wds. Sannazaro); 8. Lasso, dicea 'Perché venisti Amore'; 9. Madonna, sua mercè, pur una parte (Wds. Sannazzaro); 10. Menando giorno gl'agni presso un fiume (Wds. Sannazzaro); 11. Non al suo amante più Diana piacque (Wds. Petrarch); 12. Non vidi mai dopo notturna pioggia (Wds. Petrarch); 13. Nova angeletta sovra l'ale accorta (Wds. Petrarch); 14. O bella man, che mi distringi 'l core (Wds. Petrarch); 15. Sul carro de la mente auriga siedi (Wds. Petrarch); 16. Tutto 'l dì piango (Wds. Petrarch); 17. Vedi le valli e i campi (Wds. Sannazzaro); 18. Veggo, dolce mio bene; 19. Vezzosi augelli, in fra le verdi fronde (Wds. Tasso); 20. Vienne Montan, mentre le nostre tormora (Wds. Sannazzaro); 21. Zefiro torna, e 'l bel tempo rimena (Wds. Petrarch).
Cpte *Concerto Italiano*, R. Alessandrini (r1994)
(10/94) (O111) ① **OPS30-117**
Madrigals, Book 1 (Madrigali...libro primo)—4+4vv (pub 1588)
EXCERPTS: 1. Basti fin qui le fen'e i duri affanni (wds. Sannazaro); 2. Ben me credeva, lasso (wds. Sannazaro); 3. Com'ogni rio che d'acque dolci et chiare; 4. Ecco che un'altra volta o piagge apriche (wds. Sannazaro); 5. Ecco così dicea (wds. Martinengo); 6. Fiere silvestre che per lati campi (wds. Sannazaro); 7. Fuggito è 'l sonno le mie crude notti (wds. Petrarch); 8. Interdette speranze e van desio (wds. Sannazaro); 9. O fere stelle homai datemi pace (wds. Sannazaro); 10. Ov'è condotto il mio amoroso stile (wds. Petrarch); 11. Piango che Amor con disusato oltraggio; 12. Se la mie vita da l'aspro tormento (wds. Petrarch); 13. Senza il mio sole in tenebre e martiri (wds. Sannazaro); 14. Senza il mio vago sol (wds. Trojano); 15. Valli riposte e sole (wds. Sannazore).

9, 11. Consort of Musicke, A. Rooley (r1987-88) *Concert*
(1/94) (MOSC) ① **070992**
Madrigals, Book 1 (Il primo libro de madrigali)—5vv (pub 1580)
EXCERPTS: 1. Cantatava la più vaga pastorella; 2. Che fa hoggi il mio sole; 3. Dolorosi martir, fieri tormenti (wds. Tansillo); 4. Lasso ch'io ardo e 'l mio bel sole ardente; 5. Liquide perle Amor da gli occhi sparse (wds. Pasqualino); 6. Madonna mia gentil ringratio Amore; 7. Ohime, dov'è 'l mio ben, dov'è 'l mio core (wds. B. Tasso); 8. O tu che fra le selve occulta vivi; 9. Partirò dunque, ohime mi manca il core; 10. Quando i vostri begl'occhi un caro velo (wds. Sannazaro); 11. Questa di verd'herbette; 12. Spuntavan già per far il mondo adorno; 13. Tirsi morir volea (wds. Guarini); 14. Venuta era Madonna al mio languire (wds. Sannazaro).
3, 5. Consort of Musicke, A. Rooley (r1987-88) *Concert*
(1/94) (MOSC) ① **070992**
Madrigals, Book 2 (Il secondo libro de madrigali)—5vv (pub 1581)
EXCERPTS: 1. Al vago del mio sole; 2. Amor io non potrei (Wds. Ariosto); 3. Amor, poiche non vuole (Wds. Parabosco); 4. Fillida mia più che i ligustri bianca (Wds. Sannazaro); 5. Già Febo il tuo splendor rendeva chiaro; 6. Già torna a rallegrar l'aria e la terra; 7. I' piango; ed ella il volto (Wds. Petrarch); 8. Itene a l'ombra de gli ameni faggi (Wds. Sannazaro); 9. La bella ninfa mia ch'al Tebro infiora (Wds. Molza); 10. Mi fa lasso languire (Wds. Cassola); 11. O voi che sospirate a miglior note (Wds. Petrarch); 12. Perche di pioggia 'l ciel non si distille; 13. Quando sorge l'aurora; 14. Se 'l pensier che mi strugge (Wds. Petrarch); 15. Strider faceva le zampogne a l'aura.
3. M. Arruabarrena, K. van Laethem, M. Valenta, J. Benet, M. van Altena, J. Cabré, T. de Zwart, A. Pols, R. Van Der Meer, K. Junghänel (lte/dir) *Concert*
(1/92) (ACCE) ① **ACC8864D**
11. Consort of Musicke, A. Rooley (r1987-88) *Concert*
(1/94) (MOSC) ① **070992**
Madrigals, Book 5 (Il quinto libro de madrigali)—5vv (pub 1585)
EXCERPTS: 1. Basciami basciami mille mille volte; 2. Chi vuol veder Amore; 3. Consumando mi vo di piaggi'in piaggia (wds. Petrarch); 4. Dolor tant'è la gioia che mi dai; 5. Due rose fresche, e colte in Paradiso (wds. Petrarch); 6. Il suo vago gioioso e lieto manto; 7. L'alto e nobil pensier che si sovente (wds. Sannazaro); 8. La rete fu di queste fila d'oro (wds. Ariosto); 9. Liete, verdi, fiorite e fresche valli (wds. Sannazaro); 10. Occhi miei che miraste si bel sole; 11. Ohime, l'antica fiamma (wds. Guarini); 12. Quella che lieta del mio duolo (wds. della Casa); 13. Se voi sete cor mio; 14. S'io vissi cieco e grave fall'indegno (wds. della Casa); 15. Sola angioletta starsi in treccie a l'ombra (wds. Sannazaro); 16. Sotto l'ombra de tuoi pregiati rami.
5. Consort of Musicke, A. Rooley (r1987-88) *Concert*
(1/94) (MOSC) ① **070992**
Madrigals, Book 5 (Il quinto libro de madrigali)—6vv (pub 1591)
EXCERPTS: 1. Amatemi ben mio...per che sdegn'il mio core (Wds. Tasso); 2. Baci soavi e cari (Wds. Guarini); 3. Come fuggir per selv'ombrosa e folta (Wds. della Casa); 4. Con la sua man la mia; 5. Ecco che 'l ciel a noi chiar'et sereno (Wds. Trojano); 6. Giunt'a un bel font'io trasmutato in fiore; 7. Leggiadre ninfe e pastorelli amanti (Wds. Guicciardi); 8. Leggiadrissima eterna primavera; 9. Nel dolce seno della bella Clori (Wds. Tasso); 10. S'a veder voi non vengo alma mia luce; 11. Spiri dolce Favonio Arabi odori (Wds. Trojano); 12. Vivrò dunque lontano.
2. Consort of Musicke, A. Rooley (r1987-88) *Concert*
(1/94) (MOSC) ① **070992**
Madrigals, Book 6 (Il sesto libro de madrigali)—6vv (pub 1595)
EXCERPTS: 1. Giovane donna sott'un verde lauro (wds. Petrarch); 2. La dove sono i pargoletti Amori (wds. Tasso); 3. Lucida perla a cui fu conca il cielo (wds. Guarini); 4. O verdi selv'o dolci fonti o rivi (wds. Tasso); 5. Se quel dolor che va inanzi al morire (wds. Tansillo).
5. Consort of Musicke, A. Rooley (r1987-88) *Concert*
(1/94) (MOSC) ① **070992**
Magnificat—8vv
King's College Ch, D. Briggs, S. Cleobury *Concert*
(5/85) (EMI) ① **CDC7 47065-2**
O figlie di Piero—madrigal (18vv) - Intermedio 2, La Pellegrina (c1589) (Wds. O. Rinuccini)
Taverner Consort, Taverner Plyrs, A. Parrott *Concert*
(8/88) (EMI) ① **CDC7 47998-2**

O mille volte mille—madrigal (8vv) - Intermedio 3, La Pellegrina (c1589) (Wds. O. Rinuccini)
Taverner Consort, Taverner Plyrs, A. Parrott *Concert*
(8/88) (EMI) ① **CDC7 47998-2**
O valoroso Dio—madrigal (4vv) - Intermedio 3, La Pellegrina (c1589) (Wds. O. Rinuccini)
Taverner Consort, Taverner Plyrs, A. Parrott *Concert*
(8/88) (EMI) ① **CDC7 47998-2**
Passando con pensier per un boschetto—madrigal (6vv) (pub 1584) (Wds. Sacchetti)
Consort of Musicke, A. Rooley *Concert*
(12/91) (DHM) ① **RD77154**
Questi vaghi concenti—madrigal (5vv) (pub 1595)
C. Janequin Ens *Concert*
(11/90) (HARM) ① **HMC90 1281**
Qui di carne si sfama—madrigal (12vv) - Intermedio 3, La Pellegrina (c1589) (Wds. O. Rinuccini)
Taverner Consort, Taverner Plyrs, A. Parrott *Concert*
(8/88) (EMI) ① **CDC7 47998-2**
Rose bianche e vermiglie—madrigal: 5vv (1582)
M. Arruabarrena, K. van Laethem, M. Valenta, J. Benet, M. van Altena, J. Cabré, T. de Zwart, A. Pols, R. Van Der Meer, K. Junghänel (lte/dir) *Concert*
(1/92) (ACCE) ① **ACC8864D**
Se nelle voci nostre—madrigal (12vv) - Intermedio 3, La Pellegrina (c1589) (Wds. O. Rinuccini)
Taverner Consort, Taverner Plyrs, A. Parrott *Concert*
(8/88) (EMI) ① **CDC7 47998-2**
Se quel dolor che va inanzi al morire—'capitolo' madrigal (6vv) (pub 1595) (Wds. L. Tansillo)
C. Janequin Ens *Concert*
(11/90) (HARM) ① **HMC90 1281**

MARIE, Gabriel *(1852–1928)*
France

SECTION I: ORCHESTRAL

La Cinquantaine
H. Kreisler, F. Kreisler (arr vc/pf: r1923) *Concert*
(7/90) (BIDD) ① [2] **LAB009/10**

MARIE DE FRANCE *(12–13th Cent) France*

SECTION III: INSTRUMENTAL

La danse de gupil—instrumental piece derived from 'D'un gupil' (comp Shira Kammen)
S. Kammen (r1993) *Concert*
(11/94) (ERAT) ① **4509-94830-2**

SECTION IV: VOCAL AND CHORAL

D'un gupil—poem
A. Azéma, S. Kammen (r1993; music anon, ed. Cohen) *Concert* (11/94) (ERAT) ① **4509-94830-2**
Issi avint qu'un cers—poem
A. Azéma, S. Kammen (r1993; music anon, ed. Cohen) *Concert* (11/94) (ERAT) ① **4509-94830-2**

MARÍN, José *(?1619–1699)*
Spain

SECTION IV: VOCAL AND CHORAL

Ojos, que me desdenais
M. Figueras, Hespèrion XX, J. Savall *Concert*
(2/92) (ASTR) ① **E8729**
Romanesca (r1991-2) *Concert*
(11/94) (GLOS) ① **GCD920201**
Song Collection—1v and guitar (pub 1690)
1. Desengañemonos; 2. Filis no cantes; 3. Aquella sierra nevada; 4. Menguilla, yo me muriera (Juan de Celis); 5. Sin duda piensa menguilla (Juan Hidalgo); 6. No piense menguilla ya.
M.D.M. Fernández Doval, Extempore Stg Ens *Concert* (7/92) (HYPE) ① **CDA66327**
3, 6. Romanesca (r1991-2) *Concert*
(11/94) (GLOS) ① **GCD920201**

MARINI, Biagio *(c1587–1685)*
Italy

SECTION II: CHAMBER

Eco a tre violini
Gabrieli Players, P. McCreesh (r1990; ed Bartlett) *Concert* (4/93) (ARCH) ① [2] **437 552-2AH2**

J. Holloway, S. Ritchie, A. Manze, N. North, M. Springfels, J. Toll (r1993) *Concert*
(2/94) (HARM) ① **HMU90 7091**

Passacaglia a 4
Capriccio Stravaganze, S. Sempé (hpd/dir) *Concert*
(10/91) (DHM) ① **RD77220**

Sonata—two instruments and continuo (unidentified)
Palladian Ens (r1992) *Concert*
(7/93) (LINN) ① **CKD010**

Sonata a tre—two violins and continuo, Op. 22 (Fugge dolente core)
J. Holloway, S. Ritchie, A. Manze, N. North, M. Springfels, J. Toll (r1993) *Concert*
(2/94) (HARM) ① **HMU90 7091**

SECTION IV: VOCAL AND CHORAL

Concerto terzo delle musiche da camera—3-6vv and continuo, Op. 16 (pub 1649)
1. Gite sospiri miei; 2. O Cloride; 3. Men vivo amante; 4. Non vuoi chio t'amai; 5. Mentre fissando il guardo; 6. Ardimi, struggimi 'l cor; 7. Gia son amante no'l niego più; 8. Languir per un bel volto; 9. Ninfa; 10. Amanti che fareno; 11. Grotte ambrosi, antri foschi; 12a. Balletto primo a tre e a cinque.
Cpte Consort of Musicke, A. Rooley (r1990)
(3/94) (MOSC) ① **070994**

SECTION V: STAGE WORKS

Ei l'armi cinesi—balletto (3vv) (pub 1649) (Wds. cpsr)
Consort of Musicke, A. Rooley *Concert*
(12/90) (VIRG) ① **VC7 59606-2**

MARIO, E. A. *(1884–?) Italy*
---

pseudonym of Giovanni Gaeta

SECTION IV: VOCAL AND CHORAL

La Leggenda di Piave—song
G. Martinelli, orch. R. Bourdon (r1926) *Concert*
(10/92) (TEST) ① **SBT1005**

Santa Lucia luntana—song (1919) (Wds. cpsr)
B. Gigli, orch, N. Shilkret (r1926) *Concert*
(9/88) (PEAR) ① **GEMMCD9316**

MARKEVITCH, Igor *(1912–1983) Russia/Italy*

SECTION II: CHAMBER

L' Envol d'Icare, '(The) Flight of Icarus'—2 pianos and percussion (1932) (arr from orchestral piece)
1. Prélude; 2. Jeux des Adolescents; 3. Icare attrape deux colombes; 4. Icare se fait fixer des ailes; 5. L'Envol d'Icare; 6. Où l'on apprend la chute d'Icare; 7. La mort d'Icare.
K. Lessing, C. Lyndon-Gee, F. Lang, J. Gagelmann, R. Haeger (r1993) *Concert*
(10/95) (LARG) ① **Largo 5127**

Galop—fl, ob, cl, bn, cor, perc, pf, vn, vc (1932)
Cologne Markevitch Ens (r1993) *Concert*
(10/95) (LARG) ① **Largo 5127**

Serenade—vn, cl, bn (1930)
K. Lessing, W. Meyer, D. Jensen (r1993) *Concert*
(10/95) (LARG) ① **Largo 5127**

SECTION III: INSTRUMENTAL

Noces—piano (1925)
1. Préambule; 2. A l'église; 3. Réjouissances.
K. Lessing (r1993) *Concert*
(10/95) (LARG) ① **Largo 5127**

SECTION IV: VOCAL AND CHORAL

Psaume—soprano, small choir and orchestra (1933)
1. Exaltation de la Divinité; 2. Solitude de l'Etre et Prière; 3. Laudate; 4. Majesté cosmique du Divin.
S. von Osten, Suisse Romande Rad Ch, SRO, I. Markevitch (pp1982) *Stravinsky: Rite of Spring*.
(11/92) (CASC) ① **VEL2004**

MARSCHNER, Heinrich (August) *(1795–1861) Germany*

SECTION I: ORCHESTRAL

Grande Ouverture solenne on 'God save the King'—concert overture, Op. 78 (1842)
Košice St PO, A. Walter (r1993) *Concert*
(9/95) (MARC) ① **8 223342**

SECTION V: STAGE WORKS

Der Bäbu—comic opera: 3 acts, Op. 98 (1838—Hanover) (Lib. W A Wohlbrück)
EXCERPTS: 1. Overture.
1. Košice St PO, A. Walter (r1994) *Concert*
(9/95) (MARC) ① **8 223342**

Des Falkners Braut—comic opera: 3 acts (1832—Dresden)
EXCERPTS: 1. Overture.
1. Košice St PO, A. Walter (r1993) *Concert*
(9/95) (MARC) ① **8 223342**

Der Goldschmied von Ulm—incidental music to Mosenthal's play (1856—Dresden)
EXCERPTS: 1. Overture.
1. Košice St PO, A. Walter (r1993) *Concert*
(9/95) (MARC) ① **8 223342**

Hans Heiling—romantic opera: prologue and 3 acts (1833—Berlin) (Lib. E. Devrient)
EXCERPTS: PROLOGUE: 1a. Rastlos geschafft; 1b. Genug, beendet euer emsig Treiben; 2. Overture. ACT 1: 3. O bleib' bei mir!; 4. Ha, welche Zeichen!; 5. An jenem Tag; 6. Wohlan, wohlan!; 7. Juchheisa!; 8. Ein sprödes allerliebstes Kind; 9. Wie hüpft mir vor Freude das Herz. ACT 2: 10. Einst war so tiefer Friede; 11. Aus der Klüfte; 12. Wohl durch den grünen Wald; 13. Ha dieses Wort; 14. Des Nachts wohl auf der Haide; 15. Ihr hört es! ACT 3: 16a. O Mutter, hätt ich dir geglaubt; 16b. Herauf, ihr Geister aus Höhl'; 17. Peasants' Wedding March; 18. Es wollte vor Zeiten; 19. Segne Allmächtiger; 20. Nun bist du mein; 21. So wollen wir auf kurze Zeit.
Cpte T. Mohr, M. Hajóssyová, E. Seniglová, M. Eklöf, K. Markus, L. Neshyba, Slovak Phil Chor, Slovak PO, E. Körner (omits dialogue)
(11/91) (MARC) ① [2] **8 223306/7**
5. B. Weikl, Munich RO, H. Wallberg *Concert*
(3/89) (ACAN) ① **43 266**
5. H. Schlusnus, Berlin St Op Orch, L. Blech (r1935) *Concert*
(9/90) (PREI) ① **89006**
5. T. Hampson, Munich RO, F. Luisi (r1994) *Concert*
(9/95) (EMI) ① **CDC5 55233-2**
5. H. Schlusnus, orch (r1917) *Concert*
(10/95) (NIMB) ① **NI7867**
5. H. Hermann Nissen, Berlin SO, F. Zweig (r1929) *Concert*
(12/95) (PREI) ① **89090**

Kaiser Adolph von Nassau—romantic opera: 4 acts, Op. 130 (1845—Dresden) (Lib. H Rau)
EXCERPTS: 1. Overture.
1. Košice St PO, A. Walter (r1993) *Concert*
(9/95) (MARC) ① **8 223342**

Lukretia—opera: 2 acts, Op. 67 (1827—Danzing) (Lib. A Eckschlager)
EXCERPTS: 1. Overture.
1. Košice St PO, A. Walter (r1993) *Concert*
(9/95) (MARC) ① **8 223342**

Prinz Friedrich von Homburg—incidental music to H von Kleist's play, Op. 56 (1821—Dresden)
EXCERPTS: 1. Overture.
1. Košice St PO, A. Walter (r1993) *Concert*
(9/95) (MARC) ① **8 223342**

Der Templer und die Jüdin—romantic opera: 3 acts, Op. 60 (1829—Leipzig) (Lib. W A Wohlbrück)
EXCERPTS: 1. Overture.
1. Košice St PO, A. Walter (r1994) *Concert*
(9/95) (MARC) ① **8 223342**

Der Vampyr—romantic opera (1828—Leipzig) (Lib. W. A. Wohlbrück, after C. Nodier)
EXCERPTS: 1. Overture.
Ha, noch einen ganzen Tag...Ha, welche Lust B. Weikl, Munich RO, H. Wallberg *Concert*
(3/89) (ACAN) ① **43 266**
Ha! Noch einen ganzen Tag T. Hampson, Munich RO, F. Luisi (r1994) *Concert*
(9/95) (EMI) ① **CDC5 55233-2**

MARSH, John *(1752–1828) England*

SECTION I: ORCHESTRAL

A Conversation Symphony for two orchestras (1784)
Chichester Concert, I. Graham-Jones *Concert*
(2/90) (OLYM) ① **OCD400**

Symphony No. 1 in B flat—2 oboes, 2 horns and strings (1783)
Chichester Concert, I. Graham-Jones *Concert*
(2/90) (OLYM) ① **OCD400**

Symphony No. 3 in D—2 oboes, 2 horns and strings (c1770)
Chichester Concert, I. Graham-Jones *Concert*
(2/90) (OLYM) ① **OCD400**

Symphony No. 4 in F—2 oboes, 2 horns and strings (c1788)
Chichester Concert, I. Graham-Jones *Concert*
(2/90) (OLYM) ① **OCD400**

Symphony No. 6 in D—orchestra (1784)
Chichester Concert, I. Graham-Jones *Concert*
(2/90) (OLYM) ① **OCD400**

MARSH, Roger *(b 1949) England*

SECTION II: CHAMBER

Ferry Music—clarinet, piano and cello (1988)
Mühlfeld Ens (r1993) *Concert*
(10/94) (CLRI) ① **CC0007**

MARSHALL, Charles *(c1859–1927) England*

SECTION IV: VOCAL AND CHORAL

I hear you calling me—song (1908) (Wds. H. Harford)
J. McCormack, E. Schneider (r1927) *Concert*
(5/93) (MMOI) ① **CDMOIR418**

MARSHALL, Ingram D(ouglass) *(b 1942) USA*

SECTION I: ORCHESTRAL

Fog Tropes—six brass, tape and live electronics (1982)
St Luke's Orch, J. Adams *Concert*
(7/91) (NONE) ① **7559-79249-2**

SECTION II: CHAMBER

Alcatraz—a musical and photgraphic tour—synthesizers, tape and piano (1984) (photos J. Bengston)
1. Prelude—the bay; 2. Introduction; 3. The approach; 4. Inside; 5. Rules and regulations; 6. Cell doors; 7. Solitary; 8. Escape; 9. End; 10. Postlude—the bay.
I. Marshall, I. Marshall (8/92) (NALB) ① **NA040CD**

MARSICK, Martin (Pierre Joseph) *(1848–1924) Belgium*

SECTION II: CHAMBER
---

2 Pieces—violin and piano, Op. 6
2. Scherzando.
2. J. Thibaud, T. Janopoulo (r1933: arr Kreisler) *Concert* (12/94) (APR) ① [2] **APR7028**

MARTA, Istvan *(b 1952) Hungary*

SECTION II: CHAMBER

Doom—string quartet
Kronos Qt *Concert* (4/91) (NONE) ① **7559-79242-2**
A Sigh—string quartet
Kronos Qt *Concert* (4/91) (NONE) ① **7559-79242-2**

MARTIN, Frank *(1890–1974) Switzerland*

SECTION I: ORCHESTRAL

Ballade—cello & small orchestra (1949)
P. Dixon, LPO, M. Bamert (r1994) *Concert*
(10/95) (CHAN) ① **CHAN9380**

Ballade—viola, wind, harpsichord & percussion (1972)
P. Dukes, R. Masters, R. Elms, LPO, M. Bamert (r1994) *Concert* (10/95) (CHAN) ① **CHAN9380**

Ballade—flute, string orchestra & piano (1939)
S. Milan, M. Dussek, CLS, R. Hickox *Concert*
(10/90) (CHAN) ① **CHAN8840**
A. Pépin, SRO, F. Martin (bp1958) *Concert*
(11/92) (CASC) ① **VEL2001**
E. Brown, C. Hoca, Philh Virtuosi, R. Kapp (r1990) *Concert* (3/94) (SCHW) ① **310832**
M. Faust, Cologne RSO, A. Francis (r1992: orch Ansermet) *Concert* (12/94) (CAPR) ① **10 495**
R. Elms, C. Chambers, LPO, M. Bamert (r1994) *Concert* (10/95) (CHAN) ① **CHAN9380**
J. Zoon, R. Brautigam, Concertgebouw, R. Chailly (r1992) *Concert* (10/95) (DECC) ① **444 455-2DH**

SECTION IV: VOCAL AND CHORAL

Light Music—song cycle (1992) (Wds. D
Manon)
P. Price Jones, P. Martin (r1995) *Concert*
(12/95) (ALTA) ① **AIR-CD-9011**
**Songs for the Four Parts of the
Night—soprano & violin** (Wds. 'Owl
Woman')
P. Price Jones, R. Colan (r1995) *Concert*
(12/95) (ALTA) ① **AIR-CD-9011**

MARTÍN Y COLL, Antonio (d. after 1734) Spain

SECTION III: INSTRUMENTAL

**Flores de música—collection of Spanish
organ pieces: 4 vols** (pub 1706-9) (most
pieces anonymous)
EXCERPTS: 1. Ruede la Vola; 2. Discurso de ecos;
3. Cancion Franzesa; 4. Diferencias sobre la gayta;
5. Canarios; 6. Folías; 7. Danza del hacha; 8. Villano.
4, 5. Romanesca (r1991-2) *Concert*
(11/94) (GLOS) ① **GCD920201**

MARTÍN Y SOLER, Vicente (1754–1806) Spain

SECTION V: STAGE WORKS

**Una Cosa rara—opera: 2 acts
(1786—Vienna)** (Lib. Da Ponte after L. Vélez
de Guevara)
(Act 1); 1. Consola le pene mia vita; 2. Dolce mi
parve un dì.
Cpte M.A. Peters, E. Palacio, M. Figueras, G.
Fabuel, I. Fresán, F. Belaza-Leoz, S. Palatchi, F.
Garrigosa, Catalan Capella Reial, Concert des
Nations, J. Savall (pp1991)
(2/92) (ASTR) ① **[3] E8760**

MARTÍNEZ-SOBRAL, Manuel (1879–1946) Guatemala

SECTION I: ORCHESTRAL

**Acuarelas Chapinas—sumphonic scenes
(1907)**
1. La Parada (The Parade); 2. Misa Mayor (High
Mass); 3. La Hora del Cocktail (Cocktail Hour); 4. La
Ventana (At the Window).
Moscow SO, A. de Almeida (r1994) *Concert*
(5/95) (MARC) ① **8 223710**

MARTINI, Giovanni Battista (1706–1784) Italy

SECTION III: INSTRUMENTAL

Toccata—keyboard
H. Hardenberger, S. Preston (arr tpt, org) *Concert*
(12/92) (PHIL) ① **434 074-2PH**
O.E. Antonsen, W. Marshall (r1992: arr tpt/org: Alain)
Concert (10/94) (EMI) ① **CDC5 55048-2**

MARTINI, Johann Paul Aegidius (1741–1816) Germany

SECTION IV: VOCAL AND CHORAL

Plaisir d'amour—romanza (Wds. Florian)
V. de los Angeles, Sinfonia of London, R. Frühbeck
de Burgos (orch Gamley) *Concert*
(10/88) (EMI) ① **CDM7 69502-2**
T. Schipa, orch, C. Sabajno (r1932) *Concert*
(2/89) (PEAR) ① **GEMMCD9322**
R. Tauber, Orch (Ger: r1928) *Concert*
(4/90) (PEAR) ① **GEMMCD9381**
E. Schwarzkopf, G. Moore (r1956) *Concert*
(12/90) (EMI) ① **CDM7 63654-2**
J. Baker, ASMF, N. Marriner *Concert*
(1/93) (PHIL) ① **434 173-2PM**
F. Araiza, Munich RSO, R. Weikert (arr Hötter)
Concert (3/93) (RCA) ① **09026 61163-2**
J. Carreras, ECO, V. Sutej (r1992; arr Agostinelli)
Concert (6/93) (PHIL) ① **434 926-2PH**
M. Horne, Martin Katz (pp1994) *Concert*
(11/95) (RCA) ① **09026 62547-2**
E. Clément, anon (r1910s) *Concert*
(8/95) (PEAR) ① **GEMMCD9161**

MARTINŮ, Bohuslav (Jan) (1890–1959) Bohemia

SECTION I: ORCHESTRAL

La Bagarre—orchestra (1926)
Pomeranian PO, T. Ukigaya *Concert*
(5/88) (THOR) ① **CTH2013**
**Concertino—cello and orchestral ensemble
(1924)**
R. Wallfisch, Czech PO, J. Bělohlávek *Concert*
(4/92) (CHAN) ① **CHAN9015**
**Concertino for Piano Trio and Orchestra No.
2 (1933)**
Berlin Göbel Trio, Pomeranian PO, T. Ukigaya
Concert (5/88) (THOR) ① **CTH2013**
**Concerto for Cello and Orchestra No. 1 (1930
rev 1955)**
R. Wallfisch, Czech PO, J. Bělohlávek *Concert*
(4/92) (CHAN) ① **CHAN9015**
P. Fournier, SRO, W. Sawallisch (pp1978) *Concert*
(11/92) (CASC) ① **VEL2009**
**Concerto for Cello and Orchestra No. 2
(1944-45)**
R. Wallfisch, Czech PO, J. Bělohlávek *Concert*
(4/92) (CHAN) ① **CHAN9015**
**Concerto for Harpsichord and Small
Orchestra (1935)**
Z. Růžičková, Slovak Radio CO, Z. Košler *Concert*
(7/94) (CAMP) ① **RRCD1321**
**Concerto for Oboe and Small Orchestra
(1955)**
L. Lencses, Stuttgart RSO, N. Marriner *Concert*
(5/90) (CAPR) ① **10 308**
I. Goritzki, Polish Chmbr PO, W. Rajski *Concert*
(9/91) (CLAV) ① **CD50-9018**
J. Anderson, Philh, S. Wright *Concert*
(12/92) (NIMB) ① **NI5330**
H. Holliger, ASMF, N. Marriner (r1991) *Concert*
(9/93) (PHIL) ① **434 105-2PH**
**Concerto for Piano and Orchestra No. 2
(1934)**
R. Firkušný, Czech PO, L. Pešek (r1993) *Concert*
(4/95) (RCA) ① **09026 61934-2**
**Concerto for Piano and Orchestra No. 3
(1947-48)**
R. Firkušný, Czech PO, L. Pešek (r1993) *Concert*
(4/95) (RCA) ① **09026 61934-2**
**Concerto for Piano and Orchestra No. 4,
'Incantations' (1955-56)**
K. Havlikova, Slovak RSO, O. Lenárd *Concert*
(7/94) (CAMP) ① **RRCD1321**
R. Firkušný, Czech PO, L. Pešek (r1993) *Concert*
(4/95) (RCA) ① **09026 61934-2**
**Concerto for Piano and Orchestra No. 5,
'Fantasia concertante' (1957)**
K. Havlikova, Slovak RSO, T. Koutnik *Concert*
(7/94) (CAMP) ① **RRCD1321**
**Concerto for Piano Trio and Orchestra No. 1
(1924)**
Berlin Göbel Trio, Pomeranian PO, T. Ukigaya
Concert (5/88) (THOR) ① **CTH2013**
**Concerto for String Quartet and Orchestra
(1931)**
Brandis Qt, FNO, J. Conlon *Concert*
(9/92) (ERAT) ① **2292-45499-2**
Cleveland Orch, C. von Dohnányi (r1992) *Concert*
(9/95) (DECC) ① **443 173-2DH**
**Concerto for Violin and Orchestra No. 1
(1930 rev 1955)**
J. Suk, Czech PO, V. Neumann (r1973) *Concert*
(11/95) (SUPR) ① **11 1969-2**
**Concerto for Violin and Orchestra No. 2
(1944-45)**
L. Kaufman, French Rad and TV Orch, J.M. Leconte
(r1955) *Concert* (8/92) (CAMB) ① **CD-1063**
J. Suk, Czech PO, V. Neumann (r1973) *Concert*
(11/95) (SUPR) ① **11 1969-2**
**Divertimento—piano left-hand and orchestra
(1926)**
J. Panenka, Prague CO, B. Gregor *Sinfonietta
giocosa.* (4/91) (SUPR) ① **11 0373-2**
**Double Concerto for 2 String Orchestras,
Piano and Timpani (1938)**
Czech PO, J. Bělohlávek *Symphony 2.*
(6/91) (CHAN) ① **CHAN8950**
I. Suslak, L. Gård, Malmö SO, J. DePreist *Concert*
(11/91) (BIS) ① **BIS-CD501**
J. Skovajska, Brno St PO, C. Mackerras *Spaliček.*
(3/92) (CONI) ① **CDCF202**
J. Skovajska, Brno St PO, C. Mackerras *Concert*
(9/92) (CONI) ① **CDCF210**
J-F. Heisser, J. Camosi, FNO, J. Conlon *Concert*
(9/92) (ERAT) ① **2292-45499-2**

3 Estampes—orchestra (1958)
Czech PO, J. Bělohlávek *Concert*
(6/91) (SUPR) ① **10 4140-2**
**Les Fresques de Piero della Francesca
(1954)**
Malmö SO, J. DePreist *Concert*
(11/91) (BIS) ① **BIS-CD501**
FNO, J. Conlon *Concert*
(9/92) (ERAT) ① **2292-45794-2**
SRO, E. Ansermet (pp1961) *Concert*
(11/92) (CASC) ① **VEL2007**
Czech PO, K. Ančerl *Concert*
(3/93) (SUPR) ① **11 1931-2**
RPO, R. Kubelík (r1958) *Concert*
(11/94) (EMI) ① **[2] CZS5 68223-2**
Half-time—orchestra (1924)
Czech PO, A. Copland (pp1973) *Concert*
(6/93) (ROMA) ① **RR1973**
Memorial to Lidice—orchestra (1943)
Czech PO, K. Ančerl (r1957) *Concert*
(3/93) (SUPR) ① **11 1931-2**
Czech PO, J. Bělohlávek *Concert*
(5/93) (CHAN) ① **CHAN9138**
Overture—orchestra (1953)
Czech PO, J. Bělohlávek *Concert*
(6/91) (SUPR) ① **10 4140-2**
The Parables—orchestra (1957-58)
1. The Parable of a Sculpture; 2. The Parable of a
Garden; 3. The Parable of a Navire.
Czech PO, J. Bělohlávek *Concert*
(6/91) (SUPR) ① **10 4140-2**
SRO, E. Ansermet (pp1962) *Concert*
(11/92) (CASC) ① **VEL2007**
Czech PO, K. Ančerl *Concert*
(3/93) (SUPR) ① **11 1931-2**
Partita—string orchestra (1931)
Prague CO, B. Novotný (r1994) *Concert*
(7/95) (DENO) ① **CO-78919**
**La Rhapsodie (Allegro
symphonique)—orchestra (1928)**
Czech PO, J. Bělohlávek *Concert*
(6/91) (SUPR) ① **10 4140-2**
**Rhapsody-Concerto for Viola and Orchestra
(1952)**
N. Imai, Malmö SO, J. DePreist *Concert*
(11/91) (BIS) ① **BIS-CD501**
M. Telecký, Slovak RSO, O. Trhlik *Concert*
(9/92) (CAMP) ① **RRCD1317**
R. Golani, Berne SO, P. Maag *Concert*
(9/92) (CONI) ① **CDCF210**
J. Suk, Czech PO, V. Neumann (r1987) *Concert*
(11/95) (SUPR) ① **11 1969-2**
**3 Ricercari—chamber orchestra with two
pianos (1938)**
J-F. Heisser, A. Planès, FNO, J. Conlon *Concert*
(9/92) (ERAT) ① **2292-45499-2**
St Paul CO, C. Hogwood *Concert*
(3/93) (DECC) ① **433 660-2DH**
**Serenade No. 4 (Divertimento)—viola, viola,
oboe, piano and strings (1932)**
Prague CO *Concert* (12/89) (SUPR) ① **11 0098-2**
V. Šimčisko, M. Telecký, Bratislava Chbr Ens, V.
Horák *Concert* (9/92) (CAMP) ① **RRCD1317**
Serenade No. 5—chamber orchestra (1930)
Prague CO *Concert* (12/89) (SUPR) ① **11 0098-2**
**Sinfonietta giocosa—piano and small
orchestra (1940)**
D. Hennig, Australian CO, C. Mackerras (r1988) *Suk:
Serenade, Op. 6.* (8/89) (CONI) ① **CDCF170**
J. Panenka, Prague CO, B. Gregor *Divertimento
(1926).* (4/91) (SUPR) ① **11 0373-2**
J. Jacobson, Bournemouth Sinfonietta, T. Vásáry
Concert (5/91) (CHAN) ① **CHAN8859**
D. Hennig, Australian CO, C. Mackerras *Concert*
(9/92) (CONI) ① **CDCF210**
**Sinfonietta, '(La) Jolla'—piano and
orchestra (1950)**
M. Singerová, Zilina St CO, J. Valta *Respighi:
Botticelli Pictures.* (8/90) (OPUS) ① **9350 1844**
J. Jacobson, Bournemouth Sinfonietta, T. Vásáry
Concert (5/91) (CHAN) ① **CHAN8859**
J-F. Heisser, FNO, J. Conlon *Concert*
(9/92) (ERAT) ① **2292-45794-2**
St Paul CO, C. Hogwood *Concert*
(3/93) (DECC) ① **433 660-2DH**
Symphony No. 1 (1942)
Bamberg SO, N. Järvi *Symphony 2.*
(9/87) (BIS) ① **BIS-CD362**
Berlin SO, C.P. Flor *Symphony 2.*
(11/90) (RCA) ① **RD60154**
Czech PO, J. Bělohlávek *Double Concerto.*
(6/91) (CHAN) ① **CHAN8950**
Czech PO, V. Neumann *Concert*
(1/92) (SUPR) ① **[3] 11 0382-2**
SNO, B. Thomson *Symphony 5.*
(1/92) (CHAN) ① **CHAN8915**

Symphony No. 2 (1943)
Bamberg SO, N. Järvi Symphony 1.
(9/87) (BIS) ① **BIS-CD362**
Berlin SO, C.P. Flor Symphony 1.
(11/90) (RCA) ① **RD60154**
Czech PO, V. Neumann Concert
(1/92) (SUPR) ① [3] **11 0382-2**
SNO, B. Thomson Symphony 6.
(1/92) (CHAN) ① **CHAN8916**
Symphony No. 3 (1944)
Bamberg SO, N. Järvi Symphony 4.
(9/87) (BIS) ① **BIS-CD363**
SNO, B. Thomson Symphony 4.
(6/91) (CHAN) ① **CHAN8917**
Czech PO, V. Neumann Concert
(1/92) (SUPR) ① [3] **11 0382-2**
Czech PO, V. Neumann (r1977) Symphony 4.
(12/95) (SUPR) ① **11 1967-2**
Symphony No. 4 (1945)
Bamberg SO, N. Järvi Symphony 3.
(9/87) (BIS) ① **BIS-CD363**
SNO, B. Thomson Symphony 3.
(6/91) (CHAN) ① **CHAN8917**
Czech PO, V. Neumann Concert
(1/92) (SUPR) ① [3] **11 0382-2**
SRO, E. Ansermet (pp1967) Concert
(11/92) (CASC) ① **VEL2007**
Czech PO, J. Bělohlávek Concert
(5/93) (CHAN) ① **CHAN9138**
Czech PO, V. Neumann (r1977) Symphony 3.
(12/95) (SUPR) ① **11 1967-2**
Symphony No. 5 (1946)
Bamberg SO, N. Järvi (r1988) Symphony 6.
(12/88) (BIS) ① **BIS-CD402**
Czech PO, V. Neumann Concert
(1/92) (SUPR) ① [3] **11 0382-2**
SNO, B. Thomson Symphony 1.
(1/92) (CHAN) ① **CHAN8915**
Czech PO, K. Ančerl (r1955) Concert
(3/93) (SUPR) ① **11 1931-2**
Symphony No. 6, 'Fantaisies symphoniques' (1951-53)
Bamberg SO, N. Järvi (r1988) Symphony 5.
(12/88) (BIS) ① **BIS-CD402**
Czech PO, J. Bělohlávek Concert
(1/91) (CHAN) ① **CHAN8897**
Czech PO, V. Neumann Concert
(1/92) (SUPR) ① [3] **11 0382-2**
SNO, B. Thomson Symphony 2.
(1/92) (CHAN) ① **CHAN8916**
Czech PO, K. Ančerl (r1956) Bouquet.
(8/95) (SUPR) ① **11 1932-2**
Toccata e due canzoni (1946)
Bournemouth Sinfonietta, T. Vásáry Concert
(5/91) (CHAN) ① **CHAN8859**
J-F. Heisser, FNO, J. Conlon Concert
(9/92) (ERAT) ① **2292-45794-2**
St Paul CO, C. Hogwood Concert
(3/93) (DECC) ① **433 660-2DH**

┌─────────────────────────────────────┐
│ SECTION II: CHAMBER │
└─────────────────────────────────────┘

Duo for Violin and Cello No. 1, H157 (1927)
E. Turovsky, Y. Turovsky Concert
(7/85) (CHAN) ① **CHAN8358**
J. Heifetz, G. Piatigorsky Concert
(9/90) (RCA) ① **GD87371**
J. Heifetz, G. Piatigorsky (r1964) Concert
(11/94) (RCA) ① [65] **09026 61778-2(44)**
Madrigal Sonata—flute, violin and piano (1942)
Dartington Ens Concert
(11/88) (HYPE) ① **CDA66133**
5 Madrigal stanzas—violin and piano (1943)
Dartington Ens Concert
(11/88) (HYPE) ① **CDA66133**
J. Suk, J. Hála Concert (8/90) (SUPR) ① **11 0099-2**
4 Madrigals—oboe, clarinet and bassoon (1937)
Dartington Ens Concert
(11/88) (HYPE) ① **CDA66133**
3 Madrigals—violin and viola (1948)
Dartington Ens Concert
(11/88) (HYPE) ① **CDA66133**
Raphael Ens Concert (7/92) (HYPE) ① **CDA66516**
Piano Quintet No. 1 (1933)
P. Frankl, Lindsay Qt Dvořák: Piano Quintet, Op.81.
(6/94) (ASV) ① **CDDCA889**
La Rêvue de Cuisine—clarinet, bassoon, trumpet, cello and piano (1927)
Chicago Pro Musica Concert
(8/89) (REFE) ① **RRCD-29**
St Paul CO, C. Hogwood Concert
(3/93) (DECC) ① **433 660-2DH**
Serenade No. 1—clarinet, horn, 3 violins and viola (1932)
Prague CO Concert (12/89) (SUPR) ① **11 0098-2**

Serenade No. 2—2 violins and viola (1932)
Prague CO Concert (12/89) (SUPR) ① **11 0098-2**
K. Sillito, M. Latchem, R. Smissen Concert
(5/90) (CHAN) ① **CHAN8771**
Serenade No. 3—oboe, clarinet, 4 violins and cello (1932)
Prague CO Concert (12/89) (SUPR) ① **11 0098-2**
Sonata for Cello and Piano No. 1 (1939)
S. Isserlis, Peter Evans Concert
(7/89) (HYPE) ① **CDA66296**
R. Dieltiens, R. Groslot Concert
(7/91) (ACCE) ① **ACC28967D**
Sonata for Cello and Piano No.2 (1941)
S. Isserlis, Peter Evans Concert
(7/89) (HYPE) ① **CDA66296**
R. Dieltiens, R. Groslot Concert
(7/91) (ACCE) ① **ACC28967D**
Sonata for Cello and Piano No. 3 (1952)
S. Isserlis, Peter Evans Concert
(7/89) (HYPE) ① **CDA66296**
R. Dieltiens, R. Groslot Concert
(7/91) (ACCE) ① **ACC28967D**
Sonata for Flute and Piano (1945)
3. Movt 3.
M. Cox, N. Clayton Concert
(3/90) (KING) ① **KCLCD2013**
J. Stinton, S. Mitchell Concert
(12/91) (COLL) ① **Coll1103-2**
G. von Bahr, K. Hindart Concert
(2/93) (BIS) ① **BIS-CD234**
J-P. Rampal, J. S. Ritter (pp1991) Concert
(9/94) (SONY) ① **SK53106**
Sonata for Violin and Piano No. 2 (1931)
J. Suk, J. Hála Concert (8/90) (SUPR) ① **11 0099-2**
Sonata for Violin and Piano No. 3 (1944)
J. Suk, J. Hála Concert (8/90) (SUPR) ① **11 0099-2**
Sonatina—two violins and piano (1930)
K. Ososostowicz, E. Kovacic, S. Tomes Concert
(9/92) (HYPE) ① **CDA66473**
String Quartet No. 1 (1918)
Panocha Qt (r1982) Concert
(9/95) (SUPR) ① [3] **11 0994-2**
String Quartet No. 2 (1925)
Panocha Qt (r1982) Concert
(9/95) (SUPR) ① [3] **11 0994-2**
String Quartet No. 3 (1929)
Panocha Qt (r1982) Concert
(9/95) (SUPR) ① [3] **11 0994-2**
String Quartet No. 4 (1937)
Panocha Qt (r1980) Concert
(9/95) (SUPR) ① [3] **11 0994-2**
String Quartet No. 5 (1938)
Panocha Qt (r1979) Concert
(9/95) (SUPR) ① [3] **11 0994-2**
String Quartet No. 6 (1946)
Panocha Qt (r1981) Concert
(9/95) (SUPR) ① [3] **11 0994-2**
String Quartet No. 7 (Concerto da camera) (1947)
Panocha Qt (r1979) Concert
(9/95) (SUPR) ① [3] **11 0994-2**
String Sextet (1932)
ASMF Chbr Ens Concert
(5/90) (CHAN) ① **CHAN8771**
Raphael Ens Concert (7/92) (HYPE) ① **CDA66516**

┌─────────────────────────────────────┐
│ SECTION III: INSTRUMENTAL │
└─────────────────────────────────────┘

Borova (7 Czech dances)—piano (1929-30)
R. Kvapil (r1991) Concert
(12/93) (UNIC) ① **DKPCD9140**
3 Czech Dances—piano (1926)
R. Kvapil (r1991) Concert
(12/93) (UNIC) ① **DKPCD9140**
12 Esquisses—piano (1931)
R. Kvapil (r1991) Concert
(12/93) (UNIC) ① **DKPCD9140**
Etudes and Polkas—piano (1945)
1. Etude in D; 2. Polka in D; 3. Etude in A; 4. Polka in A; 5. Pastorale; 6. Etude; 7. Etude in C; 8. Polka in F; 9. Danse-Etude; 10. Polka in E; 11. Etude in F; 12. Etude in A; 13. Polka in A; 14. Etude in F; 15. Polka in A; 16. Etude in F.
R. Kvapil Concert (2/93) (BIS) ① **BIS-CD234**
2 Harpsichord Impromptus (1959)
B. Harbach Concert (3/89) (KING) ① **KCLCD2005**
2 Harpsichord Pieces (1935)
B. Harbach Concert (3/89) (KING) ① **KCLCD2005**
Harpsichord Sonata (1958)
B. Harbach Concert (3/89) (KING) ① **KCLCD2005**
Merry Christmas 1941—piano
St Paul CO, C. Hogwood (arr Ruggeri) Concert
(3/93) (DECC) ① **433 660-2DH**
4 Mouvements—piano (1928)
R. Kvapil (r1991) Concert
(12/93) (UNIC) ① **DKPCD9140**

Les Ritournelles—piano (1932)
R. Kvapil (r1991) Concert
(12/93) (UNIC) ① **DKPCD9140**
Sonata for Piano (1954)
R. Kvapil Concert (2/93) (BIS) ① **BIS-CD234**
Le Train hauté—piano (1937)
B. Lerner Concert (1/89) (ETCE) ① **KTC1061**
Window on to the garden—piano (1938)
R. Kvapil (r1991) Concert
(12/93) (UNIC) ① **DKPCD9140**

┌─────────────────────────────────────┐
│ SECTION IV: VOCAL AND CHORAL │
└─────────────────────────────────────┘

Bouquet (Kytice)—solo vv and chorus (1937) (Wds. trad)
L. Domanínská, Š. Červená, L. Havlák, L. Mráz, Kühn Children's Chor, Czech Phil Chor, Czech PO, K. Ančerl (r1955) Symphony 6.
(8/95) (SUPR) ① **11 1932-2**
Idyll Czech PO, V. Neumann Concert
(9/90) (ORFE) ① **C180891A**
Czech Rhapsody—baritone, chorus and orchestra (1918) (Wds. A. Jirásek)
I. Kusnjer, Kühn Chor, Prague SO, J. Bělohlávek
(11/89) (SUPR) ① **CO-72645**
The Epic of Gilgamesh—oratorio (1954-55)
E. Dĕpoltová, S. Margita, I. Kusnjer, L. Vele, M. Karpíšek, Slovak Phil Chor, Slovak PO, Z. Košler (r1989) (4/91) (MARC) ① **8 223316**
Field Mass—baritone, male vv, wind, harmonium and percussion (1939)
V. Sítek, Czech Phil Chor, Czech PO, C. Mackerras
Janáček: Amarus. (4/86) (SUPR) ① **C37-7735**
I. Kusnjer, Czech Phil Chor, Czech PO, J. Bělohlávek Concert (5/93) (CHAN) ① **CHAN9138**
Hymn to St James—SAB, chorus, horn, strings and organ (1954) (Wds. J. Daněk)
N. Romanová, D. Drobková, R. Novák, P. Haníčinec, Prague Rad Chor, Prague SO, P. Kühn, J. Hora Concert (12/92) (SUPR) ① **11 0751-2**
Legend of the smoke from potato fires—chamber cantata (1956) (Wds. M. Bureš)
M. Čejková, M. Mrázová, I. Kusnjer, J. Stivin, V. Mareš, P. Duda, M. Bláha, Kühn Chor, P. Kühn (r1988) Concert (5/94) (SUPR) ① **11 0767-2**
Mikeš of the Mountains—chamber cantata (1959) (Wds. M. Bureš)
M. Čejková, V. Doležal, P. Messiereur, J. Kvapil, J. Talich, S. Bogunia, Kühn Chor, P. Kühn (1988) Concert (5/94) (SUPR) ① **11 0767-2**
Mount of three lights—cantata: TB, spk, male chorus and org (1954) (Wds. W. E. Morton)
V. Doležal, R. Novák, P. Haníčinec, Prague Rad Chor, Kühn Chor, P. Kühn, J. Hora Concert (12/92) (SUPR) ① **11 0751-2**
The Opening of the Wells—chamber cantata (1955) (Wds. M. Bureš)
M. Čejková, A. Čakrtová, I. Kusnjer, P. Haníčinec, P. Messiereur, J. Kvapil, J. Talich, S. Bogunia, Kühn Chor, P. Kühn (1988) Concert (5/94) (SUPR) ① **11 0767-2**
Primrose (Petrklíč)—female vv, violin and piano (1954) (Wds. trad Moravian)
1. A new hat; 2. Behind our farmyard; 3. Complaint; 4. Painted wood; 5. Midday.
Kühn Chor, P. Messiereur, S. Bogunia Concert
(4/93) (SUPR) ① [2] **11 0752-2**
The Prophecy of Isaiah—SAB, male chorus and chamber ensemble (1959) (Wds. Bible)
N. Romanová, D. Drobková, R. Novák, V. Kozderka, J. Peruška, I. Kiezlich, S. Bogunia, Prague Rad Chor, Kühn Chor, P. Kühn (12/92) (SUPR) ① **11 0751-2**
The Romance of the Dandelions—soprano and mixed voices (1957) (Wds. Bureš)
M. Čejková, Kühn Chor, Brno St PO, F. Jílek Concert (4/93) (SUPR) ① [2] **11 0752-2**
7 Songs on one page—1v and piano (1943) (Wds. trad Moravian)
1. Dew; 2. Unlocking with a word; 3. Going to my love; 4. The path; 5. At Mother's; 6. The Virgin Mary's Dream; 7. Rosemary.
G. Beňačková, R. Firkušný (r1991) Concert
(1/94) (RCA) ① **09026 60823-2**

┌─────────────────────────────────────┐
│ SECTION V: STAGE WORKS │
└─────────────────────────────────────┘

Ariane—opera: 1 act (1961—Gelsenkirchen/Brno) (Lib. cpsr, after Neveux)
Cpte C. Lindsley, N. Phillips, V. Doležal, R. Novák, M. Kopp, L. Vele, Czech PO, V. Neumann
(12/92) (SUPR) ① **10 4395-2**

The **Butterfly that stamped—ballet: 1 act
(1926)** (after R Kipling)
Kühn Chor, Prague SO, J. Bělohlávek (r1986)
(9/95) (SUPR) ① 11 0380-2
Echec au Roi—ballet (1927) (unperformed)
V. Olexa, K. Kachlíková, Prague SO, J. Bělohlávek
(r1987) *Revolt.* (5/94) (SUPR) ① 11 1415-2
The **Greek Passion—opera (4 acts)
(1961—Zurich)** (Lib. cpsr, afer Kazantzakis)
Cpte J. Mitchinson, H. Field, J. Tomlinson, P. Joll, G.
Moses, A. Davies, R. Cullis, C. Savory, J. Lawton, J.
Harris, D. Gwynne, J. Jonášová, M. Geliot, Kühn
Children's Chor, Czech Phil Chor, Brno St PO, C.
Mackerras (3/91) (SUPR) ① [2] 10 3611-2
Julietta—opera: 3 acts (1938—Prague) (Lib.
cpsr, after Neveux)
Cpte M. Tauberová, I. Žídek, A. Zlesák, Z. Otava, V.
Bednář, I. Mixová, V. Jedenáctík, J. Procházková, L.
Hanzalíková, J. Horáček, K. Kalaš, M. Čadikovičová,
S. Jelínková, V. Soukupová, J. Jindrák, J. Veverka, Z.
Švehla, M. Lemariová, K. Berman, D. Jedlička, J.
Stříška, B. Lalák, Prague Nat Th Chor, Prague Nat
Th Orch, J. Krombholc (r1964)
(6/93) (SUPR) ① [3] 10 8176-2
The **Miracles of Mary—opera: prologue and
3 parts (1935—Brno)** (Lib. cpsr, after H.
Ghéon)
Cpte A. Barová, J. Marková, V. Zítek, D. Jedlička, E.
Děpoltová, A. Kratochvílová, M. Mrázová, J. Jindrák,
Bohumil Maršík, V. Kocián, I. Kusnjer, J. Vavruška, B.
Vítková, K. Průša, Prague Children's Ch, Prague Rad
Chor, Prague SO, J. Bělohlávek (r1982/3)
(1/94) (SUPR) ① [2] 11 1802-2
Revolt—ballet (1928—Brno)
Prague SO, J. Bělohlávek (r1987) *Echec au Roi.*
(5/94) (SUPR) ① 11 1415-2
Spalíček—ballet (1933—Brno)
Cpte A. Kratochvílová, M. Kopp, R. Novák, Kantiléna
Children's Chor, Kühn Chor, Brno St PO, F. Jílek
Concert (4/93) (SUPR) ① [2] 11 0752-2
Suite Brno St PO, C. Mackerras *Double Concerto.*
(3/92) (CONI) ① CDCF202

MARTUCCI, Giuseppe
(1856–1909) Italy

SECTION I: ORCHESTRAL

**Andante—cello and orchestra, Op. 69/2
(1888 orch 1909)**
G. Ives, Philh, F. d'Avalos *Concert*
(5/90) (ASV) ① CDDCA689
Canzonetta, Op. 55/1 (1883—orch later)
Philh, F. d'Avalos *Concert*
(7/90) (ASV) ① CDDCA691
Colore orientale, Op. 44/3 (1875 orch 1880)
Philh, F. d'Avalos *Concert*
(5/90) (ASV) ① CDDCA689
**Concerto for Piano and Orchestra No. 1 in D
minor (1878)**
F. Caramiello, Philh, F. d'Avalos *Canzone dei ricordi.*
(6/91) (ASV) ① CDDCA690
**Concerto for Piano and Orchestra No. 2 in B
flat minor, Op. 66 (1884-85)**
F. Caramiello, Philh, F. d'Avalos *Concert*
(7/90) (ASV) ① CDDCA691
Gavotta, Op. 55/2 (1888, orch 1901)
Philh, F. d'Avalos *Concert*
(7/90) (ASV) ① CDDCA691
Giga, Op. 61/3 (1882, orch 1892)
Philh, F. d'Avalos *Concert*
(7/90) (ASV) ① CDDCA691
Milan La Scala PO, R. Muti (1992) *Concert*
(4/94) (SONY) ① SK53280
Minuetto, Op. 57/2 (1880, later orch)
Philh, F. d'Avalos *Concert*
(7/90) (ASV) ① CDDCA691
**Momento musicale, Op. 57/3 (1883, later
orch)**
Philh, F. d'Avalos *Concert*
(7/90) (ASV) ① CDDCA691
Milan La Scala PO, R. Muti (1992) *Concert*
(4/94) (SONY) ① SK53280
Nocturne in G flat—orchestra, Op. 70/1
ECO, A. Bonavera *Concert*
(7/88) (HYPE) ① CDA66290
Philh, F. d'Avalos *Concert*
(12/89) (ASV) ① CDDCA675
Milan La Scala PO, R. Muti (1992) *Concert*
(4/94) (SONY) ① SK53280
Novelletta, Op. 82/2 (1905 orch 1908) (orch
cpsr from piano work)
Philh, F. d'Avalos *Concert*
(12/89) (ASV) ① CDDCA675
Milan La Scala PO, R. Muti (1992) *Concert*
(4/94) (SONY) ① SK53280
NBC SO, A. Toscanini (bp1948) *Concert*
(5/94) (ATS) ① [2] ATCD100

Serenata, Op. 57/1 (1886, orch later)
Philh, F. d'Avalos *Concert*
(7/90) (ASV) ① CDDCA691
**Symphony No. 1 in D minor, Op. 75 (1888-
95)**
Philh, F. d'Avalos *Concert*
(12/89) (ASV) ① CDDCA675
Symphony No. 2 in F, Op. 81 (1904)
Philh, F. d'Avalos *Concert*
(5/90) (ASV) ① CDDCA689
Tarantella—orchestra, Op. 44/6 (c1878) (arr
from piano work)
Philh, F. d'Avalos *Concert*
(12/89) (ASV) ① CDDCA675

SECTION II: CHAMBER

Piano Trio in C, Op. 59 (1883)
M. Borciani, Giovane Quartetto Italiano (r1992) *Piano
Quintet, Op. 45.* (4/93) (CLAV) ① CD50-9210
**Quintet for Piano and Strings in C, Op. 45
(1878)**
M. Borciani, Giovane Quartetto Italiano (r1992) *Piano
Trio, Op. 59.* (4/93) (CLAV) ① CD50-9210

SECTION IV: VOCAL AND CHORAL

**Canzone dei Ricordi—poemetto lirico
(c1886-87)** (Wds. R. Pagliara)
C. Madalin, ECO, A. Bonavera *Concert*
(6/91) (ASV) ① CDA66290
R. Yakar, Philh, F. d'Avalos *Piano Concerto 1.*
(6/91) (ASV) ① CDDCA690

MARTY, Georges Eugène
(1860–1908) France

SECTION II: CHAMBER

Première fantaisie—clarinet and piano
A. Périer, anon (rc1930) *Concert*
(2/94) (CLRI) ① CC0005

MARVASI

SECTION IV: VOCAL AND CHORAL

Chi se nee scorda cchiu—song (Wds.
Barthelemy)
T. Schipa, J. Huarte (r1934) *Concert*
(12/89) (RCA) ① GD87969

MARX, Joseph *(1882–1964)*
Austria

SECTION IV: VOCAL AND CHORAL

Durch Einsamkeiten—Lied: 1v, viola & piano
(Wds. A Wildgans)
M. Shirai, T. Zimmermann, H. Höll (r1993-4) *Concert*
(9/95) (CAPR) ① 10 462
Lieder aus dem 'Pierrot Lunaire' (1909)
(Wds. Giraud and Hartleben)
1. Valse de Chopin; 2. Pierrot Dandy.
1, 2. G. Maurice, G. Johnson (pp1988) *Concert*
(5/92) (ETCE) ① KTC1099
**Lieder und Gesänge—three volumes (pub
1910-17)**
1. Leuchtende Tage (wds. L. Jacobowski); 2. Wie
einst (wds. E. Triebnigg); 3. Herbstzeitlose (wds.
Schönaich-Carolath); 4. Schliesse mir die Augen
beide (wds. T. Storm); 5. O süsser Tod (wds. A. von
Platen); 6. Sonnenland (wds. A. Ritter); 7. Die Violine
(wds. A. Giraud); 8. Japanisches Regenlied; 9. Der
Ton (wds. K. Hamsun); 10. Ein Fichtenbaum steht
einsam (wds. Heine); 11. Schlafend trägt man mich
(wds. A. Monbert); 12. Barkarole (wds. Schack); 13.
Der Bescheidene Schäfer (wds. Weisse); 14. Bitte
(wds. Hesse); 15. Christbaum (wds. Christen); 16.
Ein Drängen ist meinem Herzen (wds. Zweig); 17.
Die Elfe (wds. Eichendorff); 18. Erinnerung (wds.
Eichendorff); 19. Hat Dich die Liebe berhürt (wds.
Heyse); 20. Hochsommernacht (wds. Grief); 21. Im
Maien (wds. Rodenberg); 22. Marienlied; 23.
Nachtgebet; 24. Nocturne (wds. Hartleben); 25. Selig
Nach (wds. O. E. Hartleben); 26. Sonnenland (wds.
A. Ritter); 27. Traumegekrönt (wds. Rilke); 28. Und
gestern hat er mir Rosen gebracht (wds. Lingen); 29.
Waldseligkeit (wds. Dehmell); 30. Windräder (wds.
Falke).
6. D. Dorow, M. Damerini (pp1980) *Concert*
(8/89) (ETCE) ① KTC1044
9-15. D. Dorow, M. Damerini (pp1980) *Concert*
(8/89) (ETCE) ① KTC1044
19, 24. G. Maurice, G. Johnson (pp1988) *Concert*
(5/92) (ETCE) ① KTC1099
22. E. Schumann, Vienna St Op Orch, K. Alwin
(r1928) *Concert* (6/91) (PREI) ① 89031

Selige Nacht—Lied (1915) (Wds. O. E.
Hartleben)
G. Maurice, G. Johnson (pp1988) *Concert*
(5/92) (ETCE) ① KTC1099

MASARYK, Jan *(1886–1948)*
Czechoslovakia

SECTION IV: VOCAL AND CHORAL

**15 Songs of Lidice—Czech and Moravian
folksongs**
1. O son of mine; 2. I had a dream, my lassie; 3. Why
did you stay; 4. Green groves; 5. Two young maids
went along the road; 6. Whose is the dark-haired
lass; 7. Mountain so high; 8. Love, oh love; 9. The
water, it flows down the stream; 10. Angie, my child;
11. Nothing to comfort me; 12. In front of our window;
13. Goodnight, sweetheart; 14. A pair of black
horses; 15. I saw my county die.
J. Novotná, J. Masaryk (r1942) *Concert*
(4/93) (SUPR) ① 11 1491-2

MASCAGNI, Pietro *(1863–1945)*
Italy

SECTION IV: VOCAL AND CHORAL

Ave Maria—sacred song (wds. F. E.
Weatherly)
J. McCormack, F. Kreisler, V. O'Brien (r1914)
Concert (9/89) (PEAR) ① GEMMCD9315
T. Schipa, orch, R. Bourdon (r1927) *Concert*
(10/90) (MSCM) ① [2] MM30231
Bella cantiam l'amore—song
F. Marconi, P. Mascagni (r1903) *Concert*
(6/90) (SYMP) ① SYMCD1073
M'ama, non m'ama—song (1884) (Wds.
anon)
R. Scotto, I. Davis (pp1983) *Concert*
(10/86) (ETCE) ① KTC2002
E. Orel, anon (r c1902: Russ) *Concert*
(7/93) (SYMP) ① SYMCD1105
Salve o Maria—sacred song
B. Hendricks, Stockholm CO, E. Ericson *Concert*
(4/91) (EMI) ① CDC7 54098-2
Serenata—canzona (1883)
R. Tebaldi, R. Bonynge (r1972) *Concert*
(9/94) (DECC) ① 436 202-2DM
L. Pavarotti, NYPO, L. Magiera (pp1993) *Concert*
(2/95) (DECC) ① 444 450-2DH
Stornelli marini—song (1906)
A. Giorgini, anon (r1905) *Concert*
(4/95) (RECO) ① TRC3
La tua stella—song: 1v and piano (1882)
R. Tebaldi, R. Bonynge (r1972) *Concert*
(9/94) (DECC) ① 436 202-2DM

SECTION V: STAGE WORKS

L' amico Fritz—opera: 3 acts (1891—Rome)
(Lib. Daspuro)
EXCERPTS; 1. Preludio. ACT 1: 2. Son pochi fiori;
3. Laceri, miseri, tanti bambini. ACT 2: 4a. Suzel,
buon dì (Cherry Duet); 4b. Tutto tace; 5. Intermezzo.
ACT 3: 6. O pallida, che un giorno mi guardasti; 7a.
Ed anchè Beppe amò; 7b. O Amore, o bella luce; 8.
Non mi resta che il pianto.
Cpte M. Freni, L. Pavarotti, L. Didier Gambardella, V.
Sardinero, B. di Bella, L. Pontiggia, M. Major, ROH
Chor, ROHO, G. Gavazzeni
(8/87) (EMI) ① [3] CDS7 47905-8
2. C. Muzio, orch (r1923) *Concert*
(5/90) (BOGR) ① [2] BIM705-2
2. C. Muzio, anon (r1923) *Concert*
(1/94) (ROMO) ① [2] 81005-2
2. M. Favero, La Scala Orch, G. Antonicelli (r1936)
Concert (4/94) (EMI) ① [3] CHS7 64864-2(2)
3. E. Stignani, EIAR Orch, U. Tansini (r1941) *Concert*
(1/91) (PREI) ① 89014
4a, 4b A. Morelli, P. Domingo, NYPO, Z. Mehta
(pp1988) *Concert* (9/89) (SONY) ① MK44942
4a, 4b M. Favero, T. Schipa, La Scala Orch, G.
Antonicelli (r1937) *Concert*
(10/89) (NIMB) ① NI7801
4a, 4b M. Favero, T. Schipa, La Scala Orch, G.
Antonicelli (r1937) *Concert*
(4/90) (EMI) ① CDH7 63200-2
4a, 4b R. Pampanini, D. Borgioli, orch, L. Molajoli
(r1930) *Concert* (8/93) (PREI) ① 89063
4a, 4b M. Freni, L. Pavarotti, Ater Orch, L. Magiera
(pp) *Concert* (5/94) (DECC) ① [2] 443 018-2DF2
4a, 4b, 7a, 7b Ferruccio Tagliavini, M. Olivero, EIAR
Orch, U. Tansini (r1940) *Concert*
(3/94) (CENT) ① CRC2164
4a, 7b D. Borgioli, R. Pampanini, orch (r1928)
Concert (12/90) (CLUB) ① CL99-014

4b M. Fleta, L. Bori, orch (r1924) *Concert* (2/90) (PREI) Ⓓ **89002**
4b L. Bori, M. Fleta, C. Linton, orch, R. Bourdon (r1924) *Concert* (4/94) (RCA) Ⓓ [6] **09026 61580-2(2)**
5. BPO, H. von Karajan *Concert* (10/87) (DG) Ⓓ [3] **419 257-2GH3**
5. Gothenburg SO, N. Järvi *Concert* (6/90) (DG) Ⓓ **429 494-2GDC**
7a, 7b B. Gigli, orch, R. Zamboni (r1948) *Concert* (5/90) (EMI) Ⓓ **CDH7 61052-2**

Cavalleria Rusticana—opera: 1 act (1890—Rome) (Lib. Targioni-Tozzetti and Menasci)

1. Prelude; 2. O Lola (Siciliana); 3. Gli aranci olezzano; 4. Dite, mamma Lucia; 5a. Il cavallo scalpita; 5b. Beato voi; 6a. Regina coeli; 6b. Inneggiamo, il Signor (Easter Hymn); 7. Voi lo sapete; 8. Tu qui, Santuzza?; 9. Fior di giaggiolo; 10. No, no, Turiddu, rimani; 11. Oh! Il Signore vi manda; 12. Comare Santa; 13. Intermezzo; 14. A casa, a casa; 15a. Viva il vino (Brindisi); 15b. A voi tutti salute!; 16. Mamma, quel vino è generoso.

Cpte E. Obraztsova, P. Domingo, R. Bruson, A. Gall, F. Barbieri, La Scala Chor, La Scala Orch, G. Prêtre (2/86) (PHIL) Ⓓ **416 137-2PH**
Cpte M. Callas, G. di Stefano, R. Panerai, A.M. Canali, E. Ticozzi, La Scala Chor, La Scala Orch, T. Serafin (r1953) *Leoncavallo: Pagliacci.* (10/87) (EMI) Ⓓ [3] **CDS7 47981-8**
Cpte F. Cossotto, C. Bergonzi, G. Guelfi, A. Martino, M.G. Allegri, La Scala Chor, La Scala Orch, H. von Karajan *Concert* (10/87) (DG) Ⓓ [3] **419 257-2GH3**
Cpte Z. Milanov, J. Björling, R. Merrill, C. Smith, M. Roggero, R. Shaw Chorale, RCA Orch, R. Cellini (r1953) (8/88) (RCA) Ⓓ **GD86510**
Cpte J. Varady, L. Pavarotti, P. Cappuccilli, C. Gonzales, I. Bormida, London Voices, National PO, G. Gavazzeni *Leoncavallo: Pagliacci.* (1/89) (DECC) Ⓓ [2] **414 590-2DH2**
Cpte A. Baltsa, P. Domingo, J. Pons, S. Mentzer, W. Baniewicz, ROH Chor, Philh, G. Sinopoli (12/90) (DG) Ⓓ **429 568-2GH**
Cpte M. Caballé, J. Carreras, M. Manuguerra, J. Hamari, A. Varnay, Southend Boys' Ch, Ambrosian Op Chor, Philh, R. Muti (r1979) *Leoncavallo: Pagliacci.* (3/91) (EMI) Ⓓ [2] **CMS7 63650-2**
Cpte J. Norman, G. Giacomini, D. Hvorostovsky, M. Senn, R. Laghezza, Paris Orch Chor, Paris Orch, S. Bychkov (12/91) (PHIL) Ⓓ **432 105-2PH**
Cpte V. de los Angeles, F. Corelli, M. Sereni, A. Lazzarini, C. Vozza, Rome Op Chor, Rome Op Orch, G. Santini (r1962) *Leoncavallo: Pagliacci.* (3/92) (EMI) Ⓓ [2] **CMS7 63967-2**
Cpte S. Evstatieva, G. Aragall, E. Tumagian, A. di Mauro, A. Michalková, Slovak Phil Chor, Bratislava RSO, A. Rahbari (r1992) (3/93) (NAXO) Ⓓ **8 660022**
Cpte L.B. Rasa, A. Melandri, A. Poli, M. Meloni, R.G. Toscani, Holland Italian Op Chor, Holland Italian Op Orch, P. Mascagni (pp1938) (1/94) (BONG) Ⓓ **GB1050-2**
Excs G. Cernay, G. Micheletti, A. Endrèze, A. Hena, M. Arty, chor, orch, G. Cloëz (French: r c1932) *Concert* (11/92) (MSCM) Ⓓ **MM30451**
Excs M. Jeritza, H. Roswaenge, E. Schipper, B. Paalen, M. Bokor, Vienna St Op Chor, Vienna St Op Orch, H. Reichenberger (pp1933: Ger) *Concert* (11/95) (SCHW) Ⓓ [2] **314622**
1, 2. E. Caruso, BNOC Orch, A. Buesst (r1910/32) *Concert* (5/94) (CLAR) Ⓓ **CDGSE78-50-52**
1, 2, 15b A. di Mauro, G. Aragall, E. Tumagian, Bratislava RSO, A. Rahbari (r1992) *Concert* (12/94) (NAXO) Ⓓ **8 550684**
2. E. Caruso, S. Cottone (r1902) *Concert* (5/89) (EMI) Ⓓ **CDH7 61046-2**
2. G. Martinelli, F. Lapitino, orch, J. Pasternack (r1915) *Concert* (10/89) (NIMB) Ⓓ **NI7804**
2. T. Schipa, orch, C. Sabajno (r1913) *Concert* (4/90) (EMI) Ⓓ **CDH7 63200-2**
2. B. Gigli, Anon (hp), P. Mascagni (r1940) *Concert* (5/90) (EMI) Ⓓ **CDH7 61052-2**
2. E. Caruso, anon (r1904) *Concert* (12/90) (PEAR) Ⓓ [3] **EVC1(1)**
2. E. Caruso, S. Cottone (r1902) *Concert* (12/90) (PEAR) Ⓓ [3] **EVC1(1)**
2. E. Caruso, anon (r1903) *Concert* (12/90) (PEAR) Ⓓ [3] **EVC1(1)**
2. E. Caruso, orch (r1910) *Concert* (3/91) (PEAR) Ⓓ [3] **EVC2**
2. E. Caruso, F. Lapitino (r1910) *Concert* (7/91) (RCA) Ⓓ [12] **GD60495(3)**
2. E. Caruso, anon (r1903) *Concert* (7/91) (RCA) Ⓓ [12] **GD60495(1)**
2. E. Caruso, anon (r1904) *Concert* (7/91) (RCA) Ⓓ [12] **GD60495(1)**
2. E. Caruso, S. Cottone (r1902) *Concert* (7/91) (RCA) Ⓓ [12] **GD60495(1)**
2. A. Cortis, La Scala Orch, C. Sabajno (r1929) *Concert* (10/91) (PREI) Ⓓ **89043**
2. H. Roswaenge, orch (r1928: Ger) *Concert* (2/92) (PREI) Ⓓ [2] **89201**
2. G. Lugo, orch, F. Weiss (Fr: r1933) *Concert* (2/92) (PREI) Ⓓ **89034**
2. F. de Lucia, orch (r1920) *Concert* (7/92) (PEAR) Ⓓ [3] **GEMMCDS9923(1)**
2. E. Caruso, anon (r1904) *Concert* (7/92) (PEAR) Ⓓ [3] **GEMMCDS9923(2)**
2. J. Björling, Stockholm Royal Op Orch, N. Grevillius (r1948) *Concert* (8/92) (BLUE) Ⓓ **ABCD016**
2. F. Valero, anon (r1903) *Concert* (11/92) (MEMO) Ⓓ [2] **HR4408/9(1)**
2. G. Martinelli, orch, R. Bourdon (r1927) *Concert* (3/93) (PREI) Ⓓ **89062**
2. A. Davidov, anon (r1901: Russ) *Concert* (6/93) (PEAR) Ⓓ [3] **GEMMCDS9007/9(1)**
2. J. Björling, Stockholm Royal Op Orch, N. Grevillius (r1948) *Concert* (10/93) (EMI) Ⓓ **CDH7 64707-2**
2. A. Cortis, La Scala Orch, C. Sabajno (r1929) *Concert* (3/94) (NIMB) Ⓓ **NI7850**
2. G. Anselmi, anon (r1907) *Concert* (4/94) (EMI) Ⓓ [3] **CHS7 64860-2(2)**
2. G. Zenatello, orch (r1912) *Concert* (5/94) (PEAR) Ⓓ [4] **GEMMCDS9074(1)**
2. A. Pertile, orch (r1923) *Concert* (9/94) (NIMB) Ⓓ **NI7856**
2. F. de Lucia, anon (r1903) *Concert* (1/95) (SYMP) Ⓓ **SYMCD1149**
2. G. Anselmi, anon (r1907) *Concert* (7/95) (SYMP) Ⓓ **SYMCD1170**
2. E. Clément, anon (r c1911: Fr) *Concert* (8/95) (PEAR) Ⓓ **GEMMCD9161**
2, 14, 15a, 16. H. Nash, M. Parry, J. Griffiths, BNOC Chor, BNOC Orch, A. Buesst (r1928: Eng) *Concert* (11/95) (PEAR) Ⓓ **GEMMCD9175**
2, 15a F. Valero, anon (r1903) *Concert* (6/90) (SYMP) Ⓓ **SYMCD1073**
6a, 6b H. Field, ROH Chor, ROHO, B. Haitink *Concert* (12/89) (EMI) Ⓓ **CDC7 49849-2**
7. E. Turner, orch, T. Beecham (r1928) *Concert* (9/89) (EMI) Ⓓ **CDH7 69791-2**
7. G. Bellincioni, S. Cottone (r1903) *Concert* (6/90) (SYMP) Ⓓ **SYMCD1073**
7. V. de los Angeles, Rome Op Orch, G. Morelli (r1954) *Concert* (8/90) (EMI) Ⓓ **CDH7 63495-2**
7. G. Arangi-Lombardi, La Scala Orch, L. Molajoli (r1930) *Concert* (10/90) (PREI) Ⓓ **89013**
7. E. Burzio, orch (r c1906) *Concert* (1/91) (CLUB) Ⓓ [2] **CL99-587/8**
7. C. Muzio, orch, L. Molajoli (r1934) *Concert* (4/91) (NIMB) Ⓓ **NI7814**
7. J. Gadski, orch (r1908) *Concert* (7/91) (CLUB) Ⓓ **CL99-109**
7. R. Tebaldi, New Philh, O. de Fabritiis *Concert* (8/91) (DECC) Ⓓ [2] **430 481-2DX2**
7. E. Calvé, orch (r1907) *Concert* (7/92) (PEAR) Ⓓ [3] **GEMMCDS9923(1)**
7. G. Bellincioni, S. Cottone (r1903) *Concert* (7/92) (PEAR) Ⓓ [3] **GEMMCDS9923(1)**
7. M. Freni, Venice La Fenice Orch, R. Abbado *Concert* (9/92) (DECC) Ⓓ **433 316-2DH**
7. X. Belmas, orch, A. Kitschin (r1928) *Concert* (10/92) (PREI) Ⓓ **89047**
7. G. Bellincioni, anon (r1903) *Concert* (11/92) (MEMO) Ⓓ [2] **HR4408/9(2)**
7. L. Price, E. Bainbridge, New Philh, N. Santi (r1977) *Concert* (12/92) (RCA) Ⓓ [4] **09026 61236-2**
7. E. Calvé, anon (r1902) *Concert* (3/93) (SYMP) Ⓓ **SYMCD1100**
7. E. Carelli, S. Cottone (r1904) *Concert* (8/93) (SYMP) Ⓓ **SYMCD1111**
7. A. Pinto, anon (r1902) *Concert* (8/93) (SYMP) Ⓓ **SYMCD1111**
7. R. Ponselle, orch, R. Romani (r1919) *Concert* (10/93) (NIMB) Ⓓ **NI7846**
7. E. Eames, orch (r1906: two vers) *Concert* (11/93) (ROMO) Ⓓ [2] **81001-2**
7. R. Raisa, orch (r1933) *Concert* (1/94) (CLUB) Ⓓ **CL99-052**
7. M. Jeritza, orch (r1923) *Concert* (4/94) (PREI) Ⓓ **89079**
7. E. Destinn, orch (r1911) *Concert* (5/94) (SUPR) Ⓓ **11 1337-2**
7. F. Litvinne, anon (r1905) *Concert* (12/94) (SYMP) Ⓓ **SYMCD1128**
7. E. Destinn, orch (r1912) *Concert* (12/94) (SUPR) Ⓓ [12] **11 2136-2(4)**
7. E. Destinn, orch, B. Seidler-Winkler (r1908: Ger) *Concert* (12/94) (SUPR) Ⓓ [12] **11 2136-2(1)**
7. E. Destinn, orch, B. Seidler-Winkler (r1908: Ger) *Concert* (12/94) (SUPR) Ⓓ [12] **11 2136-2(2)**
7. E. Destinn, orch, F. Kark (r1908: Ger) *Concert* (12/94) (SUPR) Ⓓ [12] **11 2136-2(2)**
7. C. Muzio, orch (r1918) *Concert* (1/95) (ROMO) Ⓓ [2] **81010-2**
7. E. Rethberg, Berlin SO, F. Weissmann (r1933) *Concert* (10/95) (ROMO) Ⓓ [2] **81014-2**
7, 11. E. Destinn, D. Gilly, orch (r1911) *Concert* (12/94) (SUPR) Ⓓ [12] **11 2136-2(4)**
7, 8. M. Callas, A.M. Canali, E. Ticozzi, G. di Stefano, La Scala Chor, La Scala Orch, T. Serafin (r1953) *Concert* (2/90) (EMI) Ⓓ [4] **CMS7 63244-2**
8. H. Spani, P. Masini, orch (r1925) *Concert* (9/90) (CLUB) Ⓓ [2] **CL99-509/10**
8. B. Gigli, D. Giannini, La Scala Orch, C. Sabajno (r1932) *Concert* (6/93) (MMOI) Ⓓ **CDMOIR417**
8(pt) G. Zenatello, E. Mazzoleni, orch (r c1911) *Concert* (5/94) (SYMP) Ⓓ **SYMCD1158**
8. G. Zenatello, M. Gay, orch (r1911) *Concert* (5/94) (PEAR) Ⓓ [4] **GEMMCDS9074(1)**
8. J. Johnston, A. Shuard, Philh, M. Mudie (r1951: Eng) *Concert* (4/95) (TEST) Ⓓ **SBT1058**
8, 10. E. Burzio, G. Acerbi, orch (r1915) *Concert* (1/91) (CLUB) Ⓓ [2] **CL99-587/8**
8(pt), 10. G. Zenatello, E. Mazzoleni, orch (r1911) *Concert* (5/94) (PEAR) Ⓓ [4] **GEMMCDS9074(1)**
8, 12, 15a, 16. J. Björling, A. Nordmo-Løvberg, B. Björling, M. Sehlmark, G. Svedenbrant, Stockholm Royal Op Chor, Stockholm Royal Op Orch, K. Bendix (pp1954) *Concert* (3/92) (BLUE) Ⓓ **ABCD028**
8, 15a, 16. J. Björling, R. Tebaldi, L. Dani, R. Corsi, MMF Chor, MMF Orch, A. Erede (r1959) *Concert* (10/95) (DECC) Ⓓ **443 930-2DM**
10. D. Giannini, B. Gigli, La Scala Orch, C. Sabajno (r1932) *Concert* (5/90) (EMI) Ⓓ **CDH7 61052-2**
10. H. Roswaenge, M. Jeritza, Vienna St Op Orch, H. Reichenberger (pp1933: Ger) *Concert* (6/94) (SCHW) Ⓓ **314502**
11. X. Belmas, W. Domgraf-Fassbaender, orch, A. Kitschin (r1929) *Concert* (10/92) (PREI) Ⓓ **89047**
11(pt), 12. R. Raisa, G. Rimini, orch (r1929) *Concert* (1/94) (CLUB) Ⓓ **CL99-052**
13. Gothenburg SO, N. Järvi *Concert* (6/90) (DG) Ⓓ **429 494-2GDC**
13. SO, T. Beecham (r c1912) *Concert* (11/91) (SYMP) Ⓓ [2] **SYMCD1096/7**
15a D. Smirnov, orch (r1913) *Concert* (7/90) (CLUB) Ⓓ **CL99-031**
15a E. Caruso, anon (r1905) *Concert* (12/90) (PEAR) Ⓓ [3] **EVC1(1)**
15a E. Caruso, anon (r1905) *Concert* (7/91) (RCA) Ⓓ [12] **GD60495(1)**
15a F. Valero, anon (r1903) *Concert* (7/92) (PEAR) Ⓓ [3] **GEMMCDS9923(2)**
15a F. Valero, anon (r1903) *Concert* (4/94) (EMI) Ⓓ [3] **CHS7 64860-2(1)**
15a G. Zenatello, orch (r1911) *Concert* (5/94) (PEAR) Ⓓ [4] **GEMMCDS9074(1)**
15a E. Caruso, anon (r1905) *Concert* (7/95) (NIMB) Ⓓ **NI7866**
15a, 15b(pt) A. Piccaver, E. Schipper, Vienna St Op Chor, Vienna St Op Orch, K. Alwin (pp1937: Ger) *Concert* (6/95) (SCHW) Ⓓ [2] **314632**
15a, 16. F. Merli, orch, L. Molajoli (r1926) *Concert* (1/91) (PREI) Ⓓ **89026**
15a, 16. G. Lauri-Volpi, orch (r1923) *Concert* (7/93) (NIMB) Ⓓ **NI7845**
16. B. Gigli, La Scala Orch, C. Sabajno (r1933) *Concert* (9/88) (EMI) Ⓓ **CDH7 61051-2**
16. P. Dvorský, M. Nitranová, Bratislava RSO, Czech RSO, O. Lenárd *Concert* (10/89) (OPUS) Ⓓ **9156 1824**
16. G. Martinelli, orch, J. Pasternack (r1927) *Concert* (10/89) (NIMB) Ⓓ **NI7804**
16. J. Varady, I. Bormida, L. Pavarotti, London Op Chor, National PO, G. Gavazzeni *Concert* (7/90) (DECC) Ⓓ [2] **425 681-2DM2**
16. E. Caruso, orch (r1913) *Concert* (7/91) (RCA) Ⓓ [12] **GD60495(4)**
16. E. Caruso, orch (r1913) *Concert* (7/91) (MSCM) Ⓓ **MM30352**
16. E. Caruso, orch (r1913) *Concert* (10/91) (PEAR) Ⓓ [3] **EVC3(1)**
16. J. Björling, orch, N. Grevillius (r1944) *Concert* (8/92) (BLUE) Ⓓ **ABCD016**
16. J. Hislop, orch, J. Barbirolli (r1928) *Concert* (1/93) (PEAR) Ⓓ **GEMMCD9956**
16. G. Martinelli, orch, R. Bourdon (r1927) *Concert* (3/93) (PREI) Ⓓ **89062**
16. J. Björling, orch, N. Grevillius (r1944) *Concert* (10/93) (EMI) Ⓓ **CDH7 64707-2**
16. A. Piccaver, orch, M. Gurlitt (r c1929) *Concert* (12/93) (NIMB) Ⓓ **NI7851**
16. G. Zenatello, orch (r1908) *Concert* (5/94) (SYMP) Ⓓ **SYMCD1158**

16. G. Zenatello, orch (r1908) *Concert*
(5/94) (PEAR) ① [4] **GEMMCDS9073(2)**
16. J. Johnston, O. Price, orch, M. Mudie (r1948:
Eng) *Concert* (4/95) (TEST) ① **SBT1058**
**Guglielmo Ratcliff—opera: four parts
(1895—Milan)** (Lib. H. Heine, trans A. Maffei)
EXCERPTS: 1a. Introduction. PART 1: 1b. Ucciso
ho la mia cara; 2a. Sposo e sposa voi siete; 2b. È
sempre il vecchio andazzo; 3. Sia lode al mio saio
scozzese; 4. Apro, piccina; 5. Io n'ho stupore; 6.
Vecchia volpe è quest'uomo. PART 2: 7. Willie, sai
recitarmi; 8. Che intendere voleste; 9. Il Dugla
viene?; 10. Quando fanciullo ancora; 11. Ti scendo
ora alfin nel pensier. PART 3: 12. Oh, come il vento
fischia; 13. Non m'è nuova la voce; 14. Intermezzo;
15. Non altro che delirio. PART 4: 16. Ah! Ah! Ah!
Ah!; 17. O buon Dio, quale angoscia; 18. D'indole
dolce e manusueta; 19. O Sancta vergine; 20. I tuoi
sembianti son più belli; 21. T'arresta, e non fuggirmi.
2. C. Galeffi, La Scala Orch, L. Molajoli (r1928)
Concert (2/92) (PREI) ① **89040**
2. G. Pacini, anon (r1904) *Concert*
(4/94) (EMI) ① [3] **CHS7 64860-2(1)**
Iris—opera: 3 acts (1898—Rome) (Lib. Illica)
EXCERPTS - ACT 1: 1. La notte—I primi albori; 2. I
fiori; 3. L'aurora: Son io la vita! (Hymn to the Sun); 4.
Ho fatto un triste sogno; 5. È lei! È lei!; 6. Voglio
posare; 7. Al rio! Al rio!; 8. In pure stille; 9. Giù per la
vita; 10. Io son Danjuro; 11. Misera! Ognor dunque;
12. Apri la tua finestra!; 13. È questa poesia; 14. La
bellezza; La morte; Il vampiro; 15. Grazie, mousmè!;
16. Vieni! Dammi il braccio! ACT 2: 17. (Una quècha,
susurrando); 18. Là che ci fate; 19. Donne, vampiri;
20. Ognora sogni; 21. Io prego; 22. A un cenno mio;
23. Un di (ero piccina); 24. Or dammi il braccio; 25.
Da un'ora; 26. Annotta!; 27. Oh, maraviglia; 28.
Datemi il passo! ACT 3: 29. Introduzione; 30. La
notte—Ad ora bruna; 31. Perchè? Perchè?; 32.
Ancora il triste sogno; 33. Un grand'occhio mi
guarda!.
Cpte I. Tokody, P. Domingo, J. Pons, B. Giaiotti, G.
Ferroni, C. Antuñano, S. Tedesco, H. Weber,
Bavarian Rad Chor, Munich RO, G. Patanè
(9/89) (SONY) ① [2] **M2K45526**
12. E. Caruso, S. Cottone (r1902) *Concert*
(5/89) (EMI) ① **CDH7 61046-2**
12. G. Martinelli, F. Lapitino, orch, J. Pasternack
(1917) *Concert* (10/89) (NIMB) ① **NI7804**
12. B. Gigli, orch (r1921) *Concert*
(5/90) (NIMB) ① **NI7807**
12. E. Caruso, S. Cottone (r1902) *Concert*
(12/90) (PEAR) ① [3] **EVC1(1)**
12. E. Caruso, S. Cottone (r1902) *Concert*
(7/91) (RCA) ① [12] **GD60495(1)**
12. A. Cortis, La Scala Orch, C. Sabajno (r1929)
Concert (10/91) (PREI) ① **89043**
12. A. Cortis, La Scala Orch, C. Sabajno (r1929)
Concert (3/94) (NIMB) ① **NI7850**
12. F. De Lucia, anon (r1920) *Concert*
(4/94) (EMI) ① [3] **CHS7 64860-2(1)**
12. G. Anselmi, anon (r1907) *Concert*
(7/95) (SYMP) ① **SYMCD1170**
21. M. Farneti, orch (r1931) *Concert*
(11/92) (MEMO) ① [2] **HR4408/9(1)**
23. M. Freni, Venice La Fenice Orch, R. Abbado
Concert (9/92) (DECC) ① **433 316-2DH**
23. R. Pampanini, EIAR Orch, U. Tansini (r1940)
Concert (8/93) (PREI) ① **89063**
23. E. Carelli, S. Cottone (r1904) *Concert*
(8/93) (SYMP) ① **SYMCD1111**
**Isabeau—opera: 3 acts (1911—Buenos
Aires)** (Lib. Illica, after Lady Godiva legend)
EXCERPTS: ACT 1: 1. L'ecchio à cieco; 2. Il sogno
à Dio; 3. Non colombelle. ACT 2: 4. O solo ritorno; 5.
E passera la viva creatura. ACT 3: 6. Fu vile l'editto;
7. I tuoi occhi.
E passerà la viva creatura B. De Muro, orch (r1912)
Concert (4/94) (EMI) ① [3] **CHS7 64860-2(2)**
Lodoletta—opera: 3 acts (1917—Rome) (Lib.
Forzano)
EXCERPTS. ACT 1: 1. Coro delle olandesine. ACT
2: 2. Che corsa. ACT 3: 3a. Se Franz dicesse il vero;
3b. Ah! ritrolva; 4a. Ah! il suo name; 4b. Flammen,
perdonami.
Cpte M. Spacagna, A. Ulbrich, Z. Bazsinka, J. Sánta,
P. Kelen, K. Szilágyi, M. Kálmándi, L. Polgár, A.
Laczó, J. Mukk, Hungarian St Op Children's Chor,
Hungarian Rad & TV Chor, Hungarian St Orch, C.
Rosekrans (6/91) (HUNG) ① [2] **HCD31307/8**
3a, 3b B. Gigli, D. Giannini, U. Berrettoni (r1941)
Concert (5/90) (EMI) ① **CDH7 61052-2**
4a, 4b M. Freni, Venice La Fenice Orch, R. Abbado
Concert (9/92) (DECC) ① **433 316-2DH**

Nerone—opera: 3 acts (1935—Milan) (Lib.
Targioni-Tozzetti, after Cossa)
Perchè dovrei tremare? R. Scotto, I. Davis (pp1983)
Concert (10/86) (ETCE) ① **KTC2002**
Vergini Muse...Quando al soave anelito P.
Domingo, National PO, E. Kohn *Concert*
(11/90) (EMI) ① **CDC7 54053-2**
Vergini Muse...Quando al soave anelito P.
Domingo, National PO, E. Kohn (r1989) *Concert*
(6/94) (EMI) ① **CDC5 55017-2**
I Rantzau—opera: 4 acts (1892—Florence)
(Lib. Targioni-Tozzetti and Tenasci)
Cpte B. Anderson, G. Boldrini, D. Colaianni, O.
Garaventa, C. Bosi, R. Lantieri, F. Bertoli, Livorno
Cel-Teatro Chor, Livorno Cel-Teatro Orch, B. Rigacci
(pp1992) (12/95) (FONE) ① [2] **93F13**
Zanetto—opera: 1 act (1896—Pesaro) (Lib.
Targioni-Tozzetti and Tenasci, after Coppée)
Senti bambino R. Scotto, I. Davis (pp1983) *Concert*
(10/86) (ETCE) ① **KTC2002**

MASCHERONI, Angelo
(1855–1905) Italy

SECTION IV: VOCAL AND CHORAL

Eternamente—song with violin obbligato
(Wds. P. Mazzoni)
C. Muzio, A. Spalding, R. Gaylor (r1921) *Concert*
(5/90) (BOGR) ① [2] **BIM705-2**
E. Caruso, orch (r1911) *Concert*
(3/91) (PEAR) ① [3] **EVC2**
E. Caruso, orch (r1911) *Concert*
(7/91) (RCA) ① [12] **GD60495(4)**
C. Muzio, A. Spalding, R. Gaylor (r1921) *Concert*
(1/94) (ROMO) ① [2] **81005-2**
C. Muzio, A. Spalding, orch (r1920: Eng) *Concert*
(1/95) (ROMO) ① [2] **81010-2**

MASCHERONI, Edoardo
(1859–1941) Italy

SECTION V: STAGE WORKS

Lorenza—opera (1901—Rome) (Lib. I. Illica)
Susanna al bagno E. Carelli, M. Sammarco, E.
Mascheroni (r1904) *Concert*
(8/93) (SYMP) ① **SYMCD1111**

MASINI, Francesco *(1804–1863)
Italy*

SECTION IV: VOCAL AND CHORAL

I Mulattieri—song
F. Marconi, A. Cotogni, anon (r1908) *Concert*
(10/90) (SYMP) ① **SYMCD1069**

MASON, Benedict *(b 1954)
England*

SECTION I: ORCHESTRAL

**Double Concerto—horn, trombone and
ensemble (1989)**
M. Thompson, D. Purser, London Sinfonietta, D.
Masson (r1992) *Concert*
(10/94) (BRID) ① **BCD9045**

SECTION II: CHAMBER

String Quartet No. 1 (1987)
Arditti Qt (r1993) *Concert*
(10/94) (BRID) ① **BCD9045**

SECTION IV: VOCAL AND CHORAL

**Self-Referential Songs and Realistic
Virelais—soprano and chamber ensemble
(1990)** (Wds cpsr)
EXCERPTS: 1. Partial Baffles; 2. Ah...never on the
drumhead; 3. Whiffling seesaw rhythms; 4.
Metallurgical Rules: 5. aahk pit-it-it skaaak!; 6.
Temporary Deviations; 7. Del penicille qui c'est escrit.
C. Whittlesey, Modern Ens, I. Metzmacher (pp1990)
Concert (10/94) (BRID) ① **BCD9045**

MASON, Lowell *(1792–1872)
USA*

SECTION IV: VOCAL AND CHORAL

Nearer, my God, to Thee—hymn (1859) (Wds.
S Adams, 1841; music based on hymn
'Bethany')
R. Jose, Broadway Cast (r1906) *Concert*
(5/94) (PEAR) ① [2] **GEMMCDS9050/2(1)**

MASSÉ, Victor *(1822–1884)
France*

SECTION V: STAGE WORKS

**Les Noces de Jeannette—opéra-comique: 1
act (1853—Paris)** (Lib. J. Barbier & M. Carré)
Air du rossignol P. Gallois, London Fest Orch, R.
Pople (r1993: arr fl: F.Pierre) *Concert*
(5/95) (DG) ① **445 822-2GH**
Paul et Virginie—opera: 3 acts (1876—Paris)
(Lib. Barbier and Carré)
L'oiseau s'envoie J. Lassalle, anon (r1902) *Concert*
(9/91) (SYMP) ① **SYMCD1089**
**La Reine Topaze—opéra-comique: 3 acts
(1856—Paris)** (Lib. J P Lockroy & L Battu)
EXCERPTS: 1. Ninette est jeune et belle, 'Carnaval
de Venise'.
1. S. Jo, ECO, R. Bonynge (r1993) *Concert*
(9/94) (DECC) ① **440 679-2DH**
Les Saisons—opera: 3 acts (1855—Paris)
(Lib. J Barbier & M Carré)
Chanson de blé. L. Fugère, orch (r1928) *Concert*
(6/93) (SYMP) ① **SYMCD1125**

MASSENET, Jules (Emile
Frédéric) *(1842–1912) France*

SECTION I: ORCHESTRAL

Fantaisie—cello and orchestra
S. Rolland, BBC PO, G. Varga *Concert*
(12/93) (ASV) ① **CDDCA867**
Suite No. 1—orchestra, Op. 13 (1865)
1. Pastorale and Fugue; 2. Variations; 3. Nocturne;
4. Marche et Strette.
Hong Kong PO, K. Jean *Concert*
(1/92) (MARC) ① **8 223354**
NZ SO, J-Y. Ossonce (r1994) *Concert*
(9/95) (NAXO) ① **8 553124**
**Suite No. 2, 'Scènes hongroises'—orchestra
(1871)**
1. Entrée en forme de danse; 2. Intermède; 3. Adieux
à la fiancée; 4. Cortège; 5. Bénédiction nuptiale; 6.
Sortie de l'église.
NZ SO, J-Y. Ossonce (r1994) *Concert*
(9/95) (NAXO) ① **8 553124**
**Suite No. 3, 'Scènes
dramatiques'—orchestra (1873)**
1. Prélude et divertissement: La Tempête; 2.
Mélodrame: Le sommeil de Desdémone; 3. Scène
finale: Macbeth.
Monte Carlo Op Orch, J.E. Gardiner *Concert*
(2/93) (ERAT) ① **2292-45858-2**
NZ SO, J-Y. Ossonce (r1994) *Concert*
(9/95) (NAXO) ① **8 553124**
**Suite No. 4, 'Scènes
pittoresques'—orchestra (1874)**
1. Marche; 2. Air de ballet; 3. Angelus; 4. Fête
bohème.
Monte Carlo Op Orch, J.E. Gardiner *Concert*
(2/93) (ERAT) ① **2292-45859-2**
NZ SO, J-Y. Ossonce (r1994) *Concert*
(9/95) (NAXO) ① **8 553125**
4. La Scala Orch, A. Toscanini (r1943) *Concert*
(11/92) (RCA) ① **GD60315**
**Suite No. 5, 'Scènes
napolitaines'—orchestra (1876)**
1. La danse; 2. La procession; 3. La fête.
NZ SO, J-Y. Ossonce (r1994) *Concert*
(9/95) (NAXO) ① **8 553125**
**Suite No. 6, 'Scènes de féerie'—orchestra
(1879)**
1. Cortège; 2. Ballet; 3. Apparition; 4. Bacchanale.
Monte Carlo Op Orch, J.E. Gardiner *Concert*
(2/93) (ERAT) ① **2292-45858-2**
NZ SO, J-Y. Ossonce (r1994) *Concert*
(9/95) (NAXO) ① **8 553125**
**Suite No. 7, 'Scènes
alsaciennes'—orchestra (1881)**
1. Dimanche matin; 2. Au cabaret; 3. Sous les tilleuls;
4. Dimanche soir.
National PO, R. Bonynge *Don Quichotte.*
(4/92) (DECC) ① [2] **430 636-2DM2**
Monte Carlo Op Orch, J.E. Gardiner *Concert*
(2/93) (ERAT) ① **2292-45859-2**
NZ SO, J-Y. Ossonce (r1994) *Concert*
(9/95) (NAXO) ① **8 553125**

SECTION IV: VOCAL AND CHORAL

Les Alcyons—mélodie (1887) (Wds. J.
Autran)
B. Kruysen, N. Lee *Concert*
(2/88) (ARIO) ① **ARN68009**

L' âme des fleurs—song: 1v and piano (pub 1891) (Wds. P Delaire)
P. Aramis, anon (r1905: Greek) *Concert*
(12/94) (SYMP) ① **SYMCD1172**
Aubade—mélodie (1877) (Wds. G. Prevost)
B. Kruysen, N. Lee *Concert*
(2/88) (ARIO) ① **ARN68009**
3 Chants intimes—songs: 1-3vv and piano
(pub 1869) (Wds. G Chouquet)
1. Dédication; 2. A Mignonne; 3. Berceuse.
3. J. van Dam, J-P. Collard (r1992) *Concert*
(3/94) (EMI) ① **CDC7 54818-2**
La Crépuscule—song (1872) (Wds.
Silvestre)
A. Galli-Curci, orch, J. Pasternack (r1918) *Concert*
(3/94) (ROMO) ① [2] **81003-2**
Élégie—mélodie (c1869) (Wds. L. Gallet)
E. Caruso, M. Elman, P. Kahn (r1913) *Concert*
(7/91) (RCA) ① [12] **GD60495(4)**
M. Maisky, P. Gililov (arr vc/pf) *Concert*
(7/91) (DG) ① **431 544-2GH**
E. Caruso, M. Elman, P. Kahn (r1913) *Concert*
(10/91) (PEAR) ① [3] **EVC3(1)**
E. Caruso, M. Elman, P. Kahn (r1913) *Concert*
(10/91) (BIDD) ① **LAB039**
P. Domingo, I. Perlman, NY Studio Orch, J. Tunick
(r1990) *Concert* (3/92) (EMI) ① **CDC7 54266-2**
F. Chaliapin, C. Sharpe, I. Newton (r1931) *Concert*
(6/93) (PREI) ① [2] **89207**
L. Sibiriakov, anon (r1905: Russ) *Concert*
(6/93) (GEMM) ① [3] **GEMMCDS9001/3(2)**
R. Ponselle, orch, R. Bourdon (r1926) *Concert*
(10/93) (NIMB) ① **NI7846**
E. Eames, J. Hollman, anon (r1906) *Concert*
(11/93) (ROMO) ① [2] **81001-2**
E. Eames, anon, anon (r1905) *Concert*
(11/93) (ROMO) ① [2] **81001-2**
J. van Dam, G. Rogué, J-P. Collard (r1992) *Concert*
(3/94) (EMI) ① **CDC7 54818-2**
E. Caruso, M. Elman, P. Kahn (r1913/92) *Concert*
(5/94) (CLAR) ① **CDGSE78-50-52**
M. Teyte, J. Whitehead, G. Moore (r1944) *Concert*
(10/94) (EMI) ① [2] **CHS5 65198-2**
W. Fernandez, Brodsky Qt (r1994; arr Cassidy)
Concert (10/94) (SILV) ① **SILKD6001**
R. Ponselle, orch, R. Bourdon (r1926 (2 vers)
Concert (11/94) (ROMO) ① [2] **81007-2**
E. Rethberg, M. Rosen, F. Persson (r1926: Eng)
Concert (2/95) (ROMO) ① [2] **81012-2**
E. Rethberg, F. Fradkin, anon (r1925: Eng) *Concert*
(2/95) (ROMO) ① [2] **81012-2**
P. Domingo, I. Perlman, NY Studio Orch, J. Tunick
(r1990) *Concert*
(6/95) (EMI) ① [20] **CZS5 83177-2(3)**
Les Fleurs—soprano, baritone and piano
(pub 1894) (wds. J. Normand)
C. Alliot-Lugaz, F. Le Roux, J. Cohen *Concert*
(4/91) (REM) ① **REM311086**
Horace et Lydie—2vv and piano (1886) (wds
A. de Musset, after Horace)
C. Alliot-Lugaz, F. Le Roux, J. Cohen *Concert*
(4/91) (REM) ① **REM311086**
Joie!—duet (1868) (Wds. C. Distel)
F. Lott, A. Murray, G. Johnson (r1991) *Concert*
(7/92) (EMI) ① **CDC7 54411-2**
Les Mains—song:1v and piano (Wds. N
Bazan)
J. van Dam, J-P. Collard (r1992) *Concert*
(3/94) (EMI) ① **CDC7 54818-2**
Marquise—mélodie (1888) (Wds. A.
Silvestre)
B. Kruysen, N. Lee *Concert*
(2/88) (ARIO) ① **ARN68009**
V. Maurel, anon (r1903) *Concert*
(10/92) (SYMP) ① **SYMCD1101**
La Mort de la cigale—song: 1v and piano
(pub 1911) (Wds. M Faure)
J. van Dam, J-P. Collard (r1992) *Concert*
(3/94) (EMI) ① **CDC7 54818-2**
Oh! si les fleurs avaient des yeux—mélodie
(Wds. G. Buchillot)
B. Kruysen, N. Lee *Concert*
(2/88) (ARIO) ① **ARN68009**
Pensée d'automne—song (pub 1888) (wds.
Silvestre)
J. Lassalle, anon (r1903) *Concert*
(9/91) (SYMP) ① **SYMCD1089**
Poème d'Avril, Op. 14 (1866) (Wds. A.
Silvestre)
1. Prélude; 2. Sonnet matinal; 3. Voici que les
grandes lys; 4. Riez-vous?; 5. Vous aimeres demain;
6. Que l'heure est donc brève; 7. Sur la source; 8.
Adieu.
B. Kruysen, N. Lee *Concert*
(2/88) (ARIO) ① **ARN68009**

2. E. Clément, F. La Forge (r1911) *Concert*
(8/95) (ROMO) ① **82002-2**
2. E. Clément, anon (r1910s) *Concert*
(8/95) (PEAR) ① **GEMMCD9161**
6. D. Fischer-Dieskau, H. Höll (r c1987) *Concert*
(12/95) (TELD) ① **4509-97457-2**
Poème d'Octobre—songs (1876) (Wds. P.
Collin)
1. Prélude; 2. Les Profitons bien des jours d'Octobre;
3. Les marroniers; 4. Qu' importe; 5. Belle frileuses;
6. Pareils à des oiseaux.
B. Kruysen, N. Lee *Concert*
(2/88) (ARIO) ① **ARN68009**
Poème du souvenir (1868) (Wds. A.
Silvestre)
1. A la trépassée; 2. L'air du soir; 3. Un souffle de
parfums; 4. Dans l'air plain de fils de soie; 5. Pour
qu'à l'espérance; 6. Epitaphe.
B. Kruysen, N. Lee *Concert*
(2/88) (ARIO) ① **ARN68009**
Le Poète et le fantôme—mélodie (1891)
B. Kruysen, N. Lee *Concert*
(2/88) (ARIO) ① **ARN68009**
C. Alliot-Lugaz, F. Le Roux, J. Cohen (arr sop & bar)
Concert (4/91) (REM) ① **REM311086**
Le Printemps visite la terre—mélodie (1901)
(wds. J. Chaffotte)
B. Kruysen, N. Lee *Concert*
(2/88) (ARIO) ① **ARN68009**
Rêvons c'est l'heure—soprano, tenor and
piano (pub 1872) (wds. P. Verlaine)
C. Alliot-Lugaz, F. Le Roux, J. Cohen (sop & bar)
Concert (4/91) (REM) ① **REM311086**
F. Lott, A. Murray, G. Johnson (r1991) *Concert*
(7/92) (EMI) ① **CDC7 54411-2**
Si tu l'oses—mélodie (1897) (Wds. D. G.
Mansilla)
B. Kruysen, N. Lee *Concert*
(2/88) (ARIO) ① **ARN68009**
Si tu veux, Mignonne—song (1876) (Wds.
Abbé C. G. Boyer)
S. Varcoe, G. Johnson *Concert*
(6/88) (HYPE) ① **CDA66248**
J. Lassalle, anon (r1902) *Concert*
(9/91) (SYMP) ① **SYMCD1089**
P. Plançon, anon (r1905) *Concert*
(9/91) (PEAR) ① **GEMMCD9497**
P. Plançon, anon (r1905) *Concert*
(12/94) (ROMO) ① [2] **82001-2**
Souvenir de Venise—song (1865) (Wds. de
Musset)
A. Rolfe Johnson, G. Johnson *Concert*
(3/88) (HYPE) ① **CDA66112**
La Vierge—sacred legend: 4 acts (1880)
(Wds. C. Grandmaougin)
SCENE 1: 1. Prelude; 2. Le sonneil n'a pas quitté
notre maison; 3. Les Messager du Roi des Pois
paraît; 4. Je viens te saleur. SCENE 2: 5. Buvons! ah!
quel sumptueux festin; 6. Danse galilenne? 7.
Miracle! O prodige! J'en frémis encore!; 8a. O mes
fils! on t'acclame et la foule t'envire!; 8b. Gloire au
Maître des cités! SCENE 3: 9. Là-bas du côté du
prétoire. SCENE 4: 10. Le dernier sommeil de la
Vierge (Last Sleep of the Virgin); 11. Dans nos
choeurs quelle douleur profonde!; 12. Marie! Viens!
éveille toi du grand sommeil; 13. Rêve infini! divine
extase; 14. Magnificat anima mea Dominum...Gloire
à Dieu...Consolez-vous.
Cpte M. Command, M. Castets, M. Olmeda, M-T.
Keller, P. Salmon, M. Hacquard, Lyon Nat Orch Chor,
St Etienne Maîtrise Scholachoeur, Prague SO, P.
Fournillier (5/92) (SCHW) ① [2] **313084**
10. P. Tortelier (vc/dir), ECO *Concert*
(7/88) (VIRG) ① **VC7 59668-2**
10. RPO, T. Beecham (r1947) *Concert*
(4/92) (EMI) ① **CDM7 63401-2**
10. Monte Carlo Op Orch, J.E. Gardiner *Concert*
(2/93) (ERAT) ① **2292-45858-2**
Les Yeux clos—mélodie (1905) (Wds. G.
Buchillot)
B. Kruysen, N. Lee *Concert*
(2/88) (ARIO) ① **ARN68009**

SECTION V: STAGE WORKS

Amadis—opera: 4 acts (1922—Monte Carlo)
(Lib. Claretia)
Cpte H. Perraguin, D. Streiff, D. Henry, A. Garcin, N.
Chabrier, P. Descombes, Hauts-de-Seine Maîtrise,
Paris Op Chor, Paris Op Orch, P. Fournillier
(8/96) (FORL) ① [2] **UCD16578/9**
Ariane—opera: 5 acts (1906—Paris) (Lib. C
Mendes)
EXCERPTS: 1. Andante et Menuet des Graces; 2.
Ce Sarrasin disait (Air des roses); 3. Lamento
d'Ariane.

4, 5. L. Muratore, orch (r1910s) *Concert*
(8/95) (IRCC) ① **IRCC-CD802**
Le Carillon—ballet (1892—Vienna)
National PO, R. Bonynge Delibes: Coppélia.
(1/90) (DECC) ① [2] **425 472-2DM2**
Cendrillon—concert suite from opera
1. Marche des princesses; 2. Les filles de noblesse;
3. Menuet de Cendrillon.
Hong Kong PO, K. Jean *Concert*
(1/92) (MARC) ① **8 223354**
Cendrillon, 'Cinderella'—opera: 4 acts
(1899—Paris) (Lib. Cain. after Perrault)
Cpte F. von Stade, N. Gedda, J. Berbié, J. Bastin, R.
Welting, T. Cahill, E. Bainbridge, C. Meloni, P. Crook,
C. du Plessis, J. Noble, Ambrosian Op Chor, Philh, J.
Rudel (9/89) (SONY) ① [2] **M2K79323**
Valse RPO, T. Beecham (r1957) *Concert*
(9/92) (EMI) ① **CDM7 63401-2**
Chérubin—opera: 3 acts (1903—Monte
Carlo) (Lib. F. de Croisset & H. Cain)
Cpte F. von Stade, S. Ramey, J. Anderson, D.
Upshaw, J-M. Ivaldi, H. Garetti, M. Trempont, B.
Balleys, M. Sénéchal, C.H. Ahnsjö, A. Arapian, R.
Scholze, Bavarian St Op Chor, Munich RSO, P.
Steinberg (12/92) (RCA) ① [2] **09026 60593-2**
Viva amour E. Eames, anon (r1908) *Concert*
(11/93) (ROMO) ① [2] **81001-2**
Le Cid—opera: 4 acts (1885—Paris) (Lib.
d'Ennery, Blau and Gallet)
EXCERPTS. ACT 1: 1. O noble isème étincelante.
ACT 2: BALLET MUSIC: 2a. Castillane; 2b.
Andalouse; 2c. Aragonaise; 2d. Aubade; 2e.
Catalane; 2f. Madrilène; 2g. Navarraise. ACT 3: 3a.
De cet affreux combat; 3b. Pleurez, mes yeux; 4a.
Ah! tout est bien fini; 4b. O souverain, ô juge, ô père.
ACT 4: 5. Il a fait noblement.
Cpte G. Ingram, T. Hodges, A. Voketaitis, G.
Bumbry, E. Bergquist, J. Gardner, P. Domingo, P.
Plishka, P. Lightfoot, J. Adams, Byrne Camp Chorale,
NY Op Orch, E. Queler (pp1976)
(2/90) (SONY) ① [2] **M2K79300**
1. G. Thill, orch, E. Bigot (r1933) *Concert*
(8/95) (FORL) ① **UCD16727**
1, 4a, 4b G. Thill, orch, E. Bigot (r1933) *Concert*
(12/88) (EMI) ① **CDM7 69548-2**
2a-g National PO, R. Bonynge Delibes: Sylvia.
(1/90) (DECC) ① [2] **425 475-2DM2**
3a, 3b M. Callas, FRNO, G. Prêtre *Concert*
(2/88) (EMI) ① **CDC7 49059-2**
3a, 3b K. Te Kanawa, ROHO, J. Tate *Concert*
(2/90) (EMI) ① **CDC7 49863-2**
3b G. Bumbry, Stuttgart RSO, S. Soltesz *Concert*
(11/86) (ORFE) ① **C081841A**
3b M. Callas, FRNO, G. Prêtre *Concert*
(2/90) (EMI) ① **CDM7 63182-2**
3b F. Litvinne, anon (r1903) *Concert*
(4/94) (PREI) ① **89079**
3b M. Jeritza, orch (r1925) *Concert*
(12/94) (SYMP) ① **SYMCD1128**
3b D. Visse, Camargue PO, Reinhardt Wagner
(r1995: arr R Wagner) *Concert*
(8/95) (HARM) ① **HMC90 1552**
4a, 4b J. Schmidt, orch (r1932: Ger) *Concert*
(4/90) (EMI) ① **CDM7 69478-2**
4a, 4b E. Caruso, orch, W.B. Rogers (r1916) *Concert*
(7/91) (RCA) ① [12] **GD60495(5)**
4a, 4b E. Caruso, orch, W.B. Rogers (r1916) *Concert*
(10/91) (PEAR) ① [3] **EVC3(2)**
4a, 4b L. Escalais, anon (r1906) *Concert*
(12/93) (SYMP) ① **SYMCD1126**
4a, 4b B. Heppner, Munich RO, R. Abbado (r1993/4)
Concert (11/95) (RCA) ① **09026 62504-2**
4b J. Carreras, Los Angeles PO, Z. Mehta (pp1994)
Concert (12/96) (TELD) ① **4509-96200-2**
Le Cigale—ballet: 2 acts (1904—Paris)
E. Hartle, London Voices, National PO, R. Bonynge
Tchaikovsky: Swan Lake.
(7/90) (DECC) ① [2] **425 413-2DM3**
Cléopâtre—opera: 4 acts (1914—Monte
Carlo) (Lib. L. Payen)
Cpte K. Harries, D. Henry, J-L. Maurette, D. Streiff,
M. Olmeda, M. Hacquard, C. Massoz, P. Georges,
Massenet Fest Chor, Saint-Etienne Nouvel Orch, P.
Fournillier (pp1990)
(5/94) (SCHW) ① [2] **310322**
A-t-il dit vrai?...Solitaire sur ma terrasse Vanni-
Marcoux, orch (r1931) *Concert*
(1/94) (CLUB) ① **CL99-101**
Don César de Bazan—comic opera
(1872—Paris) (Lib. D'Ennery, Dumanoir and
Chantepie)
EXCERPTS: 2. A Séville, belles Señoras (Sevillana);
3. Entr'acte (Act 3).

15c, 24a, 24b Alfredo Kraus, Toulouse Capitole Orch, M. Plasson *Concert* (10/89) (EMI) ① **CDM7 63104-2**
15c, 24b E. Clément, anon (r1905) *Concert* (8/95) (ROMO) ① **82002-2**
19a-c N. Vallin, orch, F. Ruhlmann (r1932) *Concert* (2/92) (MMOI) ① **CDMOIR408**
19b A. Arteta, Paris Opéra-Bastille Orch, E. Kohn (pp1992) *Concert* (6/94) (SONY) ① **SK46691**
19c A. Galli-Curci, orch (r1923) *Concert* (2/89) (PEAR) ① **GEMMCD9308**
19c A. Galli-Curci, orch (r1923) *Concert* (10/89) (NIMB) ① **NI7802**
19c Lotte Lehmann, orch (Ger: r1917) *Concert* (6/92) (PREI) ① [3] **89302**
19c L. Schöne, Berlin St Op Orch, L. Blech (r c1929: Ger) *Concert* (1/94) (CLUB) ① **CL99-020**
19c R. Crooks, RCA SO, W. Pelletier (r1938) *Concert* (4/94) (RCA) ① [6] **09026 61580-2(4)**
19c A. Galli-Curci, orch, R. Bourdon (r1923) *Concert* (8/94) (ROMO) ① [2] **81004-2**
19c C. Muzio, orch (r1918) *Concert* (1/95) (ROMO) ① [2] **81010-2**
24a, 24b J. Björling, Stockholm Royal Op Orch, N. Grevillius (r1945) *Concert* (10/88) (EMI) ① **CDH7 61053-2**
24a, 24b E. Caruso, orch (r1911) *Concert* (10/89) (NIMB) ① **NI7803**
24a, 24b T. Schipa, La Scala Orch, F. Ghione (r1934; Ital) *Concert* (4/90) (EMI) ① **CDH7 63200-2**
24a, 24b B. Gigli, ROHO, R. Zamboni (r1946; Ital) *Concert* (5/90) (EMI) ① **CDH7 61052-2**
24a, 24b E. Caruso, orch (r1911) *Concert* (3/91) (PEAR) ① [3] **EVC2**
24a, 24b E. Caruso, orch, W.B. Rogers (r1911) *Concert* (7/91) (RCA) ① [12] **GD60495(4)**
24b J. Patzak, orch, M. Gurlitt (Ger: r1929) *Concert* (3/90) (PEAR) ① **GEMMCD9383**
24b D. Smirnov, orch (Ital: r c1928) *Concert* (7/90) (CLUB) ① **CL99-031**
24b D. Smirnov, orch (r1910) *Concert* (7/90) (CLUB) ① **CL99-031**
24b A. Cortis, La Scala Orch, C. Sabajno (Ital: r1929) *Concert* (10/91) (PREI) ① **89043**
24b G. Lugo, orch, E. Cohen (r1935) *Concert* (2/92) (PREI) ① **89034**
24b A. Cortis, La Scala Orch, C. Sabajno (r1929: Ital) *Concert* (3/94) (NIMB) ① **NI7850**
24b G. Thill, orch, E. Bigot (r c1936) *Concert* (9/94) (NIMB) ① **NI7856**
24b H. Roswaenge, BPO, F.A. Schmidt (r1933: Ger) *Concert* (4/95) (PREI) ① [2] **89209**
25a F. Heldy, F. Ansseau, orch, P. Coppola (r1927) *Concert* (7/92) (PEAR) ① [3] **GEMMCDS9926(1)**
29. G. Féraldy, orch (r1928) *Manon.* (11/90) (EPM) ① [2] **150 012**

Panurge—operetta: 3 acts (1913—Paris) (Lib. M. Boukay & G. Spitzmüller, after Rabelais)
Touraine est un pays Vanni-Marcoux, anon (r1931) *Concert* (1/94) (CLUB) ① **CL99-101**

Le **Roi de Lahore—opéra: 5 acts (1877—Paris)** (Lib. Gallet)
EXCERPTS: ACT 3: 1. Adagio and Waltz. ACT 4: 2. Promesse de mon avenir (O casto fior). ACT 5: 3. Entr'acte.
Cpte L. Lima, J. Sutherland, S. Milnes, N. Ghiaurov, J. Morris, H. Tourangeau, London Voices, National PO, R. Bonynge (2/93) (DECC) ① [2] **433 851-2DMO2**
2. R. Stracciari, orch (r1925: Ital) *Concert* (2/90) (PREI) ① **89003**
2. J. Lassalle, anon (r1902) *Concert* (9/91) (SYMP) ① **SYMCD1089**
2. J. Lassalle, anon (r1902) *Concert* (7/92) (PEAR) ① [3] **GEMMCDS9923(1)**
2. A. Cotogni, anon (Ital: r1908) *Concert* (11/92) (MEMO) ① [2] **HR4408/9(1)**
2. A. Endrèze, orch, H. Defosse (r c1931) *Concert* (11/92) (MSCM) ① **MM30451**
2. T. Ruffo, orch (Ital: r1920) *Concert* (2/93) (PREI) ① [3] **89303(2)**
2. G. De Luca, anon (Ital: r1902) *Concert* (8/93) (SYMP) ① **SYMCD1111**
2. G. Pacini, anon (r1904: Ital) *Concert* (4/94) (EMI) ① [3] **CHS7 64860-2(1)**
2. M. Renaud, orch (r1906) *Concert* (10/95) (NIMB) ① **NI7867**

Roma—opera: 5 acts (1912—Monte Carlo) (Lib. H. Cain, after A. Parodi)
Le soleil se couchait L. Dupré, orch (r1912) *Concert* (8/92) (IRCC) ① **IRCC-CD802**
Soir admirable L. Beyle, orch (r1912) *Concert* (8/92) (IRCC) ① **IRCC-CD802**

Sapho—pièce lyrique (1897—Monte Carlo) (Lib. Cain and Bernède)
Ah! qu'il est loin mon pays G. Thill, orch, E. Bigot (r1930) *Concert* (8/95) (FORL) ① **UCD16727**

Thaïs—comédie lyrique: 3 acts (1894—Paris) (Lib. Gallet, after France)
EXCERPTS. ACT 1: 1a. Hélas! enfant encore; 1b. Toi qui mis la pitié; 2a. Va mendiant!; 2b. Voilà donc la terrible cité. ACT 2: 3a. Ah! je suis seule; 3b. Dis-moi que je suis belle; 4a. Étranger, te voila; 4b. Ah! pitié; 5. Méditation; 6. L'amour est une vertu rare. ACT 3: 7a. L'ardent soleil; 7b. O messager de Dieu; 7c. Baigne d'eau; 8. Que te fait si sévère; 9. Te souvient-il.
1a, 1b, 2a, 2b M. Journet, M. Cozette, SO, P. Coppola (r1928) *Concert* (1/94) (CLUB) ① **CL99-034**
1a, 2b T. Ruffo, orch (Ital: r1914) *Concert* (2/93) (PREI) ① [3] **89303(1)**
1a, 2b C. Formichi, orch, H. Harty (r1924) *Concert* (11/94) (PREI) ① **89055**
2b T. Ruffo, orch, W.B. Rogers (Ital: r1914) *Concert* (11/90) (NIMB) ① **NI7810**
3a, 3b J. Hammond, Philh, S. Robinson (r1951) *Concert* (12/92) (TEST) ① **SBT1013**
3a, 3b L. Price, LSO, E. Downes *Concert* (12/92) (RCA) ① [4] **09026 61236-2**
3b, 6. M. Jeritza, orch (r1926) *Concert* (4/94) (PREI) ① **89079**
5. A. Dumay, Monte Carlo PO, A. Dumay *Concert* (6/87) (EMI) ① **CDC7 47544-2**
5. BPO, H. von Karajan *Concert* (10/87) (DG) ① [3] **419 257-2GH3**
5. J-L. Garcia, ECO, P. Tortelier *Concert* (7/88) (VIRG) ① **VC7 59668-2**
5. F. Kreisler, C. Lamson (arr Marsick: vn/pf; r1928) *Concert* (1/90) (PEAR) ① **GEMMCD9324**
5. Gothenburg SO, N. Järvi *Concert* (6/90) (DG) ① **429 494-2GDC**
5. LPO, T. Beecham (bp1939) *Concert* (11/91) (SYMP) ① [2] **SYMCD1096/7**
5. N. Kennedy, National PO, R. Bonynge *Brahms: Violin Concerto.* (1/92) (DECC) ① **433 604-2DSP**
5. J. Bell, RPO, A. Litton *Concert* (1/92) (DECC) ① **433 519-2DH**
5. N. Kennedy, National PO, R. Bonynge (r1983) *Concert* (5/92) (DECC) ① **433 220-2DWO**
5. J. Hassid, G. Moore (arr Marsick: r1940) *Concert* (10/92) (PEAR) ① **GEMMCD9939**
5. J. Hassid, G. Moore (arr Marsick: r1940) *Concert* (10/92) (TEST) ① **SBT1010**
5. Chee-Yun, A. Eguchi (trans Marsick: vn, pf) *Concert* (12/93) (DENO) ① **CO-75118**
5. F. Kreisler, C. Lamson (r1928: arr Marsick: two vers) *Concert* (12/93) (BIDD) ① **LAB080**
5. A-S. Mutter, VPO, James Levine (r1992) *Concert* (12/93) (DG) ① **437 544-2GH**
5. A.A. Meyers, Philh, A. Litton (r1993) *Concert* (2/94) (RCA) ① **09026 61700-2**
5. N. Milstein, L. Pommers (r1956: arr Marsick) *Concert* (5/94) (EMI) ① [6] **ZDMF7 64830-2**
5. J. Bálint, N. Mercz (r1992: arr fl/hp: Mercz) *Concert* (12/94) (NAXO) ① **8 550741**
5. BBC SO, A. Davis (r1994) *Concert* (2/95) (TELD) ① **4509-97868-2**
5. P. Gallois, London Fest Orch, R. Pople (r1993: arr fl: Prezman) *Concert* (5/95) (DG) ① **445 822-2GH**
6. M. Garden, orch (r c1913) *Concert* (8/93) (SYMP) ① **SYMCD1136**
7c C. Formichi, G. Holst, orch (r1927) *Concert* (11/94) (PREI) ① **89055**
7c E. Katulskaya, L. Sibiriakov, orch (r1913: Russ) *Concert* (3/95) (NIMB) ① **NI7865**

Werther—opera: 4 acts (1892—Vienna) (Lib. Blau, Milliet and Hartmann)
ACT 1: 1. Prelude; 2. Assez! Assez!; 3a. Je ne sais si je veille; 3b. O nature, pleine de grâce; 4. Jésus vient de naître!; 5. O spectacle idéal d'amour; 6. Sophie! Albert!; 7a. Elle m'aime; 7b. Interlude (Clair de lune); 7c. Il faut nous séparer; 7d. Si vous l'aviez connue!. ACT 2: 8a. Prelude; 8b. Vivat Bacchus!; 9. Trois mois!; 10a. Un autre est son époux!; 10b. J'aurais sur ma poitrine; 11a. Au bonheur; 11b. Je vous sais un coeur loyal et fort; 12a. Frère, voyez le beau bouquet!; 12b. Du gai soleil, plein de flamme; 12c. Va porter ton bouquet; 13a. Ah! qu'il est loin ce jour; 13b. N'est-il donc pas d'autre femme; 14. Lorsque l'enfant revient d'un voyage. ACT 3: 15a. Werther! Qui m'aurait dit la place; 15b. Des cris joyeux; 16. Bonjour, grande soeur!; 17. Ah! le rire est béni; 18a. Va! Laisse couler; 18b. Les larmes qu'on ne pleure pas; 19. Ah! mon courage m'abandonne; 20. Oui, c'est moi!; 21a. Traduire; 21b. Pourquoi me réveiller?; 22. N'achevez pas!; 23. Werther est de retour. ACT 4: 24a. Prelude (Le nuit de Noël); 24b. Werther!...Rien!...Dieu! Ah! du sang!; 25. Noël! Noël!; 26. Là-bas, au fond du cimetière. 27. Finale.
Cpte J. Carreras, F. von Stade, T. Allen, I. Buchanan, R. Lloyd, P. Crook, M. King, L. Humphries, D. Bell, ROHO, Colin Davis (r1980) (2/87) (PHIL) ① [2] **416 654-2PH2**
Cpte Alfredo Kraus, T. Troyanos, M. Manuguerra, C. Barbaux, J. Bastin, P. Langridge, J-P. Lafont, L. Richardson, M. Lewis, Covent Garden Sngrs, LPO, M. PLasson (4/89) (EMI) ① [2] **CMS7 69573-2**
Cpte G. Thill, N. Vallin, M. Roque, G. Féraldy, A. Narçon, H. Niel, L. Guénot, Cantoria Children's Ch, Paris Opéra-Comique Chor, Paris Opéra-Comique Orch, E. Cohen (r1931) (3/90) (EMI) ① [2] **CHS7 63195-2**
Cpte N. Gedda, V. de los Angeles, R. Soyer, M. Mesplé, J-C. Benoit, A. Mallabrera, C. Grigoriou, French Rad Maîtrise, Paris Orch, G. Prêtre (5/92) (EMI) ① [2] **CMS7 63973-2**
3a G. Thill, Orch, F. Heurteur (r1927) *Concert* (1/89) (EMI) ① **CDM7 69548-2**
3a, 3b T. Schipa, orch, M. Cordone (r1942; Ital) *Concert* (4/90) (EMI) ① **CDH7 63200-2**
3a, 3b G. Thill, orch, F. Heurteur (r1927) *Concert* (10/92) (TEST) ① **SBT1005**
3a, 3b P. Domingo, Cologne RSO, R. Chailly (r1979) *Concert* (6/94) (BELA) ① **450 121-2**
3a, 3b, 21a, 21b Alfredo Kraus, LPO, M. Plasson *Concert* (10/89) (EMI) ① **CDM7 63104-2**
3b T. Schipa, orch, M. Cordone (r1942: Ital) *Concert* (9/94) (NIMB) ① **NI7856**
3b, 10b F. Ansseau, orch (r1927) *Concert* (1/91) (PREI) ① **89022**
3b, 21b A. Piccaver, orch (r1914: Ger) *Concert* (8/93) (PREI) ① **89060**
10a A. Giorgini, orch (r1908: Ital) *Concert* (4/95) (RECO) ① **TRC3**
10a, 10b G. Thill, Orch, M. Frigara (r1927) *Concert* (1/89) (EMI) ① **CDM7 69548-2**
10a, 10b R. Jobin, Paris Opéra-Comique Orch, A. Cluytens (r1948) *Concert* (4/92) (EMI) ① [7] **CHS7 69741-2(3)**
15a G. Simionato, Milan SO, A. Quadri (Ital: r1951) *Concert* (4/92) (EMI) ① [7] **CHS7 69741-2(7)**
15a, 15b M. Lipovšek, Munich RO, G. Patanè *Concert* (6/90) (ORFE) ① **C179891A**
18a, 18b B. Fassbaender, Stuttgart RSO, H. Graf *Concert* (11/86) (ORFE) ① **C096841A**
21a, 21b T. Schipa, orch (r1925) *Concert* (2/89) (PEAR) ① **GEMMCD9322**
21a, 21b T. Schipa, La Scala Orch, F. Ghione (r1934; Ital) *Concert* (4/90) (EMI) ① **CDH7 63200-2**
21b P. Dvorský, Bratislava RSO, Czech RSO, O. Lenárd *Concert* (10/89) (OPUS) ① **9156 1824**
21b T. Schipa, orch, R. Bourdon (r1925) *Concert* (12/89) (RCA) ① **GD87969**
21b J. Patzak, orch (Ger: r1937) *Concert* (3/90) (PEAR) ① **GEMMCD9383**
21b B. Gigli, ROHO, R. Zamboni (Ital: r1946) *Concert* (5/90) (EMI) ① **CDH7 61052-2**
21b L. Pavarotti, National PO, O. de Fabritiis *Concert* (7/90) (DECC) ① [2] **425 681-2DM2**
21b A. Cortis, La Scala Orch, C. Sabajno (Ital: r1929) *Concert* (10/91) (PREI) ① **89043**
21b G. Lugo, orch, F. Weiss (r1933) *Concert* (2/92) (PREI) ① **89034**
21b G. Prandelli, Milan SO, A. Quadri (Ital: r1949) *Concert* (4/92) (EMI) ① [7] **CHS7 69741-2(7)**
21b P. Dvorský, Bratislava RSO, O. Lenárd *Concert* (5/92) (NAXO) ① **8 550343**
21b M. Battistini, orch, C. Sabajno (Ital: r1911) *Concert* (10/92) (NIMB) ① **NI7831**
21b M. Battistini, orch, C. Sabajno (Ital: r1911) *Concert* (10/92) (PEAR) ① **GEMMCD9936**
21b J. Hislop, orch, G.W. Byng (r1926) *Concert* (1/93) (PEAR) ① **GEMMCD9956**
21b L. Sobinov, orch (r1910: Russ) *Concert* (6/93) (PEAR) ① [3] **GEMMCDS9997/9(2)**
21b G. Lauri-Volpi, orch (r1922: Ital) *Concert* (7/93) (NIMB) ① **NI7845**
21b G. di Stefano, Zurich Tonhalle Orch, F. Patanè (r1958) *Concert* (10/93) (DECC) ① **436 463-2DM**
21b A. Cortis, La Scala Orch, C. Sabajno (r1929: Ital) *Concert* (3/94) (NIMB) ① **NI7850**
21b T. Schipa, La Scala Orch, F. Ghione (r1934: Ital) *Concert* (4/94) (EMI) ① [3] **CHS7 64864-2(2)**
21b L. Pavarotti, Ater Orch, L. Magiera (pp) *Concert* (5/94) (DECC) ① [2] **443 018-2DF2**
21b E. Van Dyck, anon (r1905) *Concert* (12/94) (SYMP) ① **SYMCD1172**
21b L. Pavarotti, Los Angeles PO, Z. Mehta (pp1994) *Concert* (12/94) (TELD) ① **4509-96200-2**
21b F. de Lucia, anon (r1903: Ital) *Concert* (1/95) (SYMP) ① **SYMCD1149**
21b L. Pavarotti, NYPO, L. Magiera (pp1993) *Concert* (2/95) (DECC) ① **444 450-2DH**

21b G. Anselmi, anon (r1907: Ital) *Concert*
    (7/95) (SYMP) ① **SYMCD1170**
21b E. Clément, orch (r1911) *Concert*
    (8/95) (ROMO) ① **82002-2**
21b E. Clément, orch (r1911) *Concert*
    (8/95) (PEAR) ① **GEMMCD9161**
21b R. Alagna, LPO, R. Armstrong *Concert*
    (12/95) (EMI) ① **CDC5 55540-2**

MASSENZIO, Domenico (d 1650) Italy

SECTION IV: VOCAL AND CHORAL

The **Office of Compline—2-8vv and continuo, Op. 8 (pub 1630)**
Ecs St John's College Ch, G. Guest
    (4/88) (MERI) ① **CDE84121**

MASUMOTO, Kikuko (b 1937) Japan

SECTION III: INSTRUMENTAL

Pastorale—recorder (1973)
D. Laurin (r1993) *Concert*
    (8/94) (BIS) ① **BIS-CD655**

MASZYNSKI, P. (1855–1934) Poland

SECTION IV: VOCAL AND CHORAL

Bagpiper's song (Wds. Mickiewicz)
A. Didur, anon (r1901) *Concert*
    (6/93) (PEAR) ① [3] **GEMMCDS9997/9(2)**

MATAČIĆ, Lovro von (1899–1985) Yugoslavia

SECTION III: INSTRUMENTAL

Miniature Variations—piano
L. Rév *Concert*   (7/87) (HYPE) ① **CDA66185**

MATHEUS DE SANCTO JOHANNE (fl 1365–?1389) France

SECTION IV: VOCAL AND CHORAL

Fortune, faulce, parverse—rondeau (4vv)
Gothic Voices, I. Barford, C. Page *Concert*
    (12/86) (HYPE) ① **CDA66144**
Inclite flos orti Gebenensis—ballade: 3vv
Orlando Consort (bp1994) *Concert*
    (11/95) (METR) ① **METCD1008**

MATHIAS, William (James) (1934–1992) Wales

SECTION I: ORCHESTRAL

Concerto for Clarinet and Orchestra, Op. 68 (1975)
G. de Peyer, New Philh, D. Atherton (r1977) *Concert*
    (7/95) (LYRI) ① **SRCD325**
Concerto for Harp and Orchestra, Op. 50 (1970)
O. Ellis, LSO, D. Atherton (r1971) *Concert*
    (7/95) (LYRI) ① **SRCD325**
Concerto for Harp and Orchestra, Op. 50 (1970)
A. H. Pilot, ECO, I. Jackson (r1993) *Ginastera: Harp Concerto.*   (12/94) (KOCH) ① **37261-2**
Concerto for Piano and Orchestra No. 3 (1968)
P. Katin, LSO, D. Atherton (r1971) *Concert*
    (7/95) (LYRI) ① **SRCD325**
Symphony No. 1, Op. 31 (1965)
BBC Welsh SO, W. Mathias *Symphony 2.*
    (12/90) (NIMB) ① **NI5260**
Symphony No. 2, 'Summer Night', Op. 90 (1983)
BBC Welsh SO, W. Mathias *Symphony 1.*
    (12/90) (NIMB) ① **NI5260**

SECTION II: CHAMBER

String Quartet No. 1, Op. 38 (1967)
Medea Qt (r1993) *Concert*
    (10/95) (METI) ① **MSVCD92005**
String Quartet No. 2, Op. 84 (1980)
Medea Qt (r1993) *Concert*
    (10/95) (METI) ① **MSVCD92005**
String Quartet No. 3, Op. 97 (1986)
Medea Qt (r1993) *Concert*
    (10/95) (METI) ① **MSVCD92005**

SECTION III: INSTRUMENTAL

Antiphonies—organ, Op. 88/2 (1982)
John Scott (r1993) *Concert*
    (6/93) (NIMB) ① **NI5367**
Berceuse—organ, Op. 95/3 (1985)
J. Lancelot *Concert*   (8/88) (PRIO) ① **PRCD228**
    (6/93) (NIMB) ① **NI5367**
Canzonetta—organ, Op. 78/2 (1978)
S. Lawford *Concert*   (9/90) (NIMB) ① **NI5243**
Chorale—organ (1966)
John Scott (r1993) *Concert*
    (6/93) (NIMB) ① **NI5367**
Fanfare—organ (1987)
John Scott (r1993) *Concert*
    (6/93) (NIMB) ① **NI5367**
Fantasy—organ, Op. 78 (1978)
John Scott (r1993) *Concert*
    (6/93) (NIMB) ① **NI5367**
Fenestra—organ (1989)
John Scott (r1993) *Concert*
    (6/93) (NIMB) ① **NI5367**
Invocations—organ, Op. 35 (1967)
John Scott (r1993) *Concert*
    (6/93) (NIMB) ① **NI5367**
Jubilate—organ, Op. 67/2 (1974)
John Scott (r1993) *Concert*
    (6/93) (NIMB) ① **NI5367**
Processional—organ (1964)
John Scott (r1993) *Concert*
    (6/93) (NIMB) ① **NI5367**
Recessional—organ, Op. 96/4 (1986)
John Scott (r1993) *Concert*
    (6/93) (NIMB) ① **NI5367**

SECTION IV: VOCAL AND CHORAL

As truly as God is our Father—chorus and organ (1987) (Wds. Julian of Norwich)
Oxford Christ Church Cath Ch, S. Lawford, S. Darlington *Concert*   (9/90) (NIMB) ① **NI5243**
St Paul's Cath Ch, John Scott *Concert*
    (4/92) (HYPE) ① **CDA66519**
Ave Rex—chorus and orchestra, Op. 45 (1969)
1. Ave Rex; 2. Alleluja, A new work is come to hand; 3. There is no rose of such virtue; 4. Sir Christèmas.
Oxford Christ Church Cath Ch, S. Lawford, S. Darlington *Concert*   (9/90) (NIMB) ① **NI5243**
WNO Chor, LSO, D. Atherton (r1973) *Concert*
    (2/95) (LYRI) ① **SRCD324**
A Babe is born—chorus and orchestra, Op. 53 (1971) (Wds. 15th Cent Anon)
Sheffield Chorale, Sheaf Concert Orch, J. Kirkwood *Concert*   (12/89) (CHOR) ① **EECD109**
York Minster Ch *Concert*   (12/91) (YORK) ① **CD846**
Elegy for a Prince—baritone and orchestra, Op. 59 (1972) (Wds. G ab yr Ynad Coch, trans A Conran)
G. Evans, New Philh, D. Atherton (r1977) *Concert*
    (2/95) (LYRI) ① **SRCD324**
A Grace—chorus a capella, Op. 89/3 (1982)
Oxford Christ Church Cath Ch, S. Darlington *Concert*
    (9/90) (NIMB) ① **NI5243**
I will celebrate—chorus and organ (1988) (Wds. from Jerusalem Bible: Psalms 89 & 90)
Oxford Christ Church Cath Ch, S. Lawford, S. Darlington *Concert*   (9/90) (NIMB) ① **NI5243**
Jesus College Service—chorus and organ, Op. 53 (1971)
EVENING CANTICLES; 1. Magnificat; 2. Nunc dimittis.
Oxford Christ Church Cath Ch, S. Lawford, S. Darlington *Concert*   (9/90) (NIMB) ① **NI5243**
Let the people praise Thee, O God—royal wedding anthem, Op. 87 (1981) (for wedding of Prince Charles & Lady Diana Spencer)
Oxford Christ Church Cath Ch, S. Lawford, S. Darlington *Concert*   (9/90) (NIMB) ① **NI5243**
St Paul's Cath Ch, John Scott, Andrew Lucas (r1993) *Concert*   (6/94) (HYPE) ① **CDA66678**
Lux aeterna—sop, mezzo, contr, choir and orch (1982)
F. Lott, M. Cable, P. Walker, Bach Ch, St George's Chapel Ch, LSO, D. Willcocks
    (11/89) (CHAN) ① **CHAN8695**
Missa Aedis Christi—chorus and organ, Op. 92 (1984)
Oxford Christ Church Cath Ch, S. Lawford, S. Darlington *Concert*   (9/90) (NIMB) ① **NI5243**
O how amiable—chorus and organ, Op. 90/3 (1983) (Wds. Psalm 84)
Oxford Christ Church Cath Ch, S. Lawford, S. Darlington *Concert*   (9/90) (NIMB) ① **NI5243**

Rex gloriae—four motets: chorus a capella, Op. 83
1. Laetentur coeli; 2. Vicitimae paschali; 3. O nata lux; 4. O rex gloriae.
Oxford Christ Church Cath Ch, S. Darlington *Concert*
    (9/90) (NIMB) ① **NI5243**
This Worlde's Joie—cantata: soloists, chorus and orchestra, Op. 67 (1974) (Wds. medieval anon)
J. Price, K. Bowen, M. Rippon, Bach Ch, St George's Chapel Ch, New Philh, D. Willcocks (r1976) *Concert*
    (2/95) (LYRI) ① **SRCD324**

MATIELLI, Giovanni Antonio (c1733–1805) Italy

SECTION III: INSTRUMENTAL

Adagio—keyboard
L. Laskine (r1963; arr hp) *Concert*
    (12/93) (ERAT) ① **4509-92131-2**

MATTEIS, Nicola (d ?1707 or later) Italy/England

SECTION I: ORCHESTRAL

Concerto di Trombe e tre Trombette (pub 1607) (from Other Ayres and Pieces for the Violin)
S. Keavy, C. Steele-Perkins, Parley of Instr *Concert*
    (1/89) (HYPE) ① **CDA66255**

SECTION II: CHAMBER

Ayres for the Violin, Book 1—1-2 vns and continuo (pub 1676)
BOOK 1 (C minor); 46. Preludio; 47. Aria; 48. Aria—Allegro; 49. Gavotta.
Arcadian Academy, N. McGegan (hpd/dir) *Concert*
    (7/93) (HARM) ① **HMU90 7067**
Aria spagnuola a due corde; Diverse bizzarie
Palladian Ens (r1992) *Concert*
    (7/93) (LINN) ① **CKD010**
Ayres for the Violin, Book 2—1-2 vns and continuo (pub 1676)
BOOK 2 (G minor); 10. Preludio in ostinatione; 11. Passaggio rotto; 12. Andamento malinconico; 13. Ricercata; 14. Corrente da orecchie; 15. Corrente da piedi; 16. Sarabanda; 17. Giga; 18. Fuga; 22. Fantasia 'a violino solo; 23. Pavana Armoniosa; 24. Il Russignolo; 25. Allemanda ad imitatione d'un tartaglia; 26. Movimento incognito—Variatione; 27. Movimento rotto; 28. Fantasia—Violino solo senza basso; 29. Aria burlesca con molte bizzarie; 30. Sonata; 31. Aria—Variata; 32. Corrente.
Arcadian Academy, N. McGegan (hpd/dir) *Concert*
    (9/92) (HARM) ① **HMU90 7067**
22-32. Arcadian Academy (r1993) *Concert*
    (3/95) (HARM) ① **HMU90 7108**
Ayres for the Violin, Book 3—1-2 violins and continuo (1685)
7. Preludio—Prestissimo; 8. Sarabanda—Adagio—Vivace; 9. Gavotta con divisione; 23. Preludio—Allegro; 24. Aria con divisione—Presto; 25. Adagio; 26. Minuetto; 27. Allegro—Adagio; 28. Aria con divisione, 'For the flute'; 29. Aria per Ballare—Vivace; 30. Corrente alla maniera Francese; 31. Aria—Adagio—Presto; 32. Jigg—Prestissimo; 41. Preludio—Grave; 42. Aria con divisione per la fa mano; 43. Corrente; 44. Aria sminuita per la fa mano.
7-9, 23-32, 41-44. Arcadian Academy (r1993) *Concert*   (3/95) (HARM) ① **HMU90 7108**
Ayres for the Violin, Book 4—1-2 vns and continuo (pub 1685)
BOOK 4 (A major); 1. Preludio—Presto; 2. Andamento con divisione; 3. Aria facile—Presto; 4. Serio—Adagio; 5. Aria in Passaggio; 6. Corrente—Allegro; 7. Jigg—Allegro; 8. Preludio a due corde; 9. Fuga—Adagio; 10. Andamento affetuoso; 11. Minuetto con sua divisione (C major); 12. Sonata—Adagio; 13. Fuga; 14. Vivace; 15. Fuga—Presto; 16. Allemanda, per far la mano; 17. Aria; 18. Aria—Allegro (C minor); 21. Preludio semplice—Adagio; 22. Motivo—Presto; 23. Fuga a due corde; 24. Aria—Presto; 25. Passaggio a solo; 26. Allegro—Prestissimo; 27. Ground sopra un basso Malinconico; 28. Aria Amorosa—Adagio (D minor); 30. Bizzarrie all'Umor Scozzese—Allegro; 31. Un poco di Grave—Adagio; 32. Aria for the Flute—Presto; 33. Preludio in D la sol re—Prestissimo; 34. Fuga in Fantasia—Presto; 35. Grave—Adagio; 36. Ground in D la sol re (sopra un basso per fare un poco di mano); 43. Preludio; 44. Aria Allegra; 45. Sarabanda—Adagio; 46. Aria ò pur Rondeau—Prestissimo.

Arcadian Academy, N. McGegan (hpd/dir) *Concert*
(9/92) (HARM) ① **HMU90 7067**
Ground after the Scotch Humour Sonnerie Trio, S.
Stubbs (r1992) *Concert*
(5/94) (TELD) ① **4509-90841-2**
2, 28, 35, 36, 27. Palladian Ens (r1992) *Concert*
(7/93) (LINN) ① **CKD010**
25, 26, 27, 28, 36. Sonnerie Trio, S. Stubbs, A.
Lawrence-King (r1992) *Concert*
(5/94) (TELD) ① **4509-90841-2**
30-32, 43-46. Arcadian Academy (r1993) *Concert*
(3/95) (HARM) ① **HMU90 7108**
Divisions on a Ground in D minor—3 violins,
bass and continuo
Parley of Instr, R. Goodman, P. Holman *Concert*
(11/88) (HYPE) ① **CDA66108**
Ground after the Scotch Humour—recorder
and continuo (arr from 'Ayres for the Violin', Bk
4)
D. Munrow, O. Brookes, C. Hogwood (r1973) *Concert*
(10/95) (DECC) ① **440 079-2DM**

MATTEO DA PERUGIA (d before 1418) Italy

SECTION IV: VOCAL AND CHORAL

Belle sans per
Gothic Voices, C. Page (r1994) *Concert*
(2/95) (HYPE) ① **CDA66739**
Le Greygnour bien—ballade: 3vv
P. Memelsdorff, K. Boeke, S. Fomina, C. Deslignes,
K-E. Schröder, J. Feldman, H. Rodriguez (r1993)
Concert (4/95) (ARCA) ① **A21**

MATTHESON, Johann (1681-1764) Germany

SECTION II: CHAMBER

12 Sonatas for 2 and 3 Recorders without
Continuo, (Op. 1) (1708)
EXCERPTS: 3. G minor (3 recorders).
3. F. Brüggen, J. van Wingerden, K. Boeke (r1978)
Concert (10/95) (TELD) ① **4509-97467-2**

SECTION III: INSTRUMENTAL

12 Suites—keyboard (pub 1714)
5. C minor.
5 (Air) R. Ricci, C. Fürstner (arr Burmeister: r1938)
Concert (12/91) (BIDD) ① **LAB044**
5 (Air) BBC PO, M. Bamert (r1994: orch Stokowski)
Concert (6/95) (CHAN) ① **CHAN9349**

MATTHEWS, Colin (b 1946) England

SECTION III: INSTRUMENTAL

5 Studies—piano (1974-76)
A. Goldstone *Concert*
(3/92) (GAMU) ① **GAMCD526**

SECTION IV: VOCAL AND CHORAL

Cantata on the death of Anthony (Wds.
Cassius)
M. Wiegold, Composers Ens, D. Muldowney *Concert*
(4/92) (NMC) ① **NMCD003**
Strugnell's Haiku—song (Wds. Cope)
M. Wiegold, Composers Ens, D. Muldowney *Concert*
(4/92) (NMC) ① **NMCD003**

MATTHEWS, David (b 1943) England

SECTION II: CHAMBER

Adagio—string quartet (1990)
Brodsky Qt (r1994) *Concert*
(10/94) (SILV) ① **SILKD6001**
The flaying of Marsyas—concertino: oboe
and string quartet (1986-87)
N. Daniel, Brindisi Qt (r1994) *Concert*
(2/95) (METR) ① **METCD1005**
String Quartet No. 3 (1977)
Brindisi Qt (r1994) *Concert*
(2/95) (METR) ① **METCD1005**
String Quartet No. 6 (1991)
Brindisi Qt (r1994) *Concert*
(2/95) (METR) ① **METCD1005**

SECTION III: INSTRUMENTAL

A little threnody—cor anglais (1993)
N. Daniel (r1994) *Concert*
(2/95) (METR) ① **METCD1005**

MAW, (John) Nicholas (b 1935) England

SECTION I: ORCHESTRAL

Odyssey—orchestra (1985)
CBSO, S. Rattle (pp1990)
(9/91) (EMI) ① [2] **CDS7 54277-2**

SECTION II: CHAMBER

Flute Quartet (1981)
J. Pearce, M. Rush, P. Coletti, M. Wexler (r1994)
Piano Trio. (6/95) (ASV) ① **CDDCA920**
Piano Trio (1991)
Monticello Trio (r1993) *Flute Quartet.*
(6/95) (ASV) ① **CDDCA920**

SECTION IV: VOCAL AND CHORAL

One foot in Eden still, I stand—anthem
(1990) (Wds. E. Muir)
King's College Ch, S. Cleobury (r1991) *Concert*
(6/93) (EMI) ① **CDC7 54418-2**

MAWBY, Colin (b 1936) England

SECTION IV: VOCAL AND CHORAL

Ave verum corpus—motet
Westminster Cath Ch, J. O'Donnell, I. Simcock
(r1993) *Concert* (3/94) (HYPE) ① **CDA66669**

MAXWELL DAVIES, Sir Peter (b 1934) England

SECTION I: ORCHESTRAL

Chat Moss (1993)
BBC PO, P. Maxwell Davies (r1994) *Concert*
(6/95) (COLL) ① **Coll1460-2**
Concerto for Trumpet and Orchestra (1988)
J. Wallace, SNO, P. Maxwell Davies *Symphony 4.*
(6/91) (COLL) ① **Coll1181-2**
H. Hardenberger, BBC PO, E. Howarth *Concert*
(6/91) (PHIL) ① **432 075-2PH**
Cross Lane Fair (1994)
BBC PO, P. Maxwell Davies (r1994) *Concert*
(6/95) (COLL) ① **Coll1460-2**
Jimmack the Postie—orchestra (1986)
Scottish CO, P. Maxwell Davies *Concert*
(12/88) (UNIC) ① **DKPCD9070**
5 Klee Pictures (1959/76)
Philh, P. Maxwell Davies (r1994) *Concert*
(6/95) (COLL) ① **Coll1460-2**
Ojai Festival Overture (1991)
BBC PO, P. Maxwell Davies (pp1991) *Concert*
(4/92) (COLL) ① **Coll1308-2**
An Orkney Wedding, with
Sunrise—orchestra with bagpipe solo
(1985)
G. McIlwham, Scottish CO, P. Maxwell Davies
Concert (12/88) (UNIC) ① **DKPCD9070**
Sinfonia—chamber orchestra (1962)
Scottish CO, P. Maxwell Davies *Sinfonia concertante.*
(3/90) (UNIC) ① **UKCD2026**
Sinfonia Concertante—wind quintet and
chamber orchestra (1982)
D. Nicholson, R. Miller, L. Morrison, G. Newman, R.
Cooke, T. Fry, Scottish CO, P. Maxwell Davies
Sinfonia. (3/90) (UNIC) ① **UKCD2026**
Sinfonietta Accademica—chamber orchestra
(1983)
Scottish CO, P. Maxwell Davies *Into the Labyrinth.*
(10/89) (UNIC) ① **UKCD2022**
Sir Charles his Pavan (1992) (in memory of Sir
Charles Groves)
BBC PO, P. Maxwell Davies (r1992) *Concert*
(3/94) (COLL) ① **Coll1390-2**
A Spell for Green Corn: The MacDonald
Dances—violin and orchestra (1993)
J. Clark, Scottish CO, P. Maxwell Davies (r1993)
Concert (9/94) (COLL) ① **Coll1396-2**
St Thomas Wake—foxtrot for orchestra on a
pavan by John Bull (1968)
BBC PO, P. Maxwell Davies (pp1991) *Concert*
(4/92) (COLL) ① **Coll1308-2**
Strathclyde Concerto No. 1—oboe and
orchestra (1987)
R. Miller, Scottish CO, P. Maxwell Davies *Strathclyde*
Concerto 2. (1/90) (UNIC) ① **DKPCD9085**
Strathclyde Concerto No. 2—cello and
orchestra (1988)
W. Conway, Scottish CO, P. Maxwell Davies
Strathclyde Concerto 1.
(1/90) (UNIC) ① **DKPCD9085**

Strathclyde Concerto No. 3—horn, trumpet
and orchestra (1989)
R. Cook, P. Franks, Scottish CO, P. Maxwell Davies
Strathclyde Concerto 4.
(10/92) (COLL) ① **Coll1239-2**
Strathclyde Concerto No. 4—clarinet and
orchestra (1990)
L. Morrison, Scottish CO, P. Maxwell Davies
Strathclyde Concerto 3.
(10/92) (COLL) ① **Coll1239-2**
Strathclyde Concerto No. 5—violin, viola and
string orchestra (1991)
J. Clark, C. Marwood, Scottish CO, P. Maxwell
Davies (r1993) *Strathclyde Concerto 6.*
(5/94) (COLL) ① **Coll1303-2**
Strathclyde Concerto No. 6—flute and
orchestra (1991)
D. Nicholson, Scottish CO, P. Maxwell Davies
(r1993) *Strathclyde Concerto 5.*
(5/94) (COLL) ① **Coll1303-2**
Strathclyde Concerto No. 7—double-bass
and orchestra (1992)
D. McTier, Scottish CO, P. Maxwell Davies (r1993)
Concert (9/94) (COLL) ① **Coll1396-2**
Strathclyde Concerto No. 8—bassoon and
orchestra (1993)
U. Leveaux, Scottish CO, P. Maxwell Davies (r1993)
Concert (9/94) (COLL) ① **Coll1396-2**
Symphony No. 1 (1973-74)
BBC PO, P. Maxwell Davies (r1994)
(12/95) (COLL) ① **Coll1435-2**
Symphony No. 2 in B minor (1980)
BBC PO, P. Maxwell Davies (r1993)
(9/94) (COLL) ① **Coll1403-2**
Symphony No. 3 (1984)
BBC PO, P. Maxwell Davies (r1993)
(1/95) (COLL) ① **Coll1416-2**
Symphony No. 4 (1989)
Scottish CO, P. Maxwell Davies *Trumpet Concerto.*
(6/91) (COLL) ① **Coll1181-2**
Symphony No. 5 (1994)
Philh, P. Maxwell Davies (r1994) *Concert*
(6/95) (COLL) ① **Coll1460-2**
Threnody on a Plainsong for Michael Vyner
(1989)
BBC PO, P. Maxwell Davies (pp1991) *Concert*
(4/92) (COLL) ① **Coll1308-2**
Worldes Blis—motet: orchestra (1964)
C. Mowat, RPO, P. Maxwell Davies (r1993) *Concert*
(3/94) (COLL) ① **Coll1390-2**

SECTION II: CHAMBER

Ave Maris Stella—fl, cl, va, vc, pf, marimba
(1975)
Fires of London *Concert*
(3/91) (UNIC) ① **UKCD2038**
The Bairns of Brugh—instrumental
ensemble (1981)
Fires of London, P. Maxwell Davies (r1984) *Concert*
(2/95) (UNIC) ① **UKCD2068**
Image, Reflection, Shadow—fl, cl, vn, vc, pf
and perc (1982)
Fires of London *Concert*
(3/91) (UNIC) ① **UKCD2038**
Kinloche his Fantassie—fl, cl, hpd,
glockenspiel, vn & vc (1976) (realisation of W
Kinloch's 17th cent work)
Scottish CO, P. Maxwell Davies *Concert*
(12/88) (UNIC) ① **DKPCD9070**
Renaissance Scottish Dances—six
instruments (1973)
Scottish CO, P. Maxwell Davies *Concert*
(12/88) (UNIC) ① **DKPCD9070**
Runes from a Holy Island—fl, cl, vn, vc, pf
and perc (1977)
Fires of London, P. Maxwell Davies *Concert*
(3/91) (UNIC) ① **UKCD2038**
Fires of London, P. Maxwell Davies (r1984) *Concert*
(2/95) (UNIC) ① **UKCD2068**
Sonata for Trumpet and Piano, Op. 1 (1955)
H. Hardenberger, R. Pöntinen *Concert*
(11/85) (BIS) ① **BIS-CD287**
G. Ashton, J. Lenehan (r1992) *Concert*
(4/94) (VIRG) ① **VC5 45003-2**
Vesalii icones—cello, small instrumental
ensemble and dancer (1969)
Fires of London, P. Maxwell Davies (r1970) *Concert*
(2/95) (UNIC) ① **UKCD2068**

SECTION III: INSTRUMENTAL

Farewell to Stromness—piano (1980) (piano
interlude from 'The Yellow Cake Revue')
P. Maxwell Davies *Concert*
(12/88) (UNIC) ① **DKPCD9070**

Hill Runes—guitar (1981)
J. Bream (r1981-2) *Concert*
(8/93) (RCA) ① [28] 09026 61583-2(4)
J. Bream (r1981-2) *Concert*
(9/94) (RCA) ① 09026 61597-2
Sea Eagle—horn (1982)
M. Thompson *Concert*
(9/92) (EMI) ① CDC7 54420-2
**Yesnaby Ground—piano (1980) (piano
interlude from 'The Yellow Cake Revue')**
P. Maxwell Davies *Concert*
(12/88) (UNIC) ① DKPCD9070

SECTION IV: VOCAL AND CHORAL

**Ave Rex Angelorum—4vv and organ (ad lib)
(1977)**
Elysian Sngrs, M. Greenall *Concert*
(12/91) (CNTI) ① CCD1043
**Black Pentecost—mezzo, baritone and
orchestra (1979)** (Wds. G. Mackay Brown)
D. Jones, D. Wilson-Johnson, BBC PO, P. Maxwell
Davies (r1992) *Stone Litany.*
(8/93) (COLL) ① Coll1366-2
**Into the Labyrinth—cantata: tenor and
orchestra (1983)** (Wds. G. Mackay Brown,
adapted cpsr)
N. Mackie, Scottish CO, P. Maxwell Davies
Sinfonietta Accademica.
(10/89) (UNIC) ① UKCD2022
Lullaby for Lucy—4vv a cappella (1981)
(Wds. G. Mackay Brown)
St Mary's Edinburgh Ch, P. Maxwell Davies *Concert*
(12/88) (UNIC) ① DKPCD9070
**O magnum mysterium—carol sequence (4vv,
wind qnt, perc & org) (1960)** (Wds. Latin/15th
Cent English)
The Sixteen, Margaret Phillips, The Sixteen Orch, H.
Christophers *Concert*
(12/90) (COLL) ① Coll1270-2
**Seven Songs Home—children's choir
(1981)**
St Mary's Edinburgh Ch, P. Maxwell Davies *Concert*
(12/88) (UNIC) ① DKPCD9070
**Stone Litany: Runes from a House of the
Dead—mezzo-soprano and orchestra (1973)**
(Wds. from Orkney Norn)
D. Jones, BBC PO, P. Maxwell Davies (r1992) *Black
Pentecost.* (8/93) (COLL) ① Coll1366-2
**The Turn of the Tide—children's voices and
orchestra (1972)**
Manchester Cath Ch, BBC PO, P. Maxwell Davies
(r1992) *Concert* (3/94) (COLL) ① Coll1390-2

SECTION V: STAGE WORKS

**Caroline Mathilde—concert suite from Act 1
of ballet (1991)**
1. A Public Square; 2. Inside the Castle; 3. The
Queen's Chamber; 4. The Royal Chambers.
BBC PO, P. Maxwell Davies (pp1991) *Concert*
(4/92) (COLL) ① Coll1308-2
Eight Songs for a Mad King (1969) (Wds. R Stow &
King George III)
J. Eastman, Fires of London, P. Maxwell Davies *Miss
Donnithorne's Maggot.*
(3/88) (UNIC) ① DKPCD9052
**The Lighthouse—opera: prologue, 1 act
(1980—Edinburgh)** (Lib. cpsr)
Cpte N. Mackie, C. Keyte, I. Comboy, BBC PO, P.
Maxwell Davies (pp1994)
(1/95) (COLL) ① Coll1415-2
**The Martyrdom of St Magnus—chamber
opera: 9 scenes (1977—Orkney)** (Lib. cpsr,
after George Mackay Brown)
Cpte T. Dives, C. Gillett, P. Thomson, R. Morris, K.
Thomas, Scottish Chbr Op Ens, M. Rafferty
(3/91) (UNIC) ① DKPCD9100
**Miss Donnithorne's Maggot—music theatre
work: mezzo and ensemble (1974)** (Lib. R.
Stow)
M. Thomas, Fires of London, P. Maxwell Davies
Eight Songs for a Mad King.
(3/88) (UNIC) ① DKPCD9052
**Resurrection—opera: prologue & one act
(1987—Darmstadt)** (Wds. cpsr)
Cpte D. Jones, C. Robson, M. Hill, N. Jenkins, H.
Herford, G. Finley, J. Best, BBC PO, P. Maxwell
Davies (r1994) (8/95) (COLL) ① [2] Coll7034-2
**The Two Fiddlers—children's opera: 2 acts
(1978—Kirkwall)** (Lib. cpsr, after G. Mackay
Brown)
Dances Scottish CO, P. Maxwell Davies *Concert*
(12/88) (UNIC) ① DKPCD9070

MAY, Brian (20th cent) Australia

SECTION V: STAGE WORKS

**Mad Max 2: The Road Warrior—film score
(1981)**
EXCERPTS: 1. Opening Titles; 2. Montage; 3.
Confrontation; 4. Marauder's Massacre; 5. Max
Enters Compound; 6. Feral Boy Strikes; 7. Gyro
Saves Max; 8. Gyro Flight; 9. Breakout; 10. The
Chase Continues; 11. Journey Over the Mountain;
12. Finale and Largo; 13. End Title.
11. Prague City PO, W. Motzing (r1993) *Concert*
(8/94) (SILV) ① FILMCD146
Missing in Action II—film score (1985)
EXCERPTS: 1. End Titles.
1. OST *Concert* (5/93) (SILV) ① SILVAD3001
Thirst—film score (1979)
EXCERPTS: 1. Vampire Ceremony and Initiation
Ritual.
1. OST, B. May (r1979) *Concert*
(10/93) (SILV) ① FILMCD127

MAY, Hans (1886–1958)
Germany

SECTION V: STAGE WORKS

**Ein Lied geht um die Welt—film score (Eng:
My song goes round the world)**
1. Ein Lied geht um die Welt (My song goes round the
world); 2. Frag' nicht (One life, one love).
Ein Lied geht um die Welt J. Schmidt, orch (r1933)
Concert (4/90) (EMI) ① CDM7 69478-2
Ein Lied geht um die Welt F. Wunderlich, R. Lamy
Sngrs, Graunke SO, H. Carste *Concert*
(5/93) (DG) ① 431 110-2GB
Ein Stern fällt vom Himmel—film score
EXCERPTS: 1. I'm happy when it's raining; 2. Ich
singe dir ein Liebeslied (I'll sing a song of love to
you); 3. Ein Stern fällt vom Himmel (A star falls from
heaven); 4. Wo beim Wein ein Walzer klingt.
4. J. Schmidt, orch, F. Günther (r1934) *Concert*
(4/90) (EMI) ① CDM7 69478-2

MAYERL, Billy (1902–1959)
England

SECTION I: ORCHESTRAL

**Aquarium Suite—piano and orchestra
(1927)**
1. Willow moss; 2. Moorish idol; 3. Fantail; 4.
Whirligig.
Bratislava RSO, G. Carpenter (r1992) *Concert*
(12/94) (MARC) ① 8 223514
Busybody—orchestra (1956)
Bratislava RSO, G. Carpenter (r1992) *Concert*
(12/94) (MARC) ① 8 223514
Marigold—piano and orchestra (1927) (orch
cpsr from pf work)
A. Ball, Bratislava RSO, G. Carpenter (r1992)
Concert (12/94) (MARC) ① 8 223514
Minuet by Candlelight—orchestra (1956)
Bratislava RSO, G. Carpenter (r1992) *Concert*
(12/94) (MARC) ① 8 223514
Waltz for a lonely heart—orchestra (1956)
Bratislava RSO, G. Carpenter (r1992) *Concert*
(12/94) (MARC) ① 8 223514

SECTION III: INSTRUMENTAL

April's Fool—piano (pub 1945)
E. Parkin *Concert* (6/88) (CHAN) ① CHAN8560
Aquarium Suite—piano (1937)
1. Willow Moss; 2. Moorish Idol; 3. Fantail; 4.
Whirligig.
E. Parkin *Concert* (11/90) (CHAN) ① CHAN8848
Autumn Crocus—idylle: piano (pub 1932)
E. Parkin *Concert* (11/90) (CHAN) ① CHAN8848
Bratislava RSO, G. Carpenter (r1992: orch H Finck)
Concert (12/94) (MARC) ① 8 223514
Bats in the Belfry—piano (pub 1935) (on a
theme by Austen Croom-Johnson)
E. Parkin *Concert* (11/90) (CHAN) ① CHAN8848
Bratislava RSO, G. Carpenter (r1992: orch G Wind)
Concert (12/94) (MARC) ① 8 223514
Beguine Impromptu—piano (pub 1952)
E. Parkin (r1991) *Concert*
(9/93) (CHAN) ① CHAN9141
**The Big Top—five circus sketches: piano
(pub 1948)**
1. The Ringmaster; 2. Clowning; 3. Entrance; 4.
Dancing Horse; 5. Trapeze.
E. Parkin (r1991) *Concert*
(9/93) (CHAN) ① CHAN9141

**3 Contrasts—suite: piano, Op. 24 (pub
1929)**
1. Ladybird; 2. Pastoral; 3. Fiddle Dance.
Peter Jacobs *Concert* (3/93) (PRIO) ① PRCD399
3 Dances in syncopation—piano, Op.73
1. ENglish Dance; 2. Cricket Dance; 3. Harmonica
Dance.
E. Parkin *Concert* (11/90) (CHAN) ① CHAN8848
The Errant Errand Boy—piano (pub 1954)
Peter Jacobs *Concert* (3/93) (PRIO) ① PRCD399
Evening Primrose—piano (pub 1945)
Peter Jacobs *Concert* (3/93) (PRIO) ① PRCD399
Filigree—piano (pub 1955)
E. Parkin (r1991) *Concert*
(9/93) (CHAN) ① CHAN9141
Fireside Fusiliers—piano (pub 1943)
Peter Jacobs *Concert* (3/93) (PRIO) ① PRCD399
Bratislava RSO, G. Carpenter (r1992: orch A Nichols)
Concert (12/94) (MARC) ① 8 223514
Four Aces—suite: piano (pub 1933)
1. Ace of Clubs; 2. Ace of Hearts; 3. Ace of
Diamonds; 4. Ace of Spades.
A. Ball, Bratislava RSO, G. Carpenter (r1992: orch R
Noble) *Concert* (12/94) (MARC) ① 8 223514
1, 4. E. Parkin *Concert*
(11/90) (CHAN) ① CHAN8848
2, 3. E. Parkin *Concert*
(6/88) (CHAN) ① CHAN8560
From a Spanish lattice—piano (pub 1938)
E. Parkin *Concert* (6/88) (CHAN) ① CHAN8560
Bratislava RSO, G. Carpenter (r1992: orch H Bath)
Concert (12/94) (MARC) ① 8 223514
Funny Peculiar—piano (pub 1957)
Peter Jacobs *Concert* (3/93) (PRIO) ① PRCD399
Green Tulips—piano (pub 1935) (on a theme
of Austen Croom-Johnson)
E. Parkin *Concert* (11/90) (CHAN) ① CHAN8848
The Harp of the winds—piano
E. Parkin *Concert* (6/88) (CHAN) ① CHAN8560
**Hollyhock—syncopated impression: piano
(1927)**
E. Parkin *Concert* (11/90) (CHAN) ① CHAN8848
**Honky-tonk: a rhythmical
absurdity—syncopated impression (pub
1928)**
E. Parkin (r1991) *Concert*
(9/93) (CHAN) ① CHAN9141
Hop-'O-My-Thumb—piano (1934)
E. Parkin *Concert* (11/90) (CHAN) ① CHAN8848
**In my Garden - Springtime—suite: piano
(pub 1947)**
1. Cherry Blossom; 2. Carpet of Yellow; 3. April
Showers.
Peter Jacobs *Concert* (3/93) (PRIO) ① PRCD399
**In my Garden - Wintertime—suite: piano
(pub 1946)**
1. Christmas Rose; 2. The First Snowdrop; 3.
Evergreen.
Peter Jacobs *Concert* (3/93) (PRIO) ① PRCD399
**In My Garden—Autumntime—piano (pub
1946)**
1. Misty lawn; 2. Amber leaves; 3. Hollyberry.
E. Parkin (r1991) *Concert*
(9/93) (CHAN) ① CHAN9141
**In My Garden—Summertime—piano (pub
1947)**
1. Meadowsweet; 2. Japonica; 3. Alpine Bluebell.
E. Parkin (r1991) *Concert*
(9/93) (CHAN) ① CHAN9141
4 Insect Oddities—piano (pub 1940)
1. Praying Mantis; 2. Ladybird Lullaby; 3. Wedding of
an Ant; 4. Beetle in the Bottle.
E. Parkin (r1991) *Concert*
(9/93) (CHAN) ① CHAN9141
**3 Japanese Pictures—piano, Op. 25 (pub
1930)**
1. Almond Blossom; 2. A Temple in Kyoto; 3. The
Cherry Dance.
1. E. Parkin *Concert* (6/88) (CHAN) ① CHAN8560
2, 3. E. Parkin (r1991) *Concert*
(9/93) (CHAN) ① CHAN9141
Jill all alone—piano (1955) (?transcription)
E. Parkin *Concert* (11/90) (CHAN) ① CHAN8848
The Joker—piano (1934) (a further
contribution to 'Four Aces')
E. Parkin *Concert* (6/88) (CHAN) ① CHAN8560
The Legends of King Arthur—piano (1929)
1. Prelude; 2. Merlin the Wizard; 3. The Sword
Excalibur; 4. Lady of the Lake; 5. Guinevere; 6. The
Passing of Arthur.
1, 2, 4, 6. E. Parkin *Concert*
(6/88) (CHAN) ① CHAN8560
3, 5. E. Parkin (r1991) *Concert*
(9/93) (CHAN) ① CHAN9141

Leprechaun's Leap—piano (pub 1940)
E. Parkin (r1991) *Concert*
       (9/93) (CHAN) ① **CHAN9141**
A Lily Pond—piano (pub 1929)
Bratislava RSO, G. Carpenter (r1992: orch F
Adlington) *Concert*   (12/94) (MARC) ① **8 223514**
Marigold—syncopated impression: piano,
  Op. 78 (pub 1927)
E. Parkin *Concert*   (6/88) (CHAN) ① **CHAN8560**
Mignonette—syncopated impression: piano
  (pub 1931)
Peter Jacobs *Concert*   (3/93) (PRIO) ① **PRCD399**
3 Miniatures in syncopation—piano, Op. 76
  (pub 1928)
1. Cobweb; 2. Muffin man; 3. Clockwork.
E. Parkin (r1991) *Concert*
       (9/93) (CHAN) ① **CHAN9141**
Mistletoe—piano (pub 1935)
E. Parkin *Concert*   (11/90) (CHAN) ① **CHAN8848**
Nimble-Fingered Gentleman—piano (pub
  1934)
E. Parkin *Concert*   (6/88) (CHAN) ① **CHAN8560**
The Parade of the Sandwich-Board
  Men—piano (pub 1938)
E. Parkin *Concert*   (11/90) (CHAN) ① **CHAN8848**
Bratislava RSO, G. Carpenter (r1992: orch G
Windeatt) *Concert*   (12/94) (MARC) ① **8 223514**
Pastoral Sketches—piano
1. A legend; 2. Lover's lane; 3. A village festival.
Bratislava RSO, G. Carpenter (r1992: orch A Wood)
Concert   (12/94) (MARC) ① **8 223514**
Penny Whistle—a novelette: piano (pub
  1932)
Peter Jacobs *Concert*   (3/93) (PRIO) ① **PRCD399**
Piano Exaggerations—piano (pub 1926)
1. Antiquary; 2. Loose Elbows; 3. Jack-in; 4. Sleepy
Piano.
4. Peter Jacobs *Concert*
       (3/93) (PRIO) ① **PRCD399**
Piano Transcriptions—songs by other
  composers (originally published in the Mayerl
  School Magazine)
1. At the Balalaika (G Posford); 2. Body and Soul (J
W Green); 3. Deep Henderson (F Rose); 4. The Girl
with the Dreamy eyes (Carr/Pola); 5. Limehouse
Blues (P Braham); 6. Peg o'my heart (F Fisher); 7.
Phil the Fluter's Ball (P French); 8. Please believe me
(A Jacob); 9. Smoke gets in your eyes (J Kern); 10.
Tormented; 11. Sing, you sinners (Harling & Coslow);
12. Any time's the time to fall in love (Janis, King &
Coslow); 13. Balloons (Magine); 14. The match
parade (Wehle); 15. Did you ever see a dream
walking? (Gordon/Revel); 16. Thanks
(Johnston/Coslow); 17. Love locked out
(Noble/Kester); 18. On the other side of Lovers' Lane
(Miller/Gibbons); 19. I cover the waterfront
(Heyman/Green); 20. Weep no more my baby
(Heyman/Green); 21. We belong together
(Kern/Hammerstein II); 22. Close your eyes
(Petkere); 23. Masquerading in the name of love
(Sigler/Goodhart/Hoffman); 24. Two cigarettes in the
dark (Webster/Pollack); 25. Oceans of time
(Heyman/Green); 26. April in Paris (Duke/Harburg);
27. Arlene (Seymour/Pollack); 28. Love thy neighbour
(Gordon/Revel); 29. Say it (Schwartz/Adlam); 30.
Other people's babies (Ellis/Herbert); 31. June in
January (Robin/Rainger); 32. The Continental
(Magidson/Conrad); 33. With my eyes wide open I'm
dreaming (Gordon/Revel); 34. Chasing shadows
(Davis/Silver); 35. Cheek to cheek (Berlin); 36. You
hit the spot (Gordon/Revel); 37. Anything goes
(Porter); 38. I feel like a feather in the breeze
(Gordon/Revel); 39. Love me forever
(Schertzinger/Kahn); 40. Please believe me
(Jacobs/Yoell); 41. Ev'rything's been done before
(Adamson/Knopf/King); 42. Without a word of
warning (Gordon/Revel); 43. Fatal fascination
(Thompson/Gensler); 44. Will I ever know?
(Gordon/Revel); 45. A penny in my pocket
(Robin/Rainger); 46. I'm in a dancing mood
(Sigler/Goodhart/Hoffman); 47. Without rhythm
(Sigler/Goodhart/Hoffman); 48. My first thrill
(sigler/Goodhart/Hoffman); 49. Lambeth Walk
(Gay/Furber); 50. Everything's in rhythm with my
heart (Sigler/Goodhart/Hoffman); 51. Ten cents a
dance (Hart/Rodgers); 52. Baby's birthday party
(Ronell).
1, 5, 9, 36-50. E. Parkin (r1993) *Piano Transcriptions
III.*   (5/95) (PRIO) ① **PRCD467**
4, 13, 15-35. E. Parkin (r1993) *Piano Transcriptions
III.*   (1/95) (PRIO) ① **PRCD466**
7. E. Parkin (r1993) *Concert*
       (7/95) (PRIO) ① **PRCD468**

Piano Transcriptions—Mayerl's own
  compositions
EXCERPTS: 1. Imaginary Foxtrot; 2. I breathe on
windows (from Over She Goes); 3. Turn on the taps
(from Over She Goes); 4. The dance goes on (from
Over She Goes); 5. Stranger in a cup of tea (from
Crazy Days); 6. You're not too bad yourself (from
Crazy Days); 7. There's a star in the sky; 8. Like a cat
with a mouse (from Runaway Love).
1. E. Parkin (r1993) *Piano Transcriptions.*
       (1/95) (PRIO) ① **PRCD466**
2-7. E. Parkin (r1993) *Piano Transcriptions.*
       (5/95) (PRIO) ① **PRCD467**
7. E. Parkin (r1993) *Concert*
       (7/95) (PRIO) ① **PRCD468**
8. E. Parkin (r1993) *Concert*
       (7/95) (PRIO) ① **PRCD468**
Postman's knock—piano (pub 1941)
Peter Jacobs *Concert*   (3/93) (PRIO) ① **PRCD399**
Railroad rhythm—piano (pub 1938)
E. Parkin *Concert*   (6/88) (CHAN) ① **CHAN8560**
Robots—syncopated impression: piano (pub
  1928)
Peter Jacobs *Concert*   (3/93) (PRIO) ① **PRCD399**
Romanesque—piano (pub 1947)
E. Parkin (r1991) *Concert*
       (9/93) (CHAN) ① **CHAN9141**
Scallywag—syncopated impression: piano
  (pub 1931)
Peter Jacobs *Concert*   (3/93) (PRIO) ① **PRCD399**
Shallow waters—piano
E. Parkin *Concert*   (6/88) (CHAN) ① **CHAN8560**
Siberian lament—piano (pub 1934)
E. Parkin (r1991) *Concert*
       (9/93) (CHAN) ① **CHAN9141**
Song of the Fir-Tree—a Swedish impression:
  piano (pub 1938)
E. Parkin *Concert*   (6/88) (CHAN) ① **CHAN8560**
Sweet William—piano (pub 1938)
E. Parkin *Concert*   (11/90) (CHAN) ① **CHAN8848**
3 Syncopated Rambles—piano (pub 1933)
1. The Junior Apprentice (Intermezzo); 2. The
Printer's Devil (Theme and Transcription); 3. 6
am—The Milkman (Scherzo).
Peter Jacobs *Concert*   (3/93) (PRIO) ① **PRCD399**
Weeping Willow—an idylle: piano (pub
  1932)
Peter Jacobs *Concert*   (3/93) (PRIO) ① **PRCD399**
White heather—piano (1932)
E. Parkin *Concert*   (11/90) (CHAN) ① **CHAN8848**

MAYNARD, John *(1577–after 1614) England*

SECTION IV: VOCAL AND CHORAL

12 Wonders of the World—satirical songs
  (pub 1611)
1. The Batchelar: How many things?; 2. The Maide: I
marriage would forsweare.
1, 2. C. Bott, M. George, New London Consort, P.
Pickett (r1992) *Concert*   (4/94) (LINN) ① **CKD011**

MAYONE, Ascanio *(c1565–1627) Italy*

SECTION III: INSTRUMENTAL

Primo libro di diversi capricci per
  sonare—keyboard (pub 1603)
TOCCATAS: 1a. Prima; 1b. Second; 1c. Terza; 1d.
Quarta le Quinta. RICERCARS: 2a. Primo; 2b.
Secondo; 2c. Terzo; 2d. Quarto. CANZON
FRANCESE: 3a. Prima; 3b. Seconda; 3c. Terza.
PARTITE: 4a. sopra 'Rogiere'; 4b. sopra 'Fidele'; 5.
Madrigale passaggiato: 'Ancidetemi pur'.
4b R. Alessandrini (r1994) *Concert*
       (9/95) (O111) ① **OPS30-118**
Toccata prima—harp/lute
A. Lawrence-King *Concert*
       (9/87) (HYPE) ① **CDA66229**

MAYOR, Simon *(20th Cent) England*

SECTION II: CHAMBER

The Buttermere Waltz—mandolin
  ensemble
S. Mayor, H. James *Concert*
       (3/92) (ACOU) ① **CDACS014**
Dead Sea Dances—mandolin ensemble
S. Mayor, H. James *Concert*
       (3/92) (ACOU) ① **CDACS014**
The Exchange—mandolin ensemble
S. Mayor *Concert*   (3/92) (ACOU) ① **CDACS012**

The Great Bear—mandolin ensemble
S. Mayor *Concert*   (3/92) (ACOU) ① **CDACS014**
The Hoppings—jig: mandolin ensemble
S. Mayor *Concert*   (3/92) (ACOU) ① **CDACS014**
Jericho Waltz—mandolin ensemble
S. Mayor, H. James *Concert*
       (3/92) (ACOU) ① **CDACS012**
Jump the Gun/Reelin' over the
  rooftops—reels: mandolin ensemble
S. Mayor, H. James *Concert*
       (3/92) (ACOU) ① **CDACS012**
Maple Flames—mandolin ensemble
S. Mayor, H. James *Concert*
       (3/92) (ACOU) ① **CDACS012**
The Mosstrooper Medley—mandolin
  ensemble
1. Jig; 2. March; 3. Reel.
S. Mayor *Concert*   (3/92) (ACOU) ① **CDACS014**
The Old Man of the Mountains—mandolin
  ensemble
S. Mayor, H. James, S. Price *Concert*
       (3/92) (ACOU) ① **CDACS014**
Pipped at the Post—mandolin ensemble
S. Mayor, H. James *Concert*
       (3/92) (ACOU) ① **CDACS012**
Tune for a Mop Fair—mandolin ensemble
S. Mayor, H. James *Concert*
       (3/92) (ACOU) ① **CDACS012**
Two Days in Tuscany—mandolin ensemble
S. Mayor, H. James, A. Whetton *Concert*
       (3/92) (ACOU) ① **CDACS014**
Two Seagulls call from my birch
  tree—mandoline ensemble
S. Mayor *Concert*   (3/92) (ACOU) ① **CDACS012**
Wheelin' and Dealin'—mandolin ensemble
S. Mayor, H. James *Concert*
       (3/92) (ACOU) ① **CDACS012**

SECTION IV: VOCAL AND CHORAL

When Summer comes again—song:
  mandoline ensemble (comp in collaboration
  with H. James)
S. Mayor, H. James, H. James *Concert*
       (3/92) (ACOU) ① **CDACS012**

MAYR, Rupert Ignaz *(1646–1712) Germany*

SECTION IV: VOCAL AND CHORAL

Dominus regnavit—motet
Niederaltaicher Scholaren, K. Ruhland (r1992)
Concert   (10/93) (SONY) ① **SK53117**

MAYR, (Johannes) Simon *(1763–1845) Germany*

also known as Giovanni Simone Mayr

SECTION V: STAGE WORKS

Alfredo il Grande—opera: 2 acts
  (1818—Rome) (Lib. Morelli, after Rossi)
Ov'2 la bella vergine? D. Montague, K. John, M.
Moreno, R. Smythe, Philh, D. Parry *Concert*
       (10/90) (OPRA) ① **[3] ORCH103**
Cora—opera: 2 acts (1815—Naples) (Lib.
  Salfa-Benco)
Sempre uniti insiem saremo Y. Kenny, P. Doghan,
K. John, R. Leggate, R. Smythe, Philh, D. Parry
Concert   (10/90) (OPRA) ① **[3] ORCH103**
Elena (e Costantino)—opera: 2 acts
  (1814—Naples) (Lib. Tottola)
Ah! se mirar potessi R. Smythe, Philh, D. Parry
Concert   (10/90) (OPRA) ① **[3] ORCH103**
Fedra—opera: 2 acts (1820—Milan) (Lib.
  Romanelli)
Se fiero, Ippolito P. Walker, Philh, D. Parry *Concert*
       (9/95) (OPRA) ① **[3] ORCH104**
Medea in Corinto—opera: 2 acts
  (1813—Naples) (Lib. Romani)
Cpte J. Eaglen, Y. Kenny, B. Ford, R. Giménez, A.
Miles, A. Mason, P. Nilon, N. Archer, G. Mitchell Ch,
Philh, D. Parry (r1993)
       (11/94) (OPRA) ① **[3] ORC011**
Amiche cingete; Caro albergo Y. Kenny, G.
Mitchell Ch, S. Drake, Philh, D. Parry *Concert*
       (10/90) (OPRA) ① **[3] ORCH103**
La Rosa bianca e la rosa rossa—opera: 2
  acts (1813—Genoa) (Lib. Romani)
Cpte S. Anselmi, D. Serraiocco, A. C. Antonacci, L.
Canonici, S. Mazzoni, E. Facini, Milan Academia
Chor, Bergamo House Orch, T. Briccetti (pp1990)
       (12/94) (FONI) ① **[2] RFCD2007**

Dov'è la destra? infida! Y. Kenny, P. Walker, P.
Doghan, Philh, D. Parry *Concert*
(10/90) (OPRA) ① [3] **ORCH103**

MAYUZUMI, Toshiro (b 1929)
Japan

SECTION II: CHAMBER

Prelude—string quartet (1961)
LaSalle Qt *Concert* (8/88) (DG) ① **423 245-2GC**

MAZÁK, Alberich (1609–1661)
Czechoslovakia

SECTION IV: VOCAL AND CHORAL

Magnificat anima mea Dominum—motet
Niederaltaicher Scholaren, K. Ruhland (r1992)
Concert (10/93) (SONY) ① **SK53117**

MAZZOCCHI, Domenico
(1592–1665) Italy

SECTION IV: VOCAL AND CHORAL

**Nasceris, alme puer—motet: 2vv and
continuo (pub 1638)**
Gabrieli Consort, Gabrieli Players, P. McCreesh, T.
Roberts (r1992-3) *Concert*
(1/94) (ARCH) ① **437 833-2AH**

MEDINS, Janis (1890–1968)
Russia/Latvia

SECTION I: ORCHESTRAL

Symphonic Suite No. 1
Aria Detroit SO, N. Järvi (r1993) *Concert*
(8/94) (CHAN) ① **CHAN9227**

MEDTNER, Nikolay Karlovich
(1880–1951) Russia

SECTION I: ORCHESTRAL

**Concerto for Piano and Orchestra No. 1 in C
minor, Op. 33 (c1914-18)**
G. Tozer, LPO, N. Järvi *Concert*
(4/92) (CHAN) ① [2] **CHAN9040**
G. Tozer, LPO, N. Järvi *Sonata-Ballada, Op. 27.*
(4/92) (CHAN) ① **CHAN9039**
G.D. Madge, Rubinstein PO, I. Stupel *Piano Sonata,
Op. 22.* (11/92) (DANA) ① **DACOCD401**
I. Zhukov, USSR TV & Rad Orch, A. Dmitriev (r1973)
Concert (2/94) (MEZH) ① **MK417087**
D. Alexeev, BBC SO, A. Lazarev (r1994) *Piano
Quintet.* (3/95) (HYPE) ① **CDA66744**
**Concerto for Piano and Orchestra No. 2 in C
minor, Op. 50 (c1920-27)**
N. Demidenko, BBC Scottish SO, J. Maksymiuk
Piano Concerto 3. (4/92) (HYPE) ① **CDA66580**
G. Tozer, LPO, N. Järvi *Concert*
(4/92) (CHAN) ① [2] **CHAN9040**
G. Tozer, LPO, N. Järvi *Piano Concerto 3.*
(4/92) (CHAN) ① **CHAN9038**
G.D. Madge, Rubinstein PO, I. Stupel *Forgotten
Melodies, Op. 39.* (11/92) (DANA) ① **DACOCD402**
N. Medtner, Philh, I. Dobrowen (r1947) *Concert*
(4/94) (TEST) ① **SBT1027**
**Concerto for Piano and Orchestra No. 3 in E
minor, Op. 60 (c1940-43)**
N. Demidenko, BBC Scottish SO, J. Maksymiuk
Piano Concerto 2. (4/92) (HYPE) ① **CDA66580**
G. Tozer, LPO, N. Järvi *Piano Concerto 2.*
(4/92) (CHAN) ① **CHAN9038**
G. Tozer, LPO, N. Järvi *Concert*
(4/92) (CHAN) ① [2] **CHAN9040**
G.D. Madge, Rubinstein PO, I. Stupel *Forgotten
Melodies, Op. 38.* (11/92) (DANA) ① **DACOCD403**
M. Ponti, Luxembourg RSO, P. Cao *Concert*
(5/93) (VOX) ① **115714-2**
N. Medtner, Philh, I. Dobrowen (r1947) *Concert*
(4/94) (TEST) ① **SBT1027**

SECTION II: CHAMBER

**Canzonas and Danzas—violin and piano, Op.
43 (1924)**
1. Canzona No. 1 in C; 2. Danza No. 1 in C; 3.
Canzona No. 2 in B minor; 4. Danza No. 2 in B minor.
A. Shirinsky, D. Galynin (r1992) *Concert*
(11/93) (MEZH) ① [2] **MK417109**
M. Parikian, H. Milne (bp1987) *Concert*
(12/95) (CRD) ① [2] **CRD3493/4**
Knight Errant—two pianos, Op. 58/2 (1940)
D. Alexeev, N. Demidenko (r1993) *Concert*
(10/94) (HYPE) ① **CDA66654**

**3 Nocturnes—violin and piano, Op. 16
(1908)**
1. D minor; 2. G minor; 3. C minor.
A. Shirinsky, D. Galynin (r1992) *Concert*
(11/93) (MEZH) ① [2] **MK417109**
M. Parikian, H. Milne (bp1987) *Concert*
(12/95) (CRD) ① [2] **CRD3493/4**
**Quintet for Piano and Strings in C, Op. posth
(1904-49)**
D. Alexeev, New Budapest Qt (r1994) *Piano
Concerto 1.* (3/95) (HYPE) ① **CDA66744**
**Russian Round Dance (A Tale)—two pianos,
Op. 58/1 (c1940)**
N. Medtner, B. Moiseiwitsch (r1946) *Concert*
(10/93) (EMI) ① **CDC7 54839-2**
D. Alexeev, N. Demidenko (r1993) *Concert*
(10/94) (HYPE) ① **CDA66654**
**Sonata for Violin and Piano No. 1 in B minor,
Op. 21 (1909-10)**
A. Shirinsky, D. Galynin (r1992) *Concert*
(11/93) (MEZH) ① [2] **MK417109**
L. Mordkovitch, G. Tozer *Violin Sonata 2.*
(11/94) (CHAN) ① **CHAN9293**
M. Parikian, H. Milne (bp1986) *Concert*
(12/95) (CRD) ① [2] **CRD3493/4**
**Sonata for Violin and Piano No. 2 in G, Op.
44 (1926)**
A. Shirinsky, D. Galynin (r1992) *Concert*
(11/93) (MEZH) ① [2] **MK417109**
L. Mordkovitch, G. Tozer *Violin Sonata 1.*
(11/94) (CHAN) ① **CHAN9293**
M. Parikian, H. Milne (bp1985) *Concert*
(12/95) (CRD) ① [2] **CRD3493/4**
**Sonata for Violin and Piano No. 3 in E minor,
'Epica', Op. 57 (1938)**
A. Shirinsky, D. Galynin (r1992) *Concert*
(11/93) (MEZH) ① [2] **MK417109**
M. Parikian, H. Milne (bp1986) *Concert*
(12/95) (CRD) ① [2] **CRD3493/4**

SECTION III: INSTRUMENTAL

3 Arabesques—piano, Op. 7 (?1904)
1. Ein Idyll; 2. Tragoedie-Fragment in A minor; 3.
Tragoedie-Fragment in G minor.
2. N. Medtner (r1947) *Concert*
(4/94) (TEST) ① **SBT1027**
3 Dithyrambs—piano, Op. 10 (1898-1906)
1. D; 2. E flat; 3. E.
2. N. Demidenko (r1992) *Concert*
(9/93) (HYPE) ① **CDA66636**
Fairy Tale in D minor—piano (1915)
G. Tozer *Concert* (11/92) (CHAN) ① **CHAN9050**
2 Fairy Tales—piano, Op. 8 (1905)
EXCERPTS: 2. No 2.
H. Milne *Concert* (3/90) (CRD) ① **CRD3460**
2 Fairy Tales—piano, Op. 20 (1909)
1. B flat minor; 2. B minor.
N. Medtner (r1936) *Concert*
(10/93) (EMI) ① **CDC7 54839-2**
E. Petri (pp1958) *Concert*
(3/94) (MUSI) ① [4] **MACD-772**
1. N. Demidenko (r1992) *Concert*
(9/93) (HYPE) ① **CDA66636**
1. J. Heifetz, E. Bay (r1946) *Concert*
(11/94) (RCA) ① [65] **09026 61778-2(06)**
4 Fairy Tales—piano, Op. 26 (?1912)
1. E flat; 2. E flat; 3. F minor; 4. F sharp minor.
2. G. Tozer *Concert* (11/92) (CHAN) ① **CHAN9050**
3. N. Medtner (r1947) *Concert*
(4/94) (TEST) ① **SBT1027**
4. K. Lifschitz (r1990) *Concert*
(12/94) (DENO) ① **CO-78907**
4 Fairy Tales—piano, Op. 34 (?1916-17)
1. B minor; 2. E minor; 3. A minor; 4. D minor.
2. B. Moiseiwitsch (r1928) *Concert*
(10/91) (KOCH) ① **37035-2**
2. G. Tozer *Concert* (11/92) (CHAN) ① **CHAN9050**
3. K. Lifschitz (r1990) *Concert*
(12/94) (DENO) ① **CO-78907**
3 Fairy Tales—piano, Op. 42 (?1921-23)
1. F minor; 2. C minor; 3. G sharp minor.
1. G. Tozer *Concert* (11/92) (CHAN) ① **CHAN9050**
2 Fairy Tales—piano, Op. 48 (?1926)
1. C; 2. G minor.
1. G. Tozer *Concert* (11/92) (CHAN) ① **CHAN9050**
6 Fairy Tales—piano, Op. 51 (?1928)
1. D minor; 2. A minor; 3. A; 4. F sharp minor; 5. F
sharp minor; 6. G.
1. G. Tozer *Concert* (11/92) (CHAN) ① **CHAN9050**
1. N. Medtner (r1947) *Concert*
(10/93) (EMI) ① **CDC7 54839-2**
2, 3. N. Medtner (r1936) *Concert*
(10/93) (EMI) ① **CDC7 54839-2**
3. V. Horowitz (r1969) *Concert*
(11/92) (SONY) ① **SK48093**

---

3. V. Horowitz (r1969) *Concert*
(7/94) (SONY) ① **SK53472**
**Forgotten Melodies, Set I—piano, Op. 38
(?1918-20)**
1. Sonata reminiscenza; 2. Danza graziosoa; 3.
Danza festiva; 4. Canzona fluviale; 5. Danza rustica;
6. Canzona serenata; 7. Danza silvestra, alla
Reminscenza.
1. A. Fellegi *Concert* (4/92) (MARC) ① **8 223372**
1. G.D. Madge *Piano Concerto 3.*
(11/92) (DANA) ① **DACOCD403**
1. G. Tozer *Concert* (11/92) (CHAN) ① **CHAN9050**
1. Emil Gilels (pp1968) *Concert*
(4/93) (MEZH) ① **MK417072**
1, 6. N. Demidenko (r1992) *Concert*
(9/93) (HYPE) ① **CDA66636**
3. N. Medtner (r1936) *Concert*
(10/93) (EMI) ① **CDC7 54839-2**
3. E. Petri (pp1958) *Concert*
(3/94) (MUSI) ① [4] **MACD-772**
3. M-A. Hamelin (pp1994) *Concert*
(3/95) (HYPE) ① **CDA66765**
3, 6. L. Zilberstein (r1992) *Concert*
(8/94) (DG) ① **437 805-2GH**
**Forgotten Melodies, Set II—piano, Op. 39
(?1918-20)**
1. Meditazione; 2. Romanza; 3. Primavera; 4.
Canzona matinata; 5. Sonata tragica.
E. Wild *Concert* (9/91) (CHES) ① **Chesky AD1**
4, 5. N. Demidenko (r1992) *Concert*
(9/93) (HYPE) ① **CDA66636**
4, 5. L. Zilberstein (r1992) *Concert*
(8/94) (DG) ① **437 805-2GH**
5. A. Fellegi *Concert* (4/92) (MARC) ① **8 223372**
5. G.D. Madge *Piano Concerto 2.*
(11/92) (DANA) ① **DACOCD402**
3 Morceaux—piano, Op. 31 (?1914-15)
1. Improvisation; 2. Funeral March; 3. Fairy Tale.
2, 3. G. Tozer *Concert*
(11/92) (CHAN) ① **CHAN9050**
3. K. Lifschitz (r1990) *Concert*
(12/94) (DENO) ① **CO-78907**
3 Novelles—piano, Op. 17 (1908)
1. G; 2. C minor; 3. E.
H. Milne *Concert* (3/90) (CRD) ① **CRD3460**
2. A. Goldenweiser (r1955) *Concert*
(8/95) (MELO) ① **74321 25173-2**
2. A. Goldenweiser (r1955) *Concert*
(8/95) (MELO) ① [11] **74321 25172-2(1)**
**Piano Sonata in E minor, '(The) Night Wind',
Op. 25/2 (1911)**
A. Fellegi *Concert* (5/92) (MARC) ① **8 223371**
**Romantic sketches for the Young—piano,
Op. 54 (?1932)**
BOOK 1: 1a. Prélude (Pastorale); 1b. Bird's Tale.
BOOK 2: 2a. Prélude (Tempo di Sarabande); 2b.
Tale. BOOK 3: 3a. Prélude (Tender Reproach); 3b.
The Barrel-organ player. BOOK 4: 4a. Prélude; 4b.
The Beggar.
1a, 1b, 4a, 4b H. Milne *Concert*
(3/90) (CRD) ① **CRD3460**
3b G. Tozer *Concert*
(11/92) (CHAN) ① **CHAN9050**
**Second Improvisation (in variation
form)—piano, Op. 47 (1926)**
H. Milne *Piano Sonata, Op.47.*
(3/90) (CRD) ① **CRD3461**
E. Wild *Concert* (9/91) (CHES) ① **Chesky AD1**
**Sonata for Piano in A minor, Op. 30 (?1914-
15)**
H. Milne *Concert* (3/90) (CRD) ① **CRD3460**
**Sonata for Piano in C minor, 'Sonata-
Skazka', Op. 25/1 (1910-11)**
A. Fellegi *Concert* (5/92) (MARC) ① **8 223371**
**Sonata for Piano in F minor, Op. 5 (1896-
1903)**
H. Milne *Improvisation, Op.47.*
(3/90) (CRD) ① **CRD3461**
**Sonata for Piano in G minor, Op. 22 (?1919-
20)**
H. Milne *Concert* (3/90) (CRD) ① **CRD3460**
A. Fellegi *Concert* (5/92) (MARC) ① **8 223371**
G.D. Madge *Piano Concerto 1.*
(11/92) (DANA) ① **DACOCD401**
G. Tozer *Concert* (11/92) (CHAN) ① **CHAN9050**
Sonata Triad—piano, Op. 11 (1904-08)
1. A flat; 2. D minor; Elegy; 3. C.
2. N. Demidenko (r1992) *Concert*
(9/93) (HYPE) ① **CDA66636**
**Sonata-Ballada in F sharp—piano, Op. 27
(?1912-14)**
A. Fellegi *Concert* (4/92) (MARC) ① **8 223372**
G. Tozer *Concert* (4/92) (CHAN) ① [2] **CHAN9040**
G. Tozer *Piano Concerto 1.*
(4/92) (CHAN) ① **CHAN9039**

Sonate-Idylle in G—piano, Op. 56 (?1937)
E. Wild *Concert*　　　(9/91) (CHES) ① **Chesky AD1**
A. Fellegi *Concert*　　(4/92) (MARC) ① **8 223372**
Theme and Variations in C sharp
minor—piano, Op. 55 (c1933)
N. Demidenko (r1992) *Concert*
　　　　　　　　　(9/93) (HYPE) ① **CDA66636**

SECTION IV: VOCAL AND CHORAL

Angel—song: 1v and piano, Op. 1a (?1908)
(Wds. Lermontov)
L. Andrew, G. Tozer (r1993) *Concert*
　　　　　　　　　(12/95) (CHAN) ① **CHAN9327**
Noon—song: 1v and piano, Op. 59/1 (1946)
(Wds. Tyutchev)
L. Andrew, G. Tozer (r1993) *Concert*
　　　　　　　　　(12/95) (CHAN) ① **CHAN9327**
9 Songs—1v and piano, Op. 6 (1904-05)
(Wds. J. W. Goethe)
1. Wandrers Nachtlied; 2. Mailied; 3. Elfenliedchen;
4. Im Vorübergehn; 5. Aus 'Claudine von Villa-Bella';
6. Aus 'Erwin und Elmire' I; 7. Aus 'Erwin und Elmire'
II; 8. Erster Verlust; 9. Gefunden.
3, 4. E. Schwarzkopf. N. Medtner (1950: Ger)
Concert　　(10/93) (EMI) ① **CDC7 54839-2**
2 Songs—1v and piano, Op. 13 (1903-07)
1. Winterabend (wds. Pushkin); 2. Das Epitaph (wds.
Belïy).
1. T. Makushina, N. Medtner (r1947) *Concert*
　　　　　　　　　(10/93) (EMI) ① **CDC7 54839-2**
1. L. Andrew, G. Tozer (r1993) *Concert*
　　　　　　　　　(12/95) (CHAN) ① **CHAN9327**
12 Songs—1v and piano, Op. 15 (1907-08)
(Wds. J. W. Goethe)
1. Wandrers Nachtlied I; 2. An die Türen will ich; 3.
Selbstbetrug; 4. Aus 'Erwin und Elmire'; 5. Aus 'Lila';
6. Vor Gericht; 7. Meeresstille; 8. Glückliche Fahrt; 9.
Nähe des Geliebten; 10. Der untreue Knabe; 11.
Gleich und Gleich; 12. Geistergruss.
3, 5, 7, 8. E. Schwarzkopf. N. Medtner (1950: Ger)
Concert　　(10/93) (EMI) ① **CDC7 54839-2**
6 Songs—1v and piano, Op. 18 (1908-09)
(Wds. J. W. Goethe)
1. Die Sprode; 2. Die Bekehrte; 3. Einsamkeit; 4.
Mignon; 5. Das Veilchen; 6. Jägers Abendlied.
3. E. Schwarzkopf. N. Medtner (1950: Ger) *Concert*
　　　　　　　　　(10/93) (EMI) ① **CDC7 54839-2**
8 Songs—1v and piano, Op. 24 (1911)
1. Day and night; 2. Willow, why forever bending?
(wds. Tyuchev); 3. Sea-swell and memories; 4.
Twilight; 5. O'er thee I bend; 6. When my glances thy
smile chance to meet; 7. Whis'pring, Nature faintly
stirring (wds. Fet; 8. Greeting.
L. Andrew, G. Tozer (r1993) *Concert*
　　　　　　　　　(12/95) (CHAN) ① **CHAN9327**
2, 7. O. Slobodskaya, N. Medtner (r1947) *Concert*
　　　　　　　　　(10/93) (EMI) ① **CDC7 54839-2**
7 Songs—1v and piano, Op. 28 (1913-14)
1. Der ungehnte Regen (wds. Fet); 2. Jedes Mal hör'
ich dies Vöglein singen, 'Serenade' (wds. Fet); 3. Der
Schmetterling (wds. Fet); 4. Auf dem Kirchhof, da es
öd (wds. Bryusov); 5. Die Frühlingsberuhigung (wds.
Tyutchev, after Uhland); 6. Ich sitz' si einsam am
-Kamin (Wds. Tyutchev); 7. Gott, sende jedem seine
Labe (wds. Tyutchev).
2. O. Slobodskaya, N. Medtner (r1947) *Concert*
　　　　　　　　　(10/93) (EMI) ① **CDC7 54839-2**
2, 3, 4, 5. L. Andrew, G. Tozer (r1993) *Concert*
　　　　　　　　　(12/95) (CHAN) ① **CHAN9327**
7 Songs—1v and piano, Op. 29 (1913) (Wds.
Pushkin)
1. The muse; 2. The singer; 3. Lines written during a
sleepless night; 4. The horse; 5. Gone are my heart's
desires; 6. The rose; 7. The call.
1, 6. E. Schwarzkopf. N. Medtner (1950: Eng)
Concert　　(10/93) (EMI) ① **CDC7 54839-2**
6. L. Andrew, G. Tozer (r1993) *Concert*
　　　　　　　　　(12/95) (CHAN) ① **CHAN9327**
6 Songs—1v and piano, Op. 32 (1915) (Wds.
Pushkin)
1. Echo; 2. Remembrance; 3. Funeral song; 4. I loved
thee well; 5. The waltz; 6. To a dreamer.
4. L. Andrew, G. Tozer (r1993) *Concert*
　　　　　　　　　(12/95) (CHAN) ① **CHAN9327**
5. E. Schwarzkopf. N. Medtner (1950: Eng) *Concert*
　　　　　　　　　(10/93) (EMI) ① **CDC7 54839-2**
6. O. Slobodskaya, N. Medtner (r1947) *Concert*
　　　　　　　　　(10/93) (EMI) ① **CDC7 54839-2**
6 Songs—1v and piano, Op. 36 (Wds.
Pushkin)
1. Der Engel; 2. Die Blume; 3. Kaum welken hier die
Rosen; 4. Spanische Romanze; 5. Nachts; 6. Arion.
3. E. Schwarzkopf. N. Medtner (1950: Eng) *Concert*
　　　　　　　　　(10/93) (EMI) ① **CDC7 54839-2**
5. L. Andrew, G. Tozer (r1993) *Concert*
　　　　　　　　　(12/95) (CHAN) ① **CHAN9327**

5 Songs—1v and piano, Op. 37 (Wds.
Pushkin)
1. Schlaflosigkeit; 2. Tränen; 3. Waltz; 4. Waltz; 5.
Was heulst du, Wind, um Mitternacht?.
1. L. Andrew, G. Tozer (r1993) *Concert*
　　　　　　　　　(12/95) (CHAN) ① **CHAN9327**
4 Songs—1v and piano, Op. 45 (1923-24)
1. Elégie (wds. Pushkin); 2. Der Karren des Lebens
(wds. Pushkin); 3. Das Nachtlied (wds. Tyutchev); 4.
Unsere Zeit (wds. Tyutchev).
2. O. Slobodskaya, N. Medtner (r1947) *Concert*
　　　　　　　　　(10/93) (EMI) ① **CDC7 54839-2**
7 Songs—1v and piano, Op. 46 (1925-26)
1. Praeludium (wds. Goethe); 2. The sacred grove
(wds. Goethe); 3. Serenade (wds. Eichendorff); 4. In
the forest (wds. Eichendorff); 5. Winter Night (wds.
Eichendorff); 6. The Fountain (wds. Chamisso); 7.
Gaily singing (wds. Chamisso).
1, 5, 6. E. Schwarzkopf. N. Medtner (r1950: Ger)
Concert　　(10/93) (EMI) ① **CDC7 54839-2**
7 Songs—1v and piano, Op. 52 (1929-30)
(Wds. Pushkin)
1. Das Fenster; 2. Der Rabe; 3. Elegie; 4. Zeichnen;
5. Spanische Romanze; 6. Serenade; 7. Der
Gefangene.
1. L. Andrew, G. Tozer (r1993) *Concert*
　　　　　　　　　(12/95) (CHAN) ① **CHAN9327**
2. O. Slobodskaya, N. Medtner (r1947) *Concert*
　　　　　　　　　(10/93) (EMI) ① **CDC7 54839-2**

MÉHUL, Nicholas Etienne (1763–1817) France

SECTION I: ORCHESTRAL

Symphony No. 1 in G minor (1808-09)
Lisbon Gulbenkian Orch, M. Swierczewski *Concert*
　　　　　　　　　(7/89) (NIMB) ① [2] **NI5184/5**
Symphony No. 2 in D (1808-09)
Lisbon Gulbenkian Orch, M. Swierczewski *Concert*
　　　　　　　　　(7/89) (NIMB) ① [2] **NI5184/5**
Symphony No. 3 in C (1809)
Lisbon Gulbenkian Orch, M. Swierczewski *Concert*
　　　　　　　　　(7/89) (NIMB) ① [2] **NI5184/5**
Symphony No. 4 in E (1810)
Lisbon Gulbenkian Orch, M. Swierczewski *Concert*
　　　　　　　　　(7/89) (NIMB) ① [2] **NI5184/5**

SECTION V: STAGE WORKS

La chasse de jeune Henri—opera: 2 acts
(1797—Paris) (Lib. J P Bouilly)
EXCERPTS: 1. Overture.
1. Lisbon Gulbenkian Orch, M. Swierczewski *Concert*
　　　　　　　　　(7/89) (NIMB) ① [2] **NI5184/5**
Joseph—opera (2 acts) (1807—Paris) (Lib.
Marsollier)
Champs paternels R. Tauber, orch. H. Geehl (Ger:
r1945) *Concert*　　(3/92) (EMI) ① **CDH7 64029-2**
Vainement Pharaon G. Thill, orch, E. Bigot (r1930)
Concert　　(8/95) (FORL) ① **UCD16727**
Le Trésor supposé—opera (1 act)
(1802—Paris) (Lib. F-B. Hofmann)
Overture Lisbon Gulbenkian Orch, M. Swierczewski
Concert　　(7/89) (NIMB) ① [2] **NI5184/5**

MEIJERING, Chiel (b 1954) The Netherlands

SECTION III: INSTRUMENTAL

La Belle Dame Sans Merci—cello (1992)
P. Wispelwey (r1993) *Concert*
　　　　　　　　　(7/95) (CHNN) ① **CCS7495**

MEISTER, F. (19th Cent)

SECTION I: ORCHESTRAL

Erwin Fantaisie—clarinet and band
H. Lefèbvre, Garde Republicaine Band (rc1913)
Concert　　(2/94) (CLRI) ① **CC0005**

MELACHRINO, George (1909–1965) England

SECTION V: STAGE WORKS

Starlight Roof—musical revue
(1947—London)
EXCERPTS: 1. Waltz; 2. Violins in the Night.
1. RTE Concert Orch, E. Tomlinson (r1993) *Concert*
　　　　　　　　　(12/95) (MARC) ① **8 223522**

MELANI, Alessandro (1639–1703) Italy

SECTION I: ORCHESTRAL

Sinfonia a 5
D. Ferry, K. Gohl, J. Rubin, G. Murray, C. Bianchi, E.
Gatti, C. Stein (r1983) *Concert*
　　　　　　　　　(5/87) (HARM) ① **HMA190 5137**

SECTION IV: VOCAL AND CHORAL

All armi, pensieri—cantata: soprano, trumpet
and strings
J. Nelson, D. Ferry, K. Gohl, J. Rubin, G. Murray
(r1983) *Concert*　　(5/87) (HARM) ① **HMA190 5137**

MELARTIN, Erkki (1875–1937) Finland

SECTION I: ORCHESTRAL

Symphony No. 2 (1904)
Tampere PO, L. Grin (r1993) *Symphony 4.*
　　　　　　　　　(12/94) (ONDI) ① **ODE822-2**
Symphony No. 4, 'Summer', Op. 80 (1912)
P. Freund, L. Paasikivi, L. Nykänen, Tampere PO, L.
Grin (r1993) *Symphony 2.*
　　　　　　　　　(12/94) (ONDI) ① **ODE822-2**
Symphony No. 5, 'Sinfonia brevis', Op. 90
(1916)
Tampere PO, L. Grin (r1992) *Symphony 6.*
　　　　　　　　　(12/94) (ONDI) ① **ODE799-2**
Symphony No. 6, Op. 100 (1925)
Tampere PO, L. Grin (r1992) *Symphony 5.*
　　　　　　　　　(12/94) (ONDI) ① **ODE799-2**

SECTION IV: VOCAL AND CHORAL

Twenty years—song, Op. 162/5 (Wds. J.
Hemmer)
B. Nilsson, G. Parsons (pp1974) *Concert*
　　　　　　　　　(6/92) (BLUE) ① **ABCD009**

MELBA, Dame Nellie (1861–1931) Australia

SECTION IV: VOCAL AND CHORAL

Farewell speech at the Royal Opera House,
Covent Garden (1926)
N. Melba (pp1926) *Concert*
　　　　　　　　　(3/89) (LARR) ① **CDLRH221**

MELCER-SZCZAWIŃSKI, Henryk (1869–1928) Poland

SECTION I: ORCHESTRAL

Concerto for Piano and Orchestra No. 1 in E
minor (1895)
M. Ponti, Warsaw Nat PO, T. Strugała (r1992)
Paderewski: Piano Concerto.
　　　　　　　　　(7/94) (OLYM) ① **OCD398**

MELGÁS, Diogo Dias (1638–1700) Portugal

SECTION IV: VOCAL AND CHORAL

Adiuva nos—motet
PCA, M. Brown (r1994) *Concert*
　　　　　　　　　(11/94) (HYPE) ① **CDA66715**
Ecce ascendimus—motet
PCA, M. Brown (r1994) *Concert*
　　　　　　　　　(11/94) (HYPE) ① **CDA66715**
Ego sum resurrectio—motet
PCA, M. Brown (r1994) *Concert*
　　　　　　　　　(11/94) (HYPE) ① **CDA66715**
Ille homo—motet
PCA, M. Brown (r1994) *Concert*
　　　　　　　　　(11/94) (HYPE) ① **CDA66715**
In ieiunio et fletu—motet
PCA, M. Brown (r1994) *Concert*
　　　　　　　　　(11/94) (HYPE) ① **CDA66715**
In Monte Oliveti—motet
PCA, M. Brown (r1994) *Concert*
　　　　　　　　　(11/94) (HYPE) ① **CDA66715**
Lamentations (Incipit lamentatio Ieremiae
Prophetae)—Lamentations of Jeremiah
PCA, M. Brown (r1994) *Concert*
　　　　　　　　　(11/94) (HYPE) ① **CDA66715**
Magister volumus—motet
PCA, M. Brown (r1994) *Concert*
　　　　　　　　　(11/94) (HYPE) ① **CDA66715**
Memento homo—motet
PCA, M. Brown (r1994) *Concert*
　　　　　　　　　(11/94) (HYPE) ① **CDA66715**

O vos omnes—motet
PCA, M. Brown (r1994) *Concert*
(11/94) (HYPE) ① **CDA66715**
Pia et dolorosa Mater—motet
PCA, M. Brown (r1994) *Concert*
(11/94) (HYPE) ① **CDA66715**
Recordare Virgo Mater—motet
PCA, M. Brown (r1994) *Concert*
(11/94) (HYPE) ① **CDA66715**
Rex tremendae maiestatis—motet
PCA, M. Brown (r1994) *Concert*
(11/94) (HYPE) ① **CDA66715**
Salve Regina—motet
PCA, M. Brown (r1994) *Concert*
(11/94) (HYPE) ① **CDA66715**

MELLI, Pietro Paolo (c1575–1620) Italy

> **SECTION III: INSTRUMENTAL**

Capriccio chromatico—lute
K. Junghänel (r1985) *Concert*
(5/87) (HARM) ① **HMA190 1183**

MELLNÄS, Arne (b 1933) Sweden

> **SECTION I: ORCHESTRAL**

Blow—wind orchestra (1974)
Stockholm Sym Wind Orch, B. Priestman *Concert*
(3/93) (CPRI) ① **CAP21415**

MELNOTTE, Claude (1840–1923) Germany/USA

pseudonym of Charles Kunkel

> **SECTION IV: VOCAL AND CHORAL**

Angels' Visits—song (1869) (Wds. C. Spooner)
K. Battle, L. Skrobacs (r1977) *Concert*
(2/94) (NEW) ① **80220-2**

MELVILL, David (17th cent) England

> **SECTION IV: VOCAL AND CHORAL**

O lusty May—song (c1600)
C. Bott, M. George, New London Consort, P. Pickett (r1992) *Concert* (4/94) (LINN) ① **CKD011**

MENA, Gabriel (fl 1511–1516) Spain

> **SECTION IV: VOCAL AND CHORAL**

A sonbra de mis cabellos (Cancionero de Palacio)
Hespèrion XX, J. Savall *Concert*
(7/92) (ASTR) ① **E8762**
Aquella mora garrida (Cancionero de Palacio)
Hespèrion XX, J. Savall *Concert*
(7/92) (ASTR) ① **E8762**
La Bella malmaridada (Cancionero de Palacio)
Hespèrion XX, J. Savall *Concert*
(7/92) (ASTR) ① **E8762**
Gothic Voices, C. Page (r1993) *Concert*
(2/94) (HYPE) ① **CDA66653**
Yo creo que n'os dió Dios—villancico: 4vv
Gothic Voices, C. Page (r1993) *Concert*
(2/94) (HYPE) ① **CDA66653**

MENDELSSOHN (-BARTHOLDY), (Jakob Ludwig) Felix (1809–1847) Germany

> **SECTION I: ORCHESTRAL**

Capriccio brillant in B minor—concert piece for piano and orchestra, Op. 22 (?1825)
I. Margalit, LSO, B. Thomson *Brahms: Piano Concerto 1.* (11/89) (CHAN) ① **CHAN8724**
S. Edelman, Bamberg SO, C.P. Flor *Concert*
(12/89) (RCA) ① **RD87988**
A. Kuerti, LPO, P. Freeman *Concert*
(12/91) (CARL) ① **PCD953**
M. Ponti, Berlin SO, V. Schmidt-Gertenbach *Concert*
(5/93) (VOX) ① **115713-2**
LMP, H. Shelley (pf/dir) *Concert*
(4/94) (CHAN) ① **CHAN9215**

B. Frith, Košice St PO, R. Stankovsky (r1992) *Concert* (4/94) (NAXO) ① **8 550681**
Concert Piece in D minor—clarinet, basset-horn and orchestra, Op. 114 (1832) (?orch C Baermann: Bav St Lib MS)
T. King, G. Dobrée, LSO, A. Francis (r1980) *Concert* (1/88) (HYPE) ① **CDA66022**
Concert Piece in F—clarinet, basset-horn and orchestra, Op. 113 (1832-33) (orig with pf accomp)
T. King, G. Dobrée, LSO, A. Francis (r1980) *Concert* (1/88) (HYPE) ① **CDA66022**
Concerto for Piano and Orchestra No. 1 in G minor, Op. 25 (1831)
A. Schiff, BRSO, C. Dutoit *Piano Concerto 2.*
(5/86) (DECC) ① **414 672-2DH**
M. Perahia, ASMF, N. Marriner *Concert*
(11/87) (SONY) ① **MK42401**
J. Kalichstein, Scottish CO, J. Laredo *Concert*
(3/89) (NIMB) ① **NI5112**
C. Kite, Hanover Band, R. Goodman *Concert*
(6/89) (NIMB) ① **NI5158**
S. Edelman, Bamberg SO, C.P. Flor *Concert*
(12/89) (RCA) ① **RD87988**
I. Černecká, Slovak PO, O. Dohnányi *Piano Concerto 2.*
(2/90) (OPUS) ① **9350 1677**
A. Kuerti, LPO, P. Freeman *Concert*
(12/91) (CARL) ① **PCD953**
C. Katsaris, Leipzig Gewandhaus, K. Masur *Concert* (6/92) (TELD) ① **9031-75860-2**
LMP, H. Shelley (pf/dir) *Concert*
(4/94) (CHAN) ① **CHAN9215**
B. Frith, Košice St PO, R. Stankovsky (r1992) *Concert* (4/94) (NAXO) ① **8 550681**
Concerto for Piano and Orchestra No. 2 in D minor, Op. 40 (1837)
A. Schiff, BRSO, C. Dutoit *Piano Concerto 1.*
(5/86) (DECC) ① **414 672-2DH**
M. Perahia, ASMF, N. Marriner *Concert*
(11/87) (SONY) ① **MK42401**
J. Kalichstein, Scottish CO, J. Laredo *Concert*
(3/89) (NIMB) ① **NI5112**
S. Edelman, Bamberg SO, C.P. Flor *Concert*
(12/89) (RCA) ① **RD87988**
I. Černecká, Slovak PO, O. Dohnányi *Piano Concerto 1.*
(2/90) (OPUS) ① **9350 1677**
A. Kuerti, LPO, P. Freeman *Concert*
(12/91) (CARL) ① **PCD953**
C. Katsaris, Leipzig Gewandhaus, K. Masur *Concert* (6/92) (TELD) ① **9031-75860-2**
LMP, H. Shelley (pf/dir) *Concert*
(4/94) (CHAN) ① **CHAN9215**
B. Frith, Košice St PO, R. Stankovsky (r1992) *Concert* (4/94) (NAXO) ① **8 550681**
Concerto for Piano and Strings in A minor (1822)
C. Katsaris, F. Liszt CO, J. Rolla *Concert*
(6/92) (TELD) ① **9031-75860-2**
J. Ogdon, ASMF, N. Marriner *Concert*
(5/93) (DECC) ① **433 729-2DM**
Concerto for Two Pianos and Orchestra in A flat (1824)
S. Coombs, I. Munro, BBC Scottish SO, J. Maksymiuk *2-Piano Concerto in E.*
(9/92) (HYPE) ① **CDA66567**
Concerto for Two Pianos and Orchestra in E (1823)
S. Coombs, I. Munro, BBC Scottish SO, J. Maksymiuk *2-Piano Concerto in A flat.*
(9/92) (HYPE) ① **CDA66567**
J. Ogdon, B. Lucas, ASMF, N. Marriner *Concert*
(5/93) (DECC) ① **433 729-2DM**
K. Labèque, M. Labèque, Philh, S. Bychkov (r1990) *Bruch: 2-Piano Concerto.*
(7/93) (PHIL) ① **432 095-2PH**
Concerto for Violin and Orchestra in E minor, Op. 64 (1844)
1. Allegro molto appassionato; 2. Andante; 3. Allegretto non troppo—Allegro molto vivace.
A-S. Mutter, BPO, H. von Karajan *Bruch: Violin Concerto 1.*
(3/83) (DG) ① **400 031-2GH**
K-W. Chung, Montreal SO, C. Dutoit (r1981) *Tchaikovsky: Violin Concerto.*
(8/83) (DECC) ① **410 011-2DH**
I. Perlman, Concertgebouw, B. Haitink (r1983) *Bruch: Violin Concerto 1.* (12/85) (EMI) ① **CDC7 47074-2**
N. Milstein, VPO, C. Abbado *Tchaikovsky: Violin Concerto.* (8/87) (DG) ① **419 067-2GGA**
S. Mintz, Chicago SO, C. Abbado *Concert*
(2/87) (DG) ① **419 629-2GH**
A-S. Mutter, BPO, H. von Karajan *Concert*
(3/88) (DG) ① [4] **415 565-2GX4**
J. Bell, ASMF, N. Marriner *Bruch: Violin Concerto 1.*
(5/88) (DECC) ① **421 145-2DH**
Y. Menuhin, Philh, E. Kurtz (r1958) *Bruch: Violin Concerto 1.* (1/89) (EMI) ① **CDM7 69003-2**

N. Kennedy, ECO, J. Tate *Concert*
(1/89) (EMI) ① **CDC7 49663-2**
I. Perlman, Concertgebouw, B. Haitink *Brahms: Double Concerto.* (5/89) (EMI) ① **CDC7 49486-2**
B. Hudson, Hanover Band, R. Goodman *Concert*
(6/89) (NIMB) ① **NI5158**
Y. Menuhin, BPO, W. Furtwängler (r1952) *Beethoven: Violin Concerto.*
(10/89) (EMI) ① **CDH7 69799-2**
Z. Francescatti, Cleveland Orch, G. Szell (r1961) *Tchaikovsky: Violin Concerto.*
(2/90) (SONY) ① **MPK45700**
G. Shaham, Philh, G. Sinopoli *Bruch: Violin Concerto 1.* (3/90) (DG) ① **427 656-2GH**
E. Verhey, Budapest SO, A. Joó *Bruch: Violin Concerto 1.* (3/91) (LASE) ① **15 615**
X. Wei, LPO, I. Bolton *Brahms: Violin Concerto.*
(4/91) (ASV) ① **CDDCA748**
V. Mullova, ASMF, N. Marriner *Violin Concerto (1822).* (5/91) (PHIL) ① **432 077-2PH**
J. Szigeti, LPO, T. Beecham (r1933) *Concert*
(10/91) (MSCM) ① **MM30272**
Y. Menuhin, Philh, E. Kurtz *Concert*
(11/91) (EMI) ① [3] **CZS7 67310-2**
F. Kreisler, LPO, L. Ronald (r1935) *Schumann: Violin Concerto.* (12/91) (BIDD) ① **LAB047**
F. Kreisler, Berlin St Op Orch, L. Blech (r1926) *Concert* (12/91) (BIDD) ① [2] **LAB049/50**
A. Spalding, Philadelphia, E. Ormandy (r1941) *Concert* (10/92) (BIDD) ① **LAB054**
K-W. Chung, Montreal SO, C. Dutoit *Beethoven: Violin Concerto.* (2/93) (DECC) ① **430 752-2DM**
P. Zukerman, NYPO, L. Bernstein (r1969) *Concert*
(8/93) (SONY) ① **SMK47592**
F. Kreisler, Berlin St Op Orch, L. Blech (r1926) *Concert* (9/93) (PEAR) ① [2] **GEMMCDS9996**
I. Gitlis, Vienna Pro Musica orch, H. Swarowsky (r1950s) *Concert* (11/93) (VOX) ① [2] **CDX2 5505**
I. Perlman, Chicago SO, D. Barenboim (pp1993) *Prokofiev: Violin Concerto 2.*
(1/94) (ERAT) ① **4509-91732-2**
J. Szigeti, LPO, T. Beecham (r1933) *Concert*
(2/94) (EMI) ① **CDH7 64562-2**
A.A. Meyers, Philh, A. Litton (r1993) *Concert*
(2/94) (RCA) ① **09026 61700-2**
I. Perlman, Concertgebouw, B. Haitink (r1983) *Concert* (4/94) (EMI) ① [3] **CMS7 64922-2**
M. Huggett, OAE, C. Mackerras (r1992) *Beethoven: Violin Concerto.* (4/94) (EMIN) ① **CD-EMX2217**
M. Vengerov, Leipzig Gewandhaus, K. Masur (r1993) *Bruch: Violin Concerto 1.*
(4/94) (TELD) ① **4509-90875-2**
G. Kulenkampff, BPO, H. Schmidt-Isserstedt (r1935) *Schumann: Violin Concerto.*
(9/94) (TELD) ① **4509-93672-2**
J. Martzy, Philh, P. Kletzki (r1955) *Brahms: Violin Concerto.* (9/94) (TEST) ① **SBT1037**
A. Grumiaux, Concertgebouw, B. Haitink (r1960) *Concert* (9/94) (PHIL) ① [2] **442 287-2PM2**
J. Heifetz, RPO, T. Beecham (r1949) *Concert*
(10/94) (EMI) ① **CDH5 65191-2**
S. Accardo, LPO, C. Dutoit (r1975) *Concert*
(10/94) (PHIL) ① [2] **442 302-2PM2**
A. Campoli, LPO, A. Boult (r1958) *Elgar: Violin Concerto.* (10/94) (BEUL) ① **1PD10**
J-P. Wallez, Luxembourg Rad & TV SO, D. Chorafas (r1981) *Bruch: Violin Concerto 1.*
(11/94) (FORL) ① **FF041**
J. Heifetz, Boston SO, C. Munch (r1959) *Concert*
(11/94) (RCA) ① [65] **09026 61778-2(11-15)**
J. Heifetz, RPO, T. Beecham (r1949) *Concert*
(11/94) (RCA) ① [65] **09026 61778-2(18)**
A-S. Mutter, BPO, H. von Karajan (r1980) *Brahms: Violin Concerto.* (11/94) (DG) ① **445 515-2GMA**
Chee-Yun, LPO, J. López-Cobos (r1994) *Vieuxtemps: Violin Concerto 5.*
(1/95) (DENO) ① **CO-78913**
K. Takezawa, Bamberg SO, C.P. Flor (r1994) *Violin Concerto (1822).* (2/95) (RCA) ① **09026 62512-2**
I. Perlman, Concertgebouw, B. Haitink (r1983) *Concert* (6/95) (EMI) ① [20] **CZS4 83177-2(1)**
J. Laredo (vn/dir), Scottish CO (r c1986) *Bruch: Violin Concerto 1.* · (10/95) (CARL) ① **PCD2005**
2, 3. B. Huberman, P. Frenkel (r1924) *Concert*
(12/91) (BIDD) ① **LAB077/8**
3. J. Heifetz, S. Chotzinoff (r1920) *Concert*
(11/94) (RCA) ① [65] **09026 61778-2(01)**
Concerto for Violin and Strings in D minor (1822)
R. Thomas (vn/dir), Soloists of Australia (ed Menuhin) *String Symphony 9.*
(2/89) (CHAN) ① **CHAN8644**
G. Kremer, Orpheus CO (r1988) *Violin and Piano Concerto.* (9/89) (DG) ① **427 338-2GH**
V. Mullova, ASMF, N. Marriner *Violin Concerto, Op. 64.* (5/91) (PHIL) ① **432 077-2PH**

K. Takezawa, Bamberg SO, C. P. Flor (r1994) *Violin Concerto, Op. 64.*   (2/95) (RCA) ① **09026 62512-2**
Concerto for Violin, Piano and Strings in D minor (1823)
G. Kremer, M. Argerich, Orpheus CO (r1988) *Violin Concerto (1822).*   (9/89) (DG) ① **427 338-2GH**
O. Rudner, P. Entremont (pf/dir), Vienna CO *Viotti: Piano Concerto 3.*   (6/90) (SCHW) ① **311047**
P. Csaba (vn/dir), R. Gothóni, Kuhmo Virtuosi (r1993) *Haydn: Violin and Keyboard Concerto, HobXVIII/6.*
   (1/95) (ONDI) ① **ODE810-2**
The Hebrides, 'Fingal's Cave'—overture, Op. 26 (1830)
SNO, A. Gibson *Concert*
   (9/85) (CHAN) ① **CHAN8379**
LSO, C. Abbado *Concert*
   (1/86) (DG) ① [4] **415 353-2GH4**
Berne SO, P. Maag *Concert*
   (6/86) (CARL) ① **PCD824**
LSO, C. Abbado *Concert*
   (5/88) (DG) ① **423 104-2GH**
BPO, H. von Karajan *Symphony 3.*
   (10/88) (DG) ① **419 477-2GGA**
Bamberg SO, C.P. Flor *Concert*
   (1/89) (RCA) ① **RD87905**
Scottish CO, J. Laredo *Concert*
   (3/89) (NIMB) ① **NI5112**
SNO, A. Gibson *Concert*
   (10/91) (CHAN) ① **CHAN6538**
BPO, W. Furtwängler (r1930) *Concert*
   (4/92) (KOCH) ① [2] **37073-2**
Philh, W. Weller *Concert*
   (2/93) (CHAN) ① **CHAN9099**
LPO, T. Beecham (r1938) *Concert*
   (7/93) (DUTT) ① **CDLX7001**
NYPO, L. Bernstein (r1966) *Concert*
   (8/93) (SONY) ① **SMK47592**
Israel PO, L. Bernstein (pp1979) *Concert*
   (3/94) (DG) ① **439 411-2GCL**
SRO, A. Jordan (r1993) *Concert*
   (5/94) (ERAT) ① **4509-91734-2**
BBC SO, Colin Davis (r1970) *Concert*
   (10/94) (PHIL) ① [2] **442 302-2PM2**
Paris Champs-Élysées Orch, P. Herreweghe (r1994) *Midsummer Night's Dream.*
   (4/95) (HARM) ① **HMC90 1502**
LSO, P. Maag (r1960) *Concert*
   (7/95) (DECC) ① **443 578-2DCS**
Chicago SO, F. Reiner (r1956) *Concert*
   (9/95) (RCA) ① **09026 61793-2**
Exc BPO, W. Furtwängler (r1930) *Concert*
   (3/95) (TAHR) ① [4] **FURT1008/11**
Meeresstille und glückliche Fahrt, 'Calm Sea and Prosperous Voyage'—overture, Op. 27 (1828)
LSO, C. Abbado *Concert*
   (5/88) (DG) ① **423 104-2GH**
Bamberg SO, C.P. Flor *Concert*
   (1/89) (RCA) ① **RD87905**
Overture for wind instruments, Op. 24 (1824)
LSO, C. Abbado *Concert*
   (5/88) (DG) ① **423 104-2GH**
Rondo brilliant in E flat—piano and orchestra, Op. 29 (1834)
B. Frith, Košice St PO, R. Stankovsky (r1992) *Concert*   (9/94) (NAXO) ① **8 550681**
Ruy Blas—overture to Victor Hugo's play, Op. 95 (1839)
LSO, C. Abbado *Concert*
   (5/88) (DG) ① **423 104-2GH**
Bamberg SO, C.P. Flor *Concert*
   (1/89) (RCA) ① **RD87905**
LPO, T. Beecham (r1939) *Concert*
   (7/93) (DUTT) ① **CDLX7001**
New Philh, W. Sawallisch (r1967) *Concert*
   (10/94) (PHIL) ① [2] **442 302-2PM2**
Die Schöne Melusine—overture, after Grillparzer, Op. 32 (1833)
LSO, C. Abbado (r1984) *Concert*
   (1/86) (DG) ① [4] **415 353-2GH4**
Berne SO, P. Maag *Concert*
   (6/86) (CARL) ① **PCD824**
LSO, C. Abbado *Concert*
   (5/88) (DG) ① **423 104-2GH**
SRO, A. Jordan (r1993) *Concert*
   (5/94) (ERAT) ① **4509-91734-2**
Philh, F. D'Avalos (r1993) *Midsummer Night's Dream.*   (7/94) (CARL) ① **MCD78**
Symphony for Strings No. 1 in C (1821)
English Stg Orch, W. Boughton *Concert*
   (3/89) (NIMB) ① **NI5141**
Amadeus CO, A. Duczmal *Concert*
   (7/91) (EURM) ① [4] **350204**
London Fest Orch, R. Pople *Concert*
   (12/91) (HYPE) ① [3] **CDA66561/3**

Amsterdam Nieuw Sinfonietta, L. Markiz (r1994) *Concert*   (9/95) (BIS) ① **BIS-CD683**
Symphony for Strings No. 2 in D (1821)
English Stg Orch, W. Boughton *Concert*
   (3/89) (NIMB) ① **NI5141**
Amadeus CO, A. Duczmal *Concert*
   (7/91) (EURM) ① [4] **350204**
London Fest Orch, R. Pople *Concert*
   (12/91) (HYPE) ① [3] **CDA66561/3**
Amsterdam Nieuw Sinfonietta, L. Markiz (r1993) *Concert*   (6/94) (BIS) ① **BIS-CD643**
Symphony for Strings No. 3 in E minor (1821)
English Stg Orch, W. Boughton *Concert*
   (3/89) (NIMB) ① **NI5141**
Amadeus CO, A. Duczmal *Concert*
   (7/91) (EURM) ① [4] **350204**
London Fest Orch, R. Pople *Concert*
   (12/91) (HYPE) ① [3] **CDA66561/3**
Amsterdam Nieuw Sinfonietta, L. Markiz (r1993) *Concert*   (6/94) (BIS) ① **BIS-CD643**
Symphony for Strings No. 4 in C minor (1821)
English Stg Orch, W. Boughton *Concert*
   (3/89) (NIMB) ① **NI5141**
Amadeus CO, A. Duczmal *Concert*
   (7/91) (EURM) ① [4] **350204**
London Fest Orch, R. Pople *Concert*
   (12/91) (HYPE) ① [3] **CDA66561/3**
Symphony for Strings No. 5 in B flat (1821)
English Stg Orch, W. Boughton *Concert*
   (3/89) (NIMB) ① **NI5141**
Amadeus CO, A. Duczmal *Concert*
   (7/91) (EURM) ① [4] **350204**
London Fest Orch, R. Pople *Concert*
   (12/91) (HYPE) ① [3] **CDA66561/3**
Symphony for Strings No. 6 in E flat (1821)
English Stg Orch, W. Boughton *Concert*
   (3/89) (NIMB) ① **NI5141**
Solisti Italiani *Concert*   (4/90) (DENO) ① **CO-73185**
Amadeus CO, A. Duczmal *Concert*
   (7/91) (EURM) ① [4] **350204**
London Fest Orch, R. Pople *Concert*
   (12/91) (HYPE) ① [3] **CDA66561/3**
Amsterdam Nieuw Sinfonietta, L. Markiz (r1994) *Concert*   (9/95) (BIS) ① **BIS-CD683**
Symphony for Strings No. 7 in D minor (?1821-22)
English Stg Orch, W. Boughton *Concert*
   (3/89) (NIMB) ① **NI5142**
Amadeus CO, A. Duczmal *Concert*
   (7/91) (EURM) ① [4] **350204**
London Fest Orch, R. Pople *Concert*
   (12/91) (HYPE) ① [3] **CDA66561/3**
Goldberg Ens, M. Layfield *Concert*
   (3/92) (MERI) ① **CDE84193**
Amsterdam Nieuw Sinfonietta, L. Markiz (r1994) *Concert*   (9/95) (BIS) ① **BIS-CD683**
Symphony for Strings No. 8 in D (1822)
English Stg Orch, W. Boughton *Concert*
   (3/89) (NIMB) ① **NI5142**
Amadeus CO, A. Duczmal *Concert*
   (7/91) (EURM) ① [4] **350204**
London Fest Orch, R. Pople *Concert*
   (12/91) (HYPE) ① [3] **CDA66561/3**
Goldberg Ens, M. Layfield *Concert*
   (3/92) (MERI) ① **CDE84193**
Orpheus CO (r1991) *Concert*
   (8/93) (DG) ① **437 528-2GH**
Cologne Concerto (r1994) *Concert*
   (12/94) (TELD) ① **4509-94565-2**
Symphony for Strings No. 9 in C (1823)
Soloists of Australia, R. Thomas *Violin Concerto (1822).*   (2/89) (CHAN) ① **CHAN8644**
English Stg Orch, W. Boughton *Concert*
   (3/89) (NIMB) ① **NI5143**
Amadeus CO, A. Duczmal *Concert*
   (7/91) (EURM) ① [4] **350204**
London Fest Orch, R. Pople *Concert*
   (12/91) (HYPE) ① [3] **CDA66561/3**
Orpheus CO (r1991) *Concert*
   (8/93) (DG) ① **437 528-2GH**
Amsterdam Nieuw Sinfonietta, L. Markiz (r1993) *Concert*   (6/94) (BIS) ① **BIS-CD643**
Cologne Concerto (r1994) *Concert*
   (12/94) (TELD) ① **4509-94565-2**
Symphony for Strings No. 10 in B minor (1823)
English Stg Orch, W. Boughton *Concert*
   (3/89) (NIMB) ① **NI5142**
Solisti Italiani *Concert*   (4/90) (DENO) ① **CO-73185**
Amadeus CO, A. Duczmal *Concert*
   (7/91) (EURM) ① [4] **350204**
London Fest Orch, R. Pople *Concert*
   (12/91) (HYPE) ① [3] **CDA66561/3**

Orpheus CO (r1991) *Concert*
   (8/93) (DG) ① **437 528-2GH**
Amsterdam Nieuw Sinfonietta, L. Markiz (r1993) *Concert*   (6/94) (BIS) ① **BIS-CD643**
Cologne Concerto (r1994) *Concert*
   (12/94) (TELD) ① **4509-94565-2**
Symphony for Strings No. 11 in F (1823)
English Stg Orch, W. Boughton *Concert*
   (3/89) (NIMB) ① **NI5143**
Amadeus CO, A. Duczmal *Concert*
   (7/91) (EURM) ① [4] **350204**
London Fest Orch, R. Pople *Concert*
   (12/91) (HYPE) ① [3] **CDA66561/3**
Symphony for Strings No. 12 in G minor (1823)
English Stg Orch, W. Boughton *Concert*
   (3/89) (NIMB) ① **NI5143**
Amadeus CO, A. Duczmal *Concert*
   (7/91) (EURM) ① [4] **350204**
London Fest Orch, R. Pople *Concert*
   (12/91) (HYPE) ① [3] **CDA66561/3**
ASMF, N. Marriner *Concert*
   (5/93) (DECC) ① **433 729-2DM**
Amsterdam Nieuw Sinfonietta, L. Markiz (r1994) *Concert*   (9/95) (BIS) ① **BIS-CD683**
Symphony No. 1 in C minor, Op. 11 (1824)
LSO, C. Abbado *Concert*
   (1/86) (DG) ① [4] **415 353-2GH4**
BPO, H. von Karajan (r1972) *Concert*
   (8/91) (DG) ① [3] **429 664-2GSE3**
New Philh, W. Sawallisch *Concert*
   (8/91) (PHIL) ① [3] **432 598-2PB3**
Milton Keynes CO, H.D. Wetton *Symphony 5.*
   (2/93) (UNIC) ① **DKPCD9117**
Philh, W. Weller *Concert*
   (2/93) (CHAN) ① **CHAN9099**
Berlin Deutsches SO, Vladimir Ashkenazy (r1994) *Symphony 5.*   (6/95) (DECC) ① **444 428-2DH**
Leipzig Gewandhaus, K. Masur (r1972) *Concert*
   (8/95) (RCA) ① [3] **74321 20286-2**
Symphony No. 2 in B flat, 'Hymn of Praise'—SST, chorus and orchestra, Op.52 (1840)
1. Sinfonia; 2a. Alles, was Odemhat, lobe den Herrn; 2b. Lobet den Herrn, meine Seele; 3a. Saget es die ihr erlöst; 3b. Er zählet unsre Tränen; 4. Sagt es, die ihr erlöset seid; 5. Ich harrete des Herrn (I waited for the Lord); 6. Stricke des Todes hatten uns umfangen; 7. Die Nacht ist vergangen; 8. Nun danket alle Gott; 9. Drum sing' ich mit meinen Leide; 10. Ihr Völker, bringet her dem Herrn.
E. Connell, K. Mattila, H-P. Blochwitz, LSC, LSO, C. Abbado (r1985) *Concert*
   (1/86) (DG) ① [4] **415 353-2GH4**
K. Laki, M. Shirai, P. Seiffert, Düsseldorf Musikverein, BPO, W. Sawallisch (pp1987)
   (9/90) (EMI) ① **CDC7 49764-2**
L. Popp, J. Kaufmann, J. Protschka, Bamberg Sym Chor, Bamberg SO, C.P. Flor
   (9/90) (RCA) ① **RD60248**
E. Mathis, L. Rebmann, W. Hollweg, Berlin Deutsche Op Chor, BPO, H. von Karajan (r1972)
   (8/91) (DG) ① [3] **429 664-2GSE3**
E. Mathis, L. Rebmann, W. Hollweg, Berlin Deutsche Op Chor, BPO, H. von Karajan
   (8/91) (DG) ① **431 471-2GGA**
H. Donath, R. Hansmann, W. Kmentt, New Philh Chor, New Philh, W. Sawallisch *Concert*
   (8/91) (PHIL) ① [3] **432 598-2PB3**
C. Haymon, A. Hagley, P. Straka, Philh Chor, Philh, W. Weller   (5/92) (CHAN) ① **CHAN8995**
S. Isokoski, M. Bach, F. Lang, Cologne Chorus Musicus, Neue Orch, C. Spering (r1993)
   (9/94) (O111) ① **OPS30-98**
C. Casapietra, A. Stolte, P. Schreier, Leipzig Rad Chor, Leipzig Gewandhaus, K. Masur (r1972)
   (8/95) (RCA) ① [3] **74321 20286-2**
5. Westminster Cath Ch, J. O'Donnell, I. Simcock (r1993) *Concert*   (3/94) (HYPE) ① **CDA66669**
5. Southwark Cath Ch, P. Wright, S. Layton (r1992; Eng) *Concert*   (9/94) (PRIO) ① **PRCD435**
Symphony No. 3 in A minor, 'Scottish', Op. 56 (1842)
BRSO, Colin Davis *Midsummer Night's Dream.*
   (3/85) (ORFE) ① **C089841A**
LSO, C. Abbado (r1984) *Concert*
   (1/86) (DG) ① [4] **415 353-2GH4**
St John's Smith Square Orch, J. Lubbock *Symphony 4.*   (12/87) (ASV) ① **CDQS6004**
BPO, H. von Karajan *Hebrides.*
   (10/88) (DG) ① **419 477-2GGA**
Cleveland Orch, C. von Dohnányi (1988) *Erste Walpurgisnacht.*   (3/89) (TELA) ① **CD80184**
LSO, C. Abbado *Symphony 4.*
   (2/90) (DG) ① **427 810-2GDC**

M. Vengerov, A. Markovich *Concert*
(3/93) (TELD) ① **9031-76349-2**
Y. Zivoni, A. Goldstone (r1990s) *Concert*
(9/93) (MERI) ① **CDE84229**
Sonata for Violin and Piano in F minor, Op. 4 (1825)
S. Mintz, P. Ostrovsky *Violin Sonata (1838)*.
(8/87) (DG) ① **419 244-2GH**
Y. Zivoni, A. Goldstone (r1990s) *Concert*
(9/93) (MERI) ① **CDE84229**
J. Schröder, C. Hogwood *Concert*
(9/94) (L'OI) ① **443 196-2OM**
Sonata in E flat—clarinet and piano (1824)
A. Hacker, R. Burnett (r1989) *Concert*
(4/90) (AMON) ① **CD-SAR38**
C. Neidich, R. Levin (r1993) *Concert*
(9/95) (SONY) ① **SK64302**
Song without words—cello and piano, Op. 109 (1845)
M. Maisky, P. Gililov *Concert*
(7/91) (DG) ① **431 544-2GH**
F-J. Sellheim, E. Sellheim *Concert*
(10/92) (SONY) ① **SBK48171**
M. Kliegel, K. Merscher (r1992) *Concert*
(7/94) (NAXO) ① **8 550655**
N. Rosen, D. Stevenson *Concert*
(3/95) (JMR) ① **JMR5**
S. Isserlis, M. Tan (r1994) *Concert*
(3/95) (RCA) ① **09026 62553-2**
J. Du Pré, G. Moore (r1962) *Concert*
(11/95) (EMI) ① **CDC5 55529-2**
String Quartet in E flat (1823)
Melos Qt (r1981) *Concert*
(12/87) (DG) ① [3] **415 883-2GCM3**
Bartholdy Qt *Concert*
(12/89) (ACAN) ① [3] **43 075**
Artis Qt *Concert*   (5/90) (ACCO) ① **20067-2**
Coull Qt (r1991) *Concert*
(11/92) (HYPE) ① **CDA66579**
Coull Qt (r1991) *Concert*
(6/94) (HYPE) ① [3] **CDS44051/3**
Aurora Qt (r1993) *Concert*
(10/94) (NAXO) ① **8 550862**
String Quartet No. 1 in E flat, Op. 12 (1829)
1. Adagio non troppo—Allegro non tardante; 2. Canzonetta; 3. Andante espressivo; 4. Molto allegro e vivace.
Melos Qt (r1976) *Concert*
(12/87) (DG) ① [3] **415 883-2GCM3**
Bartholdy Qt *Concert*
(12/89) (ACAN) ① [3] **43 075**
Artis Qt *Concert*   (5/90) (ACCO) ① **20067-2**
Gabrieli Qt (r1989) *String Quartet 2*.
(1/92) (CHAN) ① **CHAN8827**
Coull Qt *Concert*   (1/92) (HYPE) ① **CDA66397**
Cherubini Qt (r1990) *Concert*
(8/93) (EMI) ① [3] **CDS7 54514-2**
Coull Qt (r1989) *Concert*
(6/94) (HYPE) ① [3] **CDS44051/3**
Aurora Qt (r1993) *Concert*
(10/94) (NAXO) ① **8 550862**
Moraguès Qnt (r1994; trans wind quintet) *String Quartet 2*. (11/95) (AUVI) ① **V4719**
Canzonetta A. Segovia (arr Segovia; r1936) *Concert*
(5/89) (EMI) ① [2] **CHS7 61047-2**
2. J. Bream (r1970; arr Bream) *Concert*
(8/93) (RCA) ① [28] **09026 61583-2(4)**
2. J. Bream (r1970; arr Bream) *Concert*
(6/94) (RCA) ① **09026 61594-2**
2. D. Laval (r1994: arr pf) *Concert*
(7/95) (AUVI) ① **V4729**
String Quartet No. 2 in A minor, Op. 13 (1827)
Melos Qt (r1980) *Concert*
(12/87) (DG) ① [3] **415 883-2GCM3**
Cleveland Qt *Octet, Op.20*.
(1/88) (TELA) ① **CD80142**
Medici Qt *Shostakovich: Piano Quintet, Op.57*.
(5/89) (NIMB) ① **NI5156**
Bartholdy Qt *Concert*
(12/89) (ACAN) ① [3] **43 075**
Albeni Qt *Schumann: String Quartet 3*.
(1/90) (CRD) ① **CRD3317**
Artis Qt *Concert*   (5/90) (ACCO) ① **20034-2**
Gabrieli Qt (r1989) *String Quartet 1*.
(1/92) (CHAN) ① **CHAN8827**
Coull Qt *Concert*   (1/92) (HYPE) ① **CDA66397**
Carmina Qt (r1991) *String Quartet 6*.
(3/92) (DENO) ① **CO-79527**
Cherubini Qt (r1989) *Concert*
(8/93) (EMI) ① [3] **CDS7 54514-2**
Coull Qt (r1989) *Concert*
(6/94) (HYPE) ① [3] **CDS44051/3**
Shanghai Qt (r1993) *Grieg: String Quartet, Op. 27*.
(6/94) (DELO) ① **DE3153**

Aurora Qt (r1993) *Concert*
(12/94) (NAXO) ① **8 550863**
Hausmusik *String Quintet 2*.
(5/95) (VIRG) ① **VC5 45104-2**
Talich Qt (r1985) *Concert*
(11/95) (CALL) ① **CAL6698**
Moraguès Qnt (r1994; trans wind quintet) *String Quartet 1*. (11/95) (AUVI) ① **V4719**
String Quartet No. 3 in D, Op. 44/1 (1838)
Melos Qt (r1981) *Concert*
(12/87) (DG) ① [3] **415 883-2GCM3**
Roth Qt *String Quartet 5*.
(5/88) (PEAR) ① **SHECD9603**
Bartholdy Qt *Concert*
(12/89) (ACAN) ① [3] **43 075**
Artis Qt *Concert*   (5/90) (ACCO) ① **20068-2**
Coull Qt (r1992) *Concert*
(8/93) (HYPE) ① **CDA66615**
Cherubini Qt (r1990) *Concert*
(8/93) (EMI) ① [3] **CDS7 54514-2**
Coull Qt (r1993) *Concert*
(6/94) (HYPE) ① [3] **CDS44051/3**
Aurora Qt (r1993) *Concert*
(12/94) (NAXO) ① **8 550861**
String Quartet No. 4 in E minor, Op. 44/2 (1837)
Melos Qt (r1977) *Concert*
(12/87) (DG) ① [3] **415 883-2GCM3**
English Qt *String Quartet 5*.
(4/89) (MERI) ① **CDE84152**
Bartholdy Qt *Concert*
(12/89) (ACAN) ① [3] **43 075**
Artis Qt *Concert*   (5/90) (ACCO) ① **20067-2**
Coull Qt (r1991) *Concert*
(11/92) (HYPE) ① **CDA66579**
Cherubini Qt (r1990) *Concert*
(8/93) (EMI) ① [3] **CDS7 54514-2**
Coull Qt (r1991) *Concert*
(6/94) (HYPE) ① [3] **CDS44051/3**
Aurora Qt (r1993) *Concert*
(10/94) (NAXO) ① **8 550862**
String Quartet No. 5 in E flat, Op. 44/3 (1838)
Melos Qt (r1980) *Concert*
(12/87) (DG) ① [3] **415 883-2GCM3**
Roth Qt *String Quartet 3*.
(5/88) (PEAR) ① **SHECD9603**
English Qt *String Quartet 4*.
(4/89) (MERI) ① **CDE84152**
Bartholdy Qt *Concert*
(12/89) (ACAN) ① [3] **43 075**
Artis Qt *Concert*   (5/90) (ACCO) ① **20068-2**
Coull Qt (r1992) *Concert*
(8/93) (HYPE) ① **CDA66615**
Cherubini Qt (r1989) *Concert*
(8/93) (EMI) ① [3] **CDS7 54514-2**
Coull Qt (r1993) *Concert*
(6/94) (HYPE) ① [3] **CDS44051/3**
Aurora Qt (r1993) *Concert*
(12/94) (NAXO) ① **8 550863**
String Quartet No. 6 in F minor, Op. 80 (1847)
Melos Qt (r1980) *Concert*
(12/87) (DG) ① [3] **415 883-2GCM3**
Bartholdy Qt *Concert*
(12/89) (ACAN) ① [3] **43 075**
Artis Qt *Concert*   (5/90) (ACCO) ① **20034-2**
Carmina Qt (r1991) *String Quartet 2*.
(3/92) (DENO) ① **CO-79527**
Coull Qt (r1991) *Concert*
(11/92) (HYPE) ① **CDA66579**
Cherubini Qt (r1990) *Concert*
(8/93) (EMI) ① [3] **CDS7 54514-2**
Coull Qt (r1991) *Concert*
(6/94) (HYPE) ① [3] **CDS44051/3**
Aurora Qt (r1993) *Concert*
(12/94) (NAXO) ① **8 550861**
String Quintet No. 1 in A, Op. 18 (1826, rev 1832)
Hausmusik *Octet, Op.20*.
(9/90) (EMI) ① **CDC7 49958-2**
J. Laredo, A. Kavafian, H. Ohyama, K. Kashkashian, S. Robinson *String Quintet 2*.
(9/90) (SONY) ① **MPK45883**
String Quintet No. 2 in B flat, Op. 87 (1845)
ASMF Chbr Ens (r1978) *Octet, Op. 20*.
(11/87) (PHIL) ① **420 400-2PH**
J. Laredo, A. Kavafian, H. Ohyama, K. Kashkashian, S. Robinson *String Quintet 1*.
(10/90) (SONY) ① **MPK45883**
S. Accardo, M. Batjer, T. Hoffman, S. Gazeau, G. Hoffman *Beethoven: String Quintet, Op. 29*.
(6/91) (NUOV) ① **6870**
Hausmusik *String Quartet 2*.
(5/95) (VIRG) ① **VC5 45104-2**

Variations concertantes—cello and piano, Op. 17 (1829)
F-J. Sellheim, E. Sellheim *Concert*
(10/92) (SONY) ① **SBK48171**
M. Kliegel, K. Merscher (r1992) *Concert*
(7/94) (NAXO) ① **8 550655**
S. Isserlis, M. Tan (r1994) *Concert*
(3/95) (RCA) ① **09026 62553-2**
Variations in B flat—piano duet, Op. 83a (1841)
Y. Tal, A. Groethuysen (r1991) *Concert*
(6/93) (SONY) ① **SK48494**
Variations on a march from Weber's 'La preciosa'—two pianos (?1833) (comp with Moscheles)
A. Goldstone, C. Clemmow (r1988) *Concert*
(4/89) (SYMP) ① **SYMCD1037**

SECTION III: INSTRUMENTAL

Albumblatt (Lied ohne Worte) in E minor—piano, Op. 117 (?1837)
D. Barenboim *Concert*
(10/94) (DG) ① [2] **437 470-2GX2**
Andante and rondo capriccioso—piano, Op. 14 (1830/1824)
M. Perahia *Concert*   (11/87) (SONY) ① **MK42401**
L. Godowsky (r1926) *Concert*
(4/89) (APR) ① [2] **APR7011**
A. Servadei *Concert*   (7/91) (CARL) ① **PCD949**
R. de Waal (r1989) *Concert*
(6/93) (CHNN) ① **CG9106**
I. Scharrer (r1930) *Concert*
(7/94) (PEAR) ① **GEMMCD9978**
3 Caprices—piano, Op. 33 (1833-35)
1. A minor; 2. E; 3. B flat minor.
B. Frith (r1994) *Concert*
(11/95) (NAXO) ① **8 550939**
7 Characteristic Pieces—piano, Op. 7 (pub 1827)
1. E minor; 2. B minor; 3. D; 4. A; 5. A; 6. E minor; 7. E.
4. H. Bauer (r1939) *Concert*
(4/94) (BIDD) ① **LHW009**
Chorale Variations, 'Wie gross ist des Allmächt'gen Güte'—organ (1823)
P. Planyavsky *Concert*
(10/92) (MOTE) ① **CD11271**
3 Fantaisies (or caprices)—piano, Op. 16 (1829)
1. A minor; 2. E minor; 3. E.
1. B. Moiseiwitsch (r1941) *Concert*
(9/90) (APR) ① [2] **APR7005**
2. A. Servadei *Concert*   (7/91) (CARL) ① **PCD949**
2. A. Cortot (r1923) *Concert*
(10/94) (BIDD) ① [2] **LHW014/5**
2. A. Brailowsky (r c1931) *Concert*
(2/95) (PEAR) ① **GEMMCD9132**
2. A. Brailowsky (r1931) *Concert*
(11/95) (DANA) ① [2] **DACOCD338/9**
Fantasy in F sharp minor, 'Sonate écossaise'—piano, Op. 28 (1833)
N. Petrov *Concert*   (7/88) (OLYM) ① **OCD198**
R. de Waal (r1989) *Concert*
(6/93) (CHNN) ① **CG9106**
N. Demidenko (pp1993) *Concert*
(1/94) (HYPE) ① **CDA66781/2**
2 Fugues—organ (1839)
1. E minor; 2. F minor.
John Scott *Concert*
(5/92) (HYPE) ① **CDA66491/2**
Gondellied (Barcarolle) in A—piano (1837)
R. Burnett (r1989) *Concert*
(4/90) (AMON) ① **CD-SAR38**
D. Barenboim *Concert*
(10/94) (DG) ① [2] **437 470-2GX2**
Kinderstücke, 'Christmas Pieces'—piano, Op. 72 (pub 1847)
1. G; 2. E flat; 3. E; 4. D; 5. G minor; 6. F.
J. Galway, Munich RO, J. Georgiadis (arr. D. Overton) *Concert*   (12/91) (RCA) ① **RD60736**
D. Barenboim *Concert*
(10/94) (DG) ① [2] **437 470-2GX2**
2. A. Servadei *Concert*   (7/91) (CARL) ① **PCD949**
2 Klavierstücke
D. Barenboim *Concert*
(10/94) (DG) ① [2] **437 470-2GX2**
4 Little Pieces—organ (1844)
1. Trio (andante) in F; 2. Praeludium (allegretto) in D minor; 3. Nachspiel (andante) in D; 4. Allegro (chorale and fugue) in D minor/major.
1, 4. John Scott *Concert*
(5/92) (HYPE) ① [2] **CDA66491/2**
1, 4. P. Planyavsky *Concert*
(10/92) (MOTE) ① **CD11271**
3. S. Ridgely-Whitehouse *Concert*
(8/91) (HERI) ① **HRCD901**

2 Little pieces—organ (1823)
1. Andante in D; 2. Ostinato in C minor.
1. P. Planyavsky *Concert*
(10/92) (MOTE) ① CD11271
6 Little Pieces—organ (1820-21)
1. Fugue in D minor; 2. Fugue in G minor; 3. Minuet in D minor; 4. Fugue in D minor; 5. D minor; 6. Prelude in D minor.
1. P. Planyavsky *Concert*
(10/92) (MOTE) ① CD11271
Perpetuum mobile in C—piano, Op. 119 (pub 1873)
B. Frith (r1994) *Concert*
(11/95) (NAXO) ① 8 550939
Piano Sonata in B flat, Op. 106 (1827)
F. Chiu (r1993) *Concert*
(5/94) (HARM) ① HMU90 7117
Piano Sonata in E, Op. 6 (1826)
F. Chiu (r1993) *Concert*
(5/94) (HARM) ① HMU90 7117
Piano Sonata in G minor, Op. 105 (1821)
F. Chiu (r1993) *Concert*
(5/94) (HARM) ① HMU90 7117
2 Pieces—organ (1844)
1. Andante with variations in D; 2. Allegro in B flat.
John Scott *Concert*
(5/92) (HYPE) ① [2] CDA66491/2
1. P. Planyavsky *Concert*
(10/92) (MOTE) ① CD11271
6 Preludes and Fugues—piano, Op. 35 (pub 1837)
1. E minor:E; 2. D; 3. B minor; 4. A flat; 5. F minor; 6. B flat.
D. Laval (1994) *Concert* (7/95) (AUVI) ① V4729
B. Frith (r1994) *Concert*
(11/95) (NAXO) ① 8 550939
1. M. Perahia *Concert* (11/87) (SONY) ① MK42401
1. A. Servadei *Concert* (7/91) (CARL) ① PCD949
1. J. Bolet (1988) *Concert*
(4/94) (DECC) ① 436 648-2DH
1, 3. R. de Waal (1989) *Concert*
(6/93) (CHNN) ① CG9106
3 Preludes and Fugues—organ, Op. 37 (1837)
1. C minor; 2. G, D minor; 3. D minor.
John Scott *Concert*
(5/92) (HYPE) ① [2] CDA66491/2
P. Hurford (r1985) *Concert*
(10/95) (DECC) ① 444 570-2DM
2. P. Planyavsky *Concert*
(10/92) (MOTE) ① CD11271
Rondo capriccioso in E—piano, Op. 14 (1824)
M. Levitzki (r1933) *Concert*
(6/92) (APR) ① [2] APR7020
F. Chiu (r1993) *Concert*
(5/94) (HARM) ① HMU90 7117
A. Cortot (r1923) *Concert*
(10/94) (BIDD) ① [2] LHW014/5
W. Haas (r1972) *Concert*
(10/94) (PHIL) ① [2] 442 302-2PM2
D. Laval (r1994) *Concert* (7/95) (AUVI) ① V4729
Scherzo a capriccio in F sharp minor—piano (?1835-36)
R. de Waal (1989) *Concert*
(6/93) (CHNN) ① CG9106
Sonatas for Organ, Op. 65 (1844-45)
1. F major:minor; 2. C major:minor; 3. A; 4. B flat; 5. D; 6. D major:minor.
H. Gurtner (7/91) (CLAV) ① CD50-0715
John Scott *Concert*
(5/92) (HYPE) ① CDA66491/2
1, 2. P. Planyavsky *Concert*
(10/92) (MOTE) ① CD11271
2. J. Lancelot (8/88) (PRIO) ① PRCD228
2. P. Kee *Concert* (10/93) (CHAN) ① CHAN9188
2, 3, 6. P. Hurford (r1985) *Concert*
(10/95) (DECC) ① 444 570-2DM
3. S. Cleobury *Concert* (3/87) (PRIO) ① PRCD185
3. John Scott *Concert* (12/87) (CIRR) ① CICD1007
3 (Chorale) S. Ridgley-Whitehouse *Concert*
(8/91) (HERI) ① HRCD901
3. Andrew Lucas (r1991) *Concert*
(2/94) (MIRA) ① MRCD905
6. C. Crozier *Concert* (7/91) (DELO) ① DE3090
Songs without Words—piano (1825-45)
BOOK 1—Op. 19: 1. Andante con moto, E; 2. Andante espressivo; 3. Molto allegro, A; 'Jägerlied'; 4. Moderato, A (1825); 5. Agitato, F sharp minor; 6. Andante sostenuto, G minor, 'Venetian Gondola Song' (1830). BOOK 2—Op. 30: 7. Andante espressivo, E flat; 8. Allegro di molto, B flat minor; 9. Andante sostenuto, E; 10. Agitato e con fuoco, B minor; 11. Andante grazioso, D; 12. Allegretto, F sharp minor, 'Venetian Gondola Song'. BOOK 3—Op. 38: 13. Con moto, E flat; 14. Allegro non

troppo, C minor; 15. Presto, E; 16. Andante, A; 17. Agitato, A minor; 18. Andante con moto, A flat, 'Duetto'. BOOK 4—Op. 53: 19. Andante con moto, A flat; 20. Allegro non troppo, E flat; 21. Presto agitato, G minor; 22. Adagio, F; 23. Allegro, A minor, 'Volkslied'; 24. Molto allegro vivace, A. BOOK 5—Op. 62: 25. Andante espressivo, G; 26. Allegro con fuoco, B; 27. Andante maestoso, E, 'Trauermarsch'; 28. Allegro con anima, G; 29. Andante, A minor, 'Venetian Gondola Song'; 30. Andante grazioso, A, 'Frühlingslied'. BOOK 6—Op. 67: 31. Andante, E flat; 32. Allegro leggiero, F sharp minor; 33. Andante tranquillo, B flat; 34. Presto, C, 'Spinnerlied: The Bee's Wedding'; 35. Moderato, B minor; 36. Allegro non troppo, E. BOOK 7— (Op. 85): 37. Andante espressivo, F; 38. Allegro agitato, A minor; 39. Presto, E flat; 40. Andante sostenuto, D; 41. Allegretto, A; 42. Allegretto con moto, B flat. BOOK 8— (Op. 102): 43. Andante un poco agitato, E minor; 44. Adagio, D; 45. Presto, C; 46. Un poco agitato, G minor; 47. Allegro vivace, A minor, 'Kinderstück'; 48. Andante, C.
L. Rév (12/87) (HYPE) ① [2] CDA66221/2
L. Edlina (4/92) (CHAN) ① [2] CHAN8948/9
D. Barenboim *Concert*
(10/94) (DG) ① [2] 437 470-2GX2
1. A. Cortot (r1937) *Concert*
(6/92) (BIDD) ① LHW002
1. R. Tureck (pp1992) *Concert*
(8/93) (VAI) ① [2] VAIA1024
1. J. Heifetz, E. Bay (r1946) *Concert*
(11/94) (RCA) ① [65] 09026 61778-2(06)
1, 12, 18, 25, 29, 30, 34, 35, 48. D. Barenboim
Concert (7/85) (DG) ① 415 118-2GH
1, 2, 11, 12, 25, 30, 34-36. W. Haas (r1972) *Concert*
(10/94) (PHIL) ① [2] 442 302-2PM2
1, 2, 4-6, 9-14, 18-21, 25, 30, 34, 36, 42, 45, 47. A. Schiff (5/88) (DECC) ① 421 119-2DH
1, 6, 8, 18, 30. A. Servadei *Concert*
(7/91) (CARL) ① PCD949
5, 41. C. Dowdie *Concert*
(8/91) (HERI) ① HRCD901
6. J. Bream (r1970; arr Bream) *Concert*
(8/93) (RCA) ① [28] 09026 61583-2(4)
6. J. Bream (r1970; arr Bream) *Concert*
6. and (RCA) ① 09026 61583-2(4)
7, 21, 35, 44, 45. English Gtr Qt (arr Gallery) *Concert*
(10/90) (SAYD) ① CD-SDL379
18. M. Hess (r1928) *Concert*
(5/91) (PEAR) ① GEMMCD9462
18, 34. M. Hess (r1929) *Concert*
(3/95) (BIDD) ① LHW024
22, 30, 32, 34. R. Burnett (1989) *Concert*
(4/90) (AMON) ① CD-SAR38
25. F. Kreisler, A. Sándor (arr Kreisler: vn/pf; r1926)
Concert (1/90) (PEAR) ① GEMMCD9324
25. X. Wei, Pam Nicholson (arr Kreisler) *Concert*
(9/90) (ASV) ① CDDCA698
25. G. Piatigorsky, K. Szreter (arr Kreisler: r c1928)
Concert (3/92) (MUSI) ① MACD-674
25. F. Kreisler, A. Sándor (arr Kreisler: r1926)
Concert (9/92) (BIDD) ① [2] LAB049/50
25. V. Horowitz (r1946) *Concert*
(1/93) (RCA) ① GD60463
25, 34. L. Godowsky (r1913) *Concert*
(4/89) (APR) ① [2] APR7011
29. R. Burnett (1989) *Concert*
(4/90) (AMON) ① CD-SAR38
30. E. Feuermann, W. Rebner (arr vc/pf: r1936)
Concert (10/91) (PEAR) ① GEMMCD9443
33. Philippa Davies, T. Owen *Concert*
(3/87) (CARL) ① PCD835
34. S. Rachmaninov (r1928) *Concert*
(11/91) (MSCM) ① MM30271
34. SO, T. Beecham (r c1912: arr orch) *Concert*
(11/91) (SYMP) ① [2] SYMCD1096/7
34. S. Rachmaninov (1920) *Concert*
(3/93) (RCA) ① [10] 09026 61265-2(3)
34. S. Rachmaninov (1928) *Concert*
(3/93) (RCA) ① [10] 09026 61265-2(1)
34. J. Hofmann (pp1937) *Concert*
(5/93) (VAI) ① [2] VAIA1020
34. I. Scharrer (r1909) *Concert*
(7/94) (PEAR) ① GEMMCD9978
34. A. Brailowsky (r1931) *Concert*
(11/95) (DANA) ① [2] DACOCD338/9
42. C. Dowdie, S. Ridgley-Whitehouse (arr cpsr)
Concert (8/91) (HERI) ① HRCD901
3 Studies—piano, Op. 104b
1. B flat minor (1836); 2. F (1834); 3. A minor (?1838).
2, 3. S. Rachmaninov (r1927) *Concert*
(3/93) (RCA) ① [10] 09026 61265-2(1)
3. V. Horowitz (pp1967) *Concert*
(7/94) (SONY) ① SK53471

Variations sérieuses in D minor—piano, Op. 54 (1841)
M. Perahia *Concert* (11/87) (SONY) ① MK42401
R. Burnett (1989) *Concert*
(4/90) (AMON) ① CD-SAR38
V. Horowitz (r1946) *Concert*
(11/91) (RCA) ① GD60451
A. Cortot (r1937) *Concert* (6/92) (BIDD) ① LHW002
R. de Waal (1989) *Concert*
(6/93) (CHNN) ① CG9106
W. Haas (r1972) *Concert*
(10/94) (PHIL) ① [2] 442 302-2PM2
D. Laval (r1994) *Concert* (7/95) (AUVI) ① V4729

SECTION IV: VOCAL AND CHORAL

Abendlied—folksong (Wds. Heine)
B. Fassbaender, K. Moll, C. Garben *Concert*
(9/91) (HARM) ① HMC90 5210
F. Lott, A. Murray, G. Johnson (r1991) *Concert*
(7/92) (EMI) ① CDC7 54411-2
M. Horne, F. von Stade, Martin Katz (r1992) *Concert*
(3/94) (RCA) ① 09026 61681-2
6 Anthems, Op. 79 (1843-44)
1. Rejoice, O ye people; 2. Thou, Lord, our refuge hast been; 3. Above all praises; 4. Lord, on our offences; 5. Let our hearts be joyful; 6. For our offences.
Cpte Corydon Sngrs, M. Best *Concert*
(4/90) (HYPE) ① CDA66359
King's College Ch, S. Cleobury (r1990) *Concert*
(3/94) (ARGO) ① 433 452-2ZH
Der Blumenkranz (The Garland)—Lied, Op. posth (1829) (Wds. T. Moore)
D. Fischer-Dieskau, W. Sawallisch (r1970) *Concert*
(12/93) (EMI) ① [2] CMS7 64827-2
6 Duets, Op. 63 (1845)
1. Ich woll't meine Lieb (wds. Heine); 2. Abschiedslied der Zugvögel (wds. von Fallerstein); 3. Gruss (wds. Eichendorff); 4. Herbstlied (wds. Klingemann); 5. Volkslied (wds. Burns); 6. Maiglöckchen und die Blümelein.
1. K. Ferrier, I. Baillie, G. Moore (r1945: Eng) *Concert*
(6/88) (EMI) ① CDH7 61003-2
1. R. Tauber, Orch (r1933) *Concert*
(4/90) (PEAR) ① GEMMCD9381
1, 3, 5. M. Horne, F. von Stade, Martin Katz (r1992)
Concert (3/94) (RCA) ① 09026 61681-2
1-5. H. Komatsu, K. Moll, C. Garben *Concert*
(9/91) (HARM) ① HMC90 5210
3. S. Gritton, J. Bowen, C. Dowdie *Concert*
(8/91) (HERI) ① HRCD901
5, 6. F. Lott, A. Murray, G. Johnson (r1991) *Concert*
(7/92) (EMI) ① CDC7 54411-2
Ehre sei Gott in der Höhe—double chorus
Corydon Sngrs, M. Best *Concert*
(4/90) (HYPE) ① CDA66359
Elias—oratorio: German text version of Elijah (1846) (Wds. Schubring trans Bartholemew)
PART I: 1a. Overture; 1b. Hilf, Herr!; 1c. Die Tiefe ist versiegelt!; 2. Herr, höre unser Gebet!; 3. Zerreisset eure Herzen; 4. So ihr mich von ganzem Herzen suchet; 5. Aber der Herr sieht es nicht; 6. Elias! gehe weg von hinnen; 7a. Denn er hat seinen Engeln befohlen; 7b. Nun auch der Bach vertrocknet ist; 8. Was hast du an mir getan; 9. Wohl dem, der den Herrn fürchtet; 10a. Herr Gott Abrahams; 10b. Seht! Er kommt, Herr Zebaoth lebet; 11. Baal, erhöre uns!; 12a. Rufet lauter!; 12b. Baal, erhöre uns, wache auf!; 13a. Rufet lauter! Er hört euch nicht!; 13b. Baal! Gib uns Antwort!; 14. Herr Gott Abrahams; 15. Wirf dein Anliegen auf den Herrn; 16. Der du deine Diener machst; 17. Ist nicht des Herrn Wort; 18. Weh ihnen, dass sie von mir weichen!; 19a. Hilf deinen Volk; 19b. O Herr! du hast nun deine Feinde verworfen; 20. Dank sei dir, Gott. PART 2: 21. Höre, Israel, höre des Herrn Stimme!; 22. Fürchte dich nicht; 23. Der Herr hat dich erhoben; 24. Wehe ihm, er muss sterben!; 25. Du Mann Gottes, lass meine Rede; 26. Es ist genug!; 27. Siehe, er schläft unter dem Wacholder; 28. Hebe deine Augen auf zu den Bergen; 29. Siehe, der Hüter Israels; 30. Stehe du auf Elias; 31. Sei stille dem Herrn; 32. Wer bis and das Ende beharrt; 33. Herr, es wird Nacht um mich; 34. Der Herr ging vorüber; 35. Seraphim standen über ihm; 36a. Gehe wiederum hinab!; 36b. Ich gehe hinab!; 37. Ja, es sollen wohl Berge; 38. Und der Prophet Elias brach hervor; 39. Dann werden die Gerechten leuchten; 40. Darum ward gesendet der Prophet Elias; 41a. Aber einer erwacht von Mitternacht; 41b. Wohlan, alle die ihr durstig seid; 42. Alsdann wird euer Licht.
Cpte H. Donath, K. Klein, J. van Nes, D. George, A. Miles, Leipzig Rad Chor, Israel PO, K. Masur (pp1992) (5/93) (TELD) ① [2] 9031-73131-2

Cpte E. Ameling, R. Krahmer, A. Burmeister, G. Schröter, P. Schreier, H.J. Rotzsch, T. Adam, H.C. Polster, Leipzig Rad Chor, Leipzig Gewandhaus, W. Sawallisch (r1968)
(8/93) (PHIL) Ⓓ [2] **438 368-2PM2**

Cpte S. Isokoski, D. Collot, M. Groop, J.M. Ainsley, P. Salomaa, Collegium Vocale, Chapelle Royale Ch, Chapelle Royale Orch, Paris Champs-Élysées Orch, P. Herreweghe (pp1993)
(11/93) (HARM) Ⓓ [2] **HMC90 1463/4**

Cpte C. James, N. Maultsby, K. Lewis, J. van Dam, Brussels Théâtre de la Monnaie Chor, Brussels Théâtre de la Monnaie Orch, A. Pappano (r1994)
(7/95) (FORL) Ⓓ [2] **UCD16734/5**

Cpte C. Schäfer, C. Kallisch, M. Schade, W. Schöne, Stuttgart Gächinger Kantorei, Stuttgart Bach Collegium, H. Rilling (r1994)
(9/95) (HANS) Ⓓ [2] **98 928**

3, 4, 39. U. Heilmann, Leipzig Gewandhaus, P. Schreier (r1993) *Concert*
(3/95) (DECC) Ⓓ **440 680-2DH**

7a Dresden Kreuzchor, M. Flämig *Concert*
(9/92) (CAPR) Ⓓ **10 367**

14. F. Schorr, LSO, J. Barbirolli (r1931) *Concert*
(9/91) (PEAR) Ⓓ **GEMMCD9398**

14. F. Schorr, LSO, J. Barbirolli (r1931) *Concert*
(1/93) (MMOI) Ⓓ **CDMOIR411**

17, 26. F. Schorr, New SO, A. Coates (r1930) *Concert* (9/91) (PEAR) Ⓓ **GEMMCD9398**

31. R. Anday, LSO, R. Heger (r1929) *Concert*
(5/92) (PREI) Ⓓ **89046**

Elijah—oratorio: English text version of Elias (1846) (Wds. Schubring trans Bartholomew)

PART 1: 1a. Overture; 1b. Help, Lord!; 1c. The deep affords no water; 2. Lord! bow Thine ear; 3. Ye people, rend your hearts; 4. If with all your hearts; 5. Yet doth the Lord see it not; 6. Elijah! get thee hence; 7a. For He shall give his angels; 7b. Now Cherith's brook is dried up; 8. What have I to do with thee?; 9. Blessed are the men that fear Him; 10. As God the Lord; 11. Baal, we cry to thee; 12a. Call him louder; 12b. Hear our cry, O Baal; 13a. Call him louder!; 13b. Hear and answer, Baal!; 14. Lord God of Abraham; 15. Cast thy burden upon the Lord; 16. O Thou, who makest Thine angels spirits; 17. Is not his word like a fire?; 18. Woe unto them; 19a. O man of God; 19b. O Lord, Thou hast overthrown; 20. Thanks be to God!. PART 2: 21. Hear ye, Israel; 22. Be not afraid; 23. The Lord hath exalted thee; 24. Woe to him; 25. Man of God; 26. It is enough; 27. See, now he sleepeth; 28. Lift thine eyes; 29. He, watching over Israel; 30. Arise, Elijah; 31. O rest in the Lord; 32. He that shall endure to the end; 33. Night falleth round me; 34. Behold! God the Lord passeth by!; 35. Above Him stood the Seraphim; 36a. Go, return upon thy way!; 36b. I go on my way; 37. For the mountains shall depart; 38. Then did Elijah; 39. Then shall the righteous shine forth; 40. Behold, God hath sent Elijah; 41a. But the Lord; 41b. O come everyone that thirsteth; 42. And then shall your light break forth.

Cpte R. Plowright, J. Budd, L. Finnie, A. Davies, W. White, LSC, LSO, R. Hickox (r1989)
(2/90) (CHAN) Ⓓ [2] **CHAN8774/5**

Cpte Y. Kenny, Anne Dawson, A.S. von Otter, J. Rigby, A. Rolfe Johnson, K. Begley, T. Allen, J. Connell, J. Hopkins, ASMF Chor, ASMF, N. Marriner (r1991) (10/92) (PHIL) Ⓓ [2] **432 984-2PH2**

14. D. Fischer-Dieskau, New Philh, R. Frühbeck de Burgos *Concert* (8/89) (CFP) Ⓓ **CD-CFP4532**

18, 31. K. Ferrier, Boyd Neel Orch, B. Neel (r1946) *Concert* (6/91) (DECC) Ⓓ **430 096-2DWO**

18, 31. K. Ferrier, Boyd Neel Orch, B. Neel (r1946) *Concert* (6/92) (DECC) Ⓓ **433 470-2DM**

21. I. Baillie, orch (r1928) *Concert*
(7/95) (DUTT) Ⓓ **CDLX7013**

21, 22. J. Uys, Cape Town Melodic Ch, Cape Town SO, A. Coates (pp1952) *Concert*
(2/95) (CLAR) Ⓓ **CDGSE78-50-54**

31. J. Baker, New Philh, R. Frühbeck de Burgos *Concert* (8/89) (CFP) Ⓓ **CD-CFP4532**

Die **erste Walpurgisnacht—cantata: chorus and orchestra, Op. 60 (1832)** (Wds. Goethe)

EXCERPTS: 1. Ouvertüre; 2. Es lacht der Mai; 3. Könnt ihr so verwegen handeln; 4. Wer Opfer heut zu bringen scheut; 5. Verteilt euch, wackre Männer hier; 6. Diese dumpfen Pfaffenchristen; 7. Kommt mit Zacken und mit Gabeln (bass); 8. Kommt mit Zacken und mit Gabeln (chor); 9. So weit gebracht, dass wir bei Nacht; 10. Hilf, ach hilf mir, Krieggeselle; 11. Die Flamme reinigt sich vom Rauch.

C. Cairns, J. Garrison, T. Krause, Cleveland Orch Chor, Cleveland Orch, C. von Dohnányi (r1988) *Symphony 3.* (3/89) (TELA) Ⓓ **CD80184**

B. Remmert, U. Heilmann, T. Hampson, R. Pape, A. Schoenberg Ch, COE, N. Harnoncourt (pp1992) *Midsummer Night's Dream.*
(2/94) (TELD) Ⓓ **9031-74882-2**

J. Rigby, R. Tear, A. Michaels-Moore, R. Van Allan, Philh Chor, Philh, F. D'Avalos (r1993) *Symphony 5.*
(3/94) (CARL) Ⓓ **MCD68**

The **Garland (Der Blumenkranz)—Lied (1829)** (Wds. T. Moore)

N. Stutzmann, D. Baldwin *Concert*
(5/91) (ERAT) Ⓓ **2292-45583-2**

Hear my prayer—hymn for soprano, chorus and organ (1844) (Wds. W. Bartholomew)

1. O, for the wings of a dove.

Salisbury Cath Ch, C. Walsh, R. Seal *Concert*
(9/87) (MERI) Ⓓ **CDE84025**

Anne Dawson, Corydon Sngrs, John Scott, M. Best *Concert* (4/90) (HYPE) Ⓓ **CDA66359**

B. Hendricks, E. Ericson Chbr Ch, E. Lundkvist, E. Ericson *Concert* (4/91) (EMI) Ⓓ **CDC7 54098-2**

Heritage Sngrs, S. Ridgley-Whitehouse (org/dir) *Concert* (8/91) (HERI) Ⓓ **HRCD901**

J. Budd, St Paul's Cath Ch, Adrian Lucas, John Scott *Concert* (10/91) (HYPE) Ⓓ **CDA66439**

U. Selbig, Dresden Kreuzchor, M. Flämig, M-C. Winkler *Concert* (9/92) (CAPR) Ⓓ **10 367**

C. Studer, Ambrosian Sngrs, LSO, I. Marin *Concert*
(11/92) (DG) Ⓓ **435 387-2GH**

Trinity Coll Ch, Cambridge, R. Marlow (r1993) *Concert* (2/94) (CONI) Ⓓ **CDCF219**

King's College Ch, S. Cleobury, C. Hughes (r1990; Ger) *Concert* (3/94) (ARGO) Ⓓ **433 452-2ZH**

1. E. Mason, orch (r1926) *Concert*
(8/93) (SYMP) Ⓓ **SYMCD1136**

1. E. Mason, orch, F. Black (r1926) *Concert*
(8/94) (ROMO) Ⓓ **81009-2**

Heilig, heilig ist Gott der Herr Zebaoth—double choir

Corydon Sngrs, M. Best *Concert*
(4/90) (HYPE) Ⓓ **CDA66359**

Dresden Kreuzchor, M. Flämig *Concert*
(9/92) (CAPR) Ⓓ **10 367**

Das **Hohelied** (unidentied)

E. Destinn, anon (r1905) *Concert*
(12/94) (SUPR) Ⓓ [12] **11 2136-2(1)**

Im Grünen—choral songs, Op. 59 (1844)

1. Im Grünen (wds. von Chezy); 2. Frühzeitiger Frühling (wds. Goethe); 3. Abschied vom Wald (wds. Eichendorff); 4. Die Nachtigall (wds. Goethe); 5. Ruhetal (wds. Uhland); 6. Jagdlied (wds. Eichendorff).

3. R. Tauber, Orch, F. Weissmann (r1932) *Concert*
(4/90) (PEAR) Ⓓ **GEMMCD9381**

Infelice—concert aria: soprano and orchestra, Op. 94 (1834-43) (Wds. P. Metastasio)

H. Kwon, Hamburg PO, G. Albrecht (r1992) *Concert*
(8/94) (CAPR) Ⓓ **10 449**

Keine von der Erde schönen—Lied, Op. posth (1834) (Wds. Byron)

J. Protschka, H. Deutsch *Concert*
(6/92) (CAPR) Ⓓ **10 366**

Kyrie in A—double choir, Op. posth (?1846)

Corydon Sngrs, M. Best *Concert*
(4/90) (HYPE) Ⓓ **CDA66359**

12 Lieder, Op. 8 (1828)

1. Minnelied (wds. Hölty); 2. Das Heimweh (wds. Robert); 3. Italien (wds. Grillparzer); 4. Erntelied (wds. trad); 5. Pilgerspruch (wds. Flemming); 6. Frühlingslied (wds. Robert); 7. Maienlied (wds. von der Warte); 8. Andres Maienlied or Hexenlied (wds. Hölty); 9. Abendlied (wds. Voss); 10. Romanze (from the Spanish); 11. Im Grünen (wds. Voss); 12. Suleika und Hatem (2vv; wds. Goethe).

1, 4, 5, 7. J. Protschka, H. Deutsch *Concert*
(6/92) (CAPR) Ⓓ **10 366**

1, 9, 11. J. Protschka, H. Deutsch *Concert*
(10/92) (CAPR) Ⓓ **10 363**

3, 5, 8, 12. S. Gritton, C. Dowdle *Concert*
(8/91) (HERI) Ⓓ **HRCD901**

4, 8. D. Fischer-Dieskau, W. Sawallisch (r1970) *Concert* (12/93) (EMI) Ⓓ [2] **CMS7 64827-2**

6, 10. G. Anselmi, Bettinelli (r1910: Ital) *Concert*
(7/95) (SYMP) Ⓓ **SYMCD1170**

7, 8. M. Price, G. Johnson (r1993) *Concert*
(3/94) (HYPE) Ⓓ **CDA66666**

8. N. Stutzmann, D. Baldwin *Concert*
(5/91) (ERAT) Ⓓ **2292-45583-2**

8, 10. B. Bonney, G. Parsons (r1991) *Concert*
(2/93) (TELD) Ⓓ **2292-44946-2**

12 Lieder, Op. 9 (1830)

1. Frage (wds. Voss); 2. Geständnis (wds. Anon); 3. Wartend (wds. Anon); 4. Im Frühling (wds. Anon); 5. Im Herbst (wds. Klingemann); 6. Scheidend (wds. Voss); 7. Sehnsucht (wds. Droysen); 8. Frühlingsglaube (wds. Uhland); 9. Ferne (wds. Droysen); 10. Verlust (wds. Heine); 11. Entsagung (wds. Droysen); 12. Die Nonne (wds. Uhland).

1, 2, 8. M. Price, G. Johnson (r1993) *Concert*
(3/94) (HYPE) Ⓓ **CDA66666**

1, 3-6, 8, 9, 11. J. Protschka, H. Deutsch *Concert*
(10/92) (CAPR) Ⓓ **10 363**

1, 5, 7-10, 12. B. Bonney, G. Parsons (r1991) *Concert* (2/93) (TELD) Ⓓ **2292-44946-2**

6. W. Holzmair, A. Wagner *Concert*
(7/91) (PREI) Ⓓ **93368**

6. D. Fischer-Dieskau, W. Sawallisch (r1970) *Concert*
(12/93) (EMI) Ⓓ [2] **CMS7 64827-2**

6, 9. N. Stutzmann, D. Baldwin *Concert*
(5/91) (ERAT) Ⓓ **2292-45583-2**

8. J. Bowen, S. Ridgley-Whitehouse *Concert*
(8/91) (HERI) Ⓓ **HRCD901**

6 Lieder, Op. 19a (1834)

1. Frühlingslied (wds. von Lichtenstein); 2. Das erste Veilchen (wds. Ebert); 3. Winterlied (from the Swedish); 4. Neue Liebe (wds. Heine); 5. Gruss (wds. Heine); 6. Reiselied (wds. Ebert).

D. Fischer-Dieskau, W. Sawallisch (r1970) *Concert*
(12/93) (EMI) Ⓓ [2] **CMS7 64827-2**

1, 3-5. W. Holzmair, A. Wagner *Concert*
(7/91) (PREI) Ⓓ **93368**

2, 3, 6. J. Protschka, H. Deutsch *Concert*
(10/92) (CAPR) Ⓓ **10 363**

3, 4. B. Bonney, G. Parsons (r1991) *Concert*
(2/93) (TELD) Ⓓ **2292-44946-2**

4. F. Lott, G. Johnson (r1991) *Concert*
(7/92) (EMI) Ⓓ **CDC7 54411-2**

4, 5. J. Protschka, H. Deutsch *Concert*
(6/92) (CAPR) Ⓓ **10 366**

4, 5. K. McMillan, M. McMahon (r1992) *Concert*
(6/93) (CBC) Ⓓ **MVCD1052**

4, 5. M. Price, G. Johnson (r1993) *Concert*
(3/94) (HYPE) Ⓓ **CDA66666**

4, 5. C. Prégardien, A. Staier (r1993) *Concert*
(12/94) (DHM) Ⓓ **05472 77319-2**

4, 6. N. Stutzmann, D. Baldwin *Concert*
(5/91) (ERAT) Ⓓ **2292-45583-2**

5. O. Bär, G. Parsons (r1993/4) *Concert*
(12/95) (EMI) Ⓓ **CDC5 55345-2**

6 Lieder, Op. 34 (1836)

1. Minnelied (old German); 2. Auf Flügeln des Gesanges (wds. Heine); 3. Frühlingslied (wds. Klingemann); 4. Suleika (wds. Goethe); 5. Sonntagslied (wds. Klingemann); 6. Reiselied (wds. Heine).

1, 2, 3, 6. D. Fischer-Dieskau, W. Sawallisch (r1970) *Concert* (12/93) (EMI) Ⓓ [2] **CMS7 64827-2**

1, 2, 6. J. Protschka, H. Deutsch *Concert*
(6/92) (CAPR) Ⓓ **10 366**

2. K. Te Kanawa, ECO, Barry Rose *Concert*
(5/85) (PHIL) Ⓓ **412 629-2PH**

2. T. Reilly, ASMF Chbr Ens (arr. G. Langford) *Concert* (12/86) (CHAN) Ⓓ **CHAN8486**

2. H. Prey, L. Hokanson *Concert*
(6/87) (DENO) Ⓓ **CO-1254**

2. V. de los Angeles, Sinfonia of London, R. Frühbeck de Burgos (orch Gamley) *Concert*
(10/88) (EMI) Ⓓ **CDM7 69502-2**

2. I. Stern, Columbia SO, F. Brieff (arr Harris) *Concert* (7/90) (SONY) Ⓓ **SK45816**

2. J. Heifetz, A. Benoist (r1918: arr Achron) *Concert*
(1/91) (BIDD) Ⓓ **LAB015**

2. A. Murray, G. Johnson (r1991) *Concert*
(7/92) (EMI) Ⓓ **CDC7 54411-2**

2. K. McMillan, M. McMahon (r1992) *Concert*
(6/93) (CBC) Ⓓ **MVCD1052**

2. H. Schlusnus, F. Rupp (r1932) *Concert*
(1/94) (PREI) Ⓓ [2] **89205**

2. J. Heifetz, E. Bay (r1949) *Concert*
(11/94) (RCA) Ⓓ [65] **09026 61778-2(40)**

2. J. Heifetz, I. Achron (r1928) *Concert*
(11/94) (RCA) Ⓓ [65] **09026 61778-2(02)**

2. J. Heifetz, A. Benoist (r1918) *Concert*
(11/94) (RCA) Ⓓ [65] **09026 61778-2(01)**

2. E. Rethberg, orch (r1924) *Concert*
(2/95) (ROMO) Ⓓ [2] **81012-2**

2. E. Rethberg, K. Ruhrseitz (r1932) *Concert*
(10/95) (ROMO) Ⓓ [2] **81014-2**

2. O. Bär, G. Parsons (r1993/4) *Concert*
(12/95) (EMI) Ⓓ **CDC5 55345-2**

2-4. S. Gritton, C. Dowdle *Concert*
(8/91) (HERI) Ⓓ **HRCD901**

2-4. M. Price, G. Johnson (r1993) *Concert*
(3/94) (HYPE) Ⓓ **CDA66666**

2, 4, 6. N. Stutzmann, D. Baldwin *Concert*
(5/91) (ERAT) Ⓓ **2292-45583-2**

2-5. B. Bonney, G. Parsons (r1991) *Concert*
(2/93) (TELD) Ⓓ **2292-44946-2**

2, 6. W. Holzmair, A. Wagner *Concert*
(7/91) (PREI) Ⓓ **93368**

2, 6. C. Prégardien, A. Staier (r1993) *Concert*
(12/94) (DHM) Ⓓ **05472 77319-2**

F. Lott, A. Murray, G. Johnson (r1991) *Concert*
(7/92) (EMI) ① **CDC7 54411-2**
Wie Kann ich froh und lustig sein—duet
(Wds. Kaufmann)
H. Komatsu, K. Moll, C. Garben *Concert*
(9/91) (HARM) ① **HMC90 5210**

SECTION V: STAGE WORKS

Antigone—incidental music to Sophocles'
play, Op. 85 (1841—Potsdam)
Cpte R. Pape, T. Hämer, K. Piontek, G. Schoss, W.
Unterzaucher, Berlin Rad Chor, Weber Men's Ch,
Berlin RSO, S. Soltesz (r1991)
(3/94) (CAPR) ① **10 392**
Athalie—incidental music to Racine's play,
Op. 74 (1845—Berlin-Charlottenburg)
EXCERPTS: 1. Overture; 2. War March of the
Priests.
1. Bamberg SO, C.P. Flor *Concert*
(1/89) (RCA) ① **RD87905**
2. T. Trotter (arr.Best) *Concert*
(11/87) (HYPE) ① **CDA66216**
1. Boston Pops, A. Fiedler (r1958) *Concert*
(1/94) (RCA) ① **09026 61249-2**
Der Heimkehr aus der Fremde, 'Son and
Stranger'—Liederspiel: 1 act (1829—Berlin)
(Lib. K Klingemann)
EXCERPTS: 1. Overture; 2. Ich bin ein veilgereister
Mann (I'm a roamer bold).
1. Berne SO, P. Maag *Concert*
(6/86) (CARL) ① **PCD824**
Die Hochzeit des Camacho—opera: 2 acts,
Op. 10 (1827—Berlin) (Lib. K. Klingemann,
after Cervantes: dialogue lost)
Cpte R. Schudel, C. Swanson, C. Bieber, W. Mok, V.
Horn, R. Lukas, J. Becker, W. Murray, F. Molsberger,
Berlin RIAS Chbr Ch, BRSO, B. Klee
(9/91) (SCHW) ① [2] **314042**
Cpte R. Hofman, A. Ulbrich, S. Weir, H. Rhys-Evans,
N. van der Meel, W. Wild, U. Malmberg, U. Cold,
Aachen Youth Ch, Modus Novus Ch, Anima Eterna,
J. van Immerseel (r1992)
(12/93) (CHNN) ① [2] **CCS5593**
Overture Bamberg SO, C.P. Flor *Concert*
(1/89) (RCA) ① **RD87905**
A Midsummer Night's Dream—incidental
music to Shakespeare's play, Opp. 21 and 61
(1826/1842)
1. Overture, Op. 21; 2. Scherzo (Entr'acte to Act 2);
3. Melodram: 'Over hill, over dale' and March of the
Elves (Act 2); 4. Song with chorus: 'You spotted
snakes' (Act 2); 5. The Speels (Melodram: Act 2); 6.
Entr'acte/Intermezzo (Hermia seeks Lysander; Entry
of the Rustics: Act 3); 7. Melodram: 'What hempen
homespuns' (Act 3); 8. Nocturne (Act 3); 9.
Melodram: 'The Removal of the Spells' (Act 4); 10.
Wedding March (Entr'acte to Act 5); 11. Fanfare and
Funeral March (Act 5); 12. Bergomask (Dance of the
Rustics: Act 5); 13. Wedding March—reprise (Act 5);
14. Finale: 'Through the house' (Act 5).
Cpte L. Watson, D. Wallis, Finchley Children's Music
Group, LSO, A. Previn
(9/86) (EMI) ① **CDC7 47163-2**
Cpte S. Piau, D. Collot, Chapelle Royale Ch,
Collegium Vocale, Paris Champs-Elysées Orch, P.
Herreweghe (r1994) *Hebrides.*
(4/95) (HARM) ① **HMC90 1502**
1. BRSO, Colin Davis *Symphony 3.*
(3/85) (ORFE) ① **C089841A**
1. LSO, C. Abbado (r1984) *Concert*
(1/86) (DG) ① [4] **415 353-2GH4**
1. LSO, C. Abbado *Concert*
(5/88) (DG) ① **423 104-2GH**
1. Bamberg SO, C.P. Flor *Concert*
(1/89) (RCA) ① **RD87905**
1. BPO, W. Furtwängler *Concert*
(4/92) (KOCH) ① [2] **37073-2**
1. T. Trotter (r1992: trans org: S P Warren) *Concert*
(4/94) (DECC) ① **436 656-2DH**
1, 2, 3, 4, 6, 8, 10, 11, 12, 13, 14. L. Popp, M.
Lipovšek, Bamberg Sym Chor, Bamberg SO, C.P.
Flor (r1987) (10/88) (RCA) ① **RD87764**
1, 2, 3, 4, 6, 8, 10, 11, 12, 14. L. Dawson, D.
Schaechter, Berlin Rad Chor, Berlin Deutsches SO,
Vladimir Ashkenazy (r1992) *Octet, Op. 20.*
(8/94) (DECC) ① **440 296-2DH**
1, 2, 3, 4, 6, 8, 10, 11, 12, 14. K. Battle, F. von
Stade, J. Dench, Tanglewood Fest Chor, Boston SO,
S. Ozawa (r1993) (10/94) (DG) ① **439 897-2GH**
1, 2, 4, 6, 8, 10, 11, 12, 13, 14. K. Toyoda, Y. Ohkura, Tokyo
Metropolitan SO Chor, Tokyo Metropolitan SO, P.
Maag (1/86) (DENO) ① **C37-7564**
1, 2, 4, 6, 8, 10, 11, 12, 13, 14. E. Eustis, F. Kirk,
Pennsylvania Univ Glee Club, Philadelphia, A.
Toscanini (r1942: Eng) *Concert*
(6/91) (RCA) ① [4] **GD60328**

1, 2, 4, 6, 8, 10, 11, 12, 13, 14. L. Dawson, S.
Mentzer, Rotterdam Phil Chor Women's Voices,
Rotterdam PO, J. Tate
(3/92) (EMI) ① **CDC7 54393-2**
1, 2, 4, 6, 8, 10, 11, 12, 13, 14. H. Harper, J. Baker,
Philh Chor, Philh, O. Klemperer *Concert*
(9/92) (EMI) ① **CDM7 64144-2**
1, 2, 4, 6, 8, 10, 11, 12, 13, 14. E. Wiens, Sarah
Walker, LP Ch, LPO, A. Litton
(9/92) (CFP) ① **CD-CFP4593**
1, 2, 4, 6, 8, 10, 11, 12, 13, 14. P. Coburn, E. von
Magnus, C. Bantzer, COE, N. Harnoncourt (pp1992)
Erste Walpurgisnacht.
(2/94) (TELD) ① **9031-74882-2**
1, 2, 4, 6, 8, 10, 11, 12, 13, 14. J. Howarth, J. Rigby,
Bach Ch, Philh, F. D'Avalos (r1993) *Fair Melusina.*
(7/94) (CARL) ① **MCD78**
1, 2, 4, 6, 8, 10, 11, 12, 13, 14. C. Schäfer, I. Danz,
Oregon Bach Fest Women's Chor, Oregon Bach Fest
Orch, H. Rilling (r1993) (8/94) (HANS) ① **98 922**
1, 2, 5, 6. Boston SO, Colin Davis (r1976) *Concert*
(10/94) (PHIL) ① [2] **442 302-2PM2**
1, 2, 6, 8, 10. Atlanta SO, Y. Levi *Symphony 4.*
(5/93) (TELA) ① **CD80318**
1, 2, 6, 8, 10, 11. SRO, A. Jordan (1993) *Concert*
(5/94) (ERAT) ① **9509-91734-2**
1, 2, 8. BBC SO, W. Mengelberg (pp1938) *Concert*
(12/93) (ARHI) ① **ADCD111**
1, 2, 8, 10. BRSO, R. Kubelík (r1964) *Concert*
(3/94) (DG) ① **439 411-2GCL**
1, 2, 8, 10. LSO, P. Maag (r1957) *Concert*
(7/95) (DECC) ① **443 578-2DCS**
1, 2, 8, 10. Concertgebouw, G. Szell (1957) *Concert*
(11/95) (PHIL) ① [2] **442 727-2PM2**
2. T. Trotter (trans org: Warren) *Concert*
(11/87) (HYPE) ① **CDA66216**
2. H. Shelley (r1980: trans pf: Rachmaninov) *Concert*
(10/88) (HYPE) ① **CDA66009**
2. NYPSO, A. Toscanini (r1929) *Concert*
(3/90) (PEAR) ① [3] **GEMMCDS9373**
2. S. Rachmaninov (r1935: arr pf: Rachmaninov)
Concert (5/90) (RCA) ① **GD87766**
2. LPO, T. Beecham (bp1939) *Concert*
(11/91) (SYMP) ① [2] **SYMCD1096/7**
2. H. Shelley (r1991: arr pf: Rachmaninov) *Concert*
(3/92) (HYPE) ① **CDA66486**
2. NBC SO, A. Toscanini (r1946) *Concert*
(6/92) (RCA) ① **GD60284**
2. NYPSO, A. Toscanini (r1929) *Concert*
(11/92) (RCA) ① **GD60316**
2. S. Rachmaninov (r1935: arr pf: Rachmaninov)
Concert (8/92) (RCA) ① [10] **09026 61265-2(2)**
2. J. Weber (r1992: arr pf: Rachmaninov) *Concert*
(12/93) (CARL) ① **PCD1051**
2. H. Shelley (r1980: trans pf: Rachmaninov) *Concert*
(3/94) (HYPE) ① [8] **CDS44041/8**
2. H. Shelley (r1991: trans pf: Rachmaninov) *Concert*
(3/94) (HYPE) ① [8] **CDS44041/8**
2. LPO, T. Beecham (bp1939) *Concert*
(6/94) (DUTT) ① **CDLX7003**
2. O. Yablonskaya (r1992: arr pf: Rachmaninov)
Concert (6/94) (CONN) ① **CD4194**
2. N. Lugansky (r1993: arr pf: Rachmaninov) *Concert*
(1/95) (VANG) ① **08.99009**
2. G. Cziffra (r1971: trans Rachmaninov: pf) *Concert*
(3/95) (EMI) ① **CDM5 65255-2**
2. B. Moiseiwitsch (r1939: arr pf: Rachmaninov)
Concert (10/95) (APR) ① **APR5505**
2, 10. La Scala Orch, A. Toscanini (r1921) *Concert*
(11/92) (RCA) ① **GD60315**
2, 8. NYPSO, A. Toscanini (r1926) *Concert*
(3/90) (PEAR) ① [3] **GEMMCDS9373**
2, 8. NYPSO, A. Toscanini (r1926) *Concert*
(11/92) (RCA) ① **GD60317**
2, 8. BBC SO, A. Toscanini (pp1935) *Concert*
(4/93) (TEST) ① **SBT1015**
8, 10. LPO, T. Beecham (r1936) *Concert*
(6/94) (DUTT) ① **CDLX7003**
10. St Louis SO, L. Slatkin *Concert*
(6/89) (RCA) ① **RD87716**
10. P. Hurford (trans org) *Concert*
(8/91) (DECC) ① **430 710-2DM**
10. P. Hurford (r1982: trans org) *Concert*
(6/93) (DECC) ① **436 402-2DWO**
Oedipus at Colonos—incidental music to
Sophocles' play, Op. 93 (1845)
Cpte R. Pape, O. Sander, T. Hämer, F. Pigulla, K.
Piontek, W. Unterzaucher, G. Schoss, Berlin Rad
Chor, Weber Men's Ch, BRSO, S. Soltesz (r1991)
(1/95) (CAPR) ① **10 393**

MENDELSSOHN-HENSEL, Fanny (1805–1847) Germany

SECTION I: ORCHESTRAL

Overture in C—orchestra (c1830)
Women's PO, J. Falletta *Concert*
(2/93) (KOCH) ① **37169-2**

SECTION II: CHAMBER

Piano Trio in G minor, Op.11 (?1847)
Cologne Clementi Trio R. Clarke: *Piano Trio.*
(3/87) (LARG) ① **Largo 5103**
Dartington Trio C. Schumann: *Piano Trio.*
(3/90) (HYPE) ① **CDA66331**
Macalester Trio *Concert*
(10/94) (VOX) ① [2] **115845-2**
3 Pieces for Piano Duet (c1840s)
1. Allegretto; 2. Allegro molto; 3. Allegretto grazioso.
Y. Tal, A. Groethuysen (1991) *Concert*
(6/93) (SONY) ① **SK48494**

SECTION III: INSTRUMENTAL

Das Jahr—12 Charakterstücke (1841)
L. Serbescu *Nachspiel.*
(7/89) (CPO) ① **CPO999 013-2**
4 Lieder ohne Worte—piano, Op. 6
3. Andante espressivo; 4. Saltarello Romano—Allegro
molto.
3, 4. L. Serbescu *Concert*
(7/89) (CPO) ① **CPO999 015-2**
Nachspiel—piano
L. Serbescu *Jahr.* (7/89) (CPO) ① **CPO999 013-2**
Piano Sonata in C minor (1843)
L. Serbescu *Concert*
(7/89) (CPO) ① **CPO999 015-2**
Piano Sonata in G minor (1843)
L. Serbescu *Concert*
(7/89) (CPO) ① **CPO999 015-2**
Sonata Movement in E—piano (1824)
L. Serbescu *Concert*
(7/89) (CPO) ① **CPO999 015-2**

SECTION IV: VOCAL AND CHORAL

6 Gartenlieder—4vv, Op. 3 (1846)
1. Hörst du nicht die Bäume rauschen; 2. Schöne
Fremde; 3. Im Herbste; 4. Morgengruss; 5. Abendlich
schon rauscht der Wald; 6. Im Wald.
Heidelberg Madrigal Ch, G. Kegelmann *Concert*
(4/90) (BAYE) ① **BR100041**
Io d'amor, oh Dio, mio moro—concert aria:
soprano and orchestra (1835)
H. Kwon, Hamburg PO, G. Albrecht (1992) *Concert*
(8/94) (CAPR) ① **10 449**
Nachtreigen—unaccompanied choir (8vv)
(1829) (Wds. H. Hensel)
Heidelberg Madrigal Ch, G. Kegelmann *Concert*
(4/90) (BAYE) ① **BR100041**
Oratorium nach Bildern der Bibel
I. Lippitz, A. Fischer-Kunz, H. Hatano, T.
Thomaschke, Cologne Kurrende Chor, Cologne
Kurrende Orch, E.M. Blankenburg
(3/89) (CPO) ① **CPO999 009-2**

MENDOZA Y CORTEZ, Quirino (1862–1957) Mexico

SECTION IV: VOCAL AND CHORAL

Cielito lindo, 'Ay, Ay, Ay, AY,'—Mexican
folksong setting (1919) (Wds. anon)
J. Carreras, P. Domingo, L. Pavarotti, MMF Orch,
Rome Op Orch, Z. Mehta (pp1990) *Concert*
(10/90) (DECC) ① **430 433-2DH**

MENGELBERG, Rudolf (1892–1959) The Netherlands

SECTION I: ORCHESTRAL

Praeludium on the Dutch National Anthem
NYPO, W. Mengelberg (r1924) *Concert*
(4/92) (PEAR) ① [3] **GEMMCDS9922**

MENKEN, Alan (20th Cent) USA

SECTION V: STAGE WORKS

Aladdin—film score (1992) (Lyrics Howard
Ashman & Tim Rice)
EXCERPTS: 1. One Jump Ahead (Lyrics Tim Rice);
2. A Whole New World (Lyrics Tim Rice); 3. Prince Ali
(Lyrics Howard Ashman).
3. Millar Brass Ens, V. Cichowicz (r1994-5; arr
Fraser) *Concert* (12/95) (DELO) ① **DE3186**

Beauty and the Beast—musical film (1991)
(Lyrics H. Ashman)
EXCERPTS: 1. Beauty and the Beast.
1. C. Rosenberger, ECO, D. Fraser (r1994-5; arr
Fraser) *Concert*　　(12/95) (DELO) ① **DE3186**
The Little Mermaid—musical film (1989)
(Lyrics H. Ashman)
EXCERPTS: 1. Poor Unfortunate Souls; 2. Part Of
Your World; 3. Under the Sea.
3. Millar Brass Ens, V. Cichowicz (r1994-5; arr
Fraser) *Concert*　　(12/95) (DELO) ① **DE3186**
Little Shop of Horrors—musical show
(1982—New York) (Lyrics H. Ashman. Based
on 1961 Roger Corman film)
EXCERPTS: 1. Prologue: Little Shop of Horrors; 2.
Skid Row; 3. Da-Doo; 4. Grow for Me; 5. Ya Never
Know; 6. Mushnick and Son; 7. Dentist!; 8.
Somewhere That's Green; 9. Feed Me: Git It; 10.
Now: It's Just the Gas; 11. Closed for Renovation;
12. Suddenly Seymour; 13. Suppertime; 14. The
Meek Shall Inherit; 15. Sominex/Suppertime II; 16.
Finale: Don't Feed the Plants. ADDITIONAL ITEM:
17. We'll Have Tomorrow (cut from original
production).
8. M. Patinkin, Orch, E. Stern (r1993; orch Troob, arr
Ford) *Concert*　　(11/94) (NONE) ① **7559-79330-2**
Pocahontas—musical film (1995) (Lyrics
Stephen Schwartz)
EXCERPTS: 1. Colors of the Wind.
1. ECO, D. Fraser (r1994-5; arr Fraser) *Concert*
　　(12/95) (DELO) ① **DE3186**

MENOTTI, Gian Carlo (b 1911)
Italy/USA

SECTION I: ORCHESTRAL

Apocalypse—large orchestra (1951)
Oregon SO, J. DePreist *Concert*
　　(1/93) (KOCH) ① **37156-2**
**Cantilena e scherzo—orchestra and harp
(1977)**
M. R. Hays, San Diego CO, D. Barra (r1993) *Concert*
　　(8/94) (KOCH) ① **37215-2**
Concerto in F—piano and orchestra (1945)
E. Wild, Sym of the Air, J. Mester *Copland: Piano
Concerto.*　　(2/92) (VANG) ① **08.4029.71**

SECTION II: CHAMBER

**Cantilena e Scherzo—harp and string
quartet (1977)**
H. Storck, A. Lutz, M. Salevic, S. Blaumer, K. Kühr
Concert　　(8/88) (ETCE) ① **KTC1045**

SECTION IV: VOCAL AND CHORAL

**Canti della lontananza—song cycle: soprano
and piano (1967)**
K. Armstrong, H. Francesch *Concert*
　　(7/88) (ETCE) ① **KTC1045**
4 English songs—voice and piano (1982)
1. The idle gift; 2. The swing; 3. The eternal prismer;
4. The longest wait.
K. Armstrong, H. Francesch *Concert*
　　(7/88) (ETCE) ① **KTC1045**
**Notturno—1v, harp and string quartet
(1982)**
K. Armstrong, H. Storck, A. Lutz, M. Salevic, S.
Blaumer, K. Kühr *Concert*
　　(7/88) (ETCE) ① **KTC1045**

SECTION V: STAGE WORKS

**Amahl and the Night Visitors—opera: 1 act
(1951—NBC (New York)** (Lib. cpsr)
Cpte J. Rainbird, L. Haywood, J. Dobson, D.
Maxwell, Curtis Watson, C. Painter, ROH Chor,
ROHO, D. Syrus　　(7/88) (TER) ① **CDTER1124**
Introduction; March; Shepherd's Dance NZ SO, A.
Schenck (r1989) *Concert*
　　(9/90) (KOCH) ① **37005-2**
**Amelia al ballo—opera: 1 act
(1937—Philadelphia)** (Lib. cpsr)
Overture NY Met Op Orch, J. Conlon (pp1991)
Concert　　(6/93) (RCA) ① **09026 61509-2**
While I waste these precious hours L. Price, New
Philh, N. Santi (r1977) *Concert*
　　(12/92) (RCA) ① **[4] 09026 61236-2**
**The Consul—opera: 3 acts
(1950—Philadelphia)** (Lib. cpsr)
My child is dead! I. Borkh, Berlin St Op Orch, A.
Rother (Ger: r1951) *Concert*
　　(4/92) (EMI) ① **[7] CHS7 69741-2(4)**
**Errand into the Maze—ballet (1947—New
York)**
Atlantic Sinfonietta, A. Schenck (r1990) *Concert*
　　(4/92) (KOCH) ① **37051-2**

Sebastian—ballet: 1 act (1944—New York)
Cpte LSO, J. Serebrier *Concert*
　　(5/91) (ASV) ① **CDDCA741**
Sebastian—concert suite from ballet (1947)
EXCERPTS: 1. Introduction; 2. Barcarole; 3. Baruffa;
4. Cortège; 5. Sebastian's Dance; 6. Dance of the
Wounded Courtesan; 7. Pavanne.
NZ SO, A. Schenck (r1989) *Concert*
　　(9/90) (KOCH) ① **37005-2**

MENU, Pierre (1896–1919)
France

SECTION II: CHAMBER

Sonatine—string quartet
Parisii Qt (r1994) *Concert*　　(10/95) (AUVI) ① **V4730**

MERCADANTE, (Giuseppe)
Saverio (Raffaele) (1795–1870)
Italy

SECTION I: ORCHESTRAL

**Concerto for Clarinet and Orchestra in B flat,
Op. 101 (?1819)**
T. Friedli, South-West German CO, P. Angerer
Concert　　(9/86) (CLAV) ① **CD50-0813**
**Concerto for Flute and Orchestra in D
(c1819)**
J. Galway, Solisti Veneti, C. Scimone (r1987) *Concert*
　　(4/94) (RCA) ① **09026 61447-2**
**Concerto for Flute and Orchestra in E
(c1819)**
J. Galway, Solisti Veneti, C. Scimone (r1987) *Concert*
　　(4/94) (RCA) ① **09026 61447-2**
**Concerto for Flute and Orchestra in E minor
(c1819)**
J. Galway, Solisti Veneti, C. Scimone (r1987) *Concert*
　　(4/94) (RCA) ① **09026 61447-2**

SECTION IV: VOCAL AND CHORAL

Il cardellino—Neapolitan song
J. Carreras, ECO, V. Sutej (r1992; arr Agostinelli)
Concert　　(6/93) (PHIL) ① **434 926-2PH**
Salve Maria—soprano and piano (c1864)
arr. trbn and pno C. Lindberg, R. Pöntinen *Concert*
　　(9/85) (BIS) ① **BIS-CD298**
**Le Sette Ultime parole di Nostro Signore
sulla croce—Oratorio (1838)**
5. Qual'ciglio candido.
5. L. Pavarotti, National PO, K.H. Adler (arr Gamley)
Concert　　(12/91) (DECC) ① **433 710-2DH**
**La sposa del marinaro—song: 1v and
piano**
R. Tebaldi, R. Bonynge (r1972) *Concert*
　　(9/94) (DECC) ① **436 202-2DM**

SECTION V: STAGE WORKS

**Amleto—melodramma tragico: 2 acts
(1822—Milan)** (Lib. F Romani)
Qui fu commesso, o popull S. McCulloch, T. Goble,
D. Montague, I. Thompson, A. Thorburn, G. Mitchell
Ch, Philh, D. Parry *Concert*
　　(8/95) (OPRA) ① **[3] ORCH104**
**L' Apoteosi d'Ercole—opera: 2 acts
(1819—Naples)** (Lib. Schmidt)
Ambo unite!...Come palpiti cor mio! G. Dolton, E.
Harrhy, D. Jones, P. Nilon, Philh, D. Parry *Concert*
　　(10/90) (OPRA) ① **[3] ORCH103**
**Gabriella di Vergy—dramma tragico: 2 acts
(1828—Lisbon)** (Lib. A L Tottola, adapted A
Profumo)
Ah che dicil!...Quant'immagini crudeli C. Daniels,
J. Rhys-Davies, P. Nilon, I. Sharpe, K. M. Daymond,
J. Viera, Philh, D. Parry *Concert*
　　(8/95) (OPRA) ① **[3] ORCH104**
**Nitocri—melodramma serio: 2 acts
(1824—Turin)** (Lib. Poissaco, after Zeno)
EXCERPTS: 1. Overture.
1. Overture Philh, D. Parry *Concert*
　　(8/95) (OPRA) ① **[3] ORCH104**
Numi, che intesi mai?...Se m'abbandoni D. Jones,
Philh, D. Parry *Concert*
　　(8/95) (OPRA) ① **[3] ORCH104**
**Orazi e Curiazi—tregedia lirica: 3 acts
(1846—Naples)** (Lib. Cammarano)
Cpte N. Miricioiu, A. Michaels-Moore, M. Jerome, A.
Miles, J. Rhys-Davies, P. Nilon, G. Mitchell Ch, Philh,
D. Parry (r1993)　　(12/95) (OPRA) ① **[3] ORC12**
**La Testa di bronzo—melodramma eroi-
comico: 2 acts (1827—Laranjeiras)** (Lib. F
Romani)
Overture Philh, D. Parry *Concert*
　　(8/95) (OPRA) ① **[3] ORCH104**

MERILÄINEN, Usko (b 1930)
Finland

SECTION II: CHAMBER

**Metamorfora per 7—vn, db, cl, bn, tpt, tbn &
perc (1968)**
K. Mattila, Lahti Chbr Ens, O. Vänskä *Concert*
　　(8/93) (ONDI) ① **ODE792-2**

MERKEL, Gustav Adolf
(1827–1885) Germany

SECTION III: INSTRUMENTAL

Sonata for Organ, Op. 30
H. Fagius, D. Sanger *Concert*
　　(10/85) (BIS) ① **BIS-CD273**

MERTEL, Elias (c1551–1626)
Germany

SECTION III: INSTRUMENTAL

So wünsch ich ihr eine gute Nacht—lute
L. Kirchhof *Concert*　　(11/92) (SONY) ① **SK48068**

MERTZ, Johann Kaspar
(1806–1856) Hungary

SECTION III: INSTRUMENTAL

Bardenklänge—guitar, Op. 13
EXCERPTS: 1. BOOK ONE: 1a. An Malvina; 1b.
Romanze; 2. BOOK TWO: 2a. Abendlied; 2b.
Unruhe; 2c. Elfenreigen; 3. BOOK THREE: 3a. An
die Entferute; 3b. Etude; 3c. Capriccio; 4. BOOK
FOUR: 4a. Gondoliera; 4b. Liebeslied; 5. BOOK
FIVE: 5a. Fingals-Höhle; 5b. Gebeth; 6. BOOK SIX:
Tarantelle; 7. BOOK SEVEN: Variations Mignonnes;
8. BOOK EIGHT: Kindermärchen; 11a. Lied ohne
Worte.
1-8. R. Savino (r1993)
　　(10/94) (HARM) ① **HMU90 7115**
Lied ohne Worte
N. North *Concert*　　(6/87) (AMON) ① **CD-SAR18**
6 Schubertian Songs—guitar (1845)
1. Ständchen; 2. Liebesbotschaft; 3. Die Post; 4.
Aufenthalt; 5. Das Fischermädchen; 6. Lob der
Tränen.
T. Kerstens (r1992-3) *Concert*
　　(9/94) (CONI) ① **CDCF518**

MERULA, Tarquinio
(1594/5–1665) Italy

SECTION II: CHAMBER

Chiaccona a 2
Capriccio Stravagante, S. Sempé (hpd/dir) *Concert*
　　(10/91) (DHM) ① **RD772220**
La Lusignuola—canzon
Amsterdam Loeki Stardust Qt *Concert*
　　(10/94) (L'OI) ① **440 207-2OM**

SECTION III: INSTRUMENTAL

Capriccio cromatico—keyboard
R. Alessandrini (r1994) *Concert*
　　(4/95) (O111) ① **OPS30-118**
Capriccio cromatico—keyboard
T. Koopman (r1992) *Concert*
　　(1/94) (ASTR) ① **E8503**
Toccata del secondo tono—keyboard
A. Lawrence-King (r1992) *Concert*
　　(1/94) (ASTR) ① **E8503**

SECTION IV: VOCAL AND CHORAL

**Curtio precipitato et altri capricci, libro
secondo—madrigal collection: 1v, Op. 13
(pub 1638)**
1. Folle è ben che si crede; 2. Chi vuol ch'io
m'inamori; 3. Un bambin chi va alla scola; 4. Quando
gli uccelli portaranno i Zoccoli; 5. Sentirete una
canzonetta; 6. Menti lingua bugiarda; 7. Ho ch'è
tempo di dormire.
1, 2, 3, 4, 5, 6, 7. M. Figueras, J-P. Canihac, R.
Lawrence-King, R. Lislevand, L. Duftschmid, J.
Savall, T. Koopman (1992) *Concert*
　　(1/94) (ASTR) ① **E8503**
**Madrigali et altre musiche concertate, libro
secondo—1-5vv, Op. 10 (pub 1633)**
1. Aria di Ciaccona, 'Su la cetra amorosa'.
1. M. Figueras, J-P. Canihac, A. Lawrence-King, R.
Lislevand, L. Duftschmid, J. Savall, T. Koopman
(r1992) *Concert*　　(1/94) (ASTR) ① **E8503**

ll **Primo libro de motetti, e sonate concertati—2-5vv and instruments, Op. 6** (1624)
EXCERPTS: 1. Sonata prima a 2 (instrumental); 2. Sonata seconda a 2 (instrumental).
  1. B. Dickey, Tragicomedia *Concert*
    (6/92) (ACCE) ① ACC9173D

MESSAGER, André (Charles Prosper) (1853–1929) France

SECTION II: CHAMBER

Solo de concours—clarinet and flute (1899)
C. Bradbury, O. Davies *Concert*
    (6/90) (ASV) ① CDDCA701
M. Collins, K. Stott *Concert*
    (9/92) (EMI) ① CDC7 54419-2

SECTION V: STAGE WORKS

L' amour masqué—operetta (1923—Paris)
(Lib. Guitry)
EXCERPTS: 1. Overture; 2. Veuillez accepter cette rose; 3. Vingt ans, vingt ans; 4. J'ai deux amants; 5. Valentine a perdu la tête; 6. Kartoum bella; 7. Toute l'histoire en quatre mots; 8. Voulez-vous voir un homme extremement heureux; 9. Viens, s'il est vrai que tu m'attends; 10. Ah, Colette, les bonnes; 11. Chant birman; 12. Le Koutchiska, c'est le ragout; 13. Il était pour moi; 14. Ah! quelle nuit; 15. Excellente combinaison; 16. C'était vous.
  4. B. Hendricks, Philh, L. Foster (r1992) *Concert*
    (8/93) (EMI) ① CDC7 54626-2
La Basoche—opéra-comique (1890—Pris)
(Lib. A. Carré)
EXCERPTS: 1. Prelude. ACT 1: 2. C'est aujord'hui que la Basoche; 3. En attendant l'heure de la bataille; 4. Quand tu connaitras Colette; 5. Midi, c'est l'heure; 6. Bonjour, amil; 7. Dans ce grand Paris; 8. Trop lourd est le poids du veuvage; 9. Vive le roi; 10. Quoi, se dire un simple mortel! ACT 2: 11. Voici le guet qui passe; 12. Il était une fois; 13. Ah, Colette, c'est toil; 14. A table aupres de moi; 15. Eh! que ne parliez-vous?; 16. Il faut agir adroitment. ACT 3: 17. Jour de liesse et de réjouissance; 18. El l'honneur de hyménée; 19. Elle m'aime; 20. A ton amour simple et sincère; 21. Arrêtez, s'il s'agit d'être pendul.
Cpte N. Sautereau, C. Maurane, I. Jaumillot, L. Noguera, L. Lovano, A. Doniat, J. Scellier, Génio, G. Parat, A. Martineau, J. Vilisech, P. Saugey, French Rad Lyric Chor, French Rad Lyric Orch, T. Aubin (bp1960)   (4/94) (MUSD) ① [2] 202572
Elle m'aime; Trop lourd le poids L. Fugère, orch (r1928) *Concert*
    (6/93) (SYMP) ① SYMCD1125
Quand tu connaîtras Collette G. Soulacroix, anon (r1900) *Concert* (9/91) (SYMP) ① SYMCD1089
Coups de Roulis—operetta: 3 acts (1928—Paris) (Lib. A. Willemetz, after M. Larrouy)
Cpte L. Dachary, C. Collart, G. Rey, D. Tirmont, A. Doniat, J. Pruvost, P. Saugey, M. Fauchey, R. Lenoty, C. Daguerressar, Génio, J. Hoffmann, ORTF Lyric Chorale, ORTF Lyric Orch, M. Cariven (bp1963) (11/93) (MUSD) ① [2] 20238-2
Les Deux pigeons, '(The) Two Pigeons'—ballet: 2 acts (1886—Paris)
Cpte WNO Orch, R. Bonynge (r1991)
    (10/93) (DECC) ① 433 700-2DH
Fortunio—operetta: 5 acts (1907—Paris) (Lib. de Caillavet and de Flers)
J'aimais ma vieille maison grise G. Thill, orch, P. Chagnon (r1932) *Concert*
    (8/95) (FORL) ① UCD16727
Madame Chrysanthème—operetta: 4 acts (1893—Paris) (Lib. G Hartmann & A Alexandre, after P Loti)
EXCERPTS: 1. Le jour sous le soleil béni.
  1. B. Hendricks, Philh, L. Foster (r1992) *Concert*
    (8/93) (EMI) ① CDC7 54626-2
  1. S. Jo, ECO, R. Bonynge (r1994) *Concert*
    (9/94) (DECC) ① 440 679-2DH
Monsieur Beaucaire—opérette romantique: prologue and 3 acts (1919—London) (Eng lib. Lonsdale, trans Rivoire & Veber)
EXCERPTS: 1. Introduction. ACT 1: 2a. Au jardin où les fleurs; 2b. O rose; 3. Pour faire une prisonnière; 4a. Souhaitons la bienvenue; 4b. Vous me reprochez ma tiredeur; 5. Qui donc vient là-bas vers nous; 6. Vous me demander une rose. ACT 2: 7. A femme jolie; 8a. Le jour diminue; 8b. Ah! rossignol; 9. Quoi si doux. ACT 3: 10. Je connais une belle; 11. Quand vous series fée; 12. Oh! mer écumante.

Cpte W. Clément, L. Dachary, N. Broissin, R. Lenoty, L. Lovano, H. Bedex, J. Pruvost, G. Foix, M. Enot, A. Balbon, G. Moryn, French Rad Lyric Chor, French Rad Lyric Orch, J. Gressier (bp1958)
    (11/93) (MUSD) ① [2] 20241-2
  9. M. Hill Smith, Chandos Sngrs, Chandos Concert Orch, S. Barry (Eng) *Concert*
    (2/90) (CHAN) ① CHAN8759
  10. M. Hill Smith, P. Morrison, Chandos Concert Orch, S. Barry (Eng) *Concert*
    (7/88) (CHAN) ① CHAN8561
Passionêment—operetta: 3 acts (1926—Paris) (Lib. M. Hennequin & A. Willemetz)
Cpte L. Dachary, C. Harbell, C. Collart, A. Doniat, D. Tirmont, G. Friedmann, Hieronimus, R. Lenoty, ORTF Lyric Orch, J-P. Kreder (bp1964) *P'tites Michu.*
    (3/92) (MUSD) ① [2] 20135-2
Les P'tites Michu—operetta: 3 acts (1897—Paris) (Lib. A. Vanloo & G. Duval)
Excs C. Collart, C. Harbell, C. Maurane, A. Devos, French Rad Lyric Orch, R. Ellis (bp1958)
    Passionêment. (3/92) (MUSD) ① [2] 20135-2
Véronique—opéra-comique: 3 acts (1898—Paris) (Lib. Vanloo and Duval)
EXCERPTS: 1. Overture. ACT 1: 2. La bel état que celui de fleuriste; 3. Ah! la charmante promenade; 4. Vrai Dieu, mes bons amis!; 5. Petite dinde; 6. Les voitures sont à la porte. ACT 2: 7. De-ci, de là; 8. Duo de l'escarpolette; 9. Lisette avait peur du loup; 10. Une grisette mignonne; 11. Adieu, je pars. ACT 3: 12. Chut, chut; 13. Voyons, ma tante; 14. Ma foi! pour venir de province; 15. Eh bien! par ordre procédons; 16. Par une faveur insigne; 17. Voyons, par ordre procédons (final duet).
  5. M. Hill Smith, P. Morrison, Chandos Concert Orch, S. Barry (Eng) *Concert*
    (6/85) (CHAN) ① CHAN8362
  6. E. Eames, E. de Gogorza, orch (r1911: Eng) *Concert* (11/93) (ROMO) ① [2] 81001-2
  7, 8. B. Hendricks, G. Quilico, Lyon Op Orch, L. Foster (r1993) *Concert*
    (6/95) (EMI) ① CDC5 55151-2

MESSIAEN, Olivier (1908–1992) France

SECTION I: ORCHESTRAL

L' Ascension—four meditations for orchestra (1933)
1. Majesté du Christ demandant sa gloire à son Père; 2. Alleluias sereins d'une âme qui désire le ciel; 3. Alléluia sur la trompette, alléluia sur la cymbale; 4. Prière du Christ montant vers son Père.
Paris Opéra-Bastille Orch, Myung-Whun Chung (r1991) *Saint-Saëns: Symphony 3.*
    (8/93) (DG) ① 435 854-2GH
Des Canyons aux étoiles—piano, horn and orchestra (1970-74)
P. Crossley, London Sinfonietta, E-P. Salonen *Concert* (2/89) (SONY) ① [2] M2K44762
Marja Bon, H. Dullaert, G. de Zeeuw, W. Vos, Asko Ens, Schoenberg Ens, Hague Perc Ens, R. de Leeuw (pp1990) (4/95) (AUVI) ① MO782035
Chronochromie—orchestra (1960)
BBC SO, A. Dorati *Concert*
    (3/92) (EMI) ① CDM7 63948-2
Cleveland Orch, P. Boulez (r1993) *Concert*
    (4/95) (DG) ① 445 827-2GH
Concert à quatre—flute, oboe, cello, piano & orchestra (1990-91)
C. Cantin, H. Holliger, M. Rostropovich, Y. Loriod, Paris Opéra-Bastille Orch, Myung-Whun Chung (r1994) *Concert* (8/95) (DG) ① 445 947-2GH
Couleurs de la cité céleste—piano, wind and percussion (1963)
P. Crossley, London Sinfonietta, E-P. Salonen *Concert* (2/89) (SONY) ① [2] M2K44762
Y. Loriod, Paris InterContemporain Ens, P. Boulez (pp1988) *Concert* (8/89) (MONT) ① 781111
P. Donohoe, Netherlands Wind Ens, R. de Leeuw (pp1994) *Concert*
    (1/95) (CHAN) ① [2] CHAN9301/2
Éclairs sur l'Au-Delà—orchestra (1987-91)
Katowice RSO, A. Wit (pp1993)
    (6/94) (JADE) ① JADC099
Paris Opéra-Bastille Orch, Myung-Whun Chung (r1990s) (12/94) (DG) ① 439 929-2GH
Et exspecto resurrectionem mortuorum—wind, brass and percussion (1964)
Paris Orch, S. Baudo *Concert*
    (3/92) (EMI) ① CDM7 63948-2
Berlin RSO, K. A. Rickenbacher (r1993) *Concert*
    (12/94) (SCHW) ① 311232

Netherlands Wind Ens, R. de Leeuw (pp1994) *Concert* (1/95) (CHAN) ① [2] CHAN9301/2
Cleveland Orch, P. Boulez (r1993) *Concert*
    (4/95) (DG) ① 445 827-2GH
7 Haïkaï—piano, wind, percussion and strings (1962)
1. Introduction; 2. Le parc de Nara et les lanternes de pierre; 3. Yamanaka-Cadenza; 4. Gagaku; 5. Miyajima et le torii dans la mer; 6. Les oiseaux de Karuizawa; 7. Coda.
Y. Loriod, Paris InterContemporain Ens, P. Boulez (pp1988) *Concert* (8/89) (MONT) ① 781111
P. Donohoe, Netherlands Wind Ens, R. de Leeuw (pp1993) *Concert*
    (1/95) (CHAN) ① [2] CHAN9301/2
Hymne au Saint Sacrement—orchestra (1932)
French Rad New PO, M. Constant (r1971) *Concert* (4/89) (ERAT) ① 4509-91707-2
Les Offrandes oubliées—méditation symphonique (1930)
French Rad New PO, M. Constant (r1971) *Concert* (4/89) (ERAT) ① 4509-91707-2
Paris Orch, S. Baudo *Concert*
    (5/91) (EMI) ① CZS7 62669-2
Paris Opéra-Bastille Orch, Myung-Whun Chung (r1994) *Concert* (8/95) (DG) ① 445 947-2GH
Oiseaux exotiques—piano, wind and percussion (1955-56)
P. Crossley, London Sinfonietta, E-P. Salonen *Concert* (2/89) (SONY) ① [2] M2K44762
Y. Loriod, Paris InterContemporain Ens, P. Boulez (pp1988) *Concert* (8/89) (MONT) ① 781111
Y. Loriod, BRSO, K. A. Rickenbacher (r1985) *Concert* (12/94) (SCHW) ① 311232
P. Donohoe, Netherlands Wind Ens, R. de Leeuw (pp1993) *Concert*
    (1/95) (CHAN) ① [2] CHAN9301/2
Un sourire—orchestra (1991)
French Rad PO, M. Janowski (r1992) *Concert*
    (11/93) (RCA) ① [2] 09026 61520-2
Berlin RSO, K. A. Rickenbacher (r1993) *Concert* (12/94) (SCHW) ① 311232
Paris Opéra-Bastille Orch, Myung-Whun Chung (r1994) *Concert* (8/95) (DG) ① 445 947-2GH
Le Tombeau resplendissant—orchestra (1931)
Paris Opéra-Bastille Orch, Myung-Whun Chung (r1994) *Concert* (8/95) (DG) ① 445 947-2GH
Turangalîla Symphony—piano, ondes martenot and orchestra (1946-48)
Y. Loriod, J. Loriod, Paris Bastille Orch, Myung-Whun Chung (11/91) (DG) ① 431 781-2GH
R. Muraro, V. Hartmann-Claverie, French Rad PO, M. Janowski (r1992) *Concert*
    (11/93) (RCA) ① [2] 09026 61520-2
J-Y. Thibaudet, T. Harada, Concertgebouw, R. Chailly (r1992: rev edit)
    (11/93) (DECC) ① 436 626-2DH
La ville d'en Haut—piano and orchestra (1987-88)
Y. Loriod, Berlin RSO, K. A. Rickenbacher (r1993) *Concert* (12/94) (SCHW) ① 311232
Netherlands Wind Ens, R. de Leeuw (pp1994) *Concert* (1/95) (CHAN) ① [2] CHAN9301/2
Cleveland Orch, P. Boulez (r1993) *Concert*
    (4/95) (DG) ① 445 827-2GH
Un Vitrail et des oiseaux—piano, wind, trumpet and percussion (1986)
Y. Loriod, Paris InterContemporain Ens, P. Boulez (pp1988) *Concert* (8/89) (MONT) ① 781111
Y. Loriod, Berlin RSO, K. A. Rickenbacher (r1993) *Concert* (12/94) (SCHW) ① 311232
Netherlands Wind Ens, R. de Leeuw (pp1994) *Concert* (1/95) (CHAN) ① [2] CHAN9301/2

SECTION II: CHAMBER

Le Merle noir—flute and piano (1951)
K. Zöller, Aloys Kontarsky *Quatuor.*
    (3/88) (EMI) ① CDM7 63947-2
Quatuor pour la fin du temps, 'Quartet for the End of Time'—clarinet, piano, viola and cello (1940)
1. Liturgie de cristal; 2. Vocalise pour l'Ange qui annonce la fin du Temps; 3. Abîme des oiseaux; Interméde; 5. Lovange á l'Éternité de Jésus; 6. Danse de la fureur, pour les sept trompettes; 7. Fouilles d'arcs-en-ciel, pour l'ange qui annonce la fin du Temps; 8. Lovange à L'Immortalité de Jésus.
Chbr Music NW *Bartók: Contrasts.*
    (6/87) (DELO) ① DE3043
L. Yordanoff, A. Tétard, C. Desurmont, D. Barenboim (r1978) (7/88) (DG) ① 423 247-2GC
G. Deplus, H. Fernandez, J. Neilz, M-M. Petit (r1963) *Rechants.* (4/89) (ERAT) ① 4509-91708-2
W. Boeykens Ens (10/91) (HARM) ① HMC90 1348

E. Gruenberg, G. de Peyer, W. Pleeth, M. Béroff
Merle noir. (3/92) (EMI) ① **CDM7 63947-2**
C. Poppen, W. Meyer, M. Fischer-Dieskau, Y. Loriod
Thème et variations. (3/92) (EMI) ① **CDC7 54395-2**
E. Brunner, Fontenay Trio
(12/92) (TELD) ① **9031-73239-2**
J. MacGregor, M. Mitchell, C. Van Kampen, D.
Campbell (r1993) *Krauze: Quatuor pour la
Naissance.* (6/94) (COLL) ① **Coll1393-2**
Messiaen Qt (r1987) (8/94) (PIER) ① **PV794012**
J.B. Yeh, M. Beaver, M. Johnson, A. Swan (pp1994)
Dvořák: String Quartet 9.
(4/95) (NAIM) ① **NAIMCD008**
Louange à l'Éternité de Jésus N. Fischer, J.K.
Fischer Concert (9/91) (NORT) ① **NR238-CD**
Louange à l'Éternité de Jésus J. Lloyd Webber, J.
Lenehan (r1992) *Concert*
(10/93) (PHIL) ① **434 917-2PH**
Louange à l'Éternité de Jésus M. Bachmann, J.
Klibonoff (r1993) *Concert*
(12/93) (CATA) ① **09026 61824-2**
3. P. Meyer (r1993) *Concert*
(7/95) (DENO) ① **CO-78917**
**Thème et Variations—violin and piano
(1932)**
G. Kremer, M. Argerich *Concert*
(1/91) (DG) ① **427 351-2GH**
C. Poppen, Y. Loriod *Quatuor.*
(3/92) (EMI) ① **CDC7 54395-2**
L. Mordkovitch, M. Gusak-Grin *Concert*
(4/93) (CHAN) ① **CHAN9109**
M. Vengerov, I. Golan (r1993) *Concert*
(4/94) (TELD) ① **9031-77351-2**
Visions de l'Amen—two pianos (1943)
K. Labèque, M. Labèque (r1969) *Concert*
(4/89) (ERAT) ① **4509-91707-2**
T. Lønskov, R. Llambias (4/90) (KONT) ① **32031**
A. Rabinovitch, M. Argerich
(12/90) (EMI) ① **CDC7 54050-2**
Y. Loriod, O. Messiaen (r1962) *Cantéyodjayá.*
(6/92) (ADES) ① **13233-2**
E. Niemann, N. Tilles (11/92) (NALB) ① **NA045CD**
Pianoduo *Concert* (5/93) (CHNN) ① **CCS4592**
P. Hill, B. Frith (1992) *Concert*
(6/94) (UNIC) ① **DKPCD9144**

SECTION III: INSTRUMENTAL

**Apparition de l'église éternelle—organ
(1932)**
L. Thiry *Concert* (9/87) (CALL) ① **CAL9928**
F. Klinda *Concert* (6/89) (OPUS) ① **9351 2020**
J. Bate *Concert* (8/89) (UNIC) ① **DKPCD9028**
H.-O. Ericsson *Concert* (9/89) (BIS) ① **BIS-CD409**
E. Krapp *Concert* (3/92) (WERG) ① **WER6199-2**
O. Messiaen (r1956) *Concert*
(6/92) (EMI) ① **[4] CZS7 67400-2**
T. Trotter (r1991) *Concert*
(9/93) (DECC) ① **436 400-2DH**
G. Weir (r1994) *Concert*
(12/94) (COLL) ① **[7] Coll7031-2**
O. Messiaen (r1956) *Nativité du Seigneur.*
(6/95) (EMI) ① **CDC5 55222-2**
M. Keiser *Concert* (7/91) (GOTH) ① **G49037**
**L' Ascension—four meditations for organ
(1933 arr 1934)**
1. Majesté du Christ demandant sa gloire à son Père;
2. Alléluias sereins d'une âme qui désire le ciel; 3.
Transports de joie d'une âme devant la gloire du
Christ qui est la sienne; 4. Prière du Christ montant
vers son Père.
J. Bate *Concert*
(5/89) (UNIC) ① **[2] DKPCD9024/5**
H.-O. Ericsson *Concert* (9/89) (BIS) ① **BIS-CD409**
E. Boström (pp1988) *Concert*
(3/92) (PROP) ① **PRCD9010**
A. Rössler *Concert* (3/92) (SCHW) ① **315024**
E. Krapp *Concert* (3/92) (WERG) ① **WER6199-2**
O. Messiaen (r1956) *Concert*
(6/92) (EMI) ① **[4] CZS7 67400-2**
T. Trotter (r1991) *Concert*
(9/93) (DECC) ① **436 400-2DH**
O. Messiaen (r1956) *Concert*
(5/94) (EMI) ① **CDC5 55037-2**
G. Weir (r1994) *Concert*
(12/94) (COLL) ① **[7] Coll7031-2**
3. F. Klinda *Concert* (6/89) (OPUS) ① **9351 2020**
3. T. Mechler *Concert* (9/90) (MOTE) ① **CD10881**
Le Banquet céleste—organ (1928)
L. Thiry *Concert* (9/87) (CALL) ① **CAL9928**
J. Bate *Nativité du Seigneur.*
(2/88) (UNIC) ① **DKPCD9005**
H.-O. Ericsson *Concert* (9/89) (BIS) ① **BIS-CD409**
E. Krapp *Concert* (3/92) (WERG) ① **WER6199-2**
O. Messiaen (r1956) *Concert*
(6/92) (EMI) ① **[4] CZS7 67400-2**

O. Messiaen (r1956) *Concert*
(5/94) (EMI) ① **CDC5 55037-2**
G. Weir (r1994) *Concert*
(12/94) (COLL) ① **[7] Coll7031-2**
Cantéyodjayâ—piano (1948)
P. Hill *Concert* (9/89) (UNIC) ① **DKPCD9078**
Y. Loriod (r1958) *Visions de l'Amen.*
(6/92) (ADES) ① **13233-2**
R. Hind (1994) *Concert* (12/94) (UNIT) ① **88019-2**
G. Cheng (r1993) *Concert*
(9/95) (KOCH) ① **37267-2**
Catalogue d'oiseaux—piano (1956-58)
1. Le chocard des alpes; 2. Le loriot; 3. Le merle
bleu; 4. Le traquet stapazin; 5. La chouette hulotte; 6.
L'alouette lulu; 7. La rousserolle effarvatte; 8.
L'alouette calandrelle; 9. La bouscarle; 10. La merle
de roche; 11. La buse variable; 12. La traquet rieur;
13. Le courlis cendré.
A. Ugorski (r1993) *Fauvette des Jardins.*
(5/94) (DG) ① **[3] 439 214-2GH3**
C.-A. Dominique (r1992) *Concert*
(10/94) (BIS) ① **[3] BIS-CD594/6**
1-6. P. Hill (5/88) (UNIC) ① **DKPCD9062**
7-10. P. Hill (9/89) (UNIC) ① **DKPCD9075**
11-13. P. Hill *Fauvette des jardins.*
(8/90) (UNIC) ① **DKPCD9090**
12, 13. R. Hind (1994) *Concert*
(12/94) (UNIT) ① **88019-2**
Les Corps glorieux—organ (1939)
1. Subtilité des corps glorieux; 2. Les eaux de la
grâce; 3. Les anges aux parfums; 4. Combat de la
mort et de la vie; 5. Force et agilité des corps
glorieux; 6. Joie et clarté des corps glorieux; 7. Le
mystère de la Sainte Trinité.
J. Bate *Diptyque.* (5/89) (UNIC) ① **DKPCD9004**
A. Rössler *Messe de la Pentecôte.*
(8/91) (SCHW) ① **315003**
O. Messiaen (r1956) *Concert*
(6/92) (EMI) ① **[4] CZS7 67400-2**
G. Weir (r1994) *Concert*
(12/94) (COLL) ① **[7] Coll7031-2**
6. F. Klinda *Concert* (6/89) (OPUS) ① **9351 2020**
6. P. Kee *Concert* (10/93) (CHAN) ① **CHAN9188**
Diptyque—organ (1930)
J. Bate *Corps glorieux.*
(5/89) (UNIC) ① **DKPCD9004**
H.-O. Ericsson *Concert* (9/89) (BIS) ① **BIS-CD409**
O. Messiaen (r1956) *Concert*
(6/92) (EMI) ① **[4] CZS7 67400-2**
T. Trotter (r1991) *Concert*
(9/93) (DECC) ① **436 400-2DH**
G. Weir (r1994) *Concert*
(12/94) (COLL) ① **[7] Coll7031-2**
4 Etudes de rythme—piano (1949)
1. Ile de feu; 2. Ile de feu II; 3. Mode de valeurs et
d'intensités; 4. Neumes rythmiques.
Y. Takahashi *Concert* (11/86) (DENO) ① **CO-1052**
P. Hill *Concert* (9/89) (UNIC) ① **DKPCD9078**
Y. Loriod (r1968) *Concert*
(12/94) (ERAT) ① **[3] 4509-96222-2**
G. Cheng (r1993) *Concert*
(9/95) (KOCH) ① **37267-2**
1, 2. R. Hind (1994) *Concert*
(12/94) (UNIT) ① **88019-2**
Fantaisie burlesque—piano (1932)
P. Hill (1985) *Concert*
(6/94) (UNIC) ① **DKPCD9144**
La Fauvette des jardins—piano (1972)
P. Hill *Catalogue d'oiseaux.*
(8/90) (UNIC) ① **DKPCD9090**
A. Ugorski (1993) *Catalogue d'oiseaux.*
(5/94) (DG) ① **[3] 439 214-2GH3**
C.-A. Dominique (r1992) *Concert*
(10/94) (BIS) ① **[3] BIS-CD594/6**
Livre d'orgue—organ (1951)
1. Reprises par interventions; 2. Pièce en trio; 3. Les
mains de l'abîme; 4. Chants d'oiseaux; 5. Pièce en
trio; 6. Les yeux dans les roues; 7. 64 durées.
J. Bate *Concert* (8/89) (UNIC) ① **DKPCD9028**
A. Rössler *Concert* (3/92) (SCHW) ① **315024**
O. Messiaen (r1956) *Concert*
(6/92) (EMI) ① **[4] CZS7 67400-2**
G. Weir (r1994) *Concert*
(12/94) (COLL) ① **[7] Coll7031-2**
3. F. Klinda *Concert* (6/89) (OPUS) ① **9351 2020**
Le Livre du Saint Sacrement—organ (1984)
J. Bate (8/87) (UNIC) ① **[2] DKPCD9067/8**
H.-O. Ericsson (with recordings of birdsong used in
organ music) (10/92) (BIS) ① **[2] BIS-CD491/2**
G. Weir (r1994) *Concert*
(12/94) (COLL) ① **[7] Coll7031-2**
**9 Méditations sur le mystère de la Sainte
Trinité—organ (1969)**
J. Bate *Concert*
(5/89) (UNIC) ① **[2] DKPCD9024/5**
H.-O. Ericsson (3/92) (BIS) ① **BIS-CD464**

G. Weir (r1994) *Concert*
(12/94) (COLL) ① **[7] Coll7031-2**
5. F. Klinda *Concert* (6/89) (OPUS) ① **9351 2020**
Messe de la Pentecôte—organ (1950)
1. Entrée: Les langues de feu; 2. Offertoire: Les
choses visibles et invisibles; 3. Consécration: Le don
de la sagesse; 4. Communion: Les oiseaux et les
sources; 5. Sortie: Le vent de l'esprit.
J. Bate *Concert*
(5/89) (UNIC) ① **[2] DKPCD9024/5**
A. Rössler *Corps glorieux.*
(8/91) (SCHW) ① **315023**
E. Boström (pp1988) *Concert*
(3/92) (PROP) ① **PRCD9010**
O. Messiaen (r1956) *Concert*
(6/92) (EMI) ① **[4] CZS7 67400-2**
T. Trotter (r1991) *Concert*
(9/93) (DECC) ① **436 400-2DH**
G. Weir (r1994) *Concert*
(12/94) (COLL) ① **[7] Coll7031-2**
C. Crozier (r1993) *Concert*
(2/95) (DELO) ① **DE3147**
4. F. Klinda *Concert* (6/89) (OPUS) ① **9351 2020**
La Nativité du Seigneur—organ (1935)
1. La vierge et l'enfant; 2. Les bergers; 3. Desseins
éternels; 4. Le verbe; 5. Les enfants de Dieu; 6. Les
anges; 7. Jésus accepte la souffrance; 8. Les mages;
9. Dieu parmi nous.
L. Thiry *Concert* (9/87) (CALL) ① **CAL9928**
J. Bate *Banquet céleste.*
(2/88) (UNIC) ① **DKPCD9005**
H.-O. Ericsson (9/89) (BIS) ① **BIS-CD410**
K. Bowyer (9/90) (CNTI) ① **CCD1012**
O. Messiaen (r1956) *Concert*
(6/92) (EMI) ① **[4] CZS7 67400-2**
G. Weir (r1994) *Concert*
(12/94) (COLL) ① **[7] Coll7031-2**
O. Messiaen (r1956) *Apparition de l'église éternelle.*
(6/95) (EMI) ① **CDC5 55222-2**
2, 9. F. Klinda *Concert* (6/89) (OPUS) ① **9351 2020**
5. M. Keiser *Concert* (7/91) (GOTH) ① **G49037**
9. R. Noehren *Concert* (11/87) (DELO) ① **DE3045**
**6 Petites esquisses d'oiseaux—piano
(1985)**
1. Le rouge-gorge; 2. Le merle-noir; 3. Le rouge-
gorge; 4. La grue-musicienne; 5. Le rouge-gorge; 6.
L'alouette des champs.
P. Hill (1992) *Concert*
(6/94) (UNIC) ① **DKPCD9144**
C.-A. Dominique (r1992) *Concert*
(10/94) (BIS) ① **[3] BIS-CD594/6**
Y. Loriod (r1986) *Concert*
(12/94) (ERAT) ① **[3] 4509-96222-2**
G. Cheng (r1993) *Concert*
(9/95) (KOCH) ① **37267-2**
**Pièce pour le tombeau de Paul
Dukas—piano (1935)**
P. Hill (r1984) *Concert*
(6/94) (UNIC) ① **DKPCD9144**
G. Cheng (r1993) *Concert*
(9/95) (KOCH) ① **37267-2**
8 Préludes—piano (1929)
1. La colombe; 2. Chant d'extase dans un paysage
triste; 3. Le nombre léger; 4. Instants défunts; 5. Les
sons impalpables du rêve; 6. Cloches d'angoisse et
larmes d'adieu; 7. Plainte calme; 8. Un reflet dans le
vent.
P. Hill *Concert* (9/89) (UNIC) ① **DKPCD9078**
Y. Loriod (r1968) *Concert*
(12/94) (ERAT) ① **[3] 4509-96222-2**
1, 3, 6. R. Hind (1994) *Concert*
(12/94) (UNIT) ① **88019-2**
**20 Regards sur l'enfant Jésus—piano
(1944)**
1. Regard du Père; 2. Regard de l'étoile; 3.
L'échange; 4. Regard de la Vierge; 5. Regard du Fils
sur le Fils; 6. Par Lui a été fait; 7. Regard de la Croix;
8. Regard des hauteurs; 9. Regard du Temps; 10.
Regard de l'Esprit de joie; 11. Première communion
de la Vierge; 12. La parole toute puissante; 13. Noël;
14. Regards des Anges; 15. Le baiser de l'Enfant-
Jésus; 16. Regard des prophètes, des bergers et des
Mages; 17. Regard du silence; 18. Regard de
l'Onction terrible; 19. Je dors, mais mon coeur veille;
20. Regard de l'Église d'amour.
Y. Loriod (r1973)
(4/89) (ERAT) ① **[2] 4509-91705-2**
M. Troup (9/89) (CNTI) ① **[2] CCD1004/5**
P. Hill (r1991) (9/92) (UNIC) ① **[2] DKPCD9122/3**
M. Chauveau (r1992-3)
(9/94) (FORL) ① **[2] UCD16709/10**
Y. Loriod (r1973) *Concert*
(12/94) (ERAT) ① **[3] 4509-96222-2**
H. Austbø (r1993)
(12/94) (NAXO) ① **[2] 8 550829/30**

1, 6, 16. R. Hind (r1994) *Concert*
(12/94) (UNIT) ① 88019-2
Rondeau—piano (1943)
P. Hill (r1985) *Concert*
(6/94) (UNIC) ① DKPCD9144
Verset pour la fête de la dédicace—organ (1960)
J. Bate *Concert*   (8/89) (UNIC) ① DKPCD9028
E. Boström (pp1988) *Concert*
(3/92) (PROP) ① PRCD9010
A. Rössler *Concert*   (3/92) (SCHW) ① 315024
G. Weir (r1994) *Concert*
(12/94) (COLL) ① [7] Coll7031-2

SECTION IV: VOCAL AND CHORAL

Harawi—soprano and piano (1945) (Wds. cpsr)
1. La ville qui dormait, toi; 2. Bonjour toi, colombe verte; 3. Montagnes; 4. Doundou tchil; 5. L'amour de Piroutcha; 6. Répétition planétaire; 7. Adieu; 8. Syllabes; 9. L'escalier redit, gestes du soleil; 10. Amour oiseau d'étoile; 11. Katchikatchi les étoiles; 12. Dans le noir.
D. Dorow, C-A. Dominique *Poèmes pour Mi.*
(5/88) (BIS) ① BIS-CD086
O sacrum convivium!—SATB a capella/soprano and organ (1937)
Trinity Coll Ch, Cambridge, R. Marlow *Concert*
(10/90) (CONI) ① CDCF176
France Groupe Vocal *Concert*
(10/90) (ARIO) ① ARN68084
London Sinfonietta Voices, T. Edwards *Concert*
(11/91) (VIRG) ① VC7 59051-2
Musica Sacra, R. Westenburg (r1993) *Concert*
(12/93) (CATA) ① 09026 61822-2
BBC Sym Chor, S. Jackson, J. Filsell (r1993) *Concert*
(1/95) (ASV) ① CDDCA900
3 Petites liturgies de la Présence Divine—18 sops, ondes martenot, cel, vib, perc & stgs (1944) (Wds. cpsr)
1. Antienne de la conversation intérieure; 2. Séquence du verbe, cantique divin; 3. Psalmodie de l'ubiquité par amour.
London Sinfonietta Chor, London Sinfonietta, T. Edwards *Concert*   (11/91) (VIRG) ① VC7 59051-2
Poèmes pour Mi—soprano and piano (1936 orch 1937) (Wds. cpsr)
BOOK 1: 1. Action des grâces; 2. Paysages; 3. La maison; 4. Epouvante. BOOK 2: 5. L'épose; 6. Ta voix; 7. Les deux guerriers; 8. le collier; 9. Prière exaucée.
1-4. J. Delman, L. Negro *Harawi.*
(5/88) (BIS) ① BIS-CD086
5 Rechants—12vv (1949) (Wds. cpsr)
French Rad Chor Sols, M. Couraud (r1968) *Quatuor.*
(4/89) (ERAT) ① 4509-91708-2
France Groupe Vocal *Concert*
(10/90) (ARIO) ① ARN68084
London Sinfonietta Voices, T. Edwards *Concert*
(11/91) (VIRG) ① VC7 59051-2

SECTION V: STAGE WORKS

Saint François d'Assisi—opera (Paris)
Cpte F. Eda-Pierre, J. Van Dam, K. Riegel, M. Philippe, G. Gautier, M. Sénéchal, J-P. Courtis, Paris Op Chor, Paris Op Orch, S. Ozawa (pp)
(12/88) (CYBE) ① [4] CY833/6

MESTRES, Antonio *(?18th Cent)*

SECTION III: INSTRUMENTAL

Cantabile Amoroso—organ
J. van Oortmerssen *Concert*
(11/87) (BIS) ① BIS-CD316
Toccata pastoril—organ
J. van Oortmerssen *Concert*
(11/87) (BIS) ① BIS-CD316
Toccata sexto tono—organ
J. van Oortmerssen *Concert*
(11/87) (BIS) ① BIS-CD316

MEYER, Jean *(19th Cent) Germany/Sweden*

SECTION I: ORCHESTRAL

Jernvägs—galop (1868)
Košice St PO, M. Eichenholz (r1992) *Concert*
(2/94) (MARC) ① 8 223470

MEYER, Philippe-Jacques *(1737–1819) France/England*

SECTION II: CHAMBER

Duet in D minor on Scottish Airs—harp & piano (c1810) (Duets, First Set No. 2)
F. Kelly, T. Roberts (r1994) *Concert*
(3/95) (HYPE) ① CDA66740

MEYERBEER, Giacomo *(1791–1864) Germany*

SECTION I: ORCHESTRAL

Coronation March—two orchestras (1861) (for the coronation of Kaiser Wilhelm I)
Detroit SO, P. Paray (r1959) *Concert*
(11/93) (MERC) ① 434 332-2MM

SECTION IV: VOCAL AND CHORAL

À la jeune mère—song: 1v and piano (Wds. P Durand)
N. Liang, I. Ranta (r1994) *Concert*
(7/95) (CPO) ① CPO999 269-2
Gli Amori di Teolinda—monodrama: soprano, clarinet and orchestra (1806) (Wds. G. Rossi)
J. Varady, J. Fadle, Berlin RIAS Chbr Ch, Berlin RSO, G. Albrecht   (10/92) (ORFE) ① C054831A
La Barque légère—song (pub 1829) (Wds. Naudet)
T. Hampson, G. Parsons *Concert*
(4/92) (EMI) ① CDC7 54436-2
6 Canzonette italiane—1v and piano (Wds. P Metastasio)
1. Scegliar fra mille un core; 2. Da voi, cari lumi; 3. Giura il nocchier; 4. Bei labbri che amore; 5. Se non ti moro allato; 6. Basta dir ch'io sono amante.
N. Liang, I. Ranta (r1994) *Concert*
(7/95) (CPO) ① CPO999 269-2
La Chanson de Maître Floh—song (1839) (Wds. H. Blaze de Bury)
S. Varcoe, G. Johnson *Concert*
(6/88) (HYPE) ① CDA66248
T. Hampson, G. Parsons *Concert*
(4/92) (EMI) ① CDC7 54436-2
Chant de Mai—song: 1v and piano (Wds. H Blaze)
N. Liang, I. Ranta (r1994) *Concert*
(7/95) (CPO) ① CPO999 269-2
Chant des moissonneurs vendéens—song (1839) (Wds. H. Blaze)
T. Hampson, G. Parsons *Concert*
(4/92) (EMI) ① CDC7 54436-2
Fantaisie—song: 1v and piano (Wds. H Blaze)
N. Liang, I. Ranta (r1994) *Concert*
(7/95) (CPO) ① CPO999 269-2
La Fille de l'air—song: 1v and piano (Wds. J Méry)
N. Liang, I. Ranta (r1994) *Concert*
(7/95) (CPO) ① CPO999 269-2
La Folle de St Joséph—song: 1v and piano (Wds. A de Custine)
N. Liang, I. Ranta (r1994) *Concert*
(7/95) (CPO) ① CPO999 269-2
Der Garten des Herzens—song (1839) (Wds. W. Müller)
T. Hampson, G. Parsons *Concert*
(4/92) (EMI) ① CDC7 54436-2
Hör' ich das Liedchen klingen—song (1837) (Wds. H. Heine)
T. Hampson, G. Parsons *Concert*
(4/92) (EMI) ① CDC7 54436-2
Komm! di schönes Fischermädchen—song (1837) (Wds. H. Heine)
T. Hampson, G. Parsons *Concert*
(4/92) (EMI) ① CDC7 54436-2
La Lavandière—song: 1v and piano (Wds. M. Carré)
N. Liang, I. Ranta (r1994) *Concert*
(7/95) (CPO) ① CPO999 269-2
Lied des venezianischen Gondoliers—song (?1837) (Wds. M. Beer)
T. Hampson, G. Parsons *Concert*
(4/92) (EMI) ① CDC7 54436-2
La Marguerite du poète—song: 1v and piano (Wds. H Blaze)
N. Liang, I. Ranta (r1994) *Concert*
(7/95) (CPO) ① CPO999 269-2
Meeresstille—Lied: 1v and piano (Wds. W. Müller)
N. Liang, I. Ranta (r1994) *Concert*
(7/95) (CPO) ① CPO999 269-2

Menschenfeindlich—song (1837) (Wds. M. Beer)
T. Hampson, G. Parsons *Concert*
(4/92) (EMI) ① CDC7 54436-2
Le Poète mourant—song (1836) (Wds. C. Millevoye)
T. Hampson, G. Parsons *Concert*
(4/92) (EMI) ① CDC7 54436-2
Le Revenant du vieux Château—song: 1v and piano (Wds. J. Méry)
N. Liang, I. Ranta (r1994) *Concert*
(7/95) (CPO) ① CPO999 269-2
La Ricordanza—song (Wds. G. Rossi)
N. Liang, I. Ranta (r1994) *Concert*
(7/95) (CPO) ① CPO999 269-2
Die Rose, die Lilie, die Taube—song (1838) (Wds. H. Heine)
T. Hampson, G. Parsons *Concert*
(4/92) (EMI) ① CDC7 54436-2
Scirocco—Lied: 1v and piano (Wds. M Beer)
N. Liang, I. Ranta (r1994) *Concert*
(7/95) (CPO) ① CPO999 269-2
Sicilienne—song (?1845) (Wds. Méry)
T. Hampson, G. Parsons *Concert*
(4/92) (EMI) ① CDC7 54436-2
Sie und Ich—song (1835) (Wds. F. Rückert)
T. Hampson, G. Parsons *Concert*
(4/92) (EMI) ① CDC7 54436-2
N. Liang, I. Ranta (r1994) *Concert*
(7/95) (CPO) ① CPO999 269-2
Temptation—song
L. Sibiriakov, M.T. Manasevich, anon (r1905: Russ) *Concert*
(6/93) (PEAR) ① [3] GEMMCDS9001/3(2)

SECTION V: STAGE WORKS

L' Africaine, '(The) African Maid'—opera: 5 acts (1865—Paris) (Lib. Scribe and Fétis)
ACT 1: 1. Overture; 2. Adieu, mon doux rivage. ACT 2: 3. Sur mes genoux; 4. Fille des rois; 5. Combien tu m'es chère. ACT 3: 6. Holà! Matelots; 7. Adamastor, roi des vagues. ACT 4: 8. Prelude; 9a. Pays merveilleux; 9b. O Paradis; 9c. Conduisez-moi; 10. L'avoir tant adorée (Averla tanto amata). ACT 5: 11. Erreur fatal.
2. E. Rethberg, orch (r1920: Ger) *Concert*
(7/94) (PREI) ① 89051
2. E. Rethberg, Berlin SO, F. Weissmann (r1933: Ger) *Concert*   (10/95) (ROMO) ① [2] 81014-2
3. R. Ponselle, orch, R. Bourdon (Ital: r1925) *Concert*
(1/90) (RCA) ① GD87810
3. C. Muzio, orch (r1922) *Concert*
(5/90) (BOGR) ① [2] BIM705-2
3. E. Burzio, orch (Ital: r1913) *Concert*
(1/91) (CLUB) ① [2] CL99-587/8
3. L. Price, RCA Italiana Op Orch, F. Molinari-Pradelli *Concert*   (12/92) (RCA) ① [4] 09026 61236-2
3. R. Raisa, orch (r1917: Ital) *Concert*
(1/94) (CLUB) ① CL99-052
3. C. Muzio, orch (r1922: Ital) *Concert*
(1/94) (ROMO) ① [2] 81005-2
3. R. Ponselle, orch, R. Bourdon (r1925: 2 vers: Ital) *Concert*   (11/94) (ROMO) ① [2] 81006-2
3. F. Litvinne, anon (r1905) *Concert*
(12/94) (SYMP) ① SYMCD1128
3. F. Litvinne, orch (r1907) *Concert*
(12/94) (SYMP) ① SYMCD1128
3. E. Destinn, orch, F. Kark (r1908: Ger) *Concert*
(12/94) (SUPR) ① [12] 11 2136-2(2)
4. L. Melchissédec, orch (r1907) *Concert*
(9/91) (SYMP) ① SYMCD1089
4. H. Hermann Nissen, Berlin SO, F. Zweig (r1929: Ger) *Concert*   (12/95) (PREI) ① 89090
4. H. Schlusnus, orch (r1921: Ger) *Concert*
(12/95) (PREI) ① 89110
6. T. Ruffo, orch, W.B. Rogers (Ital: r1915) *Concert*
(11/90) (NIMB) ① NI7810
6. T. Ruffo, orch (Ital: r1915) *Concert*
(2/93) (PREI) ① [3] 89303(1)
6. P. Gailhard (r1904) *Concert*
(12/94) (SYMP) ① SYMCD1172
6, 11. G. Campanari, orch (r1904: Ital) *Concert*
(4/94) (RCA) ① [6] 09026 61580-2(1)
7. R. Stracciari, orch (r1925: Ital) *Concert*
(2/90) (PREI) ① 89003
7. T. Ruffo, orch (Ital: r1920) *Concert*
(2/93) (PREI) ① [3] 89303(1)
7. T. Ruffo, orch (Ital: r1929) *Concert*
(2/93) (PREI) ① [3] 89303(2)
9a-c J. Björling, Hilversum RO, F. Weissmann (pp1939; Ital) *Concert*   (8/88) (BLUE) ① ABCD006
9a-c J. Björling, orch, N. Grevillius (r1937: Ital) *Concert*   (10/88) (EMI) ① CDH7 61053-2
9a-c P. Domingo, ROHO, J. Barker (pp1988) *Concert*
(9/89) (EMI) ① CDC7 49811-2

9a-c F. Völker, Berlin St Op Orch, J. Prüwer (r1928: Ger) *Concert* (2/90) (PREI) ① **89005**
9a-c J. Schmidt, Berlin St Op Orch, C. Schmalstich (r1929; Ger) *Concert* (4/90) (EMI) ① **CDM7 69478-2**
9a-c E. Caruso, orch (r1907: Ital) *Concert* (12/90) (PEAR) ① [3] **EVC1(2)**
9a-c E. Caruso, orch (r1907: Ital) *Concert* (7/91) (RCA) ① [12] **GD60495(2)**
9a-c B. Gigli, orch, R. Bourdon (r1923; Ital) *Concert* (4/94) (RCA) ① [6] **09026 61580-2(3)**
9a-c H. Roswaenge, BPO, F.A. Schmidt (r1933: Ger) *Concert* (4/95) (PREI) ① [2] **89209**
9a, 9b L. Melchior, LSO, J. Barbirolli (Ger: r1930) *Concert* (8/88) (DANA) ① [2] **DACOCD315/6**
9a, 9b B. Gigli, orch, R. Bourdon (Ital: r1928) *Concert* (9/88) (PEAR) ① **GEMMCD9316**
9a, 9b E. Caruso, orch (r1907: Ital) *Concert* (10/89) (NIMB) ① **NI7803**
9a, 9b P. Domingo, MMF Orch, Rome Op Orch, Z. Mehta (pp1990) *Concert* (10/90) (DECC) ① **430 433-2DH**
9a, 9b C. Bergonzi, Santa Cecilia Academy Orch, G. Gavazzeni (r1957: Ital) *Concert* (10/93) (DECC) ① **436 463-2DM**
9a, 9b L. Pavarotti, Ater Orch, L. Magiera (pp: Ital) *Concert* (5/94) (DECC) ① [2] **443 018-2DF2**
9a, 9b P. Domingo, Paris Opéra-Bastille Orch, E. Kohn (pp1992) *Concert* (6/94) (SONY) ① **SK46691**
9a, 9b P. Domingo, ROHO, J. Barker (pp1988) *Concert* (6/94) (EMI) ① **CDC5 55017-2**
9a, 9b B. Heppner, Munich RO, R. Abbado (r1993/4) *Concert* (11/95) (RCA) ① **09026 62504-2**
9b L. Melchior, orch (Ger: r1926) *Concert* (8/88) (DANA) ① [2] **DACOCD313/4**
9b E. Caruso, orch (r1907) *Concert* (5/89) (PEAR) ① **GEMMCD9309**
9b H. Nash, orch (Eng: r1926) *Concert* (8/89) (PEAR) ① **GEMMCD9319**
9b M. Fleta, orch (r1927: Ital) *Concert* (2/90) (PREI) ① **89002**
9b B. Gigli, orch, R. Bourdon (Ital: r1923) *Concert* (5/90) (NIMB) ① **NI7807**
9b L. Pavarotti, National PO, O. de Fabritiis (Ital) *Concert* (7/90) (DECC) ① [2] **425 681-2DM2**
9b G. Lauri-Volpi, La Scala Orch, F. Ghione (Ital: r1934) *Concert* (9/90) (PREI) ① **89012**
9b F. Marconi, S. Cottone (r1903: Ital) *Concert* (10/90) (SYMP) ① **SYMCD1069**
9b F. Marconi, orch (r1908: Ital) *Concert* (10/90) (SYMP) ① **SYMCD1069**
9b F. Ansseau, orch (r1923) *Concert* (1/91) (PREI) ① **89022**
9b F. Merli, orch, L. Molajoli (Ital: r1926) *Concert* (1/91) (PREI) ① **89026**
9b A. Cortis, La Scala Orch, C. Sabajno (Ital: r1930) *Concert* (10/91) (PREI) ① **89043**
9b J. Björling, orch, N. Grevillius (r1937: Ital) *Concert* (9/92) (MMOI) ① **CDMOIR409**
9b F. Viñas, anon (Ital: r1905) *Concert* (11/92) (MEMO) ① [2] **HR4408/9(1)**
9b B. Gigli, orch, R. Bourdon (Ital: r1928) *Concert* (6/93) (MMOI) ① **CDMOIR417**
9b A. Davidov, anon (r1901: Russ) *Concert* (6/93) (PEAR) ① [3] **GEMMCDS9007/9(1)**
9b G. Lauri-Volpi, La Scala Orch, F. Ghione (r1934: Ital) *Concert* (7/93) (NIMB) ① **NI7845**
9b L. Escalais, anon (r1905) *Concert* (12/93) (SYMP) ① **SYMCD1126**
9b J. Björling, orch, N. Grevillius (r1937: Ital) *Concert* (9/94) (CARL) ① **GLRS103**
9b J. Björling, orch, N. Grevillius (r1937: Ital) *Concert* (9/94) (CONI) ① **CDHD214**
9b A. Giorgini, anon (r1904: Ital) *Concert* (4/95) (RECO) ① **TRC3**
9c E. Caruso, orch, J. Pasternack (Ital: r1920) *Concert* (7/91) (RCA) ① [12] **GD60495(6)**
9c E. Caruso, orch, J. Pasternack (Ital: r1920) *Concert* (10/91) (PEAR) ① [3] **EVC4(2)**
9c E. Caruso, orch (r1920: Ital) *Concert* (7/95) (NIMB) ① **NI7866**
10. H. Schlusnus, orch (r1922: Ger) *Concert* (12/95) (PREI) ① **89110**

Il **Crociato in Egitto—opera: 2 acts (1824—Venice)** (Lib. G. Rossi)
Cpte I. Platt, B. Ford, D. Montague, Y. Kenny, D. Jones, L. Kitchen, U. Benelli, G. Mitchell Ch, RPO, D. Parry (9/92) (OPRA) ① [4] **ORC010**
Popoli dell'Egitto Alfredo Kraus, WNO Chor, WNO Orch, C. Rizzi (r1994) *Concert* (8/95) (PHIL) ① **442 785-2PH**

Dinorah, '(Le) pardon de Ploërmel'—opera: 3 acts (1859—Paris) (Lib. Barbier and Carré)
EXCERPTS: 1. Overture. ACT 1: 2. Le jour radieux; 3. Bellah! ma chèvre chérie!; 4. Dors petite; 5. Je suis chez moi!; 6. Dieu nous donne è chacun; 7. Qui va là?; 8. Sonne, sonne, gai sonneur?; 9. Holà! hé! vieil Alain!; 10. O puissante magie!; 11. Me voici!; 13. Un trésor!; 14. Ce tintement que l'on entend. ACT 2: 15. Qu'il est bon; 16. Dites-moi, dites vite; 17. Me voici! me voici!; 18. Ombre légère (Shadow Song); 19. Arrive!; 20. Ah! que j'ai froid!; 21. Grand Dieu! Quelqu'un!; 22. Quand l'heure sonnera; 23. Tu frémis? Que m'importe; 24. Taisez-vous!; 25. De l'oiseau dans le bocage. ACT 3: 26. En chasse, piqueurs adroits!; 27. Les blés sont sons è faucher; 28. Sous les génèvriers; 29. Bonjour, faucher!; 30. La force m'abandonne; 31. Ah! mon remaords te venge; 32. Grand Dieu! son teint s'anime; 33. Vois!...regarde ces lieux!; 34. Sainte Marie!.
Cpte D. Cook, C. du Plessis, A. Oliver, D. Jones, M. Hill Smith, R. Earle, I. Caley, G. Mitchell Ch, Philh, J. Judd (r1979) (4/94) (OPRA) ① [3] **ORC005**
Dors, petite A. Galli-Curci, orch, R. Bourdon (r1924: Ital) *Concert* (8/94) (ROMO) ① [2] **81004-2**
En chasse P. Plançon, anon (r1905) *Concert* (12/94) (ROMO) ① [2] **82001-2**
1. NBC SO, A. Toscanini (bp1938) *Concert* (6/90) (DELL) ① **CDDA9021**
2, 3. G. Huguet, orch (r1906: Ital) *Concert* (9/92) (IRCC) ① **IRCC-CD800**
3, 31. A. Galli-Curci, orch, R. Bourdon, Folkmann (r1924: Ital) *Concert* (4/94) (RCA) ① [6] **09026 61580-2(3)**
18. M. Callas, Philh, T. Serafin (Ital: r1954) *Concert* (11/86) (EMI) ① **CDC7 47282-2**
18. A. Galli-Curci, orch, R. Bourdon (r1917: Ital) *Concert* (5/90) (NIMB) ① **NI7806**
18. L. Pons, Columbia SO, P. Cimara (r1942) *Concert* (7/90) (SONY) ① **MPK45694**
18. Dilbèr, Estonia Op Orch, E. Klas *Concert* (9/92) (ONDI) ① **ODE768-2**
18. F. Hempel, orch (r1918: Ital) *Concert* (9/92) (IRCC) ① **IRCC-CD800**
18. L. Tetrazzini, orch, P. Pitt (Ital: r1907) *Concert* (9/92) (EMI) ① [3] **CHS7 63802-2(1)**
18. L. Tetrazzini, orch (r1913: Ital) *Concert* (9/92) (PEAR) ① **GEMMCD9224**
18. L. Tetrazzini, orch, P. Pitt (r1907: Ital) *Concert* (9/92) (PEAR) ① **GEMMCD9221**
18. M. Korjus, Berlin St Op Orch, F. Schönbaumsfeld (r1934: Ger) *Concert* (10/93) (PREI) ① **89054**
18. M. Barrientos, anon (r1904: Ital) *Concert* (12/93) (SYMP) ① **SYMCD1113**
18. A. Galli-Curci, orch, J. Pasternack (r1917: Ital) *Concert* (3/94) (ROMO) ① [2] **81003-2**
18. S. Jo, Monte Carlo PO, P. Olmi (r1994) *Concert* (6/95) (ERAT) ① **4509-97239-2**
22. J. Hadley, T. Hampson, WNO Orch, C. Rizzi (r1992) *Concert* (11/93) (TELD) ① **9031-73283-2**
26. L. Fugère, orch (r1928) *Concert* (9/92) (IRCC) ① **IRCC-CD800**
26. L. Fugère, orch (r1930) *Concert* (6/93) (SYMP) ① **SYMCD1125**
26. P. Plançon, anon (r1905) *Concert* (1/95) (NIMB) ① **NI7860**
31. R. Stracciari, orch (r1925: Ital) *Concert* (2/90) (PREI) ① **89003**
31. G. De Luca, orch (r1924: Ital) *Concert* (1/92) (PREI) ① **89036**
31. M. Ancona, orch (r1908: Ital) *Concert* (9/92) (IRCC) ① **IRCC-CD800**
31. T. Ruffo, orch (r1914: Ital) *Concert* (2/93) (PREI) ① [3] **89303(1)**

Emma—opera: 2 acts (1819—Venice) (Lib. Rossi)
Di gioja, di pace B. Mills, D. Montague, P. Nilon, H. Nichol, G. Dolton, M. Bovino, Philh, D. Parry *Concert* (10/90) (OPRA) ① [3] **ORCH103**

L' **Esule di Granata—melodramma serio: 2 acts (1822—Milan)** (Lib. F Romani)
Sì, mel credi P. Spence, A. Miles, G. Mitchell Ch, Philh, D. Parry *Concert* (8/95) (OPRA) ① [3] **ORCH104**

L' **Etoile du nord—opera: 3 acts (1854—Paris)** (Lib. Scribe)
La, la, la L. Tetrazzini, orch (Ital: r1913) *Concert* (9/92) (EMI) ① [3] **CHS7 63802-2(2)**
La, la, la L. Tetrazzini, orch (Ital: r1913) *Concert* (9/92) (PEAR) ① **GEMMCD9223**
O jours heureux P. Plançon, orch (r1908) *Concert* (9/91) (PEAR) ① **GEMMCD9497**
O jours heureux P. Plançon, orch (r1908) *Concert* (12/94) (ROMO) ① [2] **82001-2**
O jours heureux P. Plançon, orch (r1908) *Concert* (1/95) (NIMB) ① **NI7860**
Veille sur eux A. Galli-Curci, orch (r1922) *Concert* (2/89) (PEAR) ① **GEMMCD9308**
Veille sur eux A. Galli-Curci, orch, J. Pasternack (r1922) *Concert* (8/94) (ROMO) ① [2] **81004-2**

Les **Huguenots—opera: 5 acts (1836—Paris)** (Lib. Scribe and Deschamps)
ACT 1: 1. Overture; 2. Des beaux jours; 3a. De ces lieux enchanteurs; 3b. Sous le beau ciel de Touraine; 4. Bonheur de la table; 5a. Non loin des vieilles tours; 5b. Ah! quel spectacle; 5c. Plus blanche que la blanche hermine; 6a. Quelle étrange figure; 6b. Seigneur, rempart et seul; 7. Eh! mais-plus je le vois; 8. Piff paff, piff paff; 9. Au maitre de ces lieux; 10. L'aventure est singulière; 11. Honneur au conquérant; 12a. Nobles seigneurs; 12b. Une dame noble et sage; 13a. Trop de mérite aussi; 13b. Vous savez si je suis un ami; 13c. Les plaisirs, les honneurs. ACT 2: 14. Entracte; 15a. O beau pays de la Touraine; 15b. Belle forêt; 15c. Sombre chimère; 15d. A cet mot seul s'anime; 16. Jeunes beautés; 17. Non, non, non, vous n'avez jamais; 18a. Le voici, du silence; 18b. Pareille loyauté; 19a. Beauté divine; 19b. Preux doit vivre; 19c. Si j'étais coquette; 19d. A vous et ma vie et mon ame; 20. Allons! toujours le page; 21. Par l'honneur, par le nom; 22a. Et maintenant je dois offrir; 22b. O transport. ACT 3: 23. Entracte; 24. C'est le jour de dimanche; 25a. Rataplan; 25b. Prenant son sabre de batailles; 26. Vierge Marie; 27. Profanes, impies; 28a. Gypsy Round; 28b. Gypsy Dance; 29. Pour remplir un voeu solennel; 30. Rentrez, habitants de Paris; 31a. O terreur! Je tressaille; 31b. Dans la nuit; 31c. Ah! l'ingrat; 31d. Ah! tu ne peux; 32. Un danger le menace; 33. En mon bon droit j'ai confiance; 34. Nous voila! félons, arrière; 35a. Ma fille; 35b. Au banquet. ACT 4: 36. Entracte; 37a. Je suis seule; 37b. Parmi les pleurs; 38. Juste ciel! est-ce lui; 39a. Des troubles renaissants; 39b. Qu'en ce riche quartier; 40. Gloire au grand Dieu vengeur; 41a. O ciel! Où courez vous; 41b. Tu l'as dit. ACT 5: 42. Entracte and Ball; 43a. Aux armes!; 43b. A la lueur de leurs torches; 44. C'est toi; 45. Dieu Seigneur, rempart et seul soutien; 46. Savez-vous qu'en joignant vos mains; 47. Abjurez, huguenots!; 48. Ah! voyez, le ciel s'ouvre; 49. Par le fer et par l'incendie.
Dieu le veut J-F. Delmas, chor, orch (r1907) *Concert* (9/92) (IRCC) ① **IRCC-CD800**
3b E. Caruso, anon (r1903) *Concert* (5/89) (EMI) ① **CDH7 61046-2**
3b E. Caruso, anon (Ital: r1903) *Concert* (12/90) (PEAR) ① [3] **EVC1(1)**
3b E. Caruso, anon (Ital: r1903) *Concert* (7/91) (RCA) ① [12] **GD60495(1)**
5a-c G. Morino, Warmia Nat PO, B. Amaducci (Ital) *Concert* (10/90) (NUOV) ① **6851**
5b, 5c E. Caruso, anon (Ital: r1905) *Concert* (12/90) (PEAR) ① [3] **EVC1(1)**
5b, 5c E. Caruso, orch, W.B. Rogers (r1909: Ital) *Concert* (7/91) (RCA) ① [12] **GD60495(3)**
5b, 5c E. Caruso, anon (Ital: r1905) *Concert* (7/91) (RCA) ① [12] **GD60495(1)**
5b, 5c G. Zenatello, orch (r1910: Ital) *Concert* (5/94) (PEAR) ① [4] **GEMMCDS9073(2)**
5c L. Slezak, orch (Ger: r1907) *Concert* (2/91) (PREI) ① **89020**
5c E. Caruso, orch (Ital: r1909) *Concert* (3/91) (PEAR) ① [3] **EVC2**
5c I. Ershov, anon (r1903: Russ) *Concert* (6/93) (PEAR) ① [3] **GEMMCDS9997/9(1)**
5c D. Yuzhin, anon (r1902: Russ) *Concert* (6/93) (PEAR) ① [3] **GEMMCDS9001/3(1)**
5c A. Labinsky, anon (Russ: r1905) *Concert* (7/93) (SYMP) ① **SYMCD1105**
5c G. Lauri-Volpi, orch, R. Bourdon (r1929: Ital) *Concert* (7/93) (NIMB) ① **NI7845**
5c G. Zenatello, orch (r1910: Ital) *Concert* (5/94) (SYMP) ① **SYMCD1168**
5c H. Roswaenge, Berlin St Op Orch, F.A. Schmidt (r1932: Ger) *Concert* (4/95) (PREI) ① [2] **89209**
5c E. Caruso, orch (r1909: Ital) *Concert* (7/95) (NIMB) ① **NI7866**
5c G. Thill, orch, E. Bigot (r1931) *Concert* (8/95) (FORL) ① **UCD16727**
6b I. Andrésen, orch (Ger: r1929) *Concert* (10/90) (PREI) ① **89028**
6b A. Kipnis, Berlin Charlottenburg Op Orch, J. Heidenreich (Ger: r1923) *Concert* (10/91) (PEAR) ① **GEMMCD9451**
6b L. Sibiriakov, orch (r1908: Russ) *Concert* (6/93) (PEAR) ① [3] **GEMMCDS9001/3(2)**
8. T. Pasero, orch, L. Molajoli (Ital: r1928) *Concert* (6/90) (PREI) ① **89010**
8. L. Sibiriakov, orch (Russ: r1909) *Concert* (7/92) (PEAR) ① [3] **GEMMCDS9925(1)**
8. P. Plançon, anon (r1902) *Concert* (3/93) (SYMP) ① **SYMCD1100**
8. A. Didur, anon (r1900: Ital) *Concert* (6/93) (PEAR) ① [3] **GEMMCDS9997/9(2)**
8. A. Didur, S. Cottone (r1903: Ital) *Concert* (6/93) (PEAR) ① [3] **GEMMCDS9997/9(2)**

Symphony No. 5 in D, Op. 18 (1918)
BBC PO, E. Downes (pp1992) *Symphony 9.*
(7/94) (MARC) ① **8 223499**
Symphony No. 6 in E flat minor, 'Revolutionary', Op. 23 (1921-23)
Bratislava Nat Op Chor, Bratislava RSO, R. Stankovsky
(11/92) (MARC) ① **8 223301**
Russia SO, Anima Chbr Ch, V. Dudarova
(11/92) (OLYM) ① **OCD510**
Yurlov Russian Ch, USSR SO, K. Kondrashin (r1959)
(10/94) (RUSS) ① **RDCD15008**
Symphony No. 7 in B minor, Op. 24 (1922)
Slovak PO, M. Halász (r1987) *Symphony 10.*
(7/89) (MARC) ① **8 223113**
Symphony No. 8 in A, Op. 26 (1924-25)
Czech RSO, R. Stankovsky
(4/92) (MARC) ① **8 223297**
Symphony No. 9 in E minor, Op. 28 (1926-7)
BBC PO, E. Downes (pp1992) *Symphony 5.*
(7/94) (MARC) ① **8 223499**
Symphony No. 10 in F minor, Op. 30 (1927)
Slovak PO, M. Halász (r1987) *Symphony 7.*
(7/89) (MARC) ① **8 223113**
Symphony No. 12 in G minor, Op. 35 (1931-32)
Bratislava RSO, R. Stankovsky *Silence, Op. 9.*
(10/91) (MARC) ① **8 223302**
Symphony No. 19 in E flat—symphonic band, Op. 46 (1939)
Russian St Brass Orch, N. Sergeyev *Symphony 1.*
(3/94) (RUSS) ① **RDCD11007**
Symphony No. 21, 'Fantasy in F sharp minor', Op. 51 (1941)
New Philh, D. Measham (r1973) *Concert*
(2/95) (UNIC) ① **UKCD2066**
Theme and Variations—string orchestra
St Petersburg Chbr Ens, R. Melia (r1994) *Concert*
(10/95) (ASV) ① **CDDCA928**

SECTION II: CHAMBER

Sonata for Cello and Piano No. 1 in D, Op. 12 (1911)
M. Tarasova, A. Polezhaev (r1994) *Concert*
(12/94) (OLYM) ① **OCD530**
Sonata for Cello and Piano No. 2 in A minor, Op. 81 (1948-49) (also scored for va and pf)
Y. Turovsky, L. Edlina *Rachmaninov: Cello Sonata.*
(10/88) (CHAN) ① **CHAN8523**
M. Tarasova, A. Polezhaev (r1994) *Concert*
(12/94) (OLYM) ① **OCD530**

SECTION III: INSTRUMENTAL

Prelude in B flat minor (Song and Rhapsody)—piano, Op. 58 (1942)
M. McLachlan *Concert* (3/89) (OLYM) ① **OCD217**
Sonata for Piano No. 1 in D minor, Op. 6 (1907-09)
M. McLachlan *Concert* (12/88) (OLYM) ① **OCD214**
E. Hegedüs (r1990-91) *Piano Sonata 4.*
(10/93) (MARC) ① **8 223469**
Sonata for Piano No. 2 in F sharp minor, Op. 13 (1912)
M. McLachlan *Concert* (12/88) (OLYM) ① **OCD214**
E. Hegedüs *Concert* (10/90) (MARC) ① **8 223156**
Sonata for Piano No. 3 in C minor, Op. 19 (1920)
M. McLachlan *Concert* (12/88) (OLYM) ① **OCD214**
E. Hegedüs *Concert* (10/90) (MARC) ① **8 223156**
S. Richter (pp1973) *Concert*
(10/92) (PYRA) ① **PYR13503**
Sonata for Piano No. 4 in C minor, Op. 24 (1924)
M. McLachlan *Concert* (12/88) (OLYM) ① **OCD217**
E. Hegedüs (r1990-91) *Piano Sonata 1.*
(10/93) (MARC) ① **8 223469**
Sonata for Piano No. 5 in B, Op. 64/1 (1907-44)
M. McLachlan *Concert* (3/89) (OLYM) ① **OCD217**
E. Hegedüs *Concert* (10/90) (MARC) ① **8 223156**
Sonata for Piano No. 6 in A flat, Op. 64/2 (1908-44)
M. McLachlan *Concert* (12/88) (OLYM) ① **OCD214**
E. Hegedüs *Concert* (10/90) (MARC) ① **8 223178**
Sonata for Piano No. 7 in C, Op. 82 (1949)
E. Hegedüs *Concert* (10/90) (MARC) ① **8 223178**
Sonata for Piano No. 8 in D minor, Op. 83 (1949)
E. Hegedüs *Concert* (10/90) (MARC) ① **8 223178**
Sonata for Piano No. 9 in F, Op. 84 (1949)
E. Hegedüs *Concert* (10/90) (MARC) ① **8 223178**
Sonatina for Piano in E minor, Op. 57 (1942)
M. McLachlan *Concert* (3/89) (OLYM) ① **OCD217**

MÍČA, František Adam (1746–1811) Moravia

SECTION II: CHAMBER

String Quartet No. 6 in C
Talich Qt (r1985) *Concert*
(11/95) (CALL) ① **CAL6698**

MICHI, Orazio (1594/5–1641) Italy

also known as Michi dell'Arpa

SECTION IV: VOCAL AND CHORAL

Arie spirituali—song collection (pub 1640)
1. Su duro tronco; 2. I diletti di mundo; 3. Quel signor.
1-3. A. Lawrence-King *Concert*
(6/92) (HYPE) ① **CDA66518**

MIHALOVICI, Marcel (1898–1985) Romania/France

SECTION III: INSTRUMENTAL

Un Danseur roumain—piano
B. Lerner *Concert* (1/89) (ETCE) ① **KTC1061**

MIKI, Minoru (b 1930) Japan

SECTION II: CHAMBER

Marimba spiritual—marimba and percussion (1984)
E. Glennie, Ens *Concert* (1/92) (RCA) ① **RD60557**
E. Glennie, BBC SO (r1994) *Concert*
(2/95) (TELD) ① **4509-97868-2**
Marimba Spiritual II—percussion duo (1983-84)
Safri Duo (r1994) *Concert*
(4/95) (CHAN) ① **CHAN9330**

MILÁN, Luis de (1500–c1561 or later) Spain

SECTION III: INSTRUMENTAL

Divisions on the Spanish Pavan—improvisation
A. Lawrence-King *Concert*
(6/92) (HYPE) ① **CDA66518**
El Maestro—Fantasías—vihuela (pub 1536)
EXCERPTS: 1. Fantasía I; 2. Fantasía II; 3. Fantasía III; 4. Fantasía IV; 5. Fantasía V; 8. Fantasía VIII; 9. Fantasía IX; 10. Fantasía X; 11. Fantasía XI; 12. Fantasía XII; 13. Fantasía XIII; 15. Fantasía XV; 16. Fantasía XVI; 17. Fantasía XVII; 18. Fantasía XVIII; 22. Fantasía XXII; 39. Fantasía del quarto tono; 40. Fantasía de consonancias y redobles.
8, 10-13, 15, 16, 18, 22. H. Smith *Concert*
(5/91) (ASTR) ① **E7748**
8, 9, 12, 16. J. Bream (r1979) *Concert*
(8/93) (RCA) ① [28] **09026 61583-2(6)**
8, 9, 12, 16. J. Bream (r1979) *Concert*
(9/94) (RCA) ① **09026 61606-2**
10, 18. C. Wilson (r1993) *Concert*
(2/94) (HYPE) ① **CDA66653**
12. A. Lawrence-King (r1993) *Concert*
(2/94) (HYPE) ① **CDA66653**
16. P. Romero (r1993; trans P. Romero) *Concert*
(4/95) (PHIL) ① **442 150-2PH**
22. J. Bream (r1983) *Concert*
(8/93) (RCA) ① [28] **09026 61583-2(6)**
22. J. Bream (r1983) *Concert*
(8/93) (RCA) ① **09026 61610-2**
39. N. North *Concert* (6/87) (AMON) ① **CD-SAR18**
40. A. Lawrence-King *Concert*
(6/92) (HYPE) ① **CDA66518**
El Maestro—Pavanas—vihuela (pub 1536)
EXCERPTS: 1. Pavana I; 2. Pavana II; 4. Pavana IV; 5. Pavana V; 6. Pavana VI; 10. Pavana e Galliarda.
1, 2, 4, 5. H. Smith *Concert*
(5/91) (ASTR) ① **E7748**
1, 4-6. J. Bream (r1979) *Concert*
(8/93) (RCA) ① [28] **09026 61583-2(6)**
1, 4-6. J. Bream (r1979) *Concert*
(9/94) (RCA) ① **09026 61606-2**
2. J. M. Moreno *Concert*
(8/95) (GLOS) ① **GCD920103**
El Maestro—Tentos—vihuela (pub 1536)
EXCERPTS: 1. Tento I; 2. Tento II; 4. Tento IV.
1. J. Bream (r1979) *Concert*
(8/93) (RCA) ① [28] **09026 61583-2(6)**
1. J. Bream (r1979) *Concert*
(9/94) (RCA) ① **09026 61606-2**
1, 2, 4. H. Smith *Concert* (5/91) (ASTR) ① **E7748**

SECTION IV: VOCAL AND CHORAL

El Maestro—Romances—soprano and vihuela (pub 1536)
1. Triste esteva muy quexosa; 2. Sospirastes Baldovinos; 3. Con pauor recordo; 4. Durandarte.
1-4. M. Figueras, H. Smith *Concert*
(5/91) (AUVI) ① **E7777**
El Maestro—Sonetos—soprano and vihuela (pub 1536)
1. Gentil mia donna; 2. Nova angelta; 3. Madonna per voi ardo; 4. O gelosia d'amanti; 5. Toda di mi vida os amé.
1-4. M. Figueras, H. Smith *Concert*
(5/91) (AUVI) ① **E7777**
5. T. Berganza, N. Yepes *Concert*
(12/92) (DG) ① [2] **435 848-2GX2**
El Maestro—Villancicos—soprano and vihuela (pub 1536)
1. Leuay me amor; 2. Al amor quiero vencer; 3. Agora viniesse un viento; 4. Falai miña amor; 5. Amor que tan bien sirviendo; 6. Quien amores ten; 7. Perdido teñyo la calor; 8. A quel cauallero madre.
1-8. M. Figueras, H. Smith *Concert*
(5/91) (AUVI) ① **E7777**
8. T. Berganza, N. Yepes *Concert*
(12/92) (DG) ① [2] **435 848-2GX2**
Mios fueron, mi coraçon—3vv (from the Palacio Song Book)
Hespèrion XX, J. Savall *Concert*
(7/92) (ASTR) ① **E8762**

MILANO, Francesco (1497–1543) Italy

SECTION III: INSTRUMENTAL

Fantasia—lute (Castelfranco MS)
P. O'Dette (r1990-2) *Concert*
(10/95) (HARM) ① **HMU90 7043**
Fantasia di M. Francesco Milanese—lute (1559) (from 'Intavolatura de Leuto': Matelart)
L. Kirchhof *Concert* (11/92) (SONY) ① **SK48068**
Fantasia dolcissima et amorosa—lute
P. O'Dette (r1990-2) *Concert*
(10/95) (HARM) ① **HMU90 7043**
Fantasias—lute (numbering from Arthur Ness, 1971)
EXCERPTS: 1. No. 1 in C minor; 2. No. 2 in F; 3. No. 3 in G minor; 4. No. 4, 'La Campagna'; 5. No. 5 in C; 6. No. 6 in F; 7. No. 7 in F; 8. No. 8 in G; 13. No. 13; 16. No. 16; 26. No. 26; 28. No. 28; 30. No. 30; 31. No. 31; 33. No. 33; 38. No. 38; 39. No. 39; 42. No. 42; 55. No. 55; 56. No. 56; 63. No. 63; 64. No. 64; 65. No. 65; 67. No. 67; 81. No. 81; 83. No. 83.
1-8. J. Bream (r1972) *Concert*
(8/93) (RCA) ① [28] **09026 61583-2(2)**
1-8. J. Bream (r1972) *Concert*
(6/94) (RCA) ① **09026 61587-2**
8, 13, 26, 39, 56, 83. P. O'Dette (r1990-2) *Concert*
(10/95) (HARM) ① **HMU90 7043**
28, 33, 64. J. Lindberg *Concert*
(10/89) (BIS) ① **BIS-CD399**
30, 31, 38, 42. J. Lindberg (r1991) *Concert*
(11/93) (BIS) ① **BIS-CD599**
Ricercars—lute (numbering from Arthur Ness, 1971)
EXCERPTS: 1. No. 1; 2. No. 2; 4. No. 4; 10. No. 10; 12. No. 12; 13. No. 13; 16. No. 16; 34. No. 34; 51. No. 51; 69. No. 69; 70. No. 70; 73. No. 73; 76. No. 76; 79. No. 79; 84. No. 84.
13. P. O'Dette (r1990-2) *Concert*
(10/95) (HARM) ① **HMU90 7043**
16, 51. J. Lindberg *Concert*
(10/89) (BIS) ① **BIS-CD399**

MILANUZZI, Carlo (c1590–c1647) Italy

SECTION IV: VOCAL AND CHORAL

Ut re mi—Scherzo boscareccio (Primo Scherzo delle Ariose Vaghezze), Op. 7 (1622)
T. Berganza, Ens, J.E. Dähler (hpd/dir) *Concert*
(3/84) (CLAV) ① **CD50-8206**

MILFORD, Robin (1903–1959) England

SECTION IV: VOCAL AND CHORAL

The Colour—song, Op. 48/2 (1938) (Wds. T. Hardy)
I. Partridge, C. Benson *Concert*
(9/91) (HYPE) ① **CDA66015**

**If it's ever Spring again—song, Op. 48/3
(1938)** (Wds. T. Hardy)
I. Partridge, C. Benson *Concert*
(9/91) (HYPE) ① **CDA66015**
**So sweet love seemed—song, Op. 36/1
(1933)** (Wds. R. Bridges)
I. Partridge, C. Benson *Concert*
(9/91) (HYPE) ① **CDA66015**

MILHAUD, Darius (1892–1974)
France

SECTION I: ORCHESTRAL

**Ballade—piano and orchestra, Op. 61
(1920)**
C. Helffer, FNO, D. Robertson (r1991-92) *Concert*
(6/93) (ERAT) ① **2292-45992-2**
**Le carnaval d'Aix—piano and orchestra, Op.
83b (1926)** (after ballet 'Salade', Op 83)
J. Gibbons, New London Orch, R. Corp *Concert*
(12/92) (HYPE) ① **CDA66594**
C. Helffer, FNO, D. Robertson (r1991-92) *Concert*
(6/93) (ERAT) ① **2292-45992-2**
**Le carnaval de Londres—orchestra, Op. 172
(1937)**
New London Orch, R. Corp *Concert*
(12/92) (HYPE) ① **CDA66594**
Capella Cracoviensis, K.A. Rickenbacher *Concert*
(12/92) (SCHW) ① **311382**
**Chamber Symphony No. 1, 'Le printemps',
Op. 43 (1917)**
Capella Cracoviensis, K.A. Rickenbacher *Concert*
(5/93) (SCHW) ① **311392**
**Chamber Symphony No. 2, 'Pastorale', Op.
49 (1918)**
Capella Cracoviensis, K.A. Rickenbacher *Concert*
(5/93) (SCHW) ① **311392**
**Chamber Symphony No. 3, 'Serenade', Op.
71 (1921)**
Capella Cracoviensis, K.A. Rickenbacher *Concert*
(5/93) (SCHW) ① **311392**
Chamber Symphony No. 4, Op. 74 (1921)
NY Harmonie Ens, S. Richman *Concert*
(7/92) (MUSI) ① **MACD-649**
Capella Cracoviensis, K.A. Rickenbacher *Concert*
(5/93) (SCHW) ① **311392**
**Chamber Symphony No. 5—wind
instruments, Op. 75 (1922)**
Capella Cracoviensis, K.A. Rickenbacher *Concert*
(5/93) (SCHW) ① **311392**
**Chamber Symphony No. 6—STB, oboe and
cello, Op. 79 (1923)**
Capella Cracoviensis, K.A. Rickenbacher *Concert*
(5/93) (SCHW) ① **311392**
**Concertino de printemps—violin and
chamber orchestra, Op. 135 (1934)**
L. Kaufman, FRNO, D. Milhaud (r1949) *Concert*
(12/90) (MUSI) ① **MACD-620**
Y. Astruc, orch, D. Milhaud (r1935) *Concert*
(9/93) (EPM) ① [3] **150 122**
M. Guttman, RPO, J. Serebrier *Concert*
(10/93) (ASV) ① **CDDCA855**
**Concertino d'hiver—trombone and strings,
Op. 327 (1953)**
C. Lindberg, New Stockholm CO, O. Kamu *Concert*
(8/88) (BIS) ① **BIS-CD348**
**Concerto for Cello and Orchestra No. 1, Op.
136 (1934)**
M. Rostropovich, USSR TV & Rad Orch, G.
Rozhdestvensky (pp1964) *Concert*
(7/94) (RUSS) ① **RDCD11104**
J. Starker, Philh, W. Susskind (r1956) *Concert*
(12/95) (EMI) ① [6] **CZS5 68485-2**
**Concerto for Harp and Orchestra, Op. 323
(1953)**
F. Cambreling, Lyon Op Orch, K. Nagano *Concert*
(2/93) (ERAT) ① **2292-45820-2**
**Concerto for Percussion and Chamber
Orchestra, Op. 109 (1929-30)**
E. Glennie, Scottish CO, P. Daniel *Concert*
(4/93) (RCA) ① **09026 61277-2**
South-West German RSO, L. Stokowski (bp1955)
Concert (2/94) (MUSI) ① **MACD-778**
**Concerto for Piano and Orchestra No. 1, Op.
127 (1933)**
C. Helffer, FNO, D. Robertson (r1991-92) *Concert*
(6/93) (ERAT) ① **2292-45992-2**
M. Long, FRNO, D. Milhaud (r1935) *Concert*
(9/93) (EPM) ① [3] **150 122**
**Concerto for Piano and Orchestra No. 4, Op.
295 (1949)**
C. Helffer, FNO, D. Robertson (r1991-92) *Concert*
(6/93) (ERAT) ① **2292-45992-2**

**Concerto for Violin and Orchestra No. 2, Op.
255 (1945)**
L. Kaufman, FRNO, D. Milhaud (r1949) *Concert*
(12/90) (MUSI) ① **MACD-620**
**5 Etudes—piano and orchestra, Op. 63
(1920)**
C. Helffer, FNO, D. Robertson (r1991-92) *Concert*
(6/93) (ERAT) ① **2292-45992-2**
**Introduction et marche funèbre, Op. 153
(1936)** (finale to Act 1 of Rolland's 'Fourth of
July')
Paris PO, D. Milhaud (r1956) *Concert*
(9/92) (CHNT) ① **LDC278 1069**
Overture méditerranéenne, Op. 330 (1953)
Toulouse Capitole Orch, M. Plasson (r1992) *Concert*
(6/95) (DG) ① **439 939-2GH**
3 Rag Caprices—orchestra, Op. 78 (1922)
(orch cpsr from piano work)
Capella Cracoviensis, K.A. Rickenbacher *Concert*
(12/92) (SCHW) ① **311382**
**Saudades do Brasil—dance suite, Op. 67
(1920 orch 1921)**
1. Overture—Sorocabo; 2. Botafogo; 3. Leme; 4.
Copacabana; 5. Ipanema; 6. Gavea; 7. Corcovado; 8.
Tijuca; 9. Sumaré; 10. Paineras; 11. Laranjeiras; 12.
Paysandu.
Capella Cracoviensis, K.A. Rickenbacher *Concert*
(12/92) (SCHW) ① **311382**
Concert Arts Orch, D. Milhaud (r1956) *Concert*
(4/93) (EMI) ① **CDC7 54604-2**
7, 8. J. Szigeti, K. Ruhrseitz (r1926/7) *Concert*
(1/90) (BIDD) ① [2] **LAB005/6**
7-9, 11. FNO, L. Bernstein *Concert*
(10/87) (EMI) ① **CDC7 47845-2**
**Suite française—concert band, Op. 248
(1944)**
1. Normandie; 2. Bretagne; 3. Ile de France; 4.
Alsace-Lorraine; 5. Provence.
London Wind Orch, D. Wick *Concert*
(11/92) (ASV) ① **CDWHL2067**
**Suite provençale—orchestra, Op. 152b
(1936)**
Toulouse Capitole Orch, M. Plasson (r1992) *Concert*
(7/92) (DG) ① **435 437-2GH**
Paris Cons, S. Baudo *Concert*
(9/92) (CHNT) ① **LDC278 1069**
Detroit SO, N. Järvi *Concert*
(12/92) (CHAN) ① **CHAN9072**
Concert Arts Orch, D. Milhaud (r1956) *Concert*
(4/93) (EMI) ① **CDC7 54604-2**
FRNO, R. Desormière (r1938) *Concert*
(9/93) (EPM) ① [3] **150 122**
Symphony No. 1, Op. 210 (1939)
Toulouse Capitole Orch, M. Plasson *Concert*
(7/92) (DG) ① **435 437-2GH**
Symphony No. 2, Op. 247 (1944)
Toulouse Capitole Orch, M. Plasson *Concert*
(7/92) (DG) ① **435 437-2GH**
Symphony No. 4, Op. 281 (1947)
FRNO, D. Milhaud (r1968) *Symphony 8.*
(4/93) (ERAT) ① **2292-45841-2**
Symphony No. 6, Op. 343 (1955)
Toulouse Capitole Orch, M. Plasson (r1992) *Concert*
(6/95) (DG) ① **439 939-2GH**
Symphony No. 7, Op. 344 (1955)
Basle RSO, A. Francis (r1993) *Concert*
(6/95) (CPO) ① **CPO999 166-2**
Toulouse Capitole Orch, M. Plasson (r1992) *Concert*
(6/95) (DG) ① **439 939-2GH**
**Symphony No. 8, 'Rhodanienne', Op. 362
(1957)**
FRNO, D. Milhaud (r1968) *Symphony 4.*
(4/93) (ERAT) ① **2292-45841-2**
Basle RSO, A. Francis (r1993) *Concert*
(6/95) (CPO) ① **CPO999 166-2**
Symphony No. 9, Op. 350 (1959)
Basle RSO, A. Francis (r1993) *Concert*
(6/95) (CPO) ① **CPO999 166-2**

SECTION II: CHAMBER

**L' apothéose de Molière—suite: hpd, fl, ob,
cl, bn & stgs, Op. 286 (1948)**
J. Gibbons, New London Orch, R. Corp *Concert*
(12/92) (HYPE) ① **CDA66594**
**Caprice—clarinet and piano, Op. 335a
(1954)**
P. Meyer, E. Le Sage *Concert*
(9/92) (DENO) ① **CO-79282**
J. Cohler, J. Gordon *Concert*
(5/95) (CRYS) ① **Crystal CD733**
**La Cheminée du roi René—suite: wind
quintet, Op. 205 (1939)**
Athena Ens *Concert* (10/91) (CHAN) ① **CHAN6536**
Pro Arte Wind Quintet *Concert*
(1/93) (NIMB) ① **NI5327**

Berlin Phil Wind Qnt *Concert*
(4/93) (BIS) ① **BIS-CD536**
Reykjavik Wind Qnt (r1993) *Concert*
(10/95) (CHAN) ① **CHAN9362**
**La Création du monde—suite de concert
(1923)**
1. Prélude: Modéré; 2. Fugue; 3. Romance: Tendre
et doux; 4. Scherzo; 5. Final: Modéré.
A. Kavafian, J. Rosenfeld, T. Hoffman, C. Brey, A.
Previn (r1993) *Concert*
(11/95) (RCA) ① **09026 68181-2**
**Danses de Jacaremirim (Danses du petit
alligator)—violin and piano, Op. 256 (1945)**
L. Kaufman, A. Balsam (r1949) *Concert*
(12/90) (MUSI) ① **MACD-620**
**Divertissement—wind quintet, Op. 229b
(1958)** (after film score 'Gauguin')
Athena Ens *Concert* (10/91) (CHAN) ① **CHAN6536**
Duo—two violins, Op. 258 (1945)
(Americanum No 42)
K. Ososstowicz, E. Kovacic *Concert*
(9/92) (HYPE) ① **CDA66473**
**Duo concertante—clarinet and piano, Op.
351 (1956)**
E. Johnson, G. Back *Concert*
(10/88) (ASV) ① **CDDCA621**
P. Meyer, E. Le Sage *Concert*
(9/92) (DENO) ① **CO-79282**
V. Soames, J. Drake *Concert*
(9/92) (CLRI) ① **CC0001**
J. Cohler, J. Gordon (r1993) *Concert*
(5/95) (CRYS) ① **Crystal CD733**
**Pastorale—oboe, clarinet and bassoon, Op.
147 (1935)**
Athena Ens *Concert* (10/91) (CHAN) ① **CHAN6536**
London Wind Trio *Concert*
(9/92) (CARL) ① **MCD38**
**Le printemps—violin and piano, Op. 18
(1914)**
J. Szigeti, K. Ruhrseitz (r1926) *Concert*
(1/90) (BIDD) ① [2] **LAB005/6**
Scaramouche—two pianos, Op. 165b (1937)
(after incid music to 'Le médicin valant')
I. Hobson, C. Hobson *Concert*
(5/88) (ARAB) ① **Z6569**
K. Labèque, M. Labèque *Concert*
(8/91) (PHIL) ① **426 284-2PH**
D. Milhaud, M. Meyer (r1938) *Concert*
(4/93) (EMI) ① **CDC7 54604-2**
D. Milhaud, M. Meyer (r1938) *Concert*
(9/93) (EPM) ① [3] **150 122**
Pro Arte Gtr Trio (arr gtr trio) *Concert*
(1/94) (ASV) ① **CDWHL2079**
P. Corre, E. Exerjean *Concert*
(5/94) (PIER) ① **PV786091**
Brazileira E. Johnson, G. Back *Concert*
(10/88) (ASV) ① **CDDCA621**
2 Sketches—wind quintet, Op. 227b (1941)
1. Madrigal; 2. Pastoral.
Athena Ens *Concert* (10/91) (CHAN) ① **CHAN6536**
**Sonata for Flute, Oboe, Clarinet and Piano,
Op. 47 (1918)**
A. Nicolet, H. Holliger, E. Brunner, O. Maisenberg
Concert (2/87) (ORFE) ① **C060831A**
**Sonata for Two Violins and Piano, Op. 15
(1914)**
K. Ososstowicz, E. Kovacic, S. Tomes *Concert*
(9/92) (HYPE) ① **CDA66473**
**Sonata for Violin and Piano No. 2, Op. 40
(1917)**
F.P. Zimmermann, A. Lonquich (r1991) *Concert*
(1/95) (EMI) ① **CDC7 54541-2**
**Sonatina for Clarinet and Piano, Op. 100
(1927)**
E. Brunner, O. Maisenberg *Concert*
(2/87) (ORFE) ① **C060831A**
V. Soames, J. Drake *Concert*
(9/92) (CLRI) ① **CC0001**
P. Meyer, E. Le Sage *Concert*
(9/92) (DENO) ① **CO-79282**
J. Cohler, R. Hodgkinson (r1993) *Concert*
(11/94) (ONGA) ① **024-102**
Sonatina for Flute and Piano, Op. 76 (1922)
A. Nicolet, O. Maisenberg *Concert*
(2/87) (ORFE) ① **C060831A**
**Sonatina for Oboe and Piano, Op. 337
(1954)**
H. Holliger, O. Maisenberg *Concert*
(2/87) (ORFE) ① **C060831A**
String Quartet No. 1, Op. 5 (1912)
F. Mendelssohn Qt (r1994) *Concert*
(15/95) (TROU) ① **TRO-CD01409**
Arriaga Qt (r1994) *String Quartet 2.*
(11/95) (DINT) ① **DICD920290**

String Quartet No. 2, Op. 16 (1914-15)
F. Mendelssohn Qt (r1994) *Concert*
(5/95) (TROU) ① TRO-CD01409
Arriaga Qt (r1994) *String Quartet 1.*
(11/95) (DINT) ① DICD920290
String Quartet No. 5, Op. 64 (1920)
Quatuor National d'Aquitaine *Concert*
(4/87) (CYBE) ① CY805
String Quartet No. 8, Op. 121 (1932)
Quatuor National d'Aquitaine *Concert*
(4/87) (CYBE) ① CY805
String Quartet No. 11, Op. 232 (1942)
Quatuor National d'Aquitaine *Concert*
(4/87) (CYBE) ① CY805
String Quartet No. 13, Op. 268 (1946)
Quatuor National d'Aquitaine *Concert*
(4/87) (CYBE) ① CY805
Suite—violin, clarinet and piano, Op. 157b (1936) (from Anouilh's 'Le voyageur sans bagages')
H. Klug, C. Tait, I. Hobson *Concert*
(5/88) (ARAB) ① Z6569
Suite d'après Corrette—oboe, clarinet and bassoon, Op. 161b (1937) (after incid music for 'Jules César')
Athena Ens *Concert*   (10/91) (CHAN) ① CHAN6536
London Wind Trio *Concert*
(9/92) (CARL) ① MCD38

SECTION III: INSTRUMENTAL

L' automne—piano, Op. 115 (1932)
EXCERPTS: 1. Septembre; 2. Alfama; 3. Adieu.
B. Eidi (r1989) *Concert*
(2/95) (DINT) ① DICD920167
2. M. Long (r1935) *Concert*
(9/93) (EPM) ① [3] 150 122
Caramel Mou—piano, Op. 68 (1920)
I. Hobson *Concert*   (5/88) (ARAB) ① Z6569
Les charmes de la vie—suite: piano, Op. 360 (1957) (adapted from orch suite)
1. Pastorale; 2. L'Indifferent; 3. Plaisirs champêtres;
4. Sérénade; 5. Musette; 6. Masquerade.
B. Sharon (r1994) *Concert*
(5/95) (UNIC) ① DKPCD9155
Chorale—piano (1941)
S. Lechevalier (r1994) *Concert*
(7/95) (LARG) ① [2] Largo5130
4 esquisses—piano, Op. 227 (1941)
EXCERPTS: 1. Eglogue; 2. Madrigal; 3. Alameda; 4. Sobre la Loma.
B. Eidi (r1989) *Concert*
(2/95) (DINT) ① DICD920167
B. Sharon (r1994) *Concert*
(5/95) (UNIC) ① DKPCD9155
Madame Bovary—piano, Op. 128 (1933) (adapted from film score)
1. Trois valses (Op. 128c); 2. L'album de Madame Bovary (Op. 128b).
B. Sharon (r1994) *Concert*
(5/95) (UNIC) ① DKPCD9155
Pastorale—organ, Op. 229 (1941)
G. Barber *Concert*   (9/93) (PRIO) ① PRCD391
Polka—piano, Op. 95 (1928) (adapted from 'L'éventail de Jeanne')
B. Sharon (r1994) *Concert*
(5/95) (UNIC) ① DKPCD9155
9 Preludes—organ, Op. 231b (1942) (after incid music for 'L'announce faite à Marie')
1, 2. C. Bowers-Broadbent (r1992) *Concert*
(5/93) (ECM) ① 437 956-2
Printemps, Vol. 1—piano, Op. 25 (1915-19)
1. Modéré; 2. Souple; 3. Doucement.
D. Milhaud (r1930) *Concert*
(9/93) (EPM) ① [3] 150 122
B. Eidi (r1989) *Concert*
(2/95) (DINT) ① DICD920167
Printemps, Vol. 2—piano, Op. 66 (1920)
B. Eidi (r1989) *Concert*
(2/95) (DINT) ① DICD920167
3 Rag Caprices—piano, Op. 78 (1922)
I. Hobson *Concert*   (5/88) (ARAB) ① Z6569
B. Sharon (r1994) *Concert*
(5/95) (UNIC) ① DKPCD9155
Saudades do Brasil—suite for piano, Op. 67 (1920-21)
1a. Overture; 1b. Soracaba; 2. Botafogo; 3. Leme; 4. Copacabana; 5. Ipanema; 6. Gávea; 7. Corcovado; 8. Tijuca; 9. Sumaré; 10. Paineras; 11. Laranjeiras; 12. Paysandú.
M. Bratke (r1992) *Concert*
(8/93) (OLYM) ① OCD427
B. Sharon (r1994) *Concert*
(5/95) (UNIC) ① DKPCD9155
1b, 5, 7, 9. D. Milhaud (r1928/30) *Concert*
(9/93) (EPM) ① [3] 150 122
4. C. Ortiz *Concert*   (6/87) (CARL) ① PCD846

---

7. J. Heifetz, E. Bay (r1946) *Concert*
(11/94) (RCA) ① [65] 09026 61778-2(06)
9. J. Szigeti, A. Foldes (r1940: arr vn/pf: Levy)
Concert   (7/94) (BIDD) ① [2] LAB070/1
9. J. Heifetz, A. Sándor (r1934) *Concert*
(11/94) (RCA) ① [65] 09026 61778-2(02)
12. M. Long (r1935) *Concert*
(9/93) (EPM) ① [3] 150 122
Sonata for Piano No. 1, Op. 33 (1916)
B. Eidi (r1989) *Concert*
(2/95) (DINT) ① DICD920167
Sonatina—piano, Op. 354 (1956)
B. Eidi (r1989) *Concert*
(2/95) (DINT) ① DICD920167
Tango des Fratellini—piano, Op. 58c (adapted from 'Le boeuf sut le toit')
B. Sharon (r1994) *Concert*
(5/95) (UNIC) ① DKPCD9155
Le Tour de l'Exposition—piano, Op. 162 (1933)
B. Lerner *Concert*   (1/89) (ETCE) ① KTC1061

SECTION IV: VOCAL AND CHORAL

Alissa—song cycle, Op. 9 (1913 rev 1931) (Wds. A. Gide)
1. Jerome; 2. Jerome and Alissa 1; 3. Jerome and Alissa 2; 4. Letter from Jerome a; 5. Jerome and Alissa 3; 6. Letter from Alissa b; 7. Alissa's Journal.
C. Farley, J. Constable *Concert*
(3/93) (ASV) ① CDDCA810
L' amour chante, Op. 409 (1964)
C. Farley, J. Constable *Concert*
(3/93) (ASV) ① CDDCA810
Les Amours de Ronsard—chorus/4vv and orchestra, Op. 132 (1934)
1. La rose; 2. La tourterelle; 3. L'aubépine; 4. Le rossignol.
1, 3, 4. R. Mahé, E. Schenneberg, C. Rouquetty, P. Froumenty, orch. D. Milhaud (r1936) *Concert*
(9/93) (EPM) ① [3] 150 122
Catalogue de fleurs—song cycle, Op. 60 (1920) (Wds. L. Daudet)
1. La violette; 2. Le bégonia; 3. Les Fritillaires; 4. Les jacinthes; 5. Les crocus; 6. Le brachycome; 7. L'eremunis.
Paris PO, D. Milhaud (r1953) *Concert*
(9/92) (CHNT) ① LDC278 1069
4 Chansons de Ronsard—1v and piano/orchestra, Op. 223 (1941)
1. A une fontaine; 2. A Cupidon; 3. Tais-toi, babillarde; 4. Dieu vous gard'.
B. Hoch, Hong Kong PO, K. Schermerhorn *Concert*
(11/86) (CARL) ① PCD827
R. Streich, E. Werba (r1957) *Concert*
(10/94) (DG) ① [2] 437 680-2GDO2
6 chants populaires hébraïques—1v and piano/orchestra, Op. 86 (1925)
2. Chant de délivrance; 3. Berceuse; 4. Chant du veilleur.
M. Singher, D. Milhaud (r1932) *Concert*
(9/93) (EPM) ① [3] 150 122
Le Château de feu—cantata: chorus and orchestra, Op. 338 (1954) (Wds. Cassou)
Paris PO, D. Milhaud (r1956) *Concert*
(9/92) (CHNT) ① LDC278 1069
3 Elégies—soprano, tenor and strings, Op. 199 (1939) (Wds. Jammes)
1. Dis-moi, dis-moi; 2. Sur le sable des allées; 3. Mon amour, disais-tu.
K. Livingstone, N. Mackie, J.J. Blakely *Concert*
(2/89) (VANG) ① UKCD2009
La Mort du tyran—chorus, wind & percussion, Op. 116 (1932) (Wds. Lampride, trans Diderot)
Paris PO, D. Milhaud (r1956) *Concert*
(9/92) (CHNT) ① LDC278 1069
Pacem in Terris—choral symphony, Op. 404 (1963)
F. Kopleff, L. Quilico, Utah Univ Chor, Utah SO, M. Abravanel *Homme et son désir.*
(11/93) (VANG) ① 08.9070.71
3 Poèmes de Jean Cocteau, Op. 59 (1920)
1. Fumée; 2. Fête de Bordeaux; 3. Fête de Montmatre.
J. Bathori, D. Milhaud (r1929) *Concert*
(9/93) (EPM) ① [3] 150 122
U. Sonntag, R. Jansen (r1994) *Concert*
(5/95) (TROU) ① TRO-CD01409
4 Poèmes de Léo Latil—songs, Op. 20 (1914)
1. L'abandon; 2. Ma douleur; 3. Le rossignol; 4. La tourterelle.
U. Sonntag, R. Jansen (r1994) *Concert*
(5/95) (TROU) ① TRO-CD01409

Poèmes Juifs—song cycle, Op. 34 (1916)
1. Chant de Nourrice; 5. Chant de Résignation; 6. Chant d'Amour; 8. Lamentation.
C. Farley, J. Constable *Concert*
(3/93) (ASV) ① CDDCA810
1. P. Frijsh, C. Dougherty (r1940) *Concert*
(4/95) (PEAR) ① [2] GEMMCDS9095(1)
1, 5, 6. J. Bathori, D. Milhaud (r1929) *Concert*
(9/93) (EPM) ① [3] 150 122
3 Psaumes de David—chorus a cappella, Op. 339 (1954)
Je me suis fondue de joie Orphei Drängar Ch, E. Ericson *Concert*   (7/88) (BIS) ① BIS-CD383
Quatrain à Albert Roussel, Op. 106 (1929) (Wds. F. Jammes)
M. Cable, M. Fingerhut *Concert*
(9/88) (CHAN) ① CHAN8578
Les Soirées de Pétrograd—12 poèmes, Op. 55 (1919) (Wds. R. Chalupt)
Excs J. Bathori, D. Milhaud (r1928) *Concert*
(9/93) (EPM) ① [3] 150 122

SECTION V: STAGE WORKS

L' Abandon d'Ariane—opéra-minute: 5 scenes, Op. 98 (1927) (Lib. H. Hoppenot)
Capella Cracoviensis, K.A. Rickenbacher *Concert*
(5/93) (SCHW) ① 311392
J. Bathori, J. Planel, G. Petit, M. Brega, Pro Musica Ens, D. Milhaud (r1929) *Concert*
(9/93) (EPM) ① [3] 150 122
Le Boeuf sur le toit, '(The) Bull on the Roof'—ballet, Op. 58 (1920—Paris)
FNO, L. Bernstein *Concert*
(10/87) (EMI) ① CDC7 47845-2
Ulster Orch, Y. P. Tortelier *Concert*
(9/92) (CHAN) ① CHAN9023
New London Orch, R. Corp *Concert*
(12/92) (HYPE) ① CDA66594
Lyon Op Orch, K. Nagano *Concert*
(2/93) (ERAT) ① 2292-45820-2
Paris Champs-Élysées Orch, D. Milhaud (r1958) *Concert*
(4/93) (EMI) ① CDC7 54604-2
R. Bénédetti, J. Wiener (r1928: vn/pf vers) *Concert*
(9/93) (EPM) ① [3] 150 122
Paris Orch, S. Bychkov *Concert*
(3/94) (PHIL) ① 432 993-2PH
F. Iaciu, Lille Nat Orch, J-C. Casadesus (pp1993)
Six: Mariés de la Tour Eiffel.
(5/94) (HARM) ① HMC90 1473
P. Corre, E. Exerjean (trans pf duet) *Concert*
(5/94) (PIER) ① PV786091
Les Choéphores—incidental music, Op. 24 (1915) (Wds. Claudel, after Aeschylus)
EXCERPTS: 1. Vociferation funèbre; 2. Libation; 5. Exhortation; 7. Conclusion.
1, 2, 5, 7. C. Croiza, Antwerp Caecilia Chorale, Antwerp Concerts Orch, L. de Vocht (r1928/9) *Concert*   (9/93) (EPM) ① [3] 150 122
Christophe Colomb—opera: 2 parts, Op. 102 (1930—Berlin) (Lib. P. Claudel)
Cpte R. Massard, J. Micheau, X. Depraz, X. Depraz, J. Marchat, J. Davy, J. Davy, L. Lovano, L. Lovano, L. Lovano, J. Giraudeau, J. Giraudeau, J. Peyron, P. Germain, J. Chalude, French Rad Chor, French Rad Lyric Orch, M. Rosenthal (pp1956)
(5/88) (MONT) ① [2] TCE8750
La Création du monde—ballet, Op. 81a (1923—Paris)
FNO, L. Bernstein *Concert*
(10/87) (EMI) ① CDC7 47845-2
J. Harle, London Sinfonietta, S. Rattle *Concert*
(12/87) (EMI) ① CDC7 47991-2
Sinfonia da Camera, I. Hobson *Concert*
(5/88) (ARAB) ① Z6569
Prague SO, V. Neumann *Concert*
(11/90) (SUPR) ① 11 1105-2
Paris Cons, G. Prêtre *Concert*
(3/92) (EMI) ① CDM7 63945-2
Ulster Orch, Y. P. Tortelier *Concert*
(9/92) (CHAN) ① CHAN9023
Lyon Op Orch, K. Nagano *Concert*
(2/93) (ERAT) ① 2292-45820-2
orch. D. Milhaud (r1932) *Concert*
(4/93) (EMI) ① CDC7 54604-2
orch. D. Milhaud (r1932) *Concert*
(9/93) (EPM) ① [3] 150 122
Lausanne CO, A. Zedda (r1989) *Concert*
(10/95) (VIRG) ① CUV5 61206-2
La Délivrance de Thésée—opéra-minute: 6 scenes, Op. 99 (1927) (Wds. H. Hoppenot)
Capella Cracoviensis, K.A. Rickenbacher *Concert*
(5/93) (SCHW) ① 311392
J. Bathori, J. Planel, G. Petit, A. Valencin, J. Hazart, Pro Musica Ens, D. Milhaud (r1929) *Concert*
(9/93) (EPM) ① [3] 150 122

L' Enlèvement d'Europe—opéra-minute: 8
scenes, Op. 94 (1927)
Capella Cracoviensis, K.A. Rickenbacher *Concert*
(5/93) (SCHW) ① **311392**
J. Bathori, J. Planel, G. Petit, J. Hazart, Pro Musica
Ens, D. Milhaud (r1929) *Concert*
(9/93) (EPM) ① [3] **150 122**
Les Euménides—incidental music, Op. 41
(1917-22) (Wds. Claudel, after Aeschylus)
Processionnal Antwerp Caecilia Chorale, Antwerp
Concerts Orch, L. de Vocht (r1929) *Concert*
(9/93) (EPM) ① [3] **150 122**
La Fête de la musique—ballet (light and
water spectacle), Op. 159 (1937—Paris)
(Wds. Claudel)
E. Fels, E. Schenneberg, R. Gourgues, J. Claverie,
orch, D. Milhaud (r1937) *Concert*
(9/93) (EPM) ① [3] **150 122**
L' homme et son désir—ballet, Op. 48
(1918)
Desormiere Ens, D. Milhaud (r1948) *Concert*
(9/93) (EPM) ① [3] **150 122**
B. Christensen, M. Nixon, R. Christensen, P.
Chartand, Utah SO, M. Abravanel (r1960s) *Pacem in
Terris.*
(11/93) (VANG) ① **08.9070.71**
Les Malheurs d'Orphée—opera: 3 acts, Op.
85 (1926—Brussels) (Lib. A. Lunel)
Cpte M. Walker, A. Steiger, P. Harrhy, P. Donnelly,
M. Best, Gaynor Morgan, P. Bardon, S. Bickley,
Matrix Ens, R. Ziegler *Concert*
(7/91) (ASV) ① **CDDCA758**
Salade—ballet, Op. 83 (1924—Paris)
Tango R. Mahé, C. Rouquetty, E. Chastenet, P.
Froumenty, orch, D. Milhaud (r1936) *Concert*
(9/93) (EPM) ① [3] **150 122**
Les Songes—ballet, Op. 124 (1933—Paris)
Paris SO, D. Milhaud (r1934) *Concert*
(9/93) (EPM) ① [3] **150 122**

MILLÖCKER, Carl (1842–1899) Austria

SECTION I: ORCHESTRAL

Jonathan-Marsch (1890)
LJSO, J. Rothstein *Concert*
(1/86) (CHAN) ① **CHAN8381**
Klopf' an!—polka française (1887) (Eng:
Knock on the door!)
London Viennese Orch, J. Rothstein *Concert*
(5/93) (CHAN) ① **CHAN9127**
Die Sieben Schwaben-Marsch (1887) (Seven
Swabian March)
LJSO, J. Rothstein *Concert*
(1/86) (CHAN) ① **CHAN8381**

SECTION IV: VOCAL AND CHORAL

I und mei Bua—yodelling song
E. Schumann-Heink, orch (r1908) *Concert*
(2/91) (NIMB) ① **NI7811**

SECTION V: STAGE WORKS

Der Arme Jonathan—operetta (3 acts)
(1890—Vienna) (Lib. Wittmann and Bauer)
Ach, wir armen Primadonnen! L. Schöne, orch
(r1925) *Concert* (9/94) (NIMB) ① **NI7833**
The Doleful Prima Donna M. Hill Smith, Chandos
Concert Orch, S. Barry *Concert*
(7/88) (CHAN) ① **CHAN8561**
Der Bettlestudent, '(The) Beggar
Student'—operetta: 3 acts, Vienna (1882)
(Lib. Zell and Genée)
ACT 1: 1. Ach unsre Lieben sperrte man ein; 2a.
Und da soll man noch galant sein; 2b. Ach ich hab'
sie ja nur auf die Schulter geküsst; 3. Die Welt hat
das geniaiste Streben; 4. Juchheissa, hurra! Die
Messe beginnt; 5. Einkäufe machen sollten wir
eigentlich; 6. Ich knüpfte manche zarte Bande; 7. Bei
solchem Feste (finale). ACT 2: 8. Einem Mann hat sie
(hab' ich) gefunden; 9. Durch diesen Kuss sei unser
Bund geweiht!; 10a. Soll ich reden, darf ich
schweigen?; 10b. Ich setz' sen Fall; 11. Glückliche
Braut! Dir strahlet hell das Leben; 12. Mit Geld und
guten Worten; 13. Ach, ich hab' sie ja nur auf die
Schulter geküsst. ACT 3: 14. Lumpen, Bagage,
Bettelstudent; 15. Der Fürst soll nur ein Bettler sein;
16. Ich hab' kein Geld, bin vogelfrei; 17a. Still, man,
kommt!...Dort steht der Patron; 17b. Die halbe
Stunde ist vorbei; 17c. Jetzt lach' ich jeglicher
Gefahr; 18. Befreit das Land! Geknüpft das Band!.
Cpte G. Litz, R. Streich, R. Holm, H. Prey, G. Unger,
N. Gedda, K.H. Bennert, Bavarian Rad Chor,
Graunke SO, F. Allers (r1967/73: with dialogue)
(2/95) (EMI) ① [2] **CMS5 65387-2**

Nur das Eine bitt'ich dich Raphaele Concert Orch,
P. Walden (arr Waldenmaier) *Concert*
(5/91) (MOZA) ① **MECD1002**
6. F. Völker, orch (r1934) *Concert*
(3/90) (PEAR) ① **GEMMCD9383**
16. J. Björling, orch, N. Grevillius (r1938: Swed)
Concert (8/92) (BLUE) ① **ABCD016**
16. J. Björling, orch, N. Grevillius (r1938: Swed)
Concert (9/92) (MMOI) ① **CDMOIR409**
16. J. Björling, orch, N. Grevillius (r1938: Swed)
Concert (10/93) (NIMB) ① **NI7842**
16. J. Björling, orch, N. Grevillius (r1938: Swed)
Concert (12/93) (NIMB) ① **NI7851**
16. J. Björling, orch, N. Grevillius (r1938: Swed)
Concert (9/94) (CARL) ① **GLRS103**
16. J. Björling, orch, N. Grevillius (r1938: Swed)
Concert (9/94) (CONI) ① **CDHD214**
Die Dubarry—operetta (1931) (pastiche made
by Theo Mackeben)
EXCERPTS: 1a. Introduction; 1b. Immer nahen,
immer nähen; 2. Heut' hab ich Glück; 3. Aber wenn
es Feierabend. SCENE 2: 4. Seht, wie sich alles
schön; 5. Heut' hab ich Glück; 6. Stets verliebt; 7a.
Der Frühling zieht ins Land; 7b. Es lockt die Nacht; 8.
Stets verliebt (chorus). SCENE 3: 9. Wie schön ist
alles!; 10. Liebe, kleine Jeanne. SCENE 4: 11.
Blicken dich zwei Augen an. SCENE 5: 12. Der
Geige Klange lockt zur Nacht von Paris; 13. In
dunkler Nacht zog mich Gesang; 14a. Ja, es ist ein
alter Vorgang; 14b. Wenn verliebte bummeln gehr;
15a. Ich habe Liebe schon genossen; 15b. Ich
schenk mein' Herz nur einem Mann; 16. Arme kleine
Jeanne. SCENE 7: 17. Ob man gefällt oder nicht
gefällt; 18a. Ügerglück macht die Liebe; 18b. Ich
denk zürück an jene Zeit; 19. Der uns führen soll ins
grosse Glück!. SCENE 8: 20. Ich habe Liebe schon
genossen (reprise); 21. Ich schenk mein' Herz
(reprise). SCENE 9: 22. Im Park von Trianon; 23a.
Was ich im Leben beginne; 23b. Ja, so ist die, die
Dubarry; 24a. Die Uniform freut mich enorm; 24b. Ich
nehem' die Trommel an; 25. Mein Weg führt immer
mich zu Dir zurück.
1a, 1b, 8, 9, 17, 18b, 23a, 23b E. Köth, H. Wilhelm,
Günther Arndt Ch, Berlin SO, F. Fox *Fall: Rose von
Stambul.* (2/91) (EURO) ① **GD69023**
9. H. Nash, orch (r1932: Eng) *Concert*
(9/91) (PEAR) ① **GEMMCD9473**
15b L. Popp, ASMF, N. Marriner *Concert*
(6/88) (EMI) ① **CDC7 49700-2**
15b Raphaele Concert Orch, P. Walden (arr
Waldenmaier) *Concert*
(5/91) (MOZA) ① **MECD1002**
15b, 23a, 23b E. Schwarzkopf, chor, Philh, O.
Ackermann (1/86) (EMI) ① **CDC7 47284-2**
Gasparone—operetta: 3 acts (1884—Vienna)
(Lib. F. Zell and R. Genée)
Cpte A. Rothenberger, G. Wewel, W. Brokmeier, H.
Prey, G.W. Dieberitz, M. Finke, G. Fuchs, Bavarian
St Op Chor, Munich RO, H. Wallberg (r1981: with
dialogue) (2/95) (EMI) ① [2] **CMS5 65363-2**
Canzonetta J. Patzak, orch, M. Gurlitt (r1929)
Concert (3/90) (PEAR) ① **GEMMCD9383**
Er soll dein Herr sein Raphaele Concert Orch, E.
Rondell (arr Waldenmaier) *Concert*
(5/91) (MOZA) ① **MECD1002**
Wie freu'ich mich, Sie hier zu seh'n...Hüten Sie
sich B. Hendricks, G. Quilico, Lyon Op Orch, L.
Foster (r1993) *Concert*
(6/95) (EMI) ① **CDC5 55151-2**
Das Verwunschene Schloss—operetta: 3
acts (1878—Vienna) (Lib. Berla)
Polonaise Raphaele Concert Orch, E. Rondell (arr
Waldenmaier) *Concert*
(5/91) (MOZA) ① **MECD1002**

MINISCALCHI, Guglielmo (fl 1622–30) Italy

SECTION IV: VOCAL AND CHORAL

Fuggir pur mi convien—Aria (Book 1)
(1625)
T. Berganza, Ens, J.E. Dähler (hpd/dir) *Concert*
(3/84) (CLAV) ① **CD50-8206**
Fuggir voglio—Aria (Book 3) (1630)
T. Berganza, Ens, J.E. Dähler (hpd/dir) *Concert*
(3/84) (CLAV) ① **CD50-8206**
Io me ne vo—Aria (Book 2) (1625)
T. Berganza, Ens, J.E. Dähler (hpd/dir) *Concert*
(3/84) (CLAV) ① **CD50-8206**

MINKUS, Léon (Fyodorovich) (1826–1917) Czechoslovakia or Poland

SECTION I: ORCHESTRAL

Grand Pas—ballet music (1881) (orig comp for
Delvedez's 'Paquita')
English Concert Orch, R. Bonynge (arr March)
Concert (11/90) (DECC) ① [2] **421 818-2DH2**

SECTION V: STAGE WORKS

La Bayadère—ballet (1877—St Petersburg)
Cpte ECO, R. Bonynge (r1992)
(7/94) (DECC) ① [2] **436 917-2DH2**
Excs Sofia National Op Orch, B. Spassov (r1994)
Paquita. (12/95) (CAPR) ① **10 544**
Don Quixote—ballet: 4 acts
(1869—Moscow)
1. Pas de deux.
Cpte Sofia National Op Orch, B. Spassov (r1994)
(5/95) (CAPR) ① [2] **10 540/1**
1. English Concert Orch, R. Bonynge (arr March)
Concert (11/90) (DECC) ① [2] **421 818-2DH2**
Paquita—ballet (1881—St. Petersburg)
(interpolated into Deldevez's ballet)
Cpte Sofia National Op Orch, B. Spassov (r1994)
Bayadère. (12/95) (CAPR) ① **10 544**

MIRA FORNES, Rafael Angel (b 1951) Spain

SECTION II: CHAMBER

Caramelos para Zoe—string quartet
Arditti Qt *Concert* (12/91) (MONT) ① **789006**

MIRZOYAN, Edward (Mik'aeli) (b 1921) USSR

SECTION I: ORCHESTRAL

Poem Epitaph (in memory of Aram
Khachaturian)—orchestra
St Petersburg Chbr Ens, R. Melia *Concert*
(7/95) (ASV) ① **CDDCA916**
Symphony for Tympani and Strings (1962)
St Petersburg Chbr Ens, R. Melia *Concert*
(7/95) (ASV) ① **CDDCA916**
Theme and Variations—orchestra (1947)
St Petersburg Chbr Ens, R. Melia *Concert*
(7/95) (ASV) ① **CDDCA916**

MISSA, Edmond (1861–1910) France

pseudonym of Marius Michel

SECTION V: STAGE WORKS

Muguette
Minuet SO, T. Beecham (r c1912) *Concert*
(11/91) (SYMP) ① [2] **SYMCD1096/7**

MIYOSHI, Akira (b 1933) Japan

SECTION I: ORCHESTRAL

Concerto for Marimba and Strings (1969)
E. Glennie, Scottish CO, P. Daniel *Concert*
(4/93) (RCA) ① **09026 61277-2**

MOERAN, E(rnest) J(ohn) (1894–1950) England

SECTION I: ORCHESTRAL

Concerto for Cello and Orchestra (1945)
R. Wallfisch, Bournemouth Sinfonietta, N. del Mar
Sinfonietta. (9/87) (CHAN) ① **CHAN8456**
Concerto for Violin and Orchestra (1937-41)
L. Mordkovitch, Ulster Orch, V. Handley *Pieces for
small orchestra.* (9/90) (CHAN) ① **CHAN8807**
In the Mountain Country—symphonic
impression (1921)
Ulster Orch, V. Handley *Concert*
(9/89) (CHAN) ① **CHAN8639**
Overture to a Masque (1944)
Ulster Orch, V. Handley *Symphony.*
(4/88) (CHAN) ① **CHAN8577**
2 Pieces for Small Orchestra
1. Lonely waters (?1924); 2. Whythorne's Shadow
(?1931).
Ulster Orch, V. Handley *Violin Concerto.*
(9/90) (CHAN) ① **CHAN8807**

Rhapsody No. 1 in F—orchestra (1922)
Ulster Orch, V. Handley Concert
(9/89) (CHAN) ① **CHAN8639**
Rhapsody No. 2 in E—orchestra (1924 rev 1940-41)
Ulster Orch, V. Handley Concert
(9/89) (CHAN) ① **CHAN8639**
Rhapsody No. 3 in F sharp—piano and orchestra (1942-43)
M. Fingerhut, Ulster Orch, V. Handley Concert
(9/89) (CHAN) ① **CHAN8639**
Serenade in G—orchestra (1948)
Ulster Orch, V. Handley Concert
(3/91) (CHAN) ① **CHAN8808**
Northern Sinfonia, R. Hickox (1988) Concert
(8/94) (EMI) ① **CDM7 64721-2**
Sinfonietta—orchestra (1944)
Bournemouth Sinfonietta, de del Mar Cello Concerto.
(9/87) (CHAN) ① **CHAN8456**
Northern Sinfonia, R. Hickox (1988) Concert
(8/94) (EMI) ① **CDM7 64721-2**
Symphony in G minor (1924-37)
Ulster Orch, V. Handley Masque Ov.
(4/88) (CHAN) ① **CHAN8577**
Hallé, L. Heward (r1942) Ireland: Piano Concerto.
(5/93) (DUTT) ① **CDAX8001**

SECTION II: CHAMBER

Fantasy-Quartet—oboe, violin, viola and cello (1946)
S. Francis, English Qt Concert
(7/87) (CHAN) ① **CHAN8392**
Sonata for Cello and Piano (1947)
R. Wallfisch, J. York (r1994) Concert
(8/95) (MARC) ① **8 223718**
Sonata for Violin and Piano in E minor (1923)
D. Scotts, J. Talbot String Quartet 1.
(9/87) (CHAN) ① **CHAN8465**
May Harrison, C. Lynch (r1937) Concert
(12/90) (SYMP) ① **SYMCD1075**
String Quartet No. 1 in A minor (1921)
Melbourne Qt Violin Sonata in E minor.
(9/87) (CHAN) ① **CHAN8465**
String Trio in G (1931)
J. Pougnet, F. Riddle, A. Pini (r1941) Concert
(12/95) (DUTT) ① **CDAX8014**

SECTION III: INSTRUMENTAL

Summer Valley—piano (1925)
C. Headington Concert
(11/90) (KING) ① **KCLCD2017**

SECTION IV: VOCAL AND CHORAL

Far in a Western Brookland—song: 1v and piano (1925) (Wds. A E Housman)
A. Rolfe Johnson, G. Johnson (r c1994) Concert
(8/95) (HYPE) ① [2] **CDA66471/2**
Nocturne—baritone, chorus and orchestra (1934) (Wds. R. Nichols)
H. Mackey, Renaissance Sngrs, Ulster Orch, V. Handley Concert
(3/91) (CHAN) ① **CHAN8808**
O Fair Enough are Sky and Plain—song: 1v and piano (mid-late 1940s) (Wds. A E Housman)
A. Rolfe Johnson, G. Johnson (r c1994) Concert
(8/95) (HYPE) ① [2] **CDA66471/2**
Phyllida and Corydon—choral suite: chorus a cappella (1939)
1. Madrigal: Phyllida and Corydon (wds. Breton); 2. Madrigal: Beauty sat Bathing (wds. Munday); 3. Pastoral: On a Hill There Grows a Flower (wds. Breton); 4. Air: Phyllis Amorata (wds. anon); 5. Ballet: Said I that Amaryllis (wds. anon); 6. Canzonet: The Treasure of my heart (wds. Sidney).
Finzi Sngrs, P. Spicer (r1992) Concert
(10/93) (CHAN) ① **CHAN9182**
The Sailor and Young Nancy—Norfolk folksong arrangement (1924)
Cambridge Sngrs, J. Rutter Concert
(4/87) (CLLE) ① **COLCD104**
Songs of Springtime—chorus a cappella (1930)
1. Under the Greenwood Tree (wds. Shakespeare); 2. The River-God's Song (wds. J. Fletcher); 3. Spring, the sweet Spring (wds. S. Daniel); 4. Love is a sickness (wds. T. Maske); 5. Sigh no more, Ladies (wds. Shakespeare); 6. Good wine (wds. W. Browne); 7. To daffodils (wds. R. Herrick).
Finzi Sngrs, P. Spicer (r1992) Concert
(10/93) (CHAN) ① **CHAN9182**
3, 7. King's Sngrs Concert
(6/88) (EMI) ① **CDC7 49765-2**
Te Deum and Jubilate in E flat (1931)
Norwich Cath Ch, M. Nicholas, N. Taylor (r1993) Concert
(10/94) (PRIO) ① **PRCD470**

MOHR, J.

SECTION II: CHAMBER

Air varié—clarinet and piano
C. Draper, wind band (rc1908) Concert
(2/94) (CLRI) ① **CC0005**

MOLINARO, Simone (c1565–1615) Italy

SECTION III: INSTRUMENTAL

Intavolatura di liuto libro primo—lute (pub 1599) (also pieces by Gostena)
1. FANTASIAS: 1a. prima; 1b. seconda; 1c. terza; 1e. quinta; 1f. sesta; 1g. settima; 1h. ottava; 1i. nona; 1j. decima; 1m. decima quarta; 2. SALTARELLOS: 2a. primo; 2e. quinto; 2g. settimo; 2h. del predetto ballo; 3. CANZONE FRANCESE: 3a. Ung gaij bergier (Crequillon); 3b. Rosignolet (Crequillon); 3c. Frais e Gaillard (Clemens non Papa); 4. Ballo detto il Conte Orlando; 5. Pass'e mezzo in quattro modi; 6. Gagliarda in tre modi.
1a, 2h, 4. J. Bream (r1966) Concert
(8/93) (RCA) ① [28] **09026 61583-2(1)**
1a, 2h, 4. J. Bream (r1966) Concert
(6/94) (RCA) ① **09026 61585-2**
1i Y. Imamura Concert
(3/84) (CLAV) ① **CD50-8206**
1i, 5, 6. J. Lindberg (r1991) Concert
(11/93) (BIS) ① **BIS-CD599**
2a-h, 4. K. Ragossnig Concert
(2/86) (ARCH) ① **415 294-2AH**
2h, 4. P. O'Dette Concert
(4/88) (HYPE) ① **CDA66228**
4. Kithara (r1993) Concert
(3/95) (CHAN) ① **CHAN0562**

MOLIQUE, (Wilhelm) Bernhard (1802–1869) Germnay

SECTION I: ORCHESTRAL

Concertino in G minor—oboe and orchestra
B. Glaetzner, Berlin SO, C.P. Flor Concert
(5/90) (CAPR) ① **10 281**

MØLLER, Peter (b 1947) Denmark

SECTION III: INSTRUMENTAL

Sonata VIII—piano (c1792)
W. Naboré (r1992) Concert
(8/94) (DORO) ① **DRC3001**

MOLLIN, Fred (20th cent) USA

SECTION V: STAGE WORKS

Forever Knight—film score (1992)
EXCERPTS: 1. Main Title.
1. OST, F. Mollin (r1992) Concert
(10/93) (SILV) ① **FILMCD127**

MOLLOY, James (1839–1909) England

SECTION IV: VOCAL AND CHORAL

Kerry dance—song
E. Schumann-Heink, orch (r1913) Concert
(2/91) (NIMB) ① **NI7811**
Love's old sweet song—song
A. Galli-Curci, orch, R. Bourdon (r1923) Concert
(9/94) (ROMO) ① [2] **81004-2**
Tomorrow will be Friday—partsong (Wds. C. Marlowe)
Hilliard Ens, L-L. Kiesel Concert
(12/91) (MERI) ① **DUOCD89009**

MOLTER, Johann Melchior (1696–1765) Germany

SECTION I: ORCHESTRAL

Concerto for Clarinet and Strings No. 1 in D
A.O. Popa, Iaşi Moldova PO, P. Popescu Concert
(9/92) (OLYM) ① **OCD418**
Concerto for Clarinet and Strings No. 6 in D
T. Friedli, South-West German CO, P. Angerer Concert
(9/86) (CLAV) ① **CD50-0813**
Concerto for Trumpet and Strings No. 1 in D, MWV IV. 12 (after 1743)
H. Hardenberger, LPO, E. Howarth Concert
(3/91) (PHIL) ① **426 311-2PH**

G. Touvron, Slovak CO, B. Warchal Concert
(9/91) (OPUS) ① **9350 1710**
G. Touvron, Württemberg CO, J. Faerber Concert
(5/93) (RCA) ① **09026 61200-2**
Concerto for Trumpet and Strings No. 2 in D
W. Marsalis, ECO, R. Leppard Concert
(1/86) (SONY) ① **MK39061**
J. Wallace, Philh, S. Wright Concert
(4/89) (NIMB) ① **NI5121**
G. Touvron, Württemberg CO, J. Faerber Concert
(5/93) (RCA) ① **09026 61200-2**
Concerto for Trumpet and Strings No. 3 in D, MWVIV/14a
L. Güttler, F. Kircheis, Leipzig New Bach Collegium Musicum, M. Pommer (r1986) Concert
(8/89) (CAPR) ① **10 051**
G. Touvron, Württemberg CO, J. Faerber Concert
(5/93) (RCA) ① **09026 61200-2**
Concerto Pastorale in G
English Concert, T. Pinnock (hpd/dir) Concert
(12/91) (ARCH) ① **435 262-2AH**
5 Concertos for Trumpet and Strings in D, MWVIV.7-11 (1440s)
4. No 4 in D, MWVIV.10; 5. No 5 in D, MWVIV.11; 5a. Adagio.
4. G. Touvron, G. Messler, Württemberg CO, J. Faerber Concert (5/93) (RCA) ① **09026 61200-2**

MOLTKE, Cuno, Count von (1847–1923) Germany

SECTION I: ORCHESTRAL

Grosser Kurfürsten Reitermarsch—wind band (Eng: Great Elector's Cavalry)
Berlin Phil Wind Qnt, H. von Karajan (r1973) Concert
(5/94) (DG) ① **439 346-2GX2**

MOMPOU, Federico (1893–1987) Spain

SECTION III: INSTRUMENTAL

Cançons i danses—piano (or guitar where marked)
1. I (1921); 2. II (1918-24); 3. III (1926); 4. IV (1928); 5. V (1952); 6. VI (1942); 7. VII (1944); 8. VIII (1946); 9. IX (1948); 10. X (1953); 11. XI (1961); 12. XII (1962); 13. XIII (guitar: 1972); 14. XIV (1948-62).
G. Soriano (r1950s) Concert
(12/92) (EMI) ① **CDM7 64470-2**
A. de Larrocha (r1992) Preludes.
(11/94) (RCA) ① **09026 62554-2**
Excs A. de Larrocha Concert
(9/92) (DECC) ① [2] **433 929-2DM2**
1. A.B. Michelangeli (r1942) Concert
(8/93) (CHAN) ① **CDH7 64490-2**
1. A. Rubinstein (1955) Concert
(9/93) (RCA) ① **09026 61261-2**
5, 6, 8. F. Mompou (r1950) Concert
(11/93) (EMI) ① **CDC7 54836-2**
6. A. Rubinstein (r1954) Concert
(9/93) (RCA) ① **09026 61261-2**
Fêtes lointaines—piano (1920)
1. Calme; 2. Vif I; 3. Rythmé; 4. Vif II; 5. Lentement; 6. Vif III.
C. Bravo (r1950s) Concert
(12/92) (EMI) ① **CDM7 64470-2**
Impressions intimes—piano (1911-14)
1. Planys; 2. Pájaro triste; 3. La barca; 4. Cuna; 5. Secreto; 6. Gitano.
A. de Larrocha Concert
(9/92) (DECC) ① [2] **433 929-2DM2**
5. A. de Larrocha Concert
(7/90) (DECC) ① **417 795-2DM**
Musica callada—four books: piano (1959-67)
1. BOOK ONE (1959): 1a. Angélico; 1b. Lent; 1c. Placide; 1d. Afflito e penoso; 1e. Legato metallico; 1f. Lento, molto cantabile; 1g. Lento, profond; 1h. Semplice; 1i. Lento; 2. BOOK TWO (1962): 2a. Lento-Cantabile; 2b. Allegretto; 2c. Lento; 2d. Tranqille-Très calme; 2e. Severo-S-e1rieux; 2f. Lento-Plaintif; 2g. Calme; 3. BOOK THREE (1965): 3a. Lento; 3b. Luminoso; 3c. Tranquillo; 3d. Calme; 3e. Lento; 4. BOOK FOUR (1967): 4a. Molto lento e tranquillo; 4b. Calme, avec clarté; 4c. Moderato; 4d. Lento molto; 4e. Lento; 4f. Lento molto; 4g. Lento.
H. Henck (r1993) (9/95) (ECM) ① **445 699-2**
4. A. de Larrocha Concert
(9/92) (DECC) ① [2] **433 929-2DM2**
Paisajes—piano (1942-60)
1. La fuente i la campana (1942); 2. El lago (1947); 3. Carros de Galicia (1960).

C. Bravo (r1950s) *Concert*
(12/92) (EMI) ① **CDM7 64470-2**
1. F. Mompou (r1950) *Concert*
(11/93) (EMI) ① **CDC7 54836-2**
Pessebres—piano (1914-17)
1. Pessebres; 2. L'Ermita; 3. El pastor.
C. Bravo (r1950s) *Concert*
(12/92) (EMI) ① **CDM7 64470-2**
12 Preludes—piano
1. I (1927-28); 2. II (1927-28); 3. III (1927-28); 4. IV
(1927-28); 5. V (1930); 6. VI (1930); 7. VII,
'Fireworks' (1931); 8. VIII (1943); 9. IX (1943); 10. X
(1944); 11. XI (1960: unpub); 12. XII (1960: unpub).
5-7, 11. A. de Larrocha (r1993) *Cançons i danses.*
(11/94) (RCA) ① **09026 62554-2**
Préludio a Alicia de Larrocha—piano (1949)
A. de Larrocha *Concert*
(9/92) (DECC) ① [2] **433 929-2DM2**
Scènes d'enfants—piano (1915-18)
1. Cris dans le rue; 2. Jeux I; 3. Jeux II; 4. Jeux sur la
plage; 5. Jeunes filles au jardin.
C. Bravo (r1950s) *Concert*
(12/92) (EMI) ① **CDM7 64470-2**
Teatre Lliure CO, J. Pons (r1993; orch Tansman)
Concert (4/94) (HARM) ① **HMC90 1482**
5. F. Mompou (r1950) *Concert*
(11/93) (EMI) ① **CDC7 54836-2**
Souvenirs de l'exposition—piano (1937)
1. Entrée; 2. Tableaux de statistiques; 3. Planétaire;
4. Pavillon de l'élégance.
B. Lerner *Concert* (1/89) (ETCE) ① **KTC1061**
Suburbis—piano (1916-17)
1. El carrer, el guitarrista i el vell cavall; 2. Gitanes I;
3. Gitanes II; 4. La ceguetta; 5. L'home de l'aristó.
C. Bravo (r1950s) *Concert*
(12/92) (EMI) ① **CDM7 64470-2**
Teatre Lliure CO, J. Pons (r1993; orch Rosenthal)
Concert (4/94) (HARM) ① **HMC90 1482**
1. F. Mompou (r1950) *Concert*
(11/93) (EMI) ① **CDC7 54836-2**
Suite compostelana
J. Bream (r1983) *Concert*
(8/93) (RCA) ① [28] **09026 61583-2(4)**
J. Bream (r1983) *Concert*
(6/94) (RCA) ① **09026 61596-2**

SECTION IV: VOCAL AND CHORAL

**Combat del somni—1v, piano/orch (1942-8,
orch 1965)** (Wds. J. Janès)
EXCERPTS: 1. Damunt de tu, només les flors; 2.
Aquesta nit un mateix vent; 3. Jo et pressentia com la
mar.
V. de los Angeles, Lamoureux Orch, A. Ros-Marbà
(r1969: arr Ros-Marbà) *Concert*
(4/94) (EMI) ① [4] **CMS5 65061-2(1)**
V. Parramon, Teatre Lliure CO, J. Pons (r1993)
Concert (4/94) (HARM) ① **HMC90 1482**
**Improperiae (Los Improperios)—oratorio:
baritone, chorus and orchestra (1964)**
V. Parramon, J. Artysz, Valencia Ch, Teatre Lliure
CO, J. Pons (r1993) *Concert*
(4/94) (HARM) ① **HMC90 1482**

MONAHAN, Gordon *(20th Cent)*

SECTION IV: VOCAL AND CHORAL

Shepherd's love—song
C. Muzio, orch (r1924) *Concert*
(5/90) (BOGR) ① [2] **BIM705-2**
C. Muzio, orch (r1924) *Concert*
(1/94) (ROMO) ① [2] **81005-2**

MONASTERIO, Jesús
(1836–1903) Spain

SECTION II: CHAMBER

Sierra Morena—violin and piano
Y. Menuhin, L. Persinger (r1928) *Concert*
(4/91) (BIDD) ① **LAB031**

MONCAYO GARCÍA, José Pablo
(1912–1958) Mexico

SECTION I: ORCHESTRAL

Huapango—orchestra (1941)
Xalapa SO, H. de la Fuente *Concert*
(12/93) (CARL) ① **MCD63**

**MONCKTON, (John) Lionel
(Alexander)** *(1861–1924)
England*

SECTION V: STAGE WORKS

The **Arcadians—musical comedy: 3 acts**
(1909—London) (Lib. Ambient, Thompson,
Courtneidge and Wimperis.)
EXCERPTS: 1. Overture. ACT 1: 2. Who's for the
woods?; 3. Arcadians are we; 4. I quite forgot
Acardia; 5. The joy of life; 6. Look what hovers above
us; 7. The pipes of Pan are calling; 8. All a lie!; 9.
Sweet Simplicitas; 10. To all and each. ACT 2: 11.
That's all over; 12. Back your fancy; 13. The girl with
the brogue; 14. This is really altogether too
provoking; 15. Acardy is ever young; 16. Somewhere;
17. Charming weather; 18. Fickle fortune; 19. The
horses are out. ACT 3: 20. Plant your posies; 21. I
like London; 22. My motter—always merry and bright;
23. Half past two; 24. Cheer for Simplicitas; 25. All
down Piccadilly; 26. Truth is so beautiful; 27. My
heart flies home.
7. M. Hill Smith, Southern Fest Orch, R. White
Concert (5/93) (CHAN) ① **CHAN9110**
17. M. Hill Smith, P. Morrison, Chandos Concert
Orch, S. Barry *Concert*
(6/85) (CHAN) ① **CHAN8362**
**Our Miss Gibbs—musical show
(1909—London)**
Moonstruck M. Hill Smith, Southern Fest Orch, R.
White *Concert* (5/93) (CHAN) ① **CHAN9110**
The **Quaker Girl—musical play
(1910—London)** (Lib. Greenbank)
A Bad Boy and a Good Girl M. Hill Smith, P.
Morrison, Chandos Concert Orch, S. Barry *Concert*
(7/88) (CHAN) ① **CHAN8561**
A **Runaway Girl—musical show
(1898—London)**
Soldiers in the park Southern Fest Orch, R. White
Concert (5/93) (CHAN) ① **CHAN9110**

MONDÉJAR, Alonso de *(fl
1502–1505) Spain*

SECTION IV: VOCAL AND CHORAL

**Un solo fin de mis males/Non so yo quien la
descubre—canción: 1v**
C. Bott, New London Consort, P. Pickett *Concert*
(7/92) (LINN) ① **CKD007**

**MONDONVILLE, Jean-Joseph
Cassanéa de** *(1711–1772)
France*

SECTION II: CHAMBER

**Pièces de clavecin—harpsichord and violin
(pub 1734)**
1. G minor; 2. F; 3. B flat; 4. C; 5. G; 6. A.
5. S. Standage, L.U. Mortensen (r1993) *Concert*
(6/93) (CHAN) ① **CHAN0531**

SECTION IV: VOCAL AND CHORAL

Benefac Domine—petit motet
G. Fisher, London Baroque, E. Higginbottom *Concert*
(11/88) (HYPE) ① **CDA66269**
De Profundis—grand motet (1748)
G. Fisher, C. Daniels, S. Varcoe, New College Ch,
London Baroque, E. Higginbottom *Concert*
(11/88) (HYPE) ① **CDA66269**
In decachordo psalterio—petit motet
G. Fisher, London Baroque, E. Higginbottom *Concert*
(11/88) (HYPE) ① **CDA66269**
Regina terrae—petit motet
G. Fisher, London Baroque, E. Higginbottom *Concert*
(11/88) (HYPE) ① **CDA66269**
Venite exultemus—grand motet (1740)
G. Fisher, C. Daniels, S. Varcoe, New College Ch,
London Baroque, E. Higginbottom *Concert*
(11/88) (HYPE) ① **CDA66269**

SECTION V: STAGE WORKS

**Titon et aurore—heroic pastorale: prologue
and 3 acts (1753—Paris)** (Lib. La Marre &
Voiserion)
Cpte J-P. Fouchécourt, C. Napoli, P. Huttenlocher, J.
Smith, A. Monoyios, F. Herr Voc Ens, Musiciens du
Louvre, M. Minkowski (pp1991)
(10/92) (ERAT) ① [2] **2292-45715-2**

MONIOT DE PARIS *(13th Cent)
France*

SECTION IV: VOCAL AND CHORAL

Je chevauchoie l'autrier—song
A. Azéma, C. A. Fulton, S. Kammen (r1993) *Concert*
(11/94) (ERAT) ① **4509-94830-2**

MONIUSZKO, Stanisław
(1819–1872) Poland

SECTION I: ORCHESTRAL

Concert Polonaise in A (1866)
Warsaw Nat PO, W. Rowicki (r1964) *Concert*
(8/93) (OLYM) ① **OCD386**
The **Fairy tale—concert overture (1848)**
Warsaw Nat PO, W. Rowicki (r1964) *Concert*
(8/93) (OLYM) ① **OCD386**
Bydgoszcz PSO, R. Satanowski (r1991) *Concert*
(8/93) (CPO) ① **CPO999 113-2**

SECTION IV: VOCAL AND CHORAL

O mother—song
A. Didur, anon (r1900) *Concert*
(6/93) (PEAR) ① [3] **GEMMCDS9997/9(2)**
A. Didur, anon (r1901) *Concert*
(6/93) (PEAR) ① [3] **GEMMCDS9997/9(2)**
A. Didur, orch (r1928) *Concert*
(1/94) (CLUB) ① **CL99-089**
Old age—song
A. Didur, anon (r1901) *Concert*
(6/93) (PEAR) ① [3] **GEMMCDS9997/9(2)**
Phantoms—cantata (before 1859) (wds. after
A. Mickiewicz)
Children! don't you recognize me? A. Didur, anon
(r1901) *Concert*
(6/93) (PEAR) ① [3] **GEMMCDS9997/9(2)**
The **Quack's prophecy—song**
A. Didur, anon (r1900) *Concert*
(6/93) (PEAR) ① [3] **GEMMCDS9997/9(2)**
A. Didur, anon (r1901) *Concert*
(6/93) (PEAR) ① [3] **GEMMCDS9997/9(2)**
Sail! young raftsmen—song
A. Didur, anon (r1901) *Concert*
(6/93) (PEAR) ① [3] **GEMMCDS9997/9(2)**

SECTION V: STAGE WORKS

The **Countess—opera: 4 acts
(1859—Warsaw)** (Lib. W. Wolski)
Overture Katowice RSO, J. Krenz (r1952) *Concert*
(8/93) (OLYM) ① **OCD386**
Overture Bydgoszcz PSO, R. Satanowski (r1991)
Concert (8/93) (CPO) ① **CPO999 113-2**
**Halka—opera: 2 acts rev 4 acts (1848 rev
1858—Vilnius; Warsaw)** (Lib. Wolski)
Janusz's aria N. Shevelev, anon (r1901) *Concert*
(6/93) (PEAR) ① [3] **GEMMCDS9007/9(2)**
Like the shrub in the whirlwind J. Korolewicz-
Wayda, orch, O.I. Arkadiev (r1908) *Concert*
(6/93) (PEAR) ① [3] **GEMMCDS9004/6(1)**
Like the wind in the hills A. Labinsky, orch (r1908)
Concert (3/95) (NIMB) ① **NI7865**
Overture Bydgoszcz PSO, R. Satanowski (r1991)
Concert (8/93) (CPO) ① **CPO999 113-2**
Overture; Mazurka Warsaw Nat PO, W. Rowicki
(r1964) *Concert* (8/93) (OLYM) ① **OCD386**
Polonaise A. Didur, anon (r1901) *Concert*
(6/93) (PEAR) ① [3] **GEMMCDS9997/9(2)**
The **wind whistles** L. Sobinov, anon (r1901) *Concert*
(6/93) (PEAR) ① [3] **GEMMCDS9997/9(1)**
The **wind whistles** D. Yuzhin, anon (r1902) *Concert*
(6/93) (PEAR) ① [3] **GEMMCDS9001/3(1)**
The **Haunted Manor—opera (4 acts)
(1865—Warsaw)** (Lib. Checiński)
When I looked into her eyes A. Didur, anon (r1900)
Concert
(6/93) (PEAR) ① [3] **GEMMCDS9997/9(2)**
Jawnuta—operetta (1852 rev 1860—Warsaw)
(Lib. F D Kniaznin: rev of 'The Gypsies')
Overture Bydgoszcz PSO, R. Satanowski (r1991)
Concert (8/93) (CPO) ① **CPO999 113-2**
**Paria—opera: prologue and 3 acts
(1869—Warsaw)** (Lib. Checiński)
Overture Bydgoszcz PSO, R. Satanowski (r1991)
Concert (8/93) (CPO) ① **CPO999 113-2**
Overture Katowice RSO, G. Fitelberg (r1952)
Concert (8/93) (OLYM) ① **OCD386**
The **Raftsman—opera: 1 act (1858—Warsaw)**
(Lib. W. Boguslawski)
Overture Bydgoszcz PSO, R. Satanowski (r1991)
Concert (8/93) (CPO) ① **CPO999 113-2**
Overture Warsaw Nat PO, W. Rowicki (r1964)
Concert (8/93) (OLYM) ① **OCD386**

Rokiczana—opera: 3 acts (1858-59)
1. Ballad of Florian the Grey.
A. Didur, anon (r1901) Concert
(6/93) (PEAR) ① [3] GEMMCDS9997/9(2)
Verbum nobile—opera: 1 act
(1860—Warsaw) (Lib. J. Checiński)
Overture Bydgoszcz PSO, R. Satanowski (r1991)
Concert (8/93) (CPO) ① CPO999 113-2
Overture Katowice RSO, G. Fitelberg (r1952)
Concert (8/93) (OLYM) ① OCD386
Serwacy's Polonaise A. Didur, anon (r1901)
Concert
(6/93) (PEAR) ① [3] GEMMCDS9997/9(2)

MONK, Edwin George (1819–1900) England

SECTION IV: VOCAL AND CHORAL

Angel voices ever singing (tune: Angel voices)
St Paul's Cath Ch, C. Dearnley, John Scott Concert
(7/90) (HYPE) ① CDH88036

MONK, Meredith (b 1943) USA

SECTION IV: VOCAL AND CHORAL

Return to earth—chorus a capella
Musica Sacra, R. Westenburg (r1993) Concert
(12/93) (CATA) ① 09026 61822-2

SECTION V: STAGE WORKS

Atlas—opera: 3 acts (1991)
Cpte C. Arávalo, T. Bogdan, J. Brenner, S-Z. Chen, A. Easter, R. Een, D. Emerson, E. Eyre, K. Geissinger, C. Gonzalez, D. Hanchard, W. Hill, S. Kalm, M. Monk, R. Osborne, W. Pauley, R. Wong, Orch, W. Hankin (r1992)
(10/93) (ECM) ① [2] 437 773-2

MONK, Theolonious (1917–1982) USA

SECTION III: INSTRUMENTAL

Monk's Point—piano
J. MacGregor (trans MacGregor) Concert
(8/89) (COLL) ① Coll1299-2
Round Midnight—piano
J. MacGregor (trans MacGregor) Concert
(8/89) (COLL) ① Coll1299-2

MONK OF SALZBURG (13th Cent) Austria

SECTION IV: VOCAL AND CHORAL

Kum senfter Trost—song
E. Lamandier Concert (2/88) (ALIE) ① AL1019

MONKMAN, Francis (20th Cent) England

SECTION V: STAGE WORKS

The Long Good Friday—film score (1981)
EXCERPTS: 1. Main Title; 2. Overture; 3. The Scene is Set; 4. At the Pool; 5. Discovery; 6. The Icehouse; 7. Talking to the Police; 8. Guitar Interludes; 9. Realization; 10. Fury; 11. Taken.
11. OST Concert (5/93) (SILV) ① SILVAD3001

MONN, Matthias Georg (1717–1750) Austria

SECTION I: ORCHESTRAL

Concerto for Cello and Orchestra in G minor
J. Du Pré, LSO, J. Barbirolli (r1968) Concert
(8/94) (EMI) ① CZS5 68132-2

SECTION IV: VOCAL AND CHORAL

Deutsche Marienlieder—alto and continuo
J. Bowman, King's Consort, R. King Concert
(3/87) (MERI) ① CDE84126

MONNIKENDAM, Marius (1896–1977) The Netherlands

SECTION III: INSTRUMENTAL

Toccata No. 2—organ (1971)
C. Herrick Concert (7/86) (HYPE) ① CDA66121

MONRO, George (d 1731) England

SECTION IV: VOCAL AND CHORAL

My lovely Celia—song
D. Lloyd, G. Moore (r1943: arr Lane Wilson) Concert
(4/92) (EMI) ① [7] CHS7 69741-2(2)
R. Ponselle, orch, R. Bourdon (r1924) Concert
(11/94) (ROMO) ① [2] 81006-2

MONSIGNY, Pierre-Alexandre (1729–1817) France

SECTION V: STAGE WORKS

Aline, reine de Golconde—opera: 3 acts (Paris) (Lib. M-J. Sedaine)
Rigaudon Y. Menuhin, H. Giesen (arr Franko: r1930) Concert (4/91) (BIDD) ① LAB032

MONTAGUE, Stephen (b 1943) USA

SECTION I: ORCHESTRAL

From the White Edge of Phrygia—orchestra (1983-4)
Florida Orch, J. Ling (r1993) Concert
(4/95) (CNTI) ① CCD1061

SECTION II: CHAMBER

String Quartet No. 1, 'in memoriam Barry Anderson and Tomasz Sikorski'—str qt, live electronics & computer generated tape (1989-93)
S. Montague, Smith Qt (r1993) Concert
(4/95) (CNTI) ① CCD1061

SECTION III: INSTRUMENTAL

Haiku—prepared pf, live electronics & tape (1987)
S. Montague, P. Mead (r1993) Concert
(4/95) (CNTI) ① CCD1061

SECTION IV: VOCAL AND CHORAL

Tigida Pipa—4vv, perc & tape (1983-9)
S. Montague, Singcircle, G. Rose (r1993) Concert
(4/95) (CNTI) ① CCD1061

MONTANARI (19th–20th cent) Italy

SECTION IV: VOCAL AND CHORAL

Serenatella—song
G. Zenatello, orch (r1911) Concert
(5/94) (PEAR) ① [4] GEMMCDS9073(2)

MONTE, Philippus de (1521–1603) Netherlands

SECTION IV: VOCAL AND CHORAL

Leggiadre ninfe—madrigal
Amaryllis Consort Concert
(6/86) (CARL) ① PCD822
Occhi vaghi amorosi—madrigal: 5vv
M. Arruabarrena, K. van Laethem, M. Valenta, J. Benet, M. van Altena, J. Cabré, T. de Zwart, A. Pols, R. Van Der Meer, K. Junghänel (lte/dir) Concert
(1/92) (ACCE) ① ACC8864D
Le premier jour du mois de mai—chanson: 5vv (pub 1575) (Wds Ronsard)
C. Janequin Ens, D. Visse (r1993) Concert
(2/95) (HARM) ① HMC90 1491
Quand de ta lèvre—chanson: 5vv (pub 1575) (Wds Ronsard)
C. Janequin Ens, D. Visse (r1993) Concert
(2/95) (HARM) ① HMC90 1491
Si trop souvent—chanson: 5vv (pub 1575) (Wds Ronsard)
C. Janequin Ens, D. Visse (r1993) Concert
(2/95) (HARM) ① HMC90 1491

MONTÉCLAIR, Michel Pignolet de (1667–1737) France

SECTION IV: VOCAL AND CHORAL

La Bergère—cantata: 1v (pub 1728)
J. Baird, American Baroque, S. Schultz Concert
(9/92) (KOCH) ① 37096-2

Il Dispetto in amor—cantata (1v) (pub c1716)
G. Lesne, Arts Florissants Instr Ens, W. Christie
Concert (6/89) (HARM) ① HMC90 1280
La Mort de Didon—cantata (1v) (pub c1716)
A. Mellon, Arts Florissants Instr Ens, W. Christie
Concert (6/89) (HARM) ① HMC90 1280
J. Baird, American Baroque, S. Schultz Concert
(9/92) (KOCH) ① 37096-2
Morte di Lucretia—cantata (1v) (pub 1728)
M. Zanetti, Arts Florissants Instr Ens, W. Christie
Concert (6/89) (HARM) ① HMC90 1280
Pan et Syrinx—cantata: 1v
J. Baird, American Baroque, S. Schultz Concert
(9/92) (KOCH) ① 37096-2
Pyrame et Thisbé—cantata (3vv) (pub c1716)
M. Zanetti, J-P. Fouchécourt, J-F. Gardeil, Arts Florissants Instr Ens, W. Christie Concert
(6/89) (HARM) ① HMC90 1280
Le Triomphe de l'amour—cantata (1v) (pub c1716)
J-P. Fouchécourt, Arts Florissants Instr Ens, W. Christie Concert (6/89) (HARM) ① HMC90 1280

SECTION V: STAGE WORKS

Jephté—tragédie lyrique: prologue and 5 acts (1732—Paris) (Lib. S-J. Pellegrin)
Cpte J. Bona, S. Daneman, C. Brua, N. Rivenq, M. Padmore, B. Loonen, J-C. Saragosse, S. Pitour, S. Colas, M. Saint-Palais, F. Bazola-Minori, P. Foucher, A. Pichard, Arts Florissants Chor, Arts Florissants Orch, W. Christie
(1/93) (HARM) ① [2] HMC90 1424/5

MONTEVERDI, Claudio (Giovanni Antonio) (1567–1643) Italy

SECTION IV: VOCAL AND CHORAL

Adoramus te, Christe—motet: 5vv (pub 1620)
A. Wright, Westminster Cath Ch, S. Cleobury (ed Arnold) Concert (7/83) (ARGO) ① 410 005-2ZH
Arts Florissants Voc Ens, Arts Florissants Instr Ens, W. Christie (r1986) Concert
(7/87) (HARM) ① HMC90 1250
Taverner Ch, Taverner Consort, Taverner Plyrs, A. Parrott Concert (8/91) (EMI) ① CDC7 54117-2
Trinity Coll Ch, Cambridge, R. Marlow Concert
(11/92) (CONI) ① CDCF212
Monteverdi Ch, A. Davis, C. Van Kampen, S. Carrington, J. E. Gardiner (r1969) Concert
(2/94) (DECC) ① 440 032-2DM
Cantate Domino—motet: 6vv (pub 1620)
A. Wright, Westminster Cath Ch, S. Cleobury (ed Arnold) Concert (7/83) (ARGO) ① 410 005-2ZH
Trinity Coll Ch, Cambridge, R. Marlow Concert
(11/92) (CONI) ① CDCF212
Cantate Domino—motet: 2vv (pub 1615)
E. Kirkby, E. Tubb, Consort of Musicke, A. Rooley Concert (4/88) (CARL) ① PCD881
Monteverdi Ch, A. Davis, C. Van Kampen, S. Carrington, J. E. Gardiner (r1969) Concert
(2/94) (DECC) ① 440 032-2DM
Christe, adoramus te—motet: 5vv and continuo (1620)
Taverner Ch, Taverner Consort, Taverner Plyrs, A. Parrott Concert (8/91) (EMI) ① CDC7 54117-2
Trinity Coll Ch, Cambridge, R. Marlow Concert
(11/92) (CONI) ① CDCF212
Il Combattimento di Tancredi e Clorinda—secular oratorio: 3vv and instruments (pub 1624) (Wds. Tasso)
E. Kirkby, E. Tubb, M. Nichols, A. King, P. Agnew, A. Ewing, Consort of Musicke, A. Rooley Concert
(12/90) (VIRG) ① VC7 59606-2
Red Byrd, Parley of Instr, P. Holman Concert
(9/92) (HYPE) ① CDA66475
B. Borden, D. Nasrawi, C. Righetti, Tragicomedia, S. Stubbs (r1992) Concert
(10/93) (TELD) ① 4509-90798-2
Arts Florissants Chor, Arts Florissants Orch, W. Christie (r1992) Concert
(10/93) (HARM) ① HMC90 1426
T. Malakate, J. Aymonino, K. Paliatsaras, Capriccio Stravagante, S. Sempé (hpd/dir) Concert
(2/94) (DHM) ① 05472 77190-2
T. Schmidt, K. Equiluz, W. Hollweg, VCM, N. Harnoncourt (r1984) Monteverdi, Bk 8.
(2/94) (TELD) ① 4509-92181-2
C. Bott, A. King, J. M. Ainsley, New London Consort, P. Pickett (r1993) Concert
(6/95) (L'OI) ① 440 637-2OH

Confitebor tibi, Domine—motet: 1v and 5 viols (Upsala ed. Attrib.)
Arts Florissants Voc Ens, Arts Florissants Instr Ens, W. Christie (r1986) *Concert*
(7/87) (HARM) ① HMC90 1250

Currite populi—motet: 1v (pub 1625)
Jeffrey Thomas *Concert*
(8/91) (EMI) ① CDC7 54117-2

Domine, ne in furore—motet: 6vv (pub 1620)
Trinity Coll Ch, Cambridge, R. Marlow *Concert*
(11/92) (CONI) ① CDCF212
The Sixteen, H. Christophers, L. Cummings, R. Jeffrey (r1992) *Concert*
(10/93) (COLL) ① Coll1360-2
Monteverdi Ch, A. Davis, C. Van Kampen, S. Carrington, J. E. Gardiner (r1969) *Concert*
(2/94) (DECC) ① 440 032-2DM

Ego flos campi—motet: 1v (pub 1624)
J. Bowman, S. Sempé, J. Bernfeld *Concert*
(9/89) (ARIO) ① ARN68046
G. Lesne, Tragicomedia *Concert*
(5/91) (VIRG) ① VC7 59602-2

Ego sum pastor bonus—motet: 3vv (pub 1582)
G. Lesne, J. Benet, J. Cabré *Concert*
(5/91) (VIRG) ① VC7 59602-2

Exulta, filia Sion—motet: 1v and organ (pub 1629)
E. Kirkby, Consort of Musicke, A. Rooley *Concert*
(4/88) (CARL) ① PCD881
J. Benet, Seminario Musicale, Tragicomedia *Concert*
(5/91) (VIRG) ① VC7 59602-2
E. Van Evera, Taverner Ch, Taverner Consort, Taverner Plyrs, A. Parrott *Concert*
(8/91) (EMI) ① CDC7 54117-2

Fuge, fuge, anima mea, mundum—motet: 2vv and violin (pub 1620)
B. Lesne, G. Lesne, Seminario Musicale, Tragicomedia *Concert*
(5/91) (VIRG) ① VC7 59602-2

Heus, bone vir—contrafacta on 'Armato il cor': 2vv (pub 1642)
Consort of Musicke, A. Rooley (lte/dir) (r1992-3) *Concert*
(3/94) (MOSC) ① 070995

Justi tulerunt spolia impiorum—motet: 3vv (pub 1582)
G. Lesne, J. Benet, J. Cabré *Concert*
(5/91) (VIRG) ① VC7 59602-2

Lamento d'Arianna—madrigal: 1v (pub 1623) (Wds. Rinuccini)
1. Lasciatemi morire; 2. O Teseo, Teseo mio; 3. Dove, dove'e la fede; 4. Ahio, ch'ei non pur risponde.
T. Berganza, ECO, M. Viotti *Concert*
(3/91) (CLAV) ① CD50-9016
A.S. von Otter, Drottningholm Baroque Ens, A. Öhrwall *Concert* (10/91) (PROP) ① PRCD9008
G. Laurens, Capriccio Stravagante, S. Sempé (hpd/dir) *Concert* (2/94) (DHM) ① 05472 77190-2
S. le Sage, M. Worthley, A. Deller, P. Todd, M. Bevan, Deller Consort, A. Deller (r1950s) *Ballo delle ingrate.*
(3/95) (VANG) ① 08.5063.71

Lamento d'Olimpia—madrigal: 1v (pub 1620)
1. Voglio morir; 2. Anzi che non amarmi; 3. Ma perchè, o ciel.
E. Kirkby, A. Rooley *Concert*
(2/87) (HYPE) ① CDA66106

Lapidabant Stephanum—motet: 3vv (pub 1582)
G. Lesne, J. Benet, J. Cabré *Concert*
(5/91) (VIRG) ① VC7 59602-2

Longe, mi Jesu—contrafacta on 'Parlo, miser'o taccio': 3vv (pub 1649)
Consort of Musicke, A. Rooley (lte/dir) (r1992-3) *Concert* (3/94) (MOSC) ① 070995

Madrigals, Book 1 (Il primo libro de madrigali)—5vv (pub 1587)
1. A che tormi il ben mio; 2. Amor per tua mercè vatene a quella; 3. Amor, s'il tuo ferire; 4. Ardo, si, ma non t'amo; 5. Baci soave e cari (wds. Guarini); 6. Ch'io ami la mia vita; 7. Donna, s'io miro voi giaccio divengo; 8. Filli cara e amata (Parma); 9. Fumia la pastorella (Allegretti); 10. La vaga pastorella; 11. Poi che del mio dolore; 12. Questa bella di laccio (Strozzi); 13. Se nel partir da voi, vita mia; 14. Se per haverui oimè; 15. Se pur non mi consenti; 16. Tra mille fiamme e tra mille cathene.
5. E. Schwarzkopf, I. Seefried, G. Moore (r1955) *Concert* (3/89) (EMI) ① CDH7 69793-2

Madrigals, Book 2 (Il secondo libro de madrigali)—5vv (pub 1590)
1. Bevea Fillide mia (wds. Casoni); 2. Cantai un tempo (wds. Bembo); 3. Crudel, perchè mi fuggi (wds. Tasso); 4. Dolcemente dormiva la mia Clori (wds. Tasso); 5. Dolcissimi legami di parole amorose

(wds. Tasso); 6. Donna, nel mio ritorno (wds. Tasso); 7. Ecco mormorar l'onde (wds. Tasso); 8. Intorno a due vermiglie; 9. La bocc'onde l'asprissime (wds. Bentiviglio); 10. Mentre io miravo fiso (wds. Tasso); 11. Non giacinti o narcisi (wds. Casoni); 12. Non m'è grave'l morire; 13. Non si levev'ancor (wds. Tasso); 14. Non sono in queste rive fiori (wds. Tasso); 15. Quell'ombra esser vorrei (wds. Casoni); 16. Questo specchio ti dono, Rosa; 17. S'andasse amor a caccia (wds. Tasso); 18. Se tu mi lassi, perfida (wds. Tasso; 19. Ti spontò l'ali amor (wds. Alberti); 20. Tutte le bocche belle (wds. Alberti).
Cpte Consort of Musicke, A. Rooley (lte/dir) (r1990-91) (10/93) (VIRG) ① VC7 59282-2
Concerto Italiano, R. Alessandrini (r1994)
(8/95) (O111) ① OPS30-111
7. Boulanger Ens, N. Boulanger (r1937) *Concert*
(1/89) (EMI) ① CDH7 61025-2

Madrigals, Book 3 (Il terzo libro de madrigali)—5vv (pub 1592)
1. Ch'io non t'ami, cor mio (wds. Guarini); 2. La giovinetta pianta; 3. Lumi miei, cari lumi (wds. Guarini); 4. Occhi un tempo, mia vita (wds. Guarini); 5. O come è gran martire (wds. Guarini); 6. O dolce anima mia (wds. Guarini); 7. O rossignuol ch'in queste verdi fronde (wds. Guarini); 8. Perfidissimo volto (wds. Guarini); 9. Perfidissimo volto (Celiano); 11. Se per estremo ardore (wds. Guarini); 12. Sovra tenere herbette; 13. Stracciami pur il core (wds. Guarini); 14. Vattene pur, crudel, con quella pace (wds. Tasso); 15. Vivrò fra i miei tormenti (wds. Tasso).
Cpte Consort of Musicke, A. Rooley (lte/dir) (r1990-91) (10/93) (VIRG) ① VC7 59283-2

Madrigals, Book 4 (Il quarto libro de madrigali)—5vv (pub 1603)
1. Ah dolente partita (wds. Guarini); 2. Anima del mio cor; 3. Anima dolorosa; 4. Anima mia, perdona; 5. A un giro sol de' bell'occhi lucenti (wds. Guarini); 6. Cor mio, mentre vi miro (wds. Guarini); 7. Cor mio, non mori?; 8. Io mi son giovinetta; 9. La piaga c'ho nel core; 10. Longe da te, cor mio; 11. Luci serene e chiare; 12. Non più guerra, pietate (wds. Guarini); 13. Ohimè, se tanto amate (wds. Guarini); 14. Piange e sospira; 15. Quel augellin che canta; 16. Sfogava con le stelle (wds. Rinuccini); 17. Si ch'io vorrei morire; 18. Voi pur da me partite (wds. Guarini); 19. Volgea l'anima mia soavemente (wds. Guarini).
Cpte Consort of Musicke, A. Rooley
(2/87) (L'OI) ① 414 148-2OH
Cpte Concerto Italiano, R. Alessandrini (r1993)
(12/93) (O111) ① OPS30-81
4, 8, 15, 16, 17. Consort of Musicke, A. Rooley (lte/dir) (r1992-3) *Concert*
(3/94) (MOSC) ① 070995
11. Concerto Vocale *Concert*
(5/87) (HARM) ① HMA190 1084
13. Monteverdi Ch, J. E. Gardiner (r1969) *Concert*
(2/94) (DECC) ① 440 032-2DM
15. Amaryllis Consort *Concert*
(6/86) (CARL) ① PCD822

Madrigals, Book 5 (Il quinto libro de madrigali)—5vv and continuo (pub 1605)
1. Ahi, com'a un vago sol; 2. Amor, se giusto sei; 3. Che dar più vi poss'io?; 4. Ch'io t'ami e t'ami (wds. Guarini); 5. Cruda Amarilli (wds. Guarini); 6. Ecco Silvio (wds. Guarini); 7. E cosi a poc'a poco (wds. Guarini); 8. Era l'anima mia (wds. Guarini); 9. M'e piu dolce il penar per Amarilli (wds. Guarini); 10. O Mirtillo, Mirtill'anima mia (wds. Guarini); 11. Questi vaghi concenti; 12. T'amo mia vita (wds. Guarini); 13. Troppo ben puo questo tiranno amore (wds. Guarini).
1, 7, 8, 10, 12, 13. Concerto Vocale *Concert*
(5/87) (HARM) ① HMA190 1084
8. Monteverdi Ch, J. E. Gardiner (r1969) *Concert*
(2/94) (DECC) ① 440 032-2DM
11. H. Schütz Ch, R. Norrington *Concert*
(5/92) (DECC) ① 433 174-2DM

Madrigals, Book 6 (Il sesto libro de madrigali)—5vv, dialogue, 7vv, continuo (1614)
1. A Dio, Florida bella (wds. Marini); 2. Batto qui pianse Ergasto (wds. Marini); 3. Lamento d'Arianna: Lasciatemi morire (wds. Rinuccini); 4. Misero Alceo; 5. Ohimè, il bel viso (wds. Petrach); 6. Presso un fiume tranquillo (wds. Marini); 7. Qui rise, O Tirsi (wds. Tirsi); 8. Sestina: Lagrime d'amante (wds. Agnelli); 9. Una donna fra l'altre; 10. Zefiro torna: 5vv (wds. Petrach).
Cpte Consort of Musicke, A. Rooley
(12/90) (VIRG) ① VC7 59605-2
Cpte Concerto Italiano Voc Ens, R. Alessandrini (r1992) (7/93) (ARCA) ① A66
1. Concerto Vocale *Concert*
(5/87) (HARM) ① HMA190 1084

3. Amaryllis Consort *Concert*
(6/86) (CARL) ① PCD822
3. Boulanger Ens, N. Boulanger (r1937) *Concert*
(1/89) (EMI) ① CDH7 61025-2
5, 7, 8. Cantus Cölln, K. Junghänel (lte/dir) (r1992) *Concert* (10/93) (DHM) ① 05472 77282-2
6. Arts Florissants Chor, Arts Florissants Orch, W. Christie (r1992) *Concert*
(10/93) (HARM) ① HMC90 1426
8. Arts Florissants Voc Ens, Arts Florissants Instr Ens, W. Christie *Ballo delle ingrate.*
(8/85) (HARM) ① HMC90 1108
8. Schütz Consort, R. Norrington *Concert*
(5/92) (DECC) ① 433 174-2DM
10. Capriccio Stravagante, S. Sempé (hpd/dir) (arr Strings) *Concert* (10/91) (DHM) ① RD77220
10. Monteverdi Ch, J. E. Gardiner (r1969) *Concert*
(2/94) (DECC) ① 440 032-2DM

Madrigals, Book 7 (Concerto: settimo libro de madrigali)—1–4, 6vv and continuo (1619)
1. Ah, non che non si conviene romper la fede?; 2. Al lume delle stelle (wds. Tasso); 3. Amor che deggio far?; 4. A quest'olmo, a quest'ombra (wds. Marini); 5. Augellin, che la voce al canto spieghi; 6. Chiome d'oro, bei thesoro; 7. Con che soavita (wds. Guarini); 8. Dice la mia bellissima Licori (wds. Guarini); 9. Eccomi pronta ai baci (wds. Marini); 10. Ecco vicine, o bella tigre; 11. Interotte speranze (wds. Guarini); 12. Io son pur vezzosetta pastorella (wds. Guarini); 13. Io son pur vezzosetta pastorella (wds. degl'Atti); 14. Non è mai le stelle augellino (wds. Guarini); 15. O come sei gentile, caro augellino (wds. Guarini); 16. Ohimè, dovè il mio ben? (wds. B. Tasso); 17. O viva fiamma; 18. Parlo, miser'o taccio? (wds. Guarini); 19. Perchè fuggi tra salci, ritrosetta? (wds. Marini); 20. Se i languidi miei sguardi (Lettera amorosa); 21. S'el vostro cor, madonna (wds. Marini); 22. se pur destina e vole il cielo; 23. Soave libertate (wds. Chiabrera); 24. Tempro la cetra (wds. Marini); 25. Tornate, o cari baci (wds. Marini); 26. Tu dormi? Ah crudo core; 27. Vaga su spina ascosa (wds. Chiabrera); 28. Vorrei baciarti, O Filli (wds. Marini).
3, 6. Arts Florissants Voc Ens, Arts Florissants Instr Ens, W. Christie *Concert*
(12/87) (HARM) ① HMA190 1068
5, 9, 10, 19, 21, 23, 25, 27. Tragicomedia, S. Stubbs (r1993) *Concert* (1/94) (TELD) ① 4509-91971-2
6, 12, 13, 15, 16, 22. E. Kirkby, E. Tubb, Consort of Musicke, A. Rooley *Concert*
(4/88) (CARL) ① PCD881
6, 16. Boulanger Ens, N. Boulanger (r1937) *Concert*
(1/89) (EMI) ① CDH7 61025-2
6, 7, 16, 18, 21, 24, 25. E. Kirkby, J. Nelson, P. Holden, P. Elliott, A. King, D. Thomas, R. Wistreich, Consort of Musicke, A. Rooley *Concert*
(5/89) (L'OI) ① 421 480-2OH
7, 15, 26. Arts Florissants Chor, Arts Florissants Orch, W. Christie (r1992) *Concert*
(10/93) (HARM) ① HMC90 1426
7, 24. G. Laurens, Capriccio Stravagante, S. Sempé (hpd/dir) *Concert* (10/91) (DHM) ① RD77220
12. E. Schwarzkopf, I. Seefried, G. Moore (r1955) *Concert* (3/89) (EMI) ① CDH7 69793-2
13, 15, 16, 21, 23, 26. Cantus Cölln, K. Junghänel (lte/dir) (r1992) *Concert*
(10/93) (DHM) ① 05472 77282-2
18. Consort of Musicke, A. Rooley (lte/dir) (r1992-3) *Concert* (3/94) (MOSC) ① 070995
20. C. Berberian, B. Canino *Concert*
(7/89) (WERG) ① WER60054-50
22. Concerto Vocale *Concert*
(5/87) (HARM) ① HMA190 1084
24. J. Potter, Tragicomedia, S. Stubbs (r1992) *Concert* (10/93) (TELD) ① 4509-90798-2
27. N. Rogers, I. Partridge, C. Keyte, Inst Ens, J. Jürgens (r1971) *Concert*
(1/93) (ARCH) ① 437 075-2AT

Madrigals, Book 8 (Madrigali guerrieri et amorosi...libro ottavo)—1–8vv, instruments and continuo (pub 1638)
WAR: 1. Altri canti d'amor; 2. Ardo, avvampo, mi struggo; 3. Gira il nemico insidioso; 4. Hor ch'el ciel e la terra (wds. Petrarch); 5. Ogni amante è guerrier; 6. Se vittorie si belle. LOVE: 7. Altri canti de Marte (wds. Guarini); 8. Ardo e scoprir; 9. Chi vol haver felice (wds. Guarini); 10. Dolcissimo uscignolo (wds. Guarini); 11. Lamento della ninfa: Non havea Febo ancora (wds. Rinuccini); 12. Mentre vaga Angioletta ogn'anima (wds. Guarini); 13. Ninfa che scalza il piede; 14. Non partir, ritrosetta; 15. O sia tranquill'il mare; 16. Perchè t'en fuggi, O Filide?; 17. Su su su pastorelli vezzosi; 18. Vago augelletto, che cantando vai (wds. Petrarch).
Cpte Glyndebourne Fest Chor, ECO, R. Leppard *Scherzi musicali (1632).*
(7/92) (PHIL) ① [2] 432 503-2PM2

Veni in hortum meum—motet: 3vv (pub 1582)
G. Lesne, J. Benet, J. Cabré Concert
(5/91) (VIRG) ① **VC7 59602-2**

Vespro della Beata Vergine, 'Vespers' (pub 1610) (selection and order of movements may vary)
1. Domine ad adiuvandum a 6; 2. Dixit Dominus a 6; 3. Nigra sum a 1; 4. Laudate, pueri, Dominum a 8; 5. Pulchra es a 2; 6. Laetatus sum a 6; 7. Duo Seraphim a 3; 8. Nisi Dominus a 10; 9. Audi coelum a 8; 10. Lauda Jerusalem a 7; 11. Sonata sopra Sancta Maria a 1; 12. Ave maris stella a 8; 13. Magnificat I a 7; 14. Magnificat II a 6.
Taverner Consort, Taverner Ch, Taverner Plyrs, A. Parrott (ed Parrott/Keyte)
(10/85) (EMI) ① [2] **CDS7 47078-8**
A. Mellon, G. Laurens, V. Darras, H. Crook, W. Kendall, G. O'Byrne, P. Kooy, D. Thomas, Ghent Collegium Vocale, Toulouse Saqueboutiers, Paris Chapelle Royale Chor, Paris Chapelle Royale Orch, P. Herreweghe
(2/88) (HARM) ① [2] **HMC90 1247/8**
N. Jenkin, M. Seers, C. Royall, A. Murgatroyd, N. MacKenzie, M. Padmore, S. Birchall, J. White, The Sixteen, The Sixteen Orch, H. Christophers Concert
(4/89) (HYPE) ① [2] **CDA66311/2**
M. Zanetti, G. Fisher, D. Cordier, J. Elwes, W. Kendall, N. van der Meel, P. Kooy, P. Cantor, Stuttgart Chbr Ch, Cologne Musica Fiata, F. Bernius
(2/90) (DHM) ① [2] **RD77760**
M. Figueras, M.C. Kiehr, L. Picotti, P. Costa, G. de Mey, G. Fagotto, G. Türk, P. Spagnoli, R. Abbondanza, D. Carnovich, Padua Centro Musica Antica Ch, J. Savall (2/90) (ASTR) ① [2] **E8719**
A. Monoyios, M. Pennicchi, M. Chance, M. Tucker, N. Robson, S. Naglia, B. Terfel, A. Miles, Monteverdi Ch, His Majesties Sagbutts and Cornetts, EBS, J.E. Gardiner
(1/91) (ARCH) ① [2] **429 565-2AH2**
C. Bott, T. Bonner, C. Robson, A. King, J.M. Ainsley, M. George, S. Grant, New London Consort, P. Pickett
(3/91) (L'OI) ① [2] **425 823-2OH2**
M. Bach, B. Fleckenstein, C. Prégardien, P. Schmitz, K. Mertens, M. George, Frankfurt Voc Ens, Basso Instr Ens, R. Otto (r1993) (8/95) (CAPR) ① **10 516**
3. A. Lawrence-King Concert
(6/92) (HYPE) ① **CDA66518**
3, 5. Tragicomedia Concert
(5/91) (VIRG) ① **VC7 59602-2**

Voglio di vita uscir—madrigal: 1v (pub 1630) (Wds. ?Ferrari)
E. Kirkby, A. Rooley Concert
(2/87) (HYPE) ① **CDA66106**
E. Kirkby, A. Rooley Concert
(9/87) (HYPE) ① **CDA66227**

SECTION V: STAGE WORKS

L' Arianna—opera (1608—Mantua) (Lib. Rinuccini)
Lasciatemi morire H. Sheppard, S. Le Sage, M. Worthley, P. Todd, M. Deller (alto/dir), M. Bevan, Deller Consort Ballo delle ingrate.
(4/94) (VANG) ① **08.2030.71**
Lasciatemi morire a 1
E. Pinza, F. Kitzinger (r1940) Concert
(9/93) (RCA) ① **09026 61245-2**

Il Ballo delle ingrate—ballet (1608—Mantua) (Wds. Rinuccini)
Cpte C. Bott, T. Bonner, M. George, Chor, New London Consort, P. Pickett (r1993) Concert
(6/95) (L'OI) ① **440 637-2OH**
Arts Florissants Voc Ens, Arts Florissants Instr Ens, W. Christie Madrigals, Bk.6.
(8/85) (HARM) ① **HMC90 1108**
Boulanger Ens, N. Boulanger (r1937) Concert
(1/89) (EMI) ① **CDH7 61025-2**
E. Tubb, M. Nichols, A. Ewing Concert
(12/90) (VIRG) ① **VC7 59606-2**
H. Schütz Ch, R. Norrington Concert
(5/92) (DECC) ① **433 174-2DM**
Red Byrd, Parley of Instr, P. Holman Concert
(9/92) (HYPE) ① **CDA66475**
B. Borden, S. Le Blanc, J. Järvlö, H. van der Kamp, Tragicomedia, S. Stubbs (r1992) Concert
(10/93) (TELD) ① **4509-90798-2**
A. Cantelo, E. McLoughlin, A. Deller (alto/dir), D. Ward, J. Bream, D. Dupré, D. Vaughan, Ambrosian Sngrs, London Chbr Plyrs L'Arianna.
(4/94) (VANG) ① **08.2030.71**
A. Deller, E. McLoughlin, A. Cantelo, D. Ward, Ambrosian Sngrs, London Chbr Plyrs, A. Deller (r1950s) Lamento d'Arianna a 1.
(3/95) (VANG) ① **08.5063.71**

L' Incoronazione di Poppea, '(The) Coronation of Poppea'—opera (1642—Venice) (Lib. Busenello)
Cpte D. Borst, G. Laurens, J. Larmore, A. Köhler, M. Schopper, L. Lootens, M.C. Kiehr, H.M. Ørbaek, C. Homberger, G. de Mey, A. Lebeda, R. Jakobi, M. Bovet, G. Türk, C. Högman, Concerto Vocale, R. Jacobs (4/91) (HARM) ① [3] **HMC90 1330/2**
Adagiati Poppea; Eri già tutta mia R. Jacobs, K. Junghänel (r1985) Concert
(5/87) (HARM) ① **HMA190 1183**
Oblivion soave E. Pinza, F. Kitzinger (r1940) Concert
(9/93) (RCA) ① **09026 61245-2**
Pur ti miro M. László, Richard Lewis, RPO, J. Pritchard (r1963) Concert
(6/94) (EMI) ① **CDH5 65072-2**

L' Orfeo—favola in musica (1607—Mantua) (Lib. Striggio)
Cpte L. Kozma, R. Hansmann, C. Berberian, E. Katanosaka, N. Simkowsky, J. Villisech, M. van Egmond, G. Theuring, N. Rogers, K. Equiluz, VCM, N. Harnoncourt (7/85) (TELD) ① [2] **2292-42494-2**
Cpte A. Rolfe Johnson, J. Baird, L. Dawson, A.S. von Otter, N. Argenta, M. Nichols, J. Tomlinson, D. Montague, W. White, M. Tucker, N. Robson, M. Chance, S. Birchall, H. Milner, N. Robertson, Monteverdi Ch, EBS, His Majesties Sagbutts and Cornetts, J.E. Gardiner
(12/87) (ARCH) ① [2] **419 250-2AH2**
Cpte J.M. Ainsley, J. Gooding, C. Bott, T. Bonner, C. Robson, A. King, R. Evans, M. George, S. Grant, New London Consort, P. Pickett (r1991)
(2/93) (L'OI) ① [2] **433 545-2OH2**
Cpte N. Rogers, P. Kwella, E. Kirkby, J. Smith, H. Afonso, C. Denley, G. Laurens, M. Bolognesi, R. Covey-Crump, J. Potter, S. Varcoe, D. Thomas, T. Edwards, G. Shaw, Chiaroscuro, London Cornett and Sackbutt Ens, T. Caudle, London Baroque, C. Medlam (r1983) (4/94) (EMI) ① [2] **CMS7 64947-2**
Cpte L. Dale, E. Ben-Nun, J. Larmore, A. Scholl, P. Gérimon, B. Fink, H. Peeters, N. Rivenq, Concerto Vocale, R. Jacobs (r1995)
(12/95) (HARM) ① [2] **HMC90 1553/4**

Il Ritorno d'Ulisse in Patria—opera: prologue and 3 acts (1641—Venice) (Lib. G. Badoaro)
Cpte C. Prégardien, B. Fink, C. Högman, M. Hill, J. Taillon, D. Visse, M. Tucker, D. Thomas, G. de Mey, F. Subrata, J. Dürmüller, L. Hunt, M. Schopper, O. Lallouette, C. McFadden, M. Bovet, Concerto Vocale, R. Jacobs (r1992)
(3/93) (HARM) ① [3] **HMC90 1427/9**
Di misera Regina (Lamento di Penelope) E. Tubb, Consort of Musicke, A. Rooley Concert
(4/88) (CARL) ① **PCD881**

Tirsi e Clori—ballet (1616—Mantua)
Cpte C. Bott, A. King, Chor, New London Consort, P. Pickett (r1993) Concert
(6/95) (L'OI) ① **440 637-2OH**
Arts Florissants Voc Ens, Arts Florissants Instr Ens, W. Christie Concert
(12/87) (HARM) ① **HMA190 1068**
S. Le Blanc, J. Potter, Tragicomedia, S. Stubbs (r1992) Concert (10/93) (TELD) ① **4509-90798-2**

Volgendo il ciel—ballet (?1636, pub 1638—Vienna) (Wds. Rinuccini. Published in Madrigals, Book 8)
E. Kirkby, A. King, P. Agnew, Consort of Musicke, A. Rooley Concert (12/90) (VIRG) ① **VC7 59606-2**
Red Byrd, Parley of Instr, P. Holman Concert
(9/92) (HYPE) ① **CDA66475**
Taverner Consort, Taverner Plyrs, A. Parrott Madrigals, Bk 8. (12/92) (EMI) ① **CDC7 54333-2**

SECTION III: INSTRUMENTAL

Granaína—flamenco guitar
P. Peña Concert (9/88) (NIMB) ① **NI5093**
Minera—flamenco guitar
P. Peña Concert (9/88) (NIMB) ① **NI5093**
Rondeña—flamenco guitar
P. Peña Concert (9/88) (NIMB) ① **NI5093**
La Rosa (Alegría)—flamenco guitar
P. Peña Concert (9/88) (NIMB) ① **NI5093**
Soleá—flamenco guitar
P. Peña Concert (9/88) (NIMB) ① **NI5093**
Tango mayor y menor—flamenco guitar
P. Peña Concert (9/88) (NIMB) ① **NI5093**

SECTION I: ORCHESTRAL

Concierto breve—piano and orchestra (1953)
L. Morales, Madrid SO, A. R. Marbà (pp1993) Concert (8/95) (MARC) ① **8 223753**

SECTION III: INSTRUMENTAL

Berceuse a la memoria de Oscar Esplá—piano left hand
A. de Larrocha (r1992) Concert
(9/94) (RCA) ① **09026 61389-2**
Divagación—piano (1950)
A. de Larrocha (r1992) Concert
(9/94) (RCA) ① **09026 61389-2**
Divertimento No. 2, 'Habanera'—piano (1941)
A. de Larrocha Concert
(9/92) (DECC) ① [2] **433 929-2DM2**
3 Divertimentos on Themes of Forgotten Composers—piano
1. Con decisión; 2. Muy dolce; 3. Vivo.
A. de Larrocha (r1992) Concert
(9/94) (RCA) ① **09026 61389-2**
Si, à Mompou—piano left hand
A. de Larrocha Concert
(9/94) (RCA) ① **09026 61389-2**
Sonatina para Yvette—piano (1962)
A. de Larrocha Concert
(9/92) (DECC) ① [2] **433 929-2DM2**
Sonatine pour Yvette—piano (1962)
A. de Larrocha (r1992) Concert
(9/94) (RCA) ① **09026 61389-2**

SECTION IV: VOCAL AND CHORAL

5 Canciones negras—1v and piano (1945)
1. Cuba dento de un piano (wds. Alberti); 2. Punto de Habanera (wds. Luján); 3. Chévere (wds. Guillén); 4. Canción de cuna para dormir a un negrito (wds. Valdés); 5. Canto negro (wds. Guillén).
Y. Pappas, Israel SO, G. Stern Concert
(2/88) (MERI) ① **CDE84134**
V. de los Angeles, Paris Cons, R. Frühbeck de Burgos Concert (10/88) (EMI) ① **CDM7 69502-2**
T. Berganza, F. Lavilla Concert
(12/92) (DG) ① [2] **435 848-2GX2**
V. de los Angeles, Paris Cons, R. Frühbeck de Burgos (r1962) Concert
(4/94) (EMI) ① [4] **CMS5 65061-2(1)**
D. Jones, M. Martineau (r1993) Concert
(9/94) (CHAN) ① **CHAN9277**
Sinfonía de réquiem—soprano and orchestra (1985)
C. Moncloa, Madrid SO, A. R. Marbà (pp1993) Concert (9/95) (MARC) ① **8 223753**

SECTION I: ORCHESTRAL

Bulgarian Wedding—harmonica and strings
T. Reilly, ASMF Chbr Ens Concert
(12/86) (CHAN) ① **CHAN8486**
Little Suite—harmonica and orchestra
T. Reilly, ASMF, N. Marriner Concert
(10/88) (CHAN) ① **CHAN8617**
Toledo: a Spanish fantasy—harmonica and orchestra (1960)
T. Reilly, Munich RO, R. Farnon (r1977) Concert
(5/94) (CHAN) ① **CHAN9248**

SECTION II: CHAMBER

Quintet for Harmonica and String Quartet (1972)
T. Reilly, Hindar Qt Concert
(10/90) (CHAN) ① **CHAN8802**
Suite dans le style français—harmonica and harp (1979)
T. Reilly, S. Kanga Concert
(10/90) (CHAN) ① **CHAN8802**

SECTION I: ORCHESTRAL

Pageant of P. T. Barnum—suite (1924)
EXCERPTS: 1. Boyhood at Bethel; 2. Joice Heth—161 Year Old Negress; 3. General and Mrs. Tom Thumb; 4. Jenny Lind; 5. Circus Parade.

Eastman-Rochester Orch, H. Hanson (r1958)
Concert   (2/93) (MERC) ① **434 319-2MM**

Carry Nation—opera: 2 acts
(1966—Lawrence) (Lib. W N Jayme)
Cpte B. Wolff, A. Voketaitis, E. Faull, J. Patrick, J.
Bittner, E. Pierson, NYC Op Chor, NYC Op Orch, S.
Krachmalnick   (7/90) (BAY) ① [2] **BCD-1012/3**

MOORE, Graham Ponsonby
(1859–1916) Australia

Lullaby—piano
A. Etherden Concert
                    (7/93) (HUNT) ① **HMPCD0589**

MOORE, Thomas (1779–1852)
Ireland

Irish Melodies—traditional tunes with new
lyrics: 10 vols (pub 1807-34) (Vols 1-7, music
arr J.A. Stevenson; Vols 8-10 arr H. Bishop)
EXCERPTS: 1. VOLUME 1: 1a. Erin! the tear and
the smile in thine eyes; 1b. Silent, oh Moyle! (The
Song of Fionnuala); 1c. Rich and rare were the gems
she wore; 1d. The harp that once thro' Tara's halls; 2.
VOLUME 2: 2a. How dear to me the hour; 3.
VOLUME 3: 3a. 'Tis believed that this land (The
Origin of the Harp); 3b. She is far from the land; 4.
VOLUME 4: 4a. Avenging and bright; 4b. What the
bee is to the floweret; 5. VOLUME 5: 5a. The valley
lay smiling before me (The Son of O'Ruark); 5b. The
Minstrel Boy; 5c. 'Tis the last rose of summer; 6.
VOLUME 6: 6a. Dear harp of my country (The
Farewell to my Harp); 6b. Come, rest in this bosom;
6c. Come o'er the sea; 6d. At the mid hour of night;
6e. Fill the bumper fair!; 8. VOLUME 8: 8a. How
sweet the answer Echo makes; 11. UNSPECIFIED
VOLUMES: 11a. Believe me if all those endearing
young charms; 11b. The Meeting of the Waters; 11c.
They tell me thou'rt the favoured guest; 11d. When
Love is Kind; 11e. Love thee, dearest, love thee.
5c W. Marsalis, Eastman Wind Ens, D. Hunsberger
(arr tpt/wind: D Hunsberger) Concert
                    (9/87) (SONY) ① **MK42137**
5c R. A. Morgan Concert
                    (12/87) (ETCE) ① **KTC1049**
5c A. Patti, L. Ronald (r1905) Concert
                    (4/90) (PEAR) ① **GEMMCD9312**
5c M. Elman, A. Loesser (arr Auer; r1921) Concert
                    (12/91) (APR) ① [2] **APR7015**
5c L. Tetrazzini, orch (r1911) Concert
                    (9/92) (PEAR) ① **GEMMCD9223**
5c A. Murray, G. Johnson (r1992) Concert
                    (8/93) (HYPE) ① **CDA66627**

MORAGO, Estâvão Lopes
(c1575–after 1630) Portugal

Commissa mea—motet: 6vv
PCA, M. Brown (r1994) Concert
                    (11/94) (HYPE) ① **CDA66715**
De profundis—motet
PCA, M. Brown (r1994) Concert
                    (11/94) (HYPE) ① **CDA66715**
Esto mihi—motet
PCA, M. Brown (r1994) Concert
                    (11/94) (HYPE) ① **CDA66715**
Exsurge—motet
PCA, M. Brown (r1994) Concert
                    (11/94) (HYPE) ① **CDA66715**
Laetentur caeli—motet
PCA, M. Brown (r1994) Concert
                    (11/94) (HYPE) ① **CDA66715**
Montes Israel—motet
PCA, M. Brown (r1994) Concert
                    (11/94) (HYPE) ① **CDA66715**
Oculi mei—motet: 4vv
PCA, M. Brown (r1994) Concert
                    (11/94) (HYPE) ① **CDA66715**
Parce Domine—motet
PCA, M. Brown (r1994) Concert
                    (11/94) (HYPE) ① **CDA66715**
Revelabitur gloria Domini—motet
PCA, M. Brown (r1994) Concert
                    (11/94) (HYPE) ① **CDA66715**
Versa est in luctum—motet
PCA, M. Brown (r1994) Concert
                    (11/94) (HYPE) ① **CDA66715**

MORALES, Cristóbal de
(c1500–1553) Spain

Lamentabatur Jacob—motet
Taverner Consort, A. Parrott Concert
                    (8/87) (EMI) ① **CDC7 47699-2**
Magnificat octavi toni
Oxford Camerata, J. Summerly (r1993) Concert
                    (3/95) (NAXO) ① **8 550843**
Missa pro defunctis—5vv (pub 1544)
Catalan Capella Reial, Hespèrion XX, J. Savall
(r1991) Officium defunctorum.
                    (10/93) (ASTR) ① **E8765**
Officium defunctorum
Catalan Capella Reial, Hespèrion XX, J. Savall
(r1991) Missa pro defunctis a 5.
                    (10/93) (ASTR) ① **E8765**
Parce mihi domine—motet
J. Garbarek, Hilliard Ens (r1993: 3 vers) Concert
                    (10/94) (ECM) ① **445 369-2**

MORAN, Robert (b 1937) USA

3 Dances—six pianos
1. Anatasia's Two-Step (1986); 2. Miami City Slink
(1986); 3. Lithuanian Spin (1983).
Piano Circus (r1992) Concert
                    (1/94) (ARGO) ① **440 294-2ZH**
Music from the Towers of the Moon—string
quartet
Balanescu Qt (r1992) Concert
                    (3/93) (ARGO) ① **436 565-2ZH**
Open Veins—violin and ensemble (1986)
A. Balanescu, Piano Circus Band, R. Moran Concert
                    (8/92) (ARGO) ① **436 128-2ZH**
Ten Miles high over Albania—eight harps
(1983)
M. Falco, R. Moran Concert
                    (8/92) (ARGO) ① **436 128-2ZH**

Seven Sounds Unseen—chorus a cappella
Musica Sacra, R. Westenburg (r1993) Concert
                    (12/93) (CATA) ① **09026 61822-2**

Desert of Roses—opera (1982)
EXCERPTS: 1. Movement 1; 2. I can go? I can go to
my father?; 3. Movement 3; 4. Look into my eyes; 5.
Movement 5.
1-5. J. West, Piano Circus Band, C. Smith Concert
                    (8/92) (ARGO) ① **436 128-2ZH**
Points of Departure—ballet
Baltimore SO, D. Zinman (r1994) Concert
                    (7/95) (ARGO) ① **444 454-2ZH**

MORATA, Ginés (16th Cent)
Spain

Pués que me tienes—song
Hespèrion XX, J. Savall (r1991-92) Concert
                    (6/93) (ASTR) ① **E8764**
Pues que no puedo olvidarte—song
Hespèrion XX, J. Savall (r1991-92) Concert
                    (6/93) (ASTR) ① **E8764**

MORAVEC, Paul (b 1957) USA

Sonata for Violin and Piano (1992)
M. Bachmann, J. Klibonoff (r1993) Concert
                    (12/93) (CATA) ① **09026 61824-2**

MORAWETZ, Oscar (b 1917)
Czechoslovakia/Canada

Fantasy in D minor—piano (1948)
G. Gould Concert   (3/93) (SONY) ① **SMK52677**

MOREL, Jacques (fl c1700–1740)
France

Premier livre de pièces de viole (pub 1710)
1. Chaconne en trio; 2. Suite in D minor: 2a. Prélude;
2b. Allemande La Jolie; 2c. Courante La Dacier; 2d.
Sarabande; 2e. Gigue L'Inconstante; 2f. Le Folet; 2g.

La Fanchonette.
1. Royal Trio (r1991) Concert
                    (8/93) (DHM) ① **05472 77176-2**

MOREL, Jorge (b 1931) Mexico

Danza Braziliera—flute/guitar
V. Taylor, T. Kain Concert   (9/92) (TALL) ① **TP003**

MORENO TORROBA, Federico
(1891–1982) Spain

Aires de la Mancha—guitar
1. Jerigonza; 2. Ya llega el Invieno; 3. Copilla; 4. La
Pastora; 5. La Seguidilla.
P. Romero (r1993) Concert
                    (4/95) (PHIL) ① **442 150-2PH**
Madroños—guitar (1954)
W. Lendle Concert   (7/92) (TELD) ① **9031-75864-2**
J. Bream (r1962) Concert
                    (8/93) (RCA) ① [28] **09026 61583-2(3)**
J. Bream (r1962) Concert
                    (8/93) (RCA) ① **09026 61591-2**
Nocturno—guitar (1926)
M. Kayath Concert   (5/88) (CARL) ① **PCD876**
A. Segovia (r1930) Concert
                    (5/89) (EMI) ① [2] **CHS7 61047-2**
W. Lendle Concert   (7/92) (TELD) ① **9031-75864-2**
Prelude in E—guitar
M. Kayath Concert   (5/88) (CARL) ① **PCD876**
A. Segovia (r1928) Concert
                    (5/89) (EMI) ① [2] **CHS7 61047-2**
Sonatina in A—guitar (1965)
M. Kayath Concert   (5/88) (CARL) ① **PCD876**
J. Bream (r1983) Concert
                    (8/93) (RCA) ① [28] **09026 61583-2(4)**
J. Bream (r1983) Concert
                    (6/94) (RCA) ① **09026 61596-2**
Movt 1. A. Segovia (r1927) Concert
                    (5/89) (EMI) ① [2] **CHS7 61047-2**
Suite castellana—guitar (1926)
1. Fandanguillo; 2. Arada; 3. Danza.
A-S. Ramírez (r1991) Concert
                    (2/94) (DENO) ① **CO-75357**
1. A. Segovia (r1928) Concert
                    (5/89) (EMI) ① [2] **CHS7 61047-2**

La Chulapona—zarzuela (1934—Madrid)
Noche madrileña P. Domingo, ROHO, J. Barker
(pp1988) Concert   (9/89) (EMI) ① **CDC7 49811-2**
Luisa Fernanda—zarzuela (1932—Madrid)
EXCERPTS: 1. De este apacible rincón; 2. Caballero
del alto plumero; 3. Bien venidos, los vareadores.
Cpte T. Toumé, E. Alsina, R. Cesari, P. Lavirgen, J.
Bermejo, A. Fernandez, P. Tamayo, J.R. Henche, A.
Curros, S. Videras, V. Larrea, R. Campos, Hispavox
Lyric Chor, Madrid Concerts Orch, F. Moreno
Torroba   (10/92) (HISP) ① **CDZ7 67329-2**
Coro de Vareadores P. Domingo, chor, Madrid SO,
E. G. Asensio (pp1991) Concert
                    (11/92) (CARL) ① **MCD45**
3. P. Domingo, Madrid Zarzuela Chor, Madrid SO, M.
Moreno-Buendia (r1987) Concert
                    (1/89) (EMI) ① **CDC7 49148-2**
Maravilla—zarzuela (1941) (Lib A Quintero & J
M Arozamena)
Amor, vida de mi vida P. Domingo, Madrid SO, M.
Moreno-Buendia (r1987) Concert
                    (1/89) (EMI) ① **CDC7 49148-2**
Amor, vida de mi Vida P. Domingo, Los Angeles
PO, Z. Mehta (pp1994) Concert
                    (12/94) (TELD) ① **4509-96200-2**

MORET, Norbert (b 1921)
Switzerland

En rêve—violin and chamber orchestra
(1988)
A-S. Mutter, Boston SO, S. Ozawa Bartók: Violin
Concerto 2.   (11/91) (DG) ① **431 626-2GH**
A-S. Mutter, Boston SO, S. Ozawa (r1991) Concert
                    (12/94) (DG) ① [3] **445 487-2GX3**

MORGAN, Thomas (late 17th cent) England

SECTION I: ORCHESTRAL

Mr Henry Purcell's Farewell Tune—2 oboes, bassoons and strings (1695-96) (from suite for A Behn's 'The Younger Brother')
Parley of Instr, R. Goodman Concert
(3/93) (HYPE) ① CDA66578

MORHARDT, Peter (?–1685) Germany

SECTION III: INSTRUMENTAL

Aus tiefer Not schrei ich zu Dir—organ
G. Leonhardt Concert (10/94) (SONY) ① SK53371

MORIN, Jean-Baptiste (1677–1754) France

SECTION IV: VOCAL AND CHORAL

Regina coeli—motet: 2 trebles (pub 1704)
V. Gens, N. Rime, Arts Florissants Chor, Arts Florissants Orch, W. Christie Concert
(4/93) (HARM) ① HMC90 1416

MORITZ, Landgrave of Hessen-Kassel (1572–1632) Germany

SECTION II: CHAMBER

Canzon à 8—brass and continuo
Musica Fiata, R. Wilson (r1991) Concert
(8/93) (DHM) ① 05472 77183-2

SECTION III: INSTRUMENTAL

Pavan—lute (pub 1610) (from 'Varietie of Lute-Lessons')
P. O'Dette (r1992) Concert
(8/93) (HYPE) ① CDA66637
J. Bream (r1966) Concert
(8/93) (RCA) ① [28] 09026 61583-2(1)
J. Bream (r1966) Concert
(6/94) (RCA) ① 09026 61585-2

MORLACCHI, Francesco (1784–1841) Italy

SECTION V: STAGE WORKS

Il Nuovo barbiere di Siviglia—opera (4 acts) (1816—Dresden) (Lib. Petrosellini)
Giusto cielo!... Buona sera M. Hill Smith, K. John, P. Guy-Bromley, J. Best, R. Smythe, Philh, D. Parry Concert (10/90) (OPRA) ① [3] ORCH103

MORLAYE, Guillaume (c1510–after 1558) France

SECTION III: INSTRUMENTAL

Guitar Works, Book 1 (Premier livre de tabulature de Guiterne) (pub 1552)
EXCERPTS: 1. Gaillarde 'Les cinq pas'; 2. Fantasie; 3. Conte Clare; 4. Bransle.
1-4. F. Marincola (r1993) Concert
(2/95) (PIER) ① PV794052
Guitar Works, Book 2 (Second livre de tabulature de Guiterne) (pub 1553)
EXCERPTS: 1. Fantasie; 2. Villanesque; 3. Tin que tin tin.
1-3. F. Marincola (r1993) Concert
(2/95) (PIER) ① PV794052
Guitar Works, Book 4 (Quatriesme livre de tabulature de Guiterne) (pub 1552)
EXCERPTS: 1. Si iay du bien (after Sandrin); 2. Paduane 'Au ioly bois'; 3. Si son esperit; 4. Gaillarde; 5. Bransle 'Scaramella'.
1-5. F. Marincola (r1993) Concert
(2/95) (PIER) ① PV794052
Lute Pieces (from Uppsala MS no. 412)
EXCERPTS: 1. Gaillarde piemontoise; 2. Qui souhetes (after Sandrin); 3. Praelude Romanesque; 4. Pavane de Romanesque; 5. Romaine.
1-5. F. Marincola (r1993) Concert
(2/95) (PIER) ① PV794052
Lute Works, Book 1 (Premier livre de tabulature de leut) (pub 1552)
EXCERPTS: 1. Gaillarde; 2. Pavane; 3. Gaillarde; 4. Fantasie; 5. Sans liberté (after Magdelain).
1-5. F. Marincola (r1993) Concert
(2/95) (PIER) ① PV794052

Lute Works, Book 2 (Second livre de tabulature de leut) (pub 1552)
EXCERPTS: 1. Fantasie; 2. Ta privauilté (after Arcadelt); 3. Pavane des Dieux; 4. Gaillarde des Dieux.
1-4. F. Marincola (r1993) Concert
(2/95) (PIER) ① PV794052
Lute Works, Book 3 (Troisième livre de tabulature de leut) (pub 1558)
EXCERPTS: 1. Fantasie.
1. F. Marincola (r1993) Concert
(2/95) (PIER) ① PV794052

MORLEY, Thomas (1557/8–1602) England

SECTION II: CHAMBER

9 Fantasie—consort
1. Il doloroso; 2. La Girondola; 3. La rondinella; 4. Il grillo; 5. Il lamento; 6. La caccia; 7. La sampogna; 8. La sirena; 9. La torello (Tortella).
J. Bream Consort (r1962) Concert
(9/94) (RCA) ① 09026 61589-2
2, 5, 6. F. Brüggen, Brüggen Consort (r1967/79) Concert (10/95) (TELD) ① 4509-97465-2
3. J. Bream, J. Bream Consort (r1962) Concert
(8/93) (RCA) ① [28] 09026 61583-2(2)
The Frog galliard—consort lesson (1599)
J. Bream, J. Bream Consort (r1962) Concert
(8/93) (RCA) ① [28] 09026 61583-2(2)
J. Bream Consort (r1962) Concert
(9/94) (RCA) ① 09026 61589-2
Galliard to the Sacred End (pub 1609)
J. Bream, J. Bream Consort (r1987; ed Edwards) Concert (8/93) (RCA) ① [28] 09026 61583-2(3)
J. Bream Consort (r1987; ed Edwards) Concert
(9/94) (RCA) ① 09026 61590-2
Joyne hands—consort lesson (pub 1599) (arr of ayre 'See, see, myne owne sweet jewell')
D. Cordier, Tragicomedia, S. Stubbs Concert
(1/90) (HYPE) ① CDA66307
Tragicomedia, S. Stubbs Concert
(1/90) (HYPE) ① CDA66307
J. Bream, J. Bream Consort (r1962) Concert
(8/93) (RCA) ① [28] 09026 61583-2(2)
J. Bream, J. Bream Consort (r1987; ed Beck) Concert (8/93) (RCA) ① [28] 09026 61583-2(3)
J. Bream Consort (r1962) Concert
(9/94) (RCA) ① 09026 61589-2
J. Bream Consort (r1987; ed Beck) Concert
(9/94) (RCA) ① 09026 61590-2
O mistress mine—consort lesson (1599)
J. Bream, J. Bream Consort (r1962) Concert
(8/93) (RCA) ① [28] 09026 61583-2(2)
J. Bream Consort (r1962) Concert
(9/94) (RCA) ① 09026 61589-2
Sacred End Pavin—consort lesson (pub 1609)
J. Bream, J. Bream Consort (r1987; ed Edwards) Concert (8/93) (RCA) ① [28] 09026 61583-2(3)
J. Bream, J. Bream Consort (r1987; ed Edwards) Concert (9/94) (RCA) ① 09026 61590-2

SECTION III: INSTRUMENTAL

Alman, C—keyboard
Z. Růžičková Concert
(10/89) (ORFE) ① C139861A

SECTION IV: VOCAL AND CHORAL

The First Booke of Ayres or Little Short Songs—1v, lute and bass viol (pub 1600)
1. Absence, hear thou my protestation; 2. A painted tale; 3. Can I forget what reasons's force; 4. Come, sorrow, come; 5. Faire in a morne; 6. I saw my ladye weeping; 7. It was a lover and his lasse; 8. Love winged my hopes; 9. Misteresse mine, well may you fare; 10. Thirsis and Milla; 11. What if my mistresse now; 12. Who is it that this darke night; 13. With my love my life was nestled.
1, 7, 12. P. Pears, J. Bream (r1969) Concert
(8/93) (RCA) ① [28] 09026 61583-2(5)
1, 7, 12. P. Pears, J. Bream (r1969) Concert
(8/93) (RCA) ① 09026 61602-2
6. E. Kirkby, A. Rooley Concert
(8/91) (L'OI) ① 425 892-2OH
7, 9. J. Elwes, S. Stubbs Concert
(9/93) (HYPE) ① PV787092
7, 9. C. Bott, New London Consort, P. Pickett (r1992) Concert (4/94) (LINN) ① CKD011
10. R. Tear, J. Bream Consort (r1987; ed Fellows) Concert (8/93) (RCA) ① [28] 09026 61583-2(3)
10. R. Tear, J. Bream Consort (r1987; ed Fellows) Concert (9/94) (RCA) ① 09026 61590-2

The First Booke of Balletts to Five Voyces (pub 1595)
1. About the may-pole new; 2. Fyer, fyer; 3. O love, alas, I love thee; 4. I saw my lovely Phillis; 5. Ladie, those cherris plentie; 6. Leave, alas, this tormenting; 7. Lo, she flyes; 8. My bonny lasse she smyleth; 9. My lovely wanton jewell; 10. No, no, Nigella; 11. Now is the month of maying; 12. Phillis, I faine wold die now (dialogue: 7vv); 13. Shoot, false love, I care not; 14. Singing alone satte my sweet Amarillis; 15. Sing wee and chaunt it; 16. Those dainty daffadillies; 17. Thus saith my Galatea; 18. What saith my daintie darling?; 19. Why weepes, alas, my lady?; 20. You that won't to my pipes' sound.
2, 8. Amaryllis Consort, C. Brett Concert
(3/88) (CARL) ① PCD873
2, 8, 11. Cambridge Sngrs, J. Rutter Concert
(11/87) (CLLE) ① COLCD105
11. Magdalen (Oxford) Coll, G. Ives Concert
(11/92) (CNTO) ① CRCD2366
11. C. Bott, M. George, New London Consort, P. Pickett (r1992; arr Rosseter) Concert
(4/94) (LINN) ① CKD011
Canzonets or Little Short Aers to Five and Sixe Voices (pub 1597) (5vv unless otherwise indicated)
1. Adiew, adiew, you kind and cruel; 2. Ay me, the fatall arrow; 3. Cruell, wilt thou persever?; 4. Daintie fine sweet nimphe; 5. Damon and Phyllis squared; 6. False love did me inveagle; 7. Fly love, that art so sprightly; 8. Good love, then flie thou toe her (6vv); 9. Harke, Alleluia cheerely (6vv); 10. I follow, loe, the footing; 11. Ladies, you see time flieth (6vv); 12. Lady, you thinke you spite me; 13. Love's folke in greene arraying; 14. Love tooke his bowe and arrow; 15. Lo, where with floury head; 16. My nymph, the deere; 17. O griefe, even on the bud; 18. Our bonny bootes could toote it; 19. Sayd I that Amarillis; 20. Sov'raign of my delight; 21. Stay, hart, runne not so fast (6vv); 22. You blacke bright starres.
17. Hilliard Ens, P. Hillier Concert
(2/89) (EMI) ① CDC7 49197-2
The First Booke of Canzonets to Two Voyces (pub 1595)
1. Flora, wilt thou torment mee?; 2. Fyre and lightning from heaven; 3. Goe yee, my canzonets; 4. I goe before, my darling; 5. In nets of goulden wyers; 6. I should for griefe and anguish; 7. Leave now, mine eyes lamenting; 8. Loe heere another love; 9. Miraculous love's wounding; 10. O thou that art so cruel; 11. Sweet nimphe, come to thy lover; 12. When, loe, by breake of morning.
2, 5, 9, 11. Hilliard Ens, P. Hillier Concert
(2/89) (EMI) ① CDC7 49197-2
I am the resurrection and the life—anthem (1695) (for the funeral of Queen Mary)
The Sixteen, The Sixteen Orch, H. Christophers (r1994) Concert (1/95) (COLL) ① Coll1425-2
E. Kirkby, E. Tubb, M. Chance, I. Bostridge, S. Richardson, S. Birchall, Westminster Abbey Ch, New London Consort, M. Neary (r1994) Concert
(3/95) (SONY) ① SK66243
I heard a voice from Heaven—anthem
The Sixteen, The Sixteen Orch, H. Christophers (r1994) Concert (1/95) (COLL) ① Coll1425-2
E. Kirkby, E. Tubb, M. Chance, I. Bostridge, S. Richardson, S. Birchall, Westminster Abbey Ch, New London Consort, M. Neary (r1994) Concert
(3/95) (SONY) ① SK66243
I know that my Redeemer liveth—anthem
The Sixteen, The Sixteen Orch, H. Christophers (r1994) Concert (1/95) (COLL) ① Coll1425-2
E. Kirkby, E. Tubb, M. Chance, I. Bostridge, S. Richardson, S. Birchall, Westminster Abbey Ch, New London Consort, M. Neary (r1994) Concert
(3/95) (SONY) ① SK66243
In the midst of life—anthem
The Sixteen, The Sixteen Orch, H. Christophers (r1994) Concert (1/95) (COLL) ① Coll1425-2
E. Kirkby, E. Tubb, M. Chance, I. Bostridge, S. Richardson, S. Birchall, Westminster Abbey Ch, New London Consort, M. Neary (r1994) Concert
(3/95) (SONY) ① SK66243
Madrigals to Four Voyces: the First Booke (pub 1594 enlarged 1600)
1. Aprill is in my mistris face; 2. Beesides a fountaine; 3. Clorinda false, adieu; 4. Come, lovers, follow me; 5. Dye now, my heart; 6. Hark, jolly shepheards; 7. Help, I fall, ladie; 8. Hoe, who comes here?; 9. In dewe of roses; 10. In every place; 11. I will no more come to thee; 12. Lady, why grieve you still mee?; 13. No, no, thou doest but flout me; 14. Now is the gentle season; 15. On a faire morning; 16. Round about a wood; 17. Say, gentle nymphes; 18. Since my teares and lamenting; 19. Sport wee, my lovely treasure; 20. Why sit I heere complaining?.

1. Hilliard Ens, P. Hillier *Concert*
(2/89) (EMI) ① **CDC7 49197-2**

Man that is born of a woman—anthem
The Sixteen, The Sixteen Orch, H. Christophers
(r1994) *Concert* (1/95) (COLL) ① **Coll1425-2**
E. Kirkby, E. Tubb, M. Chance, I. Bostridge, S.
Richardson, S. Birchall, Westminster Abbey Ch, New
London Consort, M. Neary (r1994) *Concert*
(3/95) (SONY) ① **SK66243**

Nolo mortem peccatoris—full anthem (4vv)
(pub 1616)
Magdalen Oxford Coll Ch, J. Harper *Concert*
(11/91) (ABBE) ① **CDCA901**
Cambridge Sngrs, J. Rutter *Concert*
(4/92) (CLLE) ① **COLCD113**

Out of the deep—verse anthem (1/5vv) (pub
1641)
Magdalen Oxford Coll Ch, J. Harper *Concert*
(11/91) (ABBE) ① **CDCA901**

We brought nothing into this
world—anthem
The Sixteen, The Sixteen Orch, H. Christophers
(r1994) *Concert* (1/95) (COLL) ① **Coll1425-2**
E. Kirkby, E. Tubb, M. Chance, I. Bostridge, S.
Richardson, S. Birchall, Westminster Abbey Ch, New
London Consort, M. Neary (r1994) *Concert*
(3/95) (SONY) ① **SK66243**

When lo by break of morning—madrigal
(2vv) (pub 1595)
Hilliard Ens, P. Hillier *Concert*
(2/89) (EMI) ① **CDC7 49197-2**

MOROSS, Jerome *(1913–1983)*
USA

SECTION I: ORCHESTRAL

Symphony No. 1 (1942)
LSO, J. Falletta (r1993) *Concert*
(10/93) (KOCH) ① **37188-2**
Variations on a Waltz—orchestra (1966)
LSO, J. Falletta (r1993) *Concert*
(10/93) (KOCH) ① **37188-2**

SECTION II: CHAMBER

Sonata in G—piano duet and string quartet
(1975)
N. Weems, J. Jensen, Lyric Art Qt *Concert*
(10/90) (BAY) ① **BCD-1014**

SECTION V: STAGE WORKS

The Big Country—film score (1958)
EXCERPTS: 1. Main Title; 2. Julie's House; 3. The
Welcoming; 4. Courtin' Time; 5. Old Thunder; 6. The
Raid and Capture; 7. Major Terrill's Party: 7a. Dance
I; 7b. Dance II; 7c. Waltz; 7d. Polka; 8a. McKay's
Ride; 8b. McKay is Missing; 8c. The Old House; 9.
Waiting; 10. The Big Muddy; 11a. McKay Alone; 11b.
Night at Ladder Ranch; 11c. The Fight; 12. Cattle at
the River; 13. Attempted Rape; 14a. The War Party
Gathers; 14b. McKay in Blanco Canyon; 14c. The
Major Alone; 15a. The Duel (The Stalking); 15b. The
Death of Buck Hannassey; 16. End Title.
Suite Philh, T. Bremner *Concert*
(5/93) (SILV) ① **SILVAD3002**
The Last Judgement—ballet (1953)
LSO, J. Falletta (r1993) *Concert*
(10/93) (KOCH) ① **37188-2**

MORRICONE, Ennio *(b 1928)*
Italy

SECTION I: ORCHESTRAL

Essercizi per dieci archi (1992-3)
Solisti Italiani (r1994) *Concert*
(10/95) (DENO) ① **CO-78949**

SECTION V: STAGE WORKS

Cinema Paradiso—film score (1988)
EXCERPTS: 1. Main Theme; 2. First Youth; 3. Love
Theme (comp Andrea Morricone).
1. OST (1989) *Concert* (9/95) (VIR2) ① **CDV2774**
1-3. Mancini Pops Orch, H. Mancini (r1990; arr
Mancini) *Concert* (11/91) (RCA) ① **RD60706**
Hamlet—film score (1990)
EXCERPTS: 1. Main Theme.
1. OST (r1991) *Concert* (9/95) (VIR2) ① **CDV2774**
The Mission—film score (1986)
EXCERPTS: 1. Main Theme; 2. Gabriel's Oboe; 3.
On Earth as it is in Heaven.
2. Mancini Pops Orch, H. Mancini (r1990; arr
Mancini) *Concert* (11/91) (RCA) ① **RD60706**
3. OST (r1986) *Concert* (9/95) (VIR2) ① **CDV2774**

Once Upon a Time in America—film score
(1983)
EXCERPTS: 1. Deborah's Theme.
1. Mancini Pops Orch, H. Mancini (r1990; arr
Mancini) *Concert* (11/91) (RCA) ① **RD60706**
Once Upon a Time in the West—film score
(1968)
EXCERPTS: 1. Main Title; 2. Man With a
Harmonica.
1, 2. Mancini Pops Orch, H. Mancini (r1990; arr
Mancini) *Concert* (11/91) (RCA) ① **RD60706**
The Untouchables—film score (1987)
EXCERPTS: 1. The Ness Family Theme; 2. Death
Theme; 3. Main Title; 4. Al Capone.
3. Mancini Pops Orch, H. Mancini (r1990; arr
Mancini) *Concert* (11/91) (RCA) ① **RD60706**

MORRIS, R(eginald) O(wen)
(1886–1948) England

SECTION II: CHAMBER

Canzoni Ricertati—string quartet (1931)
1. Risoluto; 6. Lento sostenuto.
1, 6. Lindsay Qt (r1992) *Concert*
(1/94) (ASV) ① **CDDCA879**

SECTION IV: VOCAL AND CHORAL

Blow away the morning dew—part-song
(Wds. Trad)
King's Sngrs *Concert*
(6/88) (EMI) ① **CDC7 49765-2**

MORSE, Theodore *(1873–1924)*
USA

SECTION I: ORCHESTRAL

Up the Street—march (orig pf duet: orch
cpsr)
Boston Pops, A. Fiedler (r1958) *Concert*
(1/94) (RCA) ① **09026 61249-2**

MORSE, Woolson *(19th–20th*
Cent) USA

SECTION V: STAGE WORKS

Wang—musical show (1891—New York)
(Lyrics J Cheever Goodwin)
EXCERPTS: 1. A Pretty Girl.
1. Cincinnati Uni Sngrs, Cincinnati Uni Th Orch, E.
Rivers (r1978) *Concert* (4/94) (NEW) ① **80221-2**

MORTENSEN, Carl *(1832–1893)*
Denmark

SECTION IV: VOCAL AND CHORAL

the Dimlit fogs of night—song (Wds. C.
Ploug)
L. Melchior, Orch (r1915) *Concert*
(8/88) (DANA) ① [2] **DACOCD311/2**

MORTON, Jelly Roll *(1890–1941)*
USA

Ferdinand Joseph Lamothe/Lemott

SECTION III: INSTRUMENTAL

Mamanita—piano (1917-22)
A. Feinberg (r1994; trans James Dapogny) *Concert*
(11/95) (ARGO) ① **444 457-2ZH**

MOSCA, Luigi *(1775–1824) Italy*

SECTION V: STAGE WORKS

Le Bestie in uomini—opera (2 acts)
(1812—Milan) (Lib. Anelli)
Mentre guardo, oh Dio! me stessa D. Montague, G.
Mitchell Ch, Philh, D. Parry *Concert*
(10/90) (OPRA) ① [3] **ORCH103**

MOSCAGLIA, Giovanni Battista *(fl*
1559–1590) Italy

SECTION IV: VOCAL AND CHORAL

Mentre te fui si cara—madrigal: 5vv (stanza II
of a 6-stanza cycle by various comps)
M. Arruabarrena, K. van Laethem, M. Valenta, J.
Benet, M. van Altena, J. Cabré, T. de Zwart, A. Pols,
R. Van Der Meer, K. Junghänel (lte/dir) *Concert*
(1/92) (ACCE) ① **ACC8864D**

MOSCHELES, Ignaz *(1794–1870)*
Bohemia

SECTION I: ORCHESTRAL

Concerto for Piano and Orchestra in G
minor, Op. 60 (1820)
M. Ponti, Philh Hungarica, O. Maga *Concert*
(5/93) (VOX) ① **115712-2**

SECTION II: CHAMBER

Grande Sonate in E flat—piano duet, Op. 47
(1816)
A. Goldstone, C. Clemmow *Concert*
(7/93) (MERI) ① **CDE84237**

SECTION III: INSTRUMENTAL

Romance and Tarantelle brillante in F/A
minor—piano, Op. 101
I. Hobson *Concert* (3/89) (ARAB) ① **Z6596**

MOSOLOV, Alexandr Vasil'yevich
(1900–1973) Russia/USSR

SECTION I: ORCHESTRAL

Zavod, '(The) Foundry'—orchestra, Op. 19
(1926-28) (orch episode from ballet 'Stal')
Concertgebouw, R. Chailly (r1992) *Concert*
(11/94) (DECC) ① **436 640-2DH**

MOSONYI, Mihaly *(1815–1870)*
Hungary

formerly Michael Brand

SECTION I: ORCHESTRAL

Concerto for Piano and Orchestra in E minor
(1844)
J. Rose, Luxembourg RSO, P. Cao *Concert*
(5/93) (VOX) ① **115708-2**
K. Körmendi, Košice St. PO, R. Stankovsky (r1993)
Symphony 1. (3/95) (MARC) ① **8 223539**
Symphony No. 1 in D (1842-44)
Bratislava RSO, R. Stankovsky (r1993) *Piano*
Concerto in E minor. (3/95) (MARC) ① **8 223539**

SECTION II: CHAMBER

3 Colours of Burning Love—piano: 4 hands
(1864)
1. Andantino (The red rose: A piros rózsa); 2.
Allegretto(The lily: A liliom); 3. Allegro maestoso (The
lurel: A babér).
I. Kassai, K. Körmendi (r1992) *Concert*
(12/94) (MARC) ① **8 223558**
Festival music (Ünnepi zene)—piano: 4
hands (1861) (trans cpsr from orch work:
1860)
I. Kassai, K. Körmendi (r1992) *Concert*
(12/94) (MARC) ① **8 223558**
Grand Duo in F minor—piano: 4 hands
(1837-38)
I. Kassai, K. Körmendi (r1992) *Concert*
(12/94) (MARC) ① **8 223558**

SECTION III: INSTRUMENTAL

Hungarian Children's World—12 genres for
piano (1859)
I. Kassai (r1992) *Hungarian Development Studies.*
(9/94) (MARC) ① **8 223557**
20 Studies for Development in the
Performance of Hungarian Music—piano
(1860)
I. Kassai (r1992) *Hungarian Children's World.*
(9/94) (MARC) ① **8 223557**

MOSSI, Giovanni *(fl 1700) Italy*

SECTION I: ORCHESTRAL

12 Concerti a 6 e 10 (c1726)
12. G minor (4 vns).
12. Cologne Musica Antiqua, R. Goebel *Concert*
(9/92) (ARCH) ① **435 393-2AH**

MOSZKOWSKI, Moritz
(1854–1925) Germany

SECTION I: ORCHESTRAL

Concerto for Piano and Orchestra in E, Op.
59
P. Lane, BBC Scottish SO, J. Maksymiuk
Paderewski: Piano Concerto.
(2/92) (HYPE) ① **CDA66452**

M. Ponti, Philh Hungarica, H.R. Stracke *F. X.*
Scharwenka: Piano Concerto, Op.56.
(5/93) (VOX) ① **115710-2**
M. Raekallio, Tampere PO, L. Grin (r1993)
Rubinstein: Piano Concerto 4.
(2/95) (ONDI) ① **ODE818-2**

SECTION II: CHAMBER

**5 Danzas españolas—piano 4 hands, Op.
12**
EXCERPTS: 1. No 1; 2. No 2; 3. No 3; 4. No 4; 5. No
5.
LSO, A. Argenta (r1956; arr orch) *Concert*
(6/93) (DECC) ① [2] **433 911-2DM2**
LSO, A. Argenta (r1957: orch ?) *Concert*
(5/95) (DECC) ① **443 580-2DCS**
1, 3. B. Eden, A. Tamir *Concert*
(6/90) (CARL) ① **PWK1134**
6 Klavierstücke—piano—four hands, Op. 15
1. Serenata.
1. J. McCormack, F. Kreisler, Victor Orch, W.B.
Rogers (r1915; arr. voice, vn and orch) *Concert*
(9/89) (PEAR) ① **GEMMCD9315**

SECTION III: INSTRUMENTAL

Albumblatt—piano, Op. 2
S. Tanyel (r1993) *Concert*
(10/95) (COLL) ① **Coll1412-2**
**Barcarolle aus Hoffmans Erzählungen
(Offenbach)—piano**
S. Tanyel (r1993) *Concert*
(10/95) (COLL) ① **Coll1412-2**
Caprice espagnole—piano, Op. 37
S. Hough (r1986) *Concert*
(1/89) (VIRG) ① **VC7 59509-2**
J. Hofmann (pp1937) *Concert*
(5/93) (VAI) ① [2] **VAIA1020**
**Chanson bohème de l'opéra 'Carmen' de
Georges Bizet—piano**
S. Tanyel (r1993) *Concert*
(10/95) (COLL) ① **Coll1412-2**
8 Characteristic Pieces—piano, Op. 36
2. Rêverie; 3. Expansion; 4. En Autoumne; 5. Air de
Ballet; 6. Etincelles.
2-5. S. Tanyel (r1993) *Concert*
(10/95) (COLL) ① **Coll1412-2**
6. V. Horowitz (pp1985) *Concert*
(12/86) (DG) ① **419 499-2GH**
3 Etudes—piano, Op. 24
1. G flat.
1. M. Hambourg (r1909) *Concert*
(6/95) (PEAR) ① **GEMMCD9147**
Etudes de virtuosité—piano, Op. 72
1. E; 2. G minor; 3. G; 4. C; 5. C; 6. F; 7. E flat; 8. C;
9. D minor; 10. C; 11. A flat; 12. D flat; 13. A flat
minor; 14. C minor; 15. B.
6. V. Horowitz *Concert* (5/86) (DG) ① **419 045-2GH**
11. V. Horowitz (pp1965) *Concert*
(7/94) (SONY) ① [3] **S3K53461**
La Jongleuse—piano, Op. 52/4
M. Levitzki (r1927) *Concert*
(6/92) (APR) ① [2] **APR7020**
M. Levitzki (r1923) *Concert*
(1/93) (APR) ① [2] **APR7014**
S. Rachmaninov (r1923) *Concert*
(3/93) (RCA) ① [10] **09026 61265-2(3)**
S. Tanyel (r1993) *Concert*
(10/95) (COLL) ① **Coll1412-2**
Liebeswalzer in A flat—piano, Op. 57/5
S. Cherkassky (pp1991) *Concert*
(6/93) (DECC) ① **433 651-2DH**
2 Pieces—piano, Op. 45
2. Guitarre.
2. I. Perlman, S. Sanders (arr Sarasate; trans
Heifetz) *Concert* (12/89) (EMI) ① **CDC7 49604-2**
2. J. Heifetz, A. Benoist (r1918: arr Sarasate) *Concert*
(1/91) (BIDD) ① **LAB015**
2. A. Campoli, S. Crooke (arr Sarasate) *Concert*
(10/91) (PEAR) ① **PASTCD9744**
2(Guitarre) J. Heifetz, A. Benoist (arr Sarasate;
r1918) *Concert* (12/91) (APR) ① [2] **APR7015**
2. Y. Menuhin, A. Balsam (r1932) *Concert*
(12/91) (BIDD) ① **LAB046**
2. G. Piatigorsky, K. Szreter (arr Piatigorsky: r c1927)
Concert (3/92) (MUSI) ① **MACD-674**
2. K. Daeshik Kang, M. Rahkonen (r1992; arr
Sarasate) *Concert* (9/93) (NIMB) ① **NI5358**
2. J. Heifetz, A. Sándor (r1934) *Concert*
(11/94) (RCA) ① [65] **09026 61778-2(02)**
2. J. Heifetz, A. Benoist (r1918) *Concert*
(11/94) (RCA) ① [65] **09026 61778-2(01)**
2. I. Perlman, S. Sanders (r1988: arr Sarasate: ed .
Heifetz) *Concert*
(6/95) (EMI) ① [20] **CZS4 83177-2(3)**

4 Pieces—piano, Op. 68
1. Nocturne; 2. Minuetto; 3. Au crepuscule; 4. Danse
russe.
S. Tanyel (r1993) *Concert*
(10/95) (COLL) ① **Coll1412-2**
Poème de Mai—piano, Op. 67/1
S. Tanyel (r1993) *Concert*
(10/95) (COLL) ① **Coll1412-2**
Près de Berceau—piano, Op. 58/3
S. Tanyel (r1993) *Concert*
(10/95) (COLL) ① **Coll1412-2**
Serenata—piano, Op. 15/1
R. Tauber, orch (r1932: arr as Liebe kleine
Nachtigall) *Concert* (12/94) (MMOI) ① **CDMOIR425**
S. Tanyel (r1993) *Concert*
(10/95) (COLL) ① **Coll1412-2**
Siciliano—piano, Op. 42/2
S. Hough (r1987) *Concert*
(1/89) (VIRG) ① **VC7 59509-2**
Tarantella—piano, Op. 27/2
S. Tanyel (r1993) *Concert*
(10/95) (COLL) ① **Coll1412-2**
Valse mignonne—piano
S. Tanyel (r1993) *Concert*
(10/95) (COLL) ① **Coll1412-2**

MOURANT, Walter *(b 1910) USA*

SECTION I: ORCHESTRAL

**The Pied Piper—clarinet, strings and
celesta**
G. Macdonald, Northern Sinfonia, S. Bedford *Concert*
(2/88) (ASV) ① **CDDCA568**

**MOURET, Jean-Joseph
*(1682–1738) France***

SECTION I: ORCHESTRAL

**Symphonies de Fanfares—brass and strings
(c1729)**
EXCERPTS: 1. Rondeau; 2. Air; 3. Fanfares; 4.
Marcia & Allegro.
1-3. J. Freeman-Attwood, I. Simcock (r1993; arr
tpt/org) *Concert* (5/94) (PROU) ① **PROUCD135**

SECTION V: STAGE WORKS

**Les amours de Ragonde ou La soirée de
village—comédie lyrique: 3 acts (1714 rev
1742—Sceaux)** (Lib. Mericault-Destouches)
Cpte M. Verschaeve, J-P. Fouchécourt, S. Marin-
Degor, J-L. Bindi, N. Rime, G. Ragon, J-L. Serre,
Musiciens du Louvre, M. Minkowski
(12/92) (ERAT) ① **2292-45823-2**

**MOUTON, Jean *(c1459–1522)
France***

SECTION III: INSTRUMENTAL

Menuet—lute
L. Kirchhof *Concert* (11/92) (SONY) ① **SK48068**
Prélude/Chaconne—lute
L. Kirchhof *Concert* (11/92) (SONY) ① **SK48068**

SECTION IV: VOCAL AND CHORAL

Ave Maria gemma virginum—motet: 8vv
Theatre of Voices, P. Hillier (r1993) *Concert*
(11/95) (HARM) ① **HMU90 7136**
Ave Maria gratia plena—motet: 4vv
Chanticleer (r1990) *Concert*
(12/94) (CHTI) ① **CR-8803**
Ave Maria virgo serena—motet: 5vv
Theatre of Voices, P. Hillier (r1993) *Concert*
(11/95) (HARM) ① **HMU90 7136**
Ave sanctissima Maria—motet: 4vv
Theatre of Voices, P. Hillier (r1993) *Concert*
(11/95) (HARM) ① **HMU90 7136**
Nesciens mater—motet (8vv) (pub 1555)
The Sixteen, H. Christophers *Concert*
(12/88) (HYPE) ① **CDA66263**
Theatre of Voices, P. Hillier (r1993) *Concert*
(11/95) (HARM) ① **HMU90 7136**
O Maria piissima—motet: 6vv (pub 1555)
Theatre of Voices, P. Hillier (r1993) *Concert*
(11/95) (HARM) ① **HMU90 7136**

**MOZART, (Johann Georg) Leopold
*(1719–1787) South
Germany/Austria***

Numbers from Eisen's Thematic Catalogue

SECTION I: ORCHESTRAL

**Cassation in G, 'Toy Symphony' (now
thought to be arr. L. Mozart from Anon:)**
ASMF, N. Marriner *Concert*
(11/87) (PHIL) ① **416 386-2PH**
NBC SO, A. Toscanini (bp1941) *Concert*
(1/91) (RCA) ① **GD60308**
**Concerto for Trumpet and Orchestra in D
(1762)**
W. Marsalis, National PO, R. Leppard *Concert*
(5/85) (SONY) ① **SK37846**
M. André, BPO, H. von Karajan (ed. Seiffert) *Concert*
(2/89) (EMI) ① **CDC7 49237-2**
J. Wallace, Philh, S. Wright *Concert*
(4/89) (NIMB) ① **NI5121**
H. Hardenberger, LPO, E. Howarth *Concert*
(3/91) (PHIL) ① **426 311-2PH**
F. Immer, VCM, N. Harnoncourt *Concert*
(12/92) (TELD) ① **9031-77603-2**
R. Friedrich, ASMF, N. Marriner *Concert*
(6/93) (CAPR) ① **10 436**
A. Sandoval, LSO, L. Haza (r1993) *Concert*
(1/95) (GRP) ① **GRK75002**
W. Marsalis, ECO, R. Leppard (r1993) *Concert*
(5/95) (SONY) ① **SK57497**
**Concerto for 2 Horns and Orchestra in E flat
(1752)**
B. Tylšar, Z. Tylšar, Slovak CO, B. Warchal *Concert*
(9/90) (OPUS) ① **9150 1473**
**Sinfonia da caccia in G, 'Jagd
Symphonie'—four horns, percussion and
strings**
R. Beránek, Z. Divoký, Slovak CO, B. Warchal
Concert (9/90) (OPUS) ① **9150 1473**

SECTION II: CHAMBER

**6 Sonate per chiesa e da camera—2 violins
and continuo**
4. G.
4. London Baroque *Concert*
(11/92) (HARM) ① **HMC90 1395**

**MOZART, Wolfgang Amadeus
*(1756–1791) Austria***

K–Numbers used in L. von Koechel's W.A. Mozarts
Werke

SECTION I: ORCHESTRAL

**Adagio and Fugue in C minor—string
orchestra, K546 (1788) (Fugue arr from K426
for two pfs)**
Berlin RSO, F. Fricsay (r1960) *Requiem.*
(11/94) (DG) ① **445 408-2GDO**
Berlin RSO, F. Fricsay (r1951) *Concert*
(11/94) (DG) ① [11] **445 400-2GDO10**
Sinfonia Varsovia, E. Krivine (r1990) *Concert*
(3/95) (DENO) ① **CO-75597**
**Adagio for Violin and Orchestra in E, K261
(1776)**
J-J. Kantorow, Netherlands CO, L. Hager *Concert*
(12/85) (DENO) ① **C37-7505**
I. Perlman, VPO, James Levine *Concert*
(2/90) (DG) ① **427 813-2GDC**
F. Gulli, Venice and Padua CO, B. Giuranna *Concert*
(3/91) (CLAV) ① [2] **CD50-8913/4**
A. Grumiaux, New Philh, R. Leppard *Concert*
(4/91) (PHIL) ① **426 977-2PCC**
H. Szeryng, New Philh, A. Gibson *Concert*
(6/91) (PHIL) ① [4] **422 508-2PME4**
A-S. Mutter, ASMF, N. Marriner *Concert*
(1/92) (EMI) ① **CDC7 54302-2**
S. Standage, AAM, C. Hogwood *Concert*
(4/92) (L'OI) ① [2] **433 045-2OH2**
O. Renardy, W. Robert (r1940) *Concert*
(12/92) (BIDD) ① [2] **LAB061/2**
J. Bell, ECO, P. Maag *Concert*
(3/93) (DECC) ① **436 376-2DH**
A. Grumiaux, New Philh, R. Leppard (r1960s)
Concert (9/93) (PHIL) ① [2] **438 323-2PM2**
D. Oistrakh (vn/dir), BPO (r1971) *Concert*
(3/94) (EMI) ① **CDM7 64868-2**
M. Fujikawa, RPO, W. Weller (r1980) *Concert*
(5/94) (DECC) ① **440 621-2DF2**
J. Suk, Prague CO, L. Hlaváček (r1972) *Concert*
(1/95) (RCA) ① **74321 21278-2**
I. Perlman, VPO, James Levine (r1985) *Concert*
(1/95) (DG) ① [2] **445 535-2GMA2**

M. Huggett (vn/dir), OAE Concert
(3/95) (VIRG) ① **VC5 45060-2**

D. Garrett, A. Markovich (r1993) Concert
(4/95) (DG) ① **445 657-2GH**

Andante for Flute and Orchestra in C, K315/285e (1778)

P-L. Graf, ECO, R. Leppard Concert
(9/86) (CLAV) ① **CD50-8505**

L. Beznosiuk, AAM, C. Hogwood Concert
(5/88) (L'OI) ① **417 622-2OH**

M. Helasvuo, Ostrobothnian CO, J. Kangas Concert
(4/89) (BIS) ① **BIS-CD368**

S. Milan, ECO, R. Leppard Concert
(4/89) (CHAN) ① **CHAN8613**

J. Galway (fl/dir), COE Concert
(7/89) (RCA) ① [2] **RD87861**

S. Palma, Orpheus CO Concert
(3/90) (DG) ① **427 677-2GH**

M. Grauwels, Québec Violons du Roy, B. Labadie
Concert (3/90) (HYPE) ① **CDA66393**

I. Grafenauer, ASMF, N. Marriner Concert
(7/91) (PHIL) ① [5] **422 509-2PME5**

S. Palma, Orpheus CO Concert
(7/91) (DG) ① [3] **431 665-2GX3**

M. Debost, Paris Orch, D. Barenboim Concert
(10/91) (EMI) ① [2] **CZS7 67306-2**

W. Tast, CPE Bach Orch, Hans Haenchen Concert
(11/91) (CAPR) ① [3] **10 805**

J-P. Rampal, Vienna SO, T. Guschlbauer Concert
(8/92) (ERAT) ① [2] **4509-95361-2**

A. Nicolet, Concertgebouw, D. Zinman Concert
(10/94) (PHIL) ① [2] **442 299-2PM2**

J. Bálint, N. Mercz (r1992: arr fl/hp: Mercz) Concert
(12/94) (NAXO) ① **8 550741**

Andante in D, K297/K300a (1778) (original slow movement for Symphony 31)

ASMF, N. Marriner Concert
(12/90) (PHIL) ① [6] **422 502-2PME6**

Cassation in B flat, K99/K63a (1769)

Salzburg Camerata, S. Végh Concert
(3/88) (CAPR) ① **10 192**

ASMF, N. Marriner Concert
(12/90) (PHIL) ① [7] **422 503-2PME7**

Salzburg CO, H. Nerat (r1992) Concert
(4/93) (NAXO) ① **8 550609**

Cassation in D, K100/K62a (?1769)

ASMF, N. Marriner Concert
(12/90) (PHIL) ① [7] **422 503-2PME7**

Salzburg CO, H. Nerat (r1992) Concert
(4/93) (NAXO) ① **8 550609**

Cassation in G, 'Final-Musik'—violin and orchestra, K63 (1769)

1. Marche; 2. Allegro; 3. Andante; 4. Menuet; 5. Adagio; 6. Menuet; 7. Allegro assai.

Salzburg Camerata, S. Végh Concert
(3/88) (CAPR) ① **10 192**

J-J. Kantorow, Auvergne Orch, L. Hager Serenade, K203. (10/90) (DENO) ① **CO-73676**

K. Sillito, ASMF, N. Marriner Concert
(12/90) (PHIL) ① [7] **422 503-2PME7**

Salzburg CO, H. Nerat (r1992) Concert
(4/93) (NAXO) ① **8 550609**

Concerti for Horn and Orchestra

1. D, K412:K386b (1791); 2. E flat, K417 (1783); 3. E flat, K447 (?1784-7); 4. E flat, K495 (1786).

B. Tuckwell (hn/dir), ECO
(9/85) (DECC) ① **410 284-2DH**

Z. Tylšar, Prague CO (r1982) Rondo, K371.
(6/86) (DENO) ① **C37-7432**

J. Williams, COE, A. Schneider
(4/87) (ASV) ① **CDCOE805**

M. Petr, Musici de Praga, L. Hlaváček Adagio and Fugue, K546. (12/87) (SUPR) ① **2SUP0005**

R. Watkins, CLS, R. Hickox Rondo, K371.
(12/87) (CARL) ① **PCD865**

D. Brain, Philh, H. von Karajan (r1953)
(2/88) (EMI) ① **CDH7 61013-2**

A. Halstead, Hanover Band, R. Goodman Horn Concerto, KAnh98a/K494a.
(8/88) (NIMB) ① **NI5104**

M-L. Neunecker, Berne Camerata, T. Füri (vn/dir) (r1988) (11/88) (NOVA) ① **150 030-2**

B. Tuckwell, ASMF, N. Marriner Concert
(1/89) (EMI) ① **CDM7 69569-2**

L. Greer, Philh Baroque Orch, N. McGegan Concert
(3/89) (HARM) ① **HMU90 7012**

T. Brown, OAE, S. Kuijken Concert
(8/90) (VIRG) ① **VC7 59558-2**

A. Civil, Philh, O. Klemperer
(2/91) (EMIL) ① **CDZ7 67012-2**

P. Damm, ASMF, N. Marriner Concert
(7/91) (PHIL) ① [5] **422 509-2PME5**

S. Weigle, Dresden PO, J-P. Weigle (with alt Movt 2 of K412) Concert (11/91) (CAPR) ① [3] **10 805**

C. Briggs, RLPO, S. Kovacevich Haydn: Trumpet Concerto. (1/92) (CFP) ① **CD-CFP4589**

A. Koster, Tafelmusik, B. Weil (r1992-93) Rondo, K371. (2/94) (SONY) ① **SK53369**

W. Ver Meulen, Houston SO, C. Eschenbach (r1993)
Concert (4/94) (CARL) ① [3] **TCD77**

R. Vlatkovič, ECO, J. Tate (r1985) Concert
(10/94) (EMI) ① **CDM7 64851-2**

E. Ruske, Scottish CO, C. Mackerras (r1993) Concert
(10/94) (TELA) ① **CD80367**

A. Civil, ASMF, N. Marriner (r1972) Rondo, K371.
(12/94) (PHIL) ① **442 397-2PM**

A. Halstead, AAM, C. Hogwood (r1993) Concert
(8/95) (L'OI) ① **443 216-2OH**

1, 4. D. Jolley, Orpheus CO Clarinet Concerto, K622.
(6/88) (DG) ① **423 377-2GH**

1, 4. D. Jolley, Orpheus CO Concert
(7/91) (DG) ① [3] **431 665-2GX3**

2, 3. W. Purvis, Orpheus CO Concert
(7/91) (DG) ① [3] **431 665-2GX3**

Concerto for Bassoon and Orchestra in B flat, K191 (1774)

K. Thunemann, Zurich CO, E. de Stoutz Clarinet Concerto, K622. (2/86) (CLAV) ① **CD50-8205**

D. Bond, AAM, C. Hogwood Concert
(5/88) (L'OI) ① **417 622-2OH**

K. Walker, LMP, J. Glover Concert
(8/89) (GALL) ① **CD-499**

K. Thunemann, ASMF, N. Marriner Concert
(7/91) (PHIL) ① [5] **422 509-2PME5**

F. Morelli, Orpheus CO Concert
(7/91) (DG) ① [3] **431 665-2GX3**

M. Wilkie, COE, S. Végh Concert
(9/91) (ASV) ① **CDCOE813**

K. Hellmann, Vienna Mozart Ens, Herbert Kraus Concert (11/91) (CAPR) ① [3] **10 805**

M. Turkovic, VCM, N. Harnoncourt Concert
(12/92) (TELD) ① **9031-77603-2**

P. Hongne, Bamberg SO, T. Guschlbauer Concert
(6/93) (ERAT) ① **2292-45937-2**

S. Azzolini, ECCO, E. Aadland (r1992) Concert
(12/93) (CARL) ① **PCD1054**

B. Kamins, Houston SO, C. Eschenbach (r1993)
Concert (4/94) (CARL) ① [3] **TCD77**

P. Hongne, Bamberg SO, T. Guschlbauer Concert
(8/94) (ERAT) ① [2] **4509-95361-2**

E. Marschall, BRSO, Colin Davis (pp1992) Serenade, K320. (9/94) (RCA) ① **09026 61927-2**

Concerto for Clarinet and Orchestra in A, K622 (1791)

1. Allegro; 2. Adagio; 3. Rondo (Allegro).

A. Prinz, VPO, K. Böhm Flute and Harp Concerto, K299. (5/85) (DG) ① **413 552-2GH**

T. Friedli, Zurich CO, E. de Stoutz Bassoon Concerto, K191. (2/86) (CLAV) ① **CD50-8205**

A. Pay, AAM, C. Hogwood (hpd/dir) Oboe Concerto, K314. (5/86) (L'OI) ① **414 339-2OH**

T. King, ECO, J. Tate (basset clarinet version) Clarinet Quintet, K581.
(9/86) (HYPE) ① **CDA66199**

D. Shifrin, Mostly Mozart Orch, G. Schwarz Clarinet Quintet, K581. (3/87) (DELO) ① **DE3020**

C. Neidich, Orpheus CO Horn Concerti.
(6/88) (DG) ① **423 377-2GH**

J. Brymer, ASMF, N. Marriner Oboe Concerto, K314.
(10/88) (PHIL) ① **416 483-2PH**

T. King, ECO, A. Francis Spohr: Clarinet Concerto 4.
(10/88) (MERI) ① **CDE84022**

R. Hosford, COE, A. Schneider Concert
(10/89) (ASV) ① **CDCOE811**

A. Prinz, VPO, K. Münchinger Flute and Harp Concerto, K299. (3/90) (DECC) ① **421 023-2DC**

J. Farrell, Divertimenti, P. Daniel Concert
(6/90) (MERI) ① **CDE84169**

P. Schmidl, VPO, L. Bernstein (pp1987) Concert
(8/90) (DG) ① **429 221-2GH**

J. Brymer, RPO, T. Beecham Flute and Harp Concerto, K299. (7/91) (EMIL) ① **CDZ7 67007-2**

K. Leister, ASMF, N. Marriner Concert
(7/91) (PHIL) ① [5] **422 509-2PME5**

C. Neidich, Orpheus CO Concert
(7/91) (DG) ① [3] **431 665-2GX3**

R. Hosford, COE, A. Schneider Concert
(9/91) (ASV) ① **CDCOE814**

D. Glazer, ECO, G. Simon Concert
(11/91) (CAPR) ① [3] **10 805**

S. Meyer, Staatskapelle Dresden, H. Vonk (basset cl vers) Sinfonia Concertante, K297b.
(3/92) (EMI) ① **CDC7 54138-2**

K. Kell, LPO, M. Sargent (r1940) Concert
(8/92) (TEST) ① **SBT1007**

J. Campbell, Canadian Nat Arts Centre Orch, F-P. Decker Concert (9/92) (CBC) ① **SMCD5096**

A. Malmsbury, LMP, J. Glover Concert
(9/92) (ASV) ① **CDDCA795**

J. Lancelot, ECO, J-P. Rampal Concert
(6/93) (ERAT) ① **2292-45937-2**

G. de Peyer, LSO, P. Maag Concert
(7/93) (DECC) ① **433 727-2DM**

P. Meyer, ECO, D. Zinman (1992) Concert
(11/93) (DENO) ① **CO-75289**

M. Carulli, ECCO, E. Aadland (1992) Concert
(12/93) (CARL) ① **PCD1054**

D. Peck, Houston SO, C. Eschenbach (r1993)
Concert (4/94) (CARL) ① [3] **TCD77**

E. Ottensamer, VPO, Colin Davis Concert
(6/94) (PHIL) ① **438 868-2PH**

J. Lancelot, J-F Paillard CO, J-F. Paillard Concert
(8/94) (ERAT) ① [2] **4509-95361-2**

D. Campbell, CLS, R. Hickox (r1986) Flute and Harp
Concerto, K299. (10/95) (CARL) ① **PCD2011**

2. G. de Peyer, LSO, P. Maag Concert
(6/91) (DECC) ① **430 498-2DWO**

2. H.P. Draper, SO, C. Raybould (r1931) Concert
(2/94) (CLRI) ① **CC0005**

Concerto for Flute and Orchestra No. 1 in G, K313/K285c (1778)

1. Allegro maestoso; 2. Adagio non troppo; 3. Rondo (tempo di menuetto).

P-L. Graf, ECO, R. Leppard Concert
(9/86) (CLAV) ① **CD50-8505**

J. Hall, Philh, Peter Thomas Flute Concerto, K314.
(2/88) (CARL) ① **PCD871**

L. Beznosiuk, AAM, C. Hogwood Concert
(5/88) (L'OI) ① **417 622-2OH**

M. Helasvuo, Ostrobothnian CO, J. Kangas Concert
(4/89) (BIS) ① **BIS-CD368**

S. Milan, ECO, R. Leppard Concert
(4/89) (CHAN) ① **CHAN8613**

J. Galway (fl/dir), COE Concert
(7/89) (RCA) ① [2] **RD87861**

S. Palma, Orpheus CO Concert
(3/90) (DG) ① **427 677-2GH**

M. Grauwels, Québec Violons du Roy, B. Labadie
Concert (3/90) (HYPE) ① **CDA66393**

T. Indermühle, ECO, L. Hager (r1989: arr ob/orch: Holliger) Concert (4/90) (NOVA) ① **150 043-2**

I. Grafenauer, ASMF, N. Marriner Concert
(7/91) (PHIL) ① [5] **422 509-2PME5**

S. Palma, Orpheus CO Concert
(7/91) (DG) ① [3] **431 665-2GX3**

T. Fischer (fl/dir), COE Concert
(9/91) (ASV) ① **CDCOE813**

M. Debost, Paris Orch, D. Barenboim Concert
(10/91) (EMI) ① [2] **CZS7 67306-2**

W. Tast, CPE Bach Orch, Hans Haenchen Concert
(11/91) (CAPR) ① [3] **10 805**

J-P. Rampal, Israel PO, Z. Mehta Concert
(8/92) (SONY) ① [3] **SK48184**

Philippa Davies, LMP, J. Glover Concert
(9/92) (ASV) ① **CDDCA795**

S. Coles, ECO, Y. Menuhin (1990) Concert
(1/94) (VIRG) ① **VJ5 61108-2**

A. Dorough, Houston SO, C. Eschenbach (r1993)
Concert (4/94) (CARL) ① [3] **TCD77**

J-P. Rampal, Vienna SO, T. Guschlbauer Concert
(8/94) (ERAT) ① [2] **4509-95361-2**

A. Nicolet, Concertgebouw, D. Zinman Concert
(10/94) (PHIL) ① [2] **442 299-2PM2**

Concerto for Flute and Orchestra No. 2 in C, K314/K285d (1778)

P-L. Graf, ECO, R. Leppard Concert
(9/86) (CLAV) ① **CD50-8505**

J. Hall, Philh, Peter Thomas Flute Concerto, K313.
(2/88) (CARL) ① **PCD871**

M. Helasvuo, Ostrobothnian CO, J. Kangas Concert
(4/89) (BIS) ① **BIS-CD368**

S. Milan, ECO, R. Leppard Concert
(4/89) (CHAN) ① **CHAN8613**

J. Galway (fl/dir), COE Concert
(7/89) (RCA) ① [2] **RD87861**

I. Grafenauer, ASMF, N. Marriner Concert
(7/91) (PHIL) ① [5] **422 509-2PME5**

W. Tast, CPE Bach Orch, Hans Haenchen Concert
(11/91) (CAPR) ① [3] **10 805**

J-P. Rampal, Israel PO, Z. Mehta Concert
(8/92) (SONY) ① [3] **SK48184**

S. Coles, ECO, Y. Menuhin (1990) Concert
(1/94) (VIRG) ① **VJ5 61108-2**

A. Nicolet, Concertgebouw, D. Zinman Concert
(10/94) (PHIL) ① [2] **442 299-2PM2**

Concerto for Flute, Harp and Orchestra in C, K299/K297c (1778)

1. Allegro; 2. Andantino; 3. Rondeau (Allegro).

W. Schulz, N. Zabaleta, VPO, K. Böhm Clarinet Concerto, K622. (5/85) (DG) ① **413 552-2GH**

U. Holliger, ECO, P-L. Graf (fl/dir) Spohr: Violin and Harp Concerto 1. (12/87) (CLAV) ① **CD50-0208**

L. Beznosiuk, F. Kelly, AAM, C. Hogwood Concert
(5/88) (L'OI) ① **417 622-2OH**

J. Galway (fl/dir), M. Robles, COE Concert
(7/89) (RCA) ① [2] **RD87861**

W. Tripp, H. Jellinek, VPO, K. Münchinger *Clarinet Concerto, K622.* (3/90) (DECC) ① **421 023-2DC**
S. Palma, N. Allen, Orpheus CO *Concert*
(3/90) (DG) ① **427 677-2GH**
M. Grauwels, G. Herbert, Québec Violons du Roy, B. Labadie *Concert* (3/90) (HYPE) ① **CDA66393**
E. Shaffer, M. Costello, Philh, Y. Menuhin *Clarinet Concerto, K622.* (7/91) (EMI) ① **CDZ7 67007-2**
I. Grafenauer, M. Graf, ASMF, N. Marriner *Concert*
(7/91) (PHIL) ① **[5] 422 509-2PME5**
S. Palma, N. Allen, Orpheus CO *Concert*
(7/91) (DG) ① **[3] 431 665-2GX3**
T. Fischer (fl/dir), C. Sprenkels, COE *Concert*
(9/91) (ASV) ① **CDCOE813**
H. Friedrich, A. Berger, Vienna Mozart Ens, Herbert Kraus *Concert* (11/91) (CAPR) ① **[3] 10 805**
J-P. Rampal, M. Nordmann, F. Liszt CO, J. Rolla (vn/dir) *Concert* (8/92) (SONY) ① **[2] SK48184**
S. Milan, S. Kanga, CLS, R. Hickox *Concert*
(11/92) (CHAN) ① **CHAN9051**
J. Galway, M. Robles, LSO, M. Tilson Thomas (r1992) *Concert*
(12/93) (RCA) ① **[3] 09026 61677-2**
J. Galway, M. Robles, LSO, M. Tilson Thomas (r1992) *Concert* (12/93) (RCA) ① **09026 61789-2**
S. Coles, N. Yoshino, ECO, Y. Menuhin (r1990) *Concert* (1/94) (VIRG) ① **VJ5 61108-2**
L. Laskine, J-P. Rampal, J-F Paillard CO, J-F. Paillard *Concert*
(8/94) (ERAT) ① **[2] 4509-95361-2**
H. Barwahser, O. Ellis, LSO, Colin Davis *Concert*
(10/94)' (PHIL) ① **[2] 442 299-2PM2**
J. Smith, L. Wellbaum, Cleveland Orch, C. von Dohnányi (r1993) *Concert*
(2/95) (DECC) ① **443 175-2DH**
Philippa Davies, R. Masters, CLS, R. Hickox (r1986) *Clarinet Concerto, K622.*
(10/95) (CARL) ① **PCD2011**

Concerto for Horn and Orchestra No. 1 in E, KAnh98a/K494a (1786) (incomplete: fragment only)
A. Halstead, Hanover Band, R. Goodman (recons. J.Humphries and R.Goodman) *Horn Concerti.*
(8/88) (NIMB) ① **NI5104**
B. Tuckwell, ASMF, N. Marriner *Concert*
(1/89) (EMI) ① **CDM7 69569-2**
T. Brown, OAE, S. Kuijken *Concert*
(8/90) (VIRG) ① **VC7 59558-2**
S. Weigle, Dresden PO, J-P. Weigle *Concert*
(11/91) (CAPR) ① **[3] 10 805**
E. Ruske, Scottish CO, C. Mackerras (r1993: ed J Humphries) *Concert* (10/94) (TELA) ① **CD80367**

Concerto for Keyboard and Orchestra No. 1 in F, K37 (1767) (arr from movts by Raupach & Honaur)
M. Perahia (pf/dir), ECO *Concert*
(1/86) (SONY) ① **SK39225**
G. Anda (pf/dir), Salzburg Mozarteum Camerata Academica (r1968) *Concert*
(6/90) (DG) ① **[10] 429 001-2GX10**
D. Barenboim (pf/dir), ECO (r1974) *Concert*
(6/90) (EMI) ① **[10] CZS7 62825-2**
I. Haebler, VCA, E. Melkus (r1973) *Concert*
(5/91) (PHIL) ① **[12] 422 507-2PME12**
Vladimir Ashkenazy (pf/dir), Philh (r1988) *Concert*
(9/95) (LOND) ① **[10] 443 727-2LC10**
Vladimir Ashkenazy (pf/dir), Philh (r1987) *Concert*
(9/95) (DECC) ① **425 089-2DM**

Concerto for Keyboard and Orchestra No. 2 in B flat, K39 (1767) (arr from movts by Raupach & Schobert)
M. Perahia (pf/dir), ECO *Concert*
(1/86) (SONY) ① **SK39225**
G. Anda (pf/dir), Salzburg Mozarteum Camerata Academica (r1968) *Concert*
(6/90) (DG) ① **[10] 429 001-2GX10**
D. Barenboim (pf/dir), ECO (r1974) *Concert*
(6/90) (EMI) ① **[10] CZS7 62825-2**
I. Haebler, VCA, E. Melkus (r1973) *Concert*
(5/91) (PHIL) ① **[12] 422 507-2PME12**
Vladimir Ashkenazy (pf/dir), Philh (r1988) *Concert*
(9/95) (LOND) ① **[10] 443 727-2LC10**
Vladimir Ashkenazy (pf/dir), Philh (r1987) *Concert*
(9/95) (DECC) ① **425 092-2DM**

Concerto for Keyboard and Orchestra No. 3 in D, K40 (1767) (arr from movts by Honauer, Eckard & C.P.E. Bach)
M. Perahia (pf/dir), ECO *Concert*
(1/86) (SONY) ① **SK39225**
G. Anda (pf/dir), Salzburg Mozarteum Camerata Academica (r1968) *Concert*
(6/90) (DG) ① **[10] 429 001-2GX10**
D. Barenboim (pf/dir), ECO (r1974) *Concert*
(6/90) (EMI) ① **[10] CZS7 62825-2**
I. Haebler, VCA, E. Melkus (r1973) *Concert*
(5/91) (PHIL) ① **[12] 422 507-2PME12**

Vladimir Ashkenazy (pf/dir), Philh (r1988) *Concert*
(9/95) (LOND) ① **[10] 443 727-2LC10**
Vladimir Ashkenazy (pf/dir), Philh (r1987) *Concert*
(9/95) (DECC) ① **425 093-2DM**

Concerto for Keyboard and Orchestra No. 4 in G, K41 (1767) (arr from movts by Honauer & Raupach)
M. Perahia (pf/dir), ECO *Concert*
(1/86) (SONY) ① **SK39225**
G. Anda (pf/dir), Salzburg Mozarteum Camerata Academica (r1968) *Concert*
(6/90) (DG) ① **[10] 429 001-2GX10**
D. Barenboim (pf/dir), ECO (r1974) *Concert*
(6/90) (EMI) ① **[10] CZS7 62825-2**
I. Haebler, VCA, E. Melkus (r1973) *Concert*
(5/91) (PHIL) ① **[12] 422 507-2PME12**
Vladimir Ashkenazy (pf/dir), Philh (r1988) *Concert*
(9/95) (LOND) ① **[10] 443 727-2LC10**
Vladimir Ashkenazy (pf/dir), Philh (r1987) *Concert*
(9/95) (DECC) ① **425 095-2DM**

Concerto for Keyboard and Orchestra No. 5 in D, K175 (1773)
G. Anda (pf/dir), Salzburg Mozarteum Camerata Academica (r1968) *Concert*
(6/90) (DG) ① **[10] 429 001-2GX10**
D. Barenboim (pf/dir), ECO (r1969) *Concert*
(6/90) (EMI) ① **[10] CZS7 62825-2**
A. Brendel, ASMF, N. Marriner (r1984) *Concert*
(5/91) (PHIL) ① **[12] 422 507-2PME12**
Anima Eterna, J. Van Immerseel (fp/dir) *Piano Concerto 9.* (10/92) (CHNN) ① **CCS0590**
J. Van Immerseel (fp/dir), Anima Eterna *Concert*
(10/92) (CHNN) ① **[10] CCSBOX10**
Vladimir Ashkenazy (pf/dir), Philh (r1986) *Concert*
(9/95) (LOND) ① **[10] 443 727-2LC10**
Vladimir Ashkenazy (pf/dir), Philh (r1986) *Concert*
(9/95) (DECC) ① **425 088-2DM**

Concerto for Keyboard and Orchestra No. 6 in B flat, K238 (1776)
M. Perahia (pf/dir), ECO *Piano Concerto 13.*
(10/85) (SONY) ① **SK39223**
G. Anda (pf/dir), Salzburg Mozarteum Camerata Academica (r1962) *Concert*
(6/90) (DG) ① **[10] 429 001-2GX10**
D. Barenboim (pf/dir), ECO (r1973) *Concert*
(6/90) (EMI) ① **[10] CZS7 62825-2**
A. Brendel, ASMF, N. Marriner (r1984) *Concert*
(5/91) (PHIL) ① **[12] 422 507-2PME12**
Anima Eterna, J. Van Immerseel (fp/dir) *Piano Concerto 17.* (10/92) (CHNN) ① **CCS1891**
J. Van Immerseel (fp/dir), Anima Eterna *Concert*
(10/92) (CHNN) ① **[10] CCSBOX10**
Vladimir Ashkenazy (pf/dir), Philh (r1986) *Concert*
(9/95) (LOND) ① **[10] 443 727-2LC10**
Vladimir Ashkenazy (pf/dir), Philh (r1986) *Concert*
(9/95) (DECC) ① **425 088-2DM**

Concerto for Keyboard and Orchestra No. 8 in C, K246 (1776)
G. Anda (pf/dir), Salzburg Mozarteum Camerata Academica (r1968) *Concert*
(6/90) (DG) ① **[10] 429 001-2GX10**
D. Barenboim (pf/dir), ECO (r1973) *Concert*
(6/90) (EMI) ① **[10] CZS7 62825-2**
A. Brendel, ASMF, N. Marriner (r1983) *Concert*
(5/91) (PHIL) ① **[12] 422 507-2PME12**
P. Bruni, ECCO, E. Aadland *Concert*
(3/92) (CARL) ① **PCD964**
M. Uchida, ECO, J. Tate *Piano Concerto 9.*
(7/92) (PHIL) ① **432 086-2PH**
Anima Eterna, J. Van Immerseel (fp/dir) *Concert*
(10/92) (CHNN) ① **CCS0690**
J. Van Immerseel (fp/dir), Anima Eterna *Concert*
(10/92) (CHNN) ① **[10] CCSBOX10**
A. Schiff, Salzburg Mozarteum Camerata Academica, S. Végh *Concert* (5/93) (DECC) ① **433 042-2DH**
W. Kempff, BPO, F. Leitner (r c1962) *Concert*
(5/95) (DG) ① **[2] 439 699-2GX2**
Vladimir Ashkenazy, LSO, I. Kertész (r1966) *Concert*
(5/95) (DECC) ① **443 576-2DCS**
Vladimir Ashkenazy (pf/dir), Philh (r1985) *Concert*
(9/95) (LOND) ① **[10] 443 727-2LC10**
Vladimir Ashkenazy (pf/dir), Philh (r1985) *Concert*
(9/95) (DECC) ① **425 089-2DM**

Concerto for Keyboard and Orchestra No. 9 in E flat, K271 (1777)
EXCERPTS: 1. Allegro; 2. Andantino; 3. Presto.
M. Perahia (pf/dir), ECO *Piano Concerto 21.*
(6/87) (SONY) ① **SK34562**
S. Hough, Hallé, B. Thomson *Piano Concerto 21.*
(2/88) (CFP) ① **CD-CFP9016**
G. Anda (pf/dir), Salzburg Mozarteum Camerata Academica (r1969) *Concert*
(6/90) (DG) ① **[10] 429 001-2GX10**
D. Barenboim (pf/dir), ECO (r1967) *Concert*
(6/90) (EMI) ① **[10] CZS7 62825-2**

A. Schiff, Salzburg Mozarteum Camerata Academica, S. Végh *Piano Concerto 13.*
(7/90) (DECC) ① **425 466-2DH**
J. Jandó, Concentus Hungaricus, A. Ligeti *Piano Concerto 27.* (10/90) (NAXO) ① **8 550203**
A. Brendel, ASMF, N. Marriner (r1978) *Concert*
(5/91) (PHIL) ① **[12] 422 507-2PME12**
A. de Larrocha, ECO, Colin Davis *Piano Concerto 21.*
(1/92) (RCA) ① **RD60825**
M. Uchida, ECO, J. Tate *Piano Concerto 8.*
(7/92) (PHIL) ① **432 086-2PH**
Anima Eterna, J. Van Immerseel (fp/dir) *Piano Concerto 5.* (10/92) (CHNN) ① **CCS0590**
J. Van Immerseel (fp/dir), Anima Eterna *Concert*
(10/92) (CHNN) ① **[10] CCSBOX10**
H. Shelley (pf/dir), LMP *Piano Concerto 17.*
(11/92) (CHAN) ① **CHAN9068**
BPO, D. Barenboim (pf/dir) *Piano Concerto 17.*
(11/92) (TELD) ① **9031-73128-2**
W. Gieseking, Paris Nat Orch, I. Markevitch (pp1955) *Concert* (3/94) (PEAR) ① **GEMMCD9038**
R. Levin, AAM, C. Hogwood *Piano Concerto 17.*
(7/94) (L'OI) ① **443 328-2OH**
R. Firkušný, South-West German RSO, E. Bour (r1994) *Concert* (8/94) (INTE) ① **INT820 547**
F. Ts'ong (pf/dir), Polish CO (r1986) *Piano Concerto 12.* (9/94) (CARL) ① **MCD84**
M. Horszowski, Musica aeterna, F. Waldman (r1962-72) *Concert* (3/95) (PEAR) ① **[2] GEMMCDS9138**
A. Brendel, ASMF, N. Marriner (r1978) *Concert*
(4/95) (PHIL) ① **[2] 442 571-2PM2**
W. Gieseking, Berlin St Op Orch, H. Rosbaud (r1936) *Concert* (5/95) (APR) ① **APR5511**
Vladimir Ashkenazy, LSO, I. Kertész (r1966) *Concert*
(5/95) (DECC) ① **443 576-2DCS**
Vladimir Ashkenazy (pf/dir), Philh (r1984) *Concert*
(9/95) (LOND) ① **[10] 443 727-2LC10**
Vladimir Ashkenazy (pf/dir), Philh (r1984) *Concert*
(9/95) (DECC) ① **425 089-2DM**
C. Haskil, Vienna SO, P. Sacher (r1954) *Concert*
(11/95) (PHIL) ① **[12] 442 685-2PM12**
C. Haskil, Vienna SO, P. Sacher (r1954) *Concert*
(11/95) (PHIL) ① **[4] 442 631-2PM4**
M. Bilson, EBS, J. E. Gardiner (r1984) *Concert*
(12/95) (ARCH) ① **447 291-2AMA**
2. E. Petri (pp1958: arr Busoni) *Concert*
(3/94) (MUSI) ① **[4] MACD-772**

Concerto for Keyboard and Orchestra No. 11 in F, K413/387a (1782-3)
M. Perahia (pf/dir), ECO *Concert*
(9/87) (SONY) ① **SK42243**
G. Anda (pf/dir), Salzburg Mozarteum Camerata Academica *Concert*
(6/90) (DG) ① **[10] 429 001-2GX10**
D. Barenboim (pf/dir), ECO (r1972/3) *Concert*
(6/90) (EMI) ① **[10] CZS7 62825-2**
A. Brendel, ASMF, N. Marriner (r1984) *Concert*
(5/91) (PHIL) ① **[12] 422 507-2PME12**
P. Frankl, ECO Sols *Concert*
(9/91) (ASV) ① **CDDCA764**
J. Plowright, Capital Virtuosi *Concert*
(1/92) (SPRO) ① **SPCV1001**
Anima Eterna, J. Van Immerseel (fp/dir) *Concert*
(10/92) (CHNN) ① **CCS0990**
J. Van Immerseel (fp/dir), Anima Eterna *Concert*
(10/92) (CHNN) ① **[10] CCSBOX10**
A. Schiff, Salzburg Mozarteum Camerata Academica, S. Végh *Concert* (5/93) (DECC) ① **433 042-2DH**
Vladimir Ashkenazy (pf/dir), Philh (r1986) *Concert*
(9/95) (LOND) ① **[10] 443 727-2LC10**
Vladimir Ashkenazy (pf/dir), Philh (r1986) *Concert*
(9/95) (DECC) ① **425 090-2DM**
R. Levin, AAM, C. Hogwood (r1994) *Concert*
(9/95) (L'OI) ① **444 571-2OH**

Concerto for Keyboard and Orchestra No. 12 in A, K414/K385p (1782)
L. Lortie, Montreal I Musici, Y. Turovsky *Piano Concerto 14.* (1/87) (CHAN) ① **CHAN8455**
S. Lubin (fp/dir), Mozartean Players *Piano Concerto 15.* (3/87) (ARAB) ① **Z6552**
M. Perahia (pf/dir), ECO *Concert*
(9/87) (SONY) ① **SK42243**
A. Schiff, Salzburg Mozarteum Camerata Academica, S. Végh *Piano Concerto 14.*
(12/89) (DECC) ① **417 886-2DH**
G. Anda (pf/dir), Salzburg Mozarteum Camerata Academica (r1965) *Concert*
(6/90) (DG) ① **[10] 429 001-2GX10**
D. Barenboim (pf/dir), ECO (r1972/3) *Concert*
(6/90) (EMI) ① **[10] CZS7 62825-2**
J. Jandó, Concentus Hungaricus, A. Ligeti *Concert*
(10/90) (NAXO) ① **8 550202**
A. Brendel, ASMF, N. Marriner (r1978) *Concert*
(5/91) (PHIL) ① **[12] 422 507-2PME12**
P. Frankl, ECO Sols *Concert*
(9/91) (ASV) ① **CDDCA764**

Anima Eterna, J. Van Immerseel (fp/dir) *Concert*
(10/92) (CHNN) ① **CCS0690**
J. Van Immerseel (fp/dir), Anima Eterna *Concert*
(10/92) (CHNN) ① [10] **CCSBOX10**
E. Kissin, Moscow Virtuosi, V. Spivakov *Concert*
(2/93) (RCA) ① **09026 60400-2**
LMP, H. Shelley (pf/dir) (r1993) *Piano Concerto 19.*
(6/94) (CHAN) ① **CHAN9256**
R. Levin, AAM, C. Hogwood *Piano Concerto 9.*
(7/94) (L'OI) ① **443 328-2OH**
F. Ts'ong (pf/dir), Polish CO (r1986) *Piano Concerto 9.*
(9/94) (CARL) ① **MCD84**
M. Horszowski, Musica aeterna, F. Waldman (r1962-72) *Concert* (3/95) (PEAR) ① [2] **GEMMCDS9138**
Vladimir Ashkenazy (pf/dir), Philh (r1980) *Concert*
(9/95) (LOND) ① [10] **443 727-2LC10**
Vladimir Ashkenazy (pf/dir), Philh (r1980) *Concert*
(9/95) (DECC) ① **425 090-2DM**
Concerto for Keyboard and Orchestra No. 13 in C, K415/K387b (1782-3)
M. Perahia (pf/dir), ECO *Piano Concerto 6.*
(10/85) (SONY) ① **SK39223**
G. Anda (pf/dir), Salzburg Mozarteum Camerata Academica (r1967) *Concert*
(6/90) (DG) ① [10] **429 001-2GX10**
D. Barenboim (pf/dir), ECO (r1967) *Concert*
(6/90) (EMI) ① [10] **CZS7 62825-2**
A. Schiff, Salzburg Mozarteum Camerata Academica, S. Végh *Piano Concerto 9.*
(7/90) (DECC) ① **425 466-2DH**
J. Jandó, Concentus Hungaricus, A. Ligeti *Piano Concerto 9.* (10/90) (NAXO) ① **8 550201**
A.B. Michelangeli, N German RSO, C. Garben (pp1990) *Piano Concerto 15.*
(2/91) (DG) ① **431 097-2GH**
A. Brendel, ASMF, N. Marriner (r1978) *Concert*
(5/91) (PHIL) ① [12] **422 507-2PME12**
P. Frankl, ECO Sols *Concert*
(9/91) (ASV) ① **CDDCA764**
Anima Eterna, J. Van Immerseel (fp/dir) *Concert*
(10/92) (CHNN) ① **CCS0990**
J. Van Immerseel (fp/dir), Anima Eterna *Concert*
(10/92) (CHNN) ① [10] **CCSBOX10**
H. Shelley (pf/dir), LMP *Piano Concerto 24.*
(1/95) (CHAN) ① **CHAN9326**
M. Horszowski, Musica aeterna, F. Waldman (r1962-72) *Concert* (3/95) (PEAR) ① [2] **GEMMCDS9138**
Vladimir Ashkenazy (pf/dir), Philh (r1980) *Concert*
(9/95) (LOND) ① [10] **443 727-2LC10**
Vladimir Ashkenazy (pf/dir), Philh (r1981) *Concert*
(9/95) (DECC) ① **425 091-2DM**
R. Levin, AAM, C. Hogwood (r1994) *Concert*
(9/95) (L'OI) ① **444 K51-2OH**
Concerto for Keyboard and Orchestra No. 14 in E flat, K449 (1784)
D. Ambache (pf/dir), Ambache Chbr Ens *Piano Concerto 18.* (9/85) (MERI) ① **ECD84086**
L. Lortie, Montreal I Musici, Y. Turovsky *Piano Concerto 12.* (1/87) (CHAN) ① **CHAN8455**
M. Perahia (pf/dir), ECO *Concert*
(9/87) (SONY) ① **SK42243**
D. Barenboim (pf/dir), ECO (r1968) *Concert*
(12/88) (EMI) ① **CDM7 69124-2**
A. Schiff, Salzburg Mozarteum Camerata Academica, S. Végh *Piano Concerto 12.*
(12/89) (DECC) ① **417 886-2DH**
G. Anda (pf/dir), Salzburg Mozarteum Camerata Academica (r1966) *Concert*
(6/90) (DG) ① [10] **429 001-2GX10**
D. Barenboim (pf/dir), ECO (r1968) *Concert*
(6/90) (EMI) ① [10] **CZS7 62825-2**
J. Jandó, Concentus Hungaricus, A. Ligeti *Concert*
(10/90) (NAXO) ① **8 550202**
A. Brendel, ASMF, N. Marriner (r1978) *Concert*
(5/91) (PHIL) ① [12] **422 507-2PME12**
Anima Eterna, J. Van Immerseel (fp/dir) *Concert*
(10/92) (CHNN) ① **CCS0990**
J. Van Immerseel (fp/dir), Anima Eterna *Concert*
(10/92) (CHNN) ① [10] **CCSBOX10**
LMP, H. Shelley (pf/dir) (r1992) *Piano Concerto 27.*
(6/93) (CHAN) ① **CHAN9137**
M-J. Pires, VPO, C. Abbado (r1992) *Piano Concerto 26.* (3/94) (DG) ① **437 529-2GH**
E. Istomin, Perpignan Fest Orch, P. Casals (r1951) *Concert* (5/94) (SONY) ① **SMK58984**
M. Horszowski, Musica aeterna, F. Waldman (r1962-72) *Concert* (3/95) (PEAR) ① [2] **GEMMCDS9138**
Vladimir Ashkenazy (pf/dir), Philh (r1986) *Concert*
(9/95) (LOND) ① [10] **443 727-2LC10**
Vladimir Ashkenazy (pf/dir), Philh (r1986) *Concert*
(9/95) (DECC) ① **425 091-2DM**
Concerto for Keyboard and Orchestra No. 15 in B flat, K450 (1784)
A. Brendel, ASMF, N. Marriner *Piano Concerto 21.*
(3/83) (PHIL) ① **400 018-2PH**

S. Lubin (fp/dir), Mozartean Players *Piano Concerto 12.* (3/87) (ARAB) ① **Z6552**
D. Barenboim (pf/dir), ECO (r1968) *Concert*
(12/88) (EMI) ① **CDM7 69124-2**
G. Anda (pf/dir), Salzburg Mozarteum Camerata Academica (r1968) *Concert*
(6/90) (DG) ① [10] **429 001-2GX10**
D. Barenboim (pf/dir), ECO (r1968) *Concert*
(6/90) (EMI) ① [10] **CZS7 62825-2**
A.B. Michelangeli, N German RSO, C. Garben (pp1990) *Piano Concerto 13.*
(2/91) (DG) ① **431 097-2GH**
A. Brendel, ASMF, N. Marriner (r1981) *Concert*
(5/91) (PHIL) ① [12] **422 507-2PME12**
Anima Eterna, J. Van Immerseel (fp/dir) *Piano Concerto 16.* (10/92) (CHNN) ① **CCS1791**
J. Van Immerseel (fp/dir), Anima Eterna *Concert*
(10/92) (CHNN) ① [10] **CCSBOX10**
A. Schiff, Salzburg Mozarteum Camerata Academica, S. Végh *Piano Concerto 16.*
(10/92) (DECC) ① **433 374-2DH**
A. Brendel, ASMF, N. Marriner (r1981) *Concert*
(4/95) (PHIL) ① [2] **442 571-2PM2**
Vladimir Ashkenazy (pf/dir), Philh (r1982) *Concert*
(9/95) (LOND) ① [10] **443 727-2LC10**
Vladimir Ashkenazy (pf/dir), Philh (r1983) *Concert*
(9/95) (DECC) ① **425 091-2DM**
Concerto for Keyboard and Orchestra No. 16 in D, K451 (1784)
D. Barenboim (pf/dir), ECO (r1973) *Concert*
(12/88) (EMI) ① **CDM7 69124-2**
G. Anda (pf/dir), Salzburg Mozarteum Camerata Academica (r1963) *Concert*
(6/90) (DG) ① [10] **429 001-2GX10**
D. Barenboim (pf/dir), ECO (r1973) *Concert*
(6/90) (EMI) ① [10] **CZS7 62825-2**
C. Zacharias, Stuttgart RSO, N. Marriner *Piano Concerto 19.* (9/90) (EMI) ① **CDC7 49982-2**
A. Brendel, ASMF, N. Marriner (r1984) *Concert*
(5/91) (PHIL) ① [12] **422 507-2PME12**
Anima Eterna, J. Van Immerseel (fp/dir) *Piano Concerto 15.* (10/92) (CHNN) ① **CCS1791**
J. Van Immerseel (fp/dir), Anima Eterna *Concert*
(10/92) (CHNN) ① [10] **CCSBOX10**
A. Schiff, Salzburg Mozarteum Camerata Academica, S. Végh *Piano Concerto 15.*
(10/92) (DECC) ① **433 374-2DH**
R. Firkušný, South-West German RSO, E. Bour *Piano Concerto 20.* (8/94) (INTE) ① **INT820 546**
Vladimir Ashkenazy (pf/dir), Philh (r1979) *Concert*
(9/95) (LOND) ① [10] **443 727-2LC10**
Vladimir Ashkenazy (pf/dir), Philh (r1979) *Concert*
(9/95) (DECC) ① **425 092-2DM**
Concerto for Keyboard and Orchestra No. 17 in G, K453 (1784)
EXCERPTS: 1. Allegro; 2. Andante; 3. Allegretto.
M. Perahia (pf/dir), ECO *Piano Concerto 18.*
(9/85) (SONY) ① **SK36686**
A. Schiff, Salzburg Mozarteum Camerata Academica, S. Végh *Piano Concerto 18.*
(5/86) (DECC) ① **414 289-2DH**
G. Anda (pf/dir), Salzburg Mozarteum Camerata Academica (r1961) *Concert*
(6/90) (DG) ① [10] **429 001-2GX10**
D. Barenboim (pf/dir), ECO (r1967) *Concert*
(6/90) (EMI) ① [10] **CZS7 62825-2**
J. Jandó, Concentus Hungaricus, M. Antal *Piano Concerto 18.* (10/90) (NAXO) ① **8 550205**
A. Brendel, ASMF, N. Marriner (r1970) *Concert*
(5/91) (PHIL) ① [12] **422 507-2PME12**
E. Dohnányi (pf/dir), Budapest PO (r1928) *Concert*
(1/92) (SCHW) ① **311136**
Anima Eterna, J. Van Immerseel (fp/dir) *Piano Concerto 6.* (10/92) (CHNN) ① **CCS1891**
J. Van Immerseel (fp/dir), Anima Eterna *Concert*
(10/92) (CHNN) ① [10] **CCSBOX10**
J. O'Conor, Scottish CO, C. Mackerras *Piano Concerto 24.* (10/92) (TELA) ① **CD80306**
H. Shelley (pf/dir), LMP *Piano Concerto 9.*
(11/92) (CHAN) ① **CHAN9068**
BPO, D. Barenboim (pf/dir) *Concert*
(11/92) (TELD) ① **9031-73128-2**
Vladimir Ashkenazy (pf/dir), Philh (r1977) *Concert*
(9/95) (LOND) ① [10] **443 727-2LC10**
Vladimir Ashkenazy (pf/dir), Philh (r1977) *Concert*
(9/95) (DECC) ① **425 092-2DM**
M. Bilson, EBS, J. E. Gardiner (fp) *Concert*
(12/95) (ARCH) ① **447 291-2AMA**
Concerto for Keyboard and Orchestra No. 18 in B flat, K456 (1784)
D. Ambache (pf/dir), Ambache Chbr Ens *Piano Concerto 14.* (9/85) (MERI) ① **ECD84086**
M. Perahia (pf/dir), ECO *Piano Concerto 17.*
(9/85) (SONY) ① **SK36686**

A. Schiff, Salzburg Mozarteum Camerata Academica, S. Végh *Piano Concerto 17.*
(5/86) (DECC) ① **414 289-2DH**
G. Anda (pf/dir), Salzburg Mozarteum Camerata Academica (r c1964) *Concert*
(6/90) (DG) ① [10] **429 001-2GX10**
D. Barenboim (pf/dir), ECO (r1972) *Concert*
(6/90) (EMI) ① [10] **CZS7 62825-2**
M. Uchida, ECO, J. Tate *Piano Concerto 19.*
(7/90) (PHIL) ① **422 348-2PH**
J. Jandó, Concentus Hungaricus, M. Antal *Piano Concerto 17.* (10/90) (NAXO) ① **8 550205**
A. Brendel, ASMF, N. Marriner (r1974) *Concert*
(5/91) (PHIL) ① [12] **422 507-2PME12**
Anima Eterna, J. Van Immerseel (fp/dir) *Piano Concerto 19.* (10/92) (CHNN) ① **CCS1991**
J. Van Immerseel (fp/dir), Anima Eterna *Concert*
(10/92) (CHNN) ① [10] **CCSBOX10**
R. Firkušný, South-West German RSO, E. Bour *Piano Concerto 25.* (8/94) (INTE) ① **INT820 548**
D. Barenboim (pf/dir), BPO (r1993) *Concert*
(4/95) (TELD) ① **4509-90674-2**
Vladimir Ashkenazy (pf/dir), Philh (r1984) *Concert*
(9/95) (LOND) ① [10] **443 727-2LC10**
Vladimir Ashkenazy (pf/dir), Philh (r1984) *Concert*
(9/95) (DECC) ① **425 093-2DM**
Concerto for Keyboard and Orchestra No. 19 in F, K459 (1784)
M. Perahia (pf/dir), ECO *Piano Concerto 23.*
(1/86) (SONY) ① **SK39064**
M. Pollini, VPO, K. Böhm *Piano Concerto 23.*
(1/86) (DG) ① **413 793-2GH**
P. Štěpán, Musici de Praga, L. Hlaváček *Piano Concerto 27.* (12/88) (SUPR) ① **2SUP0029**
A. Schiff, Salzburg Mozarteum Camerata Academica, S. Végh *Piano Concerto 27.*
(3/89) (DECC) ① **421 259-2DH**
G. Anda (pf/dir), Salzburg Mozarteum Camerata Academica (r1967) *Concert*
(6/90) (DG) ① [10] **429 001-2GX10**
D. Barenboim (pf/dir), ECO (r1972/3) *Concert*
(6/90) (EMI) ① [10] **CZS7 62825-2**
M. Uchida, ECO, J. Tate *Piano Concerto 18.*
(7/90) (PHIL) ① **422 348-2PH**
C. Zacharias, Stuttgart RSO, N. Marriner *Piano Concerto 16.* (9/90) (EMI) ① **CDC7 49982-2**
A. Brendel, ASMF, N. Marriner (r1971) *Concert*
(5/91) (PHIL) ① [12] **422 507-2PME12**
A. Schnabel, LSO, M. Sargent (r1937) *Concert*
(6/91) (EMI) ① [3] **CHS7 63703-2**
J. O'Conor, Scottish CO, C. Mackerras *Concert*
(11/91) (TELA) ① **CD80285**
Anima Eterna, J. Van Immerseel (fp/dir) *Piano Concerto 18.* (10/92) (CHNN) ① **CCS1991**
J. Van Immerseel (fp/dir), Anima Eterna *Concert*
(10/92) (CHNN) ① [10] **CCSBOX10**
LMP, H. Shelley (pf/dir) (r1993) *Piano Concerto 12.*
(6/94) (CHAN) ① **CHAN9256**
A. Brendel, ASMF, N. Marriner (r1971) *Concert*
(10/94) (PHIL) ① [2] **442 269-2PM2**
M. Horszowski, Musica aeterna, F. Waldman (r1962-72) *Concert* (3/95) (PEAR) ① [2] **GEMMCDS9138**
D. Barenboim (pf/dir), BPO (r1994) *Concert*
(4/95) (TELD) ① **4509-90674-2**
Vladimir Ashkenazy (pf/dir), Philh (r1978) *Concert*
(9/95) (LOND) ① [10] **443 727-2LC10**
Vladimir Ashkenazy (pf/dir), Philh (r1978) *Concert*
(9/95) (DECC) ① **425 093-2DM**
Concerto for Keyboard and Orchestra No. 20 in D minor, K466 (1785)
EXCERPTS: 1. Allegro; 2. Romanze; 3. Allegro assai.
E. Westenholz, Collegium Musicum, M. Schønwandt *Piano Concerto 23.* (7/86) (BIS) ① **BIS-CD283**
M. Uchida, ECO, J. Tate *Piano Concerto 21.*
(7/86) (PHIL) ① **416 381-2PH**
C. Curzon, ECO, B. Britten (r1970) *Piano Concerto 27.* (10/86) (DECC) ① **417 288-2DH**
F. Guida, VPO, C. Abbado *Piano Concerto 21.*
(4/87) (DG) ① **415 842-2GGA**
M. Perahia (pf/dir), ECO *Piano Concerto 27.*
(9/87) (SONY) ① **SK42243**
M. Bilson, EBS, J.E. Gardiner (fp) *Piano Concerto 21.*
(1/88) (ARCH) ① **419 609-2AH**
D. Barenboim (pf/dir), ECO *Piano Concerto 24.*
(4/88) (EMI) ① **CDC7 49007-2**
S. Lubin, Mozartean Players, R. Wilson (fp) *Piano Concerto 23.* (5/88) (ARAB) ① **Z6530**
G. Anda (pf/dir), Salzburg Mozarteum Camerata Academica (r c1964) *Concert*
(6/90) (DG) ① [10] **429 001-2GX10**
D. Barenboim (pf/dir), ECO (r1967) *Concert*
(6/90) (EMI) ① [10] **CZS7 62825-2**
J. Frantz, Bamberg SO, C.P. Flor *Piano Concerto 24.*
(9/90) (EURO) ① **RD69000**

J. Jandó, Concentus Hungaricus, A. Ligeti *Piano Concerto 13.* (10/90) (NAXO) ① **8 550201**
G. Solti (pf/dir), ECO *Concert* (11/90) (DECC) ① **430 232-2DH**
A. Brendel, ASMF, N. Marriner (r1973) *Concert* (5/91) (PHIL) ① [12] **422 507-2PME12**
A. Schnabel, Philh, W. Susskind (r1948) *Concert* (6/91) (EMI) ① [3] **CHS7 63703-2**
A. Schiff, Salzburg Mozarteum Camerata Academica, S. Végh *Piano Concerto 21.* (10/91) (DECC) ① **430 510-2DH**
H. Shelley (pf/dir), LMP *Piano Concerto 23.* (1/92) (CHAN) ① **CHAN8992**
J. Van Immerseel (fp/dir), Anima Eterna *Concert* (10/92) (CHNN) ① [10] **CCSBOX10**
J. Van Immerseel (fp/dir), Anima Eterna *Piano Concerto 21.* (10/92) (CHNN) ① **CCS2391**
D. Barenboim (pf/dir), BPO *Piano Concerto 21.* (11/92) (TELD) ① **9031-75710-2**
E. Kissin, Moscow Virtuosi, V. Spivakov *Concert* (2/93) (RCA) ① **09026 60400-2**
J. O'Conor, Scottish CO, C. Mackerras (r1991) *Piano Concerto 22.* (11/93) (TELA) ① **CD80308**
B. Walter (pf/dir), VPO (r1937) *Concert* (3/94) (PEAR) ① **GEMMCD9940**
B. Walter (pf/dir), VPO (r1937) *Concert* (3/94) (PREI) ① **90141**
R. Firkušný, South-West German RSO, E. Bour *Piano Concerto 16.* (8/94) (INTE) ① **INT820 546**
A. Previn (pf/dir), LSO (r1976) *2-Piano Concerto, K365.* (9/94) (EMI) ① **CDM5 65180-2**
A. Brendel, ASMF, N. Marriner (r1973) *Concert* (10/94) (PHIL) ① [2] **442 269-2PM2**
G. Anda (pf/dir), Vienna SO (r1973) *Concert* (1/95) (RCA) ① **74321 17888-2**
S. Vladar, ASMF, N. Marriner (r1993) *Concert* (3/95) (SONY) ① **SMK64251**
Vladimir Ashkenazy (pf/dir), Philh (r1983) *Concert* (9/95) (LOND) ① [10] **443 727-2LC10**
Vladimir Ashkenazy (pf/dir), Philh (r1983) *Piano Concerto 22.* (9/95) (DECC) ① **425 094-2DM**
C. Haskil, Vienna SO, B. Paumgartner (r1954) *Concert* (11/95) (PHIL) ① [12] **442 685-2PM12**
C. Haskil, Lamoureux Concerts Orch, I. Markevitch (r1960) *Concert* (11/95) (PHIL) ① [4] **442 631-2PM4**
C. Haskil, Lamoureux Concerts Orch, I. Markevitch (r1960) *Concert* (11/95) (PHIL) ① [12] **442 685-2PM12**
C. Haskil, Vienna SO, B. Paumgartner (r1954) *Concert* (11/95) (PHIL) ① [4] **442 631-2PM4**

Concerto for Keyboard and Orchestra No. 21 in C, 'Elvira Madigan', K467 (1785) (informally named after film which used slow movt as theme tune)

EXCERPTS: 1. Allegro maestoso; 2. Andante; 3. Allegro vivace assai.

A. Brendel, ASMF, N. Marriner *Piano Concerto 15.* (3/83) (PHIL) ① **400 018-2PH**
M. Uchida, ECO, J. Tate *Piano Concerto 20.* (7/86) (PHIL) ① **416 381-2PH**
D. Barenboim (pf/dir), ECO *Piano Concerto 27.* (4/87) (EMI) ① **CDC7 47269-2**
F. Gulda, VPO, C. Abbado *Piano Concerto 20.* (4/87) (DG) ① **415 842-2GGA**
M. Perahia (pf/dir), ECO *Piano Concerto 9.* (6/87) (SONY) ① **SK34562**
M. Bilson, EBS, J.E. Gardiner (fp) *Piano Concerto 20.* (1/88) (ARCH) ① **419 609-2AH**
S. Hough, Hallé, B. Thomson *Piano Concerto 9.* (2/88) (CFP) ① **CD-CFP9016**
D. Lipatti, Lucerne Fest Orch, H. von Karajan (pp1950) *Schumann: Piano Concerto.* (7/89) (EMI) ① **CDH7 69792-2**
S. Kovacevich, LSO, Colin Davis (r1972) *Piano Concerto 25.* (2/90) (PHIL) ① **426 077-2PCC**
G. Anda (pf/dir), Salzburg Mozarteum Camerata Academica (r1961) *Concert* (6/90) (DG) ① [10] **429 001-2GX10**
D. Barenboim (pf/dir), ECO (r1968) *Concert* (6/90) (EMI) ① [10] **CZS7 62825-2**
M. Hess, Hallé, L. Heward (r1942) *Concert* (8/90) (APR) ① [2] **APR7012**
J. O'Conor, Scottish CO, C. Mackerras (r1989) *Piano Concerto 27.* (9/90) (TELA) ① **CD80219**
J. Frantz, Bamberg SO, C.P. Flor *Piano Concerto 23.* (9/90) (EURO) ① **RD69076**
J. Jandó, Concentus Hungaricus, A. Ligeti *Concert* (10/90) (NAXO) ① **8 550202**
A. Brendel, ASMF, N. Marriner (r1981) *Concert* (5/91) (PHIL) ① [12] **422 507-2PME12**
A. Schnabel, LSO, M. Sargent (r1937) *Concert* (6/91) (EMI) ① [3] **CHS7 63703-2**
A. Fischer, Philh, W. Sawallisch *Piano Concerto 22.* (7/91) (EMIL) ① **CDZ7 67002-2**
M. Perahia (pf/dir), COE *Piano Concerto 27.* (8/91) (SONY) ① **SK46485**
R. Casadesus, Cleveland Orch, G. Szell *Concert* (9/91) (SONY) ① **SM3K46519**
A. Schiff, Salzburg Mozarteum Camerata Academica, S. Végh *Piano Concerto 20.* (10/91) (DECC) ① **430 510-2DH**
D. Ambache (pf/dir), Ambache CO *Piano Concerto 25.* (12/91) (VIRG) ① **VJ7 59647-2**
A. de Larrocha, ECO, Colin Davis *Piano Concerto 9.* (1/92) (RCA) ① **RD60825**
J. Van Immerseel (fp/dir), Anima Eterna *Piano Concerto 20.* (10/92) (CHNN) ① **CCS2391**
J. Van Immerseel (fp/dir), Anima Eterna *Concert* (10/92) (CHNN) ① [10] **CCSBOX10**
D. Barenboim (pf/dir), BPO *Piano Concerto 20.* (11/92) (TELD) ① **9031-75710-2**
Emil Gilels, USSR SO, K. Kondrashin (pp1959) *Tchaikovsky: Piano Concerto 2.* (5/93) (MEZH) ① **MK417106**
Sinfonia Varsovia, F. Ts'ong (pf/dir) (r1991) *Piano Concerto 27.* (3/94) (CARL) ① **MCD74**
A. Brendel, ASMF, N. Marriner (r1981) *Concert* (10/94) (PHIL) ① [2] **442 269-2PM2**
R. Serkin, LSO, C. Abbado (r1982) *Piano Concerto 27.* (1/95) (DG) ① **445 516-2GMA**
G. Anda (pf/dir), Vienna SO (r1973) *Concert* (1/95) (RCA) ① **74321 17888-2**
H. Francesch, Nice PO, K. Weise (pp1991) *Piano Concerto 22.* (2/95) (KONT) ① **32189**
Vladimir Ashkenazy (pf/dir), Philh (r1977) *Concert* (9/95) (LOND) ① [10] **443 727-2LC10**
Vladimir Ashkenazy (pf/dir), Philh (r1977) *Concert* (9/95) (DECC) ① **425 095-2DM**
H. Shelley (pf/dir), CLS (r1980s) *Piano Concerto 24.* (10/95) (CARL) ① **PCD2007**
2. T. Nishizaki, Capella Istropolitana, J. Wildner (arr Saint-Saëns) *Concert* (4/91) (NAXO) ① **8 550414**
2. Vladimir Ashkenazy (pf/dir), Philh *Concert* (6/91) (DECC) ① **430 498-2DWO**
2. J. Thibaud, T. Janopoulo (r1930: arr vn/pf: Saint-Saëns) *Concert* (12/94) (APR) ① [2] **APR7028**

Concerto for Keyboard and Orchestra No. 22 in E flat, K482 (1785)

EXCERPTS: 1. Allegro; 2. Andante; 3. Allegro.

C. Zacharias, Staatskapelle Dresden, D. Zinman *Piano Concerto 23.* (4/87) (EMI) ① **CDC7 47428-2**
M. Uchida, ECO, J. Tate (r1986) *Piano Concerto 23.* (8/87) (PHIL) ① **420 187-2PH**
M. Perahia (pf/dir), ECO *Piano Concerto 24.* (8/87) (SONY) ① **SK42242**
G. Anda (pf/dir), Salzburg Mozarteum Camerata Academica (r1962) *Concert* (6/90) (DG) ① [10] **429 001-2GX10**
D. Barenboim (pf/dir), ECO (r1971) *Concert* (6/90) (EMI) ① [10] **CZS7 62825-2**
J. Frantz, Bamberg SO, C.P. Flor *Piano Concerto 27.* (9/90) (EURO) ① **RD69075**
A. Brendel, ASMF, N. Marriner (r1975) *Concert* (5/91) (PHIL) ① [12] **422 507-2PME12**
A. Fischer, Philh, W. Sawallisch *Piano Concerto 21.* (7/91) (EMIL) ① **CDZ7 67002-2**
A. Schiff, Salzburg Mozarteum Camerata Academica, S. Végh *Piano Concerto 23.* (7/91) (DECC) ① **425 855-2DH**
R. Casadesus, Columbia SO, G. Szell *Concert* (9/91) (SONY) ① **SM3K46519**
Anima Eterna, J. Van Immerseel (fp/dir) *Piano Concerto 23.* (10/92) (CHNN) ① **CCS2491**
J. Van Immerseel (fp/dir), Anima Eterna *Concert* (10/92) (CHNN) ① [10] **CCSBOX10**
BPO, D. Barenboim (pf/dir) *Piano Concerto 23.* (11/92) (TELD) ① **9031-75711-2**
J. O'Conor, Scottish CO, C. Mackerras (r1991) *Piano Concerto 20.* (11/93) (TELA) ① **CD80308**
Sinfonia Varsovia, F. Ts'Ong (pf/dir) (r1991) *Piano Concerto 24.* (6/94) (CARL) ① **MCD79**
A. de Larrocha, ECO, Colin Davis (r1992) *Piano Concerto 26.* (7/94) (RCA) ① **09026 61698-2**
T. Fellner, Lausanne CO, U. Segal (r1993) *Concert* (9/94) (CLAV) ① **CD50-9328**
H. Francesch, Nice PO, K. Weise (pp1991) *Piano Concerto 21.* (2/95) (KONT) ① **32189**
A. Brendel, ASMF, N. Marriner (r1975) *Concert* (4/95) (PHIL) ① [2] **442 571-2PM2**
Vladimir Ashkenazy (pf/dir), Philh (r1978) *Concert* (9/95) (LOND) ① [10] **443 727-2LC10**
Vladimir Ashkenazy (pf/dir), Philh (r1983) *Piano Concerto 20.* (9/95) (DECC) ① **425 094-2DM**

Concerto for Keyboard and Orchestra No. 23 in A, K488 (1786)

EXCERPTS: 1. Allegro; 2. Adagio; 3. Allegro assai.

M. Perahia (pf/dir), ECO *Piano Concerto 19.* (1/86) (SONY) ① **SK39064**
M. Pollini, VPO, K. Böhm *Piano Concerto 19.* (1/86) (DG) ① **413 793-2GH**
E. Westenholz, Collegium Musicum, M. Schønwandt *Piano Concerto 20.* (7/86) (BIS) ① **BIS-CD283**
C. Zacharias, Staatskapelle Dresden, D. Zinman *Piano Concerto 22.* (4/87) (EMI) ① **CDC7 47428-2**
M. Uchida, ECO, J. Tate (r1986) *Piano Concerto 22.* (8/87) (PHIL) ① **420 187-2PH**
V. Horowitz, La Scala Orch, C.M. Giulini *Piano Sonata, K333.* (11/87) (DG) ① **423 287-2GH**
S. Lubin (fp/dir), Mozartean Players *Piano Concerto 20.* (5/88) (ARAB) ① **Z6530**
I. Moravec, Czech CO, J. Vlach *Concert* (12/88) (SUPR) ① **2SUP0027**
W. Kempff, Bamberg SO, F. Leitner *Piano Concerto 24.* (12/88) (DG) ① **423 885-2GGA**
G. Anda (pf/dir), Salzburg Mozarteum Camerata Academica (r1963) *Concert* (6/90) (DG) ① [10] **429 001-2GX10**
D. Barenboim (pf/dir), ECO (r1967) *Concert* (6/90) (EMI) ① [10] **CZS7 62825-2**
J. Frantz, Bamberg SO, C.P. Flor *Piano Concerto 21.* (9/90) (EURO) ① **RD69076**
R. Casadesus, Columbia SO, G. Szell *Piano Concerto 26.* (10/90) (SONY) ① **MPK45884**
J. Jandó, Concentus Hungaricus, M. Antal *Piano Concerto 24.* (10/90) (NAXO) ① **8 550204**
A. Brendel, ASMF, N. Marriner (r1971) *Concert* (5/91) (PHIL) ① [12] **422 507-2PME12**
A. Schiff, Salzburg Mozarteum Camerata Academica, S. Végh *Piano Concerto 22.* (7/91) (DECC) ① **425 855-2DH**
R. Casadesus, Columbia SO, G. Szell *Concert* (9/91) (SONY) ① **SM3K46519**
J. O'Conor, Scottish CO, C. Mackerras *Concert* (11/91) (TELA) ① **CD80285**
H. Shelley (pf/dir), LMP *Piano Concerto 20.* (1/92) (CHAN) ① **CHAN8992**
J. Van Immerseel (fp/dir), Anima Eterna *Concert* (10/92) (CHNN) ① [10] **CCSBOX10**
Anima Eterna, J. Van Immerseel (fp/dir) *Piano Concerto 22.* (10/92) (CHNN) ① **CCS2491**
BPO, D. Barenboim (pf/dir) *Piano Concerto 22.* (11/92) (TELD) ① **9031-75711-2**
A. de Larrocha, ECO, Colin Davis *Piano Concerto 24.* (3/93) (RCA) ① **09026 60989-2**
M. Pletnev (pf/dir), Deutsche Kammerphilharmonie (r1991) *Piano Concerto 24.* (6/93) (VIRG) ① **VC7 59280-2**
F. Gulda, Concertgebouw, N. Harnoncourt (r1983) *Piano Concerto 26.* (2/94) (TELD) ① **4509-92150-2**
A. Brendel, ASMF, N. Marriner (r1971) *Concert* (10/94) (PHIL) ① [2] **442 269-2PM2**
A. Brendel, ASMF, N. Marriner (r1971) *Piano Concerto 27.* (12/94) (PHIL) ① **442 391-2PM**
W. Kempff, Bamberg SO, F. Leitner (r c1960) *Concert* (5/95) (DG) ① [2] **439 699-2GX2**
M. Uchida, ECO, J. Tate (r c1987) *Piano Concerto 24.* (7/95) (PHIL) ① **442 648-2PM**
Vladimir Ashkenazy (pf/dir), Philh (r1980) *Concert* (9/95) (LOND) ① [10] **443 727-2LC10**
Vladimir Ashkenazy (pf/dir), Philh (r1980) *Concert* (9/95) (DECC) ① **425 095-2DM**
C. Haskil, Vienna SO, P. Sacher (r1954) *Concert* (11/95) (PHIL) ① [4] **442 631-2PM4**
C. Haskil, Vienna SO, P. Sacher (r1954) *Concert* (11/95) (PHIL) ① [12] **442 685-2PM12**

Concerto for Keyboard and Orchestra No. 24 in C minor, K491 (1786)

EXCERPTS: 1. Allegro; 2. Larghetto; 3. Allegretto.

C. Zacharias, N German RSO, G. Wand *Piano Concerto 27.* (6/87) (EMI) ① **CDC7 47432-2**
M. Perahia (pf/dir), ECO *Piano Concerto 22.* (8/87) (SONY) ① **SK42242**
D. Barenboim (pf/dir), ECO *Piano Concerto 20.* (3/88) (EMI) ① **CDC7 49007-2**
P. Badura-Skoda (pf/dir), Prague CO *Concert* (12/88) (SUPR) ① **2SUP0027**
W. Kempff, Bamberg SO, F. Leitner *Piano Concerto 23.* (12/88) (DG) ① **423 885-2GGA**
M. Uchida, ECO, J. Tate (r1988) *Piano Concerto 25.* (8/89) (PHIL) ① **422 331-2PH**
G. Anda (pf/dir), Salzburg Mozarteum Camerata Academica (r1966) *Concert* (6/90) (DG) ① [10] **429 001-2GX10**
D. Barenboim (pf/dir), ECO (r1971) *Concert* (6/90) (EMI) ① [10] **CZS7 62825-2**
J. Frantz, Bamberg SO, C.P. Flor *Piano Concerto 20.* (9/90) (EURO) ① **RD69000**
J. Jandó, Concentus Hungaricus, M. Antal *Piano Concerto 23.* (10/90) (NAXO) ① **8 550204**
A. Brendel, ASMF, N. Marriner (r1973) *Concert* (5/91) (PHIL) ① [12] **422 507-2PME12**
A. Schnabel, Philh, W. Susskind (r1948) *Concert* (6/91) (EMI) ① [3] **CHS7 63703-2**
A. Schiff, Salzburg Mozarteum Camerata Academica, S. Végh *Piano Concerto 25.* (7/91) (DECC) ① **425 791-2DH**

J. Suk (vn/dir), Suk CO *Concert*
    (6/91) (VANG) ① **08.7001.71**
S. Accardo (vn/dir), Prague CO *Violin Concerto, K216.*
    (6/91) (NUOV) ① **6902**
T. Zehetmair (vn/dir), Philh *Concert*
    (9/91) (TELD) ① **2292-46340-2**
S. Standage, AAM, C. Hogwood *Concert*
    (4/92) (L'OI) ① [2] **433 045-2OH2**
A. Cappelletti, ECCO, E. Aadland *Concert*
    (5/92) (SCHW) ① [2] **311164**
A. Grumiaux, LSO, Colin Davis (r1964) *Concert*
    (9/93) (PHIL) ① [2] **438 323-2PM2**
M. Fujikawa, RPO, W. Weller (r1980) *Concert*
    (5/94) (DECC) ① [2] **440 621-2DF2**
M. Huggett (vn/dir), OAE (r1991) *Concert*
    (9/94) (VIRG) ① **VC5 45010-2**
J. Suk, Prague CO, L. Hlaváček (r1972) *Concert*
    (1/95) (RCA) ① **74321 21277-2**
I. Perlman, VPO, James Levine (r1985) *Concert*
    (1/95) (DG) ① [2] **445 535-2GMA2**
Concerto for Violin and Orchestra No. 3 in G, K216 (1775)
J-J. Kantorow, Netherlands CO, L. Hager *Violin Concerto, K219.*
    (12/85) (DENO) ① **C37-7504**
A-S. Mutter, BPO, H. von Karajan (r1977) *Violin Concerto, K219.*
    (3/86) (DG) ① **415 327-2GH**
K. Sjøgren, Copenhagen Collegium Musicum, M. Schønwandt (r1983) *Violin Concerto, K219.*
    (7/86) (BIS) ① **BIS-CD282**
D. Sitkovetsky (vn/dir), ECO *Concert*
    (11/87) (NOVA) ① **150 012-2**
A-S. Mutter, BPO, H. von Karajan *Concert*
    (3/88) (DG) ① [4] **415 565-2GX4**
A. Dumay, Warsaw Sinfonia, E. Krivine *Concert*
    (3/89) (EMI) ① **CDC7 49160-2**
B. Huberman, VPO, I. Dobroven (r1935) *Concert*
    (8/89) (PEAR) ① **GEMMCD9341**
Y. Menuhin, Paris SO, G. Enescu (r1935) *Concert*
    (1/90) (BIDD) ① **LAB004**
W. Schneiderhan (vn/dir), BPO *Concert*
    (2/90) (DG) ① **429 159-2GR**
C. Altenburger, German Bach Sols, H. Winschermann *Concert* (5/90) (LASE) ① **15 525**
F. Gulli, Venice and Padua CO, B. Giuranna *Concert*
    (3/91) (CLAV) ① [2] **CD50-8913/4**
T. Nishizaki, Capella Istropolitana, S. Gunzenhauser *Violin Concerto, K219.* (4/91) (NAXO) ① **8 550063**
Y. Menuhin, Paris SO, G. Enescu (r1935) *Concert*
    (4/91) (EMI) ① **CDH7 63718-2**
Y. Menuhin, Bath Fest Orch *Concert*
    (6/91) (EMIL) ① **CDZ7 67004-2**
H. Szeryng, New Philh, A. Gibson *Concert*
    (6/91) (PHIL) ① [4] **422 508-2PME4**
J. Suk (vn/dir), Suk CO *Concert*
    (6/91) (VANG) ① **08.7001.71**
S. Accardo (vn/dir), Prague CO *Violin Concerto, K211.*
    (6/91) (NUOV) ① **6902**
T. Zehetmair (vn/dir), Philh *Concert*
    (9/91) (TELD) ① **2292-46340-2**
Y. Menuhin (vn/dir), C. Ferras *Concert*
    (11/91) (EMI) ① [3] **CZS7 67310-2**
D. Oistrakh, Czech PO, K. Ančerl (r1954) *Concert*
    (12/91) (SUPR) ① **11 0582-2**
S. Standage, AAM, C. Hogwood *Concert*
    (4/92) (L'OI) ① [2] **433 045-2OH2**
A. Cappelletti, ECCO, E. Aadland *Concert*
    (5/92) (SCHW) ① [2] **311164**
J. Bell, ECO, P. Maag *Concert*
    (3/93) (DECC) ① **436 376-2DH**
A. Grumiaux, LSO, Colin Davis (r1961) *Concert*
    (9/93) (PHIL) ① [2] **438 323-2PM2**
S. Chase, Hanover Band, R. Goodman (r1992) *Concert* (12/93) (CALA) ① [2] **CACD1014**
S. Goldberg, Philh, W. Susskind (r1951) *Concert*
    (4/94) (TEST) ① **SBT1028**
M. Fujikawa, RPO, W. Weller (r1979) *Concert*
    (5/94) (DECC) ① [2] **440 621-2DF2**
J. Suk, Prague CO, L. Hlaváček (r1972) *Concert*
    (1/95) (RCA) ① **74321 21277-2**
I. Perlman, VPO, James Levine (r1982) *Concert*
    (1/95) (DG) ① [2] **445 535-2GMA2**
M. Huggett (vn/dir), OAE *Concert*
    (3/95) (VIRG) ① **VC5 45060-2**
Z. Francescatti, Columbia So, B. Walter *Concert*
    (8/95) (SONY) ① **SMK64468**
Movt 2. Y. Menuhin, L. Persinger (r1929) *Concert*
    (4/91) (BIDD) ① **LAB031**
Concerto for Violin and Orchestra No. 4 in D, K218 (1775)
1. Allegro moderato; 2. Andante; 3. Rondo (Allegro).
A-S. Mutter, RPO, R. Muti (r1981) *Violin Concerto, K211.* (3/84) (EMI) ① **CDC7 47011-2**
O. Shumsky, Scottish CO, Y.P. Tortelier *Violin Concerto, K219.* (3/84) (NIMB) ① **NI5009**
J-J. Kantorow, Netherlands CO, L. Hager *Concert*
    (12/85) (DENO) ① **C37-7505**

I. Perlman, VPO, James Levine (r1985) *Violin Concerto, K211.*   (12/86) (DG) ① **415 975-2GH**
D. Sitkovetsky (vn/dir), ECO *Violin Concerto, K219.*
    (11/87) (NOVA) ① **150 007-2**
W. Schneiderhan (vn/dir), BPO *Concert*
    (2/90) (DG) ① **429 159-2GR**
C. Altenburger, German Bach Sols, H. Winschermann *Concert* (5/90) (LASE) ① **15 525**
F. Kreisler, orch, L. Ronald (r1924) *Concert*
    (7/90) (BIDD) ① [2] **LAB009/10**
F. Kreisler, LPO, M. Sargent (r1939) *Violin Concerto, K268.* (9/90) (BIDD) ① **LAB016**
F. Gulli, Venice and Padua CO, B. Giuranna *Concert*
    (3/91) (CLAV) ① [2] **CD50-8913/4**
T. Nishizaki, Capella Istropolitana, S. Gunzenhauser *Sinfonia Concertante, K364.*
    (4/91) (NAXO) ① **8 550332**
Y. Menuhin (vn/dir), Bath Fest orch *Concert*
    (6/91) (EMIL) ① **CDZ7 67005-2**
H. Szeryng, New Philh, A. Gibson *Concert*
    (6/91) (PHIL) ① [4] **422 508-2PME4**
S. Accardo (vn/dir), Prague CO *Violin Concerto, K207.* (6/91) (NUOV) ① **6926**
S. Standage, AAM, C. Hogwood *Concert*
    (4/92) (L'OI) ① [2] **433 045-2OH2**
A. Cappelletti, ECCO, E. Aadland *Concert*
    (5/92) (SCHW) ① [2] **311164**
F. Kreisler, LSO, L. Ronald (r1924) *Concert*
    (9/93) (PEAR) ① [2] **GEMMCDS9996**
A. Grumiaux, LSO, Colin Davis (r1962) *Concert*
    (9/93) (PHIL) ① [2] **438 323-2PM2**
J. Szigeti, LPO, T. Beecham (r1934) *Concert*
    (2/94) (EMI) ① **CDH7 64562-2**
D. Oistrakh, BPO (r1970) *Concert*
    (3/94) (EMI) ① **CDM7 64868-2**
S. Goldberg, Philh, W. Susskind (r1951) *Concert*
    (4/94) (TEST) ① **SBT1028**
M. Fujikawa, RPO, W. Weller (r1980) *Concert*
    (5/94) (DECC) ① [2] **440 621-2DF2**
J. Heifetz, New SO, M. Sargent (r1962) *Concert*
    (11/94) (RCA) ① [65] **09026 61778-2(30)**
J. Heifetz, RPO, T. Beecham (r1947) *Concert*
    (11/94) (RCA) ① [65] **09026 61778-2(18)**
J. Suk, Prague CO, L. Hlaváček (r1972) *Concert*
    (1/95) (RCA) ① **74321 21278-2**
I. Perlman, VPO, James Levine (r1985) *Concert*
    (1/95) (DG) ① [2] **445 535-2GMA2**
M. Huggett (vn/dir), OAE *Concert*
    (3/95) (VIRG) ① **VC5 45060-2**
Z. Francescatti, Columbia So, B. Walter *Concert*
    (8/95) (SONY) ① **SMK64468**
Concerto for Violin and Orchestra No. 5 in A, 'Turkish', K219 (1775)
1. Allegro aperto; 2. Adagio; 3. Rondo (tempo di menuetto).
O. Shumsky, Scottish CO, Y.P. Tortelier *Violin Concerto, K218.* (3/84) (NIMB) ① **NI5009**
J-J. Kantorow, Netherlands CO, L. Hager *Violin Concerto, K216.* (12/85) (DENO) ① **C37-7504**
A-S. Mutter, BPO, H. von Karajan (r1977) *Violin Concerto, K216.* (3/86) (DG) ① **415 327-2GH**
K. Sjøgren, Copenhagen Collegium Musicum, M. Schønwandt (r1983) *Violin Concerto, K216.*
    (7/86) (BIS) ① **BIS-CD282**
D. Sitkovetsky (vn/dir), ECO *Violin Concerto, K218.*
    (11/87) (NOVA) ① **150 007-2**
A-S. Mutter, BPO, H. von Karajan *Concert*
    (3/88) (DG) ① [4] **415 565-2GX4**
I. Perlman, VPO, James Levine *Concert*
    (2/90) (DG) ① **427 813-2GDC**
W. Schneiderhan (vn/dir), BPO *Concert*
    (2/90) (DG) ① **429 159-2GR**
C. Altenburger, German Bach Sols, H. Winschermann *Concert* (5/90) (LASE) ① **15 525**
F. Gulli, Venice and Padua CO, B. Giuranna *Concert*
    (3/91) (CLAV) ① [2] **CD50-8913/4**
T. Nishizaki, Capella Istropolitana, S. Gunzenhauser *Violin Concerto, K216.* (4/91) (NAXO) ① **8 550063**
Y. Menuhin, Bath Fest Orch *Concert*
    (6/91) (EMIL) ① **CDZ7 67004-2**
H. Szeryng, New Philh, A. Gibson *Concert*
    (6/91) (PHIL) ① [4] **422 508-2PME4**
T. Zehetmair (vn/dir), Philh *Concert*
    (9/91) (TELD) ① **2292-46340-2**
Y. Menuhin (vn/dir), C. Ferras *Concert*
    (11/91) (EMI) ① [3] **CZS7 67310-2**
S. Standage, AAM, C. Hogwood *Concert*
    (4/92) (L'OI) ① [2] **433 045-2OH2**
A. Cappelletti, ECCO, E. Aadland *Concert*
    (5/92) (SCHW) ① [2] **311164**
J. Bell, ECO, P. Maag *Concert*
    (3/93) (DECC) ① **436 376-2DH**
A. Grumiaux, LSO, Colin Davis (r1961) *Concert*
    (9/93) (PHIL) ① [2] **438 323-2PM2**
T. Varga (vn/dir), Varga Fest Orch (r1976) *Symphony 36.* (11/93) (CLAV) ① **CD50-9312**

Varga Fest Orch, T. Varga (vn/dir) (r1976) *Concert*
    (11/93) (CLAV) ① [4] **CD50-9300/4**
S. Chase, Hanover Band, R. Goodman (r1992) *Concert* (12/93) (CALA) ① [2] **CACD1014**
D. Oistrakh (vn/dir), BPO (r1970) *Concert*
    (3/94) (EMI) ① **CDM7 64868-2**
S. Goldberg, Philh, W. Susskind (r1951) *Concert*
    (4/94) (TEST) ① **SBT1028**
E. Morini, Perpignan Fest Orch, P. Casals (r1951) *Sinfonia concertante, K364.*
    (5/94) (SONY) ① **SMK58983**
M. Fujikawa, RPO, W. Weller (r1980) *Concert*
    (5/94) (DECC) ① [2] **440 621-2DF2**
M. Huggett (vn/dir), OAE (r1991) *Concert*
    (9/94) (VIRG) ① **VC5 45010-2**
J. Heifetz, LPO, J. Barbirolli (r1934) *Concert*
    (10/94) (EMI) ① **CDH5 65191-2**
J. Heifetz, LSO, M. Sargent (r1951) *Concert*
    (11/94) (RCA) ① [65] **09026 61778-2(10)**
J. Heifetz, LPO, J. Barbirolli (r1934) *Concert*
    (11/94) (RCA) ① [65] **09026 61778-2(26)**
J. Heifetz, CO (r1963) *Concert*
    (11/94) (RCA) ① [65] **09026 61778-2(02)**
J. Suk, Prague CO, L. Hlaváček (r1972) *Concert*
    (1/95) (RCA) ① **74321 21278-2**
I. Perlman, VPO, James Levine (r1982) *Concert*
    (1/95) (DG) ① [2] **445 535-2GMA2**
R. Pasquier, Liège PO, P. Bartholomée (r1994) *Sinfonia Concertante, K364.*
    (7/95) (AUVI) ① **V4712**
B. Belkin, Salzburg Chbr Sols (r1994) *Concert*
    (7/95) (DENO) ① **CO-78918**
W. Schneiderhan (vn/dir), BPO (r1967) *Beethoven: Violin Concerto.* (9/95) (DG) ① **447 403-2GOR**
J. Heifetz, LPO, J. Barbirolli (r1934) *Concert*
    (11/95) (PEAR) ① [2] **GEMMCDS9157**
Concerto for Violin, Keyboard and Orchestra in D, K Anh56/K315f (1778) (fragment only)
J-J. Kantorow, G. Wilson, Netherlands CO, L. Hager *Concert* (12/85) (DENO) ① **C37-7505**
H. Shelley, ASMF, I. Brown (vn/dir) (recons Wilby) *Concert* (6/91) (PHIL) ① [4] **422 508-2PME4**
Concerto for 2 Keyboards and Orchestra in E flat, K365/K316a (1779) (Keyboard Concerto No 10)
1. Allegro; 2. Andante; 3. Rondo (allegro).
K. Labèque, M. Labèque, BPO, S. Bychkov (1989) *3-Piano Concerto, K242.*
    (9/90) (PHIL) ① **426 241-2PH**
D. Barenboim, G. Solti (pf/dir), ECO *Concert*
    (11/90) (DECC) ① **430 232-2DH**
A. Brendel, I. Cooper, ASMF, N. Marriner (r1977) *Concert* (5/91) (PHIL) ① [12] **422 507-2PME12**
A. Schnabel, K.U. Schnabel, LSO, A. Boult (r1936) *Concert* (6/91) (EMI) ① [3] **CHS7 63703-2**
R. Casadesus, G. Casadesus, Philadelphia, E. Ormandy *Concert* (9/91) (SONY) ① **SM3K46519**
M. Perahia, R. Lupu, ECO *Concert*
    (10/91) (SONY) ① **SK44915**
Vladimir Ashkenazy, D. Barenboim (pf/dir), ECO *Concert* (2/93) (DECC) ① **425 044-2DM**
A. Previn (pf/dir), R. Lupu, LSO (r1975) *Piano Concerto 20.* (9/94) (EMI) ① **CDM5 65180-2**
Vladimir Ashkenazy, D. Barenboim (pf/dir), ECO (r1972) *Concert*
    (9/95) (LOND) ① [10] **443 727-2LC10**
Vladimir Ashkenazy (pf/dir), D. Barenboim, ECO (r1972) *Concert* ① **425 090-2DM**
A. de Larrocha, A. Previn (pf/dir), St Luke's Orch (r1993) *Piano Sonata, K448.*
    (9/95) (RCA) ① **09026 68044-2**
Concerto for 2 Keyboards and Orchestra in F, K242 (1776) (arr of 3-Keyboard Concerto, K242)
A. Brendel, I. Cooper, ASMF, N. Marriner (r1984) *Concert* (5/91) (PHIL) ① [12] **422 507-2PME12**
M. Perahia, R. Lupu, ECO *Concert*
    (10/91) (SONY) ① **SK44915**
Concerto for 3 Keyboards and Orchestra in F, K242 (1776) (Keyboard Concerto No 7)
K. Labèque, M. Labèque, S. Bychkov (pf/dir), BPO (1989) *2-Piano Concerto, K365.*
    (9/90) (PHIL) ① **426 241-2PH**
A. Schiff, D. Barenboim, G. Solti (pf/dir), ECO
    (11/90) (DECC) ① **430 232-2DH**
K. Labèque, M. Labèque, S. Bychkov (pf/dir), BPO (1989) *Concert*
    (5/91) (PHIL) ① [12] **422 507-2PME12**
Vladimir Ashkenazy, D. Barenboim (pf/dir), F. Ts'ong, ECO *Concert* (2/93) (DECC) ① **425 044-2DM**
Vladimir Ashkenazy, D. Barenboim (pf/dir), F. Ts'Ong, ECO (r1972) *Concert*
    (9/95) (LOND) ① [10] **443 727-2LC10**
Vladimir Ashkenazy, D. Barenboim, F. T'Song (pf/dir) (r1986) *Concert*
    (9/95) (DECC) ① **425 088-2DM**

Concertone in C—2 violins, oboe, cello and orchestra, K190/186E (1774)
N. Brainin, P. Schidlof, N. Black, O. Hegedus, ECO, A. Gibson (r1983) Sinfonia Concertante, K364.
(1/85) (CHAN) ① CHAN8315
I. Perlman, P. Zukerman, Israel PO, Z. Mehta Sinfonia Concertante, K364.
(12/85) (DG) ① 415 486-2GH
H. Szeryng, G. Poulet, New Philh, A. Gibson Concert
(6/91) (PHIL) ① [4] 422 508-2PME4
S. Accardo (vn/dir), M. Batjer, Prague CO Sinfonia Concertante, K364. (6/91) (NUOV) ① 6949
J-P. Rampal (fl/dir), S. Kudo, W. Schlachter, J. Schneider, Salzburg Mozarteum Orch (2 fls) Concert
(2/92) (SONY) ① SK45930
C-L. Lin, J. Laredo, ECO, R. Leppard Sinfonia concertante, K364. (6/92) (SONY) ① SK47693
B. Garlitski, Moscow Virtuosi, V. Spivakov (vn/dir) (r1990) Sinfonia Concertante, K364.
(10/93) (RCA) ① 09026 60467-2
3 Concertos for Keyboard and Strings, K107 (1772)
1. D (after J. C. Bach's Keyboard Sonata, Op. 5:2); 2. G (after J. C. Bach's Keyboard Sonata, Op. 5:3); 3. E flat (after J. C. Bach's Keyboard Sonata, Op. 5:4).
M. Perahia (pf/dir), ECO Schröter: Piano Concerto, Op. 3/3. (1/86) (SONY) ① SK39222
T. Koopman (hpd/dir), Amsterdam Baroque Orch, K. Labèque (r1989) Concert
(5/91) (PHIL) ① [12] 422 507-2PME12
London Baroque Concert
(11/92) (HARM) ① HMC90 1395
1. T. Pinnock (hpd/dir), English Concert Concert
(5/89) (CRD) ① CRD3311
Contredanse in B flat, K535b (1788) (cpted E. Smith)
ASMF, N. Marriner Concert
(12/91) (PHIL) ① [3] 422 545-2PME3
Contredanse in C, '(La) Bataille'—orchestra, K535 (1788)
Salzburg Mozarteum Orch, H. Graf Concert
(10/91) (CAPR) ① [3] 10 809
Contredanse in C, '(Der) Sieg des Helden Koburg'—orchestra, K587 (1789)
Orpheus CO Concert (4/91) (DG) ① 429 783-2GH
Salzburg Mozarteum Orch, H. Graf Concert
(10/91) (CAPR) ① [3] 10 809
Contredanse in D, K565a (cpted E. Smith)
ASMF, N. Marriner Concert
(12/91) (PHIL) ① [3] 422 545-2PME3
Contredanse in D, '(Das) Donnerwetter'—orchestra, K534 (1788)
Salzburg Mozarteum Orch, H. Graf Concert
(10/91) (CAPR) ① [3] 10 809
Contredanse in E flat, '(Il) trionfo delle dame'—orchestra, K607/605a (1791) (orig with German Dances, K606)
Orpheus CO Concert (4/91) (DG) ① 429 783-2GH
Contredanse in G, '(Les) filles malicieuses'—orchestra, K610 (1783)
Orpheus CO Concert (4/91) (DG) ① 429 783-2GH
6 Contredanses, K462/K448b (?1783)
1. C; 2. E flat; 3. B flat; 4. D; 5. B flat; 6. F.
Salzburg Mozarteum Orch, H. Graf Concert
(10/91) (CAPR) ① [3] 10 809
2 Contredanses—orchestra, K603 (1791)
1. D; 2. B flat.
Salzburg Mozarteum Orch, H. Graf Concert
(10/91) (CAPR) ① [3] 10 809
5 Contredanses, K609 (1787-88)
1. C (Non più andrai); 2. E flat; 3. D; 4. C; 5. G.
Salzburg Mozarteum Camerata Academica, S. Végh Concert (10/91) (CAPR) ① [3] 10 302
1, 3. VPO, C. Abbado (pp1991) Concert
(4/91) (DG) ① 431 628-2GH
Divertimenti for Strings, 'Salzburg Symphonies' (1772)
1. D, K136&K125a; 2. B flat, K137&K125b; 3. F, K138&K125c.
Slovak PO, L. Pešek (9/88) (CAVA) ① CAVCD020
Amadeus Qt
(1/89) (DG) ① [6] 423 300-2GCM6
Amsterdam Baroque Orch, T. Koopman Divertimento, K251.
(12/90) (ERAT) ① 2292-45471-2
ASMF Chbr Ens Concert
(12/90) (PHIL) ① [5] 422 504-2PME5
Hagen Qt Concert
(6/91) (DG) ① [3] 431 645-2GH3
Mirring Qt Concert (10/91) (CAPR) ① [3] 10 801
Eder Qt (r1991) String Quartet, K465.
(9/93) (NAXO) ① 8 550543
Sinfonia Varsovia, E. Krivine (r1990) Concert
(3/95) (DENO) ① CO-75597
Hagen Qt (r1990) Serenade, K525.
(4/95) (DG) ① 439 940-2GH

1. COE, J. Judd Concert (8/85) (CARL) ① PCD805
1. Orpheus CO Concert
(12/86) (DG) ① 419 192-2GH
1. Norwegian CO, I. Brown Concert
(1/89) (SIMA) ① PSC1035
1. Aeolian Qt Clarinet Quintet, K581.
(3/94) (SAGA) ① EC3387-2
1. Saito Kinen Orch, S. Ozawa (r1992) Concert
(9/94) (PHIL) ① 438 137-2PH
1. Lausanne CO, Y. Menuhin (r1989) Concert
(10/95) (VIRG) ① CUV5 61204-2
1, 2. Salzburg Mozarteum Camerata Academica, S. Végh Concert (11/87) (CAPR) ① 10 185
3. Salzburg Mozarteum Camerata Academica, S. Végh Concert (6/87) (CAPR) ① 10 153
3. Polish CO, J. Stanienda (vn/dir) (pp1990) Concert
(12/91) (LINN) ① CKD001
Divertimento in E flat—two oboes, two horns and two bassoons, K289/271g (1777)
Octophoros Concert (11/89) (ACCE) ① ACC8856D
Divertimento No. 1 in E flat—wind and strings, K113 (1771)
ASMF Chbr Ens Concert
(12/90) (PHIL) ① [5] 422 504-2PME5
Salzburg Camerata Academica, S. Végh Concert
(10/91) (CAPR) ① [3] 10 801
Divertimento No. 2 in D—flute, oboe, bassoon, 4 horns and strings, K131 (1772)
ASMF, N. Marriner Concert
(12/90) (PHIL) ① [7] 422 503-2PME7
Salzburg Camerata Academica, S. Végh Concert
(10/91) (CAPR) ① [3] 10 801
Capella Istropolitana, H. Nerat (r1994) Divertimento, K287. (6/95) (NAXO) ① 8 550996
Divertimento No. 5—2 flutes, 5 trumpets and timpani, K187/C17.12 (c1773) (arr L. Mozart from dances by Starzer & Gluck)
J. Wallace, Philh, S. Wright Concert
(4/89) (NIMB) ① NI5121
Divertimento No. 6 in C—2 flutes, 5 trumpets and timpani, K188/K240b (1773)
J. Wallace, Philh, S. Wright Concert
(4/89) (NIMB) ① NI5121
Divertimento No. 7 in D—2 horns, bassoon and strings, K205/167A (?1773)
Salzburg Mozarteum Camerata Academica, S. Végh Divertimento, K287. (11/89) (CAPR) ① 10 271
ASMF Chbr Ens Concert
(12/90) (PHIL) ① [5] 422 504-2PME5
Salzburg Camerata Academica, S. Végh Concert
(10/91) (CAPR) ① [3] 10 801
Salzburg Chbr Sols (r1994) Concert
(7/95) (DENO) ① CO-78918
Divertimento No. 8 in F—2 oboes, 2 bassoons and 2 horns, K213 (1775)
Berlin Phil Wind Qnt Concert
(12/87) (ORFE) ① C152861A
Octophoros Concert (11/89) (ACCE) ① ACC8856D
SNO Wind Ens, P. Järvi Serenade, K361.
(11/93) (CHAN) ① CHAN6575
Divertimento No. 9 in B flat—2 oboes, 2 bassoons and 2 horns, K240 (1776)
Berlin Phil Wind Qnt Concert
(12/87) (ORFE) ① C152861A
Octophoros Concert (11/89) (ACCE) ① ACC8856D
Divertimento No. 10 in F—two horns and strings, K247 (1776)
Salzburg Mozarteum Camerata Academica, S. Végh Divertimento, K251. (1/89) (CAPR) ① 10 203
Berne Camerata (r1988) Divertimento, K247.
(3/90) (NOVA) ① 150 040-2
ASMF Chbr Ens Concert
(12/90) (PHIL) ① [5] 422 504-2PME5
Salzburg Mozarteum Camerata Academica, S. Végh Concert (10/91) (CAPR) ① [3] 10 801
Divertimento No. 11 in D—oboe, two horns and strings, K251 (1776)
Salzburg Mozarteum Camerata Academica, S. Végh Divertimento, K247. (1/89) (CAPR) ① 10 203
R. Canter, A. Halstead, R. Diaz, London Baroque Concert (6/89) (AMON) ① CD-SAR34
VCM, N. Harnoncourt (orig. instr.) Concert
(6/90) (TELD) ① 2292-44809-2
Amsterdam Baroque Orch, T. Koopman Divertimenti, K136-8. (12/90) (ERAT) ① 2292-45471-2
ASMF Chbr Ens Concert
(12/90) (PHIL) ① [5] 422 504-2PME5
Amadeus Ens Concert
(9/91) (UNIC) ① DKPCD9107
Salzburg Mozarteum Camerata Academica, S. Végh Concert (10/91) (CAPR) ① [3] 10 801
Vienna-Berlin Ens Concert
(3/93) (DG) ① 431 782-2GH
BPO, C. Abbado (r1992) Concert
(3/94) (SONY) ① SK53277

Divertimento No. 12 in E flat—two oboes, two bassoons and two horns, K252/K240a (1776)
Orpheus CO Concert (12/86) (DG) ① 419 192-2GH
Berlin Phil Wind Qnt Concert
(12/87) (ORFE) ① C152861A
Octophoros Concert (11/89) (ACCE) ① ACC8856D
Linos Ens (r1993) Serenade, K361.
(7/95) (CAPR) ① 10 472
Divertimento No. 14 in B flat—two oboes, two bassoons and two horns, K270 (1777)
1. Allegro molto; 2. Andantino; 3. Menuetto; 4. Presto.
Berlin Phil Wind Qnt Concert
(12/87) (ORFE) ① C152861A
Octophoros Concert (11/89) (ACCE) ① ACC8856D
Divertimento No. 15 in B flat—two horns and strings, K287/K271H (1777)
EXCERPTS: 1. Allegro; 2. Adagio; 3. Menuetto; 4. Adagio.
Salzburg Mozarteum Camerata Academica, S. Végh Divertimento, K205. (11/89) (CAPR) ① 10 271
Berne Camerata (r1988) Divertimento, K247.
(3/90) (NOVA) ① 150 040-2
ASMF Chbr Ens Concert
(12/90) (PHIL) ① [5] 422 504-2PME5
J. Szigeti, Orch, M. Goberman (r1938) Concert
(11/92) (BIDD) ① LAB064
Capella Istropolitana, H. Nerat (r1994) Divertimento, K131. (6/95) (NAXO) ① 8 550996
Divertimento No. 17 in D—two horns and strings, K334/K320b (1779-80)
1. Allegro; 2. Tema con variazioni (Andante); 3. Menuetto I; 4. Adagio; 5. Menuetto II; 6. Rondo (Allegro).
Salzburg Mozarteum Camerata Academica, S. Végh Divertimenti, K136-8. (6/87) (CAPR) ① 10 153
ASMF Chbr Ens Concert
(12/90) (PHIL) ① [5] 422 504-2PME5
J-P. Rampal, A. Cazalet, J-M. Vinit, R. Pasquier, B. Pasquier, R. Pidoux Concert
(11/91) (SONY) ① SK47230
3. J. Galway (fl/dir), COE (arr Galway) Concert
(7/89) (RCA) ① [2] RD87861
3. J. Heifetz, E. Bay (r1947) Concert
(11/94) (RCA) ① [65] 09026 61778-2(06)
3. J. Heifetz, S. Chotzinoff (r1919) Concert
(11/94) (RCA) ① [65] 09026 61778-2(01)
Fragment for Horn and Orchestra in E flat (Concerto Movement), K370b
S. Weigle, Dresden PO, J-P. Weigle (ed H. Jeurissen) Concert (11/91) (DG) ① [3] 10 805
6 German Dances, K509 (1787)
1. D; 2. G; 3. E flat; 4. F; 5. A flat.
Salzburg Mozarteum Orch, H. Graf Concert
(10/91) (CAPR) ① [3] 10 809
Tafelmusik, B. Weil Concert
(5/92) (SONY) ① SK46696
6 German Dances, K536 (1788)
1. C; 2. G; 3. B flat; 4. D; 5. F; 6. F.
Tafelmusik, B. Weil Concert
(5/92) (SONY) ① SK46696
6 German Dances, K567 (1788)
1. B flat; 2. E flat; 3. G; 4. D; 5. A; 6. C.
Orpheus CO Concert (4/91) (DG) ① 429 783-2GH
Tafelmusik, B. Weil Concert
(5/92) (SONY) ① SK46696
6 German Dances, K571 (1789)
1. D; 2. A; 3. C; 4. G; 5. B flat; 6. D.
Tafelmusik, B. Weil Concert
(5/92) (SONY) ① SK46696
12 German Dances, K586 (1789)
1. C; 2. G; 3. B flat; 4. F; 5. A; 6. D; 7. G; 8. E flat; 9. B flat; 10. F; 11. A; 12. C.
Tafelmusik, B. Weil Concert
(5/92) (SONY) ① SK46696
6 German Dances, K600 (1791)
1. C; 2. F; 3. B flat; 4. F flat; 5. G; 6. D.
N. German RSO, G. Wand Serenade, K250.
(1/91) (RCA) ① RD60068
Salzburg Mozarteum Orch, H. Graf Concert
(10/91) (CAPR) ① [3] 10 809
4 German Dances, K602 (1791)
1. B flat; 2. F; 3. C (Die Leyerer); 4. A.
3. Orpheus CO Concert
(4/91) (DG) ① 429 783-2GH
3 German Dances, K605 (1791)
1. D; 2. G; 3. C (Die Schlittenfahrt).
Orpheus CO Concert (4/91) (DG) ① 429 783-2GH
Salzburg Mozarteum Orch, H. Graf Concert
(10/91) (CAPR) ① [3] 10 809
VPO, B. Walter (r1937) Concert
(3/94) (PEAR) ① GEMMCD9940
3. VPO, C. Abbado (pp1991) Concert
(4/91) (DG) ① 431 628-2GH

March in C, K214 (1775)
Salzburg Mozarteum Orch, H. Graf *Concert*
(11/89) (CAPR) ① **10 253**
Salzburg Mozarteum Orch, H. Graf *Concert*
(10/91) (CAPR) ① [3] **10 809**
March in D, K62 (1769)
Salzburg Mozarteum Orch, H. Graf *Concert*
(11/89) (CAPR) ① **10 253**
ASMF, N. Marriner *Concert*
(12/90) (PHIL) ① [7] **422 503-2PME7**
Salzburg Mozarteum Orch, H. Graf *Concert*
(10/91) (CAPR) ① [3] **10 809**
March in D, K189/K167b (1773)
Salzburg Mozarteum Orch, H. Graf *Concert*
(11/89) (CAPR) ① **10 253**
ASMF, N. Marriner *Concert*
(12/90) (PHIL) ① [7] **422 503-2PME7**
Salzburg Mozarteum Camerata Academica, S. Végh
Concert (10/91) (CAPR) ① **10 302**
Salzburg Mozarteum Orch, H. Graf *Concert*
(10/91) (CAPR) ① [3] **10 809**
March in D, K215/K213b (1775)
Salzburg Mozarteum Orch, H. Graf *Concert*
(11/89) (CAPR) ① **10 253**
ASMF, N. Marriner *Concert*
(12/90) (PHIL) ① [7] **422 503-2PME7**
Salzburg Mozarteum Orch, H. Graf *Concert*
(10/91) (CAPR) ① [3] **10 809**
VCM, N. Harnoncourt *Concert*
(5/92) (TELD) ① **9031-72289-2**
March in D, K237/189c (1774)
ASMF, N. Marriner *Concert*
(12/90) (PHIL) ① [7] **422 503-2PME7**
Salzburg Mozarteum Orch, H. Graf *Concert*
(10/91) (CAPR) ① [3] **10 809**
VCM, N. Harnoncourt (r1992) *Concert*
(10/94) (TELD) ① **4509-90842-2**
March in D, K249 (1776)
Salzburg Mozarteum Orch, H. Graf *Concert*
(11/89) (CAPR) ① **10 253**
Amsterdam Baroque Orch, T. Koopman (r1988)
Serenade, K250. (2/90) (ERAT) ① **2292-45436-2**
ASMF, N. Marriner *Concert*
(12/90) (PHIL) ① [7] **422 503-2PME7**
Salzburg Mozarteum Orch, H. Graf *Concert*
(10/91) (CAPR) ① [3] **10 809**
March in D, K290/K167AB (1772)
ASMF Chbr Ens *Concert*
(12/90) (PHIL) ① [5] **422 504-2PME5**
Archibudelli *Concert* (12/91) (SONY) ① **SK46702**
March in D, K445/K320c (1780)
Salzburg Mozarteum Orch, H. Graf *Concert*
(11/89) (CAPR) ① **10 253**
ASMF Chbr Ens *Concert*
(12/90) (PHIL) ① [5] **422 504-2PME5**
Salzburg Mozarteum Orch, H. Graf *Concert*
(10/91) (CAPR) ① [3] **10 809**
Archibudelli *Concert* (12/91) (SONY) ① **SK46702**
March in F, K248 (1776)
Salzburg Mozarteum Orch, H. Graf *Concert*
(11/89) (CAPR) ① **10 253**
ASMF Chbr Ens *Concert*
(12/90) (PHIL) ① [5] **422 504-2PME5**
Salzburg Mozarteum Orch, H. Graf *Concert*
(10/91) (CAPR) ① [3] **10 809**
Archibudelli *Concert* (12/91) (SONY) ① **SK46702**
March to 'Die Entführung aus dem Serail', Kdeest
ASMF *Concert*
(12/91) (PHIL) ① [3] **422 545-2PME3**
2 Marches, K335/K320a (1779)
1. D; 2. D.
Salzburg Mozarteum Orch, H. Graf *Concert*
(11/89) (CAPR) ① **10 253**
ASMF, N. Marriner *Concert*
(12/90) (PHIL) ① [7] **422 503-2PME7**
Orpheus CO *Concert* (4/91) (DG) ① **429 783-2GH**
Salzburg Mozarteum Orch, H. Graf *Concert*
(10/91) (CAPR) ① [3] **10 809**
BPO, C. Abbado (r1992) *Concert*
(3/94) (SONY) ① **SK53277**
3 Marches (1782)
1. C, K408:1/K383e; 2. D, K408:2/K385a; 3. C,
K408:3/K383F.
Salzburg Mozarteum Orch, H. Graf *Concert*
(11/89) (CAPR) ① **10 253**
Salzburg Mozarteum Orch, H. Graf *Concert*
(10/91) (CAPR) ① [3] **10 809**
Maurerische Trauermusik in C minor, 'Masonic Funeral Music', K477/K479a (1785)
Bamberg SO, E. Jochum *Symphony 41*.
(9/86) (ORFE) ① **C045902A**
LSO, I. Kertész *Concert*
(11/90) (DECC) ① **425 722-2DM**

LSO, I. Kertész *Concert*
(6/91) (DECC) ① **430 498-2DWO**
LMP, J. Glover *Requiem*.
. (12/91) (ASV) ① **CDDCA757**
Staatskapelle Dresden, P. Schreier *Concert*
(4/92) (PHIL) ① [6] **422 522-2PME6**
Concert des Nations, J. Savall *Requiem*.
(11/92) (ASTR) ① **E8759**
LCP, R. Norrington *Concert*
(11/92) (EMI) ① **CDC7 54525-2**
Vienna Academy Orch, M. Haselböck (r1991)
Concert (10/93) (NOVA) ① **150 081-2**
BPO, C. Abbado (r1992) *Concert*
(5/95) (SONY) ① **SK48385**
Minuet in A, K61g/1 (1770) (doubtful)
ASMF, N. Marriner *Concert*
(12/90) (PHIL) ① [6] **422 501-2PME6**
Minuet in C, K409/K383f (1782) (? for Symphony 34, K338)
ASMF, N. Marriner *Concert*
(12/90) (PHIL) ① [6] **422 502-2PME6**
5 Minuets, K461/K448a (1784)
1. C; 2. E flat; 3. G; 4. B flat; 5. F.
Salzburg Mozarteum Orch, H. Graf *Concert*
(10/91) (CAPR) ① [3] **10 809**
2 Minuets with Contredanses, K463/K448c (1783)
1. F; 2. B flat.
Salzburg Mozarteum Orch, H. Graf *Concert*
(10/91) (CAPR) ① [3] **10 809**
Ein Musikalischer Spass, '(A) Musical Joke'—two horns and strings, K522 (1787)
VCM, N. Harnoncourt (orig. instr.) *Concert*
(6/90) (TELD) ① **2292-44809-2**
ASMF Chbr Ens *Concert*
(12/90) (PHIL) ① [5] **422 504-2PME5**
Orpheus CO *Concert* (4/91) (DG) ① **429 783-2GH**
Archibudelli *Concert* (12/91) (SONY) ① **SK46702**
Philh, G. Cantelli (r1955) *Concert*
(11/94) (EMI) ① [2] **CZS5 68217-2**
Movt 4. Vienna Mozart Ens, W. Boskovsky *Concert*
(6/91) (DECC) ① **430 498-2DWO**
Notturno in D—4 groups each of 2 horns and strings, K286/269a (1776-77)
ASMF, N. Marriner *Concert*
(12/90) (PHIL) ① [7] **422 503-2PME7**
Salzburg Mozarteum Camerata Academica, S. Végh
Concert (10/91) (CAPR) ① **10 302**
VCM, N. Harnoncourt *Concert*
(12/92) (TELD) ① **9031-77603-2**
Rondo for Flute and Orchestra in D, KAnh184 (?spurious)
M. Helasvuo, Ostrobothnian CO, J. Kangas *Concert*
(4/89) (BIS) ① **BIS-CD368**
S. Milan, ECO, R. Leppard *Concert*
(4/89) (CHAN) ① **CHAN8613**
Rondo for Horn and Orchestra in D, K514 (?1792) (incompl movt originally intended for K412)
L. Greer, Philh Baroque Orch, N. McGegan *Concert*
(3/89) (HARM) ① **HMU90 7012**
A. Halstead, AAM, C. Hogwood (r1993) *Concert*
(8/95) (L'OI) ① [2] **443 216-2OH**
Rondo for Horn and Orchestra in E flat, 'Concert Rondo', K371 (1781) (incomplete)
Z. Tylšar, Prague CO (r1982) *Horn Concerti*.
(6/86) (DENO) ① **C37-7432**
R. Watkins, CLS, R. Hickox (cpted Süssmayr) *Horn Concerti*.
(12/87) (CARL) ① **PCD865**
B. Tuckwell, ASMF, N. Marriner (cpted Tuckwell)
Concert (1/89) (EMI) ① **CDM7 69569-2**
L. Greer, Philh Baroque Orch, N. McGegan *Concert*
(3/89) (HARM) ① **HMU90 7012**
J. Williams, COE, A. Schneider (pp1988) *Concert*
(4/89) (ASV) ① **CDCOE810**
T. Brown, OAE, S. Kuijken *Concert*
(8/90) (VIRG) ① **VC7 59558-2**
P. Damm, ASMF, N. Marriner *Concert*
(7/91) (PHIL) ① [5] **422 509-2PME5**
S. Weigle, Dresden PO, J-P. Weigle (ed P. Damm)
Concert (11/91) (CAPR) ① [3] **10 805**
T. Brown, ASMF, K. Sillito (compl & orch: E. Smith)
Concert (12/91) (PHIL) ① [3] **422 545-2PME3**
A. Koster, Tafelmusik, B. Weil (r1993: arr R Levin)
Horn Concerti. (2/94) (SONY) ① **SK53369**
R. Vlatkovič, ECO, J. Tate (r1985: arr Tuckwell)
Concert (10/94) (EMI) ① **CDM7 64851-2**
E. Ruske, Scottish CO, C. Mackerras (r1993: ed J
Humphries) *Concert* (10/94) (TELA) ① **CD80367**
A. Civil, ASMF, N. Marriner (r1972; completed A.
Civil) *Horn Concerti*.
(12/94) (PHIL) ① **442 397-2PM**
A. Halstead, AAM, C. Hogwood (r1993) *Concert*
(8/95) (L'OI) ① **443 216-2OH**

Rondo for Keyboard and Orchestra in A, K386 (1782)
M. Perahia (pf/dir), ECO *Concert*
(11/85) (SONY) ① **SK39224**
A. Brendel, ASMF, N. Marriner (r1975) *Concert*
(5/91) (PHIL) ① [12] **422 507-2PME12**
J. O'Conor, Scottish CO, C. Mackerras (arr
Mackerras/Badura-Skoda) *Concert*
(11/91) (TELA) ① **CD80285**
Vladimir Ashkenazy, LSO, I. Kertész *Concert*
(2/93) (DECC) ① **425 044-2DM**
A. Schiff, Salzburg Mozarteum Camerata Academica,
S. Végh *Concert* (5/93) (DECC) ① **433 042-2DH**
A. Brendel, ASMF, N. Marriner (r1975; completed E.
Smith & A. Brendel) *Concert*
(10/94) (PHIL) ① [2] **442 269-2PM2**
Vladimir Ashkenazy, LSO, I. Kertész (r1966: ed C
Mackerras & P Badura-Skoda) *Concert*
(5/95) (DECC) ① **433 576-2DCS**
Vladimir Ashkenazy, LSO, I. Kertész (r1966) *Concert*
(9/95) (LOND) ① [10] **443 727-2LC10**
Vladimir Ashkenazy, LSO, I. Kertész (r1966; ed
Mackerras & Badura-Skoda) *Concert*
(9/95) (DECC) ① **425 097-2DM**
R. Levin, AAM, C. Hogwood (r1994) *Concert*
(9/95) (L'OI) ① **444 571-2OH**
C. Haskil, Vienna SO, B. Paumgartner (r1954)
Concert (11/95) (PHIL) ① [12] **442 685-2PM12**
C. Haskil, Vienna SO, B. Paumgartner (r1954)
Concert (11/95) (PHIL) ① [4] **442 631-2PM4**
Rondo for Keyboard and Orchestra in D, K382 (1782)
M. Perahia (pf/dir), ECO *Concert*
(11/85) (SONY) ① **SK39224**
D. Barenboim (pf/dir), ECO (r1971) *Concert*
(6/90) (EMI) ① [10] **CZS7 62825-2**
A. Brendel, ASMF, N. Marriner (r1975) *Concert*
(5/91) (PHIL) ① [12] **422 507-2PME12**
Anima Eterna, J. Van Immerseel (fp/dir) *Concert*
(10/92) (CHNN) ① **CCS0690**
J. Van Immerseel (fp/dir), Anima Eterna *Concert*
(10/92) (CHNN) ① [10] **CCSBOX10**
Vladimir Ashkenazy (pf/dir), Philh *Concert*
(2/93) (DECC) ① **425 044-2DM**
E. Kissin, Moscow Virtuosi, V. Spivakov *Concert*
(2/93) (RCA) ① **09026 60400-2**
A. Brendel, ASMF, N. Marriner (r1975) *Concert*
(10/94) (PHIL) ① [2] **442 269-2PM2**
S. Vladar, ASMF, N. Marriner (r1993) *Concert*
(3/95) (SONY) ① **SMK64251**
D. Barenboim (pf/dir), BPO (r1994) *Concert*
(4/95) (PHIL) ① [4] **4509-90674-2**
Vladimir Ashkenazy (pf/dir), Philh (r1980) *Concert*
(9/95) (LOND) ① [10] **443 727-2LC10**
Vladimir Ashkenazy (pf/dir), Philh (r1980) *Concert*
(9/95) (DECC) ① **425 096-2DM**
M. Bilson, EBS, J. E. Gardiner (r1986) *Concert*
(12/95) (ARCH) ① **447 291-2AMA**
Rondo for Violin and Orchestra in B flat, K269/K261a (1775-77)
J-J. Kantorow, Netherlands CO, L. Hager *Concert*
(12/86) (DENO) ① **C37-7506**
F. Gulli, Venice and Padua CO, B. Giuranna *Concert*
(3/91) (CLAV) ① [2] **CD50-8913/4**
T. Nishizaki, Capella Istropolitana, J. Wildner *Concert*
(4/91) (NAXO) ① **8 550414**
H. Szeryng, New Philh, A. Gibson *Concert*
(6/91) (PHIL) ① [4] **422 508-2PME4**
S. Standage, AAM, C. Hogwood *Concert*
(4/92) (L'OI) ① [2] **433 045-2OH2**
D. Oistrakh (vn/dir), BPO (r1971) *Concert*
(3/94) (EMI) ① **CDM7 64868-2**
M. Fujikawa, RPO, W. Weller (r1980) *Concert*
(5/94) (DECC) ① [2] **440 621-2DF2**
J. Suk, Prague CO, L. Hlaváček (r1972) *Concert*
(1/95) (RCA) ① **74321 21278-2**
I. Perlman, VPO, James Levine (r1985) *Concert*
(1/95) (DG) ① [2] **445 535-2GMA2**
M. Huggett (vn/dir), OAE *Concert*
(3/95) (VIRG) ① **VC5 45060-2**
Rondo for Violin and Orchestra in C, K373 (1781)
J-J. Kantorow, V. Mendelssohn, M. Fujiwara, G.
Wilson, Netherlands CO, L. Hager *Concert*
(12/85) (DENO) ① **C37-7505**
P-L. Graf, ECO, R. Leppard *Concert*
(9/86) (CLAV) ① **CD50-8505**
A. Dumay, Warsaw Sinfonia, E. Krivine *Concert*
(3/89) (EMI) ① **CDC7 49160-2**
J. Galway (fl/dir), COE (arr Galway) *Concert*
(7/89) (RCA) ① [2] **RD87861**
F. Gulli, Venice and Padua CO, B. Giuranna *Concert*
(3/91) (CLAV) ① [2] **CD50-8913/4**
A. Grumiaux, New Philh, R. Leppard *Concert*
(4/91) (PHIL) ① **426 977-2PCC**

H. Szeryng, New Philh, A. Gibson *Concert*
        (6/91) (PHIL) ① [4] 422 508-2PME4
S. Standage, AAM, C. Hogwood *Concert*
        (4/92) (L'OI) ① [2] 433 045-2OH2
J. Bell, ECO, P. Maag *Concert*
        (3/93) (DECC) ① 436 376-2DH
A. Grumiaux, New Philh, R. Leppard (r1960s)
Concert   (9/93) (PHIL) ① [2] 438 323-2PM2
D. Oistrakh (vn/dir), BPO (r1971) *Concert*
        (3/94) (EMI) ① CDM7 64868-2
M. Fujikawa, RPO, W. Weller (r1980) *Concert*
        (5/94) (DECC) ① [2] 440 621-2DF2
J. Suk, Prague CO, L. Hlaváček (r1972) *Concert*
        (1/95) (RCA) ① 74321 21277-2
I. Perlman, VPO, James Levine (r1985) *Concert*
        (1/95) (DG) ① [2] 445 535-2GMA2

Serenade No. 3 in D, K185/K167a (1773)
ASMF, N. Marriner *Concert*
        (12/90) (PHIL) ① [7] 422 503-2PME7
Salzburg Mozarteum Camerata Academica, S. Végh
Concert   (10/91) (CAPR) ① 10 302
J-J. Kantorow, Auvergne Orch, L. Hager *Serenade*,
K204.   (10/91) (DENO) ① CO-76530

**Serenade No. 4 in D—violin and orchestra,
K203/K189b (1774)**
J-J. Kantorow, Auvergne Orch, L. Hager *Cassation*,
K63.   (10/90) (DENO) ① CO-73676
I. Brown, ASMF, N. Marriner *Concert*
        (12/90) (PHIL) ① [7] 422 503-2PME7
VCM, N. Harnoncourt (r1992) *Concert*
        (10/94) (TELD) ① 4509-90842-2

**Serenade No. 5 in D—violin and orchestra,
K204/K213a (1775)**
K. Sillito, ASMF, N. Marriner *Concert*
        (12/90) (PHIL) ① [7] 422 503-2PME7
J-J. Kantorow, Auvergne Orch, L. Hager *Serenade*,
K185.   (10/91) (DENO) ① CO-76530
VCM, N. Harnoncourt *Concert*
        (5/92) (TELD) ① 9031-72289-2

**Serenade No. 6 in D, 'Serenata notturna',
K239 (1776)**
Soloists of Australia, R.Thomas (vn/dir) *Concert*
        (4/87) (CHAN) ① CHAN8498
Salzburg Mozarteum Camerata Academica, S. Végh
Concert   (11/87) (CAPR) ① 10 185
BRSO, Colin Davis *Serenade*, K320.
        (11/87) (NOVA) ① 150 013-2
Serenata of London *Concert*
        (11/87) (CARL) ① PCD861
Prague CO, C. Mackerras (r1987) *Serenade*, K250.
        (11/88) (TELA) ① CD80161
ASMF, N. Marriner *Concert*
        (12/90) (PHIL) ① [7] 422 503-2PME7
Berlin CO, P. Wohlert *Concert*
        (10/91) (CAPR) ① . [3] 10 801
Czech PO, H. Scherchen (pp1951) *Concert*
        (1/92) (MULT) ① 310077-2
VCM, N. Harnoncourt *Concert*
        (12/92) (TELD) ① 9031-77603-2
Vienna Mozart Ens, W. Boskovsky (r1978) *Concert*
        (9/95) (DECC) ① [2] 443 458-2DF2
ECO, B. Britten (r1968) *Concert*
        (9/95) (DECC) ① [2] 444 323-2DF2
Lausanne CO, Y. Menuhin (r1989) *Concert*
        (10/95) (VIRG) ① CUV5 61204-2
Movts 2, 3. Cologne CO, H. Abendroth (r1933)
Concert   (9/94) (TAHR) ① [2] TAH102

**Serenade No. 7 in D, 'Haffner'—violin and
orchestra, K250/K248b (1776)**
1. Allegro maestoso—Allegro molto; 2. Andante; 3.
Menuetto; 4. Rondo (Allegro); 5. Menuetto galante; 6.
Andante; 7. Menuetto; 8. Adagio—Allegro assai.
J. Suk, Prague CO, L. Hlaváček
        (12/87) (SUPR) ① 2SUP0006
O. Vlček, Prague CO, C. Mackerras (r1987)
Serenade, K239.   (11/88) (TELA) ① CD80161
BRSO, Colin Davis (1988) *Symphony 32.*
        (11/88) (NOVA) ① 150 027-2
Amsterdam Baroque Orch, T. Koopman *March*,
K249.   (2/90) (ERAT) ① 2292-45436-2
J-J. Kantorow, Auvergne Orch, L. Hager (1988)
        (10/90) (DENO) ① CO-73870
I. Brown, ASMF, N. Marriner *Concert*
        (12/90) (PHIL) ① [7] 422 503-2PME7
R. Greutter, N. German RSO, G. Wand *German
Dances*, K600.   (1/91) (RCA) ① RD60068
Vienna Mozart Ens, W. Boskovsky (r1972) *Concert*
        (9/95) (DECC) ① [2] 443 458-2DF2
*4. J. Thibaud, T. Janopoulo (r1936: arr vn/pf:
Kreisler) Concert*   (10/91) (MSCM) ① MM30321
4. J. Heifetz, B. Smith (r1970) Concert
        (11/94) (RCA) ① [65] 09026 61778-2(28)
4. J. Heifetz, S. Chotzinoff (r1920) Concert
        (11/94) (RCA) ① [65] 09026 61778-2(01)
*4. J. Thibaud, T. Janopoulo (r1936: arr vn/pf:
Kreisler) Concert*   (12/94) (APR) ① APR7028

**Serenade No. 9 in D, 'Posthorn', K320
(1779)**
Z. Tylšar, Prague CO, C. Mackerras (r1984)
Serenade, K525.   (8/85) (TELA) ① CD80108
BPO, K. Böhm *Serenade*, K525.
        (8/87) (DG) ① 415 843-2GGA
BRSO, Colin Davis *Serenade*, K239.
        (11/87) (NOVA) ① 150 013-2
ASMF, N. Marriner *Concert*
        (12/90) (PHIL) ① [7] 422 503-2PME7
BPO, C. Abbado (pp1992) *Concert*
        (3/94) (SONY) ① SK53277
BRSO, Colin Davis (pp1992) *Bassoon Concerto*,
K191.   (9/94) (RCA) ① 09026 61927-2
Vienna Mozart Ens, W. Boskovsky (r1973) *Concert*
        (9/95) (DECC) ① [2] 443 458-2DF2

**Serenade No. 10 in B flat, 'Gran Partita'—13
wind instruments, K361/K370a (1781-84)**
EXCERPTS: 1. Largo—Molto allegro; 2. Menuetto;
3. Adagio; 4. Menuetto; 5.
Adagio—Allegretto—Adagio; 6. Tema con variazioni;
7. Molto allegro.
COE, A. Schneider   (4/87) (ASV) ① CDCOE804
ASMF, N. Marriner   (5/87) (PHIL) ① 412 726-2PH
Octophoros, Barthold Kuijken
        (9/87) (ACCE) ① ACC68642D
Albion Ens   (3/89) (HYPE) ① CDA66285
London Wind Qnt and Ens, O. Klemperer *Serenade*,
K375.   (4/90) (EMI) ① CDM7 63349-2
Amadeus Wind Ens   (10/90) (NAXO) ① 8 550060
Collegium Aureum   (7/91) (DHM) ① VD77540
ECO, D. Barenboim *Concert*
        (10/91) (EMI) ① [2] CZS7 67306-2
SNO Wind Ens, P. Järvi *Divertimento*, K213.
        (11/93) (CHAN) ① CHAN6575
Budapest Wind Ens, Z. Kocsis (r c1992) *Serenade*,
K388.   (8/94) (HARM) ① HMA190 3051
St Luke's Orch, C. Mackerras (r1993)
        (8/94) (TELA) ① CD80359
Linos Ens (r1993) *Divertimento*, K252.
        (7/95) (CAPR) ① 10 472
BPO, Z. Mehta (r1993)   (9/95) (SONY) ① SK58950
1, 5-7. Czech PO, V. Talich (pp1954) *Concert*
        (1/92) (MULT) ① 310078-2
5, 6. Czech PO, H. Scherchen (pp1951) *Concert*
        (1/92) (MULT) ① 310077-2

**Serenade No. 11 in E flat—two oboes, two
clarinets, two bassoons & two horns, K375
(1781)**
1. Allegro maestoso; 2. Menuetto I; 3. Adagio; 4.
Menuetto II; 5. Allegro.
Albion Ens *Serenade*, K388.
        (6/86) (MERI) ① CDE84107
COE, A. Schneider *Serenade*, K388.
        (5/88) (ASV) ① CDCOE802
New Philh Wind Ens, O. Klemperer *Serenade*, K361.
        (4/90) (EMI) ① CDM7 63349-2
Orpheus CO *Serenade*, K388.
        (9/91) (DG) ① 431 683-2GH
Moragües Qnt (r1992: arr qnt: David Walter) *Concert*
        (11/93) (AUVI) ① V4684
Vienna Wind Sols (r1992) *Concert*
        (3/95) (DECC) ① 436 654-2DH
Netherlands Wind Ens (r1993) *Concert*
        (5/95) (CHAN) ① CHAN9284
Mozzafiato, C. Neidich (cl/dir) (r1994: orig sextet
vers) *Concert*   (9/95) (SONY) ① SK64306

**Serenade No. 12 in C minor—two oboes, two
clarinets, two bassoons & two horns,
K388/K384a (1782 or 1783)**
1. Allegro; 2. Andante; 3. Menuetto in canone; 4.
Allegro.
Albion Ens *Serenade*, K375.
        (6/86) (MERI) ① CDE84107
COE, A. Schneider *Serenade*, K375.
        (5/88) (ASV) ① CDCOE802
Norwegian Wind Ens *Serenade*, K375.
        (7/89) (SIMA) ① PSC1037
Orpheus CO *Serenade*, K375.
        (9/91) (DG) ① 431 683-2GH
Moragües Qnt (r1992: arr qnt: David Walter) *Concert*
        (11/93) (AUVI) ① V4684
Budapest Wind Ens, Z. Kocsis (r c1992) *Serenade*,
K361.   (8/94) (HARM) ① HMA190 3051
Vienna Wind Sols (r1992) *Concert*
        (3/95) (DECC) ① 436 654-2DH
Netherlands Wind Ens (r1993) *Concert*
        (5/95) (CHAN) ① CHAN9284

**Serenade No. 13 in G, 'Eine kleine
Nachtmusik'—string orchestra, K525 (1787)**
(A Little Night Music)
EXCERPTS: 1. Allegro; 2. Andante; 3. Menuetto; 4.
Allegro.
I Musici *Concert*   (12/83) (PHIL) ① 410 606-2PH
Prague CO, C. Mackerras (r1984) *Serenade*, K320.
        (8/85) (TELA) ① CD80108

Orpheus CO *Concert*   (12/86) (DG) ① 419 192-2GH
VPO, K. Böhm *Serenade*, K320.
        (8/87) (DG) ① 415 843-2GGA
ASMF, N. Marriner *Concert*
        (11/87) (PHIL) ① 416 386-2PH
Salzburg Mozarteum Camerata Academica, S. Végh
Concert   (11/87) (CAPR) ① 10 185
Serenata of London *Concert*
        (11/87) (CARL) ① PCD861
Czech CO, J. Vlach *Concert*
        (12/88) (SUPR) ① 2SUP0027
COE, J. Galway *Concert*
        (7/89) (RCA) ① [2] RD87861
VCM, N. Harnoncourt (orig. instr.) *Concert*
        (6/90) (TELD) ① 2292-44809-2
ASMF Chbr Ens *Concert*
        (12/90) (PHIL) ① [5] 422 504-2PME5
ASMF, N. Marriner *Concert*
        (12/90) (PHIL) ① [7] 422 503-2PME7
Vienna Mozart Ens, Herbert Kraus *Concert*
        (10/91) (CAPR) ① [3] 10 801
Julius Levine, Budapest Qt *Concert*
        (3/92) (SONY) ① [3] SM3K46527
Barbirolli CO, J. Barbirolli (r1928) *Concert*
        (3/92) (KOCH) ① 37077-2
BPO, W. Furtwängler (r1936/7) *Concert*
        (4/92) (KOCH) ① [2] 37059-2
Tafelmusik, B. Weil *Concert*
        (5/92) (SONY) ① SK46695
VPO, D. Oistrakh (pp1972) *Tchaikovsky: Symphony
5.*   (6/93) (ORFE) ① C302921B
VPO, B. Walter (r1936) *Concert*
        (3/94) (PEAR) ① GEMMCD9940
Saito Kinen Orch, S. Ozawa (r1992) *Concert*
        (9/94) (PHIL) ① 438 137-2PH
Bamberg SO, E. Jochum (r1983) *Concert*
        (9/94) (RCA) ① 74321 17888-2
Cleveland Orch, C. von Dohnányi (r1991) *Concert*
        (2/95) (DECC) ① 443 175-2DH
Sinfonia Varsovia, E. Krivine (r1990) *Concert*
        (3/95) (DENO) ① CO-75597
Hagen Qt, A. Posch (r1994) *Divertimento*, K136-8.
        (4/95) (DG) ① 439 940-2GH
Concertgebouw, W. Mengelberg (r1942) *Concert*
        (5/95) (ARHI) ① ADCD112
Columbia So, B. Walter *Concert*
        (8/95) (SONY) ① SMK64468
Vienna Mozart Ens, W. Boskovsky (1968) *Concert*
        (9/95) (DECC) ① [2] 443 458-2DF2
1. ASMF, N. Marriner *Concert*
        (11/87) (DECC) ① 430 498-2DWO
1, 2. Medici Qt (featured as part of play Mozart's
Journey to Prague) *Concert*
        (11/92) (MEDI) ① MQCD6005

**Sinfonia Concertante in A—violin, viola,
cello and orchestra, K Anh104/K320e (1779-
80) (fragment only)**
J-J. Kantorow, V. Mendelssohn, M. Fujiwara,
Netherlands CO, L. Hager *Concert*
        (12/85) (DENO) ① C37-7505
S. Orton, ASMF, I. Brown (vn/dir) (recons Wilby)
Concert   (6/91) (PHIL) ① [4] 422 508-2PME4

**Sinfonia Concertante in E flat—oboe,
clarinet, bassoon, horn and orchestra,
K297b/KAnh9/C14.01 (1778) (doubtful)**
EXCERPTS: 1. Allegro; 2. Adagio; 3. Andantino con
variazioni.
COE, A. Schneider (pp1984) *Concert*
        (3/87) (ASV) ① CDCOE803
T. Indermühle, J-E. Lluna, F. Lloyd, R. O'Neill, ECO,
L. Hager (r1989) *Concert*
        (4/90) (NOVA) ① 150 043-2
C. O'Neal, K. Puddy, B. Sewell, M. Baines, English
Sinfonia, C. Groves *Concert*
        (11/90) (CARL) ① PCD939
S. Taylor, D. Singer, S. Dibner, W. Purvis, Orpheus
CO *Sinfonia Concertante*, K364.
        (4/91) (DG) ① 429 784-2GH
N. Black, J. Brymer, A. Civil, M. Chapman, ASMF, N.
Marriner *Concert*
        (7/91) (PHIL) ① [5] 422 509-2PME5
H. Holliger, A. Nicolet, K. Baumann, K. Thunemann,
ASMF, N. Marriner (recons R. D. Levin) *Concert*
        (7/91) (PHIL) ① [5] 422 509-2PME5
S. Taylor, D. Singer, S. Dibner, W. Purvis, Orpheus
CO *Concert*   (7/91) (DG) ① [3] 431 665-2GX3
Mainz Wind Ens, K.R. Schöll (arr Egk) *Concert*
        (7/91) (WERG) ① WER60179-50
D. Boyd, R. Hosford, R. O'Neill, J. Williams, COE, A.
Schneider *Concert*   (9/91) (ASV) ① CDCOE814
P. Graeme, T. King, I. James, M. Gatt, ECO, D.
Barenboim *Concert*
        (10/91) (EMI) ① [2] CZS7 67306-2
D. Jonas, S. Meyer, B. Schneider, S. Azzolini,
Staatskapelle Dresden, H. Vonk *Clarinet Concerto*,
K622.   (3/92) (EMI) ① CDC7 54138-2

COE, A. Schneider *Symphony 39.*
(3/87) (ASV) ① **CDCOE806**
Prague CO, C. Mackerras *Symphony 36.*
(10/87) (TELA) ① **CD80148**
FNO, B. Walter (pp1955) *Brahms: Symphony 2.*
(5/89) (MONT) ① **TCE8831**
LMP, J. Glover *Concert*
(8/89) (ASV) ① **CDDCA647**
BPO, K. Böhm *Concert*
(11/89) (DG) ① [12] **427 241-2GX12**
Salzburg Mozarteum Orch, H. Graf *Concert*
(12/89) (CAPR) ① **10 269**
Warsaw Sinfonia, Y. Menuhin *Symphony 39.*
(3/90) (VIRG) ① **VC7 59561-2**
Philh, O. Klemperer *Concert*
(4/90) (EMI) ① [4] **CMS7 63272-2**
ASMF, N. Marriner *Concert*
(12/90) (PHIL) ① [6] **422 502-2PME6**
EBS, J.E. Gardiner *Symphony 39.*
(2/91) (PHIL) ① **426 283-2PH**
Capela Istropolitana, B. Wordsworth *Concert*
(4/91) (NAXO) ① **8 550119**
Czech PO, V. Talich (pp1954) *Concert*
(1/92) (MULT) ① **310078-2**
VPO, B. Walter (pp1955) *Mahler: Symphony 4.*
(2/92) (DG) ① **435 334-2GWP**
VPO, B. Walter (pp1955) *Concert*
(2/92) (DG) ① [12] **435 321-2GWP12**
Czech PO, R. Kubelík (pp1991) *Dvořák: Symphony 9.*
(7/92) (DENO) ① **CO-79728**
LCP, R. Norrington *Symphony 40.*
(11/92) (EMI) ① **CDC7 54336-2**
Concertgebouw, N. Harnoncourt *Symphony 39.*
(12/92) (TELD) ① **9031-77596-2**
Amsterdam Baroque Orch, T. Koopman *Concert*
(4/93) (ERAT) ① [2] **2292-45857-2**
VPO, B. Walter (r1936) *Concert*
(3/94) (PEAR) ① **GEMMCD9940**
EBS, J. E. Gardiner (1988) *Concert*
(3/95) (PHIL) ① [5] **442 604-2PH5**
ECO, B. Britten (r1970) *Concert*
(9/95) (DECC) ① [2] **444 323-2DF2**
BPO, K. Böhm (r1959) *Concert*
(11/95) (DG) ① [2] **447 416-2GOR2**
English Concert, T. Pinnock (hpd/dir) (r1993) *Concert*
(12/95) (ARCH) ① [4] **447 043-2AH4**

Symphony No. 39 in E flat, K543 (1788)
EXCERPTS: 1. Adagio—Allegro; 2. Andante con moto; 3. Menuetto; 4. Allegro.
Bamberg SO, E. Jochum (r1982) *Symphony 40.*
(10/85) (ORFE) ① **C045901A**
COE, A. Schneider *Symphony 38.*
(3/87) (ASV) ① **CDCOE806**
LMP, J. Glover *Concert*
(7/88) (ASV) ① **CDDCA615**
BPO, K. Böhm *Concert*
(11/89) (DG) ① [12] **427 241-2GX12**
Warsaw Sinfonia, Y. Menuhin *Symphony 38.*
(3/90) (VIRG) ① **VC7 59561-2**
Philh, O. Klemperer *Concert*
(4/90) (EMI) ① [4] **CMS7 63272-2**
ASMF, N. Marriner *Concert*
(12/90) (PHIL) ① [6] **422 502-2PME6**
Berlin St Op Orch, E. Kleiber (r1927) *Concert*
(1/91) (KOCH) ① **37011-2**
EBS, J.E. Gardiner *Symphony 38.*
(2/91) (PHIL) ① **426 283-2PH**
Capela Istropolitana, B. Wordsworth *Concert*
(4/91) (NAXO) ① **8 550186**
Prague CO, C. Mackerras *Concert*
(4/91) (TELA) ① **CD80203**
Hamburg RSO, G. Wand (pp1990) *Symphony 41.*
(4/91) (RCA) ① **RD60714**
LCP, R. Norrington *Symphony 41.*
(6/91) (EMI) ① **CDC7 54090-2**
ECO, D. Barenboim *Concert*
(7/91) (EMIL) ① **CDZ7 67011-2**
Scottish CO, J-P. Saraste (r1990) *Symphony 41.*
(12/91) (VIRG) ① **VJ7 59649-2**
Berlin St Op Orch, R. Strauss (r1926) *Concert*
(3/92) (KOCH) ① **37076-2**
COE, N. Harnoncourt (pp1991) *Concert*
(5/92) (TELD) ① [2] **9031-74858-2**
Leningrad PO, E. Mravinsky (pp1972) *Symphony 33.*
(6/92) (ERAT) ① **2292-45758-2**
Leningrad PO, E. Mravinsky (pp1972) *Concert*
(6/92) (ERAT) ① [11] **2292-45763-2**
SRO, T. Beecham (pp1958) *Concert*
(11/92) (CASC) ① **VEL2002**
NBC SO, A. Toscanini (bp1948) *Concert*
(11/92) (RCA) ① **GD60285**
Concertgebouw, N. Harnoncourt *Symphony 38.*
(12/92) (TELD) ① **9031-77596-2**
Czech PO, V. Talich (r1955) *Tchaikovsky: Symphony 6.*
(4/94) (SUPR) ① **11 1908-2**

Berlin St Op Orch, H. Knappertsbusch (r1929) *Concert*
(5/94) (PREI) ① **90951**
EBS, J. E. Gardiner (r1988) *Concert*
(3/95) (PHIL) ① [5] **442 604-2PH5**
BPO, K. Böhm (r1966) *Concert*
(11/95) (DG) ① [2] **447 416-2GOR2**
English Concert, T. Pinnock (hpd/dir) (r1994) *Concert*
(12/95) (ARCH) ① [4] **447 043-2AH4**
3, 4. La Scala Orch, A. Toscanini (r1920) *Concert*
(11/92) (RCA) ① **GD60315**

Symphony No. 40 in G minor, K550 (1788)
(two versions—second with clarinets)
EXCERPTS: 1. Molto allegro; 2. Andante; 3. Menuetto; 4. Allegro assai.
Bamberg SO, E. Jochum (1982) *Symphony 39.*
(10/85) (ORFE) ① **C045901A**
St John's Smith Square Orch, J. Lubbock *Haydn: Symphony 44.*
(8/86) (CARL) ① **PCD820**
LSO, C. Abbado *Symphony 41.*
(4/87) (DG) ① **415 841-2GGA**
Prague CO, C. Mackerras (r1986) *Symphony 41.*
(5/87) (TELA) ① **CD80139**
FNO, J. Krips (pp1965) *Brahms: Symphony 4.*
(5/89) (MONT) ① **TCE8821**
BPO, K. Böhm *Concert*
(10/89) (DG) ① **427 210-2GR**
BPO, K. Böhm *Concert*
(11/89) (DG) ① [12] **427 241-2GX12**
BPO *Concert*
(11/89) (RCA) ① **RD60032**
Philh, O. Klemperer *Concert*
(4/90) (EMI) ① [4] **CMS7 63272-2**
LPO, J. Sándor *Concert*
(5/90) (LASE) ① **15 511**
LPO, C. Mackerras *Symphony 41.*
(11/90) (CFP) ① **CD-CFP4253**
ASMF, N. Marriner *Concert*
(12/90) (PHIL) ① [6] **422 502-2PME6**
Cleveland Orch, G. Szell *Concert*
(3/91) (SONY) ① **SBK46333**
Capela Istropolitana, B. Wordsworth *Concert*
(4/91) (NAXO) ① **8 550164**
VPO, James Levine *Symphony 41.*
(4/91) (DG) ① **429 731-2GH**
Capela Istropolitana, B. Wordsworth *Symphony 41.*
(4/91) (NAXO) ① **8 550299**
LMP, J. Glover *Concert*
(4/91) (ASV) ① **CDDCA761**
ECO, D. Barenboim *Concert*
(7/91) (EMIL) ① **CDZ7 67011-2**
Stuttgart RSO, G. Gelmetti *Sinfonia Concertante, K364.*
(7/91) (EMI) ① **CDC7 54196-2**
English Classical Players, J. Brett *Schubert: Symphony 5.*
(11/91) (LINN) ① **CKD003**
Berlin St Op Orch, R. Strauss (r1927) *Concert*
(3/92) (KOCH) ① **37076-2**
BPO, C.M. Giulini *Symphony 41.*
(3/92) (SONY) ① **SK47264**
COE, N. Harnoncourt (pp1991) *Concert*
(5/92) (TELD) ① [2] **9031-74858-2**
BPO, H. von Karajan *Symphony 41.*
(9/92) (DG) ① **435 592-2GGA**
NBC SO, A. Toscanini (r1950) *Beethoven: Symphony 3.*
(10/92) (RCA) ① **GD60271**
NBC SO, A. Toscanini (r1938/9) *Concert*
(11/92) (RCA) ① **GD60285**
EBS, J.E. Gardiner *Symphony 41.*
(11/92) (PHIL) ① **426 315-2PH**
LCP, R. Norrington *Symphony 38.*
(11/92) (EMI) ① **CDC7 54336-2**
ASMF, N. Marriner (r1986) *Concert*
(6/93) (EMI) ① [2] **CZS7 67564-2**
VPO, H. Knappertsbusch (bp1941) *Concert*
(5/94) (PREI) ① **90951**
Sinfonia Varsovia, Y. Menuhin *Symphony 41.*
(11/94) (VIRG) ① **CUV5 61133-2**
EBS, J. E. Gardiner (1989) *Concert*
(3/95) (PHIL) ① [5] **442 604-2PH5**
N. German Orch, G. Wand (pp1994) *Tchaikovsky: Symphony 5.*
(6/95) (RCA) ① **09026 68032-2**
ECO, B. Britten (r1968) *Concert*
(9/95) (DECC) ① [2] **444 323-2DF2**
BPO, K. Böhm (r1961-2) *Concert*
(11/95) (DG) ① [2] **447 416-2GOR2**
English Concert, T. Pinnock (hpd/dir) (r1994) *Concert*
(12/95) (ARCH) ① [4] **447 043-2AH4**
English Concert, T. Pinnock (hpd/dir) (r1994) *Symphony 41.*
(12/95) (ARCH) ① [4] **447 048-2AH**
1. COE, G. Solti *Concert*
(6/91) (DECC) ① **430 498-2DWO**

Symphony No. 41 in C, 'Jupiter', K551 (1788)
EXCERPTS: 1. Allegro vivace; 2. Andante cantabile; 3. Menuetto; 4. Molto allegro.
Bamberg SO, E. Jochum *Maurerische Trauermusik, K477.*
(9/86) (ORFE) ① **C045902A**
LSO, C. Abbado *Symphony 40.*
(4/87) (DG) ① **415 841-2GGA**

Prague CO, C. Mackerras (r1986) *Symphony 40.*
(5/87) (TELA) ① **CD80139**
BPO, K. Böhm *Concert*
(10/89) (DG) ① **427 210-2GR**
BPO, K. Böhm *Concert*
(11/89) (DG) ① [12] **427 241-2GX12**
Philh, O. Klemperer *Concert*
(4/90) (EMI) ① [4] **CMS7 63272-2**
LPO, J. Sándor *Concert*
(5/90) (LASE) ① **15 511**
LPO, C. Mackerras *Symphony 40.*
(11/90) (CFP) ① **CD-CFP4253**
ASMF, N. Marriner *Concert*
(12/90) (PHIL) ① [6] **422 502-2PME6**
Cleveland Orch, G. Szell *Concert*
(3/91) (SONY) ① **SBK46333**
Capela Istropolitana, B. Wordsworth *Concert*
(4/91) (NAXO) ① **8 550113**
ECO, L. Hager *Concert*
(4/91) (NOVA) ① **150 053-2**
VPO, James Levine *Symphony 40.*
(4/91) (DG) ① **429 731-2GH**
Hamburg RSO, G. Wand (pp1990) *Symphony 39.*
(4/91) (RCA) ① **RD60714**
LMP, J. Glover *Concert*
(4/91) (ASV) ① **CDDCA761**
Capela Istropolitana, B. Wordsworth *Symphony 40.*
(4/91) (NAXO) ① **8 550299**
LCP, R. Norrington *Symphony 39.*
(6/91) (EMI) ① **CDC7 54090-2**
Scottish CO, J-P. Saraste (r1990) *Symphony 39.*
(12/91) (VIRG) ① **VJ7 59649-2**
Berlin St Op Orch, R. Strauss (r1926) *Concert*
(3/92) (KOCH) ① **37076-2**
BPO, C.M. Giulini *Symphony 40.*
(3/92) (SONY) ① **SK47264**
COE, N. Harnoncourt (pp1991) *Concert*
(5/92) (TELD) ① [2] **9031-74858-2**
BPO, H. von Karajan *Symphony 40.*
(9/92) (DG) ① **435 592-2GGA**
NBC SO, A. Toscanini (r1945/6) *Concert*
(11/92) (RCA) ① **GD60285**
EBS, J.E. Gardiner *Symphony 40.*
(11/92) (PHIL) ① **426 315-2PH**
Amsterdam Baroque Orch, T. Koopman *Concert*
(4/93) (ERAT) ① [2] **2292-45857-2**
ASMF, N. Marriner (r1984) *Concert*
(6/93) (EMI) ① [2] **CZS7 67564-2**
VPO, B. Walter (r1938) *Concert*
(3/94) (PREI) ① **90141**
VPO, H. Knappertsbusch (bp1941) *Concert*
(5/94) (PREI) ① **90951**
LSO, A. Coates (r1927) *Beethoven: Symphony 3.*
(6/94) (CLAR) ① **CDGSE78-50-55**
Sinfonia Varsovia, Y. Menuhin *Concert*
(11/94) (VIRG) ① **CUV5 61133-2**
EBS, J. E. Gardiner (1989) *Concert*
(3/95) (PHIL) ① [5] **442 604-2PH5**
VPO, R. Muti (r1993) *Symphony 31.*
(7/95) (PHIL) ① **442 126-2PH**
BPO, K. Böhm (r1961-2) *Concert*
(11/95) (DG) ① [2] **447 416-2GOR2**
English Concert, T. Pinnock (hpd/dir) (r1994) *Symphony 40.* (12/95) (ARCH) ① [4] **447 048-2AH**
English Concert, T. Pinnock (hpd/dir) (r1995) *Concert*
(12/95) (ARCH) ① [4] **447 043-2AH4**

SECTION II: CHAMBER

Adagio and Fugue in C minor—strings, K546 (1788)
ASMF, N. Marriner *Concert*
(11/87) (PHIL) ① **416 386-2PH**
Czech CO, J. Vlach (r1965) *Horn Concertos.*
(12/87) (SUPR) ① **2SUP0005**
Salzburg Camerata, S. Végh *Concert*
(3/88) (CAPR) ① **10 192**
Amadeus Qt *Schubert: String Quintet.*
(9/88) (DG) ① **423 543-2GM**
M. Haselböck *Concert* (10/91) (SCHW) ① **317003**
Staatskapelle Dresden, P. Schreier *Concert*
(4/92) (PHIL) ① [6] **422 522-2PME6**
Talich Qt (r1992) *Concert*
(11/93) (CALL) ① **CAL9245**
Eder Qt (r1993) *Concert*
(4/95) (NAXO) ① **8 550547**

Adagio and Rondo in C minor—glass harmonica, flute, oboe, viola and cello, K617 (1791)
M. Grauwels, D. James, Brussels Virtuosi *Flute Quartets.*
(4/90) (HYPE) ① **CDA66392**
Nash Ens *Concert* (4/90) (VIRG) ① **VC7 59560-2**
B. Hoffmann, A. Nicolet, K. Schouten, J. Decroos *Concert*
(9/91) (PHIL) ① [5] **422 514-2PME5**
M. Haselböck *Concert* (10/91) (SCHW) ① **317003**
J.S. Ritter, J-P. Rampal, P. Pierlot, B. Pasquier, R. Pidoux *Concert*
(11/91) (SONY) ① **SK47230**

Vienna-Berlin Ens *Concert*
(3/93) (DG) ① **431 782-2GH**
J. Jandó, I. Kovács, J. Kiss, G. Konrád, T. Koó
Concert (4/93) (NAXO) ① **8 550511**
**Adagio in B flat—two clarinets and three
basset-horns, K411/484a (?1782-83)**
Moraguès Qnt (r1992: arr qnt: David Walter) *Concert*
(11/93) (AUVI) ① **V4684**
Netherlands Wind Ens (r1993) *Concert*
(5/95) (CHAN) ① **CHAN9284**
**Adagio in C—cor anglais, violin, viola and
cello, KAnh94/K580a**
H. Schellenberger, Berlin Philh Qt *Concert*
(9/85) (DENO) ① **C37-7034**
I. Goritzki, Berne Qt *Concert*
(9/85) (CLAV) ① **CD50-8406**
Netherlands Wind Ens (r1993) *Concert*
(5/95) (CHAN) ① **CHAN9284**
**Adagio in F—clarinet and three basset-
horns, KAnh94/580a (?1788)** (fragment only)
Netherlands Sols Ens (r1992) *Concert*
(10/94) (EMER) ① **[2] EC3992-2**
**Allegro assai in B flat—two clarinets and
three basset-horns, KAnh95/484b** (Fragment
only)
Netherlands Sols Ens (r1992) *Concert*
(10/94) (EMER) ① **[2] EC3992-2**
**Allegro in F—two horns and strings,
K288/K246c (?1776)** (sketch only)
ASMF Chbr Ens (cptd E.Smith) *Concert*
(9/91) (PHIL) ① **[3] 422 510-2PME3**
Netherlands Sols Ens (r1992) *Concert*
(10/94) (EMER) ① **[2] EC3992-2**
**Andante and Variations in G—keyboard
duet, K501 (1786)**
M. Perahia, R. Lupu *Concert*
(10/91) (SONY) ① **SK44915**
I. Haebler, L. Hoffmann *Concert*
(11/91) (PHIL) ① **[2] 422 516-2PME2**
I. Beyer, H. Dagul *Concert*
(5/92) (FOUR) ① **FHMD9111**
C. Eschenbach, J. Frantz *Concert*
(6/92) (DG) ① **[2] 435 042-2GX2**
P. Frankl, T. Vásáry *Concert*
(9/92) (ASV) ① **CDDCA792**
O. Ouziel, D. Ouziel *Concert*
(1/93) (PAVA) ① **[2] ADW7244/5**
L. Lortie, H. Mercier (r1992) *Concert*
(7/93) (CHAN) ① **CHAN9162**
A. Schiff, G. Malcolm (r1993) *Concert*
(6/94) (DECC) ① **440 474-2DH**
M. Argerich, A. Rabinovitch (r1992/3) *Concert*
(1/95) (TELD) ① **4509-91378-2**
**Andantino in B flat—cello and orchestra,
KAnh46/K374g (?1782-83)** (Fragment: 33
bars)
Netherlands Sols Ens (r1992) *Concert*
(10/94) (EMER) ① **[2] EC3992-2**
**5 Divertimenti in B flat—two basset-hns/cls
& bassoon or 3 basset-hns, KAnh229/439b
(1781-82 or 1785)**
1. No 1: 1a. Allegro; 1b. Minuet; 1c. Adagio; 1d.
Minuet; 1e. Rondo; 2. No 2: 2a. Allegro; 2b. Minuet;
2c. Larghetto; 2d. Minuet; 2e. Rondo; 3. No 3: 3a.
Allegro; 3b. Minuet; 3c. Adagio; 3d. Minuet; 3e.
Rondo; 4. No 4: 4a. Allegro; 4b. Larghetto; 4c.
Minuet; 4d. Adagio; 4e. Allegro; 5. No 5: 5a. Adagio;
5b. Minuet; 5c. Adagio; 5d. Andante; 5e. Polonaise.
Thurston Cl Qt (arr Whewell) *Concert*
(10/93) (ASV) ① **CDWHL2076**
Larghetto & Allegro J. Bream (r1967-8; ed Bream)
Concert (8/93) (RCA) ① **[28] 09026 61583-2(3)**
Larghetto & Allegro J. Bream (r1967-8; ed Bream)
Concert (8/93) (RCA) ① **09026 61591-2**
1-4. Classical Winds (3/87) (AMON) ① **CD-SAR25**
**Divertimento in B flat—keyboard trio, K254
(1776)**
London Fp Trio *Piano Trio, K548.*
(11/86) (HYPE) ① **CDA66093**
Borodin Trio *Concert*
(2/88) (CHAN) ① **[2] CHAN8536/7**
Beaux Arts Trio *Concert*
(11/88) (PHIL) ① **[3] 422 079-2PH3**
Beaux Arts Trio *Concert*
(9/91) (PHIL) ① **[5] 422 514-2PME5**
Arion Trio *Concert*
(11/91) (BIS) ① **[2] BIS-CD513/4**
Mozartean Players (r1990) *Concert*
(8/93) (HARM) ① **[2] HMU90 7033/4**
Beaux Arts Trio (r c1967) *Concert*
(8/95) (PHIL) ① **[2] 446 154-2PM2**
**Divertimento in E flat—violin, viola and cello,
K563 (1788)**
Cummings Trio (9/86) (MERI) ① **ECD84079**
A. Dumay, G. Caussé, G. Hoffman
(10/91) (EMI) ① **CDC7 54009-2**

J. Heifetz, W. Primrose, E. Feuermann (r1941)
Concert (11/94) (RCA) ① **[65] 09026 61778-2(09)**
**Divertimento in F—two oboes, two horns
and two bassoons, K253 (1776)**
Octophoros *Concert* (11/89) (ACCE) ① **ACC8856D**
**Duo in B flat—bassoon and cello, K292/196c
(1775)**
K. Thunemann, S. Orton *Concert*
(9/91) (PHIL) ① **[3] 422 510-2PME3**
M. Turkovic, G. Faust *Concert*
(3/93) (DG) ① **431 782-2GH**
Duo in B flat—violin and viola, K424 (1783)
I. Perlman, P. Zukerman *Concert*
(12/91) (RCA) ① **RD60735**
V. Beths, G. Beths *Concert*
(4/92) (SONY) ① **SK46631**
S. Goldberg, P. Hindemith (r1934) *Concert*
(4/92) (MUSI) ① **[3] MACD-665**
J. Heifetz, W. Primrose (r1941) *Concert*
(11/94) (RCA) ① **[65] 09026 61778-2(09)**
Duo in G—violin and viola, K423 (1783)
I. Perlman, P. Zukerman *Concert*
(12/91) (RCA) ① **RD60735**
V. Beths, G. Beths *Concert*
(4/92) (SONY) ① **SK46631**
S. Goldberg, F. Riddle (r1948) *Concert*
(4/92) (MUSI) ① **[3] MACD-665**
**12 Duos—two horns/basset-horns,
K487/496a (1786)**
1. Allegro; 2. Menuetto (Allegretto); 3. Andante; 4.
Polonaise; 5. Larghetto; 6. Menuetto; 7. Adagio; 8.
Allegro; 9. Menuetto; 10. Andante; 11. Menuetto; 12.
Allegro.
2, 5, 8, 10. Archibudelli *Concert*
(12/91) (SONY) ① **SK46702**
Fugue in C minor—two pianos, K426 (1783)
I. Haebler, L. Hoffmann *Concert*
(11/91) (PHIL) ① **[2] 422 516-2PME2**
O. Ouziel, D. Ouziel *Concert*
(1/93) (PAVA) ① **[2] ADW7244/5**
Fugue in G—string trio, K443/404b (1782)
(cpted M. Stadler)
M. Haselböck *Concert* (10/91) (SCHW) ① **317003**
**Gallimathias musicum—keyboard, 2 oboes,
2 horns, 2 bassoons, strings, K32 (1766)**
Orpheus CO *Concert* (4/91) (DG) ① **429 783-2GH**
**3 Keyboard Trio Movements, K442 (c1766-
91)** (fragments: cpted M Stadler)
1. D minor; 2. G; 3. D.
Beaux Arts Trio *Concert*
(11/88) (PHIL) ① **[3] 422 079-2PH3**
Beaux Arts Trio *Concert*
(9/91) (PHIL) ① **[5] 422 514-2PME5**
Netherlands Sols Ens (r1992) *Concert*
(10/94) (EMER) ① **[2] EC3992-2**
Keyboard Trio No. 1 in G, K496 (1786)
Borodin Trio *Concert*
(2/88) (CHAN) ① **[2] CHAN8536/7**
London Fp Trio *Piano Trio, K542.*
(7/88) (HYPE) ① **CDA66148**
Beaux Arts Trio *Concert*
(11/88) (PHIL) ① **[3] 422 079-2PH3**
Beaux Arts Trio *Concert*
(9/91) (PHIL) ① **[5] 422 514-2PME5**
Arion Trio *Concert*
(11/91) (BIS) ① **[2] BIS-CD513/4**
Mozartean Players (r1990) *Concert*
(8/93) (HARM) ① **[2] HMU90 7033/4**
J. Balogh, Danubius Qt (r1992: arr cl/stgs) *Concert*
(2/94) (NAXO) ① **8 550439**
Beaux Arts Trio (r c1967) *Concert*
(8/95) (PHIL) ① **[2] 446 154-2PM2**
**Keyboard Trio No. 2 in E flat,
'Kegelstatt'—piano, clarinet/violin and viola,
K498 (1786)**
Borodin Trio, J. Campbell *Concert*
(6/89) (CHAN) ① **CHAN8655**
A. Pay, R. Chase, I. Brown *Concert*
(6/89) (CRD) ① **CRD3411**
S. Meyer, T. Zimmermann, H. Höll *Concert*
(8/89) (EMI) ① **CDC7 49736-2**
Nash Ens *Concert* (4/90) (VIRG) ① **VC7 59560-2**
J. Farrell, G. Jackson, G. Johnson *Concert*
(6/90) (MERI) ① **CDE84169**
J. Hilton, N. Imai, R. Vignoles *Concert*
(4/91) (CHAN) ① **CHAN8776**
S. Kovacevich, J. Brymer, P. Ireland *Concert*
(9/91) (PHIL) ① **[5] 422 514-2PME5**
I. von Alpenheim, A. Morf, C. Veress *Concert*
(11/91) (BIS) ① **[2] BIS-CD513/4**
R. Kell, F. Riddle, L. Kentner (r1941) *Concert*
(8/92) (TEST) ① **SBT1007**
W. Boeykens, W. Boeykens Ens *Clarinet Quintet,
K581.* (3/93) (HARM) ① **HMC90 1384**
K. Leister, W. Christ, James Levine *Concert*
(3/93) (DG) ① **431 782-2GH**

H. de Graaf, I. Shimon, D. Wayenberg *Concert*
(4/93) (CHNN) ① **CG9107**
W. Meyer, A. Mitterer, P. Cohen (r1992) *Clarinet
Quintet, K581.* (8/93) (ASTR) ① **E8736**
B. Kovács, G. Konrád, J. Jandó (r1991) *Concert*
(2/94) (NAXO) ① **8 550439**
C. Neidich, R. Levin, A. Bylsma (r1992) *Concert*
(5/94) (SONY) ① **SK53366**
J. Brymer, P. Ireland, S. Kovacevich (r1969) *Concert*
(8/95) (PHIL) ① **[2] 446 154-2PM2**
Keyboard Trio No. 3 in E flat, K502 (1786)
London Fp Trio *Piano Trio, K548.*
(7/87) (HYPE) ① **CDA66125**
Borodin Trio *Concert*
(2/88) (CHAN) ① **[2] CHAN8536/7**
Beaux Arts Trio *Concert*
(11/88) (PHIL) ① **[3] 422 079-2PH3**
Beaux Arts Trio *Concert*
(9/91) (PHIL) ① **[5] 422 514-2PME5**
Arion Trio *Concert*
(11/91) (BIS) ① **[2] BIS-CD513/4**
Mozartean Players (r1990) *Concert*
(8/93) (HARM) ① **HMU90 7033/4**
Beaux Arts Trio (r c1967) *Concert*
(8/95) (PHIL) ① **[2] 446 154-2PM2**
Keyboard Trio No. 4 in E, K542 (1788)
Borodin Trio *Concert*
(2/88) (CHAN) ① **[2] CHAN8536/7**
London Fp Trio (r1984) *Piano Trio, K496.*
(7/88) (HYPE) ① **CDA66148**
Beaux Arts Trio *Concert*
(11/88) (PHIL) ① **[3] 422 079-2PH3**
Ambache Chbr Ens *Concert*
(12/88) (MERI) ① **CDE84142**
Beaux Arts Trio *Concert*
(9/91) (PHIL) ① **[5] 422 514-2PME5**
Arion Trio *Concert*
(11/91) (BIS) ① **[2] BIS-CD513/4**
Mozartean Players (r1990) *Concert*
(8/93) (HARM) ① **HMU90 7033/4**
Beaux Arts Trio (r c1967) *Concert*
(8/95) (PHIL) ① **[2] 446 154-2PM2**
Keyboard Trio No. 5 in C, K548 (1788)
London Fp Trio *Divertimento, K254.*
(11/86) (HYPE) ① **CDA66093**
Borodin Trio *Concert*
(2/88) (CHAN) ① **[2] CHAN8536/7**
Beaux Arts Trio *Concert*
(11/88) (PHIL) ① **[3] 422 079-2PH3**
Beaux Arts Trio *Concert*
(9/91) (PHIL) ① **[5] 422 514-2PME5**
Arion Trio *Concert*
(11/91) (BIS) ① **[2] BIS-CD513/4**
Mozartean Players (r1990) *Concert*
(8/93) (HARM) ① **HMU90 7033/4**
Beaux Arts Trio (r c1967) *Concert*
(8/95) (PHIL) ① **[2] 446 154-2PM2**
Keyboard Trio No. 6 in E, K564 (1788)
London Fp Trio *Piano Trio, K502.*
(7/87) (HYPE) ① **CDA66125**
Borodin Trio *Concert*
(2/88) (CHAN) ① **[2] CHAN8536/7**
Beaux Arts Trio *Concert*
(11/88) (PHIL) ① **[3] 422 079-2PH3**
Beaux Arts Trio *Concert*
(9/91) (PHIL) ① **[5] 422 514-2PME5**
Arion Trio *Concert*
(11/91) (BIS) ① **[2] BIS-CD513/4**
Mozartean Players (r1990) *Concert*
(8/93) (HARM) ① **HMU90 7033/4**
Beaux Arts Trio (r c1967) *Concert*
(8/95) (PHIL) ① **[2] 446 154-2PM2**
**Larghetto and Allegro in E flat—two
keyboards, Kdeest (?1782-83)** (fragment
cpted M Stadler)
J. Demus, P. Badura-Skoda (cpted Badura-Skoda)
Concert (11/91) (PHIL) ① **[2] 422 516-2PME2**
O. Ouziel, D. Ouziel *Concert*
(1/93) (PAVA) ① **[2] ADW7244/5**
Minuet in F—string quartet, K168a (?1775)
ASMF Chbr Ens *Concert*
(9/91) (PHIL) ① **[3] 422 510-2PME3**
A Musical Dice Game, K561f (1787)
N. Marriner, E. Smith *Concert*
(12/91) (PHIL) ① **[3] 422 545-2PME3**
**Quartet for Keyboard, Violin, Viola and Cello
in E flat, K493 (1786)**
Beaux Arts Trio, B. Giuranna (r1983) *Piano Quartet,
K478.* (12/84) (PHIL) ① **410 391-2PH**
J. Rouvier, Mozart Trio *Piano Quartet, K478.*
(9/87) (DENO) ① **CO-1374**
R. Burnett, Salomon Qt *Piano Quartet, K478.*
(1/88) (AMON) ① **CD-SAR31**
Ambache Chbr Ens *Concert*
(12/88) (MERI) ① **CDE84142**

Minuet in F—keyboard, K2 (1762)
T. Koopman *Concert*
(10/91) (PHIL) ① [5] 422 518-2PME5
G. Penson *Concert*
(12/92) (RICE) ① [3] RIC105081
G. Tozer *Concert* (12/92) (TALL) ① TP001
M. Souter (r1994-5) *Concert*
(12/95) (ISIS) ① ISISCD010

Minuet in F—keyboard, K4 (1762)
T. Koopman *Concert*
(10/91) (PHIL) ① [5] 422 518-2PME5
G. Penson *Concert*
(12/92) (RICE) ① [3] RIC105081
G. Tozer *Concert* (12/92) (TALL) ① TP001
M. Souter (r1994-5) *Concert*
(12/95) (ISIS) ① ISISCD010

Minuet in F—keyboard, K5 (1762)
T. Koopman *Concert*
(10/91) (PHIL) ① [5] 422 518-2PME5
G. Penson *Concert*
(12/92) (RICE) ① [3] RIC105081
M. Souter (r1994-5) *Concert*
(12/95) (ISIS) ① ISISCD010

Minuet in G—keyboard, K1/1e (1761-62)
T. Koopman *Concert*
(10/91) (PHIL) ① [5] 422 518-2PME5
G. Penson *Concert*
(12/92) (RICE) ① [3] RIC105081
G. Tozer *Concert* (12/92) (TALL) ① TP001

8 Minuets—keyboard, K315a (1773)
1. C; 2. G; 3. D; 4. G; 5. C; 6. F; 7. D; 8. A.
G. Penson *Concert*
(12/92) (RICE) ① [3] RIC105081

Modulierendis Präludium—keyboard, Kdeest
E. Smith *Concert*
(12/91) (PHIL) ① [3] 422 545-2PME3

Orgelstück (Fantasia) für eine Uhr—mechanical organ, K608 (1791)
1. Allegro; 2. Andante; 3. Allegro.
S. Cleobury *Concert* (3/87) (PRIO) ① PRCD185
John Scott *Concert* (12/87) (CIRR) ① CICD1007
K. John *Concert* (5/89) (PRIO) ① PRCD235
I. Tracey (r1990; arr Tracey) *Concert*
(4/91) (MIRA) ① MRCD901
S. Preston *Concert*
(6/91) (DECC) ① 430 091-2DWO
M. Haselböck *Concert*
(10/91) (NOVA) ① 150 054-2
M. Haselböck *Concert* (10/91) (SCHW) ① 317003
M. Perahia, R. Lupu, ECO (arr Busoni) *Concert*
(10/91) (SONY) ① SK44915
D. Chorzempa *Concert*
(12/91) (PHIL) ① [2] 422 521-2PME2
C. Eschenbach, J. Frantz *Concert*
(6/92) (DG) ① [2] 435 042-2GX2
P. Frankl, T. Vásáry (r1992; arr pf 4 hands) *Concert*
(5/93) (ASV) ① CDDCA799
A. Schiff, G. Malcolm (r1993: trans pf 4 hands)
Concert (6/94) (DECC) ① 440 474-2DH
C. Herrick (r1993) *Concert*
(8/94) (HYPE) ① CDA66676
T. Trotter (r1993; ed Trotter) *Concert*
(10/95) (LOND) ① 443 451-2LH

Prelude and Fugue in C—keyboard, K394/383a (1782)
L. Devos *Concert*
(12/92) (RICE) ① [3] RIC105081
T. Trotter (r993) *Concert*
(10/95) (LOND) ① 443 451-2LH

Romanze in A flat—keyboard, KAnh205 (spurious)
J. Kubelík, G. Lapierre (arr Kubelík: r1912) *Concert*
(6/91) (BIDD) ① [2] LAB033/4

Rondo in A minor—keyboard, K511 (1787)
M. Uchida *Concert* (2/85) (PHIL) ① 412 122-2PH
J. van Immerseel *Concert*
(9/86) (ACCE) ① ACC58018D
M. Uchida *Concert*
(2/89) (PHIL) ① [6] 422 115-2PH6
A. Schnabel (r1946) *Concert*
(6/91) (EMI) ① [3] CHS7 63703-2
M. Uchida *Concert*
(10/91) (PHIL) ① [5] 422 518-2PME5
I. Paderewski (r1937) *Concert*
(11/91) (PEAR) ① GEMMCD9499
A. Brendel *Concert* (2/92) (VANG) ① 08.4025.71
Vladimir Ashkenazy *Concert*
(2/92) (DECC) ① 425 031-2DM
C. Arrau *Concert*
(3/92) (PHIL) ① [7] 432 306-2PM7
A. Schiff *Concert* (5/92) (L'OI) ① 433 328-2OH
A. Brendel *Concert* (8/92) (PHIL) ① 434 663-2PH
L. Devos *Concert*
(12/92) (RICE) ① [3] RIC105081
M. Dalberto *Concert* (12/92) (DENO) ① CO-79477

M. Uchida (pp1991) *Concert*
(4/93) (PHIL) ① [2] 432 989-2PH2
T. Fellner (r1993) *Concert*
(9/94) (CLAV) ① CD50-9328
K. Lifschitz (pp1993) *Concert*
(12/94) (DENO) ① CO-78908
H. Neuhaus (r1950) *Concert*
(8/95) (MELO) ① 74321 25174-2
H. Neuhaus (r1950) *Concert*
(8/95) (MELO) ① [11] 74321 25172-2(1)

Rondo in D—keyboard, K485 (1786)
M. Uchida *Concert* (7/87) (PHIL) ① 420 185-2PH
M. Uchida *Concert*
(2/89) (PHIL) ① [6] 422 115-2PH6
M. Uchida *Concert*
(10/91) (PHIL) ① [5] 422 518-2PME5
C. Arrau *Concert*
(3/92) (PHIL) ① [7] 432 306-2PM7
A. Schiff *Concert* (5/92) (L'OI) ① 433 328-2OH
L. Devos *Concert*
(12/92) (RICE) ① [3] RIC105081
A. de Larrocha *Concert*
(4/93) (RCA) ① 09026 60453-2
V. Horowitz (r1980s) *Concert*
(1/95) (DG) ① 445 517-2GMA

Sonata for Keyboard in F, K46e (1768) (also exists as keyboard/vn son)
C. Eschenbach (r1970) *Concert*
(3/94) (DG) ① [5] 419 445-2GX5

Sonata for Keyboard No. 1 in C, K279/K189d (1775)
M. Uchida *Concert* (1/86) (PHIL) ① 412 617-2PH
M. Uchida *Concert*
(2/89) (PHIL) ① [6] 422 115-2PH6
T. Vesselinova *Concert*
(7/89) (ACCE) ① [2] ACC8849/50
P. Katin *Concert* (5/90) (OLYM) ① OCD232
M. Uchida *Concert*
(9/91) (PHIL) ① [5] 422 517-2PME5
M-J. Pires *Concert*
(2/92) (DG) ① [6] 431 760-2GH6
C. Arrau *Concert*
(3/92) (PHIL) ① [7] 432 306-2PM7
D. Barenboim *Concert*
(4/92) (EMI) ① [5] CZS7 67294-2
M-J. Pires *Concert* (2/93) (DG) ① 435 882-2GH
A. de Larrocha *Concert*
(4/93) (RCA) ① 09026 60453-2
C. Eschenbach (r1969) *Concert*
(3/94) (DG) ① [5] 419 445-2GX5

Sonata for Keyboard No. 2 in F, K280/K189e (1775)
M. Uchida *Concert* (4/88) (PHIL) ① 420 186-2PH
M. Uchida *Concert*
(2/89) (PHIL) ① [6] 422 115-2PH6
T. Vesselinova *Concert*
(7/89) (ACCE) ① [2] ACC8849/50
P. Katin *Concert* (5/90) (OLYM) ① OCD232
M. Uchida *Concert*
(9/91) (PHIL) ① [5] 422 517-2PME5
M-J. Pires *Concert*
(2/92) (DG) ① [6] 431 760-2GH6
C. Arrau *Concert*
(3/92) (PHIL) ① [7] 432 306-2PM7
D. Barenboim *Concert*
(4/92) (EMI) ① [5] CZS7 67294-2
M-J. Pires *Concert* (2/93) (DG) ① 435 882-2GH
A. de Larrocha *Concert*
(4/93) (RCA) ① 09026 60453-2
C. Eschenbach (r1969) *Concert*
(3/94) (DG) ① [5] 419 445-2GX5
S. Richter (pp1966) *Concert*
(8/94) (PHIL) ① [2] 438 480-2PH2

Sonata for Keyboard No. 3 in B flat, K281/189f (1775)
M. Uchida *Concert* (4/88) (PHIL) ① 420 186-2PH
M. Uchida *Concert*
(2/89) (PHIL) ① [6] 422 115-2PH6
T. Vesselinova *Concert*
(7/89) (ACCE) ① [2] ACC8849/50
V. Horowitz *Concert* (11/89) (DG) ① 427 772-2GH
P. Katin *Concert* (5/90) (OLYM) ① OCD234
M. Uchida *Concert*
(9/91) (PHIL) ① [5] 422 517-2PME5
A. de Larrocha *Concert* (10/91) (RCA) ① RD60709
M-J. Pires *Concert*
(2/92) (DG) ① [6] 431 760-2GH6
C. Arrau *Concert*
(3/92) (PHIL) ① [7] 432 306-2PM7
D. Barenboim *Concert*
(4/92) (EMI) ① [5] CZS7 67294-2
M-J. Pires (r1990) *Concert*
(7/93) (DG) ① 437 546-2GH
C. Eschenbach (r1969) *Concert*
(3/94) (DG) ① [5] 419 445-2GX5

V. Horowitz (r1980s) *Concert*
(1/95) (DG) ① 445 517-2GMA

Sonata for Keyboard No. 4 in E flat, K282/K189g (1775)
M. Uchida *Concert* (4/88) (PHIL) ① 420 186-2PH
M. Uchida *Concert*
(2/89) (PHIL) ① [6] 422 115-2PH6
T. Vesselinova *Concert*
(7/89) (ACCE) ① [2] ACC8849/50
P. Katin *Concert* (5/90) (OLYM) ① OCD234
M. Uchida *Concert*
(9/91) (PHIL) ① [5] 422 517-2PME5
A. de Larrocha *Concert* (10/91) (RCA) ① RD60709
M-J. Pires *Concert*
(2/92) (DG) ① [6] 431 760-2GH6
C. Arrau *Concert*
(3/92) (PHIL) ① [7] 432 306-2PM7
D. Barenboim *Concert*
(4/92) (EMI) ① [5] CZS7 67294-2
A. Brendel *Concert* (8/92) (PHIL) ① 434 663-2PH
M-J. Pires (r1990) *Concert*
(7/93) (DG) ① 437 546-2GH
C. Eschenbach (r1968) *Concert*
(3/94) (DG) ① [5] 419 445-2GX5
S. Feinberg (r1953) *Concert*
(8/95) (MELO) ① [11] 74321 25172-2(1)
S. Feinberg (r1953) *Concert*
(8/95) (MELO) ① 74321 25175-2

Sonata for Keyboard No. 5 in G, K283/K189h (1775)
M. Uchida *Concert* (4/88) (PHIL) ① 420 186-2PH
M. Uchida *Concert*
(2/89) (PHIL) ① [6] 422 115-2PH6
T. Vesselinova *Concert*
(7/89) (ACCE) ① [2] ACC8849/50
P. Katin *Concert* (5/90) (OLYM) ① OCD234
M. Uchida *Concert*
(9/91) (PHIL) ① [5] 422 517-2PME5
M-J. Pires *Concert*
(2/92) (DG) ① [6] 431 760-2GH6
C. Arrau *Concert*
(3/92) (PHIL) ① [7] 432 306-2PM7
D. Barenboim *Concert*
(4/92) (EMI) ① [5] CZS7 67294-2
M-J. Pires (r1990) *Concert*
(3/94) (DG) ① 437 791-2GH
C. Eschenbach (r1969) *Concert*
(3/94) (DG) ① [5] 419 445-2GX5
S. Richter (pp1986) *Concert*
(8/94) (PHIL) ① [2] 438 480-2PH2
I. Pogorelich (r1992) *Concert*
(8/95) (DG) ① 437 763-2GH

Sonata for Keyboard No. 6 in D, K284/K205b (1775)
M. Uchida *Concert* (7/87) (PHIL) ① 420 185-2PH
M. Uchida *Concert*
(2/89) (PHIL) ① [6] 422 115-2PH6
T. Vesselinova *Concert*
(7/89) (ACCE) ① [2] ACC8849/50
P. Katin *Concert* (5/90) (OLYM) ① OCD233
M. Uchida *Concert*
(9/91) (PHIL) ① [5] 422 517-2PME5
A. de Larrocha *Concert* (10/91) (RCA) ① RD60709
M-J. Pires *Concert*
(2/92) (DG) ① [6] 431 760-2GH6
C. Arrau *Concert*
(3/92) (PHIL) ① [7] 432 306-2PM7
D. Barenboim *Concert*
(4/92) (EMI) ① [5] CZS7 67294-2
M-J. Pires (r1990) *Concert*
(3/94) (DG) ① 437 791-2GH
C. Eschenbach (r1970) *Concert*
(3/94) (DG) ① [5] 419 445-2GX5

Sonata for Keyboard No. 7 in C, K309/284b (1777)
M. Uchida *Concert* (7/86) (PHIL) ① 412 741-2PH
M. Uchida *Concert*
(2/89) (PHIL) ① [6] 422 115-2PH6
P. Katin *Concert* (5/90) (OLYM) ① OCD232
M. Uchida *Concert*
(9/91) (PHIL) ① [5] 422 517-2PME5
M-J. Pires *Concert*
(2/92) (DG) ① [6] 431 760-2GH6
C. Arrau *Concert*
(3/92) (PHIL) ① [7] 432 306-2PM7
D. Barenboim *Concert*
(4/92) (EMI) ① [5] CZS7 67294-2
A. de Larrocha *Concert* (7/92) (RCA) ① RD60454
C. Eschenbach (r1969) *Concert*
(3/94) (DG) ① [5] 419 445-2GX5

Sonata for Keyboard No. 8 in A minor, K310/K300d (1778)
M. Uchida *Concert* (7/86) (PHIL) ① 412 741-2PH
I. Haebler *Concert* (8/88) (DENO) ① CO-1517
M. Uchida *Concert*
(2/89) (PHIL) ① [6] 422 115-2PH6

M-J. Pires *Concert*
(2/92) (DG) ① [6] **431 760-2GH6**
C. Arrau *Concert*
(3/92) (PHIL) ① [7] **432 306-2PM7**
D. Barenboim *Concert*
(4/92) (EMI) ① [5] **CZS7 67294-2**
A. Schiff *Concert* (5/92) (L'OI) ① **433 328-2OH**
C. Eschenbach (r1969) *Concert*
(3/94) (DG) ① [5] **419 445-2GX5**
W. Kapell (bp c1947) *Concert*
(11/94) (VAI) ① **VAIA1048**
W. Gieseking (r1936) *Concert*
(5/95) (APR) ① **APR5511**
M. Pletnev (r1984) *Concert*
(8/95) (MELO) ① [11] **74321 25181-2**
M. Pletnev (r1984) *Concert*
(8/95) (MELO) ① [11] **74321 25172-2(2)**
**Sonata for Keyboard No. 18 in D, K576
(1789)**
M. Uchida *Concert* (1/86) (PHIL) ① **412 617-2PH**
P. Badura-Skoda *Concert*
(3/86) (ASTR) ① [2] **E7703/4**
M. Uchida *Concert*
(2/89) (PHIL) ① [6] **422 115-2PH6**
I. Haebler *Concert* (7/89) (DENO) ① **CO-73087**
P. Katin *Concert* (5/90) (OLYM) ① **OCD234**
W. Gieseking (bp1944) *Concert*
(11/90) (MUSI) ① **MACD-612**
A. Lubimov *Concert*
(4/91) (ERAT) ① **2292-45510-2**
M. Uchida *Concert*
(9/91) (PHIL) ① [5] **422 517-2PME5**
M-J. Pires *Concert*
(2/92) (DG) ① [6] **431 760-2GH6**
Vladimir Ashkenazy *Concert*
(2/92) (DECC) ① **425 031-2DM**
C. Arrau *Concert*
(3/92) (PHIL) ① [7] **432 306-2PM7**
D. Barenboim *Concert*
(4/92) (EMI) ① [5] **CZS7 67294-2**
M-J. Pires *Concert* (2/93) (DG) ① [5] **435 882-2GH**
M. Uchida (pp1991) *Concert*
(4/93) (PHIL) ① [2] **432 989-2PH2**
W. Landowska (r1938) *Concert*
(10/93) (BIDD) ① **LHW013**
M. Horszowski (r1980s) *Concert*
(12/93) (NONE) ① [3] **7559-79261-2**
C. Eschenbach (r1970) *Concert*
(3/94) (DG) ① [5] **419 445-2GX5**
S. Feinberg (1952) *Concert*
(8/95) (MELO) ① [11] **74321 25172-2(1)**
S. Feinberg (1952) *Concert*
(8/95) (MELO) ① [11] **74321 25175-2**
**Suite in the style of Handel in C—keyboard,
K399 (71782)**
1. Overture.
M. Haselböck *Concert*
(10/91) (NOVA) ① **150 054-2**
M. Haselböck *Concert* (10/91) (SCHW) ① **317003**
T. Koopman *Concert*
(10/91) (PHIL) ① [5] **422 518-2PME5**
G. Penson *Concert*
(12/92) (RICE) ① [3] **RIC105081**
1. T. Trotter (r1993) *Concert*
(10/95) (LOND) ① **443 451-2LH**
**8 Variations in A on 'Come un angello' by G.
Sarti—keyboard, K460/K454a (1784)**
T. Koopman *Concert*
(10/91) (PHIL) ① [5] **422 518-2PME5**
F. Nicolosi (r1991) *Concert*
(9/94) (NAXO) ① **8 550613**
**12 Variations in C on a minuet by J. C.
Fischer—keyboard, K179/189a (1774)**
I. Haebler *Concert*
(10/91) (PHIL) ① [5] **422 518-2PME5**
D. Barenboim *Concert*
(4/92) (EMI) ① [3] **CDS7 54362-2**
F. Nicolosi (r1991) *Concert*
(9/94) (NAXO) ① **8 550611**
**12 Variations in C on 'Ah, vous dirai-je,
Maman'—keyboard, K265/K300e (1781-82)**
J. van Immerseel *Concert*
(9/86) (ACCE) ① **ACC58018D**
L. Rév *Concert* (7/87) (HYPE) ① **CDA66185**
I. Haebler *Concert*
(10/91) (PHIL) ① [5] **422 518-2PME5**
D. Barenboim *Concert*
(4/92) (EMI) ① [3] **CDS7 54362-2**
M. Dalberto *Concert* (12/92) (DENO) ① **CO-79477**
F. Nicolosi (r1991) *Concert*
(9/94) (NAXO) ① **8 550612**
**9 Variations in D on a minuet by J. P.
Duport—keyboard, K573 (1789)** (transc from
Duport Cello Sonata, Op. 4/6)
I. Haebler *Concert*
(10/91) (PHIL) ① [5] **422 518-2PME5**

A. Brendel *Concert* (2/92) (VANG) ① **08.4025.71**
D. Barenboim *Concert*
(4/92) (EMI) ① [3] **CDS7 54362-2**
M. Dalberto *Concert* (12/92) (DENO) ① **CO-79477**
F. Nicolosi (r1991) *Concert*
(9/94) (NAXO) ① **8 550613**
C. Haskil (r1954) *Concert*
(11/95) (PHIL) ① [3] **442 635-2PM3**
C. Haskil (r1954) *Concert*
(11/95) (PHIL) ① [12] **442 685-2PM12**
**7 Variations in D on 'Willem van
Nassau'—keyboard, K25 (1766)**
I. Haebler *Concert*
(10/91) (PHIL) ① [5] **422 518-2PME5**
D. Barenboim *Concert*
(4/92) (EMI) ① [3] **CDS7 54362-2**
F. Nicolosi (r1991) *Concert*
(9/94) (NAXO) ① **8 550611**
**12 Variations in E flat on 'Je suis Lindor' by
A. L. Baudron—keyboard, K354/K299a
(1778)**
I. Haebler *Concert*
(10/91) (PHIL) ① [5] **422 518-2PME5**
D. Barenboim *Concert*
(4/92) (EMI) ① [3] **CDS7 54362-2**
F. Nicolosi (r1991) *Concert*
(9/94) (NAXO) ① **8 550611**
**12 Variations in E flat on 'La belle
Françoise'—keyboard, K353/K300f (1781-82)**
I. Haebler *Concert*
(10/91) (PHIL) ① [5] **422 518-2PME5**
D. Barenboim *Concert*
(4/92) (EMI) ① [3] **CDS7 54362-2**
F. Nicolosi (r1991) *Concert*
(9/94) (NAXO) ① **8 550612**
M. Dalberto *Concert* (6/95) (DENO) ① **CO-78909**
**6 Variations in F on an allegretto—keyboard,
K54/K547b (1788)**
D. Barenboim *Concert*
(4/92) (EMI) ① [3] **CDS7 54362-2**
F. Nicolosi (r1991) *Concert*
(9/94) (NAXO) ① **8 550611**
**8 Variations in F on 'Dieu d'amour' by
Grétry—keyboard, K352/K374c (1781)**
I. Haebler *Concert*
(10/91) (PHIL) ① [5] **422 518-2PME5**
D. Barenboim *Concert*
(4/92) (EMI) ① [3] **CDS7 54362-2**
F. Nicolosi (r1991) *Concert*
(9/94) (NAXO) ① **8 550613**
**8 Variations in F on 'Ein Weib ist das
herrlichste Ding' by B. Schack or F.
Gerl—keyboard, K613 (1791)**
I. Haebler *Concert*
(10/91) (PHIL) ① [5] **422 518-2PME5**
D. Barenboim *Concert*
(4/92) (EMI) ① [3] **CDS7 54362-2**
F. Nicolosi (r1991) *Concert*
(9/94) (NAXO) ① **8 550613**
**6 Variations in F on 'Salve tu, Domine' by
Paisiello—keyboard, K398/K416e (1782)**
I. Haebler *Concert*
(10/91) (PHIL) ① [5] **422 518-2PME5**
D. Barenboim *Concert*
(4/92) (EMI) ① [3] **CDS7 54362-2**
M. Dalberto *Concert* (12/92) (DENO) ① **CO-79477**
F. Nicolosi (r1991) *Concert*
(9/94) (NAXO) ① **8 550612**
**8 Variations in G on a Dutch song, 'Laat ons
juichen' (C.E. Graaf)—keyboard, K24 (1766)**
I. Haebler *Concert*
(10/91) (PHIL) ① [5] **422 518-2PME5**
D. Barenboim *Concert*
(4/92) (EMI) ① [3] **CDS7 54362-2**
F. Nicolosi (r1991) *Concert*
(9/94) (NAXO) ① **8 550611**
**6 Variations in G on 'Mio caro Adone' by
Salieri—keyboard, K180/K173c (1773)**
I. Haebler *Concert*
(10/91) (PHIL) ① [5] **422 518-2PME5**
D. Barenboim *Concert*
(4/92) (EMI) ① [3] **CDS7 54362-2**
F. Nicolosi (r1991) *Concert*
(9/94) (NAXO) ① **8 550611**
**10 Variations in G on 'Unser dummer Pöbel
meint' by Gluck—keyboard, K455 (1784)**
I. Haebler *Concert*
(10/91) (PHIL) ① [5] **422 518-2PME5**
D. Barenboim *Concert*
(4/92) (EMI) ① [3] **CDS7 54362-2**
M. Uchida (pp1991) *Concert*
(4/93) (PHIL) ① [2] **432 989-2PH2**
M. Horszowski (pp1969) *Concert*
(12/93) (PEAR) ① [2] **GEMMCDS9979**

F. Nicolosi (r1991) *Concert*
(9/94) (NAXO) ① **8 550613**
M. Dalberto (r1993) *Concert*
(6/95) (DENO) ① **CO-78909**
**9 Variations on 'Lison dormait' from
Dezède's 'Julie'—keyboard, K264/315d
(1778)**
I. Haebler *Concert*
(10/91) (PHIL) ① [5] **422 518-2PME5**
D. Barenboim *Concert*
(4/92) (EMI) ① [3] **CDS7 54362-2**
F. Nicolosi (r1991) *Concert*
(9/94) (NAXO) ① **8 550612**

SECTION IV: VOCAL AND CHORAL

A questo seno—concert aria, K374 (1781)
(Wds. G. de Gamerra)
E. Gruberová, COE, N. Harnoncourt (pp1991)
Concert (5/92) (TELD) ① **9031-72302-2**
G. Janowitz, Vienna SO, W. Boettcher (r1966)
Concert (12/95) (DG) ① [2] **447 352-2GDB2**
Abendempfindung—Lied, K523 (1787) (Wds.
?J.H. Campe)
R. Alexander, G. Wilson *Concert*
(3/87) (ETCE) ① **KTC1035**
R. Jacobs, K. Junghänel (r1985) *Concert*
(5/87) (HARM) ① **HMA190 1183**
M. Shirai, H. Höll *Concert* (7/87) (CAPR) ① **10 098**
E. Mathis, K. Engel *Concert*
(9/87) (NOVA) ① **150 010-2**
E. Schwarzkopf, W. Gieseking *Concert*
(12/90) (EMI) ① **CDH7 63702-2**
B. Hendricks, M-J. Pires *Concert*
(7/91) (EMI) ① **CDC7 54007-2**
B. Bonney, G. Parsons *Concert*
(1/92) (TELD) ① **2292-46334-2**
J. Kowalski, S. Katz *Concert*
(12/92) (CAPR) ① **10 359**
J. Varady, E. Bashkirova *Concert*
(5/93) (ORFE) ① **C248921A**
I. Seefried, E. Werba (r1957) *Concert*
(7/93) (DG) ① [2] **437 348-2GDO2**
A. Auger, J. Revzen (pp1986) *Concert*
(4/94) (KOCH) ① **37248-2**
I. Seefried, G. Moore (1950) *Concert*
(4/94) (TEST) ① **SBT1026**
J. Protschka, H. Deutsch (r1991) *Concert*
(10/94) (CAPR) ① [2] **10 446/7**
O. Bär, G. Parsons (r1993/4) *Concert*
(12/95) (EMI) ① **CDC5 55345-2**
**Ah, lo previdi...Ah, t'invola—concert aria:
soprano, K272 (1777)** (Wds. V.A. Cigna-Santi)
B. Hendricks, ECO, J. Tate *Concert*
(6/85) (EMI) ① **CDC7 47122-2**
E. Kirkby, AAM, C. Hogwood *Concert*
(4/91) (L'OI) ① **425 835-2OH**
G. Janowitz, Vienna SO, W. Boettcher (r1966)
Concert (12/95) (DG) ① [2] **447 352-2GDB2**
**Ah! se in ciel, benigne stelle—concert aria:
soprano, K538 (1788)** (Wds. Metastasio)
E. Gruberová, COE, N. Harnoncourt (pp1991)
Concert (5/92) (TELD) ① **9031-72302-2**
**Ah, spiegarti, o Dio—concert aria: soprano,
K178/417e (1783)**
R. Alexander, G. Wilson *Concert*
(3/87) (ETCE) ① **KTC1035**
**Al desio—interpolation aria (Mozart's La
nozze di Figaro), K577 (1789)** (Wds. ?L. da
Ponte)
T. Berganza, Vienna CO, G. Fischer *Concert*
(4/93) (DECC) ① **421 899-2DA**
M. Price, LPO, J. Lockhart (r1975) *Concert*
(5/95) (RCA) ① [2] **09026 61635-2**
**Alma grande e nobil core—insertion aria
(Cimarosa's 'I due baroni', K578 (1789)**
(Wds. G. Palomba)
E. Schwarzkopf, LSO, G. Szell *Concert*
(12/90) (EMI) ① **CDH7 63702-2**
C. Bartoli, Vienna CO, G. Fischer *Concert*
(12/91) (DECC) ① **430 513-2DH**
G. Janowitz, Vienna SO, W. Boettcher (r1966)
Concert (12/95) (DG) ① [2] **447 352-2GDB2**
A. Roocroft, ASMF, N. Marriner *Concert*
(12/95) (EMI) ① **CDC5 55396-2**
Als Luise die Briefe—Lied, K520 (1787) (Wds.
G. von Baumberg)
R. Alexander, G. Wilson *Concert*
(3/87) (ETCE) ① **KTC1035**
M. Shirai, H. Höll *Concert* (7/87) (CAPR) ① **10 098**
E. Mathis, K. Engel *Concert*
(9/87) (NOVA) ① **150 010-2**
E. Schwarzkopf, W. Gieseking *Concert*
(12/90) (EMI) ① **CDH7 63702-2**
B. Hendricks, M-J. Pires *Concert*
(7/91) (EMI) ① **CDC7 54007-2**

B. Bonney, English Concert, T. Pinnock (r1993)
Concert   (10/94) (ARCH) ① 445 353-2AH
C. Bartoli, Vienna CO, G. Fischer (r1993) Concert
          (11/94) (DECC) ① 443 452-2DH
M. Stader, Berlin RSO, F. Fricsay (r1960)
Entführung.   (7/95) (DG) ① [2] 445 412-2GDO2
3. L. Popp, ECO, G. Fischer Concert
          (8/89) (CFP) ① CD-CFP4532
3. E. Schumann, orch. G.W. Byng (r1926) Concert
          (6/91) (PREI) ① 89031
3. K. Battle, Orch. A. Previn (r1991) Concert
          (12/92) (SONY) ① SK48235
3. E. Schumann, orch. G.W. Byng (r1926) Concert
          (1/93) (MMOI) ① CDMOIR411
3. L. Price, VPO, H. von Karajan (r1961) Concert
          (6/93) (DECC) ① 436 402-2DWO
**2 German Church Songs, K343/K336c
(?1787)**
1. O Lammes Gott; 2. Als aus Aegypten.
J. Protschka, H. Deutsch (r1991) Concert
          (10/94) (CAPR) ① [2] 10 446/7
1. B. Bonney, G. Parsons Concert
          (1/92) (TELD) ① 2292-46334-2
**Grabmusik—cantata: soprano, bass, choir
and orchestra, K42a/K35a (1772) (Wds. ?J.A.
Schachtner)**
A. Murray, S. Varcoe, South German Rad Chor,
Stuttgart RSO, N. Marriner Concert
          (4/92) (PHIL) ① [6] 422 522-2PME6
Betracht dies Herz B. Hendricks, ASMF, N. Marriner
Concert   (5/88) (EMI) ① CDC7 49283-2
**Ich würd' auf meinem Pfad (An die
Hoffnung)—Lied, K390/K340c (1781-82)**
(Wds. J.T. Hermes)
M. Shirai, H. Höll Concert   (7/87) (CAPR) ① 10 098
E. Mathis, K. Engel Concert
          (9/87) (NOVA) ① 150 010-2
B. Hendricks, M-J. Pires Concert
          (7/91) (EMI) ① CDC7 54007-2
H. Hagegård, T. Schuback (r1976) Concert
          (5/94) (BIS) ① BIS-CD054
J. Protschka, H. Deutsch (r1991) Concert
          (10/94) (CAPR) ① [2] 10 446/7
**Ihr unsre neuen Leiter—Lied: tenor, chorus
and organ, K484 (1785-86) (Wds. A.V.
Schlittersberg)**
W. Krenn, Edinburgh Fest Chor, G. Fischer Concert
          (11/90) (DECC) ① 425 722-2DM
P. Schreier, Leipzig Rad Chor, R. Alpermann Concert
          (4/92) (PHIL) ① [6] 422 522-2PME6
C. Prégardien, Chorus Viennensis, M. Haselböck
(r1991) Concert   (10/93) (NOVA) ① 150 081-2
**Im Frühlingsanfang—Lied, K597 (1791) (Wds.
C.C. Sturm)**
R. Alexander, G. Wilson Concert
          (3/87) (ETCE) ① KTC1035
M. Shirai, H. Höll Concert   (7/87) (CAPR) ① 10 098
E. Mathis, K. Engel Concert
          (9/87) (NOVA) ① 150 010-2
E. Schwarzkopf, W. Gieseking Concert
          (12/90) (EMI) ① CDH7 63702-2
B. Bonney, G. Parsons Concert
          (1/92) (TELD) ① 2292-46334-2
J. Protschka, H. Deutsch (r1991) Concert
          (10/94) (CAPR) ① [2] 10 446/7
**Inter natos mulierum in G—offertory:
chorus, two trumpets, strings & organ,
K72/K74f (1771)**
Berlin RIAS Chbr Ch, Berlin RSO, M. Creed Concert
          (8/89) (CAPR) ① 10 169
**Das Kinderspiel—Lied, K598 (1791) (Wds.
C.A. Overbeck)**
E. Mathis, K. Engel Concert
          (9/87) (NOVA) ① 150 010-2
E. Schwarzkopf, W. Gieseking Concert
          (12/90) (EMI) ① CDH7 63702-2
B. Bonney, G. Parsons Concert
          (1/92) (TELD) ① 2292-46334-2
I. Seefried, E. Werba (r1957) Concert
          (7/93) (DG) ① [2] 437 348-2GDO2
I. Seefried, E. Werba (pp1957) Concert
          (9/93) (ORFE) ① C297921B
I. Seefried, E. Moore (r1950) Concert
          (4/94) (TEST) ① SBT1026
R. Streich, E. Werba (r1956) Concert
          (10/94) (DG) ① [2] 437 680-2GDO2
J. Protschka, H. Deutsch (r1991) Concert
          (10/94) (CAPR) ① [2] 10 446/7
**Eine Kleine deutsche Kantate, '(Die) ihr des
unermesslichen Weltalls'—soprano/tenor
and keyboard, K619 (1791) (Wds. F.H.
Ziegenhagen)**
W. Krenn, G. Fischer Concert
          (11/90) (DECC) ① 425 722-2DM
B. Hendricks, M-J. Pires Concert
          (7/91) (EMI) ① CDC7 54007-2

H-P. Blochwitz, R. Jansen Concert
          (4/92) (PHIL) ① [6] 422 522-2PME6
H. Wildhaber, M. Haselböck (r1991) Concert
          (10/93) (NOVA) ① 150 081-2
J. Protschka, H. Deutsch (r1991) Concert
          (10/94) (CAPR) ① [2] 10 446/7
M. Price, J. Lockhart (r1970) Concert
          (5/95) (RCA) ① [2] 09026 61635-2
**Eine Kleine Freimaurer-Kantate, 'Laut
verkünde unsre Freude'—Masonic cantata:
TTB, chorus and orchestra, K623 (1791)
(Wds. E. Schikaneder)**
W. Krenn, T. Krause, Edinburgh Fest Chor, LSO, I.
Kertész Concert   (11/90) (DECC) ① 425 722-2DM
J. Bryden, M. Westerbrook-Geha, W. Hite, W.
Bastian, W. Sharp, S. Richardson, Boston Early
Music Fest Chor, Boston Early Music Fest Orch, A.
Parrott Requiem.   (12/91) (DENO) ① CO-77152
H-P. Blochwitz, A. Schmidt, Leipzig Rad Chor,
Staatskapelle Dresden Concert
          (4/92) (PHIL) ① [6] 422 522-2PME6
C. Prégardien, H. Wildhaber, G. Hornik, Chorus
Viennensis, Vienna Academy Orch, M. Haselböck
(r1991) Concert   (10/93) (NOVA) ① 150 081-2
**Das Kleine Spinnerin—Lied, K531 (1787)
(Wds. ?D. Jäger)**
M. Shirai, H. Höll Concert   (7/87) (CAPR) ① 10 098
E. Mathis, K. Engel Concert
          (9/87) (NOVA) ① 150 010-2
E. Schwarzkopf, W. Gieseking Concert
          (12/90) (EMI) ① CDH7 63702-2
B. Hendricks, M-J. Pires Concert
          (7/91) (EMI) ① CDC7 54007-2
I. Seefried, E. Werba (r1957) Concert
          (7/93) (DG) ① [2] 437 348-2GDO2
I. Seefried, E. Moore (r1950) Concert
          (4/94) (TEST) ① SBT1026
R. Streich, E. Werba (r1956) Concert
          (10/94) (DG) ① [2] 437 680-2GDO2
M. Shirai, H. Höll (r1991) Concert
          (10/94) (CAPR) ① [2] 10 446/7
**Der Kleinen Friedrichs Geburtstag—Lied,
K529 (1787) (Wds. J.E.F. Schall/J.H. Campe)**
J. Protschka, H. Deutsch (r1991) Concert
          (10/94) (CAPR) ① [2] 10 446/7
**Komm, liebe Zither—Lied, K351/K367b
(1780-81) (Wds. Anon)**
M. Shirai, H. Höll Concert   (7/87) (CAPR) ① 10 098
P. Schreier, K. Ragossnig Concert
          (10/89) (NOVA) ① 150 039-2
B. Hendricks, G. Söllscher Concert
          (7/91) (EMI) ① CDC7 54007-2
B. Bonney, G. Parsons Concert
          (1/92) (TELD) ① 2292-46334-2
A. Stephens, P. Holden Concert
          (3/92) (AMON) ① CD-SAR53
D. Orieschnig, W. Würdinger (r1986) Concert
          (5/92) (PHIL) ① 422 527-2PME
J. Protschka, H. Deutsch (r1991) Concert
          (10/94) (CAPR) ① [2] 10 446/7
**Kommt her, ihr frechen Sünder—aria:
soprano, strings and organ, K146/317b
(1779)**
A. Murray, Stuttgart RSO, N. Marriner Concert
          (4/92) (PHIL) ① [6] 422 522-2PME6
**Kyrie in D minor—chorus and orchestra,
K341/K368a (1781)**
LSC, LSO, Colin Davis (r1971) Concert
          (3/86) (PHIL) ① 412 873-2PH
Monteverdi Ch, EBS, J.E. Gardiner Requiem.
          (11/87) (PHIL) ① 420 197-2PH
Stuttgart Gächinger Kantorei, Stuttgart Bach
Collegium, H. Rilling Concert
          (9/92) (HANS) ① [2] 98 979
Cologne Chbr Ch, Collegium Cartusianum, P.
Neumann (r1989) Mass, K427.
          (7/95) (VIRG) ① VER5 61167-2
**Lasst uns mit geschlungen Händen—chorus
and organ, K623a (1791) (fragment of 32
bars)**
Edinburgh Fest Chor, G. Fischer Concert
          (11/90) (DECC) ① 425 722-2DM
Leipzig Rad Chor, R. Alpermann Concert
          (4/92) (PHIL) ① [6] 422 522-2PME6
Lied der Freiheit—Lied, K506 (1785)
(Wds. Blumauer)
B. Bonney, G. Parsons Concert
          (1/92) (TELD) ① 2292-46334-2
J. Protschka, H. Deutsch (r1991) Concert
          (10/94) (CAPR) ① [2] 10 446/7
**Das Lied der Trennung—Lied, K519 (1787)
(Wds. Schmitt)**
R. Alexander, G. Wilson Concert
          (3/87) (ETCE) ① KTC1035
M. Shirai, H. Höll Concert   (7/87) (CAPR) ① 10 098

E. Schwarzkopf, W. Gieseking Concert
          (12/90) (EMI) ① CDH7 63702-2
B. Hendricks, M-J. Pires Concert
          (7/91) (EMI) ① CDC7 54007-2
B. Bonney, G. Parsons Concert
          (1/92) (TELD) ① 2292-46334-2
J. Kowalski, S. Katz Concert
          (12/92) (CAPR) ① 10 359
I. Seefried, E. Werba (r1957) Concert
          (7/93) (DG) ① [2] 437 348-2GDO2
A. Auger, J. Revzen (pp1986) Concert
          (4/94) (KOCH) ① 37248-2
R. Streich, E. Werba (r1956) Concert
          (10/94) (DG) ① [2] 437 680-2GDO2
J. Protschka, H. Deutsch (r1991) Concert
          (10/94) (CAPR) ① [2] 10 446/7
Lied zur Gesellenreise—Lied, K468 (1785)
(Wds. J. F. von Ratschky)
M. Shirai, H. Höll Concert   (7/87) (CAPR) ① 10 098
W. Krenn, G. Fischer Concert
          (11/90) (DECC) ① 425 722-2DM
H-P. Blochwitz, R. Jansen Concert
          (4/92) (PHIL) ① [6] 422 522-2PME6
H. Wildhaber, M. Haselböck (r1991) Concert
          (10/93) (NOVA) ① 150 081-2
J. Protschka, H. Deutsch (r1991) Concert
          (10/94) (CAPR) ① [2] 10 446/7
**Litaniae de venerabili altaris
sacramento—SATB, chorus and orchestra,
K125 (1772)**
B. Bonney, E. von Magnus, U. Heilmann, G.
Cachemaille, A. Schoenberg Ch, VCM, N.
Harnoncourt (r1992) Concert
          (8/93) (TELD) ① 4509-90494-2
**Litaniae de venerabili altaris sacramento,
K243 (1775)**
1. Kyrie; 2. Panis vivus; 3. Verbum caro factum; 4.
Hostia sancta; 5. Tremendum; 6. Dulcissimum
convivium; 7. Viaticum; 8. Pignus futurae gloriae; 9.
Agnus Dei; 10. Miserere.
M. Marshall, M. Cable, W. Evans, S. Roberts, St
John's College Ch, Wren Orch, G. Guest Haydn:
Mass 9.   (6/91) (DECC) ① 430 158-2DM
A.M. Blasi, E. von Magnus, D. van der Walt, A. Miles,
A. Schoenberg Ch, VCM, N. Harnoncourt (r1991)
Mass, K257.   (6/93) (TELD) ① 9031-72304-2
2. U. Heilmann, Leipzig Gewandhaus, P. Schreier
(r1993) Concert   (3/95) (DECC) ① 440 680-2DH
6. B. Hendricks, ASMF, N. Marriner Concert
          (5/88) (EMI) ① CDC7 49283-2
**Litaniae Lauretanae BVM—SATB, chorus
and orchestra, K195/186d (1774)**
I. Cotrubas, H. Watts, R. Tear, J. Shirley-Quirk,
Oxford Schola Cantorum, ASMF, N. Marriner (r1971)
Concert   (5/94) (DECC) ① [2] 443 009-2DF2
Agnus Dei B. Hendricks, ASMF Chor, ASMF, N.
Marriner Concert   (5/88) (EMI) ① CDC7 49283-2
**Lobesgesang auf die feierliche
Johannislogie—Lied, K148/K125h (?1775-76)**
(Wds.Lenz)
H-P. Blochwitz, R. Jansen Concert
          (4/92) (PHIL) ① [6] 422 522-2PME6
H. Wildhaber, M. Haselböck (r1991) Concert
          (10/93) (NOVA) ① 150 081-2
**Mass No. 4 in C minor, 'Waisenhausmesse',
K139/47a (1768)**
G. Janowitz, F. von Stade, W. Ochman, K. Moll,
Vienna St Op Chor, VPO, C. Abbado
          (8/89) (DG) ① 427 255-2GGA
C. Lindsley, G. Schreckenbach, W. Hollweg, W.
Grönroos, Berlin RIAS Chbr Ch, Berlin RSO, M.
Creed Concert   (8/89) (CAPR) ① 10 169
**Mass No. 10 in C, 'Spatzenmesse'—Missa
brevis, K220/K196b (1775-76)**
R. Hansmann, A. Bartelloni, M. Sénéchal, R. Soyer,
M-C. Alain Concert
          (8/94) (ERAT) ① 4509-95362-2
**Mass No. 11 in C, 'Credo Mass'—SATB,
chorus and orchestra, K257 (1776)**
A. Monoyios, E. Graf, O. Pfaff, F-J. Selig, Cologne
Chbr Ch, Collegium Cartusianum, P. Neumann
Concert   (10/91) (EMI) ① CDC7 54037-2
A.M. Blasi, E. von Magnus, D. van der Walt, A. Miles,
A. Schoenberg Ch, VCM, N. Harnoncourt (r1991)
Litanies, K243.   (6/93) (TELD) ① 9031-72304-2
**Mass No. 12 in C, 'Spaurmesse'—Missa
brevis, K258 (1776)**
F. Palmer, M. Cable, P. Langridge, S. Roberts, St
John's College Ch, Wren Orch, G. Guest Haydn:
Mass 13.   (6/91) (DECC) ① 430 161-2DM
B. Schlick, U. Groenewold, M. Schäfer, K. Mertens,
Cologne Chbr Ch, Collegium Cartusianum, P.
Neumann (10/91) (EMI) ① CDC7 54037-2

**Mass No. 13 in C, 'Organ solo'—SATB,
chorus and orchestra, K259 (1775 or 1776)**
A. Monoyios, E. Graf, O. Pfaff, F-J. Selig, Cologne
Chbr Ch, Collegium Cartusianum, P. Neumann
Concert   (10/91) (EMI) ① CDC7 54037-2
**Mass No. 15 in B flat, 'Missa brevis',
K275/K272b (1777)**
Benedictus M. Haselböck (arr V. Novello) *Concert*
   (10/91) (SCHW) ① 317003
Mass No. 16 in C, 'Coronation', K317 (1779)
E. Moser, J. Hamari, N. Gedda, D. Fischer-Dieskau,
Bavarian Rad Chor, BRSO, E. Jochum *Vespers,
K339.*   (9/87) (EMI) ① CDM7 69023-2
A. Tomowa-Sintow, A. Baltsa, W. Krenn, J. Van Dam,
Vienna Singverein, BPO, H. von Karajan *Beethoven:
Missa Solemnis.*
   (2/89) (DG) ① [2] 423 913-2GGA2
M. Stader, O. Dominguez, E. Haefliger, M. Roux, E.
Brasseur Ch, Lamoureux Orch, I. Markevitch (r1960)
Beethoven: Mass in C.
   (6/90) (DG) ① 429 510-2GR
S. McNair, D. Ziegler, H-P. Blochwitz, A. Schmidt,
Berlin RIAS Chbr Ch, BPO, James Levine (pp)
Haydn: Mass 10.   (9/92) (DG) ① 435 853-2GH
E. Kirkby, C. Robbin, J.M. Ainsley, M. George,
Winchester Cath Ch, Winchester Quiristers, AAM, C.
Hogwood (r1990) *Concert*
   (4/93) (L'OI) ① 436 585-2OH
P. Coles, A. di Mauro, J. Dickie, A. Martin, Košice
Teachers Ch, Camerata Cassovia, J. Wildner
Concert   (5/93) (NAXO) ① 8 550495
M. Marshall, A. Murray, R. Covey-Crump, D. Wilson-
Johnson, King's College Ch, ECO, S. Cleobury
(r1983) *Haydn: Mass 11.*
   (5/93) (DECC) ① 436 470-2DM
E. Mathis, J. Rappé, H-P. Blochwitz, T. Quasthoff,
Leipzig Rad Chor, Staatskapelle Dresden, P.
Schreier (r1989) *Concert*
   (2/94) (PHIL) ① 426 275-2PH
H. Donath, G. Knight, R. Davies, S. Dean, John Alldis
Ch, LSO, Colin Davis (r1971) *Concert*
   (3/94) (PHIL) ① [2] 438 800-2PM2
I. Cotrubas, H. Watts, R. Tear, J. Shirley-Quirk,
Oxford Schola Cantorum, ASMF, N. Marriner (r1971)
Concert   (5/94) (DECC) ① [2] 443 009-2DF2
P. Wise, M. Bürgener, M. Cousins, H.K. Ecker,
Lisbon Gulbenkian Chor, Lisbon Gulbenkian Orch, T.
Guschlbauer *Concert*
   (8/94) (ERAT) ① [2] 4509-95362-2
B. Bonney, C. Wyn-Rogers, J. MacDougall, S. Gadd,
English Concert Ch, English Concert, T. Pinnock
(r1993) *Concert*   (10/94) (ARCH) ① 445 353-2AH
M. Pennicchi, C. Patriasz, Z. Vandersteene, J.
Draijer, Netherlands Chbr Ch, Eighteenth Century
Orch, F. Brüggen (r1991) *Concert*
   (6/95) (PHIL) ① 434 799-2PH
Agnus Dei B. Hendricks, ASMF, N. Marriner *Concert.*
Marriner *Concert*   (5/88) (EMI) ① CDC7 49283-2
**Mass No. 17 in C, 'Missa brevis', K337
(1780)**
B. Bonney, E. von Magnus, U. Heilmann, G.
Cachemaille, A. Schoenberg Ch, VCM, N.
Harnoncourt (r1992) *Concert*
   (8/93) (TELD) ① 4509-90494-2
**Mass No. 18 in C minor, 'Great'—SSTB,
chorus and orchestra, K427/K417a (1782-3)**
(incomplete)
1. Kyrie; 2. Gloria: 2a. Gloria in excelsis Deo; 2b.
Laudamus te; 2c. Gratias agimus tibi; 2d. Domine
Deus; 2e. Qui tollis; 2f. Quoniam; 2g. Jesu Christe;
2h. Cum Sancto Spirito; 3. Credo: 3a. Credo; 3b. Et
incarnatus est; 4. Sanctus: 4a. Sanctus; 4b.
Benedictus.
I. Cotrubas, K. Te Kanawa, W. Krenn, H. Sotin, John
Alldis Ch, New Philh, R. Leppard
   (10/86) (EMI) ① CDC7 47385-2
S. McNair, D. Montague, A. Rolfe Johnson, C.
Hauptmann, Monteverdi Ch, EBS, J.E. Gardiner
(ed.Schmitt/Gardiner)
   (5/88) (PHIL) ① 420 210-2PH
E. Wiens, D. Ziegler, J. Aler, W. Stone, Atlanta Sym
Chor, Atlanta SO, Robert Shaw (r1987) *Beethoven:
Missa Solemnis.*   (11/88) (TELA) ① [2] CD80150
A. Auger, L. Dawson, J.M. Ainsley, D. Thomas,
Winchester Cath Ch, Winchester Quiristers, AAM, C.
Hogwood (ed. Maunder)
   (7/90) (L'OI) ① 425 528-2OH
B. Bonney, A. Auger, H-P. Blochwitz, R. Holl, Berlin
Rad Chor, BPO, C. Abbado (ed Eder)
   (10/91) (SONY) ① SK46671
K. Battle, L. Cuberli, G. Seiffert, K. Moll, Vienna St
Op Chor, VPO, James Levine
   (11/91) (DG) ① 423 664-2GH
A. Auger, F. von Stade, F. Lopardo, C. Hauptmann,
Bavarian Rad Chor, BRSO, L. Bernstein (pp) *Concert*
   (12/91) (DG) ① 431 791-2GH

E. Norberg-Schulz, A.S. von Otter, U. Heilmann, R.
Pape, Vienna St Op Concert Ch, VPO, G. Solti (ed
Robbins Landon)   (2/92) (DECC) ① 433 749-2DH
N. Armstrong, D. Labelle, Jeffrey Thomas, R.
Morrison, J. Christie, Handel & Haydn Soc Chor,
Boston Early Music Fest Orch, A. Parrott (pp1991)
Church Sonatas.   (9/92) (DENO) ① CO-79573
C. Oelze, J. Larmore, S. Weir, P. Kooy, Collegium
Vocale, Chapelle Royale Ch, Paris Champs-Élysées
Orch, P. Herreweghe *Missa Hostermusik*, K477.
   (9/92) (HARM) ① HMC90 1393
C. Oelze, I. Verebics, S. Weir, O. Widmer, Stuttgart
Gächinger Kantorei, Stuttgart Bach Collegium, H.
Rilling (cptd Eder) *Concert*
   (9/92) (HANS) ① [2] 98 979
H. Donath, H. Harper, R. Davies, S. Dean, LSC,
LSO, Colin Davis (r1971) *Concert*
   (3/94) (PHIL) ① [2] 438 800-2PM2
K. te Kanawa, A. S. von Otter, A. Rolfe Johnson, R.
Lloyd, ASMF Chor, ASMF, N. Marriner (r1993) *Ave
verum corpus, K618.*
   (12/94) (PHIL) ① 438 999-2PH
B. Schlick, M. Frimmer, C. Prégardien, K. Mertens,
Cologne Chbr Ch, Collegium Cartusianum, P.
Neumann (r1989) *Kyrie, K341.*
   (7/95) (VIRG) ① VER5 61167-2
2b K. Te Kanawa, New Philh, R. Leppard *Concert*
   (8/89) (CFP) ① CD-CFP4532
3b B. Hendricks, ASMF, N. Marriner *Concert*
   (5/88) (EMI) ① CDC7 49283-2
**Mass No. 19 in D minor, 'Requiem'—SATB,
chorus and orchestra, K626 (1791)**
(incomplete)
1. Introitus: Requiem; 2. Kyrie; 3. Sequentia: 3a. Dies
irae; 3b. Rex tremendae; 3d. Recordare; 3e.
Confutatis; 3f. Lacrimosa; 4. Offertorium: 4a. Domine
Jesu; 4b. Hostias; 5. Sanctus; 6. Benedictus; 7.
Agnus Dei; 8. Communio: Lux aeterna.
M. Price, T. Schmidt, F. Araiza, T. Adam, Leipzig Rad
Chor, Staatskapelle Dresden, P. Schreier (cptd
Süssmayr)   (6/84) (PHIL) ① 411 420-2PH
E. Kirkby, C. Watkinson, A. Rolfe Johnson, D.
Thomas, Westminster Cath Boys' Ch, AAM Chor,
AAM, C. Hogwood (ed Maunder)
   (11/84) (L'OI) ① 411 712-2OH
E. Mathis, J. Hamari, W. Ochman, K. Ridderbusch,
Vienna St Op Chor, VPO, K. Böhm (ed Süssmayr)
   (2/86) (DG) ① 413 553-2GH
R. Yakar, O. Wenkel, K. Equiluz, R. Holl, Vienna St.
Op. Chor, VCM, N. Harnoncourt (ed Beyer)
   (5/86) (TELD) ① 2292-42911-2
K. Battle, A. Murray, D. Rendall, M. Salminen, Paris
Chor, Paris Orch, D. Barenboim (ed Süssmayr)
   (9/86) (EMI) ① CDC7 47342-2
I. Schmithüsen, C. Patriasz, N. Mackie, M. Hölle,
Netherlands Chbr Ch, Petite Bande, S. Kuijken (ed
Beyer: pp1986)   (4/87) (ACCE) ① ACC68645D
A. Auger, D. Ziegler, J. Hadley, T. Krause, Atlanta
Sym Chor, Atlanta SO, Robert Shaw (r1986; ed
Beyer)   (5/87) (TELA) ① CD80128
B. Bonney, A.S. von Otter, H-P. Blochwitz, W. White,
Monteverdi Ch, EBS, J.E. Gardiner (cptd Süssmayr)
Kyrie, K341.   (11/87) (PHIL) ① 420 197-2PH
K. Equiluz, G. Eder, Vienna Boys' Ch, Vienna
Hofmusikkapelle Ch, Vienna St Op Chor, Vienna
Hofmusikkapelle Orch, H. Gillesberger (r1982)
Süssmayr) Concert   (11/87) (RCA) ① GD86535
H. Donath, Y. Minton, R. Davies, G. Nienstedt, John
Alldis Ch, BBC SO, Colin Davis (r1967; cptd
Süssmayr)   (2/88) (PHIL) ① 420 353-2PM
Y. Kenny, Sarah Walker, W. Kendall, D. Wilson-
Johnson, St John's College Ch, ECO, M. Guest (ed
Süssmayr)   (2/88) (CHAN) ① CHAN8574
P. Pace, W. Meier, F. Lopardo, J. Morris, Swedish
Rad Ch, Stockholm Chbr Ch, BPO, R. Muti (ed
Süssmayr) *Ave verum corpus, K618.*
   (3/88) (EMI) ① CDC7 49640-2
M. McLaughlin, M. Ewing, J. Hadley, C. Hauptmann,
Bavarian Rad Chor, BRSO, L. Bernstein (pp1988; ed
Beyer)   (10/89) (DG) ① 427 353-2GH
A. Tomowa-Sintow, A. Baltsa, W. Krenn, J. Van Dam,
Vienna Singverein, BPO, H. von Karajan (ed
Süssmayr)   (11/89) (DG) ① 419 867-2GGA
G. Janowitz, J. Bernheimer, M. Hill, D. Thomas,
Hanover Band Chor, Hanover Band, R. Goodman (ed
Robbins Landon)   (7/90) (NIMB) ① NI5241
I. Seefried, A. Kupper, L. Fehenberger, K. Borg,
Bavarian Rad Chor, BRSO, E. Jochum (pp1956)
   (8/90) (ORFE) ① C205891A
L. Dawson, J. van Nes, K. Lewis, S. Estes, Philh
Chor, Philh, C.M. Giulini (ed Süssmayr)
   (8/90) (SONY) ① SK45577
S. Armstrong, J. Baker, N. Gedda, D. Fischer-
Dieskau, John Alldis Ch, ECO, D. Barenboim (ed
Süssmayr) *Verdi: Requiem.*
   (10/90) (EMI) ① CZS7 62892-2

B. Schlick, C. Watkinson, C. Prégardien, H. van der
Kamp, Netherlands Bach Soc Ch, Amsterdam
Baroque Orch, T. Koopman (ed Süssmayr: pp1989)
   (12/90) (ERAT) ① 2292-45472-2
T. Zylis-Gara, O. Dominguez, P. Schreier, F. Crass,
South German Madrigal Ch, Consortium Musicum,
W. Gönnenwein (ed Süssmayr)
   (7/91) (EMI) ① CDZ7 67014-2
D. Montague, M. Chance, C. Prégardien, F-J. Selig,
Cologne Chbr Ch, Collegium Cartusianum, P.
Neumann (ed Süssmayr) *Ave verum corpus, K618.*
   (11/91) (EMI) ① CDC7 54306-2
S. McNair, C. Watkinson, F. Araiza, R. Lloyd, ASMF
Chor, ASMF, N. Marriner (ed Süssmayr)
   (12/91) (PHIL) ① 432 087-2PH
J. Howarth, D. Montague, M. Davies, S. Roberts,
BBC Sngrs, LMP, J. Glover (ed Süssmayr)
Maurerische Trauermusik, K477.
   (12/91) (ASV) ① CDDCA757
J. Bryden, M. Westerbrook-Geha, W. Hite, W.
Bastian, W. Sharp, S. Richardson, Boston Early
Music Fest Chor, Boston Early Music Fest Orch, A.
Parrott (ed Süssmayr) *Kleine Freimaurer-Kantate,
K623.*   (12/91) (DENO) ① CO-77152
A. Auger, C. Bartoli, V. Cole, R. Pape, Vienna St Op
Chor, VPO, G. Solti (with prayers: pp1991)
   (3/92) (DECC) ① 433 688-2DH
C. Oelze, I. Danz, S. Weir, A. Schmidt, Stuttgart
Gächinger Kantorei, Stuttgart Bach Collegium, H.
Rilling (ed Levin) *Concert*
   (9/92) (HANS) ① [2] 98 979
M. Figueras, C. Schubert, G. Türk, S.
Schreckenberger, Capella Reial Voc Ens, Concert
des Nations, J. Savall *Maurerische trauermusik,
K477.*   (11/92) (ASTR) ① E8759
A.M. Blasi, M. Lipovšek, U. Heilmann, J-H. Rootering,
Bavarian Rad Chor, BRSO, Colin Davis (ed
Süssmayr)   (11/92) (RCA) ① RD60599
N. Argenta, C. Robbin, J.M. Ainsley, A. Miles, London
Schütz Ch, Schütz Consort, LCP, R. Norrington (ed
Druce) *Concert*   (11/92) (EMI) ① CDC7 54525-2
H. Donath, Y. Minton, R. Davies, G. Nienstedt, John
Alldis Ch, BBC SO, Colin Davis (r1967) *Concert*
   (3/94) (PHIL) ① [2] 438 800-2PM2
I. Cotrubas, H. Watts, R. Tear, J. Shirley-Quirk,
ASMF Chor, ASMF, N. Marriner (ed Beyer: r1977)
Concert   (5/94) (DECC) ① [2] 443 009-2DF2
E. Grümmer, M. Höffgen, H. Krebs, G. Frick, Berlin St
Hedwig's Cath Ch, BPO, R. Kempe (r1955) *Bruckner:
Te Deum.*   (10/94) (EMI) ① CDH5 65202-2
E. Grümmer, G. Pitzinger, H. Krebs, H. Hotter, Berlin
RIAS Chbr Ch, Berlin St Hedwig's Cath Ch, Berlin
RIAS Orch, F. Fricsay (r1951) *Adagio and Fugue,
K546.*   (11/94) (DG) ① 445 408-2GDO
E. Grümmer, G. Pitzinger, H. Krebs, H. Hotter, Berlin
RIAS Chbr Ch, Berlin St Hedwig's Cath Ch, VPO, F.
Fricsay (r1951) *Concert*
   (11/94) (DG) ① [11] 445 400-2GDO10
A. M. Panzarella, N. Stutzmann, C. Prégardien, N.
Berg, Arts Florissants Chor, Arts Florissants Orch, W.
Christie (r1994: ed Süssmayr) *Ave verum corpus,
K618.*   (11/95) (ERAT) ① 0630-10697-2
R. Ziesak, N. Maultsby, R. Croft, D. Arnold, Boston
Baroque, M. Pearlman (r1994: ed R Levin)
   (11/95) (TELA) ① CD80410
3e, 3f ASMF Chor, ASMF, N. Marriner *Concert*
   (6/91) (DECC) ① 430 498-2DWO
**Die Maurerfreude—cantata: tenor, male
chorus and orchestra, K471 (1785)** (Wds. F.
Petran)
W. Krenn, Edinburgh Fest Chor, LSO, I. Kertész
Concert   (11/90) (DECC) ① 425 722-2DM
Leipzig Rad Chor, Staatskapelle Dresden, P.
Schreier (ten/dir) *Concert*
   (4/92) (PHIL) ① [6] 422 522-2PME6
C. Prégardien, Chorus Viennensis, Vienna Academy
Orch, M. Haselböck (r1991) *Concert*
   (10/93) (NOVA) ① 150 081-2
**Meistermusik—male chorus and orchestra,
K477 (1785)** (hypothetical vers of Traurermusik,
K477: Autexier)
Collegium Vocale, Chapelle Royale Ch, Paris
Champs-Élysées Orch, P. Herreweghe *Mass, K427.*
   (9/92) (HARM) ① HMC90 1393
Mentre ti lascio—concert aria, K513 (1787)
(Wds.Morbilli)
J. Van Dam, Paris Orch Ens, J-P. Wallez (pp)
Concert   (5/88) (NOVA) ① 150 014-2
E. Pinza, NY Met Op Orch, B. Walter (r1946) *Concert*
   (4/90) (SONY) ① MPK45693
L. Polgár, F. Liszt CO, R. Leppard (r1989) *Concert*
   (1/91) (SONY) ① SK45855

O. Bär, G. Parsons (r1993/4) *Concert*
(12/95) (EMI) ① **CDC5 55345-2**

Venite populi—offertory: chorus and orchestra, K260/248a (1776)
Berlin RIAS Chbr Ch, Berlin RSO, M. Creed *Concert*
(8/89) (CAPR) ① **10 169**

Verdankt sei es dem Glanz der Grossen—Lied, K392/K340a (1781-82) (Wds. Hermes)
J. Protschka, H. Deutsch (r1991) *Concert*
(10/94) (CAPR) ① [2] **10 446/7**

Der Verschweigung—Lied, K518 (1787) (Wds. Weisse)
R. Alexander, G. Wilson *Concert*
(3/87) (ETCE) ① **KTC1035**
E. Schwarzkopf, M. Raucheisen (bp1944) *Concert*
(6/87) (ACAN) ① **43 801**
M. Shirai, H. Höll *Concert* (7/87) (CAPR) ① **10 098**
E. Mathis, K. Engel *Concert*
(9/87) (NOVA) ① **150 010-2**
B. Hendricks, M-J. Pires *Concert*
(7/91) (EMI) ① **CDC7 54007-2**
B. Bonney, G. Parsons *Concert*
(1/92) (TELD) ① **2292-46334-2**
I. Seefried, E. Werba (r1957) *Concert*
(7/93) (DG) ① [2] **437 348-2GDO2**
R. Streich, E. Werba (r1956) *Concert*
(10/94) (DG) ① [2] **437 680-2GDO2**
J. Protschka, H. Deutsch (r1991) *Concert*
(10/94) (CAPR) ① [2] **10 446/7**

Vesperae de Domenica, K321 (1779)
1. Dixit Dominus; 2. Confitebor; 3. Beatus vir; 4. Laudate pueri; 5. Laudate Dominum; 6. Magnificat.
L. Dawson, D. James, R. Covey-Crump, P. Hillier, King's College Ch, Cambridge Classical Plyrs, S. Cleobury *Concert* (9/89) (EMI) ① **CDC7 49672-2**
M. Marshall, M. Cable, W. Evans, S. Roberts, St John's College Ch, Wren Orch, G. Guest *Haydn: Mass 14.* (6/91) (DECC) ① **430 162-2DM**
P. Wise, M. Bürgener, M. Cousins, H.K. Ecker, Lisbon Gulbenkian Chor, Lisbon Gulbenkian Orch, T. Guschlbauer *Concert*
(8/94) (ERAT) ① [2] **4509-95362-2**
5. B. Hendricks, ASMF, N. Marriner *Concert*
(5/88) (EMI) ① **CDC7 49283-2**
5. L. Popp, L. Pearson, ECO, G. Fischer (r1967) *Concert* (10/88) (EMI) ① **CDM7 69546-2**
5. Vienna Boys' Ch, U.C. Harrer *Concert*
(12/91) (PHIL) ① **426 307-2PH**

Vesperae solennes de confessore in C, 'Solemn Vespers'—soloists, chorus and orchestra, K339 (1780)
1. Dixit Dominus; 2. Confitebor; 3. Beatus vir; 4. Laudate pueri; 5. Laudate Dominum; 6. Magnificat.
K. Te Kanawa, E. Bainbridge, R. Davies, G. Howell, LSC, LSO, Colin Davis (r1971) *Concert*
(3/86) (PHIL) ① **412 873-2PH**
E. Moser, J. Hamari, N. Gedda, D. Fischer-Dieskau, Bavarian Rad Chor, BRSO, E. Jochum *Mass, K317.*
(9/87) (DG) ① **CDM7 69023-2**
L. Dawson, D. James, R. Covey-Crump, P. Hillier, King's College Ch, Cambridge Classical Plyrs, S. Cleobury *Concert* (9/89) (EMI) ① **CDC7 49672-2**
F. Palmer, M. Cable, P. Langridge, S. Roberts, St John's College Ch, Wren Orch, G. Guest *Haydn: Mass 10.* (6/91) (DECC) ① **430 157-2DM**
E. Kirkby, C. Robbin, J.M. Ainsley, M. George, Winchester Cath Ch, Winchester Quiristers, AAM, C. Hogwood (r1990; ed Maunder) *Concert*
(4/93) (L'OI) ① **436 585-2OH**
E. Mathis, J. Rappé, H-P. Blochwitz, T. Quasthoff, Leipzig Rad Chor, Staatskapelle Dresden, P. Schreier (r1989) *Concert*
(2/94) (PHIL) ① **426 275-2PH**
R. Hansmann, A. Bartelloni, M. Sénéchal, R. Soyer, M-C. Alain *Concert*
(8/94) (ERAT) ① [2] **4509-95362-2**
B. Bonney, C. Wyn-Rogers, J. MacDougall, S. Gadd, English Concert Ch, English Concert, T. Pinnock (1993) *Concert* (10/94) (ARCH) ① **445 353-2AH**
M. Pennicchi, C. Patriasz, Z. Vandersteene, J. Draijer, Netherlands Chbr Ch, Eighteenth Century Orch, F. Brüggen (r1991) *Concert*
(6/95) (PHIL) ① **434 799-2PH**
4. F. Palmer, St John's College Ch, Wren Orch, G. Guest (r1979) *Concert*
(6/93) (DECC) ① **436 402-2DWO**
5. K. Te Kanawa, St Paul's Cath Ch, ECO, Barry Rose *Concert* (5/85) (PHIL) ① **412 629-2PH**
5. B. Hendricks, ASMF Chor, ASMF, N. Marriner *Concert* (5/88) (EMI) ① **CDC7 49283-2**
5. L. Popp, Ambrosian Sngrs, ECO, G. Fischer (r1967) *Concert* (10/88) (EMI) ① **CDM7 69546-2**
5. Ghislaine Morgan, St Bride's Ch, Fleet St, C. Etherington, R. Jones *Concert*
(2/91) (REGE) ① **REGSB701CD**

5. C. Studer, Ambrosian Sngrs, LSO, I. Marin *Concert* (11/92) (DG) ① **435 387-2GH**
5. K. te Kanawa, LSC, LSO, Colin Davis *Puccini: Messa di Gloria.* (1/93) (PHIL) ① **434 170-2PM**
5. P. Coles, Košice Teachers Ch, Camerata Cassovia, J. Wildner *Concert*
(5/93) (NAXO) ① **8 550495**

Voi avete un cor fedele—concert aria, K217 (1775)
F. Lott, LMP, J. Glover *Concert*
(2/90) (ASV) ① **CDDCA683**
E. Kirkby, AAM, C. Hogwood *Concert*
(4/91) (L'OI) ① **425 835-2OH**
E. Gruberová, COE, N. Harnoncourt (pp1991) *Concert* (5/92) (TELD) ① **9031-72302-2**

Vorrei spiegarvi, oh Dio—soprano, K418 (1783) (insertion aria for Anfossi's 'Il curioso indiscreto')
B. Hoch, Hong Kong PO, K. Schermerhorn *Concert* (11/86) (CARL) ① **PCD827**
K. Battle, RPO, A. Previn *Concert*
(12/86) (PHIL) ① **CDC7 47355-2**
E. Gruberová, COE, N. Harnoncourt (pp1991) *Concert* (5/92) (TELD) ① **9031-72302-2**
T. Dahl, Calgary PO, M. Bernardi (r1992) *Concert* (12/94) (CBC) ① **SMCD5125**
M. Price, LPO, J. Lockhart (r1975) *Concert*
(5/95) (RCA) ① [2] **09026 61635-2**

Warnung—arietta, K433a (1783) (Trans. Müller from Männer suchen stets zu naschen, K433 (incomplete)
E. Schumann, G. Reeves (r1930) *Concert*
(6/91) (PREI) ① **89031**
B. Bonney, G. Parsons *Concert*
(1/92) (TELD) ① **2292-46334-2**
I. Seefried, E. Moore (r1950) *Concert*
(4/94) (TEST) ① **SBT1026**
R. Streich, E. Werba (r1956) *Concert*
(10/94) (DG) ① [2] **437 680-2GDO2**

Wie unglücklich bin ich nit—Lied, K147/K125g (?1772-76) (Wds. Anon)
E. Mathis, K. Engel *Concert*
(9/87) (NOVA) ① **150 010-2**
J. Protschka, H. Deutsch (r1991) *Concert*
(10/94) (CAPR) ① [2] **10 446/7**

Der Zauberer—Lied, K472 (1785) (Wds. Weisse)
R. Alexander, G. Wilson *Concert*
(3/87) (ETCE) ① **KTC1035**
M. Shirai, H. Höll *Concert* (7/87) (CAPR) ① **10 098**
E. Mathis, K. Engel *Concert*
(9/87) (NOVA) ① **150 010-2**
E. Schwarzkopf, W. Gieseking *Concert*
(12/90) (EMI) ① **CDH7 63702-2**
B. Hendricks, M-J. Pires *Concert*
(7/91) (EMI) ① **CDC7 54007-2**
B. Bonney, G. Parsons *Concert*
(1/92) (TELD) ① **2292-46334-2**
J. Varady, E. Bashkirova *Concert*
(5/93) (ORFE) ① **C248921A**
I. Seefried, E. Moore (r1950) *Concert*
(4/94) (TEST) ① **SBT1026**
R. Streich, E. Werba (r1956) *Concert*
(10/94) (DG) ① [2] **437 680-2GDO2**
M. Shirai, H. Höll (r1991) *Concert*
(10/94) (CAPR) ① [2] **10 446/7**

Zerfliesset heut' geliebte Brüder—Lied: tenor, chorus and organ, K483 (1785) (Wds. J. W. Goethe)
W. Krenn, Edinburgh Fest Chor, G. Fischer *Concert* (11/90) (DECC) ① **425 722-2DM**
P. Schreier, Leipzig Rad Chor, R. Alpermann *Concert* (4/92) (PHIL) ① [6] **422 522-2PME6**
C. Prégardien, Chorus Viennensis, M. Haselböck (r1991) *Concert* (10/93) (NOVA) ① **150 081-2**

Die Zufriedenheit—Lied, K349 (1780-81) (Wds. Miller)
M. Shirai, H. Höll (r1991) *Concert* (7/87) (CAPR) ① **10 098**
E. Mathis, K. Engel *Concert*
(9/87) (NOVA) ① **150 010-2**
P. Schreier, K. Ragossnig *Concert*
(10/89) (NOVA) ① **150 039-2**
E. Schwarzkopf, W. Gieseking *Concert*
(12/90) (EMI) ① **CDH7 63702-2**
A. Stephens, P. Holden *Concert*
(3/92) (AMON) ① **CD-SAR51**
D. Orieschnig, W. Würdinger (r1986) *Concert*
(5/92) (PHIL) ① **422 527-2PME**
I. Seefried, E. Moore (r1950) *Concert*
(4/94) (TEST) ① **SBT1026**
J. Protschka, H. Deutsch (r1991) *Concert*
(10/94) (CAPR) ① [2] **10 446/7**

Die Zufriedenheit—Lied, K473 (1785) (Wds. Weisse)
R. Alexander, G. Wilson *Concert*
(3/87) (ETCE) ① **KTC1035**

M. Shirai, H. Höll *Concert* (7/87) (CAPR) ① **10 098**
E. Mathis, K. Engel *Concert*
(9/87) (NOVA) ① **150 010-2**
B. Hendricks, M-J. Pires *Concert*
(7/91) (EMI) ① **CDC7 54007-2**
B. Bonney, G. Parsons *Concert*
(1/92) (TELD) ① **2292-46334-2**
J. Protschka, H. Deutsch (r1991) *Concert*
(10/94) (CAPR) ① [2] **10 446/7**

SECTION V: STAGE WORKS

Apollo et Hyacinthus—Latin intermezzo, K38 (1767—Salzburg) (Wds. ?P. F. Widl)
EXCERPTS: 1. Overture. ACT ONE: 2. Amice! iam parata sunt omnia; 3. Numen o Latonium!; 4a. Heu me! perimus!; 4b. Saepe terrent Numina; 5a. Ah nate! vera loqueris; 5b. Iam pastor Apollo. ACT TWO: 6a. Amare numquid filia; 6b. Laetari, iocari; 7a. Rex! de salute filii est actum; 7b. En! duos conspicis; 8a. Heu! Numen! eccel; 8b. Discede crudelis!. ACT THREE: 9a. Non est - Quis ergo; 9b. Ut navis in aequore luxuriante; 10a. Quocumque me converto; 10b. Natus cadit; 11a. Rex! me redire cogit; 11b. Tandem post turbida fulmina.
Cpte C. Günther, S. Pratschke, M. Schäfer, C. Fliegner, P. Cieslewicz, Nice Baroque Ens, G. Schmidt-Gaden
(11/91) (PAVA) ① [2] **ADW7236/7**
Cpte C. Wulkopf, E. Mathis, A. Rolfe Johnson, A. Auger, H. Schwarz, Salzburg Chbr Ch, Salzburg Mozarteum Orch, L. Hager (r1981)
(11/91) (PHIL) ① [2] **422 526-2PME2**

Ascanio in Alba—festa teatrale: 2 acts, K111 (1771—Milan) (Lib. G. Parini)
EXCERPTS: 1a. Overture. PART ONE: 1b. Andante grazioso; 2. Di te più amabile; 3a. Geni, Grazie, ed Amori; 3b. L'ombra de' rami tuoi; 4a. Ma la Ninfa gentil; 4b. L'augelletto; 5a. Perché tacer degg'io?; 5b. Cara, lontano ancora; 6. Venga, de' sommi Eroi; 7a. Ma qual cita risona?; 7b. Venga, de' sommi Eroi; 8a. Ma tu, chi sei, che ignoto qui t'aggiri fra noi?; 8b. Se il labbro più non dice; 9a. Quanto soavi al core de la man; 9b. Hai di Diana il core; 10a. Oh, generosa Diva; 10b. Venga, de' sommi Eroi; 11a. Di propria man la Dea vi tuole donerà; 11b. Venga, de' sommi Eroi; 12a. Oh mia gloria, oh mia cura; 12b. Per la gioia in questo seno; 13a. Misera! Che farò?; 13b. Si, ma d'un altro amante; 14a. Ah no, Silvia t'inganni; 14b. Come è felice stato; 15a. Silvia, mira, che il sole oma s'avanza; 15b. Venga, de' sommi Eroi; 16a. Cielo! Che vidi mai?; 16b. Ah di sì nobil alma; 17a. Un'altra prova a te mirar conviene; 17b. Al chiaror di quel bei rai; 18. Di te più amabile; 19a. Star lontana non so; 19b. Spiega il desio; 20. Già l'ore van volando; 21a. Cerco di dois te loco; 21b. Silvia, ove sei?; 21c. Dal tuo gentil sembiante; 22a. Ahimè! Che veggio mai?; 22b. Al mio ben mi veggio avanti; 23a. Ferma, aspetta, ove mi veggio?; 23b. Infelici affetti miei; 24a. Anima grande; 24b. Che strano evento; 25a. Ahi la crudel; 25b. Torna mia bene, ascolta; 26a. Venga, de' sommi Eroi; 27a. Che strana meraviglia; 27b. Sento, che il cor mi dice; 28a. Si, Padre, alfin mi taccia; 28b. Scendi, celeste Venere; 29a. Ma, s'allontani almen; 29b. Scendi celeste Venere; 30a. Scendi ingombran l'altare; 30b. Scendi, celeste Venere; 31a. Invoca, o figlia; 31b. Ah caro sposo, oh Dio!; 32a. Eccovi al fin di vostre pene; 32b. Che bel piacer io sento; 33a. Ah chi nodi più forti; 33b. Alma Dea, tutto il mondo governa.
Cpte A. Baltsa, E. Mathis, P. Schreier, L. Sukis, A. Auger, Salzburg Chbr Ch, Salzburg Mozarteum Orch, L. Hager (r1976)
(1/92) (PHIL) ① [3] **422 530-2PME3**
Cpte M. Chance, J. Feldman, H. Milner, L. Windsor, R. Mannion, Paris Sorbonne Uni Ch, Concerto Armonico, J. Grimbert (1990)
(12/95) (NAXO) ① **8 660040/1**
1a Staatskapelle Dresden, H. Vonk *Concert*
(10/91) (CAPR) ① [3] **10 809**
5a, 5b, 16b J. Kowalski, Berlin RSO, H. Fricke *Concert* (2/91) (CAPR) ① **10 416**

Bastien und Bastienne—Singspiel: 1 act, K50/K46b (1768—Vienna) (Lib. F. W. Weiskern & J. A. Sachtner)
EXCERPTS: 1. Overture; 2. Mein liebster Freund hat mich verlassen; 3. Ich geh jetzt auf die Weide; 4. Entry of Colas; 5. Befraget mich ein zartes Kind; 6. Wenn mein Bastien einst in Scherze; 7. Würd ich auch, wie manche Buhlerinnen; 8. Auf den Rat, den ich gegeben; 9. Grossen Dank dir abzustatten; 10. Geh! du sagst mir eine Fabel; 11. Diggi, daggi; 12. Meiner Liebsten schöne Wangen; 13. Er war mir sonst treu und gewogen; 14. Geh hin! - Ich will mich in die Stadt begeben; 15. Dein Trotz vermehrt sich durch mein Leiden?; 16. Geh! Herz von Flandern!;

17. Kinderl Kinder.
Cpte V. Cole, E. Gruberová, L. Polgár, F. Liszt CO,
R. Leppard (r1989) *Concert*
(1/91) (SONY) ① **SK45855**
Cpte G. Nigl, D. Orieschnig, D. Busch, Vienna SO,
U.C. Harrer (r1986) *Concert*
(5/92) (PHIL) ① **422 527-2PME**
La **Clemenza di Tito—opera seria: 2 acts,**
K621 (1791—Prague) (Lib. C. Mazzolà)
EXCERPTS: 1. Overture. ACT ONE: 2. Come ti
piace, imponi; 3. Deh se piacer; 4. Deh prendi un
dolce amplesso; 5. Marcia; 6. Serbate, o Dei custodi;
7. Del più sublime soglio; 8. Ah perdona al primo
affetto; 9. Ah, se fosse; 10. Parto, parto; 11. Vengo...
aspettate... 12a. Oh Dei, che smania è questa; 12b.
Deh conservate, oh Dei! (Finale). ACT TWO: 13.
Torna di Tito a lato; 14. Se al volto mai ti senti; 15. Ah
grazie si rendano; 16. Tardi s'avvede; 17. Tu fosti
tradito; 18. Quello di Tito è il volto; 19. Deh per
questo istante; 20. Se all'impero; 21. S'altro che
lagrime; 22a. Ecco il punto, oh Vitellia; 22b. Non più
di fiori; 23. Che del ciel; 24a. Ma che giomo è mai
questo?; 24b. Tu, è ver, m'assolvi Augusto (Finale).
Cpte P. Schreier, J. Varady, T. Berganza, M. Schiml,
E. Mathis, T. Adam, Leipzig Rad Chor, Staatskapelle
Dresden, K. Böhm (r1979)
(12/90) (DG) ① [2] **429 878-2GX2**
Cpte A. Rolfe Johnson, J. Varady, A.S. von Otter, C.
Robbin, S. McNair, C. Hauptmann, Monteverdi Ch,
EBS, J.E. Gardiner (pp1991)
(12/91) (ARCH) ① [2] **431 806-2AH2**
Cpte S. Burrows, J. Baker, Y. Minton, F. von Stade,
L. Popp, R. Lloyd, ROH Chor, ROHO, Colin Davis
(r1976) (4/92) (PHIL) ① [2] **422 544-2PME2**
Cpte P. Langridge, L. Popp, A. Murray, D. Ziegler, R.
Ziesak, L. Polgár, Zurich Op Hse Chor, Zurich Op
Orch, N. Harnoncourt (r1993)
(5/94) (TELD) ① [2] **4509-90857-2**
Cpte U. Heilmann, D. Jones, C. Bartoli, D. Montague,
B. Bonney, G. Cachemaille, AAM Chor, AAM, C.
Hogwood (r1993)
(3/95) (L'OI) ① [2] **444 131-2OHO2**
Cpte G. Winbergh, C. Vaness, D. Ziegler, M. Senn,
C. Barbaux, L. Polgár, Vienna St Op Chor, VPO, R.
Muti (pp1988) (10/95) (EMI) ① [2] **CDS5 55489-2**
1. ASMF, N. Marriner *Concert*
(4/84) (EMI) ① **CDC7 47014-2**
1. Staatskapelle Dresden, B. Vonk *Concert*
(10/91) (CAPR) ① [3] **10 809**
1. Tafelmusik, B. Weil *Concert*
(5/92) (SONY) ① **SK46695**
7, 9, 20. J. Dickie, Capella Istropolitana, J. Wildner
Concert (12/91) (NAXO) ① **8 550383**
9. G. Sabbatini, NHK Chbr Sols, R. Paternostro
(pp1990) *Concert* (10/91) (CAPR) ① **10 348**
9. P. Domingo, Munich RO, E. Kohn *Concert*
(3/92) (EMI) ① **CDC7 54329-2**
9. L. Simoneau, Vienna SO, B. Paumgartner (r1954)
Concert (11/94) (PHIL) ① [2] **438 953-2PM2**
10. B. Fassbaender, Stuttgart RSO, H. Graf *Concert*
(11/86) (ORFE) ① **C096841A**
10. M. Lipovšek, Munich RO, G. Patanè *Concert*
(6/90) (ORFE) ① **C179891A**
10. D. Soffel, Swedish CO, M. Liljefors (pp1988)
Concert (4/93) (CPRI) ① **CAP21428**
10. T. Berganza, Vienna St Op Orch, I. Kertész
(r1966/7) *Concert* (4/93) (DECC) ① **421 899-2DA**
10. T. Berganza, LSO, J. Pritchard (r1962) *Concert*
(4/93) (DECC) ① **421 899-2DA**
10. E. Ritchie, V. Soames, J. Purvis (r1992; arr
Bergmann) *Concert* (4/93) (CLRI) ① **CC0006**
10. M. Price, ECO, J. Lockhart (r1973) *Concert*
(5/95) (RCA) ① [2] **09026 61635-2**
10, 19. J. Larmore, Lausanne CO, J. López-Cobos
(r1994) *Concert* (12/95) (TELD) ① **4509-96800-2**
10, 19, 22b C. Bartoli, Vienna CO, G. Fischer
Concert (12/91) (DECC) ① **430 513-2DH**
14. K. Te Kanawa, LSO, Colin Davis *Concert*
(3/84) (PHIL) ① **411 148-2PH**
20. J. Protschka, Munich RO, K. Eichhorn *Concert*
(3/89) (CAPR) ① **10 109**
20. R. Blake, LSO, N. McGegan *Concert*
(3/89) (ARAB) ① **Z6598**
20. L. Simoneau, Paris Champs-Élysées Orch, A.
Jouve (r1955) *Concert*
(3/91) (EMI) ① [2] **CHS7 63715-2**
22b L. Popp, Munich RO, L. Slatkin (r1983) *Concert*
(8/84) (EMI) ① **CDC7 47019-2**
22b C. Studer, ASMF, N. Marriner *Concert*
(9/94) (PHIL) ① **442 410-2PM**
Così fan tutte—opera buffa: 2 acts, K588
(1790—Vienna) (Lib. L. da Ponte).
EXCERPTS: 1. Overture. ACT 1: 2. La mia
Dorabella; 3a. Fuor la spadal; 3b. È la fede; 4a.
Scioccherie di poetil; 4b. Una bella serenata; 5. Ah
guarda, sorella; 6. Vorrei dir; 7. Sento, o Dio; 8. Al

---

fato dan legge; 9. Bella vita militar!; 10. Di scrivermi;
11. Soave sia il vento; 12. Smanie implacabili; 13. In
uomini; 14. Alla bella Despinetta; 15a. Temerari!
Sortite fuori di questo loco!; 15b. Come scoglio; 16.
Non siate ritrosi; 17. Rivolgete a lui lo sguardo
(alternative aria for No. 16); 18. E voi ridete?; 19. Un'
aura amorosa; 20. Ah, che tutta in momento; 21.
Dove son? Che loco è questo?. ACT 2: 22a. Andate
là; 22b. Una donna a quindici anni; 23a. Sorella, cosa
dici?; 23b. Prenderò quel brunettino; 24. Secondate,
aurette amiche; 25. La mano a me date; 26. Il core vi
dono; 27a. Barbara! Perchè fuggi?; 27b. Ah, lo
veggio; 28a. Ei parte...senti; 28b. Per pietà, ben mio;
29. Donne mie, la fate a tanti; 30a. In qual foreo
contrasto; 30b. Tradito, schernito dal perfido cor; 31.
È Amore un ladroncello; 32. Fra gli amplessi; 33.
Tutti accusan le donne; 34. Richiamati, da regio
contrordine; 35. Fortunato l'uom che prende (Finale).
Cpte M. Caballé, J. Baker, I. Cotrubas, N. Gedda, W.
Ganzarolli, R. Van Allan, ROH Chor, ROHO, Colin
Davis (4/87) (PHIL) ① [3] **416 633-2PH3**
Cpte C. Vaness, D. Ziegler, L. Watson, J. Aler, D.
Duesing, C. Desderi, Glyndebourne Fest Chor, LPO,
B. Haitink (r1986)
(7/87) (EMI) ① [3] **CDS7 47727-8**
Cpte L. Price, T. Troyanos, J. Raskin, G. Shirley, S.
Milnes, E. Flagello, Ambrosian Op Chor, New Philh,
E. Leinsdorf (1967) (9/88) (RCA) ① [3] **GD86677**
Cpte E. Schwarzkopf, C. Ludwig, H. Steffek, Alfredo
Kraus, G. Taddei, W. Berry, Philh Chor, Philh, K.
Böhm (r1962) (11/88) (EMI) ① [3] **CMS7 69330-2**
Cpte E. Schwarzkopf, N. Merriman, L. Otto, L.
Simoneau, R. Panerai, S. Bruscantini, Chor, Philh, H.
von Karajan (r1954)
(12/88) (EMI) ① [3] **CHS7 69635-2**
Cpte L. Cuberli, C. Bartoli, J. Rodgers, K. Streit, F.
Furlanetto, J. Tomlinson, Berlin RIAS Chbr Ch, BPO,
D. Barenboim (1989)
(10/90) (ERAT) ① [3] **2292-45475-2**
Cpte K. Mattila, A.S. von Otter, E. Szmytka, F.
Araiza, T. Allen, J. Van Dam, Ambrosian Op Chor,
ASMF, N. Marriner (r1988-9)
(11/90) (PHIL) ① [3] **422 381-2PH3**
Cpte G. Janowitz, B. Fassbaender, R. Grist, P.
Schreier, H. Prey, R. Panerai, Vienna St Op Chor,
VPO, K. Böhm (pp1974)
(12/90) (DG) ① [3] **429 874-2GX2**
Cpte J. Borowska, R. Yachmi-Caucig, P. Coles, J.
Dickie, A. Martin, P. Mikuláš, Slovak Phil Chor,
Capella Istropolitana, J. Wildner (r1990)
(3/91) (NAXO) ① [3] **8 660008/10**
Cpte I. Souez, L. Helletsgruber, I. Eisinger, H. Nash,
W. Domgraf-Fassbaender, J. Brownlee,
Glyndebourne Fest Chor, Glyndebourne Fest Orch,
F. Busch r1935)
(3/91) (PEAR) ① [3] **GEMMCDS9406**
Cpte I. Souez, L. Helletsgruber, I. Eisinger, H. Nash,
W. Domgraf-Fassbaender, J. Brownlee,
Glyndebourne Fest Chor, Glyndebourne Fest Orch,
F. Busch r1935)
(9/91) (EMI) ① [2] **CHS7 63864-2**
Cpte M. Price, Y. Minton, L. Popp, L. Alva, G. Evans,
H. Sotin, John Alldis Ch, New Philh, K. Klemperer
(9/91) (EMI) ① [3] **CMS7 63845-2**
Cpte C. Margiono, D. Ziegler, A. Steiger, D. van der
Walt, G. Cachemaille, T. Hampson, Netherlands Op
Chor, Concertgebouw, N. Harnoncourt (r1991)
(11/91) (TELD) ① [3] **9031-71381-2**
Cpte M. Caballé, J. Baker, I. Cotrubas, N. Gedda, W.
Ganzarolli, R. Van Allan, ROH Chor, ROHO, Colin
Davis (1974) (1/92) (PHIL) ① [3] **422 542-2PME3**
Cpte A.C. Antonacci, M. Bacelli, L. Cherici, R.
Decker, A. Dohmen, S. Bruscantini, Marchigiano V.
Bellini Lyric Chor, Marchigiano PO, G. Kuhn (pp1990)
(10/92) (ORFE) ① [3] **C243913F**
Cpte S. Isokoski, M. Groop, N. Argenta, M. Schäfer,
P. Vollestad, H. Claessens, Petite Bande Chor, Petite
Bande, S. Kuijken (pp1992)
(2/94) (ACCE) ① [3] **ACC9296/8D**
Cpte A. Roocroft, R. Mannion, E. James, R. Trost, R.
Gilfry, C. Feller, Monteverdi Ch, EBS, J. E. Gardiner
(pp1992) (2/94) (ARCH) ① [3] **437 829-2AH3**
Cpte F. Lott, M. McLaughlin, N. Focile, J. Hadley, A.
Corbelli, G. Cachemaille, Edinburgh Fest Chor,
Scottish CO, C. Mackerras (r1993)
(4/94) (TELA) ① [3] **CD80360**
Cpte I. Seefried, D. Hermann, L. Otto, A. Dermota, E.
Kunz, P. Schoeffler, Vienna St Op Chor, VPO, K.
Böhm (pp1954) (2/95) (ORFE) ① [2] **C357942I**
1. ASMF, N. Marriner *Concert*
(4/84) (EMI) ① **CDC7 47014-2**
1. Staatskapelle Dresden, B. Vonk *Concert*
(10/91) (CAPR) ① [3] **10 809**
1. Tafelmusik, B. Weil *Concert*
(5/92) (SONY) ① **SK46695**

---

1. LSO, J. Krips (r1951) *Concert*
(7/95) (DECC) ① [2] **443 530-2LF2**
1, 16, 29. J. Van Dam, Paris Orch Ens, J-P. Wallez
(pp) *Concert* (5/88) (NOVA) ① **150 014-2**
2, 3a, 3b, 4a, 4b, 5, 7, 10, 11, 15b, 23b, 26, 28a,
28b, 32. S. Jurinac, B. Thebom, Richard Lewis, E.
Kunz, M. Borriello, Glyndebourne Fest Orch, F.
Busch (r1950): inc rehearsals for 23b,28b,32) Così fan
tutte. (6/94) (TEST) ① **SBT1040**
4b H. Nash, W. Domgraf-Fassbaender, J. Brownlee,
Glyndebourne Fest Orch, F. Busch (r1935) *Concert*
(6/94) (EMI) ① **CDH5 65072-2**
5, 15b, 28a, 28b S. Jurinac, B. Thebom,
Glyndebourne Fest Orch, F. Busch (r1950) *Concert*
(1/90) (EMI) ① **CDH7 63199-2**
5, 23b, 25, 26, 32. A. Martin, D. Robin, Capella
Istropolitana, J. Wildner *Concert*
(12/91) (NAXO) ① **8 550435**
11. L. Popp, B. Fassbaender, T. Krause, Vienna Op
Orch, I. Kertész *Concert*
(6/91) (DECC) ① **430 498-2DWO**
11. C. Vaness, D. Ziegler, C. Desderi, LPO, B.
Haitink (r1986) *Concert*
(6/94) (EMI) ① **CDH5 65072-2**
11, 19. M. Marshall, A. Baltsa, J. Van Dam, F. Araiza,
VPO, R. Muti *Concert*
(7/91) (EMIL) ① **CDZ7 67015-2**
12. M. Lipovšek, Munich RO, G. Patanè *Concert*
(6/90) (ORFE) ① **C179891A**
12. T. Berganza, LPO, G. Solti (r1973) *Concert*
(4/93) (DECC) ① **421 899-2DA**
12. J. Larmore, Lausanne CO, J. López-Cobos
(r1994) *Concert* (12/95) (TELD) ① **4509-96800-2**
13, 15a, 15b, 28a, 28b C. Bartoli, Vienna CO, G.
Fischer (r1993) *Concert*
(11/94) (DECC) ① **443 452-2DH**
13, 22b A. Noni, Glyndebourne Fest Orch, F. Busch
(r1950) Così fan
tutte. (6/94) (TEST) ① **SBT1040**
15a, 15b C. Studer, ASMF, N. Marriner *Concert*
(9/94) (PHIL) ① **442 410-2PM**
15a, 15b A. Roocroft, LPO, F. Welser-Möst *Concert*
(10/94) (EMI) ① **CDC5 55090-2**
15a, 15b, 28a, 28b, 31. T. Berganza, LSO, J.
Pritchard (r1962) *Concert*
(4/93) (DECC) ① **421 899-2DA**
15a, 15b, 28a, 28b I. Seefried, Vienna SO, F. Leitner
(r1953) *Concert*
(9/93) (DG) ① [2] **437 677-2GDO2**
15b L. Popp, Munich RO, L. Slatkin (r1983) *Concert*
(8/84) (EMI) ① **CDC7 47019-2**
15b C. Vaness, LPO, B. Haitink *Concert*
(7/91) (EMIL) ① **CDZ7 67015-2**
15b K. Te Kanawa, Strasbourg PO, A. Lombard
(r1972) *Concert*
(4/94) (RCA) ① [6] **09026 61580-2(8)**
16, 17, 29. H. Prey, Salzburg Mozarteum Orch, B.
Weil *Concert* (5/88) (DENO) ① **CO-1741**
17, 29. F. Furlanetto, Vienna SO, I. Marin *Concert*
(3/89) (ARAB) ① **Z6598**
19. R. Blake, LSO, N. McGegan *Concert*
(3/89) (ARAB) ① **Z6598**
19. Alfredo Kraus, Philh, K. Böhm *Concert*
(10/89) (EMI) ① **CDM7 63104-2**
19. H. Roswaenge, Berlin St Op Orch, F. Weissmann
(Ger. r1928) *Concert*
(5/90) (PEAR) ① **GEMMCD9394**
19. G. Sabbatini, NHK Chbr Sols, R. Paternostro
(pp1990) *Concert* (10/91) (CAPR) ① **10 348**
19. H. Roswaenge, orch (r1928: Ger) *Concert*
(2/92) (PREI) ① [2] **89201**
19. P. Domingo, Munich RO, E. Kohn (r1991)
Concert (6/94) (EMI) ① **CDC5 55017-2**
19. L. Simoneau, Vienna SO, B. Paumgartner (r1954)
Concert (11/94) (PHIL) ① [2] **438 953-2PM2**
19. H. Nash, Glyndebourne Fest Orch, F. Busch
(r1935) *Concert* (2/95) (DUTT) ① **CDLX7012**
19. W. Ludwig, Berlin St Op Orch, B. Seidler-Winkler
(r1936: Ger) *Concert* (7/95) (PREI) ① **89088**
19, 27b, 30a, 30b J. Dickie, Capella Istropolitana, J.
Wildner *Concert* (12/91) (NAXO) ① **8 550383**
19, 30a, 30b J. Protschka, Munich RO, K. Eichhorn
Concert (3/89) (CAPR) ① **10 109**
19, 30a, 30b P. Domingo, Munich RO, E. Kohn
Concert (3/92) (EMI) ① **CDC7 54329-2**
22b L. Schöne, Berlin St Op Orch, F. Zweig (r1928:
Ger) *Concert* (1/94) (CLUB) ① **CL99-020**
23a, 23b I. Seefried, N. Merriman, BPO, E. Jochum
(r1962) *Concert*
(9/93) (DG) ① [2] **437 677-2GDO2**
26. E. Kunz, B. Thebom, Glyndebourne Fest Orch, F.
Busch (r1950) *Concert*
(6/94) (EMI) ① **CDH5 65072-2**
28a, 28b K. Te Kanawa, LSO, Colin Davis *Concert*
(3/84) (PHIL) ① **411 148-2PH**
28a, 28b A. Tomowa-Sintow, Munich RO, P. Sommer
Concert (11/86) (ORFE) ① **C106841A**

28a, 28b A. Roocroft, ASMF, N. Marriner Concert
(12/95) (EMI) ① CDC5 55396-2
28b E. Schwarzkopf, Philh, H. von Karajan (r1954)
Concert (12/90) (EMI) ① CDM7 63657-2
29. G. Taddei, Philh, K. Böhm Concert
(7/91) (EMIL) ① CDZ7 67015-2
29. M. Rothmüller, Philh, J. Robertson (r1950)
Concert (4/92) (EMI) ① [7] CHS7 69741-2(4)
29. G. Hüsch, Berlin St Op Orch, H.U. Müller (r1939:
Ger) Concert (4/92) (PREI) ① 89071
30b G. Morino, Warnia Nat PO, B. Amaducci
Concert (10/90) (NUOV) ① 6851
31. C. Bartoli, Vienna CO, G. Fischer Concert
(12/91) (DECC) ① 430 513-2DH
32. P. Domingo, C. Vaness, Munich RO, E. Kohn
Concert (3/92) (EMI) ① CDC7 54329-2
32. I. Souez, H. Nash, orch, C. Raybould (r1934)
Concert (2/95) (DUTT) ① CDLX7012
Don Giovanni—dramma giocoso: 2 acts,
K527 (1787—Prague) (Lib. L. da Ponte)
EXCERPTS: 1a. Overture. ACT ONE: 1b. Notte e
giorno; 2a. Ma qual mai s'offre; 2b. Fuggi, crudele; 3.
Ah, chi mi dice; 4. Madamina il catalogo; 5.
Giovinette, che fate all' amore; 6. Ho capito; 7. Là ci
darem la mano; 8. Ah, fuggi il traditor; 9. Non ti fidar;
10a. Don Ottavio, son morta; 10b. Or sai chi l'onore;
10c. Dalla sua pace; 11. Finch' han dal vino; 12.
Batti, batti; 13. Presto, presto; 13a. Minuet. ACT
TWO: 14. Eh via, buffone; 15. Ah, taci in giusto core;
16. Deh! vieni alla finestra; 17a. Metà di voi; 17b. Se
un uom e una ragazza; 18. Vedrai, carino; 19. Sola
sola; 20. Ah pietà; 21. Il mio tesoro; 22. Per queste
tue manine; 23a. In quali eccessi; 23b. Mi tradì quell'
alma ingrata; 24. O statua gentilissima; 25a. Crudele!
Ah no mio bene; 25b. Non mi dir; 26. Gia la mensa è
preparata; 27. Ah, dovè il perfido?.
Cpte T. Allen, C. Vaness, M. Ewing, E. Gale, K.
Lewis, R. Van Allan, J. Rawnsley, D. Kavrakos,
Glyndebourne Fest Chor, LPO, B. Haitink
(12/84) (EMI) ① [3] CDS7 47037-8
Cpte S. Ramey, A. Tomowa-Sintow, A. Baltsa, K.
Battle, G. Winbergh, F. Furlanetto, A. Malta, P.
Burchuladze, Berlin Deutsche Op Chor, BPO, H. von
Karajan (r1985) (10/86) (DG) ① [3] 419 179-2GH3
Cpte R. Raimondi, E. Moser, K. Te Kanawa, T.
Berganza, K. Riegel, J. Van Dam, M. King, J.
Macurdy, Paris Op Chor, Paris Op Orch, L. Maazel
(r1979) (11/87) (SONY) ① [3] M3K35192
Cpte E. Waechter, J. Sutherland, E. Schwarzkopf, G.
Sciutti, L. Alva, G. Taddei, P. Cappuccilli, G. Frick,
Philh Chor, Philh, C.M. Giulini (r1959)
(12/87) (EMI) ① [3] CDS7 47260-8
Cpte J. Brownlee, I. Souez, L. Helletsgruber, A.
Mildmay, K. von Pataky, S. Baccaloni, Roy
Henderson, D. Franklin, Glyndebourne Fest Chor,
Glyndebourne Fest Orch, F. Busch (r1936)
(3/89) (EMI) ① [3] CHS7 61030-2
Cpte C. Siepi, S. Danco, L. della Casa, H. Gueden,
A. Dermota, F. Corena, W. Berry, K. Böhme, Vienna
St Op Chor, VPO, J. Krips (r1955)
(9/89) (DECC) ① [3] 411 626-2DM3
Cpte T. Hampson, E. Gruberová, R. Alexander, B.
Bonney, H-P. Blochwitz, L. Polgár, A. Scharinger, R.
Holl, Netherlands Op Chor, Concertgebouw, N.
Harnoncourt (r1988)
(3/90) (TELD) ① [3] 2292-44184-2
Cpte D. Fischer-Dieskau, B. Nilsson, M. Arroyo, R.
Grist, P. Schreier, E. Flagello, A. Mariotti, M. Talvela,
Czech Sngrs Chor, Prague Nat Th Orch, K. Böhm
(1967) (12/90) (DG) ① [3] 429 870-2GX3
Cpte H. Hagegård, A. Auger, D. Jones, B. Bonney,
N. van der Meel, G. Cachemaille, B. Terfel, K.
Sigmundsson, Drottningholm Court Th Orch,
Drottningholm Court Th Orch, A. Östman (r1989)
(12/90) (L'OI) ① [3] 425 943-2OH3
Cpte J. Brownlee, I. Souez, L. Helletsgruber, A.
Mildmay, K. von Pataky, S. Baccaloni, Roy
Henderson, D. Franklin, Glyndebourne Fest Chor,
Glyndebourne Fest Orch, F. Busch (r1936)
(3/91) (PEAR) ① [3] GEMMCDS9369
Cpte B. Weikl, M. Price, S. Sass, L. Popp, S.
Burrows, G. Bacquier, A. Sramek, K. Moll, London
Op Chor, LPO, G. Solti
(3/91) (DECC) ① [3] 425 169-2DM3
Cpte C. Siepi, E. Grümmer, E. Schwarzkopf, E.
Berger, A. Dermota, O. Edelmann, W. Berry, D.
Ernster, Vienna St Op Chor, VPO, W. Furtwängler
(pp1954) (7/91) (EMI) ① [3] CHS7 63860-2
Cpte M. Shimell, C. Studer, C. Vaness, S. Mentzer,
F. Lopardo, S. Ramey, N. de Carolis, J-H. Rootering,
Vienna St Op Concert Ch, VPO, R. Muti
(7/91) (EMI) ① [3] CDS7 54255-2
Cpte N. Ghiaurov, C. Watson, C. Ludwig, M. Freni,
N. Gedda, W. Berry, P. Montarsolo, F. Crass, New
Philh Chor, New Philh, O. Klemperer (r1966)
(9/91) (EMI) ① [3] CMS7 63841-2

Cpte I. Wixell, M. Arroyo, K. Te Kanawa, M. Freni, S.
Burrows, W. Ganzarolli, R. Van Allan, L. Roni, ROH
Chor, ROHO, Colin Davis (r1973)
(1/92) (PHIL) ① [3] 422 541-2PME3
Cpte T. Allen, S. Sweet, K. Mattila, M. McLaughlin, F.
Araiza, S. Alaimo, C. Otelli, R. Lloyd, Ambrosian Op
Chor, ASMF, N. Marriner (r1990)
(1/92) (PHIL) ① [3] 432 129-2PH3
Cpte F. Furlanetto, L. Cuberli, W. Meier, J. Rodgers,
U. Heilmann, J. Tomlinson, M. Pertusi, M. Salminen,
Berlin RIAS Chbr Ch, BPO, D. Barenboim
(3/92) (ERAT) ① [3] 2292-45588-2
Cpte R. Bruson, S. Ghazarian, G. Ottenthal, P. Pace,
G. Sabbatini, N. Ghiuselev, S. Rinaldi-Miliani, F. de
Grandis, Cologne Rad Chor, Cologne RSO, N. Järvi
(r1990) (5/92) (CHAN) ① [3] CHAN8920/2
Cpte A. Dohmen, F. Pedaci, I. Galgani, B. Lucarini,
M. Berti, E. Turco, A. Cauli, A. Silvestrelli,
Marchigiano V. Bellini Lyric Chor, Marchigiano PO,
G. Kuhn (pp1991) (5/92) (SCHW) ① [3] 314088
Cpte D. Fischer-Dieskau, S. Jurinac, M. Stader, I.
Seefried, E. Haefliger, K.C. Kohn, I. Sardi, W.
Kreppel, Berlin RIAS Chbr Ch, Berlin RSO, F. Fricsay
(r1958) (5/93) (DG) ① [3] 437 341-2GDO3
Cpte A. Schmidt, A. Halgrimson, L. Dawson, N.
Argenta, J.M. Ainsley, G. Yurisich, G. Finley, A.
Miles, London Schütz Ch, LCP, R. Norrington (r1992)
(10/93) (EMI) ① [3] CDS7 54859-2
Cpte E. Grümmer, L. Orgonášová, C. Margiono, E.
James, C. Prégardien, I. D'Arcangelo, J. Clarkson, A.
Silvestrelli, Monteverdi Ch, EBS, J. E. Gardiner
(pp1994) (8/95) (ARCH) ① [3] 445 870-2AH3
Cpte R. Gilfry, L. Orgonášová, C. Margiono, E.
James, C. Prégardien, I. D'Arcangelo, J. Clarkson, A.
Silvestrelli, Monteverdi Ch, EBS, J. E. Gardiner
(pp1994) (8/95) (ARCH) ① [3] 445 870-2AH3
1a ASMF, N. Marriner (concert ending Mozart)
Concert (4/84) (EMI) ① CDC7 47014-2
1a Staatskapelle Dresden, H. Vonk Concert
(10/91) (CAPR) ① [3] 10 809
1a National PO, L. Stokowski Concert
(4/92) (EMI) ① CDM7 64140-2
1a Tafelmusik, B. Weil Concert
(5/92) (SONY) ① SK46695
1a LPO, T. Beecham (r1939/40) Concert
(1/94) (DUTT) ① CDLX7009
1a LSO, J. Krips (r1951) Concert
(7/95) (DECC) ① [2] 443 530-2LF2
1a, 1b, 3-5, 7, 9, 10c, 11-16, 17a, 18, 22, 23b, 25b,
26. Athena Ens (arr 8 wind instr: Triebensee)
(4/94) (CHAN) ① CHAN6597
Concert (12/91) (PHIL) ① [3] 422 545-2PME3
2a, 2b P. Domingo, C. Vaness, Munich RO, E. Kohn
Concert (3/92) (EMI) ① CDC7 54329-2
4. F. Chaliapin, orch, J. Barbirolli (1928) Concert
(12/89) (PEAR) ① GEMMCD9314
4. E. Pinza, NY Met Op Orch, B. Walter (r1946)
Concert (4/90) (SONY) ① MPK45693
4. A. Kipnis, Berlin St Op Orch, C. Schmalstich (Ger:
r1930) Concert (4/90) (PREI) ① 89019
4. R. Bruson, NHK Chbr Sols, R. Paternostro
(pp1990) Concert (10/91) (CAPR) ① 10 348
4. O. Natzke, orch (r1940s) Concert
(12/92) (ODE) ① CDODE1365
4. L. Fugère, orch (French: r1929) Concert
(6/93) (SYMP) ① SYMCD1125
4. T. Pasero, La Scala Orch, A. Sabino (r1941)
Concert (4/95) (PREI) ① 89074
4. E. Kunz, VPO, O. Ackermann (r1951) Concert
(9/95) (TEST) ① SBT1059
4, 11, 16. J. Van Dam, Paris Orch Ens, J-P. Wallez
(pp) Concert (5/88) (NOVA) ① 150 014-2
4, 6, 11, 16, 17a, 17b H. Prey, Salzburg Mozarteum
Orch, B. Weil Concert (5/88) (DENO) ① CO-1741
4, 6, 11, 16, 17a F. Furlanetto, Vienna SO, I. Marin
Concert (3/92) (SONY) ① SK47192
4, 7, 10b, 10c, 11, 12, 13, 16, 18, 21, 23a, 23b, 25b,
26. G. Harman, R. Brünner, R. Knoll, Salzburg
Mozarteum Chor, Salzburg Mozarteum Orch, K.
Prestel (r1966) (5/94) (BELA) ① 450 080-2
4, 7, 16, 18. A. Martin, D. Robin, Vienna Mozart Orch,
K. Leitner Concert (12/91) (NAXO) ① 8 550349
7. R. Soyer, H. Donath, ECO, D. Barenboim Concert
(7/91) (EMIL) ① CDZ7 67015-2
7. S. Ghazarian, R. Bruson, NHK Chbr Sols, R.
Paternostro (pp1990) Concert
(10/91) (CAPR) ① 10 348
7. E. Berger, H. Schlusnus, Berlin St Op Orch, C.
Krauss (Ger: r1936) Concert
(12/91) (PREI) ① 89035
7. M. Battistini, E. Corsi, orch (r1906) Concert
(2/92) (PREI) ① 89045
7. Lotte Lehmann, H. Schlusnus, orch (Ger: r1920)
Concert (6/92) (PREI) ① [3] 89302

7. M. Battistini, E. Corsi, orch, C. Sabajno (r1906)
Concert (7/92) (PEAR) ① [3] GEMMCDS9924(1)
7. E. Eames, E. de Gogorza, orch (r1906/7: two vers)
Concert (11/93) (ROMO) ① [2] 81001-2
7. T. Allen, E. Gale, LPO, B. Haitink (r1984) Concert
(6/94) (EMI) ① CDH5 65072-2
7. I. Muia-Tchako, K. Youn, Paris Opéra-Bastille
Orch, E. Kohn (pp1992) Concert
(6/94) (SONY) ① SK46691
7. E. Eames, E. de Gogorza, orch (r1906) Concert
(1/95) (NIMB) ① NI7860
7. E. Kunz, I. Seefried, VPO, H. von Karajan (r1947)
Concert (9/95) (TEST) ① SBT1059
10a, 10b L. Price, P. de Palma, RCA Italiana Op
Orch, F. Molinari-Pradelli Concert
(12/92) (RCA) ① [4] 09026 61236-2
10a, 10b L. Price, P. de Palma, RCA Italiana Op
Orch, F. Molinari-Pradelli Concert
(6/93) (RCA) ① 09026 61357-2
10a, 10b, 25b K. Te Kanawa, ECO, J. Tate Concert
(10/88) (PHIL) ① 420 950-2PH
10b F. Leider, orch, J. Barbirolli (r1928) Concert
(2/90) (PREI) ① 89004
10b F. Leider, orch (r1925: Ger) Concert
(5/91) (PREI) ① [3] 89301
10b, 25a, 25b M. Cebotari, VPO, H. von Karajan
(r1947) Concert (12/90) (PREI) ① 90034
10c R. Tauber, orch (Ger: r1922) Concert
(7/89) (EMI) ① CDM7 69476-2
10c R. Tauber, orch (Ger: r1922) Concert
(7/89) (PEAR) ① GEMMCD9327
10c R. Tauber, orch (Ger: r1922) Concert
(3/92) (EMI) ① CDH7 64029-2
10c W. Midgley, ROHO, R. Goodall (r1951) Concert
(4/92) (EMI) ① [7] CHS7 69741-2(2)
10c H. Nash, orch (r1929) Concert
(7/92) (PEAR) ① GEMMCDS9926(1)
10c A. Bonci, anon (r1905) Concert
(12/92) (NIMB) ① NI7830
10c A. Bonci, anon (r1905) Concert
(12/93) (SYMP) ① SYMCD1113
10c W. Ludwig, orch, H. von Benda (r1934: Ger)
Concert (7/95) (PREI) ① 89088
10c, 21. J. Protschka, Munich RO, K. Eichhorn
Concert (3/89) (CAPR) ① 10 109
10c, 21. R. Blake, LSO, N. McGegan Concert
(3/89) (ARAB) ① Z6598
10c, 21. H. Nash, orch (r1929) Concert
(8/89) (PEAR) ① GEMMCD9319
10c, 21. T. Schipa, orch, R. Bourdon (1927) Concert
(12/89) (RCA) ① GD87969
10c, 21. J. Dickie, Capella Istropolitana, J. Wildner
Concert (12/91) (NAXO) ① 8 550383
10c, 21. H. Roswaenge, orch (r1928: Ger) Concert
(2/92) (PREI) ① [2] 89201
10c, 21. P. Domingo, Munich RO, E. Kohn Concert
(3/92) (EMI) ① CDC7 54329-2
10c, 21. P. Domingo, Munich RO, E. Kohn (r1991)
Concert (6/94) (EMI) ① CDC5 55017-2
10c, 21. L. Simoneau, Vienna SO, B. Paumgartner
(r1954) Concert
(11/94) (PHIL) ① [2] 438 953-2PM2
10c, 21. H. Nash, orch, C. Raybould (1929) Concert
(2/95) (DUTT) ① CDLX7012
11. E. Pinza, orch, R. Bourdon (r1930) Concert
(7/91) (MMOI) ① CDMOIR404
11. F. d'Andrade, orch (r1907) Concert
(7/92) (PEAR) ① [3] GEMMCDS9923(1)
11. A. Scotti, orch (r1904) Concert
(7/92) (PEAR) ① [3] GEMMCDS9923(2)
11. T. Ruffo, orch (r1914) Concert
(2/93) (PREI) ① [3] 89303(1)
11. M. Battistini, anon (r1902) Concert
(7/93) (NIMB) ① NI7840/1
11. E. Pinza, orch, R. Bourdon (r1930) Concert
(9/93) (RCA) ① 09026 61245-2
11, 16. E. Pinza, Cibelli, orch, R. Bourdon (r1930)
Concert (2/89) (PEAR) ① GEMMCD9306
11, 16. J. Hynninen, Estonian SO, E. Klas Concert
(4/90) (ONDI) ① ODE731-2
11, 16. E. Pinza, orch, R. Bourdon (r1930) Concert
(3/92) (PREI) ① 89050
11, 16. M. Battistini, anon (r1902) Concert
(10/92) (PEAR) ① GEMMCD9936
11, 16. A. Scotti, orch (r1902) Concert
(3/93) (SYMP) ① SYMCD1100
11, 23b T. Allen, M. Ewing, LPO, B. Haitink Concert
(7/91) (EMIL) ① CDZ7 67015-2
12. A. Patti, L. Ronald (r1905) Concert
(4/90) (PEAR) ① GEMMCD9312
12. L. Tetrazzini, orch, P. Pitt (r1907) Concert
(9/92) (EMI) ① [3] CHS7 63802-2(1)
12. L. Tetrazzini, orch (r1911) Concert
(9/92) (EMI) ① [3] CHS7 63802-2(1)

12. L. Tetrazzini, orch, P. Pitt (r1907) *Concert* (9/92) (PEAR) Ⓓ **GEMMCD9221**
12. L. Tetrazzini, orch (r1911) *Concert* (9/92) (PEAR) Ⓓ **GEMMCD9222**
12. A. Patti, L. Ronald (r1905) *Concert* (7/93) (NIMB) Ⓓ [2] **NI7840/1**
12. G. Farrar, orch (r1908) *Concert* (10/94) (NIMB) Ⓓ **NI7857**
12. E. Rethberg, Victor SO, R. Bourdon (r1930) *Concert* (10/95) (ROMO) Ⓓ [2] **81014-2**
12, 18. E. Schumann, orch, G.W. Byng (r1926) *Concert* (6/91) (PREI) Ⓓ **89031**
12, 23a, 23b C. Bartoli, Vienna CO, G. Fischer (r1993) *Concert* (11/94) (DECC) Ⓓ **443 452-2DH**
16. L. Howard (trans Busoni) *Concert* (12/86) (HYPE) Ⓓ **CDA66090**
16. E. Petri (r1938: arr Busoni) *Concert* (4/90) (PEAR) Ⓓ **GEMMCD9347**
16. E. Pinza, NY Met Op Orch, F. Cleva (r1947) *Concert* (4/90) (SONY) Ⓓ **MPK45693**
16. J. Lassalle, anon (French: r1902) *Concert* (9/91) (SYMP) Ⓓ **SYMCD1089**
16. M. Renaud, orch (r1908) *Concert* (7/92) (PEAR) Ⓓ [3] **GEMMCDS9923(2)**
16. V. Maurel, anon (r1904) *Concert* (7/92) (PEAR) Ⓓ [3] **GEMMCDS9923(1)**
16. G. De Luca, anon (r1907) *Concert* (7/92) (PEAR) Ⓓ [3] **GEMMCDS9925(1)**
16. E. Pinza, NY Met Op Orch, B. Walter (pp1942) *Concert* (7/92) (PEAR) Ⓓ [3] **GEMMCDS9926(2)**
16. T. Ruffo, orch (r1920) *Concert* (2/93) (PREI) Ⓓ [3] **89303(1)**
16. T. Ruffo, orch (r1912) *Concert* (2/93) (PREI) Ⓓ [3] **89303(1)**
16. V. Maurel, anon (r1907) *Concert* (7/93) (NIMB) Ⓓ [2] **NI7840/1**
16. G. De Luca, anon (r1902) *Concert* (8/93) (SYMP) Ⓓ **SYMCD1111**
16. T. Gobbi, La Scala Orch, U. Berrettoni (r1942) *Concert* (8/93) (TEST) Ⓓ **SBT1019**
16. Vanni-Marcoux, orch (r1927: French) *Concert* (1/94) (CLUB) Ⓓ **CL99-101**
16. E. Pinza, Cibelli, orch, R. Bourdon (r1930) *Concert* (4/94) (RCA) Ⓓ [6] **09026 61580-2(3)**
16. V. Maurel, anon (r1905) *Concert* (12/94) (SYMP) Ⓓ **SYMCD1128**
16. P. Schoeffler, National SO, C. Krauss (r1947) *Concert* (1/95) (PREI) Ⓓ **90190**
16. E. Petri (r1938: arr Busoni) *Concert* (8/95) (APR) Ⓓ [2] **APR7027**
16. H. Schlusnus, orch (r1925: Ger) *Concert* (12/95) (PREI) Ⓓ **89110**
16. E. Wild (r1995: trans pf: W Backhaus) *Concert* (12/95) (SONY) Ⓓ **SK62036**
18. C. Bartoli, Vienna CO, G. Fischer *Concert* (12/91) (DECC) Ⓓ **430 513-2DH**
18. I. Seefried, D. Fischer-Dieskau, I. Sardi, Berlin RSO, F. Fricsay (r1958) *Concert* (9/93) (DG) Ⓓ [2] **437 677-2GDO2**
21. J. McCormack, orch, W.B. Rogers (r1916) *Concert* (10/89) (NIMB) Ⓓ **NI7801**
21. H. Roswaenge, Berlin St Op Orch, F. Weissmann (Ger: r1928) *Concert* (5/90) (PEAR) Ⓓ **GEMMCD9394**
21. N. Gedda, New Philh, O. Klemperer *Concert* (7/91) (EMIL) Ⓓ **CDZ7 67015-2**
21. R. Tauber, orch, W. Goehr (r1939) *Concert* (3/92) (EMI) Ⓓ **CDH7 64029-2**
21. H. Meyer-Welfing, VPO, R. Moralt (Ger: r1946) *Concert* (4/92) (EMI) Ⓓ [7] **CHS7 69741-2(4)**
21. J. McCormack, orch (r1916) *Concert* (7/92) (PEAR) Ⓓ [3] **GEMMCDS9924(2)**
21. J. McCormack, orch, W.B. Rogers (r1916) *Concert* (5/93) (MMOI) Ⓓ **CDMOIR418**
21. R. Crooks, orch, W. Pelletier (r1937) *Concert* (5/94) (CLAR) Ⓓ **CDGSE78-50-52**
21. R. Tauber, orch, W. Goehr (r1939) *Concert* (9/94) (NIMB) Ⓓ **NI7856**
23a, 23b C. Studer, ASMF, N. Marriner *Concert* (9/94) (PHIL) Ⓓ **442 410-2PM**
23a, 23b H. Konetzni, Vienna SO, H. Swarowsky (r1950) *Concert* (1/95) (PREI) Ⓓ **90078**
23a, 23b, 25a, 25b L. Popp, Munich RO, L. Slatkin (r1983) *Concert* (8/84) (EMI) Ⓓ **CDC7 47019-2**
23a, 23b, 25a, 25b M. Price, ECO, J. Lockhart (r1973) *Concert* (5/95) (RCA) Ⓓ [2] **09026 61635-2**
23b E. Schwarzkopf, VPO, W. Furtwängler (pp1954) *Concert* (12/90) (EMI) Ⓓ **CDM7 63657-2**
23b S. Ghazarian, NHK Chbr Sols, R. Paternostro (pp1990) *Concert* (10/91) (CAPR) Ⓓ **10 348**
23b A. Roocroft, ASMF, N. Marriner *Concert* (12/95) (EMI) Ⓓ **CDC5 55396-2**
24. M. Sammarco, O. Luppi, anon (r1905) *Concert* (7/92) (PEAR) Ⓓ [3] **GEMMCDS9924(2)**
25a, 25b L. Price, LSO, E. Downes *Concert* (12/92) (RCA) Ⓓ [4] **09026 61236-2**
25a, 25b L. Price, LSO, E. Downes *Concert* (6/93) (RCA) Ⓓ **09026 61357-2**
25b M. Callas, MMF Orch, T. Serafin (r1953) *Concert* (2/93) (EMI) Ⓓ **CDC7 54437-2**
27. L. Helletsgruber, A. Mildmay, K. von Pataky, Roy Henderson, I. Souez, S. Baccaloni, Glyndebourne Fest Orch, F. Busch (r1936) *Concert* (6/94) (EMI) Ⓓ **CDH5 65072-2**

Die **Entführung aus dem Serail, '(The) Abduction from the hareem'—singspiel: 3 acts, K384 (1782—Vienna)** (Lib. C F Bretzner & J G Stephanie jr)

EXCERPTS: 1. Overture. ACT 1: 2. Hier soll ich dich denn sehen; 3. Wer ein Liebchen hat gefunden; 4. Solche hergelaufne Laffen; 5. Konstanze...O wie ängstlich; 6. Singt dem grossen Bassa Lieder; 7. Ach ich liebte; 8. Konstanze! dich wiederzusehen...O wie ängstlich; 9. Durch Zärtlichkeit; 10. Ich gehe, doch rate ich dir; 11a. Welcher Kummer; 11b. Traurigkeit; 12. Martern aller Arten; 13. Welche Wonne, welche Lust; 14. Frisch zum Kampfe!; 15. Vivat Bacchus!; 16. Wenn der Freude Tränen fliessen; 17. Ach, Belmonte! ach mein Leben! (Quartet). ACT 3: 18. Ich baue ganz auf deine Stärke; 19. In Mohrenland gefangen war; 20. Ha, wie will ich triumphieren; 21a. Welch ein Geschick!; 21b. Ha, du solltest für mich sterben; 22. Nie werd' ich deine Huld verkennen (Vaudeville); 23. Chorus of Janissaries.

Cpte E. Gruberová, K. Battle, G. Winbergh, H. Zednik, M. Talvela, W. Quadflieg, Vienna St Op Concert Ch, VPO, G. Solti (r1985: with dialogue) (4/87) (DECC) Ⓓ [2] **417 402-2DH2**
Cpte Y. Kenny, L. Watson, P. Schreier, W. Gamlich, M. Salminen, W. Reichmann, Zurich Op. Hse Chor, Zurich Op Hse Mozart Orch, N. Harnoncourt (with dialogue) (5/88) (TELD) Ⓓ [3] **2292-42643-2**
Cpte A. Rothenberger, L. Popp, N. Gedda, G. Unger, G. Frick, L. Rudolf, Vienna St Op Chor, VPO, J. Krips (with dialogue) (12/89) (EMI) Ⓓ [2] **CMS7 63263-2**
Cpte A. Auger, R. Grist, P. Schreier, H. Neukirch, K. Moll, O. Mellies, Leipzig Rad Chor, Staatskapelle Dresden, K. Böhm (with dialogue) (12/90) (DG) Ⓓ [2] **429 868-2GX2**
Cpte L. Marshall, I. Hollweg, L. Simoneau, G. Unger, G. Frick, H. Laubenthal, Beecham Choral Soc, RPO, T. Beecham (with dialogue) *Concert* (3/91) (EMI) Ⓓ [2] **CHS7 63715-2**
Cpte C. Eda-Pierre, N. Burrowes, S. Burrows, R. Tear, R. Lloyd, C. Jürgens, John Alldis Ch, ASMF, Colin Davis (r1978: with dialogue) (4/92) (PHIL) Ⓓ [2] **422 538-2PME2**
Cpte C. Studer, E. Szmytka, K. Streit, R. Gambill, G. Missenhardt, M. Heltau, Vienna St Op Chor, Vienna SO, B. Weil (5/92) (SONY) Ⓓ [2] **S2K48053**
Cpte L. Orgonášová, C. Sieden, S. Olsen, U. Peper, C. Hauptmann, H-P. Minetti, Monteverdi Ch, EBS, J.E. Gardiner (r1991: with dialogue) (12/92) (ARCH) Ⓓ [2] **435 857-2AH2**
Cpte M. Stader, R. Streich, E. Haefliger, M. Vantin, J. Greindl, W. Franck, Berlin RIAS Chbr Ch, Berlin RIAS Orch, F. Fricsay (r1954: with dialogue) *Exsultate, jubilate, K165.* (7/95) (DG) Ⓓ [2] **445 412-2GDO2**
Cpte E. Köth, L. Schädle, F. Wunderlich, F. Lenz, K. Böhme, R. Boysen, Bavarian St Op Chor, BRSO, E. Jochum (with dialogue) (7/95) (DG) Ⓓ [2] **439 708-2GX2**
Cpte W. Lipp, E. Loose, W. Ludwig, P. Klein, E. Koréh, H. Woester, Vienna St Op Chor, VPO, J. Krips (r1950: omits dialogue) *Concert* (7/95) (DECC) Ⓓ [2] **443 530-2LF2**
Cpte E. Gruberová, G. Ebel, F. Araiza, N. Orth, R. Bracht, H. Leipnitz, Bavarian Rad Chor, Munich RO, H. Wallberg (r1978) (10/95) (RCA) Ⓓ [2] **74321 25283-2**
1. ASMF, N. Marriner (concert ending André) *Concert* (4/84) (EMI) Ⓓ **CDC7 47014-2**
1. Staatskapelle Dresden, H. Vonk *Concert* (10/91) (CAPR) Ⓓ [3] **10 809**
1. BPO, W. Furtwängler (r1933) *Concert* (4/92) (KOCH) Ⓓ [2] **37059-2**
1. Tafelmusik, B. Weil *Concert* (5/92) (SONY) Ⓓ **SK46695**
1, 2, 9, 10, 13, 15, 16, 20. Netherlands Wind Ens (arr 8 wind instr: Wendt?) *Concert* (12/91) (PHIL) Ⓓ [3] **422 545-2PME3**
2. H. Roswaenge, Berlin St Op Orch, B. Seidler-Winkler (r1937) *Concert* (4/95) (PREI) Ⓓ [2] **89209**
2, 16. F. Wunderlich, Bavarian St Orch, E. Jochum *Concert* (5/93) (DG) Ⓓ **431 110-2GB**
2, 16. P. Anders, Berlin Staatskapelle, R. Heger (bp1945) *Concert* (8/93) (ACAN) Ⓓ **43 268**
2, 5, 16, 18, 19. J. Dickie, Capella Istropolitana, J. Wildner *Concert* (12/91) (NAXO) Ⓓ **8 550383**
3. A. Kipnis, Berlin St Op Orch, E. Orthmann (r1931) *Concert* (12/90) (PREI) Ⓓ **89019**
3, 4, 20. M. Salminen, Lahti SO, E. Klas *Concert* (8/92) (BIS) Ⓓ **BIS-CD520**
5. H.E. Groh, orch (r1936) *Concert* (3/92) (PEAR) Ⓓ **GEMMCD9419**
5. W. Ludwig, Berlin St Op Orch, B. Seidler-Winkler (r1936) *Concert* (7/95) (PREI) Ⓓ **89088**
5, 14. P. Domingo, Munich RO, E. Kohn *Concert* (3/92) (EMI) Ⓓ **CDC7 54329-2**
5, 16, 18. J. Protschka, Munich RO, K. Eichhorn *Concert* (3/89) (CAPR) Ⓓ **10 109**
7. M. Perras, Berlin St Op Orch, B. Seidler-Winkler (r1930s) *Concert* (10/93) (NIMB) Ⓓ **NI7848**
7. M. Price, LPO, J. Pritchard (r1972) *Concert* (6/94) (EMI) Ⓓ **CDH5 65072-2**
7, 12. M. Németh, orch (r c1930) *Concert* (1/94) (CLUB) Ⓓ **CL99-007**
9. A. Martin, D. Robin, Vienna Mozart Orch, K. Leitner *Concert* (12/91) (NAXO) Ⓓ **8 550435**
9. T. Dahl, Calgary PO, M. Bernardi (r1992) *Concert* (12/94) (CBC) Ⓓ **SMCD5125**
11a, 11b L. Popp, Munich RO, L. Slatkin (r1983) *Concert* (8/84) (EMI) Ⓓ **CDC7 47019-2**
11a, 11b, 12. K. Te Kanawa, ECO, J. Tate *Concert* (10/88) (PHIL) Ⓓ **420 950-2PH**
12. M. André, Toulouse Capitole Orch, M. Plasson (arr tpt) *Concert* (1/89) (EMI) Ⓓ **CDC7 49219-2**
12. J. Sutherland, ROHO, F. Molinari-Pradelli *Concert* (1/90) (DECC) Ⓓ [2] **425 493-2DM2**
12. M. Ivogün, orch (r1919) *Concert* (7/92) (PEAR) Ⓓ [3] **GEMMCDS9926(1)**
12. M. Callas, Rome RAI Orch, A. Simonetto (Ital: pp1954) *Concert* (2/93) (EMI) Ⓓ **CDC7 54437-2**
12. M. Ivogün, orch (r c1925) *Concert* (1/94) (CLUB) Ⓓ **CL99-020**
12. C. Studer, ASMF, N. Marriner *Concert* (9/94) (PHIL) Ⓓ **442 410-2PM**
12. M. Price, ECO, J. Lockhart (r1973) *Concert* (5/95) (RCA) Ⓓ [2] **09026 61635-2**
12, 20. A. Rothenberger, G. Frick, VPO, J. Krips *Concert* (7/91) (EMIL) Ⓓ **CDZ7 67015-2**
13. I. Hollweg, RPO, T. Beecham *Concert* (7/91) (EMIL) Ⓓ **CDZ7 67015-2**
16. W. Ludwig, orch, H. von Benda (r1934) *Concert* (7/95) (PREI) Ⓓ **89088**
18. R. Blake, LSO, N. McGegan *Concert* (3/89) (ARAB) Ⓓ **Z6598**
18. L. Simoneau, Paris Champs-Élysées Orch, A. Jouve (r1955) *Concert* (3/91) (EMI) Ⓓ [2] **CHS7 63715-2**
20. E. Pinza, NY Met Op Orch, B. Walter (r1946: Ital) *Concert* (4/90) (SONY) Ⓓ **MPK45693**
21a, 21b P. Anders, E. Berger, Berlin Staatskapelle, K. Schmidt (bp1946) *Concert* (8/93) (ACAN) Ⓓ **43 268**

La **finta giardiniera—opera buffa: 3 acts, K196 (1775—Munich)** (Lib. G. Petrosellini)

EXCERPTS: 1. Overture. ACT 1: 2. Che lieto giorno, che contentezza; 3. Se l'augellin sen fugge; 4. Dentro il mio petto; 5. Noi donne poverine, tapine sfortunate; 6. A forza di martelli; 7. Che beltà, che leggiadria; 8. Si promette facilmente dagl'amanti; 9. Da scirocco a tramontana; 10a. Un marito! Oh Dio, vorrei; 10b. Un marito! Oh Dio! vorrei (alternative version); 11. Appena mi vedon chi cade chi sviene; 12. Geme la tortorella; 13. Numi! che incanto è questo. ACT 2: 14. Vorrei punirti, indegno; 15. Con un vezzo all'italiana; 16. Care pupille, pupille belle; 17. Una voce sento al core; 18. Una damina, una nipote?; 19. Dolce d'amor compagna; 20a. Ah non partir m'ascolta; 20b. Già di vento freddo; 21. Chi vuol godere il mondo; 22. Crudel, oh! Dio, fermate; 23. Ah dal pianto, dal singhiozzo; 24. Fra quest'ombre e quest'oscuro; 25. Mirate, che contrasto fa il sole; 26. Mio padronne, io dir volevo; 27. Và pure ad altri in braccio; 28a. Dove mai son!; 28b. Tu me lasci? o fiero istante; 29. Viva pur la giardiniera!.

Cpte J. Kozlowska, U. Benelli, M. Torzewski, M. Major, L. Poulson, E. Szmytka, R. Smythe, Brussels Théâtre de la Monnaie Orch, S. Cambreling (pp1989) (4/90) (RICE) Ⓓ [3] **RIS066045/7**
Cpte H. Donath, G. Unger, W. Hollweg, J. Norman, T. Troyanos, I. Cotrubas, H. Prey, N German Rad Chor, N German RSO, H. Schmidt-Isserstedt (r1972: Ger) (5/92) (PHIL) Ⓓ [3] **422 534-2PME3**
Cpte J. Conwell, E. di Cesare, T. Moser, L. Sukis, B. Fassbaender, J-R. Ihloff, B. McDaniel, Salzburg Mozarteum Orch, L. Hager (r1980) (5/92) (PHIL) Ⓓ [3] **422 533-2PME3**
Cpte E. Gruberová, T. Moser, U. Heilmann, C. Margiono, M. Bacelli, D. Upshaw, A. Scharinger, VCM, N. Harnoncourt (pp1991) (3/93) (TELD) Ⓓ [3] **9031-72309-2**

1. English Sinfonia, C. Groves *Concert* (11/90) (CARL) Ⓓ **PCD939**

1. Staatskapelle Dresden, H. Vonk *Concert* (10/91) (CAPR) Ⓓ [3] **10 809**

5. I. Baillie, CBO, B. Cameron (r1941: Eng) *Concert* (7/95) (DUTT) Ⓓ **CDLX7013**

6, 15. H. Prey, Salzburg Mozarteum Orch, B. Weil (Ger) *Concert* (5/88) (DENO) Ⓓ **CO-1741**

7. P. Domingo, Munich RO, E. Kohn *Concert* (3/92) (EMI) Ⓓ **CDC7 54329-2**

20a J. Protschka, Munich RO, K. Eichhorn (Ger) *Concert* (3/89) (CAPR) Ⓓ **10 109**

22. K. Te Kanawa, LSO, Colin Davis *Concert* (3/84) (PHIL) Ⓓ **411 148-2PH**

27. J. Larmore, Lausanne CO, J. López-Cobos (r1994) *Concert* (12/95) (TELD) Ⓓ **4509-96800-2**

La **finta semplice—opera buffa: 3 acts, K51/K46a (1769—Salzburg)** (Lib. M. Coltellini, after C. Goldini)

EXCERPTS: 1. Overture. ACT ONE: 2. Bella cosa è far l'amore!; 3a. Ritiriamoci, amici!; 3b. Troppa briga a prender moglie; 4a. L'un de' patroni è alzato; 4b. Marito io vorrei; 5a. Oh, starem male insieme; 5b. Non c'è al mondo altro che donne; 6a. Con chi l'ha Don Cassandro?; 6b. Guarda la donna in viso; 7a. Eh! ben ben, ci vedremo; 7b. Colla bocca, e non col core; 8a. Sicché m'avete inteso?; 8b. Oh, la prendo da vero; 8c. Cosa ha mai la donna indosso; 9a. Grand'uomo che son io; 9b. Ella vuole ed io torrei; 10a. Eh ben, sorella mia?; 10b. Senti l'eco, ove t'aggiri; 11a. Ninetta - Che volete?; 11b. Chi mi vuol bene; 12a. Adesso è fatto tutto; 12b. Dove avete la creanza? ACT TWO: 13a. Sono i padroni miei; 13b. Un marito, donne care; 14a. Eh, quando sia mia sposa; 14b. Con certe persone vuol esser bastone; 15a. Non mi marito più; 15b. Se a maritarmi arrivo; 16a. Quando avrò moglie anch'io; 16b. Amoretti, che ascosi qui siete; 17a. Vado subitamente; 17b. Ubriaco non son io; 18a. Egli è venuto; 18b. Sposa cara, sposa bella; 19a. Mia signora Madama; 19b. Me ne vo' prender spasso; 19c. Ehi...dormite, signore?; 19d. Ho sentito a dir da tutte; 20a. Di voi cercavo appunto; 20b. Cospetton, cospettonaccio!; 21a. Dove andate, signore?; 21b. Siam quasi in porto adesso; 21c. Vieni a tempo, Simone; 21d. In voi, belle, è leggiadria; 22. T'ho detto, buffone. ACT THREE: 23. Vieni, vieni, oh mia Ninetta; 24a. Io non ho gran paura; 24b. Sono in amore, voglio marito; 25. Che scompiglio, che flagello; 26a. Che smorfie, che paura!; 26b. Nelle guerre d'amore; 27a. E così, Baronessa?; 27b. Eh ben, quando facciamo queste nozze, signora?; 27c. Se le pupille io giro.

Cpte H. Donath, A. Rolfe Johnson, T. Berganza, R. Holl, J-R. Ihloff, T. Moser, R. Lloyd, Salzburg Mozarteum Orch, L. Hager (r1983) (8/89) (ORFE) Ⓓ [3] **C085843F**

Cpte B. Hendricks, S. Lorenz, D. Johnson, A. Murray, E. Lind, H-P. Blochwitz, A. Schmidt, CPE Bach Orch, P. Schreier (r1988) (11/91) (PHIL) Ⓓ [2] **422 528-2PME2**

25. J. Larmore, Lausanne CO, J. López-Cobos (r1994) *Concert* (12/95) (TELD) Ⓓ **4509-96800-2**

Idomeneo, Rè di Creta, 'Idomeneo, King of Crete'—opera seria: 3 acts, K366 (1781—Munich) (Lib. G Varesco)

EXCERPTS - MUNICH VERSION: 1. Overture. ACT 1: 2a. Quando avran; 2b. Padre, germani, addio!; 3. Non ho colpa, e mi codanni; 4. Godiam la pace, trionfi Amore; 5a. Estinto è Idomeneo?; 5b. Tutte nel cor vi sento; 6. Pietà, Numi, pietà!; 7. Vedrommi intorno; 8a. Spietatissimi Dei!; 8b. Il padre adorato ritrovo; 9a. March in D; 9b. Ballet in G; 10. Nettuno s'onori! ACT 2: 11a. Tutto m'è noto; 11b. Se il tuo duol; 12. Se il padre perdei; 13a. Qual mi conturba i sensi equivoca favella; 13b. Fuor del mar; 14a. Chi mai del mio provò piacer più dolce; 14b. Idol mio, se ritroso; 15. March in C; 16. Placidò il mar; 17. Pria di partir, O Dio!; 18. Qual nuovo terrore!; 19. Corriamo, fuggiamo quel mostro spietato. ACT 3: 20a. Solitudini amiche; 20b. Zeffiretti lusinghieri; 21. S'io non moro a questi accenti; 22. Andrò ramingo e solo (quartet); 23. Se solà ne' fati è scritto; 24a. Volgi intorno lo sguardo; 24b. O, o voto tremendo; 25. March in F; 26. Accogli, o rè del mar; 27a. Padre, mio caro padre!; 27b. No, la morte io non pavento; 28a. Ma che più tradi? Idomeneo cessi esser rè; 28b. Ha vinto amore; 29a. O ciel pietoso!; 29b. Oh smania! oh furie!; 30. Popoli! A Voi l'ultima legge; 31. Torna la pace al core; 32. Scenda Amor, scende Imeneo. VARIANT ARIAS: 50. Spiegarti non poss'io, K489 (21); 51. Non più. Tutto ascoltai, K490 (11a); 52. Non temer, amato bene, K490 (11b); 53. D'Oreste, d'Aiace (29b); 54. Torna la pace (31); 55. Gavotte; 56. Ballet Music, K367.

Cpte W. Hollweg, T. Schmidt, R. Yakar, F. Palmer, K. Equiluz, R. Tear, S. Estes, Zurich Op Hse Chor, Zurich Op Hse Mozart Orch, N. Harnoncourt (3/86) (TELD) Ⓓ [3] **2292-42600-2**

Cpte L. Pavarotti, A. Baltsa, L. Popp, E. Gruberová, L. Nucci, Timothy Jenkins, N. Storozhev, Vienna St Op Concert Ch, VPO, J. Pritchard (4/88) (DECC) Ⓓ [3] **411 805-2DH3**

Cpte W. Ochman, P. Schreier, E. Mathis, J. Varady, H. Winkler, E. Büchner, S. Vogel, Leipzig Rad Chor, Staatskapelle Dresden, K. Böhm (r1977) (12/90) (DG) Ⓓ [3] **429 864-2GX3**

Cpte A. Rolfe Johnson, A.S. von Otter, S. McNair, H. Martinpelto, N. Robson, G. Winslade, C. Hauptmann, Monteverdi Ch, EBS, J.E. Gardiner (pp1990) (6/91) (ARCH) Ⓓ [3] **431 674-2AH3**

Cpte F. Araiza, S. Mentzer, B. Hendricks, R. Alexander, U. Heilmann, W. Hollweg, H. Peeters, Bavarian Rad Chor, BRSO, Colin Davis (r1991) (12/91) (PHIL) Ⓓ [3] **422 537-2PME3**

Cpte W. Kmentt, E. Haefliger, P. Lorengar, E. Grümmer, R. Capecchi, E. Waechter, G. Littasy, Vienna St Op Chor, VPO, F. Fricsay (pp1961: Paumgartner vers) (9/95) (DG) Ⓓ [3] **447 662-2GX3**

1. ASMF, N. Marriner *Concert* (4/84) (EMI) Ⓓ **CDC7 47014-2**

1. Staatskapelle Dresden, H. Vonk *Concert* (10/91) (CAPR) Ⓓ [3] **10 809**

1. Tafelmusik, B. Weil *Concert* (5/92) (SONY) Ⓓ **SK46695**

1, 12, 29a, 29b, 30-32. J. Sabel, E. Réthy, E. Böttcher, A. Konetzni, E. Kunz, M. Rus, H. Alsen, Vienna St Op Chor, Vienna St Op Orch, R. Strauss (pp1941: Ger: arr R Strauss) *Concert* (11/94) (SCHW) Ⓓ [2] **314532**

2a, 2b B. Hendricks, L. Pearson, ECO, J. Tate *Concert* (6/85) (EMI) Ⓓ **CDC7 47122-2**

2a, 2b, 12, 20b S. Jurinac, Glyndebourne Fest Orch, F. Busch (r1951) *Concert* (1/90) (EMI) Ⓓ **CDH7 63199-2**

3. A. Baltsa, VPO, J. Pritchard (r1983) *Concert* (10/93) (DECC) Ⓓ **436 462-2DM**

5b R. Hunter, Tasmanian SO, D. Franks (r1989) *Concert* (10/95) (ABCC) Ⓓ **8 7000 10**

7. Richard Lewis, Glyndebourne Fest Orch, F. Busch (r1951) *Concert* (6/94) (EMI) Ⓓ **CDH5 65072-2**

7, 31. J. Protschka, Munich RO, K. Eichhorn *Concert* (3/89) (CAPR) Ⓓ **10 109**

7, 8a, 8b G. Sabbatini, NHK Chbr Sols, R. Paternostro (pp1990) *Concert* (10/91) (CAPR) Ⓓ **10 348**

9a, 15, 25. Salzburg Mozarteum Orch, H. Graf *Concert* (11/89) (CAPR) Ⓓ **10 253**

9a, 15, 25. Salzburg Mozarteum Orch, H. Graf *Concert* (10/91) (CAPR) Ⓓ [3] **10 809**

12. K. Te Kanawa, LSO, Colin Davis *Concert* (3/84) (PHIL) Ⓓ **411 148-2PH**

12. L. Price, New Philh, P.H. Adler *Concert* (6/93) (RCA) Ⓓ **09026 61357-2**

12. A. Roocroft, ASMF, N. Marriner *Concert* (12/95) (EMI) Ⓓ **CDC5 55396-2**

13a, 13b L. Simoneau, Vienna SO, B. Paumgartner (r1954) *Concert* (11/94) (PHIL) Ⓓ [2] **438 953-2PM2**

13b R. Blake, LSO, N. McGegan *Concert* (3/89) (ARAB) Ⓓ **Z6598**

13b P. Domingo, Munich RO, E. Kohn *Concert* (3/92) (EMI) Ⓓ **CDC7 54329-2**

14a, 14b M. Price, ECO, J. Lockhart (r1973) *Concert* (5/95) (RCA) Ⓓ [2] **09026 61635-2**

20a, 20b L. Popp, Munich RO, L. Slatkin (r1983) *Concert* (8/84) (EMI) Ⓓ **CDC7 47019-2**

20a, 20b A. Roocroft, LPO, F. Welser-Möst *Concert* (10/94) (EMI) Ⓓ **CDC5 55090-2**

29b, 29c L. Price, Philh, H. Lewis (r1979) *Concert* (12/92) (RCA) Ⓓ [4] **09026 61236-2**

29b, 53. L. Price, New Philh, N. Santi *Concert* (6/93) (RCA) Ⓓ **09026 61357-2**

29b, 53. C. Studer, ASMF, N. Marriner *Concert* (9/94) (PHIL) Ⓓ **442 410-2PM**

31. L. Simoneau, Paris Champs-Élysées Orch, A. Jouve (r1955) *Concert* (3/91) (EMI) Ⓓ [2] **CHS7 63715-2**

50. S. Jurinac, L. Simoneau, Glyndebourne Fest Orch, J. Pritchard (r1956) *Concert* (6/94) (EMI) Ⓓ **CDH5 65072-2**

52. B. Hendricks, J-L. Garcia, ECO, J. Tate *Concert* (6/85) (EMI) Ⓓ **CDC7 47122-2**

52. K. Battle, D. Harris, B. Griffiths, RPO, A. Previn *Concert* (12/86) (EMI) Ⓓ **CDC7 47355-2**

52. B. Hendricks, S. Mentzer, A. Röhn, BRSO, Colin Davis *Concert* (12/91) (PHIL) Ⓓ [3] **422 545-2PME3**

52. I. Seefried, Vienna SO, F. Leitner (r1952) *Concert* (9/93) (DG) Ⓓ [2] **437 677-2GDO2**

52. L. Simoneau, Vienna SO, B. Paumgartner (r1954) *Concert* (11/94) (PHIL) Ⓓ [2] **438 953-2PM2**

56. NHK Chbr Sols, R. Paternostro (pp1990) *Concert* (10/91) (CAPR) Ⓓ **10 348**

Lucio Silla—opera seria: 3 acts, K135 (1772—Milan) (Lib. G. de Gamerra)

EXCERPTS: 1. Overture. ACT 1: 2. Vieni ov'amour t'invita; 3a. Dunque sperar; 3b. Il tenero momento; 4. Se lusinghiera speme; 5. Dalla sponda tenebrosa; 6a. Mi piace? E il cor di Silla; 6b. Il desio di vendetta; 7a. Morte fatal; 7b. Fuor di queste urne; 8a. Se l'empio Silla; 8b. D'Eliso in sen m'attendi. ACT 2: 9. Guerrier, che d'un acciaro; 10a. Ah corri, vola, Cecilio a che t'arresti; 10b. Quest'improvviso tremito; 11. Se il labbro tumido; 12a. Vanne t'affretta; 12b. Ah se il crudel periglio; 13a. Ah sì, scuotasi omai; 13b. Nel fortunato istante; 14. D'ogni pietà mi spoglio perfida; 15a. Chi sa che non sia questa; 15b. Ah se morir mi chiama; 16. Quando sugl'arsi campi; 17a. In un istante; 17b. Parto m'affretto; 18. Se gloria in crin ti cinse; 19. Quell'orgoglioso sdegno. ACT 3: 20. Strider sento la procella; 21. De' più superbi il core; 22. Pupille amate non lagrimate; 23a. Sposo, mia vita. Ah dove. Dove vai?; 23b. Fra i pensier più funesti; 24. Il gran Silla che a Roma in seno.

Cpte P. Schreier, E. Gruberová, C. Bartoli, Y. Kenny, D. Upshaw, A. Schoenberg Ch, VCM, N. Harnoncourt (pp1989) (3/91) (TELD) Ⓓ [2] **2292-44928-2**

Cpte A. Rolfe Johnson, L. Cuberli, A. Murray, B-M. Aruhn, C. Barbaux, A. Van Baasbank, Brussels Théâtre de la Monnaie Chor, Brussels Théâtre de la Monnaie Orch, S. Cambreling (pp1985) (2/92) (RICE) Ⓓ [3] **RIS090072/4**

Cpte P. Schreier, A. Auger, J. Varady, E. Mathis, H. Donath, W. Krenn, Salzburg Rad Chor, Salzburg Mozarteum Chor, Salzburg Mozarteum Orch, L. Hager (r1975) (2/92) (PHIL) Ⓓ [3] **422 532-2PME3**

1. ASMF, N. Marriner *Concert* (4/84) (EMI) Ⓓ **CDC7 47014-2**

1. Staatskapelle Dresden, H. Vonk *Concert* (10/91) (CAPR) Ⓓ [3] **10 809**

12a, 12b E. Gruberová, Munich RO, L. Gardelli *Concert* (11/86) (ORFE) Ⓓ **C101841A**

22. K. Te Kanawa, LSO, Colin Davis *Concert* (3/84) (PHIL) Ⓓ **411 148-2PH**

23b B. Hendricks, ECO, J. Tate *Concert* (6/85) (EMI) Ⓓ **CDC7 47122-2**

Mitridate, rè di Ponto—opera seria: 3 acts, K87 (1770—Milan) (Lib. V. A. Cigna-Santi)

EXCERPTS: 1. Overture. ACT 1: 2. Al destin, che la minaccia; 3a. Qual tumulto; 3b. Soffre il mio cor con pace; 4. L'odio nel cor frenate; 5. Nel sen mi palpita dolente il core; 6. Parto: nel gran cimento; 7. Venga pur, minacci; 8. March; 9. Se di lauri il crine adorno; 10. In faccia all'oggetto che'marde; 11a. Respira alfin, respira; 11b. Quel ribelle e quell'ingrato. ACT 2: 12. Va, va, l'error mio palesa; 13. Tu, che fedel mi sei; 14a. Non più Regina; 14b. Lungi da te, mio bene, se vuoi ch'io porti il piede; 15a. Grazie ai numi parti; 15b. Nel grave tormento; 16. So, quanto a te dispiace; 17. Son reo, l'error confesso e degno del tuo sdegno; 18. Già di pietà mi spoglio; 19a. Io sposa di quel mostro; 19b. Se viver non degg'io. ACT 3: 20. Tu sai per chi m'accese; 21. Vado incontro al fato estremo; 22. Se il rigor d'ingrata sorte; 23a. Ah ben ne fui presaga!; 23b. Pallid'ombre, che scorgete; 24. Se di regnar sei vago; 25a. Vadasi, oh ciel; 25b. Già dagli occhi il velo è tolto; 26. Non si ceda al Campidoglio.

Cpte W. Hollweg, A. Auger, E. Gruberová, A. Baltsa, I. Cotrubas, D. Kuebler, C. Weidinger, Salzburg Mozarteum Orch, L. Hager (r1977) (2/92) (PHIL) Ⓓ [3] **422 529-2PME3**

7, 12, 17, 25b J. Kowalski, CPE Bach Orch, Hartmut Haenchen *Concert* (3/88) (CAPR) Ⓓ **10 213**

9, 21. R. Blake, LSO, N. McGegan *Concert* (3/89) (ARAB) Ⓓ **Z6598**

11b J. Protschka, Munich RO, K. Eichhorn *Concert* (3/89) (CAPR) Ⓓ **10 109**

14b K. Te Kanawa, ECO, J. Tate *Concert* (10/88) (PHIL) Ⓓ **420 950-2PH**

14b F. Lott, LMP, J. Glover *Concert* (2/90) (ASV) Ⓓ **CDDCA683**

25b J. Larmore, Lausanne CO, J. López-Cobos (r1994) *Concert* (12/95) (TELD) Ⓓ **4509-96800-2**

Le **Nozze di Figaro, '(The) Marriage of Figaro'—opera buffa: 4 acts, K492 (1786—Vienna)** (Lib. L. da Ponte, after Beaumarchais)

EXCERPTS: 1. Overture. ACT 1: 2. Cinque dieci; 3a. Cosa stai misurando; 3b. Se a cosa madama; 4a. Bravo, signor padrone!; 4b. Se vuol ballare; 5. La vendetta; 6. Via, resti servita; 7. Non so più cosa son; 8. Cosa sento!; 9. Giovani liete; 10. Non più andrai. ACT 2: 11. Porgi, amor; 12. Voi che sapete; 13a.

Bravo! che bella voce; 13b. Venite inginocchiatevi; 14. Quante buffonerie!; 15a. Che novità!; 15b. Susanna, or via, sortite; 16a. Dunque voi non aprite?; 16b. Aprite, presto, aprite; 17a. Tutto è come il lasciai; 17b. Esci, ormai, garzon malnato; 18. Dunque?...o ciel (Finale). ACT 3: 19. Crudel! perchè finora; 20a. 'Hai già vinta la causa!'; 20b. Vedrò mentr'io sospiro; 21. Riconosci in quest'amplesso; 22a. E Susanna non vien!; 22b. Dove sono; 23a. Cosa mi narri?; 23b. Sull'aria; 24. Ricevete o padroncina; 25. Ecco la marcia (Wedding March). ACT 4: 26. L'ho perduta; 27. Il capro e la capretta; 28. In quegli anni; 29a. Tutto è disposto; 29b. Aprite un po' quegl'occhi; 30a. Giunse alfin il momento; 30b. Deh vieni, non tardar; 31. Pian pianino; 32. Pace, pace, mio dolce tesoro!; 33. Contessa, perdono. VARIANTS: V1. Signora mia garbata, K492g (Act 1: Marcellina); V2. Un moto di gioia, K579 (Act 2: Susanna); V3. Aprite, presto, aprite (Act 2: Susanna and Cherubino); V4. Ah no, lasciarti in pace, K577d (high version: Act 3: Almaviva); V5. Dove sono (second part: Act 3: Countess: 1789 version); V6. Al desio di chi t'adora, K577a (Act 4: Susanna).

Cpte S. Ramey, L. Popp, T. Allen, K. Te Kanawa, F. von Stade, J. Berbié, K. Moll, R. Tear, P. Langridge, G. Tadeo, Y. Kenny, London Op Chor, LPO, G. Solti (4/84) (DECC) ① [3] **410 150-2DH3**

Cpte J. Van Dam, B. Hendricks, R. Raimondi, L. Popp, A. Baltsa, F. Palmer, R. Lloyd, A. Baldin, N. Jenkins, D. Maxwell, C. Pope, Ambrosian Op Chor, ASMF, N. Marriner (r1985) (7/86) (PHIL) ① [3] **416 370-2PH3**

Cpte J. Van Dam, I. Cotrubas, T. Krause, A. Tomowa-Sintow, F. von Stade, J. Berbié, J. Bastin, H. Zednik, K. Equiluz, Z. Kélémen, C. Barbaux, Vienna St Op Chor, VPO, H. von Karajan (7/88) (DECC) ① [3] **421 125-2DH3**

Cpte C. Desderi, G. Rolandi, R. Stilwell, F. Lott, F. Esham, A. Mason, A. Korn, U. Benelli, A. Oliver, F. Davià, Anne Dawson, Glyndebourne Fest Chor, LPO, B. Haitink (7/88) (EMI) ① [3] **CDS7 49753-2**

Cpte P. Salomaa, B. Bonney, H. Hagegård, A. Auger, A. Nafé, D. Jones, C. Feller, E. Gimenez, F. Egerton, E. Florimo, N. Argenta, Drottningholm Court Th Chor, Drottningholm Court Th Orch, A. Östman (also contains alternative arias) (12/88) (L'OI) ① [3] **421 333-2OH3**

Cpte G. Taddei, A. Moffo, E. Waechter, E. Schwarzkopf, F. Cossotto, D. Gatta, I. Vinco, R. Ercolani, P. Cappuccilli, E. Fusco, Philh Chor, Philh, C.M. Giulini (r1959) (1/90) (EMI) ① [2] **CMS7 63266-2**

Cpte C. Siepi, H. Gueden, A. Poell, L. della Casa, S. Danco, H. Rössl-Majdan, F. Corena, M. Dickie, H. Meyer-Welfing, H. Pröglhöf, A. Felbermayer, Vienna St Op Chor, VPO, E. Kleiber (r1955) (2/90) (DECC) ① [3] **417 315-2DM3**

Cpte P. Schoeffler, M. Cebotari, M. Ahlersmeyer, M. Teschemacher, A. Kolniak, E. Waldenau, K. Böhme, K. Wessely, H. Buchta, H.H. Fiedler, H. Franck, Stuttgart Rad Chor, Stuttgart RO, K. Böhm (Ger: bp1938) (11/90) (PREI) ① [2] **90035**

Cpte H. Prey, E. Mathis, D. Fischer-Dieskau, G. Janowitz, T. Troyanos, P. Johnson, P. Lagger, E. Wohlfahrt, M. Vantin, K. Hirte, B. Vogel, Berlin Deutsche Op Chor, Berlin Deutsche Op Orch, K. Böhm (12/90) (DG) ① [3] **429 869-2GX3**

Cpte G. Evans, J. Blegen, D. Fischer-Dieskau, H. Harper, T. Berganza, B. Finnilä, W. McCue, J. Fryatt, J. Robertson, M. Donnelly, E. Gale, John Alldis Ch, ECO, D. Barenboim (5/91) (EMI) ① [3] **CMS7 63646-2**

Cpte J. Tomlinson, J. Rodgers, A. Schmidt, L. Cuberli, C. Bartoli, P. Pancella, G. von Kannen, G. Clark, R. Brunner, P. Rose, H. Leidland, Berlin RIAS Chbr Ch, BPO, D. Barenboim (5/91) (ERAT) ① [3] **2292-45501-2**

Cpte G. Evans, R. Grist, G. Bacquier, E. Söderström, T. Berganza, A. Burmeister, M. Langdon, W. Hollweg, W. Brokmeier, C. Grant, M. Price, John Alldis Ch, New Philh, O. Klemperer (9/91) (EMI) ① [3] **CMS7 63849-2**

Cpte S. Bruscantini, G. Sciutti, F. Calabrese, S. Jurinac, R. Stevens, M. Sinclair, I. Wallace, H. Cuénod, D. McCoshan, G. Griffiths, J. Sinclair, Glyndebourne Fest Chor, Glyndebourne Fest Orch, V. Gui (r1955) (9/91) (CFP) ① [2] **CD-CFPD4724**

Cpte A. Titus, H. Donath, F. Furlanetto, J. Varady, M. Schmiege, C. Kallisch, S. Nimsgern, H. Zednik, C.H. Ahnsjö, G. Auer, I. Kertesi, Bavarian Rad Chor, BRSO, Colin Davis (9/91) (RCA) ① [3] **RD60440**

Cpte F. Furlanetto, D. Upshaw, T. Hampson, K. Te Kanawa, A.S. von Otter, T. Troyanos, P. Plishka, A. Laciura, M. Forrest, R. Capecchi, H. Grant-Murphy, NY Met Op Chor, NY Met Op Orch, James Levine (9/91) (DG) ① [3] **431 619-2GH3**

Cpte W. Ganzarolli, M. Freni, I. Wixell, J. Norman, Y. Minton, M. Casula, C. Grant, R. Tear, D. Lennox, P. Hudson, L. Watson, BBC Chor, BBC SO, Colin Davis (r1971) (1/92) (PHIL) ① [3] **422 540-2PME3**

Cpte M. Pertusi, M. McLaughlin, L. Gallo, K. Mattila, M. Bacelli, N. Curiel, A. Nosotti, U. Benelli, G. Sica, G. Tadeo, MMF Chor, MMF Orch, Z. Mehta (r1992) (6/94) (SONY) ① [3] **S3K53286**

Cpte B. Terfel, A. Hagley, R. Gilfry, H. Martinpelto, P. H. Stephen, S. McCulloch, C. Feller, F. Egerton, J. Clarkson, C. Backes, Monteverdi Ch, EBS, J. E. Gardiner (pp1993) (8/94) (ARCH) ① [3] **439 871-2AH3**

Cpte R. Capecchi, I. Seefried, D. Fischer-Dieskau, M. Stader, H. Töpper, L. Benningsen, I. Sardi, P. Kuen, F. Lenz, G. Wieter, R. Schwaiger, Berlin RIAS Chbr Ch, Berlin RSO, F. Fricsay (r1960) (10/94) (DG) ① [3] **437 671-2GDO3**

Cpte W. Berry, R. Streich, P. Schoeffler, S. Jurinac, C. Ludwig, I. Malaniuk, O. Czerwenka, E. Majkut, M. Dickie, K. Dönch, R. Schwaiger, Vienna St Op Chor, Vienna SO, K. Böhm (r1956) (10/94) (PHIL) ① [3] **438 670-2PM3**

Cpte A. Scharinger, B. Bonney, T. Hampson, C. Margiono, P. Lang, A. Murray, K. Moll, P. Langridge, C. Späth, K. Langan, I. Rey, Netherlands Op Chor, Concertgebouw, N. Harnoncourt (r1993) (10/94) (TELD) ① [3] **4509-90861-2**

Cpte A. Miles, N. Focile, A. Corbelli, C. Vaness, S. Mentzer, S. Murphy, A. Antoniozzi, R. Davies, R. Evans, Scottish Chbr Chor, Scottish CO, C. Mackerras (r1994; with appendices) (8/95) (TELA) ① [3] **CD80388**

Cpte L. Gallo, S. McNair, B. Skovhus, C. Studer, C. Bartoli, A. C. Antonacci, I. d'Arcangelo, C. Allemano, P. Jelosits, I. Gáti, A. Rost, Vienna St Op Chor, VPO, C. Abbado (r1994) (10/95) (DG) ① [3] **445 903-2GH3**

Excs M. Ahlersmeyer, M. Reining, M. Cebotari, M. Rohs, Vienna St Op Orch, K. Böhm (pp1941: Ger) *Concert* (3/95) (SCHW) ① [2] **314602**

1. ASMF, N. Marriner *Concert* (4/84) (EMI) ① **CDC7 47014-2**

1. RPO, E. Bátiz *Concert* (11/89) (ASV) ① **CDQS6033**

1. BPO *Concert* (11/89) (RCA) ① **RD60032**

1. English Sinfonia, C. Groves *Concert* (11/90) (CARL) ① **PCD939**

1. Staatskapelle Dresden, H. Vonk *Concert* (10/91) (CAPR) ① [3] **10 809**

1. BPO, W. Furtwängler (r1933) *Concert* (4/92) (KOCH) ① [2] **37059-2**

1. Tafelmusik, B. Weil *Concert* (5/92) (SONY) ① **SK46695**

1. NYPO, L. Bernstein (r1968) *Concert* (9/93) (SONY) ① **SMK47601**

1. LPO, T. Beecham (r1937) *Concert* (10/94) (DUTT) ① **CDLX7009**

1. LSO, J. Krips (r1951) *Concert* (7/95) (DECC) ① [2] **443 530-2LF2**

1, 20a, 20b J. Van Dam, Paris Orch Ens, J-P. Wallez (pp) *Concert* (5/88) (NOVA) ① **150 014-2**

1, 22b K. Te Kanawa, LPO, G. Solti *Concert* (6/91) (DECC) ① **430 498-2DWO**

1, 2, 9, 10, 19(pt), 33. A. Jerger, M. Reining, P. Schoeffler, M. Perras, D. With, O. Levko-Antosch, K. Ettl, W. Wernigk, H. Gallos, V. Madin, D. Komarek, Vienna St Op Chor, Vienna St Op Orch, W. Loibner (pp1938: Ger) *Concert* (6/95) (SCHW) ① [2] **314632**

1, 8. SO, T. Beecham (r c1912/6) *Concert* (11/91) (SYMP) ① [2] **SYMCD1096/7**

2. G. Rolandi, C. Desderi, LPO, B. Haitink (r1987) *Concert* (6/94) (EMI) ① **CDH5 65072-2**

4a, 4b, 5, 10, 20a, 20b, 29a, 29b F. Furlanetto, Vienna SO, I. Marin *Concert* (3/92) (SONY) ① **SK47192**

4b G. De Luca, orch (r1917) *Concert* (1/92) (PREI) ① **89036**

4b P. Schoeffler, National SO, C. Krauss (r1947) *Concert* (1/95) (PREI) ① **90190**

4b, 10, 20a, 20b, 22b H. Prey, Salzburg Mozarteum Orch, B. Weil *Concert* (5/88) (DENO) ① **CO-1741**

4b, 29b E. Pinza, NY Met Op Orch, B. Walter (r1946) *Concert* (4/90) (SONY) ① **MPK45693**

5. A. Kipnis, E. Ruziczka, Berlin St Op Orch, E. Orthmann (Ger: r1931) *Concert* (12/90) (PREI) ① **89019**

5. A. Kipnis, E. Ruziczka, Berlin St Op Orch, E. Orthmann (Ger: r1931) *Concert* (10/91) (PEAR) ① **GEMMCD9451**

7. A. Galli-Curci, orch (r1917) *Concert* (2/89) (PEAR) ① **GEMMCD9308**

7. P. McCann, Black Dyke Mills Band, P. Parkes (r1984: arr P Parkes) *Concert* (11/92) (CHAN) ① **CHAN4501**

7. A. Galli-Curci, orch, J. Pasternack (r1917) *Concert* (3/94) (ROMO) ① [2] **81003-2**

7, 12. C. Supervia, orch, A. Albergoni (r1928) *Concert* (9/90) (CLUB) ① **CL99-074**

7, 12. C. Supervia, orch, A. Albergoni (r1928) *Concert* (9/90) (PREI) ① **89023**

7, 12. T. Berganza, LSO, J. Pritchard (r1962) *Concert* (4/93) (DECC) ① **421 899-2DA**

7, 12, 13b, 30b E. Schumann, orch, G.W. Byng (r1926) *Concert* (6/91) (PREI) ① **89031**

7, 12, 30a, 30b C. Bartoli, Vienna CO, G. Fischer *Concert* (12/91) (DECC) ① **430 513-2DH**

10. E. Pinza, orch, B. Reibold (r1939) *Concert* (7/91) (MMOI) ① **CDMOIR404**

10. C. Desderi, LPO, B. Haitink *Concert* (7/91) (EMIL) ① **CDZ7 67015-2**

10. C. Santley, anon (r1903) *Concert* (10/92) (SYMP) ① **SYMCD1093**

10. T. Gobbi, Philh, J. Robertson (r1950) *Concert* (8/93) (TEST) ① **SBT1019**

10. S. Ramey, LPO, G. Solti (r1981) *Concert* (10/93) (DECC) ① **436 464-2DM**

10. P. Schoeffler, Vienna St Op Orch, W. Loibner (pp1938: Ger) *Concert* (6/94) (SCHW) ① **314502**

10. E. Kunz, VPO, H. von Karajan (r1947) *Concert* (9/95) (TEST) ① **SBT1059**

10, 19, 30b A. Martin, D. Robin, Vienna Mozart Orch, K. Leitner *Concert* (12/91) (NAXO) ① **8 550435**

10, 20a, 20b R. Bruson, NHK Chbr Sols, R. Paternostro (pp1990) *Concert* (10/91) (CAPR) ① **10 348**

11. V. de los Angeles, Philh, W. Susskind (r1949) *Concert* (8/90) (EMI) ① **CDH7 63495-2**

11. E. Schwarzkopf, VPO, H. von Karajan (r1950) *Concert* (12/90) (EMI) ① **CDM7 63657-2**

11. F. Leider, orch (r1925: Ger) *Concert* (5/91) (PREI) ① [3] **89301**

11. J. Gadski, orch (r1910) *Concert* (7/91) (CLUB) ① **CL99-109**

11. M. Price, VPO, R. Muti *Concert* (7/91) (EMIL) ① **CDZ7 67015-2**

11. Lotte Lehmann, orch (Ger: r1917) *Concert* (7/92) (PEAR) ① [3] **GEMMCDS9925(2)**

11. Lilli Lehmann, orch (r1907: Ger) *Concert* (7/93) (NIMB) ① [2] **NI7840/1**

11. E. Rethberg, orch (r1921: Ger) *Concert* (7/94) (PREI) ① **89051**

11. E. Destinn, orch, F. Kark (r1906: Ger) *Concert* (12/94) (SUPR) ① [12] **11 2136-2(1)**

11. E. Rethberg, Berlin SO, F. Weissmann (r1930: Ger) *Concert* (10/95) (ROMO) ① [2] **81014-2**

11. R. Hunter, Tasmanian SO, D. Franks (r1989) *Concert* (10/95) (ABCC) ① **8 7000 10**

11, 12, 30a, 30b L. Popp, Munich RO, L. Slatkin (r1983) *Concert* (8/84) (EMI) ① **CDC7 47019-2**

11, 22a, 22b M. Reining, VPO, J. Krips (r1950; Ger) *Concert* (9/92) (PREI) ① **90083**

11, 22a, 22b, 30a, 30b M. Reining, Prussian St Orch, H.U. Müller (r1942: Ger) *Concert* (9/94) (PREI) ① **89065**

11, 22a, 22b C. Studer, ASMF, N. Marriner *Concert* (9/94) (PHIL) ① **442 410-2PM**

11, 22b T. Lemnitz, BPO, B. Seidler-Winkler (r1938) *Concert* (10/90) (PREI) ① **89025**

11, 22b F. Leider, orch (r1921: Ger) *Concert* (5/91) (PREI) ① [3] **89301**

11, 22b S. Ghazarian, NHK Chbr Sols, R. Paternostro (pp1990) *Concert* (10/91) (CAPR) ① **10 348**

11, 30a, 30b L. Price, New Philh, P.H. Adler *Concert* (6/93) (RCA) ① **09026 61357-2**

11, 30b Lotte Lehmann, orch (Ger: r1917) *Concert* (6/92) (PREI) ① [3] **89302**

12. N. Melba, orch, W.B. Rogers (r1910) *Concert* (3/89) (LARR) ① **CDLRH221**

12. A. Patti, L. Ronald (r1905) *Concert* (4/90) (PEAR) ① **GEMMCD9312**

12. L. Garrett, Philh, A. Greenwood (r1990-1) *Concert* (11/91) (SILV) ① **SONGCD903**

12. Lotte Lehmann, orch (Ger: r1921) *Concert* (6/92) (PREI) ① [3] **89302**

12. L. Tetrazzini, orch, P. Pitt (r1907) *Concert* (9/92) (EMI) ① [3] **CHS7 63802-2(1)**

12. L. Tetrazzini, orch, P. Pitt (r1907) *Concert* (9/92) (PEAR) ① **GEMMCD9221**

12. A. Patti, L. Ronald (r1905) *Concert* (7/93) (NIMB) ① [2] **NI7840/1**

12. F. von Stade, LPO, G. Solti (r1981) *Concert* (10/93) (DECC) ① **436 462-2DM**

12. G. Farrar, orch (r1908) *Concert* (10/94) (NIMB) ① **NI7857**

12. N. Melba, orch, W.B. Rogers (r1910) *Concert* (5/95) (ROMO) ① [3] **81011-2(2)**

12. N. Melba, orch, W.B. Rogers (r1907) *Concert* (5/95) (ROMO) ① [3] **81011-2(1)**

12. J. Larmore, Lausanne CO, J. López-Cobos (r1994) *Concert* (12/95) (TELD) ① **4509-96800-2**
12, 22a, 22b, 30a, 30b M. Price, ECO, J. Lockhart (r1973) *Concert* (5/95) (RCA) ① [2] **09026 61635-2**
12, 30b F. Cossotto, A. Moffo, Philh, C.M. Giulini *Concert* (7/91) (EMIL) ① **CDZ7 67015-2**
13b E. Schumann, orch (r1927) *Concert* (7/92) (PEAR) ① [3] **GEMMCDS9925(2)**
19. Lotte Lehmann, H. Schlusnus, orch (Ger: r1920) *Concert* (6/92) (PREI) ① [3] **89302**
19. E. Eames, E. de Gogorza, orch (r1909) *Concert* (11/93) (ROMO) ① [2] **81001-2**
19. E. Eames, E. de Gogorza, orch (r1909) *Concert* (1/95) (NIMB) ① **NI7860**
20a, 20b J. Hynninen, Estonian SO, E. Klas *Concert* (4/90) (ONDI) ① **ODE731-2**
20a, 20b G. Hüsch, Berlin St Op Orch, H.U. Müller (r1939: Ger) *Concert* (3/94) (PREI) ① **89071**
20b T. Pasero, orch, A. Sabino (r1943) *Concert* (4/95) (PREI) ① **89074**
21. M. Sinclair, S. Bruscantini, I. Wallace, D. McCoshan, F. Calabrese, G. Sciutti, Glyndebourne Fest Orch, V. Gui (r1955) *Concert* (6/94) (EMI) ① **CDH5 65072-2**
22a, 22b B. Hendricks, ECO, J. Tate *Concert* (6/85) (EMI) ① **CDC7 47122-2**
22a, 22b M. Freni, Rome Op Orch, F. Ferraris *Concert* (10/89) (EMI) ① **CDM7 63110-2**
22a, 22b M. Cebotari, Philh, J. Krips (r1947) *Concert* (12/90) (PREI) ① **90034**
22a, 22b L. Price, RCA Italiana Op Orch, F. Molinari-Pradelli *Concert* (12/92) (RCA) ① [4] **09026 61236-2**
22a, 22b L. Price, RCA Italiana Op Orch, F. Molinari-Pradelli *Concert* (6/93) (RCA) ① **09026 61357-2**
22a, 22b K. Te Kanawa, LPO, G. Solti (r1981) *Concert* (10/93) (DECC) ① **436 461-2DM**
22a, 22b, 30a, V6. C. Bartoli, Vienna CO, G. Fischer (r1993) *Concert* (11/94) (DECC) ① **443 452-2DH**
22b K. Te Kanawa, LPO, G. Solti *Concert* (11/87) (DECC) ① **417 645-2DH**
22b E. Destinn, orch, B. Seidler-Winkler (r1908: Ger) *Concert* (5/94) (SUPR) ① **11 1337-2**
22b E. Destinn, orch, B. Seidler-Winkler (r1908: Ger) *Concert* (12/94) (SUPR) ① [12] **11 2136-2(2)**
22b E. Destinn, orch, F. Kark (r1908: Ger) *Concert* (12/94) (SUPR) ① [12] **11 2136-2(2)**
22b S. Bullock, A. Bryn Parri (r1994) *Concert* (11/95) (SAIN) ① **SCDC2070**
22b, 23b M. Teschemacher, I. Beilke, Berlin St Op Orch, B. Seidler-Winkler (Ger: r1939) *Concert* (11/92) (PREI) ① **89049**
23b E. Berger, V. Ursuleac, Berlin St Op Orch, C. Krauss (Ger: r1936) *Concert* (12/91) (PREI) ① **89035**
23b E. Eames, M. Sembrich, orch (r1908) *Concert* (11/93) (ROMO) ① [2] **81001-2**
23b E. Eames, M. Sembrich, orch (r1908) *Concert* (1/95) (NIMB) ① **NI7860**
23b, 24. A. Mildmay, A. Rautawaara, Glyndebourne Fest Chor, Glyndebourne Fest Orch, F. Busch (r1934) *Concert* (6/94) (EMI) ① **CDH5 65072-2**
23b, 24. A. Arteta, N. Stemme, Paris Opéra-Bastille Orch, E. Kohn (pp1992) *Concert* (6/94) (SONY) ① **SK46691**
25. Salzburg Mozarteum Orch, H. Graf *Concert* (11/89) (CAPR) ① **10 253**
25. Salzburg Mozarteum Orch, H. Graf *Concert* (10/91) (CAPR) ① [3] **10 809**
28. P. Domingo, Munich RO, E. Kohn *Concert* (3/92) (EMI) ① **CDC7 54329-2**
29b T. Gobbi, Philh, J. Robertson (r1950) *Concert* (10/89) (EMI) ① **CDM7 63109-2**
29b A. Kipnis, orch (Ger: r c1916) *Concert* (10/91) (PEAR) ① **GEMMCD9451**
30a, 30b E. Gruberová, F. Liszt CO, R. Leppard (r1989) *Concert* (1/91) (SONY) ① **SK45855**
30a, 30b I. Seefried, Berlin RSO, F. Fricsay (r1960) *Concert* (9/93) (DG) ① [2] **437 677-2GDO2**
30a, 30b B. Sayão, RCA SO, W. Pelletier (r1940) *Concert* (4/94) (RCA) ① [6] **09026 61580-2(4)**
30b A. Pandolfini, S. Cottone (r1903) *Concert* (6/90) (SYMP) ① **SYMCD1073**
30b E. Schumann, orch, G.W. Byng (r1926) *Concert* (2/92) (MMOI) ① **CDMOIR408**
30b F. Hempel, orch (r1911) *Concert* (3/94) (NIMB) ① **NI7849**
30b E. Rethberg, orch (r1927) *Concert* (2/95) (ROMO) ① [2] **81012-2**
30b I. Baillie, orch (r1927) *Concert* (7/95) (DUTT) ① **CDLX7013**

L' **oca del Cairo, '(The) Cairo Goose'—opera buffa: 2 acts, K422 (1783)** (Lib. Varesco: incomplete)
Cpte D. Fischer-Dieskau, E. Wiens, P. Schreier, D. Johnson, P. Coburn, A. Scharinger, I. Nielsen, CPE Bach Orch, P. Schreier (r1990) *Sposo deluso.* (5/92) (PHIL) ① **422 539-2PME**

Il **rè pastore, '(The) Shepherd king'—serenata: 2 acts, K208 (1775—Salzburg)** (Lib. P. Metastasio)
EXCERPTS—; 1. Overture. ACT 1: 2. Intendo, amico rio; 3. Alla selva, al prato, al fonte; 4a. Ditelo voi pastori; 4b. Aer tranquillo e dì sereni; 5. Si spande al sole in faccia; 6. Per me rispondete; 7. Di tante sue procelle; 8a. Che! m'affretti; 8b. Vanne a regnar, ben mio. ACT 2: 9. Barbaro, oh Dio, mi vedi; 10. Se vincendo vi rendo felici; 11. L'amerò, sarò costante; 12. Se tu di me fai dono; 13. Sol può dir, come si trova; 14. Voi che fausti ognor donate; 15. Viva! l'invito duce!.
Cpte A.M. Blasi, S. McNair, I. Vermillion, J. Hadley, C.H. Ahnsjö, ASMF, N. Marriner (r1989) (12/91) (PHIL) ① [2] **422 535-2PME2**
4b, 11. E. Kirkby, AAM, C. Hogwood *Concert* (4/91) (L'OI) ① **425 835-2OH**
11. K. Te Kanawa, LSO, Colin Davis *Concert* (3/84) (PHIL) ① **411 148-2PH**
11. L. Popp, Munich RO, L. Slatkin (r1983) *Concert* (8/84) (EMI) ① **CDC7 47019-2**
11. K. Battle, B. Griffiths, RPO, A. Previn *Concert* (12/86) (EMI) ① **CDC7 47355-2**
11. E. Schumann, orch, G.W. Byng (r1926) *Concert* (6/91) (PREI) ① **89031**
11. L. Price, New Philh, P.H. Adler *Concert* (6/93) (RCA) ① **09026 61357-2**
11. N. Melba, J. Kubelík, G. Lapierre (r1913) *Concert* (9/93) (RCA) ① **09026 61412-2**
11. I. Seefried, Vienna SO, F. Leitner (r1952) *Concert* (9/93) (DG) ① [2] **437 677-2GDO2**
11. M. Ivogün, orch (r c1924) *Concert* (1/94) (CLUB) ① **CL99-020**
11. N. Melba, J. Kubelík, G. Lapierre (r1913) *Concert* (5/95) (ROMO) ① [3] **81011-2(2)**
11. M. Price, ECO, J. Lockhart (r1973) *Concert* (5/95) (RCA) ① [2] **09026 61635-2**
11. E. Rethberg, Victor SO, R. Bourdon (r1930) *Concert* (10/95) (ROMO) ① [2] **81014-2**

Der **Schauspieldirektor, '(The) Impresario'—Singspiel: 1 act, K486 (1786—Vienna)** (Lib. J. G. Stephanie jr)
EXCERPTS: 1. Overture; 2. Da schlägt die Abschiedsstunde; 3. Bester Jüngling! mit Entzükken; 4. Ich bin die erste Sängerin; 5. Jeder Künstler strebt nach Ehre.
Cpte R. Grist, A. Auger, P. Schreier, K. Moll, Staatskapelle Dresden, K. Böhm (omits dialogue) *Zauberflöte.* (12/90) (DG) ① [3] **429 877-2GX3**
Cpte R. Welting, I. Cotrubas, A. Rolfe Johnson, C. Grant, LSO, Colin Davis (r1975: omits dialogue) *Zaïde.* (4/92) (PHIL) ① [2] **422 536-2PME2**
Cpte M. Nador, K. Laki, T. Hampson, H. van der Kamp, Concertgebouw, N. Harnoncourt (r1986) *Thamos, K345.* (3/95) (TELD) ① **4509-95979-2**
1. ASMF, N. Marriner *Concert* (4/84) (EMI) ① **CDC7 47014-2**
1. Staatskapelle Dresden, H. Vonk *Concert* (10/91) (CAPR) ① [3] **10 809**
1. Tafelmusik, B. Weil *Concert* (5/92) (SONY) ① **SK46695**
1. LSO, J. Krips (r1951) *Concert* (7/95) (DECC) ① [2] **443 530-2LF2**

Il **sogno di Scipione, 'Scipio's dream'—azione teatrale: 1 act, K126 (1772—Salzburg)** (Lib. P. Metastasio)
Cpte P. Schreier, L. Popp, E. Gruberová, C.H. Ahnsjö, T. Moser, E. Mathis, Salzburg Chbr Ch, Salzburg Mozarteum Orch, L. Hager (r1979) (1/92) (PHIL) ① [2] **422 531-2PME2**

Lo **Sposo deluso, '(The) Deluded Spouse'—opera buffa: 2 acts, K430/K424a (?1784)** (Lib. ?L. da Ponte: unfinished)
1. Overture; 2. Trio; 3. Quartet.
Cpte F. Palmer, I. Cotrubas, R. Tear, A. Rolfe Johnson, C. Grant, LSO, Colin Davis (r1975) *Oca del Cairo.* (5/92) (PHIL) ① **422 539-2PME**

Thamos, König in Ägypten, 'Thamos, King of Egypt'—play with music: 5 acts, K345 (1774—Salzburg) (Wds. T P von Gebler)
EXCERPTS—; 1. Schon weichet dir, Sonne (chorus); 2. Intermezzo No. 1; 3. Intermezzo No. 2; 4. Intermezzo No. 3; 5. Intermezzo No. 4; 6. Gottheit, Gottheit, über alle mätchting (chorus); 7. Intermezzo No. 5; 8. Ihr (Wie) Kinder des Straubes, erzittert und behet (chorus); 9. Final Music for Act 5.
Cpte A. Miles, Monteverdi Ch, EBS, J.E. Gardiner (r1991) (2/94) (ARCH) ① **437 556-2AH**
Cpte T. Thomaschke, J. Perry, A-M. Mühle, M. van Altena, H. van der Kamp, Collegium Vocale, Netherlands Chbr Ch, Concertgebouw, N. Harnoncourt (r1980) *Schauspieldirektor.* (3/95) (TELD) ① **4509-95979-2**

Zaïde—Singspiel: 2 acts, K344/336b (1779-80—Salzburg) (Lib. J. A. Schachtner)
EXCERPTS: ACT ONE: 2. Unerforschliche Fügung; 3. Ruhe sanft, meine holdes Leben; 4. Rase Schicksal, wüte immer; 5. Meine Seele hüpft vor Freuden; 6. Herr und Freund!; 7. Nur mutig, mein Herz; 8. O selige Wonne! ACT TWO: 9a. Zaide entflohen!; 9b. Der stolze Löw'; 10. Wer hungrig bei der Tafel sitzt; 11. Ich bin so bös' als gut; 12. Trostlos schluchzet Philomele; 13. Tiger! wetze nur die Klauen; 14. Ihr Mächtigen seht ungerührt; 15. Freundin! stille deine Tränen.
Cpte J. Blegen, W. Hollweg, W. Schöne, T. Moser, R. Holl, W. Bellon, Salzburg Mozarteum Orch, L. Hager (with dialogue) (5/91) (ORFE) ① [2] **C055832I**
Cpte E. Mathis, P. Schreier, I. Wixell, W. Hollweg, R. Süss, A. Ude, Berlin Staatskapelle, B. Klee (r1973: with dialogue) *Schauspieldirektor.* (4/92) (PHIL) ① [2] **422 536-2PME2**
3. K. Te Kanawa, LSO, Colin Davis *Concert* (3/84) (PHIL) ① **411 148-2PH**
3. F. Wunderlich, Stuttgart RSO, A. Rischner (bp1956) *Concert* (10/89) (ACAN) ① **43 267**
3. F. Lott, LMP, J. Glover *Concert* (2/90) (ASV) ① **CDDCA683**
3. I. Seefried, LMP, H. Blech (r1953) *Concert* (4/94) (TEST) ① **SBT1026**
3. T. Dahl, Calgary PO, M. Bernardi (r1992) *Concert* (12/94) (CBC) ① **SMCD5125**
3, 12. E. Kirkby, AAM, C. Hogwood *Concert* (4/91) (L'OI) ① **425 835-2OH**

Die **Zauberflöte, '(The) Magic Flute'—singspiel: 2 acts, K620 (1791—Vienna)** (Lib. E. Schikaneder)
EXCERPTS: 1a. Overture. ACT 1: 1b. Zu Hilfe; 2. Der Vogelfänger bin ich ja; 3. Dies Bildnis ist bezaubernd schön; 4a. O zitt're nicht; 4b. Zum leiden; 5. H'm H'm H'm; 6. Du feines Täubchen; 7. Bei Männern; 8a. Zum Ziele führt dich; 8b. Wie stark ist nicht dein Zauberton; 9a. Schnelle Füsse; 9b. Das klinget so herrlich—könnte jeder brave Mann; 9c. Es lebe Sarastro. ACT 2: 10a. March; 10b. O, Isis und Osiris (aria); 11. Bewahret euch vor Weibertücken; 12. Wie? Wie? Wie?; 13. Alles fühlt der Liebe Freuden; 14. Der Hölle Rache; 15. In diesen heil'gen Hallen; 16. Seid uns zum zweitenmal willkommen; 17. Ach, ich fühl's; 18. O, Isis und Osiris (chorus); 19. Soll ich dich, Teurer, nicht mehr sehen?; 20. Ein Mädchen oder Weibchen; 21. Bald prangt; 22. Der, welcher wandert; 23. Papagena Weibchen; 24. Pa-Pa-Pa-Papagena; 25. Nur stille. 26. Die Strahlen der Sonne.
Cpte E. Mathis, K. Ott, F. Araiza, G. Hornik, J. Van Dam, C. Nicolai, H. Kruse, J. Perry, A. Tomowa-Sintow, A. Baltsa, H. Schwarz, W. Bünten, C. Schulz, T. Pfülb, V. Horn, V. von Halem, H. Hopfner, L. Valenta, Berlin Deutsche Op Chor, BPO, H. von Karajan (r1980: with dialogue) (1/85) (DG) ① [3] **410 967-2GH3**
Cpte L. Popp, E. Gruberová, S. Jerusalem, W. Brendel, R. Bracht, N. Bailey, H. Zednik, B. Lindner, M. Richardson, D. Soffel, O. Wenkel, P. Hofmann, A. Haugland, W. Kmentt, E. Kunz, A. von Mattoni, Tolz Boys' Ch, Bavarian Rad Chor, BRSO, B. Haitink (with dialogue) (3/88) (EMI) ① [3] **CDS7 47951-8**
Cpte K. Moll, E. Moser, A. Rothenberger, P. Schreier, W. Berry, O. Miljakovic, T. Adam, W. Brokmeier, W. Badorek, G. Wewel, W. Badorek, G. Wewel, L. Kirschstein, I. Gramatzki, B. Fassbaender, W. Gampert, P. Hinterreiter, A. Stein, Bavarian St Op Chor, Bavarian St Op Orch, W. Sawallisch (with dialogue) (3/88) (EMI) ① [2] **CDS7 47827-8**
Cpte I. Seefried, W. Lipp, A. Dermota, E. Kunz, L. Weber, G. London, P. Klein, E. Loose, S. Jurinac, F. Riegler, E. Schürhoff, H. Steinmassl, E. Dörpinghans, A. Stückl, E. Majkut, L. Pantscheff, H. Pröglhöf, Vienna Singverein, VPO, H. von Karajan (r1950: omits dialogue) (1/89) (EMI) ① [2] **CHS7 69631-2**
Cpte B. Bonney, E. Gruberová, H-P. Blochwitz, A. Scharinger, M. Salminen, T. Hampson, P. Keller, E. Schmid, P. Coburn, D. Ziegler, M. Lipovšek, S. Gienger, M. Baur, A. Fischer, T. Moser, A. Suhonen, A. Maly, W. Kmentt, Vienna Singverein, G. Jesserer, Zurich Op Hse Chor, Zurich Op Orch, N. Harnoncourt (r1987; with narration) (7/89) (TELD) ① [2] **2292-42716-2**

17. E. Destinn, orch, W.B Rogers (r1915) *Concert*
(12/94) (SUPR) ① [12] **11 2136-2(5)**
17. E. Destinn, orch, B. Seidler-Winkler (r1908)
Concert (12/94) (SUPR) ① [12] **11 2136-2(2)**
17. E. Destinn, Odeon Orch, A. Pilz (r1908) *Concert*
(12/94) (SUPR) ① [12] **11 2136-2(2)**
17. E. Rethberg, orch (r1927) *Concert*
(2/95) (ROMO) ① [2] **81012-2**
17. I. Galante, Latvian Nat SO, A. Vilumanis (r1994)
Concert (11/95) (CAMP) ① **RRCD1335**
18. Berlin Deutsche Op Chor, Berlin Deutsche Op
Orch, G. Sinopoli *Concert*
(10/85) (DG) ① **415 283-2GH**
19. P. Anders, T. Eipperle, G. Hann, Berlin RSO, A.
Rother (bp1944) *Concert*   (8/93) (ACAN) ① **43 268**

MUCZYNSKI, Robert (b 1929)
USA

SECTION II: CHAMBER

Sonata for Flute and Piano, Op. 14 (1960-61)
A. Still, S. De Witt Smith (r1992) *Concert*
(4/94) (KOCH) ① **37144-2**

MUDARRA, Alonso (c1510–1580)
Spain

SECTION II: CHAMBER

Pavan et Galliard d'Alexandra
Circa 1500, N. Hadden *Concert*
(9/92) (VIRG) ① **VC7 59071-2**

SECTION III: INSTRUMENTAL

Divisions on Spagnoletta—improvisation
A. Lawrence-King *Concert*
(6/92) (HYPE) ① **CDA66518**
Fantasía X
J. Bream (r1983) *Concert*
(8/93) (RCA) ① [28] **09026 61583-2(6)**
J. Bream (r1983) *Concert*
(8/93) (RCA) ① **09026 61610-2**
Fantasía XIV
J. Bream (r1983) *Concert*
(8/93) (RCA) ① [28] **09026 61583-2(6)**
J. Bream (r1983) *Concert*
(8/93) (RCA) ① **09026 61610-2**
2 Fantasías—vihuela
Fantasía J. Bream, J. Bream, G. Malcolm, Melos
Ens, Cremona Qt (r1966) *Concert*
(8/93) (RCA) ① [28] **09026 61583-2(4)**
Fantasías J. Bream (r1983) *Concert*
(9/94) (RCA) ① **09026 61606-2**
Tres libros en Cifras para vihuela—vihuela/guitar (pub 1546)
VIHUELA: 1. Pavana de Alexandre, Gallarda; 2. Una
Pavana; 3. Fantasia; 4. Fantasia para desenvolver
las manos; 5. Fantasia de pasos largos para
desenvolver las manos; 6. Conde Claros en doze
maneras; 7. Fantasia de pasos para desenvolver las
manos; 8. Fantasia que contrahaze la harpa en la
manera de Ludovico; 9. Tiento del quinto tono; 10.
Seven tonos; 11. Two fantasias facils. GUITAR: 12.
Una Pavana; 13. Fantasia del primer tono; 14.
Fantasia del quarto tono; 15. Fantasia del quinto
tono; 16. Romanesca o Guardame las vacas.
Cpte H. Smith   (7/92) (ASTR) ① **E8740**
1, 8. J. M. Moreno (r1994) *Concert*
(8/95) (GLOS) ① **GCD920103**
8. A. Lawrence-King *Concert*
(6/92) (HYPE) ① **CDA66518**
8. Tragicomedia *Concert*
(9/92) (EMI) ① **CDC7 54191-2**
8. L. Kirchhof *Concert*   (11/92) (SONY) ① **SK48068**
8. P. Romero (r1993; trans P. Romero) *Concert*
(4/95) (PHIL) ① **442 150-2PH**
8, 14, 16. N. North *Concert*
(6/87) (AMON) ① **CD-SAR18**

SECTION IV: VOCAL AND CHORAL

Tres libros de musica en cifras y canto—vocal works in the collection of vihuela pieces (pub 1546)
EXCERPTS: 1. Villancicos: 1a. Si me llaman a mi;
1b. Si viesse e melevasse; 1c. Isabel, perdista la tu
faxa; 1d. Gentil, cavallero; 2. Romances: 2a. Triste
estava el rey David; 2b. Israel, mira tus montes; 3.
Canciones: 3a. Claros y frescos rios (Wds. Boscan);
3b. Recuerde el alma dormida (Wds. Manrique); 4.
Sonnets: 4a. Por asperos caminos (Wds. Garcilaso
de la Vega); 4b. Que llantos son aquestos; 4c. La
vita fugge (Wds. Petrarch); 4d. O gelosia d'amanti
(Wds. Sannazaro); 5. Latin Texts: 5a. Beatus ille
(Wds. Horace); 5b. Dulces consord (Wds. Virgil); 5c.
Regia qui mesto.

Cpte M. Figueras, H. Smith (r1994)
(5/95) (ASTR) ① **E8533**
1a Kithara (r1993) *Concert*
(3/95) (CHAN) ① **CHAN0562**
1a, 1c, 2a, 3a T. Berganza, N. Yepes *Concert*
(12/92) (DG) ① [2] **435 848-2GX2**
3a Hespèrion XX, J. Savall (r1991-92) *Concert*
(6/93) (ASTR) ① **E8764**

MUFFAT, Georg (1653–1704)
Germany

SECTION I: ORCHESTRAL

Armonico tributo—sonatas: strings and continuo (pub 1682)
1. D; 2. G minor; 3. A; 4. E minor; 5. G.
2, 5. Freiburg Baroque Orch Consort (r1993) *Biber:*
Sonatas.   (10/94) (DHM) ① **05472 77303-2**
5. London Baroque, C. Medlam (r1985) *Concert*
(11/87) (HARM) ① **HMA190 1220**
Concerto grosso in A, 'Cor vigilans' (1701)
Cantilena, A. Shepherd *Concert*
(4/88) (CHAN) ① [2] **CHAN8448/9**
Concerto grosso in A minor, 'Bona Nova' (c1701)
VCM, N. Harnoncourt (r1965) *Concert*
(1/93) (ARCH) ① **437 081-2AT**
Concerto Grosso in E minor (1701)
Cantilena, A. Shepherd *Concert*
(9/84) (CHAN) ① **CHAN8319**
Cantilena, A. Shepherd *Concert*
(4/88) (CHAN) ① [2] **CHAN8448/9**
Concerto grosso in G, 'Propitia Sydera' (1701)
Cantilena, A. Shepherd *Concert*
(4/88) (CHAN) ① [2] **CHAN8448/9**
Suite in G (1698)
Cantilena, A. Shepherd *Concert*
(4/88) (CHAN) ① [2] **CHAN8448/9**
Suite No. 3 in D minor, 'Gratitudo' (1695)
Cantilena, A. Shepherd *Concert*
(4/88) (CHAN) ① [2] **CHAN8448/9**
Suite No. 4 in B flat, 'Impatienta' (1695)
Cantilena, A. Shepherd *Concert*
(4/88) (CHAN) ① [2] **CHAN8448/9**
Suite No. 8 in E, 'Indissolubilis Amicitia' (pub 1698) (from Florilegium II)
VCM, N. Harnoncourt (r1965) *Concert*
(1/93) (ARCH) ① **437 081-2AT**
J. Freeman-Attwood, I. Simcock (r1993; arr tpt/org)
Concert   (5/94) (PROU) ① **PROUCD135**

SECTION II: CHAMBER

Sonata and Violin and Continuo (pub. 1677)
London Baroque, C. Medlam (r1985) *Concert*
(11/87) (HARM) ① **HMA190 1220**

SECTION III: INSTRUMENTAL

Toccata octava
W.R. Schuster *Concert*   (3/86) (MOTE) ① **CD10601**

MUGNONE, Leopoldo (1858–1941) Italy

SECTION IV: VOCAL AND CHORAL

Mattinata—song
G. Anselmi, L. Mugnone (r1910) *Concert*
(7/95) (SYMP) ① **SYMCD1170**
Spes ultima Dea—song
G. Anselmi, L. Mugnone (r1910) *Concert*
(7/95) (SYMP) ① **SYMCD1170**

SECTION V: STAGE WORKS

Vita brettone—opera: 3 acts (1905—Naples)
(Lib. E. Golisciani)
Vivea nel tempo antico A. Didur, orch (r1906)
Concert   (1/94) (CLUB) ① **CL99-089**

MÜHLBERGER, Karl (1857–1944)
Austria

SECTION I: ORCHESTRAL

Mir sein die Kaiserjäger—march: wind band
(Eng: The Emperor's Marksmen)
Berlin Phil Wind Qnt, H. von Karajan (r1973) *Concert*
(5/94) (DG) ① **439 346-2GX2**

MULDOWNEY, Dominic (b 1952)
England

SECTION IV: VOCAL AND CHORAL

On Suicide—song (Wds. B. Brecht)
M. Wiegold, Composers Ens, D. Muldowney *Concert*
(4/92) (NMC) ① **NMCD003**

MULET, Henri (1878–1967)
France

SECTION III: INSTRUMENTAL

Carillon-sortie in D—organ (1911)
J. Parker-Smith *Concert*
(3/89) (ASV) ① **CDDCA610**
I. Shaw *Concert*   (7/91) (PRIO) ① **PRCD296**
C. Herrick (r1993) *Concert*
(8/94) (HYPE) ① **CDA66676**
10 Esquisses byzantines—organ (?1914-19)
1. Nef; 2. Vitrail; 3. Rosace; 4. Chapelle des Morts; 5.
Campanile; 6. Procession; 7. Chant funèbre; 8. Noël;
9. In Paradisum; 10. Tu es petra.
8. I. Tracey *Concert*   (1/90) (CFP) ① **CD-CFP4558**
8. S. Standage (r1993) *Concert*
(12/93) (CONI) ① **CDCF517**
10. J.S. Whiteley *Concert*   (7/87) (YORK) ① **CD101**
10. John Scott *Concert*
(4/89) (GUIL) ① **GRCD7022**
10. N. Hakim *Concert*   (10/89) (MOTE) ① **CD40081**
10. D. Flood *Concert*   (4/91) (YORK) ① **CD108**
Noël—organ
J.S. Whiteley *Concert*   (12/91) (YORK) ① **CD846**

MÜLLER, Iwan (1786–1854)
Estonia

SECTION II: CHAMBER

Quartet for Clarinet, Violin, Viola and Cello No. 2 in F sharp minor (1820)
V. Soames, A. Colman, M. Souter, A. Blayden
(r1992) *Concert*   (3/94) (CLRI) ① **CC0006**

MUNDY, John (c1555–1630)
England

SECTION III: INSTRUMENTAL

Robin—keyboard
Z. Růžičková *Concert*
(10/89) (ORFE) ① **C139861A**

MUNDY, William (c1529–1591)
England

SECTION IV: VOCAL AND CHORAL

Adolescentulus sum ego—motet (6vv)
The Sixteen, H. Christophers *Concert*
(1/90) (HYPE) ① **CDA66319**
Ah, helpless wretch—verse anthem (1/5vv and organ)
C. Royall, The Sixteen, P. Nicholson, H. Christophers
Concert   (1/90) (HYPE) ① **CDA66319**
Beatus et sanctus—motet (5vv)
The Sixteen, H. Christophers *Concert*
(1/90) (HYPE) ① **CDA66319**
Evening Service (in medio chori)—9vv
1. Magnificat; 2. Nunc dimittis.
The Sixteen, H. Christophers *Concert*
(1/90) (HYPE) ① **CDA66319**
Kyrie—4-5vv
The Sixteen, H. Christophers *Concert*
(1/90) (HYPE) ① **CDA66319**
Oxford Camerata, J. Summerly (r1993) *Concert*
(2/95) (NAXO) ① **8 550937**
Magnificat
Oxford Camerata, J. Summerly (r1993) *Concert*
(2/95) (NAXO) ① **8 550937**
O Lord, the maker of all things—anthem (4vv)
The Sixteen, H. Christophers *Concert*
(1/90) (HYPE) ① **CDA66319**
Oxford Christ Church Cath Ch, S. Preston *Concert*
(2/90) (GAMU) ① **GOUPCD153**
Worcester Cath Ch, Don Hunt *Concert*
(9/90) (CARL) ① **PCD937**
Worcester Cath Ch, Don Hunt, R. Johnston (r1993)
Concert   (2/95) (ABBE) ① **CDCA957**
O Lord, the world's saviour—anthem (4vv)
The Sixteen, H. Christophers *Concert*
(1/90) (HYPE) ① **CDA66319**

The **Secret sins—verse anthem (1/5vv and organ)**
C. Royall, The Sixteen, P. Nicholson, H. Christophers *Concert* (1/90) (HYPE) ① **CDA66319**
Sive vigilem—motet (5vv)
The Sixteen, H. Christophers *Concert* (1/90) (HYPE) ① **CDA66319**
Videte miraculum—respond (5vv)
The Sixteen, H. Christophers *Concert* (1/90) (HYPE) ① **CDA66319**
Vox patris caelestis—respond (6vv)
Tallis Scholars, P. Phillips *Concert* (7/86) (GIME) ① **CDGIM339**
The Sixteen, H. Christophers *Concert* (1/90) (HYPE) ① **CDA66319**

MURCIA, Santiago de (17th–18th Cent) Spain

SECTION III: INSTRUMENTAL

El Amor—guitar (pub 1691) (from Poema Harmonico)
W. Carter (r1993) *Concert* (1/95) (LINN) ① **CKD015**
Baroque Dances—guitar (from the Saldivar Codex No. 4)
1. Fandango; 2. Zarambegues o Muecas; 3. La Jotta; 4. Gaitas; 5. Cumbees.
T. Kerstens *Concert* (7/92) (CONI) ① **CDCF509**
3. W. Carter (r1993) *Concert* (1/95) (LINN) ① **CKD015**
5. J. M. Moreno (r1994) *Concert* (8/95) (GLOS) ① **GCD920103**
Fandango—guitar (?1730)
B. Mason *Concert* (10/90) (AMON) ① **CD-SAR45**
Giga—baroque guitar (pub 1732) (from Passacalles y Obras de Guitarra)
J. M. Moreno (r1994) *Concert* (8/95) (GLOS) ① **GCD920103**
Prelude y Allegro—guitar (pub 1714)
J. Bream (r1983) *Concert* (8/93) (RCA) ① [28] **09026 61583-2(6)**
J. Bream (r1983) *Concert* (8/93) (RCA) ① **09026 61610-2**
Suite in D minor—guitar
1. Prelude; 2. Gavotte; 3. Minuet; 4. Sarabande; 5. Gigue.
B. Mason *Concert* (10/90) (AMON) ① **CD-SAR45**

MURRAY, Lyn (b 1909) USA

SECTION V: STAGE WORKS

To Catch a Thief—film score (1955)
EXCERPTS: 1. You'll Love France; 2. My Jewels; 3. Red Convertible; 4. Riviera Car Chase; 5. Bus Stop; 6. Finale.
1-6. Prague City PO, P. Bateman (arr Bateman) *Concert* (9/95) (SILV) ① **FILMCD159**

MURRILL, Herbert (Henry John) (1909–1952) England

SECTION III: INSTRUMENTAL

Carillon for organ (1949)
Andrew Lucas (r1994) *Concert* (11/94) (NAXO) ① **8 550955**

SECTION IV: VOCAL AND CHORAL

Evening Service in E (1946)
1. Magnificat; 2. Nunc dimittis.
1, 2. St Paul's Cath Ch, C. Dearnley, John Scott *Concert* (1/89) (HYPE) ① **CDA66305**

MUSET, Colin (fl c1200–50) France

SECTION IV: VOCAL AND CHORAL

Trop volontiers chanteroie—isorhythmic poem (13th cent)
Gothic Voices, C. Page *Concert* (12/90) (HYPE) ① **CDA66423**

MUSGRAVE, Thea (b 1928) Scotland

SECTION I: ORCHESTRAL

Song of the Enchanter (1990)
Helsinki PO, S. Comissiona *Concert* (4/92) (ONDI) ① **ODE767-2**

MUSSI, Giulio (fl 1620) Italy

SECTION IV: VOCAL AND CHORAL

Il primo libro delle canzoni—5vv, Op. 5 (pub 1620)
1. L'Amaltea.
1. Capriccio Stravagante, S. Sempé (hpd/dir) *Concert* (2/94) (DHM) ① **05472 77190-2**

MUSSORGSKY, Modest Petrovich (1839–1881) Russia

SECTION I: ORCHESTRAL

The **Capture of Kars—Triumphal March (1880)**
Locke Brass Consort, J. Stobart (arr Lake) *Concert* (9/92) (CRD) ① **CRD3402**
LSO, C. Abbado (r1980) *Concert* (6/93) (RCA) ① **09026 61354-2**
A **Night on the Bare Mountain—orchestra (1867 arr & re-orch 1886) (arr Rimsky-Korsakov unless otherwise stated)**
Dallas SO, E. Mata *Concert* (6/83) (RCA) ① **RCD14439**
Cleveland Orch, L. Maazel (r1978) *Pictures*. (11/84) (TELA) ① **CD80042**
Finnish RSO, L. Segerstam *Concert* (6/87) (BIS) ① **BIS-CD325**
LPO, C. Mackerras *Concert* (11/87) (CFP) ① **CD-CFP9000**
Cincinnati Pops, E. Kunzel (orch Stokowski) *Concert* (4/88) (TELA) ① **CD80129**
B. Engerer (trans. pf) *Concert* (9/88) (HARM) ① **HMC90 1266**
Oslo PO, M. Jansons *Concert* (1/90) (EMI) ① **CDC7 49797-2**
LSO, A. Dorati *Prokofiev: Romeo and Juliet Suites*. (3/91) (MERC) ① **432 004-2MM**
Philadelphia, E. Ormandy *Concert* (3/91) (SONY) ① **SBK46329**
NYPO, G. Sinopoli (r1989) *Concert* (5/91) (DG) ① **429 785-2GH**
Slovak PO, D. Nazareth *Concert* (7/91) (NAXO) ① **8 550051**
Bergen PO, D. Kitaienko *Concert* (2/92) (VIRG) ① **VJ7 59659-2**
Philadelphia, L. Stokowski (arr Stokowski: r1940) *Concert* (2/92) (PEAR) ① **GEMMCD9488**
LSO, L. Stokowski (arr Stokowski) *Concert* (4/92) (DECC) ① **433 625-2DSP**
Atlanta SO, Y. Levi *Concert* (4/92) (TELA) ① **CD80296**
Vancouver SO, R. Barshai *Tchaikovsky: Symphony 6*. (6/92) (CBC) ① **SMCD5083**
Cleveland Orch, C. von Dohnányi *Pictures*. (12/92) (TELD) ① **9031-77600-2**
Philh, G. Simon (r1992) *Concert* (11/93) (CALA) ① **CACD1012**
Chicago SO, F. Reiner (r1959) *Concert* (8/94) (RCA) ① **09026 61958-2**
Philadelphia, L. Stokowski (r1940: arr Rimsky-Koraskov/Stokowski) *Concert* (11/94) (DUTT) ① **CDAX8009**
LPO, K. Tennstedt *Beethoven: Symphony 3*. (11/94) (EMI) ① **CDC5 55186-2**
Pictures at an Exhibition—suite (1874) (orch Ravel - from piano work - unless otherwise stated)
1a. Promenade; 1b. The gnome; 2a. Promenade; 2b. The old castle; 3a. Promenade; 3b. Tuileries; 4a. Bydlo; 4b. Promenade; 5. Unhatched chickens; 6. Samuel Goldenburg; 7. Market Place at Limoges; 8. Catacombe; 9. Baba-jaga; 10. Great Gate at Kiev.
Cleveland Orch, L. Maazel (r1978) *Night on the bare mountain*. (11/84) (TELA) ① **CD80042**
Philh, Vladimir Ashkenazy (orch Ashkenazy) *Pictures*. (5/86) (DECC) ① **414 386-2DH**
Finnish RSO, L. Segerstam (orch. Funtek) *Concert* (6/87) (BIS) ① **BIS-CD325**
Chicago SO, C.M. Giulini *Concert* (8/87) (DG) ① **415 844-2GGA**
LSO, C. Abbado *Stravinsky: Petrushka*. (3/89) (DG) ① **423 901-2GH**
FNO, E. Inbal *Concert* (6/89) (DENO) ① **CO-71799**
Oslo PO, M. Jansons *Concert* (1/90) (EMI) ① **CDC7 49797-2**
Chicago SO, N. Järvi *Scriabin: Poème de l'extase*. (9/90) (CHAN) ① **CHAN8849**
BPO, C.M. Giulini *Stravinsky: Firebird Suite (1919)*. (12/90) (SONY) ① **SK45935**
NYPO, G. Sinopoli (r1989) *Concert* (5/91) (DG) ① **429 785-2GH**
Slovak PO, D. Nazareth *Concert* (7/91) (NAXO) ① **8 550051**

Rotterdam PO, J. Conlon *Khovanshchina*. (8/91) (ERAT) ① **2292-45596-2**
NBC SO, A. Toscanini (r1953) *Elgar: Enigma Variations*. (2/92) (RCA) ① **GD60287**
RPO, Y. Temirkanov *Concert* (3/92) (RCA) ① **RD60195**
Atlanta SO, Y. Levi *Concert* (4/92) (TELA) ① **CD80296**
Philadelphia, R. Muti *Stravinsky: Rite of Spring*. (11/92) (EMI) ① **CDM7 64516-2**
Cleveland Orch, C. von Dohnányi *Night on the bare mountain*. (12/92) (TELD) ① **9031-77600-2**
New Philh, C. Mackerras *Stravinsky: Petrushka*. (4/93) (VANG) ① **08.4065.71**
Boston SO, S. Koussevitzky (r1930) *Concert* (6/93) (PEAR) ① **GEMMCD9020**
Britannia Building Soc Band, H. Snell (arr Howarth) *Concert* (7/93) (DOYE) ① **DOYCD011**
Chicago SO, F. Reiner (1957) *Concert* (8/93) (RCA) ① **09026 61401-2**
NY Met Op Orch, James Levine (r1992) *Stravinsky: Rite of Spring*. (11/93) (DG) ① **437 531-2GH**
T. Ungár, Philh, G. Simon (1992; arr pf/orch: Leonard) *Concert* (11/93) (CALA) ① **CACD1012**
Rotterdam PO, J. Conlon (r1989) *Khovanshchina*. (12/93) (ERAT) ① **4509-92870-2**
New Philh, L. Maazel (r1971) *Prokofiev: Piano Concerto 3*. (6/94) (BELA) ① **450 081-2**
Chicago SO, F. Reiner (r1957) *Concert* (8/94) (RCA) ① **09026 61958-2**
Philh, D.V. Yu (r1993) *Concert* (1/95) (CARL) ① **MCD82**
BPO, C. Abbado (pp1993) *Concert* (2/95) (DG) ① **445 238-2GH**
BPO, H. von Karajan (r1965/6) *Concert* (12/95) (DG) ① **447 426-2GOR**
1a, 1b, 2a, 2b, 4a, 4b, 5, 6, 8-10. Philadelphia, L. Stokowski (r1939: arr Stokowski) *Concert* (11/94) (DUTT) ① **CDAX8009**
9, 10. Black Dyke Mills Band, J. Watson (r1992: arr Sparke) *Concert* (9/93) (POLY) ① **QPRL053D**
Scherzo in B flat—orchestra (1858) (orch from piano work)
LSO, C. Abbado (r1980) *Concert* (6/93) (RCA) ① **09026 61354-2**
Philh, G. Simon (r1992: orch Rimsky-Korsakov) *Concert* (11/93) (CALA) ① **CACD1012**
St **John's Night on the bare mountain—orchestra (1867)**
LSO, C. Abbado (r1980) *Concert* (6/93) (RCA) ① **09026 61354-2**
BPO, C. Abbado (pp1993) *Concert* (2/95) (DG) ① **445 238-2GH**

SECTION III: INSTRUMENTAL

Au village—piano (?1880)
M. Fingerhut *Concert* (6/87) (CHAN) ① **CHAN8439**
M. Papadopoulos *Concert* (1/89) (HLCN) ① **CD-HLR143-2**
La **Capricieuse on a theme by Count L. Heyden—piano (1865)**
M. Campanella *Concert* (12/90) (NUOV) ① **6826**
Duma (Rêverie) on a theme of V. A. Loginov—piano (1865)
M. Campanella *Concert* (12/90) (NUOV) ① **6826**
Gopak—piano (1880) (arr cpsr from Ukranian folk tune in Sorochinsky Fair)
B. Engerer *Concert* (9/88) (HARM) ① **HMC90 1266**
M. Papadopoulos *Concert* (1/89) (HLCN) ① **CD-HLR143-2**
S. Rachmaninov (arr Rachmaninov: pf roll) *Concert* (6/90) (DECC) ① **425 964-2DM**
Gursuf, 'On the southern shore of the Crimea'—piano (1880)
Philh, G. Simon (r1992: orch Goehr) *Concert* (11/93) (CALA) ① **CACD1012**
Intermezzo in modo classico—piano (1860-61)
M. Papadopoulos *Concert* (1/89) (HLCN) ① **CD-HLR143-2**
Ein Kinderscherz—piano (1859 rev 1860)
M. Fingerhut *Concert* (6/87) (CHAN) ① **CHAN8439**
M. Papadopoulos *Concert* (1/89) (HLCN) ① **CD-HLR143-2**
M. Campanella *Concert* (12/90) (NUOV) ① **6826**
Une Larme—piano (1880)
M. Fingerhut *Concert* (6/87) (CHAN) ① **CHAN8439**
B. Engerer *Concert* (9/88) (HARM) ① **HMC90 1266**
M. Papadopoulos *Concert* (1/89) (HLCN) ① **CD-HLR143-2**
Pictures at an Exhibition—suite for piano (1874)
1a. Promenade; 1b. The gnome; 2a. Promenade; 2b. The old castle; 3a. Promenade; 3b. Tuileries; 4a. Bydlo; 4b. Promenade; 5. Unhatched chickens; 6. Samuel Goldenburg; 7. Market Place at Limoges; 8.

Catacombe; 9. Baba-jaga; 10. Great Gate at Kiev.
Vladimir Ashkenazy *Pictures.*
(5/86) (DECC) ① **414 386-2DH**
P-Y. Asselin (trans org) Widor: *Symphony 5.*
(3/87) (DENO) ① **CO-1028**
B. Engerer *Concert* (9/88) (HARM) ① **HMC90 1266**
A. Weissenberg *Tchaikovsky: Piano Concerto 1.*
(11/88) (EMI) ① **CDM7 69381-2**
M. Papadopoulos *Concert*
(1/89) (HLCN) ① **CD-HLR143-2**
K. John (trans John) *Alain: Danses (1937/9).*
(4/89) (PRIO) ① **PRCD262**
R. Smith *Concert* (8/89) (NIMB) ① **NI5187**
B. Moiseiwitsch (r1945) *Concert*
(9/90) (APR) ② **APR7005**
M. Pletnev *Tchaikovsky: Sleeping Beauty.*
(4/91) (VIRG) ① **VC7 59611-2**
V. Horowitz (pp1951) *Concert*
(1/92) (RCA) ① **GD60449**
J. Boyk (1/92) (PERF) ① **PRCD-7**
A. Ugorski *Stravinsky: Petrushka.*
(4/92) (DG) ① **435 616-2GH**
V. Horowitz (r1947) *Concert*
(1/93) (RCA) ① **GD60526**
O. Mustonen *Concert*
(2/93) (DECC) ① **436 255-2DH**
V. Horowitz (arr Horowitz: pp1951) *Tchaikovsky: Piano Concerto 1.* (9/93) (RCA) ① **GD60321**
L. Vogt (r1991) *Concert*
(11/93) (EMI) ① **CDC7 54548-2**
N. Grubert (r1992) *Concert*
(7/94) (EMER) ① **EC3993-2**
L. Zilberstein (r1993) *Concert*
(8/94) (DG) ① **437 805-2GH**
W. Kapell (bp1953) *Concert*
(11/94) (VAI) ① **VAIA1048**
9, 10. Vladimir Ashkenazy (r1982) *Concert*
(7/93) (DECC) ① **430 759-2DM**
Scherzo in C sharp minor—piano (1858)
B. Engerer *Concert* (9/88) (HARM) ① **HMC90 1266**
The Seamstress—scherzino for piano (1871)
M. Campanella *Concert* (12/90) (NUOV) ① **6826**
N. Milstein, L. Mittman (r1938: arr vn/pf: Milstein) *Concert* (9/95) (BIDD) ① **LAB096**
Souvenir d'enfance—piano (1857)
B. Engerer *Concert* (9/88) (HARM) ① **HMC90 1266**
Souvenirs d'enfance—piano (1865)
1. Nurse and I; 2. First punishment: Nurse shuts me in a dark room.
M. Fingerhut *Concert* (6/87) (CHAN) ① **CHAN8439**
M. Campanella *Concert* (12/90) (NUOV) ① **6826**
1. B. Engerer *Concert*
(9/88) (HARM) ① **HMC90 1266**
2. M. Papadopoulos *Concert*
(1/89) (HLCN) ① **CD-HLR143-2**

SECTION IV: VOCAL AND CHORAL

But if I could meet thee again—song (1863)
(Wds. V. Kurochkin)
B. Christoff, A. Labinsky (r c1956) *Concert*
(8/89) (EMI) ① [3] **CHS7 63025-2**
A. Haugland, P. Rosenbaum (r1994) *Concert*
(4/95) (CHAN) ① [3] **CHAN9336/8**
K. Vayne, C. Tilney (r1966) *Concert*
(6/95) (PREI) ① **89996**
Child's song (1868) (Wds. Mey)
B. Christoff, A. Labinsky *Concert*
(8/89) (EMI) ① [3] **CHS7 63025-2**
A. Haugland, P. Rosenbaum (r1994) *Concert*
(4/95) (CHAN) ① [3] **CHAN9336/8**
The Classicist—song (1867) (Wds. Mussorgsky)
B. Christoff, A. Labinsky *Concert*
(8/89) (EMI) ① [3] **CHS7 63025-2**
A. Haugland, P. Rosenbaum (r1994) *Concert*
(4/95) (CHAN) ① [3] **CHAN9336/8**
S. Leiferkus, S. Skigin *Concert*
(12/95) (CONI) ① **75605 51248-2**
Darling Savishna—song (1866) (Wds. cpsr)
B. Christoff, A. Labinsky (r c1956) *Concert*
(8/89) (EMI) ① [3] **CHS7 63025-2**
S. Leiferkus, S. Skigin (r1993) *Concert*
(2/95) (CONI) ① **CDCF229**
A. Haugland, P. Rosenbaum (r1994) *Concert*
(4/95) (CHAN) ① [3] **CHAN9336/8**
Dear one, why are thine eyes sometimes so cold?—song (1866) (Wds. Pleshcheyev)
B. Christoff, A. Labinsky (r c1956) *Concert*
(8/89) (EMI) ① [3] **CHS7 63025-2**
A. Haugland, P. Rosenbaum (r1994) *Concert*
(4/95) (CHAN) ① [3] **CHAN9336/8**
The Destruction of Sennacherib—chorus and orchestra (1866-67 rev 1874)
LSC, LSO, C. Abbado (r1980) *Concert*
(6/93) (RCA) ① **09026 61354-2**

Prague Phil Chor, BPO, C. Abbado (pp1993) *Concert*
(2/95) (DG) ① **445 238-2GH**
Epitaph—song (1874) (Wds. cpsr)
B. Christoff, A. Labinsky *Concert*
(8/89) (EMI) ① [3] **CHS7 63025-2**
S. Leiferkus, S. Skigin *Concert*
(12/95) (CONI) ① **75605 51248-2**
Eremushka's lullaby—song (1868) (Wds. Nekrasov)
B. Christoff, A. Labinsky *Concert*
(8/89) (EMI) ① [3] **CHS7 63025-2**
A. Haugland, P. Rosenbaum (r1994) *Concert*
(4/95) (CHAN) ① [3] **CHAN9336/8**
S. Leiferkus, S. Skigin *Concert*
(12/95) (CONI) ① **75605 51248-2**
Evening Song—song (1871) (Wds. ?Pleshcheyev)
B. Christoff, A. Labinsky *Concert*
(8/89) (EMI) ① [3] **CHS7 63025-2**
A. Haugland, P. Rosenbaum (r1994) *Concert*
(4/95) (CHAN) ① [3] **CHAN9336/8**
The Feast—song (1867) (Wds. A. Kol'tsov)
B. Christoff, A. Labinsky *Concert*
(8/89) (EMI) ① [3] **CHS7 63025-2**
A. Haugland, P. Rosenbaum (r1994) *Concert*
(4/95) (CHAN) ① [3] **CHAN9336/8**
S. Leiferkus, S. Skigin *Concert*
(12/95) (CONI) ① **75605 51248-2**
Forgotten—song (1874) (Wds. Golenishchev-Kutuzov)
B. Christoff, A. Labinsky *Concert*
(8/89) (EMI) ① [3] **CHS7 63025-2**
S. Leiferkus, S. Skigin (r1993) *Concert*
(2/95) (CONI) ① **CDCF229**
A. Haugland, P. Rosenbaum (r1994) *Concert*
(4/95) (CHAN) ① [3] **CHAN9336/8**
From my tears—song (1866) (Wds. Heine, trans M. Michaylov)
B. Christoff, A. Labinsky (r c1956) *Concert*
(8/89) (EMI) ① [3] **CHS7 63025-2**
Philh, G. Simon (r1992: orch Kindler) *Concert*
(11/93) (CALA) ① **CACD1012**
A. Haugland, P. Rosenbaum (r1994) *Concert*
(4/95) (CHAN) ① [3] **CHAN9336/8**
A. Haugland, P. Rosenbaum (r1994) *Concert*
(4/95) (CHAN) ① [3] **CHAN9336/8**
S. Leiferkus, S. Skigin *Concert*
(12/95) (CONI) ① **75605 51248-2**
The Garden by the Don—song (1867) (Wds. Kol'tsov)
B. Christoff, A. Labinsky *Concert*
(8/89) (EMI) ① [3] **CHS7 63025-2**
K. Borg, E. Werba (r1959) *Concert*
(12/94) (FINL) ① [3] **4509-95606-2**
A. Haugland, P. Rosenbaum (r1994) *Concert*
(4/95) (CHAN) ① [3] **CHAN9336/8**
K. Vayne, C. Tilney (r1966) *Concert*
(6/95) (PREI) ① **89996**
Gathering mushrooms—song (1867) (Wds. Mey)
B. Christoff, A. Labinsky *Concert*
(8/89) (EMI) ① [3] **CHS7 63025-2**
A. Haugland, P. Rosenbaum (r1994) *Concert*
(4/95) (CHAN) ① [3] **CHAN9336/8**
Gopak—song (1866 rev with orch, 1868) (Wds. Shevchenko, trans Mey)
B. Christoff, FRNO, G. Tzipine (r c1956) *Concert*
(8/89) (EMI) ① [3] **CHS7 63025-2**
Detroit SO, N. Järvi (r1993: arr orch) *Concert*
(8/94) (CHAN) ① **CHAN9227**
N. Ghiaurov, P. Dokovska (1993) *Concert*
(1/95) (RCA) ① **09026 62501-2**
A. Haugland, P. Rosenbaum (r1994) *Concert*
(4/95) (CHAN) ① [3] **CHAN9336/8**
Hebrew song—song (1866) (Wds. cpsr)
B. Christoff, A. Labinsky *Concert*
(8/89) (EMI) ① [3] **CHS7 63025-2**
A. Haugland, P. Rosenbaum (r1994) *Concert*
(4/95) (CHAN) ① [3] **CHAN9336/8**
The he-goat: a worldly story—song (1867) (Wds. Mussorgsky)
B. Christoff, A. Labinsky *Concert*
(8/89) (EMI) ① [3] **CHS7 63025-2**
S. Leiferkus, S. Skigin (r1993) *Concert*
(2/95) (CONI) ① **CDCF229**
A. Haugland, P. Rosenbaum (r1994) *Concert*
(4/95) (CHAN) ① [3] **CHAN9336/8**
Hour of jollity—song (1858) (Wds. A. Kol'tsov)
B. Christoff, A. Labinsky (r c1956) *Concert*
(8/89) (EMI) ① [3] **CHS7 63025-2**
A. Haugland, P. Rosenbaum (r1994) *Concert*
(4/95) (CHAN) ① [3] **CHAN9336/8**

I have many palaces and gardens—song (1863) (Wds. A. Kol'stov)
B. Christoff, A. Labinsky (r c1956) *Concert*
(8/89) (EMI) ① [3] **CHS7 63025-2**
A. Haugland, P. Rosenbaum (r1994) *Concert*
(4/95) (CHAN) ① [3] **CHAN9336/8**
Is spinning man's work—song (1877) (Wds. A. K. Tolstoy)
B. Christoff, A. Labinsky *Concert*
(8/89) (EMI) ① [3] **CHS7 63025-2**
A. Haugland, P. Rosenbaum (r1994) *Concert*
(4/95) (CHAN) ① [3] **CHAN9336/8**
S. Leiferkus, S. Skigin *Concert*
(12/95) (CONI) ① **75605 51248-2**
It scatters and breaks—song (1877) (Wds. A. K. Tolstoy)
B. Christoff, A. Labinsky *Concert*
(8/89) (EMI) ① [3] **CHS7 63025-2**
A. Haugland, P. Rosenbaum (r1994) *Concert*
(4/95) (CHAN) ① [3] **CHAN9336/8**
S. Leiferkus, S. Skigin *Concert*
(12/95) (CONI) ① **75605 51248-2**
Joshua—mezzo-soprano, chorus and orchestra
Z. Gal, LSC, LSO, C. Abbado (r1980) *Concert*
(6/93) (RCA) ① **09026 61354-2**
E. Zaremba, Prague Phil Chor, BPO, C. Abbado (pp1993) *Concert* (2/95) (DG) ① **445 238-2GH**
Kalistratushka—song (1864) (Wds. Nekrasov)
B. Christoff, A. Labinsky (r c1956) *Concert*
(8/89) (EMI) ① [3] **CHS7 63025-2**
A. Haugland, P. Rosenbaum (r1994) *Concert*
(4/95) (CHAN) ① [3] **CHAN9336/8**
King Saul—song (1863) (Wds. Byron, trans P. Kozlov)
B. Christoff, FRNO, G. Tzipine (r c1956) *Concert*
(8/89) (EMI) ① [3] **CHS7 63025-2**
A. Haugland, P. Rosenbaum (r1994) *Concert*
(4/95) (CHAN) ① [3] **CHAN9336/8**
Lullaby—song (1865) (Wds. Ostrovsky)
B. Christoff, A. Labinsky (r c1956) *Concert*
(8/89) (EMI) ① [3] **CHS7 63025-2**
A. Haugland, P. Rosenbaum (r1994) *Concert*
(4/95) (CHAN) ① [3] **CHAN9336/8**
K. Vayne, C. Tilney (r1966) *Concert*
(6/95) (PREI) ① **89996**
The Magpie—song (1867) (Wds. Pushkin)
B. Christoff, A. Labinsky *Concert*
(8/89) (EMI) ① [3] **CHS7 63025-2**
A. Haugland, P. Rosenbaum (r1994) *Concert*
(4/95) (CHAN) ① [3] **CHAN9336/8**
Meines Herzen Sehnsucht—song (1858) (Wds. anon)
A. Haugland, P. Rosenbaum (r1994) *Concert*
(4/95) (CHAN) ① [3] **CHAN9336/8**
Mephistopheles' song of the flea—song (1879) (Wds. Goethe, trans A. Strugovshchikov)
B. Christoff, FRNO, G. Tzipine *Concert*
(8/89) (EMI) ① [3] **CHS7 63025-2**
F. Chaliapin, orch, E. Goossens (r1926) *Concert*
(12/89) (PEAR) ① **GEMMCD9314**
E. Pinza, orch (bp1944) *Concert*
(7/91) (MMOI) ① **CDMOIR404**
A. Kipnis, Victor SO, N. Berezowski (r1946) *Concert*
(9/92) (RCA) ① **GD60522**
O. Natzke, orch (Eng: r1940s) *Concert*
(12/92) (ODE) ① **CDODE1365**
F. Chaliapin, orch, R. Bourdon (r1927) *Concert*
(6/93) (PREI) ① **89207**
B. Christoff, Philh, I. Dobroven (r1950) *Concert*
(6/93) (EMI) ① **CDH7 64252-2**
H. Schlusnus, Berlin St Op Orch, A. Melichar (r1932: Ger) *Concert* (1/94) (PREI) ① **89205**
K. Borg, E. Werba (r1959) *Concert*
(12/94) (FINL) ① [3] **4509-95606-2**
N. Ghiaurov, P. Dokovska (r1993) *Concert*
(1/95) (RCA) ① **09026 62501-2**
S. Leiferkus, S. Skigin (r1993) *Concert*
(2/95) (CONI) ① **CDCF229**
A. Haugland, P. Rosenbaum (r1994) *Concert*
(4/95) (CHAN) ① [3] **CHAN9336/8**
Night—song (1864 orch 1870) (Wds. after Pushkin)
B. Christoff, A. Labinsky (r c1956) *Concert*
(8/89) (EMI) ① [3] **CHS7 63025-2**
M. Predit, G. Moore (r1949) *Concert*
(4/92) (EMI) ① [7] **CHS7 69741-2(6)**
A. Haugland, P. Rosenbaum (r1994) *Concert*
(4/95) (CHAN) ① [3] **CHAN9336/8**
O. Borodina, L. Gergieva (r1994) *Concert*
(8/95) (PHIL) ① **442 780-2PH**

Not like thunder, trouble struck—song (1877) (Wds. A. K. Tolstoy)
B. Christoff, A. Labinsky *Concert*
(8/89) (EMI) ① [3] **CHS7 63025-2**
A. Haugland, P. Rosenbaum (r1994) *Concert*
(4/95) (CHAN) ① [3] **CHAN9336/8**
S. Leiferkus, S. Skigin *Concert*
(12/95) (CONI) ① **75605 51248-2**

The Nursery—song cycle (1870-72) (Wds. cpsr)
1. With nurse; 2. In the corner; 3. The cockchafer; 4. With the doll; 5. Going to sleep; 6. On the hobbyhorse; 7. The cat Sailor.
B. Christoff, A. Labinsky (r c1956) *Concert*
(8/89) (EMI) ① [3] **CHS7 63025-2**
I. Seefried, E. Werba (Ger: pp1953) *Concert*
(7/93) (DG) ① [2] **437 348-2GDO2**
S. Leiferkus, S. Skigin (r1993) *Concert*
(2/95) (CONI) ① **CDCF229**
A. Haugland, P. Rosenbaum (r1994) *Concert*
(4/95) (CHAN) ① [3] **CHAN9336/8**
E. Podles, G. Johnson *Concert*
(5/95) (FORL) ① **UCD16683**
M. Price, J. Lockhart (r1970) *Concert*
(5/95) (RCA) ① [2] **09026 61635-2**

Old man's song—song (1863) (Wds. Goethe)
B. Christoff, A. Labinsky (r c1956) *Concert*
(8/89) (EMI) ① [3] **CHS7 63025-2**
A. Haugland, P. Rosenbaum (r1994) *Concert*
(4/95) (CHAN) ① [3] **CHAN9336/8**

On the Dnieper—song (1862 lost); 1879) (Wds. Shevchenko, trans Mey)
B. Christoff, A. Labinsky *Concert*
(8/89) (EMI) ① [3] **CHS7 63025-2**
A. Haugland, P. Rosenbaum (r1994) *Concert*
(4/95) (CHAN) ① [3] **CHAN9336/8**
S. Leiferkus, S. Skigin *Concert*
(12/95) (CONI) ① **75605 51248-2**

The Orphan—song (1868) (Wds. cpsr)
B. Christoff, A. Labinsky *Concert*
(8/89) (EMI) ① [3] **CHS7 63025-2**
A. Haugland, P. Rosenbaum (r1994) *Concert*
(4/95) (CHAN) ① [3] **CHAN9336/8**

The Outcast—song (1865) (Wds. I. Holz-Miller)
B. Christoff, A. Labinsky *Concert*
(8/89) (EMI) ① [3] **CHS7 63025-2**
A. Haugland, P. Rosenbaum (r1994) *Concert*
(4/95) (CHAN) ① [3] **CHAN9336/8**

The Peepshow—song (1870) (Wds. cpsr)
B. Christoff, A. Labinsky *Concert*
(8/89) (EMI) ① [3] **CHS7 63025-2**
S. Leiferkus, S. Skigin (r1993) *Concert*
(2/95) (CONI) ① **CDCF229**

A Prayer—song (1865) (Wds. Lermontov)
B. Christoff, A. Labinsky (r c1956) *Concert*
(8/89) (EMI) ① [3] **CHS7 63025-2**
A. Haugland, P. Rosenbaum (r1994) *Concert*
(4/95) (CHAN) ① [3] **CHAN9336/8**

Pride—song (1877) (Wds. A. K. Tolstoy)
B. Christoff, A. Labinsky *Concert*
(8/89) (EMI) ① [3] **CHS7 63025-2**
A. Haugland, P. Rosenbaum (r1994) *Concert*
(4/95) (CHAN) ① [3] **CHAN9336/8**
S. Leiferkus, S. Skigin *Concert*
(12/95) (CONI) ① **75605 51248-2**

The Ragamuffin—song (1867) (Wds. cpsr)
B. Christoff, A. Labinsky *Concert*
(8/89) (EMI) ① [3] **CHS7 63025-2**
A. Haugland, P. Rosenbaum (r1994) *Concert*
(4/95) (CHAN) ① [3] **CHAN9336/8**

Sadly rustled the leaves—song (1859) (after Pleshcheyev)
B. Christoff, G. Moore (r1951) *Concert*
(8/89) (EMI) ① [3] **CHS7 63025-2**
A. Haugland, P. Rosenbaum (r1994) *Concert*
(4/95) (CHAN) ① [3] **CHAN9336/8**

The Seminarist—song (1866) (Wds. Mussorgsky)
B. Christoff, A. Labinsky *Concert*
(8/89) (EMI) ① [3] **CHS7 63025-2**
S. Leiferkus, S. Skigin (r1993) *Concert*
(2/95) (CONI) ① **CDCF229**
A. Haugland, P. Rosenbaum (r1994) *Concert*
(4/95) (CHAN) ① [3] **CHAN9336/8**

Softly the spirit flew up to heaven—song (1877) (Wds. A. K. Tolstoy)
B. Christoff, A. Labinsky *Concert*
(8/89) (EMI) ① [3] **CHS7 63025-2**
B. Christoff, G. Moore (r1951) *Concert*
(6/93) (EMI) ① **CDH7 64252-2**
A. Haugland, P. Rosenbaum (r1994) *Concert*
(4/95) (CHAN) ① [3] **CHAN9336/8**
S. Leiferkus, S. Skigin *Concert*
(12/95) (CONI) ① **75605 51248-2**

Songs and Dances of Death (1877) (Wds. Golenishchev and Kutuvoz)
1. Lullaby (1875); 2. Serenade (1875); 3. Trepak (1875); 4. The field-marshal (1877).
M. Talvela, Finnish RSO, N. Järvi (arr. Aho) *Concert*
(6/87) (BIS) ① **BIS-CD325**
B. Christoff, FRNO, G. Tzipine (r c1956) *Concert*
(8/89) (EMI) ① [3] **CHS7 63025-2**
M. Rothmüller, S. Gyr (Ger: r1943) *Concert*
(11/91) (SYMP) ① [2] **SYMCD1098/9**
S. Leiferkus, RPO, Y. Temirkanov (arr Shostakovich) *Concert*
(3/92) (RCA) ① **RD60195**
B. Fassbaender, Gothenburg SO, N. Järvi (r1992) *Shostakovich: Symphony 14.*
(2/94) (DG) ① **437 785-2GH**
D. Hvorostovsky, Kirov Th Orch, V. Gergiev (r1993) *Concert*
(5/94) (PHIL) ① [3] **438 872-2PH**
K. Borg, E. Werba (r1956: Ger) *Concert*
(12/94) (FINL) ① [3] **4509-95606-2**
N. Ghiaurov, P. Dokovska (r1993) *Concert*
(1/95) (RCA) ① **09026 62501-2**
S. Leiferkus, S. Skigin (r1993) *Concert*
(2/95) (CONI) ① **CDCF229**
A. Kocherga, BPO, C. Abbado (pp1994: orch D Shostakovich) *Tchaikovsky/Mussorgsky 5.*
(3/95) (SONY) ① **SK66276**
A. Haugland, P. Rosenbaum (r1994) *Concert*
(4/95) (CHAN) ① [3] **CHAN9336/8**
E. Podles, G. Johnson *Concert*
(5/95) (FORL) ① **UCD16683**
R. Lloyd, Philadelphia, M. Jansons (r1994: orch Shostakovich) *Shostakovich: Symphony 10.*
(6/95) (EMI) ① **CDC5 55232-2**
3. F. Chaliapin, orch, L. Collingwood (r1929) *Concert*
(6/93) (PREI) ① [2] **89207**
4. I. Ershov, anon (r1903) *Concert*
(6/93) (PEAR) ① [3] **GEMMCDS9997/9(1)**
4. B. Christoff, G. Moore (r1951) *Concert*
(6/93) (EMI) ① **CDH7 64252-2**

The Sphinx—song (1875) (Wds. cpsr)
B. Christoff, A. Labinsky *Concert*
(8/89) (EMI) ① [3] **CHS7 63025-2**
A. Haugland, P. Rosenbaum (r1994) *Concert*
(4/95) (CHAN) ① [3] **CHAN9336/8**
S. Leiferkus, S. Skigin *Concert*
(12/95) (CONI) ① **75605 51248-2**

Sunless—song cycle (1874) (Wds. Golenishchev-Kutuzov)
1. Between four walls; 2. Thou didst not know me in the crowd; 3. The idle, noisy day is ended; 4. Boredom; 5. Elegy; 6. On the river.
Cpte A. Orda, J. Lee (bp1961) *Concert*
(12/89) (SYMP) ① **SYMCD1067**
B. Christoff, A. Labinsky (r c1956) *Concert*
(8/89) (EMI) ① [3] **CHS7 63025-2**
A. Haugland, P. Rosenbaum (r1994) *Concert*
(4/95) (CHAN) ① [3] **CHAN9336/8**
S. Leiferkus, S. Skigin *Concert*
(12/95) (CONI) ① **75605 51248-2**
6. V. Horowitz (arr Horowitz: r1947) *Concert*
(1/92) (RCA) ① **GD60449**

Tell me why, o maiden—song (1858)
B. Christoff, A. Labinsky *Concert*
(8/89) (EMI) ① [3] **CHS7 63025-2**
A. Haugland, P. Rosenbaum (r1994) *Concert*
(4/95) (CHAN) ① [3] **CHAN9336/8**

The Vision—song (1877) (Wds. Golenishchev and Kutuzov)
B. Christoff, A. Labinsky *Concert*
(8/89) (EMI) ① [3] **CHS7 63025-2**
A. Haugland, P. Rosenbaum (r1994) *Concert*
(4/95) (CHAN) ① [3] **CHAN9336/8**
S. Leiferkus, S. Skigin *Concert*
(12/95) (CONI) ① **75605 51248-2**

The Wanderer—song (1878) (Wds. Rückert trans Pleshcheyev)
B. Christoff, A. Labinsky *Concert*
(8/89) (EMI) ① [3] **CHS7 63025-2**
A. Haugland, P. Rosenbaum (r1994) *Concert*
(4/95) (CHAN) ① [3] **CHAN9336/8**

What are words of love to you?—song (1860) (Wds. A. Ammosov)
D. Christoff, A. Labinsky (r c1956) *Concert*
(8/89) (EMI) ① [3] **CHS7 63025-2**
A. Haugland, P. Rosenbaum (r1994) *Concert*
(4/95) (CHAN) ① [3] **CHAN9336/8**
O. Borodina, L. Gergieva (r1994) *Concert*
(8/95) (PHIL) ① **442 780-2PH**

Where art thou, little star—song (1858) (Wds. N. Grekov)
B. Christoff, A. Labinsky (r c1956) *Concert*
(8/89) (EMI) ① [3] **CHS7 63025-2**
K. Borg, E. Werba (r1959) *Concert*
(12/94) (FINL) ① [3] **4509-95606-2**
A. Haugland, P. Rosenbaum (r1994) *Concert*
(4/95) (CHAN) ① [3] **CHAN9336/8**

The Wild wind blows—song (1864) (Wds. A. Kol'stov)
B. Christoff, FRNO, G. Tzipine (r c1956) *Concert*
(8/89) (EMI) ① [3] **CHS7 63025-2**
A. Haugland, P. Rosenbaum (r1994) *Concert*
(4/95) (CHAN) ① [3] **CHAN9336/8**

You drunken sot—song (1866) (Wds. cpsr)
A. Haugland, P. Rosenbaum (r1994) *Concert*
(4/95) (CHAN) ① [3] **CHAN9336/8**

SECTION V: STAGE WORKS

Boris Godunov—opera: prologue and 4 acts (1874—St Petersburg) (Lib. cpsr)
PROLOGUE: 1a. To whom are you abandoning us; 1b. Mityukha, what are we bawling about?; 1c. True Believers; 1d. The Angel of the Lord spake to the world; 2a. Like to the red sun; 2b. I am sick at heart (Coronation Scene). ACT 1: 3a. Yet one last tale; 3b. You have been writing; 4a. I caught a dove-coloured drake; 4b. For the building of a church; 4c. Once in the town of Kazan; 4d. How he rides...Hostess, where does this road lead?; 4e. Why, from here, for instance; 5. Who are you? Eh?. ACT 2: 6a. Where are you, my bridegroom?; 6b. Once a gnat was sawing wood; 6c. A tale of this and that; 7a. And you, my son, what are you busy with?; 7b. I have attained the highest power; 7c. Our poll parrot was sitting with the nannies; 7d. Your Majesty, I make obeisance; 7e. Ugh, it's oppressive (Clock Scene). ACT 3: 8a. On the banks of the azure Vistula; 8b. Enough! The beauteous lady is grateful; 8c. Marina's bored; 8d. Oh, it's you, father; 9a. At midnight in the garden; 9b. Tsarevich!...At my heels again; 9c. I don't believe in your passion (Polonaise and Chorus); 9d. The crafty Jesuit squeezed me hard; 9e. Oh tsarevich, I implore. ACT 4: 10a. Is the mass over, then?; 10b. Trrrr Tin hat; 10c. The moon is going; 10d. What is he crying for?; 10e. Gush forth, bitter tears; 11a. Well, let's put it to the vote; 11b. Your pardon, my lords; 11c. One day at the hour of vespers (Pimen's monologue); 11d. Farewell, my son, I am dying; 12a. Bring him down here; 12b. No falcon flies across the skies; 12c. The sun and moon have gone dark; 12d. Unleashed, raging our might has been; 12e. Oh Lord, save the king; 12f. Hail to thee, tsarevich; 12g. Gush forth, bitter tears.
Cpte N. Ghiaurov, L. Spiess, G. Vishnevskaya, M. Talvela, A. Diakov, A. Maslennikov, M. Paunov, Z. Kélémen, O. Miljakovic, N. Dobrianova, B. Cvejic, M. Lilowa, A. Maslennikov, S. Markov, S.R. Frese, P. Karolidis, Vienna Boys' Ch, Sofia Rad Chor, Vienna St Op Chor, Vienna PO, H. von Karajan (arr Rimsky-Korsakov/Ippolitov-Ivanov)
(11/88) (DECC) ① [3] **411 862-2DH3**
Cpte R. Raimondi, V. Polozov, G. Vishnevskaya, P. Plishka, R. Tesarowicz, K. Riegel, M. Raitzin, N. Storozhev, M.A. Fish, C. Dubosc, M. Zaremba, E. Gedda, L. Miller, Chevy Chase Sch Ch, Washington Oratorio Soc, Washington Chor Arts Soc, Washington NSO, M. Rostropovich
(6/90) (ERAT) ① [3] **2292-45418-2**
Abridged A. Haugland, S.F. Andersen, H. Zednik, E. Harbo, A. Møller, S. Lillesøe, M. Myhus, G. Paevatalu, DR Rad Ch, DR RSO, D. Kitaienko (bp1986)
(6/90) (KONT) ① [2] **32036/7**
Cpte N. Ghiaurov, M. Svetlev, S. Mineva, N. Ghiuselev, D. Petkov, J. Franck, Angel Petkov, S. Martinovich, R. Troeva-Mircheva, L. Hadjieva, S. Popangelova, P. Dilova, M. Popov, Bodra Smyana Children's Ch, Sofia National Op Chor, Sofia Fest Orch, E. Tchakarov (1872 vers)
(4/92) (SONY) ① [3] **S3K45763**
Cpte M. Talvela, N. Gedda, B. Kinasz, L. Mróz, A. Haugland, B. Paprocki, K. Pustelak, A. Hiolski, W. Baniewicz, H. Lukomska, B. Brun-Barańska, S. Toczyska, P. Raptis, W. Zalewski, J. Góralski, Cracow Boys' Ch, Polish Rad Chor, Cracow RSO, J. Semkow (r1976)
(5/94) (EMI) ① [3] **CDS7 54377-2**
Cpte A. Kocherga, S. Larin, M. Lipovšek, S. Ramey, G. Nikolsky, P. Langridge, H. Wildhaber, S. Leiferkus, L. Nichiteanu, V. Valente, Y. Gorokhovskaya, E. Zaremba, A. Fedin, A. Shagidullin, M. Krutikov, W. Drabowicz, Slovak Phil Chor, Berlin Rad Chor, Tolz Boys' Ch, BPO, C. Abbado (r1993: orig ver)
(5/94) (SONY) ① [3] **S3K58977**
Cpte B. Christoff, N. Gedda, E. Zareska, A. Bielecki, K. Borg, L. Lebedeva, L. Romanova, W. Pasternak, R. Bonte, E. Bousquet, Paris Russian Chor, FRNO, I. Dobroven (r1952: arr Rimsky-Korsakov)
(12/94) (EMI) ① [3] **CHS5 65192-2**
Forest scene Bolshoi Th Chor, Bolshoi SO, A. Lazarev (r1993) *Concert*
(5/94) (ERAT) ① **4509-91723-2**

Symphonic Synthesis Philadelphia, L. Stokowski
(r1936: arr Stokowski) *Concert*
(11/94) (DUTT) ① **CDAX8009**
2a, 2b, 4c, 4d, 7b, 7d, 7e, 11d A. Kipnis, A. Leskaya,
I. Tamarin, Victor Chorale, Victor SO, N. Berezowski
(r1945/6) *Concert* (9/92) (RCA) ① **GD60522**
2b F. Chaliapin, Paris Russian Op Chor, Paris
Russian Op Orch, M. Steinmann, chor, orch, E.
Goossens (r1926/31) *Concert*
(6/88) (EMI) ① **CDH7 61009-2**
2b Vanni-Marcoux, orch (r1934: French) *Concert*
(1/94) (GLUB) ① **CL99-101**
2b Kirov Th Chor, Kirov Th Orch, V. Gergiev (r1993;
arr Shostakovich; includes bonus sampler CD)
Concert (7/95) (PHIL) ① **442 775-2PH**
3a F. Chaliapin, orch, G.W. Byng (r1922) *Concert*
(12/89) (PEAR) ① **GEMMCD9314**
3a B. Christoff, Philh, N. Malko (r1949) *Concert*
(6/93) (EMI) ① **CDH7 64252-2**
3a, 3b D. Smirnov, K.E. Kaidanov, orch (r1924)
Concert
(6/93) (PEAR) ① [3] **GEMMCDS9004/6(2)**
4c F. Chaliapin, orch, R. Bourdon (1927) *Concert*
(12/89) (PEAR) ① **GEMMCD9314**
4c B. Christoff, Philh, H. von Karajan (r1949) *Concert*
(6/93) (EMI) ① **CDH7 64252-2**
4c L. Sibiriakov, orch (r1910) *Concert*
(6/93) (PEAR) ① [3] **GEMMCDS9007/9(2)**
7b E. Pinza, NY Met Op Chor, NY Met Op Orch, E.
Cooper (r1944: Ital) *Concert*
(4/90) (SONY) ① **MPK45693**
7b E. Pinza, NY Met Op Orch, E. Panizza (Ital:
bp1939) *Concert* (7/91) (MMOI) ① **CDMOIR404**
7b T. Pasero, orch (Ital: r1944) *Concert*
(4/92) (EMI) ① [7] **CHS7 69741-2(7)**
7b G. London, NY Pleasants (r1950) *Concert*
(4/92) (EMI) ① [7] **CHS7 69741-2(2)**
7b F. Chaliapin, orch, V. Bellezza (pp1928) *Concert*
(7/92) (PEAR) ① [3] **GEMMCDS9926(1)**
7b M. Reizen, Bolshoi Th Orch, N. Golovanov
(r1948) *Concert* (12/92) (PREI) ① **89059**
7b T. Pasero, SO, D. Marzollo (r1944: Ital) *Concert*
(4/95) (PREI) ① **89074**
7b, 7e F. Chaliapin, LSO, M. Steinmann (r1931)
Concert (6/88) (EMI) ① **CDH7 61009-2**
7b, 7e F. Chaliapin, LSO, M. Steinmann (r1931)
Concert (12/89) (PEAR) ① **GEMMCD9314**
7b, 7e, 11d Vanni-Marcoux, orch (r1927: French)
Concert (1/94) (CLUB) ① **CL99-101**
7b, 11c, 11d K. Borg, Berlin RSO, H. Stein (r1963)
Concert (4/94) (RCA) ① [6] **09026 61580-2(5)**
7b, 11d B. Christoff, ROH Chor, Philh, I. Dobrowen
(r1949) *Concert* (6/93) (EMI) ① **CDH7 64252-2**
7e A. Kipnis, RCA SO, N. Berezowski (r1945)
Concert (4/94) (RCA) ① [6] **09026 61580-2(5)**
11d F. Chaliapin, ROH Chor, ROHO, V. Bellezza
(pp1928) *Concert* (6/88) (EMI) ① **CDH7 61009-2**
11d F. Chaliapin, orch, L. Collingwood (r1927)
Concert (12/89) (PEAR) ① **GEMMCD9314**
11d E. Pinza, Twentieth Cent Fox Chor, Twentieth
Cent Fox SO, Alfred Newman (r1952) *Concert*
(9/93) (RCA) ① **09026 61245-2**
11d O. Miljakovic, N. Ghiaurov, Vienna St Op Chor,
Sofia Rad Chor, VPO, H. von Karajan (r1970)
Concert (10/93) (DECC) ① **436 464-2DM**
11d M. Reizen, B. Zlatogorova, Bolshoi Th Orch, N.
Golovanov (r1948) *Concert* (2/95) (PREI) ① **89080**
19a, 19b P. Althouse, M. Ober, orch, W.B. Rogers
(r1915: Ital) *Concert*
(4/94) (RCA) ① [6] **09026 61580-2(2)**
**The Fair at Sorochintsï, 'Sorochinskaya
yarmarka'—opera (1913—Moscow)** (Lib. after
Gogol opera finished Lyadov)
Gopak S. Rachmaninov (r1925; arr Rachmaninov:
pf) *Concert* (5/90) (RCA) ① **GD87766**
Gopak H. Shelley (1991: arr pf: Rachmaninov)
Concert (3/92) (HYPE) ① **CDA66486**
Gopak LSO, A. Coates (1929) *Concert*
(12/92) (KOCH) ① **37700-2**
Gopak S. Rachmaninov (r1925; arr Rachmaninov:
pf) *Concert* (3/93) (RCA) ① [10] **09026 61265-2(2)**
Gopak Philh, G. Simon (r1992: orch Liadov) *Concert*
(11/93) (CALA) ① **CACD1012**
Gopak H. Shelley (1991: arr pf: Rachmaninov)
Concert (HYPE) ① [8] **CDS44041/8**
Gopak N. Milstein, orch, R. Irving (r1962: arr Jones)
Concert (5/94) (EMI) ① [6] **ZDMF7 64830-2**
Gopak J. Szigeti, A. Foldes (r1941: arr vn/pf:
Dushkin) *Concert* (7/94) (BIDD) ① [2] **LAB070/1**
Gopak J. Starker, G. Moore (r1958: arr vc/pf:
Stutschewsky) *Concert*
(12/95) (EMI) ① [6] **CZS5 68485-2**
Why, my sad heart G. Vinogradov, Bolshoi Th Orch,
S. Samosud (r c1948) *Concert*
(4/92) (EMI) ① [7] **CHS7 69741-2(6)**

Why, my sad heart D. Smirnov, orch (r1924: Fr)
Concert
(6/93) (PEAR) ① [3] **GEMMCDS9004/6(2)**
**Khovanshchina—opera: 5 acts (1872-80—St
Petersburg)** (Lib. cpsr)
1. Prelude (Dawn over the Moscow River). ACT 2:
14b. Mysterious forces (Marfa's divination). ACT 3:
21a. I walked all through the meadows (Marfa's aria):
24. The lair of the Streltsi is sunk in sleep
(Shaklovity's aria). ACT 4: 34. Dance of the Persian
Slave Girls; 36. Prelude (Scene 2). ACT 5: 41. Here
on this spot (Dosifei's aria). ADDITIONAL ITEMS: 46.
Intermezzo; 47. Golitsyn's journey.
Cpte N. Ghiaurov, Z. Gadjev, K. Kaludov, S. Popov,
N. Ghiuselev, A. Milcheva, M.P. Popova, Angel
Petkov, M. Dimchewska, D. Stanchev, S. Georgiev,
R. Doikov, A. Selimski, Sofia National Op Chor, Sofia
National Op Orch, E. Tchakarov
(10/90) (SONY) ① [3] **S3K45831**
Cpte A. Haugland, V. Atlantov, V. Popov, A.
Kocherga, P. Burchuladze, M. Lipovšek, B.
Poschner-Klebel, H. Zednik, J. Borowska, W.
Gahmlich, Vienna Boys' Ch, Slovak Phil Chor,
Vienna St Op Chor, Vienna St Op Orch, C. Abbado
(pp1989) (11/90) (DG) ① [3] **429 758-2GH3**
Cpte B. Minzhilkiev, V. Galusin, A. Steblianko, V.
Alexeev, N. Okhotnikov, O. Borodina, E. Tselovalnik,
K. Pluzhnikov, J. Prokina, N. Gassiev, V. Gerelo,
Leningrad Kirov Th Chor, Leningrad Kirov Th Orch,
V. Gergiev (6/92) (PHIL) ① [3] **432 147-2PH3**
Excs Rotterdam PO, J. Conlon Pictures.
(8/91) (ERAT) ① **2292-45596-2**
1. Moscow PO, L. Leighton Smith *Concert*
(2/88) (SHEF) ① **CD25**
1. Oslo PO, M. Jansons *Concert*
(1/90) (EMI) ① **CDC7 49797-2**
1. RPO, Vladimir Ashkenazy (pp1989) *Concert*
(5/90) (RPO) ① **CDRPO7014**
1. RPO, Y. Temirkanov (arr Rimsky-Korsakov)
Concert (3/90) (RCA) ① **RD60195**
1. Atlanta SO, Y. Levi *Concert*
(4/92) (TELA) ① **CD80296**
1. Leningrad PO, E. Mravinsky (pp1981) *Concert*
(6/92) (ERAT) ① **2292-45757-2**
1. Leningrad PO, E. Mravinsky (pp1981) *Concert*
(6/92) (ERAT) ① [11] **2292-45763-2**
1. Russian Nat Orch, M. Pletnev *Concert*
(12/94) (DG) ① **439 892-2GH**
1, 34, 47. Rotterdam PO, J. Conlon (1989) *Pictures.*
(12/93) (ERAT) ① **4509-92870-2**
1, 47. LSO, C. Abbado (r1980) *Concert*
(6/93) (RCA) ① **09026 61354-2**
1, 47. Philh, G. Simon (r1992: orch Rimsky-
Korsakov/Stokowski) *Concert*
(11/93) (CALA) ① **CACD1012**
14b Z. Dolukhanova, orch (r1950s) *Concert*
(4/92) (EMI) ① [7] **CHS7 69741-2(6)**
36. Philadelphia, L. Stokowski (r1927: arr Stokowski)
(11/94) (DUTT) ① **CDAX8009**
41. M. Reizen, Bolshoi Th Orch, V. Nebolsin (r1953)
Concert (12/92) (PREI) ① **89059**
41. B. Christoff, Philh, I. Dobrowen (r1950) *Concert*
(6/93) (EMI) ① **CDH7 64252-2**
41. K. Borg, Berlin RSO, H. Stein (r1963) *Concert*
(12/94) (FINL) ① [3] **4509-95606-2**
46. Gothenburg SO, N. Järvi *Concert*
(6/90) (DG) ① **429 494-2GDC**
**The Marriage—comic opera: 1 act (1909—St.
Petersburg)** (Lib. Gogol: opera unfinished)
Cpte V. Khrulev, A. Podbolotov, L. Kolmakova, V.
Ribasenko, USSR Ministry of Culture SO, G.
Rozhdestvensky (r1982: orch Rozhdestvensky)
Rimsky-Korsakov: Mozart and Salieri.
(9/93) (OLYM) ① **OCD145**
**Oedipus in Athens—opera (projected) (1858-
60)** (Lib. cpsr, after Ozerov)
Chorus of people in the temple LSC, LSO, C.
Abbado (r1980) *Concert*
(6/93) (RCA) ① **09026 61354-2**
Chorus of people in the temple Prague Phil Chor,
BPO, C. Abbado (pp1993) *Concert*
(2/95) (DG) ① **445 238-2GH**
Salammbô—opera (incomplete) (1863-66)
(Lib. cpsr, after Flaubert)
Balearic Song B. Christoff, A. Labinsky (r c1956)
Concert (8/89) (EMI) ① [3] **CHS7 63025-2**
Balearic Song A. Haugland, P. Rosenbaum (r1994)
Concert (4/95) (CHAN) ① [3] **CHAN9336/8**
Chorus of priestesses LSC, LSO, C. Abbado
(r1980) *Concert* (6/93) (RCA) ① **09026 61354-2**
Chorus of priestesses Prague Phil Chor, BPO, C.
Abbado (pp1993) *Concert*
(2/95) (DG) ① **445 238-2GH**

Trio—clarinet, bassoon and piano (1942)
Modern Ens, I. Metzmacher (r1992) *Concert*
(11/93) (RCA) ℗ **09026 61180-2**

SECTION III: INSTRUMENTAL

Blues—piano (1935)
J. MacGregor *Concert* (8/89) (COLL) ℗ **Coll1299-2**
Prelude—piano (1935)
J. MacGregor *Concert* (8/89) (COLL) ℗ **Coll1299-2**
M. Legrand (r1994) *Concert*
(7/95) (ERAT) ℗ **4509-96386-2**
Studies for Player Piano (1950-)
No 6. A. Feinberg, D. Druckman (r1994; trans Daniel
Druckman) *Concert*
(11/95) (ARGO) ℗ **444 457-2ZH**
Vol.1: Nos. 3a, 3b, 3c, 3d, 3e, 20, 44, 41a, 41b, 41c
C. Nancarrow (r1988) *Concert*
(3/92) (WERG) ℗ [2] **WER6168-2**
Vol.2 Nos: 5, 6, 14, 22, 26, 31, 35, 4, 32, 37, 40a,
40b C. Nancarrow (r1988) *Concert*
(3/92) (WERG) ℗ [2] **WER6168-2**
Vol. 5: Nos 42, 45a, 45b, 45c, 48a, 48b, 48c, 49a,
49b, 49c C. Nancarrow
(8/89) (WERG) ℗ **WER60165-50**
Vols 3 & 4 Nos 1, 2a, 2b, 7, 8, 9, 10, 11, 12, 13, 15,
16, 17, 18, 19, 21, 23, 24, 25, 27, 28, 29, 33, 34, 36,
43, 46, 47, 50. C. Nancarrow
(7/91) (WERG) ℗ [2] **WER60166/7-50**
(No) 1, 2, 3c, 5, 6, 7, 9, 12, 14, 18, 19. Modern Ens,
I. Metzmacher (r1992; arr Y. Mikhashoff) *Concert*
(11/93) (RCA) ℗ **09026 61180-2**
Tango?—piano (1984)
U. Oppens *Concert* (5/90) (MUSI) ℗ **MACD-604**
C. Nancarrow (r1988) *Concert*
(3/92) (WERG) ℗ [2] **WER6168-2**
Modern Ens, I. Metzmacher (r1992; arr Y.
Mikhashoff) *Concert*
(11/93) (RCA) ℗ **09026 61180-2**

NANINO, Giovanni Maria (1543 or 1544–1607) Italy

SECTION IV: VOCAL AND CHORAL

Adoramus te, Christe—motet (5vv)
King's College Ch, S. Cleobury *Concert*
(5/85) (EMI) ℗ **CDC7 47065-2**

Haec Dies—motet
Westminster Abbey Ch, S. Preston *Concert*
(5/86) (ARCH) ℗ **415 517-2AH**

NAOUMOFF, Emile (b 1962) France

SECTION II: CHAMBER

In memoriam Lili Boulanger—bassoon and piano (1993)
C. Marchèse, E. Naoumoff (r1993) *Concert*
(9/94) (MARC) ℗ **8 223636**

NÁPRAVNÍK, Eduard (1839–1916) Moravia

SECTION V: STAGE WORKS

**Dubrovsky—opera (4 acts), Op. 58 (1895—St
Petersburg)** (Lib. M. I. Tchaikovsky, after
Pushkin)
Give me oblivion I. Kozlovsky, Bolshoi Th Orch, A.
Orlov (r1939) *Concert*
(4/92) (EMI) ℗ [7] **CHS7 69741-2(6)**
Give me oblivion A. Labinsky, anon (r1901) *Concert*
(6/93) (PEAR) ℗ [3] **GEMMCDS9001/3(1)**
Give me oblivion D. Smirnov, orch (r1912) *Concert*
(6/93) (PEAR) ℗ [3] **GEMMCDS9004/6(1)**
Give me oblivion A. Davidov, anon (r1902) *Concert*
(6/93) (PEAR) ℗ [3] **GEMMCDS9007/9(1)**
Ne jamais la voir ni l'entendre M. Mei-Figner, N.
Figner, anon (r1901: Fr) *Concert*
(6/93) (PEAR) ℗ [3] **GEMMCDS9997/9(1)**
**Harold—opera: 5 acts, Op. 45 (1886—St.
Petersburg)** (Lib. P P Weinberg, after E von
Wildenbruch)
Berceuse d'Harold F. Litvinne, A. Cortot (r1902)
Concert (10/92) (SYMP) ℗ **SYMCD1101**
Hush thee, dear one, slumber well M. Mei-Figner,
anon (r1901) *Concert*
(6/93) (PEAR) ℗ [3] **GEMMCDS9997/9(1)**
Hush thee, dear one, slumber well A. Nezhdanova,
anon, anon (r1907) *Concert*
(6/93) (PEAR) ℗ [3] **GEMMCDS9007/9(1)**

NARBUTAITE, Onute (b 1956) USSR/Lithuania

SECTION I: ORCHESTRAL

**Opus Lugubre, '(A) Sad Creation'—22
strings (1991)**
Ostrobothnian CO, J. Kangas (r1994) *Concert*
(11/95) (FINL) ℗ **4509-97892-2**

NARDINI, Pietro (1722–1793) Italy

SECTION II: CHAMBER

7 Sonatas—violin and continuo
7. B Flat.
7(Larghetto) N. Milstein, L. Mittman (arr David:
r1938) *Concert* (10/92) (BIDD) ℗ **LAB055**

NARES, James (1715–1783) England

SECTION II: CHAMBER

**Sonata for Harpsichord, Two Violins and
Continuo, Op. 2 No. 6 (pub 1759)** (from solo
hpd lessons, Op. 2)
P. Nicholson (kybds/dir), Parley of Instr, P. Holman
(r1993) *Concert* (8/94) (HYPE) ℗ **CDA66700**

SECTION III: INSTRUMENTAL

Introduction and Fugue—keyboard (1772)
T. Dart (r1957) *Concert* (5/95) (JMS) ℗ **JMSCD1**
**Introduction and Fugue in A—keyboard
(1767)**
Margaret Phillips *Concert*
(5/91) (GAMU) ℗ **GAMCD514**
**Introduction and Fugue in F—keyboard (pub
1728)**
J. Bate *Concert* (5/91) (UNIC) ℗ **DKPCD9099**
8 Setts of Lessons—harpsichord (1747)
2. D.
2. T. Pinnock (r1978) *Concert*
(4/89) (CRD) ℗ **CRD3347**

NARITA, Tamezo (1893–1945) Japan

SECTION IV: VOCAL AND CHORAL

The Song of the Seashore—song (Wds. K.
Hayashi)
J. Lloyd Webber, RPO, N. Cleobury *Concert*
(3/87) (PHIL) ℗ **416 698-2PH**

NARVÁEZ, Luys de (fl 1530–1550) Spain

SECTION III: INSTRUMENTAL

Paseávase el rey moro—vihuela (pub 1538)
(from book ? of Seys libros del delphin)
A. Lawrence-King (r1993) *Concert*
(2/94) (HYPE) ℗ **CDA66653**
J. M. Moreno (r1994) *Concert*
(8/95) (GLOS) ℗ **GCD920103**
**Los Seys libros del delphin—vihuela (pub
1538)**
Libro 1: 1a. Fantasía I tono; 1b. Fantasía II tono; 1c.
Fantasía III tono; 1d. Fantasía IV tono; 1e. Fantasía V
tono; 1f. Fantasía VI tono en Fa ut mi re; 1g. Fantasía
VII tono on Ut re mi mi; 1h. Fantasía VIII tono. Libro
2: 2a. Fantasía I tono 1; 2b. Fantasía I tono 2; 2c.
Fantasía IV tono; 2d. Fantasía V tono. Libro 3: 3a. La
cancion del Emperador: on Josquin Desprez's 'Mille
regretz'; 3b. Je veux laisser melancolie de Ricafort;
3c. Sanctus and Osanna from Josquin Desprez's
Missa 'Faisant regretz'; 3d. Sanctus and Osanna
from Josquin Desprez's Missa Hercules Dux Ferrarie;
3e. Una cancion de Gombert; 3f. Cum sancto spiritu
from Josquin Desprez's Missa ad fugam. Libro 4: 4a.
Diferencias on 'O gloriosa domina'; 4b. Diferencias
on 'Pange lingua'. Libro 5: 5a. Arde corçon arde; 5b.
Ya se asiente el Rey Ramiro; 5c. Fantasía VII tono
on 'Ut re mi fa mi'; 5d. Diferencias on 'Y la mi cinta
dorada'. Libro 6: 6a. Diferencias on 'Conde claros';
6b. Diferencias on 'Guárdame las vacas'; 6c. Una
baxa de contrapunto; 6d. Tres diferencias por otra
parte.
1a–h, 2a–d, 3a–f, 4a, 6a–d H. Smith
(3/90) (ASTR) ℗ **E8706**
1b, 1c C. Wilson (r1993) *Concert*
(2/94) (HYPE) ℗ **CDA66653**
1e, 2d, 3a, 3e, 4a, 5a, 5b, 6a–d J. Bream (r1979)
Concert (8/93) (RCA) ℗ [28] **09026 61583-2(5)**

1e, 2d, 3a, 3e, 4a, 5a, 5b, 6a–d J. Bream (r1979)
Concert (9/94) (RCA) ℗ **09026 61606-2**
3a N. North *Concert* (6/87) (AMON) ℗ **CD-SAR18**
3a, 6a J. Bream (r1983) *Concert*
(8/93) (RCA) ℗ [28] **09026 61583-2(6)**
3a, 6a J. Bream (r1983) *Concert*
(8/93) (RCA) ℗ **09026 61610-2**
3a, 6b J. M. Moreno (r1994) *Concert*
(8/95) (GLOS) ℗ **GCD920103**

SECTION IV: VOCAL AND CHORAL

Con qué la lavaré?—song
T. Berganza, N. Yepes *Concert*
(12/92) (DG) ℗ [2] **435 848-2GX2**

NASH, Peter Paul (b 1950) England

SECTION IV: VOCAL AND CHORAL

**In a walled garden—songs: 1v and
instrumental ensemble (1988)** (Wds. A
Tennyson)
1. Her tears fell with the dews at even; 2. Upon the
middle of the night; 3. And ever when the moon was
low; 4. All day within the dreamy house; 5. The
sparrow's chirrup on the roof.
J. Manning, Jane's Minstrels, R. Montgomery (r1993)
Concert (10/95) (NMC) ℗ **NMCD025**

NATH, Pandit Pran (b 1918) Pakistan

SECTION IV: VOCAL AND CHORAL

**It is my turn, oh Lord (Aba kee tayk
Hameree)—voice, string quartet and
percussion (1992)**
Kronos Qt, P.P. Nath, K. Bhatt, T. Riley, J. Constant
(r1992) *Concert* (8/93) (NONE) ℗ **7559-79310-2**

NAUDOT, Jacques-Christophe (c1690–1762) France

SECTION I: ORCHESTRAL

Concertos for Recorder and Strings, Op. 17
3. C; 5. G.
5. F. Brüggen, VCM, N. Harnoncourt (r1968) *Concert*
(2/94) (TELD) ℗ **4509-92180-2**
5. F. Brüggen, VCM, N. Harnoncourt, F. Brüggen (r
c1969) *Concert* (10/95) (TELD) ℗ **4509-97474-2**

NAUWACH, Johann (c1595–c1630) Germany

SECTION IV: VOCAL AND CHORAL

**Teutsche Villanellen—Lieder collection (pub
1627)**
1. Jetzund kömpt die Nacht herbey (Wds. Opitz); 2.
Ach Liebste, lass uns eilen (Wds. Opitz).
1, 2. A. Scholl, A. Verzier, K. E. Schröder, M. Märkl
(r1994) *Concert* (5/95) (HARM) ℗ **HMC90 1505**

NAYLOR, Edward (Woodall) (1867–1934) England

SECTION IV: VOCAL AND CHORAL

Evening Service in A—choir a cappella
Chichester Cath Ch, A. Thurlow, J. Thomas (r1994)
Concert (5/95) (PRIO) ℗ **PRCD511**
Final responses—choir
King's College Ch, S. Cleobury (pp1991 with Choral
Evensong) *Concert*
(10/92) (EMI) ℗ **CDC7 54412-2**
Vox dicentis: Clama—anthem (1911) (Wds.
Liturgy of St.James)
St Paul's Cath Ch, Andrew Lucas, John Scott
Concert (9/90) (HYPE) ℗ **CDA66374**
Norwich Cath Ch, M. Nicholas, N. Taylor *Concert*
(3/92) (PRIO) ℗ **PRCD351**
King's College Ch, S. Cleobury (r1991) *Concert*
(6/93) (EMI) ℗ **CDC7 54418-2**

NAZARETH, Ernesto (1863–1934) Brazil

SECTION III: INSTRUMENTAL

Ameno resedá—tango
M. Bratke (r1992) *Concert*
(8/93) (OLYM) ℗ **OCD427**
Apanhei-te, Cavaquinho—Polka (1915)
M. Verzoni *Concert* (4/90) (SCHW) ℗ **310019**
J. Rifkin *Concert* (4/92) (DECC) ℗ **425 225-2DH**

M. Bratke (r1992) *Concert*
   (8/93) (OLYM) ① **OCD427**
Bambino—Tango (1909)
M. Verzoni *Concert* (4/90) (SCHW) ① **310019**
Batuque—Tango (1906)
M. Bratke (r1992) *Concert*
   (8/93) (OLYM) ① **OCD427**
Brejeiro—Tango (1893)
M. Bratke (r1992) *Concert*
   (8/93) (OLYM) ① **OCD427**
Cubanos—piano
J. Rifkin *Concert* (4/92) (DECC) ① **425 225-2DH**
M. Bratke (r1992) *Concert*
   (8/93) (OLYM) ① **OCD427**
Duvidoso—Tango
M. Verzoni *Concert* (4/90) (SCHW) ① **310019**
Escorregando—Tango brasileiro (1923)
M. Verzoni *Concert* (4/90) (SCHW) ① **310019**
Faceira—waltz—piano
M. Verzoni *Concert* (4/90) (SCHW) ① **310019**
Favorito—tango—piano
M. Verzoni *Concert* (4/90) (SCHW) ① **310019**
Fon-Fon—Tango (1910)
J. Rifkin *Concert* (4/92) (DECC) ① **425 225-2DH**
M. Bratke (r1992) *Concert*
   (8/93) (OLYM) ① **OCD427**
Garoto—piano
M. Verzoni *Concert* (4/90) (SCHW) ① **310019**
Guerreiro—tango
J. Rifkin *Concert* (4/92) (DECC) ① **425 225-2DH**
Labirinto—tango
J. Rifkin *Concert* (4/92) (DECC) ① **425 225-2DH**
Nove de Julho—tango argentino
J. Rifkin *Concert* (4/92) (DECC) ① **425 225-2DH**
Odeon—Tango (1910)
J. Rifkin *Concert* (4/92) (DECC) ① **425 225-2DH**
M. Bratke (r1992) *Concert*
   (8/93) (OLYM) ① **OCD427**
Plangente—tango come estilo de Habanera
J. Rifkin *Concert* (4/92) (DECC) ① **425 225-2DH**
Remando—tango—piano
M. Verzoni *Concert* (4/90) (SCHW) ① **310019**
Sarambeque—Tango (1916)
M. Bratke (r1992) *Concert*
   (8/93) (OLYM) ① **OCD427**
Tenebroso—tango
M. Bratke (r1992) *Concert*
   (8/93) (OLYM) ① **OCD427**
Travesso—tango
M. Bratke (r1992) *Concert*
   (8/93) (OLYM) ① **OCD427**
Vitorioso—tango
J. Rifkin *Concert* (4/92) (DECC) ① **425 225-2DH**

NEAR, Gerald (b 1942) USA

SECTION IV: VOCAL AND CHORAL

And all in the morning—chorus (Wds &
 melody trad English)
St John's Episcopal Cath Ch, D. Pearson *Concert*
   (10/92) (DELO) ① **DE3125**

NEDBAL, Oskar (1874–1930) Bohemia

SECTION I: ORCHESTRAL

Die Glocken des Waldes—Waltz
Czech PO, V. Neumann *Concert*
   (6/87) (ORFE) ① **C107201A**
Im Urwald—Polka
Czech PO, V. Neumann *Concert*
   (6/87) (ORFE) ① **C107201A**
Valse triste
Czech PO, V. Neumann *Concert*
   (6/87) (ORFE) ① **C107201A**
Czech PO, V. Neumann *Concert*
   (9/90) (ORFE) ① **C180891A**
RLPO, L. Pešek (r1990) *Concert*
   (11/94) (VIRG) ① **VC 59285-2**

SECTION V: STAGE WORKS

Polenblut—operetta (1913—Vienna)
Mazurka Czech PO, V. Neumann *Concert*
   (9/90) (ORFE) ① **C180891A**

NEGRI, Cesare de' (c1535–after 1604) Italy

SECTION II: CHAMBER

**Le Gratie d'amore—dance collection (pub
1602)** (same contents as 'Nuove Inventione di
Balli', 1604)
1. La catena d'amore; 2. Bassa gioiosa; 3. La
Nizzarda; 4. Il canario; 5. Ballo del fiore; 6.

Spagnoletta; 7. Vilanicco di spagna; 8. Pavaniglia di
spagna; 9. Spagnoletto da capo.
1-5. Broadside Band, J. Barlow *Concert*
   (3/88) (HYPE) ① **CDA66244**

SECTION III: INSTRUMENTAL

La Barriera—harp/lute
A. Lawrence-King *Concert*
   (9/87) (HYPE) ① **CDA66229**
**Brando per quattro pastore e quattro
ninfe—harp/lute**
A. Lawrence-King *Concert*
   (9/87) (HYPE) ① **CDA66229**

NEGRI, Marc'Antonio (?–?1621) Italy

SECTION IV: VOCAL AND CHORAL

Alte mendozza
Amaryllis Consort *Concert*
   (6/86) (CARL) ① **PCD822**
Leggiadra Marina
Amaryllis Consort *Concert*
   (6/86) (CARL) ① **PCD822**
Torneo amoroso
Amaryllis Consort *Concert*
   (6/86) (CARL) ① **PCD822**

NELSON, Havelock (b 1917) Eire

SECTION IV: VOCAL AND CHORAL

Dirty work, 'John o' the North'—song
Sarah Walker, R. Vignoles *Concert*
   (10/92) (CRD) ① **CRD3473**

NEPOMUNECO, Alberto (1864–1920) Brazil

SECTION III: INSTRUMENTAL

Improviso—piano, Op. 27/2 (1915)
M. I. Guimarães (r1993) *Concert*
   (2/95) (MARC) ① **8 223548**
Nocturne—piano, Op. 33 (1907)
M. I. Guimarães (r1993) *Concert*
   (2/95) (MARC) ① **8 223548**
2 Nocturnes—piano: left-hand (?1919)
1. C; 2. G.
M. I. Guimarães (r1993) *Concert*
   (2/95) (MARC) ① **8 223548**
4 peças lyricas—piano, Op. 13 (1894)
1. Anhelo; 2. Diálogo; 3. Valsa; 4. Galhofeira.
4. M. I. Guimarães (r1993) *Concert*
   (2/95) (MARC) ① **8 223548**
**5 pequenas peças (Five little pieces)—piano
(1906)**
1. Barcarola; 2. Melodia; 3. Dança; 4. Brincando; 5.
Pola.
M. I. Guimarães (r1993) *Concert*
   (2/95) (MARC) ① **8 223548**
Piano Sonata in F minor, Op. 9 (1893)
M. I. Guimarães (r1993) *Concert*
   (2/95) (MARC) ① **8 223548**
Suíte antiga—piano, Op. 11 (1893)
1. Prélude; 2. Menuet; 3. Air; 4. Rigaudon.
M. I. Guimarães (r1993) *Concert*
   (2/95) (MARC) ① **8 223548**

NERUDA, Johann Baptist Georg (c1707–c1780) Czechoslovakia/Germany

SECTION I: ORCHESTRAL

**Concerto for Trumpet and Orchestra in E
flat**
C. Steele-Perkins, ECO, A. Halstead *Concert*
   (6/86) (CARL) ① **PCD821**
**Concerto for Trumpet and Strings in E flat
(c1770)**
O.E. Antonsen, ECO, J. Tate (r1993) *Concert*
   (2/94) (EMI) ① **CDC7 54897-2**
J. Wallace, Philh, C. Warren-Green (r1986) *Concert*
   (2/95) (NIMB) ① **NI7016**

NESBET, John (d ?1488) England

SECTION IV: VOCAL AND CHORAL

Magnificat—5vv (Eton Choirbook)
The Sixteen, H. Christophers (r1993) *Concert*
   (2/94) (COLL) ① **Coll1395-2**
Eton Coll Chapel Ch, R. Allwood (r1991) *Concert*
   (5/95) (FUTU) ① **FCM1004**

NESSLER, Viktor E(rnst) (1841–1890) Alsace

SECTION V: STAGE WORKS

Der Trompeter von Säckingen—opera (1884)
(Lib. R. Bunge, after V. von Scheffel)
Behüt' dich Gott! L. Melchior, Orch (Danish: r1913)
Concert (8/88) (DANA) ① **[2] DACOCD311/2**
Behüt' dich Gott H.E. Groh, orch (r1938) *Concert*
   (3/92) (PEAR) ① **GEMMCD9419**
Behüt' dich Gott R. Tauber, Berlin Schauspielhaus
Orch, E. Hauke (r1928) *Concert*
   (12/92) (NIMB) ① **NI7833**

NEUKOMM, Sigismond von (1788–1858) Austria

SECTION II: CHAMBER

**Serenade in B flat—wind octet with double-
bass (1796)**
Consortium Classicum *Concert*
   (9/90) (SCHW) ① **310002**

SECTION IV: VOCAL AND CHORAL

Poor Adele—song (pub 1825) (Wds.
Cornwall)
D. Fischer-Dieskau, D. Klöcker, H. Höll *Concert*
   (4/88) (ORFE) ① **C153861A**

NEUNER, Carl Borromäus (1778–1830) Germany

SECTION I: ORCHESTRAL

Concerto for Oboe and Orchestra in C
P.W. Feit, Württemberg CO, J. Faerber *Winter: Oboe
Concerto.* (10/89) (SCHW) ① **311027**

NEUSIDLER, Hans (c1508/9–1563) Slovakia

SECTION III: INSTRUMENTAL

Hie' folget ein Welscher Tanz—lute
J. Bream (r1966) *Concert*
   (8/93) (RCA) ① **[28] 09026 61583-2(1)**
J. Bream (r1966) *Concert*
   (6/94) (RCA) ① **09026 61585-2**
Ich klag' den Tag—lute intabulation
J. Bream (r1966) *Concert*
   (8/93) (RCA) ① **[28] 09026 61583-2(1)**
J. Bream (r1966) *Concert*
   (6/94) (RCA) ① **09026 61585-2**
Judentanz
K. Ragossnig *Concert*
   (2/86) (ARCH) ① **415 294-2AH**
J. Bream (r1966) *Concert*
   (8/93) (RCA) ① **[28] 09026 61583-2(1)**
J. Bream (r1966) *Concert*
   (6/94) (RCA) ① **09026 61585-2**
**Mein herz hat sich mit Lieb' verpflicht—lute
intabulation**
J. Bream (r1966) *Concert*
   (8/93) (RCA) ① **[28] 09026 61583-2(1)**
J. Bream (r1966) *Concert*
   (6/94) (RCA) ① **09026 61585-2**
**Welscher Tanz Wascha
mesa/Hupfauff—lute**
K. Ragossnig *Concert*
   (2/86) (ARCH) ① **415 294-2AH**

NEVHAUSER, F. (1861–1936)

SECTION IV: VOCAL AND CHORAL

For good night—song
I. Bohuss, anon (r1902) *Concert*
   (6/93) (PEAR) ① **[3] GEMMCDS9004/6(1)**

NEVIN, Ethelbert (1862–1901) USA

SECTION IV: VOCAL AND CHORAL

I once had a sweet little doll—song
E. Eames, anon (r1908) *Concert*
   (11/93) (ROMO) ① **[2] 81001-2**
Mighty lak' a rose—song (1901) (Wds. F L
Stanton)
F. Kreisler, C. Lamson (r1928: arr Kreisler) *Concert*
   (12/93) (BIDD) ① **LAB080**
E. Mason, orch, F. Black (r1928) *Concert*
   (8/94) (ROMO) ① **81009-2**

The **Rosary**—song (pub 1898) (Wds. R C Rogers)
F. Kreisler, C. Lamson (r1928: arr Kreisler) *Concert*
(12/93) (BIDD) ① **LAB080**
R. Ponselle, orch, J. Pasternack (r1925) *Concert*
(11/94) (ROMO) ① [2] **81006-2**

NEWMAN, Alfred *(1900–1970)* USA

SECTION I: ORCHESTRAL

Selznick International Pictures Fanfare
National PO, C. Gerhardt (1973) *Steiner: Gone with the Wind.*
(6/90) (RCA) ① **GD80452**
Bratislava RSO, Adriano (r1990) *Waxman: Rebecca.*
(10/92) (MARC) ① **8 223399**
National PO, C. Gerhardt *Concert*
(10/92) (RCA) ① **GD82792**
20th Century Fox Fanfare (1935, rev 1954)
('Cinemascope' extension added 1954)
Hollywood Bowl SO, J. Mauceri (1991) *Concert*
(9/91) (PHIL) ① **432 109-2PH**
National PO, C. Gerhardt *Concert*
(10/92) (RCA) ① **GD82792**
OST, LSO, J. T. Williams *Concert*
(11/94) (FOX) ① [4] **07822 11012-2**
OST, L. Hayton (1968; with Cinemascope extension)
Various: Star!. (11/94) (FOX) ① **07822 11009-2**
OST, Alfred Newman (r1951) *Herrmann: Day the Earth Stood Still.* (11/94) (FOX) ① **07822 11010-2**
OST, Alfred Newman (r1953) *Robe.*
(11/94) (FOX) ① **07822 11011-2**
OST, Alfred Newman (r1941) *How Green Was My Valley.* (11/94) (FOX) ① **07822 11008-2**
OST, Alfred Newman (r1943) *Various: Stormy Weather.* (11/94) (FOX) ① **07822 11007-2**
orch, Alfred Newman (r1953) *Concert*
(11/94) (FOX) ① **07822 11006-2**
Prague City PO, P. Bateman *Concert*
(9/95) (SILV) ① **FILMCD159**

SECTION V: STAGE WORKS

Airport—film score (1970)
1. Main Title.
OST (r1970) (8/94) (VARE) ① **VSD5436**
All about Eve—film score (1950)
EXCERPTS: 1. Main Title.
1. National PO, C. Gerhardt *Concert*
(3/90) (RCA) ① **GD80183**
Anastasia—film score (1956)
EXCERPTS: 1. Main Title.
OST (r1956) (8/94) (VARE) ① **VSD5422**
Captain from Castile—film score (1947)
EXCERPTS: 1. Pedro and Cataña; 2. Conquest march.
Suite Orch, Anthony Newman
(2/91) (FACE) ① **FE8103**
How Green Was My Valley—film score (1941)
EXCERPTS: 1. Main Title/Huw's Theme; 2. The Family and Bronwen; 3. The Strike/Mother and Huw in Broken Ice; 4. Treasure Island/The Spring Birds; 5. Angharad and Mister Gruffydd; 6. Command from the Queen; 7. Huw Walks Among the Daffodils; 8. Angharad with the Minister; 9. Love Denied; 10. School; 11. Huw's Lesson/The Mine Tragedy; 12. Two More Brothers Leave; 13. The House on the Hill/Gossip; 14. Goodbyes; 15. Huw Finds His Father; 16. Finale/End Title.
1-16. OST, Alfred Newman (r1941) *20th Century Fox Fanfare.* (11/94) (FOX) ① **07822 11008-2**
How the West Was Won—film score (1962)
(songs arr Newman & Darby unless stated)
EXCERPTS: 1. Overture: 1a. I'm Bound for the Promised Land; 1b. Shenandoah; 1c. Endless Prairie; 1d. The Ox Driver; 2. Main Title—How the West Was Won; 3. Bereavement and Fulfillment; 4. The River Pirates; 5. Home in the Meadow (Music R.E. Dolan; Lyrics S. Cahn); 6. Cleve and the Rocky; 7. Raise a Ruckus (Music R.E. Dolan; Lyrics J. Mercer); 8. Come Share My Life; 9. The Marriage Proposal (Tune: Greensleeves); 10. Entr'acte: 10a. Home in the Meadow; 10b. 900 Miles; 10c. On the Banks of the Sacramento; 10d. When Johnny Comes Marching Home; 10e. I'm Bound for the Promised Land; 10f. Battle Hymn of the Republic; 11. Cheyennes; 12. He's Linus' Boy; 13. Climb a Higher Hill; 14. What Was Your Name in the States? (Music Dolan; Lyrics Mercer); 15. No Goodbye; 16. Finale—How the West Was Won.
2. Prague City PO, P. Bateman (r1994; arr Palmer) *Concert* (11/94) (SILV) ① **FILMCD153**
The **Robe**—film score (1953)
EXCERPTS: 1. Prelude/Main Title; 2. The Slave Market—Diana; 3. Caligula's Arrival (Entrance of

Caligula); 4. Caligula's Departure; 5. Farewell to Diana; 6. The Map of Jerusalem; 7. Palm Sunday; 8. The Carriage of the Cross; 9. The Crucifixion; 10. Marcellus Returns to Capri; 11. Attempted Suicide; 12. Tiberius' Palace; 13. The Market Place; 14. Elegy; 15. Village of Cana; 16. The Song of Resurrection; 17. Miriam; 18. Marcellus' Redemption; 19. Justus' Death (Lament of Justus); 20. Hymn for the Dead; 21. In His Service; 22. The Big Fisherman; 23. The Catacombs; 24. Room in the Catacombs; 25. Hope; 26. Demetrius' Rescue; 27. Gallio's House; 28. Peter Heals Demetrius (The Miracle); 29. Marcellus' Farewell; 30. Interior Dungeon; 31. Finale/Hallelujah (The Better Kingdom).
1-4, 6-8, 10-14, 18-21, 23-31. OST, Alfred Newman (r1953; stereo soundtrack) *20th Century Fox Fanfare.*
(11/94) (FOX) ① **07822 11011-2**
Street Scene—film score (1931)
EXCERPTS: 1. Main Theme (revised & used in several later films).
1. Hollywood Bowl SO, J. Mauceri (1991) *Concert*
(9/91) (PHIL) ① **432 109-2PH**

NEWSOME, Roy *(b 1930)* England

SECTION I: ORCHESTRAL

Concorde—Variations on an original melody—cornet and brass band (1973)
P. McCann, Black Dyke Mills Band, R. Newsome *Concert* (10/91) (CHAN) ① **CHAN6539**

NEWTON, Rodney *(20th cent)* England

SECTION I: ORCHESTRAL

Variations for Percussion and Brass Band
Sellers Engin Band, N. Law (r1993) *Concert*
(11/95) (CHAN) ① **CHAN4531**

NICHOLLS, David *(b 1955)* England

SECTION II: CHAMBER

Winter Landscape with Skaters and Birdtrap—string quartet (1989-90)
Bingham Qt *Concert* (11/92) (NMC) ① **NMCD006**

NICHOLSON, Charles *(1795–1837)* England

SECTION IV: VOCAL AND CHORAL

Home sweet home—theme and variations for flute and piano
S. Preston, L. Carolan *Concert*
(3/87) (AMON) ① **CD-SAR19**

NICHOLSON, Richard *(fl 1595; d 1639)* England

SECTION II: CHAMBER

The **Jew's Dance**—consort
J. Bream, J. Bream Consort (1987; ed Beck) *Concert* (8/93) (RCA) ① [28] **09026 61583-2(3)**
J. Bream Consort (r1987; ed Beck) *Concert*
(11/94) (RCA) ① **09026 61590-2**

SECTION IV: VOCAL AND CHORAL

In a merry May morn—ayre (1v and consort)
D. Cordier, Tragicomedia, S. Stubbs *Concert*
(1/90) (HYPE) ① **CDA66307**
A. Deller, SCB, A. Wenzinger (r1956: arr P Warlock) *Concert* (4/95) (VANG) ① **08.5068.71**

NICOLAI, Johann Michael *(1629–1685)* Germany

SECTION II: CHAMBER

Sonata for Three Viola da gambas in A minor
Ricercar Consort, P. Pierlot (va da gamba/dir) (r1992) *Concert* (8/94) (RICE) ① **RIC098112**

NICOLAI, (Carl) Otto (Ehrenfried) *(1810–1849)* Germany

SECTION IV: VOCAL AND CHORAL

Das Blümchen—Lied
E. Van Dyck, anon (r1905: Dutch) *Concert*
(12/94) (SYMP) ① **SYMCD1172**

SECTION V: STAGE WORKS

Die Lustigen Weiber von Windsor, '(The) Merry Wives of Windsor'—opera: 3 acts (1849—Berlin) (Lib. Mosenthal, after Shakespeare)
EXCERPTS: 1. Overture. ACT 1: 2. Nein, das ist wirklich doch zu keck!; 3. So geht indes hinein - Eure Tochter!; 4. Nun eilt herbei; 5a. So hab' ich dich errungen; 5b. Herein! Kommt all herein!. ACT 2: 6. Als Büblein klein; 7a. Gott grüss Euch, Sir!; 7b. In einem Waschkorb?; 8a. Dies ist die Stunde; 8b. Horch, die Lerche singt im Hain!; 8c. Fenton! - Mein Mädchen; 8d. Bestürmen denn die läst'gen Freier; 9. Sol Jetzt hätt' ich ihn gefangen!; 10. Wer klopft? - Mach auf, Herr Fluth!. ACT 3: 11. Vom Jäger Herne die Mär ist alt; 12. Wohl dehn, gefasst ist der Entschluss!; 13. O süsser Mond!; 14. Die Glocke schlug schon Mitternacht; 15a. Ihr Elfen, weiss und rot und grau; 15b. Die Menschheit schläft; 16. Mücken, Wespen, Fliegenchor; 17a. Er gesteht noch immer nicht!; 17b. Fasst ihn, Geister, nach der Reih'; 18. So hat denn der Schwank der fröhlichen Nacht.
Cpte R-M. Pütz, G. Litz, E. Mathis, G. Frick, E. Gutstein, K. Engen, F. Wunderlich, F. Lenz, C. Hoppe, Bavarian St Op Chor, Bavarian St Orch, R. Heger (r1963) (7/89) (EMI) ① [2] **CMS7 69348-2**
Excs L. Hofmann, A. Jerger, K. Bollhammer, E. Majkut, Vienna St Op Chor, Vienna St Op Orch, F. Weingartner (pp1935) *Concert*
(3/95) (SCHW) ① [2] **314602**
1. VPO, C. Kleiber (pp1992) *Concert*
(4/92) (SONY) ① **SK48376**
1. LPO, T. Beecham (r1936) *Concert*
(7/93) (DUTT) ① **CDLX7001**
1. Black Dyke Mills Band, D. Hurst (arr brass band: G Langford) *Concert* (9/93) (CHAN) ① **CHAN4514**
1. NYPO, L. Bernstein (r1967) *Concert*
(9/93) (SONY) ① **SMK47601**
1. LSO, C. Mackerras (r1961) *Concert*
(12/95) (MERC) ① **434 352-2MM**
2. E. Berger, C. Müller, Berlin City Op Orch, W.F. Reuss (r1933) *Concert* (12/91) (PREI) ① **89035**
4. M. Cebotari, VPO, F. Prohaska (r1949) *Concert*
(12/90) (PREI) ① **90034**
4. Lotte Lehmann, orch (r1919) *Concert*
(6/92) (PREI) ① [3] **89302**
4. M. Ivogün, orch (r1917) *Concert*
(8/92) (NIMB) ① **NI7832**
4. L. Schöne, Berlin St Op Orch, E. Orthmann (r c1930) *Concert* (1/94) (CLUB) ① **CL99-020**
6. A. Kipnis, Berlin St Op Orch, E. Orthmann (r1931) *Concert* (12/90) (PREI) ① **89019**
7b G. Hüsch, E. Fuchs, Berlin City Op Orch, A. von Zemlinsky (r1932) *Concert* (3/94) (PREI) ① **89071**
8b J. Patzak, orch (r1936) *Concert*
(3/90) (PEAR) ① **GEMMCD9383**
8b H.E. Groh, orch (r1933) *Concert*
(3/92) (PEAR) ① **GEMMCD9419**
8b P. Anders, Berlin St Op Orch, J. Schüler (bp1942) *Concert* (8/93) (ACAN) ① **43 268**
8b W. Ludwig, Berlin St Op Orch, B. Seidler-Winkler (r1936) *Concert* (7/95) (PREI) ① **89088**

NICOLAI, Philipp *(1556–1608)* Germany

SECTION IV: VOCAL AND CHORAL

Wachet auf, ruft uns die Stimme—chorale
Trinity Coll Ch, Cambridge, R. Marlow (Eng) *Concert*
(12/90) (CONI) ① **CDCF501**

NIEDERMEYER, (Abraham) Louis *(1802–1861)* Switzerland

SECTION IV: VOCAL AND CHORAL

Le lac—song (Wds. Lamartine)
P. Plançon, anon (r1904) *Concert*
(12/94) (ROMO) ① [2] **82001-2**
Pietà, Signore—Sacred Aria (attrib Stradella and also Rossini)
J. Björling, Bergen SO, C. Garaguly (pp1954) *Concert* (8/88) (BLUE) ① **ABCD006**
E. Caruso, orch, J. Pasternack (r1918) *Concert*
(12/90) (NIMB) ① **NI7809**

B. Hendricks, Stockholm CO, E. Ericson *Concert*
(4/91) (EMI) ① **CDC7 54098-2**
E. Caruso, orch, J. Pastemack (r1918) *Concert*
(7/91) (RCA) ① [12] **GD60495(6)**
E. Caruso, orch, J. Pastemack (r1918) *Concert*
(10/91) (PEAR) ① [3] **EVC4(1)**
L. Pavarotti, National PO, K.H. Adler (arr Gamley)
Concert (12/91) (DECC) ① **433 710-2DH**
J. Carreras, ECO, V. Sutej (r1992; arr Agostinelli)
Concert (6/93) (PHIL) ① **434 926-2PH**
T. Pasero, orch, A. Sabino (r1943) *Concert*
(4/95) (PREI) ① **89074**

NIELSEN, Carl (August) (1865–1931) Denmark

FS—Numbers used in D. Fog and D. Schousboe,
Carl Nielsen (1965)

SECTION I: ORCHESTRAL

Bøhmisk-dansk folketone—paraphrase: strings, FS130 (1928)
Danish Nat RSO, G. Rozhdestvensky *Concert*
(9/94) (CHAN) ① **CHAN9287**
Odense SO, E. Serov (r1993) *Concert*
(9/95) (KONT) ① **32171**
Concerto for Clarinet and Orchestra, FS129 (Op. 57) (1928)
O. Schill, Gothenburg SO, Myung-Whun Chung
Concert (8/86) (BIS) ① **BIS-CD321**
J. Hilton, SNO, M. Bamert *Concert*
(10/88) (CHAN) ① **CHAN8618**
N. Thomsen, Danish Nat RSO, M. Schønwandt
Concert (9/94) (CHAN) ① **CHAN8894**
L. Cahuzac, Copenhagen Op Orch, J. Frandsen
(r1947) *Concert* (3/93) (CLRI) ① **CC0002**
O. Schill, Gothenburg SO, Myung-Whun Chung
(r1985) *Concert* (7/93) (BIS) ① **BIS-CD616**
O. Schill, Gothenburg SO, Myung-Whun Chung
(r1985) *Concert* (7/93) (BIS) ① [4] **BIS-CD614/6**
S. Drucker, NYPO, L. Bernstein (r1966) *Concert*
(7/93) (SONY) ① **SMK47599**
H. Rosengren, Swedish RSO, E-P. Salonen (r1992)
Concert (4/94) (SONY) ① **SK53276**
W. Boeykens, Beethoven Academy, J. Caeyers
(r1993) *Concert* (6/94) (HARM) ① **HMC90 1489**
Concerto for Flute and Orchestra, FS119 (1926)
P. Gallois, Gothenburg SO, Myung-Whun Chung
Concert (8/90) (BIS) ① **BIS-CD454**
T. Lund Christiansen, Danish Nat RSO, M.
Schønwandt *Concert* (4/91) (CHAN) ① **CHAN8894**
J. Stinton, Scottish CO, S. Bedford *Concert*
(8/91) (COLL) ① **Coll1210-2**
P. Gallois, Gothenburg SO, Myung-Whun Chung
(r1989) *Concert* (7/93) (BIS) ① **BIS-CD616**
P. Gallois, Gothenburg SO, Myung-Whun Chung
(r1989) *Concert* (7/93) (BIS) ① [4] **BIS-CD614/6**
J. Baker, NYPO, L. Bernstein (r1967) *Concert*
(7/93) (SONY) ① **SMK47599**
P. Alanko, Finnish RSO, J-P. Saraste (r1992)
Concert (11/93) (ONDI) ① **ODE802-2**
P. Flemström, Swedish RSO, E-P. Salonen (r1991)
Concert (4/94) (SONY) ① **SK53276**
M. Faust, Cologne RSO, A. Francis (r1991) *Concert*
(12/94) (CAPR) ① **10 495**
Concerto for Violin and Orchestra, FS61 (Op. 33) (1911)
D-S. Kang, Gothenburg SO, Myung-Whun Chung
Symphony 5. (12/87) (BIS) ① **BIS-CD370**
C-L. Lin, Swedish RSO, E-P. Salonen *Sibelius: Violin
Concerto.* (9/89) (SONY) ① **SK44548**
K. Sjøgren, Danish Nat RSO, M. Schønwandt
Concert (4/91) (CHAN) ① **CHAN8894**
Y. Menuhin, Danish St RSO, M. Wöldike (r1952)
Sibelius: Violin Concerto.
(4/91) (EMI) ① **CDM7 63987-2**
D-S. Kang, Gothenburg SO, Myung-Whun Chung
(1987) *Concert* (7/93) (BIS) ① **BIS-CD616**
D-S. Kang, Gothenburg SO, Myung-Whun Chung
(1987) *Concert* (7/93) (BIS) ① [4] **BIS-CD614/6**
A. Telleftsen, RPO, Y. Menuhin (r1988/9) *Symphony
4.* (11/94) (VIRG) ① **CUV5 61136-2**
Helios—overture, FS32 (Op. 17) (1903)
SNO, A. Gibson *Concert*
(10/91) (CHAN) ① **CHAN6533**
Danish Nat RSO, G. Rozhdestvensky *Concert*
(9/94) (CHAN) ① **CHAN9287**
Danish St RSO, E. Tuxen (r1952) *Concert*
(7/95) (DUTT) ① **CDLXT2502**
Little Suite in A minor—string orchestra, FS6 (Op. 1) (1888 rev 1889)
Scottish Baroque Ens, Lionel Friedman *Concert*
(10/87) (CRD) ① **CRD3342**
Musica Vitae CO, W. Rajski *Concert*
(6/90) (BIS) ① **BIS-CD461**

London Little Orch, L. Jones *Concert*
(9/92) (UNIC) ① **UKCD2047**
Beethoven Academy, J. Caeyers (r1993) *Concert*
(6/94) (HARM) ① **HMC90 1489**
Pan and Syrinx, FS87 (Op. 49) (1917-18)
CBSO, S. Rattle (r1984) *Concert*
(11/90) (EMI) ① **CDM7 64737-2**
Beethoven Academy, J. Caeyers (r1993) *Concert*
(6/94) (HARM) ① **HMC90 1489**
Danish Nat RSO, G. Rozhdestvensky *Concert*
(9/94) (CHAN) ① **CHAN9287**
Paraphrase on 'Nearer my God to Thee'—wind ensemble, FS63 (1912)
Danish Nat RSO, G. Rozhdestvensky *Concert*
(9/94) (CHAN) ① **CHAN9287**
Rhapsody Overture: an imaginary trip to the Faroe Islands, FS123 (1927)
Gothenburg SO, Myung-Whun Chung *Concert*
(8/90) (BIS) ① **BIS-CD454**
Swedish RSO, E-P. Salonen (r1992) *Concert*
(4/94) (SONY) ① **SK53276**
Danish Nat RSO, G. Rozhdestvensky *Concert*
(9/94) (CHAN) ① **CHAN9287**
**Saga-Drøm—tone poem, FS46 (Op. 39) (1908)
(Eng: The Dream of Gunnar)**
New Philh, J. Horenstein *Symphony 5.*
(10/89) (UNIC) ① **UKCD2023**
Danish Nat RSO, G. Rozhdestvensky *Concert*
(9/94) (CHAN) ① **CHAN9287**
**Symphonic Rhapsody in F, FS7 (1888)
(unpub)**
Danish Nat RSO, G. Rozhdestvensky *Concert*
(9/94) (CHAN) ① **CHAN9287**
Odense SO, E. Serov (r1993) *Concert*
(9/95) (KONT) ① **32171**
Symphony No. 1 in G minor, FS16 (Op. 7) (1890-92)
San Francisco SO, H. Blomstedt *Symphony 6.*
(2/90) (DECC) ① **425 607-2DH**
Gothenburg SO, Myung-Whun Chung *Concert*
(8/90) (BIS) ① **BIS-CD454**
SNO, B. Thomson *Symphony 2.*
(6/92) (CHAN) ① **CHAN8880**
Gothenburg SO, Myung-Whun Chung (r1989)
Concert (7/93) (BIS) ① [4] **BIS-CD614/6**
Gothenburg SO, N. Järvi (r1992) *Concert*
(12/93) (DG) ① [3] **437 507-2GH3**
Stockholm PO, G. Rozhdestvensky (r1992)
Symphony 4. (5/94) (CHAN) ① **CHAN9260**
Danish RSO, E. Tuxen (bp1957) *Concert*
(4/95) (DANA) ① [3] **DACOCD351/3**
Danish St RSO, T. Jensen (r1952) *Concert*
(7/95) (DUTT) ① **CDLXT2502**
Royal Danish Orch, P. Berglund (r1987) *Concert*
(8/95) (RCA) ① [3] **74321 20290-2**
Ireland National SO, A. Leaper (r1994) *Symphony 6.*
(12/95) (NAXO) ① **8 550826**
Symphony No. 2, '(The) Four Temperaments', FS29 (Op. 16) (1901-02)
Gothenburg SO, Myung-Whun Chung *Aladdin Suite.*
(5/84) (BIS) ① **BIS-CD247**
San Francisco SO, H. Blomstedt *Symphony 3.*
(8/90) (DECC) ① **430 280-2DH**
SNO, B. Thomson *Symphony 1.*
(6/92) (CHAN) ① **CHAN8880**
NYPO, L. Bernstein (r1973) *Symphony 4.*
(7/93) (SONY) ① **SMK47597**
Gothenburg SO, Myung-Whun Chung (r1983)
Concert (7/93) (BIS) ① [4] **BIS-CD614/6**
Gothenburg SO, N. Järvi (r1991) *Concert*
(12/93) (DG) ① [3] **437 507-2GH3**
Odense SO, E. Serov (r1993) *Concert*
(11/94) (KONT) ① **32178**
Stockholm PO, G. Rozhdestvensky (r1993)
Symphony 3. (12/94) (CHAN) ① **CHAN9300**
Danish RSO, L. Grøndahl (bp1956) *Concert*
(4/95) (DANA) ① [3] **DACOCD351/3**
Royal Danish Orch, P. Berglund (r1988) *Concert*
(8/95) (RCA) ① [3] **74321 20290-2**
Ireland National SO, A. Leaper (r1994) *Symphony 3.*
(11/95) (NAXO) ① **8 550825**
Symphony No. 3, 'Sinfonia espansiva', FS60 (Op. 27) (1910-11)
P. Raanoja, K. Skram, Gothenburg SO, Myung-Whun
Chung *Concert* (8/86) (BIS) ① **BIS-CD321**
N.W. Kromm, M. McMillan, San Francisco SO, H.
Blomstedt *Symphony 2.*
(8/90) (DECC) ① **430 280-2DH**
Royal Danish Orch, P. Berglund *Symphony 6.*
(4/92) (RCA) ① **RD60427**
C. Bott, S. Roberts, SNO, B. Thomson *Symphony 5.*
(2/93) (CHAN) ① **CHAN9067**
P. Raanoja, K. Skram, Gothenburg SO, Myung-Whun
Chung (r1985) *Concert*
(7/93) (BIS) ① [4] **BIS-CD614/6**

R. Guldbaek, N. Møller, Royal Danish Orch, L.
Bernstein (r1965) *Symphony 5.*
(7/93) (SONY) ① **SMK47598**
S. Isokoski, J. Hynninen, Gothenburg SO, N. Järvi
(r1991) *Concert*
(12/93) (DG) ① [3] **437 507-2GH3**
S. Kringelborn, K-M. Fredriksson, Stockholm PO, G.
Rozhdestvensky (r1993) *Symphony 2.*
(12/94) (CHAN) ① **CHAN9300**
Danish RSO, T. Jensen (bp1959) *Concert*
(4/95) (DANA) ① [3] **DACOCD351/3**
Royal Danish Orch, P. Berglund (r1989) *Concert*
(8/95) (RCA) ① [3] **74321 20290-2**
Odense SO, E. Serov *Concert*
(11/95) (KONT) ① **32203**
Ireland National SO, A. Leaper (r1994) *Symphony 2.*
(11/95) (NAXO) ① **8 550825**
K. Schultz, P. Rasmussen, Danish RSO, H.
Blomstedt (r1973) *Concert*
(12/95) (EMI) ① **CDM5 65415-2**
Symphony No. 4, '(The) inextinguishable', FS76 (Op. 29) (1914-16)
San Francisco SO, H. Blomstedt *Symphony 5.*
(10/88) (DECC) ① **421 524-2DH**
BBC SO, A. Davis *Concert*
(4/91) (VIRG) ① **VC7 59618-2**
SNO, B. Thomson *Symphony 6.*
(3/93) (CHAN) ① **CHAN9047**
Gothenburg SO, N. Järvi (r1990) *Symphony 6.*
(7/93) (BIS) ① **BIS-CD600**
NYPO, L. Bernstein (r1970) *Symphony 2.*
(7/93) (SONY) ① **SMK47597**
Gothenburg SO, N. Järvi (r1990) *Concert*
(7/93) (BIS) ① [4] **BIS-CD614/6**
CBSO, S. Rattle (r1984) *Concert*
(11/93) (EMI) ① **CDM7 64737-2**
Gothenburg SO, N. Järvi (r1990) *Concert*
(12/93) (DG) ① [3] **437 507-2GH3**
Stockholm PO, G. Rozhdestvensky (r1993)
Symphony 1. (5/94) (CHAN) ① **CHAN9260**
Ireland National SO, A. Leaper (r1992) *Symphony 5.*
(10/94) (NAXO) ① **8 550743**
RPO, Y. Menuhin (r1988/9) *Violin Concerto.*
(11/94) (VIRG) ① **CUV5 61136-2**
BPO, H. von Karajan (r1981) *Sibelius: Tapiola.*
(1/95) (DG) ① **445 518-2GMA**
Danish RSO, T. Jensen (bp1952) *Concert*
(4/95) (DANA) ① [3] **DACOCD351/3**
Royal Danish Orch, P. Berglund (r1987) *Concert*
(8/95) (RCA) ① [3] **74321 20290-2**
Danish RSO, H. Blomstedt (r1974) *Concert*
(12/95) (EMI) ① **CDM5 65415-2**
Symphony No. 5, FS97 (Op. 50) (1921-22)
Gothenburg SO, Myung-Whun Chung *Violin
Concerto.* (12/87) (BIS) ① **BIS-CD370**
San Francisco SO, H. Blomstedt *Symphony 4.*
(10/88) (DECC) ① **421 524-2DH**
New Philh, J. Horenstein *Saga-Drøm.*
(10/89) (UNIC) ① **UKCD2023**
BBC SO, A. Davis *Concert*
(4/91) (VIRG) ① **VC7 59618-2**
SNO, A. Gibson *Concert*
(10/91) (CHAN) ① **CHAN6533**
SNO, B. Thomson *Symphony 3.*
(2/93) (CHAN) ① **CHAN9067**
Gothenburg SO, Myung-Whun Chung (r1987)
Concert (7/93) (BIS) ① [4] **BIS-CD614/6**
NYPO, L. Bernstein (r1962) *Symphony 3.*
(7/93) (SONY) ① **SMK47598**
Gothenburg SO, N. Järvi (r1991) *Concert*
(12/93) (DG) ① [3] **437 507-2GH3**
Danish RSO, R. Kubelík (pp1983) *Concert*
(10/94) (EMI) ① **CDM5 65182-2**
Ireland National SO, A. Leaper (r1992) *Symphony 4.*
(10/94) (NAXO) ① **8 550743**
Danish RSO, E. Tuxen (pp1955) *Concert*
(4/95) (DANA) ① [3] **DACOCD351/3**
Danish St RSO, T. Jensen (r1954) *Concert*
(7/95) (DUTT) ① **CDLXT2502**
Royal Danish Orch, P. Berglund (r1988) *Concert*
(8/95) (RCA) ① [3] **74321 20290-2**
Odense SO, E. Serov (r1993) *Concert*
(9/95) (KONT) ① **32171**
Stockholm PO, G. Rozhdestvensky (r1994)
Symphony 6. (9/95) (CHAN) ① **CHAN9367**
Symphony No. 6, 'Sinfonia semplice', FS116 (1924-25)
San Francisco SO, H. Blomstedt *Symphony 1.*
(2/90) (DECC) ① **425 607-2DH**
Royal Danish Orch, P. Berglund *Symphony 3.*
(4/92) (RCA) ① **RD60427**
SNO, B. Thomson *Symphony 4.*
(3/93) (CHAN) ① **CHAN9047**
Gothenburg SO, N. Järvi (r1992) *Symphony 4.*
(7/93) (BIS) ① **BIS-CD600**

Gothenburg SO, N. Järvi (r1992) *Concert*
(7/93) (BIS) ① [4] **BIS-CD614/6**
Gothenburg SO, N. Järvi (r1992) *Concert*
(12/93) (DG) ① [3] **437 507-2GH3**
Danish RSO, T. Jensen (r1952) *Concert*
(4/95) (DANA) ① [3] **DACOCD351/3**
Royal Danish Orch, P. Berglund (1989) *Concert*
(8/95) (RCA) ① [3] **74321 20290-2**
Stockholm PO, G. Rozhdestvensky (r1994)
Symphony 5. (9/95) (CHAN) ① **CHAN9367**
Ireland National SO, A. Leaper (r1994) *Symphony 1.*
(12/95) (NAXO) ① **8 550826**

SECTION II: CHAMBER

Allegretto in F—two recorders, FS157 (1931)
G. Sandvik, P. Hannevold *Concert*
(9/89) (BIS) ① **BIS-CD428**
At the bier of a young artist (Ved en ung kunstners baare)—string quartet and double-bass, FS58 (1910)
Kontra Qt, J. Johansson *Concert*
(4/92) (BIS) ① [2] **BIS-CD503/4**
Danish RSO, H. Blomstedt (r1975) *Concert*
(12/95) (EMI) ① **CDM5 65415-2**
Canto serioso—horn and piano, FS132 (1913)
Athena Ens *Concert* (2/89) (CHAN) ① **CHAN8680**
V. Olsen, L.O. Andsnes *Concert*
(9/89) (BIS) ① **BIS-CD428**
Faith and Hope are playing—flute and viola (1921 rev 1959) (from The Mother, Op. 41)
Athena Ens *Concert* (2/89) (CHAN) ① **CHAN8680**
G. Sandvik, L.A. Tomter *Concert*
(9/89) (BIS) ① **BIS-CD428**
Fantasy Piece in G minor—clarinet and piano, FS3h (c1885)
L.K. Holm Brynildsen, L.O. Andsnes *Concert*
(9/89) (BIS) ① **BIS-CD428**
2 Fantasy Pieces—oboe and piano, FS8 (Op. 2) (1889)
1. Romanze; 2. Humoresque.
Athena Ens *Concert* (2/89) (CHAN) ① **CHAN8680**
S. Hannevold, L.O. Andsnes *Concert*
(9/89) (BIS) ① **BIS-CD428**
Movements for String Quartet, FS3c (1883-87) (unpub)
1. Andante in B flat; 2. Minuet in D minor; 3. Allegro in F; 4. Scherzo in D minor; 5. Andante in F sharp minor.
Danish Qt (r1992) *Concert*
(10/93) (KONT) ① [2] **32150/1**
1, 4. Odense SO, E. Serov *Concert*
(11/95) (KONT) ① **32203**
Seranata in vano—clarinet, bassoon, horn, cello and double-bass, FS68 (1914)
Athena Ens *Concert* (2/89) (CHAN) ① **CHAN8680**
V. Olsen, P. Hannevold *Concert*
(9/89) (BIS) ① **BIS-CD428**
A. Oxenvad, H. Sørensen, K. Larsson, L. Jensen, L. Hegner (r1937) *Concert* (3/93) (CLRI) ① **CC0002**
Lahti Chbr Ens *Concert*
(8/93) (ONDI) ① **ODE792-2**
Sonata for Violin and Piano in A, FS20 (Op. 9) (1895)
L. Mordkovitch, C. Benson *Violin Sonata 2.*
(9/89) (CHAN) ① **CHAN8598**
S. Elbaek, M. Mogensen (r1994) *Concert*
(7/95) (KONT) ① **32200**
Sonata for Violin and Piano No. 2, FS64 (Op. 35) (1912)
L. Mordkovitch, C. Benson *Violin Sonata, Op.9.*
(9/89) (CHAN) ① **CHAN8598**
S. Elbaek, M. Mogensen (r1994) *Concert*
(7/95) (KONT) ① **32200**
C. Tetzlaff, L. O. Andsnes (r1994) *Concert*
(11/95) (VIRG) ① **VC5 45122-2**
String Quartet No. 1 in G minor, FS4 (Op. 13) (1887-88 rev 1897-98)
Kontra Qt *Concert*
(4/92) (BIS) ① [2] **BIS-CD503/4**
Danish Qt (r1992) *Concert*
(10/93) (KONT) ① [2] **32150/1**
String Quartet No. 2 in F minor, FS11 (Op. 5) (1890)
Kontra Qt *Concert*
(4/92) (BIS) ① [2] **BIS-CD503/4**
Danish Qt (r1992) *Concert*
(10/93) (KONT) ① [2] **32150/1**
String Quartet No. 3 in E flat, FS23 (Op. 14) (1897-98)
Kontra Qt *Concert*
(4/92) (BIS) ① [2] **BIS-CD503/4**
Danish Qt (r1992) *Concert*
(10/93) (KONT) ① [2] **32150/1**

String Quartet No. 4 in F, FS36 (Op. 44) (1919) (revision of Piacevolezza, Op. 19 of 1906)
Kontra Qt *Concert*
(4/92) (BIS) ① [2] **BIS-CD503/4**
Danish Qt (r1992) *Concert*
(10/93) (KONT) ① [2] **32150/1**
String Quintet in G, FS5 (1888)
Kontra Qt, P. Naegele *Concert*
(4/92) (BIS) ① [2] **BIS-CD503/4**
ASMF Chbr Ens (r1993) *Concert*
(5/94) (CHAN) ① **CHAN9258**
Wind Quintet, FS100 (Op. 43) (1922)
Athena Ens *Concert* (2/89) (CHAN) ① **CHAN8680**
Bergen Wind Qnt *Concert*
(9/89) (BIS) ① **BIS-CD428**
H.G. Jespersen, S.C. Felumb, A. Oxenvad, H. Sørensen, K. Larsson (r1936) *Concert*
(3/93) (CLRI) ① **CC0002**
Chbr Music NW (r1992) *Concert*
(12/93) (DELO) ① **DE3136**
Oslo Wind Qnt (r1993) *Concert*
(3/95) (NAXO) ① **8 553050**

SECTION III: INSTRUMENTAL

Chaconne—piano, FS79 (Op. 32) (1916)
E. Westenholz *Concert*
(5/90) (BIS) ① [2] **BIS-CD167/8**
E. Katahn *Concert* (10/90) (KING) ① **KCLCD2019**
The Children are playing—flute (1921 rev 1959) (from The Mother, Op. 41)
Athena Ens *Concert* (2/89) (CHAN) ① **CHAN8680**
G. Sandvik *Concert* (9/89) (BIS) ① **BIS-CD428**
Commotio—organ, FS155 (Op. 58) (1931)
E. Westenholz *Concert* (9/90) (BIS) ① **BIS-CD131**
U. Spang-Hanssen *Concert*
(9/90) (PAUL) ① **PACD55**
C. Herrick (r1993) *Concert*
(8/94) (HYPE) ① **CDA66676**
Dream of 'Silent Night' (Drømmen om 'Glade Jul')—piano, FS34 (1905)
E. Westenholz *Concert*
(5/90) (BIS) ① [2] **BIS-CD167/8**
Festival Prelude, 'Ved Aarhundredskiftet'—piano, FS24 (1900)
E. Westenholz *Concert*
(5/90) (BIS) ① [2] **BIS-CD167/8**
Humoresque Bagatelles—piano, FS22 (Op. 11) (1894-97)
E. Westenholz *Concert*
(5/90) (BIS) ① [2] **BIS-CD167/8**
E. Katahn *Concert* (10/90) (KING) ① **KCLCD2019**
29 Little Preludes—organ, FS136 (Op. 51) (1929)
E. Westenholz *Concert* (9/90) (BIS) ① **BIS-CD131**
U. Spang-Hanssen *Concert*
(9/90) (PAUL) ① **PACD55**
Piano Music for Young and Old (Klavermusik for smaa og store), FS148 (Op. 53) (1930)
1. Vol 1; 2. Vol 2.
E. Westenholz *Concert*
(5/90) (BIS) ① [2] **BIS-CD167/8**
Piece in C—piano, FS159 (1931)
E. Westenholz *Concert*
(5/90) (BIS) ① [2] **BIS-CD167/8**
5 Pieces—piano, FS10 (Op. 3) (1890)
E. Westenholz *Concert*
(5/90) (BIS) ① [2] **BIS-CD167/8**
E. Katahn *Concert* (10/90) (KING) ① **KCLCD2019**
3 Pieces—piano, FS131 (Op. 59) (1928)
E. Westenholz *Concert*
(5/90) (BIS) ① [2] **BIS-CD167/8**
E. Katahn *Concert* (10/90) (KING) ① **KCLCD2019**
Prelude and Theme with Variations—violin, FS104 (Op. 48) (1923)
S. Elbaek (r1994) *Concert* (7/95) (KONT) ① **32200**
2 Preludes—organ, FS137 (1930)
E. Westenholz *Concert* (9/90) (BIS) ① **BIS-CD131**
U. Spang-Hanssen *Concert*
(9/90) (PAUL) ① **PACD55**
Preludio e Presto—violin, FS128 (Op. 52) (1927-8)
S. Elbaek (r1994) *Concert* (7/95) (KONT) ① **32200**
Suite—piano, FS91 (Op. 45) (1919-20) (originally titled 'Den Luciferiske')
E. Westenholz *Concert*
(5/90) (BIS) ① [2] **BIS-CD167/8**
E. Katahn *Concert* (10/90) (KING) ① **KCLCD2019**
Symphonic Suite—piano, FS19 (Op. 8) (1894)
E. Westenholz *Concert*
(5/90) (BIS) ① [2] **BIS-CD167/8**
Theme with Variations—piano, FS81 (Op. 40) (1917)
E. Westenholz *Concert*
(5/90) (BIS) ① [2] **BIS-CD167/8**

E. Katahn *Concert* (10/90) (KING) ① **KCLCD2019**

SECTION IV: VOCAL AND CHORAL

Ariel's Song, FS80 (1916) (Wds. H. Rode)
P. Severin, D. Kirkeskov *Concert*
(1/91) (ROND) ① **RCD8319**
The Ballad of the Bear, 'Balladen om Bjørnen', FS109 (Op. 47) (1923) (Wds. A. Bernsten after C.J.L. Almquist)
J. Klint, R. Bevan *Concert*
(12/90) (PAUL) ① **PACD56**
P. Severin, D. Kirkeskov *Concert*
(1/91) (ROND) ① **RCD8319**
Cantata for the Centenary of the Merchant's Committee, FS86 (1917) (Wds. V. Rødam)
L.T. Bertelsen, T. Lønskov *Concert*
(1/91) (ROND) ① **RCD8325**
2. J. Klint, R. Bevan *Concert*
(12/90) (PAUL) ① **PACD56**
Come Yule to Earth, 'Kom, Jul til Jord'—Christmas Carol, FS107 (1923) (Wds. J. Wiberg)
E. Rehling, D. Kirkeskov (r1988) *Concert*
(1/91) (ROND) ① **RCD8323**
Danish Songs Volumes 1 and 2, FS70 and FS78 (1914-17)
1. Farewell, my Blessed Town of my Birth/Farvel min velsignede Fødeby; 2. The Refnaes Lads, the Samsø Lasses/De Refnaesdrenge, de Samsøpiger; 3. She knows me not/Hun mig har glemt; 4. My little bird/Min lille Fugl; 5. Look around, one Summer Day/Se dig ud en Sommerdag; 6. The Groves are shining green now/Ny lyser Løv i Lunde; 7. Morning dew which gently trembles/Morgendyg der sagte baever; 8. In cooling shadows/I kølende Skygger; 9. My native soil/Hjemstavn; 10. I bear my yoke with a smile/Jeg baerer min Byrde med Smil; 11. Now the day is full of song/Nu er dagen fuld af Sang; 12. How sweetly on this Summer Evening/Hvor sødt i Sommeraftenstunden; 13. Often I'm happy/Tidt er jeg glad; 14. Spring has come now/Nu er da Vaaren kommen; 15. Strangest breeze of twilight hours/Underlige Aftenlufte; 16. The Swallow/Svalen; 17. Sleep sweetly, little Baby mine/En moder med sit Barn paa en Baenk; 18. In shadow we wander/I Skyggen vi vanke; 19. Now leaps the Spring from its bed/Nu springer Våren fra sin Seng; 20. The Snow Queen/Snedronningen; 21. There lived a man in Ribe Town/Der boede en Mand i Ribe By; 22. Bjarke's Lay/Bjarkemaal; 23. You are setting out on Life's journey/Ud gaar du nu paa Livets Vej; 24. If luck should abandon you/Vender sig Lykken fra dig; 25. I praise our world a thousandfold/Vor Verden priser jeg; 26. The rose now blooms in Dana's garden/Rosen blusser alt i Danas Have; 27. Out of the mist emerges my native soil/Der dukker af Disen.
1, 2, 5, 10-12, 14, 15, 18, 23, 24, 27. K. Westi, H. Metz *Concert* (7/91) (KONT) ① **32047**
1-9. P. Severin, D. Kirkeskov *Concert*
(1/91) (ROND) ① **RCD8319**
4-6, 10. J. Klint, R. Bevan *Concert*
(12/90) (PAUL) ① **PACD56**
10-21. P. Severin, E. Rehling, D. Kirkeskov (1988) *Concert* (1/91) (ROND) ① **RCD8323**
22-27. L.T. Bertelsen, T. Lønskov *Concert*
(1/91) (ROND) ① **RCD8325**
Danish Weather, 'Dansk Vejr'—song, FS122 (1927) (Wds. O. Rode)
P. Severin, D. Kirkeskov *Concert*
(1/91) (ROND) ① **RCD8319**
Dawn, 'Gry'—song, FS93 (Wds. H. Lorenzen)
1-3. E.H. Thaysen, T. Lønskov *Concert*
(1/91) (ROND) ① **RCD8329**
Denmark, Now Sleeps the Light Night, 'Danmark nu blunder den lyse Nat'—song, FS146 (1929) (Wds. T. Larsen)
P. Severin, D. Kirkeskov *Concert*
(1/91) (ROND) ① **RCD8319**
Denmark Songbook, FS111 (c1928) (Wds Various)
1. I was a lad keeping watch o'er the sheep/Jeg gik i Marken, og vogtede Faar.
1. L.T. Bertelsen, T. Lønskov *Concert*
(1/91) (ROND) ① **RCD8325**
The Flower Song, 'Blomstervise', FS84 (1917) (Wds. L. Holstein)
E. Rehling, D. Kirkeskov (r1988) *Concert*
(1/91) (ROND) ① **RCD8323**
The Golden River, 'Guldfloden'—song, FS127 (1927) (Wds. B.S. Ingemann)
P. Severin, D. Kirkeskov *Concert*
(1/91) (ROND) ① **RCD8319**

Heaven Darkens, Great and Silent, 'Himlen mørkner stor og stum'—Christmas Song, FS106 (Wds. M. Falck)
L.T. Bertelsen, T. Lønskov *Concert*
　　　　　　　(1/91) (ROND) ① **RCD8325**
His Words I Can Never Forget, 'Aldrig hans ord kan jeg glemme'—song, FS13a (Wds. F. Paludan-Müller; unpub.)
E. Rehling, D. Kirkeskov (r1988) *Concert*
　　　　　　　(1/91) (ROND) ① **RCD8323**
49 Hymns and sacred songs, FS83 (1913-14) (Wds. various)
1. Strange to say/Forunderligt at sige; 2. Maria sat on hay an straw/Maria sad paa Hø og Straa; 3. God's Angels sing in chorus/Guds Engle i Flok; 4. Now the sun in the East/Nu sol i Øst oprinder mild; 5. Alas, my rose/Ak, min Rose visner bort; 6. Standing in Pain under the Cross/Under Korset stod med smerte; 7. It is a Wonder/Der er et Under paa Verdens Ø; 8. Jesus mine, let my heart savour/Min Jesus, lad mit Hjerte faa; 9. The sign and word of the Cross/Korsets Tegn og Korsets Ord; 10. Of all the flowers that grow on earth/Utalige Blomster paa Jorderig gro; 11. As the golden sun breaks through/Som den gyldne Sol frembryder; 12. There is a path/Der er en Vej; 13. It is no great struggle/Det koster ej for megen Strid; 14. Daffodil, why are you here?/Paaskeblomst, hvad vil du her?.
1. J. Klint, R. Bevan *Concert*
　　　　　　　(12/90) (PAUL) ① **PACD56**
1-8. E. Rehling, J.E. Hansen *Concert*
　　　　　　　(1/91) (ROND) ① **RCD8327**
9-13. L.T. Bertelsen, F. Stengaard *Concert*
　　　　　　　(1/91) (ROND) ① **RCD8329**
Hymnus amoris—STBB, chorus and orchestra, FS21 (Op. 12) (1896-97) (Wds. A. Olrik, trans. J.L. Heiberg)
I. Nielsen, P. Elming, A. Elkrog, P. Høyer, J. Ditlevsen, Copenhagen Boys' Ch, Danish Nat Rad Ch, Danish Nat RSO, L. Segerstam *Concert*
　　　　　　　(4/91) (CHAN) ① **CHAN8853**
In the Land of Dreams, 'I Drømmenes Land'—song (1891) (Wds. J.P. Jacobsen)
P. Severin, D. Kirkeskov (r1988) *Concert*
　　　　　　　(1/91) (ROND) ① **RCD8323**
It is Autumn, 'Det är Höst'—song (1929) (Wds. A. Rogberg)
E. Rehling, D. Kirkeskov (r1988) *Concert*
　　　　　　　(1/91) (ROND) ① **RCD8323**
Joyously, With Jubilant Chorus, 'Frydeligt med Jubelkor'—May Song, FS34a (1906) (Wds. M. Børup & F. Moth)
L.T. Bertelsen, T. Lønskov *Concert*
　　　　　　　(1/91) (ROND) ① **RCD8329**
4 Jutish songs, FS115 (1924-5) (Wds. A. Bernsten)
1. Jens Madsen to An-Sofi/Jens Madsen å An-Sofi; 2. Our daughter/Wo Daetter; 3. One and the Other/Den Jenn aaden Anden; 4. The Haypole/Ae Lastraa.
P. Severin, D. Kirkeskov *Concert*
　　　　　　　(1/91) (ROND) ① **RCD8319**
The Land of the Future, 'Fremtidens Land'—song, FS145 (Wds. B. Bjørnsson)
P. Severin, D. Kirkeskov *Concert*
　　　　　　　(1/91) (ROND) ① **RCD8319**
10 Little Danish Songs, FS114 (1923-4) (Wds. Various)
1. I know a lark's nest/Jeg ved en Laerkerede; 2. The sun is so red, Mother/Solen er saa rød Mor; 3. As quietly as the stream runs in the meadow/Tyst som Aa i Engen rinder; 4. The sparrow sits in silence behind the gable/Spurren sidder stum bag Kvist; 5. The fiddler is playing his fiddle/Den Spillemand spiller paa Strengel; 6. When children whimper at Eventide/Naa Smaabørn klynker ved Aftentide; 7. Green is the hedge in Spring/Grøn er Vaarens Hak; 8. I settle down to sleep so snugly/Jeg laegger mig ass trygt til Ro; 9. O, today I am so happy/O, hvor jeg er gladi Dag!; 10. The Danish Song/Den danske Sang.
Cpte E. Rehling, P. Severin, D. Kirkeskov *Concert*
　　　　　　　(1/91) (ROND) ① **RCD8327**
1, 10. J. Klint, R. Bevan *Concert*
　　　　　　　(12/90) (PAUL) ① **PACD56**
1, 2, 5, 7, 8, 10. K. Westi, H. Metz *Concert*
　　　　　　　(7/91) (KONT) ① **32047**
3 Motets—a cappella choir, FS139 (Op. 55) (1929)
1. Afflictus sum (wds. Psalm 38); 2. Dominus regit me (wds. Psalm 22); 3. Benedictus Dominus (wds. Psalm 30).
Camerata Chbr Ch, P. Enevold *Concert*
　　　　　　　(9/90) (BIS) ① **BIS-CD131**
Danish Nat Rad Ch, S. Parkman *Concert*
　　　　　　　(4/91) (CHAN) ① **CHAN8853**

O Danish Man, 'Du danske Mand'—patriotic song, FS35 (1906) (Wds. H. Drachmann)
L.T. Bertelsen, T. Lønskov *Concert*
　　　　　　　(1/91) (ROND) ① **RCD8325**
20 Popular Melodies, FS95 (1917-21) (Wds. Various)
1. Gone are the days of Old/Udrundne er de gamle dage; 2. On the ground/Paa det Jaevne; 3. That tiny lark/Hedelaerken; 4. The noble nature-lover/Naturens aedle Dryker; 5. A Fisherman sat so pensive/Der Sad en Fisker, saa tankefuld; 6. I only looked back/Jeg saa kun tilbage; 7. Like the deepest well/Som dybets Brønd; 8. Freedom is the purest gold/Frihed er det bedste Guld; 9. The barques meet/De Snaekker mødtes; 10. Heavy, sombre clouds of night/Tunge, mørke Natteskyer; 11. The great Master comes/Den store Mester Kommer; 12. Our eyes may rejoice/Derfor kan vort Øje glaedes; 13. When Summer's song is sung/Naar Somrens Sang er sungen; 14. Earth in whose embrace/Jord, i hvis Favn; 15. See my fragile web/Betragt mit svage spind.
1-10. L.T. Bertelsen, T. Lønskov *Concert*
　　　　　　　(1/91) (ROND) ① **RCD8325**
11-15. E.H. Thaysen, M. Ejsing, T. Lønskov *Concert*
　　　　　　　(1/91) (ROND) ① **RCD8329**
4 Popular Melodies, FS101 (1922) (Wds. Various)
1. Now shall it be revealed/Nu skal det aabenbares; 2. The song casts light/Sangen har Lysning; 3. Of what you are singing?/Hvad synger du om?; 4. Teach me, o stars of night/Laer mig Nattens Stjerne.
1, 2. L.T. Bertelsen, T. Lønskov *Concert*
　　　　　　　(1/91) (ROND) ① **RCD8325**
3, 4. E.H. Thaysen, T. Lønskov *Concert*
　　　　　　　(1/91) (ROND) ① **RCD8329**
The Power that Gave Me My Little Song, 'Den Magt som gav min lille sang'—song (Wds. B. Bjørnson)
E.H. Thaysen, T. Lønskov *Concert*
　　　　　　　(1/91) (ROND) ① **RCD8329**
Reunion, 'Gensyn'—song, FS151 (1930) (Wds. F. Paludon-Müller)
P. Severin, D. Kirkeskov *Concert*
　　　　　　　(1/91) (ROND) ① **RCD8319**
The Sleep, 'Søvnen'—chorus and orchestra, FS33 (Op. 18) (1903-04) (Wds. J. Jørgensen)
Danish Nat Rad Ch, Danish Nat RSO, L. Segerstam *Concert*
　　　　　　　(4/91) (CHAN) ① **CHAN8853**
6 Songs, FS3 (1887-8) (Wds. various)
1. To the Queen of my Heart/Til mit hjertes dronning; 2. Angst (Hold me tighter); 3. The stars going/Vej viseren synger; 4. My soul is dark (Min Sjael er mørk); 5. Serenade (The blue waves sleep); 6. Beware, O Bonnie Ann!/Tag Jer i agt for Anna.
P. Severin, D. Kirkeskov (r1988) *Concert*
　　　　　　　(1/91) (ROND) ① **RCD8323**
5 Songs, FS12 (Op. 4) (1891) (J. P. Jacobsen)
1. Sunset/Solnedgang; 2. In the Seraglio garden/I seraillets have; 3. To Asali/Til Asali; 4. Irmelin Rose; 5. Has the day gathered all its sorrow/Har Dagen sanket al sein sorg.
J. Klint, R. Bevan *Concert*
　　　　　　　(12/90) (PAUL) ① **PACD56**
P. Severin, D. Kirkeskov *Concert*
　　　　　　　(1/91) (ROND) ① **RCD8327**
6 Songs, FS18 (Op. 10) (1894) (Wds. L. Holstein)
1. Apple Blossom/Aebleblomst; 2. Lake of Memories/Erindringens so; 3. Summer Song/Sommersang; 4. Song behind the plough/Sang bag ploven; 5. This evening/I aften; 6. Greeting/Hilsen.
P. Severin, E. Rehling, D. Kirkeskov (r1988) *Concert*
　　　　　　　(1/91) (ROND) ① **RCD8323**
4, 5. J. Klint, R. Bevan *Concert*
　　　　　　　(12/90) (PAUL) ① **PACD56**
Songs, FS143 (c1929) (Wds. Various)
1. Sign of Light/Lysets Tegen.
1. L.T. Bertelsen, T. Lønskov *Concert*
　　　　　　　(1/91) (ROND) ① **RCD8325**
Songs and Verses, FS14 (Op. 6) (1891) (Wds. J.P. Jacobsen)
1. Genre piece/Genrebillede; 2. The Seraphs/Serafeme; 3. Silken shoes on a golden last/Silkesko over gylden Laest; 4. A moment of pleasure/Det bødes der for; 5. Song from Mogens/Vise af Mogens.
P. Severin, D. Kirkeskov *Concert*
　　　　　　　(1/91) (ROND) ① **RCD8319**
4. J. Klint, R. Bevan *Concert*
　　　　　　　(12/90) (PAUL) ① **PACD56**

Springtime in Funen, 'Fynsk Forar'—soloists, chorus and orchestra, FS96 (Op. 42) (1921) (Wds. A. Berntsen)
1. Springtime in Funen; 2. The day, with sun (Den milde dag); 3. The old bachelor; 4. The blind musician; 5. The old people; 6. Dance ballad.
I. Nielsen, K. von Binzer, J. Klint, St Klemens Sch Children's Ch, Little Muko Univ Ch, Odense SO, T. Vetö *Aladdin Suite*.　(6/86) (UNIC) ① **DKPCD9054**
I. Nielsen, P. Grønlund, S. Byriel, St Anne's Gymnasium Children's Chor, Danish Nat Rad Ch, Danish Nat RSO, L. Segerstam *Concert*
　　　　　　　(4/91) (CHAN) ① **CHAN8853**
A. Båverstam, L. Ekdahl, A. Thors, K. M. Sandve, P. Høyer, Swedish Boys' Ch, Swedish Rad Ch, Swedish RSO, E-P. Salonen (r1992) *Concert*
　　　　　　　(4/94) (SONY) ① **SK53276**
The blind musician J. Klint, R. Bevan *Concert*
　　　　　　　(12/90) (PAUL) ① **PACD56**
Strophic Songs, FS42 (Op. 21) (1902-07) (Wds. various)
VOLUME 1: 1a. Shall the Flowers wither then? / Skal blomsterne da visne (wds. Rode); 1b. The Hawk / Høgen (wds. Aakjaer); 1c. Jens the road mender / Jens Vejmand (wds. Aakjaer). VOLUME 2: 2a. Bow your head, O flower / Saenk kun dit hoved, du blomst (wds. Jørgensen; 2b. The first lark / Den første laerke (wds. Aakjaer); 2c. Homeless / Husvild (wds. Jensen); 2d. Good Night / Godnat (wds. Jensen).
1a, 1b, 2c, 2d P. Severin, D. Kirkeskov *Concert*
　　　　　　　(1/91) (ROND) ① **RCD8319**
1c J. Klint, R. Bevan *Concert*
　　　　　　　(12/90) (PAUL) ① **PACD56**
1c, 2a K. Westi, H. Metz *Concert*
　　　　　　　(7/91) (KONT) ① **32047**
1c, 2b P. Severin, D. Kirkeskov *Concert*
　　　　　　　(1/91) (ROND) ① **RCD8319**
2a E. Rehling, D. Kirkeskov (r1988) *Concert*
　　　　　　　(1/91) (ROND) ① **RCD8323**
Study from Nature, 'Studie efter Naturen'—song, FS82 (1916) (Wds. H.C. Andersen)
P. Severin, D. Kirkeskov *Concert*
　　　　　　　(1/91) (ROND) ① **RCD8319**
Supplement to the High School Songbook, FS125 (1927)
1. The very best/Villeste; 2. We mention a name/Vi naevner et Nam; 3. Breezy morning/Frisk Morgen!; 4. Do you notice, it is brightening/Laer I maerke det lysner.
1. J. Klint, R. Bevan *Concert*
　　　　　　　(12/90) (PAUL) ① **PACD56**
2-4. L.T. Bertelsen, T. Lønskov *Concert*
　　　　　　　(1/91) (ROND) ① **RCD8325**
There is a Lovely Land, 'Der er et yndigt Land'—a cappella choir, FS110 (1924) (Wds. A. Oehlenschläger)
L.T. Bertelsen, T. Lønskov *Concert*
　　　　　　　(1/91) (ROND) ① **RCD8325**
Vocalise-Etude pour voix élevée, FS124 (1927)
E.H. Thaysen, T. Lønskov *Concert*
　　　　　　　(1/91) (ROND) ① **RCD8329**

　　　　　　SECTION V: STAGE WORKS

Aladdin—incidental music, FS89 (Op. 34) (1918-19) (Wds. A. Oehlenschläger)
1. Gulnare's song; 2. Aladdin's Lullaby/Aladdins Vuggevise; 3. Fatima's song.
Cpte M. Ejsing, G. Paevatalu, Danish Rad Chbr Ch, Danish Nat RSO, G. Rozhdestvensky (r1992)
　　　　　　　(5/93) (CHAN) ① **CHAN9135**
1-3. E. Rehling, P. Severin, D. Kirkeskov *Concert*
　　　　　　　(1/91) (ROND) ① **RCD8327**
Aladdin—concert suite from incidental music, FS89 (Op. 34) (1918-19)
1. Oriental festive march; 2. Aladdin's dream and dance of the morning mist; 3. Hindu dance; 4. Chinese dance; 5. The market in Ispahan; 6. Dance of the prisoners; 7. Negro dance.
Gothenburg SO, Myung-Whun Chung *Symphony 2*.
　　　　　　　(5/84) (BIS) ① **BIS-CD247**
Odense SO, T. Vetö *Springtime in Funen*.
　　　　　　　(6/86) (UNIC) ① **DKPCD9054**
Amor and the Poet, 'Amor og Digteren'—incidental music to S Michaelis' play, FS150 (1930)
1. Overture; 2. Italian Shepherd's song/Italiensk Hyrdearie; 3. We love you, our lofty north/Vi elsker dig vort høje Nord!; 4. Allegretto con brio.
1. Odense SO, E. Serov (r1993) *Concert*
　　　　　　　(11/94) (KONT) ① **32178**
2, 3. E.H. Thaysen, T. Lønskov *Concert*
　　　　　　　(1/91) (ROND) ① **RCD8329**
4. Beethoven Academy, J. Caeyers (r1993) *Concert*
　　　　　　　(6/94) (HARM) ① **HMC90 1489**

Cosmus—incidental music, FS98 (1921-2)
(Wds. E. Christiansen)
1. The sun springs out like a rose/Solen springer ud
som en Rose.
1. J. Laursen, T. Lønskov *Concert*
(1/91) (ROND) ① **RCD8329**

Ebbe Skammelsen—incidental music to Bergstedt's play, SF117 (1925—Copenhagen)
H. Bonde-Hansen, L.T. Bertelsen, L. Lind, N.B.
Mikkelsen, Funen Acad Children's Ch, Odense Phil
Ch, Odense SO, T. Vetö (r c1994) *Concert*
(3/95) (KONT) ① **32188**

An Evening at Giske, 'En after paa Giske'—concert suite from incidental music, FS9 (1890)
Danish Nat RSO, G. Rozhdestvensky *Concert*
(9/94) (CHAN) ① **CHAN9287**

Hagbarth and Signe—incidental music, FS57 (1910) (Wds. A. Oehlenschläger)
1. My helmet is too shiny and too heavy/Min Helim er
mig for blank og tung.
H. Bonde-Hansen, L.T. Bertelsen, L. Lind, N.B.
Mikkelsen, Funen Acad Children's Ch, Odense Phil
Ch, Odense SO, T. Vetö (r c1994) *Concert*
(3/95) (KONT) ① **32188**
1. L.T. Bertelsen, T. Lønskov *Concert*
(1/91) (ROND) ① **RCD8325**

The Liar (Løgneren)—incidental music, FS88 (1918) (Wds. J. Sigurjonsson)
1. The Bard's Lay/Skjaldens Drapa.
1. L.T. Bertelsen, T. Lønskov *Concert*
(1/91) (ROND) ① **RCD8325**

Maskarade—opera, FS39 (1906—Copenhagen) (Lib. V. Andersen, after Holberg)
EXCERPTS -; 1. Prelude, Act 1; 2. Prelude, Act 2; 3.
Dance of the Cockerels.
Cpte I. Hansen, G. Plesner, T. Landy, M. Schmidt
Johansen, C. Sørensen, G. Bastian, E. Brodersen, T.
Hyldgaard, J. Klint, O.V. Hansen, A. Haugland,
Danish Rad Chor, Danish RSO, J. Frandsen
(12/88) (UNIC) ① [2] **DKPCD9073/4**
E.H. Thaysen, L.T. Bertelsen, Odense SO, E. Serov
Concert (11/95) (KONT) ① **32203**
1. Gothenburg SO, Myung-Whun Chung *Concert*
(8/86) (BIS) ① **BIS-CD321**
1. BBC SO, A. Davis *Concert*
(4/91) (VIRG) ① **VC7 59618-2**
4. J. Klint, R. Bevan *Concert*
(12/90) (PAUL) ① **PACD56**

Master Oluf Rides, 'Hr. Oluf han Rider'—incidental music to Drachman's play, FS37 (1906)
PROLOGUE: 1. Prelude; 2. Vanderens Monologue.
ACT 1: 3. I Rosenluden (Prelude); 4. Nissens Song;
5. Helleildens Song. ACT 2: 6. Elvemat (Prelude); 7.
Alvens Monologue; 8. Oluf's Song; 9. Elverdans. ACT
3: 10. Prelude; 11. Sidsel's Song. ACT 4: 12.
Prelude; 13. Dance-Song.
5, 8, 13. M. Ejsing, L.T. Bertelsen, T. Lønskov
Concert (1/91) (ROND) ① **RCD8329**

The Mother—incidental music to play by H. Rode, FS94 (Op. 41) (1920—Copenhagen)
1. The storm wages over the dark waters/Vildt gaar
Storm mod sorte Vande; 2. My girl is fair as
amber/Min Pige er saa lys som Rav; 3. The day the
eagle was ready to fly/Den Gang Ørnen var flyveklar;
4. A mother was told at the feast/Ved Festen fik en
Moder Bud; 5. The thistle crop looks
promising/Tidselhøsten tegner godt; 6. Once when
Death was awaited/Dengang Døden var i Vente; 7.
So bitter was my heart/Saa bittert var mit Hjerte; 8.
Like a Venturous Fleet at anchor/Som en rejselysten
Flaade; 9. The fog is lifting/Taagen Letter (flute and
harp); 10. The Children are playing/Børnene spiller.
1-8. J. Laursen, L.T. Bertelsen, T. Lønskov *Concert*
(1/91) (ROND) ① **RCD8329**
2. K. Westi, H. Metz *Concert*
(7/91) (KONT) ① **32047**
9. Athena Ens *Concert*
(2/89) (CHAN) ① **CHAN8680**
9. G. Sandvik, T. Kniejski *Concert*
(9/89) (BIS) ① **BIS-CD428**

Saul and David—opera: 4 acts, FS25 (1902—Copenhagen) (Lib. E. Christiansen)
Cpte A. Haugland, P. Lindroos, T. Kiberg, K. Westi,
A. Gjevang, C. Christiansen, J. Klint, Danish Nat Rad
Chor, Danish Nat RSO, N. Järvi
(3/91) (CHAN) ① [2] **CHAN8911/2**
2. Swedish RSO, E-P. Salonen (r1992) *Concert*
(4/94) (SONY) ① **SK53276**

Snefrid—melodram, FS17 (1893—Copenhagen) (Wds. H Drachmann)
Odense SO, E. Serov (r1993) *Concert*
(11/94) (KONT) ① **32178**

Son of Wolf (Ulvens Søn)—incidental music, FS50 (1909) (Wds. J. Aakjaer)
1. There stands a stunted tree/Der Staar en Purle; 2.
Are you coming soon, you cottagers/Kommer I snart,
I Husmaend.
1, 2. L.T. Bertelsen, T. Lønskov *Concert*
(1/91) (ROND) ① **RCD8325**

St John's Eve play (Sankt Hansaffenspil)—incidental music to Oehlenschläger's play, FS65 (1913)
H. Bonde-Hansen, L.T. Bertelsen, L. Lind, N.B.
Mikkelsen, Funen Acad Children's Ch, Odense Phil
Ch, Odense SO, T. Vetö (r c1994) *Concert*
(3/95) (KONT) ① **32188**

Tove—incidental music to Holstein's play, FS43 (1906-08)
1. We sons of the plains/Vi Sletternes Sønner; 2. Bird
catcher's song/Fuglefaengervise; 3. Tove's song; 4.
The Hunter's song/Jaegersang.
1. J. Klint, R. Bevan *Concert*
(12/90) (PAUL) ① **PACD56**
1-4. E. Rehling, P. Severin, D. Kirkeskov *Concert*
(1/91) (ROND) ① **RCD8327**

Willemoes—incidental music, FS44 (1907-8) (Wds. L.C. Nielsen)
1. Vieke's song/Vibekes sang; 2. Song of the
Sea/Havets sang; 3. Ja, tag os; 4. Havet, omuring
Danmark; 5. ACT 3: Prelude.
1, 2. E. Rehling, P. Severin, D. Kirkeskov *Concert*
(1/91) (ROND) ① **RCD8327**

NIELSEN, Hans *(c1580–c1626)* Denmark

also known as Giovanni Fonteio

SECTION IV: VOCAL AND CHORAL

T'amo, mia vita—madrigal: 5vv (pub 1606)
Consort of Musicke, A. Rooley (lte/dir) *Concert*
(2/89) (BIS) ① **BIS-CD392**

NIETZSCHE, Friedrich *(1844–1900)* Germany

SECTION II: CHAMBER

Monodie à deux: Lob der Barmherzigkeit—piano duet (1873)
J.B. Young, C. Keene *Concert*
(12/92) (NEWP) ① **NPD85513**

Nachklang einer Sylvesternacht, mit Prozessionslied, Bauerntanz und Glockengeläut—piano duet (1871)
J.B. Young, C. Keene *Concert*
(12/92) (NEWP) ① **NPD85513**

SECTION III: INSTRUMENTAL

Da geht ein Bach—piano (1862)
J.B. Young *Concert* (12/92) (NEWP) ① **NPD85513**
Edes Titok—piano (1862)
J.B. Young *Concert* (12/92) (NEWP) ① **NPD85513**
Einleitung—piano (1861)
J.B. Young *Concert* (12/92) (NEWP) ① **NPD85513**
Ermanarich—symphonic poem: piano (1862)
J.B. Young *Concert* (12/92) (NEWP) ① **NPD85513**
Heldenklage—piano (1862)
J.B. Young *Concert* (12/92) (NEWP) ① **NPD85513**
Hymnus an die Freudenschaft—piano (1874)
1. Prologue; 2. Festival of Friends at the Temple of
Friendship.
J.B. Young *Concert* (12/92) (NEWP) ① **NPD85513**
Im Mondschein auf der Puszta—piano (1862)
J.B. Young *Concert* (12/92) (NEWP) ① **NPD85513**
2 Polish Dances—piano (1862)
1. Mazurka; 2. Aus der Czarda.
J.B. Young *Concert* (12/92) (NEWP) ① **NPD85513**
So lach doch mal—piano (1862)
J.B. Young *Concert* (12/92) (NEWP) ① **NPD85513**
Ungarischer Marsch—piano (1862)
J.B. Young *Concert* (12/92) (NEWP) ① **NPD85513**
Das zerbrochene Ringlein—piano (1863)
J.B. Young *Concert* (12/92) (NEWP) ① **NPD85513**

SECTION IV: VOCAL AND CHORAL

Aus der Jugendzeit—Lied (1862) (Wds. F. Rückert)
J.B. Young (arr Young) *Concert*
(12/92) (NEWP) ① **NPD85513**
Nachspiel—Lied (1862) (Wds. S. Petöfi)
J.B. Young (arr Young) *Concert*
(12/92) (NEWP) ① **NPD85513**
Unendlich—Lied (1862) (Wds. S. Petöfi)
J.B. Young (arr Young) *Concert*
(12/92) (NEWP) ① **NPD85513**

NIEWIADOMSKI, Stanislaw *(1859–1936)* Poland

SECTION IV: VOCAL AND CHORAL

Sophia—song
I. Bohuss, anon (r1902) *Concert*
(6/93) (PEAR) ① [3] **GEMMCDS9004/6(1)**

NIKOLAYEV, Leonid (Vladimirovich) *(1878–1942)* Russia

SECTION IV: VOCAL AND CHORAL

I cannot banish grief—song
L. Sobinov, anon (r1901) *Concert*
(6/93) (PEAR) ① [3] **GEMMCDS9997/9(1)**
Rest—song
L. Sobinov, D.G. Komilov (r1904) *Concert*
(6/93) (PEAR) ① [3] **GEMMCDS9997/9(2)**

NIKOLSKY, Yuri Sergeyevich *(1895–1962)* Russia/USSR

SECTION IV: VOCAL AND CHORAL

The eternally begotten and co-eternal Son—Russian liturgical chant
N. Gedda, Paris Russian Orthodox Cath Ch, E. Evetz
Concert (1/93) (PHIL) ① **434 174-2PM**

NILSSON, Torsten *(b 1920)* Sweden

SECTION I: ORCHESTRAL

Concerto for Piano and Orchestra No. 1, Op. 63 (1974-78)
H. Pålsson, Malmö SO, V. Handley (r1986) *Concert*
(5/93) (CPRI) ① **CAP21417**
On the Threshold (Steget över Tröskeln)—concerto for piano and wind instruments, Op. 67 (1975)
H. Pålsson, Stockholm PO, J. Panula (r1983)
Concert (5/93) (CPRI) ① **CAP21417**

SECTION III: INSTRUMENTAL

Suite for Piano, Op. 121 (1988)
H. Pålsson *Concert* (5/93) (CPRI) ① **CAP21417**

NIN (Y CASTELLANOS), Joaquín *(1879–1949)* Cuba

SECTION IV: VOCAL AND CHORAL

El amor es como un niña—song (trans from Anon work)
M. Bayo, J.A. Alvarez-Parejo (r1992) *Concert*
(6/93) (CLAV) ① **CD50-9205**
20 Cantos populares españolas (1923)
1. Tonada de Valdovinos; 3. Tonada de la niña
perdida; 4. Montañesa; 5. Tonada del Conde Sol; 6.
Malagueña; 7. Granadina; 8. Saeta; 9. Jota tortosina;
14. Asturiana; 15. Paño murciano; 16. Villancico
Catalán; 17. El Canto de los pájaros; 18. El Vito; 19.
Canto andaluz; 20. Polo.
3, 4, 6, 7, 19, 20. N. Vallin, J. Nin (r1929) *Concert*
(11/93) (EMI) ① **CDC7 54836-2**
4. H. Spani, orch, G. Nastrucci (r1930) *Concert*
(9/90) (CLUB) ① [2] **CL99-509/10**
4, 20. M. Bayo, J.A. Alvarez-Parejo (r1992) *Concert*
(6/93) (CLAV) ① **CD50-9205**
14. J. Heifetz, E. Bay (r1946) *Concert*
(11/94) (RCA) ① [65] **09026 61778-2(06)**
Confiado jilguerillo—song (trans from Laserna's Aci e Galatea')
M. Bayo, J.A. Alvarez-Parejo (r1992) *Concert*
(6/93) (CLAV) ① **CD50-9205**
Las majas de Paris—song
M. Bayo, J.A. Alvarez-Parejo (r1992) *Concert*
(6/93) (CLAV) ① **CD50-9205**
Tirana—song (trans from Laserna's 'Tirana')
M. Bayo, J.A. Alvarez-Parejo (r1992) *Concert*
(6/93) (CLAV) ① **CD50-9205**
10 Villancicos (noëls espagnols)—voice and piano (1932)
1. Villancico Castellano; 2. Villancico Asturiano; 3.
Villancico Andaluz; 4. Jesús de Nazaret; 5. Villancico
Vasco.
5. I. Gorin, A. Baller (r1941) *Concert*
(4/92) (EMI) ① [7] **CHS7 69741-2(2)**

NIN-CULMELL, Joaquin (b 1908) USA

SECTION III: INSTRUMENTAL

48 Tonadas—piano (1956-61)
VOL. I; 1. Arada de Salamanca; 2. Diferencia sobre
la arada de Salamanca; 3. Baile de Burgos; 4. Jota
alicantina. VOL II: 6. Canción del labrador (León); 7.
Copla castellana; 8. Canción otoñal (País Vasco); 9.
Seguidilla murciana; 10. Canción de trilla (Murcia);
11. Muñeira (Galicia). VOL III: 12. Motivo de Santo
Domingo (Canarias). VOL IV: 13. Canción
(Vascongadas); 14. Zortzico (Vascongadas); 15. Jota
castellana.
6-11. A. de Larrocha *Concert*
    (9/92) (DECC) ① [2] **433 929-2DM2**

NINOT LE PETIT (16th Cent) France

SECTION IV: VOCAL AND CHORAL

N'as tu point—chanson: 4vv
C. Janequin Ens, D. Visse (r1994) *Concert*
    (5/95) (HARM) ① **HMC90 1453**

NITZSCHE, Jack (b 1937) USA

SECTION V: STAGE WORKS

Revenge—film score (1990)
EXCERPTS: 1. Love Theme; 2. Friendship; 3.
Miryea; 4. Betrayal; 5. Jeep Ride; 6. On the Beach; 7.
Illicit Love; 8. Tibey's Revenge; 9. Whorehouse &
Healing; 10. Dead Texan; 11. Confrontation; 12.
Miryea's Death.
1. OST (r1990) *Concert*
    (5/93) (SILV) ① **SILVAD3001**

NIVERS, Guillaume Gabriel (c1632–1714) France

SECTION III: INSTRUMENTAL

**Livre d'orgue des huit tons de l'Eglise
III—organ (pub 1675)**
4. Suite du 4ème ton.
4. A. Isoir *Concert*   (6/90) (CALL) ① **CAL9916**

SECTION IV: VOCAL AND CHORAL

Dominus illuminatio mea
A. Mellon, G. Lesne, I. Honeyman, J. Bona (r1990s;
with faux-bourdon by Charpentier, H226) *Concert*
    (9/95) (VIRG) ① **VC7 59295-2**
**Miserere mei—Psalm 50: plainchant (ed
Nivers)**
A. Mellon, G. Lesne, I. Honeyman, J. Bona,
Seminario musicale (r1990s; with faux-bourdon by
Charpentier, H156) *Concert*
    (9/95) (VIRG) ① **VC7 59295-2**

NOBLE, Thomas Tertius (1867–1953) England/USA

SECTION IV: VOCAL AND CHORAL

Evening Service, Op. 6 (pub 1896)
1. Magnificat; 2. Nunc dimittis.
1, 2. St Paul's Cath Ch, C. Dearnley, John Scott
Concert   (1/89) (HYPE) ① **CDA66305**
Evening Service in A minor, Op. 17
1. Magnificat; 2. Nunc dimittis.
1, 2. Ely Cath Ch, P. Trepte *Concert*
    (2/92) (GAMU) ① **GAMCD527**

NOLA, Giovanni Domenico del Giovane da (1510/20–1592) Italy

SECTION IV: VOCAL AND CHORAL

Chi la gagliarda
King's Sngrs, Tragicomedia *Concert*
    (9/92) (EMI) ① **CDC7 54191-2**
Cingari simo venit'a giocare
Kithara (r1993) *Concert*
    (3/95) (CHAN) ① **CHAN0562**
Fuggit Amore
London Musica Antiqua, M. Uridge (r1980-83)
  Concert   (12/93) (SYMP) ① **SYMCD1157**
Tri ciechi siamo—frottola
King's Sngrs *Concert*
    (9/92) (EMI) ① **CDC7 54191-2**

NONO, Luigi (1924–1990) Italy

SECTION II: CHAMBER

**'Hay que caminar' sognando—two violins
(1989)**
G. Kremer, T. Grindenko *Lontananza nostalgica.*
    (9/92) (DG) ① **435 870-2GH**
**La Lontananza nostalgica utopica
futura—violin and magnetic tape (1988-89)**
G. Kremer, S. Gubaidulina *Hay que caminar.*
    (9/92) (DG) ① **435 870-2GH**

SECTION IV: VOCAL AND CHORAL

**Il canto sospeso—sop, alto, ten, narrs,
chorus & orchestra (1955-56)** (Wds. various)
S. Lothar, B. Ganz, B. Bonney, S. Otto, M.
Torzewski, Berlin Rad Chor, BPO, C. Abbado
(pp1992) *Concert*   (10/93) (SONY) ① **SK53360**
Liebeslied—chorus and orchestra (1954)
(Wds. cpsr)
Vienna Jeunesse Ch, VPO, C. Abbado (pp1988)
Concert   (4/90) (DG) ① **429 260-2GH**

SECTION V: STAGE WORKS

**Intolleranza 1960—scenic action: 2 acts
(1961—Venice)** (Wds. from various texts)
Cpte D. Rampy, U. Koszut, K. Harries, J. van der
Schaaf, W. Probst, J. Dieken, C. Hoening, C. Otto, H.
Wenning, Stuttgart Op Chor, Stuttgart Op Orch, B.
Kontarsky (pp1993)
    (10/95) (TELD) ① **4509-97304-2**
**Prometeo: Tragedia dell'ascolto—opera
(1984—Venice)** (Lib. Cacciari)
Cpte I. Ade-Jesemann, M. Bair-Ivenz, P. Hall,
Freiburg Sols Ch, Modern Ens, I. Metzmacher
(pp1993)   (12/95) (EMI) ① [2] **CDS5 55209-2**
Promoteo—vocal suite from opera (1992)
1. 3 voci, 'Ascolta! Cogli quest'anima (wds. after W
Benjamin); 2. Isola seconda, 'Doch uns ist gegeben'
(wds. Hölderlin).
1, 2. I. Ade-Jesemann, M. Bair-Ivenz, S. Otto, P. Hall,
U. Krumbiegel, M. Schadock, M. Hasel, M. Preis, C.
Gössling, Freiburg Sols Ch, BPO, C. Abbado
(pp1992) *Concert*   (1/95) (SONY) ① **SK53978**

NOORDT, Anthoni van (1620–1675) Netherlands

SECTION III: INSTRUMENTAL

Fantasia II—keyboard (1659)
B. van Asperen (r1990) *Concert*
    (3/91) (SONY) ① **SK46349**

NOORDT, Sybrant (Sybrandus) (1659–1705) The Netherlands

SECTION III: INSTRUMENTAL

Sonata a Cimbalo solo (c1702)
B. van Asperen (r1990; recons B. van Asperen)
  Concert   (3/91) (SONY) ① **SK46349**

NORDENSTEN, Frank Tveor (b 1955) Norway

SECTION I: ORCHESTRAL

Ricochet, Op. 75 (1990)
Borealis Ens, C. Eggen (r1990s) *Concert*
    (9/92) (AURO) ① **ACD4973**

NORDHEIM, Arne (b 1931) Norway

SECTION I: ORCHESTRAL

**Boomerang—concerto for oboe and
chamber orchestra (1984-85)**
E. Larsen, Norwegian CO, T. Tønnesen (vn/dir)
  Concert   (10/91) (VICT) ① **VCD19014**
Magma—orchestra (1988)
Oslo PO, Y. Talmi *Tenebrae.*
    (12/92) (AURO) ① **ACD4966**
**Rendezvous for strings (arr cpsr from String
Quartet, 1956)**
Norwegian CO, T. Tønnesen (vn/dir) *Concert*
    (10/91) (VICT) ① **VCD19014**
Tenebrae—cello and orchestra (1982)
T. Mørk, Oslo PO, Y. Talmi *Magma.*
    (12/92) (AURO) ① **ACD4966**

NORDINE, Ken (20th Cent) USA

SECTION II: CHAMBER

**A Cage Went In Search of a
Bird—synthesisers (1993)** (in memoriam John
Cage)
K. Nordine (r1993) *Concert*
    (8/94) (KOCH) ① [2] **37238-2**

NORDRAAK, Rikard (1842–1866) Norway

SECTION IV: VOCAL AND CHORAL

Ingrid Sletten av Sillejord—song
K. Flagstad, orch (r1930) *Concert*
    (12/95) (SIMA) ① [3] **PSC1821(1)**

NØRGÅRD, Per (b 1932) Denmark

SECTION I: ORCHESTRAL

**Between—three movements for cello and
orchestra (1984-85)**
1. In between; 2. Turning point; 3. Among.
M. Zeuthen, Danish Nat RSO, J. Panula
Remembering Child.
    (11/92) (MARC) ① **DCCD9002**
**Concerto for Percussion and Orchestra, 'For
a Change' (1982-83)** (based on 'I Ching')
G. Mortensen, Danish Nat RSO, J. Latham-König
(r1984) *Siddhartha.*
    (12/95) (DACA) ① [2] **8 224031/2**
**Remembering Child—viola and chamber
orchestra (1985)**
P. Zukerman, Danish Nat RSO, J. Panula *Between.*
    (11/92) (MARC) ① **DCCD9002**
Twilight—orchestra (1977)
Aarhus RAM Orch, S.K. Hansen (r1994) *Concert*
    (7/95) (KONT) ① **32194**
**Voyage into the Golden Screen—chamber
orchestra (1969)**
Danish RSO, O. Knussen *Gilgamesh.*
    (1/93) (MARC) ① [2] **DCCD9001**

SECTION II: CHAMBER

Echo Zone I-III—percussion duo (1993)
Safri Duo (r1994) *Concert*
    (4/95) (CHAN) ① **CHAN9330**

SECTION III: INSTRUMENTAL

Achilles and the Tortoise—piano (1983)
P. Salo (r1992) *Concert*   (8/93) (KONT) ① **32147**
Grooving—piano (1968)
P. Salo (r1992) *Concert*   (8/93) (KONT) ① **32147**
I Ching—percussion (1983)
G. Mortensen *Concert*   (4/89) (BIS) ① **BIS-CD256**
Sonata for Piano No. 2, Op. 20 (1957)
P. Salo (r1992) *Concert*   (8/93) (KONT) ① **32147**
Turn—piano (1973)
P. Salo (r1992) *Concert*   (8/93) (KONT) ① **32147**

SECTION IV: VOCAL AND CHORAL

**And time shall be no more—mixed choir
(1994)**
1. Ritual (Rit: wds. L Lundkvist); 2. Gravesong and
Gravediggers' Mazurka (Grab-Lied und Tootagreb'r-
Mazurka); 3. We are leaving this world (Biz Düyaden
Gider Olduk: wds Y Emre); 4. Time (Tid: wds J G
Brandt).
Danish Nat Rad Ch, S. Parkman (r1994) *Concert*
    (4/95) (CHAN) ① **CHAN9264**
Wie ein Kind—chorus a capella (1979-80)
(Wds. A. Wölfi & R. M. Rilke)
1. Wiigen Lied; 2. Frühlings-Lied; 3. Trauermarsch
mit ein Unglüchsfall.
Danish Nat Rad Chbr Ch, S. Parkman *Concert*
    (12/91) (CHAN) ① **CHAN8963**

SECTION V: STAGE WORKS

**Gilgamesh—opera in six days and seven
nights (1973—Århus)** (Lib. cpsr)
Cpte B. Haugan, H. Lannerbäck, B-M. Aruhn, J.
Hviid, R. Eckhoff, M. Baekkelund, B. Eriksson, S.
Grippe, A. Bartler, R. Leanderson, chor, Swedish
RSO, T. Vetö *Voyage into the Golden Screen.*
    (1/93) (MARC) ① [2] **DCCD9001**

Siddhartha: Play for the Expected One—opera ballet: 3 acts (1983—Stockholm) (Lib. O Sarvig)
Cpte S. F. Andersen, A. Haugland, E. Guillaume, E. Harbo, K. Janken, C. Christiansen, P. Elming, T. Kiberg, A. Frellesvig, M. Nyhus, G. Mortensen, Danish Nat Rad Ch, Danish Nat Rad Childrens' Ch, Danish Nat RSO, J. Latham-König (r1984) For a Change. (12/95) (DACA) ① [2] 8 224031/2

NØRHOLM, Ib (b 1931) Denmark

SECTION I: ORCHESTRAL

Concerto for Cello and Orchestra, Op. 108 (1989)
E.B. Bengtsson, Aalborg SO, T. Vetö (r1991) Violin Concerto. (9/93) (KONT) ① 32099
Concerto for Violin and Orchestra, Op. 60 (1974)
K. Suzumi, Aalborg SO, T. Vetö (r1991) Cello Concerto. (9/93) (KONT) ① 32099
Symphony No. 1, Op. 10 (1958)
Odense SO, E. Serov Symphony 3.
(9/93) (KONT) ① 32132
Symphony No. 2, 'Isola Bella', Op. 50 (1968-71)
A. Nyborg, Odense SO, E. Serov (r1993)
(12/94) (KONT) ① 32182
Symphony No. 3, 'Day's Nightmare', Op. 57 (1973)
Odense SO, E. Serov Symphony 1.
(9/93) (KONT) ① 32132
Symphony No. 4, 'Decreation', Op. 76 (1978-78)
N. Pavlovski, S. Dahlberg, P. Høyer, I. Nørholm, Danish Nat Rad Ch, Odense SO, E. Serov (r1995) Symphony 5. (10/95) (KONT) ① 32212
Symphony No. 5, '(The) Elements', Op. 80 (1980)
Odense SO, E. Serov (r1995) Symphony 4.
(10/95) (KONT) ① 32212
Symphony No. 6, 'Moralities, or There may be many miles to the nearest spider', Op. 85 (1981)
1. A Song for occupations; 2. The Time has not come it is Passed; 3. Letter in April; 4. Critique of Insight; 5. Good-bye my Fancy!.
M. Bjerno, P. Høyer, U. Henriksen, U. Seel, Odense SO, E. Serov (r1993) Symphony 8.
(2/94) (KONT) ① 32162
Symphony No. 7, 'Ecliptic Instincts', Op. 88 (1982)
Odense SO, E. Serov Symphony 9.
(9/93) (KONT) ① 32112
Symphony No. 8, 'Faith and Longing', Op. 114 (1990)
P. Høyer, Odense SO, E. Serov (r1993) Symphony 6.
(9/93) (KONT) ① 32162
Symphony No. 9, 'The Sun Garden in Three Shades of Light', Op. 116 (1990)
Odense SO, E. Serov Symphony 7.
(9/93) (KONT) ① 32112

SECTION II: CHAMBER

String Quartet No. 3, 'From my green herbarium', Op. 35 (1966)
Danish Qt Concert (12/94) (KONT) ① 32049
String Quartet No. 4, 'September—October—November', Op. 38 (1966)
Danish Qt Concert (12/94) (KONT) ① 32049
String Quartet No. 7, 'En Passant', Op. 94 (1985)
Danish Qt Concert (12/94) (KONT) ① 32049
String Quartet No. 8, 'Memories', Op. 107 (1988)
Danish Qt Concert (12/94) (KONT) ① 32049

NORTH, Alex (1910–1991) USA

SECTION V: STAGE WORKS

The Agony and the Ecstasy—film score (1965)
EXCERPTS: 1. The Mountains of Carrara; 2. The Warrior Pope; 3. Festivity in St Peter's Square; 4. The Medici; 5. Michelangelo's Recovery; 6. The Contessina; 7. The Sketch of the Apostles; 8. Genesis; 9. The Sistine Chapel; 10. The Agony; 11. The War; 12. Michelangelo's Magnificent Achievement (comp Franco Potenza).
1-12. OST, A. North (r1965) Anthøil: Pride and the Passion. (4/92) (CLOU) ① CNS5001
Cleopatra—film score (1963)
EXCERPTS: 1. Caesar & Cleopatra; 2. Antony and Cleopatra (Love Theme); 3. Cleopatra Enters Rome.

2. National PO, C. Gerhardt Concert
(6/90) (VARE) ① VSD5207
Dragonslayer—film score (1981)
EXCERPTS: 1. The White Horse; 2. Into the Sunset.
1, 2. OST Concert (5/93) (SILV) ① SILVAD3003
Who's Afraid of Virginia Woolf—film score (1966)
EXCERPTS: 1. Main Theme.
1. National PO, C. Gerhardt Concert
(6/90) (VARE) ① VSD5207
2001—film score (1967) (not used in completed film)
EXCERPTS: 1. Main Title; 2. The Foraging; 3. The Dawn of Man; 4. Piangono al pianger mio le fere (Rad Meat and the Kill; 7. Space Station Docking; 8. Space Talk; 9. Interior Orion; 10. Trip to the Moon; 11. Moon Rocket Bus; 12. Main Theme Entr'acte.
1-12. National PO, J. Goldsmith (r1993)
(3/94) (VARE) ① VSD5400

NORTHCOTT, Bayan (b 1940) England

SECTION IV: VOCAL AND CHORAL

'The Maidens came...'—song (Wds. 16th cent anon)
M. Wiegold, Composers Ens, D. Muldowney Concert
(4/92) (NMC) ① NMCD003

NORTON, Caroline (1808–1877) England

SECTION IV: VOCAL AND CHORAL

Juanita—song (1851) (Wds cpsr)
A. Rolfe Johnson, G. Johnson (r1991/3) Concert
(8/94) (HYPE) ① CDA66709

NORTON, (George) Frederic(k) (1869–1946) England

SECTION V: STAGE WORKS

Chu Chin Chow—musical tale of the East: 2 acts (1916—London) (Lyrics L. Ashe)
EXCERPTS: ACT ONE: 1. Prelude; 2. Here Be Oysters; 3. I Am Chu Chin Chow; 4. Cleopatra's Nile; 5. I'll Sing and Dance; 6. Corraline; 7. When a Pullet is Plump; 8. I Love Thee So; 9. Behold; 10. The Robbers' March. ACT TWO: 11. I Long for the Sun (added 1917); 12. Mahbubah; 13. I Built a Fairy Palace in the Sky (added 1918); 14. Anytime's Kissing Time; 15. The Cobbler's Song; 16. We Bring Ye Fruits; 17. Finale.
1, 12, 13. M. Grimaldi, E. Darling, U. Connors, I. Humphris, Chor, Sinfonia of London, J. Hollingsworth (r1961) Concert (11/94) (EMI) ① CDANGEL 5
2-11, 14-17. J. Bryan, B. Leigh, I. te Wiata, C. Young, Orch, M. Collins (r1959) Concert
(11/94) (EMI) ① CDANGEL 5
3, 9. M. McEachern, Gaumont British Orch, Anon (cond) (r1934; film version) Concert
(11/94) (EMI) ① CDANGEL 5
4, 7, 8, 14, 15. V. Essex, C. Pounds, F. Cochrane, Orig London Cast, Percy Fletcher (r1916) Concert
(11/94) (EMI) ① CDANGEL 5

NORWORTH, Jack (1879–1959) USA

SECTION V: STAGE WORKS

The Jolly Bachelors—additional songs for Hubbell's show (1910—New York) (Lyrics Nora Bayes)
EXCERPTS: 1. Come Along, My Mandy; 2. Young America; 3. College Medley; 4. How Can They Tell That Oi'm Irish?.
1-4. N. Bayes, Orig Broadway Cast (r1910) Concert
(5/94) (PEAR) ① [3] GEMMCDS9053/5
Little Miss Fix-It—musical show (1911—New York) (Music & Lyrics collab with Nora Bayes)
EXCERPTS: 1. Strawberries; 2. For Months and Months and Months; 3. Turn Off Your Light, Mister Moon-Man.
1-3. N. Bayes, J. Norworth, Orig Broadway Cast (r1910-11) Concert
(5/94) (PEAR) ① [3] GEMMCDS9053/5

NOSKOWSKI, Zygmunt (1846–1909) Poland

SECTION IV: VOCAL AND CHORAL

Our mountaineers—song
A. Didur, anon (r1901) Concert
(6/93) (PEAR) ① [3] GEMMCDS9997/9(2)
A. Didur, orch (r1928) Concert
(1/94) (CLUB) ① CL99-089

NOTARI, Angelo (1556–1663) Italy

SECTION IV: VOCAL AND CHORAL

Prime musiche nuove—madrigal collection (pub 1613)
1. Intenerite voi, lagrime mie (Wds Rinuccini); 2. Occhi miei (Wds Guarini); 3. Su la riva del Tebro (Wds Anon); 4. Piangono al pianger mio le fere (Wds Rinuccini); 5. Occhi, un tempo mia vita (Wds Guarini); 6. Girate, ochi, girate (Wds Chiabrera); 7. Ahi, che s'accresce in me (Wds Anon); 8. Che farai, Meliseo? (Wds Sannazzaro); 9. Musa, Amor porta novella (Wds Anon); 10. Sì da me pur mi desviano (Wds Chiabrera); 11. Ecco, ch'un'altra volta (Wds Sannazzaro); 12. Se nasce in cielo (Wds Anon); 13. O bella Clori (Wds Anon); 14. Mesta ti scorgo (Wds Anon); 15. Anima eletta (Wds Sannazzaro); 16. Con esperanças espero (Wds Anon); 17. Così di ben amar (Wds Petrarch); 18. Ben qui si mostra il ciel (Wds Anon).
Cpte Consort of Musicke, A. Rooley (r1984)
(8/95) (MOSC) ① 070983
1. M. Chance, D. Cordier, Tragicomedia, S. Stubbs Concert (12/90) (HYPE) ① CDA66335

NOUGUÈS, Jean (1875–1932) France

SECTION V: STAGE WORKS

L' Aigle—opera: 3 acts (1912—Rouen) (Lib. H. Cain & L. Payen)
Ah! mes fidèles H. Albers, orch (r1911) Concert
(8/92) (IRCC) ① IRCC-CD802
Quo vadis?—opera
Amici, l'ora attesa e questa; Errar sull'ampio M. Battistini, orch, C. Sabajno (Ital: r1912) Concert
(10/92) (PEAR) ① GEMMCD9936
Errar sull'ampio mar M. Battistini, orch, C. Sabajno (Ital: r1912) Concert (10/92) (NIMB) ① NI7831

NOVÁČEK, Ottokar (Eugen) (1866–1900) Hungary/USA

SECTION II: CHAMBER

8 Concert caprices—violin and piano, Op. 5
4. Perpetuum mobile.
4. K-W. Chung, P. Moll Concert
(9/87) (DECC) ① 417 289-2DH
4. Y. Menuhin, H. Giesen (r1930) Concert
(4/91) (BIDD) ① LAB032
4. Y. Menuhin, H. Giesen (r1930) Concert
(9/91) (TEST) ① SBT1003
4. I. Perlman, S. Sanders Concert
(6/95) (EMI) ① [20] CZS4 83177-2(3)

NOVÁČEK, Rudolf (1860–1929)

SECTION I: ORCHESTRAL

Castaldo March—Regimental March of the 28th Infantry Regiment (1884)
Czech PO, V. Neumann Concert
(6/87) (ORFE) ① C107101A

NOVÁK, Jan František (?–1771) Bohemia

SECTION II: CHAMBER

Sonata for Violin and Piano in A minor (1891)
J. Suk, J. Panenka Concert
(5/90) (SUPR) ① 11 0705-2

NOVÁK, Vítězslav (Augustín Rudolf) *(1870–1949)* Bohemia

SECTION I: ORCHESTRAL

Eternal Longing—symphonic poem, Op. 33 (1903-05)
Czech PO, K. Sejna (r1966) *Concert*
(6/93) (SUPR) ① **11 0682-2**
In the Tatra Mountains—symphonic poem, Op. 26 (1902)
Czech PO, K. Sejna (r1966) *Concert*
(6/93) (SUPR) ① **11 0682-2**
Slovak Suite—small orchestra, Op. 32 (1903)
Brno St PO, K. Sejna (r1968) *Concert*
(6/93) (SUPR) ① **11 0682-2**
Czech PO, V. Talich (r1953) *Concert*
(1/94) (SUPR) ① **11 1905-2**

SECTION III: INSTRUMENTAL

Pan—tone poem, Op. 43 (1910)
Slovak PO, Z. Bílek (arr orch)
(10/91) (MARC) ⑧ **8 223325**

SECTION V: STAGE WORKS

Nicotina—ballet pantomine: 7 scenes (1930—Prague)
Brno Madrigal Sngrs, Brno St PO, F. Jílek
(11/89) (SUPR) ① **CO-2198**

NOVELLO, Ivor *(1893–1951)* Wales

SECTION IV: VOCAL AND CHORAL

Fairy laughter—song (Wds. D. Furber)
M. Hill Smith, G. Langford, Chandos Concert Orch, S. Barry *Concert* (8/93) (CHAN) ① **CHAN9142**
Keep the Home fires burning (till the boys come home)—song (1915) (Wds. L. G. Ford)
M. Hill Smith, G. Langford, Chandos Concert Orch, S. Barry *Concert* (8/93) (CHAN) ① **CHAN9142**
The Little Damozel—song
M. Hill Smith, G. Langford, Chandos Concert Orch, S. Barry *Concert* (8/93) (CHAN) ① **CHAN9142**
Spring of the Year—song (pub 1910)
M. Hill Smith, G. Langford, Chandos Concert Orch, S. Barry *Concert* (8/93) (CHAN) ① **CHAN9142**

SECTION V: STAGE WORKS

Arc de Triomphe—musical play (1943—London) (Lyrics C. Hassell)
EXCERPTS: 1. Dark music.
1. M. Hill Smith, G. Langford, Chandos Concert Orch, S. Barry *Concert* (8/93) (CHAN) ① **CHAN9142**
Careless Rapture—musical play (1936—London) (Lyrics C. Hassell)
EXCERPTS: 1. Music in May; 2. WHy is there ever Goodbye?.
1, 2. M. Hill Smith, G. Langford, Chandos Concert Orch, S. Barry *Concert*
(8/93) (CHAN) ① **CHAN9142**
The Dancing Years—musical play: 3 acts (1939—London) (Lyrics C. Hassell)
EXCERPTS: 1. Overture; 2. My dearest dear; 3. Waltz of my heart; 4. Wings of sleep; 5. My life belongs to you; 6. Chorale and Tyrolese dance; 7. Leap year Waltz; 8. When it's Spring in Vienna; 9. I can give you the starlight; 10. Primrose; 11. My dearest dear (reprise).
1, 2. M. Hill Smith, G. Langford, Chandos Concert Orch, S. Barry *Concert*
(8/93) (CHAN) ① **CHAN9142**
3, 9. M. Hill Smith, National SO, J.O. Edwards (r1989-91) *Concert* (10/91) (TER) ① **CDVIR8314**
Gay's the Word—musical play (1951—London) (Lyrics A. Melville)
EXCERPTS: 1. On such a night as this; 2. Finder, please return.
1, 2. M. Hill Smith, G. Langford, Chandos Concert Orch, S. Barry *Concert*
(8/93) (CHAN) ① **CHAN9142**
Glamorous Night—musical play: 2 acts (1935—London) (Wds. Hassall)
EXCERPTS: 1. Glamorous night.
1. M. Hill Smith, G. Langford, Chandos Concert Orch, S. Barry *Concert* (8/93) (CHAN) ① **CHAN9142**
King's Rhapsody—musical show: 3 acts (1949—Manchester) (Lyrics C. Hassall)
EXCERPTS: 1. When the gypsy played; 2. Fly home, little heart; 3. When the violins begin to play; 4. The gates of Paradise.
1-3. M. Hill Smith, G. Langford, Chandos Concert Orch, S. Barry *Concert*
(8/93) (CHAN) ① **CHAN9142**

Perchance to dream—musical play: 3 acts (1945—London) (Book and Lyrics cpsr)
EXCERPTS: 1. Love is my reason; 2. When I curtsied to the King; 3. We'll gather lilacs.
1, 2, 3. M. Hill Smith, G. Langford, Chandos Concert Orch, S. Barry *Concert*
(8/93) (CHAN) ① **CHAN9142**
Valley of Song—musical show (cpted R Hamner: 1964)
EXCERPTS: 1. Look in my heart.
1. M. Hill Smith, G. Langford, Chandos Concert Orch, S. Barry *Concert* (8/93) (CHAN) ① **CHAN9142**

NUCIUS, Johannes *(c1556–1620)* Germany

SECTION IV: VOCAL AND CHORAL

Dum complerentur—motet: 5vv
Schola Gregoriana, M. Berry (r1992) *Concert*
(11/93) (HERA) ① **HAVPCD161**

NUTILE, E. *(19th Cent)* Italy

SECTION IV: VOCAL AND CHORAL

Mamma mia, che vo' sapè—song (Wds. F. Russo)
B. Gigli, orch, R. Bourdon (r1930) *Concert*
(5/90) (PEAR) ① **GEMMCD9367**
E. Caruso, orch (r1909) *Concert*
(3/91) (PEAR) ① [3] **EVC2**
E. Caruso, orch, W.B. Rogers (r1909) *Concert*
(7/91) (RCA) ① [12] **GD60495(3)**

NUYTS, Frank *(b 1954)* Belgium

SECTION I: ORCHESTRAL

Woodnotes—marimba and orchestra (1987)
1. Part I; 2. Part II.
R. van Sice, Bruges Collegium Instr, F. Nuyts *Concert* (6/90) (ETCE) ① **KTC1085**

NYBLOM, Carl Göran *(1867–1920)* Sweden

SECTION IV: VOCAL AND CHORAL

Flaming golden stream—song (Wds. cpsr)
J. Björling, orch, N. Grevillius (r1933) *Concert*
(8/92) (BLUE) ① **ABCD016**

NYIREGHÁZI, Ervin *(1903–1987)* Hungary/USA

SECTION III: INSTRUMENTAL

Un ballo in maschera (Verdi)—piano transcription
E. Nyiregházi (r1978) *Concert*
(12/93) (VAI) ① **VAIA1003**
Eugene Onegin (Tchaikovsky)—piano transcription
E. Nyiregházi (r1978) *Concert*
(12/93) (VAI) ① **VAIA1003**
Otello (Verdi)—piano transcription (with interpolated 'Pagliacci': Leoncavallo)
E. Nyiregházi (r1978) *Concert*
(12/93) (VAI) ① **VAIA1003**
Pagliacci (Leoncavallo)—piano paraphrase
E. Nyiregházi (r1978) *Concert*
(12/93) (VAI) ① **VAIA1003**
Rienzi and Lohengrin (Wagner)—piano transcription
E. Nyiregházi (r1978) *Concert*
(12/93) (VAI) ① **VAIA1003**
Il trovatore (Verdi)—piano transcription
E. Nyiregházi (r1978) *Concert*
(12/93) (VAI) ① **VAIA1003**

NYMAN, Michael *(b 1948)* England

SECTION I: ORCHESTRAL

MGV (Musique à Grande Vitesse) (1993) (for the inauguration of the TGV North-European line)
Nyman Band, Orch, M. Nyman (r1993) *Piano Concerto.* (9/94) (ARGO) ① **443 382-2ZH**
The Piano Concerto (1993) (arr of themes from film score)
EXCERPTS: 1. The Beach; 2. The Woods; 3. The Hut; 4. The Release.
K. Stott, RLPO, M. Nyman (r1994) *MGV.*
(9/94) (ARGO) ① **443 382-2ZH**

Where the Bee dances—saxophone and orchestra
J. Harle, Bournemouth Sinfonietta, I. Bolton *Concert*
(7/92) (ARGO) ① **433 847-2ZH**

SECTION II: CHAMBER

Flugal and Piano (1991)
G. Ashton, J. Lenehan (r1992) *Concert*
(4/94) (VIRG) ① **VC5 45003-2**
For John Cage—brass ensemble (1992)
London Brass (r1992) *Concert*
(7/93) (ARGO) ① **440 282-2ZH**
4 Songs for Tony (Simons)—saxophones (1992-93)
1. First Song; 2. Second Song; 3. Third Song; 4. Fourth Song.
Apollo Sax Qt (r1993) *Concert*
(8/95) (ARGO) ① **443 903-2ZH**
String Quartet No. 1 (1985)
Balanescu Qt *Concert*
(8/91) (ARGO) ① **433 093-2ZH**
String Quartet No. 2 (1988)
Balanescu Qt *Concert*
(8/91) (ARGO) ① **433 093-2ZH**
String Quartet No. 3 (1990)
Balanescu Qt *Concert*
(8/91) (ARGO) ① **433 093-2ZH**
Time will pronounce—violin, cello and piano (1992)
London Trio (r1992) *Concert*
(7/93) (ARGO) ① **440 282-2ZH**
1-100—multiple pianos (1976)
Piano Circus *Concert*
(7/92) (ARGO) ① **433 522-2ZH**

SECTION III: INSTRUMENTAL

The convertilibity of lute strings—harpsichord (1992)
V. Black (r1992) *Concert*
(7/93) (ARGO) ① **440 282-2ZH**

SECTION IV: VOCAL AND CHORAL

Noises, Sounds and Sweet Airs—soloists and orchestra (1993) (Wds. Shakespeare)
Cpte C. Bott, H. Summers, I. Bostridge, Basse-Normandie Ens, D. Debart (r1993)
(4/95) (ARGO) ① **440 842-2ZH**
Self-laudatory hymn of Inanna and her omnipotence—alto and viols (1992) (Wds. Sumerian, trans Kramer)
J. Bowman, Fretwork (r1992) *Concert*
(7/93) (ARGO) ① **440 282-2ZH**

SECTION V: STAGE WORKS

The Draughtsman's Contract—film score (1982)
EXCERPTS: 1. Chasing Sheep is Best Left to Shepherds; 2. An Eye for Optical Theory; 3. The Garden is Becoming a Robe Room.
1. OST (1989) (9/95) (VIR2) ① **CDV2774**
The Man who mistook his Wife for a Hat—chamber opera (Lib. C. Rawlence)
Cpte E. Belcourt, S. Leonard, F. Westcott, Inst Ens, M. Nyman (r1988) (11/88) (SONY) ① **MK44669**
The Piano—film score (1993)
EXCERPTS: 1. To the Edge of the Earth; 2. Big My Secret; 3. A Wild and Distant Shore; 4. The Heart asks Pleasure First; 5. Here to There; 6. The Promise; 7. A Bed of Ferns; 8. The Fling; 9. The Scent of Love; 10. Deep Into the Forest; 11. The Mood that Passes Through You; 12. Lost and Found; 13. The Embrace; 14. Little Impulse; 15. The Sacrifice; 16. I Clipped Your Wing; 17. The Wounded; 18. All Imperfect Things; 19. Dreams of a Journey.
1-19. OST, Munich PO, M. Nyman (pf/dir) (r1993)
(8/94) (VIR2) ① **CDVE919**
4, 6. OST (r1993) *Concert*
(9/95) (VIR2) ① **CDV2774**
Prospero's Books—film score (1991) (Wds. Shakespeare)
EXCERPTS—: 1. Full fathom five; 2. Prospero's curse; 3. While you here do snoring lie; 4. Prospero's magic; 5. Miranda; 6. Come unto these yellow sands; 7. Come unto thee you; 8. History of Sycorax; 9. Come and go; 10. Cornfield; 11. Where the bee sucks; 12. Caliban's pit; 13. Reconciliation; 14. The Masque.
S. Leonard, M. Angel, U. Lemper, D. Conway, Nyman Band, M. Nyman (pf/dir)
(11/91) (DECC) ① **425 224-2DH**
A Zed and two noughts—film score (1985)
1. Prawn-watching; 2. Time lapse.
OST, S. Leonard, A. Balanescu, E. Perry, M. Nyman, Zoo Orch (3/86) (TER) ① **CDTER1106**

NYSTEDT, Knut (b 1915) Norway

SECTION I: ORCHESTRAL

Pia memoria—nine brass instruments and percussion, Op. 65 (1971)
Brass Ens, K. Nystedt Concert
(5/93) (AURO) ① [2] ACD4971

SECTION II: CHAMBER

Rhapsody in Green—brass quintet, Op. 82 (1978)
Norwegian Brass Quintet Concert
(5/93) (AURO) ① [2] ACD4971

SECTION IV: VOCAL AND CHORAL

Lucis creator optime—soprano, baritone, choir and orchestra, Op. 58 (1968)
E. Skaug, O. Eriksen, Norwegian Sols Ch, Oslo PO, K. Nystedt Concert
(5/93) (AURO) ① [2] ACD4971

19 Motets—choir a capella (1950-1980s)
1. Neslandskyrkja; 2. Ikke ved makt; 3. Dyp av nåde; 4. Blessed be he (Velsignet vaere han); 5. I am the bread of life (Eg er livsens brod); 6. He has risen (Han er oppstanden); 7. Fader, jeg vil; 8. A krist, som i bryllaup gjesta; 9. Vaer ikke bekymret; 10. Jeg er verdens lys; 11. Den seg selv opphøyer; 12. If you receive my words; 13. Get you up; 14. Thou, O Lord; 15. Sing and rejoice; 16. Peace I leave with you; 17. I will praise Thee, O Lord; 18. Yet a little while; 19. Cry out and shout.
Bergen Cath Ch, M. Mangersnes Concert
(5/93) (AURO) ① [2] ACD4971

NYSTROEM, Gösta (1890–1966) Sweden

SECTION I: ORCHESTRAL

The Arctic Ocean, 'Ishavet'—symphonic poem (1924-25)
Stockholm PO, P. Erös Concert
(4/90) (CPRI) ① CAP21332
Malmö SO, P. Järvi (r1994) Concert
(4/95) (BIS) ① BIS-CD682

Concerto for Viola and Orchestra, 'Hommage à la France' (1940)
N. Imai, Malmö SO, P. Järvi (r1993) Concert
(4/95) (BIS) ① BIS-CD682

Sinfonia Concertante—cello and orchestra (1940-44)
N. Ullner, Malmö SO, P. Järvi (r1994) Concert
(4/95) (BIS) ① BIS-CD682

Symphony No. 1, 'Sinfonia breve' (1929-31)
Gothenburg SO, S. Ehrling Concert
(4/90) (CPRI) ① CAP21332

Symphony No. 5, 'Sinfonia seria' (1963)
Stockholm PO, J-P. Saraste Concert
(4/90) (CPRI) ① CAP21332

OAKELEY, Sir Herbert (Stanley) (1830–1903) England

SECTION IV: VOCAL AND CHORAL

Sun of my Soul—hymn (tune: Abends)
St Paul's Cath Ch, C. Dearnley, John Scott Concert
(7/90) (HYPE) ① CDH88036

OBRADORS, Fernando J (1897–1945) Spain

SECTION IV: VOCAL AND CHORAL

Aquel Sombrero de monte—song
V. de los Angeles, G. Parsons (pp1990) Concert
(12/91) (COLL) ① Coll1247-2

Canciones clásicas españolas—1v and piano (1920)
1. Al amor; 2. Corazón, por qué pasáis; 3. Con amores, la mi madre; 4. Dos cantares populares; 5. Copla de curro dolce; 6. El majo celoso; 7. Del cabello más sutil; 8. La mi sola Laureola; 9. La mia sola, Laureola.
1, 3, 6-8. P. Rozario, M. Troop Concert
(12/92) (COLL) ① Coll3052-2
1-6, 9. M. Bayo, J.A. Alvarez-Parejo (r1992) Concert
(6/93) (CLAV) ① CD50-9205
1, 7, 8. K. Battle, M. Garrett (pp1991) Concert
(9/94) (SONY) ① SK53106
2, 6, 7, 8. D. Jones, M. Martineau (r1993) Concert
(9/94) (CHAN) ① CHAN9277

Chiquitita la novia—song
K. Battle, M. Garrett (pp1994) Concert
(9/94) (SONY) ① SK53106

Coplas de curro dulce—song
H. Spani, orch, G. Nastrucci (r1930) Concert
(9/90) (CLUB) ① [2] CL99-509/10

El Molondrón—song
V. de los Angeles, G. Parsons (pp1990) Concert
(12/91) (COLL) ① Coll1247-2

El Vito—song
V. de los Angeles, G. Parsons (pp1990) Concert
(12/91) (COLL) ① Coll1247-2
D. Jones, M. Martineau (r1993) Concert
(9/94) (CHAN) ① CHAN9277
J. Gomez, J. Constable (r1994) Concert
(9/94) (CONI) ① CDCF243

OBRECHT, Jacob (c1450–1505) The Netherlands

SECTION IV: VOCAL AND CHORAL

Factor orbis—motet: 5vv
New London Chmbr Ch, J. Wood Concert
(3/93) (AMON) ① CD-SAR56

Omnes spiritus laudet—motet: 5vv (from Segovia MS)
Daedalus Ens Concert
(12/92) (ACCE) ① ACC9176D

Pater noster—4vv
Lower Rhine Choral Soc, H. Schmitt Concert
(2/90) (SCHW) ① 313001

Quod Chorus Vatum/Haec Deum Caelii
Clerk's Group, E. Wickham (r1994) Concert
(3/95) (ASV) ① CDGAU139

Salve crux—motet: 5vv (late 1480s)
New London Chmbr Ch, J. Wood Concert
(3/93) (AMON) ① CD-SAR56

Salve regina—motet: 6vv
Clerks' Group, E. Wickham (r1993) Concert
(10/93) (PROU) ① PROUCD133

OCHS, Siegfried (1858–1929) Germany

SECTION IV: VOCAL AND CHORAL

Dank sei dir, Herr—song (previously attrib Handel)
J. Norman, G. Parsons (pp1987) Concert
(8/88) (PHIL) ① 422 048-2PH
R. Anday, Vienna St Op Orch, K. Alwin (r1929) Concert
(5/92) (PREI) ① 89046
K. Flagstad, Philh, W. Braithwaite (r1948) Concert
(7/93) (TEST) ① SBT1018
H. Schlusnus, Berlin St Op Orch, H. Weigert (r1930) Concert
(1/94) (PREI) ① 89205

OCKEGHEM, Johannes (c1410–1497) Flanders

SECTION IV: VOCAL AND CHORAL

Alma redemptoris mater—motet: 4vv
Clerk's Group, E. Wickham (r1994) Concert
(3/95) (ASV) ① CDGAU139

Au travail suis—chanson: 3vv
London Medieval Ens Concert
(9/93) (L'OI) ① [2] 436 194-2OH2

L' aultre d'antan l'autrier—chanson: 3vv
London Medieval Ens Concert
(9/93) (L'OI) ① [2] 436 194-2OH2

Aultre venus estés—chanson: 3vv
London Medieval Ens Concert
(9/93) (L'OI) ① [2] 436 194-2OH2

Ave Maria—motet: 4vv
Clerks' Group, E. Wickham (r1993) Concert
(10/93) (PROU) ① PROUCD133

Baisiés moy dont fort—chanson: 3vv
London Medieval Ens Concert
(9/93) (L'OI) ① [2] 436 194-2OH2

Ce n'est pas jeu—chanson: 3vv (attrib)
London Medieval Ens Concert
(9/93) (L'OI) ① [2] 436 194-2OH2

Credo—mass movement: 4vv (possibly 'Patrem de village', copied 1475)
Capella Alamire, P. Urquhart (r1993) Concert
(11/95) (DORI) ① DIS80131

Departés vous, male touche—chanson: 3vv (attrib)
London Medieval Ens Concert
(9/93) (L'OI) ① [2] 436 194-2OH2

Les Deséaux ont la saison—chanson: 3vv
London Medieval Ens Concert
(9/93) (L'OI) ① [2] 436 194-2OH2

La despourveue et la bannie—chanson: 3vv
London Medieval Ens Concert
(9/93) (L'OI) ① [2] 436 194-2OH2

D'un aultre amer—chanson: 3vv
London Medieval Ens Concert
(9/93) (L'OI) ① [2] 436 194-2OH2

D'un aultre la, 'Rondeau royal'—chanson: 3vv
London Medieval Ens Concert
(9/93) (L'OI) ① [2] 436 194-2OH2

Fors seulement contre ce qu'ay promys—chanson: 3vv
London Medieval Ens Concert
(9/93) (L'OI) ① [2] 436 194-2OH2

Fors seulement l'attente—chanson: 3vv
London Medieval Ens Concert
(9/93) (L'OI) ① [2] 436 194-2OH2

Il ne m'en chault plus—chanson: 3vv
London Medieval Ens Concert
(9/93) (L'OI) ① [2] 436 194-2OH2

Intemerata Dei mater—motet: 5vv
Clerks' Group, E. Wickham (r1993) Concert
(10/93) (PROU) ① PROUCD133
Oxford Camerata, J. Summerly (r1993) Concert
(3/95) (NAXO) ① 8 550843

Je n'ay dueil que je ne suis morte—chanson: 4vv (doubtful)
London Medieval Ens Concert
(9/93) (L'OI) ① [2] 436 194-2OH2

Ma bouche rit—chanson: 3vv
London Medieval Ens Concert
(9/93) (L'OI) ① [2] 436 194-2OH2

Ma maistresse et ma plus grant amye—chanson: 3vv
London Medieval Ens Concert
(9/93) (L'OI) ① [2] 436 194-2OH2

Malheur me bat—chanson: 3vv
London Medieval Ens Concert
(9/93) (L'OI) ① [2] 436 194-2OH2

Missa Ecce ancilla Domini—4vv
Clerks' Group, E. Wickham (r1993) Concert
(10/93) (PROU) ① PROUCD133

Missa, 'Mi-Mi' (quarti toni)—4vv (copied 1475-76)
Clerk's Group, E. Wickham (r1994) Concert
(3/95) (ASV) ① CDGAU139

Missa Pro defunctis—3-4vv (?c1461)
PCA, B. Turner Josquin Desprez: Missa L'homme armé super voces musicales.
(4/86) (ARCH) ① 415 293-2AH

Missa prolationum—4vv
Cappella Nova, R. Taruskin Lupi: Ergone conticuit.
(2/87) (ASV) ① CDGAU103

Mort tu as navre—chanson: 4vv (c1460)
London Medieval Ens Concert
(9/93) (L'OI) ① [2] 436 194-2OH2

O rosa bella o dolce anima mia—chanson: 2vv (arr after Bedyngham or Dunstable)
London Medieval Ens Concert
(9/93) (L'OI) ① [2] 436 194-2OH2

Prenez sur moi vostre exemple—chanson: 3vv
London Medieval Ens Concert
(9/93) (L'OI) ① [2] 436 194-2OH2

Presque transi—chanson: 3vv
London Medieval Ens Concert
(9/93) (L'OI) ① [2] 436 194-2OH2

Quant ce viendra—chanson: 3vv (doubtful)
London Medieval Ens Concert
(9/93) (L'OI) ① [2] 436 194-2OH2

Quant de vous seul—chanson: 3vv
London Medieval Ens Concert
(9/93) (L'OI) ① [2] 436 194-2OH2

Qu'es mi vida preguntoys—chanson: 4vv (after 3vv setting by Cornago)
London Medieval Ens Concert
(9/93) (L'OI) ① [2] 436 194-2OH2

Requiem—4vv (?1461)
1. Introitus: Requiem aeternam.
Organum Ens, M. Pérès (r1992; with plainchant)
(2/94) (HARM) ① HMC90 1441

Resjois toy terre de France—chanson: 4vv (doubtful)
London Medieval Ens Concert
(9/93) (L'OI) ① [2] 436 194-2OH2

Salve regina I—motet: 4vv (Ms Cappella Sistina 42)
Clerk's Group, E. Wickham (r1994) Concert
(3/95) (ASV) ① CDGAU139

Se vostre cuer eslongne—chanson: 3vv
London Medieval Ens Concert
(9/93) (L'OI) ① [2] 436 194-2OH2

S'elle m'amera—chanson: 4vv
London Medieval Ens Concert
(9/93) (L'OI) ① [2] 436 194-2OH2

Tant fuz gentement—chanson: 3vv
London Medieval Ens Concert
(9/93) (L'OI) ① [2] 436 194-2OH2

O'DONNELL, Bertram Walton
(1887–1939) England

SECTION I: ORCHESTRAL

2 Songs of the Gael, '(A) Gaelic Fantasy'—wind brass, Op. 31
Coldstream Guards Band, R.A. Ridings *Concert*
(4/87) (BAND) ① **BNA5002**
Theme and Variations—wind band, Op. 26
Coldstream Guards Band, R.A. Ridings *Concert*
(4/87) (BAND) ① **BNA5002**

OFFENBACH, Jacques
(1819–1880) Germany/France

SECTION I: ORCHESTRAL

Les **belles américaines**—orchestral waltzes
(arr cpsr from piano work)
Cincinnati Pops, E. Kunzel *Concert*
(11/92) (TELA) ① **CD80294**
Boston Pops, A. Fiedler (r1956; arr R. R. Bennett)
Concert (1/94) (RCA) ① **09026 61429-2**
Concerto-rondò—cello and orchestra (c1850)
O. Harnoy, Cincinnati SO, E. Kunzel *Concert*
(11/86) (RCA) ① **RD71003**
Musette—Air de Ballet du 17me siècle, Op. 24 (1843)
Boston Pops, A. Fiedler (r1956) *Concert*
(1/94) (RCA) ① **09026 61429-2**

SECTION II: CHAMBER

Danse bohémienne—cello and piano, Op. 28 (c1846)
M. Kliegel, R. Havenith *Concert*
(9/92) (MARC) ① **8 223403**

SECTION V: STAGE WORKS

Barbe-Bleue—operetta: 3 acts (1866—Paris)
(Lib. Meilhac and Halévy)
EXCERPTS: 1. Overture; 2. Y a p't-êtr' des bergèr's dans l'village; 3. V'la z'encor' de drôl's de jeunesses.
Or depuis la rose nouvelle...Tous les deux, amoureux B. Hendricks, G. Quilico, Lyon Op Orch, L. Foster (r1993) *Concert*
(6/95) (EMI) ① **CDC5 55151-2**
Overture BPO, H. von Karajan (German version)
Concert (3/83) (DG) ① **400 044-2GH**
1. Vienna SO, B. Weil (r1992: arr F Hoffmann)
Concert (1/94) (SONY) ① **SK53288**
La **Belle Hélène, 'Beautiful Helen'**—operetta: 3 acts (1864—Paris) (Lib. Meilhac and Halévy)
1a. Overture (prep. E. Haensch). ACT 1: 1b. Vers tes autels, Jupin (chorus); 1c. C'est le devoir des jeunes filles (Chorus of girls); 2a. Amours divins! (Helen); 2b. Entrez, vite, Grande Reine! (Calchas, Helen); 3a. Au cabaret du labyrinthe (Oreste, Calchas, chorus); 3b. Tzing la la (Oreste, chorus); 4. Quoi?...Là-bas dans l'azur (melodrame); 5. Homme de 20 ans (melodrame); 6. Au mont Ida (Paris); 7a. Voici les rois de la Grèce (chorus); 7b. Ces rois remplis de vaillance (Kings); 7c. Nous commençons (ensemble); 7d. Fanfare! (Helen, chorus); 8. Gloire (finale). ACT 2: 9. Entr'acte; 10. Ô Reine, en ce jour (Helen, Bacchus, chorus); 11. Je ne nomme Hélène la Blonde (Helen); 12. Le voici le Roi des Rois (March of the goose); 13. Vous le voyez (Gambling Scene); 14. En couronnes, tressons les roses (Helen, Paris, chorus); 15. C'est le ciel qui m'envoie (Helen, Paris); 16. A moi! Rois de la Grèce (finale: ensemble). ACT 3: 17. Entr'acte; 18a. Dansons, buvons (Oreste, chorus); 18b. Vénus au fond de notre âme (Oreste, chorus); 18c. Oh mais alors ce n'était pas un rêve (melodrame); 19. Là vrai, je ne suis pas coupable (Hélène); 20. Lorsque le Grèce (Menelaus, Calchas, Agamemnon); 21a. La galère de Cythère (chorus); 21b. Et tout d'abord, ô vile multitude (Paris, chorus); 22. Helen vient, c'est elle (finale: ensemble).
Cpte J. Norman, J. Aler, C. Burles, G. Bacquier, J-P. Lafont, C. Alliot-Lugaz, J. Loreau, R. Trentin, G. Desroches, N. Carreras, A. Levallier, Toulouse Capitole Chor, Toulouse Capitole Orch, M. Plasson (9/86) (EMI) ① [2] **CDS7 47157-8**
1a BPO, H. von Karajan *Concert*
(3/83) (DG) ① **400 044-2GH**
1a Berlin St Op Orch, O. Klemperer (r1929) *Concert*
(2/89) (SYMP) ① **SYMCD1042**
1a Detroit SO, P. Paray (r1959) *Concert*
(11/93) (MERC) ① **434 332-2MM**
1a Boston Pops, A. Fiedler (r1956) *Concert*
(1/94) (RCA) ① **09026 61429-2**
1a Vienna SO, B. Weil (r1992: arr F Leiner) *Concert*
(1/94) (SONY) ① **SK53288**

1a, 15. Raphaele Concert Orch, P. Walden (arr Waldenmaier) *Concert*
(5/91) (MOZA) ① **MECD1002**
1c, 6, 7a, 7b, 8, 11, 15, 18b, 20, 21b, 22. C. Devos, Duvaleix, M. Roux, B. Demigny, G. Rey, A. Doniat, W. Clément, D. Dassy, L. Berton, Raymond St Paul Chor, Lamoureux Orch, J. Gressier (r1950s) *Concert*
(5/93) (EMI) ① [2] **CZS7 67515-2**
6. H. Nash, orch (Eng: r1932) *Concert*
(9/91) (PEAR) ① **GEMMCD9473**
6. J. Björling, orch, N. Grevillius (r1938: Swed) *Concert*
(8/92) (BLUE) ① **ABCD016**
6. J. Björling, orch, N. Grevillius (r1938: Swed) *Concert*
(10/93) (NIMB) ① **NI7842**
6. J. Björling, orch, N. Grevillius (r1938: Swed) *Concert*
(10/93) (EMI) ① **CDH7 64707-2**
6. J. Björling, orch, N. Grevillius (r1938: Swed) *Concert*
(9/94) (CARL) ① **GLRS103**
6. J. Björling, orch, N. Grevillius (r1938: Swed) *Concert*
(12/94) (MMOI) ① **CDMOIR425**
Les **Brigands**—operetta: 3 acts (1869—Paris) (Lib. Meilhac and Halévy)
Cpte T. Raffalli, G. Raphanel, C. Alliot-Lugaz, M. Trempont, C. Jean, F. Dudziak, P-Y. Le Maigat, V. Millot, M. Fockenoy, J-L. Viala, T. Dran, F. le Roux, B. Pisani, R. Schirrer, J. Loreau, Lyon Op Chor, Lyon Op Orch, J.E. Gardiner (r1988)
(2/90) (EMI) ① [2] **CDS7 49830-2**
La **Chanson de Fortunio**—operetta: 1 act (1861—Paris) (Lib. Crémieux and Halévy)
Cpte L. Lovano, L. Dachary, M. Hamel, R. Amade, F. Betti, A. Doniat, R. Destain, J. Pruvost, P. Saugey, ORTF Lyric Orch, J-C. Hartemann (bp1963) *Madame l'Archiduc.* (3/92) (MUSD) ① [2] **20138-2**
Christopher Columbus—opera pastiche (1976—Belfast) (Lib. D White: music arr P Schmid)
Cpte M. Arthur, J. Roberts, J. Peters, L. Gray, M. Hill Smith, C. du Plessis, A. Opie, Anna Dawson, A. Bregonzi, C. Harré, J. Duxbury, R. Ashe, C. Kite, K. Smales, A. Dixey, G. Mitchell Ch, LMP, A. Francis (r1977: Eng) (4/93) (OPRA) ① [2] **ORC002**
Les **Contes d'Hoffmann, '(The) Tales of Hoffmann'**—opera: prologue, 3 acts, epilogue (1881—Paris) (Lib. Barbier. Score completed Guiraud)
PROLOGUE: 1. Prelude; 2. Glou! glou! glou!; 3a. Le conseilleur Lindorf, morbleu!; 3b. Dans les rôles d'amoureux langoureux; 4. Deux heures devant moi; 5. Drig, drig, drig; 6. Il était une fois à la cour d'Eisenach (Legend of Kleinsach); 7. Peuh! cette bière est détestable. ACT 1: 8. Entr'acte; 9. Là! dors en paix; 10a. Allons! courage et confiance; 10b. C'est elle!; 10c. Ah! vivre deux!; 11a. C'est moi, Coppélius (Je me nomme Coppélius); 11b. J'ai des yeux; 12. Non aucun hôte vraiment; 13. Les oiseaux dans la charmille (Doll's Song); 14a. Le souper vous attend; 14b. Ils se sont éloignés enfin!; 15. Voici les valseurs (Waltz). ACT 2: 16. Belle nuit, ô nuit d'amour (Barcarolle); 17a. Et moi, ce n'est pa la; 17b. Que d'un brûlant désir; 18a. Scintille diamant!; 18b. Cher ange!; 19a. Malhureux!; 19b. O Dieu! de quelle ivresse; 20. Hélas! mon coeur s'égare encore!; 21. Ecoutez, messieurs!. ACT 3: 22. Elle a fui, la tourterelle; 23. Jour et nuit; 24a. C'est une chanson d'amour; 24b. J'ai le bonheur dans l'âme; 25. Qu'as-tu donc?; 26. Pour conjurer le danger; 27a. Ne chanteras plus?; 27b. Écoute! Antonia! Dieu, ma mère; 28. Mon enfant! ma fille! Antonia! (Finale). 29. Entr'acte. EPILOGUE: 30. Voilà quelle fut l'histoire; 31. Vidons les tonneaux; 32a. Et moi?; 32b. O Dieu! de quelle ivresse; 33. Non, ivre mort. 34. Barcarolle (orchestral version).
Cpte P. Domingo, J. Sutherland, H. Tourangeau, G. Bacquier, J. Charon, A. Neury, P. Plishka, M. Lilowa, H. Cuénod, R. Jacques, Suisse Romande Rad Ch, SRO, R. Bonynge (with dialogue)
(11/86) (DECC) ① [2] **417 363-2DH2**
Cpte N. Shicoff, L. Serra, J. Norman, R. Plowright, D. Bryant, A. Murray, J. van Dam, A. Oliver, D. Duesing, K. Rydl, J. Taillon, R. Tear, A. Murray, K. Rydl, Brussels Nat Op Chor, Brussels Nat Op Orch, S. Cambreling (1988)
(12/88) (EMI) ① [3] **CDS7 49641-2**
Cpte N. Gedda, G. d'Angelo, E. Schwarzkopf, V. de los Angeles, J-C. Benoit, N. Ghiuselev, G. London, E. Blanc, M. Sénéchal, J-P. Laffage, R. Geay, C. Gayraud, J. Collard, R. Duclos Ch, Paris Cons, A. Cluytens (r1964/5)
(11/88) (EMI) ① **CMS7 63222-2**
Cpte P. Domingo, E. Gruberová, C. Eder, A. Schmidt, G. Bacquier, J. Diaz, J. Morris, G. Friedmann, R. Van Allan, H. Stamm, C. Ludwig, R. Gambill, P. Crook, M. Sénéchal, K. Rydl, R. Lloyd, U. Malmberg, French Rad Chor, FNO, S. Ozawa (r1986)
(3/90) (DG) ① [2] **427 682-2GH2**

Cpte R. Jobin, R. Doria, V. Bovy, G. Boué, F. Revoil, R. Faure, L. Musy, A. Pernet, C. Soix, R. Bourdin, R. Lapelletrie, C. Cambon, A. Philippe, S. Borghese, Bourvil, A. Vessières, R. Amade, C. Maurane, H. Delahaye, Paris Opéra-Comique Chor, Paris Opéra-Comique Orch, A. Cluytens (r1948)
(9/95) (EMI) ① [2] **CMS5 65260-2**
1. Detroit SO, P. Paray (r1959) *Concert*
(11/93) (MERC) ① **434 332-2MM**
6. P. Domingo, SRO, R. Bonynge *Concert*
(7/86) (DG) ① **415 366-2GH**
6. G. Lauri-Volpi, NY Met Op Chor, NY Met Op Orch, G. Setti (r1929) *Concert* (9/90) (PREI) ① **89012**
6. G. Lauri-Volpi, NY Met Op Chor, NY Met Op Orch, G. Setti (r1929) *Concert* (7/93) (NIMB) ① **NI7845**
6. P. Domingo, Suisse Romande Rad Chor, Lausanne Pro Arte Ch, SRO, R. Bonynge (r1972) *Concert* (10/93) (DECC) ① **436 463-2DM**
6. Alfredo Kraus, P. Gyton, WNO Chor, WNO Orch, C. Rizzi (r1994) *Concert*
(8/95) (PHIL) ① **442 785-2PH**
6, 19b R. Tauber, orch (Ger: r1928) *Concert*
(7/89) (PEAR) ① **GEMMCD9327**
6, 19b R. Tauber, chor, Berlin Staatskapelle, E. Hauke (Ger: r1928) *Concert*
(3/92) (EMI) ① **CDH7 64029-2**
6, 19b R. Tauber, chor, Berlin Staatskapelle, E. Hauke (Ger: r1928) *Concert*
(12/94) (NIMB) ① **NI7830**
6, 32b J. Patzak, Berlin St Op Orch, H. Weigert (Ger: r1930) *Concert* (3/90) (PEAR) ① **GEMMCD9383**
8. Boston Pops, A. Fiedler (r1956) *Concert*
(1/94) (RCA) ① **09026 61429-2**
8, 16, 19a, 29. LPO, T. Beecham (r1936) *Concert*
(7/94) (PEAR) ① **GEMMCD9065**
8, 19a, 29, 34. LPO, T. Beecham (r1936) *Concert*
(6/94) (DUTT) ① **CDLX7003**
11a A. Didur, orch (r c1916) *Concert*
(1/94) (CLUB) ① **CL99-089**
13. M. André, Toulouse Capitole Chor, Toulouse Capitole Orch, M. Plasson (arr tpt) *Concert*
(1/89) (EMI) ① **CDC7 49219-2**
13. L. Pons, orch, G. Cloëz (r1929) *Concert*
(4/92) (MSOU) ① **DFCDI-111**
13. F. Saville, anon (Ger: r c1902) *Concert*
(10/92) (SYMP) ① **SYMCD1093**
13. M. Korjus, Berlin St Op Orch, F. Schönbaumsfeld (Ger: r1934) *Concert* (10/93) (PREI) ① **89054**
13. F. Hempel, orch (r1913) *Concert*
(3/94) (NIMB) ① **NI7849**
13. P. Alarie, Lamoureux Orch, P. Dervaux (r1953) *Concert* (11/94) (PHIL) ① [2] **438 953-2PM2**
13. I. Baillie, orch, S. Robinson (r1930: Eng) *Concert*
(7/95) (DUTT) ① **CDLX7013**
13, 34. T. Dahl, Calgary PO, M. Bernardi (r1992) *Concert* (12/94) (CBC) ① **SMCD5125**
16. G. Saba (trs. Msockowski) *Concert*
(10/87) (CARL) ① **PCD858**
16. J. McCormack, F. Kreisler, E. Schneider (Eng: r1916) *Concert* (9/89) (PEAR) ① **GEMMCD9315**
16. L. Garrett, Philh, A. Greenwood (r1990-1) *Concert* (11/91) (SILV) ① **SONGCD903**
16. P. Domingo, I. Perlman, NY Studio Orch, J. Tunick (r1990: arr ten/vn) *Concert*
(3/92) (EMI) ① **CDC7 54266-2**
16. M. Caballé, S. Verrett, New Philh, A. Guadagno (5/92) (RCA) ① **GD60818**
16. C. Muzio, K. Howard, orch (r1918) *Concert*
(1/95) (ROMO) ① [2] **81010-2**
17a, 17b, 19b C. Kullman, Berlin St Op Orch, O. Dobrindt (Ger: r1931) *Concert*
(11/93) (PREI) ① **89057**
18a H. Hasslo, orch, N. Grevillius (r1941: Swed) *Concert* (4/92) (EMI) ① [7] **CHS7 69741-2(5)**
18a H. Schlusnus, orch (r1925: Ger) *Concert*
(12/95) (PREI) ① **89110**
19b A. Piccaver, orch (r1920: Ger) *Concert*
(8/93) (PREI) ① **89060**
19b R. Tauber, orch (r1928: Ger) *Concert*
(12/94) (MMOI) ① **CDMOIR427**
22. K. Te Kanawa, ROHO, J. Tate *Concert*
(2/90) (EMI) ① **CDC7 49863-2**
22. C. Muzio, orch (r1924) *Concert*
(5/90) (BOGR) ① [2] **BIM705-2**
22. Lotte Lehmann, orch (r1921) *Concert*
(6/92) (PREI) ① [3] **89302**
22. J. Hammond, Philh, V. Tausky (r1952) *Concert*
(12/92) (TEST) ① **SBT1013**
22. C. Muzio, orch (r1924) *Concert*
(1/94) (ROMO) ① [2] **81005-2**
22. J. Novotná, RCA SO, F. Weissmann (r1945) *Concert* (4/94) (RCA) ① [6] **09026 61580-2(5)**
24a, 24b H. Roswaenge, H. von Debička, Berlin St Op Orch, H. Weigert (Ger: r1931: Ger) *Concert*
(4/95) (PREI) ① [2] **89209**

24b H.E. Groh, E. Bettendorf, orch (Ger: r1931) *Concert* (3/92) (PEAR) ① **GEMMCD9419**
34. BPO, H. von Karajan (arr M Rosenthal) *Concert* (3/83) (DG) ① **400 044-2GH**
34. Gothenburg SO, N. Järvi *Concert* (6/90) (DG) ① **429 494-2GDC**
34. BPO, H. von Karajan (arr M Rosenthal) *Concert* (8/91) (DG) ① **431 160-2GR**
34. Black Dyke Mills Band, G. Brand (arr G Langford) *Concert* (10/91) (CHAN) ① **CHAN6539**

La **Fille du tambour-major—operetta: 3 acts (1879—Paris)** (Lib. Chivot and Duru)
EXCERPTS: 1. Overture; 2. Chanson de la fille du tambour-major.
1. Vienna SO, B. Weil (r1992) *Concert* (1/94) (SONY) ① **SK53288**

Gaîté Parisienne—ballet (1938) (arr M. Rosenthal)
1. Overture (La Vie Parisienne); 2. Allegro moderato (Mesdames de la Halle); 3. Polka (Voyage dans la Lune); 4. Ländler (Lieschen et Fritzchen); 5. Mazurka (La Vie Parisienne); 6. Valse (La Vie Parisienne); 7. Entrée du Brésilien (La Vie Parisienne); 8. Polka (La belle Hélène); 9. Valse (Orphée aux enfers); 10. Marche (Tromb-al-Cazar); 11. Valse (La Vie Parisienne); 12. Entrée du Brésilien); 13. Valse (Les Contes d'Hoffmann); 14. Duel (composed Rosenthal); 15. Valse (La Périchole); 16. Prélude au Can-Can (composed Rosenthal); 17. Can-Can Scène 1 (Orphée aux enfers; Robinson Crusoe); 18. Can-Can Scène 2—Polka (Orphée aux enfers); 19. Can-Can Scène 3 (potpourri).
Cpte Monte Carlo PO, M. Rosenthal *Concert* (12/89) (EMI) ① **CDM7 63136-2**
Cpte Montreal SO, C. Dutoit *Gounod: Faust.* (8/91) (DECC) ① **430 718-2DM**
Cpte Cincinnati Pops, E. Kunzel (arr Rosenthal) *Concert* (11/92) (TELA) ① **CD80294**
Cpte Boston Pops, A. Fiedler (r1954) *Rossini: Boutique fantasque.* (2/94) (RCA) ① **09026 61847-2**
Excs BPO, H. von Karajan *Concert* (5/90) (DG) ① **429 163-2GR**
Excs BPO, H. von Karajan (r1971) *Concert* (10/94) (DG) ① [2] **437 404-2GX2**
Suite NYPO, L. Bernstein *Concert* (11/92) (SONY) ① **SMK47532**
1-3, 13, 15, 17-19. Philadelphia, E. Ormandy (r1963) *Concert* (6/93) (SONY) ① **SBK48279**

Geneviève de Brabant—operetta: 2 acts (1859—Paris) (Lib. Jaime and Tréfeu)
Galop Cincinnati Pops, E. Kunzel *Concert* (11/92) (TELA) ① **CD80294**
Galop Boston Pops, A. Fiedler (r1956) *Concert* (1/94) (RCA) ① **09026 61429-2**

Der **Goldschmied von Toledo—operetta: 3 acts** (pastiche of Offenbach works: 1919)
EXCERPTS: 1. Lieblichste alle Frauen.
1. J. Patzak, Berlin St Op Chor, Berlin St Op Orch, J. Prüwer (r1931) *Concert* (3/90) (PEAR) ① **GEMMCD9383**

La **Grande-Duchesse de Gérolstein—operetta: 3 acts (1867—Paris)** (Lib. Meilhac and Halévy)
EXCERPTS: 1. Overture. ACT 1: 2. Tournons et valsons?; 3a. O mon Fritz; 3b. Allez, jeunes filles; 4. Pif, Paf, Pouf; 5. Me voici! me voici!; 6. Portez armes; 7a. Vous aimez le danger; 7b. Ah! Que j'aime les militaires; 8. Ah! c'est un fameux régiment; 9. Pour epouser une princesse (Chronique de la Gazette de Hollande); 9a. Ils vont tous partir; 9b. Voici le sabre de mon père. ACT 2: 10a. Enfin la guerre est terminée; 10b. Je t'ai sur mon coeur; 10c. Ah! lettre adorée; 11. Après le victoire; 12. En très bon ordre; 13a. Oui, Général; 13b. Dites-lui qu'on l'a remarqué distigué; 14a. Ne devinez-vous pas; 14b. Max était soldat de fortune; 15. Logeons-la donc. ACT 3: 16. Ce qu'on a fait; 17. Sortez, sortez; 18a. Nous amenons la jeune femme; 18b. Bonne nuit, monsieur; 19a. On peut être aimable; 19b. Ouvrez, ouvres; 19c. À cheval, à cheval; 19d. Notre auguste maîtresse; 20. Au repas comme à la Bataille; 21. Il était un de mes aïoux (Légende du Verre); 22. Voici revenir; 23. Enfin j'ai repris la panache.
1. BPO, H. von Karajan (arr F Hoffmann) *Concert* (3/83) (DG) ① **400 044-2GH**
1. Boston Pops, A. Fiedler (r1956) *Concert* (1/94) (RCA) ① **09026 61429-2**
1. Vienna SO, B. Weil (r1992: arr F Hoffmann) *Concert* (1/94) (SONY) ① **SK53288**

M. Choufleuri restera chèz lui—operetta: 1 act (1861—Paris) (Lib. various)
Cpte J-P. Lafont, M. Mesplé, C. Burles, M. Trempont, M. Hamel, E. Greger, J. Laforge Choral Ens, Monte Carlo PO, M. Rosenthal *Concert* (10/89) (EMI) ① [2] **CDS7 49361-2**

Madame l'archiduc—operetta: 3 acts (1874—Paris) (Lib. Meilhac, Halévy & Millaud)
EXCERPTS: 1. Couplet de l'Alphabet.
Cpte L. Dachary, J. Levasseur, R. Bredy, D. Tirmont, P. Miguel, R. Amade, G. Rey, A. Doniat, R. Lenoty, J. Pruvost, M. Martin, M. Fauchey, M. Vigneron, ORTF Lyric Chorale, ORTF Lyric Orch, J-C. Hartemann (bp1963) *Chanson de Fortunio.* (3/92) (MUSD) ① [2] **20138-2**

Le **Mari à la porte—operetta: 1 act (1859—Paris)** (Lib. A Delacour & L Morand)
EXCERPTS: 1. J'entends, ma belle, 'Valse tyrolienne'.
1. S. Jo, ECO, R. Bonynge (r1993) *Concert* (9/94) (DECC) ① **440 679-2DH**

Mesdames de la Halle—operetta: 1 act (1853—Paris) (Lib. A. Lapointe)
Cpte M. Hamel, J-P. Lafont, M. Trempont, M. Pouradier-Duteil, O. Dumaine, M. Quillevéré, C. Burles, J-M. Frémeau, L. Pezzino, M. Mesplé, J. Laforge Choral Ens, Monte Carlo PO, M. Rosenthal *Concert* (10/89) (EMI) ① [2] **CDS7 49361-2**

Monsieur et Madame Denis—operetta: 1 act (1862—Paris) (Lib. M. Laurencin & M. Delaporte)
EXCERPTS: 1. Overture.
1. Vienna SO, B. Weil (r1992) *Concert* (1/94) (SONY) ① **SK53288**

Orphée aux enfers, 'Orpheus in the Underworld'—operetta: 2 (later 4) acts (1858 rev 1874—Paris) (Lib. H Crémieux & L Halévy)
EXCERPTS: 1. Overture; 1a. Can-can. ACT 1: 3. La femme dont le coeur; 4. Ah! c'est ainsi!; 5. Ballet pastoral; 6a. Moi, je suis Aristée; 6b. Voici le tendre Aristée; 6c. Mélodrame; 7a. La mort m'apparaît; 7b. Violà une plume (Mélodrame); 8. Libre! ô bonheur. ACT 2: 9. Entr'acte and Chorus of Sleep; 10. Je suis Vénus!; 11. Tzing, tzing, tzing; 12. Par Saturne!; 13a. Eh hop! Eh hop!; 13b. Entry of Pluto; 14. Comme il me regarde!; 15. Aux armes, dieux et demi-dieux!; 16. Pour séduire Alcmène... 17. Il approche! Il s'avance...Le violà, oui, c'est bien lui!; 18. Entr'acte. ACT 3: 19. Ah! quelle triste destinée; 20a. Quand j'étais roi de Béotie; 20b. Ah! tenez, Madame (Mélodrame); 21. Ah! mon bras! (Mélodrame); 22. Nez au vent, oeil au guet; 23. Allons, mes fins limiers; 24. Le beau bourdon que voilà; 25. Il m'a semblé sur mon épaule; 26a. Si j'étais roi de Béotie; 26b. Galop. ACT 4: 27. Vive le vin! Vive Pluton!; 28. J'ai vu le Dieu Bacchus; 29. Maintenant, je veux, moi qui (Menuet et Galop infernal); 30. Elle est assez bonne! (Mélodrame); 31. Ne regarde pas en arrière! (finale).
Cpte M. Sénéchal, M. Mesplé, C. Burles, M. Trempont, D. Castaing, J. Rhodes, B. Brewer, M. Command, J. Berbié, M. Péna, J-P. Lafont, A. Mallabrera, H. Brambilla, J-C. Bonnafous, R. Trentin, H. Amiel, Petits Chanteurs à la Croix Potencée, Toulouse Capitole Chor, Toulouse Capitole Orch, M. Plasson (r1978) (1/89) (EMI) ① [2] **CDS7 49647-2**
Excs A. Doniat, M. Roux, C. Devos, C. Collart, A. Grandjean, H. Prudon, D. Dassy, F. Betti, L. Berton, Raymond St Paul Chor, Lamoureux Orch, J. Gressier (r1950s) *Concert* (5/93) (EMI) ① [2] **CZS7 67515-2**
1. BPO, H. von Karajan *Concert* (3/83) (DG) ① **400 044-2GH**
1. Raphaele Concert Orch, P. Walden (arr Waldenmaier) *Concert* (5/91) (MOZA) ① **MECD1002**
1. BPO, H. von Karajan *Concert* (8/91) (DG) ① **431 160-2GR**
1. NYPO, L. Bernstein *Concert* (11/92) (SONY) ① **SMK47532**
1. Detroit SO, P. Paray (r1959) *Concert* (11/93) (MERC) ① **434 332-2MM**
1. Boston Pops, A. Fiedler (r1956) *Concert* (1/94) (RCA) ① **09026 61429-2**
1. Vienna SO, B. Weil (r1992: arr Binder/Busch) *Concert* (1/94) (SONY) ① **SK53288**
1. LSO, C. Mackerras (r1961) *Concert* (12/95) (MERC) ① **434 352-2MM**
1a Empire Brass (r1992; arr. R. Smedvig) *Concert* (1/94) (TELA) ① **CD80305**

Le **Papillon—ballet: 2 acts (1860—Paris)**
Excs English Concert Orch, R. Bonynge (arr Bonynge) *Concert* (11/90) (DECC) ① [2] **421 818-2DH2**

La **Périchole—operetta: 2 (later 3) acts (1868 rev 1874—Paris)** (Lib. Meilhac and Halévy)
EXCERPTS: 1a. Overture. ACT 1: 1b. Du vice-roi c'est aujourd'hui la fête; 1c. Promptes à servir la pratique; 1d. Ah! Qu'on y fait gaîment glouglou; 2. C'est lui, c'est notre vice-roi!; 3. Dis-moi, Piquillo? (Marche indienne); 4. Le conquérant dir à la jeune indienne; 5. Vous a-t-on dit souvent (Seguidille); 6. Levez-vous et prenez vos rangs; 7. O mon cher amant, je te jure; 8a. Ah! mon Dieu! (melodrame); 8b. Holà! hé!...holà! de là-bas; 8c. Et prenez les bras de vos clercs!; 8d. Ah! quel dîner je viens de faire!; 8e. C'est un ange, messieurs!; 8f. Ah! les autres; 8g. Pourrais-je vous prier; 8h. Mon Dieu!...que de cérémonie; 8i. Et maintenant, séparez-les. ACT 2: 9. Entr'acte; 10. Cher seigneur, revenez à vous; 11. On vante partout son sourire; 12. Quel marché sa bassesse; 13a. Et là, maintenant que que nous sommes seuls; 13b. Est-ce bientôt cette présentation?; 13c. Son Altesse à l'heure ordinaire; 14a. Nous allons donc voir un mari; 14b. Que veulent dire ces colères; 14c. C'est vrai, j'ai tort de m'emporter; 14d. Sautez dessus!; 14e. Conduisez-le, bons courtisans. ACT 3: 15. Les maris courbaient le tête (Boléro); 16. On me proposait d;être infâme; 17a. Qui va là?; 17b. Dans ces couloirs obscurs; 17c. Tu n'es pas beau, tu n'es pas riche; 17d. Je t'adore, brigand, j'ai honte à l'avour; 18. Je suis le joli geôlier; 19. Roi pas plus haut qu' une botte!; 20a. Tais-toi!; 20b. Elle m'adore; 21a. En avant! en avant soldat!; 21b. Pauvres gens, où sont-ils?; 22. Écoutez, peup d'Amérique; 23. Tous deux, au temps de peine et de misère.
Cpte T. Berganza, J. Carreras, G. Bacquier, M. Sénéchal, M. Trempont, P. Delange, M. Command, S. Nigoghossian, H. Brambilla, H. Amiel, Toulouse Capitole Chor, Toulouse Capitole Orch, M. Plasson (r1981) (3/87) (EMI) ① [2] **CDS7 47362-8**
Cpte R. Crespin, A. Vanzo, J. Bastin, G. Friedmann, J. Trigeau, A. Besançon, P. Guigue, R. Roberts, E. Saurova, G. Baudoz, I. Meister, Rhine Op Chor, Strasbourg PO, A. Lombard (5/92) (ERAT) ① [2] **2292-45686-2**
Medley Boston Pops, A. Fiedler (r1956) *Concert* (1/94) (RCA) ① **09026 61429-2**
8d C. Novikova, orch (Russ: r1940s) *Concert* (4/92) (EMI) ① [7] **CHS7 69741-2(6)**
8d D. Visse, Camargue PO, Reinhardt Wagner (r1995: arr R Wagner) *Concert* (8/95) (HARM) ① **HMC90 1552**
17c M. Teyte, orch (r1932) *Concert* (2/92) (MMOI) ① **CDMOIR408**
17c L. Price, LSO, E. Downes *Concert* (12/92) (RCA) ① [4] **09026 61236-2**

Pomme d'api—operetta: 1 act (1873—Paris) (Lib. Halévy and W. Busnach)
EXCERPTS: 1. Overture; 2. Bonjour, Monsieur...Je suis la bonne; 3. J'en prenderai un, deux, trois.
Cpte J-P. Lafont, L. Pezzino, M. Mesplé, Monte Carlo PO, M. Rosenthal *Concert* (10/89) (EMI) ① [2] **CDS7 49361-2**

Robinson Crusoé—operetta (1867—Paris) (Lib. Cormon and Crémieux)
Cpte J. Brecknock, Y. Kenny, R. Kennedy, E. Hartle, M. Hill Smith, A. Oliver, S. Browne, A. Opie, W. Parfitt, G. Mitchell Ch, RPO, A. Francis (r1980: Eng) (8/94) (OPRA) ① [3] **ORC007**

Vert-vert—operetta: 3 acts (1869—Paris) (Lib. Meilhac and Nuitter)
Overture BPO, H. von Karajan *Concert* (3/83) (DG) ① **400 044-2GH**
Overture Vienna SO, B. Weil (r1992: arr F Hoffmann) *Concert* (1/94) (SONY) ① **SK53288**

La **Vie parisienne—operetta: 5 (later 4) acts (1866—Paris)** (Lib. Meilhac and Halévy)
EXCERPTS: 1. Overture; 2. Rondeau et valse.
Autrefois plus d'un amant B. Hendricks, Philh, L. Foster (r1992) *Concert* (8/93) (EMI) ① **CDC7 54626-2**
Excs E. Waechter, M. Schramm, F. Gruber, P. Alexander, L. della Casa, R. Schock, I. Hallstein, G. Unger, B. Mira, D. Chryst, K-E. Mercker, K. Böhme, U. Schirrmacher, G. Guarente, C. von Schuch, Berlin Deutsche Op Chor, Berlin SO, F. Allers (Ger) (2/91) (EURO) ① **GD69020**
Excs M. Roux, M. Hamel, W. Clément, L. Dachary, N. Renaux, L. Berton, D. Dassy, Raymond St Paul Chor, Lamoureux Orch, J. Gressier (r1950s) *Concert* (5/93) (EMI) ① [2] **CZS7 67515-2**
1. Vienna SO, B. Weil (r1992: arr B Wolff) *Concert* (1/94) (SONY) ① **SK53288**

Le **Voyage dans la lune—fairy opera: 4 acts (1875—Paris)** (Lib. Leyerrier, Vanloo and A. Mortier)
Monde charmant B. Hendricks, Philh, L. Foster (r1992) *Concert* (8/93) (EMI) ① **CDC7 54626-2**

OGDON, John Howard Andrew *(1937–1989) UK*

SECTION III: INSTRUMENTAL

5 Preludes—piano (c1960)
1. Bagatelle; 2. Pensée héroïque; 3. Homage; 4.
Pensée Militaire; 5. In modo Napolitano.
B. Lucas *Concert*   (3/92) (GAMU) ① **GAMCD528**
25 Preludes—piano (1985)
1. C; 2. Funeral of a Doll; 3. C sharp; 4. C sharp
minor; 5. D; 6. Homage to Dave Brubeck; 7.
Celebrating the return to good health of HRH
Princess Margaret; 8. A tribute to Nicholas Medtner,
known as the 'Russian Brahms'; 9. In memory of
Claud Biggs, an extraordinary teacher of Bach; 10.
Pop song; 11. Based on the Song of the Faraway
Hills; 12. Based on Chopin's Prelude No. 18; 13. In
memory of Bernard Hermann; 14. A tribute to Daniel
Barenboim; 15. G; 16. In the Latin verse rhythm of
the Dactyl and Spondee; 17. In Iambic Pentameter;
18. A vigil, in memory of Norman Andrew; 19.
Homage to Muzio Clementi; 20. A minor; 21. B flat;
22. Serenade; 23. Gallop; 24. Spinning Song; 25.
Epilogue.
B. Lucas *Concert*   (3/92) (GAMU) ① **GAMCD528**
Sonata No. 4, 'An American Sonata'—piano (1984)
B. Lucas *Concert*   (3/92) (GAMU) ① **GAMCD528**
Sonatina, 'To Brenda'—piano (1965)
B. Lucas *Concert*   (3/92) (GAMU) ① **GAMCD528**

OGERMANN, Claus *(b 1930) USA*

SECTION IV: VOCAL AND CHORAL

Tagore-Lieder—voice and piano (1975) (Wds.
Tagore)
1. Es war gerade an dem Tag; 2. Der Tag ist schon
dahin; 3. Zeit ist endlos, Herr; 4. Das ist nun so; 5.
Wolken; 6. Er kommt; 7. Letztes Lied.
B. Fassbaender, J. Wustman *Concert*
(9/88) (ACAN) ① **43 579**

OHANA, Maurice *(b 1914) France*

SECTION III: INSTRUMENTAL

Tiento
J. Bream (r1983) *Concert*
(8/93) (RCA) ① [28] **09026 61583-2(4)**
J. Bream (r1983) *Concert*
(6/94) (RCA) ① **09026 61596-2**

SECTION IV: VOCAL AND CHORAL

Cantigas—6 songs (1953-54) (Wds. 13th/14th
Cent)
M. Quercia, F. Atlan, Choeur Contemporain,
Strasbourg Percussions, R. Hayrabedian (r1986)
Stravinsky: *Noces*.   (10/87) (PIER) ① **PV787032**

O'HARA, Geoffrey *(1882–1967) Canada*

SECTION IV: VOCAL AND CHORAL

**Your eyes have told me what I did not
know—song** (wds. F. G. Bowles)
E. Caruso, orch (r1913) *Concert*
(7/91) (RCA) ① [12] **GD60495(4)**
E. Caruso, orch (r1913) *Concert*
(10/91) (PEAR) ① [3] **EVC3(1)**

OLCOTT, Chauncey *(1858–1932) USA*

SECTION V: STAGE WORKS

The **Irish Artist—musical show (1894—New
York)** (Lyrics cpsr)
EXCERPTS: 1. My Beautiful Irish Maid.
1. C. Olcott, Broadway Cast (r1913) *Concert*
(5/94) (PEAR) ① [3] **GEMMCDS9050/2(1)**
A **Romance of Athione—musical show
(1899—New York)** (Lyrics cpsr)
EXCERPTS: 1. My Wild Irish Rose.
1. C. Olcott, Broadway Cast (r1913) *Concert*
(5/94) (PEAR) ① [3] **GEMMCDS9050/2(1)**
**Sweet Inniscarra—musical show (1897—New
York)** (Lyrics cpsr)
EXCERPTS: 1. Sweet Inniscarra.
1. C. Olcott, Broadway Cast (r1913) *Concert*
(5/94) (PEAR) ① [3] **GEMMCDS9050/2(1)**

OLDFIELD, Mike *(b 1953) England*

SECTION V: STAGE WORKS

The **Killing Fields—film score (1984)**
EXCERPTS: 1. Etude (Tárrega, arr Oldfield).
1. OST (r1984) *Concert*   (9/95) (VIR2) ① **CDV2774**

OLDHAM, Kevin *(1960–1993) USA*

SECTION I: ORCHESTRAL

**Concerto for Piano and Orchestra, Op. 14
(1993)** (orch S Cohen from sketches)
I. Hobson, Kansas City SO, W. McGlaughlin (r1993)
Concert   (7/94) (CATA) ① **09026 61979-2**

OLIVIERI, Dino *(19th/20th Cent) Italy*

SECTION IV: VOCAL AND CHORAL

Inno di Garibaldi—song (Wds. L Mercantini)
E. Caruso, orch, J. Pasternack (r1918) *Concert*
(7/91) (RCA) ① [12] **GD60495(6)**
E. Caruso, orch, J. Pasternack (r1918) *Concert*
(10/91) (PEAR) ① [3] **EVC4(1)**
J. Peerce, NBC SO, A. Toscanini (bp1943) *Concert*
(5/94) (ATS) ① [2] **ATCD100**
C. Muzio, orch (r1917) *Concert*
(1/95) (ROMO) ① [2] **81010-2**
J'attendrai—song (Wds. Poterat)
L. Pons, orch (bp1945) *Concert*
(4/92) (MSOU) ① **DFCDI-111**

OLSEN, Carl Gustav Sparre *(1903–1984) Norway*

SECTION IV: VOCAL AND CHORAL

Canto amoroso—song, Op. 36/1
O.E. Antonsen, W. Marshall (r1992: arr tpt/org)
Concert   (10/94) (EMI) ① **CDC5 55048-2**

OLSSON, Otto (Emanuel) *(1879–1964) Sweden*

SECTION IV: VOCAL AND CHORAL

**Te Deum—chorus, strings, harp and organ,
1906 (Op. 25)**
A. Stångberg, E. Lundkvist, Täby Church Ch,
Orpheus Chbr Ens, K. Ek *Langlais: Messe
solennelle.*   (8/86) (BIS) ① **BIS-CD289**

ONO, Yoko *(b 1933) Japan/USA*

SECTION IV: VOCAL AND CHORAL

**Georgia Stone—various sampled sounds,
speech etc (1987)**
Y. Ono (r1987-93) *Concert*
(8/94) (KOCH) ① [2] **37238-2**

ONSLOW, (André) Georges (Louis) *(1784–1853) England/France*

SECTION II: CHAMBER

**Septet in B flat—wind quintet, piano and
double-bass, Op. 79**
Stalder Qnt, W. Bärtschi, R. Frei *Wind Quintet,
Op.81/3.*   (11/88) (JECK) ① **JD554-2**
Wind Quintet in F, Op. 81/3
Stalder Qnt *Septet.*   (11/88) (JECK) ① **JD554-2**

OPENSHAW, John *(1880–?) England*

SECTION IV: VOCAL AND CHORAL

**Love sends a little gift of roses—song
(1919)**
F. Kreisler, C. Lamson (r1924: arr Kreisler) *Concert*
(9/93) (BIDD) ① **LAB068/9**

OPERTI, Giuseppe *(19th Cent) USA*

SECTION V: STAGE WORKS

The **Black Crook—musical show
(1866—New York)** (Book C. M. Barras: lyrics
various)
EXCERPTS: 1. Amazons' March; 2. The Broadway,
Opera and Bowery Crawl (wds. P. Stoner).
1, 2. Cincinnati Uni Sngrs, Cincinnati Uni Th Orch, E.
Rivers (r1978) *Concert*   (4/94) (NEW) ① **80221-2**

OREGON *USA*

group comprising Ralph Towner, Paul McCandless,
Glen Moore

SECTION II: CHAMBER

**Chance/Choice—winds, double bass &
synths (1993)** (in memory of John Cage)
Oregon (r1993) *Concert*
(8/94) (KOCH) ① [2] **37238-2**

ORFF, Carl *(1895–1982) Germany*

SECTION II: CHAMBER

**Orff-Schulwerk—instrumental & vocal
exercises for children** (expanded version of
Musik für Kinder; collab with Keetman)
Cpte Tolz Boys' Ch, G. Schmidt-Gaden, Munich
Hochschule Chbr Ch, F. Schieri, Stuttgart
Sprechchor, H. Mende, Ens, G. Orff-Büchtemann, C.
Orff (r1963-71) (8/95) (RCA) ① [6] **09026 68031-2**

SECTION IV: VOCAL AND CHORAL

**Carmina Burana—cantiones profanae: STB,
chor & orch (1936)** (Wds. 13th cent poems)
1. O Fortuna; 2. O Fortune plango vulnera; 3. Veris
leta facies; 4. Omnia sol temperat; 5. Ecce gratium;
6. Tanz; 7. Floret silva; 8. Chramer, gip die varwe
mir; 9. Reie; 10. Swaz hie gat umbe—Chume, chum
geselle min; 11. Were diu werlt alle min; 12. Estuans
interius; 13. Olim lacus colueram; 14. Ego sum
abbas; 15. In taberna quando sumus; 16. Amor volat
undique; 17. Dies, nox et omnia; 18. Stetit puella; 19.
Circa mea pectora; 20. Si puer cum puellula; 21.
Veni, veni, venias; 22. In trutina; 23. Tempus est
iocundum; 24. Dulcissime; 25. Ave formosissima; 26.
O Fortuna.
Cpte L. Griffith, U. Ress, T. Mohr, Frankfurt
Singakademie, Figuralchor, Goethegymnasiums
Children's Ch, Frankfurt Children's Ch, Royal
Flanders PO, M. Tang (pp1993) *Concert*
(8/95) (WERG) ① [3] **WER6275-2**
J. Blegen, William Brown, H. Hagegård, Atlanta Sym
Chor, Atlanta SO, Robert Shaw (r1980)
(12/83) (TELA) ① **CD80056**
S. Greenberg, J. Bowman, S. Roberts, Berlin Rad
Sym Chor, Berlin Cath Boys' Ch, Berlin RSO, R.
Chailly   (10/84) (DECC) ① **411 702-2DH**
A. Auger, J. van Kesteren, J. Summers, Philh Chor,
Philh, R. Muti (r1980)
(4/85) (EMI) ① **CDC7 47100-2**
J. Anderson, P. Creech, B. Weikl, Glen Ellyn
Children's Choir, Chicago Sym Chor, Chicago SO,
James Levine   (12/86) (DG) ① **415 136-2GH**
S. Armstrong, G. English, T. Allen, St Clement Danes
Sch Ch, LSC, LSO, A. Previn (r1974)
(12/86) (EMI) ① **CDC7 47411-2**
N. Burrowes, L. Devos, J. Shirley-Quirk, Southend
Boys' Ch, Brighton Fest Chor, RPO, A. Dorati
(7/87) (DECC) ① **417 714-2DM**
P. Walmsley-Clark, J. Graham-Hall, D. Maxwell, LSC,
LSO, R. Hickox (r1986) (7/87) (CARL) ① **PCD855**
S. Armstrong, P. Hall, B. Rayner Cook, Manchester
GS Boys' Ch, Hallé Ch, Hallé, M. Handford
(11/87) (CFP) ① **CD-CFP9005**
G. Janowitz, G. Stolze, D. Fischer-Dieskau,
Schöneberg Boys' Ch, Berlin Deutsche Op Chor,
Berlin Deutsche Op Orch, E. Jochum
(11/88) (DG) ① **423 886-2GGA**
M. Šubrtová, J. Tománek, T. Šrubař, Czech Phil
Chor, Czech PO, V. Smetáček *Concert*
(11/88) (SUPR) ① **2SUP0025**
E. Gruberová, J. Aler, T. Hampson, Shin-yu Kai Ch,
Berlin Cath Boys' Ch, BPO, S. Ozawa (r1988)
(7/89) (PHIL) ① **422 363-2PH**
E. Jenisová, V. Doležal, I. Kusnjer, Slovak Phil Chor,
Bratislava RSO, S. Gunzenhauser
(10/90) (NAXO) ① **8 550196**
B. Hendricks, M. Chance, J. Black, St Albans Abbey
Ch, LP Chor, LPO, F. Welser-Möst (r1989)
(11/90) (EMI) ① **CDC7 54054-2**

L. Dawson, J. Daniecki, K. McMillan, San Francisco Girls' Chor, San Francisco Boys' Chor, San Francisco Sym Chor, San Francisco SO, H. Blomstedt (12/91) (DECC) ① **430 509-2DH**
L. Popp, G. Unger, R. Wolansky, J. Noble, Wandsworth Sch Boys' Ch, New Philh Chor, New Philh, R. Frühbeck de Burgos (r1965) *Ravel: Boléro.* (11/92) (EMI) ① **CDM7 64328-2**
E. Mandac, S. Kolk, S. Milnes, New England Cons Chor, New England Child Chor, Boston SO, S. Ozawa (r1969) (7/93) (RCA) ① **07863 56533-2**
S. Jo, J. Kowalski, B. Skovhus, Southend Boys' Ch, LP Ch, LPO, Z. Mehta (r1992) (2/94) (TELD) ① **9031-74886-2**
B. Bonney, F. Lopardo, A. Michaels-Moore, Vienna Boys' Ch, A. Schoenberg Ch, VPO, A. Previn (pp1993) (1/95) (DG) ① **439 950-2GH**
V. Babikian, C. Hager, G. Gardner, Houston Boys' Ch, Houston Chorale, Houston SO, L. Stokowski (r1958) *Stravinsky: Firebird Suite (1919).* (4/95) (EMI) ① **CDM5 65207-2**
S. McNair, J. Aler, H. Hagegård, St Louis Sym Chor, St Louis SO, L. Slatkin (r1992) (4/95) (RCA) ① **09026 61673-2**
G. Janowitz, G. Stolze, D. Fischer-Dieskau, Schöneberg Boys' Ch, Berlin Deutsche Op Chor, Berlin Deutsche Op Orch, E. Jochum (r1967) (12/95) (DG) ① **447 437-2GOR**
Catulli carmina—ludi scaenici (1930 rev 1943) (Wds. Catullus)
Cpte L. Griffith, T. Dewald, Frankfurt Kantorei, A. Ickstadt, E. Krämer, K. Rarichs, F. Walther-Lindqvist, Royal Flanders Phil Perc Ens, W. Schäfer (pp1993) *Concert* (8/95) (WERG) ① [3] **WER6275-2**
M. Schäfer, R. Ziesak, R. Hoffmann, F. Walther-Lindqvist, E. Krämer, K. Rarichs, Frankfurt Kantorei, W. Schäfer (r1988) *Stravinsky: Noces.* (7/91) (SCHW) ① **314021**
Der Gute Mensch—cantata (1930) (Wds. F. Werfel)
Czech Phil Chor, Inst. Ens, V. Smetáček *Concert* (11/88) (SUPR) ① **2SUP0025**
Trionfo di Afrodite—concerto scenico (1953) (Wds. Catulli, Sappho & Euripides)
Cpte S. Roberts, T. Dewald, L. Griffith, U. Ress, T. Mohr, Frankfurt Singakademie, Frankfurt Kantorei, Figuralchor, Caecilia Chorale, Royal Flanders PO, M. Tang (pp1993) *Concert* (8/95) (WERG) ① [3] **WER6275-2**
Veni, Creator Spritus—cantata (1930) (Wds. F. Werfel)
Czech Phil Chor, Inst. Ens, V. Smetáček *Concert* (11/88) (SUPR) ① **2SUP0025**
Die Weihnachtsgeschichte—chorus and instrumental ens (music arr G. Keetman)
Tolz Boys' Ch, G. Schmidt-Gaden, Inst Ens, Salzburg Shepherd Boys, T. Reiser, Munich Chmbr Chor, F. Schieri, Cologne Children's Ch, H-G. Lenders *Keetman: Weihnachtslieder.* (12/90) (DHM) ① **RD77139**

SECTION V: STAGE WORKS

Antigonae—Trauerspiel: 1 act (1949—Salzburg) (Wds. Sophocles, after Hölderlin)
Cpte I. Borkh, C. Hellmann, C. Alexander, G. Stolze, F. Uhl, E. Haefliger, K. Borg, H. Plümacher, K. Engen, Bavarian Rad Chor, BRSO, F. Leitner (r1961) (8/93) (DG) ① [3] **437 721-2GC3**
Die Kluge—opera: 1 act (1943—Frankfurt)
Cpte T. Stewart, G. Frick, L. Popp, R. Kogel, M. Schmidt, C. Nicolai, F. Gruber, H. Friedrich, K. Böhme, Munich RO, K. Eichhorn *Mond.* (3/91) (EURO) ① [2] **GD69069**
Cpte M. Cordes, G. Frick, E. Schwarzkopf, G. Wieter, R. Christ, B. Kusche, P. Kuen, H. Prey, G. Neidlinger, Philh, W. Sawallisch *Mond.* (3/91) (EMI) ① [2] **CMS7 63712-2**
Der Mond—opera: 1 act (1939—Munich) (Lib. cpsr, after Brothers Grimm)
Cpte J. van Kesteren, H. Friedrich, R. Kogel, F. Gruber, B. Kusche, R. Grumbach, F. Crass, H. Buchta, R. Kiermeyer Children's Ch, Bavarian Rad Chor, Munich RO, K. Eichhorn *Kluge.* (3/91) (EURO) ① [2] **GD69069**
Cpte R. Christ, K. Schmitt-Walter, H. Graml, P. Kuen, P. Lagger, A. Peter, H. Hotter, Childrens' Chor, Philh, W. Sawallisch *Kluge.* (3/91) (EMI) ① [2] **CMS7 63712-2**

O Saviour of the world
Magdalen Oxford Coll Ch, J. Harper *Concert*
(11/91) (ABBE) ① **CDCA913**
St Paul's Cath Ch, John Scott *Concert*
(4/92) (HYPE) ① **CDA66519**

OVALLE, Jaime (1894–1955) Brazil

SECTION IV: VOCAL AND CHORAL

Azulão—song
V. de los Angeles, Sinfonia of London, R. Frühbeck de Burgos (orch Gamley) *Concert*
(10/88) (EMI) ① **CDM7 69502-2**

OWEN, Elwyn

SECTION III: INSTRUMENTAL

Invocation—piano
F. Kreisler, C. Lamson (r1926: arr Kreisler) *Concert*
(12/93) (BIDD) ① **LAB075**

OZAITA, María Luisa (b 1937) Spain

SECTION III: INSTRUMENTAL

Tema con variaciones—piano (1983)
S. Marin *Concert*
(4/93) (RNE) ① **M3/03**

PABLO, Luis de (b 1930) Spain

SECTION II: CHAMBER

Fragmento—string quartet (1985-86)
Arditti Qt *Concert*
(12/91) (MONT) ① **789006**

PABST, Paul (1834–1897) Germany

SECTION III: INSTRUMENTAL

Concert Paraphrase from Tchaikovsky's 'Eugene Onegin'—piano, Op. 81
S. Cherkassky (pp1991) *Concert*
(1/93) (DECC) ① **433 654-2DH**
Paraphrase on 'Sleeping Beauty' (Tchaikovsky)—piano
E. Wild (r1995) *Concert*
(12/95) (SONY) ① **SK62036**

PACH, Walter (1905–1977) Austria

SECTION III: INSTRUMENTAL

Introduction and Fugue—organ
A. Fletcher *Concert*
(11/91) (MIRA) ① **MRCD903**

PACHELBEL, Johann (1653–1706) Germany

SECTION I: ORCHESTRAL

Canon and Gigue in D—string orchestra (orig 3 violins and continuo) (orch version unless indicated)
AAM, C. Hogwood *Concert*
(12/83) (L'OI) ① **410 553-2OH**
English Concert, T. Pinnock (hpd/dir) *Concert*
(1/86) (ARCH) ① **415 518-2AH**
BPO, H. von Karajan *Concert*
(8/87) (DG) ① **419 046-2GGA**
ASMF, N. Marriner *Concert*
(11/87) (PHIL) ① **416 386-2PH**
Taverner Plyrs, A. Parrott *Concert*
(12/88) (EMI) ① **CDM7 69853-2**
Cologne Musica Antiqua, R. Goebel (orig version) *Concert*
(6/89) (ARCH) ① **427 118-2AGA**
Scottish Ens, J. Rees (r1991) *Concert*
(12/91) (VIRG) ① **VJ7 59652-2**
Cologne Musica Antiqua, R. Goebel (r1980) *Concert*
(1/93) (ARCH) ① **437 089-2AT**
Guildhall Str Ens, R. Salter (vn/dir) (r1992) *Concert*
(2/94) (RCA) ① **09026 61275-2**
J. Holloway, S. Ritchie, A. Manze, N. North, M. Springfels, J. Toll (r1993; orig vers) *Concert*
(2/94) (HARM) ① **HMU90 7091**
I Musici (r1984) *Concert*
(9/94) (PHIL) ① **442 396-2PM**
Canon I Musici *Concert*
(12/83) (PHIL) ① **410 606-2PH**
Canon St Louis SO, L. Slatkin *Concert*
(1/84) (TELA) ① **CD80080**
Canon Cantilena, A. Shepherd *Concert*
(9/84) (CHAN) ① **CHAN8319**

Canon W. Marsalis, ECO, R. Leppard *Concert*
(6/88) (SONY) ① **SK42478**
Canon ASMF, N. Marriner *Concert*
(1/89) (EMIL) ① **CDZ114**
Canon Solisti Italiani *Concert*
(10/89) (DENO) ① **CO-73335**
Canon ASMF, N. Marriner *Concert*
(11/89) (CFP) ① **CD-CFP4557**
Canon D. Flood (trans org) *Concert*
(4/91) (YORK) ① **CD108**
Canon Stuttgart CO, K. Münchinger *Concert*
(8/91) (DECC) ① **430 706-2DM**
Canon J. Galway, Munich RO, J. Georgiadis *Concert*
(12/91) (RCA) ① **RD60736**
Canon Capital Virtuosi *Concert*
(1/92) (SPRO) ① **SPCV1001**
Canon London CO, C. Warren-Green (vn/dir) (r1988) *Concert*
(11/94) (VIRG) ① **CUV5 61145-2**

SECTION II: CHAMBER

Musicalische Ergötzung, 'Musical entertainment'—6 Partien for 2 scordatura violins & continuo (pub 1695)
EXCERPTS: 1. Partie I in F; 2. Partie II in C minor; 3. Partie III in E flat; 4. Partie IV in E minor; 5. Partie V in C; 6. Partie VI in B flat.
Cyclopes (r1994) *Concert*
(7/95) (PIER) ① **PV794111**
4. Cologne Musica Antiqua, R. Goebel *Concert*
(6/89) (ARCH) ① **427 118-2AGA**
Partie in G (Suite)—2 violins, 2 violas, cello and contino
Cologne Musica Antiqua, R. Goebel *Concert*
(6/89) (ARCH) ① **427 118-2AGA**
Cologne Musica Antiqua, R. Goebel (r1980) *Concert*
(1/93) (ARCH) ① **437 089-2AT**

SECTION III: INSTRUMENTAL

Aria con variazioni in A—keyboard (pub 1689)
Cologne Musica Antiqua, R. Goebel (arr Goebel) *Concert*
(6/89) (ARCH) ① **427 118-2AGA**
Aria Sebaldina in F minor—organ (pub 1699)
H. Balli *Concert*
(9/85) (DENO) ① **C37-7068**
W. Jacob (r1988) *Concert*
(4/90) (VIRG) ① **VC7 59197-2**
Christus, der ist mein leben—chorale variations
W. Jacob (r1988) *Concert*
(4/90) (VIRG) ① **VC7 59197-2**
Ciaccona in F minor—organ
W. Jacob (r1988) *Concert*
(4/90) (VIRG) ① **VC7 59197-2**
J. Butt *Concert*
(5/91) (HARM) ① **HMU90 7029**
Ciaconna I in D—organ
J. Butt *Concert*
(5/91) (HARM) ① **HMU90 7029**
Ein feste Burg—chorale fantasia (3-part cantus firmus)
H. Balli *Concert*
(9/85) (DENO) ① **C37-7068**
Gelobet seist du, Jesu Christ—chorale prelude
W. Jacob (r1988) *Concert*
(4/90) (VIRG) ① **VC7 59197-2**
Hexachordum Apollinis—organ (pub 1699)
1. Aria prima in D minor; 2. Aria secunda in E minor; 3. Aria tertia in F; 4. Aria quarta in G minor; 5. Aria quinta in A minor; 6. Aria sexta in F minor, 'Aria Sebaldina'.
J. Butt *Concert*
(5/91) (HARM) ① **HMU90 7029**
Magnificat-Fugue—organ
W. Jacob (r1988) *Concert*
(4/90) (VIRG) ① **VC7 59197-2**
Meine Seele erhebet den Herren—organ
W. Jacob (r1988) *Concert*
(4/90) (VIRG) ① **VC7 59197-2**
Nun komm, der Heiden Heiland—chorale prelude
W. Jacob (r1988) *Concert*
(4/90) (VIRG) ① **VC7 59197-2**
Prelude and Fugue in C minor—organ
W. Jacob (r1988) *Concert*
(4/90) (VIRG) ① **VC7 59197-2**
Prelude, Fugue and Chaconne in D minor—organ
W. Jacob (r1988) *Concert*
(4/90) (VIRG) ① **VC7 59197-2**
Toccata and Ricercare in C minor—organ
W. Jacob (r1988) *Concert*
(4/90) (VIRG) ① **VC7 59197-2**
Toccata in F—organ
W. Jacob (r1988) *Concert*
(4/90) (VIRG) ① **VC7 59197-2**
Von Himmel hoch, da komm ich her I—chorale prelude
W. Jacob (r1988) *Concert*
(4/90) (VIRG) ① **VC7 59197-2**

Von Himmel hoch, da komm ich her II—chorale prelude
W. Jacob (r1988) *Concert*
(4/90) (VIRG) ① **VC7 59197-2**
Wie schön leuchtet der Morgenstern—chorale prelude
W. Jacob (r1988) *Concert*
(4/90) (VIRG) ① **VC7 59197-2**

SECTION IV: VOCAL AND CHORAL

Exsurgat Deus—motet
Cantus Cölln, K. Junghänel (lte/dir) (r1993) *Concert*
(7/94) (DHM) ① **05472 77305-2**
Der Herr ist König und herrlich geschmückt—motet
Cantus Cölln, K. Junghänel (lte/dir) (r1993) *Concert*
(7/94) (DHM) ① **05472 77305-2**
Jauchzet dem Herrn—motet
Cantus Cölln, K. Junghänel (lte/dir) (r1993) *Concert*
(7/94) (DHM) ① **05472 77305-2**
Jauchzet Gott, alle Lande—motet
Cantus Cölln, K. Junghänel (lte/dir) (r1993) *Concert*
(7/94) (DHM) ① **05472 77305-2**
Magnificat—4vv
Cantus Cölln, K. Junghänel (lte/dir) (r1993) *Concert*
(7/94) (DHM) ① **05472 77305-2**
Nun danket alle Gott—motet
Cantus Cölln, K. Junghänel (lte/dir) (r1993) *Concert*
(7/94) (DHM) ① **05472 77305-2**
Singet dem Herrn—motet
Cantus Cölln, K. Junghänel (lte/dir) (r1993) *Concert*
(7/94) (DHM) ① **05472 77305-2**
Tröste uns Gott—motet
Cantus Cölln, K. Junghänel (lte/dir) (r1993) *Concert*
(7/94) (DHM) ① **05472 77305-2**

PACINI, Giovanni (1796–1867) Italy

SECTION V: STAGE WORKS

Adelaide e Comingio—opera: 2 acts (1817—Milan) (Lib. Rossi)
Overture Philh, D. Parry *Concert*
(10/90) (OPRA) ① **[3] ORCH103**
Annetta e Lucindo—opera: 1 act (1813—Milan) (Lib. Marconi)
Fra l'orror di notte oscura E. Harrhy, P. Nilon, J. Cashmore, G. Dolton, Philh, D. Parry *Concert*
(10/90) (OPRA) ① **[3] ORCH103**
Il Contestabile di Chesner, ovvero I Fidanzati—melo-dramma romantico: 3 parts (1829—Naples) (Lib. Gilardoni)
Ah sì ch'lo t'amo...Là sotto il salice Y. Kenny, S. McCulloch, G. Mitchell Ch, Philh, D. Parry *Concert*
(8/95) (OPRA) ① **[3] ORCH104**
Saffo—opera: 3 acts (1840—Naples) (Lib. S. Cammarano)
L'ama ognor E. Burzio, orch (r1913) *Concert*
(1/91) (CLUB) ① **[2] CL99-587/8**

PACOLINI, Giovanni (16th–17th Cent) Italy

SECTION II: CHAMBER

Passemezzo della battaglia
J. Lindberg, R. Meunier, P. O'Dette *Concert*
(12/86) (BIS) ① **BIS-CD341**
Passemezzo di zorzi
J. Lindberg, R. Meunier, N. North, P. O'Dette *Concert*
(12/86) (BIS) ① **BIS-CD341**
Passemezzo milanese
J. Lindberg, N. North, P. O'Dette *Concert*
(12/86) (BIS) ① **BIS-CD341**

PADEREWSKI, Ignacy Jan (1860–1941) Poland

SECTION I: ORCHESTRAL

Concerto for Piano and Orchestra in A minor, Op. 17 (1888)
P. Lane, BBC Scottish SO, J. Maksymiuk
Moszkowski: Piano Concerto.
(2/92) (HYPE) ① **CDA66452**
P. Paleczny, Polish Nat RSO, T. Strugala (r1982)
Melcer-Szczawiński: Piano Concerto 1.
(7/94) (OLYM) ① **OCD398**

SECTION III: INSTRUMENTAL

Chants du Voyageur—piano, Op. 8 (c1883)
3. Mélodie.
3. I. Paderewski (r1938) *Concert*
(11/91) (PEAR) ① **GEMMCD9499**

Humoresques de concert—piano, Op. 14 (1887-88)
LIVRE 1 (à l'antique): 1. Menuet célèbre; 2. Sarabande; 3. Caprice in the style of Scarlatti. LIVRE 2 (moderne): 4. Burlesque; 5. Intermezzo polacco; 6. Cracovienne fantastique.
1. S. Hough (r1986) *Concert*
(1/89) (VIRG) ① **VC7 59509-2**
1. I. Paderewski (r1937) *Concert*
(11/91) (PEAR) ① **GEMMCD9499**
1. M. Lympany *Concert* (1/92) (EMIL) ① **CDZ111**
1. I. Paderewski (r1937) *Concert*
(3/93) (RCA) ① **GD60923**
1. S. Rachmaninov (r1927) *Concert*
(3/93) (RCA) ① [10] **09026 61265-2(1)**
1. S. Cherkassky (bp1979) *Concert*
(6/93) (DECC) ① **433 651-2DH**
6. I. Paderewski (r1922) *Concert*
(11/91) (PEAR) ① **GEMMCD9499**
Miscellanea—piano, Op. 16 (c1888-94)
1. Légende No. 1 in A flat; 2. Mélodie in G flat; 3. Thème varié in A; 4. Nocturne in B flat; 5. Légende No. 2 in A; 6. Un moment musical; 7. Menuet in A.
2. F. Kreisler, C. Lamson (r1923: arr Kreisler) *Concert* (9/93) (BIDD) ① [2] **LAB068/9**
3. E. Wild *Concert* (8/92) (VANG) ① **08.4033.71**
4. S. Hough (r1987) *Concert*
(1/89) (VIRG) ① **VC7 59509-2**
4. I. Paderewski (r1922) *Concert*
(11/91) (PEAR) ① **GEMMCD9499**

Manru—opera: 3 acts, Op. 20
(1901—Dresden) (Lib. A Nossig, after J I Kraszewski)
Come al sol cocente G. Anselmi, anon (r1907: Ital) *Concert* (7/95) (SYMP) ① **SYMCD1170**

PADILLA, José (1889-1960)
Spain

Missa Ego flos campi—8vv
Mixylodian, P. Schmidt *Concert*
(5/92) (CARL) ① **PCD970**
Princesita—song
T. Schipa, orch (r1926) *Concert*
(2/89) (PEAR) ① **GEMMCD9322**
T. Schipa, orch, J. Pasternack (r1926) *Concert*
(12/89) (RCA) ① **GD87969**
El Relicario—song
T. Ruffo, orch (r1922) *Concert*
(2/93) (PREI) ① [3] **89303(2)**
Stabat mater—4vv
Mixylodian, P. Schmidt *Concert*
(5/92) (CARL) ① **PCD970**
Valencia—song
T. Schipa, orch (r1926) *Concert*
(2/89) (PEAR) ① **GEMMCD9322**

PADILLA, Juan Guitiérrez de (c1590-1664) Mexico

Domine ad adjuvandum—choir and instrumental ensemble
Westminster Cath Ch, A. Watts, A. Lawrence-King, I. Simcock, J. O'Donnell *Concert*
(12/90) (HYPE) ① **CDA66330**
Lamentations of Jeremiah—6vv a capella
Westminster Cath Ch, J. O'Donnell *Concert*
(12/90) (HYPE) ① **CDA66330**
Mirabilia testimonia—choir and organ
Westminster Cath Ch, I. Simcock, J. O'Donnell *Concert* (12/90) (HYPE) ① **CDA66330**
Salve Regina—choir a capella
Westminster Cath Ch, J. O'Donnell *Concert*
(12/90) (HYPE) ① **CDA66330**

PADOVANO, Annibale (1527-1575) Italy

Toccata VI toni—organ (c1604)
R. Micconi *Concert* (3/90) (MOTE) ① **CD10561**

PAER, Ferdinando (1771-1839)
Italy

Le Maître de chapelle—opéra-comique: 2 acts (1821—Paris) (Lib. S. Gay)
Ah quel plaisir L. Fugère, orch (r1930) *Concert*
(6/93) (SYMP) ① **SYMCD1125**
Air G. Soulacroix, anon (r1904) *Concert*
(9/91) (SYMP) ① **SYMCD1089**
Sargino, ossia L'allievo dell'amore—dramma eroicomico: 2 acts (1803—Dresden) (Lib. Foppa)
Una voca al cor mi parla E. Ritchie, V. Soames, J. Purvis, r1992; arr Waxman/Voxman) *Concert*
(3/94) (CLRI) ① **CC0006**

PAGANINI, Nicolò (1782-1840)
Italy

MS—Nos in Moretti & Sorrento, pub 1982

Concerto for Violin and Orchestra No. 1 in E flat, Op. 6 (?1817) (usually trans into D)
I. Perlman, RPO, L. Foster *Sarasate: Carmen Fantasy.* (4/85) (EMI) ① **CDC7 47101-2**
S. Accardo, LPO, C. Dutoit *Violin Concerto 2.*
(2/87) (DG) ① **415 378-2GH**
Y. Menuhin, RPO, A. Erede (Cad. Foster) *Violin Concerto 2.* (1/88) (EMI) ① **CDC7 47088-2**
M. Kaplan, LSO, M. Miller (r1988) *Wieniawski: Violin Concerto 2.* (7/89) (ARAB) ① **Z6597**
V. Mullova, ASMF, N. Marriner *Vieuxtemps: Violin Concerto 5.* (10/89) (PHIL) ① **422 332-2PH**
G. Shaham, NYPO, G. Sinopoli *Saint-Saëns: Violin Concerto 3.* (5/91) (DG) ① **429 786-2GH**
Z. Francescatti, Philadelphia, E. Ormandy (r1950) *Saint-Saëns: Violin Concerto 3.*
(12/91) (SONY) ① **MPK46728**
Auvergne Orch, J-J. Kantorow (vn/dir) *Violin Concerto 2.* (4/92) (DENO) ① **CO-77611**
M. Vengerov, Israel PO, Z. Mehta *Concert*
(5/92) (TELD) ① **9031-73266-2**
A. Markov, Saarbrücken RSO, M. Viotti *Violin Concerto 2.* (3/93) (ERAT) ① **2292-45788-2**
I. Kaler, Polish Nat RSO, S. Gunzenhauser (r1992) *Violin Concerto 2.* (12/93) (NAXO) ① **8 550649**
I. Perlman, RPO, L. Foster (r1971) *Concert*
(4/94) (EMI) ① [3] **CMS7 64922-2**
J-J. Kantorow, B. Thomas CO, B. Thomas (r1982) *Violin Concerto 2.* (11/94) (FORL) ① **FF053**
S. Chang, Philadelphia, W. Sawallisch *Concert*
(1/95) (EMI) ① **CDC5 55026-2**
S. Accardo, LPO, C. Dutoit (r1975) *Concert*
(3/95) (DG) ① **439 981-2GGA**
Cadenza J. Kubelík (r1910) *Concert*
(6/91) (BIDD) ① [2] **LAB033/4**
Rondo E. Friedman, Chicago SO, W. Hendl *Concert*
(8/93) (RCA) ① **09026 61210-2**
Concerto for Violin and Orchestra No. 2 in B minor, Op. 7 (1826)
3. Rondo à la clochette, 'La campanella'.
S. Accardo, LPO, C. Dutoit *Violin Concerto 1.*
(2/87) (DG) ① **415 378-2GH**
Y. Menuhin, RPO, A. Erede (Cad. Balier) *Violin Concerto 1.* (1/88) (EMI) ① **CDC7 47088-2**
Auvergne Orch, J-J. Kantorow (vn/dir) *Violin Concerto 1.* (4/92) (DENO) ① **CO-77611**
A. Markov, Saarbrücken RSO, M. Viotti *Violin Concerto 1.* (3/93) (ERAT) ① **2292-45788-2**
I. Kaler, Polish Nat RSO, S. Gunzenhauser (r1992) *Violin Concerto 1.* (12/93) (NAXO) ① **8 550649**
N. Hall, LMP, A. Litton (r1992: trans gtr/orch: N Hall) *Concert* (3/94) (DECC) ① **440 293-2DH**
J-J. Kantorow, B. Thomas CO, B. Thomas (r1982) *Violin Concerto 1.* (11/94) (FORL) ① **FF053**
Movt 3. B. Huberman, P. Frenkel (r1923: arr Wilhelmj) *Concert* (3/94) (BIDD) ① [2] **LAB077/8**
3. Y. Menuhin, H. Giesen (arr Wilhelmj: r1930) *Concert* (4/91) (BIDD) ① **LAB032**
3. Y. Menuhin, H. Giesen (arr Wilhelmj: r1930) *Concert* (9/91) (TEST) ① **SBT1003**
3. W. Primrose, H. Isaacs (r1937) *Concert*
(10/91) (PEAR) ① **GEMMCD9453**
3. R. Ricci, C. Fürstner (arr Kochanski: r1938) *Concert* (12/91) (BIDD) ① **LAB044**
3. N. Milstein, L. Mittman (r1936: arr Kreisler) *Concert* (7/93) (APR) ① [2] **APR7016**
3. N. Milstein, L. Mittman (r1936: arr vn/pf: Kreisler) *Concert* (9/95) (BIDD) ① **LAB096**

Concerto for Violin and Orchestra No. 5 in A minor (1830)
S. Accardo, LPO, C. Dutoit *Concert*
(10/88) (DG) ① **423 578-2GH**
Concerto for Violin and Orchestra No. 6 in E minor, Op. posth (c1815)
S. Accardo, LPO, C. Dutoit *Concert*
(5/89) (DG) ① **423 717-2GH**
Introduction and Variations on 'Dal tuo stellato soglio' from Rossini's 'Mosé'—violin and orchestra, Op. 24 (1818-19)
G. Karr, Philh, G. Simon (arr. Karr) *Concert*
(3/87) (CALA) ① [2] **CACD0101**
R. Ricci, C. Fürstner (r1938) *Concert*
(12/91) (BIDD) ① **LAB044**
T. Varga, H. Greenslade (r1947: arr vn/pf) *Concert*
(11/93) (CLAV) ① **CD50-9314**
5. T. Varga, H. Greenslade (r1947: arr vn/pf) *Concert* (11/93) (CLAV) ① [4] **CD50-9300/4**
Introduction and Variations on 'Non più mesta' from Rossini's 'La cenerentola'—violin and orchestra, Op. 12 (1819)
S. Accardo, LPO, C. Dutoit *Concert*
(5/89) (DG) ① **423 717-2GH**
Maestoso sentimentale: Variations on the Austrian national hymn—violin and orchestra (1828)
S. Accardo, LPO, C. Dutoit *Concert*
(10/88) (DG) ① **423 578-2GH**
Moto perpetuo in C, 'Perpetual Motion'—Allegro di concert: violin & orchestra, Op. 11 (after 1830)
W. Marsalis, Eastman Wind Ens, D. Hunsberger (arr D Hunsberger) *Concert* (9/87) (SONY) ① **MK42137**
NBC SO, A. Toscanini (orch Toscanini: bp1940) *Concert* (9/90) (DELL) ① **CDDA9020**
J. Heifetz, A. Benoist (r1918) *Concert*
(1/91) (BIDD) ① **LAB015**
NBC SO, A. Toscanini (arr Toscanini: r1939) *Concert* (1/91) (RCA) ① **GD60308**
T. Papavrami, C. Larrieu *Concert*
(3/91) (HARM) ① **HMC90 5207**
J. Kubelík, anon (r1905) *Concert*
(6/91) (BIDD) ① [2] **LAB033/4**
Y. Menuhin, M. Gazelle (r1934) *Concert*
(9/91) (TEST) ① **SBT1003**
K. Parlow, Anon (pf) (arr vn,pf: r1909) *Concert*
(12/91) (APR) ① [2] **APR7015**
R. Childs, N. Childs, Besses o' the Barn Band, R. Newsome (pp1987: arr H Snell) *Concert*
(11/93) (CHAN) ① **CHAN4513**
G. Shaham, G. Söllscher (r1992: arr vn/gtr: Hannibal) *Concert* (4/94) (DG) ① **437 837-2GH**
J. Heifetz, A. Benoist (r1918) *Concert*
(11/94) (RCA) ① [65] **09026 61778-2(01)**
Chicago SO, F. Stock (r1941: orch Stock) *Concert*
(2/95) (BIDD) ① [2] **WHL021/2**
S. Nakarjakov, A. Markovich (r1994: arr tpt/pf) *Concert* (6/95) (TELD) ① **4509-94554-2**
I palpiti—Introduction and Variations on 'Di tanti palpiti' from Rossini's 'Tancredi'—violin and orchestra, Op. 13 (1819)
A. Grumiaux, R. Castagnone (r1958: arr vn/pf) *Concert* (11/93) (PHIL) ① [3] **438 516-2PM3**
M. Vengerov, I. Golan (r1993: arranged by Kreisler) *Concert* (4/94) (TELD) ① **9031-77351-2**
S. Accardo, LPO, C. Dutoit (r1976) *Concert*
(3/95) (DG) ① **439 981-2GGA**
Perpetuela (Sonata à mouvement perpétuel)—violin and orchestra/piano (after 1830) (ed G Kinsky & F Rothschild: pub 1922)
S. Accardo, LPO, C. Dutoit (r1976) *Concert*
(3/95) (DG) ① **439 981-2GGA**
La primavera—sonata: violin and orchestra (?1838)
S. Accardo, LPO, C. Dutoit *Concert*
(10/88) (DG) ① **423 578-2GH**
Sonata and Variations on a theme by Joseph Weigl—violin and orchestra (1828)
S. Accardo, LPO, C. Dutoit *Concert*
(5/89) (DG) ① **423 717-2GH**
Sonata Napoleone in E flat—violin and orchestra (1807)
S. Accardo, LPO, C. Dutoit (r1976) *Concert*
(3/95) (DG) ① **439 981-2GGA**
Le Streghe: variations on a song by Süssmayr—violin and orchestra, Op. 8 (1813)
S. Accardo, LPO, C. Dutoit *Concert*
(5/89) (DG) ① **423 717-2GH**
K. Daeshik Kang, M. Rahkonen (r1992: arr Daeshik Kang) *Concert* (9/93) (NIMB) ① **NI5358**

A. Grumiaux, R. Castagnone (r1958; arr vn/pf)
Concert   (11/93) (PHIL) ① [3] **438 516-2PM3**
**Variations on 'God save the King'—violin
and orchestra (or piano), Op. 9 (1829)**
R. Ricci, M. Argerich (arr vn/pf) Concert
        (9/86) (ETCE) ① **KTC1038**
J. Kubelík, anon (r1905) Concert
        (6/91) (BIDD) ① [2] **LAB033/4**

┌─────────────────────────────┐
│ **SECTION II: CHAMBER** │
└─────────────────────────────┘

**Cantabile e Valtz—violin and guitar, Op. 19
(1823 or 1824)**
S. St John, S. Wynberg (r1993) Concert
        (12/94) (NAXO) ① **8 550759**
**Cantabile in D—violin and guitar, Op. 17
(1823)**
J. Williams, I. Perlman Concert
        (7/87) (SONY) ① **MK34508**
Midori, R. McDonald (r1992) Concert
        (6/93) (SONY) ① **SK52568**
G. Shaham, G. Söllscher (r1992) Concert
        (4/94) (DG) ① **437 837-2GH**
S. St John, S. Wynberg (r1993) Concert
        (12/94) (NAXO) ① **8 550690**
**18 centone di sonate—violin and guitar (after
1828)**
1. No 1 in A; 2. No 2 in D; 3. No 3; 4. No 4 in A; 5. No
5; 6. No 6; 7. No 7; 8. No 8; 9. No 9; 10. No 10; 11.
No 11; 12. No 12; 13. No 13 in F; 14. No 14 in G; 15.
No 15 in A; 16. No 16 in C; 17. No 17 in A minor; 18.
No 18 in D.
1. J. Williams, I. Perlman Concert
        (7/87) (SONY) ① **MK34508**
1-6. M. Hammer, N. Kraft (r1994)
        (5/95) (NAXO) ① **8 553141**
2, 4. G. Shaham, G. Söllscher (r1992) Concert
        (4/94) (DG) ① **437 837-2GH**
Duetto amoroso—violin and guitar (?1807)
S. St John, S. Wynberg (r1993) Concert
        (12/94) (NAXO) ① **8 550759**
**Grand Sonata for Violin and Guitar in A, Op.
posth**
O. Renardy, W. Robert (arr vn/pf: r1940) Concert
        (12/92) (BIDD) ① [2] **LAB061/2**
N. Kraft (arr gtr solo: Kraft) Concert
        (8/93) (CHAN) ① **CHAN9033**
J. Bream (r1970; arr Bream) Concert
        (8/93) (RCA) ① [28] **09026 61583-2(4)**
G. Shaham, G. Söllscher (r1992) Concert
        (4/94) (DG) ① **437 837-2GH**
J. Bream (r1970; arr Bream) Concert
        (6/94) (RCA) ① **09026 61594-2**
M. Huggett, R. Savino (r1993) Concert
        (5/95) (HARM) ① **HMU90 7116**
Second & Third Movts T. Kerstens (r1992-3; Urtext
Ed) Concert   (9/94) (CONI) ① **CDCF518**
Sonata—large viola and guitar (1834) (arr
from va/orch vers)
S. St John, S. Wynberg (r1993) Concert
        (12/94) (NAXO) ① **8 550759**
Sonata a preghiera—violin and piano (based
on Variations, Op. 24)
G. Shaham, G. Söllscher (r1992: arr vn/gtr: Hannibal)
Concert   (4/94) (DG) ① **437 837-2GH**
**Sonata concertata in A—guitar and violin,
Op. 61 (1804)**
J. Williams, I. Perlman Concert
        (7/87) (SONY) ① **MK34508**
G. Shaham, G. Söllscher (r1992) Concert
        (4/94) (DG) ① **437 837-2GH**
S. St John, S. Wynberg (r1993) Concert
        (12/94) (NAXO) ① **8 550690**
M. Huggett, R. Savino (r1993) Concert
        (5/95) (HARM) ① **HMU90 7116**
**6 Sonatas for Guitar and Violin, Op. 2 (c1801-
04)**
1. A; 2. C; 3. D minor; 4. A; 5. D; 6. D minor.
S. St John, S. Wynberg (r1993) Concert
        (12/94) (NAXO) ① **8 550759**
**6 Sonatas for Guitar and Violin, Op. 3 (c1801-
04)**
1. A; 2. G; 3. D; 4. A minor; 5. A; 6. E minor.
S. St John, S. Wynberg (r1993) Concert
        (12/94) (NAXO) ① **8 550690**
1, 4, 6. G. Shaham, G. Söllscher (r1992) Concert
        (4/94) (DG) ① **437 837-2GH**
6. J. Williams, I. Perlman Concert
        (7/87) (SONY) ① **MK34508**
**36 Sonatas for Violin and Guitar, 'Lucca
Sonatas'—6 sets of 6 sonatas (1806-09)**
(rediscovered 1982)
1. Set I: Dedicated to Madame Frassinet; 2. Set II:
Dedicated to M. Frassinet; 3. Set III: No violin part
extant; 4. Set IV: Dedicated to Felice Baciocchi; 5.
Set V: Dedicated to Madame T; 6. Set VI: Dedicated
to Principessa Napoleone.

L.A. Bianchi, M. Preda (r1985)
        (11/93) (DYNA) ① [2] **CDS43/1-2**
**60 Variations on 'Barucabà'—violin and
guitar, Op. 14 (1835)**
S. St John, S. Wynberg (r1993) Concert
        (12/94) (NAXO) ① **8 550690**
**Variazioni di bravura on Caprice No.
24—violin and guitar (pub 1959)**
S. St John, S. Wynberg (r1993) Concert
        (12/94) (NAXO) ① **8 550759**

┌─────────────────────────────┐
│ **SECTION III: INSTRUMENTAL** │
└─────────────────────────────┘

24 Caprices—violin, Op. 1 (1801-07)
1. E; 2. B minor; 3. E minor; 4. C minor; 5. A minor; 6.
G minor; 7. A minor; 8. E flat; 9. E; 10. G minor; 11.
C; 12. A flat; 13. B flat; 14. E flat; 15. E minor; 16. G
minor; 17. E flat; 18. C; 19. E flat; 20. D; 21. A; 22. F;
23. E flat; 24. A minor.
S. Mintz   (4/85) (DG) ① **415 043-2GH**
I. Perlman   (7/88) (EMI) ① **CDC7 47171-2**
Midori   (3/90) (SONY) ① **SK49944**
S. Accardo   (9/90) (DG) ① **429 714-2GGA**
P. Gallois (arr fl)   (10/92) (DG) ① **435 768-2GH**
O. Renardy, W. Robert (arr vn/pf: r1940) Concert
        (12/92) (BIDD) ① [2] **LAB061/2**
M. Rabin (r1958)   (9/93) (EMI) ① **CDM7 64560-2**
L. Kavacos   (9/93) (DYNA) ① **CDS66**
I. Kaler (r1992)   (10/93) (NAXO) ① **8 550717**
T. Zehetmair (r1992)
        (5/94) (TELD) ① **9031-76259-2**
I. Perlman Concert
        (6/95) (EMI) ① [20] **CZS4 83177-2(2)**
1, 15. S. Chang, S. Rivers Concert
        (1/93) (EMI) ① **CDC7 54352-2**
1, 2, 5, 9, 18. T. Papavrami Concert
        (3/91) (HARM) ① **HMC90 5207**
2. J. Szigeti (r1935) Concert
        (1/90) (BIDD) ① [2] **LAB005/6**
5, 13. W. Primrose (r1939) Concert
        (10/91) (PEAR) ① **GEMMCD9453**
5, 17. N. Milstein (bp1933) Concert
        (8/92) (DANA) ① **DACOCD303**
6. J. Kubelík (r1910) Concert
        (6/91) (BIDD) ① [2] **LAB033/4**
9. J. Szigeti (r1933) Concert
        (1/90) (BIDD) ① [2] **LAB005/6**
9. Y. Menuhin (r1936) Concert
        (9/91) (TEST) ① **SBT1003**
9. J. Szigeti (r1933) Concert
        (10/91) (MSCM) ① **MM30272**
13. R. Ricci (r1959) Concert
        (5/92) (DECC) ① **433 220-2DWO**
13. J. Heifetz, S. Chotzinoff (r1920) Concert
        (11/94) (RCA) ① [65] **09026 61778-2(01)**
13. N. Milstein (pp1986) Concert
        (5/94) (TELD) ① **4509-95998-2**
13. J. Starker, G. Moore (r1958: arr vc/pf: Kreisler)
Concert   (12/95) (EMI) ① [6] **CZS5 68485-2**
13, 20. J. Heifetz, B. Smith (r1956) Concert
        (11/94) (RCA) ① [65] **09026 61778-2(24)**
13, 24. J. Heifetz, A. Sándor (r1934) Concert
        (11/94) (RCA) ① [65] **09026 61778-2(02)**
17. W. Primrose, Anon (pf) (r1934) Concert
        (10/91) (PEAR) ① **GEMMCD9453**
17. S. Nakarjakov, A. Markovich (r1994: arr tpt/pf)
Concert   (6/95) (TELD) ① **4509-94554-2**
20. J. Heifetz, A. Benoist (r1918: arr Kreisler) Concert
        (1/91) (BIDD) ① **LAB015**
20. C. Flesch, I. Strasfogel (arr Kreisler; r1929)
Concert   (12/91) (BIDD) ① **LAB045**
20. J. Heifetz, A. Sándor (r1934) Concert
        (11/94) (RCA) ① [65] **09026 61778-2(03)**
20. J. Heifetz, A. Benoist (r1918) Concert
        (11/94) (RCA) ① [65] **09026 61778-2(01)**
24. J. Szigeti, K. Ruhrseitz (arr vn/pf: r1928) Concert
        (1/90) (BIDD) ① [2] **LAB005/6**
24. J. Szigeti, K. Ruhrseitz (arr vn/pf: r1926) Concert
        (1/90) (BIDD) ① [2] **LAB005/6**
24. Y. Menuhin (r1932) Concert
        (9/91) (TEST) ① **SBT1003**
24. N. Hall (arr gtr) Concert
        (5/92) (DECC) ① **430 839-2DH**
43 Ghiribizzi, MS43 (1820)
1. Allegretto: A; 2. Andantino: C; 3. Valtz: C; 4.
Allegretto: A; 5. Moderato: D; 6. Andantino: G; 7.
Valtz: E; 8. Andante: C; 9. Andantino: C; 10.
Allegretto: C; 11. Allegretto: A; 12. Andante: C; 13.
Allegro: C; 14. Allegro assai: C; 15. Allegro: G; 16.
Larghetto: G—(Paisiello: In cor più non mi sento); 17.
Andantino: D—(Glissani: Le streghe); 18.
Andantino: D minor; 19. Corrente: G; 20. Andante:
C—(Mozart: Là ci darem la mano); 21. Allegretto: A;
22. Larghetto: A; 23. Allegro: A; 24. Andante: A; 25.
Andante: C; 26. Arietta: D; 27. Andantino: D; 28.
Allegretto: D; 29. Marcia: D; 30. Allegretto: D; 31.
Minuetto (Andante): A; 32. Allegretto: A; 33.

Allegretto: A; 34. Valtz: A; 35. Valtz: D; 36. Allegretto:
C; 37. Adagetto con espressione: A
(Paganini/Rossini); 38. Vivace: A; 39. Allgretto: D; 40.
Andante: A; 41. Allegro: C; 42. Valtz: A; 43.
Andantino: A minor.
20, 37. T. Kerstens (r1992-3) Concert
        (9/94) (CONI) ① **CDCF518**
**Introduction and Variations on 'Nel cor più
non mi sento' from Paisiello's 'La
Molinara'—violin (?1820)**
T. Papavrami Concert
        (3/91) (HARM) ① **HMC90 5207**
J. Kubelík (r1903) Concert
        (6/91) (BIDD) ① [2] **LAB033/4**
5 Sonatinas for Guitar, MS85
1. C; 2. C; 3. D; 4. C; 5. C.
1. T. Kerstens (r1992-3) Concert
        (9/94) (CONI) ① **CDCF518**

┌─────────────────────────────┐
│ **PAINE, John Knowles
(1839–1906) USA** │
└─────────────────────────────┘

┌─────────────────────────────┐
│ **SECTION I: ORCHESTRAL** │
└─────────────────────────────┘

**Symphony No. 2 in A, 'In the Spring', Op. 34
(1879-80)**
NYPO, Z. Mehta   (5/88) (NEW) ① **NW350-2**

┌─────────────────────────────┐
│ **PAISIBLE, James (d 1721)
France/Britain** │
└─────────────────────────────┘

┌─────────────────────────────┐
│ **SECTION I: ORCHESTRAL** │
└─────────────────────────────┘

The Queen's Farewell—march (1695) (for the
funeral of Queen Mary)
The Sixteen, The Sixteen Orch, H. Christophers
(r1994) Concert   (1/95) (COLL) ① **Coll1425-2**
New London Consort, M. Neary (r1994) Concert
        (3/95) (SONY) ① **SK66243**

┌─────────────────────────────┐
│ **PAISIELLO, Giovanni
(1740–1816) Italy** │
└─────────────────────────────┘

┌─────────────────────────────┐
│ **SECTION I: ORCHESTRAL** │
└─────────────────────────────┘

Concerto for Harp and Orchestra in A (arr of
keyboard concerto)
J.C. Merlak, ECCO, D. Demetriades Concert
        (8/88) (HYPE) ① **CDH88015**
Concerto for Mandolin and Strings in C
U. Orlandi, Solisti Veneti, C. Scimone (r1985)
Concert   (12/93) (ERAT) ① **4509-92132-2**
Concerto for Mandolin and Strings in E flat
U. Orlandi, Solisti Veneti, C. Scimone (r1985)
Concert   (12/93) (ERAT) ① **4509-92132-2**
**Concerto for Piano and Orchestra No. 1 in
C**
M. Monetti, ECO, S. Gonley Concert
        (8/94) (ASV) ① **CDDCA873**
**Concerto for Piano and Orchestra No. 2 in
F**
M. Monetti, ECO, S. Gonley Concert
        (2/94) (ASV) ① **CDDCA872**
**Concerto for Piano and Orchestra No. 3 in
A**
M. Monetti, ECO, S. Gonley (ed Spada) Concert
        (2/94) (ASV) ① **CDDCA872**
**Concerto for Piano and Orchestra No. 4 in G
minor**
M. Monetti, ECO, S. Gonley (ed Spada) Concert
        (2/94) (ASV) ① **CDDCA872**
**Concerto for Piano and Orchestra No. 5 in
D**
M. Monetti, ECO, S. Gonley (ed Spada) Concert
        (8/94) (ASV) ① **CDDCA873**
**Concerto for Piano and Orchestra No. 6 in B
flat**
M. Monetti, ECO, S. Gonley (ed Spada) Concert
        (2/94) (ASV) ① **CDDCA872**
**Concerto for Piano and Orchestra No. 7 in
A**
M. Monetti, ECO, S. Gonley (ed Spada) Concert
        (8/94) (ASV) ① **CDDCA873**
**Concerto for Piano and Orchestra No. 8 in
C**
M. Monetti, ECO, S. Gonley (ed Spada) Concert
        (8/94) (ASV) ① **CDDCA873**

┌─────────────────────────────┐
│ **SECTION IV: VOCAL AND CHORAL** │
└─────────────────────────────┘

Gloria Patri—motet
E. Petricola, Czech Rad Chor, Prague SO, E. Brizio
(r1994) Concert   (11/95) (STUD) ① **SM12 2389**
**Missa in pastorale per il Natale per la
cappella del Primo Consolo (1802)**
L. Bersiani, E. Petricola, S. Salvati, C. Putelli, C.
Lepore, Czech Rad Chor, Prague SO, E. Brizio
(r1994) Concert   (11/95) (STUD) ① **SM12 2389**

Tantum ergo—motet
L. Bersiani, Czech Rad Chor, Prague SO, E. Brizio
(r1994) *Concert*   (11/95) (STUD) ① **SM12 2389**
Tecum principium—motet
R. N. Zucchi, Czech Rad Chor, Prague SO, E. Brizio
(r1994) *Concert*   (11/95) (STUD) ① **SM12 2389**

SECTION V: STAGE WORKS

L' Amor contrastato, 'La Molinara'—opera: 3 acts (1789—Naples) (Lib. G. Palomba)
EXCERPTS: 1. Nel cor più non mi sento.
1. E. Pinza, orch, D. Voorhees (bp1950) *Concert*
(7/91) (MMOI) ① **CDMOIR404**
1. C. Bartoli, G. Fischer *Concert*
(12/92) (DECC) ① **436 267-2DH**
1. J. Baker, ASMF, N. Marriner *Concert*
(1/93) (PHIL) ① **434 173-2PM**
1. E. Pinza, F. Kitzinger (r1940) *Concert*
(9/93) (RCA) ① **09026 61245-2**
Don Chisciotte della Mancia—opera: 3 acts (1769—Naples) (Lib. G.B. Lorenzi)
Cpte P. Barbacini, R. Franceschetto, M.A. Peters, E.
Zilio, M. Bolognesi, B. Praticò, B. Lucarini, F. Arnone,
Ann Rossi, Rome Op Orch, P.G. Morandi (pp1990)
(4/92) (NUOV) ① [2] **6994/5**
**Nina, o sia La pazza per amore—commedia
in prosa e versi: 1 act (1789—Naples)** (Lib. G.
Carpani, after B. J. Mersollier)
EXCERPTS: 1. Overture; 2. Il mio ben quando verrà.
Cpte M. Bolgan, D. Bernardini, F. Musinu, F.
Pediconi, G. Surian, C. Bosi, B. Cegile, Catania
Teatro Massimo Bellini Chor, Catania Teatro
Massimo Bellini Orch, R. Bonynge (pp1989)
(9/91) (NUOV) ① [2] **6872/3**
2. C. Bartoli, G. Fischer *Concert*
(12/92) (DECC) ① **436 267-2DH**
**La Serva Padrona—intermezzo: 2 acts
(1781—Tsarskoye Selo)** (Lib. G.A. Federico)
Cpte A.V. Banks, G.L. Ricci, Milan CO, P. Vaglieri
(2/93) (NUOV) ① **7043**
**Il Zingari in fiera—commedia per musica: 2
acts (1789—Naples)** (Lib. Palomba)
EXCERPTS: 1. Overture; 2. Chi vuol la zingarella.
2. V. de los Angeles, G. Parsons (pp1990) *Concert*
(12/91) (COLL) ① **Coll1247-2**
2. C. Bartoli, G. Fischer (r1990-1) *Concert*
(12/92) (DECC) ① **436 267-2DH**

PAIVA, Heliodoro *(c1500–1552) Portugal*

SECTION IV: VOCAL AND CHORAL

Alleluia (Santa Cruz, Coimbra MS)
A Capella Portvgvesa, O. Rees (r1994) *Concert*
(11/94) (HYPE) ① **CDA66735**

PALADILHE, Emil *(1844–1926) France*

SECTION IV: VOCAL AND CHORAL

Au bord de l'eau—duet (Wds. S.
Prudhomme)
F. Lott, A. Murray, G. Johnson (r1991) *Concert*
(7/92) (EMI) ① **CDC7 54411-2**
Mandolinata—song
V. Maurel, anon (r1904) *Concert*
(9/91) (SYMP) ① **SYMCD1089**
V. Maurel, anon (r1905) *Concert*
(12/94) (SYMP) ① **SYMCD1128**

SECTION V: STAGE WORKS

Patrie!—opera: 5 acts (1886—Paris) (Lib.
Sardou and Gallet)
Pauvre martyr obscur T. Ruffo, orch (r1920)
Concert   (2/93) (PREI) ① [3] **89303(1)**
Pauvre martyr obscur J-F. Delmas, orch (r1904)
Concert   (12/94) (SYMP) ① **SYMCD1172**
**Suzanne—opéra-comique: 3 acts
(1878—Paris)** (Lib. Lockroy & E Cormon)
Comme un petit oiseau T. Schipa, orch, Mr Prince
(r1924) *Concert*   (12/89) (RCA) ① **GD87969**

PALENZ ?Norway

SECTION IV: VOCAL AND CHORAL

A.B.C.-Viser, 'A.B.C. songs'—song
K. Flagstad, orch (r1930) *Concert*
(12/95) (SIMA) ① [3] **PSC1821(1)**

PALERO, Fernández *(15th–16th cent) Spain*

SECTION III: INSTRUMENTAL

**Paseávase el rey moro—instrumental
ballade**
A. Lawrence-King (r1993) *Concert*
(2/94) (HYPE) ① **CDA66653**

PALESTRINA, Giovanni Pierluigi da *(1525/6–1594) Italy*

SECTION IV: VOCAL AND CHORAL

Alma Redemptoris mater—8vv (from Cappella
Giulia MS XIII)
Akademia, F. Lasserre, L. Stewart (r1994) *Concert*
(9/94) (PIER) ① **PV794041**
Tallis Scholars, P. Phillips (pp1994) *Concert*
(9/94) (GIME) ① **CDGIM994**
Assumpta est Maria—motet: 6vv
Tallis Scholars, P. Phillips *Concert*
(9/90) (GIME) ① **CDGIM020**
St John's College Ch, G. Guest *Concert*
(10/92) (DECC) ① **433 678-2DH**
Tallis Scholars, P. Phillips (r1989) *Concert*
(1/94) (GIME) ① [4] **CDGIMB400**
Ave mundi spes—motet: 8vv (c1584) (from
Cappella Giulia MS XIII 24)
Akademia, F. Lasserre, L. Stewart (r1994) *Concert*
(9/94) (PIER) ① **PV794041**
**Coelestis urbs Jerusalem—Vespers hymn:
4vv**
Gradus ad Parnassum, K. Junghänel (r1994) *Concert*
(7/95) (DHM) ① **05472 77326-2**
**Domine Jesus in qua nocte—5vv (pub
1572)**
PCA, B. Turner *Concert*
(12/92) (ASV) ① **CDQS6086**
Dum complerentur—motet: 6vv (pub 1569)
Taverner Consort, A. Parrott *Concert*
(8/87) (EMI) ① **CDC7 47699-2**
Oxford Christ Church Cath Ch, S. Darlington *Concert*
(11/88) (NIMB) ① **NI5100**
Exsultate Deo—motet: 5vv (pub 1584)
Westminster Cath Ch, S. Cleobury (ed Washington)
Concert   (7/83) (ARGO) ① **410 005-2ZH**
Oxford Christ Church Cath Ch, S. Darlington *Concert*
(11/88) (NIMB) ① **NI5100**
Gaude, Barbara—motet: 5vv (pub 1572)
N. Jenkin, M. Seers, C. Royall, A. Murgatroyd, N.
MacKenzie, M. Padmore, S. Birchall, The Sixteen,
The Sixteen Orch, H. Christophers *Concert*
(4/89) (HYPE) ① [2] **CDA66311/2**
Chanticleer (r1994) *Concert*
(2/95) (TELD) ① **4509-94561-2**
Hodie beata virgo—motet: 4vv (pub 1563)
King's College Ch, D. Willcocks *Concert*
(5/89) (DECC) ① **421 147-2DM**
**Lamentationum Hieremiae prophetae liber
primus (1588)**
Oxford Camerata, J. Summerly *Concert*
(4/93) (NAXO) ① **8 550572**
Amsterdam Loeki Stardust Qt *Concert*
(L'OI) ① **440 207-2OM**
Litaniae de Beata Virgine Maria—8vv
King's College Ch, D. Willcocks *Concert*
(5/89) (DECC) ① **421 147-2DM**
**Madrigals, Book 1 (Il primo libro di
madrigali)—secular: 5vv (pub 1581)**
EXCERPTS: 1. Amor, senza il tuo dono; 2. Dunque,
divin; 3. E tu, anima mia; 4. Giammai non resti; 5. Ma
so ben, Signor mio; 6. Non basta ch'una volta; 7. O
cibo di dolcezza; 8. O Jesu dolce; 9. O amava
saporito; 10. O refrigerio acceso; 11. O
sol'incoronato; 12. Paraclito amoroso; 13. Per
questo, Signor mio; 14. Questo più T'offend'io; 15.
Signor, dammi scienza; 16. S'io non Ti conoscessi;
17. Spirito santo, amore; 18. Tu sei soave fiume; 19.
Vergine bella (Wds Petrarch).
19. Akademia, F. Lasserre, L. Stewart (r1994)
Concert   (9/94) (PIER) ① **PV794041**
Magnificat—8vv
King's College Ch, D. Willcocks *Concert*
(5/89) (DECC) ① **421 147-2DM**
Akademia, F. Lasserre, L. Stewart (r1994) *Concert*
(9/94) (PIER) ① **PV794041**
Magnificat Primi Toni—4vv (pub 1591)
Tallis Scholars, P. Phillips (pp1994) *Concert*
(9/94) (GIME) ① **CDGIM994**
Magnificat VI toni—6vv
St John's College Ch, G. Guest *Concert*
(10/92) (DECC) ① **433 678-2DH**

**Missa Aeterna Christi munera—4vv (pub
1590)**
Oxford Camerata, J. Summerly *Missa Papae
Marcelli.*   (12/92) (NAXO) ① **8 550573**
PCA, B. Turner (r1974) *Concert*
(1/93) (ARCH) ① **437 072-2AT**
Missa Assumpta est Maria—6vv
Paris Chapelle Royale Chor, P. Herreweghe *Concert*
(4/89) (RICE) ① **RIC008029**
Tallis Scholars, P. Phillips *Concert*
(9/90) (GIME) ① **CDGIM020**
St John's College Ch, G. Guest *Concert*
(10/92) (DECC) ① **433 678-2DH**
Tallis Scholars, P. Phillips (r1989) *Concert*
(1/94) (GIME) ① [4] **CDGIMB400**
**Missa Benedicta es (after Josquin Desprez,
1520)**
Tallis Scholars, P. Phillips *Concert*
(7/90) (GIME) ① **CDGIM001**
Tallis Scholars, P. Phillips (r1981) *Concert*
(1/94) (GIME) ① [4] **CDGIMB400**
Missa brevis—4vv (pub 1570)
Tallis Scholars, P. Phillips *Concert*
(1/87) (GIME) ① **CDGIM008**
Westminster Cath Ch, D. Hill (r1987) *Missa Papae
Marcelli.*   (5/88) (HYPE) ① **CDA66266**
Tallis Scholars, P. Phillips (r1986) *Concert*
(1/94) (GIME) ① [4] **CDGIMB400**
Missa Dum complerentur—6vv (pub 1599)
Oxford Christ Church Cath Ch, S. Darlington *Concert*
(11/88) (NIMB) ① **NI5100**
**Missa Hodie Christus natus est—8vv (pub
1601)**
Gabrieli Consort, Gabrieli Players, P. McCreesh, T.
Roberts (r1992-3) *Concert*
(1/94) (ARCH) ① **437 833-2AH**
Oxford Schola Cantorum, J. Summerly (r1993)
Concert   (6/94) (NAXO) ① **8 550836**
Missa in festis Apostolorum I—5vv (1578-9)
('Mantuan' mass)
San Petronio Cappella Musicale Sols, S. Vartolo,
Nova Schola Gregoriana, A. Turco (r1994) *Concert*
(5/95) (BONG) ① [2] **GB5544/5-2**
Missa in festis Apostolorum II—5vv (1578-9)
('Mantuan' mass)
San Petronio Cappella Musicale Sols, S. Vartolo,
Nova Schola Gregoriana, A. Turco (r1994) *Concert*
(5/95) (BONG) ① [2] **GB5544/5-2**
**Missa in Semiduplicibus Maioribus I—5vv
(1578-9)** ('Mantuan' mass)
San Petronio Cappella Musicale Sols, S. Vartolo,
Nova Schola Gregoriana, A. Turco (r1994) *Concert*
(5/95) (BONG) ① [2] **GB5544/5-2**
**Missa in Semiduplicibus Maioribus II—5vv
(1578-9)** ('Mantuan' mass)
San Petronio Cappella Musicale Sols, S. Vartolo,
Nova Schola Gregoriana, A. Turco (r1994) *Concert*
(5/95) (BONG) ① [2] **GB5544/5-2**
Missa Nasce la gioia mia—6vv (pub 1590)
Tallis Scholars, P. Phillips *Concert*
(1/87) (GIME) ① **CDGIM008**
Tallis Scholars, P. Phillips (r1986) *Concert*
(1/94) (GIME) ① [4] **CDGIMB400**
Missa Nigra sum—5vv (pub 1590)
Tallis Scholars, P. Phillips *Concert*
(8/87) (GIME) ① **CDGIM003**
Tallis Scholars, P. Phillips (r1983) *Concert*
(1/94) (GIME) ① [4] **CDGIMB400**
Missa O Rex gloriae—4vv (pub 1601)
Westminster Cath Ch, J. O'Donnell *Concert*
(1/90) (HYPE) ① **CDA66316**
Missa Papae Marcelli—6vv (pub 1567)
Westminster Abbey Ch, S. Preston *Concert*
(5/86) (ARCH) ① **415 517-2AH**
Tallis Scholars, P. Phillips *Concert*
(7/86) (GIME) ① **CDGIM339**
PCA, M. Brown *Stabat mater a 8.*
(1/87) (CARL) ① **PCD863**
Westminster Cath Ch, D. Hill (r1987) *Missa brevis.*
(5/88) (HYPE) ① **CDA66266**
The Sixteen, H. Christophers *Concert*
(10/90) (COLL) ① **Coll5009-2**
Oxford Camerata, J. Summerly *Missa Aeterna Christi
Munera.*   (12/92) (NAXO) ① **8 550573**
PCA, B. Turner *Concert*
(12/92) (ASV) ① **CDQS6086**
Tallis Scholars, P. Phillips (r1980) *Concert*
(1/94) (GIME) ① [4] **CDGIMB400**
Tallis Scholars, P. Phillips (pp1994) *Concert*
(9/94) (GIME) ① **CDGIM994**
**Missa pro defunctis (Requiem)—5vv (pub
1591)**
Chanticleer (r1994) *Concert*
(2/95) (TELD) ① **4509-94561-2**

Missa Sicut lilium inter spinas—5vv (pub 1590)
Tallis Scholars, P. Phillips *Concert*
(9/90) (GIME) ① **CDGIM020**
Tallis Scholars, P. Phillips (r1989) *Concert*
(1/94) (GIME) ① [4] **CDGIMB400**
Missa Sine Nomine—5vv (1578-9) ('Mantuan' mass)
San Petronio Cappella Musicale Sols, S. Vartolo,
Nova Schola Gregoriana, A. Turco (r1994) *Concert*
(5/95) (BONG) ① [2] **GB5544/5-2**
Missa Veni sponsa Christi—4vv (pub 1599)
St John's College Ch, G. Guest *Concert*
(10/92) (DECC) ① **433 678-2DH**
Missa Viri Galilaei—6vv (pub 1601)
Westminster Cath Ch, J. O'Donnell *Concert*
(1/90) (HYPE) ① **CDA66316**
Motets, Book 2—4vv (pub 1581)
EXCERPTS: 1. Ad Dominum cum tribularer; 2.
Adoramus te Christe; 3. Ad te levavi; 4. Alma
Redemptoris mater; 5. Ave Maria; 6. Ave regina
coelorum; 7. Confitemini Domino; 8. Domine quando
veneris; 9. Ecce, nunc benedicite; 10. Ego sum panis
vivus ... Patres; 11. Fundamenta ejus; 12. Gloriosi
principes; 13. Haec dies; 14. Heu mihi Domine; 15.
Pueri Hebraeorum; 16. Quia vidisti me, Thoma; 17.
Salve regina misericordiae; 18. Sicut cervus; 18a.
secunda pars: Sitivit anima mea; 19. Sub tuum
praesidium; 20. Super flumina Babylonis.
4. PCA, B. Turner *Concert*
(12/92) (ASV) ① **CDQS6086**
5, 17, 19. Akademia, F. Lasserre, L. Stewart (r1994)
Concert (9/94) (PIER) ① **PV794041**
13, 18. Oxford Christ Church Cath Ch, S. Darlington
Concert (11/88) (NIMB) ① **NI5100**
18. Paris Chapelle Royale Chor, P. Herreweghe
Concert (4/89) (RICE) ① **RIC008029**
18, 20. PCA, B. Turner (r1974) *Concert*
(1/93) (ARCH) ① **437 072-2AT**
Motets, Book 3—5,6 & 8vv (pub 1575)
EXCERPTS: 1. Accepit Jesus (6vv); 2. Angelus
Domini (5vv); 3. Ave Maria (5vv); 4. Ave regina
coelorum (8vv); 5. Cantantibus organis (5vv); 6. Caro
mea (5vv); 7. Columna es (6vv); 8. Congrega,
Domine, dispersionem (5vv); 9. Cum ortus fuerit
(6vv); 10. Deus, qui ecclesiam tuam (6vv); 11.
Domine Deus, qui conteris (5vv); 12. Haec dies (6vv);
13. Hodie Christus natus est (8vv); 14. Jubilate Deo
omnis terra (5vv); 15. Jubilate Deo omnis terra (8vv);
16. Judica me, Deus (6vv); 17. Lauda Sion
salvatorem (8vv); 18. Manifesto vobis (5vv); 19. O
bone Jesu (6vv); 20. O lux et decus (5vv); 21.
Omnipotens sempiterne Deus (5vv); 22. O quam
metuendus est (5vv); 23. O sancte praesul Nicolaë
(5vv); 24. Pater noster (5vv); 25. Quid habes, Hester
(5vv); 26. Rex pacificus magnificatus est (6vv); 27.
Sanctificat Dominus (5vv); 28. Surge illuminare
Jerusalem (8vv); 29. Susanna ab improbis (6vv); 30.
Tradent enim vos (5vv); 31. Veni Sancte Spiritus
(8vv).
3, 19. Paris Chapelle Royale Chor, P. Herreweghe
Concert (4/89) (RICE) ① **RIC008029**
4. Akademia, F. Lasserre, L. Stewart (r1994) *Concert*
(9/94) (PIER) ① **PV794041**
13. Kings College Ch, D. Willcocks *Concert*
(12/91) (EMI) ① **CDM7 64130-2**
13. Gabrieli Consort, Gabrieli Players, P. McCreesh,
T. Roberts (r1992/3) *Concert*
(1/94) (ARCH) ① **437 833-2AH**
13. Oxford Schola Cantorum, J. Summerly (r1993)
Concert (6/94) (NAXO) ① **8 550836**
15. Taverner Consort, A. Parrott *Concert*
(8/87) (EMI) ① **CDC7 47699-2**
19. Oxford Christ Church Cath Ch, S. Darlington
Concert (11/88) (NIMB) ① **NI5100**
19. PCA, B. Turner (r1974) *Concert*
(1/93) (ARCH) ① **437 072-2AT**
19. Chanticleer (r1994) *Concert*
(2/95) (TELD) ① **4509-94561-2**
28. Tallis Scholars, P. Phillips (pp1994) *Concert*
(9/94) (GIME) ① **CDGIM994**
Motets, Book 4, 'Canticis Canticorum'—5vv (pub 1584)
EXCERPTS: 1. Osculetur me; 2. Trahe me; 3. Nigra
sum; 4. Vineam meam non custodivi; 5. Si ignoras; 6.
Pulchrae sunt genae tuae; 7. Fasciculus myrrae; 8.
Ecce tu pulcher es; 9. Tota pulchra es; 10. Vulnerasti
cor meum; 11. Sicut lilium inter spinas; 12. Introduxit
me rex; 13. Laeva ejus; 14. Vox dilecti mei; 15.
Surge, propera; 16. Surge, amica mea; 17. Dilectus
meus mihi; 18. Surgam et circuibo civitatem; 19.
Adjuro vos; 20. Caput ejus; 21. Dilectus meus
descendit; 22. Pulchra es; 23. Quae es ista; 24.
Descendi in hortum nucum; 25. Quam pulchri sunt;
26. Duo ubera tua; 27. Quam pulchra es; 28. Guttur
tuum; 29. Veni, dilecte mi.

Cpte Cambridge Sngrs, J. Rutter (r1993)
(9/94) (CLLE) ① **COLCD122**
2, 3, 15, 16, 27, 29. Chanticleer (r1994) *Concert*
(2/95) (TELD) ① **4509-94561-2**
5. Oxford Camerata, J. Summerly (r1993) *Concert*
(3/95) (NAXO) ① **8 550843**
Motettorum liber quintus—5vv (pub 1584)
1. Gaude gloriosa; 2. Salve regina; 3. Ave Regina
coelorum.
1. Chanticleer (r1994) *Concert*
(2/95) (TELD) ① **4509-94561-2**
2. Chanticleer (r1994) *Concert*
(2/95) (TELD) ① **4509-94561-2**
Nunc dimittis—motet: 8vv
Tallis Scholars, P. Phillips (pp1994) *Concert*
(9/94) (GIME) ① **CDGIM994**
O beata et benedicta—motet: 5vv (pub 1569)
Taverner Consort, A. Parrott *Concert*
(8/87) (EMI) ① **CDC7 47699-2**
Paris Chapelle Royale Chor, P. Herreweghe *Concert*
(4/89) (RICE) ① **RIC008029**
O Rex gloriae—motet: 4vv (pub 1563)
Westminster Cath Ch, J. O'Donnell *Concert*
(1/90) (HYPE) ① **CDA66316**
Pange lingua—hymn: 4vv (1589) (from 'Hymni totius anni')
Chanticleer (r1994) *Concert*
(2/95) (TELD) ① **4509-94561-2**
Peccantem me quotidie—motet: 5vv (pub 1572)
Westminster Cath Ch, S. Cleobury *Concert*
(7/83) (ARGO) ① **410 005-2ZH**
Paris Chapelle Royale Chor, P. Herreweghe *Concert*
(4/89) (RICE) ① **RIC008029**
PCA, B. Turner *Concert*
(12/92) (ASV) ① **CDQS6086**
Regina coeli—8vv (from Cappella Giulia MS XIII)
Akademia, F. Lasserre, L. Stewart (r1994) *Concert*
(9/94) (PIER) ① **PV794041**
Salve regina—motet, 4 settings: 8vv (c1584) (from Cappella Giulia MS XIII 2a)
Akademia, F. Lasserre, L. Stewart (r1994) *Concert*
(9/94) (PIER) ① **PV794041**
Senex puerum portabat—motet: 5vv (pub 1569)
King's College Ch, D. Willcocks *Concert*
(5/89) (DECC) ① **421 147-2DM**
Sicut lilium inter spinas I—motet: 5vv (pub 1569)
Tallis Scholars, P. Phillips *Concert*
(9/90) (GIME) ① **CDGIM020**
Tallis Scholars, P. Phillips (r1989) *Concert*
(1/94) (GIME) ① [4] **CDGIMB400**
Stabat mater—motet: 8vv
Taverner Consort, A. Parrott *Concert*
(8/87) (EMI) ① **CDC7 47699-2**
PCA, M. Brown *Missa Papae Marcelli.*
(11/87) (CARL) ① **PCD863**
King's College Ch, D. Willcocks *Concert*
(5/89) (DECC) ① **421 147-2DM**
The Sixteen, H. Christophers *Concert*
(10/90) (COLL) ① **Coll5009-2**
Cambridge Sngrs, J. Rutter *Concert*
(4/92) (CLLE) ① **COLCD116**
PCA, B. Turner *Concert*
(12/92) (ASV) ① **CDQS6086**
Oxford Schola Cantorum, J. Summerly (r1993)
Concert (6/94) (NAXO) ① **8 550836**
Tallis Scholars, P. Phillips (pp1994) *Concert*
(9/94) (GIME) ① **CDGIM994**
Tu es Petrus—motet: 6vv (pub 1572)
Westminster Cath Ch, S. Cleobury (ed. Collins)
Concert (7/83) (ARGO) ① **410 005-2ZH**
Westminster Abbey Ch, S. Preston *Concert*
(5/86) (ARCH) ① **415 517-2AH**
Veni sponsa Christi—antiphon: 6vv
St John's College Ch, G. Guest *Concert*
(10/92) (DECC) ① **433 678-2DH**
Veni sponsa Christi—motet: 4vv (pub 1563)
St John's College Ch, G. Guest *Concert*
(10/92) (DECC) ① **433 678-2DH**
Vestiva i colli—secular madrigal: 5vv (pub 1566) (trans Bartolomé de Selma, 1638)
Ens *Concert* (3/84) (CLAV) ① **CD50-8206**
Viri Galilaei—motet: 6vv (pub 1559)
Westminster Cath Ch, J. O'Donnell *Concert*
(1/90) (HYPE) ① **CDA66316**

PALLAVICINO, Carlo *(1630–1688)* Italy

SECTION V: STAGE WORKS

Il Diocletiano—opera (1674—Venice)
Sinfonia C. Steele-Perkins, Parley of Instr *Concert*
(1/89) (HYPE) ① **CDA66255**

PALMGREN, Selim *(1878–1951)* Finland

SECTION III: INSTRUMENTAL

En route—piano, Op. 9
S. Hough (r1986) *Concert*
(1/89) (VIRG) ① **VC7 59509-2**
24 Preludes—piano, Op. 17
9. Cradle song; 12. The Sea; 19. Bird's song.
9. M. Hess (r1931) *Concert*
(3/95) (BIDD) ① **LHW024**

PALONI

SECTION IV: VOCAL AND CHORAL

Non guardarmi così—song
F. Marconi, S. Cottone (r1903) *Concert*
(6/90) (SYMP) ① **SYMCD1073**

PAMINGER, Leonhard *(1495–1567)* Austria

SECTION IV: VOCAL AND CHORAL

Pater noster—4vv
Lower Rhine Choral Soc, H. Schmitt *Concert*
(2/90) (SCHW) ① **313001**

PANDOLFI (MEALLI), Giovanni Antonio *(fl 1660–1669)* Italy

SECTION II: CHAMBER

6 Sonatas for Violin and Continuo, Op. 4 (1660)
1. La Bernabea, E minor; 2. La Viviana, A minor; 3.
La Monella Romanesca, G minor; 4. La Biancuccia,
D minor; 5. La Stella, D minor; 6. La Vinciolina, D
minor.
1, 4, 6. A. Manze, R. Egarr, F. Jacobs (r1992)
Concert (7/94) (CHNN) ① **CCS5894**
6 Sonatas per chiesa e camera—violin and continuo, Op. 3 (pub 1660)
1. La Stella, A minor; 2. La Cesta, A minor; 3. La
Melana, D; 4. La Castella, D; 5. La Clemente, E
minor; 6. La Sabbatina, C.
2, 4-6. A. Manze, R. Egarr, F. Jacobs (r1992)
Concert (7/94) (CHNN) ① **CCS5894**

PANIZZA, Giacomo *(1804–1860)* Italy

SECTION II: CHAMBER

Ballabile con Variazioni bel ballo 'Ettore Feramosca'—clarinet and piano (1837)
C. Bradbury, O. Davies *Concert*
(6/90) (ASV) ① **CDDCA701**

PANUFNIK, Sir Andrzej *(1914–1991)* Poland/Britain

SECTION I: ORCHESTRAL

Arbor cosmica—orchestra (1983)
NY Chbr SO, A. Panufnik (r1988) *Sinfonia sacra.*
(5/91) (NONE) ① **7559-79228-2**
Autumn Music—orchestra (1962 rev 1965)
A. Peebles, LSO, J. Horenstein *Concert*
(4/89) (UNIC) ① **UKCD2016**
Concerto festivo—orchestra (1979)
LSO, A. Panufnik *Concert*
(8/89) (UNIC) ① **UKCD2020**
Concerto for Bassoon and Orchestra (1985)
(to the memory of Fr. Jerzy Popiełuszko)
R. Thompson, London Musici, M. Stephenson
Concert (7/90) (CONI) ① **CDCF182**
Concerto for Piano and Orchestra (1962 rev 1982)
E. Pobłocka, LSO, A. Panufnik *Symphony 9.*
(5/92) (CONI) ① **CDCF206**
Concerto for Timpani, Percussion and Strings (1980)
K-H. Goedicke, M. Frye, LSO, A. Panufnik *Concert*
(8/89) (UNIC) ① **UKCD2020**

R. Benjafield, G. Cole, London Musici, M.
Stephenson (r1993) *Concert*
(8/94) (CONI) ① **CDCF217**
Concerto for Violin and Strings (1971)
K. Smietana, London Musici, M. Stephenson *Concert*
(7/90) (CONI) ① **CDCF182**
**Harmony—a poem for chamber orchestra
(1989)**
London Musici, M. Stephenson (r1993) *Concert*
(8/94) (CONI) ① **CDCF217**
Heroic Overture—orchestra (1952 rev 1955)
LSO, J. Horenstein *Concert*
(4/89) (UNIC) ① **UKCD2016**
**Hommage à Chopin—flute and strings
(1966)**
K. Jones, London Musici, M. Stephenson *Concert*
(7/90) (CONI) ① **CDCF182**
Katyń Epitaph—orchestra (1967)
LSO, A. Panufnik *Concert*
(8/89) (UNIC) ① **UKCD2020**
Landscape—orchestra (1962)
LSO, A. Panufnik *Concert*
(8/89) (UNIC) ① **UKCD2020**
Nocturne—orchestra (1947 rev 1955)
A. Peebles, LSO, J. Horenstein *Concert*
(4/89) (UNIC) ① **UKCD2016**
**Sinfonia Concertante—flute, harp and
strings (1973)**
K. Jones, R. Masters, London Musici, M. Stephenson
(r1993) *Concert* (8/94) (CONI) ① **CDCF217**
Sinfonia rustica (1948 rev 1955)
Monte Carlo Op Orch, A. Panufnik *Concert*
(4/89) (UNIC) ① **UKCD2016**
Sinfonia sacra (1963)
Monte Carlo Op Orch, A. Panufnik *Concert*
(8/89) (UNIC) ① **UKCD2020**
NY Chbr SO, A. Panufnik (r1987) *Arbor cosmica*.
(5/91) (NONE) ① **7559-79228-2**
Symphony No. 8, 'Sinfonia Votiva' (1981)
Boston SO, S. Ozawa (r1982) *Sessions: Concerto for
Orchestra*. (7/89) (HYPE) ① **CDA66050**
BBC SO, A. Panufnik (pp1983) *Concert*
(12/95) (BBCR) ① **BBCRD9124**
**Symphony No. 9, 'Sinfonia della speranza'
(1986 rev 1990)**
LSO, A. Panufnik *Piano Concerto*.
(5/92) (CONI) ① **CDCF206**
**Tragic Overture—orchestra (1942, recons
1945, rev 1955)**
LSO, J. Horenstein *Concert*
(4/89) (UNIC) ① **UKCD2016**

SECTION II: CHAMBER

Song to the Virgin Mary—string sextet (1969)
(rev from choral version, 1964)
Chilingirian Qt, R. Chase, S. Orton (r1993) *Concert*
(12/93) (CONI) ① **CDCF218**
String Quartet No. 1 (1976-77)
1. Prelude (1976); 2. Transformation (1976); 3.
Postlude (1977).
Chilingirian Qt (r1993) *Concert*
(12/93) (CONI) ① **CDCF218**
String Quartet No. 2 (1980)
Chilingirian Qt (r1993) *Concert*
(12/93) (CONI) ① **CDCF218**
String Quartet No. 3 (1991)
Chilingirian Qt (r1993) *Concert*
(12/93) (CONI) ① **CDCF218**
String Sextet (1988)
Chilingirian Qt, R. Chase, S. Orton (r1993) *Concert*
(12/93) (CONI) ① **CDCF218**

PAPE, Andy *(b 1955) Denmark*

SECTION II: CHAMBER

CaDance 4 2—percussion duo
Safri Duo (r1994) *Concert*
(4/95) (CHAN) ① **CHAN9330**

PARADIES, Maria Theresia von
(1759–1824) Austria

SECTION II: CHAMBER

Sicilienne in E flat—violin & piano
X. Wei, Pam Nicholson *Concert*
(9/90) (ASV) ① **CDDCA698**
N. Hall (arr gtr) *Concert*
(5/92) (DECC) ① **430 839-2DH**
G. Neveu, B. Seidler-Winkler (arr Dushkin: r1938)
Concert (10/92) (TEST) ① **SBT1010**
J. Thibaud, T. Janopoulo (r1930: arr vn/pf: Dushkin)
Concert (12/94) (APR) ① [2] **APR7028**
A. A. Meyers, S. Rivers (r1993) *Concert*
(4/95) (RCA) ① **09026 62546-2**

I. Perlman, S. Sanders (arr Dushkin) *Concert*
(6/95) (EMI) ① [20] **CZS4 83177-2(3)**
J. Du Pré, G. Moore (r1962: arr vc/pf: Dushkin)
Concert (11/95) (EMI) ① **CDC5 55529-2**

PARADIS (PARADIES), Pietro
Domenico *(1707–1791) Italy*

SECTION III: INSTRUMENTAL

**12 Sonate di gravicembalo—keyboard (pub
1754)**
EXCERPTS: 6. Sonata in A; 6a. Toccata; 6b.
Allegro.
6. T. Pinnock (r1978) *Concert*
(4/89) (CRD) ① **CRD3347**
6. G. Gifford *Concert* (5/90) (LIBR) ① **LRCD156**
6a R. Aldwinckle *Concert*
(7/87) (CARL) ① **PCD850**
6a I. Perlman, S. Sanders (trans Heifetz) *Concert*
(12/89) (EMI) ① **CDC7 49604-2**
6a V. Black *Concert* (5/91) (COLL) ① **Coll5024-2**
6a I. Perlman, S. Sanders (r1988: arr vn/pf: Heifetz)
Concert (6/95) (EMI) ① [20] **CZS4 83177-2(3)**
6a G. Malcolm (r1962) *Concert*
(11/95) (DECC) ① **444 390-2DWO**

SECTION IV: VOCAL AND CHORAL

M'ha presa alla sua ragna—song
R. Tebaldi, R. Bonynge (r1972) *Concert*
(9/94) (DECC) ① **436 202-2DM**
Quel ruscelletto—song
H. Spani, orch, G. Nastrucci (r1930) *Concert*
(9/90) (CLUB) ① [2] **CL99-509/10**

PARAY, Paul *(1886–1979)
France/USA*

SECTION IV: VOCAL AND CHORAL

**Mass for the 500th Anniversary of the Death
of Joan of Arc—SATB, chorus and orchestra
(1931)**
F. Yeend, F. Bible, D. Lloyd, Yi-Kwei-Sze, Rackham
Sym Ch, Detroit SO, P. Paray (r1956) *Saint-Saëns:
Symphony 3*. (9/92) (MERC) ① **432 719-2MM**

PARCHAM, Andrew *(17th–18th
Cent) England*

SECTION II: CHAMBER

Solo (Suite) in G—recorder and continuo
D. Munrow, O. Brookes, C. Hogwood (r1973) *Concert*
(10/95) (DECC) ① **440 079-2DM**
F. Brüggen, N. Harnoncourt (r1967/79) *Concert*
(10/95) (TELD) ① **4509-97465-2**

PARISH ALVARS, Elias
(1808–1849) England

SECTION I: ORCHESTRAL

**Concerto for Harp and Orchestra in G minor,
Op. 81**
M. Nordmann, F. Liszt CO, J-P. Rampal (r1993)
Concert (10/95) (SONY) ① **SK58919**

SECTION III: INSTRUMENTAL

Divertissement—harp, Op. 38
S. Drake *Concert* (9/86) (HYPE) ① **CDA66038**
**Grande Fantaisie et Variations di
Bravure—harp**
S. Drake *Concert* (1988)
(2/90) (HYPE) ① **CDA66340**
Mandoline—harp
S. McDonald (arr McDonald) *Concert*
(10/84) (DELO) ① **DE3005**
Serenade—harp
T. Owen *Concert* (3/87) (CARL) ① **PCD835**

PARISOTTI, Alessandro
(1835–1913) Italy

SECTION IV: VOCAL AND CHORAL

Se tu m'ami—aria, C xxii, 68 (previously attrib
Pergolesi)
C. Muzio, orch (r1925) *Concert*
(5/90) (BOGR) ① [2] **BIM705-2**
H. Spani, orch, G. Nastrucci (r1930) *Concert*
(9/90) (CLUB) ① [2] **CL99-509/10**
C. Muzio, orch, L. Molajoli (r1935) *Concert*
(4/91) (NIMB) ① **NI7814**
C. Ferrani, anon (r1902) *Concert*
(5/91) (SYMP) ① **SYMCD1077**

V. de los Angeles, G. Parsons (pp1990) *Concert*
(12/91) (COLL) ① **Coll1247-2**
C. Bartoli, G. Fischer *Concert*
(12/92) (DECC) ① **436 267-2DH**
A. Bonci, anon (r1905) *Concert*
(12/93) (SYMP) ① **SYMCD1113**
C. Muzio, orch (r1925) *Concert*
(1/94) (ROMO) ① [2] **81005-2**
R. Tebaldi, R. Bonynge (r1972) *Concert*
(9/94) (DECC) ① **436 202-2DM**

PARKER, Clifton *(1905–1989)
England*

SECTION V: STAGE WORKS

Sink the Bismarck!—film score (1960)
EXCERPTS: 1. Main Theme.
1. Prague City PO, P. Bateman (r1994) *Concert*
(11/94) (SILV) ① **FILMCD151**
Western Approaches—film score (1944)
EXERPTS: 1. Seascape.
1. LSO, M. Mathieson (r1945) *Concert*
(9/94) (EMI) ① **CDGO 2059**

PARKER, Horatio William
(1863–1919) USA

SECTION I: ORCHESTRAL

**A Northern Ballad—symphonic poem, Op.
49 (1899)**
Albany SO, J. Heygi *Chadwick: Symphony 2*.
(9/87) (NEW) ① **NW339-2**

SECTION III: INSTRUMENTAL

Sonata in E flat—organ, Op. 65 (1908)
G. Weir *Concert* (12/92) (KOSS) ① **KC1013**

SECTION IV: VOCAL AND CHORAL

Love in May—song, Op. 51/4 (1901) (Wds.
Higginson)
E. Eames, anon (r1908) *Concert*
(11/93) (ROMO) ① [2] **81001-2**

PARRY, Sir (Charles) Hubert
(Hastings) *(1848–1918) England*

SECTION I: ORCHESTRAL

Concertstück in G minor—orchestra (1877)
(incomplete: cpted B. Benoliel, 1981)
LPO, M. Bamert *Symphony 1*.
(7/92) (CHAN) ① **CHAN9062**
Elegy for Brahms—orchestra (1897)
LPO, M. Bamert *Concert*
(9/91) (CHAN) ① **CHAN8955**
An English Suite—string orchestra (1921)
1. Prelude; 2. In Minuet Style; 3. Caprice; 4.
Caprice; 5. Pastoral; 6. Air; 7. Frolic.
English Stg Orch, W. Boughton (r1992) *Concert*
(8/93) (NIMB) ① **NI5366**
**From Death to Life—symphonic poem in two
connected movements (1914)**
1. Via Mortis; 2. Via Vite.
LPO, M. Bamert *Concert*
(9/91) (CHAN) ① **CHAN8955**
English SO, W. Boughton *Symphony 1*.
(5/92) (NIMB) ① **NI5296**
**Lady Radnor's Suite—string orchestra
(1894)**
1. Prelude; 2. Allemande; 3. Sarabande; 4. Slow
Minuet; 5. Bourrée; 6. Gigue.
English Stg Orch, W. Boughton *Concert*
(10/88) (NIMB) ① **NI5068**
**Overture to an Unwritten
Tragedy—orchestra (1894)**
English Northern Philh, D. Lloyd-Jones *Concert*
(1/92) (HYPE) ① **CDA66515**
Symphonic Variations—orchestra (1897)
LPO, M. Bamert *Symphony 2*.
(10/91) (CHAN) ① **CHAN8961**
Symphony No. 1 in G minor (1882)
English SO, W. Boughton *From Death to Life*.
(5/92) (NIMB) ① **NI5296**
LPO, M. Bamert *Concertstück*.
(7/92) (CHAN) ① **CHAN9062**
Symphony No. 2 in F, 'Cambridge' (1883)
LPO, M. Bamert *Symphonic Variations*.
(10/91) (CHAN) ① **CHAN8961**
Symphony No. 3 in C, 'English' (1889)
LPO, M. Bamert *Symphony 4*.
(1/91) (CHAN) ① **CHAN8896**
Symphony No. 4 in E minor (1889)
LPO, M. Bamert *Symphony 3*.
(1/91) (CHAN) ① **CHAN8896**

Symphony No. 5 in B minor, 'Symphonic Fantasia' (1912)
LPO, M. Bamert *Concert*
(9/91) (CHAN) ① **CHAN8955**

SECTION II: CHAMBER

Fantasie-Sonata in B minor—violin and piano (1878)
E. Gruenberg, R. Vignoles *Concert*
(9/91) (HYPE) ① **CDA66157**

Nonet in B flat—fl, ob, cor ang, 2 cls, 2 bns, 2 hns (1877)
Capricorn (r1987; ed Dibble) *Stanford: Serenade.*
(9/89) (HYPE) ① **CDA66291**

Piano Quartet in A flat (1879)
Deakin Pf Trio, Y. Inoue *Piano Trio 1.*
(7/94) (MERI) ① **CDE84248**

Piano Trio No. 1 in E minor (1878)
Deakin Pf Trio *Piano Quartet.*
(7/94) (MERI) ① **CDE84248**

Piano Trio No. 2 in B minor (1884)
Deakin Pf Trio (r1993) *Piano Trio 3.*
(7/94) (MERI) ① **CDE84255**

Piano Trio No. 3 in G (c1884-90)
Deakin Pf Trio (r1993) *Piano Trio 2.*
(7/94) (MERI) ① **CDE84255**

12 Short Pieces (1895)
BOOK 1: 1. Idyll; 2. Romance; 3. Capriccio; 4. Lullaby. BOOK 2: 5. Prelude; 6. Romance; 7. Capriccio; 8. Envoi. BOOK 3: 9. Preamble; 10. Romance; 11. Capriccio; 12. Envoi.
E. Gruenberg, R. Vignoles *Concert*
(9/91) (HYPE) ① **CDA66157**

Sonata for Violin and Piano in D (?1888-89)
E. Gruenberg, R. Vignoles *Concert*
(9/91) (HYPE) ① **CDA66157**

SECTION III: INSTRUMENTAL

7 Chorale Preludes—Set 2—organ (pub 1916)
EXCERPTS: 1. Ye boundless realms of joy (Croft's 136th); 2. Martyrdom; 3. St Thomas; 4. St Mary; 5. Eventide; 6. St Cross; 7. Hanover.
3. D. Briggs *Concert* (7/91) (PRIO) ① **PRCD322**
5. C. Curley (r1991) *Concert*
(4/92) (ARGO) ① **433 450-2ZH**

Hands across the Centuries—suite: piano (1916-)
1. Prelude; 2. The Passionate Allemande; 3. The Wistful Courant-Capriccioso; 4. Quasi Sarabande; 5. Gavotte and Musette; 6. Quasi Minuetto; 7. The Whirling Jig.
Peter Jacobs (r1992) *Concert*
(10/95) (PRIO) ① **PRCD451**

Shulbrede Tunes—piano (pub 1914)
1. Shulbrede; 2. Elizabeth; 3. Dolly (No. 1); 4. Bogies and Sprites that Gambold by Nights; 5. Matthew; 6. Prior's Chamber by Firelight; 7. Children's Pranks; 8. Dolly (No. 2); 9. In the Garden with the Dew on the Grass; 10. Father Playmate.
Peter Jacobs (r1992) *Concert*
(10/95) (PRIO) ① **PRCD451**

Theme and 19 Variations in D minor—piano (1878-1885)
Peter Jacobs (r1992) *Concert*
(10/95) (PRIO) ① **PRCD451**

Toccata and Fugue in G (Wanderer)—organ (1921)
G. Barber *Concert* (7/91) (PRIO) ① **PRCD314**

SECTION IV: VOCAL AND CHORAL

Choric Song from Tennyson's 'Lotos Eaters'—soprano, chorus and orchestra (1892)
D. Jones, LP Ch, LPO, M. Bamert *Soul's Ransom.*
(1/92) (CHAN) ① **CHAN8990**

Crossing the Bar—motet (1908) (Wds. A. Tennyson)
Wellington College Chs, T. Byram-Wigfield, S. Anderson *Concert* (10/92) (HERA) ① **HAVPCD153**

Dear Lord and Father of Mankind—hymn (Wds. Whittier)
St Paul's Cath Ch, C. Dearnley, John Scott *Concert*
(7/90) (HYPE) ① **CDH88036**

English Lyrics, Set 2—voice and piano (1886-87) (Wds. Shakespeare)
1. O mistress mine; 2. Take, o take; 3. No longer mourn for me; 4. Blow, blow, thou sinter wind; 5. When icles hang by the wall.
1. Sarah Walker, J. Constable *Concert*
(4/92) (GAMU) ① **GAMD506**
1. J. Baker, G. Moore (r1967) *Concert*
(11/94) (EMI) ① **CDM5 65009-2**

English Lyrics, Set 5—voice and piano (pub 1902) (Wds. various)
1. A stray nymph of Dian (wds. J. Sturgis); 2. Proud Maisie (wds. Scott); 3. Crabbed age and youth (wds. Shakespeare); 4. Lay a garland (wds. Beaumont/Fletcher); 5. Love and laughter (wds. A. Butler); 6. A girl to her glass (wds. J. Sturgis); 7. A Welsh lullaby (wds. C. O. Jones).
2. J. Baker, G. Moore *Concert*
(11/94) (EMI) ① **CDM5 65009-2**

English Lyrics, Set 6—voice and piano (pub 1902) (Wds. various)
1. When comes my Gwen (wds. E. O. Jones); 2. And yet I love till I die (wds. Anon); 3. Love is a bable (wds. Anon); 4. A lover's garland (wds. A. P. Graves); 5. At the hour the long day ends (wds. A. P. Graves); 6. Under the greenwood tree (wds. Shakespeare).
3. L. Finnie, A. Legge *Concert*
(4/90) (CHAN) ① **CHAN8749**
3. K. Ferrier, F. Stone (bp1952) *Concert*
(7/91) (LOND) ① **430 061-2LM**
3. K. Ferrier, F. Stone (bp1952) *Concert*
(6/92) (DECC) ① **433 473-2DM**

Evening Service in D (c1882)
1. Magnificat; 2. Nunc dimittis.
St. George's Chapel Ch, R. Judd, C. Robinson *Concert*
(9/88) (HYPE) ① **CDA66273**

Hear my words, ye people—anthem: chorus and orchestra (1894)
St. George's Chapel Ch, R. Judd, C. Robinson *Concert*
(9/88) (HYPE) ① **CDA66273**
St Paul's Cath Ch, John Scott, Andrew Lucas (r1993) *Concert*
(6/94) (HYPE) ① **CDA66678**
1. St Bride's Ch, Fleet St, C. Etherington, R. Jones *Concert*
(2/91) (REGE) ① **REGSB701CD**

I was glad—anthem for the Coronation of King Edward VII (1902)
Salisbury Cath Ch, C. Walsh, R. Seal *Concert*
(9/87) (MERI) ① **CDE84025**
St. George's Chapel Ch, R. Judd, C. Robinson *Concert*
(9/88) (HYPE) ① **CDA66273**
LSC, LSO, R. Hickox (r1988) *Concert*
(2/89) (CHAN) ① [2] **CHAN8641/2**
Westminster Abbey Ch, London Brass, M. Neary *Concert*
(10/89) (CARL) ① **PCD919**
Winchester Cath Ch, Waynflete Sngrs, T. Byram-Wigfield, Bournemouth SO, D. Hill (orch Elgar) *Concert*
(4/92) (ARGO) ① **430 836-2ZH**
Westminster Abbey Ch, S. Preston (r1962) *Concert*
(6/93) (DECC) ① **436 403-2DWO**
Trinity Coll Ch, Cambridge, R. Marlow (r1993) *Concert*
(2/94) (CONI) ① **CDCF219**
Westminster Abbey Ch, M. Baker, M. Neary (r1993/4) *Concert* (9/94) (CNTO) ① **CSACD3050**
St Paul's Cath Ch, John Scott, Andrew Lucas (r1994) *Concert*
(5/95) (HYPE) ① **CDA66758**

Invocation to Music—STB, chorus and orchestra (1895) (Wds. R. Bridges)
Anne Dawson, A. Davies, B. Rayner Cook, LP Ch, LPO, M. Bamert
(6/92) (CHAN) ① **CHAN9025**

Jerusalem—choral song (1916) (Wds. W. Blake)
St. George's Chapel Ch, R. Judd, C. Robinson *Concert*
(9/88) (HYPE) ① **CDA66273**
I. Tracey (r1990; arr Tracey) *Concert*
(4/91) (MIRA) ① **MRCD901**
Winchester Cath Ch, Waynflete Sngrs, T. Byram-Wigfield, Bournemouth SO, D. Hill (orch Elgar) *Concert*
(4/92) (ARGO) ① **430 836-2ZH**
Trinity Coll Ch, Cambridge, R. Marlow (r1993) *Concert*
(2/94) (CONI) ① **CDCF219**
BBC Sngrs, BBC Sym Chor, BBC SO, A. Davis (r1994; arr Elgar) *Concert*
(2/95) (TELD) ① **4509-97868-2**

Judith—oratorio: SATB, chorus and orchestra (1888) (Wds. Apocrypha and cpsr)
Long since in Egypt's plenteous Land Winchester Cath Ch, Waynflete Sngrs, T. Byram-Wigfield, Bournemouth SO, D. Hill *Concert*
(4/92) (ARGO) ① **430 836-2ZH**

Ode at a Solemn Music, 'Blest Pair of Sirens'—chorus and orchestra (1887) (Wds. J Milton)
LSC, LSO, R. Hickox (r1988) *Concert*
(2/89) (CHAN) ① [2] **CHAN8641/2**
Winchester Cath Ch, Waynflete Sngrs, T. Byram-Wigfield, Bournemouth SO, D. Hill *Concert*
(4/92) (ARGO) ① **430 836-2ZH**

7 Partsongs—male voice choir (1904-12) (Wds. various)
1. Hand fear, cast away care (wds. cpsr: 1906); 2. Love wakes and weeps (wds. W. Scott: 1906); 3. The mad dog (wds. O. Goldsmith: 1906); 4. There art very wise man, old Aesop (wds. C. Dickens: 1912); 5. Orpheus (wds. cpsr: 1904); 6. Out upon it! (wds. T. Suckling); 7. An Analogy (wds. cpsr: 1911).

Hilliard Ens, L-L. Kiesel *Concert*
(12/91) (MERI) ① **DUOCD89009**

7 Partsongs—4-6vv a capella (pub 1909) (Wds. various)
1. In a harbour grene (4vv: wds. R. Weber); 2. Sweet day, so cool (4vv: wds. G. Herbert); 3. Sorrow and Pain (6vv: wds. Lady C. Elliott); 4. Wrong not, sweet Empress (4vv: wds. W. Raleigh); 5. Prithee, why? (4vv: wds. J. Suckling); 6. My delight and thy delight (4vv: wds. R. Bridges).
2. King's Sngrs *Concert*
(6/88) (EMI) ① **CDC7 49765-2**

6 Songs of Farewell—chorus (4vv-8vv) (1916-18) (Wds. various)
1. My soul, there's a country (Wds. Vaughan); 2. I know my soul hath power (Wds. Davies); 3. Never weatherbeaten sail (Wds. Campion); 4. There is an old belief (Wds. Lockhart); 5. At the round earth's imagined corners (Wds. Donne); 6. Lord, let me know mine end.
Cpte Trinity Coll Ch, Cambridge, R. Marlow *Concert*
(9/87) (CONI) ① **CDCF155**
Cpte St. George's Chapel Ch, R. Judd, C. Robinson *Concert*
(9/88) (HYPE) ① **CDA66273**
1. St Bride's Ch, Fleet St, R. Jones *Concert*
(2/91) (REGE) ① **REGSB701CD**
1. Magdalen Oxford Coll Ch, J. Harper *Concert*
(11/91) (ABBE) ① **CDCA913**
4. St Paul's Cath Ch, John Scott, Adrian Lucas (r1991) *Concert* (8/93) (HYPE) ① **CDA66618**
6. King's College Ch, S. Cleobury (pp1991 with Choral Evensong) *Concert*
(10/92) (EMI) ① **CDC7 54412-2**

4 Sonnets by Shakespeare (1873-82)
1. When in disgrace with fortune and men's eyes; 2. Farewell, thou art toodear for my possessing; 3. Shall I compare thee to a summer's day?; 4. When to the sessions of sweet silent thought.
1, 2. A. Rolfe Johnson, G. Johnson *Concert*
(5/92) (HYPE) ① **CDA66480**

The Soul's Ransom—sinfonia sacra: SB, chorus and orchestra (1906) (Wds. Ezekiel and cpsr)
D. Jones, D. Wilson-Johnson, LP Ch, LPO, M. Bamert *Lotos Eaters.* (1/92) (CHAN) ① **CHAN8990**

SECTION V: STAGE WORKS

The Birds—incidental music to Aristophanes's play (1883—Cambridge)
EXCERPTS: 1. Bridal March.
1. A. Lumsden (trans org: Alcock) *Concert*
(4/91) (GUIL) ① **GRCD7025**

PARRY, John (c1710–1782)
Wales

SECTION III: INSTRUMENTAL

Lesson No. 2—harp
1. Siciliana; 2. Allegro assai.
1, 2. F. Kelly (r1992) *Concert*
(9/94) (MOSC) ① **070987**

PARSONS, Robert I (c1530–1570)
England

SECTION II: CHAMBER

In Nomine a 5—consort (5 parts)
Fretwork *Concert* (3/88) (AMON) ① **CD-SAR29**

The Songe called Trumpetts—6 violas da gamba (also known as 'Lusti gallant' and 'Cante cantate')
J. Lindberg, N. North, P. O'Dette *Concert*
(12/86) (BIS) ① **BIS-CD341**

Ut re me fa sol—consort (4 parts)
Fretwork *Concert* (3/88) (AMON) ① **CD-SAR29**
Amsterdam Loeki Stardust Qt (r1991) *Concert*
(2/94) (L'OI) ① **436 155-2OH**

SECTION IV: VOCAL AND CHORAL

Ave Maria—motet: 5vv
Cambridge Sngrs, J. Rutter *Concert*
(6/88) (CLLE) ① **COLCD107**
Oxford Christ Church Cath Ch, S. Preston *Concert*
(2/90) (GAMU) ① **GOUPCD153**
Oxford Christ Church Cath Ch, S. Darlington *Concert*
(10/92) (NIMB) ① **NI5328**

Pour down, you powr'rs divine (Pandolpho)—consort song: 1v and viols
A. Deller, SCB, A. Wenzinger (r1956: arr P Warlock) *Concert* (4/95) (VANG) ① **08.5068.71**

PÄRT, Arvo (b 1935)
Estonia/Austria

SECTION I: ORCHESTRAL

Arbos—brass ensemble with percussion (1977-86)
Stuttgart St Orch Brass Ens, D.R. Davies *Concert*
(9/87) (ECM) ① 831 959-2
Cantus in memory of Benjamin Britten—string orchestra and bell (1976)
Bergen PO, N. Järvi *Concert*
(6/89) (BIS) ① BIS-CD420
SNO, N. Järvi *Concert*
(11/89) (CHAN) ① CHAN8656
Bournemouth Sinfonietta, R. Studt (vn/dir) (r1993)
Concert (6/94) (EMIN) ① CD-EMX2221
Fiamminghi *Concert* (6/95) (TELA) ① CD80387
BBC SO, G. Rozhdestvensky (pp1979) *Concert*
(10/95) (BBCR) ① BBCRD9129
Moscow Virtuosi, V. Spivakov (r1993) *Concert*
(12/95) (RCA) ① 09026 68061-2
Collage on the theme B-A-C-H—oboe, strings, harpsichord & piano (1964)
1. Toccata; 2. Sarabande; 3. Ricercar.
Philh, N. Järvi *Concert*
(6/93) (CHAN) ① CHAN9134
Moscow Virtuosi, V. Spivakov (r1993) *Concert*
(12/95) (RCA) ① 09026 68061-2
Concerto for Cello and Orchestra, 'Pro et contra' (1966)
F. Helmerson, Bamberg SO, N. Järvi *Concert*
(9/89) (BIS) ① BIS-CD434
Festina lente—adagio: strings with harp (ad lib) (1988-90)
Bonn Beethovenhalle Orch, D. R. Davies *Concert*
(1/92) (ECM) ① 847 539-2
Philh, N. Järvi (r1992) *Concert*
(6/93) (CHAN) ① CHAN9134
Bournemouth Sinfonietta, R. Studt (vn/dir) (r1993)
Concert (6/94) (EMIN) ① CD-EMX2221
Fiamminghi *Concert* (6/95) (TELA) ① CD80387
Fratres—12 cellos (1980)
Philh, N. Järvi (r1992) *Concert*
(6/93) (CHAN) ① CHAN9134
Fratres—strings and percussion
Fiamminghi *Concert* (6/95) (TELA) ① CD80387
Fratres—violin, strings and percussion
P. Manning, Fiamminghi *Concert*
(6/95) (TELA) ① CD80387
Fratres—wind octet and percussion
Fiamminghi *Concert* (6/95) (TELA) ① CD80387
If Bach had been a Beekeeper—harpsichord, electric bass, orchestra & tape (1976)
Philh, N. Järvi (r1992) *Concert*
(6/93) (CHAN) ① CHAN9134
Perpetuum mobile—orchestra, Op. 10 (1963)
Bamberg SO, N. Järvi *Concert*
(9/89) (BIS) ① BIS-CD434
Summa—strings
Bournemouth Sinfonietta, R. Studt (vn/dir) (r1993)
Concert (6/94) (EMIN) ① CD-EMX2221
Fiamminghi *Concert* (6/95) (TELA) ① CD80387
Symphony No. 1, 'Polyphonic' (1964)
Bamberg SO, N. Järvi *Concert*
(9/89) (BIS) ① BIS-CD434
Symphony No. 2 (1966)
Bamberg SO, N. Järvi *Concert*
(9/89) (BIS) ① BIS-CD434
Philh, N. Järvi (r1992) *Concert*
(6/93) (CHAN) ① CHAN9134
Symphony No. 3 (1971)
Bamberg SO, N. Järvi *Concert*
(9/89) (BIS) ① BIS-CD434
Tabula rasa—two violins, prepared piano and chamber orchestra (1976)
T. Little, Bournemouth Sinfonietta, R. Studt (vn/dir)
(r1993) *Concert* (6/94) (EMIN) ① CD-EMX2221

SECTION II: CHAMBER

Fratres—violin and piano (1977)
M. Bachmann, J. Klibonoff (r1993) *Concert*
(12/93) (CATA) ① 09026 61824-2
Tallinn Qt (r1992) *Concert*
(1/94) (BIS) ① BIS-CD574
Chilingirian Qt (arr 1991 stg qt;r1993) *Concert*
(5/94) (VIRG) ① VC5 45023-2
T. Little, M. Roscoe (r1993) *Concert*
(6/94) (EMIN) ① CD-EMX2221
Fratres—cello and piano
F. Springuel, M. Gleizes *Concert*
(6/95) (TELA) ① CD80387
Fratres—eight cellos
Fiamminghi *Concert* (6/95) (TELA) ① CD80387

Fratres—string quartet
Fiamminghi *Concert* (6/95) (TELA) ① CD80387
Spiegel im Spiegel—cello and piano (1978)
T. Little, M. Roscoe (r1993) *Concert*
(6/94) (EMIN) ① CD-EMX2221

SECTION III: INSTRUMENTAL

Pari intervalli—organ (1976)
C. Bowers-Broadbent *Concert*
(9/87) (ECM) ① 831 959-2
Partita—piano (1958-59)
1. Toccatino, Fughetta; 2. Larghetto, Ostinato.
L. Väinmaa (r1993) *Concert*
(7/95) (FINL) ① 4509-95704-2

SECTION IV: VOCAL AND CHORAL

An den Wassern zu Babel—4vv and organ (1976-84) (Wds. Psalm 137)
Hilliard Ens *Concert* (9/87) (ECM) ① 831 959-2
The Beatitudes—choir and organ (1990 rev 1991)
Kings College Ch, S. Cleobury, D. Goode (r1994)
Concert (12/94) (EMI) ① CDC5 55096-2
Berliner Messe—choir and orchestra/organ (1990-92)
Estonian Phil Chbr Ch, Tallinn CO, T. Kaljuste
(r1993) (ECM) ① 439 162-2
L. DenBeste, L. Crockett, D. Vanderwal, K. Blume, M.
Lewis, Oregon Repertory Sngrs, G. Seeley (r1992) L.
Harrison: St Anthony Mass.
(4/94) (KOCH) ① 37177-2
Credo—mixed chorus, piano and orchestra (1968)
Boris Berman, Philh Chor, Philh, N. Järvi (r1992)
Concert (6/93) (CHAN) ① CHAN9134
De profundis—4vv, organ and percussion (1980) (Wds. Psalm 130)
Hilliard Ens *Concert* (9/87) (ECM) ① 831 959-2
Es sang vor langen Jahren—motet: 1v, violin and viola (1984)
S. Bickley, G. Kremer, V. Mendelssohn *Concert*
(9/87) (ECM) ① 831 959-2
Magnificat—choir a cappella (1989)
Estonian Phil Chbr Ch, T. Kaljuste (r1993) *Concert*
(11/93) (ECM) ① 439 162-2
Oxford Pro Musica Sngrs, M. Smedley (r1993)
Concert (12/94) (PROU) ① PROUCD136
Kings College Ch, S. Cleobury (r1994) *Concert*
(12/94) (EMI) ① CDC5 55096-2
Miserere (1989)
Western Wind Chbr Ch, Hilliard Ens, P. Hillier
Concert (1/92) (ECM) ① 847 539-2
Passio Domini nostri Jesu Christi secundum Johannem (1982)
M. George, J. Potter, L. Dawson, D. James, R.
Covey-Crump, Gordon Jones, E. Layton, M. Maxwell,
E. Wilson, C. Duckett, C. Bowers-Broadbent,
Western Wind Chbr Ch, P. Hillier
(2/89) (ECM) ① 837 109-2
Sarah was ninety-years old—three soloists, chorus, organ and timpani (1977) (Wds. Genesis vv16-18 & 21)
Hilliard Ens, P. Hillier *Concert*
(1/92) (ECM) ① 847 539-2
Silouans Song, 'My soul yearns after the Lord ... ' (1991)
Estonian Phil Chbr Ch, Tallinn CO, T. Kaljuste
(r1993) *Concert* (11/93) (ECM) ① 439 162-2
Stabat mater—vocal and string trios (1985)
L. Dawson, D. James, R. Covey-Crump, G. Kremer,
V. Mendelssohn, T. Demenga (r1993)
(9/87) (ECM) ① 831 959-2
Summa—tenor, bass/chorus and six instruments (1978)
Hilliard Ens *Concert* (9/87) (ECM) ① 831 959-2
Philh Chor, Philh, N. Järvi (r1992) *Concert*
(6/93) (CHAN) ① CHAN9134
Chilingirian Qt (arr 1991 stg qt;r1993) *Concert*
(5/94) (VIRG) ① VC5 45023-2
Oxford Pro Musica Sngrs, M. Smedley (r1993)
Concert (12/94) (PROU) ① PROUCD136
Te Deum—three choirs, strings, prepared piano and tape (1984-85 rev 1986)
Estonian Phil Chbr Ch, Tallinn CO, T. Kaljuste
(r1993) *Concert* (11/93) (ECM) ① 439 162-2

PASATIERI, Thomas (b 1945)
USA

SECTION IV: VOCAL AND CHORAL

Alleluia
T. Hampson, St Paul CO, H. Wolff *Concert*
(12/91) (TELD) ① 9031-73135-2

PASCHA, Edmund (1714-1772)
Slovakia

SECTION IV: VOCAL AND CHORAL

Christmas Mass in F (from Harmonia Pastoralis)
1. Kyrie; 2. Gloria; 3. Credo; 4. Sanctus; 5.
Benedictus; 6. Agnus Dei.
Prague Madrigal Sngrs, M. Venhoda (arr. Venhoda)
Prosae Pastorales. (12/91) (CAMP) ① RRCD1305
Prosae Pastorales—Christmas carols
1. To the Mountains, follows; 2. Get up, shepherds
(Pro nocte Natali Domini); 3. Oh, shepherds, get up;
4. The new year's coming; 5. A new thing unheard of;
6. Menalka et Dometa (Pro nocte Nativitatis Domini);
7. A strange thing has happened; 8. What does that
sign mean (Pro Epiphania Domini); 9. To the forest,
to the mountains, shepherds.
Musica Bohemica, J. Krček (arr. Krcek) *Christmas
Mass*. (12/91) (CAMP) ① RRCD1305

PASCULLI, Antonio (1842-1924)
Italy

SECTION I: ORCHESTRAL

Concerto sopra motivi dell'opera 'La Favorita' di Donizetti—oboe and strings
B. Glaetzner, Berlin SO, C.P. Flor (orch Zani)
Concert (5/90) (CAPR) ① 10 281

SECTION II: CHAMBER

Gran Concerto sopra dell' opera 'I vespri siciliani'—oboe and piano
R. Canter, R. Burnett *Concert*
(4/87) (AMON) ① CD-SAR22
Omàggio a Bellini—cor anglais and harp
H. Schellenberger, M-A. Süss *Concert*
(12/91) (DENO) ① CO-76611

PASQUALI, Niccolo (c1718-1757)
Italy

SECTION III: INSTRUMENTAL

Lesson No. 4 in A—keyboard
G. Gifford *Concert* (5/90) (LIBR) ① LRCD156

PASQUINI, Bernardo (1637-1710)
Italy

SECTION III: INSTRUMENTAL

Toccata I—keyboard
T. Roberts (r1992-3) *Concert*
(1/94) (ARCH) ① 437 833-2AH

PASSEREAU, Pierre (fl. 1509-1547) France

SECTION IV: VOCAL AND CHORAL

Il est bel et bon—chanson
Scholars (r1993) *Concert*
(2/95) (NAXO) ① 8 550880

PATÁKY, Hubert (1892-1953)
Germany

SECTION IV: VOCAL AND CHORAL

Die Einsame—Lied
E. Rethberg, anon (r1920) *Concert*
(7/94) (PREI) ① 89051

PATTERSON, Johnny (c1840-1899) Ireland

SECTION IV: VOCAL AND CHORAL

The Garden where the praties grow—song (Wds. cpsr)
J. McCormack, E. Schneider (r1930) *Concert*
(5/93) (MMOI) ① CDMOIR418

PATTERSON, Paul (b 1947)
England

SECTION II: CHAMBER

Duologue—oboe and piano (1984)
N. Daniel, J. Drake *Concert*
(10/93) (LEMA) ① LC44801

SECTION III: INSTRUMENTAL

A **Tunnel of Time—piano, Op. 66 (1988)**
(reworking of Spiders, Op. 48)
C. Headington *Concert*
(11/90) (KING) ① **KCLCD2017**

PATTI, Adelina (1843–1919) Spain

SECTION IV: VOCAL AND CHORAL

A **New Year's Message** (to her husband,
Baron Rolf Cederström)
A. Patti (r1905) *Concert*
(4/90) (PEAR) ① **GEMMCD9312**
On parting—song
A. Patti, L. Ronald (r1905) *Concert*
(4/90) (PEAR) ① **GEMMCD9312**

PAULOS, Peregrino (20th Cent) Argentina

SECTION IV: VOCAL AND CHORAL

Inspiracion—tango (Wds. L. Rubinstein)
Buenos Aires Qnt, RPO, E. Stratta (arr J. Calandrelli)
Concert (1/93) (TELD) ① **9031-76997-2**

PAULUS, Stephen (b 1949) USA

SECTION IV: VOCAL AND CHORAL

All my pretty ones—song cycle (1978-83)
(Wds. M. D. Browne)
1. In a tree a dawn; 2. And the birds arrive; 3. Purple
finch; 4. Feeder; 5. Little life; 6. The bird inside; 7.
Night bird; 8. All my pretty ones.
R. Jacobson, P. Schoenfield *Concert*
(5/92) (ALBA) ① **TROY036-2**
Artsongs (1983) (Wds. various)
1. Archaic Torso of Apollo (wds. R. M. Rilke, trans S.
Mitchell); 2. The dance (wds. W. C. Williams); 3.
Museum piece (wds. R. Wilbur); 4. Seurat (wds. I.
Sadoff); 5. On seeing Larry's river (wds. F. O'Hara);
6. Moor swan (wds. J. Logan); 7. Warrior with shield
(wds. M. D. Browne).
P. Sperry, I. Vallecillo *Concert*
(5/92) (ALBA) ① **TROY036-2**
Bittersuite (1987) (Wds. O. Nash)
1. For the good dog; 2. The middle; 3. Time marches
on; 4. Old men.
H. Hagegård, W. Jones *Concert*
(5/92) (ALBA) ① **TROY036-2**

PAVESI, Stefano (1779–1850) Italy

SECTION V: STAGE WORKS

Aginta, o la Virtu Premiata—opera: 2 acts
(1814—Milan) (Lib. Fiorini)
Come Paride alle Grazie M. Hill Smith, A. Bolton, G.
Dolton, Philh, D. Parry *Concert*
(10/90) (OPRA) ① [3] **ORCH103**

PAWŁOWSKI, Jakub (late 18th Cent) Poland

SECTION I: ORCHESTRAL

Allegro
Warsaw CO, M. Sewen *Concert*
(8/94) (OLYM) ① **OCD380**

PAXTON, William (1738–1781) England

SECTION IV: VOCAL AND CHORAL

Breathe soft, ye winds—partsong (Wds.
anon)
PCA, M. Brown *Concert* (3/87) (CONI) ① **CDCF145**

PAYNE, Anthony (Edward) (b 1936) England

SECTION IV: VOCAL AND CHORAL

**Adlestrop—song: soprano, piano and string
quaret (1989)** (Wds. E Thomas)
J. Manning, Jane's Minstrels, R. Montgomery (r1993)
Concert (10/95) (NMC) ① **NMCD025**

PEARSALL, Robert Lucas (1795–1856) England

SECTION IV: VOCAL AND CHORAL

Lay a garland on her hearse—madrigal: 8vv
(1840) (Wds. Beaumont and Fletcher)
Cambridge Sngrs, J. Rutter (r1992) *Concert*
(11/93) (CLLE) ① **COLCD119**
O who will o'er the downs so free—catch
PCA, M. Brown *Concert* (3/87) (CONI) ① **CDCF145**
There is a paradise on earth—catch
Hilliard Ens, L-L. Kiesel *Concert*
(12/91) (MERI) ① **DUOCD89009**
Waters of Elle—partsong (Wds.Unknown)
PCA, M. Brown *Concert* (3/87) (CONI) ① **CDCF145**
**Who shall have my lady fair?—ante-
madrigal: 4vv**
Magdalen (Oxford) Coll Ch, G. Ives *Concert*
(11/92) (CNTO) ① **CRCD2366**

PEARSON, Donald (20th Cent) USA

SECTION IV: VOCAL AND CHORAL

Advent procession—chorus (Wds. St
Ambrose, J M Neale & others)
St John's Episcopal Cath Ch, D. Pearson *Concert*
(10/92) (DELO) ① **DE3125**

PEARSON, Leslie (20th Cent) England

SECTION III: INSTRUMENTAL

Fantasy Variations—tenor horn
Britannia Building Soc Band, H. Snell (r1990) *Concert*
(8/92) (DOYE) ① **DOYCD004**

PECI, Alexander (b 1953) Albania

SECTION II: CHAMBER

3 Albanian dances—violin and piano
T. Papavrami, C. Larrieu *Concert*
(3/91) (HARM) ① **HMC90 5207**

PEDERSØN, Mogens (c1580–1628) Denmark

SECTION IV: VOCAL AND CHORAL

Madrigali, libro secondo—5vv (pub 1611)
(remainder lost)
1. Tu fuggi e col fuggire; 2. Lasso io prima morira; 3.
Udite, amanti, udite; 4. Non garir, Augellino; 5.
importun, Augellino; 6. S'ancor tu amante sei; 7. Son
morta; 8. La mia cruda Brunetta; 9. Ardo, sospira e
piango; 10. Lasso, perchè mi fuggi.
1-10. Consort of Musicke, A. Rooley (lte/dir) *Concert*
(2/89) (BIS) ① **BIS-CD392**
Mass—5vv (pub 1620) (from 'Pratum
Spirituale')
Hilliard Ens, P. Hillier *Concert*
(2/89) (BIS) ① **BIS-CD389**
T'amo mia vita—madrigal: 5vv (pub 1608)
Consort of Musicke, A. Rooley (lte/dir) *Concert*
(2/89) (BIS) ① **BIS-CD392**

PEEL, Graham (1877–1937) England

SECTION IV: VOCAL AND CHORAL

The **Early morning—song** (Wds. H. Belloc)
F. Lott, G. Johnson *Concert*
(7/90) (CHAN) ① **CHAN8722**
In Summertime on Bredon—song (Wds. A. E.
Housman)
G. Trew, R. Vignoles, Coull Qt *Concert*
(11/90) (MERI) ① **CDE84185**
R. Irwin, G. Moore (r1948) *Concert*
(4/92) (EMI) ① [7] **CHS7 69741-2(2)**
Reveille—song (Wds. A. E. Housman)
G. Trew, R. Vignoles, Coull Qt *Concert*
(11/90) (MERI) ① **CDE84185**
When the lad for longing sighs—song (Wds.
A. E. Housman)
G. Trew, R. Vignoles, Coull Qt *Concert*
(11/90) (MERI) ① **CDE84185**

PEERSON, Martin (1571/3–1651) England

SECTION III: INSTRUMENTAL

Keyboard Works—virginals
1. Alman; 2. Fall of the Leaf; 3. Piper's Paven; 4.
Primrose.
2. Z. Růžičková *Concert*
(10/89) (ORFE) ① **C139861A**

SECTION IV: VOCAL AND CHORAL

The **Primrose—madrigal**
Amaryllis Consort, C. Brett *Concert*
(3/88) (CARL) ① **PCD873**
**Upon my lap my soveraigne sits—ayre (pub
1620)** (Wds. Verstegan)
Red Byrd, Rose Consort *Concert*
(12/91) (AMON) ① **CD-SAR46**

PEETERS, Flor (1903–1986) Belgium

SECTION III: INSTRUMENTAL

Aria—organ, Op. 51 (1945)
A. Fletcher *Concert* (11/91) (MIRA) ① **MRCD903**
J. Watts *Concert* (8/94) (PRIO) ① **PRCD377**
Andrew Lucas (r1994) *Concert*
(11/94) (NAXO) ① **8 550955**
Concert Piece—organ, Op. 52a (1952)
J. Watts *Concert* (8/94) (PRIO) ① **PRCD377**
Élégie—organ, Op. 38 (1935)
J. Watts *Concert* (8/94) (PRIO) ① **PRCD377**
**Preludium, Canzona et Ciacona—organ, Op.
83 (1955)**
J. Watts *Concert* (8/94) (PRIO) ① **PRCD377**
**Variations on an Original Theme—organ, Op.
58 (1945)**
A. Fletcher *Concert* (11/91) (MIRA) ① **MRCD903**

PELLEGRINI, Domenico (17th Cent) Italy

SECTION III: INSTRUMENTAL

Armoniosi concerti—guitar (1650)
1. Ricercata; 2. Corrente; 3. Sarabande; 4. Battaglia
Francese.
B. Mason *Concert* (10/90) (AMON) ① **CD-SAR45**

PEÑALOSA, Francisco de (c1470–1528) Spain

SECTION IV: VOCAL AND CHORAL

Missa Ave Maria peregrina—4vv
Westminster Cath Ch, J. O'Donnell *Concert*
(6/93) (HYPE) ① **CDA66629**
Missa Nunc fue pena mayor—4vv (on
Urreda's viliancico)
Westminster Cath Ch, J. O'Donnell *Concert*
(6/93) (HYPE) ① **CDA66629**
Motets—3-5vv
1. Inter vestibulum et altare; 2. Tribularer, si
nescirem; 3. Ne reminiscaris; 4. Versa est in luctum;
5. Domine, secundum actum meum; 6. Adoro te,
Domine Iesu Christe; 7. Ave, verum corpus natum; 8.
Nigra sum, sed formosa; 9. Sancta Maria; 10. Unica
est colomba mea; 11. Ave, vera caro Christi; 12. Ave,
vere sanguis Domini; 13. In passione positus; 14.
Precor te, Domine Iesu Christe; 15. Pater noster; 16.
Ave Regina caelorum; 17. Sancta Mater, istud agas;
18. O Domina sanctissima; 19. Emendemus in
melius; 20. Deus, qui manus tuas; 21. Domine Iesu
Christe, qui neminem; 22. Transeunte Domino Iesu;
23. Memorae piissima.
1-22. PCA, B. Turner (7/92) (HYPE) ① **CDA66574**
3, 9, 14. Gothic Voices, C. Page (r1993) *Concert*
(2/94) (HYPE) ① **CDA66653**
17. Hilliard Ens *Concert*
(6/91) (HYPE) ① **CDA66370**
Por las sierras de Madrid—quodilibet: 6vv
(from the Polacio Song Book)
Hespèrion XX, J. Savall *Concert*
(2/92) (ASTR) ① **E8762**
Gothic Voices, C. Page (r1993) *Concert*
(2/94) (HYPE) ① **CDA66653**
Sacris solemniis—hymn: 4vv
Westminster Cath Ch, J. O'Donnell *Concert*
(6/93) (HYPE) ① **CDA66629**

PENDERECKI, Krzysztof *(b 1933) Poland*

SECTION I: ORCHESTRAL

Anaklasis—strings and percussion (1960)
LSO, K. Penderecki (r1973) *Concert*
(10/94) (EMI) ① **CDM5 65077-2**
Capriccio—oboe and 11 strings (1965)
M. Pedzialek, Poznan Amadeus CO, A. Duczmal
Concert (9/90) (WERG) ① **WER60172-50**
A. Utkin, Moscow Virtuosi, V. Spivakov (vn/dir)
Concert (10/90) (RCA) ① **RD60370**
Capriccio—violin and orchestra (1967)
W. Wilkomirska, Polish Nat RSO, K. Penderecki
(r1972) *Concert* (10/94) (EMI) ① **CDM5 65077-2**
Concerto for Cello and Orchestra No. 2 (1982)
I. Monighetti, Polish Nat RO, A. Wit *Concert*
(6/90) (POLS) ① **PNCD020**
Concerto for Viola and Orchestra (1983)
G. Zhislin, Polish Radio & TV SO, S. Kawalla *Concert*
(1/90) (CONI) ① **CDCF168**
S. Kamasa, Polish Nat RSO, K. Penderecki
(6/90) (POLS) ① **PNCD020**
T. Zimmermann, Poznan Amadeus CO, A. Duczmal
Concert (9/90) (WERG) ① **WER60172-50**
K. Kashkashian, Stuttgart CO, D.R. Davies (r1992)
Concert (11/93) (ECM) ① **439 611-2**
Concerto for Violin and Orchestra (1976)
C. Edinger, Katowice RSO, K. Penderecki
(3/88) (THOR) ① **CTH2017**
S. Accardo, Italian Youth Orch, K. Penderecki
Shostakovich: Symphony 6.
(11/88) (NUOV) ① **6705**
De Natura Sonoris I—orchestra (1966)
Polish Nat RSO, K. Penderecki (r1975) *Concert*
(10/94) (EMI) ① **CDM5 65077-2**
De Natura Sonoris II—orchestra (1971)
Polish Nat RSO, K. Penderecki (r1972) *Concert*
(10/94) (EMI) ① **CDM5 65077-2**
Dream of Jacob—orchestra (1974)
Polish Nat RO, A. Wit *Concert*
(6/90) (POLS) ① **PNCD020**
Polish Nat RSO, K. Penderecki (r1975) *Concert*
(10/94) (EMI) ① **CDM5 65077-2**
Fonogrammi—orchestra (1961)
Polish Nat RSO, K. Penderecki (r1972) *Concert*
(10/94) (EMI) ① **CDM5 65077-2**
Intermezzo—24 strings (1973)
Poznan Amadeus CO, A. Duczmal *Concert*
(9/90) (WERG) ① **WER60172-50**
3 Pieces in the antique style—orchestra (1963)
1. Aria; 2. Minuet I; 3. Minuet II.
Poznan Amadeus CO, A. Duczmal *Concert*
(9/90) (WERG) ① **WER60172-50**
Threnody for the Victims of Hiroshima—orchestra (1960)
Polish Radio & TV SO, S. Kawalla *Concert*
(1/90) (CONI) ① **CDCF168**
Polish Nat RSO, K. Penderecki (r1975) *Concert*
(10/94) (EMI) ① **CDM5 65077-2**

SECTION II: CHAMBER

Quartet for Clarinet and String Trio (1993)
M. Fröst, P. Swedrup, I. Kierkegaard, H. Nilsson
(r1994) *Concert* (5/95) (BIS) ① **BIS-CD652**
String Quartet No. 1 (1960)
LaSalle Qt *Concert* (8/88) (DG) ① **423 245-2GC**
Tale Qt (r1994) *Concert* (5/95) (BIS) ① **BIS-CD652**
String Quartet No. 2 (1968)
Varsovia Qt *Concert* (6/89) (OLYM) ① **OCD328**
Tale Qt (r1994) *Concert* (5/95) (BIS) ① **BIS-CD652**
String Trio (1990-91)
T. Olsson, I. Kierkegaard, H. Nilsson (r1994) *Concert*
(5/95) (BIS) ① **BIS-CD652**
Der unterbrochene Gedanke—string quartet (1988)
Tale Qt (r1994) *Concert* (5/95) (BIS) ① **BIS-CD652**

SECTION III: INSTRUMENTAL

Prelude—clarinet (1987)
M. Fröst (r1994) *Concert*
(5/95) (BIS) ① **BIS-CD652**

SECTION IV: VOCAL AND CHORAL

Canticum Canticorum Salomonis—chorus and chamber orchestra (1972)
Cracow Phil Chor, Polish Nat RSO, K. Penderecki
(r1975) *Concert* (10/94) (EMI) ① **CDM5 65077-2**

Polish Requiem—SATB, 2 choirs and orchestra (1980-84)
1. Agnus Dei (8-part choir a capella).
I. Haubold, G. Winogrodska, Z. Terzakis, M. Smith, N
German Rad Chor, Bavarian Rad Chor, N German
RSO, K. Penderecki (pp1989)
(3/91) (DG) ① [2] **429 720-2GH2**
Lacrimosa B. Hendricks, E. Ericson Chbr Ch,
Swedish RSO, E. Ericson *Concert*
(4/91) (EMI) ① **CDC7 54098-2**
Strophes—soprano, narrator and 10 instruments (1959)
O. Szwajgier, Poznan Amadeus CO, A. Duczmal
Concert (9/90) (WERG) ① **WER60172-50**

SECTION V: STAGE WORKS

Paradise Lost—sacra rappresentazione: 2 acts (1978—Chicago) (Lib. C Fry, after J
Milton)
Polish Nat RO, A. Wit (Adagietto) *Concert*
(6/90) (POLS) ① **PNCD020**

PENELLA, Manuel *(1880–1939) Spain*

SECTION V: STAGE WORKS

El Gato Montés—opera: 3 acts (1916—Madrid) (Lib. cpsr)
Cpte J. Pons, P. Domingo, V. Villarroel, T. Berganza,
C. Chausson, M. Pereistein, A. Barrio, C. Alvarez, P.
Farrés, M.L. Galindo, C. Bergasa, Angeles Blancas,
R. Muñiz, Madrid Zarzuela Chor, Madrid SO, M. Roa
(9/92) (DG) ① [2] **435 776-2GH2**
Me llamabas, Rafaeliyo? A. Arteta, P. Domingo,
Paris Opéra-Bastille Orch, E. Kohn (pp1992) *Concert*
(6/94) (SONY) ① **SK46691**
Si Torero quiero sé. J. Carreras, I. Rey, ECO, E.
Ricci (r1994) *Concert*
(2/95) (ERAT) ① **4509-95789-2**

PENNARIO, Leonard *(b 1924) USA*

SECTION V: STAGE WORKS

Julie—film score (1956)
Midnight on the Cliffs National PO, C. Gerhardt
Concert (6/90) (VARE) ① **VSD5207**

PENNINO, Gaetano Errico *(20th Cent) Italy*

SECTION IV: VOCAL AND CHORAL

Pecchè?—song (Wds. C. De Flaviis)
L. Pavarotti, Teatro Communale Orch, A. Guadagno
Concert (8/83) (DECC) ① **410 015-2DH**
E. Caruso, orch, W.B. Rogers (r1915) *Concert*
(12/90) (NIMB) ① **NI7809**
E. Caruso, orch, W.B. Rogers (r1915) *Concert*
(7/91) (RCA) ① [12] **GD60495(5)**
E. Caruso, orch, W.B. Rogers (r1915) *Concert*
(10/91) (PEAR) ① [3] **EVC3(2)**

PENTLAND, Barbara (Lally) *(b 1912) Canada*

SECTION III: INSTRUMENTAL

Shadows/Ombres—piano
G. Gould *Concert* (3/93) (SONY) ① **SMK52677**

PEPPING, Ernst *(1901–1981) Germany*

SECTION III: INSTRUMENTAL

Concerto No. 2—organ (1941)
W. Stockmeier *Concert*
(7/91) (CPO) ① **CPO999 039-2**
4 Fugues—organ (1942)
1. D; 2. C minor; 3. E flat; 4. F minor.
W. Stockmeier *Concert*
(7/91) (CPO) ① **CPO999 039-2**
3 Fugues on BACH—organ (1943)
1. Allegro sostenuto; 2. Andante; 3. Maestoso
passionato.
K. Bowyer (r1993) *Concert* (1/95) (NIMB) ① **NI5411**
Partita No. 1, 'Ach wie flüchtig'—organ (1953)
W. Stockmeier *Concert*
(7/91) (CPO) ① **CPO999 039-2**
Wie schön leuchtet der Morgenstern—chorale partita: organ (1933)
W. Stockmeier *Concert*
(7/91) (CPO) ① **CPO999 039-2**

SECTION IV: VOCAL AND CHORAL

Passionsbericht des Matthäus—double choir (1950)
Cpte Danish Nat Rad Ch, S. Parkman
(9/92) (CHAN) ① **CHAN8854**

PEPUSCH, Johann Christoph *(1667–1752) Germany/England*

SECTION I: ORCHESTRAL

Kammer-Sinfonie for strings in D minor
Cantilena, A. Shepherd *Concert*
(9/84) (CHAN) ① **CHAN8319**

SECTION II: CHAMBER

Sonata No. 4 for Recorder and Continuo in F (source unidentified)
F. Brüggen, A. Bylsma, G. Leonhardt (r1967/79)
Concert (10/95) (TELD) ① **4509-97465-2**

PERGOLESI, Giovanni Battista *(1710–1736) Italy*

SECTION I: ORCHESTRAL

Concertino for Strings and Continuo No. 2 in G (also attrib Ricciotti)
J-W. Audoli Inst Ens, J-W. Audoli *Concert*
(12/89) (ARIO) ① **ARN68026**
Concerto for Violin and Strings in B flat
Y. Naganuma, J-W. Audoli Inst Ens, J-W. Audoli
Concert (12/89) (ARIO) ① **ARN68026**
A. Keller, Cologne Concerto (r1992) *Concert*
(1/94) (CAPR) ① **10 378**
Concerto in G—flute and strings (extremely doubtful)
W. Bennett, ECO, I. Watson (hpd/dir) *Concert*
(12/91) (VIRG) ① **VJ7 59656-2**
J. Galway, Solisti Veneti, C. Scimone (r1991) *Concert*
(4/94) (RCA) ① **09026 61164-2**

SECTION IV: VOCAL AND CHORAL

In coelestibus regnis—alto and strings
M. Chance, King's Consort, R. King *Concert*
(11/88) (HYPE) ① **CDA66294**
Magnificat in C—SATB, chorus and orchestra (attrib. Durante)
E. Harwood, J. Baker, I. Partridge, C. Keyte, King's
College Ch, ASMF, D. Willcocks (r1966) *Concert*
(7/95) (DECC) ① [2] **443 868-2DF2**
Miserere II in C minor—SATB, chorus, organ and strings
I. Wolf, D. James, R. Covey-Crump, R. Suart,
Magdalen Oxford Coll Ch, S. Lawford, Wren Orch,
Bernard Rose (r1978) *Concert*
(7/91) (DECC) ① **430 359-2DM**
Orfeo—chamber cantata: soprano, strings and continuo (1735)
R. Klepper, Bamberg Qt, S. Adelmann, B. Höps
(1993) *Stabat Mater.* (7/95) (CAPR) ① **10 517**
J. Faulkner, Budapest Camerata, M. Halász (r1994)
Stabat Mater. (9/95) (NAXO) ① **8 550766**
Pro Jesu dum vivo—motet: 2vv & continuo
I. Poulenard, J-L. Comoretto, Grande Ecurie, J-C.
Malgoire (r1994) *Stabat Mater.*
(12/95) (ASTR) ① **E8556**
Salve Regina in A minor—soprano, strings and organ (1736)
G. Fisher, King's Consort, R. King *Concert*
(11/88) (HYPE) ① **CDA66294**
J. Anderson, C. Bartoli, Montreal Sinfonietta, C.
Dutoit (r1991) *Concert*
(8/93) (DECC) ① **436 209-2DH**
B. Schlick, Europa Galante, F. Biondi (vn/dir) (r1993)
Concert (4/94) (O111) ① **OPS30-88**
I. Åkerlund, Accademia Bizantina, C. Chiarappa
(r1992) *Concert* (2/95) (DENO) ① **CO-78904**
Salve Regina in C minor—soprano, strings and organ (1736)
E. Kirkby, AAM, C. Hogwood *Stabat mater.*
(2/90) (L'OI) ① **425 692-2OH**
B. Schlick, Europa Galante, F. Biondi (vn/dir) (r1993)
Concert (4/94) (O111) ① **OPS30-88**
Salve Regina in F minor—alto, strings and organ (1736)
J. Bowman, King's Consort, R. King (org/dir) *Concert*
(6/87) (MERI) ① **CDE84138**
J. Bowman, J-W. Audoli Inst Ens, J-W. Audoli
Concert (12/89) (ARIO) ① **ARN68026**
N. Stutzmann, Hanover Band, R. Goodman (r1992)
Stabat Mater. (1/94) (RCA) ① **09026 61215-2**
Stabat Mater—soprano, alto, strings and organ (1736)
1. Stabat Mater dolorosa; 2. Cujus animam
gementem; 3. O quam tristis et afflicta; 4. Quae

moerabat et dolebat; 5. Quis est homo, qui non fleret;
6. Vidit suum dulcem Natum; 7. Eja Mater, fons
amoris; 8. Fac et ardeat cor meum; 9. Sancta Mater
istud agas; 10. Fac ut portem Christi mortem; 11.
Inflammatus et accensus; 12. Quando corpus
morietur.
M. Marshall, L.V. Terrani, LSO, C. Abbado
(4/85) (DG) ① 415 103-2GH
G. Fisher, M. Chance, King's Consort, R. King
Concert   (11/88) (HYPE) ① CDA66294
J. Raskin, M. Lehane, Naples Rossini Orch, F.
Caracciolo Rossini: Petite messe solennelle.
(6/89) (DECC) ① [2] 421 645-2DM2
E. Kirkby, J. Bowman, AAM, C. Hogwood Salve
Regina in C minor.   (2/90) (L'OI) ① 425 692-2OH
J. Taylor, K. Ferrier, Nottingham Oriana Ch, Boyd
Neel Orch, Roy Henderson (orch K Scott: r1946)
Concert   (6/92) (DECC) ① 433 470-2DM
J. Anderson, C. Bartoli, Montreal Sinfonietta, C.
Dutoit (r1991) Concert
(8/93) (DECC) ① 436 209-2DH
E. Norberg-Schulz, N. Stutzmann, Hanover Band, R.
Goodman (r1992) Salve Regina in F minor.
(1/94) (RCA) ① 09026 61215-2
E. Mei, M. Lipovšek, VCM, N. Harnoncourt (r1993)
Vivaldi: Gloria, RV589.
(7/94) (TELD) ① 9031-76989-2
L. Åkerlund, G. Zambon, Accademia Bizantina, C.
Chiarappa (r1992) Concert
(2/95) (DENO) ① CO-78904
R. Klepper, M. Borst, Bamberg Qt, S. Adelmann, B.
Höps (r1993) Orfeo   (7/95) (CAPR) ① 10 517
F. Palmer, A. Hodgson, St John's College Ch, Argo
CO, G. Guest (r1978) Concert
(7/95) (DECC) ① [2] 443 868-2DF2
J. Faulkner, A. Gonda, Budapest Camerata, M.
Halász (r1994) Orfeo. (9/95) (NAXO) ① 8 550766
I. Poulenard, J-L. Comoretto, Grande Ecurie, J-C.
Malgoire (r1994; ed J-C. Malgoire) Pro Jesu dum
vivo.   (12/95) (ASTR) ① E8556
4. D. Soffel, Swedish CO, M. Liljefors (pp1987)
Concert   (4/93) (CPRI) ① CAP21428
Tre giorni son che Nina—song (also possibly
by Ciampi)
F. Kreisler, H. Kreisler, C. Keith (r1924: arr. Kreisler)
Concert   (7/90) (BIDD) ① [2] LAB009/10
L. Tetrazzini, orch (r1914) Concert
(10/90) (NIMB) ① NI7808
E. Caruso, orch, J. Pasternack (r1919) Concert
(12/90) (NIMB) ① NI7809
E. Caruso, orch, J. Pasternack (r1919) Concert
(7/91) (RCA) ① [12] GD60495(6)
E. Caruso, orch, J. Pasternack (r1919) Concert
(10/91) (PEAR) ① [3] EVC4(2)
L. Tetrazzini, orch (r1914) Concert
(9/92) (EMI) ① [3] CHS7 63802-2(2)
L. Tetrazzini, orch (r1914) Concert
(9/92) (PEAR) ① GEMMCD9225

SECTION V: STAGE WORKS

Lo Frate 'nnamorato—commedia musicale:
3 acts (1732—Naples) (Lib. G. G. Federico)
Cpte A. Felle, N. Focile, A. Corbelli, B. de Simone, B.
Manca di Nissa, N. Curiel, E. Norberg-Schulz, L.
d'Intino, E di Cesare, La Scala Orch, R. Muti
(pp1989)   (7/91) (EMI) ① [3] CDS7 54240-2
Ogni pena più spietata J. Baker, ASMF, N. Marriner
Concert   (1/93) (PHIL) ① 434 173-2PM
La Serva Padrona—intermezzo: 2 acts
(1733—Naples) (Lib. G A Federico)
M. Bonifaccio, S. Nimsgern, Collegium Aureum, F.
Maier (vn/dir)   (9/92) (DHM) ① RD77184
Stizzoso, mio stizzoso V. de los Angeles, G.
Parsons (pp1990) Concert
(12/91) (COLL) ① Coll1247-2

PERI, Jacopo (1561–1633) Italy

SECTION IV: VOCAL AND CHORAL

Dunque fra turbido onde—aria (1v) -
Intermedio 5, La Pellegrina (c1589) (Wds.
after Rinuccini)
N. Rogers, Taverner Plyrs, A. Parrott Concert
(8/88) (EMI) ① CDC7 47998-2
Le varie musiche—song collection: 1v and
continuo (pub 1609)
1. Bellissima regina (wds. O. Rinuccini); 2. O durezza
di ferro (wds. anon); 3. Tra le donne (wds. anon).
1-3. N. Rogers, C. Tilney, A. Bailes, J. Savall, P. Ros
(r1975) Concert   (1/93) (ARCH) ① 437 075-2AT

PÉRIER, E. ?France

SECTION IV: VOCAL AND CHORAL

Dors, mon enfant—song
J. Périer, anon (r1905) Concert
(9/91) (SYMP) ① SYMCD1089

PERLE, George (b 1915) USA

SECTION I: ORCHESTRAL

Concerto for Piano and Orchestra No. 2
(1992)
M. Boriskin, Utah SO, J. Silverstein (r1993) Concert
(5/95) (HARM) ① HMU90 7124

SECTION II: CHAMBER

Wind Quintet No. 1—flute, oboe, clarinet,
horn and bassoon, op. 57 (1959)
Dorian Qnt Concert   (10/88) (NEW) ① NW359-2
Wind Quintet No. 2—flute, oboe, clarinet,
horn and bassoon, Op. 41 (1960)
Dorian Qnt Concert   (10/88) (NEW) ① NW359-2
Wind Quintet No. 3—flute, oboe, clarinet,
horn and bassoon (1967)
Dorian Qnt Concert   (10/88) (NEW) ① NW359-2
Wind Quintet No. 4—flute, oboe, clarinet,
horn and bassoon (1984)
Dorian Qnt Concert   (10/88) (NEW) ① NW359-2

SECTION III: INSTRUMENTAL

6 Etudes—piano (1973-76)
M. Boriskin (r1994) Concert
(5/95) (HARM) ① HMU90 7124

PERNAMBUCO, João
(1883–1947) Brazil

also known as João Guimarães

SECTION III: INSTRUMENTAL

Interrogando—guitar
M. Kayath Concert   (9/87) (CARL) ① PCD853
Sonho de magia—waltz: guitar
M. Kayath Concert   (9/87) (CARL) ① PCD853
Sons de carrilhoes—piano
M. Kayath Concert   (9/87) (CARL) ① PCD853

PÉROTIN (c 1160–c1225)
France

aka Perotinus

SECTION IV: VOCAL AND CHORAL

Alleluia, Nativitas—organum (3vv) (Nativity of
the Blessed Virgin Mary)
Hilliard Ens, P. Hillier Concert
(2/90) (ECM) ① 837 751-2
Alleluia, Posui adiutorium—organum (3vv)
(Confessor-Bishop)
Hilliard Ens, P. Hillier Concert
(2/90) (ECM) ① 837 751-2
Beata viscera—conductus (1v) (Wds. Philippe
the Chancellor)
Hilliard Ens, P. Hillier Concert
(2/90) (ECM) ① 837 751-2
J. Garbarek, Hilliard Ens (r1993) Concert
(10/94) (ECM) ① 445 369-2
Dum sigillum summi patris—conductus
(2vv)
Hilliard Ens, P. Hillier Concert
(2/90) (ECM) ① 837 751-2
Presul nostri temporis—conductus
Gothic Voices, C. Page (r1994) Concert
(2/95) (HYPE) ① CDA66739
Sederunt principes V. Adiuva—organum
(4vv) (gradual for St. Stephen)
Hilliard Ens, P. Hillier Concert
(2/90) (ECM) ① 837 751-2
Viderunt omnes V. Notum fecit—organum
(4vv) (gradual for Christmas and Circumcision)
London Early Music Consort, D. Munrow Concert
(8/85) (ARCH) ① 415 292-2AH
Hilliard Ens, P. Hillier Concert
(2/90) (ECM) ① 837 751-2

PERRIN, Jean (1920–1989)
Switzerland

SECTION I: ORCHESTRAL

Concerto for Cello and Orchestra, Op. 27
(1972)
A. Gutu, Timişoara Banatul PO, J-F. Antonioli (r1992)
De Profundis, Op. 26. (4/94) (CLAV) ① CD50-9315

SECTION IV: VOCAL AND CHORAL

De Profundis—oratorio: soloists, chorus and
orchestra, op. 26 (1968-70)
I. Bentoiu, L. Bizineche, F. Diaconescu, I. Tibrea,
Timişoara Banatul Phil Chor, Timişoara Banatul PO,
J-F. Antonioli (r1992) Cello Concerto.
(4/94) (CLAV) ① CD50-9315

PERRY, Jean-Jacques (20th Cent)
?USA

SECTION V: STAGE WORKS

Main Street Electrical Parade: Baroque
Hoedown—Disneyland attraction (Lyrics
Gershon Kingsley)
LAGQ (r1994-5; arr Fraser) Concert
(12/95) (DELO) ① DE3186

PERSICHETTI, Vincent
(1915–1987) USA

SECTION I: ORCHESTRAL

Choral Prelude: O God Unseen—wind band,
Op. 160 (1984)
LSO Winds, D. Amos (r1993) Concert
(10/94) (HARM) ① HMU90 7092
Concerto for Piano and Orchestra, Op. 90
(1962)
R. Taub, Philadelphia, C. Dutoit Symphony 5.
(3/91) (NEW) ① NW370-2
Divertimento for Band, Op. 42 (1949-50)
EXCERPTS: 1. Prologue; 2. Song; 3. Dance; 4.
Burlesque; 5. Soliloquy; 6. March.
LSO Winds, D. Amos (r1993) Concert
(10/94) (HARM) ① HMU90 7092
The Hollow Men—trumpet and strings
(1944)
Manhattan CO, R.A. Clark (r1994) Concert
(7/95) (KOCH) ① 37282-2
Masquerade for Band, Op. 102 (1965)
LSO Winds, D. Amos (r1993) Concert
(10/94) (HARM) ① HMU90 7092
Night Dances, Op. 114 (1970)
Juilliard Orch, J. DePreist Concert
(7/91) (NEW) ① 80396-2
O Cool is the Valley—wind band, Op. 118
(1971) (inspired by Joyce's poem)
LSO Winds, D. Amos (r1993) Concert
(10/94) (HARM) ① HMU90 7092
Pageant—wind band, Op. 59 (1953)
LSO Winds, D. Amos (r1993) Concert
(10/94) (HARM) ① HMU90 7092
Parable for Band, Op. 121 (1972)
LSO Winds, D. Amos (r1993) Concert
(10/94) (HARM) ① HMU90 7092
Psalm for Band, Op. 53 (1952)
LSO Winds, D. Amos (r1993) Concert
(10/94) (HARM) ① HMU90 7092
Symphony No. 5, 'Symphony for Strings',
Op. 61 (1953)
Philadelphia, R. Muti Piano Concerto.
(3/91) (NEW) ① NW370-2
Symphony No. 8—orchestra, Op. 106 (1967)
Louisville Orch, J. Mester Concert
(6/90) (ALBA) ① TROY024-2

SECTION II: CHAMBER

Serenade No. 10—flute and harp, Op. 79
(1957)
J. Stinton, A. Brewer Concert
(4/92) (COLL) ① Coll1297-2

SECTION III: INSTRUMENTAL

Harpsichord Sonata No. 7, Op. 156 (1983-
84)
B. Harbach Concert   (3/89) (KING) ① KCLCD2005

PERTI, Giacomo Antonio
(1661–1756) Italy

SECTION IV: VOCAL AND CHORAL

Sperar io non dovrei—solo cantata
J. Carreras, ECO, V. Sutej (r1992; arr Agostinelli)
Concert   (6/93) (PHIL) ① 434 926-2PH

PESSARD, Emile (1843–1917)
France

SECTION IV: VOCAL AND CHORAL

L' Adieu du matin—song
E. Clément, F. La Forge (r1911) Concert
(8/95) (ROMO) ① 82002-2

E. Clément, F. la Forge (r1911) *Concert*
(8/95) (PEAR) ① **GEMMCD9161**

PETER VON ABERG (13th Cent)
Germany

SECTION IV: VOCAL AND CHORAL
O starker Got—song
E. Lamandier *Concert*   (2/88) (ALIE) ① **AL1019**

PETER VON SACHSEN (13th Cent)
Germany

SECTION IV: VOCAL AND CHORAL
Maria gnuchtig—song
E. Lamandier *Concert*   (2/88) (ALIE) ① **AL1019**

PETERSON, Wayne (b 1927)
USA

SECTION II: CHAMBER
String Quartet No. 1 (1983)
Group for Contemporary Music (r1991) *Concert*
(7/93) (KOCH) ① **37121-2**

PETERSON-BERGER, Wilhelm (1867–1942) Sweden

SECTION IV: VOCAL AND CHORAL
On the fell in sunshine—chorus
Orphei Drängar Ch, E. Ericson *Concert*
(7/88) (BIS) ① **BIS-CD383**

PETIT, Jean-Claude (20th Cent)
France

SECTION V: STAGE WORKS
Jean de Florette—film score (1986)
EXCERPTS: 1. Theme (inspired by Verdi's La Forza
del Destino Overture).
1. OST (r1986) *Concert*   (9/95) (VIR2) ① **CDV2774**

PETRALI, Vincenzo (1832–1889)
Italy

SECTION III: INSTRUMENTAL
Messe Solennelle—organ
1. Gloria.
1. L. Benedetti (1992) *Concert*
(4/95) (PRIO) ① **PRCD427**

PETRELLA, Errico (1813–1877)
Italy

SECTION V: STAGE WORKS
**La Contessa d'Amalfi—opera: 4 acts
(1864—Turin)** (Lib. G Peruzzini)
Fra i rami fulgida A. Santini, orch (r1908) *Concert*
(6/94) (IRCC) ① **IRCC-CD808**
**Jone, o L'ultimo giorno di Pompeo—opera: 4
acts (1858—Milan)** (Lib. Peruzzini, after
Bulwer-Lytton)
Della corona egizia; Sinistro è il ciel F. Corradetti,
anon (r1907) *Concert*
(12/94) (BONG) ① **GB1043-2**
O Jone di quest'anima A. Scampini, orch (r1908)
Concert   (6/94) (IRCC) ① **IRCC-CD808**

PETRUCCI, Ottaviano del
(1466–1539) Italy

SECTION IV: VOCAL AND CHORAL
**Salve, regina di misericordia—lauda (pub
1508)** (Laude Libro primo. Wds. Belcari)
Daedalus Ens (r1992) *Concert*
(11/93) (ACCE) ① **ACC9289D**

PETRUS DE CRUCE (d c1299)
France

SECTION IV: VOCAL AND CHORAL
**Aucun on trouvé/Lonc tans—13th century
motet (3vv)**
London Early Music Consort, D. Munrow *Concert*
(8/85) (ARCH) ① **415 292-2AH**

PETTERSSON, (Gustaf) Allan
(1911–1980) Sweden

SECTION I: ORCHESTRAL
Concerto for Viola and Orchestra (1979)
N. Imai, Malmö SO, L. Markiz *Symphony 5.*
(2/91) (BIS) ① **BIS-CD480**
Symphonic Movement—orchestra (1973)
BBC Scottish SO, A. Francis (r1994) *Symphony 2.*
(9/95) (CPO) ① **CPO999 281-2**
Symphony No. 2 (1952-53)
BBC Scottish SO, A. Francis (r1994) *Symphonic
Movement.*   (9/95) (CPO) ① **CPO999 281-2**
Symphony No. 3 (1954-5)
Saarbrücken RSO, A. Francis (r1994) *Symphony 4.*
(12/95) (CPO) ① **CPO999 223-2**
Symphony No. 4 (1958-9)
Saarbrücken RSO, A. Francis (r1994) *Symphony 3.*
(12/95) (CPO) ① **CPO999 223-2**
Symphony No. 5 (1960-62)
Malmö SO, M. Atzmon *Viola Concerto.*
(2/91) (BIS) ① **BIS-CD480**
Symphony No. 7 (1966-67)
Norrköping SO, L. Segerstam (r1992) *Symphony 11.*
(4/94) (BIS) ① **BIS-CD580**
Hamburg PO, G. Albrecht (pp1991)
(10/94) (CPO) ① **CPO999 190-2**
Symphony No. 8 (1968-69)
Berlin RSO, T. Sanderling (bp1984)
(10/94) (CPO) ① **CPQ999 085-2**
Symphony No. 9 (1970)
Berlin Deutsches SO, A. Francis (r1993)
(9/95) (CPO) ① **CPO999 231-2**
Symphony No. 11 (1973)
Norrköping SO, L. Segerstam (r1992) *Symphony 7.*
(4/94) (BIS) ① **BIS-CD580**
Symphony No. 13 (1976)
BBC Scottish SO, A. Francis (r1993)
(3/94) (CPO) ① **CPO999 224-2**
Symphony No. 14 (1978)
Berlin RSO, J. Arnell (pp1988)
(10/94) (CPO) ① **CPO999 191-2**
Symphony No. 15 (1978)
Berlin RSO, P. Ruzicka (r1993) *Ruzicka: Orchestral
Sketches.*   (12/95) (CPO) ① **CPO999 095-2**

SECTION II: CHAMBER
7 Sonatas—2 violins (1951)
J. Grünfarb, K-O. Mannberg
(10/91) (CPRI) ① **CAP21401**

PEZEL, Johann Christoph
(1639–1694) Germany

SECTION I: ORCHESTRAL
Suite à 5 for strings (orig for 2 cornetti & 3
sackbuts)
Cantilena, A. Shepherd *Concert*
(9/84) (CHAN) ① **CHAN8319**

PFITZNER, Hans (Erich)
(1869–1949) Germany

SECTION I: ORCHESTRAL
**Concerto for Cello and Orchestra, Op.
posth**
D. Geringas, Bamberg SO, W.A. Albert (r1992)
Concert   (4/94) (CPO) ① **CPO999 135-2**
**Concerto for Cello and Orchestra in A minor,
Op. 52 (1943)**
D. Geringas, Bamberg SO, W.A. Albert (r1992)
Concert   (4/94) (CPO) ① **CPO999 135-2**
**Concerto for Cello and Orchestra in G, Op.
42 (1935)**
D. Geringas, Bamberg SO, W.A. Albert (r1992)
Concert   (4/94) (CPO) ① **CPO999 135-2**
**Concerto for Piano and Orchestra in E flat,
Op. 31 (1922)**
W. Harden, Bratislava RSO, H. Beissel *Concert*
(7/89) (MARC) ① **8 223162**
**Concerto for Violin and Orchestra in B
minor, Op. 34 (1923)**
S. Gawriloff, Bamberg SO, W.A. Albert *Concert*
(5/91) (CPO) ① **CPO999 079-2**
**Duo for Violin, Cello and Small Orchestra,
Op. 43 (1937)**
S. Gawriloff, J. Berger, Bamberg SO, W.A. Albert
Concert   (5/91) (CPO) ① **CPO999 079-2**
M. Strub, L. Hoelscher, Berlin St Op Orch, H. Pfitzner
(r1938) *Concert*   (9/90) (PREI) ① **90029**
M. Strub, L. Hoelscher, Berlin St Op Orch, H. Pfitzner
(r1938) *Concert*   (5/95) (EMI) ① **CDC5 55225-2**

**Elegie und Reigen—orchestra, Op. 45
(1940)**
Bamberg SO, W.A. Albert *Concert*
(7/93) (CPO) ① **CPO999 136-2**
Fantasie—orchestra, Op. 56 (1947)
Bamberg SO, W.A. Albert *Concert*
(7/93) (CPO) ① **CPO999 136-2**
Kleine Sinfonie in G, Op. 44 (1939)
Bamberg SO, W.A. Albert *Concert*
(5/91) (CPO) ① **CPO999 080-2**
Scherzo in C minor—orchestra (1887)
Bamberg SO, W.A. Albert *Concert*
(5/91) (CPO) ① **CPO999 079-2**
Symphony in C, Op. 46 (1940)
Bamberg SO, W.A. Albert *Concert*
(5/91) (CPO) ① **CPO999 080-2**
BPO, H. Pfitzner (r1940) *Concert*
(7/91) (PREI) ① **90029**
Symphony in C sharp minor, Op. 32a (1932)
(after String Quartet No. 2)
Bamberg SO, W.A. Albert *Concert*
(7/93) (CPO) ① **CPO999 136-2**

SECTION IV: VOCAL AND CHORAL
An den Mond—Lied, Op. 18 (1906) (Wds.
Goethe)
D. Fischer-Dieskau, A. Reimann *Concert*
(9/90) (EMI) ① **CDM7 63569-2**
**Der Blumen Rache—ballad: mezzo, female
vv and orchestra (1888)** (Wds. cpsr after F
Freiligrath)
Y. Jänicke, Berlin Rad Chor, Berlin RSO, R. Reuter
(r1993) *Concert*   (4/95) (CPO) ① **CPO999 158-2**
**Das dunkle Reich—choral fantasia: solo vv,
orchestra and organ, Op. 38 (1929)** (Wds.
Michelangelo, Goethe, Meyer & Dehmel)
Y. Wiedstruck, Y. Windmüller, S. Bruns, Berlin RSO,
R. Reuter (r1993) *Concert*
(4/95) (CPO) ① **CPO999 158-2**
**Fons salutifer—hymn: choir, organ &
orchestra, Op. 48 (1941)** (Wds. E G
Kolbenheyer)
S. Bruns, Berlin Rad Chor, Berlin RSO, R. Reuter
(r1993) *Concert*   (4/95) (CPO) ① **CPO999 158-2**
7 Lieder—Lieder, Op. 2 (1888-89)
1. In der Früh (wds Leander); 2. Ist der Himmel
darum im Lenz so blau (wds Leander); 3. Kalt und
schneidend weht der Wind (wds Lingg); 4. Im tiefen
Wald verborgen (wds anon); 5. Ich hör' ein Vöglein
locken' (wds Böttger); 6. Immer leiser wird mein
Schlummer (wds Lingg); 7. Verrat (wds Kaufmann).
2. F. Beckmann, B. Seidler-Winkler (r1939) *Concert*
(4/92) (EMI) ① **[7] CHS7 69741-2(4)**
2. C. Ludwig, E. Werba (pp1968) *Concert*
(7/94) (ORFE) ① **C331931A**
2, 6. L. Popp, I. Gage *Concert*
(4/92) (RCA) ① **RD60950**
5 Lieder—1v and piano, Op. 7 (1888-89)
1. Hast du von den Fischerkindern (wds Müller von
Königswinter); 2. Nachtwanderer (wds Eichendorff);
3. Über ein Stündlein (wds Heyse); 4. Lockung (wds
Eichendorff); 5. Wie Frühlingsahnung (wds J Grun).
1. G. Hüsch, H. Pfitzner (r1938) *Concert*
(7/91) (PREI) ① **90029**
1. C. Ludwig, E. Werba (pp1968) *Concert*
(7/94) (ORFE) ① **C331931A**
1. G. Hüsch, H. Pfitzner (r1938) *Concert*
(5/95) (EMI) ① **CDC5 55225-2**
2, 4. D. Fischer-Dieskau, K. Engel *Concert*
(9/90) (EMI) ① **CDM7 63569-2**
4. D. Fischer-Dieskau, W. Sawallisch (pp1975)
Concert   (1/90) (ORFE) ① **C185891A**
5 Lieder—1v and piano, Op. 9 (1894-95)
(Wds. Eichendorff)
1. Der Gärtner; 2. Die Einsame; 3. Im Herbst; 4. Der
Kühne; 5. Abschied.
D. Fischer-Dieskau, K. Engel *Concert*
(9/90) (EMI) ① **CDM7 63569-2**
1. H. Hermann Nissen, B. Seidler-Winkler (r1939)
Concert   (12/95) (PREI) ① **89090**
1, 2. G. Hüsch, H. Pfitzner (r1939) *Concert*
(7/91) (PREI) ① **90090**
1, 2. G. Hüsch, H. Pfitzner (r1939) *Concert*
(5/95) (EMI) ① **CDC5 55225-2**
2. L. Popp, I. Gage *Concert*
(4/92) (RCA) ① **RD60950**
3 Lieder—1v and piano, Op. 10 (1901)
1. Sehnsucht (wds D von Liliencron); 2. Müde (wds D
von Liliencron); 3. Zum Abschied meiner Tochter
(wds Eichendorff).
3. D. Fischer-Dieskau, W. Sawallisch (pp1975)
Concert   (1/90) (ORFE) ① **C185891A**
3. D. Fischer-Dieskau, K. Engel *Concert*
(9/90) (EMI) ① **CDM7 63569-2**

3. G. Hüsch, H. Pfitzner (r1939) *Concert*
(7/91) (PREI) ① **90029**
3. C. Ludwig, E. Werba (pp1968) *Concert*
(7/94) (ORFE) ① **C331931A**
3. G. Hüsch, H. Pfitzner (r1939) *Concert*
(5/95) (EMI) ① **CDC5 55225-2**
5 Lieder—1v and piano, Op. 11 (1901)
1. Ich und du (wds Hebbel); 2. Ich aber weiss (M M
gewidmet: wds Jakobowski); 3. Studenfahrt(wds
Eichendorff); 4. Venus Mater (wds R Dehmel); 5.
Gretel (wds Busse).
2. R. Holl, Konrad Richter *Concert*
(2/90) (PREI) ① **93331**
3. D. Fischer-Dieskau, K. Engel *Concert*
(9/90) (EMI) ① **CDM7 63569-2**
4. L. Popp, I. Gage *Concert*
(4/92) (RCA) ① **RD60950**
4, 5. C. Ludwig, E. Werba (pp1968) *Concert*
(7/94) (ORFE) ① **C331931A**
4 Lieder—1v and piano, Op. 15 (1904)
1. Leierkastenmann (wds Busse); 2. Korn (wds
Eichendorff); 3. An die Musik (wds I von Stach); 4.
Sonst (wds Eichendorff).
2, 4. D. Fischer-Dieskau, K. Engel *Concert*
(9/90) (EMI) ① **CDM7 63569-2**
2 Lieder—1v and piano, Op. 19 (1905) (Wds.
Busse)
1. Stimme der Sehnsucht; 2. Michaelskirchplatz.
2. G. Hüsch, H. Pfitzner (r1938) *Concert*
(7/91) (PREI) ① **90029**
2. G. Hüsch, H. Pfitzner (r1939) *Concert*
(5/95) (EMI) ① **CDC5 55225-2**
2 Lieder—1v and piano, Op. 21 (1907)
1. Herbstlied (wds Hebbel); 2. Die Nachtigallen (wds
Eichendorff).
2. D. Fischer-Dieskau, K. Engel *Concert*
(9/90) (EMI) ① **CDM7 63569-2**
5 Lieder—1v and piano, Op. 22 (1907)
1. In Danzig (wds Eichendorff); 2. Tragische
Geschichte (wds Chamisso); 3. Schön' Suschen (wds
Bürger); 4. Gegenliebe (wds Bürger); 5. An die
Bienen (wds Bürgen).
1. D. Fischer-Dieskau, W. Sawallisch (pp1975)
Concert (1/90) (ORFE) ① **C185891A**
1. R. Holl, Konrad Richter *Concert*
(2/90) (PREI) ① **93331**
1. D. Fischer-Dieskau, K. Engel *Concert*
(9/90) (EMI) ① **CDM7 63569-2**
1. G. Hüsch, H. Pfitzner (r1939) *Concert*
(7/91) (PREI) ① **90029**
1. G. Hüsch, H. Pfitzner (r1939) *Concert*
(5/95) (EMI) ① **CDC5 55225-2**
5 Lieder—1v and piano, Op. 26 (1916)
1. Gebet (wds Hebbel); 2. Nachts (wds Eichendorff);
3. Neue Liebe (wds Eichendorff); 4. Trauerstille (wds
Bürger); 5. Mailied (wds Goethe).
2. D. Fischer-Dieskau, W. Sawallisch (pp1975)
Concert (1/90) (ORFE) ① **C185891A**
2. R. Holl, Konrad Richter *Concert*
(2/90) (PREI) ① **93331**
2. G. Hüsch, H. Pfitzner (r1939) *Concert*
(7/91) (PREI) ① **90029**
2. G. Hüsch, H. Pfitzner (r1939) *Concert*
(5/95) (EMI) ① **CDC5 55225-2**
2, 3. D. Fischer-Dieskau, K. Engel *Concert*
(9/90) (EMI) ① **CDM7 63569-2**
5. D. Fischer-Dieskau, A. Reimann *Concert*
(9/90) (EMI) ① **CDM7 63569-2**
4 Lieder—1v and piano, Op. 29 (1922)
1. Abbitte (wds Hölderlin); 2. Herbsthauch (wds
Rückert); 3. Wilkommen und Abschied (wds Goethe);
4. Die stille Stadt (wds Dehmel).
R. Holl, Konrad Richter *Concert*
(2/90) (PREI) ① **93331**
1. G. Hüsch, H. Pfitzner (r1939) *Concert*
(7/91) (PREI) ① **90029**
1. M. Shirai, H. Höll *Concert*
(12/94) (CAPR) ① **10 534**
1. G. Hüsch, H. Pfitzner (r1939) *Concert*
(5/95) (EMI) ① **CDC5 55225-2**
1. W. Sharp, S. Blier (r1991) *Concert*
(7/93) (KOCH) ① **37086-2**
4 Lieder—1v and piano, Op. 30 (1922)
1. Sehsucht nach Vergessen (wds. Lenau); 2. Das
verlassene Mägdelein (wds E Mörike); 3. Denk' es, o
Seele (wds E Mörike); 4. Der Arbeitsmann (wds
Dehmel).
2. L. Popp, I. Gage *Concert*
(4/92) (RCA) ① **RD60950**
**4 Lieder—baritone/bass and piano, Op. 32
(1923)** (Wds C F Meyer)
1. Hussens Kerker; 2. Säerspruch; 3. Eingelegte
Ruder; 4. Lass scharren deiner Rosse Huf.
R. Holl, Konrad Richter *Concert*
(2/90) (PREI) ① **93331**

---

1. D. Fischer-Dieskau, H. Reutter *Concert*
(9/90) (EMI) ① **CDM7 63569-2**
1, 2. G. Hüsch, H. Pfitzner (r1938) *Concert*
(7/91) (PREI) ① **90029**
1, 2. G. Hüsch, H. Pfitzner (r1938) *Concert*
(5/95) (EMI) ① **CDC5 55225-2**
6 Lieder—1v and piano, Op. 40 (1931)
1. Leuchtende Tage (wds Jakobowski); 2. Wenn ich
Llebes von dir lösen will (wds Bartel); 3. Sehsucht
(wds R Huch); 4. Herbstgefühl (wds anon); 5.
Wanderers Nachtlied (wds Goethe); 6. Der Weckruf
(wds Eichendorff).
R. Holl, Konrad Richter *Concert*
(2/90) (PREI) ① **93331**
1, 4. G. Hüsch, H. Pfitzner (r1938) *Concert*
(7/91) (PREI) ① **90029**
1, 4. G. Hüsch, H. Pfitzner (r1938) *Concert*
(5/95) (EMI) ① **CDC5 55225-2**
3 Sonnets—1v and piano, Op. 41 (1931)
1. Auf die Morgenröte (wds Bürger); 2. Der
verspätete Wanderer (wds Eichendorff); 3. Das Alter
(wds Eichendorff).
R. Holl, Konrad Richter *Concert*
(2/90) (PREI) ① **93331**
2. D. Fischer-Dieskau, W. Sawallisch (pp1975)
Concert (1/90) (ORFE) ① **C185891A**
2, 3. D. Fischer-Dieskau, K. Engel *Concert*
(9/90) (EMI) ① **CDM7 63569-2**
**Von deutscher Seele—cantata: soloists,
chorus and orchestra, Op. 28 (1921)** (Wds.
Eichendorff)
Cpte A. Habereder, I. Most, J. Protschka, V. von
Halem, Düsseldorf Musikverein, Düsseldorf SO, H.
Hollreiser (pp1988) (10/89) (SCHW) ① [2] **314027**

SECTION V: STAGE WORKS

**Das Christ-Elflein—opera: 1 act, Op. 20
(1906—Munich)** (Lib. I von Stach & cpsr: work
rev 1917)
Overture Bratislava RSO, H. Beissel *Concert*
(7/89) (MARC) ① **8 223162**
Overture Berlin St Op Orch, H. Pfitzner (r1927)
Concert (5/95) (EMI) ① **CDC5 55225-2**
**Das Fest auf Solhaug—incidental music to
Ibsen's play (1890—Mainz)**
Bamberg SO, W.A. Albert *Concert*
(5/91) (CPO) ① **CPO999 080-2**
**Das Herz—music drama: 3 acts, Op. 39
(1931—Berlin & Munich)** (Lib. H Mahner-
Mons)
Cpte A. Wenhold, V. Horn, R. Cunningham, B.
Johanning, K. Quandt, R. Dressler, L. Chioreanu, I.
Melle, R. Atanasova, L. Hübel, I. Christoph, N.
Barowski, Thüringian Landestheater Chor, Thüringian
SO, R. Reuter (r1993)
(11/94) (MARC) ① [2] **8 223627/8**
Love theme Bratislava RSO, H. Beissel *Concert*
(7/89) (MARC) ① **8 223162**
Palestrina—opera: 3 acts (1917—Munich)
(Lib. cpsr)
Cpte N. Gedda, K. Ridderbusch, B. Weikl, H.
Steinbach, D. Fischer-Dieskau, V. von Halem, J. van
Kesteren, P. Meven, H. Prey, F. Lenz, Adalbert
Kraus, F. Mazura, H. Donath, B. Fassbaender, G.
Nienstedt, R. Freyer, Tolz Boys' Ch, Bavarian Rad
Chor, BRSO, R. Kubelik (r1970s)
(7/89) (DG) ① [3] **427 417-2GC3**
Excs J. Witt, A. Jerger, M. Bokor, E. Réthy, E.
Szánthó, H. Alsen, K. Ettl, F. Destal, G. Maikl, W.
Wernigk, D. Komarek, A. Gregorig, Vienna St Op
Chor, Vienna St Op Orch, B. Walter (pp1937)
Concert (2/95) (SCHW) ① [2] **314572**
Preludes to Acts 1-3. Berlin St Op Orch, H. Pfitzner
(r1931) *Concert* (5/95) (EMI) ① **CDC5 55225-2**

**PHALÈSE, Pierre I (c1510–1573/6)
The Netherlands**

SECTION II: CHAMBER

Alemande de Liège—consort (pub 1571)
Baltimore Consort (r1992; arr Baltimore Consort)
Concert (4/95) (DORI) ① **DOR90177**
**Danserye—collection of dance tunes (pub
1571)**
EXCERPTS: 1. Pavane de la garde; 2. Allemande;
3. Chanson du bouffon; 4. Rocque gaillarde; 5.
Pavane Lesquercarde.
4. Baltimore Consort (r1992; arr Baltimore Consort)
Concert (4/95) (DORI) ① **DOR90177**
Gaillarde d'escosse—consort (pub 1571)
Baltimore Consort (r1992; arr Baltimore Consort)
Concert (4/95) (DORI) ① **DOR90177**
Passamezzo d'Italye
Ulsamer Collegium, J. Ulsamer *Concert*
(2/86) (ARCH) ① **415 294-2AH**

**PHILIDOR, André Danican
(c1647–1730) France**

SECTION II: CHAMBER

**Sonata for Recorder and Continuo in D
minor**
F. Brüggen, A. Bylsma, G. Leonhardt (r1970) *Concert*
(10/95) (TELD) ① **4509-97469-2**

SECTION V: STAGE WORKS

**Le Mariage de la Grosse Cathos, 'Fat Kate's
Wedding'—opéra-ballet (1688—Versailles)**
London Ob Band, M-A. Petit, P. Goodwin (r1994)
Concert (4/95) (HARM) ① **HMU90 7122**

**PHILIDOR, Jacques Danican (le
Cadet) (1657–1708) France**

SECTION III: INSTRUMENTAL

Marche de timbales—drums
M-A. Petit *Concert* (9/89) (HARM) ① **HMC90 1298**

**PHILIDOR, Pierre Danican
(1681–1731) France**

SECTION II: CHAMBER

Premier Oeuvre—oboe and continuo (1717)
No 5. P. Dombrecht, W. Kuijken, R. Kohnen *Concert*
(9/90) (ACCE) ① **ACC8537D**

**PHILIPP, Adolf (1864–1936)
Germany/USA**

aka Jean Briquet and Paul Hervé

SECTION V: STAGE WORKS

**Alma, Where Do You Live?—musical show
(1910—New York)** (Lyrics George V. Hobart)
EXCERPTS: 1. Alma; 2. Sail Home.
1, 2. T. Shattuck, Orig Broadway Cast (r1911)
Concert (5/94) (PEAR) ① [3] **GEMMCDS9053/5**
**The Midnight Girl—English version of 'Das
Mitternachtsmaedel' (1913—New York)**
(Lyrics Paulton)
EXCERPTS: 1. Oh! Gustave. INTERPOLATION
SONGS: 2. Your Eyes (Johnson/Anderson); 3. Can't
You Hear Me Calling, Caroline? (Roma/Gardner).
1-3. G. MacFarlane, M. Romaine, Orig Broadway
Cast (r1914) *Concert*
(5/94) (PEAR) ① [3] **GEMMCDS9056/8**

**PHILIPPE DE THAON (fl c1130)
France**

SECTION IV: VOCAL AND CHORAL

Monosceros—poem
A. Azéma, S. Kammen (r1993) *Concert*
(11/94) (ERAT) ① **4509-94830-2**
Serena en mer hante—poem
A. Azéma, C. A. Fulton, S. Kammen (r1993) *Concert*
(11/94) (ERAT) ① **4509-94830-2**

**PHILIPPE DE VITRY (1291–1361)
France**

SECTION III: INSTRUMENTAL

Firmissime fidem teneamus—intabulation
Sequentia *Concert* (1/92) (DHM) ① **RD77095**
Tribum, que non abhorruit—intabulation
Sequentia *Concert* (1/92) (DHM) ① **RD77095**

SECTION IV: VOCAL AND CHORAL

**Aman novi/Heu fortuna/Heu me, tristis est
anima mea—motet (1315/16)**
A. Azéma, S. Kammen (r1993) *Concert*
(11/94) (DHM) ① **RD77095**
Ay, amours! tant me dure—chanson (attrib.
From Roman de Fauvel MS)
Sequentia *Concert* (1/92) (DHM) ① **RD77095**
**Colla iugo/Bona conduit/Libera me
Domine—motet (c1320)**
Sequentia *Concert* (1/92) (DHM) ① **RD77095**
**Cum statua/Hugo, Hugo,
princeps—isorhythmic motet (3vv)**
London Early Music Consort, D. Munrow *Concert*
(8/85) (ARCH) ① **415 292-2AH**
**Cum statua/Hugo/Magister invidie—motet
(c1330)**
Sequentia *Concert* (1/92) (DHM) ① **RD77095**
**Douce playsence/Garison/Neuma quinti
toni—motet (c1317)**
Sequentia *Concert* (1/92) (DHM) ① **RD77095**

Firmissime/Adesto/Alleluya,
Benedictus—motet (by mid-1314)
Sequentia Concert   (1/92) (DHM) ① RD77095
Floret/Fiorens/Neuma—motet (1314)
Sequentia Concert   (1/92) (DHM) ① RD77095
Garrit gallus/In nova fert/Neuma—motet
(1314)
Sequentia Concert   (1/92) (DHM) ① RD77095
Gratissima virginis/Vos qui
admiramini/Gaude gloriosa—isorhythmic
motet (4vv)
Gothic Voices, C. Page Concert
                           (11/87) (HYPE) ① CDA66238
Impudenter circuivi/Virtutibus—motet
(c1330)
Sequentia Concert   (1/92) (DHM) ① RD77095
Impudenter circumivi/Virtutibus
laudabilis—isorhythmic motet (4vv)
London Early Music Consort, D. Munrow Concert
                           (8/85) (ARCH) ① 415 292-2AH
Je qui paoir selue ai de conforter—Descort
(attrib. From Roman de Fauvel MS)
Sequentia Concert   (1/92) (DHM) ① RD77095
O canenda/Rex quem/Rex regum—motet
(1330s)
Sequentia Concert   (1/92) (DHM) ① RD77095
Petre clemens/Lugentium—motet (1342 or
1350)
Sequentia Concert   (1/92) (DHM) ① RD77095
Providencia la senée—virelai (attrib. From
Roman de Fauvel MS)
Sequentia Concert   (1/92) (DHM) ① RD77095
Se j'onques a mon vivant—chanson (attrib.
From Roman de Fauvel MS)
Sequentia Concert   (1/92) (DHM) ① RD77095
Talant j'ai que d'obeir—Lai (attrib. From
Roman de Fauvel MS)
Sequentia Concert   (1/92) (DHM) ① RD77095
Tribum/Quoniam secta/Merito hec
patimur—motet (1315)
Sequentia Concert   (1/92) (DHM) ① RD77095
Tuba sacrae fidei/In arboris/Virgo
sum—motet (c1320)
Sequentia Concert   (1/92) (DHM) ① RD77095
Vos quid admiramini/Gratissima/Gaude
gloriosa—motet (1330s)
Sequentia Concert   (1/92) (DHM) ① RD77095

PHILIPPUS DE CASERTA (14th Cent) Flanders

SECTION IV: VOCAL AND CHORAL

Par les bons Gedeons—ballade: 3vv
Orlando Consort (bp1994) Concert
                           (11/95) (METR) ① METCD1008

PHILIPS, Peter (1560/1–1628) England

SECTION II: CHAMBER

Almand, 'Tregian'—consort: 5 parts
Parley of Instr Concert
                           (1/89) (HYPE) ① CDA66240
Aria—consort (5 parts) (arr T. Simpson)
Parley of Instr Concert
                           (1/89) (HYPE) ① CDA66240
Aria del Gran Duca Ferdinando di
Toscana—consort (5 parts) (after Cavalieri)
Parley of Instr Concert
                           (1/89) (HYPE) ① CDA66240
Balla d'amore—consort (5 parts) (after
Tregian)
Parley of Instr Concert
                           (1/89) (HYPE) ① CDA66240
Galliard (Coranto)—consort (5 parts) (after
Bassano)
Parley of Instr Concert
                           (1/89) (HYPE) ① CDA66240
Galliard—consort (5 parts)
Parley of Instr Concert
                           (1/89) (HYPE) ① CDA66240
Pavan—consort (2 parts) (1580)
Parley of Instr Concert
                           (1/89) (HYPE) ① CDA66240
Pavan and Galliard—consort (5 parts) (after
Bassano. Spurious)
Parley of Instr Concert
                           (1/89) (HYPE) ① CDA66240
Pavan and Galliard—consort (5 parts) (after
Morley)
Parley of Instr Concert
                           (1/89) (HYPE) ① CDA66240

Pavan and Galliard—consort: 5 parts (1580)
Parley of Instr (reconstr Holman) Concert
                           (1/89) (HYPE) ① CDA66240
Pavan and Galliard, 'Dolorosa'—consort: 5
parts (1593)
Parley of Instr Concert
                           (1/89) (HYPE) ① CDA66240
Pavan and Galliard in F—consort: 5 parts
Parley of Instr Concert
                           (1/89) (HYPE) ① CDA66240
Pavan and Galliard, 'Paget'—consort: 5
parts (?1590)
Parley of Instr Concert
                           (1/89) (HYPE) ① CDA66240
Pavan, 'Passamezzo'—consort: 5 parts
Parley of Instr Concert
                           (1/89) (HYPE) ① CDA66240

SECTION III: INSTRUMENTAL

Chromatic Pavan and Galliard—lute
J. Bream (r1966) Concert
                           (8/93) (RCA) ① [28] 09026 61583-2(1)
J. Bream (r1966) Concert
                           (6/94) (RCA) ① 09026 61585-2
Pavan in G—keyboard (1580) ('the first one
Philips made')
C. Wilson (lte) Concert
                           (11/91) (VIRG) ① VC7 59034-2
Philips Pavan—lute
J. Bream, J. Bream Consort (r1962) Concert
                           (8/93) (RCA) ① [28] 09026 61583-2(2)
J. Bream, J. Bream Consort (r1987; ed Beck)
Concert   (8/93) (RCA) ① [28] 09026 61583-2(3)
J. Bream Consort (r1962; arr consort) Concert
                           (9/94) (RCA) ① 09026 61589-2
J. Bream Consort (r1987; ed Beck) Concert
                           (9/94) (RCA) ① 09026 61590-2

SECTION IV: VOCAL AND CHORAL

Ascendit Deus—motet: 5vv (pub 1612)
Oxford Christ Church Cath Ch, S. Preston Concert
                           (2/90) (GAMU) ① GOUPCD153
Winchester Cath Ch, Parley of Instr, D. Hill (r1992)
Concert   (11/93) (HYPE) ① CDA66643
Ave Jesu Christe—motet: 8vv (pub 1613)
Salisbury Cath Ch, R. Seal Concert
                           (11/90) (MERI) ① CDE84180
Winchester Cath Ch, Parley of Instr, D. Hill (r1992)
Concert   (11/93) (HYPE) ① CDA66643
Cantatibus organis—5vv and continuo (pub
1612)
Winchester Cath Ch, Parley of Instr, D. Hill (r1992)
Concert   (11/93) (HYPE) ① CDA66643
Christus resurgens—5vv and continuo (pub
1612)
Winchester Cath Ch, Parley of Instr, D. Hill (r1992)
Concert   (11/93) (HYPE) ① CDA66643
Ecce vicit Leo—anthem: 8vv (1613)
Salisbury Cath Ch, R. Seal Concert
                           (11/90) (MERI) ① CDE84180
Winchester Cath Ch, Parley of Instr, D. Hill (r1992)
Concert   (11/93) (HYPE) ① CDA66643
Hodie concepta est—8vv and continuo (pub
1613)
Winchester Cath Ch, Parley of Instr, D. Hill (r1992)
Concert   (11/93) (HYPE) ① CDA66643
Litania duodecima—9vv and continuo (pub
1623)
Winchester Cath Ch, Parley of Instr, D. Hill (r1992)
Concert   (11/93) (HYPE) ① CDA66643
O beatum et sacrosanctum diem—motet:
5vv (1612)
Cambridge Sngrs, J. Rutter Concert
                           (4/92) (CLLE) ① COLCD113
O crux splendidior—5vv (pub 1612)
Winchester Cath Ch, Parley of Instr, D. Hill (r1992)
Concert   (11/93) (HYPE) ① CDA66643
O quam suavis est I—8vv and continuo (pub
1613)
Winchester Cath Ch, Parley of Instr, D. Hill (r1992)
Concert   (11/93) (HYPE) ① CDA66643
O quam suavis est II—8vv and continuo (pub
1613)
Winchester Cath Ch, Parley of Instr, D. Hill (r1992)
Concert   (11/93) (HYPE) ① CDA66643
Salve regina, vita dulcedo—8vv and
continuo (pub 1613)
Winchester Cath Ch, Parley of Instr, D. Hill (r1992)
Concert   (11/93) (HYPE) ① CDA66643
Tibi laus, tibi gloria—5vv and continuo (pub
1612)
Winchester Cath Ch, Parley of Instr, D. Hill (r1992)
Concert   (11/93) (HYPE) ① CDA66643

Tristitia vestra—5vv and continuo (pub
1612)
Winchester Cath Ch, Parley of Instr, D. Hill (r1992)
Concert   (11/93) (HYPE) ① CDA66643
Tu es Petrus—8vv and continuo (pub 1613)
Winchester Cath Ch, Parley of Instr, D. Hill (r1992)
Concert   (11/93) (HYPE) ① CDA66643

PHILIPS, Thomas (19th Cent) England

SECTION IV: VOCAL AND CHORAL

Crows in the cornfield—glee
Hilliard Ens, L-L. Kiesel Concert
                           (12/91) (MERI) ① DUOCD89009

PHILLIPS, Burrill (1907–1988) USA

SECTION I: ORCHESTRAL

Selections from McGuffey's Reader—suite
(1933)
EXCERPTS: 1. The One-Horse Shay; 2. John Alden
and Priscilla; 3. Midnight Ride of Paul Revere.
Eastman-Rochester Orch, H. Hanson (r1956)
Concert   (2/93) (MERC) ① 434 319-2MM

PHILLIPS, John W.

SECTION I: ORCHESTRAL

Romance—two euphoniums and brass band
(1989)
R. Childs, N. Childs, Britannia Building Soc Band, H.
Snell Concert   (2/91) (DOYE) ① DOYCD002

PHILLIPS, Montague F(awcett) (1885–1969) England

SECTION IV: VOCAL AND CHORAL

Open your window to the morn—song (Wds.
Royden)
R. Crooks, orch (r1937) Concert
                           (9/93) (CLAR) ① CDGSE78-50-50
Wimmen oh wimmen—song
O. Natzke, H. Greenslade (r1940) Concert
                           (12/92) (ODE) ① CDODE1365

SECTION V: STAGE WORKS

The Rebel Maid—romantic light opera
(1921—London) (Lib. G. Dodson and A. M.
Thomson)
Sail my ships M. Hill Smith, Southern Fest Orch, R.
White Concert   (5/93) (CHAN) ① CHAN9110

PHILLIPS, Sid (1907–1973) England

SECTION III: INSTRUMENTAL

Cadenza—clarinet
Thurston Cl Qt (arr Harvey) Concert
                           (10/93) (ASV) ① CDWHL2076

PIACENTINO, Antonio (18th Cent) Italy

SECTION I: ORCHESTRAL

Concerto for Flute and Orchestra in G
(source: Karlsruhe MS)
J. Galway, Solisti Veneti, C. Scimone (r1991) Concert
                           (4/94) (RCA) ① 09026 61164-2

PIAZZOLLA, Astor (1921–1992) Argentina

SECTION I: ORCHESTRAL

Tangazo—orchestra (1988)
New World Sym, M. Tilson Thomas (r1992) Concert
                           (6/93) (ARGO) ① 436 737-2ZH

SECTION II: CHAMBER

Le Grand Tango—cello and piano
Pro Arte Gtr Trio (arr gtr trio) Concert
                           (1/94) (ASV) ① CDWHL2079
M. Kliegel, B. Glemser (r1993) Concert
                           (1/95) (NAXO) ① 8 550785
Histoire du Tango—flute and guitar (1986)
1. Bordel 1900; 2. Café 1930; 3. Nightclub 1960; 4.
Concert d'Aujourd'hui.
M. Helasvuo, J. Savijoki Concert
                           (12/92) (ONDI) ① ODE781-2

A. Noakes, J. Woodrow *Concert*
(12/92) (KING) ① **KCLCD2027**

SECTION III: INSTRUMENTAL

Adios Nonino—tango: guitar
Buenos Aires Qnt, RPO, E. Stratta (arr J. Calandrelli)
Concert (1/93) (TELD) ① **9031-76997-2**
Contrabajaendo—tango: guitar
J. Oraison (trans gtr: Oraison) *Concert*
(10/92) (ETCE) ① **KTC1023**
6 Etudes tanguistiques
M. Helasvuo *Concert* (12/92) (ONDI) ① **ODE781-2**
Jacinto Chiciano—milonga: piano
J. Oraison (trans gtr: Oraison) *Concert*
(10/92) (ETCE) ① **KTC1023**
Milogna en ay Menor—piano
J. Oraison (trans gtr: Oraison) *Concert*
(10/92) (ETCE) ① **KTC1023**
Milonga del Angel—piano
J. Oraison (trans gtr: Oraison) *Concert*
(10/92) (ETCE) ① **KTC1023**
La Muerte del Angel—tango: guitar
M. Kayath (arr. Carlevaro) *Concert*
(9/87) (CARL) ① **PCD853**
J. Oraison (trans gtr: Oraison) *Concert*
(10/92) (ETCE) ① **KTC1023**
Oblivion—tango
Buenos Aires Qnt, RPO, E. Stratta (arr J. Calandrelli)
Concert (1/93) (TELD) ① **9031-76997-2**
Otoño Porteño—tango: piano
J. Oraison (trans gtr: Oraison) *Concert*
(10/92) (ETCE) ① **KTC1023**
5 Pieces—guitar (1980)
1. Campero; 2. Romántico; 3. Acentuado; 4. Tristón;
5. Compadre.
J. Oraison *Concert* (10/92) (ETCE) ① **KTC1023**
J. Savijoki *Concert* (12/92) (ONDI) ① **ODE781-2**
Retrato de Alfredo Gobbi—tango: piano
J. Oraison (trans gtr: Oraison) *Concert*
(10/92) (ETCE) ① **KTC1023**
Verano porteño—guitar
J. Williams *Concert* (8/89) (SONY) ① **SK44898**

PICCHI, Giovanni (fl 1575–1630)
Italy

SECTION II: CHAMBER

19 Canzoni da sonar—2-4, 6 and 8
instruments and continuo (pub 1625)
1. Canzon I; 6. Sonata VI; 12. Canzon XII; 14.
Canzon XIV; 15. Canzon XV; 17. Canzon XVII.
1, 6, 12, 14, 16, 17. Musica Fiata, Roland Wilson
(r1992) *Monteverdi: Selva morale e spirituale.*
(7/94) (SONY) ① **SK53363**

SECTION III: INSTRUMENTAL

Intavolatura di Balli d'Arpicordo—dance
collection (pub 1621)
1. Saltarello del pass'e mezo; 2. Ballo ongaro; 3.
Ballo alla polacha; 4. Todesca; 5. Padoana ditta la
Ongara; 6. Ballo ditto il Picchi.
1, 2. Broadside Band, J. Barlow *Concert*
(3/88) (HYPE) ① **CDA66244**
2. Kithara (r1993) *Concert*
(3/95) (CHAN) ① **CHAN0562**
2, 3, 6. R. Alessandrini (r1994) *Concert*
(4/95) (O111) ① **OPS30-118**
3. C. Farr *Concert* (1/90) (ETCE) ① **KTC1056**
Toccata—keyboard
C. Farr *Concert* (1/90) (ETCE) ① **KTC1056**

PICCININI, Alessandro
(1566–c1638) Italy

SECTION II: CHAMBER

Canzone a tre liutti
J. Lindberg, N. North, P. O'Dette *Concert*
(12/86) (BIS) ① **BIS-CD341**
Chiaccone
Kithara (r1993) *Concert*
(3/95) (CHAN) ① **CHAN0562**
Colascione—chitarrone & tambourine
Tragicomedia *Concert*
(9/92) (EMI) ① **CDC7 54191-2**

SECTION III: INSTRUMENTAL

Intavolutura di liuto et di chitarrone libro
primo (pub 1623)
EXCERPTS: 1. TOCCATAS: 1a. Toccata I; 1b.
Toccata II; 1f. Toccata VI; 1j. Toccata X; 1k. Toccata
XI; 1l. Toccata cromatica XII; 1m. Toccata XIII; 1o.
Toccata XV; 1t. Toccata XX; 1x. Toccata XXIV; 1y.
Toccata cromatica; 2. CORRENTI: 2a. Corrente I; 2f.
Corrente VI sopra l'Alemana; 2k. Corrente XI; 2m.
Corrente XIII; 3. GAGLIARDE: 3a. Gagliarda I; 3b.

Gagliarda II; 3c. Gagliarda III; 4. ARIE: 4a. Aria I
affetuosa; 4b. Aria di Saravande in varie partite; 4c.
Aria III con parte variate; 5. CANZONI: 5a. Canzone
I; 6. PARTITE: 6a. Partite sopra La folia aria
Romanesca; 6b. Partite variate sopra quest'Aria
francese detta l'Alemana; 7. OTHER PIECES: 7a.
Chiaccona in partite variate; 7b. Romanesca con
partite variate; 7c. Sarabanda alla Francese.
1b, 1f, 1j, 1l, 1m, 1o, 1t, 1y, 2a, 2f, 2k, 2m, 3a-c, 4a-
c, 5a, 6a, 6b, 7a-c N. North (r1994)
(8/95) (ARCA) ① **A06**

PICCINNI, (Vito) Niccolò (Marcello
Antonio Giacomo) (1728–1800)
Italy

SECTION V: STAGE WORKS

Le faux Lord—opéra-comique: 1 acts
(1783—Paris) (Lib. G. M. Piccinni)
EXCERPTS: 1. O notte, o dea del mistro.
1. J. Baker, ASMF, N. Marriner *Concert*
(1/93) (PHIL) ① **434 173-2PM**

PICCOLO, Anthony (b 1946)
USA

SECTION IV: VOCAL AND CHORAL

O hear us, Lord—chorus (Wds. J. Donne)
St John's Episcopal Cath Ch, D. Pearson *Concert*
(10/92) (DELO) ① **DE3125**

PICHL, Václav (1741–1805)
Bohemia
aka Wenzel Pichel

SECTION I: ORCHESTRAL

Symphonie concertante in D, Apollo', Op. 6
Oradea PO, R. Rîmbu (r1993) *Concert*
(5/94) (OLYM) ① **OCD434**
Symphony in B flat, Op. 1/5
Oradea PO, R. Rîmbu (r1993) *Concert*
(5/94) (OLYM) ① **OCD434**
Symphony in D, Op. 17
Oradea PO, R. Rîmbu (r1993) *Concert*
(5/94) (OLYM) ① **OCD434**
Symphony in D, 'Mars'
Oradea PO, R. Rîmbu (r1993) *Concert*
(5/94) (OLYM) ① **OCD434**

PICK, ? (19th Cent) Germany

SECTION IV: VOCAL AND CHORAL

Wiener Fiakerlied—song
E. Kunz, Kemmeter-Faltl Schrammel Ens (r1949)
Concert (9/95) (TEST) ① **SBT1059**

PICKER, Tobias (b 1954) USA

SECTION I: ORCHESTRAL

Old and Lost Rivers—orchestra (1986)
Houston SO, C. Eschenbach *Concert*
(7/91) (VIRG) ① **VC7 59007-2**
Romances and Interludes—oboe and
orchestra (1989) (based on Schumann's
Romanzen, Op 94)
R. Atherholt, Houston SO, C. Eschenbach *Concert*
(7/91) (VIRG) ① **VC7 59007-2**
Séance (1990)
Helsinki PO, S. Comissiona *Concert*
(4/92) (ONDI) ① **ODE767-2**

SECTION III: INSTRUMENTAL

Old and Lost Rivers—piano (1986)
C. Eschenbach *Concert*
(7/91) (VIRG) ① **VC7 59007-2**

SECTION IV: VOCAL AND CHORAL

Encantadas—narrator and orchestra (1983)
(wds. Melville)
J. Gielgud, Houston SO, C. Eschenbach *Concert*
(7/91) (VIRG) ① **VC7 59007-2**

PIEFKE, Gottfried (1817–1884)
Germany

SECTION I: ORCHESTRAL

Königrätz Marsch—wind band (1866)
Berlin Phil Wind Qnt, H. von Karajan (r1973) *Concert*
(5/94) (DG) ① **439 346-2GX2**

Preussens Gloria—march
Berlin Phil Wind Qnt, H. von Karajan (r1973) *Concert*
(5/94) (DG) ① **439 346-2GX2**

PIERNÉ, (Henri Constant) Gabriel
(1863–1937) France

SECTION I: ORCHESTRAL

Cathédrales—orchestra, with chorus ad lib
(after E. Morand)
1. Prélude.
1. Loire PO, P. Dervaux *Concert*
(3/92) (EMI) ① **CDM7 63950-2**
Concerto for Piano and Orchestra in C
minor, Op. 42 (c1887)
D. Achatz, Lorraine PO, J. Houtmann *Ramuntcho.*
(8/88) (BIS) ① **BIS-CD381**
Konzertstück for harp and orchestra, Op. 39
(1903)
A. Challan, Paris Cons, A. Cluytens (r1964) *Concert*
(11/94) (EMI) ① [2] **CZS5 68220-2**
March of the Little Lead Soldiers
ECO, P. Tortelier *Concert*
(7/88) (VIRG) ① **VC7 59668-2**
Paysages Franciscains—symphonic poems,
Op. 43 (1920) (after J. Joergensen)
Loire PO, P. Dervaux *Concert*
(3/92) (EMI) ① **CDM7 63950-2**
Viennoise—divertissement for orchestra
(1932) (earlier vers of 'Images')
Loire PO, P. Dervaux *Concert*
(3/92) (EMI) ① **CDM7 63950-2**

SECTION II: CHAMBER

Canzonetta—clarinet and piano, Op. 19
E. Johnson, G. Back *Concert*
(10/88) (ASV) ① **CDDCA621**
Pastorale—wind quintet, Op. 41
1. No. 1.
Selandia Ens *Concert* (6/90) (KONT) ① **32032**
1. Reykjavik Wind Qnt (r1993) *Concert*
(10/95) (CHAN) ① **CHAN9362**
Sonata for Flute and Piano, Op. 36 (1900)
I. Matuz, N. Szelecsényi (r1988) *Piano Trio, Op.45.*
(10/90) (MARC) ① **8 223189**
Sonata for Violin and Piano (1900)
G. Poulet, N. Lee (r1993) *Concert*
(9/94) (ARIO) ① **ARN68228**
Trio—violin, cello and piano, Op. 45 (1920-
21)
B. Bánfalvi, K. Vass, N. Szelecsényi (r1988) *Flute*
Sonata, Op. 36. (10/90) (MARC) ① **8 223189**
Variations, libres et finale—flute, violin,
viola, cello and harp, Op. 51 (1933)
Netherlands Harp Ens *Concert*
(5/89) (ETCE) ① **KTC1021**

SECTION III: INSTRUMENTAL

Impromptu-caprice, Op. 9
S. Drake (r1988) *Concert*
(2/90) (HYPE) ① **CDA66340**
M. Robles *Concert*
(2/93) (DECC) ① **433 869-2DWO**
M. Klinko *Concert* (8/93) (EMI) ① **CDC7 54467-2**

SECTION IV: VOCAL AND CHORAL

Sérénade—song
A. Galli-Curci, orch. R. Bourdon (r1924) *Concert*
(8/94) (ROMO) ① [2] **81004-2**
D. Fischer-Dieskau, H. Höll (r c1987) *Concert*
(12/95) (TELD) ① **4509-97457-2**

SECTION V: STAGE WORKS

Cydalise et la chèvre-pied—ballet (1923)
Entrance of the Little Fauns St Louis SO, L. Slatkin
Concert (6/89) (RCA) ① **RD87716**
Images—ballet, Op. 49 (1935)
Loire PO, P. Dervaux *Concert*
(3/92) (EMI) ① **CDM7 63950-2**
Ramuntcho—musique de scène pour le
drame de Pierre Loti (1908)
Stes Nos 1 and 2. Lorraine PO, J. Houtmann *Piano*
Concerto. (8/88) (BIS) ① **BIS-CD381**

PIERRE DES MOLINS (fl
?1190–1220)

SECTION IV: VOCAL AND CHORAL

De ce que fol pense—ballade (3vv)
Gothic Voices, C. Page *Concert*
(11/87) (HYPE) ① **CDA66238**

PIERSON, Henry Hugo (1815–1873) England/Germany

SECTION I: ORCHESTRAL

Romeo and Juliet—overture, Op. 86 (1874)
English Northern Philh, D. Lloyd-Jones *Concert*
(1/92) (HYPE) ① **CDA66515**

PIETRI, Giuseppe (1886–1946) Italy

SECTION V: STAGE WORKS

Maristella—opera (1934—Naples) (Lib. M Salvini, after S Di Giacomo)
Io conosco un giardino B. Gigli, orch, U. Berrettoni
(r1940) *Concert* (9/88) (EMI) ① **CDH7 61051-2**
Uno strano senso arcano; Oh! la mia casa R.
Pampanini, orch, L. Molajoli (r1934) *Concert*
(8/93) (PREI) ① **89063**

PIGARELLI, Luigi Italy

SECTION IV: VOCAL AND CHORAL

La montarana—song (Wds. Ortelli)
T. Gobbi, Inst Ens (r1950) *Concert*
(8/93) (TEST) ① **SBT1019**

PIGOTT, Francis (c1665–1704) England

SECTION IV: VOCAL AND CHORAL

Ask me not—song (Wds Cowley)
Consort of Musicke, A. Rooley (lte/dir) (r1993)
Concert (1/95) (MOSC) ① **070986**

PIJPER, Willem (1894–1947) The Netherlands

SECTION II: CHAMBER

String Quartet No. 1 in F minor (1914)
Schoenberg Qt (r1994) *Concert*
(2/95) (OLYM) ① **OCD457**
String Quartet No. 2 (1920)
Schoenberg Qt (r1994) *Concert*
(2/95) (OLYM) ① **OCD457**
String Quartet No. 3 (1923)
Schoenberg Qt (r1994) *Concert*
(2/95) (OLYM) ① **OCD457**
String Quartet No. 4 (1928)
Schoenberg Qt (r1994) *Concert*
(2/95) (OLYM) ① **OCD457**
String Quartet No. 5 (1946) (unfinished)
Schoenberg Qt (r1994) *Concert*
(2/95) (OLYM) ① **OCD457**

PILKINGTON, Francis (c1570–1638) England

SECTION III: INSTRUMENTAL

Go from my window—variations: lute
S. Stubbs *Concert* (9/93) (PIER) ① **PV787092**

SECTION IV: VOCAL AND CHORAL

Come all ye—song
E. Kirkby, A. Rooley *Concert*
(8/91) (L'OI) ① **425 892-2OH**
Musick deare solace—song
E. Kirkby, A. Rooley *Concert*
(8/91) (L'OI) ① **425 892-2OH**
Rest, sweet nymphs—song (pub 1605)
E. Kirkby, A. Rooley *Concert*
(8/91) (L'OI) ① **425 892-2OH**
J. Elwes, S. Stubbs *Concert*
(9/93) (PIER) ① **PV787092**

PINI-CORSI, Antonio (1859–1918) Italy

SECTION IV: VOCAL AND CHORAL

Tu non mi vuoi più ben—song (Wds. F. Carbonetti)
E. Caruso, anon (r1903) *Concert*
(5/89) (EMI) ① **CDH7 61046-2**
E. Caruso, anon (r1903) *Concert*
(12/90) (PEAR) ① [3] **EVC1(1)**
E. Caruso, anon (r1903) *Concert*
(7/91) (RCA) ① [12] **GD60495(1)**

PINKHAM, Daniel (b 1923) USA

SECTION I: ORCHESTRAL

Sonata No. 3—organ & string orchestra (1987)
J. D. Christie, LSO, J. Sedares (r1994) *Concert*
(8/95) (KOCH) ① **37179-2**
Symphony No. 3—orchestra (1985)
LSO, J. Sedares (r1994) *Concert*
(8/95) (KOCH) ① **37179-2**
Symphony No. 4—orchestra (1990)
LSO, J. Sedares (r1994) *Concert*
(8/95) (KOCH) ① **37179-2**

SECTION II: CHAMBER

Introduction, Nocturne and Rondo—mandolin and guitar (1984)
W. Buonocore, J. Curtis (r1992) *Concert*
(1/94) (KOCH) ① **37180-2**
Serenades—trumpet & wind ensemble (1980)
M. Murphy, LSO, J. Sedares (r1994) *Concert*
(8/95) (KOCH) ① **37179-2**
String Quartet (1990)
Boston Cpsrs Qt (r1992) *Concert*
(1/94) (KOCH) ① **37180-2**

SECTION IV: VOCAL AND CHORAL

Advent Cantata—chorus, wind quintet & harp (1991)
C. Baum, Ariel Wind Qnt, Boston Cecilia, D. Teeters
(r1992) *Concert* (1/94) (KOCH) ① **37180-2**
Christmas Cantata—chorus, brass qt & organ/double brass choirs (1958)
Lenox Brass, J. Christie, Boston Cecilia, D. Teeters
(r1992) *Concert* (1/94) (KOCH) ① **37180-2**
Wedding Cantata—chorus and piano (1959)
B. Bruns, Boston Cecilia, D. Teeters (r1992) *Concert*
(1/94) (KOCH) ① **37180-2**

PINTO, George Frederick (1785–1806) England

SECTION III: INSTRUMENTAL

Minuetto in A flat (in 'The Harmonicon', ii, 1824)
T. Roberts *Concert* (12/91) (HYPE) ① **CDA66497**
Piano Sonata in C minor (1802-03)
I. Hobson *Concert* (3/89) (ARAB) ① **Z6595**
Rondo in E flat—piano (c1805, pub 1826)
T. Roberts (r1994) *Concert*
(3/95) (HYPE) ① **CDA66740**

SECTION IV: VOCAL AND CHORAL

4 Canzonets
1. Oh! think on my fate (The Galley Slave); 2. Alas! what pains (Absence); 3. Soon as the letters (A Canzonett...from Pope's 'Abelard and Eloisa'); 4. Oh! he was almost speechless (A Canzonett on the Death of a Friend).
3. E. Kirkby, T. Roberts *Concert*
(12/91) (HYPE) ① **CDA66497**
6 Canzonets (pub ?1803)
1. It was a winter's evening (The Distress'd Mother); 2. A shepherd love a nymph so fair; 3. The smiling plains; 4. Nature! sweet mistress (Invocation to Nature); 5. Little warbler chearful be; 6. From thee, Eliza, I must go.
1. Invocation (r1994) *Concert*
(3/95) (HYPE) ① **CDA66740**
2. R. Müller, T. Roberts *Concert*
(12/91) (HYPE) ① **CDA66497**
4. E. Kirkby, T. Roberts *Concert*
(12/91) (HYPE) ① **CDA66497**
6. R. Müller, T. Roberts *Concert*
(12/91) (HYPE) ① **CDA66497**

PIPELARE, Matthaeus (c1450–c1515) The Netherlands

SECTION IV: VOCAL AND CHORAL

Fors seulement—chanson (from Chanson album of Marguerite)
C. Janequin Ens, D. Visse (r1994) *Concert*
(5/95) (HARM) ① **HMC90 1453**

PISENDEL, Johann Georg (1687–1755) Bohemia

SECTION I: ORCHESTRAL

Concerto for Violin and Orchestra in D
Freiburg Baroque Orch, G. von der Goltz (r1994)
Concert (10/95) (DHM) ① **05472 77339-2**
Sonata in C minor—2 oboes, strings & continuo
Freiburg Baroque Orch, G. von der Goltz (r1994)
Concert (10/95) (DHM) ① **05472 77339-2**

PISTON, Walter (Hamor) (1894–1976) USA

SECTION I: ORCHESTRAL

Capriccio—harp and string orchestra (1963)
T.E. Wunrow, Seattle SO, G. Schwarz *Concert*
(7/92) (DELO) ① **DE3106**
Ceremonial Fanfare—brass ensemble (1970)
LPO, J. Mester *Concert* (7/91) (KOCH) ① **37012-2**
Concerto for String Quartet, Wind Instruments and Percussion (1976)
Juilliard Qt, Seattle SO, G. Schwarz (r1992) *Concert*
(2/94) (DELO) ① **DE3126**
Concerto for 2 Pianos and Orchestra (1958)
J. Pierce, D. Jonas, RPO, D. Amos (r1989) *Concert*
(10/90) (KOCH) ① **37002-2**
Fanfare for the Fighting French—brass ensemble (1943)
LPO, J. Mester *Concert* (7/91) (KOCH) ① **37012-2**
Fantasy for English Horn, Harp and Strings (1953)
G. Danielson, T. E. Wunrow, Seattle SO, G. Schwarz
(1991) *Concert* (2/94) (DELO) ① **DE3126**
3 New England Sketches—orchestra (1959)
St. Louis SO, L. Slatkin *Concert*
(1/92) (RCA) ① **RD60798**
Seattle SO, G. Schwarz *Concert*
(7/92) (DELO) ① **DE3106**
Serenata—orchestra (1956)
NY Chbr SO, G. Schwarz *Concert*
(7/92) (DELO) ① **DE3106**
Sinfonietta—orchestra (1941)
NY Chbr SO, G. Schwarz *Concert*
(9/90) (DELO) ① **DE3074**
Suite for orchestra (1929)
Seattle SO, G. Schwarz (r1992) *Concert*
(2/94) (DELO) ① **DE3126**
Symphony No. 2 (1943)
Seattle SO, G. Schwarz *Concert*
(9/90) (DELO) ① **DE3074**
Symphony No. 4 (1950)
Seattle SO, G. Schwarz *Concert*
(7/92) (DELO) ① **DE3106**
Symphony No. 6 (1955)
Seattle SO, G. Schwarz *Concert*
(9/90) (DELO) ① **DE3074**
St. Louis SO, L. Slatkin *Concert*
(1/92) (RCA) ① **RD60798**

SECTION II: CHAMBER

Quintet for Piano and Strings (1949)
L. Hokanson, Portland Qt *Concert*
(9/90) (NORT) ① **NR232-CD**
Sonatina for Violin and Piano (1945)
R. Davidovici, S. de Groote *Concert*
(11/87) (NEW) ① **NW334-2**
String Quartet No. 1 (1933)
Portland Qt *Concert* (9/90) (NORT) ① **NR9001-CD**
Chester Qt *Concert* (11/92) (KOCH) ① **37069-2**
String Quartet No. 2 (1935)
Portland Qt *Concert* (9/90) (NORT) ① **NR9001-CD**
String Quartet No. 3 (1947)
Portland Qt *Concert* (9/90) (NORT) ① **NR9001-CD**

SECTION III: INSTRUMENTAL

Improvisation—piano (1945)
L. Hokanson *Concert* (9/90) (NORT) ① **NR232-CD**
Passacaglia—piano (1943)
L. Hokanson *Concert* (9/90) (NORT) ① **NR232-CD**
Sonata for Piano (1926)
L. Hokanson *Concert* (9/90) (NORT) ① **NR232-CD**

SECTION IV: VOCAL AND CHORAL

Psalm and Prayer of David—chorus (Wds. Psalms 86 & 96)
Seattle Sym Chorale, Seattle SO, G. Schwarz
(r1991) *Concert* (2/94) (DELO) ① **DE3126**

PISTON (continued)

SECTION V: STAGE WORKS

The **Incredible Flutist—ballet (1938—Boston)**
Cpte Louisville Orch, J. Mester *Gottschalk: Cakewalk.*
(3/90) (ALBA) ① **TROY016-2**

The **Incredible Flutist—concert suite from ballet (1938)**
Moscow PO, D. Kitaienko *Concert*
(2/88) (SHEF) ① **CD26**
St. Louis SO, L. Slatkin *Concert*
(1/92) (RCA) ① **RD60798**
S. Goff, Seattle Sym Chorale, Seattle SO (r1992) *Concert*
(2/94) (DELO) ① **DE3126**

PIZZETTI, Ildebrando (1880–1968) Italy

SECTION I: ORCHESTRAL

La Pisanelle—suite (1917)
2. Le quai du porte de Famagouste.
2. La Scala Orch, A. Toscanini (r1920) *Concert*
(11/92) (RCA) ① **GD60315**

SECTION II: CHAMBER

3 canti ad una giovane fidanzata—violin and piano (1924)
1. Affetuoso; 2. Quasi grave e commosso; 3. Appassionato.
1. N. Milstein, L. Mittman (r1938) *Concert*
(9/95) (BIDD) ① **LAB096**

SECTION IV: VOCAL AND CHORAL

3 Composizione corali—chorus a capella (1942-43)
Danish Nat Rad Chbr Ch, S. Parkman *Concert*
(5/92) (CHAN) ① **CHAN8964**
2 Composizione corali—chorus a capella (1961) (Wds. Sappho, trans M. Valgimiglia)
Danish Nat Rad Chbr Ch, S. Parkman *Concert*
(5/92) (CHAN) ① **CHAN8964**
Messa di Requiem—unaccompanied chorus (1922)
Danish Nat Rad Chbr Ch, S. Parkman *Concert*
(5/92) (CHAN) ① **CHAN8964**

PLANQUETTE, (Jean) Robert (1848–1903) France

SECTION I: ORCHESTRAL

Sambre-et-Meuse—march
Boston Pops, A. Fiedler (r1958) *Concert*
(1/94) (RCA) ① **09026 61249-2**

SECTION IV: VOCAL AND CHORAL

Le Régiment de Sambre et Meuse—song (wds. P. Cézano)
E. Caruso, orch, J. Pasternack (r1919) *Concert*
(7/91) (RCA) ① **[12] GD60495(6)**
E. Caruso, orch, J. Pasternack (r1919) *Concert*
(10/91) (PEAR) ① **[3] EVC4(2)**

SECTION V: STAGE WORKS

Rip van Winkle—operetta: 3 acts (1882—London) (Lib. H. B. Farnie)
Cpte C. Daguerressar, L. Dachary, J. Pruvost, F. Betti, L. Lovano, R. Lenoty, J. Peyron, C. Collart, J. Pierre, P. Oriadey, J. Giovannetti, French Rad Lyric Chor, French Rad Lyric Orch, M. Cariven (with dialogue: bp1961)
(3/92) (MUSD) ① **20160-2**

PLANSON, Jean (c1559–after 1612) France

SECTION IV: VOCAL AND CHORAL

Une jeune fillette—chanson (pub 1587)
Baltimore Consort (r1992; arr Baltimore Consort) *Concert*
(4/95) (DORI) ① **DOR90177**
Ma bergère, ma lumière—chanson (pub 1578)
Baltimore Consort (r1992; arr Baltimore Consort) *Concert*
(4/95) (DORI) ① **DOR90177**

PLATTI, Giovanni Benedetto (1697–1763) Italy

SECTION II: CHAMBER

6 Sonatas—flute, cello and continuo, Op. 3 (?1743)
1. D; 2. G; 3. E minor; 4. A; 5. C; 6. G.
6. Barthold Kuijken, W. Kuijken, R. Kohnen *Concert*
(5/92) (ACCE) ① **ACC9177D**

PLAYFORD, John I (1623–1686) England

SECTION II: CHAMBER

The **(English) Dancing Master, Appendix** (wks in later eds: several revs up to 1728)
1. The boon companion; 2. La bourée; 3. Bouzer Castle (1686); 4. Cheshire Rounds; 5. Childgrove (1695); 6. Excuse me (1686); 7. Go from my window; 8. Hunt the Squirrel (1709); 9. The Indian Queen (The New Bourée); 10. Jocobella; 11. La Chabott; 12. Lady Catherine Ogle (1686); 13. The merry companion; 14. Miller's Jig (1686); 15. Mr Lane's Minuet; 16. My mother's ay glow'ring o'er me; 17. Never love thee more (1686); 18. Paul's Steeple (1670 rev) 19. The Scotchman's dance (1686); 20. Trumpet Tune; 21. With Ally; 22. On the cold ground (1665); 23. The queen's delight (1665); 24. Tune upon a jig.
3, 4, 5, 6, 8, 10, 11, 12, 14, 15, 17, 18, 19, 21. Broadside Band *Concert*
(3/88) (AMON) ① **CD-SAR28**
The **English Dancing Master, Part One—country dance collection (pub 1651)** (excs from 1651 ed: alternative names in brackets)
1. Upon a Summer's Day (The Garland; Gipsie's Round); 2. Blew Cap; 3. The Night Peece (Dance of Death; Shaking of the Sheets); 4. The Boate man; 5. The Begger Boy; 6. Parsons farewell; 7. Bobbing Joe; 8. The New Exchange (Durham Stable); 9. The Whist (The Whisk); 10. Stingo (The Oyle of Barly; Cold and Raw); 11. The Wherligig; 12. Picking of Sticks; 13. The Old Mole; 14. Grimstock; 15. Wooddicock (Gigge-a-Gogge); 16. Greenwood (The Huntsman); 17. The Saraband; 18. Hit and misse; 19. Confesse (Court Lady); 20. Mage on a Cree; 21. A Health to Betty; 22. Millisons Jegge; 23. The Spanish Jeepsie (Come follow); 24. Lady Spellor; 25. Kemps Jegg (Roland); 26. The Cherping of the Larke (Muscadin; Kemp's Morris); 27. If all the World were Paper; 28. Adsons Saraband; 29. Nonesuch—version I (a la mode de la France: version I); 30. Daphne (The Shepherdess); 31. The merry merry Milke Maids; 32. Mill-field; 33. The fine Companion; 34. Skellamefago; 35. Cast a Bell; 36. The Spanyard; 37. Rose is white and Rose is red; 38. Have at thy Coat old woman; 39. Drive the cold winter away; 40. The Gun; 41. Peppers Black; 42. The Maid peept out at the window (The Frier in the Well); 43. Halfe Hannikin; 44. Lord of Carnarvans Jegg; 45. Irish Trot; 46. Faine I would (Parthenia; King's Complaint); 47. Once I loved a Maiden faire; 48. The Irish Lady (Anniseed-water Robin); 49. A la mode de France—version II (Nonsuch—version II); 50. My Lady Cullen; 51. The Bath; 53. Goddesses (Quodling's delight).
9, 16, 30, 46. Broadside Band *Concert*
(3/88) (AMON) ① **CD-SAR28**
10, 14. Musicians of Swanne Alley *Concert*
(11/89) (VIRG) ① **VC7 59534-2**
The **English Dancing Master, Part Two—country dance collection (pub 1651)**
1. Jog on; 2. Hearts Ease; 3. The Health (Merry Wassail; Merry Frolic); 4. Jack Pudding; 5. Prince Ruperts March; 6. Argeers; 7. Dissembling Love; 8. The London Gentlewoman (The Hemp-Dresser; The sun has loos'd; Winchester); 9. Lavena; 10. Mayden Lane; 11. Jack a Lent; 12. Chirping of the Nightingale; 13. Souldiers life; 14. Saint Martins (Lady Martin's Almaine); 15. Cuckolds all a row; 16. Petticoat wag; 17. Pauls Steeple (I am the Duke of Norfolk); 18. Rufty tufty; 19. All in a Garden green; 20. Sedany (Dargason; Shropshire Wakes); 21. The Punks Delight (The New Way); 22. Aye me (The Simphony); 23. Broome, the bonny bonny Broome (O, the Broom); 24. The Milke-Mayds Bobb; 25. An Old man is a Bed full of bones (Cock Lorrel); 26. Newcastle; 27. Cherily and merrily (Mr Webb's Fancy); 28. The Countrey Coll; 29. Saturday night and Sunday morn; 30. Dull Sir John; 31. Hockley in the hole; 32. New Boe peep (Pickadilla); 33. The Fryar and the Nun (Wilshire Wedding; London 'prentice; All on a misty; 34. Chestnut (The Doves Figary); 35. Pauls Wharfe; 36. Stanes Morris; 37. Tom Tinker; 38. Kettle Drum; 39. Mundesse; 40. Hide Parke; 41. Lady lye neare mee (Green Garter); 42. Lulle me beyond thee (Northern Turtle); 43. The Glory of the West; 44. Jenny Pluck Pears; 45. Gathering Peascods (Alleyn's Jig; Johnson's Almaine); 46. Up Tailes all; 47. New New Nothing; 48. Scotch Cap; 49. Step Stately; 50. Shepheards Holyday (Labour in Vaine); 51. Row all ye Marriners; 52. Graises Inne Maske (Mad Tom; Poor Tom); 53. The Slip.
2, 5, 14. Broadside Band *Concert*
(3/88) (AMON) ① **CD-SAR28**
Musick's Delight on the Cithren, Restored and Refined—collection for the cithren (pub 1666)
1. The Lady Nevils Delight.
1. Broadside Band *Concert*
(3/88) (AMON) ① **CD-SAR28**
Musick's Hande-Maide—lessons for virginals (pub 1663 and 1678) (2 vols)
1. An Italian Rant; 2. A New Riguadon; 3. The Grange; 4. The Lord Monck's March; 5. Gerard's Mistress.
1, 2. Broadside Band *Concert*
(3/88) (AMON) ① **CD-SAR28**
3, 4, 5. T. Pinnock (r1978) *Concert*
(4/89) (CRD) ① **CRD3347**
Musick's Recreation on the Lyra viol—collection (pub 1652)
1. The Granadees March; 2. Saraband by Mr Simon Ives.
1, 2. Broadside Band *Concert*
(3/88) (AMON) ① **CD-SAR28**

PLEYEL, Ignace Joseph (1757–1831) Austria/France

Ben—Nos. from Thematic Catalogue by R. Benton

SECTION I: ORCHESTRAL

Clarinet Concerto in C, Ben 106 (1797)
T. Friedli, South-West German CO, P. Angerer *Concert*
(9/86) (CLAV) ① **CD50-0813**

SECTION II: CHAMBER

Sextet in E flat—2 clarinets, 2 horns & 2 bassoons
Mozzafiato, C. Neidich (cl/dir) (r1994) *Concert*
(9/95) (SONY) ① **SK64306**

PLOTNIKOV ?Russia

SECTION IV: VOCAL AND CHORAL

With the sweet scent of lilacs—song
D. Yuzhin, anon (r1902) *Concert*
(6/93) (PEAR) ① **[3] GEMMCDS9001/3(1)**

PLUMMER, John (c1418–c1484) England

SECTION IV: VOCAL AND CHORAL

Anna mater matris Christi—motet: 4vv (from 'Eton Choirbook')
Hilliard Ens *Concert*
(5/87) (HARM) ① **HMA190 1106**

PLUMSTEAD, Mary (1905–1980) England

SECTION IV: VOCAL AND CHORAL

Close thine eyes—song
L. Finnie, A. Legge *Concert*
(4/90) (CHAN) ① **CHAN8749**

POGLIETTI, Alessandro (1641–1683) Austria

SECTION IV: VOCAL AND CHORAL

Ave regina coelorum—motet
Niederaltaicher Scholaren, K. Ruhland (r1992) *Concert*
(10/93) (SONY) ① **SK53117**

POHLE, David (1624–1695) Germany

SECTION II: CHAMBER

Sonata à 6 (attrib in Kassel MS)
Musica Fiata, R. Wilson (r1991) *Concert*
(8/93) (DHM) ① **05472 77183-2**
Sonata à 6—two violins, 4 trombones & continuo (Kassel MS)
Musica Fiata, R. Wilson (r1991) *Concert*
(8/93) (DHM) ① **05472 77183-2**

POISE, (Jean Alexandre) Ferdinand (1828–1892) France

SECTION V: STAGE WORKS

Joli Gilles—opéra-comique: 2 acts (1884—Paris) (Lib. Monselet, after S d'Allainval)
Voici le matin la grive a chanté. A. Ghasne, orch
(r1906) Concert   (9/91) (SYMP) ① SYMCD1089

POKORNÝ, František Xaver Jan (1797–1850) Bohemia

SECTION I: ORCHESTRAL

Concerto for Flute and Orchestra in D
P-L. Graf, Zurich Camerata, R. Tschupp Concert
(11/87) (JECK) ① JD506-2
Concerto for Two Horns and Orchestra in F
Z. Tylšar, B. Tylšar, Capella Istropolitana, F. Vajnar
Concert   (3/93) (NAXO) ① 8 550459

POLDINI, Ede (1869–1957) Hungary

SECTION III: INSTRUMENTAL

7 Marionnettes—piano
2. Poupée valsante.
2. K-W. Chung, P. Moll (arr vn/pf) Concert
(9/87) (DECC) ① 417 289-2DH
2. F. Kreisler, C. Lamson (r1924: arr Kreisler)
Concert   (9/93) (BIDD) ① [2] LAB068/9
2. F. Kreisler, F. Rupp (r1938: arr Kreisler) Concert
(12/93) (EMI) ① CDH7 64701-2
2. J. Thibaud, T. Janopoulo (r1933: arr vn/pf:
Kreisler) Concert   (12/94) (APR) ① [2] APR7028

PÕLDMÄE, Alo (b 1945)

SECTION II: CHAMBER

Sonatina—alto flute and guitar (1975)
Tallinn Camerata (r1993) Concert
(5/95) (FINL) ① 4509-95705-2

POLDOWSKI (1880–1932)

pseudonym of Irene Regine Wieniawska

SECTION II: CHAMBER

Tango—violin and piano
J. Heifetz, E. Bay (r1946) Concert
(11/94) (RCA) ① [65] 09026 61778-2(06)

POLEDOURIS, Basil (b 1945) USA

SECTION V: STAGE WORKS

The Hunt for Red October—film score (1990)
EXCERPTS: 1. Hymn to Red October (Main Title); 2. Nuclear Scam; 3. Putin's Demise; 4. Course Two-Five-Zero; 5. Ancestral Aid; 6. Chopper; 7. Two Wives; 8. Plane Route I; 9. Plane Crash; 10. Kaboom!!!
ADDITIONAL ITEM: 11. Hymn of the Red Army (Traditional).
11. San Diego SO, L. Schifrin Concert
(5/93) (SILV) ① SILVAD3001

POLLACK, Lew (1896–1946) USA

SECTION IV: VOCAL AND CHORAL

My Yiddishe Momma—song (1925) (comp with J. Yellen: wds. J. Yellen)
I. Perlman, Israel PO, D. Seltzer (r1986: arr Seltzer)
Concert   (5/93) (EMI) ① [4] CMS7 64617-2
I. Perlman, Israel PO, D. Seltzer (r1986: arr Seltzer)
Concert   (0/95) (EMI) ① [20] CZS4 83177-2(3)

PONCE, Juan (c1480–after 1521) Spain

SECTION IV: VOCAL AND CHORAL

Ave color vini clari—4vv (Cancionero de Palacio)
Hespèrion XX, J. Savall Concert
(7/92) (ASTR) ① E8762
Como está, sola mi vida—canción: 1vv
C. Bott, New London Consort, P. Pickett Concert
(7/92) (LINN) ① CKD007

Torre de la niña (Cancionero de Palacio)
Hespèrion XX, J. Savall Concert
(7/92) (ASTR) ① E8762

PONCE, Manuel (Maria) (1882–1948) Mexico

SECTION III: INSTRUMENTAL

Arrulladora—piano
J. F. Osorio (r1993) Concert
(5/95) (ASV) ① CDDCA874
Balada mexicana—piano (1914)
J. F. Osorio (r1993) Concert
(5/95) (ASV) ① CDDCA874
Gavota—piano (1900)
J. F. Osorio (r1993) Concert
(5/95) (ASV) ① CDDCA874
Intermezzo No. 1—piano
J. F. Osorio (r1993) Concert
(5/95) (ASV) ① CDDCA874
Mazurka—guitar
A. Segovia (r1935) Concert
(5/89) (EMI) ① [2] CHS7 61047-2
Mazurkas—guitar
1, 2, 4-7, 10. J. F. Osorio (r1993) Concert
(5/95) (ASV) ① CDDCA874
Postlude—guitar
A. Segovia (r1930) Concert
(5/89) (EMI) ① [2] CHS7 61047-2
Prelude y Fuga sobre un tema de Handel—piano
J. F. Osorio (r1993) Concert
(5/95) (ASV) ① CDDCA874
3 Rapsodias cubanas—piano (1916)
1. J. F. Osorio (r1993) Concert
(5/95) (ASV) ① CDDCA874
Romanza de amor—piano
J. F. Osorio (r1993) Concert
(5/95) (ASV) ① CDDCA874
Scherzino Mexicano—guitar
J. Williams Concert   (8/89) (SONY) ① SK44898
J. F. Osorio (r1993: trans pf) Concert
(5/95) (ASV) ① CDDCA874
Sonata No. 3—guitar (1927)
T. Korhonen Concert   (7/92) (ONDI) ① ODE770-2
Movts. 1 and 2. A. Segovia (r1930) Concert
(5/89) (EMI) ① [2] CHS7 61047-2
Sonata romántica, 'Hommage à Franz Schubert'—guitar (1929)
N. Kraft Concert   (8/93) (CHAN) ① CHAN9033
Sonatina meridional—guitar (1932)
T. Korhonen Concert   (7/92) (ONDI) ① ODE770-2
Suite in A minor—guitar (1929)
A. Segovia (r1930) Concert
(5/89) (EMI) ① [2] CHS7 61047-2
Tema mexicano variado—piano
J. F. Osorio (r1993) Concert
(5/95) (ASV) ① CDDCA874
Tema variado y final
T. Korhonen Concert   (7/92) (ONDI) ① ODE770-2
Valse—guitar
M. Kayath (arr. Segovia) Concert
(9/87) (CARL) ① PCD853
A. Segovia (arr Segovia; r1935) Concert
(5/89) (EMI) ① [2] CHS7 61047-2
Variations and Fugue on 'La Folia'—guitar (c1928-31)
J. Freire Concert   (7/92) (LEMA) ① LC42601
T. Korhonen Concert   (7/92) (ONDI) ① ODE770-2

SECTION IV: VOCAL AND CHORAL

Estrellita—song
I. Perlman, S. Sanders (trans. Heifetz) Concert
(5/89) (EMI) ① CDC7 49604-2
L. Pons, orch, A. Kostelanetz (r1947) Concert
(7/90) (SONY) ① MPK45694
P. Domingo, I. Perlman, NY Studio Orch, J. Tunick
(r1990) Concert   (3/92) (EMI) ① CDC7 54266-2
F. Araiza, Munich RSO, R. Weikert (arr Sommerlatte)
Concert   (3/93) (RCA) ① 09026 61163-2
I. Perlman, S. Sanders (arr Heifetz) Concert
(5/93) (EMI) ① [4] CMS7 64617-2
A. Galli-Curci, orch, R. Bourdon (r1924) Concert
(8/94) (ROMO) ① [2] 81004-2
J. Heifetz, I. Achron (r1928) Concert
(11/94) (RCA) ① [65] 09026 61778-2(2)
J. Heifetz, E. Bay (r1946) Concert
(11/94) (RCA) ① [65] 09026 61778-2(40)
P. Domingo, I. Perlman, NY Studio Orch, J. Tunick
(r1990)   (6/95) (EMI) ① [20] CZS4 83177-2(3)
I. Perlman, S. Sanders (r1988: arr vn/pf: Heifetz)
Concert   (6/95) (EMI) ① [20] CZS4 83177-2(3)

PONCHIELLI, Amilcare (1834–1886) Italy

SECTION I: ORCHESTRAL

Capriccio—oboe and orchestra
B. Glaetzner, Berlin SO, C.P. Flor (recons. Hohensee) Concert   (5/90) (CAPR) ① 10 281
Elegia, 'Sulla tomba di Garibaldi'—band (1882)
Minsk PO, S. Frontalini (r1990: ed & orch Frontalini)
Concert   (1/94) (BONG) ① GB2115-2
Scena campestre—symphony (1852)
Minsk PO, S. Frontalini (r1990; ed & orch Frontalini)
Concert   (1/94) (BONG) ① GB2115-2
Sinfonia (ed & orch Frontalini from unidentified work)
Minsk PO, S. Frontalini (r1990) Concert
(1/94) (BONG) ① GB2115-2

SECTION II: CHAMBER

Il Convegno—Divertimento—2 clarinets (1868)
C. Bradbury, D. Watson Concert
(6/90) (ASV) ① CDDCA701
Sinfonia—piano duet (1884)
Minsk PO, S. Frontalini (r1990; ed & orch Frontalini)
Concert   (1/94) (BONG) ① GB2115-2

SECTION III: INSTRUMENTAL

Gavotte poudrée—piano (1884)
Minsk PO, S. Frontalini (r1990; ed & orch Frontalini)
Concert   (1/94) (BONG) ① GB2115-2

SECTION IV: VOCAL AND CHORAL

Noi leggevamo insieme—song: 1v and piano (pub 1889) (Wds. Ghislanzoni)
R. Tebaldi, R. Bonynge (r1972) Concert
(9/94) (DECC) ① 436 202-2DM

SECTION V: STAGE WORKS

La Gioconda—opera: 4 acts (1876—Milan) (Lib. T Gorrio (A Boito)
ACT 1: 1. Prelude; 2. Feste! Pane!; 3. Figlia, che reggi; 4a. La vidi stamane; 4b. Assassini!; 5a. Voce di donna; 5b. A te questo rosario; 6a. Enzo Grimaldo, Principe di Santafior; 6b. Oh grido di quest'anima; 7. Oh monumento!; 8. Angele Dei. ACT 2: 9a. Ho! He!; 9b. Pescator, affonda l'esca; 10. Cielo e mar!; 11a. Deh! non turbare; 11b. Deh! non tremar; 11c. Laggiù nelle nebbie remote; 12. Stella del marinar!; 13a. E un anatema!; 13b. L'amo come il fulgor del creato!; 14a. Laura, Laura! ove sei?; 14b. Vedi là, nel canal morto. ACT 3: 15a. Sì! morir ella de'!; 15b. Là turbini e farnetichi; 15c. Bella così, madonna; 16. Benvenuti, messeri!; 17. Dance of the hours; 18a. D'un vampiro fatal; 18b. Già ti veggo. ACT 4: 19a. Suicidio!; 19b. Ecco il velen; 20a. Gioconda!...Enzo!; 20b. Oh furibonda; 20c. Oh gioia!; 21a. Ecco la barca; 21b. Quest'ultimo bacio!; 22. Ora posso morir; 23a. Così mantieni il patto?; 23b. Ebbrezza! delirio!.
Cpte M. Caballé, L. Pavarotti, S. Milnes, A. Hodgson, N. Ghiaurov, A. Baltsa, J. Del Carlo, R. Romani, N. Jenkins, S. Varcoe, London Op Chor, Finchley Children's Music Group, National PO, B. Bartoletti
(7/85) (DECC) ① [3] 414 349-2DH3
Cpte M. Callas, P.M. Ferraro, P. Cappuccilli, I. Companeez, I. Vinco, F. Cossotto, L. Monreale, R. Ercolani, C. Forti, La Scala Chor, La Scala Orch, A. Votto (r1959)   (2/88) (EMI) ① [3] CDS7 49518-2
Cpte A. Cerquetti, M. del Monaco, E. Bastianini, F. Sacchi, C. Siepi, G. Simionato, G. Giorgetti, A. Cesarini, MMF Chor, MMF Orch, G. Gavazzeni
(r1957)   (9/93) (DECC) ① [2] 433 770-2DMO2
3, 5a, 11c, 13b I. Minghini-Cattaneo, D. de Martis, L. Cecil, A. Granforte, La Scala Orch, C. Sabajno
(r1930) Concert   (6/90) (PREI) ① 89008
4b G. Lauri-Volpi, NY Met Op Chor, NY Met Op Orch, G. Setti (r1929) Concert   (9/90) (PREI) ① 89012
5a K. Branzell, orch (r1927) Concert
(8/92) (PREI) ① 89039
5a L. Homer, orch (r1912) Concert
(4/94) (RCA) ① [6] 09026 61580-2(1)
5a E. Petri, chor, orch (r1908) Concert
(4/94) (EMI) ① [3] CHS7 64860-2(2)
6a B. Gigli, orch, R. Bourdon (r1929) Concert
(5/90) (PEAR) ① GEMMCD9367
6a B. Gigli, T. Ruffo, orch, R. Bourdon (r1926)
Concert   (10/90) (RCA) ① GD87811
6a B. Gigli, T. Ruffo, orch, R. Bourdon (r1926)
Concert   (11/90) (NIMB) ① NI7810
6a T. Ruffo, B. Gigli, orch (r1926) Concert
(2/93) (PREI) ① [3] 89303(2)
6a G. De Luca, B. Gigli, orch, R. Bourdon (r1927)
Concert   (10/94) (PREI) ① 89073

587

6a G. Aragall, E. Tumagian, Bratislava RSO, A. Rahbari (r1992) *Concert*
(12/94) (NAXO) ① **8 550684**
6a, 6b B. Gigli, G. De Luca, orch, R. Bourdon (r1927) *Concert* (9/88) (PEAR) ① **GEMMCD9316**
6a, 6b G. Zenatello, P. Amato, anon (r1907) *Concert*
(12/93) (SYMP) ① **SYMCD1148**
6a, 6b P. Amato, R. Grassi, orch (r1909) *Concert*
(4/94) (EMI) ① [3] **CHS7 64860-2(2)**
6a, 6b G. Zenatello, P. Amato, anon (r1907) *Concert*
(5/94) (PEAR) ① [4] **GEMMCDS9073(1)**
7. R. Stracciari, orch (r1925) *Concert*
(2/90) (PREI) ① **89003**
7. T. Ruffo, orch, C. Sabajno (r1912) *Concert*
(11/90) (NIMB) ① **NI7810**
7. G. De Luca, anon (r1907) *Concert*
(7/92) (PEAR) ① [3] **GEMMCDS9924(2)**
8(pt) G. Arangi-Lombardi, G. Zinetti, La Scala Orch, L. Molajoli (r1929) *Concert* (10/90) (PREI) ① **89013**
9b T. Ruffo, orch, C. Sabajno (r1912) *Concert*
(11/90) (NIMB) ① **NI7810**
9b G. De Luca, NY Met Op Chor, NY Met Op Orch, G. Setti (r1928) *Concert* (10/94) (PREI) ① **89073**
10. L. Pavarotti, New Philh, L. Magiera *Concert*
(7/86) (DECC) ① [2] **417 011-2DH2**
10. M. André, Toulouse Capitole Orch, M. Plasson (arr tpt) *Concert* (1/89) (EMI) ① **CDC7 49219-2**
10. E. Caruso, S. Cottone (r1902) *Concert*
(5/89) (EMI) ① **CDH7 61046-2**
10. T. Schipa, orch, C. Sabajno (r1913) *Concert*
(4/90) (EMI) ① **CDH7 63200-2**
10. B. Gigli, T. Ruffo, orch, R. Bourdon (r1926) *Concert* (5/90) (PEAR) ① **GEMMCD9367**
10. B. Gigli, orch, C. Sabajno (r1918) *Concert*
(5/90) (NIMB) ① **NI7807**
10. F. Marconi, S. Cottone (r1903) *Concert*
(5/90) (SYMP) ① **SYMCD1073**
10. L. Pavarotti, New Philh, L. Magiera *Concert*
(7/90) (DECC) ① [2] **425 681-2DM2**
10. A. Pertile, La Scala Orch, C. Sabajno (r1928) *Concert* (9/90) (PREI) ① **89007**
10. B. Gigli, orch, R. Bourdon (r1929) *Concert*
(10/90) (RCA) ① **GD87811**
10. E. Caruso, S. Cottone (r1902) *Concert*
(12/90) (PEAR) ① [3] **EVC1(1)**
10. E. Caruso, anon (r1905) *Concert*
(12/90) (PEAR) ① [3] **EVC1(1)**
10. F. Merli, orch, L. Molajoli (r1928) *Concert*
(1/91) (PREI) ① **89026**
10. E. Caruso, orch (r1910) *Concert*
(3/91) (PEAR) ① [3] **EVC2**
10. E. Caruso, anon (r1905) *Concert*
(7/91) (RCA) ① [12] **GD60495(1)**
10. E. Caruso, S. Cottone (r1902) *Concert*
(7/91) (RCA) ① [12] **GD60495(1)**
10. E. Caruso, anon (r1905) *Concert*
(7/91) (RCA) ① [12] **GD60495(3)**
10. R. Tucker, NY Met Op Orch, E. Cooper (r1947) *Concert* (4/92) (EMI) ① [7] **CHS7 69741-2(2)**
10. F. Marconi, S. Cottone (r1903) *Concert*
(7/92) (PEAR) ① [3] **GEMMCDS9923(1)**
10. B. Gigli, orch (r1929) *Concert*
(9/92) (MMOI) ① **CDMOIR409**
10. J. Björling, orch, N. Grevillius (r1937) *Concert*
(10/92) (TEST) ① **SBT1005**
10. D. Yuzhin, anon (r1902: Russ) *Concert*
(6/93) (PEAR) ① [3] **GEMMCDS9001/3(1)**
10. J. Björling, MMF Orch, A. Erede (r1957) *Concert*
(10/93) (DECC) ① **436 463-2DM**
10. J. Björling, Stockholm Royal Op Orch, N. Grevillius (r1937) *Concert*
(10/93) (EMI) ① **CDH7 64707-2**
10. A. Bonci, anon (r1905) *Concert*
(12/93) (SYMP) ① **SYMCD1113**
10. J. Björling, orch, N. Grevillius (r1937) *Concert*
(12/93) (NIMB) ① **NI7851**
10. G. Zenatello, orch (r1908) *Concert*
(12/93) (SYMP) ① **SYMCD1148**
10. F. Marconi, S. Cottone (r1903) *Concert*
(4/94) (EMI) ① [3] **CHS7 64860-2(1)**
10. G. Zenatello, anon (r1907) *Concert*
(5/94) (PEAR) ① [4] **GEMMCDS9073(1)**
10. G. Zenatello, orch (r1908) *Concert*
(5/94) (PEAR) ① [4] **GEMMCDS9073(1)**
10. L. Pavarotti, Ater Orch, L. Magiera (pp) *Concert*
(5/94) (DECC) ① [2] **443 018-2DF2**
10. G. Zenatello, orch (r1911) *Concert*
(5/94) (PEAR) ① [4] **GEMMCDS9074(1)**
10. J. Björling, orch, N. Grevillius (r1937) *Concert*
(9/94) (CONI) ① **CDHD214**
10. D. Yuzhin, orch (r1908: Russ) *Concert*
(11/94) (NIMB) ① **NI7865**
10. J. Björling, MMF Orch, A. Erede (r1959) *Concert*
(10/95) (DECC) ① **443 930-2DM**

11c R. Tebaldi, F. Corelli, R. Cambiata, SRO, A. Guadagno (r1972) *Concert*
(10/93) (DECC) ① **436 301-2DA**
13a, 13b M. Caballé, A. Baltsa, L. Pavarotti, S. Milnes, National PO, B. Bartoletti *Concert*
(12/91) (DECC) ① **430 724-2DM**
13a, 13b M. Caballé, S. Verrett, New Philh, A. Guadagno (r1972) *Concert* (5/92) (RCA) ① **GD60818**
13b G. Cigna, C. Elmo, EIAR Orch, U. Tansini
(r1941) *Concert* (11/90) (PREI) ① **89016**
13b E. Destinn, L. Kirkby-Lunn, orch, P. Pitt (r1911) *Concert* (12/94) (SUPR) ① [12] **11 2136-2(4)**
14a, 14b, 20a G. Zenatello, E. Mazzoleni, orch (r c1910) *Concert* (12/93) (SYMP) ① **SYMCD1148**
14a, 20a G. Zenatello, E. Mazzoleni, orch (r1911) *Concert* (5/94) (PEAR) ① [4] **GEMMCDS9074(1)**
15a T. Pasero, orch, L. Molajoli (r1928) *Concert*
(6/90) (PREI) ① **89010**
15b G. Gravina, anon (r1902) *Concert*
(12/89) (SYMP) ① **SYMCD1065**
17. Gothenburg SO, N. Järvi *Concert*
(6/90) (DG) ① **429 494-2GDC**
17. NBC SO, A. Toscanini (r1952) *Concert*
(1/91) (RCA) ① **GD60308**
17. NYPO, L. Bernstein (r1967) *Concert*
(9/93) (SONY) ① **SMK47600**
18b E. Turner, E. Rubadi, F. Ciniselli, L. Paci, B. Carmassi, La Scala Chor, orch, L. Molajoli (r1926) *Concert* (9/89) (EMI) ① **CDH7 69791-2**
18b E. Mazzoleni, G. Armanini, R. Stracciari, N. de Angelis, orch (r1910) *Concert*
(12/93) (SYMP) ① **SYMCD1113**
19a E. Turner, orch, L. Molajoli (r1926) *Concert*
(9/89) (EMI) ① **CDH7 69791-2**
19a R. Ponselle, orch, R. Bourdon (r1925) *Concert*
(10/89) (NIMB) ① **NI7805**
19a R. Ponselle, orch, R. Bourdon (r1925) *Concert*
(1/90) (RCA) ① **GD87810**
19a M. Callas, La Scala Orch, A. Votto *Concert*
(2/90) (EMI) ① **CDM7 63182-2**
19a M. Callas, C. Forti, La Scala Chor, La Scala Orch, A. Votto *Concert*
(2/90) (EMI) ① [4] **CMS7 63244-2**
19a G. Cigna, orch, L. Molajoli (r1931) *Concert*
(11/90) (LYRC) ① **SRO805**
19a R. Tebaldi, New Philh, O. de Fabritiis *Concert*
(8/91) (DECC) ① [2] **430 481-2DX2**
19a R. Ponselle, orch (r1925) *Concert*
(7/92) (PEAR) ① [3] **GEMMCDS9926(1)**
19a A. Pinto, anon (r1902) *Concert*
(8/93) (SYMP) ① **SYMCD1111**
19a M. Caballé, R. Tebaldi, B. Bartoletti (r1980) *Concert* (10/93) (DECC) ① **436 461-2DM**
19a E. Destinn, orch (r1914) *Concert*
(11/93) (ROMO) ① [2] **81002-2**
19a R. Raisa, orch (r1933) *Concert*
(1/94) (CLUB) ① **CL99-052**
19a R. Raisa, orch (r1923) *Concert*
(1/94) (CLUB) ① **CL99-052**
19a M. Jeritza, orch (r1923) *Concert*
(4/94) (PREI) ① **89079**
19a G. Cigna, orch, L. Molajoli (r1932) *Concert*
(4/94) (EMI) ① [3] **CHS7 64864-2(2)**
19a G. Cobelli, orch (r1905) *Concert*
(4/94) (EMI) ① [3] **CHS7 64864-2(1)**
19a E. Destinn, orch, W.B. Rogers (r1914) *Concert*
(5/94) (SUPR) ① **11 1337-2**
19a R. Ponselle, orch, R. Bourdon (r1925: 2 vers) *Concert* (11/94) (ROMO) ① [2] **81006-2**
19a E. Destinn, orch (r1911) *Concert*
(12/94) (SUPR) ① [12] **11 2136-2(4)**
19a E. Destinn, orch, W.B Rogers (r1914) *Concert*
(12/94) (SUPR) ① [12] **11 2136-2(5)**
19a C. Muzio, orch (r1917) *Concert*
(1/95) (ROMO) ① [2] **81010-2**
19a R. Hunter, Tasmanian SO, D. Franks (1989)
(10/95) (ABCC) ① **8 7000 10**
19a, 19b G. Bumbry, Stuttgart RSO, S. Soltesz
(11/86) (ORFE) ① **C081841A**
21a E. Teodorini, anon (r1903) *Concert*
(5/91) (SYMP) ① **SYMCD1077**
21b E. Burzio, orch (r1913) *Concert*
(1/91) (CLUB) ① [2] **CL99-587/8**
23a G. Arangi-Lombardi, E. Molinari, La Scala Orch, L. Molajoli (r1929) *Concert* (10/90) (PREI) ① **89013**
23a E. Burzio, G. De Luca, orch (r c1906) *Concert*
(1/91) (CLUB) ① [2] **CL99-587/8**
23a G. De Luca, E. Burzio, anon (r1907) *Concert*
(4/94) (EMI) ① [3] **CHS7 64860-2(2)**
Lina—opera (1877—Milan) (Lib. C D'Ormeville: revision of 'La savoiarda')
La madre mia M. Carosio, orch (r1946) *Concert*
(6/94) (IRCC) ① **IRCC-CD808**

I Lituani—opera: prologue & 3 acts (1874—Milan) (Lib. S Ghislanzoni)
Sinfonia Minsk PO, S. Frontalini (r1990) *Concert*
(1/94) (BONG) ① **GB2115-2**
I promessi sposi—melodramma: 4 parts (1856—Cremona) (Lib. after Manzoni)
Al tuo trono E. Vannuccini, orch (r1910s) *Concert*
(6/94) (IRCC) ① **IRCC-CD808**
Sinfonia Minsk PO, S. Frontalini (r1990) *Concert*
(1/94) (BONG) ① **GB2115-2**

PÖNTINEN, Roland (b 1963) Sweden

SECTION I: ORCHESTRAL

Blå Vinter (Blue Winter)—trombone and strings (1987)
C. Lindberg, New Stockholm CO *Concert*
(8/88) (BIS) ① **BIS-CD348**

POPPER, David (1843–1913) Bohemia

SECTION II: CHAMBER

Characterstücke—cello and piano, Op. 3 (pub 1880)
1. Arlequin; 4. Papillon.
1. B. Harrison, Margaret Harrison (r1929) *Concert*
(3/93) (CLAR) ① **CDGSE78-50-47**
Fantasy on Little Russian Songs—cello and piano, Op. 43
M. Kliegel, R. Havenith *Concert*
(9/92) (MARC) ① **8 223403**
Gavotte No. 2 in D—cello and piano, Op. 23
B. Harrison, Margaret Harrison (r1919) *Concert*
(3/93) (SYMP) ① **SYMCD1140**
M. Kliegel, B. Glemser (r1993) *Concert*
(1/95) (NAXO) ① **8 550785**
Hungarian Rhapsody—cello and piano, Op. 68 (pub 1894)
J. Starker, G. Moore (r1958) *Concert*
(12/95) (EMI) ① [6] **CZS5 68485-2**
Menuetto—cello and piano, Op. 65/2
M. Kliegel, B. Glemser (r1993) *Concert*
(1/95) (NAXO) ① **8 550785**
Serenade—cello and piano, Op. 54/2
M. Kliegel, R. Havenith *Concert*
(9/92) (MARC) ① **8 223403**
3 Stücke—cello and piano, Op. 11 (pub 1874)
3. Mazurka in G minor.
3. P. Casals, N. Mednikoff (r1928) *Concert*
(10/91) (BIDD) ① **LAB017**
3. M. Kliegel, B. Glemser (r1993) *Concert*
(1/95) (NAXO) ① **8 550785**
Suite—cello and piano, Op. 50
4. Gnomentanz.
2. M. Kliegel, B. Glemser (r1993) *Concert*
(1/95) (NAXO) ① **8 550785**
Tarantella—cello and piano, Op. 33 (also version for vc and stgs)
M. Kliegel, B. Glemser (r1993) *Concert*
(1/95) (NAXO) ① **8 550785**
Vito (Spanish dance)—cello and piano, Op. 54/5
P. Casals, N. Mednikoff (r1928) *Concert*
(10/91) (BIDD) ① **LAB017**
B. Harrison, May Harrison (r1919) *Concert*
(3/93) (SYMP) ① **SYMCD1140**

PORENA, Boris (b 1927) Italy

SECTION I: ORCHESTRAL

Vivaldi—string orchestra (1988)
Solisti Italiani (r1994) *Concert*
(10/95) (DENO) ① **CO-78949**

PORRINO, Ennio (1910–1959) Italy

SECTION V: STAGE WORKS

Gli orazi—opera: 1 act (1941—Milan) (Lib. C Guastalla)
Io per l'antico diritto T. Pasero, SO, D. Marzollo (r1944) *Concert* (4/95) (PREI) ① **89074**

PORTER, Cole (Albert) (1891–1964) USA

SECTION IV: VOCAL AND CHORAL

Bull Dog—song (1911) (football song for Yale College)
T. Hampson, LSO, J. McGlinn *Concert*
(10/91) (EMI) ① **CDC7 54203-2**
Don't Fence Me In—song for the film 'Hollywood Canteen' (1944) (Lyrics cpsr)
T. Hampson, LSO, J. McGlinn *Concert*
(10/91) (EMI) ① **CDC7 54203-2**
A Fool there was—song (1937) (originally written for 'Rosalie')
T. Hampson, LSO, J. McGlinn *Concert*
(10/91) (EMI) ① **CDC7 54203-2**
Miss Otis Regrets—song (1934)
J. Gomez, Martin Jones (r1992) *Concert*
(9/93) (UNIC) ① **DKPCD9138**
Who said Gay Paree?—song (1953) (originally intended for 'Can-can')
T. Hampson, LSO, J. McGlinn *Concert*
(10/91) (EMI) ① **CDC7 54203-2**

SECTION V: STAGE WORKS

Anything Goes—musical show (1934—Boston) (Lyrics cpsr; Book Guy Bolton & P G Wodehouse)
EXCERPTS: 1. Overture. ACT 1: 2. I Get a Kick Out of You; 3. Bon Voyage; 4. All Through the Night; 5. There'll Always Be a Lady Fair; 6. Where are the Men?; 7. You're the Top; 8. There'll Always Be a Lady Fair (reprise); 9. Anything Goes; 10. Finale; 11. Entr'acte. ACT 2: 12. Public Enemy Number One; 13. What a Joy to Be Young; 14. Blow, Gabriel, Blow; 15. Be Like the Bluebird; 16. Buddie, Beware; 17. The Gypsy in Me; 18. Finale. ADDITIONAL NUMBERS CUT FROM FINAL SHOW: 19. There's No Cure like Travel; 20. Kate the Great; 21. Waltz Down the Aisle.
Cpte K. Criswell, C. Groenendaal, F. von Stade, J. Gilford, J. Green, R. Caine, S. Green, B. Landrine, M.B. Wailing, B. Hubbard, D-B. Bach, P. Ossafee, D. Stacks, Ambrosian Chor, LSO, J. McGlinn (orig vers)
(12/89) (EMI) ① **CDC7 49848-2**
Born to Dance—musical film (1936) (Lyrics cpsr)
EXCERPTS: 1. Title Music; 2. Rolling Home; 3. Rap-Tap on Wood; 4. Hey, Babe, Hey; 5. Love Me, Love My Pekinese; 6. Easy to Love; 7. I've Got You Under My Skin; 8. Easy to Love (reprise); 9. Dance; 10. Swingin' the Jinx Away; 11. Easy to Love (2nd reprise); 12. Finale.
6, 7. T. Hampson, LSO, J. McGlinn *Concert*
(10/91) (EMI) ① **CDC7 54203-2**
7. K. Te Kanawa, New World Phil, P. Matz (r1993) *Concert*
(7/94) (EMI) ① **CDC5 55050-2**
Broadway Melody of 1940—musical film (1940) (Lyrics cpsr)
EXCERPTS: 1. Opening Titles; 2. Please Don't Monkey with Broadway; 3. I Am the Captain (Rocked in the Cradle of the Deep); 4. Between You and Me; 5. I've Got My Eyes on You; 6. Juke Box Dance; 7. I Concentrate on You; 8. Begin the Beguine; 9. I've Got My Eyes on You (chorus); 10. End Titles.
1. T. Hampson, LSO, J. McGlinn *Concert*
(10/91) (EMI) ① **CDC7 54203-2**
7. K. Te Kanawa, New World Phil, P. Matz (r1993) *Concert*
(7/94) (EMI) ① **CDC5 55050-2**
Can-Can—musical show (1953—Philadelphia) (Lyrics cpsr)
EXCERPTS: 1. Introduction—Maidens Typical of France; 2. Never Give Anything Away; 3. Quadrille; 4. C'est Magnifique; 5. Come Along With Me; 6. Live and Let Love; 7. I Am In Love; 8. If You Loved Me Truly; 9. Montmart'; 10. Allez-vous-en, Go Away; 11. Never, Never Be An Artist; 12. It's All Right With Me; 13. Every Man Is a Stupid Man; 14. I Love Paris; 15. Can-Can. ADDITIONAL ITEM: 16. The Garden of Eden Ballet.
Cpte G. Verdon, Lilo, P. Cookson, Orig Broadway Cast, M. Rosenstock (r1953)
(11/93) (EMI) ① **ZDM7 64664-2**
12, 14. K. Criswell, Ambrosian Sngrs, London Sinfonietta, J. McGlinn (r1992) *Concert*
(4/94) (EMI) ① **CDC7 54802-2**
12, 14. K. Te Kanawa, New World Phil, P. Matz (r1993) *Concert* (7/94) (EMI) ① **CDC5 55050-2**
Du Barry was a Lady—musical show (1939—New Haven) (Lyrics cpsr)
EXCERPTS: 1. Overture; 2. Do I love you?; 3. Friendship; 4. It Ain't Etiquette; 5. Give him the Oo-la-la; 6. Katie went to Haiti; 10. Ballet.
4. T. Hampson, LSO, J. McGlinn *Concert*
(10/91) (EMI) ① **CDC7 54203-2**

5, 6. K. Criswell, London Sinfonietta, J. McGlinn (r1992) *Concert*
(4/94) (EMI) ① **CDC7 54802-2**
Gay Divorce—musical show (1932—Boston) (Lyrics cpsr)
EXCERPTS: 1. Overture; 2. Night and Day; 3. How's your Romance?; 4. After you.
2. J. Gomez, Martin Jones (r1992) *Concert*
(9/93) (UNIC) ① **DKPCD9138**
2, 3. T. Hampson, LSO, J. McGlinn *Concert*
(10/91) (EMI) ① **CDC7 54203-2**
2, 4. K. Te Kanawa, New World Phil, P. Matz (r1993) *Concert*
(7/94) (EMI) ① **CDC5 55050-2**
Greenwich Village Follies of 1924—musical revue (1924—New York)
EXCERPTS: 1. Overture; 2. I'm in love again; 3. Two little babes in the wood.
3. T. Hampson, LSO, J. McGlinn *Concert*
(10/91) (EMI) ① **CDC7 54203-2**
High Society—musical film (1956) (Lyrics cpsr)
EXCERPTS: 1. Overture; 2. Calypso; 3. Little One; 4. Who Wants to Be a Millionaire; 5. True Love; 6. You're Sensational; 7. I Love You, Samantha; 8. Now You Has Jazz; 9. Well Did You Evah?; 10. Mind If I Make Love to You.
5. K. Te Kanawa, New World Phil, P. Matz (r1993) *Concert*
(7/94) (EMI) ① **CDC5 55050-2**
Hitchy-Koo of 1919—musical revue (1919—New York) (Wds. G.V. Hobart)
EXCERPTS: 1. Overture; 2. Old fashioned garden; 3. When I had a uniform on; 4. Bring me back my Butterfly; 5. My cozy little corner in the Ritz.
3-5. T. Hampson, LSO, J. McGlinn *Concert*
(10/91) (EMI) ① **CDC7 54203-2**
Jubilee—musical show (1935—New York) (Lyrics cpsr)
EXCERPTS: 1. Overture; 2. Begin the Beguine; 3. Just one of those things.
2. T. Hampson, LSO, J. McGlinn *Concert*
(10/91) (EMI) ① **CDC7 54203-2**
3. K. Te Kanawa, New World Phil, P. Matz (r1993) *Concert*
(7/94) (EMI) ① **CDC5 55050-2**
Kiss Me, Kate—musical show (1948—Philadelphia) (Lyrics cpsr; Book B. & S. Spewack, after Shakespeare)
EXCERPTS: 1. Overture; 2. Another Op'nin', Another Show; 3. Why Can't You Behave?; 4. Wunderbar; 5. So in Love Am I; 6. We Open In Venice; 7. Tom, Dick or Harry; 8. I've Come to Wive It Wealthily in Padua; 9. I Hate Men; 10. Were Thine That Special Face; 11. Kiss Me, Kate; 12. Too Darn Hot; 13. Where is the Life That Late I Led?; 14. Always True to You (In My Fashion); 15. Bianca; 16. Brush Up Your Shakespeare; 17. I Am Ashamed That Women Are So Simple.
Cpte J. Barstow, T. Hampson, K. Criswell, G. Dvorsky, K. Burns, D. Evans, R. Nichols, D. Garrison, D. Gaines, J.M. Ainsley, Ambrosian Chor, London Sinfonietta, J. McGlinn
(12/90) (EMI) ① **[2] CDS7 54033-2**
Cpte L. Kirk, P. Morison, A. Drake, Orig Broadway Cast
(11/93) (EMI) ① **ZDM7 64760-2**
5. K. Te Kanawa, New World Phil, P. Matz (r1993) *Concert*
(7/94) (EMI) ① **CDC5 55050-2**
Leave it to Me—musical show (1938—New Haven) (Lyrics cpsr)
EXCERPTS: 1. Overture; 2. My heart belongs to daddy; 3. Get out of town.
2. J. Gomez, Martin Jones (r1992) *Concert*
(9/93) (UNIC) ① **DKPCD9138**
Nymph Errant—musical show (1933—London) (Lyrics cpsr; Book R. Bent, after Laver)
EXCERPTS: 1. The Physician; 2. Experiment.
1. J. Gomez, Martin Jones (r1992) *Concert*
(9/93) (UNIC) ① **DKPCD9138**
2. M. Patinkin, Orch, E. Stern (r1993; orch Troob, arr Ford) *Concert* (11/94) (NONE) ① **7559-79330-2**
Paris—musical show (1928) (Lyrics Brown)
EXCERPTS: 1. Let's do it; 2. Don't look at me this way.
1. J. Gomez, Martin Jones (r1992) *Concert*
(9/93) (UNIC) ① **DKPCD9138**
1, 2. K. Te Kanawa, New World Phil, P. Matz (r1993) *Concert* (7/94) (EMI) ① **CDC5 55050-2**
Red, Hot and Blue—musical show (1936—New York) (Lyrics cpsr)
EXCERPTS: 1. Overture; 2. Down in the Depths; 3. It's De-lovely; 4. Ridin' High; 5. Red, Hot and Blue.
4. K. Te Kanawa, New World Phil, P. Matz (r1993) *Concert* (7/94) (EMI) ① **CDC5 55050-2**
Rosalie—songs for the film (1937)
EXCERPTS: 1. In the still of the night; 2. Rosalie.
1. T. Hampson, LSO, J. McGlinn *Concert*
(10/91) (EMI) ① **CDC7 54203-2**

1. K. Te Kanawa, New World Phil, P. Matz (r1993) *Concert*
(7/94) (EMI) ① **CDC5 55050-2**
Seven Lively Arts—musical revue (1944—New York) (Lyrics cpsr)
EXCERPTS: 1. Overture; 2. Ev'ry time we say goodbye; 3. Drink.
2. K. Criswell, London Sinfonietta, J. McGlinn (r1992) *Concert*
(4/94) (EMI) ① **CDC7 54802-2**
2. K. Te Kanawa, New World Phil, P. Matz (r1993) *Concert*
(7/94) (EMI) ① **CDC5 55050-2**
3. T. Hampson, LSO, J. McGlinn *Concert*
(10/91) (EMI) ① **CDC7 54203-2**
Something For the Boys—musical show (1942—Boston) (Lyrics cpsr)
EXCERPTS: 1. Overture; 2. When My Baby Goes to Town; 3. He's the Right Guy; 4. The Leader of the Big-Time Band; 5. Hey Good Lookin'; 6. Something For the Boys.
2. T. Hampson, LSO, J. McGlinn *Concert*
(10/91) (EMI) ① **CDC7 54203-2**
3, 4. K. Criswell, London Sinfonietta, J. McGlinn (r1992) *Concert* (4/94) (EMI) ① **CDC7 54802-2**
Something to Shout About—songs for the film (1943)
EXCERPTS: 1. You'd be so nice to come home to.
1. K. Te Kanawa, New World Phil, P. Matz (r1993) *Concert* (7/94) (EMI) ① **CDC5 55050-2**

PORTER, (William) Quincy (1907–1966) USA

SECTION I: ORCHESTRAL

Ukrainian Suite—orchestra (1925)
San Diego CO, D. Barra (r1992) *Concert*
(12/94) (KOCH) ① **37196-2**

SECTION II: CHAMBER

Blues lointains—flute and piano (1928)
A. Still, S. De Witt Smith (r1992) *Concert*
(12/94) (KOCH) ① **37144-2**
String Quartet No. 3 (1930)
Chester Qt *Concert* (11/92) (KOCH) ① **37069-2**

POSADAS, Guillermo

SECTION IV: VOCAL AND CHORAL

Noche feliz—song
E. Caruso, orch, J. Pasternack (ed Cornejo: r1920) *Concert* (7/91) (RCA) ① **[12] GD60495(6)**
E. Caruso, orch, J. Pasternack (r1920) *Concert*
(10/91) (PEAR) ① **[3] EVC4(2)**

POSCH, Isaac (d 1622 or 1623) Germany

SECTION II: CHAMBER

Musicalische Tafelfreudt—dance collection (pub 1621)
5a. Paduana VI; 5b. Gagliarda V.
5. Ricercar Consort, P. Pierlot (va da gamba/dir) (r1992) *Concert* (8/94) (RICE) ① **RIC098112**

POSFORD, George (1906–1976) England

SECTION V: STAGE WORKS

Balalaika—musical comedy (1936—London) (Book & Lyrics E. Maschwitz)
At the Balalaika P. Morrison, Chandos Concert Orch, S. Barry *Concert*
(7/88) (CHAN) ① **CHAN8561**

POSTON, Elizabeth (1905–1987) England

SECTION IV: VOCAL AND CHORAL

In Praise of Woman (pub 1928) (from Five Songs. Wds Anon)
A. Rolfe Johnson, G. Johnson (r1991/3) *Concert*
(8/94) (HYPE) ① **CDA66709**

POTT, Francis (b 1957) England

SECTION III: INSTRUMENTAL

Christus—passion symphony: organ (1986-90)
I. Simcock (7/92) (PRIO) ① **[2] PRCD390**

R. Pöntinen, L. Derwinger (r1993) *Concert*
(11/93) (BIS) ① **BIS-CD593**
P. Rogé, J-P. Collard (r1992) *Concert*
(10/95) (DECC) ① **443 968-2DH**
Sonata for Violin and Piano (1942-43 rev 1949)
Y. Menuhin, J. Février *Concert*
(12/89) (EMI) ① [2] **CZS7 62736-2**
J. Suk, J. Panenka *Concert*
(5/90) (SUPR) ① **11 0710-2**
D-S. Kang, P. Devoyon *Concert*
(11/90) (NAXO) ① **8 550276**
L. Kaufman, H. Pognari (r1954) *Concert*
(12/90) (MUSI) ① **MACD-620**
J. Prat, J-P. Armengaud (r1990) *Concert*
(9/93) (ACCO) ① [2] **20202-2**
F.P. Zimmermann, A. Lonquich (r1991) *Concert*
(1/95) (EMI) ① **CDC7 54541-2**
I. van Keulen, R. Brautigam (r1993) *Concert*
(10/95) (SCHW) ① **315272**
C. Juillet, P. Rogé (r1994) *Concert*
(10/95) (DECC) ① **443 968-2DH**
T. Little, P. Lane (r1995) *Concert*
(12/95) (EMIN) ① **CD-EMX2244**
Trio for Oboe, Bassoon and Piano (1926)
Nash Ens *Concert*
(10/86) (CRD) ① **CRD3437**
F. Poulenc, R. Lamorlette, G. Dhérin (r1928) *Concert*
(10/88) (PEAR) ① **GEMMCD9311**
M. Bourgue, A. Wallez, P. Rogé *Concert*
(8/89) (DECC) ① **421 581-2DH**
James Levine, H. Schellenberger, M. Turkovic *Concert*
(11/89) (DG) ① **427 639-2GH**
J. Février, R. Casier, G. Faisandier *Concert*
(12/89) (EMI) ① [2] **CZS7 62736-2**
J. Vandeville, A. Randon, J-P. Armengaud (r1992) *Concert*
(9/93) (ACCO) ① [2] **20202-2**
R. Lamorlette, G. Dhérin, F. Poulenc (r1928) *Concert*
(6/94) (EMI) ① **CDC5 55036-2**
N. Daniel, R. Gough, J. Drake (r1994) *Concert*
(2/95) (CALA) ① [2] **CACD1018**
Villanelle—flute and piano (1934)
T. Prévost, J-P. Armengaud (r1992) *Concert*
(9/93) (ACCO) ① [2] **20202-2**
W. Bennett, C. Benson (r1994) *Concert*
(2/95) (CALA) ① [2] **CACD1018**

SECTION III: INSTRUMENTAL

Badinage—piano (1934)
E. Parkin (r1986) *Concert*
(10/88) (CHAN) ① **CHAN8637**
P. Crossley *Concert*
(3/90) (SONY) ① [3] **CD44921**
Les Biches—piano transcriptions of ballet music
1. Adagietto; 2. Rondeau.
1. E. Parkin (r1986) *Concert*
(10/88) (CHAN) ① **CHAN8637**
1, 2. F. Poulenc (r1928) *Concert*
(10/88) (PEAR) ① **GEMMCD9311**
Bourrée au pavillon d'Auvergne—piano (1937)
P. Crossley *Concert*
(3/90) (SONY) ① [3] **CD44921**
Bourrée au pavillon d'Auvergne—piano (1937)
B. Lerner *Concert* (1/89) (ETCE) ① **KTC1061**
Caprice after finale of 'Le Bal masqué'—piano (1932)
F. Poulenc (r1932) *Concert*
(10/88) (PEAR) ① **GEMMCD9311**
3 Feuillets d'album—piano (1933)
1. Ariette; 2. Rêve; 3. Gigue.
P. Crossley *Concert*
(3/90) (SONY) ① [3] **CD44921**
Française—piano
P. Crossley *Concert*
(3/90) (SONY) ① [3] **CD44921**
Humoresque—piano (1934)
P. Crossley *Concert*
(3/90) (SONY) ① [3] **CD44921**
E. Parkin *Concert* (12/90) (CHAN) ① **CHAN8847**
P. Rogé *Concert* (4/91) (DECC) ① **425 862-2DH**
5 Impromptus—piano (1920)
P. Crossley *Concert*
(3/90) (SONY) ① [3] **CD44921**
15 Improvisations—piano (1932-59)
1. B minor; 2. A flat; 3. B minor; 4. A flat; 5. A minor; 6. B flat; 7. C; 8. A minor; 9. D; 10. F (Eloge des gammes); 11. G minor; 12. E flat (Hommage à Schubert); 13. A minor; 14. D flat; 15. C minor (Hommage à Edith Piaf).
P. Crossley *Concert*
(3/90) (SONY) ① [3] **CD44921**
E. Parkin *Concert* (12/90) (CHAN) ① **CHAN8847**
1-3, 6-8, 12-13, 15. P. Rogé *Concert*
(7/87) (DECC) ① **417 438-2DH**

2, 5, 9, 10. F. Poulenc (r1934) *Concert*
(10/88) (PEAR) ① **GEMMCD9311**
2, 5, 9, 10. F. Poulenc (r1934) *Concert*
(6/94) (EMI) ① **CDC5 55036-2**
4, 5, 9-11, 14. P. Rogé *Concert*
(4/91) (DECC) ① **425 862-2DH**
10, 12, 15. K.W. Paik *Concert*
(12/91) (VIRG) ① **VJ7 59653-2**
3 Intermezzi—piano
1. C (1934); 2. D flat (1934); 3. A flat (1944).
P. Crossley *Concert*
(3/90) (SONY) ① [3] **CD44921**
E. Parkin *Concert* (12/90) (CHAN) ① **CHAN8847**
P. Rogé *Concert* (4/91) (DECC) ① **425 862-2DH**
2. K.W. Paik *Concert*
(12/91) (VIRG) ① **VJ7 59653-2**
2, 3. A. Rubinstein (r1963) *Concert*
(10/93) (RCA) ① **09026 61446-2**
3. E. Parkin (r1986) *Concert*
(10/88) (CHAN) ① **CHAN8637**
Mélancolie—piano (1940)
C. Ortiz *Concert* (6/87) (CARL) ① **PCD846**
P. Crossley *Concert*
(3/90) (SONY) ① [3] **CD44921**
3 Mouvements perpétuels—piano (1918)
1. Assez modéré; 2. Très modéré; 3. Alerte.
P. Rogé *Concert* (7/87) (DECC) ① **417 438-2DH**
E. Parkin (r1986) *Concert*
(10/88) (CHAN) ① **CHAN8637**
F. Poulenc (r1927) *Concert*
(10/88) (PEAR) ① **GEMMCD9311**
P. Crossley *Concert*
(3/90) (SONY) ① [3] **CD44921**
K.W. Paik *Concert* (12/91) (VIRG) ① **VJ7 59653-2**
A. Rubinstein (r1963) *Concert*
(10/93) (RCA) ① **09026 61446-2**
F. Poulenc (r1928) *Concert*
(6/94) (EMI) ① **CDC5 55036-2**
1. J. Heifetz, E. Bay (r1937) *Concert*
(11/94) (RCA) ① [65] **09026 61778-2(03)**
1. J. Heifetz, B. Smith (r1965) *Concert*
(11/94) (RCA) ① [65] **09026 61778-2(45)**
Napoli—suite for piano (1925)
1. Barcarolle; 2. Nocturne; 3. Caprice italien.
E. Parkin (r1986) *Concert*
(10/88) (CHAN) ① **CHAN8637**
P. Crossley *Concert*
(3/90) (CHAN) ① [3] **CD44921**
8 Nocturnes—piano (1929-38)
1. C; 2. A (Bal de jeunes filles); 3. F; 4. C minor; 5. D minor; 6. G; 7. E flat; 8. without key.
P. Crossley *Concert*
(3/90) (SONY) ① [3] **CD44921**
P. Rogé *Concert* (4/91) (DECC) ① **425 862-2DH**
1, 2, 4. F. Poulenc (r1934) *Concert*
(10/88) (PEAR) ① **GEMMCD9311**
1, 2, 4. F. Poulenc (r1934) *Concert*
(6/94) (EMI) ① **CDC5 55036-2**
1, 5, 6. K.W. Paik *Concert*
(12/91) (VIRG) ① **VJ7 59653-2**
Novelette sur un thème de Falla in E minor—piano (1959)
P. Rogé *Concert* (7/87) (DECC) ① **417 438-2DH**
E. Parkin *Concert* (12/90) (CHAN) ① **CHAN8847**
2 Novelettes—piano (1927-28)
1. C; 2. B flat minor.
P. Rogé *Concert* (7/87) (DECC) ① **417 438-2DH**
F. Poulenc *Concert*
(10/88) (PEAR) ① **GEMMCD9311**
P. Crossley *Concert*
(3/90) (SONY) ① [3] **CD44921**
E. Parkin *Concert* (12/90) (CHAN) ① **CHAN8847**
F. Poulenc (r1932) *Concert*
(6/94) (EMI) ① **CDC5 55036-2**
1. Reykjavik Wind Qnt (r1993; arr wind qnt: G. Emerson) *Concert* (10/95) (CHAN) ① **CHAN9362**
Pastourelle—piano (1927) (arr of ballet music)
P. Rogé *Concert* (7/87) (DECC) ① **417 438-2DH**
P. Crossley *Concert*
(3/90) (SONY) ① [3] **CD44921**
11. V. Horowitz (r1932) *Concert*
(3/90) (EMI) ① [3] **CHS7 63538-2**
Pièce brève sur le nom d'Albert Roussel—piano (1929)
M. Fingerhut *Concert* (9/88) (CHAN) ① **CHAN8578**
P. Crossley *Concert*
(3/90) (SONY) ① [3] **CD44921**
3 Pièces—piano (1928)
1. Pastorale; 2. Toccata; 3. Hymne.
P. Rogé *Concert* (7/87) (DECC) ① **417 438-2DH**
E. Parkin (r1986) *Concert*
(10/88) (CHAN) ① **CHAN8637**
P. Crossley *Concert*
(3/90) (SONY) ① [3] **CD44921**

---

2. V. Horowitz (r1932) *Concert*
(3/90) (EMI) ① [3] **CHS7 63538-2**
Presto in B flat—piano (1934)
I. Perlman, S. Sanders (trans. Heifetz) *Concert*
(12/89) (EMI) ① **CDC7 49604-2**
P. Crossley *Concert*
(3/90) (SONY) ① [3] **CD44921**
E. Parkin *Concert* (12/90) (CHAN) ① **CHAN8847**
P. Rogé *Concert* (4/91) (DECC) ① **425 862-2DH**
K.W. Paik *Concert* (12/91) (VIRG) ① **VJ7 59653-2**
V. Horowitz (r1947) *Concert*
(6/92) (RCA) ① **GD60377**
J. Heifetz, E. Bay (r1946) *Concert*
(11/94) (RCA) ① [65] **09026 61778-2(40)**
I. Perlman, S. Sanders (r1988: arr vn/pf: Heifetz) *Concert* (6/95) (EMI) ① [20] **CZS4 83177-2(3)**
10 Promenades—piano (1921)
1. A pied; 2. En auto; 3. A cheval; 4. En bateau; 5. En avion; 6. En autbus; 7. En voiture; 8. En chemin de fer; 9. A bicyclette; 10. En diligence.
P. Crossley *Concert*
(3/90) (SONY) ① [3] **CD44921**
Les Soirées de Nazelles—piano (1930-36)
1. Préambule; 2. Variations; 3. Cadence; 4. Finale.
P. Rogé *Concert* (7/87) (DECC) ① **417 438-2DH**
E. Parkin (r1986) *Concert*
(10/88) (CHAN) ① **CHAN8637**
P. Crossley *Concert*
(3/90) (SONY) ① [3] **CD44921**
Suite française—piano (1936) (arr cpsr from orch work)
P. Crossley *Concert*
(3/90) (SONY) ① [3] **CD44921**
E. Parkin *Concert* (12/90) (CHAN) ① **CHAN8847**
Suite in C—piano (1920)
1. Presto; 2. Andantino; 3. Vif.
E. Parkin (r1986) *Concert*
(10/88) (CHAN) ① **CHAN8637**
P. Crossley *Concert*
(3/90) (SONY) ① [3] **CD44921**
P. Rogé *Concert* (4/91) (DECC) ① **425 862-2DH**
Thème varié—piano (1951)
P. Crossley *Concert*
(3/90) (SONY) ① [3] **CD44921**
E. Parkin *Concert* (12/90) (CHAN) ① **CHAN8847**
P. Rogé *Concert* (4/91) (DECC) ① **425 862-2DH**
Valse—piano (1919)
P. Rogé *Concert* (7/87) (DECC) ① **417 438-2DH**
P. Crossley *Concert*
(3/90) (SONY) ① [3] **CD44921**
Valse-improvisation sur le nom de Bach—piano (1932)
E. Parkin (r1986) *Concert*
(10/88) (CHAN) ① **CHAN8637**
P. Crossley *Concert*
(3/90) (SONY) ① [3] **CD44921**
Villageoises—piano (1923)
1. Valse tyrolienne; 2. Staccato; 3. Rustique; 4. Polka; 5. Petite ronde; 6. Coda.
P. Crossley *Concert*
(3/90) (SONY) ① [3] **CD44921**
E. Parkin *Concert* (12/90) (CHAN) ① **CHAN8847**
P. Rogé *Concert* (4/91) (DECC) ① **425 862-2DH**

SECTION IV: VOCAL AND CHORAL

À sa guitare—song (1935) (Wds. Ronsard)
F. Lott, G. Johnson (r1994) *Concert*
(8/96) (FORL) ① **UCD16730**
Airs chantés—songs (1927-28) (Wds. Moréas)
1. Air romantique; 2. Air champêtre; 3. Air grave; 4. Air vif.
S. Peignot, F. Poulenc (r1930) *Concert*
(10/88) (PEAR) ① **GEMMCD9311**
4. G. Souzay, D. Baldwin (r1963) *Concert*
(3/95) (PHIL) ① [4] **438 964-2PM4(1)**
Ave verum corpus—female voices (1952)
Cambridge Sngrs, J. Rutter *Concert*
(10/88) (CLLE) ① **COLCD108**
Trinity Coll Ch, Cambridge, R. Marlow *Concert*
(10/88) (CONI) ① **CDCF151**
The Sixteen, H. Christophers (r1991) *Concert*
(12/93) (VIRG) ① **VC7 59311-2**
Le Bal masqué—cantata (voice and chamber ensemble) (1932) (Wds. Jacob)
1. Préambule et air de bravoure; 2. Intermède; 3. Malvina; 4. Bagatelle; 5. La dame aveugle; 6. Finale.
T. Allen, Nash Ens *Concert*
(10/86) (CRD) ① **CRD3437**
D. Henry, Stamitz Ens *Concert*
(10/91) (REM) ① **REM311105**
J. van Dam, Lyon Op Orch, K. Nagano *Concert*
(2/93) (VIRG) ① **VC7 59236-2**
J-C. Benoit, M. Charpentier, Paris Cons, G. Prêtre (r1965) *Mamelles de Tirésias*.
(12/95) (EMI) ① **CDM5 65565-2**

Banalités—song cycle (1940) (Wds.
Apollinaire)
1. Chanson d'Orkenise; 2. Hôtel; 3. Fagnes de
Wallonies; 4. Voyage à Paris; 5. Sanglots.
P. Bernac, F. Poulenc *Concert*
(8/90) (ADES) ① 14114-2
D. Jones, M. Martineau (r1992) *Concert*
(6/93) (CHAN) ① CHAN9147
F. Lott, G. Johnson (r1994) *Concert*
(8/94) (FORL) ① UCD16730
G. Cachemaille, P. Rogé (r1992) *Concert*
(11/94) (DECC) ① 436 991-2DH
1, 2. R. Crespin, J. Wustman *Concert*
(11/88) (DECC) ① 417 813-2DH
4. J. Norman, D. Baldwin *Concert*
(12/86) (PHIL) ① 416 445-2PH

Le Bestiaire ou Cortège d'Orphée, 'Book of
Beasts'—song cycle (voice and chamber
ensemble/piano) (1918-19 orch before 1922)
(wds. G. Apollinaire)
1. Le dromadaire; 2. La chèvre du Thibet; 3. La
sauterelle; 4. Le dauphin; 5. L'écrevisse; 6. La carpe.
T. Allen, Nash Ens *Concert*
(10/86) (CRD) ① CRD3437
C. Croiza, F. Poulenc (r1928) *Concert*
(10/88) (PEAR) ① GEMMCD9311
P. Bernac, F. Poulenc *Concert*
(8/90) (ADES) ① 14114-2
D. Henry, Stamitz Ens *Concert*
(10/91) (REM) ① REM311105
P. Bernac, F. Poulenc (r1945) *Concert*
(4/93) (EMI) ① CDC7 54605-2
D. Jones, M. Martineau (r1992) *Concert*
(6/93) (CHAN) ① CHAN9147
F. Lott, G. Johnson (r1994) *Concert*
(8/94) (FORL) ① UCD16730
G. Cachemaille, P. Rogé (r1992) *Concert*
(11/94) (DECC) ① 436 991-2DH

Calligrammes—song cycle (1948) (Wds.
Apollinaire)
1. L'espionne; 2. Mutation; 3. Vers le sud; 4. Il pleut;
5. La grâce exilée; 6. Aussi bien que les cigales; 7.
Voyage.
P. Bernac, F. Poulenc *Concert*
(8/90) (ADES) ① 14114-2
D. Henry, A. Pondepeyre *Concert*
(10/91) (REM) ① REM311105
G. Souzay, D. Baldwin (r1966) *Concert*
(3/95) (PHIL) ① [4] 438 964-2PM4(1)

Ce doux petit visage—song (1939)
(Wds.Eluard)
L. Price, D. Garvey (r1959) *Concert*
(5/93) (RCA) ① 09026 61499-2
C. Dubosc, P. Rogé (r1992) *Concert*
(11/94) (DECC) ① 436 991-2DH

Chanson à boire—male chorus (1922)
The Sixteen, H. Christophers (r1991) *Concert*
(12/93) (VIRG) ① VC7 59311-2
New London Chbr Ch, J. Wood (r1995) *Concert*
(12/95) (HYPE) ① CDA66798

7 Chansons—chorus (1936)
1. La blanche neige (wds. Apollinaire); 2. A peine
défigurée (wds. Eluard); 3. Par une nuit nouvelle
(wds. Eluard); 4. Tous les préts (wds. Eluard); 5.
Belle et ressemblante (wds. Eluard); 6. Marie (wds.
Apollinaire); 7. Luire (wds. Apollinaire).
The Sixteen, H. Christophers (r1991) *Concert*
(12/93) (VIRG) ① VC7 59311-2
New London Chbr Ch, J. Wood (r19954) *Concert*
(12/95) (HYPE) ① CDA66798

Chansons françaises—chorus a cappella
(1945-46)
1. Margoton va t'a l'eau; 2. La belle se siet au pied de
la tour; 3. Pilons l'orge; 4. Clic, clac, dansez sabots;
5. C'est la petit' fill' du prince; 6. LA belle si nous
étions; 7. Ah! mon beau laboureau; 8. Les tisserands.
Cambridge Sngrs, J. Rutter (r1992) *Concert*
(11/93) (CLLE) ① COLCD119
The Sixteen, H. Christophers (r1991) *Concert*
(12/93) (VIRG) ① VC7 59311-2
New London Chbr Ch, J. Wood (r19954) *Concert*
(12/95) (HYPE) ① CDA66798

Chansons gaillardes—song cycle (1925-26)
(Wds. 17th cent. Anon)
1. La maîtresse volage; 2. Chanson à boire; 3.
Madrigal; 4. Invocation aux parques; 5. Couplets
bachiques; 6. L'offrande; 7. La belle jeunesse; 8.
Sérénade.
J. Van Dam, J-P. Collard *Concert*
(1/90) (EMI) ① CDC7 49288-2
P. Bernac, F. Poulenc *Concert*
(8/90) (ADES) ① 14114-2
B. Kruysen, N. Lee (r1983) *Concert*
(3/94) (ARIO) ① ARN68258
G. Cachemaille, P. Rogé (r1992) *Concert*
(11/94) (DECC) ① 436 991-2DH

4, 7. P. Bernac, F. Poulenc (r1936) *Concert*
(4/93) (EMI) ① CDC7 54605-2

Chansons villageoises (1942) (Wds. M.
Fombeure)
1. Chanson du clair tamis; 2. Les gars qui vont à la
fête; 3. C'est le joli: printemps; 4. Le mendiant; 5.
Chanson de la fille frivole; 6. Le retour du sergent.
G. Souzay, D. Baldwin (r1966) *Concert*
(3/95) (PHIL) ① [4] 438 964-2PM4(1)
2. R. Crespin, J. Wustman *Concert*
(11/88) (DECC) ① 417 813-2DH

Les Chemins de l'amour—valse chantée
(1940) (Wds. Anouilh)
J. Norman, D. Baldwin *Concert*
(12/86) (PHIL) ① 416 445-2PH
D. Jones, M. Martineau (r1992) *Concert*
(6/93) (CHAN) ① CHAN9147
C. Dubosc, P. Rogé (r1992) *Concert*
(11/94) (DECC) ① 436 991-2DH

Cocardes—songs (1919) (wds. J. Cocteau)
1. Miel de Narbonne; 2. Bonne d'enfant; 3. Enfant de
troupe.
D. Henry, Stamitz Ens *Concert*
(10/91) (REM) ① REM311105
F. Lott, G. Johnson (r1994) *Concert*
(8/94) (FORL) ① UCD16730

Colloque—song (1940) (Wds. Valéry)
C. Alliot-Lugaz, F. Le Roux, J. Cohen *Concert*
(4/91) (REM) ① REM311105
C. Dubosc, G. Cachemaille, P. Rogé (r1992) *Concert*
(11/94) (DECC) ① 436 991-2DH

La Courte paille—songs (1960) (Wds.
Carème)
1. Le sommeil; 2. Quelle aventure; 3. La reine de
coeur; 4. Ba, be, bi, bo, bu; 5. Les anges musiciens;
6. Le carafon; 7. Lune d'avril.
3, 6. R. Crespin, J. Wustman *Concert*
(11/88) (DECC) ① 417 813-2DH

La Dame de Monte Carlo—soprano and
orchestra (1961) (Wds. Cocteau)
F. Lott, G. Johnson (r1994) *Concert*
(8/94) (FORL) ① UCD16730

Dernier poème—song (1956) (Wds. R.
Desnos)
P. Thirion-Vallet, D. Baldwin *Concert*
(6/95) (ARCO) ① AAOC93232

Le Disparu—song (1947) (Wds. Desnos)
P. Bernac, F. Poulenc *Concert*
(8/90) (ADES) ① 14115-2
P. Thirion-Vallet, D. Baldwin *Concert*
(6/95) (ARCO) ① AAOC93232

Epitaphe—song (1930) (Wds. Malherbe)
P. Bernac, F. Poulenc *Concert*
(8/90) (ADES) ① 14114-2

Exultate Deo—motet pour les fêtes
solennelles: 4vv (1941)
Cambridge Sngrs, J. Rutter *Concert*
(10/88) (CLLE) ① COLCD108
Trinity Coll Ch, Cambridge, R. Marlow *Concert*
(10/88) (CONI) ① CDCF151
The Sixteen, H. Christophers (r1991) *Concert*
(12/93) (VIRG) ① VC7 59311-2
Westminster Cath Ch, J. O'Donnell (r1993) *Concert*
(6/94) (HYPE) ① CDA66664
St John's College Ch, G. Guest (r1976) *Concert*
(7/94) (DECC) ① [2] 436 486-2DF2

Fiançailles pour rire—songs (1939) (Wds. de
Vilmorin)
1. La dame d'André; 2. Dans l'herbe; 3. Il voie; 4.
Mon cadavre est doux comme un gant; 5. Violon; 6.
Fleurs.
Cpte Y. Kenny, L. Skrobacs (pp1984) *Concert*
(7/90) (ETCE) ① KTC1029
C. Dubosc, P. Rogé (r1992) *Concert*
(11/94) (DECC) ① 436 991-2DH

Figure humaine—cantata: 12vv (1943) (Wds.
Eluard)
Provence Voc Ens, H. Guy *Concert*
(12/89) (PIER) ① PV788111
The Sixteen, H. Christophers *Concert*
(12/93) (VIRG) ① VC7 59192-2
Danish Nat Rad Chbr Ch, S. Parkman *Concert*
(12/91) (CHAN) ① CHAN8963
New London Chbr Ch, J. Wood (r1995) *Concert*
(12/95) (HYPE) ① CDA66798

La Fraîcheur et le feu—songs (1950) (Wds.
Eluard)
1. Rayon des yeux; 2. Le matin les branches attisent;
3. Tout disparut; 4. Dans les ténèbres du jardin; 5.
Unis la fraîcheur et le feu; 6. Homme au sourir
tendre; 7. La grande rivière qui va.
P. Bernac, F. Poulenc *Concert*
(8/90) (ADES) ① 14115-2
G. Souzay, D. Baldwin (r1966) *Concert*
(3/95) (PHIL) ① [4] 438 964-2PM4(1)

Gloria—soprano, chorus and orchestra
(1959)
1. Gloria in excelsis Deo; 2. Laudamus te; 3. Domine
Deus, Rex coelestis; 4. Domine Fili unigenite; 5.
Domine Deus, Agnus Dei; 6. Qui sedes ad dexteram
Patris.
Cpte R. Carteri, French Rad Chor, FRNO, G. Prêtre
Concert (11/87) (EMI) ① CDC7 47723-2
Cpte D. Deam, CLS, J. Rutter *Concert*
(10/88) (CLLE) ① COLCD108
Cpte N. Burrowes, CBSO Chor, CBSO, L. Frémaux
Concert (10/89) (EMI) ① CDM7 69644-2
Cpte K. Battle, Tanglewood Fest Chor, Boston SO,
S. Ozawa (r1987) *Stabat mater.*
(9/89) (DG) ① 427 304-2GH
Cpte B. Hendricks, French Rad Chor, FNO, G. Prêtre
Stabat Mater. (12/89) (EMI) ① CDC7 49851-2
Cpte S. Greenberg, Lausanne Pro Arte Ch, Suisse
Romande Rad Ch, SRO, J. López-Cobos *Concert*
(7/90) (DECC) ① 425 627-2DM
C. Dubosc, Westminster Sngrs, CLS, R. Hickox
Concert (2/93) (VIRG) ① VC7 59286-2
J. Blegen, Westminster Ch, NYPO, L. Bernstein
(r1976) *Janáček: Glagolitic Mass.*
(5/93) (SONY) ① SMK47569
S. Greenberg, Suisse Romande Rad
Ch, Lausanne Pro Arte Ch, SRO, J.López-Cobos
(r1982) *Saint-Saëns: Mass, Op. 4.*
(8/93) (DECC) ① 425 077-2DM
J. Watson, BBC Sngrs, BBC PO, Y. P. Tortelier
(r1994) *Stabat Mater.* (8/95) (CHAN) ① CHAN9341
D. Borst, Ile de France Regional Ch, Orch de la Cité,
M. Piquemal (r1992) *Concert*
(10/95) (NAXO) ① 8 553176
3. C. Studer, Ambrosian Sngrs, LSO, I. Marin
(r1992) (DG) ① 435 387-2GH

La Grenouillère—song (1938) (Wds.
Apollinaire)
J. Norman, D. Baldwin *Concert*
(12/86) (PHIL) ① 416 445-2PH
P. Bernac, F. Poulenc *Concert*
(8/90) (ADES) ① 14114-2
G. Souzay, D. Baldwin (r1966) *Concert*
(3/95) (PHIL) ① [4] 438 964-2PM4(1)

Hyde Park—song (1945) (Wds. Apollinaire)
G. Cachemaille, P. Rogé (r1992) *Concert*
(11/94) (DECC) ① 436 991-2DH

Hymne—song (1947) (Wds. J. Racine)
P. Thirion-Vallet, D. Baldwin *Concert*
(6/95) (ARCO) ① AAOC93232

Laudes de Saint Antoine de Padoue—male
voices (1957-59)
1. O Jésu; 2. O proles; 3. Laus regi; 4. Si quaeris.
Trinity Coll Ch, Cambridge, R. Marlow *Concert*
(10/88) (CONI) ① CDCF151
The Sixteen, H. Christophers *Concert*
(3/90) (VIRG) ① VC7 59192-2
Wells Cath Vicars Choral, A. Nethsingha *Concert*
(9/92) (ABBE) ① CDCA924

Litanies à la vierge noire—female voices and
organ (1936 orch 1947)
Lyon Nat Ch, Lyon Nat Orch, S. Baudo *Concert*
(7/85) (HARM) ① HMC90 5149
Cambridge Sngrs, CLS, J. Rutter *Concert*
(10/88) (CLLE) ① COLCD108
Westminster Sngrs, CLS, R. Hickox *Concert*
(2/93) (VIRG) ① VC7 59286-2
Westminster Cath Ch, J. O'Donnell, I. Simcock
Concert (6/94) (HYPE) ① CDA66664
St John's College Ch, S. Cleobury, G. Guest (r1976)
Concert (7/94) (DECC) ① [2] 436 486-2DF2
E. Lebrun, Ile de France Regional Ch, Orch de la
Cité, M. Piquemal (r1992) *Concert*
(10/95) (NAXO) ① 8 553176

Main dominée par le coeur—song (1947)
(Wds. Eluard)
L. Price, D. Garvey (r1959) *Concert*
(5/93) (RCA) ① 09026 61499-2
C. Dubosc, P. Rogé *Concert*
(11/94) (DECC) ① 436 991-2DH

Mass in G (1937)
1. Agnus Dei.
Regent Chbr Ch, G. Cole *Concert*
(10/88) (REGE) ① REGCD101
Trinity Coll Ch, Cambridge, R. Marlow *Concert*
(10/88) (CONI) ① CDCF151
Oxford Christ Church Cath Ch, S. Darlington (r1989)
Concert (12/89) (NIMB) ① NI5197
R. Shaw Fest Sngrs, Robert Shaw *Concert*
(10/90) (TELA) ① CD80236
J. Bond, St John's College Ch, G. Guest *Concert*
(9/91) (DECC) ① 430 360-2DM
The Sixteen, H. Christophers (r1991) *Concert*
(12/93) (VIRG) ① VC7 59311-2
M. Kennedy, Westminster Cath Ch, J. O'Donnell
(r1993) *Concert* (6/94) (HYPE) ① CDA66664

Mes filles, violà s'schève L. Price, LSO, E. Downes
  Concert   (12/92) (RCA) ① [4] 09026 61236-2
**L' invitation au château—incidental music to
Anouilh's play (1947)**
J. Campbell, P. Carter, J. Elias, J. Guter, J. York
  (1994) Concert   (2/95) (CALA) ① [2] CACD1018
**Les Mamelles de Tirésias—opéra bouffe:
prologue & 2 acts (1947—Paris)** (Lib.
Apollinaire)
Cpte D. Duval, M. Legouhy, J. Giraudeau, E.
  Rousseau, R. Jeantet, J. Thirache, F. Leprin, S.
  Rallier, J. Hivert, G. Jullia, Paris Opéra-Comique
  Chor, Paris Opéra-Comique Orch, A. Cluytens
  (r1953) Bal masqué.
                         (12/95) (EMI) ① CDM5 65565-2
**Les Mariés de la tour Eiffel—play-ballet
(1921—Paris)** (see also under Les Six)
EXCERPTS—: 1. Discours du Général; 2. La
  Baigneuse de Trouville.
South-West German RSO, M. Viotti Concert
  (5/92) (CLAV) ① CD50-9111
W. Marsalis, J.L. Stillman (1992;trans D. Stewart for
  2 tpts) Concert   (5/94) (SONY) ① SK47193
**La Voix humaine—tragédie lyrique: 1 act
(1959—Paris)** (Lib. Cocteau)
Cpte F. Pollet, Lille Nat Orch, J-C. Casadesus
  (r1993)   (7/94) (HARM) ① HMC90 1474
Cpte D. Duval, Paris Opéra-Comique Orch, G. Prêtre
  (r1959) Cocteau: Bel indifférent.
                     (10/94) (EMI) ① CDM5 65156-2

POWELL, Bud (1924–1966) USA

SECTION III: INSTRUMENTAL

Dusk in Sandi—piano
A. Feinberg (r1994; trans Martin Brody) Concert
  (11/95) (ARGO) ① 444 457-2ZH

POWELL, Roy (20th cent)

SECTION II: CHAMBER

**Bow-out—saxophone quartet and keyboards
(1990s)**
Apollo Sax Qt, R. Powell (r1992) Concert
  (8/95) (ARGO) ① 443 903-2ZH

POWER, Leonel (c1370–1445) England

SECTION IV: VOCAL AND CHORAL

Sanctus—mass movement (4vv) (?c1410) (on
Sarum Sanctus III)
Gothic Voices, C. Page Concert
  (11/87) (HYPE) ① CDA66238

POWERS, Anthony (b 1953) England

SECTION II: CHAMBER

Trio—clarinet, cello and piano (1988)
Mühlfeld Ens (r1993) Concert
  (10/94) (CLRI) ① CC0007

POZZOLI, Ettore (1873–1957) Italy

SECTION III: INSTRUMENTAL

Deep River—piano
L. Laskine (r1975; trans Salzedo: hp) Concert
  (12/93) (ERAT) ① 4509-92131-2
Etude—piano
L. Laskine (r1975; arr hp) Concert
  (12/93) (ERAT) ① 4509-92131-2

PRAETORIUS, Bartholomaeus (c1590–1623) Germany

SECTION II: CHAMBER

**Neue liebliche Paduanen und Galliarden—26
paired dances (pub 1616)**
1a. Paduan I; 1b. Galliard I; 2a. Paduan II; 2b.
  Galliard II; 7a. Paduan VII; 7b. Galliard VIII; 8a.
  Paduan VIII; 8b. Galliard VIII; 21a. Paduan XXI; 21b.
  Galliard XXI.
1a, 2b, 7a, 8b, 21a, 21b Lautten Compagney
  (r1990/1) Concert   (6/93) (CAPR) ① 10 431

PRAETORIUS, Hieronymus (1560–1629) Germany

SECTION IV: VOCAL AND CHORAL

In dulci jubilo—motet
Tallis Scholars, P. Phillips Concert
  (12/86) (GIME) ① CDGIM010
Joseph, lieber Joseph mein—motet
Tallis Scholars, P. Phillips Concert
  (12/86) (GIME) ① CDGIM010

PRAETORIUS, Michael (1571–1621) Germany

SECTION I: ORCHESTRAL

**Terpsichore—musarum aoniarum quinta: a
4-6 (pub 1612)**
Excs New London Consort, P. Pickett
  (11/86) (L'OI) ① 414 633-2OH
Excs Parley of Instr, D. Hill (r1986) Concert
  (6/87) (HYPE) ① CDA66200
Suite C. Parkening, I. Brown, L. Handy, J. Constable
  (r1993) Concert   (10/94) (EMI) ① CDC5 55052-2
Three Branles; Volte Baltimore Consort (r1992; arr
  Baltimore Consort) Concert
  (4/95) (DORI) ① DOR90177

SECTION III: INSTRUMENTAL

Galliard de Monsiuer Wustron
K. Ragossnig, Ulsamer Collegium, J. Ulsamer
  Concert   (2/86) (ARCH) ① 415 294-2AH
Galliarde de la guerre
Ulsamer Collegium, J. Ulsamer Concert
  (2/86) (ARCH) ① 415 294-2AH
Reprinse
Ulsamer Collegium, J. Ulsamer Concert
  (2/86) (ARCH) ① 415 294-2AH

SECTION IV: VOCAL AND CHORAL

Den die Hirten lobeten sehre
J. Baird, M. Bleeke, P. Becker, W. Pauley, NY Cornet
  and Sacbut Ens Concert
  (12/91) (NEWP) ① NC60021
En natus est Emmanuel
Lichfield Cath Ch, J. Rees-Williams Concert
  (12/90) (ABBE) ① CDCA903
Es ist ein Ros' entsprungen—carol
Tallis Scholars, P. Phillips Concert
  (12/86) (GIME) ① CDGIM010
M. Petri, Westminster Abbey Ch, National PO, M.
  Neary Concert   (12/91) (RCA) ① RD60060
Regensburg Cath Ch Concert
  (12/91) (RCA) ① RD60736
York Minster Ch (wds translated J.M. Neale) Concert
  (12/91) (YORK) ① CD846
T. Hampson, St Paul CO, H. Wolff (arr Pasatieri)
  Concert   (12/91) (TELD) ① 9031-73135-2
F. von Stade, Chor, A. Previn (pp1991) Concert
  (12/92) (SONY) ① SK48235
Birmingham Bach Ch, Fine Arts Brass Ens, P. Spicer
  (r1992; arr Saint) Concert
  (12/93) (BIRM) ① BBCCD2
Gelobet seist du, Jesus Christ
J. Baird, M. Bleeke, P. Becker, W. Pauley, NY Cornet
  and Sacbut Ens Concert
  (12/91) (NEWP) ① NC60021
In dulci jubilo—motet: 3vv (pub 1619) (Wds.
anon)
Taverner Consort, Taverner Ch, Taverner Plyrs, A.
  Parrott Concert   (8/88) (EMI) ① CDC7 47633-2
J. Baird, M. Bleeke, P. Becker, W. Pauley, NY Cornet
  and Sacbut Ens Concert
  (12/91) (NEWP) ① NC60021
Alberquerque Música Antigua Concert
  (8/93) (DORI) ① DIS80104
Chanticleer (r1990) Concert
  (12/94) (CHTI) ① CR-8803
Lutheran Christmas Mass (cspd with S Scheit
& J H Schein)
Roskilde Cath Ch, Gabrieli Consort, Gabrieli Players,
  P. McCreesh   (12/94) (ARCH) ① 439 250-2AH
**Musae Sioniae - sechster Theil—psalms and
songs (1609)**
53. Westminster Cath Ch, Parley of Instr, D. Hill
  (r1986) Concert   (6/87) (HYPE) ① CDA66200
Nun komm, der ist so freudenreich
J. Baird, M. Bleeke, P. Becker, W. Pauley, NY Cornet
  and Sacbut Ens Concert
  (12/91) (NEWP) ① NC60021
Omnis mundus jocundetur—motet
Cambridge Clare College Ch, Cambridge Clare
  College Orch, J. Rutter Concert
  (12/89) (DECC) ① 425 500-2DM

**Polyhymnia caduceatrix et panegyrica
(1619)**
9, 10, 12, 17. Westminster Cath Ch, Parley of Instr,
  D. Hill (r1986) Concert
  (6/87) (HYPE) ① CDA66200
Psallite unigenito
Kings College Ch, D. Willcocks Concert
  (12/91) (CFP) ① CD-CFP4586
Puer natus in Bethlehem—motet (pub 1619)
Taverner Consort, Taverner Ch, Taverner Plyrs, A.
  Parrott Concert   (8/88) (EMI) ① CDC7 47633-2
J. Baird, M. Bleeke, P. Becker, W. Pauley, NY Cornet
  and Sacbut Ens Concert
  (12/91) (NEWP) ① NC60021
London Musica Antiqua, M. Uridge (r1980-83; 2 vers)
  Concert   (12/93) (SYMP) ① SYMCD1157
Puer nobis nascitur—carol
M. Petri, Westminster Abbey Ch, National PO, M.
  Neary Concert   (12/91) (RCA) ① RD60060
**Puericinium—3-14vv and contiuno (pub
1621)**
1. Pueri nostri (Singt und klinget); 2. Quem pastores
  laudavere; 3. Nun helft mir Gottes; 4. Meine Seele
  erhebt den Herren.
1-3. Westminster Cath Ch, Parley of Instr, D. Hill
  (r1986) Concert   (6/87) (HYPE) ① CDA66200
4. Schütz Academy, H. Arman (r1991) Concert
  (5/93) (CAPR) ① 10 409
**Resonet in laudibus—motet (7vv) (pub
1619)**
J. Baird, R. Barrows, NY Cornet and Sacbut Ens
  Concert   (12/91) (NEWP) ① NC60021
Der Tag, der ist so freudenreich
J. Baird, M. Bleeke, P. Becker, W. Pauley, NY Cornet
  and Sacbut Ens Concert
  (12/91) (NEWP) ① NC60021
Veni, Redemptor genitum—hymn (Wds. St
Ambrose)
Charterhouse Special Ch, R. Burton, R. Wells (arr
  Wells) Concert   (12/91) (HERA) ① HAVPCD142
Vom Himmel kommt—chorale
Alberquerque Música Antigua Concert
  (8/93) (DORI) ① DIS80104
Von Himmel hoch
J. Baird, M. Bleeke, P. Becker, W. Pauley, NY Cornet
  and Sacbut Ens Concert
  (12/91) (NEWP) ① NC60021
**Wachet auf, ruft uns die Stimme—motet (pub
1619)**
Tallis Scholars, P. Phillips (ed Bach) Concert
  (12/86) (GIME) ① CDGIM010
Taverner Consort, Taverner Ch, Taverner Plyrs, A.
  Parrott Concert   (8/88) (EMI) ① CDC7 47633-2
**Wie schön leuchtet der Morgenstern—motet
(pub 1619)** (Wds. P. Nicolai)
Taverner Consort, Taverner Plyrs, A. Parrott Concert
  (8/88) (EMI) ① CDC7 47633-2

PRATT, Charles E. (1841–1902) USA

SECTION IV: VOCAL AND CHORAL

Put my little shoes away—song (pub 1870)
(Wds. S N Mitchell)
R. Taylor, Harmoneion Sngrs, N. Bruce, L. Skrobacs
  (r1977) Concert   (2/94) (NEW) ① 80220-2

PREDIERI, Luca Antonio (1688–1767) Italy

SECTION V: STAGE WORKS

Zenobia—opera (1740—Vienna) (Lib.
Metastasio)
Pace una volta K. Battle, W. Marsalis, St Luke's
  Orch, J. Nelson Concert
  (8/92) (SONY) ① SK46672

PREISNER, Zbigniew (20th Cent) Poland

SECTION V: STAGE WORKS

The Secret Garden—film score (1993)
EXCERPTS: 1. Main Title; 2. Leaving the Docks; 3.
  Mary Downstairs; 4. First Time Outside; 5. Skipping
  Rope; 6. Entering the Garden; 7. Walking Through
  the Garden; 8. Mary and Robin Together; 9. Shows
  Dickon Garden; 10. Awakening of Spring; 11. Craven
  Leaves; 12. Taking Colin to the Garden; 13. Colin
  Opens His Eyes; 14. Colin Tries Standing; 15. Colin
  Loves Mary; 16. Craven's Return; 17. Looking at
  Photos; 18. Craven to the Garden; 19. Colin Senses
  Craven; 20. Happily Ever After.

1-20. OST, Cracow Boys' Ch, Sinfonia Varsovia, W. Michniewski (r1993) (8/94) (VARE) ① **VSD5443**

PRESTON, Simon (John) (b 1938) England

SECTION III: INSTRUMENTAL

Alleluyas—carol for organ (1960s)
C. Herrick Concert (7/86) (HYPE) ① **CDA66121**
A. Lumsden Concert (4/91) (GUIL) ① **GRCD7025**
J. Watts (r1994) Concert
 (10/95) (PRIO) ① **PRCD491**
Fantasia, '(The) Christmas Light'—organ (1985)
J. Watts (r1994) Concert
 (10/95) (PRIO) ① **PRCD491**

PRESTON, Thomas (after 1559) England

SECTION II: CHAMBER

O lux beata trinitas—consort (3 parts)
C. Wilson, Fretwork Concert
 (3/88) (AMON) ① **CD-SAR29**

PREVIN, André (George) (b 1929) Germany/USA/England

SECTION I: ORCHESTRAL

Triolet for brass (1984)
PJBE Concert (2/88) (CHAN) ① **CHAN8490**

SECTION II: CHAMBER

Bowing and scraping—jazz ensemble
I. Perlman, A. Previn, S. Manne, J. Hall, R. Mitchell (r1980) Concert (5/93) (EMI) ① [4] **CMS7 64617-2**
Chocolate apricot—jazz ensemble
I. Perlman, J. Hall, S. Manne, R. Mitchell, A. Previn
Concert (6/95) (EMI) ① [20] **CZS4 83177-2(3)**
A Different kind of blues—jazz ensemble
I. Perlman, J. Hall, S. Manne, R. Mitchell, A. Previn
Concert (6/95) (EMI) ① [20] **CZS4 83177-2(3)**
The Five of us—jazz ensemble
I. Perlman, J. Hall, S. Manne, R. Mitchell, A. Previn
Concert (6/95) (EMI) ① [20] **CZS4 83177-2(3)**
It's a breeze—jazz ensemble
I. Perlman, J. Hall, S. Manne, R. Mitchell, A. Previn
Concert (6/95) (EMI) ① [20] **CZS4 83177-2(3)**
Look at him go—jazz ensemble
I. Perlman, A. Previn, S. Manne, J. Hall, R. Mitchell (r1980) Concert (5/93) (EMI) ① [4] **CMS7 64617-2**

SECTION III: INSTRUMENTAL

The Invisible Drummer—piano (pub 1974)
J. McCabe Concert
 (6/91) (CNTI) ① [2] **CCD1028/9**

PRÉVOST, Henri (b 1934) Canada

SECTION I: ORCHESTRAL

Scherzo for Strings
Montreal I Musici, Y. Turovsky Concert
 (7/87) (CHAN) ① **CHAN8515**

PRIETO, Maria Teresa (1910–1982) Spain

SECTION III: INSTRUMENTAL

12 variaciones seriales—piano (1961)
S. Marin Concert (4/93) (RNE) ① **M3/03**
12 variaciones tonales—piano (1962)
S. Marin Concert (4/93) (RNE) ① **M3/03**

PRIMAVERA, Giovanni Leonardo (c1540/45–after 1585) Italy

SECTION IV: VOCAL AND CHORAL

Nasce la gioia mia—6vv
Tallis Scholars, P. Phillips Concert
 (1/87) (GIME) ① **CDGIM008**
Tallis Scholars, P. Phillips (r1986) Concert
 (1/94) (GIME) ① [4] **CDGIMB400**

PRIN, Jean Baptiste (c1650–after 1742) France

SECTION II: CHAMBER

L' Echo de Psyché - Suite—trumpet, timpani and organ
N. Bardach, G. Touvron, W. Karius Concert
 (10/88) (SCHW) ① **311052**

PRINCIPE, Remy (1889–?) Italy

SECTION II: CHAMBER

El campielo—violin and piano (1932)
T. Varga, G. Moore (r1947) Concert
 (11/93) (CLAV) ① **CD50-9314**
T. Varga, G. Moore (r1947) Concert
 (11/93) (CLAV) ① [4] **CD50-9300/4**

PROCH, Heinrich (1809–1878) Austria

SECTION IV: VOCAL AND CHORAL

Deh! torna mio bene—air and variations: soprano and orchestra, Op. 164
B. Hoch, Hong Kong PO, K. Schermerhorn Concert
 (11/86) (CARL) ① **PCD827**
N. Miricioiu, D. Harper (pp1985) Concert
 (5/90) (ETCE) ① **KTC1041**
L. Tetrazzini, orch (r1911) Concert
 (10/90) (NIMB) ① **NI7808**
L. Pons, orch, G. Cloëz (1929) Concert
 (4/92) (MSOU) ① **DFCDI-111**
L. Tetrazzini, orch (r1911) Concert
 (9/92) (EMI) ① [3] **CHS7 63802-2(1)**
L. Tetrazzini, orch (r1911) Concert
 (9/92) (PEAR) ① **GEMMCD9224**
L. Tetrazzini, orch (r1911) Concert
 (9/92) (PEAR) ① **GEMMCD9222**
M. Korjus, Berlin RO, J. Müller (r1934) Concert
 (10/93) (PREI) ① **89054**
A. Galli-Curci, orch, J. Pasternack (r1917) Concert
 (3/94) (ROMO) ① [2] **81003-2**
A. Galli-Curci, orch (r1917) Concert
 (8/94) (NIMB) ① **NI7852**

PROKOFIEV, Sergey (Sergeyevich) (1891–1953) Russia/USSR

SECTION I: ORCHESTRAL

Andante—orchestra, Op. 29b (1934) (trans cpsr from Piano Sonata No. 4)
SNO, N. Järvi Concert
 (3/90) (CHAN) ① **CHAN8728**
Andante—strings, Op. 50 bis (?1930) (from unpub String Quartet No. 1)
SNO, N. Järvi Concert
 (2/91) (CHAN) ① **CHAN8806**
Autumnal sketch—small orchestra, Op. 8 (1910 rev 1914, 1935)
SNO, N. Järvi Concert
 (2/91) (CHAN) ① **CHAN8806**
Scottish CO, J. Serebrier Concert
 (7/91) (ASV) ① **CDDCA760**
Concertino for Cello and Orchestra in G minor, Op. 132 (1952) (cpted Rostropovich & Kabalevsky)
L. Harrell, RPO, Vladimir Ashkenazy (r1991)
Symphony-Concerto.
 (5/94) (DECC) ① **436 233-2DH**
Concerto for Cello and Orchestra in E minor, Op. 58 (1933-38)
J. Starker, Philh, W. Susskind (r1956) Concert
 (12/95) (EMI) ① **CZS5 68485-2**
Concerto for Piano and Orchestra No. 1 in D flat, Op. 10 (1911-12)
M. Lympany, Philh, W. Susskind (r1956) Concert
 (3/88) (OLYM) ① **OCD190**
M. Béroff, Leipzig Gewandhaus, K. Masur Concert
 (7/89) (EMI) ① [2] **CMS7 62542-2**
V. Feltsman, LSO, M. Tilson Thomas Concert
 (8/89) (SONY) ① **MK44818**
Vladimir Ashkenazy, LSO, A. Previn Concert
 (3/90) (DECC) ① [2] **425 570-2DM2**
Boris Berman, Concertgebouw, N. Järvi Concert
 (10/90) (CHAN) ① **CHAN8791**
M. Kodama, Philh, K. Nagano Concert
 (4/92) (ASV) ① **CDDCA786**
A. Gavrilov, LSO, S. Rattle (r1977) Concert
 (4/92) (EMI) ① **CDM7 64329-2**
K.W Paik, Polish Nat RSO, A. Wit Concert
 (11/92) (NAXO) ① **8 550566**

V. Krainev, Frankfurt RSO, D. Kitaienko (r1991)
Concert (7/93) (TELD) ① [2] **9031-73257-2**
Y. Bronfman, Israel PO, Z. Mehta (r1992) Concert
 (12/93) (SONY) ① **SK52483**
E. Kissin, BPO, C. Abbado (r1993) Piano Concerto 3.
 (12/94) (DG) ① **439 898-2GH**
Concerto for Piano and Orchestra No. 2 in G minor, Op. 16 (1912-13 rev 1923)
M. Béroff, Leipzig Gewandhaus, K. Masur Concert
 (7/89) (EMI) ① [2] **CMS7 62542-2**
V. Feltsman, LSO, M. Tilson Thomas Concert
 (8/89) (SONY) ① **MK44818**
Vladimir Ashkenazy, LSO, A. Previn Concert
 (3/90) (DECC) ① [2] **425 570-2DM2**
H. Gutiérrez, Concertgebouw, N. Järvi Piano
Concerto 3. (5/91) (CHAN) ① **CHAN8889**
K.W. Paik, Polish Nat RSO, A. Wit Piano Concerto 5.
 (11/92) (NAXO) ① **8 550565**
V. Krainev, Frankfurt RSO, D. Kitaienko (r1992)
Concert (7/93) (TELD) ① [2] **9031-73257-2**
Y. Bronfman, Israel PO, Z. Mehta (r1993) Concert
 (5/95) (SONY) ① **SK58966**
Concerto for Piano and Orchestra No. 3 in C, Op. 26 (1917-21)
M. Argerich, BPO, C. Abbado Tchaikovsky: Piano
Concerto 1. (5/85) (DG) ① **415 062-2GH**
J.K. Parker, RPO, A. Previn (r1985) Tchaikovsky:
Piano Concerto 1. (12/86) (TELA) ① **CD80124**
J. Vakarelis, RPO, W. Rowicki Liszt: Piano Concerto 2. (1/87) (RPO) ① **CDRPO5001**
M. Lympany, Philh, W. Susskind (r1956)
Rachmaninov: Piano Concerto 3.
 (3/88) (OLYM) ① **OCD191**
T. Barto, LPO, A. Davis Concert
 (1/89) (EMI) ① **CDC7 49495-2**
M. Béroff, Leipzig Gewandhaus, K. Masur Concert
 (7/89) (EMI) ① [2] **CMS7 62542-2**
Vladimir Ashkenazy, LSO, A. Previn Concert
 (3/90) (DECC) ① [2] **425 570-2DM2**
H. Gutiérrez, Concertgebouw, N. Järvi Piano
Concerto 2. (5/91) (CHAN) ① **CHAN8889**
S. Prokofiev, LSO, P. Coppola (r1932) Concert
 (11/91) (PEAR) ① **GEMMCD9470**
M. Kodama, Philh, K. Nagano Concert
 (4/92) (ASV) ① **CDDCA786**
K.W Paik, Polish Nat RSO, A. Wit Concert
 (11/92) (NAXO) ① **8 550566**
V. Krainev, Frankfurt RSO, D. Kitaienko (r1991)
Concert (7/93) (TELD) ① [2] **9031-73257-2**
Y. Bronfman, Israel PO, Z. Mehta (r1992) Concert
 (12/93) (SONY) ① **SK52483**
M. Argerich, BPO, C. Abbado (r1967) Concert
 (1/94) (DG) ① **439 413-2GCL**
I. Margalit, New Philh, L. Maazel (r1971) Mussorgsky:
Pictures. (6/94) (BELA) ① **450 081-2**
W. Kapell, NYPSO, L. Stokowski (bp1949)
Rachmaninov: Symphony 2.
 (7/94) (MUSI) ① **MACD-769**
D. Atamian, Seattle SO, G. Schwarz (r1993)
Khachaturian: Piano Concerto.
 (12/94) (DELO) ① **DE3155**
E. Kissin, BPO, C. Abbado (pp1993) Piano Concerto 1. (12/94) (DG) ① **439 898-2GH**
W. Kapell, Dallas SO, A. Dorati (r1949) Concert
 (5/95) (RCA) ① **GD60921**
S. Prokofiev, LSO, P. Coppola (r1932) Concert
 (5/95) (EMI) ① **CDC5 55223-2**
M. Argerich, BPO, C. Abbado (r1967) Concert
 (12/95) (DG) ① **447 438-2GOR**
Concerto for Piano (left-hand) and Orchestra No. 4 in B flat, Op. 53 (1931)
M. Béroff, Leipzig Gewandhaus, K. Masur Concert
 (7/89) (EMI) ① [2] **CMS7 62542-2**
Vladimir Ashkenazy, LSO, A. Previn Concert
 (3/90) (DECC) ① [2] **425 570-2DM2**
Boris Berman, Concertgebouw, N. Järvi Concert
 (10/90) (CHAN) ① **CHAN8791**
R. Serkin, Philadelphia, E. Ormandy (r1958) Reger:
Piano Concerto. (12/91) (SONY) ① **MPK46452**
K.W Paik, Polish Nat RSO, A. Wit Concert
 (11/92) (NAXO) ① **8 550566**
L. Fleisher, Boston SO, S. Ozawa Concert
 (4/93) (SONY) ① **SK47188**
V. Krainev, Frankfurt RSO, D. Kitaienko (r1992)
Concert (7/93) (TELD) ① [2] **9031-73257-2**
Y. Bronfman, Israel PO, Z. Mehta (r1993) Concert
 (5/95) (SONY) ① **SK58966**
Concerto for Piano and Orchestra No. 5 in G minor, Op. 55 (1931-32)
S. Richter, Warsaw Nat PO, W. Rowicki (r1958)
Rachmaninov: Piano Concerto 2.
 (6/85) (DG) ① **415 119-2GH**
M. Béroff, Leipzig Gewandhaus, K. Masur Concert
 (7/89) (EMI) ① [2] **CMS7 62542-2**
Vladimir Ashkenazy, LSO, A. Previn Concert
 (3/90) (DECC) ① [2] **425 570-2DM2**

Boris Berman, Concertgebouw, N. Järvi *Concert*
 (10/90) (CHAN) ① **CHAN8791**
K.W. Paik, Polish Nat RSO, A. Wit *Piano Concerto 2.*
 (11/92) (NAXO) ① **8 550565**
S. Richter, LSO, L. Maazel *Concert*
 (3/93) (EMI) ① [4] **CMS7 64429-2**
V. Krainev, Frankfurt RSO, D. Kitaienko (r1992)
 Concert (7/93) (TELD) ① [2] **9031-73257-2**
Y. Bronfman, Israel PO, Z. Mehta (r1992) *Concert*
 (12/93) (SONY) ① **SK52483**

Concerto for Violin and Orchestra No. 1 in D,
Op. 19 (1916-17)
S. Mintz, Chicago SO, C. Abbado *Violin Concerto 2.*
 (4/84) (DG) ① **410 524-2GH**
I. Perlman, BBC SO, G. Rozhdestvensky *Violin*
 Concerto 2. (9/84) (EMI) ① **CDC7 47025-2**
P. Hofer, FNO, G. Tzipine (pp1963) *Bartók: Violin*
 Concerto 2. (12/87) (INA) ① **MHC291059**
F.P. Zimmermann, BPO, L. Maazel *Tchaikovsky:*
 Violin Concerto. (12/88) (EMI) ① **CDC7 49758-2**
L. Mordkovitch, SNO, N. Järvi *Violin Concerto 2.*
 (5/89) (CHAN) ① **CHAN8709**
H. Kun, English Stg Orch, Y. Menuhin *Concert*
 (11/89) (NIMB) ① **NI5192**
K-W. Chung, LSO, A. Previn *Concert*
 (7/90) (DECC) ① **425 003-2DM**
V. Spivakov, RPO, Y. Temirkanov (r1991)
 Tchaikovsky: Violin Concerto.
 (12/93) (RCA) ① **09026 60990-2**
S. Mintz, Chicago SO, C. Abbado (r1983) *Concert*
 (1/94) (DG) ① **439 413-2GCL**
J. Bell, Montreal SO, C. Dutoit (r1992) *Concert*
 (1/94) (DECC) ① **440 331-2DH**
J. Szigeti, LPO, T. Beecham (r1935) *Concert*
 (2/94) (EMI) ① **CDH7 64562-2**
M. Vengerov, LSO, M. Rostropovich (r1994)
 Shostakovich: Violin Concerto 1.
 (2/95) (TELD) ① **4509-92256-2**
B. Belkin, Zurich Tonhalle Orch, M. Stern (r1993)
 Violin Concerto 2. (3/95) (DENO) ① **CO-75891**
C-L. Lin, Los Angeles PO, E-P. Salonen (r1992)
 Concert (3/95) (SONY) ① **SK53969**
I. Perlman, BBC SO, G. Rozhdestvensky *Concert*
 (6/95) (EMI) ① [20] **CZS4 83177-2(2)**
J. Rachlin, Moscow RSO, V. Fedoseyev (pp1994)
 Tchaikovsky: Violin Concerto.
 (8/95) (SONY) ① **SK66567**

Concerto for Violin and Orchestra No. 2 in G
minor, Op. 63 (1935)
S. Mintz, Chicago SO, C. Abbado *Violin Concerto 1.*
 (4/84) (DG) ① **410 524-2GH**
I. Perlman, BBC SO, G. Rozhdestvensky *Violin*
 Concerto 1. (9/84) (EMI) ① **CDC7 47025-2**
L. Mordkovitch, SNO, N. Järvi *Violin Concerto 1.*
 (5/89) (CHAN) ① **CHAN8709**
K-W. Chung, LSO, A. Previn *Concert*
 (7/90) (DECC) ① **425 003-2DM**
F.P. Zimmermann, BPO, L. Maazel *Sibelius: Violin*
 Concerto. (7/92) (EMI) ① **CDC7 54454-2**
K. Takezawa, Moscow RSO, V. Fedoseyev
 Tchaikovsky: Violin Concerto.
 (12/93) (RCA) ① **09026 60759-2**
J. Bell, Montreal SO, C. Dutoit (r1992) *Concert*
 (1/94) (DECC) ① **440 331-2DH**
I. Perlman, Chicago SO, D. Barenboim (pp1993)
 Mendelssohn: Violin Concerto, Op.64.
 (1/94) (ERAT) ① **4509-91732-2**
N. Milstein, New Philh, E. Frühbeck de Burgos
 (r1965) *Concert*
 (5/94) (EMI) ① [6] **ZDMF7 64830-2**
I. Perlman, Boston SO, E. Leinsdorf (r1966) *Concert*
 (9/94) (RCA) ① **09026 61454-2**
J. Heifetz, Boston SO, S. Koussevitzky (r1937)
 Concert (11/94) (RCA) ① [65] **61778-2(04)**
J. Heifetz, Boston SO, C. Munch (r1959) *Concert*
 (11/94) (RCA) ① [65] **09026 61778-2(11-15)**
B. Belkin, Zurich Tonhalle Orch, M. Stern (r1993)
 Violin Concerto 1. (3/95) (DENO) ① **CO-75891**
C-L. Lin, Los Angeles PO, E-P. Salonen (r1992)
 Concert (3/95) (SONY) ① **SK53969**
J. Heifetz, Boston SO, S. Koussevitzky (r1937)
 Concert (11/95) (PEAR) ① **GEMMCDS9167**

Divertissement—orchestra, Op. 43 (1925-
29)
SNO, N. Järvi *Concert*
 (3/90) (CHAN) ① **CHAN8728**

Dreams—symphonic tableau, Op. 6 (1910)
SNO, N. Järvi *Concert*
 (1/87) (CHAN) ① **CHAN8472**

March in B flat—military band, Op. 99 (1943-
44)
COE, C. Abbado *Concert*
 (4/91) (DG) ① **429 396-2GH**

Overture on Jewish Themes, Op. 34b (1934)
 (arr cpsr from chbr version)
London Musici, M. Stephenson *Concert*
 (3/91) (CONI) ① **CDCF173**
COE, C. Abbado *Concert*
 (4/91) (DG) ① **429 396-2GH**

Peter and the Wolf—tale for children with
narrator and orchestra, Op. 67 (1936) (Wds.
 cpsr)
RPO, A. Previn, A. Previn *Concert*
 (10/87) (TELA) ① **CD80126**
L. Prokofiev, SNO, N. Järvi *Concert*
 (10/87) (CHAN) ① **CHAN8511**
C. Lee, English Stg Orch, Y. Menuhin *Concert*
 (11/89) (NIMB) ① **NI5192**
W. Rushton, LPO, S. Edwards *Concert*
 (2/91) (EMIN) ① **CD-EMX2165**
Sting, COE, C. Abbado *Concert*
 (4/91) (DG) ① **429 396-2GH**
O. Prokofiev, New London Orch, R. Corp *Concert*
 (12/91) (HYPE) ① **CDA66499**
R. Richardson, LSO, M. Sargent *Concert*
 (1/92) (DECC) ① **433 612-2DSP**
E. Shilling, Czech PO, K. Ančerl (r1963) *Concert*
 (3/93) (SUPR) ① **11 1945-2**
J. Gielgud, London Academy, R. Stamp (r1987/8)
 Saint-Saëns: Carnaval des animaux.
 (11/94) (VIRG) ① **CUV5 61137-2**
P. Stewart, Lyon Op Orch, K. Nagano (r1993)
 Debussy: Boîte à joujoux.
 (8/95) (ERAT) ① **4509-97418-2**
J. Gielgud, RPO, A. Licata *Concert*
 (11/95) (TRIN) ① **TRP046**

4 Portraits and Dénoument from 'The
Gambler'—orchestra, Op. 49 (1931)
 1. Alexis; 2. La Grand'mère; 3. Le Général; 4.
 Pauline; 5. Dénoument.
SNO, N. Järvi *Semyon Kotko, op 81 bis.*
 (10/87) (CHAN) ① **CHAN8803**

Pushkin Waltzes—orchestra, Op. 120 (1949)
 EXCERPTS: 1. No 1; 2. No 2.
SNO, N. Järvi *Concert*
 (1/87) (CHAN) ① **CHAN8472**
2. Seattle SO, G. Schwarz *Romeo and Juliet Suites.*
 (9/87) (DELO) ① **DE3050**

Russian Overture, Op. 72 (1936 rev 1937)
Philh, N. Järvi (r1991) *Concert*
 (3/93) (CHAN) ① **CHAN9096**

Scythian Suite, Op. 20 (1915)
SNO, N. Järvi *Alexander Nevsky.*
 (5/88) (CHAN) ① **CHAN8584**
Danish Nat RSO, D. Kitaienko *Alexander Nevsky.*
 (5/92) (CHAN) ① **CHAN9001**
Leipzig Gewandhaus, K. Masur (pp1991) *Alexander*
 Nevsky. (5/92) (TELD) ① **9031-73284-2**
CBSO, S. Rattle (r1992) *Symphony 5.*
 (6/93) (EMI) ① **CDC7 54577-2**
Ukrainian St SO, T. Kuchar (r1994) *Concert*
 (4/95) (NAXO) ① [2] **8 550968/9**
Chicago SO, C. Abbado (r1977) *Concert*
 (6/95) (DG) ① **447 419-2GOR**

Semyon Kotko—symphonic
suite—orchestra, Op. 81bis (1941)
 1. Introduction; 2. Semyon and his mother; 3. The
 Betrothal; 4. The Southern Night; 5. Execution; 6.
 The Village is burning; 7. Funeral; 8. Ours have
 come.
SNO, N. Järvi *Gambler Portraits, op 49.*
 (9/90) (CHAN) ① **CHAN8803**
4. Hollywood Bowl SO, J. Mauceri (r1991) *Concert*
 (11/94) (PHIL) ① **432 109-2PH**

Sinfonietta in A, Op. 48 (1909 rev 1929)
SNO, N. Järvi *Symphony 7.*
 (7/88) (CHAN) ① **CHAN8442**
Lausanne CO, A. Zedda (r1989) *Concert*
 (10/95) (VIRG) ① **CUV5 61206-2**

A Summer Day—children's suite for small
orchestra, Op. 65bis (1941) (from Music for
 Children, Op 65—7 mvts)
 1. Morning; 2. Tag; 3. Waltz; 4. Repentance; 5.
 March; 6. Evening; 7. The moon sails o'er the
 meadows.
Scottish CO, J. Serebrier *Concert*
 (7/91) (ASV) ① **CDDCA760**
New London Orch, R. Corp *Concert*
 (12/91) (HYPE) ① **CDA66499**

Summer night—suite from 'The Duenna',
Op. 123 (1950)
Philh, N. Järvi (r1991) *Concert*
 (3/93) (CHAN) ① **CHAN9096**
Russian Nat Orch, M. Pletnev *Cinderella.*
 (6/95) (DG) ① [2] **445 830-2GH2**

Symphonic Song—orchestra, Op. 57 (1933)
SNO, N. Järvi *Concert*
 (3/90) (CHAN) ① **CHAN8728**

Symphony No. 1 in D, 'Classical', Op. 25
(1916-17)
 1. Allegro; 2. Larghetto; 3. Gavotte; 4. Molto vivace.
Los Angeles CO, G. Schwarz *Concert*
 (10/84) (DELO) ① **DE3021**
SNO, N. Järvi *Symphony 4.*
 (3/86) (CHAN) ① **CHAN8400**
Orpheus CO *Concert* (1/89) (DG) ① **423 624-2GH**
English Stg Orch, Y. Menuhin *Concert*
 (11/89) (NIMB) ① **NI5192**
LSO, N. Marriner *Concert*
 (11/90) (PHIL) ① **426 640-2PSL**
London Musici, M. Stephenson *Concert*
 (3/91) (CONI) ① **CDCF173**
COE, C. Abbado *Concert*
 (4/91) (DG) ① **429 396-2GH**
Scottish CO, J. Serebrier *Concert*
 (7/91) (ASV) ① **CDDCA760**
Chicago SO, G. Solti *Romeo and Juliet.*
 (8/91) (DECC) ① **430 731-2DM**
Atlanta SO, Y. Levi *Symphony 5.*
 (10/91) (TELA) ① **CD80289**
LSO, M. Sargent *Concert*
 (1/92) (DECC) ① **433 612-2DSP**
BPO, S. Ozawa *Symphony 6.*
 (10/92) (DG) ① **435 026-2GH**
NBC SO, A. Toscanini (r1951) *Concert*
 (11/92) (RCA) ① **GD60323**
BPO, H. von Karajan *Symphony 5.*
 (1/93) (DG) ① **437 253-2GGA**
LPO, L. Slatkin *Symphony 5.*
 (3/93) (RCA) ① **09026 61350-2**
LSO, M. Tilson Thomas *Symphony 5.*
 (3/93) (SONY) ① **SK48239**
NYPO, L. Bernstein (1968) *Symphony 5.*
 (7/93) (SONY) ① **SMK47602**
Philh, E. Kurtz (r1957) *Concert*
 (9/93) (EMI) ① [2] **CZS7 67729-2**
St Paul CO, H. Wolff (r1992) *Concert*
 (2/94) (TELD) ① **9031-77309-2**
Los Angeles PO, A. Previn *Symphony 5.*
 (9/94) (PHIL) ① **442 399-2PM**
Chicago SO, James Levine (1992) *Symphony 5.*
 (1/95) (DG) ① **439 912-2GH**
Boston SO, S. Koussevitzky (1947) *Concert*
 (4/95) (RCA) ① **09026 61657-2**
Lausanne CO, A. Zedda (1989) *Concert*
 (10/95) (VIRG) ① **CUV5 61206-2**
Movt 3. S. Prokofiev (r1935: arr pf) *Concert*
 (5/95) (EMI) ① **CDC5 55223-2**
3. J. Szigeti, N. Magaloff (1937: arr Grunes) *Concert*
 (1/90) (BIDD) ① [2] **LAB007/8**
3. S. Prokofiev (r1935: arr pf) *Concert*
 (11/91) (PEAR) ① **GEMMCD9470**
3. Brodsky Qt (arr M. Thomas) *Concert*
 (4/92) (TELD) ① **2292-46015-2**

Symphony No. 2 in D minor, Op. 40 (1924-
25)
SNO, N. Järvi *Romeo and Juliet Suites.*
 (10/85) (CHAN) ① **CHAN8368**
BPO, S. Ozawa *Symphony 4.*
 (10/91) (DG) ① **435 027-2GH**

Symphony No. 3 in C minor, Op. 44 (1928)
 (material from 'The Fiery Angel')
SNO, N. Järvi *Symphony 4.*
 (5/86) (CHAN) ① **CHAN8401**
Moscow SO, D. Kitaienko (1985) *Symphony 4.*
 (11/94) (OLYM) ① **OCD260**
Concertgebouw, R. Chailly (r1991) *Concert*
 (11/94) (DECC) ① **436 640-2DH**
BPO, S. Ozawa (r1990/1) *Symphony 7.*
 (9/95) (DG) ① **437 838-2GH**
Ukraine Nat SO, T. Kuchar (1994) *Symphony 7.*
 (9/95) (NAXO) ① **8 553054**

Symphony No. 4 in C, Opp. 47/112 (1929-30
rev 1947) (material from 'The Prodigal Son')
SNO, N. Järvi (rev. version) *Symphony 1.*
 (3/86) (CHAN) ① **CHAN8400**
SNO, N. Järvi (orig. version) *Symphony 3.*
 (5/86) (CHAN) ① **CHAN8401**
Moscow SO, D. Kitaienko (1985; rev version)
 Symphony 3. (11/94) (OLYM) ① **OCD260**
BPO, S. Ozawa (r1992) *Symphony 3.*
 (9/95) (DG) ① **437 838-2GH**

Symphony No. 5 in B flat, Op. 100 (1944)
SNO, N. Järvi *Waltz Suite.*
 (7/86) (CHAN) ① **CHAN8450**
Leningrad PO, M. Jansons
 (5/88) (CHAN) ① **CHAN8576**
BRSO, D. Mitropoulos (pp1954) *Schoenberg: Violin*
 Concerto. (8/90) (ORFE) ① **C204891A**
Atlanta SO, Y. Levi *Symphony 1.*
 (10/91) (TELA) ① **CD80289**
BPO, S. Ozawa *Lt. Kijé Suite.*
 (5/92) (DG) ① **435 029-2GH**

BPO, H. von Karajan *Symphony 1.*
(1/93) (DG) ① **437 253-2GGA**
St Louis SO, L. Slatkin *Symphony 1.*
(3/93) (RCA) ① **09026 61350-2**
LSO, M. Tilson Thomas *Symphony 1.*
(3/93) (SONY) ① **SK48239**
CBSO, S. Rattle (r1992) *Scythian Suite.*
(6/93) (EMI) ① **CDC7 54577-2**
NYPO, L. Bernstein (r1966) *Symphony 1.*
(7/93) (SONY) ① **SMK47602**
Los Angeles PO, A. Previn *Symphony 1.*
(9/94) (PHIL) ① **442 399-2PM**
Chicago SO, James Levine (r1992) *Symphony 1.*
(1/95) (DG) ① **439 912-2GH**
Boston SO, S. Koussevitzky (r1946) *Concert*
(4/95) (RCA) ① **09026 61657-2**
Symphony No. 6 in E flat, Op. 111 (1945-47)
SNO, N. Järvi *Waltz Suite.*
(7/85) (CHAN) ① **CHAN8359**
BPO, S. Ozawa *Symphony 1.*
(10/92) (DG) ① **435 026-2GH**
Leningrad PO, E. Mravinsky (bp1958) *Stravinsky:*
Petrushka. (8/94) (MULT) ① **310189-2**
Cleveland Orch, Vladimir Ashkenazy (r1993)
Symphony 7. (4/95) (DECC) ① **443 325-2DH**
Symphony No. 7 in C sharp minor, Op. 131
(1951-52)
SNO, N. Järvi *Sinfonietta.*
(7/86) (CHAN) ① **CHAN8442**
BPO, S. Ozawa *Symphony 2.*
(10/91) (DG) ① **435 027-2GH**
Cleveland Orch, Vladimir Ashkenazy (r1993)
Symphony 6. (4/95) (DECC) ① **443 325-2DH**
Ukraine Nat SO, T. Kuchar (r1994) *Symphony 3.*
(10/95) (NAXO) ① **8 553054**
Symphony-Concerto for Cello and Orchestra
in E minor, Op. 125 (1950-51 rev 1952) (after
Cello Concerto Op. 58)
R. Wallfisch, SNO, N. Järvi *Romeo and Juliet Suites.*
(5/87) (CHAN) ① **CHAN8508**
Y-Y. Ma, Pittsburgh SO, L. Maazel *Concert*
(11/92) (SONY) ① **SK48382**
L. Harrell, RPO, Vladimir Ashkenazy (1989) *Cello*
Concertino. (5/94) (DECC) ① **436 233-2DH**
Waltz Suite, Op. 110 (1946)
1. Since we met (War and Peace); 2. In the Palace
(Cinderella); 3. Mephisto Waltz (Lermontov); 4. End
of the Fairy Tale (Cinderella); 5. New Year's Eve Ball
(War and Peace); 6. Happiness (Cinderella).
1, 3, 4. SNO, N. Järvi *Symphony 5.*
(7/86) (CHAN) ① **CHAN8450**
2, 5, 6. SNO, N. Järvi *Symphony 6.*
(7/85) (CHAN) ① **CHAN8359**
Wedding Suite, Op. 126 (1951) (from 'The
Tale of the Stone Flower')
1. Amourous dance; 2. Dance of the fiancée's girl-
friends; 3. Maidens' dance; 4. Ceremonial dance; 5.
Wedding dance.
SNO, N. Järvi *Concert*
(2/91) (CHAN) ① **CHAN8806**

SECTION II: CHAMBER

Adagio—cello and piano, Op. 97b (1944)
(transc cpsr from 'Cinderella')
D. Ferschtman, R. Brautigam *Concert*
(10/88) (ETCE) ① **KTC1059**
S. Wieder-Atherton, L. Cabasso (r1992) *Concert*
(4/94) (AUVI) ① **V4666**
Ballade in C minor—cello and piano, Op. 15
(1912)
D. Ferschtman, R. Brautigam *Concert*
(10/88) (ETCE) ① **KTC1059**
S. Wieder-Atherton, L. Cabasso (r1992) *Concert*
(4/94) (AUVI) ① **V4666**
Humoresque scherzo—four bassoons, Op.
12b (1915) (after No 9 of 10 Piano Pieces, Op
10)
M. Gatt, M. Alexander, M. Mackie, J. Orford *Concert*
(3/91) (CONI) ① **CDCF173**
5 Melodies—violin and piano, Op.35b (1925)
(arr from 5 Songs, Op.35)
D. Sitkovetsky, P. Gililov (r1990) *Concert*
(11/71) (VIRG) ① **VC5 45074-2**
L. Mordkovitch, M. Gusak-Grin *Concert*
(3/87) (CHAN) ① **CHAN8500**
M. Fujikawa, C. Sheppard *Concert*
(11/89) (ASV) ① **CDDCA667**
G. Kremer, M. Argerich *Concert*
(10/92) (DG) ① **431 803-2GH**
N. Madojan, E. Westenholz (r1994) *Concert*
(9/94) (KONT) ① **32185**
J. Bell, O. Mustonen (r1994) *Concert*
(5/95) (DECC) ① **440 926-2DH**

Overture on Hebrew Themes in C
minor—clarinet, string quartet and piano,
Op. 34 (1919)
M. Béroff, M. Portal, Parrenin Qt *Concert*
(7/89) (EMI) ① **[2] CMS7 62542-2**
Montreal I Musici, Y. Turovsky *Concert*
(7/90) (CHAN) ① **CHAN8800**
Moscow Virtuosi, V. Spivakov (vn/dir) *Concert*
(10/90) (RCA) ① **RD60370**
Borodin Trio, E. Turovsky, R. Golani, J. Campbell
Concert (10/91) (CHAN) ① **CHAN8924**
Camerata Vistula *Concert*
(11/91) (OLYM) ① **OCD343**
A. Malsbury, D. Pettit, Coull Qt *Concert*
(9/92) (HYPE) ① **CDA66573**
W. Boeykens Ens (r1992) *Concert*
(6/93) (HARM) ① **HMC90 1419**
Berlin Sols (r1991) *Concert*
(6/93) (TELD) ① **9031-73400-2**
Y. Bronfman, G. Feidman, Juilliard Qt (r1994)
Concert (5/95) (SONY) ① **SK58966**
Quintet in G minor—oboe, clarinet, violin,
viola and double-bass, Op. 39 (1924)
W. Boeykens Ens (r1992) *Concert*
(6/93) (HARM) ① **HMC90 1419**
Berlin Sols (r1991) *Concert*
(6/93) (TELD) ① **9031-73400-2**
Chbr Music NW (r1992) *Concert*
(12/93) (DELO) ① **DE3136**
Sonata for Cello and Piano in C, Op. 119
(1949)
Y. Turovsky, L. Edlina *Shostakovich: Cello Sonata,*
Op. 40. (4/85) (CHAN) ① **CHAN8340**
D. Ferschtman, R. Brautigam *Concert*
(10/88) (ETCE) ① **KTC1059**
P. Marleyn, S. Morley *Concert*
(1/94) (UNIT) ① **88006-2**
M. Grebanier, J. Guggenheim (r1993) *Concert*
(6/95) (NAXO) ① **8 553136**
Sonata for Flute and Piano in D, Op. 94
(1943)
M. Wiesler, R. Pöntinen *Concert*
(6/90) (BIS) ① **BIS-CD419**
J. Snowden, London Musici, M. Stephenson (orch
Palmer) *Concert* (3/91) (CONI) ① **CDCF173**
J. Stinton, S. Mitchell *Concert*
(12/91) (COLL) ① **Coll1103-2**
P. E. Davies, J. Alley *Concert*
(7/94) (EMI) ① **CDC5 55085-2**
Sonata for Violin and Piano No. 1 in F minor,
Op. 80 (1938-46)
D. Sitkovetsky, P. Gililov (r1990) *Concert*
(11/71) (VIRG) ① **VC5 45074-2**
M. Fujikawa, C. Sheppard *Concert*
(11/89) (ASV) ① **CDDCA667**
N. Gotkovsky, I. Gotkovsky *Concert*
(9/91) (PYRA) ① **PYR13496**
A. Hardy, L. Devos *Concert*
(6/92) (OLYM) ① **OCD355**
G. Kremer, M. Argerich *Concert*
(10/92) (DG) ① **431 803-2GH**
N. Madojan, E. Westenholz (r1994) *Concert*
(9/94) (KONT) ① **32185**
I. Perlman, Vladimir Ashkenazy (r1969) *Concert*
(9/94) (RCA) ① **09026 61454-2**
J. Bell, O. Mustonen (r1994) *Concert*
(5/95) (DECC) ① **440 926-2DH**
S. Mintz, Y. Bronfman (1987) *Concert*
(11/95) (DG) ① **445 557-2GMA**
Sonata for Violin and Piano No. 2 in D, Op.
94a (1944) (arr cpsr from Flute Sonata, Op.
94)
D. Sitkovetsky, P. Gililov (r1990) *Concert*
(11/71) (VIRG) ① **VC5 45074-2**
R. Ricci, M. Argerich *Concert*
(9/86) (ETCE) ① **KTC1038**
M. Fujikawa, C. Sheppard *Concert*
(11/89) (ASV) ① **CDDCA667**
A. Hardy, L. Devos *Concert*
(6/92) (OLYM) ① **OCD355**
P. Berman, L. Berman (pp1990) *Concert*
(8/92) (AUDI) ① **CD72040**
G. Kremer, M. Argerich *Concert*
(10/92) (DG) ① **431 803-2GH**
N. Milstein, A. Balsam (1955) *Concert*
(5/94) (EMI) ① **[6] ZDMF7 64830-2**
N. Madojan, E. Westenholz (r1994) *Concert*
(9/94) (KONT) ① **32185**
I. Perlman, Vladimir Ashkenazy (r1969) *Concert*
(9/94) (RCA) ① **09026 61454-2**
J. Bell, O. Mustonen (r1994) *Concert*
(5/95) (DECC) ① **440 926-2DH**
S. Mintz, Y. Bronfman (1987) *Concert*
(11/95) (DG) ① **445 557-2GMA**

Sonata for 2 Violins in C, Op. 56 (1932)
E. Turovsky, Y. Turovsky (arr vn/vc D.Oistrakh)
Concert (7/89) (CHAN) ① **CHAN8652**
E. Drucker, P. Setzer *Concert*
(10/91) (DG) ① **431 772-2GH**
L. Mordkovitch, E. Young, C. Benson
(12/91) (CHAN) ① **CHAN8988**
K. Osostowicz, E. Kovacic, S. Tomes *Concert*
(9/92) (HYPE) ① **CDA66473**
Sonata in D—flute and piano (1943)
S. Wieder-Atherton, L. Cabasso (r1992) *Concert*
(4/94) (AUVI) ① **V4666**
String Quartet No. 1 in B minor, Op.50
(1930)
American Qt (r1982) *String Quartet 2.*
(2/90) (OLYM) ① **OCD340**
Chilingirian Qt *String Quartet 2.*
(7/91) (CHAN) ① **CHAN8929**
Emerson Qt *Concert* (10/91) (DG) ① **431 772-2GH**
Britten Qt *String Quartet 2.*
(1/92) (COLL) ① **Coll1189-2**
Coull Qt *Concert* (9/92) (HYPE) ① **CDA66573**
Aurora Qt (r1994) *Concert*
(6/95) (NAXO) ① **8 553136**
String Quartet No. 2 in F, Op. 92 (1941)
American Qt (r1982) *String Quartet 1.*
(2/90) (OLYM) ① **OCD340**
Chilingirian Qt *String Quartet 1.*
(7/91) (CHAN) ① **CHAN8929**
Emerson Qt *Concert* (10/91) (DG) ① **431 772-2GH**
Britten Qt *String Quartet 1.*
(1/92) (COLL) ① **Coll1189-2**
Coull Qt *Concert* (9/92) (HYPE) ① **CDA66573**
Hollywood Qt (r1951) *Concert*
(3/95) (TEST) ① **SBT1052**
Aurora Qt (r1994) *Concert*
(6/95) (NAXO) ① **8 553136**

SECTION III: INSTRUMENTAL

Dumka—piano (?1910s)
Boris Berman *Concert*
(4/93) (CHAN) ① **CHAN9119**
O. Marshev (r1991) *Concert*
(1/94) (DANA) ① **DACOCD391**
4 Etudes—piano, Op. 2 (1909)
3. Concert.
3. E. Kissin (pp1990) *Concert*
(3/91) (RCA) ① **[2] RD60443**
Gavotte from 'Hamlet'—piano, Op. 77bis
(1938)
Boris Berman *Concert*
(11/92) (CHAN) ① **CHAN9017**
March and Scherzo from 'The Love for
Three Oranges'—piano, Op. 33ter (1922)
Boris Berman *Concert*
(2/91) (CHAN) ① **CHAN8851**
T. Joselson *Concert* (10/92) (OLYM) ① **OCD453**
March Barry Douglas (r1991) *Concert*
(3/92) (RCA) ① **RD60779**
Music for Children—12 pieces: piano, Op. 65
(1935)
1. Morning; 2. Promenade; 3. Little fairy tale; 4.
Tarantella; 5. Regrets; 6. Waltz; 7. March of the
grasshoppers; 8. The rain and the rainbow; 9.
'Playing tag'; 10. March; 11. Evening; 12. Moonlit
meadows.
Boris Berman *Concert*
(6/91) (CHAN) ① **CHAN8926**
March D. Ferschtman, R. Brautigam (trans. G.
Piatigorsky) *Concert* (10/88) (ETCE) ① **KTC1059**
March Brodsky Qt (arr M. Thomas) *Concert*
(4/92) (TELD) ① **2292-46015-2**
Waltz L. Rév *Concert* (7/87) (HYPE) ① **CDA66185**
1, 2, 4, 5, 7, 9, 10. G. Tozer *Concert*
(12/92) (TALL) ① **TP001**
3 Pensées—piano, Op. 62 (1933-34)
Boris Berman *Concert*
(11/92) (CHAN) ① **CHAN9069**
4 Pieces—piano, Op. 3 (1911) (rev by cpsr of 4
Pieces, 1907-08)
1. Story; 2. Jest; 3. March; 4. Phantom.
Boris Berman *Concert*
(11/91) (CHAN) ① **CHAN8976**
O. Marshev (r1992) *Concert*
(1/94) (DANA) ① **DACOCD392**
4 Pieces—piano, Op. 4 (1910-12) (revision of 4
Pieces, 1908)
1. Reminiscences; 2. Ardor; 3. Despair; 4.
Temptation (Suggestion diabolique).
M. McLachlan *Concert* (3/90) (OLYM) ① **OCD257**
B. Nissman *Concert* (6/91) (NEWP) ① **NCD60094**
Boris Berman *Concert*
(11/92) (CHAN) ① **CHAN9017**
4. B. Moiseiwitsch (r1928) *Concert*
(10/91) (KOCH) ① **37035-2**

Vladimir Ashkenazy (r1994) *Concert*
　　　(6/95) (DECC) ① **444 408-2DH**
M. Pollini (r1971) *Concert*
　　　(6/95) (DG) ① **447 431-2GOR**
M. Pletnev (r1978) *Concert*
　　　(8/95) (MELO) ① [11] **74321 25172-2(2)**
M. Pletnev (r1978) *Concert*
　　　(8/95) (MELO) ① **74321 25181-2**
Movt 3. V. Horowitz (pp1953) *Concert*
　　　(1/93) (RCA) ① **GD60526**
Sonata for Piano No. 8 in B flat, Op. 84 (1939-44)
S. Richter *Concert*　　(9/88) (DG) ① **423 573-2GDO**
M. McLachlan *Concert*　(3/90) (OLYM) ① **OCD256**
J. Lill *Concert*　　　(4/91) (ASV) ① **CDDCA755**
B. Nissman *Concert*　(6/91) (NEWP) ① **NCD60093**
Boris Berman *Concert*
　　　(11/91) (CHAN) ① **CHAN8976**
P. Donohoe *Concert*
　　　(11/91) (EMI) ① **CDC7 54281-2**
A. Gavrilov *Concert*　(6/92) (DG) ① **435 439-2GH**
S. Richter (pp1973) *Concert*
　　　(10/92) (PYRA) ① **PYR13503**
F. Chiu *Concert*
　　　(1/94) (HARM) ① [3] **HMU90 7086/8**
O. Marshev (r1992) *Concert*
　　　(1/94) (DANA) ① **DACOCD392**
V. Ovchinikov (r c1992) *Concert*
　　　(3/95) (EMI) ① [3] **CDS5 55127-2**
Vladimir Ashkenazy (r1993) *Concert*
　　　(6/95) (DECC) ① **444 408-2DH**
S. Richter (r1961) *Concert*
　　　(12/95) (DG) ① [2] **447 355-2GDB2**
Sonata for Piano No. 9 in C, Op. 103 (1947)
J. Lill *Concert*　　　(4/91) (ASV) ① **CDDCA755**
B. Nissman *Concert*　(6/91) (NEWP) ① **NCD60094**
F. Chiu *Concert*
　　　(1/94) (HARM) ① [3] **HMU90 7086/8**
V. Ovchinikov (r c1992) *Concert*
　　　(3/95) (EMI) ① [3] **CDS5 55127-2**
Sonata for Piano No. 10 in E minor, Op. 137 (incomplete fragment)
M. McLachlan *Concert*　(3/90) (OLYM) ① **OCD255**
B. Nissman *Concert*　(6/91) (NEWP) ① **NCD60094**
Sonata in D—violin/unison violins, Op. 115 (1947)
D. Sitkovetsky (r1990) *Concert*
　　　(11/71) (VIRG) ① **VC5 45074-2**
London Musici, M. Stephenson *Concert*
　　　(3/91) (CONI) ① **CDCF173**
N. Gotkovsky *Concert*　(9/91) (PYRA) ① **PYR13496**
2 Sonatinas—piano, Op. 54 (1931-32)
1. E minor; 2. G.
J. Lill *Concert*　　　(9/91) (ASV) ① **CDDCA753**
Boris Berman *Concert*
　　　(11/92) (CHAN) ① **CHAN9017**
1. M. McLachlan *Concert*
　　　(3/90) (OLYM) ① **OCD257**
The Tales of an old grandmother—piano, Op. 31 (1918)
1. Moderato; 2. Andantino; 3. Andante assai; 4. Sostenuto.
Boris Berman *Concert*
　　　(2/91) (CHAN) ① **CHAN8881**
B. Vodenicharov *Concert*
　　　(7/92) (ETCE) ① **KTC1122**
O. Marshev (r1992) *Concert*
　　　(1/94) (DANA) ① **DACOCD392**
V. Sofronitzky (r1946) *Concert*
　　　(8/95) (MELO) ① [11] **74321 25172-2(1)**
V. Sofronitzky (r1946) *Concert*
　　　(8/95) (MELO) ① [2] **74321 25177-2**
2, 3. S. Prokofiev (r1935) *Concert*
　　　(11/91) (PEAR) ① **GEMMCD9470**
2, 3. N. Milstein, G. Pludermacher (pp1986: arr vn/pf) *Concert*
　　　(5/95) (TELD) ① **4509-95998-2**
Toccata in C—piano, Op. 11 (1912)
R. Pöntinen *Concert*　(9/85) (BIS) ① **BIS-CD276**
T. Trotter (arr.Guillou) *Concert*
　　　(11/87) (HYPE) ① **CDA66216**
V. Horowitz (r1930) *Concert*
　　　(3/90) (EMI) ① [3] **CHS7 63538-2**
B. Nissman *Concert*　(6/91) (NEWP) ① **NCD60094**
V. Horowitz (r1947) *Concert*
　　　(6/92) (RCA) ① **GD60377**
B. Vodenicharov *Concert*
　　　(7/92) (ETCE) ① **KTC1122**
V. Ovchinikov (r c1992) *Concert*
　　　(3/95) (EMI) ① [3] **CDS5 55127-2**
M. Argerich (r1960) *Concert*
　　　(6/95) (DG) ① **447 430-2GOR**
Visions fugitives—20 pieces: piano, Op. 22 (1915-17)
1. Largamente; 2. Andante; 3. Allegretto; 4. Animato; 5. Molto giocoso; 6. Con eleganza; 7. Pittoresco; 8. Commodo; 9. Allegretto tranquillo; 10.

Ridiculosamente; 11. Con vivacita; 12. Assai moderato; 13. Allegretto; 14. Feroce; 15. Inquieto; 16. Dolente; 17. Poetico; 18. Con una dolce lentezza; 19. Presto agitatissimo e molto accentuato; 20. Lento irrealmente.
M. Béroff *Concert*
　　　(7/89) (EMI) ① [2] **CMS7 62542-2**
M. Raekallio *Concert*　(5/90) (ONDI) ① **ODE729-2**
Boris Berman *Concert*
　　　(2/91) (CHAN) ① **CHAN8881**
B. Nissman *Concert*　(6/91) (NEWP) ① **NCD60094**
N. Demidenko *Concert*　(8/91) (CONI) ① **CDCF204**
J. Lill *Concert*　　　(9/91) (ASV) ① **CDDCA753**
B. Vodenicharov *Concert*
　　　(7/92) (ETCE) ① **KTC1122**
L. Cabasso *Concert*　(11/92) (AUVI) ① **V4655**
O. Marshev (r1991) *Concert*
　　　(1/94) (DANA) ① **DACOCD391**
H. Neuhaus (r1956) *Concert*
　　　(8/95) (MELO) ① [11] **74321 25172-2(1)**
H. Neuhaus (r1956) *Concert*
　　　(8/95) (MELO) ① **74321 25174-2**
1, 2, 3, 6, 7, 9, 10, 11, 12, 13, 14, 16. A. Rubinstein (pp1961) *Concert*　(10/93) (RCA) ① **09026 61445-2**
1, 3, 5, 11. Emil Gilels (pp1968) *Concert*
　　　(8/95) (MELO) ① **74321 25179-2**
1, 3, 5, 11. Emil Gilels (r1968) *Concert*
　　　(8/95) (MELO) ① [11] **74321 25172-2(1)**
3, 5, 6, 9-11, 16-18. S. Prokofiev (r1935) *Concert*
　　　(11/91) (PEAR) ① **GEMMCD9470**
3, 5, 6, 9-11, 16-18. S. Prokofiev (r1935) *Concert*
　　　(5/95) (EMI) ① **CDC5 55223-2**
3-6, 8, 9, 11, 14, 15, 18. S Richter *Concert*
　　　(8/94) (PHIL) ① [2] **438 627-2PH2**
3, 6, 9. S. Richter (pp1962) *Concert*
　　　(9/88) (DG) ① **423 573-2GDO**
3, 6, 9. S. Richter (pp1962) *Concert*
　　　(12/95) (DG) ① [2] **447 355-2GDB2**
7. V. Sofronitzky (pp1953) *Concert*
　　　(8/95) (MELO) ① **74321 25177-2**
7. V. Sofronitzky (pp1953) *Concert*
　　　(8/95) (MELO) ① [11] **74321 25172-2(1)**
10, 11, 16, 17. E. Kissin (pp1984) *Concert*
　　　(8/95) (MELO) ① [11] **74321 25172-2(2)**
10, 11, 16, 17. E. Kissin (pp1984) *Concert*
　　　(8/95) (MELO) ① **74321 25182-2**
Waltzes Suite (Schubert)—piano arrangement (1920)
Boris Berman *Concert*
　　　(4/93) (CHAN) ① **CHAN9119**

SECTION IV: VOCAL AND CHORAL

5 Akhmatova Poems, Op. 27 (1916)
1. The sun has filled my room; 2. True tenderness; 3. Memory of the sun; 4. Greetings; 5. The king with grey eyes.
C. Farley, A. Aronov *Concert*
　　　(5/87) (CHAN) ① **CHAN8509**
Alexander Nevsky—cantata after film score: mez, chor & orch, Op. 78 (1939) (Wds. cpsr & Lugorsky)
EXCERPTS: 1. Russia Under the Mongolian Yoke; 2. Song About Alexander Nevsky; 3. The Crusaders in Pskov; 4. Arise, Ye Russian People; 5. The Battle On the Ice; 6. The Field of the Dead; 7. Alexander's Entry into Pskov.
E. Obraztsova, LSC, LSO, C. Abbado (r1979) *Lt Kijé Suite*.　　　(6/87) (DG) ① **419 603-2GH**
C. Cairns, Los Angeles Master Chorale, Los Angeles PO, A. Previn *Lt. Kijé Suite*.
L. Finnie, Scottish Nat Chor, SNO, N. Järvi *Scythian Suite*.　　　(5/88) (CHAN) ① **CHAN8584**
A. Reynolds, LSC, LSO, A. Previn (r1971) *Rachmaninov: Bells*.
　　　(10/89) (EMI) ① **CDM7 63114-2**
R. Elias, Chicago Sym Chor, Chicago SO, F. Reiner (Eng) *Concert*　(1/90) (RCA) ① **GD60176**
L. Chookasian, Westminster Ch, NYPO, T. Schippers *Romeo and Juliet*.　(10/90) (SONY) ① **MPK45557**
L. Schemtchuk, Danish Nat Rad Ch, Danish Nat RSO, D. Kitaienko *Scythian Suite*.
　　　(5/92) (CHAN) ① **CHAN9001**
C. Watkinson, Latvija Chor, Leipzig Gewandhaus, K. Masur (pp1991) *Scythian Suite*.
　　　(5/92) (TELD) ① **9031-73284-2**
D. Zajick, LSC, LSO, M. Rostropovich (r1991) *Ivan the Terrible Suite*.　(4/93) (SONY) ① [2] **S2K48387**
E. Obraztsova, LSC, LSO, C. Abbado (r1979) *Concert*　(6/95) (DG) ① **447 419-2GOR**
Cantata for the 20th anniversary of the October Revolution—narr, military, accordion & perc band, chor & orch, Op. 74 (1936-37) (Wds. Marx, Lenin & Stalin)
G. Rozhdestvensky, Philh Chor, Philh, N. Järvi *Stone Flower*.　(3/93) (CHAN) ① **CHAN9095**

3 Children's Songs, Op. 68 (1936)
1. Chatterbox; 2. Sweet song; 3. The little pig.
Cpte C. Farley, R. Vignoles *Concert*
　　　(11/89) (ASV) ① **CDDCA669**
Ivan the Terrible—oratorio after film score, Op. 116 (1942-45) (arr. Abram Stasevich, 1961)
V. Zorova, D. Stanchev, B. Morgunov, Danube Sounds Ch, Rousse PSO, A. Naydenov (pp1984)
　　　(8/85) (FORL) ① **UCD16530**
I. Arkhipova, A. Mokrenko, B. Morgunov, Ambrosian Chor, Philh, R. Muti　(4/89) (EMI) ① **CDM7 69584-2**
5 Poems, Op. 36 (1921) (Wds. Bal'mont)
1. Incantation, fire and water; 2. Birdsong; 3. The Butterfly; 4. Remember me; 5. The Pylons.
C. Farley, A. Aronov *Concert*
　　　(5/87) (CHAN) ① **CHAN8509**
2 Poems, Op. 9 (1910-11)
1. It is of other planets (Wds. Bal'mont); 2. The drifting boat (Wds. A. Apukhtin).
C. Farley, A. Aronov *Concert*
　　　(5/87) (CHAN) ① **CHAN8509**
5 Poems, Op. 23 (1915) (Wds. Bal'mont)
1. Under the roof; 2. The little grey dress; 3. Follow me; 4. In my garden; 5. The prophet.
Cpte C. Farley, R. Vignoles *Concert*
　　　(11/89) (ASV) ① **CDDCA669**
3 Romances, Op. 73 (1936) (Wds. Pushkin)
1. Pine Trees; 2. With a blush; 3. In your brightness.
C. Farley, A. Aronov *Concert*
　　　(5/87) (CHAN) ① **CHAN8509**
12 Russian Folksongs, Op. 104 (1944)
1. Guelder Rose (Snowdrop-tree); 2. Green Glade; 3. Guelder Rose on the Hill (Wedding Song); 4. White Snow (Snowflakes); 5. Brown Eyes; 6. Katerina; 7. The Dream; 8. Beyond the Woods; 9. Dunyushka; 10. The Beloved is Gone; 11. Sashenska; 12. The Monk.
1, 2. C. Farley, R. Vignoles *Concert*
　　　(11/89) (ASV) ① **CDDCA669**
3, 4, 12. L. Popp, G. Parsons (pp1981) *Concert*
　　　(6/95) (ORFE) ① **C363941B**
5 Songs without words, Op. 35 (1920)
1. The magician.
Cpte C. Farley, R. Vignoles *Concert*
　　　(11/89) (ASV) ① **CDDCA669**
The Ugly Duckling—song, Op. 18 (1914) (wds after H C Andersen).
C. Farley, R. Vignoles *Concert*
　　　(11/89) (ASV) ① **CDDCA669**
C. Farley, Scottish CO, J. Serebrier *Concert*
　　　(7/91) (ASV) ① **CDDCA760**
P. Walmsley-Clark, New London Orch, R. Corp *Concert*　(12/91) (HYPE) ① **CDA66499**
Winter Bonfire—children's suite, Op. 122 (1949-50)
1. Departure; 2. Snow outside the window; 3. Waltz on the ice; 4. The Bonfire; 5. Chorus of the Pioneers; 6. Winter Evening; 7. March; 8. The Return.
Paisley Abbey Ch, Scottish CO, J. Serebrier *Concert*
　　　(7/91) (ASV) ① **CDDCA760**
O. Prokofiev, G. Prokofiev, Finchley Children's Music Group, New London Orch, R. Corp *Concert*
　　　(12/91) (HYPE) ① **CDA66499**

SECTION V: STAGE WORKS

Alexander Nevsky—film score (1938) (reconstructed from original soundtrack) & Cantata, Op. 78 by W D Brohn)
EXCERPTS: 1. Prelude; 2. The 13th Century; 3. Plescheyevo Lake (Song about Alexander Nevsky); 4. Pskov in Flames; 5. 'Death to the Blasphemer!' (Peregrinus expectavi); 6. Arise, People of Russia; 7. The Teutonic Camp (Peregrinus expectavi); 8. Nevsky's Camp: Night Before the Battle; 9. The Battle on the Ice: 9a. April 5, 1242 (Peregrinus expectavi); 9b. Fight for Russia!; 9c. Spears and Arrows (Peregrinus expectavi); 9d. The Duel with the Grand Master; 9e. The Battle is Won; 9f. The Ice Breaks; 10. The Field of the Dead; 11. Pskov: Procession of the Fallen & Judgement of the Prisoners; 12. 'And Now Let's Celebrate!'; 13. Final Chorus.
1-13. Y. Gorokhovskaya, St Petersburg Teleradio Chor, St Petersburg Chbr Ch, St Petersburg Chor Capella, St Petersburg PO, Y. Temirkanov (r1993)
　　　(6/95) (RCA) ① **09026 61926-2**
Boris Godunov—incidental music to Pushkin's play, Op. 70b (1936)
Excs SNO, N. Järvi *Concert*
　　　(1/87) (CHAN) ① **CHAN8472**
Cinderella—ballet: 3 acts, Op. 87 (1945—Moscow)
ACT 1; 1. Introduction; 2. Pas de châle; 3. Cinderella; 4. The Father; 5. The Fairy Godmother; 6. The Sisters' new clothes; 7. The Dancing Lesson; 8. Departure for the Ball; 9. Cinderella dreams of the

Ball; 10. Gavotte; 11. Fairy Godmother returns; 12.
Spring Fairy; 13. Summer Fairy; 14. Grasshoppers
and Dragonflies; 15. Autumn Fairy; 16. Winter Fairy;
17. Interrupted departure; 18. Clock Scene; 19.
Cinderella's departure for the Ball. ACT 2; 20. Dance
of the Courtiers; 21. Court Dance (Passepied); 22.
Cavaliers' Dance; 23. Skinny's variation; 24. Dumpy's
variation; 25. Court Dance (repeat); 26. Mazurka and
Entrance of the Prince; 27. Dance of the Prince's
Companion; 28. Mazurka; 29. Cinderella's arrival at
the Ball; 30. Grand Waltz; 31. Promenade; 32.
Cinderella's variation; 33. The Prince's variation; 34.
Refreshments for the Guests; 35. Duet of the Sisters
with their Oranges; 36. Duet of the Prince and
Cinderella; 37. Waltz-Coda; 38. Midnight. ACT 3; 39.
The Prince and the Shoemakers; 40. First Galop; 41.
Temptation; 42. Second Galop; 43. Oriental Dance;
44. Third Galop; 45. Cinderella awakes; 46. The
Morning after the Ball; 47. The Prince's visit; 48. The
Prince finds Cinderella; 49. Slow Waltz; 50. Amoroso.
Cpte Cleveland Orch, Vladimir Ashkenazy
(8/86) (DECC) ① [2] **410 162-2DH2**
Cpte Russian Nat Orch, M. Pletnev *Summer Night,*
Op.123. (6/95) (DG) ① [2] **445 830-2GH2**
Adagio Y. Turovsky, P. Pettinger *(arr. vc/pf) Concert*
(4/88) (CHAN) ① **CHAN8555**
37. Hollywood Bowl SO, J. Mauceri (r1993) *Concert*
(6/94) (PHIL) ① **438 685-2PH**

Cinderella Suite No. 1—concert suite from
ballet, Op. 107 (1946)
EXCERPTS: 1. Introduction; 2. Pas de chat; 3.
Quarrel; 4. Fairy Godmother and Fairy Winter; 5.
Mazurka; 6. Cinderella Goes to the Ball; 7.
Cinderella's Waltz; 8. Midnight.
Košice St PO, A. Mogrelia *Concert*
(9/91) (NAXO) ① **8 550381**
Ukrainian St SO, T. Kuchar *Concert*
(4/95) (NAXO) ① [2] **550968/9**
1, 3. SNO, N. Järvi *Concert*
(10/87) (CHAN) ① **CHAN8511**

Cinderella Suite No. 2—concert suite from
ballet, Op. 108 (1946)
SNO, N. Järvi *Cinderella Suite 3.*
(9/91) (CHAN) ① **CHAN8939**
Ukrainian St SO, T. Kuchar (r1994) *Concert*
(4/95) (NAXO) ① [2] **550968/9**

Cinderella Suite No. 3—concert suite from
ballet, Op. 109 (1946)
EXCERPTS: 1. Pavane; 2. Cinderella and the
Prince; 3. Three Oranges; 4. Dance of Seduction; 5.
Orientalia; 6. The Prince finds Cinderella; 7. End of
the Fairy-Tale; 8. Amoroso.
SNO, N. Järvi *Cinderella Suite 2.*
(9/91) (CHAN) ① **CHAN8939**
Ukrainian St SO, T. Kuchar (r1994) *Concert*
(4/95) (NAXO) ① [2] **550968/9**
1-5, 8. SNO, N. Järvi *Concert*
(10/87) (CHAN) ① **CHAN8511**

Eugene Onegin—incidental music to
Pushkin's play, Op. 71 (1936)
Cpte L. Koroleva, B. Stetsenko, Blagovest Ch,
Moscow Maly SO, V. Ponkin *Concert*
(9/92) (CDM) ① [2] **LDC288 027/8**
Cpte T. West, S. West, N. Cusack, New Company,
Sinfonia 21, E. Downes
(1/94) (CHAN) ① [2] **CHAN9318/9**
Excs SNO, N. Järvi *Concert*
(1/87) (CHAN) ① **CHAN8472**

The Fiery Angel—opera: 5 acts, Op. 37
(1954—Paris) (Lib. V. Bryusov)
Cpte N. Secunde, S. Lorenz, H. Zednik, P. Salomaa,
K. Moll, G. Zachrisson, B. Terfel, R. Lang, R. Engert-
Ely, C.G. Holmgren, Ohlin Voc Ens, Gothenburg Pro
Musica Chbr Ch, Gothenburg SO, N. Järvi
(7/91) (DG) ① [2] **431 669-2GH2**

Hamlet—music for Shakespeare's play, Op.
77 (1939)
L. Koroleva, B. Stetsenko, Blagovest Ch, Moscow
Maly SO, V. Ponkin *Concert*
(9/92) (CDM) ① [2] **LDC288 027/8**

Ivan the Terrible—concert suite from film
score (see also Ivan the Terrible oratorio, Op.
116)
L. Finnie, N. Storozhev, Philh Chor, Philh, N. Järvi
(r1991; arr Christopher Palmer)
(11/91) (CHAN) ① **CHAN8977**
T. Sinyavskaya, S. Leiferkus, C. Plummer, New
London Children's Ch, LSC, LSO, M. Rostropovich
(r1991; arr M. Lankester) *Alexander Nevsky.*
(4/93) (SONY) ① [2] **S2K48387**

Lieutenant Kijé—concert suite from film
score, Op. 60 (1934)
EXCERPTS: 1. Birth of Kijé; 2. Romance; 3. Kijé's
Wedding; 4. Troika; 5. Burial of Kijé.
Chicago SO, C. Abbado *Alexander Nevsky.*
(6/87) (DG) ① **419 603-2GH**

Los Angeles PO, A. Previn *Alexander Nevsky.*
(2/88) (TELA) ① **CD80143**
Chicago SO, F. Reiner *Concert*
(1/90) (RCA) ① **GD60176**
LSO, N. Marriner *Concert*
(11/90) (PHIL) ① **426 640-2PSL**
SNO, N. Järvi *Concert*
(2/91) (CHAN) ① **CHAN8806**
Košice St PO, A. Mogrelia *Concert*
(9/91) (NAXO) ① **8 550381**
Paris Cons, A. Boult *Concert*
(1/92) (DECC) ① **433 612-2DSP**
A. Schmidt, BPO, S. Ozawa *Symphony 5.*
(5/92) (DG) ① **435 029-2GH**
Moscow Maly SO, V. Ponkin *Concert*
(9/92) (CDM) ① [2] **LDC288 027/8**
LPO, T. Yuasa (r1990) *Rimsky-Korsakov:*
Scheherazade. (12/93) (EMIN) ① **CD-EMX2214**
Chicago SO, C. Abbado (r1977) *Concert*
(1/94) (DG) ① **439 413-2GCL**
Chicago SO, C. Abbado (r1977) *Concert*
(6/95) (DG) ① **447 419-2GOR**
Chicago SO, F. Reiner (r1958) *Concert*
(9/95) (RCA) ① **09026 61957-2**
2, 3. F. Chiu (trans Chiu) *Concert*
(1/94) (HARM) ① [3] **HMU90 7086/8**
2, 3, 4. Tetra (r1989-91; arr Goss: gtr qt) *Concert*
(11/93) (CONI) ① **CDCF903**
4. Fine Arts Brass Ens, P. Spicer (r1992; arr Roberts)
Concert (12/93) (BIRM) ① **BBCCD2**
4. Prince of Wales Brass (arr Harrison) *Concert*
(12/93) (ASV) ① **CDWHL2083**

The Love for Three Oranges—opera:
prologue & 4 acts, Op. 33 (1919—Chicago)
SUITE—; 1. Les ridicules; 2. Scène infernale; 3.
Marche; 4. Scherzo; 5. Le Prince et la Princesse; 6.
La fruite.
Cpte G. Bacquier, J-L. Viala, H. Perraguin, V. Le
Texier, G. Gautier, D. Henry, G. Reinhart, M.
Lagrange, C. Caroli, B. Fournier, C. Dubosc, J.
Bastin, B. Uria-Monzon, Lyon Op Chor, Lyon Op
Orch, K. Nagano (Fr)
(12/89) (VIRG) ① [2] **VCD7 59566-2**
3. Empire Brass (r1992; arr. E. Smedvig) *Concert*
(1/94) (TELA) ① **CD80305**

The Love for Three Oranges—concert suite
from opera
EXCERPTS: 1. Les ridicules; 2. Scène infernale; 3.
March; 4. Scherzo; 5. Le Prince et la Princesse; 6. La
fruite.
SNO, N. Järvi *Concert*
(9/89) (CHAN) ① **CHAN8729**
LSO, N. Marriner *Concert*
(11/90) (PHIL) ① **426 640-2PSL**
Montreal SO, C. Dutoit (r1992) *Concert*
(1/94) (DECC) ① **440 331-2DH**
Philadelphia, E. Ormandy (r1963) *Concert*
(7/94) (SONY) ① **SBK53261**
1-5. LPO, W. Weller *Concert*
(1/92) (DECC) ① **433 612-2DSP**
3. R. Pöntinen (arr pf) *Concert*
(11/85) (BIS) ① **BIS-CD300**
3. A. Rubinstein (arr.Rubinstein) *Concert*
(10/87) (RCA) ① **RD85666**
3. St Louis SO, L. Slatkin *Concert*
(6/89) (RCA) ① **RD87716**
3. X. Wei, Pam Nicholson (arr Heifetz) *Concert*
(2/91) (RCA) ① **CDDCA698**
3. I. Perlman, J.G. Guggenheim (pp1990) *Concert*
(2/91) (EMI) ① **CDC7 54108-2**
3. S. Chang, S. Rivers (arr Heifetz) *Concert*
(1/93) (EMI) ① **CDC7 54352-2**
3. Midori, R. McDonald (1992: arr vn/pf Heifetz)
Concert (6/93) (SONY) ① **SK52568**
3. A. Rubinstein (r1961; arr pf) *Concert*
(8/94) (RCA) ① **09026 61863-2**
3. J. Heifetz, E. Bay (r1945) *Concert*
(11/94) (RCA) ① [2] **09026 61778-2(19)**
3. J. Heifetz, B. Smith (r1970) *Concert*
(11/94) (RCA) ① [65] **09026 61778-2(40)**
3-5. Košice St PO, A. Mogrelia *Concert*
(9/91) (NAXO) ① **8 550381**

On the Dnieper—concert suite from ballet,
Op. 51 (1933-34)
Ukrainian St SO, T. Kuchar (r1994) *Concert*
(4/95) (NAXO) ① [2] **8 550968/9**

Le Pas d'acier—ballet: 2 scenes, Op. 41
(1927—Paris)
SNO, N. Järvi *Concert*
(9/89) (CHAN) ① **CHAN8729**

The Prodigal Son—ballet: 3 scenes, Op. 46
(1929—Paris)
SNO, N. Järvi *Concert*
(3/90) (CHAN) ① **CHAN8728**

Romeo and Juliet—ballet: 3 acts and
epilogue, Op. 64 (1938—Brno)
ACT 1; 1. Introduction; 2. Romeo; 3. The street
awakens; 4. Morning Dance; 5. The Quarrel; 6. The
Fight; 7. The Prince gives his order; 8. Interlude; 9.
Preparing for the Ball (Juliet and the Nurse); 10.
Juliet as a young girl; 11. Arrival of the guests
(Minuet); 12. Masks; 13. Dance of the Knights; 14.
Juliet's Variation; 15. Mercutio; 16. Madrigal; 17.
Tybalt recognizes Romeo; 18. Departure of the
guests (Gavotte); 19. Balcony scene; 20. Romeo's
Variation; 21. Love Dance. ACT 2; 22. Folk Dance;
23. Romeo and Mercutio; 24. Dance of the five
couples; 25. Dance with the five mandolins; 26. The
Nurse; 27. The Nurse gives Romeo the note from
Juliet; 28. Romeo with Friar Laurence; 29. Juliet with
Friar Laurence; 30. The people continue to make
merry; 31. A Folk Dance again; 32. Tybalt meets
Mercutio; 33. Tybalt and Mercutio fight; 34. Mercutio
dies; 35. Romeo decides to avenge Mercutio's death;
36. Finale. ACT 3; 37. Introduction; 38. Romeo and
Juliet (Juliet's bedroom); 39. The last farewell; 40.
The Nurse; 41. Juliet refuses to marry Paris; 42.
Juliet alone; 43. Interlude; 44. At Friar Laurence's;
45. Interlude; 46. Again in Juliet's bedroom; 47. Juliet
alone; 48. Morning Serenade; 49. Dance of the girls
with the lilies; 50. At Juliet's bedside. (EPILOGUE);
51. Juliet's funeral; 52. Death of Juliet.
Cpte Cleveland Orch, L. Maazel
(2/87) (DECC) ① [2] **417 510-2DH2**
Cpte Boston SO, S. Ozawa (r1986)
(2/88) (DG) ① [2] **423 268-2GH2**
Cpte Bolshoi Th Orch, A. Ziuraitis
(5/89) (CFP) ① [2] **CD-CFPD4452**
Cpte Kirov Th Orch, V. Gergiev
(12/91) (PHIL) ① [2] **432 166-2PH2**
Cpte ROHO, M. Ermler (r1993)
(11/94) (ROH) ① [2] **ROH309/10**
Cpte Danish Nat RSO, D. Kitaienko (r1993)
(4/95) (CHAN) ① [2] **CHAN9322/3**
Excs NYPO, D. Mitropoulos *Alexander Nevsky.*
(10/90) (SONY) ① **MPK45557**
Excs Montreal SO, C. Dutoit
(1/91) (DECC) ① **430 279-2DH**
1, 10, 11, 13, 18, 35-37, 39, 43-45. Los Angeles PO,
E. Leinsdorf *Concert* (8/87) (SHEF) ① **CD-7/8**
1, 3, 4, 10, 12, 13, 18-21, 25, 28, 30, 33, 34, 39,
48, 51, 52. RLPO, L. Pešek (r1989)
(10/93) (VIRG) ① **VC7 59278-2**
1-4, 13, 14, 19-21, 33-38, 52. Chicago SO, G. Solti
Symphony 1. (8/91) (DECC) ① **430 731-2DM**
5, 6, 25. LSO, C. Abbado *Concert*
(4/85) (DG) ① **425 027-2GM**
7-13, 19-22, 25, 33, 35, 36, 39, 48, 51, 52. BPO, E-P.
Salonen (8/88) (SONY) ① **SK42662**
49. Y. Turovsky, P. Pettinger *(arr Vlasov: vc/pf)*
Concert (4/88) (CHAN) ① **CHAN8555**

Romeo and Juliet—concert suites from
ballet
SUITE 1, Op. 64a (1936): 1. Folk Dance; 2. Scene;
3. Madrigal; 4. Minuet; 5. Masks; 6. Balcony Scene;
7. Death of Tybalt. SUITE 2, Op. 64b (1936): 8.
Montagues and Capulets; 9. Juliet, the little girl; 10.
Friar Laurence; 11. Dance; 12. Romeo and Juliet
before parting; 13. Dance of the maids with lilies; 14.
Romeo at Juliet's grave. SUITE 3, Op. 101 (1947):
15. Romeo at the fountain; 16. Morning Dance; 17.
Juliet prepares for the ball; 18. The Nurse; 19.
Aubade; 20. The Death of Juliet.
Minneapolis SO, S. Skrowaczewski *Mussorgsky:*
Night on the bare Mountain.
(3/91) (MERC) ① **432 004-2MM**
SNO, N. Järvi (9/91) (CHAN) ① **CHAN8940**
SRO, A. Jordan (7/93) (ERAT) ① **2292-45817-2**
Leipzig Gewandhaus, K. Ančerl (r1993) *Rimsky-*
Korsakov: Scheherazade.
(11/95) (TAHR) ① **TAH119**
1-10, 12, 14. Philadelphia, R. Muti
(2/84) (EMI) ① **CDC7 47004-2**
1-14. Washington NSO, M. Rostropovich
(9/83) (DG) ① **410 519-2GH**
1-14. Seattle SO, G. Schwarz *Pushkin Waltzes.*
(9/87) (DELO) ① **DE3050**
1-14. Oslo PO, M. Jansons (r1988)
(5/89) (EMI) ① **CDC7 49289-2**
1-14, 20. Concertgebouw, Myung-Whun Chung
(r1993) (9/94) (DG) ① **439 870-2GH**
1, 5-14. Cleveland Orch, Y. Levi
(2/87) (TELA) ① **CD80089**
1-7. SNO, N. Järvi *Symphony 2.*
(8/95) (CHAN) ① **CHAN8368**
2, 4-8, 10, 12, 14-18, 20. Košice St PO, A. Mogrelia
(9/91) (NAXO) ① **8 550380**
3-10, 12, 14, 19, 20. Philh, C.P. Flor (r1992)
(10/93) (RCA) ① **09026 61388-2**

3, 13. Košice St PO, A. Mogrelia *Concert*
(9/91) (NAXO) ① **8 550381**
3-9, 11, 12, 14. SRO, E. Ansermet (r1961)
Tchaikovsky: Swan Lake.
(9/95) (DECC) ① [2] **440 630-2DF2**
7, 8, 11, 13, 16, 19. LSO, C. Abbado *Concert*
(6/91) (DECC) ① **425 027-2DM**
8-14. SNO, N. Järvi *Concert*
(1/87) (CHAN) ① **CHAN8472**
8-14. Leningrad PO, E. Mravinsky (pp) *Shostakovich:*
Symphony 5. (7/95) (RUSS) ① **RDCD11180**
8, 9, 11, 14. Boston SO, S. Koussevitzky (r1945)
Concert (4/95) (RCA) ① **09026 61657-2**
15-20. SNO, N. Järvi *Symphony-Concerto.*
(5/87) (CHAN) ① **CHAN8508**
Semyon Kotko—opera: 5 acts, Op. 81
(1940—Moscow) (Lib. V Katayev & cpsr)
EXCERPTS: 1. Overture.
1. Russian Nat Orch, M. Pletnev *Concert*
(12/94) (DG) ① **439 892-2GH**
The **Tale of the Buffoon, 'Chout'**—ballet: 6
scenes, Op. 21 (1921—Paris)
Danse finale Boston SO, S. Koussevitzky (r1947)
Concert (4/95) (RCA) ① **09026 61657-2**
Suite Y. Turovsky, P. Pettinger (arr Sapojnikov:
vc/pf) *Concert* (4/88) (CHAN) ① **CHAN8555**
Suite D. Ferschtman, R. Brautigam (arr. vc/pf
Sapojnikov) *Concert* (10/88) (ETCE) ① **KTC1059**
Suite SNO, N. Järvi *Concert*
(9/89) (CHAN) ① **CHAN8729**
Suite LSO, C. Abbado *Concert*
(6/91) (DECC) ① **425 027-2DM**
The **Tale of the Stone Flower**—ballet: 4 acts,
Op. 118 (1954—Moscow)
EXCERPTS: ACT 3: 29. Ural Rhapsody; 31. Russian
Dance; 32. Gypsy Dance; 33. Severyan's Dance; 34.
Solo of the Gypsy Girl and Coda. ACT 4: 39. Katerina
sits by the fire; 40. Scene and Dance of Katerina.
Prologue; Scene and waltz of the diamonds;
Waltz SNO, N. Järvi *Concert*
(2/91) (CHAN) ① **CHAN8806**
Waltz Y. Turovsky, P. Pettinger (arr. Knushevitsky)
Concert (4/88) (CHAN) ① **CHAN8555**
Waltz D. Ferschtman, R. Brautigam (trans. G.
Piatigorsky) *Concert* (10/88) (ETCE) ① **KTC1059**
29, 31-34, 39, 40. Philh, N. Järvi *Cantata, Op. 74.*
(3/93) (CHAN) ① **CHAN9095**
War and Peace—opera: 5 acts & epigraph,
Op. 91 (1944—Moscow) (Lib. cpsr, after
Tolstoy)
EXCERPTS: 1. Overture; 2. Scene 1: The radiance
of the sky (Svetlaje vesenneje neba); 3. Scene 2: 3a.
Ballet Music; 3b. Chorus! let the chorus begin! (Horl
Pust' nachinajet hor!); 4. Scene 3: The young prince's
fiancée (Nevesta maladova kn'az'a); 5. Scene 4: The
charming, delightful Natasha! (Maja prelesnaja); 6.
Scene 5: At ten o'clock in the evening (Vecheram v
des'at'); 7. Scene 6: Oh, my dear Miss Natasha (Oj,
baryshn'a); 8. Scene 7: Picture the scene, Countess
(Padumajte, grafin'a); 9. Epigraph (chorus): The
forces of two and ten European nations; 10. Scene 8:
Come on, lads! (Pashla rib'atal); 11. Scene 9: The
wine is uncorked (Vino atkuporena); 12. Scene 10:
And so, gentlemen (Itak, gospoda); 13. Scene 11:
Moscow's deserted! (Maskva pustal); 14. Scene 12:
It's stretching higher and further (T'anesta); 15.
Scene 13: We've burnt our bridges (Karabli sazheny).
Cpte L. Miller, G. Vishnevskaya, Katherine Ciesinski,
M. Paunova, D. Petkov, W. Ochman, S. Toczyska, N.
Gedda, V. de Kanel, M. Smith, N. Ghiuselev, E.
Tumagian, French Rad Chor, FNO, M. Rostropovich
(r1986) (4/92) (ERAT) ① [4] **2292-45331-2**
Cpte A. Gergalov, Y. Prokina, S. Volkova, L.
Kanunnikova, S. Alexashkin, G. Gregorian, O.
Borodina, Y. Marusin, A. Morozov, M. Kit, N.
Okhotnikov, V. Gerelo, Kirov Th Chor, Kirov Th Orch,
V. Gergiev (r1991)
(6/93) (PHIL) ① [3] **434 097-2PH3**
What right have they? L. Popp, Munich RO, S.
Soltesz (r1987) *Concert*
(4/89) (EMI) ① **CDC7 49319-2**
War and Peace—concert suite from the
opera (arr. C Palmer)
EXCERPTS: 1. The Ball: 1a. Fanfare and Polonaise;
1b. Waltz; 1c. Mazurka; 2. Intermezzo—May Night; 3.
Finale: 3a. Snowstorm; 3b. Battle; 3c. Victory.
Philh, N. Järvi (r1991) *Concert*
(3/93) (CHAN) ① **CHAN9096**

PROVOST, Heinz

SECTION V: STAGE WORKS

Intermezzo—film score (1939)
T. Seidel, E. Kusmiak (r c1940) *Concert*
(7/93) (APR) ① [2] **APR7016**

**PRUDEN, Larry (1925–1982) New
Zealand**

SECTION I: ORCHESTRAL

Soliloquy—string orchestra (1952)
New Zealand CO (r1993) *Concert*
(9/95) (KOCH) ① **37260-2**

**PRYOR, Arthur (1870–1942)
USA**

SECTION IV: VOCAL AND CHORAL

Travel, Travel, Little Star—song for the show
'The Old Town' (1910) (Lyrics Bryan)
Montgomery & Stone, Orig Broadway Cast (r1911)
Concert (5/94) (PEAR) ① [3] **GEMMCDS9053/5**

**PUCCINI, Giacomo (Antonia
Domenico Michele Secondo
Maria) (1858–1924) Italy**

SECTION I: ORCHESTRAL

Capriccio sinfonico (1883)
Monte Carlo Op Orch, C. Scimone (r1978) *Concert*
(6/93) (ERAT) ① **2292-45942-2**
Preludio sinfonico in A (1876)
Monte Carlo Op Orch, C. Scimone (r1978) *Concert*
(6/93) (ERAT) ① **2292-45942-2**

SECTION II: CHAMBER

Crisantemi—string quartet (pub 1890)
Camerata Lysy *Concert*
(3/87) (CLAV) ① **CD50-8507**
Raphael Qt *Concert* (5/88) (ETCE) ① **KTC1050**
Israel CO, Y. Talmi (arr. str. orch.) *Concert*
(8/88) (CHAN) ① **CHAN8593**
Alberni Qt *Concert* (5/89) (CRD) ① **CRD3366**
Rasumovsky Qt *Concert*
(12/92) (IMPE) ① **RAZCD901**
Hagen Qt (r1993) *Concert*
(12/95) (DG) ① **447 069-2GH**
3 Minuets—string quartet (pub 1892)
1. A (Moderato); 2. Allegretto; 3. A (Assai mosso).
Raphael Qt *Concert* (5/88) (ETCE) ① **KTC1050**
Scherzo in A minor—string quartet (c1880-
83)
Raphael Qt *Concert* (5/88) (ETCE) ① **KTC1050**
String Quartet in D (c1880-83)
Raphael Qt *Concert* (5/88) (ETCE) ① **KTC1050**

SECTION III: INSTRUMENTAL

Foglio d'album—piano (?1907)
T. Crone *Concert* (5/88) (ETCE) ① **KTC1050**
Piccolo tango—piano (?1907)
T. Crone *Concert* (5/88) (ETCE) ① **KTC1050**

SECTION IV: VOCAL AND CHORAL

Ad te—song (Wds. unknown)
P. Domingo, J. Rudel *Concert*
(3/90) (SONY) ① **SK44981**
Ad una mortal—song (Wds. A. Ghislanzoni)
P. Domingo, J. Rudel *Concert*
(3/90) (SONY) ① **SK44981**
Avanti; Urania!—song (pub 1899) (Wds.
Fucini)
R. Alexander, T. Crone *Concert*
(5/88) (ETCE) ① **KTC1050**
P. Domingo, J. Rudel *Concert*
(3/90) (SONY) ① **SK44981**
Canto d'anime—song (Wds. L. Illica)
P. Domingo, J. Rudel *Concert*
(3/90) (SONY) ① **SK44981**
Casa mia, casa mia—song (Wds. unknown)
P. Domingo, J. Rudel *Concert*
(3/90) (SONY) ① **SK44981**
È l'uccellino (Ninna-Nanna)—song (pub
1899) (Wds. Fucini)
R. Alexander, T. Crone *Concert*
(5/88) (ETCE) ① **KTC1050**
P. Domingo, J. Rudel *Concert*
(3/90) (SONY) ① **SK44981**
J. Van Dam, C. Musquer (r1992) *Concert*
(8/93) (FORL) ① **UCD16681**
R. Tebaldi, R. Bonynge (r1972) *Concert*
(9/94) (DECC) ① **436 202-2DM**
Inno a Diana—song (pub 1899) (Wds.
Abenicar)
R. Alexander, T. Crone *Concert*
(5/88) (ETCE) ① **KTC1050**
P. Domingo, J. Rudel *Concert*
(3/90) (SONY) ① **SK44981**

Inno a Roma—song (1923) (Wds. Salvatori)
P. Domingo, J. Rudel *Concert*
(3/90) (SONY) ① **SK44981**
Menti all'avviso—romanza (1883) (Wds.
cpsr)
R. Alexander, T. Crone *Concert*
(5/88) (ETCE) ① **KTC1050**
P. Domingo, J. Rudel *Concert*
(3/90) (SONY) ① **SK44981**
Messa di Gloria in A flat—tenor, baritone,
chorus and orchestra (1880)
K. Lövaas, W. Hollweg, B. McDaniel, W German Rad
Chor, Frankfurt RSO, E. Inbal *Mozart: Vespers,*
K339. (1/93) (PHIL) ① **434 170-2PM**
W. Johns, P. Huttenlocher, Lisbon Gulbenkian Chor,
Lisbon Gulbenkian Orch, M. Corboz (r1974) *Concert*
(6/93) (ERAT) ① **2292-45942-2**
Morire?—song (pub c1917) (Wds. Adami)
R. Alexander, T. Crone *Concert*
(5/88) (ETCE) ① **KTC1050**
P. Domingo, J. Rudel *Concert*
(3/90) (SONY) ① **SK44981**
Requiem—STB, organ/harmonium (before
1905)
Gonville & Caius College Ch, G. Webber (r1994; ed
Spada) *Concert* (6/95) (ASV) ① **CDDCA914**
Salve del ciel regina (before 1880) (Wds. A.
Ghislanzoni)
R. Alexander, T. Crone *Concert*
(5/88) (ETCE) ① **KTC1050**
P. Domingo, J. Rudel *Concert*
(3/90) (SONY) ① **SK44981**
Gonville & Caius College Ch, G. Webber (r1994; ed
Kaye) *Concert* (6/95) (ASV) ① **CDDCA914**
Sole e amore—song (1888) (Wds. cpsr)
R. Alexander, T. Crone *Concert*
(5/88) (ETCE) ① **KTC1050**
P. Domingo, J. Rudel *Concert*
(3/90) (SONY) ① **SK44981**
Storiella d'amore—song (1883) (Wds. A.
Ghislanzoni)
R. Scotto, I. Davis (pp1983) *Concert*
(10/86) (ETCE) ① **KTC2002**
R. Alexander, T. Crone *Concert*
(5/88) (ETCE) ① **KTC1050**
P. Domingo, J. Rudel *Concert*
(3/90) (SONY) ① **SK44981**
Terra e mare—song (pub 1902) (Wds. E.
Panzacchi)
R. Alexander, T. Crone *Concert*
(5/88) (ETCE) ① **KTC1050**
P. Domingo, J. Rudel *Concert*
(3/90) (SONY) ① **SK44981**
Vexilla regis—two voices and organ (1874-
1880) (Wds. V. H. Fortunatus)
P. Domingo, J. Diaz, J. Rudel *Concert*
(3/90) (SONY) ① **SK44981**
Gonville & Caius College Ch, G. Webber (r1994)
Concert (6/95) (ASV) ① **CDDCA914**

SECTION V: STAGE WORKS

La Bohème, 'Bohemian Life'—opera: 4 acts
(1896—Turin) (Lib. Illica and Giacosa)
EXCERPTS: ACT 1: 1a. Questo Mar Rosso; 1b. Nei
cieli bigi; 1c. Pensier profondo! Giusto color!; 1d.
Legna! Sigari! Bordo!; 1e. Si può? Chi è là? Benoit!;
1f. Io resto per terminar l'articolo; 1g. Non sono in
vena. Chi è là!; 1h. Si sente meglio? Sì. Qui cè tanto
freddo; 2. Che gelida manina; 3. Sì. Mi chiamano
Mimì; 4. O soave fanciulla. ACT 2: 5. Aranci, datteri!;
6a. Chi guardi?; 6b. Eccoci qui!; 7a. Come un
facchino; 7b. Quando me'n vo' soletta (Musetta's
Waltz). ACT 3: 8. Ohè, là, le guardie; 9.
Mimì?!...Speravo di trovarvi; 10a.
Marcello...Finalmente; 10b. Mimì è una civetta; 11.
Donde lieta uscì (Mimì's Farewell); 12. Addio dolce
svegliare. ACT 4: 13a. In un coupé?; 13b. O Mimì, tu
più non torni; 14. Che ora sia?; 15. Musetta!...C'è
Mimì; 16. Vecchia zimarra (Coat song); 17a. Sono
andati?; 17b. Tornò al nido; 17c. Oh Dio! Mimì!
Cpte M. Caballé, P. Domingo, J. Blegen, S. Milnes,
V. Sardinero, R. Raimondi, N. Mangin, N. Castel, A.
Byers, F. Whiteley, W. Mason, Wandsworth Sch
Boys' Ch, John Alldis Ch, LPO, G. Solti
(9/86) (RCA) ① [2] **RD80371**
Cpte K. Ricciarelli, J. Carreras, A. Putnam, I. Wixell,
H. Hagegård, R. Lloyd, G. de Angelis, W. Elvin, F.
Egerton, R. Hazell, D. Whelan, ROH Chor, ROHO,
Colin Davis (r1979)
(5/87) (PHIL) ① [2] **416 492-2PH2**
Cpte V. de los Angeles, J. Björling, L. Amara, R.
Merrill, J. Reardon, G. Tozzi, F. Corena, W. Nahr, G.
del Monte, T. Powell, Columbus Boychoir, RCA
Victor Chor, RCA Victor SO, T. Beecham (r1956)
(6/87) (EMI) ① [2] **CDS7 47235-8**

12. J. Schmidt, Berlin St Op Orch, F. Weissmann (Ger: r1933) *Concert* (4/90) (EMI) ① **CDM7 69478-2**
12. L. Pavarotti, National PO, O. de Fabritiis *Concert* (7/90) (DECC) ① [2] **425 681-2DM2**
12. G. Campora, Rome Op Orch, G. Santini *Concert* (8/90) (CFP) ① **CD-CFP4569**
12. I. Calleja, orch (Eng: r1914) *Concert* (11/92) (MEMO) ① [2] **HR4408/9(2)**
12. P. Domingo, ROHO, Z. Mehta *Concert* (5/93) (DG) ① **431 104-2GB**
12. G. Lauri-Volpi, SO, M. Cordone (r1942) *Concert* (7/93) (NIMB) ① **NI7845**
12. A. Piccaver, orch (r1914: Ger) *Concert* (8/93) (PREI) ① **89060**
12. J. Björling, orch, N. Grevillius (r1937) *Concert* (10/93) (NIMB) ① **NI7842**
12. G. Zenatello, orch (r1911) *Concert* (5/94) (PEAR) ① [4] **GEMMCDS9073(2)**
12. P. Domingo, ROHO, J. Barker (pp1988) *Concert* (6/94) (EMI) ① **CDC5 55017-2**
12. J. Björling, orch, N. Grevillius (r1937) *Concert* (9/94) (CARL) ① **GLRS103**
12. J. Björling, orch, N. Grevillius (r1937) *Concert* (9/94) (CONI) ① **CDHD214**
12. T. Ralf, Saxon St Orch, K. Böhm (r1941: Ger) *Concert* (10/94) (PREI) ① **89077**
12(pt) A. Giorgini, orch (r1924) *Concert* (4/95) (RECO) ① **TRC3**
12. A. Piccaver, Vienna St Op Orch, H. Duhan (pp1937: Ger) *Concert* (6/95) (SCHW) ① [2] **314632**
12. J. Björling, MMF Orch, A. Erede (r1959) *Concert* (10/95) (DECC) ① **443 930-2DM**
12. B. Heppner, Munich RO, R. Abbado (r1993/4) *Concert* (11/95) (RCA) ① **09026 62504-2**

Gianni Schicchi—opera: 1 act (1918—New York) (Lib. Adami)

1. Firenze è come un albero fiorito; 2. O mio babbino caro; 3. Lauretta mia.

Cpte T. Gobbi, I. Cotrubas, P. Domingo, A. di Stasio, F. Andreolli, S. Fortunato, A. Domingo, A. Mariotti, G. Luccardi, C. del Bosco, S. Malagù, LSO, L. Maazel *Concert* (11/88) (SONY) ① [3] **M3K79312**
Cpte R. Panerai, H. Donath, P. Seiffert, W. Baniewicz, T. Pane, V. Errante, C. Kunz, G. Auer, F. Federici, R. Riener, M. Georg, Bavarian Rad Chor, Munich RO, G. Patanè *Concert* (4/90) (EURO) ① [3] **GD69043**
Cpte F. Corena, R. Tebaldi, A. Lazzari, L. Danieli, R. Ercolani, D. Carral, A. di Ninno, G. Foiani, P. Washington, S. Maionica, M.T. Pace, MMF Chor, MMF Orch, L. Gardelli *Concert* (2/91) (DECC) ① [3] **411 665-2DM3**
Cpte T. Gobbi, V. de los Angeles, C. del Monte, A.M. Canali, A. Zagonara, L. Marimpietri, C. Cornoldi, S. Meletti, P. Montarsolo, F. Valentini, G. Raymondi, Rome Op Orch, G. Santini (r1958) *Concert* (6/93) (EMI) ① [3] **CMS7 64165-2**
Cpte E. Tumagian, M. Gauci, Y. Ramiro, M. Perelstein, F. Careccia, D. Verdoodt, O. Van De Voorde, F. Van Eetveldt, M. Rosca, M. Meersman, R. Fabry, J. Joris, Brussels BRT PO, A. Rahbari (r1993) (7/94) (DINT) ① **DICD920119**
Cpte L. Nucci, M. Freni, R. Alagna, E. Podles, R. Cassinelli, B. Frittoli, B. Guerrini, G. Giorgetti, E. Fissore, O. Mori, N. Curiel, C. Cue, A. Mariotti, D. Jenis, D. Serraiocco, MMF Chor, MMF Orch, B. Bartoletti (r1991) *Concert* (8/94) (DECC) ① [3] **436 261-2DHO3**
Cpte R. Panerai, H. Donath, P. Seiffert, W. Baniewicz, T. Pane, V. Errante, C. Kunz, G. Auer, F. Federici, R. Riener, M. Georg, Bavarian Rad Chor, Munich RO, G. Patanè (r1987) (6/95) (RCA) ① **74321 25285-2**
Cpte R. Capecchi, B. Rizzoli, A. Lazzari, V. Palombini, P. de Palma, O. Rovero, N. Tarallo, P. Clabassi, G. Modesti, A. La Porta, M. Minetto, F. Mazzoli, G. Onesti, G. Gaudioso, Naples San Carlo Op Chor, Naples San Carlo Op Orch, F. Molinari-Pradelli (r1956) *Bohème.* (12/95) (PHIL) ① [2] **442 106-2PM2**
Excs A. Jerger, E. Réthy, D. With, E. Godin, W. Wernigk, M. Schober, O. Drapal, N. Zec, V. Madin, F. Worff, W. Achsel, K. Ettl, F. Skokan, F. Schramm, Vienna St Op Orch, W. Loibner (pp1938: Ger) *Concert* (3/95) (SCHW) ① [2] **314602**
2. K. Te Kanawa, LPO, J. Pritchard *Concert* (5/85) (SONY) ① **MK37298**
2. K. Te Kanawa, LPO, J. Pritchard *Concert* (8/86) (SONY) ① **MK39097**
2. M. Caballé, LSO, C. Mackerras *Concert* (10/87) (EMI) ① **CDC7 47841-2**
2. M. Callas, Philh, T. Serafin (r1954) *Concert* (12/87) (EMI) ① **CDC7 47966-2**
2. M. Freni, Hamburg PO, L. Magiera *Concert* (11/88) (ACAN) ① **49 384**
2. F. Weathers, Vienna Op. Orch, A. Quadri *Concert* (1/89) (DECC) ① **417 686-2DC**
2. A. Morelli, NYPO, Z. Mehta (pp1988) *Concert* (9/89) (SONY) ① **MK44942**
2. M. Freni, Orch, L. Magiera *Concert* (10/89) (EMI) ① **CDM7 63110-2**
2. A. Stella, LSO, A. Erede *Concert* (8/90) (CFP) ① **CD-CFP4569**
2. V. Masterson, RPO, R. Stapleton *Concert* (10/90) (CARL) ① **MCD15**
2. R. Tebaldi, MMF Orch, L. Gardelli *Concert* (8/91) (DECC) ① [2] **430 481-2DX2**
2. L. Garrett, Philh, A. Greenwood (r1990-1) *Concert* (11/91) (SILV) ① **SONGCD903**
2. M. Freni, Venice La Fenice Orch, R. Abbado *Concert* (9/92) (DECC) ① **433 316-2DH**
2. P. McCann, Black Dyke Mills Band, P. Parkes (r1984: arr G Langford) *Concert* (11/92) (CHAN) ① **CHAN4501**
2. M. Gauci, Belgian Rad & TV Orch, A. Rahbari *Concert* (11/92) (NAXO) ① **8 550606**
2. J. Hammond, Hallé, L. Heward (r1941: Eng) *Concert* (12/92) (TEST) ① **SBT1013**
2. L. Price, LSO, E. Downes *Concert* (12/92) (RCA) ① [4] **09026 61236-2**
2. L. Orgonášová, Bratislava RSO, W. Humburg *Concert* (2/93) (NAXO) ① **8 550605**
2. A. Roocroft, LPO, F. Welser-Möst *Concert* (10/94) (EMI) ① **CDC5 55090-2**
2. C. Muzio, orch (r1918) *Concert* (1/95) (ROMO) ① [2] **81010-2**
2. J. Varady, Berlin RSO, M. Viotti (r1993) *Concert* (5/95) (ORFE) ① **C323941A**
2. L. Popp, G. Parsons (pp1981) *Concert* (6/95) (ORFE) ① **C363941B**
2. E. Steber, orch, H. Barlow (bp1949) *Concert* (11/95) (VAI) ① **VAIA1072**
2. I. Galante, Latvian Nat SO, A. Vilumanis (r1994) *Concert* (11/95) (CAMP) ① **RRCD1335**
3. M. Freni, F. Bonisolli, Hamburg PO, L. Magiera *Concert* (11/88) (ACAN) ① **49 384**

Madama Butterfly—opera: 2 acts (1904—Milan) (Lib. Giacosa and Illica)

EXCERPTS: ACT 1: 1a. E soffitto; 1b. Questa è la cameriera; 2. Dovunque al mondo; 3a. Ed è bella la sposa?; 3b. Amore o grillo; 4a. Ah! ah! quanto cielo!; 4b. Ancora un passo; 5a. Gran ventura; 5b. L'Imperial Commissario; 6. Vieni, amor mio!; 7a. Ieri son salita tutta sola; 7b. Ed eccoci in famiglia; 8a. Viene la sera; 8b. Bimba, dagli occhi; 8c. Vogliatemi bene; 8d. Un po' di vero c'è. ACT 2: 9. E Izaghi e Izanami; 10. Un bel dì vedremo; 11a. C'è. Entrate; 11b. Ora a noi; 11c. Ebbene, che fareste; 11d. E questo?; 12. Che tua madre; 13a. Il cannone del porto!; 13b. Scuoti quella fronda; 13c. Tutti i fior; 13d. Or vienmi ad adornar; 14. Humming Chorus; 15. Intermezzo; 16. Già il sole!; 17a. Povera Butterfly; 17b. Ve lo dissi?; 17c. Io so che alle sue pene; 18a. Non ve l'avevo detto?; 18b. Addio, fiorito asil; 18c. Glielo dirai?; 19a. Che vuol da me; 19b. Come una mosca prigioniera; 20a. Con onor muore; 20b. Tu? tu? piccolo iddio.

Cpte M. Freni, L. Pavarotti, R. Kerns, C. Ludwig, M. Sénéchal, G. Stendoro, E. Schary, M. Rintzler, H. Helm, S.R. Frese, Vienna St Op Chor, VPO, H. von Karajan (r1974) (6/87) (DECC) ① [3] **417 577-2DH3**
Cpte R. Scotto, P. Domingo, I. Wixell, G. Knight, F. Andreolli, J. Summers, A. Murray, M. King, C. Keyte, A. Byers, Ambrosian Op Chor, Philh, L. Maazel (6/87) (SONY) ① [2] **M2K35181**
Cpte M. Callas, N. Gedda, M. Borriello, L. Danieli, R. Ercolani, Mario Carlin, L. Villa, P. Clabassi, E. Campi, La Scala Chor, La Scala Orch, H. von Karajan (r1955) (10/87) (EMI) ① [2] **CDS7 47959-8**
Cpte L. Price, R. Tucker, P. Maero, R. Elias, P. de Palma, R. Kerns, A. di Stasio, V. Carbonari, A. la Porta, M. Rinaudo, RCA Italiana Op Chor, RCA Italiana Op Orch, E. Leinsdorf (3/88) (RCA) ① [2] **RD86160**
Cpte A. Moffo, C. Valletti, R. Cesari, R. Elias, Mario Carlin, N. Catalani, M.T. Pace, F. Corena, L. Monreale, Rome Op Chor, Rome Op Orch, E. Leinsdorf (r1957) (9/88) (RCA) ① [2] **GD84145**
Cpte M. Freni, J. Carreras, J. Pons, T. Berganza, A. Laciura, M. Curtis, M. Rørholm, K. Rydl, P. Salomaa, H. Komatsu, Ambrosian Op Chor, Philh, G. Sinopoli (r1987) (12/88) (DG) ① [3] **423 567-2GH3**
Cpte R. Scotto, C. Bergonzi, R. Panerai, A. di Stasio, P. de Palma, G. Morresi, S. Padoan, P. Montarsolo, M. Rinaudo, Rome Op Chor, Rome Op Orch, J. Barbirolli (r1966) (5/89) (EMI) ① [2] **CMS7 69654-2**
Cpte R. Tebaldi, C. Bergonzi, E. Sordello, F. Cossotto, A. Mercuriali, M. Cazzato, L. Nerozzi, P. Washington, O. Nanni, V. Carbonari, Santa Cecilia Academy Chor, Santa Cecilia Academy Orch, T. Serafin (3/90) (DECC) ① [2] **425 531-2DM2**
Cpte V. de los Angeles, J. Björling, M. Sereni, M. Pirazzini, P. de Palma, A. la Porta, S. Bertona, P. Montarsolo, B. Giaiotti, A. Sacchetti, P. Caroli, Rome Op. Chor, Rome Op. Orch, G. Santini (3/91) (EMI) ① [2] **CMS7 63634-2**
Cpte M. Gauci, Y. Ramiro, G. Tichy, N. Boschková, J. Abel, R. Szücs, A. Michalková, J. Špaček, V. Kubovčik, Slovak Phil Chor, Bratislava RSO, A. Rahbari (5/92) (NAXO) ① [2] **8 660015/6**
2, 3b J. Hislop, W. Parnis, D. Gilly, orch, J. Harrison (r1923) *Concert* (1/93) (PEAR) ① **GEMMCD9956**
3b J. Hislop, D. Gilly, orch (r1923) *Concert* (7/92) (PEAR) ① [3] **GEMMCDS9925(1)**
3b, 18a E. Caruso, A. Scotti, orch (r1910) *Concert* (3/91) (PEAR) ① [3] **EVC2**
3b, 18a E. Caruso, A. Scotti, orch (r1910) *Concert* (10/94) (NIMB) ① **NI7857**
3b, 18a, 18b E. Caruso, A. Scotti, orch (r1910) *Concert* (7/91) (RCA) ① [12] **GD60495(3)**
3b, 18b W. Ludwig, G. Hüsch, Berlin St Op Orch, F. Zaun (r1934: Ger) *Concert* (7/95) (PREI) ① **89088**
4a, 10. Lotte Lehmann, orch (Ger: r1917) *Concert* (6/92) (PREI) ① [3] **89302**
4b E. Mason, orch (r1924) *Concert* (8/93) (SYMP) ① **SYMCD1136**
4b E. Mason, orch, F. Black (r1924) *Concert* (8/94) (ROMO) ① **81009-2**
4b C. Muzio, orch (r1917) *Concert* (1/95) (ROMO) ① [2] **81010-2**
4b, 7a, 10, 12, 20a G. Farrar, orch (r1909) *Concert* (10/94) (NIMB) ① **NI7857**
4b, 10. E. Mason, orch, F. Black (r1925) *Concert* (8/94) (ROMO) ① **81009-2**
8a-d R. Tauber, E. Rethberg, orch (Ger: r1922) *Concert* (3/92) (EMI) ① **CDH7 64029-2**
8a-d R. Pampanini, F. Ciniselli, orch, E. Panizza (r1928) *Concert* (8/93) (PREI) ① **89063**
8a-d M. Freni, C. Ludwig, L. Pavarotti, VPO, H. von Karajan (r1974) *Concert* (12/93) (DECC) ① **433 439-2DA**
8a-d E. Rethberg, R. Tauber, orch (r1922: Ger) *Concert* (7/94) (PREI) ① **89051**
8b M. Freni, F. Bonisolli, Hamburg PO, L. Magiera *Concert* (11/88) (ACAN) ① **49 384**
8b H. von Debička, H. Roswaenge, orch (r1929: Ger) *Concert* (2/92) (PREI) ① [2] **89201**
8b M. Sheridan, A. Pertile, La Scala Orch, C. Sabajno (r1927) *Concert* (7/92) (PEAR) ① [3] **GEMMCDS9925(2)**
8b-d M. Callas, N. Gedda, La Scala Chor, La Scala Orch, H. von Karajan (r1955) *Concert* (2/90) (EMI) ① [4] **CMS7 63244-2**
8b-d H. von Debička, H. Roswaenge, Berlin St Op Orch, M. Gurlitt (Ger: r1929) *Concert* (5/90) (PEAR) ① **GEMMCD9394**
8b, 10. S. Bullock, A. Davies, A. Bryn Parri (r1994) *Concert* (11/95) (SAIN) ① **SCDC2070**
8c R. Tauber, V. Schwarz, orch (Ger: r1930) *Concert* (7/89) (EMI) ① **CDM7 69476-2**
8c G. Zenatello, L. Cannetti, orch (r1911) *Concert* (5/94) (SYMP) ① **SYMCD1158**
8c J. Johnston, J. Gartside, ROHO, L. Collingwood (r1947: Eng) *Concert* (4/95) (TEST) ① **SBT1058**
8c, 8d G. Zenatello, L. Cannetti, orch (r1911) *Concert* (5/94) (PEAR) ① [4] **GEMMCDS9073(2)**
8d G. Farrar, E. Caruso, orch, W.B. Rogers (r1908) *Concert* (12/90) (PEAR) ① [3] **EVC1(2)**
8d G. Farrar, E. Caruso, orch, W.B. Rogers (r1908) *Concert* (7/91) (RCA) ① [12] **GD60495(2)**
8d G. Farrar, E. Caruso, orch (r1908) *Concert* (10/94) (NIMB) ① **NI7857**
10. K. Te Kanawa, LPO, J. Pritchard *Concert* (5/85) (SONY) ① **MK37298**
10. K. Te Kanawa, LPO, J. Pritchard *Concert* (8/86) (SONY) ① **MK39097**
10. M. Freni, Hamburg PO, L. Magiera *Concert* (11/88) (ACAN) ① **49 384**
10. F. Weathers, Vienna Op. Orch, A. Quadri *Concert* (1/89) (DECC) ① **417 686-2DC**
10. E. Turner, orch, J. Batten (r1933: Eng) *Concert* (9/89) (EMI) ① **CDH7 69791-2**
10. R. Ponselle, orch, R. Romani (r1919) *Concert* (10/89) (NIMB) ① **NI7802**
10. M. Freni, Orch, L. Magiera *Concert* (8/90) (CFP) ① **CD-CFP4569**
10. H. Spani, orch (r1925) *Concert* (9/90) (CLUB) ① [2] **CL99-509/10**
10. V. Masterson, RPO, R. Stapleton *Concert* (10/90) (CARL) ① **MCD15**

11a M. Caballé, B. Marti, LSO *Concert* (8/90) (CFP) Ⓓ **CD-CFP4569**

11a, 11b M. Callas, G. di Stefano, La Scala Orch, T. Serafin *Concert* (10/88) (EMI) Ⓓ **CDM7 69543-2**

11a, 11b K. Te Kanawa, J. Carreras, Bologna Teatro Comunale Orch, R. Chailly *Concert* (12/91) (DECC) Ⓓ **430 724-2DM**

11a, 11b P. Domingo, M. Caballé, NY Met Op Orch, James Levine *Concert* (5/93) (DG) Ⓓ **431 104-2GB**

11a, 11b M. Caballé, P. Domingo, NY Met Op Orch, James Levine (pp) *Concert* (5/93) (DG) Ⓓ **431 103-2GB**

11a, 11b R. Tebaldi, F. Corelli, SRO, A. Guadagno (r1972) *Concert* (10/93) (DECC) Ⓓ **436 301-2DA**

11a, 11b R. Tebaldi, F. Corelli, SRO, A. Guadagno (r1972) *Concert* (12/93) (DECC) Ⓓ **433 439-2DA**

11a, 11b A. Pertile, M. Sheridan, La Scala Orch, C. Sabajno (r1928) *Concert* (10/94) (PREI) Ⓓ **89072**

12. A. Pertile, La Scala Orch, C. Sabajno (r1930) *Concert* (9/90) (PREI) Ⓓ **89007**

12. G. Zenatello, orch, R. Bourdon (r1929) *Concert* (11/91) (CLUB) Ⓓ **CL99-025**

12. G. Zenatello, orch, R. Bourdon (r1929) *Concert* (11/91) (PREI) Ⓓ **89038**

12. G. Zenatello, orch (r1909) *Concert* (7/92) (PEAR) Ⓓ [3] **GEMMCDS9924(1)**

12. P. Schiavazzi, orch (r1910) *Concert* (11/92) (MEMO) Ⓓ [2] **HR4408/9(2)**

12. G. Zenatello, orch, R. Bourdon (r1929) *Concert* (5/94) (PEAR) Ⓓ [4] **GEMMCDS9074(2)**

12. A. Pertile, La Scala Orch, C. Sabajno (r1930) *Concert* (10/94) (PREI) Ⓓ **89072**

13. BPO, H. von Karajan *Concert* (10/87) (DG) Ⓓ [3] **419 257-2GH3**

13. Gothenburg SO, N. Järvi *Concert* (6/90) (DG) Ⓓ **429 494-2GDC**

15a E. Garbin, S. Cottone (r1902) *Concert* (4/94) (EMI) Ⓓ [3] **CHS7 64860-2(1)**

15a A. Pertile, A. Granforte, La Scala Orch, C. Sabajno (r1927) *Concert* (10/94) (PREI) Ⓓ **89072**

15a, 15b G. Lauri-Volpi, L. Borgonovo, La Scala Orch, F. Ghione (r1934) *Concert* (9/90) (PREI) Ⓓ **89012**

15a, 15b G. Lauri-Volpi, L. Borgonovo, La Scala Orch, F. Ghione (r1934) *Concert* (7/93) (NIMB) Ⓓ **NI7845**

15a, 15b J. Björling, E. Campi, Rome Op Orch, Rome Op Chor, J. Perlea (r1954) *Concert* (4/94) (RCA) Ⓓ [6] **09026 61580-2(5)**

18. R. Scotto, LSO, G. Gavazzeni *Concert* (8/86) (SONY) Ⓓ **MK39097**

18. A. Stella, LSO, A. Erede *Concert* (8/90) (CFP) Ⓓ **CD-CFP4569**

18. R. Pampanini, EIAR Orch, U. Tansini (r1940) *Concert* (8/93) (PREI) Ⓓ **89063**

La **Rondine, '(The) Swallow'—opera: 3 acts (1917—Monte Carlo)** (Lib. Adami)

EXCERPTS: ACT ONE: 1. Ah! no! no!; 2. Chi il bel sogno di Doretta; 3. Dolcessa! Ebbrezza!; 4. La Doretta della mia fantasia; 5. Denaro! Nient'altro che denaro!; 6. Ore dolci e divine; 7. E poi? Basta. È finito; 8. O mio giovine amico; 9. Forse, come la rondine. ACT TWO: 10. Fiori freschi!; 11. Chi è? Mai vista!; 12. Scusatemi, scusate; 13. Che caldo! Che sete!; 14. Perchè mai cercate di saper; 15. Zitti! Non disturbiamoli!; 16. Bevo al tuo fresco sorriso; 17. Rambaldo! Ah, M'aiutate!; 18. Nella trepida luce d'un mattin. ACT THREE: 19. Senti? Anche il mare respira sommesso; 20. E siam fuggiti qui per nasconderlo!; 21. Dimmi che vuoi seguirmi; 22. Che più dirgli? Che fare?; 23. È qui? Non so!; 24. Ma come voi?; 25. Amore mio! Mia madre!.

Cpte K. Te Kanawa, P. Domingo, M. Nicolesco, D. Rendall, L. Nucci, L. Watson, G. Knight, L. Finnie, E. Gale, O. Broome, M. Midgley, M. Thomas, U. Connors, B. Ogston, V. Midgley, L. Benson, D. Beavan, A. Byers, W. Evans, Ambrosian Op. Chor, LSO, L. Maazel (r1981) (10/85) (SONY) Ⓓ [2] **M2K37852**

Cpte A. Moffo, D. Barioni, G. Sciutti, P. de Palma, M. Sereni, S. Brigham-Dimiziani, V. de Notaristefani, F. Mattiucci, M. Basiola II, F. Iacopucci, R. El Hage, RCA Italiana Op Chor, RCA Italiana Op Orch, F. Molinari-Pradelli (r1966) (9/90) (RCA) Ⓓ [2] **GD60459**

2. K. Te Kanawa, LPO, J. Pritchard *Concert* (5/85) (SONY) Ⓓ **MK37298**

2. K. Te Kanawa, LPO, J. Pritchard *Concert* (8/86) (SONY) Ⓓ **MK39097**

2. M. Caballé, LSO, C. Mackerras (r1970) *Concert* (10/87) (EMI) Ⓓ **CDC7 47841-2**

2. M. Freni, Orch, L. Magiera *Concert* (10/89) (EMI) Ⓓ **CDM7 63110-2**

2. N. Miricioiu, D. Harper (pp1985) *Concert* (5/90) (ETCE) Ⓓ **KTC1041**

2. R. Tebaldi, New Philh, O. de Fabritiis *Concert* (8/91) (DECC) Ⓓ [2] **430 481-2DX2**

2. D. Kirsten, RCA Victor Orch, J-P. Morel (r1949) *Concert* (4/92) (EMI) Ⓓ [7] **CHS7 69741-2(1)**

2. L. Orgonášová, Bratislava RSO, W. Humburg *Concert* (2/93) (NAXO) Ⓓ **8 550605**

2. A. Roocroft, LPO, F. Welser-Möst *Concert* (10/94) (EMI) Ⓓ **CDC5 55090-2**

2. J. Varady, Berlin RSO, M. Viotti (r1993) *Concert* (5/95) (ORFE) Ⓓ **C323941A**

2. I. Galante, Latvian Nat SO, A. Vilumanis (r1994) *Concert* (11/95) (CAMP) Ⓓ **RRCD1335**

Suor Angelica, 'Sister Angelica'—opera: 1 act (1918—New York) (Wds. Forzano)

EXCERPTS. 1. Tutto ho offerto; 2. Intermezzo; 3. Senza mamma, O bimbo; 4. Amici fiori che nel.

Cpte R. Scotto, M. Horne, P. Payne, G. Knight, A. Howard, I. Cotrubas, D. Cryer, M. Cable, E. Bainbridge, S. Minty, G. Jennings, U. Connors, A. Gunson, D. Jones, Desborough School Ch, Ambrosian Op Chor, New Philh, L. Maazel *Concert* (11/88) (SONY) Ⓓ [3] **M3K79312**

Cpte L. Popp, M. Lipovšek, M. Schiml, D. Jennings, B. Calm, M.G. Ferroni, M. Georg, V. Errante, E. van Lier, K. Hautermann, M. Schmitt, A. Schiller, Bavarian Rad Chor, Munich RO, G. Patanè *Concert* (4/90) (EURO) Ⓓ [3] **GD69043**

Cpte R. Tebaldi, G. Simionato, L. Danieli, M.T. Pace, A. di Stasio, D. Carral, J. Valtriani, G. Tavolaccini, MMF Chor, MMF Orch, L. Gardelli *Concert* (2/91) (DECC) Ⓓ [3] **411 665-2DM3**

Cpte V. de los Angeles, F. Barbieri, M. Doro, C. Vozza, L. Marimpietri, S. Chissari, A. Marcangeli, T. Cantarini, S. Bertona, M. Huder, Rome Op Chor, Rome Op Orch, T. Serafin (r1957) *Concert* (6/93) (EMI) Ⓓ [3] **CMS7 64165-2**

Cpte M. Gauci, L. Van Deyck, M. Karadjian, R. Fabry, D. Grossberger, B. Degelin, D. Verdoodt, M. Vliegen, J. Greggoor Chor, Brussels BRT PO, A. Rahbari (r1993) (7/94) (DINT) Ⓓ **DICD920120**

Cpte M. Freni, E. Suliotis, G. Scalchi, E. Podles, N. Curiel, B. Frittoli, V. Esposito, O. Romanko, D. Beronesi, L. Cherici, S. Macculi, Prato Voci Bianche Chor, MMF Chor, MMF Orch, B. Bartoletti (r1991) *Concert* (8/94) (DECC) Ⓓ [3] **436 261-2DHO3**

2. BPO, H. von Karajan *Concert* (10/87) (DG) Ⓓ [3] **419 257-2GH3**

2. Gothenburg SO, N. Järvi *Concert* (6/90) (DG) Ⓓ **429 494-2GDC**

3. R. Scotto, New Philh, L. Maazel *Concert* (8/86) (SONY) Ⓓ **MK39097**

3. M. Callas, Philh, T. Serafin (r1954) *Concert* (12/87) (EMI) Ⓓ **CDC7 47966-2**

3. M. Freni, Rome Op Orch, F. Ferraris *Concert* (10/89) (EMI) Ⓓ **CDM7 63110-2**

3. F. Cavalli, RPO, A. Fistoulari *Concert* (8/90) (CFP) Ⓓ **CD-CFP4569**

3. K. Te Kanawa, LSO, Myung-Whun Chung *Concert* (11/90) (EMI) Ⓓ **CDC7 54062-2**

3. R. Tebaldi, MMF Orch, L. Gardelli *Concert* (8/91) (DECC) Ⓓ [2] **430 481-2DX2**

3. M. Gauci, Belgian Rad & TV Orch, A. Rahbari *Concert* (11/92) (NAXO) Ⓓ **8 550606**

3. L. Price, RCA Italiana Op Orch, F. Molinari-Pradelli *Concert* (12/92) (RCA) Ⓓ [4] **09026 61236-2**

3. A. Oltrabella, orch, G. Antonicelli (r1936) *Concert* (4/94) (EMI) Ⓓ [3] **CHS7 64864-2(2)**

3. C. Muzio, orch (r1918) *Concert* (1/95) (ROMO) Ⓓ [2] **81010-2**

3. J. Varady, Berlin RSO, M. Viotti (r1993) *Concert* (5/95) (ORFE) Ⓓ **C323941A**

3, 4. Lotte Lehmann, orch (Ger: r1920) *Concert* (6/92) (PREI) Ⓓ [3] **89302**

Il **Tabarro, '(The) Cloak'—opera: 1 act (1918—New York)** (Lib. Adami)

EXCERPTS. 1. Hai ben ragione; 2a. È ben altro il mio sogno!; 2b. Ma chi lascia il sobborgo; 2c. O Luigi!; 2d. Folle di gelosia!; 3. Perchè non m'ami più; 4a. Scorri, fiume eterno (original version of Michele's aria); 4b. Nulla! Silenzio! (replacement version of Michele's aria).

Cpte I. Wixell, R. Scotto, P. Domingo, M. Sénéchal, D. Wicks, G. Knight, Ambrosian Op Chor, New Philh, L. Maazel *Concert* (11/88) (SONY) Ⓓ [3] **M3K79312**

Cpte S. Nimsgern, I. Tokody, G. Lamberti, T. Pane, G. Auer, W. Baniewicz, Bavarian Rad Chor, Munich RO, G. Patanè *Concert* (4/90) (EURO) Ⓓ [3] **GD69043**

Cpte R. Merrill, R. Tebaldi, M. del Monaco, R. Ercolani, S. Maionica, L. Danieli, MMF Chor, MMF Orch, L. Gardelli *Concert* (2/91) (DECC) Ⓓ [3] **411 665-2DM3**

Cpte T. Gobbi, M. Mas, G. Prandelli, P. de Palma, P. Clabassi, M. Pirazzini, Rome Op Chor, Rome Op Orch, V. Bellezza (r1955) *Concert* (6/93) (EMI) Ⓓ [3] **CMS7 64165-2**

Cpte J. Pons, M. Freni, G. Giacomini, P. de Palma, F. de Grandis, G. Scalchi, R. Cassinelli, B. Frittoli, R. Emili, MMF Chor, MMF Orch, B. Bartoletti (r1991) *Concert* (8/94) (DECC) Ⓓ [3] **436 261-2DHO3**

Cpte E. Tumagian, M. Slatinaru, N. Martinucci, A. Leonel, M. Rosca, L. van Deyck, J. Gregoor Ch, Brussels BRT Phil Chor, Brussels BRT PO, A. Rahbari (r1994) (4/95) (DINT) Ⓓ **DICD920209**

1. D. Smirnov, orch (r1921) *Concert* (7/90) (CLUB) Ⓓ **CL99-031**

4a L. Tibbett, orch (pp1935) *Concert* (3/91) (PEAR) Ⓓ [2] **GEMMCDS9452**

Tosca—opera: 3 acts (1900—Rome) (Lib. Illica and Giacosa)

ACT 1: 1a. Ah! Finalmente!; 1b. E sempre lava!; 1c. Sante ampolle!; 2. Recondita armonia; 3a. Mario!; 3b. Perchè chiuso?; 3c. Ora stammi a sentir; 3d. Non la sospiri; 3e. Or lasciami al lavoro; 3f. Ah, quegli occhi!; 4. È buona la mia Tosca; 5. Sommo giubilo; 6a. Un tal baccano in chiesa!; 6b. Fu grave sbaglio; 7a. Or tutto è chiaro; 7b. Tosca divina; 7c. O che v'offende; 8. Tre sbirri (Te Deum). ACT 2: 9a. Tosca è un buon falco; 9b. Ella verrà; 10a. Sale, ascende...A te quest'inno (Cantata); 10b. Mario, tu qui?; 11a. La povera mia cena; 11b. Già, mi dicon venal; 11c. Se la giurata; 12. Vissi d'arte; 13a. Sei troppo bella; 13b. Tosca. finalmente mia!. ACT 3: 14. Prelude; 15a. Io de' sospiri; 15b. Mario Cavaradossi?; 16. E lucevan le stelle; 17a. Franchigia a Floria Tosca; 17b. O dolci mani; 17c. Senti, l'ora è vicina; 18a. Amaro sol per te; 18b. Trionfal...Di nova speme; 19a. Son pronto; 19b. Com'è lunga l'attesa!.

Cpte K. Ricciarelli, J. Carreras, R. Raimondi, G. Hornik, H. Zednik, F. Corena, V. von Halem, W. Bünten, Berlin Deutsche Op Chor, BPO, H. von Karajan (3/85) (DG) Ⓓ [2] **413 815-2GH2**

Cpte M. Callas, G. di Stefano, T. Gobbi, F. Calabrese, A. Mercuriali, M. Luise, D. Caselli, A. Cordova, La Scala Chor, La Scala Orch, V. de Sabata (r1953) (9/85) (EMI) Ⓓ [2] **CDS7 47175-8**

Cpte M. Caballé, J. Carreras, I. Wixell, S. Ramey, P. de Palma, D. Trimarchi, W. Elvin, A. Murray, ROH Chor, ROHO, Colin Davis (4/86) (PHIL) Ⓓ [2] **412 885-2PH2**

Cpte K. Te Kanawa, G. Aragall, L. Nucci, M. King, P. de Palma, S. Malas, P. Hudson, N. Folwell, I. Martinez, ROH Children's Chor, WNO Chor, National PO, G. Solti (11/86) (DECC) Ⓓ [2] **414 597-2DH2**

Cpte L. Price, P. Domingo, S. Milnes, C. Grant, F. Egerton, P. Plishka, J. Gibbs, M. Rippon, D. Pearl, Wandsworth Sch Boys' Ch, John Alldis Ch, New Philh, Z. Mehta (11/86) (RCA) Ⓓ [2] **RD80105**

Cpte Z. Milanov, J. Björling, L. Warren, L. Monreale, Mario Carlin, F. Corena, N. Catalani, V. Preziosa, G. Bianchini, Rome Op Chor, Rome Op Orch, E. Leinsdorf (1/89) (RCA) Ⓓ [2] **GD84514**

Cpte M. Freni, L. Pavarotti, S. Milnes, R. Van Allan, M. Sénéchal, I. Tajo, P. Hudson, J. Tomlinson, W. Baratti, Wandsworth Sch Boys' Ch, London Op Chor, National PO, N. Rescigno (1/89) (DECC) Ⓓ [2] **414 036-2DH2**

Cpte R. Scotto, P. Domingo, R. Bruson, J. Cheek, A. Velis, R. Capecchi, P. Hudson, I. Perlman, D. Martinez, Ambrosian Op Chor, St Clement Danes Sch Ch, Philh, James Levine (r1980) (1/89) (EMI) Ⓓ [2] **CDS7 49364-2**

Cpte L. Price, G. di Stefano, G. Taddei, C. Cava, P. de Palma, F. Corena, L. Monreale, A. Mariotti, H. Weiss, Vienna St Op Chor, VPO, H. von Karajan (1/89) (DECC) Ⓓ [2] **421 670-2DM2**

Cpte M. Callas, C. Bergonzi, T. Gobbi, L. Monreale, R. Ercolani, G. Tadeo, U. Trama, D. Sellar, Paris Op Chor, Paris Cons, G. Prêtre (r1964) (8/89) (EMI) Ⓓ [2] **CMS7 69974-2**

Cpte E. Marton, J. Carreras, J. Pons, I. Gáti, F. Gerdesits, I. Tajo, J. Német, J. Gregor, B. Héja, Hungarian Rad & TV Chor, Hungarian St Orch, M. Tilson Thomas (10/90) (SONY) Ⓓ [2] **S2K45847**

Cpte R. Tebaldi, M. del Monaco, G. London, S. Maionica, P. de Palma, F. Corena, G. Morese, E. Palerini, Santa Cecilia Academy Chor, Santa Cecilia Academy Orch, F. Molinari-Pradelli (8/91) (DECC) Ⓓ [2] **411 871-2DM2**

Cpte N. Miricioiu, G. Lamberti, S. Carroli, A. Piccinni, M. Dvorský, J. Špaček, J. Durco, S. Benacka, Slovak Phil Chor, Bratislava RSO, A. Rahbari (10/91) (NAXO) Ⓓ [2] **8 660001/2**

Cpte M. Freni, P. Domingo, S. Ramey, B. Terfel, A. Laciura, A. Veccia, R. Lukas, B. Secombe, L. Tiernan, ROH Chor, Philh, G. Sinopoli (r1990) (7/92) (DG) Ⓓ [2] **431 775-2GH2**

**Turandot—opera: 3 acts (1926—Milan) (cpted
Alfano: Lib. Adami and Simoni)**
ACT 1: 1. Popolo di Pekino!; 2. Gira la cote!; 3.
Perchè tarda la luna?; 4. O giovinetto!; 5.
Principessa! Pietà!; 6. Fermo! che fai?; 7. Non
indugiare!; 8. Signore, ascolta!; 9. Non piangere, Liù!;
10. Ah! per l'ultima volta!. ACT 2. 11a. Olà, Pang!
Olà, Pong!; 11b. O China; 11c. Ho una casa; 11d. Vi
ricordate il principe regal; 11e. Addio, amore; 12a.
Gravi, enormi; 12b. Un giuramento; 12c. Popolo di
Pekino!; 13a. In questa Reggia; 13b. O Principe, che
a lunghe carovane; 14. Straniero, ascolta!; 15. Tre
enigmi. ACT 3: 16. Così comanda Turandot; 17.
Nessun dorma!; 18. Tu che guardi le stelle; 19.
Principessa divina!; 20. Tanto amore; 21. Tu, che di
gel sei cinta; 22. Liù!; 23. Principessa di morte!; 24a.
Del primo pianto; 24b. Diecimila anni al nostro
Imperatore!.

17. L. Pavarotti, Grudgionz Fest Chor, Grudgionz
Fest Orch, G-F. Masini (pp1964) *Concert*
(10/95) (RCA) ① **09026 68014-2**
17. B. Heppner, Bavarian Rad Chor, Munich RO, R.
Abbado (r1993/4) *Concert*
(11/95) (RCA) ① **09026 62504-2**
20, 21. E. Norena, orch, P. Coppola (r1932) *Concert*
(3/91) (PREI) ① **89041**
21. K. Ricciarelli, J. Carreras, Vienna St Op Chor,
Vienna St Op Orch, L. Maazel *Concert*
(8/86) (SONY) ① **MK39097**
21. A. Tomowa-Sintow, Munich RO, P. Sommer
Concert (11/86) (ORFE) ① **C106841A**
21. M. Freni, Rome Op Orch, F. Ferraris *Concert*
(8/90) (CFP) ① **CD-CFP4569**
21. E. Arizmendi, orch, J.E. Martini (r c1953) *Concert*
(4/92) (EMI) ① **[7] CHS7 69741-2(7)**
21. K. Ricciarelli, Verona Arena Orch, B. Martinotti
(pp) *Concert* (5/94) (DECC) ① **[2] 443 018-2DF2**
23, 24a, 24b L. Kelm, J.F. West, chor, orch, C.
Keene (pp1985: original Alfano conclusion) *Alfano:
Risurrezione.* (10/93) (LYRC) ① **[2] SRO839**
Le **Villi—opera: 2 acts (1884—Milan)** (Lib.
Fontana)
EXCERPTS. ACT 1: 1. Prelude; 2. Evviva! Evviva!;
3. Se come voi piccina io fossi; 4. Non esser, Anna
mia; 5. Presto! Presto in vaggio. ACT 2: 6.
L'Abbandono; 7. La Tregenda; 8. No, possibil non è;
9a. Ecco la casa; 9b. Torna ai felice; 10. Roberto!.
Cpte L. Nucci, R. Scotto, P. Domingo, T. Gobbi,
Ambrosian Op Chor, National PO, L. Maazel
(5/88) (SONY) ① **MK76890**
1. P. Dvorský, Bratislava RSO, O. Lenárd *Concert*
(5/92) (NAXO) ① **8 550343**
3. K. Te Kanawa, LPO, J. Pritchard *Concert*
(5/85) (SONY) ① **MK37298**
3. K. Te Kanawa, LPO, J. Pritchard *Concert*
(8/86) (SONY) ① **MK39097**
3. M. Caballé, LSO, C. Mackerras *Concert*
(10/87) (EMI) ① **CDC7 47841-2**
3. M. Gauci, Belgian Rad & TV Orch, A. Rahbari
Concert (11/92) (NAXO) ① **8 550606**

PUCITTA (PUCCITTA), Vincenzo
(1778–1861) Italy

SECTION V: STAGE WORKS

La **Vestale—opera: 2 acts (1810—London)**
Viva di Roma...Guldò Marte i nostri passi P. Nilon,
G. Mitchell Ch, Philh, D. Parry *Concert*
(10/90) (OPRA) ① **[3] ORCH103**

PUGNACCI

SECTION IV: VOCAL AND CHORAL

Il **Gitano Re—song**
T. Ruffo, orch (r1929) *Concert*
(2/93) (PREI) ① **[3] 89303(2)**

PUGNANI, (Giulio) Gaetano
(Gerolamo) *(1731–1798) Italy*

SECTION II: CHAMBER

**6 Sonatas—violin and continuo, Op. 7
(ZT106-111) (c1770)** (pub as Op. 5 in
Amsterdam & Op. 6 in Paris)
1. E.
1. H. Temianka, J. Graudan (arr Alard: r1937)
Concert (2/93) (BIDD) ① **[2] LAB059/60**

SECTION III: INSTRUMENTAL

**6 Sonatas—violin, Op. 8 (ZT112-117) (before
1774)**
3. D.
3 (Largo espressivo) G. Enescu, S. Schlüssel (arr
Moffat: r1929) *Concert*
(12/91) (MSCM) ① **MM30322**
3(Largo espressivo) G. Enescu, S. Schlüssel (arr
Moffat: r1929) *Concert* (6/93) (BIDD) ① **LAB066**

PUGNI, Cesare *(1802–1870)*
Italy

SECTION V: STAGE WORKS

Esmerelda—ballet (1844—London) (additional
numbers by Drigo for 1886 revival)
1. Diane et Actéon: pas de deux (comp Drigo).
1. English Concert Orch, R. Bonynge (arr March)
Concert (11/90) (DECC) ① **[2] 421 818-2DH2**
**Pas de quatre—ballet divertissement
(1845—London)**
English Concert Orch, R. Bonynge (arr March)
Concert (11/90) (DECC) ① **[2] 421 818-2DH2**

PUJOL, Maximo Diego *(b 1957)*
Argentina

SECTION III: INSTRUMENTAL

Candombe en mi—guitar
E. Kotzia *Concert* (6/89) (PEAR) ① **SHECD9609**
Preludio tristón—guitar
E. Kotzia *Concert* (6/89) (PEAR) ① **SHECD9609**
Sevilla—guitar
W. Lendle *Concert* (7/92) (TELD) ① **9031-75864-2**
Tristango en vos—guitar
E. Kotzia *Concert* (6/89) (PEAR) ① **SHECD9609**

PUJOL VILARRUBÍ, Emilio
(1886–1980) Spain

SECTION III: INSTRUMENTAL

3 Spanish Pieces—guitar
1. Tonadilla; 2. Guajira; 3. Tango.
T. Kerstens *Concert* (7/92) (CONI) ① **CDCF509**
2, 3. J. Bream (r1983-90) *Concert*
(8/93) (RCA) ① **[28] 09026 61583-2(6)**
2, 3. J. Bream (r1983-90) *Concert*
(6/94) (RCA) ① **09026 61609-2**

PURCELL, Daniel *(c1660–1717)*
England

SECTION II: CHAMBER

Sonata for Two Trumpets and Strings
English Tpt Virtuosi, A. Hoskins (tpt/dir), M. Hoskins
(tpt/dir) (r1994) *Concert* (10/95) (MOSC) ① **070979**
**Sonata in D minor—recorder and continuo
(pub 1698)**
D. Munrow, O. Brookes, C. Hogwood (r1973) *Concert*
(10/95) (DECC) ① **440 079-2DM**

SECTION IV: VOCAL AND CHORAL

**Evening Service in E minor—choir and
organ**
Chichester Cath Ch, A. Thurlow, J. Thomas (r1994)
Concert (5/95) (PRIO) ① **PRCD511**

SECTION V: STAGE WORKS

**Achilles, or Iphgenia in Aulis—incidental
music (1699—London)** (Wds. Boyce)
EXCERPTS: 1. O Morpheus, thou gentle God.
1. C. Bott, D. Roblou, M. Levy (r1990) *Concert*
(2/93) (L'OI) ① **433 187-2OH**
1. E. Tubb, F. Kelly (r1992) *Concert*
(9/94) (MOSC) ① **070987**
The **Pilgrim—secular masque
(1700—London)** (Wds. Dryden)
EXCERPTS: 1. With horns and hounds.
1. E. Kirkby, English Tpt Virtuosi, A. Hoskins (tpt/dir),
M. Hoskins (tpt/dir) (r1994) *Concert*
(10/95) (MOSC) ① **070979**

PURCELL, Henry II *(1659–1695)*
England

Z–Numbers from F.F. Zimmerman's Analytic
Catalogue, 1963

SECTION I: ORCHESTRAL

Chaconne in G minor for strings, Z730
English Concert, T. Pinnock (hpd/dir) *Concert*
(1/86) (ARCH) ① **415 518-2AH**
Parley of Instr, P. Holman *Concert*
(9/87) (HYPE) ① **CDA66212**
ASMF, N. Marriner *Concert*
(11/89) (CFP) ① **CD-CFP4557**
London Baroque *Concert*
(10/90) (HARM) ① **HMC90 1327**
Eighteenth Century Orch, F. Brüggen *Concert*
(4/91) (PHIL) ① **426 714-2PH**
AAM, C. Hogwood *Concert*
(4/91) (L'OI) ① **[6] 425 893-2OM6(2)**
Scottish Ens, J. Rees (r1991) *Concert*
(1/92) (VIRG) ① **VJ7 59652-2**
Freiburg Baroque Orch, T. Hengelbrock *Concert*
(3/92) (DHM) ① **RD77231**
Capriccio Stravagante, S. Sempé (hpd/dir) *Concert*
(9/92) (DHM) ① **RD77252**
Leonhardt Consort, G. Leonhardt (r1969) *Concert*
(9/93) (TELD) ① **[2] 9031-77608-2**
Guildhall Str Ens, R. Salter (vn/dir) (r1992; arr Britten)
Concert (2/94) (RCA) ① **09026 61275-2**
LPO, L. Slatkin (1989; arr Britten) *Concert*
(3/94) (RCA) ① **09026 61226-2**
Parley of Instr, P. Holman (r1993) *Concert*
(6/94) (HYPE) ① **CDA66667**

London Baroque (r1989) *Concert*
(7/95) (HARM) ① **[6] HMX290 1528/33(1)**
English Concert, T. Pinnock (r1983) *Concert*
(7/95) (ARCH) ① **447 153-2AP**
AAM, C. Hogwood (r1994) *Concert*
(9/95) (PHIL) ① **446 081-2PH**
R. Browder, Purcell Qt *Concert*
(10/89) (CHAN) ① **CHAN8663**
**March and Canzona in C minor—for the
funeral of Queen Mary II, Z860 (1692)** (orig
from 'The Libertine', Z600)
ECO, S. Cleobury, J. Ryan, Symphoniae Sacrae, G.
Guest *Concert* (7/91) (DECC) ① **430 263-2DM**
ECO, G. Guest (r1972) *Concert*
(6/93) (DECC) ① **436 403-2DWO**
Collegium Vocale, P. Herreweghe (r1993) *Concert*
(2/94) (HARM) ① **HMC90 1462**
King's Consort, R. King (r1993) *Concert*
(6/94) (HYPE) ① **CDA66677**
London Baroque Brass, D. Hill (r1992) *Concert*
(6/94) (ARGO) ① **436 833-2ZH**
The Sixteen, The Sixteen Orch, H. Christophers
(r1994) *Concert* (1/95) (COLL) ① **Coll1425-2**
New London Consort, M. Neary (r1994) *Concert*
(3/95) (SONY) ① **SK66243**
Collegium Vocale, P. Herreweghe (r1993) *Concert*
(7/95) (HARM) ① **[6] HMX290 1528/33(1)**
Taverner Plyrs, A. Parrott (1988) *Concert*
(12/95) (VIRG) ① **VC5 45159-2**
Sonata for Trumpet and Strings No. 1 in D
(ov to lost ode, 'Light of the world')
A. Stringer, N. Rawsthorne (r1974) *Concert*
(11/87) (CRD) ① **CRD3308**
P. Hurford, M. Laird Brass Ens (r1990: arr Hurford)
Concert (9/94) (ARGO) ① **433 451-2ZH**
Suite—wind and strings (arr Barbirolli:
1930s)
1. Andante maestoso—Allegro (The Gordian Knot
Untied: Overture); 2. Tempo di minuetto (The
Virtuous Wife: Minuet); 3. Andantino (King Arthur:
Fairest Isle); 4. Allegro giocoso (Abdelazar: Air); 5.
Largo (Dido and Aeneas: Dido's Lament); 6. Allegro
(King Arthur: Allegro from second music).
NYPSO, J. Barbirolli (r1938) *Concert*
(4/92) (PEAR) ① **GEMMCDS9922**
Suite of Instrumental Pieces (arr. Hogwood
from various sources)
1. Cebell; 2. To Arms; 3. Slow Air; 4. We Come to
Sing; 5. Trumpet Tune; 6. Jig; 7. Hear, Mighty Love.
C. Steele-Perkins, AAM, C. Hogwood (r1994)
Concert (9/95) (PHIL) ① **446 081-2PH**

SECTION II: CHAMBER

Chaconne in F—recorders and continuo
(unidentified)
F. Brüggen, K. Boeke, W. van Hauwe, W. Möller, B.
van Asperen (r1979) *Concert*
(10/95) (TELD) ① **4509-97465-2**
**Fantasia in A minor (incomplete)—four
violas da gamba** (r1994) *Concert*
Fretwork (r1994) *Concert*
(5/95) (VIRG) ① **VC5 45062-2**
**Fantasia in F, 'Upon one note'—five viols,
Z745 (c1680)**
Eighteenth Century Orch, F. Brüggen *Concert*
(4/91) (PHIL) ① **426 714-2PH**
Baroque Plyrs (r1950s) *Concert*
(9/93) (VANG) ① **[2] 08.2003.72**
Fretwork (r1994) *Concert*
(5/95) (VIRG) ① **VC5 45062-2**
VCM (r1960s) *Concert*
(7/95) (ARCH) ① **447 153-2AP**
SCB (r1954) *Concert*
(7/95) (ARCH) ① **447 156-2AP**
Fantasia upon a Ground, Z731 (c1680)
Taverner Plyrs, A. Parrott *Concert*
(12/88) (EMI) ① **CDM7 69853-2**
R. Browder, Purcell Qt *Concert*
(10/89) (CHAN) ① **CHAN8663**
London Baroque *Concert*
(10/90) (HARM) ① **HMC90 1327**
Eighteenth Century Orch, F. Brüggen *Concert*
(4/91) (PHIL) ① **426 714-2PH**
Capriccio Stravagante, S. Sempé (hpd/dir) *Concert*
(9/92) (DHM) ① **RD77252**
N. Marriner, P. Gibbs, G. Jones, D. Dupré, G.
Malcolm (r1950s) *Concert*
(9/93) (VANG) ① **[2] 08.2003.72**
J. Holloway, S. Ritchie, A. Manze, N. North, M.
Springfels, J. Toll (r1993) *Concert*
(2/94) (HARM) ① **HMU90 7091**
Scaramouche, K. Junghänel, F. Kooistra (r1992)
Concert (5/94) (CHNN) ① **CCS4792**
London Baroque (r1989) *Concert*
(7/95) (HARM) ① **[6] HMX290 1528/33(1)**

Prelude in G minor—violin, Z N773
C. Mackintosh *Concert*

(12/89) (CHAN) ① **CHAN8763**
The **Second Part of Musick's Hand-maid**—keyboard (pub 1687) (works by Purcell in Playford's Collection)

1. Song Tune in C, Z T694 (Ah! how pleasant, Z353); 2. Song Tune in C, Z695 (Sylvia now your scorn, Z420); 3a. March in C, Z647; 3b. March in C, Z648; 4. A New Minuet in D minor, Z T689; 5a. Minuet in A minor, Z649; 5b. Minuet in A minor, Z650; 6. Minuet in D minor, Z T682 (Welcome to all the pleasures, Z339); 7. A New Scotch Tune in G, Z655; 8. A New Ground in E minor, Z T682 (Welcome to all the pleasures, Z339); 9. A New Irish Tune in G, Z646 (Lilliburlero); 10. Rigadoon in C, Z653; 11. Sefauchi's Farewell in D minor, Z656; 12. Suite in C, Z665.

1, 3a, 3b, 4, 5a, 5b, 6, 7, 8, 9, 10, 11. G. Malcolm
(1950s) *Concert* (9/93) (HYPE) ① [2] **08.2003.72**
8. K. Gilbert *Concert* (6/88) (NOVA) ① **150 018-2**
8. C. Rousset (r1992) *Concert*
(9/93) (ASTR) ① **E8757**
8. K. Gilbert (r1993) *Concert*
(5/95) (HARM) ① **HMC90 1496**
9. T. Pinnock (r1978) *Concert*
(4/89) (CRD) ① **CRD3347**
9. B. Wissick (r1991) *Concert*
(10/95) (ALBA) ① **TROY127-2**
9, 11. G. Leonhardt (r1967) *Concert*
(9/93) (TELD) ① [2] **9031-77608-2**
12. D. Moroney (r1995) *Concert*
(5/95) (VIRG) ① **VC5 45166-2**
Trumpet Tune in D—organ (pub c1780) (ed Cooper)
J. Butt (r1992) *Concert*
(6/94) (HARM) ① **HMU90 7103**
J. Butt (r1992) *Concert*
(7/95) (HARM) ① [6] **HMX290 1528/33(2)**
Unidentified Verset—keyboard (possibly spurious)
T. Dart (1957) *Concert* (5/95) (JMS) ① **JMSCD1**
Verse in F—organ, Z716
J. Butt (r1992) *Concert*
(6/94) (HARM) ① **HMU90 7103**
R. Woolley (r1993) *Concert*
(9/94) (CHAN) ① **CHAN0553**
T. Dart (1957) *Concert* (5/95) (JMS) ① **JMSCD1**
J. Butt (r1992) *Concert*
(7/95) (HARM) ① [6] **HMX290 1528/33(2)**
4 Voluntaries—organ, Z717-20
1. C; 2. D minor; 3. D minor (double organ); 4. G.
J. Butt (r1992) *Concert*
(6/94) (HARM) ① **HMU90 7103**
J. Butt (r1992) *Concert*
(7/95) (HARM) ① [6] **HMX290 1528/33(2)**
1, 2, 4. L. Cummings (r1994) *Concert*
(2/95) (NAXO) ① **8 553129**
1, 3, 4. R. Woolley (r1993) *Concert*
(9/94) (CHAN) ① **CHAN0553**
1, 4. D. Hill (r1992) *Concert*
(6/94) (ARGO) ① **436 833-2ZH**
1, 4. T. Dart (1957) *Concert*
(5/95) (JMS) ① **JMSCD1**
1, 4. T. Roberts *Concert*
(7/95) (ARCH) ① **445 824-2AH**
2, 4. R. Woolley *Concert*
(12/89) (CHAN) ① **CHAN8763**
3. T. Koopman *Concert* (5/91) (CAPR) ① **10 254**
3, 4. S. Preston (r1984/5) *Choice Collection of Lessons.* (7/95) (ARCH) ① **447 154-2AP**
Voluntary in A (on the Old 100th)—organ, Z721
A. Lumsden *Concert* (4/91) (GUIL) ① **GRCD7025**
J. Butt (r1992) *Concert*
(6/94) (HARM) ① **HMU90 7103**
T. Dart (1957) *Concert* (5/95) (JMS) ① **JMSCD1**
J. Butt (r1992) *Concert*
(7/95) (HARM) ① [6] **HMX290 1528/33(2)**

SECTION IV: VOCAL AND CHORAL

A thousand sev'ral ways I tried—song, Z359 (c1681, pub 1684)
R. Covey-Crump, M. Caudle, D. Miller, R. King (r1993) *Concert* (9/94) (HYPE) ① **CDA66710**
Ah! cruel nymph, you give despair—song (1v), Z352
R. Jacobs, W. Kuijken, K. Junghänel *Concert*
(8/85) (ACCE) ① **ACC57802D**
P. Esswood, J. Sonnleitner, C. Medlam *Concert*
(12/89) (HYPE) ① **CDA66070**
R. Covey-Crump, King's Consort (r1993) *Concert*
(10/94) (HYPE) ① **CDA66720**
Ah! how pleasant 'tis to love—song (1v), Z353 (pub 1688)
B. Bonney, M. Caudle, D. Miller, R. King (r1993) *Concert* (9/94) (HYPE) ① **CDA66710**

Amidst the shades and cool refreshing streams—song, Z355 (1687)
B. Bonney, M. Caudle, D. Miller, R. King (r1993) *Concert* (9/94) (HYPE) ① **CDA66710**
Amintas, to my grief I see—song, Z356 (1679)
R. Covey-Crump, S. Pell, D. Miller, R. King (r1993-4) *Concert* (1/95) (HYPE) ① **CDA66730**
Amintor, heedless of his flocks—song, Z357 (1681)
C. Daniels, M. Caudle, D. Miller, R. King (r1993-4) *Concert* (1/95) (HYPE) ① **CDA66730**
Anacreon's Defeat, 'This poet sings the Trojan wars'—song, Z423 (1688)
M. George, M. Caudle, D. Miller, R. King (r1993) *Concert* (9/94) (HYPE) ① **CDA66710**
Ask me to love no more—song, Z358 (1694) (Wds A. Hammond)
J. Bowman, M. Caudle, D. Miller, R. King (r1993-4) *Concert* (1/95) (HYPE) ① **CDA66730**
Awake and with attention hear—devotional song: bass and continuo, Z181 (1688) (Wds. A. Cowley)
M. George, King's Consort, R. King (r1992-3) *Concert* (2/94) (HYPE) ① **CDA66656**
H. van der Kamp, G. Leonhardt (r1994) *Concert*
(11/95) (SONY) ① **SK53981**
Awake, awake, put on thy strength—verse anthem, Z1 (c1682-85)
R. Covey-Crump, C. Daniels, M. George, King's Consort, R. King (r1993/4) *Concert*
(3/95) (HYPE) ① **CDA66716**
Awake, ye dead—sacred song: 2vv, Z182 (1688) (wds. N. Tate)
M. George, M. Evans, King's Consort, R. King (r1992-3) *Concert* (9/93) (HYPE) ① **CDA66644**
Gabrieli Consort, Gabrieli Players, P. McCreesh *Concert* (7/95) (ARCH) ① **445 829-2AH**
Bacchus is a pow'r divine—song, Z360
M. George, M. Caudle, D. Miller, R. King (r1993-4) *Concert* (1/95) (HYPE) ① **CDA66730**
Be merciful unto me—verse anthem, Z4 (? before 1683)
R. Covey-Crump, C. Daniels, M. George, King's Consort Ch, King's Consort, R. King (r1993-4) *Concert* (10/94) (HYPE) ① **CDA66686**
Beati omnes qui timent Dominum—Psalm 128, Z131 (c1680)
New College Ch, E. Higginbottom, S. Cunningham, H. Moody *Concert* (7/88) (MERI) ① **CDE84112**
M. Kennedy, King's Consort, R. Covey-Crump, M. George, King's Consort, R. King (r1993) *Concert*
(6/94) (HYPE) ① **CDA66677**
Taverner Consort, Taverner Plyrs, A. Parrott (1984) *Concert* (6/95) (VIRG) ① **VC5 45061-2**
Begin the song, and strike the living lyre—bass and orchestra, Z183 (1693) (Wds. Cowley)
M. George, King's Consort, R. King *Concert*
(4/93) (HYPE) ① **CDA66623**
Behold, I bring you glad tidings—verse anthem, Z2 (1687)
J. Bowman, C. Daniels, M. George, King's Consort, R. King (r1992-3) *Concert*
(9/93) (HYPE) ① **CDA66644**
Interludes Seattle NW CO, A. Francis *Concert*
(12/88) (HYPE) ① **CDH88028**
Behold now, praise the Lord—verse anthem, Z3 (c1680)
J. Bowman, R. Covey-Crump, M. George, New College Ch, King's Consort, R. King *Concert*
(11/92) (HYPE) ① **CDA66609**
The Bell Anthem, 'Rejoice in the Lord alway'—verse anthem, Z49 (c1682-85)
Salisbury Cath Ch, C. Walsh, R. Seal *Concert*
(9/87) (MERI) ① **CDE84025**
King's College Ch, ASMF, P. Ledger, F. Grier *Concert* (1/91) (CFP) ① **CD-CFP4570**
J. Bowman, N. Rogers, M. van Egmond, King's College Ch, D. Willcocks, Leonhardt Consort, G. Leonhardt (r1969) *Concert*
(9/93) (TELD) ① [2] **9031-77608-2**
J. Bowman, C. Daniels, M. George, New College Ch, King's Consort, R. King (r1992-3) *Concert*
(2/94) (HYPE) ① **CDA66656**
T. Bonner, P. Kwella, K. Wessel, P. Agnew, W. Kendall, P. Kooy, S. Roberts, Winchester Cath Ch, Brandenburg Consort, D. Hill (r1992) *Concert*
(6/94) (ARGO) ① **436 833-2ZH**
A. Deller (alto/dir), Deller Consort, Oriana Concert Orch (r1962) *Concert* (7/95) (VANG) ① **08.5060.71**

T. Bonner, P. Kwella, K. Wessel, P. Agnew, W. Kendall, P. Kooy, Collegium Vocale, P. Herreweghe (r1993) *Concert*
(7/95) (HARM) ① [6] **HMX290 1528/33(1)**
D. Cordier, J. Elwes, P. Kooy, Tolz Boys' Ch, Chbr Ens, G. Leonhardt (org/dir) (r1994) *Concert*
(11/95) (SONY) ① **SK53981**
Bell Barr, 'I love and I must'—1v and continuo, Z382
A. Cantelo, G. Malcolm (r1950s) *Concert*
(9/93) (VANG) ① [2] **08.2003.72**
B. Bonney, King's Consort (r1993) *Concert*
(10/94) (HYPE) ① **CDA66720**
Beneath a dark and melancholy grove—song, Z461 (c1681)
S. Gritton, M. George, M. Caudle, D. Miller, R. King (r1993) *Concert* (9/94) (HYPE) ① **CDA66710**
Bess of Bedlam, 'From silent shades'—song: 1v and continuo, Z370 (1682)
E. Kirkby, C. Hogwood, A. Rooley, R. Campbell, C. Mackintosh *Concert* (9/86) (L'OI) ① **417 123-2OH**
K. Ferrier, P. Spurr (bp1949) *Concert*
(6/92) (DECC) ① **433 473-2DM**
J. Feldman, N. North, S. Cunningham *Concert*
(1/93) (ARCA) ① **A02**
D. Minter, P. O'Dette, M. Springfels *Concert*
(1/93) (HARM) ① **HMU90 7035**
C. Bott, D. Roblou (r1990) *Concert*
(2/93) (L'OI) ① **433 187-2OH**
A. Mellon, W. Kuijken, C. Rousset (r1992) *Concert*
(9/93) (ASTR) ① **E8757**
N. Argenta, N. North, R. Boothby, P. Nicholson (r1992) *Concert* (6/94) (VIRG) ① **VC7 59324-2**
S. Gritton, S. Pell, D. Miller, R. King (r1993-4) *Concert* (1/95) (HYPE) ① **CDA66730**
M. Hill, A. Ball (1994; arr Tippett & Bergmann) *Concert* (4/95) (HYPE) ① **CDA66749**
Sarah Walker, G. Johnson (1995; arr Britten) *Concert* (11/95) (HYPE) ① [2] **CDA67061/2**
Beware, poor shepherds—song, Z361 (1684)
C. Daniels, M. Caudle, D. Miller, R. King (r1993) *Concert* (9/94) (HYPE) ① **CDA66710**
Birthday Ode, 'Celebrate this festival'—for Mary II, Z321 (1693) (Wds. N. Tate)
G. Fisher, T. Bonner, J. Bowman, J. Kenny, R. Covey-Crump, R. Müller, M. George, C. Pott, King's Consort, R. King *Concert*
(11/90) (HYPE) ① **CDA66412**
Crown the altar, deck the shrine E. Kirkby, C. Hogwood, A. Rooley, R. Campbell, C. Mackintosh *Concert* (9/86) (L'OI) ① **417 123-2OH**
Crown the altar, deck the shrine D. Minter, M. Meyerson *Concert* (1/93) (HARM) ① **HMU90 7035**
Crown the altar, deck the shrine
A. Deller, W. Bergmann (r1950s) *Concert*
(9/93) (VANG) ① [2] **08.2003.72**
Birthday Ode, 'Come ye sons of art away'—for Mary II, Z323 (1694) (Wds. ?N. Tate)
1. Sound the trumpet.
G. Fisher, T. Bonner, J. Bowman, M. Chance, M. Padmore, J.M. Ainsley, M. George, R. Evans, New College Ch, King's Consort, R. King *Concert*
(3/93) (HYPE) ① **CDA66598**
J. Gooding, J. Bowman, C. Robson, H. Crook, D. Wilson-Johnson, M. George, Age of Enlightenment Ch, OAE, G. Leonhardt (r1991) *Concert*
(6/93) (VIRG) ① **VC7 59243-2**
A. Deller (alto/dir), Deller Consort, Oriana Concert Ch, Oriana Concert Orch (r1962) *Concert*
(7/95) (VANG) ① **08.5060.71**
F. Lott, C. Brett, J. Williams, T. Allen, Monteverdi Ch, Monteverdi Orch, Equale Brass, J.E. Gardiner (r1976) *Funeral Sentences.*
(7/95) (ERAT) ① **4509-96553-2**
F. Lott, C. Brett, J. Williams, T. Allen, Monteverdi Ch, Monteverdi Orch, Equale Brass, J.E. Gardiner (r1976) *Concert* (7/95) (ERAT) ① [8] **4509-96371-2**
E. Van Evera, T. Wilson, J.M. Ainsley, C. Daniels, D. Thomas, Taverner Consort, Taverner Ch, Taverner Plyrs, A. Parrott (1988) *Concert*
(12/95) (VIRG) ① **VC5 45159-2**
Sound the trumpet E. Gruberová, W. Marsalis, ECO, R. Leppard *Concert*
(1/86) (SONY) ① **MK39061**
Sound the trumpet K. Ferrier, I. Baillie, G. Moore (r1945) *Concert* (6/88) (EMI) ① **CDH7 61003-2**
Sound the trumpet M. Chance, J. Bowman, King's Consort, R. King *Concert*
(7/88) (HYPE) ① **CDA66253**
Sound the trumpet F. Lott, A. Murray, G. Johnson (r1991) *Concert* (7/92) (EMI) ① **CDC7 54411-2**
Strike the viol J. Feldman, N. North, S. Cunningham *Concert* (1/93) (ARCA) ① **A02**

1. Gabrieli Consort, Gabrieli Players, P. McCreesh
Concert   (7/95) (ARCH) ① **445 829-2AH**

1, 2, 3. The Sixteen, The Sixteen Orch, H.
Christophers (r1994) Concert
(1/95) (COLL) ① **Coll1425-2**

1, 3. Oxford Christ Church Cath Ch, English Concert,
S. Preston (r1980) Concert
(7/95) (ARCH) ① [2] **447 150-2AP2**

1-4. T. Bonner, P. Kwella, K. Wessel, P. Agnew, W.
Kendall, P. Kooy, Collegium Vocale, P. Herreweghe
(r1993) Concert   (2/94) (HARM) ① **HMC90 1462**

1-4. M. Kennedy, R. Covey-Crump, C. Daniels, M.
George, King's Consort Ch, King's Consort, R. King
(r1993; Z17b, Z58b, Z58c) Concert
(6/94) (HYPE) ① **CDA66677**

1-4. T. Bonner, P. Kwella, K. Wessel, P. Agnew, W.
Kendall, P. Kooy, Collegium Vocale, P. Herreweghe
(r1993) Concert
(7/95) (HARM) ① [6] **HMX290 1528/33(1)**

3. Trinity Coll Ch, Cambridge, C. Matthews, G.
Jackson, R. Marlow Concert
(9/87) (CONI) ① **CDCF152**

3. Cambridge Sngrs, J. Rutter Concert
(6/88) (CLLE) ① **COLCD107**

3. St John's College Ch, G. Guest Concert
(7/91) (DECC) ① **430 263-2DM**

3. St John's College Ch, ECO, G. Guest (r1972)
Concert   (6/93) (DECC) ① **436 403-2DWO**

3. The Sixteen, The Sixteen Orch, H. Christophers
(r1994) Concert   (1/95) (COLL) ① **Coll1425-2**

3. E. Kirkby, E. Tubb, M. Chance, I. Bostridge, S.
Richardson, S. Birchall, Westminster Abbey Ch, New
London Consort, M. Neary (r1994) Concert
(3/95) (SONY) ① **SK66243**

3(Z58c) Taverner Consort, Taverner Ch, Taverner
Plyrs, A. Parrott (r1988) Concert
(12/95) (VIRG) ① **VC5 45159-2**

**Gentle shepherds, you that know—elegy on
the death of John Playford, Z464 (1687)**
(Wds. Tate)
A. Mellon, W. Kuijken, C. Rousset (r1992) Concert
(9/93) (ASTR) ① **E8757**
S. Gritton, M. George, King's Consort (r1993)
Concert   (10/94) (HYPE) ① **CDA66720**

**Give sentence with me, O Lord—verse
anthem: 3vv and continuo, Z12 (1681)**
W. Kendall, P. Butterfield, D. Sweeney, D. Dunnett,
D. Hill (r1992) Concert
(6/94) (ARGO) ① **436 833-2ZH**

**Go, tell Amynta, gentle swain—song: 2vv,
Z489** (Wds. J. Dryden)
E. Kirkby, D. Thomas, A. Rooley Concert
(6/88) (HYPE) ① **CDA66056**

**Great God and just—devotional song, Z186
(1688)**
M. Kennedy, E. O'Dwyer, M. George, New College
Ch, King's Consort, R. King (r1992-3) Concert
(2/94) (HYPE) ① **CDA66663**

**Hark, Damon, hark—symphony song: 3vv &
instr, Z541 (r1683)**
Red Byrd, Parley of Instr, P. Holman (r1993) Concert
(8/95) (HYPE) ① **CDA66750**

**Hark how the wild musicians
sing—symphony song: 3vv & instr, Z542
(r1683)**
Red Byrd, Parley of Instr, P. Holman (r1993) Concert
(8/95) (HYPE) ① **CDA66750**

**He himself courts his own ruin—song, Z372
(1684)**
J. Bowman, M. Caudle, D. Miller, R. King (r1993-4)
Concert   (1/95) (HYPE) ① **CDA66730**

**A Health to the nut brown lass—catch: 4vv,
Z240 (pub 1685)** (Wds. J. Suckling)
Deller Consort, A. Deller Concert
(3/86) (HARM) ① **HMC90 242**

**Hear me, O Lord, and that soon—full
anthem, Z13a/Z13b (c1679-80)**
M. Kennedy, J. Bowman, C. Daniels, M. George,
King's Consort Ch, King's Consort, R. King (r1993/4)
Concert   (3/95) (HYPE) ① **CDA66716**

**Hear me, O Lord, the great
support—devotional song, Z133 (1680-82)**
C. Daniels, P. Agnew, M. George, New College Ch,
King's Consort, R. King (r1992-3) Concert
(6/94) (HYPE) ① **CDA66663**

**Hear my prayer, O God—verse anthem, Z14
(before 1682)**
R. Covey-Crump, C. Daniels, M. George, King's
Consort Ch, King's Consort, R. King (r1994) Concert
(3/95) (HYPE) ① **CDA66707**

**Hear my prayer, O Lord—full anthem, Z15
(c1680-2)**
Trinity Coll Ch, Cambridge, C. Matthews, G. Jackson,
R. Marlow Concert   (9/87) (CONI) ① **CDCF152**
Cambridge Sngrs, J. Rutter Concert
(6/88) (CLLE) ① **COLCD107**

Magdalen Oxford Coll Ch, J. Harper Concert
(11/91) (ABBE) ① **CDCA912**
Norwich Cath Ch, M. Nicholas, N. Taylor Concert
(3/92) (PRIO) ① **PRCD351**
King's Consort Ch, King's Consort, R. King Concert
(4/93) (HYPE) ① **CDA66623**
T. Bonner, P. Kwella, K. Wessel, P. Agnew, W.
Kendall, P. Kooy, Collegium Vocale, P. Herreweghe
(r1993) Concert   (2/94) (HARM) ① **HMC90 1462**
Trinity Coll Ch, Cambridge, R. Marlow (r1993)
Concert   (2/94) (CONI) ① **CDCF219**
Winchester Cath Ch, D. Hill (r1992) Concert
(6/94) (ARGO) ① **436 833-2ZH**
L. Cummings, Oxford Camerata, J. Summerly (r1994)
Concert   (2/95) (NAXO) ① **8 553129**
T. Bonner, P. Kwella, K. Wessel, P. Agnew, W.
Kendall, P. Kooy, Collegium Vocale, P. Herreweghe
(r1993) Concert
(7/95) (HARM) ① [6] **HMX290 1528/33(1)**

**Hence, fond deceiver—song: 2vv, Z492 (pub
1687)**
E. Kirkby, D. Thomas, A. Rooley Concert
(6/88) (HYPE) ① **CDA66056**

**High on a throne of glitt'ring ore—ode to the
Queen: 2vv, Z465 (1690)** (Wds. T. D'Urfey)
B. Bonney, M. George, King's Consort (r1993)
Concert   (10/94) (HYPE) ① **CDA66720**

**Hosanna to the highest—bass, chorus and
orchestra, Z187**
M. George, King's Consort Ch, King's Consort, R.
King Concert   (4/93) (HYPE) ① **CDA66623**

**How delightful's the life of an innocent
swain—song: 1v, Z373**
S. Gritton, M. George, King's Consort (r1993)
Concert   (10/94) (HYPE) ① **CDA66720**

**How have I stray'd—devotional song, Z188
(1688)**
S. Gritton, M. George, King's Consort, R. King
(r1994) Concert   (3/95) (HYPE) ① **CDA66707**

**How I sigh when I think of the
charms—song, Z374 (1681)**
S. Gritton, M. Caudle, D. Miller, R. King (r1993)
Concert   (1/95) (HYPE) ① **CDA66710**

**How long, great God—sacred song: 1v, Z189
(pub 1688)** (Wds. J. Norris)
J. Bowman, King's Consort, R. King Concert
(7/89) (HYPE) ① **CDA66288**
N. Witcomb, King's Consort, R. King (r1992-3)
Concert   (2/94) (HYPE) ① **CDA66656**

**How pleasant is this flowery
plain—symphony song: 2vv & instr, Z543
(r1682)**
Saltire Sngrs, Inst Ens, H. Oppenheim (r1955)
Concert   (7/95) (ARCH) ① **447 156-2AP**
Red Byrd, Parley of Instr, P. Holman (r1993) Concert
(8/95) (HYPE) ① **CDA66750**

**I came, I saw, and was undone—1v and
continuo, Z375** (Wds. A. Cowley)
A. Mellon, W. Kuijken, C. Rousset (r1992) Concert
(9/93) (ASTR) ① **E8757**
Consort of Musicke, A. Rooley (lte/dir) (r1993)
Concert   (1/95) (MOSC) ① **070986**
B. Bonney, M. Caudle, D. Miller, R. King (r1993-4)
Concert   (1/95) (HYPE) ① **CDA66730**

**I gave her cakes and I gave her ale—catch:
3vv, Z256 (pub 1690)**
Deller Consort, A. Deller Concert
(3/86) (HARM) ① **HMC90 242**

I lov'd fair Celia—song: 1v, Z381 (by 1693)
(Wds. B. Howard)
R. Jacobs, W. Kuijken, K. Junghänel Concert
(8/85) (ACCE) ① **ACC57802D**
R. Covey-Crump, M. Caudle, D. Miller, R. King
(r1993) Concert   (9/94) (HYPE) ① **CDA66710**

**I resolve against cringing and
whining—song: 1v, Z386 (1679)**
C. Daniels, King's Consort (r1993) Concert
(10/94) (HYPE) ① **CDA66720**

**I spy Celia, Celia eyes me—song: 2vv &
continuo, Z499**
I. Bostridge, R. Jackson, G. Johnson (r1995; arr
Britten) Concert
(11/95) (HYPE) ① [2] **CDA67061/2**

**I take no pleasure in the sun's bright
beams—song: 1v, Z388 (1681)**
B. Bonney, King's Consort (r1993) Concert
(10/94) (HYPE) ① **CDA66720**
I. Bostridge, G. Johnson (r1995; arr Britten) Concert
(11/95) (HYPE) ① [2] **CDA67061/2**

**I was glad when they said unto me—full
anthem (1685)** (incorrectly attrib to Blow)
Trinity Coll Ch, Cambridge, C. Matthews, G. Jackson,
R. Marlow Concert   (9/87) (CONI) ① **CDCF152**
P. Esswood, I. Partridge, St John's College Ch, S.
Dean, Stg Orch, John Scott, G. Guest Concert
(7/91) (DECC) ① **430 263-2DM**

Magdalen Oxford Coll Ch, J. Harper Concert
(11/91) (ABBE) ① **CDCA912**
P. Esswood, I. Partridge, S. Dean, St John's College
Ch, John Scott, G. Guest (r1975) Concert
(6/93) (DECC) ① **436 403-2DWO**
King's Consort Ch, King's Consort, R. King (r1993)
Concert   (6/94) (HYPE) ① **CDA66677**
Westminster Abbey Ch, orch, S. Preston (1986)
Concert   (7/95) (ARCH) ① **447 155-2AP**

**I was glad when they said unto me—verse
anthem, Z19 (1682-3)**
R. Covey-Crump, C. Daniels, M. George, New
College Ch, King's Consort, R. King (r1993) Concert
(6/94) (HYPE) ① **CDA66677**
E. Kirkby, E. Tubb, M. Chance, I. Bostridge, S.
Richardson, S. Birchall, Westminster Abbey Ch, New
London Consort, M. Neary (r1994) Concert
(3/95) (SONY) ① **SK66243**

**I will give thanks unto the Lord as long as I
live—verse anthem, Z21 (?c1685)**
C. Daniels, C. Campbell, M. George, King's Consort
Ch, King's Consort, R. King (r1994) Concert
(3/95) (HYPE) ① **CDA66707**

**I will give thanks unto Thee, O Lord—verse
anthem, Z20 (c1682-85)**
J. Bowman, R. Covey-Crump, M. George, New
College Ch, King's Consort, R. King Concert
(11/92) (HYPE) ① **CDA66609**

**I will love thee, O Lord—verse anthem, ZN67
(?1679)**
M. George, New College Ch, King's Consort, R. King
(r1992-3) Concert   (2/94) (HYPE) ① **CDA66663**

**I will sing unto the Lord—full anthem, Z22
(by 1679)**
Trinity Coll Ch, Cambridge, C. Matthews, G. Jackson,
R. Marlow Concert   (9/87) (CONI) ① **CDCF152**
L. Cummings, Oxford Camerata, J. Summerly (r1994)
Concert   (2/95) (NAXO) ① **8 553129**
E. O'Dwyer, M. Kennedy, J. Bowman, C. Daniels, M.
Milhofer, M. George, King's Consort Ch, King's
Consort, R. King (r1994) Concert
(3/95) (HYPE) ① **CDA66707**

**If ever I more riches did desire—symphony
song: 4vv & instr, Z544 (1686-7)** (Wds. A.
Cowley)
Deller Consort, A. Deller Concert
(3/86) (HARM) ① **HMC90 242**
Red Byrd, Parley of Instr, P. Holman (1993) Concert
(8/95) (HYPE) ① **CDA66750**

**If grief has any power to kill—song: 1v, Z378
(1685)**
R. Covey-Crump, King's Consort (r1993) Concert
(10/94) (HYPE) ① **CDA66720**

**If music be the food of love—song: 1v,
Z379/1 (1692)** (Wds. H. Heveningham)
J. Bowman, King's Consort, R. King Concert
(7/89) (HYPE) ① **CDA66288**
H. Crook, Capriccio Stravagante, S. Sempé (hpd/dir)
Concert   (9/92) (DHM) ① **RD77252**
A. Deller, W. Bergmann (r1950s) Concert
(9/93) (VANG) ① [2] **08.2003.72**
N. Argenta, R. Boothby, P. Nicholson (r1992) Concert
(6/94) (VIRG) ① **VC7 59324-2**
K. Battle, M. Lutzke, Anthony Newman (pp1991)
Concert   (9/94) (SONY) ① **SK53106**
R. Covey-Crump, M. Caudle, D. Miller, R. King
(r1993) Concert   (9/94) (HYPE) ① **CDA66710**
N. Argenta, Freiburg Baroque Orch, G. von der Goltz
(r1993) Concert   (10/94) (DHM) ① **05472 77295-2**
A. Deller, W. Kuijken, W. Christie, R. Skeaping
(r1979) Concert
(7/95) (HARM) ① [6] **HMX290 1528/33(2)**
F. Lott, G. Johnson (r1995; arr Britten) Concert
(11/95) (HYPE) ① [2] **CDA67061/2**

**If music be the food of love—song: 1v,
Z379/2 (1693)** (Wds. H. Heveningham)
P. Esswood, J. Sonnleitner, C. Medlam Concert
(12/89) (HYPE) ① **CDA66070**
R. Covey-Crump, King's Consort (r1993) Concert
(10/94) (HYPE) ① **CDA66720**
M. Hill, A. Ball (r1994; arr Tippett & Bergmann)
Concert   (4/95) (HYPE) ① **CDA66749**

**If music be the food of love—song: 2vv,
Z379/3 (1695)** (Wds. H. Heveningham)
E. Kirkby, C. Hogwood, A. Rooley, R. Campbell, C.
Mackintosh Concert   (9/86) (L'OI) ① **417 123-2OH**
P. Esswood, J. Sonnleitner, C. Medlam Concert
(12/89) (HYPE) ① **CDA66070**
J. Feldman, N. North, S. Cunningham Concert
(1/93) (ARCA) ① **A02**
D. Minter, P. O'Dette, M. Springfels Concert
(1/93) (HARM) ① **HMU90 7035**
A. Mellon, W. Kuijken, C. Rousset (1992) Concert
(9/93) (ASTR) ① **E8757**
A. Auger, J. Revzen (pp1989; arr Britten) Concert
(4/94) (KOCH) ① **37248-2**

G. Fisher, J. Bowman, R. Covey-Crump, J.M.
Ainsley, M. George, S. Keenlyside, New College Ch,
King's Consort, R. King *Birthday Ode*, Z342.
(7/90) (HYPE) ① **CDA66349**
Fiori Musicali Ch, Fiori Musicali, P. Rapson *Caldara:
Laudate pueri Dominum*.
(10/91) (UNIC) ① **DKPCD9109**
J. Smith, A. Stafford, B. Gordon, P. Elliott, S. Varcoe,
D. Thomas, Monteverdi Ch, EBS, J.E.Gardiner
(r1982) *Concert*
(7/95) (ERAT) ① [8] **4509-96371-2**
J. Smith, A. Stafford, B. Gordon, P. Elliott, S. Varcoe,
D. Thomas, Monteverdi Ch, EBS, J.E. Gardiner
(r1982) (7/95) (ERAT) ① **4509-96554-2**
S. Woolf, P. Esswood, R. Tatnell, A. Young, J.
Shirley-Quirk, M. Rippon, Tiffin Ch, Ambrosian Sngrs,
ECO, C. Mackerras (r1969) *Married Beau*, Z603.
(7/95) (ARCH) ① **447 149-2AP**
Gabrieli Consort, Gabrieli Players, P. McCreesh
(r1994) *Concert* (10/95) (ARCH) ① **445 882-2AH**
4. R. Jacobs, W. Kuijken, K. Junghänel *Concert*
(8/85) (ACCE) ① **ACC57802D**
4. H. Crook, Capriccio Stravagante, S. Sempé
(hpd/dir) *Concert* (9/92) (DHM) ① **RD77252**
4. J. Feldman, N. North, S. Cunningham *Concert*
(1/93) (ARCA) ① **A02**
4. D. Minter, P. O'Dette, M. Meyerson *Concert*
(1/93) (HARM) ① **HMU90 7035**
4. S. Sanford, B. Wissick, R. Erickson (r1991)
Concert (10/95) (ALBA) ① **TROY127-2**
10. J. Bowman, M. Chance, King's Consort, R. King
Concert (7/88) (HYPE) ① **CDA66253**
St Cecilia's Day Ode, 'Laudate Ceciliam',
Z329 (1683)
G. Fisher, M. Seers, J. Bowman, N. Short, M.
Padmore, A. Tusa, M. George, M. Evans, King's
Consort, R. King *Concert*
(3/93) (HYPE) ① **CDA66494**
St Cecilia's Day Ode, 'Raise, raise the
voice', Z334 (c1685)
1. Mark, how readily each pliant string.
G. Fisher, M. Seers, J. Bowman, N. Short, M.
Padmore, A. Tusa, M. George, M. Evans, King's
Consort, R. King *Concert*
(3/93) (HYPE) ① **CDA66494**
B. Borden, D. Nasrawi, S. Grant, Tragicomedia
(r1994) *Concert* (7/95) (TELD) ① **4509-95068-2**
St Cecilia's Day Ode, 'Welcome to all the
pleasures', Z339 (1683) (Wds. C. Fishburn)
G. Fisher, T. Bonner, J. Bowman, M. Chance, C.
Daniels, J.M. Ainsley, M. George, King's Consort, R.
King *Concert* (2/89) (HYPE) ① **CDA66314**
R. Holton, N. Jenkin, M. Chance, P. Tindall, G.
Mosley, Monteverdi Ch, EBS, J. E Gardiner (r1990)
Dido. (3/94) (PHIL) ① **432 114-2PH**
A. Deller (alto/dir), Deller Consort, Kalmar CO, W.
Bergmann (r1962) *Concert*
(7/95) (VANG) ① **08.5060.71**
J.M. Ainsley, C. Daniels, Taverner Consort, Taverner
Ch, Taverner Plyrs, A. Parrott (1988) *Concert*
(12/95) (VIRG) ① **VC5 45159-2**
Here the deities approve J. Bowman, King's
Consort, R. King *Concert*
(7/89) (HYPE) ① **CDA66288**
Here the deities approve D. Minter, P. O'Dette
Concert (1/93) (HARM) ① **HMU90 7035**
Strip of their green our groves
appear—song: 1v, Z444 (pub 1692) (Wds.
P.A. Motteux)
E. Kirkby, A. Rooley *Concert*
(9/87) (HYPE) ① **CDA66227**
E. Kirkby, A. Rooley *Concert*
(6/88) (HYPE) ① **CDA66056**
N. Argenta, N. North, R. Boothby, P. Nicholson
(r1992) *Concert* (6/94) (VIRG) ① **VC7 59324-2**
E. Kirkby, E. Tubb, M. Chance, I. Bostridge, S.
Richardson, S. Birchall, Westminster Abbey Ch, New
London Consort, M. Neary (r1994) *Concert*
(3/95) (SONY) ① **SK66243**
Sylvia, now your scorn give over—song: 1v,
Z420 (pub 1688)
J. Bowman, King's Consort (r1993) *Concert*
(7/95) (HYPE) ① **CDA66720**
Sylvia, 'tis true you're fair—song: 2vv, Z512
(1686)
C. Daniels, M. George, M. Caudle, D. Miller, R. King
(r1993-4) *Concert* (7/95) (HYPE) ① **CDA66730**
Te Deum and Jubilate in D, Z232 (1694)
1. Te Deum - We praise thee, O God; 1a. Vouchsafe,
O Lord; 2. Jubilate - O be joyful in the Lord.
Oxford Christ Church Cath Ch, English Concert, S.
Preston *Concert* (5/89) (ARCH) ① **427 124-2AGA**

M. Creese, S. Keenlyside, R. King, R. Smith, Paul
Williams, J. Bowman, C. Brett, I. Partridge, F.
Robinson, ECO, S. Cleobury, J. Ryan, Symphoniae
Sacrae, St John's College Ch, G. Guest *Concert*
(7/91) (DECC) ① **430 263-2DM**
J. Bowman, R. Covey-Crump, M. George, New
College Ch, King's Consort, R. King *Concert*
(11/92) (HYPE) ① **CDA66609**
Taverner Consort, Taverner Plyrs, A. Parrott (r1994)
Concert (6/95) (VIRG) ① **VC5 45061-2**
Oxford Christ Church Cath Ch, English Concert, S.
Preston (r1980) *Concert*
(7/95) (ARCH) ① [2] **447 150-2AP2**
1. T. Bonner, P. Kwella, K. Wessel, P. Agnew, W.
Kendall, P. Kooy, Collegium Vocale, P. Herreweghe
(r1993) *Concert* (2/94) (HARM) ① **HMC90 1462**
1. T. Bonner, P. Kwella, K. Wessel, P. Agnew, W.
Kendall, P. Kooy, Collegium Vocale, P. Herreweghe
(r1993) *Concert*
(7/95) (HARM) ① [6] **HMX290 1528/33(1)**
2. Trinity Coll Ch, Cambridge, C. Matthews, G.
Jackson, R. Marlow *Concert*
(9/87) (CONI) ① **CDCF152**
They say you're angry—song, Z422 (1685)
(Wds Cowley)
C. Daniels, M. Caudle, D. Miller, R. King (r1993)
Concert (9/94) (HYPE) ① **CDA66710**
Consort of Musicke, A. Rooley (lte/dir) (r1993)
Concert (1/95) (MOSC) ① **070986**
They that go down to the sea in
ships—verse anthem, Z57 (1685)
Oxford Christ Church Cath Ch, English Concert, S.
Preston (5/89) (ARCH) ① **427 124-2AGA**
J. Bowman, M. George, King's Consort Ch, King's
Consort (r1993-4) *Concert*
(10/94) (HYPE) ① **CDA66686**
D. Thomas, Oxford Christ Church Cath Ch, English
Concert, S. Preston (r1980) *Concert*
(7/95) (ARCH) ① [2] **447 150-2AP2**
Through mournful shades and solitary
groves—song: 1v, Z424 (1684) (Wds R.
Duke)
B. Bonney, King's Consort (r1993) *Concert*
(10/94) (HYPE) ① **CDA66720**
Thy Way, O God, is Holy—verse anthem: alto
and bass, Z60 (1687)
C. Daniels, M. George, King's Consort, R. King
(r1993) *Concert* (6/94) (HYPE) ① **CDA66677**
Thy word is a lantern unto my feet—verse
anthem, Z61
J. Bowman, C. Daniels, M. George, King's Consort
Ch, King's Consort, R. King *Concert*
(4/93) (HYPE) ① **CDA66623**
Southwark Cath Ch, P. Wright, S. Layton (r1992)
Concert (7/94) (PRIO) ① **PRCD435**
'Tis wine was made to rule the day—drinking
song: soprano and chorus, Z546 (pub 1702)
Saltire Sngrs, Inst Ens, H. Oppenheim (r1955)
Concert (7/95) (ARCH) ① **447 156-2AP**
'Tis women makes us love—catch: 4vv, Z281
(pub 1685)
Deller Consort, A. Deller *Concert*
(3/86) (HARM) ① **HMC90 242**
Turn then thine eyes—song: 1v, Z425 (Wds.
?E. Settle. Solo version)
J. M. Ainsley, G. Johnson (r1995; arr Britten) *Concert*
(11/95) (HYPE) ① [2] **CDA67061/2**
Turn thou us, O good Lord—verse anthem,
Z62
C. Daniels, M. Padmore, M. George, King's Consort
Ch, King's Consort, R. King (r1993/4) *Concert*
(3/95) (HYPE) ① **CDA66716**
Under this stone lies Gabriel John—catch:
3vv, Z286 (pub 1686)
Deller Consort, A. Deller *Concert*
(3/86) (HARM) ① **HMC90 242**
Unto Thee will I cry—verse anthem, Z63
(c1682-5)
J. Bowman, C. Daniels, M. George, King's Consort
Ch, King's Consort, R. King (r1994) *Concert*
(3/95) (HYPE) ① **CDA66707**
Urge me no more—song: 1v, Z426
E. Kirkby, C. Hogwood, A. Rooley, R. Campbell, C.
Mackintosh *Concert* (9/86) (L'OI) ① **417 123-2OH**
S. Gritton, M. Caudle, D. Miller, R. King (r1993)
Concert (9/94) (HYPE) ① **CDA66710**
The Way of God is an undefiled way—verse
anthem, Z56 (1694)
J. Bowman, R. Covey-Crump, M. George, New
College Ch, King's Consort, R. King (r1992-3)
Concert (9/93) (HYPE) ① **CDA66644**
We reap all the pleasures—symphony song:
3vv & instr, Z547 (r1682)
Red Byrd, Parley of Instr, P. Holman (r1993) *Concert*
(8/95) (HYPE) ① **CDA66750**

We sing to him whose wisdom form'd the
ear—sacred song: 1v, Z199 (pub 1688) (Wds.
N. Ingelo)
J. Bowman, King's Consort, R. King *Concert*
(7/89) (HYPE) ① **CDA66288**
S. Gritton, King's Consort, R. King (r1992-3) *Concert*
(2/94) (HYPE) ① **CDA66656**
J. Bowman, G. Johnson (r1995; arr Britten) *Concert*
(11/95) (HYPE) ① [2] **CDA67061/2**
Wedding Ode, 'From hardy climes and
dangerous toils of war'—for Prince George
of Denmark & Princess Anne, Z325 (1683)
1. The sparrow and the gentle dove.
G. Fisher, T. Bonner, R. Covey-Crump, C. Daniels,
M. George, King's Consort, R. King *Concert*
(5/92) (HYPE) ① **CDA66456**
The sparrow and the gentle dove P. Esswood, J.
Sonnleitner, C. Medlam *Concert*
(12/89) (HYPE) ① **CDA66070**
Weeping, 'See where she sits'—symphony
song: 2vv & instr, Z508 (?1683) (Wds
Cowley)
Red Byrd, Parley of Instr, P. Holman (r1993) *Concert*
(8/95) (HYPE) ① **CDA66750**
Welcome Song, 'Fly, bold rebellion', Z324
(1683)
1. Be welcome then, great Sir.
G. Fisher, T. Bonner, J. Bowman, J. Kenny, R.
Covey-Crump, R. Müller, M. George, C. Pott, King's
Consort, R. King *Concert*
(11/90) (HYPE) ① **CDA66412**
Be welcome then, great Sir D. Minter, P. O'Dette,
M. Meyerson, M. Springfels *Concert*
(1/93) (HARM) ① **HMU90 7035**
Welcome Song, 'From those serene and
rapturous joys'—for Charles II, Z326 (1684)
(Wds. T. Flatman)
G. Fisher, M. Seers, J. Bowman, N. Short, M.
Padmore, A. Tusa, M. George, M. Evans, King's
Consort, R. King *Concert*
(3/93) (HYPE) ① **CDA66494**
Welcome Song, 'Sound the trumpet'—for
James II, Z335 (1687)
J. Bowman, J. Kenny, R. Covey-Crump, R. Müller, M.
George, C. Pott, King's Consort, R. King *Concert*
(11/90) (HYPE) ① **CDA66412**
E. Söderström, K. Meyer, J. Eyron (1974) *Concert*
(3/90) (BIS) ① **BIS-CD017**
Welcome Song, '(The) summer's absence
unconcerned we bear'—for Charles II, Z337
(1682)
G. Fisher, E. Tubb, J. Bowman, N. Short, R. Covey-
Crump, J.M. Ainsley, M. George, C. Pott, King's
Consort, R. King *Concert*
(5/92) (HYPE) ① **CDA66476**
Welcome Song, 'Swifter Isis, swifter
flow'—for Charles II, Z336 (1681)
G. Fisher, S. Hamilton, J. Bowman, N. Short, R.
Covey-Crump, C. Daniels, M. George, R. Evans,
King's Consort, R. King *Concert*
(3/93) (HYPE) ① **CDA66587**
Overture London Baroque *Concert*
(10/90) (HARM) ① **HMC90 1327**
Overture London Baroque (1989) *Concert*
(7/95) (HARM) ① [6] **HMX290 1528/33(1)**
Welcome Song, 'Welcome, vicegerent of the
mighty king'—for Charles II, Z340 (1680)
G. Fisher, T. Bonner, J. Bowman, M. Chance, M.
Padmore, J.M. Ainsley, M. George, R. Evans, New
College Ch, King's Consort, R. King *Concert*
(3/93) (HYPE) ① **CDA66598**
Suzie Le Blanc, B. Borden, S. Dugardin, D. Nasrawi,
H. van der Kamp, S. Grant, Tragicomedia (r1994)
Concert (7/95) (TELD) ① **4509-95068-2**
Welcome Song, 'What, what shall be done in
behalf of man?'—for the Duke of York, Z341
(1682)
G. Fisher, S. Hamilton, J. Bowman, N. Short, R.
Covey-Crump, C. Daniels, M. George, R. Evans,
King's Consort, R. King *Concert*
(3/93) (HYPE) ① **CDA66587**
Welcome Song, 'Why, are all the Muses
mute?'—for James II, Z343 (1685)
1. O how blest is the Isle.
G. Fisher, T. Bonner, J. Bowman, M. Chance, M.
Padmore, J.M. Ainsley, M. George, R. Evans, New
College Ch, King's Consort, R. King *Concert*
(3/93) (HYPE) ① **CDA66598**
Suzie Le Blanc, B. Borden, S. Dugardin, D. Nasrawi,
H. van der Kamp, S. Grant, Tragicomedia (r1994)
Concert (7/95) (TELD) ① **4509-95068-2**
Welcome Song, 'Ye tuneful Muses'—for
James II (1686)
G. Fisher, J. Bowman, R. Covey-Crump, C. Daniels,
M. George, C. Pott, King's Consort, R. King *Concert*
(5/92) (HYPE) ① **CDA66456**

Cpte C. Bott, J. M. Ainsley, E. Kirkby, D. Thomas, E. Priday, S. Stowe, J. Baird, D. Lochmann, M. Chance, AAM Chor, AAM, C. Hogwood (r1992)
(7/94) (L'OI) Ⓓ **436 992-2OHO**
Cpte L. Hunt, M. Dean, L. Saffer, E. Rabiner, D. Deam, C. Brandes, R. Rainero, P. Elliott, Cambridge Clare College Ch, Philh Baroque Orch (r1993) *Gordian Knot Unty'd, Z597.*
(4/95) (HARM) Ⓓ **HMU90 7110**
Cpte V. Gens, N. Berg, S. Marin-Degor, C. Brua, S. Daneman, G. Mechaly, J-P. Fouchécourt, Arts Florissants Voc Ens, Arts Florissants Instr Ens, W. Christie (r1994) (6/95) (ERAT) Ⓓ **4509-98477-2**
Cpte G. Laurens, P. Cantor, J. Feldman, D. Visse, A. Mellon, B. Borden, E. Lestrigant, M. Laplénie, Arts Florissants Voc Ens, Arts Florissants Instr Ens, W. Christie (r1985) *Concert*
(7/95) (HARM) Ⓓ [6] **HMX290 1528/33(1)**
Cpte T. Troyanos, B. McDaniel, S. Armstrong, P. Johnson, Margaret Baker, M. Lensky, P. Esswood, N. Rogers, Hamburg Monteverdi Ch, Hamburg NDR CO, C. Mackerras (r1967)
(7/95) (ARCH) Ⓓ **447 148-2AP**
Excs Freiburg Baroque Orch, T. Hengelbrock (arr Hengelbrock) *Concert* (3/92) (DHM) Ⓓ **RD77231**
1. Taverner Plyrs, A. Parrott *Concert*
(7/83) (CHAN) Ⓓ **CHAN8301**
1, 43. C. Watkinson, Amsterdam Bach Sols, J.W. de Vriend *Concert* (3/89) (ETCE) Ⓓ **KTC1064**
2. J. Feldman, N. North, S. Cunningham *Concert*
(1/93) (ARCA) Ⓓ **A02**
42, 43. L. Price, RCA Italiana Op Orch, F. Molinari-Pradelli *Concert*
(12/92) (RCA) Ⓓ [4] **09026 61236-2**
42, 43. K. Flagstad, Philh, W. Braithwaite (r1948) *Concert* (7/93) (TEST) Ⓓ **SBT1018**
42-44. J. Baker, St Anthony Sngrs, ECO, A. Lewis (r1961) *Concert* (10/93) (DECC) Ⓓ **436 462-2DM**
43. G. Fisher, King's Consort, R. King *Concert*
(8/88) (CARL) Ⓓ **PCD894**
43. K. Flagstad, Philh, W. Braithwaite (r1948) *Concert* (4/92) (EMI) Ⓓ [7] **CHS7 69741-2(5)**

The History of **Dioclesian, or The Prophetess—instrumental suite, Z627**
EXCERPTS: 1a. Overture; 1b. Dance; 1c. Dance of Bacchanals; 1d. Trumpet tune; 1e. Prelude; 1f. Hornpipe; 1g. Dance of the Furies; 1h. First music; 1i. Prelude; 1j. Act tune; 1k. Chaconne; 1l. Second music; 1m. Paspe; 1n. Chair dance.
1a-n Freiburg Baroque Orch, G. von der Goltz (r1993) *Concert* (10/94) (DHM) Ⓓ **05472 77295-2**

The History of **Dioclesian, or The Prophetess—instrumental suite, Z627 (pub 1697)** (from A Collection of Ayres, compos'd for the Theatre)
EXCERPTS: 1. Overture; 2. Preludio; 3. Song Tune: Let the soldiers rejoice; 4. Trumpet Tune; 5. Country Dance; 6. Aire; 7. Hornpipe; 8. Aire; 9. Canaries.
Parley of Instr Baroque Orch (r1994) *Concert*
(10/95) (HYPE) Ⓓ [3] **CDA67001/3**

The History of **Dioclesian, or The Prophetess—semi-opera: 5 acts, Z627 (1691—London)** (Lib. T Betterton. Work rev 1694)
EXCERPTS: 1. First Musick; 2. Second Musick; 3. Overture. ACT 1: 4. First Act Tune (Hornpipe). ACT 2: 5a. Great Diocles the Boar has kill'd (song: bass); 5b. Sing Iôs! (chorus); 6. Charon the peaceful Shade invites (song: soprano); 7. Symphony (trumpets and violins); 8. Let all mankind the pleasure share (duet: soprano, bass); 9a. Let the soldiers rejoice, 'Martial song' (tenor); 9b. Rejoice with a general voice (2 tenors, bass); 9c. Retornello I (trumpets and oboes); 9d. To Mars let 'em raise...Rejoice with a general voice (TTB); 9e. Retornello II (trumpets and oboes); 10a. A Symphony of Flutes; 10b. Since the toils and the hazards (song: alto); 10c. Let the priests (SATB); 10d. All sing (chorus); 11. Dance of Furies; 12. Second Act Tune. ACT 3: 13a. Two in one upon a Ground; 13b. Chaconne for Flutes; 14. The Chair Dance; 15a. Prelude for Oboes; 15b. What I shall do? (song: tenor); 16. Third Act Tune. ACT 4: 17. Butterfly Dance; 18. Tune for Trumpets; 19. Sound Fame, thy brazen trumpet sound (song: tenor); 20. Let all rehearse (chorus); 21. Fourth Act Tune. APPENDICES: 22. Country Dance in the Fifth Act; 23. Since from my dear Astrea's sight (song: soprano); 24. When first I saw (song: tenor); 25. MASQUE: 26. Call the nymphs (Cupid, chorus); 27. Come, come away (duet); 28. Behold, O mighty'st of Gods (chorus); 29. Paspe (The first entry of heros on the stage); 30. Oh, the sweet delights of love! (duet); 31. Let mortals fight (Fawn, chorus); 32a. Make room...(2 Bacchanals, Bacchus: the second entry); 32b. Dance of Bacchanals; 33. Still I'm wishing (Follower of Cupid); 34. Canaries; 35. Tell me why (Shepherd, Shepherdess: The third entry); 36. Dance; 37a. All our days...(A Pleasure, Chorus: the fourth entry); 37b. Let us dance; 37c. Dance; 38. Triumph, victorious Love (Trio, chorus: the last entry).
Cpte C. Pierard, J. Bowman, J. M. Ainsley, M. Padmore, M. George, Collegium Musicum 90 Chor, Collegium Musicum 90, R. Hickox (r1994)
(7/95) (CHAN) Ⓓ **CHAN0568**
Cpte N. Argenta, A. Monoyios, P. Agnew, R. Edgar-Wilson, S. Gadd, S. Birchall, L. Wallington, B. Bannatyne-Scott, English Concert Ch, English Concert, T. Pinnock (r1994) *Timon of Athens, Z632.*
(12/95) (ARCH) Ⓓ [2] **447 071-2AH2**
1-24. L. Dawson, G. Fisher, R. Covey-Crump, P. Elliott, M. George, S. Varcoe, Monteverdi Ch, EBS, J.E. Gardiner (r1987) *Timon of Athens, Z632.*
(7/95) (ERAT) Ⓓ [2] **4509-96556-2**
1-24. L. Dawson, G. Fisher, R. Covey-Crump, P. Elliott, M. George, S. Varcoe, Monteverdi Ch, EBS, J.E.Gardiner (r1987) *Concert*
(7/95) (ERAT) Ⓓ [8] **4509-96371-2**
3. P. Esswood, J. Sonnleitner, C. Medlam *Concert*
(12/89) (HYPE) Ⓓ **CDA66070**
3. N. Argenta, N. North, R. Boothby, P. Nicholson (r1992) *Concert* (6/94) (VIRG) Ⓓ **VC7 59324-2**
9a M. Chance, Freiburg Baroque Orch, G. von der Goltz (r1993) *Concert*
(10/94) (DHM) Ⓓ **05472 77295-2**
15b A. Deller, W. Bergmann (r1950s) *Concert*
(9/93) (VANG) Ⓓ [2] **08.2003.72**
15b, 23. J. Bowman, King's Consort, R. King *Concert*
(7/89) (HYPE) Ⓓ **CDA66288**
19. E. Kirkby, English Tpt Virtuosi, A. Hoskins (tpt/dir), M. Hoskins (tpt/dir) (r1994) *Concert*
(10/95) (MOSC) Ⓓ **070979**
23. R. Jacobs, W. Kuijken, K. Junghänel *Concert*
(8/85) (ACCE) Ⓓ **ACC57802D**
23. J. Feldman, N. North, S. Cunningham *Concert*
(1/93) (ARCA) Ⓓ **A02**
23. A. Mellon, W. Kuijken, C. Rousset (r1992) *Concert* (9/93) (ASTR) Ⓓ **E8757**
23. A. Deller, W. Kuijken, W. Christie, R. Skeaping (r1979) *Concert*
(7/95) (HARM) Ⓓ [6] **HMX290 1528/33(2)**
25. C. Pierard, J. Bowman, J. M. Ainsley, I. Bostridge, M. George, M. Brook, N. Berg, Collegium Musicum 90, R. Hickox (r1993) *Timon of Athens, Z632.* (11/94) (CHAN) Ⓓ **CHAN0558**
35. E. Kirkby, D. Thomas, A. Rooley *Concert*
(6/88) (HYPE) Ⓓ **CDA66056**
37c S. Sanford, B. Wissick, R. Erickson (r1991) *Concert* (10/95) (ALBA) Ⓓ **TROY127-2**

Distressed Innocence—incidental music, Z577 (1690—London) (Wds. E. Settle)
1. Overture; 2. Air; 3. Slow Air; 4. Air; 5. Hornpipe or Jig; 6. Rondeau; 7. Air; 8. Menuet.
Parley of Instr (r1994) *Concert*
(10/95) (HYPE) Ⓓ [3] **CDA67001/3**
1-8. AAM, C. Hogwood *Concert*
(4/91) (L'OI) Ⓓ [6] **425 893-2OM6(1)**

The Comical History of **Don Quixote—incidental music, Z578 (1694-95—London)** (incomplete: wds T. D'Urfey)
1. Overtures; 2. Sing all ye muses; 3. When the world first knew creation; 4. Let the dreadful engines; 5. With this sacred charming wand; 6. Since times are so bad; 7. Genius of England; 8. Lads and lasses; 9. From rosy bow'rs.
1-9. J. Nelson, E. Kirkby, J. Bowman, M. Hill, D. Thomas, AAM, C. Hogwood *Concert*
(4/91) (L'OI) Ⓓ [6] **425 893-2OM6(1)**
4. A. Opie, R. Vignoles (arr Britten) *Concert*
(5/92) (HYPE) Ⓓ **CDA66498**
4. M. Bevan, G. Malcolm (r1950s) *Concert*
(9/93) (VANG) Ⓓ [2] **08.2003.72**
4. S. Keenlyside, G. Johnson (r1995; arr Britten) *Concert* (11/95) (HYPE) Ⓓ [2] **CDA67061/2**
4, 9. C. Bott, D. Roblou, M. Levy, A. Pleeth, P. Chateauneuf, T. Finucane (r1990) *Concert*
(2/93) (L'OI) Ⓓ **433 187-2OH**
9. J. Feldman, N. North, S. Cunningham *Concert*
(1/93) (ARCA) Ⓓ **A02**
9. A. Deller, W. Bergmann (r1950s) *Concert*
(9/93) (VANG) Ⓓ [2] **08.2003.72**
9. A. Mellon, W. Kuijken, C. Rousset (r1992) *Concert*
(9/93) (ASTR) Ⓓ **E8757**
9. N. Argenta, N. North, R. Boothby, P. Nicholson (r1992) *Concert* (6/94) (VIRG) Ⓓ **VC7 59324-2**
9. A. Deller, W. Kuijken, W. Christie, R. Skeaping (r1979) *Concert*
(7/95) (HARM) Ⓓ [6] **HMX290 1528/33(2)**
9. S. Sanford, B. Wissick, R. Erickson (r1991) *Concert* (10/95) (ALBA) Ⓓ **TROY127-2**

Don Quixote: The Musical—music by Purcell & others (1995) (Book & revised lyrics Don Taylor)
EXCERPTS: ACT ONE: 1. Fanfare (J Eccles); 2. Overture (Anon); 3. Knighting music (Anon); 4. Sing all ye muses; 5. Knighting music (Anon); 6. Funeral entrance music (J Eccles); 7. Young Chrysostom (J Eccles); 8. The dirge (J Eccles); 9. The Barber's song (Anon); 10. When the world first knew creation; 11. Let the dreadful engines; 12. 'Twas early one morning (J Eccles); 13. With this sacred charming wand; 14. Pastoral Suite (J Lenton). ACT TWO: 15a. Slow pastoral (J Lenton); 15b. Artful Shepherds (J Stanley); 16. If you will love me (Anon); 17. Ye nymphs and sylvan gods (J Eccles); 18. Damon, let a friend (Colonel Pack); 19. Riding through the whistling air; 20. Hornpipe (T Tollet); 21. Lads and lasses; 22. Masque overture (Mr Orme); 23. Vertumnus Flora (R Courtville); 24. Here is Hymen (R Courtville); 25. Cease, Hymne, cease (R Courtville); 26. Happy mortals (B Compton); 27. Come tell what befell (Anon); 28. The old wife (Anon); 29. Theresa was as sweet (Anon); 30. Marcella's distraught narrative; 31. I burn, I burn (J Eccles); 32. You can never trust a Frenchman (Anon); 33. Genius of England; 34. From rosy bowers; 35a. Puppet overture(T Tollet); 35b. Sweetheart, my passion (Anon); 36. Now sleep my knight; 37. While thus we bow.
Cpte P. Scofield, R. Hudd, E. Kirkby, E. Tubb, D. Thomas, Consort of Musicke, City Waites, Purcell Simfony, A. Rooley (r1995)
(10/95) (MOSC) Ⓓ [2] **070973**

The **Double Dealer—incidental music, Z592 (1693—London)** (Wds. W. Congreve)
1. Overture; 2. Hornpipe; 3. Menuet; 4. Air; 5. Hornpipe; 6. Cynthia frowns (song); 7. Menuet; 8. Menuet; 9. Air.
1-5, 7-9. Parley of Instr (r1994) *Concert*
(10/95) (HYPE) Ⓓ [3] **CDA67001/3**
1-9. J. Nelson, AAM, C. Hogwood *Concert*
(4/91) (L'OI) Ⓓ [6] **425 893-2OM6(1)**
6. P. Esswood, J. Sonnleitner, C. Medlam *Concert*
(12/89) (HYPE) Ⓓ **CDA66070**

Epsom Wells—incidental music, Z579 (1693—London) (Wds. T. Shadwell)
Leave these useless arts (duet)
J. Nelson, D. Thomas, AAM, C. Hogwood *Concert*
(4/91) (L'OI) Ⓓ [6] **425 893-2OM6(2)**

The **Fairy Queen—instrumental suite, Z629 (pub 1697)** (from A Collection of Ayres, compos'd for the Theatre)
EXCERPTS: 1. Overture; 2. Hornpipe; 3. Aire; 4. Aire; 5. Rondeau; 6. Preludio; 7. Hornpipe; 8. Overture; 9. Song Tune: If love's a sweet passion; 10. Jigg; 11. Dance for Furies (Fairies); 12. Aire 4 in 2 (Dance for the Followers of Night); 13. Song Tune: Sing while we trip it; 14. Aire; 15. Aire; 16. Song Tune: Thus happy and free; 17. Chacone; 18. Aire.
Parley of Instr Baroque Orch (r1994) *Concert*
(10/95) (HYPE) Ⓓ [3] **CDA67001/3**

The **Fairy Queen—semi-opera: 5 acts, Z629 (1692—London)** (Lib. ?E. Settle, after Shakespeare)
EXCERPTS: 1. First Musick: 1a. Prelude; 1b. Hornpipe; 2. Second Musick: 2a. Air; 2b. Rondeau; 2c. Overture. ACT 1: 3. Come let us leave the town; 4. Fill up the bowl (Scene of the Drunken Poet); 5. First Act Tune: Jig. ACT 2: 6a. Prelude; 6b. Come all ye songsters of the sky; 7a. May the God of Wit inspire; 7b. Echo (trumpet); 8. Now join your warbling voices all; 9a. Sing while we trip it; 9b. Dance of the Fairies; 10. See, even Night herself is here; 11. I am come to lock all fast; 12. One charming night; 13. Hush, no more; 14. Dance of the followers of Night; 15. Second Act Tune: Air. ACT 3: 16. If love's a sweet passion; 17. Symphony while the swans come forward; 18. Dance of the Fairies; 19. Dance of the Green Men; 20. Ye gentle spirits of the air; 21. Now the maids and the men (Coridon and Mopsa Dialogue); 22. Dance of the Haymakers; 23. When I have often heard; 24. A thousand ways; 25. Third Act Tune: Hornpipe. ACT 4: 26. Symphony; 27. Now the night is chased away; 28. Let the fifes and the clarions; 29. Entry of Phoebus; 30. When a cruel long winter; 31. Hail! Great parent of us all; 32. Thus ever grateful Spring; 33. Here's the Summer; 34. See my many coloured fields; 35. Next Winter comes slowly; 36. Hail! Great parent (reprise); 37. Fourth Act Tune: Air. ACT 5: 38. Prelude; 39. Thrice happy lovers (Epithalamium); 40. O let me weep (The Plaint); 41. Entry Dance; 42. Symphony; 43. Thus the gloomy world; 44. Thus happy and free; 45. Yes, Xansi; 46. Monkeys' Dance; 47. Hark! now all things; 48. Hark! the echoing air; 49. Sure the dull God of Marriage; 50. Prelude; 51a. See, I obey; 51b. Turn

then thine eyes; 51c. My torch indeed; 52. They shall be as happy as they're fair (Trio); 53. Chaconne: Dance of the Chinese Man and Woman; 54. They shall be as happy (chorus).

Cpte E. Harrhy, J. Smith, J. Nelson, T. Penrose, A. Stafford, W. Evans, M. Hill, S. Varcoe, D. Thomas, Monteverdi Ch, EBS, J.E. Gardiner (8/87) (ARCH) ① [2] **419 221-2AH2**

Cpte N. Argenta, L. Dawson, I. Desrochers, W. van Gent, V. Gens, S. Piau, N. Rime, C. Daniels, J-P. Fouchécourt, M. le Brocq, C. le Paludier, B. Loonen, F. Piolino, T. Randle, F. Bazola-Minori, J. Corréas, G. Banks-Martin, B. Delétré, T. Lander, R. Taylor, Arts Florissants Chor, Arts Florissants Orch, W. Christie (r1989) (1/90) (HARM) ① [2] **HMC90 1308/9**

Cpte G. Fisher, L. Anderson, A. Murray, M. Chance, J.M. Ainsley, I. Partridge, R. Suart, M. George, The Sixteen, The Sixteen Orch, H. Christophers (4/92) (COLL) ① [2] **Coll7013-2**

Cpte J. Vyvyan, M. Wells, N. Burrowes, A. Hodgson, J. Bowman, C. Brett, P. Pears, I. Partridge, O. Brannigan, J. Shirley-Quirk, Ambrosian Op Chor, ECO, B. Britten (r1970: ed/arr Britten, I Holst, Ledger & Pears) (5/92) (DECC) ① [2] **433 163-2DM2**

Cpte Scholars Baroque Ens (r1992) (7/94) (NAXO) ① [2] **8 550660/1**

Cpte L. Hunt, C. Pierard, S. Bickley, H. Crook, M. Padmore, D. Wilson-Johnson, R. Wistreich, London Schütz Ch, LCP, R. Norrington (r1993) (2/95) (EMI) ① [2] **CDS5 55234-2**

C. Bott, Jeffrey Thomas, M. Schopper, Amsterdam Baroque Ch, Amsterdam Baroque Orch, T. Koopman (r1994) (6/95) (ERAT) ① [2] **4509-98507-2**

Excs Freiburg Baroque Orch, T. Hengelbrock (arr Hengelbrock) *Concert* (3/92) (DHM) ① **RD77231**

Excs M. André, H. Bilgram (tpt/org) *Concert* (1/93) (EMI) ① **CDC7 54330-2**

Suite English Gtr Qt (arr Gallery) *Concert* (11/91) (SAYD) ① **CD-SDL386**

1-4. E. Kirkby, C. Hogwood, A. Rooley, R. Campbell, C. Mackintosh *Concert* (9/86) (L'OI) ① **417 123-2OH**

1, 5. J. Bowman, King's Consort, R. King *Concert* (7/89) (HYPE) ① **CDA66288**

2, 3, 8. D. Minter, P. O'Dette, M. Springfels *Concert* (1/93) (HARM) ① **HMU90 7035**

2-4. J. Feldman, N. North, S. Cunningham *Concert* (1/93) (ARCA) ① **A02**

2, 48. H. Crook, Capriccio Stravagante, S. Sempé (hpd/dir) *Concert* (9/92) (DHM) ① **RD77252**

8. K. Ferrier, P. Spurr (bp1949) *Concert* (6/92) (DECC) ① **433 473-2DM**

16, 20, 48. S. Sanford, B. Wissick, R. Erickson (r1991) *Concert* (10/95) (ALBA) ① **TROY127-2**

39. A. Deller, G. Malcolm (r1950s) *Concert* (9/93) (VANG) ① [2] **08.2003.72**

39. A. Mellon, W. Kuijken, C. Rousset (r1992) *Concert* (9/93) (ASTR) ① **E8757**

39. M. Hill, A. Ball (r1994; arr Tippett & Bergmann) *Concert* (4/95) (HYPE) ① **CDA66749**

39, 40. A. Deller, W. Kuijken, W. Christie, R. Skeaping (r1979) *Concert* (7/95) (HARM) ① [6] **HMX290 1528/33(2)**

40. Suzie Le Blanc, Tragicomedia (r1994) *Concert* (7/95) (TELD) ① **4509-95068-2**

40, 48. S. McNair, C. Steele-Perkins, S. Standage, AAM, C. Hogwood (r1994) *Concert* (9/95) (PHIL) ① **446 081-2PH**

48. N. Argenta, N. North, R. Boothby, P. Nicholson (r1992) *Concert* (6/94) (VIRG) ① **VC7 59324-2**

48. F. Lott, G. Johnson (r1995; arr Britten) *Concert* (11/95) (HYPE) ① [2] **CDA67061/2**

The **Fatal Marriage—incidental music, Z595 (1694—London)** (Wds. T. Southerne)

1. The danger is over; 2. I sigh'd and owned my love.

1, 2. J. Nelson, AAM, C. Hogwood *Concert* (4/91) (L'OI) ① [6] **425 893-2OM6(2)**

The **Female Vertuosos—incidental music, Z596 (1693—London)** (Wds. T. Wright, after Molière)

Love, thou art best (duet)

E. Kirkby, AAM, C. Hogwood *Concert* (4/91) (L'OI) ① [6] **425 893-2OM6(2)**

A **Fool's Preferment—incidental music, Z571 (1688—London)** (Wds. T. D'Urfey)

1. I'll sail upon the dog star.

J. Nelson, R. Covey-Crump, AAM, C. Hogwood *Concert* (4/91) (L'OI) ① [6] **425 893-2OM6(2)**

1. C. Bott, D. Roblou (r1990) *Concert* (2/93) (L'OI) ① **433 187-2OH**

1. R. Jackson, G. Johnson (r1995; arr Britten) *Concert* (11/95) (HYPE) ① [2] **CDA67061/2**

The **Gordian Knot Unty'd—incidental music, Z597 (1691—London)**

1. Overture; 2. Air; 3. Rondeau menuet; 4. Air; 5. Jig; 6. Chaconne; 7. Air; 8. Menuet.

Parley of Instr (r1994) *Concert* (10/95) (HYPE) ① [3] **CDA67001/3**

Suite Parley of Instr, P. Holman *Concert* (9/87) (HYPE) ① **CDA66212**

1-8. AAM, C. Hogwood *Concert* (4/91) (L'OI) ① [6] **425 893-2OM6(1)**

1-8. Cologne Stravaganza *Concert* (12/92) (DENO) ① **CO-79250**

1-8. Cambridge Clare College Ch, Philh Baroque Orch (r1993) *Dido.* (4/95) (HARM) ① **HMU90 7110**

6. Taverner Plyrs, A. Parrott *Concert* (12/88) (EMI) ① **CDM7 69853-2**

Henry the Second, King of England—incidental music, Z580 (1692—London) (Wds. ?W. Mountfort and J. Bancroft)

In vain 'gainst love I strove (song)

J. Nelson, E. Kirkby, AAM, C. Hogwood *Concert* (4/91) (L'OI) ① [6] **425 893-2OM6(1)**

The **History of King Richard II—incidental music, Z581 (1681—London)** (Wds. N. Tate, after Shakespeare)

Retired from any mortal's sight

R. Jacobs, W. Kuijken, K. Junghänel *Concert* (8/85) (ACCE) ① **ACC57802D**

J. Nelson, AAM, C. Hogwood *Concert* (4/91) (L'OI) ① [6] **425 893-2OM6(1)**

A. Deller, B. Lam, T. Weil (r1953) *Concert* (4/92) (EMI) ① [7] **CHS7 69741-2(2)**

A. Deller, W. Kuijken, W. Christie, R. Skeaping (r1979) *Concert* (7/95) (HARM) ① [6] **HMX290 1528/33(2)**

The **Indian Emperor—incidental music, Z598 (1691)** (wds J. Dryden & R. Howard)

I look and saw within

E. Kirkby, AAM, C. Hogwood *Concert* (4/91) (L'OI) ① [6] **425 893-2OM6(2)**

The **Indian Queen—instrumental suite, Z630**

1. Overture; 2. Trumpet Tune; 3. Trumpet Tune (I come to sing great Zempoalla's story); 4. Air; 5. Hornpipe; 6. Air; 7. Hornpipe; 8. Air; 9. Song Tune (We are the spirits of the air); 10. Rondeau.

Parley of Instr Baroque Orch (r1994) *Concert* (10/95) (HYPE) ① [3] **CDA67001/3**

The **Indian Queen—semi-opera (final masque by D. Purcell), Z630 (1695—London)** (Lib. J. Dryden and R. Howard)

EXCERPTS: 1. First Music; 2. Second Music; 3. Overture; 4. Trumpet Tune. PROLOGUE: 5. Wake, Quivera; 6. Why should men quarrel; 7. By ancient prophecies; 8. Trumpet tune (reprise). ACT 2: 9. Symphony; 10. I come to sing great Zempoalla's Story; 11. What flattering noise is this; 12. Scorn'd envy, here's nothing; 13. I fly from the place; 14. Begone, curst fiends of hell; 15. I come to sing. ACT 3: 16. Air; 17. Minuet; 18. Ye twice ten thousand deities; 19. Symphony; 20. Seek not to know; 21. Trumpet Overture; 22. Ah, how happy are we; 23. We the Spirits of the Air; 24. I attempt from love's sickness; 25. Third Act Tune. ACT 4: 26. They tell us that your mighty powers; 27. Fourth Act Tune. ACT 5: 28. While thus we bow.

Cpte M. Bevan, H. Sheppard, M. Deller, P. Elliott, A. Deller, Deller Ch, King's Musick, A. Deller (omits final masque) (8/87) (HARM) ① **HMC90 243**

Cpte S. Varcoe, J. Smith, M. Hill, J. Elwes, R. Hardy, G. Fisher, A. Stafford, D. Thomas, D. Harris, Monteverdi Ch, EBS, J.E.Gardiner (r1979) *Concert* (7/95) (ERAT) ① [8] **4509-96371-2**

Cpte R. Hardy, M. Hill, J. Elwes, A. Stafford, D. Thomas, S. Varcoe, G. Fisher, D. Harris, J. Smith, Monteverdi Ch, EBS, J.E. Gardiner (r1979) (7/95) (ERAT) ① **4509-96551-2**

Cpte T. Bonner, C. Bott, R. Covey-Crump, P. Harvey, Purcell Simfony Voices, Purcell Simfony (r1994) (9/95) (LINN) ① **CKD035**

Let us wander K. Ferrier, I. Baillie, G. Moore (r1945) *Concert* (6/88) (EMI) ① **CDH7 61003-2**

Let us wander E. Söderström, K. Meyer, J. Eyron (r1974) *Concert* (9/93) (BIS) ① **BIS-CD017**

Let us wander V. de los Angeles, D. Fischer-Dieskau, G. Moore (r1960: arr Moffat) *Concert* (4/94) (EMI) ① [4] **CMS5 65061-2(2)**

1, 3, 4. W. Marsalis, ECO, R. Leppard *Concert* (1/86) (SONY) ① **MK39061**

1-3, 5, 9, 10, 17-22, 24, 26, 28. C. Keyte, A. Cantelo, Wilfred Brown, I. Partridge, R. Tear, St Anthony Sngrs, ECO, C. Mackerras (r1965) *King Arthur, Z628.* (5/92) (DECC) ① [2] **433 166-2DM2**

8, 9. Taverner Plyrs, A. Parrott *Concert* (12/88) (EMI) ① **CDM7 69853-2**

19. Parley of Instr Baroque Orch (r1994) *Concert* (10/95) (HYPE) ① [3] **CDA67001/3**

24. A. Murray, G. Johnson (r1991) *Concert* (7/92) (EMI) ① **CDC7 54411-2**

24. J. Feldman, N. North, S. Cunningham *Concert* (1/93) (ARCA) ① **A02**

24. D. Minter, M. Meyerson *Concert* (1/93) (HARM) ① **HMU90 7035**

24. A. Deller, W. Bergmann (r1950s) *Concert* (9/93) (VANG) ① [2] **08.2003.72**

24. N. Argenta, P. Nicholson (r1992) *Concert* (6/94) (VIRG) ① **VC7 59324-2**

24. A. Deller, W. Kuijken, W. Christie, R. Skeaping (r1979) *Concert* (7/95) (HARM) ① [6] **HMX290 1528/33(2)**

24. S. McNair, AAM, C. Hogwood (r1994) *Concert* (9/95) (PHIL) ① **446 081-2PH**

24. S. Sanford, B. Wissick, R. Erickson (r1991) *Concert* (10/95) (ALBA) ① **TROY127-2**

24. S. Gritton, G. Johnson (r1995; arr Britten) *Concert* (11/95) (HYPE) ① [2] **CDA67061/2**

King Arthur—instrumental suite, Z628 (pub 1697) (from A Collection of Ayres, compos'd for the Theatre)

EXCERPTS: 1. Overture; 2. Aire; 3. Aire; 4. Song Tune: Fairest Isle; 5. Hornpipe; 6. Aire; 7. Song Tune: How blest are shepherds; 8. Aire; 9. Song Tune: Round thy coast; 10. Song Tune: Come, if you dare; 11. Trumpet Tune; 12. Trumpet Tune; 13. Chaconne.

Parley of Instr Baroque Orch (r1994) *Concert* (10/95) (HYPE) ① [3] **CDA67001/3**

King Arthur—semi-opera, Z628 (1691—London) (Lib. J. Dryden)

EXCERPTS: 1. First Music; 2. Second Music; 3. Overture. ACT 1: 4. SACRIFICE SCENE: 4a. Woden, first to thee; 4b. The White Horse neigh'd aloud; 4c. The Lot is cast; 4d. Brave souls; 5. Come if you care; 6. First Act Tune: Come if you date. ACT 2: 7a. Hither this way; 7b. Let not a Moon-born Elf; 7c. Hither this way (chorus); 7d. Come follow me; 8a. How blest are the Shepherds; 8b. Shepherd, shepherd, leave Decoying; 8c. Come shepherds; 8d. Hornpipe; 9. Second Act Tune: Air. ACT 3: 10. FROST SCENE: 10a. What ho; 10b. What Power art thou; 10c. Thou Doting Fool; 10d. Great love; 10e. No part of my Dominion; 10f. Prelude; 10g. See, see, we assemble; 10h. 'Tis I that have warm'd ye; 10i. Sound a Parley; 11. Third Act Tune: Hornpipe. ACT 4: 12. Two daughters; 13a. Passacaglia; 13b. How happy the Lover; 13c. For love ev'ry creature; 14. Fourth Act Tune: Air. ACT 5: 15. Trumpet Tune; 16. Ye blust'ring Brethren; 17. Symphony; 18. Round the coast; 19. For folded flocks; 20. Your Hay it is Mow'd (Harvest Home); 21. Fairest isle; 22. You say,Tis love; 23. Warlike Consort; 24a. Saint George, the patron of our isle; 24b. Our natives not alone appear.

Cpte E. Morison, H. Harper, M. Thomas, J. Whitworth, D. Galliver, Wilfred Brown, J. Cameron, H. Alan, T. Anthony, St Anthony Sngrs, Philomusica of London, A. Lewis (r1958) *Indian Queen, Z630.* (5/92) (DECC) ① [2] **433 166-2DM2**

Cpte N. Argenta, J. Gooding, L. Perillo, J. MacDougall, M. Tucker, B. Bannatyne-Scott, G. Finley, English Concert Ch, English Concert, T. Pinnock (9/92) (ARCH) ① [2] **435 490-2AH2**

Cpte V. Gens, C. McFadden, S. Piau, S. Waters, M. Padmore, I. Paton, J. Best, P. Salomaa, F. Bazola-Minori, Arts Florissants Chor, Arts Florissants Orch, W. Christie (6/95) (ERAT) ① [2] **4509-98535-2**

Cpte J. Smith, G. Fisher, E. Priday, G. Ross, A. Stafford, P. Elliott, S. Varcoe, Monteverdi Ch, EBS, J.E.Gardiner (r1983) *Concert* (7/95) (ERAT) ① [8] **4509-96371-2**

Cpte J. Smith, G. Fisher, E. Priday, G. Ross, A. Stafford, P. Elliott, S. Varcoe, Monteverdi Ch, EBS, J.E. Gardiner (r1983) (7/95) (ERAT) ① [2] **4509-96552-2**

Excs Freiburg Baroque Orch, T. Hengelbrock (arr Hengelbrock) *Concert* (3/92) (DHM) ① **RD77231**

Excs H. Sheppard, J. Knibbs, R. Hardy, A. Deller, M. Deller, P. Elliott, L. Nixon, M. Bevan, N. Beavan, Deller Ch, King's Musick, A. Deller (r1978) *Concert* (7/95) (HARM) ① [6] **HMX290 1528/33(2)**

8a, 8b, 21. F. Lott, S. Gritton, Sarah Walker, J. M. Ainsley, G. Johnson (r1995; arr Britten) *Concert* (11/95) (HYPE) ① [2] **CDA67061/2**

8b K. Ferrier, I. Baillie, G. Moore (r1945) *Concert* (6/88) (EMI) ① **CDH7 61003-2**

12. E. Söderström, K. Meyer, J. Eyron (r1974) *Concert* (9/93) (BIS) ① **BIS-CD017**

13c, 22. E. Kirkby, D. Thomas, A. Rooley *Concert* (6/88) (HYPE) ① **CDA66056**

20. L. Skeaping, J. Potter, Broadside Band, J. Barlow (r1992; arr J. Barlow) *Concert* (6/93) (SAYD) ① **CD-SDL400**

21. W. Marsalis, ECO, R. Leppard *Concert* (1/86) (SONY) ① **MK39061**

21. J. Bowman, King's Consort, R. King *Concert* (7/89) (HYPE) ① **CDA66288**

21. P. Esswood, J. Sonnleitner, C. Medlam *Concert*
(12/89) (HYPE) ① **CDA66070**
21. F. Lott, G. Johnson (r1991) *Concert*
(7/92) (EMI) ① **CDC7 54411-2**
21. J. Feldman, N. North, S. Cunningham *Concert*
(1/93) (ARCA) ① **A02**
21. A. Deller, W. Bergmann (r1950s) *Concert*
(9/93) (VANG) ① [2] **08.2003.72**
21. A. Mellon, W. Kuijken, C. Rousset (r1992)
is he (song). (9/93) (ASTR) ① **E8757**
21. N. Argenta, N. North (r1992) *Concert*
(6/94) (VIRG) ① **VC7 59324-2**
21. A. Deller, W. Kuijken, W. Christie, R. Skeaping
(r1979) *Concert*
(7/95) (HARM) ① [6] **HMX290 1528/33(2)**
21. S. McNair, AAM, C. Hogwood (r1994) *Concert*
(9/95) (PHIL) ① **446 081-2PH**
The **Libertine—incidental music, Z600**
(?1692—London) (Wds. T. Shadwell)
1. Nymphs and shepherds; 2. We come; 3. Prelude:
Flatt trumpets; 4. Prepare, prepare, new guests draw
near; 5. To arms, heroic prince.
1. A. Auger, J. Revzen (pp1989; arr Britten) *Concert*
(4/94) (KOCH) ① **37248-2**
1-5. J. Nelson, J. Bowman, M. Hill, D. Thomas, AAM,
C. Hogwood *Concert*
(4/91) (L'OI) ① [6] **425 893-2OM6(1)**
5. S. McNair, C. Steele-Perkins, AAM, C. Hogwood
(r1994) *Concert* (9/95) (PHIL) ① **446 081-2PH**
Love Triumphant—incidental music, Z582
(1694—London) (Wds. J. Dryden)
How happy the husband
J. Nelson, J. Bowman, M. Hill, AAM, C. Hogwood
Concert (4/91) (L'OI) ① [6] **425 893-2OM6(2)**
The **Maid's Last Prayer—incidental music,**
Z601 (1693—London) (Wds. T. Southerne)
1. Though you make no return (song); 2. No,
resistance is but vain (duet).
1, 2, 3. J. Nelson, J. Bowman, M. Hill, D. Thomas,
AAM, C. Hogwood *Concert*
(4/91) (L'OI) ① [6] **425 893-2OM6(2)**
2. J. Bowman, M. Chance, King's Consort, R. King
Concert (7/88) (HYPE) ① **CDA66253**
2. Sarah Walker, R. Jackson, G. Johnson (r1995; arr
Britten) *Concert*
(11/95) (HYPE) ① [2] **CDA67061/2**
The **Marriage-Hater Match'd—incidental**
music, Z602 (1602) (wds. T. D'Urfey)
1. As soon as the chaos; 2. How vile are the sordid
intrigues.
1, 2. E. Kirkby, M. Hill, R. Covey-Crump, D. Thomas,
AAM, C. Hogwood *Concert*
(4/91) (L'OI) ① [6] **425 893-2OM6(2)**
The **Married Beau—incidental music, Z603**
(1694—London) (Wds. J. Crowne)
1. Overture; 2. Slow air; 3. Hornpipe; 4. Air; 5.
Hornpipe; 6. Jig; 7. Trumpet air; 8. March; 9.
Hornpipe on a ground; 10. See where repenting Celia
lies (song).
1-10. J. Roberts, AAM, C. Hogwood *Concert*
(4/91) (L'OI) ① [6] **425 893-2OM6(1)**
1-9. Cologne Stravaganza *Concert*
(12/92) (DENO) ① **CO-79250**
1-9. Lucerne Fest Strings, R. Baumgartner (r1959) *St*
Cecilia's Day Ode, Z328.
(7/95) (ARCH) ① **447 149-2AP**
1-9. Parley of Instr (r1994) *Concert*
(10/95) (HYPE) ① [3] **CDA67001/3**
3. Barbirolli CO, J. Barbirolli (r1928) *Concert*
(3/92) (KOCH) ① **37077-2**
Massacre of Paris—incidental music, Z604
(1690—London) (Wds. N. Lee)
1. Thy genius, lo! (first setting); 2. Thy genius, lo!
(second setting).
1, 2. J. Nelson, AAM, C. Hogwood *Concert*
(4/91) (L'OI) ① [6] **425 893-2OM6(1)**
The **Mock Marriage—incidental music, Z605**
(1695—London) (Wds. T. Scott)
1. Oh! how you protest (song); 2. 'Twas within a
furlong (song); 3. Man is for woman made (song).
1-3. R. Covey-Crump, AAM, C. Hogwood *Concert*
(4/91) (L'OI) ① [6] **425 893-2OM6(2)**
3. A. Rolfe Johnson, G. Johnson (r1995; arr Britten)
Concert (11/95) (HYPE) ① [2] **CDA67061/2**
Oedipus—incidental music, Z583
(?1692—London) (Wds. J. Dryden and N.
Lee)
1. (ACT 3) Hear ye sullen powers below (trio); 2.
Music for a while (song); 3. Come away, do not stay
(solo and trio).
1-3. J. Bowman, M. Hill, D. Thomas, AAM, C.
Hogwood *Concert*
(4/91) (L'OI) ① [6] **425 893-2OM6(1)**
2. R. Jacobs, W. Kuijken, K. Junghänel *Concert*
(8/85) (ACCE) ① **ACC57802D**

2. R. Jacobs, K. Junghänel (r1985) *Concert*
(5/87) (HARM) ① **HMA190 1183**
2. J. Bowman, King's Consort, R. King *Concert*
(7/89) (HYPE) ① **CDA66288**
2. P. Esswood, J. Sonnleitner, C. Medlam *Concert*
(12/89) (HYPE) ① **CDA66070**
2. Sarah Walker, J. Constable *Concert*
(4/92) (GAMU) ① **GAMD506**
2. H. Crook, Capriccio Stravagante, S. Sempé
(hpd/dir) *Concert* (9/92) (DHM) ① **RD77252**
2. J. Feldman, N. North, S. Cunningham *Concert*
(1/93) (ARCA) ① **A02**
2. D. Minter, P. O'Dette *Concert*
(1/93) (HARM) ① **HMU90 7035**
2. A. Deller, W. Bergmann (r1950s) *Concert*
(9/93) (VANG) ① [2] **08.2003.72**
2. K. Battle, M. Lutzke, Anthony Newman (pp1991)
Concert (9/93) (SONY) ① **SK53106**
2. A. Deller, W. Kuijken, W. Christie, R. Skeaping
(r1979) *Concert*
(7/95) (HARM) ① [6] **HMX290 1528/33(2)**
2. S. McNair, AAM, C. Hogwood (r1994) *Concert*
(9/95) (PHIL) ① **446 081-2PH**
2. S. Sanford, B. Wissick (1991) *Concert*
(10/95) (ALBA) ① **TROY127-2**
2. Sarah Walker, G. Johnson (r1995; arr Britten)
Concert (11/95) (HYPE) ① [2] **CDA67061/2**
The **Old Bachelor—incidental music, Z607**
(1693—London) (Wds. W. Congreve).
1. Overture; 2. Hornpipe; 3. Thus to a ripe consenting
maid (song); 4. Slow air; 5. Hornpipe; 6. As Amoret
and Thysis (duet); 7. Rondeau; 8. Menuet; 9.
Bourrée; 10. March; 11. Jig.
1-11. J. Nelson, M. Hill, S. Keyte, AAM, C. Hogwood
Concert (4/91) (L'OI) ① [6] **425 893-2OM6(1)**
1, 2, 4, 5, 7-11. Parley of Instr (r1994) *Concert*
(10/95) (HYPE) ① [3] **CDA67001/3**
6. R. Jacobs, W. Kuijken, K. Junghänel *Concert*
(8/85) (ACCE) ① **ACC57802D**
6. E. Kirkby, D. Thomas, A. Rooley *Concert*
(6/88) (HYPE) ① **CDA66056**
Oroonoko—incidental music, Z584
(1695—London) (Wds. T. Southerne)
Clemene, pray tell me
E. Kirkby, J. Nelson, AAM, C. Hogwood *Concert*
(4/91) (L'OI) ① [6] **425 893-2OM6(2)**
S. Gritton, I. Bostridge, G. Johnson (r1995; arr
Britten) *Concert*
(11/95) (HYPE) ① [2] **CDA67061/2**
Overture in G minor, Z631/1 (possibly
composed for the prologue of 'Dido and
Aeneas')
Parley of Instr (r1994) *Concert*
(10/95) (HYPE) ① [3] **CDA67001/3**
Pausanias—incidental music, Z585
(1695—London) (Wds. Norton)
1. Sweeter than roses (song); 2. My dearest, my
fairest (duet).
1. R. Jacobs, W. Kuijken, K. Junghänel *Concert*
(8/85) (ACCE) ① **ACC57802D**
1. E. Kirkby, C. Hogwood, A. Rooley, R. Campbell, C.
Mackinson *Concert* (9/86) (L'OI) ① **417 123-2OH**
1. R. Jacobs, K. Junghänel (r1985) *Concert*
(5/87) (HARM) ① **HMA190 1183**
1. P. Esswood, J. Sonnleitner, C. Medlam *Concert*
(12/89) (HYPE) ① **CDA66070**
1. J. Feldman, N. North, S. Cunningham *Concert*
(1/93) (ARCA) ① **A02**
1. D. Minter, P. O'Dette, M. Springfels *Concert*
(1/93) (HARM) ① **HMU90 7035**
1. A. Deller, W. Bergmann (r1950s) *Concert*
(9/93) (VANG) ① [2] **08.2003.72**
1. A. Mellon, W. Kuijken, C. Rousset (r1992) *Concert*
(9/93) (ASTR) ① **E8757**
1. A. Auger, J. Revzen (pp1989; arr Britten) *Concert*
(4/94) (KOCH) ① **37248-2**
1. N. Argenta, N. North, R. Boothby (r1992) *Concert*
(6/94) (VIRG) ① **VC7 59324-2**
1. M. Hill, A. Ball (r1994; arr Tippett & Bergmann)
Concert (4/95) (HYPE) ① **CDA66749**
1. A. Deller, W. Kuijken, W. Christie, R. Skeaping
(r1979) *Concert*
(7/95) (HARM) ① [6] **HMX290 1528/33(2)**
1. S. McNair, AAM, C. Hogwood (r1994) *Concert*
(9/95) (PHIL) ① **446 081-2PH**
1. F. Lott, G. Johnson (r1995; arr Britten) *Concert*
(11/95) (HYPE) ① [2] **CDA67061/2**
1, 2. J. Nelson, P. Elliott, A. Byers, P. Bamber, AAM,
C. Hogwood *Concert*
(4/91) (L'OI) ① [6] **425 893-2OM6(2)**
Regulus—incidental music, Z586 (1692)
(wds. J. Crowne)
Ah me! to many deaths
J. Nelson, AAM, C. Hogwood *Concert*
(4/91) (L'OI) ① [6] **425 893-2OM6(2)**

The **Richmond Heiress—incidental music,**
Z608 (1693—London) (Wds. T. D'Urfey)
Behold the man
J. Nelson, D. Thomas, AAM, C. Hogwood *Concert*
(4/91) (L'OI) ① [6] **425 893-2OM6(1)**
The **Rival Sisters—incidental music, Z609**
(1695—London) (Wds. R. Gould)
1. Overture; 2. Celia has a thousand charms (song);
3. Take not a woman's anger ill (song); 4. How happy
is she (song).
1-4. J. Nelson, Taverner Ch, AAM, C. Hogwood
Concert (4/91) (L'OI) ① [6] **425 893-2OM6(1)**
2. J. Bowman, King's Consort, R. King *Concert*
(7/89) (HYPE) ① **CDA66288**
2. D. Minter, P. O'Dette, M. Springfels *Concert*
(1/93) (HARM) ① **HMU90 7035**
2. A. Mellon, W. Kuijken, C. Rousset (r1992) *Concert*
(9/93) (ASTR) ① **E8757**
3. J. M. Ainsley, G. Johnson (r1995; arr Britten)
Concert (11/95) (HYPE) ① [2] **CDA67061/2**
Rule a Wife and Have a Wife—incidental
music, Z587 (1693—London) (Wds. J.
Fletcher)
There's not a swain
J. Nelson, D. Thomas, AAM, C. Hogwood *Concert*
(4/91) (L'OI) ① [6] **425 893-2OM6(2)**
K. Battle, M. Lutzke, Anthony Newman (pp1991)
Concert (9/94) (SONY) ① **SK53106**
I. Bostridge, G. Johnson (r1995; arr Britten) *Concert*
(11/95) (HYPE) ① [2] **CDA67061/2**
Sir Anthony Love—incidental music, Z588
(1690—London) (Wds. T. Southerne)
1. Overture; 2. Pursuing Beauty; 3. No more, Sir, no
more; 4. In vain Clemene; 5. Ground.
1. Parley of Instr (r1994) *Concert*
(10/95) (HYPE) ① [3] **CDA67001/3**
1-5. J. Nelson, C. Keyte, AAM, C. Hogwood *Concert*
(4/91) (L'OI) ① [6] **425 893-2OM6(1)**
Sir Barnaby Whigg—incidental music, Z589
(1681) (wds. T. D'Urfey)
Blow, Boreas, blow
R. Covey-Crump, D. Thomas, AAM, C. Hogwood
Concert (4/91) (L'OI) ① [6] **425 893-2OM6(1)**
Sonata While the Sun Rises in 'The Indian
Queen'—suite of music from Act IV,
Z629/27
1. Allegro; 2. Canzona; 3. Adagio; 4. Allegro-Adagio-
Allegro.
Parley of Instr Baroque Orch (r1994) *Concert*
(10/95) (HYPE) ① [3] **CDA67001/3**
Sophonisba—incidental music, Z590
(?1685—London) (Wds. N. Lee)
Beneath the poplar's shadow
P. Esswood, J. Sonnleitner, C. Medlam *Concert*
(12/89) (HYPE) ① **CDA66070**
J. Nelson, AAM, C. Hogwood *Concert*
(4/91) (L'OI) ① [6] **425 893-2OM6(1)**
N. Argenta, N. North, R. Boothby (r1992) *Concert*
(6/94) (VIRG) ① **VC7 59324-2**
The **Spanish Friar—incidental music, Z610**
(1694-95—London) (Wds. J. Dryden)
Whilst I with grief J. Feldman, N. North, S.
Cunningham *Concert* (1/93) (ARCA) ① **A02**
Whilst I with grief
R. Covey-Crump, AAM, C. Hogwood *Concert*
(4/91) (L'OI) ① [6] **425 893-2OM6(2)**
The **Tempest—semi-opera, Z631 (c1695)**
(Lib. Shadwell)
1. Dear pretty youth; 2. Full fathom five; 3. Come
unto these yellow sands; 4. Dry those eyes (attrib).
Cpte D. Thomas, R. Earle, C. Hall, R. Hardy, J.
Smith, S. Varcoe, J. Elwes, Monteverdi Ch,
Monteverdi Orch, J.E. Gardiner (1979)
(7/95) (ERAT) ① **4509-96555-2**
Cpte J. Smith, R. Hardy, C. Hall, J. Elwes, S. Varcoe,
D. Thomas, R. Earle, Monteverdi Ch, EBS,
J.E.Gardiner (1979) *Concert*
(7/95) (ERAT) ① [8] **4509-96371-2**
1. E. Kirkby, C. Hogwood, A. Rooley, R. Campbell, C.
Mackinson *Concert* (9/86) (L'OI) ① **417 123-2OH**
1. J. Feldman, N. North, S. Cunningham *Concert*
(1/93) (ARCA) ① **A02**
1. N. Argenta, N. North, R. Boothby (r1992) *Concert*
(6/94) (VIRG) ① **VC7 59324-2**
1. S. Sanford, B. Wissick, R. Erickson (r1991)
Concert (10/95) (ALBA) ① **TROY127-2**
Theodosius—incidental music, Z606
(1680—London) (Wds. N. Lee)
1. Prepare, the rites begin; 2. Can'st thou, Marina; 3.
The gate to bliss; 4. Hark, behold the heav'nly choir;
5. Now the fight's done; 6. Sad as death at dead of
night; 7. Dance no more of pleasure past; 8. Hail to
the myrtle shade; 9. Ah! Cruel, bloody fate.
1-9. J. Nelson, E. Kirkby, J. Bowman, M. Hill,
Taverner Ch, AAM, C. Hogwood *Concert*
(4/91) (L'OI) ① [6] **425 893-2OM6(1)**

Timon of Athens—incidental music, Z632
(1694—London) (Wds. T. Shadwell, after
Shakespeare)
1. Overture; 2. Hark! how the songsters; 3. Love in
their little veins; 4. Hence with your trifling deity; 5.
Come all to me; 6. Return, revolting rebels; 7. The
cares of lovers; 8. Love quickly is pall'd; 8. Come let
us agree; 9. Curtain tune.
Cpte L. Dawson, G. Fisher, R. Covey-Crump, P.
Elliott, M. George, S. Varcoe, Monteverdi Ch, EBS,
J.E.Gardiner (r1987) Concert
(7/95) (ERAT) ① [8] 4509-96371-2
Cpte L. Dawson, G. Fisher, R. Covey-Crump, P.
Elliott, M. George, S. Varcoe, Monteverdi Ch, EBS,
J.E. Gardiner (r1987) Dioclesian, Z627.
(7/95) (ERAT) ① [2] 4509-96556-2
Cpte N. Argenta, A. Monoyios, P. Agnew, B.
Bannatyne-Scott, C. Foster, English Concert Ch,
English Concert, T. Pinnock (r1994) Dioclesian,
Z627.   (12/95) (ARCH) ① [2] 447 071-2AH2
1, 9. Parley of Instr, P. Holman Concert
(9/87) (HYPE) ① CDA66212
1-9. I. Davies, C. de la Hoyde, J. Bowman, J. M.
Ainsley, I. Bostridge, Collegium Musicum 90, R.
Hickox (r1993) Dioclesian, Z627.
(11/94) (CHAN) ① CHAN0558
1, 9. Parley of Instr (r1994) Concert
(10/95) (HYPE) ① [3] CDA67001/3
2. M. Chance, J. Bowman, King's Consort, R.
Concert   (7/88) (HYPE) ① CDA66253
3. A. Mellon, W. Kuijken, C. Rousset (r1992) Concert
(9/93) (ASTR) ① E8757
6. M. van Egmond, Leonhardt Consort, G. Leonhardt
(r1967) Concert
(9/93) (TELD) ① [2] 9031-77608-2
7. E. Kirkby, C. Hogwood, A. Rooley, R. Campbell, C.
Mackintosh Concert (9/86) (L'OI) ① 417 123-2OH
7. J. Feldman, N. North, S. Cunningham Concert
(1/93) (ARCA) ① A02
Tyrannic Love—incidental music, Z613
(1694—London) (Wds. J. Dryden)
1. Hark, my Damilcar (duet); 2. Ah! how sweet it is to
love (song).
1, 2. J. Nelson, E. Kirkby, AAM, C. Hogwood Concert
(4/91) (L'OI) ① [6] 425 893-2OM6(1)
2. J. Bowman, King's Consort, R. King Concert
(7/89) (HYPE) ① CDA66288
2. J. Feldman, N. North, S. Cunningham Concert
(1/93) (ARCA) ① A02
2. A. Mellon, W. Kuijken, C. Rousset (r1992) Concert
(9/93) (ASTR) ① E8757
2. N. Argenta, R. Boothby, P. Nicholson (r1992)
Concert   (6/94) (VIRG) ① VC7 59324-2
2. S. Sanford, B. Wissick, R. Erickson (r1991)
Concert   (10/95) (ALBA) ① TROY127-2
The Virtuous Wife—incidental music, Z611
(?1694—London) (Wds. T. D'Urfey)
1. Overture; 2. Song tune; 3. Slow air; 4. Air; 5.
Preludio; 6. Hornpipe; 7. Menuet; 8. Menuet; 9. Act I
tune.
Parley of Instr (r1994) Concert
(10/95) (HYPE) ① [3] CDA67001/3
Suite Parley of Instr, P. Holman Concert
(9/87) (HYPE) ① CDA66212
1-9. AAM, C. Hogwood Concert
(4/91) (L'OI) ① [6] 425 893-2OM6(1)
The Wife's Excuse—incidental music, Z612
(1691) (wds. T. Southern)
EXCERPTS: 1. Ingrateful love; 2. Hang this whining
way wooing; 3. Saty, cruel Amoret; 4. Corinna, I
excuse thy face.
1, 2, 3. E. Kirkby, M. Hill, R. Covey-Crump, AAM, C.
Hogwood Concert
(4/91) (L'OI) ① [6] 425 893-2OM6(2)

PURCELL-COCKRAM, Edward (d
1932) England

SECTION IV: VOCAL AND CHORAL

Passing by—song (Wds. anon English:
spuriously attrib to Herrick)
P. McCann, I. Robertson (r1984: arr P McCann)
Concert   (11/92) (CHAN) ① CHAN4501

PURVIS, Richard (b 1915) USA

SECTION III: INSTRUMENTAL

Capriccio on the notes of the
Cuckoo—organ
J. Jones Concert   (8/91) (MOTE) ① CD11491

PYAMOUR, John (fl c1418 d1431)
England

SECTION IV: VOCAL AND CHORAL

Quam pulchra es—motet (3vv)
Gothic Voices, C. Page Concert
(11/87) (HYPE) ① CDA66238

PYCARD, ?Thomas (fl c1340)
England

SECTION IV: VOCAL AND CHORAL

Credo—4vv
Gothic Voices, C. Page (lte/dir) Concert
(9/92) (HYPE) ① CDA66588
Gloria
Gothic Voices, C. Page Concert
(11/87) (HYPE) ① CDA66238
Gothic Voices, C. Page, A. Lawrence-King Concert
(6/93) (HYPE) ① CDA66619

PYGOTT, Richard (16th Cent)
England

SECTION IV: VOCAL AND CHORAL

Quid petis, o fili—carol (4vv)
Cambridge Taverner Ch, O. Rees (r1993) Concert
(12/93) (PAST) ① 3589

PYKINI (fl. ?1370) France

SECTION IV: VOCAL AND CHORAL

Plaisance, or tost
Gothic Voices, C. Page (r1994) Concert
(2/95) (HYPE) ① CDA66739

QUANTZ, Johann Joachim
(1697–1773) Germany

SECTION I: ORCHESTRAL

Concerto for Flute and Orchestra in C
J. Galway, Württemberg CO, J. Faerber Concert
(11/91) (RCA) ① RD60247
Concerto for Flute and Orchestra in D, 'pour
Potsdam'
J. Galway, Württemberg CO, J. Faerber Concert
(11/91) (RCA) ① RD60247
Concerto for Flute and Orchestra in G
J. Galway, Württemberg CO, J. Faerber Concert
(11/91) (RCA) ① RD60247
P. Gallois, CPE Bach CO, P. Schreier (r1993)
Concert   (2/95) (DG) ① 439 895-2GH
Concerto for Flute and Orchestra in G
minor
J. Galway, Württemberg CO, J. Faerber Concert
(11/91) (RCA) ① RD60247
Concerto for Flute and Strings in A
R. Brown, M. Comberti, J. Coe, L.U. Mortensen, S.
Standage (vn/dir) Concert
(5/94) (CHAN) ① CHAN0541

SECTION II: CHAMBER

Sonata for Flute and Harpsichord in D
S. Preston, L. Carolan Concert
(3/87) (AMON) ① CD-SAR19
Trio Sonata in C—recorder, flute and
continuo
F. Brüggen, F. Vester, B. Pollard, A. Bylsma, G.
Leonhardt (r1963) Concert
(10/95) (TELD) ① 4509-97467-2

QUILTER, Roger (1877–1953)
England

SECTION I: ORCHESTRAL

A Children's Overture—orchestra, Op. 17
(1919)
Light Music Soc Orch, V. Dunn Concert
(12/91) (EMI) ① CDM7 64131-2
Bratislava RSO, A. Leaper (r1992) Concert
(8/94) (MARC) ① 8 223444
Concert Waltz from 'Rosmé'—orchestra
(1936) (adapted from opera 'Julia')
Bratislava RSO, A. Leaper (r1992) Concert
(8/94) (MARC) ① 8 223444
3 English Dances—small orchestra, Op. 11
(1910)
Bratislava RSO, A. Leaper (r1992) Concert
(8/94) (MARC) ① 8 223444

SECTION III: INSTRUMENTAL

Country Pieces—piano (1923)
1. Shepherd Song; 2. Goblins; 3. Forest Lullaby; 4.
Pipe and Tabor.
Bratislava RSO, A. Leaper (r1992) Concert
(8/94) (MARC) ① 8 223444

SECTION IV: VOCAL AND CHORAL

The Arnold Book of Old Songs—song
arrangements (pub 1947)
1. Drink to me only with thine eyes (wds ⊃ Jonson);
2. Over the mountains (wds from Percy's 'Reliques');
3. My Lady Greensleeves (wds J Irvine); 4. Believe
me, if all those endearing young charms (wds T
Moore); 5. Oh! 'tis sweet to think (wds T Moore); 6.
Ye banks and braes (wds R Burns); 7. Charlie is my
darling (wds anon); 8. Ca'the yowes to the knowes
(wds R Burns); 9. The man behind the plough (wds R
Bennett); 10. My lady's garden (wds R Bennett); 11.
Pretty month of May (wds anon); 12. The jolly miller
(wds anon); 13. Barbara Allen (wds trad); 14. Three
poor mariners (wds anon); 15. Since first I saw your
face (wds anon); 16. The ash grove (wds R Bennett).
1. E. Schwarzkopf, G. Moore (r1956) Concert
(12/90) (EMI) ① CDM7 63654-2
2. K. Ferrier, P. Spurr (r1951) Concert
(6/92) (DECC) ① 433 475-2DM
At close of day—song (1904) (Wds. L.
Binyon)
B. Luxon, D. Willison Concert
(3/90) (CHAN) ① CHAN8782
7 Elizabethan Lyrics—voice and piano, Op.
12 (1908) (Wds. various)
1. Weep you no more (wds. Anon); 2. My life's delight
(wds. T. Campion); 3. Damask roses (wds. Anon); 4.
The faithless shepherdess (wds. Anon); 5. Brown is
my love (wds. Anon); 6. By a fountainside (wds. B.
Jonson); 7. Fair house of joy (wds. Anon).
B. Luxon, D. Willison Concert
(3/90) (CHAN) ① CHAN8782
1, 7. L. Finnie, A. Legge Concert
(4/90) (CHAN) ① CHAN8749
7. K. Ferrier, P. Spurr (r1951) Concert
(6/92) (DECC) ① 433 475-2DM
I arise from dreams of thee—song, Op. 29
(1931) (Wds. P B Shelley)
B. Luxon, D. Willison Concert
(3/90) (CHAN) ① CHAN8782
3 Shakespeare Songs, Op. 6 (1905 orch
1944-45)
1. Come Away Death; 2. O Mistress mine; 3. Blow,
Blow, thou winter Wind.
S. Varcoe, CLS, R. Hickox Concert
(1/90) (CHAN) ① CHAN8743
B. Luxon, D. Willison Concert
(3/90) (CHAN) ① CHAN8782
1. A. Rolfe Johnson, G. Johnson Concert
(5/92) (HYPE) ① CDA66480
5 Shakespeare Songs, Op. 23 (1919-21)
1. Fear no more the heat of the sun; 2. Under the
greenwood tree; 3. It was a lover and his lass; 4.
Take, o take those lips away; 5. Hey, ho, the wind
and the rain.
1, 3, 4. A. Rolfe Johnson, G. Johnson Concert
(5/92) (HYPE) ① CDA66480
3. F. Lott, A. Murray, G. Johnson (r1991) Concert
(7/92) (EMI) ① CDC7 54411-2
3 Songs, Op. 3
1. Love's philosophy (wds. P B Shelley: 1905); 2.
Now sleeps the crimson petal (wds. A Tennyson:
1904); 3. Fill a glass with golden wine (wds W E
Henley: 1905).
1. J. Baker, G. Moore (r1967) Concert
(11/94) (EMI) ① CDM5 65009-2
1, 2. B. Luxon, D. Willison Concert
(3/90) (CHAN) ① CHAN8782
1, 2. L. Finnie, A. Legge Concert
(4/90) (CHAN) ① CHAN8749
2. S. Hough (r1986: arr pf: Hough) Concert
(1/89) (VIRG) ① VC7 59509-2
2. V. Masterson, J. Constable Concert
(4/92) (GAMU) ① GAMD506
2. K. Ferrier, P. Spurr (r1951) Concert
(6/92) (DECC) ① 433 475-2DM
2. Sarah Walker, R. Vignoles Concert
(10/92) (CRD) ① CRD3473
4 Songs, Op. 14 (1910) (Wds. various)
1. Autumn Evening (wds. A. Maquarie); 2. April (wds.
W. Watson); 3. A Last Year's Rose (wds. E.
Henley); 4. Song of the Blackbird (wds. W. E.
Henley).
B. Luxon, D. Willison Concert
(3/90) (CHAN) ① CHAN8782

5 Songs, Op. 24
1. There be none of beauty'sdaughters (wds. Byron: 1922); 2. Morning song (wds. Heywood: 1922); 3. Go, lovely rose (wds E Waller: 1923); 4. O, the month of May (wds T Dekker: 1927); 5. The time of roses (wds. T. Hood: 1928).
3. B. Luxon, D. Willison *Concert*
(3/90) (CHAN) ① **CHAN8782**
3. G. Maurice, G. Johnson (pp1988) *Concert*
(5/92) (ETCE) ① **KTC1099**
6 Songs, Op. 25 (1922-27)
1. Song of the stream (wds. A Williams: 1922); 2. The fuschia tree (wds. Manx ballad: 1923); 3. An old carol: 'I sing of a maiden' (wds 15th cent anon); 4. Arab love song (wds. P B Shelley: 1925); 5. Music, when soft voices die (wds P B Shelley); 6. In the bud of the morning-O (wds J Stephens: 1927).
2. S. Hough (r1987: arr pf: Hough) *Concert*
(1/89) (VIRG) ① **VC7 59509-2**
4, 5, 6. B. Luxon, D. Willison *Concert*
(3/90) (CHAN) ① **CHAN8782**
3 Songs of William Blake, Op. 20 (1917)
1. Dream Valley; 2. The Wild Flower's Song; 3. Daybreak.
B. Luxon, D. Willison *Concert*
(3/90) (CHAN) ① **CHAN8782**
To Julia—songs, Op. 8 (1905) (Wds. Herrick)
Interlude; 1. The Bracelet; 2. The Maiden Blush; 3. To Daisies; 4. The Night Piece; 5. Julia's Hair. Interlude; 6. Cherry Ripe.
B. Luxon, D. Willison *Concert*
(3/90) (CHAN) ① **CHAN8782**
3. K. Ferrier, P. Spurr (r1951) *Concert*
(6/92) (DECC) ① **433 475-2DM**

SECTION V: STAGE WORKS

As You Like It—concert suite from incidental music, Op. 21 (1922)
EXCERPTS: 1. Shepherd's holiday; 2. Evening in the forest; 3. Merry pranks; 4. Country dance.
Bratislava RSO, A. Leaper (r1992) *Concert*
(8/94) (MARC) ① **8 223444**
The Rake—concert suite from ballet (1925)
EXCERPTS: 1. Dance at the feast; 2. The light-hearted lady; 3. The frolicsome friend; 4. Allurement; 5. Midnight revels.
Bratislava RSO, A. Leaper (r1992) *Concert*
(8/94) (MARC) ① **8 223444**
Where the Rainbow Ends—concert suite from incidental music (1911) (arr from children's fairy play)
1. Rainbow Land; 2. Will o' the Wisp; 3. Rosamund; 4. Fairy Frolic; 5. Goblin Forest.
Bratislava RSO, A. Leaper (r1992) *Concert*
(8/94) (MARC) ① **8 223444**

RÄÄTS, Jaan (b 1932) Estonia

SECTION III: INSTRUMENTAL

Toccata—piano (1968)
L. Väinmaa (r1993) *Concert*
(7/95) (FINL) ① **4509-95704-2**

RABAUD, Henri (1873–1949) France

SECTION I: ORCHESTRAL

Divertissement on Russian songs—orchestra, Op. 2 (1899)
Loire PO, P. Dervaux *Concert*
(3/92) (EMI) ① **CDM7 63951-2**
Rhineland-Pfalz State PO, L. Segerstam (r1990) *Concert*
(1/95) (MARC) ① **8 223503**
Églogue—Virgilian poem for orchestra, Op. 7 (1894)
Loire PO, P. Dervaux *Concert*
(3/92) (EMI) ① **CDM7 63951-2**
Rhineland-Pfalz State PO, L. Segerstam (r1990) *Concert*
(1/05) (MARC) ① **8 223503**
Procession nocturne—symphonic poem after Lenau's 'Faust', Op. 6 (1897)
Loire PO, P. Dervaux *Concert*
(3/92) (EMI) ① **CDM7 63951-2**
Rhineland-Pfalz State PO, L. Segerstam (r1990) *Concert*
(1/95) (MARC) ① **8 223503**
Suite anglaise No. 2—from incidental music for 'The Merchant of Venice' (arr/orch from various cpsrs)
1. Allegro (W. Byrd); 2. Andante (Anon); 3. Allegro maestoso.
Rhineland-Pfalz State PO, L. Segerstam (r1990) *Concert*
(1/95) (MARC) ① **8 223503**

Suite anglaise No. 3—from incidental music for 'The Merchant of Venice' (arr/orch from various cpsrs)
1. Maestoso (Anon); 2. Moderato (G Farnaby); 3. Allegro (G Farnaby); 4. Andante (Anon); 5. Maestoso (Anon).
Rhineland-Pfalz State PO, L. Segerstam (r1990) *Concert*
(1/95) (MARC) ① **8 223503**

SECTION V: STAGE WORKS

Mârouf, savetier du Caire—opera: 5 acts (1914—Paris) (Lib. L Népoty)
A travers le désert R. Alagna, LPO, R. Armstrong *Concert*
(12/95) (EMI) ① **CDC5 55540-2**
Dances Loire PO, P. Dervaux *Concert*
(3/92) (EMI) ① **CDM7 63951-2**
Dances Rhineland-Pfalz State PO, L. Segerstam (r1990) *Concert*
(1/95) (MARC) ① **8 223503**

RABE, Folke (Alvar Harald Reinhold) (b 1935) Sweden

SECTION II: CHAMBER

Shazam
H. Hardenberger, R. Pöntinen *Concert*
(11/85) (BIS) ① **BIS-CD287**

RABEY, René (1878–?)

SECTION IV: VOCAL AND CHORAL

Dans tes yeux en pleurs—song
F. Alda, M. Elman, F. La Forge (r1915) *Concert*
(10/91) (BIDD) ① **LAB039**

RACHMANINOV, Sergey (Vasil'yevich) (1873–1943) Russia/USA

SECTION I: ORCHESTRAL

Concerto for Piano and Orchestra No. 1 in F sharp minor, Op. 1 (1891 rev 1917)
E. Wild, RPO, J. Horenstein (r1965) *Concert*
(9/87) (CHAN) ① **[2] CHAN8521/2**
Vladimir Ashkenazy, Concertgebouw, B. Haitink *Paganini Rhapsody.*
(12/87) (DECC) ① **417 613-2DH**
M. Lympany, Philh, N. Malko (r1951) *Concert*
(3/88) (OLYM) ① **OCD190**
M. Pletnev, Philh, L. Pešek *Paganini Rhapsody.*
(12/88) (VIRG) ① **VC7 59506-2**
Vladimir Ashkenazy, LSO, A. Previn *Piano Concerto 4.*
(7/90) (DECC) ① **425 004-2DM**
H. Shelley, SNO, B. Thomson *Concert*
(4/91) (CHAN) ① **[2] CHAN8882/3**
T. Vásáry, LSO, Y. Ahronovitch *Concert*
(12/91) (DG) ① **[2] 413 850-2GW2**
S. Rachmaninov, Philadelphia, E. Ormandy (r1939/40) *Concert*
(3/93) (RCA) ① **[10] 09026 61265-2(1)**
M. Rudy, St Petersburg PO, M. Jansons (r1993) *Piano Concerto 4.*
(2/95) (EMI) ① **CDC5 55188-2**
J-Y. Thibaudet, Cleveland Orch, Vladimir Ashkenazy (r1994) *Piano Concerto*
(10/95) (DECC) ① **448 219-2DH**
Concerto for Piano and Orchestra No. 2 in C minor, Op. 18 (1900-01)
S. Richter, Warsaw Nat PO, S. Wislocki (r1959) *Prokofiev: Piano Concerto 5.*
(6/85) (DG) ① **415 119-2GH**
Vladimir Ashkenazy, Concertgebouw, B. Haitink *Piano Concerto 4.*
(4/86) (DECC) ① **414 475-2DH**
C. Ortiz, RPO, M. Atzmon *Concert*
(9/86) (DECC) ① **414 348-2DH**
Vladimir Ashkenazy, LSO, A. Previn *Paganini Rhapsody.*
(7/87) (DECC) ① **417 702-2DM**
E. Wild, RPO, J. Horenstein (r1965) *Concert*
(9/87) (CHAN) ① **[2] CHAN8521/2**
P. Fowke, RPO, Y. Temirkanov *Paganini Rhapsody.*
(10/87) (EMIN) ① **CD-EMX9509**
M. Lympany, Philh, N. Malko (r1951) *Concert*
(3/88) (OLYM) ① **OCD190**
T. Vásáry, LSO, Y. Ahronovitch *Piano Concerto 4.*
(9/88) (DG) ① **419 061-2GGA**
M. Tirimo, Philh, Y. Levi (r1982) *Paganini Rhapsody.*
(9/88) (EMI) ① **CD-CFP9017**
S. Rachmaninov, Philadelphia, L. Stokowski (r1929) *Piano Concerto 3.*
(10/88) (RCA) ① **RD85997**
Vladimir Ashkenazy, Concertgebouw, B. Haitink *Concert*
(4/89) (DECC) ① **[2] 421 590-2DH2**
S. Barere, Orch (pp1940s) *Concert*
(11/89) (APR) ① **[2] APR7008**

J. Jandó, Budapest SO, G. Lehel *Paganini Rhapsody.*
(10/90) (NAXO) ① **8 550117**
E. Wild, RPO, J. Horenstein (r1965) *Piano Concerto 3.*
(2/91) (CHAN) ① **CHAN6507**
H. Shelley, SNO, B. Thomson *Concert*
(4/91) (CHAN) ① **[2] CHAN8882/3**
A. Gavrilov, Philadelphia, R. Muti *Paganini Rhapsody.*
(10/91) (EMI) ① **CDC7 49966-2**
T. Vásáry, LSO, Y. Ahronovitch *Concert*
(12/91) (DG) ① **[2] 413 850-2GW2**
M. Rudy, Leningrad PO, M. Jansons *Tchaikovsky: Piano Concerto 1.*
(4/92) (EMI) ① **CDC7 54232-2**
B. Janis, Minneapolis SO, A. Dorati *Concert*
(9/92) (MERC) ① **432 759-2MM**
Y. Bronfman, Philh, E-P. Salonen *Piano Concerto 3.*
(9/92) (SONY) ① **SK47183**
S. Rachmaninov, Philadelphia, L. Stokowski (r1929) *Concert*
(3/93) (RCA) ① **[10] 09026 61265-2(1)**
S. Rachmaninov, Philadelphia, L. Stokowski (1924: side 3 r1929) *Concert*
(3/93) (RCA) ① **[10] 09026 61265-2(2)**
S. Rachmaninov, Philadelphia, L. Stokowski (r1929) *Concert*
(11/93) (CARL) ① **GLRS104**
Barry Douglas, LSO, M. Tilson Thomas (r1992) *Concert*
(12/93) (RCA) ① **[3] 09026 61677-2**
Barry Douglas, LSO, M. Tilson Thomas (1992) *Preludes.*
(12/93) (RCA) ① **09026 61679-2**
F-R. Duchâble, Strasbourg PO, T. Guschlbauer *Grieg: Piano Concerto.*
(12/93) (ERAT) ① **4509-92872-2**
S. Costa, RPO, C. Seaman (r1993) *Piano Concerto 4.*
(4/94) (RPO) ① **CDRPO7022**
H. Grimaud, RPO, J. López-Cobos (r1992) *Ravel: Piano Concerto.*
(4/94) (DENO) ① **CO-75368**
J-Y. Thibaudet, Cleveland Orch, Vladimir Ashkenazy *Paganini Rhapsody.*
(12/94) (DECC) ① **440 653-2DH**
L. Zilberstein, BPO, C. Abbado (pp1991) *Piano Concerto 3.*
(2/95) (DG) ① **439 930-2GH**
S. Richter, Warsaw PO, S. Wislocki (1959) *Tchaikovsky: Piano Concerto 1.*
(7/95) (DG) ① **447 420-2GOR**
B. Moiseiwitsch, LPO, W. Goehr (r1937) *Concert*
(10/95) (APR) ① **APR5505**
G. Anda, Philh, A. Galliera (r1953) *Concert*
(10/95) (TEST) ① **SBT1064**
Movt 3. Martin Jones (1989: trans pf: Grainger) *Concert*
(7/90) (NIMB) ① **NI5232**
Concerto for Piano and Orchestra No. 3 in D minor, Op. 30 (1909)
Vladimir Ashkenazy, Concertgebouw, B. Haitink *Concert*
(11/86) (DECC) ① **417 239-2DH**
E. Wild, RPO, J. Horenstein (r1965) *Concert*
(9/87) (CHAN) ① **[2] CHAN8521/2**
S. Rachmaninov, Philadelphia, E. Ormandy *Paganini Rhapsody.*
(11/87) (RCA) ① **GD86524**
A. Gavrilov, Philadelphia, R. Muti *Concert*
(12/87) (EMI) ① **CDC7 49049-2**
M. Lympany, New SO, A. Collins (r1952) *Prokofiev: Piano Concerto 3.*
(3/88) (OLYM) ① **OCD191**
Vladimir Ashkenazy, LSO, A. Previn *Preludes.*
(10/88) (DECC) ① **417 764-2DM**
S. Rachmaninov, Philadelphia, E. Ormandy (r1939/40) *Piano Concerto 2.*
(10/88) (RCA) ① **RD85997**
Vladimir Ashkenazy, Concertgebouw, B. Haitink *Concert*
(4/89) (DECC) ① **[2] 421 590-2DH2**
T. Barto, LPO, C. Eschenbach *Bartók: Concert*
(1/90) (EMI) ① **CDC7 49861-2**
V. Horowitz, LSO, A. Coates (r1930) *Concert*
(3/90) (EMI) ① **[3] CHS7 63538-2**
E. Wild, RPO, J. Horenstein (r1965) *Piano Concerto 2.*
(2/91) (CHAN) ① **CHAN6507**
H. Shelley, SNO, B. Thomson *Concert*
(4/91) (CHAN) ① **[2] CHAN8882/3**
B. Janis, LSO, A. Dorati *Concert*
(9/92) (MERC) ① **432 759-2MM**
Y. Bronfman, Philh, E-P. Salonen *Piano Concerto 2.*
(9/92) (SONY) ① **SK47183**
B. Berezovsky, Philh, E. Inbal *Preludes.*
(9/92) (TELD) ① **9031-73797-2**
S. Rachmaninov, Philadelphia, E. Ormandy (r1939/40) *Concert*
(3/93) (RCA) ① **[10] 09026 61265-2(1)**
V. Horowitz, NYPO, E. Ormandy (pp1978) *Concert*
(7/93) (RCA) ① **09026 61564-2**
E. Kissin, Boston SO, S. Ozawa (pp1993) *Concert*
(8/93) (RCA) ① **09026 61548-2**
M. Rudy, St Petersburg PO, M. Jansons (1992) *Paganini Rhapsody.*
(2/95) (EMI) ① **CDC7 54880-2**
Emil Gilels, Paris Cons, A. Cluytens (r1955) *Concert*
(2/94) (TEST) ① **SBT1029**
J. Lill, BBC Nat Orch of Wales, T. Otaka (r1993) *Piano Sonata 2.*
(10/94) (NIMB) ① **NI5348**

4, 5. C. Ludwig, G. Parsons *Concert*
(9/92) (EMI) ① [4] **CMS7 64074-2(2)**

6 Songs, Op. 8 (1893)
1. The waterlily (wds. Heine); 2. Child, thou art as
beautiful as a flower (wds. Heine); 3. Brooding (wds.
Shevchenko); 4. I have grown fond of sorrow: The
soldier's bride (wds. Shevchenko); 5. The dream
(wds. Heine); 6. A prayer (wds. Goethe).
Cpte E. Söderström, Vladimir Ashkenazy (r1975/7)
Concert (5/94) (DECC) ① [3] **436 920-2DM**
2. L. Howard (trans cpsr) *Concert*
(12/86) (HYPE) ① **CDA66090**
2. D. Hvorostovsky, M. Arkadiov *Concert*
(2/95) (PHIL) ① **442 536-2PH**
2, 3. S. Leiferkus, H. Shelley (r1994) *Concert*
(10/95) (CHAN) ① **CHAN9374**
4. A. El-Tour, anon (r1910) *Concert*
(6/93) (PEAR) ① [3] **GEMMCDS9004/6(1)**
4. Mozart Qt, Moz-art Qt (r1993) *Concert*
(8/94) (ETCE) ① **KTC1171**
5. D. Hvorostovsky, O. Boshniakovich *Concert*
(10/91) (PHIL) ① **432 119-2PH**

12 Songs, Op. 14 (1896)
1. I wait for thee (wds. Davidova) (1894); 2. The isle
(wds. Shelley); 3. For long there has been little
consolation in love (wds. Fet); 4. I was with her (wds.
Koltsov); 5. These summer nights (wds. Rathaus); 6.
How everyone loves thee (wds. Tolstoy); 7. Believe
me not, friend (wds. Tolstoy); 8. Oh, do not grieve
(wds. Apukhtin); 9. She is as lovely as the moon
(wds. Minsky); 10. In my soul (wds. Minsky); 11.
Spring waters (wds. Tyutchev); 12. 'Tis time (wds.
Nadson).
Cpte E. Söderström, Vladimir Ashkenazy (r1975/7/8-
9) *Concert* (5/94) (DECC) ① [3] **436 920-2DM**
1, 2. Mozart Qt, Moz-art Qt (r1993) *Concert*
(8/94) (ETCE) ① **KTC1171**
1, 8, 9, 11. E. Podles, G. Johnson *Concert*
(5/95) (FORL) ① **UCD16683**
2, 5, 11. E. Wild (trans pf Wild) *Concert*
(11/87) (DELL) ① **CDDBS7001**
4, 6, 9, 11, 12. S. Leiferkus, H. Shelley (r1994)
Concert (10/95) (CHAN) ① **CHAN9374**
5. E. Wild (r1995: trans pf: Wild) *Concert*
(12/95) (SONY) ① **SK62036**
8, 11. E. Wild (trans Wild) *Concert*
(9/92) (CHES) ① **Chesky CD58**
9. D. Hvorostovsky, O. Boshniakovich *Concert*
(10/91) (PHIL) ① **432 119-2PH**
11. A. Orda, E. Lush (bp1968) *Concert*
(12/89) (SYMP) ① **SYMCD1067**
11. D. Hvorostovsky, M. Arkadiov *Concert*
(2/95) (PHIL) ① **442 536-2PH**
11. K. Vayne, C. Tilney (r1966) *Concert*
(6/95) (PREI) ① **89996**

12 Songs, Op. 21 (1902)
1. Fate (wds. Apukhtin) (1900); 2. By the fresh grave
(wds. Nadson); 3. Twilight (wds. Guyot trans.
Tkhorzhevsky); 4. They answered (wds. Hugo trans.
Mey); 5. Lilacs (wds. Beketova); 6. Fragment from
Musset (wds. Apukhtin); 7. How fair this spot (wds.
Galina); 8. On the death of a linnet (wds. Zhukovsky);
9. Melody (wds. Nadson); 10. Before the icon (wds.
Golenishchev-Kutuzov); 11. No prophet I (wds.
Kruglov); 12. How painful for me (wds. Galina).
Cpte E. Söderström, Vladimir Ashkenazy (r1974/5/6)
Concert (5/94) (DECC) ① [3] **436 920-2DM**
1, 2, 5, 10, 11. S. Leiferkus, H. Shelley (r1995)
Concert (10/95) (CHAN) ① **CHAN9374**
3. Mozart Qt, Moz-art Qt (r1993) *Concert*
(8/94) (ETCE) ① **KTC1171**
5. X. Wei, Pam Nicholson (arr Heifetz/Palmer)
Concert (9/90) (ASV) ① **CDDCA698**
5. J. Björling, Stockholm Concert Soc Orch, N.
Grevillius (r1947) *Concert*
(10/93) (EMI) ① **CDH7 64707-2**
5. L. Popp, G. Parsons (pp1981) *Concert*
(6/95) (ORFE) ① **C363941B**
5. K. Vayne, C. Tilney (r1966) *Concert*
(6/95) (PREI) ① **89996**
5, 12. A. Orda, E. Lush (bp1968) *Concert*
(12/89) (SYMP) ① **SYMCD1067**
6. D. Hvorostovsky, O. Boshniakovich *Concert*
(10/91) (PHIL) ① **432 119-2PH**
7. I. Perlman, S. Sanders (trans. Heifetz) *Concert*
(12/89) (EMI) ① **CDC7 49604-2**
7. K. Battle, M. Garrett (pp1991) *Concert*
(7/92) (DG) ① **435 440-2GH**
7. A. Nezhdanova, anon (r1914) *Concert*
(6/93) (PEAR) ① [3] **GEMMCDS9007/9(2)**
7. V. Spivakov, S. Bezrodny (r1991-2; arr Heifetz)
Concert (5/95) (RCA) ① **09026 62524-2**
7. I. Perlman, S. Sanders (r1988: arr vn/pf: Heifetz)
Concert (6/95) (EMI) ① [20] **CZS4 83177-2(2)**
7, 8, 12. E. Wild (trans pf Wild) *Concert*
(11/87) (DELL) ① **CDDBS7001**

12. D. Hvorostovsky, M. Arkadiov *Concert*
(2/95) (PHIL) ① **442 536-2PH**

15 Songs, Op. 26 (1906)
1. There are many sounds (wds. Tolstoy); 2. He took
all from me (wds. Tyutchev); 3. Let us rest (wds.
Chekov); 4. Two partings (wds. Koltsov) (bar & sop);
5. Beloved, let us fly (wds. Golenischev-Kutuzov); 6.
Christ is risen (wds. Merezhkovsky); 7. To the
children (wds. Khomyakov); 8. I beg for mercy (wds.
Merezhkovsky); 9. Again I am alone (wds.
Shevchenko trans. Bunin); 10. Before my window
(wds. Galina); 11. The fountain (wds. Tyutchev); 12.
Night is mournful (wds. Bunin); 13. When yesterday
we met (wds. Polonsky); 14. The ring (wds. Koltsov);
15. All things pass by (wds. Rathaus).
Cpte E. Söderström, J. Shirley-Quirk, Vladimir
Ashkenazy (r1976/7/8-9) *Concert*
(5/94) (DECC) ① [3] **436 920-2DM**
2, 3, 6, 13, 15. S. Leiferkus, H. Shelley (r1995)
Concert (10/95) (CHAN) ① **CHAN9374**
2, 6, 10, 15. A. Orda, E. Lush (bp1968) *Concert*
(12/89) (SYMP) ① **SYMCD1067**
2, 6, 13. D. Hvorostovsky, O. Boshniakovich *Concert*
(10/91) (PHIL) ① **432 119-2PH**
5, 10, 12. Mozart Qt, Moz-art Qt (r1993) *Concert*
(8/94) (ETCE) ① **KTC1171**
6. E. Podles, G. Johnson *Concert*
(5/95) (FORL) ① **UCD16683**
7. E. Wild (trans pf Wild) *Concert*
(11/87) (DELL) ① **CDDBS7001**
7. J. McCormack, F. Kreisler, E. Schneider (r1924)
Concert (10/92) (TEST) ① **SBT1005**
7, 10. J. McCormack, F. Kreisler, E. Schneider
(r1924) *Concert* (9/89) (PEAR) ① **GEMMCD9315**
7, 10. J. McCormack, F. Kreisler, E. Schneider
(r1924) *Concert* (9/93) (BIDD) ① [2] **LAB068/9**
10. J. McCormack, F. Kreisler, E. Schneider *Concert*
(5/93) (MMOI) ① **CDMOIR418**
10. D. Smirnov, anon (r1912) *Concert*
(6/93) (PEAR) ① [3] **GEMMCDS9004/6(2)**

14 Songs, Op. 34 (1912)
1. The muse (wds. Pushkin); 2. In the soul of each of
us (wds. Korinfsky); 3. The storm (wds. Pushkin); 4.
The migrant wind (wds. Bal'mont); 5. Arion (wds.
Pushkin); 6. The raising of Lazarus (wds.
Khomyakov); 7. It cannot be (wds. Maykov); 8. Music
(wds. Polonsky); 9. You knew him (wds. Tyutchev);
10. I remember that day (wds. Tyutchev); 11. The
peasant (wds. Fet); 12. What happiness (wds. Fet);
13. Discord (wds. Polonsky); 14. Vocalise (wordless)
(rev 1915).
Cpte E. Söderström, Vladimir Ashkenazy (r1974/5/8-
9) *Concert* (5/94) (DECC) ① [3] **436 920-2DM**
1, 14. E. Wild (trans pf Wild) *Concert*
(11/87) (DELL) ① **CDDBS7001**
2, 6, 9, 11. S. Leiferkus, H. Shelley (r1995) *Concert*
(10/95) (CHAN) ① **CHAN9374**
14. S. Murphy, K. Lewis, SNO, N. Järvi (orch cpsr)
Concert (2/87) (CHAN) ① **CHAN8476**
14. A. Moffo, American SO, L. Stokowski (arr
Dubensky) *Concert* (6/89) (RCA) ① **GD87831**
14. K. Walker, J. Drake (arr bn) *Concert*
(10/89) (REGE) ① **REGCD104**
14. I. Stern, Columbia SO, F. Brieff (arr Harris)
Concert (7/90) (SONY) ① **SK45816**
14. L. Mordkovitch, M. Gusak-Grin (arr Rose)
Concert (11/90) (CHAN) ① **CHAN8748**
14. M. Maisky, P. Gililov (arr vc/pf) *Concert*
(7/91) (DG) ① **431 544-2GH**
14. R. Ricci, L. Persinger (arr Press: r1938) *Concert*
(12/91) (BIDD) ① **LAB044**
14. H. Shelley (r1991: arr pf: Kocsis) *Concert*
(3/92) (HYPE) ① **CDA66486**
14. K. Battle, M. Garrett (pp1991) *Concert*
(7/92) (DG) ① **435 440-2GH**
14. E. Wild (trans Wild) *Concert*
(9/92) (CHES) ① **Chesky CD58**
14. M. Kliegel, R. Havenith (arr vc/pf) *Concert*
(9/92) (MARC) ① **8 223403**
14. S. McNair, Baltimore SO, D. Zinman *Symphony
2.* *Concert* (10/92) (TELA) ① **CD80312**
14. I. Perlman, S. Sanders (r1972: arr Press/Gingold)
Concert (5/93) (EMI) ① [4] **CMS7 64617-2**
14. E. Kissin (pp1993: arr Richardson) *Concert*
(8/93) (RCA) ① **09026 61548-2**
14. Chee-Yun, A. Eguchi (trans Press) *Concert*
(12/93) (DENO) ① **CO-75118**
14. J. Weber (r1992: arr pf: Richardson) *Concert*
(12/93) (CARL) ① **PCD1051**
14. H. Shelley (r1991: arr pf: Kocsis) *Concert*
(3/94) (HYPE) ① [8] **CDS44041/8**
14. St Petersburg PO, Y. Temirkanov (r1991: arr
Sanderling: string orch) *Symphony 2.*
(9/94) (RCA) ① **09026 61281-2**

14. O.E. Antonsen, W. Marshall (r1992: arr tpt/org:
Antonsen/Marshall) *Concert*
(11/94) (EMI) ① **CDC5 55048-2**
14. J. Heifetz, E. Bay (r1947) *Concert*
(11/94) (RCA) ① [65] **09026 61778-2(40)**
14. R. A. Swenson, W. Jones (pp1994) *Concert*
(1/95) (RCA) ① **09026 62547-2**
14. N. Lee, Novosibirsk PO, A. Kaz (r1984/5) *Concert*
(2/95) (SONY) ① **SMK57660**
14. A. A. Meyers, S. Rivers (r1993; trans Press:
vn/pf) *Concert* (4/95) (RCA) ① **09026 62546-2**
14. V. Spivakov, S. Bezrodny (r1991-2; arr Heifetz)
Concert (5/95) (RCA) ① **09026 62524-2**
14. I. Perlman, S. Sanders (r1972: arr vn/pf:
Press/Gingold) *Concert*
(6/95) (EMI) ① [20] **CZS4 83177-2(2)**
14. LPO Vcs, RPO Vcs, BBC SO Vcs, Philh Vcs, G.
Simon (r1993; arr Balcombe) *Concert*
(9/95) (CALA) ① **CACD0104**

6 Songs, Op. 38 (1916)
1. In my garden at night (wds. Isaakian trans. Blok);
2. To her (wds. Belly); 3. Daisies (wds. Severianin);
4. The rat-catcher (wds. Bryusov); 5. A dream (wds.
Sologub); 6. A-u! (wds. Bal'mont).
Cpte E. Söderström, Vladimir Ashkenazy (r1974)
Concert (5/94) (DECC) ① [3] **436 920-2DM**
3. X. Wei, Pam Nicholson (arr Heifetz/Palmer)
Concert (9/90) (ASV) ① **CDDCA698**
3. F. Kreisler, C. Lamson (r1926: arr Kreisler)
Concert (12/93) (BIDD) ① **LAB075**
3. J. Heifetz, B. Smith (r1967) *Concert*
(11/94) (RCA) ① [65] **09026 61778-2(40)**
3. J. Heifetz, B. Smith (r1970) *Concert*
(11/94) (RCA) ① [65] **09026 61778-2(35)**
3. J. Heifetz, E. Bay (r1946) *Concert*
(11/94) (RCA) ① [65] **09026 61778-2(05)**
3. I. Perlman, S. Sanders (r1985: arr vn/pf: Kreisler)
Concert (6/95) (EMI) ① [20] **CZS4 83177-2(2)**
5. E. Wild (trans pf Wild) *Concert*
(11/87) (DELL) ① **CDDBS7001**

**Spring—cantata (baritone, chorus and
orchestra), Op. 20 (1902)** (Wds. Nekrasov)
J. Hynninen, Danish Nat Rad Ch, Danish Nat RSO,
D. Kitaienko *Bells.* (2/92) (CHAN) ① **CHAN8966**
S. Leiferkus, Philadelphia Choral Arts Soc,
Philadelphia, C. Dutoit (r1992) *Concert*
(8/94) (DECC) ① **440 355-2DH**

Twilight has fallen—song (1891) (Wds. A. K.
Tolstoy)
E. Söderström, Vladimir Ashkenazy (r1977) *Concert*
(5/94) (DECC) ① [3] **436 920-2DM**

**Vespers, 'All-Night Vigil'—chorus a capella,
Op. 37 (1915)**
1. O come, let us worship; 2. Bless the Lord, O my
soul; 3. Blessed is the man; 4. Hail, gladdening light;
5. Lord, now let your servant depart (Nunc dimittis);
6. Hail Mary (Ave Maria); 7. Hexapsalmos: Glory to
God; 8. Praise the name of the Lord; 9. You are
blessed, O Lord; 10. The Veneration of the Cross; 11.
My soul magnifies the Lord (Magnificat); 12. Glory to
God (Gloria in excelsis); 13. Salvation has come
(hymn); 14. When you, O Lord (hymn); 15. Hymn to
the mother of God.
Cpte M. Forrester, G. Tucker, Washington Chor Arts
Soc, M. Rostropovich
(1/89) (ERAT) ① **2292-45269-2**
Cpte J. Polvtsova, S. Rokozitsa, Leningrad Glinka
Acad Ch, V. Chernushenko
(12/89) (OLYM) ① **OCD247**
Cpte K. Dent, R. Shaw Fest Sngrs, Robert Shaw
(10/90) (TELA) ① **CD80172**
Cpte Corydon Sngrs, M. Best
(7/91) (HYPE) ① **CDA66460**
Cpte St Petersburg Cappella, V. Chernushenko
(5/93) (CDM) ① **LDC288 050**
Cpte O. Borodina, V. Mostowoy, St Petersburg Chbr
Ch, N. Korniev (r1993)
(11/94) (PHIL) ① **442 344-2PH**
Cpte Swedish Rad Ch, T. Kaljuste
(4/95) (VIRG) ① **VC5 45124-2**
Cpte Berlin Rad Chor, R. Gritton (r1994)
(9/95) (CPO) ① **CPO999 292-2**
Cpte S. Fryer, P. Butterfield, Philh Chor, D. Hill
(r1993) (12/95) (NIMB) ① **NI5432**
5. St Petersburg Glinka Acad Ch, V. Chernushenko
Concert (3/92) (TELD) ① **9031-73241-2**

Were you hiccoughing—song (1899) (Wds. P.
Vyazemsky)
E. Söderström, Vladimir Ashkenazy (r1978-9)
Concert (5/94) (DECC) ① [3] **436 920-2DM**
S. Leiferkus, H. Shelley (r1994) *Concert*
(10/95) (CHAN) ① **CHAN9374**

SECTION V: STAGE WORKS

Aleko—opera: 1 act (1893—Moscow) (Lib.
Nemirovich-Danchenko, after Pushkin)
EXCERPTS—; 1. Intermezzo; 2. Gipsy chorus; 3.
Old Gipsy's story; 4. Scena and chorus; 5. Gipsy
Girls' dance; 6. Men's dance; 7. Chorus; 8. Duet; 9.
Zemfira's song; 10. Aleko's cavatina; 11. Intermezzo;
12. Young Gipsy's song; 13. Duet and finale.
Cpte V. Matorin, N. Erassova, V. Pochapsky, V.
Tarashchenko, G. Borisova, Russian St Ch, Orch, A.
Chistiakov (r1993)   (10/94) (CDM) ① **LDC288 079**
1. BPO, L. Maazel *Concert*
(9/92) (DG) ① **435 594-2GGA**
1. St Petersburg PO, Y. Temirkanov (r1992) *Concert*
(4/95) (RCA) ① **09026 62710-2**
1, 5. LSO, A. Previn (r1976) *Concert*
(10/93) (EMI) ① [3] **CMS7 64530-2**
3, 10. M. Reizen, Bolshoi Th Orch, V. Nebolsin
(r1955) *Concert*   (12/92) (PREI) ① **89059**
10. F. Chaliapin, orch, L. Collingwood (r1929)
Concert   (6/88) (EMI) ① **CDH7 61009-2**
10. D. Hvorostovsky, Kirov Th Orch, V. Gergiev
(r1993) *Concert*   (5/94) (PHIL) ① **438 872-2PH**
**The miserly knight—opera: 3 scenes, Op. 24
(1906—Moscow)** (Lib. Pushkin)
Cpte M. Krutikov, V. Kudriashov, A. Arkhipov, V.
Verestnikov, P. Gluboky, Bolshoi Th Orch, A.
Chistiakov (r1993)   (10/94) (CDM) ① **LDC288 080**
**Monna Vanna—opera: act 1 in piano score;
act 2 sketch only (1907)** (Lib. Slonov, after
Maeterlinck)
Act 1. S. Milnes, S. McCoy, B. Walker, N.
Karousatos, J. Thorsteinsson, Icelandic Op Chor,
Iceland SO, I. Buketoff (orch Buketoff) *Piano
Concerto 4.*   (3/92) (CHAN) ① **CHAN8987**

RACKHAM, Simon *(20th Cent)*
United Kingdom

SECTION II: CHAMBER

**Which ever way your nose bends—six
pianos (1989)**
Piano Circus *Concert*
(7/92) (ARGO) ① **433 522-2ZH**

RADCLIFFE, Philip (FitzHugh)
(1905–1985) England

SECTION IV: VOCAL AND CHORAL

God be in my head—anthem: 8vv (Wds. from
the Sarum Primer)
St Paul's Cath Ch, John Scott, Andrew Lucas (r1994)
Concert   (5/95) (HYPE) ① **CDA66758**
Versicles and Responses (1972)
King's College Ch, S. Cleobury, C. Hughes (pp1991
with Choral Evensong) *Concert*
(10/92) (EMI) ① **CDC7 54412-2**

RADECK, Ferdinand *(1828–1903)*
Germany

SECTION I: ORCHESTRAL

Fridericus-Rex—march (after Lied by Loewe)
Berlin Phil Wind Qnt, H. von Karajan (r1973) *Concert*
(5/94) (DG) ① **439 346-2GX2**

RAFF, (Joseph) Joachim
(1822–1882)
Switzerland/Germany

SECTION I: ORCHESTRAL

Abends-Rhapsodie—orchestra
Philh, F. d'Avalos *Concert*
(10/92) (ASV) ① **CDDCA793**
**Concert Overture in F—orchestra, Op. 123
(1862)**
Košice St PO, U. Schneider (r1993) *Symphony 7.*
(8/94) (MARC) ① **8 223506**
**Concerto for Piano and Orchestra in C
minor, Op. 185 (1873)**
J-F. Antonioli, Lausanne CO, L. Foster *Concert*
(8/89) (CLAV) ① **CD50-8806**
M. Ponti, Hamburg SO, R. Kapp *Concert*
(5/93) (VOX) ① **115708-2**
**Ein feste Burg ist unser Gott—overture, Op.
127 (1854-55)**
Košice St PO, U. Schneider (r1993) *Symphony 5.*
(2/95) (MARC) ① **8 223455**

**Ode au printemps in G—piano and
orchestra, Op. 76 (1857)**
J-F. Antonioli, Lausanne CO, L. Foster *Concert*
(8/89) (CLAV) ① **CD50-8806**
Overtures to Shakespeare plays (1879)
1. The Tempest; 2. Macbeth; 3. Romeo and Juliet; 4.
Othello.
2. Philh, F. d'Avalos *Concert*
(10/92) (ASV) ① **CDDCA793**
2, 3. Košice St PO, U. Schneider (r1994) *Symphony
2.*   (7/95) (MARC) ① **8 223630**
Symphony No. 1 in D, 'An das Vaterland'
Rhenish PO, S. Friedman (r1988)
(11/89) (MARC) ① **8 223165**
Symphony No. 2 in C, Op. 140 (1869)
Košice St PO, U. Schneider (r1993) *Shakespeare
Overtures.*   (7/95) (MARC) ① **8 223630**
**Symphony No. 3 in F, 'Im Walde', Op. 153
(1869)**
Philh, F. d'Avalos *Concert*
(10/92) (ASV) ① **CDDCA793**
Symphony No. 4 in G minor, Op. 167 (1871)
Košice St PO, U. Schneider (r1993) *Symphony 11.*
(2/95) (MARC) ① **8 223529**
**Symphony No. 5 in E, 'Leonore', Op. 177
(1873)**
LPO, B. Herrmann   (10/90) (UNIC) ① **UKCD2031**
Košice St PO, U. Schneider (r1992) *Ein feste Burg
Overture.*   (2/95) (MARC) ① **8 223455**
**Symphony No. 7 in B flat, 'In den Alpen', Op.
201 (1875)**
Košice St PO, U. Schneider (r1993) *Concert
Overture, Op. 123.*   (8/94) (MARC) ① **8 223506**
**Symphony No. 8 in A, 'Frühlingsklänge', Op.
205 (1876)**
Košice St PO, U. Schneider *Symphony 9.*
(11/92) (MARC) ① **8 223362**
**Symphony No. 9 in E minor, 'Im Sommer',
Op. 208 (1878)**
Košice St PO, U. Schneider *Symphony 8.*
(11/92) (MARC) ① **8 223362**
**Symphony No. 11 in A minor, 'Der Winter',
Op. 214 (1876)**
Košice St PO, U. Schneider (r1992) *Symphony 4.*
(2/95) (MARC) ① **8 223529**

SECTION II: CHAMBER

Octet in C—strings, Op. 176 (1872)
ASMF Chbr Ens *Mendelssohn: Octet, Op. 20.*
(3/90) (CHAN) ① **CHAN8790**
6 Pieces—violin and piano, Op. 85 (1859)
3. Cavatina.
3. J. Kubelík, anon (r1907) *Concert*
(6/91) (BIDD) ① [2] **LAB033/4**
3 String Quartets, Op. 192 (1874)
2 (The Mill) A. Campoli, Welbeck Light Qt *Concert*
(10/91) (PEAR) ① **PASTCD9744**

SECTION III: INSTRUMENTAL

2 Pieces—piano, Op. 157 (1870)
1. Cavatine; 2. La fileuse.
1. I. Perlman, S. Sanders (arr vn/pf) *Concert*
(6/95) (EMI) ① [20] **CZS4 83177-2(3)**
La Polka de la Reine—piano, Op. 95 (1861)
A. Etherden *Concert*
(7/93) (HUNT) ① **HMPCD0589**
Serenade—piano, Op. 1
J. McCormack, F. Kreisler, E. Schneider (r1916: arr.
voice, vn and pf-Rosier) *Concert*
(9/89) (PEAR) ① **GEMMCD9315**

RAID, Kaljo *(b 1922)* Estonia

SECTION I: ORCHESTRAL

Symphony No. 1 in C minor (1944)
SNO, N. Järvi *Concert*
(11/89) (CHAN) ① **CHAN8525**

RAIMON DE MIRAVAL
(1191–1229) France

SECTION IV: VOCAL AND CHORAL

Aissi cum es genser pascors—chanson
P. Hillier, S. Stubbs, A. Lawrence-King, E. Headley
Concert   (7/89) (ECM) ① **837 360-2**

RAINIER, Priaulx *(1903–1986)*
South Africa

SECTION I: ORCHESTRAL

Ploërmel—wind and percussion (1972-73)
RNCM Wind Ens *Concert*
(11/92) (REDC) ① **RR007**

SECTION II: CHAMBER

Quanta—oboe and string trio (1961-62)
Redcliffe Ens *Concert*   (11/92) (REDC) ① **RR007**
String Quartet (1939)
Edinburgh Qt *Concert*   (11/92) (REDC) ① **RR007**
String Trio (1965-66)
Redcliffe Ens *Concert*   (11/92) (REDC) ① **RR007**

RAISON, André *(before
1650–1719) France*

SECTION III: INSTRUMENTAL

Premier livre d'orgue (pub 1688)
1. Messe du huitième ton: 1a. Elevation, C minor; 2.
Offerte, en action de grâce.
Trio en passacaille; Grand plein jeu P. Bardon
Concert   (3/87) (PIER) ① [2] **PV785051/2**
1a J. Payne (r1994) *Concert*
(10/95) (NAXO) ① **8 553215**
P. Bardon *Concert*   (5/84) (PIER) ① **PV784011**
A. Isoir *Concert*   (6/90) (CALL) ① **CAL9916**
Second livre d'orgue (pub 1614)
1. Prélude; 2. Christe; 3. Kyrie II; 4. Elevation; 5.
Dialogue; 6. Joseph est bien marié.
Excs B. Foccroulle *Concert*
(1/89) (RICE) ① **RIC052034**
6. D. Ferran *Concert*   (4/88) (ARIO) ① **ARN68015**

RAJNA, Thomas *(b 1928)*
Hungary/South Africa

SECTION I: ORCHESTRAL

Concerto for Harp and Orchestra (1990)
M. Wright, SA Nat SO, A. Stephenson (r1991) *Piano
Concerto 2.*   (11/93) (CLAR) ① **CDGSE1526**
**Concerto for Piano and Orchestra No. 2
(1984)**
T. Rajna, SA Nat SO, A. Stephenson (r1991) *Harp
Concerto.*   (11/93) (CLAR) ① **CDGSE1526**

RAK, Štěpan *(b 1945)*
Czechoslovakia

SECTION III: INSTRUMENTAL

Cry of the guitar—guitar
S. Rak *Concert*   (9/88) (CHAN) ① **CHAN8622**
The Czech Chorale—guitar
S. Rak *Concert*   (9/88) (CHAN) ① **CHAN8622**
Danza Mauretana—guitar
S. Rak *Concert*   (9/88) (CHAN) ① **CHAN8622**
First love—guitar
S. Rak *Concert*   (9/88) (CHAN) ① **CHAN8622**
Hiroshima—guitar
S. Rak *Concert*   (9/88) (CHAN) ① **CHAN8622**
Hora/Czardas—guitar
S. Rak *Concert*   (9/88) (CHAN) ① **CHAN8622**
Pavanne—guitar
S. Rak *Concert*   (9/88) (CHAN) ① **CHAN8622**
Remembering Prague—guitar
S. Rak *Concert*   (9/88) (CHAN) ① **CHAN8622**

RAKSIN, David *(b 1912) USA*

SECTION V: STAGE WORKS

Laura—film score (1944)
EXCERPTS: 1. Main Theme (Lyrics Johnny Mercer).
Suite: Theme and Variations OST, Alfred Newman
(r1944) *Concert*   (11/94) (FOX) ① **07822 11006-2**

RAMEAU, Jean-Philippe
(1683–1764) France

SECTION II: CHAMBER

**5 Pièces de clavecin en
concerts—harpsichord, flute/violin and viola
da gamba/violin (pub 1741 rev 1752)**
1. Premier concert: 1a. La Coulicam; 1b. La Livri; 1c.
Le Vézinet. 2. Deuxième concert: 2a. La Laborde; 2b.
La Boucon; 2c. L'agaçante; 2d. Menuet I; 2e. Menuet
II. 3. Troisième concert: 3a. La Poplinière; 3b. La
timide, rondeau I; 3c. La timide, rondeau II; 3d.
Tambourin I; 3e. Tambourin II. 4. Quatrième concert:
4a. La pantomime; 4b. L'indiscrète; 4c. La Rameau.
5. Cinquième concert: 5a. La Forqueray; 5b. La
Cupis; 5c. La Marais.
Sonnerie Trio   (9/89) (VIRG) ① **VC7 59154-2**
C. Arita, N. Wakamatsu, M. Arita, W. Kuijken
(9/92) (DENO) ① **CO-79045**
R. Terakado, K. Uemura, C. Rousset (r1992)
(4/93) (HARM) ① **HMC90 1418**

F. Brüggen, S. Kuijken, W. Kuijken, G. Leonhardt
(r1971)　　(7/93) (TELD) ① 9031-77618-2
L. Frydén, N. Harnoncourt, G. Leonhardt (r1955)
(3/94) (VANG) ① 08.2023.71
C. Mackintosh, L. Dreyfus, K. Haugsand (r1992)
(6/94) (SIMA) ① PSC1095
R. Kohnen, B. Kuijken, S. Kuijken, W. Kuijken (r1994)
(8/95) (ACCE) ① ACC9493D
1. Music's Recreation *Concert*
(6/88) (MERI) ① CDE84114
4a T. Pinnock (trans hpd) *Pièces de clavecin.*
(8/88) (CRD) ① CRD3320
5. R. Brown, M Caudle, J. Johnstone *Concert*
(2/94) (CHAN) ① CHAN0544

SECTION III: INSTRUMENTAL

Harpsichord works (For purposes of this catalogue Rameau's harpsichord works are numbered serially. They comprise 3 volumes published in the composer's lifetime—Vol. 1: 1-10; Vol. 2: 11-31 (but note No. 11 included in error and not intended for performance); Vol. 3: 32-47 and also No. 48 (written for the wedding of the Dauphin and Maria-Josepha of Saxony) and Nos. 49-53 which are arrangements from the Pièces de clavecin en concerts.)

(Premier Livre de Pièces, Suite in A minor-major, 1706): 1. Prélude; 2. Allemande I; 3. Allemande II; 4. Courante; 5. Gigue; 6. Sarabande I; 7. Sarabande II; 8. Vénetienne; 9. Gavotte; 10. Menuet. (Suite in E minor, 1724 rev 1731): 11. Menuet en rondeau; 12. Allemande; 13. Courante; 14. Gigue en rondeau I; 15. Gigue en rondeau II; 16. La rappel des oiseaux; 17. Rigaudon; 18. Rigaudon avec double; 19. Musette en rondeau; 20. Tambourin; 21. La villageoise. (Suite in D minor-major, 1724 rev 1731): 22. Les tendres plaintes; 23. Les niais de Sologne avec doubles; 24. Les soupirs; 25. La joyeuse; 26. La follette; 27. L'entretien des muses; 28. Les tourbillons; 29. Les cyclopes; 30. Le lardon; 31. La boiteuse. (Suite in A minor-major, c1728): 32. Allemande; 33. Courante; 34. Sarabande; 35. Les trois mains; 36. Fanfarinette; 37. la triomphante; 38. Gavotte avec six doubles. (Suite in G major-minor, c1728): 39. Les tricotets; 40. L'indifférente; 41. Menuet majeur; 42. Menuet mineur; 43. La poule; 44. Les triolets; 45. Les sauvages; 46. L'enharmonique; 47. L'Egyptienne. 48. La Dauphine (1747). (Pièces de clavecin en concert, 1741): 49. La Livri; 50. L'agaçante; 51. La timide, rondeau I; 52. La timide rondeau II. 53. L'indiscrète.

K. Gilbert　　(3/90) (ARCH) ① [2] 427 176-2AGA2
1-10, 48-53. T. Pinnock *Pièces de clavecin en concerts.*　　(8/88) (CRD) ① CRD3320
1-35, 39-53. M. Meyer (r1953/6) *Concert*
(6/95) (EMI) ① [4] CZS5 68092-2
1-48. C. Rousset
(12/91) (L'OI) ① [2] 425 886-2OH2
9, 16, 20, 23, 43, 48. R. Veyron-Lacroix (r1970) *Concert*　　(12/91) (ERAT) ① 4509-92135-2
10. L. Laskine (r1975; arr hp) *Concert*
(12/91) (ERAT) ① 4509-92131-2
12, 14-17, 19, 22, 26, 29, 30. S. Assad, O. Assad (r1991; arr 2 gtrs) *Concert*
(10/93) (NONE) ① 7559-79292-2
12-21, 32-38. T. Pinnock　　(8/88) (CRD) ① CRD3310
12-47. W. Christie (r1983)
(1/84) (HARM) ① [2] HMA190 1120/1
16, 20, 43. G. Malcolm (r1966) *Concert*
(11/95) (DECC) ① 444 390-2DWO
16, 20, 43, 47. G. Cziffra (r1980-81) *Concert*
(3/95) (EMI) ① CDM5 65253-2
17. I. Perlman, S. Sanders (trans. Heifetz) *Concert*
(12/89) (EMI) ① CDC7 49604-2
19, 20, 43, 46. R. Aldwinckle *Concert*
(7/87) (CARL) ① PCD850
20. L. Fugère, anon (1928: arr Tiersot) *Concert*
(7/93) (NIMB) ① [2] NI7840/1
22, 26-28, 34, 41, 42, 46. G. Leonhardt *Concert*
(5/92) (DHM) ① RD77924
22-31, 39-47. T. Pinnock　(8/88) (CRD) ① CRD3330
29. V. Black *Concert*　　(5/91) (COLL) ① Coll5024-2
37. T. Pinnock *Concert*
(11/84) (ARCH) ① 413 591-2AH
38. M. Novello (r1927) *Concert*
(4/89) (OPAL) ① OPALCD9839
38. New Philh, O. Klemperer (orch Klemperer) *Concert*　　(9/92) (EMI) ① [3] CMS7 64150-2
46-48. S. Yates (r1993) *Concert*
(11/93) (CHAN) ① CHAN0545

SECTION IV: VOCAL AND CHORAL

Deus noster refugium—grand motet: 6vv and instruments (1713-15)
V. Gens, I. Desrochers, J-P. Fouchécourt, H. Lamy, P. Harvey, M. Loureiro de Sà, S. Imbodem, Concert Spirituel Orch, H. Niquet (r1992) *Concert*
(2/94) (FNAC) ① 592096
S. Daneman, N. Rime, P. Agnew, N. Rivenq, N. Cavallier, Arts Florissants Chor, Arts Florissants Orch, W. Christie (r1994) *Concert*
(8/95) (ERAT) ① 4509-96967-2
In convertendo—grand motet: 3/6vv and instruments (c1718)
V. Gens, I. Desrochers, J-P. Fouchécourt, H. Lamy, P. Harvey, M. Loureiro de Sà, S. Imbodem, Concert Spirituel Orch, H. Niquet (r1992) *Concert*
(2/94) (FNAC) ① 592096
S. Daneman, N. Rime, P. Agnew, N. Rivenq, N. Cavallier, Arts Florissants Chor, Arts Florissants Orch, W. Christie (r1994) *Concert*
(8/95) (ERAT) ① 4509-96967-2
Quam dilecta—motet: 5/6vv and instruments (c1720)
V. Gens, I. Desrochers, J-P. Fouchécourt, H. Lamy, P. Harvey, M. Loureiro de Sà, S. Imbodem, Concert Spirituel Orch, H. Niquet (r1992) *Concert*
(2/94) (FNAC) ① 592096
S. Daneman, N. Rime, P. Agnew, N. Rivenq, N. Cavallier, Arts Florissants Chor, Arts Florissants Orch, W. Christie (r1994) *Concert*
(8/95) (ERAT) ① 4509-96967-2
Rossignols amoureux—arietta: soprano, flute, violin and continuo
K. Battle, J-P. Rampal, M. Lutzke, Anthony Newman (pp1991) *Concert*　　(9/94) (SONY) ① SK53106

SECTION V: STAGE WORKS

Abaris (Les Boréades)—tragédie lyrique: 5 acts (Lib. anon, attrib Cahusac)
Orchestral Suite Eighteenth Century Orch, F. Brüggen *Dardanus*　　(11/87) (PHIL) ① 420 240-2PH
Anacréon—acte de ballet: 1 act (1754—Fontainbleau) (Lib. Cahusac)
Cpte R. Schirrer, A. Mellon, J. Feldman, D. Visse, M. Laplénie, Arts Florissants Voc Ens, Arts Florissants Instr Ens, W. Christie
(12/87) (HARM) ① HMA190 1090
Castor et Pollux—tragédie en musique: prologue & 5 acts (1737 rev 1754—Paris) (Lib. Bernard)
EXCERPTS: 1. Ouverture. PROLOGUE: 2. Vénus, ô Vénus; 3. Symphonie; 4. Je vous revois, belle Déesse; 5a. Gavottes; 5b. Renais, plus brillante; 6a. Premier Menuet & Tambourin; 6b. Naissez, dons de Flore; 7a. Deuxième Menuet & Tambourin; 7b. D'un spectacle nouveau. ACT ONE: 8. Que tout gémisse; 9. Où courez-vous?; 10. Tristes apprêts, pâles flambeaux; 11a. Symphonie. ACT THREE: 12. D'où partent ces cris nouveaux?; 11c. Eclatez, fières trompettes (Premier Air des Athlètes); 12. Deuxième et Troisième Airs des Athlètes; 13. Je Remets à vos pieds. ACT TWO: 14. Nature, Amour, qui partagez mon coeur; 15. Le souverain des Dieux; 16. Ma voix, puissant maître du monde; 17. Connaissez notre puissance; 18. Qu'Hébé de fleurs; 19. Voici des Dieux. ACT THREE: 20. Rassemblez-vous, peuples; 21. Son char a reculé; 22. Sortez d'esclavage; 23. Brisons tous nos fers; 24. Tout cède à ce héros vainqueur. ACT FOUR: 25. Séjour de l'éternelle paix; 26. Qu'il soit heureux comme nous?; 27. Ici se lève l'aurore; 28a. Gavotte; 28b. Sur les Ombres fugitives; 29a. Passepieds; 29b. Autant d'amours que de fleurs; 30. Fuyez, Ombres légères; 31. Rassurez-vous, habitants fortunés; 32. Mais, qui s'offre à mes yeux; 33. Revenez sur les rivages sombres. ACT FIVE: 34. Castor revoit le jour; 35. Le Ciel est donc touché; 36. Vivez, heureux époux; 37. Peuples, éloignez-vous; 38. Eh quoi! tous ces objets; 39. Qu'ai-je entendu!; 40. Les Destins sont contents; 41. Mon frère...ô Ciel!; 42. Palais de ma grandeur; 43. Tant de vertus doivent prétendre; 44. Entrée des Astres. Gigue; 45a. Ariette; 45b. Brillez, Astres nouveaux; 46a. Chaconne; 46b. Que les Cieux.
Cpte H. Crook, J. Corréas, A. Mellon, V. Gens, R. Schirrer, S. Piau, M. Padmore, C. Brua, S. Daneman, A. Brand, J-C. Sarragosse, Arts Florissants Chor, Arts Florissants Orch, W. Christie (r1992)
(7/93) (HARM) ① [3] HMC90 1435/7
Cpte P. Jeffes, P. Huttenlocher, J. Smith, C. Buchan, L. Wallington, B. Parsons, J. Rees, G. Fisher, J. Hancorn, H. Herford, English Bach Fest Chor, English Bach Fest Baroque Orch, C. Farncombe (r1982)　(5/95) (ERAT) ① [2] 4509-95311-2
Suite Eighteenth Century Orch, F. Brüggen *Concert*
(4/91) (PHIL) ① 426 714-2PH

Dardanus—tragédie en musique: prologue & 5 acts (1739 rev 1744—Paris) (Lib. Le Clerc de la Bruyère)
1. Ouverture; 2. Entrée pour les Guerriers; 3. Bruit de guerre; 4. Premier Air: Grave; 5. Deuxième Air: Vivement; 6. Tambourins; 7. Les songes; 8. Chaconne.
Cpte C. Eda-Pierre, F. von Stade, G. Gautier, M. Devlin, R. Soyer, J. Van Dam, V. Dietschy, H. Garetti, A. Dutertre, M. Marandon, J-P. Courtis, Paris Op Chor, Paris Op Orch, R. Leppard (r1980)
(5/95) (ERAT) ① [2] 4509-95312-2
Rigaudon. G. Cziffra (r1980-81; arr pf) *Concert*
(3/95) (EMI) ① CDM5 65253-2
Rigaudon. G. Cziffra (r1969; arr pf) *Concert*
(3/95) (EMI) ① CDM5 65255-2
Suite Collegium Aureum, R. Peters (r1964) *Indes galantes.*　　(8/93) (DHM) ① 05472 77269-2
1-8. Eighteenth Century Orch, F. Brüggen *Abaris.*
(11/87) (PHIL) ① 420 240-2PH
Les Fêtes d'Hébé—opéra-ballet: prologue & 3 entrées (1739—Paris)
Tambourin Queen's Hall Orch, Henry Wood (r1923) *Concert*　　(1/94) (BEUL) ① 1PD3
Hippolyte et Aricie—tragédie en musique: prologue & 5 acts (1733—Paris) (Lib. Pellegrin)
Cpte J-P. Fouchécourt, V. Gens, B. Fink, R. Smythe, T. Feighan, A. Massis, L. Naouri, F. Katz, J-L. Georgel, L. Coadou, J-L. Meunier, J-F. Loiseleur des Longchamps, J. Varnier, M. Simon, S. van Dyck, K. Okada, M. Hall, Sagittarius Ens, Musiciens du Louvre, M. Minkowski (pp1994)
(9/95) (ARCH) ① [3] 445 853-2AH3
Nightingale Song E. Schwarzkopf, G. Scheck, M. Raucheisen (Ger: bp1944) *Concert*
(6/87) (ACAN) ① 43 801
Suite Petite Bande, S. Kuijken (r1978)
(7/90) (DHM) ① GD77009
Les Indes galantes—opéra-ballet: prologue & 4 entrées (1735-1761—Paris) (Lib. Fuzelier)
Cpte C. McFadden, J. Corréas, I. Poulenard, N. Rivenq, M. Ruggeri, H. Crook, B. Delétré, J-P. Fouchécourt, S. Piau, N. Rime, Arts Florissants Chor, Arts Florissants Orch, W. Christie
(2/92) (HARM) ① [3] HMC90 1367/9
Cpte G. Hartmann, P. Huttenlocher, J. Smith, L. Devos, J. Elwes, Valencia Voc Ens, J-F. Paillard CO, J-F. Paillard (r1974)
(5/95) (ERAT) ① [3] 4509-95310-2
Orchestral Suite Eighteenth Century Orch, F. Brüggen　　(8/94) (PHIL) ① 438 946-2PH
Suite Collegium Aureum, R. Peters (r1967) *Dardanus.*　　(8/93) (DHM) ① 05472 77269-2
Naïs—pastorale-héroïque: 3 acts (1749—Paris) (Lib. Cahusac)
1. Overture; 2. Entrée majesteuse; 3. Sarabande; 4. Gavotte Vive; 5. Riguadons; 6. Entrée des Lutteures; 7. Chaconne; 8. Air de Triomphe; 9. Menuets; 10. Tambourins; 11. Musette; 12. Sarabande; 13. Gavottes; 14. Pas de deux; 15. Air gai; 16. Tambourins; 17. Menuets; 18. Contredanse général.
Cpte L. Russell, I Caley, I. Caddy, J. Tomlinson, R. Jackson, B. Parsons, A. Ransome, A. Mackay, J. Smith, English Bach Fest Chor, English Bach Fest Orch, N. McGegan (r1980)
(11/95) (ERAT) ① [2] 4509-98532-2
1-18. Philh Baroque Orch, N. McGegan (r1994)
(7/95) (HARM) ① HMU90 7121
Temple de la Gloire.
Nélé et Myrtgis—acte de ballet: 1 act (?) (Lib. anon)
Cpte A. Mellon, J. Corréas, F. Semellaz, D. Michel-Dansac, C. Pelon, Arts Florissants Chor, Arts Florissants Orch, W. Christie *Pygmalion.*
(7/92) (HARM) ① HMC90 1381
Les Paladins—comédie-ballet (1760) (Lib. de Monticourt)
Suite OAE, G. Leonhardt (hpd/dir) (r1991)
(9/92) (PHIL) ① 432 968-2PH
Platée—comédie-lyrique: prologue & 3 acts (1745—Versailles) (Lib. J Autreau & A J Le Valois d'Orville)
Cpte G. Ragon, J. Smith, G. de Mey, V. le Texier, G. Laurens, B. Delétré, V. Gens, M. Verschaeve, F. Herr Voc Ens, Musiciens du Louvre, M. Minkowski (1988)
(9/90) (ERAT) ① [2] 2292-45028-2
Pygmalion—acte de ballet: 1 act (1748) (Lib. Ballot de Savot, after de La Motte)
Cpte J. Elwes, M. van der Sluis, F. Vanhecke, R. Yakar, Paris Chapelle Royale Chor, Petite Bande, G. Leonhardt (r1980)　　(7/90) (DHM) ① GD77143

Cpte H. Crook, S. Piau, A. Mellon, D. Michel-Dansac, Arts Florissants Chor, Arts Florissants Orch, W. Christie *Nélée et Myrthis*.
　(7/92) (HARM) ① **HMC90 1381**
Cpte J-P. Fouchécourt, G. de Reyghere, N. Fournié, S. Piau, Concert Spirituel Orch, H. Niquet (r1992) *Temple de la gloire*.　(10/93) (FNAC) ① **592196**
Ouverture; Pantomime; Gigue; Contredanse K. Gilbert (trans Balbastre) *Concert*
　(7/92) (NOVA) ① **150 018-2**
Le temple de la gloire—opéra-ballet: 5 acts (1745—Versailles) (Lib. Voltaire)
1. Overture; 2. Air tendre pour les Muses; 3. Musette en Rondeau; 4. Gavotte en Musette; 5. Air; 6. Gigue un peu gai; 7. Air de Triomphe; 8. Gigue vive; 9. Passacaille; 10. Entrée des Bergers et Bergères; 11. Loure Grave pour une Entrée Brillante; 12. Air Gai; 13. Entrée de la Jeunesse; 14. Suite de la Passacaille; 15. Air très gai.
Airs gay; Ramages Concert Spirituel Orch, H. Niquet (r1992) *Pygmalion*.
　(10/93) (FNAC) ① **592196**
1-15. Philh Baroque Orch, N. McGegan (r1994) *Naïs*.
　(7/95) (HARM) ① **HMU90 7121**
Zoroastre—tragédie en musique: prologue & (1749 rev 1756—Paris) (Lib. Cahusac)
Cpte J. Elwes, G. de Reyghere, M. van der Sluis, A. Mellon, G. Reinhart, J. Bona, M. Verschaeve, F. Fauché, P. Cantor, Ghent Collegium Vocale, Petite Bande, S. Kuijken (6/91) (DHM) ① [3] **GD77144**

RAMEY, Phillip (b 1939) USA

SECTION III: INSTRUMENTAL

Canzona—piano
B. Lerner *Concert*　(12/89) (ETCE) ① **KTC1036**
Piano Fantasy (1969-72)
B. Lerner *Concert*　(12/88) (ETCE) ① **KTC1019**

RAMIREZ, Ariel (b 1921) Argentina

SECTION IV: VOCAL AND CHORAL

Misa Criolla (1964)
J. Carreras, A. Ramirez, Laredo Choral Salvé, Bilbao Choral Soc, Inst Ens, J.L. Ocejo *Concert*
　(11/88) (PHIL) ① **420 955-2PH**
Navidad en Verano—tenor and choir (1964) (Wds. F. Luna)
J. Carreras, Laredo Choral Salvé, Bilbao Choral Soc, A. Ramirez, D. Sanchez *Concert*
　(11/88) (PHIL) ① **420 955-2PH**
Navidad nuestra—cantata (1964) (Wds. F. Luna)
J. Carreras, A. Ramirez, Laredo Choral Salvé, Bilbao Choral Soc, Inst Ens, D. Sanchez *Concert*
　(11/88) (PHIL) ① **420 955-2PH**

RAMOS, Ramon (b 1954) Spain

SECTION II: CHAMBER

Pas encore—string quartet
Arditti Qt *Concert*　(12/91) (MONT) ① **789006**

RAMSEY, Robert (c1612–1644) England

SECTION IV: VOCAL AND CHORAL

Almighty and everlasting God, we humbly beseech—anthem: 5vv
Magnificat Ch, Magnificat Players, P. Cave (r1994) *Concert*　(7/95) (ASV) ① **CDGAU138**
Go perjured man—song: 1v and continuo (Wds. R Herrick)
Magnificat Ch, Magnificat Players, P. Cave (r1994) *Concert*　(7/95) (ASV) ① **CDGAU138**
How are the mighty fallen—anthem: 6vv
Magnificat Ch, Magnificat Players, P. Cave (r1994) *Concert*　(7/95) (ASV) ① **CDGAU138**
In guilty night—dialogue: 3vv and continuo
Magnificat Ch, Magnificat Players, P. Cave (r1994) *Concert*　(7/95) (ASV) ① **CDGAU138**
In Monte Oliveti—motet: 6vv
Magnificat Ch, Magnificat Players, P. Cave (r1994) *Concert*　(7/95) (ASV) ① **CDGAU138**
Inclina, Domine—motet: 8vv
Magnificat Ch, Magnificat Players, P. Cave (r1994) *Concert*　(7/95) (ASV) ① **CDGAU138**
O come, let us sing unto the Lord—anthem: 5vv
Magnificat Ch, Magnificat Players, P. Cave (r1994) *Concert*　(7/95) (ASV) ① **CDGAU138**

O Sapientia—motet: 5vv
Magnificat Ch, Magnificat Players, P. Cave (r1994) *Concert*　(7/95) (ASV) ① **CDGAU138**
O vos omnes—motet: 6vv
Magnificat Ch, Magnificat Players, P. Cave (r1994) *Concert*　(7/95) (ASV) ① **CDGAU138**
Service—4vv
1. Te Deum; 2. Jubilate Deo; 3. Kyrie; 4. Litany; 5. Creed; 6. Magnificat; 7. Nunc Dimittis.
6, 7. Magnificat Ch, Magnificat Players, P. Cave (r1994) *Concert*　(7/95) (ASV) ① **CDGAU138**
Sleep, fleshy birth—madrigal: 6vv
Cambridge Sngrs, J. Rutter *Concert*
　(11/87) (CLLE) ① **COLCD105**
Amaryllis Consort, C. Brett *Concert*
　(3/88) (CARL) ① **PCD873**
Magnificat Ch, Magnificat Players, P. Cave (r1994) *Concert*　(7/95) (ASV) ① **CDGAU138**
Te Deum and Jubilate—Latin settings: 5vv
Magnificat Ch, Magnificat Players, P. Cave (r1994) *Concert*　(7/95) (ASV) ① **CDGAU138**
Thou maist be proud—song: 1v and continuo (Wds. R Herrick)
Magnificat Ch, Magnificat Players, P. Cave (r1994) *Concert*　(7/95) (ASV) ① **CDGAU138**
What tears, dear Prince—song: 1v and continuo (Wds. Sir Walter Raleigh)
Magnificat Ch, Magnificat Players, P. Cave (r1994) *Concert*　(7/95) (ASV) ① **CDGAU138**
When David heard—anthem: 6vv
Magnificat Ch, Magnificat Players, P. Cave (r1994) *Concert*　(7/95) (ASV) ① **CDGAU138**

RANDEGGER, Alberto Iginio (1880–1918) Italy

SECTION II: CHAMBER

Bohemian Dance—violin and piano, Op. 22
F. Macmillen, anon (r1909) *Concert*
　(7/93) (APR) ① [2] **APR7016**
Pierrot sérénade—violin and piano, Op. 33/1
J. Kubelík, anon (r1910) *Concert*
　(6/91) (BIDD) ① [2] **LAB033/4**
J. Kubelík, anon (r1911) *Concert*
　(6/91) (BIDD) ① [2] **LAB033/4**
Saltarello-caprice—violin and piano, Op. 17/2
F. Macmillen, anon (r1909) *Concert*
　(7/93) (APR) ① [2] **APR7016**

RANGSTRÖM, (Anders Johan) Ture (1884–1947) Sweden

SECTION IV: VOCAL AND CHORAL

The Amazon—song (Wds. K. Boye)
B. Nilsson, G. Parsons (pp1974) *Concert*
　(6/92) (BLUE) ① **ABCD009**
The Girl under the New Moon—song (Wds. B. Bergman)
B. Nilsson, G. Parsons (pp1974) *Concert*
　(6/92) (BLUE) ① **ABCD009**

RANISH, John Frederick (1692/3–1777) England

SECTION II: CHAMBER

Sonata in B minor—flute and continuo
K. Smith, P. Rhodes *Concert*
　(1/91) (ASV) ① **CDDCA739**

RASKATOV, Alexander (b 1953) USSR

SECTION I: ORCHESTRAL

7 Sentimental Sequences—13 performers (1986)
Moscow Contemp Music Ens, A. Vinogradov (r1992) *Concert*　(9/93) (CDM) ① **LDC288 059**

SECTION II: CHAMBER

Dolce Farniente—cello and piano (1991)
Moscow Contemp Music Ens, A. Vinogradov (r1992) *Concert*　(9/93) (CDM) ① **LDC288 059**
Misteria Brevis—piano and percussion (1992)
Moscow Contemp Music Ens, A. Vinogradov (r1992) *Concert*　(9/93) (CDM) ① **LDC288 059**

SECTION IV: VOCAL AND CHORAL

Let there be night—five fragments to poems by S-T. Coleridge (1989)
Moscow Contemp Music Ens, A. Vinogradov (r1992) *Concert*　(9/93) (CDM) ① **LDC288 059**
Song Circle I—1v, cello and keyboards (1984) (Wds. V. Jukovsky)
Moscow Contemp Music Ens, A. Vinogradov (r1992) *Concert*　(9/93) (CDM) ① **LDC288 059**
txetrU (Urtext)—1v, bass clarinet and string trio (1992) (Wds Bible: Old Testament)
Moscow Contemp Music Ens, A. Vinogradov (r1992) *Concert*　(9/93) (CDM) ① **LDC288 059**

RASMUSSEN, Karl Aage (b 1947) Denmark

SECTION II: CHAMBER

Solos and Shadows—string quartet (1983)
Arditti Qt *Concert*
　(11/92) (MARC) ① [2] **DCCD9003**
Surrounded by Scales—string quartet (1985)
Arditti Qt *Concert*
　(11/92) (MARC) ① [2] **DCCD9003**

RATHGEBER, Johann Valentin (1682–1750) Germany

SECTION I: ORCHESTRAL

Concerto for 2 Trumpets and Strings in E flat, Op. 6/15
H. Läubin, B. Läubin, ECO, S. Preston (hpd/dir) *Concert*　(12/91) (DG) ① **431 817-2GH**

RAUTAVAARA, Einojuhani (b 1928) Finland

SECTION I: ORCHESTRAL

Concerto for Cello and Orchestra, Op. 41 (1968)
M. Ylönen, Helsinki PO, M. Pommer (r1993) *Symphony 6*.　(12/94) (ONDI) ① **ODE819-2**
The Fiddlers (Pelimannit)—string orchestra, Op. 1 (1952) (orig comp pf: arr stgs 1973)
1. Närböläisten Braa Speli; 2. Kopsin Jonas; 3. Klockar Samuel Dikström; 4. Pirum Polska; 5. Hypyt.
Musica Vitae CO, W. Rajski *Concert*
　(6/90) (BIS) ① **BIS-CD460**
Playgrounds for Angels—brass ensemble (1981)
PJBE *Concert*　(2/88) (CHAN) ① **CHAN8490**
Symphony No. 6, 'Vincentiana' (1992)
Helsinki PO, M. Pommer (r1993) *Cello Concerto*.
　(12/94) (ONDI) ① **ODE819-2**

SECTION IV: VOCAL AND CHORAL

The Myth of Sampo—male chorus, soloists & tape (1982) (based on epic 'Kalevala')
T. Nyman, S. Tiilikainen, A. Suhonen, Helsinki Univ Chor, M. Hyökki (r1994)
　(12/95) (ONDI) ① **ODE842-2**
Suite de Lorca—chorus a capella, Op. 72 (1973)
1. Cancion de jinete; 2. El grito; 3. La luna asoma; 4. Malaguena.
Danish Nat Rad Ch, S. Parkman (r1994) *Concert*
　(4/95) (CHAN) ① **CHAN9264**

RAVANELLO, Oreste (19th Cent) Italy

SECTION III: INSTRUMENTAL

Theme and Variations in B minor—organ
K. John *Concert*　(11/92) (PRIO) ① **PRCD370**

RAVEL, (Joseph) Maurice (1875–1937) France

SECTION I: ORCHESTRAL

Alborada del gracioso (1905) (from 'Miroirs')
Montreal SO, C. Dutoit *Concert*
　(8/83) (DECC) ① **410 010-2DH**
Boston SO, S. Ozawa *Concert*
　(8/87) (DG) ① **415 845-2GGA**
FNO, E. Inbal *Concert*　(6/88) (DENO) ① **CO-1797**
Cincinnati SO, J. López-Cobos *Concert*
　(12/88) (TELA) ① **CD80171**
Berlin St Op Orch, O. Klemperer (r1926) *Concert*
　(2/89) (SYMP) ① **SYMCD1042**

Philh, G. Cantelli (r1952) *Concert*
(7/93) (TEST) ① **SBT1017**
B. Fromanger, M. Klinko (r1993: arr fl/hp: Maganini)
Concert (2/94) (EMI) ① **CDC7 54884-2**
Atlanta SO, Y. Levi (r1993) *Daphnis et Chloé.*
(3/94) (TELA) ① **CD80352**
Boston SO, S. Ozawa (r1974) *Concert*
(5/94) (BELA) ① **450 129-2**
Paris Orch, S. Bychkov (r1992) *Concert*
(12/94) (PHIL) ① **438 209-2PH**
English Sinfonia, C. Groves (r1988) *Concert*
(10/95) (CARL) ① **PCD2017**
Concertgebouw, C. M. Giulini (pp1995) *Concert*
(11/95) (SONY) ① **SK66832**
Rapsodie espagnole (1907)
1. Prélude à la nuit; 2. Malagueña; 3. Habañéra; 4.
Feria.
Montreal SO, C. Dutoit *Concert*
(8/83) (DECC) ① **410 010-2DH**
Paris Orch, C. Munch *Concert*
(5/86) (EMI) ① **CDC7 47356-2**
LSO, C. Abbado *Concert*
(12/86) (DG) ① **415 972-2GH**
Los Angeles PO, C.M. Giulini *Concert*
(8/87) (DG) ① **415 844-2GGA**
FNO, E. Inbal *Concert* (6/88) (DENO) ① **CO-1797**
Cincinnati SO, J. López-Cobos *Concert*
(12/88) (TELA) ① **CD80171**
Chicago SO, F. Reiner *Concert*
(1/90) (RCA) ① **GD60179**
LSO, P. Monteux (r1961) *Concert*
(5/90) (DECC) ① **425 956-2DM**
BRSO, C. Krauss (pp1953) *Concert*
(8/90) (ORFE) ① **C196891A**
Ulster Orch, Y.P. Tortelier *Concert*
(10/90) (CHAN) ① **CHAN8850**
Cleveland Orch, P. Boulez *Concert*
(2/91) (SONY) ① [3] **SM3K45842**
Dallas SO, E. Mata *Concert*
(2/91) (RCA) ① **VD60485**
Detroit SO, P. Paray *Concert*
(4/91) (MERC) ① **432 003-2MM**
Philh, G. Simon *Concert*
(11/91) (CALA) ① **CACD1005**
Paris Cons, A. Cluytens *Concert*
(7/92) (EMI) ① [2] **CZS7 67474-2**
Chicago SO, D. Barenboim *Concert*
(12/92) (ERAT) ① **2292-45766-2**
Chicago SO, F. Reiner (r1956) *Concert*
(4/93) (RCA) ① **09026 61250-2**
SRO, E. Ansermet (r1960) *Concert*
(6/93) (DECC) ① [2] **433 911-2DM2**
NYPO, L. Bernstein (r1973) *Concert*
(7/93) (SONY) ① **SMK47603**
SRO, A. Jordan (r1986) *Concert*
(8/94) (ERAT) ① [2] **4509-91934-2**
BPO, P. Boulez (r1993) *Concert*
(9/94) (DG) ① **439 859-2GH**
M. Argerich, N. Freire, P. Sadlo, E. Guggeis (r1993:
arr 2 pfs/perc: P. Sadlo) *Concert*
(10/94) (DG) ① **439 867-2GH**
VPO, C. Silvestri (r1959) *Concert*
(11/94) (EMI) ① **CZS5 68229-2**
Paris Orch, S. Bychkov (r1992) *Concert*
(12/94) (PHIL) ① **438 209-2PH**
Boston SO, C. Munch (r1956) *Concert*
(12/94) (RCA) ① **09026 61956-2**
New Philh, L. Stokowski (pp1974) *Concert*
(3/95) (BBCR) ① **BBCRD9107**
Philadelphia, L. Stokowski (r1934) *Concert*
(8/95) (BIDD) ① **WHL013**
3. J. Bálint, N. Mercz (r1992: arr fl/hp: Mercz) *Concert*
(12/94) (NAXO) ① **8 550741**
Shéhérazade—fairy overture (1898)
LSO, C. Abbado *Concert*
(7/89) (DG) ① **427 314-2GH**
NYPO, P. Boulez *Concert*
(2/91) (SONY) ① [3] **SM3K45842**
Ulster Orch, Y.P. Tortelier *Concert*
(10/91) (CHAN) ① **CHAN8914**
Ulster Orch, Y.P. Tortelier *Concert*
(10/91) (CHAN) ① **CHAN8914**
Montreal SO, C. Dutoit (r1992) *Concert*
(10/95) (DECC) ① **440 333-2DH**
Le **Tombeau de Couperin (1917)** (orch
Ravel—1919)
Montreal SO, C. Dutoit *Concert*
(11/84) (DECC) ① **410 254-2DH**
ASMF, N. Marriner *Concert*
(2/85) (ASV) ① **CDDCA517**
LSO, C. Abbado *Concert*
(2/89) (DG) ① **423 665-2GH**
NYPO, P. Boulez *Concert*
(2/91) (SONY) ① [3] **SM3K45842**
Dallas SO, E. Mata *Concert*
(2/91) (RCA) ① **VD60485**

Detroit SO, P. Paray *Concert*
(4/91) (MERC) ① **432 003-2MM**
St Paul CO, H. Wolff *Concert*
(10/92) (TELD) ① **9031-74006-2**
LSO, C. Abbado (r1987) *Concert*
(6/94) (DG) ① **439 414-2GCL**
SRO, A. Jordan (r1986) *Concert*
(8/94) (ERAT) ① [2] **4509-91934-2**
**Tzigane—rapsodie de concert for violin and
orchestra (1924)**
A. Dumay, Monte Carlo PO, A. Dumay *Concert*
(6/87) (EMI) ① **CDC7 47544-2**
I. Perlman, Paris Orch, J. Martinon *Concert*
(12/87) (EMI) ① **CDC7 47725-2**
I. Perlman, NYPO, Z. Mehta *Concert*
(12/87) (DG) ① **423 063-2GH**
S. Accardo, LSO, C. Abbado *Concert*
(7/89) (DG) ① **427 314-2GH**
S. Chase, Philh, G. Simon *Concert*
(11/91) (CALA) ① **CACD1004**
J. Bell, RPO, A. Litton *Concert*
(1/92) (DECC) ① **433 519-2DH**
F.P. Zimmermann, Stuttgart RSO, G. Gelmetti
Concert (3/92) (EMI) ① **CDC7 54248-2**
Y.P. Tortelier (vn/dir), Ulster Orch *Concert*
(9/92) (CHAN) ① **CHAN8972**
Z. Francescatti, NYPO, L. Bernstein *Concert*
(5/93) (SONY) ① **SMK47548**
I. Perlman, LSO, A. Previn (r1968) *Concert*
(7/93) (RCA) ① **07863 56520-2**
E. Friedman, LSO, M. Sargent *Concert*
(8/93) (RCA) ① **09026 61210-2**
M. Bisengaliev, Polish Nat RSO, J. Wildner (r1992)
Concert (12/93) (NAXO) ① **8 550494**
A-S. Mutter, VPO, James Levine (r1992) *Concert*
(12/93) (DG) ① **437 544-2GH**
S. Accardo, LSO, C. Abbado (r1987) *Concert*
(6/94) (DG) ① **439 414-2GCL**
J. Heifetz, Los Angeles PO, A. Wallenstein (r1953)
Concert (11/94) (RCA) ① [65] **09026 61778-2(08)**
I. Perlman, Paris Orch, J. Martinon (r1974) *Concert*
(6/95) (EMI) ① [20] **CZS4 83177-2(1)**
Valses nobles et sentimentales (1912)
(adapted from piano work)
Montreal SO, C. Dutoit *Concert*
(11/84) (DECC) ① **410 254-2DH**
Toulouse Capitole Orch, M. Plasson *Concert*
(7/87) (EMI) ① **CDC7 47648-2**
Cincinnati SO, J. López-Cobos *Concert*
(12/88) (TELA) ① **CD80171**
FNO, E. Inbal *Concert* (6/89) (DENO) ① **CO-71799**
Chicago SO, F. Reiner *Concert*
(1/90) (RCA) ① **GD60179**
LSO, C. Abbado (r1988) *Daphnis et Chloé.*
(4/90) (DG) ① **427 679-2GH**
NYPO, P. Boulez *Concert*
(2/91) (SONY) ① [3] **SM3K45842**
NYPO, G. Sinopoli (r1989) *Concert*
(5/91) (DG) ① **429 785-2GH**
Boston SO, S. Ozawa (r1974) *Daphnis et Chloé.*
(7/93) (DG) ① **437 648-2GGA**
Paris Cons, P. Coppola (r1934) *Concert*
(9/93) (KOCH) ① **37702-2**
San Francisco SO, P. Monteux (r1946) *Concert*
(9/94) (RCA) ① [15] **09026 61893-2**

SECTION II: CHAMBER

**Berceuse sur le nom de Gabriel
Fauré—violin and piano (1922)**
K. Sillito, M. Fingerhut *Concert*
(9/88) (CHAN) ① **CHAN8578**
R. Pasquier, B. Engerer *Concert*
(8/92) (HARM) ① **HMC90 1364**
A. Dumay, M-J. Pires (r1993) *Concert*
(10/95) (DG) ① **445 880-2GH**
Boléro—2 pianos (1930) (transcr cpsr from
orch work)
I. Thorson, J. Thurber *Concert*
(10/88) (PAUL) ① [2] **PACD51**
W. Jordans, L. Van Doesselaar *Concert*
(11/88) (ETCE) ① **KTC1054**
L. Lortie, H. Mercier *Concert*
(3/91) (CHAN) ① **CHAN8905**
D. Achatz, Y. Nagai *Concert*
(10/91) (BIS) ① **BIS-CD489**
**Fanfare pour 'L'éventail de Jeanne'—piano
duet** (arr from ballet score)
I. Thorson, J. Thurber *Concert*
(10/88) (PAUL) ① [2] **PACD51**
W. Jordans, L. Van Doesselaar *Concert*
(11/88) (ETCE) ① **KTC1054**
Frontispice—2 pianos (1918)
I. Thorson, J. Thurber, G. Gardiner *Concert*
(10/88) (PAUL) ① [2] **PACD51**
S. Coombs, Cyril Scott *Concert*
(2/91) (GAMU) ① **GAMCD517**

**Introduction and Allegro for flute, clarinet,
harp and string quartet (1905)**
Nash Ens *Concert* (6/88) (CRD) ① **CRD3446**
I. Thorson, J. Thurber (arr. 2 pfs) *Concert*
(10/88) (PAUL) ① [2] **PACD51**
S. Kanga, ASMF Chbr Ens *Concert*
(12/88) (CHAN) ① **CHAN8621**
Melos Ens *Concert* (1/89) (DECC) ① **421 154-2DM**
M. Jurkovič, J. Luptáčik, K. Nováková, Phil Qt
Concert (9/89) (OPUS) ① **9351 1894**
Prometheus Ens *Concert*
(11/89) (ASV) ① **CDDCA664**
A. Giles, E. Talmi, A. Arnheim, R. Kaminkovsky, R.
Mozes, Y. Kaminkovsky, Y. Alperin *Concert*
(6/90) (CARL) ① **PWK1141**
S. Coombs, Cyril Scott (arr 2 pfs) *Concert*
(2/91) (GAMU) ① **GAMCD517**
Vienna-Berlin Ens *Concert*
(3/91) (DG) ① **429 738-2GGA**
L. Lortie, H. Mercier *Concert*
(3/91) (CHAN) ① **CHAN8905**
R. Masters, Ulster Orch, Y.P. Tortelier *Concert*
(9/92) (CHAN) ① **CHAN8972**
B. Fromanger, M. Gabai, M. Klinko, F. Laroque, G.
Torgomian, P. Lénert, C. Lacrouts (r1993) *Concert*
(2/94) (EMI) ① **CDC7 54884-2**
W. Bennett, J. Campbell, I. Jones, Allegri Qt (r1994)
Concert (2/95) (CALA) ① [2] **CACD1018**
A. Gleghorn, M. Lurie, A.M. Stockton, Hollywood Qt
(1951) *Concert* (3/95) (TEST) ① **SBT1053**
J. Galway, R. Stoltzman, H. Lehwalder, Tokyo Qt
(1988) *Concert* (4/95) (RCA) ① **09026 62552-2**
Ma mère l'oye—piano duet (1908-10)
K. Labèque, M. Labèque *Concert*
(11/87) (PHIL) ① **420 159-2PH**
T. Paraskivesco, J. Rouvier *Concert*
(8/88) (CALL) ① [4] **CAL9831/4**
I. Thorson, J. Thurber *Concert*
(10/88) (PAUL) ① [2] **PACD51**
W. Jordans, L. Van Doesselaar *Concert*
(11/88) (ETCE) ① **KTC1054**
B. Eden, A. Tamir (r1983) *Concert*
(3/91) (CRD) ① **CRD3424**
L. Lortie, H. Mercier *Concert*
(3/91) (CHAN) ① **CHAN8905**
D. Achatz, Y. Nagai *Concert*
(10/91) (BIS) ① **BIS-CD489**
P. Rogé, D-F. Rogé (r1974) *Concert*
(10/94) (DECC) ① [2] **440 836-2DF2**
Pavane; Laideronnette Brodsky Qt (arr M. Thomas)
Concert (4/92) (TELD) ① **2292-46015-2**
2-6. H. Snell Brass, H. Snell (arr Sparke) *Concert*
(9/91) (POLY) ① **QPRZ005D**
Piano Trio (1914)
Beaux Arts Trio Chausson: *Piano Trio.*
(4/85) (PHIL) ① **411 141-2PH**
Borodin Trio *Concert* (5/87) (CHAN) ① **CHAN8458**
Parnassus Trio Debussy: *Piano Trio.*
(12/87) (MDG) ① **L3272**
M. Crayford, C. van Kampen, I. Brown *Concert*
(6/88) (CRD) ① **CRD3446**
J-J. Kantorow, P. Muller, J. Rouvier *Concert*
(2/89) (DENO) ① **CO-72508**
Trio di Milano *Concert* (5/89) (DYNA) ① **CDS49**
G. Van Blerk, V. Beths, A. Bylsma *Concert*
(5/90) (BAYE) ① **BR100009**
J. Heifetz, G. Piatigorsky, A. Rubinstein (r1950)
Concert (9/90) (RCA) ① **GD87871**
Y. Menuhin, G. Cassadó, L. Kentner *Concert*
(4/91) (EMI) ① **CDM7 63986-2**
Solomon Trio *Concert* (7/92) (CARL) ① **MCD41**
Fontenay Trio *Concert*
(7/92) (TELD) ① **2292-44937-2**
Ulster Orch, Y. P. Tortelier (orch Y P Tortelier)
Concert (9/93) (CHAN) ① **CHAN9114**
Nash Ens (1990) *Concert*
(6/94) (VIRG) ① **VC5 45016-2**
J. Heifetz, G. Piatigorsky, A. Rubinstein (r1950)
Concert (11/94) (RCA) ① [65] **09026 61778-2(44)**
Joachim Trio (r1993) *Concert*
(8/95) (NAXO) ① **8 550934**
A. Previn, J. Rosenfeld. G. Hoffman (r1992)
Debussy: *Piano Trio.*
(11/95) (RCA) ① **09026 68062-2**
I. Perlman, L. Harrell, Vladimir Ashkenazy *Concert*
(12/95) (DECC) ① **444 318-2DH**
**Pièce en forme de habanera—violin and
piano**
E. Johnson, G. Back (arr. Back) *Concert*
(10/88) (ASV) ① **CDDCA621**
J. Szigeti, N. Magaloff (arr Leduc: r1936) *Concert*
(1/90) (BIDD) ① [2] **LAB007/8**
G. Neveu, J. Neveu (r1946) *Concert*
(8/90) (EMI) ① **CDH7 63493-2**
H. de Vries, Philh, G. Simon (arr. Hoérée) *Concert*
(11/91) (CALA) ① **CACD1005**

R. Pasquier, B. Engerer (arr Kreisler) *Concert*
(8/92) (HARM) ① **HMC90 1364**
V. Taylor, T. Kain (fl/gtr) *Concert*
(9/92) (TALL) ① **TP003**
P. Fournier, E. Lush (r1951) *Concert*
(7/93) (TEST) ① **SBT1016**
Empire Brass (r1991) *Concert*
(11/93) (TELA) ① **CD80301**
F. Laroque, M. Klinko (r1993: arr vn/hp) *Concert*
(2/94) (EMI) ① **CDC7 54884-2**
W. Marsalis, J.L. Stillman (tpt/pf) *Concert*
(5/94) (SONY) ① **SK47193**
J. Heifetz, M. Kaye (r1944) *Concert*
(11/94) (RCA) ① **[65] 09026 61778-2(19)**
J. Campbell, J. York (r1994) *Concert*
(2/95) (CALA) ① **[2] CACD1018**
A. A. Meyers, S. Rivers (r1993) *Concert*
(4/95) (RCA) ① **09026 62546-2**
A. Janigro, D. Lipatti (r1947: arr vc/pf) *Concert*
(10/95) (ARCI) ① **[2] ARC112/3**
A. Dumay, M-J. Pires (r1993) *Concert*
(10/95) (DG) ① **445 880-2GH**

Rapsodie espagnole—two pianos
I. Thorson, J. Thurber *Concert*
(10/88) (PAUL) ① **[2] PACD51**
W. Jordans, L. Van Doeselaar *Concert*
(11/88) (ETCE) ① **KTC1054**
S. Coombs, Cyril Scott *Concert*
(2/91) (GAMU) ① **GAMCD517**
B. Eden, A. Tamir (r1983) *Concert*
(3/91) (CRD) ① **CRD3424**
L. Lortie, H. Mercier *Concert*
(3/91) (CHAN) ① **CHAN8905**
D. Achatz, Y. Nagai *Concert*
(10/91) (BIS) ① **BIS-CD489**

Shéhérazade—piano duet (arr from song cycle)
Overture I. Thorson, J. Thurber *Concert*
(10/88) (PAUL) ① **[2] PACD51**
Overture S. Coombs, Cyril Scott (2 pfs) *Concert*
(2/91) (GAMU) ① **GAMCD517**

Sites auriculaires—2 pianos (1895-97)
1. Habanera; 2. Entre cloches.
Entre Cloches I. Thorson, J. Thurber *Concert*
(10/88) (PAUL) ① **[2] PACD51**
Entre Cloches S. Coombs, Cyril Scott *Concert*
(2/91) (GAMU) ① **GAMCD517**
Habanera T. Paraskivesco, J. Rouvier *Concert*
(8/88) (CALL) ① **[4] CAL9831/4**
1. M. Kliegel, R. Havenith (arr vc/pf) *Concert*
(9/92) (MARC) ① **8 223403**

Sonata for Violin and Cello (1920-22)
E. Turovsky, Y. Turovsky *Concert*
(7/85) (CHAN) ① **CHAN8358**
M. Crayford, C. van Kampen *Concert*
(6/88) (CRD) ① **CRD3446**
V. Beths, A. Bylsma *Concert*
(5/90) (BAYE) ① **BR100009**
G. Hetzel, G. Faust *Concert*
(3/91) (DG) ① **429 738-2GH**
M. Crayford, C. van Kampen (r1990) *Concert*
(6/94) (VIRG) ① **VC5 45016-2**

Sonata for Violin and Piano (1897)
J-J. Kantorow, J. Rouvier *Concert*
(8/89) (DENO) ① **CO-72718**
D-S. Kang, P. Devoyon *Concert*
(11/90) (NAXO) ① **8 550276**
F.P. Zimmermann, A. Lonquich *Concert*
(6/92) (EMI) ① **CDC7 54305-2**
R. Pasquier, B. Engerer *Concert*
(8/92) (HARM) ① **HMC90 1364**
G. Poulet, N. Lee (r1993) *Concert*
(9/94) (ARIO) ① **ARN68228**
L. Mordkovitch, C. Benson (r1994) *Concert*
(6/95) (CHAN) ① **CHAN9351**
J. Suk, J. Hála (r1994) *Concert*
(11/95) (DINT) ① **DICD920306**

Sonata for Violin and Piano in G (1923-27)
F.P. Zimmermann, A. Lonquich *Concert*
(6/92) (EMI) ① **CDC7 54305-2**
R. Pasquier, B. Engerer *Concert*
(8/92) (HARM) ① **HMC90 1364**
J. Szigeti, C. Bussotti (r1953) *Concert*
(5/93) (SONY) ① **MPK52569**
K. Takezawa, R. de Silva (r1992) *Concert*
(9/94) (RCA) ① **09026 61386-2**
G. Poulet, N. Lee (r1993) *Concert*
(9/94) (ARIO) ① **ARN68228**
L. Mordkovitch, C. Benson (r1994) *Concert*
(6/95) (CHAN) ① **CHAN9351**
C. Tetzlaff, L. O. Andsnes (r1994) *Concert*
(11/95) (VIRG) ① **VC5 45122-2**
S. Mintz, Y. Bronfman (r1985) *Concert*
(11/95) (DG) ① **445 557-2GMA**
T. Little, P. Lane (r1995) *Concert*
(12/95) (EMIN) ① **CD-EMX2244**

String Quartet in F (1902-3)
1. Moderato très doux; 2. Assez vif-très rhthmé; 3. Très lent; 4. Vif et agité.
Sequoia Qt Bartók: *String Quartet 3.*
(11/84) (DELO) ① **DE3004**
Alban Berg Qt (r1984) Debussy: *String Quartet.*
(8/86) (EMI) ① **CDC7 47347-2**
Cleveland Qt (r1985) Debussy: *String Quartet.*
(3/87) (TELA) ① **CD80111**
Viotti Qt *Concert*
(3/87) (PIER) ① **PV786102**
Quartetto Italiano (r1965) Debussy: *String Quartet.*
(10/88) (PHIL) ① **420 894-2PSL**
Talich Qt *Concert*
(11/89) (CALL) ① **CAL9893**
Budapest Qt Debussy: *string quartet.*
(10/90) (SONY) ① **MPK44843**
New World Qt *Concert*
(1/91) (CARL) ① **MCD17**
Talich Qt Debussy: *String Quartet.*
(4/91) (SUPR) ① **10 4110-2**
Britten Qt *Concert*
(2/92) (EMI) ① **CDC7 54346-2**
Danish Qt Debussy: *String Quartet.*
(8/92) (AUVI) ① **V4409**
LaSalle Qt Debussy: *String Quartet.*
(9/92) (DG) ① **435 589-2GGA**
Carmina Qt Debussy: *String Quartet.*
(3/93) (DENO) ① **CO-75164**
Juilliard Qt (r1992) *Concert*
(3/94) (SONY) ① **SK52554**
Hagen Qt (r1992-3) *Concert*
(6/94) (DG) ① **437 836-2GH**
Sharon Qt (r1988) *Concert*
(10/94) (DINT) ① **DICD920171**
Emerson Qt (r1984) Debussy: *String Quartet.*
(12/94) (DG) ① **445 509-2GMA**
Keller Qt (r1993) Debussy: *String Quartet.*
(2/95) (ERAT) ① **4509-96361-2**
Tokyo Qt (r1992/4) *Concert*
(4/95) (RCA) ① **09026 62552-2**
Parisii Qt (r1994) *Concert* (10/95) (AUVI) ① **V4730**
Lindsay Qt (r1994) *Concert*
(12/95) (ASV) ① **CDDCA930**

Tzigane—rapsodie de concert for violin and piano (1924)
M. Vengerov, I. Vinogradova *Concert*
(4/90) (BIDD) ① **LAW001**
G. Neveu, J. Neveu (r1946) *Concert*
(8/90) (EMI) ① **CDH7 63493-2**
Y. Menuhin, A. Balsam (r1932) *Concert*
(9/91) (TEST) ① **SBT1003**
Y. Menuhin, A. Balsam (r1932) *Concert*
(12/91) (BIDD) ① **LAB046**
R. Pasquier, B. Engerer *Concert*
(8/92) (HARM) ① **HMC90 1364**
I. Haendel, I. Newton (r1941) *Concert*
(10/92) (PEAR) ① **GEMMCD9939**
J. Heifetz, B. Smith (r1972) *Concert*
(11/94) (RCA) ① **[65] 09026 61778-2(46)**
J. Heifetz, A. Sándor (r1934) *Concert*
(11/94) (RCA) ① **[65] 09026 61778-2(02)**
A. Dumay, M-J. Pires (r1993) *Concert*
(10/95) (DG) ① **445 880-2GH**
T. Little, P. Lane (r1991) *Concert*
(12/95) (EMIN) ① **CD-EMX2244**

La Valse (1921) (transcr composer for two pianos, 1921)
I. Thorson, J. Thurber *Concert*
(10/88) (PAUL) ① **[2] PACD51**
S. Coombs, Cyril Scott *Concert*
(2/91) (GAMU) ① **GAMCD517**
B. Eden, A. Tamir (r1983) *Concert*
(3/91) (CRD) ① **CRD3424**
L. Lortie, H. Mercier *Concert*
(3/91) (CHAN) ① **CHAN8905**

SECTION III: INSTRUMENTAL

A la manière de Borodine—piano (1913)
P. Crossley *Concert* (7/88) (CRD) ① **CRD3384**
L. Lortie *Concert* (10/89) (CHAN) ① **CHAN8647**
K.W. Paik *Concert*
(10/92) (DANT) ① **[2] PSG9123/4**
J-Y. Thibaudet *Concert*
(11/92) (DECC) ① **[2] 433 515-2DH2**
G. Fergus-Thompson *Concert*
(10/93) (ASV) ① **CDDCA809**
A. Queffélec (r1992) *Concert*
(3/94) (VIRG) ① **VC7 59322-2**
W. Haas (r1964) *Concert*
(10/94) (PHIL) ① **[2] 438 353-2PM2**
P. Rogé (r1974) *Concert*
(10/94) (DECC) ① **[2] 440 836-2DF2**
F-J. Thiollier (r1993) *Concert*
(2/95) (NAXO) ① **8 550683**

A la manière de Chabrier—piano (1913)
P. Crossley *Concert* (7/88) (CRD) ① **CRD3384**
L. Lortie *Concert* (10/89) (CHAN) ① **CHAN8647**
K.W. Paik *Concert*
(10/92) (DANT) ① **[2] PSG9123/4**

J-Y. Thibaudet *Concert*
(11/92) (DECC) ① **[2] 433 515-2DH2**
G. Fergus-Thompson *Concert*
(10/93) (ASV) ① **CDDCA809**
A. Queffélec (r1992) *Concert*
(3/94) (VIRG) ① **VC7 59322-2**
A. Planès (r1993) *Concert*
(5/94) (HARM) ① **HMC90 1465**
W. Haas (r1964) *Concert*
(10/94) (PHIL) ① **[2] 438 353-2PM2**
P. Rogé (r1974) *Concert*
(10/94) (DECC) ① **[2] 440 836-2DF2**
F-J. Thiollier (r1993) *Concert*
(2/95) (NAXO) ① **8 550683**

Gaspard de la nuit—piano (1908)
1. Ondine; 2. Le gibet; 3. Scarbo.
V. Perlemuter *Concert* (1/84) (NIMB) ① **NI5005**
I. Pogorelich Prokofiev: *Piano Sonata 6.*
(11/84) (DG) ① **413 363-2GH**
S. François *Concert*
(10/86) (EMI) ① **CDC7 47368-2**
M. Argerich Piano Concerto.
(12/87) (DG) ① **419 062-2GGA**
P. Crossley *Concert* (7/88) (CRD) ① **CRD3384**
L. Lortie *Concert* (10/89) (CHAN) ① **CHAN8647**
M. Nojima *Miroirs.* (10/90) (REFE) ① **RRCD-35**
W. Gieseking (r1930s) *Concert*
(4/91) (PEAR) ① **GEMMCD9449**
K. Stott *Concert* (6/92) (CONI) ① **CDCF191**
K.W. Paik *Concert*
(10/92) (DANT) ① **[2] PSG9123/4**
J-Y. Thibaudet *Concert*
(11/92) (DECC) ① **[2] 433 515-2DH2**
G. Fergus-Thompson *Concert*
(12/92) (ASV) ① **CDDCA805**
A. Gavrilov *Concert*
(11/93) (DG) ① **437 532-2GH**
A. Queffélec (r1992) *Concert*
(3/94) (VIRG) ① **VC7 59322-2**
W. Haas (r1964) *Concert*
(10/94) (PHIL) ① **[2] 438 353-2PM2**
P. Rogé (r1974) *Concert*
(10/94) (DECC) ① **[2] 440 836-2DF2**
Vladimir Ashkenazy (r1982) *Concert*
(10/94) (DECC) ① **425 081-2DM**
K. Lifschitz (pp1993) *Concert*
(12/94) (DENO) ① **CO-78908**
B. Berezovsky (r1994) *Concert*
(3/95) (TELD) ① **4509-94539-2**
F-J. Thiollier (r1993) *Concert*
(7/95) (NAXO) ① **8 553008**
A.B. Michelangeli (pp1987) *Concert*
(10/95) (MEMR) ① **[4] 999001**
M. Argerich (r1974) *Concert*
(12/95) (DG) ① **447 438-2GOR**
1. C. Rosenberger *Concert*
(6/86) (DELO) ① **DE3006**
1. W. Gieseking (bp1944) *Concert*
(11/90) (MUSI) ① **MACD-612**
2. Philh, G. Simon (arr. Goossens) *Concert*
(11/91) (CALA) ① **CACD1005**

Jeux d'eau—piano (1901)
V. Perlemuter *Concert* (1/84) (NIMB) ① **NI5005**
C. Rosenberger *Concert* (6/86) (DELO) ① **DE3006**
C. Ortiz *Concert* (6/87) (CARL) ① **PCD846**
P. Crossley *Concert* (7/88) (CRD) ① **CRD3384**
L. Lortie *Concert* (5/89) (CHAN) ① **CHAN8620**
Philh, G. Simon (arr. Viacava) *Concert*
(11/91) (CALA) ① **CACD1004**
M. Lympany *Concert* (1/92) (EMIL) ① **CDZ111**
K. Stott *Concert* (6/92) (CONI) ① **CDCF191**
A. Cortot (r1931) *Concert* (6/92) (BIDD) ① **LHW006**
K.W. Paik *Concert*
(10/92) (DANT) ① **[2] PSG9123/4**
J-Y. Thibaudet *Concert*
(11/92) (DECC) ① **[2] 433 515-2DH2**
G. Fergus-Thompson *Concert*
(12/92) (ASV) ① **CDDCA805**
A. Queffélec (r1992) *Concert*
(3/94) (VIRG) ① **VC7 59322-2**
W. Gieseking (r1923) *Concert*
(3/94) (PEAR) ① **GEMMCD9038**
W. Haas (r1964) *Concert*
(10/94) (PHIL) ① **[2] 438 353-2PM2**
A. Cortot (r1920/23: 2 vers) *Concert*
(10/94) (BIDD) ① **[2] LHW014/5**
P. Rogé (r1974) *Concert*
(10/94) (DECC) ① **[2] 440 836-2DF2**
F-J. Thiollier (r1993) *Concert*
(2/95) (NAXO) ① **8 550683**
L. Zilberstein *Concert* (2/95) (DG) ① **439 927-2GH**
G. Cziffra (r1974) *Concert*
(3/95) (EMI) ① **CDM5 65253-2**
M. Argerich (r1960) *Concert*
(6/95) (DG) ① **447 430-2GOR**

Menuet antique—piano (1895)
P. Crossley (r1983) *Concert*
　　　　(7/88) (CRD) ① **CRD3383**
L. Lortie *Concert*　(10/89) (CHAN) ① **CHAN8647**
K.W. Paik *Concert*
　　　　(10/92) (DANT) ① [2] **PSG9123/4**
J-Y. Thibaudet *Concert*
　　　　(11/92) (DECC) ① [2] **433 515-2DH2**
A. Queffélec *Concert*
　　　　(4/93) (VIRG) ① **VC7 59233-2**
G. Fergus-Thompson *Concert*
　　　　(10/93) (ASV) ① **CDDCA809**
W. Haas (r1964) *Concert*
　　　　(10/94) (PHIL) ① [2] **438 353-2PM2**
P. Rogé (r1974) *Concert*
　　　　(10/94) (DECC) ① [2] **440 836-2DF2**
F-J. Thiollier (r1993) *Concert*
　　　　(2/95) (NAXO) ① **8 550683**

Menuet sur le nom de Haydn—piano (1909)
P. Crossley *Concert*　(7/88) (CRD) ① **CRD3384**
M. Fingerhut *Concert*　(9/88) (CHAN) ① **CHAN8578**
L. Lortie *Concert*　(10/89) (CHAN) ① **CHAN8647**
K.W. Paik *Concert*
　　　　(10/92) (DANT) ① [2] **PSG9123/4**
J-Y. Thibaudet *Concert*
　　　　(11/92) (DECC) ① [2] **433 515-2DH2**
G. Fergus-Thompson *Concert*
　　　　(10/93) (ASV) ① **CDDCA809**
A. Queffélec (r1992) *Concert*
　　　　(3/94) (VIRG) ① **VC7 59322-2**
W. Haas (r1964) *Concert*
　　　　(10/94) (PHIL) ① [2] **438 353-2PM2**
P. Rogé (r1974) *Concert*
　　　　(10/94) (DECC) ① [2] **440 836-2DF2**
F-J. Thiollier (r1993) *Concert*
　　　　(2/95) (NAXO) ① **8 550683**

Miroirs—piano (1905)
1. Noctuelles; 2. Oiseaux tristes; 3. Une barque sur
l'océan; 4. Alborada del gracioso; 5. La vallée des
cloches.
V. Perlemuter *Concert*　(1/84) (NIMB) ① **NI5005**
Y. Nagai (r1983) *Tombeau de Couperin.*
　　　　(6/85) (BIS) ① **BIS-CD246**
P. Crossley (r1983) *Concert*
　　　　(7/88) (CRD) ① **CRD3383**
L. Lortie *Concert*　(10/89) (CHAN) ① **CHAN8647**
M. Nojima *Gaspard de la nuit.*
　　　　(10/90) (REFE) ① **RRCD-35**
K.W. Paik *Concert*
　　　　(10/92) (DANT) ① [2] **PSG9123/4**
J-Y. Thibaudet *Concert*
　　　　(11/92) (DECC) ① [2] **433 515-2DH2**
A. Queffélec *Concert*
　　　　(4/93) (VIRG) ① **VC7 59233-2**
G. Fergus-Thompson *Concert*
　　　　(10/93) (ASV) ① **CDDCA809**
W. Haas (r1964) *Concert*
　　　　(10/94) (PHIL) ① [2] **438 353-2PM2**
P. Rogé (r1974) *Concert*
　　　　(10/94) (DECC) ① [2] **440 836-2DF2**
F-J. Thiollier (r1993) *Concert*
　　　　(2/95) (NAXO) ① **8 550683**
L. Zilberstein *Concert*　(2/95) (DG) ① **439 927-2GH**
4. C. Ortiz *Concert*　(6/87) (CARL) ① **PCD846**
4. D. Lipatti (r1948) *Concert*
　　　　(11/89) (EMI) ① **CDH7 63038-2**
4. J. MacGregor (r1993) *Concert*
　　　　(8/94) (COLL) ① **Coll1404-2**
4, 5. W. Gieseking (r1930s) *Concert*
　　　　(4/91) (PEAR) ① **GEMMCD9449**
5. CBSO, S. Rattle (arr Grainger) *Concert*
　　　　(8/91) (EMI) ① **CDC7 54204-2**
5. Philh, G. Simon (arr. Grainger) *Concert*
　　　　(11/91) (CALA) ① **CACD1004**
5. A. Rubinstein (r1963) *Concert*
　　　　(10/93) (RCA) ① **09026 61446-2**

La parade—piano (c1898)
F-J. Thiollier (r1993) *Concert*
　　　　(2/95) (NAXO) ① **8 550683**

Pavane pour une infante défunte—piano (1899)
V. Perlemuter *Concert*　(1/84) (NIMB) ① **NI5005**
P. Crossley (r1983) *Concert*
　　　　(7/88) (CRD) ① **CRD3383**
E. Johnson, G. Back (arr. Back) *Concert*
　　　　(10/88) (ASV) ① **CDDCA621**
L. Lortie *Concert*　(5/89) (CHAN) ① **CHAN8620**
K. Stott *Concert*　(6/92) (CONI) ① **CDCF191**
K.W. Paik *Concert*
　　　　(10/92) (DANT) ① [2] **PSG9123/4**
G. Fergus-Thompson *Concert*
　　　　(10/93) (ASV) ① **CDWHL2066**
J-Y. Thibaudet *Concert*
　　　　(11/92) (DECC) ① [2] **433 515-2DH2**
A. Queffélec *Concert*
　　　　(4/93) (VIRG) ① **VC7 59233-2**

Vladimir Ashkenazy (r1983) *Concert*
　　　　(7/93) (DECC) ① **430 759-2DM**
J. Bream (r1959; arr Bream) *Concert*
　　　　(8/93) (RCA) ① [28] **09026 61583-2(4)**
G. Fergus-Thompson *Concert*
　　　　(10/93) (ASV) ① **CDDCA809**
J. Bream, J. Williams (r1971; arr Bream) *Concert*
　　　　(11/93) (RCA) ① **09026 61450-2**
A. Gavrilov (r1992) *Concert*
　　　　(11/93) (DG) ① **437 532-2GH**
J. MacGregor (r1993) *Concert*
　　　　(8/94) (COLL) ① **Coll1404-2**
W. Haas (r1964) *Concert*
　　　　(10/94) (PHIL) ① [2] **438 353-2PM2**
P. Rogé (r1974) *Concert*
　　　　(10/94) (DECC) ① [2] **440 836-2DF2**
Vladimir Ashkenazy (r1982) *Concert*
　　　　(10/94) (DECC) ① **425 081-2DM**
F-J. Thiollier (r1993) *Concert*
　　　　(2/95) (NAXO) ① **8 550683**
M. Hess (r1928) *Concert*　(3/95) (BIDD) ① **LHW024**
1, 5. J. Bream (r1959; arr Bream) *Concert*
　　　　(6/94) (RCA) ① **09026 61594-2**

Prélude—piano (1913)
P. Crossley *Concert*　(7/88) (CRD) ① **CRD3384**
L. Lortie *Concert*　(10/89) (CHAN) ① **CHAN8647**
K.W. Paik *Concert*
　　　　(10/92) (DANT) ① [2] **PSG9123/4**
J-Y. Thibaudet *Concert*
　　　　(11/92) (DECC) ① [2] **433 515-2DH2**
G. Fergus-Thompson *Concert*
　　　　(10/93) (ASV) ① **CDDCA809**
A. Queffélec (r1992) *Concert*
　　　　(3/94) (VIRG) ① **VC7 59322-2**
W. Haas (r1964) *Concert*
　　　　(10/94) (PHIL) ① [2] **438 353-2PM2**
P. Rogé (r1974) *Concert*
　　　　(10/94) (DECC) ① [2] **440 836-2DF2**
F-J. Thiollier (r1993) *Concert*
　　　　(2/95) (NAXO) ① **8 550683**

Sérénade grotesque—piano (c1893)
P. Crossley *Concert*　(7/88) (CRD) ① **CRD3384**
L. Lortie *Concert*　(5/89) (CHAN) ① **CHAN8620**
J-Y. Thibaudet *Concert*
　　　　(11/92) (DECC) ① [2] **433 515-2DH2**
G. Fergus-Thompson *Concert*
　　　　(10/93) (ASV) ① **CDDCA809**
A. Queffélec (r1992) *Concert*
　　　　(3/94) (VIRG) ① **VC7 59322-2**
F-J. Thiollier (r1993) *Concert*
　　　　(2/95) (NAXO) ① **8 550683**

Sonatine—piano (1903-5)
P. Crossley (r1983) *Concert*
　　　　(7/88) (CRD) ① **CRD3383**
Netherlands Harp Ens (arr Salzedo: fl/vc/hp) *Concert*
　　　　(5/89) (ETCE) ① **KTC1021**
L. Lortie *Concert*　(10/89) (CHAN) ① **CHAN8647**
K. Stott *Concert*　(6/92) (CONI) ① **CDCF191**
A. Cortot (r1931) *Concert*　(6/92) (BIDD) ① **LHW006**
K.W. Paik *Concert*
　　　　(10/92) (DANT) ① [2] **PSG9123/4**
J-Y. Thibaudet *Concert*
　　　　(11/92) (DECC) ① [2] **433 515-2DH2**
Auréole (r1991: arr Salzedo) *Concert*
　　　　(7/93) (KOCH) ① **37102-2**
G. Fergus-Thompson *Concert*
　　　　(10/93) (ASV) ① **CDDCA809**
A. de Larrocha (r1991) *Concert*
　　　　(12/93) (RCA) ① **09026 60985-2**
A. Queffélec (r1992) *Concert*
　　　　(3/94) (VIRG) ① **VC7 59322-2**
W. Haas (r1964) *Concert*
　　　　(10/94) (PHIL) ① [2] **438 353-2PM2**
P. Rogé (r1973) *Concert*
　　　　(10/94) (DECC) ① [2] **440 836-2DF2**
F-J. Thiollier (r1993) *Concert*
　　　　(2/95) (NAXO) ① **8 550683**
L. Zilberstein *Concert*　(2/95) (DG) ① **439 927-2GH**
G. Cziffra (r1968) *Concert*
　　　　(3/95) (EMI) ① **CDM5 65253-2**
B. Berezovsky (r1994) *Concert*
　　　　(3/95) (TELD) ① **4509-94539-2**
C. Haskil (r1951) *Concert*
　　　　(11/95) (PHIL) ① [3] **442 635-2PM3**
C. Haskil (r1951) *Concert*
　　　　(11/95) (PHIL) ① [12] **442 685-2PM12**
Menuet J. Heifetz, E. Bay (arr Roques: r1947)
Concert　　　　(9/90) (RCA) ① **GD87871**
Menuet J. Heifetz, E. Bay (r1947) *Concert*
　　　　(11/94) (RCA) ① [65] **09026 61778-2(44)**

Le Tombeau de Couperin—piano (1913/17)
1. Prélude; 2. Fugue; 3. Forlane; 4. Rigaudon; 5.
Menuet; 6. Toccata.
Y. Nagai (r1983) *Miroirs.*
　　　　(6/85) (BIS) ① **BIS-CD246**
P. Crossley *Concert*　(7/88) (CRD) ① **CRD3384**

L. Lortie *Concert*　(5/89) (CHAN) ① **CHAN8620**
C. Ousset *Concert*　(7/91) (EMI) ① **CDC7 54158-2**
K. Stott *Concert*　(6/92) (CONI) ① **CDCF191**
K.W. Paik *Concert*
　　　　(10/92) (DANT) ① [2] **PSG9123/4**
J-Y. Thibaudet *Concert*
　　　　(11/92) (DECC) ① [2] **433 515-2DH2**
G. Fergus-Thompson *Concert*
　　　　(12/92) (ASV) ① **CDDCA805**
A. Queffélec *Concert*
　　　　(4/93) (VIRG) ① **VC7 59233-2**
W. Haas (r1964) *Concert*
　　　　(10/94) (PHIL) ① [2] **438 353-2PM2**
P. Rogé (r1973) *Concert*
　　　　(10/94) (DECC) ① [2] **440 836-2DF2**
F-J. Thiollier (r1994) *Concert*
　　　　(7/95) (NAXO) ① **8 553008**
3. G. Fergus-Thompson *Concert*
　　　　(10/92) (ASV) ① **CDWHL2066**
3. A. Rubinstein (r1961) *Concert*
　　　　(10/93) (RCA) ① **09026 61446-2**
6. B. Moiseiwitsch (r1946) *Concert*
　　　　(9/90) (APR) ① [2] **APR7005**
6. G. Cziffra (r1968) *Concert*
　　　　(3/95) (EMI) ① **CDM5 65253-2**

La Valse—piano transcription (1921)
G. Saba *Concert*　(10/87) (CARL) ① **PCD858**
L. Lortie *Concert*　(5/89) (CHAN) ① **CHAN8620**
L. Lortie *Concert*　(9/89) (CHAN) ① **CHAN8733**
B. Berezovsky (r1994) *Concert*
　　　　(3/95) (TELD) ① **4509-94539-2**

La Valse—piano (1920)
F-J. Thiollier (r1994) *Concert*
　　　　(7/95) (NAXO) ① **8 553008**

Valses nobles et sentimentales—piano (1911)
1. Moderé - très franc; 2. Assez lent; 3. Moderé; 4.
Assez animé; 5. Presque lent; 6. Vif; 7. Moins vif; 8.
Lent.
P. Crossley (r1983) *Concert*
　　　　(7/88) (CRD) ① **CRD3383**
L. Lortie *Concert*　(5/89) (CHAN) ① **CHAN8620**
K.W. Paik *Concert*
　　　　(10/92) (DANT) ① [2] **PSG9123/4**
J-Y. Thibaudet *Concert*
　　　　(11/92) (DECC) ① [2] **433 515-2DH2**
G. Fergus-Thompson *Concert*
　　　　(12/92) (ASV) ① **CDDCA805**
A. Rubinstein (r1963) *Concert*
　　　　(10/93) (RCA) ① **09026 61446-2**
A. de Larrocha (r1991) *Concert*
　　　　(12/93) (RCA) ① **09026 60985-2**
A. Queffélec (r1992) *Concert*
　　　　(3/94) (VIRG) ① **VC7 59322-2**
J. MacGregor (r1993) *Concert*
　　　　(8/94) (COLL) ① **Coll1404-2**
W. Haas (r1964) *Concert*
　　　　(10/94) (PHIL) ① [2] **438 353-2PM2**
P. Rogé (r1973) *Concert*
　　　　(10/94) (DECC) ① [2] **440 836-2DF2**
Vladimir Ashkenazy (r1982) *Concert*
　　　　(10/94) (DECC) ① **425 081-2DM**
B. Berezovsky (r1994) *Concert*
　　　　(3/95) (TELD) ① **4509-94539-2**
F-J. Thiollier (r1994) *Concert*
　　　　(7/95) (NAXO) ① **8 553008**
P. Fowke (r1988) *Concert*
　　　　(7/95) (CFP) ① **CD-CFP4667**
1. Empire Brass (r1991) *Concert*
　　　　(11/93) (TELA) ① **CD80301**
6, 7. I. Perlman, S. Sanders (trans. Heifetz) *Concert*
　　　　(2/89) (EMI) ① **CDC7 49604-2**
6, 7. J. Heifetz, E. Bay (r1946) *Concert*
　　　　(11/94) (RCA) ① [65] **09026 61778-2(06)**
6, 7. J. Heifetz, B. Smith (r1965) *Concert*
　　　　(11/94) (RCA) ① [65] **09026 61778-2(45)**

SECTION IV: VOCAL AND CHORAL

Alcyone—cantata (1902) (Wds. E. and E.
Adénis)
1. Air d'Alcyone.
1. M. Atger, Monte Carlo PO, M. Constant *Concert*
　　　　(4/92) (AUVI) ① **V4644**

L' Aurore—tenor, chorus & orchestra (1905)
(Wds. J Barbier)
M. Duguay, Paris Sorbonne Chor, Paris Sorbonne
Orch, J. Grimbert (r1993/4) *Concert*
　　　　(10/95) (MARC) ① **8 223755**

Les Bayadères—soprano, chorus & orchestra (1900)
B. Desnoues, Paris Sorbonne Chor, Paris Sorbonne
Orch, J. Grimbert (r1993/4) *Concert*
　　　　(10/95) (MARC) ① **8 223755**

RAYMOND, Fred *(1900–1954)*
Germany

SECTION V: STAGE WORKS

Maske in Blau—operetta (1937—Berlin) (Lib.
    H. Hentschke & G. Schwann)
Excs M. Schramm, M. Rökk, R. Schock, K-E.
    Mercker, Berlin Deutsche Op Chor, Berlin SO, W.
    Schmidt-Boelcke   (2/91) (EURO) ① **GD69029**

RAZZI, Giovanni *(1531–1611)*
Italy

also known as Serafino Razzi

SECTION IV: VOCAL AND CHORAL

**O Vergin Santa non m'abbandonare—lauda
    (pub 1563)** (Libro primo della laudi spirituali)
Daedalus Ens (r1992) *Concert*
            (11/93) (ACCE) ① **ACC9289D**

READE, Paul *(b 1943)* **England**

SECTION V: STAGE WORKS

**Hobson's Choice—ballet
    (1989—Birmingham)**
Cpte Royal Ballet Sinfonia, B. Wordsworth
            (11/93) (ASV) ① **CDWHL2080**

READING II, John *(c1685–1764)*
England

SECTION III: INSTRUMENTAL

Air for French Horns and Flutes—organ
J. Bate *Concert*   (2/91) (UNIC) ① **DKPCD9096**

REALE, Paul *(b 1943)* **USA**

SECTION II: CHAMBER

Trio—violin, cello and piano (1980)
Mirecourt Trio *Concert*
            (11/91) (MUSI) ① **MACD-635**

REBEL, Jean-Féry *(1666–1747)*
France

SECTION I: ORCHESTRAL

Les Élémens—ballet (1737)
Musiciens du Louvre, M. Minkowski (r1992) *Concert*
            (11/93) (ERAT) ① **2292-45974-2**
Cologne Musica Antiqua, R. Goebel (r1994) *Concert*
            (12/95) (ARCH) ① **445 824-2AH**

SECTION II: CHAMBER

**Les caractères de la danse—fantaisie: 2
    violins and continuo (vv ad lib) (1715)**
Musiciens du Louvre, M. Minkowski (r1992) *Concert*
            (11/93) (ERAT) ① **2292-45974-2**
**Deuxième Suite en D La Ré B mol—violin
    and continuo**
Concert Royal, P. Bismuth (vn/dir) (r1992) *Collasse:
    Racine Canticles.*   (4/94) (ASTR) ① **E8756**
**Le Tombeau de Monsieur de Lully—2
    violins, viola da gamba and continuo (pub
    1712)**
Cologne Musica Antiqua, R. Goebel (r1978) *Concert*
            (1/93) (ARCH) ① **437 086-2AT**
Musiciens du Louvre, M. Minkowski (r1992) *Concert*
            (11/93) (ERAT) ① **2292-45974-2**

REBIKOV, Vladimir Ivanovich
(1866–1920) Russia

SECTION III: INSTRUMENTAL

The Christmas tree—piano
S. Cherkassky (bp1989) *Concert*
            (6/93) (DECC) ① **433 651-2DH**

REBOULOT, Antoine *(b 1914)*
Canada/France

SECTION III: INSTRUMENTAL

**Choral orné sur le 'Pater Noster'
    grégorien—organ**
J-G. Proulx *Concert*   (8/91) (REM) ① **REM311078**

REDHEAD, Robert *(20th cent)*
England

SECTION I: ORCHESTRAL

A Pastoral Symphony—brass band
Sellers Engin Band, P. McCann (r1993) *Concert*
            (11/95) (CHAN) ① **CHAN4531**

REFICE, Licinio *(1885–1954)*
Italy

SECTION IV: VOCAL AND CHORAL

Ombra di Nube—song (Wds. E. Mucci)
C. Muzio, orch, L. Refice (r1935) *Concert*
            (10/89) (NIMB) ① **NI7801**
C. Muzio, orch, L. Refice (r1935) *Concert*
            (4/91) (NIMB) ① **NI7814**

SECTION V: STAGE WORKS

Cecilia—opera (1922—Rome) (Lib. E Mucci)
Grazie sorelle R. Tebaldi, Santa Cecilia Academy
    Orch, A. Erede *Concert*
            (8/91) (DECC) ① [2] **430 481-2DX2**

**REGER, (Johann Baptist Joseph)
Max(imilian)** *(1873–1916)*
Germany

SECTION I: ORCHESTRAL

Eine Ballettsuite in D, Op. 130 (1913)
BRSO, Colin Davis *Hiller Variations.*
            (4/87) (ORFE) ① **C090841A**
Bamberg SO, H. Stein *Hiller Variations.*
            (3/92) (SCHW) ① **311150**
Norrköping SO, L. Segerstam (r1993) *Concert*
            (6/94) (BIS) ① **BIS-CD601**
**Concerto for Piano and Orchestra, Op. 114
    (1910)**
R. Serkin, Philadelphia, E. Ormandy (r1959)
    Prokofiev: Piano Concerto 4.
            (12/91) (SONY) ① **MPK46452**
**Konzert im alten Stil in F—orchestra, Op. 123
    (1912)**
P. Rosenberg, H. Orlovsky, Bamberg SO, H. Stein
    (r1993) *Sinfonietta, Op. 90.*
            (8/94) (KOCH) ① **313542**
**Eine Romantische Suite, after Eichendorff,
    Op. 125 (1912)**
N German RSO, H. Schmidt-Isserstedt *Symphonic
    Poems, Op.128.*   (8/89) (ACAN) ① **43 077**
Berlin RSO, G. Albrecht *Symphonic Poems, Op.128.*
            (8/89) (SCHW) ① **311011**
**Sinfonietta in A—orchestra, Op. 90 (1904–
    05)**
P. Rosenberg, Bamberg SO, H. Stein (r1992/3)
    Konzert im alten Stil.   (8/94) (KOCH) ① **313542**
**Suite in A minor—violin and orchestra, Op.
    103a (1908)**
H. Maile, Berlin RSO, U. Lajovic *Concert*
            (7/90) (SCHW) ① **311122**
**4 Symphonic Poems, after A. Böcklin, Op.
    128 (1913)**
Berlin RSO, G. Albrecht *Romantische Suite.*
            (8/89) (SCHW) ① **311011**
N German RSO, H. Schmidt-Isserstedt *Romantische
    Suite.*   (8/89) (ACAN) ① **43 077**
Concertgebouw, N. Järvi *Symphonic Poems.*
            (3/90) (CHAN) ① **CHAN8794**
Dresden PO, J-P. Weigle *Mozart Variations, Op.132.*
            (11/92) (CAPR) ① **10 307**
Norrköping SO, L. Segerstam (r1993) *Concert*
            (6/94) (BIS) ① **BIS-CD601**
**Variations and Fugue on a Theme of
    Beethoven—orchestra, Op. 86 (1915)** (arr
    cpsr from two-piano work)
LPO, N. Järvi *Bruckner: Symphony 8.*
            (6/90) (CHAN) ① [2] **CHAN8843/4**
Norrköping SO, L. Segerstam (r1993) *Concert*
            (6/94) (BIS) ① **BIS-CD601**
**Variations and Fugue on a theme of J. A.
    Hiller—orchestra, Op. 100 (1907)**
BRSO, Colin Davis *Ballettsuite.*
            (4/87) (ORFE) ① **C090841A**
Concertgebouw, N. Järvi *Symphonic Poems, Op.128.*
            (3/90) (CHAN) ① **CHAN8794**
Bamberg SO, H. Stein *Ballettsuite.*
            (3/92) (SCHW) ① **311150**
Czech PO, V. Neumann (pp1992) *Zemlinsky:
    Maeterlinck Songs, Op.13.*
            (7/93) (SUPR) ① **11 1811-2**
NZ SO, F-P. Decker (r1994) *Mozart Variations, Op.
    132.*   (7/95) (NAXO) ① **8 553079**

**Variations and Fugue on a theme of
    Mozart—orchestra, Op. 132 (1914)**
BRSO, Colin Davis *Hindemith: Symphonic
    Metamorphosis.*   (9/90) (PHIL) ① **422 347-2PH**
Dresden PO, J-P. Weigle *Symphonic Poems,
    Op.128.*   (11/92) (CAPR) ① **10 307**
NYPO, K. Masur (pp1991) *Concert*
            (12/92) (TELD) ① **9031-74007-2**
NZ SO, F-P. Decker (r1994) *Hiller Variations.*
            (7/95) (NAXO) ① **8 553079**

SECTION II: CHAMBER

Piano Trio in B minor, Op. 2 (1891)
H. Maile, Y. Noda, H. Göbel *Piano Trio, op 102.*
            (7/90) (ETCE) ① **KTC1077**
Piano Trio in E minor, Op. 102 (1907-08)
C. Ragaz, R. Häusler, J. Buttrick
            (7/87) (JECK) ① **JD604-2**
Göbel Trio, Berlin *Piano Trio, op 2.*
            (7/90) (ETCE) ① **KTC1077**
**Serenade in D—flute, violin and viola, Op.
    77a (1904)**
P-L. Graf, S. Végh, R. Moog *Flute Serenade, Op.
    141a.*   (10/91) (CLAV) ① **CD50-8104**
A. Noakes, B. Wilde, G. Robertson *Concert*
            (9/94) (ASV) ① **CDDCA875**
**Serenade in G—flute/violin, violin and viola,
    Op. 141a (1915)**
P-L. Graf, S. Végh, R. Moog *Flute Serenade, Op.
    77a.*   (10/91) (CLAV) ① **CD50-8104**
A. Noakes, B. Wilde, G. Robertson *Concert*
            (9/94) (ASV) ① **CDDCA875**
**Sonata for Violin and Piano No. 6 in E minor,
    Op. 122 (1911)**
H. Schneeberger, J-J. Dünki *Violin Sonata 7.*
            (5/93) (JECK) ① **JD649-2**
**Sonata for Violin and Piano No. 7 in C minor,
    Op. 139 (1915)**
H. Schneeberger, J-J. Dünki *Violin Sonata 6.*
            (5/93) (JECK) ① **JD649-2**

SECTION III: INSTRUMENTAL

**Blätter und Blüten—piano: 12 pieces, Op. 58
    (1900)**
J. Martin (r1994) *Concert*
            (10/95) (NAXO) ① **8 550932**
2 Chorale Fantasias—organ, Op. 40 (1899)
1. Wie schön leucht't uns der Morgenstern; 2. Straf
    mich nicht in deinem Zorn.
1. G. Barber (r1990) *Concert*
            (11/93) (PRIO) ① **PRCD315**
3 Chorale Fantasias—organ, Op. 52 (1900)
1. Alle Menschen müssen sterben; 2. Wachet auf,
    ruft uns die Stimme; 3. Hallelujah! Gott zu loben,
    bleibe meine Seelenfreud.
3. D. Matrone *Concert*
            (8/91) (REM) ① **REM311068**
**52 Easy Chorale Preludes—organ, Op. 67
    (1902)**
1. Allein Gott, in der Höh sei Ehr; 2. Alles ist an
    Gottes Segen; 3. Aus tiefer Not schrei ich zu dir; 4.
    Aus meinem Herzens Grunde; 5. Christus, der ist
    mein Leben; 6. Ein fest Burg ist unser Gott; 7. Dir, dir,
    Jehova will ich singen; 8. Erscheinen ist der herrliche
    Tag; 9. Herr Jesu Christ, dich zu uns wend; 10. Es ist
    das Heil uns kommen her; 11. Freu dich sehr, o
    meine Seele; 12. Gott des Himmels und der Erden;
    13. Herr, du willst so schicks mit mir; 14. Herzlich tut
    mich verlangen; 15. Jauchz, Erd und Himmel singe
    hell; 16. Ich dank dir, lieber Herre Gott; 17. Ich will
    dich lieben, meine Stärke; 18. Jerusalem, du
    hochgebaute Stadt; 19. Jesu Leiden, Pein und Not;
    20. Jesus, meine Zuversicht; 21. Jesu, meine
    Freude; 22. Komm, o komm, du Geist des Lebens;
    23. Lobt Gott, ihr Christen alle gleich; 24. Lobe den
    Herren; 25. Machs mit mir, Gott, nach deiner Güt; 26.
    Meinem Jesum lass ich nicht; 27. Nun danket alle
    Gott; 28. Nun freut euch, lieben Christen; 29. Nun
    komm, der Heiden Heiland; 30. O Jesu Christ, du
    Geist des Lebens; 31. O Gott, du frommer Gott; 32.
    O Lamm Gottes, unschuldig; 33. O Welt, ich muss
    dich lassen; 34. Schmücke dich, o liebe Seele; 35.
    Seelenbräutigam; 36. Sollt ich meinem Gott nicht
    singen; 37. Straf mich nicht in deinem Zorn; 38. Valet
    will ich dir geben; 39. Vater unser im Himmelreich;
    40. Vom Himmel hoch da komm ich her; 41. Wachet
    auf! ruft uns die Stimme; 42. Von Gott will ich nicht
    lassen; 43. Warum sollt ich mich denn grämen; 44.
    Was Gott tut, das ist wohlgetan; 45. Wer nur den
    lieben Gott lässt walten; 46. Wer nur den lieben Gott
    lässt walten; 47. Werde munter, mein Gemüte; 48.
    Wer weiss, wie nahe mir mein Ende; 49. Wie wohl ist
    leuchtet der Morgenstern; 50. Wie wohl ist mir, o
    Freund der Seelen; 51. Jesus ist kommen; 52. O wie
    selig seid ihr doch, ihr Frommen.
3. P. Kee *Concert*   (12/92) (CHAN) ① **CHAN9097**

5 Easy Preludes and Fugues—organ, Op. 56
(1904)
1. E; 2. D minor; 3. G; 4. C.
1. K. John *Concert*   (11/92) (PRIO) ① **PRCD370**
Fantasia and Fugue in D minor—organ, Op.
135b (1916)
D. Matrone *Concert*   (8/91) (REM) ① **REM311068**
Introduction and Passacaglia in D
minor—organ (1899)
J. Lancelot *Concert*   (8/88) (PRIO) ① **PRCD228**
I. Tracey *Concert*   (1/90) (CFP) ① **CD-CFP4558**
P. Kee *Concert*   (12/92) (CHAN) ① **CHAN9097**
P. Hurford (r1982) *Concert*
(10/95) (DECC) ① **444 567-2DM**
Introduction, Passacaglia and Fugue in E
minor—organ, Op. 127 (1913)
D. Matrone *Concert*   (8/91) (REM) ① **REM311068**
6 Morceaux—piano, Op. 24 (1898)
J. Martin (r1994) *Concert*
(10/95) (NAXO) ① **8 550932**
Organ Sonata No. 2 in D minor, Op. 60
(1901)
W.R. Schuster *Concert*   (3/86) (MOTE) ① **CD10601**
G. Barber *Concert*   (5/91) (PRIO) ① **PRCD297**
D. Craighead *Vierne: Symphony 6.*
(7/91) (DELO) ① **DE3096**
12 Pieces—organ, Op. 59 (1901)
1. Prelude in E minor; 2. Pastorale in F; 3.
Intermezzo; 4. Canon; 5. Toccata in D minor; 6.
Fugue in D; 7. Kyrie eleison; 8. Gloria in exelsis Deo;
9. Benedictus; 10. Capriccio (Scherzo); 11. Melodia;
12. Te Deum.
5, 6. M.H. Long *Concert*   (4/91) (KOCH) ① **37008-2**
5, 6, 9. Andrew Lucas (r1994) *Concert*
(11/94) (NAXO) ① **8 550955**
9. A. Fletcher *Concert*   (11/91) (MIRA) ① **MRCD903**
9. P. Hurford (r1987) *Concert*
(10/95) (DECC) ① **444 567-2DM**
12 Pieces—organ, Op. 65 (1902)
1. Toccata and Fugue in D minor; 4. Consolation in
E; 7. Prelude in D minor; 8. Fugue in D; 9. Canzone
in E flat; 10. Scherzo in D minor; 11. Toccata in D
minor; 12. Fugue in E.
7. P. Kee *Concert*   (12/92) (CHAN) ① **CHAN9097**
10. G. Weir *Concert*   (12/92) (KOSS) ① **KC1013**
9 Pieces—organ, Op. 129 (1913)
1. Toccata in D minor; 2. Fugue in D minor; 4.
Melodia in B flat; 5. Capriccio in G minor; 7.
Intermezzo in F minor.
7. P. Kee *Concert*   (12/92) (CHAN) ① **CHAN9097**
7 Pieces—organ, Op. 145 (1915-16)
1. Trauerode; 2. Dankpsalm; 3. Weihnachten; 4.
Passion; 5. Ostern; 6. Pfingsten; 7. Siegesfeier.
2. S. Cleobury *Concert*   (3/87) (PRIO) ① **PRCD185**
2. Andrew Lucas (r1991) *Concert*
(2/94) (MIRA) ① **MRCD905**
8 Preludes and Fugues—violin, Op. 117
(1909-12)
1. B minor; 2. G minor; 3. E minor; 4. G minor
(Chaconne); 5. G; 6. D minor; 7. A minor; 8. E minor.
1-3, 5-8. M. Marinkovic (r1993) *Preludes and Fugues,*
Op. 131a.   (9/94) (ASV) ① **[2] CDDCA876**
6 Preludes and Fugues—violin, Op. 131a
(1914)
1. A minor; 2. D minor. 3. G; 4. G minor; 5. D; 6. E
minor.
M. Marinkovic (r1993) *Preludes and Fugues, Op.*
117.   (9/94) (ASV) ① **[2] CDDCA876**
7 Silhouetten—piano, Op. 53 (1900)
J. Martin (r1994) *Concert*
(10/95) (NAXO) ① **8 550932**
Suite in G minor—organ, Op. 92 (1905)
Y. Bashmet (va/dir), Moscow Sols Ens (orch
Poltoratsky) *Concert*   (6/91) (RCA) ① **RD60464**
3 Suites—cello, Op. 131c (1915)
1. G; 2. D minor; 3. A minor.
1. E. Feuermann (r1939) *Concert*
(10/91) (PEAR) ① **GEMMCD9443**
1. M. Haimovitz *Concert*
(1/92) (DG) ① **431 813-2GH**
3 Suites—viola, Op. 131d (1915)
1. G minor; 2. D; 3. E minor.
G. Robertson *Concert*   (9/94) (ASV) ① **CDDCA875**
Variations and Fugue on a theme of J. S
Bach—piano, Op. 81 (1904)
W. Harden *Schumann: Humoreske.*
(3/87) (MARC) ① **8 220408**
A. Schiff (pp1994) *Concert*
(11/95) (TELD) ① **4509-99051-2**

SECTION IV: VOCAL AND CHORAL
An das Meer—chorus
Orphei Drängar Ch, E. Ericson *Concert*
(7/88) (BIS) ① **BIS-CD383**
An die Hoffnung—contralto and orchestra,
Op. 124 (1912) (Wds. Hölderlin)
D. Fischer-Dieskau, Hamburg PO, G. Albrecht
Concert   (2/91) (ORFE) ① **C209901A**
K. Mattila, BPO, C. Abbado (pp1993) *Concert*
(3/95) (SONY) ① **SK53975**
3 Duets—soprano, alto and piano, Op. 111a
(1909)
1. Waldesstille; 2. Frühlingsfeier; 3. Abendgang.
J. Banse, B. Fassbaender, C. Garben (r1993)
Concert   (8/95) (SCHW) ① **312592**
Der Einsiedler—baritone, chorus and
orchestra, Op. 144a (1915) (Wds. J. von
Eichendorff)
D. Fischer-Dieskau, Hamburg St Michaelis Ch,
Hamburg Monteverdi Ch, Hamburg PO, G. Albrecht
Concert   (2/91) (ORFE) ① **C209901A**
3 Geistliche Gesänge—5vv (pub 1912)
1. Mein Odem ist schwach; 2. Ach, Herr, stafe mich
nicht; 3. O Tod, wie bitte bist du.
Danish Nat Rad Ch, S. Parkman *Concert*, Op. 39.
(10/94) (CHAN) ① **CHAN9298**
8 Geistliche Gesänge—4-8vv, Op. 138
(1914)
1. Der Mensch lebt und bestehet nur eine kleine Zeit;
2. Morgengesang; 3. Nachtlied; 4. Unser lieben
Frauen Traum; 5. Kreuzfahrerlied; 6. Das Agnus Dei;
7. Schlachtgesang; 8. Wir glauben an einen Gott.
Frankfurt Voc Ens, R. Otto *Martin: Mass.*
(10/90) (BAYE) ① **BR100084**
3 Gesänge—6vv a cappella, Op. 39 (1899)
Danish Nat Rad Ch, S. Parkman *Geistliche Gesänge,*
Op. 110.   (10/94) (CHAN) ① **CHAN9298**
Hymnus der Liebe—baritone/mezzo soprano
and orchestra, Op. 136 (1914) (Wds. L.
Jacobwoski)
D. Fischer-Dieskau, Hamburg PO, G. Albrecht
Concert   (2/91) (ORFE) ① **C209901A**
6 Lieder, Op. 31 (1898) (Wds. A. Ritter)
2. Ich glaub', lieber Schatz.
2. E. Schwarzkopf, M. Raucheisen (bp1944) *Concert*
(5/93) (ACAN) ① **43 128**
15 Lieder, Op. 55 (1900-01)
11. E. Schwarzkopf, M. Raucheisen (bp1944)
Concert   (5/93) (ACAN) ① **43 128**
16 Lieder, Op. 62 (1901)
2. Waldseligkeit (wds. R. Dehmel).
2. E. Schwarzkopf, M. Raucheisen (bp1944) *Concert*
(5/93) (ACAN) ① **43 128**
17 Lieder, Op. 70 (1902-02)
1. Die Verschmähte (wds. G. Falke).
8. E. Schwarzkopf, M. Raucheisen (bp1943) *Concert*
(5/93) (ACAN) ① **43 128**
Pater noster—11vv a capella (1911)
Lower Rhine Choral Soc, H. Schmitt *Concert*
(2/90) (SCHW) ① **313001**
Requiem—contralto/baritone, chorus and
orchestra, Op. 144b (1915) (Wds. Hebbel)
D. Fischer-Dieskau, Hamburg St Michaelis Ch,
Hamburg Monteverdi Ch, Hamburg PO, G. Albrecht
Concert   (2/91) (ORFE) ① **C209901A**
60 Schlichte Weisen—Lieder: voice and
piano, Op. 76 (1903-12)
3. Waldeinsamkeit; 8. Der Brief (wds. R. Burns/T.
Storm); 12. Mit Rosen bestreut (wds. Bern); 45.
Lutschemäulchen (wds. Boelitz); 47. Schlaf's ein
(wds. Boelitz); 49. Ein Tänzchen (wds. Boelitz); 52.
Maria Wiegenlied (wds. Boelitz); 59. Zum Schlafen
(wds. Schellenberg).
3, 8. C. Ludwig, G. Moore *Concert*
(9/92) (EMI) ① **[4] CMS7 64074-2(1)**
52. L. Howard (trans pf: cpsr) *Concert*
(12/86) (HYPE) ① **CDA66090**
52. C. Muzio, orch, L. Molajoli (r1935: Ital) *Concert*
(4/91) (NIMB) ① **NI7814**
52. E. Grümmer, H. Diez (r1948) *Concert*
(4/92) (EMI) ① **[7] CHS7 69741-2(4)**
Wiegenlied—Lied, Op. 142/1 (1915)
E. Schwarzkopf, M. Raucheisen (bp1943) *Concert*
(6/87) (ACAN) ① **43 801**

REGGIO, Pietro (Francesco)
(1632–1685) Italy

SECTION IV: VOCAL AND CHORAL
By Heav'n I'll tell her boldly—song (pub
1680) (Wds Cowley)
Consort of Musicke, A. Rooley (lte/dir) (r1993)
Concert   (1/95) (MOSC) ① **070986**

I thought, I'll swear—song (pub 1680) (Wds
Cowley)
Consort of Musicke, A. Rooley (lte/dir) (r1993)
Concert   (1/95) (MOSC) ① **070986**
Now by my Love—song (pub 1680) (Wds
Cowley)
Consort of Musicke, A. Rooley (lte/dir) (r1993)
Concert   (1/95) (MOSC) ① **070986**
Then like some wealthy Island—song (pub
1680) (Wds Cowley)
Consort of Musicke, A. Rooley (lte/dir) (r1993)
Concert   (1/95) (MOSC) ① **070986**
Though all thy gestures—song (pub 1680)
(Wds Cowley)
Consort of Musicke, A. Rooley (lte/dir) (r1993)
Concert   (1/95) (MOSC) ① **070986**
'Tis a strnge kind of Ignorance—song (pub
1680) (Wds Cowley)
Consort of Musicke, A. Rooley (lte/dir) (r1993)
Concert   (1/95) (MOSC) ① **070986**
'Tis well, 'tis well with them—song (pub
1680) (Wds Cowley)
Consort of Musicke, A. Rooley (lte/dir) (r1993)
Concert   (1/95) (MOSC) ① **070986**
Unhurt, untouch't—song (pub 1680) (Wds
Cowley)
Consort of Musicke, A. Rooley (lte/dir) (r1993)
Concert   (1/95) (MOSC) ① **070986**

REGIS, Johannes (c1430–c1485)
The Netherlands

SECTION IV: VOCAL AND CHORAL
O admirabile commercium/Verbum
caro—Christmas motet: 5vv
New London Chmbr Ch, J. Wood *Concert*
(3/93) (AMON) ① **CD-SAR56**

REGNARD, François
(c1530–c1600) France

SECTION IV: VOCAL AND CHORAL
Bois Janin à moi—chanson: 6vv (pub 1574)
(Wds Ronsard)
C. Janequin Ens, D. Visse (r1993) *Concert*
(2/95) (HARM) ① **HMC90 1491**
Contre mon gré—chanson: 5vv (pub 1574)
(Wds Ronsard)
C. Janequin Ens, D. Visse (r1993) *Concert*
(2/95) (HARM) ① **HMC90 1491**
Dedans ce bois—chanson: 5vv (pub 1574)
(Wds Ronsard)
C. Janequin Ens, D. Visse (r1993) *Concert*
(2/95) (HARM) ① **HMC90 1491**
Heureux ennui—chanson: 5vv (pub 1574)
(Wds Ronsard)
C. Janequin Ens, D. Visse (r1993) *Concert*
(2/95) (HARM) ① **HMC90 1491**
Las, toi qui es de moi—chanson: 5vv (pub
1574) (Wds Ronsard)
C. Janequin Ens, D. Visse (r1993) *Concert*
(2/95) (HARM) ① **HMC90 1491**
Mon triste coeur—chanson: 5vv (pub 1574)
(Wds Ronsard)
C. Janequin Ens, D. Visse (r1993) *Concert*
(2/95) (HARM) ① **HMC90 1491**
Ni nuit ne jour—chanson: 5vv (pub 1574)
(Wds Ronsard)
C. Janequin Ens, D. Visse (r1993) *Concert*
(2/95) (HARM) ① **HMC90 1491**

REGONDI, Giulio (1822–1872)
Italy

SECTION II: CHAMBER
12 Leisure moments—treble concertina and
piano (pub 1857)
1. Andante—Larghetto; 2. Andantino; 4. Allegretto; 5.
Andante cantabile—Allegretto; 7.
Allegretto—Larghetto; 8. Allegretto giocoso.
2, 3, 4, 5, 7, 8. D. Rogers, J. Lustman (r1994)
Concert   (12/95) (BRID) ① **BCD9055**
Morceau de Concert in B flat, '(Les)
Oiseaux'—concertina and piano, Op. 12
(?1851)
D. Rogers, J. Lustman (r1993) *Concert*
(12/95) (BRID) ① **BCD9039**
Serenade in A—concertina and piano
D. Rogers, J. Lustman (r1993) *Concert*
(12/95) (BRID) ① **BCD9039**

SECTION III: INSTRUMENTAL

10 Etudes—guitar (rediscovered 1989)
EXCERPTS: 1. C; 2. A minor; 3. A; 4. E; 5. A; 6. D
minor; 7. D; 8. G; 9. E; 10. A.
D. Starobin (r1992) *Concert*
(12/95) (BRID) ① **BCD9039**

Introduction and Caprice—guitar, Op. 23
T. Kerstens (r1992-3) *Concert*
(9/94) (CONI) ① **CDCF518**
D. Starobin (r1994) *Concert*
(12/95) (BRID) ① **BCD9055**

Remembrance—baritone concertina
D. Rogers (r1994) *Concert*
(12/95) (BRID) ① **BCD9055**

Rêverie nocturne—guitar, Op. 19 (pub
1864)
D. Starobin (r1994) *Concert*
(12/95) (BRID) ① **BCD9055**

SECTION IV: VOCAL AND CHORAL

Absence—song: 1v and piano (Wds. C M)
D'A. Fortunato, J. Lustman (r1994) *Concert*
(12/95) (BRID) ① **BCD9055**

**As Slowly Part the Shades of Night—song:
1v & piano** (Wds. N Smith)
D'A. Fortunato, J. Lustman (r1994) *Concert*
(12/95) (BRID) ① **BCD9055**

L' Avviso—song: 1v and piano (Wds. anon)
D'A. Fortunato, J. Lustman (r1994) *Concert*
(12/95) (BRID) ① **BCD9055**

**Tell me heart! Why so depressing—song: 1v
and piano** (Wds. G Stirling)
D'A. Fortunato, J. Lustman (r1994) *Concert*
(12/95) (BRID) ① **BCD9055**

REICH, Steve (Michael) (b 1936)
USA

SECTION I: ORCHESTRAL

The Four Sections
LSO, M. Tilson Thomas *Music for Mallet Instruments,
Voices and Organ.* (6/91) (NONE) ① **7559-79220-2**

Variations—wind, strings and keyboards
(1980)
San Francisco SO, E. de Waart *J. Adams: Shaker
Loops.* (9/86) (PHIL) ① **412 214-2PH**

SECTION II: CHAMBER

Clapping music—2 performers (1972)
The Sixteen, H. Christophers *Concert*
(4/92) (COLL) ① **Coll1287-2**

Music for Pieces of Wood (1973)
Amadinda Perc Group *Concert*
(6/91) (HUNG) ① **HCD31288**

4 Organs (1970)
Piano Circus (r1992) *Concert*
(1/94) (ARGO) ① **440 294-2ZH**

6 Pianos (1973)
S. Reich and Musicians *Concert*
(9/89) (DG) ① [2] **427 428-2GC2**
Piano Circus *Riley: In C.*
(6/91) (ARGO) ① **430 380-2ZH**

Reed Phase—saxophone and tape (1967)
J. Gibson (r1992) *Concert*
(6/93) (PNT) ① **434 873-2PTH**

Sextet—4 percussion instrs and 2 pianos
(1984-85)
Amadinda Perc Group *Concert*
(6/91) (HUNG) ① **HCD31358**

SECTION IV: VOCAL AND CHORAL

Drumming—2vv, piccolo and percussion
(1970-71)
S. Reich and Musicians *Concert*
(9/89) (DG) ① [2] **427 428-2GC2**

**Music for Mallet Instruments, Voices and
Organ** (1973)
S. Reich and Musicians *Concert*
(9/89) (DG) ① [2] **427 428-2GC2**
S. Reich and Musicians *Four Sections.*
(6/91) (NONE) ① **7559-79220-2**
Amadinda Perc Group *Concert*
(6/91) (HUNG) ① **HCD31358**

REICHA, Antoine(-Joseph)
(1770-1836) Bohemia/France

SECTION II: CHAMBER

**2 Andantes and Adagio—cor anglais, flute,
clarinet, bassoon and horn** (1817-19)
1. Andante No. 1 in E flat; 2. Andante No. 2 in F; 3.
Adagio in D minor.
1. A. Schweitzer Qnt (r1988) *Concert*
(3/91) (CPO) ① **CPO999 029-2**

---

3. A. Schweitzer Qnt *Concert*
(3/89) (CPO) ① **CPO999 024-2**

**6 Quartets for Flute, Violin, Viola and Cello,
Op. 98** (c1813)
1. G minor; 2. C; 3. G; 6. G.
6. Adieux (r1992) *Oboe Quintet, Op.107.*
(9/93) (DHM) ① **05472 77287-2**

Quintet for Bassoon and String Quartet
(1826)
Daniel Smith, Coull Qt *Concert*
(10/88) (ASV) ① **CDDCA613**

Quintet for Cello and String Quartet in E
(1807)
A. Bylsma, Archibudelli (r1992) *Cello and Viola
Quintets.* (10/93) (SONY) ① **SK53118**

**Quintet for Clarinet and Strings in B flat, Op.
89** (c1809)
C. Neidich, Archibudelli (r1993) *Concert*
(9/95) (SONY) ① **SK57968**

**Quintet for Oboe and String Quartet in F, Op.
107** (pub 1829)
Adieux (r1992) *Flute Quintets, Op.98.*
(9/93) (DHM) ① **05472 77287-2**

**6 Quintets for Cello or Viola and String
Quartet** (1805-07) (Nos 1-2 for vc; 3-6 for va)
1. A; 2. F.
1, 2. A. Bylsma, Archibudelli (r1992) *Cello Quintet*
(1807). (10/93) (SONY) ① **SK53118**

**12 Trios—two horns and bassoon/cello, Op.
93** (pub 1815-20)
Z. Tylšar, B. Tylšar, F. Herman *Concert*
(3/93) (SUPR) ① **11 1445-2**

6 Wind Quintets, Op. 88 (1811-17)
1. E minor; 2. E flat; 3. G; 4. D minor; 5. B flat; 6. F.
1, 5. A. Schweitzer Qnt (r1986) *Wind Quintets,
Op.99.* (3/89) (CPO) ① **CPO999 022-2**
3, 4. A. Schweitzer Qnt (r1987) *Wind Quintets,
Op.91.* (3/89) (CPO) ① **CPO999 023-2**
5. Prague Acad Wind Qnt *Wind Quintets, Op.91.*
(3/91) (HYPE) ① **CDA66379**
6. A. Schweitzer Qnt (r1988) *Concert*
(3/91) (CPO) ① **CPO999 026-2**

6 Wind Quintets, Op. 91 (pub ?1817-19)
1. C; 2. A minor; 3. D; 4. G minor; 5. A; 6. C minor.
1. A. Schweitzer Qnt (r1988) *Concert*
(3/91) (CPO) ① **CPO999 027-2**
3. A. Schweitzer Qnt (r1988) *Concert*
(3/91) (CPO) ① **CPO999 026-2**
4. A. Schweitzer Qnt (r1989) *Concert*
(3/89) (CPO) ① **CPO999 024-2**
5. A. Schweitzer Qnt (r1987) *Wind Quintets, Op.88.*
(3/89) (CPO) ① **CPO999 023-2**
5. Prague Acad Wind Qnt *Wind Quintets, Op.88.*
(3/91) (HYPE) ① **CDA66379**
6. A. Schweitzer Qnt (r1988) *Concert*
(3/91) (CPO) ① **CPO999 029-2**

6 Wind Quintets, Op. 99 (1811-19)
1. C; 2. F minor; 3. F; 4. D; 5. B minor; 6. G.
2. A. Schweitzer Qnt (r1986) *Wind Quintets, Op.88.*
(3/89) (CPO) ① **CPO999 022-2**
4, 5. A. Schweitzer Qnt (r1987)
(3/89) (CPO) ① **CPO999 025-2**
6. A. Schweitzer Qnt (r1988) *Concert*
(3/91) (CPO) ① **CPO999 027-2**

6 Wind Quintets, Op. 100 (71820)
1. F; 2. D minor; 3. E flat; 4. E minor; 5. A minor; 6. B
flat.
1. A. Schweitzer Qnt (r1987) *Concert*
(3/91) (CPO) ① **CPO999 024-2**
3. A. Schweitzer Qnt (r1988) *Concert*
(3/91) (CPO) ① **CPO999 026-2**
5. Aulos Wind Qnt *Concert*
(10/89) (SCHW) ① **310011**
5. A. Schweitzer Qnt (r1988) *Concert*
(3/91) (CPO) ① **CPO999 027-2**
6. A. Schweitzer Qnt (r1988) *Concert*
(3/91) (CPO) ① **CPO999 029-2**

REILLY, David (20th Cent)
England

SECTION II: CHAMBER

Aviator—harmonica and strings
T. Reilly, ASMF Chbr Ens *Concert*
(12/86) (CHAN) ① **CHAN8486**

REILLY, Tommy (Rundle) (b 1919)
Canada/England

SECTION III: INSTRUMENTAL

Serenade—harmonica
T. Reilly *Concert* (12/86) (CHAN) ① **CHAN8486**

REIMANN, Aribert (b 1936)
Germany

SECTION III: INSTRUMENTAL

Variations—piano (1979)
D. Levine *Unrevealed.*
(3/89) (CPO) ① **CPO999 031-2**

SECTION IV: VOCAL AND CHORAL

Kinderlieder—soprano and piano (1961)
(Wds. Reinert)
C. Schäfer, A. Bauni *Concert*
(9/90) (WERG) ① **WER60183-50**

**Nacht-Räume—piano duet with soprano
voice** (1988)
C. Schäfer, A. Bauni, A. Reimann *Concert*
(9/90) (WERG) ① **WER60183-50**

3 Poems of Michelangelo—1v, piano (1985)
1. Sol io ardendo; 2. Che fie di me?; 3. L'alma
inquieta e confusa.
D. Fischer-Dieskau, A. Reimann (r1986)
Shostakovich: Michelangelo Suite, op. 145.
(12/95) (TELD) ① **4509-97460-2**

**Shine and Dark—baritone and piano left-
hand** (wds. J. Joyce)
D. Fischer-Dieskau, A. Reimann *Unrevealed.*
(10/91) (ORFE) ① **C212901A**

**9 Sonnets of Louis Labé—mezzo-soprano
and piano** (1986) (Wds. trans Fahrenbach-
Wachendorff)
L. Himmelheber, A. Bauni *Concert*
(9/90) (WERG) ① **WER60183-50**

Unrevealed—baritone and string quartet
(1980) (Wds. Lord Byron to Augusta Leigh)
R. Salter, Kreuzberger Qt *Variations.*
(3/89) (CPO) ① **CPO999 031-2**
D. Fischer-Dieskau, Cherubini Qt *Shine and Dark.*
(10/91) (ORFE) ① **C212901A**

REIMANN, Heinrich (1850-1906)
Germany

SECTION IV: VOCAL AND CHORAL

Spinnerliedchen—Lied
E. Schumann-Heink, J. Hofmann (r1913) *Concert*
(2/91) (NIMB) ① **NI7811**

REINAGLE, Alexander
(1756-1809) USA

SECTION III: INSTRUMENTAL

4 Philadelphia Sonatas—piano
1. D; 2. E.
1, 2. W. Naboré (r1992) *Concert*
(8/94) (DORO) ① **DRC3001**

REINCKEN, Johann Adam
(1623-1722) Netherlands or
Germany

SECTION II: CHAMBER

**Hortus musicus—suites: 2 vns, va da gamba
and continuo** (pub 1687)
EXCERPTS: 1. Sonata I (arr Bach as Sonata,
BWV965).
1. Cologne Musica Antiqua, R. Goebel (r1980)
Concert (1/93) (ARCH) ① **437 089-2AT**

SECTION III: INSTRUMENTAL

Fugue in G minor—organ
G. Leonhardt *Concert* (10/94) (SONY) ① **SK53371**

REINDL, Constantin (1738-1799)
Germany

SECTION I: ORCHESTRAL

**Sinfonia Concertante in D—violin and
orchestra** (c1789)
J-L. Garcia, ECO, H. Griffiths *Concert*
(9/89) (NOVA) ① **150 031-2**

REINECKE, Carl (Heinrich
Carsten) (1824-1910) Germany

SECTION I: ORCHESTRAL

**Concerto for Piano and Orchestra No. 1 in F
sharp minor, Op. 72** (1879)
M. Ponti, Luxembourg RSO, P. Cao *Concert*
(5/93) (VOX) ① **115713-2**

SECTION II: CHAMBER

3 Phantasiestücke—viola & piano, Op. 43
G. Caussé, F-R. Duchâble (r1994) *Concert*
(7/95) (EMI) ① **CDC5 55166-2**
Piano Trio in A minor—piano, oboe and horn, Op. 188 (1887)
R. Requejo, I. Goritzki, B. Tuckwell *Herzogenberg: Piano Trio in D, Op. 61.*
(6/87) (CLAV) ① **CD50-0803**

SECTION IV: VOCAL AND CHORAL

4 Duets—2 sopranos & piano, Op. 12 (1847)
1. Winter (R von Liliencron); 2. Trennung (Heine); 3. Im Wald (Vogl); 4. Das Veilchen (Haltaus).
E. Mathis, H. Komatsu, C. Garben (r1994) *Concert*
(11/95) (CPO) ① **CPO999 262-2**
6 Duets—two female v & piano, Op. 109 (1870) (Wds. J Altmann)
1. Duften nicht Jasminenlauben; 2. Volkslied; 3. Die Mühle im Thale; 4. Abendfriede; 5. Du Himmel so blau; 6. Grüss Gott, Du goldgrüner Hain.
E. Mathis, H. Komatsu, C. Garben (r1994) *Concert*
(11/95) (CPO) ① **CPO999 262-2**

REINHARDT, Heinrich (1865–1922) Austria

SECTION V: STAGE WORKS

The Spring Maid—operetta (1910) (Lyrics Harry B. Smith)
EXCERPTS: 1. The Three Trees; 2. Two Little Love Bees; 3. Day Dreams, Visions of Bliss.
1-3. C. McDonald, T. McNaughton, Orig Broadway Cast (r1911) *Concert*
(5/94) (PEAR) ① [3] **GEMMCDS9053/5**

REIS, Dilermando (1918–1976) Brazil

SECTION III: INSTRUMENTAL

Courante—lute
L. Kirchhof *Concert* (11/92) (SONY) ① **SK48068**
Si ela perguntar—slow waltz: guitar
M. Kayath *Concert* (9/87) (CARL) ① **PCD853**

REISSIGER, Carl Gottlieb (1798–1859) Germany

SECTION I: ORCHESTRAL

Concertino for Clarinet and Orchestra in E flat, Op. 63
D. Klöcker, Berlin RSO, J. López-Cobos *Concert*
(11/88) (SCHW) ① **311045**

SECTION IV: VOCAL AND CHORAL

Abendständchen an die Geliebte—Lied (Wds. Heine)
D. Fischer-Dieskau, K. Wallendorf, H. Höll *Concert*
(4/88) (ORFE) ① **C153861A**
Heimweh—Lied (Wds. Rasmus)
D. Fischer-Dieskau, K. Wallendorf, H. Höll *Concert*
(4/88) (ORFE) ① **C153861A**

REIZENSTEIN, Franz (Theodor) (1911–1968) Germany/England

SECTION II: CHAMBER

Arabesques—clarinet and piano, Op. 47 (1968)
T. King, C. Benson *Concert*
(11/89) (HYPE) ① **CDA66044**
Quintet for piano and strings, Op. 23 (1948)
Melos Ens *Concert* (11/91) (CNTI) ① **CCD1024**
Sonata for Violin and Piano, Op. 20 (1945)
E. Gruenberg, D. Wilde *Concert*
(11/91) (CNTI) ① **CCD1024**
Sonatina for Oboe and Piano, Op. 11 (1937)
E. Gruenberg, D. Wilde *Concert*
(11/91) (CNTI) ① **CCD1024**

SECTION III: INSTRUMENTAL

Legend—piano, Op. 24 (1949)
P. Martin *Concert* (2/90) (CNTI) ① **CCD1007**
Piano Sonata No. 2 in A flat, Op. 40 (1964)
P. Martin *Concert* (2/90) (CNTI) ① **CCD1007**
Scherzo in A—piano, Op. 21 (1947)
P. Martin *Concert* (2/90) (CNTI) ① **CCD1007**
Suite—piano, Op. 6 (1936)
P. Martin *Concert* (2/90) (CNTI) ① **CCD1007**
Variations on 'The Lambeth Walk'—piano
(trans P. Martin from cpsr's own recording)
P. Martin *Concert* (2/90) (CNTI) ① **CCD1007**

REKAŠIUS, Antanas (b 1928) Lithuania/USSR

SECTION I: ORCHESTRAL

Music for Strings (1992)
Ostrobothnian CO, J. Kangas (r1994) *Concert*
(11/95) (FINL) ① **4509-97893-2**

RENARD, Jean (19th Cent) France

SECTION II: CHAMBER

Marche grotesque—four clarinets
4. M. Gomez, C. Draper, H.P. Draper, Renard Cl Qt, R. Kell, F. Thurston, R. Clarke, Griller Qt, A. Umbach, C. Esberger, R. Quaranta, A. Giammatteo, F.J. Brissett, B. Goodman, G. Hamelin, A. Périer, H. Lefèbvre, anon, wind band, SO, C. Raybould, G. Moore, Budapest Qt, orch, P. Coppola, Garde Republicaine Band (rc1915) *Concert*
(2/94) (CLRI) ① **CC0005**

RENAUD, Albert (1855–?) France

SECTION III: INSTRUMENTAL

Toccata in D minor—organ
J. Parker-Smith *Concert*
(3/89) (ASV) ① **CDDCA610**

RENTARO, Taki (1879–1903) Japan

SECTION IV: VOCAL AND CHORAL

Kojyo No Tsuki—song
A. A. Meyers, S. Rivers (r1993; arr Sigeaki: vn/pf) *Concert*
(4/95) (RCA) ① **09026 62546-2**

RESPIGHI, Ottorino (1879–1936) Italy

SECTION I: ORCHESTRAL

Adagio con variazioni—cello and orchestra (1920) (arr from early work for cello and piano)
R. Wallfisch, Bournemouth Sinfonietta, T. Vásáry *Concert* (4/92) (CHAN) ① **CHAN8913**
M. Maisky, Paris Orch, S. Bychkov *Concert*
(10/92) (DG) ① **435 781-2GH**
A. Baillie, Philh, G. Simon *Concert*
(3/93) (CALA) ① **CACD1007**
G. Cassadó, Vienna Pro Musica Orch, J. Perlea (r1950s) *Concert* (11/93) (VOX) ① [2] **CDX2 5502**
M. Rostropovich, Moscow PO, G. Rozhdestvensky (pp1964) *Concert* (7/94) (RUSS) ① **RDCD11104**
Antiche danze ed arie per liuto, 'Ancient Airs and Dances' (based on lute works by Molinaro & Galilei)
SUITE NO. 1 (1917): 1a. Balletto detto 'Il Conte Orlando' (Molinaro); 1b. Gagliaiarda (V. Galilei); 1c. Villanella (Anon: c1600); 1d. Finale: Passo mezzo e mascherada (Anon: c1600). SUITE NO. 2 (1924): 2a. 'Laura Soave'—Balletto con gagliarda, saltarello e canario (Caroso); 2b. Danza rustica (Besard); 2c. 'Campanae Parisiennses'—Aria: Les cloches de Paris; 2d. Bergamasca (Gianoncelli). SUITE NO. 3 (1932: strings only); 3a. Italiana (Anon: c1600); 3b. Arie di corte (Besard); 3c. Siciliana (Anon: c1600); 3d. Passacaglia (Roncalli).
Lausanne CO, J. López-Cobos *Botticelli Pictures.*
(9/92) (TELA) ① **CD80309**
St Paul CO, H. Wolff (r1994) *Concert*
(1/95) (TELD) ① **4509-91729-2**
1a-d, 3a-d Orpheus CO (r1991) *Concert*
(7/93) (DG) ① **437 533-2GH**
1b La Scala Orch, A. Toscanini (r1920) *Concert*
(11/92) (RCA) ① **GD60315**
3a-d BPO, H. von Karajan *Concert*
(1/85) (DG) ① **413 822-2GH**
3a-d Accademia Bizantina, C. Chiarappa (vn/dir) (r1993) *Concert* (3/95) (DENO) ① **CO-78916**
Ballata delle gnomidi, 'Ballad of the Gnomes'—orchestra (1918-20)
Philh, G. Simon *Concert*
(3/93) (CALA) ① **CACD1007**
BBC PO, E. Downes (r1993) *Concert*
(4/94) (CHAN) ① **CHAN9232**
Belfagor—concert overture (1925) (based on themes from opera)
BBC PO, E. Downes (r1994) *Concert*
(1/95) (CHAN) ① **CHAN9311**

Burlesca—orchestra (1906)
Bratislava RSO, Adriano *Concert*
(5/92) (MARC) ① **8 223348**
Carnival Overture—orchestra (1913)
Bratislava RSO, Adriano *Concert*
(5/92) (MARC) ① **8 223348**
Chaconne—violin, organ and strings (1908) (arr/ed after Vitali)
I. Turban, ECO, M. Viotti *Concert*
(10/91) (CLAV) ① **CD50-9017**
Concerto a cinque—ob, tpt, vn, db, pf and strings (1933)
I. Turban, N. Black, G. Ashton, S. Williams, I. Watson, ECO, M. Viotti *Concert*
(10/91) (CLAV) ① **CD50-9017**
Concerto all'antica—violin and orchestra (pub 1923)
I. Turban, ECO, M. Viotti *Concert*
(10/91) (CLAV) ① **CD50-9017**
A. Cappelletti, Philh, M. Bamert (r1993) *Gregorian Concerto.* (8/94) (SCHW) ① **311242**
Concerto for Piano and Orchestra in A minor (1902)
G. Tozer, BBC PO, E. Downes (r1994) *Concerto in modo misolidio.* (8/94) (CHAN) ① **CHAN9285**
K. Scherbakov, Slovak RSO, H. Griffiths (r1994) *Concert* (11/95) (NAXO) ① **8 553207**
Concerto gregoriano—violin and orchestra (1921)
L. Mordkovitch, BBC PO, E. Downes (r1993) *Concert*
(4/94) (CHAN) ① **CHAN9232**
A. Cappelletti, Philh, M. Bamert (r1993) *Concerto all'antica.* (8/94) (SCHW) ① **311242**
P. Amoyal, FNO, C. Dutoit (r1993) *Concert*
(7/95) (DECC) ① **443 324-2DH**
Concerto in modo misolidio—piano and orchestra (1925)
G. Tozer, BBC PO, E. Downes (r1994) *Piano Concerto in A minor.* (8/94) (CHAN) ① **CHAN9285**
Fantasia slava—piano and orchestra (c1902)
G. Tozer, BBC PO, E. Downes (r1994) *Concert*
(1/95) (CHAN) ① **CHAN9311**
K. Scherbakov, Slovak RSO, H. Griffiths (r1994) *Concert* (11/95) (NAXO) ① **8 553207**
Feste romane, 'Roman Festivals'—symphonic poem (1928)
Philadelphia, R. Muti *Concert*
(3/86) (EMI) ① **CDC7 47316-2**
Oslo PO, M. Jansons *Concert*
(4/90) (EMI) ① **CDC7 49964-2**
NBC SO, A. Toscanini (r1949) *Concert*
(1/91) (RCA) ① **GD60262**
Philadelphia, E. Ormandy *Concert*
(2/91) (RCA) ① **VD60486**
Philadelphia, A. Toscanini (r1941) *Concert*
(6/91) (RCA) ① [4] **GD60328**
Philh, Y. P. Tortelier *Concert*
(4/92) (CHAN) ① **CHAN8989**
RPO, E. Bátiz *Concert* (8/92) (NAXO) ① **8 550539**
BPO, V. de Sabata (r1939) *Concert*
(11/92) (KOCH) ① **37126-2**
NYPO, G. Sinopoli (r1991) *Concert*
(9/93) (DG) ① **437 534-2GH**
Cleveland Orch, L. Maazel (r1976) *Concert*
(11/93) (DECC) ① **425 052-2DM**
Cincinnati SO, J. López-Cobos (r1993) *Concert*
(7/94) (TELA) ① **CD80356**
Montreal SO, C. Dutoit (r1982) *Concert*
(8/94) (DECC) ① **430 729-2DM**
Fontane di Roma, 'Fountains of Rome'—symphonic poem (1914-16)
1. La fontana di Valle Giulia all'alba; 2. La fontana del Tritone mattino; 3. La fontana di Trevi al meriggio; 4. La fontana di Villa Medici al tramonto.
BPO, H. von Karajan *Concert*
(1/85) (DG) ① **413 822-2GH**
Atlanta SO, L. Lane *Concert*
(5/85) (TELA) ① **CD80085**
Philadelphia, R. Muti *Concert*
(3/86) (EMI) ① **CDC7 47316-2**
NBC SO, A. Toscanini (r1951) *Concert*
(1/91) (RCA) ① **GD60262**
Philadelphia, E. Ormandy *Concert*
(2/91) (RCA) ① **VD60486**
Minneapolis SO, A. Dorati *Concert*
(2/91) (MERC) ① **432 007-2MM**
Philh, Y. P. Tortelier *Concert*
(4/92) (CHAN) ① **CHAN8989**
NYPSO, J. Barbirolli (r1939) *Concert*
(4/92) (PEAR) ① [3] **GEMMCDS9922**
RPO, E. Bátiz *Concert* (8/92) (NAXO) ① **8 550539**
LSO, A. Coates (r1927/8) *Concert*
(4/93) (KOCH) ① [2] **37704-2**
Chicago SO, F. Reiner (r1959) *Concert*
(8/93) (RCA) ① **09026 61401-2**

Scherzo veneziano (Le astuzie di Colombina)—ballet (1920—Rome)
EXCERPTS: 1. Quandro primo (Tableau 1); 2. Intermezzo; 3. Quadro secondo (Tableau 2).
Bratislava RSO, Adriano Concert
(11/92) (MARC) ① **8 223346**
Semirama—opera: 3 acts (1910—Bologna)
(Lib. A Cerè)
Cpte E. Marton, V. Kincses, L. Bartolini, L. Miller, L. Polgár, T. Clementis, Hungarian Rad & TV Chor, Hungarian St Orch, L. Gardelli (r1990)
(7/93) (HUNG) ① [2] **HCD31197/8**
Sèvres de la vieille France—ballet-pastiche (1920—Rome)
EXCERPTS: 1. Menuet; 2. Tambourin; 3. Bergère légère; 4. Gavotte.
Bratislava RSO, Adriano Concert
(11/92) (MARC) ① **8 223346**

REUBKE, (Friedrich) Julius (1834–1858) Germany

SECTION III: INSTRUMENTAL

Sonata in B flat minor—piano (1857)
C. Tanski Organ Sonata.   (11/89) (MDG) ① **L3344**
Sonata on the 94th Psalm in C minor—organ (1857)
M. Lagache Concert   (4/89) (MOTE) ① **CD11111**
M. Sander Piano Sonata.   (11/89) (MDG) ① **L3344**
K. John Concert   (4/90) (PRIO) ① **PRCD264**
K. Bowyer (r1992) Schumann: B-A-C-H Fugues, Op.60.   (2/94) (NIMB) ① **NI5361**
C. Crozier Concert   (7/91) (DELO) ① **DE3090**

REUSNER, Esaias (1636–1679) Germany

SECTION III: INSTRUMENTAL

Neue Lauten-Früchte—lute suites (pub 1676)
(Eng: New Fruits for the Lute)
1. D MINOR; 1a. Praeludium; 1b. Paduan; 1d. Couranta; 1e. Saraband; 1f. Gavotte; 1g. Gigue; 2. C MINOR; 2a. Allemand; 2b. Courant; 2c. Sarabande; 2d. Gavotte; 2e. Gigue; 3. D; 3a. Sonatina; 3b. Allemanda; 3c. Courant; 3d. Sarabanda; 3e. Gavotte; 3f. Gigue; 3g. Passacaglia; 4. G MINOR; 4a. Allemanda; 4b. Courant; 4c. Sarabanda; 4d. Arias I-II; 4e. Ballett; 4f. Gigue; 5. C MINOR; 5a. Paduan; 5b. Allemanda; 5c. Couranto; 5d. Sarabande; 5e. Gigue; 6. E MINOR; 6a. Allemanda; 6b. Couranta; 6c. Sarabanda; 6d. Gigue.
K. Junghänel   (9/92) (DHM) ① **RD77230**
1, 2. Lautten Compagney (r1990/1; arr Stanley, 1668) Concert   (6/93) (CAPR) ① **10 431**

REUTTER, Hermann (1900–1985) Germany

SECTION IV: VOCAL AND CHORAL

5 Antike Oden—1v, viola & piano, Op. 57 (c1940) (Wds. Sappho)
1. Wie hernieder vom Berge; 2. Hinunter ist schon der Mond; 3. Singet, ihr Mädchen, das Lied; 4. Seelenlos liegt dereinst da; 5. Aphroditel.
M. Shirai, T. Zimmermann, H. Höll (r1993-4) Concert   (9/95) (CAPR) ① **10 462**
3 Hölderlin Lieder, Op. 67 (pub 1947) (Wds Hölderlin)
EXCERPTS: 1. Sonnenuntergang; 2. Die Nacht; 3. Lebenslauf.
M. Shirai, H. Höll Concert
(12/94) (CAPR) ① **10 534**

REVUELTAS, Silvestre (1899–1940) Mexico

SECTION I: ORCHESTRAL

Alcancías (1932)
London Sinfonietta, D. Atherton (r1979) Concert
(2/05) (CATA) ① **09026 62672-2**
Caminos (Itinerarios)—orchestra (1934)
Mexico City PO, E. Bátiz Concert
(8/89) (ASV) ① **CDDCA653**
Homenaje a Federico García Lorca (1937)
New Philh, E. Mata (r1975) Concert
(2/95) (CATA) ① **09026 62672-2**
Musica para Charlar—orchestra (1938) (orig for film 'Ferrocariles de baja California')
1. SUITE 1: Construction of the Railroad; 1a. Sleepers and rails; 1b. Home Land; 1c. Mexicali; 1d. Telegraph Poles; 2. SUITE 2: The Desert; 2a. Cactus; 2b. Twilight; 2c. Sand and Water; 2d. Tractors; 2e. Hymn to the Home Land.

Mexico City PO, E. Bátiz Concert
(8/89) (ASV) ① **CDDCA653**
Planos (1933)
London Sinfonietta, D. Atherton (r1979) Concert
(2/95) (CATA) ① **09026 62672-2**
Sensemayá—orchestra (1938)
NYPO, L. Bernstein (r1963) Concert
(5/93) (SONY) ① **SMK47544**
New World Sym, M. Tilson Thomas (r1992) Concert
(6/93) (ARGO) ① **436 737-2ZH**
Xalapa SO, H. de la Fuente Concert
(12/93) (CARL) ① **MCD63**
New Philh, E. Mata (r1975) Concert
(2/95) (CATA) ① **09026 62672-2**
Toccata (1933)
London Sinfonietta, D. Atherton (r1979) Concert
(2/95) (CATA) ① **09026 62672-2**
Ventanas—orchestra (1932)
Mexico City PO, E. Bátiz Concert
(8/89) (ASV) ① **CDDCA653**

SECTION II: CHAMBER

Ocho x Radio—eight instruments (1933)
Xalapa SO, H. de la Fuente Concert
(12/93) (CARL) ① **MCD63**
London Sinfonietta, D. Atherton (r1979) Concert
(2/95) (CATA) ① **09026 62672-2**
String Quartet No. 1
Latin American Qt (r1993) Concert
(6/94) (NALB) ① **NA062CD**
String Quartet No. 2, 'Magueyes' (1931)
Latin American Qt (r1993) Concert
(6/94) (NALB) ① **NA062CD**
String Quartet No. 3
Latin American Qt (r1993) Concert
(6/94) (NALB) ① **NA062CD**
String Quartet No. 4, 'Musica de Feria' (1932)
Latin American Qt (r1993) Concert
(6/94) (NALB) ① **NA062CD**

SECTION V: STAGE WORKS

La Noche de los Mayas—concert suite from film score (1939)
EXCERPTS: 1. La noche de los Mayas; 2. La noche de Jaranas; 3. La noche de Yucatán; 4. La noche de encantamiento.
Xalapa SO, H. de la Fuente (r1980) Concert
(2/95) (CATA) ① **09026 62672-2**

REYER, (Louis-Etienne-)Ernest (1823–1909) France

SECTION IV: VOCAL AND CHORAL

Le Sélam—oriental symphony in five pictures (1850) (Eng: The Greeting)
G. Ottenthal, B. Lazzaretti, W. Glashof, Berlin St Hedwig's Cath Ch, Berlin RSO Concert
(5/92) (CAPR) ① **10 380**

SECTION V: STAGE WORKS

Sigurd—opera: 4 acts (1884—Brussels) (Lib. du Locle and Blau)
EXCERPTS: 1. Overture. ACT 1: 2. Brodons des étendards; 3. Ma mère, un songe malgré moi; 4. Fille des rois, que te sert d'être belle?; 5. Les destins n'ont pas de secrets; 6. Quand on court depuis le matin; 7. J'aime à voir assis; 8. Il est une île sombre; 9. Prince du Rhin, nous partons; 10. Prince du Rhin, au pays de mon père; 11. O file de Sigemon. ACT 2: 12. Dieux terribles qui vous plaisez; 13. Et toi, Freia, déesse de l'amour; 14. O Brunehild, ô vierge armée; 15. Et bien, puisqu'ici-bas; 16. Lequel de nous va tenter l'aventure?; 17. Lequel de vous, guerriers; 18a. Le bruit des chants s'éteint; 18b. Esprits gardiens; 19. Mais non! Point de triste présage; 20. Je suis vainquuer!; 21. Salut, splendeur du jour!; 22. O Gunther mon ami. ACT 3: 23. À la voix des esprits de l'air; 24. Oui, Sigurd est vainqueur!; 25. La viôla donc, la déesse; 26. Je suis Gunther, Roi des Burgondes; 27. Les premiers feux du matin; 28. Au nom du roi Gunther, peuple; 29. Roi Gunther, digne fils; 30. Frappons les airs joyeux. ACT 4: 31. Emplissons nos urnes; 32. O palais radieux; 33. Jeune reine, ma soeur; 34. Compagnons, parmi les sentiers; 35. La nuit sera belle; 36. Un souvenir poignant; 37. Sigurd, les dieux dans leur clémence; 38. La nuit sera belle; 39. De nos pères suivant l'usage; 40. O prodigel...Oubliez les maux.
10. M. Renaud, anon (r1903) Concert
(9/91) (SYMP) ① **SYMCD1089**
13. M. Renaud, anon (r1903) Concert
(8/92) (IRCC) ① **IRCC-CD802**
21. G. Lubin, orch, H. Defosse (r1929) Concert
(5/91) (CLUB) ① **CL99-022**

21, 32. M. Lawrence, Pasdeloup Orch, P. Coppola (r1934) Concert   (5/90) (PREI) ① **89011**
37. R. Caron, anon (r1904) Concert
(8/92) (IRCC) ① **IRCC-CD802**
37(pt) A. Talexis, L. Escalais, anon (r1905) Concert
(8/92) (IRCC) ① **IRCC-CD802**
37 (pt) L. Escalais, A. Talexis, anon (r1906) Concert
(12/93) (SYMP) ① **SYMCD1126**
37. R. Caron, anon (r1904) Concert
(12/94) (SYMP) ① **SYMCD1172**

REYNEAU, Gacian (?c1370–fl before 1429) France

SECTION IV: VOCAL AND CHORAL

Va t'en, mon cuer—rondeau
Gothic Voices, I. Barford, C. Page Concert
(12/86) (HYPE) ① **CDA66144**

REYNOLDS, Roger (b 1934) USA

SECTION II: CHAMBER

Coconino...a shattered landscape—string quartet (1985)
Arditti Qt Concert   (11/90) (GVIS) ① **GV79440-2**

REYS, Jacob (c1540–c1605) Poland

also known as 'Le Polonios'

SECTION III: INSTRUMENTAL

Courante sur le Courante de Perrichon—lute
P. O'Dette Concert   (4/93) (HARM) ① **HMU90 7068**
Sarabande—lute (in Lord Herbert of Cherbury's Lute Book)
P. O'Dette Concert   (4/93) (HARM) ① **HMU90 7068**

REZNIČEK, E(mil) N(ikolaus) von (1860–1945) Austria

SECTION V: STAGE WORKS

Donna Diana—opera: 3 acts (1894—Prague)
(Lib. cpsr)
Overture VPO, C. Abbado (pp1988) Concert
(7/88) (DG) ① **423 662-2GH**
Overture NYPO, Z. Mehta (pp1988) Concert
(9/89) (SONY) ① **MK44942**
Overture NYPO, L. Bernstein (r1967) Concert
(9/93) (SONY) ① **SMK47601**
Overture BPO, E. Kleiber (r1932) Concert
(5/94) (ARCI) ① **ARC102**

RHEINBERGER, Joseph (Gabriel) (1839–1901) Germany/Lichtenstein

SECTION I: ORCHESTRAL

Concerto for Organ and Orchestra No. 1 in F, Op. 137
M. Murray, RPO, J. Ling (r1986) Dupré: Organ Symphony, Op. 25.   (6/87) (TELA) ① **CD80136**
Concerto for Piano and Orchestra in A flat, Op. 94
M. Ponti, Berlin SO, V. Schmidt-Gertenbach Concert
(8/92) (VOX) ① **115713-2**

SECTION III: INSTRUMENTAL

Organ Sonata No. 3 in G, 'Pastorale', Op. 88
G. Barber Concert   (6/90) (PRIO) ① **PRCD269**
Organ Sonata No. 4 in A minor, Op. 98
T. Mechler Concert   (9/90) (MOTE) ① **CD10881**
Organ Sonata No. 8 in E minor, Op. 132
Scherzoso J. Jones Concert
(8/91) (MOTE) ① **CD11491**
Organ Sonata No. 10 in B minor, Op. 146
G. Barber Concert   (6/90) (PRIO) ① **PRCD269**
Organ Sonata No. 11 in D minor, Op. 148
G. Barber Concert   (6/90) (PRIO) ① **PRCD269**
Cantilène J. Lancelot Concert
(4/88) (PRIO) ① **PRCD228**
Organ Sonata No. 13 in E flat, Op. 161
G. Barber Concert   (5/91) (PRIO) ① **PRCD297**
Organ Sonata No. 17 in B flat, Op. 81
Intermezzo J. Jones Concert
(8/91) (MOTE) ① **CD11491**

RICARDO, Niño *Spain*

SECTION III: INSTRUMENTAL

Alegrías—flamenco guitar
P. Peña *Concert*   (9/88) (NIMB) ① **NI5093**
Bulerías—flamenco guitar
P. Peña *Concert*   (9/88) (NIMB) ① **NI5093**
Fandangos—flamenco guitar
P. Peña *Concert*   (9/88) (NIMB) ① **NI5093**
Farrucas—flamenco guitar
P. Peña *Concert*   (9/88) (NIMB) ① **NI5093**
Seguiriyas—flamenco guitar
P. Peña *Concert*   (9/88) (NIMB) ① **NI5093**
Tarantas—flamenco guitar
P. Peña *Concert*   (9/88) (NIMB) ① **NI5093**
Zambra—flamenco guitar
P. Peña *Concert*   (9/88) (NIMB) ① **NI5093**

RICCI, Federico *(1809–1877)* Italy

SECTION IV: VOCAL AND CHORAL

Il carrettiere del Vomero—song
R. Tebaldi, R. Bonynge (r1972) *Concert*
          (9/94) (DECC) ① **436 202-2DM**

SECTION V: STAGE WORKS

**Crispino e la comare—melodramma
fantastico-giocoso: 4 acts (1850—Venice)**
(Lib. F Piave: comp with L Ricci)
  Io non sono l. Tetrazzini, orch (r1913) *Concert*
          (9/92) (EMI) ① [3] **CHS7 63802-2(2)**
  Io non sono l. Tetrazzini, orch (r1913) *Concert*
          (9/92) (PEAR) ① **GEMMCD9223**

RICCI, Luigi *(1805–1859)* Italy

SECTION V: STAGE WORKS

**Il diavolo condannato nel mondo a prender
moglie—azione comica spettacolosa: 3 acts**
(1827—Naples) (Lib. A L Tottola)
  Io ti ho dato il sangue mio P. Nilon, J. Rawnsley, A.
  Viera, A. Thorburn, Philh, D. Parry *Concert*
          (8/95) (OPRA) ① [3] **ORCH104**

RICCIARDI, V

SECTION IV: VOCAL AND CHORAL

Amor mio—song (wds. G. E. Gaeta)
E. Caruso, orch, W.B. Rogers (r1914) *Concert*
          (7/91) (RCA) ① [12] **GD60495(5)**
E. Caruso, orch, W.B. Rogers (r1914) *Concert*
          (10/91) (PEAR) ① [3] **EVC3(1)**

RICCIO, Giovanni Battista *(fl 1609/21)* Italy

SECTION II: CHAMBER

**Canzon a doi soprani in echo
proposta—echo sonata**
Capriccio Stravagante, S. Sempé (hpd/dir) *Concert*
          (10/95) (DHM) ① **RD77220**
Canzon a 4 in A—3 recorders & continuo
(Unidentified)
F. Brüggen, K. Boeke, W. van Hauwe, W. Möller, B.
van Asperen (r1978) *Concert*
          (10/95) (TELD) ① **4509-97466-2**
**Canzon in A, '(La) Rosignola'—3 recorders
& continuo**
F. Brüggen, K. Boeke, W. van Hauwe, W. Möller, B.
van Asperen (r c1960s) *Concert*
          (10/95) (TELD) ① **4509-97466-2**

RICE, Edward Everett *(1849–1924)* USA

SECTION V: STAGE WORKS

Conrad the Corsair—musical show
(1887—New York) (comp with John Braham.
Lyrics H E Dixey)
EXCERPTS: 1. Buckets of Gore.
  1. Cincinnati Uni Sngrs, Cincinnati Uni Th Orch, E.
  Rivers (r1978) *Concert*   (4/94) (NEW) ① **80221-2**
**Evangeline—musical show (1874—New
York)** (Lyrics J Cheever Goodwin. Book Rice &
Goodwin)
EXCERPTS: 1. My Heart (added for 1885 revival).
  1. Cincinnati Uni Sngrs, Cincinnati Uni Th Orch, E.
  Rivers (r1978) *Concert*   (4/94) (NEW) ① **80221-2**

RICHARDSON, Clive *(b 1909)
England*

SECTION I: ORCHESTRAL

Beachcomber—orchestra (1948)
RTE Concert Orch, E. Tomlinson (r1993) *Concert*
          (12/95) (MARC) ① **8 223522**

SECTION II: CHAMBER

Roundelay for clarinet and piano (1936)
G. de Peyer, G. Pryor *Concert*
          (11/87) (CHAN) ① **CHAN8549**

RICHART *(fl late 12th or early 13th
cent) France*

SECTION IV: VOCAL AND CHORAL

Je chevauchai—pastourelle: 1v and lute
Gothic Voices, C. Page (r1994) *Concert*
          (8/95) (HYPE) ① **CDA66773**

RICHART DE FOURNIVAL *(d 1260)
France*

SECTION II: CHAMBER

Onques n'amai tant con je fui amee—dance
M. Kiek, Sinfonye, S. Wishart *Concert*
          (6/88) (HYPE) ① **CDA66283**

SECTION IV: VOCAL AND CHORAL

**Onques n'amai tant con je fui amee—13th
Cent motet**
M. Kiek, Sinfonye, S. Wishart *Concert*
          (6/88) (HYPE) ① **CDA66283**

RICHTER, Franz Xaver *(1709–1789) Moravia/Germany*

SECTION I: ORCHESTRAL

Concerto for Flute and Strings in E minor
Barthold Kuijken, Tafelmusik, J. Lamon (r1991)
Concert   (7/93) (SONY) ① **SK48045**
**Concerto for Trumpet and Strings in D
(1760s)**
L. Güttler, C. Schornsheim, Leipzig New Bach
Collegium Musicum, M. Pommer (r1986) *Concert*
          (8/89) (CAPR) ① **10 051**
H. Hardenberger, LPO, E. Howarth *Concert*
          (3/91) (PHIL) ① **426 311-2PH**
Symphony in G
Slovak CO, B. Warchal *Concert*
          (11/89) (OPUS) ① **9350 1812**

SECTION II: CHAMBER

String Quartet in B flat, Op. 5/2
VCM, N. Harnoncourt (r1967) *Concert*
          (7/93) (TELD) ① **4509-91002-2**

RICHTER, Max *(20th Cent)*

SECTION II: CHAMBER

Cake Music—six pianos (1990s)
Piano Circus (r1992-93) *Concert*
          (2/95) (ARGO) ① **443 527-2ZH**
**Gongstream—five pianos, prepared piano
and typewriter (1990s)**
Piano Circus (r1992-93) *Concert*
          (2/95) (ARGO) ① **443 527-2ZH**
Rain, Sun, etc—six pianos (1990s)
Piano Circus (r1992-93) *Concert*
          (2/95) (ARGO) ① **443 527-2ZH**

RIDOUT, Alan (John) *(b 1934)
England*

SECTION IV: VOCAL AND CHORAL

Epitaph for Amy—song (1969) (Wds. anon)
J. Bowman, Downshire Players, P. Ash *Concert*
          (3/89) (MERI) ① **CDE84158**
Ferdinand—narrator and violin (Wds. Munro
Leaf)
L. Mordkovitch, G. Woolf *Concert*
          (11/90) (CHAN) ① **CHAN8748**
The Prism of Life—song (Wds. J. A.
Symons)
J. Bowman, Downshire Players, P. Ash *Concert*
          (3/89) (MERI) ① **CDE84158**
3 Sonnets of Cecil Day Lewis (1971)
  1. For infants, time is like a humming shell; 2. Our
  youth-time passes down a colonnade; 3. To travel

like a bird.
J. Bowman, Downshire Players, P. Ash *Concert*
          (3/89) (MERI) ① **CDE84158**

RIDOUT, Godfrey *(1918–1984)
Canada*

SECTION IV: VOCAL AND CHORAL

**Folksongs of Eastern Canada—soprano and
orchestra (1967)**
  1. J'ai cueilli la belle rose; 2. She's like the swallow;
  3. I'll give my love an apple; 4. Ah! si mon maine
  voulait danser!.
  4. C. Robbin, M. McMahon (r1985) *Concert*
          (7/94) (MARQ) ① **ERAD113**

RIEDEL, Georg *(1676–1738)
Germany*

SECTION IV: VOCAL AND CHORAL

**Harmonische freude frommer
seelen—funeral cantata: 4vv (1706)** (Wds.
Luke XV: vv11-32)
G. de Reyghere, J. Bowman, G. de Mey, M. van
Egmond, Ricercar Consort *Concert*
          (7/91) (RICE) ① **RIC079061**

RIES, Franz *(1846–1932)
Germany*

SECTION II: CHAMBER

La Capricciosa—violin and piano
Y. Menuhin, L. Persinger (r1928) *Concert*
          (4/91) (BIDD) ① **LAB031**
Y. Menuhin, L. Persinger (r1928) *Concert*
          (9/91) (TEST) ① **SBT1003**
Suite No. 3 in G—violin and piano, Op. 34
  3. Adagio; 4. Gondoliera; 5. Perpetuum mobile.
  5. J. Kubelík, anon (r1911) *Concert*
          (6/91) (BIDD) ① **LAB033/4**

RIETI, Vittorio *(1898–1994)
Italy/USA*

SECTION I: ORCHESTRAL

**Symphony No. 4, 'Sinfonia Tripartita'
(1944)**
NBC SO, A. Toscanini (bp1945) *Concert*
          (5/94) (ATS) ① [2] **ATCD100**

SECTION III: INSTRUMENTAL

La Danseuse aux lions—piano
B. Lerner *Concert*   (1/89) (ETCE) ① **KTC1061**

RIETZ, Julius *(1812–1877)
Germany*

SECTION I: ORCHESTRAL

**Concerto for Clarinet and Orchestra in G
minor, Op. 29**
T. King, ECO, A. Litton *Concert*
          (4/90) (HYPE) ① **CDA66300**

RIGATTI, Giovanni Antonio *(1615–1649)* Italy

SECTION IV: VOCAL AND CHORAL

**Messa e salmi ariosi—3vv with instruments
ad lib (pub 1643)**
  1. Salve regina.
  1. Gabrieli Consort, Gabrieli Players, P. McCreesh
  (r1990; ed Roche) *Concert*
          (4/93) (ARCH) ① [2] **437 552-2AH2**
**Messa e salmi parte concertati—3-8vv, 2
violins with instruments ad lib (pub 1640)**
  1. Dixit Dominus (double choir); 2. Magnificat (8vv);
  3. Nisi Dominus (3vv).
  1-3. Gabrieli Consort, Gabrieli Players, P. McCreesh
  (r1990; ed Bartlett, Roche) *Concert*
          (4/93) (ARCH) ① [2] **437 552-2AH2**

RIHM, Wolfgang *(b 1952)
Germany*

SECTION I: ORCHESTRAL

**Gesungene Zeit—violin and orchestra (1991-
92)**
A-S. Mutter, Chicago SO, James Levine *Berg: Violin
Concerto.*   (1/93) (DG) ① **437 093-2GH**

A-S. Mutter, Chicago SO, James Levine (r1992)
Concert   (12/94) (DG) ① [3] 445 487-2GX3

SECTION II: CHAMBER

Fremde Szenen I-III—attempts: piano trio (1982-84)
Ravensburg Beethoven Trio (r1991)
          (2/94) (CPO) ① CPO999 119-2
Sine nomine—brass quintet (1985)
R. Friedrich, W. Bauer, W. Wipfler, O. Seifert, U.
Füssel (r1991-2) Concert   (6/93) (CAPR) ① 10 482
String Quartet No. 4 (1979-81)
Alban Berg Qt (pp1990) Schnittke: String Quartet 4.
          (4/93) (EMI) ① CDC7 54660-2

SECTION IV: VOCAL AND CHORAL

Départ—chorus and orchestra (1988) (Wds.
A. Rimbaud)
Vienna Jeunesse Ch, VPO, C. Abbado (pp1988)
Concert   (4/90) (DG) ① 429 260-2GH
Hölderlin-Fragmente—voice and piano (1976-77)
J. M. Kösters, BPO, C. Abbado (pp1993) Concert
          (3/95) (SONY) ① SK53975

RIISAGER, Knudage (1897–1974) Denmark

SECTION II: CHAMBER

Divertimento—flute, oboe, bassoon and horn
Selandia Ens Concert   (6/90) (KONT) ① 32032

RILEY, Terry (b 1935) USA

SECTION II: CHAMBER

In C—unspecified instruments (1964)
Piano Circus Reich: Pianos.
          (6/91) (ARGO) ① 430 380-2ZH
New Music Th, Life on the Water, T. Riley, L. Rush
(pp1990)   (11/95) (NALB) ① NA071CD
Salome Dances for Peace—string quartet (1985-86)
1. Anthem of the Great Spirit; 1a. The Summons; 1b.
Peace dance; 1c. Fanfare in the Minimal Kingdom;
1d. Ceremonial Night Race; 1e. At the ancient Aztec
Corn Races; 1f. More Ceremonial Races; 1g.
Oldtimers at the Races; 1h. Half Wolf Dances Mad in
Moonlight; 2. Conquest of the War Demons; 2a. Way
of the Warrior; 2b. Salome and Half Wolf descend
through the gates; 2c. Breakthrough to the realm of
the War Demons; 2d. Combat Dance; 2e. Victory:
Salome re-enacts for Half Wolf her deeds of valour;
2f. Discovery of Peace; 2g. The underworld arising;
3. The Gift; 3a. Echoes of Primordial Time; 3b.
Mongolian Winds; 4. The Ecstasy; 4a. Processional;
4b. Seduction of the Bear Father; 4c. The Gathering;
4d. At the Summit; 4e. Recessional; 5. Good
Medicine; 5a. Good Medicine Dance.
Kronos Qt (r1988)
          (9/90) (NONE) ① [2] 7559-79217-2
Tread on the Trail—no specific instruments (1964-65) (no specific method of performance)
J. Gibson, M. Riesman (r1992) Concert
          (6/93) (PNT) ① 434 873-2PTH

RIMMER, William (1862–1936) England

SECTION I: ORCHESTRAL

The Australasian—march
Glasgow CWS Band, H. Snell Concert
          (9/92) (DOYE) ① DOYCD005

RIMSKY-KORSAKOV, Nikolay Andreyevich (1844–1908) Russia

SECTION I: ORCHESTRAL

Capriccio espagnol—orchestra, Op. 34 (1887)
LSO, G. Simon Concert
          (3/87) (CALA) ① CACD0101
Gothenburg SO, N. Järvi Concert
          (2/89) (DG) ① [2] 423 604-2GH2
NYPO, Z. Mehta (pp1988) Concert
          (9/89) (SONY) ① MK44942
LSO, R. Frühbeck de Burgos Concert
          (11/89) (CARL) ① PCD924
Hungarian St. Orch, J. Sándor Scheherazade.
          (10/90) (LASE) ① 15 608
LSO, C. Mackerras (r1990) Scheherazade.
          (10/90) (TELA) ① CD80208

Gothenburg SO, N. Järvi Concert
          (3/91) (DG) ① 429 984-2GH
New Philh, L. Stokowski Concert
          (4/92) (DECC) ① 433 625-2DSP
LSO, A. Argenta (r1956) Concert
          (6/93) (DECC) ① [2] 433 911-2DM2
Black Dyke Mills Band, J. Watson (r1992: arr
Wilkinson) Concert   (9/93) (POLY) ① QPRL053D
Bergen PO, D. Kitaienko Concert
          (11/93) (CHAN) ① CHAN9178
BPO, L. Maazel (r1958) Concert
          (5/94) (BELA) ① 450 129-2
Bolshoi SO, A. Lazarev (r1992) Concert
          (8/94) (ERAT) ① 4509-94808-2
LSO, A. Argenta (r1957) Concert
          (5/95) (DECC) ① 443 580-2DCS
LSO, I. Markevitch (r1963) Concert
          (6/95) (PHIL) ① 442 643-2PM
LPO, M. Jansons (r1994) Scheherazade.
          (7/95) (EMI) ① CDC5 55227-2
Concerto for Piano and Orchestra in C sharp minor, Op. 30 (1884)
M. Binns, English Northern Philh, D. Lloyd-Jones
Concert   (7/93) (HYPE) ① CDA66640
I. Zhukov, USSR TV & Rad Orch, G. Rozhdestvensky
(r1968) Concert   (2/94) (MEZH) ① MK417087
G. Tozer, Bergen SO, D. Kitaienko (r1993) Concert
          (7/94) (CHAN) ① CHAN9229
Concerto for Trombone and Military Band in B flat (1877)
N. Law, Black Dyke Mills Band, P. Parkes (r1989: arr
G Langford) Concert
          (10/94) (CHAN) ① CHAN4523
Conzertstück for Clarinet and Military Band in E flat (1878)
K. Fagéus, Stockholm Sym Wind Orch, O. Vänskä
Concert   (3/93) (CPRI) ① CAP21415
Dubinushka—orchestra, Op. 62 (1905-06)
LSO, N. Järvi Concert
          (2/90) (CHAN) ① CHAN8783
LSO, A. Coates (r1932) Concert
          (12/92) (KOCH) ① 37700-2
Philh, E. Kurtz (r1963) Concert
          (9/93) (EMI) ① [2] CZS7 67729-2
SRO, E. Ansermet (r1958) Concert
          (9/95) (DECC) ① [2] 443 464-2DF2
Fairy Tale (Skazka), Op. 29 (1879-80)
LSO, Y. Butt Symphony 3.
          (9/87) (ASV) ① CDDCA538
Fantasia on Two Russian Themes—violin and orchestra, Op. 33 (1886-87)
C. Pavlík, Dvořák CO, V. Válek Concert
          (4/92) (SUPR) ① 11 0111-2
N. Milstein, orch, R. Irving (r1962) Concert
          (5/94) (EMI) ① [6] ZDMF7 64830-2
Russian Easter Festival Overture, Op. 36 (1888)
St. Louis SO, L. Slatkin Concert
          (12/83) (TELA) ① CD80072
Gothenburg SO, N. Järvi Concert
          (2/89) (DG) ① [2] 423 604-2GH2
Philh, E. Svetlanov Symphony 2.
          (9/90) (HYPE) ① CDA66399
Gothenburg SO, N. Järvi Concert
          (3/91) (DG) ① 429 984-2GH
Cleveland Orch, L. Maazel Scheherazade.
          (1/92) (DECC) ① 433 615-2DSP
NYPO, Y. Temirkanov (r1991) Scheherazade.
          (5/93) (RCA) ① 09026 61173-2
Philadelphia, L. Stokowski (1929) Concert
          (3/94) (BIDD) ① WHL010
Philh, G. Sinopoli (r1992) Tchaikovsky: Symphony 5.
          (3/94) (DG) ① 437 542-2GH
Bergen SO, D. Kitaienko (r1993) Concert
          (7/94) (CHAN) ① CHAN9229
Bolshoi SO, A. Lazarev (r1992) Concert
          (8/94) (ERAT) ① 4509-94808-2
LSO, I. Markevitch (r1965) Concert
          (6/95) (PHIL) ① 442 643-2PM
SRO, E. Ansermet (r1959) Concert
          (9/95) (DECC) ① [2] 443 464-2DF2
Baltimore SO, D. Zinman (r1991) Concert
          (12/95) (TELA) ① CD80378
Boston Pops, A. Fiedler (r1957) Concert
          (12/95) (RCA) ① 09026 68132-2
Sadko—Musical picture, Op. 5 (1869 rev 1892)
Bratislava RSO, O. Lenárd Concert
          (10/90) (NAXO) ① 8 550098
SRO, E. Ansermet Concert
          (6/94) (BELA) ① 450 132-2
Bergen SO, D. Kitaienko (r1993) Concert
          (7/94) (CHAN) ① CHAN9229
San Francisco SO, P. Monteux (r1945) Concert
          (9/94) (RCA) ① [15] 09026 61893-2

SRO, E. Ansermet (r1958) Concert
          (9/95) (DECC) ① [2] 443 464-2DF2
Russian St SO, E. Svetlanov (r1993) Concert
          (10/95) (RCA) ① 09026 62684-2
Scheherazade—symphonic suite after 1001 Nights, Op. 35 (1888)
1. The Sea and Sinbad's Ship; 2. The Kalender
Prince; 3. The Young Prince and Princess; 4. Festival
at Baghdad—The Sea—The Shipwreck.
Philadelphia, R. Muti
          (2/85) (EMI) ① CDC7 47023-2
SNO, N. Järvi Glazunov: Stenka Razin.
          (2/87) (CHAN) ① CHAN8479
BPO, H. von Karajan Borodin: Prince Igor.
          (4/87) (DG) ① 419 063-2GGA
RPO, T. Beecham (r1957) Borodin: Prince Igor.
          (9/87) (EMI) ① CDC7 47717-2
LSO, J. Mauceri   (5/88) (CARL) ① PCD880
Bratislava RSO, O. Lenárd Concert
          (10/90) (NAXO) ① 8 550098
Hungarian St. Orch, J. Sándor Capriccio Espagnol.
          (10/90) (LASE) ① 15 608
LSO, C. Mackerras (r1990) Capriccio espagnol.
          (10/90) (TELA) ① CD80208
LPO, A. Litton (r1988) Ravel: Boléro.
          (12/91) (VIRG) ① VJ7 59658-2
Cleveland Orch, L. Maazel Russian Easter Festival
Ov.   (1/92) (DECC) ① 433 615-2DSP
Berlin RSO, H.M. Schneidt Ravel: Shéhérazade.
          (5/92) (CAPR) ① 10 381
BPO, O. Fried (r1928) Concert
          (2/93) (KOCH) ① 37146-2
NYPO, Y. Temirkanov (r1991) Russian Easter
Festival Ov.   (5/93) (RCA) ① 09026 61173-2
Chicago SO, D. Barenboim (r1993) Tale of Tsar
Saltan.   (12/93) (ERAT) ① 4509-91717-2
LPO, T. Yuasa (r1990) Prokofiev: Lt. Kijé Suite.
          (12/93) (EMIN) ① CD-EMX2214
Philadelphia, L. Stokowski (1927: incl alt takes)
Concert   (3/94) (BIDD) ① WHL010
Philh, E. Bátiz (r1992) Tale of Tsar Saltan.
          (6/94) (NAXO) ① 8 550726
LSO, P. Monteux (r1950s) Concert
          (6/94) (BELA) ① 450 132-2
San Francisco SO, P. Monteux (r1942) Concert
          (9/94) (RCA) ① [15] 09026 61893-2
Concertgebouw, R. Chailly Stravinsky: Scherzo
fantastique.   (10/94) (DECC) ① 443 703-2DH
Concertgebouw, K. Kondrashin (r1980) Concert
          (6/95) (PHIL) ① 442 643-2PM
LPO, M. Jansons (r1994) Capriccio espagnol.
          (7/95) (EMI) ① CDC5 55227-2
SRO, E. Ansermet (r1960) Concert
          (9/95) (DECC) ① [2] 443 464-2DF2
Berlin RSO, K. Ančerl (r1957) Prokofiev: Romeo and
Juliet Suites.   (11/95) (TAHR) ① TAH119
3(Chanson arabe) T. Seidel, E. Bay (r1927: arr
Kreisler) Concert   (7/93) (APR) ① [2] APR7016
3, 4. F. Kreisler, C. Lamson (1922: arr Kreisler)
Concert   (9/93) (BIDD) ① [2] LAB068/9
Symphony No. 1, Op. 1 (1865 rev 1884)
Gothenburg SO, N. Järvi Concert
          (2/89) (DG) ① [2] 423 604-2GH2
Bergen PO, D. Kitaienko Concert
          (11/93) (CHAN) ① CHAN9178
Russian St SO, E. Svetlanov (r1993) Symphony 2.
          (10/95) (RCA) ① 09026 62558-2
Symphony No. 2, 'Antar', Op. 9 (1868, rev 1875 and 1897)
Pittsburgh SO, L. Maazel (1986) Tchaikovsky:
Symphony 2.   (11/87) (TELA) ① CD80131
Gothenburg SO, N. Järvi Concert
          (2/89) (DG) ① [2] 423 604-2GH2
Philh, E. Svetlanov Russian Easter Festival Ov.
          (9/90) (HYPE) ① CDA66399
Bergen PO, D. Kitaienko Concert
          (11/93) (CHAN) ① CHAN9178
San Francisco SO, P. Monteux (r1946) Concert
          (9/94) (RCA) ① [15] 09026 61893-2
Russian St SO, E. Svetlanov (r1993) Symphony 1.
          (11/94) (RCA) ① 09026 62558-2
Symphony No. 3 in C, Op. 32 (1866-73 rev 1886)
LSO, Y. Butt Fairy Tale, Op. 29.
          (9/87) (ASV) ① CDDCA538
Gothenburg SO, N. Järvi Concert
          (2/89) (DG) ① [2] 423 604-2GH2
Bergen SO, D. Kitaienko (r1993: 1886 ver) Concert
          (7/94) (CHAN) ① CHAN9229
Russian St SO, E. Svetlanov (r1993) Concert
          (10/95) (RCA) ① 09026 62684-2

SECTION II: CHAMBER

Nocturne in F—four horns (c1888)
London Gabrieli Brass Ens, C. Larkin Concert
          (4/92) (HYPE) ① CDA66470

Quintet for Piano, Flute, Clarinet, Horn and Bassoon in B flat (1876)
Capricorn Glinka: Sextet in E flat.
(12/86) (HYPE) ① **CDA66163**
Nash Ens *Arensky: Piano Trio 1.*
(6/92) (CRD) ① **CRD3409**

SECTION III: INSTRUMENTAL

Little Song—piano
M. Fingerhut *Concert* (6/87) (CHAN) ① **CHAN8439**
4 Pieces—piano, Op. 11 (1876-77)
1. Impromptu; 2. Novellette; 3. Scherzino; 4. Etude.
2, 3. M. Fingerhut
(6/87) (CHAN) ① **CHAN8439**

SECTION IV: VOCAL AND CHORAL

By the sea—song cycle: 1v and piano, Op. 46 (1897) (Wds. A. K. Tolstoy)
1. The wave breaks into spray; 2. Not a sound from the sea; 3. The sea is tossing; 4. Do not believe, friend; 5. The waves rise up.
1. D. Hvorostovsky, M. Arkadiov *Concert*
(2/95) (PHIL) ① **442 536-2PH**
1, 2. A. El-Tour, anon (r1910) *Concert*
(6/93) (PEAR) ① [3] **GEMMCDS9004/6(1)**
1, 2. M. Lanskoy, I. Scheps *Concert*
(7/93) (CDM) ① [3] **LDC288 038/40**
3, 5. S. Baikov, I. Scheps *Concert*
(7/93) (CDM) ① [3] **LDC288 038/40**
4. A. Martynov, A. Konstantinidi *Concert*
(7/93) (CDM) ① [3] **LDC288 038/40**

In spring—song cycle: 1v and piano, Op. 43 (1897)
1. The lark sings louder (wds. A. K. Tolstoy); 2. Not the wind, blowing from the heights (wds. A. K. Tolstoy); 3. Cool and fragant is thy garland (wds. A. Fet); 4. Early spring (wds. A. K. Tolstoy).
1. N. Shevelev, anon (r1901) *Concert*
(6/93) (PEAR) ① [3] **GEMMCDS9007/9(2)**
1, 2. N. Gerassimova, V. Skanavi *Concert*
(7/93) (CDM) ① [3] **LDC288 038/40**
1, 2. O. Borodina, L. Gergieva (r1994) *Concert*
(8/95) (PHIL) ① **442 780-2PH**
3, 4. A. Martynov, A. Konstantinidi *Concert*
(7/93) (CDM) ① [3] **LDC288 038/40**

4 Songs—1v and piano, Op. 2 (1865-66)
1. Lean thy cheek to mine (wds. Heine, trans M. Mikhaylov: 1865); 2. Enslaved by the rose, the nightingale (wds. A. Klo'tsov: 1866); 3. Lullaby (wds. L. Mey: 1866); 4. From my tears (wds. Heine, trans M. Mikhaylov: 1866).
1. M. Lanskoy, I. Scheps *Concert*
(7/93) (CDM) ① [3] **LDC288 038/40**
2. R. Ponselle, R. Romani (r1939) *Concert*
(10/89) (NIMB) ① **NI7805**
2. R. Ponselle, R. Romani (r1939) *Concert*
(1/90) (RCA) ① **GD87810**
2. T. Schipa, orch. C. Sabajno (Fr: r1932) *Concert*
(10/90) (MSCM) ① [2] **MM30231**
2. R. Doria, T. Janopoulo (Fr: r1949) *Concert*
(4/92) (EMI) ① [7] **CHS7 69741-2(3)**
2. D. Smirnov, anon (r1913) *Concert*
(6/93) (PEAR) ① [3] **GEMMCDS9004/6(2)**
2. A. Nezhdanova, anon (r1914) *Concert*
(6/93) (PEAR) ① [3] **GEMMCDS9007/9(2)**
2. F. Kreisler, C. Lamson (r1926: arr Gordon) *Concert*
(12/93) (BIDD) ① **LAB075**
2. R. Ponselle, orch. R. Bourdon (r1927: Eng) *Concert*
(11/94) (ROMO) ① [2] **81007-2**
2. O. Borodina, L. Gergieva (r1994) *Concert*
(8/95) (PHIL) ① **442 780-2PH**
2, 3. N. Gerassimova, V. Skanavi *Concert*
(7/93) (CDM) ① [3] **LDC288 038/40**
4. A. Martynov, A. Konstantinidi *Concert*
(7/93) (CDM) ① [3] **LDC288 038/40**

4 Songs—1v and piano, Op. 3 (1866)
1. The pine and the palm (wds. Heine, trans M. Mikhaylov); 2. Southern night (wds. N. Shcherbina); 3. The golden cloud had slept (wds. Lermontov); 4. On the hills of Georgia (wds. Pushkin).
1, 2. M. Shutova, E. Cheglakova *Concert*
(7/93) (CDM) ① [3] **LDC288 038/40**
3. S. Baikov, I. Scheps *Concert*
(7/93) (CDM) ① [3] **LDC288 038/40**
4. A. Martynov, A. Konstantinidi *Concert*
(7/93) (CDM) ① [3] **LDC288 038/40**
4. V. Bogachev, Montreal I Musici, Y. Turovsky (r1992: orch V. Milman) *Concert*
(9/93) (CHAN) ① **CHAN9149**

4 Songs—1v and piano, Op. 4 (1866)
1. What is my name to thee? (wds. Pushkin); 2. The messenger (wds. Heine, trans Mikhaylov); 3. In the dark grove the nightingale is silent (wds. I. Nitkin); 4. Quietly evening falls (wds. A. Fet).
1, 3. A. Martynov, A. Konstantinidi *Concert*
(7/93) (CDM) ① [3] **LDC288 038/40**

2. S. Baikov, I. Scheps *Concert*
(7/93) (CDM) ① [3] **LDC288 038/40**
4. N. Gerassimova, V. Skanavi *Concert*
(7/93) (CDM) ① [3] **LDC288 038/40**

4 Songs—1v and piano, Op. 7 (1867)
1. My voice for thee is sweet and languid (wds. Pushkin); 2. Hebrew song (wds. L. Mey); 3. Switezianka (wds. Mickiewicz, trans L. Mey); 4. Thy glance is radiant as the heavens (wds. Lermontov).
1, 2. M. Shutova, E. Cheglakova *Concert*
(7/93) (CDM) ① [3] **LDC288 038/40**
3. N. Gerassimova, V. Skanavi *Concert*
(7/93) (CDM) ① [3] **LDC288 038/40**
4. M. Lanskoy, I. Scheps *Concert*
(7/93) (CDM) ① [3] **LDC288 038/40**

6 Songs—1v and piano, Op. 8 (1868-1870)
1. Where thou art, my thoughts flies to thee (wds. anon: 1870); 2. Night (wds. Pleshcheyev: 1868); 3. The secret (wds. after Chamisso: 1868); 4. Arise, come down! (wds. L. Mey: 1868); 5. In the kingdom of roses and wine (wds. A. Fet: 1870); 6. I believe I love (wds. Pushkin: 1870).
1, 2. M. Shutova, E. Cheglakova *Concert*
(7/93) (CDM) ① [3] **LDC288 038/40**
3. N. Gerassimova, V. Skanavi *Concert*
(7/93) (CDM) ① [3] **LDC288 038/40**
4, 6. M. Lanskoy, I. Scheps *Concert*
(7/93) (CDM) ① [3] **LDC288 038/40**
5. N. Zabela-Vrubel, anon (r1912) *Concert*
(6/93) (PEAR) ① [3] **GEMMCDS9004/6(1)**
5. A. Martynov, A. Konstantinidi *Concert*
(7/93) (CDM) ① [3] **LDC288 038/40**

2 Songs—1v and piano, Op. 25 (Wds. Heine, trans M. Mikhaylov)
1. To my song (1870); 2. When I gaze into thy eyes (1876).
1. S. Baikov, I. Scheps *Concert*
(7/93) (CDM) ① [3] **LDC288 038/40**
2. A. Martynov, A. Konstantinidi *Concert*
(7/93) (CDM) ① [3] **LDC288 038/40**

4 Songs—1v and piano, Op. 26 (1882)
1. In moment to delight devotes (wds. Byron, trans I. Kozlov); 2. Evocation (wds. Pushkin); 3. For the shores of thy far native land (wds. Pushkin); 4. Zuleika's song (wds. Byron, trans I. Kozlov).
1. A. Martynov, A. Konstantinidi *Concert*
(7/93) (CDM) ① [3] **LDC288 038/40**
2, 3. M. Lanskoy, I. Scheps *Concert*
(7/93) (CDM) ① [3] **LDC288 038/40**
4. M. Shutova, E. Cheglakova *Concert*
(7/93) (CDM) ① [3] **LDC288 038/40**

4 Songs—1v and piano, Op. 27 (1883)
1. Softly the spirit flew up to heaven (wds. A. K. Tolstoy); 2. The echo (wds. F. Coupée, trans S. Andreyevsky); 3. Thou and you (wds. Pushkin); 4. Forgive! Remember not these tearful days (wds. N. Nekrasov).
1, 4. N. Gerassimova, V. Skanavi *Concert*
(7/93) (CDM) ① [3] **LDC288 038/40**
2. A. Martynov, A. Konstantinidi *Concert*
(7/93) (CDM) ① [3] **LDC288 038/40**
3. A. Martynov, A. Konstantinidi *Concert*
(7/93) (CDM) ① [3] **LDC288 038/40**

4 Songs—1v and piano, Op. 39 (1897) (Wds. A. K. Tolstoy)
1. Oh, if thou couldst for one moment; 2. The west dies out in pallid rose; 3. Silence descends on the golden cornfields; 4. Sleep, my poor friend.
1, 4. M. Lanskoy, I. Scheps *Concert*
(7/93) (CDM) ① [3] **LDC288 038/40**
2, 3. S. Baikov, I. Scheps *Concert*
(7/93) (CDM) ① [3] **LDC288 038/40**

4 Songs—1v and piano, Op. 40 (1897)
1. When the golden cornfield waves (wds. Lermontov); 2. Across the midnight sky (wds. Lermontov); 3. Of what I dream in the quiet sky (wds. A. Maykov); 4. I waited for thee in the grotto at the appointed hour (wds. A. Maykov).
1, 2. S. Baikov, I. Scheps *Concert*
(7/93) (CDM) ① [3] **LDC288 038/40**
3. N. Gerassimova, V. Skanavi *Concert*
(7/93) (CDM) ① [3] **LDC288 038/40**
3. O. Borodina, L. Gergieva (r1994) *Concert*
(8/95) (PHIL) ① **442 780-2PH**
4. M. Lanskoy, I. Scheps *Concert*
(7/93) (CDM) ① [3] **LDC288 038/40**

4 Songs—1v and piano, Op. 41 (1897)
1. Sun of the sleepless (wds. A. K. Tolstoy, after Byron); 2. I am unhappy (wds. Lermontov); 3. I love thee, moon (wds. A. Maykov); 4. Look in thy garden (wds. A. Maykov).
1, 3, 4. A. Martynov, A. Konstantinidi *Concert*
(7/93) (CDM) ① [3] **LDC288 038/40**
2. M. Lanskoy, I. Scheps *Concert*
(7/93) (CDM) ① [3] **LDC288 038/40**

4 Songs—1v and piano, Op. 42 (1897)
1. A whisper, a gentle breath (wds. A. Fet); 2. I have come to greet thee (wds. A. Fet); 3. The clouds begin to scatter (wds. Pushkin); 4. My spoiled darling (wds. Mickiewicz, trans Mey).
1, 2, 4. A. Martynov, A. Konstantinidi *Concert*
(7/93) (CDM) ① [3] **LDC288 038/40**
3. N. Gerassimova, V. Skanavi *Concert*
(7/93) (CDM) ① [3] **LDC288 038/40**
3. V. Bogachev, Montreal I Musici, Y. Turovsky (r1992: orch V. Milman) *Concert*
(9/93) (CHAN) ① **CHAN9149**
3. D. Hvorostovsky, M. Arkadiov *Concert*
(2/95) (PHIL) ① **442 536-2PH**
3. O. Borodina, L. Gergieva (r1994) *Concert*
(8/95) (PHIL) ① **442 780-2PH**

2 Songs—1v and piano, Op. 49 (1882-97) (Wds. Pushkin)
1. The upas tree; 2. The prophet.
2. F. Chaliapin, orch. A. Coates (r1927) *Concert*
(6/93) (PREI) ① [2] **89207**

4 Songs—1v and piano, Op. 50 (1897-98) (Wds. Myakov, after modern Greek poets)
1. The maiden and the sun (1897); 2. The singer (1897); 3. Quiet is ther blue sea (1897); 4. I an still filled, dear friend (1898).
1. N. Gerassimova, V. Skanavi *Concert*
(7/93) (CDM) ① [3] **LDC288 038/40**
2-4. A. Martynov, A. Konstantinidi *Concert*
(7/93) (CDM) ① [3] **LDC288 038/40**

5 Songs—1v and piano, Op.51 (1897) (Wds. Pushkin)
1. Slowly drag my days; 2. Do not sing to me, o lovely one; 3. Withered flower; 4. The beauty; 5. The rainy day has waned.
1, 3. N. Gerassimova, V. Skanavi *Concert*
(7/93) (CDM) ① [3] **LDC288 038/40**
2, 4. A. Martynov, A. Konstantinidi *Concert*
(7/93) (CDM) ① [3] **LDC288 038/40**
5. M. Lanskoy, I. Scheps *Concert*
(7/93) (CDM) ① [3] **LDC288 038/40**

4 Songs—1v and piano, Op. 55 (1897-98)
1. Awakening (wds. Pushkin: 1897); 2. To the Grecian girl (wds. Pushkin: 1898); 3. The dream (wds. Pushkin: 1898); 4. I died from happiness (wds. L. Uhland, trans ?Zhukovsky).
Cpte A. Martynov, A. Konstantinidi *Concert*
(7/93) (CDM) ① [3] **LDC288 038/40**

2 Songs—1v and piano, Op. 56 (Wds. Maykov)
1. The nymph; 2. Summer night's dream.
Cpte N. Gerassimova, V. Skanavi *Concert*
(7/93) (CDM) ① [3] **LDC288 038/40**

To the poet—song cycle: 1v and piano, Op. 45 (1897-99)
1. The echo (wds. Pushkin: 1897); 2. Art (wds. A. Maykov: 1897); 3. The octave (wds. A. Maykov: 1897); 4. Doubt (wds. A. Maykov: 1897); 5. The poet (wds. Pushkin: 1899).
1, 2, 5. A. Martynov, A. Konstantinidi *Concert*
(7/93) (CDM) ① [3] **LDC288 038/40**
3. D. Hvorostovsky, M. Arkadiov *Concert*
(2/95) (PHIL) ① **442 536-2PH**
3. O. Borodina, L. Gergieva (r1994) *Concert*
(8/95) (PHIL) ① **442 780-2PH**
3, 4. N. Gerassimova, V. Skanavi *Concert*
(7/93) (CDM) ① [3] **LDC288 038/40**

SECTION V: STAGE WORKS

Christmas Eve—opera: 4 acts (1895—St Petersburg) (Lib. cpsr, after Gogol)
1. Christmas night; 2. Ballet of the stars; 3. Witches' sabbath and ride on the Devil's back; 4. Polonaise; 5. Vakula and the slippers.
Koliadka Bolshoi Th Chor, Bolshoi SO, A. Lazarev (r1993) *Concert* (5/94) (ERAT) ① **4509-91723-2**
1-5. Armenian PO, L. Tjeknavorian *Concert*
(9/92) (ASV) ① **CDDCA772**
1-5. SRO, E. Ansermet (r1958) *Concert*
(9/95) (DECC) ① [2] **443 464-2DF2**

The Golden Cockerel—concert suite from opera (prep. Glazunov & M. Steinberg)
1. Introduction and Dodon's sleep; 2. King Dodon on the battlefield; 3. Queen of Shemakha's Dance; King Dodon's Dance; 4. Wedding Feast, Death of King Dodon and Finale.
1, 4 (pt) Bratislava RSO, O. Lénárd *Concert*
(10/90) (NAXO) ① **8 550098**
1-4. Armenian PO, L. Tjeknavorian *Concert*
(9/92) (ASV) ① **CDDCA772**
1-4. Bratislava RSO, D. Johanos *Concert*
(9/92) (NAXO) ① **8 550486**
1-4. Philh, E. Kurtz (r1961) *Concert*
(9/93) (EMI) ① **CZS7 67729-2**
1-4. Bolshoi SO, A. Lazarev (r1992) *Concert*
(8/94) (ERAT) ① **4509-94808-2**

The **Golden Cockerel, '(Le) Coq d'Or'—opera: 3 acts (1909—Moscow)** (Lib. Bel'sky, sfter Pushkin)
EXCERPTS: 1. Overture. ACT 2: 2. Hymn to the Sun. ACT 3: 3. Wedding March.
2. L. Pons, orch, A. Kostelanetz (r1940: French) *Concert*   (4/92) (MSOU) ① **DFCDI-111**
2. L. Kaufman, P. Ulanowsky (r1950s: trans vn/pf: Kreisler) *Concert*   (8/92) (CAMB) ① **CD-1063**
2. A. Nezhdanova, orch (r1910) *Concert*   (6/93) (PEAR) ① [3] **GEMMCDS9007/9(2)**
2. F. Kreisler, C. Lamson (r1921: trans vn/pf: Kreisler) (9/93) (BIDD) ① [2] **LAB068/9**
2. M. Korjus, Berlin St Op Orch, B. Seidler-Winkler (r1936: Ger) *Concert*   (10/93) (PREI) ① **89054**
2. A. Galli-Curci, orch (r1921) *Concert*   (3/94) (CONI) ① **CDHD201**
2. L. Pons, RCA SO, A. Kostelanetz (r1940: Fr) *Concert*   (4/94) (RCA) ① [6] **09026 61580-2(4)**
2. A. Galli-Curci, orch (r1921) *Concert*   (8/94) (NIMB) ① **NI7852**
2. A. Galli-Curci, orch, J. Pasternack (r1921) *Concert*   (8/94) (ROMO) ① [2] **81004-2**
2. J. Heifetz, E. Bay (r1945) *Concert*
Kaschey the Deathless—autumnal parable: 1 act (1902—Moscow) (Lib. cpsr, after E M Petrovsky)
EXCERPTS: 1. Kashcheyevna's Aria; 2. Prince Ivan Karalevich's Aria: In this, night's darkest hour.
2. D. Hvorostovsky, Kirov Th Orch, V. Gergiev (r1993) *Concert*   (5/94) (PHIL) ① **438 872-2PH**
Legend of the Invisible City of Kitezh and the Maiden Fevronia—opera: 4 acts (1907—St Petersburg) (Lib. Bel'sky, after various)
1. Prelude: A Hymn to Nature; 2. Wedding Procession; 3. Tartar invasion and Battle of Kershenets; 4. Death of Fevronia and Apotheosis of the Invisible City.
O vain illusion of glory and grandeur B. Christoff, Philh, W. Schüchter (r1952) *Concert*   (6/93) (EMI) ① **CDH7 64252-2**
The disaster is approaching Bolshoi Th Chor, Bolshoi SO, A. Lazarev (r1993) *Concert*   (5/94) (ERAT) ① **4509-91723-2**
1-4. Saarbrücken RSO, Myung-Whun Chung (r1985) *Shostakovich: Symphony 6.*   (2/92) (SCHW) ① **311202**
The **Maid of Pskov (Ivan the Terrible)—incidental music to L. A. Mey's play (1877 rev 1882: pub 1951)**
EXCERPTS: 1. Overture.
Storm Music LSO, A. Coates (r1932) *Concert*   (12/92) (KOCH) ① **37700-2**
Storm Music Philadelphia, L. Stokowski (r1939) *Concert*   (3/94) (BIDD) ① **WHL010**
1. Russian St SO, E. Svetlanov (r1993) *Concert*   (10/95) (RCA) ① **09026 62684-2**
May Night—opera: 3 acts (1880—St. Petersburg) (Lib. cpsr, after Gogol)
1. Overture.
Sleep, my beauty L. Sobinov, anon (r1901) *Concert*   (6/93) (PEAR) ① [3] **GEMMCDS9997/9(1)**
Sleep, my beauty D. Yuzhin, anon (r1902) *Concert*   (6/93) (PEAR) ① [3] **GEMMCDS9001/3(1)**
Sleep, my beauty L. Sobinov, orch (r1910) *Concert*   (9/94) (NIMB) ① **NI7856**
1. LSO, A. Coates (r1929) *Concert*   (12/92) (KOCH) ① **37700-2**
1. SRO, E. Ansermet *Concert*   (6/94) (BELA) ① **450 132-2**
1. Bolshoi SO, A. Lazarev (r1993) *Concert*   (8/94) (ERAT) ① **4509-94808-2**
1. Philh, C. Silvestri (r1959) *Concert*   (11/94) (EMI) ① [2] **CZS5 68229-2**
1. SRO, E. Ansermet (r1959) *Concert*   (9/95) (DECC) ① [2] **443 464-2DF2**
Mlada—opera-ballet (1872) (collab with Borodin, Cui, Mussorgsky & Minkus)
1. Introduction; 2. Redowa; 3. A Bohemian Dance; 4. Lithuanian Dance; 5. Indian Dance; 6. Procession of the Nobles.
Suite Philh, E. Svetlanov *Holst: Planets.*   (9/92) (COLL) ① **Coll1348-2**
1, 2, 4-6. Bratislava RSO, D. Johanos *Concert*   (9/92) (NAXO) ① **8 550486**
6. Cincinnati Pops, E. Kunzel *Concert*   (9/86) (TELA) ① **CD80115**
6. LSO, A. Coates (r1930) *Concert*   (12/92) (KOCH) ① **37700-2**
6. Bolshoi Th Chor, Bolshoi SO, A. Lazarev (r1993) *Concert*   (5/94) (ERAT) ① **4509-91723-2**
6. Russian St SO, E. Svetlanov (r1993) *Concert*   (10/95) (RCA) ① **09026 62684-2**

Mozart and Salieri—opera: 1 act, Op. 48 (1898—Moscow) (Lib. Pushkin)
Cpte A. Fedin, E. Nesterenko, Bolshoi Th Orch, M. Ermler (r1986) *Mussorgsky: Marriage.*   (9/93) (OLYM) ① **OCD145**
Cpte V. Bogachev, N. Storozhev, Montreal I Musici, Y. Turovsky (r1992) *Concert*   (9/93) (CHAN) ① **CHAN9149**
Sadko—opera: 7 scenes (1898—Moscow) (Lib. cpsr and Bel'sky)
EXCERPTS -; 1. Greetings, ye merchants of Novgorod; 2. O you dark forests (Sadko's aria); 3. O fearful crags (Song of the Viking Guest); 4. Song of the Indian Guest; 5. Song of the Venetian Guest; 6. Farewell, my friends (Sadko's aria); 7. Sleep went along the river (Berceuse); 8. Songs of the Venetian Merchant: 8a. The paragon of cities; 8b. Beautiful city!.
Cpte V. Galusin, V. Tsidipova, S. Alexashkin, M. Tarassova, L. Dyadkova, B. Minzhilkiev, G. Grigorian, A. Gergalov, V. Ognovenko, N. Gassiev, N. Putilin, Y. Boitsov, G. Bezebenkov, Kirov Th Chor, Kirov Th Orch, V. Gergiev (pp1993)   (1/95) (PHIL) ① [3] **442 138-2PH3**
Excs G. Morskoi, anon (r1901) *Concert*   (6/93) (PEAR) ① [3] **GEMMCDS9001/3(1)**
3. F. Chaliapin, orch, A. Coates (r1927) *Concert*   (6/88) (EMI) ① **CDH7 61009-2**
3. A. Kipnis, Victor SO, N. Berezowski (r1945) *Concert*   (9/92) (RCA) ① **GD60522**
3. M. Reizen, Bolshoi Th Orch, N. Golovanov (r1952) *Concert*   (12/92) (PREI) ① **89059**
3. B. Christoff, Philh, I. Dobrowen (r1950) *Concert*   (6/93) (EMI) ① **CDH7 64252-2**
3. L. Sibiriakov, orch (r1905) *Concert*   (6/93) (PEAR) ① [3] **GEMMCDS9001/3(2)**
4. J. Lloyd Webber, RPO, N. Cleobury (arr vc) *Concert*   (3/87) (PHIL) ① **416 698-2PH**
4. A. Galli-Curci, orch (r1922) *Concert*   (2/89) (PEAR) ① **GEMMCD9308**
4. B. Gigli, orch, N. Shilkret (French: r1932) *Concert*   (5/90) (PEAR) ① **GEMMCD9367**
4. E. Feuermann, G. Moore (arr vc/pf: r1939) *Concert*   (10/91) (PEAR) ① **GEMMCD9443**
4. L. Pons, orch, A. Kostelanetz (Fr: r1941) *Concert*   (4/92) (MSOU) ① **DFCDI-111**
4. I. Alchevsky, anon (r1900s) *Concert*   (7/93) (SYMP) ① **SYMCD1105**
4. M. Korjus, Berlin St Op Orch, B. Seidler-Winkler (Ger: r1936) *Concert*   (10/93) (PREI) ① **89054**
4. R. Ponselle, orch, R. Romani (r1920) *Concert*   (9/93) (NIMB) ① **NI7846**
4. F. Kreisler, F. Rupp (r1938: arr Kreisler) *Concert*   (12/93) (EMI) ① **CDH7 64701-2**
4. A. Galli-Curci, orch (r1922) *Concert*   (8/94) (NIMB) ① **NI7852**
4. A. Galli-Curci, orch, J. Pasternack (r1922) *Concert*   (8/94) (ROMO) ① [2] **81004-2**
4. J. Bálint, N. Mercz (r1992: arr fl/hp: Mercz) *Concert*   (12/94) (NAXO) ① **8 550741**
5. P. Lisitsian, Bolshoi Th Orch, N. Golovanov (r c1953) *Concert*   (4/92) (EMI) ① [7] **CHS7 69741-2(6)**
5. P. Lisitsian, Bolshoi Th Orch, N. Golovanov (r1952) *Concert*   (8/93) (PREI) ① **89061**
7. N. Koshetz, orch (r1928) *Concert*   (10/89) (NIMB) ① **NI7802**
7. N. Zabela-Vrubel, anon (r1912) *Concert*   (6/93) (PEAR) ① [3] **GEMMCDS9004/6(1)**
7. A. Nezhdanova, anon (r1907) *Concert*   (6/93) (PEAR) ① [3] **GEMMCDS9007/9(1)**
7. L. Garrett, RPO, P. Robinson (r1994) *Concert*   (4/95) (SILV) ① **SILKD6004**
8a, 8b D. Hvorostovsky, Kirov Th Orch, V. Gergiev (r1993) *Concert*   (5/94) (PHIL) ① **438 872-2PH**
Snow Maiden (second version)—opera: 4 acts (1898—St. Petersburg) (Lib. cpsr, after Ostrovsky)
1. Introduction; 2. Danse des oiseaux; 3. Cortège; 4. Danse des bouffons.
Carnival Procession; Chorus of Blind Psalterists; Song of the Grain Bolshoi Th Chor, Bolshoi SO, A. Lazarev (r1993) *Concert*   (5/94) (ERAT) ① **4509-91723-2**
Clouds plotted with thunder E. Zbrueva, anon (r1903) *Concert*   (6/93) (PEAR) ① [3] **GEMMCDS9004/6(2)**
Going berrying X. Belmas, orch, A. Kitschin (r1929) *Concert*   (10/92) (PREI) ① **89047**
How painful here; But what ails me? L. Lipkowska, orch (r1912) *Concert*   (6/93) (PEAR) ① [3] **GEMMCDS9004/6(1)**
How painful E. Orel, anon (r c1902) *Concert*   (7/93) (SYMP) ① **SYMCD1105**
How painful L. Lipkowska, orch (r1912) *Concert*   (3/95) (NIMB) ① **NI7865**

Joyous day departs L. Sobinov, orch (r1911) *Concert*   (6/93) (PEAR) ① [3] **GEMMCDS9997/9(2)**
Mighty nature, full of wonder L. Sobinov, anon (r1901) *Concert*   (6/93) (PEAR) ① [3] **GEMMCDS9997/9(1)**
Mizgir's Aria: Under the warm blue sea D. Hvorostovsky, Kirov Th Orch, V. Gergiev (r1993) *Concert*   (5/94) (PHIL) ① **438 872-2PH**
So full of wonder I. Zhadan, Bolshoi Th Orch, A. Orlov (r1937) *Concert*   (4/92) (EMI) ① [7] **CHS7 69741-2(6)**
So full of wonder D. Smirnov, orch, J. Harrison (r1924) *Concert*   (6/93) (PEAR) ① [3] **GEMMCDS9004/6(2)**
With friends to gather berries A. Nezhdanova, orch (r1908) *Concert*   (6/93) (PEAR) ① [3] **GEMMCDS9007/9(2)**
1-4. Bratislava RSO, D. Johanos *Concert*   (9/92) (NAXO) ① **8 550486**
1-4. Philh, E. Kurtz (r1963) *Concert*   (9/93) (EMI) ① [2] **CZS7 67729-2**
1-4. Geneva Motet Ch, SRO, E. Ansermet (r1957) *Concert*   (9/95) (DECC) ① [2] **443 464-2DF2**
4. Cincinnati Pops, E. Kunzel *Concert*   (9/86) (TELA) ① **CD80115**
4. LSO, A. Coates (r1932) *Concert*   (12/92) (KOCH) ① **37700-2**
4. NYPO, L. Bernstein (r1967) *Concert*   (9/93) (SONY) ① **SMK47600**
The **Tale of Tsar Saltan—opera: prologue & 4 acts (1900—Moscow)** (Lib. Bel'sky, after Pushkin)
1. Tsar's farewell and departure; 2. Tsarina in a barrel at sea; 3. Flight of the bumble-bee; 4. The three wonders; 5. March.
1, 2, 4. Philh, P. Kletzki (r1958) *Concert*   (9/93) (EMI) ① [2] **CZS7 67726-2**
1, 2, 4. Chicago SO, D. Barenboim (r1993) *Scheherazade.*   (12/93) (ERAT) ① **4509-91717-2**
1, 2, 4. Philh, E. Bátiz (r1992) *Scheherazade.*   (6/94) (NAXO) ① **8 550726**
1, 2, 4. SRO, E. Ansermet (r1959) *Concert*   (9/95) (DECC) ① [2] **443 464-2DF2**
1-4. Armenian PO, L. Tjeknavorian *Concert*   (9/92) (ASV) ① **CDDCA772**
3. J. Lloyd Webber, ECO, N. Cleobury (arr C Palmer) *Concert*   (3/85) (PHIL) ① **412 231-2PH**
3. W. Marsalis, Eastman Wind Ens, D. Hunsberger (arr D Hunsberger) *Concert*   (9/87) (SONY) ① **MK42137**
3. K. Walker, J. Drake (arr bn Waterhouse) *Concert*   (10/89) (REGE) ① **REGCD104**
3. J. Szigeti, N. Magaloff (arr Hartmann: r1933) *Concert*   (1/90) (BIDD) ① [2] **LAB007/8**
3. V. Horowitz (arr Rachmaninov: r1932) *Concert*   (3/90) (EMI) ① [3] **CHS7 63538-2**
3. S. Rachmaninov (r1929: arr Rachmaninov: pf) *Concert*   (5/90) (RCA) ① **GD87766**
3. S. Rachmaninov (arr Rachmaninov: pf roll) *Concert*   (6/90) (DECC) ① **425 964-2DM**
3. I. Stern, Columbia SO, M. Katims (arr Harris) *Concert*   (7/90) (SONY) ① **SK45816**
3. Y. Menuhin, A. Balsam (arr Hartmann: r1932) *Concert*   (9/91) (TEST) ① **SBT1003**
3. J. Heifetz, E. Bay (arr Heifetz: r1932) *Concert*   (12/91) (APR) ① [2] **APR7015**
3. Y. Menuhin, A. Balsam (arr Hartmann: r1932) *Concert*   (12/91) (BIDD) ① **LAB046**
3. H. Shelley (1991: arr pf: Rachmaninov) *Concert*   (3/92) (HYPE) ① **CDA66486**
3. S. Rachmaninov (r1929: arr Rachmaninov: pf) *Concert*   (3/93) (RCA) ① [10] **09026 61265-2(2)**
3. S. Nakarjakov, A. Markovich (arr tpt/pf) *Concert*   (5/93) (TELD) ① **9031-77705-2**
3. N. Milstein, G. Moore (r1932: arr Hartmann) *Concert*   (7/93) (APR) ① [2] **APR7016**
3. W. Lang, M. Murphy, J. Shepherd, P. McCann, Black Dyke Mills Band, P. Parkes (pp1987: arr Woodfield) *Concert*   (11/93) (CHAN) ① **CHAN4513**
3. Chee-Yun, A. Eguchi (trans Heifetz) *Concert*   (12/93) (DENO) ① **CO-75118**
3. J. Weber (1992: arr pf: Rachmaninov) *Concert*   (12/93) (CARL) ① **PCD1051**
3. H. Shelley (1991: arr pf: Rachmaninov) *Concert*   (3/94) (HYPE) ① [8] **CDS44041/8**
3. N. Milstein, L. Pommers (r1956: arr Hartmann) *Concert*   (5/94) (RCA) ① [6] **ZDMF7 64830-2**
3. J. Heifetz, A. Sándor (r1934) *Concert*   (11/94) (RCA) ① [65] **09026 61778-2(02)**
3. J. Heifetz, E. Bay (r1946) *Concert*   (11/94) (RCA) ① [65] **09026 61778-2(06)**
3. Philh, D.V. Yu (r1993) *Concert*   (1/95) (CARL) ① **MCD82**
3. SRO, E. Ansermet (r1958) *Concert*   (9/95) (DECC) ① [2] **443 464-2DF2**

3. A. Janigro, D. Lipatti (r1947: arr vc/pf) *Concert*
(10/95) (ARCI) ① **ARC112/3**
3. G. Malcolm (r1962; arr Malcolm) *Concert*
(11/95) (DECC) ① **444 390-2DWO**
3. Boston Pops, A. Fiedler (r1958) *Concert*
(12/95) (RCA) ① **09026 68132-2**
4. Russian St SO, E. Svetlanov (r1993) *Concert*
(10/95) (RCA) ① **09026 62684-2**
5. RPO, A. Previn (r1984) *Tchaikovsky: Symphony 5.*
(5/85) (TELA) ① **CD80107**

The **Tsar's Bride—opera: 4 acts**
(1899—Moscow) (Lib. I F Tyumnrrv, after
May)
EXCERPTS: 1. Overture.
Cpte P. Gluboky, E. Kudriavchenko, V. Verestinkov,
N. Nizinenko, A. Mishenkin, N. Terentieva, V.
Kudriashov, I. Udalova, E. Okolycheva, T. Pechuria,
V. Pashinsky, N. Larionova, Y. Markelov, Russian
Academy Ch, Bolshoi Th Orch, A. Chistiakov
(r1992) (8/93) (CDM) ① [2] **LDC288 056/7**
All the livelong day L. Lipkowska, orch (r1912)
Concert
(6/93) (PEAR) ① [3] **GEMMCDS9004/6(1)**
Gryaznoy's Aria: Still the beauty haunts my mind
D. Hvorostovsky, Kirov Th Orch, V. Gergiev (r1993)
Concert (8/94) (PHIL) ① **438 872-2PH**
Haste thee, mother mine Y. Menuhin, H. Giesen
(arr Franko: r1930) *Concert*
(4/91) (BIDD) ① **LAB032**
Haste thee, mother mine Y. Menuhin, H. Giesen
(arr Franko: r1930) *Concert*
(9/91) (TEST) ① **SBT1003**
Hop-Picker's Chorus Bolshoi Th Chor, Bolshoi SO,
A. Lazarev (r1993) *Concert*
(5/94) (ERAT) ① **4509-91723-2**
In Novgorod M. Korjus, Berlin St Op Orch, B.
Seidler-Winkler (Ger: r1936) *Concert*
(10/93) (PREI) ① **89054**
Ivan Sergeivich, come into the garden M.
Seinemeyer, Berlin St Op Orch, F. Weissmann (Ger:
r1927) *Concert* (11/90) (PREI) ① **89029**
Look there, above your head A. Nezhdanova, orch
(r1912) *Concert*
(6/93) (PEAR) ① [3] **GEMMCDS9007/9(2)**
Overture Bolshoi SO, A. Lazarev (r1992) *Concert*
(5/94) (ERAT) ① **4509-94808-2**
Overture Russian Nat Orch, M. Pletnev *Concert*
(12/94) (DG) ① **439 892-2GH**
She lay asleep L. Sibiriakov, anon (r1905) *Concert*
(6/93) (PEAR) ① [3] **GEMMCDS9001/3(2)**
The threatening cloud has passed away G.
Morskoi, anon (r1901) *Concert*
(6/93) (PEAR) ① [3] **GEMMCDS9001/3(1)**
1. Russian St SO, E. Svetlanov (r1993) *Concert*
(10/95) (RCA) ① **09026 62684-2**

RIPA, Alberto da (c1500–1551)
Italy

sometimes known as Ripa da Mantova

SECTION III: INSTRUMENTAL

L' Eccho—lute intabulation (after Gentian)
P. O'Dette (r1990-2) *Concert*
(10/95) (HARM) ① **HMU90 7043**
Fantasias—lute (numbering from Jean-Michel
Vaccaro, 1975)
EXCERPTS: 8. No. VIII; 22. No. XXII; 23. No. XXIII;
24. No. XXIV.
8, 22. P. O'Dette (r1990-2) *Concert*
(10/95) (HARM) ① **HMU90 7043**

RIPPE, Albert de (c1500–c1551)
France

SECTION III: INSTRUMENTAL

Fantasie II—lute (1552)
E. Bellocq (r1993) *Concert*
(2/95) (HARM) ① **HMC90 1491**

RIQUIER, Guiraut (c1230–c1300)
France

SECTION IV: VOCAL AND CHORAL

Be.m degra de chantar tener—chanson
P. Hillier, S. Stubbs, A. Lawrence-King, E. Headley
Concert (7/89) (ECM) ① **837 360-2**
Jhesu Cristz filh de Dieu vlu—chanson
(1275)
E. Lamandier *Concert* (2/88) (ALIE) ① **AL1019**

RITTER, Christian (1645/50–after
1717) Germany

SECTION III: INSTRUMENTAL

Sonatina in D minor—organ
G. Leonhardt *Concert* (10/94) (SONY) ① **SK53371**

RITTLER, Philipp Jakob
(c1637–1690) Germany

SECTION IV: VOCAL AND CHORAL

Ave regina coelorum—motet
Niederaltaicher Scholaren, K. Ruhland (r1992)
Concert (10/93) (SONY) ① **SK53117**

RIVIER, Jean (1896–1987)
France

SECTION II: CHAMBER

Sonatina for violin and cello (1937)
E. Turovsky, Y. Turovsky *Concert*
(7/85) (CHAN) ① **CHAN8358**

ROBAUDI, Vincenzo (1819–1882)
Italy

SECTION IV: VOCAL AND CHORAL

Alla stella confidente—song
F. Corradetti, anon (r1907) *Concert*
(12/94) (BONG) ① **GB1043-2**

ROBBINS, Richard (20th cent)
USA

SECTION V: STAGE WORKS

The **Remains of the Day—film score (1993)**
EXCERPTS: 1. Opening Titles: Darlington Hall; 2.
The Keyhole and the Chinaman; 3. Tradition and
Order; 4. The Conference Begins; 5. Sei mir
Gegrüsst (Schubert); 6. The Cooks in the Kitchen; 7.
Sir Geoffrey Wren and Stevens, Sr; 8. You Mean a
Great Deal to this House; 9. Loss and Separation; 10.
Blue Moon (Rodgers); 11a. Sentimental Love Story;
11b. Appeasement; 11c. In the Rain; 12a. A Portrait
Returns; 12b. Darlington Hall; 12c. End Credits.
1. OST (r1993) *Concert* (9/95) (VIR2) ① **CDV2774**
1-10, 11a-c, 12a-c OST, H. Rabinowitz (r1993)
(8/94) (EMI) ① **CDQ5 55029-2**
A **Room With a View—film score (1986)**
EXCERPTS: 1. The Pensione Bertollini.
1. OST (r1986) *Concert* (9/95) (VIR2) ① **CDV2774**

ROBERDAY, François
(1624–1689) France

SECTION III: INSTRUMENTAL

Fugue and Caprice No. 3—organ (c1660)
J. Payne (r1994) *Concert*
(10/95) (NAXO) ① **8 553215**

ROBERTON, Sir Hugh S
(1874–1952) Scotland

SECTION IV: VOCAL AND CHORAL

The **Fidgety bairn—song**
L. Finnie, A. Legge *Concert*
(4/90) (CHAN) ① **CHAN8749**
O hush thee, my babie—song
L. Finnie, A. Legge *Concert*
(4/90) (CHAN) ① **CHAN8749**

ROBERTS, John (1822–1877)
Wales

SECTION IV: VOCAL AND CHORAL

Immortal, invisible, God only wise—hymn
(tune: St Denio)
St Paul's Cath Ch, C. Dearnley, John Scott *Concert*
(7/90) (HYPE) ① **CDH88036**

ROBERTS, Myron J. (b 1912)
USA

SECTION III: INSTRUMENTAL

Pastorale and Aviary—organ
J. Jones *Concert* (8/91) (MOTE) ① **CD11491**

ROBINSON, Thomas (fl
1589–1609) England

SECTION III: INSTRUMENTAL

The **Spanish pavan—lute (pub 1603)** (from
The Schoole of Musicke)
C. Wilson *Concert* (11/91) (VIRG) ① **VC7 59034-2**

ROBYN, Alfred George
(1860–1935) USA

SECTION V: STAGE WORKS

The **Yankee Consul—musical show**
(1904—New York) (Lyrics Blossom)
EXCERPTS: 1. Ain't it Funny What a Difference Just
a Few Hours Make?; 2. In the Days of Old.
1, 2. R. Hitchcock, Broadway Cast (r1910) *Concert*
(5/94) (PEAR) ① [3] **GEMMCDS9050/2(2)**

ROCHBERG, George (b 1918)
USA

SECTION I: ORCHESTRAL

Concerto for Oboe and Orchestra (1984)
J. Robinson, NYPO, Z. Mehta *Druckman: Prism.*
(9/87) (NEW) ① **NW335-2**

SECTION II: CHAMBER

Between Two Worlds (Ukiyo-e III)—five
images: flute and piano (1982)
1. Fantasia; 2. Scherzoso (Fast Dance); 3. Night
Scene A; 4. Sarabande (Slow Dance); 5. Night Scene
B.
A. Still, S. De Witt Smith (r1992) *Concert*
(4/94) (KOCH) ① **37144-2**
Piano Quartet (1983)
American Chbr Players *Concert*
(7/91) (KOCH) ① **37027-2**

SECTION III: INSTRUMENTAL

Carnival Music—piano (1969)
1. Fanfares and March; 2. Blues; 3. Largo Doloroso;
4. Stumato; 5. Toccata Rag.
J. McCabe *Concert*
(6/91) (CNTI) ① [2] **CCD1028/9**

RODE, Pierre Jacques Joseph
(1744–1830) France

SECTION III: INSTRUMENTAL

24 Caprices—violin, Op. 24
2. A minor; 8. F sharp minor; 17. A flat; 18. F minor,
'Minute Caprice'; 21. B flat.
O. Shumsky (1/89) (EBS) ① **EBS6007**

RODGERS, Richard (1902–1979)
USA

SECTION V: STAGE WORKS

Allegro—musical show (1947—New York)
(Lyrics O. Hammerstein II)
EXCERPTS: 1. Overture.
1. Hollywood Bowl SO, J. Mauceri *Concert*
(9/92) (PHIL) ① **434 127-2PH**
Babes in Arms—musical show, later film
(1937; film, 1939—New York) (Lyrics L. Hart)
EXCERPTS: 1. The Lady is a Tramp; 2. Johnny One
Note; 3. Where or When; 4. I Wish I Were in Love
Again; 5. My Funny Valentine.
My funny Valentine; Where or when F. von Stade,
LSO, J. McGlinn *Concert*
(2/91) (EMI) ① **CDC7 54071-2**
2. K. Criswell, London Sinfonietta, J. McGlinn (1992)
Concert (4/94) (EMI) ① **CDC7 54802-2**
3. M. Patinkin, Orch, E. Stern (r1993; orch Troob, arr
Ford) *Concert* (11/94) (NONE) ① **7559-79330-2**
3-5. J. Andrews, London Musicians Orch, I. Fraser
(r1994; orch B. Byers & I. Fraser) *Concert*
(1/95) (PHIL) ① **442 603-2PH**
Betsy—musical show (1926—New York)
(lyrics L. Hart)
If you were there F. von Stade, R. Ashe, L.
Richardson, P. Bartlett, LSO, J. McGlinn *Concert*
(2/91) (EMI) ① **CDC7 54071-2**
The **Boys from Syracuse—musical show**
(1938—New York) (lyrics L. Hart, after
Shakespeare)
EXCERPTS: 1. Overture. ACT ONE: 2. He Had
Twins; 3. Dear Old Syracuse; 4. What Can You Do
With a Man?; 5. Falling in Love With Love; 6. The
Shortest Day of the Year; 7. This Can't Be Love. ACT

TWO: 8. Ladies of the Evening; 9. He and She; 10. You Have Cast Your Shadow on the Sea; 11. Come With Me; 12. The Ballet; 13. Sing for Your Supper; 14. Oh, Diogenes; 15. Finale.
Cpte Revival Cast (11/93) (EMI) ① **ZDM7 64695-2**
5. F. von Stade, Ambrosian Chor, LSO, J. McGlinn Concert (2/91) (EMI) ① **CDC7 54071-2**
5. J. Norman, J.T. Williams (r1987) Concert (4/92) (PHIL) ① **422 401-2PH**
7. J. Andrews, London Musicians Orch, I. Fraser (r1994; orch B. Florence) Concert (1/95) (PHIL) ① **442 603-2PH**

Carousel—musical show (1945—New York) (Lyrics O. Hammerstein II)
EXCERPTS: 1. Introduction (Heaven). ACT 1: 2. The Carousel Waltz; 3. You're a queer one, Julie Jordan; 4. Mister Snow; 5. If I loved you; 6. June is bustin' out all over; 7. When the children are asleep; 8. Blow high, blow low; 9. Soliloquy. ACT 2: 10. This a real nice clambake; 11. When the children are asleep; 11a. Geraniums in the winter; 11b. Stonecutters cut in stone; 12. What's the use of wond'rin'; 13. There's nothing so bad for a woman; 14. You'll never walk alone; 15. The Highest Judge of All; 16. You'll never walk alone (reprise).
1, 2. Hollywood Bowl SO, J. Mauceri (r1991) Concert (9/91) (PHIL) ① **432 109-2PH**
1, 4-10, 11a, 11b, 12, 14. London Cast (r1993) (5/94) (FRST) ① **CASTCD40**
2. J. Andrews, London Musicians Orch, I. Fraser (r1994; medley orch B. Byers) Concert (1/95) (PHIL) ① **442 603-2PH**
5. Hollywood Bowl SO, J. Mauceri Concert (9/92) (PHIL) ① **434 127-2PH**
5. V. Masterson, T. Allen, Philh, J.O. Edwards (r1990) Concert (5/94) (TER) ① **CDVIR8317**
5. J. Andrews, London Musicians Orch, I. Fraser (r1994; orch A. Morley) Concert (1/95) (PHIL) ① **442 603-2PH**
14. Glasgow CWS Band, H. Snell (arr Snell) Concert (9/92) (DOYE) ① **DOYCD005**

Carousel—musical show based on show (1956) (Lyrics O Hammerstein II)
EXCERPTS: 1. The Carousel Waltz; 2. You're a Queer One, Julie Jordan; 3. Mr Snow; 4. If I Loved You; 5. When the Children Are Asleep; 6. June is Bustin' Out All Over; 7. Soliloquy; 8. Blow High, Blow Low; 9. A Real Nice Clambake; 10. Stonecutters Cut It On Stone; 11. What's the use of Wond'rin; 12. You'll Never Walk Alone; 13. If I Loved You (reprise); 14. Finale: You'll Never Walk Alone (chorus).
Cpte G. MacRae, Shirley Jones, Orig Film Cast, Alfred Newman (r1956) (11/93) (EMI) ① **ZDM7 64692-2**

Chee-Chee—musical show (1928—New York) (lyrics L. Hart)
I must love you; Moon of my delight F. von Stade, LSO, J. McGlinn Concert (2/91) (EMI) ① **CDC7 54071-2**

Cinderella—television musical (1957) (Lyrics O. Hammerstein II, after Perrault)
EXCERPTS: 1. Overture; 2. Waltz for a Ball; 3. In My Own Little Corner; 4. Do I Love You Because You're So Beautiful?.
1. Hollywood Bowl SO, J. Mauceri Concert (9/92) (PHIL) ① **434 127-2PH**

A Connecticut Yankee—musical show (1927, revived 1943—New York) (Lyrics L. Hart, after Mark Twain)
EXCERPTS: 1. Overture; 2. My Heart Stood Still; 3. Thou Swell; 4. On a Desert Island; 5. To Keep My Love Alive; 6. Can't You Do a Friend a Favor?; 7. I Feel at Home With You; 8. You Always Love the Same Girl; 9. Finale.
To keep my love alive F. von Stade, LSO, J. McGlinn Concert (2/91) (EMI) ① **CDC7 54071-2**
3. J. Andrews, London Musicians Orch, I. Fraser (r1994; orch B. Florence) Concert (1/95) (PHIL) ① **442 603-2PH**

Dearest Enemy—musical show (1925) (lyrics L. Hart)
Bye and bye F. von Stade, LSO, J. McGlinn Concert (2/91) (EMI) ① **CDC7 54071-2**

Do I Hear a Waltz?—musical show (1965—New York) (Lyrics S. Sondheim; Book A. Laurents)
EXCERPTS: ACT ONE: 1. Someone Woke Up; 2. This Week, Americans; 3. What Do We Do? We Fly!; 4. Someone Like You; 5. Bargaining; 6. Here We Are Again; 7. Thinking; 8. No Understand; 9. Take the Moment. ACT TWO: 10. Moon in My Window; 11. We're Gonna Be All Right; 12. Do I Hear a Waltz?; 13. Stay; 14. Perfectly Lovely Couple; 15. Thank You So Much.

12. J. Andrews, London Musicians Orch, I. Fraser (r1994; medley orch B. Byers) Concert (1/95) (PHIL) ① **442 603-2PH**

Flower Drum Song—musical show (1958—New York) (Books/Lyrics J. Field & O. Hammerstein II)
EXCERPTS: 1. Overture. ACT ONE: 2. You Are Beautiful; 3. A Hundred Million Miracles; 4. I Enjoy Being a Girl; 5. I Am Going To Like It Here; 6. Like A God; 7. Chop Suey; 8. Don't Marry Me; 9. Grant Avenue; 10. Love Look Away; 11. Fan tan Fannie; 12. Gliding Through My Memoree. ACT TWO: 13. The Other Generation; 14. Sunday; 15. The Other Generation (reprise); 16. Finale.
Cpte Orig London Cast, R. Lowe (r1960) (12/94) (EMI) ① **CDANGEL 7**
1. Hollywood Bowl SO, J. Mauceri Concert (9/92) (PHIL) ① **434 127-2PH**

Heads Up!—musical show (1929—New York) (lyrics L. Hart)
A ship without a sail F. von Stade, LSO, J. McGlinn Concert (2/91) (EMI) ① **CDC7 54071-2**

Higher and Higher—musical show (1940—New York) (Lyrics L. Hart)
EXCERPTS: 1. It Never Entered My Mind.
1. K. Criswell, London Sinfonietta, J. McGlinn (r1992) Concert (4/94) (EMI) ① **CDC7 54802-2**
1. J. Andrews, London Musicians Orch, I. Fraser (r1994; orch B. Byers) Concert (1/95) (PHIL) ① **442 603-2PH**

I'd Rather Be Right—musical show (1937—New York) (lyrics L. Hart)
Ev'rybody loves you F. von Stade, LSO, J. McGlinn Concert (2/91) (EMI) ① **CDC7 54071-2**

The King and I—musical show (1951—New York) (Lyrics O. Hammerstein II)
EXCERPTS: 1. Overture; 2. I Whistle a Happy Tune; 3. My Lord and Master; 4. Hello, Young Lovers; 5. March of the Royal Siamese Children; 6. A Puzzlement; 7. Getting to Know You; 8. We Kiss in a Shadow; 9. Shall I Tell You What I Think of You?; 10. Something Wonderful; 11. Western People Funny; 12. I Have Dreamed; 13. Shall We Dance?; 14. Dance of Anna and Sir Edward. ADDITIONAL ITEMS: 15. Arrival at Bangkok; 16. Children Sing, Priests Chant; 17. The Royal Bangkok Academy; 18. So Big a World; 19. Act 1 Finale; 20. Finale.
Cpte J. Andrews, B. Kingsley, P. Bryson, L. Salonga, M. Horne, R. Moore, M. Sheen, Hollywood Bowl Orch, J. Mauceri (10/92) (PHIL) ① **438 007-2PH**
1. Hollywood Bowl SO, J. Mauceri Concert (9/92) (PHIL) ① **434 127-2PH**
4. V. Masterson, Philh, J.O. Edwards (r1990) Concert (5/94) (TER) ① **CDVIR8317**
5. Boston Pops, A. Fiedler (r1964) (1/94) (RCA) ① **09026 61249-2**
12. V. Masterson, T. Allen, Philh, J.O. Edwards (r1990) Concert (5/94) (TER) ① **CDVIR8317**
12. J. Andrews, London Musicians Orch, I. Fraser (r1994; orch E. Karam) Concert (1/95) (PHIL) ① **442 603-2PH**

The King and I—musical film based on show (1956) (Lyrics O Hammerstein II)
EXCERPTS: 1. Overture; 2. I Whistle a Happy Tune; 3. My Lord and Master; 4. Hello, Young Lovers; 5. The March of the Siamese Children; 6. A Puzzlement; 7. Getting to Know You; 8. We Kiss in a Shadow; 9. I Have Dreamed; 10. Shall I Tell You What I Think of You?; 11. Something Wonderful; 12. Song of the King; 13. Shall We Dance?; 14. Something Wonderful (chorus).
Cpte Y. Brynner, M. Nixon, Orig Film Cast (r1956) (11/93) (EMI) ① **ZDM7 64693-2**

Lido Lady—musical show (1926—London) (Lyrics L. Hart)
EXCERPTS: 1. Here In My Arms.
Atlantic blues F. von Stade, LSO, J. McGlinn Concert (2/91) (EMI) ① **CDC7 54071-2**

Love Me Tonight—musical film (1932) (Lyrics L. Hart)
EXCERPTS: 1. That's the Song of Paree; 2. Isn't It Romantic?; 3. Lover; 4. Mimi; 5. A Woman Needs Something; 6. The Poor Apache; 7. Love Me Tonight.
3. J. Norman, J.T. Williams (r1987) Concert (4/92) (PHIL) ① **422 401-2PH**

Me and Juliet—musical show (1953—New York) (Lyrics O. Hammerstein II)
EXCERPTS: 1. Overture.
1. Hollywood Bowl SO, J. Mauceri Concert (9/92) (PHIL) ① **434 127-2PH**

No Strings—musical show (1962—New York) (Lyrics cpsr)
EXCERPTS: 1. Nobody Told Me.
Cpte R. Kiley, Diahann Carroll, Orig Broadway Cast (11/93) (EMI) ① **ZDM7 64694-2**

1. J. Andrews, London Musicians Orch, I. Fraser (r1994; orch E. Karam) Concert (1/95) (PHIL) ① **442 603-2PH**

Oklahoma!—musical show (1943) (Lyrics O. Hammerstein)
EXCERPTS: 1. Overture; 2. Oh, What a Beautiful Mornin'; 3. I Caint Say No; 4. Kansas City; 5. Oklahoma; 6. People Will Say We're In Love; 7. The Surrey with the Fringe on Top; 8. Out of My Dreams; 9. Pore Jud is Daid; 10. All er Nothin'; 11. The Farmer and the Cowman; 12. Many a New Day.
1. Hollywood Bowl SO, J. Mauceri Concert (9/92) (PHIL) ① **434 127-2PH**
2. H. Donath, K. Donath (pp1994; parody version) (1/95) (RCA) ① **09026 62547-2**
2, 8. J. Andrews, London Musicians Orch, I. Fraser (r1994; medley orch B. Byers) Concert (1/95) (PHIL) ① **442 603-2PH**
6. V. Masterson, T. Allen, Philh, J.O. Edwards (r1990) Concert (5/94) (TER) ① **CDVIR8317**
8. M. Hill Smith, Philh, J.O. Edwards (r1989-91) Concert (10/91) (TER) ① **CDVIR8314**

Oklahoma!—musical film based on show (1955) (Lyrics O. Hammerstein II)
EXCERPTS: 1. Overture; 2. Oh, What a Beautiful Mornin'; 3. The Surrey With the Fringe on Top; 4. Kansas City; 5. I Cain't Say No; 6. Many a New Day; 7. People Will Say We're in Love; 8. Poor Jud is Daid; 9. Out of My Dreams; 10. The Farmer and the Cowman; 11. All er Nothin'; 12. Oklahoma.
Cpte G. MacRae, Shirley Jones, Orig Film Cast (r1955) (11/93) (EMI) ① **ZDM7 64691-2**

On Your Toes—musical show (1936, revived 1983—New York) (Lyrics L. Hart)
EXCERPTS: 1. Overture; 2. Two a Day for Keith; 3. Questions and Answers; 4. It's Got to be Love; 5. Too Good for the Average Man; 6. There's a Small Hotel; 7. La Princesse Zenobia Ballet; 8. The Heart is Quicker Than the Eye; 9. Glad to be Unhappy; 10. Quiet Night; 11. On Your Toes; 12. Slaughter on Tenth Avenue.
Quiet night F. von Stade, LSO, J. McGlinn Concert (2/91) (EMI) ① **CDC7 54071-2**

Pal Joey—musical show (1940—New York) (Lyrics L. Hart; Book J. O'Hara)
EXCERPTS: 1. Overture; 2. You Mustn't Kick It Around; 3. I Could Write a Book; 4. Chicago; 5. That Terrific Rainbow; 6. What Is a Man; 7. Happy Hunting Horn; 8. Bewitched, Bothered and Bewildered; 9. Pal Joey; 10. Flower Garden of My Heart; 11. Zip; 12. Plant You Now, Dig You Later; 13. In Our Little Den; 14. Do It the Hard Way; 15. Take Him; 16. Bewitched (reprise); 17. Finale (I Could Write a Book).
Cpte S. Phillips, D. Lawson, London Cast, T. York (r1980) (4/92) (TER) ① **CDTER1005**
Cpte Broadway Cast, M. Meth (r1952) (11/93) (EMI) ① **ZDM7 64696-2**
Bewitched, Bothered and Bewildered F. von Stade, LSO, J. McGlinn Concert (2/91) (EMI) ① **CDC7 54071-2**
8. J. Andrews, London Musicians Orch, I. Fraser (r1994; orch E. Karam) Concert (1/95) (PHIL) ① **442 603-2PH**

Pipe Dream—musical show (1955—New York) (Lyrics O. Hammerstein II)
EXCERPTS: 1. Overture.
1. Hollywood Bowl SO, J. Mauceri Concert (9/92) (PHIL) ① **434 127-2PH**

Simple Simon—musical show (1930—New York) (Lyrics L. Hart)
EXCERPTS: 1. Ten cents a Dance.
Ten cents a dance K. Criswell, London Sinfonietta, J. McGlinn (r1992) Concert (4/94) (EMI) ① **CDC7 54802-2**

The Sound of Music—musical show (1959—New York) (Lyrics O. Hammerstein II)
EXCERPTS: 1. Overture; 2. The Sound of Music; 3. Maria; 4. My Favourite Things; 5. Do Re Mi; 6. Sixteen Going on Seventeen; 7. The Lonely Goatherd; 8. How Can Love Survive? (not in film); 9. So Long, Farewell; 10. Climb Every Mountain; 11. No Way to Stop It (not in film); 12. An Ordinary Couple (not in film); 13. Edelweiss.
Cpte F. von Stade, H. Hagegård, E. Farrell, B. Daniels, May Fest Chor, Cincinnati Pops, E. Kunzel (r1987; includes all items from stage & film version) (12/88) (TELA) ① **CD80162**
Entr'acte Hollywood Bowl SO, J. Mauceri Concert (9/92) (PHIL) ① **434 127-2PH**
2, 13. J. Andrews, London Musicians Orch, I. Fraser (r1994; orch A. Morley) Concert (1/95) (PHIL) ① **442 603-2PH**
4. S. Hough (r1986: arr Hough) Concert (1/89) (VIRG) ① **VC7 59509-2**
4. F. von Stade, Orch, A. Previn (pp1991) Concert (12/92) (SONY) ① **SK48235**

South Pacific—musical show (1949—New York) (Lyrics O. Hammerstein II)
EXCERPTS: 1. Overture; 2. Dites-Moi; 3. A Cock-Eyed Optimist; 4. Some Enchanted Evening; 5. Bloody Mary; 6. There is Nothin' Like a Dame; 7. Bali Ha'i; 8. I'm Gonna Wash That Man Right Outa My Hair; 9. I'm in Love With a Wonderful Guy; 10. Younger Than Springtime; 11. Happy Talk; 12. Honey Bun; 13. Carefully Taught; 14. This Nearly Was Mine.
1. Hollywood Bowl SO, J. Mauceri *Concert*
(9/92) (PHIL) ① **434 127-2PH**
3. J. Andrews, London Musicians Orch, I. Fraser (r1994; orch B. Byers) *Concert*
(1/95) (PHIL) ① **442 603-2PH**
4. T. Allen, Philh, J.O. Edwards (r1990) *Concert*
(5/94) (TER) ① **CDVIR8317**
9, 14. J. Andrews, London Musicians Orch, I. Fraser (r1994; medley orch B. Byers) *Concert*
(1/95) (PHIL) ① **442 603-2PH**
Spring Is Here—musical show (1929—New York) (Lyrics L. Hart)
EXCERPTS: 1. Spring Is Here; 2. With a Song In My Heart.
1. J. Andrews, London Musicians Orch, I. Fraser (r1994; orch B. Byers) *Concert*
(1/95) (PHIL) ① **442 603-2PH**
2. J. Carreras, Los Angeles PO, Z. Mehta (pp1994) *Concert*
(12/94) (PHIL) ① **4509-96200-2**
State Fair—musical show (1945) (Lyrics O. Hammerstein)
EXCERPTS: 1. It might as well be spring; 2. It's a grand night for singing.
Suite Hollywood Bowl SO, J. Mauceri *Concert*
(9/92) (PHIL) ① **434 127-2PH**
2. J. Andrews, London Musicians Orch, I. Fraser (r1994; medley orch B. Byers) *Concert*
(1/95) (PHIL) ① **442 603-2PH**
Too Many Girls—musical show (1939—New York) (Lyrics L. Hart)
EXCERPTS: 1. I Didn't Know What Time It Was.
I didn't know what time it was; Love never went to college; You're nearer F. von Stade, LSO, J. McGlinn *Concert*
(2/91) (EMI) ① **CDC7 54071-2**
Two Weeks with Pay—musical show (1940—New York) (lyrics L. Hart)
Now that I know you F. von Stade, LSO, J. McGlinn *Concert*
(2/91) (EMI) ① **CDC7 54071-2**

RODRIGO, Joaquín (b 1901)
Spain

SECTION I: ORCHESTRAL

A la busca del más allá—orchestra (1976)
LSO, E. Bátiz *Concert*
(9/92) (EMI) ① [4] **CZS7 67435-2**
Cançoneta—violin and string orchestra (1923)
A. L. Ara, ASMF, N. Marriner (r1992) *Concert*
(8/94) (PHIL) ① **438 016-2PH**
Concierto andaluz—4 guitars and orchestra (1967)
A. Moreno, M. Garibay, C. López, J. Ruiz, Mexico St SO, E. Bátiz *Concert*
(9/92) (EMI) ① [4] **CZS7 67435-2**
Concierto de Aranjuez—guitar and orchestra (1939)
1. Allegro con spirito; 2. Adagio; 3. Allegro gentile.
J. Williams, Philh, L. Frémaux (r1983) *Fantasía.*
(7/85) (SONY) ① **SK37848**
N. Yepes, Philh, G. Navarro *Fantasía.*
(3/86) (DG) ① **415 349-2GH**
M. Conn, St John's Smith Square Orch, J. Lubbock *Arnold: Guitar Concerto, Op.67.*
(8/87) (CARL) ① **PCD859**
G. Söllscher, Orpheus CO *Concert*
(6/90) (DG) ① **429 232-2GH**
C. Bonell, Montreal SO, C. Dutoit *Concert*
(8/91) (DECC) ① **430 703-2DM**
S. Isbin, Lausanne CO, L. Foster *Concert*
(11/91) (VIRG) ① **VC7 59024-2**
P. Romero, ASMF, N. Marriner *Concert*
(7/92) (PHIL) ① **432 828-2PM**
A. Diaz, Spanish Nat Orch, R. Frühbeck de Burgos *Concert*
(7/92) (EMI) ① [2] **CZS7 67474-2**
A. Moreno, Mexico St SO, E. Bátiz *Concert*
(9/92) (EMI) ① [4] **CZS7 67435-2**
J. Bream, CBSO, S. Rattle (r1990) *Concert*
(7/93) (EMI) ① **CDC7 54661-2**
J. Bream, Melos Ens (r1963) *Concert*
(8/93) (RCA) ① [28] **09026 61583-2(4)**
J. Bream, Monteverdi Orch, J.E. Gardiner (r1974) *Concert*
(8/93) (RCA) ① [28] **09026 61583-2(5)**
J. Bream, COE, J.E. Gardiner (r1982) *Concert*
(8/93) (RCA) ① [28] **09026 61583-2(6)**

J. Bream, COE, J.E. Gardiner (r1982) *Concert*
(8/93) (RCA) ① **09026 61611-2**
C. Parkening, RPO, A. Litton (r1992) *Concert*
(9/93) (EMI) ① **CDC7 54665-2**
N. Kraft, Northern CO, N. Ward (r1992) *Concert*
(4/94) (NAXO) ① **8 550729**
J. Bream, Melos Ens, Colin Davis (r1963) *Concert*
(6/94) (RCA) ① **09026 61598-2**
P. Romero, ASMF, N. Marriner (r1992) *Concert*
(8/94) (PHIL) ① **438 016-2PH**
J. Bream, Monteverdi Orch, J. E. Gardiner (r1974) *Concert*
(8/94) (RCA) ① **09026 61605-2**
A. Moreno, Mexico St SO, E. Bátiz (r1994) *Concert*
(12/95) (ASV) ① **CDDCA887**
2. Empire Brass, E. Flower (r1991) *Concert*
(11/93) (TELA) ① **CD80301**
2. J. Williams, Seville SO (r1992) *Concert*
(1/94) (SONY) ① **SK53359**
Concierto de estío—violin and orchestra (1943)
A.L. Ara, LSO, E. Bátiz *Concert*
(9/92) (EMI) ① [4] **CZS7 67435-2**
M. Guttman, RPO, J. Serebrier *Concert*
(10/93) (ASV) ① **CDDCA855**
Concierto en modo galante—cello and orchestra (1949)
R. Cohen, LSO, E. Bátiz *Concert*
(9/92) (EMI) ① [4] **CZS7 67435-2**
Concierto heróico—piano and orchestra (1942)
J.F. Osorio, RPO, E. Bátiz *Concert*
(9/92) (EMI) ① [4] **CZS7 67435-2**
Concierto madrigal—2 guitars and orchestra (1969)
P. Romero, ASMF, N. Marriner *Concert*
(7/92) (PHIL) ① **432 828-2PM**
A. Moreno, D. Mariotti, LSO, E. Bátiz *Concert*
(9/92) (EMI) ① [4] **CZS7 67435-2**
Concierto para una fiesta—guitar and orchestra (1982)
A. Moreno, Mexico St SO, E. Bátiz (r1994) *Concert*
(12/95) (ASV) ① **CDDCA887**
Concierto pastoral—flute and orchestra (1977)
L. Hansen, RPO, E. Bátiz *Concert*
(9/92) (EMI) ① [4] **CZS7 67435-2**
P. Gallois, Philh, I. Marin *Khachaturian: Violin Concerto.*
(10/92) (DG) ① **435 767-2GH**
Concierto serenata—harp and orchestra (1952)
N. Allen, RPO, E. Bátiz *Concert*
(9/92) (EMI) ① [4] **CZS7 67435-2**
Fantasía para un gentilhombre—guitar and orchestra (1954)
1. Villano y Ricercare; 2. Españoleta; 3. Fanfare de la Caballería de Nápoles; 4. Danza de las Hachas; 5. Canario.
J. Williams, Philh, L. Frémaux (r1983) *Concierto de Aranjuez.*
(7/85) (SONY) ① **SK37848**
N. Yepes, ECO, G. Navarro *Concierto de Aranjuez.*
(3/86) (DG) ① **415 349-2GH**
G. Söllscher, Orpheus CO *Concert*
(6/90) (DG) ① **429 232-2GH**
N. Kraft, B. Silver (arr gtr/hpd) *Concert*
(11/91) (CHAN) ① **CHAN8937**
S. Isbin, Lausanne CO, L. Foster *Concert*
(11/91) (VIRG) ① **VC7 59024-2**
P. Romero, ASMF, N. Marriner *Concert*
(7/92) (PHIL) ① **432 828-2PM**
A. Moreno, Mexico St SO, E. Bátiz *Concert*
(9/92) (EMI) ① [4] **CZS7 67435-2**
J. Bream, RCA Victor CO, L. Brouwer (r1987) *Concert*
(8/93) (RCA) ① [28] **09026 61583-2(6)**
J. Bream, RCA Victor CO, L. Brouwer (r1987) *Concert*
(8/93) (RCA) ① **09026 61611-2**
C. Parkening, RPO, A. Litton (r1992) *Concert*
(9/93) (EMI) ① **CDC7 54665-2**
P. Romero, ASMF, N. Marriner (r1992) *Concert*
(8/94) (PHIL) ① **438 016-2PH**
A. Moreno, Mexico St SO, E. Bátiz (r1994; ed Segovia) *Concert*
(12/95) (ASV) ① **CDDCA887**
Música para un jardín—orchestra (1957)
LSO, E. Bátiz *Concert*
(9/92) (EMI) ① [4] **CZS7 67435-2**
Per la flor del lliri blau—symphonic poem (1934)
LSO, E. Bátiz *Concert*
(9/92) (EMI) ① [4] **CZS7 67435-2**
5 Piezas infantiles—orchestra (1924)
1. Son chicos que pasan; 2. Despues de un cuento; 3. Mazurka; 4. Plegaria; 5. Gritería Finale.
RPO, E. Bátiz *Concert*
(9/92) (EMI) ① [4] **CZS7 67435-2**
Soleriana—orchestra (1953)
4, 5. RPO, E. Bátiz *Concert*
(9/92) (EMI) ① [4] **CZS7 67435-2**

Zarabanda lejana y villancico—orchestra (1929) (orch cpsr from gtr/pf work)
LSO, E. Bátiz *Concert*
(9/92) (EMI) ① [4] **CZS7 67435-2**
Madrid SO, A. R. Marbà (pp1993) *Concert*
(9/95) (MARC) ① **8 223753**

SECTION II: CHAMBER

Atardecer—piano: four hands (1975)
G. Allen, A. Nel *Concert*
(7/92) (BRID) ① [2] **BCD9027**
Gran Marcha de los Subsecretarios—piano: four hands (1943)
G. Allen, A. Nel *Concert*
(7/92) (BRID) ① [2] **BCD9027**
5 Piezas Infantiles—two pianos (1924)
1. Son chicos que pasan; 2. Después de un cuento; 3. Mazurka; 4. Plegaria; 5. Gritería final.
G. Allen, A. Nel *Concert*
(7/92) (BRID) ① [2] **BCD9027**
Serenata al Alba del Dia—flute/violin and piano (1982)
V. Taylor, T. Kain *Concert* (9/92) (TALL) ① **TP003**
Sonatina para dos Muñecas—piano: 4 hands (1977)
G. Allen, A. Nel *Concert*
(7/92) (BRID) ① [2] **BCD9027**

SECTION III: INSTRUMENTAL

A l'ombre de Torre Bermeja—piano (1945)
G. Allen *Concert* (7/92) (BRID) ① [2] **BCD9027**
A. Pizarro (r1994) *Concert*
(6/95) (COLL) ① **Coll1434-2**
Air de Ballet sur le nom d'une Jeune Fille—piano (1930)
G. Allen *Concert* (7/92) (BRID) ① [2] **BCD9027**
El Album de Cecilia (6 Piezas para manos pequeñas)—piano (1948)
1. María de los Reyes; 2. A la jota—Jota de las Palomas; 3. Canción del hada rubia; 4. Canción del hada morena; 5. El negrito Pepo; 6. Borriquillos a Belén.
G. Allen *Concert* (7/92) (BRID) ① [2] **BCD9027**
Bagatela—piano (1926)
G. Allen *Concert* (7/92) (BRID) ① [2] **BCD9027**
Berceuse de Otoño—piano (1923)
G. Allen *Concert* (7/92) (BRID) ① [2] **BCD9027**
A. Pizarro (r1994) *Concert*
(6/95) (COLL) ① **Coll1434-2**
Berceuse de primavera—piano (1928)
G. Allen *Concert* (7/92) (BRID) ① [2] **BCD9027**
A. Pizarro (r1994) *Concert*
(6/95) (COLL) ① **Coll1434-2**
Danza de la Amapola—piano (1978)
G. Allen *Concert* (7/92) (BRID) ① [2] **BCD9027**
3 Danzas de España—piano (1941)
1. Rústica; 2. Danza de tres doncellas; 3. Serrana.
G. Allen *Concert* (7/92) (BRID) ① [2] **BCD9027**
En tierras de Jerez—guitar (1972)
W. Lendle *Concert* (7/92) (TELD) ① **9031-75864-2**
4 Estampas andaluzas—piano (1954)
G. Allen *Concert* (7/92) (BRID) ① [2] **BCD9027**
A. Pizarro (r1994) *Concert*
(6/95) (COLL) ① **Coll1434-2**
3 Evocaciones—piano (1981)
1. Tarde en el parque; 2. Noche en el Guaralquivir; 3. Mañana en Triana.
G. Allen *Concert* (7/92) (BRID) ① [2] **BCD9027**
A. Pizarro (r1994) *Concert*
(6/95) (COLL) ① **Coll1434-2**
Invocación y danza—guitar (1962)
S. Isbin *Concert* (10/90) (VIRG) ① **VC7 59591-2**
J. Williams *Concert* (7/92) (SONY) ① **SK48480**
J. Bream (r1982-3) *Concert*
(8/93) (RCA) ① [28] **09026 61583-2(6)**
J. Bream (r1982-3) *Concert*
(8/93) (RCA) ① **09026 61611-2**
A-S. Ramírez (r1991) *Concert*
(2/94) (DENO) ① **CO-75357**
P. Romero 1992) *Concert*
(8/94) (PHIL) ① **438 016-2PH**
Pastorale—piano (1926)
G. Allen *Concert* (7/92) (BRID) ① [2] **BCD9027**
3 Pequeñas piezas—guitar (1971)
1. Ya se van los pastores; 2. Por Caminos de Santiago; 3. Pequeña Sevillana.
P. Romero 1992) *Concert*
(8/94) (PHIL) ① **438 016-2PH**
4 Piezas—piano (1938)
1. Caleseras (Homenaje a Chuecca); 2. Fandango del ventorrillo; 3. Plegaria de la Infanta de Castilla; 4. Danza valenciana.
G. Allen *Concert* (7/92) (BRID) ① [2] **BCD9027**
A. Pizarro (r1994) *Concert*
(6/95) (COLL) ① **Coll1434-2**

5 Piezas del siglo XVI—piano (1937)
1. Diferencias sobre el Canto del Caballero
(Cabezón); 2. Pavana (Milán); 3. Zapateado.
Pavana (Valderrábano); 5. Fantasía (Mudarra).
A. Pizarro (r1994) *Concert*
(6/95) (COLL) ① **Coll1434-2**
3 Piezas españolas—guitar (1954)
1. Fandango; 2. Passacaglia; 3. Zapateado.
T. Kerstens *Concert* (7/92) (CONI) ① **CDCF509**
J. Bream (r1982-3) *Concert*
(8/93) (RCA) ① **[28] 09026 61583-2(6)**
J. Bream (r1982-3) *Concert*
(8/93) (RCA) ① **09026 61611-2**
2. M. Kayath *Concert* (5/88) (CARL) ① **PCD876**
Por los campos de España—guitar
1. En los trigales (1939); 2. Entre olivares (1942).
1. J. Williams *Concert* (7/92) (SONY) ① **SK48480**
1. J. Bream (r1959) *Concert*
(8/93) (RCA) ① **[28] 09026 61583-2(3)**
1. J. Bream (r1959) *Concert*
(8/93) (RCA) ① **09026 61591-2**
3. A-S. Ramírez (r1991) *Concert*
(2/94) (DENO) ① **CO-75357**
Por tierras de Jerez—guitar (1972)
P. Romero (r1993) *Concert*
(4/95) (PHIL) ① **442 150-2PH**
2 Preludes—guitar (1977)
1. Adagio; 2. Allegro.
W. Lendle *Concert* (7/92) (TELD) ① **9031-75864-2**
Preludio al gallo mañanero—piano (1926)
G. Allen *Concert* (7/92) (BRID) ① **[2] BCD9027**
Preludio de Añoranza—piano (1987)
G. Allen *Concert* (7/92) (BRID) ① **[2] BCD9027**
Romance de Durandarte—guitar (transc. from
ballet Pavana Real (1955)
A-S. Ramírez (r1991) *Concert*
(2/94) (DENO) ① **CO-75357**
Serenata española—piano (1931)
G. Allen *Concert* (7/92) (BRID) ① **[2] BCD9027**
**Sonada de adiós, 'Hommage à Paul
Dukas'—piano (1935)**
G. Allen *Concert* (7/92) (BRID) ① **[2] BCD9027**
**5 Sonatas de Castilla con toccata a modo de
prégon—piano (1951)**
1. Sonata; 2. Sonata en Fa sostenido menor; 3.
Sonata en Re; 4. Sonata como un tiento; 5. Sonata
en La.
G. Allen *Concert* (7/92) (BRID) ① **[2] BCD9027**
Suite—piano (1923)
G. Allen *Concert* (7/92) (BRID) ① **[2] BCD9027**
Zarabanda lejana—guitar (1926)
G. Allen *Concert* (7/92) (BRID) ① **[2] BCD9027**

SECTION IV: VOCAL AND CHORAL

**Canción del grumete—voice and piano
(1938)** (Wds. Anónimo)
P. Rozario, M. Troop *Concert*
(12/92) (COLL) ① **Coll3052-2**
**12 Cançiones populares españolas—voice
and piano (1965)** (Wds. trad)
1. Viva la novia y el novio; 2. De ronda; 3. Una
palomita blanca; 4. Canción de baile con pandero; 5.
Porque toco el pandero; 6. Tararán; 7. En las
montañas de Asturias; 8. Estando en mi majada;
9. Adela; 10. En Jerez de la Frontera; 11. San José y
Maria; 12. Canción de cuna.
2, 3, 9, 10. P. Rozario, M. Troop *Concert*
(12/92) (COLL) ① **Coll3052-2**
9. J. Gomez, J. Constable (r1994) *Concert*
(9/94) (CONI) ① **CDCF243**
**Cántico de la esposa—voice and
piano/orchestra (1934)** (Wds. S. J. de la
Cruz)
P. Rozario, M. Troop *Concert*
(12/92) (COLL) ① **Coll3052-2**
**Esta niña se lleva la flor—voice and piano
(1934)** (Wds. F. de Figueroa)
P. Rozario, M. Troop *Concert*
(12/92) (COLL) ① **Coll3052-2**
**4 Madrigales amatorios—voice and
piano/orchestra (1948)**
1. E conquá la lavaré?; 2. Vós me matasteis; 3. De
dónde venís, amores?; 4. De los álamos vengo,
madre.
Cpte V. de los Angeles, Paris Cons, R. Frühbeck de
Burgos *Concert* (10/88) (EMI) ① **CDM7 69502-2**
Cpte Y. Kenny, L. Skrobacs (pp1984) *Concert*
(7/90) (ETCE) ① **KTC1029**
Cpte P. Rozario, M. Troop *Concert*
(12/92) (COLL) ① **Coll3052-2**
Cpte M. Bayo, J.A. Alvarez-Parejo (r1992) *Concert*
(6/93) (CLAV) ① **CD50-9205**
Cpte V. de los Angeles, Paris Cons, R. Frühbeck de
Burgos (r1962) *Concert*
(4/94) (EMI) ① **[4] CMS5 65061-2(1)**

**Tríptic de Mosén Cinto—songs: 1v and
orchestra (1936)** (Wds. J Verdagner)
1. L'harpa sagrada; 2. Lo violi de San Franesch; 3.
San Franesch i la cigala.
V. de los Angeles, Lamoureux Orch, A. Ros-Marbà
(r1969) *Concert*
(4/94) (EMI) ① **[4] CMS5 65061-2(1)**
**3 Villancicos—soprano and piano/orchestra
(1952)**
1. Pastorcito Santo (wds Lope de Vega); 2. Copillas
de Belén (wds V Kamhi); 3. Aire y donaire (wds
Anónimo).
1. V. de los Angeles, G. Soriano (r1961/2) *Concert*
(4/94) (EMI) ① **[4] CMS5 65061-2(2)**
1, 2. P. Rozario, M. Troop *Concert*
(12/92) (COLL) ① **Coll3052-2**

RODRIGUES COELHO, Manuel
(c1555–c1635) Portugal

SECTION III: INSTRUMENTAL

Tiento para arpa—harp
A. Lawrence-King *Concert*
(9/92) (VIRG) ① **VC7 59071-2**

RODRIGUEZ, Gerardo *(20th Cent)
Argentina*

SECTION IV: VOCAL AND CHORAL

La Cumparsita—tango (Wds. ?Contursi &
Maroni)
Buenos Aires Qnt, RPO, E. Stratta (arr J. Calandrelli)
Concert (1/93) (TELD) ① **9031-76997-2**

ROGER-DUCASSE, Jean (Jules
Aimable) *(1873–1954) France*

SECTION I: ORCHESTRAL

Sarabande—symphonic poem (1910)
Chor, NBC SO, A. Toscanini (bp1946) *Concert*
(1/90) (DELL) ① **CDDA9020**

SECTION II: CHAMBER

Hommage à Gabriel Fauré—two pianos
M. Fingerhut, C. Benson *Concert*
(9/88) (CHAN) ① **CHAN8578**

ROGERS, Benjamin *(1614–1698)
England*

SECTION IV: VOCAL AND CHORAL

**Hymnus eucharisticus, 'Te deum patrem
colimus'—Magdalen College hymn (1660)**
Magdalen (Oxford) Coll Ch, G. Ives *Concert*
(11/92) (CNTO) ① **CRCD2366**

ROGERS, Bernard *(1893–1968)
USA*

SECTION I: ORCHESTRAL

**Once Upon a Time (Five Fairy Tales)—suite
(1934)**
EXCERPTS: 1. The Tinder-Box Soldier; 2. The Song
of Rapunzel; 3. The Story of a Darning Needle; 4.
Dance of the Twelve Princesses; 5. The Ride of
Koschei the Deathless.
Eastman-Rochester Orch, H. Hanson (r1957)
Concert (2/93) (MERC) ① **434 319-2MM**

ROGERS, Clara Kathleen
(1844–1931) England/USA

also used pseudonym Clara Doria

SECTION II: CHAMBER

Sonata for Violin and Piano, Op. 25 (1903)
E. Skorodin, K. Schmidt (r1991) *Concert*
(12/93) (KOCH) ① **37240-2**

SECTION IV: VOCAL AND CHORAL

**Out of my own great woe—song: 1v and
piano**
S. Mentzer, K. Schmidt (r1991) *Concert*
(12/93) (KOCH) ① **37240-2**

ROGERS, James Hotchkiss
(1857–1940) USA

SECTION IV: VOCAL AND CHORAL

At parting—song: 1v and piano
M. Garden, J. Dansereau (r1926) *Concert*
(8/94) (ROMO) ① **81008-2**
K. Flagstad, E. McArthur (r1937) *Concert*
(12/95) (NIMB) ① **NI7871**

ROGIER, Philippe *(c1561–1596)
Netherlands/Spain*

SECTION IV: VOCAL AND CHORAL

Laboravi in gemitu meo—motet (pub 1595)
Oxford Camerata, J. Summerly (r1993) *Concert*
(3/95) (NAXO) ① **8 550843**

ROGNONI TAEGGIO, Francesco
(c1585–c1624) Italy

SECTION IV: VOCAL AND CHORAL

Selva di varii passaggi (1620) (treatise on
ormentation: vocal & instr)
1. Pulchra es amica mea (Palestrina).
1. B. Dickey, Tragicomedia *Concert*
(6/92) (ACCE) ① **ACC9173D**

ROLDÁN, Amadeo *(1900–1939)
Cuba*

SECTION I: ORCHESTRAL

Ritmica V—percussion ensemble (1930)
New World Sym, M. Tilson Thomas (r1992) *Concert*
(6/93) (ARGO) ① **436 737-2ZH**

SECTION V: STAGE WORKS

**Le Rebambaramba—concert suite from
ballet (1928)**
1. Final del primer cuadro; 2. Comparsa lucumí; 3.
Comparsa de la culebra; 4. Final de la obra.
New World Sym, M. Tilson Thomas (r1992) *Concert*
(6/93) (ARGO) ① **436 737-2ZH**

ROLLA, Alessando *(1757–1841)
Italy*

SECTION I: ORCHESTRAL

Concertino for Viola and Strings in E flat
M. Paris, I Musici (r1993; rev M Paris) *Concert*
(11/95) (PHIL) ① **442 154-2PH**
**Concerto for Viola and Orchestra in E flat,
Op. 3**
M. Paris, I Musici (r1993) *Concert*
(11/95) (PHIL) ① **442 154-2PH**
Divertimento for Viola and Strings in F
M. Paris, I Musici (r1993; rev F Sciannameo) *Concert*
(11/95) (PHIL) ① **442 154-2PH**
Rondo for Viola and Orchestra in G
M. Paris, I Musici (r1993; rev F Sciannameo & M
Paris) *Concert* (11/95) (PHIL) ① **442 154-2PH**

ROMÁN *(late 15th Cent) Spain*

SECTION IV: VOCAL AND CHORAL

O voy (from the Polacio Song Book)
Hespérion XX, J. Savall *Concert*
(7/92) (ASTR) ① **E8762**

ROMAN, Johan Helmich
(1694–1758) Sweden

SECTION I: ORCHESTRAL

**Concerto for Violin and Strings in D minor,
BeRI/49**
Orpheus Chbr Ens, N-E. Sparf *Concert*
(9/86) (BIS) ① **BIS-CD284**
**Concerto for Violin and Strings in E flat,
BeRI/50**
Orpheus Chbr Ens, N-E. Sparf *Concert*
(9/86) (BIS) ① **BIS-CD284**
**Concerto for Violin and Strings in F minor,
BeRI/52**
Orpheus Chbr Ens, N-E. Sparf *Concert*
(9/86) (BIS) ① **BIS-CD284**
**Concerto Grosso in B flat—oboe and
strings, BeR146**
Musica Vitae CO, W. Rajski, H. Jahren *Concert*
(6/90) (BIS) ① **BIS-CD460**

Drottningholm Music, 'Royal Wedding
  Music'—suite (1744)
  Suite in D Stockholm Nat Museum CO, C. Génetay
    Concert   (1/93) (MSVE) ① MSCD417
Sinfonia in A, BeRI/26
  Orpheus Chbr Ens, N-E. Sparf Concert
                     (9/86) (BIS) ① BIS-CD284
Sinfonia in D, BeRI/14
  Orpheus Chbr Ens, N-E. Sparf Concert
                     (9/86) (BIS) ① BIS-CD284
Sinfonia in F, BeRI/17
  Orpheus Chbr Ens, N-E. Sparf Concert
                     (9/86) (BIS) ① BIS-CD284
Suite in G minor (Sjukmans Musiquen)
  (c1730)
  Stockholm Nat Museum CO, C. Génetay Concert
                     (1/93) (MSVE) ① MSCD417

SECTION III: INSTRUMENTAL

12 Suites—harpsichord
  J. Payne (r1994) (2/95) (BIS) ① [2] BIS-CD669/70
  No 2. A. Stringer, N. Rawsthorne (r1974) Concert
                     (11/87) (CRD) ① CRD3308

SECTION IV: VOCAL AND CHORAL

Piante amiche—cantata (?1735-37)
  P-M. Nilsson, Stockholm Nat Museum CO, C.
    Génetay Concert (1/93) (MSVE) ① MSCD417
Swedish Mass—chorus and orchestra
  (1752)
  H. Martinpelto, A.S. von Otter, M. Samuelson, A.
    Fredriks Bach Ch, Drottningholm Baroque Ens, A.
    Öhrwall (pp1983) (9/90) (PROP) ① PRCD9920
  O Herre Gud Guds Lamb A.S. von Otter,
    Drottningholm Baroque Ens, A. Öhrwall (pp1983)
    Concert   (10/91) (PROP) ① PRCD9008

ROMANO, Enrico (1877–?) Italy

SECTION V: STAGE WORKS

Zulma—opera
  Da tanto tempo; O si ricordiamo E. Burzio, orch
    (r1913) Concert   (1/91) (CLUB) ① [2] CL99-587/8

ROMANS, Beatriz de (?13th Cent) France

SECTION IV: VOCAL AND CHORAL

Na Maria—trobairitz canso
  Sinfonye, S. Wishart (r1992) Concert
                     (8/93) (HYPE) ① CDA66625

ROMBERG, Andreas Jakob (1767–1821) Germany

SECTION II: CHAMBER

Quintet in E flat—clarinet and string quartet,
  Op. 57
  T. King, Britten Qt Concert
                     (7/92) (HYPE) ① CDA66479

SECTION IV: VOCAL AND CHORAL

Black clouds—song
  L. Sibiriakov, M.T. Manasevich, anon (r1905) Concert
                     (6/93) (PEAR) ① [3] GEMMCDS9001/3(2)
Das Lied von der Glocke—soloists, chorus
  & orchestra, Op. 25 (Wds. Schiller)
  B. Schlick, M. Georg, F. Lang, K. Mertens, Cologne
    Chorus Musicus, Neue Orch, C. Spering (r1992)
                     (7/93) (O111) ① OPS30-67

ROMBERG, Sigmund (1887–1951) Hungary/USA

SECTION IV: VOCAL AND CHORAL

I love to go swimmin' with wimmin'—song
  (Lyrics Ballard MacDonald)
  J. Hadley, T. Randall, American Th Orch, P.
    Gemignani (r1993; orch W. D. Brohn) Concert
                     (12/95) (RCA) ① 09026 62681-2

SECTION V: STAGE WORKS

The Desert Song—musical play: 2 acts
  (1926—New York) (Wds. O Harbach, O
  Hammerstein II & F Mandel)
  EXCERPTS: 1. Overture. ACT 1: 2. I'll be a buoyant
  girl; 3. Why did we ever marry soldiers?; 4. French
  military marching song; 5a. Romance; 5b. Then you
  will know; 6. I want a kiss; 7. The Desert Song. ACT
  2: 8. My little Castagnette; 9. Song of the Brass Key;
  10. One good man gone wrong; 11a. Let love go;
  11b. One flower grows alone in your garden; 12. One
  alone; 13. Duet; 14. Sabre Song; 15. All hail to the

General; 16. It; 17. Finale: The Desert Song (reprise).
  4. M. Hill Smith, Philh, J.O. Edwards (1989-91)
    Concert   (10/91) (TER) ① CDVIR8314
  7. B. Hendricks, G. Quilico, Lyon Op Orch, L. Foster
    (r1993) Concert   (6/95) (EMI) ① CDC5 55151-2
  7, 12. J. Hadley, American Th Orch, P. Gemignani
    (r1993; orch W. D. Brohn) Concert
                     (12/95) (RCA) ① 09026 62681-2
  12. R. Tauber, orch (r1940) Concert
                     (2/92) (LYRC) ① [2] SRO830
Maytime—operetta (1917) (Lib. R. J. Young)
  EXCERPTS: 1. Will You Remember?.
  1. J. C. Thomas, Orig Broadway Cast (r1922)
    Concert   (5/94) (PEAR) ① [3] GEMMCDS9059/61
The New Moon—operetta: 2 acts
  (1928—New York) (Lyrics O. Hammerstein, F.
  Mandel & L. Schwarz)
  EXCERPTS: 1. Overture. ACT 1: 2. Dainty wisp of
  thistledown; 3. Marianne; 4. The girl on the prow; 5.
  An interrupted love song; 6. Tavern song; 7. Softly,
  as in a morning sunrise; 8. Stout-hearted men; 9.
  One kiss; 10. The trial; 11. Wanting you. ACT 2: 12.
  Funny little sailor men; 13. Lover, come back to me;
  14. Love is quite a simple thing; 15a. Marriage
  number; 15b. Try her out at dances; 16a. Never for
  you; 16b. Lover, come back to me (reprise); 17a. One
  kiss (reprise); 17b. Wanting you (reprise).
  3, 7, 8. J. Hadley, Harvard Glee Club, American Th
    Orch, P. Gemignani (r1993; orch W. D. Brohn)
    Concert   (12/95) (RCA) ① 09026 62681-2
  9, 13. B. Hendricks, Ambrosian Sngrs, Philh, L.
    Foster, G. Quilico (r1992) Concert
                     (8/93) (EMI) ① CDC7 54626-2
  11. B. Hendricks, G. Quilico, Lyon Op Orch, L. Foster
    (r1993) Concert   (6/95) (EMI) ① CDC5 55151-2
The Night is Young—songs for film (1935)
  (Lyrics Hammerstein)
  EXCERPTS: 1. When I Grow too Old to Dream.
  1. J. Hadley, American Th Orch, P. Gemignani
    (r1993; orch W. D. Brohn) Concert
                     (12/95) (RCA) ① 09026 62681-2
The Student Prince—operetta (1924) (Lib.
  Donnelly)
  EXCERPTS: 1. Overture. ACT 1: 2. Prologue - By
  our bearing so sedate; 3. Golden days; 4. Garlands
  bright; 5. To the Inn we're marching (Entrance of
  Students and Kathie); 6. Drinking song; 7. I'm
  coming at your call; 8. A student has a happy lot; 9.
  Come boys, let's all be gay, boys; 10. Entrance of the
  Prince and Engel; 11. Heidelberg, beloved vision; 12.
  In Heidelberg fair; 13. Gaudeamus igitur; 14. Drinking
  Song (reprise); 15. Golden days (reprise); 16. Deep
  in my heart, dear; 17. Come sir, will you join our
  noble Saxon corps; 18. To our native land of
  freedom; 19. Come answer to our call; 20. Drinking
  song (reprise); 21. Serenade; 22. Carnival of
  Springtime; 23. Come boys, let's all be gay, boys.
  ACT 2: 24. Introduction; 25. Farmer Jacob lay a-
  snoring; 26. Student life; 27. Thoughts will come to
  me of days; 28. We're off to Paris, city of joy; 29.
  Deep in my heart, dear (reprise). ACT 3: 30.
  Opening; 31. Ballet; 32. Waltz; 33. Just we two; 34.
  The flag that flies above; 35. Gavotte; 36. Never
  more will come again those days of youth; 37.
  Serenade Intermezzo. ACT 4: 38. Let us sing a song;
  39. To the Inn we're marching (reprise); 40. The flag
  that flies above us (reprise); 41. Serenade (reprise);
  42. Come boys, let's all be gay, boys (reprise); 43.
  Scene; 44. Deep in my heart, dear (reprise).
  Cpte D. Rendall, M. Hill Smith, N. Bailey, D.
    Montague, J. Howard, R. Ashe, N. Jenkins, D.
    Maxwell, B. Bottone, Leon Greene, S. Page, A.
    Mutis, N. Colicos, S. Green, B. Rankin, R. Hart, R.
    Lock, M. Friedman, Ambrosian Chor, Philh, J.O.
    Edwards   (3/91) (TER) ① [2] CDTER2 1172
  3. J. Hadley, M. Lanza, American Th Orch, P.
    Gemignani (r1993; orch W. D. Brohn; Lanza's vocal
    r1952) Concert   (12/95) (RCA) ① 09026 62681-2
  6, 21. J. Hadley, Harvard Glee Club, American Th
    Orch, P. Gemignani (r1993; orch W. D. Brohn)
    Concert   (12/95) (RCA) ① 09026 62681-2
  16. M. Hill Smith, Philh, J.O. Edwards (1989-91)
    Concert   (10/91) (TER) ① CDVIR8314
  16. F. Kreisler, C. Lamson (r1926: arr Kreisler)
    Concert   (12/93) (BIDD) ① LAB075
  16. B. Hendricks, G. Quilico, Lyon Op Orch, L. Foster
    (r1993) Concert   (6/95) (EMI) ① CDC5 55151-2
  21. P. Domingo, I. Perlman, NY Studio Orch, J.
    Tunick (r1990) Concert
                     (3/92) (EMI) ① CDC7 54266-2

ROMERO, Celedonio (b 1918) Spain

SECTION III: INSTRUMENTAL

Los Maestros—guitar
  EXCERPTS: 1. Copla; 2. La rueda; 3. Baile.
  P. Romero (r1993) Concert
                     (4/95) (PHIL) ① 442 150-2PH
Suite Andaluza—guitar
  A. Romero Concert (4/90) (TELA) ① CD80213

ROMERO, Mateo (1575–1647) Spain

SECTION IV: VOCAL AND CHORAL

Caiase de un espino
  M. Figueras, Hespèrion XX, J. Savall Concert
                     (2/92) (ASTR) ① E8729

RONALD, Sir Landon (1873–1938) England

SECTION IV: VOCAL AND CHORAL

Cycle of Life—songs (pub 1906) (Wds. H
  Simpson)
  1. Prelude; 2. Down in the forest (Spring); 3. Love I
  have won you (Summer); 4. The winds are calling
  (Autumn); 5. Drift down, drift down (Winter).
  2. N. Melba, anon (r1909) Concert
                     (5/95) (ROMO) ① [3] 81011-2(1)
In Sunshine and Shadow—songs (pub
  1905)
  1. The dove (wds. J Keats); 2. 'Tis June (wds. N
  Hurst); 3. As a dream (wds. H Simpson); 4. As
  southern song (wds. B Deane-Freeman); 5. The
  white sea mist (wds. H Simpson); 6. Peace and rest
  (wds. F E Weatherly).
  5. N. Melba, anon (r1909) Concert
                     (5/95) (ROMO) ① [3] 81011-2(1)
Sérénade espagnole—song (pub 1905) (Wds.
  G. Ferrari)
  E. Caruso, orch, W.B. Rogers (r1914) Concert
                     (7/91) (RCA) ① [12] GD60495(5)
  E. Caruso, orch, W.B. Rogers (r1914) Concert
                     (10/91) (PEAR) ① [3] EVC3(1)
Summertime—songs (pub 1901) (Wds. E
  Teschemacher)
  EXCERPTS: 1. Daybreak; 2. Morning; 3. Evening; 4.
  O lovely night.
  4. E. Turner, orch (r1926) Concert
                     (9/89) (EMI) ① CDH7 69791-2
  4. N. Melba, orch, W.B. Rogers (r1910) Concert
                     (5/95) (ROMO) ① [3] 81011-2(2)
  4. N. Melba, orch, W.B. Rogers (r1909) Concert
                     (5/95) (ROMO) ① [3] 81011-2(1)
  4. K. Flagstad, E. McArthur (r1936) Concert
                     (12/95) (PEAR) ① GEMMCD9092

RONCALLI, Conte Ludovico (fl late 17th Cent) Italy

SECTION III: INSTRUMENTAL

Passacaglia—guitar
  P. O'Dette Concert (4/88) (HYPE) ① CDA66228
  J. Williams (trans J.Williams) Concert
                     (8/88) (SONY) ① SK44518
Sonata No. 8 in C, 'Quinto Tono'—guitar
  (pub 1692) (from 'Capricci Armonici')
  J. Lindberg (r1986) Concert
                     (11/87) (BIS) ① BIS-CD327

RÖNTGEN, Julius (1855–1932) The Netherlands

SECTION II: CHAMBER

Sonata for Oboe and Piano No. 1 (1918)
  P. Bree, P. Komen Concert
                     (2/90) (ETCE) ① KTC1074

ROPARTZ, Joseph Guy (Marie) (1864–1955) France

SECTION II: CHAMBER

Pièce in E flat minor—trombone and piano
  C. Lindberg, R. Pöntinen Concert
                     (9/85) (BIS) ① BIS-CD298

SECTION IV: VOCAL AND CHORAL

4 Poèmes de l'intermezzo de Heine—songs: 1v and piano (1899) (Wds. H. Heine)
1. Lent: Tendrement enlacés; 2. Lent: Pourquoi vois-je pâlir; 3. Assez lent: Ceux qui, parmi les morts d'amour; 4. Funèbre: Depuis que nul rayon.
J. Van Dam, J-P. Collard *Concert*
(1/90) (EMI) ① CDC7 49288-2
P. Thirion-Vallet, D. Baldwin *Concert*
(6/95) (ARCO) ① AAOC93232

ROQUES, Jean-Louis (20th Cent) France

SECTION V: STAGE WORKS

Germinal—film score (1993)
EXCERPTS: 1. Opening Titles.
1. OST (r1993) *Concert* (9/95) (VIR2) ① CDV2774

RORE, Cipriano de (1515/6–1565) Flanders/Italy

SECTION IV: VOCAL AND CHORAL

Amor, se cosi dolce—madrigal (8vv) (pub 1557)
J. Lindberg, R. Meunier, N. North, P. O'Dette, D. Miller, E. Van Evera, M. Nichols, R. Covey-Crump, P. Long, J.L. Nixon, P. Elliott, A. King *Concert*
(12/86) (BIS) ① BIS-CD341
Anchor che col partire—Book 4 of Cantatas and Solo Vocal Lists (1584) (trans Girolamo dalla Casa)
Ens *Concert* (3/84) (CLAV) ① CD50-8206
Ave regina—motet: 7vv
Tallis Scholars, P. Phillips *Concert*
(6/94) (GIME) ① CDGIM029
Descendi in ortum meum—motet: 7vv
Tallis Scholars, P. Phillips *Concert*
(6/94) (GIME) ① CDGIM029
Madrigals, Book 5 (Il quinto libro de madrigali)—7vv (pub 1566)
1. Convien ch'ovunque (wds. Ariosto); 2. Da le belle contrade; 3. Mentre lumi maggior; 4. Non è lasso martire (wds. Spiro); 5. O santo fior felice; 6. Qualhor rivolgo il basso; 7. Se com'il biondo crin.
Cpte Consort of Musicke, A. Rooley (r1991) *Concert*
(1/94) (MOSC) ① 070991
Missa Praeter rerum seriem—7vv (on Josquin's motet)
Tallis Scholars, P. Phillips *Concert*
(6/94) (GIME) ① CDGIM029
O voi che sotto—madrigal: 5vv
Consort of Musicke, A. Rooley (1991) *Concert*
(1/94) (MOSC) ① 070991
Qual donna attende à gloriosa fama—madrigal (5vv) (pub 1548) (Wds. Petrarch)
Oxford Christ Church Cath Chr, S. Darlington *Concert*
(4/89) (NIMB) ① NI5150
Sacrae cantiones—motets: 5-7vv (pub 1595)
EXCERPTS: 1. Beatam me dicent (5vv); 2. Expectans expectavi (5vv); 3. Hic est panis (5vv); 4. Infelix ego (6vv); 5. Iubilate Deo (5vv); 6. In coelum (5vv); 7. O salutaris hostia (5vv); 8. Parce mihi (5vv); 8a. 2nd Part: Peccavi quid faciam; 9. Salve crux pretiosa (5vv); 10. Virtute magna (5vv); 11. Vere me ad Dominum (5vv).
4, 8. Tallis Scholars, P. Phillips *Concert*
(6/94) (GIME) ① CDGIM029
Le vive fiamme de' vaghi e dilettevoli madrigali—4-5vv (pub 1565)
1. Alma real, se come fida stella; 2. Alma Susanna; 3. Amor cha 'tho fatt'io; 4. Candido e vago fiore; 5. Chi vol veder tutta (wds. Parabosco: also attrib Ingegneri); 6. Di l'estrem' orizonte; 7. Felice sei Trevigi; 8. Fera gentil; 9. Poi che m'invita amore; 10. Quest'affanato; 11. Spesso in parte (wds. Gonzaga: also attrib Ingegneri); 12. Tra più beati; 13. Vaghi pensieri.
1, 2, 3, 6, 8, 13. Consort of Musicke, A. Rooley (r1991) *Concert* (1/94) (MOSC) ① 070991

ROREM, Ned (b 1923) USA

SECTION I: ORCHESTRAL

Concerto for Piano (Left Hand) and Orchestra (1991)
G. Graffman, Curtis Inst Student Orch, A. Previn (r1993) *Eleven Studies.* (2/95) (NEW) ① 80445-2
Concerto for Violin and Orchestra (1984)
G. Kremer, NYPO, L. Bernstein (pp1988) *Concert*
(1/92) (DG) ① 429 231-2GH

Eleven Studies for Eleven Players (1959-60)
E. Ostling, K. Lord, G. Raden, J. Sutte, S. Copes, C-J. Chang, J. Lastrapes, K. Englichova, R. Uchida, A. Lafargue, R. Leveille, R. Milanov (r1993) *Left Hand Concerto.* (2/95) (NEW) ① 80445-2

SECTION II: CHAMBER

Bright Music—flute, 2 violins, cello and piano (1987)
1. Fandango; 2. Piernot; 3. Dance-Song-Dance; 4. Another Dream; 5. Chopin.
M. Martin, A. Kavafian, I. Kavafian, F. Sherry, A-M. Schub *Winter Pages.* (10/92) (NEW) ① 80416-2
Day Music—violin and piano (1971)
1. Wedges and Doubles; 2. Pearls; 3. Extreme Leisure; 4. Bats; 5. Billet Doux; 6. Another Ground; 7. Yellows; 8. A Game of Chess four centuries ago.
J. Laredo, R. Laredo (r1973) *Night Music.*
(9/94) (PHOE) ① PHCD123
Night Music—violin and piano (1972)
1. Answers; 2. Mosquitoes and Earthworms; 3. Gnats; 4. The Lighthouse; 5. Epeira Sclopetaria; 6. The two moths; 7. Black and Silver; 8. Saying Goodbye, Driving off.
E. Carlyss, A. Schein (r1974) *Day Music.*
(9/94) (PHOE) ① PHCD123
Winter Pages—clarinet, bassoon, violin, cello and piano (1981)
T. Palmer, L. Morelli, I. Kavafian, F. Sherry, C. Wadsworth *Bright Music.*
(10/92) (NEW) ① 80416-2

SECTION III: INSTRUMENTAL

A Quaker Reader—organ (1976)
1. First-Day Thoughts; 2. Mary Dyer did hang as a flag... 3. Evidence of things not seen; 4. There is a Spirit that Delights to do no Evil; 5. The World of Silence; 6. Bewitching attire of the most charming simplicity; 7. A Secret Power; 8. No darkness at all; 9. One Sigh Rightly Begotten; 10. Return Home to Within; 11. Ocean of Light.
C. Crozier *Oldest House.* (5/90) (DELO) ① DE3076
Views from the Oldest House—organ (1981)
1. Sunrise on Sunset Hill; 2. Elms; 3. The Nest in Old North Church; 4. Spires; 5. Rain over the Quaker Graveyard; 6. Sunday Night.
C. Crozier *Quaker Reader.*
(5/90) (DELO) ① DE3076

SECTION V: STAGE WORKS

A Childhood Miracle—opera: 1 act (1956—Philadelphia) (Lib. E Stein)
Cpte D. Dunn, M. Couture, M. Tsingopoulos, P. Castaldi, M. Cidoni, P. Greene, Magic Circle CO, R. Evans Harrell (r c1994) *Three Sisters Who Are Not Sisters.* (10/95) (NEWP) ① NPD85594
Three Sisters Who Are Not Sisters—opera: 1 act (1971—Philadelphia) (Lib. G Stein)
Cpte A. Matthews, F. Urrey, C. Flamm, M. Tsingopoulos, M. Singer, J. van Buskirk, Magic Circle CO, R. Evans Harrell (r c1994) *Childhood Miracle.*
(10/95) (NEWP) ① NPD85594

ROSA, Salvatore (1615–1673) Italy

SECTION IV: VOCAL AND CHORAL

Star vicino—song
G. Zenatello, anon (r1911) *Concert*
(5/94) (PEAR) ① [4] GEMMCDS9073(2)
G. Zenatello, anon (r1911) *Concert*
(5/94) (SYMP) ① SYMCD1168

ROSAURO, Ney (b 1952) Brazil

SECTION I: ORCHESTRAL

Concerto for Marimba and Strings
E. Glennie, Scottish CO, P. Daniel *Concert*
(4/93) (RCA) ① 09026 61277-2

SECTION III: INSTRUMENTAL

Cenas Amerindias—percussion
1. Brasiliana; 2. Eldorado.
2. E. Glennie *Concert* (1/92) (RCA) ① RD60557

ROSE, Barry (Michael) (b 1934) England

SECTION IV: VOCAL AND CHORAL

Psalm 121
Truro Cath Chr, D. Briggs, H. Doughty *Concert*
(7/91) (PRIO) ① PRCD322

ROSE, Bernard (William George) (b 1916) England

SECTION IV: VOCAL AND CHORAL

Feast Song for St. Cecilia—anthem: SAT, choir (1975) (Wds. G. Rose)
J. Budd, St Paul's Cath Chr, John Scott *Concert*
(10/91) (HYPE) ① CDA66439
New College Chr, E. Higginbottom *Concert*
(9/92) (MERI) ① CDE84123
Praise ye the Lord—choir and organ
Magdalen Oxford Coll Chr, G. Webber *Concert*
(11/91) (ABBE) ① CDCA914

ROSE, David (1910–1990) England/USA

SECTION I: ORCHESTRAL

Holiday for Strings
Glasgow CWS Band, H. Snell (arr Farr) *Concert*
(9/92) (DOYE) ① DOYCD005

ROSEINGRAVE, Thomas (1688–1766) England

SECTION I: ORCHESTRAL

Concerto for Harpsichord, Two Trumpets, Timpani and Strings in D (before 1750)
(reconstructed from surviving hpd part)
P. Nicholson (kybds/dir), Parley of Instr, P. Holman (r1993; recons P. Holman) *Concert*
(8/94) (HYPE) ① CDA66700

SECTION III: INSTRUMENTAL

Concerto in D—harpsichord (reduction of a lost orchestral concerto)
P. Nicholson *Concert* (9/92) (HYPE) ① CDA66564
6 Double Fugues—keyboard (pub 1750)
3. F; 4. E minor.
3, 4. P. Nicholson *Concert*
(9/92) (HYPE) ① CDA66564
8 Suits of Lessons—keyboard (pub 1725)
1. E flat; 5. F minor; 6. E minor; 7. G.
1, 5, 6, 7. P. Nicholson *Concert*
(9/92) (HYPE) ① CDA66564
Voluntarys and Fugues made on purpose for the Organ or Harpsichord (pub 1728)
1. Voluntary in C minor; 2. Voluntary in G minor; 4. Voluntary in G minor; 6. Fugue in F; 7. Voluntary in G minor; 8. Voluntary in G minor; 10. Fugue in G; 13. Fugue in E minor.
1. Margaret Phillips *Concert*
(5/91) (GAMU) ① GAMCD514
2. J. Bate *Concert* (2/91) (UNIC) ① DKPCD9096
4, 6, 7, 8, 10. P. Nicholson *Concert*
(9/92) (HYPE) ① CDA66564
13. J. Bate *Concert* (7/91) (UNIC) ① DKPCD9104

ROSENBERG, Hilding (Constantin) (1892–1985) Sweden

SECTION I: ORCHESTRAL

Concerto for Violin and Orchestra No. 1, Op. 22 (1924)
C. Barkel, Stockholm Concert Soc Orch, H. Rosenberg (r1924) *Concert*
(5/93) (CPRI) ① [3] CAP21510
Orpheus in Town—dance suite (1938)
Radiotjänst Entertainment Orch, Stockholm Concert Soc Orch, H. Rosenberg (r1948) *Concert*
(5/93) (CPRI) ① [3] CAP21510
Overture and Dance Suite—orchestra (1938)
(from the opera 'Marionetter')
1. Overture; 2. Suite.
Malmö SO, J. DePreist *Concert*
(1/93) (BIS) ① BIS-CD570
Sinfonia Concertante—vn, va, ob, bn, 2 hn, 2 tpt & stgs (1935)
Stockholm Concert Soc Orch, H. Rosenberg (r1949) *Concert* (5/93) (CPRI) ① [3] CAP21510
Symphony No. 3—narrator and orchestra (1939-50) (Wds. R. Rolland)
H. Rosenberg, Radiotjänst SO, H. Rosenberg (ver 1: abbrev: r1948) *Concert*
(5/93) (CPRI) ① [3] CAP21510

**Symphony No. 4 (Johannes uppenbarelse),
'The Revelation of St. John'—baritone,
chorus and orchestra (1940)**
H. Hagegård, Swedish Rad Ch, Pro Musica Ch, Rilke
Ens, Gothenburg SO, S. Ehrling
(5/93) (CPRI) ① **CAP21429**
fragments A. de Wahl, Swedish Rad Ch, Swedish
Rad Orch, H. Rosenberg (orig ver: r1940-44) *Concert*
(5/93) (CPRI) ① [3] **CAP21510**

**Symphony No. 5, 'Hortulanus'
(Örtagårdsmästaren)—contralto, chorus and
orchestra (1944)**
L. Lail, Swedish Rad Ch, Swedish Rad Orch, H.
Rosenberg (r1944) *Concert*
(5/93) (CPRI) ① [3] **CAP21510**

SECTION II: CHAMBER

Suite in D—violin and piano, Op. 13 (1922)
4. Pastorale.
4. L. Andréason, H. Rosenberg (r1935) *Concert*
(5/93) (CPRI) ① [3] **CAP21510**

SECTION IV: VOCAL AND CHORAL

**The Holy Night (Den heliga
natten)—narrator, SATBBB, chorus and
orchestra (1936)**
O. Widgren, K. Lindberg-Torlind, L. Lail, A. Ohlson,
E. Saedén, L. Björker, H. Nilsson, Stockholm Chbr
Ch, Swedish Rad Orch, H. Rosenberg (r1949)
Concert (5/93) (CPRI) ① [3] **CAP21510**

ROSENFELDT ?Norway

SECTION IV: VOCAL AND CHORAL

Ingalill—song
K. Flagstad, orch (r1914) *Concert*
(12/95) (SIMA) ① [3] **PSC1821(1)**

ROSENMAN, Leonard (b 1924) USA

SECTION V: STAGE WORKS

**Battle for the Planet of the Apes—film score
(1973)**
EXCERPTS: 1. Main Title.
1. Prague City PO, W. Motzing (r1993) *Concert*
(8/94) (SILV) ① **FILMCD146**

Countdown—film score (1967)
EXCERPTS: 1. Main Theme.
1. Prague City PO, W. Motzing (r1993) *Concert*
(8/94) (SILV) ① **FILMCD146**

Fantastic Voyage—film score (1966)
EXCERPTS: 1. Ocean of Life.
1. Prague City PO, W. Motzing (r1993) *Concert*
(8/94) (SILV) ① **FILMCD146**

The Lord of the Rings—film score (1978)
EXCERPTS: 1. History of the Ring; 2. Gandalf
Throws the Ring; 3. The Journey Begins/Encounter
with the Ringwraiths; 4. Trying to Kill Hobbits; 5.
Escape to Rivendell; 6. Company of the Ring; 7.
Mines of Moria; 8. The Battle in the Mines/The
Balrog; 9. Mithrandir; 10. Frodo Disappears; 11.
Following Orcs; 12. Fleeing Orcs; 13. Attack of the
Orcs; 14. Gandalf Remembers; 15. Riders of Rohan;
16. Helm's Deep; 17. The Dawn Battle/Theoden's
Victory; 18. The Voyage to Mordor/Main Theme.
1-18. OST, L. Rosenman (r1978)
(5/93) (INTD) ① **FMT8003D**

ROSENMÜLLER, Johann (1619–1684) Germany

SECTION II: CHAMBER

**Sonata à 3—two violins, dulcian & continuo
(pub 1682)**
Musica Fiata, R. Wilson (r1991) *Concert*
(8/93) (DHM) ① **05472 77183-2**

**12 Sonate a 2, 3, 4 e 5 stromenti da arco e
altri e Basso continuo (1682)**
2. Sonata in E minor: 2 violins and continuo; 7. D
minor; 9. D; 11. A.
2. Cologne Musica Antiqua, R. Goebel (r1980)
Concert (1/93) (ARCH) ① **437 089-2AT**

Sonate da Camera (pub 1667)
1. F; 2. a 5, D; 4. G minor.
2. Parley of Instr, R. Goodman, P. Holman *Concert*
(9/91) (HYPE) ① **CDA66074**

SECTION IV: VOCAL AND CHORAL

**Beatus vir qui timet Dominum—4vv, strings
and continuo (Wds. Psalm 111)**
Cantus Cölln, K. Junghänel (lte/dir) (r1991) *Concert*
(6/93) (DHM) ① **05472 77181-2**

**Benedicam Dominum—3vv and continuo
(Wds. Psalm 33)**
Cantus Cölln, K. Junghänel (lte/dir) (r1991) *Concert*
(6/93) (DHM) ① **05472 77181-2**

**Confitebor (4vv, 5 stgs)—4vv, strings and
continuo**
Cantus Cölln, K. Junghänel (lte/dir) (r1991) *Concert*
(6/93) (DHM) ① **05472 77181-2**

**De profundis clamavi—4vv, strings and
continuo**
Cantus Cölln, K. Junghänel (lte/dir) (r1991) *Concert*
(6/93) (DHM) ① **05472 77181-2**

**Gloria in excelsis Deo—4vv, strings, brass
and continuo**
Cantus Cölln, K. Junghänel (lte/dir) (r1991) *Concert*
(6/93) (DHM) ① **05472 77181-2**

Magnificat—5vv, strings and continuo, 5vv
Cantus Cölln, K. Junghänel (lte/dir) (r1991) *Concert*
(6/93) (DHM) ① **05472 77181-2**

ROSENTHAL, Moritz (1862–1946) Poland

SECTION III: INSTRUMENTAL

**New Carneval de Vienne—piano (based on
waltz tunes by J Strauss II)**
M. Rosenthal (r1934) *Concert*
(9/93) (APR) ① [2] **APR7002**
M. Rosenthal (r1935) *Concert*
(9/93) (APR) ① [2] **APR7002**

Papillons—piano
S. Hough (r1986) *Concert*
(1/89) (VIRG) ① **VC7 59509-2**
M. Rosenthal (r1930) *Concert*
(10/92) (APR) ① **APR7013**
M. Rosenthal (r1937) *Concert*
(9/93) (APR) ① [2] **APR7002**
M. Rosenthal (r1930) *Concert*
(9/93) (PEAR) ① **GEMMCD9963**

**Paraphrase on 'An der schönen, blauen
Donau' (J. Strauss II)—piano**
M. Rosenthal (r1920s/30s) *Concert*
(10/92) (APR) ① [2] **APR7013**

**Vienna Carnival—piano (based on waltz tunes
by J. Strauss II)**
M. Rosenthal (r1930) *Concert*
(4/89) (PEAR) ① **GEMMCD9339**

ROSETTI, (Francesco) Antonio (1746–1792) Bohemia

orig name: František Antonín Rössler. K numbers
denote Kaul catalogue

SECTION I: ORCHESTRAL

**Concerto for Two Horns and Orchestra in A
flat**
Z. Tylšar, B. Tylšar, Capella Istropolitana, F. Vajnar
Concert (3/93) (NAXO) ① **8 550459**

**Concerto for Two Horns and Orchestra in E
flat**
Z. Tylšar, B. Tylšar, Capella Istropolitana, F. Vajnar
Concert (3/93) (NAXO) ① **8 550459**

Partita in F—12 wind instruments (1785)
Octophoros, P. Dombrecht *Concert*
(2/90) (ACCE) ① **ACC8860D**

Sinfonia in B flat, K1:25
Cologne Concerto (r1995) *Concert*
(12/95) (TELD) ① **4509-98420-2**

Sinfonia in E flat, K1:23
Cologne Concerto (r1995) *Concert*
(12/95) (TELD) ① **4509-98420-2**

Sinfonia in E flat, K1:32
Cologne Concerto (r1995) *Concert*
(12/95) (TELD) ① **4509-98420-2**

Sinfonia in G minor, K1:27
Cologne Concerto (r1995) *Concert*
(12/95) (TELD) ① **4509-98420-2**

ROSIER, Carl (1640–1725) Flanders

SECTION II: CHAMBER

Suite for 3 Violins and Continuo (pub 1679)
(from 'Antwerpsche Vrede-vreught')
J. Holloway, S. Ritchie, A. Manze, N. North, M.
Springfels, J. Toll (r1993) *Concert*
(2/94) (HARM) ① **HMU90 7091**

ROSLAVETS, Nikolay Andreyevich (1881–1944) Russia

SECTION II: CHAMBER

Sonata for Viola and Piano No. 1 (1925) (lost:
reconstructed Raskatov)
Y. Bashmet, M. Muntian *Concert*
(3/93) (RCA) ① **09026 61273-2**

ROSSETER, Philip (1567/8–1623) England

SECTION III: INSTRUMENTAL

Galliard—lute
J. Bream (r1960) *Concert*
(8/93) (RCA) ① [28] **09026 61583-2(1)**
J. Bream (r1960) *Concert*
(8/93) (RCA) ① **09026 61584-2**

Pavane—lute
J. Bream (r1960) *Concert*
(8/93) (RCA) ① [28] **09026 61583-2(1)**
J. Bream (r1960) *Concert*
(8/93) (RCA) ① **09026 61584-2**

SECTION IV: VOCAL AND CHORAL

If she forsake me—ayre
P. Pears, J. Bream (r1969) *Concert*
(8/93) (RCA) ① [28] **09026 61583-2(5)**
P. Pears, J. Bream (r1969) *Concert*
(8/93) (RCA) ① **09026 61602-2**
J. Elwes, S. Stubbs *Concert*
(9/93) (PIER) ① **PV787092**

No grave for woe—ayre
M. Chance, C. Wilson (r1992) *Concert*
(10/94) (CHAN) ① **CHAN0538**

**Shall I come if I swim?—song: 1v and lute
(pub 1601)**
M. Chance, C. Wilson (r1992) *Concert*
(10/94) (CHAN) ① **CHAN0538**

Sweet, come again—ayre
J. Elwes, S. Stubbs *Concert*
(9/93) (PIER) ① **PV787092**

**What then is love but mourning—ayre (pub
1601)**
E. Kirkby, A. Rooley (pp1985) *Concert*
(6/87) (HYPE) ① **CDA66186**
P. Pears, J. Bream (r1969) *Concert*
(8/93) (RCA) ① [28] **09026 61583-2(5)**
P. Pears, J. Bream (r1969) *Concert*
(8/93) (RCA) ① **09026 61602-2**
M. Chance, C. Wilson (r1992) *Concert*
(10/94) (CHAN) ① **CHAN0538**

When Laura smiles—ayre (pub 1603)
P. Pears, J. Bream (r1969) *Concert*
(8/93) (RCA) ① [28] **09026 61583-2(5)**
P. Pears, J. Bream (r1969) *Concert*
(8/93) (RCA) ① **09026 61602-2**

ROSSI, Luigi (c1597–1653) Italy

SECTION II: CHAMBER

Arie di passacaglia
Tragicomedia (r1992) *Concert*
(10/93) (TELD) ① **4509-90799-2**
Kithara (r1993) *Concert*
(3/95) (CHAN) ① **CHAN0562**

Balletto (attrib)
Tragicomedia (r1992) *Concert*
(10/93) (TELD) ① **4509-90799-2**

Sarabanda (attrib)
Tragicomedia (r1992) *Concert*
(10/93) (TELD) ① **4509-90799-2**

SECTION III: INSTRUMENTAL

Passacaille del seigneur Luigi
Tragicomedia (r1992) *Concert*
(10/93) (TELD) ① **4509-90799-2**

SECTION IV: VOCAL AND CHORAL

**Ai sospiri, al dolore—cantata: 2vv and
continuo**
Tragicomedia (r1992) *Concert*
(10/93) (TELD) ① **4509-90799-2**

Disperate speranza—cantata: 3vv
Tragicomedia (r1992) *Concert*
(10/93) (TELD) ① **4509-90799-2**

Fan battaglia—cantata: 3vv
Tragicomedia (r1992) *Concert*
(10/93) (TELD) ① **4509-90799-2**

Infelice pensier, che ne conforta—cantata: 2vv and continuo
Tragicomedia (r1992) *Concert*
(10/93) (TELD) ① **4509-90799-2**

Noi siam tre donzellette semplicette—cantata: 3vv
1. Perchè piangete Amanti; 2. Amanti a giocare; 3. Pene, pene, ahi, chi vuol pene.
Tragicomedia (r1992) *Concert*
(10/93) (TELD) ① **4509-90799-2**

Occhi belli, occhi miei cari—cantata: 2vv and continuo
Tragicomedia (r1992) *Concert*
(10/93) (TELD) ① **4509-90799-2**

Piango, prego e sospiro—cantata: 3vv
Tragicomedia (r1992) *Concert*
(10/93) (TELD) ① **4509-90799-2**

Poi che mancò speranza—cantata
Tragicomedia (r1992) *Concert*
(10/93) (TELD) ① **4509-90799-2**

Speranza al tuo pallore—cantata: 2vv and continuo
Tragicomedia (r1992) *Concert*
(10/93) (TELD) ① **4509-90799-2**

SECTION V: STAGE WORKS

Il palazzo incantato, overo La guerriera amante—opera (1642—Rome)
Corrente Tragicomedia (r1992) *Concert*
(10/93) (TELD) ① **4509-90799-2**

ROSSI, Michelangelo (1601/2–1656) Italy

SECTION III: INSTRUMENTAL

Toccata settima—keyboard
R. Alessandrini (r1994) *Concert*
(4/95) (O111) ① **OPS30-118**

ROSSINI, Gioachino (Antonio) (1792–1868) Italy

SECTION I: ORCHESTRAL

Introduction, Theme and Variations in B flat—clarinet and orchestra (unidentified)
E. Johnson, ECO, C. Groves *Concert*
(11/86) (ASV) ① **CDDCA559**

Overture obbligata and contrabasso in D—orchestra (c1807-10)
Bologna Teatro Comunale Orch, R. Chailly (r1992) *Concert*
(8/94) (DECC) ① **436 832-2DH**

Sinfonia in D, 'al Conventello' (c1806-07) (discovered 1970s)
Bologna Teatro Comunale Orch, R. Chailly (r1992: ed P Gossett) *Concert*
(8/94) (DECC) ① **436 832-2DH**
1. ASMF, N. Marriner (r1979) *Concert*
(10/92) (PHIL) ① [3] **434 016-2PM3**

Sinfonia (Overture) in D, 'Bologna'—orchestra (1808)
Bologna Teatro Comunale Orch, R. Chailly (r1992: ed P Gossett) *Concert*
(8/94) (DECC) ① **436 832-2DH**
1. ASMF, N. Marriner (r1979) *Concert*
(10/92) (PHIL) ① [3] **434 016-2PM3**

Variations in C—clarinet and small orchestra (1810)
A.O. Popa, Iaşi Moldova PO, P. Popescu *Concert*
(9/92) (OLYM) ① **OCD418**

SECTION II: CHAMBER

Péchés de vieillesse Book 9—12 pieces: piano, violin, cello, harmonium & horn (1857-68)
1. Mélodie candide, A: piano; 2. Chansonette, E flat: piano; 3. La savoie aimante, A minor: piano; 4. Un mot à Paganini—élégie, D: violin and piano; 5. Impromptu tarantellisé, F: piano; 6. Echantillon du chant de Noël à la'italienne, E flat: piano; 7. Marche et reminiscences pour mon dernier voyage, A flat: piano; 8. Prélude, thème et variations, E: horn and piano; 9. Prélude italien, A flat: piano; 10. Una larme: thème variations, A minor: cello and piano; 11. Enchantillon de blague mélodique, E flat and piano; 12. Petite fanfare à quatre mains, E flat: piano 2 or 4 hands.
2, 3, 5, 7. A. Portugheis (r1994) *Concert*
(11/94) (ASV) ① **CDDCA901**
3. J. Swann *Concert* (7/91) (AKAD) ① **CDAK103**
3. M. Meyer (r1953/6) *Concert*
(6/95) (EMI) ① [4] **CZS5 68092-2**
7. H. Antoni *Concert* (11/91) (ETCE) ① **KTC1107**

Quintet (Harmoniemusik) in F—2 clarinets, 2 horns and bassoon (unidentified)
Mozzafiato (r1992-93) *Concert*
(3/94) (SONY) ① **SK53965**

6 Sonate a quattro—two violins, viola and double-bass (c1804)
1. G; 2. A; 3. C; 4. B flat; 5. E flat; 6. D.
Solisti Italiani *Concert*
(5/88) (DENO) ① [2] **CO-1846/7**
Serenata of London (10/91) (ASV) ① **CDDCA767**
Elizabeth Wallfisch, M. Marcus, R. Tunnicliffe, C-C. Nwanoku (10/92) (HYPE) ① **CDA66595**
I. Musici (1/93) (PHIL) ① [2] **434 734-2PM2**
Vienna/Berlin Ens (r1992: arr wind qt: Berr)
(11/93) (SONY) ① **SK52524**
Kremlin CO, M. Rachlevsky (r1992)
(11/93) (CLAV) ① **CD50-9222**
ASMF, N. Marriner (r1966/7) *Concert*
(7/95) (DECC) ① [2] **443 838-2DF2**
1, 2, 4-6. Munich Residenz Qnt (arr Berr)
(10/87) (CALI) ① **CAL50850**
1-3. Budapest Rossini Ens *Donizetti: Sinfonia in C.*
(5/93) (NAXO) ① **8 550621**
1, 3-5. Berne Camerata, T. Füri (r1992)
(7/85) (DG) ① **413 310-2GH**
1, 3-5. London Musici, M. Stephenson
(3/91) (CONI) ① **CDCF181**
2, 4, 5. Bologna Teatro Comunale Orch, R. Chailly (r1992: ed N Gallino) *Concert*
(8/94) (DECC) ① **436 832-2DH**
4-6. Budapest Rossini Ens
(5/93) (NAXO) ① **8 550622**
6. Aulos Wind Qnt (arr wind qnt) *Concert*
(10/91) (SCHW) ① **310087**

SECTION III: INSTRUMENTAL

Danse sibérienne—piano (1864)
H. Antoni *Concert* (11/91) (ETCE) ① **KTC1107**

Péchés de vieillesse Book 4—piano (1857-68)
1. Quatre mendiants; 1a. Les figues sèches; 1b. Les amandes, G; 1c. Les raisins, C; 1d. Les noisettes, B minor; 2. Quatre hors d'oeuvres; 2a. Les radis, A minor; 2b. Les anchois, D; 2c. Les cornochons, E flat; 2d. Le beurre, B flat.
1, 2b-d J. Swann *Concert*
(7/91) (AKAD) ① **CDAK103**

Péchés de Vieillesse, Book 5, 'Album pour les enfants adolescents'—piano (1857-60)
1. Première Communion, E flat; 2. Thème naïf et variations idem, G; 3. Saltarello à italienne, A flat; 4. Prélude moresque, E minor; 5. Valse lugubre, C; 6. Impromptu anodin, F; 7. L'innocence italienne—La candeur française, A minor; 8. Prélude convulsif, C; 9. La lagune de Venise à l'expiration de l'année 1861, G flat; 10. Ouf! les petits pois, B; 11. Un sauté, D; 12. Hachis romantique, A minor.
1, 9. A. Portugheis (r1994) *Concert*
(11/94) (ASV) ① **CDDCA901**
2. H. Antoni *Concert* (11/91) (ETCE) ① **KTC1107**
7, 10. J. Swann *Concert* (7/91) (AKAD) ① **CDAK103**
10, 11. M. Meyer (r1953/6) *Concert*
(6/95) (EMI) ① [4] **CZS5 68092-2**

Péchés de Vieillesse, Book 6, 'Album pour les enfants dégourdis'—piano (1857-68)
1. Mon prélude hygiégique du matin, C; 2. Prélude baroque, A minor; 3. Memento homo, C minor; 4. Assez de meneto: dansons, F; 5. La pesarese, B flat; 6. Valse torturée, D; 7. Une caresse à ma femme, G; 8. Barcarole, E flat; 9. Un petit train de plaisir comico-imitatif, C; 10. Fausse couche de polka-mazurka, A flat; 11. Étude asthmatique, E; 12. Un enterrement en Carnaval, D.
1, 3, 4, 7. J. Swann *Concert*
(7/91) (AKAD) ① **CDAK103**
7-9. H. Antoni *Concert* (11/91) (ETCE) ① **KTC1107**

Péchés de Vieillesse, Book 7, 'Album de chaumière'—piano (1857-68)
1. Gymnastique d'ecartement, A flat; 2. Prélude fugassaé, E; 3. Petite polka chinoise, B minor; 4. Petite valse de boudoir, A flat; 5. Prélude inoffensif, C; 6. Petite valse, 'L'huile de Ricin', E; 7. Un profond sommeil—Un reveil en sursaut, B minor; 8. Plein-chant chinois—Scherzo, B minor; 9. Un cauchemar, E; 10. Valse boiteuse, D flat; 11. Une pensée à Florence, A minor; 12. Marche, C.
5. J. Swann *Concert* (7/91) (AKAD) ① **CDAK103**
6. H. Antoni *Concert* (11/91) (ETCE) ① **KTC1107**

Péchés de Vieillesse, Book 8, 'Album de Château'—12 pieces: piano (1860s)
1. Spécimen de l'ancien régime: E flat; 2. Prélude rococo: G; 3. Un regret: Un espoir; E; 4. Boléro tartare: A minor; 5. Prélude prétentieux: C minor; 6. Spécimen de mon temps: A flat; 7. Valse anti-dansante: F; 8. Prélude semipastorale: A; 9. Tarantelle pur sang (avec Traversée de la procession): B minor; 10. Un rêve: B minor; 11. Prélude soi-disant dramatique: F sharp; 12. Spécimen de l'avenir: E flat.

2, 3. A. Portugheis (r1994) *Concert*
(11/94) (ASV) ① **CDDCA901**
3, 5. M. Meyer (r1953/6) *Concert*
(6/95) (EMI) ① [4] **CZS5 68092-2**

Péchés de Vieillesse, Book 10, 'Miscellanée pour piano'—piano (1857-68)
1. Prélude blageur, A minor; 2. Des tritons s'il vous plait (montée-descente), C; 3. Petite pensée, E flat; 4. Une bagatelle, E flat; 5. Mélodie italienne: une bagatelle (In nomine Patris), A flat; 6. Petite caprice (style Offenbach), C.
6. L. Howard *Concert*
(12/86) (HYPE) ① **CDA66090**

Péchés de Vieillesse, Book 12, 'Quelques rien pour album'—24 pieces: piano (1860s)
1. Un rien (Allegretto); 2. Un rien (Allegro moderato); 3. Un rien (Allegro moderato); 4. Un rien (Andantino sostenuto—Allegretto—primo tempo); 5. Un rien (Allegretto moderato); 6. Un rien (Andante maetoso—Allegro brillante); 7. Un rien (Andantino mosso); 8. Un rien (Andantino sostenuto); 9. Un rien (Allegretto moderato); 10. Un rien (Andantino mosso); 11. Andantino mosso—Allegretto mosso—primo tempo); 12. Un rien (Danse Sibérienne—Allegretto moderato); 13. Un rien (Allegretto brillante); 14. Un rien (Allegretto vivace); 15. Petite Galette Allemande (Allegro brillante); 16. Douces reminiscences offertes a mon ami Carafa; 17. Un rien—A piacere (Andantino mosso quasi Allegretto); 18. Un rien (Andantino mosso—Allegretto—primo tempo); 19. Un rien (Allegretto moderato); 20. Un rien (Allegro brillante); 21. Un rien (Andantino sostenuto); 22. Thème et Variations sur le Mode Mineur (Andantino mosso—Allegretto—Largo; 23. Thème et Variations sur le Mode Majeur (Allegretto moderato—Più mosso); 24. Un Rien sur le Mode Enharmonique.
B. Mezzena (8/89) (DYNA) ① [2] **CDS42**
3, 5, 12, 16, 24. A. Portugheis (r1994) *Concert*
(11/94) (ASV) ① **CDDCA901**

Petite promenade de Passy à Courbevoie—piano
H. Antoni *Concert* (11/91) (ETCE) ① **KTC1107**

SECTION IV: VOCAL AND CHORAL

Ah! per pietà t'arresta—two sopranos and orchestra (1817) (written for Nicolini's opera 'Quinto fabio')
D. Montague, Y. Kenny, Philh, D. Parry *Concert*
(10/90) (OPRA) ① [3] **ORCH103**

Album de Musique, offert par Mme. Louise Carlier—song collection compiled by Rossini (1835)
EXCERPTS: 1. Rossini: Mi lagnerò tacendo in A; 2. Bellini: Dolente immagine; 3. Paer: Ange à la voix tendre (Romance); 4. Bruguière: Le printemps arrive (Ronde villageoise); 5. Panseron: Il n'aurait pas du venir (Romance); 6. Tadolini: Com'è soave à l'anima (Arietta); 7. M. Costa: Trova un sol, mia bella Clori; 8. Marliani: La gita in gondola; 9. Mercadante: Aure amiche, ahl non spirate; 10. Morlacchi: La rosa apassita (Romanza in forma di elegia); 11. Meyerberr: Soave l'istante (Arietta); 12. Berton: Air à trois notes; 13. Bertin: Ah, dors en pais, mon bel enfant; 14. Cherubini: La pietosa bugia (Arietta); 15. Spontini: L'adieu (Romance); 16. Onslow: Le bater dans le paradis; 17. Gordigiani: Ognuno tira l'acqua al suo mulino (Canto popolare toscano); 18. Bazzini: Parmi!?.
Cpte S. Danco, E. Orel, F. Molinari-Pradelli (1956)
(9/94) (PHIL) ① **438 952-2PM**

L' Âme délaissée—soprano and piano (1844) (wds. C. Delavinge)
C. Bartoli, S. Spencer *Concert*
(4/91) (DECC) ① **430 518-2DH**
M. Horne, Martin Katz *Concert*
(4/92) (RCA) ① **RD60811**

Aragonese, 'Mi lagnerò tacendo'—1v and piano (Wds. Metastasio)
6. A. Auger, D. Baldwin *Concert*
(4/93) (ARAB) ① **Z6623**

Ariette à l'ancienne—mezzo-soprano and piano (1857-68) (wds. J-J. Rousseau)
C. Bartoli, S. Spencer *Concert*
(4/91) (DECC) ① **430 518-2DH**

Beltà crudele—soprano and piano (1821) (wds. N. di Santo-Magno)
C. Bartoli, S. Spencer *Concert*
(4/91) (DECC) ① **430 518-2DH**
M. Horne, Martin Katz *Concert*
(4/92) (RCA) ① **RD60811**

Overture ASMF, N. Marriner (r1979) *Concert*
(10/92) (PHIL) Ⓓ [3] **434 016-2PM3**
Tu non sai qual colpo atroce D. Jones, CLS, R. Hickox *Concert* (2/91) (CHAN) Ⓓ **CHAN8865**

La **Boutique Fantasque—ballet (1919—London)** (arr/orch Respighi from misc pieces by Rossini)
EXCERPTS: 1. Overture; 2. Scene; 3. Vivo; 4. Tarantella; 5. Mazurka; 6. Scene; 7. Cossack Dance; 8. Valse brillante; 9. Can-Can; 10. Andantino mosso; 11. Valse lente; 12. Scene; 13. Nocturne; 14. Galop; 15. Finale.
Philadelphia, E. Ormandy *Tchaikovsky: Sleeping Beauty.* (3/91) (SONY) Ⓓ **SBK46340**
Boston Pops, A. Fiedler (r1956) *Offenbach: Gaîté Parisienne.* (2/94) (RCA) Ⓓ **09026 61847-2**
1. Plovdiv PO, R. Raychev *Concert*
(10/90) (LASE) Ⓓ **15 520**
1, 4, 5, 7, 9, 11, 13, 14. SNO, A. Gibson (r1972) *Concert* (3/91) (CHAN) Ⓓ **CHAN6503**
4. Black Dyke Mills Band, P. Parkes (arr Langford) *Concert* (7/93) (CHAN) Ⓓ **CHAN4505**
8. Britannia Building Soc Band, H. Snell (r1990; arr Snell: brass band) *Concert*
(8/92) (DOYE) Ⓓ **DOYCD004**

La **cambiale di matrimonio—farsa comica: 1 act (1810—Venice)** (Lib. G. Rossi)
EXCERPTS: 1. Overture; 2. Non c'è il vecchio sussurrone; 3. Chi mai trova il dritto, il fondo; 4. Ecco un lettera per voi, signore; 5a. Ma, signore, questa lettera; 5b. Isacchetto!; 5c. Signor et caetera et caetera; 5d. Povera Miss Fanny!; 6. Tornami a dir che m'ami; 7a. Sì cara mia, speriam; 7b. Avete voi veduto; 8. Presto, presto; 9. Grazie ... grazie ... 10. Sicchè, dunque, istruitemi; 11a. Servo! proprio in Europa; 11b. Volea dirlo ... sicchè dunque saprete; 12. Darei per si'bel fondo; 13. Quell'amabile visino; 14a. Non si farà; 14b. Anch'io son giovine; 15. Eccolo appunto; 16. Ipotecato! - Diavolo! - Madama; 17. Dite presto, dove sta questa gran difficoltà; 18. Venite, sono andati; 19a. Bravi! Bravi!; 19b. Ragazzi miei; 20a. Come tacer; 20b. Vorrei spiegarvi; 21. Eppur lo cred'anch'io che il far del bene; 22a. Metti là tutto, e parti; 22b. Porterò così il cappello; 23. Qual'ira, oh ciel; 24. Vi prego un momento, signore.
Cpte B. Praticò, Alessandra Rossi, M. Comencini, B. de Simone, F. Facini, V. Baiano, ECO, M. Viotti (r1990) (7/91) (CLAV) Ⓓ **CD50-9101**
1. ASMF, N. Marriner *Concert*
(2/89) (EMI) Ⓓ **CDC7 49155-2**
1. Plovdiv PO, R. Raychev *Concert*
(10/90) (LASE) Ⓓ **15 520**
1. ASMF, N. Marriner (r1974) *Concert*
(10/92) (PHIL) Ⓓ [3] **434 016-2PM3**
1. National PO, R. Chailly (r1984) *Concert*
(9/95) (DECC) Ⓓ [2] **443 850-2DF2**

La **Cenerentola, or La bontà in trionfo, 'Cinderella'—dramma giocoso: 2 acts (1817—Rome)** (Lib. G. Ferretti)
EXCERPTS: 1. Overture. ACT 1: 2a. No, no, no; 2b. Una volta c'era un re; 2c. Un tantin di carità; 2d. O figlie amabili; 2e. Cenerentola, vien qua; 3. Miei rampolli femminini; 4a. Tutto è deserto; 4b. Un soave non so che; 5a. Non so che dir; 5b. Scegli la sposa, affrettati; 5c. Come un'ape ne' giorni d'aprile; 6. Signor, una parola; 7. Là del ciel nell'arcano profondo; 8. Zitto, zitto, piano, piano; 8a. Conciossiacosacche; 8b. Noi Don Magnifico; 8c. Zitto, zitto, piano, piano; 8d. Signor...Altezza, è in tavolo. ACT 2: 9a. Mi par che quei birbanti; 9b. Sia qualunque delle figlie; 10a. Ah! questa bella incognita; 10b. E allor... 10c. Sì, ritrovarla io giuro; 11a. Ma dunque io son un ex; 11b. Un segreto d'importanza; 12a. Ma ve l'avevo detto; 12b. Temporale; 13a. Son qui; 13b. Siete voi?; 14a. Della Fortuna; 14b. Nacqui all'affanno, al pianto; 14c. Non più mesta accanto al fuoco.
Cpte A. Baltsa, F. Araiza, S. Alaimo, R. Raimondi, C. Malone, F. Palmer, J. del Carlo, Ambrosian Op Chor, ASMF, N. Marriner (r1987)
(11/88) (PHIL) Ⓓ [3] **420 468-2PH3**
Cpte L.V. Terrani, F. Araiza, D. Trimarchi, E. Dara, E. Ravaglia, M. Schmiege, A. Corbelli, W German Rad Chor, Cappella Coloniensis, G. Ferro
(6/91) (SONY) Ⓓ [2] **S2K46433**
Cpte M. de Gabarain, J. Oncina, S. Bruscantini, I. Wallace, A. Noni, F. Cadoni, H. Alan, Glyndebourne Fest Chor, Glyndebourne Fest Orch, V. Gui, B. Balkwill (r1953/4)
(5/92) (EMI) Ⓓ [2] **CMS7 64183-2**
Cpte C. Bartoli, W. Matteuzzi, A. Corbelli, E. Dara, F. Costa, G. Banditelli, M. Pertusi, Bologna Teatro Comunale Chor, Bologna Teatro Comunale Orch, R. Chailly (r1992)
(11/93) (DECC) Ⓓ [2] **436 902-2DHO2**
Cpte J. Larmore, R. Giménez, G. Quilico, A. Corbelli, A. Scarabelli, L. Polverelli, A. Miles, ROH Chor, ROHO, C. Rizzi (r1994)
(4/95) (TELD) Ⓓ [2] **4509-94553-2**
1. Philh, C.M. Giulini *Concert*
(12/87) (EMI) Ⓓ **CDM7 69042-2**
1. LSO, C. Abbado *Concert*
(5/88) (DG) Ⓓ **419 869-2GGA**
1. ASMF, N. Marriner *Concert*
(2/89) (EMI) Ⓓ **CDC7 49155-2**
1. Chicago SO, F. Reiner *Concert*
(9/90) (RCA) Ⓓ **GD60387**
1. Plovdiv PO, R. Raychev *Concert*
(10/90) (LASE) Ⓓ **15 520**
1. COE, C. Abbado *Concert*
(5/91) (DG) Ⓓ **431 653-2GH**
1. ASMF, N. Marriner (r1976) *Concert*
(10/92) (PHIL) Ⓓ [3] **434 016-2PM3**
1. NBC SO, A. Toscanini (r1945) *Concert*
(11/92) (RCA) Ⓓ **GD60289**
1. Black Dyke Mills Band, P. Parkes (arr Parkes) *Concert* (7/93) (CHAN) Ⓓ **CHAN4505**
1. ASMF, N. Marriner (r1976) *Concert*
(12/95) (PHIL) Ⓓ **446 196-2PM**
3. A. Rossi, orch (r1905) *Concert*
(12/92) (TEST) Ⓓ **SBT1008**
6. J. Oncina, M. de Gabarain, I. Wallace, S. Bruscantini, Glyndebourne Fest Orch, V. Gui (r1953) *Concert* (6/94) (EMI) Ⓓ **CDH5 65072-2**
10b(pt), 10c R. Giménez, Scottish Phil Sngrs, Scottish CO, M. Veltri *Concert*
(8/88) (NIMB) Ⓓ **NI5106**
14a-c F. von Stade, J. Opalach, C. Estep, M. Fortuna, M. Lerner, H. Runey, NY Concert Chorale, St Luke's Orch, R. Norrington (pp1992) *Concert*
(12/94) (EMI) Ⓓ **CDC7 54643-2**
14b C. Supervia, orch, A. Albergoni (r1927) *Concert*
(7/92) (PEAR) Ⓓ [3] **GEMMCDS9926(2)**
14b, 14c C. Bartoli, Vienna Volksoper Orch, G. Patanè *Concert* (9/89) (DECC) Ⓓ **425 430-2DH**
14b, 14c V. de los Angeles, Rome Op Orch, G. Morelli (r1954) *Concert*
(8/90) (EMI) Ⓓ **CDH7 63495-2**
14b, 14c C. Supervia, orch, A. Albergoni (r1927) *Concert* (9/90) (PREI) Ⓓ **89023**
14b, 14c D. Jones, C. Smith, K. Steffan, H. Nicholl, G. Finley, S. Birchall, Richard Hickox Sngrs, CLS, R. Hickox *Concert* (2/91) (CHAN) Ⓓ **CHAN8865**
14b, 14c C. Supervia, orch, A. Albergoni (r1927) *Concert* (12/92) (TEST) Ⓓ **SBT1008**
14b, 14c C. Supervia, orch, A. Albergoni (r1927) *Concert* (3/93) (NIMB) Ⓓ [2] **NI7836/7**
14b, 14c M. Horne, ROHO, H. Lewis (r1964) *Concert*
(10/93) (DECC) Ⓓ **436 462-2DM**

Le **Comte Ory—opéra/opéra comique: 2 acts (1828—Paris)** (Lib. E. Scribe & C.G. Delestre-Poirson)
EXCERPTS: 1. Overture. ACT 1: 2. Jouvencelles, venez vite; 3. Que les destins prospères; 4. Moi, je réclame; 5. De grâce, encore un mot; 6. Je ne puis plus longtemps; 7. Veiller sans cesse; 8. Vous, notre appui; 9. Cette aventure fort singulière; 10. Cet ermite, ma belle enfant; 11. Une dame de haut parage; 12. Isolier dans ces lieux; 13. En proie à la tristesse; 14. Vous avez entendu sa touchante prière; 15a. Ô bon ermite; 15b. C'est bien, je suis content; 16. Ciel! - Ô terreur, ô peine extrême; 17. Cet écrit, noble châtelaine; 18. Venez amis, retirons-nous. ACT 2: 19a. Dans ce séjour calme et tranquille; 19b. Noble châtelaine; 19c. Quand tomberont sur lui; 20. Ah! quel respect, Madame; 21. Ce téméraire; 22. Voici vos compagnes fidèles; 23. Ah! la bonne folie!; 24. Eh! mais, quelle triste observance; 25. Dans ce lieu solitaire; 26. Buvons, buvons; 27. Elle revient ... silence!; 28. A la faveur de cette nuit obscure; 29. J'entends d'ici le bruit des armes; 30. Ecoutez ces chants de victoire.
Cpte J. Aler, S. Jo, G. Cachemaille, D. Montague, G. Quilico, R. Pierotti, M. Castets, F. Dudziak, N. Rivenq, Lyon Op Chor, Lyon Op Orch, J.E. Gardiner
(10/89) (PHIL) Ⓓ [2] **422 406-2PH2**
Cpte J. Oncina, S. Barabas, I. Wallace, C. Canne-Meijer, M. Roux, M. Sinclair, J. Sinclair, D. Troy, Glyndebourne Fest Chor, Glyndebourne Fest Orch, V. Gui (r1956) (5/92) (EMI) Ⓓ [2] **CMS7 64180-2**
3. R. Blake, LSO, J. McCarthy *Concert*
(4/88) (ARAB) Ⓓ **Z6582**
15a C. Canne-Meijer, J. Oncina, S. Barabas, Glyndebourne Fest Chor, Glyndebourne Fest Orch, V. Gui (r1956) *Concert*
(6/94) (EMI) Ⓓ **CDH5 65072-2**

Demetrio e Polibio—dramma serio: 2 acts (1812—Rome) (Lib. V. Viganò-Mombelli)
EXCERPTS: 1. Overture.
1. ASMF, N. Marriner (r1979) *Concert*
(10/92) (PHIL) Ⓓ [3] **434 016-2PM3**

La **Donna del lago, '(The) Lady of the Lake'—melodramma: 2 acts (1819—Naples)** (Lib. A.L. Tottola, after Sir Walter Scott)
EXCERPTS: 1. Overture. ACT 1: 2. O, mattutini albori; 3. Qual suon!; 4. Uberto! Ah! Dove t'ascondi?; 5. Sei già nel tetto mio; 6. D'Inibaca Donzella; 7. Sei già sposa?; 8. Quali accenti!... 9. Ma son sorpreso... 10. Mura felici; 11. Elena! o tu, che chiamo!; 12. O quante lacrime; 13. Figlia! È così; 14. Taci, lo voglio; 15. E nel fatal conflitto; 16. Vivere io non potrò; 17. Qual rapido torrente; 18. Eccomi a voi; 19. Ma dov'è colei; 20. Se a'miei voti; 21. Alfin mi è dato; 22. Vieni, o stella; 23. Quanto a quest'alma; 24. La mia spada; 25. Quest'amplesso; 26. Crudele sospetto... 27. Sul colle a Morve; 28. Già un raggio; 29. Su...amici!. ACT 2: 30. O fiamma soave; 31. Va, non temer; 32. Alla ragion deh rieda; 33. Numi, se a'miei sospiri... 34. Vincesti!...Addio!... 35. Qual pena in me; 36. Parla...che sei?; 37. Io son la misera; 38. Quante sciagure; 39. Ah! Si pera; 40. Douglas! Douglas! Ti salva!; 41. Che sento!; 42. Attendi: Il Re fra poco; 43. Che sento! Qual soave armonia!; 44. Stelle! Sembra egli stesso!; 45. Eccolo! Amica sorte; 46. Impogna il Re: 47. Ah! Che vedo!; 48. Tanti affetti; 49. Fra il padre.
Cpte K. Ricciarelli, L.V. Terrani, D. Gonzalez, D. Raffanti, S. Ramey, C. Valdenassi, O. di Credico, A. d'Uva, Prague Philharmonic Ch, COE, M. Pollini (r1983) (8/88) (SONY) Ⓓ [3] **S2K39311**
Cpte J. Anderson, M. Dupuy, R. Blake, C. Merritt, G. Surian, M. Laurenza, E. Gavazzi, F. Poggi, La Scala Chor, La Scala Orch, R. Muti (pp1992)
(2/95) (PHIL) Ⓓ [2] **438 211-2PH2**
10. M. Horne, St Luke's Orch, R. Norrington (pp1992) *Concert* (12/94) (EMI) Ⓓ **CDC7 54643-2**
10, 11. C. Bartoli, Vienna Volksoper Orch, G. Patanè *Concert* (9/89) (DECC) Ⓓ **425 430-2DH**
10-12. D. Jones, CLS, R. Hickox *Concert*
(2/91) (CHAN) Ⓓ **CHAN8865**
18. R. Vargas, ECO, M. Viotti *Concert*
(11/92) (CLAV) Ⓓ **CD50-9202**
30. R. Blake, LSO, J. McCarthy *Concert*
(4/88) (ARAB) Ⓓ **Z6582**
48. C. Bartoli, Venice La Fenice Chor, Venice La Fenice Orch, I. Martin *Concert*
(2/92) (DECC) Ⓓ **436 075-2DH**
48. M. Caballé, RCA Italiana Op Chor, RCA Italiana Op Orch, C.F. Cillario *Concert*
(11/92) (RCA) Ⓓ [2] **GD60941**
48. D. Soffel, Swedish CO, M. Liljefors (pp1988) *Concert* (4/93) (CPRI) Ⓓ **CAP21428**

Edipo a Colono—incidental music (before 1817)
EXCERPTS: 1. Overture.
1. ASMF, N. Marriner (r1979) *Concert*
(10/92) (PHIL) Ⓓ [3] **434 016-2PM3**

Eduardo e Cristina—dramma: 2 acts (1819—Venice) (Lib. G. Schmidt, after Pavesi)
EXCERPTS: 1. Overture.
1. ASMF, N. Marriner (r1979) *Concert*
(10/92) (PHIL) Ⓓ [3] **434 016-2PM3**

Elisabetta, Regina d'Inghilterra—dramma: 2 acts (1815—Naples) (Lib. G. Schmidt, after Federici)
EXCERPTS: 1. Overture. ACT 1: 2. Più lieta, più bella; 3. Nel giubilo comun, signore; 4a. Esulta, Elisa, omai; 4b. Qant'è grato all'alma mia; 4c. Questo cor ben lo comprende; 5a. Grandi del regno; 5b. Vieni, o prode; 6. Alta Regina; 7. Incauta, che festi!; 8a. Sconsigliata!; 8b. Sento un'interna voce; 9. Che intesi!; 10b. Perché mai, destin crudele; 10c. Misera! A quale stato; 11. Guglielmo, ascolta; 12a. Che penso; 12b. Se mi serbasti il soglio; 12c. Qual colpo inaspettato; 12d. Duce, il tal guisa. ACT 2: 13a. Dov'è Matilde?; 13b. Pensa che sol per poco; 13c. Non bastan quelle lagrime; 14a. Misero me!...La sposa; 14b. L'avverso mio destino; 14c. Ah! Fra poco, in faccia a morte; 15. Chiede Norfolk a te l'accesso; 16. Qui soffermiamo il piè; 17a. Che intesi!...Oh annunzio!; 17b. Deh! Troncate i ceppi suoi; 18a. Della cieca fortuna; 18b. Sposa amata; 19a. E l'adorata sposa; 19b. Deh! scusa i trasporti; 20a. Tu regina!...deh! come; 20b. Fellon, la pena avrai; 20c. Bell'alme generose; 20d. Leicester!.
Cpte M. Caballé, J. Carreras, V. Masterson, R. Creffield, U. Benelli, N. Jenkins, Ambrosian Sngrs, LSO, G-F. Masini
(12/92) (PHIL) Ⓓ [2] **432 453-2PM2**
4b K. Ricciarelli, Lyon Op Chor, Lyon Op Orch, G. Ferro (r1989) *Concert*
(11/94) (VIRG) Ⓓ **CUV5 61139-2**
4b, 20b C. Bartoli, Venice La Fenice Chor, Venice La Fenice Orch, I. Martin *Concert*
(2/92) (DECC) Ⓓ **436 075-2DH**
17a R. Blake, LSO, J. McCarthy *Concert*
(4/88) (ARAB) Ⓓ **Z6582**

18a C. Merritt, Munich RSO, J. Fiore (r1993) *Concert* (9/94) (PHIL) ⦶ **434 102-2PH**

Ermione—azione tragica: 2 acts (1819—Naples) (Lib. A.L. Tottola, after Racine)

EXCERPTS: 1. Overture. ACT 1: 1a. Mi guarda, e impallidisce!; 2. Troja! qual fosti un di!; 3. Mia delizia! un solo istante; 4. All'ombra del tuo sposo; 5. Dall'Oriente l'astro del giorno; 6a. A tante cure, o amiche; 6b. Non proseguir; 7. Sul lido di Agamennone; 8. Venga il Greco Orator; 9a. Reggia abborrita; 9b. Che sorda al mesto pianto; 9c. Ah! come nascondere; 9d. Che fai di te; 10. March; 11a. Mi guarda e impallidisce; 11b. Balena in man del figlio; 12a. Deh serena i mesti rai; 12b. Non pavento: quest'alma; 12c. Periglioso e il restar; 13a. E Pirro ancor; 13b. Amarti?; 14. Alfin l'Eroe da forte; 15. Sperar poss'io; 16. A me Astianatte. ACT 2: 17a. Liete novelle; 17b. Ombra del caro sposo; 17c. Vieni a giurar; 18a. Sia compiuto il mio fato; 18b. Essa corre al trionfo; 18c. Di, che vedesti piangere; 19a. Il voglia il Ciel; 19b. Amata, l'amai; 20a. Ma che ascolto?; 20b. Un'empia mel rapi; 21. Il tuo dolor ei affretta; 22a. Ah! qual sovrasta a Pirro; 22b. A così triste immagine; 23a. Che feci? dove son?; 23b. Parmi, che ad ogn'istante; 25. Ah! ti rinvenni!.

1. ASMF, N. Marriner (r1979) *Concert* (10/92) (PHIL) ⦶ [3] **434 016-2PM3**

9a-c R. Blake, P. Jeffes, LSO, M. Valdes *Concert* (12/89) (ARAB) ⦶ **Z6612**

11b C. Merritt, Munich RSO, J. Fiore (r1993) *Concert* (9/94) (PHIL) ⦶ **434 102-2PH**

La **Gazza ladra, '(The) Thieving Magpie'—melodramma: 2 acts (1817—Milan)** (Lib. G. Gheradini, after d'Aubigny & Caigniez)

EXCERPTS: 1. Overture. ACT 1: 2. Oh che giorno fortunato; 3. Marmotte, che fate; 4. Egli viene, o mia Lucia; 5. Là, seduto l'amato Giannetto; 6. Oh cospetto! Undici ore già passate; 7. Di piacer mi balza il cor; 8. Tutto sorridere; 9. Alfin sei giunta; 10. Stringhe e ferri; 11. Oh, senti il vecchio Isacco; 12a. Ma qual suono; 12b. Bravo, bravo! Ben tornato; 13. Vieni fra queste braccia; 14. Bravo, bravo. Ma quel piacer; 15. Tocchiamo, beviamo; 16a. Oh madre, ancor no mi diceste; 16b. Idol mio!; 17. Ieri, sul tramontar del sole; 18. Come frenare il pianto; 19. Per questo amplesso; 20. Io tremo, pavento; 21. Il mio piano è preparato; 22. Sì, sì, Ninetta; 23a. Un altro, un altro; 23b. Questo piego presante; 23c. Ah! Padre udiste?; 24. M'affretto di mandarvi; 25. Respiro ... Mia cara!; 26. Siamo soli: Amor seconda; 27. Non so quel che farei!; 28a. Stringhe e ferri da calzette; 28b. Ecco la gabbia; 28c. Andiam tosto; 28d. Eccovi, o miei signori; 28e. E sopra sotto; 29. In casa di Messere; 30. Iasacco chiamaste; 31. Mi sento opprimere; 32. In prigione costei. ACT 2: 32b. Ahimè; 33a. In quell'orrendo; 33c. Oh troppe grazie!; 34. Forse un dì conoscerete; 35. Oh mio signor partite; 36. Ah destino crudel; 37a. Sì per voi, pupille amate; 37b. Chi m'aiuta?; 38. Udrai la sentenza; 39. Podestà, Poedstà!; 40. Deh pensa domani; 41. Infelice Ninetta; 42. Chi è? Fernando!; 43. Eterni Dei, che sento!; 44. Ah lungi, il timore!; 45a. Ora mi par che il core; 45b. A questo seno; 45c. Saprò correggerre; 46. A pieni voti; 47. Tremate, o popoli; 48. Infelice donzella; 49. Aspettate sopendete; 50. Ah no! Fermate!; 51. Sino il pianto è negato; 52a. Che razza di villaggio; 52b. Ora che nel castagno; 53. Infelice, sventurata; 54. Deh tu reggi in tal momento; 55. Giorgio, Giorgio?; 56. Che scampanare è questo?; 57. Figlia mia!; 58. Ecco cessato il vento.

Cpte K. Ricciarelli, W. Matteuzzi, S. Ramey, B. Manca di Nissa, L. d'Intino, F. Furlanetto, R. Coviello, O. di Credico, P. Lefebre, F. Musinu, M. Lippi, Prague Phil Chor, Turin RSO, G. Gelmetti (pp1989) (10/90) (SONY) ⦶ [3] **S3K45850**

1. Philh, C.M. Giulini *Concert* (12/87) (EMI) ⦶ **CDM7 69042-2**

1. LSO, C. Abbado *Concert* (5/88) (DG) ⦶ **419 869-2GGA**

1. ASMF, N. Marriner *Concert* (2/89) (EMI) ⦶ **CDC7 49155-2**

1. Philh, H. von Karajan *Concert* (11/89) (EMI) ⦶ **CDM7 63113-2**

1. BPO, H. von Karajan *Concert* (5/90) (DG) ⦶ **429 164-2GR**

1. Chicago SO, F. Reiner *Concert* (9/90) (RCA) ⦶ **GD60387**

1. Plovdiv PO, R. Raychev *Concert* (10/90) (LASE) ⦶ **15 506**

1. LCP, R. Norrington *Concert* (4/91) (EMI) ⦶ **CDC7 54091-2**

1. COE, C. Abbado *Concert* (5/91) (DG) ⦶ **431 653-2GH**

1. BPO, W. Furtwängler (r1930) *Concert* (4/92) (KOCH) ⦶ [2] **37059-2**

1. ASMF, N. Marriner (r1976) *Concert* (10/92) (PHIL) ⦶ [3] **434 016-2PM3**

1. NBC SO, A. Toscanini (r1945) *Concert* (11/92) (RCA) ⦶ **GD60289**

1. LPO, T. Beecham (r1934) *Concert* (7/93) (DUTT) ⦶ **CDLX7001**

1. Philh, G. Cantelli (r1952) *Concert* (11/94) (TEST) ⦶ **SBT1034**

1. Atlanta SO, Y. Levi (r1993) *Concert* (11/94) (TELA) ⦶ **CD80334**

1. Berlin RIAS Orch, F. Fricsay (r1953) *Concert* (11/94) (DG) ⦶ **445 406-2GDO**

1. I. Seefried, M. Forrester, E. Haefliger, D. Fischer-Dieskau, Berlin St Hedwig's Cath Ch, BPO, F. Fricsay, H. Krebs, T. Varga, Berlin RIAS Chbr Ch, Berlin RIAS Orch, H. Geusser, W. Fugmann, M. Weber, G. Herzog, Berlin RSO, VPO, E. Grümmer, G. Pitzinger, H. Hotter, Y. Menuhin (r1953) *Concert* (11/94) (DG) ⦶ [11] **445 400-2GDO10**

1. National PO, R. Chailly (r1981) *Concert* (9/95) (DECC) ⦶ [2] **443 850-2DF2**

1. ASMF, N. Marriner (r1976) *Concert* (12/95) (PHIL) ⦶ **446 196-2PM**

13. R. Blake, Ambrosian Sngrs, LSO, M. Valdes *Concert* (12/89) (ARAB) ⦶ **Z6612**

Guillaume Tell—opéra: 4 acts (1829—Paris) (Lib. E de Jouy, H-L-F Bris et al)

EXCERPTS: 1. Overture. ACT 1: 2. Quel jour serein le ciel présage! (È il ciel seren); 3. Accours dans ma nacelle (Il piccol legno ascendi); 4. On entend des montagnes (Oh! quale alta d'intorno); 6. Près des torrents qui grondent; 8. Le mien, dit-il, jamais le mien!; 9a. Où va-tu?; 9b. Ah! Mathilde, idole de mon âme (Ah! Matilde, io t'amo); 10. Du danger quand sonnera l'heure; 11a. O Ciel, tu sais si Mathilde m'est chère!; 11b. Bridal Procession; 12. Sur nos têtes le soleil brille; 13. Quand le Ciel entend votre promesse; 14. Des antiques vertus vous nous rendez l'exemple; 16. Hymenée, ta journée fortunée (Cinto che il crine); 17. Pas de six (Passo a sei); 18. Gloire, honneur au fils de Teil; 19. Pâle et tremblant, se soutenant à peine; 21. Dieu de bonté, Dieu tout-puissant (Nume pietoso); 22. Ils vont parler; 23. Comme lui nous aurions dû faire. ACT 2: 25. Quel est ce bruit?; 26. Ils s'éloignent enfin (S'allontanano alfine!); 27. Sombre fôret (Selva opaca); 28. Ma présence pour vous est peut-être un outrage? (Se il mio giunger); 29. Oui, vous l'arrachez à mon âme; 30. Doux aveu! ce tendre langage; 31. Il est digne de mon amour, oui...Dans celle que j'aime; 33. Ciel! Walter et Guillaume oui...Tu n'étais pas seul; 34. Quand l'Helvétie est un champ de supplices (Allor che scorre); 35. Ses jours qu'ils ont osé proscrire; 36. Il est donc vrai!; 37. Des profondeurs du bois immense; 38. En ces temps de malheurs; 40. De prompts effets la promesse est suive; 41. L'avalanche roulant (Scène de la conjuration). ACT 3: 42. Arnold, d'où naît ce désespoir?; 43. Pour notre amour plus espérance; 45. Sur la rive étrangère; 46. Gloire au pouvoir suprême!; 47. Vainement dans son insolence; 48. Que l'empire germain de votre obéissance; 49a. Pas de trois; 49b. Toi que l'oiseau ne suivrant pas (Tyrolienne); 50. Danse (Allegretto et maestoso); 51. Toi que l'oiseau ne suivrant pas; 52. Pas de Soldats (Soldiers' March); 53. Audacieux, incline-toi!; 54. C'est là cet archer redoutable; 55. Réjoins ta mère, je l'ordonne; 56. Je te bénis en répandant des larmes (Ti benedico); 57. Sois immobile, et vers la terre (Resta immobile); 59. Au nom de souverain, je le prends sous ma garde; 60. Quand l'orgueil les égare. ACT 4: 61. Ne m'abandonne pas (Non mi lasciere); 62. Asile héridiitaire (O muto asil); 63. Vengeance! Vengeance!; 64. Amis, amis, secondez ma vengeance (Corriam, voliam); 72. Pourquoi ta pr

Cpte S. Milnes, M. Freni, L. Pavarotti, N. Ghiaurov, J. Tomlinson, D. Jones, E. Connell, F. Mazzoli, C.A. Suarez, P. de Palma, R. Van Allan, Ambrosian Op Chor, National PO, R. Chailly (Ital) (2/87) (DECC) ⦶ [4] **417 154-2DH4**

Cpte G. Bacquier, M. Caballé, N. Gedda, K. Kováts, G. Howell, M. Mesplé, J. Taillon, L. Hendrikx, C. Burles, R. Cassinelli, N. Christov, Ambrosian Op Chor, RPO, L. Gardelli (r1972: also includes item 73) (3/89) (EMI) ⦶ [4] **CMS7 69951-2**

Excs Consortium Classicum (arr wind ens: Sedlak) (4/89) (CLAV) ⦶ **CD50-8804**

Excs P. Gallois, London Fest Orch, R. Pople (r1993: arr fl: Demersseman/Berthelemy/Gallois) *Concert* (5/95) (DG) ⦶ **445 822-2GH**

1. LSO, G. Simon *Concert* (3/87) (CALA) ⦶ [2] **CACD0101**

1. Philh, C.M. Giulini *Concert* (12/87) (EMI) ⦶ **CDM7 69042-2**

1. ASMF, N. Marriner *Concert* (2/89) (EMI) ⦶ **CDC7 49155-2**

1. Chicago SO, F. Reiner *Concert* (9/90) (RCA) ⦶ **GD60387**

1. Plovdiv PO, R. Raychev *Concert* (10/90) (LASE) ⦶ **15 520**

1. LCP, R. Norrington *Concert* (4/91) (EMI) ⦶ **CDC7 54091-2**

1. COE, C. Abbado *Concert* (5/91) (DG) ⦶ **431 653-2GH**

1(pt) SO, T. Beecham (r c1912) *Concert* (11/91) (SYMP) ⦶ [2] **SYMCD1096/7**

1. National PO, L. Stokowski *Concert* (4/92) (EMI) ⦶ **CDM7 64140-2**

1. ASMF, N. Marriner (r1976) *Concert* (10/92) (PHIL) ⦶ [3] **434 016-2PM3**

1. NBC SO, A. Toscanini (r1953) *Concert* (11/92) (RCA) ⦶ **GD60289**

1. Black Dyke Mills Band, T. Walmsley (arr Grant) *Concert* (7/93) (CHAN) ⦶ **CHAN4505**

1. LPO, T. Beecham (r1934) *Concert* (7/93) (DUTT) ⦶ **CDLX7001**

1. Detroit SO, P. Paray (r1959) *Concert* (11/93) (MERC) ⦶ **434 332-2MM**

1. T. Trotter (r1992: trans org: E Lemare) *Concert* (4/94) (DECC) ⦶ **436 656-2DH**

1. Atlanta SO, Y. Levi (r1993) *Concert* (11/94) (TELA) ⦶ **CD80334**

1. National PO, R. Chailly (r1981) *Concert* (9/95) (DECC) ⦶ [2] **443 850-2DF2**

1. Santa Cecilia Academy Orch, V. de Sabata (r1948) *Concert* (9/95) (EMI) ⦶ [2] **CHS5 65506-2**

1. ASMF, N. Marriner (r1976) *Concert* (12/95) (PHIL) ⦶ **446 196-2PM**

1, 49a, 49b Philh, H. von Karajan *Concert* (11/89) (EMI) ⦶ **CDM7 63113-2**

4a H. Schlusnus, R. Hutt, orch (r1921: Ger) *Concert* (12/95) (PREI) ⦶ **89110**

9a, 9b J. Lotrič, I. Morozov, Slovak RSO, J. Wildner (r1994) *Concert* (2/95) (NAXO) ⦶ **8 553030**

9b A. Pertile, B. Franci, La Scala Orch, C. Sabajno (Ital: r1930) *Concert* (9/90) (PREI) ⦶ **89007**

9b L. Slezak, L. Demuth, orch (Ger: r1908) *Concert* (2/91) (PREI) ⦶ **89020**

9b C. Muzio, orch (r1918: Ital) *Concert* (1/95) (ROMO) ⦶ [2] **81010-2**

26, 27. R. Tebaldi, Santa Cecilia Academy Orch, A. Erede (Ital) *Concert* (8/91) (DECC) ⦶ [2] **430 481-2DX2**

26, 27. K. Ricciarelli, Lyon Op Chor, Lyon Op Orch, G. Ferro (r1989) *Concert* (11/94) (VIRG) ⦶ **CUV5 61139-2**

27. G. Martinelli, orch, N. Shilkret (Ital: r1923) *Concert* (10/89) (NIMB) ⦶ **NI7804**

27. E. Norena, orch, H. Defosse (r1930) *Concert* (3/91) (PREI) ⦶ **89041**

27. L. Pagliughi, orch (Ital: r c1938) *Concert* (12/92) (TEST) ⦶ **SBT1008**

35. G. Martinelli, G. De Luca, J. Mardones, orch (Ital: r1923) *Concert* (12/92) (TEST) ⦶ **SBT1008**

35. L. Escalais, O. Luppi, A. Magini-Coletti, anon (Ital: r1905) *Concert* (12/93) (SYMP) ⦶ **SYMCD1126**

35. L. Escalais, anon (r1905) *Concert* (12/93) (SYMP) ⦶ **SYMCD1126**

37. H. Spani, La Scala Orch, C. Sabajno (r1931: Ital) *Concert* (4/94) (EMI) ⦶ [3] **CHS7 64864-2(2)**

57. T. Gobbi, Philh, A. Erede (r1963: Ital) *Concert* (10/89) (EMI) ⦶ **CDM7 63109-2**

57. G. De Luca, orch (Ital: r1923) *Concert* (1/92) (PREI) ⦶ **89036**

57. A. Endrèze, orch, F. Ruhlmann (r c1932) *Concert* (11/92) (MSCM) ⦶ **MM30451**

57. A. Sved, orch (Ital: r1940) *Concert* (12/92) (TEST) ⦶ **SBT1008**

57. J. Van Dam, Loire PO, M. Soustrot (r1992; Ital) *Concert* (8/93) (FORL) ⦶ **UCD16681**

57. D. Hvorostovsky, Philh, I. Marin (r1992) *Concert* (9/94) (PHIL) ⦶ **434 912-2PH**

61, 62. C. Merritt, NY Concert Chorale, St Luke's Orch, R. Norrington (pp1992) *Concert* (12/94) (EMI) ⦶ **CDC7 54643-2**

61, 62. R. Alagna, LPO, R. Armstrong *Concert* (12/95) (EMI) ⦶ **CDC5 55540-2**

61-64. L. Pavarotti, Vienna Op Chor, Vienna Op Orch, N. Rescigno (r1969: Ital) *Concert* (12/93) (DECC) ⦶ **433 437-2DA**

62. G. Thill, Orch, E. Bigot (r1931) *Concert* (1/89) (EMI) ⦶ **CDM7 69548-2**

62. F. Signorini, orch (Ital: r1908) *Concert* (11/92) (MEMO) ⦶ [2] **HR4408/9(1)**

62. A. d'Arkor, orch (r1930) *Concert* (12/92) (TEST) ⦶ **SBT1008**

62. G. Thill, orch, E. Bigot (r1931) *Concert* (8/95) (FORL) ⦶ **UCD16727**

62, 64. F. Tamagno, Anon (pf) (r1903-04) *Concert* (2/92) (OPAL) ⦶ **OPALCD9846**

64. F. Tamagno, anon (Ital: r1903) *Concert* (12/92) (TEST) ⦶ **SBT1008**

L' **Inganno felice—farsa: 1 act (1812—Venice)** (Lib. G. Foppa after Paisiello)
EXCERPTS: 1. Overture; 2a. Cosa dite! ma cosa dite!; 2b. Ebben, che ascendi; 3a. Qual tenero diletto; 3b. Né posson due lustri; 4. Ebben, che tenta; 5. Chi mi chiama?; 6a. Prima d'andar; 6b. Una voce m'ha colpito; 7. Egli restò indeciso; 8. Ciel protettor; 9a. Oh, Cielo; 9b. Quel sembiante, quello sguardo; 10. Oh, l'impressione è fatta; 11a. Quale inchiesta!; 11b. Tu mi conosci, e sai che; 12a. Mel pagherà tua vita!; 12b. Va taluno mormorando; 13. È deciso!; 14a. Al nuovo dì col mio fedele; 14b. Al più dolce e caro oggetto; 15. Son fuor di me!; 16. Oarmi tutto disposto; 17. Finale: Tacita notte amica, deh.
Cpte N. de Carolis, A. Felle, I. Zennaro, F. Previati, D. Serraiocco, ECO, M. Viotti (r1992) (5/93) (CLAV) ① **CD50-9211**
Cpte E. Cundari, F. Jacopucci, P. Montarsolo, G. Tadeo, Sergio Pezzetti, Naples RAI Orch, C. Franci (5/93) (NOTE) ① [2] **PGP21001**
1. ASMF, N. Marriner (r1974) *Concert* (10/92) (PHIL) ① [3] **434 016-2PM3**

L' **Italiana in Algeri, '(The) Italian Girl in Algiers'—dramma giocoso: 2 acts (1816—Rome)** (Lib. A. Anelli)
EXCERPTS: 1. Overture. ACT 1: 2. Serenate il mesto ciglio; 3. Il mio schiavo italian; 4. Languir per una bella; 5a. Ah, quando fia; 5b. Se inclinassi a prender moglie; 6a. Quanta roba!; 6b. Cruda sorte!; 7. Misericordia; 8a. Ah! Isabella; 8b. Ai capricci della sorte; 9a. E ricusar potresti; 9b. Ascoltami, italiano; 9c. Dunque degg'io lasciarvi?; 10. Già d'insolito; 11a. Viva, viva; 11b. O! Che muso; 12a. Vo' star con mia; 12b. Pria di dividerci. ACT 2: 13a. Uno stupido; 13b. Amiche, andate a dir all'italiana; 13c. Qual disdetta; 14. Ah, come il cor di giubilo; 15a. Viva il grande Kaimakan; 15b. Ho un gran peso; 16a. Dunque a momenti; 16b. Per lui che adoro; 17a. Io non resisto più; 17b. Ti presento; 18a. Con tutta la sua boria; 18b. La femmine d'Italia; 19. E tu speri di togliere Isabella; 20. Orsù, la tua nipote; 21a. Pappataci; 21b. Voi mi deste; 22. E può la tua padrone; 23a. Tutti i nostri Italiani; 23b. Pronti abbiamo; 23c. Amici, in ogni evento; 23d. Pensa alla patria; 23e. Qual piacer!; 24a. Che bel cor; 24b. Dei Pappataci; 25a. Non sei tu che il grado eletto; 25b. Son l'aure seconde; 25c. Mio Signore. ADDITIONAL ARIA: 26. Concedi, concedi, amor pietoso.
Cpte L.V. Terrani, F. Araiza, E. Dara, W. Ganzarolli, J.M. Bima, L. Rizzi, A. Corbelli, W German Rad Chor, Cappella Coloniensis, G. Ferro (8/88) (SONY) ① [2] **S2K39048**
Cpte T. Berganza, L. Alva, R. Panerai, F. Corena, G. Tavolaccini, M.T. Pace, P. Montarsolo, MMF Chor, MMF Orch, S. Varviso (7/89) (DECC) ① [2] **417 828-2DM2**
Cpte A. Baltsa, F. Lopardo, E. Dara, R. Raimondi, P. Pace, A. Gonda, A. Corbelli, Vienna St Op Chor, VPO, C. Abbado (r1987) (10/89) (DG) ① [2] **427 331-2GH2**
Cpte G. Simionato, C. Valletti, M. Cortis, M. Petri, G. Sciutti, M. Masini, E. Campi, La Scala Chor, La Scala Orch, C.M. Giulini (r1954) (11/91) (EMI) ① [2] **CHS7 64041-2**
Cpte M. Horne, E. Palacio, D. Trimarchi, S. Ramey, K. Battle, C. Foti, N. Zaccaria, Prague Phil Chor, Solisti Veneti, C. Scimone (1/92) (ERAT) ① [2] **2292-45404-2**
1. Philh, C.M. Giulini *Concert* (12/87) (EMI) ① **CDM7 69042-2**
1. LSO, C. Abbado *Concert* (5/88) (DG) ① **419 869-2GGA**
1. Philh, H. von Karajan *Concert* (11/89) (EMI) ① **CDM7 63113-2**
1. NYPSO, A. Toscanini (r1936) *Concert* (3/90) (PEAR) ① [3] **GEMMCDS9373**
1. BPO, H. von Karajan *Concert* (5/90) (DG) ① **429 164-2GR**
1. Plovdiv PO, R. Raychev *Concert* (10/90) (LASE) ① **15 506**
1. LCP, R. Norrington *Concert* (4/91) (EMI) ① **CDC7 54091-2**
1. COE, C. Abbado *Concert* (5/91) (DG) ① **431 653-2GH**
1. ASMF, N. Marriner (r1974) *Concert* (10/92) (PHIL) ① [3] **434 016-2PM3**
1. NBC SO, A. Toscanini (pp1950) *Concert* (11/92) (RCA) ① **GD60289**
1. NYPO, A. Toscanini (r1936) *Concert* (11/92) (RCA) ① **GD60318**
1. Black Dyke Mills Band, P. Parkes (arr brass band: P Parkes) *Concert* (9/93) (CHAN) ① **CHAN4514**
1. Atlanta SO, Y. Levi (r1993) *Concert* (11/94) (TELA) ① **CD80334**
1. National PO, R. Chailly (r1981) *Concert* (9/95) (DECC) ① [2] **443 850-2DF2**
1. ASMF, N. Marriner (r1974) *Concert* (12/95) (PHIL) ① **446 196-2PM**
4. R. Blake, LSO, J. McCarthy *Concert* (4/88) (ARAB) ① **Z6582**
4. R. Vargas, ECO, M. Viotti *Concert* (11/92) (CLAV) ① **CD50-9202**
4, 26. R. Giménez, Scottish CO, M. Veltri *Concert* (8/88) (NIMB) ① **NI5106**
6a, 6b D. Jones, Richard Hickox Sngrs, CLS, R. Hickox *Concert* (2/91) (CHAN) ① **CHAN8865**
6b D. Soffel, Swedish CO, M. Liljefors (pp1984) *Concert* (4/93) (CPRI) ① **CAP21428**
6b M. Horne, Solisti Veneti, C. Scimone (r1980) *Concert* (4/94) (RCA) ① [6] **09026 61580-2(8)**
6b, 23b-d C. Bartoli, A. Schoenberg Ch, Vienna Volksoper Orch, G. Patanè *Concert* (9/89) (DECC) ① **425 430-2DH**
8b C. Supervia, C. Scattola, orch, A. Albergoni (r1927) *Concert* (3/93) (NIMB) ① [2] **NI7836/7**
23d G. Fabbri, S. Cottone (r1903) *Concert* (12/89) (SYMP) ① **SYMCD1065**

Maometto Secondo—dramma: 2 acts (1820—Naples) (Lib. C. della Valle)
EXCERPTS: 1. Overture. ACT 1: 2. Al tou cenno, Erisso; 3. Risponda a te primiero; 4. Sì, giuriam!; 5. Ah! che invan su questo ciglio; 6. Petoso ciel; 7a. No, tacer non deggio; 7b. Ohimè, qual fulmine; 7c. Dal cor l'iniquo affetto; 7d. Misere! ... or dove, ahimè; 8a. Giusto Cielo, in tal periglio; 8b. Ahi padre!; 9. Figlia, mi lascia; 10. Mira, signor, quel pianto; 11. Dal ferro, dal foco; 12. Sorgete, sorgete; 13. Del mondo al vincitor; 14a. Compiuta ancor del tutto; 14b. Signor, di liete nuove; 14c. Appressatevi, o prodi; 15. Giusto Ciel, che strazio è questo!; 16. Guardie, olà, costor si traggano; 17. Rendemi il padre, o barbaro; 18. Ah! perchè fra le spade nemiche. ACT 2: 19. È follia sul fior degli anni; 20. Tacete. - Ahimè!; 21. Anna, tu piangi?; 22. Gli estremi sensi ascolta; 23. Ma qual tumulto ascolto?; 24a. Ah che più tardi ancor?; 24b. All'invito generoso; 24c. Dell'araba tromba; 25. Sieguimi, o Calbo; 26. Tenera sposa; 27. Non temer: d'un basso affetto; 28. Del periglio al fiero aspetto; 29. Oh, come al cor soavi; 30. In questi estremi istanti; 31a. Alfin compita è la metà; 31b. Nume, cui'l sole è trono; 32. Sventurata! fuggir sol ti resta; 33. Quella morte che s'avanza; 34. Sì, ferite: il chieggo, il merto; 35. Già fra le tombe?.
Cpte J. Anderson, M. Zimmermann, E. Palacio, S. Ramey, L. Dale, Ambrosian Op. Chor, Philh, C. Scimone (9/85) (PHIL) ① [3] **412 148-2PH3**
1. ASMF, N. Marriner (r1979) *Concert* (10/92) (PHIL) ① [3] **434 016-2PM3**
5, 8a C. Bartoli, Venice La Fenice Chor, Venice La Fenice Orch, I. Martin *Concert* (2/92) (DECC) ① **436 075-2DH**
27. D. Soffel, Swedish CO, M. Liljefors (pp1984) *Concert* (4/93) (CPRI) ① **CAP21428**

Matilde di Shabran (or Bellezza e cuor di ferro)—melodramma giocoso: 2 acts (1821—Rome) (Lib. G. Ferretti)
EXCERPTS: 1. Overture.
Overture Plovdiv PO, R. Raychev *Concert* (10/90) (LASE) ① **15 520**

Mosè—opera: 3 acts (1827—Rome) (Italian version of Moïse et Pharaon')
Cpte N. Rossi-Lemeni, A. Lazzari, G. Taddei, M. Filippeschi, P. de Palma, P. Clabassi, L. Danieli, C. Mancini, B. Rizzoli, F. Mazzoli, Naples San Carlo Op Chor, Naples San Carlo Op Orch, T. Serafin (r1956) (3/95) (PHIL) ① [2] **442 100-2PM2**

Mosè in Egitto—azione tragico-sacra: 3 acts (1818—Naples) (Lib. A.L. Tottola, after Ringhieri)
EXCERPTS: 1. Introduction. ACT 1: 2. Mano ultrice d'un Dio; 3. Eterno! immenso!; 4a. Celeste man placata!; 4b. Egizi! Faraone!; 4c. Voci di giubilo; 5. E avete, avverse stelle; 6a. Ah! se puoi così lasciarmi; 6b. Non è ver che stringa il cielo; 6c. Ah! quel suon già d'Israele; 7. Ah! dov'è Faraone?; 8a. Cade dal ciglio in velo; 8b. Ove m'ascondo?; 9. All'etra, al ciel; 10. Tutto mi ride intorno; 11a. Che narri?...Il ver; 11b. All'idea di tanto eccesso; 11c. Padre...Signor... ACT 2: 12. Ecco in tua mano, Aronne; 13a. Parlar, spiegar non posso; 13b. (Non merta più consiglio); 14. Gentil Regina, oh quanto; 15a. La pace mia smarrita; 15b. Deh, ti consola e spera; 16. Nuove sciagure, o mio german!; 17a. Dove mi guidi?; 17b. Quale assalto, qual cimento!; 17c. Ah mira!...Oh ciel!; 17d. Involto in fiamma rea; 17e. Mi manca la voce; 17f. Fiera guerra mi sento nel seno; 18. Che potrai dir?; 19. Tu di ceppi m'aggravi; 20. O Nume Osiri; 21. Se a mitigar tue cure; 22. Sì, popoli d'Egitto; 23a. Porgi la destra amata; 23b. E ancor resisti?; 23c. Tormenti, affanni e smanie; 24. Eccone in salvo, o figli; 25a. Dal tuo stellato soglio; 25b. Ma qual fragor!; 25c. Son fuggiti! Oh cieli, che miro!.
Cpte R. Raimondi, J. Anderson, Z. Gal, S. Browne, S. Fisichella, E. Palacio, K. Lewis, S. Nimsgern, Ambrosian Op Chor, Philh, C. Scimone (1819 vers) (12/92) (PHIL) ① [2] **420 109-2PM2**
Prayer Ambrosian Op. Chor, Philh, C. Scimone *Petite messe solennelle.* (12/85) (PHIL) ① [2] **412 548-2PH2**
3. N. De Angelis, orch (r1929) *Concert* (4/94) (EMI) ① [3] **CHS7 64864-2(1)**
3, 25a E. Cheni, I. Mannarini, E. Venturini, N. de Angelis, orch, L. Molajoli (r1929) *Concert* (7/92) (PREI) ① **89042**
25a E. Pinza, A.M. Turchetti, chor, orch (r1923) *Concert* (12/92) (TEST) ① **SBT1008**

L' **Occasione fa il ladro—burletta: 1 act (1812—Venice)** (Lib. L. Prividali)
EXCERPTS: 1. Overture; 2. Frema in cielo il nembo irato; 3a. Il tuo rigore insano; 3b. Grato conforto è l'incontrar per viaggio; 4a. Paghiamo il conto; 4b. Che sorte, che accidente; 5. Non lo permetto; 6a. Vicino è il momento; 6b. Sposarsi ad un; 7. Eccomi al gran cimento; 8a. Alma coraggio!; 8b. Quel gentil, quel vago oggetto; 9. Se non m'inganna il core; 10. Dov'è questo aposo?; 11. Non so più cosa far; 12a. Qual strano caso è il mio!; 12b. D'ogni più sacro impegno; 13a. Per conoscer l'inganno; 13b. Voi la sposa!; 14a. Qui non c'è scampo; 14b. Il mio padrone è un uomo; 15. Voi qui appunto io cercava; 16a. Qual chiasso è questo?; 16b. Ma se incerti voi siete; 16c. Fermatevi; 17a. Il suo trascorso alfine; 17b. Quello, ch'io fui, ritorno; 18. On quanto son grate; 19. Finale: Miei signore, allegramente.
Cpte M. Bayo, N. de Carolis, I. Zennaro, F. Provvisionato, F. Previati, F. Massa, ECO, M. Viotti (r1992) (5/93) (CLAV) ① [2] **CD50-9208/9**
12b R. Giménez, Scottish CO, M. Veltri *Concert* (8/88) (NIMB) ① **NI5106**
12b R. Vargas, ECO, M. Viotti *Concert* (11/92) (CLAV) ① **CD50-9202**

Otello (or Il moro di Venezia)—dramma: 3 acts (1816—Naples) (Lib. F. Berio di Salsa, after Shakespeare)
EXCERPTS: 1. Overture. ACT 1: 2. Viva Otello, via il prode; 3a. Vincemmo, prodi; 3b. Ah! sì, per voi già sento; 4a. Rodrigo! Elmiro!; 4b. No, no temer, serena; 5a. Inutile è quel pianto; 5b. Ah! ch'io pavento; 6a. Ma che miro?; 6b. Giunto è Rodrigo, il fortunato istante; 6c. Padre, permetti; 6d. Dove son? Che mai veggio; 6f. L'infida, ahimè che miro?; 6g. Padre!...Non v'è perdono. ACT 2: 7a. Lasciami; 7b. Che ascolto? ahimè, che dici?; 8a. M'abbandò, disparve; 8b. Che feci?; 9a. E a tanto giunger puote; 9b. Ahimè! fermate, udite; 10a. Desdemona! che veggo!; 10b. Qual nuova a me recate? ACT 3: 11a. Ah! Dagli affani oppressa; 11b. Assia a piè d'un salice; 11c. Che dissi!; 11d. Deh calma, o ciel, nel sonno; 12a. Eccomi giunto inosservato, e solo; 12b. Che miro! ahimè!; 12c. Non arrestare il colpo; 12d. Per me la tua colpa. ADDITIONAL ITEM FOR 1844 PARIS REVIVAL: 13. Ballet.
Cpte J. Carreras, F. von Stade, G. Pastine, S. Fisichella, N. Condò, S. Ramey, K. Lewis, A. Leoz, Ambrosian Op Chor, Philh, J. López-Cobos (12/92) (PHIL) ① [2] **432 456-2PM2**
1. ASMF, N. Marriner (r1979) *Concert* (10/92) (PHIL) ① [3] **434 016-2PM3**
1. National PO, R. Chailly (r1984) *Concert* (9/95) (DECC) ① [2] **443 850-2DF2**
2. C. Bartoli, Vienna Volksoper Orch, G. Patanè *Concert* (9/89) (DECC) ① **425 430-2DH**
3b C. Merritt, Munich RSO, J. Fiore (r1993) *Concert* (9/94) (PHIL) ① **434 102-2PH**
7b R. Blake, LSO, M. Valdes *Concert* (12/89) (ARAB) ① **Z6612**
11a-d M. Caballé, C. Vozza, RCA Italiana Op Orch, C.F. Cillario *Concert* (11/92) (RCA) ① [2] **GD60941**
11b D. Jones, C. Smith, CLS, R. Hickox *Concert* (2/91) (CHAN) ① **CHAN8865**
11b-d K. Ricciarelli, Lyon Op Chor, Lyon Op Orch, G. Ferro (r1989) *Concert* (11/94) (VIRG) ① **CUV5 61139-2**

La **pietra del paragone—melodramma giocoso: 2 acts (1812—Milan)** (Lib. L. Romanelli)
Cpte J. Carreras, B. Wolff, E. Bonazzi, A. Elgar, J. Reardon, A. Foldi, J. Diaz, R. Murcell, Clarion Concerts Chor, Clarion Concerts Orch, N. Jenkins (12/92) (VANG) ① [3] **08.9031.73**
Cpte P. Barbacini, H. Müller-Molinari, A. Trovarelli, M.C. Nocentini, R. Scaltriti, V. di Matteo, P. Rumetz, A. Svab, Modena Teatro Comunale Chor, Camerata Musicale Orch, C. Desderi (pp1992) (5/93) (NUOV) ① [2] **7132/3**

Oh, come il fosco ...Quell'alme pupille R. Giménez, Scottish CO, M. Veltri *Concert* (8/88) (NIMB) ① **NI5106**

Se l'Italie contrade...Se per voi lo care lo torno C. Bartoli, A. Schoenberg Ch, Vienna Volksoper Orch, G. Patanè *Concert* (9/89) (DECC) ① **425 430-2DH**

Ricciardo e Zoriade—dramma: 2 acts (1818—Naples) (Lib. F. Berio di Salsa)

Contro cento, e cento prodi D. Montague, P. Doghan, P. Nilon, G. Dolton, G. Mitchell Ch, Philh, D. Parry *Concert* (10/90) (OPRA) ① [3] **ORCH103**

Overture Ambrosian Sngrs, ASMF, N. Marriner (r1979) *Concert* (10/92) (PHIL) ① [3] **434 016-2PM3**

S'ella m'è ognor fedele R. Blake, P. Jeffes, LSO, M. Valdes *Concert* (12/89) (ARAB) ① **Z6612**

La **Scala di seta, '(The) Silken Ladder'—farsa comica: 1 act (1812—Venice)** (Lib. G Foppa, after Gaveaux)

EXCERPTS: 1. Overture; 2. Va' sciocco, non seccarmi; 3. Siamo sicuri. Uscite!; 4. Egli è sceso... 5a. Signor padron; 5b. Io so ch'hai buon core; 6. Oh senza ceremonia... 7a. E che? tu ti mariti?; 7b. Va lesto; 7c. Vedrò qual sommo incanto; 8a. Io non so conquistare un cor di donna?; 8b. Si che unito a cara sposa; 9. Va' là presto; 10a. Or andiam dal tutor... 10b. Sento talor nell'anima; 11. Bellissima! il cassetto è proprio nuovo!; 12. E ognum mi dice sciocco!; 13a. Sollecitiam perchè Blansac; 13b. Ma se mai; 13c. Il mio ben sospiro e chiamo; 14a. Brava! vada, si serva... 15. Come? come?; 16. Buono! non c'è persona; 17. Dorme ognuno in queste soglie; 18. Finale: Finir conviene la scena.

Cpte A. Corbelli, T. Ringholz, R. Vargas, N. de Carolis, F. Provvisionato, F. Massa, ECO, M. Viotti (r1992) (5/93) (CLAV) ① [2] **CD50-9219/20**

1. Philh, C.M. Giulini *Concert* (12/87) (EMI) ① **CDM7 69042-2**

1. ASMF, N. Marriner *Concert* (2/89) (EMI) ① **CDC7 49155-2**

1. Philh, H. von Karajan *Concert* (11/89) (EMI) ① **CDM7 63113-2**

1. BPO, H. von Karajan *Concert* (5/90) (DG) ① **429 164-2GR**

1. Chicago SO, F. Reiner *Concert* (9/90) (RCA) ① **GD60387**

1. Plovdiv PO, R. Raychev *Concert* (10/90) (LASE) ① **15 506**

1. LCP, R. Norrington *Concert* (4/91) (EMI) ① **CDC7 54091-2**

1. COE, C. Abbado *Concert* (5/91) (DG) ① **431 653-2GH**

1. ASMF, N. Marriner (r1974) *Concert* (10/92) (PHIL) ① [3] **434 016-2PM3**

1. Black Dyke Mills Band, P. Parkes (arr Parkes) *Concert* (7/93) (CHAN) ① **CHAN4505**

1. LPO, T. Beecham (r1933) *Concert* (7/93) (DUTT) ① **CDLX7001**

1. BBC SO, A. Toscanini (r1938) *Concert* (5/94) (BIDD) ① [2] **WHL008/9**

1. LPO, T. Beecham (r1933) *Concert* (10/94) (DUTT) ① **CDLX7009**

1. Atlanta SO, Y. Levi (r1993) *Concert* (11/94) (TELA) ① **CD80334**

1. National PO, R. Chailly (r1981) *Concert* (9/95) (DECC) ① [2] **443 850-2DF2**

1. ASMF, N. Marriner (r1974) *Concert* (12/95) (PHIL) ① **446 196-2PM**

Semiramide—melodramma tragico: 2 acts (1823—Venice) (Lib. G. Rossi, after Voltaire)

EXCERPTS: 1. Overture. ACT 1: 2. Sì...gran Nume...t'intesi; 3. Suoni festevoli; 4. Là dal Gange a te primiero; 5. Di plausi qual clamor; 6. Di tanti regi e populi; 7. Ah! già il sacro foco è spento; 8. Eccomi alfine in Babilonia; 9. Ah! quel giorno ognor rammento; 10. Io t'attendeva, Arsace; 11. Bella imago; 12. Serena i vaghi rai; 13a. Bel raggio lusinghier; 13b. Dolce pensiero; 13c. Mitrane! E che rechi?; 14. Serbami ognor sì fido; 15. Alle più calde immagini; 16. March; 17. Ergi omai la fronte altera; 18. I vostri voti omai; 19. L'alto eroe; 20. Qual mesto gemito; 21. D'un semidio che adoro; 22. Ah! Sconvolta nell'ordine eterno. ACT 2: 23. Assur, i cenni miei; 24. Se la vita; 25. Quekka, ricordati; 26. La forza primiera; 27. Ebben, compiasi omai; 28. In sì barbara sciagura; 29. Su, ti scuoti; 30. No: non ti lascio; 31. Ebben...a tei; ferisci; 32. Giorno d'orrore!; 33. Madre—addio; 34. La speranza più soave; 35. Sì, sperar voglio contento; 36. Il di già cade; 37. Deh! ti ferma; 38. Que' numi furenti; 39. Qual densa notte!; 40. Al mio pregar t'arrendi; 41. Dei! qual sospiro!; 42. Ninia, ferisci!.

Cpte J. Sutherland, M. Horne, J. Rouleau, J. Serge, P. Clark, S. Malas, M. Langdon, L. Fyson, Ambrosian Op Chor, LSO, R. Bonynge (2/90) (DECC) ① [3] **425 481-2DM3**

Cpte C. Studer, J. Larmore, S. Ramey, F. Lopardo, J. Faulkner, J-H. Rootering, R. Tesarowicz, O. Arévalo, Ambrosian Op Chor, LSO, I. Marin (2/94) (DG) ① [3] **437 797-2GH3**

1. Philh, C.M. Giulini *Concert* (12/87) (EMI) ① **CDM7 69042-2**

1. ASMF, N. Marriner *Concert* (2/89) (EMI) ① **CDC7 49155-2**

1. Philh, H. von Karajan *Concert* (11/89) (EMI) ① **CDM7 63113-2**

1. NYPSO, A. Toscanini (r1936) *Concert* (3/90) (PEAR) ① [3] **GEMMCDS9373**

1. Plovdiv PO, R. Raychev *Concert* (10/90) (LASE) ① **15 506**

1. LCP, R. Norrington *Concert* (4/91) (EMI) ① **CDC7 54091-2**

1. COE, C. Abbado *Concert* (5/91) (DG) ① **431 653-2GH**

1. ASMF, N. Marriner (r1976) *Concert* (10/92) (PHIL) ① [3] **434 016-2PM3**

1. NBC SO, A. Toscanini (r1951) *Concert* (11/92) (RCA) ① **GD60289**

1. NYPO, A. Toscanini (r1936) *Concert* (11/92) (RCA) ① **GD60318**

1. BBC SO, A. Toscanini (pp1935) *Concert* (4/93) (TEST) ① **SBT1015**

1. LPO, T. Beecham (r1939) *Concert* (7/93) (DUTT) ① **CDLX7001**

1. Berlin RIAS Orch, F. Fricsay (r1951) *Concert* (11/94) (DG) ① **445 406-2GDO**

1. I. Seefried, M. Forrester, E. Haefliger, D. Fischer-Dieskau, Berlin St Hedwig's Cath Ch, BPO, F. Fricsay, H. Krebs, T. Varga, Berlin RIAS Chbr Ch, Berlin RIAS Orch, H. Geusser, W. Fugmann, M. Weber, G. Herzog, Berlin RSO, VPO, E. Grümmer, G. Pitzinger, H. Hotter, Y. Menuhin (r1951) *Concert* (11/94) (DG) ① [11] **445 400-2GDO10**

1. Atlanta SO, Y. Levi (r1993) *Concert* (11/94) (TELA) ① **CD80334**

1. National PO, R. Chailly (r1984) *Concert* (9/95) (DECC) ① [2] **443 850-2DF2**

1. ASMF, N. Marriner (r1976) *Concert* (12/95) (PHIL) ① **446 196-2PM**

9. G. Fabbri, S. Cottone (r1903) *Concert* (12/89) (SYMP) ① **SYMCD1065**

9. E. Stignani, EIAR Orch, A. la Rosa Parodi (r1940) *Concert* (1/91) (PREI) ① **89014**

12, 13a, 13b K. Ricciarelli, Lyon Op Chor, Lyon Op Orch, G. Ferro (r1989) *Concert* (11/94) (VIRG) ① **CUV5 61139-2**

13a M. André, Toulouse Capitole Orch, M. Plasson (arr tpt) *Concert* (1/89) (EMI) ① **CDC7 49219-2**

13a L. Tetrazzini, orch, P. Pitt (r1910) *Concert* (9/92) (EMI) ① [3] **CHS7 63802-2(1)**

13a L. Tetrazzini, orch, P. Pitt (r1910) *Concert* (9/92) (PEAR) ① **GEMMCD9222**

13a C. Boninsegna, orch (r1910) *Concert* (12/92) (TEST) ① **SBT1008**

13a A. Galli-Curci, orch (r1924) *Concert* (3/94) (CONI) ① **CDHD201**

13a A. Galli-Curci, orch, R. Bourdon (r1924) *Concert* (8/94) (ROMO) ① [2] **81004-2**

13a A. Pendachanska, Sofia SO, M. Angelov (r1994) *Concert* (12/95) (CAPR) ① **10 706**

13a-c J. Sutherland, ROHO, F. Molinari-Pradelli *Concert* (1/90) (DECC) ① [2] **425 493-2DM2**

13a, 13b J. Anderson, Paris Op Orch, M. Veltri (pp1987) *Concert* (12/88) (EMI) ① **CDC7 49067-2**

13a, 13b C. Bartoli, Venice La Fenice Chor, Venice La Fenice Orch, I. Martin *Concert* (2/92) (DECC) ① **436 075-2DH**

13a, 14, 15, 30-33. J. Sutherland, M. Horne, L. Fyson, LSO, R. Bonynge (r1965) *Bellini: Norma.* (10/93) (DECC) ① **436 303-2DA**

13b E. Stignani, orch (r c1938) *Concert* (12/92) (TEST) ① **SBT1008**

14, 15. M. Caballé, S. Verrett, New Philh, A. Guadagno *Concert* (5/92) (RCA) ① **GD60818**

34. R. Blake, Ambrosian Sngrs, LSO, M. Valdes *Concert* (12/89) (ARAB) ① **Z6612**

37. T. Pasero, EIAR Orch, U. Tansini (r1940) *Concert* (4/95) (PREI) ① **89074**

Le **Siège de Corinthe, 'Assedio di Corinto'—tragédie lyrique: 3 acts (1826—Paris)** (Lib. L. Balocchi)

EXCERPTS: 1. Overture. ACT 1: 2. Ta noble voix seigneur; 3. Ta fille m'est promise; 4. La ville coupable; 5. Qu'à ma voix la victoire s'arrête; 6. Nous avons triomphé. ACT 2: 7. L'hymen lui donne une couronne; 8. Que vais-je devenir; 9. Rassure-toi mon pouvoir t'environne; 10. Air de danse; 11. Divin prophète entends nos voeux; 12. Il est mon frère; 13. Corinthe nous défie. ACT 3: 14. Avançons, oui ces murs; 15. Oh toi qui tout révère; 16. Grand Dieu faut-il qu'un peuple qui t'adore; 17. Céleste providence; 18. Je viens de parcourir; 19. Répondons à ce cri de victoire; 20a. L'heure fatale approche; 20b. Juste ciel! ah, ta clémence est ma seule espérance; 21. Mais quels accens se font entendre.

Cpte B. Sills, S. Verrett, J. Diaz, H. Theyard, G. Howell, R. Lloyd, D. Wallis, G. Scano, Ambrosian Op Chor, LSO, T. Schippers (r1974: Ital) (4/93) (EMI) ① [3] **CMS7 64335-2**

Cpte L. Serra, M. Lippi, M. Comencini, D. Raffanti, A. Gaforio, V. Martino, F. Facini, F. Provvisionato, Prague Phil Chor, Genoa Carlo Felice Th Chor, Genoa Carlo Felice Th Orch, P. Olmi (pp1992) (5/93) (NUOV) ① [3] **7140/2**

1. LSO, C. Abbado *Concert* (5/88) (DG) ① **419 869-2GGA**

1. Plovdiv PO, R. Raychev *Concert* (10/90) (LASE) ① **15 506**

1. ASMF, N. Marriner (r1976) *Concert* (10/92) (PHIL) ① [3] **434 016-2PM3**

1. NBC SO, A. Toscanini (r1945) *Concert* (11/92) (RCA) ① **GD60289**

1. Santa Cecilia Academy Orch, G. Cantelli (r1949) *Concert* (7/93) (TEST) ① **SBT1017**

1. National PO, R. Chailly (r1984) *Concert* (9/95) (DECC) ① [2] **443 850-2DF2**

5. S. Ramey, NY Concert Chorale, St Luke's Orch, R. Norrington (pp1992) *Concert* (12/94) (EMI) ① **CDC7 54643-2**

14. D. Soffel, Swedish CO, M. Liljefors (pp1984; Ital) *Concert* (4/93) (CPRI) ① **CAP21428**

20a, 20b M. Caballé, RCA Italiana Op Chor, RCA Italiana Op Orch, C.F. Cillario (Ital) *Concert* (11/92) (RCA) ① [2] **GD60941**

20a, 20b K. Ricciarelli, Lyon Op Chor, Lyon Op Orch, G. Ferro (r1989) *Concert* (11/94) (VIRG) ① **CUV5 61139-2**

Il **Signor Bruschino (or Il figlio per azzardo)—farsa giocosa: 1 act (1813—Venice)** (Lib. G. Foppa, after Chazet & Maurice Ourry)

EXCERPTS: 1. Overture; 2a. Deh! tu m'assisti amore; 2b. Marianna! ... Voi signore?; 2c. Quanto è dolce a un'alma amante; 3. A voi lieto ritorno; 4. Ah se il colpo arrivo a fare; 5. A noi su, trasformiamoci; 6. Nel teatro del gran mondo; 7a. Ho trovato a Sofia un buon partito; 7b. Lasciatemi... che violenza!; 8. Per un figlio già pentito; 9a. Impaziente son io; 9b. Sì, tentiamo; 10. Ah donate il caro sposo; 11. Qui convien finirla; 12. Ho la testa, o è andata via?; 13. Va tutto ben; 14. È bel nodo, che due cori; 15. Ebben, ragion, dovere; 16. È tornato Filiberto.

Cpte B. Praticò, N. de Carolis, P. Orciani, L. Canonici, P. Spagnoli, K. Lytting, F. Massa, Turin PO, M. Viotti (r1988) (10/89) (CLAV) ① [2] **CD50-8904/5**

Cpte J. Mahler, J. Wolański, A. Słowakiewicz, K. Myrlak, D. Niemirowicz, H. Górzyńska, K. Moleda, B. Jaszkowski, Warsaw Chbr Op Orch, J. Kaspszyk (5/93) (PAVA) ① **ADW7158**

Cpte S. Ramey, C. Desderi, K. Battle, F. Lopardo, M. Pertusi, J. Larmore, O. Arévalo, ECO, I. Marin (r1991) (12/93) (DG) ① **435 865-2GH**

1. Philh, C.M. Giulini *Concert* (12/87) (EMI) ① **CDM7 69042-2**

1. LSO, C. Abbado *Concert* (5/88) (DG) ① **419 869-2GGA**

1. Chicago SO, F. Reiner *Concert* (9/90) (RCA) ① **GD60387**

1. LCP, R. Norrington *Concert* (4/91) (EMI) ① **CDC7 54091-2**

1. ASMF, N. Marriner (r1974) *Concert* (10/92) (PHIL) ① [3] **434 016-2PM3**

1. NBC SO, A. Toscanini (r1945) *Concert* (11/92) (RCA) ① **GD60289**

1. Berlin RIAS Orch, F. Fricsay (r1951) *Concert* (11/94) (DG) ① **445 406-2GDO**

1. I. Seefried, M. Forrester, E. Haefliger, D. Fischer-Dieskau, Berlin St Hedwig's Cath Ch, BPO, F. Fricsay, H. Krebs, T. Varga, Berlin RIAS Chbr Ch, Berlin RIAS Orch, H. Geusser, W. Fugmann, M. Weber, G. Herzog, Berlin RSO, VPO, E. Grümmer, G. Pitzinger, H. Hotter, Y. Menuhin (r1951) *Concert* (11/94) (DG) ① [11] **445 400-2GDO10**

1. National PO, R. Chailly (r1981) *Concert* (9/95) (DECC) ① [2] **443 850-2DF2**

1. ASMF, N. Marriner (r1974) *Concert* (12/95) (PHIL) ① **446 196-2PM**

2a-c R. Giménez, Scottish CO, M. Veltri *Concert* (8/88) (NIMB) ① **NI5106**

10. D. Jones, CLS, R. Hickox *Concert* (2/91) (CHAN) ① **CHAN8865**

Tancredi—melodramma eroico: 2 acts (1813—Venice) (Lib. G. Rossi, after Voltaire)

EXCERPTS: 1. Overture. ACT 1: 2. Pace, onore, fede amore; 3. Se amistà verace; 4a. Più dolci e placide; 4b. Come dolce all'alma mia; 5. Amenaide sventurata!; 6a. Oh patria!; 6b. Di tanti palpiti; 7. E voi

nella gran piazza; 8a. Andante, al gran tempi'; 8b. Pensa, pensa che sei mia figlia; 9a. Che feci! incauta!; 9b. L'aura che intorno spiri; 10. Amori scendete; 11. Alla gloria, al trionfo; 11e. Si, la patria si difenda; 12. Amici, Cavalieri; 13a. E morte infame; 13b. Ciel! che feci!; 13c. Ah! se giusto, o ciel. ACT 2: 14. Vedesti? L'indegna!; 15a. Io padre più non sono; 15b. Oh Dio! Crudel!; 15c. Ah! segnar invano; 16a. Trionfa, esulta; 16b. Tu che i miseri; 17a. Di mia vita infelice; 17b. No, che il morir non è; 18. Di già l'ora; 19. Fermate!; 20a. M'abbraccia, Argirio; 20b. Ah! se de'mali; 20c. Ecco le trome; 21. Ov'è? ... dov'è?; 22a. Gran Dio! Deh! tu proteggi; 22b. Giusto Dio; 23. Plaudite, o popoli; 24a. T'arresta; 24b. Lasciami: non t'ascolto; 24c. Ah! come mai quell'anima; 24d. Dunque? ... Addio; 25. Infelice Tancredi!; 26a. S'avverassero pure; 26b. Torni alfin; 27a. Dove son io?; 27b. Ah! che scordar; 27c. Regna il terror; 28a. Ecco, amici; 28b. Perchè turbar; 28c. Traitrice; 29. Quanti tormenti; 30a. Gran Dio!; 30b. Muore il prode; 30c. Oh Dio ... lasciarti; 30d. Amenaide ... serbami. REPLACEMENT ARIAS: 31a. A sospirato lido!; 31b. Dolci d'amor parole; 31c. Voce, che tenera; 32a. Qual suon? che miro?; 32b. Solamir d'Amenaide; 32c. Va, palese è troppo omai; 32d. E' questa la fede; 32e. Si, la patria si difenda.

Cpte M. Horne, L. Cuberli, E. Palacio, N. Zaccaria, B. Manca di Nissa, P. Schuman, Venice La Fenice Chor, Venice La Fenice Orch, R. Weikert (pp1983) (8/88) (SONY) ① [3] **S3K39073**

Cpte P. Price, H. Francis, K. Lewis, T. McDonnell, E. Stokes, P. Jeffes, London Voices, Centre d'Action Musicale de l'Ouest Orch, J. Perras (pp1976) (5/94) (ARIO) ① [3] **ARN368200**

Cpte E. Podles, S. Jo, S. Olsen, P. Spagnoli, A. M. di Micco, L. Lendi, L. Baert, F. Coryn, E. Demeyere, Capella Brugensis, Collegium Instr Brugense, A. Zedda (r1994) (11/95) (NAXO) ① [2] **8 660037/8**

1. Plovdiv PO, R. Raychev *Concert* (10/90) (LASE) ① **15 506**

1. ASMF, N. Marriner (r1974) *Concert* (10/92) (PHIL) ① [3] **434 016-2PM3**

1. Black Dyke Mills Band, T. Walmsley (arr Rimmer) *Concert* (7/93) (CHAN) ① **CHAN4505**

1. Berlin RIAS Orch, F. Fricsay (r1952) *Concert* (11/94) (DG) ① **445 406-2GDO**

1. I. Seefried, M. Forrester, E. Haefliger, D. Fischer-Dieskau, Berlin St Hedwig's Cath Ch, BPO, F. Fricsay, H. Krebs, T. Varga, Berlin RIAS Chbr Ch, Berlin RIAS Orch, H. Geusser, W. Fugmann, M. Weber, G. Herzog, Berlin RSO, VPO, E. Grümmer, G. Pitzinger, H. Hotter, Y. Menuhin (r1952) *Concert* (11/94) (DG) ① [11] **445 400-2GDO10**

1. Atlanta SO, Y. Levi (r1993) *Concert* (11/94) (TELA) ① **CD80334**

1. National PO, R. Chailly (r1984) *Concert* (9/95) (DECC) ① [2] **443 850-2DF2**

4a, 4b K. Ricciarelli, Lyon Op Chor, Lyon Op Orch, G. Ferro (r1989) *Concert* (11/94) (VIRG) ① **CUV5 61139-2**

6a, 6b C. Bartoli, Vienna Volksoper Orch, G. Patanè *Concert* (9/89) (DECC) ① **425 430-2DH**

6a, 6b M. Caballé, RCA Italiana Op Orch, C.F. Cillario *Concert* (11/92) (RCA) ① [2] **GD60941**

6a, 6b, 27a, 27b J. Kowalski, Berlin RSO, H. Fricke *Concert* (10/92) (CAPR) ① **10 416**

6b D. Soffel, Swedish CO, M. Liljefors (pp1984) *Concert* (4/93) (CPRI) ① **CAP21428**

15b, 15c R. Giménez, Scottish Phil Sngrs, Scottish CO, M. Veltri *Concert* (8/88) (NIMB) ① **NI5106**

22a, 22b K. Battle, Ambrosian Op Chor, LPO, B. Campanella (r1991) *Concert* (12/93) (DG) ① **435 866-2GH**

Torvaldo e Dorliska—dramma semiserio: 2 acts (1815—Rome) (Lib. C. Sterbini)

EXCERPTS: 1. Overture. ACT ONE: 2. È un bel dir che tutto al mondo; 3. Dunque invano; 4. Il padrone? Ben tornato eccellenza!; 5. Ormondo, la mia gente; 6. Dove son? chi m'aita; 7. Oh, giusto Ciel; 8. Ah! per pietà; 9. Ella... oh Ciel!; 10. Dove corri, sconsigliata?; 11. Ella più non mi fugge; 12a. Tutto è silenzio; 12b. Fra un istante; 13. Finché niun qui m'osserva; 14. Ah qual raggio di speranza; 15. A Dorliska tu n'andrai; 16. Dunqu... Andiamo; 17. Delle nostre notturne bagattelle; 18. Sopra quell'albero; 19. Oh! via, Signora mia; 20. Immota, stolida; 21. Ella manca. ACT TWO: 22. Bravi, bravi; quà venite; 23. Oh, Giorgio; 24. Dille, che solo a lei; 25. No, pentirsi non giova; 26. Ferma, costante, immobile; 27. Ah!... morir pel caro sposo; 28. Insensata!... e non vede; 29. Una voce lusinghiera; 30. Ah non posso!; 31. Dunque tu vuoi ch'io parta?; 32. Quest'ultimo addio; 33. Alme ree! tremate! invano; 34. Vieni; 35. Cedi... 36. Grazie al destin pietoso.

Cpte E. Palacio, F. Pediconi, S. Antonucci, M. Buda, N. Ciliento, A. Marani, Cantemus, Lugano Rad & TV Ch, Lugano Rad & TV Orch, M. de Bernart (pp1992) (11/94) (AKAD) ① [2] **2CDAK123**

1. ASMF, N. Marriner (r1979) *Concert* (10/92) (PHIL) ① [3] **434 016-2PM3**

1. National PO, R. Chailly (r1984) *Concert* (9/95) (DECC) ① [2] **443 850-2DF2**

12a, 12b C. Merritt, Philh, D. Parry *Concert* (10/90) (OPRA) ① [3] **ORCH103**

Il Turco in Italia—dramma buffo: 2 acts (1814—Milan) (Lib. F. Romani)

EXCERPTS: 1. Overture (Sinfonia). ACT 1: 2a. Nostra patria è il mondo intero; 2b. Ho da far un dramma buffo; 3a. Ah! se di questi zingari l'arrivo; 3b. Vado in traccia d'una Zingara; 3c. Ah! mia moglie; 4a. Brava! Intesi ogni cosa; 4b. Non si dà follia maggiore; 4c. Voga, voga; 4e. Bella Italia, alfin ti miro; 4f. Serva...Servo; 4g. Della Zingara amante; 4h. Un vago sembiante; 4i. Amici...Soccorretemi; 5. Un marito scimunito!; 6a. Olà: tosto il caffè; 6b. Siete dei Turchi; 6c. Io stupisco, mi sorprende; 6d. Come! Sì grave torto; 7a. Sono arrivato tardi; 7b. Per piacere alla signora; 7c. Non mia vita, mio tesoro; 8a. Ho quasi del mio dramma; 8b. Gran maraviglie; 8c. Per la fuga è tutto lesto; 8d. Perchè mai se son tradito; 8e. Evviva d'amore; 8f. Chi servir non brama amor; 8g. Qui mia moglie ha da venire; 8h. Ah! che il cor non m'ingannava; 8i. Vada via: si guardi bene; 8j. Quando il vento. ACT 2: 9a. Via...cosa serve?; 9b. D'un bell'uso in Turchia; 9c. Se Fiorilla di vender bramate; 9d. Ed invece di pagarla; 10a. Credeva che questa scena; 10b. Non v'è piacer perfetto; 11a. Che Turca impertinente!; 11b. Credete alla femmine; 11c. In Italia certamente; 12a. Sentite!; 12b. Intesi: ah! tutto intesi; 12c. Oh! che fatica! che cervello duro!; 12d. Zaida infelice!; 12e. Ah! sarebbe troppo dolce; 13. Amor la danza mova; 14a. Eccomi qui; 14b. Oh! quardate che accidente; 14c. Dunque seguitemi; 14d. Questo vecchio maledetto; 15a. Benedetta la festa; 15b. I vostri cenci vi mando; 15c. Squallida veste; 15d. Caro padre, madre amata; 16a. Che dramma!; 16b. Son la vite campo appassita; 16c. Rida a voi sereno il Cielo.

Cpte N. Rossi-Lemeni, M. Callas, F. Calabrese, N. Gedda, J. Gardino, P. de Palma, M. Stabile, La Scala Chor, La Scala Orch, G. Gavazzeni (r1954) (12/87) (EMI) ① [2] **CDS7 49344-2**

Cpte S. Ramey, M. Caballé, E. Dara, E. Palacio, J. Berbié, P. Barbacini, L. Nucci, Ambrosian Op Chor, National PO, R. Chailly (r1981) (9/89) (SONY) ① [2] **S2K37859**

Cpte S. Alaimo, S. Jo, E. Fissore, R. Giménez, S. Mentzer, P. Bronder, A. Corbelli, Ambrosian Op Chor, ASMF, N. Marriner (12/92) (PHIL) ① [2] **434 128-2PH2**

1. ASMF, N. Marriner (r1974) *Concert* (10/92) (PHIL) ① [3] **434 016-2PM3**

1. National PO, R. Chailly (r1981) *Concert* (9/95) (DECC) ① [2] **443 850-2DF2**

1. ASMF, N. Marriner (r1974) *Concert* (12/95) (PHIL) ① **446 196-2PM**

11a-c M. Callas, F. Calabrese, La Scala Orch, G. Gavazzeni (r1954) *Concert* (2/90) (EMI) ① [4] **CMS7 63244-2**

12b R. Blake, LSO, J. McCarthy *Concert* (4/88) (ARAB) ① **Z6582**

Ugo re d'Italia—opera ("lost' opera for London, 1825)

Vieni, o cara B. Ford, P. Nilon, Philh, D. Parry *Concert* (8/95) (OPRA) ① [3] **ORCH104**

Il viaggio a Reims (or L'albergo del giglio d'oro)—dramma giocoso: 1 act (1825—Paris) (Lib. L. Balocchi)

EXCERPTS: 1. Overture. 2a. Presto, presto, su coraggio; 2b. Benché grazie al mio talento; 3. Di vaghi raggi adorno; 4a. Partire io pur vorrei; 4b. Amabil Contessina; 4c. Che accede; 5a. Ahimè! sta in gran pericolo; 5b. Partir, oh ciel! desio; 5c. Che miro! ah! qual sorpresa; 5d. Eh! senti, mastro Antonio; 6a. Sì, di matti una gran gabbia; 6b. La mia quota a voi consegno; 6c. Donna ingrata; 6d. Naturale è l'impazienza; 7. Non pavento alcun periglio; 8. Arpa gentil; 9. Zitti. Non canta più; 10a. Ah! perchè la conobbi?; 10b. Invan strappar dal core; 11. Milord, una parola; 12a. Sola ritrovo alfin la bella Dea; 12b. Nel suo divin sembiante; 12c. Bravo il signor Ganimede!; 13a. Medaglie incomparabili; 13b. Vedeste il Cavaliere?; 14a. Ah! A tal colpo inaspettato; 14b. Signor, ecco una lettera; 14c. Son qua, cosa comanda?; 15a. Di che son reo?; 15b. D'alma celeste, oh Dio; 15c. Madama qui mi manda; 16a. Or che regna; 16b. Ai prodi guerrieri; 16c. Onore, gloria ed alto omaggio; 16d. Omaggio all'Augusto Duce; 16e. Dell'aurea pianta; 16f. Madre el nuovo Enrico; 16g. Più vivace e più fecondo; 17a. Corinna, or tacca a voi; 17b. All'ombra amena; 18. Viva il diletto augusto Regnator.

Cpte C. Gasdia, K. Ricciarelli, L. Cuberli, L.V. Terrani, E. Gimenez, F. Araiza, S. Ramey, R. Raimondi, E. Dara, G. Surian, L. Nucci, Prague Phil Chor, COE, C. Abbado (pp1984) (1/86) (DG) ① [2] **415 498-2GH2**

Cpte S. McNair, C. Studer, L. Serra, L.V. Terrani, R. Giménez, W. Matteuzzi, S. Ramey, R. Raimondi, E. Dara, G. Surian, L. Gallo, Berlin Rad Chor, BPO, C. Abbado (pp1992) (12/93) (SONY) ① [2] **S2K53336**

1. Plovdiv PO, R. Raychev *Concert* (10/90) (LASE) ① **15 520**

1. ASMF, N. Marriner (r1976) *Concert* (10/92) (PHIL) ① [3] **434 016-2PM3**

1. National PO, R. Chailly (r1981) *Concert* (9/95) (DECC) ① [2] **443 850-2DF2**

5b K. Battle, Ambrosian Op Chor, LPO, B. Campanella (r1991) *Concert* (12/93) (DG) ① **435 866-2GH**

14a, 14b M. Fortuna, D. Voigt, M. Horne, K. Kuhlmann, M. Lerner, F. von Stade, R. Blake, C. Estep, C. Merritt, T. Hampson, J. Opalach, H. Runey, G. Hogan, S. Ramey, St Luke's Orch, R. Norrington (pp1992) *Concert* (12/94) (EMI) ① **CDC7 54643-2**

Zelmira—dramma: 2 acts (1822—Naples) (Lib. A.L. Tottola, after Dormont de Belloy)

EXCERPTS: 1. Overture. ACT 1: 2. Oh, sciagura!; 3. Che vidi amici!; 4. Della tenda real; 5. Non fuggirmi ... 6. Ah! gia trascorse il dì; 7. Ma m'illude il desio?; 8. S'intessano agli allori; 9a. Terra amica; 9b. Godi, o Signor; 10. O cielo! Egli è fra suoi; 11. Dimmi ... al tuo padre; 12. T'intendo, istabil Diva; 13. Mentre qual fiera ingorda; 14. Di luce sfavillante; 15a. Emma fedel; 15b. Perche mi guardi; 16. Si sparga di fiori; 17. Si figli miei; 18. Il figlio mio; 19. La sorpresa ... lo stupore; 20. Alla strage ognor ti guida. ACT 2: 21a. Gran cose, o Re!; 21b. Pian, piano inoltrisi; 22. Ciel, pietoso, ciel clemente; 23a. A che difendi; 23b. In estasi di gioja; 24. Chi sciolse i lacci miei; 25. Ne lacci miei cadesti; 26. Di Azor le ceneri; 27. Perigliosi; 28. Riedi al soglio; 29. Fa piu grato. ADDITIONAL ARIA: 30. Da te spero.

Cpte C. Gasdia, B. Fink, W. Matteuzzi, C. Merritt, J. Garcia, B. Senator, V. Midgley, L. Fyson, Ambrosian Sngrs, Solisti Veneti, C. Scimone (6/90) (ERAT) ① [2] **2292-45419-2**

Prchè mi guardi, e piangi? E. Harrhy, D. Jones, Philh, D. Parry *Concert* (8/95) (OPRA) ① [3] **ORCH104**

8, 9a R. Blake, Ambrosian Sngrs, LSO, M. Valdes *Concert* (12/89) (ARAB) ① **Z6612**

9a R. Blake, NY Concert Chorale, St Luke's Orch, R. Norrington (pp1992) *Concert* (12/94) (EMI) ① **CDC7 54643-2**

28. C. Bartoli, Venice La Fenice Chor, Venice La Fenice Orch, I. Martin *Concert* (2/92) (DECC) ① **436 075-2DH**

ROTA, Nino *(1911–1979) Italy*

SECTION I: ORCHESTRAL

Concerto for Strings (1964-5)

Accademia Bizantina, C. Chiarappa (vn/dir) (r1993) *Concert* (3/95) (DENO) ① **CO-78916**

Milan La Scala PO, R. Muti (r1994) *Concert* (8/95) (SONY) ① **SK66279**

Solisti Italiani (r1994) *Concert* (10/95) (DENO) ① **CO-78949**

SECTION III: INSTRUMENTAL

Casonova Suite—piano (arr cpsr from film score)

L. Bacalov *Preludes.* (1/94) (CAM) ① **MB016**

7 Difficult Pieces for Children—piano (1972)

D. Laval (r1993) *Concert* (1/94) (AUVI) ① **V4698**

Ippolito gioco—piano (1930)

D. Laval (r1993) *Concert* (1/94) (AUVI) ① **V4698**

15 Preludes—piano (1966)

L. Bacalov *Casanova Suite.* (1/94) (CAM) ① **MB016**

D. Laval (r1993) *Concert* (1/94) (AUVI) ① **V4698**

Variations and Fugue on B-A-C-H—piano (1950)

D. Laval (r1993) *Concert* (1/94) (AUVI) ① **V4698**

2 Waltzes on B-A-C-H—piano

1. Circus Waltz; 2. Valzer Carillon.

D. Laval (r1993) *Concert* (1/94) (AUVI) ① **V4698**

SECTION V: STAGE WORKS

Amarcord—film score (1973)

EXCERPTS: 1. Main Theme.

Suite Czech SO, D. Wadsworth (r1993; arr Wadsworth) *Concert* (10/93) (SILV) ① **FILMCD129**

1. Mancini Pops Orch, H. Mancini (r1990; arr Mancini) *Concert* (11/91) (RCA) ① **RD60706**

Il **Bidone—film score (1955)**

Suite Czech SO, D. Wadsworth (r1993; arr Wadsworth) *Concert* (10/93) (SILV) ① **FILMCD129**

Boccaccio '70—film score (1962)

EXCERPTS: 1. Bevete più latte! (Drink more milk).

Suite Czech SO, D. Wadsworth (r1993; arr Wadsworth) *Concert* (10/93) (SILV) ① **FILMCD129**

1. Mancini Pops Orch, H. Mancini (r1990; arr Mancini) *Concert* (11/91) (RCA) ① **RD60706**

Il **Casanova—film score (1976)**

Suite Czech SO, D. Wadsworth (r1993; arr Wadsworth) *Concert* (10/93) (SILV) ① **FILMCD129**

I **Clowns—film score (1970)**

EXCERPTS: 1. Theme.

Suite Czech SO, D. Wadsworth (r1993; arr Wadsworth) *Concert* (10/93) (SILV) ① **FILMCD129**

1. Mancini Pops Orch, H. Mancini (r1990; arr Mancini) *Concert* (11/91) (RCA) ① **RD60706**

La **Dolce Vita—film score (1959)**

EXCERPTS: 1. Titoli di Testa; 2. La Dolce Vita—Arrivederci Roma; 3. La Dolce Vita—Via Veneto; 4. Patrizia; 5. Lola; 6. Via Veneto e i Nobili; 7. Blues; 8. Notturno o Mattutino; 9. La Dolce Vita—La bella malinconia; 10. La Dolce Vita nella Villa di Fregene; 11. Why Wait.

Suite Czech SO, D. Wadsworth (r1993; arr Wadsworth) *Concert* (10/93) (SILV) ① **FILMCD129**

1. Mancini Pops Orch, H. Mancini (r1990; arr Mancini) *Concert* (11/91) (RCA) ① **RD60706**

Fellini Satyricon—film score (1969)

Suite Czech SO, D. Wadsworth (r1993; arr Wadsworth) *Concert* (10/93) (SILV) ① **FILMCD129**

Il **Gattopardo, '(The) Leopard'—film score (1963)**

EXCERPTS: 1a. Titoli di Testa; 1b. Viaggio a Donnafugata; 2. Angelica e Tancredi; 3a. I Sogni del Principe; 3b. Giovani eroi; 3c. Partenza di Tancredi; 3d. Amore e ambizione; 3e. Quasi in porto; 3f. Finale; 4. Mazurka; 5. Controdanza; 6. Valzer Brillante (Verdi); 7. Polka; 8. Quadriglia; 9. Galop; 10. Valzer del Commiato.

4-10. Milan La Scala PO, R. Muti (r1994: arr N Scardicchio) *Concert* (8/95) (SONY) ① **SK66279**

Il **Gattopardo, '(The) Leopard'—concert suite from film score (1963)**

1. Allegro maestoso; 2. Allegro impetuoso; 3. Sostenuto appassionato.

1-3. Monte Carlo PO, G. Gelmetti *Concert* (3/93) (EMI) ① **CDC7 54528-2**

Giulietta degli Spirit, 'Juliet of the Spirits'—film score (1965)

Suite Czech SO, D. Wadsworth (r1993; arr Wadsworth) *Concert* (10/93) (SILV) ① **FILMCD129**

The **Godfather—film score (1972)** (collab with Carmine Coppola)

EXCERPTS: 1. Love Theme (Rota); 2. The Godfather's Tarantella (Coppola); 3. The Godfather's Mazurka (Coppola); 4. Every Time I Look In Your Eyes (Coppola); 5. The Godfather Waltz (Rota); 6. Michael's Theme (Rota); 7. The Godfather's Foxtrot (Coppola); 8. The Godfather Theme (Rota).

5, 6, 8. Mancini Pops Orch, H. Mancini (r1990; arr Mancini) *Concert* (11/91) (RCA) ① **RD60706**

The **Godfather, Part II—film score (1974)** (collab with Carmine Coppola & Francesco Pennino)

EXCERPTS: 1. Senza Mamma (Pennino); 2. Napule Ve Salute (Pennino); 3. Marcia Religiosa (Coppola; also used in Godfather III); 4. Festa March (Copppola); 5. Kay's Theme (Rota); 6. A New Carpet (Rota); 7. The Immigrant—Main Theme (Rota).

7. Milan Philh, C. Coppola *Concert* (5/93) (SILV) ① **SILVAD3001**

Le **Notte di Cabiria, '(The) Nights of Cabiria'—film score (1957)**

Suite Czech SO, D. Wadsworth (r1993; arr Wadsworth) *Concert* (10/93) (SILV) ① **FILMCD129**

Prova d'Orchestra, 'Orchestra Rehearsal'—film score (1978)

Suite Czech SO, D. Wadsworth (r1993; arr Wadsworth) *Concert* (10/93) (SILV) ① **FILMCD129**

Roma—film score (1971)

Suite Czech SO, D. Wadsworth (r1993; arr Wadsworth) *Concert* (10/93) (SILV) ① **FILMCD129**

Romeo and Juliet—film score (1968)

EXCERPTS: 1. Prologue and Fanfare; 2. Romeo; 3. Juliet; 4. The Feast at the House of Capulet; 5. Their first meeting; 6. What is a youth? (song); 7. What light through yonder window breaks; 8. Parting is such sweet sorrow; 9. But this I pray... 10. Romeo and Juliet are wed; 11. The Death of Mercutio and Tybalt; 12. Night's candle are burnt out; 13. Adieu; 14. The likeness of death; 15. The ride from Mantua; 16. Death...hath sucked the honey from thy breath; 17. Love Theme; 18. O, happy dagger!; 19. Epilogue.

1-19. OST, G. Weston, N. Rota (r1968) (4/92) (CLOU) ① **CNS5000**

17. Mancini Pops Orch, H. Mancini (r1990; arr Mancini) *Concert* (11/91) (RCA) ① **RD60706**

Lo **Sceicco Bianco, '(The) White Sheikh'—film score (1952)**

Suite Czech SO, D. Wadsworth (r1993; arr Wadsworth) *Concert* (10/93) (SILV) ① **FILMCD129**

La **Strada—film score (1954)**

Suite Czech SO, D. Wadsworth (r1993; arr Wadsworth) *Concert* (10/93) (SILV) ① **FILMCD129**

La **Strada—concert suite from the ballet (1966)** (based on the film score)

1. Country wedding; 2. The three musicians and the 'Madman' on the tightrope; 3a. Rumba; 3b. The circus—The jugglers; 4. Zampano's anger; 5. Zampano kills the 'Madman'; 6. The last show in the snow; 7. Zampano alone and in tears.

Monte Carlo PO, G. Gelmetti *Concert* (3/93) (EMI) ① **CDC7 54528-2**

Milan La Scala PO, R. Muti (r1994) *Concert* (8/95) (SONY) ① **SK66279**

I **Vitelloni—film score (1953)**

Suite Czech SO, D. Wadsworth (r1993; arr Wadsworth) *Concert* (10/93) (SILV) ① **FILMCD129**

War and Peace—concert suite from film score (1956)

1a. Introduction; 1b. Natasha's Waltz; 2. La rosa di Novgorod; 3. Finale.

1a, 1b, 2, 3. Monte Carlo PO, G. Gelmetti *Concert* (3/93) (EMI) ① **CDC7 54528-2**

Waterloo—concert suite from film score (1973)

1. Andante eroico—Tempo di Valzer; 2. Andante alla marcia—Mosso, non troppo; 3. Andante con moto—Alla marcia.

1-3. Monte Carlo PO, G. Gelmetti *Concert* (3/93) (EMI) ① **CDC7 54528-2**

8 1/2, 'Otto e Mezzo'—film score (1963)

Suite Czech SO, D. Wadsworth (r1993; arr Wadsworth) *Concert* (10/93) (SILV) ① **FILMCD129**

ROTHCHILD

SECTION IV: VOCAL AND CHORAL

Si vous n'avez rien à me dire—song

A. Patti, L. Ronald (r1905) *Concert* (4/90) (PEAR) ① **GEMMCD9312**

ROTOLI, Augusto *(1847–1904) Italy*

SECTION IV: VOCAL AND CHORAL

Mia sposa sarà la mia bandiera—song

E. Caruso, orch, W.B. Rogers (r1916) *Concert* (7/91) (RCA) ① [12] **GD60495(5)**

E. Caruso, orch, W.B. Rogers (r1916) *Concert* (10/91) (PEAR) ① [3] **EVC3(2)**

T. Ruffo, orch (r1925) *Concert* (2/93) (PREI) ① [3] **89303(2)**

G. Zenatello, anon (r1909) *Concert* (5/94) (SYMP) ① **SYMCD1168**

G. Zenatello, anon (r1909) *Concert* (5/94) (PEAR) ① [4] **GEMMCDS9073(2)**

Serenata—song

A. Scotti, anon (r1902) *Concert* (3/93) (SYMP) ① **SYMCD1100**

ROTT, Hans *(1858–1884) Austria*

SECTION I: ORCHESTRAL

Symphony in E (1878-80)

Cincinnati Philh, G. Samuel (r1989; ed Banks) (12/89) (HYPE) ① **CDA66366**

Norrköping SO, L. Segerstam (11/92) (BIS) ① **BIS-CD563**

ROUSE, Christopher *(b 1949) USA*

SECTION II: CHAMBER

Bonham—eight percussionists (1988)

Baltimore SO, D. Zinman (r1994) *Concert* (7/95) (ARGO) ① **444 454-2ZH**

ROUSSEL, Albert (Charles Paul Marie) *(1869–1937) France*

SECTION I: ORCHESTRAL

Concertino—cello and orchestra, Op. 57 (1936)

A. Tétard, Paris Orch, J-P. Jacquillat (r1969) *Concert* (7/95) (EMI) ① **CDM5 65154-2**

Concerto for Piano and Orchestra in G, Op. 36 (1928)

D. Laval, Paris Orch, J-P. Jacquillat (r1969) *Concert* (7/95) (EMI) ① **CDM5 65154-2**

Le **Festin de l'araignée, 'Spider's Feast'—symphonic fragments from the ballet, Op. 17 (1912)**

Czech PO, Z. Košler (r1982) *Chausson: Symphony, Op. 20.* (8/88) (SUPR) ① **CO-1472**

orch, A. Roussel (r1929) *Concert* (9/93) (EMI) ① **CDC7 54840-2**

Paris Cons, A. Cluytens (r1963) *Concert* (11/94) (EMI) ① [2] **CZS5 68220-2**

Flemish Rhapsody—orchestra, Op. 56 (1936)

Belgian Rad & TV Orch, A. Rahbari (r1992) *Concert* (8/94) (DINT) ① **DICD920101**

Pour une fête de printemps—symphonic poem, Op. 22 (1920)

Paris Orch, J-P. Jacquillat (r1969) *Concert* (7/95) (EMI) ① **CDM5 65154-2**

Sinfonietta—string orchestra, Op. 52 (1934)

Detroit SO, N. Järvi *Concert* (12/92) (CHAN) ① **CHAN9072**

Tapiola Sinfonietta, P. Järvi (r1993) *Concert* (6/94) (BIS) ① **BIS-CD630**

Paris Cons, A. Cluytens (r1963) *Concert* (11/94) (EMI) ① [2] **CZS5 68220-2**

Suite in F, Op. 33 (1926)

Paris Orch, J-P. Jacquillat (r1969) *Concert* (7/95) (EMI) ① **CDM5 65154-2**

Symphony No. 3 in G minor, Op. 42 (1929-30)

FNO, C. Munch (pp1964) *Concert* (11/88) (MONT) ① **MUN2041**

Detroit SO, N. Järvi *Concert* (3/92) (CHAN) ① **CHAN8996**

Brno St PO, V. Neumann (r1963) *Concert* (5/93) (SUPR) ① **11 0681-2**

NYPO, P. Boulez (r1975) *Concert* (5/95) (SONY) ① **SMK64107**

FNO, L. Bernstein (pp1981) *Franck: Symphony.* (10/95) (DG) ① **445 512-2GMA**

Symphony No. 4 in F, Op. 53 (1934)

FNO, C. Munch (pp1966) *Concert* (11/88) (MONT) ① **MUN2041**

Detroit SO, N. Järvi *Concert* (12/92) (CHAN) ① **CHAN9072**

SECTION II: CHAMBER

Andante—oboe, clarinet and bassoon (1937) (orig planned as movt of unfinished Trio)

H. Roerade, F. van den Brink, J. de Lange (r1994) *Concert* (11/95) (OLYM) ① **OCD460**

Andante and Scherzo—flute and piano, Op. 51 (1934)

P. Lloyd, R. Holt *Concert* (9/92) (CARL) ① **PCD991**

P. Verhey, J. Röling (r1994) *Concert* (11/95) (OLYM) ① **OCD460**

Duo—bassoon and double-bass/cello (1925)

J. de Lange, Q. van Regteren Altena (r1994) *Concert* (9/95) (OLYM) ① **OCD459**

Joueurs de flûte—flute and piano, Op. 27 (1924)

P. Verhey, J. Röling (r1994) *Concert* (9/95) (OLYM) ① **OCD459**

Pipe in D—piccolo & piano (1934)

P. Verhey, J. Röling (r1994) *Concert* (11/95) (OLYM) ① **OCD460**

Sérénade—flute, violin, viola, cello and harp, Op. 30 (1925)

S. Kanga, ASMF Chbr Ens *Concert* (12/88) (CHAN) ① **CHAN8621**

Netherlands Harp Ens *Concert* (5/89) (ETCE) ① **KTC1021**

M. Jurkovič, K. Nováková, Phil Qt *Concert* (9/89) (OPUS) ① **9351 1894**

Prometheus Ens *Concert* (11/89) (ASV) ① **CDDCA664**

P. Verhey, E. Waardenburg, Schoenberg Qt (r1994) *Concert* (9/95) (OLYM) ① **OCD459**

Sonata for Violin and Piano No. 2 in A (1924)

J-J. Kantorow, J. Röling (r1994) *Concert* (9/95) (OLYM) ① **OCD459**

String Quartet in D, Op. 45 (1931-32)
Schoenberg Qt (r1994) *Concert*
(11/95) (OLYM) ① **OCD460**
Trio—flute, viola and cello, Op. 40 (1929)
P. Verhey, H-J. Stegenga, H. Guittart (r1994) *Concert*
(11/95) (OLYM) ① **OCD460**
Trio—violin, viola, cello, Op. 58 (1937)
Jerusalem Stg Trio *Concert*
(6/90) (CARL) ① **PWK1141**
J. van der Meer, H. Guittart, V. de Hoog (r1994)
Concert (11/95) (OLYM) ① **OCD460**

Doute—piano (1919)
E. Parkin *Concert* (10/91) (CHAN) ① **CHAN8887**
Impromptu—harp, Op. 21 (1919)
M. Klinko *Concert* (8/93) (EMI) ① **CDC7 54467-2**
E. Waardenburg (r1994) *Concert*
(9/95) (OLYM) ① **OCD459**
3 Pieces—piano, Op. 49 (1933)
E. Parkin *Concert* (10/91) (CHAN) ① **CHAN8887**
Prelude and Fughetta—organ, Op. 41 (1929)
M-B. Dufourcet (r1992) *Concert*
(6/95) (PRIO) ① **PRCD422**
Prelude and Fugue—piano, Op. 46 (1932-34)
E. Parkin *Concert* (10/91) (CHAN) ① **CHAN8887**
Rustiques—piano, Op. 5 (1904-06)
E. Parkin *Concert* (10/91) (CHAN) ① **CHAN8887**
Ségovia—guitar, Op. 29 (1925)
E. Parkin (trans pf) *Concert*
(10/91) (CHAN) ① **CHAN8887**
J. Bream (r1959) *Concert*
(8/93) (RCA) ① [28] **09026 61583-2(4)**
J. Bream (r1959) *Concert*
(6/94) (RCA) ① **09026 61595-2**
J. Goudswaard (r1994) *Concert*
(9/95) (OLYM) ① **OCD459**
Sonatine—piano, Op. 16 (1912)
E. Parkin *Concert* (10/91) (CHAN) ① **CHAN8887**
Suite in F sharp minor—piano, Op. 14 (1909)
E. Parkin *Concert* (10/91) (CHAN) ① **CHAN8887**

2 Mélodies, Op. 19 (1918)
1. Light (wds. Jean-Aubry); 2. A Farewell (wds. Oliphant).
1. C. Croiza, A. Roussel (r1928) *Concert*
(9/93) (EMI) ① **CDC7 54840-2**
3 Mélodies, Op. 20 (1919) (Wds. Chalupt)
1. Le bachelier de Salamanque; 2. Sarabande.
1. G. Souzay, D. Baldwin (r1963) *Concert*
(3/95) (PHIL) ① [4] **438 964-2PM4(2)**
2. C. Croiza, A. Roussel (r1928) *Concert*
(9/93) (EMI) ① **CDC7 54840-2**
2 Mélodies, Op. 50 (1933-34) (Wds. R. Chalupt)
1. Coeur en péril; 2. L'heure de retour.
2. P. Frijsh, C. Dougherty (r1942) *Concert*
(4/95) (PEAR) ① [2] **GEMMCDS9095(1)**
4 Poèmes, Op. 3 (1903) (Wds. H. de Régnier)
1. Le depart; 2. Voeu; 3. Le jardin mouillé; 4. Madrigal lyrique.
3. C. Croiza, A. Roussel (r1928) *Concert*
(9/93) (EMI) ① **CDC7 54840-2**
3. G. Souzay, D. Baldwin (r1963) *Concert*
(3/95) (PHIL) ① [4] **438 964-2PM4(2)**
4 Poèmes, Op. 8 (1907) (Wds. H. de Régnier)
1. Adieux; 2. Invocation; 3. Nuit d'automne; 4. Odelette.
2. C. Croiza, A. Roussel (r1929) *Concert*
(9/93) (EMI) ① **CDC7 54840-2**
2 Poèmes chinois, Op. 12 (1907-08) (Wds. H. P. Roche, after Giles)
1. Ode à un jeune gentilhomme; 2. Amoureux séparés.
2. C. Croiza, A. Roussel (r1928) *Concert*
(9/93) (EMI) ① **CDC7 54840-2**
2 Poèmes de Ronsard—songs with flute and piano, Op. 26 (1924)
1. Rossignol, mon mignon; 2. Ciel, aer et vens.
K. Battle, J-P. Rampal (pp1991) *Concert*
(9/94) (SONY) ① **SK53106**
I. Maessen, P. Verhey (r1994) *Concert*
(9/95) (OLYM) ① **OCD459**
2 Vocalises (1927-28)
2. No. 2.
2. H. Roerade, J. Röling (r1994: arr ob/pf: Hoérée)
Concert (9/95) (OLYM) ① **OCD459**

Bacchus et Ariane—concert suites from ballet, Op. 43 (1932-33)
EXCERPTS: 1. Suite No 1; 2. Suite No 2.
2. FNO, C. Munch (pp1966) *Concert*
(11/88) (MONT) ① **MUN2041**
2. BRSO, E. Ormandy (pp1959) *Concert*
(8/90) (ORFE) ① **C199891A**
2. Paris Orch, S. Baudo *Concert*
(5/91) (EMI) ① [2] **CZS7 62669-2**
2. Boston SO, C. Munch (r1952) *Ravel: Daphnis et Chloé.*
(12/91) (RCA) ① **GD60469**
2. Detroit SO, N. Järvi *Concert*
(3/92) (CHAN) ① **CHAN8996**
2. Brno St PO, V. Neumann (r1963) *Concert*
(5/93) (SUPR) ① **11 0681-2**
2. Paris Cons, A. Cluytens (r1963) *Concert*
(11/94) (EMI) ① [2] **CZS5 68220-2**
Elpénor—radio score: flute and string quartet, Op. 59 (1947)
P. Verhey, Schoenberg Qt (r1994) *Concert*
(11/95) (OLYM) ① **OCD460**
Le Festin de l'araignée, 'Spider's Feast'—ballet-pantomime: 1 act, Op. 17 (1913—Paris)
NBC SO, A. Toscanini (bp1946) *Concert*
(6/90) (DELL) ① **CDDA9021**
Prague SO, V. Smetáček (r1963) *Concert*
(5/93) (SUPR) ① **11 0681-2**
Padmâvatî—opera-ballet: 2 acts (1923—Paris) (Lib. L. Laloy)
Cpte M. Horne, N. Gedda, J. Van Dam, J. Berbié, C. Burles, M. Vento, L. Dale, Orléon Donostiarra, Toulouse Capitole Orch, M. Plasson
(9/88) (EMI) ① [2] **CDS7 47891-8**

ROUTH, Francis (John) (b 1927) England

Quartet for Oboe and Strings, Op. 34 (1977)
Redcliffe Ens *Concert* (11/92) (REDC) ① **RR006**

Tragic Interludes—oboe, Op. 43 (1983)
Redcliffe Ens *Concert* (11/92) (REDC) ① **RR006**

ROXAS, Emanuele de (1827–1891) Italy

O ben tornato, amore—song
C. Muzio, orch (r1918) *Concert*
(1/95) (ROMO) ① [2] **81010-2**

ROYER, Joseph-Nicolas-Pancrace (c1705–1755) France

La Chasse de Zaïde—keyboard (1739) (Bibliothèque Nationale MS D14218)
C. Rousset *Pièces de clavecin.*
(9/93) (L'OI) ① **436 127-2OH**
Pièces de clavecin—harpsichord (pub 1746)
1. La Majestueuse: Courante; 2. La Zaïde: Rondeau—Tendrement; 3. Les Matelots: Modérément; 4a. Premier Tambourin; 4b. Deuxième Tambourin; 5. L'Incertaine: Marqué; 6. L'Aimable: Gracieux; 7. La Bagatelle; 8. Suitte de la Bagatelle; 9. La Remouleuse: Rondeau—Modérément; 10. Les Tendres Sentiments: Rondeau; 11. Le Vertigo: Rondeau—Modérément; 12. Allemande; 13. La Sensible: Rondeau; 14. La Marche des Scythes: Fièrement.
C. Rousset *Chasse de Zaïde (D14218).*
(9/93) (L'OI) ① **436 127-2OH**
1-3. G. Leonhardt *Concert*
(5/92) (DHM) ① **RD77924**

RÓZSA, Miklós (1907–1995) Hungary/USA

Andante—string orchestra, Op. 22a (1992)
Berlin SO, I. Jackson (r1992) *Concert*
(7/93) (KOCH) ① **37152-2**
Background to Violence—concert suite from film scores
EXCERPTS: 1. Prelude to Murder (Brute Force, 1947); 2. Nocturno (Brute Force); 3. Scherzo (Brute Force); 4. Despair (The Killers, 1946); 5. Pursuit (The

Naked City, 1948); 6. Epilogue: The Song of a City (The Naked City).
1-6. Frankenland State SO, M. Rózsa (r1958) *Lust for Life.*
(10/93) (VARE) ① **VSD5405**
Concerto for String Orchestra (1943)
Berlin SO, I. Jackson (r1992) *Concert*
(7/93) (KOCH) ① **37152-2**
Concerto for Viola and Orchestra, Op. 37a (1979)
M. Newman, Nuremberg SO, R. Kaufman (r1991)
Concert (10/92) (COLO) ① **CST34 8048**
Concerto for Violin and Orchestra, Op. 24 (1956)
J. Heifetz, Dallas SO, W. Hendl (r1956) *Concert*
(4/89) (RCA) ① **GD87963**
J. Heifetz, Dallas SO, W. Hendl (r1956) *Concert*
(11/94) (RCA) ① [65] **09026 61778-2(21)**
Hungarian Nocturne—orchestra, Op. 28 (1964)
NZ SO, J. Sedares (r1992) *Concert*
(9/93) (KOCH) ① **37191-2**
3 Hungarian Sketches—orchestra, Op. 14 (1938)
NZ SO, J. Sedares (r1992) *Concert*
(9/93) (KOCH) ① **37191-2**
Overture to a Symphony Concert, Op. 26 (1957)
NZ SO, J. Sedares (r1992) *Concert*
(9/93) (KOCH) ① **37191-2**
Spellbound Concerto—piano and orchestra (1945) (reworked from the film score 'Spellbound')
Prague City PO, P. Bateman (r1993) *Concert*
(3/94) (SILV) ① **FILMCD137**
S. Hough, Hollywood Bowl SO, J. Mauceri (r1993)
Concert (1/95) (PHIL) ① **442 425-2PH**
Symphony in Three Movements, Op. 6a (1930, rev 1993)
NZ SO, J. Sedares (r1993; ed Rózsa & C. Palmer) *Vintner's Daughter, Op. 23a.*
(6/94) (KOCH) ① **37244-2**
Tema con variazioni—violin, cello and chamber orchestra, Op. 29a (1964)
J. Heifetz, G. Piatigorsky, CO (r1963) *Concert*
(4/89) (RCA) ① **GD87963**
J. Heifetz, G. Piatigorsky, CO (r1963) *Concert*
(11/94) (RCA) ① [65] **09026 61778-2(21)**
Theme, Variations and Finale—orchestra, Op. 13a (1943) (rev cpsr from Op. 13: 1933)
NZ SO, J. Sedares (r1992) *Concert*
(9/93) (KOCH) ① **37191-2**
The Vintner's Daughter, Op. 23a (1953, orch 1955) (orch cpsr from Piano work)
NZ SO, J. Sedares (r1993) *Symphony, Op. 6a.*
(6/94) (KOCH) ① **37244-2**

Duo—viola and piano, Op. 7 (1931)
I. Lippi, J. Novacek (r1994) *Concert*
(11/95) (KOCH) ① **37256-2**
North Hungarian Peasant Songs and Dances, 'Little Suite'—violin and piano, Op. 5 (1929)
I. Lippi, J. Novacek (r1994) *Concert*
(11/95) (KOCH) ① **37256-2**
String Quartet, Op. 22 (1950)
New World Qt (r1978) *Concert*
(10/93) (VOX) ① [2] **115775-2**
Variations on a Hungarian Peasant Song—violin and piano, Op. 4 (1929) (arr cpsr from orch work)
I. Lippi, J. Novacek (r1994) *Concert*
(11/95) (KOCH) ① **37256-2**

Sonata for Solo Violin, Op. 40 (1986)
S. Lautenbacher *Concert*
(11/91) (BAYE) ① **BR100058**
I. Lippi *Concert* (11/95) (KOCH) ① **37256-2**

Ben-Hur—film score (1959)
EXCERPTS: 1. Overture; 2. Prelude; 3. Star of Bethlehem; 4. Adoration of the Magi; 5. Title Music; 6. Roman March; 7. Friendship; 8. The House of Hur; 9. Love Theme; 10. Gratus' Entry into Jerusalem; 11. Messala's Revenge; 12. The Burning Desert; 13. The Rowing of the Galley Slaves; 14. Naval Battle; 15. Victory Parade; 16. Fertility Dance; 17. Arrius' Party; 18. Farewell to Rome; 19. Return to Judea; 20. Memories; 21. The Mother's Love; 22. Intermission Entr'acte Music; 23. Bread and Circus March; 24. Parade of the Charioteers; 25. Death of Messala; 26. Sermon on the Mount; 27. Valley of the Dead; 28. The Lepers' Search for the Christ; 29. Procession to Calvary; 30. Golgotha; 31. Christ Theme; 32. The

Miracle and Finale.
24. Boston Pops, A. Fiedler (r1962) *Concert*
(1/94) (RCA) ① **09026 61249-2**
Double Indemnity—film score (1944)
EXCERPTS: 1a. Mrs Dietrichson; 1b. The
Conspiracy.
1a, 1b National PO, C. Gerhardt (r1974) *Concert*
(5/91) (RCA) ① **GD80911**
El Cid—film score (1961)
EXCERPTS: 1. Overture; 2. Prelude (Main Title); 3.
Palace Music; 4. Fight for Calahorra; 5. Thirteen
Knights; 6. Pride and Sorrow; 7. Farewell (Scene
d'Amour); 8. Intermezzo: El Cid March; 9. The Twins;
10. Battle of Valencia; 11. The Cid's Death; 12. The
Legend and Epilogue; 13. Exit Music: The Falcon and
the Dove. ADDITIONAL ITEMS: 14. Love Theme (arr
cpsr as concert work); 15. Fanfare; 16. Entry of the
Nobles.
1, 2, 5-8, 15. OST, M. Rózsa (r1961) *Concert*
(10/93) (CLOU) ① **CNS5006**
The Four Feathers—film score (1939)
EXCERPTS: 1. Sunstroke; 2. River Journey.
1, 2. National PO, C. Gerhardt (r1974) *Concert*
(5/91) (RCA) ① **GD80911**
Ivanhoe—film score (1952)
EXCERPTS: 1. Prelude; 2. Ransom; 3. Rotherwood;
4. Lady Rowena; 5. Sir Cedric; 6. Squire Wamba; 7.
Rebecca; 8. The Intruder; 9. The Rivals; 10.
Sheffield; 11. Rebecca's Love; 12. Search; 13.
Torquilstone Castle; 14. Bois-Guilbert's Bargain; 15.
The Battlement; 16. Saxon Victory; 17. Farewell; 18.
Challenge and Finale.
Overture (suite) National PO, C. Gerhardt (r1974)
Concert (5/91) (RCA) ① **GD80911**
1-18. Sinfonia of London, B. Broughton (r1994;
orchestral reconstruction by D Robbins)
(5/95) (INTD) ① **MAF7055D**
Julius Caesar—film score (1953)
EXCERPTS: 1a. Julius Caesar Overture (original
unused film version); 1b. Overture (reworked concert
overture); 2. Praeludium; 3. Caesar's Procession; 4.
Flavius Arrested; 5. Feast of Lupercal; 6. Caesar and
His Train; 7. The Scolding Winds; 8. Brutus'
Soliloquy; 9. Brutus' Secret; 10. They Murder Caesar;
11. The Ides of March; 12. Black Sentence; 13.
Brutus' Camp; 14. Heavy Eyes; 15. Song: Gentle
Knave; 16. Ghost of Caesar; 17. Most Noble Brutus;
18. Battle at Philippi; 19. Titinius Enclosed; 20.
Caesar Now Be Still; 20a. Approach of Octavian's
Army; 20b. Death of Brutus; 21. Finale.
1a, 2-21. J. Emmanuel, Sinfonia Chor, Sinfonia of
London, B. Broughton (r1995; orchestral
reconstruction by D Robbins)
(12/95) (INTD) ① **MAF7056D**
1b National PO, C. Gerhardt (r1974)
(10/92) (RCA) ① **GD82792**
The Jungle Book—film score (1942)
EXCERPTS: 1. The Jungle; 2. The Animals of the
Jungle; 3. Mowgli; 4. Life in the Jungle; 5. Indian
Night; 6. Pursuit; 7. Lullaby; 8. Mowgli's Mother; 9.
Among Men; 10. Song of the Jungle; 11. Panic of the
Animals; 12. Hunt for the Shere Khan; 13. The
Python Kaa; 14. Combat; 15. Mowgli's Triumph; 16.
Finale.
1-16. Nuremberg SO, K. Seibel (r1981) *Thief of
Bagdad.* (5/91) (COLO) ① **CST34 8044**
10. Ambrosian Sngrs, National PO, C. Gerhardt
(r1974) *Concert* (5/91) (RCA) ① **GD80911**
**Knights of the Round Table—film score
(1953)**
EXCERPTS: 1. Scherzo in Flight.
1. National PO, C. Gerhardt (r1974) *Concert*
(5/91) (RCA) ① **GD80911**
1. National PO, C. Gerhardt (r1974) *Concert*
(10/92) (RCA) ① **GD82792**
The Lost Weekend—film score (1945)
EXCERPTS: 1. The Bottle: First Meeting; 2. The
Mouse and the Bat: Nightmare; 3. Love Scene and
Finale.
1-3. National PO, C. Gerhardt (r1974) *Concert*
(5/91) (RCA) ① **GD80911**
3. National PO, C. Gerhardt *Concert*
(6/90) (VARE) ① **VSD5207**
Lust for Life—film score (1956)
EXCERPTS: 1. Prelude; 2. Summer (Pastorale); 3.
Brotherly Love; 4. Sunflowers; 5. Postman Roulin; 6.
Madness; 7. Finale.
1-7. Frankenland State SO, M. Rózsa (r1958)
Background to Violence.
(10/93) (VARE) ① **VSD5405**
Madame Bovary—film score (1949)
EXCERPTS: 1. Waltz.
1. Hollywood Bowl SO, J. Mauceri (r1993; restored
Palmer) *Concert* (6/94) (PHIL) ① **438 685-2PH**

The Red House—film score (1947)
EXCERPTS: 1. Prelude; 2a. The Morgan Farm; 2b.
The New Hired Hand; 2c. Swimming Scene; 3. Meg
finds the Red House; 4. Teller shoots at Meg; 5.
Pete's Death and Finale.
1, 2a-c, 3-5. Ambrosian Sngrs, National PO, C.
Gerhardt (r1974) *Concert*
(5/91) (RCA) ① **GD80911**
Sahara—film score (1943)
EXCERPTS: 1. Main Title.
1. National PO, C. Gerhardt *Concert*
(10/90) (RCA) ① **GD80422**
Spellbound—film score (1945)
EXCERPTS: 1a. The Dream Sequence; 1b. The
Mountain Lodge.
1a, 1b National PO, C. Gerhardt (r1974) *Concert*
(5/91) (RCA) ① **GD80911**
The Thief of Bagdad—film score (1940)
EXCERPTS: 1. The King's Fanfare; 2. The Harbour
of Bagdad; 3. Procession; 4. Eternal Love: Love of
the Princess; 5. Galop of the Flying Horse; 6. Dance
of the Silvermaid; 7. The Marketplace of Basra.
1-7. Nuremberg SO, M. Rózsa *Jungle Book.*
(5/91) (COLO) ① **CST34 8044**
4. National PO, C. Gerhardt (r1974) *Concert*
(5/91) (RCA) ① **GD80911**
Time after Time—film score (1979)
EXCERPTS: 1. Warner Bros Fanfare (Steiner) &
Prelude; 2. Search for the Ripper/Decision; 3.
Vaporising Equalizer/The Time Machine; 4. Time
Travel; 5. Bank Montage; 6. Utopia; 7. The
Ripper/Pursuit; 8. Time Machine Waltz; 9. Man
Before His Time; 10. Redwoods; 11. Frightened; 12.
Murder; 13. The Fifth Victim; 14. The Last Victim; 15.
Nocturnal Visitor; 16. Dangerous Drive; 17. Journey's
End & Finale.
17. RPO, M. Rózsa *Concert*
(5/93) (SILV) ① **SILVAD3002**

RUBBRA, (Charles) Edmund
(1901-1986) England

SECTION I: ORCHESTRAL

**Concerto for Viola and Orchestra in A, Op.
75 (1952)**
R. Golani, RPO, V. Handley (r1994) *Violin Concerto.*
(10/94) (CONI) ① **CDCF225**
**Concerto for Violin and Orchestra, Op. 103
(1959)**
C. Pini, Melbourne SO, D. Measham *Ireland: Piano
Concerto.* (1/87) (UNIC) ① **DKPCD9056**
T. Little, RPO, V. Handley (r1994) *Viola Concerto.*
(10/94) (CONI) ① **CDCF225**
Festival Overture, Op. 62 (1947)
New Philh, V. Handley *Concert*
(12/92) (LYRI) ① **SRCD235**
**Improvisations on Virginal Pieces by Giles
Farnaby, Op. 50 (1939)**
Bournemouth Sinfonietta, H-H. Schönzeler (r1976)
Concert (11/93) (CHAN) ① **CHAN6599**
**Resurgam Overture—orchestra, Op. 149
(1975)**
Philh, N. del Mar *Concert*
(11/90) (LYRI) ① **SRCD202**
**Soliloquy—cello and orchestra, Op. 57
(1943-44)**
R. de Saram, LSO, V. Handley *Concert*
(10/92) (LYRI) ① **SRCD234**
Symphony No. 2 in D, Op. 45 (1937)
New Philh, V. Handley *Concert*
(12/92) (LYRI) ① **SRCD235**
Symphony No. 3, Op. 49 (1939)
Philh, N. del Mar *Concert*
(11/90) (LYRI) ① **SRCD202**
Symphony No. 4, Op. 53 (1941)
Philh, N. del Mar *Concert*
(11/90) (LYRI) ① **SRCD202**
Symphony No. 5 in B flat, Op. 63 (1947-48)
Melbourne SO, H-H. Schönzeler (r1976)
(6/92) (CHAN) ① **CHAN6576**
Symphony No. 6, Op. 80 (1954)
Philh, N. del Mar *Concert*
(10/92) (LYRI) ① **SRCD234**
Symphony No. 7 in C, Op. 88 (1957)
LPO, A. Boult *Concert* (12/92) (LYRI) ① **SRCD235**
**Symphony No. 8, 'Hommage à Teilhard de
Chardin'—1966-68, Op. 132**
Philh, N. del Mar *Concert*
(10/92) (LYRI) ① **SRCD234**
**Symphony No. 10, 'Sinfonia da camera', Op.
145 (1974)**
Bournemouth Sinfonietta, H-H. Schönzeler (r1976)
Concert (11/93) (CHAN) ① **CHAN6599**

**A Tribute (for Ralph Vaughan Williams on
his 70th birthday), Op. 56 (1942)**
Philh, N. del Mar *Concert*
(11/90) (LYRI) ① **SRCD202**
Bournemouth Sinfonietta, H-H. Schönzeler (r1976)
Concert (11/93) (CHAN) ① **CHAN6599**
**Variations on 'The Shining River'—brass
band, Op. 101 (1958)**
Black Dyke Mills Band, R. Newsome *Concert*
(7/93) (CHAN) ① **CHAN4508**

SECTION II: CHAMBER

**Duo—cor anglais and piano, Op. 156 (1900-
81)**
P. Bree, P. Komen *Concert*
(2/90) (ETCE) ① **KTC1074**
**Sonata for Cello and Piano in G minor, Op.
60 (1946)**
R. Wallfisch, J. York (r1994) *Concert*
(8/95) (MARC) ① **8 223718**
**Sonata for Oboe and Piano in C, Op. 100
(1958)**
P. Bree, P. Komen *Concert*
(2/90) (ETCE) ① **KTC1074**
J. Polmear, D. Ambache *Concert*
(9/92) (UNIC) ① **DKPCD9121**
String Quartet No. 2 in E flat (1951)
English Qt (r1992) *Concert*
(12/93) (TREM) ① **TREM102-2**

SECTION IV: VOCAL AND CHORAL

**And when the builders—anthem, Op. 125
(1964)** (Wds. Bible)
Llandaff Cath Ch, M. Smith, M. Hoeg (r1994) *Concert*
(10/95) (PRIO) ① **PRCD510**
**Beauty is but a painted hell—partsong, Op.
51/3 (1949)** (Wds. Campion)
King's Sngrs *Concert*
(6/88) (EMI) ① **CDC7 49765-2**
3 Hymn Tunes—chorus a cappella, Op. 114
1. St Colette (Prayer to Jesus); 2. St Non's (That
Virgin Child); 3. Mater Misericordia (Queen of Mercy).
Gonville & Caius College Ch, G. Webber *Concert*
(3/94) (ASV) ① **CDDCA881**
**Magnificat and Nunc Dimittis in A
flat—chorus a cappella, Op.**
Gonville & Caius College Ch, Michael Phillips, G.
Webber *Concert* (3/94) (ASV) ① **CDDCA881**
**Missa in honorem Sancti Dominici—4vv, Op.
66 (1948)**
Gonville & Caius College Ch, G. Webber *Concert*
(3/94) (ASV) ① **CDDCA881**
3 Motets—chorus a cappella, Op. 76
1. Let us now praise famous men; 2. There is a spirit;
3. Except the Lord built the house.
Gonville & Caius College Ch, G. Webber *Concert*
(3/94) (ASV) ① **CDDCA881**
My tocher's the jewel—part-song, Op. 10
(Wds. traditional Scottish)
King's Sngrs *Concert*
(6/88) (EMI) ① **CDC7 49765-2**
3 Psalms—voice and piano (1946) (Wds.
Bible)
1. Psalm 6: O Lord, rebuke me not; 2. Psalm 23: The
Lord is my Shepherd; 3. Psalm 150: Praise ye the
Lord.
K. Ferrier, E. Lush (bp1953) *Concert*
(7/91) (LOND) ① **430 061-2LM**
Salutation—chorus a cappella (1953)
Cambridge Univ Chbr Ch, T. Brown *Concert*
(4/92) (GAMU) ① **GAMCD529**

RUBENS, Paul (Alfred)
(1875-1917) England

SECTION IV: VOCAL AND CHORAL

**I Love You, Ma Chérie—song for the show
'The Parisian Model' (1906)**
H. Leoni, Broadway Cast (r1907) *Concert*
(5/94) (PEAR) ① [3] **GEMMCD9050/2(2)**

SECTION V: STAGE WORKS

**Three Little Maids—musical show
(1902—London)** (Lyrics cpsr; additional songs
by Talbot & Greenbank)
EXCERPTS: 1. Men; 2. Something Sweet About Me;
3. The Golf Scene; 4. My Gal Sal; 5. Girls, Girls; 6.
Algy's Simply Awf'lly Good at Algebra; 7. A Real
Town Lady; 8. She Was a Miller's Daughter; 9. The
Fishes in the Sea; 10. What is a Maid to Do?
1-5. G. Carroll, M. Crichton, G. P. Huntley (r1902 &
07) *Concert*
(5/94) (PEAR) ① [3] **GEMMCD9050/2(1)**

Tonight's the Night—musical show
(1914—New York) (Lyrics cpsr & Percy
Greenbank)
EXCERPTS: 1. Murders; 2. The Only Way; 3. Meet
Me 'Round the Corner; 4. Boots and Shoes.
1-4. G. Grossmith, L. Henson (r1915) *Concert*
(5/94) (PEAR) ① [3] **GEMMCDS9056/8**

RUBINSTEIN, Anton
(Grigor'yevich) (1829–1894)
Russia

SECTION I: ORCHESTRAL

Caprice russe—piano and orchestra, Op. 102
(1858)
J. Banowetz, Bratislava RSO, R. Stankovsky (r1993)
Piano Concerto 5. (2/95) (MARC) ① **8 223489**
Concerto for Piano and Orchestra No. 1 in E,
Op. 25 (1850)
J. Banowetz, Košice St PO, A. Walter (r1992) *Piano*
Concerto 2. (7/93) (MARC) ① **8 223456**
Concerto for Piano and Orchestra No. 2 in F,
Op. 35 (1851)
J. Banowetz, Košice St PO, A. Walter (r1992) *Piano*
Concerto 1. (7/93) (MARC) ① **8 223456**
A. Paley, Moscow St SO, I. Golovshin (r1993) *Piano*
Concerto 4. (2/95) (RUSS) ① **RDCD11360**
Concerto for Piano and Orchestra No. 4 in D
minor, Op. 70 (1864)
M. Ponti, Philh Hungarica, O. Maga *Thalberg: Piano*
Concerto. (5/93) (VOX) ① **115711-2**
J. Hofmann, Curtis Inst Student Orch, F. Reiner
(pp1937) *Concert* (5/93) (VAI) ① [2] **VAIA1020**
A. Paley, Moscow St SO, I. Golovshin (r1993) *Piano*
Concerto 2. (2/95) (RUSS) ① **RDCD11360**
M. Raekallio, Tampere PO, L. Grin (r1993)
Moszkowski: Piano Concerto.
(2/95) (ONDI) ① **ODE818-2**
Concerto for Piano and Orchestra No. 5 in E
flat, Op. 94 (1874)
J. Banowetz, Bratislava RSO, R. Stankovsky (r1993)
Caprice russe, Op. 102.
(2/95) (MARC) ① **8 223489**
Don Quixote—musical picture after
Cervantes, Op. 87 (1870)
Russian St SO, I. Golovshin (r1993) *Ivan the Terrible.*
(9/95) (RUSS) ① **RDCD11397**
Eroica Fantasia—orchestra, Op. 110 (1884)
Bratislava RSO, R. Stankovsky (r1993) *Symphony 3.*
(2/95) (RUSS) ① **8 223576**
Ivan the Terrible—musical picture after L. A.
Mey, Op. 79 (1869)
Russian St SO, I. Golovshin (r1993) *Don Quixote.*
(9/95) (RUSS) ① **RDCD11397**
Symphony No. 2, 'Ocean', Op. 42 (1851 rev
1863 and 1880)
Moscow St SO, I. Golovshin (r1993) *Feramors.*
(10/94) (RUSS) ① **RDCD11356**
Symphony No. 3 in A, Op. 43 (1855)
Bratislava RSO, R. Stankovsky (r1993) *Eroica*
Fantasia, Op. 110. (2/95) (RUSS) ① **8 223576**
Symphony No. 4 in D minor, 'Dramatic', Op.
95 (1874)
Russian St SO, I. Golovshin (r1993)
(6/95) (RUSS) ① **RDCD11357**
Symphony No. 6 in A minor, Op. 111 (1886)
Philh Hungarica, G. Varga (r1986)
(11/87) (MARC) ① **8 220489**

SECTION II: CHAMBER

3 Characteristic Pieces—piano: four hands,
(orig Op. 9) (1847-48)
1. Russian Song; 2. Nocturne on the Water; 3. The
Waterfall.
A. Groethuysen, Y. Tal *Concert*
(11/92) (SONY) ① **SK47199**
3 Pieces—cello and piano, Op. 11/2 (1854)
Nocturne N. Imai, R. Pöntinen *Concert*
(2/88) (BIS) ① **BIS-CD358**

SECTION III: INSTRUMENTAL

Barcarolle in G minor—piano, Op. 50/3
(1854-68) (arr of pf 4-hand version)
A. Rubinstein (r1953) *Concert*
(1/95) (RCA) ① **09026 61860-2**
Barcarolle No. 4 in G—piano
A. Rubinstein (r1953) *Concert*
(1/95) (RCA) ① **09026 61860-2**
2 Melodies—piano, Op. 3 (1852)
1. F; 2. B.
1. M. Lympany *Concert* (1/89) (EMIL) ① **CDZ110**
1. L. Godowsky (r1916) *Concert*
(4/89) (APR) ① [2] **APR7011**
1. H. Kreisler, F. Kreisler (r1923) *Concert*
(7/90) (BIDD) ① [2] **LAB009/10**

---

1. P. Casals, N. Mednikoff (arr Popper: r1926)
Concert (10/91) (BIDD) ① **LAB017**
1. S. Cherkassky (pp1975) *Concert*
(10/91) (DECC) ① **433 653-2DH**
Piano Sonata No. 1 in E minor, Op. 12
(c1848-54)
L. Howard (r1980) *Piano Sonata 3.*
(5/90) (HYPE) ① **CDA66017**
Piano Sonata No. 2 in C minor, Op. 20
(c1848-54)
L. Howard (r1982) *Piano Sonata 4.*
(5/90) (HYPE) ① **CDA66105**
Piano Sonata No. 3 in F, Op. 41 (1855)
L. Howard (r1980) *Piano Sonata 1.*
(5/90) (HYPE) ① **CDA66017**
Piano Sonata No. 4 in A minor, Op. 100
(1877)
L. Howard (r1982) *Piano Sonata 2.*
(5/90) (HYPE) ① **CDA66105**
Rocky Island—piano: 24 pieces, Op. 10
(1853-54)
22. *Rêve angélique.*
22. L. Godowsky (r1924) *Concert*
(4/89) (APR) ① [2] **APR7011**
22. H. Bauer (r1924) *Concert*
(9/93) (BIDD) ① **LHW007**
6 Soirées de Saint-Pétersbourg—piano, Op.
44 (1860)
1. Romance in E flat; 2. Scherzo in A minor; 3.
Preghiera in B flat; 4. Impromptu in G; 5. Nocturne in
F; 6. Appassionato in B minor.
L. Mordkovitch, M. Gusak-Grin (arr Wilhelmj) *Concert*
(11/94) (CHAN) ① **CHAN8748**
J. Kubelík, anon (arr Wieniawski: r1913) *Concert*
(6/91) (BIDD) ① [2] **LAB033/4**
1. L. Godowsky (r1920) *Concert*
(4/89) (APR) ① [2] **APR7011**
1. I. Stern, Columbia SO, F. Brieff (arr Harris)
Concert (7/90) (SONY) ① **SK45816**
1. A. Etherden *Concert*
(7/93) (HUNT) ① **HMPCD0589**
Soirées musicales—piano, Op. 109 (1884)
1. Prelude; 2. Valse; 3. Nocturne; 4. Scherzo; 5.
Impromptu; 6. Rêverie-caprice; 7. 8 Badinages; 9.
Theme and Variations; 9. Study.
J. Banowetz (9/90) (MARC) ① **8 223177**
6 Studies—piano, Op. 23 (1849-50)
1. F; 2. C; 3. C sharp minor; 4. E flat; 5. F; 6. G.
2. M. Levitzki (r1927) *Concert*
(6/92) (APR) ① [2] **APR7020**
2. E. Wild *Concert* (9/92) (VANG) ① **08.4033.71**
Valse caprice in E flat (1870)
L. Howard *Concert* (5/90) (HYPE) ① **CDA66090**
A. Rubinstein (r1953; arr C. Deis) *Concert*
(1/95) (RCA) ① **09026 61860-2**

SECTION IV: VOCAL AND CHORAL

Der Asra—song, Op. 32/6 (Wds. Heine)
G.B. de Negri, anon (r1902) *Concert*
(12/89) (SYMP) ① **SYMCD1065**
I. Tartakov, anon (r1901) *Concert*
(6/93) (PEAR) ① [3] **GEMMCDS9997/9(1)**
O. Kamionsky, anon (r1910) *Concert*
(6/93) (PEAR) ① [3] **GEMMCDS9001/3(1)**
The Donkey and the Nightingale—song
A. Davidov, anon (r1902) *Concert*
(6/93) (PEAR) ① [3] **GEMMCDS9007/9(1)**
Du wist wie eine Blume—song, Op. 32/5
(Wds. Heine)
E. Rethberg, F. Fradkin, D. Lieberfeld (r1928-9)
Concert (2/95) (ROMO) ① [2] **81012-2**
Der Engel—duet, Op. 48/1 (Wds. after
Lermontov)
H. Komatsu, K. Moll, C. Garben *Concert*
(9/91) (HARM) ① **HMC90 5210**
Die Lotosblume ängstigt sich—duet (Wds.
Heine)
H. Komatsu, K. Moll, C. Garben *Concert*
(9/91) (HARM) ① **HMC90 5210**
Die Nacht, '(The) Night'—song (based on
Romance, Op 44/1)
R. Tauber, Berlin Künstlertheater Orch, E. Hauke
(r1927) *Concert* (4/90) (PEAR) ① **GEMMCD9381**
M. Seinemeyer, Berlin St Op Orch, F. Weissmann
(r1929) *Concert* (11/90) (PREI) ① **89029**
R. Mei-Figner, anon (r1901) *Concert*
(6/93) (PEAR) ① [3] **GEMMCDS9997/9(1)**
12 Persian Songs, Op. 34 (1854) (Wds. Mirza-
Shafi, trans F. Bodenstedt)
1. Zuleika; 3. When I look upon your feet; 9. The
turbulent waters of Kur.
1. A. El-Tour, anon (r1910) *Concert*
(6/93) (PEAR) ① [3] **GEMMCDS9004/6(1)**
3. B. Gmyrya, L. Ostrin (r1949) *Concert*
(4/92) (EMI) ① [7] **CHS7 69741-2(6)**

---

9. F. Chaliapin, orch, L. Collingwood (r1931) *Concert*
(6/93) (PREI) ① [2] **89207**
The Prisoner—song (c1878) (Wds.
Polonsky)
F. Chaliapin, J. Bazilevsky (r1930) *Concert*
(6/93) (PREI) ① [2] **89207**
Since first I met thee—song (Wds. Watson:
based on Romance, Op 44/1)
R. Ponselle, orch, R. Bourdon (r1928) *Concert*
(11/94) (ROMO) ① [2] **81007-2**
The Voyevode—song
D. Bukhtoyarov, anon (r1902) *Concert*
(6/93) (PEAR) ① [3] **GEMMCDS9001/3(1)**
Waldlied—duet (Wds. Lenau)
H. Komatsu, K. Moll, C. Garben *Concert*
(9/91) (HARM) ① **HMC90 5210**
Wanderers Nachtlied—duet (Wds. Lermontov,
after Goethe)
B. Fassbaender, K. Moll, C. Garben *Concert*
(9/91) (HARM) ① **HMC90 5210**
We three—song
I. Tartakov, anon (r1901) *Concert*
(6/93) (PEAR) ① [3] **GEMMCDS9997/9(1)**

SECTION V: STAGE WORKS

The Demon—opera: 3 acts (1875—St
Petersburg) (Lib. Viskovatov)
EXCERPTS: 1. Overture. ACT 1: 2. Accursed world!;
3. Thou wilt be the world's queen; 4. On desire's soft,
fleeting wing. ACT 2: 5. Lezginka (Caucasian Dance);
6. Ballet Music; 7. Do not weep, my child (Demon's
aria); 8. On the airy ocean. ACT 3: 9. Calm and clear
is the night; 10. I am he whom you called; 11. I swear
by the eternal truth.
Sinodal's aria A. Labinsky, anon (r1905) *Concert*
(7/93) (SYMP) ① **SYMCD1105**
Soaring like a falcon L. Sobinov, orch (r1910)
Concert (3/95) (NIMB) ① **NI7865**
2. L. Sibiriakov, orch (r1912) *Concert*
(6/93) (PEAR) ① [3] **GEMMCDS9007/9(2)**
4. A. Bogdanovich, anon (r1903) *Concert*
(6/93) (PEAR) ① [3] **GEMMCDS9007/9(1)**
7. F. Chaliapin, orch (r1911) *Concert*
(6/88) (EMI) ① **CDH7 61009-2**
7. E. Giraldoni, anon (r1902) *Concert*
(6/90) (SYMP) ① **SYMCD1073**
7. M. Reizen, Bolshoi Th Orch, V. Nebolsin (r1955)
Concert (12/92) (PREI) ① **89059**
7. T. Ruffo, orch (r1922) *Concert*
(2/93) (PREI) ① [3] **89303(2)**
7, 10. I. Tartakov, anon (r1901) *Concert*
(6/93) (PEAR) ① [3] **GEMMCDS9997/9(1)**
7, 8. N. Shevelev, anon (r1901) *Concert*
(6/93) (PEAR) ① [3] **GEMMCDS9007/9(2)**
7, 8, 10. D. Hvorostovsky, Kirov Th Orch, V. Gergiev
(r1993) *Concert* (5/94) (PHIL) ① **438 872-2PH**
8. P. Orlov, anon (r1902) *Concert*
(6/93) (PEAR) ① [3] **GEMMCDS9001/3(1)**
Feramors—opera: 3 acts (1863—Dresden)
(Lib. J. Rodenberg, after T. Moore)
Moscow St SO, I. Golovshin (r1993) *Symphony 2.*
(10/94) (RUSS) ① **RDCD11356**
Kalashnikov the Merchant—opera: 3 acts
(1880—St Petersburg) (Lib. N. Kulikov, after
Lermontov)
Merchant's aria N. Shevelev, anon (r1901) *Concert*
(6/93) (PEAR) ① [3] **GEMMCDS9007/9(2)**
Nero—opera: 4 acts (1879—Hamburg) (Lib.
Barbier)
EXCERPTS: 1. Vindex's Epithalamium: I sing to you,
Hymen divine!.
Imen! Imen! P. Lisitsian, Bolshoi Th Orch, A. Melik-
Pashayev (1957) *Concert* (8/93) (PREI) ① **89061**
Invan, Invan F. Marconi, anon (r1907: Ital) *Concert*
(10/90) (SYMP) ① **SYMCD1069**
Invan, Invan F. Marconi, S. Cottone (r1903: Ital)
Concert (10/90) (SYMP) ① **SYMCD1069**
Oh, light of the day E. Caruso, orch, J. Pasternack
(2 vers: French: r1917) *Concert*
(7/91) (RCA) ① [12] **GD60495(6)**
Oh, light of the day E. Caruso, orch, J. Pasternack
(2 vers: French: r1917) *Concert*
(10/91) (PEAR) ① [3] **EVC4(1)**
Oh, light of the day E. Caruso, orch (r1917: Fr)
Concert (7/95) (NIMB) ① **NI7866**
Zulima's Bacchic song E. Zbrueva, chor, orch
(r1911) *Concert*
(6/93) (PEAR) ① [3] **GEMMCDS9004/6(2)**
1. D. Hvorostovsky, Kirov Th Orch, V. Gergiev
(r1993) *Concert* (5/94) (PHIL) ① **438 872-2PH**

RUDERS, Poul (b 1949) Denmark

SECTION I: ORCHESTRAL

Concerto for Clarinet and twin-Orchestra (1985)
N. Thomsen, Odense SO, T. Vetö *Concert*
(4/92) (UNIC) ① **DKPCD9114**
Concerto for Violin and Orchestra No. 1 (1981)
R. Hirsch, Odense SO, T. Vetö *Concert*
(4/92) (UNIC) ① **DKPCD9114**
Concerto for Violin and Orchestra No. 2 (1990-91)
R. Hirsch, Copenhagen Collegium Musicum, M. Schønwandt (r1992) *Dramaphonia.*
(9/94) (MARC) ① **DCCD9308**
Gong—orchestra
Danish Nat RSO, L. Segerstam (r1993) *Concert*
(10/93) (CHAN) ① **CHAN9179**
Nightshade—10 instruments (1986)
Capricorn, O. Knussen (r1987) *Concert*
(5/93) (BRID) ① **BCD9037**
Polydrama (Drama-Trilogy Part 3)—cello and orchestra (1988)
M. Zeuthen, Odense SO, T. Vetö *Concert*
(4/92) (UNIC) ① **DKPCD9114**
Psalmodies—guitar and nine instruments (1989)
1. Entrance for one; 2. Solo for Two; 3. Six in the Air; 4. A Fanfare for All; 5. With Passion for All; 6. A Chorale and a Song; 7. Cadenza for One; 8. Cadenza for All; 9. A March of Light and Darkness; 10. A Prayer with Halo; 11. Exit for One.
D. Starobin, Speculum Musicae, D. Palma (r1992) *Concert*
(5/93) (BRID) ① **BCD9037**
Symphony, 'Himmelhoch Jauchzend—zum Tode Betrübt' (1989)
Danish Nat RSO, L. Segerstam (r1993) *Concert*
(10/93) (CHAN) ① **CHAN9179**
Thus saw St. John (Saaledes saae Johannes)—orchestra (1984)
Danish Nat RSO, L. Segerstam (r1993) *Concert*
(10/93) (CHAN) ① **CHAN9179**
Tundra—orchestra (1990)
Helsinki PO, S. Comissiona *Concert*
(4/92) (ONDI) ① **ODE767-2**
Danish Nat RSO, L. Segerstam (r1991) *Concert*
(10/93) (CHAN) ① **CHAN9179**

SECTION II: CHAMBER

Dramaphonia—piano and chamber ensemble (1987)
P. Rosenbaum, Lontano, O. de la Martinez (r1990) *Violin Concerto 2.* (9/94) (MARC) ① **DCCD9308**
Vox in Rama—amplified piano, clarinet and piano (1983)
Capricorn (r1987) *Concert*
(5/93) (BRID) ① **BCD9037**

RUDOLPH, ARCHDUKE OF AUSTRIA (1788–1831)

SECTION II: CHAMBER

Sonata for Violin and Piano in F minor (c1812)
J. Suk, S. Kagan (r1992) *Variations in F.*
(7/93) (KOCH) ① **37082-2**
Variations in F on a Theme by Prince Louis Ferdinand of Prussia—violin and piano (c1810)
J. Suk, S. Kagan (r1992) *Violin Sonata.*
(7/93) (KOCH) ① **37082-2**

RUEFF, Jeanine (b 1922) France

SECTION II: CHAMBER

Sonatina for Trumpet and Piano
S. Nakarjakov, A. Markovich *Concert*
(5/93) (TELD) ① **9031-77705-2**

RUGGI, Francesco Jnr (1826–1901) Italy

SECTION V: STAGE WORKS

I due Ciabattini—opera (1860—Naples) (Lib. A Spadetta)
Arsenico! Veleno! G. De Luca, F. Corradetti, anon (r1907) *Concert* (6/94) (IRCC) ① **IRCC-CD808**

RUGGLES, Carl (Sprague) (1876–1971) USA

SECTION I: ORCHESTRAL

Men and Mountains (1924, rev 1936)
Cleveland Orch, C. von Dohnányi (r1994) *Concert*
(12/95) (DECC) ① **443 776-2DH**
Sun-treader—orchestra (1926-31)
Cleveland Orch, C. von Dohnányi (r1994) *Concert*
(12/95) (DECC) ① **443 776-2DH**

SECTION II: CHAMBER

Angels—6 tpts rev 4 tpt and 3 tbns (1938)
(from 'Men and Angels', 1920)
London Gabrieli Brass Ens, C. Larkin *Concert*
(5/92) (HYPE) ① **CDA66517**

RÜHM, Gerhard (b 1930) Germany

SECTION IV: VOCAL AND CHORAL

Foetus—6vv female vv
Bel Canto Ens, D. Spohr (r1993) *Concert*
(3/95) (SCHW) ① **314322**
Schöpfung, 'Creation'—6vv female vv (1986-87)
Bel Canto Ens, D. Spohr (r1993) *Concert*
(3/95) (SCHW) ① **314322**
Sprechquartette—spoken quartets on German folksongs (1987)
1. Frühlingsbotschaft; 2. Frühlingsankunft; 3. Der holde Mai; 4. Rätsel; 5. Gott weiss es; 6. Weihnachtslied; 7. Der Tannebaum; 8. Von den zwei Schafen; 9. Das Vöglein; 10. Wenn ich ein Vöglein wär'; 11. Kuchenbacken; 12. Von den Watschelgänschen; 13. Der Gänselied; 14. Jäger und Hase; 15. Spiellied; 16. O, du lieber Augustin.
Bel Canto Ens, D. Spohr (r1993) *Concert*
(3/95) (SCHW) ① **314322**

RUIZ DE RIBAYAZ, Lucas (before 1650–?) Spain

SECTION III: INSTRUMENTAL

Luz y norte musical para caminar—guitar and harp tutor (pub 1677)
EXCERPTS: 1. Pasacalles; 2. Xacaras por primer tono; 3. Gallardas; 4. Zarambeques; 5. Chaconas y Marionas; 6. Preludio o Capricho Arpeado (Gaspar Sanz); 7. Folias; 8. Pabanas; 9. Españoletas; 10. Achas & Buelta del Hacha; 11. Paradetas; 12. Zarabandas; 13. Rugero; 14. Bacas; 15. Villanos; 16. El Turdeon; 17. Canarios; 18. Fantasia (after Ludovico); 19. Galeria de Amor & Buelta; 20. Torneo; 21. Preludio y Fantasia con mucha Variedad de falsas (Gaspar Sanz); 22. Tatantela; 23. Matachenes; 24. Gaytas; 25. El Gran Duque & Baylete.
5, 9, 12, 19. Extempore Stg Ens *Concert*
(7/92) (HYPE) ① **CDA66327**
9. Romanesca (r1991-2) *Concert*
(11/94) (GLOS) ① **GCD920201**

RUNÓLFSSON, Karl Otto (1900–1970) Iceland

SECTION I: ORCHESTRAL

On Crossroads—suite (1939)
Iceland SO, P. Sakari (r1993) *Concert*
(10/93) (CHAN) ① **CHAN9180**

RUPÈS, Georges France

SECTION IV: VOCAL AND CHORAL

Pastorale Languedocienne—song
L. Escalaïs, anon (r1906) *Concert*
(12/93) (SYMP) ① **SYMCD1126**

RUSSELL, (George) Alexander (1880–1953) USA

SECTION IV: VOCAL AND CHORAL

Say a little prayer for me—song
A. Galli-Curci, orch, R. Bourdon (r1924: 2 vers) *Concert*
(8/94) (ROMO) ① [2] **81004-2**

RUSSELL, William (1777–1813) England

SECTION III: INSTRUMENTAL

12 Voluntaries, Set 1—keyboard (pub 1805)
2. F; 9. A minor; 11. E minor.
2. J. Bate *Concert* (11/91) (UNIC) ① **DKPCD9106**
9. J. Bate *Concert* (5/91) (UNIC) ① **DKPCD9099**
11. J. Bate *Concert* (2/91) (UNIC) ① **DKPCD9096**
Voluntaries, Set 2—keyboard (pub 1812)
7. A.
7. J. Bate *Concert* (5/91) (UNIC) ① **DKPCD9101**

RUSSELL, Willy (20th Cent) England

SECTION V: STAGE WORKS

Blood Brothers—musical show (1983—London) (Book and Lyrics cpsr)
EXCERPTS: 1. Marilyn Monroe; 2. My Child; 3. Easy Terms; 4. Shoes Upon the Table; 5. Kids Game; 6. Shoes Upon the Table (reprise); 7. Long Sunday Afternoon/My Friend; 8. Bright New Day; 9. Marilyn Monroe (reprise); 10. That Guy; 11. Summer Sequence; 12. I'm Not Saying a Word; 13. Take A Letter Miss Jones; 14. The Robbery; 15. Marilyn Monroe (2nd reprise); 16. Light Romance; 17. Madman; 18. Tell Me It's Not True.
Cpte K. Dee, London Cast, R. Edwards (r1988)
(5/89) (FRST) ① **CASTCD17**

RUSSO, William (b 1928) USA

SECTION I: ORCHESTRAL

3 Blues Pieces—blues band and symphony orchestra, Op. 50 (c1968)
Siegel-Schwall Band, San Francisco SO, S. Ozawa *Concert* (12/91) (DG) ① [2] **413 851-2GW2**

RUTTER, John (b 1945) England

SECTION I: ORCHESTRAL

Suite antique—flute, harpsichord and strings (1979)
1. Prelude; 2. Ostinato; 3. Aria; 4. Waltz; 5. Chanson; 6. Rondeau.
D. Dobing, W. Marshall, CLS, J. Rutter *Concert*
(3/93) (CLLE) ① **COLCD117**

SECTION IV: VOCAL AND CHORAL

All things bright and beautiful—anthem
Cambridge Sngrs, PJBE, J. Rutter *Concert*
(6/87) (CLLE) ① **COLCD100**
Angels' Carol, 'Have you heard the sound of the angel voices' (Wds. cpsr)
Cambridge Sngrs, CLS, J. Rutter *Concert*
(12/89) (CLLE) ① **COLCD111**
Behold, the tabernacle of God—festival anthem (1981)
Cambridge Sngrs, CLS, J. Rutter *Concert*
(4/92) (CLLE) ① **COLCD114**
Brother Heinrich's Christmas—musical fable (1982) (Wds. Cpsr)
B. Kay, Cambridge Sngrs, CLS, J. Rutter *Concert*
(12/91) (CLLE) ① **COLCD115**
Candlelight carol—choir and organ/orchestra (1984) (Wds. cpsr)
Cambridge Sngrs, CLS, J. Rutter *Concert*
(12/87) (CLLE) ① **COLCD106**
Canterbury Cath Ch, M. Harris, D. Flood *Concert*
(12/90) (YORK) ① **CD109**
St Bride's Ch, Fleet St, C. Etherington, R. Jones *Concert* (2/91) (REGE) ① **REGSB701CD**
5 Childhood Lyrics—chorus a capella (1973)
1. Monday's child (wds. trad); 2. The owl and the pussy-cat (wds. E. Lear); 3. Windy nights (wds. R. L. Stevenson); 4. Matthew, Mark, Luke amd John (wds. trad); 5. Sing a song of sixpence (wds. trad).
Cambridge Sngrs, J. Rutter *Concert*
(3/93) (CLLE) ① **COLCD117**
Christmas lullaby—brass ensemble
Cambridge Sngrs, CLS, J. Rutter (r1985) *Concert*
(12/93) (CLLE) ① **COLCD121**
Donkey Carol (Wds. cpsr)
Cambridge Clare College Ch, Cambridge Clare College Orch, J. Rutter *Concert*
(12/89) (DECC) ① **425 500-2DM**
Cambridge Sngrs, CLS, J. Rutter (r1985) *Concert*
(12/93) (CLLE) ① **COLCD121**

The **Falcon**—mixed vv, organ and orchestra (1969)
St Paul's Cath Ch, Cambridge Sngrs, Andrew Lucas, CLS, J. Rutter *Concert*
(4/92) (CLLE) ① **COLCD114**

Fancies—chorus and chamber orchestra (1971)
1. Tell me where is fancy bred (wds. Shakespeare);
2. There a a garden in her face (wds. T. Campion); 3. The urchin's dance (wds. anon); 4. Riddle song (wds. 15th cent anon); 5. Midnight's bell (wds. T. Middleton); 6. The bellman's song (wds. R. Herrick).
Cambridge Sngrs, CLS, J. Rutter *Concert*
(3/93) (CLLE) ① **COLCD117**

For the beauty of the earth—anthem
Cambridge Sngrs, PJBE, J. Rutter *Concert*
(6/87) (CLLE) ① **COLCD100**
St John's Episcopal Cath Ch, D. Pearson *Concert*
(10/92) (DELO) ① **DE3125**

A **Gaelic Blessing**—anthem
Cambridge Sngrs, PJBE, J. Rutter *Concert*
(6/87) (CLLE) ① **COLCD100**
Ex Cathedra Chbr Ch, J. Skidmore (r c1994) *Concert*
(12/94) (ASV) ① **CDDCA912**

Gloria—chorus and orchestra
Cambridge Sngrs, CLS, J. Rutter *Concert*
(6/87) (CLLE) ① **COLCD100**

God be in my head—anthem
Cambridge Sngrs, PJBE, J. Rutter *Concert*
(6/87) (CLLE) ① **COLCD100**

I will lift up mine eyes—Psalm 121: mixed chorus and orchestra (1974) (Wds. Bible)
CLS, J. Rutter *Requiem*.
(11/86) (CLLE) ① **COLCD103**

Jesus child—carol
Sheffield Chorale, Sheaf Concert Orch, J. Kirkwood *Concert* (12/89) (CHOR) ① **EECD109**
Cambridge Sngrs, CLS, J. Rutter (r1985) *Concert*
(12/93) (CLLE) ① **COLCD121**

The **Lord bless you and keep you**—anthem
Cambridge Sngrs, PJBE, J. Rutter *Concert*
(6/87) (CLLE) ① **COLCD100**

The **Lord is my shepherd**—anthem
Cambridge Sngrs, PJBE, J. Rutter *Concert*
(6/87) (CLLE) ① **COLCD100**

Loving Shepherd of Thy Sheep—hymn: 4vv with soprano solo (Wds. Leeson)
Cambridge Sngrs, J. Rutter *Concert*
(4/92) (CLLE) ① **COLCD113**

Magnificat—soprano, chorus and orchestra (1990)
P. Forbes, Cambridge Sngrs, CLS, J. Rutter *Concert*
(4/92) (CLLE) ① **COLCD114**

Mary's lullaby—carol (Wds. cpsr)
Cambridge Clare College Ch, Cambridge Clare College Orch, J. Rutter *Concert*
(12/89) (DECC) ① **425 500-2DM**
Sheffield Chorale, Sheaf Concert Orch, J. Kirkwood *Concert* (12/89) (CHOR) ① **EECD109**
Cambridge Sngrs, CLS, J. Rutter (r1985) *Concert*
(12/93) (CLLE) ① **COLCD121**

Nativity carol—choir, organ/orchestra (1963)
Cambridge Sngrs, CLS, J. Rutter *Concert*
(12/87) (CLLE) ① **COLCD106**
Sheffield Chorale, Sheaf Concert Orch, J. Kirkwood *Concert* (12/89) (CHOR) ① **EECD109**

O clap your hands—anthem
Cambridge Sngrs, PJBE, J. Rutter *Concert*
(6/87) (CLLE) ① **COLCD100**

O praise the Lord of Heaven—festival anthem (1980)
Cambridge Sngrs, John Scott, CLS, J. Rutter *Concert*
(4/92) (CLLE) ① **COLCD114**

Open thou mine eyes—anthem
Cambridge Sngrs, J. Rutter *Concert*
(6/87) (CLLE) ① **COLCD100**

Praise ye the Lord—anthem
Cambridge Sngrs, PJBE, J. Rutter *Concert*
(6/87) (CLLE) ① **COLCD100**

A **Prayer of St Patrick**—anthem
Cambridge Sngrs, J. Rutter *Concert*
(6/87) (CLLE) ① **COLCD100**

The **Reluctant Dragon**—musical fable (1978) (Wds. D. Grant based on K. Grahame)
R. Baker, J. Jackman, G. Ives, A. Holt, S. Carrington, King's Sngrs, CLS, R. Hickox *Concert*
(12/91) (CLLE) ① **COLCD115**

Requiem—chorus and orchestra/organ (1985)
C. Ashton, D. Deam, CLS, J. Rutter *I will lift up mine eyes*. (11/86) (CLLE) ① **COLCD103**

Shepherd's pipe carol
Sheffield Chorale, Sheaf Concert Orch, J. Kirkwood *Concert* (12/89) (CHOR) ① **EECD109**

Atlanta Choral Guild, W. Noll *Concert*
(12/91) (NCWP) ① **NPD65529**
St Alban's Bach Ch, A. Parnell, Barry Rose (r1992) *Concert* (12/93) (LAMM) ① **LAMM081D**
Salisbury Cath Ch, R. Seal (r1983) *Concert*
(12/93) (MERI) ① **CDE84068**
Cambridge Sngrs, CLS, J. Rutter (r1985) *Concert*
(12/93) (CLLE) ① **COLCD121**
St John's College Ch, G. Guest, S. Cleobury (r c1974) *Concert* (12/94) (BELA) ① **450 111-2**

Star carol—carol
Sheffield Chorale, Sheaf Concert Orch, J. Kirkwood *Concert* (12/89) (CHOR) ① **EECD109**
Atlanta Choral Guild, W. Noll *Concert*
(12/91) (NEWP) ① **NPD65529**
Cambridge Sngrs, CLS, J. Rutter (r1985) *Concert*
(12/93) (CLLE) ① **COLCD121**

Te Deum—chorus, brass and organ (1988)
East London Choir, Locke Brass Consort, P. Ayres, M. Kibblewhite *Concert* (12/93) (KOCH) ① **37202-2**

There is a flower—carol (Wds. J. Audelay)
Cambridge Sngrs, J. Rutter *Concert*
(12/87) (CLLE) ① **COLCD106**

5 Traditional Songs—English folksong arrangements
1. The girl I left behind me; 2. O waly, waly; 3. The British Grenadiers; 4. Golden slumbers; 5. Dashing away with the smoothing iron.
Cpte Cambridge Sngrs, CLS, J. Rutter (r1992) *Concert* (11/93) (CLLE) ① **COLCD120**

The **very best time of year**—carol (Wds. cpsr)
Cambridge Sngrs, CLS, J. Rutter (r1985) *Concert*
(12/93) (CLLE) ① **COLCD121**

What sweeter music—carol (Wds. R. Herrick)
Cambridge Sngrs, CLS, J. Rutter *Concert*
(12/89) (CLLE) ① **COLCD111**

When icicles hang—chorus and orchestra (1973)
1. Icicles (wds Shakespeare); 2. When winter nights (wds T. Campion); 3. Good ale (wds anon 15th cent); 4. Blow, blow, thou winter wind (wds Shakespeare); 5. Winter wakeneth all my care (wds anon 14th cent); 6. Hay, ay (wds English anon, c1600).
Cambridge Sngrs, CLS, J. Rutter *Concert*
(3/93) (CLLE) ① **COLCD117**

Wild wood carol (Wds. cpsr)
Cambridge Sngrs, CLS, J. Rutter (r1985) *Concert*
(12/93) (CLLE) ① **COLCD121**

The **Wind in the Willows**—musical fable (1981) (Wds. D. Grant based on K. Grahame)
R. Baker, A. Holt, A. Hume, C.S. Mason, G. Ives, S. Carrington, J. Jackman, King's Sngrs, CLS, R. Hickox *Concert* (12/91) (CLLE) ① **COLCD115**

RUZICKA, Peter (b 1948)
Germany

SECTION I: ORCHESTRAL

4 Orchestral Sketches, '...das Gesegnete, das Verfluchte'—requiem for Allan Pettersson (1991)
Berlin RSO, P. Ruzicka (r1992) *Pettersson: Symphony 15.* (12/95) (CPO) ① **CPO999 095-2**

RYGAARD, Georg (1894–1921)
Denmark

SECTION IV: VOCAL AND CHORAL

Denmark—song (Wds. A. Juel)
L. Melchior, Orch (r c1921) *Concert*
(8/88) (DANA) ① [2] **DACOCD311/2**
The **Flag**—song (Wds. A. Juel)
L. Melchior, Orch (r c1921) *Concert*
(8/88) (DANA) ① [2] **DACOCD311/2**

RYPDAL, Terje (b 1947) Norway

SECTION I: ORCHESTRAL

Largo—electric guitar, strings and gran cassa, Op. 55
T. Rypdal, Borealis Ens, C. Eggen (r1991) *Q.E.D.*
(8/93) (ECM) ① **513 374-2**

Q. E. D.—jazz orchestra, Op. 52 (1991)
T. Rypdal, Borealis Ens, C. Eggen (r1991) *Largo, Op.55.* (8/93) (ECM) ① **513 374-2**

SAARIAHO, Kaija (b 1952)
Finland

SECTION I: ORCHESTRAL

... à la fumée—alto flute, cello and orchestra (1990)
P. Alanko, A. Karttunen, Los Angeles PO, E-P. Salonen (r1992) *Concert*
(10/93) (ONDI) ① **ODE804-2**
Du cristal—orchestra (1989-90)
Los Angeles PO, E-P. Salonen (r1990) *Concert*
(10/93) (ONDI) ① **ODE804-2**

SECTION II: CHAMBER

Nymphea, 'Jardin secret III'—string quartet and electronics (1987)
Kronos Qt (r1989) *Concert*
(10/93) (ONDI) ① **ODE804-2**

SACCHINI, Antonio (1730–1786)
Italy

SECTION V: STAGE WORKS

La **contadina in Corte**—opera buffa: 2 acts (1765—Rome) (Lib. N Tassi)
Cpte C. Forte, S. Rigacci, E. Palacio, G. Gatti, Sassari SO, G. Catalucci (pp1991)
(1/95) (BONG) ① [2] **GB2145/6-2**

SACRATI, Francesco (1605–1650)
Italy

SECTION V: STAGE WORKS

Proserpina rapita—opera (1644—Venice)
E dove t'aggiri V. de los Angeles, G. Moore (r1960) *Concert* (4/94) (EMI) ① [4] **CMS5 65061-2(2)**

SADERO, Geni (1886–1961)
Italy

pseudonym of Eugenia Scarpa

SECTION IV: VOCAL AND CHORAL

Amuri, amuri—song
R. Ponselle, R. Ponselle (r1954) *Concert*
(1/90) (RCA) ① **GD87810**
Era la vo—Sicilian lullaby (Wds. Trad)
V. de los Angeles, Sinfonia di Londra, R. Frühbeck de Burgos (orch Gamley) *Concert*
(10/88) (EMI) ① **CDM7 69502-2**
Gondoliera Veneziana—song
T. Gobbi, Orch, P. Green (r1950) *Concert*
(8/93) (TEST) ① **SBT1019**

SAENGER, Gustav (1865–1935)
USA

SECTION II: CHAMBER

3 Concert Miniatures—violin and piano, Op. 130
2. Scottish pastorale.
2. Y. Menuhin, L. Persinger (arr Persinger: r1929) *Concert* (4/91) (BIDD) ① **LAB031**

SAEVERUD, Harald (Sigurd Johan) (1897–1992) Norway

SECTION I: ORCHESTRAL

Galdreslåtten—Danza sinfonica con passacaglia per orchestra, Op. 20 (1942 rev 1955)
RPO, P. Dreier *Concert*
(8/87) (AURO) ① **NCD4913**
Kjempevisesiåtten—canto rivoltso per orchestra, Op. 22a/5 (1943)
RPO, P. Dreier *Concert*
(8/87) (AURO) ① **NCD4913**
Rondo amoroso—orchestra, Op. 14/7 (1940)
L. Ward, RPO, P. Dreier *Concert*
(8/87) (AURO) ① **NCD4913**
Symphony No. 9, Op. 45 (1966)
RPO, P. Dreier *Concert*
(8/87) (AURO) ① **NCD4913**

SECTION II: CHAMBER

Slätter—piano pieces, Op. 21a (1942)
Bergen Wind Qnt *Concert*
(9/86) (BIS) ① **BIS-CD291**

SECTION III: INSTRUMENTAL

Birdcall variations (Fuglefløtvariasjoner)—piano, Op. 38
E. H. Smebye *Concert*
(12/94) (VICT) ① **VCD19086**

5 Capricci—piano, Op. 1
E. H. Smebye *Concert*
(12/94) (VICT) ① **VCD19084**

7 Easy Pieces—piano, Op. 14
1. Happy chap's frisky steps (Småsvein-gangar); 2. Peasant hierloom brooch (Syljetone); 3. Silk-sock dance (Silkesokk-slåtten); 4. Shepherd song (Gjaetle-vise); 5. Hillside melody (Li-tone); 6. The Aeolian harp (Vindharpeslåtten); 7. Rondo amoroso.
E. H. Smebye *Concert*
(12/94) (VICT) ① **VCD19084**

5 Easy Pieces—piano, Op. 18
1. Rendezvous—but she didn't come (Stevnemøte—men hun kom ikke); 2. Little bird waltz (Småfugl-vals); 3. The landing waltz (Bryggevalsen); 4. Waltz for a little girl (Vals til en liten pike); 5. Venevil: Kristin's waltz (Venevil: Kristins vals).
E. H. Smebye *Concert*
(12/94) (VICT) ① **VCD19084**

Grazietta—piano, Op. 42
E. H. Smebye *Concert*
(12/94) (VICT) ① **VCD19086**

Peer Gynt—piano transcription from incidental music, Op. 28
1. The Devils' five-hop (Fa'ens Femstag); 2. Bridal dance (Brureslåtten); 3. The threatener (Hotaren); 4. Dovretroll jog (Dovreslått); 5. Hymn against the Boyg I (Salme mot Bøygen I); 6. Hymn against the Boyg II (Salme mot Bøygen II); 7. Anitra; 8. Solveig sings (Solveig synger); 9. Burial hymn I (Gravsalme I); 10. Burial hymn II (Gravsalme II); 11. Twinnam (Tvinnan); 12. Whitsun hymn (Pinsesalme); 13. Sleep my darling, precious boy (Pinsesalme, Sov du dyreste gutter min).
E. H. Smebye *Concert*
(12/94) (VICT) ① **VCD19086**

Siljuslåtten—piano, Op. 17 (1942)
E. H. Smebye *Concert*
(12/94) (VICT) ① **VCD19084**

6 Sonatinas—piano, Op. 30
E. H. Smebye *Concert*
(12/94) (VICT) ① **VCD19086**

Tunes and Dances from Siljustøl: Suite No. 1—piano, Op. 21 (1942)
E. H. Smebye *Concert*
(12/94) (VICT) ① **VCD19085**

Tunes and Dances from Siljustøl: Suite No. 2—piano, Op. 22 (1942)
E. H. Smebye *Concert*
(12/94) (VICT) ① **VCD19085**

Tunes and Dances from Siljustøl: Suite No. 3—piano, Op. 24
1. Wedding march (Bruremarsi); 2. Shepherd boy's lonely vigil (Hjuringen 'pi Eismodal); 3. Beware of the bear (Bjønn' Stokk-Lokk); 4. Winflowers twiddle the moonbeam fiddle (Myrdunspele' på); 5. Thor the hammerer (Hamar-Tor slaåtten).
E. H. Smebye *Concert*
(12/94) (VICT) ① **VCD19085**

Tunes and Dances from Siljustøl: Suite No. 4—piano, Op. 25
1. High seat lay (Høgsetetev); 2. Dark dream (Draumeslåtten); 3. The dipper bird (Fossekallen); 4. Tone's cradle-son (Tones vuggevise); 5. Rondomoltogajo.
E. H. Smebye *Concert*
(12/94) (VICT) ① **VCD19085**

SAGRERAS, Julio (b 1933)
Spain

SECTION III: INSTRUMENTAL

El Colibrí—guitar
J. Williams *Concert*
(8/89) (SONY) ① **SK44898**

SAHL, Michael (b 1934) USA

SECTION I: ORCHESTRAL

Tango from the Exile's Café—chamber ensemble (1984)
U. Oppens (arr pf) *Concert*
(5/90) (MUSI) ① **MACD-604**

SAINTE-COLOMBE (c1691–1701)
France

SECTION II: CHAMBER

67 Concerts à deux violes esgales—two bass viols
3. Le tendre; 8. La conférence; 27. Bourrasque; 41. Le retour; 42. Dalain; 44. Tombeau les regrets; 48. La raporte; 51. La rougeville; 54. La dubois; 67. Le fuguré.
3, 8, 42, 51, 67. J. Savall, W. Kuijken (r1992)
(11/93) (ASTR) ① **E8743**
27, 41, 44, 48, 54. J. Savall, W. Kuijken (r1992)
(11/93) (ASTR) ① **E7729**
41, 44. Spectre de la Rose (r1993) *Concert*
(2/94) (NAXO) ① **8 550750**
44. P. Pierlot, R. Zipperling (r1992) *Concert*
(2/94) (RICE) ① **RIC118100**

SAINTE-COLOMBE LE FILS (fl 1713) France

SECTION III: INSTRUMENTAL

Fantaisie en Rondeau—viola da gamba (Durham Cathedral MS)
P. Pierlot (r1992) *Concert*
(2/94) (RICE) ① **RIC118100**

Tombeau pour M. de Sainte-Colombe le père—viola da gamba (Durham Cathedral MS)
P. Pierlot (r1992) *Concert*
(2/94) (RICE) ① **RIC118100**

SAINT-LUBIN, Léon de (1805–1850) France

SECTION III: INSTRUMENTAL

Sextet from Donizetti's 'Lucia di Lammermoor'—violin, Op. 56
J. Kubelík (r1902) *Concert*
(6/91) (BIDD) ① [2] **LAB033/4**
J. Kubelík (r1905) *Concert*
(6/91) (BIDD) ① [2] **LAB033/4**

SAINT-MARTIN, Léonce de (1886–1954) France

SECTION III: INSTRUMENTAL

Toccata de la Libération—organ (1944)
J. Parker-Smith *Concert*
(9/90) (ASV) ① **CDDCA702**

SAINTON, Philip (1891–1967)
England

SECTION I: ORCHESTRAL

The Island—orchestra (c1942)
Philh, M. Bamert (r1992) *Hadley: Trees so high.*
(10/93) (CHAN) ① **CHAN9181**

SAINT-SAËNS, (Charles) Camille (1835–1921) France

SECTION I: ORCHESTRAL

Allegro appassionato in B minor—cello and orchestra, Op. 43 (1875)
J. Lloyd Webber, ECO, Y.P. Tortelier *Concert*
(6/91) (PHIL) ① **432 084-2PH**

Caprice andalous in G—violin and orchestra, Op. 122 (1904)
U. Hoelscher, New Philh, P. Dervaux (r1977) *Concert*
(9/94) (EMI) ① [2] **CMS7 64790-2**
D-S. Kang, Katowice RSO, A. Wit (r1993) *Concert*
(10/94) (NAXO) ① **8 550752**

Le Carnaval des animaux, 'Carnival of the Animals'—zoological fantasy (1886)
1. Introduction and royal march of the lion; 2. Cocks and hens; 3. Wild asses; 4. Tortoises; 5. Elephants; 6. Kangaroos; 7. Aquarium; 8. People with long ears; 9. Cuckoo in the heart of the woods; 10. Aviary; 11. Pianists; 12. Fossils; 13. The swan; 14. Finale.
J. Villa, P. Jennings, Pittsburgh SO, A. Previn *Ravel: Ma Mère l'Oye.*
(4/83) (PHIL) ① **400 016-2PH**
P. Rogé, C. Ortiz, London Sinfonietta, C. Dutoit *Concert*
(1/87) (DECC) ① **414 460-2DH**
A. Ciccolini, A. Weissenberg, M. Debost, R. Cordier, J. Cazauran, Paris Cons, G. Prêtre *Concert*
(6/88) (EMI) ① **CDM7 69112-2**
C. Hobson, I. Hobson (pf/dir), Sinfonia da Camera *Concert*
(10/89) (ARAB) ① **Z6570**

G. Salvador I, G. Salvador II, Mexico City PO, E. Bátiz *Concert*
(1/90) (ASV) ① **CDDCA665**
P. Rogé, C. Ortiz, London Sinfonietta, C. Dutoit *Symphony 3.*
(12/91) (DECC) ① **430 720-2DM**
P. Pierlot, G. Dangain, J-M. Conquer, A. Flammer, J. Dupouy, A. Meunier, G. Lauridon, D. Benetti, J-F. Heisser, V. Postnikova, G. Rozhdestvensky *Concert*
(4/93) (ERAT) ① **2292-45772-2**
Musique Oblique Ens (r1993) *Concert*
(3/94) (HARM) ① **HMC90 1472**
London Academy, R. Stamp (r1987/8) *Prokofiev: Peter and the Wolf.*
(11/94) (VIRG) ① **CUV5 61137-2**
M. Rawicz, W. Landauer, Hallé, J. Barbirolli (r1954) *Concert*
(7/95) (DUTT) ① **CDSJB1002**
O. Barabini, M.B. Montgomery, Philadelphia, L. Stokowski (r1929) *Concert*
(8/95) (BIDD) ① **WHL012**
J. Ogdon, B. Lucas, CBSO, L. Frémaux (r1971) *Concert*
(11/95) (EMI) ① [2] **CES5 68525-2**
RPO, A. Licata *Concert*
(11/95) (TRIN) ① **TRP046**
H. Downs, L. Litwin, S. Lipman, Boston Pops, A. Fiedler (r1961/3: wds O Nash) *Concert*
(12/95) (RCA) ① **09026 68131-2**
13. J. Lloyd Webber, ECO, N. Cleobury (arr C Palmer) *Concert*
(3/85) (PHIL) ① **412 231-2PH**
13. Philippa Davies, T. Owen *Concert*
(3/87) (CARL) ① **PCD835**
13. T. Trotter (arr.Guilmant) *Concert*
(11/87) (HYPE) ① **CDA66216**
13. P. Tortelier (vc/dir), M. Reeves, ECO *Concert*
(7/88) (VIRG) ① **VC7 59668-2**
13. P. Tortelier (vc/dir), ECO *Concert*
(1/89) (VIRG) ① **VC7 59509-2**
13. R. Tauber, orch (wds Balan: r1933) *Concert*
(7/89) (EMI) ① **CDM7 69476-2**
13. I. Perlman, S. Sanders (trans. Heifetz) *Concert*
(12/89) (EMI) ① **CDC7 49604-2**
13. B. Gigli (wds ?: r1923) *Concert*
(5/90) (NIMB) ① **NI7807**
13. J. Kubelík, anon (r1910) *Concert*
(6/91) (BIDD) ① [2] **LAB033/4**
13. M. Maisky, P. Gililov (arr vc/pf) *Concert*
(7/91) (DG) ① **431 544-2GH**
13. P. Casals, N. Mednikoff (r1926) *Concert*
(10/91) (BIDD) ① **LAB017**
13. E. Feuermann, M. Taube (arr vn/pf; r c1930) *Concert*
(10/91) (PEAR) ① **GEMMCD9446**
13. L. Blake, C. Palmer *Concert*
(4/92) (ETCE) ① **KTC1111**
13. G. Fergus-Thompson (arr Godowsky) *Concert*
(10/92) (ASV) ① **CDWHL2066**
13. M. Maisky, Paris Orch, S. Bychkov *Concert*
(10/92) (DG) ① **435 781-2GH**
13. S. Rachmaninov (r1924) *Concert*
(3/93) (RCA) ① [10] **09026 61265-2(3)**
13. E. Zimbalist, S. Chotzinoff (r1912) *Concert*
(7/93) (APR) ① [2] **APR7016**
13. P. Fournier, G. Moore (r1946) *Concert*
(7/93) (TEST) ① **SBT1016**
13. S. Isserlis, D. Moore (r1992: arr vc/pf) *Concert*
(12/93) (RCA) ① **09026 61678-2**
13. M. Dupré (r c1928: arr org) *Concert*
(9/94) (BEUL) ① **1PD5**
13. R. Goss-Custard (r c1930: arr org) *Concert*
(9/94) (BEUL) ① **1PD5**
13. S. Cherkassky (r1956: arr pf: Godowsky) *Concert*
(9/94) (TEST) ① **SBT1033**
13. J. Heifetz, B. Smith (1965) *Concert*
(11/94) (RCA) ① [65] **09026 61778-2(45)**
13. J. Heifetz, E. Bay (1945) *Concert*
(11/94) (RCA) ① [65] **09026 61778-2(19)**
13. S. Nakarjakov, A. Markovich (r1994: arr tpt/pf) *Concert*
(6/95) (TELD) ① **4509-94554-2**
13. I. Perlman, S. Sanders (r1988: arr vn/pf: Heifetz) *Concert*
(6/95) (EMI) ① [20] **CZS4 83177-2(3)**
13. LPO Vcs, RPO Vcs, BBC SO Vcs, Philh Vcs, G. Simon (r1993: arr Balcombe) *Concert*
(9/95) (CALA) ① **CACD0104**
13. J. Du Pré, O. Ellis (r1962: arr vc/hp) *Concert*
(11/95) (EMI) ① **CDC5 55529-2**

Concerto for Cello and Orchestra No. 1 in A minor, Op. 33 (1872)
O. Harnoy, Victoria SO, P. Freeman *Concert*
(11/86) (RCA) ① **RD71003**
M. Rostropovich, LPO, C.M. Giulini *Dvořák: Cello Concerto.*
(2/88) (EMI) ① **CDC7 49306-2**
M. Haimovitz, Chicago SO, James Levine *Concert*
(8/89) (DG) ① **427 323-2GH**
J. Lloyd Webber, ECO, Y.P. Tortelier *Concert*
(6/91) (PHIL) ① **432 084-2PH**
H. Schiff, New Philh, C. Mackerras *Concert*
(8/91) (DG) ① **431 166-2GR**
J. Starker, LSO, A. Dorati *Concert*
(4/92) (MERC) ① **432 010-2MM**

7 Improvisations—organ, Op. 150 (1916-17)
1. E; 2. B minor; 3. B flat; 4. A; 5. G minor; 6. B minor; 7. A minor.
7. C. Herrick *Concert*   (9/91) (HYPE) ① **CDA66457**

Odelette—flute, Op. 162 (1920)
W. Bennett, C. Benson (r1994: arr fl/pf) *Concert*
(2/95) (CALA) ① [2] **CACD1017**

Préludes et fugues—organ, Op. 99 (1894)
1. B; 2. E; 3. E flat.
H. Fagius *Concert*   (4/93) (BIS) ① **BIS-CD556**
A. Partington (r1991) *Concert*
(8/94) (PRIO) ① **PRCD384**
3(Prélude) M. Dupré (r c1928) *Concert*
(9/94) (BEUL) ① **1PD5**

Préludes et fugues—organ, Op. 109 (1898)
1. D minor; 2. G minor; 3. C.
Margaret Phillips *Concert*   (5/91) (YORK) ① **CD110**
H. Fagius *Concert*   (4/93) (BIS) ① **BIS-CD556**
A. Partington (r1991) *Concert*
(8/94) (PRIO) ① **PRCD384**
3. J. Parker-Smith *Concert*
(3/89) (ASV) ① **CDDCA610**

3 Rhapsodies sur des cantiques bretons—organ, Op. 7 (1866)
1. E; 2. D; 3. F.
C. Herrick *Concert*   (3/89) (MERI) ① **CDE84148**
Margaret Phillips *Concert*   (5/91) (YORK) ① **CD110**
H. Fagius (r1992) *Concert*
(7/93) (BIS) ① **BIS-CD555**

Romance in D flat—flute/violin, Op. 37 (1871)
W. Bennett, C. Benson (r1994: arr fl/pf) *Concert*
(2/95) (CALA) ① [2] **CACD1017**

SECTION IV: VOCAL AND CHORAL

L' Attente—song (1v and orchestra) (c1855) (Wds. V. Hugo)
D. Fischer-Dieskau, H. Höll (r c1987) *Concert*
(12/95) (TELD) ① **4509-97457-2**

Chanson à boire du vieux temps—song (1885) (Wds. Boileau)
P. Thirion-Vallet, D. Baldwin *Concert*
(6/95) (ARCO) ① **AAOC93232**

2 Choeurs—chorus & piano ad lib, Op. 68 (1882) (Wds. cpsr)
1. Calme des nuits; 2. Les fleurs et les arbres.
Cambridge Clare College Ch, R. Egarr, T. Brown *Concert*   (12/88) (MERI) ① **CDE84153**
Monteverdi Ch, J. E. Gardiner (r1992) *Concert*
(9/94) (PHIL) ① [4] **438 149-2PH**

2 Choeurs—chorus, Op. 141 (1913)
1. Des pas dans l'allée; 2. Trinquons.
1. Monteverdi Ch, J. E. Gardiner (r1992) *Concert*
(9/94) (PHIL) ① [4] **438 149-2PH**

La Cigal et la fourmi—song (1865) (Wds. J. de Lafontaine)
S. Varcoe, G. Johnson *Concert*
(6/88) (HYPE) ① **CDA66248**

Clair de lune—song (c1865) (Wds. C. Mendès)
J. van Dam, J.-P. Collard *Concert*
(3/94) (EMI) ① **CDC7 54818-2**
D. Fischer-Dieskau, H. Höll (r c1987) *Concert*
(12/95) (TELD) ① **4509-97457-2**

La Cloche—song (c1855) (Wds. V. Hugo)
D. Fischer-Dieskau, H. Höll (r c1987) *Concert*
(12/95) (TELD) ① **4509-97457-2**

Les Cloches de la mer—song: 1v and piano (1900) (Wds. cpsr)
J. van Dam, J.-P. Collard *Concert*
(3/94) (EMI) ① **CDC7 54818-2**

Danse macabre—song: voice and orchestra (1872) (Wds. Cazalis)
J. van Dam, J.-P. Collard *Concert* (1992) *Concert*
(3/94) (EMI) ① **CDC7 54818-2**
P. Thirion-Vallet, D. Baldwin *Concert*
(6/95) (ARCO) ① **AAOC93232**

Le Déluge—oratorio, Op. 45 (1875)
Prélude Paris Orch, D. Barenboim *Concert*
(4/87) (DG) ① **415 847-2GGA**
Prélude A. Dumay, Monte Carlo PO, A. Dumay *Concert*   (6/87) (EMI) ① **CDC7 47544-2**
Prélude J. Thibaud, G. de Lausnay (r1929) *Concert*
(10/91) (MSCM) ① **MM30321**
Prélude E. Zimbalist, F. Moore (r1918) *Concert*
(7/93) (APR) ① [2] **APR7016**
Prélude U. Hoelscher, New Philh, P. Dervaux
(1977) *Concert* (9/94) (EMI) ① [2] **CMS7 64790-2**
Prélude J. Thibaud, G. de Lausnay (r1929) *Concert*
(12/94) (APR) ① [2] **APR7028**

El Desdichado—duet (1871)
F. Lott, A. Murray, G. Johnson *Concert*
(11/90) (EMI) ① **CDC7 49930-2**

Extase—song (c1860) (Wds. V. Hugo)
J. van Dam, J.-P. Collard (r1992) *Concert*
(3/94) (EMI) ① **CDC7 54818-2**

La Fiancée du timbalier—song (1v and orchestra) (1887) (Wds. V. Hugo)
F. Lott, G. Johnson (r1984) *Concert*
(5/87) (HARM) ① **HMA190 1138**

La Flûte invisible—song (1885) (Wds. V. Hugo)
C. Ludwig, D. Whittaker, G. Parsons *Concert*
(9/92) (EMI) ① [4] **CMS7 64074-2(2)**
K. Battle, J.-P. Rampal, M. Garrett (pp1991) *Concert*
(9/94) (SONY) ① **SK53106**

Guitares et mandolines—song (1890) (Wds. cpsr)
J. Gomez, J. Constable (r1994) *Concert*
(4/94) (CONI) ① **CDCF243**

Le Lever de la lune—song: 1v and piano (1855) (Wds. Ossian)
J. van Dam, J.-P. Collard (r1992) *Concert*
(3/94) (EMI) ① **CDC7 54818-2**

Mass—soloists, choir, organ and orchestra, Op. 4 (1855)
S. Colston, A. de Rivaz, J. Vickers, T. Owen, B. Harvey, Worcester Cath Ch, R. Massey, P. Trepte, Don Hunt (r1978) *Poulenc: Gloria.*
(9/94) (DECC) ① **425 077-2DM**

Oratorio de Noël—solo voices, chorus, string quartet, harp and orchestra, Op. 12 (1858)
U. Selbig, E. Wilkie, A. Markert, A. Ude, E. Junghanns, J Zoff, M-C. Winkler, Dresden Kreuzchor, Dresden PO, M. Flämig *Mendelssohn: Vom Himmel hoch.*   (3/88) (CAPR) ① **10 216**
V. Schweizer, E. Wiens, H. Jungwirth, F. Melzer, K. Widmer, B. Biermann, Mainz Bach Ch, Mainz Bach Orch, D. Hellmann   (12/91) (CALI) ① **CAL50512**

Le pas d'armes du Roi Jean—song (1852) (Wds. V. Hugo)
C. Panzéra, orch, P. Coppola (r1926) *Concert*
(3/93) (EMI) ① **CDH7 64254-2**
J. van Dam, J.-P. Collard (r1992) *Concert*
(3/94) (EMI) ① **CDC7 54818-2**
P. Thirion-Vallet, D. Baldwin *Concert*
(6/95) (ARCO) ① **AAOC93232**
D. Fischer-Dieskau, H. Höll (r c1987) *Concert*
(12/95) (TELD) ① **4509-97457-2**

Pastorale—duet (1855) (Wds. Destouches)
F. Lott, A. Murray, G. Johnson *Concert*
(11/90) (EMI) ① **CDC7 49930-2**
V. de los Angeles, F. Fischer-Dieskau, G. Moore (r1960) *Concert*
(4/94) (EMI) ① [4] **CMS5 65061-2(2)**

Revêrie—song: 1v and piano (1851) (Wds. V. Hugo)
J. van Dam, J.-P. Collard (r1992) *Concert*
(3/94) (EMI) ① **CDC7 54818-2**

Saltarelle—4 male vv, Op. 74 (1885) (Wds. Deschamps)
Orphei Drängar Ch, E. Ericson *Concert*
(7/88) (BIS) ① **BIS-CD383**

Si vous n'avez rien à me dire—song (1870) (Wds. V. Hugo)
J. van Dam, J.-P. Collard (r1992) *Concert*
(3/94) (EMI) ① **CDC7 54818-2**

Soirée en mer—song (1862) (Wds. V. Hugo)
F. Lott, G. Johnson (r1984) *Concert*
(5/87) (HARM) ① **HMA190 1138**

Sonnet—song: 1v and piano (1898) (Wds. cpsr)
J. van Dam, J.-P. Collard (r1992) *Concert*
(3/94) (EMI) ① **CDC7 54818-2**

SECTION V: STAGE WORKS

Ascanio—opéra: 5 acts (1890—Paris) (Lib. Gallet, after P Meierice)
EXCERPTS: ACT 1: 1. Enfants, je ne vous en veux; 2. Airs de ballet: 2a. Adagio et Variation; 2g. Valse-finale.
1. J. Lassalle, anon (r1902) *Concert*
(9/91) (SYMP) ① **SYMCD1089**
2. W. Bennett, ECO, S. Bedford *Concert*
(10/89) (ASV) ① **CDDCA652**
2. S. Milan, CLS, T. Hickox *Concert*
(10/90) (CHAN) ① **CHAN8840**
2. K. Lovano, S. Edwards (r1993: arr fl/pf) *Concert*
(10/94) (CONI) ① [2] **CDCF905**

L' assassinat du Duc de Guise—film score, Op. 128 (1908)
Musique Oblique Ens (r1993) *Concert*
(3/94) (HARM) ① **HMC90 1472**

Les Barbares—opéra: 3 acts (1901—Paris) (Lib. V. Sardou & P. B. Gheusi)
N'oublions pas les sacrifices C. Rousselière, anon (r1903) *Concert* (9/92) (IRCC) ① **IRCC-CD802**

Etienne Marcel—opera: 4 acts (1879—Lyon) (Lib. L. Gallet)
O beaux rêves évanouis J. Hammond, Philh, W. Susskind (r1953) *Concert*
(12/92) (TEST) ① **SBT1013**

Henry VIII—opéra: 4 acts (1883—Paris) (Lib. L Détroyat & A Silvestre)
EXCERPTS: ACT 1: 4. Qui donc commande, quand il aime. ACT 2: 14. Chère Anne; 18. Ballet-divertissement: 18a. Introduction—Entré des Clans; 18b. Idylle écossaise; 18c. La fête du houblon; 18d. Danse de la gitane; 18e. Scherzetto; 18f. Gigue et Finale; 22a. O souvenirs cruell.
Cpte P. Rouillon, M. Command, L. Vignon, A. Gabriel, P. Bohée, A. Laiter, G. Serkoyan, J-M. Loisel, Rouen Théâtre des Arts Chor, French Lyrique Orch, A. Guingal (4/93) (CHNT) ① [3] **LDC278 1083/5**

Samson et Dalila—opéra: 3 acts (1877—Weimar) (Lib. F. Lemaire)
ACT 1: 1. Dieu d'Israël!; 2. Arrêtez, ô mes frères; 3. Qui donc élève ici la voix?; 4. Que vois-je?; 5. Maudite à jamais; 6. Hymne de joie; 7. Je viens célébrer la victoire; 8. Danse des prêtresses de Dagon; 9. Printemps qui commence. ACT 2: 10. Prelude; 11a. Samson, recherchant; 11b. Amour! viens aider ma faiblesse!; 12a. J'ai gravi la montagne; 12a. La victoire facile; 13a. En ces lieux, malgré moi; 13b. Mon coeur s'ouvre à ta voix. ACT3: 14. Vois ma misère; 15. L'aube qui blanchit; 16. Bacchanale; 17. Gloire à Dagon.
Cpte J. Vickers, R. Gorr, E. Blanc, A. Diakov, A. Diakov, R. Corazza, J. Potier, J-P. Hurteau, R. Duclos Ch, Paris Op Orch, G. Prêtre
(7/88) (EMI) ① [2] **CDS7 47895-8**
Cpte J. Carreras, A. Baltsa, J. Summers, S. Estes, P. Burchuladze, R. Swensen, D.G. Smith, U. Malmberg, Bavarian Rad Chor, BRSO, Colin Davis (r1989)
(1/91) (PHIL) ① [2] **426 243-2PH2**
Cpte P. Domingo, E. Obraztsova, R. Bruson, P. Thau, R. Lloyd, G. Friedmann, C. Zaharia, M. Huber, Paris Orch Chor, Paris Orch, D. Barenboim
(11/91) (DG) ① [2] **413 297-2GX2**
Cpte P. Domingo, W. Meier, A. Fondary, J-P. Courtis, S. Ramey, C. Papis, D. Galvez-Vallejo, F. Harismendy, Paris Opéra-Bastille Chor, Paris Opéra-Bastille Orch, Myung-Whun Chung
(2/93) (EMI) ① [2] **CDS7 54470-2**
Cpte J. Luccioni, H. Bouvier, P. Cabanel, C. Cambon, Paris Op Chor, Paris Op Orch, L. Fourestier (r1946)   (9/95) (EMI) ① [2] **CMS5 65263-2**
Excs R. Anday, R. Maison, Vienna St Op Orch, H. Reichenberger (pp1933) *Concert*
(12/94) (SCHW) ① [2] **314542**
2. F. Tamagno, Anon (pf) (r1903-04) *Concert*
(2/92) (OPAL) ① **OPALCD9846**
2. L. Escalais, anon (r1905) *Concert*
(12/93) (SYMP) ① **SYMCD1126**
2. G. Zenatello, orch (r1908: Ital) *Concert*
(5/94) (SYMP) ① **SYMCD1168**
2. G. Zenatello, orch (r1908: Ital) *Concert*
(5/94) (PEAR) ① [3] **GEMMCDS9073(1)**
3(pt) A. Paoli, chor, orch (r1907: Ital) *Concert*
(4/94) (EMI) ① [3] **CHS7 64860-2(2)**
5. C. Formichi, orch, H. Harty (r1924) *Concert*
(11/94) (PREI) ① **89055**
7. L. Homer, E. Caruso, M. Journet, orch, J. Pasternack (r1919) *Concert*
(7/91) (RCA) ① [12] **GD60495(6)**
7. L. Homer, E. Caruso, M. Journet, orch, J. Pasternack (r1919) *Concert*
(10/91) (PEAR) ① [3] **EVC4(2)**
8. B. Fassbaender, Stuttgart RSO, H. Graf *Concert*
(11/86) (ORFE) ① **C096841A**
9. M. Callas, FRNO, G. Prêtre *Concert*
(2/90) (EMIN) ① **CD-EMX2123**
9. C. Supervia, orch, A. Albergoni (1927: Ital) *Concert*   (9/90) (CLUB) ① **CL99-074**
9. C. Supervia, orch, A. Albergoni (Ital: r1927) *Concert*   (9/90) (PREI) ① **89023**
9. R. Anday, Berlin St Op Orch, J. Prüwer (1928) *Concert*   (5/92) (PREI) ① **89046**
9. L. Kirkby-Lunn, orch, P. Pitt (r1915) *Concert*
(7/92) (PEAR) ① [3] **GEMMCDS9924(2)**
9. E. Thornton, orch (Eng: r1908) *Concert*
(7/92) (PEAR) ① [3] **GEMMCDS9925(1)**
9. K. Branzell, orch (r1928) *Concert*
(8/92) (PREI) ① **89039**
9. C. Supervia, orch, G. Cloëz (r1931) *Concert*
(3/93) (NIMB) ① [2] **NI7836/7**
9. A. Parsi-Pettinella, orch (Ital: r1904) *Concert*
(12/93) (SYMP) ① **SYMCD1113**
9. A. Parsi-Pettinella, orch (r1907: Ital) *Concert*
(4/94) (EMI) ① [3] **CHS7 64860-2(1)**
9, 11a, 11b, 13b M. Callas, FRNO, G. Prêtre *Concert*   (2/88) (EMI) ① **CDC7 49059-2**
9, 11a, 11b, 13. M. Lipovšek, Munich RO, G. Patanè *Concert*   (6/90) (ORFE) ① **C179891A**
9, 11b E. Stignani, EIAR Orch, U. Tansini (Ital: r1937) *Concert*   (1/91) (PREI) ① **89014**

9, 13b S. Onegin, Berlin St Op Orch, L. Blech (Ger: r1929) *Concert* (2/91) (PREI) ① **89027**
11b H. Bouvier, Paris Op Orch, L. Fourestier (r1946) *Concert* (4/92) (EMI) ① [7] **CHS7 69741-2(3)**
11b, 13b R. Anday, Vienna St Op Orch, K. Alwin (Ger: r1931) *Concert* (5/92) (PREI) ① **89046**
11b, 13b K. Branzell, orch (Ger: r1927) *Concert* (8/92) (PREI) ① **89039**
13b M. Anderson, orch, L. Collingwood (Eng: r1930) *Concert* (10/89) (NIMB) ① **NI7801**
13b M. Callas, FRNO, G. Prêtre *Concert* (2/90) (EMI) ① **CDM7 63182-2**
13b I. Minghini-Cattaneo, orch, J. Barbirolli (Ital: r1929) *Concert* (6/90) (PREI) ① **89008**
13b B. Thebom, LSO, W. Braithwaite (r1950) *Concert* (4/92) (EMI) ① [7] **CHS7 69741-2(1)**
13b F. Litvinne, anon (r1903) *Concert* (10/92) (SYMP) ① **SYMCD1101**
13b F. Litvinne, A. Cortot (r1902) *Concert* (10/92) (SYMP) ① **SYMCD1101**
13b Grimethorpe Colliery Band, E. Howarth (arr Langford) *Concert* (12/92) (DOYE) ① **DOYCD013**
13b R. Resnik, ROHO, E. Downes (r1961) *Concert* (10/93) (DECC) ① **436 462-2DM**
13b F. Litvinne, orch (r1907) *Concert* (12/94) (SYMP) ① **SYMCD1128**
13b E. Destinn, orch (r1911: Ger) *Concert* (12/94) (SUPR) ① [12] **11 2136-2(4)**
13b K. Thorborg, Berlin St Op Orch, F. Weissmann (r1933: Ger) *Concert* (4/95) (PREI) ① **89084**
13b M. Klose, Berlin St Op Orch, F.A. Schmidt (r1932: Ger) *Concert* (7/95) (PREI) ① **89082**
13b P. Bertin, Camargue PO, Reinhardt Wagner (r1995: arr R Wagner) *Concert* (8/95) (HARM) ① **HMC90 1552**
14. G. Thill, Orch, P. Gaubert (r1936) *Concert* (1/89) (EMI) ① **CDM7 69548-2**
14. E. Caruso, NY Met Op Chor, orch, J. Pasternack (r1916) *Concert* (7/91) (RCA) ① [12] **GD60495(5)**
14. E. Caruso, NY Met Op Chor, orch, J. Pasternack (r1916) *Concert* (10/91) (PEAR) ① [3] **EVC4(1)**
14. G. Thill, chor, orch, P. Gaubert (r1936) *Concert* (7/92) (PEAR) ① [3] **GEMMCDS9926(1)**
14. P. Franz, chor, orch (r1919) *Concert* (7/92) (PEAR) ① [3] **GEMMCDS9925(1)**
16. Cincinnati Pops, E. Kunzel *Concert* (9/86) (TELA) ① **CD80115**
16. Paris Orch, D. Barenboim *Concert* (4/87) (DG) ① **415 847-2GGA**
16. Paris Op Orch, G. Prêtre *Concert* (6/88) (EMI) ① **CDM7 69112-2**
16. Montreal SO, C. Dutoit *Concert* (6/89) (DECC) ① **421 527-2DH**
16. H. Fagius, Stockholm PO, J. DePreist (r1992) *Concert* (7/93) (BIS) ① **BIS-CD555**
16. NYPO, L. Bemstein (r1967) *Concert* (9/93) (SONY) ① **SMK47600**
16. Empire Brass (r1992; arr. R. Smedvig) *Concert* (1/94) (TELA) ① **CD80305**
16. Philadelphia, L. Stokowski (r1927) *Concert* (8/95) (BIDD) ① **WHL012**

SAINZ DE LA MAZA, Eduardo *(b 1903) Spain*

SECTION III: INSTRUMENTAL

Campanas del Alba—guitar
W. Lendle *Concert* (7/92) (TELD) ① **9031-75864-2**
Homage a la guitarra—solo guitar
W. Lendle *Concert* (7/92) (TELD) ① **9031-75864-2**
Zapateado—guitar
S. Isbin *Concert* (10/90) (VIRG) ① **VC7 59591-2**

SAKAMOTO, Ryuichi *(b 1952) Japan*

SECTION II: CHAMBER

Haiku FM—synthesisers (1993)
R. Sakamoto (r1993) *Concert* (8/94) (KOCH) ① [2] **37238-2**

SECTION V: STAGE WORKS

The **Sheltering Sky—film score (1990)**
EXCERPTS: 1. Main Theme.
1. OST (r1990) *Concert* (9/95) (VIR2) ① **CDV2774**

SALAZAR, Antonio de *(c1650–c1715) Mexico*

SECTION IV: VOCAL AND CHORAL

O sacrum convivium—choir & organ
Westminster Cath Ch, I. Simcock, J. O'Donnell *Concert* (12/90) (HYPE) ① **CDA66330**

SALAZAR, Diego José de *(?–1709) Spain*

SECTION IV: VOCAL AND CHORAL

Salga el Torillo—villancico
Cordoba Children's Ch, Elyma Ens, G. Garrido (r1992) *Concert* (9/93) (K617) ① **K617025**

SALIERI, Antonio *(1750–1825) Italy/Austria*

SECTION I: ORCHESTRAL

Concerto for Flute, Oboe and Orchestra in C (pub 1774)
S. Milan, D. Theodore, CLS, R. Hickox *Concert* (11/92) (CHAN) ① **CHAN9051**
Concerto for Keyboard and Orchestra in B flat (1773)
A. Staier, Cologne Concerto (r1994) *Concert* (11/95) (TELD) ① **4509-94569-2**
Concerto for Keyboard and Orchestra in C (1773)
A. Staier, Cologne Concerto (r1994) *Concert* (11/95) (TELD) ① **4509-94569-2**

SECTION V: STAGE WORKS

L' **Angiolina, ossia Il Matrimonio per sussurro—opera buffa: 2 acts (1800—Vienna)** (Lib. C.P. Defranceschi)
Overture Bratislava RSO, M. Dittrich (r1992) *Concert* (1/94) (MARC) ① **8 223381**
Armida—opera seria: 3 acts (1771) (Lib. Coltellini)
Overture Bratislava RSO, M. Dittrich (r1992) *Concert* (1/94) (MARC) ① **8 223381**
Axur, Re d'Ormus—opera: 4 acts (1788—Vienna) (Lib. Da Ponte)
Cpte A. Martin, C. Rayam, E. Mei, E. Nova, A. Vespasiani, M. Valentini, M. Porcelli, M. Cecchetti, S. Turchetta, G.B. Palmieri, Guido d'Arezzo Ch, Russian PO, R. Clemencic (hpd/dir) (12/90) (NUOV) ① [3] **6852/4**
Overture Bratislava RSO, M. Dittrich (r1991) *Concert* (1/94) (MARC) ① **8 223381**
Cesare in Farmacusa—opera eroico-comica: 2 acts (1800—Vienna) (Lib. C.P. Defranceschi)
Overture Bratislava RSO, M. Dittrich (r1991) *Concert* (1/94) (MARC) ① **8 223381**
Les **Danaides—opera: 5 acts (1784—Paris)** (Lib. Du Roullet and Tschudi)
Overture Bratislava RSO, M. Dittrich (r1991) *Concert* (1/94) (MARC) ① **8 223381**
Don Chisciotte alle nozze di Gamace—divertimento teatrale: 1 act (1770—Vienna) (Lib. G. Boccherini)
Overture Bratislava RSO, M. Dittrich (r1992) *Concert* (1/94) (MARC) ① **8 223381**
Eraclito e Democrito—opera filosofico-buffa: 2 acts (1795—Vienna) (Lib. Gamerra)
Overture Bratislava RSO, M. Dittrich (r1991) *Concert* (1/94) (MARC) ① **8 223381**
La **grotta di Trofonio—opera: 2 acts (1785—Vienna)** (Lib. G.B. Casti)
Overture Bratislava RSO, M. Dittrich (r1991) *Concert* (1/94) (MARC) ① **8 223381**
Il **moro—opera buffa: 2 acts (1796—Vienna)** (Lib. Gamerra)
Overture Bratislava RSO, M. Dittrich (r1991) *Concert* (1/94) (MARC) ① **8 223381**
Il **ricco d'un giorno—opera buffa: 3 acts (1784—Vienna)** (Lib. Da Ponte)
Overture Bratislava RSO, M. Dittrich (r1991) *Concert* (1/94) (MARC) ① **8 223381**
La **secchia rapita—opera buffa: 3 acts (1772—Vienna)** (Lib. G. Boccherini)
Overture Bratislava RSO, M. Dittrich (r1991) *Concert* (1/94) (MARC) ① **8 223381**
Il **talismano—opera buffa: 3 acts (1788—Vienna)** (Lib. Da Ponte)
Overture Bratislava RSO, M. Dittrich (r1991) *Concert* (1/94) (MARC) ① **8 223381**

SALLINEN, Aulis *(b 1935) Finland*

SECTION I: ORCHESTRAL

Some **Aspects of Peltoniemi Hintrik's Funeral March—string orchestra (1981)** (arr cpsr from String Quartet No 3)
Musica Vitae CO, W. Rajski *Concert* (6/90) (BIS) ① **BIS-CD461**

T. Thedéen, Tapiola Sinfonietta, O. Vänskä *Concert* (6/93) (BIS) ① **BIS-CD560**
Chamber Music III, '(The) Nocturnal Dances of Don Juanquixote'—cello and strings, Op. 58 (1986)
Tapiola Sinfonietta, O. Vänskä *Concert* (6/93) (BIS) ① **BIS-CD560**
Concerto for Violin and Orchestra, Op. 18 (1968)
E. Koskinen, Tapiola Sinfonietta, O. Vänskä *Concert* (6/93) (BIS) ① **BIS-CD560**
Shadows—orchestral prelude, Op. 52 (1982)
Malmö SO, J. DePreist (r1993) *Concert* (12/94) (BIS) ① **BIS-CD607**
Symphony No. 4, Op. 49 (1979)
Malmö SO, J. DePreist (r1993) *Concert* (12/94) (BIS) ① **BIS-CD607**
Symphony No. 5, 'Washington Mosaics', Op. 57 (1985-87)
Malmö SO, J. DePreist (r1993) *Concert* (12/94) (BIS) ① **BIS-CD607**
Variations for Orchestra, Op. 8 (1963)
Tapiola Sinfonietta, O. Vänskä *Concert* (6/93) (BIS) ① **BIS-CD560**

SECTION II: CHAMBER

String Quartet No. 1, Op. 14 (1958)
J. Sibelius Qt (r1994) *Concert* (12/95) (ONDI) ① **ODE831-2**
String Quartet No. 2, 'Canzona' (1960)
J. Sibelius Qt (r1994) *Concert* (12/95) (ONDI) ① **ODE831-2**
String Quartet No. 3, 'Aspects of Peltoniemi Hintrik's Funeral March', Op. 19 (1969)
J. Sibelius Qt (r1994) *Concert* (12/95) (ONDI) ① **ODE831-2**
String Quartet No. 4, 'Silent Songs' (1971)
J. Sibelius Qt (r1994) *Concert* (12/95) (ONDI) ① **ODE831-2**
String Quartet No. 5, 'Pieces of Mosaic' (1983)
J. Sibelius Qt (r1994) *Concert* (12/95) (ONDI) ① **ODE831-2**

SECTION IV: VOCAL AND CHORAL

Songs of Life and Death—baritone, chorus & orchestra, Op. 69 (1993) (Wds. L Nummi)
1. Like flood waters the days of my life; 2. We wander here; 3. I, unborn; 4. Tuba mirum; 5. I can think you departed; 6. Dies irae; 7. While you are still on this shore; 8. Live a full life.
J. Hynninen, Op Fest Chor, Helsinki PO, O. Kamu (r1995) *Iron Age Suite.* (12/95) (ONDI) ① **ODE844-2**

SECTION V: STAGE WORKS

The **Iron Age, 'Rauta-aika'—concert suite from film score: sop, chor & orch, Op. 55 (1982)**
EXCERPTS: 1. Wedding procession; 2. The song of Aino; 3. Lemminki in Pohjola; 4. Lemminki hunts the Devil's elk; 5. Lemminki in Tuonela; 6. Väinö's song; 7. Lemminki and the maidens of the island.
M. Papunen, Op Fest Chor, E. Helsinki Music Inst Ch, Helsinki PO, O. Kamu (r1995) *Songs of Life and Death.* (12/95) (ONDI) ① **ODE844-2**
Kullervo—opera: 2 acts (1988—Los Angeles) (Lib. cpsr)
Cpte J. Hynninen, E-L. Saarinen, M. Salminen, J. Silvasti, S. Vihavainen, A-L. Jakobson, P. Mäkelä, J. Kotilainen, E. Etelävuori, M. Putkonen, M. Heinikari, E. Ruuttunen, V-M. Loiri, Finnish Nat Op Chor, Finnish Nat Op Orch, U. Söderblom (8/92) (ONDI) ① [3] **ODE780-2**

SALMHOFER, Franz *(1900–1975) Austria*

SECTION V: STAGE WORKS

Iwan Tarassenko—opera: prologue & 1 act (1938—Vienna)
Excs A. Konetzni, T. Mazaroff, A. Jerger, G. Monthy, K. Ettl, K. Kolowratnik, R. Tomek, F. Szkokan, J. Sawka, Vienna St Op Chor, Vienna St Op Orch, W. Loibner (pp1938) *Concert* (6/95) (SCHW) ① [2] **314632**

SALOMON, Johann Peter *(1745–1815) Germany*

SECTION I: ORCHESTRAL

Romance in D—violin and strings (?1810)
S. Standage, English Concert, T. Pinnock *Concert* (5/89) (ARCH) ① **427 316-2AH**

SECTION IV: VOCAL AND CHORAL

Go, lovely rose—song (Wds. E. Waller)
R. Müller, T. Roberts *Concert*
(12/91) (HYPE) ① **CDA66497**
O tuneful voice—song (pub 1801) (Wds. A.
Hunter: from Six English Canzonets)
R. Müller, T. Roberts *Concert*
(12/91) (HYPE) ① **CDA66497**
Why still before these streaming eyes—song
(Wds. A. Hunter)
E. Kirkby, T. Roberts *Concert*
(12/91) (HYPE) ① **CDA66497**

SALTER, Hans J. (1896–1994) Austria/USA

SECTION V: STAGE WORKS

Ghost of Frankenstein—film score (1942)
(orch & reconstructed John Morgan)
EXCERPTS: 1. Main Title; 2. Blowing Up the Castle;
3. Freeing the Monster; 4. Frankenstein's Castle; 5.
Arrival at Vasario; 6. Erik's Dilemma; 7. Baron
Frankenstein's Dialogue; 8. The Monster's Trial; 9.
Elsa's Discovery; 10. Dr Kettering's Death; 11. Igor's
Scheme; 12. Dr Frankenstein's Advice; 13. Searching
the Castle; 14. Mob Psychology; 15. Monster Talks;
16. Death of the Unholy Three; 17. End Cast.
1-17. RTE Concert Orch, A. Penny (r1992) *House of
Frankenstein.* (8/94) (MARC) ① **8 223477**
House of Frankenstein—film score (1944)
(orch & reconstructed John Morgan)
EXCERPTS: 1. Main Title; 2. Gruesome Twosome
Escape; 3. Dracula Restored; 4. Rendezvous with
Dracula; 5. Dracula Pursued; 6. Dracula Destroyed;
7. Dan's Love; 8. The Monstrosities; 9. Full Moon; 10.
Silver Bullet; 11. Dr Niemann Successful; 12. Larry at
Peace; 13. Dr Niemann Attacked; 14. Death of the
Unholy Two; 15. End Cast.
1-15. RTE Concert Orch, A. Penny (r1992) *Ghost of
Frankenstein.* (8/94) (MARC) ① **8 223477**

SALVATORE, Giovanni (?1610–?1675) Italy

SECTION III: INSTRUMENTAL

Canzon Francese Terza—keyboard
R. Alessandrini (r1994) *Concert*
(4/95) (O111) ① **OPS30-118**
2 Correnti—keyboard
1. Prima; 2. Seconda.
R. Alessandrini (r1994) *Concert*
(4/95) (O111) ① **OPS30-118**
Toccata prima—keyboard
R. Alessandrini (r1994) *Concert*
(4/95) (O111) ① **OPS30-118**

SALZEDO, Carlos (Léon) (1885–1961) France/USA

SECTION III: INSTRUMENTAL

Chanson dans la nuit—harp
S. McDonald *Concert* (10/84) (DELO) ① **DE3005**
M. Robles *Concert*
(2/93) (DECC) ① **433 869-2DWO**

SAMAZEUILH, Gustave (1887–1967) France

SECTION II: CHAMBER

Chant d'Espagne—violin and piano
Y. Menuhin, L. Persinger (r1929) *Concert*
(4/91) (BIDD) ① **LAB031**

SECTION III: INSTRUMENTAL

Prélude—organ (pub 1921)
N. Kynaston *Concert* (4/89) (HYPE) ① **CDA66265**

SAMMARTINI, Giovanni Battista (1700–1775) Italy

SECTION I: ORCHESTRAL

Symphony in D, JC14
Ens 415, C. Banchini (vn/dir) (r1986) *Concert*
(4/87) (HARM) ① **HMA190 1245**
Symphony in G, JC39
Ens 415, C. Banchini (vn/dir) (r1986) *Concert*
(4/87) (HARM) ① **HMA190 1245**

SECTION II: CHAMBER

**Sonata for Flute, Two Violins and Continuo
in D**
Cologne Camerata (r1994) *Concert*
(8/95) (DHM) ① **05472 77323-2**
6 Sonatas for Cello and Continuo, Op. 4 (pub
1742)
1. B flat; 2. G; 3. B flat; 4. G; 5. F; 6. G (? doubtful).
1. Cologne Camerata (r1994) *Concert*
(10/93) (DHM) ① **05472 77283-2**
String Quintet No. 3 in G (1773)
Ens 415, C. Banchini (vn/dir) (r1986) *Concert*
(4/87) (HARM) ① **HMA190 1245**
Trio for Two Flutes and Continuo in D
Cologne Camerata (r1994) *Concert*
(8/95) (DHM) ① **05472 77323-2**

SECTION III: INSTRUMENTAL

Sonata for Harpsichord in A
S. Bauer (r1992) *Concert*
(10/93) (DHM) ① **05472 77283-2**
Sonata for Organ No. 6 in C
S. Bauer (r1992) *Concert*
(10/93) (DHM) ① **05472 77283-2**

SECTION IV: VOCAL AND CHORAL

Weisse Schäfchen—old French folksong
E. Schwarzkopf, M. Raucheisen (Ger: bp1944)
Concert (6/87) (ACAN) ① **43 801**

SAMMARTINI, Giuseppe (Francesco Gaspare Melchiorre Baldassare) (1695–1750) Italy

SECTION I: ORCHESTRAL

Concerti grossi, Op. 5 (MS: British Museum,
London)
6. Christmas Concerto.
6. Ens 415, C. Banchini (vn/dir) (r1986) *Concert*
(4/87) (HARM) ① **HMA190 1245**
6(Pastorale) English Concert, T. Pinnock (hpd/dir)
Concert (12/91) (ARCH) ① **435 262-2AH**
Concerto for Oboe and Strings in D
H. Holliger, I Musici *Concert*
(4/88) (PHIL) ① **420 189-2PH**
Concerto for Oboe and Strings in E flat
H. Schellenberger, Solisti Italiani *Concert*
(2/89) (DENO) ① **CO-2301**
Cologne Camerata (r1994) *Concert*
(8/95) (DHM) ① **05472 77323-2**
**Concerto for Piccolo Cello, Strings and
Continuo in C**
Cologne Camerata (r1994) *Concert*
(8/95) (DHM) ① **05472 77323-2**
Concerto for Recorder and Strings in F
M. Petri, ASMF, I. Brown *Concert*
(7/83) (PHIL) ① **400 075-2PH**
C. Steinmann, Ens 415, C. Banchini (vn/dir) (r1986)
Concert (4/87) (HARM) ① **HMA190 1245**
R. Harvey, London Vivaldi Orch, M. Huggett *Concert*
(5/88) (ASV) ① **CDGAU111**
Cologne Camerata (r1994) *Concert*
(8/95) (DHM) ① **05472 77323-2**
F. Brüggen, VCM, N. Harnoncourt, F. Brüggen (r
c1969) *Concert* (10/95) (TELD) ① **4509-97474-2**
Sinfonia (No. 5) in A—strings (pub 1747)
Capella Istropolitana, J. Krechek (r1993) *Concert*
(3/95) (NAXO) ① **8 550877**

SECTION II: CHAMBER

**6 Solos for Flute, Violin/Oboe and Continuo,
Op. 13** (c1760)
1. G; 2. G; 3. G; 4. G; 5. G minor; 6. G.
1, 4. Cologne Camerata (r1992) *Concert*
(10/93) (DHM) ① **05472 77283-2**
4. M. Petri, G. Malcolm *Concert*
(10/86) (PHIL) ① **412 632-2PH**
**Sonata for Recorder and Continuo in F
minor** (c1726) (Sibley MS No. 15)
Cologne Camerata (r1992) *Concert*
(10/93) (DHM) ① **05472 77283-2**
Sonata for Recorder and Continuo in G
(c1726) (Silbey MS No. 24)
Cologne Camerata (r1992) *Concert*
(10/93) (DHM) ① **05472 77283-2**
6 Sonatas—strings, Op. 1 (pub. 1744)
1. A; 2. E flat; 3. E flat; 4. A; 5. F; 6. D.
1(Serenade) M. Elman, P. Kahn (arr Elman; r1914)
Concert (12/91) (APR) ① **[2] APR7015**
6 Sonatas for Flute and Continuo, Op. 2
(c1745)
1. G; 2. C; 3. E minor; 4. G; 5. D; 6. A minor.
3. Cologne Camerata (r1992) *Concert*
(10/93) (DHM) ① **05472 77283-2**

Trio for Two Recorders and Continuo in F
Cologne Camerata (r1994) *Concert*
(8/95) (DHM) ① **05472 77323-2**

SAMUEL-ROUSSEAU, Marcel (1882–1955) France

SECTION V: STAGE WORKS

Tarass Boulba—opera: 5 acts (1919—Paris)
Non, je n'ai pas sommeil M. Kuznetsova, orch
(r1920) *Concert*
(6/93) (PEAR) ① **[3] GEMMCDS9004/6(1)**

SAMUELS, Homer (1889–?) USA

SECTION IV: VOCAL AND CHORAL

When Chloris sleeps—song
A. Galli-Curci, orch, J. Pasternack (r1919) *Concert*
(3/94) (ROMO) ① **[2] 81003-2**

SANCAN, Pierre (b 1916) France

SECTION II: CHAMBER

Sonatine—flute and piano
S. Milan, I. Brown *Concert*
(11/88) (CHAN) ① **CHAN8609**

SANCES, Giovanni Felice (c1600–1679) Italy

SECTION IV: VOCAL AND CHORAL

**Miserà, hor sì ch'il pianto—Cantata (Book 2,
Part 1)** (1633)
T. Berganza, Ens, J.E. Dähler (hpd/dir) *Concert*
(3/84) (CLAV) ① **CD50-8206**
**O perduti diletti—Cantata and Aria for solo
voice** (1636)
T. Berganza, Ens, J.E. Dähler (hpd/dir) *Concert*
(3/84) (CLAV) ① **CD50-8206**

SANDERS, Alma M. (1882–1956) USA

SECTION IV: VOCAL AND CHORAL

Little Town in the Ould Country—song (Wds.
R. Pascoe & M. Carlo)
J. McCormack, orch, J. Pasternack (r1921) *Concert*
(5/93) (MMOI) ① **CDMOIR418**

SANDERSON, Wilfred (1878–1935) England

SECTION III: INSTRUMENTAL

Sincerité—piano
A. Etherden *Concert*
(7/93) (HUNT) ① **HMPCD0589**

SECTION IV: VOCAL AND CHORAL

Until—song
R. Crooks, orch (r1933) *Concert*
(9/93) (CLAR) ① **CDGSE78-50-50**
C. Muzio, orch (r1918) *Concert*
(1/95) (ROMO) ① **[2] 81010-2**

SANDOVAL, Arturo (b 1949) Cuba

SECTION I: ORCHESTRAL

Concerto for Trumpet and Orchestra (orch
Zito Zelanti)
A. Sandoval, LSO, L. Haza (r1993) *Concert*
(1/95) (GRP) ① **GRK75002**

SANDOVAL, Miguel (1903–1953) USA

SECTION IV: VOCAL AND CHORAL

Eres tú—song
B. Gigli, orch (r1932) *Concert*
(12/94) (MMOI) ① **CDMOIR425**

SANDRIN (c1490–after 1561)
France

SECTION IV: VOCAL AND CHORAL

Je ne le croy—chanson
Scholars (r1993) *Concert*
          (2/95) (NAXO) ① **8 550880**

SANDSTRÖM, Sven David (b 1942)
Sweden

SECTION II: CHAMBER

Drums—percussion ensemble (1980)
M. Wiesler, R. Pilat, Kroumata Perc Ens *Concert*
          (2/86) (BIS) ① **BIS-CD272**

SECTION IV: VOCAL AND CHORAL

A Cradle Song/The Tyger—mixed vv a cappella (Wds. W Blake)
Danish Nat Rad Ch, S. Parkman (r1994) *Concert*
          (4/95) (CHAN) ① **CHAN9264**

SANZ, Gaspar (1640–1710)
Spain

SECTION II: CHAMBER

Granduque—consort
Extempore Stg Ens (arr consort) *Concert*
          (7/92) (HYPE) ① **CDA66327**

SECTION III: INSTRUMENTAL

Instrucción de música sobre la guitarra española I—guitar (pub 1674)
1. Alemanda, 'La Preciosa'; 2. Ballata; 3. Canarios;
4. Coriente; 5. Danzas de las Hachas; 6. Españoleta;
7. Fuga I, por Primer Tono al Ayre Español; 8. Fuga
II, al Ayre de Jiga; 9. Gallarda; 10. Jiga al Ayre
Ingles; 11. Mariona; 12. Passacalle Sobre in D; 13.
Pavana; 14. Preludio o Capricho, arpendo por la; 15.
Preludio y Fantasia; 16. Sesquiáleta; 17. Tornea; 18.
Villano; 19. Zarabanda Francesca; 20. Alemanda, 'La
Serenissima'.
1. N. North *Concert*   (6/87) (AMON) ① **CD-SAR18**
1. B. Mason *Concert*
          (10/90) (AMON) ① **CD-SAR45**
1. Extempore Stg Ens *Concert*
          (7/92) (HYPE) ① **CDA66327**
1, 3. Celedonio Romero (trans. P. Romero) *Concert*
          (2/87) (DELO) ① **DE1005**
1, 3. T. Kerstens *Concert*
          (7/92) (CONI) ① **CDCF509**
1-6. A. Romero (arr & incl Prologo A. Romero)
Concert   (4/90) (TELA) ① **CD80213**
3. J. Bream (r1965) *Concert*
          (8/93) (RCA) ① **[28] 09026 61583-2(3)**
3. J. Bream (r1965) *Concert*
          (8/93) (RCA) ① **09026 61591-2**
3. Romanesca (r1991-2) *Concert*
          (11/94) (GLOS) ① **GCD920201**
3, 9. J. Bream (r1983-4) *Concert*
          (8/93) (RCA) ① **[28] 09026 61583-2(4)**
3, 9. J. Bream (r1983-4) *Concert*
          (6/94) (RCA) ① **09026 61592-2**

Instrucción de música sobre la guitarra española II—guitar (pub 1674)
1. Bailete Frances; 2. Canciones; 3. Canarios I; 4.
Españoleta IV; 5. Chacona; 6. Clarin des los
Mosqueteros del Rey de Francia; 7. Clarines y
Trompetas; 8. Las Trompetas de la Reyna de Suecia;
9. Españoleta I; 10. Españoleta II; 11. Españoleta III;
12. Españoleta IV; 13a. Folías; 14. Gallardas; 15.
Jácaras; 16. Jiga Inglesa; 17. La Buelta; 18. La
Cavalleria de Nápoles con dos Clarines; 19. La
Coquina Francesca; 20. La Esfachata de Nápoles;
21. La Garzona; 22. La Miñona de Portugal; 23. La
Miñona de Cataluña; 24. Lantururu; 25. Marçapolos;
26. Las Hachas; 27. Matachin; 28. Paradetas; 29.
Passacalles I; 30. Passacalles por la O; 31. Pavanas
por la D con Partidas al Aire Español; 32. Pavena por
la O; 33. Rujero.
2, 3. B. Mason *Concert*
          (10/90) (AMON) ① **CD-SAR45**
2, 4-7, 10-12. A. Romero (arr A. Romero) *Concert*
          (4/90) (TELA) ① **CD80213**
3, 13, 24, 31. J. M. Moreno (r1994) *Concert*
          (8/95) (GLOS) ① **GCD920103**
5-7, 10, 12. Celedonio Romero (trans P. Romero)
Concert   (2/87) (DELO) ① **DE1005**
7, 10. Extempore Stg Ens *Concert*
          (7/92) (HYPE) ① **CDA66327**
8. N. North *Concert*   (6/87) (AMON) ① **CD-SAR18**
8, 11. T. Kerstens *Concert*
          (7/92) (CONI) ① **CDCF509**

13, 24. Romanesca (r1991-2) *Concert*
          (11/94) (GLOS) ① **GCD920201**
29. J. Bream (r1983-4) *Concert*
          (8/93) (RCA) ① **[28] 09026 61583-2(4)**
29. J. Bream (r1983-4) *Concert*
          (6/94) (RCA) ① **09026 61592-2**
Pavanas—guitar
B. Mason *Concert*   (10/90) (AMON) ① **CD-SAR45**
T. Kerstens *Concert*   (7/92) (CONI) ① **CDCF509**
J. Bream (r1966) *Concert*
          (8/93) (RCA) ① **[28] 09026 61583-2(3)**
J. Bream (r1966) *Concert*
          (6/94) (RCA) ① **09026 61592-2**

SARACINI, Claudio (1586–1649)
Italy

SECTION IV: VOCAL AND CHORAL

Le musiche—madrigals and arias: 1-2 vv and continuo (pub 1614)
1. Deh, come invan chiedete (wds. G. Guarini); 2.
Giovinetta vezzosetta (wds. anon); 3. Io moro, ecco
ch'io moro (wds. G. Marino).
1-3. N. Rogers, C. Tilney, A. Bailes, J. Savall, P. Ros
(r1975) *Concert*   (1/93) (ARCH) ① **437 075-2AT**

Le seconde musiche—madrigals and arias: 1v and continuo (pub 1620)
1. Da te parto (wds. anon); 2. Quest'amore,
quest'arsura (wds. anon).
1, 2. N. Rogers, C. Tilney, A. Bailes, J. Savall, P. Ros
(r1975) *Concert*   (1/93) (ARCH) ① **437 075-2AT**

SARASATE (Y NAVASCUÉZ), Pablo (Martín Melatón) (1844–1908) Spain

SECTION I: ORCHESTRAL

Concert Fantasy on Carmen—violin and orchestra, Op. 25 (?1883) (based on themes from Bizet's 'Carmen')
I. Perlman, RPO, L. Foster *Concert: Violin Concerto 1.*   (4/85) (EMI) ① **CDC7 47101-2**
I. Perlman, NYPO, Z. Mehta *Concert*
          (12/87) (DG) ① **423 063-2GH**
I. Perlman, RPO, L. Foster *Concert*
          (11/90) (EMI) ① **CDM7 63533-2**
B. Huberman, S. Schultze (r1926) *Concert*
          (10/91) (EPM) ① **150 032**
I. Perlman, RPO, L. Foster (r1971) *Concert*
          (5/93) (EMI) ① **[4] CMS7 64617-2**
A-S. Mutter, VPO, James Levine (r1992) *Concert*
          (12/93) (DG) ① **437 544-2GH**
J. Heifetz, I. Achron (r1924) *Concert*
          (11/94) (RCA) ① **[65] 09026 61778-2(01)**

Zigeunerweisen—violin and orchestra, Op. 20 (1878)
A-S. Mutter, FNO, S. Ozawa *Lalo: Symphonie
espagnole.*   (1/86) (EMI) ① **CDC7 47318-2**
I. Perlman, Pittsburgh SO, A. Previn *Concert*
          (11/90) (EMI) ① **CDM7 63533-2**
G. Shaham, LSO, L. Foster *Concert*
          (12/91) (DG) ① **431 815-2GH**
J. Bell, RPO, A. Litton *Concert*
          (12/91) (DECC) ① **433 519-2DH**
C. Pavlík, Dvořák CO, V. Válek *Concert*
          (4/92) (SUPR) ① **11 0111-2**
R. Ricci, LSO, P. Gamba (r1959) *Concert*
          (5/92) (DECC) ① **433 220-2DWO**
J. Heifetz, LSO, J. Barbirolli (r1937) *Concert*
          (5/92) (EMI) ① **CDH7 64251-2**
E. Friedman, LSO, M. Sargent *Concert*
          (8/93) (RCA) ① **09026 61210-2**
M. Bisengaliev, Polish Nat RSO, J. Wildner (r1992)
Concert   (12/93) (NAXO) ① **8 550494**
A-S. Mutter, VPO, James Levine (r1992) *Concert*
          (12/93) (DG) ① **437 544-2GH**
N. Hall, LMP, A. Litton (r1992: trans gtr/orch: N Hall)
Concert   (3/94) (DECC) ① **440 293-2DH**
J. Heifetz, LSO, J. Barbirolli (r1937) *Concert*
          (11/94) (RCA) ① **[65] 09026 61778-2(04)**
J. Heifetz, RCA Victor SO, W. Steinberg (r1951)
Concert (11/94) (RCA) ① **[65] 09026 61778-2(22)**
S. Nakarjakov, A. Markovich (r1994: trans: arr tpt/pf)
Concert   (6/95) (TELD) ① **4509-94554-2**
J. Heifetz, LSO, J. Barbirolli (r1937) *Concert*
          (11/95) (PEAR) ① **[2] GEMMCDS9167**

SECTION II: CHAMBER

Caprice basque—violin and piano, Op. 24 (pub 1881)
P. de Sarasate, anon (r1904) *Concert*
          (8/90) (SYMP) ① **SYMCD1071**
I. Perlman, S. Sanders (arr Francescatti) *Concert*
          (11/90) (EMI) ① **CDM7 63533-2**

T. Papavrami, C. Larrieu *Concert*
          (3/91) (HARM) ① **HMC90 5207**
M. Vengerov, I. Golan (r1993) *Concert*
          (4/94) (TELD) ① **9031-77351-2**
I. Perlman, S. Sanders (r1978: arr Francescatti)
Concert   (6/95) (EMI) ① **[20] CZS4 83177-2(3)**
Concert Fantasy on Carmen—violin and piano, Op. 25 (based on themes from Bizet's 'Carmen')
H. Marteau, P. Vladigerov (r1927) *Concert*
          (8/90) (SYMP) ① **SYMCD1071**
T. Papavrami, C. Larrieu *Concert*
          (3/91) (HARM) ① **HMC90 5207**
S. Chang, S. Rivers (ed.Francescatti) *Concert*
          (1/93) (EMI) ① **CDC7 54352-2**
B. Huberman, S. Schultze (r1925) *Concert*
          (3/94) (BIDD) ① **[2] LAB077/8**
Habañera; Chanson bohème J. Kubelík, anon
(r1903) *Concert*   (6/91) (BIDD) ① **[2] LAB033/4**
Danzas españolas—violin and piano, Opp. 21, 22, 23 and 26 (pub. 1878-82)
1. Malagueña; 2. Habañera; 3. Romanza andaluze;
4. Jóta Navarra; 5. Playera; 6. Zapateado; 7. Dance
in C; 8. Dance in C.
1. J. Heifetz, A. Benoist (r1917) *Concert*
          (1/91) (BIDD) ① **LAB015**
1. J. Heifetz, A. Benoist (r1917) *Concert*
          (12/91) (APR) ① **[2] APR7015**
1. I. Menges, E. Beattie (r1925) *Concert*
          (12/91) (APR) ① **[2] APR7015**
1. J. Heifetz, A. Benoist (r1917) *Concert*
          (11/94) (RCA) ① **[65] 09026 61778-2(01)**
1. I. Perlman, S. Sanders (r1978: arr Francescatti)
Concert   (6/95) (EMI) ① **[20] CZS4 83177-2(3)**
1, 2. H. Temianka, J. Graudan (r1936) *Concert*
          (2/93) (BIDD) ① **[2] LAB059/60**
1-3, 5, 6, 8. I. Perlman, S. Sanders *Concert*
          (11/90) (EMI) ① **CDM7 63533-2**
2. P. de Sarasate, anon (r1904) *Concert*
          (8/90) (SYMP) ① **SYMCD1071**
2. R. Ricci, L. Persinger (r1938) *Concert*
          (12/91) (BIDD) ① **LAB044**
2. A. Campoli, D. Ibbott (r1976) *Concert*
          (5/92) (DECC) ① **433 220-2DWO**
2. Midori, R. McDonald (r1992) *Concert*
          (6/93) (SONY) ① **SK52568**
2. J. Heifetz, I. Achron (r1924) *Concert*
          (11/94) (RCA) ① **[65] 09026 61778-2(01)**
2, 6, T. Papavrami, C. Larrieu *Concert*
          (3/91) (HARM) ① **HMC90 5207**
3. B. Huberman, S. Schultze (r1929) *Concert*
          (10/91) (EPM) ① **150 032**
3. C. Pavlík, Dvořák CO, V. Válek (arr. Frankenberg)
Concert   (4/92) (SUPR) ① **11 0111-2**
3. B. Huberman, S. Schultze (r1929) *Concert*
          (9/94) (BIDD) ① **[2] LAB081/2**
3. J. Heifetz, E. Bay (r1946) *Concert*
          (11/94) (RCA) ① **[65] 09026 61778-2(06)**
3, 4. B. Huberman, S. Schultze (r1924) *Concert*
          (3/94) (BIDD) ① **[2] LAB077/8**
3, 6. I. Perlman, S. Sanders (r1972) *Concert*
          (6/95) (EMI) ① **[20] CZS4 83177-2(3)**
5. X. Wei, Pam Nicholson *Concert*
          (9/90) (ASV) ① **CDDCA698**
5, 6. J. Hassid, G. Moore (r1940) *Concert*
          (10/92) (PEAR) ① **GEMMCD9939**
5, 6. J. Hassid, G. Moore (r1940) *Concert*
          (10/92) (TEST) ① **SBT1010**
6. J. Dunn, anon (r1909) *Concert*
          (8/90) (SYMP) ① **SYMCD1071**
6. J. Heifetz, A. Benoist (r1918) *Concert*
          (1/91) (BIDD) ① **LAB015**
6. J. Kubelík, anon (r1911) *Concert*
          (6/91) (BIDD) ① **[2] LAB033/4**
6. J. Kubelík, anon (r1910) *Concert*
          (6/91) (BIDD) ① **[2] LAB033/4**
6. Y. Menuhin, M. Gazelle (r1936) *Concert*
          (9/91) (TEST) ① **SBT1003**
6. N. Hall (arr gtr) *Concert*
          (5/92) (DECC) ① **430 839-2DH**
6. J. Heifetz, E. Bay (r1946) *Concert*
          (11/94) (RCA) ① **[65] 09026 61778-2(40)**
6. J. Heifetz, I. Achron (r1926) *Concert*
          (11/94) (RCA) ① **[65] 09026 61778-2(02)**
6. J. Heifetz, A. Benoist (r1918) *Concert*
          (11/94) (RCA) ① **[65] 09026 61778-2(01)**
8. J. Kubelík, anon (r1913) *Concert*
          (6/91) (BIDD) ① **[2] LAB033/4**
Introduction and Tarantella—violin and piano, Op. 43 (pub. 1899)
J. Heifetz, A. Benoist (r1918) *Concert*
          (1/91) (BIDD) ① **LAB015**
R. Ricci, L. Persinger (r1938) *Concert*
          (12/91) (BIDD) ① **LAB044**
Midori, R. McDonald (r1992) *Concert*
          (6/93) (SONY) ① **SK52568**

K. Daeshik Kang, M. Rahkonen (r1992) *Concert*
(9/93) (NIMB) ① **NI5358**
T. Varga, G. Moore (r1947) *Concert*
(11/93) (CLAV) ① [4] **CD50-9300/4**
T. Varga, G. Moore (r1947) *Concert*
(11/93) (CLAV) ① **CD50-9314**
Chee-Yun, A. Eguchi *Concert*
(12/93) (DENO) ① **CO-75118**
N. Milstein, L. Pommers (r1959) *Concert*
(5/94) (EMI) ① [6] **ZDMF7 64830-2**
J. Heifetz, A. Benoist (r1918) *Concert*
(11/94) (RCA) ① [65] **09026 61778-2(01)**
N. Milstein, G. Pludermacher (pp1986) *Concert*
(5/95) (TELD) ① **4509-95998-2**
Miramar-Zortzico—violin and piano, Op. 42
(pub 1899)
P. de Sarasate, anon (r1904) *Concert*
(8/90) (SYMP) ① **SYMCD1071**
Navarra—two violins and piano, Op. 33
E. Brown, R. Totenberg, orch (r c1939) *Concert*
(7/93) (APR) ① [2] **APR7016**
Zigeunerweisen—violin and piano, Op. 20
(1878)
T. Papavrami, C. Larrieu *Concert*
(3/91) (HARM) ① **HMC90 5207**
J. Kubelik, anon (r1912) *Concert*
(6/91) (BIDD) ① [2] **LAB033/4**
J. Kubelik, anon (r1907) *Concert*
(6/91) (BIDD) ① [2] **LAB033/4**
I. Haendel, A. Kotowska (r1940) *Concert*
(10/92) (PEAR) ① **GEMMCD9939**
J. Heifetz, S. Chotzinoff (r1919) *Concert*
(11/94) (RCA) ① [65] **09026 61778-2(01)**
Allegro molto vivace R. Ricci, C. Fürstner (r1938:
two vers) *Concert*   (12/91) (BIDD) ① **LAB044**

SARGON, Simon A *(b 1938) USA*

SECTION II: CHAMBER

Deep Ellum Nights: three sketches—clarinet
and piano (1991)
1. Dark and Smokey; 2. Quiet and Easy; 3. Tempo di
Rag.
J. Cohler, J. Gordon (r1992) *Concert*
(11/94) (ONGA) ① **024-101**

SARIYEV, Valery *(b 1950)*
USSR/Russia

SECTION IV: VOCAL AND CHORAL

The Lord, our God (Wds. prayer of Macarius
the Great)
Bolshoi Children's Ch, A. Zaboronok (r1994) *Concert*
(7/95) (COLL) ① **Coll1443-2**

SARRI, Domenico *(1679–1744)*
Italy

SECTION II: CHAMBER

Concerto for Recorder, Two Violins, Viola
and Continuo in A minor
Giardino Armonico Ens, G. Antonini (rec/dir) (r1993)
Concert   (11/94) (TELD) ① **4509-93157-2**

SECTION IV: VOCAL AND CHORAL

Sen core l'agnelletta—aria
J. Baker, ASMF, N. Marriner *Concert*
(1/93) (PHIL) ① **434 173-2PM**

SARRIER, Antonio *(18th Cent)*

SECTION I: ORCHESTRAL

Symphony in D
Berlin RIAS Sinfonietta, J. Velazco *Concert*
(12/89) (SCHW) ① **311035**

SARTI, Giuseppe *(1729–1802)*
Italy

SECTION V: STAGE WORKS

Armida e Rinaldo—opera: 2 acts (1786—St
Petersburg) (Lib. M. Coltellini)
Lungi dal caro bene E. Pinza, F. Kitzinger (r1940)
Concert   (9/93) (RCA) ① **09026 61245-2**

SARTORIUS, Georg *(18th–19th*
cent) Germany

SECTION II: CHAMBER

Harmoniemusik on Mozart's 'Le nozze di
Figaro'—2 clarinets, 2 horns, 2 bassoons
and double-bass (c1800)
Mozzafiato (r1992-93) *Concert*
(3/94) (SONY) ① **SK53965**

SATIE, Erik (Alfred Leslie)
(1866–1925) France

SECTION I: ORCHESTRAL

La Belle excentrique—music-hall orchestra
(1920)
1. Grande Ritournelle; 2. Marche 'Franco-Lunaire'; 3.
Valse du 'mystérieux baiser dans l'oeil'; 4.
Cancan'Grand-Mondain'.
Toulouse Capitole Orch, M. Plasson *Concert*
(8/89) (EMI) ① **CDC7 49471-2**
Utah SO, M. Abravanel *Concert*
(5/92) (VANG) ① **08.4030.71**
5 Grimaces for 'A Midsummer Night's
Dream' (1914)
1. Modéré; 2. Peu vite; 3. Modéré; 4. Tempe de
Marche; 5. Modéré.
Toulouse Capitole Orch, M. Plasson *Concert*
(8/89) (EMI) ① **CDC7 49471-2**
Utah SO, M. Abravanel *Concert*
(5/92) (VANG) ① **08.4030.71**
J. McCabe (r1980; arr pf) *Concert*
(3/94) (SAGA) ① **EC3393-2**
B. Sharon (r1994: arr pf: Milhaud) *Concert*
(5/95) (UNIC) ① **DKPCD9155**
3 Gymnopédies (1888) (Nos. 1 and 3 orch
Debussy; No.2 orch Murrill and Roland-
Manuel)
1. Lent et douloureux; 2. Lent et triste; 3. Lent et
grave.
St Louis SO, L. Slatkin *Concert*
(12/83) (TELA) ① **CD80059**
1. J. de Lancie, LSO, A. Previn (r1966) *Concert*
(12/91) (RCA) ① **GD87989**
1, 3. ECO, P. Tortelier *Concert*
(7/88) (VIRG) ① **VC7 59668-2**
1, 3. Montreal SO, C. Dutoit *Concert*
(6/89) (DECC) ① **421 527-2DH**
1, 3. Toulouse Capitole Orch, M. Plasson *Concert*
(8/89) (EMI) ① **CDC7 49471-2**
1, 3. Utah SO, M. Abravanel *Concert*
(5/92) (VANG) ① **08.4030.71**
1, 3. Malmö SO, J. DePreist *Concert*
(1/93) (BIS) ① **BIS-CD570**
1, 3. Philadelphia, L. Stokowski (r1937) *Concert*
(8/95) (BIDD) ① **WHL011**
1, 3. English Sinfonia, C. Groves (r1988) *Concert*
(10/95) (CARL) ① **PCD2017**
2. New London Orch, R. Corp (orch Corp) *Concert*
(2/90) (HYPE) ① **CDA66365**
3. I. Stern, Columbia SO, F. Brieff (arr Harris)
Concert   (7/90) (SONY) ① **SK45816**

SECTION II: CHAMBER

Aperçus désagréables—piano (four hands)
(1908-12)
1. Pastorale; 2. Choral; 3. Fugue.
Y. Takahashi, A. Palnés *Concert*
(1/86) (DENO) ① **C37-7487**
A. Ciccolini, G. Tacchino *Concert*
(7/89) (EMI) ① **CDC7 49713-2**
K. Körmendi, G. Eckhardt (r1994) *Concert*
(6/95) (NAXO) ① **8 550699**
La Belle excentrique—piano (2 or 4 hands)
(1908-12)
Y. Takahashi, A. Palnés, Y. Murai, K. Okazaki
Concert   (1/86) (DENO) ① **C37-7487**
A. Ciccolini, G. Tacchino *Concert*
(7/89) (EMI) ① **CDC7 49760-2**
A. Queffélec, C. Collard (r1990) *Concert*
(8/93) (VIRG) ① **VC7 59296-2**
K. Körmendi, G. Eckhardt (r1994) *Concert*
(6/95) (NAXO) ① **8 550699**
Choses vues à droite et à gauche (sans
lunettes)—violin and piano (1914)
1. Choral hypocrite; 2. Fugue à tâtons; 3. Fantasise
musculaire.
Y. Takahashi, K. Mizuno *Concert*
(9/86) (DENO) ① **C37-7486**
F.P. Zimmermann, A. Lonquich (r1991) *Concert*
(1/95) (EMI) ① **CDC7 54541-2**

Cinéma—entr'acte symphonique for piano (4
hands) (1924) (arr Milhaud)
Y. Takahashi, A. Palnés *Concert*
(1/86) (DENO) ① **C37-7487**
En habit de cheval—piano duet (1911)
A. Ciccolini, G. Tacchino *Concert*
(7/89) (EMI) ① **CDC7 49713-2**
Toulouse Capitole Orch, M. Plasson (orch) *Concert*
(8/89) (EMI) ① **CDC7 49471-2**
K. Körmendi, G. Eckhardt (r1994) *Concert*
(6/95) (NAXO) ① **8 550699**
Morceaux en forme de poire, 'Pieces in the
shape of a Pear'—piano: 4 hands (1890-
1903)
1. Manière de commencement; 2. Lentement; 3.
Enlevé; 4. Brutal; 5. En plus; 6. Redite.
Y. Takahashi, A. Palnés, Y. Murai, K. Okazaki
Concert   (1/86) (DENO) ① **C37-7487**
A. Ciccolini, G. Tacchino *Concert*
(7/89) (EMI) ① **CDC7 49702-2**
Utah SO, M. Abravanel (orch Desormière) *Concert*
(5/92) (VANG) ① **08.4030.71**
A. Queffélec, C. Collard (r1990) *Concert*
(8/93) (VIRG) ① **VC7 59296-2**
K. Körmendi, G. Eckhardt (r1994) *Concert*
(6/95) (NAXO) ① **8 550699**
Musique d'ameublement—piano, three
clarinets and trombone (1920) (comp with
Milhaud)
Erwartung Ens, B. Desgraupes (r1993) *Concert*
(12/94) (FNAC) ① **592292**
Parade—ballet suite for piano (4 hands)
(1917)
1. Prelude du rideau rouge; 2. Prestidigitateur
chinois; 3. Petite fille américaine; 4. Rag-time du
Paquebot; 5. Acrobates; 6. Suite au Prelude du
rideau rouge.
Y. Takahashi, A. Palnés *Concert*
(1/86) (DENO) ① **C37-7487**
4. J. MacGregor (pf solo) *Concert*
(5/91) (COLL) ① **Coll1053-2**
3 Petites pièces montées—piano (c1920)
A. Ciccolini, G. Tacchino *Concert*
(7/89) (EMI) ① **CDC7 49702-2**
K. Körmendi, G. Eckhardt (r1994) *Concert*
(6/95) (NAXO) ① **8 550699**

SECTION III: INSTRUMENTAL

Allegro—piano (1884)
A. Ciccolini *Concert*   (7/89) (EMI) ① **CDC7 49702-2**
Avant-dernières pensées—piano (1915)
1. Idylle; 2. Aubade; 3. Méditation.
Y. Takahashi *Concert*   (9/86) (DENO) ① **C37-7486**
R. Pöntinen *Concert*   (4/87) (BIS) ① **BIS-CD317**
P. Rogé *Concert*   (5/89) (DECC) ① **421 713-2DH**
A. Queffélec *Concert*
(5/89) (VIRG) ① **VC7 59515-2**
A. Ciccolini *Concert*   (7/89) (EMI) ① **CDC7 49702-2**
J. MacGregor *Concert*   (5/91) (COLL) ① **Coll1053-2**
J. Lenehan *Concert*   (5/93) (EART) ① **CDEASM003**
M. Legrand (r1993) *Concert*
(12/93) (ERAT) ① **4509-92857-2**
J. McCabe (r1980) *Concert*
(3/94) (SAGA) ① **EC3393-2**
Caresse—piano (c1897)
A. Ciccolini *Concert*   (7/89) (EMI) ① **CDC7 49713-2**
A. Queffélec (r1990) *Concert*
(8/93) (VIRG) ① **VC7 59296-2**
M. Legrand (r1993) *Concert*
(12/93) (ERAT) ① **4509-92857-2**
K. Körmendi (r1993) *Concert*
(7/94) (NAXO) ① **8 550697**
21 Carnet d'esquisses et de croquis—piano
(1897-1914) (ed Caby)
A. Ciccolini *Concert*   (7/89) (EMI) ① **CDC7 49713-2**
Chapitres tournés en tous sens—piano
(1913)
1. Celui qui parle trop; 2. Le porteur de grosses
pierres; 3. Regrets des enfermés.
P. Rogé *Concert*   (5/89) (DECC) ① **421 713-2DH**
A. Queffélec *Concert*
(5/89) (VIRG) ① **VC7 59515-2**
A. Ciccolini *Concert*   (7/89) (EMI) ① **CDC7 49714-2**
P. Lawson *Concert*   (12/89) (CFP) ① **CD-CFP4329**
J. Lenehan *Concert*   (5/93) (EART) ① **CDEASM003**
P. Dickinson *Concert*   (5/93) (CONI) ① **CDCF512**
M. Legrand (r1993) *Concert*
(12/93) (ERAT) ① **4509-92857-2**
J. McCabe (r1980) *Concert*
(3/94) (SAGA) ① **EC3393-2**
1. K.W. Paik *Concert*
(12/91) (VIRG) ① **VJ7 59653-2**
Croquis et agaceries d'un gros bonhomme
en bois—piano (1913)
1. Tyrolienne turque; 2. Danse maigre; 3. Española.
P. Rogé *Concert*   (5/89) (DECC) ① **421 713-2DH**

K. Körmendi (r1993) *Concert*
(7/94) (NAXO) ① **8 550697**

3 Préludes du fils des étoiles—piano (1892)
A. Ciccolini *Concert* (7/89) (EMI) ① **CDC7 49703-2**
J. Lenehan *Concert* (5/93) (EART) ① **CDEASM003**
P. Dickinson *Concert* (5/93) (CONI) ① **CDCF512**
J. McCabe (r1980) *Concert*
(3/94) (SAGA) ① **EC3393-2**

2. P. Lawson *Concert*
(12/93) (CFP) ① **CD-CFP4329**

2 Préludes du Nazaréen—piano (1892)
A. Ciccolini *Concert* (7/89) (EMI) ① **CDC7 49703-2**

3 Préludes flasques—piano (1912)
A. Ciccolini *Concert* (7/89) (EMI) ① **CDC7 49714-2**
M. Legrand (r1993) *Concert*
(12/93) (ERAT) ① **4509-92857-2**
K. Körmendi (r1993) *Concert*
(7/94) (NAXO) ① **8 550697**

Premier Minuet—piano (1920)
A. Ciccolini *Concert* (7/89) (EMI) ① **CDC7 49702-2**

Première pensée Rose & Croix—piano (1891)
A. Ciccolini *Concert* (7/89) (EMI) ① **CDC7 49703-2**
J. Lenehan *Concert* (5/93) (EART) ① **CDEASM003**
A. Queffélec (r1990) *Concert*
(8/93) (VIRG) ① **VC7 59296-2**
K. Koermendi (r1992) *Concert*
(11/93) (NAXO) ① **8 550696**
J. McCabe (r1980) *Concert*
(3/94) (SAGA) ① **EC3393-2**

Prière—piano fragment (1893-95)
A. Ciccolini *Concert* (7/89) (EMI) ① **CDC7 49703-2**

Rêverie de l'enfance de Pantagruel—piano (c1920)
K. Koermendi (r1992) *Concert*
(11/93) (NAXO) ① **8 550696**

Rêverie du pauvre—piano (1900)
A. Ciccolini (ed Caby) *Concert*
(7/89) (EMI) ① **CDC7 49703-2**
J. Lenehan *Concert* (5/93) (EART) ① **CDEASM003**
K. Koermendi (r1992) *Concert*
(11/93) (NAXO) ① **8 550696**
J. McCabe (r1980) *Concert*
(3/94) (SAGA) ① **EC3393-2**

2 Rêveries nocturnes—piano (ed Caby)
P. Rogé *Concert* (5/89) (DECC) ① **421 713-2DH**
A. Ciccolini *Concert* (7/89) (EMI) ① **CDC7 49713-2**
K. Koermendi (r1992) *Concert*
(11/93) (NAXO) ① **8 550696**
M. Legrand (r1993) *Concert*
(12/93) (ERAT) ① **4509-92857-2**
J. McCabe (r1980) *Concert*
(3/94) (SAGA) ① **EC3393-2**

3 Sarabandes—piano (1887)
A. Ciccolini *Concert* (7/89) (EMI) ① **CDC7 49702-2**
K. Koermendi (r1992) *Concert*
(11/93) (NAXO) ① **8 550696**

3. R. Pöntinen *Concert* (4/87) (BIS) ① **BIS-CD317**

Sonatine bureaucratique—piano (1917)
P. Rogé *Concert* (10/84) (DECC) ① **410 220-2DH**
Y. Takahashi *Concert* (9/86) (DENO) ① **C37-7486**
R. Pöntinen *Concert* (4/87) (BIS) ① **BIS-CD317**
A. Queffélec *Concert*
(5/89) (VIRG) ① **VC7 59515-2**
A. Ciccolini *Concert* (7/89) (EMI) ① **CDC7 49714-2**
Y. Seow *Concert* (12/89) (HYPE) ① **CDA66344**
P. Lawson *Concert* (12/89) (CFP) ① **CD-CFP4329**
P. Dickinson *Concert* (5/93) (CONI) ① **CDCF512**
M. Legrand (r1993) *Concert*
(12/93) (ERAT) ① **4509-92857-2**

Sonneries de la Rose & Croix—piano (1892)
3. Air du Grand Prieur.
A. Ciccolini *Concert* (7/89) (EMI) ① **CDC7 49703-2**
K. Koermendi (r1992) *Concert*
(11/93) (NAXO) ① **8 550696**

Sports et divertissements—piano (1914)
1. Choral inappétissant; 2. La balançoire; 3. La chasse; 4. Le comédie italienne; 5. Le réveil de la mariée; 6. Colin-Maillard; 7. La pêche; 8. Le yachting; 9. Le bain de mer; 10. Le carnaval; 11. Le golf; 12. Le pieuvre; 13. Les courses; 14. Les quatre-coins; 15. Le pique-nique; 16. Le water-chute; 17. Le tango; 18. Le traîneau; 19. Le flirt; 20. Le feu d'artifico; 21. Le tennis.
Y. Takahashi *Concert* (9/86) (DENO) ① **C37-7486**
A. Queffélec *Concert*
(5/89) (VIRG) ① **VC7 59515-2**
A. Ciccolini *Concert* (7/89) (EMI) ① **CDC7 49714-2**
Y. Seow *Concert* (12/89) (HYPE) ① **CDA66344**
J. MacGregor *Concert* (5/91) (COLL) ① **Coll1053-2**
P. Dickinson *Concert* (5/93) (CONI) ① **CDCF512**
M. Legrand (r1993) *Concert*
(12/93) (ERAT) ① **4509-92857-2**

Valse-ballet—piano (1885)
A. Ciccolini *Concert* (7/89) (EMI) ① **CDC7 49702-2**

A. Queffélec (r1990) *Concert*
(8/93) (VIRG) ① **VC7 59296-2**
J. McCabe (r1980) *Concert*
(3/94) (SAGA) ① **EC3393-2**

3 Valses du précieux dégoûté—piano (1914)
1. Sa taille; 2. Son bincole; 3. Ses jambes.
Y. Takahashi *Concert* (9/86) (DENO) ① **C37-7486**
R. Pöntinen *Concert* (4/87) (BIS) ① **BIS-CD317**
P. Rogé *Concert* (5/89) (DECC) ① **421 713-2DH**
A. Ciccolini *Concert* (7/89) (EMI) ① **CDC7 49714-2**
Y. Seow *Concert* (12/89) (HYPE) ① **CDA66344**
J. MacGregor *Concert* (5/91) (COLL) ① **Coll1053-2**
A. Queffélec (r1990) *Concert*
(8/93) (VIRG) ① **VC7 59296-2**
J. McCabe (r1980) *Concert*
(3/94) (SAGA) ① **EC3393-2**

3 Véritables préludes flasques—piano (1912)
1. Sévère reprimande; 2. Seul à la maison; 3. On jou.
P. Rogé *Concert* (10/84) (DECC) ① **410 220-2DH**
Y. Takahashi *Concert* (9/86) (DENO) ① **C37-7486**
R. Pöntinen *Concert* (4/87) (BIS) ① **BIS-CD317**
P. Rogé *Concert* (5/89) (DECC) ① **421 713-2DH**
A. Queffélec *Concert*
(5/89) (VIRG) ① **VC7 59515-2**
A. Ciccolini *Concert* (7/89) (EMI) ① **CDC7 49714-2**
J. MacGregor *Concert* (5/91) (COLL) ① **Coll1053-2**
P. Dickinson *Concert* (5/93) (CONI) ① **CDCF512**

Versets laïques et somptueux—piano
A. Ciccolini *Concert* (7/89) (EMI) ① **CDC7 49703-2**

Vexations—piano (c1893)
A. Ciccolini *Concert* (7/89) (EMI) ① **CDC7 49703-2**
P. Dickinson *Concert* (5/93) (CONI) ① **CDCF512**

Vieux séquins et vieilles cuirasses—piano (1913)
1. Chez le marchand d'or; 2. Danse cuirassée; 3. La Défaite des cimbres.
P. Rogé *Concert* (10/84) (DECC) ① **410 220-2DH**
A. Queffélec *Concert*
(5/89) (VIRG) ① **VC7 59515-2**
A. Ciccolini *Concert* (7/89) (EMI) ① **CDC7 49714-2**
J. MacGregor *Concert* (5/91) (COLL) ① **Coll1053-2**
K. Körmendi *Concert* (6/95) (NAXO) ① **3 550699**

SECTION IV: VOCAL AND CHORAL

Allons-y Chochotte—café-concert song
(Wds. D. Durante)
J. Gomez, J. Constable *Concert*
(6/88) (UNIC) ① **DKPCD9055**

La Diva de l'Empire—café-concert song (marche chantée) (c1900) (Wds. Bonnaud and Blès. From revue 'Dévidons la Bobine')
J. Gomez, J. Constable *Concert*
(6/88) (UNIC) ① **DKPCD9055**
D. Jones, M. Martineau (1992) *Concert*
(6/93) (CHAN) ① **CHAN9147**

Je te veux—café-concert song (valse chantée) (c1900) (Wds. H. Pacory)
J. Norman, D. Baldwin *Concert*
(12/86) (PHIL) ① **416 445-2PH**
C. Alliot-Lugaz, F. Le Roux, J. Cohen *Concert*
(4/91) (REM) ① **REM311086**

Ludions—songs (1923) (Wds. L-P. Fargue)
1. Air du rat; 2. Spleen; 3. La grenouille américaine; 4. Air du poète; 5. Chanson du chat.
D. Jones, M. Martineau (1992) *Concert*
(6/93) (CHAN) ① **CHAN9147**

3 Mélodies—1v and piano (1916)
1. Daphénéo (Wds. M. God); 2. La statue de bronze (Wds. Fargue); 3. Le chapelier (Wds. Chalput).
J. Norman, D. Baldwin *Concert*
(12/86) (PHIL) ① **416 445-2PH**
D. Jones, M. Martineau (1992) *Concert*
(6/93) (CHAN) ① **CHAN9147**
J. Bathori, D. Milhaud (1929) *Concert*
(9/93) (EPM) ① [3] **150 122**

Messe des Pauvres—chorus and organ/piano (c1893-95) (Wds. Latin Mass and psalms)
B. Bowers-Broadbent (1992; organ part only) *Concert* (5/93) (ECM) ① **437 956-2**

3 Poèmes d'amour—songs (1914) (Wds. cpsr)
1. Ne suis que grain de sable; 2. Suis chauve de naissance; 3. Ta parure est secrète.
S. Varcoe, G. Johnson *Concert*
(6/88) (HYPE) ① **CDA66248**

Socrate—drame symphonique: 4vv and orchestra (1919) (Wds. Plato trans Cousin)
1. Portrait de Socrate; 2. Les Bords de l'Ilissus; 3. Mort de Socrate.
J-P. Fouchécourt, Erwartung Ens, B. Desgraupes (r1993) *Concert* (12/94) (FNAC) ① **592292**

SECTION V: STAGE WORKS

Les Aventures de Mercure—ballet (1924—Paris)
Cpte New London Orch, R. Corp *Concert*
(2/90) (HYPE) ① **CDA66365**
Cpte Utah SO, M. Abravanel *Concert*
(5/92) (VANG) ① **08.4030.71**

Parade—ballet réaliste (1917—Paris)
1. Choral-Prélude du rideau rouge; 2. Prestidateur chinois; 3. Petite fille américaine; 4. Acrobates; 5. Final—Suite au 'Prélude du rideau rouge'.
Cpte New London Orch, R. Corp *Concert*
(2/90) (HYPE) ① **CDA66365**
Cpte Utah SO, M. Abravanel *Concert*
(5/92) (VANG) ① **08.4030.71**
Toulouse Capitole Orch, M. Plasson *Concert*
(8/89) (EMI) ① **CDC7 49471-2**

Le Piège de Méduse—play with music: 1 act (1913) EXCERPTS: 1. Quadrille; 2. Valse; 3. Pas vite; 4. Mazurka; 5. Un peu vif; 6. Polka; 7. Quadrille.
Cpte Erwartung Ens, B. Desgraupes (r1993) *Concert*
(12/94) (FNAC) ① **592292**

Relâche—ballet instantanéiste (2 acts and cinematogrphic entr'acte) (1924—Paris)
Cpte New London Orch, R. Corp *Concert*
(2/90) (HYPE) ① **CDA66365**
Cpte Utah SO, M. Abravanel *Concert*
(5/92) (VANG) ① **08.4030.71**
Cpte Erwartung Ens, B. Desgraupes (r1993) *Concert*
(12/94) (FNAC) ① **592292**
Toulouse Capitole Orch, M. Plasson *Concert*
(8/89) (EMI) ① **CDC7 49471-2**

SATOH, Somei (b 1947) USA

SECTION II: CHAMBER

Birds in warped time II—violin and piano (1980)
F. Almond, M. Leng Tan *Concert*
(9/90) (NALB) ① **NA008CD**

Litania—two pianos with tape delay (1973)
M. Leng Tan *Concert* (9/90) (NALB) ① **NA008CD**

SECTION III: INSTRUMENTAL

A Gate into the stars—piano (1962)
M. Leng Tan *Concert* (9/90) (NALB) ① **NA008CD**

Incarnation II—piano with tape delay (1977)
M. Leng Tan *Concert* (9/90) (NALB) ① **NA008CD**

SECTION IV: VOCAL AND CHORAL

The Heavenly spheres are illuminated by lights—soprano, piano and percussion (1979)
L. Messier, M. Pugliese, M. Leng Tan *Concert*
(9/90) (NALB) ① **NA008CD**

Mantra—voice and electronics (1986)
S. Satoh (pp1987) *Stabat Mater (1987).*

Stabat Mater—soprano and chorus a capella (1987)
J. Thorngren, Pro Arte Chorale, G. Manahan (pp1987) *Mantra (1986).*
(9/90) (NALB) ① **NA016CD**

SAUER, Emil von (1862–1942) Germany

SECTION I: ORCHESTRAL

Concerto for Piano and Orchestra No. 1 in E minor (1900)
S. Hough, CBSO, L. Foster (r1994) *F. X. Scharwenka: Piano Concerto 4.*
(11/95) (HYPE) ① **CDA66790**

SAUGUET, Henri(-Pierre) (1901–1989) France

SECTION I: ORCHESTRAL

Concerto d'Orphée—violin and orchestra (1953)
L. Kaufman, FRNO, J.M. Leconte *Concert*
(12/90) (MUSI) ① **MACD-620**

Garden Concerto—harmonica abd chamber orchestra (1970)
J. Vandeville, J-W. Audoli Inst Ens, J-W. Audoli (arr ob) *Concert* (8/90) (ARIO) ① **ARN68071**

Sonate d'église—organ and strings (1984-85)
J-P. Brosse, J-W. Audoli Inst Ens, J-W. Audoli *Concert* (8/90) (ARIO) ① **ARN68071**

SECTION III: INSTRUMENTAL

Nuit colonaile—piano (1937)
B. Lerner *Concert*   (1/89) (ETCE) ℗ **KTC1061**

SECTION IV: VOCAL AND CHORAL

L' Oiseau a vut tout cela—cantata: baritone and strings (1960) (Wds. Cayrol)
M. Piquemal, J-W. Audoli Inst Ens, J-W. Audoli
Concert   (8/90) (ARIO) ℗ **ARN68071**

SAVINO, Domenico (20th Cent) USA

collab with Sam Perry

SECTION V: STAGE WORKS

The **Phantom of the Opera—film score (1930)** (score for 1930 sound version of 1925 silent film)
EXCERPTS: 1. Through the Looking Glass.
1. Hollywood Bowl SO, J. Mauceri (r1993) *Concert*
      (1/95) (PHIL) ℗ **442 425-2PH**

SAXTON, Robert (b 1953) England

SECTION I: ORCHESTRAL

In the Beginning—orchestra (1987)
1. Slow, sustained, mysterious; 2. Agitated, quick; 3. Fast, joyful.
BBC SO, M. Bamert *Concert*
      (4/92) (COLL) ℗ **Coll1283-2**
Music to celebrate the Resurrection of Christ
ECO, S. Bedford *Concert*
      (2/91) (COLL) ℗ **Coll1102-2**
Violin Concerto (1990)
T. Little, BBC SO, M. Bamert *Concert*
      (4/92) (COLL) ℗ **Coll1283-2**

SECTION IV: VOCAL AND CHORAL

At the round earth's imagined corners—chorus (1992) (Wds. J. Donne)
St Paul's Cath Ch, John Scott, Adrian Lucas (r1991)
Concert   (8/93) (HYPE) ℗ **CDA66618**
I will awake the dawn—28vv unaccompanied (1987)
BBC Sngrs, J. Poole *Concert*
      (4/92) (COLL) ℗ **Coll1283-2**

SECTION V: STAGE WORKS

Caritas—opera: 2 acts (1991—Wakefield) (Lib. A. Wesker)
Cpte E. Davies, J. Best, C. Ventris, L. Hibberd, R. Bryson, D. Gwynne, P. Wilson, G. Bell, B. Budd, B. Cookson, L. Ormiston, English Northern Philh, D. Masson (pp1991)   (7/92) (COLL) ℗ **Coll1350-2**

SAYGUN, Ahmet Adnan (1907–1991) Turkey

SECTION I: ORCHESTRAL

Concerto for Viola and Orchestra, Op. 78 (1978)
R. Günes, LPO, G. Aykal *Elgar: In the South.*
      (4/90) (SCHW) ℗ **311002**

SCANLAN, William J. (1856–1898) USA

SECTION V: STAGE WORKS

Mavourneen—musical show (1891—New York)
EXCERPTS: 1. Molly O! (or Mavourneen).
1. C. Olcott, Broadway Cast (r1913) *Concert*
      (5/94) (PEAR) ℗ **GEMMCDS9050/2(1)**

SCARLATTI, (Pietro) Alessandro (Gaspare) (1660–1725) Italy

SECTION I: ORCHESTRAL

6 Concerti grossi—strings (pub 1740)
1. F minor; 2. C minor; 3. F; 4. G minor; 5. D minor; 6. E.
3. Capella Istropolitana, J. Krechek (r1993) *Concert*
      (3/95) (NAXO) ℗ **8 550877**
12 Sinfonie di concerto grosso (1720)
1. F; 2. D; 3. D minor; 4. E minor; 5. D minor; 6. A minor; 7. G G minor; 8. G; 9. G minor; 10. A minor; 11. C; 12. C minor.
3. R. Harvey, London Vivaldi Orch, M. Huggett *Concert*   (5/88) (ASV) ℗ **CDGAU111**

Sonatas for Flute and Strings (pub 1725)
1. D; 2. A minor; 3. C minor; 4. A minor; 5. A; 6. C; 7. G minor.
3, 4. E. Berardi, Brewer CO, R. Palmer (r1992)
Ishmael.   (7/94) (NEWP) ℗ [2] **NPD85558**

SECTION II: CHAMBER

Sonata for Recorder, Two Violins and Continuo in A minor
Giardino Armonico Ens, G. Antonini (rec/dir) (r1993)
Concert   (11/94) (TELD) ℗ **4509-93157-2**
Sonata in F—3 recorders and continuo
F. Brüggen, K. Boeke, W. van Hauwe, W. Möller, B. van Asperen (r1978) *Concert*
      (10/95) (TELD) ℗ **4509-97467-2**

SECTION III: INSTRUMENTAL

Toccata per cembalo d'ottava stesa—harpsichord (1723)
Variations on 'La Folia'
R. Woolley *Concert*   (3/90) (HYPE) ℗ **CDA66254**
Toccata per il cembalo
R. Alessandrini (r1994) *Concert*
      (4/95) (O111) ℗ **OPS30-118**

SECTION IV: VOCAL AND CHORAL

Agar et Ismaele esiliati, 'Ishmael'—oratorio: 5vv, strings & continuo (1683) (aka L'Abramo; Ismaele soccorso dall'angelo; Il sacrificio di Abramo)
J. Baird, B. Harris, E. Mills, D. Fortunato, J. Ostendorf, Brewer CO, R. Palmer (r1992) *Flute Sonatas.*   (7/94) (NEWP) ℗ [2] **NPD85558**
Bellezza, che s'ama
R. Scotto, I. Davis (pp1983) *Concert*
      (10/86) (ETCE) ℗ **KTC2002**
Cara e dolce
R. Scotto, I. Davis (pp1983) *Concert*
      (10/86) (ETCE) ℗ **KTC2002**
Clori e Mirtillo, 'Mentre sul carro aurato'—cantata: 2vv & continuo
V. Dietschy, A. Zaepffel, Gradiva Ens (r1992)
Concert   (9/93) (ADES) ℗ **20217-2**
Con voce festiva—aria: soprano, trumpet and strings
J. Nelson, D. Ferry, K. Gohl, J. Rubin, G. Murray (r1983) *Concert*   (5/87) (HARM) ℗ **HMA190 5137**
K. Battle, W. Marsalis, St Luke's Orch, J. Nelson
Concert   (8/92) (SONY) ℗ **SK46672**
Cor mio, deh, non languire—madrigal: 5vv
Consort of Musicke, A. Rooley *Concert*
      (12/91) (DHM) ℗ **RD77154**
Correa nel seno amato—cantata: 1v, 2vns & continuo (before 1694)
L. Dawson, Purcell Qt *Concert*
      (3/90) (HYPE) ℗ **CDA66254**
J. Nicolas, S. Deeks, X. Julien-Laferriere, A. Verzier, M. Bothwell, P. Ramin *Concert*
      (9/90) (PIER) ℗ **PV790013**
De tenebroso lacu—motet: alto and strings
G. Lesne, Seminario Musicale (r1993) *Concert*
      (6/95) (VIRG) ℗ **VC5 45103-2**
Diana ed Endimione, 'Voi solitarie piante'—serenata: 2vv & continuo (c1680-85)
J. Nicolas, A. Aubin, S. Deeks, X. Julien-Laferriere, H. Williams, A. Verzier, M. Bothwell, P. Ramin *Concert*   (9/90) (PIER) ℗ **PV790013**
Dixit Dominus II—motet: 5vv
N. Argenta, A. Stafford, S. Varcoe, English Concert Ch, English Concert, T. Pinnock *Vivaldi: Gloria, RV589.*   (5/88) (ARCH) ℗ **423 386-2AH**
Domine refugium factus es nobis—motet: 5vv
London Schütz Ch, R. Norrington (r1973) *Concert*
      (7/95) (DECC) ℗ [2] **443 868-2DF2**
Doralbo e Niso, 'Perchè sospiri, o Niso?'—cantata: 2vv & continuo
V. Dietschy, A. Zaepffel, Gradiva Ens (r1992)
Concert   (9/93) (ADES) ℗ **20217-2**
Ero ed Leandro, 'Leandro, anima mia'—cantata: 1v & continuo
A. Aubin, A. Verzier, M. Bothwell, P. Ramin *Concert*   (9/90) (PIER) ℗ **PV790013**
Exultate Deo adjutori—motet: 4vv
E. Futral, J. Malafronte, F. Urrey, W. Pauley, Musica Sacra, R. Westenburg *Concert*
      (1/93) (RCA) ℗ **09026 60970-2**
Farò la vendetta—aria: 1v, tpt & continuo
J. Nelson, D. Ferry, K. Gohl, J. Rubin, G. Murray (r1983) *Concert*   (5/87) (HARM) ℗ **HMA190 5137**
Già lusingato applena—cantata: 1v, 2 violins and continuo
L. Dawson, Purcell Qt *Concert*
      (3/90) (HYPE) ℗ **CDA66254**

In terra la guerra—aria: soprano, trumpet and strings
J. Nelson, D. Ferry, K. Gohl, J. Rubin, G. Murray (r1983) *Concert*   (5/87) (HARM) ℗ **HMA190 5137**
Infirmata, vulnerata—motet: alto and strings (1702)
G. Lesne, Seminario Musicale (r1993) *Concert*
      (6/95) (VIRG) ℗ **VC5 45103-2**
Lamentazioni per la Settimana Santa—soprano and strings (?1708)
1. WEDNESDAY: 1a. First Lesson: Incipit lamentatio Jeremiae; 1b. Third Lesson: Jod—Manum Suam; 2. THURSDAY: 2a. First Lesson: De lamentatione; 2b. Second Lesson: Malmed—Matribus suis dixerunt; 3. FRIDAY: 3a. First Lesson: De lamentatione; 3b. Second Lesson: Aleph—Quomodo obscuratum est.
Cpte C. Miatello, G. Fagotto, Aurora Ens (r1992)
      (10/93) (SYPH) ℗ [2] **SY92D17**
1, 2. N. Rime, M. Lins, Parlement de Musique, M. Gester (r1992)   (8/93) (O111) ℗ **OPS30-66**
Marc'Antonio e Cleopatra, 'Cleopatra, mia Reina'—cantata: 2vv & continuo
V. Dietschy, A. Zaepffel, Gradiva Ens (r1992)
Concert   (9/93) (ADES) ℗ **20217-2**
Mio tesoro, per te moro—aria: 1v, trumpet and continuo
J. Nelson, D. Ferry, K. Gohl, J. Rubin, G. Murray (r1983) *Concert*   (5/87) (HARM) ℗ **HMA190 5137**
K. Battle, W. Marsalis, St Luke's Orch, J. Nelson
Concert   (8/92) (SONY) ℗ **SK46672**
O di Betlemme altera povertà—Christmas cantata
N. Argenta, English Concert, T. Pinnock (r1992)
Concert   (3/94) (ARCH) ℗ **437 834-2AH**
O Magnum Mysterium—motet: 8vv (1707)
London Schütz Ch, R. Norrington (r1973) *Concert*
      (7/95) (DECC) ℗ [2] **443 868-2DF2**
Rompe sprezza con un sospir—aria: soprano, trumpet and strings
J. Nelson, D. Ferry, K. Gohl, J. Rubin, G. Murray (r1983) *Concert*   (5/87) (HARM) ℗ **HMA190 5137**
K. Battle, W. Marsalis, St Luke's Orch, J. Nelson
Concert   (8/92) (SONY) ℗ **SK46672**
Salve Regina in F minor—soprano, contralto and strings (attrib)
J. Anderson, C. Bartoli, Montreal Sinfonietta, C. Dutoit (r1991) *Concert*
      (8/93) (DECC) ℗ **436 209-2DH**
V. Gens, G. Lesne, Seminario Musicale (r1993)
Concert   (6/95) (VIRG) ℗ **VC5 45103-2**
Sento nel core—arietta
T. Schipa, orch, C. Sabajno (r1932) *Concert*
      (4/90) (EMI) ℗ **CDH7 63200-2**
J. Baker, ASMF, N. Marriner *Concert*
      (1/93) (PHIL) ℗ **434 173-2PM**
Si riscaldi il Tebro—aria: soprano, trumpet and strings
J. Nelson, D. Ferry, K. Gohl, J. Rubin, G. Murray (r1983) *Concert*   (5/87) (HARM) ℗ **HMA190 5137**
Si suoni la tromba—aria: soprano, trumpet and strings
J. Nelson, D. Ferry, K. Gohl, J. Rubin, G. Murray (r1983) *Concert*   (5/87) (HARM) ℗ **HMA190 5137**
K. Battle, W. Marsalis, St Luke's Orch, J. Nelson
Concert   (8/92) (SONY) ℗ **SK46672**
Solitudini amene, apriche collinette—cantata: soprano, flute and continuo
Io vi miro ancor A. Galli-Curci, orch (r1929) *Concert*
      (3/94) (CONI) ℗ **CDHD201**
Il sonno, 'Questo silenzio ombrosio'—cantata: 2vv & continuo (1707)
V. Dietschy, A. Zaepffel, Gradiva Ens (r1992)
Concert   (9/93) (ADES) ℗ **20217-2**
Spesso vibra per suo gioco—aria
C. Bartoli, G. Fischer *Concert*
      (12/92) (DECC) ℗ **436 267-2DH**
J. Baker, ASMF, N. Marriner *Concert*
      (1/93) (PHIL) ℗ **434 173-2PM**
Su le sponde del Tebro—cantata: soprano, 2 violins, trumpet and continuo
K. Battle, W. Marsalis, St Luke's Orch, J. Nelson
Concert   (8/92) (SONY) ℗ **SK46672**
Su venite e consiglio
M. László, L. Cortese (r1950) *Concert*
      (4/92) (EMI) ℗ [7] **CHS7 69741-2(7)**
Totus amore languens—motet: alto and strings
G. Lesne, Seminario Musicale (r1993) *Concert*
      (6/95) (VIRG) ℗ **VC5 45103-2**
Il Trionfo della grazia, '(La) Maddalena'—oratorio: 3vv and strings (1685) (Wds B. Pamphili)
Cpte S. Piccollo, R. Bertini, G. Banditelli, Europa Galante, F. Biondi (r1993)
      (10/94) (O111) ℗ **OPS30-96**

Venere e Adoni—Il giardino d'amore, 'Care selve, amati orrori'—serenata: 2vv & continuo (c1700-05)
L. Åkerlund, D.L. Ragin, Clemencic Consort, R. Clemenčić (5/90) (ACCO) ① **20008-2**

SECTION V: STAGE WORKS

La Donna ancora è fedele—dramma per musica: 3 acts (1698—Naples) (Lib. after Contini)
EXCERPTS: 1. Son tutta duolo; 2. Se Florindo è fedele.
1. T. Schipa, orch. D. Olivieri (r1939) Concert
(4/90) (EMI) ① **CDH7 63200-2**
1, 2. C. Bartoli, G. Fischer Concert
(12/92) (DECC) ① **436 267-2DH**
2. H. Spani, orch, G. Nastrucci (r1929) Concert
(9/90) (CLUB) ① **CL99-509/10**

Il Flavio—dramma per musica: 3 acts (1688—Naples) (Lib. after M Noris)
Che vuole innamorarsi E. Pinza, F. Kitzinger (r1940) Concert (9/93) (RCA) ① **09026 61245-2**

L' Honestà negli amore—dramma per musica: 3 acts (1680—Rome) (Lib. F Parnasso)
EXCERPTS: 1. Già il sole dal Gange.
1. C. Bartoli, G. Fischer Concert
(12/92) (DECC) ① **436 267-2DH**
1. J. Baker, ASMF, N. Marriner Concert
(1/93) (PHIL) ① **434 173-2PM**

Il Pirro e Demetrio—dramma per musica: 3 acts (1694—Naples) (Lib. Morselli)
Le Violette V. de los Angeles, G. Parsons (pp1990) Concert (1/91) (COLL) ① **Coll1247-2**
Le violette V. de los Angeles, G. Moore (r1960) Concert (4/94) (EMI) ① **CMS5 65061-2(2)**
Rugladose, odorose T. Schipa, orch, D. Olivieri (r1939) Concert (4/90) (EMI) ① **CDH7 63200-2**

Il Pompeo—dramma per musica: 3 acts (1683—Rome) (Lib. N Minato)
EXCERPTS: 1. O cessate di piagarmi; 2. Toglietemi la vita ancor; 3. Già il sole dal Gange.
1. C. Bartoli, G. Fischer Concert
(12/92) (DECC) ① **436 267-2DH**
1. R. Tebaldi, R. Bonynge (r1972) Concert
(9/94) (DECC) ① **436 202-2DM**
1-3. J. Carreras, ECO, V. Sutej (r1992; arr Agostinelli) Concert (6/93) (PHIL) ① **434 926-2PH**

SCARLATTI, (Giuseppe) Domenico (1685–1757) Italy/Spain

SECTION I: ORCHESTRAL

Concerto No. 1 in G—oboe and strings (trans G Bayan: from Sonatas Nos 318,376,380,471)
B. Hoff, ECO, I. Watson Concert
(2/90) (SIMA) ① **PSC1049**
Sinfonia in A
Cologne Concerto (r1992) Concert
(1/94) (CAPR) ① **10 378**
Sinfonia in C
Cologne Concerto (r1992) Concert
(1/94) (CAPR) ① **10 378**
Sinfonia in G
Cologne Concerto (r1992) Concert
(1/94) (CAPR) ① **10 378**

SECTION III: INSTRUMENTAL

Keyboard Sonatas (unpub: not listed under Kirkpatrick numbering)
1. C, Prestissimo (doubtful); 2. G; 3. C; 4. G; 5. D minor; 6. A; 7. A; 8. A; 9. E; 10. A; 11. A; 12. Version in D of Kk96; 13. G; 14. Fandango, D minor.
1-14. M. Soné (10/94) (ERAT) ① **4509-94806-2**
Keyboard Sonatas Nos 1-555 (Kk - numbering system adopted by Ralph Kirkpatrick)
S. Ross (6/88) (ERAT) ① [34] **2292-45309-2**
Kk1, 8, 11, 13, 20, 87, 98, 119, 135, 159, 380, 450, 487, 529. I. Pogorelich
(1/93) (DG) ① **435 855-2GH**
Kk1, 9, 11, 14, 19, 39, 125, 146, 159, 259, 466, 551. D. Tomšič (11/93) (VIEN) ① **160106**
Kk1, 9, 30, 69, 113, 127, 132, 133, 141, 159, 175, 215, 380, 430, 481, 492, 502. J. MacGregor
(8/92) (COLL) ① **Coll1322-2**
Kk2, 9, 11, 14, 15, 20, 21, 23, 24. M. Souter Handel: Keyboard Suites Set I. (3/93) (ISIS) ① **ISISCD001**
Kk3, 52, 184, 185, 191-193, 208, 209, 227, 238, 239, 252, 253. G. Leonhardt (r1978)
(10/89) (RCA) ① **GD71955**
Kk7, 84, 185, 187, 193, 208, 491, 492. V. Black Concert (8/94) (UNIT) ① **88005-2**

Kk8, 11, 52, 87, 159, 169, 202, 206, 208, 209, 215, 377, 380, 415, 430, 446. B. van Asperen
(12/92) (DHM) ① **CDC7 54483-2**
Kk8, 20, 107, 124, 159, 247, 328, 380, 397, 430, 447, 519. W. Landowska (r1934) Concert
(8/94) (EMI) ① **CDH7 64934-2**
Kk9. S. Rachmaninov (arr Tausig: r1919) Concert
(10/92) (APR) ① [2] **APR7013**
Kk9. S. Rachmaninov (r1919; arr Tausig) Concert
(3/93) (RCA) ① [10] **09026 61265-2(3)**
Kk9, 11. A.B. Michelangeli (r1942) Concert
(8/93) (EMI) ① **CDH7 64490-2**
Kk9, 13, 17, 27, 29, 30, 32, 64, 69, 87, 96, 114, 119, 125, 159, 175, 202, 245, 279, 377, 380, 427, 430, 432, 446, 450, 474, 478, 492, 519, 523, 533. M. Meyer (r1953/6) Concert
(6/95) (EMI) ① [4] **CZS5 68092-2**
Kk9, 20. A. Brailowsky (r1938) Concert
(8/94) (APR) ① **APR5501**
Kk9, 20. A. Brailowsky (r1928) Concert
(2/95) (PEAR) ① **GEMMCD9132**
Kk9, 20. A. Brailowsky (r1928: arr Tausig) Concert
(11/95) (DANA) ① [2] **DACOCD338/9**
Kk9, 27, 30, 33, 69, 87, 96, 159, 193, 247, 492, 531. A. Queffélec (r1970)
(3/95) (ERAT) ① **4509-96960-2**
Kk9, 380. D. Lipatti (r1947) Concert
(6/89) (EMI) ① **CDH7 69800-2**
Kk9, 54, 96, 140, 141, 162, 251, 432, 466, 531. S. Assad, O. Assad (r1991; arr 2 gtrs) Concert
(10/93) (NONE) ① **7559-79292-2**
Kk11, 159. I. Scharrer (r c1926) Concert
(7/94) (PEAR) ① **GEMMCD9978**
Kk11, 159. M. Hess (r1928) Concert
(3/95) (BIDD) ① **LHW024**
Kk11, 377. N. Demidenko (pp1993) Concert
(1/94) (HYPE) ① [2] **CDA66781/2**
Kk11, 87. J. Bream (r1959; arr Segovia) Concert
(8/93) (RCA) ① [28] **09026 61583-2(4)**
Kk11, 87. J. Bream (r1959; arr Segovia) Concert
(6/94) (RCA) ① **09026 61592-2**
Kk14. D. Lipatti (r1941) Concert
(10/95) (ARCI) ① [2] **ARC112/3**
Kk18, 30, 27, 69, 87, 113, 119, 120, 187, 299, 461, 463, 474, 545. G. Wilson
(3/95) (TELD) ① **2292-46419-2**
Kk18, 43, 56, 58, 87, 122, 141, 144, 145, 151, 158, 204a, 208, 248, 340, 415, 437, 450, 456, 472, 525, 532. P. Hantaï (4/93) (ASTR) ① **E8502**
Kk20. V. Horowitz (arr Tausig: r1928) Concert
(1/93) (APR) ① [2] **APR7014**
Kk20. V. Horowitz (r1928: arr Tausig) Concert
(7/94) (RCA) ① **09026 60986-2**
Kk24, 113, 119, 120, 146, 213, 318, 319, 380, 381, 466, 501, 502. V. Black (CRD) ① **CRD3442**
Kk25, 52, 197, 201, 303, 547. V. Horowitz (r1964) Concert (11/92) (SONY) ① **SK48093**
Kk25, 52, 197, 201, 303, 547. V. Horowitz (r1964) Keyboard Sonatas. (7/94) (SONY) ① **SK53460**
Kk27, 141, 263, 264, 318, 319, 380, 381, 417, 446, 550, 551. M. Cole (2/87) (AMON) ① **CD-SAR27**
Kk30. R. Aldwinckle Concert
(7/87) (CARL) ① **PCD850**
Kk30. M. Hamburg (r1913) Concert
(4/89) (OPAL) ① **OPALCD9839**
Kk30, 46, 87, 119, 132, 133, 208, 213, 215, 259, 260, 278, 380, 429, 517, 544, 545. C. Booth
(3/95) (OLYM) ① **OCD251**
Kk32, 109, 234, 256, 259, 440, 490, 515. W. Landowska (r1940) Concert
(8/94) (EMI) ① **CDH7 64934-2**
Kk33, 54, 96, 146, 162, 198, 391, 466, 474, 481, 491, 525. V. Horowitz (r1964) Keyboard Sonatas. (7/94) (SONY) ① **SK53460**
Kk46, 322, 380, 455. V. Horowitz (r1946) Concert
(7/94) (RCA) ① **09026 60986-2**
Kk46, 87, 95, 99, 124, 201, 204a, 490-492, 513, 520, 521. T. Pinnock (12/86) (CRD) ① **CRD3368**
Kk52, 211, 212, 248, 249, 261-264, 318, 319, 347, 348, 416, 417, 490-492. E. Thornburgh (r1989)
(10/91) (KOCH) ① **37014-2**
Kk55, 380. V. Horowitz (pp1968) Concert
(7/94) (SONY) ① **SK53465**
Kk62, 108, 118, 123, 156, 157, 185, 186, 197, 215, 216, 240, 241, 268, 269, 277, 278, 302-305, 364, 365, 426, 427, 468, 469, 522, 523, 550, 551. G. Rowland (12/95) (KING) ① [2] **KLCD5005/6**
Kk64, 87, 96, 132, 133, 175, 202, 213, 214, 263, 264, 277, 278, 420, 421, 460, 461. A. Staier (r1991)
(3/93) (DHM) ① **05472 77274-2**
Kk82, 165-6, 211-2, 217-8, 228-9, 234-5, 244-5, 270-1, 294-5, 314-5, 362-3, 422-3, 466-7, 495-6, 499, 500, 511-2, 540-1, 534-5. G. Rowland
(12/95) (KING) ① [2] **KLCD5007/8**
Kk87, 101, 127, 135, 184, 466. V. Horowitz (pp1981) Concert (5/93) (RCA) ① **09026 61416-2**

Kk87, 125. V. Horowitz (r1935) Concert
(3/90) (EMI) ① [3] **CHS7 63538-2**
Kk87, 135. V. Horowitz Concert
(6/86) (DG) ① **419 217-2GH**
Kk87, 193, 386. C. Haskil (r1951) Concert
(11/95) (PHIL) ① [3] **442 635-2PM3**
Kk87, 193, 386. C. Haskil (r1951) Concert
(11/95) (PHIL) ① [12] **442 685-2PM12**
Kk87, 531. V. Horowitz (r1947) Concert
(7/94) (RCA) ① **09026 60986-2**
Kk90. Giardino Armonico Ens, G. Antonini (rec/dir) (r1993; arr anon) Concert
(11/94) (TELD) ① **4509-93157-2**
Kk96, 113, 159. G. Cziffra (r1956/1969) Concert
(3/95) (EMI) ① **CDM5 65255-2**
Kk98, 123, 124, 147, 198, 326, 327, 428, 429, 454, 466, 467. C. Tilney (10/94) (L'OI) ① **443 179-2OM**
Kk108, 118, 119, 141, 198, 203, 454, 455, 490-492, 501, 502, 516-519. A. Staier
(2/92) (DHM) ① **RD77224**
Kk113. M. Levitzki (r1928) Concert
(11/95) (APR) ① [2] **APR7020**
Kk113. S. Barere (bp1920s/30s) Concert
(1/93) (APR) ① [2] **APR7014**
Kk113. H. Bauer (r1939) Concert
(4/94) (BIDD) ① **LHW009**
Kk115, 116, 144, 175, 402, 403, 449, 450, 474, 475, 513, 516, 517, 544, 545. A. Schiff
(3/89) (DECC) ① **421 422-2DH**
Kk141, 144, 145. K. Heindel (lute-hpd) Concert
(2/91) (KING) ① **KCLCD2020**
Kk141, 423, 481, 492. W. Landowska (r1939) Concert (8/94) (EMI) ① **CDH7 64934-2**
Kk159, 175, 213, 380, 448. J. Williams (trans J.Williams) Concert (8/89) (SONY) ① **SK44518**
Kk159, 337, 380. V. Black Concert
(5/91) (COLL) ① **Coll5024-2**
Kk175. J. Henry Concert
(10/92) (VICT) ① **VCD19013**
Kk184, 206, 492. K. Gilbert Concert
(6/88) (NOVA) ① **150 018-2**
Kk185, 300, 440, 511. R. Veyron-Lacroix (r1978 & 1989) Concert (12/93) (ERAT) ① **4509-92135-2**
Kk188, 322. V. Horowitz (r1951) Concert
(3/90) (EMI) ① [3] **CHS7 63538-2**
Kk213. J. Williams (r1992: arr J Williams) Concert
(1/94) (SONY) ① **SK53359**
Kk254, 255, 287, 288, 328. F. Grier (arr. organ) Concert (12/89) (HYPE) ① **CDA66182**
Kk260, 319. V. Horowitz (pp1969: pf) Concert
(7/94) (SONY) ① **SK53466**
Kk322. S. Mayor (arr Mayor: Mandolin ens) Concert
(3/92) (ACOU) ① **CDACS014**
Kk322, 455, 531. V. Horowitz (r1962) Concert
(7/94) (SONY) ① [2] **S2K53457**
Kk380. V. Horowitz (pp1985) Concert
(12/86) (DG) ① **419 499-2GH**
Kk380, 381. T. Pinnock Concert
(11/84) (ARCH) ① **413 591-2AH**
Kk380, 427. W. Gieseking (bp1944) Concert
(11/90) (MUSI) ① **MACD-612**
Kk460, 461, 478, 479, 502, 516, 517, 518, 519, 529, 544, 545, 546, 547. T. Pinnock
(9/87) (ARCH) ① **419 632-2AH**

SECTION IV: VOCAL AND CHORAL

Che vidi, o ciel—cantata (1v, 2 violins and continuo)
K. Eckersley, Fiori Musicali, P. Rapson Concert
(11/90) (UNIC) ① **DKPCD9095**
Con qual cor—cantata: 1v and continuo
Musica Fiammante Concert
(9/92) (UNIC) ① **DKPCD9124**
Consolati e spera—1v and strings
G. Anselmi, Bettinelli (r1910) Concert
(7/95) (SYMP) ① **SYMCD1170**
Dir vorrei—cantata: soprano, 2 vns & vc
K. Eckersley, Fiori Musicali, P. Rapson Concert
(5/92) (UNIC) ① **DKPCD9119**
No, non fuggire o Nice—cantata: 1v and continuo
Musica Fiammante Concert
(9/92) (UNIC) ① **DKPCD9124**
O qual meco Nice cangiata—cantata: soprano, 2 vns & vc
K. Eckersley, Fiori Musicali, P. Rapson Concert
(5/92) (UNIC) ① **DKPCD9119**
Pinagete, occhi dolenti—cantata (1v, 2 violins and continuo)
K. Eckersley, Fiori Musicali, P. Rapson Concert
(11/90) (UNIC) ① **DKPCD9095**
Pur nel sonno almen tal'ora—cantata (1v) (Wds. P. Metastasio)
K. Eckersley, Fiori Musicali, P. Rapson Concert
(11/90) (UNIC) ① **DKPCD9095**

Qual pensier, quale ardire—cantata: 1v and continuo
Musica Fiammante *Concert*
(9/92) (UNIC) ① **DKPCD9124**
Salve Regina
C. Harris, N. Clapton, Oxford Christ Church Cath Ch,
F. Grier *Concert* (12/89) (HYPE) ① **CDA66182**
Scritte con falso inganno—cantata: soprano, 2 vns & vc
K. Eckersley, Fiori Musicali, P. Rapson *Concert*
(5/92) (UNIC) ① **DKPCD9119**
Se fedele tu m'adori—cantata (1v, 2 violins and continuo)
K. Eckersley, Fiori Musicali, P. Rapson *Concert*
(11/90) (UNIC) ① **DKPCD9095**
Stabat mater in C minor—10vv
Monteverdi Ch, EBS, J.E. Gardiner *Concert*
(7/85) (ERAT) ① **2292-45219-2**
Oxford Christ Church Cath Ch, F. Grier *Concert*
(12/89) (HYPE) ① **CDA66182**
Currende Voc Ens, Currende Instr Ens, E. van Nevel
Esteves: Mass for eight voices.
(5/92) (ACCE) ① **ACC9069D**
London Schütz Ch, R. Norrington (r1973) *Concert*
(7/95) (DECC) ① [2] **443 868-2DF2**
Ti ricorda o bella irene—cantata: 1v and continuo
Musica Fiammante *Concert*
(9/92) (UNIC) ① **DKPCD9124**
Tinte a note di sangue—cantata: soprano, 2 vns & vc
K. Eckersley, Fiori Musicali, P. Rapson *Concert*
(5/92) (UNIC) ① **DKPCD9119**
Tirsi caro—cantata: 2vv and continuo
E. van Evera, Musica Fiammante *Concert*
(9/92) (UNIC) ① **DKPCD9124**

SCELSI, Giacinto *(1905–1988) Italy*

SECTION I: ORCHESTRAL

Anahit—violin and 18 instruments (1965)
C. Fournier, Cracow Rad & TV Orch, J. Wyttenbach
Concert (8/90) (ACCO) ① **20061-2**
4 Pezzi—orchestra (1959) ('Ciascuno su una nota sola')
Cracow Rad & TV Orch, J. Wyttenbach *Concert*
(8/90) (ACCO) ① **20061-2**

SECTION II: CHAMBER

Elegia per Ty—viola and cello (1966)
C. Schiller, P. Demenga *Concert*
(9/90) (ACCO) ① **20062-2**
String Quartet No. 1 (1944)
Arditti Qt *Concert* (9/90) (SALA) ① [2] **SCD8904/5**
String Quartet No. 2 (1961)
Arditti Qt *Concert* (9/90) (SALA) ① [2] **SCD8904/5**
String Quartet No. 3 (1963)
Arditti Qt *Concert* (9/90) (SALA) ① [2] **SCD8904/5**
String Quartet No. 4 (1964)
Arditti Qt *Concert* (9/90) (SALA) ① [2] **SCD8904/5**
String Quartet No. 5 (1974-85)
Arditti Qt *Concert* (9/90) (SALA) ① [2] **SCD8904/5**
String Trio—violin, viola and cello (1958)
R. Zimansky, C. Schiller, P. Demenga *Concert*
(9/90) (ACCO) ① **20062-2**
Arditti Qt *Concert* (9/90) (SALA) ① [2] **SCD8904/5**

SECTION III: INSTRUMENTAL

Coelocanth—viola (1955)
C. Schiller *Concert* (9/90) (ACCO) ① **20062-2**
Divertimento No. 3—violin (mid 1950s)
R. Zimansky *Concert* (9/90) (ACCO) ① **20062-2**
Ko-Tha—six-stringed cello (1978)
F-M. Uitti *Trilogia.* (11/92) (ETCE) ① **KTC1136**
L'ame ailée—violin (1973)
R. Zimansky *Concert* (9/90) (ACCO) ① **20062-2**
L'ame ouverte—violin (1973)
R. Zimansky *Concert* (9/90) (ACCO) ① **20062-2**
4 Pezzi—trumpet (1956)
R. Friedrich (r1991-2) *Concert*
(6/93) (CAPR) ① **10 482**
Trilogia—cello (1957-61)
1. Triphon; 2. Dithome; 3. Ygghur.
F-M. Uitti *Ko-Tha.* (11/92) (ETCE) ① **KTC1136**

SECTION IV: VOCAL AND CHORAL

Khoom—soprano and six instruments (1962) (Wds. M. Hirayama)
M. Hirayama, F. Lloyd, M. Ben Omar, Arditti Qt, A.
Brizzi *Concert* (9/90) (SALA) ① [2] **SCD8904/5**
Uaxuctum—chorus, ondes martenot and orchestra (1966)
T. Murail, Cracow Rad & TV Chor, Cracow Rad & TV
Orch, J. Wyttenbach *Concert*
(8/90) (ACCO) ① **20061-2**

SCHAFER, R(aymond) Murray *(b 1933) Canada*

SECTION III: INSTRUMENTAL

Le Cri de Merlin—guitar (1987)
N. Kraft *Concert* (1/90) (CHAN) ① **CHAN8784**

SCHARWENKA, (Franz) Xaver *(1850–1924) Poland*

SECTION I: ORCHESTRAL

Concerto for Piano and Orchestra in C minor, Op. 56 (1881)
M. Ponti, Hamburg SO, R. Kapp *Moszkowski: Piano Concerto.* (5/93) (VOX) ① **115710-2**
Concerto for Piano and Orchestra No. 4 in F minor, Op. 82 (1908)
S. Hough, CBSO, L. Foster (r1994) *Sauer: Piano Concerto 1.* (11/95) (HYPE) ① **CDA66790**

SECTION II: CHAMBER

Piano Trio in A minor, Op. 45 (1876-78)
S. Tanyel, L. Chilingirian, I-J. van der Werff, G.
Atmacayan (r1994) *Piano Quartet, Op. 37.*
(3/95) (COLL) ① **Coll1419-2**
Piano Trio No. 1 in F sharp minor—piano, violin & cello, Op. 1 (1869)
S. Tanyel, L. Mordkovitch, C. Carr (r1995) *Concert*
(10/95) (COLL) ① **Coll1448-2**
Quartet in F—piano, violin, viola and cello, Op. 37 (1876-78)
S. Tanyel, L. Chilingirian, I-J. van der Werff, G.
Atmacayan (r1994) *Piano Trio, Op. 45.*
(3/95) (COLL) ① **Coll1419-2**
Serenade—violin & piano, Op. 70 (1895)
S. Tanyel, L. Mordkovitch (r1995) *Concert*
(10/95) (COLL) ① **Coll1448-2**
Sonata for Cello and Piano in E minor, Op. 46a (1878)
S. Tanyel, C. Carr (r1995) *Concert*
(10/95) (COLL) ① **Coll1448-2**
Sonata for Violin and Piano in D minor, Op. 2 (1869)
S. Tanyel, L. Mordkovitch (r1995) *Concert*
(10/95) (COLL) ① **Coll1448-2**

SECTION III: INSTRUMENTAL

Barcarolle in E minor—piano, Op. 14 (1879)
S. Tanyel (r1992) *Concert*
(9/93) (COLL) ① **Coll1365-2**
2 Danses Polonaises—piano, Op. 29 (1876)
1. C sharp minor; 2. B minor.
S. Tanyel (r1992) *Concert*
(9/93) (COLL) ① **Coll1352-2**
Eglantine Waltz—piano, Op. 84 (1913)
S. Tanyel *Concert* (9/92) (COLL) ① **Coll1325-2**
First Polonaise—piano, Op. 12
S. Tanyel *Concert* (9/92) (COLL) ① **Coll1325-2**
Impromptu—piano, Op. 17
S. Tanyel *Concert* (9/92) (COLL) ① **Coll1325-2**
2 Pieces—piano, Op. 22 (1875)
1. Novelette; 2. Melodie.
S. Tanyel (r1992) *Concert*
(9/93) (COLL) ① **Coll1365-2**
5 Polish Dances—piano, Op. 3 (1869)
S. Tanyel *Concert* (9/92) (COLL) ① **Coll1325-2**
4 Polish Dances—piano, Op. 58 (1881)
S. Tanyel (r1992) *Concert*
(9/93) (COLL) ① **Coll1365-2**
Polonaise—piano, Op. 42
S. Tanyel *Concert* (9/92) (COLL) ① **Coll1325-2**
Romanzero—piano, Op. 33 (1877)
S. Tanyel (r1992) *Concert*
(9/93) (COLL) ① **Coll1352-2**
Scherzo in G—piano, Op. 4 (1869)
S. Tanyel (r1992) *Concert*
(9/93) (COLL) ① **Coll1365-2**
Sonata No. 1 in C sharp minor—piano, Op. 6 (1872)
S. Tanyel (r1992) *Concert*
(9/93) (COLL) ① **Coll1352-2**
Sonata No. 2 in E flat—piano, Op. 36 (1878)
S. Tanyel (r1992) *Concert*
(9/93) (COLL) ① **Coll1352-2**
2 Sonatinas—piano, Op. 52 (1880)
1. E minor.
1. S. Tanyel (r1992) *Concert*
(9/93) (COLL) ① **Coll1352-2**
Theme and Variations—piano, Op. 48
S. Tanyel (r1992) *Concert*
(9/93) (COLL) ① **Coll1365-2**
Valse-Caprice—piano, Op. 31
S. Tanyel *Concert* (9/92) (COLL) ① **Coll1325-2**

SCHAT, Peter *(b 1935) Holland*

SECTION I: ORCHESTRAL

The Heavens—symphonic variations, Op. 37 (1989-90)
Concertgebouw, R. Chailly (pp1992) *Concert*
(7/94) (NMCL) ① **NM92033**

SCHATTENBERG, Thomas *(c1580–after 1622) Denmark*

SECTION IV: VOCAL AND CHORAL

Amor Jesu dulcissimus—motet: 4vv (pub 1620)
Hilliard Ens, P. Hillier *Concert*
(2/89) (BIS) ① **BIS-CD389**
Jesu decus Angelicum—motet: 4vv (pub 1620)
Hilliard Ens, P. Hillier *Concert*
(2/89) (BIS) ① **BIS-CD389**
Jesu tua dilectio—motet (4vv) (pub 1620)
Hilliard Ens, P. Hillier *Concert*
(2/89) (BIS) ① **BIS-CD389**
O Jesu mi dulcissime—motet: 4vv (pub 1620)
Hilliard Ens, P. Hillier *Concert*
(2/89) (BIS) ① **BIS-CD389**

SCHEIBE, Johann Adolph *(1708–1776) Germany*

SECTION I: ORCHESTRAL

Concerto for Flute and Strings in A
M. Bania, Concerto Copenhagen, A. Manze (r1992)
Concert (6/93) (CHAN) ① **CHAN0535**
Concerto for Flute and Strings in D
I. Spranger, Concerto Copenhagen, A. Manze
(r1992) *Concert* (6/93) (CHAN) ① **CHAN0535**
Sinfonia a 4 in A—strings (MS Kungliga Musikaliska Akademien)
Concerto Copenhagen, A. Manze (vn/dir) (r1993)
Concert (7/94) (CHAN) ① **CHAN0550**
Sinfonia a 4 in B flat I—strings (MS Lund/Kraus coll)
EXCERPTS: 1. Allegro assai; 2. Andante; 3. Presto.
Concerto Copenhagen, A. Manze (vn/dir) (r1993)
Concert (7/94) (CHAN) ① **CHAN0550**
Sinfonia a 4 in B flat II—strings (MS Lund/Engelhart coll)
EXCERPTS: 1. Allegro; 2. Adagio, amoroso molto; 3. Presto.
Concerto Copenhagen, A. Manze (vn/dir) (r1993)
Concert (7/94) (CHAN) ① **CHAN0550**
Sinfonia a 16 in D—orchestra (Mecklenburgische Landesbibliothek Schwerin, MS 4852)
Concerto Copenhagen, A. Manze (vn/dir) (r1993)
Concert (7/94) (CHAN) ① **CHAN0550**

SECTION IV: VOCAL AND CHORAL

Sörge- og Klagesange over Dronning Lovise—Mourning Cantata for Queen Lovise (1766)
EXCERPTS: 1. Sinfonia in B minor.
1. Concerto Copenhagen, A. Manze (vn/dir) (r1993)
Concert (7/94) (CHAN) ① **CHAN0550**
Sörgesange over Kong Frederik V (Wds J. Evald)
EXCERPTS: 1. Introduzzione in E flat.
1. Concerto Copenhagen, A. Manze (vn/dir) (r1993)
Concert (7/94) (CHAN) ① **CHAN0550**
Der Tempel des Ruhmes—Homage Cantata to Queen Juliana Maria (1752)
EXCERPTS: 1. Sinfonia in D.
1. Concerto Copenhagen, A. Manze (vn/dir) (r1993)
Concert (7/94) (CHAN) ① **CHAN0550**

SCHEIDEMANN, Heinrich *(c1595–1663) Germany*

SECTION III: INSTRUMENTAL

Benedicam Dominum—chorale : organ
K. Eichhorn *Concert* (10/89) (THOR) ① **CTH2035**
Dic nobis Maria—organ
K. Eichhorn *Concert* (10/89) (THOR) ① **CTH2035**
Englische Mascarada oder Judentanz—keyboard
L.U. Mortensen *Concert* (2/89) (BIS) ① **BIS-CD391**
Galliarda in D minor—organ
G. Leonhardt *Concert* (10/94) (SONY) ① **SK53371**
Praeludium in F—organ
G. Leonhardt *Concert* (10/94) (SONY) ① **SK53371**

SCHEIDT, Samuel (1587–1654) Germany

SECTION I: ORCHESTRAL

Pavane (unidentified)
F. Brüggen, K. Boeke, W. van Hauwe, W. Möller, B. van Asperen (r c1960s) *Concert*
(10/95) (TELD) ① **4509-97466-2**

SECTION II: CHAMBER

Canzon à Cornet vel viol—two cornetts, two violins & continuo (pub 1629) (from 'Ludorum musicalium')
Musica Fiata, R. Wilson (r1991) *Concert*
(8/93) (DHM) ① **05472 77183-2**
Canzon à 4 tromboni—four trombones and continuo (pub 1629) (from 'Ludorum musicalium')
Musica Fiata, R. Wilson (r1991) *Concert*
(8/93) (DHM) ① **05472 77183-2**
Canzon super Cantionem Gallicam—organ and brass ensemble (pub. 1621)
A. Ross, His Majesties Sagbutts and Cornetts *Concert* (9/87) (MERI) ① **CDE84096**
Canzon super Intradam Aechiopicam—organ and brass ensemble (pub. 1621)
A. Ross, His Majesties Sagbutts and Cornetts *Concert* (9/87) (MERI) ① **CDE84096**
Canzon super O Nachbar Roland—viols (dpub 1621)
Ricercar Consort, P. Pierlot (va da gamba/dir) (r1992) *Concert* (8/94) (RICE) ① **RIC098112**
Galliard battaglia a 5—organ and brass ensemble (pub 1621)
A. Ross, His Majesties Sagbutts and Cornetts *Concert* (9/87) (MERI) ① **CDE84096**
Intrada a 5—brass ensemble (pub 1621)
His Majesties Sagbutts and Cornetts *Concert*
(9/87) (MERI) ① **CDE84096**

SECTION III: INSTRUMENTAL

Ach du feiner Reiter (Cantio belgica)—organ (1624)
K. Eichhorn *Concert* (10/89) (THOR) ① **CTH2035**
Alamanda—organ
K. Eichhorn *Concert* (10/89) (THOR) ① **CTH2035**
Benedicamus Domino a 6 (modus pleno organo pedaliter)—organ (1624)
K. Eichhorn *Concert* (10/89) (THOR) ① **CTH2035**
Est-ce Mars, 'Canto gallica'—organ (1624)
K. Eichhorn *Concert* (10/89) (THOR) ① **CTH2035**
Galliarda after John Dowland—organ
K. Eichhorn *Concert* (10/89) (THOR) ① **CTH2035**
Margaret Phillips (r1989) *Concert*
(4/91) (REGE) ① **REGCD105**
Magnificat (Tone 9, tonus pergrinus)—keyboard (pub 1624)
D. Wagler *Concert* (10/91) (PRIO) ① **PRCD332**
Modus ludendi pleno organo pedaliter—organ (1624)
K. Eichhorn *Concert* (10/89) (THOR) ① **CTH2035**
Toccata in G minor—organ
K. Eichhorn *Concert* (10/89) (THOR) ① **CTH2035**
Vom Himmel hoch da komm ich her—chorale
London Musica Antiqua, M. Uridge (r1980-83) *Concert* (12/93) (SYMP) ① **SYMCD1157**

SCHEIN, Johann Hermann (1586–1630) Germany

SECTION II: CHAMBER

Canzona a 5—organ and brass ensemble (pub 1609)
A. Ross, His Majesties Sagbutts and Cornetts *Concert* (9/87) (MERI) ① **CDE84096**
Padouana in D minor—brass and continuo (pub 1617) (pub in Banchetto musicale newer)
A. Ross, His Majesties Sagbutts and Cornetts *Concert* (9/87) (MERI) ① **CDE84096**
Suite No. 7 a 4—brass ensemble (pub 1617)
His Majesties Sagbutts and Cornetts *Concert*
(9/87) (MERI) ① **CDE84096**

SECTION IV: VOCAL AND CHORAL

Christ unser Herr zum Jordan kam—cantata (2vv, strings and continuo) (pub 1618)
G. de Reyghere, A. Mellon, Ricercar Consort *Concert*
(1/90) (RICE) ① **RIC046023**
Diletti pastorali—madrigals (5vv) (pub 1624)
1. O Amarilli zart; 2. Aurora schön mit ihrem Haar; 3. Als Filli schön und fromm; 4. In Filli schönen Äugelein; 5. Unlängst dem blinden Göttelein; 6. Wie kömmt's, o zarte Filli mein; 7. Cupido blind, das

Venuskind; 8. Wenn Filli ihre Liebesstrahl; 9. O Amarilli, schönste Zier; 10. All wilden Tier im grünen Wald; 11. O, Venus und Cupido blind; 12. Amor, das liebe Räuberlein; 13. Mirtillo hat ein Schäfelein; 14. Die Vöglein singen; 15. Mein Schifflein lief im wilden Meer.
1-15. Cantus Cölln, K. Junghänel (lte/dir) *Concert*
(10/90) (DHM) ① **RD77088**
Frischauf, ihr Kosterbrüder mein—madrigal (5vv) (pub 162)
Cantus Cölln, K. Junghänel (lte/dir) *Concert*
(10/90) (DHM) ① **RD77088**
Gelobet seist du, Jesu Christ—cantata (3vv and continuo) (pub 1618)
G. de Reyghere, A. Mellon, G. de Mey, Ricercar Consort (r1989) *Concert*
(5/90) (RICE) ① **RIC060048**
Heulen und schmerzlichs Weinen—madrigal (5vv) (pub 1609)
Cantus Cölln, K. Junghänel (lte/dir) *Concert*
(10/90) (DHM) ① **RD77088**
Ihr Brüder, lieben Brüder mein—madrigal (5vv) (pub 1626)
Cantus Cölln, K. Junghänel (lte/dir) *Concert*
(10/90) (DHM) ① **RD77088**
Kickehihi, kakakanei—madrigal (5vv) (pub 1621)
Cantus Cölln, K. Junghänel (lte/dir) *Concert*
(10/90) (DHM) ① **RD77088**
Maria, gegrüsset seist du, Holdselige—cantata (2vv and instruments) (pub 1626)
G. de Reyghere, G. de Mey, Ricercar Consort (r1989) *Concert* (5/90) (RICE) ① **RIC060048**
Nun komm, der Heiden Heiland—cantata (3vv and instruments)
G. de Reyghere, A. Mellon, G. de Mey, Ricercar Consort (r1989) *Concert*
(5/90) (RICE) ① **RIC060048**
O Jesu Christe, Gottes Sohn—cantata (1v, strings and continuo) (pub 1618)
G. de Reyghere, Ricercar Consort *Concert*
(1/90) (RICE) ① **RIC046023**
O Jesulein, mein Jesulein—cantata (2vv and continuo) (pub 1626)
G. de Reyghere, A. Mellon, Ricercar Consort (r1989) *Concert* (5/90) (RICE) ① **RIC060048**
O Scheiden, O bitter Scheiden—secular choral work (pub 1621ty)
R. Jacobs, K. Junghänel (r1985) *Concert*
(5/87) (HARM) ① **HMA190 1183**
Cantus Cölln, K. Junghänel (lte/dir) *Concert*
(10/90) (DHM) ① **RD77088**
O seidne Härelein—madrigal (5vv) (pub 1621)
Cantus Cölln, K. Junghänel (lte/dir) *Concert*
(10/90) (DHM) ① **RD77088**
Ringstum mich schwebet Traurigkeit—madrigal (5vv) (pub 1609)
Cantus Cölln, K. Junghänel (lte/dir) *Concert*
(10/90) (DHM) ① **RD77088**
Uns ist ein Kind geboren—cantata (3vv and continuo) (pub 1626)
G. de Reyghere, A. Mellon, G. de Mey, Ricercar Consort (r1989) *Concert*
(5/90) (RICE) ① **RIC060048**

SCHELLE, Johann (1648–1701) Germany

SECTION II: CHAMBER

Nun komm der Heiden Heiland—canon a 6
Cologne Musica Fiata, R. Wilson (r1993) *Concert*
(5/94) (DHM) ① **05472 77298-2**

SECTION IV: VOCAL AND CHORAL

Ach mein herzliebes Jesulein—two voices and continuo
Capella Ducale, Cologne Musica Fiata, R. Wilson
(r1993) *Concert* (5/94) (DHM) ① **05472 77298-2**
Actus musicus auf Weyh-Nachten—6vv and instruments
Capella Ducale, Cologne Musica Fiata, R. Wilson
(r1993) *Concert* (5/94) (DHM) ① **05472 77298-2**
Machet die Thore weit—4vv and instruments
Capella Ducale, Cologne Musica Fiata, R. Wilson
(r1993) *Concert* (5/94) (DHM) ① **05472 77298-2**
Uns ist ein kind geboren—5vv and instruments
Capella Ducale, Cologne Musica Fiata, R. Wilson
(r1993) *Concert* (5/94) (DHM) ① **05472 77298-2**

Vom Himmel kam der Engel Schar—5vv and instruments
Capella Ducale, Cologne Musica Fiata, R. Wilson
(r1993) *Concert* (5/94) (DHM) ① **05472 77298-2**

SCHELLING, Ernest (1876–1939) USA

SECTION I: ORCHESTRAL

A Victory Ball—symphonic poem (pub 1925)
NYPO, W. Mengelberg (r1925) *Concert*
(4/92) (PEAR) ① **[3] GEMMCDS9922**

SECTION III: INSTRUMENTAL

Nocturne (Ragusa)—piano
I. Paderewski (r1926) *Concert*
(3/93) (PEAR) ① **GEMMCD9943**

SCHENCK, Johannes (1660–1712) Germany

SECTION II: CHAMBER

Scherzi musicali—viola da gamba and continuo, Op. 6
1. Suite in A; 2. Suite in A minor.
2. Ricercar Consort, P. Pierlot (va da gamba/dir) (r1992) *Concert* (8/94) (RICE) ① **RIC098112**

SCHIASSI, Gaetano Maria (1698–1754) Italy

SECTION II: CHAMBER

Sinfonia in D, 'Sinfonia pastorale per il SS Natale'—2 violins, cello and continuo
Seattle NW CO, A. Francis *Concert*
(12/88) (HYPE) ① **CDH88028**

SCHICKELE, Peter (b 1935) USA

see also P.D.Q. Bach

SECTION I: ORCHESTRAL

Pentangle—five songs for horn and orchestra (1976)
1. Cottonwood Grove; 2. Tom on the Town; 3. Noonsong; 4. Ladies and Gentlemen, the amazing and amusing Professor Presto; 5. Riddling Knight.
K. Albrecht, Louisville Orch, J. Mester *Concert*
(6/90) (ALBA) ① **TROY024-2**

SCHICKHARDT, Johann Christian (c1682–1762) Germany

SECTION II: CHAMBER

6 Concerts—four recorders and continuo, Op. 19 (c1713-15)
2. D minor; 3. G.
2, 3. Amsterdam Loeki Stardust Qt, AAM, C. Hogwood (r1992) *Concert*
(7/94) (L'OI) ① **436 905-2OH**

SCHIFF, David (b 1945) USA

SECTION I: ORCHESTRAL

Stomp—orchestra (1990)
Baltimore SO, D. Zinman (r1994) *Concert*
(7/95) (ARGO) ① **444 454-2ZH**

SCHIFRIN, Lalo (Boris) (b 1932) Argentina/USA

SECTION IV: VOCAL AND CHORAL

Around the World—medley
1. America (Bernstein from 'West Side Story'); 2. All I ask of you (A Lloyd Webber from 'The Phantom of the Opera'); 3. Funiculì, Funiculà (Denza); 4. Sous les ponts de Paris (Scotto); 5. Brazil (Barroso); 6. Be my love (Brodszky from 'The Toast of New Orleans'); 7. Marechiare (Tosti); 8. Lippen schweigen (Lehár from 'Die lustige Witwe'); 9. Santa Lucia luntana (Mario); 10. Those were the days (Raslin); 11. Te Quiero Dijiste (Grever); 12. Torna a Surriento (De Curtis).
J. Carreras, P. Domingo, L. Pavarotti, Los Angeles Music Center Op Chor, Los Angeles PO, Z. Mehta
(pp1994) *Concert* (12/94) (TELD) ① **4509-96200-2**
A Tribute to Hollywood—medley
1. My Way (Revaux); 2. Moon River (Mancini from 'Breakfast at Tiffany's'); 3. Because (D'Hardelot); 4. Singin' in the Rain (Brown from 'Singin' in the Rain').

J. Carreras, P. Domingo, L. Pavarotti, Los Angeles
Music Center Op Chor, Los Angeles PO, Z. Mehta
(pp1994) *Concert* (12/94) (TELD) ① **4509-96200-2**

SECTION V: STAGE WORKS

Cool Hand Luke—film score (1967)
EXCERPTS: 1. Symphonic Sketches.
1. Rochester Pops, L. Schifrin *Concert*
(5/93) (SILV) ① **SILVAD3001**
The **Schifrin Suite—film & TV scores** (arr
cpsr)
1. Rollercoaster—Amusement Park Theme; 2.
Bullitt—Main Theme; 3. Dirty Harry Suite (Dirty Harry,
Magnum Force & The Dead Pool); 4.
Mannix—Theme; 5. Mission Impossible—Theme &
The Plot.
1-5. San Diego SO, L. Schifrin (1990) *Concert*
(11/91) (PRO) ① **CDS524**
2, 3. San Diego SO, L. Schifrin *Concert*
(5/93) (SILV) ① **SILVAD3001**

SCHILDT, Melchior (1592/3–1667) Germany

SECTION III: INSTRUMENTAL

Gleich wie das Feuer—variations: keyboard
L.U. Mortensen *Concert* (2/89) (BIS) ① **BIS-CD391**
Gleichwie das Feuwer—harpsichord
G. Leonhardt *Concert* (10/94) (SONY) ① **SK53371**
Paduana Lacrymae—variations: keyboard
L.U. Mortensen *Concert* (2/89) (BIS) ① **BIS-CD391**

SCHILLINGS, Max von (1868–1933) Germany

SECTION I: ORCHESTRAL

**Concerto for Violin and Orchestra, Op. 25
(1910)**
E. Rozsa, Košice St PO, A. Walter *Concert*
(4/92) (MARC) ① **8 223324**
**Symphonic Prologue to the Oedipus
Tyrannus of Sophocles, Op. 11 (1900)**
Košice St PO, A. Walter *Concert*
(4/92) (MARC) ① **8 223324**

SECTION IV: VOCAL AND CHORAL

Das **Eleusische Fest—melodrama: narrator
and orchestra, Op. 9/2 (1900)** (Wds. F
Schiller)
M. Neubauer, Thüringian SO, K. Bach (r1993/4)
Concert (2/95) (MARC) ① **8 223660**
**Glockenlieder—tenor and orchestra, Op. 22
(1908)** (Wds. C. Spittler)
2, 3, 4. T. Lemnitz, P. Anders, Berlin Staatskapelle,
R. Heger (bp1943) *Wagner: Wesendonk Lieder.*
(7/89) (ACAN) ① **43 275**
**Kassandra—melodrama: narrator and
orchestra, Op. 9/1 (1900)** (Wds. F Schiller)
M. Neubauer, Thüringian SO, K. Bach (r1993/4: orch
K Bach) *Concert* (2/95) (MARC) ① **8 223660**

SECTION V: STAGE WORKS

Moloch—opera (1906—Dresden) (Lib. E.
Gerhäuser)
Harvest festival Košice St PO, A. Walter *Concert*
(4/92) (MARC) ① **8 223324**
**Mona Lisa—opera: 2 acts, Op. 31
(1915—Vienna)** (Lib. B Dovsky)
Cpte B. Bilandzija, K. Wallprecht, A. Bonnema, M.
Gasztecki, K. Russ, U. Köberle, J. Sabrowski, B.
Gebhardt, E. Reimer, A. Lawrence, G. Kosbahn, Kiel
Op Chor, Kiel PO, K. Seibel (r1994)
(8/95) (CPO) ① [2] **CPO999 303-2**

SCHIPA, Tito (1888–1965) Italy

SECTION IV: VOCAL AND CHORAL

Pianefforte è notte—song (Wds. Di
Giacomo)
T. Schipa, orch, M. Campanino (r1955) *Concert*
(12/89) (RCA) ① **GD87969**

SCHIPA-HUA

SECTION IV: VOCAL AND CHORAL

Cubanita—song
T. Ruffo, orch (r1925) *Concert*
(2/93) (PREI) ① [3] **89303(2)**

SCHMALSTICH, Clemens (1880–1960) Germany

SECTION I: ORCHESTRAL

Sehnsucht—orchestra
Berlin Ens *Concert* (5/91) (ORFE) ① **C126901A**

SCHMELZER, Johann Heinrich (c1620/23–1680) Austria

SECTION I: ORCHESTRAL

Sonata natalis
Virtuosi Saxoniae, L. Güttler *Concert*
(12/89) (CAPR) ① **10 225**

SECTION II: CHAMBER

Duodena selectarum sonatarum
9. London Baroque, C. Medlam (r1985) *Concert*
(11/87) (HARM) ① **HMA190 1220**
**Sacro-Profanus Concentus Musicus (pub
1662)**
8. Sonata a 5, G; 12. Sonata XII.
8. Parley of Instr, R. Goodman, P. Holman *Concert*
(9/91) (HYPE) ① **CDA66074**
12. Gradus ad Parnassum, K. Junghänel (r1994)
Concert (7/95) (DHM) ① **05472 77326-2**
Sonata a tre
London Baroque, C. Medlam (r1985) *Concert*
(11/87) (HARM) ① **HMA190 1220**
J. Holloway, S. Ritchie, A. Manze, N. North, M.
Springfels, J. Toll (r1993) *Concert*
(2/94) (HARM) ① **HMU90 7091**
Sonata a tre, 'Lanterly'
London Baroque, C. Medlam (r1985) *Concert*
(11/87) (HARM) ① **HMA190 1220**
**Sonata for 3 Violins and Continuo (pub
1677)**
London Baroque, C. Medlam (r1985) *Concert*
(11/87) (HARM) ① **HMA190 1220**
Sonata on the death of Ferdinand III
London Baroque, C. Medlam (r1985) *Concert*
(11/87) (HARM) ① **HMA190 1220**
**Sonata per Chiesa et Camera—5 trumpets,
strings & continuo**
Gradus ad Parnassum, K. Junghänel (r1994) *Concert*
(7/95) (DHM) ① **05472 77326-2**

SECTION IV: VOCAL AND CHORAL

Inquietum est cor meum—motet
Niederaltaicher Scholaren, K. Ruhland (r1992)
Concert (10/93) (SONY) ① **SK53117**
Vespers, 'Vesperae sollennes'
Vienna Hofburgkapella Schola, Concerto Palatino,
Gradus ad Parnassum, K. Junghänel (r1994) *Concert*
(7/95) (DHM) ① **05472 77326-2**

SCHMIDT, Franz (1874–1939) Austria

SECTION I: ORCHESTRAL

Symphony No. 1 in E (1896-9)
Bratislava RSO, L. Rajter *Concert*
(2/88) (OPUS) ① [4] **9350 1851/4**
Bratislava RSO, L. Rajter
(2/88) (OPUS) ① **9350 1851**
Symphony No. 2 in E flat (1911-2)
Bratislava RSO, L. Rajter
(2/88) (OPUS) ① **9350 1852**
Bratislava RSO, L. Rajter *Concert*
(2/88) (OPUS) ① [4] **9350 1851/4**
Chicago SO, N. Järvi (pp1989)
(3/90) (CHAN) ① **CHAN8779**
Symphony No. 3 in A (1927-28)
Bratislava RSO, L. Rajter *Concert*
(2/88) (OPUS) ① [4] **9350 1851/4**
Bratislava RSO, L. Rajter
(2/88) (OPUS) ① **9350 1853**
Slovak PO, L. Pešek (2/88) (SUPR) ① **CO-1668**
Chicago SO, N. Järvi (pp1991) *Hindemith: Concerto
for Orchestra.* (3/92) (CHAN) ① **CHAN9000**
Symphony No. 4 in C (1932-3)
Bratislava RSO, L. Rajter
(2/88) (OPUS) ① **9350 1854**
Bratislava RSO, L. Rajter *Concert*
(2/88) (OPUS) ① [4] **9350 1851/4**
VPO, Z. Mehta (1971) *Mahler: Symphony 2.*
(5/94) (DECC) ① [2] **440 615-2DF2**
**Variationen über ein Husarenlied—orchestra
(1930-31)**
VPO, H. Knappertsbusch (pp1957) *Schubert:
Symphony 9.* (2/92) (DG) ① **435 328-2GWP**
VPO, H. Knappertsbusch (pp1957) *Concert*
(2/92) (DG) ① [12] **435 321-2GWP12**

SECTION II: CHAMBER

**3 Phantasiestücke nach ungarischen
Nationalmelodien—cello and piano (1892)**
J. Slávik, D. Rusó (r1991) *Concert*
(7/94) (MARC) ① **8 223415**
N. Green, F. Moyer (r1993) *Brahms: Hungarian
Dances.* (5/95) (BIDD) ① **LAW010**
**Quintet for Clarinet and Piano Quartet No. 1
in B flat (1932)**
A. Jánoska, F. Török, A. Lakatos, J. Slávik, D. Rusó
(r1990) *Concert* (7/94) (MARC) ① **8 223415**
**Quintet for Clarinet and Piano Quartet No. 2
in A (1938)**
Vienna Kammermusiker (2/89) (PREI) ① **93357**
A. Jánoska, S. Mucha, A. Lakatos, J. Slávik, D. Rusó
(10/92) (MARC) ① **8 223414**

SECTION III: INSTRUMENTAL

Chaconne in C sharp minor—organ (1925)
A. Juffinger *Concert* (9/89) (CAPR) ① **10 262**
K. John *Concert* (11/92) (PRIO) ① **PRCD370**
**Chorale-prelude on 'Der Heiland ist
erstanden'—organ (1933)**
A. Juffinger *Concert* (9/89) (CAPR) ① **10 264**
**Chorale-prelude on Haydn's 'Gott
erhalte'—organ (1933)**
A. Juffinger *Concert* (9/89) (CAPR) ① **10 264**
4 Chorale-Preludes—organ (1926)
1. O Ewigkeit, du Donnerwort; 2. Was mein Gott will;
3. O wie selig seid ihr doch, ihr Frommen; 4. Nun
danket alle Gott.
A. Juffinger *Concert* (9/89) (CAPR) ① **10 262**
Fantasia and Fugue in D—organ (1924)
A. Juffinger *Concert* (9/89) (CAPR) ① **10 262**
Fugue in F—organ (1927)
A. Juffinger *Concert* (9/89) (CAPR) ① **10 263**
4 Little Preludes and Fugues—organ (1928)
1. B flat; 2. C minor; 3. G; 4. D, 'Halleluja'.
A. Juffinger *Concert* (9/89) (CAPR) ① **10 263**
4. A. Fletcher *Concert* (11/91) (MIRA) ① **MRCD903**
Prelude and Fugue in A—organ (1934)
A. Juffinger *Concert* (9/89) (CAPR) ① **10 264**
Prelude and Fugue in C—organ
A. Juffinger *Concert* (9/89) (CAPR) ① **10 263**
Prelude and Fugue in E flat—organ (1924)
A. Juffinger *Concert* (9/89) (CAPR) ① **10 261**
H. Binder *Concert* (3/90) (MOTE) ① **CD11191**
Romance in A—piano (1922)
D. Rusó (r1991) *Concert*
(7/94) (MARC) ① **8 223415**
Toccata and Fugue in A flat—organ (1935)
A. Juffinger *Concert* (9/89) (CAPR) ① **10 264**
H. Binder *Concert* (3/90) (MOTE) ① **CD11191**
Toccata in C—organ
A. Juffinger *Concert* (9/89) (CAPR) ① **10 261**
H. Binder *Concert* (3/90) (MOTE) ① **CD11191**
Toccata in D minor—piano left-hand (1938)
D. Rusó (r1991) *Concert*
(7/94) (MARC) ① **8 223415**
**Variations and Fugue on an original
theme—organ (1916-24)**
A. Juffinger *Concert* (9/89) (CAPR) ① **10 261**

SECTION IV: VOCAL AND CHORAL

**Das Buch mit Sieben Siegeln—Oratorio
(1935-37)** (Wds. Apocalypse)
S. Greenberg, C. Watkinson, P. Schreier, T. Moser,
R. Holl, K. Rydl, M. Haselböck, Vienna St Op *Concert*
Ch, Austrian RSO, L. Zagrosek
(2/88) (ORFE) ① [2] **C143862H**

SECTION V: STAGE WORKS

Notre Dame—opera: 2 acts (1902-04) (Lib.
cpsr after Hugo)
Cpte G. Jones, J. King, H. Laubenthal, H. Welker, K.
Moll, H. Helm, K. Borris, Berlin St Hedwig's Cath Ch,
Berlin RIAS Chbr Ch, Berlin RSO, C. Perick
(5/89) (CAPR) ① [2] **10 248/9**
Excs A. Jerger, H. Alsen, K. Friedrich, J. Witt, E.
Schulz, G. Monthy, Vienna St Op Chor, Vienna St Op
Orch, R. Moralt (pp1943) *Concert*
(2/95) (SCHW) ① [2] **314572**
Intermezzo BPO, H. von Karajan *Concert*
(10/87) (DG) ① [3] **419 257-2GH3**
Intermezzo Gothenburg SO, N. Järvi *Concert*
(6/90) (DG) ① **429 494-2GDC**
Intermezzo Vienna St Op Orch, W. Loibner (pp1938)
Concert (6/94) (SCHW) ① **314502**
Intermezzo Vienna St Op Orch, W. Loibner (pp1938)
Concert (6/95) (SCHW) ① [2] **314632**

SCHMIDT, Harvey Lester (b 1929)
USA

SECTION V: STAGE WORKS

110 in the Shade—musical show (1963—New York) (Lyrics T. Jones)
EXCERPTS: 1a. Overture; 1b. Gonna be another hot day; 2. Lizzie's comin home; 3. Love, don't turn away; 4. Poker Polka; 5. Hungry men; 6. Rain song; 7. You're not follin' me; 8. Raunchy; 9. A man and a woman; 10. Old maid; 11. Everything beautiful happens at night; 12. Melisande; 13. Simple little things; 14. Little red hat; 15. Is is really me?; 16. Womderful music; 17. Rain song Finale.
  15. M. Hill Smith, Philh, J.O. Edwards (r1989-91)
    Concert   (10/91) (TER) ① **CDVIR8314**

SCHMIDT & JANSSON, Ole & Gunnar (b 1928 & 1944)
Denmark/Sweden

SECTION IV: VOCAL AND CHORAL

The Öresund Symphony—sop, ten, chor & orchestra (1993) (Movts I & IV by Schmidt, II & III by Jansson)
K. Hamnoy, A. Lundh, Ars Nova, Malmö SO, O. Schmidt (r1994) *Gade: Violin Concerto, Op. 56.*
     (6/95) (BIS) ① **BIS-CD672**

SCHMITT, Florent (1870–1958)
France

SECTION I: ORCHESTRAL

Danse d'Abisag—piano, Op. 75 (1925)
Rhineland-Pfalz State PO, L. Segerstam (r1992) *Concert*   (3/95) (MARC) ① **8 223689**
Dionysiaques—concert band, Op. 62/1 (1914-25)
Gardiens de la Paix Orch, D. Dondeyne *Concert*
     (8/88) (CALL) ① **CAL9859**
Habeyssée—suite: violin and orchestra, Op. 110 (1947)
H. Segerstam, Rhineland-Pfalz State PO, L. Segerstam (r1988) *Concert*
     (3/95) (MARC) ① **8 223689**
Le Palais hanté, Op. 49 (1900-04)
Monte Carlo PO, G. Prêtre (r1983) *Concert*
     (9/93) (EMI) ① **CDM7 64687-2**
Rêves—orchestra, Op. 65 (1913)
Monte Carlo PO, D. Robertson (r1993) *Concert*
     (9/94) (AUVI) ① **V4687**
Rhineland-Pfalz State PO, L. Segerstam (r1987) *Concert*   (3/95) (MARC) ① **8 223689**
Soirs—eight short pieces for small orchestra, Op. 5 (arr cpsr from 'Soirs' for piano)
1. En rêvant; 2. Spleen; 3. Gaiety; 4. Après l'été; 5. Parfum exotique; 6. Sur l'onde; 7. Un soir; 8. Eglogue.
Monte Carlo PO, D. Robertson (r1993) *Concert*
     (9/94) (AUVI) ① **V4687**
Symphonie concertante—piano and orchestra, Op. 82 (1931)
H. Sermet, Monte Carlo PO, D. Robertson (r1993) *Concert*   (9/94) (AUVI) ① **V4687**
Symphony No. 2, Op. 137 (1958)
Rhineland-Pfalz State PO, L. Segerstam (r1988) *Concert*   (3/95) (MARC) ① **8 223689**
La tragédie de Salomé—symphonic poem, Op. 50 (1910) (based on ballet of same name)
Walther Straram Orch, F. Schmitt (r1930) *Concert*
     (9/93) (EMI) ① **CDC7 54840-2**

SECTION II: CHAMBER

Hasards—piano quartet, Op. 96 (1939-44)
R. Pasquier, B. Pasquier, R. Pidoux, H. Greif (r1992) *Concert*   (9/93) (AUVI) ① **V4679**
Quintet for Piano and Strings, Op. 51 (1902-08)
  Movt 2. F. Schmitt, Calvet Qt (r1935) *Concert*
     (9/93) (EMI) ① **CDC7 54840-2**
3 Rapsodies—two pianos, Op. 53 (1903-04)
H. Sermet, K.W. Paik (r1992) *Concert*
     (9/93) (AUVI) ① **V4679**
Sonate libre en deux parties enchaînées—violin and piano, Op. 68 (1918-19)
R. Pasquier, H. Sermet (r1992) *Concert*
     (9/93) (AUVI) ① **V4679**
Très lent—violin, cello and piano
Joachim Trio (r1993) *Concert*
     (8/95) (NAXO) ① **8 550934**

SECTION III: INSTRUMENTAL

In memoriam Gabriel Fauré—piano, Op. 72
M. Fingerhut *Concert*   (9/88) (CHAN) ① **CHAN8578**
Mirages—piano, Op.70 (1920-21)
P. Le Corre *Concert*   (3/87) (CYBE) ① **CY809**
Pièces romantiques—piano, Op.42 (1908)
P. Le Corre *Concert*   (3/87) (CYBE) ① **CY809**
Retardée—piano, Op. 90/3
B. Lerner *Concert*   (1/89) (ETCE) ① **KTC1061**
3 Valses nocturnes—piano, Op.31 (1901)
Cpte P. Le Corre *Concert*   (3/87) (CYBE) ① **CY809**

SECTION V: STAGE WORKS

Salammbô—concert suites from film score, Op. 76 (1925)
1. SUITE NO. 1—; 1a. The silent palace; The barbarians' feast; 1b. In the harem; Mathô's flight; With the sacred veil; 2. SUITE NO. 2—; 2a. In the tent; 2b. The old man's tale; The field of corpses; The Balearic rebels; 3. SUITE NO. 3—; 3a. War pact; Council of Elders; Massacre in the pass; Hamilicar's procession; 3b. Mathô's death.
1, 2, 3. French Army Chor, Ile de France Nat Orch, J. Mercier (1991)   (6/94) (ACCO) ① **20359-2**
La tragédie de Salomé—ballet: 7 scenes, Op. 50 (1907—Paris) (after R. d'Humières)
Cpte M-P. Fayt, Rhineland-Pfalz State PO, D. Davin (r1991)   (12/93) (MARC) ① **8 223448**

SCHMOOL, Barak (20th Cent)

SECTION II: CHAMBER

Stolen train—five pianos, prepared piano and typewriter (1990-93)
Piano Circus (r1992-93) *Concert*
     (2/95) (ARGO) ① **443 527-2ZH**

SCHNABEL, Artur (1882–1951)
Germany

SECTION I: ORCHESTRAL

Symphony No. 2 (1941-43)
RPO, P. Zukofsky   (9/92) (MOBS) ① **CP2104**

SECTION II: CHAMBER

Sonata for Violin and Piano (1935)
P. Zukofsky, U. Oppens *M. Feldman: Spring of Chosroes.*   (4/92) (MOBS) ① **CP2102**

SCHNITTKE, Alfred (b 1934)
USSR

SECTION I: ORCHESTRAL

Concerto for Cello and Orchestra No. 1 (1985-86)
T. Thedéen, Danish Nat RSO, L. Segerstam *Concert*
     (7/91) (BIS) ① **BIS-CD507**
M. Kliegel, Saarbrücken RSO, G. Markson *Concert*
     (1/92) (MARC) ① **8 223334**
N. Gutman, LPO, K. Masur *Schumann: Cello Concerto.*   (8/92) (EMI) ① **CDC7 54443-2**
Concerto for Cello and Orchestra No. 2 (1989-90)
M. Rostropovich, LSO, S. Ozawa *In memoriam for orchestra.*   (7/92) (SONY) ① **SK48241**
T. Thedéen, Malmö SO, L. Markiz *Concerto Grosso 2.*   (12/92) (BIS) ① **BIS-CD567**
Concerto for Oboe, Harp and Strings (1971)
H. Jahren, K.A. Lier, New Stockholm CO, L. Markiz *Concert*   (4/88) (BIS) ① **BIS-CD377**
Concerto for Piano and Strings (1979)
R. Pöntinen, New Stockholm CO, L. Markiz *Concert*
     (4/88) (BIS) ① **BIS-CD377**
V. Krainev, Moscow Virtuosi, V. Spivakov (r1991) *Concert*   (5/93) (RCA) ① **09026 60466-2**
I. Margalit, Moscow PO, D. Barra (r1992) *Concert*
     (9/93) (KOCH) ① **37159-2**
V. Krainev, Moscow Virtuosi, V. Spivakov (r1991) *Concert*   (5/94) (RCA) ① [2] **74321 24894-2**
Concerto for Viola and Orchestra (1985)
N. Imai, Malmö SO, L. Markiz *In Memoriam.*
     (12/91) (BIS) ① **BIS-CD447**
Y. Bashmet, LSO, M. Rostropovich *Trio Sonata.*
     (4/91) (RCA) ① **RD60446**
K. Kashkashian, Saarbrücken RSO, D.R. Davies *Kancheli: Vom Winde beweint.*
     (4/93) (ECM) ① **437 199-2**
T. Zimmermann, Jerusalem SO, D. Shallon (r1993) *Concert*   (8/94) (EMI) ① **CDC5 55107-2**
Y. Bashmet, LSO, M. Rostropovich (1988) *Concert*
     (5/94) (RCA) ① [2] **74321 24894-2**
I. van Keulen, Philh, H. Schiff (r1995) *Lutosławski: Chain 2.*   (11/95) (SCHW) ① **315232**

Concerto for Violin and Chamber Orchestra No. 3 (1978)
G. Kremer, COE, C. Eschenbach (r1994) *Concert*
     (2/95) (TELD) ① **4509-94540-2**
Concerto for Violin and Orchestra No. 1 (1957 rev 1963)
M. Lubotsky, Malmö SO, E. Klas *Violin Concerto 2.*
     (4/91) (BIS) ① **BIS-CD487**
Concerto for Violin and Orchestra No. 2 (1966)
M. Lubotsky, Malmö SO, E. Klas *Violin Concerto 1.*
     (4/91) (BIS) ① **BIS-CD487**
G. Kremer, COE, C. Eschenbach (r1994) *Concert*
     (2/95) (TELD) ① **4509-94540-2**
Concerto Grosso No. 1—2 violins, strings, harpsichord and piano (1977)
C. Bergqvist, P. Swedrup, R. Pöntinen, New Stockholm CO, L. Markiz *Concert*
     (4/88) (BIS) ① **BIS-CD377**
G. Kremer, T. Grindenko, LSO, G. Rozhdestvensky (r1977) *Sibelius: Violin Concerto.*
     (9/92) (RCA) ① **GD60957**
G. Kremer, T. Grindenko, Y. Smirnov, Y. Smirnov, COE, H. Schiff (pp1988) *Concert*
     (3/95) (DG) ① **445 520-2GMA**
G. Kremer, T. Grindenko, LSO, G. Rozhdestvensky (r1977) *Concert*
     (5/95) (RCA) ① [2] **74321 24894-2**
Concerto Grosso No. 2—violin, cello and orchestra (1981-82)
O. Krysa, T. Thedéen, Malmö SO, L. Markiz *Cello Concerto 2.*   (12/92) (BIS) ① **BIS-CD567**
Concerto grosso No. 3—pf/hpd, 2 vns and orch (1985)
R. Brautigam, V. Lieberman, J. Van Zweden, Concertgebouw, R. Chailly *Concerto grosso 4.*
     (2/92) (DECC) ① **430 698-2DH**
P. Swedrup, T. Olsson, Stockholm CO, L. Markiz *Concert*   (6/92) (BIS) ① **BIS-CD537**
Concerto Grosso No. 4 (Symphony No. 5)—ob, 2vns, va, vc, pf, hpd and orch (1988)
Gothenburg SO, N. Järvi *Pianissimo.*
     (8/90) (BIS) ① **BIS-CD427**
J. Spronk, J. Van Zweden, J.P. Knijff, R. Waterman, G.J. Leuverink, S. Boon, R. van den Brink, Concertgebouw, R. Chailly *Concerto grosso 3.*
     (2/92) (DECC) ① **430 698-2DH**
Concerto Grosso No. 5—violin, invisible piano and orchestra (1990-91)
G. Kremer, R. Keuschnig, VPO, C. von Dohnányi (pp1991) *Glass: Violin Concerto.*
     (10/93) (DG) ① **437 091-2GH**
Concerto Grosso No. 6—violin, piano and orchestra (1993)
S. Rozhdestvensky, V. Postnikova, Stockholm PO, G. Rozhdestvensky (r1994) *Symphony 8.*
     (7/95) (CHAN) ① **CHAN9359**
K ein Sommernachtstraum—orchestra (1985)
Malmö SO, L. Segerstam *Concert*
     (8/89) (BIS) ① **BIS-CD437**
Gogol Suite (1976) (compiled G. Rozhdestvensky)
Malmö SO, L. Markiz *Labyrinths.*
     (7/92) (BIS) ① **BIS-CD557**
In Memoriam—orchestra (1978) (orch ver of Pf Qnt, 1972-76)
Malmö SO, L. Markiz *Viola Concerto.*
     (8/90) (BIS) ① **BIS-CD447**
In memoriam—orchestra (1972-78)
LSO, M. Rostropovich *Cello Concerto 2.*
     (7/92) (SONY) ① **SK48241**
Monologue—viola and orchestra
Y. Bashmet (va/dir), Moscow Sols Ens *Concert*
     (6/91) (RCA) ① **RD60464**
T. Zimmermann, Jerusalem SO, D. Shallon (r1993) *Concert*   (8/94) (EMI) ① **CDC5 55107-2**
Y. Bashmet (va/dir), Moscow Sols Ens (r1990) *Concert*   (5/95) (RCA) ① [2] **74321 24894-2**
Moz-Art à la Haydn—game with music for various string groups (1977)
G. Kremer (vn/dir), T. Grindenko, COE (pp1988) *Concert*   (3/95) (DG) ① **445 520-2GMA**
Passacaglia—orchestra (1980)
Malmö SO, L. Segerstam *Concert*
     (8/89) (BIS) ① **BIS-CD437**
Pianissimo—large orchestra (1967-68)
Gothenburg SO, N. Järvi *Concerto grosso 4.*
     (8/90) (BIS) ① **BIS-CD427**
Quasi una sonata—violin, piano and chamber orchestra (1987)
M. Lubotsky, ECO, M. Rostropovich (r1992) *Concert*
     (4/94) (SONY) ① **SK53271**
G. Kremer (vn/dir), Y. Smirnov, COE (pp1988) *Concert*   (3/95) (DG) ① **445 520-2GMA**

6 Lieder, Op. 51 (1931-43) (Wds. Eichendorff (1-3); Mörike (4-6)
1. Nachtgruss; 2. Motto; 3. Trost; 4. Er ist's; 5. Septembermorgen; 6. Spruch.
J. Banse, D. Henschel, W. Rieger (r1992) *Concert*
(3/94) (JECK) ① **JD677-2**

Der Sänger—song cycle: 1v and piano, Op. 57 (1944-45) (Wds. H. Leuthold)
Cpte F. Lang, R. Lang-Oester (r1988)
(10/94) (SCHW) ① **310912**

Sommerabend—Lied (1921) (Wds. Müllenhof. Rediscovered 1978)
N. Tüller, C. Keller (r1992) *Concert*
(3/94) (JECK) ① **JD673-2**

Das Stille Leuchten—song cycle, Op. 60 (1946) (Wds. Meyer)
1. Das heilige Feuer; 2. Liederseelen; 3. Reisephantasie; 4. Mit einem Jugendbildnis; 5. Am Himmelstor; 6. In einer Sturmacht; 7. In Harmensnächten; 8. Lenzfahrt; 9. Frühling Triumphator; 10. Unruhige Nacht; 11. Was treibst du, Wind; 12. Hochzeitslied; 13. Der Gesang des Meeres; 14. Der römische Brunnen; 15. Das Ende des Festes; 16. Die Jungfrau; 17. Neujahrsglocken; 18. Alle; 19. Der Reisebecher; 20. Das weisse Spitzchen; 21. Göttermahl; 22. Ich würd'es hören; 23. Firnelicht; 24. Schwarzschattende Kastanie; 25. Requiem; 26. Abendwolke; 27. Nachtgeräusche; 28. Jetzt rede du!.
D. Fischer-Dieskau, H. Höll
(7/90) (CLAV) ① **CD50-8910**

Unter Sternen—song cycle, Op. 55 (1941-42) (Wds. Keller)
1. Trost der Kreatur; 2. Sonnenuntergang; 3. Siehst du den Stern; 4. Stille der Nacht; 5. Unter Sternen; 6. Abendlied an der Natur; 7. Unruhe der Nacht; 8. Waldlied I; 9. Waldlied II; 10. Stilleben; 11. Das Tal; 12. Abendlied; 13. Wir wähnten Inage recht zu leben; 14. Flackre, ew'ges Licht im Tal; 15. Die Zeit geht nicht; 16. Trübes Wetter; 17. Frühgesicht; 18. Frühlingsglaube; 19. In der Trauer; 20. Den Zweifellosen I und II; 21. Tod und Dichter; 22. An das Herz; 23. Ein Tagewerk I und II.
D. Fischer-Dieskau, H. Höll
(12/86) (CLAV) ① **CD50-8606**

Wanderung im Gebirge—song cycle (1930) (Wds. Lenau)
N. Tüller, C. Keller (r1992) *Concert*
(3/94) (JECK) ① **JD673-2**

Das Wandsbecker Liederbuch—song cycle, Op. 52 (1936) (Wds. Claudius)
1. Die Liebe; 2. Phidile; 3. Ein Wiegenlied, bei Mondschein zu singen; 4. Als er sein Weib und's Kind schlafend fand; 5. Die Natur; 6. Der Frühling; 7. Der Sternseherin; 8. Kuckuck; 9. Ein Lied, hinterm Ofen zu singen; 10. Abendlied; 11. Der Mensch; 12. Die Römer; 13. Der Schwarze in der Zuckerplantage; 14. Der Krieg; 15. Auf den Tod einer Kaiserin; 16. Der Tod; 17. Spruch.
J. Banse, D. Henschel, W. Rieger (r1992) *Concert*
(3/94) (JECK) ① **JD677-2**

Wiegenlied—Lied (1947) (Wds. & melody Jaeger)
J. Banse, W. Rieger (r1992) *Concert*
(3/94) (JECK) ① **JD677-2**

SECTION V: STAGE WORKS

Massimilla Doni—opera: 4 acts (6 scenes), Op. 50 (1937—Dresden) (Lib. Rüger, after Balzac)
Cpte E. Mathis, J. Protschka, H. Winkler, H. Stamm, R. Hermann, D. van der Walt, C. Lindsley, H. Küttenbaum, U. Ress, Cologne Rad Chor, Cologne RSO, G. Albrecht (bp1986)
(11/89) (SCHW) ① [2] **314025**

Penthesilea—opera: 1 act (1925—Dresden) (Lib. cpsr, after Kleist)
1. Suite (arr. Delfs).
Cpte H. Dernesch, J. Marsh, M. Gessendorf, M. Lipovšek, G. Sima, T. Adam, H. Hiestermann, P. Weber, Austrian Rad Chor, Austrian RSO, G. Albrecht (pp1982)
(3/91) (ORFE) ① **C364941B**
1. Swiss YSO, A. Delfs *Violin Concerto*.
(2/93) (CLAV) ① **CD50-9201**

Venus—opera: 3 acts, Op. 32 (1922—Zurich) (Lib. A. Rüeger, after Mérimée)
Cpte F. Lang, L. Popp, J. O'Neal, H. Fassbender, B. Skovhus, Z. Alfóldi, Heidelberg Chbr Ch, Basle Boys' Ch, Swiss Workshop PO, M. Venzago (r1991)
(10/94) (MGB) ① [2] **CD6112**

SCHOEMAKER, Maurice (1890–1964) Belgium

SECTION I: ORCHESTRAL

Flemish rhapsody—orchestra (1931)
Belgian Rad & TV Orch, A. Rahbari (r1992) *Concert*
(8/94) (DINT) ① **DICD920101**

SCHOENBERG, Arnold (Franz Walther) (1874–1951) Austria/USA

SECTION I: ORCHESTRAL

Begleitungsmusik zu einer Lichtspielszene, 'Accompaniment Music for a Film Scene'—orchestra, Op. 34 (1929-30)
BBC SO, P. Boulez (r1976) *Concert*
(12/93) (SONY) ① **SMK48462**
COE, H. Holliger (r1992) *Concert*
(10/94) (TELD) ① **9031-77314-2**
LSO, R. Craft (r1994) *Concert*
(6/95) (KOCH) ① **37263-2**

Chamber Symphony No. 1, Op. 9 (1906 rev 1922)
Schoenberg Ens, R. de Leeuw *Concert*
(8/89) (SCHW) ① **311009**
Orpheus CO *Concert* (7/90) (DG) ① **429 233-2GH**
A. Paratore, J. Paratore (arr Berg) *Brahms: Piano Quartet 1.* (9/90) (SCHW) ① **311034**
Nash Ens *Concert* (11/91) (VIRG) ① **VC7 59057-2**
Musique Oblique ens (trans Webern) *Pierrot lunaire.*
(8/92) (HARM) ① **HMC90 1390**
P. Gulda, Hagen Qt (r1992: arr Pf Qnt: Webern) *Brahms: Piano Quintet.*
(10/93) (DG) ① **437 804-2GH**
Paris InterContemporain Ens, P. Boulez (r1980) *Concert* (12/93) (SONY) ① **SMK48462**
Birmingham Contemp Mus Group, S. Rattle (r1993) *Concert* (4/95) (EMI) ① **CDC5 55212-2**
Arditti Qt, S. Litwin (1993: arr str qt & pf) *Concert*
(10/95) (AUVI) ① [2] **MO782025**
Tapiola Sinfonietta, J-J. Kantorow (r1994) *Concert*
(10/95) (BIS) ① [2] **BIS-CD703**

Chamber Symphony No. 2, Op. 38 (1906-39)
Orpheus CO *Concert* (7/90) (DG) ① **429 233-2GH**
Paris InterContemporain Ens, P. Boulez (r1980) *Moses und Aron.*
(12/93) (SONY) ① [2] **SM2K48456**
COE, H. Holliger (r1992) *Concert*
(10/94) (TELD) ① **9031-77314-2**

Concerto for Cello and Orchestra (1932-33) (after Monn: Keyboard Concerto in D, 1746)
H. Schiff, South-West German RSO, M. Gielen *Concert* (10/90) (WERG) ① **WER60185-50**

Concerto for Piano and Orchestra, Op. 42 (1942)
M. Pollini, BPO, C. Abbado (r1988) *Schumann: Piano Concerto.* (7/90) (DG) ① **427 771-2GH**
E. Ax, Philh, E-P. Salonen (r1992) *Concert*
(12/93) (SONY) ① **SK53289**
G. Gould, CBC SO, R. Craft (r1961) *Concert*
(4/93) (SONY) ① **SM2K52664**
A. Malling, Danish Nat RSO, M. Schønwandt (r1994) *Schumann: Piano Concerto.*
(10/95) (CHAN) ① **CHAN9375**

Concerto for Violin and Orchestra, Op. 36 (1935/6)
I. Isakadze, USSR Academy SO, A. Lazarev (r1980) *Khachaturian: Violin Concerto.*
(10/89) (OLYM) ① **OCD135**
L. Krasner, BRSO, D. Mitropoulos (pp1954) *Prokofiev: Symphony 5.*
(8/90) (ORFE) ① **C204891A**

Fanfare for a Bowl Concert—orchestra (1945)
Hollywood Bowl SO, J. Mauceri (r1991) *Concert*
(9/91) (PHIL) ① **432 109-2PH**

5 Orchestral Pieces, Op. 16 (1909)
BPO, James Levine *Concert*
(8/87) (DG) ① **419 781-2GH**
Schoenberg Ens, R. de Leeuw (arr Greissle) *Concert* (8/89) (SCHW) ① **311009**
CBSO, S. Rattle (1987/8) *Concert*
(11/89) (EMI) ① **CDC7 49857-2**
South-West German RSO, M. Gielen *Concert*
(10/90) (WERG) ① **WER60185-50**
LSO, A. Dorati *Concert*
(3/91) (MERC) ① **432 006-2MM**
D. Wilson-Johnson, P. Boulez (r1976) *Concert*
(12/93) (SONY) ① **SMK48463**
LSO, R. Craft (r1994) *Concert*
(6/95) (KOCH) ① **37263-2**

Chicago SO, D. Barenboim (r1994) *Concert*
(8/95) (TELD) ① **4509-98256-2**

Pelleas und Melisande—symphonic poem, Op. 5 (1902-03) (after Maeterlinck)
SNO, M. Bamert *Webern: Passacaglia.*
(10/88) (CHAN) ① **CHAN8619**
BPO, H. von Karajan *Concert*
(8/89) (DG) ① [3] **427 424-2GC3**
VPO, K. Böhm (pp1969) *Concert*
(2/92) (DG) ① [12] **435 321-2GWP12**
Chicago SO, P. Boulez *Variations, Op. 31.*
(4/93) (ERAT) ① **2292-45827-2**
New Philh, J. Barbirolli (r1967) *R. Strauss: Metamorphosen.* (7/94) (EMI) ① **CDM5 65078-2**
Atlanta SO, Y. Levi (r1993-4) *Verklärte Nacht.*
(3/95) (TELA) ① **CD80372**
Philh, G. Sinopoli (r1991) *Verklärte Nacht.*
(6/95) (DG) ① **439 942-2GH**

3 Pieces—chamber orchestra (1910)
Schoenberg Ens, R. de Leeuw *Concert*
(8/89) (SCHW) ① **311009**
Paris InterContemporain Ens, P. Boulez (r1980s) *Concert* (12/93) (SONY) ① **SMK48465**

String Quartet No. 2 in F sharp minor—orchestral arrangement, Op. 10 (1908, arr 1919?) (solo soprano in movts 3 & 4)
C. Högman, Tapiola Sinfonietta, J-J. Kantorow (r1994) *Concert* (10/95) (BIS) ① [2] **BIS-CD703**

Variations for Orchestra, Op. 31 (1926-28)
BPO, H. von Karajan (r1974) *Verklärte Nacht.*
(3/86) (DG) ① **415 326-2GH**
BPO, H. von Karajan *Concert*
(8/89) (DG) ① [3] **427 424-2GC3**
South-West German RSO, M. Gielen *Concert*
(10/90) (WERG) ① **WER60185-50**
Chicago SO, P. Boulez *Pelleas und Melisande.*
(4/93) (ERAT) ① **2292-45827-2**
BBC SO, P. Boulez (r1976) *Concert*
(12/93) (SONY) ① **SMK48464**
CBSO, S. Rattle (r1994) *Concert*
(4/95) (EMI) ① **CDC5 55212-2**

Verklärte Nacht, 'Transfigured Night' (1899) (arr. str. orch 1917; second ver 1943)
BPO, H. von Karajan (r1973) *Variations, Op. 31.*
(3/86) (DG) ① **415 326-2GH**
English Stg Orch, W. Boughton *R. Strauss: Metamorphosen.* (4/89) (NIMB) ① **NI5151**
BPO, H. von Karajan *Concert*
(8/89) (DG) ① [3] **427 424-2GC3**
Orpheus CO *Concert* (7/90) (DG) ① **429 233-2GH**
London Fest Orch, R. Pople *R. Strauss: Metamorphosen.* (9/91) (ASV) ① **CDDCA743**
Sinfonia Varsovia, E. Krivine *Concert*
(12/92) (DENO) ① **CO-79442**
Salzburg Mozarteum Camerata Academica, S. Végh *Brahms: String Quintet 2.*
(12/92) (CAPR) ① **10 427**
BPO, James Levine (r1991) *Concert*
(8/93) (DG) ① **435 883-2GH**
NYPO, P. Boulez (r1973) *Concert*
(12/93) (SONY) ① **SMK48464**
COE, H. Holliger (r1992) *Concert*
(10/94) (TELD) ① **9031-77314-2**
ECO, D. Barenboim (r1967) *Concert*
(12/94) (EMI) ① **CDM5 65079-2**
Atlanta SO, Y. Levi (r1993-4) *Pelleas und Melisande.*
(3/95) (TELA) ① **CD80372**
Philh, G. Sinopoli (r1992) *Pelleas und Melisande.*
(6/95) (DG) ① **439 942-2GH**
Chicago SO, D. Barenboim (r1994) *Concert*
(8/95) (TELD) ① **4509-98256-2**
Tapiola Sinfonietta, J-J. Kantorow (r1994) *Concert*
(10/95) (BIS) ① [2] **BIS-CD703**
Bamberg SO, L. Zagrosek (r1993-4) *Bruckner: String Quintet.* (11/95) (ORFE) ① **C348951**

SECTION II: CHAMBER

Phantasy—violin and piano, Op. 47 (1949)
N. Gotkovsky, I. Gotkovsky *Concert*
(9/91) (PYRA) ① **PYR13496**
Y. Menuhin, G. Gould (bp1965) *Concert*
(10/93) (SONY) ① **SMK52688**
I. Baker, G. Gould (r1964) *Concert*
(4/95) (SONY) ① [2] **SM2K52664**
I. Arditti, S. Litwin (r1993) *Concert*
(10/95) (AUVI) ① [2] **MO782025**

Presto in C—string quartet (?1896-97)
Arditti Qt (r1993) *Concert*
(10/95) (AUVI) ① [2] **MO782025**

Scherzo in F—string quartet (1897)
Arditti Qt (r1993) *Concert*
(10/95) (AUVI) ① [2] **MO782025**

String Quartet in D (1897)
LaSalle Qt *Concert*
(4/88) (DG) ① [4] **419 994-2GCM4**

Artis Qt *Zemlinsky: String Quartet 2.*
(7/90) (ORFE) ① **C194901A**
Arditti Qt (r1993) *Concert*
(10/95) (AUVI) ① [2] **MO782025**
String Quartet No. 1, Op. 7 (1905)
LaSalle Qt *Concert*
(4/88) (DG) ① [4] **419 994-2GCM4**
Schoenberg Qt (7/89) (SCHW) ① **310033**
Kolisch Qt (r1936) *Concert*
(1/94) (ARCI) ① [2] **ARC103/4**
Manfred Qt (r1990) (4/94) (PIER) ① **PV791031**
Arditti Qt (r1993) *Concert*
(1/95) (AUVI) ① [2] **MO782024**
String Quartet No. 2 in F sharp minor, Op. 10
(1907) (solo soprano in movts 3 & 4)
M. Price, LaSalle Qt *Concert*
(4/88) (DG) ① [4] **419 994-2GCM4**
C. Gifford, Kolisch Qt (r1936) *Concert*
(1/94) (ARCI) ① [2] **ARC103/4**
D. Upshaw, Arditti Qt (r1993) *Concert*
(1/95) (AUVI) ① [2] **MO782024**
C. Oelze, Brindisi Qt (r1994) *Concert*
(6/95) (METR) ① **METCD1007**
A. Roocroft, Britten Qt *Schubert: String Quartet,*
D804. (7/95) (EMI) ① **CDC5 55289-2**
String Quartet No. 3, Op. 30 (1927)
LaSalle Qt *Concert*
(4/88) (DG) ① [4] **419 994-2GCM4**
Kolisch Qt (r1936) *Concert*
(1/94) (ARCI) ① [2] **ARC103/4**
Arditti Qt (r1993) *Concert*
(1/95) (AUVI) ① [2] **MO782024**
String Quartet No. 4, Op. 37 (1936)
LaSalle Qt *Concert*
(4/88) (DG) ① [4] **419 994-2GCM4**
Kolisch Qt (r1937) *Concert*
(1/94) (ARCI) ① [2] **ARC103/4**
Arditti Qt (r1993) *Concert*
(1/95) (AUVI) ① [2] **MO782024**
String Trio, Op. 45 (1946)
W. Levin, P. Kamnitzer, L. Fiser *Verklärte Nacht.*
(9/88) (DG) ① **423 250-2GC**
Juilliard Qt *Pierrot Lunaire.*
(2/90) (SONY) ① **MPK45695**
R. Mann, S. Rhodes, J. Krosnick *Verklärte Nacht.*
(5/93) (SONY) ① **SK47690**
D. Alberman, G. Knox, R. de Saram (r1993) *Concert*
(10/95) (AUVI) ① [2] **MO782025**
Suite in E flat for nine instruments, Op. 29
(1926)
Paris InterContemporain Ens, P. Boulez (r1982)
Concert (12/93) (SONY) ① **SMK48465**
Verklärte Nacht—string sextet, Op. 4 (1899)
LaSalle Qt, D. McInnes, J. Pegis *String Trio.*
(9/88) (DG) ① **423 250-2GC**
Talich Qt, J. Najnar, V. Bernašék (r1989) *Dvořák:*
String Sextet. (1/90) (CALL) ① **CAL9217**
Raphael Ens *Korngold: String Sextet, Op. 10.*
(1/91) (HYPE) ① **CDA66425**
Nash Ens *Concert* (11/91) (VIRG) ① **VC7 59057-2**
Vienna Stg Sextet *Brahms: String Sextet 3.*
(3/92) (EMI) ① **CDC7 54140-2**
W. Trampler, Y-Y. Ma, Juilliard Qt *String Trio.*
(5/93) (SONY) ① **SK47690**
Paris InterContemporain Ens, P. Boulez (r1983)
Concert (12/93) (SONY) ① **SMK48465**
A. Dinkin, K. Reher, Hollywood Qt (r1950) *Schubert:*
String Quintet. (4/94) (TEST) ① **SBT1031**
Arditti Qt, T. Kakuska, V. Erben (r1993) *Concert*
(10/95) (AUVI) ① [2] **MO782025**
Weihnachtsmusik—2 vlns, vlc, harm, pno
(1921)
Versailles Camerata, A. du Closel *Concert*
(9/88) (AUVI) ① **AV6110**

SECTION III: INSTRUMENTAL

2 Fragments of a Sonata for Organ (1941)
1. Molto moderato; 2. Allegretto.
K. Bowyer (r1993) *Concert* (1/95) (NIMB) ① **NI5411**
Klavierstück, Op. 33a (1928-9)
M. Pollini *Concert* (6/88) (DG) ① **423 249-2GC**
K. Wolpe *Concert* (10/92) (SYMP) ① **SYMCD1107**
G. Gould (r1965) *Concert*
(4/95) (SONY) ① [2] **SM2K52664**
Klavierstück, Op. 33b (1931)
M. Pollini *Concert* (6/88) (DG) ① **423 249-2GC**
K. Wolpe *Concert* (10/92) (SYMP) ① **SYMCD1107**
G. Gould (r1965) *Concert*
(4/95) (SONY) ① [2] **SM2K52664**
3 Klavierstücke, Op. 11 (1909)
M. Pollini *Concert* (6/88) (DG) ① **423 249-2GC**
K. Wolpe *Concert* (10/92) (SYMP) ① **SYMCD1107**
G. Gould (r1958) *Concert*
(4/95) (SONY) ① [2] **SM2K52664**
D. Barenboim (r1994) *Concert*
(8/95) (TELD) ① **4509-98256-2**

No. 2. D. Barenboim (r1994: arr Busoni) *Concert*
(8/95) (TELD) ① **4509-98256-2**
6 Klavierstücke, Op. 19 (1911)
M. Pollini *Concert* (6/88) (DG) ① **423 249-2GC**
K. Wolpe *Concert* (10/92) (SYMP) ① **SYMCD1107**
G. Gould (r1965) *Concert*
(4/95) (SONY) ① [2] **SM2K52664**
D. Barenboim (r1994) *Concert*
(8/95) (TELD) ① **4509-98256-2**
G. Herzfeld (r1994) *Concert*
(11/95) (EDA) ① **EDA008-2**
5 Klavierstücke, Op. 23 (1920-23)
M. Pollini *Concert* (6/88) (DG) ① **423 249-2GC**
K. Wolpe *Concert* (10/92) (SYMP) ① **SYMCD1107**
G. Gould (r1965) *Concert*
(4/95) (SONY) ① [2] **SM2K52664**
Suite—piano, Op. 25 (1921-23)
M. Pollini *Concert* (6/88) (DG) ① **423 249-2GC**
K. Wolpe *Concert* (10/92) (SYMP) ① **SYMCD1107**
G. Gould (r1964) *Concert*
(4/95) (SONY) ① [2] **SM2K52664**
G. Gould (pp1959) *Concert*
(9/95) (SONY) ① **SMK53474**
Variations on a Recitative—organ, Op. 40
(1941)
K. Bowyer (r1993) *Concert* (1/95) (NIMB) ① **NI5411**

SECTION IV: VOCAL AND CHORAL

Am Strande—Lied (1909) (Wds. R. M. Rilke)
S. Lange, T. Lønskov *Concert*
(2/90) (KONT) ① [3] **32028/30**
D. Fischer-Dieskau, A. Reimann *Concert*
(9/90) (EMI) ① **CDM7 63570-2**
2 Balladen, Op. 12 (1907)
1. Jane Grey (wds. H. Amman); 2. Der verlorene
Haufen (wds. V. Klemperer).
S. Lange, L.T. Bertelsen, T. Lønskov *Concert*
(2/90) (KONT) ① [3] **32028/30**
2. D. Fischer-Dieskau, A. Reimann *Concert*
(9/90) (EMI) ① **CDM7 63570-2**
Der Buch der hängenden Gärten—song
cycle, Op. 15 (1908-09) (Wds. S. George)
S. Lange, T. Lønskov *Concert*
(2/90) (KONT) ① [3] **32028/30**
P. Bryn-Julson, U. Oppens *Concert*
(6/92) (MUSI) ① **MACD-650**
J. Kaufmann, I. Gage (r1992) *Concert*
(2/94) (ORFE) ① **C305931A**
Cabaret Songs—voice and chamber
ensemble (1901) (Wds. various)
1. Galathea (wds. Wedekind); 2. Gigerlette (wds. B.
Bierbaum); 3. Der genügsame Liehhaber (wds. H.
Salus); 4. Einfältiges Lied (wds. H. Salus); 5.
Mahnung (wds. G. Hochstetter); 6. Jedem das Seine
(wds. Colly); 7. Seit ich so viele Weiber sah (from
'Spiegel von Arcadia': wds. Schikaneder); 8.
Nachtwandler (wds. G. Falke).
D. Dorow, T. Crone, R. de Reede, P. Masseurs, W.
Goudswaard *Concert* (12/88) (ETCE) ① **KTC1051**
J. Norman, NY Met Op Orch, James Levine (r1990)
Erwartung. (9/93) (PHIL) ① **426 261-2PH**
1, 2, 3. M. Shirai, H. Höll (r1993) *Concert*
(5/95) (CAPR) ① **10 514**
1-7. P. Bryn-Julson, U. Oppens *Concert*
(6/92) (MUSI) ① **MACD-650**
2, 3, 5, 7. J. Gomez, J. Constable *Concert*
(6/88) (UNIC) ① **DKPCD9055**
7. F. von Stade, Martin Katz (pp1994) *Concert*
(1/95) (RCA) ① **09026 62547-2**
Deinem Blick mich zu bequemen—Lied
(1903) (Wds. Goethe)
S. Lange, T. Lønskov *Concert*
(2/90) (KONT) ① [3] **32028/30**
D. Fischer-Dieskau, A. Reimann *Concert*
(9/90) (EMI) ① **CDM7 63570-2**
3 Deutsche Volkslieder—4vv a capella
(1929)
1. Es gingen zwei Gespielen; 2. Herzlieblich Lieb,
durch Scheiden; 3. Schein uns, du liebe Sonne.
BBC Sngrs, P. Boulez *Concert*
(8/90) (SONY) ① [2] **SM2K44571**
Dreimal tausend Jahre—4vv a capella, Op.
50a (1949) (Wds. D. D. Runes)
BBC Sngrs, P. Boulez *Concert*
(8/90) (SONY) ① [2] **SM2K44571**
Drüben geht die Sonne scheiden—Lied
(1893) (Wds. N Lenau)
M. Shirai, H. Höll (r1993) *Concert*
(5/95) (CAPR) ① **10 514**
4 Folksong Arrangements (1929)
1. Der Mai tritt ein mit Freuden; 2. Es gingen zwei
Gespielen gut; 3. Mein Herz in steten Treuen; 4. Mein
Herz ist mir gemenget.
S. Lange, T. Lønskov *Concert*
(2/90) (KONT) ① [3] **32028/30**

M. Shirai, H. Höll (r1993) *Concert*
(5/95) (CAPR) ① **10 514**
Friede auf Erden—8 voices, instruments ad
lib, Op. 13 (1907-11) (Wds. C. F. Meyer)
BBC Sngrs, P. Boulez *Concert*
(8/90) (SONY) ① [2] **SM2K44571**
Danish Nat Rad Chbr Ch, S. Parkman *Concert*
(12/91) (CHAN) ① **CHAN8963**
E. Futral, J. Malafronte, F. Urrey, W. Pauley, Musica
Sacra, R. Westenburg *Concert*
(1/93) (RCA) ① **09026 60970-2**
Gedenken—Lied (before 1900) (Wds. anon)
S. Lange, T. Lønskov *Concert*
(2/90) (KONT) ① [3] **32028/30**
M. Shirai, H. Höll (r1993) *Concert*
(5/95) (CAPR) ① **10 514**
Gruss in die Ferne—Lied (1900) (Wds. H.
Lingg)
L.T. Bertelsen, T. Lønskov *Concert*
(2/90) (KONT) ① [3] **32028/30**
S. Kimbrough, D. Baldwin (r1990) *Concert*
(2/95) (SCHW) ① **310942**
Gurrelieder—soloists, narrator, chorus and
orchestra (1900-03 rev 1910-11) (Wds.
Jacobsen)
J. Norman, T. Troyanos, J. McCracken, W.
Klemperer, Tanglewood Fest Chor, Boston SO, S.
Ozawa (pp1979)
(3/85) (PHIL) ① [2] **412 511-2PH2**
S. Jerusalem, S. Dunn, B. Fassbaender, H. Becht, P.
Haage, H. Hotter, Berlin St Hedwig's Cath Ch,
Düsseldorf Musikverein, Berlin RSO, R. Chailly
(3/91) (DECC) ① [2] **430 321-2DH2**
E. Connell, J. van Nes, P. Frey, V. Vogel, W.
Grönroos, N German Rad Chor, Bavarian Rad Chor,
Frankfurt Op Chor, Frankfurt RSO, E. Inbal
(4/93) (DENO) ① [2] **CO-77066/7**
M. Napier, Y. Minton, Jess Thomas, K. Bowen, S.
Nimsgern, G. Reich, BBC Sngrs, BBC Choral Soc,
Goldsmiths' Choral Union, LP Ch, BBC SO, P.
Boulez (r1974) *Lieder, Op. 22.*
(12/93) (SONY) ① [2] **SM2K48459**
S. Sweet, M. Lipovšek, S. Jerusalem, P. Langridge,
H. Welker, B. Sukowa, A. Schoenberg Ch, Slovak
Phil Chor, Vienna St Op Chor, VPO, C. Abbado
(pp1992) (5/95) (DG) ① [2] **439 944-2GH2**
Herzgewächse—speaker, celeste,
harmonium and harp, Op. 20 (1911) (Wds.
Maeterlinck)
E. Hulse, LSO, P. Craft (r1994) *Concert*
(6/95) (KOCH) ① **37263-2**
In hellen Träumen—Lied (1893) (Wds Gold)
S. Kimbrough, D. Baldwin (r1990) *Concert*
(2/95) (SCHW) ① **310942**
Die Jakobsleiter—oratorio: soloists, chorus
and orchestra (1917-22 rev 1944) (fragment
only)
S. Nimsgern, K. Bowen, I. Partridge, P. Hudson, J.
Shirley-Quirk, A. Rolfe Johnson, O. Wenkel, M.
Mesplé, BBC Sngrs, BBC SO, P. Boulez (r1980)
Concert (12/93) (SONY) ① **SMK48462**
Kol Nidre—speaker, chorus and orchestra,
Op. 39 (1938) (Wds. Jewish liturgy, trans Eng)
J. Shirley-Quirk, BBC Chor, BBC SO, P. Boulez
Concert (8/90) (SONY) ① [2] **SM2K44571**
Lied der Waldtuabe—mezzo-soprano and 17
instruments (1900 arr 1922)
J. van Nes, Schoenberg Ens, R. de Leeuw (arr cpsr:
mezzo and chamber orchestra) *Concert*
(8/89) (SCHW) ① **311009**
J. Norman, Paris InterContemporain Ens, P. Boulez
(r1979) *Concert* (12/93) (SONY) ① **SMK48466**
2 Lieder, Op. 1 (?1898) (Wds. K. von
Levetzow)
1. Dank; 2. Abschied.
L.T. Bertelsen, T. Lønskov *Concert*
(2/90) (KONT) ① [3] **32028/30**
4 Lieder, Op.2 (1899)
1. Erwartung (wds. Dehmel); 2. Schenk mir deinen
goldenen Kamm (wds. Dehmel); 3. Erhebung (wds.
Dehmel); 4. Waldsonne (wds. Schlaf).
E. Speiser, I. Gage *Concert*
(1/89) (JECK) ① **JD561-2**
S. Lange, T. Lønskov *Concert*
(2/90) (KONT) ① [3] **32028/30**
L. Popp, I. Gage *Concert* (4/92) (RCA) ① **RD60950**
P. Bryn-Julson, U. Oppens *Concert*
(6/92) (MUSI) ① **MACD-650**
M. Shirai, H. Höll (r1993) *Concert*
(5/95) (CAPR) ① **10 514**
1, 2. D. Fischer-Dieskau, A. Reimann *Concert*
(9/90) (EMI) ① **CDM7 63570-2**
6 Lieder, Op. 3 (1899)
1. Wie Georg von Frundsberg (Wds. Knaben
Wunderhorn); 2. Die Aufgeregten (Wds. G. Keller); 3.
Warnung (Wds. R. Dehmel); 4. Hochzeitslied (Wds.

J. P. Jacobsen); 5. Geübtes Herz (Wds. G. Keller); 6. Freihold (Wds. H. Lingg).
S. Lange, L.T. Bertelsen, T. Lønskov *Concert*
(2/90) (KONT) ① [3] **32028/30**
1. T. Hampson, G. Parsons *Concert*
(10/90) (TELD) ① **2292-44923-2**
1-3, 5. D. Fischer-Dieskau, A. Reimann *Concert*
(9/90) (EMI) ① **CDM7 63570-2**
2. M. Shirai, H. Höll (r1993) *Concert*
(5/95) (CAPR) ① **10 514**

8 Lieder, Op. 6 (1903-05)
1. Traumleben (wds. J. Hart); 2. Alles (wds. R. Dehmel); 3. Mädchenlied (wds. P. Renner); 4. Verlassen (wds. H. Conradi); 5. Ghasel (wds. G. Keller); 6. Am Wegrand (wds. J. H. Mackay); 7. Lockung (wds. K. Aram); 8. Der Wanderer (wds. F. Nietzsche).
S. Lange, T. Lønskov *Concert*
(2/90) (KONT) ① [3] **32028/30**
1, 4, 8. D. Fischer-Dieskau, A. Reimann *Concert*
(9/90) (EMI) ① **CDM7 63570-2**
1, 4, 8. M. Shirai, H. Höll (r1993) *Concert*
(5/95) (CAPR) ① **10 514**

2 Lieder, Op. 12 (1907)
1. Jane Grey (wds. H.Amman); 2. Der verlorene Haufen (wds. V.Klemperer).
1. M. Shirai, H. Höll (r1993) *Concert*
(5/95) (CAPR) ① **10 514**

2 Lieder, Op. 14 (1907-08)
1. Ich darf nicht (wds. S. George); 2. In diesen Wintertagen (wds. G. Henckel).
S. Lange, T. Lønskov *Concert*
(2/90) (KONT) ① [3] **32028/30**
M. Shirai, H. Höll (r1993) *Concert*
(5/95) (CAPR) ① **10 514**
1. D. Fischer-Dieskau, A. Reimann *Concert*
(9/90) (EMI) ① **CDM7 63570-2**

4 Lieder—1v and orchestra, Op. 11 (1913)
1. Seraphita (wds. E. Dowson, trans George); 2. Alle welche dich suchen (wds. Rilke); 3. Mach mich zum Wächter deiner Weiten (wds. Rilke); 4. Vorgefühl (wds. Rilke).
Y. Minton, BBC SO, P. Boulez (r1981) *Gurrelieder*.
(12/93) (SONY) ① [2] **SM2K48459**

3 Lieder, Op. 48 (1933) (Wds. J. Haringer)
1. Sommermüd; 2. Tot; 3. Mädchenlied.
S. Lange, T. Lønskov *Concert*
(2/90) (KONT) ① [3] **32028/30**
1, 2. D. Fischer-Dieskau, A. Reimann *Concert*
(9/90) (EMI) ① **CDM7 63570-2**

Mädchenfrühling—Lied (1897) (Wds. R. Dehmel)
S. Lange, T. Lønskov *Concert*
(2/90) (KONT) ① [3] **32028/30**

Mailied—Lied (Wds Goethe)
S. Kimbrough, D. Baldwin (r1990) *Concert*
(2/95) (SCHW) ① **310942**

Mannesbangen—Lied (before 1903) (Wds. R. Dehmel)
S. Lange, T. Lønskov *Concert*
(2/90) (KONT) ① [3] **32028/30**
S. Kimbrough, D. Baldwin (r1990) *Concert*
(2/95) (SCHW) ① **310942**

Mein Herz das ist ein tiefer Schacht—Lied (before 1900) (Wds. anon)
S. Lange, T. Lønskov *Concert*
(2/90) (KONT) ① [3] **32028/30**

Moderner Psalm—speaker, chorus and orchestra, Op. 50c (1950) (Wds. cpsr)
J. Shirley-Quirk, BBC Chor, London SInfonietta, P. Boulez *Concert* (12/93) (SONY) ① **SM2K44571**
G. Reich, Bratislava Phil Ch, South-West German RSO, M. Gielen *Concert*
(10/90) (WERG) ① **WER60185-50**

Nicht doch!—Lied (before 1900) (Wds. Dehmel)
S. Lange, T. Lønskov *Concert*
(2/90) (KONT) ① [3] **32028/30**

O dass der Sinnen doch so viele sind
BBC Sngrs, P. Boulez *Concert*
(8/90) (SONY) ① [2] **SM2K44571**

Ode to Napoleon—reciter, piano and string quartet/string orchestra, Op. 41 (1942) (Wds. Byron)
T. Allen, Nash Ens *Concert*
(11/91) (VIRG) ① **VC7 59057-2**
D. Wilson-Johnson, Paris InterContemporain Ens, P. Boulez *Concert* (r1980) *Concert*
(12/93) (SONY) ① **SMK48463**
J. Horton, G. Gould, Juilliard Qt (r1965) *Concert*
(4/95) (SONY) ① [2] **SM2K52664**
Arditti Qt, S. Litwin, M. Carey (r1993) *Concert*
(10/95) (AUVI) ① [2] **MO782025**
R. Hermann, T. Vogler, F. Reinecke, S. Fehlandt, M. Sanderling, F-I. Zichner (r1993) *Concert*
(11/95) (EDA) ① **EDA008-2**

Pierrot lunaire—song cycle: speaker and chamber ensemble, Op. 21 (1912) (Wds. Giraud)
E. Sziklay, Budapest Chbr Ens, A. Mihály *Concert*
(10/87) (HUNG) ① **HCD11385**
E. Stiedry-Wagner, R. Kolisch, S. Auber, E. Steuermann, L. Posella, K. Bloch, A. Schoenberg (r1941) *String Trio.* (2/90) (SONY) ① **MPK45695**
J. Manning, Nash Ens, S. Rattle (r1977) *Webern: Concerto, Op. 24.* (8/92) (CHAN) ① **CHAN6534**
Musique Oblique ens, P. Herreweghe *Chamber Symphony 1.* (8/92) (HARM) ① **HMC90 1390**
Y. Minton, D. Barenboim, M. Debost, A. Pay, P. Zukerman, L. Harrell, P. Boulez (r1977) *Concert*
(12/93) (SONY) ① **SMK48466**
P. Rideout, G. Gould (r1975) *Concert*
(4/95) (SONY) ① [2] **SM2K52664**

Psalm 130, 'De profundis'—6vv a capella, Op. 50b (1950) (Wds. Bible)
BBC Sngrs, P. Boulez *Concert*
(8/90) (SONY) ① [2] **SM2K44571**

Sang ein Bettlerpärlein am Schenkentor (Mädchenlied)—Lied (before 1900) (Wds. P. Heyse)
S. Lange, T. Lønskov *Concert*
(2/90) (KONT) ① [3] **32028/30**

3 Satiren—4vv a capella, Op. 28 (1925) (Wds. cpsr)
1. Am Scheideweg; 2. Vielseitigkeit; 3. Der neune Klassizimus.
BBC Sngrs, London SInfonietta, P. Boulez *Concert*
(8/90) (SONY) ① [2] **SM2K44571**

Serenade—chamber ensemble with baritone, Op. 24 (1920-23)
J. Shirley-Quirk, Paris InterContemporain Ens, P. Boulez (r2979) *Concert*
(12/93) (SONY) ① **SMK48463**
S. Varcoe, Twentieth Century Classics Ens, R. Craft (r1994) *Concert* (6/95) (KOCH) ① **37263-2**
Sonett No. 217. I. Arditti, R. de Saram, S. Litwin (r1993: arr vn, vc & pf) *Concert*
(10/95) (AUVI) ① [2] **MO782025**

4 Stücke—4vv a capella, Op. 27 (1925)
1. Unentrinnbar (wds. cpsr); 2. Du sollst nicht, du musst (wds. cpsr); 3. Mond und Menschen (wds. Tschan-Jo-Su, trans. Bethge); 4. Der Wunsch des Liebhabers (wds. Hung-So-Fan, trans. trans Bethge).
BBC Sngrs, London SInfonietta, P. Boulez *Concert*
(8/90) (SONY) ① [2] **SM2K44571**

6 Stücke—male voices a capella, Op. 35 (1929-30) (Wds. cpsr)
1. Hemmung; 2. Gesetz; 3. Ausdrucksweise; 4. Glück; 5. Landsknechte; 6. Verbundenheit.
BBC Sngrs, London SInfonietta, P. Boulez *Concert*
(8/90) (SONY) ① [2] **SM2K44571**

A Survivor from Warsaw—narrator, male voices and orchestra, Op. 46 (1947) (Wds. cpsr)
G. Reich, BBC Sngrs, BBC SO, P. Boulez *Concert*
(8/90) (SONY) ① [2] **SM2K44571**
G. Hornik, Vienna St Op Chor, VPO, C. Abbado (r1989) *Concert* (5/93) (DG) ① **431 774-2GH**
S. Callow, London Voices, LSO, R. Craft (r1994) *Concert* (6/95) (KOCH) ① **37263-2**

3 Volkslieder—4vv a capella, Op. 49 (1948)
1. Es gingen zwei Gespielen gut; 2. Der Mai tritt ein mit Freuden; 3. Mein Herz in steten Treuen.
BBC Sngrs, P. Boulez *Concert*
(8/90) (SONY) ① [2] **SM2K44571**

Waldesnacht, du wunderkühle—Lied (before 1900) (Wds. P. Weyse)
S. Lange, T. Lønskov *Concert*
(2/90) (KONT) ① [3] **32028/30**

Warum bist du aufgewacht—Lied (1893-4) (Wds Pfau)
S. Kimbrough, D. Baldwin (r1990) *Concert*
(2/95) (SCHW) ① **310942**

Wenn der schwer Gedruckte klagt
BBC Sngrs, P. Boulez *Concert*
(8/90) (SONY) ① [2] **SM2K44571**

SECTION V: STAGE WORKS

Erwartung—monodrama: 1 act, Op. 17 (1909—Prague) (Lib. M. Pappenheim)
Cpte A. Silja, VPO, C. von Dohnányi *Berg: Wozzeck.*
(2/89) (DECC) ① [2] **417 348-2DH2**
Cpte J. Norman, NY Met Op Orch, James Levine (r1989) *Cabaret Songs.*
(9/93) (PHIL) ① **426 261-2PH**
Cpte J. Martin, BBC SO, P. Boulez (r1977) *Concert*
(12/93) (SONY) ① **SMK48466**
Cpte P. Bryn-Julson, CBSO, S. Rattle (r1993) *Concert*
(4/95) (EMI) ① **CDC5 55212-2**

Die glückliche Hande—drama with music: 1 act, Op. 18 (1924—Vienna) (Wds. cpsr)
S. Nimsgern, BBC Sngrs, BBC SO, P. Boulez (r1981) *Concert* (12/93) (SONY) ① **SMK48464**

Moses und Aron—opera: 3 acts (1930-32: fp 1951) (Lib. cpsr)
Cpte F. Mazura, P. Langridge, A. Haugland, B. Bonney, M. Zakai, D. Harper, T. Dymit, H. Wittges, K. Link, J. Braham, B. Pearson, C. Anderson, K. Zajac, R. Cohn, P. Grizzell, S. Schweikert, E. Gottlieb, K. Brunssen, Roald Henderson, B. Nystrom, W. Kirkwood, Glen Ellyn Children's Chor, Chicago Sym Chor, Chicago SO, G. Solti (r1984)
(1/85) (DECC) ① [2] **414 264-2DH2**
Cpte G. Reich, R. Cassilly, R. Angas, F. Palmer, G. Knight, J. Winfield, R. Hermann, J. Noble, J. Manning, G. Knight, H. Watts, P. Langridge, M. Rippon, D. Wicks, BBC Sngrs, Orpheus Boys' Ch, BBC SO, P. Boulez (r1974) *Chamber Symphony 2.*
(12/93) (SONY) ① [2] **SM2K48456**

SCHOENFIELD, Paul (b 1947) USA

SECTION I: ORCHESTRAL

Klezmer Rondos—flute, male vocalist and orchestra (1986)
C. Wincenc, New World Sym, J. Nelson (r1992) *Concert* (6/94) (ARGO) ① **440 212-2ZH**

4 Parables—piano and orchestra (1982-83)
1. Rambling till the butcher cuts us down; 2. Senility's ride; 3. Elegy; 4. Dog heaven.
J. Kahane, New World Sym, J. Nelson (r1992) *Concert* (6/94) (ARGO) ① **440 212-2ZH**

Vaudeville—piccolo trumpet and orchestra
1. Overture; 2. Bear Dance; 3. Klezmers; 4. Sketches; 5. Carmen Rivera.
W. Basch, New World Sym, J. Nelson (r1992) *Concert* (6/94) (ARGO) ① **440 212-2ZH**

SECTION II: CHAMBER

3 Country Fiddle Pieces (1980)
R. Davidovici, P. Schoenfield *Concert*
(11/87) (NEW) ① **NW334-2**

SCHOLEFIELD, Clement Cotterill (1839–1904) England

SECTION IV: VOCAL AND CHORAL

The Day thou gavest, Lord, is ended—hymn
St Paul's Cath Ch, C. Dearnley, John Scott *Concert*
(7/90) (HYPE) ① **CDH88036**

SCHOLL, Andreas (20th cent) ?Germany

SECTION IV: VOCAL AND CHORAL

White as Lilies—song
A. Scholl, K.E. Schröder (r1995: arr R Wagner) *Concert* (8/95) (HARM) ① **HMC90 1552**

SCHOLZ Germany

SECTION I: ORCHESTRAL

Torgau March—wind band (c1816)
Berlin Phil Wind Qnt, H. von Karajan (r1973) *Concert*
(5/94) (DG) ① **439 346-2GX2**

SCHÖNBERG, Claude-Michel (20th Cent) France

SECTION V: STAGE WORKS

Les Misérables—musical show (1985—London) (Lyrics H. Kretzmer; Book A. Boublil & Schönberg, after V. Hugo)
EXCERPTS: 1. Prologue; 2. At the End of the Day; 3. I Dreamed a Dream; 4. Lovely Ladies; 5. Who Am I?; 6. Come to Me; 7. Confrontation; 8. Castle On a Cloud; 9. Master of the House; 10. Stars; 11. Look Down; 12. Little People; 13. Red and Black; 14. Do You Hear the People Sing?; 15. I Saw Him Once; 16. In My Life; 17. A Heart Full of Love; 18. One Day More; 19. On My Own; 20. The Attack; 21. A Little Fall of Rain; 22. Drink With Me to Days Gone By; 23. Bring Him Home; 24. Dog Eats Dog; 25. Soliloquy; 26. Empty Chairs at Empty Tables; 27. Wedding Chorale; 28. Beggars at the Feast; 29. Finale.
Cpte International Cast, Philh, M. Koch (Symphonic Score version) (3/89) (FRST) ① [3] **MIZCD1**
3, 23. M. Patinkin, Orch, E. Stern (r1993; orch Troob, arr Ford) *Concert* (11/94) (NONE) ① **7559-79330-2**

SCHOP, Johann (c1590–1667) Germany

SECTION II: CHAMBER

Lachrime pavaen—recorder and continuo
M. Huggett, S. Cunningham, S. Stubbs (r1992)
Concert   (5/94) (TELD) ① **4509-90841-2**

SCHÖZLER

SECTION III: INSTRUMENTAL

Etudes—piano, Op. 1
2. S. Hough (r1986) Concert
          (1/89) (VIRG) ① **VC7 59509-2**

SCHRADER, Mogens Denmark

SECTION IV: VOCAL AND CHORAL

Summer night—song (Wds. Stevens)
J. Björling, orch, N. Grevillius (r1936) Concert
          (9/94) (CONI) ① **CDHD214**

SCHRAMMEL, Johann (1850 – 1893) Austria

SECTION I: ORCHESTRAL

Wien bleibt Wien—march (1884)
Berlin Phil Wind Qnt, H. von Karajan (r1973: arr
Schmidt-Petersen) Concert
          (5/94) (DG) ① **439 346-2GX2**

SCHREKER, Franz (1878–1934) Austria

SECTION I: ORCHESTRAL

Chamber Symphony (1916)
Berlin RSO, M. Gielen Concert
          (11/88) (SCHW) ① **311078**
Nachtstücke
Berlin RSO, K.A. Rickenbacher Concert
          (11/88) (SCHW) ① **311078**
Prelude to a Drama—orchestra (1914) (later
used as Prelude to 'Die Gezeichneten')
Berlin RSO, M. Gielen Concert
          (11/88) (SCHW) ① **311078**
Valse lente
Berlin RSO, K.A. Rickenbacher Concert
          (11/88) (SCHW) ① **311078**

SECTION IV: VOCAL AND CHORAL

Entführung—lied (1909) (Wds George)
S. Kimbrough, D. Baldwin (r1990) Concert
          (2/95) (SCHW) ① **310942**
Funf Gesänge (1909)
1. Ich frag' nach dir jedwede Morgen sonne (1001
Nights); 2. Dies aber mein Sehen nimmer
fassen (wds. Ronsperger); 3. Die Dunkelheit sinkt
schwer wie Blei (wds. Ronsperger); 4. Sie sind so
schön die milden, sonnenreichen (wds. Ronsperger);
5. Einst gibt ein Tag mir alles Glück zu eigen (wds.
Ronsperger).
A. Reichling, Versailles Camerata, A. du Closel (arr
Neuwirth) Concert   (9/88) (AUVI) ① **AV6110**
D. Dorow, M. Damerini (pp1980) Concert
          (8/89) (ETCE) ① **KTC1044**
4. L. Popp, I. Gage Concert
          (4/92) (RCA) ① **RD60950**
2 Gesänge, Op. 2 (before 1899)
1. Sommerfäden (wds. Leen); 2. Stimmen des Tages
(wds. Saar).
1. L. Popp, I. Gage Concert
          (4/92) (RCA) ① **RD60950**
5 Lieder, Op. 4 (before 1899)
1. Unendliche Liebe (wds. Tolstoy); 2. Frühling (wds.
Lemayer); 3. Wohl fühl' ich wie das Leben rinnt (wds.
Storm); 4. Die Liebe als Recensentin (wds. Sturm); 5.
Lenzzauber (wds. Scherenberg).
D. Dorow, M. Damerini (pp1980) Concert
          (8/89) (ETCE) ① **KTC1044**
1. L. Popp, I. Gage Concert
          (4/92) (RCA) ① **RD60950**
1-4. S. Kimbrough, D. Baldwin (1990) Concert
          (2/95) (SCHW) ① **310942**
2, 4. E. Speiser, I. Gage Concert
          (1/89) (JECK) ① **JD561-2**
8 Lieder, Op. 7 (1898-1900)
1. Wiegenliedchen (wds. Sturm); 2. Späte Reue
(wds. Sturm); 3. Traum (wds. Leen); 4. Spuk (wds.
Leen); 5. Rosentod (wds. Leen); 6. Ach, noch so jung
(wds. Scherenberg); 7. Rosengruss (wds.
Scherenberg); 8. Lied des Harfenmädchens (wds.

Storm).
1. S. Kimbrough, D. Baldwin (r1990) Concert
          (2/95) (SCHW) ① **310942**
2, 5. E. Speiser, I. Gage Concert
          (1/89) (JECK) ① **JD561-2**
5. L. Popp, I. Gage Concert
          (4/92) (RCA) ① **RD60950**
Ein Rosenblatt—lied (Wds Zusner)
S. Kimbrough, D. Baldwin (r1990) Concert
          (2/95) (SCHW) ① **310942**
**Und wie mag die Liebe dir kommen
sein?—lied (1920)** (Wds Rilke)
S. Kimbrough, D. Baldwin (r1990) Concert
          (2/95) (SCHW) ① **310942**

SECTION V: STAGE WORKS

**Der Ferne Klang—opera: 3 acts
(1912—Frankfurt)** (Lib. cpsr)
Cpte E. Grigorescu, T. Harper, A. Haller, H. Fiehl, R.
Bunse, E. Pilarl, P. Friess, W. Hahn, P.N. Kante, R.
Leisenheimer, W. Pickersgill, Hagen Op Chor, Hagen
PO, M. Halász (r1989)
          (8/90) (MARC) ① [2] **8 223270/1**
Cpte G. Schnaut, T. Moser, S. Nimsgern, H. Helm, V.
von Halem, B. Scherler, J.W. Prein, R. Hermann, G.
Saks, R. Wörle, C. Otelli, J. Juon, Berlin RIAS Chbr
Ch, Berlin Rad Chor, Berlin RSO, G. Albrecht
          (12/91) (CAPR) ① [2] **60 024-2**
In einem Lande ein bleicher König T. Hampson,
Munich RO, F. Luisi (r1994) Concert
          (9/95) (EMI) ① **CDC5 55233-2**
**Der Geburtstag der Infantin, '(The) Birthday
of the Infanta'—concert suite from the ballet
(1923)**
Leipzig Gewandhaus, L. Zagrosek (r1994) Concert
          (5/95) (DECC) ① **444 182-2DH**
**Die Gezeichneten—opera: 3 acts
(1918—Frankfurt)** (Lib. cpsr)
Cpte C. van Tassel, S. Cowan, W. Oosterkamp, M.
Schmiege, W. Cochran, H. Meens, F. Lang, E.D.
Smid, M. Dirks, E. Godding, C. van Tassel, E.
Bollongino, Dutch Rad Phil Chor, Dutch Rad PO, E.
de Waart (pp1990)
          (12/91) (MARC) ① [3] **8 223328/30**
Cpte A. Muff, M. Pederson, L. Polgár, E. Connell, H.
Kruse, R. Wörle, E. Wottrich, O. Widmer, M. Görne,
K. Sigmundsson, P. Salomaa, M. Posselt, C.
Berggold, M. Petzold, H. Lippert, R. Beyer, M.
Rüping, J. Becker, G. Schwarz, K. Borris, I. Nguyen-
Huu, R. Schudel, R. Ginzel, J. Gottschick, F.
Molsberger, P. Menzel, M. Köhler, J. Metzger, H.
Czerny, Berlin Rad Chor, Berlin Deutsches SO, L.
Zagrosek (r1993/4)
          (6/95) (DECC) ① [3] **444 442-2DHO3**
Irrelohe—opera: 3 acts (1924—Cologne) (Lib.
cpsr)
Cpte M. Pabst, L. DeVol, G. Simic, E. Randová, M.
Pederson, H. Zednik, N. Belamaric, S. Holecek, H.
Wildhaber, Vienna Singverein, Vienna SO, P. Gülke
(pp1989)   (12/95) (SONY) ① [2] **S2K66850**
**Der Schatzgräber—opera: prologue, 4 acts
& epilogue (1920—Frankfurt)** (Lib. cpsr)
Cpte J. Protschka, G. Schnaut, H. Stamm, P. Haage,
H. Helm, H. Kruse, C. Schultz, P. Galliard, U.
Malmberg, F.F. Nentwig, H. Jankun, J. Metzger, H.
Hamburg St Op Chor, Hamburg St Op Orch, G.
Albrecht (pp1989)   (5/90) (CAPR) ① [2] **60 010-2**

SCHRÖTER, Johann Samuel (c1752–1788) Germany

SECTION I: ORCHESTRAL

**Concerto for Piano and Orchestra in C, Op.
3/3 (c1774)**
M. Perahia (pf/dir), ECO Mozart: Piano Concertos,
K107.   (1/86) (SONY) ① **SK39222**

SCHUBERT, Franz (Peter) (1797–1828) Austria

SECTION I: ORCHESTRAL

**Concertstück in D—violin and orchestra,
D345 (1816)**
St. Paul CO, P.Zukerman (vn/dir) Concert
          (11/87) (PHIL) ① **420 168-2PH**
J-J. Kantorow, Netherlands PO, E. Krivine Concert
          (4/88) (DENO) ① **CO-1666**
G. Kremer, LSO, E. Tchakarov Concert
          (1/91) (DG) ① **431 168-2GGA**
V. Snitil, Prague SO, J. Hlaváček Concert
          (10/91) (SUPR) ① **11 1114-2**
G. Kremer, COE (r1991) Concert
          (8/93) (DG) ① **437 535-2GH**

**Overture in D to Albrecht's comedy 'Der
Teufel als Hydraulicus', D4 (71812)**
English Sinfonia, C. Groves Concert
          (5/92) (CARL) ① **PCD967**
**Overture in the Italian style in C, D591
(1817)**
Stockholm Sinfonietta, N. Järvi Concert
          (9/88) (BIS) ① **BIS-CD387**
VPO, I. Kertész Concert
          (4/92) (DECC) ① [4] **430 773-2DC4**
English Sinfonia, C. Groves Concert
          (5/92) (CARL) ① **PCD967**
Northern Sinfonia, H. Schiff (r1992) Concert
          (6/93) (CHAN) ① **CHAN9136**
San Francisco SO, H. Blomstedt (r1992) Symphony
9.   (10/93) (DECC) ① **436 598-2DH**
Concertgebouw, N. Harnoncourt (1992) Concert
          (12/93) (TELD) ① **4509-97509-2**
**Overture in the Italian style in D, D590
(1817)**
Stockholm Sinfonietta, N. Järvi Concert
          (4/90) (BIS) ① **BIS-CD453**
**Polonaise in B flat—violin and orchestra,
D580 (1817)**
St. Paul CO, P.Zukerman (vn/dir) Concert
          (11/87) (PHIL) ① **420 168-2PH**
J-J. Kantorow, Netherlands PO, E. Krivine Concert
          (4/88) (DENO) ① **CO-1666**
G. Kremer, LSO, E. Tchakarov Concert
          (1/91) (DG) ① **431 168-2GGA**
V. Snitil, Prague SO, J. Hrnčíř Concert
          (10/91) (SUPR) ① **11 1114-2**
G. Kremer, COE (r1991) Concert
          (8/93) (DG) ① **437 535-2GH**
**Rondo in A—violin and orchestra, D438
(1816)**
St. Paul CO, P.Zukerman (vn/dir) Concert
          (11/87) (PHIL) ① **420 168-2PH**
J-J. Kantorow, Netherlands PO, E. Krivine Concert
          (4/88) (DENO) ① **CO-1666**
N. Kennedy, ECO, J. Tate Concert
          (1/89) (EMI) ① **CDC7 49663-2**
E. Verhey, Colorado Qt Concert
          (11/90) (LASE) ① **15 522**
G. Kremer, LSO, E. Tchakarov Concert
          (1/91) (DG) ① **431 168-2GGA**
A. Grumiaux, New Philh, R. Leppard Concert
          (4/91) (PHIL) ① **426 977-2PCC**
J. Gatwood, V. Beths, L. Rautenberg, S. Dann, K.
Slowik (r1990) String Quintet.
          (9/91) (SONY) ① **SK46669**
H. Temianka (vn/dir), Temianka CO (r1937) Concert
          (3/93) (BIDD) ① [2] **LAB059/60**
G. Kremer, COE (r1991) Concert
          (8/93) (DG) ① **437 535-2GH**
Symphonic Fragment in D, D615 (1818)
(sketches for two movements)
ASMF, N. Marriner (orch. Newbould) Concert
          (3/85) (PHIL) ① [6] **412 176-2PH6**
**Symphonic Fragment in D, D708a (after
1820)** (sketches only)
ASMF, N. Marriner (cpted & orch. Newbould) Concert
          (3/85) (PHIL) ① [6] **412 176-2PH6**
Symphony No. 1 in D, D82 (1813)
ASMF, N. Marriner Concert
          (3/85) (PHIL) ① [6] **412 176-2PH6**
BPO, K. Böhm (r1971) Concert
          (5/88) (DG) ① [4] **419 318-2GH4**
COE, C. Abbado Concert
          (2/89) (DG) ① [5] **423 651-2GH5**
BPO, H. von Karajan Concert
          (2/89) (EMI) ① [4] **CMS7 69884-2**
Cologne RSO, G. Wand Concert
          (2/89) (RCA) ① [5] **GD60096**
COE, C. Abbado Symphony 2.
          (9/89) (DG) ① **423 652-2GH**
Hanover Band, R. Goodman Concert
          (3/91) (NIMB) ① [4] **NI5270/3**
VPO, R. Muti Symphony 8.
          (8/91) (EMI) ① **CDC7 54066-2**
VPO, I. Kertész Concert
          (4/92) (DECC) ① [4] **430 773-2DC4**
Concertgebouw, N. Harnoncourt (pp1992) Concert
          (12/93) (TELD) ① [4] **4509-91184-2**
Concertgebouw, N. Harnoncourt (r1992) Concert
          (12/93) (TELD) ① **4509-97509-2**
VPO, R. Muti (r1990) Concert
          (5/94) (EMI) ① [4] **CMS7 64873-2**
Budapest Failoni Orch, M. Halász (r1994) Symphony
2.   (8/95) (NAXO) ① **8 553093**
Symphony No. 2 in B flat, D125 (1814-15)
ASMF, N. Marriner Concert
          (3/85) (PHIL) ① [6] **412 176-2PH6**
BPO, K. Böhm (r1971) Concert
          (5/88) (DG) ① [4] **419 318-2GH4**

Music Group of London (8/93) (ASV) ① CDQS6098
Budapest Schubert Ens (r1992) Octet, D72.
(8/93) (NAXO) ① 8 550389
Nash Ens (r1987) (10/93) (VIRG) ① VC5 45017-2
Berlin Sols (r1987)
(11/93) (TELD) ① 4509-91448-2
Vienna Chbr Ens (r1980)
(10/94) (DG) ① 437 318-2GGA
Berlin Philh Ens (r1988)
(10/94) (DENO) ① CO-75671
Overture in F—piano duet, D675 (?1819)
I. Beyer, H. Dagul (r1993) Concert
(7/93) (FOUR) ① FHMD892
Y. Tal, A. Groethuysen (r1993) Concert
(9/94) (SONY) ① [2] S2K58955
**Piano Quintet in A, 'Trout'—piano, violin,
viola, cello and double-bass, D667 (1819)**
Emil Gilels, N. Brainin, P. Schidlof, M. Lovett, R.
Zepperitz String Quartet, D703.
(11/84) (DG) ① 413 453-2GH
A. Schiff, Hagen Qt (4/85) (DECC) ① 411 975-2DH
E. Leonskaja, Alban Berg Qt, G. Hörtnagel
(1/87) (EMI) ① CDC7 47448-2
Nash Ens Hirt auf dem Felsen, D965.
(12/87) (CARL) ① PCD868
C. Curzon, Vienna Octet String Quartet, D810.
(6/88) (DECC) ① 417 459-2DM
Nash Ens Nottumo, D897.
(5/89) (CRD) ① CRD3352
I. Haebler, Grumiaux Trio, J. Cazauran Concert
(10/89) (PHIL) ① 422 838-2PC
Schubert Ens of London Hummel: Piano Quintet, op
87. (6/90) (HYPE) ① CDH88010
Prometheus Ens Concert
(6/90) (ASV) ① CDDCA684
M. Horszowski, Budapest Qt, Julius Levine
Impromptus. (10/90) (SONY) ① MPK44847
E. Verhey, F. Erblich, J. Decroos, P. Jansen, D.
Dechenne Concert (11/90) (LASE) ① 15 522
R. Serkin, J. Laredo, P. Naegele, L. Parnas, Julius
Levine Mozart: Clarinet Quintet, K581.
(6/91) (SONY) ① SMK46252
Alberni Qt, S. Tanyel String Quartet, D810.
(10/91) (COLL) ① Coll1074-2
J. Jandó, Kodály Qt, I. Tóth Adagio and Rondo
concertante, D487. (4/93) (NAXO) ① 8 550658
S. Lubin, AAM Chbr Ens Concert
(9/93) (L'OI) ① 433 848-2OH
G. Hetzel, W. Christ, G. Faust, A. Posch, James
Levine (r1990) Guitar Quartet, D96.
(1/94) (DG) ① 431 783-2GH
Domus, C-C. Nwanoku (r1988) Adagio and Rondo
Concertante, D487.
(11/94) (VIRG) ① CUV5 61140-2
Movt 4. C. Curzon, Vienna Octet (r1957) Concert
(6/93) (DECC) ① 436 407-2DWO
**Piano Trio in B flat, D28 (1812) (one
movement only)**
Beaux Arts Trio (r1984) Concert
(7/86) (PHIL) ① 412 620-2PH2
J-P. Collard, A. Dumay, F. Lodéon Concert
(4/88) (EMI) ① CDC7 49165-2
M. Kaplan, C. Carr, D. Golub Concert
(10/88) (ARAB) ① [2] Z6580-2
Beaux Arts Trio (r1960s) Piano Trio 2.
(6/90) (PHIL) ① 426 096-2PC
Trieste Trio Concert (5/91) (NUOV) ① [2] 6857/8
Rubinstein Trio Concert
(5/91) (CHNT) ① LDC278 970/1
Castle Trio Piano Trio 2.
(11/93) (VIRG) ① VC7 59303-2
Beaux Arts Trio (r1966) Concert
(4/94) (PHIL) ① [2] 438 700-2PM2
S. Ritchie, M. Lutzke, S. Lubin (r1992) Concert
(7/94) (HARM) ① HMU90 7094
Piano Trio No. 1 in B flat, D898 (1827)
Borodin Trio (3/84) (CHAN) ① CHAN3308
Beaux Arts Trio (r1984) Concert
(7/86) (PHIL) ① 412 620-2PH2
Israel Pf Trio (12/86) (CRD) ① CRD3438
G. Oppitz, D. Sitkovetsky, D. Geringas Nottumo,
D897. (6/87) (NOVA) ① 150 002-2
J-P. Collard, A. Dumay, F. Lodéon Concert
(4/88) (EMI) ① CDC7 49165-2
M. Kaplan, C. Carr, D. Golub Concert
(10/88) (ARAB) ① [2] Z6580-2
H. Szeryng, P. Fournier, A. Rubinstein Schumann:
Piano Trio 1. (4/89) (RCA) ① GD86262
J. Thibaud, P. Casals, A. Cortot (r1926) Beethoven:
Piano Trios. (10/89) (EMI) ① CDH7 61024-2
M. Hess, d'Aranyi, F. Salmond (r c1928) Concert
(8/90) (APR) ① [2] APR7012
Trieste Trio Concert (5/91) (NUOV) ① [2] 6857/8
Rubinstein Trio Concert
(5/91) (CHNT) ① LDC278 970/1

J. Thibaud, P. Casals, A. Cortot (r1926) Concert
(12/91) (EMI) ① [3] CHS7 64057-2
London Mozart Trio Dvořák: Piano Trio 4.
(11/92) (CARL) ① PCD1006
Beaux Arts Trio (r1966) Concert
(4/94) (PHIL) ① [2] 438 700-2PM2
A. Schneider, P. Casals, E. Istomin (r1951)
Beethoven: Piano Trios.
(5/94) (SONY) ① SMK58989
S. Ritchie, M. Lutzke, S. Lubin (r1992) Concert
(7/94) (HARM) ① HMU90 7094
J. Heifetz, E. Feuermann, A. Rubinstein (r1941)
Beethoven: Piano Trios.
(11/94) (RCA) ① [65] 09026 61778-2(29)
Piano Trio No. 2 in E flat, D929 (1827)
Borodin Trio (r1981) (11/84) (CHAN) ① CHAN8324
Beaux Arts Trio (r1984) Concert
(7/86) (PHIL) ① 412 620-2PH2
G. Oppitz, D. Sitkovetsky, D. Geringas
(6/87) (NOVA) ① 150 003-2
R. Serkin, A. Busch, H. Busch (r1935) Fantasie,
D934. (4/88) (EMI) ① CDH7 61014-2
M. Kaplan, C. Carr, D. Golub Concert
(10/88) (ARAB) ① [2] Z6580-2
A. Dumay, F. Lodéon, J-P. Collard Sonata, D574.
(11/89) (EMI) ① CDC7 47553-2
Beaux Arts Trio (r1960s) Piano Trio 2.
(6/90) (PHIL) ① 426 096-2PC
Trieste Trio Concert (5/91) (NUOV) ① [2] 6857/8
Rubinstein Trio Concert
(5/91) (CHNT) ① LDC278 970/1
Castle Trio Piano Trio 2.
(11/93) (VIRG) ① VC7 59303-2
Beaux Arts Trio (r1966) Concert
(4/94) (PHIL) ① [2] 438 700-2PM2
A. Schneider, P. Casals, M. Horszowski (r1952)
Beethoven: Piano Trios.
(5/94) (SONY) ① SMK58988
J. Heifetz, G. Piatigorsky, J. Lateiner (r1965) Brahms:
Piano Trio 2.
(11/94) (RCA) ① [65] 09026 61778-2(38)
A. Busch, H. Busch, R. Serkin (r1935) Concert
(7/95) (PEAR) ① [2] GEMMCDS9141
Bekova Sisters (r c1995) Nottumo, D897.
(11/95) (CHAN) ① CHAN9414
4 Polonaises—piano duet, D599 (1818)
1. D minor; 2. B flat; 3. E; 4. F.
I. Beyer, H. Dagul Concert
(10/89) (FOUR) ① FHMD891
Crommelynck Duo Concert
(10/91) (CLAV) ① CD50-8802
6 Polonaises—piano duet, D824 (1826)
1. D minor; 2. F; 3. B flat; 4. D; 5. A; 6. E.
Y. Tal, A. Groethuysen (r1993) Concert
(9/94) (SONY) ① [2] S2K58955
I. Beyer, H. Dagul Divertissement, D823.
(12/95) (FOUR) ① FHMD895
**Quartet in G—guitar, flute, viola and cello,
D96 (1814 (discovered 1918) (after Nottumo,
Op. 21 by Matiegka)**
W. Schulz, W. Christ, G. Faust, G. Söllscher (r1993)
Trout Quintet, D667. (1/94) (DG) ① 431 783-2GH
**Rondo brillant in B minor—violin and piano,
D895 (1826)**
J. Swensen, J. Kahane Concert
(8/89) (RCA) ① RD87962
M. Rostal, C. Horsley Concert
(1/90) (SYMP) ① SYMCD1068
G. Kremer, V. Afanassiev Concert
(3/92) (DG) ① 431 654-2GH
R. Oleg, G. Wyss (r1993) Concert
(7/94) (DENO) ① CO-75636
Rondo in A—piano duet, D951 (1828)
P. Badura-Skoda, J. Demus Concert
(1/90) (AUVI) ① V4622
Crommelynck Duo (r1994) Concert
(1/95) (CLAV) ① CD50-9413
Rondo in D—piano duet, D608 (1818)
P. Badura-Skoda, J. Demus Concert
(1/90) (AUVI) ① V4622
Crommelynck Duo Concert
(10/91) (CLAV) ① CD50-8901
I. Beyer, H. Dagul (r1993) Concert
(7/93) (FOUR) ① FHMD892
Y. Tal, A. Groethuysen (r1993) Concert
(9/94) (SONY) ① [2] S2K58955
**Sonata for Arpeggione and Piano in A minor,
D821 (1824) (usually played by cello and
piano)**
M. Maisky, M. Argerich Concert
(1/86) (PHIL) ① 412 230-2PH
G. de Peyer, G. Pryor (arr/ed De Peyer and Bellison)
Concert (4/87) (CHAN) ① CHAN8506
M. Rostropovich, B. Britten (r1968) Concert
(9/87) (DECC) ① 417 833-2DH

L. Harrell, James Levine Dvořák: Cello Concerto.
(11/87) (RCA) ① GD86531
J. Swensen, K. Kahane (arr vn) Concert
(8/89) (RCA) ① RD87962
N. Imai, R. Vignoles Beethoven: Nottumo, Op.42.
(4/90) (CHAN) ① CHAN8664
English Gtr Qt (arr Gallery) Concert
(9/90) (SAYD) ① CD-SDL379
Y. Bashmet, M. Muntain Concert
(12/90) (RCA) ① RD60112
F-J. Sellheim, E. Sellheim Concert
(10/92) (SONY) ① SBK48171
M. Kliegel, K. Merscher (r1991) Concert
(7/93) (NAXO) ① 8 550654
G. Cassadó, Bamberg SO, J. Perlea (r1950s; arr
Cassadó) Concert
(11/93) (VOX) ① [2] CDX2 5502
G. Cassadó, Concertgebouw, W. Mengelberg
(pp1940: arr Cassadó) Concert
(7/94) (MUSI) ① [4] MACD-780
R. Oleg, G. Wyss (r1993) Concert
(7/94) (DENO) ① CO-75636
M. Rostropovich, B. Britten (r1968) Bridge: Cello
Sonata. (4/95) (DECC) ① 443 575-2DCS
G. Caussé, F-R. Duchâble (r1994: arr va/pf) Concert
(7/95) (EMI) ① CDC5 55166-2
Sonata for Piano Duet in B flat, D617 (1818)
C. Smith, P. Sellick Concert
(9/89) (NIMB) ① NI5178
I. Beyer, H. Dagul Concert
(10/89) (FOUR) ① FHMD891
**Sonata for Piano Duet in C, 'Grand
Duo'—two pianos, D812 (1824)**
COE, C. Abbado (orch Joachim) Concert
(2/89) (DG) ① [5] 423 651-2GH5
Crommelynck Duo Concert
(10/91) (CLAV) ① CD50-8901
E. Feuermann, G. Moore (r1937) Concert
(5/92) (EMI) ① CDH7 64250-2
I. Beyer, H. Dagul (r1993) Concert
(6/94) (FOUR) ① FHMD893
Budapest Failoni Orch, M. Halász (r1994: arr
Joachim) Symphony 4. (8/95) (NAXO) ① 8 553095
**Sonata for Violin and Piano in A, D574
(1817)**
L. Mordkovitch, G. Oppitz Fantasie, D934.
(4/89) (CHAN) ① CHAN8544
A. Dumay, J-P. Collard Piano Trio 2.
(11/89) (EMI) ① CDC7 47553-2
M. Rostal, C. Horsley Concert
(1/90) (SYMP) ① SYMCD1068
A. Chumachenco, R. Gothóni Concert
(7/91) (ONDI) ① ODE746-2
G. Kremer, V. Afanassiev Concert
(3/92) (DG) ① 431 654-2GH
R. Oleg, T. Paraskivesco (r1991) Concert
(3/93) (DENO) ① CO-75027
F. Kreisler, S. Rachmaninov (r1928) Concert
(3/93) (RCA) ① [10] 09026 61265-2(1)
A. Grumiaux, R. Castagnone (1955) Concert
(11/93) (PHIL) ① [3] 438 516-2PM3
F. Biondi, O. Tverskaya (r1995) Concert
(10/95) (O111) ① OPS30-126
**Sonat(in)a for Violin and Piano in A minor,
D385 (1816)**
M. Rostal, C. Horsley Concert
(1/90) (SYMP) ① SYMCD1068
V. Vaidman, E. Krasovsky Concert
(6/90) (CARL) ① PWK1137
A. Chumachenco, R. Gothóni Concert
(7/91) (ONDI) ① ODE746-2
R. Oleg, T. Paraskivesco (r1991) Concert
(3/93) (DENO) ① CO-75027
G. Kremer, O. Maisenberg (r1991) Concert
(4/93) (DG) ① 437 092-2GH
A. Grumiaux, R. Castagnone (r1955) Concert
(11/93) (PHIL) ① [3] 438 516-2PM3
J. Schröder, C. Hogwood Concert
(9/94) (L'OI) ① 443 196-2OM
F. Biondi, O. Tverskaya (r1995) Concert
(10/95) (O111) ① OPS30-126
**Sonat(in)a for Violin and Piano in D, D384
(1816)**
J. Swensen, J. Kahane Concert
(8/89) (RCA) ① RD87962
M. Rostal, C. Horsley Concert
(1/90) (SYMP) ① SYMCD1068
A. Chumachenco, R. Gothóni Concert
(7/91) (ONDI) ① ODE746-2
R. Oleg, T. Paraskivesco (r1991) Concert
(3/93) (DENO) ① CO-75027
G. Kremer, O. Maisenberg (r1991) Concert
(4/93) (DG) ① 437 092-2GH
A. Grumiaux, R. Castagnone (r1955) Concert
(11/93) (PHIL) ① [3] 438 516-2PM3

Valse sentimentale—transcription for violin & piano (trans. Franko from unidentified work)
V. Spivakov, S. Bezrodny (r1991-2) *Concert*
(5/95) (RCA) ① **09026 62524-2**

8 Variations in A flat—piano duet, D813 (1824)
Crommelynck Duo *Concert*
(10/91) (CLAV) ① **CD50-8901**
I. Beyer, H. Dagul (r1993) *Concert*
(6/94) (FOUR) ① **FHMD893**

Variations in B flat—piano duet, D603, later D968a (?1824)
P. Badura-Skoda, J. Demus *Concert*
(1/90) (AUVI) ① **V4622**
Y. Tal, A. Groethuysen (r1993) *Concert*
(9/94) (SONY) ① [2] **S2K58955**

8 Variations in E minor on a French song—piano four hands, D624 (1818)
I. Beyer, H. Dagul (r1993) *Concert*
(7/93) (FOUR) ① **FHMD892**
Crommelynck Duo (r1994) *Concert*
(1/95) (CLAV) ① **CD50-9413**

8 Variations on a theme from Hérold's 'Marie'—piano duet, D908 (1827)
A. Goldstone, C. Clemmow (r1988) *Concert*
(4/89) (SYMP) ① **SYMCD1037**
Y. Tal, A. Groethuysen (r1993) *Concert*
(9/94) (SONY) ① [2] **S2K58955**

SECTION III: INSTRUMENTAL

Adagio in G—piano, D178 (1815)
L. Hokanson (1/90) (NORT) ① **NR233-CD**
M. Dalberto (r1994) *Concert*
(7/95) (DENO) ① **CO-78914**

Allegretto in C minor—piano, D900 (after 1820) (fragment only)
O. Maisenberg *Concert*
(1/89) (ORFE) ① **C043831A**

Allegretto in C minor—piano, D915 (1827)
P. Berkowitz *Concert* (11/87) (MERI) ① **CDE84102**
M. Pollini *Concert*
(4/88) (DG) ① [2] **419 229-2GH2**
A. Brendel *Concert* (2/89) (PHIL) ① **422 229-2PH**
A. Schnabel (r1939) *Impromptus.*
(4/89) (EMI) ① **CDH7 61021-2**
M. Pollini *Concert* (5/89) (DG) ① **427 326-2GH**
I. Cooper *Concert* (10/90) (OTTA) ① **OTRC88821**
D. Barenboim *Concert*
(11/91) (DG) ① **435 072-2GGA**
S. Kovacevich (r1994) *Concert*
(7/95) (EMI) ① **CDC5 55359-2**
S. Richter (r1961) *Concert*
(12/95) (DG) ① [2] **447 355-2GDB2**

Andante in C—piano, D29 (1812) (arr cpsr from Str Qt, D3)
L. Hokanson (1/90) (NORT) ① **NR233-CD**
M. Dalberto (10/90) (DENO) ① **CO-76330**

Andantino in C—piano, D348 (?1816) (fragment only)
O. Maisenberg *Concert*
(1/89) (ORFE) ① **C043831A**

Cotillon in E flat—piano, D976 (1825)
1, 2, 14, 20, 22, 26, 29, 30, 31, 32, 33, 34, 35, 36. M. Dalberto (r1994) *Concert*
(7/95) (DENO) ① **CO-78914**

12 Deutsche (Ländler)—piano, D790 (1823)
1. D; 2. A; 3. D; 4. D; 5. B minor; 6. G sharp minor; 7. A flat; 8. A flat minor; 9. B; 10. B; 11. A flat; 12. E.
I. Cooper *Concert* (4/88) (OTTA) ① **OTRC68608**
M. Dalberto (r1993) *Concert*
(6/94) (DENO) ① **CO-75757**
A. Cortot (r1937) *Concert* (5/95) (BIDD) ① **LHW020**
S. Kovacevich (r1994) *Concert*
(7/95) (EMI) ① **CDC5 55359-2**
2, 3, 6-9. P. Badura-Skoda *Concert*
(2/89) (MUSI) ① **MACD-267**

6 Deutsche Tänze—piano, D820 (1824)
1. A flat; 2. A flat; 3. A flat; 4. B flat; 5. B flat; 6. B flat.
Berlin RSO, M. Bamert (orch Webern) *Concert*
(9/90) (SCHW) ① **311135**
Frankfurt RO, A. Webern (arr pf1932: orch Webern) *Concert* (6/91) (SONY) ① [3] **SM3K45845**
NY Chbr SO, G. Schwarz (orch Webern) *Concert*
(5/92) (DELO) ① **DE3067**
A. Schiff *Concert* (11/92) (DECC) ① **430 425-2DH**

2 Deutsche Tänze—piano, D841 (1825)
1. F; 2. G.
M. Dalberto (10/90) (DENO) ① **CO-76330**

16 Deutsche Tänze and 2 Ecossaises—piano, D783 (1823-24)
1. A; 2. D; 3. B flat; 4. G; 5. B minor; 6. B flat; 7. B flat; 8. E flat; 9. C; 10. A minor; 11. E minor; 12. C; 13. C; 14. F minor; 15. F minor; 16. F.
A. Brendel *Concert* (2/89) (PHIL) ① **422 229-2PH**
A. Brendel *Concert* (2/92) (VANG) ① **08.4026.71**
I. Cooper *Concert* (2/92) (OTTA) ① **OTRC87923**

M. Dalberto (r1993-4) *Concert*
(10/95) (DENO) ① **CO-78955**
5. P. Badura-Skoda *Concert*
(2/89) (MUSI) ① **MACD-267**

Ecossaise in D—piano, D782 (c1823)
M. Dalberto (r1993) *Concert*
(6/94) (DENO) ① **CO-75757**

Ecossaise in D minor/F—piano, D158 (1815)
M. Dalberto *Concert* (10/90) (DENO) ① **CO-76330**

9 Ecossaises—piano, D145 (1815-21)
1. A flat; 2. A flat; 3. B minor; 4. G; 5. B; 6. A flat; 7. B; 8. B minor; 9. G.
1-3. R. Burnett *Concert*
(5/88) (AMON) ① **CD-SAR7**

6 Ecossaises—piano, D421 (1816)
1. A flat; 2. F minor; 3. E flat; 4. B flat; 5. E flat; 6. A flat.
M. Dalberto (r1994) *Concert*
(7/95) (DENO) ① **CO-78914**
1, 2. R. Burnett *Concert*
(5/88) (AMON) ① **CD-SAR7**

8 Ecossaises—piano, D529 (1817)
1. D; 2. D; 4. D; 5. D; 6. D; 7. D; 8. D.
M. Dalberto *Concert* (6/90) (DENO) ① **CO-74499**

12 Ecossaises—piano, D781 (1823)
1. D; 2. G flat; 3. D; 4. G flat; 5. E flat; 6. A flat; 7. E flat minor; 8. B minor; 9. D; 10. B; 11. G sharp minor; 12. B minor.
2-12. I. Cooper *Concert*
(12/88) (OTTA) ① **OTRC58714**
2-12. M. Dalberto (r1993) *Concert*
(6/94) (DENO) ① **CO-75757**

Fantasie in C minor—piano, D2e (1811)
L. Hokanson *Concert* (1/90) (NORT) ① **NR233-CD**

Fantasy in C, 'Wandererfantasie'—piano, D760 (1822)
M. Perahia *Schumann: Fantasie.*
(12/86) (SONY) ① **MK42124**
A. Brendel *Piano Sonata, D960.*
(8/87) (PHIL) ① **420 644-2PM**
M. Pollini *Piano Sonata, D845.*
(8/87) (DG) ① **419 672-2GH**
S. Richter (rev. Badura-Skoda) *Dvořák: Piano Concerto.* (11/87) (EMI) ① **CDC7 47967-2**
O. Maisenberg *Concert*
(1/89) (ORFE) ① **C043831A**
A. Rubinstein *Concert* (2/89) (RCA) ① **RD86257**
P. Badura-Skoda *Concert*
(2/89) (MUSI) ① **MACD-267**
A. Brendel *Piano Sonata, D960.*
(1/90) (PHIL) ① **422 062-2PH**
R. Gothóni *Piano Sonata, D845.*
(4/91) (ONDI) ① **ODE734-2**
S. Richter *Concert*
(3/93) (EMI) ① [4] **CMS7 64429-2**
R. Orozco (r1992) *Piano Sonata, D960.*
(8/93) (AUVI) ① **V4683**
A. Ugorski (r1992) *Schumann: Davidsbündlertänze.*
(10/93) (DG) ① **437 539-2GH**
J. Jandó (r1993) *Concert*
(3/95) (NAXO) ① **8 550846**
M. Dalberto (r1993-4) *Concert*
(10/95) (DENO) ① **CO-78955**

Farewell Waltz—piano (unidentified)
P. Badura-Skoda *Concert*
(2/89) (MUSI) ① **MACD-267**

Galop and 8 Ecossaises—piano, D735 (c1822)
1. Galop in G; 2. Ecossaise in G; 3. Ecossaise in E minor; 4. Ecossaise in D; 5. Ecossaise in B flat; 6. Ecossaise in E flat; 7. Ecossaise in E flat; 8. Ecossaise in E flat; 9. Ecossaise in A flat.
Galop; Ecossaise 1. VPO, C. Abbado (orch Maderna: pp1991) *Concert*
(4/91) (DG) ① **431 628-2GH**
Galop 1. Berlin RSO, M. Bamert (orch Maderna) *Concert* (9/90) (SCHW) ① **311135**

Grazer Galopp in C—piano, D925 (1827)
Vienna Ens (arr orch: anon) *Concert*
(9/92) (SONY) ① **SK47187**
A. Schiff *Concert* (11/92) (DECC) ① **430 425-2DH**

Impromptus—piano (1828)
D899: 1. C minor; 2. E flat; 3. G flat; 4. A flat. D935: 5. F minor; 6. A flat; 7. B flat; 8. F minor. D946: 9. E flat minor; 10. E flat; 11. C.
A. Schiff *Concert* (11/92) (DECC) ① **430 425-2DH**
1-4. C. Rosenberger *Piano Sonata, D960.*
(10/90) (DELO) ① **DE3018**
1-4. I. Cooper *Concert*
(2/92) (OTTA) ① **OTRC87923**
1-8. A. Brendel (4/84) (PHIL) ① **411 040-2PH**
1-8. R. Lupu (10/84) (DECC) ① **411 711-2DH**
1-8. J.E. Dähler (1/87) (CLAV) ① **CD50-0509**
1-8. A. Schnabel (r1950) *Allegretto, D915.*
(4/89) (EMI) ① **CDH7 61021-2**

1-8. A. Brendel (r1988)
(10/89) (PHIL) ① **422 237-2PH**
1-8. K. Zimerman (5/91) (DG) ① **423 612-2GH**
1-8. L. Orkis (9/92) (VIRG) ① **VC7 59600-2**
1-8. A. Gavrilov (r1991)
(3/93) (DG) ① **435 788-2GH**
1-8. Edwin Fischer (r1938)
(5/93) (DANT) ① **HPC006**
1-8. J. O'Conor (r1993) *Waltzes, D145.*
(3/94) (TELA) ① **CD80337**
1-8. P. Katin (r1993) (1/95) (ATHN) ① **ATHCD5**
2, 3. D. Lipatti (pp1950) *Concert*
(6/89) (EMI) ① **CDH7 69800-2**
2, 3. G. Saba *Concert* (9/91) (CARL) ① **PCD950**
2, 3. D. Lipatti (pp1950) *Concert*
(12/94) (EMI) ① **CDH5 65166-2**
2, 4. S. Richter (pp1979) *Concert*
(10/92) (OLYM) ① **OCD288**
2, 4-6. V. Horowitz (r1973) *Concert*
(7/94) (SONY) ① **SK53471**
3. V. Horowitz *Concert* (6/86) (DG) ① **419 217-2GH**
3. P. Berkowitz *Concert*
(11/87) (MERI) ① **CDE84102**
3. V. Horowitz (r1953) *Concert*
(7/92) (RCA) ① **GD60523**
3. C. Curzon (r1964) *Concert*
(6/93) (DECC) ① **436 407-2DWO**
3. V. Horowitz (r1962: trans Horowitz) *Concert*
(7/94) (SONY) ① [2] **S2K53457**
3. J. Heifetz, A. Sándor (r1934) *Concert*
(11/94) (RCA) ① [65] **09026 61778-2(02)**
3, 4. A. Rubinstein *Concert*
(2/89) (RCA) ① **RD86257**
3, 4. C. Curzon (r1964) *Concert*
(4/95) (DECC) ① **443 570-2DCS**
3, 4. V. Sofronitsky (pp1960) *Concert*
(8/95) (MELO) ① [2] **74321 25177-2**
3, 4. V. Sofronitsky (pp1960) *Concert*
(8/95) (MELO) ① [11] **74321 25172-2(1)**
4. V. Horowitz *Concert* (5/86) (DG) ① **419 045-2GH**
4. S. Rachmaninov (r1925) *Concert*
(3/93) (RCA) ① [10] **09026 61265-2(1)**
4. H. Bauer (r1924) *Concert*
(9/93) (BIDD) ① **LHW007**
4. N. Demidenko (pp1993) *Piano Sonata, D845.*
(1/94) (HYPE) ① [2] **CDA66781/2**
5-8. I. Cooper *Piano Sonata, D845.*
(2/90) (OTTA) ① **OTRC88817**
5-8. R. Serkin *Trout Quintet, D667.*
(10/90) (SONY) ① **MPK44847**
5-8. M. Dalberto *Concert*
(6/93) (DENO) ① **CO-75071**
5-8. D. Barenboim (pp1992) *Piano Sonata, D960.*
(2/94) (ERAT) ① **4509-91700-2**
6. E. Leginska (r1928) *Concert*
(4/89) (OPAL) ① **OPALCD9839**
6. I. Paderewski (r1926) *Concert*
(11/91) (PEAR) ① **GEMMCD9499**
7. M. Tirimo *Concert*
(12/88) (KING) ① **KCLCD2003**
7. J. Jandó *Concert* (11/90) (LASE) ① **15 522**
7. I. Paderewski (r1924) *Concert*
(11/91) (PEAR) ① **GEMMCD9499**
9-11. M. Pollini *Concert*
(4/88) (DG) ① [2] **419 229-2GH2**
9-11. M. Pollini *Concert*
(5/89) (DG) ① **427 326-2GH**
9-11. A. Brendel *Piano Sonata, D845.*
(10/89) (PHIL) ① **422 075-2PH**
9-11. I. Cooper *Concert*
(10/90) (OTTA) ① **OTRC88821**
9-11. A. Lonquich *Piano Sonata, D958.*
(12/90) (NUOV) ① **6828**
9-11. A. Brendel (r1974) *Concert*
(5/94) (PHIL) ① [2] **438 703-2PM2**
17 Ländler—piano, D145 (1815-21)
1. E flat; 2. E flat; 3. A flat; 4. D flat; 5. D flat; 6. D flat; 7. D flat; 8. D flat; 9. A flat; 10. D flat; 11. D flat; 12. A; 13. D; 14. G; 15. G; 16. G; 17. D.
2-5. R. Burnett *Concert*
(5/88) (AMON) ① **CD-SAR7**
2, 6. M. Tirimo *Concert*
(12/88) (KING) ① **KCLCD2003**
12. S. Richter (r1961) *Concert*
(12/95) (DG) ① [2] **447 355-2GDB2**
March in E—piano, D606 (?1818)
A. Schnabel (r1939) *Concert*
(5/92) (EMI) ① [2] **CHS7 64259-2**
M. Dalberto (r1993-4) *Concert*
(10/95) (DENO) ① **CO-78955**
Minuet in C sharp minor—piano, D600 (?1814)
L. Hokanson *Concert* (1/90) (NORT) ① **NR233-CD**
M. Dalberto *Concert* (6/90) (DENO) ① **CO-74499**

6 Moments musicaux—piano, D780 (1823-28)
1. C; 2. A flat; 3. F minor; 4. C sharp minor; 5. F minor; 6. A flat.
D. Barenboim Concert (7/85) (DG) ① 415 118-2GH
J.E. Dähler Piano Sonata, D960.
(9/88) (CLAV) ① CD50-8011
I. Cooper Piano Sonata, D850.
(1/89) (OTTA) ① OTRC128715
P. Badura-Skoda Concert
(2/89) (MUSI) ① MACD-267
R. Lupu Piano Sonata, D958.
(4/89) (DECC) ① 417 785-2DM
A. Brendel Piano Sonata, D958.
(4/89) (PHIL) ① 422 076-2PH
M-J. Pires Concert (2/90) (DG) ① 427 769-2GH
M. Dalberto Concert (6/90) (DENO) ① CO-74499
D. Barenboim Concert
(11/91) (DG) ① 435 072-2GGA
A. Schnabel (r1937) Concert
(5/92) (EMI) ① [2] CHS7 64259-2
S. Richter (pp1979) Concert
(10/92) (OLYM) ① OCD286
A. Schiff Concert (11/92) (DECC) ① 430 425-2DH
Emil Gilels (pp1970) Concert
(7/94) (ORFE) ① C332931B
C. Curzon (r1971) Concert
(4/95) (DECC) ① 443 570-2DCS
J. O'Conor (r1993) Piano Sonata, D959.
(10/95) (TELA) ① CD80369
2. I. Paderewski (r1931) Concert
(11/91) (PEAR) ① GEMMCD9499
2, 3. R. Tureck (pp1992) Concert
(8/93) (VAI) ① [2] VAIA1024
3. V. Horowitz Concert
(11/89) (DG) ① 427 772-2GH
3. P. Casals, N. Mednikoff (arr Becker: r1926)
Concert (10/91) (BIDD) ① LAB017
3. S. Cherkassky (arr Godowsky: pp1975) Concert
(10/91) (DECC) ① 433 653-2DH
3. R. de Waal (arr Godowsky) Concert
(3/92) (HYPE) ① CDA66496
3. C. Curzon (r1964) Concert
(6/93) (DECC) ① 436 407-2DWO
3. M. Rosenthal (r1937) Concert
(9/93) (APR) ① [2] APR7002
3. H. Bauer (r1939) Concert
(4/94) (BIDD) ① LHW009
3. T. Kerstens (r1992-3; arr Tárrega: gtr) Concert
(9/94) (CONI) ① CDCF518
3. B. Huberman, S. Schultze (r1935: arr Auer)
Concert (9/94) (BIDD) ① [2] LAB081/2
3. B. Huberman, anon (r1899: arr Auer) Concert
(9/94) (BIDD) ① [2] LAB081/2
3. M. Maisky, D. Hovora (r1993: arr vc/pf: Maisky)
Concert (9/94) (DG) ① 439 863-2GH
3. A. Brailowsky (r1931: arr Leschetizky) Concert
(11/95) (DANA) ① [2] DACOCD338/9
3. Philadelphia, L. Stokowski (r1927: arr Stokowski)
Concert (11/95) (BIDD) ① WHL033
3. J. Starker, G. Moore (r1958: arr vc/pf: Becker)
Concert (12/95) (EMI) ① [6] CZS5 68485-2

36 Originaltänze (Waltzes)—piano, D365 (1816-21)
1. A flat; 2. A flat; 3. A flat; 4. A flat; 5. A flat; 6. A flat; 7. A flat; 8. A flat; 9. A flat; 10. A flat; 11. A flat; 12. A flat; 13. A flat; 14. D flat; 15. D flat; 16. A; 17. A; 18. A; 19. G; 20. G; 21. G; 22. B; 23. B; 24. B; 25. E; 26. E; 27. C sharp minor; 28. A; 29. D; 30. A; 31. C; 32. F; 33. F; 34. F; 35. F; 36. F.
P. Berkowitz Piano Sonata, D959.
(6/87) (MERI) ① CDE84103
1, 2, 14, 20, 22, 26, 29, 30, 31, 32, 33, 34, 35, 36. M. Dalberto (r1994) Concert
(7/95) (DENO) ① CO-78914
2. M. Tirimo Concert
(12/88) (KING) ① KCLCD2003
26. P. Badura-Skoda Concert
(2/89) (MUSI) ① MACD-267

2 Scherzi—piano, D593 (1817)
1. B flat; 2. D flat.
M-J. Pires Concert (2/90) (DG) ① 427 769-2GH
D. Barenboim Concert
(11/91) (DG) ① 435 072-2GGA
M. Dalberto (r1993) Concert
(6/94) (DENO) ① CO-75757
1. G. Tozer Concert (12/92) (TALL) ① TP001
Sonata for Piano in C, D613 (1818) (fragmentary, 2 movts: slow mvt, D612)
M. Dalberto (r1993-4) Concert
(10/95) (DENO) ① CO-78955
Sonata for Piano No. 1 in E, D157 (1815)
L. Hokanson Concert (1/90) (NORT) ① NR233-CD
A. Schiff (r1992) Concert (4/90) (DENO) ① CO-73787
R. Lupu Concert (2/92) (DECC) ① 425 033-2DM

A. Schiff (r1992) Concert
(11/95) (DECC) ① 440 311-2DH
Sonata for Piano No. 2 in C, D279 (1815)
L. Hokanson Concert (1/90) (NORT) ① NR233-CD
A. Schiff (r1992) Concert
(6/95) (DECC) ① 440 310-2DH
Sonata for Piano No. 3 in E, D459 (1816)
A. Schiff (r1993) Concert
(11/95) (DECC) ① 440 311-2DH
Sonata for Piano No. 4 in A minor, D537 (1817)
A.B. Michelangeli Brahms: Ballades.
(3/83) (DG) ① 400 043-2GH
A. Brendel Piano Sonata, D664.
(11/83) (PHIL) ① 410 605-2PH
P. Katin Piano Sonata, D960.
(10/87) (OLYM) ① OCD188
M. Dalberto Piano Sonata, D959.
(4/91) (AUVI) ① V4630
R. Gothóni (r1991) Piano Sonata, D840.
(1/95) (ONDI) ① ODE797-2
A. Schiff (r1992) Piano Sonata, D959.
(1/95) (DECC) ① 440 309-2DH
J. Jandó (r1993) Concert
(3/95) (NAXO) ① 8 550846
Sonata for Piano No. 5 in A flat, D557 (1817)
M. Dalberto Concert (6/93) (DENO) ① CO-75071
A. Schiff (r1992) Concert
(6/94) (DECC) ① 440 307-2DH
M. Endres (r1993/4) Concert
(9/95) (CAPR) ① 10 553
Sonata for Piano No. 6 in E minor, D566 (1817)
A. Schiff (r1992) Concert
(12/93) (DECC) ① 440 306-2DH
M. Dalberto (r1992) Concert
(6/94) (DENO) ① CO-75757
M. Endres (r1993/4) Concert
(9/95) (CAPR) ① 10 553
Sonata for Piano No. 7 in E flat, D568 (1817)
A. Schiff Piano Sonata, D958.
(10/94) (DECC) ① 440 308-2DH
Sonata for Piano No. 8 in F sharp minor, D571 (1817) (fragment only)
A. Schiff (r1992) Concert
(12/93) (DECC) ① 440 305-2DH
Sonata for Piano No. 9 in B, D575 (1817)
S. Richter (pp1979) Concert
(10/92) (OLYM) ① OCD286
A. Schiff (r1992) Concert
(6/94) (DECC) ① 440 307-2DH
S. Richter (r1979) Concert
(8/94) (PHIL) ① [2] 438 483-2PH2
M. Dalberto (r1994) Concert
(7/95) (DENO) ① CO-78914
M. Endres (r1993/4) Concert
(9/95) (CAPR) ① 10 553
Sonata for Piano No. 11 in F minor, D625 (1818)
G. Saba Concert (9/91) (CARL) ① PCD950
S. Richter (pp1979) Concert
(10/92) (OLYM) ① OCD286
P. Badura-Skoda (r1992) Piano Sonata, D958.
(8/93) (ARCA) ① A17
A. Schiff (r1993) Concert
(6/95) (DECC) ① 440 310-2DH
Sonata for Piano No. 13 in A, D664 (1819)
A. Brendel Piano Sonata, D537.
(11/83) (PHIL) ① 410 605-2PH
M. Hess (r1928) Concert
(8/90) (APR) ① [2] APR7012
M. Hess (r1928) Concert
(5/91) (PEAR) ① GEMMCD9462
S. Cherkassky (pp1975) Concert
(10/91) (DECC) ① 433 653-2DH
T. Leonhardt Concert
(11/91) (JECK) ① [2] J4422/3-2
S. Richter (pp1979) Concert
(10/92) (OLYM) ① OCD288
S. Richter Concert
(3/93) (EMI) ① [4] CMS7 64429-2
E. Leonskaja (r1992) Piano Sonata, D959.
(10/93) (TELD) ① 9031-74865-2
R. Lupu Piano Sonata, D960.
(11/94) (DECC) ① 440 295-2DH
J. Jandó (r1993) Concert
(3/95) (NAXO) ① 8 550846
M. Hess (r1928) Concert (3/95) (BIDD) ① LHW024
Vladimir Ashkenazy (r1966) Concert
(4/95) (DECC) ① 443 579-2DCS
M. Dalberto (r1994) Concert
(7/95) (DENO) ① CO-78914
M. Endres (r1993/4) Concert
(9/95) (CAPR) ① 10 553

A. Schiff (r1992) Concert
(11/95) (DECC) ① 440 311-2DH
M. Kazakevich (r1994) Piano Sonata, D960.
(12/95) (CONI) ① 75605 51254-2
Sonata for Piano No. 14 in A minor, D784 (1823)
I. Cooper Concert (4/88) (OTTA) ① OTRC68608
A. Brendel (r1987) Piano Sonata, D850.
(11/88) (PHIL) ① 422 063-2PH
O. Maisenberg Concert
(1/89) (ORFE) ① C043831A
M-J. Pires Concert (2/90) (DG) ① 427 769-2GH
T. Leonhardt Concert
(11/91) (JECK) ① [2] J4420/1-2
R. Lupu Concert (2/92) (DECC) ① 425 033-2DM
P. Berkowitz Piano Sonata, D894.
(4/92) (MERI) ① CDE84201
N. Grubert Piano Sonata, D960.
(7/92) (OTTA) ① OTRC78926
S. Richter (pp1979) Concert
(10/92) (OLYM) ① OCD288
J. Jandó (r1992) Concert
(6/93) (NAXO) ① 8 550730
A. Schiff (r1992) Concert
(12/93) (DECC) ① 440 306-2DH
M. Dalberto (r1992) Concert
(6/94) (DENO) ① CO-75757
Emil Gilels (pp1970) Concert
(7/94) (ORFE) ① C332931B
Vladimir Ashkenazy (r1966) Concert
(4/95) (DECC) ① 443 579-2DCS
E. Kissin (r1994) Concert
(9/95) (SONY) ① SK64538
Sonata for Piano No. 15 in C, 'Relique', D840 (1825)
I. Cooper Concert (12/88) (OTTA) ① OTRC58714
A. Brendel Piano Sonata, D894.
(10/89) (PHIL) ① 422 340-2PH
M. Dalberto Concert (10/90) (DENO) ① CO-76330
A. Brendel Concert (2/92) (VANG) ① 08.4026.71
A. Schiff (r1992) Concert
(12/93) (DECC) ① 440 305-2DH
S. Richter (r1979) Concert
(8/94) (PHIL) ① [2] 438 483-2PH2
R. Gothóni (r1991) Piano Sonata, D537.
(1/95) (ONDI) ① ODE797-2
Sonata for Piano No. 16 in A minor, D845 (1825)
R. Lupu Piano Sonata, D894.
(6/87) (DECC) ① 417 640-2DH
M. Pollini Fantasy, D760.
(8/87) (DG) ① 419 672-2GH
A. Brendel Impromptus.
(10/89) (PHIL) ① 422 075-2PH
I. Cooper Impromptus.
(2/90) (OTTA) ① OTRC88817
M. Dalberto Concert (4/90) (DENO) ① CO-73787
R. Gothóni Fantasy, D760.
(4/91) (ONDI) ① ODE734-2
T. Leonhardt Concert
(11/91) (JECK) ① [2] J4420/1-2
A. Schiff (r1992) Concert
(12/93) (DECC) ① 440 305-2DH
M. Endres (r1994) Piano Sonata, D850.
(9/95) (CAPR) ① 10 707
Sonata for Piano No. 17 in D, D850 (1825)
A. Brendel (r1987) Piano Sonata, D784.
(11/88) (PHIL) ① 422 063-2PH
I. Cooper Moments musicaux, D780.
(1/89) (OTTA) ① OTRC128715
T. Leonhardt Concert
(11/91) (JECK) ① [2] J4422/3-2
A. Schnabel (r1939) Concert
(5/92) (EMI) ① [2] CHS7 64259-2
L. Zilberstein Concert (9/92) (DG) ① 435 385-2GH
A. Schiff (r1992) Concert
(12/93) (DECC) ① 440 306-2DH
Emil Gilels (r1960) Liszt: Piano Sonata, S178.
(4/94) (RCA) ① 09026 61614-2
C. Curzon (r1964) Concert
(4/95) (DECC) ① 443 570-2DCS
M. Endres (r1994) Concert
(12/95) (CAPR) ① 10 707
Movt 4. J. Szigeti, A. Foldes (r1941: arr vn/pf: Friedberg) Concert (7/94) (BIDD) ① [2] LAB070/1
Rondo J. Szigeti, N. Magaloff (arr Friedberg: r1936) Concert (1/90) (BIDD) ① [2] LAB007/8
Rondo J. Heifetz, E. Bay (r1946) Concert
(11/94) (RCA) ① [65] 09026 61778-2(06)
Rondo J. Heifetz, I. Achron (r1926) Concert
(11/94) (RCA) ① [65] 09026 61778-2(02)
Sonata for Piano No. 18 in G, D894 (1826)
R. Lupu Piano Sonata, D845.
(6/87) (DECC) ① 417 640-2DH
I. Cooper Concert (4/88) (OTTA) ① OTRC68608

SECTION IV: VOCAL AND CHORAL

M. Shirai, H. Höll *Concert*
    (10/89) (CAPR) ① :10 171
Sarah Walker, R. Vignoles *Concert*
    (4/90) (CRD) ① **CRD3464**
C. Ludwig, I. Gage *Concert*
    (9/91) (DG) ① [2] **431 476-2GGA2**
D. Fischer-Dieskau, G. Moore (r c1967) *Concert*
    (3/93) (DG) ① [9] **437 215-2GX9(4)**
E. Ameling, D. Baldwin (r1982) *Concert*
    (4/94) (PHIL) ① [4] **438 528-2PM4(2)**
D. Upshaw, R. Goode (r1993) *Concert*
    (8/94) (NONE) ① **7559-79317-2**
H-P. Blochwitz, R. Jansen (r1992) *Concert*
    (3/95) (PHIL) ① **438 932-2PH**
**An den Mond—Lied, D468 (1816) (Wds. L.
Hölty)**
D. Fischer-Dieskau, G. Moore (r c1967) *Concert*
    (3/93) (DG) ① [9] **437 215-2GX9(5)**
L. Popp, G. Johnson (r1992) *Concert*
    (6/93) (HYPE) ① **CDJ33017**
**An den Mond in einer Herbstnacht—Lied,
D614 (1818) (Wds. A. Schreiber)**
Sarah Walker, G. Johnson (r1989) *Concert*
    (10/90) (HYPE) ① **CDJ33008**
D. Fischer-Dieskau, G. Moore (r1969) *Concert*
    (3/93) (DG) ① [9] **437 225-2GX9(1)**
**An den Schlaf—Lied, D477 (1816) (Wds. ?J.
P. Uz)**
D. Fischer-Dieskau, G. Moore (r c1967) *Concert*
    (3/93) (DG) ① [9] **437 215-2GX9(5)**
P. Schreier, G. Johnson (r1992) *Concert*
    (7/93) (HYPE) ① **CDJ33018**
**An den Tod—Lied, D518 (1817) (Wds. C F D
Schubart)**
K. Moll, C. Garben *Concert*
    (9/87) (ORFE) ① **C021821A**
B. Fassbaender, G. Johnson (r1990) *Concert*
    (8/91) (HYPE) ① **CDJ33011**
D. Fischer-Dieskau, G. Moore (r1969) *Concert*
    (3/93) (DG) ① [9] **437 225-2GX9(1)**
E. Ameling, R. Jansen (r1984) *Concert*
    (4/94) (PHIL) ① [4] **438 528-2PM4(2)**
H. Hagegård, T. Schuback (r1976) *Concert*
    (5/94) (BIS) ① **BIS-CD054**
**An die Apfelbäume—Lied, D197 (1815) (Wds.
L. Hölty)**
M. Hill, G. Johnson (r1990) *Concert*
    (5/91) (HYPE) ① **CDJ33010**
D. Fischer-Dieskau, G. Moore (r c1967) *Concert*
    (3/93) (DG) ① [9] **437 215-2GX9(2)**
**An die Entfernte—Lied, D765 (1822) (Wds.
Goethe)**
D. Fischer-Dieskau, G. Moore *Concert*
    (9/90) (EMI) ① [2] **CMS7 63566-2**
D. Fischer-Dieskau, G. Moore (r1969) *Concert*
    (3/93) (DG) ① [9] **437 225-2GX9(3)**
P. Schreier, G. Johnson (r1992) *Concert*
    (7/93) (HYPE) ① **CDJ33018**
E. Ameling, R. Jansen (r1984) *Concert*
    (4/94) (PHIL) ① [4] **438 528-2PM4(2)**
P. Pears, B. Britten (r1968/72) *Concert*
    (10/95) (DECC) ① **443 933-2DM**
T. Félix, P.Badura-Skoda (r1995) *Concert*
    (12/95) (ARCA) ① **A37**
**An die Freude—Lied, D189 (1815) (Wds. F.
von Schiller)**
D. Fischer-Dieskau, G. Moore (r c1967) *Concert*
    (3/93) (DG) ① [9] **437 215-2GX9(2)**
T. Allen, G. Johnson (r1992) *Concert*
    (3/93) (HYPE) ① **CDJ33016**
**An die Freunde—Lied, D654 (1819) (Wds. J.
Mayrhofer)**
A. Murray, G. Johnson (r1988) *Concert*
    (1/90) (HYPE) ① **CDJ33003**
D. Fischer-Dieskau, G. Moore (r1969) *Concert*
    (3/93) (DG) ① [9] **437 215-2GX9(1)**
**An die Geliebte—Lied, D303 (1815) (Wds.
Stoll)**
M. Hill, G. Johnson (r1990) *Concert*
    (5/91) (HYPE) ① **CDJ33010**
D. Fischer-Dieskau, G. Moore (r c1967) *Concert*
    (3/93) (DG) ① [9] **437 215-2GX9(3)**
**An die Harmonie—Lied, D394 (1816) (Wds.
Wds. J. G. von Salis-Seewis)**
D. Fischer-Dieskau, G. Moore (r c1967) *Concert*
    (3/93) (DG) ① [9] **437 215-2GX9(4)**
P. Schreier, G. Johnson (r1992) *Concert*
    (7/93) (HYPE) ① **CDJ33018**
**An die Laute—Lied, D905 (1827) (Wds. J.F.
Rochlitz)**
K. Battle, James Levine *Concert*
    (12/88) (DG) ① **419 237-2GH**
A. Rolfe Johnson, G. Johnson (r1989) *Concert*
    (6/90) (HYPE) ① **CDJ33006**
D. Fischer-Dieskau, G. Moore *Concert*
    (9/90) (EMI) ① [2] **CMS7 63566-2**

F. Wunderlich, H. Giesen *Concert*
    (11/90) (DG) ① **429 933-2GDO**
P. Vollestad, S. Hjelset *Concert*
    (9/92) (SIMA) ① **PSC1071**
D. Fischer-Dieskau, G. Moore (r c1967) *Concert*
    (3/93) (DG) ① [9] **437 215-2GX9(6)**
P. Pears, B. Britten (r1959) *Concert*
    (8/93) (DECC) ① **436 201-2DM**
G. Souzay, D. Baldwin (r1967) *Concert*
    (11/93) (PHIL) ① [4] **438 511-2PM4**
M. Price, G. Johnson (r1993) *Concert*
    (3/94) (FORL) ① **UCD16698**
E. Ameling, D. Baldwin (r1973) *Concert*
    (4/94) (PHIL) ① [4] **438 528-2PM4(1)**
H. Rehfuss, F. Martin (bp1964) *Concert*
    (5/94) (CLAV) ① **CD50-9327**
K. Erb, B. Seidler-Winkler (r1937) *Concert*
    (6/94) (PREI) ① [2] **89208**
B. Terfel, M. Martineau (r1994) *Concert*
    (10/94) (DG) ① **445 294-2GH**
An die Leier—Lied, D737 (1822 or 1823)
(Wds. von Bruchmann, after Anacreon)
E. Haefliger, J. E. Dähler *Concert*
    (2/88) (CLAV) ① **CD50-8611**
M. Rothmüller, S. Gyr (r1944) *Concert*
    (11/91) (SYMP) ① [2] **SYMCD1098/9**
T. Hampson, G. Johnson (r1991) *Concert*
    (4/92) (HYPE) ① **CDJ33014**
D. Fischer-Dieskau, G. Moore (r1969) *Concert*
    (3/93) (DG) ① [9] **437 225-2GX9(3)**
J. Björling, H. Ebert (r1940) *Concert*
    (10/93) (NIMB) ① **NI7842**
C. Bartoli, A. Schiff (r1992: Ital) *Concert*
    (11/93) (DECC) ① **440 297-2DH**
H. Hagegård, T. Schuback (r1976) *Concert*
    (5/94) (BIS) ① **BIS-CD054**
B. Terfel, M. Martineau (r1994) *Concert*
    (10/94) (DG) ① **445 294-2GH**
**An die Musik—Lied, D547 (1819) (Wds.
Schöber)**
D. Fischer-Dieskau, G. Moore *Concert*
    (9/85) (DG) ① **415 188-2GH**
G. Hüsch, H.U. Müller (r1938) *Concert*
    (10/90) (PREI) ① **89017**
F. Wunderlich, H. Giesen *Concert*
    (11/90) (DG) ① **429 933-2GDO**
K. Ferrier, P. Spurr (r1950) *Concert*
    (6/91) (DECC) ① **430 096-2DWO**
A. Auger, L. Orkis *Concert*
    (6/91) (VIRG) ① **VC7 59630-2**
E. Schwarzkopf, Edwin Fischer (r1952) *Concert*
    (3/92) (EMI) ① **CDH7 64026-2**
K. Ferrier, P. Spurr (r1950) *Concert*
    (6/92) (DECC) ① **433 471-2DM**
C. Ludwig, G. Parsons *Concert*
    (9/92) (EMI) ① [4] **CMS7 64074-2(1)**
T. Takács, J. Jandó *Concert*
    (3/93) (NAXO) ① **8 550476**
D. Fischer-Dieskau, G. Moore (r1969) *Concert*
    (3/93) (DG) ① [9] **437 225-2GX9(1)**
E. Wiens, R. Jansen *Concert*
    (5/93) (CBC) ① **MVCD1053**
I. Seefried, E. Werba (r1958) *Concert*
    (7/93) (DG) ① [2] **437 348-2GDO2**
G. Souzay, D. Baldwin (r1967) *Concert*
    (11/93) (PHIL) ① [4] **438 511-2PM4**
M. Price, G. Johnson (r1993) *Concert*
    (3/94) (FORL) ① **UCD16698**
V. de los Angeles, G. Moore (r1960) *Concert*
    (4/94) (EMI) ① [4] **CMS5 65061-2(2)**
E. Ameling, D. Baldwin (r1982) *Concert*
    (4/94) (PHIL) ① [4] **438 528-2PM4(2)**
H. Hagegård, T. Schuback (r1976) *Concert*
    (5/94) (BIS) ① **BIS-CD054**
E. Mathis, G. Johnson (r1992) *Concert*
    (8/94) (HYPE) ① **CDJ33021**
H. Hotter, G. Moore (r1949) *Concert*
    (10/94) (EMI) ① **CDH5 65196-2**
B. Terfel, M. Martineau (r1994) *Concert*
    (10/94) (DG) ① **445 294-2GH**
I. Baillie, G. Moore (r1941: Eng) *Concert*
    (7/95) (DUTT) ① **CDLX7013**
F. Lott, G. Johnson (r1988) *Concert*
    (10/95) (CARL) ① **PCD2016**
**An die Nachtigall—Lied, D196 (1815) (Wds. L.
Hölty)**
E. Ameling, G. Johnson (r1989) *Concert*
    (8/90) (HYPE) ① **CDJ33007**
D. Fischer-Dieskau, G. Moore (r c1967) *Concert*
    (3/93) (DG) ① [9] **437 215-2GX9(2)**
E. Ameling, D. Baldwin (r1973) *Concert*
    (4/94) (PHIL) ① [4] **438 528-2PM4(1)**
**An die Nachtigall—Lied, D497 (1816) (Wds.
M. Claudius)**
E. Mathis, K. Engel *Concert*
    (2/90) (NOVA) ① **150 026-2**

A. Auger, L. Orkis *Concert*
    (6/91) (VIRG) ① **VC7 59630-2**
C. Ludwig, I. Gage *Concert*
    (9/91) (DG) ① [2] **431 476-2GGA2**
L. Popp, G. Johnson (r1992) *Concert*
    (6/93) (HYPE) ① **CDJ33017**
E. Ameling, D. Baldwin (r1973) *Concert*
    (4/94) (PHIL) ① [4] **438 528-2PM4(1)**
**An die Natur—Lied, D372 (?1816) (Wds. F.
Leopold, Graf zu Stolberg-Stolberg)**
J. Norman, P. Moll *Concert*
    (1/86) (PHIL) ① **412 623-2PH**
J. Norman, G. Parsons (pp1987) *Concert*
    (8/88) (PHIL) ① **422 048-2PH**
E. Connell, G. Johnson (1988) *Concert*
    (9/93) (HYPE) ① **CDJ33005**
D. Fischer-Dieskau, G. Moore (r c1967) *Concert*
    (3/93) (DG) ① [9] **437 215-2GX9(4)**
**An die Sonne—Lied, D270 (1815) (Wds.
Bammberg)**
M. Price, G. Johnson (r1991) *Concert*
    (2/93) (HYPE) ① **CDJ33015**
G. Janowitz, I. Gage (r1970s) *Concert*
    (9/93) (DG) ① [2] **437 943-2GX2**
**An die Sonne—Lied, D272 (1815) (Wds. C. W.
Tiedge)**
D. Fischer-Dieskau, G. Moore (r c1967) *Concert*
    (3/93) (DG) ① [9] **437 215-2GX9(3)**
L. Anderson, G. Johnson (r1993) *Concert*
    (1/95) (HYPE) ① **CDJ33022**
An die Sonne—SATB and piano, D439 (1816)
(Wds. J. P. Uz)
E. Ameling, J. Baker, P. Schreier, D. Fischer-
Dieskau, G. Moore *Concert*
    (10/92) (DG) ① [2] **435 596-2GGA2**
**An die Türen (Harfenspieler III)—Lied, D479
(1816) (Wds. Goethe)**
G. Hüsch, H.U. Müller (r1938) *Concert*
    (10/90) (PREI) ① **89017**
D. Fischer-Dieskau, G. Moore (r c1967) *Concert*
    (3/93) (DG) ① [9] **437 215-2GX9(5)**
K. Borg, E. Werba (r1959) *Concert*
    (12/94) (FINL) ① [3] **4509-95606-2**
C. Prégardien, G. Johnson (r1994) *Concert*
    (7/95) (HYPE) ① **CDJ33023**
T. Quasthoff, C. Spencer (r1993) *Concert*
    (8/95) (RCA) ① **09026 61864-2**
T. Félix, P.Badura-Skoda (r1995) *Concert*
    (12/95) (ARCA) ① **A37**
**An die untergehende Sonne—Lied, D457
(1816-17) (Wds. L. Kosegarten)**
E. Mathis, K. Engel *Concert*
    (2/90) (NOVA) ① **150 026-2**
M. Price, G. Johnson (r1991) *Concert*
    (2/93) (HYPE) ① **CDJ33015**
D. Fischer-Dieskau, G. Moore (r c1967) *Concert*
    (3/93) (DG) ① [9] **437 215-2GX9(5)**
E. Ameling, R. Jansen (r1984) *Concert*
    (4/94) (PHIL) ① [4] **438 528-2PM4(2)**
**An eine Quelle—Lied, D530 (1817) (Wds. M.
Claudius)**
H. Hotter, H. Altmann (r1952) *Concert*
    (7/88) (PREI) ① **93145**
D. Fischer-Dieskau, G. Moore (r c1967) *Concert*
    (3/93) (DG) ① [9] **437 215-2GX9(6)**
J. M. Ainsley, S. Lubin *Concert*
    (9/93) (L'OI) ① **433 848-2OH**
E. Mathis, G. Johnson (r1992) *Concert*
    (8/94) (HYPE) ① **CDJ33021**
H-P. Blochwitz, R. Jansen (r1992) *Concert*
    (3/95) (PHIL) ① **438 932-2PH**
**An Emma—Lied, D113 (1814) (Wds. F. von
Matthisson)**
D. Fischer-Dieskau, G. Moore (r c1967) *Concert*
    (3/93) (DG) ① [9] **437 215-2GX9(1)**
T. Allen, G. Johnson (r1992) *Concert*
    (3/93) (HYPE) ① **CDJ33016**
C. Prégardien, A. Staier (r1993) *Concert*
    (1/94) (DHM) ① **05472 77296-2**
**An Laura, als sie Klopstocks
Auferstehungslied sang—Lied, D115 (1814)**
(Wds. F. von Matthisson)
Adrian Thompson, G. Johnson (r1991) *Concert*
    (2/92) (HYPE) ① **CDJ33012**
D. Fischer-Dieskau, G. Moore (r c1967) *Concert*
    (3/93) (DG) ① [9] **437 215-2GX9(1)**
**An mein Klavier—Lied, D342 (c1816) (Wds.
C.F.D. Schubart)**
E. Schwarzkopf, G. Parsons *Concert*
    (12/90) (EMI) ① **CDM7 63656-2**
D. Fischer-Dieskau, G. Moore (r c1967) *Concert*
    (3/93) (DG) ① [9] **437 215-2GX9(5)**
L. Popp, G. Johnson (r1992) *Concert*
    (6/93) (HYPE) ① **CDJ33017**

K. Borg, E. Werba (r1959) *Concert*
    (12/94) (FINL) ① [3] **4509-95606-2**
G. Souzay, J. Bonneau (r1950) *Concert*
    (1/95) (DECC) ① **440 065-2DM**
P. Frijsh, P. James Orch, P. James (bp1936) *Concert*
    (4/95) (PEAR) ① [2] **GEMMCDS9095(2)**
T. Quasthoff, C. Spencer (r1993) *Concert*
    (8/95) (RCA) ① **09026 61864-2**
Lotte Lehmann, F. Weissmann (r1930) *Concert*
    (11/95) (CLAR) ① **CDGSE78-50-57**
K. Flagstad, E. McArthur (r1956) *Concert*
    (12/95) (LOND) ① [5] **440 490-2LM5(2)**
K. Flagstad, E. McArthur (r1956) *Concert*
    (12/95) (LOND) ① **440 494-2LM**
T. Félix, P.Badura-Skoda (r1995) *Concert*
    (12/95) (ARCA) ① **A37**
Erntelied—Lied, D434 (1816) (Wds. L. Hölty)
D. Fischer-Dieskau, G. Moore (r c1967) *Concert*
    (3/93) (DG) ① [9] **437 215-2GX9(5)**
P. Schreier, G. Johnson (r1992) *Concert*
    (7/93) (HYPE) ① **CDJ33018**
Die **Erste Liebe—Lied, D182 (1815)** (Wds. J. G. Fellinger)
D. Fischer-Dieskau, G. Moore (r c1967) *Concert*
    (3/93) (DG) ① [9] **437 215-2GX9(2)**
J.M. Ainsley, G. Johnson (r1993) *Concert*
    (6/94) (HYPE) ① **CDJ33020**
Erster Verlust—Lied, D226 (1815) (Wds. Goethe)
J. Baker, G. Johnson (r1987) *Concert*
    (10/88) (HYPE) ① **CDJ33001**
E. Mathis, K. Engel *Concert*
    (2/90) (NOVA) ① **150 026-2**
D. Fischer-Dieskau, G. Moore (r c1967) *Concert*
    (3/93) (DG) ① [9] **437 215-2GX9(2)**
G. Souzay, D. Baldwin (r1967) *Concert*
    (11/93) (PHIL) ① [4] **438 511-2PM4**
E. Ameling, D. Baldwin (1982) *Concert*
    (4/94) (PHIL) ① [4] **438 528-2PM4(2)**
G. Souzay, J. Bonneau (r1956) *Concert*
    (1/95) (DECC) ① **440 065-2DM**
Die **Erwartung—Lied, D159 (1816)** (Wds. Schiller)
J. Baker, G. Johnson (r1987) *Concert*
    (10/88) (HYPE) ① **CDJ33001**
D. Fischer-Dieskau, G. Moore (r c1967) *Concert*
    (3/93) (DG) ① [9] **437 215-2GX9(1)**
Evangelium Johannis—Lied, D607 (1818)
E. Mathis, G. Johnson (r1992: cpted Van Hoorickx) *Concert*
    (8/94) (HYPE) ① **CDJ33021**
Fahrt zum Hades—Lied, D526 (1817) (Wds. J. Mayrhofer)
K. Moll, C. Garben *Concert*
    (9/87) (ORFE) ① **C021821A**
S. Varcoe, G. Johnson (r1987) *Concert*
    (1/89) (HYPE) ① **CDJ33002**
T. Herrmann, G. Moore (r c1950) *Concert*
    (4/92) (EMI) ① [7] **CHS7 69741-2(4)**
D. Fischer-Dieskau, G. Moore (r c1967) *Concert*
    (3/93) (DG) ① [9] **437 215-2GX9(6)**
Das Finden—Lied, D219 (1815) (Wds. L. Kosegarten)
D. Fischer-Dieskau, G. Moore (r c1967) *Concert*
    (3/93) (DG) ① [9] **437 215-2GX9(2)**
P. Schreier, G. Johnson (r1992) *Concert*
    (7/93) (HYPE) ① **CDJ33018**
Der Fischer—Lied, D225 (1815) (Wds. Goethe)
J. Baker, G. Johnson (r1987) *Concert*
    (10/88) (HYPE) ① **CDJ33001**
Sarah Walker, R. Vignoles *Concert*
    (4/90) (CRD) ① **CRD3464**
D. Fischer-Dieskau, K. Engel *Concert*
    (9/90) (EMI) ① [2] **CMS7 63566-2**
D. Fischer-Dieskau, G. Moore (r c1967) *Concert*
    (3/93) (DG) ① [9] **437 215-2GX9(2)**
C. Robbin, M. McMahon (1985) *Concert*
    (7/94) (MARQ) ① **ERAD113**
Fischerlied (first version)—Lied, D351 (?1816) (Wds. J. G. von Salis-Seewis)
S. Varcoe, G. Johnson (r1987) *Concert*
    (1/89) (HYPE) ① **CDJ33002**
D. Fischer-Dieskau, G. Moore (r c1967) *Concert*
    (3/93) (DG) ① [9] **437 215-2GX9(4)**
Fischerlied (second version)—Lied, D562 (1817) (Wds. J. G. von Salis-Seewis)
S. Varcoe, G. Johnson (r1987) *Concert*
    (1/89) (HYPE) ① **CDJ33002**
D. Fischer-Dieskau, G. Moore (r c1967) *Concert*
    (3/93) (DG) ① [9] **437 225-2GX9(1)**
Des Fischers Liebesglück—Lied, D933 (1827) (Wds. K.G. Leitner)
H. Hotter, H. Altmann (r1952) *Concert*
    (7/88) (PREI) ① **93145**
A. Rolfe Johnson, G. Johnson (r1989) *Concert*
    (6/90) (HYPE) ① **CDJ33006**

D. Fischer-Dieskau, G. Moore *Concert*
    (9/90) (EMI) ① [2] **CMS7 63566-2**
P. Vollestad, S. Hjelset *Concert*
    (9/92) (SIMA) ① **PSC1071**
D. Fischer-Dieskau, G. Moore (r1969) *Concert*
    (3/93) (DG) ① [9] **437 225-2GX9(4)**
A. Schmidt, R. Jansen (r1992) *Concert*
    (6/93) (DG) ① **437 536-2GH**
G. Souzay, D. Baldwin (r1967) *Concert*
    (11/93) (PHIL) ① [4] **438 511-2PM4**
K. Erb, B. Seidler-Winkler (r1936) *Concert*
    (11/93) (PHIL) ① [4] **438 511-2PM4**
D. Fischer-Dieskau, H. Höll (pp1992) *Concert*
    (9/95) (ERAT) ① **4509-98493-2**
Fischerweise—Lied, D881 (?1826) (Wds. F.X. von Schlecta)
H. Prey, L. Hokanson *Concert*
    (6/87) (DENO) ① **CO-1254**
E. Haefliger, J. E. Dähler *Concert*
    (2/88) (CLAV) ① **CD50-8611**
S. Varcoe, G. Johnson (r1987) *Concert*
    (1/89) (HYPE) ① **CDJ33002**
D. Hammond-Stroud, G. Kirkwood *Concert*
    (1/90) (SYMP) ① **SYMCD1064**
D. Fischer-Dieskau, G. Moore *Concert*
    (9/90) (EMI) ① [2] **CMS7 63566-2**
C. Ludwig, G. Moore *Concert*
    (9/92) (EMI) ① [4] **CMS7 64074-2(1)**
P. Vollestad, S. Hjelset *Concert*
    (9/92) (SIMA) ① **PSC1071**
D. Fischer-Dieskau, G. Moore (r1969) *Concert*
    (3/93) (DG) ① [9] **437 225-2GX9(4)**
E. Wiens, R. Jansen *Concert*
    (5/93) (CBC) ① **MVCD1053**
I. Seefried, E. Werba (r1958) *Concert*
    (7/93) (DG) ① [2] **437 348-2GDO2**
D. Fischer-Dieskau, S. Richter (pp1977) *Concert*
    (2/94) (ORFE) ① **C334931A**
M. Price, G. Johnson (r1993) *Concert*
    (3/94) (FORL) ① **UCD16698**
E. Ameling, D. Baldwin (1973) *Concert*
    (4/94) (PHIL) ① [4] **438 528-2PM4(1)**
G. Janowitz, I. Gage (r1970s) *Concert*
    (1/95) (DG) ① [2] **437 943-2GX2**
G. Souzay, J. Bonneau (r1950) *Concert*
    (1/95) (DECC) ① **440 065-2DM**
D. Fischer-Dieskau, H. Höll (pp1992) *Concert*
    (9/95) (ERAT) ① **4509-98493-2**
Der Flüchtling—Lied, D402 (1816) (Wds. Schiller)
J. Baker, G. Johnson (r1987) *Concert*
    (10/88) (HYPE) ① **CDJ33001**
D. Fischer-Dieskau, G. Moore (r c1967) *Concert*
    (3/93) (DG) ① [9] **437 215-2GX9(4)**
Der Flug der Zeit—Lied, D515 (1812) (Wds. L. von Széchényi)
D. Fischer-Dieskau, G. Moore (r c1967) *Concert*
    (3/93) (DG) ① [9] **437 215-2GX9(6)**
E. Mathis, G. Johnson (r1992) *Concert*
    (8/94) (HYPE) ① **CDJ33021**
Der Fluss—Lied, D693 (1820) (Wds. F. von Schlegel)
D. Fischer-Dieskau, G. Moore (r1969) *Concert*
    (3/93) (DG) ① [9] **437 225-2GX9(2)**
Die **Forelle—Lied, D550 (?1817)** (Wds. C.F.D. Schubart)
D. Fischer-Dieskau, G. Moore *Concert*
    (9/85) (DG) ① **415 188-2GH**
B. Hendricks, R. Lupu *Concert*
    (4/87) (EMI) ① **CDC7 47549-2**
H. Prey, L. Hokanson *Concert*
    (6/87) (DENO) ① **CO-1254**
F. Wunderlich, H. Giesen *Concert*
    (1/89) (DG) ① **423 956-2GDO**
E. Mathis, K. Engel *Concert*
    (2/90) (NOVA) ① **150 026-2**
A. Mackay, Y. Seow *Concert*
    (6/90) (ASV) ① **CDDCA684**
D. Fischer-Dieskau, G. Moore *Concert*
    (9/90) (EMI) ① [2] **CMS7 63566-2**
E. Schwarzkopf, G. Moore *Concert*
    (12/90) (EMI) ① **CDM7 63656-2**
D. Fischer-Dieskau, G. Moore *Concert*
    (2/91) (DG) ① **431 085-2GH**
A. Auger, L. Orkis *Concert*
    (6/91) (VIRG) ① **VC7 59630-2**
C. Ludwig, G. Parsons *Concert*
    (9/92) (EMI) ① [4] **CMS7 64074-2(1)**
T. Takács, J. Jandó *Concert*
    (3/93) (NAXO) ① **8 550476**
D. Fischer-Dieskau, G. Moore (r1969) *Concert*
    (3/93) (DG) ① [9] **437 225-2GX9(1)**
I. Seefried, E. Werba (r1958) *Concert*
    (7/93) (DG) ① [2] **437 348-2GDO2**
J. M. Ainsley, S. Lubin *Concert*
    (9/93) (L'OI) ① **433 848-2OH**

G. Souzay, D. Baldwin (r1961) *Concert*
    (11/93) (PHIL) ① [4] **438 511-2PM4**
Vanni-Marcoux, anon (r1928: French) *Concert*
    (1/94) (CLUB) ① **CL99-101**
E. Ameling, R. Jansen (r1984) *Concert*
    (4/94) (PHIL) ① [4] **438 528-2PM4(2)**
E. Mathis, G. Johnson (r1992) *Concert*
    (8/94) (HYPE) ① **CDJ33021**
R. Streich, E. Werba (r1957) *Concert*
    (10/94) (DG) ① [2] **437 680-2GDO2**
B. Terfel, M. Martineau (r1994) *Concert*
    (10/94) (DG) ① **445 294-2GH**
G. Janowitz, I. Gage (r1970s) *Concert*
    (1/95) (DG) ① [2] **437 943-2GX2**
G. Souzay, J. Bonneau (r1956) *Concert*
    (1/95) (DECC) ① **440 065-2DM**
H-P. Blochwitz, R. Jansen (r1992) *Concert*
    (3/95) (PHIL) ① **438 932-2PH**
B. Bonney, G. Parsons (r1994) *Concert*
    (3/95) (TELD) ① **4509-90873-2**
F. Lott, G. Johnson (r1988) *Concert*
    (10/95) (CARL) ① **PCD2016**
K. Flagstad, E. McArthur (r1936) *Concert*
    (12/95) (PEAR) ① **GEMMCD9092**
G. Janowitz, I. Gage (r1970s) *Concert*
    (12/95) (DG) ① [2] **447 352-2GDB2**
K. Flagstad, E. McArthur (r1937) *Concert*
    (12/95) (SIMA) ① [3] **PSC1821(2)**
Fragment aus dem Aeschylus—Lied, D450 (1816) (Wds. Aeschylus, trans J. Mayrhofer)
T. Hampson, G. Johnson (r1991) *Concert*
    (4/92) (HYPE) ① **CDJ33014**
D. Fischer-Dieskau, G. Moore (r c1967) *Concert*
    (3/93) (DG) ① [9] **437 215-2GX9(5)**
Freiwilliges Versinken—Lied, D700 (1820) (Wds. J. Mayrhofer)
T. Hampson, G. Johnson (r1991) *Concert*
    (4/92) (HYPE) ① **CDJ33014**
D. Fischer-Dieskau, G. Moore (r1969) *Concert*
    (3/93) (DG) ① [9] **437 225-2GX9(2)**
S. Keenlyside, M. Martineau *Concert*
    (8/94) (EMIN) ① **CD-EMX2224**
D. Fischer-Dieskau, H. Höll (pp1992) *Concert*
    (9/95) (ERAT) ① **4509-98493-2**
Freude aus dem Kinderjahre—Lied, D455 (1816) (Wds. F. von Köpken)
D. Fischer-Dieskau, G. Moore (r c1967) *Concert*
    (3/93) (DG) ① [9] **437 215-2GX9(5)**
C. Prégardien, G. Johnson (r1994) *Concert*
    (7/95) (HYPE) ① **CDJ33023**
Die **Fröhlichkeit—Lied, D262 (1815)** (Wds. M. J. Prandstetter)
D. Fischer-Dieskau, G. Moore (r c1967) *Concert*
    (3/93) (DG) ① [9] **437 215-2GX9(3)**
I. Bostridge, G. Johnson (r1993) *Concert*
    (6/94) (HYPE) ① **CDJ33020**
Frohsinn—Lied, D520 (1817) (Wds. I. F. Castelli)
D. Fischer-Dieskau, G. Moore (r c1967) *Concert*
    (3/93) (DG) ① [9] **437 215-2GX9(6)**
Die **Frühe Liebe—Lied, D430 (1816)** (Wds. L. Hölty)
D. Fischer-Dieskau, G. Moore (r c1967) *Concert*
    (3/93) (DG) ① [9] **437 215-2GX9(5)**
C. Prégardien, G. Johnson (r1994) *Concert*
    (7/95) (HYPE) ① **CDJ33023**
Die **Frühen Gräber—Lied, D290 (1815)** (Wds. F. G. Klopstock)
Sarah Walker, G. Johnson (r1989) *Concert*
    (10/90) (HYPE) ① **CDJ33008**
D. Fischer-Dieskau, G. Moore (r c1967) *Concert*
    (3/93) (DG) ① [9] **437 215-2GX9(3)**
Frühlingsgesang—partsong, D740 (1822) (Wds. Schober)
K. Dent, R. Clements, R. Shaw Chbr Sngrs, M. Ackerman, Robert Shaw (r1992) *Concert*
    (6/94) (TELA) ① **CD80340**
Frühlingsglaube—Lied, D686 (1820) (Wds. L. Uhland)
F. Wunderlich, H. Giesen *Concert*
    (1/89) (DG) ① **423 956-2GDO**
E. Mathis, K. Engel *Concert*
    (2/90) (NOVA) ① **150 026-2**
R. Tauber, Orch (r1933) *Concert*
    (4/90) (PEAR) ① **GEMMCD9381**
R. Tauber, Orch, A. Paulik (r1934) *Concert*
    (4/90) (PEAR) ① **GEMMCD9381**
Y. Kenny, L. Skrobacs (pp1984) *Concert*
    (7/90) (ETCE) ① **KTC1029**
E. Speiser, J. Buttrick *Concert*
    (2/91) (JECK) ① **JD630-2**
C. Ludwig, I. Gage *Concert*
    (9/91) (DG) ① [2] **431 476-2GGA2**
C. Ludwig, G. Parsons *Concert*
    (9/92) (EMI) ① [4] **CMS7 64074-2(1)**

Stimme der Liebe (second version)—Lied, D418 (1816) (Wds. F. von Matthisson)
Sarah Walker, G. Johnson (r1989) *Concert*
(10/90) (HYPE) ① **CDJ33008**
Der Strom—Lied, D565 (?1817)
K. Moll, C. Garben *Concert*
(9/87) (ORFE) ① **C021821A**
S. Varcoe, G. Johnson (r1987) *Concert*
(1/89) (HYPE) ① **CDJ33002**
D. Fischer-Dieskau, G. Moore *Concert*
(9/90) (EMI) ① [2] **CMS7 63566-2**
D. Fischer-Dieskau, G. Moore (r1969) *Concert*
(3/93) (DG) ① [9] **437 225-2GX9(1)**
D. Fischer-Dieskau, S. Richter (pp1977) *Concert*
(2/94) (ORFE) ① **C334931A**
D. Fischer-Dieskau, H. Höll (pp1992) *Concert*
(9/95) (ERAT) ① **4509-98493-2**
Suleika I—Lied, D720 (1821) (Wds. M. von Willemer, adapted by Goethe)
J. Norman, P. Moll *Concert*
(1/86) (PHIL) ① **412 623-2PH**
B. Hendricks, R. Lupu *Concert*
(4/87) (EMI) ① **CDC7 47549-2**
M. Lipovšek, G. Parsons *Concert*
(11/88) (ORFE) ① **C159871A**
K. Battle, James Levine *Concert*
(12/88) (DG) ① **419 237-2GH**
E. Mathis, K. Engel *Concert*
(2/90) (NOVA) ① **150 026-2**
Sarah Walker, R. Vignoles *Concert*
(4/90) (CRD) ① **CRD3464**
E. Schwarzkopf, G. Parsons *Concert*
(12/90) (EMI) ① **CDM7 63656-2**
A. Auger, L. Orkis *Concert*
(6/91) (VIRG) ① **VC7 59630-2**
K. Ferrier, B. Walter (pp1949) *Concert*
(6/92) (DECC) ① **433 476-2DM**
T. Takács, J. Jandó *Concert*
(3/93) (NAXO) ① **8 550476**
I. Seefried, E. Werba (pp1957) *Concert*
(9/93) (ORFE) ① **C297921B**
F. Lott, G. Johnson (r1992) *Concert*
(2/94) (HYPE) ① **CDJ33019**
M. Price, G. Johnson (r1993) *Concert*
(3/94) (FORL) ① **UCD16698**
E. Ameling, D. Baldwin (r1975) *Concert*
(4/94) (PHIL) ① [4] **438 528-2PM4(1)**
D. Upshaw, R. Goode (r1993) *Concert*
(8/94) (NONE) ① **7559-79317-2**
G. Janowitz, I. Gage (r1970s) *Concert*
(1/95) (DG) ① [2] **437 943-2GX2**
G. Janowitz, I. Gage (r1970s) *Concert*
(12/95) (DG) ① [2] **447 352-2GDB2**
Suleika II—Lied, D717 (?1824) (Wds. M. von Willemer, adapted by Goethe)
B. Hendricks, R. Lupu *Concert*
(4/87) (EMI) ① **CDC7 47549-2**
M. Lipovšek, G. Parsons *Concert*
(11/88) (ORFE) ① **C159871A**
E. Mathis, K. Engel *Concert*
(2/90) (NOVA) ① **150 026-2**
Sarah Walker, R. Vignoles *Concert*
(4/90) (CRD) ① **CRD3464**
E. Schwarzkopf, G. Parsons *Concert*
(12/90) (EMI) ① **CDM7 63656-2**
A. Auger, L. Orkis *Concert*
(6/91) (VIRG) ① **VC7 59630-2**
T. Takács, J. Jandó *Concert*
(3/93) (NAXO) ① **8 550476**
I. Seefried, E. Werba (pp1957) *Concert*
(9/93) (ORFE) ① **C297921B**
F. Lott, G. Johnson (r1992) *Concert*
(2/94) (HYPE) ① **CDJ33019**
M. Price, G. Johnson (r1993) *Concert*
(3/94) (FORL) ① **UCD16698**
E. Ameling, D. Baldwin (r1975) *Concert*
(4/94) (PHIL) ① [4] **438 528-2PM4(1)**
C. Robbin, M. McMahon (r1985) *Concert*
(7/94) (MARQ) ① **ERAD113**
G. Janowitz, I. Gage (r1970s) *Concert*
(1/95) (DG) ① [2] **437 943-2GX2**
G. Janowitz, I. Gage (r1970s) *Concert*
(12/95) (DG) ① [2] **447 352-2GDB2**
Szene aus Goethes Faust, 'Wie anders, Gretchen'—Lied, D126 (1814) (Wds. J. W. Goethe)
M. McLaughlin, T. Hampson, chor, G. Johnson (r1991) *Concert* (4/92) (HYPE) ① **CDJ33013**
J. Baker, D. Fischer-Dieskau, Berlin RIAS Chbr Ch, G. Moore *Concert*
(10/92) (DG) ① [2] **435 596-2GGA2**
E. Ameling, M. Kraak, chor, D. Baldwin, anon (r1975) *Concert* (4/94) (PHIL) ① [4] **438 528-2PM4(1)**
T. Quasthoff, C. Spencer (r1993) *Concert*
(8/95) (RCA) ① **09026 61864-2**

Täglich zu singen—Lied, D533 (1817) (Wds. M. Claudius)
E. Connell, G. Johnson (r1988) *Concert*
(2/90) (HYPE) ① **CDJ33005**
D. Fischer-Dieskau, G. Moore (r c1967) *Concert*
(3/93) (DG) ① [9] **437 215-2GX9(6)**
Tantum ergo in C—soprano, chorus and orchestra, D460 (1816)
E. Rüggeberg, Bavarian Rad Chor, BRSO, W. Sawallisch (r1980s) *Concert*
(8/94) (EMI) ① [3] **CMS7 64783-2**
Tantum ergo in C—soloists, chorus and orchestra, D461 (1816)
E. Rüggeberg, J. Falk, A. Gassner, P. Lika, Bavarian Rad Chor, BRSO, W. Sawallisch (r1980s) *Concert*
(8/94) (EMI) ① [3] **CMS7 64783-2**
Tantum ergo in C—SATB, organ/orchestra, D739 (1814)
Bavarian Rad Chor, BRSO, W. Sawallisch (r1980s) *Concert* (8/94) (EMI) ① [3] **CMS7 64783-2**
Tantum ergo in D—chorus and orchestra, D750 (1822)
Bavarian Rad Chor, BRSO, W. Sawallisch (r1980s) *Concert* (8/94) (EMI) ① [3] **CMS7 64783-2**
Tantum ergo in E flat—soloists, chorus and orchestra, D962 (1828)
L. Popp, B. Fassbaender, A. Dallapozza, D. Fischer-Dieskau, Bavarian Rad Chor, BRSO, W. Sawallisch (r1969) *Concert* (9/90) (EMI) ① **CDM7 69223-2**
B. Bonney, D. Schaechter, J. Pita, A. Schmidt, Vienna St Op Chor, COE, C. Abbado (pp1990) *Concert* (6/93) (DG) ① **435 486-2GH**
L. Popp, B. Fassbaender, A. Dallapozza, D. Fischer-Dieskau, Bavarian Rad Chor, BRSO, W. Sawallisch (r1981) *Concert* (8/94) (EMI) ① [4] **CMS7 64778-2**
Der Tanz—choral song, D826 (1828) (Wds. ?K. Schnitzer von Meerau)
E. Ameling, J. Baker, P. Schreier, D. Fischer-Dieskau, G. Moore *Concert*
(10/92) (DG) ① [2] **435 596-2GGA2**
Der Taucher—Lied, D77 (1813-14) (Wds. Schiller)
S. Varcoe, G. Johnson (r1987) *Concert*
(1/89) (HYPE) ① **CDJ33002**
D. Fischer-Dieskau, G. Moore (r c1967) *Concert*
(3/93) (DG) ① [9] **437 215-2GX9(1)**
Die Täuschung—Lied, D230 (1815) (Wds. L. Kosegarten)
D. Fischer-Dieskau, G. Moore (r c1967) *Concert*
(3/93) (DG) ① [9] **437 215-2GX9(2)**
P. Rozario, G. Johnson (r1993) *Concert*
(6/94) (HYPE) ① **CDJ33020**
Thekla: eine Geisterstimme (first version)—Lied, D73 (1813) (Wds. Schiller)
J. Baker, G. Johnson (r1987) *Concert*
(10/88) (HYPE) ① **CDJ33001**
Thekla: eine Geisterstimme (second version)—Lied, D595 (1817) (Wds. F. von Schiller)
A. Auger, G. Johnson (r1989) *Concert*
(1/91) (HYPE) ① **CDJ33009**
B. Fassbaender, G. Johnson (r1990) *Concert*
(8/91) (HYPE) ① **CDJ33011**
Tiefes Leid, 'Im Jänner 1817—Lied, D876 (1826) (Wds. E. Schulze)
D. Fischer-Dieskau, G. Moore (r1969) *Concert*
(3/93) (DG) ① [9] **437 225-2GX9(4)**
P. Schreier, G. Johnson (r1992) *Concert*
(7/93) (HYPE) ① **CDJ33018**
Tischlerlied—Lied, D274 (1815) (Wds. anon)
D. Fischer-Dieskau, G. Moore (r c1967) *Concert*
(3/93) (DG) ① [9] **437 215-2GX9(3)**
M. George, G. Johnson (r1993) *Concert*
(6/94) (HYPE) ① **CDJ33020**
Tischlied—Lied, D234 (1815) (Wds. Goethe)
D. Fischer-Dieskau, G. Moore (r c1967) *Concert*
(3/93) (DG) ① [9] **437 215-2GX9(2)**
Der Tod Oscars—Lied, D375 (1816) (Wds. Ossian)
C. Prégardien, G. Johnson (r1994) *Concert*
(7/95) (HYPE) ① **CDJ33023**
Der Tod und das Mädchen—Lied, D531 (1817) (Wds. M. Claudius)
D. Fischer-Dieskau, G. Moore *Concert*
(9/85) (DG) ① **415 188-2GH**
J. Norman, P. Moll *Concert*
(1/86) (PHIL) ① **412 623-2PH**
K. Moll, C. Garben *Concert*
(9/87) (ORFE) ① **C021821A**
J. Norman, G. Parsons (pp1987) *Concert*
(8/88) (PHIL) ① **422 048-2PH**
M. Anderson, F. Rupp (r1946) *Concert*
(1/90) (RCA) ① **GD87911**
D. Fischer-Dieskau, G. Moore *Concert*
(9/90) (EMI) ① [2] **CMS7 63566-2**

B. Fassbaender, G. Johnson (r1990) *Concert*
(8/91) (HYPE) ① **CDJ33011**
C. Ludwig, I. Gage *Concert*
(9/91) (DG) ① [2] **431 476-2GGA2**
K. Ferrier, B. Walter (pp1949) *Concert*
(6/92) (DECC) ① **433 476-2DM**
C. Ludwig, G. Parsons *Concert*
(9/92) (EMI) ① [4] **CMS7 64074-2(1)**
T. Takács, J. Jandó *Concert*
(3/93) (NAXO) ① **8 550476**
D. Fischer-Dieskau, G. Moore (r c1967) *Concert*
(3/93) (DG) ① [9] **437 215-2GX9(6)**
F. Chaliapin, orch, E. Goossens (1928) *Concert*
(6/93) (PREI) ① [2] **89207**
G. Souzay, D. Baldwin (r1967) *Concert*
(11/93) (PHIL) ① [4] **438 511-2PM4**
M. Price, G. Johnson (r1993) *Concert*
(3/94) (FORL) ① **UCD16698**
V. de los Angeles, G. Moore (r1960) *Concert*
(4/94) (EMI) ① [4] **CMS5 65061-2(2)**
B. Terfel, M. Martineau (r1994) *Concert*
(10/94) (DG) ① **445 294-2GH**
C. Ludwig, C. Spencer (pp1994) *Concert*
(3/95) (RCA) ① **09026 62652-2**
Todesmusik—Lied, D758 (1822) (Wds. F. von Schober)
D. Fischer-Dieskau, G. Moore (r1969) *Concert*
(3/93) (DG) ① [9] **437 225-2GX9(3)**
Totengräberlied—Lied, D44 (1813) (Wds. L.H.C. Hölty)
K. Moll, C. Garben *Concert*
(9/87) (ORFE) ① **C021821A**
D. Fischer-Dieskau, G. Moore (r c1967) *Concert*
(3/93) (DG) ① [9] **437 215-2GX9(1)**
Totengräbers Heimweh—Lied, D842 (1825) (Wds. J N Craigher)
D. Fischer-Dieskau, G. Moore (pp1957) *Concert*
(6/87) (ORFE) ① **C140101A**
D. Fischer-Dieskau, G. Moore (r1969) *Concert*
(3/93) (DG) ① [9] **437 225-2GX9(3)**
D. Fischer-Dieskau, S. Richter (pp1977) *Concert*
(2/94) (ORFE) ① **C334931A**
D. Fischer-Dieskau, H. Höll (pp1992) *Concert*
(9/95) (ERAT) ① **4509-98493-2**
Totengräberweise—Lied, D869 (1826) (Wds. F. X. von Schlechta)
D. Fischer-Dieskau, G. Moore (r1969) *Concert*
(3/93) (DG) ① [9] **437 225-2GX9(4)**
Totenkranz für ein Kind—Lied, D275 (1815) (Wds. F. von Matthisson)
D. Fischer-Dieskau, G. Moore (r c1967) *Concert*
(3/93) (DG) ① [9] **437 215-2GX9(3)**
P. Rozario, G. Johnson (r1993) *Concert*
(6/94) (HYPE) ① **CDJ33020**
Totenopfer—Lied, D101 (1814) (Wds. F. von Mattisson)
E. Connell, G. Johnson (r1988) *Concert*
(2/90) (HYPE) ① **CDJ33005**
D. Fischer-Dieskau, G. Moore (r c1967) *Concert*
(3/93) (DG) ① [9] **437 215-2GX9(1)**
Il traditor deluso—Lied, D902/2 (1827) (Wds. P. Metastasio)
D. Fischer-Dieskau, G. Moore (r1969) *Concert*
(3/93) (DG) ① [9] **437 225-2GX9(4)**
Trauer der Liebe—Lied, D465 (1816) (Wds. J. G. Jacobi)
Sarah Walker, G. Johnson (r1989) *Concert*
(10/90) (HYPE) ① **CDJ33008**
D. Fischer-Dieskau, G. Moore (r c1967) *Concert*
(3/93) (DG) ① [9] **437 215-2GX9(5)**
Der Traum—Lied, D213 (1815) (wds. Hölty)
M. Hill, G. Johnson (r1990) *Concert*
(5/91) (HYPE) ① **CDJ33010**
D. Fischer-Dieskau, G. Moore (r c1967) *Concert*
(3/93) (DG) ① [9] **437 215-2GX9(2)**
Trinklied—choral song, D148 (1815) (Wds. I. F. Castelli)
P. Schreier, H. Laubenthal, D. Fischer-Dieskau, G. Moore *Concert*
(10/92) (DG) ① [2] **435 596-2GGA2**
J. MacDougall, J. M. Ainsley, S. Keenlyside, M. George, G. Johnson (r1993) *Concert*
(1/95) (HYPE) ① **CDJ33022**
Trinklied—Lied, D183 (1815) (Wds. A. Zettler)
D. Fischer-Dieskau, G. Moore (r c1967) *Concert*
(3/93) (DG) ① [9] **437 215-2GX9(2)**
J.M. Ainsley, J. MacDougall, S. Keenlyside, M. George, G. Johnson (r1993) *Concert*
(6/94) (HYPE) ① **CDJ33020**
Trinklied—2 tenors, 2 basses and piano, D267 (1815) (Wds. anon)
J.M. Ainsley, J. MacDougall, S. Keenlyside, M. George, G. Johnson (r1993) *Concert*
(6/94) (HYPE) ① **CDJ33020**

5. H. Jadlowker, anon (r1927) *Concert*
(12/91) (CLUB) ① CL99-042
5. Vanni-Marcoux, anon (r1931: French) *Concert*
(1/94) (CLUB) ① CL99-101
5. H. Rehfuss, F. Martin (bp1964) *Concert*
(5/94) (CLAV) ① CD50-9327
5. H-P. Blochwitz, R. Jansen (r1992) *Concert*
(3/95) (PHIL) ① 438 932-2PH
5. C. Ludwig, C. Spencer (pp1994) *Concert*
(3/95) (RCA) ① 09026 62652-2
13. R. Tauber, M. Spoliansky (r1927) *Concert*
(7/89) (EMI) ① CDM7 69476-2
13. M. Ivogün, orch (r c1924) *Concert*
(8/92) (NIMB) ① NI7832
20. K. Erb, B. Seidler-Winkler (r1937) *Concert*
(6/94) (PREI) ① [2] 89208
21. K. Erb, B. Seidler-Winkler (r1939) *Concert*
(6/94) (PREI) ① [2] 89208

Wonne der Wehmut—Lied, D260 (1815)
(Wds. Goethe)
J. Baker, G. Johnson (r1987) *Concert*
(10/88) (HYPE) ① CDJ33001
E. Mathis, K. Engel *Concert*
(2/90) (NOVA) ① 150 026-2
D. Fischer-Dieskau, G. Moore (r c1967) *Concert*
(3/93) (DG) ① [9] 437 215-2GX9(3)

Der Zufriedene—Lied, D320 (1815) (Wds. C. L. Reissig)
D. Fischer-Dieskau, G. Moore (r c1967) *Concert*
(3/93) (DG) ① [9] 437 215-2GX9(4)
J.M. Ainsley, G. Johnson (r1993) *Concert*
(6/94) (HYPE) ① CDJ33020

Zufriedenheit—Lied, D362 (?1816) (Wds. M. Claudius)
D. Fischer-Dieskau, G. Moore (r c1967) *Concert*
(3/93) (DG) ① [9] 437 215-2GX9(6)
C. Prégardien, G. Johnson (r1994) *Concert*
(7/95) (HYPE) ① CDJ33023

Das Zügenglöcklein—Lied, D871 (?1826)
(Wds. J.G. Seidl)
M. Shirai, H. Höll *Concert*
(10/89) (CAPR) ① 10 171
O. Bär, G. Parsons *Concert*
(7/90) (EMI) ① CDC7 49997-2
D. Fischer-Dieskau, G. Moore *Concert*
(9/90) (EMI) ① [2] CMS7 63566-2
B. Fassbaender, G. Johnson (r1990) *Concert*
(8/91) (HYPE) ① CDJ33011
D. Fischer-Dieskau, G. Moore (r1969) *Concert*
(3/93) (DG) ① [9] 437 225-2GX9(4)
D. Schreier, S. Richter (pp1977) *Concert*
(2/94) (ORFE) ① C334931A
D. Fischer-Dieskau, H. Höll (pp1992) *Concert*
(4/95) (ERAT) ① 4509-98493-2

Zum Punsche—Lied, D492 (1816) (Wds. J. Mayrhofer)
D. Fischer-Dieskau, G. Moore (r c1967) *Concert*
(3/93) (DG) ① [9] 437 215-2GX9(6)

Zur guten Nacht—Lied with chorus, D903 (1827) (Wds. J. F. Rochlitz)
A. Rolfe Johnson, Chor, G. Johnson (r1989) *Concert*
(6/90) (HYPE) ① CDJ33006

Der Zürnende Barde—Lied, D785 (1823)
(Wds. F. von Bruchmann)
K. Moll, C. Garben *Concert*
(9/87) (ORFE) ① C021821A
D. Fischer-Dieskau, G. Moore *Concert*
(9/90) (EMI) ① [2] CMS7 63566-2
D. Fischer-Dieskau, G. Moore (r1969) *Concert*
(3/93) (DG) ① [9] 437 225-2GX9(3)
H. Schlusnus, F. Rupp (r1931) *Concert*
(1/94) (PREI) ① [2] 89205

Der Zürnenden Diana—Lied, D707 (1820)
(Wds. J. Mayrhofer)
I. Partridge, J. Lindberg *Concert*
(10/89) (PEAR) ① SHECD9608
T. Hampson, G. Johnson (r1991) *Concert*
(4/92) (HYPE) ① CDJ33014
D. Fischer-Dieskau, G. Moore (r1969) *Concert*
(3/93) (DG) ① [9] 437 225-2GX9(2)

Der Zwerg—Lied, D771 (?1822) (Wds. M. von Collin)
J. Norman, P. Moll *Concert*
(1/86) (PHIL) ① 412 623-2PH
D. Fischer-Dieskau, G. Moore (pp1957) *Concert*
(6/87) (ORFE) ① C140101A
A. Murray, G. Johnson (r1988) *Concert*
(1/90) (HYPE) ① CDJ33003
Sarah Walker, R. Vignoles *Concert*
(4/90) (CRD) ① CRD3464
C. Ludwig, I. Gage *Concert*
(9/91) (DG) ① [2] 431 476-2GGA2
T. Takács, J. Jandó *Concert*
(3/93) (NAXO) ① 8 550476
D. Fischer-Dieskau, G. Moore (r1969) *Concert*
(3/93) (DG) ① [9] 437 225-2GX9(3)

718

G. Souzay, D. Baldwin (r1961) *Concert*
(11/93) (PHIL) ① [4] 438 511-2PM4
T. Quasthoff, C. Spencer (r1993) *Concert*
(8/95) (RCA) ① 09026 61864-2
D. Fischer-Dieskau, H. Höll (pp1992) *Concert*
(9/95) (ERAT) ① 4509-98493-2

Claudine von Villa Bella—Singspiel: 3 acts, D239 (1913—Vienna) (Lib. Goethe. Only Overture and Act 1 complete)
1. Overture; 2. Das hast du wohl bereitet; 3. Fröhlicher, seliger, herrlicher Tag; 4. Hin und wieder fliegen die Pfeile; 5. Alle Freuden, alle Gaben; 6. Es erhebt sich eine Stimme; 7. Liebe schwärmt auf allen Wegen; 8. Mit Mädeln sich vertragen; 9. Deinem Willen nachzugeben; 10. Liebliches Kind, kannst du mir sagen; 11. Mich umfängt ein banger Schauer.
4. E. Schumann, G. Moore (r1949) *Concert*
(4/92) (EMI) ① [7] CHS7 69741-2(4)
4, 7. A. Auger, G. Johnson (r1989) *Concert*
(1/91) (HYPE) ① CDJ33009
7. K. Battle, James Levine *Concert*
(12/88) (DG) ① 419 237-2GH
7. E. Wiens, R. Jansen *Concert*
(5/93) (CBC) ① MVCD1053
7. R. Streich, E. Werba (r1959) *Concert*
(10/94) (DG) ① [2] 437 680-2GDO2
7. P. Frijsh, D. Bucktrout (r1932) *Concert*
(4/95) (PEAR) ① [2] GEMMCDS9095(2)

Fierrabras—opera: 3 acts, D796 (1897—Karlsruhe) (Lib. J Kupelwieser)
Cpte J. Protschka, K. Mattila, R. Holl, T. Hampson, R. Gambill, L. Polgár, C. Studer, B. Balleys, H. Welker, A. Schoenberg Ch, COE, C. Abbado (pp1988: omits dialogue)
(10/90) (DG) ① [2] 427 341-2GH2

Beschlossen ist's, ich löse seine Ketten! F. Wunderlich, Stuttgart Rad Chor, Berne St Orch, H. Müller-Kray (bp1959) *Concert*
(10/89) (ACAN) ① 43 267
Overture VPO, I. Kertész *Concert*
(4/92) (DECC) ① [4] 430 773-2DC4

Rosamunde, Fürstin von Zypern—incidental music to romantic play: 4 acts, D797 (1823—Vienna) (Wds. H. von Chézy)
1. Overture Die Zauberharfe (D644); 2. Entr'acte in B minor; 3. Ballet in B minor; 4. Entr'acte in D; 5. Der Vollmond strahlt; 6. Chorus of Spirits; 7. Entr'acte in B flat; 8. Shepherd's melody; 9. Chorus of Shepherds; 10. Chorus of Huntsmen; 11. Ballet in G; 12. Alfonso and Estrella Overture, D732.
1. COE, C. Abbado *Concert*
(2/89) (DECC) ① [5] 423 651-2GH5
1. Concertgebouw, W. Mengelberg (r1938) *Concert*
(7/90) (SYMP) ① SYMCD1078
1. National PO, L. Stokowski *Concert*
(4/92) (EMI) ① CDM7 64140-2
1. RPO, P. Kletzki (r1958) *Concert*
(8/95) (EMI) ① [2] CZS7 67726-2
1, 2, 7, 11. Concertgebouw, G. Szell (r1957) *Concert*
(11/95) (PHIL) ① [2] 442 727-2PM2
1, 3, 11. VPO, R. Muti (r1993) *Symphony 2.*
(1/94) (EMI) ① CDC7 54873-2
1, 3, 11. VPO, R. Muti (r1993) *Concert*
(5/94) (EMI) ① [4] CMS7 64873-2
1, 7, 11. BPO, W. Furtwängler (r1929/30) *Concert*
(4/92) (KOCH) ① [2] 37059-2
1, 7, 11. Anima Eterna, J. van Immerseel *Symphony 5.*
(3/93) (CHNN) ① CCS4292
2, 3, 11. Cologne RSO, G. Wand *Concert*
(2/89) (RCA) ① [5] GD60096
3. R. de Waal (arr Godowsky: pf) *Concert*
(3/92) (HYPE) ① CDA66496
3, 11. BPO, H. von Karajan (r1977/8) *Symphony 9.*
(11/90) (DG) ① CDM7 63529-2
5. A. Auger, G. Johnson (r1989) *Concert*
(1/91) (HYPE) ① CDJ33009
5. C. Ludwig, I. Gage *Concert*
(9/91) (DG) ① [2] 431 476-2GGA2
5. K. Ferrier, B. Walter (pp1949) *Concert*
(6/92) (DECC) ① 433 476-2DM
5. E. Ameling, D. Baldwin (r1973) *Concert*
(4/94) (PHIL) ① [4] 438 528-2PM4(1)
7. VPO, K. Münchinger (r1974) *Concert*
(6/93) (DECC) ① 436 407-2DWO
11. M. Hess (arr Ganz: r1928) *Concert*
(8/90) (APR) ① [2] APR7012
11. M. Hess (arr Ganz: r1928) *Concert*
(5/91) (PEAR) ① GEMMCD9462
11. I. Haendel, A. Kotowska (r1942) *Concert*
(10/92) (PEAR) ① GEMMCD9939
11. F. Kreisler, M. Raucheisen (r1930: arr Kreisler) *Concert*
(3/95) (EMI) ① CDH7 64701-2
11. M. Hess (arr pf: Ganz) *Concert*
(3/95) (BIDD) ① LHW024

---

11. Philadelphia, L. Stokowski (r1927: 2 vers) *Concert*
(11/95) (BIDD) ① WHL033

Des Teufels Lustschloss—opera: 3 acts, D84 (1879—Vienna) (Lib. von Kotzebue: two versions (1813-1815))
Overture VPO, I. Kertész *Concert*
(4/92) (DECC) ① [4] 430 773-2DC4
Overture L. Rose, NYPO, L. Bernstein (r1967) *Concert*
(9/93) (SONY) ① SMK47609

Die Verschworenen (Der häusliche Krieg)—Singspiel: 1 act, D787 (1861—Vienna) (Lib. F. Castelli, after Aristophanes)
EXCERPTS: 1. Overture; 3. Ich schleiche bang und still.
1. English Sinfonia, C. Groves *Concert*
(5/92) (CARL) ① PCD967
3. A. Auger, T. King, G. Johnson (r1989: ed Spiegel) *Concert*
(1/91) (HYPE) ① CDJ33009
3. E. Wiens, J. Valdepeñas, R. Jansen *Concert*
(5/93) (CBC) ① MVCD1053

Der Vierjährige Posten—Singspiel: 1 act, D190 (1896—Dresden) (Lib. T. Körner)
EXCERPTS: 5. Gott! höre meine Stimme.
5. A. Auger, G. Johnson (r1989) *Concert*
(1/91) (HYPE) ① CDJ33009

Die Zwillingsbrüder—Singspiel: 1 act, D647 (1820—Vienna) (Lib. G. von Hofmann)
Overture English Sinfonia, C. Groves *Concert*
(3/93) (CARL) ① PCD968

12 Bagatelles—violin and piano, Op. 13
9. Die Biene (L'abeille).
9. F. Kreisler, anon (r1904) *Concert*
(7/90) (BIDD) ① [2] LAB009/10
9. F. Kreisler, anon (r1904) *Concert*
(8/90) (SYMP) ① SYMCD1071
9. J. Heifetz, Anon (pf) *Concert*
(12/91) (APR) ① [2] APR7015
9. M. Kliegel, R. Havenith (arr vc/pf) *Concert*
(9/92) (MARC) ① 8 223403

Mille cherubini in coro (Lullaby)—song (Wds. Senatra: featured in film 'Forget me not')
L. Pavarotti, National PO, K.H. Adler *Concert*
(12/91) (DECC) ① 433 710-2DH
R. Tebaldi, New Philh, A. Guadagno (arr Gamley) *Concert*
(12/91) (DECC) ① 433 010-2DM

Mazurka in E flat minor—harp, Op. 12
J. Bálint, N. Mercz (1992: arr fl/hp) *Concert*
(12/94) (NAXO) ① 8 550741

Concertino for String Quartet and Orchestra (1930)
Hawthorne Qt, Deutsche Kammerphilharmonie, A. Delfs (r1994) *Concert*
(12/95) (DECC) ① 444 819-2DH

Concerto for Flute, Piano and Orchestra (1927)
B. Wild, A. Madžar, Deutsche Kammerphilharmonie, A. Delfs (r1994) *Concert*
(12/95) (DECC) ① 444 819-2DH

Concerto for Piano and Orchestra No. 1, Op. 11 (1913)
J. Simon, Prague RSO, V. Válek (r1993) *Piano Concerto 2.*
(8/95) (SUPR) ① 11 2164-2

Concerto for Piano and Orchestra No. 2 (1923)
J. Simon, Prague RSO, V. Válek (r1993) *Piano Concerto 1.*
(8/95) (SUPR) ① 11 2164-2
A. Madžar, Deutsche Kammerphilharmonie, A. Delfs (r1994) *Concert*
(12/95) (DECC) ① 444 819-2DH

Suite—chamber orchestra (1921)
1. Ragtime; 2. Valse boston; 3. Tango; 4. Shimmy; 5. Step; 6. Jazz.
Brno St PO, I. Yinon (r1993) *Concert*
(8/95) (SCHW) ① 314372

Symphony No. 1 (1925)
Philh Hungarica, G. A. Albrecht (r1993) *Concert*
(1/95) (CPO) ① **CPO999 251-2**
Brno St PO, I. Yinon (r1993) *Concert*
(8/95) (SCHW) ① **314372**
Symphony No. 2 (1932)
Philh Hungarica, G. A. Albrecht (r1993) *Concert*
(1/95) (CPO) ① **CPO999 251-2**
Symphony No. 3 (1935)
Philh Hungarica, G. A. Albrecht (r1993) *Concert*
(1/95) (CPO) ① **CPO999 251-2**

SECTION II: CHAMBER

Concertino—flute, viola and double-bass (1925)
F. Smith, M. Ludwig, E. Barker *Concert*
(5/93) (NORT) ① **NR248-CD**
T. Oepen, V. Donandt, H-U. Heinzmann (r1993)
Concert (9/95) (SCHW) ① **312322**
Divertissement—oboe, clarinet and bassoon (1926)
M. Lammers, W. Hermann, B. Groth (r1993) *Concert*
(9/95) (SCHW) ① **312322**
Duo—violin and cello (1925)
S. Wagner, B. Gmelin (r1993) *Concert*
(9/95) (SCHW) ① **311672**
G. Sussmuth, H-J. Eschenburg (r1994) *Concert*
(11/95) (CAPR) ① **10 539**
Hot-Sonata—alto saxophone and piano (1930)
D. Bensmann, M. Rische (r1988) *Concert*
(9/95) (SCHW) ① **312322**
5 Pieces—string quartet
Petersen Qt (r1992) *Concert*
(5/93) (CAPR) ① **10 463**
Kocian Qt (r1994) *Concert*
(8/95) (SUPR) ① **11 2166-2**
Sextet—2 violins, 2 violas, 2 cellos (1924)
Raphael Ens *Concert* (7/92) (HYPE) ① **CDA66516**
R. J. Kimstedt, M. Sanderling, Petersen Qt (r1994)
Concert (11/95) (CAPR) ① **10 539**
Sonata for Cello and Piano (1914)
B. Gmelin, J. Lamke (r1993) *Concert*
(9/95) (SCHW) ① **311672**
Sonata for Flute and Piano (1924-25)
F. Smith, S. Pinkas *Concert*
(5/93) (NORT) ① **NR248-CD**
H-U. Heinzmann, J. Lamke (r1993) *Concert*
(9/95) (SCHW) ① **312322**
Sonata for Violin and Piano No. 2 (1927)
S. Wagner, J. Lamke (r1993) *Concert*
(9/95) (SCHW) ① **311672**
String Quartet in G major, Op. 25 (1918)
Kocian Qt (r1994) *Concert*
(8/95) (SUPR) ① **11 2166-2**
Petersen Qt (r1994) *Concert*
(11/95) (CAPR) ① **10 539**
String Quartet No. 1 (1924)
Petersen Qt (r1992) *Concert*
(5/93) (CAPR) ① **10 463**
Hawthorne Qt *Concert*
(5/93) (NORT) ① **NR248-CD**
Brandis Qt (r1992) *Concert*
(3/95) (NIMB) ① **NI5410**
Kocian Qt (r1994) *Concert*
(8/95) (SUPR) ① **11 2166-2**
String Quartet No. 2 (1925)
Petersen Qt (r1992) *Concert*
(5/93) (CAPR) ① **10 463**
Kocian Qt (r1994) *Concert*
(8/95) (SUPR) ① **11 2166-2**

SECTION III: INSTRUMENTAL

Esquisses de jazz—piano
1. Rag; 2. Boston; 3. Tango; 4. Blues; 5. Charleston;
6. Black-bottom.
4, 5. E. Schulhoff (r1928) *Concert*
(12/95) (DECC) ① **444 819-2DH**
5 Jazz Etudes—piano (1926)
1. Charleston; 2. Blues; 3. Chanson; 4. Tango; 5.
Toccata alla the Shimmy 'Kitten on the Keys'.
2-4. E. Schulhoff (r1928) *Concert*
(12/95) (DECC) ① **444 819-2DH**
Partita—piano (pub 1925)
1. Tempo di Fox; 2. Jazz-like; 3. Tango-Rag; 4.
Tempo di Foxà la Hawai; 5. Boston; 6. Tempo di
Rag; 7. Tango; 8. Shimmy-Jazz.
3, 4, 7, 8. E. Schulhoff (r1928) *Concert*
(12/95) (DECC) ① **444 819-2DH**
Sonata for Violin (1927)
C. Muck (r1994) *Concert* (11/95) (CAPR) ① **10 539**

SECTION V: STAGE WORKS

Die Mondsüchtige, 'Moonstruck'—ballet (1931—Oxford)
Cpte Leipzig Gewandhaus, L. Zagrosek (r1994)
Concert (5/95) (DECC) ① **444 182-2DH**
Plameny, 'Flammen'—opera: 2 acts (1927-8—Prague) (Lib. K J Beneš)
1. Festliches Vorspiel (Ouvertüre).
1. Brno St PO, I. Yinon (r1994) *Concert*
(8/95) (SCHW) ① **314372**

SCHULLER, Gunther *(b 1925) USA*

SECTION I: ORCHESTRAL

Eine Kleine Posaunemusik, '(A) Little Trombone Music'—trombone and wind ensemble (1980)
C. Lindberg, Malmö SO, J. DePreist (r1993) *Concert*
(9/94) (BIS) ① **BIS-CD628**
Spectra—orchestra (1958)
Chicago SO, James Levine (1990) *Concert*
(7/94) (DG) ① **431 698-2GH**
7 Studies on Themes of Paul Klee (1957)
1. Antique harmonies; 2. Abstract trio; 3. Little blue
devil; 4. The twittering-machine; 5. Arab village; 6. An
eerie moment; 7. Pastorale.
Minneapolis SO, A. Dorati (r1960) *Concert*
(7/93) (MERC) ① **434 329-2MM**

SECTION II: CHAMBER

Recitative and Rondo—violin and piano (1954)
R. Davidovici, S. de Groote *Concert*
(11/87) (NEW) ① **NW334-2**
String Quartet No. 3 (1986)
Emerson Qt (r1991) *Concert*
(11/93) (DG) ① **437 537-2GH**
Suite—wind quintet (1945)
Reykjavik Wind Qnt (r1992) *Concert*
(11/93) (CHAN) ① **CHAN9174**

SCHULZ, Johann Abraham Peter *(1747-1800) Germany*

SECTION III: INSTRUMENTAL

6 Diverses pièces, Op. 1 (pub 1776)
EXCERPTS: 5. Allegretto; 6. Larghetto con
Variazioni.
5, 6. C. Schornsheim (r1991) *Concert*
(4/95) (CAPR) ① **10 424**

SCHULZ-EVLER, Andrey *(1854-1905) Poland*

SECTION III: INSTRUMENTAL

An die schönen Blauen Donau—concert arabesques on waltz by Johann Strauss II
P. Fowke *Concert* (8/89) (CRD) ① **CRD3396**

SCHUMAN, William (Howard) *(1910-1992) USA*

SECTION I: ORCHESTRAL

American Festival Overture (1939)
Los Angeles PO, I. Bernstein (pp 1982) *Concert*
(10/84) (DG) ① **413 324-2GH**
St Louis SO, L. Slatkin (r1991/2) *Concert*
(5/93) (RCA) ① **09026 61282-2**
Colloquies
P. Myers, NYPO, Z. Mehta *Crumb: Haunted
Landscape.* (2/88) (NEW) ① **NW326-2**
New England Triptych (1956)
Phoenix SO, J. Sedares *Herrmann: Symphony 1.*
(9/92) (KOCH) ① **37135-2**
St Louis SO, L. Slatkin (r1991/2) *Concert*
(5/93) (RCA) ① **09026 61282-2**
Czech PO, A. Copland (pp1973) *Concert*
(6/93) (ROMA) ① **RR1973**
Seattle SO, G. Schwarz *Concert*
(7/93) (DELO) ① **DE3115**
Symphony No. 5, 'Symphony for Strings' (1943)
Seattle SO, G. Schwarz *Concert*
(7/93) (DELO) ① **DE3115**
Symphony No. 10, 'American Muse' (1975)
St Louis SO, L. Slatkin (r1991/2) *Concert*
(5/93) (RCA) ① **09026 61282-2**

SECTION II: CHAMBER

String Quartet No. 2 (1937)
Lydian Qt *Concert* (8/94) (HARM) ① **HMU90 7114**

String Quartet No. 3 (1939)
Lydian Qt *Concert* (8/94) (HARM) ① **HMU90 7114**
String Quartet No. 5 (1987)
Lydian Qt *Concert* (8/94) (HARM) ① **HMU90 7114**

SECTION III: INSTRUMENTAL

Voyage—piano (1953)
B. Lerner *Concert* (12/89) (ETCE) ① **KTC1036**

SECTION V: STAGE WORKS

Judith—ballet (1949)
Seattle SO, G. Schwarz *Concert*
(7/93) (DELO) ① **DE3115**
The Mighty Casey—baseball opera: 3 scenes (1953—Hartford) (Lib. J Gury, after E L
Thayer)
Cpte S. Robinson, F. Pomponi, C. Thorpe, D.
Corman, R. Cusick, D. Dreyer, C. Conde, A. Parks, J.
Russell, K. Chester, S. Rosenbaum, Juilliard Op
Center, Juilliard Orch, G. Schwarz (pp1990) *Question
of Taste.* (9/94) (DELO) ① **DE1030**
Night Journey—ballet (1947)
Atlantic Sinfonietta, A. Schenck (r1994) *Concert*
(4/92) (KOCH) ① **37051-2**
A Question of Taste—opera: 1 act (1989—New York) (Lib. J D McClatchy, after R
Dahl)
Cpte A. Norton, E. Grohowski, T. P. Groves, E.
Bishop, D. Corman, S. Wilde, C. Scimone, Juilliard
Op Center, Juilliard Orch, G. Schwarz (pp1990)
Mighty Casey. (9/94) (DELO) ① **DE1030**

SCHUMANN, Clara (Josephine) *(1819-1896) Germany*

SECTION I: ORCHESTRAL

Concerto for Piano and Orchestra in A minor, Op. 7 (1835-36)
A. Cheng, Women's PO, J. Falletta *Concert*
(2/93) (KOCH) ① **37169-2**

SECTION II: CHAMBER

Piano Trio in G minor, Op. 17 (before 1846)
Dartington Trio (r1988) *Mendelssohn-Hensel: Piano
Trio.* (3/90) (HYPE) ① **CDA66331**
Macalester Trio *Concert*
(10/94) (VOX) ① [2] **115845-2**
3 Romances—violin and piano, Op. 22 (1853)
A. Jodry, H. Boschi *Concert*
(9/88) (CALL) ① **CAL9211**

SECTION III: INSTRUMENTAL

9 Caprices en forme de valse—piano, Op. 2 (1831-32)
1. C; 2. D; 3. E flat; 4. A Flat; 5. B flat; 6. C; 7. A flat;
8. E flat; 9. D flat.
J. de Beenhouwer *Concert*
(1/93) (PART) ① [3] **Part9293-2**
Deuxième Scherzo in C minor—piano, Op. 14 (c1841)
J. de Beenhouwer *Concert*
(1/93) (PART) ① [3] **Part9293-2**
Etude in A flat—piano (c1832)
J. de Beenhouwer *Concert*
(1/93) (PART) ① [3] **Part9293-2**
3 Fugues on Themes of Bach—piano (1845)
1. E flat; 2. E; 3. G minor.
J. de Beenhouwer *Concert*
(1/93) (PART) ① [3] **Part9293-2**
Geburtstagmarsch in E flat—piano (1879)
J. de Beenhouwer *Concert*
(1/93) (PART) ① [3] **Part9293-2**
Impromptu in E—piano (c1843)
J. de Beenhouwer *Concert*
(1/93) (PART) ① [3] **Part9293-2**
4 Pièces caractéristiques—piano, Op. 5 (1835-36)
1. Impromptu le sabbat; 2. Caprice à la boléro; 3.
Romance; 4. Scène fantastique: le ballet de
revenants.
J. de Beenhouwer *Concert*
(1/93) (PART) ① [3] **Part9293-2**
4 Pièces fugitives—piano, Op. 15 (1845)
1. Larghetto, F; 2. Un poco agitato, A minor; 3.
Andante espressivo, D; 4. Scherzo, G.
J. de Beenhouwer *Concert*
(1/93) (PART) ① [3] **Part9293-2**
3. H. Boschi *Concert* (9/88) (CALL) ① **CAL9211**
4 Polonaises—piano, Op. 1 (1828-30)
1. E flat; 2. C; 3. D; 4. C.
J. de Beenhouwer *Concert*
(1/93) (PART) ① [3] **Part9293-2**
Präludium in F minor—piano
J. de Beenhouwer *Concert*
(1/93) (PART) ① [3] **Part9293-2**

3 Preludes and Fugues—piano, Op. 21 (by 1845)
1. G minor; 2. B flat; 3. D minor.
H. Boschi *Concert* (9/88) (CALL) ① **CAL9211**
J. de Beenhouwer *Concert*
(1/93) (PART) ① [3] **Part9293-2**
Romance in A minor—piano (1853)
J. de Beenhouwer *Concert*
(1/93) (PART) ① [3] **Part9293-2**
Romance in B minor—piano (1856)
H. Boschi *Concert* (9/88) (CALL) ① **CAL9211**
J. de Beenhouwer *Concert*
(1/93) (PART) ① [3] **Part9293-2**
3 Romances—piano, Op. 11 (1839)
1. E flat minor; 2. G minor; 3. A flat.
H. Boschi *Concert* (9/88) (CALL) ① **CAL9211**
J. de Beenhouwer *Concert*
(1/93) (PART) ① [3] **Part9293-2**
3 Romances—piano, Op. 21 (1853)
1. A minor; 2. F; 3. G minor.
H. Boschi *Concert* (9/88) (CALL) ① **CAL9211**
J. de Beenhouwer *Concert*
(1/93) (PART) ① [3] **Part9293-2**
Scherzo in D minor—piano, Op. 10 (1838)
J. de Beenhouwer *Concert*
(1/93) (PART) ① [3] **Part9293-2**
Soirées musicales—piano, Op. 6 (1834-36)
1. Toccatina, A minor; 2. Notturno, F; 3. Mazurka, G minor; 4. Ballade, D minor; 5. Mazurka, G; 6. Polonaise, A minor.
J. de Beenhouwer *Concert*
(1/93) (PART) ① [3] **Part9293-2**
Sonata for Piano in G minor (1841-42)
J. de Beenhouwer *Concert*
(1/93) (PART) ① [3] **Part9293-2**
Souvenir de Vienne—impromptu: piano, Op. 9 (1838)
J. de Beenhouwer *Concert*
(1/93) (PART) ① [3] **Part9293-2**
Valses romantiques—piano, Op. 4 (1838)
J. de Beenhouwer *Concert*
(1/93) (PART) ① [3] **Part9293-2**
Variations de concert sur la cavatine du Pirate de Bellini—piano, Op. 8 (1834)
J. de Beenhouwer *Concert*
(1/93) (PART) ① [3] **Part9293-2**
Variations on a theme of Robert Schumann—piano, Op. 20 (1853)
H. Boschi *Concert* (9/88) (CALL) ① **CAL9211**
J. de Beenhouwer *Concert*
(1/93) (PART) ① [3] **Part9293-2**

SECTION IV: VOCAL AND CHORAL

3 Lieder, Op. 12 (1840) (Wds. Rückert)
pub in R. Schumann's 'Gedichte aus 'Liebesfrühling', Op. 37; 1. Er ist gekommen; 2. Liebst du um Schönheit; 3. Warum willst du and're fragen?.
2. S. Mentzer, K. Schmidt (r1991) *Concert*
(12/93) (KOCH) ① **37240-2**
3 Partsongs—unaccompanied choir (4vv) (1848) (Wds. E. Geibel)
Heidelberg Madrigal Ch, G. Kegelmann *Concert*
(4/90) (BAYE) ① **BR100041**

SCHUMANN, Robert (Alexander) (1810-1856) Germany

SECTION I: ORCHESTRAL

Concerto for Cello and Orchestra in A minor, Op. 129 (1850)
M. Maisky, VPO, L. Bernstein (pp1985) *Symphony 2.*
(11/86) (DG) ① **419 190-2GH**
M. Maisky, VPO, L. Bernstein (pp 1985) *Concert*
(3/88) (DG) ① [3] **423 099-2GH3**
Y-Y. Ma, BRSO, Colin Davis *Concert*
(10/88) (SONY) ① **SK42663**
G. Piatigorsky, LPO, J. Barbirolli (r1934) *Concert*
(10/91) (PEAR) ① **GEMMCD9447**
G. Piatigorsky, LPO, J. Barbirolli (r1934) *Concert*
(3/92) (MUSI) ① **MACD-674**
J. Starker, LSO, S. Skrowaczewski *Concert*
(4/92) (MERC) ① **432 010-2MM**
T. Thedéen, Malmö SO, L. Markiz *Elgar: Cello Concerto.*
(8/92) (BIS) ① **BIS-CD486**
L. Harrell, Cleveland Orch, N. Marriner *Cello Concerto.*
(8/92) (DECC) ① **430 743-2DM**
N. Gutman, LSO, K. Masur *Schnittke: Cello Concerto 1.*
(8/92) (EMI) ① **CDC7 54443-2**
P. Fournier, SRO, F. Fricsay (pp1957) *Concert*
(11/92) (CASC) ① **VEL2009**
J. Du Pré, New Philh, D. Barenboim *Concert*
(3/93) (EMI) ① **CDM7 64626-2**
P. Tortelier, RPO, Y.P. Tortelier (r1978) *Concert*
(8/93) (EMI) ① [2] **CZS7 67521-2**

L. Rose, NYPO, L. Bernstein (r1960) *Concert*
(9/93) (SONY) ① **SMK47609**
G. Cassadó, Bamberg SO, J. Perlea (r1950s) *Concert* (11/93) (VOX) ① [2] **CDX2 5502**
P. Casals, Prades Fest Orch, E. Ormandy (r1953) *Concert* (5/94) (SONY) ① **SMK58993**
J. Du Pré, New Philh, D. Barenboim (r1968) *Concert*
(8/94) (EMI) ① [6] **CZS5 68132-2**
A. Noras, Finnish RSO, S. Oramo (r1994) *Dvořák: Cello Concerto.* (10/95) (FINL) ① **4509-98886-2**
M. Kliegel, Ireland National SO, A. Constantine (r1994) *Brahms: Double Concerto.*
(10/95) (NAXO) ① **8 550938**
J. Starker, Bamberg SO, D. R. Davies (r1994) *Hindemith: Cello Concerto.*
(10/95) (RCA) ① **09026 68027-2**
J. Starker, Philh, C.M. Giulini (r1957) *Concert*
(12/95) (EMI) ① [6] **CZS5 68485-2**
Exc P. Fournier, BPO, W. Furtwängler (pp1943) *Concert* (3/95) (TAHR) ① [4] **FURT1008/11**
Concerto for Piano and Orchestra in A minor, Op. 54 (1841-45)
A. Brendel, LSO, C. Abbado *Weber: Konzertstück.*
(3/86) (PHIL) ① **412 251-2PH**
G. Anda, BPO, R. Kubelík *Grieg: Piano Concerto.*
(8/87) (DG) ① **415 850-2GGA**
R. Lupu, LSO, A. Previn *Grieg: Piano Concerto.*
(12/87) (DECC) ① **417 728-2DM**
I. Margalit, LPO, B. Thomson *Saint-Saëns: Piano Concerto 2.* (1/88) (CHAN) ① **CHAN8546**
J. Frantz, VPO, L. Bernstein (pp 1984) *Concert*
(3/88) (DG) ① [3] **423 099-2GH3**
F. Davies, RPS Orch, E. Ansermet (r1928) *Concert*
(5/88) (PEAR) ① **GEMMCD9291**
A. Rubinstein, Chicago SO, C.M. Giulini *Concert*
(9/88) (RCA) ① **RD86255**
S. Richter, Monte Carlo Nat Op Orch, L. von Matačić *Grieg: Piano Concerto.*
(12/88) (EMI) ① **CDC7 47164-2**
M. Perahia, BRSO, Colin Davis (pp1988) *Grieg: Piano Concerto.* (5/89) (SONY) ① **SK44899**
D. Lipatti, Philh, H. von Karajan (r1948) *Mozart: Piano Concerto 21.* (7/89) (EMI) ① **CDH7 69792-2**
D. Alexeev, RPO, Y. Temirkanov (r1988) *Grieg: Piano Concerto.* (12/89) (EMIN) ① **CD-EMX2195**
M. Pollini, BPO, C. Abbado (r1989) *Schoenberg: Piano Concerto.* (7/90) (DG) ① **427 771-2GH**
L. Fleisher, Cleveland Orch, G. Szell *Grieg: piano concerto.* (10/90) (SONY) ① **MPK44849**
P. Devoyon, LPO, J. Maksymiuk (r1990) *Grieg: Piano Concerto.* (2/91) (CFP) ① **CD-CFP4574**
B. Janis, Minneapolis SO, S. Skrowaczewski *Concert* (11/91) (MERC) ① **432 011-2MM**
F. Gulda, VPO, V. Andreae *Concert*
(1/92) (DECC) ① **433 628-2DSP**
A. Cortot, LSO, L. Ronald (r1927) *Concert*
(6/92) (BIDD) ① **LHW003**
L. Lortie, Philh, N. Järvi *Chopin: Piano Concerto 2.*
(11/92) (CHAN) ① **CHAN9061**
L. Vogt, CBSO, S. Rattle *Grieg: Piano Concerto.*
(1/93) (EMI) ① **CDC7 54746-2**
D. Barenboim, LPO, D. Fischer-Dieskau *Concert*
(3/93) (EMI) ① **CDM7 64626-2**
A. de Larrocha, VPO, Colin Davis (r1991) *Piano Quintet, Op.44.* (5/93) (RCA) ① **09026 61279-2**
M. Bergerich, Berlin Fest Orch, V. Petroschoff *Concert* (6/93) (ROSE) ① **3221**
E. Kissin, VPO, C.M. Giulini (pp1992) *Concert*
(6/93) (SONY) ① **SK52567**
D. Barenboim, LPO, D. Fischer-Dieskau *Concert*
(8/93) (EMI) ① [2] **CZS7 67521-2**
Solomon, Philh, H. Menges (r1956) *Concert*
(8/93) (EMI) ① [2] **CZS7 67735-2**
A. Rubinstein, RCA Victor SO, J. Krips (r1958) *Concert* (10/93) (RCA) ① **09026 61444-2**
M. Hess, SO, W. Goehr (r1937) *Concert*
(2/94) (DUTT) ① **CDLX7005**
M. Dalberto, Vienna SO, E. Inbal (r1993) *Concert*
(6/94) (DENO) ① **CO-75859**
J-M. Luisada, LSO, M. Tilson Thomas (r1993) *Grieg: Piano Concerto.* (12/94) (DG) ① **439 913-2GH**
M. Argerich, G. Kremer, COE, N. Harnoncourt (pp1992) *Violin Concerto.*
(1/95) (TELD) ① **4509-90696-2**
M. Pollini, BPO, C. Abbado (r1989) *Concert*
(3/95) (DG) ① **445 522-2GMA**
W. Gieseking, BPO, W. Furtwängler (pp1942) *Beethoven: Piano Concerto 5.*
(5/95) (MUSI) ① **MACD-815**
B. Davidovich, Seattle SO, G. Schwarz (r1992) *Concert* (7/95) (DELO) ① [4] **DE3146**
W. Kempff, BRSO, R. Kubelík (r1973) *Concert*
(9/95) (DG) ① **439 476-2GCL**
A. Malling, Danish Nat RSO, M. Schønwandt (r1994) *Schoenberg: Piano Concerto.*
(10/95) (CHAN) ① **CHAN9375**

A.B. Michelangeli, Rome RAI Orch, G. Gavazzeni (pp1962) *Concert* (10/95) (MEMR) ① [4] **999001**
C. Haskil, Hague PO, W. van Otterloo (r1951) *Concert* (11/95) (PHIL) ① [4] **442 631-2PM4**
C. Haskil, Hague PO, W. van Otterloo (r1951) *Concert* (11/95) (PHIL) ① [12] **442 685-2PM12**
Movt 1. Martin Jones (trans pf: Grainger) *Concert* (2/91) (NIMB) ① **NI5255**
Concerto for Violin and Orchestra in A minor, Op. 129 (arr cpsr from Cello Concerto: found 1987)
S. Gawriloff, South-West German RSO, L. Hager *Concert* (10/91) (AMAT) ① **SRR8904/1**
G. Kremer, Boston SO, S. Ozawa (pp1992: orch Shostakovich) *Shostakovich: Violin Concerto 2.*
(9/94) (DG) ① **439 890-2GH**
Concerto for Violin and Orchestra in D minor, Op. posth (1853)
J-J. Kantorow, Netherlands PO, E. Krivine *Concert*
(4/88) (DENO) ① **CO-1666**
V. Snítil, Prague SO, L. Hlaváček *Concert*
(10/91) (SUPR) ① **11 1114-2**
Y. Menuhin, NYPO, J. Barbirolli (r1938) *Mendelssohn: Violin Concerto, Op.64.*
(12/91) (BIDD) ① **LAB047**
T. Zehetmair, Philh, C. Eschenbach (r1988) *Concert*
(7/93) (TELD) ① **4509-91444-2**
G. Kremer, Philh, R. Muti (r1982) *Concert*
(8/93) (EMI) ① [2] **CZS7 67521-2**
T. Wanami, LPO, A. Leaper (r1992) *Brahms: Violin Concerto.* (4/94) (CART) ① **PCD1062**
G. Kulenkampff, BPO, H. Schmidt-Isserstedt (r1937) *Sibelius: Violin Concerto.* (9/94) (DANT) ① **LYS012**
G. Kulenkampff, BPO, H. Schmidt-Isserstedt (r1937) *Mendelssohn: Violin Concerto, Op.64.*
(9/94) (TELD) ① **4509-93672-2**
M. Argerich, G. Kremer, COE, N. Harnoncourt (pp1994) *Piano Concerto.*
(1/95) (TELD) ① **4509-90696-2**
Fantasie in C—violin and orchestra, Op. 131 (1853)
V. Snítil, Prague SO, L. Hlaváček *Concert*
(10/91) (SUPR) ① **11 1114-2**
T. Zehetmair, Philh, C. Eschenbach (r1988) *Brahms: Violin Concerto.* (7/93) (TELD) ① **4509-91443-2**
Introduction and Allegro appassionato—piano and orchestra, Op. 92 (1849)
D. Barenboim, LPO, D. Fischer-Dieskau *Concert*
(3/93) (EMI) ① **CDM7 64626-2**
D. Barenboim, LPO, D. Fischer-Dieskau (r1974) *Concert* (8/93) (EMI) ① [2] **CZS7 67521-2**
J. Jandó, Brussels BRT PO, A. Rahbari (r1992) *Brahms: Piano Concerto 2.*
(9/93) (NAXO) ① **8 550506**
M. Dalberto, Vienna SO, E. Inbal (r1993) *Concert*
(6/94) (DENO) ① **CO-75859**
Introduction and Allegro in D/D minor—piano and orchestra, Op. 134 (1853)
M. Dalberto, Vienna SO, E. Inbal (r1993) *Concert*
(6/94) (DENO) ① **CO-75859**
Julius Cäsar—overture to Shakespeare's play, Op. 128 (1851)
LSO, N. Järvi *Brahms: Symphony 2.*
(4/89) (CHAN) ① **CHAN8649**
Konzertstück in F—4 horns and orchestra, Op. 86 (1849)
R. Bonneve, M. Robbins, D. Knapp, W. Silson, Seattle SO, G. Schwarz *Concert*
(5/90) (DELO) ① **DE3084**
M. Rimon (hn/dir), Israel PO *Concert*
(2/92) (CARL) ① **MCD31**
G. Seifert, N. Hauptmann, C. Kohler, M. Klier, BPO, K. Tennstedt (r1978) *Concert*
(8/93) (EMI) ① [2] **CZS7 67521-2**
Seattle SO, G. Schwarz (r1988) *Concert*
(7/95) (DELO) ① [4] **DE3146**
Overture, Scherzo and Finale, Op. 52 (1841 rev 1845)
Stuttgart RSO, N. Marriner *Concert*
(6/86) (CAPR) ① **10 063**
Stuttgart RSO, N. Marriner *Concert*
(1/89) (CAPR) ① [3] **10 997**
LSO, N. Järvi *Brahms: Symphony 3.*
(3/89) (CHAN) ① **CHAN8646**
Staatskapelle Dresden, W. Sawallisch *Concert*
(5/89) (EMI) ① **CDM7 69471-2**
Seattle SO, G. Schwarz *Concert*
(5/90) (DELO) ① **DE3084**
BPO, H. von Karajan *Brahms: Symphony 1.*
(8/91) (DG) ① **431 161-2GR**
Staatskapelle Dresden, W. Sawallisch (r1972) *Concert* (11/93) (EMI) ① [2] **CMS7 64815-2**
Hanover Band, R. Goodman (r1993) *Concert*
(3/95) (RCA) ① [2] **09026 61931-2**

SECTION II: CHAMBER

1. B. Janis (r1962) Concert
(9/91) (MERC) ① **432 002-2MM**
1. S. Richter Concert
(11/92) (DG) ① **435 751-2GDO**
1. S. Richter Concert
(8/94) (PHIL) ① [3] **438 477-2PH3**
1, 2. Vladimir Ashkenazy (r1986) Concert
(8/88) (DECC) ① **421 010-2DH**
1, 2. A. Rubinstein Concert
(9/88) (RCA) ① **RD86255**
2. E. Joyce (r1937) Concert
(2/94) (PEAR) ① **GEMMCD9022**
2. H. Bauer (r1929) Concert
(4/94) (BIDD) ① **LHW009**
2, 4, 8. S. Richter (pp1979) Concert
(10/92) (OLYM) ① **OCD287**
8. Vladimir Ashkenazy (r1989) Concert
(4/92) (DECC) ① **425 940-2DH**
8. G. Cziffra (r1968) Concert
(3/95) (EMI) ① **CDM5 65254-2**

Papillons—piano, Op. 2 (1829-31)
A. Schiff Concert
(1/86) (DENO) ① **C37-7573**
E. Wild Concert
(2/89) (DELL) ① **CDDBS7005**
G. Oppitz Concert
(1/92) (RCA) ① **RD60856**
W. Kempff Concert
(5/92) (DG) ① [4] **435 045-2GX4**
A. Cortot (r1935) Concert
(6/92) (DANT) ① [2] **HPC004/5**
A. Cortot (r1935) Concert
(6/92) (BIDD) ① **LHW003**
A. Cortot (r1935) Concert
(9/92) (PEAR) ① **GEMMCD9932**
S. Richter (pp1962) Concert
(3/93) (EMI) ① [4] **CMS7 64429-2**
S. Richter (pp1962) Concert
(3/93) (EMI) ① **CDM7 64625-2**
M. Horszowski (r1991) Concert
(12/93) (NONE) ① **7559-79264-2**
J. Jandó (r1992) Concert
(4/94) (NAXO) ① **8 550784**
K. Lifschitz (r1990) Concert
(12/94) (DENO) ① **CO-78907**

Presto passionato in G minor—piano (?1833)
(rejected finale of Op. 22)
V. Horowitz (r1932) Concert
(3/90) (EMI) ① [3] **CHS7 63538-2**
H. Milne (r1990) Concert   (8/93) (CRD) ① **CRD3471**
B. Glemser (r1993) Concert
(10/94) (NAXO) ① **8 550715**

3 Romanzen—piano, Op. 28 (1839)
1. B flat minor; 2. F sharp; 3. B.
W. Kempff Concert
(5/92) (DG) ① [4] **435 045-2GX4**
D. Várjon (r1994) Concert
(6/95) (NAXO) ① **8 550849**
M-J. Pires (r1992) Concert
(6/95) (DG) ① **437 538-2GH**
1. H. Bauer (r1939) Concert
(4/94) (BIDD) ① **LHW009**
2. E. Wild Concert   (2/89) (DELL) ① **CDDBS7005**
2. B. Moiseiwitsch (r1941) Concert
(9/90) (APR) ① [2] **APR7005**
2. A. Servadei Concert   (7/91) (CARL) ① **PCD949**
2. B. Janis (r1962) Concert
(9/91) (MERC) ① **432 002-2MM**
2. P. Grainger (r1928) Concert
(4/93) (BIDD) ① **LHW008**

4 Sketches—pedal piano, Op. 58 (1845)
J. Bate (r1978) Concert   (7/94) (ASV) ① **CDQS6127**
O. Latry (r1991) Concert
(10/94) (SONY) ① **SK57490**

Sonata for Piano No. 1 in F sharp minor, Op. 11 (1832-35)
H. Grimaud Concert   (3/88) (DENO) ① **CO-1786**
M. Pollini Fantaisie.   (5/88) (DG) ① **423 134-2GH**
Vladimir Ashkenazy (r1987) Concert
(2/89) (DECC) ① **421 290-2DH**
E. Wild Concert   (2/89) (DELL) ① **CDDBS7005**
D. Ciani (pp) Concert   (8/89) (DYNA) ① **CDS55**
I. Hobson Concert   (3/93) (ARAB) ① [2] **Z6621/2**
V. Sofronitzky (pp1960) Concert
(8/95) (MELO) ① [2] **74321 25177-2**
V. Sofronitzky (pp1960) Concert
(8/95) (MELO) ① [11] **74321 25172-2(1)**

Sonata for Piano No. 2 in G minor, Op. 22 (1833-38)
M. Perahia Schubert: Piano Sonata, D959.
(8/88) (SONY) ① **MK44569**
P. Katin Concert   (5/89) (OLYM) ① **OCD218**
Vladimir Ashkenazy (r1989) Concert
(4/92) (DECC) ① **425 940-2DH**
W. Kempff Concert
(5/92) (DG) ① [4] **435 045-2GX4**
M. Levitzki (r1933) Concert
(6/92) (APR) ① [2] **APR7020**
M. Argerich Concert   (2/93) (DG) ① **437 252-2GGA**

S. Richter (pp1962) Concert
(3/93) (EMI) ① [4] **CMS7 64429-2**
I. Hobson Concert   (3/93) (ARAB) ① [2] **Z6621/2**
P. Grainger (r1927) Concert
(4/93) (BIDD) ① **LHW008**
H. Milne (r1990) Concert   (8/93) (CRD) ① **CRD3471**
B. Berezovsky (r1992) Concert
(8/93) (TELD) ① **9031-77476-2**
M. Kazakevich (r1993) Concert
(7/94) (CONI) ① [2] **CDCF227**
B. Glemser (r1993) Concert
(10/94) (NAXO) ① **8 550715**

Sonata for Piano No. 3 in F minor, Op. 14 (1835-36) (revision of 'Concert sans orchestre')
A. Marks Fantaisie.   (9/89) (NIMB) ① **NI5181**
C. Favre Kinderszenen.
(9/89) (CLAV) ① **CD50-8906**
S. Nagaoka (1853 Edition) Concert
(11/92) (CHNN) ① **CG9101**
I. Hobson Concert   (3/93) (ARAB) ① [2] **Z6621/2**
V. Horowitz (pp1976) Concert
(7/94) (RCA) ① **GD86680**

Movt 3. V. Horowitz (pp1951) Concert
(1/93) (RCA) ① **GD60463**

Variations N. Demidenko (pp1993) Concert
(1/94) (HYPE) ① [2] **CDA66781/2**

6 Studies—pedal piano, Op. 56 (1845)
1. C; 2. A minor; 3. E; 4. A flat; 5. B minor; 6. B.
H. C. Becker-Foss Concert   (6/93) (ROSE) ① **3221**
O. Latry (r1991) Concert
(10/94) (SONY) ① **SK57490**
5. John Scott Concert   (12/87) (CIRR) ① **CICD1007**
5. S. Preston (arr. J E West) Concert
(1/93) (DECC) ① **430 091-2DWO**

Thema in E flat—piano (1854)
A. Servadei Concert   (7/91) (CARL) ① **PCD949**

Theme and Variations on the name 'Abegg'—piano, Op. 1 (1829-30)
E. Kissin (pp1990) Concert
(3/91) (RCA) ① [2] **RD60443**
I. Cooper Concert   (5/92) (OTTA) ① **OTRC39027**
S. Richter (pp1962) Concert
(11/92) (DG) ① **435 751-2GDO**
I. Hobson Concert   (3/93) (ARAB) ① [2] **Z6621/2**
Vladimir Ashkenazy (r1991) Concert
(2/95) (DECC) ① **443 322-2DH**
C. Haskil (r1951) Concert
(11/95) (PHIL) ① [12] **442 685-2PM12**
C. Haskil (r1951) Concert
(11/95) (PHIL) ① [3] **442 635-2PM3**
S. Richter (pp1962) Concert
(12/95) (DG) ① [2] **447 355-2GDB2**

Toccata in C—piano, Op. 7 (1829-32)
I. Pogorelich Concert   (10/83) (DG) ① **410 520-2GH**
S. Barere (pp1946) Concert
(11/89) (APR) ① [2] **APR7008**
V. Horowitz (r1934) Concert
(3/90) (EMI) ① [3] **CHS7 63538-2**
H. Shelley Concert   (9/90) (CHAN) ① **CHAN8814**
S. Barere (r1935/6: LP 2 vers, CD 3 vers) Concert
(5/91) (APR) ① [2] **APR7001**
S. Richter Concert   (11/92) (DG) ① **435 751-2GDO**
S. Richter (pp1986) Concert
(3/93) (DECC) ① **436 456-2DH**
B. Berezovsky (r1992) Concert
(8/93) (TELD) ① **9031-77476-2**
V. Horowitz (r1962) Concert
(7/94) (SONY) ① [2] **S2K53457**
M. Kazakevich (r1993) Concert
(7/94) (CONI) ① [2] **CDCF227**
B. Glemser (r1993) Concert
(10/94) (NAXO) ① **8 550715**
M. Anderson (r1993) Concert
(7/95) (NIMB) ① **NI5422**

Waldszenen—piano, Op. 82 (1848-49)
1. Eintritt; 2. Jäger auf der Lauer; 3. Einsame Blumen; 4. Verrufene Stelle; 5. Freundliche Landschaft; 6. Herberge; 7. Vogel als Prophet; 8. Jagdlied; 9. Abschied.
Vladimir Ashkenazy (r1987) Concert
(2/89) (DECC) ① **421 290-2DH**
W. Kempff Concert
(5/92) (DG) ① [4] **435 045-2GX4**
C. Katsaris Concert   (6/92) (TELD) ① **9031-75863-2**
A. Haefliger (r1991) Concert
(10/92) (SONY) ① **SK48036**
S. Richter (r1956) Concert
(11/92) (DG) ① **435 751-2GDO**
S. Nagaoka Concert   (11/92) (CHNN) ① **CG9101**
P. Gulda Concert   (4/93) (NAXO) ① **8 550401**
G. Oppitz (r1991) Concert
(5/93) (RCA) ① **09026 60977-2**
V. Afanassiev (r1992) Kreisleriana.
(8/94) (DENO) ① **CO-75714**

M-J. Pires (r1994) Concert
(6/95) (DG) ① **437 538-2GH**
C. Haskil (r1954) Concert
(11/95) (PHIL) ① [3] **442 635-2PM3**
C. Haskil (r1954) Concert
(11/95) (PHIL) ① [12] **442 685-2PM12**
7. E. Wild Concert   (2/89) (DELL) ① **CDDBS7005**
7. I. Perlman, S. Sanders (trans. Heifetz) Concert
(12/89) (EMI) ① **CDC7 49604-2**
7. A. Servadei Concert   (7/91) (CARL) ① **PCD949**
7. M. Elman, P. Kahn (arr Auer; r1914) Concert
(12/91) (APR) ① [2] **APR7015**
7. M. Lympany Concert   (1/92) (EMIL) ① **CDZ111**
7. L. Laskine Concert   (1/92) (ERAT) ① **4509-92131-2**
7. J. Heifetz, E. Bay (r1945) Concert
(11/94) (RCA) ① [65] **09026 61778-2(19)**
7. M. Hess (r1931) Concert
(3/95) (BIDD) ① **LHW024**

SECTION IV: VOCAL AND CHORAL

An Anna I—Lied (1828) (Wds. Kerner)
T. Hampson, G. Parsons (r1989) Concert
(4/91) (TELD) ① **2292-44935-2**
An Anna II—Lied (1828) (Wds. Kerner)
T. Hampson, G. Parsons (r1989) Concert
(4/91) (TELD) ① **2292-44935-2**
Belsatzar—Lied, Op. 57 (1840) (Wds. Heine)
T. Quasthoff, R. Szidon (r1992) Concert
(2/94) (RCA) ① **09026 61225-2**
Dichterliebe—song cycle, Op. 48 (1840)
(Wds. Heine)
1. Im wunderschönen Monat Mai; 2. Aus meinen Tränen spriessen; 3. Die Rose, die Lilie, die Taube, die Sonne; 4. Wenn ich in deine Augen seh; 5. Ich will meine Seele tauchen; 6. Im Rhein, im heiligen Strome; 7. Ich grolle nicht; 8. Und wüssten's die Blumen, die kleinen; 9. Das ist ein Flöten und Geigen; 10. Hör ist das Liedchen klingen; 11. Ein Jüngling liebt ein Mädchen; 12. Am leuchtenden Sommermorgen; 13. Ich hab im Traum geweinet; 14. Allnächtlich im Traume; 15. Aus alten Märchen; 16. Die alten, bösen Lieder.
Cpte D. Fischer-Dieskau, C. Eschenbach Concert
(9/85) (DG) ① **415 190-2GH**
Cpte H. Prey, L. Hokanson Concert
(4/86) (DENO) ① **C37-7720**
Cpte O. Bär, G. Parsons Liederkreis, Op. 39.
(9/86) (EMI) ① **CDC7 47397-2**
Cpte H. Hotter, H. Altmann (r1954) Concert
(7/88) (PREI) ① **93145**
Cpte J. Protschka, H. Deutsch Liederkreis, Op.39.
(12/88) (CAPR) ① **10 215**
Cpte Lotte Lehmann, B. Walter (r1941) Frauenliebe und -leben, Op. 42.   (11/89) (SONY) ① **MPK44800**
Cpte J. Hynninen, R. Gothóni (pp1985) Brahms: Ernste Gesänge, Op. 121.
(10/90) (ONDI) ① **ODE738-2**
Cpte F. Wunderlich, H. Giesen Concert
(11/90) (DG) ① **429 933-2GDO**
Cpte P. Schreier, C. Eschenbach Concert
(6/91) (TELD) ① [3] **2292-46154-2**
Cpte S. Jerusalem, E. Bashkirova Liederkreis, Op. 39.   (3/92) (ERAT) ① **2292-45740-2**
Cpte C. Panzéra, A. Cortot (r1935) Concert
(6/92) (DANT) ① [2] **HPC004/5**
Cpte C. Panzéra, A. Cortot (r1935) Concert
(6/92) (BIDD) ① **LHW005**
Cpte J. Kowalski, S. Katz Concert
(12/92) (CAPR) ① **10 359**
Cpte C. Panzéra, A. Cortot (r1935) Concert
(3/93) (PEAR) ① **GEMMCD9919**
Cpte K. McMillan, M. McMahon (r1992) Concert
(3/93) (CBC) ① **MVCD1052**
Cpte N. Stutzmann, C. Collard (r1992) Concert
(8/93) (RCA) ① **09026 61187-2**
Cpte D. Fischer-Dieskau, C. Eschenbach (r1970s) Concert   (1/94) (DG) ① **439 417-2GCL**
Cpte T. Quasthoff, R. Szidon (r1992) Concert
(2/94) (RCA) ① **09026 61225-2**
Cpte I. Partridge, J. Partridge (r1970s) Liederkreis, Op.39.   (6/94) (CFP) ① **CD-CFP4651**
Cpte G. Hüsch, H.U. Müller (r1936) Concert
(11/94) (PEAR) ① **GEMMCD9119**
Cpte C. Prégardien, A. Staier (r1993) Concert
(12/94) (DHM) ① **05472 77319-2**
Cpte G. Souzay, J. Bonneau (r1953) Concert
(1/95) (DECC) ① **440 065-2DM**
Cpte T. Hampson, G. Parsons (pp1993) Concert
(1/95) (EMI) ① **CDC5 55147-2**
Cpte D. Fischer-Dieskau, H. Höll (pp1992) Concert
(1/95) (ERAT) ① **4509-98492-2**
Cpte W. Holzmair, I. Cooper (r1994) Concert
(9/95) (PHIL) ① **446 086-2PH**
Cpte P. Pears, B. Britten (r1963) Concert
(10/95) (DECC) ① **443 933-2DM**

5 Lieder, Op. 40 (1840) (Wds. 1-4: Andersen, trans Chamisso; 5: Chamisso)
1. Märzveilchen; 2. Muttertraum; 3. Der Soldat; 4. Der Spielmann; 5. Verratene Liebe.
Cpte T. Hampson, G. Parsons (r1989) *Concert*
(4/91) (TELD) ① 2292-44935-2
Cpte P. Schreier, C. Eschenbach *Concert*
(6/91) (TELD) ① [3] 2292-46154-2
A. S. von Otter, B. Forsberg (r1993) *Concert*
(11/95) (DG) ① 445 881-2GH
1. C. Ludwig, C. Spencer (pp1993) *Concert*
(10/93) (RCA) ① 09026 61547-2
1-4. R. Holl, A. Schiff (r1990) *Concert*
(7/94) (DECC) ① 436 123-2DH
1-4. A. Schmidt, R. Jansen (r1993) *Concert*
(3/95) (DG) ① 439 943-2GH
2. M. Shirai, H. Höll (r1992) *Concert*
(11/93) (CAPR) ① 10 445
3. M. Lipovšek, G. Johnson (r1994) *Concert*
(8/95) (SONY) ① SK57972
5. Sarah Walker, R. Vignoles *Concert*
(6/90) (CRD) ① CRD3401
3 Lieder—2vv and piano, Op. 43 (1840)
1. Wenn ich ein Vöglein wär (from Des Knaben Wunderhorn); 2. Herbstlied (wds. Mahlmann); 3. Schön Blümelein (wds. Reinick).
E. Mathis, H. Komatsu, C. Garben (r1994) *Concert*
(11/95) (CPO) ① CPO999 262-2
1. H. Komatsu, K. Moll, C. Garben *Concert*
(9/91) (HARM) ① HMC90 5210
7 Lieder, Op. 104 (1851) (Wds. Kulmann)
1. Mond, meiner Seele Liebling; 2. Viel Glück zur Reise Schwalben!; 3. Du nennst mich armes Mädchen; 4. Der Zeisig; 5. Reich mir die Hand, o Wolke; 6. Die letzten Blumen starben; 7. Gekämpft hat meine Barke.
2. P. Frijsh, C. Dougherty (r1939) *Concert*
(4/95) (PEAR) ① [2] GEMMCDS9095(1)
6. E. Ameling, J. Demus (r1967) *Concert*
(12/95) (DHM) ① 74321 26617-2(2)
5 Lieder und Gesänge, Op. 127 (1840-50)
1. Sängers Trost (wds. Kerner); 2. Dein Angesicht (wds. Heine); 3. Es leuchtet meine Liebe (wds. Heine); 4. Mein altes Ross (wds. Moritz); 5. Schlusslied des Narren (wds. Shakespeare, trans. Tieck & Schlegel).
1. T. Hampson, G. Parsons (r1989) *Concert*
(4/91) (TELD) ① 2292-44935-2
2. H. Prey, L. Hokanson *Concert*
(4/86) (DENO) ① C37-7720
2. P. Schreier, C. Eschenbach *Concert*
(6/91) (TELD) ① [3] 2292-46154-2
2. A. S. von Otter, B. Forsberg (r1993) *Concert*
(11/95) (DG) ① 445 881-2GH
3. D. Fischer-Dieskau, H. Höll (pp1992) *Concert*
(9/95) (ERAT) ① 4509-98492-2
Lieder und Gesänge aus Wilhelm Meister, Op. 98a (1849) (Wds. Goethe)
1. Kennst du das Land; 2. Ballade des Harfners: Was hör ich draussen vor dem Tor; 3. Nur wer die Sehnsucht kennt; 4. Wer nie sein Brot mit Tränen ass; 5. Heiss mich nicht reden; 6. Wer sich der Einsamkeit ergibt; 7. Singet nicht in Trauertönen; 8. An die Türen will ich schleichen; 9. So lasst mich scheinen.
1, 3, 5, 9. M. Shirai, H. Höll *Concert*
(6/87) (CAPR) ① 10 099
1, 5, 7. D. Upshaw, R. Goode (r1993) *Concert*
(8/94) (NONE) ① 7559-79317-2
4, 6, 8. R. Holl, A. Schiff (r1990) *Concert*
(7/94) (DECC) ① 436 123-2DH
Lieder und Gesänge I, Op. 27 (1840)
1. Sag an, o lieber Vogel (wds. Hebbel); 2. Dem roten Röslein (wds. Burns, trans. Gerhard); 3. Was soll ich sagen? (wds. Chamisso); 4. Jasminenstrauch (wds. Rückert); 5. nur ein lächelnder Blick (wds. Zimmermann).
Cpte N. Stutzmann, C. Collard (r1993) *Concert*
(8/94) (RCA) ① 09026 61728-2
Cpte I. Partridge, J. Drake (r1993/4) *Concert*
(12/94) (CHAN) ① CHAN9307
2. T. Hampson, G. Parsons (pp1993) *Concert*
(1/95) (EMI) ① CDC6 55147-2
3. K. Erb, B. Seidler-Winkler (r1937) *Concert*
(6/94) (PREI) ① [2] 89208
4. E. Ameling, J. Demus *Concert*
(5/90) (DHM) ① GD77085
4. E. Ameling, J. Demus (r1967) *Concert*
(12/95) (DHM) ① 74321 26617-2(2)
5. P. Schreier, C. Eschenbach *Concert*
(6/91) (TELD) ① [3] 2292-46154-2
Lieder und Gesänge II, Op. 51 (1840-50)
1. Sehnsucht (wds. Geibel); 2. Volksliedchen (wds. Rückert); 3. Ich wandre nicht (wds. Christern); 4. Auf dem Rhein (wds. Immermann); 5. Liebeslied (wds. Goethe).

Cpte N. Stutzmann, C. Collard (r1993) *Concert*
(8/94) (RCA) ① 09026 61728-2
1. E. Ameling, J. Demus *Concert*
(5/90) (DHM) ① GD77085
1. E. Ameling, J. Demus (r1967) *Concert*
(12/95) (DHM) ① 74321 26617-2(2)
1, 3. P. Schreier, C. Eschenbach *Concert*
(6/91) (TELD) ① [3] 2292-46154-2
2. E. Schwarzkopf, M. Raucheisen (bp c1945) *Concert*
(6/87) (ACAN) ① 43 801
2. K. Ferrier, J. Newmark (r1950) *Concert*
(6/92) (DECC) ① 433 471-2DM
2. M. Price, T. Dewey (r1993) *Concert*
(10/94) (FORL) ① UCD16711
2. A. S. von Otter, B. Forsberg (r1993) *Concert*
(11/95) (DG) ① 445 881-2GH
5. G. Lubin, E.I. Kahn (r1938) *Concert*
(5/91) (CLUB) ① CL99-022
5. G. Lubin, E.I. Kahn (r1938) *Concert*
(5/91) (EPM) ① 150 052
5. D. Upshaw, R. Goode (r1993) *Concert*
(8/94) (NONE) ① 7559-79317-2
Lieder und Gesänge III, Op. 77 (1840-50)
1. Der frohe Wandersmann (wds. Eichendorff); 2. Mein Garten (wds. Fallersleben); 3. Geisternähe (wds. Halm); 4. Stiller Vorwurf (wds. Wolff); 5. Aufträge (wds. L'Egru).
Cpte N. Stutzmann, C. Collard (r1993) *Concert*
(8/94) (RCA) ① 09026 61728-2
2, 5. E. Ameling, J. Demus (r1967) *Concert*
(12/95) (DHM) ① 74321 26617-2(2)
3. M. Shirai, H. Höll (r1992) *Concert*
(11/93) (CAPR) ① 10 445
5. E. Ameling, J. Demus *Concert*
(5/90) (DHM) ① GD77085
5. E. Schwarzkopf, G. Moore (r1954) *Concert*
(12/90) (EMI) ① CDM7 63656-2
5. E. Schumann, G. Reeves (r1930) *Concert*
(6/91) (PREI) ① 89031
5. P. Schreier, C. Eschenbach *Concert*
(6/91) (TELD) ① [3] 2292-46154-2
5. R. Streich, G. Weissenborn (r1961) *Concert*
(10/94) (DG) ① [2] 437 680-2GDO2
5. Lotte Lehmann, anon (r1928) *Concert*
(11/95) (CLAR) ① CDGSE78-50-57
Lieder und Gesänge IV, Op. 96 (1850)
1. Nachtlied (wds. Goethe); 2. Schneeglöckchen (wds. anon); 3. Ihre Stimme (wds. Platen); 4. Gesungen! (wds. Neun); 5. Himmel und Erde (wds. Neun).
Cpte N. Stutzmann, C. Collard (r1993) *Concert*
(8/94) (RCA) ① 09026 61728-2
1. R. Holl, A. Schiff (r1990) *Concert*
(7/94) (DECC) ① 436 123-2DH
1. D. Upshaw, R. Goode (r1993) *Concert*
(8/94) (NONE) ① 7559-79317-2
3. P. Frijsh, C. Dougherty (r1942) *Concert*
(4/95) (PEAR) ① [2] GEMMCDS9095(1)
Lieder-Album für die Jugend, Op. 79 (1849)
1. Der Abendstern (wds. Fallersleben); 2. Schmetterling (wds. Fallersleben); 3. Frühlingsbotschaft (wds. Fallersleben); 4. Frühlingsgruss (wds. Fallersleben); 5. Vom Schlaraffenland (wds. Fallersleben); 6. Sonntag (wds. Fallersleben); 7. Zigeunerliedchen (wds. Geibel); 7a. Unter die Soldaten; 7b. Jeden Morgen in der Frühe; 8. Des Knaben Berglied (wds. Uhland); 9. Mailied (wds. Overbeck; duet ad lib); 10. Das Käuzlein (Des Knaben Wunderhorn); 11. Hinaus ins Freie! (wds. Fallersleben); 12. Der Sandmann (wds. Kletke); 13. Marienwürmchen (Des Knaben Wunderhorn); 14. Die Waise (wds. Fallersleben); 15. Das Glück (wds. Hebbel; duet); 16. Weihnachtslied (wds. Andersen); 17. Die wandelnde Glocke (wds. Goethe); 18. Frühlingslied (wds. Fallersleben; duet ad lib); 19. Frühlings Ankunft (wds. Fallersleben); 20. Die Schwalben (Des Knaben Wunderhorn; duet); 21. Kinderwacht (wds. anon); 22. Des Sennen Abschied (wds. Schiller); 23. Er ist's (wds. Mörike); 24. Spinnelied (wds. anon; trio ad lib); 25. Des Buben Schützenlied (wds. Schiller); 26. Schneeglöckchen (wds. Rückert); 27. Lied Lyncus des Türmers (wds. Goethe); 28. Mignon (wds. Goethe).
2. E. Ameling, J. Demus (r1967) *Concert*
(12/95) (DHM) ① 74321 26617-2(2)
2, 10, 12, 13, 23, 26. E. Ameling, J. Demus (r1967) *Concert*
(5/90) (DHM) ① GD77085
4, 7, 13, 26. P. Schreier, C. Eschenbach *Concert*
(6/91) (TELD) ① [3] 2292-46154-2
5, 22, 26. A. S. von Otter, B. Forsberg (r1993) *Concert*
(11/95) (DG) ① 445 881-2GH
7a, 7b D. Fischer-Dieskau, C. Eschenbach (r1970s) *Concert*
(1/94) (DG) ① 439 417-2GCL
7, 12, 13, 17, 22, 23, 26. M. Price, T. Dewey (r1993) *Concert*
(10/94) (FORL) ① UCD16711

9, 15, 20. E. Mathis, H. Komatsu, C. Garben (r1994) *Concert*
(11/95) (CPO) ① CPO999 262-2
10, 12, 13, 23, 26. E. Ameling, J. Demus (r1967) *Concert*
(12/95) (DHM) ① [4] 74321 26617-2(1)
12, 28. Sarah Walker, R. Vignoles *Concert*
(6/90) (CRD) ① CRD3401
13. T. Hampson, G. Parsons *Concert*
(10/90) (TELD) ① 2292-44923-2
15, 19, 23, 26. F. Lott, G. Johnson *Concert*
(11/90) (EMI) ① CDC7 49930-2
23, 26. E. Schumann, G. Reeves (r1930) *Concert*
(6/91) (PREI) ① 89031
23, 28. M. Lipovšek, G. Johnson (r1994) *Concert*
(8/95) (SONY) ① SK57972
26. R. Streich, G. Weissenborn (r1961) *Concert*
(10/94) (DG) ① [2] 437 680-2GDO2
28. F. Lott, G. Johnson *Concert*
(10/91) (CARL) ① MCD22
Liederkreis—song collection, Op. 24 (1840)
(Wds. Heine)
1. Morgens steh ich auf und frage; 2. Es treibt mich hin; 3. Ich wandelte unter den Bäumen; 4. Lieb Liebchen; 5. Schöne Wiege meiner Leiden; 6. Warte, warte, wilder Schiffmann; 7. Berg und Burgen schaun herunter; 8. Anfange wollt ich fast verzagen; 9. Mit Myrten und Rosen.
Cpte B. Fassbaender, I. Gage *Concert*
(2/86) (DG) ① 415 519-2GH
Cpte H. Prey, L. Hokanson *Concert*
(4/86) (DENO) ① C37-7720
Cpte P. Vollestad, S. Hjelset *Concert*
(11/89) (SIMA) ① PSC1051
Cpte P. Schreier, C. Eschenbach *Concert*
(6/91) (TELD) ① [3] 2292-46154-2
Cpte O. Bär, G. Parsons *Gedichte, Op. 35.*
(7/91) (EMI) ① CDC7 54027-2
Cpte D. Fischer-Dieskau, H. Höll (pp1992) *Concert*
(9/95) (ERAT) ① 4509-98492-2
Cpte W. Holzmair, I. Cooper (r1994) *Concert*
(9/95) (PHIL) ① 446 086-2PH
9. I. Seefried, E. Werba (r1956) *Concert*
(7/93) (DG) ① [2] 437 348-2GDO2
Liederkreis—song collection, Op. 39 (1840)
(Wds. Eichendorff)
1. In der Fremde; 2. Intermezzo; 3. Waldesgespräch; 4. Die Stille; 5. Mondnacht; 6. Schöne Fremde; 7. Auf einer Burg; 8. In der Fremde; 9. Wehmut; 10. Zwielicht; 11. Im Walde; 12. Frühlingsnacht.
Cpte D. Fischer-Dieskau, C. Eschenbach *Concert*
(9/85) (DG) ① 415 190-2GH
Cpte O. Bär, G. Parsons *Dichterliebe, Op. 48.*
(9/86) (EMI) ① CDC7 47397-2
Cpte D. Fischer-Dieskau, G. Moore (pp1959) *Gedichte, Op. 35.* (6/87) (ORFE) ① C140301A
Cpte M. Shirai, H. Höll *Concert*
(6/87) (CAPR) ① 10 099
Cpte J. Protschka, H. Deutsch *Dichterliebe, Op. 48.*
(12/88) (CAPR) ① 10 215
Cpte P. Schreier, C. Eschenbach *Concert*
(6/91) (TELD) ① [3] 2292-46154-2
Cpte F. Lott, G. Johnson *Concert*
(10/91) (CARL) ① MCD22
Cpte S. Jerusalem, E. Bashkirova *Dichterliebe, Op. 48.*
(3/92) (ERAT) ① 2292-45740-2
Cpte T. Quasthoff, R. Szidon (r1993) *Concert*
(2/94) (RCA) ① 09026 61225-2
Cpte I. Partridge, J. Partridge (r1970s) *Dichterliebe, Op.48.*
(6/94) (CFP) ① CD-CFP4651
Cpte R. Holl, A. Schiff (r1991) *Concert*
(7/94) (DECC) ① 436 123-2DH
Cpte N. Stutzmann, C. Collard (r1993) *Concert*
(8/94) (RCA) ① 09026 61728-2
Cpte B. Fassbaender, E. Leonskaja (1992) *Concert*
(8/94) (TELD) ① 9031-74872-2
Cpte M. Price, G. Johnson (r1991) *Gedichte, Op.35.*
(11/94) (HYPE) ① CDA66596
Cpte F. Schorr, F. Kitzinger (r1937/8) *Concert*
(11/94) (PEAR) ① GEMMCD9119
Cpte A. Schmidt, R. Jansen (r1993) *Concert*
(3/95) (DG) ① 439 943-2GH
Cpte M. Lipovšek, G. Johnson (r1994) *Concert*
(8/95) (SONY) ① SK57972
E. Mathis, G. Wyss (r1995) *Concert*
(11/95) (DENO) ① CO-78947
1, 2, 6, 10, 11. D. Fischer-Dieskau, W. Sawallisch (pp1975) *Concert*
(1/90) (ORFE) ① C185891A
2, 4. R. Streich, G. Weissenborn (r1961) *Concert*
(10/94) (DG) ① [2] 437 680-2GDO2
3. E. Ameling, J. Demus *Concert*
(5/90) (DHM) ① GD77085
3. E. Ameling, J. Demus (r1967) *Concert*
(12/95) (DHM) ① 74321 26617-2(2)
3, 5. M. Price, J. Lockhart *Concert*
(11/86) (ORFE) ① C031821A
4, 5. C. Ludwig, C. Spencer (pp1993) *Concert*
(10/93) (RCA) ① 09026 61547-2

3. D. Fischer-Dieskau, C. Eschenbach (r1970s) *Concert* (1/94) (DG) ① **439 417-2GCL**
3. W. Holzmair, I. Cooper (r1994) *Concert* (9/95) (PHIL) ① **446 086-2PH**
Der **Rose Pilgerfahrt—soloists, chorus and orchestra, Op. 112 (1851)** (Wds. M Horn)
Cpte I. Nielsen, H. Hinz, A. Moller, E. Halling, D. van der Walt, G. Paevatalu, C. Christiansen, Danish Nat Rad Ch, Danish Nat RSO, G. Kuhn (r1994) (7/95) (CHAN) ① **CHAN9350**
Des **Sängers Fluch—soloists, chorus and orchestra, Op. 139 (1852)** (Wds. Pohl, afterUhland)
4. Provenzaliches Lied; 7. Ballade.
4. H. Schlusnus, F. Rupp (r1934) *Concert* (1/94) (PREI) ① [2] **89205**
Sommerruh—2vv and piano (1849) (Wds. Schad)
E. Mathis, H. Komatsu, C. Garben (r1994) *Concert* (11/95) (CPO) ① **CPO999 262-2**
Spanische Liebeslieder—1-4vv and piano, Op. 138 (1849) (Wds. Geibel)
1. Vorspiel (pf: 4 hands); 2. Tief im Herzen trag ich Pein (S); 3. O wie lieblich ist das Mädchen (T); 4. Bedeckt mich mit Blumen (S,A); 5. Flutenreicher Ebro (Bar); 6. Intermezzo (pf: four hands); 7. Weh, wie zornig ist das Mädchen (T); 8. Hoch, hoch sind die Berge (A); 9. Blaue Augen hat das Mädchen (T,B); 10. Dunkler Lichtglanz (S,A,T,B).
B. Bonney, A.S. von Otter, K. Streit, O. Bär, B. Forsberg, H. Deutsch (pp1994) *Concert* (10/95) (EMI) ① **CDC5 55430-2**
2. J. Gomez, J. Constable (r1994) *Concert* (9/94) (CONI) ① **CDCF243**
5. H. Schlusnus, F. Rupp (r1933) *Concert* (1/94) (PREI) ① [2] **89205**
Spanisches Liederspiel—1-4vv and piano, Op. 74 (1849) (Wds. Geibel, after Spanish poets)
1. Erste Begegnung (S,A); 2. Intermezzo (T,B); 3. Liebesgram (S,A); 4. In der Nacht (S,T); 5. Es ist verraten (S,A,T,B); 6. Melancholie (S); 7. Geständis (T); 8. Botschaft (S,A); 9. Ich bin geliebt (S,A,T,B); 10. Der Kontrabandiste (Bar).
2. H. Komatsu, K. Moll, C. Garben *Concert* (9/91) (HARM) ① **HMC90 5210**
3, 4. E. Mathis, H. Komatsu, C. Garben (r1994) *Concert* (11/95) (CPO) ① **CPO999 262-2**
4. K. Livingstone, N. Mackie, J.J. Blakely *Concert* (2/89) (UNIC) ① **UKCD2009**
6. M. Shirai, H. Höll (r1992) *Concert* (11/93) (CAPR) ① **10 445**
7. P. Schreier, C. Eschenbach *Concert* (6/91) (TELD) ① [3] **2292-46154-2**
10. J. Lhévinne (r1920: arr Tausig) *Concert* (10/92) (APR) ① [2] **APR7013**
10. S. Rachmaninov (r1942; arr Tausig: pf) *Concert* (3/93) (RCA) ① [10] **09026 61265-2(1)**
10. D. Fischer-Dieskau, C. Eschenbach (r1970s) *Concert* (1/94) (DG) ① **439 417-2GCL**
10. D. Fischer-Dieskau, H. Höll (pp1992) *Concert* (9/95) (ERAT) ① **4509-98492-2**
Szenen aus Goethes Faust—soloists, chorus and orchestra (1844-53) (Wds. Goethe)
1. Du kanntest mich, o kleiner Engel; 2. Ach neige, du Schmerzenreiche; 3. Wie anders, Gretchen, war dir's; 4a. Die ihr dies Haupt umschwebt im luft'gen; 4b. Des Lebens Pulse schlagen; 5a. Ich heisse der Mangel; 5b. Vier sah ich kommen; 5c. Die Nacht scheint tiefer tief hereinzudringen; 6a. Herbei, herbei! Herein, herein!; 6b. Ein Sumpf zieht am Gebirge hin; 6c. Ihn sättigt keine Lust; 7a. Waldung, sie schwankt heran; 7b. Ewiger Wonnebrand; 7c. Wie Felsenabgrund mir zu Füssen; 7d. Gerettet ist das edle Glied; 7e. Hier ist die Aussicht frei; 7f. Dir, der Unberührbaren; 7g. Alles Vergängliche ist nur ein Gleichnis.
Cpte J. Vyvyan, J. Hill, F. Palmer, E. Harwood, M. Cable, M. Dickinson, P. Stevens, A. Hodgson, J. Elwes, P. Pears, N. Jenkins, J. Noble, D. Fischer-Dieskau, J. Shirley-Quirk, R. Lloyd, Wandsworth Sch Boys' Ch, Aldeburgh Fest Sngrs, ECO, B. Britten (r1972) (7/90) (DECC) ① [2] **425 705-2DM2**
Cpte E. Mathis, B. Daniels, K. Lövaas, N. Sharp, H. Schwarz, I. Gramatzki, N. Gedda, D. Fischer-Dieskau, W. Berry, H. Stamm, Tolz Boys' Ch, Düsseldorf Musikverein, Düsseldorf SO, B. Klee (r1981) (5/95) (EMI) ① [2] **CMS7 69450-2**
Cpte K. Mattila, B. Bonney, B. Poschner-Klebel, S. Graham, I. Vermillion, E. Wottrich, H-P. Blochwitz, B. Terfel, J-H. Rootering, H. Peeters, Tolz Boys' Ch, Swedish Rad Chor, BPO, C. Abbado (pp1994) (5/95) (SONY) ① [2] **S2K66308**
Overture New Philh, O. Klemperer *Concert* (12/90) (EMI) ① [2] **CMS7 63613-2**

SECTION V: STAGE WORKS

Genoveva—opera: 4 acts, Op. 81 (1850—Leipzig) (Lib. Reinick, after Tieck and Hebbel)
1. Overture.
Cpte J. Faulkner, K. Lewis, H. Stamm, A. Titus, R. Behle, C. Schultz, J. Tilli, Hamburg St Op Chor, Hamburg PO, G. Albrecht (pp1992) (1/94) (ORFE) ① [2] **C289932H**
1. LSO, N. Järvi *Brahms: Symphony 4.* (12/88) (CHAN) ① **CHAN8595**
1. NYPO, L. Bernstein (r1963) *Concert* (9/93) (SONY) ① **SMK47609**
1. Concertgebouw, B. Haitink (r1984) *Concert* (7/94) (PHIL) ① [2] **442 079-2PB2**
Manfred—incidental music, Op. 115 (1852—Leipzig) (Wds. Byron, trans Suckow)
1. Overture.
Cpte L. Browne, J. Balcon, R. de la Torre, D. Enders, G. Holt, C. Duchesneau, N. Miller, BBC Chor, RPO, T. Beecham (r1954/6: arr Beecham) (9/91) (BEEC) ① **BEECHAM4**
Cpte J. Gudzuhn, Berlin Rad Chor, Berlin SO, M. Schønwandt (r1993) (4/95) (KONT) ① **32181**
Cpte P. Schweiger, L. Larsson, R. Jakobi, S. Davislim, T. Pursio, P. Lika, L. Heimberg, R. Renn, K.H. Russius, Basle Madrigalists, Swiss Workshop PO, M. Venzago (r1994) (10/95) (MGB) ① **CD6122**
1. Stuttgart RSO, N. Marriner *Concert* (6/86) (CAPR) ① **10 063**
1. Stuttgart RSO, N. Marriner *Concert* (1/89) (CAPR) ① [3] **10 997**
1. LSO, N. Järvi *Brahms: Symphony 1.* (5/89) (CHAN) ① **CHAN8653**
1. BPO, James Levine *Concert* (2/93) (DG) ① **435 856-2GH**
1. BRSO, R. Kubelík (r1979) *Concert* (7/93) (SONY) ① **SBK48270**
1. Chicago SO, D. Barenboim (r1977) *Concert* (7/93) (DG) ① [2] **437 641-2GGA2**
1. NYPO, L. Bernstein (r1958) *Concert* (9/93) (SONY) ① **SMK47612**
1. Philh, C.M. Giulini (r1958) *Concert* (9/93) (EMI) ① [2] **CZS7 67723-2**
1. Concertgebouw, B. Haitink (r1982) *Concert* (7/94) (PHIL) ① [2] **442 079-2PB2**
1. Leipzig Gewandhaus, H. Abendroth (bp1944) *Concert* (9/94) (TAHR) ① [2] **TAH106/7**
1. Seattle SO, G. Schwarz (r1992) *Concert* (7/95) (DELO) ① [4] **DE3146**

SCHURMANN, (Edward) Gerard *(b 1929) The Netherlands/England*

SECTION I: ORCHESTRAL

Attack and Celebration (1972) (from 'Attack on the Iron Coast' & 'Two-Headed Spy')
Philh, K. Alwyn *Concert* (2/91) (SILV) ① **FILMCD713**
Smuggler's Rhapsody (1962) (from film 'Doctor Syn')
OST, G. Schurmann (r1962) *Concert* (10/93) (CLOU) ① **CNS5005**
6 Studies of Francis Bacon—orchestra (1968-69)
5. George and the Bicycle.
5. BBC SO, G. Schurmann *Concert* (7/83) (CHAN) ① **CHAN8301**

SECTION V: STAGE WORKS

Attack on the Iron Coast—film score (1967)
EXCERPTS: 1. Prelude; 2. Celebration; 3. The Mission.
1-3. OST, G. Schurmann (r1967) *Concert* (10/93) (CLOU) ① **CNS5005**
The **Bedford Incident—film score (1965)**
EXCERPTS: 1. Atlantic Encounters.
1. OST, G. Schurmann (r1965) *Concert* (10/93) (CLOU) ① **CNS5005**
The **Ceremony—film score (1963)**
EXCERPTS: 1. Main Theme; 2. Memories of Tangier; 3. Freedom.
1-3. OST, G. Schurmann (r1965) *Concert* (10/93) (CLOU) ① **CNS5005**
Claretta—film score (1984)
EXCERPTS: 1. The Drama of Claretta; 2. Waltz; 3. Claretta's Theme & Finale.
1-3. OST, G. Schurmann (r1984) *Concert* (10/93) (CLOU) ① **CNS5005**
Cone of Silence—film score (1960)
EXCERPTS: 1. Overture.
1. OST, G. Schurmann (r1960) *Concert* (10/93) (CLOU) ① **CNS5005**
Horrors of the Black Museum—film score (1959)
EXCERPTS: 1. Prelude/Streets of London; 2. Spiked Binoculars/Investigations; 3. Headline News; 4. Tunnel of Death/Bancroft's Demise/End Credits.
1-4. OST, G. Schurmann (r1959) *Concert* (10/93) (CLOU) ① **CNS5005**
Konga—film score (1960)
EXCERPTS: 1. Konga Unchained & End Titles.
1. OST, G. Schurmann (r1960) *Concert* (10/93) (CLOU) ① **CNS5005**
The **Long Arm—film score (1956)**
EXCERPTS: 1a. Prelude; 1b. Safe-cracking; 1c. Dawn; 1d. Investigations; 1e. Tailing the Suspect; 1f. Finale.
1a-f OST, G. Schurmann (r1965) *Concert* (10/93) (CLOU) ① **CNS5005**
The **Lost Continent—film score (1968)**
EXCERPTS: 1. Sargasso Sea/Romanza; 2. Action Stations.
1, 2. OST, G. Schurmann (r1968) *Concert* (10/93) (CLOU) ① **CNS5005**

SCHUSTER, Walther R *(b 1930) Germany*

SECTION III: INSTRUMENTAL

Freie Improvisation
W.R. Schuster *Concert* (3/86) (MOTE) ① **CD10601**

SCHÜTT, Eduard *(1856–1933) Germany*

pseudonyms—Henri Marling, Arnolde Clairlie

SECTION II: CHAMBER

Impromptu-Rococo—two pianos, Op. 58/2
O. Gabrilowitsch, H. Bauer (r1929) *Concert* (4/89) (OPAL) ① **OPALCD9839**
3 Morceaux—violin and piano, Op. 53
1. Slavonic Lament.
1. F. Kreisler, C. Lamson (r1924: arr Friedberg) *Concert* (9/93) (BIDD) ① [2] **LAB068/9**

SECTION III: INSTRUMENTAL

À la bien-aimée—piano, Op. 59/2
L. Godowsky (r1920) *Concert* (4/89) (APR) ① [2] **APR7011**
H. Bauer (r1925) *Concert* (9/93) (BIDD) ① **LHW007**
Etude mignonne—piano, Op. 16/1
L. Godowsky (r1920) *Concert* (4/89) (APR) ① [2] **APR7011**
L. Laskine (r1975; arr hp) *Concert* (12/93) (ERAT) ① **4509-92131-2**

SCHÜTZ, Heinrich *(1585–1672) Germany*

SWV—numbers used in W. Bittinger, Schütz-Werke-Verzeichnis (1960).

SECTION IV: VOCAL AND CHORAL

Ach Herr, du Schöpfer aller Ding—madrigale spirituale (5vv), SWV450 (1615-27)
C. Janequin Ens, Saqueboutiers de Toulouse, K. Junghänel, J. Cable, W. Jansen *Concert* (9/88) (HARM) ① **HMC90 1255**
Die **Auferstehung unsres Herren Jesu Christi—10vv, violas da gamba and continuo, SWV50 (pub 1623)**
Concerto Vocale, R. Jacobs *Symphoniae sacrae, Op. 10.* (4/91) (HARM) ① **HMC90 1311**
Cantiones sacrae—3-4vv and continuo, SWV53-93 (Op. 4) (pub 1625)
1. O bone, o dulcis, o benigne Jesu, SWV53; 2. Et ne despicias, SWV54; 3. Deus misereatur nostri, SWV55; 4. Quid commisisti, o dulcissime puer, SWV56; 5. Ego sum tui plaga doloris, SWV57; 6. Ego enim inique ege, SWV58; 7. Quo, nate Dei, SWV59; 8. Calicem salutaris accipiam, SWV60; 9. Verba mea auribus percipe, SWV61; 10. Quoniam ad te clamabo, SWV62; 11. Ego dormio, SWV63; 12. Vulnerasti cor meum, SWV64; 13. Heu mihi, Domine, SWV65; 14. In te, Domine, speravi, SWV66; 15. Dulcissime et benignissime Christe, SWV67; 16. Sicut Moses serpentem in deserto exaltavit, SWV68; 17. Spes mea, Christe Deus, SWV69; 18. Turababor, sed non perturbabor, SWV70; 19. Ad Dominum cum tribularer clamavi, SWV71; 20. Quid detur tibi, SWV72; 21. Aspice, Pater, püssimum filium, SWV73; 22. Nonne hic est, SWV74; 23. Reduc, Domine Deus meus, SWV75; 24. Supereminet omnem scientiam, SWV76; 25. Pro hoc magno mysterio pietatis, SWV77; 26. Domine, non est exaltatum cor meum, SWV78; 27. Si non humiliter sentiebam, SWV79; 28. Speret Israel in Domino, SWV80; 29. Cantate

Domino canticum rovum, SWV81; 30. Inter brachia Salvatoris mei, SWV82; 31. Veni, rogo, in cor meum, SWV83; 32. Ecce advocatus meus apud te, SWV84; 33. Domine, ne in furore tuo, SWV85; 34. Quoniam non est in morte, SWV86; 35. Discedite a me omnes qui operamini, SWV87; 36. Occuli imnium in te sperant, SWV88; 37. Pater noster, qui es in coelis, SWV89; 38. Domine Deus, pater coelestis, SWV90; 39. Confitemini Domino, SWV91; 40. Paster noster, SWV92; 41. Gratias agimus tibi, SWV93.
4-14, 17, 19-23, 26-30. Currende Voc Ens, E. van Nevel (5/92) (ACCE) ① **ACC9174D**
4-8, 13, 16, 21-25. Emmanuel Music Chor, C. Smith Concert (5/92) (KOCH) ① **37085-2**

Christmas Story, SWV435 (1664)
Musicalische Compagney Concert (9/87) (MDG) ① **L3229**
E. Kirkby, N. Rogers, D. Thomas, Taverner Consort, Taverner Ch, Taverner Plyrs, A. Parrott Concert (8/88) (EMI) ① **CDC7 47633-2**
R. Holton, J.M. Ainsley, M. George, King's Consort Ch, King's Consort, R. King Concert (12/90) (HYPE) ① **CDA66398**
S. Rydén, M. Hummel, U. Messthaler, Chor, Inst Ens, R. Jacobs (r1989) Concert (3/91) (HARM) ① **HMC90 1310**

Das ist mir Lieb (Psalm 116), SWV51 (pub 1619)
1. Das ist mir Lieb; 2. Stricke des Todes; 3. Der Herr is gnädig; 4. Sei nun wieder zufrieden; 5. Ich will den heilsamen Kelch relimen; 6. In den Höfen am Haus des Herren.
Emmanuel Music Chor, C. Smith Concert (5/92) (KOCH) ① **37085-2**

Erbarm dich mein, O Herre Gott, SWV447 (pub. 1652)
C. Janequin Ens, Saqueboutiers de Toulouse, K. Junghänel, J. Cable, W. Jansen Concert (9/88) (HARM) ① **HMC90 1255**
M. Schopper, Cologne Musica Antiqua, R. Goebel (r1985) Concert (1/93) (ARCH) ① **437 079-2AT**

Es gingen zweene Menschen, SWV444 (1640-50)
Salisbury Cath Ch, R. Seal (Eng) Concert (11/90) (MERI) ① **CDE84180**

Freue dich des Weibes deiner Jugend, SWV453 (c1640)
Musicalische Compagney Concert (9/87) (MDG) ① **L3230**
F. Lang, Monteverdi Ch, EBS, His Majesties Sagbutts and Cornetts, J.E. Gardiner Concert (11/88) (ARCH) ① **423 405-2AH**

Geistliche Chormusik—5-7vv, SWV369-97 (Op. 11) (pub 1648) (Nos 1-12, 5vv; 13-24, 6vv; 25-29, 7vv)
1. Es wird das Szepter von Juda, SWV369; 2. Er wird sein Kleid in Wein waschen, SWV370; 3. Er ist erscheinen die heilsame Gnade Gottes, SWV371; 4. Verleih uns Frieden genädiglich, SWV372; 5. Gib unsern Fürsten, SWV373; 6. Unser keiner lebet ihm selber, SWV374; 7. Viel werdenkommen, SWV375; 8. Sammlet zuvor das Unkraut, SWV376; 9. Herr, auf dich traue ich, SWV377; 10. Die mit Tränen säen, SWV378; 11. So fahr ich hin zu Jesu Christ, SWV379; 12. Also hat Gott die Welt geliebt, SWV380; 13. O lieber Herre Gott, SWV381; 14. Tröstet, tröstet mein Volk, SWV382; 15. Ich bin eine refende Stimme, SWV383; 16. Ein Kind ist uns geboren, SWV384; 17. Das Wort ward Fleisch, SWV385; 18. Die Himmel erzählen die Ehre Gottes, SWV386; 19. Herzlich lieb hab ich dich, o Herr, SWV387; 20. Das ist je gewisslich wahr, SWV388; 21. Ich ben ein rechter Weinstock, SWV389; 22. Unser Wandel ist im Himmel, SWV391; 23. Selig sind die Toten, SWV391; 24. Was mein Gott will, das gscheh allzeit, SWV392; 25. Ich weiss, dass mein Erlöser lebt, SWV393; 26. Sehet an den Feigenbaum, SWV394; 27. Der Engel sprach zu den Hirten, SWV395; 28. Auf dem Gebirge, SWV396; 29. Du Schalksknecht, SWV397.
10. G. de Reyghere, Ricercar Consort (1989) Concert (5/90) (RICE) ① **RIC060048**
11, 18, 23. Paris Chapelle Royale Chor, Paris Chapelle Royale Orch, P. Herreweghe Concert (8/88) (HARM) ① **HMC90 1261**
11, 20, 22. Emmanuel Music Chor, C. Smith Concert (5/92) (KOCH) ① **37085-2**
12. Paris Chapelle Royale Chor, Paris Chapelle Royale Orch, P. Herreweghe Concert (8/88) (HARM) ① **HMC90 1261**
13-23, 25. Emmanuel Music Chor, C. Smith (r1992) Concert Ich weiss, das mein Erlöser lebet, SWV457. (11/93) (KOCH) ① **37174-2**
23. Salisbury Cath Ch, R. Seal Concert (11/90) (MERI) ① **CDE84180**

23. E. Futral, J. Malafronte, F. Urrey, W. Pauley, Musica Sacra, R. Westenburg Concert (1/93) (RCA) ① **09026 60970-2**
28. A. Stafford, M. Chance, His Majesties Sagbutts and Cornetts, J.E. Gardiner Concert (11/88) (ARCH) ① **423 405-2AH**

Haus und Güter erbat man von Eltern, SWV21 (1618)
Musicalische Compagney Concert (9/87) (MDG) ① **L3230**

Heute ist Christus geboren, SWV439 (1632-38)
Chor, Inst Ens, R. Jacobs (r1989) Concert (3/91) (HARM) ① **HMC90 1310**

Ich beschwöre euch, ihr Töchter zu Jerusalem, SWV339 (1641)
Musicalische Compagney Concert (9/87) (MDG) ① **L3230**

Ich weiss das mein erlöser lebet—motet: 5vv, SWV457 (before 1628)
Emmanuel Music Chor, C. Smith (r1992) Geistliche Chormusik, SWV369-97. (11/93) (KOCH) ① **37174-2**

Kleiner geistlichen Concerten, Anderer Theil—1-5vv and organ continuo, SWV306-337 (Op. 9) (pub 1639)
1. Ich will den Herren loben allezeit, SWV306; 2. Was hast du verwirket, SWV307; 3. O Jesu, nomen dulcem SWV308; 4. O misericordissime Jesu, SWV309; 5. Ich liege und schlafe, SWV310; 6. Habe deine Lust an dem Herren, SWV311; 7. Herr, ich hoffe darauf, SWV312; 8. Bone Jesu, verbum Patris, SWV313; 9. Verbum caro factum est, SWV314; 10. Hodie Christus natus est, SWV315; 11a. Wann unsre Augen schlafen ein, SWV316; 11b. Latin version—Quando se claudent lumina, SWV316; 12. Meister, wir haben die ganze Nacht gearbeitet, SWV317; 13. Die Furcht des Herren, SWV318; 14. Ich beuge meine Knie, SWV319; 15. Ich bin jung gewsen, SWV320; 16. Herr, wann ich nur dich habe, SWV321; 17. Rorate coeli desuper, SWV322; 18. Joseph, du Sohn David, SWV323; 19. Ich ben die Auferstehung, SWV324; 20. Die Seele Christi heilige mich, SWV325; 21a. Ich ruf zu die, SWV326; 21b. Latin version—Te Christe supplex invoco, SWV326; 22. Allein Gott in der Höh sei Ehr, SWV327; 23. Veni Sancte Spiritus, SWV328; 24. Ist Gott für uns, SWV329; 25. Wer will uns scheiden von der Liebe Gottes, SWV330; 26. Die Stimm des Herren, SWV331; 27. Jubilate Deo omnis terra, SWV332; 28a. Sei gegrüsset, Maria, SWV333; 28b. Latin version—Ave Maria, gratia plena, SWV333; 29. Was betrübst du dich, SWV335; 30. Quemadmodum desiderat cervus, SWV336; 31. Aufer immensam, Deus, aufer iram, SWV337.
1-10, 11a, 11b, 12-19. Tolz Boys' Ch, G. Schmidt-Gaden, R. Summereder (r1989-90) Kleiner geistlichen Concerten, SWV282-305. (4/93) (CAPR) ① **10 388**
5. R. Wistreich, A. Ross Concert (9/87) (MERI) ① **CDE84096**
10, 17, 18, 28a Chor, Inst Ens, R. Jacobs (r1989) Concert (3/91) (HARM) ① **HMC90 1310**
19. Paris Chapelle Royale Chor, Paris Chapelle Royale Orch, P. Herreweghe Concert (8/88) (HARM) ① **HMC90 1261**
20, 21a, 21b, 22-27, 28a, 28b, 29-31. Tolz Boys' Ch, G. Schmidt-Gaden (r1989/90) (5/93) (CAPR) ① **10 418**
28b G. de Reyghere, A. Mellon, D. Visse, Capella Ricercar, Ricercar Consort (r1989) Concert (5/90) (RICE) ① **RIC060048**
30. C. Janequin Ens, Saqueboutiers de Toulouse, K. Junghänel, J. Cable, W. Jansen Concert (9/88) (HARM) ① **HMC90 1255**

Kleiner geistlichen Concerten, Erster Theil—1-5vv with organ continuo, SWV282-305 (Op. 8) (1636)
1. Eile mich, Gott, zu erretten, SWV282; 2. Bringt her dem Herren, SWV283; 3. Ich danke dem Herren, SWV284; 4. O süsser, o freundlicher, SWV285; 5. Der Herr ist gross, SWV286; 6a. O lieber Herre Gott, SWV287; 6b. O lieber Herre Gott SWV287a (Dresden: 1635); 7. Ihr heiligen, lobsinget dem Herren, SWV288; 8a. Erhöre mich, wenn ich rufe, SWV289; 8b. Erhöre mich, wenn ich rufe, SWV289a (Pirna: 1625-c1635); 9. Wohl dem, der nicht wandelt, SWV290; 10. Schaffe in mir, Gott, ein reines Herz, SWV291; 11. Der Herr schauet vom Himmel, SWV292; 12. Lobet den Herren, der zu Zion wohnet, SWV293; 13. Eins bitte ich vom Herrn, SWV294; 14. O hilf, Christe, Gottes Sohn, SWV295; 15a. Fürchte dich nicht, ich bin mit dir, SWV296; 15b. Fürchte dich nicht, ich bin mit dir, SWV296a (Dresden: 1635); 16. O Herr hilf, SWV297; 17. Das Blut Jesu Christi, SWV298; 18. Die Gotteseligkeit ist zu allen

Dingen nützt, SWV299; 19. Himmel und Erde vergehen, SWV300; 20a. Num komm, der Heiden Heiland, SWV301; 20b. Nun komm, der Heiden Heiland, SWV301a (Dresden: 1635); 21a. Ein Kind ist uns geboren, SWV302; 21b. Ein Kind ist uns geboren, SWV302a (Dresden: 1635); 22. Wir gläuben all an einen Gott, SWV303; 23a. Siehe, mein Fürsprecher ist im Himmel, SWV304; 23b. Siehe, mein Fürsprecher ist im Himmel, SWV304a (Dresden: 1635); 24. Ich hab mein Sach Gott heimgestellt, SWV305.
6a Paris Chapelle Royale Chor, Paris Chapelle Royale Orch, P. Herreweghe Concert (8/88) (HARM) ① **HMC90 1261**
24. Tolz Boys' Ch, G. Schmidt-Gaden, R. Summereder (r1989-90) Kleiner geistliche Concerten, SWV306-37. (4/93) (CAPR) ① **10 388**

Magnificat, SWV468 (before 1665)
C. Janequin Ens, Saqueboutiers de Toulouse, K. Junghänel, J. Cable, W. Jansen Concert (9/88) (HARM) ① **HMC90 1255**
Schütz Academy, H. Arman (r1991) Concert (5/93) (CAPR) ① **10 409**

Musicalisches Exequien, SWV279-81 (Op. 7) (1636)
1. Nacket bin ich vom Mutterleibe kommen; 2. Herr, wenn ich nur dich habe; 3. Herr, nun lässet du deinen Deiner; Selig sind die Toten (Canticum B. Simeonis).
Paris Chapelle Royale Chor, Paris Chapelle Royale Orch, P. Herreweghe Concert (8/88) (HARM) ① **HMC90 1261**
Monteverdi Ch, EBS, His Majesties Sagbutts and Cornetts, J.E. Gardiner Concert (11/88) (ARCH) ① **423 405-2AH**

Il Primo libro di madrigali—5vv, SWV1-19 (Op. 1) (1611)
1. O primavera, SWV1; 2. O dolcezze amarissime, SWV2; 3. Selve beate, SWV3; 4. Alma afflitta, che fai, SWV4; 5. Così morir debb'io, SWV5; 6. D'orrida selce alpina, SWV6; 7. Ride la primavera, SWV7; 8. Fuggi, fuggi, o mio core, SWV8; 9. Feritevi, ferite, SWV9; 10. Fiamma ch;allacia, SWV10; 11. Quella damma son io, SWV11; 12. Mi saluta costei, SWV12; 13. Io moro, SWV13; 14. Sospir che del petto, SWV14; 15. Dunque à Dio, SWV15; 16. Tornate, o cari baci, SWV16; 17. Di marmo siete voi, SWV17; 18. Giunto è pur, Lidia, SWV18; 19. Vasto mar, nel cui seno, SWV19.
1-18. Concerto Vocale, R. Jacobs (r1984) (11/85) (HARM) ① **HMA190 1162**

Psalmen Davids sampt etlichen Moteten und Concerten, SWV22-47 (Op. 2) (pub 1619)
1. Der Herr sprach zu meinem Herren (Ps 110), SWV22; 2. Warum toben die Heiden (Ps 2), SWV23; 3. Ach Herr, strof mich nicht (Ps 6), SWV24; 4. Aus der Tiefe (Ps 130), SWV25; 5. Ich freu mich des (Ps 130), SWV25; 6. Herr, unser Herrscher (Ps 8), SWV26; 7. Wohl dem, der nicht wandelt (Ps 1), SWV28; 8. Wie lieblich sind deine Wohnunge (Ps 84), SWV29; 9. Wohl dem, der den Herren fürchtet (Ps 128), SWV30; 10. Ich hebe meine Augen auf (Ps 121), SWV31; 11. Danket dem Herren (Ps 136), SWV32; 12. Der Herr ist mein Hirt (Ps 23), SWV33; 13. Ich danke dem Herrn (Ps 111), SWV34; 14. Singet dem Herren ein neues Lied (Ps 98), SWV35; 15. Jauchzet dem Herren, alle Welt (Ps 100), SWV36; 16. An den Wassern zu Babel (Ps 137), SWV37; 17. Alleluja, lobet den Herren (Ps 150), SWV38; 18. Lobe den Herren, meine Seele (concert), SWV39; 19. List nicht Ephraim mein teurer Sohn (Moteto) SWV40; 20. Nun lob, mein Seel, den Herren (Canzon), SWV41; 21. Nicht uns Herr (Ps 115), SWV43; 23. Wohl dem der den Herren fürchtet (Ps 128), SWV44; 24. Danket dem Herren (Ps 136), SWV45; 25. Zion spricht, der Herr hat mich verlassen (Concert), SWV46; 26. Jauchzet dem Herren, alle Welt (Concert), SWV47.
1, 2, 5, 6, 8, 12, 14-17, 22-24. Trinity Coll Ch, Cambridge, His Majesties Sagbutts and Cornetts, R. Marlow (6/91) (CONI) ① **CDCF190**
13. Schütz Academy, H. Arman (r1991) Concert (5/93) (CAPR) ① **10 409**
17-26. Regensburg Cath Ch, Hamburg Early Music Wind Ens, Ulsamer Collegium, H.M. Schneidt (r1971) (1/93) (ARCH) ① **437 078-2AT**
19. Monteverdi Ch, EBS, His Majesties Sagbutts and Cornetts, J.E. Gardiner Concert (11/88) (ARCH) ① **423 405-2AH**
21. C. Janequin Ens, Saqueboutiers de Toulouse, K. Junghänel, J. Cable, W. Jansen Concert (9/88) (HARM) ① **HMC90 1255**
26. E. Futral, J. Malafronte, F. Urrey, W. Pauley, Musica Sacra, R. Westenburg Concert (1/93) (RCA) ① **09026 60970-2**

Die **Sieben Worte unseres lieben Erlösers und Seligmachers Jesu Christi—5vv and instruments, SWV478**
Musicalische Compagney *Concert*
(9/87) (MDG) ① **L3229**
C. Janequin Ens, Saquebboutiers de Toulouse, K. Junghänel, J. Cable, W. Jansen *Concert*
(9/88) (HARM) ① **HMC90 1255**
Stehe auf, meine Freundin—double choir and continuo, SWV499 (rediscovered 1972)
Schütz Academy, H. Arman (r1991) *Concert*
(5/93) (CAPR) ① **10 409**
Symphoniae sacrae, SWV341-367 (pub 1647)
1. Mein Herz ist bereit, SWV341; 2. Singet den Herren ein Lied, SWV342; 3. Herr, unser Herrscher, wie herrlich ist dein Nam', SWV343; 4. Meine Seele erhabt den Herren, SWV344; 5. Der Herr ist meine Stärke, SWV345; 6. Ich werde nicht sterben, sondern leben, SWV346; 7. Ich danke dir, Herr, von ganzen Herzen, SWV347; 8. Herzlich lieb hab ich dich, o Herr, SWV348; 9. Frohlocket mit Händen und jauchzet dem Herren, SWV349; 10. Lobet den Herrn in seinem Heiligtum, SWV350; 11. Hütet euch, dass eure Herzen nicht beschweret werden, SWV351; 12. Herr, nun lässest du deinen Diener in Friede werden, SWV352; 13. Was betrübst du dich, meine Seele?, SWV353; 14. Verleihh uns Frieden gnädiglich, SWV354; 15. Gib unserm Fürsten und aller Obrigkeit, SWV355; 16. Es steh Gott auf, dass deine Feind zerstreuet werden, SWV356; 17. Wie ein Rubin in feinem Golde leuchtet, SWV357; 18. Iss dein Brot mit Freuden, SWV358; 19. Der Herr ist mein Licht und mein Heil, SWV359; 20. Zweierlei bitte ich, von dir, SWV360; 21. Herr, neige deine Himmel und fahr herab, SWV361; 22. Von Aufgang der Sonnen, SWV362; 23. Lobet den Herrn, alle Heiden, SWV363; 24. Die so ihr den Herren fürchtet, SWV364; 25. Drei schöne Dinge seind, SWV365; 26. Von Gott will ich nicht lassen, SWV366; 27. Freuet euch des Herren, ihr Gerechten, SWV367.
Cpte E. Kirkby, S. Le Blanc, J. Bowman, N. Rogers, C. Daniels, S. Varcoe, R. Wistreich, Purcell Qt, J. West, N. Perry (r1993/4)
(4/95) (CHAN) ① [2] **CHAN0566/7**
4. Musicalische Compagney *Concert*
(9/87) (MDG) ① **L3229**
4. C. Janequin Ens, Saquebboutiers de Toulouse, K. Junghänel, J. Cable, W. Jansen *Concert*
(9/88) (HARM) ① **HMC90 1255**
4. M.C. Kiehr, R. Jacobs *Auferstehungs Histoire, SWV50.*
(4/91) (HARM) ① **HMC90 1311**
12. R. Wistreich, A. Ross, His Majesties Sagbutts and Cornetts *Concert* (9/87) (MERI) ① **CDE84096**
Symphoniae sacrae, SWV257-276 (Op. 6) (pub 1629)
1. Paratum cor meum, SWV257; 2. Exultavit cor meum in Domino, SWV258; 3. In te, Domine, speravi, SWV259; 4. Cantabo Domino in vita mea, SWV260; 5. Venite ad me, SWV261; 6. Jubilate Deo omnis terra, SWV262; 7. Anima mea liquefacta est, SWV263; 8. Adjuro vos, filiae Hierusalem, SWV264; 9. O quam tu puchra es, SWV265; 10. Veni de Libano, SWV266; 11. Benedicam Dominum in omni tempore, SWV267; 12. Exquisivi Dominum, BWV268; 13. Fili mi, Absalon, SWV269; 14. Attendite, popule meus, SWV270; 15. Domine, labia mea aperies, SWV271; 16. In lectulo per noctes, SWV272; 17. Invenerunt me custodes, SWV273; 18. Veni, dilecte mi, SWV274; 19. Buccinate in neomenia tuba, SWV275; 20. Jubilate Deo, SWV276.
7, 8. C. Janequin Ens, Saquebboutiers de Toulouse, K. Junghänel, J. Cable, W. Jansen *Concert*
(9/88) (HARM) ① **HMC90 1255**
7, 8, 16, 17, 18. Musicalische Compagney *Concert*
(9/87) (MDG) ① **L3230**
13. R. Wistreich, A. Ross *Concert*
(9/87) (MERI) ① **CDE84096**
Symphoniarum sacrarum, tertia pars—4-6vv and instruments, SWV398-418 (Op. 12) (pub 1650)
1. Der Herr ist mein Hirt, SWV398; 2. Ich hebe meine Augen auf, SWV399; 3. Wo der Herr nicht das Haus bauet, SWV400; 4. Mein Sohn, warum hast du uns das getan, SWV401; 5. O Herr hilf, SWV402; 6. Siehe es erschien der Engel des Herren, SWV403; 7. Feget den alten Sauerteig, SWV404; 8. O süsser Jesu Christ, SWV405; 9. O Jesu süss, wer dein gedenkt, SWV406; 10. Lasset uns doch den Herren, SWV407; 11. Es ging ein Sämann aus zu saën, SWV408; 12. Seid barmherzig, SWV409; 13. Siehe, dieser wird gesetzt zu einem Fall, SWV410; 14. Vater unser, der du bist im Himmel, SWV411; 15. Siehe, wie fein und lieblich ist, SWV412; 16. Hütet euch, dass eure Herzen, SWV413; 17. Meister, wir wissen, SWV414; 18. Saul, Saul, was verfolgst du mich,

SWV415; 19. Herr, wie lang willt du mein so gar vergessen, SWV416; 20. Komm, heiliger Geist, Herre Gott, SWV417; 21. Nun danket alle Gott, SWV418.
14. Lower Rhine Choral Soc, H. Schmitt *Concert*
(2/90) (SCHW) ① **313001**
18. Monteverdi Ch, EBS, His Majesties Sagbutts and Cornetts, J.E. Gardiner *Concert*
(11/88) (ARCH) ① **423 405-2AH**
18. Schütz Academy, H. Arman (r1991) *Concert*
(5/93) (CAPR) ① **10 409**
Weib, was weinest du—Dialogo per la pascua, SWV443
Musicalische Compagney *Concert*
(9/87) (MDG) ① **L3230**
Salisbury Cath Ch, R. Seal (Eng) *Concert*
(11/90) (MERI) ① **CDE84180**
Wohl dem, der ein Tugendsam Weib hat, SWV20 (1618)
Musicalische Compagney *Concert*
(9/87) (MDG) ① **L3230**

SCHWARTZ, Arthur (1900–1984) USA

SECTION V: STAGE WORKS

The Band Wagon—revue (1931—New York) (Lyrics H. Dietz)
EXCERPTS: 1. Overture; 2. Sweet music; 3. High and low; 4. Hoops; 5. Confession; 6. New sun in the sky; 7. I love Louisa; 8. Ballet music; 9. Beggar's waltz; 10. White heat; 11. Dancing in the dark.
11. D. Gaines, London Sinfonietta, J. McGlinn *Concert* (8/93) (EMI) ① **CDC7 54586-2**
Between the Devil—musical show (1937—New York) (Wds. H. Dietz)
Triplets K. Criswell, J. Kaye, G. Dvorsky, London Sinfonietta, J. McGlinn *Concert*
(8/93) (EMI) ① **CDC7 54586-2**
The Gay Life—musical show (1961—New York) (Lyrics cpsr & H Dietz)
Cpte B. Cook, W. Chiari, Orig Broadway Cast
(11/93) (EMI) ① **ZDM7 64763-2**
Revenge with Music—musical show (1934—New York) (Lyrics H. Dietz)
You and the Night and the Music K. Criswell, London Sinfonietta, J. McGlinn (r1992) *Concert*
(4/94) (EMI) ① **CDC7 54802-2**

SCHWARTZ, Jean (1878–1956) USA

SECTION V: STAGE WORKS

Fritz in Tammany Hall—musical show (1905—New York) (Lyrics William Jerome)
EXCERPTS: 1. I'm a Woman of No Importance.
1. S. Mayhew, Broadway Cast (r1910) *Concert*
(5/94) (PEAR) ① [3] **GEMMCDS9050/2(2)**
The Ham Tree—musical show (1905—New York) (Lyrics William Jerome)
EXCERPTS: 1. Good-Bye, Sweet Old Manhattan Isle; 2. On an Automobile Honeymoon; 3. Sweethearts in Every Town.
1-3. H. Tally, Broadway Cast (r1905) *Concert*
(5/94) (PEAR) ① [3] **GEMMCDS9050/2(2)**
Piff! Paff! Pouf!!!—musical show (1904—New York) (Lyrics William Jerome)
EXCERPTS: 1. Since Dolly Dimple Made a Hit.
1. G. Cameron, Broadway Cast (r1904) *Concert*
(5/94) (PEAR) ① [3] **GEMMCDS9050/2(1)**

SCHWARTZ, Stephen (b 1948) USA

SECTION V: STAGE WORKS

Godspell—musical show (1971—New York)
EXCERPTS: 1. Prologue; 2. Prepare ye the way of the Lord; 3. Save the people; 4. Day by day; 5. Learn your lessons well; 6. Bless the Lord; 7. All for the best; 8. All good gifts; 9. Light of the world; 10. Turn back old man; 11. Alas for you; 12. By my side (Wds J. Hamburger; Music P. Gordon); 13. We beseech thee; 14. On the willows; 15. Beautiful City; 16. Finale.
1-16. London Cast, S. Schwartz (r1993)
(4/94) (TER) ① **CDTER1204**

SCHWARZ-SCHILLING, Reinhard (1904–1987) Germany

SECTION IV: VOCAL AND CHORAL

Kurze Fahrt—Lied (Wds. Eichendorff)
D. Fischer-Dieskau, W. Sawallisch (pp1975) *Concert*
(1/90) (ORFE) ① **C185891A**

Marienlied—Lied (Wds. Eichendorff)
D. Fischer-Dieskau, W. Sawallisch (pp1975) *Concert*
(1/90) (ORFE) ① **C185891A**
Der Wandernde Musikant (Wds. J Eichendorff)
1. Wandern lieb' ich für mein Leben; 2. Wenn die Sonne lieblich scheine; 3. Bist du manchmal auch verstimmt; 4. Durch Feld und Buchenhallen.
3. D. Fischer-Dieskau, W. Sawallisch (pp1975) *Concert*
(1/90) (ORFE) ① **C185891A**

SCHWEHR, Cornelius (20th cent) Germany

SECTION IV: VOCAL AND CHORAL

Deutsche Tänze—five female vv (1989-90)
Bel Canto Ens, D. Spohr (r1993) *Concert*
(3/95) (SCHW) ① **314322**

SCHWERTSIK, Kurt (b 1935) Austria

SECTION II: CHAMBER

3 Späte Liebeslieder ... für Christa—3 late love songs: cello and piano
C. van Kampen, N. Meecham (r1993) *Concert*
(9/94) (LARG) ① **Largo 5125**

SECTION III: INSTRUMENTAL

5 Nocturnes—piano, Op. 10b (1964)
N. Meecham (r1993) *Concert*
(9/94) (LARG) ① **Largo 5125**

SECTION IV: VOCAL AND CHORAL

da uhu schaud me so draurech au—7 Viennese songs (Wds H.C. Artmann)
EXCERPTS: 1. da uhu schaud me so draurech so; 2. en da nocht; 3. frog me ned; 4. aum eaxtn is a ma r one dia; 5. zwa groschn aus süwa; 6. pfau; 7. fola feigaln da boista.
C. Schwertsik, K. Schwertsik (r1993) *Concert*
(9/94) (LARG) ① **Largo 5125**
Gedichte und Ljuba—5 songs by Schwertsik & a 6th by Eisler, Op. 53 (1986) (Wds P. Altenberg)
EXCERPTS: 1. Was kann er für sie tun?!?; 2. Die ruhigen Stunden; 3. Sehnsucht; 4. Ljuba; 5. Das neue Kleid; 6. Und endlich stirbt die Sehnsucht doch (Eisler).
C. Schwertsik, K. Schwertsik (r1993) *Concert*
(9/94) (LARG) ① **Largo 5125**
ich sein blumenbein—11 songs, Op. 38 (1980) (Wds E. Jandl)
EXCERPTS: 1. lied; 2. liege bett; 3. über stiegen; 4. motorradfahrer; 5. nasal; 6. dies eisenharte brot; 7. körpern und ewigen; 8. kein mund; 9. blumenbein; 10. klos; 11. während.
C. Schwertsik, K. Schwertsik (r1993) *Concert*
(9/94) (LARG) ① **Largo 5125**

SCHWINDL, Friedrich (1737–1786) Germany

SECTION I: ORCHESTRAL

Symphony 'Périodique' in F (c1770-80s)
ECCO, J. Faerber *Concert*
(10/86) (HYPE) ① **CDA66156**

SCOTT, Cyril (Meir) (1879–1970) England

SECTION I: ORCHESTRAL

Aubade—orchestra, Op. 77 (1911)
SABC SO, P. Marchbank (r1993) *Concert*
(7/94) (MARC) ① **8 223485**
3 Dances—orchestra, Op. 22
1. Allegro con brio; 2. Andante sostenuto e sempre molto cantabile; 3. Allegro energico.
SABC SO, P. Marchbank (r1993) *Concert*
(7/94) (MARC) ① **8 223485**
Neapolitan Rhapsody—orchestra (1960)
SABC SO, P. Marchbank (r1993) *Concert*
(7/94) (MARC) ① **8 223485**
2 Passacaglias on Irish Themes—orchestra (1912)
1. Allegretto alla breve; 2. Andante sostenuto.
SABC SO, P. Marchbank (r1993) *Concert*
(7/94) (MARC) ① **8 223485**
Suite Fantastique—orchestra
1. Fata Morgana; 2. Fire Dance; 3. Dance of Spectres; 4. Goblins and Elves.
SABC SO, P. Marchbank (r1993) *Concert*
(7/94) (MARC) ① **8 223485**

3 Symphonic Dances—orchestra (revison of Symphony 2, 1903)
P. Thwaites, J. Lavender (r1989-91: arr 2 pfs: Grainger) Concert (1/94) (PEAR) ① **SHECD9631**

SECTION II: CHAMBER

Extatic Shepherd—flute and piano
K. Smith, P. Rhodes Concert
(1/91) (ASV) ① **CDDCA739**
Pastoral and Reel—cello and piano
J. Lloyd Webber, J. Lenehan (r1994) Concert
(12/94) (PHIL) ① **442 530-2PH**
Tallahassee Suite—violin and piano, Op. 73 (1910)
1. Bygone memories; 2. After sundown; 3. Valse triste.
J. Heifetz, E. Bay (r1937) Concert
(11/94) (RCA) ① **[65] 09026 61778-2(03)**

SECTION III: INSTRUMENTAL

Danse nègre—piano, Op. 58/3
E. Joyce (r1937) Concert
(2/94) (PEAR) ① **GEMMCD9022**
3 Danses tristes—piano, Op. 74 (1910)
1. Danse élégiaque; 2. Danse orientale; 3. Danse languoreuse.
D. Hennig Concert (10/92) (ETCE) ① **KTC1132**
2 Pieces—piano, Op. 47 (1905)
1. Lotus Land; 2. Columbine.
D. Hennig Concert (10/92) (ETCE) ① **KTC1132**
1. F. Kreisler, A. Sándor (arr Kreisler: r1926) Concert
(9/92) (BIDD) ① **[2] LAB049/50**
1. F. Kreisler, C. Lamson (r1922: arr Kreisler) Concert (9/93) (BIDD) ① **[2] LAB068/9**
1. F. Kreisler, F. Rupp (r1938: arr Kreisler) Concert
(12/93) (EMI) ① **CDH7 64701-2**
1. V. Spivakov, S. Bezrodny (r1991-2; arr Kreisler) Concert (5/95) (RCA) ① **09026 62524-2**
Pierrette—piano (1912)
D. Hennig Concert (10/92) (ETCE) ① **KTC1132**
2 Pierrot Pieces—piano, Op. 35 (1904)
1. Pierrot triste; 2. Pierrot gai.
D. Hennig Concert (10/92) (ETCE) ① **KTC1132**
Poems—piano (1912)
1. Poppies; 2. The garden of soul-sympathy; 3. Bells; 4. The twilight of the year; 5. Paradise birds.
D. Hennig Concert (10/92) (ETCE) ① **KTC1132**
Sonata for Piano, Op. 66 (1909)
D. Hennig Concert (10/92) (ETCE) ① **KTC1132**

SECTION IV: VOCAL AND CHORAL

Cherry ripe—folksong arrangement
F. Kreisler, C. Lamson (r1922: arr Kreisler) Concert
(9/93) (BIDD) ① **[2] LAB068/9**
Lullaby—song, Op. 57/2 (Wds. C. Rossetti)
R. Ponselle, orch. R. Bourdon (r1924) Concert
(11/94) (ROMO) ① **[2] 81006-2**
K. Flagstad, E. McArthur (r1936) Concert
(12/95) (PEAR) ① **GEMMCD9092**
K. Flagstad, E. McArthur (r1936) Concert
(12/95) (NIMB) ① **NI7871**

SCOTT, James Sylvester (1885–1938) USA

SECTION III: INSTRUMENTAL

Evergreen Rag—piano (1915)
J. Rifkin Concert (4/92) (DECC) ① **425 225-2DH**
Modesty Rag—piano (1920)
J. Rifkin Concert (4/92) (DECC) ① **425 225-2DH**
Peace and Plenty Rag—piano (1919)
J. Rifkin Concert (4/92) (DECC) ① **425 225-2DH**
Troubadour Ray—piano (1919)
J. Rifkin Concert (4/92) (DECC) ① **425 225-2DH**

SCOTT, Lady Jane (1810–1900) England

christened Alicia Anne Spottiswoode

SECTION IV: VOCAL AND CHORAL

Think on me—song
L. Finnie, A. Legge Concert
(4/90) (CHAN) ① **CHAN8749**

SCRIABIN, Alexander (1872–1915) Russia

SECTION I: ORCHESTRAL

Concerto for Piano and Orchestra in F sharp minor, Op. 20 (1896)
Vladimir Ashkenazy, LPO, L. Maazel Concert
(4/89) (DECC) ① **417 252-2DH**
G. Ohlsson, Czech PO, L. Pešek Concert
(11/89) (SUPR) ① **CO-2047**

R. Pôntinen, Stockholm PO, L. Segerstam Symphony 3.
(1/91) (BIS) ① **BIS-CD475**
H. Neuhaus, Moscow All-Union RSO, N. Golovanov (r1946) Concert (8/94) (RUSS) ① **RDCD15004**
N. Demidenko, BBC SO, A. Lazarev (r1993) Tchaikovsky: Piano Concerto 1.
(10/94) (HYPE) ① **CDA66680**
G. Oppitz, Frankfurt RSO, D. Kitaienko (r1993) Concert (12/95) (RCA) ① **[3] 74321 20297-2**
Le Poème de l'extase, 'Poem of Ecstasy', Op. 54 (1905-08)
Cleveland Orch, L. Maazel Concert
(4/89) (DECC) ① **417 252-2DH**
Czech PO, L. Pešek Concert
(11/89) (SUPR) ① **CO-2047**
Chicago SO, N. Järvi Mussorgsky: Pictures.
(9/90) (CHAN) ① **CHAN8849**
Philadelphia, R. Muti Tchaikovsky: Symphony 6.
(3/91) (EMI) ① **CDC7 54061-2**
Philadelphia, R. Muti Concert
(7/91) (EMI) ① **[3] CDS7 54251-2**
Berlin RSO, Vladimir Ashkenazy Concert
(11/91) (DECC) ① **430 843-2DH**
USSR SO, E. Svetlanov (pp1990) Symphony 1.
(9/93) (RUSS) ① **RDCD11056**
Boston SO, P. Monteux (r1952) Concert
(9/94) (RCA) ① **[15] 09026 61893-2**
NYPO, P. Boulez (r1972) Concert
(9/95) (SONY) ① **[2] SM2K64100**
Frankfurt RSO, D. Kitaienko (r1991) Concert
(12/95) (RCA) ① **[3] 74321 20297-2**
Prometheus, '(Le) poeme du feu'—piano, chorus and orchestra, Op. 60 (1908-10)
Vladimir Ashkenazy, Ambrosian Sngrs, LPO, L. Maazel Concert (4/89) (DECC) ① **417 252-2DH**
D. Alexeev, Philadelphia Choral Arts Soc, Philadelphia, R. Muti Concert
(7/91) (EMI) ① **[3] CDS7 54251-2**
L. Derwinger, Stockholm Phil Ch, Stockholm PO, L. Segerstam Symphony 1.
(9/92) (BIS) ① **BIS-CD534**
M. Argerich, Berlin Singakademie, BPO, C. Abbado (pp1992) Concert (1/95) (SONY) ① **SK53978**
Frankfurt RSO, D. Kitaienko (r1994) Concert
(12/95) (RCA) ① **[3] 74321 20297-2**
Rêverie—orchestra, Op. 24 (1898)
SNO, N. Järvi Symphony 2.
(10/86) (CHAN) ① **CHAN8462**
Czech PO, L. Pešek Concert
(11/89) (SUPR) ① **CO-2047**
Berlin RSO, Vladimir Ashkenazy Concert
(11/91) (DECC) ① **430 843-2DH**
Frankfurt RSO, D. Kitaienko (r1993) Concert
(12/95) (RCA) ① **[3] 74321 20297-2**
Symphony No. 1 in E—soloists, chorus and orchestra, Op. 26 (1899-1900)
Y. Gorokhovskaya, K. Pluzhnikov, Leningrad Glinka Acad Ch, USSR RSO, V. Fedoseyev (1986)
(1/89) (OLYM) ① **OCD159**
S. Toczyska, M. Myers, Westminster Ch, Philadelphia, R. Muti Concert
(7/91) (EMI) ① **[3] CDS7 54251-2**
I. Blom, L. Magnusson, Stockholm Phil Ch, Stockholm PO, L. Segerstam Prometheus.
(9/92) (BIS) ① **BIS-CD534**
N. Gaponova, A. Salynikov, USSR Rad Chor, USSR SO, E. Svetlanov (pp1990) Poème de l'extase.
(9/93) (RUSS) ① **RDCD11056**
T. Siniawskaia, A. Fedin, Figuralchor, Frankfurt RSO, D. Kitaienko (r1992) Concert
(12/95) (RCA) ① **[3] 74321 20297-2**
Symphony No. 2 in C minor, Op. 29 (1901)
SNO, N. Järvi Rêverie, Op. 24.
(10/86) (CHAN) ① **CHAN8462**
Philadelphia, R. Muti Concert
(7/91) (EMI) ① **[3] CDS7 54251-2**
Frankfurt RSO, D. Kitaienko (r1992) Concert
(12/95) (RCA) ① **[3] 74321 20297-2**
Symphony No. 3, 'Divine Poem', Op. 43 (1902-04)
Concertgebouw, K. Kondrashin (pp1976)
(6/86) (ETCE) ① **KTC1027**
Stockholm PO, L. Segerstam Piano Concerto.
(1/91) (BIS) ① **BIS-CD475**
Philadelphia, R. Muti Concert
(7/91) (EMI) ① **[3] CDS7 54251-2**
Danish Nat RSO, N. Järvi Arensky: Suite, Op. 23.
(10/91) (CHAN) ① **CHAN8898**
Berlin RSO, Vladimir Ashkenazy Concert
(11/91) (DECC) ① **430 843-2DH**
V. Krainev, Frankfurt RSO, D. Kitaienko (r1994) Concert (12/95) (RCA) ① **[3] 74321 20297-2**

SECTION II: CHAMBER

Fantasy in A minor—two pianos (?1889)
K. Labèque, M. Labèque (r1994) Concert
(12/95) (PHIL) ① **442 778-2PH**
Romance in A minor—horn & piano (1890)
G. Piatigorsky, I. Newton (arr Piatigorsky: r1934) Concert (10/91) (MUSI) ① **MACD-644**
W. Manz, R. Plagge (r1992) Concert
(11/94) (DINT) ① **DICD920150**

SECTION III: INSTRUMENTAL

2 Danses—piano, Op. 73 (1914)
1. Guirlande; 2. Flamme sombre.
M. Rudy Concert (2/89) (CALL) ① **CAL9692**
D. Amato Concert (10/92) (ALTA) ① **AIR-CD-9020**
R. Woodward Concert (10/92) (ETCE) ① **KTC1126**
S Richter Concert
(8/94) (PHIL) ① **[2] 438 627-2PH2**
Vladimir Ashkenazy (r1977) Concert
(10/94) (DECC) ① **425 081-2DM**
12 Etudes—piano, Op. 8
1. C sharp minor; 2. F sharp minor; 3. B minor; 4. B; 5. E; 6. A; 7. B flat minor; 8. A flat; 9. C sharp minor; 10. D flat; 11. B flat minor; 12. D sharp minor.
P. Lane Concert (12/92) (HYPE) ① **CDA66607**
Y. Matsuzawa (r1993) Concert
(6/94) (PP) ① **PP10394**
G. Fergus-Thompson (r1993) Concert
(4/95) (ASV) ① **CDDCA882**
2, 10, 11. V. Horowitz (r1972) Concert
(7/94) (SONY) ① **SK53472**
2, 4, 5. N. Demidenko Concert
(8/91) (CONI) ① **CDCF204**
7. V. Horowitz (pp1953) Concert
(1/90) (RCA) ① **GD86215**
7. V. Sofronitzky (r1946-51) Concert
(5/94) (MULT) ① **310181-2**
8. V. Horowitz (r1972) Concert
(7/94) (SONY) ① **SK53472**
10. J. Szigeti, N. Magaloff (arr Szigeti: r1936) Concert
(1/90) (BIDD) ① **[2] LAB007/8**
10. Midori, R. McDonald (r1992: arr vn/pf Szigeti) Concert (6/93) (SONY) ① **SK52568**
10, 12. S. Barere (pp1947) Concert
(11/89) (APR) ① **[2] APR7008**
11. D. Ciani (pp) Concert (8/89) (DYNA) ① **CDS55**
11. J. Lloyd Webber, J. Lenehan (r1992: arr vc/pf: Piatigorsky) Concert
(10/93) (PHIL) ① **434 917-2PH**
11. V. Sofronitzky (pp1960) Concert
(8/95) (MELO) ① **[2] 74321 25177-2**
11. V. Sofronitzky (pp1960) Concert
(8/95) (MELO) ① **[11] 74321 25172-2(1)**
12. V. Horowitz Concert
(6/86) (DG) ① **419 217-2GH**
12. V. Horowitz (pp1985) Concert
(12/86) (DG) ① **419 499-2GH**
12. V. Horowitz (pp1982) Concert
(1/90) (RCA) ① **GD86215**
12. S. Barere (r1934; two versions) Concert
(5/91) (APR) ① **[2] APR7001**
12. M. Lympany Concert (1/92) (EMIL) ① **CDZ111**
12. S. Barere (bp1920s/30s) Concert
(1/93) (APR) ① **[2] APR7014**
12. V. Horowitz (pp1982) Concert
(5/93) (RCA) ① **09026 61414-2**
12. V. Horowitz (r1962) Concert
(7/94) (SONY) ① **[2] S2K53457**
12. V. Horowitz (pp1968) Concert
(7/94) (SONY) ① **SK53465**
12. A. Cortot (r1923) Concert
(10/94) (BIDD) ① **[2] LHW014/5**
12. A. Brailowsky (r1928) Concert
(2/95) (PEAR) ① **GEMMCD9132**
12. A. Brailowsky (r1928) Concert
(11/95) (DANA) ① **[2] DACOCD338/9**
8 Etudes—piano, Op. 42 (1903)
1. D flat; 2. F sharp minor; 3. F sharp minor; 4. F sharp; 5. C sharp minor; 6. D flat; 7. F minor; 8. E flat.
G. Fergus-Thompson Concert
(4/92) (ASV) ① **CDDCA776**
P. Lane Concert (12/92) (HYPE) ① **CDA66607**
3, 4, 5. V. Horowitz (r1972) Concert
(7/94) (SONY) ① **SK53472**
3, 4, 7. N. Demidenko Concert
(8/91) (CONI) ① **CDCF204**
4. G. Fergus-Thompson Concert
(4/92) (ASV) ① **CDWHL2066**
4, 6. V. Sofronitzky (r1946-51) Concert
(5/94) (MULT) ① **310181-2**
5. V. Horowitz (pp1953) Concert
(1/90) (RCA) ① **GD86215**
5. E. Kissin Concert (1/90) (DG) ① **427 485-2GH**
5. E. Kissin Concert (pp1987) Concert
(11/90) (SONY) ① **SK45931**

G. Fergus-Thompson (r1993) *Concert*
(4/95) (ASV) ① **CDDCA882**
Sonata for Piano No. 3 in F sharp minor, Op. 23 (1897-98)
G. Fergus-Thompson *Concert*
(6/88) (KING) ① **KCLCD2001**
Vladimir Ashkenazy *Concert*
(1/90) (DECC) ① [2] **425 579-2DM2**
V. Horowitz (r1954-5) *Concert*
(1/90) (RCA) ① **GD86215**
Boris Berman *Concert*   (5/90) (MUSI) ① **MACD-605**
G. Scott *Concert*   (10/91) (GAMU) ① **GAMCD520**
R. Szidon *Concert*
(4/92) (DG) ① **431 747-2GC3**
V. Sofronitzky (r1946-51) *Concert*
(5/94) (MULT) ① **310181-2**
Y. Matsuzawa (r1993) *Concert*
(6/94) (PP) ① **PP10394**
G. Fergus-Thompson (r1993) *Concert*
(4/95) (ASV) ① **CDDCA882**
Sonata for Piano No. 4 in F sharp, Op. 30 (1903)
Vladimir Ashkenazy *Concert*
(1/90) (DECC) ① [2] **425 579-2DM2**
Boris Berman *Concert*   (5/90) (MUSI) ① **MACD-605**
H. Austbø *Concert*   (5/90) (SIMA) ① **PSC1055**
R. Szidon *Concert*
(4/92) (DG) ① [3] **431 747-2GC3**
G. Fergus-Thompson *Concert*
(4/92) (ASV) ① **CDDCA776**
Emil Gilels (pp1957) *Concert*
(4/93) (MEZH) ① **MK417072**
Y. Matsuzawa (r1993) *Concert*
(6/94) (PP) ① **PP10394**
V. Sofronitzky (pp1960) *Concert*
(8/95) (MELO) ① [2] **74321 25177-2**
V. Sofronitzky (pp1960) *Concert*
(8/95) (MELO) ① [11] **74321 25172-2(1)**
Sonata for Piano No. 5, Op. 53 (1907)
S. Richter (pp1962) *Concert*
(9/88) (DG) ① **423 573-2GDO**
Vladimir Ashkenazy *Concert*
(1/90) (DECC) ① [2] **425 579-2DM2**
V. Horowitz (pp1976) *Concert*
(1/90) (RCA) ① **GD86215**
Boris Berman *Concert*   (5/90) (MUSI) ① **MACD-605**
H. Austbø *Concert*   (5/90) (SIMA) ① **PSC1055**
R. Szidon *Concert*
(4/92) (DG) ① [3] **431 747-2GC3**
G. Fergus-Thompson *Concert*
(4/92) (ASV) ① **CDDCA776**
A. Sultanov (r1990) *Concert*
(8/93) (TELD) ① **2292-46011-2**
P. Jablonski (r1992) *Concert*
(2/94) (DECC) ① **440 281-2DH**
Y. Matsuzawa (r1993) *Concert*
(6/94) (PP) ① **PP10394**
S. Richter (pp1962) *Concert*
(12/95) (DG) ① [2] **447 355-2GDB2**
Sonata for Piano No. 6 in G, Op. 62 (1911)
Vladimir Ashkenazy *Concert*
(1/90) (DECC) ① [2] **425 579-2DM2**
Boris Berman *Concert*   (6/91) (MUSI) ① **MACD-621**
R. Szidon *Concert*
(4/92) (DG) ① [3] **431 747-2GC3**
R. Woodward *Concert*   (10/92) (ETCE) ① **KTC1126**
Sonata for Piano No. 7 in F sharp, 'White Mass', Op. 64 (1911)
R. Pöntinen *Concert*   (9/85) (BIS) ① **BIS-CD276**
Vladimir Ashkenazy *Concert*
(1/90) (DECC) ① [2] **425 579-2DM2**
H. Austbø *Concert*   (5/90) (SIMA) ① **PSC1055**
Boris Berman *Concert*   (6/91) (MUSI) ① **MACD-621**
R. Szidon *Concert*
(4/92) (DG) ① [3] **431 747-2GC3**
D. Amato *Concert*   (10/92) (ALTA) ① **AIR-CD-9020**
Sonata for Piano No. 8 in A, Op. 66 (1912-13)
M. Rudy *Concert*   (2/89) (CALL) ① **CAL9692**
Vladimir Ashkenazy *Concert*
(1/90) (DECC) ① [2] **425 579-2DM2**
Boris Berman *Concert*   (6/91) (MUSI) ① **MACD-621**
R. Szidon *Concert*
(4/92) (DG) ① [3] **431 747-2GC3**
D. Amato *Concert*   (10/92) (ALTA) ① **AIR-CD-9020**
Sonata for Piano No. 9 in F, 'Black Mass', Op. 68 (1912-13)
M. Rudy *Concert*   (2/89) (CALL) ① **CAL9692**
R. Smith *Concert*   (8/89) (NIMB) ① **NI5187**
Vladimir Ashkenazy *Concert*
(1/90) (DECC) ① [2] **425 579-2DM2**
H. Austbø *Concert*   (5/90) (SIMA) ① **PSC1055**
Boris Berman *Concert*   (6/91) (MUSI) ① **MACD-621**
N. Demidenko *Concert*   (8/91) (CONI) ① **CDCF204**
G. Scott *Concert*   (10/91) (GAMU) ① **GAMCD520**
R. Szidon *Concert*
(4/92) (DG) ① [3] **431 747-2GC3**

G. Fergus-Thompson *Concert*
(4/92) (ASV) ① **CDDCA776**
D. Amato *Concert*   (10/92) (ALTA) ① **AIR-CD-9020**
V. Horowitz (pp1953) *Concert*
(1/93) (RCA) ① **GD60526**
P. Jablonski (r1992) *Concert*
(2/94) (DECC) ① **440 281-2DH**
V. Horowitz (pp1965) *Concert*
(7/94) (SONY) ① [3] **S3K53461**
Sonata for Piano No. 10 in C, Op. 70 (1913)
M. Rudy *Concert*   (2/89) (CALL) ① **CAL9692**
Vladimir Ashkenazy *Concert*
(1/90) (DECC) ① [2] **425 579-2DM2**
Boris Berman *Concert*   (6/91) (MUSI) ① **MACD-621**
R. Szidon *Concert*
(4/92) (DG) ① [3] **431 747-2GC3**
G. Fergus-Thompson *Concert*
(4/92) (ASV) ① **CDDCA776**
D. Amato *Concert*   (10/92) (ALTA) ① **AIR-CD-9020**
K.W. Paik *Concert*   (10/92) (DANT) ① **PSG9115**
R. Woodward *Concert*   (10/92) (ETCE) ① **KTC1126**
1. V. Horowitz (pp1966) *Concert*
(7/94) (SONY) ① [3] **S3K53461**
Sonate-fantaisie—piano (1886)
R. Szidon *Concert*
(4/92) (DG) ① [3] **431 747-2GC3**
Valse in A flat—piano, Op. 38 (1903)
V. Sofronitzky (pp1960) *Concert*
(8/95) (MELO) ① [2] **74321 25177-2**
V. Sofronitzky (pp1960) *Concert*
(8/95) (MELO) ① [11] **74321 25172-2(1)**
Vers la flamme—piano, Op. 72 (1914)
G. Fergus-Thompson *Concert*
(6/88) (KING) ① **KCLCD2001**
M. Rudy *Concert*   (2/89) (CALL) ① **CAL9692**
N. Demidenko *Concert*   (8/91) (CONI) ① **CDCF204**
D. Amato *Concert*   (10/92) (ALTA) ① **AIR-CD-9020**
R. Woodward *Concert*   (10/92) (ETCE) ① **KTC1126**
V. Horowitz (r1972) *Concert*
(7/94) (SONY) ① **SK53472**
S Richter *Concert*
(8/94) (PHIL) ① [2] **438 627-2PH2**

SCUDERI, Gaspare *(1889–1962)* Italy

Dormi pure—song
F. Valero, anon (r1903) *Concert*
(6/90) (SYMP) ① **SYMCD1073**

SCULTHORPE, Peter (Joshua) *(b 1929)* Australia

Earth Cry—orchestra (1986)
Sydney SO, S. Challender (r1989) *Concert*
(11/95) (ABCC) ① **8 77000 2**
Irkanda IV—solo violin, strings and percussion (1976)
Australian CO *Concert*
(6/88) (SOUT) ① **SCCD1016**
D. Hazelwood, Sydney SO, S. Challender (r1989)
Concert   (11/95) (ABCC) ① **8 77000 2**
Kakadu—orchestra (1988)
Sydney SO, S. Challender (1989) *Concert*
(11/95) (ABCC) ① **8 77000 2**
Lament for Strings (1976)
Australian CO *Concert*
(6/88) (SOUT) ① **SCCD1016**
Mangrove—orchestra (1979)
Sydney SO, S. Challender (1989) *Concert*
(11/95) (ABCC) ① **8 77000 2**
Nourlangie—guitar, strings and percussion (1989)
J. Williams, Australian CO, R. Hickox (r1990) *Concert*
(5/95) (SONY) ① **SK53361**
Port Essington—string orchestra (1977)
Australian CO *Concert*
(6/88) (SOUT) ① **SCCD1016**
Small Town—oboe and orchestra (1980) (orig part of 'The Fifth Continent', 1963)
G. Henderson, Sydney SO, S. Challender (r1989)
Concert   (11/95) (ABCC) ① **8 77000 2**
Sonata for Strings (1983)
Australian CO *Concert*
(6/88) (SOUT) ① **SCCD1016**

Lament—string sextet (1976, arr 1993) (arr cpsr from orchestral work)
Brodsky Qt, S. Monks, M. Scully (r1994) *Concert*
(10/94) (SILV) ① **SILKD6001**

From Kakadu—guitar (1993)
J. Williams (r1994) *Concert*
(5/95) (SONY) ① **SK53361**
Into the Dreaming—guitar (1994)
J. Williams (r1994) *Concert*
(5/95) (SONY) ① **SK53361**
Requiem for Cello Alone (1979)
P. Wispelwey (r1993) *Concert*
(7/95) (CHNN) ① **CCS7495**

SECCHI, Antonio *(1761–1833)* Italy

Love me or not—song (wds. T. Campion)
E. Caruso, orch. J. Pasternack (r1920) *Concert*
(7/91) (RCA) ① [12] **GD60495(6)**
E. Caruso, orch. J. Pasternack (r1920) *Concert*
(10/91) (PEAR) ① [3] **EVC4(2)**

SEDDON, Tim *(20th Cent)* United Kingdom

16—six pianos
Piano Circus *Concert*
(7/92) (ARGO) ① **433 522-2ZH**

SEDLAK, Wenzel *(1776–1851)* Bohemia

Harmoniemusik on Rossini's 'Il barbiere di Siviglia'—2 clarinets, 2 horns, 2 bassoons and double-bass (c1820)
Mozzafiato (r1992-93) *Concert*
(3/94) (SONY) ① **SK53965**

SEEGER, Ruth Crawford *(1901–1953)* USA

Andante for Strings (1931) (orchestral version of String Quartet slow movt)
Cleveland Orch, C. von Dohnányi (r1994) *Concert*
(12/95) (DECC) ① **443 776-2DH**

SEGAL, Misha *(20th Cent)* USA

Phantom of the Opera—film score (1989)
EXCERPTS: 1. Main Title; 2a. Don Juan Triumphant (Wds H. Schock); 2b. Travel Through Time; 3a. The Phantom's Lair; 3b. Hellbound (Freddy at the Opera); 3c. Maddie; 4a. Young Phantom's Piano Etude; 4b. Davis' Unpleasant Surprise; 4c. Carlotta's Head; 5a. You Are Him!; 5b. Into the Lair; 6a. The Phantom on Fire; 6b. The Phantom's Face; 7. Salon Talk (comp William Ashford); 8. The Jewel Song from Faust (Gounod); 9a. Music of the Knife; 9b. Killing Joseph; 10a. Graveyard Violin; 10b. Pact With the Devil; 10c. Richard Gets Killed; 11a. Ride to the Cemetery; 11b. The Cursed Manuscript; 11c. What's In the Closet?; 12a. The Wedding; 12b. The Intruder from Springwood; 12c. Christine's Decision; 12d. Mott Stalks the Phantom; 12e. Davis' Death; 12f. The Phantom's Fiery Death?; 13. Finale/End Title.
13. OST *Concert*   (5/93) (SILV) ① **SILVAD3003**

SEGERSTAM, Leif *(b 1944)* Finland

Symphony No. 11—piano, percussion and strings (1986) (orch diary sheet No 2: Sinf piccola No 11)
Finnish RSO, L. Segerstam (pp1989) *Symphony 14.*
(10/92) (BIS) ① **BIS-CD483**
Symphony No. 14—baritone and orchestra (1987) (orch diary sheet No 44: wds. J G Brown)
M. Samuelson, Swedish RSO, L. Segerstam (pp1989) *Symphony 11.*
(10/92) (BIS) ① **BIS-CD483**
Symphony No. 15, 'Ecliptic Thoughts' (1990)
Tampere PO, L. Segerstam *Waiting for ...*
(12/94) (KONT) ① **32125**

Waiting for...—orchestral diary sheet No. 30
(1990)
Avanti CO, L. Segerstam *Symphony 15*.
(12/94) (KONT) ① **32125**

SEGNI, Giulio *(1498–1561) Italy*

SECTION III: INSTRUMENTAL

Tiento
A. Lawrence-King (r1993) *Concert*
(2/94) (HYPE) ① **CDA66653**

SEGOVIA, Andrés *(1893–1987) Spain*

SECTION III: INSTRUMENTAL

Estudio No. 2, 'Remembranza'—guitar
W. Lendle *Concert* (7/92) (TELD) ① **9031-75864-2**
Estudio sin luz—guitar
W. Lendle *Concert* (7/92) (TELD) ① **9031-75864-2**

SEIBER, Mátyás (György) *(1905–1960) Hungary/England*

SECTION I: ORCHESTRAL

Concertino—clarinet and string orch (1951)
(arr. of Clarinet Quintet)
T. King, ECO, A. Litton *Concert*
(1/88) (HYPE) ① **CDA66215**

SECTION II: CHAMBER

Serenade for 2 clarinets, 2 bassoons and 2
horns (1925)
COE Wind Sols *Concert*
(4/90) (ASV) ① **CDCOE812**

SECTION IV: VOCAL AND CHORAL

4 French Folk Songs—1v and guitar
1. Réveillez-vous; 2. J'ai descendu; 3. Le Rossignol;
4. Marguerite, elle est malade.
P. Pears, J. Bream (r1963-4) *Concert*
(8/93) (RCA) ① **[28] 09026 61583-2(5)**
P. Pears, J. Bream (r1963-4) *Concert*
(9/94) (RCA) ① **09026 61601-2**
4 Hungarian Folksongs, 1936
Nos 1, 2, 3. Magdalen (Oxford) Coll Ch, G. Ives
Concert (11/92) (CNTO) ① **CRCD2366**

SEIFFERT, Anton *(1826–1873) Austria*

SECTION I: ORCHESTRAL

Kärntner Liedermarsch (1861) (Eng:
Carinthian songs)
Berlin Phil Wind Qnt, H. von Karajan (r1973) *Concert*
(5/94) (DG) ① **439 346-2GX2**

SEISMIT-DODA, Albano *(19th–20th Cents) Italy*

SECTION IV: VOCAL AND CHORAL

Notte lunare—song
B. Gigli, orch, B. Reibold (r1929) *Concert*
(5/90) (PEAR) ① **GEMMCD9367**
Querida—song
T. Ruffo, orch (r1921) *Concert*
(2/93) (PREI) ① **[3] 89303(2)**

SEITZ, Ernest *(1892–1978) Canada*

SECTION IV: VOCAL AND CHORAL

The world is waiting for the sunrise—song
(1919) (Wds. E. Lockhart)
F. Kreisler, C. Lamson (r1924: arr Kreisler) *Concert*
(9/93) (BIDD) ① **[2] LAB068/9**

SEIXAS, (José António) Carlos de *(1704–1742) Portugal*

Keybd sonatas numbered by Santiago Kostner

SECTION III: INSTRUMENTAL

80 Sonatas—keyboard
EXCERPTS: 1. C; 6. C; 11. C minor; 12. C minor;
13. B minor; 16. C minor; 21. D; 24. D minor; 27. D
minor; 29. D minor; 31. D minor; 32. E flat; 33. E flat;
34. E; 37. E minor; 42. F minor; 45. G; 46. G; 47. G;
50. G minor; 55. G minor; 56. G minor; 57. A; 71. A
minor; 77. B flat; 78. B flat; 79. B flat.

12, 24, 27, 32, 34, 47, 50, 57, 78. R. Woolley
Keyboard Sonatas II. (4/90) (AMON) ① **CD-SAR43**
25 Sonatas—keyboard
7. D minor; 14. F sharp minor.
7, 14. R. Woolley *Keyboard Sonatas I*.
(4/90) (AMON) ① **CD-SAR43**

SELLE, Thomas *(1599–1663) Germany*

SECTION IV: VOCAL AND CHORAL

Es begab sich aber zu der Zeit—oratorio
G. de Reyghere, G. de Mey, Capella Ricercar,
Ricercar Consort (r1989) *Concert*
(5/90) (RICE) ① **RIC060048**

SELMA Y SALAVERDE, Bartolomé de *(c1585–after 1638) Spain*

SECTION II: CHAMBER

Canzon ottavo—soprano e basso
Newberry Consort, M. Springfels *Concert*
(7/92) (HARM) ① **HMU90 7022**
Canzon prima—soprano and continuo
Newberry Consort, M. Springfels *Concert*
(7/92) (HARM) ① **HMU90 7022**
Canzon prima a due
Newberry Consort, M. Springfels *Concert*
(7/92) (HARM) ① **HMU90 7022**
Canzon terza
Newberry Consort, M. Springfels *Concert*
(7/92) (HARM) ① **HMU90 7022**
Primo libro de canzoni, fantasie and correnti
da suonnare—1-4 instruments and continuo
(pub 1638)
1. Vestiva i colli; 2. Canzon a due XI; 3. Canzon a
due XIII; 4. Corrente I-II a 2; 5a. Fantasia sobre al
'Canto del Cabellero'; 5b. Fantasia ex D.
5a Romanesca (r1991-2) *Concert*
(11/94) (GLOS) ① **GCD920201**
Susanna passeggiata—1 instrument &
continuo
Romanesca (r1991-2) *Concert*
(11/94) (GLOS) ① **GCD920201**

SENAILLÉ, Jean Baptiste *(1687–1730) France*

SECTION II: CHAMBER

Premier livre de sonates—violin and
continuo (pub 1710)
1. D minor; 5. D minor; 5a. Allegro spiritoso; 6. G
minor; 8. A.
5a M. Kliegel, R. Havenith (arr vc/pf) *Concert*
(9/92) (MARC) ① **8 223403**

SEPPILLI, Armando *(1860–1931) Italy*

SECTION IV: VOCAL AND CHORAL

Little Dorry—song
A. Galli-Curci, orch, J. Pasternack (r1917) *Concert*
(3/94) (ROMO) ① **[2] 81003-2**

SEREBRIER, José *(b 1938) Uruguay*

SECTION I: ORCHESTRAL

Momento psicologico—violin and orchestra
(1957)
M. Guttman, RPO, J. Serebrier *Concert*
(5/92) (ASV) ① **CDDCA785**
Poema elegiaca—violin and orchestra
(1958)
M. Guttman, RPO, J. Serebrier *Concert*
(5/92) (ASV) ① **CDDCA785**
Winter Concerto—violin and orchestra
(1991)
M. Guttman, RPO, J. Serebrier *Concert*
(10/93) (ASV) ① **CDDCA855**

SERLY, Tibor *(1901–1978) USA*

SECTION I: ORCHESTRAL

Concerto for Viola and Orchestra (1929)
R. Golani, Budapest SO, A. Ligeti *Concert*
(2/91) (CONI) ① **CDCF189**
Rhapsody for Viola and Orchestra (1948)
R. Golani, Budapest SO, A. Ligeti *Concert*
(2/91) (CONI) ① **CDCF189**

SERMISY, Claudin de *(c1490–1562) France*

SECTION IV: VOCAL AND CHORAL

Je ne menge point de porc—chanson: 4vv
(1538)
C. Janequin Ens, D. Visse (r1994) *Concert*
(5/95) (HARM) ① **HMC90 1453**
La, la Maistre Pierre—chanson (4vv)
Scholars (r1993) *Concert*
(2/95) (NAXO) ① **8 550880**
Las, je m'y plains, mauldicte soit
fortune—chanson (4vv)
C. Janequin Ens, D. Visse (r1994) *Concert*
(5/95) (HARM) ① **HMC90 1453**
Tant que vivray en eage florissant—chanson
(4vv) (Wds. Marot)
Scholars (r1993) *Concert*
(2/95) (NAXO) ① **8 550880**
Baltimore Consort (r1992; arr Baltimore Consort)
Concert (4/95) (DORI) ① **DOR90177**
Venez, regrets—chanson
Scholars (r1993) *Concert*
(2/95) (NAXO) ① **8 550880**
Vien tost—chanson: 4vv
C. Janequin Ens, D. Visse (r1994) *Concert*
(5/95) (HARM) ① **HMC90 1453**

SEROV, Alexander Nikolayevich *(1820–1871) Russia*

SECTION V: STAGE WORKS

Judith—opera: 5 acts (1863—St Peterburg)
(Lib. cpsr, after Bible)
Cease your grumbling L. Sibiriakov, orch (r1913)
Concert (3/95) (NIMB) ① **NI7865**
Holofernes war song V. Sharonov, anon (r1901)
Concert
(6/93) (PEAR) ① **[3] GEMMCDS9001/3(1)**
I shall don my robe of byssus N. Ermolenko-
Yuzhina, orch (r1909) *Concert*
(6/93) (PEAR) ① **[3] GEMMCDS9001/3(2)**
The Power of Evil—opera: 5 acts (1871—St
Petersburg) (cpted Soloy'nov and Serova)
Merry Shrovetide F. Chaliapin, Paris Russian Op
Chor, Balalaika Orch, O. Tchernoyarov (r1931)
Concert (12/89) (PEAR) ① **GEMMCD9314**

SERRA, Eric *(20th Cent) France*

SECTION V: STAGE WORKS

The Big Blue—film score (1988)
EXCERPTS: 1. Overture.
1. OST (1988) *Concert* (9/95) (VIR2) ① **CDV2774**

SERRANO (SIMÉON), José *(1873–1941) Spain*

SECTION V: STAGE WORKS

La Alegría del batallón—zarzuela
(1907—Madrid) (Lib. Amiches and Quintana)
A una gitana preciosa C. Supervia, orch, P. Godes
(r1932) *Concert* (3/93) (NIMB) ① **[2] NI7836/7**
Canción del soldado A. Cortis, orch (r1925) *Concert*
(3/94) (NIMB) ① **NI7850**
La Canción del Olvido—zarzuela: 1 act
(1916—Valencia) (Lib. F. Romero & G.
Fernández Shaw)
Canción de Marinella Y. Menuhin, L. Persinger (arr
Persinger: r1929) *Concert*
(4/91) (BIDD) ① **LAB031**
Junto al puente de la peña P. Domingo, Madrid SO,
M. Moreno-Buendia (r1987) *Concert*
(1/89) (EMI) ① **CDC 7 49148-2**
Los Claveles—zarzuela: 1 act
(1929—Madrid) (Lib. L. Fernández de Sevilla &
A. C. Carreño)
Romance de Rosa G. Sanchez, Madrid SO, E. G.
Asensio (pp1991) *Concert*
(11/92) (CARL) ① **MCD45**
La Dolorosa—zarzuela: 2 acts
(1930—Madrid) (Lib. Lorente)
Relato de Rafael J. Carreras, ECO, E. Ricci (r1994)
Concert (3/93) (ERAT) ① **4509-95789-2**
El Mal de Amores—zarzuela (Lib. S. & J.
Alvarez Quintero)
Canción de la gitanita C. Supervia, orch, P. Godes
(r1932) *Concert* (3/93) (NIMB) ① **[2] NI7836/7**
El Trust de los Tenorios—zarzuela
EXCERPTS: 1. Te quiero, morena; 2. Jota.
Española J. Schmidt, orch (r1930) *Concert*
(4/90) (EMI) ① **CDM7 69478-2**

1. J. Carreras, ECO, E. Ricci (r1994) *Concert*
(2/95) (ERAT) ① **4509-95789-2**

SESSIONS, Roger (Huntington) (1896–1985) USA

SECTION I: ORCHESTRAL

Concerto for Orchestra (1981)
Boston SO, S. Ozawa (r1982) *Panufnik: Sinfonia Votiva.* (7/89) (HYPE) ① **CDA66050**

Rhapsody for Orchestra (1970)
Columbus SO, C. Badea *Concert*
(10/87) (NEW) ① **NW345-2**

Symphony No. 2 (1946)
San Francisco SO, H. Blomstedt (r1993) *Concert*
(7/94) (DECC) ① **443 376-2DH**

Symphony No. 4 (1958)
Columbus SO, C. Badea *Concert*
(10/87) (NEW) ① **NW345-2**

Symphony No. 5 (1964)
Columbus SO, C. Badea *Concert*
(10/87) (NEW) ① **NW345-2**

SECTION II: CHAMBER

Canons to the memory of Stravinsky—string quartet (1971)
Group for Contemporary Music (r1992) *Concert*
(2/95) (KOCH) ① **37113-2**

Quintet—two violins, two violas and cello (1958)
Group for Contemporary Music (r1992) *Concert*
(2/95) (KOCH) ① **37113-2**

String Quartet in E minor (1938)
Group for Contemporary Music (r1992) *Concert*
(2/95) (KOCH) ① **37113-2**

SECTION III: INSTRUMENTAL

Pages From a Diary, 'From My Diary'—piano (1937-39)
B.D. Salwen *Concert* (12/92) (KOCH) ① **37106-2**

Piano Sonata No. 3 (1964-65)
B.D. Salwen *Concert* (12/92) (KOCH) ① **37106-2**

5 Pieces—piano (1974-75)
B.D. Salwen *Concert* (12/92) (KOCH) ① **37106-2**

6 Pieces for Cello (1966)
EXCERPTS: 1. Prelude (Allegro energico); 2. Dialogue (Andante); 3. Scherzo (Allegro); 4. Berceuse (Lento e dolce); 5. Capriccio (Con fantasia); 6. Epilogue (Adagio molto).
J. Gordon (r1992) *Concert*
(2/95) (KOCH) ① **37113-2**
P. Wispelwey (r1993) *Concert*
(7/95) (CHNN) ① **CCS7495**

Sonata for Piano No. 1 (1927-30)
B.D. Salwen *Concert* (12/92) (KOCH) ① **37106-2**

Sonata for Piano No. 2 (1946)
B.D. Salwen *Concert* (12/92) (KOCH) ① **37106-2**
P. Lawson (r1991) *Concert*
(2/94) (VIRG) ① **VC7 59316-2**

Waltz—piano (1977-78)
B.D. Salwen *Concert* (12/92) (KOCH) ① **37106-2**

SECTION IV: VOCAL AND CHORAL

When lilacs last in the dooryard bloom'd—cantata (Wds. W. Whitman)
E. Hinds, F. Quivar, D. Cossa, Tanglewood Fest Chor, Boston SO, S. Ozawa
(4/89) (NEW) ① **NW296-2**

SÉVERAC, (Marie-Joseph-Alexandre) Déodat de (1873–1921) France

SECTION III: INSTRUMENTAL

En vacances—small romantic pieces (1912)
1. Invocation á Schumann; 2. Les careeses de grand-maman; 3. Les petites voisnes en visite; 4. Toto déguisé en suisse d'église; 5. Mimi se déguise en marquise; 6. Rondo dands le parc; 7. Où l'on entend une vieille boîte á musique; 8. Valse romantique.
P. Katin (1990) *Concert* (7/93) (SIMA) ① **PSC1067**
8. L. Laskine (r1975; arr hp) *Concert*
(12/93) (ERAT) ① **4509-92131-2**

SECTION IV: VOCAL AND CHORAL

À l'aube dans la montagne—mélodie (1903) (Wds. cpsr)
M. Command, J. Bernier *Concert*
(7/89) (SCAL) ① **ARI142**

Aubade—Catalan song (Wds. trans M. Navarre)
G. Bacquier, J. Bernier *Concert*
(7/89) (SCAL) ① **ARI142**

La **Chanson de Blaisine—mélodie (1900)** (Wds. M. Magre)
M. Command, J. Bernier *Concert*
(7/89) (SCAL) ① **ARI142**

Chanson de Jacques—mélodie (Wds. M. Magre)
G. Bacquier, J. Bernier *Concert*
(7/89) (SCAL) ① **ARI142**

Chanson de la nuit durable—mélodie (1910) (Wds. Mme Espinasse-Mongenet)
G. Bacquier, J. Bernier *Concert*
(7/89) (SCAL) ① **ARI142**

Chanson pour le petit cheval—mélodie (Wds.P. Estieu)
G. Bacquier, J. Bernier *Concert*
(7/89) (SCAL) ① **ARI142**
C. Panzéra, M. Panzéra-Baillot (r1926) *Concert*
(3/93) (EMI) ① **CDH7 64254-2**

Chansons du XVIII Century—Collection I (coll and harmonised Séverac)
1. Chansons des bateliers de St-Cloud; 2. Musette; 3. Le beau Daphnis; 4. L'amour en cage; 5. Le vin de Catherine; 6. Nicodeme; 7. L'homme n'est jamais content; 8. La fileuse; 9. Cecilia.
M. Command, J. Bernier *Concert*
(7/89) (SCAL) ① **ARI143**

Chansons du XVIII Century—Collection II (coll and harmonised Séverac)
1. Ba be bi bo bu; 2. R'muons le cotillon; 3. Zon, zon, zon; 4. Le viel epoux; 5. Pour le jour de Rols; 6. Le berger indiscret; 7. Prière du matin; 8. V'là c'que c'est qu' d'aller au bois; 9. Ne derangez pas le monde; 10. Offrande.
O. Laure, J. Bernier *Vieilles chansons de France.*
(7/89) (SCAL) ① **ARI144**

Chant de Noël—mélodie (Wds. Languedocian theme by Goudouli)
G. Bacquier, J. Bernier *Concert*
(7/89) (SCAL) ① **ARI142**

Chevrier—mélodie (1898) (Wds.P. Rey)
G. Bacquier, J. Bernier *Concert*
(7/89) (SCAL) ① **ARI143**

Le **Ciel est, par-dessus le toit—mélodie (1897)** (Wds. P. Verlaine)
M. Command, J. Bernier *Concert*
(7/89) (SCAL) ① **ARI142**

Dans les prisons de Nantes (coll and harmonised Séverac)
G. Bacquier, J. Bernier *Concert*
(7/89) (SCAL) ① **ARI143**

L' **Éveil de Pâques—mélodie (1899)** (Wds. Verhaeren)
M. Command, J. Bernier *Concert*
(7/89) (SCAL) ① **ARI142**

Hiboux—mélodie (1898) (Wds. Baudelaire)
G. Bacquier, J. Bernier *Concert*
(7/89) (SCAL) ① **ARI142**

Les **Huns—chanson de guerre** (Wds. P. Rey)
G. Bacquier, J. Bernier *Concert*
(7/89) (SCAL) ① **ARI143**

L' **Infidèle—mélodie (1900)** (Wds.M. Maeterlinck)
M. Command, J. Bernier *Concert*
(7/89) (SCAL) ① **ARI142**

Jean des Grignottes—chanson de chasse (coll and harmonised Séverac)
G. Bacquier, J. Bernier *Concert*
(7/89) (SCAL) ① **ARI143**

Ma poupée chérie—mélodie (Wds. cpsr)
G. Bacquier, J. Bernier *Concert*
(7/89) (SCAL) ① **ARI142**
M. Angelici, M. Fauré (r1950) *Concert*
(4/92) (EMI) ① **[7] CHS7 69741-2(3)**

La **Mort y la donzella—Catalan song setting** (coll and harmonised Séverac)
G. Bacquier, J. Bernier *Concert*
(7/89) (SCAL) ① **ARI143**

Paysages tristes—mélodie (Wds. P. Verlaine)
G. Bacquier, J. Bernier *Concert*
(7/89) (SCAL) ① **ARI142**

Phillis—mélodie (Wds. Anon 18th cent)
G. Bacquier, J. Bernier *Concert*
(7/89) (SCAL) ① **ARI142**

Un **Rêve—mélodie (1902)** (Wds. E. Poe, trans S. Mallarmé)
G. Bacquier, J. Bernier *Concert*
(7/89) (SCAL) ① **ARI142**

Ritournelle—mélodie (before 1898) (Wds. F. Coppée)
G. Bacquier, J. Bernier *Concert*
(7/89) (SCAL) ① **ARI143**

Tantum ergo—motet (1920)
Westminster Cath Ch, J. O'Donnell (r1993) *Concert*
(3/94) (HYPE) ① **CDA66669**

Oxford Schola Cantorum, J. Summerly (r1993) *Concert* (9/94) (NAXO) ① **8 550765**

Temps de neige—mélodie (Wds.H. Gauthier-Villars)
G. Bacquier, J. Bernier *Concert*
(7/89) (SCAL) ① **ARI142**

Les **Vieilles chansons de France** (coll and harmonised Séverac)
1. La beureuse; 2. La ronde; 3. L'auvergnat; 4. Le manchon; 5. Ma mère, il me tuera; 6. La semaine de la mariée; 7. Les gens qui sont jeunes; 8. Le roi a fait battre tambour; 9. Le boudoir d'Aspasie; 10. Les belles manières.
M. Command, J. Bernier *Chansons du XVIII Cent II.*
(7/89) (SCAL) ① **ARI144**

SEYMER, William (1890–1964) Sweden

SECTION III: INSTRUMENTAL

Solöga
R. Pöntinen *Concert* (11/85) (BIS) ① **BIS-CD300**

SGAMBATI, Giovanni (1841–1914) Italy

SECTION II: CHAMBER

Serenata napoletana, Op. 24/2
J. Kubelík, anon (r1910) *Concert*
(6/91) (BIDD) ① **[2] LAB033/4**
P. Casals, N. Mednikoff (arr Bouman: r1928) *Concert*
(10/91) (BIDD) ① **LAB017**
J. Heifetz, B. Smith (r1954) *Concert*
(11/94) (RCA) ① **[65] 09026 61778-2(31)**

SHARP, Elliott (b 1951) USA

SECTION II: CHAMBER

Digital—string quartet (1986)
Kronos Qt (r1992) *Concert*
(8/93) (NONE) ① **7559-79310-2**

SHARPE, Trevor (20th cent) England

SECTION I: ORCHESTRAL

The **Music of George Gershwin—potpourri: brass band**
Black Dyke Mills Band, R. Newsome (1977) *Concert*
(1/94) (CHAN) ① **CHAN4528**

SHCHEDRIN, Rodion Konstantinovich (b 1932) USSR

SECTION I: ORCHESTRAL

The **Frescoes of Dionysius—tone-poem**
Bolshoi Th Sols Ens, A. Lazarev *Carmen Ballet.*
(8/87) (OLYM) ① **OCD108**

Music for the City of Cöthen—orchestra (1984)
Moscow Virtuosi, V. Spivakov (r1990) *Concert*
(5/93) (RCA) ① **09026 60466-2**

Stalin Cocktail—harpsichord and string orchestra (1992)
Moscow Virtuosi, V. Spivakov (r1993) *Concert*
(12/95) (RCA) ① **09026 58061-2**

SECTION III: INSTRUMENTAL

24 Preludes and Fugues—piano (1963-70)
1. C; 2. A minor; 3. G; 4. E minor; 5. D; 6. B minor; 7. A; 8. F sharp minor; 9. E; 10. C sharp minor; 11. B; 12. G sharp minor; 13. G flat; 14. E flat minor; 15. D flat; 16. B flat minor; 17. A flat; 18. F minor; 19. E flat; 20. C minor; 21. B flat; 22. G minor; 23. F; 24. D minor.
M. McLachlan (r1994) *Preludes and Fugues (1972).*
(3/95) (OLYM) ① **OCD438**

25 Preludes and Fugues—piano (1972)
1. Two-part Invention; 2. Canon at the octave; 3. Ostinato; 4. Fughetta; 5. Canonic Imitation; 6. Collateral parts; 7. Mirror canon; 8. Recitative and crab motion; 9. Étude (Inversion); 10. Chaconne; 11. Counterpoint; 12. Toccata collage; 13. Three-part invention; 14. Canon in augmentation; 15. Motet (double canon); 16. Basso ostinato; 17. Perpetual canon; 18. Fugue; 19. Triple counterpoint; 20. Canon on cantus firmus; 21. Passacaglia; 22. Thee-part canon; 23. Double fugue; 24. The horizontal and the vertical; 25. Polyphonic mosaic.
M. McLachlan (r1994) *Preludes and Fugues (1963-70).* (3/95) (OLYM) ① **[2] OCD438**

SECTION V: STAGE WORKS

Anna Karenina (Lyric Scenes)—ballet: 3 acts (1972) (after novel by Tolstoy)
EXCERPTS: 1. Prologue: Train Station of Nikolaevsk Railroad. ACT 1: 2. Cotillon Ball; 3. Mazurka (Anna's Solo); 4. Dance of the Anna and the Four Cavaliers; 5. Bologoya. Blizzard; 6. St Petersburg. Salon of the Duchess Betty Tverskaya; 7. Karenin's Thoughts; 8. Argument of Karenin and Anna; 9. Vronsky's Dream; 10. Anna and Vronsky. ACT 2: 11. Horse Race; 12. Start of the Riders. Vronsky falls from his horse; 13. Anna's Double Life; 14. Illness and Dream; 15. Escape to Italy. ACT 3: 16. Introduction. Duet of Anna and Vronsky in Italy; 17. Ceremonial in Palace; 18. Meeting of Anna and her Son and Anna's Monologue; 19. Scene at the Opera; 20. Last Duo with Vronsky; 21. Death of Anna.
1, 11. M. Pletnev (r1978: arr Pletnev) Concert
(8/95) (MELO) ① [11] 74321 25172-2(2)
1, 11. M. Pletnev (r1978; arr Pletnev) Concert
(8/95) (MELO) ① 74321 25181-2
The **Carmen Ballet—ballet (1968)** (music arr/adptd from Bizet's opera)
Moscow Virtuosi CO, Armenian St Chbr Ens, Armenian St Perc Ens, V. Spivakov Frescoes of Dionysius. (8/87) (OLYM) ① OCD108
Kroumata Perc Ens, Helsingborg SO, H. Farberman (r1987) Farberman: Jazz Drum Concerto.
(3/89) (BIS) ① BIS-CD382

SHELLEY, Harry Rowe (1858–1947) USA

SECTION IV: VOCAL AND CHORAL

Love's sorrow—song
R. Ponselle, orch, R. Bourdon (r1924) Concert
(11/94) (ROMO) ① [2] 81006-2

SHENG, Bright (b 1955) China/USA

SECTION I: ORCHESTRAL

H'un (Lacerations): In memoriam 1966-76 (1987)
New York Chbr SO, G. Schwarz Concert
(9/92) (NEW) ① 80407-2

SECTION III: INSTRUMENTAL

My song—suite: piano (1988)
P. Serkin Concert (9/92) (NEW) ① 80407-2
The **stream flows—violin (1990)**
L. Lin Concert (9/92) (NEW) ① 80407-2

SECTION IV: VOCAL AND CHORAL

3 Chinese Love Songs—voice, viola and piano (1988)
1. Blue flower; 2. At the hillside where horse are running; 3. The stream flows.
L. Saffer, P. Neubauer, B. Sheng Concert
(9/92) (NEW) ① 80407-2
2 Folk Songs from Chinai—choir a cappella (1990)
1. Morningstar Lily; 2. A Pair of Mules.
J. Oliver Chorale, J. Oliver (r1992) Concert
(5/95) (KOCH) ① 37178-2

SHEPHARD, Richard (b 1949) England

SECTION IV: VOCAL AND CHORAL

And when the builders—anthem (1980) (Wds. Bible)
Llandaff Cath Ch, M. Smith, M. Hoeg (r1994) Concert
(10/95) (PRIO) ① PRCD510
Ye Choirs of New Jerusalem—Easter anthem (1985)
Llandaff Cath Ch, M. Smith, M. Hoeg (r1994) Concert
(10/95) (PRIO) ① PRCD510

SHEPPARD, John (c1515–?1559/60) England

SECTION IV: VOCAL AND CHORAL

Aeterne Rex altissime—motet: 5vv
The Sixteen, H. Christophers Concert
(8/93) (HYPE) ① CDA66603
Audivi vocem de caelo—motet: 4vv
The Sixteen, H. Christophers Concert
(12/92) (HYPE) ① CDA66570

Ave maris stella—motet
The Sixteen, H. Christophers Concert
(12/92) (HYPE) ① CDA66418
Beata nobis gaudia—motet: 7vv
The Sixteen, H. Christophers Concert
(12/92) (HYPE) ① CDA66570
Christe redemptor omnium—hymn: 5vv
Tallis Scholars, P. Phillips Concert
(1/90) (GIME) ① CDGIM016
Deum transisset Sabbatum I—motet: 6vv
The Sixteen, H. Christophers Concert
(12/92) (HYPE) ① CDA66570
Deus tuorum militum II—hymn: 5vv (also attrib Tallis)
The Sixteen, H. Christophers Concert
(12/92) (HYPE) ① CDA66418
Dum transisset Sabbatum II—motet: 6vv
The Sixteen, H. Christophers Concert
(8/93) (HYPE) ① CDA66603
Filiae Jerusalem venite—repsond: 6vv
The Sixteen, H. Christophers Concert
(2/89) (HYPE) ① CDA66259
Gaude, gaude, gaude Maria virgo—motet: 6vv
The Sixteen, H. Christophers Concert
(12/92) (HYPE) ① CDA66570
Clerkes of Oxenford, D. Wulstan (r1974: trans D Wulsten & S Dunkley) Concert
(3/94) (CFP) ① CD-CFP4638
Gaude virgo Christiphera—antiphon: 6vv
Clerkes of Oxenford, D. Wulstan Concert
(5/90) (PROU) ① PROUCD126
Haec dies—gradual: 6vv
The Sixteen, H. Christophers Concert
(2/89) (HYPE) ① CDA66259
Hostis Herodes impie—motet: 6vv
The Sixteen, H. Christophers Concert
(8/93) (HYPE) ① CDA66603
Impetum fecerunt unanimes—motet: 5vv
The Sixteen, H. Christophers Concert
(12/92) (HYPE) ① CDA66570
In manus tuas I—respond: 4vv
The Sixteen, H. Christophers Concert
(2/89) (HYPE) ① CDA66259
Tallis Scholars, P. Phillips Concert
(1/90) (GIME) ① CDGIM016
Cambridge Sngrs, J. Rutter Concert
(4/92) (CLLE) ① COLCD113
Clerkes of Oxenford, D. Wulstan (r1974: trans D Wulsten & S Dunkley) Concert
(3/94) (CFP) ① CD-CFP4638
In manus tuas II—respond: 4vv
Tallis Scholars, P. Phillips Concert
(1/90) (GIME) ① CDGIM016
Clerkes of Oxenford, D. Wulstan Concert
(5/90) (PROU) ① PROUCD126
The Sixteen, H. Christophers Concert
(12/92) (HYPE) ① CDA66570
In manus tuas III—respond: 3vv
Tallis Scholars, P. Phillips Concert
(1/90) (GIME) ① CDGIM016
The Sixteen, H. Christophers Concert
(8/93) (HYPE) ① CDA66603
In pace in idipsum—respond: 4vv
The Sixteen, H. Christophers Concert
(2/89) (HYPE) ① CDA66259
Clerkes of Oxenford, D. Wulstan (r1974: trans D Wulsten & S Dunkley) Concert
(3/94) (CFP) ① CD-CFP4638
Jesu salvator seculi, redemptis—hymn: 5vv
The Sixteen, H. Christophers Concert
(12/92) (HYPE) ① CDA66418
Jesu salvator seculi, verbum—motet
The Sixteen, H. Christophers Concert
(12/92) (HYPE) ① CDA66418
Justi in perpetuum vivent—respond: 5vv
The Sixteen, H. Christophers Concert
(2/89) (HYPE) ① CDA66259
Laudem dicite Deo—respond: 5vv
The Sixteen, H. Christophers Concert
(2/89) (HYPE) ① CDA66259
Clerkes of Oxenford, D. Wulstan (r1974: trans D Wulsten & S Dunkley) Concert
(3/94) (CFP) ① CD-CFP4638
Libera nos, salva nos I—antiphon: 7vv
The Sixteen, H. Christophers Concert
(2/89) (HYPE) ① CDA66259
Clerkes of Oxenford, D. Wulstan Concert
(5/90) (PROU) ① PROUCD126
Libera nos, salva nos II—antiphon: 7vv
Clerkes of Oxenford, D. Wulstan Concert
(5/90) (PROU) ① PROUCD126
The Sixteen, H. Christophers Concert
(12/92) (HYPE) ① CDA66570

The **Lord's Prayer—5vv**
Magdalen Oxford Coll Ch, J. Harper Concert
(11/91) (ABBE) ① CDCA901
Mass, '(The) Western Wynde'—4vv
Angus Smith, St John's College Ch, I. Shaw, G. Guest Concert (12/89) (ASV) ① CDGAU114
The Sixteen, H. Christophers Concert
(8/93) (HYPE) ① CDA66603
Tallis Scholars, P. Phillips Concert
(9/93) (GIME) ① CDGIM027
Media vita—antiphon: 6vv
Tallis Scholars, P. Phillips Concert
(1/90) (GIME) ① CDGIM016
Missa 'Cantate'—6vv
The Sixteen, H. Christophers Concert
(12/92) (HYPE) ① CDA66418
Paschal Kyrie—6vv
The Sixteen, H. Christophers Concert
(2/89) (HYPE) ① CDA66259
Reges Tharsis et insulae—respond: 6vv
The Sixteen, H. Christophers Concert
(2/89) (HYPE) ① CDA66259
Tallis Scholars, P. Phillips Concert
(1/90) (GIME) ① CDGIM016
Clerkes of Oxenford, D. Wulstan Concert
(5/90) (PROU) ① PROUCD126
Sacris solemniis iuncta sit gaudia—hymn: 8vv
Tallis Scholars, P. Phillips Concert
(1/90) (GIME) ① CDGIM016
The Sixteen, H. Christophers Concert
(12/92) (HYPE) ① CDA66570
Salvator mundi Domine—6vv
The Sixteen, H. Christophers Concert
(12/92) (HYPE) ① CDA66418
Sancte Dei preciose—motet: 5vv
The Sixteen, H. Christophers Concert
(12/92) (HYPE) ① CDA66570
Second Service
1. Venite; 2. Te deum; 3. Benedictus; 4. Credo; 5. Magnificat; 6. Nunc dimittis.
5, 6. The Sixteen, H. Christophers Concert
(8/93) (HYPE) ① CDA66603
Spiritus sanctus—respond: 5vv
The Sixteen, H. Christophers Concert
(2/89) (HYPE) ① CDA66259
Spiritus Sanctus procedens II—motet: 6vv
The Sixteen, H. Christophers Concert
(12/92) (HYPE) ① CDA66570
Te Deum laudamus—motet: 6vv
The Sixteen, H. Christophers Concert
(8/93) (HYPE) ① CDA66603
Vaine, vaine, vaine—song
Theatre Of Voices, P. Hillier (r1992) Concert
(9/94) (ECM) ① 439 172-2
Verbum caro factum est—respond: 6vv
The Sixteen, H. Christophers Concert
(2/89) (HYPE) ① CDA66259
Angus Smith, St John's College Ch, G. Guest Concert (12/89) (ASV) ① CDGAU114
Tallis Scholars, P. Phillips Concert
(1/90) (GIME) ① CDGIM016
Cambridge Taverner Ch, O. Rees (r1993) Concert
(12/93) (PAST) ① 3589
Clerkes of Oxenford, D. Wulstan (r1974: trans D Wulsten & S Dunkley) Concert
(3/94) (CFP) ① CD-CFP4638

SHEREMETIEV, Boris (Sergeyevich) (1822–1906) Russia

SECTION IV: VOCAL AND CHORAL

I loved you—Russian song
N. Ghiaurov, P. Dokovska (r1993) Concert
(1/95) (RCA) ① 09026 62501-2

SHERMAN, Kim D. (b 1954) USA

SECTION IV: VOCAL AND CHORAL

Graveside—chorus a cappella (1992)
Musica Sacra, R. Westenburg (r1993) Concert
(12/93) (CATA) ① 09026 61822-2

SHERMAN, Richard M. & Robert B. (b 1928 & 1925) USA

SECTION V: STAGE WORKS

The **Jungle Book—musical film (1967)**
EXCERPTS: 1. Trust in Me; 2. Colonel Haiti's March; 3. Bare Necessities (music & lyrics Terry Gilikyson); 4. I Wanna Be Like You; 5. That's What Friends Are For; 6. My Own Home.

4. LAGQ (r1994-5; arr Fraser) *Concert* (12/95) (DELO) Ⓓ **DE3186**

Mary Poppins—musical film (1964) (Music & Lyrics Sherman & Sherman)

EXCERPTS: 1. Overture; 2. The Perfect Nanny; 3. Sister Suffragette; 4. The Life I Lead; 5. A Spoonful of Sugar; 6. Pavement Artists (Chim Chim Cheree); 7. Jolly Holiday; 8. Super-cali-fragil-istic-expi-ali-docius; 9. Stay Awake; 10. I Love to Laugh; 11. A British Bank; 12. Feed the Birds; 13. Fidelity Fiduciary Bank; 14. Chim Chim Cheree; 15. Step in Time; 16. A Man Has Dreams; 17. Let's Go Fly a Kite.

12. Shanghai Qt (r1994-5; arr Fraser) *Concert* (12/95) (DELO) Ⓓ **DE3186**

Winnie the Pooh and the Blustery Day—musical film (1967)

EXCERPTS: 1. Winnie the Pooh.

1. E. Zukerman, Shanghai Qt (r1994-5; arr Fraser) *Concert* (12/95) (DELO) Ⓓ **DE3186**

SHERYNGHAM *(fl c1500)* *England*

SECTION IV: VOCAL AND CHORAL

A gentill Jhesu—carol (4vv)

The Sixteen, H. Christophers *Concert* (4/92) (COLL) Ⓓ **Coll1316-2**

SHIELD, William *(1748–1829)* *England*

SECTION IV: VOCAL AND CHORAL

Hope and Love—voice and piano/harp (pub 1796) (Wds. W. Pearse)

E. Kirkby, T. Roberts *Concert* (12/91) (HYPE) Ⓓ **CDA66497**

'Tis only no harm to know it, you know—song (pub 1796) (Wds. J. O'Keefe)

E. Kirkby, T. Roberts *Concert* (12/91) (HYPE) Ⓓ **CDA66497**

Ye balmy breezes, gently blow—song (pub 1796) (Wds. J. Rannie)

R. Müller, F. Kelly *Concert* (12/91) (HYPE) Ⓓ **CDA66497**

SHINOHARA, Makoto *(b 1931)* *Japan*

SECTION III: INSTRUMENTAL

Fragmente—recorder (1968)

D. Laurin (r1993) *Concert* (8/94) (BIS) Ⓓ **BIS-CD655**

SHIRE, David *(b 1937)* *USA*

SECTION V: STAGE WORKS

2010: Odyssey Two—film score (1984)

EXCERPTS: 1. Finale.

1. Prague City PO, W. Motzing (r1993) *Concert* (8/94) (SILV) Ⓓ **FILMCD146**

SHORE, Howard *(b 1946)* *Canada*

SECTION V: STAGE WORKS

M. Butterfly—film score (1993) (includes music from Puccini's 'Madame Butterfly')

EXCERPTS: 1. M. Butterly; 2. Concubine; 3a. Entrance of Butterfly (Puccini); 3b. Drunken Beauty; 4. Dragonfly; 5. The Great Wall; 6. Even the Softest Skin; 7. Sha Jia Bang; 8a. Bonfire of the Vanities; 8b. Cultural Revolution; 9. He was the Perfect Father; 10. Are you my Butterfly?; 11. The Only Time I ever really existed; 12. What I loved was the Lie; 13. Everything has been destroyed; 14. Un bel dì (Puccini); 15. My Name is Rene Gallimard.

1, 2, 3a, 3b, 4-7, 8a, 8b, 9-15. OST, M. Couture, M.T. Uribe, Budapest Op Orch, A. Medveczky, RPO, LPO, H. Shore (r1992-3) (8/94) (VARE) Ⓓ **VSD5435**

SHORTALL, Harrington *(1895–?)* *USA*

SECTION II: CHAMBER

Fanfare for those who will not return—five trumpets (1942)

Wallace Collection (r1995) *Concert* (7/95) (LARG) Ⓓ [2] **Largo5130**

SHOSTAKOVICH, Dmitry (Dmitriyevich) *(1906–1975)* *USSR*

SECTION I: ORCHESTRAL

Ballet Suite No. 1 (1949)

SNO, N. Järvi *Concert* (9/89) (CHAN) Ⓓ **CHAN8730**

SNO, N. Järvi (r1988) *Concert* (5/95) (CHAN) Ⓓ [2] **CHAN7000/1**

Ballet Suite No. 2 (1951)

SNO, N. Järvi *Concert* (9/89) (CHAN) Ⓓ **CHAN8730**

SNO, N. Järvi (r1988) *Concert* (5/95) (CHAN) Ⓓ [2] **CHAN7000/1**

Ballet Suite No. 3 (1952)

SNO, N. Järvi *Concert* (9/89) (CHAN) Ⓓ **CHAN8730**

SNO, N. Järvi (r1988) *Concert* (5/95) (CHAN) Ⓓ [2] **CHAN7000/1**

Ballet Suite No. 4 (1953)

SNO, N. Järvi *Symphony 10.* (3/89) (CHAN) Ⓓ **CHAN8630**

SNO, N. Järvi (r1988) *Concert* (5/95) (CHAN) Ⓓ [2] **CHAN7000/1**

Ballet Suite No. 5, Op. 27a (1933) (arr from 'Bolt')

SNO, N. Järvi *Symphony 5.* (4/90) (CHAN) Ⓓ **CHAN8650**

SNO, N. Järvi (r1988) *Concert* (5/95) (CHAN) Ⓓ [2] **CHAN7000/1**

Chamber Symphony—chamber orchestra, Op. 83a (arr Barshai from String Quartet 4)

COE, R. Barshai *Symphony, Op.73a.* (8/92) (DG) Ⓓ **435 386-2GH**

Chamber Symphony, Op. 110a (1960) (arr Barshai from String Quartet 8)

Montreal I Musici, Y. Turovsky *Piano Concerto 1.* (4/85) (CHAN) Ⓓ **CHAN8357**

Moscow Virtuosi, V. Spivakov *Concert* (12/89) (RCA) Ⓓ **RD87947**

COE, R. Barshai (r1989) *Symphony for Strings.* (5/90) (DG) Ⓓ **429 229-2GH**

Zagreb Sols, T. Ninič *Concert* (11/92) (CARL) Ⓓ **PCD1000**

Kremlin CO, M. Rachlevsky *Concert* (3/93) (CLAV) Ⓓ **CD50-9115**

Helsinki PO, J. DePreist (r1993) *Symphony 5.* (12/94) (ONDI) Ⓓ **ODE817-2**

Chamber Symphony No. 2—chamber orchestra (arr V Milman from String Quartet 3)

Moscow Virtuosi, V. Spivakov (r1993) *Concert* (12/95) (RCA) Ⓓ **09026 68061-2**

Concerto for Cello and Orchestra No. 1 in E flat, Op. 107 (1959)

1. Allegretto; 2. Moderato; 3. Cadenza; 4. Allegro con moto.

R. Wallfisch, ECO, G. Simon (r1982) *Barber: Cello Concerto.* (2/85) (CHAN) Ⓓ **CHAN8322**

H. Schiff, BRSO, M. Shostakovich *Cello Concerto 2.* (10/85) (PHIL) Ⓓ **412 526-2PH**

M. Rostropovich, Philadelphia, E. Ormandy *Concert* (11/89) (SONY) Ⓓ **MPK44850**

N. Gutman, RPO, Y. Temirkanov *Cello Concerto 2.* (1/91) (RCA) Ⓓ **RD87918**

P. Fournier, SRO, J. Horenstein (pp1962) *Concert* (11/92) (CASC) Ⓓ **VEL2009**

M. Sádlo, Czech PO, K. Ančerl (r1968) *Symphony 5.* (8/93) (SUPR) Ⓓ **11 0676-2**

T. Thedéen, Malmö SO, J. DePreist (r1993) *Cello Concerto 2.* (7/94) (BIS) Ⓓ **BIS-CD626**

M. Maisky, LSO, M. Tilson Thomas (r1993) *Cello Concerto 2.* (4/95) (DG) Ⓓ **445 821-2GH**

Concerto for Cello and Orchestra No. 2 in G, Op. 126 (1966)

H. Schiff, BRSO, M. Shostakovich *Cello Concerto 1.* (10/85) (PHIL) Ⓓ **412 526-2PH**

N. Gutman, RPO, Y. Temirkanov *Cello Concerto 1.* (1/91) (RCA) Ⓓ **RD87918**

M. Rostropovich, Boston SO, S. Ozawa *Concert* (8/91) (DG) Ⓓ **431 475-2GGA**

T. Thedéen, Malmö SO, J. DePreist (r1992) *Cello Concerto 1.* (7/94) (BIS) Ⓓ **BIS-CD626**

M. Rostropovich, Boston SO, S. Ozawa *Concert* (10/94) (DG) Ⓓ [2] **437 952-2GX2**

M. Maisky, LSO, M. Tilson Thomas (r1993) *Cello Concerto 1.* (4/95) (DG) Ⓓ **445 821-2GH**

M. Rostropovich, Boston SO, S. Ozawa (r1975) *Symphony 5.* (9/95) (DG) Ⓓ **439 481-2GCL**

Concerto for Piano and Orchestra No 2 in F, Op. 102 (1957)

D. Shostakovich Jnr, Montreal I Musici, Montreal SO, M. Shostakovich *Symphony for Strings.* (7/86) (CHAN) Ⓓ **CHAN8443**

D. Alexeev, ECO, J. Maksymiuk *Concert* (1/89) (CFP) Ⓓ **CD-CFP4547**

L. Bernstein (pf/dir), NYPO *Concert* (11/89) (SONY) Ⓓ **MPK44850**

C. Ortiz, RPO, Vladimir Ashkenazy *Violin Concerto 1.* (8/90) (DECC) Ⓓ **425 793-2DH**

D. Shostakovich, FRNO, A. Cluytens (r1958) *Concert* (4/93) (EMI) Ⓓ **CDC7 54606-2**

E. Leonskaja, St Paul CO, H. Wolff (r1991) *Concert* (6/93) (TELD) Ⓓ **9031-73282-2**

L. Bernstein (pf/dir), NYPO (r1958) *Concert* (6/94) (SONY) Ⓓ **SMK47618**

D. Shostakovich, Moscow PO, S. Samosud (r1958) *Concert* (2/95) (RUSS) Ⓓ **RDCD15005**

Concerto for Piano, Trumpet and Strings in C minor, Op. 35 (1933)

C. Rosenberger, S. Burns, Los Angeles CO, G. Schwarz *Concert* (10/84) (DELO) Ⓓ **DE3021**

D. Shostakovich Jnr, J. Thompson, Montreal I Musici, M. Shostakovich *Chamber Symphony, Op. 110a.* (4/85) (CHAN) Ⓓ **CHAN8357**

D. Alexeev, P. Jones, ECO, J. Maksymiuk *Concert* (1/89) (CFP) Ⓓ **CD-CFP4547**

A. Previn, W. Vacchiano, NYPO, L. Bernstein *Concert* (11/89) (SONY) Ⓓ **MPK44850**

E. Kissin, V. Kan, Moscow Virtuosi, V. Spivakov *Concert* (12/89) (RCA) Ⓓ **RD87947**

G. Ohlsson, M. Murphy, Cracow PO, G. Levine *Concert* (1/90) (ARAB) Ⓓ **Z6610**

R. Simmons, P. Jablonski, RPO, Vladimir Ashkenazy *Concert* (12/92) (DECC) Ⓓ **436 239-2DH**

P. Masseurs, R. Brautigam, Concertgebouw, R. Chailly *Concert* (3/93) (DECC) Ⓓ **433 702-2DH**

D. Shostakovich, L. Vaillant, FRNO, A. Cluytens (r1958) *Concert* (4/93) (EMI) Ⓓ **CDC7 54606-2**

E. Leonskaja, St Paul CO, H. Wolff (r1991) *Concert* (6/93) (TELD) Ⓓ **9031-73282-2**

I. Margalit, M.M. Khanin, Moscow PO, D. Barra (r1992) *Concert* (9/93) (KOCH) Ⓓ **37159-2**

W. Vacchiano, A. Previn, NYPO, L. Bernstein (r1962) *Concert* (6/94) (SONY) Ⓓ **SMK47618**

M. Argerich, G. Touvron, Württemberg CO, J. Faerber (r1993) *Haydn: Keyboard Concerto, HobXVIII:11.* (1/95) (DG) Ⓓ **439 864-2GH**

D. Shostakovich, Moscow RSO, A. Gauk (pp1957) *Concert* (2/95) (RUSS) Ⓓ **RDCD15005**

E. Joyce, A. Lockwood, Hallé, L. Heward (r1941) *Concert* (2/95) (DUTT) Ⓓ **CDAX8010**

M. Rudy, O.E. Antonsen, BPO, M. Jansons (r1994) *Symphony 1.* (12/95) (EMI) Ⓓ **CDC5 55361-2**

Concerto for Violin and Orchestra No. 1 in A minor, Op. 99 (1947-48 rev 1955) (originally published as Op. 77)

I. Perlman, Israel PO, Z. Mehta (pp1988) *Glazunov: Violin Concerto.* (1/90) (EMI) Ⓓ **CDC7 49814-2**

L. Mordkovitch, SNO, N. Järvi *Violin Concerto 2.* (4/90) (CHAN) Ⓓ **CHAN8820**

B. Belkin, RPO, Vladimir Ashkenazy *Piano Concerto 2.* (8/90) (DECC) Ⓓ **425 793-2DH**

D. Sitkovetsky, BBC SO, A. Davis (r1989) *Violin Concerto 2.* (9/90) (VIRG) Ⓓ **VC7 59601-2**

N. Gotkovsky, Bulgarian RSO, V. Kazandjiev *Violin Concerto 2.* (10/91) (PYRA) Ⓓ **PYR13493**

M. Vengerov, LSO, M. Rostropovich (r1994) *Prokofiev: Violin Concerto 1.* (2/95) (TELD) Ⓓ **4509-92256-2**

I. Perlman, Israel PO, Z. Mehta (pp1988) *Concert* (6/95) (EMI) Ⓓ [20] **CZS4 83177-2(2)**

Concerto for Violin and Orchestra No. 2 in C sharp minor, Op. 129 (1967)

L. Mordkovitch, SNO, N. Järvi *Violin Concerto 1.* (4/90) (CHAN) Ⓓ **CHAN8820**

D. Sitkovetsky, BBC SO, A. Davis (r1989) *Violin Concerto 1.* (9/90) (VIRG) Ⓓ **VC7 59601-2**

N. Gotkovsky, Bulgarian RSO, V. Kazandjiev *Violin Concerto 1.* (10/91) (PYRA) Ⓓ **PYR13493**

G. Kremer, Boston SO, S. Ozawa (pp1992) *Schumann: Violin Concerto, Op.129.* (9/94) (DG) Ⓓ **439 890-2GH**

Festive Overture in A, Op. 96 (1954)

Moscow PO, L. Leighton Smith *Concert* (2/88) (SHEF) Ⓓ **CD27**

SNO, N. Järvi *Concert* (7/88) (CHAN) Ⓓ **CHAN8587**

Cincinnati Pops, E. Kunzel *Concert* (10/89) (TELA) Ⓓ **CD80170**

LSO, M. Shostakovich (r1990) *Symphony 5.* (9/90) (COLL) Ⓓ **Coll1108-2**

Helsinki PO, J. DePreist *Symphony 10.* (1/91) (DELO) Ⓓ **DE3089**

Malmö SO, J. DePreist *Concert* (1/93) (BIS) Ⓓ **BIS-CD570**

Philadelphia, R. Muti (r1992) *Symphony 5.* (12/93) (EMI) Ⓓ **CDC7 54803-2**

Empire Brass (r1992; arr. Pilafian) *Concert* (1/94) (TELA) Ⓓ **CD80305**

NYPO, L. Bernstein (r1962)
(6/94) (SONY) ① **SMK47616**
Moscow PO, K. Kondrashin (r1975)
(11/94) (MELO) ① **74321 19839-2**
Symphony No. 8 in C minor, Op. 65 (1943)
Leningrad PO, E. Mravinsky (pp1982)
(6/89) (PHIL) ① **422 442-2PH**
SNO, N. Järvi   (4/90) (CHAN) ① **CHAN8757**
LSO, M. Shostakovich   (6/92) (COLL) ① **Coll1271-2**
Helsinki PO, J. DePreist
(10/92) (ONDI) ① **ODE775-2**
Washington NSO, M. Rostropovich
(10/92) (TELD) ① **9031-74719-2**
Moscow PO, K. Kondrashin (bp1969) Overture on
Russian and Kirghiz Folk Themes.
(9/93) (PRAG) ① **PR250 040**
Bratislava RSO, L. Slovák
(11/93) (NAXO) ① **8 550628**
Concertgebouw, B. Haitink (r1982)
(11/93) (DECC) ① **425 071-2DM**
RPO, Vladimir Ashkenazy (r1981) Concert
(4/94) (DECC) ① **436 763-2DH**
Atlanta SO, Y. Levi (r1991)
(7/94) (TELA) ① **CD80291**
Moscow PO, K. Kondrashin (r1961)
(11/94) (MELO) ① **74321 19841-2**
Vienna SO, E. Inbal (r1991)
(1/95) (DENO) ① **CO-78910**
LSO, A. Previn   (3/95) (DG) ① **437 819-2GH**
Kirov Th Orch, V. Gergiev (r1994)
(8/95) (PHIL) ① **446 062-2PH**
LSO, A. Previn (r1973)
(10/95) (EMI) ① **CDM5 65521-2**
Symphony No. 9 in E flat, Op. 70 (1945)
VPO, L. Bernstein (pp1985) Symphony 6.
(11/87) (DG) ① **419 771-2GH**
SNO, N. Järvi Concert
(7/88) (CHAN) ① **CHAN8587**
NYPO, E. Kurtz (r1949) Symphony 10.
(2/90) (SONY) ① **MPK45698**
Atlanta SO, Y. Levi (r1989) Symphony 5.
(6/90) (TELA) ① **CD80215**
Brussels BRT PO, A. Rahbari Symphony 5.
(3/92) (NAXO) ① **8 550427**
Oslo PO, M. Jansons Symphony 5.
(5/92) (EMI) ① **CDC7 54339-2**
Czech PO, K. Ančerl (pp1966) Concert
(5/93) (PRAG) ① **[2] PR254 002/3**
Bratislava RSO, L. Slovák (r1988) Symphony 5.
(11/93) (NAXO) ① **8 550632**
LPO, B. Haitink (r1980) Symphony 5.
(11/93) (DECC) ① **425 066-2DM**
USSR SO, D. Oistrakh (pp1969) Symphony 14.
(1/94) (RUSS) ① **RDCD11192**
Vienna SO, E. Inbal (r1990) Symphony 3.
(2/94) (DENO) ① **CO-75444**
NYPO, L. Bernstein (r1965) Symphony 1.
(6/94) (SONY) ① **SMK47615**
Washington NSO, M. Rostropovich (r1993)
Symphony 1.   (10/94) (TELD) ① **4509-90849-2**
Moscow PO, K. Kondrashin (r1965) Symphony 15.
(11/94) (MELO) ① **74321 19846-2**
LSO, M. Sargent (r1960) Symphony 6.
(4/95) (EVER) ① **EVC9005**
Montreal SO, C. Dutoit (r1992) Symphony 5.
(11/95) (DECC) ① **448 122-2DH**
Solti Orchestral Project, M. Solti (pp1994) Concert
(12/95) (DECC) ① **444 458-2DH**
Symphony No. 10 in E minor, Op. 93 (1953)
BPO, H. von Karajan (r1981)
(8/84) (DG) ① **413 361-2GH**
SNO, N. Järvi Ballet Suite 4.
(3/89) (CHAN) ① **CHAN8630**
USSR Ministry of Culture SO, G. Rozhdestvensky
Hamlet, Op.32.   (5/89) (OLYM) ① **OCD131**
NYPO, D. Mitropoulos (r1954) Symphony 9.
(2/90) (SONY) ① **MPK45698**
BPO, H. von Karajan (r1966)
(8/90) (DG) ① **429 716-2GGA**
LSO, M. Shostakovich   (10/91) (COLL) ① **Coll1106-2**
Helsinki PO, J. DePreist Festive Overture.
(1/91) (DELO) ① **DE3089**
Atlanta SO, Y. Levi   (1/91) (TELA) ① **CD80241**
Hallé, S. Skrowaczewski
(10/91) (CARL) ① **PCD955**
LSO, M. Rostropovich
(3/92) (TELD) ① **9031-74529-2**
Leningrad PO, E. Mravinsky (r1954)
(6/92) (SAGA) ① **EC3366-2**
Concertgebouw, C.P. Flor
(6/92) (RCA) ① **RD60448**
Leningrad PO, E. Mravinsky (pp1976) Concert
(6/92) (ERAT) ① **[11] 2292-45763-2**
Leningrad PO, E. Mravinsky (pp1976)
(6/92) (ERAT) ① **2292-45753-2**
Vienna SO, E. Inbal   (9/92) (DENO) ① **CO-79474**

LPO, B. Haitink (r1977) Symphony 2.
(11/93) (DECC) ① **425 064-2DM**
Bratislava RSO, L. Slovák (r1989)
(11/93) (NAXO) ① **8 550633**
Leningrad PO, Y. Temirkanov (pp1973) Symphony 2.
(1/94) (RUSS) ① **RDCD11195**
Philh, S. Rattle (r1985) Britten: Sinfonia da Requiem.
(3/94) (EMI) ① **CDM7 64870-2**
Moscow PO, K. Kondrashin (r1973) Symphony 6.
(11/94) (MELO) ① **74321 19847-2**
LPO, A. Litton Festive Overture.
(11/94) (VIRG) ① **CUV5 61134-2**
Philadelphia, M. Jansons (r1994) Mussorgsky: Songs
and Dances of Death.
(6/95) (EMI) ① **CDC5 55232-2**
Leningrad PO, E. Mravinsky (r1983) Bolt Suite.
(9/95) (PRAG) ① **PR250 053**
**Symphony No. 11 in G minor, '(The) year
1905', Op. 103 (1957)**
Moscow PO, K. Kondrashin Concert
(5/89) (CHNT) ① **[2] LDC278 1007/8**
Helsinki PO, J. DePreist   (5/89) (DELO) ① **DE3080**
Gothenburg SO, N. Järvi
(9/90) (DG) ① **429 405-2GH**
Washington NSO, M. Rostropovich (r1992)
(8/93) (TELD) ① **9031-76262-2**
Bratislava RSO, L. Slovák (1988)
(11/93) (NAXO) ① **8 550629**
Concertgebouw, B. Haitink (r1983)
(11/93) (DECC) ① **425 072-2DM**
Leningrad PO, E. Mravinsky (pp1957)
(1/94) (RUSS) ① **RDCD11157**
Leningrad PO, E. Mravinsky (r1967)
(8/94) (PRAG) ① **PR254 018**
Moscow PO, K. Kondrashin (r1973)
(11/94) (MELO) ① **74321 19843-2**
Vienna SO, E. Inbal (r1992)
(4/95) (DENO) ① **CO-78920**
**Symphony No. 12 in D minor, '(The) year
1917', Op. 112 (1960-61)** (also subtitles 'To the
memory of Lenin')
USSR Ministry of Culture SO, G. Rozhdestvensky
Symphony 6.   (5/89) (OLYM) ① **OCD111**
Moscow PO, K. Kondrashin Concert
(5/89) (CHNT) ① **[2] LDC278 1007/8**
Gothenburg SO, N. Järvi Concert
(9/91) (DG) ① **431 688-2GH**
Leningrad PO, E. Mravinsky (pp1984) Concert
(6/92) (ERAT) ① **[11] 2292-45763-2**
Leningrad PO, E. Mravinsky (pp1984)
(6/92) (ERAT) ① **2292-45754-2**
Bratislava RSO, L. Slovák (r1989) Symphony 6.
(11/93) (NAXO) ① **8 550626**
Concertgebouw, B. Haitink (r1982) Symphony 6.
(11/93) (DECC) ① **425 067-2DM**
Leningrad PO, E. Mravinsky (pp1962) Symphony 6.
(8/94) (PRAG) ① **PR254 017**
Moscow PO, K. Kondrashin (r1972) Symphony 1.
(11/94) (MELO) ① **74321 19848-2**
RPO, Vladimir Ashkenazy (r1992) Symphony 3.
(11/94) (DECC) ① **436 760-2DH**
**Symphony No. 13 in B flat minor, 'Babiy
Yar'—bass, chorus and orchestra, Op. 113
(1962)** (Wds. Evtushenko)
N. Storozhev, CBSO Chor, City of Birmingham Ch,
Warwick Univ Chor, CBSO, O. Kamu
(12/87) (CHAN) ① **CHAN8540**
A. Safiulin, Yurlov Russian Ch, USSR Ministry of
Culture SO, G. Rozhdestvensky (1985)
(5/89) (OLYM) ① **OCD132**
A. Eisen, RSFSR Academic Russian Ch, Moscow
PO, K. Kondrashin Concert
(5/89) (CHNT) ① **[2] LDC278 1007/8**
P. Mikuláš, Slovak Phil Chor, Bratislava RSO, L.
Slovák (r1990)   (11/93) (NAXO) ① **8 550630**
M. Rintzler, Concertgebouw Ch, Concertgebouw, B.
Haitink (r1984)   (11/93) (DECC) ① **425 073-2DM**
V. Gromadsky, USSR St Academic Ch, Yurlov
Russian Ch, Moscow PO, K. Kondrashin (pp1962)
(3/94) (RUSS) ① **RDCD11191**
R. Holl, Viennensis Chor, Vienna SO, E. Inbal
(pp1993)   (9/94) (DENO) ① **CO-75887**
S. Leiferkus, NY Male Choral Artists, NYPO, K.
Masur (r1993)   (10/94) (TELD) ① **4509-90848-2**
A. Eisen, Russian Republic Chs, Moscow PO, K.
Kondrashin (r1967)
(11/94) (MELO) ① **74321 19842-2**
S. Baikov, Estonia Nat Male Ch, St Petersburg
Camerata, Lithuanian CO, S. Sondeckis (r1994)
(7/95) (SONY) ① **SM66591**
S. Aleksashkin, A. Hopkins, Chicago Sym Chor,
Chicago SO, G. Solti (pp1993)
(8/95) (DECC) ① **444 791-2DH**
J. Shirley-Quirk, Düsseldorf Musikverein, Düsseldorf
SO, D. Shallon (pp1991) (8/95) (SCHW) ① **313932**

**Symphony No. 14—soprano, bass, strings
and percussion, Op. 135 (1969)** (Wds.
various)
E. Holleque, N. Storozhev, Montreal I Musici, Y.
Turovsky   (12/88) (CHAN) ① **CHAN8607**
M. Kasrashubili, A. Safiulin, USSR Ministry of Culture
SO, G. Rozhdestvensky (r1985) King Lear, Op.58a.
(12/88) (OLYM) ① **OCD182**
M. Hajóssyová, P. Mikuláš, Bratislava RSO, L.
Slovák (r1991)   (11/93) (NAXO) ① **8 550631**
J. Varady, D. Fischer-Dieskau, Concertgebouw, B.
Haitink (r1980) Marina Tsvetaeva Poems.
(11/93) (DECC) ① **425 074-2DM**
G. Vishnevskaya, M. Reshetin, Moscow CO, R.
Barshai (pp1969) Symphony 9.
(1/94) (RUSS) ① **RDCD11192**
L. Kazarnovskaya, S. Leiferkus, Gothenburg SO, N.
Järvi (r1992) Mussorgsky: Songs and Dances of
Death.   (2/94) (DG) ① **437 785-2GH**
T. Kubiak, I. Bushkin, NYPO, L. Bernstein (r1976)
(6/94) (SONY) ① **SMK47617**
E. Tselovalnik, E. Nesterenko, Moscow PO, K.
Kondrashin (r1974) Symphony 2.
(11/94) (MELO) ① **74321 19844-2**
Symphony No. 15 in A, Op. 141 (1971)
Gothenburg SO, N. Järvi Concert
(5/91) (DG) ① **427 616-2GH**
LSO, M. Shostakovich Gadfly Suite.
(5/91) (COLL) ① **Coll1206-2**
LSO, M. Rostropovich
(3/92) (TELD) ① **9031-74560-2**
Bratislava RSO, L. Slovák Symphony 2.
(11/93) (NAXO) ① **8 550624**
LPO, B. Haitink (r1978) Jewish Folk Poetry, Op 79.
(11/93) (DECC) ① **425 069-2DM**
Montreal SO, C. Dutoit Symphony 1.
(10/94) (DECC) ① **436 838-2DH**
Moscow PO, K. Kondrashin (r1974) Symphony 9.
(11/94) (MELO) ① **74321 19846-2**
Vienna SO, E. Inbal (r1992) Symphony 1.
(12/95) (DECC) ① **CO-78948**
Taiti trot—orchestra, Op. 16 (1928) (transcr of
Youmans's song 'Tea for two')
SNO, N. Järvi Concert
(7/88) (CHAN) ① **CHAN8587**
Concertgebouw, R. Chailly Concert
(3/93) (DECC) ① **433 702-2DH**
BBC SO, G. Rozhdestvensky (pp1981) Concert
(10/95) (BBCR) ① **[2] DMCD98**
**Theme and Variations in B flat—orchestra,
Op. 3 (1921-22)**
USSR Ministry of Culture SO, G. Rozhdestvensky
Concert   (6/88) (OLYM) ① **OCD194**

SECTION II: CHAMBER

Concertino—two pianos, Op. 94 (1953)
W. Manz, R. Plagge (r1992) Concert
(11/94) (DINT) ① **DICD920150**
Piano Trio No. 1 in C minor, Op. 8 (1923)
Oslo Trio Concert   (10/88) (SIMA) ① **PSC1014**
Piano Trio No. 2 in E minor, Op. 67 (1944)
Borodin Trio Piano Quintet, Op. 57.
(4/85) (CHAN) ① **CHAN8342**
Oslo Trio Concert   (10/88) (SIMA) ① **PSC1014**
Tchaikovsky Trio Rachmaninov: Trio élégiaque,
Op.9.   (10/88) (DYNA) ① **DC-U23**
I. Stern, Y-Y. Ma, E. Ax Cello Sonata, Op.40.
(6/89) (SONY) ① **MK44664**
G. Feighin, V. Feighin, I. Yukov Concert
(6/90) (CHNT) ① **[2] LDC278 1018/9**
Beaux Arts Trio Piano Quintet, Op. 57.
(8/91) (PHIL) ① **432 079-2PH**
H. Pálsson, A. Tellefsen, F. Helmerson Concert
(9/92) (BIS) ① **BIS-CD026**
2 Pieces—string octet, Op. 11 (1924-25)
1. Prelude; 2. Scherzo.
Medici Qt, Alberni Qt Concert
(1/89) (NIMB) ① **NI5140**
Soviet Emigré Orch, L. Gozman (orch. L.Gosman)
Concert   (8/89) (OLYM) ① **OCD196**
ASMF Chbr Ens (1992) Concert
(5/93) (CHAN) ① **CHAN9131**
2. Zagreb Sols, T. Ninić Concert
(11/92) (CARL) ① **PCD1000**
2 Pieces for String Quartet (1931)
1. Elegy; 2. Polka.
Medici Qt Concert   (1/89) (NIMB) ① **NI5140**
Shostakovich Qt (1985) Concert
(9/94) (OLYM) ① **OCD531**
1. Borodin Qt (pp1991) Concert
(10/93) (RUSS) ① **RDCD11087**
**Quintet for Piano and Strings in G minor, Op.
57 (1940)**
Borodin Trio, M. Zweig, J. Horner Piano Trio 2.
(4/85) (CHAN) ① **CHAN8342**

SECTION III: INSTRUMENTAL

10, 15, 16, 24. L. Mordkovitch (arr Tsiganov) *Concert*
(11/90) (CHAN) ① **CHAN8748**

10, 15, 16, 24. Midori, R. McDonald (r1992; arr vn/pf
Tsyganow) *Concert* (6/93) (SONY) ① **SK52568**

14. Philadelphia, L. Stokowski (r1935: arr Stokowski)
Concert (5/93) (DUTT) ① **CDAX8002**

14. Philadelphia, L. Stokowski (r1935: orch
Stokowski) *Concert*
(1/94) (PEAR) ① [2] **GEMMCDS9044**

**24 Preludes and Fugues—piano, Op. 87
(1950-51)**
T. Nikolaieva (3/91) (HYPE) ① [3] **CDA66441/3**
K. Jarrett (9/92) (ECM) ① [2] **437 189-2**
T. Nikolaieva (r1987)
(2/95) (MELO) ① [3] **74321 19849-2**
1-12. M. Papadopoulos
(3/91) (KING) ① **KCLCD2023**
1, 2, 4, 15, 19. Boris Berman *Piano Sonata 2.*
(10/89) (OTTA) ① **OTRC38616**
1, 4, 5, 23, 24. D. Shostakovich (r1958) *Concert*
(4/93) (EMI) ① **CDC7 54606-2**
4, 12, 14, 15, 17, 23. S Richter *Concert*
(8/94) (PHIL) ① [2] **438 627-2PH2**
5. Emil Gilels (r1955) *Concert*
(2/94) (TEST) ① **SBT1029**
13-24. M. Papadopoulos
(3/91) (KING) ① **KCLCD2024/5**
19, 21, 22. S. Richter (pp1973) *Concert*
(10/92) (PYRA) ① **PYR13503**

SECTION IV: VOCAL AND CHORAL

**The Execution of Stepan Razin—poem:
bass, chorus and orchestra, Op. 119 (1964)**
(wds. Y. Yevtushenko)
A. Vassilev, Varna Phil Chor, Varna PO (r1989)
Sviridov: Oratorio Pathétique.
(3/91) (KOCH) ① **37017-2**

**From Jewish Folk Poetry—songs for
soprano, contralto, tenor and piano, Op. 79
(1948 orch 1964)** (Wds. Anon)
1. Lament on the dead child; 2. The thoughtful father;
3. Lullaby; 4. Before the separation; 5. Warning; 6.
The abandoned father; 7. Song on indigence; 8. The
winter; 9. A Fine life; 10. The girl's song; 11. Good
fortune.
N. Pelle, M.A. Hart, R. Nolan, Montreal I Musici, Y.
Turovsky *Concert* (7/90) (CHAN) ① **CHAN8800**
E. Söderström, O. Wenkel, R. Karczykowski,
Concertgebouw, B. Haitink (r1983) *Symphony 15.*
(11/93) (DECC) ① **425 069-2DM**
I. Orgonášová, N. Stutzmann, P. Langridge,
Gothenburg SO, N. Järvi (r1992) *Concert*
(9/94) (DG) ① **439 860-2GH**

**2 Krylov Fables—1v, women's chorus and
orchestra, Op. 4 (1922)** (Wds. I Krylov)
1. The dragonfly and the ant; 2. The ass and the
nightingale.
L. Dyadkova, Gothenburg Op Chor, Gothenburg SO,
N. Järvi (r1993) *Concert*
(9/94) (DG) ① **439 860-2GH**

**6 Marina Tsvetaeva Poems—suite: contralto
& piano/orchestra, Op. 143 (1973)**
1. My poems; 2. Where does such tendemess come
from?; 3. Hamlet's dialogue with conscience; 4. The
poet and her tsar; 5. No, the drum beat; 6. To Anna
Akhmatova.
O. Wenkel, Concertgebouw, B. Haitink (r1982)
Symphony 14. (4/93) (DECC) ① **425 074-2DM**

**7 Romances on Verses by Alexander
Blok—soprano and piano trio, Op. 127
(1967)**
1. Ophelia's Song; 2. Hamayun, the prophetic bird; 3.
We were together; 4. The city sleeps; 5. Storm; 6.
Mysterious signs; 7. Music.
N. Pelle, Borodin Trio *Concert*
(10/91) (CHAN) ① **CHAN8924**
J. Delman, E. Dekov, Å. Olofsson, L. Negro *Concert*
(9/92) (BIS) ① **BIS-CD026**

**The Song of the Forests—tenor, bass,
children's chorus and orchestra, Op. 81
(1949)** (Wds. Y. Dolmatovsky)
1. When war is ended; 2. We will clothe our
homeland with forests; 3. Memories of the past; 4.
The pioneers plant the forests; 5. The young
Communists go forth; 6. A walk in the future; 7. Glory.
M. Kotliarov, N. Storozhev, Brighton Fest Chor, New
London Children's Ch, RPO, Vladimir Ashkenazy
(r1991) *Concert* (4/94) (DECC) ① **436 762-2DH**

4 Songs—bass and piano, Op. 46 (1936)
(Wds. A Pushkin)
D. Kharitonov, CBSO, M. Elder (r1992) *No.4 orch
McBurney) Concert* (1/94) (UNIT) ① **88001-2**
S. Leiferkus, Gothenburg SO, N. Järvi (r1993)
Concert (9/94) (DG) ① **439 860-2GH**

**6 Songs on Verses by British Poets—bass
and orchestra/chamber orchestra, Op. 140
(1942 rev 1971)** (Wds. various)
1. The wood, the weed, the wag, 'To a song' (wds W
Raleigh); 2. O, wert thou in the cauld blast, 'In the
fields' (wds R Burns); 3. Macpherson before his
excution, 'Macpherson's farewell (wds R Burns); 4.
Jenny, 'Coming thro' the rye' (wds R Burns); 5.
Sonnet No. 66, 'Tired with all these' (wds
Shakespeare); 6. The King's campaign, 'The grand
old Duke of York' (wds trad).
S. Leiferkus, Gothenburg SO, N. Järvi (r1993)
Concert (9/94) (DG) ① **439 860-2GH**

**Spanish Songs—soprano and piano, Op. 100
(1956)** (Wds. Anon trans S. Bolotin and T.
Sikovsky)
1. Farewell, Granada; 2. Little Stars; 3. First Meeting;
4. Round Dance (A Birth); 5. Black Eyes; 6. Dream
(Barcarolle).
A. Eisen, A. Bogdanova *Concert*
(6/88) (OLYM) ① **OCD194**

**Suite on Verses of Michelangelo—bass &
piano/orchestra, Op. 145 (1974)** (Wds. M
Buonarrotti, trans A Efros)
1. Truth; 2. Morning; 3. Love; 4. Separation; 5. Anger;
6. Dante; 7. To the Exile; 8. Creativity; 9. Night - a
dialogue; 10. Death; 11. Immortality.
D. Fischer-Dieskau, A. Reimann (r1987) *Reimann:
Michelangelo Lieder.*
(12/95) (TELD) ① **4509-97460-2**

SECTION V: STAGE WORKS

**The Adventures of Korzinkina (A Ticket to
the Fifth Zone)—film score, Op. 59 (1940)**
USSR Ministry of Culture Chor, USSR Ministry of
Culture SO, G. Rozhdestvensky *Concert*
(6/88) (OLYM) ① **OCD194**

**The Age of Gold—concert suite from ballet,
Op. 22a (1930)**
1. Introduction; 2. Adagio; 3. Polka; 4. Dance.
Gothenburg SO, N. Järvi *Concert*
(9/91) (DG) ① **431 688-2GH**
LPO, B. Haitink *Concert*
(12/91) (DECC) ① **430 727-2DM**
1, 3, 4. Cracow PO, G. Levine *Concert*
(1/90) (ARAB) ① **Z6610**
3. Philadelphia, E. Ormandy (r1966) *Concert*
(7/94) (SONY) ① **SBK53261**

Alone—film score, Op. 26 (1930-31)
USSR Academy SO Sols Ens, G. Rozhdestvensky
Concert (6/88) (OLYM) ① **OCD194**

**The Bolt—ballet (3 acts) (1930-
31—Leningrad)**
Cpte Stockholm PO, G. Rozhdestvensky (r1994)
(6/95) (CHAN) ① [2] **CHAN9343/4**

**The Bolt—concert suite from ballet, Op. 27a
(1933)**
EXCERPTS: 1. Overture (Introduction); 2. The
Bureaucrat (Polka); 3. The Drayman's Dance
(Variations); 4. Tango: Kozelkov's Dance with
Friends; 5. Intermezzo; 6. The Dance of the Colonial
Slave; 7. The Conciliator; 8. General Dance of
Enthusiasm and Apotheosis (Finale).
1, 2, 3, 5. Czech PO, G. Rozhdestvensky (r1983)
Symphony 10. (9/95) (PRAG) ① **PR250 053**

**Counterplan—concert suite from film score,
Op. 33 (1932)**
EXCERPTS: 1. Presto; 2. Andante; 3. Andante; 4.
Song of the Meeting (1v and orchestra); 5. How long
will my heart ache? (1v, chorus and orchestra); 6.
United Nations Overture (orch arr Stokowski of No 4).
6. BBC PO, M. Bamert (r1994: orch Stokowski)
Concert (6/95) (CHAN) ① **CHAN9349**

**Five Days, Five Nights—concert suite from
film score, Op. 111a (1960)** (assembled by Lev
Atovmyan, 1961)
EXCERPTS: 1. Introduction; 2. Dresden in Ruins; 3.
Liberated Dresden; 4. Interlude; 5. Finale.
2-5. RTBF SO, J. Serebrier (r1988) *Concert*
(10/88) (RCA) ① **RD87763**

The Flea—incidental music, Op. 19 (1929)
1. March; 2. Galop; 3. Foxtrot; 4. Waltz.
2. Britannia Building Soc Band, H. Snell (1990; arr
Snell: brass band) *Concert*
(8/92) (DOYE) ① **DOYCD004**

**The Gadfly—concert suite from film score,
Op. 97a (1955)** (arr. L. Atovmyan)
Numbers quoted in paratheses identify against film
score; 1. Overture (1); 2. Contredanse (13); 3.
People's Holiday (16); 4. Interlude (17); 5. Barrel
Organ Waltz (10); 6. Galop (14); 7. Prelude (15 and 5);
8. Romance (3 and 7); 9. Intermezzo (10, 12 and 18);
10. Nocturne (23); 11. Scene (2); 12. Finale (20).
USSR Cinema SO, E. Khachaturian
(4/89) (CFP) ① **CD-CFP4463**

KBS SO, V. Jordania (r1994) *Concert*
(12/94) (KOCH) ① **37274-2**
1-3, 5-8, 10, 12. LSO, M. Shostakovich *Symphony
15.* (5/91) (COLL) ① **Coll1206-2**
3. M. Kliegel, R. Havenith (arr vc/pf) *Concert*
(9/92) (MARC) ① **8 223403**
8. Detroit SO, N. Järvi (r1993) *Concert*
(8/94) (CHAN) ① **CHAN9227**

**The Gamblers, 'Igroki'—opera: 3 acts
(1941—Wuppertal)** (Lib. N Gogol: cpted K
Meyer 1980-81)
Cpte V. Bogachev, A. Babikin, S. Suleymanov, A.
Naumenko, A. Arkhipov, N. Nizinenko, M. Krutikov,
V. Verestnikov, A. Maslennikov, NW German PO, M.
Yurovsky (r1993) *Concert* (6/95) (CAPR) ① [2] **60 062-2**

**The Golden Age—ballet: 3 acts, Op. 22
(1927-30—Leningrad)**
EXCERPTS: 1. Prelude. ACT 1: 2. Dance of the
Maître d'Hôtel and the Aristocrats; 3. Sportsmen's
Training Session; 4. Entrance of the Maître d'Hôtel
and the Aristocrats; 5. Dance of the Tennis Players
and Training Session; 6. The Maître d'Hôtel reports...
7. Preparations for the Diva's Visit; 8. Dance of the
Golden Youths; 9. Adagio; 10. Dance of the Diva and
Tanya; 11. Dance; 12. Conversation between the
Diva and Hero; 13. Dance of the Diva and the Hero;
14. Dance of the Negro and the White Man; 15.
General Dance; 16. General Confusion; 17. The
Diva's Despair; 18. Conversation between the VIP
and... 19. Fox-trot. ACT 2: 20. Gallop; 21. March; 22.
Football; 23. Interlude; 24. Dance of Tanya and
Sportsmen from U-Town; 25. Sports Contest; 26.
Scene and Exit of the Soviet; 27. Interlude; 28.
Tango; 29. Tap Dance; 30. Polka; 31. Eccentric
Dance; 32. Andante; 33. Allegro vivace. ACT 3: 34.
Adagio; 35. Adagio; 36. Allegro; 37. Finale.
Cpte Stockholm PO, G. Rozhdestvensky (r1993)
(5/94) (CHAN) ① [2] **CHAN9251/2**

**The Golden Hills—concert suite from film
score, Op. 30a (1931)**
1. Introduction; 2. Waltz; 3. Fugue; 4. Intermezzo; 5.
Funeral March; 6. Finale.
USSR Ministry of Culture SO, G. Rozhdestvensky
(r1985) *New Babylon Suite.*
(6/95) (RUSS) ① **RDCD11064**

Hamlet—incidental music, Op. 32 (1932-32)
Leningrad CO, E. Serov *Symphony 10.*
(5/89) (OLYM) ① **OCD131**

**Hamlet—concert suite from incidental
music, Op. 32a (1932)**
Gothenburg SO, N. Järvi *Concert*
(9/91) (DG) ① **431 688-2GH**

**Hamlet—concert suite from film score, Op.
116a (1963-4)** (assembled by Lev Atovmyan,
1964)
EXCERPTS: 1. Introduction; 2. Ball at the Palace; 3.
The Ghost; 4. In the Garden; 5. Scene of the
Poisoning; 6. Arrival and Scene of the Players; 7.
Ophelia; 8. The Duel and Death of Hamlet.
1, 3, 4. KBS SO, V. Jordania (r1994) *Concert*
(12/94) (KOCH) ① **37274-2**
1-3, 5, 6, 8. National PO, B. Herrmann (r1975)
Concert (2/95) (UNIC) ① **UKCD2066**
1-8. RTBF SO, J. Serebrier (r1988) *Concert*
(10/88) (RCA) ① **RD87763**

**The Human Comedy—incidental music, Op.
37 (1933-34)**
Leningrad CO, E. Serov *Concert*
(6/88) (OLYM) ① **OCD194**

**Hypothetically Murdered—concert suite from
circus show, Op. 31a (1931)** (recons G
McBurney)
EXCERPTS: 1. Gallop (Act 1: Part 1).
CBSO, M. Elder (r1992) *Concert*
(1/94) (UNIT) ① **88001-2**

**Katerina Izmaylova—opera: 4 acts, Op. 114
(1963—Moscow)** (Lib. Preys, after Leskov)
Suite SNO, N. Järvi *Concert*
(7/88) (CHAN) ① **CHAN8587**
Suite SNO, N. Järvi (r1988) *Concert*
(5/95) (CHAN) ① [2] **CHAN7000/1**

King Lear—incidental music, Op. 58a (1940)
N. Romanova, Leningrad CO, E. Serov (r1984)
Symphony 14. (12/88) (OLYM) ① **OCD182**
E. Zaremba, S. Suleymanov, Berlin Rad Chor, Berlin
RSO, M. Yurovsky *King Lear, Op. 137.*
(9/92) (CAPR) ① **10 397**

King Lear—film score, Op. 137 (1970)
RTBF SO, J. Serebrier (r1988) *Concert*
(10/88) (RCA) ① **RD87763**
Berlin RSO, M. Yurovsky *King Lear, Op. 58a.*
(9/92) (CAPR) ① **10 397**
KBS SO, V. Jordania (r1994) *Concert*
(12/94) (KOCH) ① **37274-2**

Lady Macbeth of the Mtsensk district—opera: 4 acts, Op. 29 (1934—Leningrad) (Lib cpsr & Preys, after Leskov)
Cpte G. Vishnevskaya, N. Gedda, D. Petkov, W. Krenn, R. Tear, T. Valjakka, M. Hill, L. Mróz, A. Haugland, B. Finnilä, A. Malta, L. Fyson, S. Emmerson, J. Noble, C. Appleton, A. Byers, J. Lewington, O. Broome, E. Fleet, D. Beavan, L. Richardson, Ambrosian Op Chor, LPO, M. Rostropovich (r1978)
(5/90) (EMI) ① [2] CDS7 49955-2
Cpte M. Ewing, S. Larin, A. Haugland, P. Langridge, H. Zednik, Kristine Ciesinski, I. Levinsky, R. Tesarowicz, A. Kocherga, E. Zaremba, K. Moll, G. Gritziuk, C. Alvarez, G. Petitot, J-P. Mazaloubaud, A. Woodrow, J-C. Costa, J. Savignol, J. Ochagavia, P. Duminy, M. Agnetti, J. Tilli, M.J. Wray, Paris Opéra-Bastille Chor, Paris Opéra-Bastille Orch, Myung-Whun Chung (r1992)
(12/93) (DG) ① [2] 437 511-2GH2
Passacaglia C. Herrick (arr cpsr: org) Concert
(10/92) (HYPE) ① CDA66605
Passacaglia K. John Concert
(11/92) (PRIO) ① PRCD370
The Limpid Stream—ballet: 3 acts, Op. 39 (1935—Leningrad)
Adagio J. Lloyd Webber, LSO, M. Shostakovich Concert
(5/92) (PHIL) ① 434 106-2PH
New Babylon—concert suite from film score, Op. 18a (1929)
Moscow PO, G. Rozhdestvensky (r1975) Golden Hills Suite.
(6/95) (RUSS) ① RDCD11064
The Unforgettable Year 1919—film score, Op. 89 (1951)
The Assault on beautiful Gorky D. Alexeev, ECO, J. Maksymiuk Concert
(1/89) (CFP) ① CD-CFP4547

SHOTT, Peter

SECTION II: CHAMBER

Aan de Amsterdamse Grachten—ensemble
Amsterdam Loeki Stardust Qt Concert
(10/94) (L'OI) ① 440 207-2OM

SHULMAN, Alan L. (b 1915) USA

SECTION II: CHAMBER

Suite on American Folksongs—violin and piano
EXCERPTS: 4. Cod liver 'ile.
4. J. Heifetz, B. Smith (r1955) Concert
(11/94) (RCA) ① [65] 09026 61778-2(35)

SHVEDOV, Konstantin Nikolaevich (1886–1954) Russia

SECTION IV: VOCAL AND CHORAL

Liturgy of St John Chrysostom, Op. 40 (unpub) (1935)
Cpte Slavyanka, A. Shipovalnikov (r1993)
(1/95) (HARM) ① HMU90 7105

SIBELIUS, Jean (Julian Christian) (1865–1957) Finland

SECTION I: ORCHESTRAL

Academic March—orchestra (1919)
Gothenburg SO, N. Järvi Concert
(4/87) (BIS) ① BIS-CD314
Andante festivo for strings (1922) (orig for string quartet: arr. string orch cspr)
Gothenburg SO, N. Järvi Concert
(10/84) (BIS) ① BIS-CD222
English Stg Orch, W. Boughton Concert
(8/89) (NIMB) ① NI5169
Oslo PO, M. Jansons Concert
(7/93) (EMI) ① CDC7 54804-2
Detroit SO, N. Järvi (r1991) Concert
(8/94) (CHAN) ① CHAN9227
Andante lirico—orchestra
Gothenburg SO, N. Järvi Concert
(6/87) (BIS) ① BIS-CD312
Autrefois, Op. 96/2 (1919)
E.T. Tawaststjerna (trans pf cpsr) Concert
(4/88) (BIS) ① BIS-CD367
M. Einarson, C. Forsberg, Gothenburg SO, N. Järvi Concert
(1/89) (BIS) ① BIS-CD384
Ballet Scene—orchestra (1891)
Gothenburg SO, N. Järvi Concert
(2/91) (BIS) ① BIS-CD472

The Bard—Tone poem, Op. 64 (1913 rev 1914)
SNO, A. Gibson Concert
(9/86) (CHAN) ① [2] CHAN8395/6
Gothenburg SO, N. Järvi Concert
(1/89) (BIS) ① BIS-CD384
LPO, T. Beecham (r1938) Concert
(3/92) (KOCH) ① 37061-2
LPO, T. Beecham (r1938) Concert
(3/92) (EMI) ① CDM7 64027-2
SNO, A. Gibson Concert
(11/92) (CHAN) ① CHAN6586
Canzonetta—strings, Op. 62a (1911)
Gothenburg SO, N. Järvi Concert
(11/85) (BIS) ① BIS-CD263
Gothenburg SO, N. Järvi Concert
(4/87) (BIS) ① BIS-CD311
Scottish Baroque Ens, Lionel Friedman Concert
(10/87) (CRD) ① CRD3342
Serenata of London, B. Wilde (r1994) Concert
(2/95) (CARL) ① PCD1108
Concerto for Violin and Orchestra in D minor, Op. 47 (1903 rev 1905)
1. Allegro moderato; 2. Adagio di molto; 3. Allegro ma non tanto.
I. Perlman, Pittsburgh SO, A. Previn Sinding: Suite, Op. 10.
(9/85) (EMI) ① CDC7 47167-2
V. Mullova, Boston SO, S. Ozawa Tchaikovsky: Violin Concerto.
(5/87) (PHIL) ① 416 821-2PH
S. Mintz, BPO, James Levine Dvořák: Violin Concerto.
(8/87) (DG) ① 419 618-2GH
G. Neveu, Philh, W. Susskind (r1945) Brahms: Violin Concerto.
(3/88) (EMI) ① CDH7 61011-2
S. Ishikawa, Brno St PO, J. Bělohlávek Bruch: Violin Concerto 1.
(9/88) (SUPR) ① 2SUP0002
N. Kennedy, CBSO, S. Rattle (r1987) Symphony 5.
(9/88) (EMI) ① CDC7 49717-2
S. Accardo, LSO, Colin Davis (r1979) Dvořák: Violin Concerto.
(10/88) (PHIL) ① 420 895-2PSL
C. Ferras, BPO, H. von Karajan Concert
(10/88) (DG) ① 419 871-2GGA
M. Fried, Helsinki PO, O. Kamu Concert
(10/88) (FINL) ① 4509-95856-2
C-L. Lin, Philh, E-P. Salonen Nielsen: Violin Concerto.
(1/89) (SONY) ① SK44548
S. Marcovici, Gothenburg SO, N. Järvi Concert
(1/89) (BIS) ① BIS-CD372
D. Oistrakh, Philadelphia, E. Ormandy Tchaikovsky: Violin Concerto.
(11/89) (SONY) ① MPK44854
L. Kavacos, Lahti SO, O. Vänskä Violin Concerto.
(4/91) (BIS) ① BIS-CD500
L. Kavacos, Lahti SO, O. Vänskä (orig vers) Violin Concerto.
(4/91) (BIS) ① BIS-CD500
Y. Menuhin, LPO, A. Boult (r1955) Nielsen: Violin Concerto 2.
(4/91) (EMI) ① CDM7 63987-2
F.P. Zimmermann, Philh, M. Jansons Prokofiev: Violin Concerto 2.
(7/92) (EMI) ① CDC7 54454-2
G. Kremer, LSO, G. Rozhdestvensky (r1977) Schnittke: Concerto Grosso 1.
(9/92) (RCA) ① GD60957
J. Heifetz, LPO, T. Beecham (r1935) Concert
(10/92) (EMI) ① CDH7 64030-2
Z. Francescatti, NYPO, L. Bernstein (r1963) Brahms: Violin Concerto.
(11/92) (SONY) ① SMK47540
T. Little, RLPO, V. Handley Brahms: Violin Concerto.
(2/93) (EMIN) ① CD-EMX2203
I. Perlman, Pittsburgh SO, A. Previn (r1979) Concert
(5/93) (RCA) ① [4] CMS7 64617-2
I. Perlman, Boston SO, E. Leinsdorf (r1966) Concert
(7/93) (RCA) ① 07863 56520-2
G. Shaham, Philh, G. Sinopoli (r1994) Tchaikovsky: Violin Concerto.
(9/93) (DG) ① 437 540-2GH
I. Gitlis, Vienna Pro Musica orch, J. Horenstein (r1950s) Concert
(11/93) (VOX) ① [2] CDX2 5505
J. Rachlin, Pittsburgh SO, L. Maazel (r1992) Concert
(6/94) (SONY) ① SK53272
D. Oistrakh, Stockholm Fest Orch, S. Ehrling (r1954) Beethoven: Violin Concerto.
(7/94) (TEST) ① SBT1032
G. Kulenkampff, BPO, W. Furtwängler (pp1943) Schumann: Violin Concerto.
(9/94) (DANT) ① LYS012
J. Heifetz, Chicago SO, W. Hendl (r1959) Concert
(11/94) (RCA) ① [65] 09026 61778-2(11-15)
J. Heifetz, LPO, T. Beecham (r1935) Concert
(11/94) (RCA) ① [65] 09026 61778-2(18)
Midori, Israel PO, Z. Mehta (r1993) Bruch: Scottish Fantasy.
(2/95) (SONY) ① SK58967
K-W. Chung, LSO, A. Previn (r1970) Tchaikovsky: Violin Concerto.
(5/95) (DECC) ① 425 080-2DCS
I. Perlman, Pittsburgh SO, A. Previn Concert
(6/95) (EMI) ① [20] CZS4 83177-2(1)
B. Belkin, RPO, J. Hirokami (r1994) Bruch: Violin Concerto 1.
(10/95) (DENO) ① CO-78951
J. Heifetz, LPO, T. Beecham (r1935) Concert
(11/95) (PEAR) ① [2] GEMMCDS9157

The Dryad—tone poem, Op. 45/1 (1910)
SNO, A. Gibson Concert
(9/86) (CHAN) ① [2] CHAN8395/6
Gothenburg SO, N. Järvi Concert
(10/87) (BIS) ① BIS-CD359
E.T. Tawaststjerna (trans pf cpsr) Concert
(4/88) (BIS) ① BIS-CD366
En Saga, Op. 9 (1892, rev 1902)
SNO, A. Gibson Concert
(9/86) (CHAN) ① [2] CHAN8395/6
Philh, Vladimir Ashkenazy Concert
(12/88) (DECC) ① 417 762-2DM
Helsinki RSO, O. Kamu Concert
(12/91) (DG) ① [2] 413 158-2GW2
LPO, T. Beecham (r1938/9) Concert
(3/92) (KOCH) ① 37061-2
Slovak PO, A. Leaper Concert
(4/92) (NAXO) ① 8 550200
Danish Nat RSO, L. Segerstam Concert
(4/92) (CHAN) ① CHAN8965
Helsinki PO, S. Comissiona Concert
(4/92) (ONDI) ① ODE767-2
Los Angeles PO, E-P. Salonen Legends.
(8/92) (SONY) ① SK48067
BPO, H. von Karajan Concert
(11/92) (EMI) ① CDM7 64331-2
Atlanta SO, Y. Levi (r1992) Concert
(6/93) (TELA) ① CD80320
Philh, Vladimir Ashkenazy (r1981) Concert
(7/93) (DECC) ① 430 757-2DM
Pittsburgh SO, L. Maazel (r1992) Concert
(6/94) (SONY) ① SK53272
NBC SO, A. Toscanini (bp1949) Concert
(10/95) (DELL) ① CDDA9024
Finlandia, Op. 26 (1899 rev 1900)
Gothenburg SO, N. Järvi Symphony 1.
(10/84) (BIS) ① BIS-CD221
LSO, G. Rozhdestvensky Concert
(6/86) (CSTL) ① CJCD10002
SNO, A. Gibson Concert
(9/86) (CHAN) ① [2] CHAN8395/6
Boston SO, Colin Davis Concert
(11/86) (PHIL) ① [4] 416 600-2PH4
E.T. Tawaststjerna (trans pf cpsr) Concert
(4/88) (BIS) ① BIS-CD366
BPO, H. von Karajan Concert
(10/88) (DG) ① 419 871-2GGA
Helsinki PO, O. Kamu Concert
(10/88) (FINL) ① 4509-95856-2
Finnish RSO, J-P. Saraste Concert
(11/88) (RCA) ① RD87765
Philh, Vladimir Ashkenazy Concert
(12/88) (DECC) ① 417 762-2DM
Berlin SO, C.P. Flor (pp1988) Concert
(4/90) (RCA) ① RD60119
LPO, T. Beecham (r1938) Concert
(7/90) (EMI) ① CDM7 63397-2
SNO, A. Gibson (r1977) Concert
(2/91) (CHAN) ① CHAN6508
BPO, H. von Karajan Concert
(12/91) (DG) ① [2] 413 158-2GW2
Oslo PO, M. Jansons Concert
(7/92) (EMI) ① CDC7 54273-2
Danish Nat RSO, L. Segerstam Symphony 2.
(8/92) (CHAN) ① CHAN9020
Philh, Vladimir Ashkenazy Concert
(8/92) (DECC) ① 430 737-2DM
NBC SO, A. Toscanini (r1952) Concert
(11/92) (RCA) ① GD60294
BPO, H. von Karajan Concert
(11/92) (EMI) ① CDM7 64331-2
NYPO, L. Bernstein Concert
(5/93) (SONY) ① SMK47549
Atlanta SO, Y. Levi (r1992) Concert
(6/93) (TELA) ① CD80320
Philh, Vladimir Ashkenazy (r1980) Concert
(7/93) (DECC) ① 430 757-2DM
Boston SO, Vladimir Ashkenazy (pp1992) Concert
(10/93) (DECC) ① 436 566-2DH
BPO, James Levine Concert
(3/94) (DG) ① 437 828-2GH
BPO, H. von Karajan (r1964) Concert
(6/94) (DG) ① 439 418-2GCL
C. Herrick (r1993; arr H.A. Fricker) Concert
(4/94) (HYPE) ① CDA66676
G. Thalben-Ball (r c1930: arr org) Concert
(9/94) (BEUL) ① 1PD5
Boston SO, Colin Davis Concert
(9/94) (PHIL) ① 442 389-2PM
6 Humoresques—violin and orchestra, Opp. 87/89 (1917)
Op. 87—; 1. D minor; 2. D. Op. 89—; 3. G minor; 4. G minor; 5. E flat; 6. G minor.
D-S. Kang, Gothenburg SO, N. Järvi Concert
(2/91) (BIS) ① BIS-CD472

Spagnuolo—piano (1913)
A. Servadei (r1992) *Concert*
(3/94) (CNTI) ① **CCD1059**
Valse chevaleresque—piano, Op. 96c (1919-20)
A. Servadei (r1994) *Concert*
(12/95) (CNTI) ① **CCD1071**
Valse lyrique—piano, Op. 96a (1919-20)
A. Servadei (r1994) *Concert*
(12/95) (CNTI) ① **CCD1071**

SECTION IV: VOCAL AND CHORAL

Arioso—song, Op. 3 (1893) (Wds. Runeberg)
M.A. Häggander, Gothenburg SO, J. Panula *Concert*
(2/86) (BIS) ① **BIS-CD270**
A.S. von Otter, B. Forsberg *Concert*
(6/90) (BIS) ① **BIS-CD457**
K. Flagstad, LSO, Ø. Fjeldstad (r1958) *Concert*
(12/95) (LOND) ① **440 492-2LM**
K. Flagstad, LSO, Ø. Fjeldstad (r1958) *Concert*
(12/95) (LOND) ① **[5] 440 490-2LM5(1)**
Bell Melody of Berghaill Church—partsong, Op. 65/2 (1911-12)
E.T. Tawaststjerna (trans pf cpsr) *Concert*
(4/88) (BIS) ① **BIS-CD367**
5 Christmas Songs, Op. 1 (1895-1913)
1. Now Christmas stands at the snowy gate (wds. Topelius); 2. Now Christmas comes (wds. Topelius); 3. Outside it grows dark (wds. Topelius); 4. Give me no splendour (wds. Topelius); 5. High are the snowdrifts (wds. Joukahainen).
Cpte M. Groop, L. Derwinger (r1994) *Concert*
(9/94) (BIS) ① **BIS-CD657**
Finlandia—male/mixed chorus and orchestra (c1930 rev 1948) (Wds. Koskenniemi)
Laulun Ystävät Male Ch, Gothenburg SO, N. Järvi
(arr. cpsr) *Concert* (4/87) (BIS) ① **BIS-CD314**
Helsinki Univ Male Ch, M. Hyökki *Concert*
(10/88) (FINL) ① **4509-95849-2**
K. Borg, E. Werba (1958) *Concert*
(12/94) (FINL) ① **[3] 4509-95606-2**
Fridolin's Folly—male chorus (1917) (Wds. Karlfeldt)
Helsinki Univ Male Ch, M. Hyökki *Concert*
(10/88) (FINL) ① **4509-95849-2**
Have you courage? (Har du mod?)—male chorus and orchestra, Op. 31/2 (1904)
Laulun Ystävät Male Ch, Gothenburg SO, N. Järvi
Concert (4/87) (BIS) ① **BIS-CD314**
E.T. Tawaststjerna (trans pf cpsr) *Concert*
(4/88) (BIS) ① **BIS-CD366**
Hymn to Thais—song (1900) (Wds. Borgström)
M. Groop, L. Derwinger (r1994) *Concert*
(9/94) (BIS) ① **BIS-CD657**
In the moonlight—male chorus (1916) (Wds. Suonio)
Helsinki Univ Male Ch, M. Hyökki *Concert*
(10/88) (FINL) ① **4509-95849-2**
Jonah's voyage—male chorus (1918) (Wds. Kaarlfeldt)
Helsinki Univ Male Ch, M. Hyökki *Concert*
(10/88) (FINL) ① **4509-95849-2**
Kullervo—symphony: sop, bar, male choir and orch, Op. 7 (1892) (wds. Kalevala)
1. Introduction; 2. Kullervo's Youth; 3. Kullervo and his sister; 4. Kullervo goes to War; 5. Kullervo's Death.
K. Mattila, J. Hynninen, Laulun Ystävät Male Ch, Gothenburg SO, N. Järvi
(1/87) (BIS) ① **BIS-CD313**
M. Rørholm, J. Hynninen, Helsinki Univ Chor, Los Angeles PO, E-P. Salonen (r1992)
(7/93) (SONY) ① **SK52563**
E-L. Saarinen, J. Hynninen, Estonian St Academic Male Ch, Helsinki Univ Male Ch, Helsinki PO, P. Berglund (1985) (7/94) (EMI) ① **CDM5 65080-2**
The Lover—male/mixed chorus, Op. 14 (1893 rev 1898) (Wds. Kanteletar)
P. Lindroos, Helsinki Univ Male Ch, M. Hyökki *Concert* (10/88) (FINL) ① **4509-95849-2**
Luonnotar—soprano and orchestra, Op. 70 (1913) (Wds. from Kalevala)
M.A. Häggander, Gothenburg SO, J. Panula *Concert*
(2/86) (BIS) ① **BIS-CD270**
P. Bryn-Julson, SNO, A. Gibson *Concert*
(9/86) (CHAN) ① **[2] CHAN8395/6**
P. Bryn-Julson, SNO, A. Gibson *Concert*
(11/92) (CHAN) ① **CHAN6586**
E. Söderström, Philh, Vladimir Ashkenazy (r1980)
(7/93) (DECC) ① **430 757-2DM**
G. Jones, LSO, A. Dorati (r1969) *Concert*
(10/94) (EMI) ① **CDM5 65182-2**

March of the Finnish Jaeger Battalion—male chorus and orchestra, Op.91/1 (?1917) (Wds. Nurmio)
Laulun Ystävät Male Ch, Gothenburg SO, N. Järvi
Concert (4/87) (BIS) ① **BIS-CD314**
E.T. Tawaststjerna (trans pf cpsr) *Concert*
(4/88) (BIS) ① **BIS-CD367**
Helsinki Univ Male Ch, Helsinki Garrison Band, E. Juuri (arr Kuikka) *Concert*
(10/88) (FINL) ① **4509-95849-2**
Helsinki PO, R. Kajanus (r1928) *Concert*
(2/94) (KOCH) ① **37133-2**
Narcissus—song (?1918) (Wds. B. Gripenberg)
A.S. von Otter, B. Forsberg *Concert*
(6/90) (BIS) ① **BIS-CD457**
Natus in curas—male chorus, Op. 21 (1896) (Wds. Gustafsoon)
Helsinki Univ Male Ch, M. Hyökki *Concert*
(10/88) (FINL) ① **4509-95849-2**
One hears the storm outside—male chorus (1918) (Wds. Schybergson)
Helsinki Univ Male Ch, M. Hyökki *Concert*
(10/88) (FINL) ① **4509-95849-2**
The Origin of Fire—baritone, male voices and orchestra, Op. 32 (1902 rev 1910) (Wds. Kalevala)
S. Tiilikainen, Laulun Ystävät Male Ch, Gothenburg SO, N. Järvi *Concert* (4/87) (BIS) ① **BIS-CD314**
9 Partsongs—male chorus, Op. 18 (1893-1907) (Wds. various)
1. To the Fatherland (wds. Cajander); 2. My brothers abroad (wds. Aho); 3. Fire on the island (wds. from Kanteletar, Canto 186); 4. Busy as a thrush (wds. from Kanteletar, Canto 219); 5. The woodman's song (wds. Kivi); 6. The song of my heart (wds. Kivi); 7. The broken voice (wds. from Kanteletar, Canto 57); 8. Haill moon (wds. from Kalevala); 9. The boat journey (wds. Kalevala).
1-3, 5-9. Helsinki Univ Male Ch, M. Hyökki *Concert*
(10/88) (FINL) ① **4509-95849-2**
5 Partsongs—male voices, Op. 84 (1914-15)
1. Herr Lager (wds. Fröding); 2. On the mountain (wds. Gripenberg); 3. A dream chord (wds. Fröding); 4. Eternal Eros (wds. Gripenberg); 5. To sea (wds. Reuter).
Cpte P. Saurola, Helsinki Univ Male Ch, M. Hyökki *Concert* (10/88) (FINL) ① **4509-95849-2**
2 Partsongs—male chorus, Op. 108 (1925) (Wds. Kyösti)
1. Humoresque; 2. Wanderers on the long way.
Cpte Helsinki Univ Male Ch, M. Hyökki *Concert*
(10/88) (FINL) ① **4509-95849-2**
The Rapids-Shooter's Brides—song, Op. 33 (1897) (Wds. Oksanen)
J. Hynninen, Gothenburg SO, J. Panula *Concert*
(2/86) (BIS) ① **BIS-CD270**
Resemblance—male chorus (1922) (Wds. Runeberg)
Helsinki Univ Male Ch, M. Hyökki *Concert*
(10/88) (FINL) ① **4509-95849-2**
The Roaring of a wave—male chorus (1918) (Wds. Schybergson)
Helsinki Univ Male Ch, M. Hyökki *Concert*
(10/88) (FINL) ① **4509-95849-2**
Row, row duck—song (1899) (Wds. Koskimies)
A.S. von Otter, B. Forsberg *Concert*
(6/90) (BIS) ① **BIS-CD457**
K. Borg, E. Werba (1958) *Concert*
(12/94) (FINL) ① **[3] 4509-95606-2**
Scout March—mixed vv and orchestra, Op. 91/2 (1917)
E.T. Tawaststjerna (trans pf cpsr) *Concert*
(4/88) (BIS) ① **BIS-CD367**
Serenade—song with orchestra (1895) (Wds. Stagnelius)
J. Hynninen, Gothenburg SO, J. Panula *Concert*
(2/86) (BIS) ① **BIS-CD270**
Small girls—song (1920) (Wds. Procopé)
M. Groop, L. Derwinger (r1994) *Concert*
(9/94) (BIS) ① **BIS-CD657**
Song of the Athenians—male chorus and orchestra, Op.31/3 (1899) (Wds. Rydberg)
Laulun Ystävät Male Ch, Gothenburg SO, N. Järvi
Concert (4/87) (BIS) ① **BIS-CD314**
E.T. Tawaststjerna (trans pf cpsr) *Concert*
(4/88) (BIS) ① **BIS-CD366**
7 Songs, Op. 13 (1891-92) (Wds. J. L. Runeberg)
1. 'Neath the fir trees; 2. A kiss's hope; 3. The heart's morning; 4. Spring is flying; 5. The dream; 6. To Frigga; 7. The young hunter.
2, 4. A. Gjevang, E.S. Nökleberg *Concert*
(11/91) (VICT) ① **VCD19007**

4. M.A. Häggander, Gothenburg SO, J. Panula
Concert (2/86) (BIS) ① **BIS-CD270**
4. B. Nilsson, G. Parsons (pp1974) *Concert*
(6/92) (BLUE) ① **ABCD009**
4. K. Flagstad, LSO, Ø. Fjeldstad (r1958) *Concert*
(12/95) (LOND) ① **440 492-2LM**
4. K. Flagstad, LSO, Ø. Fjeldstad (r1958) *Concert*
(12/95) (LOND) ① **[5] 440 490-2LM5(1)**
4-6. K. Borg, E. Werba (1958) *Concert*
(12/94) (FINL) ① **[3] 4509-95606-2**
6 Songs, Op. 17 (1891-98)
1. And I questioned them no further (1894: wds. J. L. Runeberg); 2. Slumber (1894: wds. K. A. Tavaststjerna); 3. Enticement (1891: wds. K. A. Tavaststjerna); 4. Astray (1894: wds. K. A. Tavaststjerna); 5. The dragonfly (?1894: wds. O. Levertin); 6. To evening (1898: wds. A. V. Forsman-Koskimies); 7. Driftwood (1898: wds. I. Calamnius).
Cpte A.S. von Otter, B. Forsberg *Concert*
(6/90) (BIS) ① **BIS-CD457**
1. M.A. Häggander, Gothenburg SO, J. Panula
Concert (2/86) (BIS) ① **BIS-CD270**
1, 6. K. Flagstad, LSO, Ø. Fjeldstad (r1958) *Concert*
(12/95) (LOND) ① **440 492-2LM**
1, 6. K. Flagstad, LSO, Ø. Fjeldstad (r1958) *Concert*
(12/95) (LOND) ① **[5] 440 490-2LM5(1)**
3, 6, 7. K. Borg, E. Werba (1958) *Concert*
(12/94) (FINL) ① **[3] 4509-95606-2**
6. B. Nilsson, G. Parsons (pp1974) *Concert*
(6/92) (BLUE) ① **ABCD009**
7. A. Gjevang, E.S. Nökleberg *Concert*
(11/91) (VICT) ① **VCD19007**
6 Songs, Op. 36 (1899)
1. Black roses (wds. E. Josephson); 2. But my bird (wds. L. Runeberg); 3. Tennis at Trianon (wds. G. Fröding); 4. Sigh, sedges, sigh (wds. G. Fröding); 5. March song (wds. J. J. Wecksell); 6. The diamond on the March snow (wds. J.J. Wecksell).
Cpte A.S. von Otter, B. Forsberg *Concert*
(6/90) (BIS) ① **BIS-CD457**
1, 2, 4, 6. K. Flagstad, LSO, Ø. Fjeldstad (r1958)
Concert (12/95) (LOND) ① **440 492-2LM**
1, 2, 4, 6. K. Flagstad, LSO, Ø. Fjeldstad (r1958)
Concert (12/95) (LOND) ① **[5] 440 490-2LM5(1)**
1, 4. J. Björling, H. Ebert (r1940) *Concert*
(10/93) (NIMB) ① **NI7842**
1, 4, 6. K. Borg, E. Werba (1958) *Concert*
(12/94) (FINL) ① **[3] 4509-95606-2**
4. J. Björling, Bergen SO, C. Garaguly (pp1954)
(8/88) (BLUE) ① **ABCD006**
4, 6. A. Gjevang, E.S. Nökleberg *Concert*
(11/91) (VICT) ① **VCD19007**
6. J. Hynninen, Gothenburg SO, J. Panula *Concert*
(2/86) (BIS) ① **BIS-CD270**
5 Songs, Op. 37 (1898-1902)
1. The first kiss (wds. J. L. Runeberg); 2. Little Lasse (wds. Z. Topelius); 3. Sunrise (wds. T. Hedberg); 4. Was it a dream? (wds. J. J. Wecksell); 5. The maiden's tryst (wds. J. L. Runeberg).
Cpte A.S. von Otter, B. Forsberg *Concert*
(6/90) (BIS) ① **BIS-CD457**
1. A. Gjevang, E.S. Nökleberg *Concert*
(11/91) (VICT) ① **VCD19007**
1. L. Lail, S-G. Andrén (r1946) *Concert*
(4/92) (EMI) ① **[7] CHS7 69741-2(5)**
1, 4. B. Nilsson, G. Parsons (pp1974) *Concert*
(6/92) (BLUE) ① **ABCD009**
1, 4, 5. K. Flagstad, LSO, Ø. Fjeldstad (r1958) *Concert*
(12/95) (LOND) ① **[5] 440 490-2LM5(1)**
1, 4, 5. K. Flagstad, LSO, Ø. Fjeldstad (r1958) *Concert*
(12/95) (LOND) ① **440 492-2LM**
3. M.A. Häggander, Gothenburg SO, J. Panula
Concert (2/86) (BIS) ① **BIS-CD270**
5 Songs, Op. 38 (1902-04)
1. Autumn evening (wds. Rydberg); 2. On a balcony by the sea (wds. Rydberg); 3. In the night (wds. Rydberg); 4. The harper and his son (wds. Rydberg); 5. I wish I dwelt in India land (wds. Fröding).
1. M.A. Häggander, Gothenburg SO, J. Panula
Concert (2/86) (BIS) ① **BIS-CD270**
1, 2. K. Flagstad, LSO, Ø. Fjeldstad (r1958) *Concert*
(12/95) (LOND) ① **440 492-2LM**
1, 2. K. Flagstad, LSO, Ø. Fjeldstad (r1958) *Concert*
(12/95) (LOND) ① **[5] 440 490-2LM5(1)**
2. J. Hynninen, Gothenburg SO, J. Panula *Concert*
(2/86) (BIS) ① **BIS-CD270**
8 Songs, Op. 57 (1909) (Wds. Josephson)
1. Alvan and the snail; 2. A little flower in the path; 3. The millwheel; 4. May; 5. The bare tree; 6. Duke Magnus; 7. The flower of friendship; 8. The elf king.
Cpte M. Groop, L. Derwinger (r1994) *Concert*
(9/94) (BIS) ① **BIS-CD657**
8 Songs, Op. 61 (1910)
1. Slowly as the evening sun (wds. Tavaststjerna); 2. Lapping waters (wds. Rydberg); 3. When I dream (wds. Tavaststjerna); 4. Romea (wds. Tavaststjerna);

5. Romance (wds. Tavastsjerna); 6. Dolce far niente
(wds. Tavastsjerna); 7. Idle wish (wds. Runeberg); 8.
Spell of springtime (wds. Gripenberg).
4. K. Borg, E. Werba (1958) *Concert*
(12/94) (FINL) ① [3] **4509-95606-2**
6 Songs, Op. 72 (1907-14)
1. Farewell (wds. Rydberg: 1914); 2. Orion's belt
(wds. Topelius: 1914); 3. The kiss (wds. Rydberg:
1915); 4. The echo nymph (wds. Kyösti: 1915); 5. Der
Wanderer und der Bach (wds. Grief: 1915); 6. A
hundred ways (wds. Runeberg: 1907).
3-6. M. Groop, L. Derwinger (r1994) *Concert*
(9/94) (BIS) ① **BIS-CD657**
6 Songs, Op. 86 (1916)
1. The coming of Spring (wds. Tavastsjerna); 2.
Longing is my heritage (wds. Karlfeldt); 3. Hidden
union (wds. Snoilsky); 4. And is there a thought?
(wds. Tavastsjerna); 5. The singer's reward (wds.
Snoilsky); 6. Ye sisters, ye brothers (wds. Lybeck).
Cpte M. Groop, L. Derwinger (r1994) *Concert*
(9/94) (BIS) ① **BIS-CD657**
6 Songs, Op. 88 (1917)
1. The anemone (wds. F. M. Franzén); 2. The two
roses (wds. F. M. Franzén); 3. The star-flower (wds.
F. M. Franzén); 4. The primrose (wds. J. L.
Runeberg); 5. The thorn (wds. J. L. Runeberg); 6.
The flower's desert (wds. J. L. Runeberg).
Cpte A.S. von Otter, B. Forsberg *Concert*
(6/90) (BIS) ① **BIS-CD457**

SECTION V: STAGE WORKS

**Belshazzar's Feast—incidental music to
Procopé's play, Op. 51** (1906)
EXCERPTS—; 1. Alla marcia; 2. Nocturne; 3. The
Jewish Girl's Song; 4. Allegretto; 5. Dance of Life; 6.
Dance of Death; 7. Tempo sostenuto; 8. Allegro.
Cpte E.T. Tawastsjerna (trans pf cpsr) *Concert*
(4/88) (BIS) ① **BIS-CD367**
1. Gothenburg SO, N. Järvi *Concert*
(10/87) (BIS) ① **BIS-CD359**
1. Slovak PO, A. Leaper *Concert*
(4/92) (NAXO) ① **8 550200**
2. J. Heifetz, B. Smith (r1967) *Concert*
(11/94) (RCA) ① [65] **09026 61778-2(33)**
**King Christian II—incidental music to A.
Paul's play, Op. 27** (1898)
EXCERPTS: 1. Nocturne; 2. Elegie; 3. Musette; 4.
Serenade; 5. Ballade; 6. Menuetto; 7. Fool's Song of
the Spider.
1-5. Gothenburg SO, N. Järvi *Symphony 3.*
(10/84) (BIS) ① **BIS-CD228**
1-5. E.T. Tawastsjerna (trans pf cpsr) *Concert*
(4/88) (BIS) ① **BIS-CD366**
1-7. S. Tiilikainen, Iceland SO, P. Sakari (r1992)
Concert (7/93) (CHAN) ① **CHAN9158**
7. J. Hynninen, Gothenburg SO, J. Panula *Concert*
(2/86) (BIS) ① **BIS-CD270**
7. M. Groop, L. Derwinger (r1994) *Concert*
(9/94) (BIS) ① **BIS-CD657**
**The Language of Birds—wedding march for
play** (1911)
Gothenburg SO, N. Järvi *Scaramouche.*
(4/92) (BIS) ① **BIS-CD502**
**The Maiden in the Tower—opera: 1 act (8
scenes)** (1896) (Lib. Hertzberg)
Cpte M.A. Häggander, E. Hagegård, J. Hynninen, T.
Kruse, Gothenburg Concert Hall Ch, Gothenburg SO,
N. Järvi *Karelia Suite.* (3/85) (BIS) ① **BIS-CD250**
**Pelleas and Melisande—incidental music to
Maeterlinck's play, Op. 46** (1905)
1. At the castle gate; 2. Melisande; 3. On the sea
shore; 4. Spring in the park; 5. Three blind sisters; 6.
Pastorale; 7. At the spinning wheel; 8. Intermezzo; 9.
Death of Melisande.
Gothenburg SO, N. Järvi *Symphony 6.*
(10/84) (BIS) ① **BIS-CD237**
E.T. Tawastsjerna (trans pf cpsr) *Concert*
(4/88) (BIS) ① **BIS-CD366**
RPO, Y. Butt *Concert* (7/89) (ASV) ① **CDDCA649**
English Stg Orch, W. Boughton *Concert*
(8/89) (NIMB) ① **NI5169**
Espoo CO, J. Lamminmäki *Concert*
(8/92) (FINL) ① **4509-95859-2**
Iceland SO, P. Sakari (r1992) *Concert*
(7/93) (CHAN) ① **CHAN9158**
2. NYPO, T. Beecham (r1942) *Concert*
(7/95) (DUTT) ① **CDAX8013**
2. NYPO, T. Beecham (r1942) *Concert*
(11/95) (BEEC) ① **BEECHAM6**
2, 6-9. LSO, A. Collins (r1954) *Concert*
(6/94) (BEUL) ① **3PD8**
4, 8, 9. LPO, T. Beecham (r1939) *Concert*
(7/95) (DUTT) ① **CDAX8013**
5. A.S. von Otter, B. Forsberg *Concert*
(6/90) (BIS) ① **BIS-CD457**

**Scaramouche—incidental music, Op. 71
(1913)** (Pantomime, P. Knudsen and
M.T.Bloch)
E.T. Tawastsjerna (trans pf cpsr) *Concert*
(4/88) (BIS) ① **BIS-CD367**
Gothenburg SO, N. Järvi *Language of Birds.*
(4/92) (BIS) ① **BIS-CD502**
Scene d'amour N-E. Sparf, B. Forsberg (arr cmpsr:
vn, pf) *Concert* (9/92) (BIS) ① **BIS-CD525**
Swanwhite—incidental music, Op. 54 (1908)
1. The Peacock; 2. The Harp; 3. The Maiden with the
Roses; 4. Listen, the Robin Sings; 5. The Prince
Alone; 6. Swanwhite and the Prince; 7. Song of
Praise.
RPO, Y. Butt *Concert* (7/89) (ASV) ① **CDDCA649**
1. Gothenburg SO, N. Järvi *Concert*
(10/87) (BIS) ① **BIS-CD359**
2, 3, 5, 6, 7. Iceland SO, P. Sakari (r1992) *Concert*
(7/93) (CHAN) ① **CHAN9158**
3. Boston SO, S. Koussevitzky (r1936) *Concert*
(7/90) (PEAR) ① [2] **GEMMCDS9408**
**The Tempest—concert suites from
incidental music, Op. 109** (1925)
1. Prelude. SUITE NO. 1: 2. The oak-tree; 3.
Humoresque; 4. Caliban's Song; 5. The Harvesters;
6. Canon; 7. Scene; 8. Intrada—Berceuse; 9.
Entr'acte; 10. Ariel's Song; 11. The Storm. SUITE
NO. 2: 12. Chorus of the Winds; 13. Intermezzo; 14.
Dance of the Nymphs; 15. Prospero; 16. Song I; 17.
Song II; 18. Miranda; 19. The Naiads; 20. Dance
Episode.
E.T. Tawastsjerna (trans pf cpsr) *Concert*
(4/88) (BIS) ① **BIS-CD367**
1. LPO, T. Beecham (r1938) *Concert*
(3/92) (EMI) ① **CDM7 64027-2**
1, 2, 3, 4, 8, 15, 18. LPO, T. Beecham (r1937/8)
Concert (7/95) (DUTT) ① **CDAX8013**
2-11. Danish Nat RSO, L. Segerstam *Symphony 4.*
(8/91) (CHAN) ① **CHAN8943**
2-4, 6-8, 11-14, 16-19. RPO, T. Beecham (r1955)
Concert (7/90) (EMI) ① **CDM7 63397-2**
8. Philadelphia, L. Stokowski (r1937) *Concert*
(6/92) (DELL) ① **CDDA9023**
**Twelfth Night—songs included in incidental
music, Op. 60 (1909—1,2)** (Wds.
Shakespeare)
1. Come, away, death; 2. When that I was and a tiny
boy.
1. J. Hynninen, Gothenburg SO, J. Panula *Concert*
(2/86) (BIS) ① **BIS-CD270**
1. K. Flagstad, LSO, Ø. Fjeldstad (r1958) *Concert*
(12/95) (LOND) ① **440 492-2LM**
1. K. Flagstad, LSO, Ø. Fjeldstad (1958) *Concert*
(12/95) (LOND) ① [5] **440 490-2LM5(1)**

SIBELLA, Gabriele

SECTION IV: VOCAL AND CHORAL

La Girometta
L. Pavarotti, NYPO, L. Magiera (pp1993) *Concert*
(2/95) (DECC) ① **444 450-2DH**

SIECZYŃSKI, Rudolf (1879–1952) Austria

SECTION IV: VOCAL AND CHORAL

Wien, du Stadt meiner Träume—song (Wds.
cpsr)
E. Schwarzkopf, chor, Philh, O. Ackermann *Concert*
(1/86) (EMI) ① **CDC7 47284-2**
P. Domingo, ECO, J. Rudel *Concert*
(2/87) (EMI) ① **CDC7 47398-2**
R. Tauber, Orch, E. Hauke (1928) *Concert*
(12/89) (EMI) ① **CDH7 69787-2**
B. Nilsson, G. Parsons (pp1974) *Concert*
(6/92) (BLUE) ① **ABCD009**
R. Tauber, orch, I. Lewis (r1935: Eng) *Concert*
(9/92) (MMOI) ① **CDMOIR409**

SIEDE

SECTION I: ORCHESTRAL

Chinese Street Serenade—orchestra
A. Campoli, Orch, W. Goehr (arr Crooke) *Concert*
(10/91) (PEAR) ① **PASTCD9744**

SIEFERT, Paul (1586–1666) Germany

SECTION II: CHAMBER

Canzon à 8 (pub 1651) (from 'Psalmorum
Davidicorum')
Musica Fiata, R. Wilson (r1991) *Concert*
(8/93) (DHM) ① **05472 77183-2**

SILBERTA, Rhea (1900–1959) USA

SECTION IV: VOCAL AND CHORAL

Beloved—song
R. Ponselle, orch, J. Pasternack (r1925) *Concert*
(11/94) (ROMO) ① [2] **81006-2**

SILCHER, (Philipp) Friedrich (1789–1860) Germany

SECTION IV: VOCAL AND CHORAL

Faithful Shepherd lead me—hymn (tune:
Paster Pastorum)
St Paul's Cath Ch, C. Dearnley, John Scott *Concert*
(7/90) (HYPE) ① **CDH88036**

SILÉSU, Lao (1883–1953) Italy

SECTION IV: VOCAL AND CHORAL

A little love, a little kiss—song (Wds. A.
Ross)
R. Crooks, orch (r1933) *Concert*
(9/93) (CLAR) ① **CDGSE78-50-50**

SILVESTRI, Alan (20th Cent) USA

SECTION V: STAGE WORKS

My Stepmother Is An Alien—film score
(1988)
EXCERPTS: 1. The Klystron.
1. Prague City PO, W. Motzing (r1993) *Concert*
(8/94) (SILV) ① **FILMCD146**

SIMON, Anton (1850–1916) France/Russia

SECTION V: STAGE WORKS

**Song of love triumphant—opera, Op. 46
(1897—Moscow)** (Lib. N. Vilde, after
Turgenev)
O pure creature N. Shevelev, anon (r1901) *Concert*
(6/93) (PEAR) ① [3] **GEMMCDS9007/9(2)**

SIMPSON, Christopher (c1605–1669) England

SECTION II: CHAMBER

**Division on a Ground in E minor—2 viola da
gambas and harpsichord**
W. Kuijken, S. Kuijken, R. Kohnen *Concert*
(1/87) (ACCE) ① **ACC68014D**
Division on a Ground in F—2 bass viols
W. Kuijken, S. Kuijken, R. Kohnen *Concert*
(1/87) (ACCE) ① **ACC68014D**
Division on a Ground in G—2 bass viols
W. Kuijken, S. Kuijken, R. Kohnen *Concert*
(1/87) (ACCE) ① **ACC68014D**
**Divisions on a Ground—bass viol and
continuo (pub 1665)** (in 'The Division Viol')
Sonnerie Trio (r1992) *Concert*
(5/94) (TELD) ① **4509-90841-2**
Scaramouche (r1992) *Concert*
(5/94) (CHNN) ① **CCS4792**
**Divisions on 'John come kiss me
now'—viola da gamba and continuo** (ed. M.
Levy)
Palladian Ens (r1992) *Concert*
(7/93) (LINN) ① **CKD010**

SECTION III: INSTRUMENTAL

Prelude—bass viol (pub 1665) (in 'The
Division Viol')
S. Cunningham (r1992) *Concert*
(5/94) (TELD) ① **4509-90841-2**
Scaramouche (r1992) *Concert*
(5/94) (CHNN) ① **CCS4792**

SIMPSON, Robert (Wilfred Levick) (b 1921) England

SECTION I: ORCHESTRAL

Energy—brass band (1971)
Desford Colliery Caterpillar Band, J. Watson *Concert*
(9/91) (HYPE) ① **CDA66449**
Desford Colliery Caterpillar Band, J. Watson
(pp1991) *Concert* (8/92) (POLY) ① **QPRL049D**
The Four Temperaments—brass band (1983)
Desford Colliery Caterpillar Band, J. Watson *Concert*
(9/91) (HYPE) ① **CDA66449**
Introduction and Allegro on a Bass by Max Reger—brass band (1987)
Desford Colliery Caterpillar Band, J. Watson *Concert*
(9/91) (HYPE) ① **CDA66449**
Symphony No. 2 (1956)
Bournemouth SO, V. Handley *Symphony 4.*
(12/92) (HYPE) ① **CDA66505**
Symphony No. 3 (1962)
RPO, V. Handley (r1994) *Symphony 5.*
(2/95) (HYPE) ① **CDA66728**
Symphony No. 4 (1971-72)
Bournemouth SO, V. Handley *Symphony 2.*
(12/92) (HYPE) ① **CDA66505**
Symphony No. 5 (1972)
RPO, V. Handley (r1994) *Symphony 3.*
(2/95) (HYPE) ① **CDA66728**
Symphony No. 6 (1977)
RLPO, V. Handley (r1987) *Symphony 7.*
(6/88) (HYPE) ① **CDA66280**
Symphony No. 7 (1977)
RLPO, V. Handley (r1987) *Symphony 6.*
(6/88) (HYPE) ① **CDA66280**
Symphony No. 9 (1987)
Bournemouth SO, V. Handley (incl talk by cmpsr)
(12/88) (HYPE) ① **CDA66299**
Symphony No. 10 (1988)
RLPO, V. Handley (10/91) (HYPE) ① **CDA66510**
Volcano—brass band (1978)
Desford Colliery Caterpillar Band, J. Watson *Concert*
(9/91) (HYPE) ① **CDA66449**
Black Dyke Mills Band, P. Parkes (pp1979) *Concert*
(3/94) (CHAN) ① **CHAN4522**
Vortex—brass band (1989)
Desford Colliery Caterpillar Band, J. Watson *Concert*
(9/91) (HYPE) ① **CDA66449**

SECTION II: CHAMBER

Quartet for Horn, Violin, Cello and Piano (1975)
R. Watkins, P. Lowbury, C. Dearnley, C. G. Armytage
(r1993) *Horn Trio.* (12/94) (HYPE) ① **CDA66695**
Quintet for Clarinet, Bass Clarinet and String Trio (1983)
J. Farrall, F. Cross, Vanbrugh Qt (r1992) *Concert*
(7/93) (HYPE) ① **CDA66626**
Sonata for Violin and Piano (1984)
P. Lowbury, C. G. Armytage (r1993) *Piano Trio*
(1988-9). (7/95) (HYPE) ① **CDA66737**
String Quartet No. 1 (1951-2)
Delmé Qt *String Quartet 4.*
(3/91) (HYPE) ① **CDA66419**
String Quartet No. 2 (in one movement) (1953)
Delmé Qt *String Quartet 5.*
(10/90) (HYPE) ① **CDA66386**
String Quartet No. 3 (1954)
Delmé Qt *Concert* (7/90) (HYPE) ① **CDA66376**
String Quartet No. 4 (1973)
Delmé Qt *String Quartet 1.*
(3/91) (HYPE) ① **CDA66419**
String Quartet No. 5 (1974)
Delmé Qt *String Quartet 2.*
(10/90) (HYPE) ① **CDA66386**
String Quartet No. 6 (1975)
Delmé Qt *Concert* (7/90) (HYPE) ① **CDA66376**
String Quartet No. 7 (1977)
Delmé Qt (r1983) *String Quartet 8.*
(2/90) (HYPE) ① **CDA66117**
String Quartet No. 8 (1979)
Delmé Qt (r1983) *String Quartet 7.*
(2/90) (HYPE) ① **CDA66117**
String Quartet No. 9, '(32) Variations and Fugue on a theme of Haydn' (1982)
Delmé Qt (r1984) (2/90) (HYPE) ① **CDA66127**
String Quartet No. 10, 'For Peace' (1983)
Coull Qt (r1986) *String Quartet 11.*
(6/88) (HYPE) ① **CDA66225**
String Quartet No. 11 (1984)
Coull Qt (r1986) *String Quartet 10.*
(6/88) (HYPE) ① **CDA66225**

String Quartet No. 12 (1987)
Coull Qt *String Quintet.*
(7/92) (HYPE) ① **CDA66503**
String Quartet No. 14 (1990)
Vanbrugh Qt (r1992) *Concert*
(7/93) (HYPE) ① **CDA66626**
String Quartet No. 15 (1991)
Vanbrugh Qt (r1992) *Concert*
(7/93) (HYPE) ① **CDA66626**
String Quintet (1989)
Coull Qt, R. Bigley *String Quartet 12.*
(7/92) (HYPE) ① **CDA66503**
String Trio, 'Prelude, Adagio and Fugue' (1987)
Delmé Qt *Concert* (7/90) (HYPE) ① **CDA66376**
Trio for Horn, Violin and Piano (1984)
R. Watkins, P. Lowbury, C. G. Armytage (r1993)
Horn Quartet. (12/94) (HYPE) ① **CDA66695**
Trio for Violin, Cello and Piano (1988-9)
Lowbury Pf Trio (r1993) *Violin Sonata (1984).*
(7/95) (HYPE) ① **CDA66737**

SIMPSON, Thomas (1582–prob after 1630) England

SECTION II: CHAMBER

Alman
Ulsamer Collegium, J. Ulsamer *Concert*
(2/86) (ARCH) ① **415 294-2AH**
Opus newer Paduanen
Pasameza J. Lindberg *Concert*
(2/89) (BIS) ① **BIS-CD390**
Ricercar, 'Bonny Sweet Robin'
F. Brüggen, Brüggen Consort (r1967/79) *Concert*
(10/95) (TELD) ① **4509-97465-2**

SINDING, Christian (August) (1856–1941) Norway

SECTION I: ORCHESTRAL

Concerto for Piano and Orchestra in D flat, Op. 6 (1889 rev 1890 and 1901)
E. Knardahl, Oslo PO, Ø. Fjeldstad *Symphony 1.*
(12/89) (NKF) ① **NKFCD50016-2**
R. Keller, Berlin SO, J. Faerber *Goetz: Piano Concerto 2.* (5/93) (VOX) ① **115715-2**
Suite for Violin and Orchestra, 'in alten Stil', Op. 10 (1889)
I. Perlman, Pittsburgh SO, A. Previn *Sibelius: Violin Concerto.* (9/85) (EMI) ① **CDC7 47167-2**
I. Perlman, Pittsburgh SO, A. Previn *Concert*
(5/93) (EMI) ① **[4] CMS7 64617-2**
J. Heifetz, Los Angeles PO, A. Wallenstein (r1953)
Concert (11/94) (RCA) ① **[65] 09026 61778-2(09)**
I. Perlman, Pittsburgh SO, A. Previn (r1979) *Concert*
(6/95) (EMI) ① **[20] CZS4 83177-2(2)**
Symphony No. 1 in D minor, Op. 21
Oslo PO, Ø. Fjeldstad *Piano Concerto.*
(12/89) (NKF) ① **NKFCD50016-2**

SECTION II: CHAMBER

Variations in E flat minor—2 pianos, Op. 2 (1882-84)
K. Baekkelund, R. Levin *Concert*
(12/89) (NKF) ① **NKFCD50017-2**

SECTION III: INSTRUMENTAL

15 Caprices—piano, Op. 44 (1898)
2, 3, 4, 12. K. Baekkelund *Concert*
(12/89) (NKF) ① **NKFCD50017-2**
Chanson—piano, Op. 34/5 (1896)
K. Baekkelund *Concert*
(12/89) (NKF) ① **NKFCD50017-2**
Crépuscules—piano, Op. 34/4 (1896)
K. Baekkelund *Concert*
(12/89) (NKF) ① **NKFCD50017-2**
Marche grotesque—piano, Op. 32/1 (1896)
K. Baekkelund *Concert*
(12/89) (NKF) ① **NKFCD50017-2**
Prélude—piano, Op. 34/1 (1896)
K. Baekkelund *Concert*
(12/89) (NKF) ① **NKFCD50017-2**
Rustle of Spring—piano, Op. 32/3 (1896)
L. Godowsky (r1924) *Concert*
(4/89) (APR) ① **APR7011**
K. Baekkelund *Concert*
(12/89) (NKF) ① **NKFCD50017-2**
S. Cherkassky (bp1985) *Concert*
(6/93) (DECC) ① **433 651-2DH**
Scherzo—piano, Op. 33/6 (1896)
K. Baekkelund *Concert*
(12/89) (NKF) ① **NKFCD50017-2**
Serenade—piano, Op. 33/4 (1896)
K. Baekkelund *Concert*
(12/89) (NKF) ① **NKFCD50017-2**

Sonata in B minor—piano, Op. 91 (1909)
K. Baekkelund *Concert*
(12/89) (NKF) ① **NKFCD50017-2**

SECTION IV: VOCAL AND CHORAL

6 Songs, Op. 18 (1892) (Wds. V Krag)
5. There screeched a bird.
5. P. Frijsh, C. Dougherty (r1939) *Concert*
(4/95) (PEAR) ① **[2] GEMMCDS9095(2)**
5 Songs, Op. 22 (1893) (Wds. Krag)
EXCERPTS: 3. May Night.
3. K. Flagstad, M. Flagstad (r1923) *Concert*
(12/95) (SIMA) ① **[3] PSC1821(1)**

SINIGAGLIA, Leone (1868–1944) Italy

SECTION I: ORCHESTRAL

Le baruffe chiozzotte—overture, Op. 32 (1907-08)
NBC SO, A. Toscanini (bp1947) *Concert*
(5/94) (ATS) ① **[2] ATCD100**
Piemonte—suite: orchestra, Op. 36 (1909)
1. Per campi e boschi; 2. Balletto rustico; 3. In montibus sanctis; 4. Carnevale piemontese.
1, 2. NBC SO, A. Toscanini (bp1941) *Concert*
(5/94) (ATS) ① **[2] ATCD100**

SIRMEN, Maddalena Lombardini (1745–1818) Italy

SECTION II: CHAMBER

String Quartet No. 1 in E flat (pub 1769)
Allegri Qt (r1994) *Concert*
(5/95) (CALA) ① **CACD1019**
String Quartet No. 2 in B flat (pub 1769)
Allegri Qt (r1994) *Concert*
(5/95) (CALA) ① **CACD1019**
String Quartet No. 3 in G minor (pub 1769)
Allegri Qt (r1994) *Concert*
(5/95) (CALA) ① **CACD1019**
String Quartet No. 4 in B flat (pub 1769)
Allegri Qt (r1994) *Concert*
(5/95) (CALA) ① **CACD1019**
String Quartet No. 5 in F minor (pub 1769)
Allegri Qt (r1994) *Concert*
(5/95) (CALA) ① **CACD1019**
String Quartet No. 6 in E (pub 1769)
Allegri Qt (r1994) *Concert*
(5/95) (CALA) ① **CACD1019**

SITWELL, Dame Edith (1887–1964) England

SECTION IV: VOCAL AND CHORAL

Poems
1. Two Kitchen Songs; 2. Five Poems; 2a. Daphne; 2b. The Peach Tree; 2c. The Strawberry; 2d. The Greengage Tree; 2e. The Nectarine Tree; 3. On the Vanity of Human Aspirations; 4. Two Poems from 'Façade'; 4a. The Drum; 4b. Clowns' Houses; 5. The Wind's Bastinado; 6. The Dark House; 7. Colonel Fantock; 8. Most Lovely Shade; 9. Heart and Mind.
P. Scales, T. West *Walton: Façade.*
(4/90) (ASV) ① **CDDCA679**

(LES) SIX France

Auric,Durey,Honegger,Milhaud,Poulenc,Tailleferre

SECTION V: STAGE WORKS

Les Mariés de la Tour Eiffel—play-ballet (1921—Paris)
1. Overture (Auric); 2. Marche nuptiale (Milhaud); 3. Discours (Poulenc); 4. La baigneuse de Trouville (Poulenc); 5. Fugue du massacre (Milhaud); 6. Valse des Dépêches (Tailleferre); 7. Marche funèbre (Honegger); 8. Quadrille (Tailleferre); 9. Ritournelles (Auric); 10. Sortie de la Noce (Milhaud).
Cpte Philh, G. Simon *Various: Eventail de Jeanne.*
(4/85) (CHAN) ① **CHAN8356**
Cpte D. Mesguich, H. Furic, Lille Nat Orch, J-C. Casadesus (pp1993) *Milhaud: Boeuf sur le toit.*
(5/94) (HARM) ① **HMC90 1473**
3, 4. Paris Orch, G. Prêtre *Concert*
(3/92) (EMI) ① **[2] CZS7 62690-2**

SJÖBERG

SECTION IV: VOCAL AND CHORAL

Tonerna—song (Wds. E. G. Geijer)
L. Melchior, orch (Ger: r1926) *Concert*
(8/88) (DANA) ① **[2] DACOCD313/4**

J. Björling, orch, N. Grevillius (r1936) *Concert*
(10/93) (NIMB) ① **NI7842**

SJÖGREN, (Johan Gustaf) Emil (1853–1918) Sweden

SECTION IV: VOCAL AND CHORAL

Der Mond schon wandelt am
Himmelszelt—Lied (Wds. Recke)
D. Fischer-Dieskau, D. Klöcker, H. Höll *Concert*
(4/88) (ORFE) ① **C153861A**

SKALKOTTAS, Nikolaos (1904–1949) Greece

SECTION I: ORCHESTRAL

Symphony, '(The) Return of Odysseus'
(1942)
Danish RSO, M. Caridis (pp1979) *Kalomiris:*
Symphony 1. (10/90) (SCHW) ① **311110**

SECTION II: CHAMBER

Concertino for Oboe and Piano (1939)
H. Holliger, B. Canino (r1994) *Concert*
(10/95) (PHIL) ① **442 795-2PH**
Concertino for Trumpet and Piano (1943)
R. Friedrich, T. Duis (r1992) *Concert*
(6/93) (CAPR) ① **10 439**
H. Hardenberger, B. Canino (r1994) *Concert*
(10/95) (PHIL) ① **442 795-2PH**
Quartet No. 1—oboe, trumpet, basson &
piano (1940-42)
H. Holliger, K. Thunemann, H. Hardenberger, B.
Canino (r1994) *Concert*
(10/95) (PHIL) ① **442 795-2PH**
Quartet No. 2—oboe, trumpet, bassoon &
piano (1940-42)
H. Holliger, K. Thunemann, H. Hardenberger, B.
Canino (r1994) *Concert*
(10/95) (PHIL) ① **442 795-2PH**
Sonata Concertante for Bassoon and Piano
K. Thunemann, B. Canino (r1994) *Concert*
(10/95) (PHIL) ① **442 795-2PH**

SKEMPTON, Howard (b 1947) England

SECTION IV: VOCAL AND CHORAL

Colomen—soprano, clarinet & piano (1990)
(Wds. Mary Webb)
Tapestry (r1994) *Concert*
(12/95) (BRIT) ① **BML012**
How slow the wind—song (Wds. E.
Dickinson)
M. Wiegold, Composers Ens, D. Muldowney *Concert*
(4/92) (NMC) ① **NMCD003**

SLADE, Julian (b 1930) England

SECTION V: STAGE WORKS

Salad Days—musical show (1954—Bristol)
(Book/lyrics cpsr & D Reynolds)
EXCERPTS: 1. The Things That Are Done By a
Don; 2. We Said We Wouldn't Look Back; 3. Find
Yourself Something to Do; 4. I Sit in the Sun; 5. Oh,
Look at Me; 6. Hush-Hush; 7. Out of Breath; 8.
Cleopatra; 9. It's Easy to Sing; 10. We're Looking for
a Piano; 11. The Time of My Life; 12. The Saucer
Song; 13. Finale.
Cpte Orig London Cast, E. Rubach, R. Docker
(r1954) (11/94) (SONY) ① **SMK66176**

SLOANE, Baldwin Alfred (1872–1926) USA

SECTION V: STAGE WORKS

Kate Kip, Buyer—musical show (1898—New
York) (Lyrics Brewster)
EXCERPTS: 1. When You Ain't Got Money, You
Needn't Come Around.
1. M. Irwin, Broadway Cast (r1907) *Concert*
(5/94) (PEAR) ① [3] **GEMMCDS9050/2(1)**

SLØGEDAL, Bjarne (b 1937) Norway

SECTION III: INSTRUMENTAL

Variations on a Norwegian Folk
Tune—organ
C. Herrick (r1993) *Concert*
(8/94) (HYPE) ① **CDA66676**

SLONOV, Mikhail (Akimovich) (1869–1930) Russia

SECTION IV: VOCAL AND CHORAL

Arise, red sun—song, Op. 10/1
F. Chaliapin, anon (r1902) *Concert*
(7/93) (SYMP) ① **SYMCD1105**
A word of farewell—song
L. Sibiriakov, anon (r1905) *Concert*
(6/93) (PEAR) ① [3] **GEMMCDS9001/3(2)**

SMART, Sir George (Thomas) (1776–1867) England

SECTION IV: VOCAL AND CHORAL

The Squirrel—partsong (Wds. Roscoe)
PCA, M. Brown *Concert* (3/87) (CONI) ① **CDCF145**

SMART, Henry Thomas (1813–1879) England

SECTION III: INSTRUMENTAL

Air and Variations and Finale Fugato—organ
(1871)
A.M. Thomas *Concert* (9/92) (PRIO) ① **PRCD368**
Andante in A—organ
Margaret Phillips *Concert*
(7/91) (GAMU) ① **GAMCD522**
A.M. Thomas *Concert* (9/92) (PRIO) ① **PRCD368**
Andante in E minor—organ
A.M. Thomas *Concert* (9/92) (PRIO) ① **PRCD368**
Andante in F—organ
Margaret Phillips *Concert*
(7/91) (GAMU) ① **GAMCD522**
Andante in G—organ
A.M. Thomas *Concert* (9/92) (PRIO) ① **PRCD368**
Fantasia with Choral—organ
Margaret Phillips *Concert*
(7/91) (GAMU) ① **GAMCD522**
Grand Solemn March in E flat—organ
A.M. Thomas *Concert* (9/92) (PRIO) ① **PRCD368**
Minuet in C—organ
A.M. Thomas *Concert* (9/92) (PRIO) ① **PRCD368**
Postlude in D—organ
A.M. Thomas *Concert* (9/92) (PRIO) ① **PRCD368**

SECTION IV: VOCAL AND CHORAL

Evening Service in G—choir and organ
Chichester Cath Ch, A. Thurlow, J. Thomas (r1994)
Concert (5/95) (PRIO) ① **PRCD511**

SMETANA, Bedřich (1824–1884) Bohemia

B nos. from Bartoš (1973); T nos. from Teige (1893)

SECTION I: ORCHESTRAL

Hakon Jarl—symphonic poem, B118 (Op. 16)
(1860-61)
BRSO, R. Kubelík *Concert*
(1/93) (DG) ① **437 254-2GGA**
Má vlast—symphonic poems
1. Vyšehrad, B110 (c1872-74); 2. Vltava, B111
(1874); 3. Šárka, B113 (1875); 4. From Bohemia's
fields and groves, B114 (1875); 5. Tábor, B120
(1878); 6. Blaník, B121 (1879).
Czech PO, V. Smetáček
(7/86) (SUPR) ① **C37-7241**
SRO, W. Sawallisch (11/86) (RCA) ① **RD83242**
Boston SO, R. Kubelík (r1971)
(4/90) (DG) ① **429 183-2GGA**
RLPO, L. Pešek (9/90) (VIRG) ① **VC7 59576-2**
Czech PO, V. Talich (r1929)
(6/91) (KOCH) ① **37032-2**
Czech PO, R. Kubelík (pp1990)
(9/91) (SUPR) ① **11 1208-2**
Israel PO, W. Weller
(1/92) (DECC) ① **433 635-2DSP**
Frankfurt RSO, E. Inbal
(6/92) (TELD) ① **9031-74778-2**
Milwaukee SO, Z. Macal (9/92) (TELA) ① **CD80265**
Czech PO, J. Bělohlávek
(3/93) (SUPR) ① **11 0957-2**
Prague RSO, J. Krombholc (pp1973)
(4/93) (MULT) ① **310152-2**
Czech PO, V. Talich (r1954)
(1/94) (SUPR) ① **11 1896-2**
Czech PO, Z. Košler (pp1992)
(3/94) (EMER) ① **EC3988-2**
Czech PO, K. Ančerl (r1963)
(7/94) (SUPR) ① **11 1925-2**
Israel PO, Z. Mehta (r1991)
(4/95) (SONY) ① **SK58944**

Polish Nat RSO, A. Wit (r1993/4)
(4/95) (NAXO) ① **8 550931**
Concertgebouw, A. Dorati (r1987)
(6/95) (PHIL) ① **442 641-2PM**
Detroit SO, N. Järvi (r1994)
(9/95) (CHAN) ① **CHAN9366**
RLPO, L. Pešek (1989)
(10/95) (VIRG) ① **CUV5 61223-2**
1, 2. Detroit SO, N. Järvi *Fibich: Symphony 1.*
(12/93) (CHAN) ① **CHAN9230**
1, 2, 4. VPO, James Levine (pp1986) *Bartered Bride.*
(8/89) (DG) ① **427 340-2GH**
2. Oslo PO, M. Jansons (r1988) *Dvořák: Symphony*
9. (1/90) (EMI) ① **CDC7 49860-2**
2. Berlin SO, C.P. Flor (pp1988) *Concert*
(4/90) (RCA) ① **RD60119**
2. NBC SO, A. Toscanini (bp1950) *Concert*
(1/91) (RCA) ① **GD60279**
2. Berlin St Op Orch, L. Blech (1928) *Concert*
(2/93) (KOCH) ① **37072-2**
2. NYPO, L. Bernstein *Concert*
(5/93) (SONY) ① **SMK47547**
2. RCA Victor SO, L. Stokowski (r1960) *Concert*
(3/94) (RCA) ① **09026 61503-2**
2. VPO, W. Furtwängler (r1951) *Concert*
(10/94) (EMI) ① **CDH5 65197-2**
2. RLPO, L. Pešek (r1989) *Concert*
(11/94) (VIRG) ① **VC7 59285-2**
2. Berlin RSO, F. Fricsay (bp1959) *Concert*
(11/94) (DG) ① [11] **445 400-2GDO10**
2. NYPO, B. Walter (r1941) *Concert*
(8/95) (SONY) ① **SMK64467**
Our lasses—polka, T49 (1862-63)
Czech PO, V. Neumann *Concert*
(9/90) (ORFE) ① **C180891A**
Prague Carnival—introduction and
polonaise (1883)
BRSO, R. Kubelík *Concert*
(1/93) (DG) ① **437 254-2GGA**
Richard III—symphonic poem, B106 (Op. 11)
(1857-58)
BRSO, R. Kubelík *Concert*
(1/93) (DG) ① **437 254-2GGA**
Wallenstein's Camp—symphonic poem,
B111 (Op. 14) (1858-59)
BRSO, R. Kubelík *Concert*
(1/93) (DG) ① **437 254-2GGA**

SECTION II: CHAMBER

From the homeland—two pieces: violin and
piano, T128 (1880)
1. Moderato; 2. Andantino.
I. Perlman, S. Sanders *Concert*
(10/86) (EMI) ① **CDC7 47399-2**
2. Margaret Harrison, R. Paul (r1929) *Concert*
(3/93) (CLAR) ① **CDGSE78-50-47**
2. Margaret Harrison, R. Paul (r1929) *Concert*
(3/93) (SYMP) ① **SYMCD1140**
2. I. Perlman, S. Sanders (r1983) *Concert*
(5/93) (EMI) ① [4] **CMS7 64617-2**
2. N. Milstein, L. Mittman (r1936) *Concert*
(7/93) (APR) ① [2] **APR7016**
2. N. Milstein, L. Mittman (r1936) *Concert*
(9/95) (BIDD) ① **LAB096**
Piano Trio in G minor, B104 (1855 rev 1857)
R. Dubinsky, Y. Turovsky, L. Edlina *Dvořák: Piano*
Trio 4. (7/87) (CHAN) ① **CHAN8445**
Suk Trio *Dvořák: Piano Trio 4.*
(5/90) (SUPR) ① **11 0704-2**
Grumiaux Pf Trio (r1993) *Arensky: Piano Trio 1.*
(1/94) (RICE) ① **RIS131117**
String Quartet No. 1 in E minor, 'From my
life' (1880)
LSO, G. Simon (orch G. Szell) *Bartered Bride.*
(8/86) (CHAN) ① **CHAN8412**
Talich Qt *Concert* (10/88) (CALL) ① **CAL9690**
Medici Qt *String Quartet 2.*
(12/88) (NIMB) ① **NI5131**
Cleveland Qt *Borodin: String Quartet 2.*
(10/89) (TELA) ① **CD80178**
Orlando Qt *Dvořák: String Quartet 12.*
(3/92) (OTTA) ① **OTRC69028**
Alban Berg Qt (pp1990) *Dvořák: String Quartet 12.*
(3/92) (EMI) ① **CDC7 54215-2**
Gabrieli Qt *Concert* (8/92) (DECC) ① **430 295-2DM**
Manfred Qt (r1994) *String Quartet 2.*
(12/95) (PIER) ① **PV795041**
String Quartet No. 2 in D minor (1882-83)
Talich Qt *Concert* (10/88) (CALL) ① **CAL9690**
Medici Qt *String Quartet 1.*
(12/88) (NIMB) ① **NI5131**
Manfred Qt (r1994) *String Quartet 1.*
(12/95) (PIER) ① **PV795041**

SECTION III: INSTRUMENTAL

Am Seegestade (concert study in G sharp minor)—piano, B119 (Op. 17) (1861)
P. Schmalfuss *Concert*
(10/89) (THOR) ① **CTH2005**

Bagatelles and Impromptus—piano, B40 (1844)
1. Innocence; 2. Depression; 3. Idyll; 4. Longing; 5. Joy; 6. Fairy Tale; 7. Love; 8. Discord.
R. Kvapil (r1992) *Czech Dances, T112.*
(10/93) (UNIC) ① **DKPCD9139**

6 Characteristic Pieces—piano, B57 (Op. 1) (c1847-48)
1. In the Forest; 2. Rising passion; 3. The Shepherdess; 4. Longing; 5. The Soldier; 6. Despair.
3, 4. P. Schmalfuss *Concert*
(10/89) (THOR) ① **CTH2005**

14 Czech Dances—piano, T112 (1877-79)
1. Polka in A major; 2. Polka in A minor; 3. Polka in F; 4. Polka in B flat; 5. Furiant; 6. The Hen; 7. The Oats; 8. The Bear; 9. Little Onion; 10. Stamping Dance; 11. The Lancer; 12. The Astride Dance; 13. The Neighbours Dance; 14. The Jump Dance.
R. Kvapil (r1992) *Bagatelles and Impromptus, B40.*
(10/93) (UNIC) ① **DKPCD9139**
5. P. Schmalfuss *Concert*
(10/89) (THOR) ① **CTH2005**

Macbeth and the Witches—piano (1859)
P. Schmalfuss *Concert*
(10/89) (THOR) ① **CTH2005**
R. Kvapil (r1994) *Concert*
(2/95) (UNIC) ① **DKPCD9152**

March of the Prague Students' Legion—piano, B58 (1848)
Czech PO, V. Neumann (orch) *Concert*
(9/90) (ORFE) ① **C180891A**

3 Polkas de Salon—piano, B94 (Op. 7) (by 1854)
R. Kvapil *Concert*　(8/88) (CALL) ① **CAL9206**
R. Kvapil *Concert*　(10/88) (CALL) ① **CAL9690**
R. Kvapil (r1994) *Concert*
(2/95) (UNIC) ① **DKPCD9152**
1, 2. P. Schmalfuss *Concert*
(10/89) (THOR) ① **CTH2005**

3 Polkas poétiques—piano, B95 (Op. 8) (by 1854)
1. E flat; 2. G minor; 3. A flat.
R. Kvapil *Concert*　(8/88) (CALL) ① **CAL9206**
R. Kvapil *Concert*　(10/88) (CALL) ① **CAL9690**
R. Kvapil (r1994) *Concert*
(2/95) (UNIC) ① **DKPCD9152**

6 Rêves—piano, T112 (1875)
P. Schmalfuss *Concert*
(10/89) (THOR) ① **CTH2005**
R. Kvapil (r1994) *Concert*
(2/95) (UNIC) ① **DKPCD9152**

4 Sketches—piano, B102 (Op. 5) (1856-57)
1. Scherzo-Polka in F sharp; 2. Melancholy in G sharp minor; 3. Pleasant Landscape in D flat; 4. Rhapsodie in F minor.
3. P. Schmalfuss *Concert*
(10/89) (THOR) ① **CTH2005**

4 Souvenirs de Bohême en forme de polka—piano, B115-16 (Opp. 12-13) (1859-60)
1. A minor; 2. E minor; 3. E minor; 4. E flat.
R. Kvapil *Concert*　(8/88) (CALL) ① **CAL9206**
R. Kvapil (r1994) *Concert*
(2/95) (UNIC) ① **DKPCD9152**
1, 2. R. Kvapil *Concert*　(10/88) (CALL) ① **CAL9690**
2-4. P. Schmalfuss *Concert*
(10/89) (THOR) ① **CTH2005**

SECTION IV: VOCAL AND CHORAL

3 Choruses—female voices, T119 (1878)
1. My star (wds. Peška); 2. Return of the swallows (wds. Sládek); 3. The sun sets behind the mountain (wds. Sládek).
Prague Chbr Ch, J. Pancik (r1994) *Concert*
(12/95) (CHAN) ① **CHAN9257**
1. J. Novotná, chbr ens (r1947) *Concert*
(4/93) (SUPR) ① **11 1491-2**

5 Evening songs, T124 (1879) (Wds. V Hálek)
1. He who can play the golden strings; 2. Do not stone the prophets!; 3. I once dreamed; 4. O what joy when dancing; 5. I'll build you a throne from my songs.
2. E. Destinn, F. Kark (r1906) *Concert*
(12/94) (SUPR) ① **[12] 11 2136-2(1)**

SECTION V: STAGE WORKS

The Bartered Bride—opera: 3 acts (1866—Prague) (Lib. Sabine)
EXCERPTS -; 1. Overture. ACT 1: 2. Let us rejoice; 3. Should I ever happen to learn; 4. While a mother's love; 5. Faithful love cannot be marred; 6. As I'm saying my dear fellow; 7. Things like these can't be fixed; 8. He is timid; 9a. You don't even suspect the hitch; 9b. And where everybody fails; 9c. Polka. ACT 2: 10. Beer's no doubt a gift; 11. Furiant; 12. My...my...mother dear; 13. I know of a maiden fair; 14. Every man maintains his wife is best; 15. I know a girl; 16a. How could they believe; 16b. Come inside, people!; 16c. Is it really true?; 16d. Quite a bargain. ACT 3: 17. I can't get it off my mind; 18. March of the Comedians; 19. Dance of the Comedians (Skočná); 20a. We will make a graceful little bear of you; 20b. What? He does not want her?; 20c. Well then, she's Mařenka; 21. Think it over, Mařenka; 22a. Oh, what a grief!; 22b. That dream of love; 23. Are you really so stubborn?; 24. Calm down, dear; 25a. Now I shall call in your parents; 25b. What have you decided, Mařenka?; 25c. Oh, he's a cunning man all right!; 25d. Ha ha ha ha.
Cpte G. Beňačková, P. Dvorský, M. Kopp, R. Novák, J. Jindrák, M. Mrázová, J. Horáček, M. Veselá, J. Jonášová, A. Hampel, K. Hanuš, Czech Phil Chor, Czech PO, Z. Košler (r1980/1)
(10/91) (SUPR) ① **[3] 10 3511-2**
Cpte H. Konetzni, R. Tauber, H. Tessmer, F. Krenn, M. Rothmüller, M. Jarred, A. Matters, S. Kalter, S. Andreva, G. Hinze, G. Clifford, ROH Chor, LPO, T. Beecham (pp1939; Ger) *Concert*
(2/92) (LYRC) ① **[2] SRO830**
Cpte L. Červinková, B. Blachut, R. Vonásek, K. Kalaš, L. Mráz, V. Krilová, J. Heriban, J. Palivcová, J. Pechová, B. Vich, J. Soumar, Prague Rad Chor, Prague RSO, K. Ančerl (r1947)
(9/94) (MULT) ① **[2] 310185-2**
Excs A. Dermota, E. Réthy, E. Kaufmann, O. Levko-Antosch, G. Monthy, E. Nikolaidi, A. Pernerstorfer, Vienna St Op Chor, Vienna St Op Orch, R. Moralt (pp1942: Ger) *Concert*
(2/95) (SCHW) ① **[2] 314572**
1. Black Dyke Mills Band, J. Watson (r1992: arr Broadbent) *Concert* (9/93) (POLY) ① **QPRL053D**
1. NYPO, L. Bernstein (r1963) *Concert*
(9/93) (SONY) ① **SMK47601**
1. RCA Victor SO, L. Stokowski (r1960) *Concert*
(3/94) (RCA) ① **09026 61503-2**
1. LSO, B. Walter (r1938) *Concert*
(8/94) (DUTT) ① **CDLX7008**
1. NBC SO, B. Walter (pp1940) *Concert*
(2/95) (PEAR) ① **GEMMCD9131**
1. Chicago SO, F. Reiner (r1955) *Concert*
(8/95) (RCA) ① **09026 62587-2**
1. LPO, H. Harty (r1933) *Concert*
(9/95) (DUTT) ① **CDLX7016**
1. Solti Orchestral Project, G. Solti (pp1994) *Concert*
(12/95) (DECC) ① **444 458-2DH**
1, 2, , 11, 18 (pt), 19. LSO, G. Simon *String Quartet 1.*
(8/86) (CHAN) ① **CHAN8412**
1, 9c, 11, 19. VPO, James Levine (r1986) *Má Vlast.*
(8/89) (DG) ① **427 340-2GH**
1, 9c, 11, 19. RLPO, L. Pešek (r1990) *Concert*
(11/94) (VIRG) ① **VC7 59285-2**
3. E. Destinn, anon (r1905) *Concert*
(12/94) (SUPR) ① **[12] 11 2136-2(1)**
3, 22a-c L. Popp, Munich RO, S. Soltesz (r1987) *Concert* (4/89) (EMI) ① **CDC7 49319-2**
5. E. Rethberg, R. Tauber, orch (Ger: r1919) *Concert* (7/94) (PREI) ① **89051**
5, 16a R. Tauber, R. Rethberg, orch (Ger: r1919) *Concert* (3/92) (EMI) ① **CDH7 64029-2**
5, 23. E. Destinn, O. Mařák, orch, B. Seidler-Winkler (r1909) *Concert*
(12/94) (SUPR) ① **[12] 11 2136-2(2)**
9c, 11, 19. Cleveland Orch, G. Szell *Concert*
(6/93) (SONY) ① **SBK48279**
11, 19. Czech PO, V. Neumann *Concert*
(9/90) (ORFE) ① **C180091A**
15. C. Kullman, E. Fuchs, Berlin City Op Orch, A. von Zemlinsky (Ger: r1931) *Concert*
(11/93) (PREI) ① **89057**
16a R. Tauber, orch (Ger: r1919) *Concert*
(7/89) (EMI) ① **CDM7 69476-2**
16a J. Patzak, orch, M. Gurlitt (Ger: r1929) *Concert*
(3/90) (PEAR) ① **GEMMCD9383**
16a R. Tauber, orch (Ger: r1919) *Concert*
(12/92) (NIMB) ① **NI7830**
19. LSO, C. Mackerras (r1961) *Concert*
(6/93) (MERC) ① **434 352-2MM**
22a-c E. Schwarzkopf, Philh, Helmut Schmidt (Ger) *Concert* (10/88) (EMI) ① **CDM7 69501-2**

22a-c S. Jurinac, Philh, W. Braithwaite (r1950; Ger) *Concert* (1/90) (EMI) ① **CDH7 63199-2**
22a-c S. Danco, SRO, I. Karr (bp1953) *Concert*
(1/93) (CASC) ① **VEL2010**
22a-c J. Novotná, orch, A. Wallenstein (bp1942) *Concert* (4/93) (SUPR) ① **11 1491-2**
22a, 22b E. Destinn, orch, B. Seidler-Winkler (r1908) *Concert* (12/94) (SUPR) ① **[12] 11 2136-2(2)**
22a, 22b H. Konetzni, VPO, H. von Karajan (r1947: Ger) *Concert* (1/95) (PREI) ① **90078**
22b E. Destinn, orch, B. Seidler-Winkler (r1908) *Concert* (5/94) (SUPR) ① **11 1337-2**

The Brandenburgers in Bohemia—opera: 3 acts (1866—Prague) (Lib. K Sabina)
Cpte K. Kalaš, J. Joran, I. Žídek, Z. Otava, A. Votava, B. Vich, M. Šubrtová, M. Fidlerová, V. Soukupová, E. Haken, J. Jindrák, Prague Nat Th Chor, Prague Nat Th Orch, J.H. Tichý (r1963)
(5/94) (SUPR) ① **[2] 11 1804-2**

Dalibor—opera: 3 acts, B133 (1868—Prague) (Lib. J. Wenzig, trans E. Špindler)
EXCERPTS: 1. Overture. ACT 1: 2. Oh no! From the prison's pit; 3. You know by now; 4a. Oh hear of what I must complain; 4b. The sun did set; 5a. I won't deny it; 5b. When Ždeňk mine; 6. Oh, didst thou hear it, friend; 7. What storm here in my bosom. ACT 2: 8. Oh yes, the gayest is this our world; 9. My dearest, my yearning; 10. Oh, how saddening is a jailer's life; 11. Oh, goodness! Now so quickly came to me; 12a. It was he again; 12b. Oh, Ždeňek, just one fleeting; 13. You're asking who I call; 14. Oh, unspeakable charm of love. ACT 3: 15. It will be near to forty years; 16a. At this late hour; 16b. Beautiful aim that any king; 17a. It's the third night; 17b. Oh, God! I'll be free again!; 18. Let so it be!.
Cpte L.M. Vodička, I. Kusnjer, E. Urbanová, V. Kříž, J. Kalendocsky, M. Kopp, J. Marková, Bohuslav Maršík, Prague Nat Th Chor, Prague Nat Th Orch, Z. Košler (r1995) (12/95) (SUPR) ① **[2] SU0077-2**
Ah, whose the spell B. Blachut, Prague Op Orch, J. Charvát (r1947)
(4/92) (EMI) ① **[7] CHS7 69741-2(6)**
How confused I feel! L. Popp, Munich RO, S. Soltesz (r1987) *Concert*
(4/89) (EMI) ① **CDC7 49319-2**
O Zdeněk; Ah, whose is the spell F. Völker, Berlin Staatskapelle, G. Steeger (r1940: Ger) *Concert*
(8/94) (PREI) ① **89070**
6. H. Winkelmann, anon (r1904: Ger) *Concert*
(7/91) (SYMP) ① **SYMCD1081**
11. E. Destin, orch, B. Seidler-Winkler (r1908) *Concert* (5/94) (SUPR) ① **11 1337-2**
11. E. Destin, orch, B. Seidler-Winkler (r1908) *Concert* (12/94) (SUPR) ① **[12] 11 2136-2(1)**
11. E. Destinn, orch, B. Seidler-Winkler (r1909: Ger) *Concert* (12/94) (SUPR) ① **[12] 11 2136-2(2)**

The Devil's Wall—comic-romantic opera: 3 acts, T129 (1882—Prague) (Lib. E Krásnohorská)
EXCERPTS: 1. Overture. ACT 1: 2. A horse without a rider; 3a. No-one? Happy me; 3b. The mom's greetings!; 4a. I bid you welcome, my maiden!; 4b. Thus to rest in your arms; 5. Ha, ha, ha, my dearest one; 6a. Welcome home ... Our commander; 6b. O, my lord!; 6c. O, woe is me!; 7a. A swift messenger is approaching; 7b. Only one lovely woman's beauty touched me. ACT 2: 8a. Who will offer shelter to the weary?; 8b. Where can I flee before so sweet an image?; 8c. Sleep, my innocent one; 9. It is hard to get accustomed to!; 10. Do something, Father; 11a. Jarek! My dear friend!; 11b. Like an orphaned bird; 12. Welcome to this castle; 13. O, what a whirl!; 14. What is your grave news? ACT 3: 15. There's the monastery; 16. Where are you taking me?; 17. My eyes have seen it!; 18. I am a good shepherd of sheep; 19. Come, quietly and stealthily; 20. Ah! Run for safety!; 21. I know why that Záviš; 22. Save yourselves!; 23. To pray alone.
Cpte V. Bednář, I. Mixová, I. Žídek, M. Šubrtová, A. Votava, L. Domanínská, K. Berman, L. Mráz, Prague Nat Th Chor, Prague Nat Th Orch, Z. Chalabala (r1960) (5/94) (SUPR) ① **[2] 11 2201-2**

The Kiss—opera: 2 acts (1876—Prague) (Lib. E. Krásnohorská after K. Světlá)
EXCERPTS: 1. Overture. ACT 1: 2a. Today with his friends he has drowned his sorrow; 2b. We are united; 3a. Let us drink now to their health; 3b. Never, never, in my despair; 3c. Here you are, my guiltless child; 3d. Till the wedding I shall wait; 3e. I only want to kiss your cheek; 4. What I've now foreseen has now arrived; 5. How could he ever forget our love; 6a. I'm, my dear girl, old by now; 6b. Cradle song; 7. Play musicians, play a jump dance. ACT 2: 8. Let's go; 9. If I knew how to redeem my guilt; 10. Just go and pray; 11. O, why ever did I believe foolishly; 12. Well did he show to me; 13. The Lark's song: Herald,

skylark, herald, a new day; 14. O yes, I forgive you,
young man.
Cpte E. Haken, E. Dépoltová, L.M Vodička, V. Zítek,
L. Márová, K. Hanuš, B. Effenberková, Z. Jankovský,
Brno Janáček Op Chor, Brno Janáček Op Orch, F.
Vajnar (r1980)   (9/95) (SUPR) ① [2] **11 2180-2**
6b S. Jurinac, Philh, W. Braithwaite (Ger: r1950)
Concert   (1/90) (EMI) ① **CDH7 63199-2**
6b J. Novotná, RCA Victor Orch, F. Weissmann
(r1945) *Concert*   (4/93) (SUPR) ① **11 1491-2**
6b E. Destinn, orch, J. Pasternack (r1921) *Concert*
(11/93) (ROMO) ① [2] **81002-2**
6b E. Destinn, orch, B. Seidler-Winkler (r1908)
Concert   (12/94) (SUPR) ① [12] **11 2136-2(2)**
6b E. Destinn, orch, J. Pasternack (r1921) *Concert*
(12/94) (SUPR) ① [12] **11 2136-2(5)**
13. J. Novotná, orch (r1926) *Concert*
(4/93) (SUPR) ① **11 1491-2**
Libuše—opera: 3 acts (1881—Prague) (Lib. J
Wenzig, trans Spindler)
EXCERPTS: 1. Prelude; 2. Eternal gods, you that
dwell above the clouds; 3. You elders, nobles. ACT 2:
4. My father; 5. When in the sweet yearning of love;
6. Without rest onwards and out in the fields; 7. The
sun is blazing; 8. O, ye lime trees; 9. Ah, look into his
face; 10. Peace be with you. ACT 3: 11. Introduction;
12. Welcome!; 13. Hail, Stronghold of Vyšehrad!; 14.
O gods almighty.
Cpte G. Beňačková, V. Zítek, A. Švorc, L.M. Vodička,
K. Průša, R. Tuček, E. Dépoltová, V. Soukupová,
Prague Nat Th Chor, Prague Nat Th Orch, Z. Košler
(pp1983)   (4/94) (SUPR) ① [3] **11 1276-2**
The Two Widows—opera: 2 acts (1874: rev
vers 1878—Prague) (Lib. E. Züngel, after P J F
Mallefille)
Cpte J. Jonášová, M. Machotková, M. Švejda, D.
Jedlička, A. Hampel, D. Šounová-Brouková, Prague
Rad Chor, Prague RSO, J. Krombholc (bp1974)
(6/93) (PRAG) ① [2] **PR250 022/3**
Cpte N. Šormová, M. Machotková, J. Zahradníček, J.
Horáček, Z. Švehla, D. Šounová-Brouková, Prague
Nat Th Chor, Prague Nat Th Orch, F. Jílek (r1975)
(10/94) (SUPR) ① [2] **11 2122-2**

SMITH, Geoff *(1966) England*

SECTION II: CHAMBER

Possess Me—keyboards
G. Smith (r1995) *Concert*
(11/95) (SONY) ① **SK66605**
The Rainpools Are Happy—keyboards
G. Smith (r1995) *Concert*
(11/95) (SONY) ① **SK66605**
To the Old Place—keyboards
G. Smith (r1995) *Concert*
(11/95) (SONY) ① **SK66605**

SECTION IV: VOCAL AND CHORAL

Fifteen Wild Decembers—song (1993) (Wds.
E Brontë)
N. Walker Smith, G. Smith (r1995) *Concert*
(11/95) (SONY) ① **SK66605**
The Last of England—song (Wds. Shelley)
N. Walker Smith, G. Smith (r1995) *Concert*
(11/95) (SONY) ① **SK66605**
Six Wings of Bliss—song (Wds. E Brontë)
N. Walker Smith, G. Smith (r1995) *Concert*
(11/95) (SONY) ① **SK66605**
Speak of the North—song (Wds. Keats)
N. Walker Smith, G. Smith (r1995) *Concert*
(11/95) (SONY) ① **SK66605**
Summer's Last Will and Testament—song
(Wds. Siddal, from 'A Year and a Day')
N. Walker Smith, G. Smith (r1995) *Concert*
(11/95) (SONY) ① **SK66605**

SMITH, John Christopher *(1712–1795) England*

SECTION V: STAGE WORKS

The Fairies—opera after Shakespeare
(1755—London) (Lib after Shakespeare,
Milton, Dryden et al)
1. You spotted snakes.
1. A. Rolfe Johnson, G. Johnson *Concert*
(5/92) (HYPE) ① **CDA66480**
The Tempest—opera after Shakespeare's
play (1756—London) (Lib after Shakespeare,
Milton, Dryden et al)
1. No more dams I'll make for fish.
1. A. Rolfe Johnson, G. Johnson *Concert*
(5/92) (HYPE) ① **CDA66480**

SMITH, Sydney *(1839–1889)* *England*

SECTION III: INSTRUMENTAL

Sleigh-Bells—piano
A. Etherden *Concert*
(7/93) (HUNT) ① **HMPCD0589**

SMITH BRINDLE, Reginald *(b 1917) England*

SECTION III: INSTRUMENTAL

El polifemo de oro—four fragments: guitar
(1956)
J. Bream (r1966) *Concert*
(8/93) (RCA) ① [28] **09026 61583-2(4)**
J. Bream (r1966) *Concert*
(6/94) (RCA) ① **09026 61595-2**

SMYTH, Dame Ethel (Mary) *(1858–1944) England*

SECTION II: CHAMBER

Sonata for Cello and Piano in A minor, Op. 5
(1887)
F. Kupsa, C. Dutilly (r1990) *Concert*
(7/94) (TROU) ① [2] **TRO-CD03**
N. Kraamwinkel, T. Gill *Concert*
(10/95) (MERI) ① **CDE84286**
Sonata for Violin and Piano in A minor, Op. 7
(1887)
R. Eggebrecht-Kupsa, C. Dutilly (r1990) *Concert*
(7/94) (TROU) ① [2] **TRO-CD03**
Chagall Trio, T. Gill *Concert*
(10/95) (MERI) ① **CDE84286**
String Quartet in E minor 1902-12
Fanny Mendelssohn Qt (r1990) *Concert*
(7/94) (TROU) ① [2] **TRO-CD03**
String Quintet in E—two violins, viola and
two cellos, Op. 1 (1884)
Fanny Mendelssohn Qt, J. Varner (r1990) *Concert*
(7/94) (TROU) ① [2] **TRO-CD03**
Trio in A—violin, horn and piano (1926) (arr
cpsr from Double Concerto)
M. Paulsen, F. Draxinger, C. Dutilly (r1992) *Concert*
(7/94) (TROU) ① **TRO-CD01405**
Trio in D minor—violin, cello & piano
Chagall Trio *Concert*   (10/95) (MERI) ① **CDE84286**

SECTION IV: VOCAL AND CHORAL

The March of the Women—soprano, chorus
and orchestra (1911) (Wds. C Hamilton)
E. Harrhy, Plymouth Music Series Chor, Plymouth
Music Series Orch, P. Brunelle *Concert*
(8/91) (VIRG) ① **VC7 59022-2**
Mass in D—soloists, chorus and orchestra
(1891 rev 1925)
E. Harrhy, J. Hardy, D. Dressen, J. Bohn, Plymouth
Music Series Chor, Plymouth Music Series Orch, P.
Brunelle *Concert*   (8/91) (VIRG) ① **VC7 59022-2**
4 Songs—mezzo-soprano and chamber
ensemble (1907)
1. Odelette (wds. H de Régnier); 2. La danse (wds. H
de Régnier); 3. Chrysilla (wds. H de Régnier); 4. Ode
Anacréontique (wds. trans L. de Lisle).
M. Paulsen, U. Siebler, R. Eggebrecht-Kupsa, G.
Georgiev, F. Kupsa, C. Zirkelbach, A.
Gotowtschikow, J. Schmeller (r1992) *Concert*
(7/94) (TROU) ① **TRO-CD01405**
3 Songs—1v and piano (1913)
1. The clowns (wds. M Baring); 2. Procession (wds. E
Carnie); 3. On the roads (wds. E Carnie).
M. Paulsen, A. Gassenhuber (r1992) *Concert*
(7/94) (TROU) ① **TRO-CD01405**
2. A. Rolfe Johnson, G. Johnson (r1991/3) *Concert*
(8/94) (HYPE) ① **CDA66709**

SECTION V: STAGE WORKS

The Boatswain's Mate—opera: 2 acts
(1916—London) (Lib. cpsr, after W W Jacobs)
EXCERPTS: 1. Overture. ACT 1: 2. When rocked on
the billows; 3. The Keeper; 4. A friend and I were on
the piece; 5a. Contrariness—Suppose you mean to
do a given thing; 5b. What if I were young again. ACT
2: 6. Oh! dear, if I had known; 7. The first thing to do
is to get rid of the body; 8. When the sun is setting.
5a, 5b E. Harrhy, Plymouth Music Series Orch, P.
Brunelle *Concert*   (8/91) (VIRG) ① **VC7 59022-2**

The Wreckers—opera: 3 acts
(1906—Leipzig) (Lib. cpsr)
EXCERPTS: 1. Overture.
Cpte P. Sidhom, D. Wilson-Johnson, B. Bannatyne-
Scott, A. Roden, A. Sand, J. Lavender, A-M. Owens,
J. Howarth, Huddersfield Choral Soc, BBC PO, O. de
la Martinez (pp1994)
(11/94) (CONI) ① [2] **CDCF250/1**

SNYDER, Ted *(1840–1912) England/USA*

SECTION IV: VOCAL AND CHORAL

How'd You Like to Be My Daddy?—song for
Romberg's show 'Sinbad' (1918)
Farber Sisters, Orig Broadway Cast (r1918) *Concert*
(5/94) (PEAR) ① [3] **GEMMCDS9059/61**
Oh, How That German Could Love—song for
the show 'The Girl and the Wizard' (1909)
(Lyrics Irving Berlin)
N. Bayes, Orig Broadway Cast (r1910) *Concert*
(5/94) (PEAR) ① [3] **GEMMCDS9053/5**
That Beautiful Rag—song for Hubbell's
show 'The Jolly Bachelors' (1910) (Lyrics
Irving Berlin)
S. Mayhew, B. Taylor, Orig Broadway Cast (r1910)
Concert   (5/94) (PEAR) ① [3] **GEMMCDS9053/5**

SÖDERLIND, Ragnar *(b 1945)* *Norway*

SECTION IV: VOCAL AND CHORAL

Kjaerleikslengt i svarmerus—1v and
ensemble (1982) (Wds. Hans Henrik Holm)
S. Torjesen, Borealis Ens, C. Eggen (r1990s)
Concert   (9/93) (AURO) ① **ACD4973**

SÖDERLUND, Gustave Frederic *(1881–1972) Sweden/USA*

SECTION I: ORCHESTRAL

Concertino for Oboe with String Orchestra
(1944)
A. Nilsson, Stockholm Sinfonietta, E-P. Salonen
Concert   (4/85) (BIS) ① **BIS-CD285**

SÖDERMAN, Johann August *(1832–1876) Sweden*

SECTION IV: VOCAL AND CHORAL

A Peasant wedding—male vv (pub 1868)
(Wds. Gustavsson)
At the bride's home Orphei Drängar Ch, E. Ericson
Concert   (7/88) (BIS) ① **BIS-CD383**

SODERO, Cesare *(1886–1947)* *Italy/USA*

SECTION IV: VOCAL AND CHORAL

Crisantemi—song
C. Muzio, orch (r1920) *Concert*
(5/90) (BOGR) ① [2] **BIM705-2**
C. Muzio, orch (r1920) *Concert*
(1/94) (ROMO) ① [2] **81005-2**

SOKOLA, Miloš *(1913–1976)* *Czechoslavakia*

SECTION III: INSTRUMENTAL

Passacaglia quasi Toccata sopra
'BACH'—organ (1966)
N. Kynaston *Concert*   (4/89) (HYPE) ① **CDA66265**

SOKOLOV, Nikolay Alexandrovich *(1859–1922) Russia*

SECTION IV: VOCAL AND CHORAL

Lord, now lettest Thou Thy servant depart in
peace (Nunc dimittis)—Russian liturgical
chant
N. Gedda, Paris Russian Orthodox Cath Ch, E. Evetz
Concert   (1/93) (PHIL) ① **434 174-2PM**

SOKOLOVSKY, Marek (1818–1884) Russia

SECTION IV: VOCAL AND CHORAL

By the blue sea—song
E. Zbrueva, anon (r1903) *Concert*
(6/93) (PEAR) ① [3] GEMMCDS9004/6(2)

SOLAGE (fl. 1370–90) France

SECTION IV: VOCAL AND CHORAL

Le Basile—chanson: 4vv
Gothic Voices, C. Page, A. Lawrence-King *Concert*
(6/93) (HYPE) ① CDA66619
Fumeux fume par fumee—rondeau (3vv)
Organum Ens, M. Pérès *Concert*
(11/87) (HARM) ① HMC90 1252
Huelgas Ens, P. van Nevel *Concert*
(2/93) (SONY) ① SK48195
Joieux de cuer en seumellant estoye—virelai
Gothic Voices, C. Page *Concert*
(3/92) (HYPE) ① CDA66463
Tres gentil cuer—3vv
Gothic Voices, C. Page (lte/dir) *Concert*
(9/92) (HYPE) ① CDA66588

SOLER (RAMOS), Antonio (Francisco Javier José) (1729–1783) Spain

Keyboard Sonatas numbered according to the edition by Samuel Rubio. M—numbers from the edition by Frederick Marvin (not included in Rubio).

SECTION II: CHAMBER

6 conciertos de dos órganos obligados
1. C; 2. A minor; 3. G; 4. F; 5. A; 6. D.
T. Mathot, T. Koopman
(7/92) (ERAT) ① 2292-45741-2
1, 6. M.G. Filippi, M. Henking (r1986) *Concert*
(10/89) (ARIO) ① ARN68047
6(Minuet) I. Tracey (r1990; arr Tracey) *Concert*
(4/91) (MIRA) ① MRCD901
6 Quintets—2 violins, viola, cello, organ/harpsichord
3. G; 4. A minor; 5. D.
3, 4, 5. Concerto Rococo (r1992)
(4/94) (PIER) ① PV792111

SECTION III: INSTRUMENTAL

The Emperor's Fanfare—keyboard (transcr Power Biggs)
M. Murray *Concert* (3/89) (TELA) ① CD80169
C. Curley *Concert* (2/91) (ARGO) ① 430 200-2ZH
Fandango—keyboard
B. van Asperen (r1991) *Concert*
(7/92) (ASTR) ① E8771
V. Black *Concert* (8/94) (UNIT) ① 88005-2
Preludes—keyboard
1. D minor; 2. G minor; 3. C; 4. F minor; 5. D; 6. G; 7. C minor; 8. F.
1. B. van Asperen (r1991) *Concert*
(7/92) (ASTR) ① E8768
3. B. van Asperen (r1991) *Concert*
(7/92) (ASTR) ① E8769
5. B. van Asperen (r1991) *Concert*
(7/92) (ASTR) ① E8771
6. B. van Asperen (r1991) *Concert*
(7/92) (ASTR) ① E8770
Sonatas for Keyboard Nos. 1-75
1. A; 2. E flat; 3. B flat; 4. G; 5. F; 6. F; 7. C; 8. C; 9. C; 10. B minor; 11. B; 12. G; 13. G; 14. G; 15. D minor; 16. E flat; 17. E flat; 18. C minor; 19. C minor; 20. C sharp minor; 21. C sharp minor; 22. D flat; 23. D flat; 24. D minor; 25. D minor; 26. E minor; 27. E minor; 28. C; 29. C; 30. G; 31. G; 32. G minor; 33. G; 34. E; 35. G; 36. C minor; 37. D; 38. C; 39. D minor; 40. -; 41. E flat; 42. G minor; 43. G; 44. -; 45. G; 46. -; 47. C minor; 48. A minor; 49. D minor; 50. C; 51. C; 52. E minor; 53. A; 54. D minor; 55. F; 56. F; 57. G minor; 58. G; 59. F; 60. C minor; 61. C; 62. B flat; 63. F; 64. -; 65. -; 66. C; 67. -; 68. -; 70. -; 71. A minor; 72. F minor; 73. D; 74. D; 75. F.
1, 3, 24, 25, 28, 29, 30, 31. B. van Asperen (r1991) *Concert* (7/92) (ASTR) ① E8768
2. Berlin RIAS Sinfonietta, J. Velazco (orch Halffter) *Concert* (12/89) (SCHW) ① 311035
2, 5, 8. Berlin RIAS Sinfonietta, J. Velazco (orch Halffter) *Concert* (12/89) (SCHW) ① 311035
7, 8, 9, 20, 21, 34. B. van Asperen (r1991) *Concert* (7/92) (ASTR) ① E8769
10, 11, 12, 13, 14, 52, 73, 74. B. van Asperen (r1991) *Concert* (7/92) (ASTR) ① E8770

15, 22, 23, 54, 61, 75. B. van Asperen (r1991) *Keyboard Sonatas II.* (7/92) (ASTR) ① E8772
18, 19, 26, 27, 36. B. van Asperen (r1991) *Keyboard Sonatas II.* (7/92) (ASTR) ① E8773
21, 39, 43, 47, 74. V. Black *Keyboard Sonatas II.* (5/89) (CRD) ① CRD3452
21, 42. A. de Larrocha *Concert*
(9/92) (DECC) ① [2] 433 920-2DM2
36, 72. V. Black *Concert* (8/94) (UNIT) ① 88005-2
37, 46, 56. B. van Asperen (r1991) *Concert*
(7/92) (ASTR) ① E8771
Sonatas for Keyboard Nos. 76-149 (Nos 121-149 from unpub Vol 7 of Rubio Edition)
1. 76, F; 2. 77, F sharp minor; 3. 78, F sharp minor; 4. 79, F sharp; 5. 80, G minor; 6. 81, G minor; 7. 82, G; 8. 83, F; 9. 84, D; 10. 85, F sharp minor; 11. 86, D; 12. 87, G minor; 13. 88, D flat; 14. 89, F; 15. 90, F sharp; 16. 91, C; 17. 92, D; 18. 93, F; 19. 94, E; 20. 95, A; 21. 96, E flat; 22. 97, A; 23. 98, B flat; 24. 99, C; 25. 100, C minor; 26. 101, F; 27. 102, -; 28. 103, C minor; 29. 104, D minor; 30. 105, -; 31. 106, E minor; 32. 107, F; 33. 108, C; 34. 109, F; 35. 110, D flat; 36. 111, -; 37. 112, C; 38. 113, E minor; 39. 114, D minor; 40. 115, D minor; 41. 116, G; 42. 117, D minor; 43. 118, A minor; 44. 119, B flat; 45. 120, D minor; 46. 121, -; 47. 122, -; 48. 123, -; 49. 124, C; 50. 125, C minor; 51. 126, C minor; 52. 127, D; 53. 128, E minor; 54. 129, -; 55. 130, G minor; 56. 131, A; 57. 132, B flat; 58. 133, -; 59. 134, -; 60. 135, -; 61. 136, -; 62. 137, -; 63. 138, -; 64. 139, -; 65. 140, -; 66. 141, -; 67. 142, -; 68. 143, -; 69. 144, -; 70. 145, -; 71. 146, -; 72. 147, -; 73. 148, -; 74. 149, -.
1, 5, 6, 9, 11. B. van Asperen (r1991) *Keyboard Sonatas I.* (7/92) (ASTR) ① E8772
2, 3, 6, 9, 15, 25, 42. V. Black *Keyboard Sonatas I.* (5/89) (CRD) ① CRD3452
8, 15, 16, 19. B. van Asperen (r1991) *Keyboard Sonatas I.* (7/92) (ASTR) ① E8773
9-12, 14. A. de Larrocha *Concert*
(9/92) (DECC) ① [2] 433 920-2DM2
17, 31. B. van Asperen (r1991) *Concert*
(7/92) (ASTR) ① E8770
20. B. van Asperen (r1991) *Concert*
(7/92) (ASTR) ① E8769
21, 43. B. van Asperen (r1991) *Concert*
(7/92) (ASTR) ① E8768
23, 25, 28, 33, 34, 37. B. van Asperen (r1991) *Concert* (7/92) (ASTR) ① E8771
42. M.G. Filippi, M. Henking (r1986) *Concert*
(10/89) (ARIO) ① ARN68047
88, 119. V. Black *Concert* (8/94) (UNIT) ① 88005-2

SOLÈRE, Etienne (1753–1817)

SECTION I: ORCHESTRAL

Sinfonie concertante in F—2 clarinets and orchestra (pub 1790)
T. King, G. Dobrée, ECO, A. Litton *Concert*
(4/90) (HYPE) ① CDA66300

SOMERVELL, Sir Arthur (1863–1937) England

SECTION IV: VOCAL AND CHORAL

Maud—song cycle (1898) (Wds. Tennyson)
Cpte D. Wilson-Johnson, D.O. Norris *Shropshire Lad.* (6/91) (HYPE) ① CDA66187
Praise to the Holiest in the Height—hymn (tune: Chorus Angelorum or Somervell)
St Paul's Cath Ch, C. Dearnley, John Scott *Concert*
(7/90) (HYPE) ① CDH88036
A Shropshire Lad—song cyle (1904) (Wds. A E Housman)
1. Loveliest of trees; 2. When I was one-and-twenty; 3. There pass the careless people; 4. In summertime on Bredon; 5. The street sounds to the soldiers' tread; 6. On the idle hill of summer; 7. White in the moon the long road lies; 8. Think no more, lad; 9. Into my heart an air that kills; 10. The lads in their hundreds.
Cpte G. Trew, R. Vignoles, Coull Qt *Concert*
(11/90) (MERI) ① CDE84185
Cpte D. Wilson-Johnson, D.O. Norris *Maud.*
(6/91) (HYPE) ① CDA66187

SONDHEIM, Stephen (Joshua) (b 1930) USA

SECTION IV: VOCAL AND CHORAL

So Many People—song from unproduced show 'Saturday Night' (1954)
M. Patinkin, Orch, E. Stern (r1993; orch Troob, arr Ford) *Concert* (11/94) (NONE) ① 7559-79330-2

SECTION V: STAGE WORKS

Anyone Can Whistle—musical show (1964—New York) (Lyrics cpsr)
EXCERPTS: 1. Overture; 2. Miracle Song; 3. Simple; 4. Anyone Can Whistle; 5. With So Little to Be Sure Of; 6. Everybody Says Don't; 7. A Parade in Town.
7. D. Upshaw, orch, E. Stern (r1993: orch L Wilcox) *Concert* (12/94) (NONE) ① 7559-79345-2
Assassins—musical play (1990) (Lyrics cpsr; Book J Weidman)
EXCERPTS: 1. Everybody's Got the Right; 2. The Ballad of Booth; 3. How I Saved Roosevelt; 4a. Gun Song; 4b. The Ballad of Czolgosz; 5. Unworthy of Your Love; 6. The Ballad of Guiteau; 7. Another National Anthem; 8. November 22, 1963; 9. Final Sequence: 9a. You Can Close the New York Stock Exchange; 9b. Everybody's Got the Right (reprise).
Cpte Orig Broadway Cast, P. Gemignani (r1991)
(4/92) (RCA) ① RD60737
Company—musical show (1970—New York) (Lyrics cpsr)
EXCERPTS: 1. Company; 2. The Little Things You Do Together; 3. Sorry-Grateful; 4. You Could Drive a Person Crazy; 5. Have I Got a Girl For You; 6. Someone Is Waiting; 7. Another Hundred People; 8. Getting Married Today; 9. Side by Side by Side; 10. What Would We Do Without You; 11. Poor Baby; 12. Tick Tock (Orchestra); 13. Barcelona; 14. The Ladies; 15. Being Alive; 16. Finale. ADDITIONAL ITEM: 17. Multitudes of Amys (cut from finished version).
6, 17. M. Patinkin, Orch, E. Stern (r1993; orch Troob, arr Ford) *Concert* (11/94) (NONE) ① 7559-79330-2
Evening Primrose—television musical (1965) (Book J Goldman, after J Collier)
EXCERPTS: 1. Take Me to the World; 2. I Remember.
1. D. Upshaw, E. Stern, L. Stifelman (r1993: orch D Troob) *Concert* (12/94) (NONE) ① 7559-79345-2
Follies—musical show (1971—New York) (Lyrics cpsr; Book J. Goldman)
EXCERPTS: 1. Prologue; 2. Beautiful Girls; 3. Don't Look at Me; 4. Waiting for the Girls Upstairs; 5. Ah, Paris!; 6. Broadway Baby; 7. The Road You Didn't Take; 8. In Buddy's Eyes; 9. Who's That Woman?; 10. I'm Still Here; 11. Too Many Mornings; 12. The Right Girl; 13. Could I Leave You?; 14. You're Gonna Love Tomorrow; 15. Love Will See Us Through; 16. The God-Why-Don't-You-Love-Me Blues; 17. Losing My Mind; 18. The Story of Lucy and Jessie; 19. Live, Laugh, Love; 20. Finale.
Cpte Alexis Smith, G. Nelson, D. Collins, J. McMartin, Orig Broadway Cast, H. Hastings (r1971)
(11/93) (EMI) ① ZDM7 64666-2
7. M. Patinkin, Orch, E. Stern (r1993; orch Troob, arr Ford) *Concert* (11/94) (NONE) ① 7559-79330-2
17. S. Bullock, A. Bryn Parri (r1994) *Concert*
(11/95) (SAIN) ① SCDC2070
The Girls of Summer—incidental music (1956) (Wds. N R Nash)
EXCERPTS: 1. The Girls of Summer.
1. D. Upshaw, E. Stern, L. Stifelman (r1993: arr E Stern) *Concert* (12/94) (NONE) ① 7559-79345-2
Into the Woods—musical play (1987—New York) (Lyrics cpsr; Book J Lapine)
EXCERPTS: ACT ONE: 1. Act One Prologue: 1a. Once Upon a Time; 1b. Into the Woods; 1c. Fly Birds, Back to the Sky; 1d. Witch's Entrance; 1e. Jack, Jack, Jack, Head in a Sack; 1f. You Wish to Have the Curse Reversed?; 1g. Our Carriage Waits; 1h. The Curse is On My House; 1i. Into the Woods; 2. Cinderella at the Grave; 3. Hello, Little Girl; 4. I Guess This is Goodbye; 5. Maybe They're Magic; 6. Our Little World; 7. I Know Things Now; 8. A Very Nice Prince; 9. First Midnight; 10. Giants in the Sky; 11. Agony; 12. It Takes Two; 13. Stay With Me; 14. On the Steps of the Palace; 15. Act One Finale: Ever After. ACT TWO: 16. Act Two Prologue: So Happy; 17. Agony; 18. Lament; 19. Any Moment; 20. Moments in the Woods; 21. Your Fault; 22. Last Midnight; 23. No More; 24. No One is Alone; 25. Finale: Children Will Listen.
Cpte J. McKenzie, I. Staunton, P. Rowlands, C. Carter, Orig London Cast, P. Stanger (r1991)
(9/91) (RCA) ① RD60752
A Little Night Music—musical play: 2 acts (1973—New York) (Lyrics H Wheller, after I Bergman)
EXCERPTS: 1. Overture. ACT 1: 2. Night Waltz; 3. Now; 4. Later; 5. Soon; 6. The glamorous life; 7. Remember; 8. You must meet my wife; 9. Liasons; 10. In praise of women; 11. Every day a little death; 12. A weekend in the country. ACT 2: 13. Night Waltz I (The sun won't set); 14. Night Waltz II (Liebeslieders); 15. It would have been wonderful; 16.

Perpetual anticipation; 17. Send in the clowns; 18. The miller's son; 19. Send in the clowns (reprise); 20. Last waltz.

13, 14. Hollywood Bowl SO, J. Mauceri (r1993; arr Mauceri/Gursky) *Concert*

(6/94) (PHIL) ① 438 685-2PH

Merrily We Roll Along—musical show (1981; rev 1985, 1990 & 1992—New York) (Lyrics cpsr, after Kaufman & Hart)

EXCERPTS: 1. Overture; 2. The Hills of Tomorrow (dropped from later revisions); 3. Merrily We Roll Along—1980; 4. Rich and Happy; 5. Merrily We Roll Along—1979—1975; 6. Old Friends; 7. Like It Was; 8. Merrily We Roll Along—1974—1973; 9. Franklin Shepard, Inc; 10. Old Friends; 11. Not a Day Goes By; 12. Now You Know; 13. Merrily We Roll Along—1964—1962; 14. Good Thing Going; 15. Merrily We Roll Along—1961—1960; 16. Bobby and Jackie and Jack; 17. Not a Day Goes By (reprise); 18. Opening Doors; 19. Our Time. ADDITIONAL NUMBERS FOR LATER PRODUCTIONS: 20. Growing Up, Parts 1 & 2; 21. That Frank; 22. The Blob (restored from preview version).

Cpte Leicester Haymarket Th Cast, P. Kerryson (r1993; 1992 version) (4/95) (TER) ① CDTER1225

7. D. Upshaw, E. Stern, L. Stifelman (r1993; arr M Starobin) *Concert* (12/94) (NONE) ① 7559-79345-2

14. M. Patinkin, Orch, E. Stern (r1993; orch Troob, arr Ford) *Concert* (11/94) (NONE) ① 7559-79330-2

Pacific Overtures—musical show: 2 acts (1976—New York) (Book and lyrics J. Weidman)

Cpte R. Angas, L. Berger, C. Booth-Jones, E. Byles, J. Cashmore, G. Christie, I. Comboy, Timothy Jenkins, J. Kitchiner, S. Masterton-Smith, H. Nicoll, M. Rivers, E. Roberts, M. Sadler, P. Strathearn, A. Woodrow, ENO Orch, J. Holmes (1987)

(8/88) (TER) ① [2] CDTER2 1152

Excs R. Angas, E. Byles, Terry Jenkins, A. Woodrow, I. Comboy, J. Cashmore, C. Booth-Jones, J. Kitchiner, S. Masterton-Smith, M. Rivers, P. Strathearn, E. Roberts, H. Nicoll, G. Fletcher, L. Berger, G. Christie, M. Sadler, ENO Orch, J. Holmes (1987) (8/88) (TER) ① CDTER1151

Passion—musical show (1994—New York) (Lyrics cpsr; Book James Lapine)

EXCERPTS: 1. Happiness; 2. First Letter; 3. Second Letter; 4. Third Letter; 5. Fourth Letter; 6. I Read; 7. Transition; 8. Garden Sequence; 9. Transition; 10. Trio; 11. Transition; 12. I Wish I Could Forget You; 13. Soldiers' Gossip; 14. Flashback; 15. Sunrise Letter; 16. Is This What You Call Love?; 17. Soldiers' Gossip; 18. Transition; 19. Forty Days; 20. Loving You; 21. Transition; 22. Soldiers' Gossip; 23. Farewell Letter; 24. No One Has Ever Loved Me; 25. Finale.

Cpte D. Murphy, J. Shea, M. Mazzie, Orig Broadway Cast, P. Gemignani (r1994)

(12/95) (EMI) ① CDQ5 55251-2

Putting It Together—musical revue (1992—Oxford) (compiled from previous shows)

EXCERPTS: ACT ONE: 1. Invocation & Intructions to the Audience (The Frogs); 2. Putting It Together (Sunday in the Park With George); 3. Rich & Happy No.1 (Merrily We Roll Along); 4a. Merrily We Roll Along (Merrily We Roll Along); 4b. Lovely (A Funny Thing Happened...); 5. Everybody Ought to Have a Maid (A Funny Thing Happened...); 6a. Sooner or Later (Dick Tracey); 6b. I'm Calm (A Funny Thing Happened...); 6c. Impossible (A Funny Thing Happened...); 6d. Ah, But Underneath (Follies); 7. Hello, Little Girl (Into the Woods); 8a. My Husband the Pig (A Little Night Music); 8b. Every Day a Little Death (A Little Night Music); 9a. Merrily We Roll Along No.2; 9b. Have I Got a Girl For You! (Company); 10. Pretty Women (Sweeney Todd); 11. Now (A Little Night Music); 12. Bang! (A Little Night Music); 13. Country House (Follies); 14a. Merrily We Roll Along No.3; 14b. Could I Leave You? (Follies) ACT TWO: 15. Back in Business (Dick Tracey); 16. Rich & Happy No.2; 17. Night Waltzes (A Little Night Music); 17a. Love Takes Time; 17b. Remember?; 17c. Perpetual Anticipation; 17d. The Sun Won't Set; 18. Game Sequence No.1; 18a. What Would We Do Without You?; 18b. Gun Song (Assassins); 19. Game Sequence No.2; A Little Night Music (Sweeney Todd); 20. The Miller's Son (A Little Night Music); 21. Live Alone & Like It (Dick Tracey); 22. Sorry-Grateful (Company); 23. Sweet Polly Plunkett (Sweeney Todd); 24. I Could Drive a Person Crazy (Company); 25. Marry Me a Little (Company); 26. Getting Married Today (Company); 27a. Merrily We Roll Along No.4; 27b. Being Alive (Company); 28. Like It Was (Merrily We Roll Along); 29a. Old Friends (Merrily We Roll Along); 29b. Merrily We Roll Along No.5.

Cpte J. Andrews, Orig Cast (r1993; arr C. Walker) (7/94) (RCA) ① [2] 09026 61729-2

Saturday Night—musical show (1954) (unperformed)

EXCERPTS: 1. What More Do I Need; 2. So Many People.

1. D. Upshaw, orch, E. Stern (r1993: orch M Starobin) *Concert* (12/94) (NONE) ① 7559-79345-2

Sunday in the Park with George—musical show (1984—New York) (Lyrics cpsr; Book J Lapine)

EXCERPTS: 1. Introduction; 2. Sunday in the Park with George; 3. No life; 4. Colour and light; 5. Gossip; 6. The day off; 7. Everybody loves Louis; 8. Finishing the hat; 9. We do not belong together; 10. Beautiful; 11. Sunday; 12. It's hot up here; 13a. Chromolume No. 7; 13b. Putting it together; 14. Children and art; 15. Lesson No. 8; 16. Move on; 17. Sunday.

Cpte Orig Broadway Cast (r1984)

(7/90) (RCA) ① RD85042

SONNTAG, Gottfried (1846–1921) Germany

SECTION I: ORCHESTRAL

Nibelungen-Marsch (after R Wagner)

Berlin Phil Wind Qnt, H. von Karajan (r1973: arr Villinger) *Concert* (5/94) (DG) ① 439 346-2GX2

SOR, (Joseph) Fernando (Macari) (1778–1839) Spain

SECTION II: CHAMBER

Divertissement, '(L')Encouragement'—two guitars, Op. 34

T. Kropat, T. Krumeich *Concert* (7/93) (CHNN) ① CG9103

J. Bream, J. Williams (r1971) *Concert* (8/93) (RCA) ① 09026 61450-2

SECTION III: INSTRUMENTAL

6 Airs from Mozart's 'Die Zauberflöte'—guitar, Op. 19

L. Eisenhardt *Concert* (1/89) (ETCE) ① KTC1025

Le calme—caprice: guitar, Op. 50

L. Eisenhardt *Concert* (1/89) (ETCE) ① KTC1025

Fantasia in D minor—guitar (c1830) (MS rediscovered 1991; unpublished)

P. Romero (r1993; ed P. Romero) *Concert* (4/95) (PHIL) ① 442 150-2PH

Fantasia No. 2—guitar, Op. 7 (pub 1814)

J. Bream (r1965) *Concert* (8/93) (RCA) ① [28] 09026 61583-2(6)

J. Bream (r1980) *Concert* (8/93) (RCA) ① [28] 09026 61583-2(6)

J. Bream (r1965) *Concert* (8/93) (RCA) ① 09026 61610-2

J. Bream (r1980) *Concert* (6/94) (RCA) ① 09026 61607-2

Fantasia No. 7—guitar, Op. 30 (pub 1828)

J. Bream (r1980) *Concert* (6/94) (RCA) ① 09026 61607-2

7. J. Bream (r1980) *Concert* (8/93) (RCA) ① [28] 09026 61583-2(6)

Fantasia No. 13, 'Fantasia élégiaque'—guitar, Op. 59 (1836)

R. Smits (r1991) *Concert* (8/93) (ACCE) ① ACC29182D

Grand Solo (Sonata prima)—guitar, Op. 14 (pub c1810-23)

J. Bream (r1967-8) *Concert* (8/93) (RCA) ① [28] 09026 61583-2(4)

J. Bream (r1967-8) *Concert* (8/93) (RCA) ① [28] 09026 61583-2(6)

J. Bream (r1967-8) *Concert* (8/93) (RCA) ① 09026 61610-2

J. Bream (r1967-8) *Concert* (6/94) (RCA) ① 09026 61593-2

Introduction and Variations on a theme by Mozart—guitar, Op. 9

N. North *Concert* (6/87) (AMON) ① CD-SAR18

A. Segovia (r1927) *Concert* (5/89) (EMI) ① [2] CHS7 61047-2

A. Gifford (r1990) *Concert* (12/92) (NATI) ① NTCD001

R. Smits (r1991) *Concert* (8/93) (ACCE) ① ACC29182D

J. Bream (r1980) *Concert* (8/93) (RCA) ① [28] 09026 61583-2(6)

J. Bream (r1983) *Concert* (8/93) (RCA) ① [28] 09026 61583-2(6)

J. Bream (r1983) *Concert* (8/93) (RCA) ① 09026 61610-2

J. Bream (r1980) *Concert* (6/94) (RCA) ① 09026 61607-2

J. M. Moreno (r1994) *Concert* (8/95) (GLOS) ① GCD920103

Introduction and Variations on 'Ye Banks and Braes'—guitar, Op. 40 (pub 1826-39)

L. Eisenhardt *Concert* (1/89) (ETCE) ① KTC1025

Minuetto—guitar, Op. 22

N. Kraft (r1993) *Concert* (1/95) (NAXO) ① 8 553007

Sonata for Guitar in C, 'Grand Sonata II', Op. 25 (pub 1826)

L. Eisenhardt *Concert* (1/89) (ETCE) ① KTC1025

J. Bream (r1974; rev Bream) *Concert* (8/93) (RCA) ① [28] 09026 61583-2(4)

J. Bream (r1974; rev Bream) *Concert* (6/94) (RCA) ① 09026 61593-2

Minuet J. Bream (r1965) *Concert* (8/93) (RCA) ① [28] 09026 61583-2(6)

Minuet J. Bream (r1965) *Concert* (8/93) (RCA) ① 09026 61610-2

12 Studies—guitar, Op. 6 (pub c1810-23)

1. D (Allegretto); 2. A (Allegretto); 3. E (Allegro moderato); 4. G; 5. C; 6. A (Allegro); 7. D; 8. C (Lento); 9. D minor (Con calma); 10. C; 11. E (Movido); 12. A (Andante).

No. 11. R. Smits (r1991) *Concert* (8/93) (ACCE) ① ACC29182D

6, 9, 11, 12. N. Kraft (r1993) *Concert* (1/95) (NAXO) ① 8 553007

24 Studies (Leçons progressives)—guitar, Op. 31 (1826-39)

EXCERPTS: 1. Mouvement de prière réligieuse; 19. Etude in A; 22. Etude in B flat.

12. R. Smits (r1991) *Concert* (8/93) (ACCE) ① ACC29182D

19. N. Kraft (r1993) *Concert* (1/95) (NAXO) ① 8 553007

24 Studies—guitar, Op. 35 (pub 1826-39)

1. C; 2. A minor; 3. A minor; 4. G; 5. G; 6. D; 7. E; 8. E; 9. A; 10. F; 11. D minor; 12. F; 13. C; 14. D minor; 15. A; 16. D minor (Andante); 17. D (Allegro grazioso); 18. E minor; 19. C; 20. A; 21. A; 22. E minor (Moderato); 23. E; 24. E.

No. 22. R. Smits (r1991) *Concert* (8/93) (ACCE) ① ACC29182D

13, 17, 22. N. Kraft (r1993) *Concert* (1/95) (NAXO) ① 8 553007

Thème variés et Douze Minuets—guitar, Op. 11 (pub c1810-23)

EXCERPTS: 4. No. 4; 6. No. 6; 9. G.

Andante maestoso; Andante expressivo J. M. Moreno (r1994) *Concert* (8/95) (GLOS) ① GCD920103

6. N. Kraft (r1993) *Concert* (1/95) (NAXO) ① 8 553007

SORABJI, Kaikhosru Shapurji (1892–1988) England

SECTION III: INSTRUMENTAL

Opus clavicembalisticum—piano (1929-30)

J. Ogdon (9/89) (ALTA) ① [4] AIR-CD-9075

Passeggiata arlecchinesca sopra un frammento di Busoni—piano (1981-2)

D. Amato (r c1994) *Concert* (4/95) (ALTA) ① AIR-CD-9025

Quaere reliqua hujus materiei inter secretiora—piano (1940)

D. Amato (r c1994) *Concert* (4/95) (ALTA) ① AIR-CD-9025

St Bertrand de Comminges, 'He was laughing in the tower'—piano (1941)

D. Amato (r c1994) *Concert* (4/95) (ALTA) ① AIR-CD-9025

2 Sutras—piano (1981 & ?1984)

EXCERPTS: 1. Sutra sul nome dell'amico Alexis; 2. Sutra, 'Per il caro amico quasi Nipote—Alexis.

D. Amato (r c1994) *Concert* (4/95) (ALTA) ① AIR-CD-9025

Symphony for Organ No. 1 (1924)

K. Bowyer (5/89) (CNTI) ① [2] CCD1001/2

Toccatinetta sopra C. G. F.—piano (1929)

D. Amato (r c1994) *Concert* (4/95) (ALTA) ① AIR-CD-9025

SØRENSEN, Bent (b 1958) Denmark

SECTION II: CHAMBER

Adieu—string quartet (1986)

Arditti Qt *Concert* (11/92) (MARC) ① [2] DCCD9003

Alman—string quartet (1983-84)
Arditti Qt *Concert*
    (11/92) (MARC) ① [2] **DCCD9003**
Angels' Music—string quartet (1987-88)
Arditti Qt *Concert*
    (11/92) (MARC) ① [2] **DCCD9003**

SORIANO, Perez *(?19th Cent)*
Spain

SECTION V: STAGE WORKS

El Guitarrico—zarzuela
El guitarrico T. Ruffo, orch (r1914) *Concert*
    (2/93) (PREI) ① [3] **89303(1)**
Jota de Perico J. Carreras, ECO, E. Ricci (r1994)
Concert   (2/95) (ERAT) ① **4509-95789-2**

SOROZÁBAL, Pablo *(1897–1988)*
Spain

SECTION V: STAGE WORKS

Del manojo de rosas—zarzuela: 2 acts (1934)
EXCERPTS: 1. Madrilena bonita.
1. P. Domingo, Madrid SO, M. Moreno-Buendia
 (r1987) *Concert*   (1/89) (EMI) ① **CDC7 49148-2**
Katiuska—zarzuela: 2 acts (1931)
Cpte P. Lorengar, Alfredo Kraus, R. Cesari, M. Gas,
 E. Serrano, S.P. Carpio, A.M. Fernandez, F. Maroto,
 J. Marin, Madrid Coros Cantores, Madrid Concerts
 Orch, P. Sorozábal
    (10/92) (HISP) ① **CDZ7 67330-2**
La Tabernera del puerto—zarzuela: 3 acts (1940—Madrid) (Lib. Fernandez & Romero)
EXCERPTS -; 1. No puede ser.
1. P. Domingo, Madrid SO, M. Moreno-Buendia
 (r1987) *Concert*   (1/89) (EMI) ① **CDC7 49148-2**
1. P. Domingo, MMF Orch, Rome Op Orch, Z. Mehta
 (pp1990) *Concert* (10/90) (DECC) ① **430 433-2DH**
1. P. Domingo, Madrid SO, E. G. Asensio (pp1991)
Concert   (11/92) (CARL) ① **MCD45**
1. P. Domingo, Paris Opéra-Bastille Orch, E. Kohn
 (pp1992) *Concert*   (6/94) (SONY) ① **SK46691**
1. J. Carreras, ECO, E. Ricci (r1994) *Concert*
    (2/95) (ERAT) ① **4509-95789-2**

SOURSBY *(fl c1430–1460)*
England

SECTION IV: VOCAL AND CHORAL

Sanctus—mass movement (3vv)
Gothic Voices, C. Page *Concert*
    (11/87) (HYPE) ① **CDA66238**

SOUSA, John Philip *(1854–1932)*
USA

SECTION I: ORCHESTRAL

The Belle of Chicago—march (1892)
Blues and Royals Band, E. W. Jeanes *Concert*
    (9/92) (CHAN) ① **CHAN6517**
El Capitan—march (1896)
Wallace Collection, J. Wallace *Concert*
    (11/88) (NIMB) ① **NI5129**
Blues and Royals Band, E. W. Jeanes *Concert*
    (9/92) (CHAN) ① **CHAN6517**
NBC SO, A. Toscanini (arr Toscanini: r1945) *Concert*
    (11/92) (RCA) ① **GD60307**
Philadelphia, L. Stokowski (r1930) *Concert*
    (10/93) (STOK) ① **LSCD20**
The Chariot race—descriptive piece (Ben Hur) (1890)
Wallace Collection, J. Wallace *Concert*
    (11/88) (NIMB) ① **NI5129**
The Coquette—caprice (1887)
Wallace Collection, J. Wallace *Concert*
    (11/88) (NIMB) ① **NI5129**
Gladiator—march (1886)
Blues and Royals Band, E. W. Jeanes *Concert*
    (9/92) (CHAN) ① **CHAN6517**
Hail to the Spirit of Liberty—march (1900)
Wallace Collection, J. Wallace *Concert*
    (11/88) (NIMB) ① **NI5129**
Hands across the sea—march (1899)
Blues and Royals Band, E. W. Jeanes *Concert*
    (9/92) (CHAN) ① **CHAN6517**
The High School Cadets—march (1890)
Blues and Royals Band, E. W. Jeanes *Concert*
    (9/92) (CHAN) ① **CHAN6517**
The Invincible Eagle—march (1901)
Blues and Royals Band, E. W. Jeanes *Concert*
    (9/92) (CHAN) ① **CHAN6517**

Jack Tar—march (1903)
Wallace Collection, J. Wallace *Concert*
    (11/88) (NIMB) ① **NI5129**
King Cotton—march (1895)
Wallace Collection, J. Wallace *Concert*
    (11/88) (NIMB) ① **NI5129**
Blues and Royals Band, E. W. Jeanes *Concert*
    (9/92) (CHAN) ① **CHAN6517**
The Liberty Bell—march (1893)
Wallace Collection, J. Wallace *Concert*
    (11/88) (NIMB) ① **NI5129**
Blues and Royals Band, E. W. Jeanes *Concert*
    (9/92) (CHAN) ① **CHAN6517**
Manhattan beach—march (1893)
Wallace Collection, J. Wallace *Concert*
    (11/88) (NIMB) ① **NI5129**
Blues and Royals Band, E. W. Jeanes *Concert*
    (9/92) (CHAN) ① **CHAN6517**
Philadelphia, L. Stokowski (r1929) *Concert*
    (10/93) (STOK) ① **LSCD20**
National Fencibles—march (1888) (The March Past of the National Fencibles)
Blues and Royals Band, E. W. Jeanes *Concert*
    (9/92) (CHAN) ① **CHAN6517**
New York Hippodrome March (1915)
Sousa's Band (r1916) *Concert*
    (5/94) (PEAR) ① [3] **GEMMCDS9056/8**
La Reine de la mer—waltzes (1886)
Wallace Collection, J. Wallace *Concert*
    (11/88) (NIMB) ① **NI5129**
Semper Fidelis—march (c1888)
Wallace Collection, J. Wallace *Concert*
    (11/88) (NIMB) ① **NI5129**
Blues and Royals Band, E. W. Jeanes *Concert*
    (9/92) (CHAN) ① **CHAN6517**
Blues and Royals Band, E. W. Jeanes *Concert*
    (9/92) (CHAN) ① **CHAN6517**
Boston Pops, A. Fiedler (r1958) *Concert*
    (1/94) (RCA) ① **09026 61249-2**
The Stars and Stripes Forever—march (1897)
Cleveland Winds, F. Fennell *Concert*
    (10/84) (TELA) ① **CD80099**
Wallace Collection, J. Wallace *Concert*
    (11/88) (NIMB) ① **NI5129**
St Louis SO, L. Slatkin *Concert*
    (6/89) (RCA) ① **RD87716**
National PO, L. Stokowski *Concert*
    (4/92) (EMI) ① **CDM7 64140-2**
NBC SO, A. Toscanini (arr Toscanini: r1945) *Concert*
    (11/92) (RCA) ① **GD60307**
V. Horowitz (arr Horowitz: r1950) *Concert*
    (1/93) (RCA) ① **GD60526**
Black Dyke Mills Band, R. Newsome (r1977) *Concert*
    (1/94) (CHAN) ① **CHAN4528**
Boston Pops, A. Fiedler (r1958) *Concert*
    (1/94) (RCA) ① **09026 61249-2**
Detroit SO, N. Järvi (r1992) *Concert*
    (8/94) (CHAN) ① **CHAN9227**
BBC PO, M. Bamert (r1994: orch Stokowski) *Concert*
    (6/95) (CHAN) ① **CHAN9349**
NBC SO, A. Toscanini (bp1943) *Concert*
    (10/95) (DELL) ① **CDDA9024**
The Thunderer—march (c1889)
Wallace Collection, J. Wallace *Concert*
    (11/88) (NIMB) ① **NI5129**
Blues and Royals Band, E. W. Jeanes *Concert*
    (9/92) (CHAN) ① **CHAN6517**
Under the Cuban Flag
Wallace Collection, J. Wallace *Concert*
    (11/88) (NIMB) ① **NI5129**
The Washington Post—march (1889)
Wallace Collection, J. Wallace *Concert*
    (11/88) (NIMB) ① **NI5129**
Blues and Royals Band, E. W. Jeanes *Concert*
    (9/92) (CHAN) ① **CHAN6517**
With Pleasure—dance hilarious (1912)
Wallace Collection, J. Wallace *Concert*
    (11/88) (NIMB) ① **NI5129**

SOUTULLO, Reveriano *(1884–1932) Spain*

SECTION V: STAGE WORKS

La Del Soto Parral—zarzuela: 2 acts (1927) (comp with J V Carbonell. Lib Carreño & Ardavín)
Ya mis horas felices P. Domingo, Madrid SO, M. Moreno-Buendia (r1987) *Concert*
    (1/89) (EMI) ① **CDC7 49148-2**
Ultimo romantico—operetta: 2 acts (Cpsd with Juan Vert)
Bella enamorada P. Domingo, Madrid SO, E. G. Asensio (pp1991) *Concert*
    (11/92) (CARL) ① **MCD45**

Noche de amor P. Domingo, ROHO, J. Barker
 (pp1988) *Concert*   (9/89) (EMI) ① **CDC7 49811-2**

SOWASH, Rick *(b 1950) USA*

SECTION III: INSTRUMENTAL

Theme and 6 Variations—harpsichord (1986)
B. Harbach *Concert*   (3/89) (KING) ① **KCLCD2005**
The Unicorn—harpsichord (1976)
B. Harbach *Concert*   (3/89) (KING) ① **KCLCD2005**

SOWERBY, Leo *(1895–1968) USA*

SECTION II: CHAMBER

Festival Musick—organ, brass and timpani (1953)
1. Fanfare; 2. Chorale; 3. Toccata on A. G. O.
J. E. Jordan Jr, Gloriae Dei Brass Ens (r1994)
Concert   (9/95) (GLOR) ① [2] **GDCD016**

SECTION III: INSTRUMENTAL

Arioso—organ (1942)
D. Chalmers (r1994) *Concert*
    (9/95) (GLOR) ① [2] **GDCD016**
Bright, Blithe and Brisk—organ (1967)
D. Chalmers (r1994) *Concert*
    (9/95) (GLOR) ① [2] **GDCD016**
Canon, Chacony and Fugue—organ (1948)
D. Chalmers (r1994) *Concert*
    (9/95) (GLOR) ① [2] **GDCD016**
Carillon—organ (1917)
D. Chalmers (r1994) *Concert*
    (9/95) (GLOR) ① [2] **GDCD016**
Comes Autumn Time—organ (1916)
G. Barber *Concert*   (3/92) (PRIO) ① **PRCD373**
Fantasy for Flute Stops—organ (1934)
C. Crozier *Concert*   (10/89) (DELO) ① **DE3075**
Passacaglia—piano (1942)
G. Quillman *Concert*   (10/89) (NEW) ① **NW376-2**
Piano Sonata (1948)
G. Quillman *Concert*   (10/89) (NEW) ① **NW376-2**
Prelude on 'Were you there?'—organ (1953-54)
D. Chalmers (r1994) *Concert*
    (9/95) (GLOR) ① [2] **GDCD016**
Requiescat in pace—organ (1920)
C. Crozier *Concert*   (10/89) (DELO) ① **DE3075**
Suite—piano (1959)
G. Quillman *Concert*   (10/89) (NEW) ① **NW376-2**
Symphony in G—organ (1930)
C. Crozier *Concert*   (10/89) (DELO) ① **DE3075**

SECTION IV: VOCAL AND CHORAL

All they from Saba shall come—anthem: tenor, choir and organ (1934) (Wds. Bible)
P. Logan, Gloriae Dei Cantores, E. C. Patterson
 (r1994) *Concert*   (9/95) (GLOR) ① [2] **GDCD016**
An Angel stood by the Altar of of the Temple—anthem: choir and organ (1955) (Wds. Bible)
3. Gloriae Dei Cantores, E. C. Patterson (r1994)
Concert   (9/95) (GLOR) ① [2] **GDCD016**
Christians, to the Paschal Victim—choir and organ (1965) (Wds. Vicitimae paschali: 14th cent)
Gloriae Dei Cantores, D. Chalmers, E. C. Patterson
 (r1994) *Concert*   (9/95) (GLOR) ① [2] **GDCD016**
Come, Holy Ghost—anthem: choir and organ (1949) (Wds Veni Creator: 10th cent, trans J Cosin)
Gloriae Dei Cantores, D. Chalmers, E. C. Patterson
 (r1994) *Concert*   (9/95) (GLOR) ① [2] **GDCD016**
Great is the Lord—anthem: choir and organ (1933) (Wds. Psalm 48)
Gloriae Dei Cantores, D. Chalmers, E. C. Patterson
 (r1994) *Concert*   (9/95) (GLOR) ① [2] **GDCD016**
Jesu, bright and morning star—choir and organ (1958) (Wds. Songs of Syon)
Gloriae Dei Cantores, D. Chalmers, E. C. Patterson
 (r1994) *Concert*   (9/95) (GLOR) ① [2] **GDCD016**
Lovely Infant—carol: choir and organ (1963) (Wds. German trad)
Gloriae Dei Cantores, D. Chalmers, E. C. Patterson
 (r1994) *Concert*   (9/95) (GLOR) ① [2] **GDCD016**
Magnificat and Nunc dimittis in E minor—choir and organ (1957)
Gloriae Dei Cantores, D. Chalmers, E. C. Patterson
 (r1994) *Concert*   (9/95) (GLOR) ① [2] **GDCD016**
O God of Light—soprano and organ (1935) (Wds. from 'Hymns of the Russian Church', trans J Brownlie)
C. Helfrich, D. Chalmers (r1994) *Concert*
    (9/95) (GLOR) ① [2] **GDCD016**

O God, the protector of all—anthem:
soprano, choir a capella, Wds. Book of
Common Prayer (1968)
C. Helfrich, Gloriae Dei Cantores, E. C. Patterson
(r1994) *Concert*   (9/95) (GLOR) ① [2] **GDCD016**
3 Psalms—bass and organ (1928)
1. Hear my cry, O God (wds. Psalm 61); 2. The Lord
is my Shepherd (wds. Psalm 23); 3. How long wilt
thou forget me (Psalm 13).
1. R. K. Pugsley, D. Chalmers (r1994) *Concert*
(9/95) (GLOR) ① [2] **GDCD016**
2. P. Norman, D. Chalmers (r1994) *Concert*
(9/95) (GLOR) ① [2] **GDCD016**
3. F. Hempel, D. Chalmers (r1994) *Concert*
(9/95) (GLOR) ① [2] **GDCD016**
Thou art my strength, O God my
Lord—soprano and organ (1933) (Wds.
Hymns of the Russian Church, trans J
Brownlie)
K. M. Hamilton, D. Chalmers (r1994) *Concert*
(9/95) (GLOR) ① [2] **GDCD016**
Turn thou to Thy God—anthem: choir and
organ (1957) (Wds. Bible)
Gloriae Dei Cantores, D. Chalmers, E. C. Patterson
(r1994) *Concert*   (9/95) (GLOR) ① [2] **GDCD016**
Whoso dewelleth—baritone and organ (1935)
(Wds. Psalm 91)
L. Norman, D. Chalmers (r1994) *Concert*
(9/95) (GLOR) ① [2] **GDCD016**

SPALDING, Albert (1888–1953) USA

SECTION II: CHAMBER

Dragonfly—violin and piano
A. Spalding, A. Benoist (r1937) *Concert*
(10/92) (BIDD) ① **LAB054**
Etchings—violin and piano, Op. 5
A. Spalding, A. Benoist (r1934) *Concert*
(10/92) (BIDD) ① **LAB054**
Wind in the Pines—violin and piano
A. Spalding, A. Benoist (r1937) *Concert*
(10/92) (BIDD) ① **LAB054**

SPARKE, Philip (b 1951) England

SECTION I: ORCHESTRAL

Capriccio—soprano cornet and brass band
G. Lindsay, Glasgow CWS Band, H. Snell *Concert*
(9/92) (DOYE) ① **DOYCD005**
Concerto Grosso—2 cornets, tenor horn,
trombone and brass band (1987-88)
R. Webster, P. Shaw, S. Smith, R. Childs, Black
Dyke Mills Band, P. Parkes (r1989) *Concert*
(10/94) (CHAN) ① **CHAN4523**
Fantasy—euphonium and brass band
(1978)
N. Childs, Britannia Building Soc Band, H. Snell
Concert   (2/91) (DOYE) ① **DOYCD002**
Partita—brass band
Britannia Building Soc Band, H. Snell (r1990) *Concert*
(8/92) (DOYE) ① **DOYCD004**
BNFL Band, R. Evans (r1993) *Concert*
(5/94) (POLY) ① **QPRL062D**

SECTION II: CHAMBER

Divertimento—brass ensemble (1990)
H. Snell Brass, H. Snell *Concert*
(9/91) (POLY) ① **QPRZ005D**

SPEAKS, Oley (1874–1948) USA

SECTION IV: VOCAL AND CHORAL

Sylvia—ballad (1914) (Wds. C. Scollard)
R. Tauber, orch (r1938) *Concert*
(7/89) (EMI) ① **CDM7 69476-2**

SPERGER, Johann Mathias (1750–1812) Germany

SECTION I: ORCHESTRAL

Concerto for Trumpet and Strings in D
(1779)
L. Güttler, C. Schornsheim, Leipzig New Bach
Collegium Musicum, M. Pommer (r1986) *Concert*
(8/89) (CAPR) ① **10 051**

SPINACINO, Francesco (fl. 1507) Italy

SECTION III: INSTRUMENAL

Adieu mes amours—chanson (pub. 1507)
(arr lute: from tune by Josquin)
J. Lindberg (arr lte from tune by Josquin) *Concert*
(10/89) (BIS) ① **BIS-CD399**
Bassadans—cantus firmus dance (pub.
1507) (tune: Il Re di Spagna)
J. Lindberg (tune: Il Re di Spagna) *Concert*
(10/89) (BIS) ① **BIS-CD399**
Recercare—lute (pub. 1507) (from
'Intabulatura de Lauto')
J. Lindberg *Concert*   (10/89) (BIS) ① **BIS-CD399**

SPIVAKOVSKY, Michael (1919–1983) England

SECTION I: ORCHESTRAL

Concerto for Harmonica and Orchestra
(1951)
T. Reilly, Munich RO, C. Gerhardt (r1977) *Concert*
(5/94) (CHAN) ① **CHAN9248**

SPOFFORTH, Reginald (1768/70–1827) England

SECTION IV: VOCAL AND CHORAL

Hail! smiling morn—glee
Hilliard Ens, L-L. Kiesel *Concert*
(12/91) (MERI) ① **DUOCD89009**

SPOHR, Louis (1784–1859) Germany

SECTION I: ORCHESTRAL

Concerto for Clarinet and Orchestra No. 1 in
C minor, Op. 26 (1808)
K. Leister, Stuttgart RSO, R. Frühbeck de Burgos
Clarinet Concerto 4. (10/86) (ORFE) ① **C088101A**
E. Johnson, ECO, G. Schwarz *Concert*
(11/89) (ASV) ① **CDDCA659**
G. de Peyer, LSO, Colin Davis *Concert*
(7/93) (DECC) ① **433 727-2DM**
E. Ottensamer, VPO, Colin Davis *Concert*
(6/94) (PHIL) ① **438 868-2PH**
E. Ottensamer, Košice St PO, J. Wildner (r1991)
Concert   (7/95) (NAXO) ① **8 550688**
Concerto for Clarinet and Orchestra No. 2 in
E flat, Op. 57 (1810)
K. Leister, Stuttgart RSO, R. Frühbeck de Burgos
Clarinet Concerto 3. (10/86) (ORFE) ① **C088201A**
E. Ottensamer, Slovak RSO, J. Wildner (r1994)
Concert   (7/95) (NAXO) ① **8 550689**
Concerto for Clarinet and Orchestra No. 3 in
F minor (1821)
K. Leister, Stuttgart RSO, R. Frühbeck de Burgos
Clarinet Concerto 2. (10/86) (ORFE) ① **C088201A**
E. Ottensamer, Košice St PO, J. Wildner (r1991)
Concert   (7/95) (NAXO) ① **8 550689**
Concerto for Clarinet and Orchestra No. 4 in
E minor (1828)
K. Leister, Stuttgart RSO, R. Frühbeck de Burgos
Clarinet Concerto 1. (10/86) (ORFE) ① **C088101A**
T. King, ECO, A. Francis Mozart: *Clarinet Concerto,*
K622.   (10/88) (MERI) ① **CDE84022**
E. Ottensamer, Slovak RSO, J. Wildner (r1994)
Concert   (7/95) (NAXO) ① **8 550689**
Concerto for String Quartet and Orchestra in
A minor, Op. 131 (1845)
E. Sebestyen, H. Ganz, H. Beyerle, M. Ostertag,
Berlin RSO, G. Albrecht *Concert*
(1/90) (SCHW) ① **311088**
Concerto for Violin and Orchestra No. 8 in A
minor, 'in modo di scena cantante', Op. 47
(1816)
1. Allegro molto; 2. Adagio; 3. Andante—Allegro
moderato.
A. Spalding, Philadelphia, E. Ormandy (r1938)
Concert   (10/92) (BIDD) ① **LAB054**
J. Heifetz, RCA Victor SO, I. Solomon (r1954)
Concert (11/94) (RCA) ① [65] **09026 61778-2(25)**
Notturno in C—wind instruments and
Turkish band, Op. 34 (1816)
Consortium Classicum (r1984) *Nonet, Op. 31.*
(9/87) (ORFE) ① **C155871A**
Octophoros, P. Dombrecht *Concert*
(2/90) (ACCE) ① **ACC8860D**

Potpourri in F—clarinet and orchestra, Op.
60 (1811)
E. Ottensamer, Bratislava RSO, J. Wildner (r1991)
Concert   (7/95) (NAXO) ① **8 550688**
Symphony No. 1 in E flat, Op. 20 (1811)
Košice St PO, A. Walter *Concert*
(12/92) (MARC) ① **8 223363**
Symphony No. 2 in D minor, Op. 49 (1820)
Singapore SO, C. Huey (r1985) *Lachner: Symphony*
1.   (10/86) (MARC) ① **8 220360**
Košice St PO, A. Walter (r1992) *Symphony 9.*
(2/94) (MARC) ① **8 223454**
Symphony No. 3 in C minor, Op. 78 (1828)
South-West German RSO, L. Hager *Concert*
(10/91) (AMAT) ① **SRR8904/1**
Košice St PO, A. Walter (r1991) *Symphony 5.*
(4/93) (MARC) ① **8 223439**
Symphony No. 5 in C minor, Op. 102 (1837)
Košice St PO, A. Walter *Symphony 1.*
(12/92) (MARC) ① **8 223363**
Symphony No. 6 in G, 'Historische Sinfonie
im Stil und Geschmack vier verschiedener
Zeitabschnitte', Op. 116 (1840)
BRSO, K.A. Rickenbacher *Symphony 9.*
(6/86) (ORFE) ① **C094841A**
Košice St PO, A. Walter (r1991) *Symphony 3.*
(4/93) (MARC) ① **8 223439**
Symphony No. 9 in B minor, '(Die)
Jahreszeiten', Op. 143 (1850)
BRSO, K.A. Rickenbacher *Symphony 6.*
(6/86) (ORFE) ① **C094841A**
Košice St PO, A. Walter (r1992) *Symphony 2.*
(2/94) (MARC) ① **8 223454**
Variations in B flat on a theme from
'Alruna'—clarinet and orchestra
H-R. Stalder, J. von Vintschger (cl/pf) *Concert*
(11/87) (JECK) ① **JD536-2**
T. King, ECO, J. Judd *Concert*
(4/90) (HYPE) ① **CDA66300**
V. Soames, J. Purvis (r1992) *Concert*
(3/94) (CLRI) ① **CC0006**
Violin and Harp Concerto No. 1 in F minor
(1807)
H. Schneeberger, U. Holliger, Lausanne CO, P-L
Graf *Mozart: Flute and Harp Concerto, K299.*
(12/87) (CLAV) ① **CD50-0208**
Waltz in A, 'Erinnerung an Marienbad', Op.
89 (1833)
ASMF Chbr Ens (r1992) *Concert*
(11/95) (PHIL) ① **438 017-2PH**

SECTION II: CHAMBER

Double Quartet No. 1 in D minor, Op. 65
(1823)
ASMF Chbr Ens *Double Quartet 2.*
(12/86) (HYPE) ① **CDA66141**
Archibudelli, Smithsonian Chbr Plyrs (r1993) *Concert*
(4/94) (SONY) ① **SK53370**
J. Heifetz, P. Amoyal, I. Baker, P. Rosenthal, M.
Thomas, A. Harshman, G. Piatigorsky, L. Lesser
(r1968) *Concert*
(11/94) (RCA) ① [65] **09026 61778-2(25)**
Double Quartet No. 2 in E flat, Op. 77 (1827)
ASMF Chbr Ens *Double Quartet 1.*
(12/86) (HYPE) ① **CDA66141**
Double Quartet No. 3 in E minor—strings,
Op. 87 (1832-33)
ASMF Chbr Ens *Double Quartet 4.*
(7/87) (HYPE) ① **CDA66142**
Double Quartet No. 4 in G Minor—strings,
Op. 136 (1847)
ASMF Chbr Ens *Double Quartet 3.*
(7/87) (HYPE) ① **CDA66142**
3 Duets—two violins, Op. 39 (1816)
1. D minor; 2. E flat; 3. E.
1 (Rondo) Y. Menuhin, L. Persinger (arr Persinger:
r1929) *Concert*   (4/91) (BIDD) ① **LAB031**
3 Duo concertanti—2 violins, Op. 67 (1824)
1. A minor; 2. D; 3. G minor.
2. I. Perlman, P. Zukerman *Concert*
(6/95) (EMI) ① [20] **CZS4 83177-2(1)**
Fantasy and Variations on a theme of
Danzi—clarinet and string quartet, Op. 81
(1814)
H-R. Stalder, Zurich Chbr Music *Concert*
(11/87) (JECK) ① **JD536-2**
C. Bradbury, O. Davies (cl/pf) *Concert*
(6/90) (ASV) ① **CDDCA701**
E. Ottensamer, Slovak RSO, J. Wildner (r1994)
Concert   (7/95) (NAXO) ① **8 550689**
Nonet in F, Op. 31 (1813)
Consortium Classicum (r1984) *Notturno, Op. 34.*
(9/87) (ORFE) ① **C155871A**
Nash Ens *Octet, Op.32.*   (3/89) (CRD) ① **CRD3354**
Gaudier Ens (r1993) *Octet, Op. 32.*
(8/94) (HYPE) ① **CDA66699**

ASMF Chbr Ens (r1992) *Concert*
(11/95) (PHIL) ① **438 017-2PH**
Octet in E, Op. 32 (1814)
Nash Ens *Nonet, Op.31.* (3/89) (CRD) ① **CRD3354**
Gaudier Ens (r1993) *Nonet, Op. 31.*
(8/94) (HYPE) ① **CDA66699**
ASMF Chbr Ens (r1992) *Concert*
(11/95) (PHIL) ① **438 017-2PH**
Piano Trio No. 1 in E minor, Op. 119 (1841)
Beethoven Broadwood Trio *Piano Trio 2.*
(3/89) (KING) ① **KCLCD2004**
Piano Trio No. 2 in F, Op. 123 (1842)
Beethoven Broadwood Trio *Piano Trio 2.*
(3/89) (KING) ① **KCLCD2004**
Piano Trio No. 3 in A minor, Op. 124 (1842)
Borodin Trio (r1994) *Piano Trio 4.*
(10/95) (CHAN) ① **CHAN9372**
Piano Trio No. 4 in B flat, Op. 133
Borodin Trio (r1994) *Piano Trio 3.*
(10/95) (CHAN) ① **CHAN9372**
Quintet in C minor—flute, clarinet, horn, bassoon and piano, Op. 52 (1820)
Nash Ens *Septet, Op.147.*
(3/89) (CRD) ① **CRD3399**
Septet in A minor—fl, cl, hn, bsn, vn, vc, pf, Op. 147 (1853)
Nash Ens *Quintet, Op.52.*
(3/89) (CRD) ① **CRD3399**
String Quartet in D minor, 'Quatuor brillant', Op. 11 (1837)
New Budapest Qt (r1990) *Concert*
(9/92) (MARC) ① **8 223254**
String Quartet in G minor, Op. 27 (1812)
New Budapest Qt (r1990) *Concert*
(9/92) (MARC) ① **8 223254**
2 String Quartets, Op. 4 (1807)
1. C; 2. G minor.
New Budapest Qt (r1990) *String Quartets, Op. 15.*
(9/92) (MARC) ① **8 223253**
2 String Quartets, Op. 15 (1808)
1. E flat; 2. D.
1. New Budapest Qt (r1990) *Concert*
(9/92) (MARC) ① **8 223254**
2. New Budapest Qt (r1990) *String Quartets, Op. 4.*
(9/92) (MARC) ① **8 223253**
3 String Quartets, Op. 29 (1813-15)
1. E flat; 2. C; 3. F minor.
1, 2. New Budapest Qt (r1990)
(9/92) (MARC) ① **8 223255**
3 String Quartets, Op. 58 (1821-22)
1. E flat; 2. A minor; 3. G.
1, 2. New Budapest Qt (r1991)
(1/93) (MARC) ① **8 223256**
2 String Quintets—two violins, two violas and cello, Op. 33 (1813-14)
2. Archibudelli, Smithsonian Chbr Plyrs (r1993)
Concert (4/94) (SONY) ① **SK53370**
String Sextet, Op. 140 (1848)
Archibudelli, Smithsonian Chbr Plyrs (r1993) *Concert*
(4/94) (SONY) ① **SK53370**
Variations in A—violin and string trio, Op. 8 (pub 1807)
E. Sebestyen, H. Ganz, W. Strehle, M. Ostertag
Concert (1/90) (SCHW) ① **311088**
Variations in D minor—violin and string trio, Op. 6 (pub c1807)
E. Sebestyen, H. Ganz, W. Strehle, M. Ostertag
Concert (1/90) (SCHW) ① **311088**

SECTION III: INSTRUMENTAL

Variations on Mehul's 'Je suis encore dans mon printemps'—harp, Op. 36 (1807)
S. Drake *Concert* (9/86) (HYPE) ① **CDA66038**

SECTION IV: VOCAL AND CHORAL

6 Lieder—1v and piano, Op. 25 (1810)
3. Scottish Lied; 3. Gretchen; 5. Zigeunerlied.
2, 5. D. Fischer-Dieskau, H. Höll *Concert*
(3/88) (ORFE) ① **C103841A**
6 Lieder—1v and piano, Op. 37 (1816)
1. Mignons Lied; 2. Gretchen; 4. Getrennte Liebe; 5. Lied beim Rundetanz.
5, 6. I. Partridge, J. Lindberg *Concert*
(10/89) (PEAR) ① **SHECD9608**
6. D. Fischer-Dieskau, H. Höll *Concert*
(3/88) (ORFE) ① **C103841A**
6 Lieder—1v and piano, Op. 41 (1818)
3. An Mignon; 6. Vanitas! vanitatum vanitas.
3, 6. D. Fischer-Dieskau, H. Höll *Concert*
(3/88) (ORFE) ① **C103841A**
6 Lieder—1v and piano, Op. 72 (1826) (Wds. various)
1. Frühlingsglaube; 2. Schifferlied der Wasserfee; 3. Ghasel; 4. Beruhigung; 5. An Rosa Maria; 6. Schlaflied.

1, 2, 4. E. Parcells, F. Justen *Concert*
(5/92) (SCHW) ① **314063**
1, 4. P. Schreier, K. Ragossnig *Concert*
(10/89) (NOVA) ① **150 039-2**
1, 4, 6. I. Partridge, J. Lindberg *Concert*
(10/89) (PEAR) ① **SHECD9608**
6. D. Fischer-Dieskau, H. Höll *Concert*
(3/88) (ORFE) ① **C103841A**
6 Lieder—1v, clarinet and piano, Op. 103 (1838)
1. Sei Still mein Herz (wds. C. von Schweizer); 2. Zweigesang (wds. Reinick); 3. Sehnsucht (wds. Geibel); 4. Wiegenlied (wds. von Fallersleben); 5. Das heimliche Leid (wds. Koch); 6. Wach auf (wds. anon).
Cpte J. Varady, H. Schöneberger, H. Höll *Concert*
(3/88) (ORFE) ① **C103841A**
Cpte E. Ritchie, V. Soames, J. Purvis (r1992)
Concert (3/94) (CLRI) ① **CC0006**
6 Lieder—baritone, violin and piano, Op. 154 (1857)
1. Abendfeier (wds H. Mahn); 2. Jagdlied (wds. F. Spohr); 3. Töne (wds. R. Otto); 4. Erlkönig (wds. Goethe); 5. Der Spielmann und seine Geige (wds. Hoppe); 6. Abendstille (wds. J. Koch).
Cpte D. Fischer-Dieskau, D. Sitkovetsky, H. Höll
Concert (3/88) (ORFE) ① **C103841A**

SECTION V: STAGE WORKS

Faust—opera: 2 (later 3) acts (1816—Prague)
(Lib. J K Bernhard)
Cpte M. Vier, E. von Jordis, D. Jennings, I. Bric, M. Eichwalder, D. Walker, U. Neuweiler, H. Kegler, W. Pugh, C. Taha, D. Abbott, M. Kowollik, Bielefeld Op Chor, Bielefeld PO, G. Moull (pp1993)
(8/94) (CPO) ① [2] **CPO999 247-2**
Cpte B. Skovhus, F. Hawlata, H. Martinpelto, A. Reiter, R. Orrego, U. Wand, R. Swensen, B. Wohlfarth, C. Späth, M. Brodt, Stuttgart Rad Chor, Kaiserslautern Rad Chor, K. Arp (r1993)
(12/94) (CAPR) ① [2] **60 049-2**
Der Hölle selbst will Ich...Liebe ist die zarte Blüte
T. Hampson, Munich RO, F. Luisi (r1994) *Concert*
(9/95) (EMI) ① **CDC5 55233-2**
Ich bin allein E. Ritchie, V. Soames, J. Purvis
(r1992) *Concert* (3/94) (CLRI) ① **CC0006**
Jessonda—opera: 3 acts, Op. 63 (1823—Kassel) (Lib. Gehe)
Cpte J. Varady, R. Behle, K. Moll, T. Moser, D. Fischer-Dieskau, P. Haage, P. Galliard, C. Meyer-Esche, Hamburg St Op Chor, Hamburg PO, G. Albrecht (11/91) (ORFE) ① [2] **C240912H**

SPOLIANSKY, Mischa (1898-1985) Russia/England

SECTION V: STAGE WORKS

Wanted for Murder—film score (1946)
EXCERPTS: 1. A Voice In the Night (Wds cpsr).
1. E. Harrison, QHLO, C. Williams (r1946) *Concert*
(9/94) (EMI) ① **CDGO 2059**

SPONTINI, Gaspare (Luigi Pacifico) (1774-1851) Italy

SECTION V: STAGE WORKS

Olimpie—tragédie lyrique: 3 acts (1821—Berlin) (Lib. Dieulafoy and Briffaut)
Cpte J. Varady, S. Toczyska, Ferruccio Tagliavini, D. Fischer-Dieskau, G. Fortune, J. Becker, Berlin RIAS Chbr Ch, Berlin Deutsche Op Chor, Berlin RSO, G. Albrecht (Ital: rev 1826)
(11/87) (ORFE) ① [3] **C137862H**
La Vestale—tragédie lyrique: 3 acts (1807—Paris) (Lib. V J E de Jouy)
EXCERPTS: 1. Overture. ACT 1: 1b. Périsse la vestale impié; 2a. Près de ce temple auguste, à Vesta consacre?; 2b. Dans le sein d'un ami fidèle; 3a. Si bien! partage donc mon crime ma fureur; 3b. Quand l'amitié seconde mon courage; 4. Fille du ciel, éternelle Vesta; 5a. Prêtresse dans ce jour, Rome victorieuse; 5b. L'amour est un mostre; 5c. Au nom de tous les Dieux; 6a. Ô d'un pouvoir funeste, invincible ascendant!; 6b. Licinius, je vais donc te revoir; 7. De lauriers couvrons les chemins. ACT 2: 8. Feu créateur, âme du monde; 9a. Du plus auguste ministre; 9b. Toi que j'implore avec effroi (Tu che invoco con orrore); 10a. Impitoyables dieux! 10b. L'arret et prononcé, ma carrière est remplie; 11a. Adieu, l'entends; 11b. Les dieux prendront pitié du sort qui nous accable; 11c. Vénus doit à l'amour son appui protecteur; 12. Quel trouble! Quels transports!; 13a. Suis moi—Quelqu' in vient; 13b. Ah! si je te suis chère;

14a. Il vivra!...D'un oeil ferme; 14b. Vengeancede leurs projects criminels; 14c. Sa bouche a prononcé l'arret. ACT 3: 15a. Qu'ai je vu! quels apprêts! quel spectacle d'horreur!; 15b. Non, non, je vis encore; 16a. Cinna, que fait l'armée?; 16b. Ce n'est plus le temps d'écouter; 17a. Mais avant de tenter un combat inégal; 17b. C'est à toi de trembler!; 18a. Différons, croyez-moi, l'instant du sacrifice; 18b. Périsse la vestale impié; 19a. Adieu, mes tendres soeurs; 20a. Sur l'autel profané de la chaste déesse; 20b. Vesta nous t'implorons pour le vierge coupable; 21a. Les dieux ont prononcé son juste châtiment; 21b. Toi, que je laisse sur la terre (Caro ogetto, il di cui nome); 22a. Arrêtez, ministres de la mort!; 22b. Ô terreur! ô disgrace!
Cpte R. Plowright, F. Araiza, P. Lefebre, G. Pasino, A. Cauli, F. de Grandis, Bavarian Rad Chor, Munich RSO, G. Kuhn (r1991)
(7/93) (ORFE) ① [2] **C256922H**
Cpte K. Huffstodt, A. M. Moore, J. P. Raftery, D. Graves, D. Kavrakos, A. Bramante, S. Sammaritano, La Scala Chor, La Scala Orch, R. Muti (pp1993)
(12/95) (SONY) ① [3] **S3K66357**
1. La Scala Orch, A. Guarnieri (r1928) *Concert*
(4/94) (EMI) ① [3] **CHS7 64864-2(1)**
9b M. Callas, La Scala Orch, T. Serafin (r1955: Ital)
Concert (2/90) (EMI) ① [4] **CMS7 63244-2**
9b R. Ponselle, orch, R. Bourdon (r1926: Ital)
Concert (2/92) (MMOI) ① **CDMOIR408**
9b E. Mazzoleni, orch (r1909/11: Ital) *Concert*
(4/94) (EMI) ① [3] **CHS7 64860-2(2)**
9b K. Vayne, orch (r1950s) *Concert*
(6/95) (PREI) ① **89996**
9b, 10a R. Ponselle, orch, R. Bourdon (r1926: Ital)
Concert (10/89) (NIMB) ① **NI7805**
9b, 10a (2 vers) R. Ponselle, orch, R. Bourdon
(r1926: Ital) *Concert*
(11/94) (ROMO) ① [2] **81007-2**
9b, 10a, 21b M. Callas, La Scala Orch, T. Serafin
(r1955: Ital) *Concert*
(11/86) (EMI) ① **CDC7 47282-2**
10a R. Ponselle, orch, R. Bourdon (r1926: Ital)
Concert (1/90) (RCA) ① **GD87810**
15a, 15b P. Domingo, National PO, E. Kohn (Ital)
Concert (11/90) (EMI) ① **CDC7 54053-2**

ST BERNARD (11–12th Cent) France

SECTION IV: VOCAL AND CHORAL

Quam pium—antiphon
Schola Gregoriana, M. Berry (r1993) *Concert*
(3/95) (HERA) ① **HAVPCD168**

ST. GODRIC

SECTION IV: VOCAL AND CHORAL

Crist and Sainte Marie
Hilliard Ens (r1984) *Concert*
(3/87) (HARM) ① **HMC90 1154**
Sainte Marie viergene
Hilliard Ens (r1984) *Concert*
(3/87) (HARM) ① **HMC90 1154**
Sainte Nicolas
Hilliard Ens (r1984) *Concert*
(3/87) (HARM) ① **HMC90 1154**

STADLMAYR, Johann (c1575–1648) Germany

SECTION IV: VOCAL AND CHORAL

Coelo rores fluunt flores—motet
Niederaltaicher Scholaren, K. Ruhland (r1992)
Concert (10/93) (SONY) ① **SK53117**

STAFFORD SMITH, John (1750–1836) England

SECTION IV: VOCAL AND CHORAL

Blest pair of sirens—serious glee: 5vv (1776) (Wds Milton)
Invocation (r1994) *Concert*
(3/95) (HYPE) ① **CDA66740**

STAINER, Sir John (1840–1901) England

SECTION IV: VOCAL AND CHORAL

Awake, awake, put on Thy strength, O Zion—saint's day anthem (1871)
How beautiful upon the mountains St Paul's Cath Ch, John Scott *Concert*
(4/92) (HYPE) ① **CDA66519**
The Crucifixion—oratorio: TB, chorus and organ (1887) (Wds. J. Sparrow-Simpson)
1. Could ye not watch with Me (bass & chorus); 2. Fling wide the gates! (tenor & chorus); 3. Cross of Sorrow (hymn); 4. King ever glorious (tenor); 5. God so loved the world (anthem); 6. Holy Jesu, by Thy passion (hymn); 7. So thou liftest Thy divine petition (duet); 8. Jesus, the Crucified, pleads for me (hymn); 9. I adore Thee (hymn); 10. From the Throne of His Cross (chorus); 11. All for Jesus (hymn).
M. Davies, D. Wilson-Johnson, St Paul's Cath Ch, Andrew Lucas, John Scott
(10/91) (CONI) ① **CDCF193**
4. R. Crooks, M. Andrews (r1930) *Concert*
(9/93) (CLAR) ① **CDGSE78-50-50**
Cupid, look about thee—partsong (Wds. from Robinson's 'New Citharen Lessons': 1609)
Hilliard Ens, L-L. Kiesel *Concert*
(12/91) (MERI) ① **DUOCD89009**
How beautiful upon the mountains—song
Wellington College Chs, T. Byram-Wigfield, S. Anderson *Concert* (10/92) (HERA) ① **HAVPCD153**
I saw the Lord—anthem (8vv)
St Paul's Cath Ch, Andrew Lucas, John Scott *Concert* (9/90) (HYPE) ① **CDA66374**
Magdalen Oxford Coll Ch, J. Harper *Concert*
(11/91) (ABBE) ① **CDCA913**
Llandaff Cath Ch, M. Smith, M. Hoeg (r1994) *Concert*
(10/95) (PRIO) ① **PRCD510**
I waited for the Lord—anthem
St Bride's Ch, Fleet St, C. Etherington, R. Jones *Concert* (2/91) (REGE) ① **REGSB701CD**
Lord Jesus think on me—hymn (tune: St Paul's)
St Paul's Cath Ch, C. Dearnley, John Scott *Concert*
(7/90) (HYPE) ① **CDH88036**
Love divine, all loves excelling—hymn (Wds. C. Wesley)
King's College Ch, R. Farnes, S. Cleobury (r1985) *Concert* (6/93) (DECC) ① **436 402-2DWO**

STALDER, Joseph Franz Xaver-Dominik (1725–1765) Switzerland

SECTION I: ORCHESTRAL

Concerto for Flute and Orchestra in B flat (c1760)
W. Bennett, ECO, H. Griffiths *Concert*
(9/89) (NOVA) ① **150 031-2**
Symphony No. 5 in G (c1756)
ECO, H. Griffiths *Concert*
(9/89) (NOVA) ① **150 031-2**

STAMITZ, Anton (Thadäus Johann Nepomuk) (1750–1789/1809) Czechoslovakia

SECTION I: ORCHESTRAL

Concerto for Two Flutes and Orchestra in G
J-P. Rampal (fl/dir), S. Kudo, Salzburg Mozarteum Orch *Concert* (2/92) (SONY) ① **SK45930**

STAMITZ, Carl (Philipp) (1745–1801) Germany

SECTION I: ORCHESTRAL

Concerto for Clarinet and Orchestra No. 3 in B flat
S. Meyer, ASMF, I. Brown (r1992) *Concert*
(11/93) (EMI) ① **CDC7 54842-2**
Concerto for Clarinet and Orchestra No. 10 in B flat
S. Meyer, ASMF, I. Brown (r1992) *Concert*
(11/93) (EMI) ① **CDC7 54842-2**
Concerto for Clarinet and Orchestra No. 11 in E flat
S. Meyer, ASMF, I. Brown (r1992) *Concert*
(11/93) (EMI) ① **CDC7 54842-2**

Concerto for Flute and Orchestra in G
Barthold Kuijken, Tafelmusik, J. Lamon (r1991) *Concert* (7/93) (SONY) ① **SK48045**
Concerto for Viola and Orchestra in D (pub 1774)
T. Zimmermann, ECCO, D. Demetriades *Concert*
(8/88) (HYPE) ① **CDH88015**
Concerto for Violin and Orchestra in B flat
Movts 2, 3. N. Milstein, A. Balsam (r1940) *Concert*
(3/93) (BIDD) ① **LAB063**
Sinfonia Concertante in C—2 violins and orchestra, Kaiser 9 (1774)
R. Friedman, S. Smith, London Fest Orch, R. Pople (r1988) *Concert* (7/95) (ASV) ① **CDQS6140**
Sinfonia Concertante in D—violin, viola and orchestra, Kaiser 19 (1780-82)
R. Friedman, R. Best, London Fest Orch, R. Pople (r1988) *Concert* (7/95) (ASV) ① **CDQS6140**
Prague Virtuosi, R. Krečmer (r1994) *Concert*
(12/95) (DINT) ① **DICD920274**
6 Symphonies, Op. 13 (pub 1777) (also pub as Op. 16)
4, 5. LMP, M. Bamert (r1994) *Concert*
(5/95) (CHAN) ① **CHAN9358**
3 Symphonies, Op. 24 (pub 1786)
3. F.
3. LMP, M. Bamert (r1994) *Concert*
(5/95) (CHAN) ① **CHAN9358**
Symphony in D, '(La) Chasse'
LMP, M. Bamert (r1994) *Concert*
(5/95) (CHAN) ① **CHAN9358**

SECTION II: CHAMBER

Sonata for Viola and Keyboard in B flat
A. B. Duetschler, U. Duetschler (r1994) *Concert*
(11/95) (CLAV) ① **CD50-9502**

STAMITZ, Jan Václav Antonín (1717–1757) Bohemia

SECTION I: ORCHESTRAL

Concerto for Clarinet and Orchestra in B flat
S. Meyer, ASMF, I. Brown (r1992) *Concert*
(11/93) (EMI) ① **CDC7 54842-2**
Concerto for Flute and Strings in G
Barthold Kuijken, Tafelmusik, J. Lamon (r1991) *Concert* (7/93) (SONY) ① **SK48045**
Concerto for Trumpet and Orchestra in D (incomplete)
H. Hardenberger, ASMF, N. Marriner (r1986; realised Boustead) *Concert* (12/87) (PHIL) ① **420 203-2PH**
6 Sonatas à trois parties concertantes—three soloists with or without orchestra, Op. 1 (pub 1755)
1. A.
1. VCM, N. Harnoncourt (r1963) *Concert*
(7/93) (TELD) ① **4509-91002-2**
Symphony in A
Slovak CO, B. Warchal *Concert*
(11/89) (OPUS) ① **9350 1812**
Symphony in B flat, 'Mannheim No. 2'
Slovak CO, B. Warchal *Concert*
(11/89) (OPUS) ① **9350 1812**
Symphony in G
Slovak CO, B. Warchal *Concert*
(11/89) (OPUS) ① **9350 1812**

STANCHINSKY, Alexey Vladimirovich (1888–1914) Russia

SECTION III: INSTRUMENTAL

3 Sketches—piano
1. Allegro moderato; 2. Allegretto; 3. Presto tempestoso.
D. Blumenthal (r1992) *Concert*
(11/94) (MARC) ① **8 223424**
12 Sketches—piano
1. Moderato; 2. Presto; 3. Vivace; 4. Lento cantabile; 5. Allegro; 6. Andante epico; 7. Adagio teneramente; 8. Molto vivace; 9. Largamente; 10. Con moto; 11. Allegro con spirito; 12. Presto assai.
D. Blumenthal (r1992) *Concert*
(11/94) (MARC) ① **8 223424**
Sonata in E flat minor—piano (1906)
D. Blumenthal (r1992) *Concert*
(11/94) (MARC) ① **8 223424**
Sonata No. 1 in F—piano (1911-12)
D. Blumenthal (r1992) *Concert*
(11/94) (MARC) ① **8 223424**

Sonata No. 2 in G—piano (1912)
D. Blumenthal (r1992) *Concert*
(11/94) (MARC) ① **8 223424**

STANFORD, Sir Charles Villiers (1852–1924) Ireland/England

SECTION I: ORCHESTRAL

Concert Piece—organ and orchestra, Op. 181 (1921)
G. Weir, Ulster Orch, V. Handley *Concert*
(11/90) (CHAN) ① **CHAN8861**
Concert Variations on 'Down upon the dead men'—piano and orchestra, Op. 71 (1898)
M. Fingerhut, Ulster Orch, V. Handley *Piano Concerto 2.* (1/90) (CHAN) ① **CHAN8736**
Concerto for Clarinet and Orchestra in A minor, Op. 80 (1904)
T. King, Philh, A. Francis (r1979) *Finzi: Clarinet Concerto.* (6/87) (HYPE) ① **CDA66001**
J. Hilton, Ulster Orch, V. Handley *Symphony 2.*
(1/92) (CHAN) ① **CHAN8991**
E. Johnson, RPO, C. Groves *Concert*
(6/92) (ASV) ① **CDDCA787**
Concerto for Piano and Orchestra No. 2 in C minor, Op. 126 (1915)
M. Fingerhut, Ulster Orch, V. Handley *Variations, Op.71.* (1/90) (CHAN) ① **CHAN8736**
Irish Rhapsody No. 1 in D minor—orchestra, Op 78 (1901)
Ulster Orch, V. Handley *Symphony 6.*
(9/88) (CHAN) ① **CHAN8627**
Irish Rhapsody No. 2 in F minor—orchestra, Op. 84 (c1903)
Ulster Orch, V. Handley *Symphony 1.*
(10/92) (CHAN) ① **CHAN9049**
Irish Rhapsody No. 3—cello and orchestra, Op. 137 (c1915)
R. Wallfisch, Ulster Orch, V. Handley *Concert*
(11/90) (CHAN) ① **CHAN8861**
Irish Rhapsody No. 4 in A minor—orchestra, Op. 141 (1914)
Ulster Orch, V. Handley *Symphony 5.*
(7/88) (CHAN) ① **CHAN8581**
Irish Rhapsody No. 5 in G minor—orchestra, Op. 147 (1917)
Ulster Orch, V. Handley *Symphony 3.*
(1/88) (CHAN) ① **CHAN8545**
Irish Rhapsody No. 6—violin and orchestra, Op. 191 (c1923)
L. Mordkovitch, Ulster Orch, V. Handley *Concert*
(3/91) (CHAN) ① **CHAN8884**
Symphony No. 1 in B flat (1875)
Ulster Orch, V. Handley *Irish Rhapsody 2.*
(10/92) (CHAN) ① **CHAN9049**
Symphony No. 2 in D minor, 'Elegiac' (1882)
Ulster Orch, V. Handley *Clarinet Concerto.*
(1/92) (CHAN) ① **CHAN8991**
Symphony No. 3 in F minor, 'Irish', Op. 28 (1887)
Ulster Orch, V. Handley *Irish Rhapsody 5.*
(1/88) (CHAN) ① **CHAN8545**
Bournemouth Sinfonietta, N. del Mar (r1982) *Elgar: Scenes from the Bavarian Highlands, Op.27.*
(7/95) (EMI) ① **CDM5 65129-2**
Symphony No. 4 in F, Op. 31 (1889)
Ulster Orch, V. Handley *Concert*
(3/91) (CHAN) ① **CHAN8884**
Symphony No. 5 in D, '(L')Allegro ed il penseroso', Op. 56 (1894)
Ulster Orch, V. Handley *Irish Rhapsody 4.*
(7/88) (CHAN) ① **CHAN8581**
Symphony No. 6 in E flat, 'in memoriam G. F. Watts', Op. 94 (c1905)
Ulster Orch, V. Handley *Irish Rhapsody 1.*
(9/88) (CHAN) ① **CHAN8627**
Symphony No. 7 in D minor, Op. 124 (1911)
Ulster Orch, V. Handley *Concert*
(11/90) (CHAN) ① **CHAN8861**

SECTION II: CHAMBER

2 Fantasy Pieces—clarinet and string quartet
T. King, Britten Qt *Concert*
(7/92) (HYPE) ① **CDA66479**
3 Intermezzos—clarinet and piano, Op. 13 (1880)
E. Johnson, M. Martineau *Concert*
(6/92) (ASV) ① **CDDCA787**
Piano Trio No. 2 in G minor, Op. 73 (1899)
Pirasti Trio (r1994) *Concert*
(9/95) (ASV) ① **CDDCA925**

Serenade (nonet) in F—fl, ob, bn, hn, 2 vns, va, vc, db, Op. 95 (c1906)
Capricorn (r1987) *Parry: Nonet.*
(9/89) (HYPE) ① **CDA66291**
Sonata—clarinet/viola and piano, Op. 129 (c1912)
T. King, C. Benson *Concert*
(7/89) (HYPE) ① **CDA66014**
E. Jóhannesson, P. Jenkins *Concert*
(1/93) (CHAN) ① **CHAN9079**
E. Johnson, M. Martineau *Concert*
(7/94) (ASV) ① **CDDCA891**
Sonata for Cello and Piano No. 2 in D minor, Op. 39 (1893)
J. Lloyd Webber, J. McCabe *Concert*
(2/93) (ASV) ① **CDDCA807**

SECTION III: INSTRUMENTAL

Fantasia and Fugue in D minor—organ, Op. 103 (1907)
F. Jackson (r1993) *Concert*
(2/95) (AMPH) ① **PHICD126**
Fantasia and Toccata in D minor—organ, Op. 57 (1894)
J. Rees-Williams *Concert*
(4/91) (ABBE) ① **CDCA902**
K. John *Concert*
(11/92) (PRIO) ① **PRCD370**
Idyll and Fantasia, 'In Festo Omnium Santorum'—organ (c1910)
J. Watts (r1992) *Concert*
(8/94) (PRIO) ① **PRCD414**
4 Irish Dances—piano, Op. 89 (1903) (from Petrie coll of Ancient Irish Music)
1. A March-Jig (Maguire's Kick); 2. A Slow Dance; 3. Leprechaun's dance; 4. A Reel.
Martin Jones (arr Grainger) *Concert*
(2/91) (NIMB) ① **NI5255**
6 Preludes—organ, Op. 88 (c1903)
EXCERPTS: 1. In form of a Minuet; 3. In form of a Toccata; 5. In form of a Pastorale.
1, 3. F. Jackson (r1993) *Concert*
(2/95) (AMPH) ① **PHICD126**
3, 5. J. Watts (r1992) *Concert*
(8/94) (PRIO) ① **PRCD414**
3 Preludes and Fugues—organ, Op. 193 (pub 1922)
EXCERPTS: 2. C minor.
2. F. Jackson (r1993) *Concert*
(2/95) (AMPH) ① **PHICD126**
6 Short Preludes and Postludes—Set 1—organ, Op. 101 (c1907)
EXCERPTS: 1. Allegretto; 2. Allegro non troppo e pesante; 3. Allegro non troppo; 4. Andante tranquillo; 5. Andante Maestoso, founded on an Irish church melody; 6. Andante con moto, founded on an Irish church melody.
F. Jackson (r1993) *Concert*
(2/95) (AMPH) ① **PHICD126**
6 Short Preludes and Postludes—Set 2—organ, Op.105 (1908)
EXCERPTS: 1. Andante tranquillo, on a theme of Orlando Gibbons; 2. Allegro, on a theme of Orlando Gibbons; 3. Lento; 4. Allegro moderato, on a theme of Orlando Gibbons; 5. Trio. Allegretto; 6. Postlude in D minor. Allegro.
D. Hunter (r1992) *Concert*
(9/94) (PRIO) ① [2] **PRCD445**
F. Jackson (r1993) *Concert*
(2/95) (AMPH) ① **PHICD126**
6. J. Bielby *Concert* (5/91) (PRIO) ① **PRCD298**
Sonata for Organ No. 1 in F, Op. 149 (1917)
D. Hunter (r1992) *Concert*
(9/94) (PRIO) ① [2] **PRCD445**
Sonata for Organ No. 2 in G minor, 'Sonata Eroica', Op. 151 (1917)
D. Hunter (r1992) *Concert*
(9/94) (PRIO) ① [2] **PRCD445**
Sonata for Organ No. 3 in D minor, 'Britannica', Op. 152 (1917)
D. Hunter (r1992) *Concert*
(9/94) (PRIO) ① [2] **PRCD445**
Sonata for Organ No. 4 in C minor, 'Celtica', Op. 153 (1918)
D. Hunter (r1992) *Concert*
(9/94) (PRIO) ① [2] **PRCD445**
Sonata for Organ No. 5 in A, 'Quasi una fantasia', Op. 159 (pub 1921)
D. Hunter (r1992) *Concert*
(9/94) (PRIO) ① [2] **PRCD445**

SECTION IV: VOCAL AND CHORAL

6 Anthems, Op. 113 (pub 1910)
1. Let us with a gladsome mind; 2. Purest and Highest; 3. In Thee is gladness; 4. Pray that Jerusalem may have; 5. Praise to the Lord, the Almighty; 6. O, for a closer walk with God.

Chichester Cath Ch, A. Thurlow, J. Suter *Concert*
(4/91) (PRIO) ① **PRCD312**
6. Cambridge Sngrs, J. Rutter, W. Marshall *Concert*
(12/92) (CLLE) ① **COLCD118**
The Beautiful City of Sligo—Irish folksong arrangement (Wds. traditional)
A. Murray, G. Johnson (r1992) *Concert*
(8/93) (HYPE) ① **CDA66627**
La Belle Dame sans merci—song (pub 1877) (Wds Keats)
J. Baker, G. Moore (r1967) *Concert*
(11/94) (EMI) ① **CDM5 65009-2**
Benedictus and Agnus Dei in F—choir and organ (1909) (additional mvts for Service, Op. 36)
Chichester Cath Ch, A. Thurlow, J. Suter *Concert*
(4/91) (PRIO) ① **PRCD312**
Durham Cath Ch, J. Lancelot, K. Wright r1992; interpolated in Services, Op. 115) *Concert*
(9/93) (PRIO) ① **PRCD437**
Clown's Songs from 'Twelfth Night', Op. 65 (1897) (Wds. Shakespeare)
1. The rain it raineth every day; 2. O mistress mine.
1. A. Rolfe Johnson, G. Johnson *Concert*
(5/92) (HYPE) ① **CDA66480**
The falling star—Irish folksong arrangement (Wds. traditional)
A. Murray, G. Johnson (r1992) *Concert*
(8/93) (HYPE) ① **CDA66627**
Festal Communion Service in B flat—chorus and orchestra/organ, Op. 128 (1911)
Gloria in excelsis Trinity Coll Ch, Cambridge, R. Marlow, S. Standage *Concert*
(6/93) (CONI) ① **CDCF214**
Gloria in excelsis Westminster Abbey Ch, M. Baker, ECO, M. Neary (r1993/4) *Concert*
(9/94) (CNTO) ② **CSACD3050**
For all the Saints—choral hymn (1908) (Tune: Engelberg)
Jesus College Ch, D. Phillips, T. Horton *Concert*
(7/93) (CNTO) ① **CRCD2367**
For lo, I raise up—anthem, Op. 145 (1914)
Norwich Cath Ch, M. Nicholas, N. Taylor *Concert*
(3/92) (PRIO) ① **PRCD351**
I heard a voice from heaven—anthem: 4vv (1910)
Cambridge Sngrs, J. Rutter, W. Marshall *Concert*
(12/92) (CLLE) ① **COLCD118**
An Irish Idyll in six miniatures—songs, Op. 77 (1901) (Wds. O'Neill)
1. Corrymeela; 2. The fairy lough; 3. Cuttin' rushes; 4. Johneen; 5. A Broken Song; 6. Back to Ireland.
2. L. Finnie, A. Legge *Concert*
(4/90) (CHAN) ① **CHAN8749**
2. K. Ferrier, F. Stone (r1952) *Concert*
(7/91) (LOND) ① **430 061-2LM**
2. K. Ferrier, F. Stone (r1952) *Concert*
(6/92) (DECC) ① **433 473-2DM**
The Lord is my Shepherd, Op. 38
Guildford Cath Ch, A. Millington, P. Wright *Concert*
(5/89) (PRIO) ① **PRCD257**
Trinity Coll Ch, Cambridge, R. Marlow, P. Rushforth (r1992) *Concert*
(6/93) (CONI) ① **CDCF214**
St Paul's Cath Ch, John Scott, Adrian Lucas (r1991) *Concert*
(8/93) (HYPE) ① **CDA66618**
Magnificat in B flat—8vv a cappella, Op. 164 (1918)
Trinity Coll Ch, Cambridge, R. Marlow *Concert*
(9/87) (CONI) ① **CDCF155**
3 Motets—4-8vv a cappella, Op. 38 (pub 1905)
1. Justorum animae; 2. Coelus ascendit; 3. Beati quorum via.
Trinity Coll Ch, Cambridge, R. Marlow *Concert*
(9/87) (CONI) ① **CDCF155**
Oxford Schola Cantorum, J. Summerly *Concert*
(4/92) (PREL) ① **PROUCD129**
1. Cambridge Sngrs, J. Rutter *Concert*
(4/92) (CLLE) ① **COLCD113**
1. St Paul's Cath Ch, John Scott *Concert*
(4/92) (HYPE) ① **CDA66519**
2. Salisbury Cath Ch, R. Seal *Concert*
(11/90) (MERI) ① **CDE84180**
2. St Paul's Cath Ch, John Scott, Andrew Lucas (r1993) *Concert* (6/94) (HYPE) ① **CDA66678**
3. Cambridge Sngrs, J. Rutter *Concert*
(6/88) (CLLE) ① **COLCD107**
3. St Paul's Cath Ch, Andrew Lucas, John Scott (9/90) (HYPE) ① **CDA66374**
3 Motets—4-8vv, Op. 135 (1913)
1. Ye holy angels (wds R Baxter); 2. Eternal Father (wds R Bridges); 3. Powerful God (wds anon).
2. Trinity Coll Ch, Cambridge, R. Marlow *Concert*
(9/87) (CONI) ① **CDCF155**
3. Magdalen Oxford Coll Ch, J. Harper *Concert*
(11/91) (ABBE) ① **CDCA913**

4 Partsongs—male 4vv a cappella, Op. 106 (pub 1908)
1. Autumn leaves (wds. C. Dickens); 2. Love's folly (wds anon); 3. To his flock (wds H Constable); 4. Fair Phyllis (wds anon).
1. King's Sngrs *Concert*
(6/88) (EMI) ① **CDC7 49765-2**
8 Partsongs—chorus a cappella, Op. 119 (1910) (Wds. M Coleridge)
1. The Witch; 2. Farewell, my joy; 3. The bluebird; 4. The train; 5. The inkbottle; 6. The swallow; 7. Chillingham; 8. My heart is thine.
3. Cambridge Sngrs, J. Rutter *Concert*
(4/87) (CLLE) ① **COLCD104**
Quick! we have but a second—Irish air arrangement
Cambridge Sngrs, J. Rutter *Concert*
(4/87) (CLLE) ① **COLCD104**
King's Sngrs *Concert*
(6/88) (EMI) ① **CDC7 49765-2**
Services in A—chorus and organ, Op. 12 (1880)
1. MORNING SERVICE: 1a. Te deum laudamus; 1b. Benedicite; 1c. Jubilate Deo; 1d. Benedictus; 2. COMMUNION SERVICE: 2a. Kyrie; 2b. Credo; 2c. Sanctus; 3. EVENING SERVICE: 3a. Magnificat; 3b. Nunc dimittis.
Durham Cath Ch, J. Lancelot, K. Wright (r1994) *Services, Op. 81.* (6/93) (PRIO) ① **PRCD514**
1a Ely Cath Ch, P. Trepte *Concert*
(2/92) (GAMU) ① **GAMCD527**
1a Hereford Cath Ch, R. Massey, G. Bowen (r1994) *Concert* (2/95) (PRIO) ① **PRCD507**
1c Ely Cath Ch, P. Trepte *Concert*
(2/92) (GAMU) ① **GAMCD527**
3a, 3b Trinity Coll Ch, Cambridge, R. Marlow, P. Rushforth (r1992) *Concert*
(6/93) (CONI) ① **CDCF214**
3a, 3b Lichfield Cath Ch, A. Lumsden, M. Shepherd (r1994) *Concert* (10/95) (PRIO) ① **PRCD505**
Services in B flat—chorus, orchestra/organ, Op. 10 (1879)
1. MORNING SERVICE: 1a. Te deum laudamus; 1b. Benedicite; 1c. Jubilate Deo; 2. COMMUNION SERVICE: 2a. Kyrie; 2b. Credo; 2c. Sanctus; 2d. Benedictus qui venit (added 1910); 2e. Agnus Dei (added 1910); 2f. Gloria in excelsis; 3. EVENING SERVICE: 3a. Magnificat; 3b. Nunc dimittis.
Cpte Durham Cath Ch, J. Lancelot, K. Wright (r1992) *Concert* (4/94) (PRIO) ① **PRCD437**
1a Westminster Abbey Ch, London Brass, I. Simcock, M. Neary *Concert*
(10/89) (CARL) ① **PCD919**
1a Winchester Cath Ch, Waynflete Sngrs, T. Byram-Wigfield, Bournemouth SO, D. Hill *Concert*
(4/92) (ARGO) ① **430 836-2ZH**
1a Trinity Coll Ch, Cambridge, R. Marlow, S. Standage (r1992) *Concert*
(6/93) (CONI) ① **CDCF214**
1a, 1c Hereford Cath Ch, R. Massey, G. Bowen (r1994) *Concert* (2/95) (PRIO) ① **PRCD507**
3a, 3b Ely Cath Ch, P. Trepte *Concert*
(2/92) (GAMU) ① **GAMCD527**
3a, 3b Winchester Cath Ch, Waynflete Sngrs, T. Byram-Wigfield, Bournemouth SO, D. Hill *Concert*
(4/92) (ARGO) ① **430 836-2ZH**
3a, 3b Cambridge Sngrs, J. Rutter, W. Marshall *Concert* (12/92) (CLLE) ① **COLCD118**
Services in C—chorus and organ, Op. 115 (1909)
1. MORNING SERVICE: 1a. Te deum laudamus; 1b. Benedicite; 1c. Jubilate Deo; 2. COMMUNION SERVICE: 2a. Kyrie; 2b. Credo; 2c. Sanctus; 2d. Gloria in excelsis; 3. EVENING SERVICE: 3a. Magnificat; 3b. Nunc dimittis.
Cpte Durham Cath Ch, J. Lancelot, K. Wright (r1992) *Concert* (4/94) (PRIO) ① **PRCD437**
1a Chichester Cath Ch, A. Thurlow, J. Suter *Concert* (4/91) (PRIO) ① **PRCD312**
1a Ely Cath Ch, P. Trepte *Concert*
(2/92) (GAMU) ① **GAMCD527**
1a Cambridge Sngrs, J. Rutter, W. Marshall *Concert* (12/92) (CLLE) ① **COLCD118**
1b Ely Cath Ch, P. Trepte *Concert*
(2/92) (GAMU) ① **GAMCD527**
1b Trinity Coll Ch, Cambridge, R. Marlow, P. Rushforth (r1992) *Concert*
(6/93) (CONI) ① **CDCF214**
3a, 3b St Paul's Cath Ch, C. Dearnley, John Scott *Concert* (3/88) (HYPE) ① **CDA66249**
3a, 3b Truro Cath Ch, D. Briggs, H. Doughty *Concert* (7/91) (PRIO) ① **PRCD322**
Services in G—chorus and organ, Op. 81 (1904)
1. MORNING SERVICE: 1a. Te deum laudamus; 1b. Benedicite; 1c. Jubilate Deo; 1d. Benedictus; 2.

COMMUNION SERVICE: 2a. Kyrie; 2b. Credo; 2c.
Sanctus; 3. EVENING SERVICE: 3a. Magnificat; 3b.
Nunc dimittis.
Durham Cath Ch, J. Lancelot, K. Wright (r1994)
  Services, Op. 12.   (6/95) (PRIO) ① **PRCD514**
3a Cambridge Sngrs, J. Rutter, W. Marshall *Concert*
      (12/92) (CLLE) ① **COLCD118**
3a, 3b New College Ch, E. Higginbottom *Concert*
      (3/87) (PROU) ① **PROUCD114**
3a, 3b J. Budd, St Paul's Cath Ch, Adrian Lucas,
John Scott *Concert*   (10/95) (HYPE) ① **CDA66439**
3a, 3b Trinity Coll Ch, Cambridge, R. Marlow, S.
Standage (r1992) *Concert*
      (6/93) (CONI) ① **CDCF214**
**A Sheaf of Songs from Leinster—1v and
piano, Op. 140 (1914)** (Wds. Letts)
1. Grandeur; 2. Thief of the world; 3. A soft day; 4.
Little Peter Morissey; 5. The bold unbiddable child; 6.
Irish skies.
3. L. Finnie, A. Legge *Concert*
      (4/90) (CHAN) ① **CHAN8749**
3. K. Ferrier, F. Stone (bp1952) *Concert*
      (7/91) (LOND) ① **430 061-2LM**
3. K. Ferrier, F. Stone (bp1952) *Concert*
      (6/92) (DECC) ① **433 473-2DM**
5. L. Finnie, A. Legge *Concert*
      (4/90) (CHAN) ① **CHAN8749**
**The stolen heart—Irish folksong
arrangement** (Wds. traditional. Air: 'Smah
dunna hoc')
A. Murray, G. Johnson (r1992) *Concert*
      (8/93) (HYPE) ① **CDA66627**
When Mary thro' the garden went—anthem
Cambridge Sngrs, J. Rutter, W. Marshall *Concert*
      (12/92) (CLLE) ① **COLCD118**
**Ye choirs of New Jerusalem—anthem, Op.
123 (1910)** (Wds. trans R. Campbell)
Trinity Coll Ch, Cambridge, R. Marlow, S. Standage
(r1992) *Concert*   (6/93) (CONI) ① **CDCF214**

SECTION V: STAGE WORKS

**Oedipus tyrannus—incidental music after
Sophocles' play, Op. 29 (1887—Cambridge)**
1. Prelude.
1. Ulster Orch, V. Handley *Concert*
      (3/91) (CHAN) ① **CHAN8884**
**Shamus O'Brien—comic opera: 2 acts, Op.
61 (1896—London)** (Lib. G H Jessop, after J S
Le Fanu)
EXCERPTS: 1. Ochone! When I Used to Be Young;
2. Where is the Man?; 3. The Song of the Banshee.
1. J. O'Mara, anon (r1901) *Concert*
      (10/92) (SYMP) ① **SYMCD1093**
1. J. O'Mara (r1901) *Concert*
      (5/94) (PEAR) ① [3] **GEMMCDS9050/2(1)**

**STANGE, Max (1856–1932)
Germany**

SECTION IV: VOCAL AND CHORAL

Die Bekehrte—Lied, Op. 13/1
E. Destinn, orch. W.B. Rogers (r1916: Eng) *Concert*
      (11/93) (ROMO) ① [2] **81002-2**
E. Destinn, orch. W.B Rogers (r1916: Eng) *Concert*
      (12/94) (SUPR) ① [12] **11 2136-2(1)**

**STANLEY, John (1712–1786)
England**

SECTION I: ORCHESTRAL

**6 Concerti for Organ and Strings, Op. 10
(pub 1775)**
1. E; 2. D; 3. B flat; 4. C minor; 5. A; 6. C.
Northern Sinfonia, G. Gifford (org/dir)
      (10/92) (CRD) ① **CRD3365**
4. London Baroque *Concert*
      (4/87) (AMON) ① **CD-SAR14**
Concertos—strings, Op. 2 (pub 1742)
1. D; 2. B minor; 3. G; 4. D minor; 5. A minor-major;
6. B flat.
Parley of Instr, R. Goodman
      (9/90) (HYPE) ① **CDA66338**
3. English Concert, T. Pinnock (hpd/dir) (r1979)
  Concert   (1/93) (ARCH) ① **437 088-2AT**

SECTION II: CHAMBER

Sonata in D minor—violin/flute and keyboard
(unidentified)
M. André, H. Bilgram *Concert*
      (1/93) (EMI) ① **CDC7 54330-2**

SECTION III: INSTRUMENTAL

10 Voluntaries, Op. 5 (1748) (Book 1)
1. C; 2. D minor; 3. G; 4. E minor; 5. D (Trumpet
Voluntary); 6. D minor; 7. G minor; 8. D minor; 9. G

minor; 10. A minor.
1. J. Bate *Concert*   (7/91) (UNIC) ① **DKPCD9105**
2, 5, 8. T. Koopman *Concert*
      (4/91) (CAPR) ① **10 256**
5. A. Stringer, N. Rawsthorne (r1974) *Concert*
      (11/87) (CRD) ① **CRD3308**
5. New College Ch, D. Burchell, E. Higginbottom
  Concert   (10/89) (MERI) ① **CDE84151**
6, 9. J. Bate *Concert*   (5/91) (UNIC) ① **DKPCD9099**
7, 10. J. Bate *Concert*
      (2/91) (UNIC) ① **DKPCD9096**
8. Margaret Phillips *Concert*
      (5/91) (GAMU) ① **GAMCD514**
8. J. Bate *Concert*   (7/91) (UNIC) ① **DKPCD9104**
10 Voluntaries, Op. 6 (1752) (Book 2)
1. D minor; 2. A minor; 3. G minor; 4. F; 5. D,D minor;
6. D; 7. G; 8. A minor; 9. E minor; 10. G minor.
1, 10. J. Bate *Concert*
      (5/91) (UNIC) ① **DKPCD9101**
2. J. Bate *Concert*   (11/91) (UNIC) ① **DKPCD9106**
2-6, 8. T. Koopman *Concert*
      (4/91) (CAPR) ① **10 256**
4. J. Bate *Concert*   (7/91) (UNIC) ① **DKPCD9105**
5. J. Bate *Concert*   (2/91) (UNIC) ① **DKPCD9096**
5, 6. P. Hurford, M. Laird Brass Ens (r1990: arr
Hurford) (9/92) (ARGO) ① **433 451-2ZH**
6. Margaret Phillips *Concert*
      (5/91) (GAMU) ① **GAMCD514**
6, 8, 9. J. Bate *Concert*
      (7/91) (UNIC) ① **DKPCD9104**
7. J. Bate *Concert*   (5/91) (UNIC) ① **DKPCD9099**
10 Voluntaries, Op. 7 (1754) (Book 3)
1. A; 2. C; 3. D minor; 4. D minor; 5. D; 6. F; 7. E
minor; 8. A minor; 9. G; 10. F.
1, 6. J. Bate *Concert*   (5/91) (UNIC) ① **DKPCD9101**
2. J. Bate *Concert*   (5/91) (UNIC) ① **DKPCD9099**
2, 6, 9. T. Koopman *Concert*
      (4/91) (CAPR) ① **10 256**
3. J. Bate *Concert*   (2/91) (UNIC) ① **DKPCD9096**
4, 9. J. Bate *Concert*
      (11/91) (UNIC) ① **DKPCD9106**
7. J. Bate *Concert*   (7/91) (UNIC) ① **DKPCD9104**
8. J. Bate *Concert*   (7/91) (UNIC) ① **DKPCD9105**
9. New College Ch, D. Burchell, E. Higginbottom
  Concert   (10/89) (MERI) ① **CDE84151**
9. T. Dart (r1957) *Concert*   (5/95) (JMS) ① **JMSCD1**

SECTION IV: VOCAL AND CHORAL

**My strength will I ascribe—anthem: soprano,
contralto, 4vv and orga**
New College Ch, D. Burchell, E. Higginbottom
  Concert   (10/89) (MERI) ① **CDE84151**

**STANTON, Walter (1891–1978)
England**

SECTION IV: VOCAL AND CHORAL

Jesu, lover of my soul—anthem (Wds. C
Wesley)
Llandaff Cath Ch, M. Smith, M. Hoeg (r1994) *Concert*
      (10/95) (PRIO) ① **PRCD510**

**STARK, Robert (1847–1922)
Germany**

SECTION II: CHAMBER

Serenade—four clarinets, Op. 55
Thurston Cl Qt *Concert*
      (10/93) (ASV) ① **CDWHL2076**

**STATHAM, Heathcote D(ickens)
(1889–1973) England**

SECTION I: ORCHESTRAL

**The Bells of St Chad's—postlude for
strings**
RPO, D. Willcocks (arr. Palmer) *Concert*
      (12/86) (UNIC) ① **DKPCD9057**

SECTION IV: VOCAL AND CHORAL

Te Deum in C (1936)
Norwich Cath Ch, M. Nicholas, N. Taylor (r1993)
  Concert   (10/94) (PRIO) ① **PRCD470**
Te Deum in D minor (1938)
Norwich Cath Ch, M. Nicholas, N. Taylor (r1993)
  Concert   (10/94) (PRIO) ① **PRCD470**

**STAUB, Victor (1872–1953)
Peru/France**

SECTION IV: VOCAL AND CHORAL

L' Heure sicilienne—song
P. Frijsh, D. Bucktrout (r1932) *Concert*
      (4/95) (PEAR) ① [2] **GEMMCDS9095(2)**

**STAVENHAGEN, Bernhard
(1862–1914) Germany**

SECTION I: ORCHESTRAL

**Concerto for Piano and Orchestra in B
minor, Op. 4**
R. Keller, Berlin SO, J. Faerber *Concert*
      (5/93) (VOX) ① **115708-2**

**STEADMAN-ALLEN, Raymond
Victor (b 1922) England**

SECTION I: ORCHESTRAL

The Beacons—brass band (1987)
Yorkshire Imperial Band, James Scott (pp1987)
  Concert   (11/93) (CHAN) ① **CHAN4513**
Centenary Fanfare—brass band (1987)
Besses o' the Barn Band, Black Dyke Mills Band,
Yorkshire Imperial Band, H. Mortimer (pp1987)
  Concert   (11/93) (CHAN) ① **CHAN4513**
**The Journeymen—four miniatures: brass
band**
1. Wayfarer; 2. Pigrim; 3. Sundowner; 4. Commuter.
BNFL Band, R. Evans (r1993) *Concert*
      (5/94) (POLY) ① **QPRL062D**

**STEFFANI, Agostino (1654–1728)
Italy**

SECTION IV: VOCAL AND CHORAL

Qui l'auretta
R. Jacobs, K. Junghänel (r1985) *Concert*
      (5/87) (HARM) ① **HMA190 1183**
**Scherzo, Guardati, 'Guardati, o core dal Dio
bambin!'—cantata: 1v, 2vns & continuo**
A. Monoyios, Berlin Barock Compagney (r1993)
  Concert   (10/95) (CAPR) ① **10 459**

**STEINER, Max (1888–1971)
Austria/USA**

SECTION I: ORCHESTRAL

Warner Bros Fanfare—orchestra (1937)
National PO, C. Gerhardt *Concert*
      (3/90) (RCA) ① **GD80183**
National PO, C. Gerhardt *Concert*
      (10/90) (RCA) ① **GD80136**
National PO, C. Gerhardt *Concert*
      (11/91) (RCA) ① **GD80912**
National PO, C. Gerhardt *Concert*
      (10/92) (RCA) ① **GD82792**

SECTION V: STAGE WORKS

**The Adventures of Don Juan—film score
(1949)**
EXCERPTS: 1. Main Title; 2. The King; 3. Don Juan;
4. The Brocade; 5. Don Juan's Serenade; 6. Parade
into London; 7. Don Juan and the Queen; 8. Final
Scene.
1-8. National PO, C. Gerhardt *Concert*
      (11/91) (RCA) ① **GD80912**
**The Adventures of Mark Twain—film score
(1948)**
EXCERPTS: 1. Overture.
1. Westminster PO, K. Alwyn (r1993; ed E. Lockett)
  Concert   (8/94) (SILV) ① **FILMCD144**
All This, and Heaven Too—film score (1940)
EXCERPTS: 1. Main Title; 2. Henriette and the
Children; 3. Love Scene; 4. Finale; 5. End Cast.
1-5. National PO, C. Gerhardt *Concert*
      (3/90) (RCA) ① **GD80183**
Beyond the Forest—film score (1949)
EXCERPTS: 1. Main Title; 2. Rosa Moline; 3. The
Train; 4. Rosa's Death.
1-4. National PO, C. Gerhardt *Concert*
      (3/90) (RCA) ① **GD80183**
The Big Sleep—film score (1946)
EXCERPTS: 1. Main Title; 2. Marlowe; 3. Bookshop;
4. Murder; 5. Chase; 6. Love Theme and Finale; 7.
Love Themes.
1-6. National PO, C. Gerhardt *Concert*
      (10/90) (RCA) ① **GD80136**

7. National PO, C. Gerhardt *Concert*
(10/90) (RCA) ① **GD80422**
The Caine Mutiny—film score (1954)
EXCERPTS: 1. Main Title; 2. March.
2. National PO, C. Gerhardt *Concert*
(10/90) (RCA) ① **GD80422**
2. National PO, C. Gerhardt *Concert*
(10/92) (RCA) ① **GD82792**
2. Westminster PO, K. Alwyn (r1993; reconstructed
M. McGurty) *Concert*   (8/94) (SILV) ① **FILMCD144**
Casablanca—film score (1942) (see also
under Hupfeld for 'As Time Goes By')
EXCERPTS: 1. Main Title; 2. The Immigrants; 3.
Morocco; 4. Song: As Time Goes By (comp Hupfeld);
5. Flashback (Paris); 6. Rick's Bar; 7. Love Scene; 8.
The Airport; 9. Major Strasser's Death; 10. Finale:
'...the beginning of a beautiful friendship'.
1, 5, 6, 8, 10. Westminster PO, K. Alwyn (r1993)
Concert   (8/94) (SILV) ① **FILMCD144**
1-9. National PO, C. Gerhardt *Concert*
(10/90) (RCA) ① **GD80422**
**The Charge of the Light Brigade—film score
(1936)**
EXCERPTS: 1. Main Title; 2. Calcutta; 3. Waltz; 4.
Love Scene; 5. March (Forward the Light Brigade); 6.
Moonlight; 7. 'Charge!'; 8. Epilogue/Cast Credits.
5. National PO, C. Gerhardt *Concert*
(10/90) (RCA) ① **GD80136**
A Distant Trumpet—film score (1964)
EXCERPTS: 1. Prelude.
1. Westminster PO, K. Alwyn (r1993) *Concert*
(8/94) (SILV) ① **FILMCD144**
Dodge City—film score (1939)
EXCERPTS: 2. The Open Paririe; 3. The Iron Horse;
4. Surrett; 5. The Comrades; 6. The Covered Wagon;
7. Grazioso; 8. Abbie and the Children; 9. Wade and
Abbie; 10. The Blarney; 11. Abbie's Theme.
2-11. National PO, C. Gerhardt *Concert*
(11/91) (RCA) ① **GD80912**
The Fountainhead—film score (1949)
EXCERPTS: 1. Main Title (Roark's Theme); 2.
Dominique's Theme; 3. The Quarry; 4.
Construction—Enright House; 5. Finale—The
Wynand Building.
1-5. National PO, C. Gerhardt *Concert*
(10/90) (RCA) ① **GD80136**
Four Wives—film score (1939)
Symphonie Moderne E. Wild, National PO, C.
Gerhardt *Concert*   (10/90) (RCA) ① **GD80136**
Gone with the Wind—film score (1939)
EXCERPTS: 1. Main Title; 1a. Dixie; 1b. Mammy;
1c. Tara; 1d. Rhett; 2. Opening Sequence: 2a. The
Twins; 2b. Katie Bell; 2c. Ashley; 2d. Mammy; 3a.
Driving Home; 3b. Gerald O'Hara; 3c. Scarlett; 3d.
Tara; 4. Dance Montage: 4a. Charleston Heel and
Toe Polka; 4b. Southern Belle Waltz; 4c. Can Can;
5a. Grazioso; 5b. Mammy; 5c. Ashley; 5d. Ashley
and Scarlett; 5e. Scarlett; 5f. Ashley and Melanie
Love Theme; 6a. Civil War; 6b. Fall of the South; 6c.
Scarlett Walks Among the Wounded; 7a. True Love;
7b. Ashley Returns to Tara from the War; 7c. Tara in
Ruins; 8. Belle Watling; 9a. Reconstruction; 9b. The
Nightingale; 9c. Tara Rebuilt; 9d. Bonnie; 9e. The
Accident; 10a. Mammy and Melanie on the Staircase;
10b. Rhett's Sorrow; 11. Apotheosis: 11a. Melanie's
Death; 11b. Scarlett and Rhett; 11c. Tara; 12. Tara
Theme—Main Theme (arr as separate piece).
National PO, C. Gerhardt (r1973) *Alf Newman:
Selznick International Pictures Fanfare.*
(6/90) (RCA) ① **GD80452**
Suite Westminster PO, K. Alwyn (r1993) *Concert*
(8/94) (SILV) ① **FILMCD144**
1. Hollywood Bowl SO, J. Mauceri (r1991) *Concert*
(9/91) (PHIL) ① **432 109-2PH**
4a National PO, C. Gerhardt *Concert*
(10/92) (RCA) ① **GD82792**
12. Rochester Pops, L. Schifrin *Concert*
(5/93) (SILV) ① **SILVAD3002**
Helen of Troy—film score (1955)
EXCERPTS: 1. Prelude; 2. The Voyage; 3. The
Gates of Troy; 4. The Siege & Aftermath; 5. Finale.
1-5. Westminster PO, K. Alwyn (r1993) *Concert*
(8/94) (SILV) ① **FILMCD144**
In This Our Life—film score (1942)
EXCERPTS: 1. Main Title; 2. Stanley and Roy; 3.
Finale.
1-3. National PO, C. Gerhardt *Concert*
(3/90) (RCA) ① **GD80183**
The Informer—film score (1935)
EXCERPTS: 1. Main Theme; 2. Love Scene; 3.
Sancta Maria.
1-3. Ambrosian Sngrs, National PO, C. Gerhardt
Concert   (10/90) (RCA) ① **GD80136**

Jezebel—film score (1938)
EXCERPTS: 1. Main Title; 2. Waltz.
2. National PO, C. Gerhardt *Concert*
(3/90) (RCA) ① **GD80183**
2. Hollywood Bowl SO, J. Mauceri (r1993; arr
Gerhardt/Freed/Mauceri) *Concert*
(6/94) (PHIL) ① **438 685-2PH**
Johnny Belinda—film score (1948)
Suite National PO, C. Gerhardt *Concert*
(10/90) (RCA) ① **GD80136**
Key Largo—film score (1948)
EXCERPTS: 1. Main Title; 2. The Bridge; 3.
McCloud and Mr Temple; 4. Reminiscene; 5.
Morning; 6. Finale.
1-6. National PO, C. Gerhardt *Concert*
(10/90) (RCA) ① **GD80422**
King Kong—film score (1933)
EXCERPTS: 1. Overture; 2. The Forgotten Island; 3.
Natives; 4. Sacrificial Dance; 5. The Gate of Kong; 6.
Kong in New York.
1. Hollywood Bowl SO, J. Mauceri (r1993) *Concert*
(1/95) (PHIL) ① **442 425-2PH**
2-6. National PO, C. Gerhardt *Concert*
(10/90) (RCA) ① **GD80136**
The Letter—film score (1940)
EXCERPTS: 1. Main Title.
1. National PO, C. Gerhardt *Concert*
(3/90) (RCA) ① **GD80183**
Now, Voyager—film score (1942)
EXCERPTS: 1. Main Title; 2. It can't be wrong; 3.
Love Scene and Finale.
2. National PO, C. Gerhardt *Concert*
(3/90) (RCA) ① **GD80183**
3. National PO, C. Gerhardt *Concert*
(10/92) (RCA) ① **GD82792**
Passage to Marseille—film score (1944)
EXCERPTS: 1. Main Title; 2. Rescue at sea.
2. National PO, C. Gerhardt *Concert*
(10/90) (RCA) ① **GD80422**
Saratoga Trunk—film score (1946)
EXCERPTS: 1. As long as I live.
1. National PO, C. Gerhardt *Concert*
(10/90) (RCA) ① **GD80136**
The Searchers—film score (1956)
EXCERPTS: 1. Opening; 2. Ethan Comes Home; 3.
Martin; 4. Texas Rangers; 5. Warparty; 6. Indian Idyll.
1-6. Prague City PO, P. Bateman (r1994; arr
Richardson) *Concert* (11/94) (SILV) ① **FILMCD153**
Since You Went Away—film score (1944)
EXCERPTS: 1. Main Title.
1. National PO, C. Gerhardt *Concert*
(10/90) (RCA) ① **GD80136**
A Stolen Life—film score (1946)
EXCERPTS: 1. Main Title.
1. National PO, C. Gerhardt *Concert*
(3/90) (RCA) ① **GD80183**
A Summer Place—film score (1959)
EXCERPTS: 1. Main Theme; 2. Young Love.
1, 2. Westminster PO, K. Alwyn (r1993) *Concert*
(8/94) (SILV) ① **FILMCD144**
**They Died with Their Boots On—film score
(1942)**
EXCERPTS: 1. Main Title Title; 2. The Farewell
Before the Battle; 3. Preparation and March; 4. The
Seventh Cavalry; 5. Garry Owen; 6. The Sioux; 7.
The Battle of Little Big Horn; 8. Custer's Last Stand.
1-8. National PO, C. Gerhardt *Concert*
(11/91) (RCA) ① **GD80912**
**The Treasure of the Sierra Madre—film
score (1948)**
EXCERPTS: 1. Main Title; 2. The Trek to the Gold;
3. Fool's Gold; 4. The Letter; 5. Finale: The Gold
scatters in the Wind.
1. Westminster PO, K. Alwyn (r1993) *Concert*
(8/94) (SILV) ① **FILMCD144**
1-5. National PO, C. Gerhardt *Concert*
(10/90) (RCA) ① **GD80422**
Virginia City—film score (1940)
EXCERPTS: 1. Main Title; 2. Stage Coach; 3. Love
Scene.
2, 3. National PO, C. Gerhardt *Concert*
(10/90) (RCA) ① **GD80422**

STELIBSKÝ, Josef
?Czechoslovakia

SECTION IV: VOCAL AND CHORAL

In the skies over Prague—song
J. Novotná, J. Stelibský (bp1952) *Concert*
(4/93) (SUPR) ① **11 1491-2**

STENHAMMAR, (Karl) Wilhelm
(Eugen) *(1871–1927) Sweden*

SECTION I: ORCHESTRAL

**Concerto for Piano and Orchestra No. 1 in B
flat minor, Op. 1 (1893)**
I. Mannheimer, Gothenburg SO, C. Dutoit *Late
Summer Nights.*   (7/90) (STER) ① **CDS1004-2**
M. Widlund, Stockholm PO, G. Rozhdestvensky (orig
version) *Symphony 3.*
(10/92) (CHAN) ① **CHAN9074**
L. Derwinger, Malmö SO, P. Järvi (r1992) *Concert*
(10/92) (BIS) ① **BIS-CD550**
**Concerto for Piano and Orchestra No. 2 in D
minor, Op. 23 (1904-07)**
C. Ortiz, Gothenburg SO, N. Järvi *Chitra.*
(2/91) (BIS) ① **BIS-CD476**
J. Sólyom, Munich PO, S. Westerberg (r1970)
(5/94) (EMI) ① **CDM5 65081-2**
**Excelsior!—symphonic overture, Op. 13
(1896)**
Gothenburg SO, N. Järvi (r1992) *Concert*
(8/95) (DG) ① [2] **445 857-2GH2**
**2 Sentimental Romances—violin and
orchestra, Op. 28 (1910)**
1. F minor; 2. A.
U. Wallin, Malmö SO, P. Järvi (r1992) *Concert*
(10/92) (BIS) ① **BIS-CD550**
Serenade in F, Op. 31
Gothenburg SO, N. Järvi
(2/87) (BIS) ① **BIS-CD310**
Swedish RSO, E-P. Salonen *Concert*
(11/90) (MSVE) ① **MSCD626**
Swedish RSO, S. Westerberg (r1974) *Concert*
(5/94) (EMI) ① **CDM5 65081-2**
Gothenburg SO, N. Järvi (r1993) *Concert*
(8/95) (DG) ① [2] **445 857-2GH2**
Symphony No. 1 in F (1902-03)
Gothenburg SO, N. Järvi (r1993) *Concert*
(8/95) (DG) ① [2] **445 857-2GH2**
**Symphony No. 2 in G minor, Op. 34 (1911-
15)**
Gothenburg SO, N. Järvi (r1993) *Concert*
(8/95) (DG) ① [2] **445 857-2GH2**
Symphony No. 3 (1918-19) (fragment only)
Stockholm PO, G. Rozhdestvensky (rev T B
Andersson) *Piano Concerto 1.*
(10/92) (CHAN) ① **CHAN9074**

SECTION III: INSTRUMENTAL

**Allegro con moto ed appassionata—piano
(1888-89)**
L. Negro (r1992) *Concert*
(3/93) (BIS) ① **BIS-CD554**
3 Fantasies—piano, Op. 11 (1895)
1. Molto appassionato, B minor; 2. Dolce scherzando,
E; 3. Molto espressivo e con intimissimo sentimento,
B minor.
L. Negro (r1992) *Concert*
(3/93) (BIS) ① **BIS-CD554**
1. R. Pöntinen *Concert*   (11/85) (BIS) ① **BIS-CD300**
**Impromptu in G flat minor—piano (pub
1898)**
L. Negro (r1992) *Concert*
(3/93) (BIS) ① **BIS-CD554**
Impromptu-Waltz—piano (pub 1895)
L. Negro (r1992) *Concert*
(3/93) (BIS) ① **BIS-CD554**
**Late Summer Nights
(Sensommarnätter)—piano, Op. 33 (1914)**
1. Tranquillo e soave; 2. Poco presto; 3. Piano. non
troppo lento; 4. Presto agitato; 5. Poco allegretto.
I. Mannheimer *Piano Concerto 1.*
(7/90) (STER) ① **CDS1004-2**
L. Negro (r1992) *Concert*
(3/93) (BIS) ① **BIS-CD554**
3 Small Piano Pieces—piano
1. Molto tranquillo semplice; 2. Allegro; 3. Polska (in
miniature).
L. Negro (r1992) *Concert*
(3/93) (BIS) ① **BIS-CD554**

SECTION IV: VOCAL AND CHORAL

Adagio—song (Wds. Bergman)
A.S. von Otter, B. Forsberg *Concert*
(7/90) (MSVE) ① **MSCD623**
**Ballad of Emperor Charles—song, Op. 32
(1910)** (Wds. Levertin)
H. Hagegård, T. Schuback *Concert*
(7/90) (MSVE) ① **MSCD623**
**Barrel-organ ballad—song, Op. 38/4 (1917-
18)** (Wds. Bergman)
H. Hagegård, T. Schuback *Concert*
(7/90) (MSVE) ① **MSCD623**

By the window—song (Wds. Bergman)
A.S. von Otter, B. Forsberg *Concert*
(7/90) (MSVE) ① **MSCD623**
Fir Tree stands alone—song, Op. 17/2
(c1890) (Wds. Heine)
A.S. von Otter, B. Forsberg *Concert*
(7/90) (MSVE) ① **MSCD623**
Florez and Blanzeflor—baritone and
orchestra, Op. 3 (1915) (Wds. O. Levertin)
P. Mattei, Malmö SO, P. Järvi *Concert*
(10/92) (BIS) ① **BIS-CD550**
I. Wixell, Swedish RSO, S. Westerberg (r1974)
Concert (5/94) (EMI) ① **CDM5 65081-2**
Fylgia—song (Wds. Fröding)
A.S. von Otter, B. Forsberg *Concert*
(7/90) (MSVE) ① **MSCD623**
Girl came from meeting her lover—song, Op.
4b/1 (1893) (Wds. Runeberg)
A.S. von Otter, B. Forsberg *Concert*
(7/90) (MSVE) ① **MSCD623**
The Girl on Midsummer eve—song (Wds.
Runeberg)
A.S. von Otter, B. Forsberg *Concert*
(7/90) (MSVE) ① **MSCD623**
In the forest—song (Wds. Gellerstedt)
A.S. von Otter, B. Forsberg *Concert*
(7/90) (MSVE) ① **MSCD623**
In the shadow of the maple tree—song (Wds.
von Heidenstam)
H. Hagegård, T. Schuback *Concert*
(7/90) (MSVE) ① **MSCD623**
The Journey to Happy Land—song (Wds.
Fröding)
H. Hagegård, T. Schuback *Concert*
(7/90) (MSVE) ① **MSCD623**
Late Harvest, 'Efterskörd'—song cycle: 1v &
piano (pub posth 1933)
1. Be blessed, tender-heartedness (Var välsignad,
milda ömsinthet); 2. Comfort (Tröst); 3. The bell
(Klockan); 4. Human eyes (Människornas ögon); 5.
The heart (Hjärtat).
Cpte P. Mattei, B-Å. Lundin (r1994) *Concert*
(9/95) (BIS) ① **BIS-CD654**
Leaning against the fence—song, Op. 8/1
(1895-96) (Wds. Runeberg)
A.S. von Otter, B. Forsberg *Concert*
(7/90) (MSVE) ① **MSCD623**
Love Song—song (1917-24) (Wds. Karlfeldt)
H. Hagegård, T. Schuback *Concert*
(7/90) (MSVE) ① **MSCD623**
Melody—song (1917-24) (Wds. Bergman)
A.S. von Otter, B. Forsberg *Concert*
(7/90) (MSVE) ① **MSCD623**
Midwinter—chorus and orchestra, Op. 24
(1907) (Wds. W. Hansen)
Swedish Rad Ch, Swedish RSO, E-P. Salonen
Concert (11/90) (BIS) ① **BIS-CD626**
Gothenburg Concert Hall Ch, Gothenburg SO, N.
Järvi *Concert* (11/90) (BIS) ① **BIS-CD438**
Mistress Blonde and Mistress Brunett—song
(Wds. Bergman)
H. Hagegård, T. Schuback *Concert*
(7/90) (MSVE) ① **MSCD623**
Moonlight—song (Wds. Bergmann)
A.S. von Otter, B. Forsberg *Concert*
(7/90) (MSVE) ① **MSCD623**
My ancestor had a great goblet—song, Op.
7/3 (1893-95) (Wds. von Heidenstam)
H. Hagegård, T. Schuback *Concert*
(7/90) (MSVE) ① **MSCD623**
7 Poems from Thoughts of Solitude—1v &
piano, Op. 7 (1893-5) (Wds. Heidenstam)
1. Within my soul (Där innerst i min ande); 2. In
loneliness my years pass by (I enslighet försvinner
mina år); 3. My ancestor had a large goblet (Min
stamfar hade en stor pokal); 4. Come friends, let us
sit down (Kom vänner, låt oss sätta oss); 5. In Rome
when I was young (I Rom, dit ung jag kom); 6. You
seek fame (Du söker rykbarhet); 7. You loved me (Du
hade mig kär).
Cpte P. Mattei, B-Å. Lundin (r1994) *Concert*
(9/95) (BIS) ① **BIS-CD654**
7. H. Hagegård, T. Schuback *Concert*
(7/90) (MSVE) ① **MSCD623**
A Ship is sailing—song (Wds. Bergman)
H. Hagegård, T. Schuback *Concert*
(7/90) (MSVE) ① **MSCD623**
Snöfrid—soloists, chorus and orchestra, Op.
5 (1891) (Wds. V. Rydberg)
U. Ahlén, G. Nilsson, G. Zackrisson, P. Enoksson,
Gothenburg Concert Hall Ch, Gothenburg SO, N.
Järvi *Concert* (11/90) (BIS) ① **BIS-CD438**

The Song—cantata, Op. 44 (1921) (Wds.
Rangström)
1. Interlude.
1. Gothenburg SO, N. Järvi *Concert*
(11/90) (BIS) ① **BIS-CD438**
Songs and Moods—1v & piano, Op. 26
(1908-9)
1. The Wanderer (Vandraren); 2. Butterfly orchid
(Nattyxne); 3. The star (Stjärnan); 4. Miss Blonde and
Miss Brunette (Jungfru Blond och Jungfru Brunett); 5.
A ship sails (Det far ett skepp); 6. When the shadow
of the casement falls (När genom rummet...); 7. Why
hurry so to rest (Varför till ro så brått); 8. To the land
of bliss (Lycklandsresan); 9. Coastal song (En
strandvisa); 10. Aladdin of the Lamp (Prins Aladin av
Lampan).
Cpte P. Mattei, B-Å. Lundin (r1994) *Concert*
(9/95) (BIS) ① **BIS-CD654**
3, 10. H. Hagegård, T. Schuback *Concert*
(7/90) (MSVE) ① **MSCD623**
5 Songs of Bo Bergman—1v & piano, Op. 20
(1903-4)
1. Stareye (Stjärnöga); 2. At the window (Vid
fönstret); 3. Ancient Dutchman (Gammal
Nederländare); 4. Moonlight (Månsken); 5. Adagio.
Cpte P. Mattei, B-Å. Lundin (r1994) *Concert*
(9/95) (BIS) ① **BIS-CD654**
3. H. Hagegård, T. Schuback *Concert*
(7/90) (MSVE) ① **MSCD623**
5 Songs to texts by Johann Ludvig
Runeberg—1v & piano, Op. 8 (1895-6)
1. Leaning on the fence (Lutad mot gärdet); 2. The
daughter said to her old mother (Dottern sade till sin
gamla moder); 3. Early sorrow (Den tidiga sorgen); 4.
To a rose (Till en ros); 5. Delights (Behagen).
Cpte P. Mattei, B-Å. Lundin (r1994) *Concert*
(9/95) (BIS) ① **BIS-CD654**
2. A.S. von Otter, B. Forsberg *Concert*
(7/90) (MSVE) ① **MSCD623**
Star-eyes—song (Wds. Bergman)
A.S. von Otter, B. Forsberg *Concert*
(7/90) (MSVE) ① **MSCD623**
4 Swedish Songs—1v & piano, Op. 16 (1893-
7) (Wds. Heidenstam, Hedberg & Fröding)
1. Let us die young (Låt oss dö unga); 2. Gold and
forests green (Guld och gröna skogar); 3. Ingalill; 4.
Fylgia.
Cpte P. Mattei, B-Å. Lundin (r1994) *Concert*
(9/95) (BIS) ① **BIS-CD654**
3. H. Hagegård, T. Schuback *Concert*
(7/90) (MSVE) ① **MSCD623**
To a rose—Lied, Op. 8/4 (1895-96) (Wds.
Runeberg)
A.S. von Otter, B. Forsberg *Concert*
(7/90) (MSVE) ① **MSCD623**
The Wanderer—song (Wds. Ekelund)
H. Hagegård, T. Schuback *Concert*
(7/90) (MSVE) ① **MSCD623**
Were I a small child—song, Op. 37/4 (1918)
(Wds. von Heidenstam)
H. Hagegård, T. Schuback *Concert*
(7/90) (MSVE) ① **MSCD623**
When through the room—song, Op. 26/6
(1906-09) (Wds. von Heidenstam)
H. Hagegård, T. Schuback *Concert*
(7/90) (MSVE) ① **MSCD623**
Why hurry to rest?—song (Wds. von
Heiderstam)
H. Hagegård, T. Schuback *Concert*
(7/90) (MSVE) ① **MSCD623**

SECTION V: STAGE WORKS

Chitra—incidental music, Op. 43 (1921)
Gothenburg SO, N. Järvi *Piano Concerto 2.*
(2/91) (BIS) ① **BIS-CD476**
Suite Swedish RSO, E-P. Salonen (arr Rosenberg)
Concert (11/90) (MSVE) ① **MSCD626**
Lodolezzi Sings—concert suite from
incidental music, Op. 39 (1911)
Gothenburg SO, N. Järvi *Concert*
(11/90) (BIS) ① **BIS-CD438**

ŠTĚPÁN *Czechoslovakia*

SECTION IV: VOCAL AND CHORAL

On my way—song
E. Destinn, orch, J. Pasternack (r1920) *Concert*
(11/93) (ROMO) ① [2] **81002-2**
E. Destinn, orch, J. Pasternack (r1920) *Concert*
(12/94) (SUPR) ① [12] **11 2136-2(5)**

ŠTĚPÁN, Josef Antonín
(1726–1797) Czechoslovakia

SECTION I: ORCHESTRAL

Concerto for Keyboard and Orchestra in B
flat (1780-90)
A. Staier, Cologne Concerto (r1994) *Concert*
(11/95) (TELD) ① **4509-94569-2**

STEPHAN, Rudi *(1887–1915)*
Germany

SECTION II: CHAMBER

Music for Seven Stringed Instruments—2
vns, va, vc, db, pf, hp
B. Hartog, I. Schliephake, S. Passaggio, G.
Donderer, A. Akahoshi, C. Tainton, M. Schmidt
Concert (9/95) (SCHW) ① **311122**

STEPHENS, Denzil

SECTION I: ORCHESTRAL

Solo Rhapsody—euphonium and brass band
(c1950s)
N. Childs, Britannia Building Soc Band, H. Snell
Concert (2/91) (DOYE) ① **DOYCD002**

STEPTOE, Roger *(b 1953)*
England

SECTION IV: VOCAL AND CHORAL

An Elegy on the Death and Burial of Cock
Robin—song (1988) (Wds. anon)
J. Bowman, Downshire Players, P. Ash *Concert*
(3/89) (MERI) ① **CDE84158**

STERN, Leo *(1862–1904)*
England

SECTION IV: VOCAL AND CHORAL

Coquette—song
S. Adams, anon (r1902) *Concert*
(3/93) (SYMP) ① **SYMCD1100**

STERNDALE BENNETT, Sir
William *(1816–1875) England*

SECTION I: ORCHESTRAL

Adagio—piano and orchestra (c1834)
(thought to be orig slow movt of Pf Conc 3)
M. Binns, Philh, N. Braithwaite (ed Cope) *Concert*
(11/90) (LYRI) ① **SRCD205**
Caprice in E—piano and orchestra, Op. 22
(1838)
M. Binns, LPO, N. Braithwaite *Concert*
(11/90) (LYRI) ① **SRCD204**
Concerto for Piano and Orchestra No. 1 in D
minor, Op. 1 (1832)
M. Binns, LPO, N. Braithwaite (ed D. Byers) *Concert*
(11/90) (LYRI) ① **SRCD204**
Concerto for Piano and Orchestra No. 2 in E
flat, Op. 4 (1833)
M. Binns, Philh, N. Braithwaite *Concert*
(11/90) (LYRI) ① **SRCD205**
Concerto for Piano and Orchestra No. 3 in C
minor, Op. 9 (1834)
M. Binns, LPO, N. Braithwaite (ed D. Byers) *Concert*
(11/90) (LYRI) ① **SRCD204**
Concerto for Piano and Orchestra No. 5 in F
minor (1836)
M. Binns, Philh, N. Braithwaite *Concert*
(11/90) (LYRI) ① **SRCD205**

SECTION II: CHAMBER

Sextet in F sharp minor—pf, 2vns, va, vc and
db, Op. 8 (1835)
A. Kiss, F. Balogh, L. Bársony, K. Botvay, P. Kubina,
I. Prunyi (r1993) *Sonata Duo, Op. 32.*
(11/94) (MARC) ① **8 223304**
Sonata Duo in A—cello and piano, Op. 32
(1852)
G. Kertész, K. Dráfi (r1993) *Piano Sextet, Op. 8.*
(11/94) (MARC) ① **8 223304**

SECTION III: INSTRUMENTAL

Capriccio in D minor—piano, Op. 2 (?1834)
I. Prunyi (r1992) *Concert*
(6/94) (MARC) ① **8 223578**

6 Impromptus—piano, Op. 12 (1836)
1. B minor; 2. E; 3. F sharp minor.
I. Prunyi (r1992) *Concert*
(6/94) (MARC) ① **8 223578**
30 Preludes and Lessons—piano, Op. 33 (1851-53)
I. Prunyi (r1992) *Concert*
(6/94) (MARC) ① **8 223578**
3 Romances—piano, Op. 14 (1837)
1. B flat minor; 2. E flat; 3. G minor.
I. Hobson *Concert* (3/89) (ARAB) ① **Z6596**
I. Prunyi (r1992) *Concert*
(6/94) (MARC) ① **8 223578**
Sonata for Piano in A flat, 'The Maid of Orleans', Op. 46 (1873)
1. In the Fields; 2. In the Field; 3. In Prison; 4. The End.
I. Hobson *Concert* (3/89) (ARAB) ① **Z6596**
Sonata for Piano in F minor, Op. 13 (1837)
I. Prunyi (r1992) *Suite de pièces, Op. 24.*
(6/94) (MARC) ① **8 223526**
Suite de pièces—piano, Op. 24 (1842)
1. Presto leggiero: C sharp minor; 2. Capricciosa: E; 3. Agitato assai: E minor; 4. Alla fantasia: A; 5. Presto agitato: F sharp minor; 6. Lento: B.
I. Prunyi (r1992) *Piano Sonata, Op. 13.*
(6/94) (MARC) ① **8 223526**

SECTION IV: VOCAL AND CHORAL

Come live with us—glee
Hilliard Ens, L-L. Kiesel *Concert*
(12/91) (MERI) ① **DUOCD89009**

STERNEFELD, Daniel (1905–1986) Belgium

SECTION I: ORCHESTRAL

Songs and dance at the court of Mary of Burgundy—orchestra (1975) (arr of dances by Susato, Phalesius & Bellerus)
Belgian Rad & TV Orch, A. Rahbari (r1992) *Concert*
(8/94) (DINT) ① **DICD920100**

STEVENS, Bernard (George) (1916–1983) England

SECTION I: ORCHESTRAL

Cello Concerto, Op.18 (1952)
A. Baillie, BBC PO, E. Downes *Symphony of Liberation.* (3/87) (MERI) ① **CDE84124**
Concerto for Piano and Orchestra, Op. 26 (1950-55)
M. Roscoe, Ireland National SO, A. Leaper (r1993) *Concert* (11/94) (MARC) ① **8 223480**
Concerto for Violin and Orchestra, Op. 4 (1943 rev 1946)
E. Kovacic, BBC PO, E. Downes *Symphony 2.*
(4/90) (MERI) ① **CDE84174**
Dance Suite—orchestra, Op. 28 (1957)
Ireland National SO, A. Leaper (r1993) *Concert*
(11/94) (MARC) ① **8 223480**
Symphony No. 2, Op. 35 (1964)
BBC PO, E. Downes *Violin Concerto.*
(4/90) (MERI) ① **CDE84174**
A Symphony of Liberation, Op.7 (1945)
BBC PO, E. Downes *Cello Concerto.*
(3/87) (MERI) ① **CDE84124**
Variations—orchestra, Op. 36 (1964)
Ireland National SO, A. Leaper (r1993) *Concert*
(11/94) (MARC) ① **8 223480**

SECTION II: CHAMBER

Lyric Suite—string trio, Op. 30 (1958)
Delmé Qt *Concert* (6/91) (UNIC) ① **DKPCD9097**
String Quartet No. 2, Op. 34 (1962)
Delmé Qt *Concert* (6/91) (UNIC) ① **DKPCD9097**
Theme and Variations—string quartet, Op. 11 (1949)
Delmé Qt *Concert* (6/91) (UNIC) ① **DKPCD9097**

SECTION IV: VOCAL AND CHORAL

Mass for double choir (1939)
Finzi Sngrs, P. Spicer *Concert*
(12/92) (CHAN) ① **CHAN9021**

STEVENS, Halsey (1908–1989) USA

SECTION II: CHAMBER

Sonata for Trumpet and Piano (1956)
W. Marsalis, J.L. Stillman (r1992) *Concert*
(5/94) (SONY) ① **SK47193**

SECTION III: INSTRUMENTAL

Intrada—piano (1954)
E. Parkin *Concert* (1/89) (PREA) ① **PRCD1776**
3 Inventions—piano (1948)
E. Parkin *Concert* (1/89) (PREA) ① **PRCD1776**

STEVENSON, Ronald (b 1928) England/Scotland

SECTION III: INSTRUMENTAL

Passacaglia on DSCH—piano (1960-62)
R. Stevenson *Concert*
(9/90) (ALTA) ① [2] **AIR-CD-9091**
R. Clarke (r1993) (9/95) (MARC) ① **8 223545**
Prelude and Fugue in themes from Busoni's 'Doktor Faust'—piano (1949-59)
R. Stevenson *Concert*
(9/90) (ALTA) ① [2] **AIR-CD-9091**
Recitative and Air—piano
R. Stevenson *Concert*
(9/90) (ALTA) ① [2] **AIR-CD-9091**
Sonatina Serenissima—piano (1977)
A. Goldstone *Concert*
(3/92) (GAMU) ① **GAMCD526**

STEWART, Haldane Campbell (1868–1942) England

SECTION IV: VOCAL AND CHORAL

King of Glory—anthem: choir and organ
Magdalen Oxford Coll Ch, G. Webber *Concert*
(11/91) (ABBE) ① **CDCA914**

STILL, William Grant (1895–1978) USA

SECTION I: ORCHESTRAL

Symphony No. 1, 'Afro-American' (1930)
Detroit SO, N. Järvi (r1992) *Ellington: River Suite.*
(4/93) (CHAN) ① **CHAN9154**
Symphony No. 2 in G minor, 'Song of a New Race' (1937)
Detroit SO, N. Järvi (r1993) *Concert*
(3/94) (CHAN) ① **CHAN9226**

SECTION II: CHAMBER

4 Danzas de Panama—string quartet/string orchestra (1948)
1. Tamborito; 2. Majorana y Socavon; 3. Punto; 4. Cumbia y Congo.
Berlin SO, I. Jackson (r1992) *Concert*
(11/93) (KOCH) ① **37154-2**
Folk Suite No. 1—string quartet, flute and piano (1962)
1. Bambalele and Espin Garda; 2. Sometimes I Feel Like A Motherless Child; 3. Two Hebraic Songs: Artsah Alinu & Ayzeh Peleh.
A. Still, S. De Witt Smith, New Zealand Qt (r1993) *Concert* (11/94) (KOCH) ① **37192-2**
Pastorela—violin and piano (1946)
A. Still, S. De Witt Smith (r1993; arr A. Still) *Concert*
(11/94) (KOCH) ① **37192-2**
Prelude—flute, string quartet and piano
A. Still, S. De Witt Smith, New Zealand Qt, M. Steer *Concert* (11/94) (KOCH) ① **37192-2**
Quit dat fool'nish—flute and piano (arr cpsr from pf work)
A. Still, S. De Witt Smith (r1992) *Concert*
(11/93) (KOCH) ① **37154-2**
A. Still, S. De Witt Smith (r1993) *Concert*
(11/94) (KOCH) ① **37192-2**
Suite for Violin and Piano (1943)
2. Movement II, suggested by Sargent Johnson's 'Mother and Child'; 3. Movement III, suggested by Augusta Savage's 'Gamin'.
2, 3. A. Still, S. De Witt Smith (r1993; ed A. Still) *Concert* (11/94) (KOCH) ① **37192-2**
Summerland—flute, harp and solo strings (1936) (arr of No 2 of '3 Visions' for pf)
A. Still, S. De Witt Smith (r1993) *Concert*
(11/93) (KOCH) ① **37154-2**
A. Still, S. De Witt Smith (r1993) *Concert*
(11/94) (KOCH) ① **37192-2**

SECTION IV: VOCAL AND CHORAL

Bayou Home—song
A. Still, S. De Witt Smith (r1993; ed A. Still) *Concert*
(11/94) (KOCH) ① **37192-2**
Here's one (1941) (arr of negro spiritual)
A. Still, S. De Witt Smith (r1993; ed A. Still) *Concert*
(11/94) (KOCH) ① **37192-2**

Song for the Lonely—song (1953) (wds. V. Arvey)
A. Still, S. De Witt Smith (r1993; ed A. Still) *Concert*
(11/94) (KOCH) ① **37192-2**
Songs of Separation (1949)
1. Idolatry (wds. A. Bontemps); 2. Poème (wds. P-T. Marcelin); 3. Parted (wds. P. L. Dunbar); 4. If you should go (wds. C. Cullen); 5. A Black Pienot (wds. L. Hughes).
4. A. Still, S. De Witt Smith (r1993; ed A. Still) *Concert* (11/94) (KOCH) ① **37192-2**

SECTION V: STAGE WORKS

La Guiablesse—ballet (1927)
Berlin SO, I. Jackson (r1992) *Concert*
(11/93) (KOCH) ① **37154-2**

STOCK, Frederick (1872–1942) Germany/USA

SECTION I: ORCHESTRAL

Waltz—orchestra, Op. 8
Chicago SO, F. Stock (r1930) *Concert*
(2/95) (BIDD) ① [2] **WHL021/2**

STOCKHAUSEN, Karlheinz (b 1928) Germany

SECTION I: ORCHESTRAL

Michaels Reise um die Erde—tpt and orch, or tpt, 9 players & sound projection (1978) (scene from Licht: Donnerstag)
M. Stockhausen, S. Stephens, I. Stuart, L. Schatzberger, M. Svoboda, K. Pasveer, A. Boettger, I. Nakamura, M. Obst, S. Stockhausen, K. Stockhausen (r1989) (3/93) (ECM) ① **437 188-2**

SECTION II: CHAMBER

Aus den sieben Tagen—15 text pieces (1968)
Verbindung; Setz die Segel zur Sonne Musique Vivante Ens, D. Masson (r1969)
(9/89) (HARM) ① **HMA190 795**
Mantra—2 pianos, percussion and ring modulators (1969-70)
Y. Mikashoff, R. Bevan, O. Ørsted
(1/91) (NALB) ① **NA025CD**

SECTION III: INSTRUMENTAL

In Freundschaft—clarinet (1977 rev 1978)
C. Lindberg *Concert* (10/89) (BIS) ① **BIS-CD388**
P. Meyer (r1993) *Concert*
(7/95) (DENO) ① **CO-78917**
14 Klavierstücke—piano
1. I (1952-53); 2. II (1952-53); 3. III (1952-53); 4. IV (1952-53); 5. V (1954-55); 6. VI (1954-55); 7. VII (1954-55); 8. VIII (1954-55); 9. IX (1954-5 rev 1961); 10. X (1954-55 rev 1961); 11. XI (1956); 12. XII (1978-79); 13. XIII (1981); 14. XIV (1984).
12-14. B. Wambach (5/90) (SCHW) ① **310015**

SECTION IV: VOCAL AND CHORAL

Stimmung—6 vocal soloists (1967) (Wds. various)
Songcircle, G. Rose (2/87) (HYPE) ① **CDA66115**

STOCKMEIER, Wolfgang (b 1931) Germany

SECTION IV: VOCAL AND CHORAL

Pater noster—chorus a capella (1969-70)
Lower Rhine Choral Soc, H. Schmitt *Concert*
(2/90) (SCHW) ① **313001**

STOJOWSKI, Zygmunt (Denis Antoni) (1870–1946) Poland

SECTION II: CHAMBER

Fantaisie (1905)
C. Lindberg, R. Pöntinen *Concert*
(9/85) (BIS) ① **BIS-CD298**

SECTION III: INSTRUMENTAL

By the brookside—piano
I. Paderewski (r1926) *Concert*
(3/93) (PEAR) ① **GEMMCD9943**
Chant d'amour—piano, Op. 26/3
I. Paderewski (r1926) *Concert*
(3/93) (PEAR) ① **GEMMCD9943**

STOKER, Richard (b 1938) England

SECTION II: CHAMBER

Sonatina—clarinet and piano (pub 1972)
E. Jóhannesson, P. Jenkins Concert
(1/93) (CHAN) ① CHAN9079

STOLL, David (b 1948) England

SECTION II: CHAMBER

Piano Quartet in A (1987)
Pro Arte Trio, N. Skinner (r1992) Concert
(10/94) (MERI) ① CDE84245
Sonata for Two Pianos in D (1990)
D. Ward, N. Skinner (r1992) Concert
(10/94) (MERI) ① CDE84245
Trio for Strings in G (1992)
Pro Arte Trio (r1992) Concert
(10/94) (MERI) ① CDE84245

SECTION III: INSTRUMENTAL

Sonata for Piano in B flat (1991)
D. Ward (r1992) Concert
(10/94) (MERI) ① CDE84245

STOLTE, Siegfried (1925–1991) Germany

SECTION II: CHAMBER

Burleske—trumpet and piano
S. Nakarjakov, A. Markovich Concert
(5/93) (TELD) ① 9031-77705-2

STOLZ, Robert (1880–1975) Austria

SECTION V: STAGE WORKS

Der Favorit—operetta: 2 acts (1916—Berlin)
(Lib. F Grünbaum & W Sterk)
Du sollst der Kaiser meiner Seele sein L. Popp,
ASMF, N. Marriner Concert
(6/88) (EMI) ① CDC7 49700-2
Du sollst der Kaiser meiner Seele sein B.
Hendricks, Philh, L. Foster, H. Bean (1992) Concert
(8/93) (EMI) ① CDC7 54626-2
Du sollst der Kaiser meiner Seele sein J. Migenes,
Vienna Volksoper Orch, L. Schifrin (r1993) Concert
(1/94) (ERAT) ① 4509-92875-2
Frühjahrsparade—operetta: 2 acts
(1964—Vienna) (Lib. Marischka and H.
Wiener)
Wien wird schön erst bei Nacht L. Popp, ASMF, N.
Marriner Concert (6/88) (EMI) ① CDC7 49700-2
Das Lied ist aus—film score (1930)
Adieu, mein kleiner Gardeoffizier R. Tauber, Orch,
F. Weissmann (r1932) Concert
(2/91) (EMI) ① CDH7 69787-2
Venus im Seide—operetta: 3 acts
(1932—Zurich) (Lib. Grünwald and L. Herzer)
Spiel auf deiner Geige J. Migenes, Vienna
Volksoper Orch, L. Schifrin (r1993) Concert
(1/94) (ERAT) ① 4509-92875-2

STONE, Richard (20th cent) USA

SECTION V: STAGE WORKS

Sundown: The Vampire in Retreat—film
score (1989)
EXCERPTS: 1. Redemption of the Damned; 2.
Finale.
1, 2. OST Concert (5/93) (SILV) ① SILVAD3003
1, 2. OST, R. Stone (r1989) Concert
(10/93) (SILV) ① FILMCD127

STONE, Robert (1516–1613) England

SECTION IV: VOCAL AND CHORAL

The Lord's Prayer—4vv (pub 1565)
Cambridge Sngrs, J. Rutter Concert
(4/92) (CLLE) ① COLCD113

STORACE, Bernardo (fl late 17th Cent) Italy

SECTION III: INSTRUMENTAL

Passamezzo—keyboard (pub 1664)
C. Farr Concert (1/90) (ETCE) ① KTC1056

Toccata and Canzon—keyboard
R. Alessandrini (r1994) Concert
(4/95) (O111) ① OPS30-118

STORACE, Stephen (John Seymour) (1762–1796) England

SECTION IV: VOCAL AND CHORAL

Captivity—ballad: 1v (1793) (Wds Rev Jeans
of Dibden)
Invocation (r1994) Concert
(3/95) (HYPE) ① CDA66740
The Curfew—song (c1782)
E. Kirkby, F. Kelly Concert
(12/91) (HYPE) ① CDA66497

STRADELLA, Alessandro (1644–1682) Italy

SECTION I: ORCHESTRAL

Sinfonia alla Serenata Il Barcheggio (pt 1)
W. Marsalis, St Luke's Orch, J. Nelson Concert
(8/92) (SONY) ① SK46672
Sonata a otto viole con una tromba—trumpet
and two string choirs (before 1675)
C. Steele-Perkins, Parley of Instr Concert
(1/89) (HYPE) ① CDA66255
Sonata a 8 con una Tromba in D—trumpet
and strings
C. Steele-Perkins, Tafelmusik, J. Lamon (vn/dir)
(r1993) Concert (4/95) (SONY) ① SK53365

SECTION III: INSTRUMENTAL

Toccata—keyboard
R. Alessandrini (r1994) Concert
(4/95) (O111) ① OPS30-118

SECTION IV: VOCAL AND CHORAL

Così amor mi fai languir—solo madrigal
J. Carreras, ECO, V. Sutej (r1992; arr Agostinelli)
Concert (6/93) (PHIL) ① 434 926-2PH
San Giovanni Battista—oratorio (1675)
Cpte A. Monoyios, M. Bach, D. Cordier, M.
Prégardien, M. Schopper, Stagione, M. Schneider
(r1989) (5/91) (DHM) ① RD77034
Cpte C. Bott, C. Batty, G. Lesne, R. Edgar-Wilson, P.
Huttenlocher, Musiciens du Louvre, M. Minkowski
(r1991) (10/92) (ERAT) ① 2292-45739-2

STRATTA, Ettore (20th Cent) ?Italy

SECTION IV: VOCAL AND CHORAL

Astoreando—tango (Wds. J. Calandrelli)
Buenos Aires Qnt, RPO, E. Stratta (arr J. Calandrelli)
Concert (1/93) (TELD) ① 9031-76997-2

STRAUS, Oscar (1870–1954) Austria

SECTION IV: VOCAL AND CHORAL

Musik kommt—song (Wds. D. von Liliencron)
B. Kusche, Berlin SO, R. Stolz Concert
(2/91) (EURO) ① GD69022

SECTION V: STAGE WORKS

Land without Music—film score (1935)
Only a simple melody R. Tauber, P. Kahn (pp or bp)
Concert (2/91) (LYRC) ① [2] SRO830
Der Letzte Walzer—operetta: 3 acts
(1920—Berlin) (Lib. J. Brammer & A.
Grünwald)
EXCERPTS: 1. Overture. ACT 1: 2. Es lebe der Herr
General!; 3. Bei Lied und Wein; 4. Rosen, die wir
nicht erreichen; 5. Mama, Mama! Wir wollen einen
Mann!; 6. O kommt, o kommt und trazt mit mir; 7.
Das ist der letzte Walzer; 8. Graf Sarrasow, Sie geh'n
zu weit (finale). ACT 2: 9. Hört ihr die liebliche,
zwingende; 10. Dann weiss der Jüngling, dass es
Zeit; 11. Tanze, vera Lisaweta; 12. Du hast zwei
Grübchen; 13. Hast du es nicht erraten?; 14. Der
ACT 3: 15. Wir sind   Klang des Guslizither (finale)
die Balletteusen; 16. Bei Lied und Wein (reprise); 17.
O du pikantes, kleines O-la-la; 18. Du lieber letzer
Walzer (finale).
Das ist der letzte Walzer M. Schramm, R. Schock,
Berlin SO, R. Stolz Concert
(2/91) (EURO) ① GD69022
La Ronde—film score (1950)
EXCERPTS: 1. Waltz.
1. Berlin SO, R. Stolz Concert
(2/91) (EURO) ① GD69022

Rund um die Liebe—operetta: 3 acts
(1914—Vienna) (Lib. R. Bodanzky & F.
Thelen)
EXCERPTS: 1. Overture; 2. Es gibt Dinge, die muss
man vergessen.
1, 2. R. Schock, Berlin SO, R. Stolz Concert
(2/91) (EURO) ① GD69022
Der Tapfere Soldat—operetta: 3 acts
(1908—Vienna) (Lib. Bernauer and Jacobson.
Eng: The Chocolate Sol)
EXCERPTS: 1. Overture. ACT 1: 2. Wir marschieren
durch die Nacht; 3. Mein Held!; 4. Wie schön ist
dieses Männerbild; 5. Komm', Komm! Held meiner
Träume; 6. In meinen Leben sah ich nie einen
Helden; 7. Ach, du kleiner Praliné-Soldat; 8a. Es ist
ein Schicksal, schwer zu tragen; 8b. Weil's Leben
süss und herlich ist; 9. Suchet alle Mann, der Serbe
nict entwischen Kann!; 10a. Drei Frauensassen am
Feuerherd; 10b. Tiralala! (finale). ACT 2: 11. Ein
Hoch ein Hoch der Heldenschar!; 12a. Ich bin
gewöhnt stets nur zu siegen; 12b. Mein
Mädchenherz, das schlägt; 13. Ich habe die Feinde
gesschlagen auf's Haupt; 14a. Ein Jeder hat es
schon erhahren; 14b. Wenn man so dürfte, wie man
wollte; 15. Ach, es ist doch ein schönes Vergnügen;
16. Es war einmal ein Fräulein; 17. Leute, Leute,
kommt herbei; 18. Ich was der Helder deiner Träume.
ACT 3: 19. Mein lieber Herr von Bumerli; 20. Pardon!
Ich steig' ja nur auf den Balcon!; 21a. Du magst dein
Köpfchen noch so heftig schütteln; 21b. Freundchen,
Freundchen nur nicht toben; 22a. Wenn ein Mann ein
Mädchen; 22b. Lieber Schwiegerpapa, liebe
Schwiegermama; 23. Ich geb' Dir morgens einem
Kuss.
Held meiner Träume M. Hill Smith, Chandos
Concert Orch, S. Barry (Eng) Concert
(6/85) (CHAN) ① CHAN8362
Komm, Held meiner Träume M. Schramm, Berlin
SO, R. Stolz Concert (2/91) (EURO) ① GD69022
Komm'! Held meiner Träume R. Tauber, P. Kahn
(pp or bp) Concert (2/92) (LYRC) ① [2] SRO830
Komm, Held meiner Träume J. Migenes, Vienna
Volksoper Orch, L. Schifrin (r1993) Concert
(1/94) (ERAT) ① 4509-92875-2
Ein Walzertraum, '(A) Waltz
Dream'—operetta: 3 acts (1907—Vienna)
(Lib. Dörmann and Jacobson)
EXCERPTS: 1. Overture. ACT 1: 2. Wir sind so
aufgerert; 3. Ein Mädchen, das so lieb und brav; 4. O
Jubel sondergleichen; 5a. Ich hab' mit Freuden
angefkehrt; 5b. Alles was kock und fesch; 6a. Vorübe
ist die Feier; 6b. Ich hab' einen Mann; 7a. Ah, was
vernehm'ich!; 7b. Und die arm Dynastie; 8a. Da
draussen im duftigen Garten; 8b. Leise, ganz leise
klingt's durch den Raum; 9. Meiner lieber Freund, du
lässt mich lang allein!. ACT 2: 10. G'stelle Mädl'n,
resch und hesch; 11a. Kom'her, du mein reizendes
Mäderl; 11b. O du liebeer, o du g'scheiter; 12a. Das
Geheimnis sollst du verraten; 12b. Temperamant!
Temperament!; 13a. Lehn'dine Wang an meine
Wang; 13b. Piccolo! Piccolo! Tsin-tsin-tsin; 14a.
Wenn zwei Menschen sich anschau'n; 14b. Du bist
der Traum, den oft ich geträumt; 15. Ich es möglich
(finale). ACT 3: 16. Es geht von Mund zu Mond; 17.
Ja, was ist denn nur los mit dir, Nikil; 18. Mann muss
manches im Leben vergessen; 19. Mächt's auf die
Tür'n, machtes auf die Fenster; 20. Einmal noch
beben, eh's wes vorbei.
6a, 6b, 8a, 8b, 10, 11a, 13b, 20. R. Schock, W. Lipp,
L. Schmidt, F. Gruber, M. Schramm, Günther Arndt
Ch, Berlin SO, R. Stolz Concert
(2/91) (EURO) ① GD69022
8a, 8b R. Tauber, Orch, F. Schönbaumsfeld (r1932)
Concert (12/89) (EMI) ① CDH7 69787-2
8a, 8b M. Hill Smith, P. Morrison, Chandos Concert
Orch, S. Barry (Eng) Concert
(2/90) (CHAN) ① CHAN8759
8b P. Domingo, ECO, J. Rudel Concert
(2/87) (EMI) ① CDC7 47398-2
8b R. Crooks, orch (r1933: Eng) Concert
(9/93) (CLAR) ① CDGSE78-50-50

STRAUSS, Eduard (1835–1916) Austria

SECTION I: ORCHESTRAL

Alpenrose—Polka mazurka, Op. 127 (1875)
(Alpine Roses)
Hallé, B. Tovey Concert
(1/94) (CFP) ① CD-CFP4577
Bahn frei—polka galop, Op. 45 (1869)
Cincinnati Pops, E. Kunzel Concert
(3/86) (TELA) ① CD80098
VPO, W. Boskovsky (r1962) Concert
(1/90) (DECC) ① 425 426-2DA

VJSO, W. Boskovsky *Concert*
(1/90) (EMI) ① [2] **CZS7 62751-2**
Košice St PO, M. Eichenholz (r1992) *Concert*
(2/94) (MARC) ① **8 223471**
Blauäuglein—polka française, Op. 254 (1887)
(Eng: Little blue eyes)
London Viennese Orch, J. Rothstein *Concert*
(5/93) (CHAN) ① **CHAN9127**
Carmen—quadrille, Op. 134 (c1875)
VPO, C. Abbado (pp1991) *Concert*
(4/91) (DG) ① **431 628-2GH**
Fesche Geister—waltz, Op. 75 (1872)
VPO, W. Boskovsky (r1970) *Concert*
(1/90) (DECC) ① **425 425-2DA**
Feuerfunken—waltz, Op. 185 (1880)
Košice St PO, M. Eichenholz (r1992) *Concert*
(2/94) (MARC) ① **8 223471**
Glockensignale—waltz, Op. 198 (1881)
Košice St PO, M. Eichenholz (r1992) *Concert*
(2/94) (MARC) ① **8 223470**
Greeting Valse, on English airs (1885)
LSO, J. Georgiadis *Concert*
(11/89) (CHAN) ① **CHAN8739**
Hectograph—Schnell-Polka, Op. 186 (1880)
LJSO, J. Rothstein *Concert*
(1/86) (CHAN) ① **CHAN8381**
Helenen-Quadrille über Motiv der komischen
Oper 'Die schöne Helena' von J. Offenbach,
Op. 14 (1865)
Berlin Ens *Concert* (5/91) (ORFE) ① **C126901A**
Knall und Fall—Polka schnell, Op. 132 (1876)
(Without warning)
LJSO, J. Rothstein *Concert*
(1/86) (CHAN) ① **CHAN8381**
Leuchtäferln, 'Glow-worms'—Waltz, Op. 161
(1877)
LJSO, J. Rothstein *Concert*
(1/86) (CHAN) ① **CHAN8381**
Lustfahrten—waltz, Op. 177 (1879)
Košice St PO, M. Eichenholz (r1992) *Concert*
(2/94) (MARC) ① **8 223470**
Mit Chic—polka schnell, Op. 221 (1884)
VPO, L. Maazel (pp1994) *Concert*
(7/94) (SONY) ① **SK46694**
Mit Dampf—polka schnell, Op. 70 (1871)
Košice St PO, M. Eichenholz (r1992) *Concert*
(2/94) (MARC) ① **8 223470**
Mit Extrapost—polka schnell, Op. 259
VPO, W. Boskovsky (r1970) *Concert*
(1/90) (DECC) ① **425 429-2DA**
Ohne Aufenthalt, 'Non-Stop'—polka schnell,
Op. 112 (1874)
VJSO, W. Boskovsky *Concert*
(1/90) (EMI) ① [2] **CZS7 62751-2**
Cincinnati Pops, E. Kunzel (1991-2) *Concert*
(7/93) (TELA) ① **CD80314**
Košice St PO, M. Eichenholz (r1992) *Concert*
(2/94) (MARC) ① **8 223471**
Ohne Bremse, 'With the Brakes Off'—polka
schnell, Op. 238 (1886)
VJSO, W. Boskovsky *Concert*
(1/90) (EMI) ① [2] **CZS7 62751-2**
Košice St PO, M. Eichenholz (r1992) *Concert*
(2/94) (MARC) ① **8 223471**
Old England for ever!—polka, Op. 239
(1885)
LSO, J. Georgiadis *Concert*
(11/89) (CHAN) ① **CHAN8739**
Österreichs Völker-Treue, 'Loyalty of
Austria's People'—march, Op. 211 (1882)
London Viennese Orch, J. Rothstein *Concert*
(5/93) (CHAN) ① **CHAN9127**
Reiselust, 'Delight in Travel'—Polka
française, Op. 166 (1878)
Košice St PO, M. Eichenholz (r1992) *Concert*
(2/94) (MARC) ① **8 223471**
Schleier und Krone—waltz, Op. 200 (1881)
(Eng: Veil and Crown)
London Viennese Orch, J. Rothstein *Concert*
(5/93) (CHAN) ① **CHAN9127**
Tour und Retour—polka française, Op. 125
(1875)
Košice St PO, M. Eichenholz (r1992) *Concert*
(2/94) (MARC) ① **8 223470**
Treuliebchen—polka française, Op. 152
(1877)
Košice St PO, M. Eichenholz (r1992) *Concert*
(2/94) (MARC) ① **8 223471**
Unter der Enns, 'Below the Enns'—Polka
schnell, Op. 121 (1874)
Hallé, B. Tovey *Concert*
(2/91) (CFP) ① **CD-CFP4577**
Von Land zu Land—polka française, Op. 140
(1876)
Košice St PO, M. Eichenholz (r1992) *Concert*
(2/94) (MARC) ① **8 223471**

STRAUSS, Franz Joseph
(1822–1905) Germany

SECTION I: ORCHESTRAL

Concerto for Horn and Orchestra, Op. 8
(1865)
I. James, Polish Nat RSO, A. Wit (r1989) *Concert*
(3/92) (EBS) ① **EBS6063**

SECTION II: CHAMBER

Nocturno—horn and piano, Op. 7
M. Thompson, P. Fowke *Concert*
(9/92) (EMI) ① **CDC7 54420-2**

STRAUSS, Johann (Baptist) I
(1804–1849) Austria

SECTION I: ORCHESTRAL

Alice—polka, Op. 238 (1848)
LSO, J. Georgiadis *Concert*
(11/89) (CHAN) ① **CHAN8739**
Almacks—quadrille, Op. 243 (1849)
LSO, J. Georgiadis *Concert*
(11/89) (CHAN) ① **CHAN8739**
Alpenkönig-Galopp, Op. 7
Vienna Biedermeier Ens *Concert*
(3/89) (DENO) ① **CO-72587**
Beliebte Annen—Polka, Op. 137
VPO, H. von Karajan (pp1987) *Concert*
(11/87) (DG) ① **419 616-2GH**
A. Posch, Alban Berg Qt (r1992: arr Weinmann)
Concert (6/94) (EMI) ① **CDC7 54881-2**
Beliebte Sperl-Polka, Op. 132 (1842)
VPO, W. Boskovsky (r1972) *Concert*
(1/90) (DECC) ① **425 427-2DA**
Cachucha—galop, Op. 97 (pub 1837)
Vienna Biedermeier Ens (trans A. Weinmann)
Concert (3/89) (DENO) ① **CO-72587**
Der Carneval in Paris—galopp, Op. 100
(1838) (Eng: Carnival in Paris)
London Viennese Orch, J. Rothstein *Concert*
(5/93) (CHAN) ① **CHAN9127**
Champagner Galopp, Op. 8 (1828)
Vienna Biedermeier Ens (M. Schönherr/H. Puffler)
Concert (3/89) (DENO) ① **CO-72587**
Chinese Galop—galop, Op. 20 (pub 1828)
Vienna Ens (arr A Weinmann) *Concert*
(9/92) (SONY) ① **SK47187**
Cincinnati Pops, E. Kunzel (1991-2) *Concert*
(7/93) (TELA) ① **CD80314**
Eisele und Beisele Sprünge—Polka, Op.
202
Vienna Biedermeier Ens (trans A. Weinmann)
Concert (3/89) (DENO) ① **CO-72587**
A. Posch, Alban Berg Qt (r1992: arr Weinmann)
Concert (6/94) (EMI) ① **CDC7 54881-2**
Eisenbahn-Lust—waltz, Op. 89 (1836)
Košice St PO, M. Eichenholz (r1992) *Concert*
(2/94) (MARC) ① **8 223470**
Exeter—polka, Op. 249 (1849)
LSO, J. Georgiadis *Concert*
(11/89) (CHAN) ① **CHAN8739**
Frederica—polka, Op. 239 (1849)
LSO, J. Georgiadis *Concert*
(11/89) (CHAN) ① **CHAN8739**
Freiheits—march, Op. 226 (1848) (Eng:
Freedom)
London Viennese Orch, J. Rothstein *Concert*
(5/93) (CHAN) ① **CHAN9127**
Gitana-Galop, Op. 108
Vienna Biedermeier Ens (trans A. Weinmann)
Concert (3/89) (DENO) ① **CO-72587**
Huldigung der Königin Victoria von
Grossbritannien—waltz, Op. 103 (1838) (Eng:
Homage to Queen Victoria of Great Britain)
LSO, J. Georgiadis *Concert*
(11/89) (CHAN) ① **CHAN8739**
Indianer-Galopp, Op. 111 (1839)
VPO, Z. Mehta (pp1990) *Concert*
(4/90) (SONY) ① **SK45808**
Kettenbrücken—Waltz No. 1, Op. 4
Vienna Biedermeier Ens (trans A. Weinmann/H.
Puffler) *Concert* (3/89) (DENO) ① **CO-72587**
Loreley-Rhein-Klänge, Op. 154 (pub 1854)
VPO, W. Boskovsky (r1961) *Concert*
(1/90) (DECC) ① **425 429-2DA**
March of the Royal Horse Guards (1849)
(piano version only)
LSO, J. Georgiadis (orch Georgiadis) *Concert*
(11/89) (CHAN) ① **CHAN8739**

Piefke und Pufke—polka française, Op. 235
(pub 1849)
VPO, W. Boskovsky (r1972) *Concert*
(1/90) (DECC) ① **425 426-2DA**
Radetzky March, Op. 228 (1848)
Cleveland Winds, F. Fennell *Concert*
(10/84) (TELA) ① **CD80099**
LSO, J. Georgiadis *Concert*
(9/87) (CARL) ① **PCD856**
VPO, H. von Karajan (pp1987) *Concert*
(11/87) (DG) ① **419 616-2GH**
VPO, C. Abbado (pp1988) *Concert*
(7/88) (DG) ① **423 662-2GH**
St Louis SO, L. Slatkin *Concert*
(6/89) (RCA) ① **RD87716**
VPO, W. Boskovsky (r1962) *Concert*
(1/90) (DECC) ① **425 426-2DA**
VJSO, W. Boskovsky *Concert*
(1/90) (EMI) ① [2] **CZS7 62751-2**
VPO, Z. Mehta (pp1990) *Concert*
(4/90) (SONY) ① **SK45808**
VPO, C. Kleiber (pp1989) *Concert*
(2/91) (SONY) ① **SK45938**
Hallé, B. Tovey *Concert*
(2/91) (CFP) ① **CD-CFP4577**
VPO, C. Abbado (pp1991) *Concert*
(4/91) (DG) ① **431 628-2GH**
VPO, C. Krauss (r1953) *Concert*
(2/92) (DG) ① [2] **435 335-2GWP2**
VPO, C. Kleiber (pp1992) *Concert*
(4/92) (SONY) ① **SK48376**
Locke Brass Consort, J. Stobart (arr Lake) *Concert*
(9/92) (CRD) ① **CRD3402**
VPO, R. Muti (pp1993) *Concert*
(3/93) (PHIL) ① **438 493-2PH**
BPO, H. von Karajan (r1966) *Concert*
(5/94) (DG) ① **439 346-2GX2**
VPO, L. Maazel (pp1994) *Concert*
(7/94) (SONY) ① **SK46694**
LSO, C. Mackerras (r1961) *Concert*
(12/95) (MERC) ① **434 352-2MM**
Reise-Galopp, Op. 85 (1836)
Košice St PO, M. Eichenholz (r1992) *Concert*
(2/94) (MARC) ① **8 223470**
Seufzer-Galopp, Op. 9 (1828)
VJSO, W. Boskovsky *Concert*
(1/90) (EMI) ① [2] **CZS7 62751-2**
VPO, C. Abbado (pp1991) *Concert*
(4/91) (DG) ① **431 628-2GH**
Souvenir de Carneval 1847—quadrille, Op.
200 (1847)
Košice St PO, M. Eichenholz (r1992) *Concert*
(2/94) (MARC) ① **8 223470**
Sperl-Galop, Op. 42 (pub 1831)
VPO, R. Muti (pp1993) *Concert*
(3/93) (PHIL) ① **438 493-2PH**
Die Vier Temperamente—waltz, Op. 59
(1832)
Vienna Ens *Concert* (9/92) (SONY) ① **SK47187**
Wettrennen—galop, Op. 29 (1829)
VPO, W. Boskovsky (r1973) *Concert*
(1/90) (DECC) ① **425 425-2DA**
Wiener Gemüths—Waltz, Op. 116
Vienna Biedermeier Ens (trans A. Weinmann)
Concert (3/89) (DENO) ① **CO-72587**
A. Posch, Alban Berg Qt (r1992: arr Weinmann)
Concert (6/94) (EMI) ① **CDC7 54881-2**

STRAUSS, Johann (Baptist) II
(1825–1899) Austria

SECTION I: ORCHESTRAL

Abschied von St Petersburg, 'Farewell to St
Petersburg'—waltz, Op. 210 (1859)
Bratislava RSO, M. Dittrich (r1992) *Concert*
(7/94) (MARC) ① **8 223234**
Abschieds-Rufe, 'Cries of farewell'—waltz,
Op. 179 (1856)
Košice St PO, J. Wildner (r1990) *Concert*
(2/94) (MARC) ① **8 223233**
Abschieds-Walzer, 'Farewell waltz', Op.
posth (1900)
Košice St PO, C. Pollack (r1992) *Concert*
(9/95) (MARC) ① **8 223239**
Accelerationen, 'Accelerations'—waltz, Op.
234 (1860)
Hallé, B. Thomson *Concert*
(12/87) (CFP) ① **CD-CFP9015**
VPO, W. Boskovsky (r1971) *Concert*
(1/90) (DECC) ① **425 429-2DA**
VPO, C. Kleiber (pp1989) *Concert*
(2/91) (SONY) ① **SK45938**
VPO, J. Krips *Concert*
(2/92) (DG) ① [2] **435 335-2GWP2**

Košice St PO, M. Eichenholz (r1992) *Concert*
(2/94) (MARC) ① **8 223471**
BPO, E. Kleiber (r1932) *Concert*
(5/94) (ARCI) ① **ARC102**
Košice St PO, J. Wildner (r1991) *Concert*
(7/94) (MARC) ① **8 223235**
VPO, L. Maazel (pp1994) *Concert*
(7/94) (SONY) ① **SK46694**
Adelen—waltz, Op. 424 (1886)
Bratislava RSO, A. Eschwé (r1989) *Concert*
(10/92) (MARC) ① **8 223217**
Aesculap-Polka, 'Aesculapius Polka', Op. 130 (1853)
Košice St PO, A. Walter (r1988) *Concert*
(1/90) (MARC) ① **8 223203**
L' Africaine—quadrille on themes from Meyerbeer's opera, Op. 299 (1865)
Košice St PO, A. Walter (r1989) *Concert*
(9/90) (MARC) ① **8 223211**
Albion-Polka, Op. 102 (1851)
Polish St PO, J. Wildner (r1989) *Concert*
(7/90) (MARC) ① **8 223209**
Alexander-Quadrille, Op. 33 (1847)
Bratislava RSO, J. Wildner (r1989) *Concert*
(2/91) (MARC) ① **8 223215**
Alexandrinen—polka française, Op. 198 (1857)
LJSO, J. Rothstein *Concert*
(1/86) (CHAN) ① **CHAN8381**
Košice St PO, A. Walter (r1991) *Concert*
(9/93) (MARC) ① **8 223230**
Alliance-Marsch, Op. 158 (1854)
Košice St PO, A. Walter (r1989) *Concert*
(5/92) (MARC) ① **8 223218**
Amazonen-Polka, 'Amazons Polka', Op. 9 (1845)
Košice St PO, A. Walter (r1988) *Concert*
(1/90) (MARC) ① **8 223203**
An der Moldau, 'By the Moldau'—polka, Op. 366 (1874)
Košice St PO, C. Pollack (r1992) *Concert*
(12/95) (MARC) ① **8 223242**
An der schönen, blauen Donau, 'Blue Danube'—waltz, Op. 314 (1867)
VJSO, W. Boskovsky *Concert*
(3/85) (EMI) ① **CDC7 47052-2**
Cincinnati Pops, E. Kunzel *Concert*
(3/86) (TELA) ① **CD80098**
LSO, J. Georgiadis *Concert*
(9/87) (CARL) ① **PCD856**
VPO, H. von Karajan (pp1987) *Concert*
(11/87) (DG) ① **419 616-2GH**
BPO, H. von Karajan *Concert*
(12/87) (EMI) ① **CDM7 69018-2**
Hallé, B. Thomson *Concert*
(12/87) (CFP) ① **CD-CFP9015**
VPO, C. Abbado (pp1988) *Concert*
(7/88) (DG) ① **423 662-2GH**
M. Rosenthal (arr Rosenthal: r1928) *Concert*
(4/89) (PEAR) ① **GEMMCD9339**
NY Voc Arts Ens, R. Beegle (arr vocal ens) *Concert*
(4/89) (ARAB) ① **Z6586**
COE, A. Schneider (pp1988) *Concert*
(4/89) (ASV) ① **CDCOE810**
VPO, W. Boskovsky (r1959) *Concert*
(1/90) (DECC) ① **425 425-2DA**
VJSO, W. Boskovsky *Concert*
(1/90) (EMI) ① [2] **CZS7 62751-2**
Chicago SO, F. Reiner *Concert*
(1/90) (RCA) ① **GD60177**
VPO, L. Maazel (pp1980) *Concert*
(4/90) (DG) ① **427 820-2GDC**
VPO, Z. Mehta (pp1990) *Concert*
(4/90) (SONY) ① **SK45808**
L. Pons, orch, A. Kostelanetz (French: r1947)
Concert (7/90) (SONY) ① **MPK45694**
Crommelynck Duo (pf duet) *Concert*
(7/90) (CLAV) ① **CD50-8915**
NBC SO, A. Toscanini (r1941/2) *Concert*
(1/91) (RCA) ① **GD60308**
VPO, C. Kleiber (pp1989) *Concert*
(2/91) (SONY) ① **SK45938**
VPO, C. Abbado (pp1991) *Concert*
(4/91) (DG) ① **431 628-2GH**
VPO, W. Boskovsky (r1959) *Concert*
(10/91) (DECC) ① **430 501-2DWO**
Berlin RSO, F. Fricsay *Concert*
(12/91) (DG) ① [2] **413 432-2GW2**
LPO, F. Welser-Möst *Concert*
(12/91) (EMI) ① **CDC7 54089-2**
VPO, G. Szell (r1934) *Concert*
(2/92) (DG) ① [2] **435 335-2GWP2**
L. Pons, orch, A. Kostelanetz (r1939) *Concert*
(4/92) (MSOU) ① **DFCDI-111**
VPO, C. Kleiber (pp1992) *Concert*
(4/92) (SONY) ① **SK48376**

M. Ivogün, Berlin St Op Orch, L. Blech (r1932)
Concert (8/92) (NIMB) ① **NI7832**
Concertgebouw, N. Harnoncourt *Concert*
(12/92) (TELD) ① **9031-74786-2**
BPO, H. von Karajan *Concert*
(1/93) (DG) ① **437 255-2GGA**
VPO, R. Muti (pp1993) *Concert*
(3/93) (PHIL) ① **438 493-2PH**
M. Ivogün, orch (r1932) *Concert*
(1/94) (CLUB) ① **CL99-020**
Berlin St Op Orch, E. Kleiber (r1923) *Concert*
(5/94) (ARCI) ① **ARC102**
Košice St PO, J. Wildner (r1990) *Concert*
(6/94) (MARC) ① **8 223233**
VPO, L. Maazel (pp1994) *Concert*
(7/94) (SONY) ① **SK46694**
Columbia SO, B. Walter (r1956) *Concert*
(8/95) (SONY) ① **SMK64467**
An der Wolga, 'By the Volga'—polka mazurka, Op. 425 (1886)
Košice St PO, J. Wildner (r1990) *Concert*
(6/94) (MARC) ① **8 223232**
An die Elbe, 'By the Elbe'—waltz, Op. 447 (1897)
Košice St PO, A. Walter (r1992) *Concert*
(9/95) (MARC) ① **8 223238**
Annen-Polka, Op. 117 (1852)
VPO, H. von Karajan (pp1987) *Concert*
(11/87) (DG) ① **419 616-2GH**
BPO, H. von Karajan *Concert*
(12/87) (EMI) ① **CDM7 69018-2**
LSO, J. Georgiadis *Concert*
(4/89) (CARL) ① **PCD902**
VPO, W. Boskovsky (r1971) *Concert*
(1/90) (DECC) ① **425 425-2DA**
Polish St PO, J. Wildner (r1989) *Concert*
(7/90) (MARC) ① **8 223209**
VPO, K. Böhm *Concert*
(12/91) (DG) ① [2] **413 432-2GW2**
VPO, C. Krauss (r1929) *Concert*
(2/92) (DG) ① [2] **435 335-2GWP2**
VPO, C. Krauss (r1929) *Concert*
(11/92) (PREI) ① **90112**
BPO, H. von Karajan *Concert*
(1/93) (DG) ① **437 255-2GGA**
Vienna Op Orch, C. Michalski *Concert*
(7/93) (ROSE) ① **3209**
Annina—polka mazur, Op. 415 (1884) (based on themes from 'Eine Nacht in Venedig')
Austrian RSO, P. Guth (r1991) *Concert*
(8/92) (MARC) ① **8 223227**
Äols-Töne—waltz, Op. 68 (1850)
Austrian RSO, P. Guth (r1991) *Concert*
(8/92) (MARC) ① **8 223227**
Architecten-Ball-Tänze, 'Architects' Ball Dances'—waltz, Op. 36 (1847)
Košice St PO, J. Wildner (r1991) *Concert*
(7/94) (MARC) ① **8 223235**
Armen-Ball-Polka, 'Poor people's ball', Op. 176 (1856)
Bratislava RSO, A. Eschwé (r1989) *Concert*
(10/92) (MARC) ① **8 223217**
Attaque, 'Attack!'—quadrille, Op. 76 (1850)
Košice St PO, A. Walter (r1991) *Concert*
(9/93) (MARC) ① **8 223230**
Auf der Jagd, 'At the Hunt'—polka schnell, Op. 373 (1875)
Cincinnati Pops, E. Kunzel *Concert*
(3/86) (TELA) ① **CD80098**
LSO, J. Georgiadis *Concert*
(4/89) (CARL) ① **PCD902**
VPO, W. Boskovsky (r1959) *Concert*
(1/90) (DECC) ① **425 425-2DA**
VJSO, W. Boskovsky *Concert*
(1/90) (EMI) ① [2] **CZS7 62751-2**
VPO, W. Boskovsky (r1959) *Concert*
(10/91) (DECC) ① **430 501-2DWO**
BPO, H. von Karajan *Concert*
(12/91) (DG) ① [2] **413 432-2GW2**
VPO, H. von Karajan *Concert*
(2/92) (DG) ① [2] **435 335-2GWP2**
BPO, H. von Karajan *Concert*
(1/93) (DG) ① **437 255-2GGA**
VPO, R. Muti (pp1993) *Concert*
(3/93) (PHIL) ① **438 493-2PH**
Košice St PO, J. Wildner (r1990) *Concert*
(6/94) (MARC) ① **8 223232**
Auf freiem Fusse—polka française, Op. 345 (1871) (based on themes from 'Indigo')
Vienna Op Ball Orch, U. Theimer *Concert*
(8/92) (DENO) ① **CO-77949**
Auf zum Tanze!, 'Let's dance'—polka schnell, Op. 436 (1888)
Košice St PO, A. Walter (r1989) *Concert*
(5/92) (MARC) ① **8 223220**

Auroraball, 'Aurora Ball'—polka, Op. 219 (1859)
Košice St PO, C. Pollack (r1992) *Concert*
(12/95) (MARC) ① **8 223242**
Aurora-Ball-Tänze, 'Aurora Ball Dances'—waltz, Op. 87 (1851)
Košice St PO, A. Walter (r1989) *Concert*
(5/92) (MARC) ① **8 223220**
Aurora-Polka, Op. 165 (1855)
Košice St PO, A. Walter (r1989) *Concert*
(9/90) (MARC) ① **8 223212**
Aus dem Bergen, 'From the mountains'—waltz, Op. 292 (1864)
Košice St PO, A. Walter (r1989) *Concert*
(9/90) (MARC) ① **8 223211**
Aus der Heimath—polka mazur, Op. 347 (1871) (based on themes from 'Indigo')
Košice St PO, J. Wildner (r1990) *Concert*
(8/92) (MARC) ① **8 223222**
Vienna Op Ball Orch, U. Theimer *Concert*
(8/92) (DENO) ① **CO-77949**
Austria-Marsch, Op. 20 (1845)
Košice St PO, R. Edlinger (r1988) *Concert*
(4/90) (MARC) ① **8 223204**
Bachus-Polka, Op. 38 (1847)
Polish St PO, O. Dohnányi (r1989) *Concert*
(7/90) (MARC) ① **8 223207**
Une Bagatelle—polka mazur, Op. 187 (1857)
Košice St PO, A. Walter (r1990) *Concert*
(9/93) (MARC) ① **8 223229**
Die Bajadere—polka schnell, Op. 351 (1871) (based on themes from 'Indigo')
Vienna Op Ball Orch, U. Theimer *Concert*
(8/92) (DENO) ① **CO-77949**
Košice St PO, A. Walter (r1990) *Concert*
(9/93) (MARC) ① **8 223229**
Bal champêtre, 'Country Ball'—quadrille sur des airs français, Op. 303 (1865)
Košice St PO, A. Walter (r1989) *Concert*
(2/91) (MARC) ① **8 223214**
Ballg'schichten, 'Tales of the Ball'—waltz, Op. 150 (1854)
Polish St PO, O. Dohnányi (r1989) *Concert*
(7/90) (MARC) ① **8 223207**
Ballsträusschen, 'Ball bouquets'—polka schnell, Op. 380 (1878)
Košice St PO, A. Walter (r1989) *Concert*
(4/90) (MARC) ① **8 223206**
Banditen-Galop, 'Bandits' Galop', Op. 378 (1875) (based on themes from 'Prinz Methusalem')
Cincinnati Pops, E. Kunzel *Concert*
(3/86) (TELA) ① **CD80098**
VPO, C. Abbado (pp1988) *Concert*
(7/88) (DG) ① **423 662-2GH**
VPO, W. Boskovsky (r1958) *Concert*
(1/90) (DECC) ① **425 428-2DA**
Polish St PO, O. Dohnányi (r1989) *Concert*
(7/90) (MARC) ① **8 223208**
Bauern-Polka, 'Peasants' Polka'—polka française, Op. 276 (1863)
Polish St PO, J. Wildner (r1989) *Concert*
(9/90) (MARC) ① **8 223210**
VPO, C. Kleiber (pp1989) *Concert*
(2/91) (SONY) ① **SK45938**
Le beau monde, 'Fashionable society'—quadrille, Op. 199 (1857)
Košice St PO, A. Walter (r1990) *Concert*
(10/92) (MARC) ① **8 223223**
Bei uns z'Haus, 'With us, at home'—waltz, Op. 361 (1873) (based on themes from 'Der Carneval in Rom')
Košice St PO, A. Walter (r1988) *Concert*
(1/90) (MARC) ① **8 223201**
La berceuse, 'Lullaby'—quadrille, Op. 194 (1857)
Košice St PO, A. Walter (r1989) *Concert*
(10/92) (MARC) ① **8 223216**
Berglieder, 'Mountain songs'—waltz, Op. 18 (1845)
Košice St PO, A. Walter (r1988) *Concert*
(1/90) (MARC) ① **8 223203**
Bijouterie-Quadrille, 'Trinkets Quadrille', Op. 169 (1855)
Bratislava RSO, J. Wildner (r1989) *Concert*
(2/91) (MARC) ① **8 223215**
Bijoux-Polka, 'Jewels Polka', Op. 242 (1860)
Bratislava RSO, J. Wildner (r1989) *Concert*
(2/91) (MARC) ① **8 223215**
Bitte schön!, 'If you please!'—polka française, Op. 372 (based on themes from 'Cagliostro')
VPO, W. Boskovsky (r1971) *Concert*
(1/90) (DECC) ① **425 429-2DA**

Košice St PO, A. Walter (r1989) *Concert*
(7/94) (MARC) ① **8 223236**
Der **Blitz**, 'Lightning flash'—quadrille, Op.
59 (1848) (based on themes from Halévy's
'L'éclair')
Košice St PO, J. Wildner (r1991: orch Babinski)
Concert (7/94) (MARC) ① **8 223235**
Bluette—polka française, Op. 271 (1862)
Košice St PO, O. Dohnányi (r1989) *Concert*
(4/90) (MARC) ① **8 223206**
Blumenfest, 'Flower festival'—polka, Op.
111 (1852)
Polish St PO, J. Wildner (r1989) *Concert*
(9/90) (MARC) ① **8 223210**
Bonvivant, 'Epicure'—quadrille, Op. 86
(1850)
Košice St PO, A. Walter (r1991) *Concert*
(6/94) (MARC) ① **8 223231**
Bouquet—quadrille, Op. 135 (1853)
Košice St PO, J. Wildner (r1990) *Concert*
(6/94) (MARC) ① **8 223233**
Bratschau, 'Looking for a bride'—polka, Op.
417 (based on themes from 'Der
Zigeunerbaron')
Vienna Op Ball Orch, U. Theimer *Concert*
(8/92) (DENO) ① **CO-77949**
Košice St PO, A. Walter (r1989) *Concert*
(10/92) (MARC) ① **8 223216**
Brünner-Nationalgarde, 'Brno National
Guard'—march, Op. 58 (1848)
Košice St PO, A. Walter (r1990) *Concert*
(9/93) (MARC) ① **8 223229**
Bürger-Ball-Polka, 'Citizens' Ball Polka', Op.
145 (1854)
Košice St PO, R. Edlinger (r1988) *Concert*
(4/90) (MARC) ① **8 223204**
Bürgersinn, 'Public spirit'—waltz, Op. 295
(1865)
Bratislava RSO, A. Eschwé (r1989) *Concert*
(10/92) (MARC) ① **8 223217**
Bürgerweisen, 'Civic airs'—waltz, Op. 306
(1866)
Košice St PO, A. Walter (r1989) *Concert*
(10/92) (MARC) ① **8 223216**
Burschen-lieder—waltz, Op. 55 (1848)
Bratislava RSO, M. Dittrich (r1993) *Concert*
(12/95) (MARC) ① **8 223241**
Burschenwanderung, 'Students
travel'—polka française, Op. 389 (1880)
Košice St PO, A. Walter (r1989) *Concert*
(5/92) (MARC) ① **8 223219**
Cagliostro—waltz, Op. 370 (1875) (based on
themes from 'Cagliostro in Wien')
Polish St PO, O. Dohnányi (r1989) *Concert*
(7/90) (MARC) ① **8 223208**
Cagliostro-Quadrille, Op. 369 (1875) (based
on themes from 'Cagliostro in Wien')
Košice St PO, A. Walter (r1989) *Concert*
(5/92) (MARC) ① **8 223218**
Camelien-Polka, 'Camelias Polka'—polka
schnell, Op. 248 (1861)
Košice St PO, O. Dohnányi (r1989) *Concert*
(4/90) (MARC) ① **8 223206**
Carnevalsbilder, 'Carnival pictures'—waltz,
Op. 357 (1873) (based on themes from 'Der
Carneval in Rom')
Polish St PO, J. Wildner (r1989) *Concert*
(7/90) (MARC) ① **8 223209**
Carnevals-Botschafter, 'Carnival's
ambassador'—waltz, Op. 270 (1862)
VPO, W. Boskovsky (r1967) *Concert*
(1/90) (DECC) ① **425 425-2DA**
Polish St PO, O. Dohnányi (r1989) *Concert*
(7/90) (MARC) ① **8 223208**
Carnevals-Spektakel, 'Carnival's
spectacle'—quadrille, Op. 152 (1854)
Košice St PO, J. Wildner (r1989) *Concert*
(8/92) (MARC) ① **8 223222**
Caroussel-Marsch, Op. 133 (1853)
Košice St PO, O. Dohnányi (r1989) *Concert*
(4/90) (MARC) ① **8 223206**
VPO, L. Maazel (pp1994) *Concert*
(7/94) (SONY) ① **SK46694**
Champagner-Polka, 'Champagne
Polka'—Musikalischer Scherz, Op. 211
(1858)
Cincinnati Pops, E. Kunzel *Concert*
(3/86) (TELA) ① **CD80098**
LSO, J. Georgiadis *Concert*
(9/87) (CARL) ① **PCD856**
VPO, W. Boskovsky (r1957) *Concert*
(1/90) (DECC) ① **425 428-2DA**
VJSO, W. Boskovsky *Concert*
(1/90) (EMI) ① [2] **CZS7 62751-2**
Košice St PO, A. Walter (r1989) *Concert*
(2/91) (MARC) ① **8 223214**

Hallé, B. Tovey *Concert*
(2/91) (CFP) ① **CD-CFP4577**
Chansonetten, 'Comic songs'—quadrille
nach Themes franösischer, Op. 259 (1861)
Košice St PO, O. Dohnányi (r1989) *Concert*
(4/90) (MARC) ① **8 223206**
Colonnen—waltz, Op. 262 (1862)
Polish St PO, O. Dohnányi (r1989) *Concert*
(7/90) (MARC) ① **8 223207**
Concordia—polka mazur, Op. 206 (pub
1858)
Košice St PO, J. Wildner (r1991) *Concert*
(9/93) (MARC) ① **8 223228**
Cycloiden, 'Cycloids'—waltz, Op. 207
(1858)
Košice St PO, J. Wildner (r1990) *Concert*
(5/92) (MARC) ① **8 223221**
Cytheren-Quadrille, Op. 6 (1844)
Košice St PO, A. Walter (r1988) *Concert*
(1/90) (MARC) ① **8 223202**
Czech-Polka, Op. 13 (1846)
Košice St PO, A. Walter (r1988) *Concert*
(1/90) (MARC) ① **8 223202**
Damenspende, '(A) Present for the
Ladies'—polka, Op. 305 (1866)
Košice St PO, A. Walter (r1992) *Concert*
(9/95) (MARC) ① **8 223238**
Dämonen-Quadrille, '(The) Demons'
Quadrille', Op. 19 (1845)
Košice St PO, A. Walter (r1988) *Concert*
(1/90) (MARC) ① **8 223203**
Debut-Quadrille, Op. 2 (1844)
1. Pantalon; 2. Été; 3. Poule; 4. Trénis; 5.
Pastourelle; 6. Finale.
Košice St PO, A. Walter (r1988) *Concert*
(1/90) (MARC) ① **8 223201**
Demi-fortune, 'One-horse carriage'—polka
française, Op. 186 (1857)
Košice St PO, A. Walter (r1990) *Concert*
(5/93) (MARC) ① **8 223224**
Demolirer-Polka, 'Demolisher Polka'—polka
française, Op. 269 (1863)
VPO, W. Boskovsky (r1962) *Concert*
(1/90) (DECC) ① **425 426-2DA**
Košice St PO, A. Walter (r1989) *Concert*
(2/91) (MARC) ① **8 223213**
Deutsche, 'German waltz'—waltz, Op. 220
(1859)
Košice St PO, A. Walter (r1990) *Concert*
(9/93) (MARC) ① **8 223229**
Deutscher Kreiger-Marsch, 'German
soldiers' March', Op. 284 (1864)
Polish St PO, O. Dohnányi (r1989) *Concert*
(7/90) (MARC) ① **8 223207**
Deutschmeister Jubiläums Marsch, 'German
Masters' Jubilee March', Op. 470 (1896)
Košice St PO, A. Walter (r1989) *Concert*
(10/92) (MARC) ① **8 223223**
Diabolin-Polka, 'Devil of a fellow', Op. 244
(1860)
Polish St PO, J. Wildner (r1989) *Concert*
(9/90) (MARC) ① **8 223210**
**Dinorah-Quadrille nach Motiven der Oper
'Die Wallfahrt nach Ploërmel von G.
Meyerbeer', Op. 224 (1859)**
Košice St PO, A. Walter (r1989) *Concert*
(5/92) (MARC) ① **8 223220**
Diplomaten-Polka, 'Diplomats' Polka', Op.
448 (1893) (based on themes from 'Fürstin
Ninetta')
VPO, R. Muti (pp1993) *Concert*
(3/93) (PHIL) ① **438 493-2PH**
Košice St PO, A. Walter (r1989) *Concert*
(7/94) (MARC) ① **8 223236**
Dividenden, 'Dividends'—waltz, Op. 252
(1861)
Košice St PO, R. Edlinger (r1988) *Concert*
(4/90) (MARC) ① **8 223204**
Dolci pianti—romance: cello and orchestra
(1863)
J. Sikora, Bratislava RSO, M. Dittrich (r1991) *Concert*
(5/93) (MARC) ① **8 223234**
Donauweibchen, 'Danube maidens'—waltz,
Op. 427 (1887) (based on themes from
'Simplicus')
VPO, Z. Mehta (pp1990) *Concert*
(4/90) (SONY) ① **SK45808**
Košice St PO, A. Walter (r1989) *Concert*
(8/92) (MARC) ① **8 223211**
Dorfgeschichten, 'Villages tales'—waltz in
Ländler-style, Op. 47 (1847)
Košice St PO, A. Walter (r1989) *Concert*
(5/92) (MARC) ① **8 223219**
Drollerie-Polka, Op. 231 (1860)
Austrian RSO, P. Guth (r1991) *Concert*
(8/92) (MARC) ① **8 223227**

Du und Du—waltz, Op. 367 (1874) (based on
themes from 'Die Fledermaus')
VPO, W. Boskovsky (r1962) *Concert*
(1/90) (DECC) ① **425 426-2DA**
Košice St PO, A. Walter (r1989) *Concert*
(2/91) (MARC) ① **8 223214**
LPO, Carl Davis *Concert*
(12/91) (VIRG) ① **VJ7 59654-2**
VPO, E. Kleiber (r1929) *Concert*
(2/92) (DG) ① [2] **435 335-2GWP2**
Vienna Op Ball Orch, U. Theimer *Concert*
(8/92) (DENO) ① **CO-77949**
VPO, E. Kleiber (r1929) *Concert*
(5/94) (ARCI) ① **ARC102**
Durch's Telephon, 'By telephone'—polka,
Op. 439 (1890)
Austrian RSO, P. Guth (r1991) *Concert*
(8/92) (MARC) ① **8 223227**
D'Woaldbuama (Die Waldbuben), '(The)
Forest lads'—waltz in Ländler style, Op. 66
(1849)
Košice St PO, A. Walter (r1991: orch Babinski)
Concert (7/94) (MARC) ① **8 223236**
Egyptischer Marsch, 'Egyptian March', Op.
335 (1870)
LJSO, J. Rothstein *Concert*
(7/83) (CHAN) ① **CHAN8301**
VPO, W. Boskovsky (r1959) *Concert*
(1/90) (DECC) ① **425 425-2DA**
Košice St PO, A. Walter (r1989) *Concert*
(2/91) (MARC) ① **8 223213**
VPO, W. Boskovsky (r1959) *Concert*
(10/91) (DECC) ① **430 501-2DWO**
BPO, H. von Karajan *Concert*
(12/91) (DG) ① [2] **413 432-2GW2**
Concertgebouw, N. Harnoncourt *Concert*
(12/92) (TELD) ① **9031-74786-2**
VPO, R. Muti (pp1993) *Concert*
(3/93) (PHIL) ① **438 493-2PH**
Cincinnati Pops Chorale, Cincinnati Pops, E. Kunzel
(r1991-2) *Concert* (7/93) (TELA) ① **CD80314**
Einheitsklänge, 'Sounds of unity'—waltz,
Op. 62 (1849)
Košice St PO, J. Wildner (r1991: arr A. Kulling)
Concert (9/93) (MARC) ① **8 223228**
Elektro-magnetische, 'Electro-
magnetic'—polka, Op. 110 (pub 1852)
Košice St PO, A. Walter (r1989) *Concert*
(5/92) (MARC) ① **8 223219**
Elektrophor, 'Electrophorus'—polka schnell,
Op. 297 (1865)
Austrian RSO, P. Guth (r1991) *Concert*
(5/93) (MARC) ① **8 223226**
Elfen-Quadrille, 'Elves Quadrille', Op. 16
(1845)
Košice St PO, A. Walter (r1991) *Concert*
(7/94) (MARC) ① **8 223236**
Elisen, 'Elise'—polka française, Op. 151
(1854)
Košice St PO, O. Dohnányi (r1989) *Concert*
(4/90) (MARC) ① **8 223205**
Eljen a Magyar!, 'Hail to Hungary'—polka,
Op. 332 (1869)
VPO, W. Boskovsky (r1958) *Concert*
(1/90) (DECC) ① **425 428-2DA**
VJSO, W. Boskovsky *Concert*
(1/90) (EMI) ① [2] **CZS7 62751-2**
VPO, C. Kleiber (pp1989) *Concert*
(2/91) (SONY) ① **SK45938**
Berlin RSO, F. Fricsay *Concert*
(12/91) (DG) ① [2] **413 432-2GW2**
Košice St PO, A. Walter (r1989) *Concert*
(10/92) (MARC) ① **8 223216**
Ella-Polka, Op. 160 (1855)
Košice St PO, A. Walter (r1989) *Concert*
(9/90) (MARC) ① **8 223212**
Die Emancipitre, '(The)
Emancipator'—polka mazur, Op. 282 (1864)
VPO, Z. Mehta (pp1990) *Concert*
(4/90) (SONY) ① **SK45808**
L' Enfantillage, 'Child's-play'—polka
française, Op. 202 (1858)
Austrian RSO, P. Guth (r1991) *Concert*
(5/93) (MARC) ① **8 223226**
VPO, L. Maazel (pp1994) *Concert*
(7/94) (SONY) ① **SK46694**
Entweder—oder!, 'Either-or!'—polka
schnell, Op. 403 (1882)
Košice St PO, A. Walter (r1989) *Concert*
(5/92) (MARC) ① **8 223218**
Episode—polka française, Op. 296 (1865)
Košice St PO, A. Walter (r1989) *Concert*
(5/92) (MARC) ① **8 223219**

Erherzog Wilhelm Genesungs—march, Op.
149 (1854) (Eng: Archduke Wilhelm's
Recovery)
Polish St PO, O. Dohnányi (r1989) *Concert*
(7/90) (MARC) ① 8 223208
Erhöhte Pulse, 'Raised pulses'—waltz, Op.
175 (1856)
Košice St PO, A. Walter (r1989) *Concert*
(5/92) (MARC) ① 8 223220
Erinnerung an Covent Garden, 'Greetings to
Covent Garden'—waltz, Op. 329 (1867)
LSO, J. Georgiadis *Concert*
(11/89) (CHAN) ① CHAN8739
Košice St PO, A. Walter (r1991) *Concert*
(9/93) (MARC) ① 8 223230
Ernte-Tänze, 'Harvest dances'—waltz, Op.
45 (1847)
Košice St PO, A. Walter (r1989) *Concert*
(2/91) (MARC) ① 8 223214
Die Ersten Curen, 'First course of
cures'—waltz, Op. 261 (1862)
Košice St PO, A. Walter (r1991) *Concert*
(6/94) (MARC) ① 8 223231
Es war so wunderschön, 'It was so
wonderful'—march, Op. 467 (1896) (based on
themes from 'Waldmeister')
Austrian RSO, P. Guth (r1991) *Concert*
(5/93) (MARC) ① 8 223226
Etwas Kleines, 'Something small'—polka
française, Op. 190 (1857)
Košice St PO, J. Wildner (r1990) *Concert*
(6/94) (MARC) ① 8 223233
Expolsionen, 'Explosions'—polka, Op. 43
(1847)
Cincinnati Pops, E. Kunzel *Concert*
(3/86) (TELA) ① CD80098
LSO, J. Georgiadis *Concert*
(4/89) (CARL) ① PCD902
VPO, W. Boskovsky (r1972) *Concert*
(1/90) (DECC) ① 425 427-2DA
VPO, Z. Mehta (pp1990) *Concert*
(4/90) (SONY) ① SK45808
Hallé, B. Tovey *Concert*
(2/91) (CFP) ① CD-CFP4577
Express—polka schnell, Op. 311 (1866)
Austrian RSO, P. Guth (r1991) *Concert*
(8/92) (MARC) ⑪ 8 223227
Die Extravaganten, '(The)
Extravagant'—waltz, Op. 205 (1858)
Košice St PO, A. Walter (r1991) *Concert*
(7/94) (MARC) ① 8 223236
Fantasiebilder, 'Fantasy pictures'—waltz,
Op. 64 (1849)
Košice St PO, J. Wildner (r1990: orch Kulling)
Concert
(6/94) (MARC) ① 8 223232
Fantasieblümchen, 'Fantasy
flowers'—polka-mazuraka, Op. 241 (1860)
Košice St PO, A. Walter (r1988) *Concert*
(1/90) (MARC) ① 8 223202
Faschings-lieder, 'Carnival songs'—waltz,
Op. 11 (1846)
Košice St PO, A. Walter (r1992: orch Kulling) *Concert*
(9/95) (MARC) ① 8 223238
Fata Morgana—polka mazur, Op. 330 (1869)
Košice St PO, A. Walter (r1989) *Concert*
(5/92) (MARC) ① 8 223220
La Favorite, '(The) Favourite'—polka-
française, Op. 217 (1859)
Bratislava RSO, M. Dittrich (r1991) *Concert*
(7/94) (MARC) ① 8 223234
Feenmärchen, 'Fairy tales'—waltz, Op. 312
(1866)
Bratislava RSO, A. Eschwé (r1989) *Concert*
(10/92) (MARC) ① 8 223217
Festival—quadrille on English themes, Op.
341 (1867)
Polish St PO, J. Wildner (r1989) *Concert*
(7/90) (MARC) ① 8 223209
Fest-Marsch, 'Festival March', Op. 49
(1847)
Košice St PO, A. Walter (r1991: orch Babinski)
Concert
(9/93) (MARC) ① 8 223230
Fest-Polonaise, 'Festival Polonaise', Op. 352
(1871)
Bratislava RSO, A. Eschwé (r1989) *Concert*
(10/92) (MARC) ① 8 223217
Fest-Quadrille, 'Festival Quadrille', Op. 44
(1847)
Košice St PO, A. Walter (r1989) *Concert*
(9/90) (MARC) ① 8 223212
Feuilleton, 'Features section'—waltz, Op.
193 (1855)
Polish St PO, J. Wildner (r1989) *Concert*
(9/90) (MARC) ① 8 223210

Fidelen-Polka, 'Jolly Folk Polka', Op. 26
(1846)
Košice St PO, A. Walter (r1989) *Concert*
(2/91) (MARC) ① 8 223213
Figaro—polka française, Op. 320 (1868)
Košice St PO, J. Wildner (r1990) *Concert*
(5/92) (MARC) ① 8 223221
Die Fledermaus—polka, Op. 362 (1873)
Košice St PO, A. Walter (r1988) *Concert*
(1/90) (MARC) ① 8 223201
LPO, Carl Davis *Concert*
(12/91) (VIRG) ① VJ7 59654-2
Vienna Op Ball Orch, U. Theimer *Concert*
(8/92) (DENO) ① CO-77949
Die Fledermaus Csárdás—orchestra
(adapted from operetta)
LPO, Carl Davis *Concert*
(12/91) (VIRG) ① VJ7 59654-2
VPO, L. Maazel (pp1994) *Concert*
(7/94) (SONY) ① SK46694
Die Fledermaus Quadrille, Op. 363 (1874)
Košice St PO, A. Walter (r1989) *Concert*
(7/94) (MARC) ① 8 223236
Flugschriften, 'Pamphlets'—waltz, Op. 300
(1866)
Košice St PO, A. Walter (r1989) *Concert*
(5/92) (MARC) ① 8 223220
Freiheits-Lieder, 'Songs of Freedom'—waltz,
Op. 52 (1848)
Bratislava RSO, A. Eschwé (r1989) *Concert*
(10/92) (MARC) ① 8 223217
Freikugeln, 'Magic bullets'—polka schnell,
Op. 326 (1869)
VPO, C. Abbado (pp1991) *Concert*
(4/91) (DG) ① 431 628-2GH
Cincinnati Pops, E. Kunzel (r1991-2) *Concert*
(7/93) (TELA) ① CD80314
Košice St PO, J. Wildner (r1990) *Concert*
(6/94) (MARC) ① 8 223233
Freiwillige vor!, 'Volunteers to the
front!'—march (1887)
Košice St PO, A. Walter (r1991) *Concert*
(9/93) (MARC) ① 8 223228
Freudengruss, 'Cheerful greeting'—polka,
Op. 217 (1853)
Košice St PO, A. Walter (r1988) *Concert*
(1/90) (MARC) ① 8 223203
Freuden-Salven, 'Salvoes of Joy'—waltz,
Op. 171 (1855)
Košice St PO, A. Walter (r1991) *Concert*
(10/92) (MARC) ① 8 223216
Freut euch des Lebens, 'Enjoy your
life'—waltz, Op. 340 (1870)
VPO, C. Abbado (pp1988) *Concert*
(7/88) (DG) ① 423 662-2GH
VPO, W. Boskovsky (r1971) *Concert*
(1/90) (DECC) ① 425 426-2DA
Košice St PO, A. Walter (r1988) *Concert*
(1/90) (MARC) ① 8 223201
Frisch heran!, 'Come on in!'—polka schnell,
Op. 386 (1880)
Košice St PO, A. Walter (r1989) *Concert*
(9/90) (MARC) ① 8 223211
Frisch in's Feld!, 'Into battle!'—march, Op.
398 (1882) (based on themes from 'Die lustige
Krieg')
Košice St PO, J. Wildner (r1991) *Concert*
(9/93) (MARC) ① 8 223228
Frohsinns-Spenden, 'Gifts of
cheerfulness'—waltz, Op. 73 (1850)
Košice St PO, A. Walter (r1989) *Concert*
(2/91) (MARC) ① 8 223214
Frühlingsstimmen, 'Voices of
Spring'—waltz, Op. 410 (1883) (orig male vv
and orch: wds Genée)
VJSO, W. Boskovsky *Concert*
(3/85) (EMI) ① CDC7 47052-2
K. Battle, VPO, H. von Karajan (pp1987) *Concert*
(11/87) (DG) ① 419 616-2GH
Hallé, B. Thomson *Concert*
(12/87) (CFP) ① CD-CFP9015
LSO, J. Georgiadis *Concert*
(4/89) (CARL) ① PCD902
NYPO, Z. Mehta (pp1988) *Concert*
(9/89) (SONY) ① MK44942
VPO, W. Boskovsky (r1959) *Concert*
(1/90) (DECC) ① 425 425-2DA
Crommelynck Duo (pf duet) *Concert*
(7/90) (CLAV) ① CD50-8915
VPO, C. Kleiber (pp1989) *Concert*
(2/91) (SONY) ① SK45938
VPO, W. Boskovsky (r1959) *Concert*
(10/91) (DECC) ① 430 501-2DWO
Vienna Boys' Ch, U.C. Harrer *Concert*
(12/91) (PHIL) ① 426 307-2PH

VPO, C. Krauss (r1950) *Concert*
(2/92) (DG) ① [2] 435 335-2GWP2
M. Ivogün, orch (r1924) *Concert*
(8/92) (NIMB) ① NI7832
Austrian RSO, P. Guth (r1991) *Concert*
(8/92) (MARC) ① 8 223227
Dilbèr, Estonia Op Orch, E. Klas *Concert*
(9/92) (ONDI) ① ODE768-2
L. Tetrazzini, P. Pitt (Ital: r1908) *Concert*
(9/92) (EMI) ① [3] CHS7 63802-2(1)
L. Tetrazzini, P. Pitt (Ital: r1908) *Concert*
(9/92) (PEAR) ① GEMMCD9221
Vienna Op Orch, C. Michalski *Concert*
(7/93) (ROSE) ① 3209
LPO, T. Beecham (r1939) *Concert*
(6/94) (DUTT) ① CDLX7003
Boston SO, S. Koussevitzky (r1928) *Concert*
(9/94) (BIDD) ① WHL019
R. A. Swenson, W. Jones (pp1994: vocal version)
Concert (1/95) (RCA) ① 09026 62547-2
First pt E. Schwarzkopf, VPO, J. Krips (r1946)
Concert (12/90) (EMI) ① CDM7 63654-2
Furioso—polka quasi galop, Op. 260 (pub
1862)
Polish St PO, O. Dohnányi (r1989) *Concert*
(7/90) (MARC) ① 8 223207
VPO, C. Abbado (pp1991) *Concert*
(4/91) (DG) ① 431 628-2GH
Fürst Bariatinsky-Marsch, 'Prince
Bariatinsky's March', Op. 212 (1858)
Košice St PO, A. Walter (r1989) *Concert*
(10/92) (MARC) ① 8 223216
Gambrinus-Tänze, 'Dances of
Gambrinus'—waltz, Op. 97 (1851)
Košice St PO, A. Walter (r1991) *Concert*
(6/94) (MARC) ① 8 223231
Gartenlaube, 'Garden Bower'—waltz, Op.
461 (1895)
Košice St PO, C. Pollack (r1992) *Concert*
(12/95) (MARC) ① 8 223242
Gavotte der Königin, '(The) Queen's
Gavotte', Op. 391 (1880)
Košice St PO, A. Walter (r1990) *Concert*
(5/93) (MARC) ① 8 223224
Gedanken auf den Alpen, 'Thoughts in the
Alps'—waltz, Op. 172 (1855)
Polish St PO, J. Wildner (r1989) *Concert*
(7/90) (MARC) ① 8 223209
Gedankenflug, 'Flight of fancy'—waltz, Op.
215 (1859)
Bratislava RSO, M. Dittrich (r1993) *Concert*
(12/95) (MARC) ① 8 223241
Geisselhiebe, 'Whiplashes'—polka, Op. 60
(1849)
Košice St PO, A. Walter (r1989) *Concert*
(2/91) (MARC) ① 8 223214
Cincinnati Pops Chorale, Cincinnati Pops, E. Kunzel
(r1991-2) *Concert* (7/93) (TELA) ① CD80314
Die Gemütlichen, '(The) Genial
ones'—waltz, Op. 70 (1849)
Košice St PO, A. Walter (r1989) *Concert*
(9/90) (MARC) ① 8 223212
Glossen, 'Marginal notes'—waltz, Op. 163
(1855)
Košice St PO, A. Walter (r1989) *Concert*
(9/90) (MARC) ① 8 223211
Glücklich ist, wer vergisst, 'Happy is he who
forgets'—polka mazurka, Op. 368 (1874)
Vienna Op Ball Orch, U. Theimer *Concert*
(8/92) (DENO) ① CO-77949
Košice St PO, A. Walter (r1990) *Concert*
(10/92) (MARC) ① 8 223223
Grillenbanner, 'Banisher of gloom'—waltz,
Op. 247 (1861)
Košice St PO, A. Walter (r1989) *Concert*
(2/91) (MARC) ① 8 223214
Grossfürstin Alexandra, 'Grand Duchess
Alexandra'—waltz, Op. 181 (1856)
Košice St PO, A. Walter (r1989) *Concert*
(5/92) (MARC) ① 8 223218
Gross-Wien, 'Great Vienna'—waltz, Op. 440
(1891)
Košice St PO, A. Walter (r1990) *Concert*
(10/92) (MARC) ① 8 223223
Gruss an Wien, 'Greetings to Vienna'—polka
française, Op. 225 (1860)
Austrian RSO, P. Guth (r1991) *Concert*
(8/92) (MARC) ① 8 223227
Grüss aus Österreich, 'Greeting from
Austria'—polka mazur, Op. 359 (1873)
Košice St PO, C. Pollack (r1992) *Concert*
(12/95) (MARC) ① 8 223242

Neu-Wien—waltz: vocal version, Op. 341 (1870) (Wds. J. Weyl)
Vienna Männergesang-Verein, Bratislava RSO, J. Wildner *Concert* (10/92) (MARC) ① **8 223250**

's gibt nur a Kaiserstadt, 's gibt nur ein Wien—polka: vocal version, Op. 291 (1874) (Wds. R. Genée)
Vienna Männergesang-Verein, Bratislava RSO, G. Track *Concert* (10/92) (MARC) ① **8 223250**

Sängerlust—polka française, Op. 328 (1868) (Wds. J. Weyl)
Vienna Männergesang-Verein, Bratislava RSO, J. Wildner *Concert* (10/92) (MARC) ① **8 223250**

Wein, Weib und Gesang—waltz: vocal version, Op. 333 (1869) (Wds. J. Weyl)
Vienna Männergesang-Verein, Bratislava RSO, J. Wildner *Concert* (10/92) (MARC) ① **8 223250**
F. Hempel, orch (r1917: Ital) *Concert*
(3/94) (NIMB) ① **NI7849**

SECTION V: STAGE WORKS

Aschenbrödel, 'Cinderella'—ballet: 3 acts (1901—Berlin) (adapted/arr J Bayer)
EXCERPTS: 1. Overture.
Piccolo March Košice St PO, C. Pollack (r1992) *Concert* (12/95) (MARC) ① **8 223242**
Prelude to Act III Bratislava RSO, M. Dittrich (r1993) *Concert* (12/95) (MARC) ① **8 223241**

Blindekuh—operetta: 3 acts (1878—Vienna) (Lib. R. Kneisel)
Overture VJSO, W. Boskovsky *Concert*
(1/90) (EMI) ① [2] **CZS7 62751-2**

Cagliostro in Wien—opera: 3 acts (1875—Vienna) (Lib. Zell and Genée)
Zigeunerkind, wie glänzt dein Haar L. Schöne, orch (r1925) *Concert* (12/92) (NIMB) ① **NI7833**

Casanova—musical comedy (1928—Berlin) (Lib. Schanzer and Welisch. Music compiled and arr.)
EXCERPTS: 1. Nuns' Chorus; 2. Laura's Song; 3. Spanish Romance; 4. Serenade.
1, 2. E. Schwarzkopf, chor, Philh, O. Ackermann *Concert* (1/86) (EMI) ① **CDC7 47284-2**
1, 2. L. Popp, Ambrosian Op. Chor, ASMF, N. Marriner *Concert* (6/88) (EMI) ① **CDC7 49700-2**
1, 2. M. Hill Smith, Ambrosian Sngrs, Chandos Concert Orch, S. Barry (Eng) *Concert* (7/88) (CHAN) ① **CHAN8561**
4. P. Morrison, Chandos Concert Orch, S. Barry (Eng) *Concert* (6/85) (CHAN) ① **CHAN8362**

Die Fledermaus, '(The) Bat'—operetta: 3 acts (1874—Vienna) (Lib. Haffner and Genée, after Meilhac and Halevy)
EXCERPTS: 1. Overture. ACT 1: 2. Täubchen, das entflattert ist; 3. Du darfst heut' nicht; 4. Nein, mit solchen Advokaten; 5. Komm' mit mir zum Souper; 6. So muss allein ich bleiben; 7. Trinke, Liebchen, trinke schnell; 8. Mein Herr, was dächten Sie; 9. Nein, nein, ich zweifle gar nicht mehr. ACT 2: 10a. Ein Souper heut uns winkt; 10b. Chacun à son goût!; 11a. Ach, meine Herr'n und Damen; 11b. Mein Herr Marquis; 12. Dieser Anstand, so manierlich; 13. Klänge der Heimat (Czardas); 14a. In Feuerstrom der Reben; 14b. Brüderlein und Schwesterlein; 15. Ballet; 16. Genug damit, genug!; ACT 3: 17. Spiel' ich die Unschuld; 18. Ich stehe voll Zagen; 19. O Fledermaus.
Cpte L. Popp, E. Lind, P. Seiffert, P. Domingo, W. Brendel, A. Baltsa, K. Rydl, H. Zednik, U. Steinsky, H. Lohner, Bavarian Rad Chor, Munich RO, P. Domingo (with dialogue) (5/87) (EMI) ① [2] **CDS7 47480-8**
Cpte H. Gueden, E. Köth, W. Kmentt, G. Zampieri, W. Berry, R. Resnik, E. Waechter, P. Klein, H. Schubert, E. Kunz, R. Tebaldi, F. Corena, B. Nilsson, M. del Monaco, T. Berganza, J. Sutherland, J. Björling, L. Price, G. Simionato, E. Bastianini, L. Welitsch, Vienna St Op Chor, VPO, H. von Karajan (with dialogue & Act 2 Gala) (12/87) (DECC) ① [2] **421 046-2DH2**
Cpte E. Schwarzkopf, R. Streich, N. Gedda, H. Krebs, E. Kunz, R. Christ, K. Dönch, E. Majkut, L. Martini, F. Böheim, Chor, Philh, H. von Karajan (r1955: with dialogue) (11/88) (EMI) ① [2] **CHS7 69531-2**
Cpte A. Rothenberger, R. Holm, N. Gedda, A. Dallapozza, D. Fischer-Dieskau, B. Fassbaender, W. Berry, J. Förster, S. Wengraf, O. Schenk, Vienna Volksoper Chor, Vienna SO, W. Boskovsky (with dialogue) (6/89) (EMI) ① [2] **CMS7 69354-2**
Cpte K. Te Kanawa, E. Gruberová, W. Brendel, R. Leech, O. Bär, B. Fassbaender, T. Krause, A. Wendler, K. Göttling, O. Schenk, Vienna St Op Chor, VPO, A. Previn (r1990: with dialogue) *Unter Donner und Blitz.* (9/91) (PHIL) ① [2] **432 157-2PH2**

Cpte G. Fontana, B. Karwautz, J. Dickie, J. Hopferwieser, A. Martin, R. Yachmi-Caucig, A. Werner, E. Wessner, H. Krämmer, A. Calix, A.E. Hollander, Bratislava City Chor, Bratislava RSO, J. Wildner (r1991) (11/94) (NAXO) ① [2] **8 660017/8**
1. VPO, H. von Karajan (pp1987) *Concert* (11/87) (DG) ① **419 616-2GH**
1. BPO, H. von Karajan *Concert* (12/87) (EMI) ① **CDM7 69018-2**
1. VPO, C. Abbado (pp1988) *Concert* (7/88) (DG) ① **423 662-2GH**
1. LSO, J. Georgiadis *Concert* (4/89) (CARL) ① **PCD902**
1. VPO, C. Kleiber (pp1989) *Concert* (2/91) (SONY) ① **SK45938**
1. Hallé, B. Tovey *Concert* (2/91) (CFP) ① **CD-CFP4577**
1. Black Dyke Mills Band, G. Brand (arr Winter) *Concert* (10/91) (CHAN) ① **CHAN6539**
1(pt) SO, T. Beecham (r1910) *Concert* (11/91) (SYMP) ① [2] **SYMCD1096/7**
1. Berlin RSO, F. Fricsay *Concert* (12/91) (DG) ① [2] **413 432-2GW2**
1. LPO, F. Welser-Möst *Concert* (12/91) (EMI) ① **CDC7 54089-2**
1. LPO, Carl Davis *Concert* (12/91) (VIRG) ① **VJ7 59654-2**
1. VPO, L. Maazel *Concert* (2/92) (DG) ① [2] **435 335-2GWP2**
1. BPO, W. Furtwängler (r1937) *Concert* (4/92) (KOCH) ① [2] **37073-2**
1. Philh, O. Klemperer *Concert* (9/92) (EMI) ① **CDM7 64144-2**
1. Vienna Ens (arr M Bjelik) *Concert* (9/92) (SONY) ① **SK47187**
1. VPO, C. Krauss (r1929) *Concert* (11/92) (PREI) ① **90112**
1. Concertgebouw, N. Harnoncourt *Concert* (9/93) (TELD) ① **9031-74786-2**
1. NYPO, L. Bernstein (r1970) *Concert* (9/93) (SONY) ① **SMK47601**
1. Columbia SO, B. Walter (r1956) *Concert* (8/95) (SONY) ① **SMK64467**
1-4, 6, 7, 10a, 10b, 11a, 11b, 12, 13, 14a, 16, 17, 19. W. Hollweg, E. Gruberová, C. Boesch, M. Lipovšek, J. Protschka, A. Scharinger, W. Kmentt, B. Bonney, E. von Magnus, Netherlands Op Chor, Concertgebouw, N. Harnoncourt (1987) (7/93) (TELD) ① **4509-91974-2**
5. J. Hadley, T. Hampson, WNO Orch, C. Rizzi (1992) (7/93) (TELD) ① **9031-73283-2**
5. H. Nash, D. Noble, orch, C. Raybould (r1930: Eng) *Concert* (2/95) (DUTT) ① **CDLX7012**
5. H. Nash, D. Noble, orch, C. Raybould (r1930: Eng) *Concert* (11/95) (PEAR) ① **GEMMCD9175**
8. Lotte Lehmann, orch, F. Weissmann (r1931) *Concert* (7/92) (PEAR) ① [3] **GEMMCDS9926(2)**
11b K. Battle, M. Garrett (pp1991) *Concert* (7/92) (DG) ① **435 440-2GH**
11b E. Schumann, orch, K. Alwin (r1927) *Concert* (7/92) (PEAR) ① [3] **GEMMCDS9926(2)**
11b T. Dahl, Calgary PO, M. Bernardi (r1992) *Concert* (12/94) (CBC) ① **SMCD5125**
11b, 13. J. Migenes, Vienna Volksoper Orch, L. Schifrin (1993) *Concert* (1/94) (ERAT) ① **4509-92875-2**
11b, 17. E. Berger, Berlin St Op Orch, W. Schütze (r1934) *Concert* (12/91) (PREI) ① **89035**
12. R. Tauber, V. Schwarz, orch (r1928) *Concert* (7/89) (PEAR) ① **GEMMCD9327**
12. R. Tauber, V. Schwarz, orch (r1928) *Concert* (7/89) (EMI) ① **CDH7 69476-2**
12. R. Tauber, V. Schwarz, Berlin Staatskapelle, F. Weissmann (r1928) *Concert* (12/89) (EMI) ① **CDH7 69787-2**
13. C. Studer, ROHO, J. Barker (pp1988) *Concert* (9/89) (EMI) ① **CDC7 49811-2**
13. E. Schwarzkopf, Philh, H. von Karajan (1955) *Concert* (12/90) (EMI) ① **CDM7 63657-2**
13. M. Ivogün, Berlin St Op Orch, L. Blech (r1932) *Concert* (8/92) (NIMB) ① **NI7832**
13. M. Reining, Berlin Deutsche Op Orch, W. Lutze (r1939) *Concert* (9/92) (PREI) ① **90083**
13. L. Price, New Philh, N. Santi (r1977) *Concert* (12/92) (RCA) ① [4] **09026 61236-2**
13. B. Hendricks, Philh, L. Foster (r1992) *Concert* (8/93) (EMI) ① **CDC7 54626-2**
13. M. Ivogün, orch (r1932) *Concert* (1/94) (CLUB) ① **CL99-020**
13. E. Rethberg, Victor SO, R. Bourdon (r1931) *Concert* (10/95) (ROMO) ① [2] **81014-2**
16. R. Tauber, Lotte Lehmann, K. Branzell, G. Merrem-Nikisch, W. Staegemann, Chor, Berlin Staatskapelle, W. Weissmann (r1928) *Concert* (12/89) (EMI) ① **CDH7 69787-2**

17. L. Schöne, orch (r1924) *Concert* (12/92) (NIMB) ① **NI7833**
19. Grimethorpe Colliery Band, E. Howarth (arr Winter) *Concert* (12/92) (DOYE) ① **DOYCD013**

Indigo und die vierzig Räuber, 'Indigo and the 40 Thieves'—operetta: 3 acts (1871—Vienna) (Lib. M Steiner)
EXCERPTS: 1. Overture. ACT 1: 2. Intermezzo; 3. Sternelied; 4. Lasst frei nun erschallen; 5. Launisches Glück (interpolated song by J Bürger, after Strauss); 6. Musik der Nacht; 7. Bacchanale.
1. VPO, R. Muti (pp1993) *Concert* (3/93) (PHIL) ① **438 493-2PH**
5. J. Schmidt, Berlin Staatskapelle, F. Weissmann (r1932) *Concert* (4/90) (EMI) ① **CDM7 69478-2**
5. C. Kullman, orch, E. Hauke (r1932) *Concert* (11/93) (PREI) ① **89057**
7. L. Schöne, orch (r1925) *Concert* (12/92) (NIMB) ① **NI7833**

Der Lustige Krieg, '(The) Merry War'—operetta: 3 acts (1882—Hamburg) (Lib. Zell and Genée)
Nur für Natur J. Patzak, orch, M. Gurlitt (r1929) *Concert* (3/90) (PEAR) ① **GEMMCD9383**
Nur für Natur E. Kunz, VPO, O. Ackermann (r1951) *Concert* (9/95) (TEST) ① **SBT1059**
Was ist an einem Kuss gelegen? L. Schöne, orch (r1925) *Concert* (12/92) (NIMB) ① **NI7833**

Eine Nacht in Venedig, '(A) Night in Venice'—operetta: 3 acts (1883—Vienna) (Lib. Zell & Genée)
EXCERPTS (1923 version by Korngold): 1. Overture. ACT 1: 2. Wenn vom Lido sacht; 3. Ihr Venetianer hört .. Drum sei fröhlich, sei selig, Venetia; 4. 'S ist wahr, ich bin nicht ... Wenn du dich kränkst; 5. Seht, oh seht! ... Frutti di mare!; 6. Evviva, Caramello! ... Willkommen, liebe Freunde!; 7. Annina! Caramello! ... Pellegrina rondinella; 8. Alle maskiert, alle maskiert; 9. Sei mir gegrüsst, du holdes Venetia!; 10. Hier ward es still ... der Mond hat schere Klag' erhoben; 11. Hast du mir ein Kostüm gebracht; 12. Komm' in die Gondel, mein Liebchen; 13. Messere Delacqua!; 14. Schnell zur Serenade!; 15. Kaum dass mein Liebchen die schaukelnde entführt. ACT 2: 16. Wo bleibt nur Caramello? ... Venedigs Frauen herzuführen; 17a. Was mir der Zufall gab; 17b. Treu sein, das liegt mir nicht; 18. Hör' mich. Annina, komm in die Gondel; 19. Sie sagten meinem Liebesflen'n; 20. Solch' ein Wirtshaus lob' ich mir ... Marietta, come va?; 21. Ninana, Ninana, hier will ich singen; 22. Lasset die Andern tanzen da, tra la la!; 23. Jetzt ist Zeit ... Horch! von San Marco der Glocken Geläut. ACT 3: 24. Karneval ruft Euch zum Ball; 25. Die Tauben von San Marco; 26. Ach, wie herrlich zu schau'n; 27. Tacke, tacke, tacke ... Aber wenn man erst gekostet hat; 28. Wie sichs gebührt, hat es gespürt.
Cpte E. Schwarzkopf, N. Gedda, E. Loose, E. Kunz, K. Dönch, P. Klein, H. Ludwig, H. Ludwig, Chor, Philh, O. Ackermann (r1954) (11/88) (EMI) ① **CDH7 69530-2**
1. VJSO, W. Boskovsky *Concert* (1/90) (EMI) ① [2] **CZS7 62751-2**
1. Raphaele Concert Orch, P. Walden (arr Waldenmaier) *Concert* (5/91) (MOZA) ① **MECD1002**
12. P. Domingo, ECO, J. Rudel *Concert* (2/87) (EMI) ① **CDC7 47398-2**
12. J. Patzak, Berlin St Op Orch, H. Weigert (r1930) *Concert* (3/90) (PEAR) ① **GEMMCD9383**
12. H.E. Groh, orch, O. Dobrindt (r1931) *Concert* (3/92) (PEAR) ① **GEMMCD9419**
12. C. Kullman, orch, E. Hauke (r1932) *Concert* (11/93) (PREI) ① **89057**
12, 26. E. Kunz, Vienna Volksoper Orch, A. Paulik (r1949) *Concert* (9/95) (TEST) ① **SBT1059**
17b E. Kunz, VPO, O. Ackermann (r1951) *Concert* (9/95) (TEST) ① **SBT1059**

Die Tänzerin Fanny Elssler, '(The) Dancer Fanny Elssler'—operetta (1934—Berlin) (arr. O. Stalla)
Draussen in Sievering L. Popp, ASMF, N. Marriner *Concert* (6/88) (EMI) ① **CDC7 49700-2**

Ein Tausend und eine Nacht, '(A) Thousand and One Nights'—operetta (1906—Vienna) (rev E Reiterer from 'Indigo')
1. Intermezzo.
1. Vienna Op Ball Orch, U. Theimer *Concert* (8/92) (DENO) ① **CO-77949**

Waldmeister—operetta (1895—Berlin) (Lib. Davis)
EXCERPTS: 1. Overture.
1. VPO, C. Abbado (pp1991) *Concert* (4/91) (DG) ① **431 628-2GH**
1. VPO, W. Boskovsky (r1957) *Concert* (2/92) (DG) ① [2] **435 335-2GWP2**

Wiener Blut, 'Vienna Blood'—operetta: 3
acts (1899—Vienna) (Lib. Léon and Stein.
Music arr. and adpted Mül)
Das eine kann ich nicht verzeih'n...Wiener Blut B.
Hendricks, G. Quilico, Lyon Op Orch, L. Foster
(r1993) Concert   (6/95) (EMI) ① CDC5 55151-2
Excs B. Kusche, R. Schock, H. Gueden, F. Liewehr,
M. Schramm, E. Kunz, W. Lipp, F. Gruber, Vienna St
Op Chor, Vienna SO, R. Stolz
                         (4/88) (EURO) ① 258 370
Grüss dich Gott, du liebes Nesterl J. Migenes,
Vienna Volksoper Orch, L. Schifrin (r1993) Concert
                         (1/94) (ERAT) ① 4509-92875-2
Der Zigeunerbaron, '(The) Gipsy
Baron'—operetta: 3 acts (1885—Vienna) (Lib.
Schnitzer, after Jókai)
1a. Overture. ACT 1: 1b. Das wär' kein rechter
Schifferknecht; 2. Als flotter Geist; 3a. So träuschte
mich die Ahnung nicht!; 3b. Ja, das Schreiben und
das Lesen; 4. Just sind es vierundzwanzig Jahre; 5a.
Dem Freier naht die Braut; 5b. Ein Falter schwirrt
ums Licht; 6. So elend und so treu; 7a. Arsena!
Arsena; 7b. Ha, was hör' ich da für Klänge; 7c. Nun
zu des bösen Nachbarn Haus (finale). ACT 2: 8a.
Entr'acte; 8b. Mein Aug' bewachte; 9a. Ein Greis ist
mir im Traum erschienen; 9b. Ha, seht, es winkt; 10.
Auf, auf, vorbei ist die Nacht; 11. Wer uns getraut;
12. Her die Hand, es muss ja sein; 13. Nach Wien!
ACT 3: 14a. Entr'acte; 15. Ein Mädchen hat es gar
nicht gut; 16. Von des Tajos Strand; 17. Hurrah, die
Schlacht mitgebracht (Entrance March); 18. Heiraten,
Vivat!.
Cpte N. Gedda, E. Schwarzkopf, E. Kunz, E. Köth,
M. Sinclair, H. Prey, W. Ferenz, J. Schmidinger, G.
Burgsthaler-Schuster, E. Paulik, Chor, Philh, O.
Ackermann (r1954)
                    (11/88) (EMI) ① [2] CHS7 69526-2
Cpte P. Coburn, H. Lippert, W. Holzmair, R.
Schasching, C. Oelze, J. Hamari, E. von Magnus, J.
Flimm, R. Florianschütz, H-J. Lazar, A. Schoenberg
Ch, Vienna SO, N. Harnoncourt (pp1994)
                    (6/95) (TELD) ① [2] 4509-94555-2
Entrance March Berlin Phil Wind Qnt, H. von
Karajan (r1973: arr Villinger) Concert
                    (5/94) (DG) ① 439 346-2GX2
1. Columbia SO, B. Walter (r1956) Concert
                    (8/95) (SONY) ① SMK64467
1a BPO, H. von Karajan Concert
                    (12/87) (EMI) ① CDM7 69018-2
1a Hallé, B. Tovey Concert
                    (2/91) (CFP) ① CD-CFP4577
1a BPO, H. von Karajan Concert
                    (12/91) (DG) ① [2] 413 432-2GW2
1a LPO, F. Welser-Möst Concert
                    (12/91) (EMI) ① CDC7 54089-2
1a VPO, C. Kleiber (pp1992) Concert
                    (4/92) (SONY) ① SK48376
1a Concertgebouw, N. Harnoncourt Concert
                    (12/92) (TELD) ① 9031-74786-2
1a BPO, E. Kleiber (r1933) Concert
                    (5/94) (ARCI) ① ARC102
2. R. Tauber, Berlin Staatskapelle, E. Hauke (r1929)
Concert   (12/89) (EMI) ① CDH7 69787-2
2. J. Schmidt, Berlin Staatskapelle, F. Weissmann
(r1932) Concert   (4/90) (EMI) ① CDM7 69478-2
2. H.E. Groh, orch (r1938) Concert
                    (3/92) (PEAR) ① GEMMCD9419
2. R. Tauber, Vienna Th Orch, A. Paulik (r1924)
Concert   (10/92) (TEST) ① SBT1005
2, 11. C. Kullman, E. Berger, Berlin St Op Orch, C.
Schmalstich (r1932) Concert
                    (11/93) (PREI) ① 89057
3b E. Kunz, Vienna Volksoper Orch, A. Paulik
(r1949) Concert   (9/95) (TEST) ① SBT1059
6. M. Cebotari, VPO, H. von Karajan (r1948) Concert
                    (12/90) (PREI) ① 90034
6. E. Rethberg, orch (r1921) Concert
                    (7/94) (PREI) ① 89051
6. E. Rethberg, Berlin SO, F. Weissmann (r1930)
Concert   (10/95) (ROMO) ① [2] 81014-2
11. R. Tauber, G. Vantoni, Berlin Staatskapelle, E.
Hauke (r1928) Concert
                    (12/89) (EMI) ① CDH7 69787-2
11. J. Björling, H. Schymberg, orch, N. Grevillius
(1938: Swed) (8/92) (BLUE) ① ABCD016
11. J. Björling, H. Schymberg, orch, N. Grevillius
(1938: Swed) (10/93) (NIMB) ① NI7842
11. J. Björling, H. Schymberg, orch, N. Grevillius
(1938: Swed) (4/94) (CARL) ① GLRS103
11. B. Hendricks, G. Quilico, Lyon Op Orch, L. Foster
(r1993) Concert   (6/95) (EMI) ① CDC5 55151-2
17. VPO, Z. Mehta (pp1990) Concert
                    (4/90) (SONY) ① SK45808
17. Raphaele Concert Orch, P. Walden (arr
Waldenmaier) Concert
                    (5/91) (MOZA) ① MECD1002

17. Vienna Op Ball Orch, U. Theimer Concert
                    (8/92) (DENO) ① CO-77949
17. VPO, C. Krauss (r1929) Concert
                    (11/92) (PREI) ① 90112

STRAUSS, Johann (Maria Eduard) III (1866–1939) Austria

SECTION I: ORCHESTRAL

Krönungs, 'Coronation Waltz'—waltz, Op. 40
(1902)
LSO, J. Georgiadis Concert
                    (11/89) (CHAN) ① CHAN8739
Unter den Linden—waltz, Op. 30 (1900) (Eng:
Under the linden trees)
London Viennese Orch, J. Rothstein Concert
                    (5/93) (CHAN) ① CHAN9127

STRAUSS, Josef (1827–1870) Austria

SECTION I: ORCHESTRAL

Allerlei, 'All sorts'—polka schnell, Op. 219
(1867)
VJSO, W. Boskovsky Concert
                    (1/90) (EMI) ① [2] CZS7 62751-2
Angelica—polka française, Op. 123 (1862)
Budapest Strauss SO, A. Walter (r1993) Concert
                    (6/95) (MARC) ① 8 223561
Aquarellen, 'Water colours'—waltz, Op. 258
(1869)
VPO, W. Boskovsky (r1965) Concert
                    (1/90) (DECC) ① 425 426-2DA
VPO, C. Abbado (pp1991) Concert
                    (4/91) (DG) ① 431 628-2GH
Auf Ferienreisen, 'Off on holiday'—polka
schnell, Op. 133 (1863)
VPO, C. Abbado (pp1988) Concert
                    (7/88) (DG) ① 423 662-2GH
VPO, W. Boskovsky (r1970) Concert
                    (1/90) (DECC) ① 425 428-2DA
Aus der Ferne, 'From far away'—polka
mazur, Op. 270 (1869)
VPO, L. Maazel (pp1994) Concert
                    (7/94) (SONY) ① SK46694
Bauern, 'Peasants'—polka mazur, Op. 10
(1856)
Budapest Strauss SO, A. Walter (r1993) Concert
                    (6/95) (MARC) ① 8 223561
Brennende Liebe, 'Ardent love'—polka
mazur, Op. 129 (1863)
VPO, C. Abbado (pp1988) Concert
                    (7/88) (DG) ① 423 662-2GH
VPO, W. Boskovsky (r1962) Concert
                    (1/90) (DECC) ① 425 426-2DA
Delirien, 'Delirious'—waltz, Op. 212 (1867)
VPO, H. von Karajan (pp1987) Concert
                    (11/87) (DG) ① 419 616-2GH
VPO, W. Boskovsky (r1976) Concert
                    (1/90) (DECC) ① 425 429-2DA
VPO, L. Maazel (pp1982) Concert
                    (4/90) (DG) ① 427 820-2GDC
BPO, H. von Karajan Concert
                    (1/93) (DG) ① 437 255-2GGA
Dorfschwalben aus Österreich, 'Village
swallows from Austria'—waltz, Op. 164
(1865)
VPO, W. Boskovsky (r1976) Concert
                    (1/90) (DECC) ① 425 428-2DA
Chicago SO, F. Reiner Concert
                    (1/90) (RCA) ① GD60177
VPO, C. Krauss (r1952) Concert
                    (2/92) (DG) ① [2] 435 335-2GWP2
VPO, C. Kleiber (pp1989) Concert
                    (4/92) (SONY) ① SK48376
Vienna Op Orch, C. Michalski Concert
                    (7/93) (ROSE) ① 3209
Dynamiden (Geheime Anziehungskräft),
'Mysterious powers of magnetism'—waltz,
Op. 173 (1865)
VPO, W. Boskovsky (r1967) Concert
                    (1/90) (DECC) ① 425 425-2DA
Eingesendet, 'Letter to the Editor'—polka
schnell, Op. 240 (1868)
VPO, W. Boskovsky (r1962) Concert
                    (1/90) (DECC) ① 425 426-2DA
VPO, Z. Mehta (pp1990) Concert
                    (4/90) (SONY) ① SK45808
Eislauf, 'Skating'—polka schnell, Op. 261
(1869)
Budapest Strauss SO, A. Walter (r1993) Concert
                    (6/95) (MARC) ① 8 223561

Elfen, 'Elves'—polka, Op. 74 (1859)
M. Hill Smith, LJSO, J. Rothstein Concert
                    (1/86) (CHAN) ① CHAN8381
Die Emanzipierte—polka mazurka, Op. 282
(1871)
VPO, W. Boskovsky (r1970) Concert
                    (1/90) (DECC) ① 425 429-2DA
Etiquette—polka française, Op. 208 (1866)
Budapest Strauss SO, A. Walter (r1993) Concert
                    (6/95) (MARC) ① 8 223561
Fantasiebilder, 'Fantasy pictures'—waltz,
Op. 151 (1864)
Budapest Strauss SO, A. Walter (r1993) Concert
                    (6/95) (MARC) ① 8 223561
Feuerfest!, 'Fireproof!'—polka schnell, Op.
269 (1870)
Cincinnati Pops, E. Kunzel Concert
                    (3/86) (TELA) ① CD80098
LSO, J. Georgiadis Concert
                    (4/89) (CARL) ① PCD902
VPO, W. Boskovsky (r1976) Concert
                    (1/90) (DECC) ① 425 425-2DA
VPO, L. Maazel (pp1994) Concert
                    (7/94) (SONY) ① SK46694
Frauenherz, 'Woman's heart'—polka
mazurka, Op. 166 (1865)
VPO, W. Boskovsky (r1971) Concert
                    (1/90) (DECC) ① 425 426-2DA
Frohes Leben, 'Joyous life'—waltz, Op. 272
(1862)
LJSO, J. Rothstein Concert
                    (1/86) (CHAN) ① CHAN8381
Gablenz-Marsch, Op. 159 (1864)
Budapest Strauss SO, A. Walter (r1993) Concert
                    (6/95) (MARC) ① 8 223561
Gruss an München, 'Greetings to
Munich'—polka française, Op. 90 (1860)
Košice St PO, M. Eichenholz (r1992) Concert
                    (2/94) (MARC) ① 8 223470
Heiterer Muth—polka française, Op. 281 (pub
1871)
VPO, W. Boskovsky (r1976) Concert
                    (1/90) (DECC) ① 425 427-2DA
Im Fluge, 'In flight'—polka schnell, Op. 230
(1868)
VPO, C. Abbado (pp1988) Concert
                    (7/88) (DG) ① 423 662-2GH
Jokey—polka schnell, Op. 278 (1871)
VPO, W. Boskovsky (r1976) Concert
                    (1/90) (DECC) ① 425 425-2DA
VPO, C. Kleiber (pp1989) Concert
                    (2/91) (SONY) ① SK45938
Cincinnati Pops, E. Kunzel (r1991-2) Concert
                    (7/93) (TELA) ① CD80314
Kakadu, 'Cockatoo'—quadrille, Op. 276
(1876)
Budapest Strauss SO, A. Walter (r1993) Concert
                    (6/95) (MARC) ① 8 223561
Künstlergruss, 'Artist's greeting'—polka
française, Op. 274 (1871)
VJSO, W. Boskovsky Concert
                    (1/90) (EMI) ① [2] CZS7 62751-2
Die Libelle, '(The) Dragonfly'—polka mazur,
Op. 204 (1867)
VPO, W. Boskovsky (r1967) Concert
                    (1/90) (DECC) ① 425 427-2DA
VPO, C. Kleiber (pp1989) Concert
                    (2/91) (SONY) ① SK45938
Marien-Klänge, 'Waltz for Marie'—waltz, Op.
214 (1867)
Budapest Strauss SO, A. Walter (r1993) Concert
                    (6/95) (MARC) ① 8 223561
Mein Lebenslauf ist Lieb und Leben, '(The)
Course of my Life is Love and
Laughter'—waltz, Op. 263 (1869)
Chicago SO, F. Reiner Concert
                    (1/90) (RCA) ① GD60177
Moulinet, 'Little mill'—polka française, Op.
57 (1858)
VPO, W. Boskovsky (r1967) Concert
                    (1/90) (DECC) ① 425 427-2DA
VPO, C. Kleiber (pp1989) Concert
                    (2/91) (SONY) ① SK45938
Budapest Strauss SO, A. Walter (r1993) Concert
                    (6/95) (MARC) ① 8 223561
Nachtschatten, 'Nightshade'—polka mazur,
Op. 229 (1867)
M. Hill Smith, LJSO, J. Rothstein Concert
                    (1/86) (CHAN) ① CHAN8381
Ohne Sorgen!, 'Without a care!'—polka
schnell, Op.271 (1870)
VPO, H. von Karajan (pp1987) Concert
                    (11/87) (DG) ① 419 616-2GH
VPO, L. Maazel (pp1994) Concert
                    (7/94) (SONY) ① SK46694

Pauline—polka mazur, Op. 190b (1866)
(second version)
London Viennese Orch, J. Rothstein *Concert*
(5/93) (CHAN) ① **CHAN9127**
Perlen der Liebe, 'Pearls of Love'—waltz, Op. 39 (1857)
VJSO, W. Boskovsky *Concert*
(1/90) (EMI) ① [2] **CZS7 62751-2**
Plappermäulchen, 'Chatterboxes'—polka schnell, Op. 245 (pub 1868)
VJSO, W. Boskovsky *Concert*
(1/90) (EMI) ① [2] **CZS7 62751-2**
VPO, C. Kleiber (pp1989) *Concert*
(2/91) (SONY) ① **SK45938**
Cincinnati Pops, E. Kunzel (r1991-2) *Concert*
(7/93) (TELA) ① **CD80314**
Die Schwätzerin, '(The) Gossip'—polka mazur, Op. 144 (1863)
VPO, W. Boskovsky (r1970) *Concert*
(1/90) (DECC) ① **425 425-2DA**
Sphären-Klänge, 'Music of the Spheres'—waltz, Op. 235 (1868)
VPO, H. von Karajan (pp1987) *Concert*
(11/87) (DG) ① **419 616-2GH**
VPO, W. Boskovsky (r1973) *Concert*
(1/90) (DECC) ① **425 425-2DA**
VPO, H. von Karajan (r1949) *Concert*
(2/92) (DG) ① [2] **435 335-2GWP2**
VPO, C. Kleiber (pp1992) *Concert*
(4/92) (SONY) ① **SK48376**
VPO, C. Krauss (r1931) *Concert*
(11/92) (PREI) ① **90112**
Cincinnati Pops, E. Kunzel (r1991-2) *Concert*
(7/93) (TELA) ① **CD80314**
Sport—polka schnell, Op. 170 (1865)
VPO, Z. Mehta (pp1990) *Concert*
(4/90) (SONY) ① **SK45808**
Sympathie—polka mazur, Op. 73 (1860)
VPO, Z. Mehta (pp1990) *Concert*
(4/90) (SONY) ① **SK45808**
Tag und Nacht, 'Day and Night'—polka schnell, Op. 93 (1860)
Vienna Biedermeier Ens (trans H. Puffler) *Concert*
(3/89) (DENO) ① **CO-72587**
Die Tanzende Muse, '(The) Dancing Muse'—polka mazur, Op. 266 (1869)
VPO, C. Abbado (pp1991) *Concert*
(4/91) (DG) ① **431 628-2GH**
Thalia—polka mazur, Op. 195 (1866)
Budapest Strauss SO, A. Walter (r1993) *Concert*
(6/95) (MARC) ① **8 223561**
Transaktionen, 'Transactions'—waltz, Op. 184 (1865)
VPO, W. Boskovsky (r1976) *Concert*
(1/90) (DECC) ① **425 427-2DA**
VPO, R. Muti (pp1993) *Concert*
(3/93) (PHIL) ① **438 493-2PH**
Vorwärts!, 'Forward!'—polka schnell, Op. 127 (1862)
M. Hill Smith, LJSO, J. Rothstein *Concert*
(1/86) (CHAN) ① **CHAN8381**
Wallonen, 'Walloons'—march, Op. 41 (1857)
London Viennese Orch, J. Rothstein *Concert*
(5/93) (CHAN) ① **CHAN9127**
Wiegenlieder, 'Cradle songs'—waltz, Op. 18 (1856)
Budapest Strauss SO, A. Walter (r1993) *Concert*
(6/95) (MARC) ① **8 223561**
Zeit-Bilder, 'Time pictures'—waltz, Op. 51 (1858)
London Viennese Orch, J. Rothstein *Concert*
(5/93) (CHAN) ① **CHAN9127**

STRAUSS, Richard (Georg)
(1864–1949) Germany

AV nos from catalogue by E.H. Mueller von Asow

SECTION I: ORCHESTRAL

Eine Alpensinfonie, 'Alpine Symphony', Op. 64 (1911-15)
Concertgebouw, B. Haitink
(7/86) (PHIL) ① **416 156-2PH**
SNO, N. Järvi *Concert*
(12/87) (CHAN) ① **CHAN8557**
Bamberg SO, H. Stein (9/89) (EURO) ① **RD69012**
San Francisco SO, H. Blomstedt *Don Juan.*
(6/90) (DECC) ① **421 815-2DH**
VPO, A. Previn (r1989) (9/90) (TELC) ① **CD80211**
ECYO, J. Judd (pp1987) (11/91) (NUOV) ① **6706**
Staatskapelle Dresden, R. Kempe (r1971) *Concert*
(12/92) (EMI) ① [3] **CMS7 64350-2**
Bavarian St Orch, R. Strauss (r1941) *Rosenkavalier film.*
(1/93) (KOCH) ① **37132-2**

Bavarian St Orch, R. Strauss (r1941) *Rosenkavalier film.*
(4/93) (EMI) ① **CDC7 54610-2**
Chicago SO, D. Barenboim (r1992) *Frau ohne schatten Fantasy.*
(6/93) (ERAT) ① **2292-45997-2**
BPO, H. von Karajan (r1980)
(6/93) (DG) ① **439 017-2GHS**
BRSO, G. Solti (r1979) *Concert*
(5/94) (DECC) ① [2] **440 618-2DF2**
Staatskapelle Dresden, G. Sinopoli
(1/95) (DG) ① **439 899-2GH**
Bavarian St Orch, R. Strauss (r1941) *Concert*
(8/95) (PREI) ① [2] **90205**
Czech PO, Z. Košler (r1994)
(12/95) (SUPR) ① **SU0005-2**
Also sprach Zarathustra, 'Thus spake Zarathustra'—tone poem after Nietzsche, Op. 30 (1895-96)
SNO, N. Järvi *Concert*
(3/88) (CHAN) ① **CHAN8538**
M. Schwalbé, BPO, H. von Karajan (r1973) *Concert*
(4/88) (DG) ① **415 853-2GGA**
Chicago SO, F. Reiner *Concert*
(7/88) (RCA) ① **GD86722**
Moscow SO, D. Kitaienko (r1985) *Rachmaninov: Symphony 3.*
(9/88) (OLYM) ① **OCD209**
Staatskapelle Dresden, H. Blomstedt *Don Juan.*
(9/88) (DENO) ① **CO-2259**
VPO, A. Previn (r1987) *Tod und Verklärung.*
(10/88) (TELA) ① **CD80167**
Seattle SO, G. Schwarz *Concert*
(9/90) (DELO) ① **DE3052**
LSO, M. Tilson Thomas *Don Juan.*
(9/91) (SONY) ① **SK45970**
Boston SO, S. Koussevitzky (r1935) *Concert*
(11/92) (RCA) ① [2] **09026 60929-2**
Chicago SO, F. Reiner (r1954) *Concert*
(12/92) (RCA) ① **09026 60930-2**
Staatskapelle Dresden, R. Kempe (r1971) *Concert*
(12/92) (EMI) ① [3] **CMS7 64346-2**
Chicago SO, F. Reiner (r1954) *Heldenleben.*
(4/93) (RCA) ① **09026 61494-2**
BPO, K. Böhm (r1958) *Concert*
(1/94) (DG) ① **439 419-2GCL**
Chicago SO, G. Solti (r1975) *Concert*
(5/94) (DECC) ① [2] **440 618-2DF2**
Chicago SO, F. Stock (r1940) *Concert*
(2/95) (BIDD) ① [2] **WHL021/2**
VPO, R. Strauss (pp1944) *Concert*
(8/95) (PREI) ① [3] **90216**
BRSO, L. Maazel (r1995) *Concert*
(10/95) (RCA) ① **09026 68225-2**
Aus Italien—symphonic fantasy, Op. 16 (1886)
EXCERPTS: 1. Auf der Campagna; 2. In Roms Ruinen; 3. Am Strande von Sorrent; 4. Neapolitanisches Volksleben.
SNO, N. Järvi *Concert*
(8/89) (CHAN) ① **CHAN8744**
Slovak PO, Z. Košler *Concert*
(2/91) (NAXO) ① **8 550342**
Aarhus SO, N. del Mar *Macbeth.*
(6/91) (ASV) ① **CDDCA750**
Staatskapelle Dresden, R. Kempe (r1974) *Concert*
(12/92) (EMI) ① [3] **CMS7 64350-2**
Movt 3. Chicago SO, F. Stock (r1941) *Concert*
(11/92) (RCA) ① [2] **09026 60929-2**
Burleske in D minor—piano and orchestra, AV85 (1885-86)
I. Hobson, Philh, N. del Mar *Concert*
(2/88) (ARAB) ① **Z6567**
S. Edelman, Stockholm PO, P. Berglund *Concert*
(11/91) (RCA) ① **RD60173**
C. Rosenberger, Seattle SO, G. Schwarz *Concert*
(10/92) (DELO) ① **DE3109**
M. Frager, Staatskapelle Dresden, R. Kempe (r1975) *Concert*
(12/92) (EMI) ① [3] **CMS7 64342-2**
M. Dalberto, Philh, J-B. Pommier *Concert*
(6/93) (DENO) ① **CO-75258**
M. Argerich, BPO, C. Abbado (pp1992) *Concert*
(7/93) (SONY) ① **SK52565**
R. Serkin, Philadelphia, E. Ormandy (r1966) *Brahms: Piano Concerto 2.*
(3/94) (SONY) ① **SBK53262**
D. Janis, Chicago SO, F. Reiner (r1957) *Don Quixote.*
(9/94) (RCA) ① **09026 61796-2**
M. Weber, Berlin RIAS Orch, F. Fricsay (r1955)
(11/94) (DG) ① **445 403-2GDO**
M. Weber, Berlin RIAS Orch, F. Fricsay (r1955)
(11/94) (DG) ① [11] **445 400-2GDO10**
J. Kahane, Cincinnati SO, J. López-Cobos (r1994) *Concert*
(12/95) (TELA) ① **CD80371**
Concerto for Horn and Orchestra No. 1 in E flat, Op. 11 (1882-83)
H. Baumann, Leipzig Gewandhaus, K. Masur *Concert*
(6/85) (PHIL) ① **412 237-2PH**
D. Brain, Philh, W. Sawallisch (r1956) *Concert*
(10/87) (EMI) ① **CDC7 47834-2**

P. Damm, Staatskapelle Dresden, R. Kempe (r1975) *Concert*
(6/89) (EMI) ① **CDM7 69661-2**
I. James, Polish Nat RSO, A. Wit (r1989) *Concert*
(3/92) (EBS) ① **EBS6063**
B. Tuckwell, RPO, Vladimir Ashkenazy *Concert*
(9/92) (DECC) ① **430 370-2DH**
D. Brain, Philh, A. Galliera (r1947) *Concert*
(10/92) (TEST) ① **SBT1009**
P. Damm, Staatskapelle Dresden, R. Kempe (r1975) *Concert*
(12/92) (EMI) ① [3] **CMS7 64342-2**
R. Vlatković, ECO, J. Tate (r1988) *Concert*
(10/94) (EMI) ① **CDM7 64851-2**
D. Pyatt, Britten Sinf, N. Cleobury (r1994) *Concert*
(8/95) (EMIN) ① **CD-EMX2238**
Concerto for Horn and Orchestra No. 2 in E flat, AV132 (1942)
H. Baumann, Leipzig Gewandhaus, K. Masur *Concert*
(6/85) (PHIL) ① **412 237-2PH**
D. Brain, Philh, W. Sawallisch (r1956) *Concert*
(10/87) (EMI) ① **CDC7 47834-2**
P. Damm, Staatskapelle Dresden, R. Kempe (r1975) *Concert*
(6/89) (EMI) ① **CDM7 69661-2**
B. Schneider, Lausanne CO, M. Aeschbacher *Concert*
(2/91) (CLAV) ① **CD50-9010**
I. James, Polish Nat RSO, A. Wit (r1989) *Concert*
(3/92) (EBS) ① **EBS6063**
B. Tuckwell, RPO, Vladimir Ashkenazy *Concert*
(9/92) (DECC) ① **430 370-2DH**
P. Damm, Staatskapelle Dresden, R. Kempe (r1975) *Concert*
(12/92) (EMI) ① [3] **CMS7 64342-2**
D. Pyatt, Britten Sinf, N. Cleobury (r1994) *Concert*
(8/95) (EMIN) ① **CD-EMX2238**
Concerto for Oboe and Orchestra, AV144 (1945 rev 1948)
D. Boyd, COE, T. Berglund *Mozart: Oboe Concerto, K314.*
(11/87) (ASV) ① **CDCOE808**
L. Koch, BPO, H. von Karajan (r1969) *Concert*
(12/88) (DG) ① **423 888-2GGA**
M. Clement, Staatskapelle Dresden, R. Kempe (r1975) *Concert*
(6/89) (EMI) ① **CDM7 69661-2**
L. Lencses, Stuttgart RSO, N. Marriner *Metamorphosen.*
(6/89) (CAPR) ① **10 231**
B.C. Nielsen, Copenhagen Collegium Musicum, M. Schønwandt *Bourgeois Gentilhomme suite.*
(9/90) (KONT) ① **32039**
A. Nilsson, Stockholm Sinfonietta, N. Järvi *Bourgeois gentilhomme Suite.*
(12/90) (BIS) ① **BIS-CD470**
I. Goritzki, Lausanne CO, M. Aeschbacher *Concert*
(2/91) (CLAV) ① **CD50-9010**
H. Schellenberger, BPO, James Levine *Concert*
(5/91) (DG) ① **429 750-2GH**
J. de Lancie, CO, M. Wilcox (r1987) *Concert*
(12/91) (RCA) ① **GD87989**
L. Goossens, Philh, A. Galliera (r1947) *Concert*
(10/92) (TEST) ① **SBT1009**
J. Anderson, Philh, S. Wright *Concert*
(12/92) (NIMB) ① **NI5330**
M. Clement, Staatskapelle Dresden, R. Kempe (r1975) *Concert*
(12/92) (EMI) ① [3] **CMS7 64342-2**
R. Canter, LSO, J. Judd (r1992) *Concert*
(10/93) (CARL) ① **MCD59**
G. Hunt, Berlin RSO, Vladimir Ashkenazy (r1991) *Concert*
(3/94) (DECC) ① **436 415-2DH**
H. Holliger, New Philh, E. de Waart (r1970) *Concert*
(7/94) (PHIL) ① [2] **438 733-2PM2**
Concerto for Violin and Orchestra in D minor, Op. 8 (1880-82)
X. Wei, LPO, J. Glover *Headington: Violin Concerto.*
(12/91) (ASV) ① **CDDCA780**
U. Hoelscher, Staatskapelle Dresden, R. Kempe (r1975) *Concert*
(12/92) (EMI) ① [3] **CMS7 64346-2**
B. Belkin, Berlin RSO, Vladimir Ashkenazy (r1991) *Concert*
(3/94) (DECC) ① **436 415-2DH**
Divertimento—small orchestra, Op. 86 (1940-41) (after Couperin)
COE, E. Leinsdorf *Bourgeois gentilhomme suite.*
(11/88) (ASV) ① **CDCOE804**
Tokyo Metropolitan O, H. Wakasugi *Dance Suite.*
(11/90) (DENO) ① **CO-76366**
Orpheus CO *Bourgeois Gentilhomme Suite.*
(3/93) (DG) ① **435 871-2GH**
Don Juan—tone poem after Lenau, Op. 20 (1888)
SNO, N. Järvi *Concert*
(3/88) (CHAN) ① **CHAN8538**
Staatskapelle Dresden, H. Blomstedt *Also sprach Zarathustra.*
(9/88) (DENO) ① **CO-2259**
Berlin St Op Orch, R. Strauss (r1929) *Concert*
(5/90) (PEAR) ① **GEMMCD9366**
Philh, O. Klemperer *Concert*
(9/90) (EMI) ① **CDM7 63350-2**
San Francisco SO, H. Blomstedt *Alpensinfonie.*
(6/90) (DECC) ① **421 815-2DH**

BBC Welsh SO, T. Otaka *Concert*
(9/90) (NIMB) ① **NI5235**
Slovak PO, Z. Košler *Concert*
(3/91) (NAXO) ① **8 550250**
Polish Nat RSO, A. Wit *Concert*
(3/91) (POLS) ① **PNCD050**
LSO, M. Tilson Thomas *Also sprach Zarathustra.*
(9/91) (SONY) ① **SK45970**
VPO, A. Previn (r1990) *Don Quixote.*
(10/91) (TELA) ① **CD80262**
Stockholm PO, P. Berglund *Concert*
(11/91) (RCA) ① **RD60173**
C. Pickler, Chicago SO *Don Quixote.*
(12/91) (ERAT) ① **2292-45625-2**
Stuttgart RSO, N. Marriner *Concert*
(9/92) (CAPR) ① **10 369**
NBC SO, A. Toscanini (r1951) *Concert*
(11/92) (RCA) ① **GD60296**
Staatskapelle Dresden, G. Sinopoli *Heldenleben.*
(11/92) (DG) ① **435 790-2GH**
Staatskapelle Dresden, R. Kempe (r1970) *Concert*
(12/92) (EMI) ① [3] **CMS7 64342-2**
LSO, A. Coates (r1926) *Concert*
(4/93) (KOCH) ① [2] **37704-2**
Cleveland Orch, G. Szell (r1957) *Concert*
(5/93) (SONY) ① **SBK48272**
BPO, C. Abbado (pp1992) *Concert*
(7/93) (SONY) ① **SK52565**
LPO, F. Busch (r1936) *Concert*
(11/93) (DUTT) ① **CDAX8005**
Concertgebouw, W. Mengelberg (r1938)
Heldenleben. (12/93) (TELD) ① **9031-76441-2**
BPO, K. Böhm (r1963) *Concert*
(1/94) (DG) ① **439 419-2GCL**
Chicago SO, G. Solti (r1973) *Concert*
(5/94) (DECC) ① [2] **440 618-2DF2**
VPO, W. Furtwängler (r1954) *Concert*
(10/94) (EMI) ① **CDH5 65197-2**
Berlin RIAS Orch, F. Fricsay (pp1952) *Concert*
(11/94) (DG) ① [11] **445 400-2GDO10**
Berlin RIAS Orch, F. Fricsay (pp1952) *Concert*
(11/94) (DG) ① **445 403-2GDO**
NY Stadium SO, L. Stokowski (r c1958) *Concert*
(4/95) (EVER) ① **EVC9004**
VPO, R. Strauss (pp1944) *Concert*
(8/95) (PREI) ① [3] **90216**
NYPO, B. Walter (r1952) *Concert*
(8/95) (SONY) ① **SMK64466**
VPO, W. Furtwängler (r1954) *Concert*
(9/95) (EMI) ① [2] **CHS5 65353-2**
BRSO, L. Maazel (r1995) *Concert*
(10/95) (RCA) ① **09026 68225-2**
Solti Orchestral Project, G. Solti (pp1994) *Concert*
(12/95) (DECC) ① **444 458-2DH**

**Don Quixote—fantastic variations for cello,
viola & orchestra, Op. 35 (1896-97)**
W. Christ, A. Meneses, BPO, H. von Karajan *Till
Eulenspiegel.* (8/87) (DG) ① **419 599-2GH**
R. Wallfisch, J. Harrington, SNO, N. Järvi *Concert*
(1/89) (CHAN) ① **CHAN8631**
M. Rostropovich, U. Koch, BPO, H. von Karajan
(8/89) (EMI) ① **CDC7 49308-2**
P. Fournier, G. Cappone, BPO, H. von Karajan *Tod
und Verklärung.* (4/90) (DG) ① **429 184-2GGA**
F. Miller, C. Cooley, NBC SO, A. Toscanini (pp1953)
Tod and Verklärung. (1/91) (RCA) ① **GD60295**
P. Bartolomey, H. Koll, VPO, A. Previn (r1990) *Don
Juan.* (10/91) (TELA) ① **CD80262**
E. Feuermann, S. Lifschey, Philadelphia, E. Ormandy
(r1940) *Bloch: Schelomo.*
(12/91) (BIDD) ① **LAB042**
J. Sharp, C. Pickler, Chicago SO *Don Juan.*
(12/91) (ERAT) ① **2292-45625-2**
A. Wallenstein, R. Pollain, NYPSO, T. Beecham
(r1932) *Concert*
(4/92) (PEAR) ① [3] **GEMMCDS9922**
J. Starker, O. Lysy, BRSO, L. Slatkin *Till
Eulenspiegel.* (4/92) (RCA) ① **RD60561**
A. Wallenstein, R. Pollain, NYPSO, T. Beecham
(r1932) *Concert*
(11/92) (RCA) ① [2] **09026 60929-2**
P. Tortelier, M. Rostal, Staatskapelle Dresden, R.
Kempe (r1973) *Concert*
(12/92) (EMI) ① [3] **CMS7 64350-2**
G. Piatigorsky, J. de Pasquale, Boston SO, C. Munch
(r1953) *Brahms: Double Concerto.*
(10/93) (RCA) ① **09026 61485-2**
P. Tortelier, R. Koeckert, G. Schmid, BRSO, R.
Kempe *Haydn: Sinfonia concertante.*
(2/94) (ORFE) ① **C267921B**
L. Munroe, W. Lincer, NYPO, L. Bernstein (r1968)
Concert (9/94) (SONY) ① **SMK47625**
A. Janigro, M. Preves, Chicago SO, F. Reiner (r1959)
Burleske. (9/94) (RCA) ① **09026 61796-2**
O. Uhl, P. Haass, Bavarian St Orch, R. Strauss
(r1941) *Concert* (8/95) (PREI) ① [2] **90205**

E. Feuermann, NBC SO, A. Toscanini (pp1938) *Tod
und Verklärung.* (9/95) (MUSI) ① **ATRA-613**
J. Du Pré, H. Downes, New Philh, A. Boult (r1968)
Lalo: Cello Concerto.
(11/95) (EMI) ① **CDC5 55528-2**
P. Tortelier, L. Rubens, RPO, T. Beecham (r1947/8)
Concert (12/95) (EMI) ① **CDH5 65502-2**

**Duett-Concertino—clarinet, bassoon, strings
and harp, AV147 (1947)**
M. Weise, W. Liebscher, Staatskapelle Dresden, R.
Kempe (r1975) *Concert*
(6/89) (EMI) ① **CDM7 69661-2**
R. Hosford, M. Wilkie, COE, T. Fischer *Concert*
(10/89) (ASV) ① **CDCOE811**
E. Brunner, M. Turkovic, Bamberg SO, L. Zagrosek
Concert (4/90) (SCHW) ① **311065**
T. Friedli, K. Thunemann, Lausanne CO, M.
Aeschbacher *Concert* (2/91) (CLAV) ① **CD50-9010**
M. Weise, W. Liebscher, Staatskapelle Dresden, R.
Kempe (r1975) *Concert*
(12/92) (EMI) ① [3] **CMS7 64342-2**
D. Ashkenazy, K. Walker, Berlin RSO, Vladimir
Ashkenazy (r1991) *Concert*
(3/94) (DECC) ① **436 415-2DH**
H. Geusser, W. Fugmann, Berlin RIAS Orch, F.
Fricsay (bp1953) *Concert*
(11/94) (DG) ① [11] **445 400-2GDO10**
H. Geusser, W. Fugmann, Berlin RIAS Orch, F.
Fricsay (bp1953) *Concert*
(11/94) (DG) ① **445 403-2GDO**
J. Farrall, J. Andrews, Britten Sinf, N. Cleobury
(r1994) *Concert* (8/95) (EMIN) ① **CD-EMX2238**

**Fanfare für die Wiener
Philharmoniker—brass and timpani, AV109
(1924)**
Locke Brass Consort, J. Stobart (orig version)
Concert (1/89) (CHAN) ① **CHAN8419**

**Fanfare zur Eröffnung der Musikwoche der
Stadt Wien—brass and timpani, AV110
(1924)**
Locke Brass Consort, J. Stobart *Concert*
(1/89) (CHAN) ① **CHAN8419**

**Feierlicher einzug der Ritter des
Johanniterordens—brass and timpani,
AV103 (1909)**
Locke Brass Consort, J. Stobart *Concert*
(1/89) (CHAN) ① **CHAN8419**

**Festliches Präludium—large orchestra and
organ, Op. 61 (1913)**
E. Power Biggs, NYPO, L. Bernstein (r1962) *Concert*
(9/94) (SONY) ① **SMK47625**
M. Chertok, Cincinnati SO, J. López-Cobos (r1994)
Concert (12/95) (TELA) ① **CD80371**

**Festmusik der Stadt Wien—brass and
timpani, AV133 (1943)**
London Brass Virtuosi, D. Honeyball *Concert*
(7/87) (HYPE) ① **CDA66189**
Locke Brass Consort, J. Stobart (orig version)
Concert (1/89) (CHAN) ① **CHAN8419**

**Festmusik zur Feier des 2600 jährigen
Bestehens des Kaiserreichs Japan, Op. 84
(1940)**
Bavarian St Orch, R. Strauss (r1940) *Concert*
(8/95) (PREI) ① [2] **90205**

**Ein Heldenleben, '(A) Hero's Life'—tone
poem, Op. 40 (1897-98)**
SNO, N. Järvi *Vier letzte Lieder.*
(8/87) (CHAN) ① **CHAN8518**
VPO, A. Previn (r1988) *Vier letzte Lieder.*
(8/89) (TELA) ① **CD80180**
Chicago SO, D. Barenboim *Till Eulenspiegel.*
(8/91) (ERAT) ① **2292-45621-2**
Seattle SO, G. Schwarz *Concert*
(5/92) (DELO) ① **DE3094**
NYPSO, W. Mengelberg (1928) *Concert*
(11/92) (RCA) ① [2] **09026 60929-2**
Staatskapelle Dresden, G. Sinopoli *Don Juan.*
(11/92) (DG) ① **435 790-2GH**
Staatskapelle Dresden, R. Kempe (r1972) *Concert*
(12/92) (EMI) ① [3] **CMS7 64342-2**
Chicago SO, F. Reiner (r1954) *Also sprach
Zarathustra.* (4/93) (RCA) ① **09026 61494-2**
Philadelphia, E. Ormandy (r1960) *Concert*
(5/93) (SONY) ① **SBK48272**
Concertgebouw, W. Mengelberg (r1941) *Don Juan.*
(12/93) (TELD) ① **9031-76441-2**
San Francisco SO, H. Blomstedt (r1992)
Metamorphosen. (5/94) (DECC) ① **436 596-2DH**
VPO, G. Solti (r1977/8) *Concert*
(5/94) (DECC) ① [2] **440 618-2DF2**
San Francisco SO, P. Monteux (r1947) *Concert*
(9/94) (RCA) ① [15] **09026 61893-2**
Bavarian St Orch, R. Strauss (r1941) *Concert*
(8/95) (PREI) ① [2] **90205**
VPO, R. Strauss (pp1944) *Concert*
(8/95) (PREI) ① [2] **90216**

**Macbeth—tone poem after Shakespeare, Op.
23 (1886-88 rev 1889-90, 1891)**
SNO, N. Järvi *Concert*
(12/90) (CHAN) ① **CHAN8834**
Aarhus SO, N. del Mar *Aus Italien.*
(6/91) (ASV) ① **CDDCA750**
Seattle SO, G. Schwarz *Concert*
(5/92) (DELO) ① **DE3094**
Staatskapelle Dresden, R. Kempe (r1973) *Concert*
(12/92) (EMI) ① [3] **CMS7 64350-2**

**Metamorphosen—study for 23 solo strings,
AV142 (1944-45)**
BPO, H. von Karajan (r1980) *Tod und Verklärung.*
(2/84) (DG) ① **410 892-2GH**
BPO, H. von Karajan (r1969) *Concert*
(12/88) (DG) ① **423 888-2GGA**
English Stg Orch, W. Boughton *Schoenberg:
Verklärte Nacht.* (4/89) (NIMB) ① **NI5151**
Stuttgart RSO, N. Marriner *Oboe Concerto.*
(6/89) (CAPR) ① **10 231**
SNO, N. Järvi *Concert*
(3/90) (CHAN) ① **CHAN8734**
Staatskapelle Dresden, H. Blomstedt *Concert*
(3/90) (DENO) ① **CO-73801**
Philh, O. Klemperer *Concert*
(5/90) (EMI) ① **CDM7 63350-2**
London Academy, R. Stamp *Concert*
(2/91) (VIRG) ① **VC7 59538-2**
London Fest Orch, R. Pople *Schoenberg: Verklärte
Nacht.* (9/91) (ASV) ① **CDDCA743**
Sinfonia Varsovia, E. Krivine *Concert*
(10/92) (DENO) ① **CO-79442**
Staatskapelle Dresden, R. Kempe (r1973) *Concert*
(12/92) (EMI) ① [3] **CMS7 64350-2**
BPO, James Levine (r1991) *Concert*
(8/93) (DG) ① **435 883-2GH**
Seattle Sym Stgs, G. Schwarz (r1992) *Concert*
(4/94) (DELO) ① **DE3121**
San Francisco SO, H. Blomstedt (r1992)
Heldenleben. (5/94) (DECC) ① **436 596-2DH**
New Philh, J. Barbirolli (r1967) *Schoenberg: Pelleas
und Melisande.* (7/94) (EMI) ① **CDM5 65078-2**
A. Posch, Vienna Stg Sextet (r1993: orig vers)
Concert (2/95) (EMI) ① **CDC5 55108-2**
New Philh, J. Barbirolli (r1967) *Mahler: Symphony 6.*
(9/95) (EMI) ① [2] **CZS7 67816-2**
Smithsonian Chbr Plyrs, K. Slowik (r1994) *Concert*
(9/95) (DHM) ① **05472 77343-2**

**Panathenäenzug: symphonische Etüden in
Form einer Passacaglia—piano left-hand
and orchestra, Op. 74 (1927)**
P. Rösel, Staatskapelle Dresden, R. Kempe (r1976)
Concert (12/92) (EMI) ① [3] **CMS7 64342-2**

2 Parade Marches—brass ensemble (1905)
1. Parademarsch des Regiments König-Jäger; 2.
Parademarsch für Kavallerie.
Locke Brass Consort, J. Stobart (orig version)
Concert (1/89) (CHAN) ① **CHAN8419**

**Parergon zur Symphonia domestica—piano
left-hand and orchestra, Op. 73 (1925)**
I. Hobson, Philh, N. del Mar *Concert*
(2/88) (ARAB) ① **Z6567**
P. Rösel, Staatskapelle Dresden, R. Kempe (r1976)
Concert (12/92) (EMI) ① [3] **CMS7 64342-2**

**Romanze in F—cello and orchestra, AV75
(1883)**
R. Wallfisch, SNO, N. Järvi *Concert*
(1/89) (CHAN) ① **CHAN8631**
M. Maisky, Paris Orch, S. Bychkov *Concert*
(10/92) (DG) ① **435 781-2GH**
M. Fujiwara, Tokyo SO, H. Wakasugi (r1993)
Symphony in F minor. (9/94) (DENO) ① **CO-75860**

**Serenade—13 wind instruments, Op. 7
(1881)**
Seattle SO, G. Schwarz *Concert*
(5/92) (DELO) ① **DE3094**
London Winds, M. Collins (r1992) *Concert*
(8/93) (HYPE) ① **CDA66731/2**
Netherlands Wind Ens, E. de Waart (r1971) *Concert*
(7/94) (PHIL) ① [2] **438 733-2PM2**
Britten Sinf, N. Cleobury (r1994) *Concert*
(8/95) (EMIN) ① **CD-EMX2238**
COE Wind Sols, H. Holliger (r1994) *Concert*
(9/95) (PHIL) ① **438 933-2PH**

**Sinfonische Fantasie aus 'Die Frau ohne
Schatten'—orchestra (1946)**
Seattle SO, G. Schwarz *Concert*
(10/92) (DELO) ① **DE3109**
Chicago SO, D. Barenboim (r1992) *Alpensinfonie.*
(3/93) (ERAT) ① **2292-45997-2**

**Sonatina No. 1 in F, 'Aus der Werkstatt
eines Invaliden'—16 wind instruments,
AV135 (1943)**
Norwegian Wind Ens, G. Oskamp *Suite, Op.4.*
(8/92) (VICT) ① **VCD19045**

1. J. Norman, G. Parsons *Concert*
(8/86) (PHIL) ① **416 298-2PH**
1. F. Schorr, anon (r1921) *Concert*
(9/91) (PEAR) ① **GEMMCD9398**
1. M. Reining, R. Strauss (bp1942) *Concert*
(10/92) (PREI) ① **93262**
1. E. Schumann, K. Alwin (r1932) *Concert*
(4/93) (EMI) ① [2] **CHS7 64487-2**
1. Lotte Lehmann, Berlin St Op Orch, F. Weissmann
(r1929) *Concert* (4/93) (EMI) ① [2] **CHS7 64487-2**
1. I. Seefried, E. Werba (r1958) *Concert*
(7/93) (DG) ① [2] **437 348-2GDO2**
1. H. Schlusnus, F. Rupp (r1930) *Concert*
(1/94) (PREI) ① [2] **89205**
1. W. Widdop, J. Lee (bp1949) *Concert*
(5/94) (CLAR) ① **CDGSE78-50-52**
1. M. Shirai, H. Höll (r1993/4) *Concert*
(2/95) (CAPR) ① **10 497**
1, 3. G. Souzay, D. Baldwin (r1963) *Concert*
(10/95) (PHIL) ① [2] **442 744-2PM2**
2. E. Schwarzkopf, M. Raucheisen (bp c1945)
Concert (6/87) (ACAN) ① **43 801**
2. B. Hendricks, R. Gothóni *Concert*
(9/88) (EMI) ① **CDC7 49318-2**
2. L. Piltti, R. Strauss (bp1942) *Concert*
(10/92) (PREI) ① **93262**
2. J. Varady, E. Bashkirova *Concert*
(5/93) (ORFE) ① **C248921A**
2. L. Price, D. Garvey (r1959) *Concert*
(5/93) (RCA) ① **09026 61499-2**
2. M. McLaughlin, G. Johnson (r1993) *Concert*
(8/95) (HYPE) ① **CDA666659**
3. C. Studer, I. Gage (pp1992) *Concert*
(10/93) (DG) ① **437 784-2GH**

4 Lieder—1v and piano, Op. 31 (1895-96)
(Wds. various)
1. Blauer Sommer (wds. Busse: 1896); 2. Wenn
(wds. Busse: 1895); 3. Weisser Jasmin (wds. Busse:
1895); 4. Stiller Gang (wds. Dehmel: 1895).
1. L. Popp, I. Gage *Concert*
(4/92) (RCA) ① **RD60950**
1, 2, 3. E. Gruberová, F. Haider *Concert*
(6/91) (TELD) ① [2] **2292-44922-2**
3. L. Popp, W. Sawallisch (r1984) *Concert*
(9/88) (EMI) ① **CDC7 49318-2**
4. J. Norman, C. Erdélyi, G. Parsons *Concert*
(8/86) (PHIL) ① **416 298-2PH**
4. M. Shirai, T. Zimmermann, H. Höll (r1993/4)
Concert (9/95) (CAPR) ① **10 462**

5 Lieder—1v and piano, Op. 32 (1896) (Wds.
various)
1. Ich trage meine Minne (wds. K. Henckell); 2.
Sehnsucht (wds. Liliencron); 3. Liebeshymnus (wds.
K. Henckell: orch 1897); 4. O süsser Mai (wds. K.
Henckell); 5. Himmelsboten (wds. Des Knaben
Wunderhorn).
1. J. Norman, G. Parsons *Concert*
(8/86) (PHIL) ① **416 298-2PH**
1. A. Dermota, R. Strauss (bp1942) *Concert*
(10/92) (PREI) ① **93262**
1. A.S. von Otter, B. Forsberg (r1993) *Concert*
(6/94) (DG) ① **437 515-2GH**
1. M. Shirai, H. Höll (r1993/4) *Concert*
(2/95) (CAPR) ① **10 497**
2. A. Dermota, R. Strauss (bp1943) *Concert*
(6/90) (PREI) ① **93261**
2. P. Anders, BPO, W. Furtwängler (pp1942) *Concert*
(7/90) (ARAB) ① **Z6082**
5. T. Hampson, G. Parsons *Concert*
(10/90) (TELD) ① **2292-44923-2**

4 Lieder—1v and piano, Op. 36 (1897-98)
(Wds. various)
1. Der Rosenband (wds. Klopstock: 1897: orch
1897); 2. Für fünfzehn Pfennige (wds. Des Knaben
Wunderhorn: 1897); 3. Hat gesagt—bleibt's nicht
dabei (wds. Des Knaben Wundhorn: 1898); 4.
Anbetung (wds. Rückert: 1898).
1. E. Schwarzkopf, LSO, G. Szell *Concert*
(12/85) (EMI) ① **CDC7 47276-2**
1. F. Lott, SNO, N. Järvi *Concert*
(8/89) (CHAN) ① **CHAN8744**
1. A. Poell, R. Strauss (bp1943) *Concert*
(6/90) (PREI) ① **93261**
1, 3. A.S. von Otter, B. Forsberg (r1993) *Concert*
(6/94) (DG) ① **437 515-2GH**
2, 3. L. Popp, W. Sawallisch (r1984) *Concert*
(9/88) (EMI) ① **CDC7 49318-2**
3. E. Schwarzkopf, G. Moore *Concert*
(12/90) (EMI) ① **CDM7 63656-2**
3. K. Te Kanawa, G. Solti *Concert*
(12/90) (DECC) ① **430 511-2DH**
3. E. Schumann, K. Alwin (r1930) *Concert*
(4/93) (EMI) ① [2] **CHS7 64487-2**

3. E. Schwarzkopf, M. Raucheisen (bp c1944-5)
Concert (5/93) (ACAN) ① **43 128**
3. L. Della Casa, S. Peschko (r1962) *Concert*
(11/94) (TEST) ① **SBT1036**

6 Lieder—1v and piano, Op. 37 (1896-98)
(Wds. various)
1. Glückes genug (wds. Liliencron: 1898); 2. Ich liebe
dich (wds. Liliencron: 1898: orch 1943); 3. Meinem
Kinde (wds. Falke: 1897: orch 1897); 4. Mein Auge
(wds. Dehmel: 1898: orch 1933); 5. Herr Lenz (wds.
Bodman: 1896); 6. Hochzeitlich Lied (wds. A.
Lindner: 1898).
1. A. Dermota, R. Strauss (bp1943) *Concert*
(6/90) (PREI) ① **93261**
1. E. Gruberová, F. Haider *Concert*
(6/91) (TELD) ① [2] **2292-44922-2**
1. J. Kaufmann, I. Gage (r1992) *Concert*
(2/94) (ORFE) ① **C305931A**
2. A. Dermota, R. Strauss (bp1942) *Concert*
(10/92) (PREI) ① **93262**
2, 4. G. Souzay, D. Baldwin (r1963) *Concert*
(10/95) (PHIL) ① [2] **442 744-2PM2**
3. J. Norman, Leipzig Gewandhaus, K. Masur
Concert (2/84) (PHIL) ① **411 052-2PH**
3. E. Schwarzkopf, LSO, G. Szell *Concert*
(12/85) (EMI) ① **CDC7 47276-2**
3. F. Lott, SNO, N. Järvi *Concert*
(12/87) (CHAN) ① **CHAN8557**
3. L. Popp, W. Sawallisch (r1984) *Concert*
(9/88) (EMI) ① **CDC7 49318-2**
3. E. Schwarzkopf, G. Parsons *Concert*
(12/90) (EMI) ① **CDM7 63656-2**
3. G. Janowitz, London Academy, R. Stamp *Concert*
(2/91) (VIRG) ① **VC7 59538-2**
3. M. Reining, R. Strauss (bp1942) *Concert*
(10/92) (PREI) ① **93262**
3. J. Varady, E. Bashkirova *Concert*
(5/93) (ORFE) ① **C248921A**
3. I. Seefried, E. Werba (r1958) *Concert*
(7/93) (DG) ① [2] **437 348-2GDO2**
3. A.S. von Otter, B. Forsberg (r1993) *Concert*
(6/94) (DG) ① **437 515-2GH**
3. M. Reining, Vienna St Op Orch, R. Moralt (r1942)
Concert (9/94) (PREI) ① **89065**
3. K. Mattila, LSO, M. Tilson Thomas (r1991) *Concert*
(11/94) (SONY) ① **SK48242**
3, 4. F. Lott, SNO, N. Järvi *Concert*
(8/92) (CHAN) ① **CHAN9054**
4. F. Lott, SNO, N. Järvi *Concert*
(8/89) (CHAN) ① **CHAN8744**

5 Lieder—1v and piano, Op. 39 (1898) (Wds.
various)
1. Leises Lied (wds. Dehmel); 2. Junghexenlied (wds.
Bierbaum); 3. Der Arbeitsmann (wds. Dehmel); 4.
Befreit (wds. Dehmel: orch 1933); 5. Lied an meinen
Sohn.
1. L. Popp, W. Sawallisch (r1984) *Concert*
(9/88) (EMI) ① **CDC7 49318-2**
1. M. McLaughlin, G. Johnson (r1993) *Concert*
(8/95) (HYPE) ① **CDA66659**
1, 2. E. Gruberová, F. Haider *Concert*
(6/91) (TELD) ① [2] **2292-44922-2**
4. J. Norman, G. Parsons *Concert*
(8/86) (PHIL) ① **416 298-2PH**
4. F. Lott, SNO, N. Järvi *Concert*
(8/89) (CHAN) ① **CHAN8744**
4. G. Janowitz, London Academy, R. Stamp *Concert*
(2/91) (VIRG) ① **VC7 59538-2**
4. B. Hendricks, R. Gothóni *Concert*
(12/91) (EMI) ① **CDC7 54381-2**
4. F. Lott, SNO, N. Järvi *Concert*
(8/92) (CHAN) ① **CHAN9054**
4. J. Varady, E. Bashkirova *Concert*
(5/93) (ORFE) ① **C248921A**
4. A.S. von Otter, B. Forsberg (r1993) *Concert*
(6/94) (DG) ① **437 515-2GH**
4. A. Roocroft, LPO, F. Welser-Möst *Concert*
(10/94) (EMI) ① **CDC5 55090-2**
4. L. Della Casa, S. Peschko (r1962) *Concert*
(11/94) (TEST) ① **SBT1036**
4. J. Baker, G. Moore (r1967) *Concert*
(11/94) (EMI) ① **CDM5 65009-2**
4. M. Shirai, H. Höll (r1993/4) *Concert*
(2/95) (CAPR) ① **10 497**

5 Lieder—1v and piano, Op. 41 (1899) (Wds.
various)
1. Wiegenlied (wds. Dehmel: orch ?1916); 2. In der
Campagna (wds. wds. Mackay); 3. Am Ufer (wds.
Dehmel); 4. Bruder Liederlich (wds. Liliencron); 5.
Leise Lieder (wds. Morgenstern).
1. J. Norman, Leipzig Gewandhaus, K. Masur
Concert (2/84) (PHIL) ① **411 052-2PH**
1. E. Schwarzkopf, LSO, G. Szell *Concert*
(12/85) (EMI) ① **CDC7 47276-2**
1. L. Popp, W. Sawallisch (r1984) *Concert*
(9/88) (EMI) ① **CDC7 49318-2**

1. Y. Kenny, L. Skrobacs (pp1984) *Concert*
(7/90) (ETCE) ① **KTC1029**
1. E. Schwarzkopf, G. Moore *Concert*
(12/90) (EMI) ① **CDM7 63656-2**
1. G. Janowitz, London Academy, R. Stamp *Concert*
(2/91) (VIRG) ① **VC7 59538-2**
1. B. Hendricks, R. Gothóni *Concert*
(12/91) (EMI) ① **CDC7 54381-2**
1. B. Nilsson, G. Parsons (pp1974) *Concert*
(6/92) (BLUE) ① **ABCD009**
1. G. Jones, Tokyo SO, R. Paternostro (pp1991)
Concert (6/92) (SCHW) ① **314081**
1. F. Lott, SNO, N. Järvi *Concert*
(8/92) (CHAN) ① **CHAN9054**
1. M. Reining, R. Strauss (bp1942) *Concert*
(9/92) (PREI) ① **90083**
1. M. Reining, R. Strauss (bp1942) *Concert*
(10/92) (PREI) ① **93262**
1. E. Schumann, I. Newton (r1927) *Concert*
(4/93) (EMI) ① [2] **CHS7 64487-2**
1. C. Studer, I. Gage (pp1992) *Concert*
(10/93) (DG) ① **437 784-2GH**
1. M. Reining, Vienna St Op Orch, R. Moralt (r1942)
Concert (9/94) (PREI) ① **89065**
2. E. Gruberová, F. Haider *Concert*
(6/91) (TELD) ① [2] **2292-44922-2**

3 Lieder—1v and piano, Op. 43 (1899) (Wds.
various)
1. An Sie (wds. Klopstock); 2. Muttertändelei (wds. G.
A. Bürger: orch 1900); 3. Die Ulme zu Hirsau (wds.
Uhland).
1. F. Lott, SNO, N. Järvi *Concert*
(3/88) (CHAN) ① **CHAN8538**
2. E. Schwarzkopf, Berlin RSO, G. Szell *Concert*
(12/85) (EMI) ① **CDC7 47276-2**
2. E. Schumann, Vienna St Op Orch, K. Alwin (r1928)
Concert (6/91) (PREI) ① **89031**
2. K. Te Kanawa, G. Solti *Concert*
(12/90) (DECC) ① **430 511-2DH**
2. F. Lott, SNO, N. Järvi *Concert*
(8/92) (CHAN) ① **CHAN9054**
2. E. Schumann, Vienna St Op Orch, K. Alwin (1928)
Concert (4/93) (EMI) ① [2] **CHS7 64487-2**
2. C. Studer, I. Gage (pp1992) *Concert*
(10/93) (DG) ① **437 784-2GH**
2. K. Mattila, LSO, M. Tilson Thomas (r1991) *Concert*
(11/94) (SONY) ① **SK48242**

5 Lieder—1v and piano, Op. 46 (1899-1900)
(Wds. F. Rückert)
1. Ein Odbach gegen Sturm und Regen (1900); 2.
Gestern war ich Atlas (1899); 3. Die sieben Siegel
(1899); 4. Morgenrot (1900); 5. Ich sehe wie in
einem Spiegel (1900).
1. L. Popp, I. Gage *Concert*
(4/92) (RCA) ① **RD60950**
1, 4. E. Gruberová, F. Haider *Concert*
(6/91) (TELD) ① [2] **2292-44922-2**
3. A.S. von Otter, B. Forsberg (r1993) *Concert*
(6/94) (DG) ① **437 515-2GH**

5 Lieder—1v and piano, Op. 47 (1900) (Wds.
Uhland)
1. Auf ein Kind; 2. Des Dichters Abendgang (orch
1918); 3. Rückleben; 4. Einkehr; 5. Von den sieben
Zechbrüdern.
4. E. Gruberová, F. Haider *Concert*
(6/91) (TELD) ① [2] **2292-44922-2**

5 Lieder—1v and piano, Op. 48 (1900)
1. Freundliche Vision (wds. Bierbaum: orch 1918); 2.
Ich schwebe (wds. Henckell); 3. Kling! (wds.
Henckell); 4. Winterweihe (wds. Henckell: orch 1918);
5. Winterliebe (wds. Henckell: orch 1918).
1. F. Lott, SNO, N. Järvi *Concert*
(12/87) (CHAN) ① **CHAN8557**
1. G. Jones, Tokyo SO, R. Paternostro (pp1991)
Concert (6/92) (SCHW) ① **314081**
1. F. Lott, SNO, N. Järvi *Concert*
(8/92) (CHAN) ① **CHAN9054**
1. E. Schumann, I. Newton (r1927) *Concert*
(4/93) (EMI) ① [2] **CHS7 64487-2**
1. L. Price, D. Garvey (r1959) *Concert*
(5/93) (RCA) ① **09026 61499-2**
1. H. Schlusnus, F. Rupp (r1930) *Concert*
(1/94) (PREI) ① [2] **89205**
1. E. Rethberg, anon (r1921) *Concert*
(7/94) (PREI) ① **89051**
1. G. Souzay, D. Baldwin (r1963) *Concert*
(10/95) (PHIL) ① [2] **442 744-2PM2**
1, 2, 4. B. Hendricks, R. Gothóni *Concert*
(12/91) (EMI) ① **CDC7 54381-2**
1-3. M. Reining, R. Strauss (bp1942) *Concert*
(10/92) (PREI) ① **93262**
1, 4. E. Schwarzkopf, Berlin RSO, G. Szell *Concert*
(12/85) (EMI) ① **CDC7 47276-2**
1, 4. G. Janowitz, London Academy, R. Stamp
Concert (2/91) (VIRG) ① **VC7 59538-2**

SECTION V: STAGE WORKS

11. L. della Casa, VPO, H. Hollreiser (r1954) *Concert* (4/90) (DECC) ① **425 959-2DM**
11. L. Price, LSO, F. Cleva *Concert* (8/90) (RCA) ① **GD60398**
11. M. Cebotari, VPO, H. von Karajan (r1948) *Concert* (12/90) (PREI) ① **90034**
11. E. Schwarzkopf, Philh, H. von Karajan (r1954) *Concert* (12/90) (EMI) ① **CDM7 63657-2**
11. F. Leider, orch (r1925) *Concert* (5/91) (PREI) ① [3] **89301**
11. Lotte Lehmann, Berlin St Op Orch, F. Weissmann (r1928) *Concert* (7/92) (PEAR) ① [3] **GEMMCDS9925(2)**
13. E. Gruberová, Munich RO, L. Gardelli *Concert* (11/86) (ORFE) ① **C101841A**
13. M. Ivogün, Berlin St Op Orch, L. Blech (r1932) *Concert* (7/92) (PEAR) ① [3] **GEMMCDS9925(2)**
13. Dilbèr, Estonia Op Orch, E. Klas *Concert* (9/92) (ONDI) ① **ODE768-2**
13. T. Dahl, Calgary PO, M. Bernardi (r1992) *Concert* (12/94) (CBC) ① **SMCD5125**
13(pt) S. Jo, Monte Carlo PO, P. Olmi (r1994) *Concert* (6/95) (ERAT) ① **4509-97239-2**

Le **Bourgeois gentilhomme—suite of incidental music to Molière's play, Op. 60 (1918—Berlin)**
1. Overture; 2. Minuet; 3. The Fencing Master; 4. Entrance and Dance of the Tailors; 5. Minuet of Lully; 6. Courante; 7. Entrance of Cléonte; 8. Prelude to Act 2 (Intermezzo); 9. The Dinner.
COE, E. Leinsdorf *Divertimento, Op.86.* (11/88) (ASV) ① **CDCOE809**
Berlin St Op Orch, R. Strauss (r1930) *Concert* (5/90) (PEAR) ① **GEMMCD9366**
Copenhagen Collegium Musicum, M. Schønwandt *Oboe Concerto.* (9/90) (KONT) ① **32039**
Stockholm Sinfonietta, N. Järvi *Oboe Concerto.* (12/90) (BIS) ① **BIS-CD470**
Limburg SO, S. Mas Conde *Stravinsky: Pulcinella Suite.* (10/92) (SCHW) ① **310272**
Chicago SO, F. Reiner (r1956) *Concert* (12/92) (RCA) ① **09026 60930-2**
Staatskapelle Dresden, R. Kempe (r1970) *Concert* (12/92) (EMI) ① [3] **CMS7 64346-2**
Orpheus CO *Divertimento, Op.86.* (3/93) (DG) ① **435 871-2GH**
VPO, C. Krauss (r1929) *Concert* (5/93) (KOCH) ① **37129-2**
VPO, R. Strauss (pp1944) *Concert* (8/95) (PREI) ① [3] **90216**
C. Juillet, R. Bertsch, Montreal SO, C. Dutoit (r1992) *Dance Suite.* (10/95) (DECC) ① **436 836-2DH**

Capriccio—conversation piece for music: 1 act, Op. 85 (1942—Munich) (Lib. C Krauss)
EXCERPTS; 1. Prelude (string sextet); 2. Kein andres (Flamand); 3. Interlude (moonlight music); 4a. Wo ist mein Bruder?; 4b. Morgen mittag um elf!; 4c. Kein andres (Countess).
Cpte E. Schwarzkopf, E. Waechter, N. Gedda, D. Fischer-Dieskau, H. Hotter, C. Ludwig, R. Christ, A. Moffo, D. Troy, K. Schmitt-Walter, Philh, W. Sawallisch (r1957/8) (11/87) (EMI) ① [2] **CDS7 49014-8**
Cpte G. Janowitz, D. Fischer-Dieskau, P. Schreier, H. Prey, K. Ridderbusch, T. Troyanos, D. Thaw, A. Auger, A. de Ridder, K.C. Kohn, BRSO, K. Böhm (r1971) (11/94) (DG) ① [2] **445 347-2GX2**
1. Stuttgart RSO, N. Marriner *Concert* (9/92) (CAPR) ① **10 369**
1. Rotterdam PO, J. Tate *Concert* (4/93) (EMI) ① **CDC7 54581-2**
1. ASMF Chbr Ens (r1992) *Concert* (5/93) (CHAN) ① **CHAN9131**
1. Vienna Stg Sextet (r1993) *Concert* (2/95) (EMI) ① **CDC5 55108-2**
1. Raphael Ens (r1993) *Concert* (3/95) (HYPE) ① **CDA66704**
1, 3. VPO, A. Previn (r1992) *Concert* (11/93) (DG) ① **437 790-2GH**
1, 3, 4b, 4c F. Lott, SNO, N. Järvi *Concert* (2/90) (CHAN) ① **CHAN8758**
2. A. Dermota, VPO, K. Böhm (r1950) *Concert* (4/92) (EMI) ① [7] **CHS7 69741-2(4)**
3. B. Tuckwell, RPO, Vladimir Ashkenazy *Concert* (9/92) (DECC) ① **430 370-2DH**
3, 4a-c L. della Casa, F. Bierbach, VPO, H. Hollreiser (r1954) *Concert* (4/90) (DECC) ① **425 959-2DM**
4a, 4b E. Schwarzkopf, K. Schmitt-Walter, Philh, W. Sawallisch (r1957) *Concert* (12/90) (EMI) ① **CDM7 63657-2**
4b, 4c E. Schwarzkopf, Philh, O. Ackermann (r1953) *Concert* (4/88) (EMI) ① **CDH7 61001-2**
4b, 4c G. Janowitz, BRSO, K. Böhm (r1971) *Concert* (4/95) (DG) ① **439 467-2GCL**

Daphne—opera: 1 act, Op. 82 (1938—Munich) (Lib. J Gregor)
EXCERPTS: 1a. Introduction; 1b. Kleontes! Adrast! Wo bleibst du?; 2a. Leb wohl, du Tag; 2b. O bleib, geliebter Tag; 3a. Leukippos, du!; 3b. Ja, ich selbst, ich war der Baum!; 4. Daphne! Mutter! Wir warten dein!; 5a. Ei, so fliegt sie vorbei; 5b. Höre uns, Brüder; 6a. Seid ihr um mich, ihr Hirten alle?; 6b. Wisset, ich sah ihn, Phoibos Apollon!; 7. Ich grüsse dich, weiser, erfahrener Fischer; 8a. Was führt dich her im niedern Gewande; 8b. Was seh ich? Was schreitet dort?; 9a. Wie bist du gewaltig, fremder Hirte; 9b. Was können an Weite menschliche Augen forschend ermessen; 10. Dieser Kuss, dies Umarmen, du nanntest dich: Bruder; 11. Allüberall blüht Dionysos; 12. O selge Dämonen; 13. Trinke, du Tochter; 14a. Furchtbare Schmach dem Gotte!; 14b. Was sagt der da?; 14c. Ein Zeichen wollt ihr?; 15a. Zu dir nun, Knabe; 15b. Ja, ich bekenne; 16. Wahrheit? Jeden heiligen Morgen; 17a. Was blendet so?; 17b. Daphne...Gespielen... 17c. Unheilvolle Daphne; 18a. Was erblicke ich? Himmlische Schönheit; 18b. Götter! Brüder im hohen Olympos!; 19. Ich komme...Ich komme, grünende Brüder.
Cpte L. Popp, R. Goldberg, K. Moll, P. Schreier, O. Wenkel, L. Baumann, A. Senger, W. Vater, M. Hölle, D. Wirtz, U-M. Flake, Bavarian Rad Chor, BRSO, B. Haitink (1/89) (EMI) ① [2] **CDS7 49309-2**
Cpte H. Gueden, J. King, P. Schoeffler, F. Wunderlich, V. Little, H. Braun, K. Equiluz, H. Pröglhöf, R. Streich, E. Mechera, Vienna St Op Chor, Vienna SO, K. Böhm (pp1964) (11/94) (DG) ① [2] **445 322-2GX2**
Cpte M. Reining, K. Friedrich, H. Alsen, A. Dermota, M. Frutschnigg, G. Monthy, R. Sallaba, H. Schweiger, H. Baier, E. Loose, M. Schober, Vienna St Op Chor, VPO, K. Böhm (pp1944) *Concert* (11/95) (PREI) ① [2] **90237**
Excs M. Reining, A. Dermota, A. Rauch, Vienna St Op Chor, Vienna St Op Orch, R. Moralt (pp1942) *Concert* (11/94) (SCHW) ① [2] **314552**
2b, 18b, 19(pt) M. Teschemacher, T. Ralf, Dresden St Op Orch, K. Böhm (r1938) *Concert* (11/95) (PREI) ① [2] **90237**
2c, 19b M. Teschemacher, Saxon St Orch, K. Böhm (r1938) *Concert* (11/92) (PREI) ① **89049**
18a M. Cebotari, Berlin RSO, A. Rother (bp1943) *Concert* (8/95) (PREI) ① **90222**
18a B. Heppner, Toronto SO, A. Davis (r1994) *Concert* (11/95) (CBC) ① **SMCD5142**
18b T. Ralf, Saxon St Orch, K. Böhm (r1938) *Concert* (10/94) (PREI) ① **89077**
19a A. Tomowa-Sintow, Munich RO, P. Sommer *Concert* (11/86) (ORFE) ① **C106841A**

Elektra—opera: 1 act, Op. 58 (1909—Dresden) (Lib. H von Hofmannsthal)
EXCERPTS: 1. Wo bleibt Elektra?; 2. Allein! Weh, ganz allein; 3. Elektra!; 4. Ich kann nicht sitzen und ins Dunkel starren; 5. Es geht ein Lärm los; 6. Was willst du? Seht doch, dort!; 7. Die Götter! bist doch selber eine Göttin; 8. Ich will nichts hören!; 9. Ich habe keine guten Nächte; 10. Wenn das rechte Blutopfer; 11. Was bluten muss?; 12. Was sagen sie ihr denn?; 13. Orest! Orest ist tot!; 14. Platz da! Wer lungert so vor einer Tür?; 15. Nun muss es hier von uns geschehen; 16. Du! Du! denn du bist stark!; 17. Nun denn, allein!; 18. Was willst du, fremder Mensch?; 19. Elektra! Elektra; 20. Orest! (Recognition Scene); 21. Du wirst es tun? Allein?; 22. Seid ihr von Sinnen; 23. Ich habe ihm das Beil nicht geben können!; 24. Es muss etwas geschehen sein; 25. He! Lichter! Lichter!; 26. Elektra! Schwester!; 27. Ob ich nich höre?; 28. Hörst du denn nicht, sie tragen ihn; 29. Schweig, und tanze.
Cpte B. Nilsson, R. Resnik, M. Collier, G. Stolze, T. Krause, T. Franc, M. Sjöstedt, M. Lilowa, G. Unger, L. Heppe, P. Tinsley, H. Watts, M. Lehane, Y. Minton, J. Cook, F. Weathers, VPO, G. Solti (r1966/7) (12/86) (DECC) ① [2] **417 345-2DH2**
Cpte H. Behrens, C. Ludwig, N. Secunde, R. Ulfung, J. Hynninen, B. Matthews, E. Rawlins, D. Labelle, B. Cresswell, M. Napier, J. Khara, W. Hillhouse, D. Kesling, C. Haymon, Tanglewood Fest Chor, Boston SO, S. Ozawa (pp1988) (4/89) (PHIL) ① [2] **422 574-2PH2**
Cpte E. Marton, M. Lipovšek, C. Studer, H. Winkler, B. Weikl, K. Moll, V. Wheeler, D. Giepel, U. Ress, A. Kuhn, C. Anhorn, D. Evangelatos, S. Close, B. Calm, J. Faulkner, C.M. Petrig, Bavarian Rad Chor, BRSO, W. Sawallisch (r1990) (12/90) (EMI) ① [2] **CDS7 54067-2**
Cpte E. Schlüter, G. Hammer, A. Kupper, P. Markwort, R. Hager, G. Neidlinger, E. Schwier, K. Lange, F. Göllnitz, H. Siegel, C. Autenrieth, M. von Ilosvay, H. Gura, M. Wulf, L. Bischof, S. Mirtsch, Hamburg St Op Chor, Hamburg PO, E. Jochum (pp1944) (7/93) (ACAN) ① [2] **ACAN44 2128-2**
Cpte I. Borkh, J. Madeira, M. Schech, F. Uhl, D. Fischer-Dieskau, F. Teschler, R. Reinecke, H. Ambros, G. Unger, S. Vogel, I. Steingruber, C. Ahlin, M. Sjöstedt, S. Wagner, J. Hellwig, G. Schreyer, Dresden St Op Chor, Staatskapelle Dresden, K. Böhm (r1960) (11/94) (DG) ① [2] **445 329-2GX2**
Excs G. Rünger, H. Konetzni, Vienna St Op Chor, Vienna St Op Orch, H. Knappertsbusch (pp1941) *Concert* (9/95) (SCHW) ① [2] **314662**
2. B. Nilsson, VPO, G. Solti (r1966/7) *Concert* (10/93) (DECC) ① **436 461-2DM**
2, 20. R. Pauly, E. Schipper, Vienna St Op Orch, H. Knappertsbusch (pp1936) *Concert* (12/95) (SCHW) ① [2] **314672**
2, 6, 26. I. Borkh, P. Schoeffler, F. Yeend, Chicago Lyric Op Chor, Chicago SO, F. Reiner (r1956) *Concert* (5/93) (RCA) ① **GD60874**

Feuersnot—opera: 1 act, Op. 50 (1901—Dresden) (Lib. E von Wolzogen)
Feuersnot! Minnegebot! J. Varady, B. Weikl, Munich RO, H. Fricke *Concert* (3/89) (ACAN) ① **43 266**
Feuersnot! Minnegebot! M. Cebotari, K. Schmitt-Walter, Berlin RSO, A. Rother (bp1943) *Concert* (8/95) (PREI) ① **90222**
Love scene Toronto SO, A. Davis (r1994) *Concert* (11/95) (CBC) ① **SMCD5142**

Die **Frau ohne Schatten—opera: 3 acts, Op. 65 (1919—Vienna)** (Lib. H von Hofmannsthal)
EXCERPTS: ACT ONE: 1. Licht überm See; 2. Amme! Wachst du?; 3. Ist mein Liebster dahin; 4. Wie soll ich denn nicht weinen?; 5. Amme, um alles, wo find' ich den Schatten?; 6. Flight down to Earth; 7. Dieb! Da nimm!; 8. Sie aus dem Hause; 9. Dritthalb Jahr bin ich dein Weib; 10. Was wollt ihr hier?; 11. Ach, Herrin, süsse Herrin!; 12. Hat es dich blutige Tränen gekostet; 13. Mutter, Mutter, lass uns nach Hause!; 14. Trag' ich die Ware selber zu Markt; 15. Sie haben es mir gesagt. ACT TWO: 16. Komm bald wieder nach Haus, mein Gebieter; 17. Was ist nun deine Rede, du Prinzessin; 18. Orchestral Interlude; 19. Falke, Falke, du wiedergefundener; 20. Stille...O weh, Falke, o weh!; 21. Es gibt derer, die haben immer Zeit; 22. Schlange, was hab' ich mit dir zu schaffen; 23. Ein Handwerk verstehst du sicher nicht; 24. Wer da?; 25. Sieh - Amme - sieh; 26. Zum Lebenswasser!; 27. Wehe, mein Mann!; 28. Es dunkelt, dass ich nicht sehe zur Arbeit; 29. Es gibt derer; 30. Das Weib ist irre; 31. Barak, ich hab' es nicht getan!. ACT THREE: 32. Schweigt doch, ihr Stimmen!; 33. Mir anvertraut; 34. Auf, geh nach oben, Mann; 35. Sie kommen!; 36. Fort mit uns; 37. Aus unsern Taten steigt ein Gericht!; 38. Was Menschen bedfürfen?; 39. Keikobad! Deine Dienerin; 40. Weh uns Armen!; 41. Vater, bist du's?; 42. Goldenen Trank; 43. Ach! Weh mir! Mein Liebster starr!; 44. Wenn das Herz aus Kristall... 45. Sind das die Cherubim; 46. Engel sind's, die von sich sagen!; 47. Trifft mich sein Lieben nicht; 48. Nun will ich jubeln; 49. Vater, dir drohet nichts.
Cpte C. Studer, R. Kollo, U. Vinzing, A. Muff, H. Schwarz, A. Schmidt, J. Kaufman, P. Frey, C. Sieden, M. Lipovšek, J-H. Rootering, K. Rydl, K. Garrison, Tolz Boys' Ch, Bavarian Rad Chor, BRSO, W. Sawallisch (r1987) (9/88) (EMI) ① [3] **CDS7 49074-2**
Cpte J. Varady, P. Domingo, H. Behrens, J. Van Dam, R. Runkel, A. Dohmen, S. Jo, R. Gambill, E. Ardam, E. Lind, G. Hornik, H. Franzen, W. Gahmlich, Vienna Boys' Ch, Vienna St Op Chor, VPO, G. Solti (5/92) (DECC) ① [3] **436 243-2DH3**
Cpte Leonie Rysanek, J. King, B. Nilsson, W. Berry, R. Hesse, P. Wimberger, Lotte Rysanek, E. Aichberger, G. Jahn, H. Helm, L. Alvary, M. Dickie, Vienna St Op Chor, Vienna St Op Orch, K. Böhm (pp1977) (11/94) (DG) ① [3] **445 325-2GX3**
Excs F. Völker, V. Ursuleac, G. Rünger, Vienna St Op Chor, Vienna St Op Orch, C. Krauss (pp1933) *Concert* (9/95) (SCHW) ① [2] **314662**
Symphonic fantasy Rotterdam PO, J. Tate *Concert* (4/93) (EMI) ① **CDC7 54581-2**
2(pt), 3, 8(pt), 9, 11, 12(pt), 15(pt), 19, 25, 31-33, 36(pt), 37, 41, 44, 47, 48. T. Ralf, H. Konetzni, E. Höngen, H. Alsen, E. Loose, W. Wenkoff, E. Boettcher, M. Frutschnigg, J. Herrmann, E. Schulz, G. Monthy, M. Rus, W. Wernigk, A. Poell, T. Neralič, R. Neumann, Vienna St Op Chor, Vienna St Op Orch, K. Böhm (pp1943) *Concert* (11/94) (SCHW) ① [2] **314552**

20b E. Ruziczka, A. Kipnis, Berlin St Op Orch, E. Orthmann (r1931) *Concert*
(10/93) (NIMB) Ⓓ **NI7848**
20c Hollywood Bowl SO, J. Mauceri (r1993) *Concert*
(6/94) (PHIL) Ⓓ **438 685-2PH**
30. M. Cebotari, P. Buchner, T. Lemnitz, Berlin RSO, A. Rother (bp1943) *Concert* (8/95) (PREI) Ⓓ **90222**
30, 31. R. Fleming, K. Battle, F. von Stade, A. Schmidt, BPO, C. Abbado (pp1992) *Concert*
(7/93) (SONY) Ⓓ **SK52565**
31. E. Berger, T. Lemnitz, Berlin St Op Orch, C. Krauss (r1936) *Concert* (12/91) (PREI) Ⓓ **89035**
31. E. Berger, T. Lemnitz, Berlin St Op Orch, C. Krauss (r1936) *Concert* (10/93) (NIMB) Ⓓ **NI7848**
31. R. Stevens, E. Berger, RCA SO, F. Reiner (r1951) *Concert*
(4/94) (RCA) Ⓓ [6] **09026 61580-2(5)**
31. E. Hadrabová, M. Gerhard, Vienna St Op Orch, C. Krauss (pp1933) *Concert*
(6/94) (SCHW) Ⓓ **314502**
32. SNO, N. Järvi *Concert*
(2/90) (CHAN) Ⓓ **CHAN8758**
32. BBC Welsh SO, T. Otaka *Concert*
(9/90) (NIMB) Ⓓ **NI5235**
32. Stuttgart RSO, N. Marriner *Concert*
(9/92) (CAPR) Ⓓ **10 369**
32. VPO, A. Previn (r1992) *Concert*
(11/93) (DG) Ⓓ **437 790-2GH**
32. Hallé, J. Barbirolli (pp1969) *Concert*
(10/95) (BBCR) Ⓓ [2] **DMCD98**
32. Cincinnati SO, J. López-Cobos (r1994) *Concert*
(12/95) (TELA) Ⓓ **CD80371**
32a-e BRSO, L. Maazel (r1995) *Concert*
(10/95) (RCA) Ⓓ **09026 68225-2**
32e Bavarian St Orch, R. Strauss (r1941) *Concert*
(8/95) (PREI) Ⓓ [2] **90205**
33. SNO, N. Järvi *Concert*
(12/90) (CHAN) Ⓓ **CHAN8834**
33. Slovak PO, Z. Košler *Concert*
(2/91) (NAXO) Ⓓ **8 550342**
33. SO, T. Beecham (r1916) *Concert*
(11/91) (SYMP) Ⓓ [2] **SYMCD1096/7**
33. Seattle SO, G. Schwarz *Concert*
(10/92) (DELO) Ⓓ **DE3109**
33. Chicago SO, F. Reiner (r1957) *Concert*
(12/92) (RCA) Ⓓ **09026 60930-2**
33. Staatskapelle Dresden, R. Kempe (r1973: arr Kempe) *Concert*
(12/92) (EMI) Ⓓ [3] **CMS7 64346-2**

Der **Rosenkavalier—music for the film version, Av112 (1925)**
Tivoli Augmented Orch, R. Strauss (r1926) *Alpensinfonie.* (1/93) (KOCH) Ⓓ **37132-2**
Tivoli Augmented Orch, R. Strauss (r1926) *Alpensinfonie.* (4/93) (EMI) Ⓓ **CDC7 54610-2**

Salome—opera: 1 act, Op. 54 (1905—Dresden) (Lib. O Wilde, trans H Lachmann)
1. Dance of the Seven Veils; 2. Ach, du wolltest mich nicht deinen Mund küssen lassen.
Cpte B. Nilsson, E. Waechter, G. Stolze, G. Hoffman, W. Kmentt, J. Veasey, T. Krause, N. Douglas, Z. Koznowski, H. Holecek, T. Kirschbichler, L. Maikl, VPO, G. Solti (7/85) (DECC) Ⓓ [2] **414 414-2DH2**
Cpte H. Behrens, J. Van Dam, K-W. Böhm, A. Baltsa, W. Ochman, H. Angervo, J. Bastin, D. Ellenbeck, G. Nienstedt, K. Rydl, H. Von Bömches, H. Nitsche, VPO, H. von Karajan
(12/87) (EMI) Ⓓ [2] **CDS7 49358-2**
Cpte M. Caballé, S. Milnes, Richard Lewis, R. Resnik, J. King, J. Hamari, M. Rippon, G. Griffiths, N. Howlett, D. Kelly, D. Wicks, E. Bainbridge, LSO, E. Leinsdorf (r1968) (9/90) (RCA) Ⓓ [2] **GD86644**
Cpte C. Studer, B. Terfel, H. Hiestermann, Leonie Rysanek, C. Bieber, M. Rørholm, F. Molsberger, R. Lukas, W. Murray, B. Rundgren, K. Lang, Berlin Deutsche Op Orch, G. Sinopoli
(9/91) (DG) Ⓓ [2] **431 810-2GH2**
Cpte I. Borkh, H. Hotter, M. Lorenz, I. Barth, L. Fehenberger, K. Sabo, M. Proebstl, A. Peter, A. Keil, F. Friedrich, C. Hoppe, G. Ebeling, Bavarian St Orch, J. Keilberth (pp1951)
(9/94) (ORFE) Ⓓ [2] **C342932I**
Cpte J. Norman, J. Morris, W. Raffeiner, K. Witt, R. Leech, A. Markert, F. Schiller, H. Peeters, J. Commichau, R. Tomaszewski, M. Henneberg, Staatskapelle Dresden, S. Ozawa (r1990)
(10/94) (PHIL) Ⓓ [2] **432 153-2PH2**
Cpte G. Jones, D. Fischer-Dieskau, R. Cassilly, M. Dunn, W. Ochman, U. Boese, H. Sotin, H. Wilhelm, K. Moll, C. Schultz, F. Grundheber, W. Hartmann, Hamburg St Op Orch, K. Böhm (pp1970)
(11/94) (DG) Ⓓ [2] **445 319-2GX2**
Cpte C. Malfitano, B. Terfel, K. Riegel, H. Schwarz, K. Begley, R. Stene, P. Rose, M. Gantner, F. Olsen, G. Paucker, W. Zeh, R. Braga, VPO, C. von Dohnányi (r1994)
(4/95) (DECC) Ⓓ [2] **444 178-2DHO2**
Cincinnati SO, J. López-Cobos (r1994) *Concert*
(12/95) (TELA) Ⓓ **CD80371**
Excs J. Witt, E. Schürhoff, E. Schulz, P. Schoeffler, A. Dermota, D. With, H. Alsen, H. Schweiger, C. Bissuti, K. Ettl, Vienna St Op Orch, R. Strauss (pp1942) *Concert* (11/94) (SCHW) Ⓓ [2] **314532**
Excs H. Hotter, E. Schulz, A. Dermota, J. Sattler, M. Bugarinovic, Vienna St Op Orch, R. Strauss (pp1942) *Concert* (11/94) (SCHW) Ⓓ [2] **314532**
Excs M. Jeritza, G. Graarud, B. Paalen, E. Schipper, G. Maikl, J. von Manowarda, Wolken, Vienna St Op Orch, H. Reichenberger (pp1933) *Concert*
(11/95) (SCHW) Ⓓ [2] **314622**
Jokanaan, ich bin verliebt J. Gadski, orch (r1908) *Concert* (7/91) (CLUB) Ⓓ **CL99-109**
Jokanaan, ich bin verliebt E. Destinn, orch, B. Seidler-Winkler (r1907) *Concert*
(5/94) (SUPR) Ⓓ **11 1337-2**
Jokanaan, ich bin verliebt E. Destinn, orch, B. Seidler-Winkler (r1907) *Concert*
(12/94) (SUPR) Ⓓ [12] **11 2136-2(1)**
1. BPO, H. von Karajan (r1972) *Concert*
(4/88) (DG) Ⓓ **415 853-2GGA**
1. SNO, N. Järvi *Concert*
(2/90) (CHAN) Ⓓ **CHAN8758**
1. Philh, O. Klemperer *Concert*
(5/90) (EMI) Ⓓ **CDM7 63350-2**
1. Seattle SO, G. Schwarz *Concert*
(9/90) (DELO) Ⓓ **DE3052**
1. Berlin St Op Orch, O. Klemperer (r1928) *Concert*
(11/91) (KOCH) Ⓓ **37053-2**
1. Berlin RSO, H.M. Schneidt *Concert*
(5/92) (CAPR) Ⓓ **10 380**
1. NBC SO, A. Toscanini (bp1939) *Concert*
(11/92) (RCA) Ⓓ **GD60296**
1. Staatskapelle Dresden, R. Kempe (r1970) *Concert*
(12/92) (EMI) Ⓓ [3] **CMS7 64346-2**
1. Chicago SO, F. Reiner (r1954) *Concert*
(5/93) (RCA) Ⓓ **GD60874**
1. VPO, C. Krauss (r1941) *Concert*
(5/93) (KOCH) Ⓓ **37129-2**
1. VPO, A. Previn (r1992) *Concert*
(11/93) (DG) Ⓓ **437 790-2GH**
1. NYPO, L. Bernstein (r1968) *Concert*
(9/94) (SONY) Ⓓ **SMK47625**
1. NY Stadium SO, L. Stokowski (r c1958) *Concert*
(4/95) (EVER) Ⓓ **EVC9004**
1, 2. L. Price, Boston SO, E. Leinsdorf *Concert*
(8/90) (RCA) Ⓓ **GD60398**
2. M. Lawrence, Pasdeloup Orch, P. Coppola (French: r1934) *Concert* (5/90) (PREI) Ⓓ **89011**
2. I. Borkh, Chicago SO, F. Reiner (r1955) *Concert*
(5/93) (RCA) Ⓓ **GD60874**
2. M. Caballé, FNO, L. Bernstein *Concert*
(5/93) (DG) Ⓓ **431 103-2GB**
2. M. Cebotari, Berlin RSO, A. Rother (bp1943) *Concert* (8/95) (PREI) Ⓓ **90222**

Salomé—opera: 1 act (1907—Paris) (Lib. O Wilde)
Cpte K. Huffstodt, J. Van Dam, J. Dupouy, H. Jossoud, J-L. Viala, H. Perraguin, J. Bastin, A. Gabriel, V. le Texier, F. Dumont, Y. Bisson, C. Goldsack, Lyon Op Orch, K. Nagano
(1/92) (VIRG) Ⓓ [2] **VCD7 59054-2**

Schlagobers—ballet: 2 acts, Op. 70 (1924—Vienna)
Tokyo Metropolitan SO, H. Wakasugi
(1/90) (DENO) Ⓓ **CO-73414**
Waltz Staatskapelle Dresden, R. Kempe (r1971) *Concert* (12/92) (EMI) Ⓓ [3] **CMS7 64346-2**

Die **Schweigsame Frau, '(The) Silent Woman'—opera: 3 acts, Op. 80 (1935—Dresden)** (Lib. S Zweig, after B Johnson)
EXCERPTS: 1. Potpourri (Overture). ACT 1: 2. Ei, die Ehre, die Ehre!; 3. Ruhe? Warum soll ich Ruhe halten?; 4. Ha! Eine schweigsame Frau? Ein Meer ohne Salz?; 5. Es wird Abend, der Ofen friert kalt; 6a. Ah! Mein Stock!; 6b. Henry?; 7a. Kleiner humoristischer Marsch; 7b. Das deine Truppen? Deine Soldaten?; 8. Ruhe! Ruhe in meinem Haus!; 9. Oh Gott, war das ein saurer Empfang!; 10. Da unten im Keller stehn allerhand Kisten; 11. Nicht am mich, an mich, Geliebter, denke; 12. Sehr rechtschaffen gedacht, junger Herr; 13a. Nun, meine Schätzchen, hätte nicht eine von euch Lust; 13b. Ich würde lachen; 13c. Ich würde singen!; 14. Hah!..Was ist?...Mir fällt etwas ein!; 15a. Seid ihr bereit?; 15b. Ja, das wollen wir probieren. ACT 2: 16. Den Paraderock mit den vergoldeten Schnüren!; 17. Euer Gnaden gehorsamster Diener!; 18. Nur das Eine lasst Euch bitten; 19. Wohl tut ihr, das Haupt zu neigen; 20. Ui je, i hab an Angst!; 21. Dieses ist ein junges Fräulein; 22. Gestattet, dass ich Euch noch dieses edle Fräulein präsentiere!; 23. Sie ist die Rechte!; 24. So stumm, mein Kind, und noch immer so scheu?; 25. Ei, ei, wie rasch das Arcanum wirkt!; 26. Anhiero gestatte ich mir, hochverehrliche Herren; 27. Ich dank Euch, ehrwürdiger, und Euch, hochgelehrter Herr; 28a. Potz Deubel, so hat die alte Hur diesmal doch; 28b. Vorwärts, brave Kameramden; 28c. Heda Nachbarn, heda Leute; 28d. Ist es möglich, Sir Morosus?; 29. Nehmt's nicht so streng als es erscheint; 30. Du bist so still und scheinst bedrückt!; 31. Ruhe! hab ich dir gesagt!!!; 32. Was geht hier vor? Sind die Türken im Haus?; 33. Siehst du, Ohm, das ist die richtige Art; 34. Aminta! Aminta! Du süssester Engel. ACT 3: 35. Introduction; 36. Hier die Spiegel, die Konsolen; 37. 'L'incoronazione di Poppea' - Sento un certo non so che; 38. Dolce amor!; 39. Seine illustre Lordschaft, der Chef-Justice, werden in wenigen Minuten; 40. Mit Reverenz! Vieledle Dame!; 41. Gnädigster Herr...zwei Karossen sind angefahren; 42a. Meinen submissesten Respekt; 42b. Es haben der hochgeborene Lord Morosus und die hochgeborene Lady Morosus; 43. Könnt ihr bezungen, dass Lady Morusus Umgang; 44. Hohes Gericht, ich habe einen weiteren Zeugen bereit; 45. Willst du wirklich mich nicht kennen?; 46a. Endlich bin ich ihrer ledig!; 46b. Ich opponiere!; 47. Teurer Ohm! Nicht länger kann ich Eure Not und Sorge schaun; 48. Wie? Was? Kameraden... 49. Die Ihr feindlich aufgenommen; 50. Wie schön ist doch die
Cpte H. Hotter, G. von Milinkovic, H. Prey, F. Wunderlich, H. Gueden, P. Alarie, H. Plümacher, J. Knapp, K. Dönch, A. Pernerstorfer, Vienna St Op Chor, VPO, K. Böhm (pp1959)
(11/94) (DG) Ⓓ [2] **445 335-2GX2**
1. Rotterdam PO, J. Tate *Concert*
(4/93) (EMI) Ⓓ **CDC7 54581-2**
1. Toronto SO, A. Davis (r1994) *Concert*
(11/95) (CBC) Ⓓ **SMCD5142**
40. M. Salminen, Lahti SO, E. Klas *Concert*
(8/92) (BIS) Ⓓ **BIS-CD520**

STRAVINSKY, Igor (Fyodorovich) *(1882–1971)* *Russia/France/USA*

SECTION I: ORCHESTRAL

Bluebird Pas-de-deux—small orchestra (1941) (arr from Tchaikovsky 'The Sleeping Beauty')
Columbia SO, I. Stravinsky *Concert*
(8/92) (SONY) Ⓓ [3] **SM3K46292**

Capriccio—piano and orchestra (1928-29)
P. Crossley, London Sinfonietta, E-P. Salonen *Concert* (10/90) (SONY) Ⓓ **SK45797**
I. Stravinsky, Walther Straram Orch, E. Ansermet (r1930) *Concert* (5/93) (EMI) Ⓓ [2] **CDS7 54607-2**
J-M. Sanromá, Boston SO, S. Koussevitzky (r1940) *Concert* (6/93) (PEAR) Ⓓ **GEMMCD9020**
O. Mustonen, Berlin Deutsches SO, Vladimir Ashkenazy (r1992) *Concert*
(1/94) (DECC) Ⓓ **440 229-2DH**
G. Tozer, SRO, N. Järvi (r1993) *Concert*
(2/94) (CHAN) Ⓓ [5] **CHAN9240**
G. Tozer, SRO, N. Järvi (r1993) *Concert*
(2/94) (CHAN) Ⓓ **CHAN9238**
J. Ogdon, ASMF, N. Marriner (r1970) *Concert*
(4/95) (DECC) Ⓓ **443 577-2DCS**
M. Haas, Berlin RIAS Orch, F. Fricsay (r1951) *Concert* (11/95) (DG) Ⓓ [2] **447 343-2GDB2**

Le **Chant du Rossignol, 'Song of the Nightingale'—symphonic poem for orchestra (1917)** (arr cpsr from Acts 2 and 3 of 'The Nightingale')
EXCERPTS: 1. The fête in the emperor of China's palace; 2. The two nightingales; 3. Illness and recovery of the emperor of China.
FNO, P. Boulez *Pulcinella.*
(5/86) (ERAT) Ⓓ **2292-45382-2**
Seattle SO, G. Schwarz *Firebird.*
(10/87) (DELO) Ⓓ **DE3051**
LSO, A. Dorati *Concert*
(11/91) (MERC) Ⓓ **432 012-2MM**
Danish Nat RSO, D. Kitaienko *Firebird.*
(9/92) (CHAN) Ⓓ **CHAN8967**
Finnish RSO, J-P. Saraste *Concert*
(9/92) (VIRG) Ⓓ **VC7 59267-2**
SRO, N. Järvi (r1993) *Concert*
(2/94) (CHAN) Ⓓ [5] **CHAN9240**
SRO, N. Järvi (r1993) *Concert*
(2/94) (CHAN) Ⓓ **CHAN9238**

Ave Maria—4vv a capella (1934 rev 1949)
(Wds. Slavonic text, rev Latin)
Tallis Scholars, P. Phillips *Concert*
　　　　　(6/91) (GIME) ① **CDGIM002**
Westminster Cath Ch, J. O'Donnell *Concert*
　　　　　(9/91) (HYPE) ① **CDA64437**
Voronezh Chbr Ch (1934 Slavonic vers) *Concert*
　　　　　(2/92) (HYPE) ① **CDA64410**
Cambridge Sngrs, J. Rutter *Concert*
　　　　　(4/92) (CLLE) ① **COLCD116**
Trinity Coll Ch, Cambridge, R. Marlow (r1994)
Concert　　(6/95) (CONI) ① **75605 51232-2**
**Babel—cantata (male chorus, male narrator
and large orchestra) (1944)** (Wds. Bible)
D. Fischer-Dieskau, Stuttgart Rad Chor, Stuttgart
RSO, G. Bertini *Concert*
　　　　　(8/87) (ORFE) ① **C015821A**
**Balanchine-Stravinsky Chorale—mixed
chorus a cappella (1946)**
Gregg Smith Sngrs, R. Craft (r1991/2) *Concert*
　　　　　(6/94) (MUSM) ① **67113-2**
**Cantata on Old English texts—soprano,
tenor, female chorus and chamber ensemble
(1952)**
Y. Kenny, J. Aler, London Sinfonietta Chor, London
Sinfonietta, E-P. Salonen *Concert*
　　　　　(10/91) (SONY) ① **SK46667**
**Canticum sacrum ad honorem Sancti Marci
nominis—TB, chorus and orchestra (1955)**
(wds. Bible)
J.M. Ainsley, S. Roberts, Westminster Cath Ch, CLS,
J. O'Donnell *Concert* (9/91) (HYPE) ① **CDA64437**
C. Ciesinski, J. Humphries, D. Evitts, M. Wait, St
Luke's Orch, R. Craft *Concert*
　　　　　(10/95) (MUSM) ① **67152-2**
**Cats' Cradle Songs—mezzo and three
clarinets (1915-16)** (Wds. trad Russian)
A. Murray, Paris InterContemporain Ens, P. Boulez
Concert　　(2/92) (DG) ① **431 751-2GC**
C. Ciesinski, St Luke's Orch, R. Craft *Concert*
　　　　　(10/95) (MUSM) ① **67152-2**
**Choral Variations on 'Vom Himmel
hoch'—chorus and orchestra (1955-56)** (orch
from J.S. Bach)
Westminster Ch, orch, I. Stravinsky *Concert*
　　　　　(12/93) (ARHI) ① **ADCD110**
Gregg Smith Sngrs, St. Luke's Orch, R. Craft
(r1991/2) *Concert* (6/94) (MUSM) ① **67113-2**
Credo—4vv a capella (1932 rev 1949 & 1964)
(Wds. Slavonic text, rev 1964: rev Latin 1949)
Westminster Cath Ch, J. O'Donnell *Concert*
　　　　　(9/91) (HYPE) ① **CDA64437**
Voronezh Chbr Ch (1964 Slavonic vers) *Concert*
　　　　　(2/92) (HYPE) ① **CDA64410**
**The Dove descending breaks—anthem: 4vv
a capella (1962)**
New London Chmbr Ch *Concert*
　　　　　(2/92) (HYPE) ① **CDA64410**
Trinity Coll Ch, Cambridge, R. Marlow (r1994)
Concert　　(6/95) (CONI) ① **75605 51232-2**
C. Ciesinski, J. Humphries, D. Evitts, M. Wait, St
Luke's Orch, R. Craft *Concert*
　　　　　(10/95) (MUSM) ① **67152-2**
**Elegy for JFK—baritone/mezzo and 3
clarinets (1964)** (Wds. Auden)
D. Fischer-Dieskau, H. Gruber, K.T. Adler, K. Berger
Concert　　(8/87) (ORFE) ① **C015821A**
J. Shirley-Quirk, Paris InterContemporain Ens, P.
Boulez *Concert* (2/92) (DG) ① **431 751-2GC**
**In memoriam Dylan Thomas: dirge canons
and song—tenor, string quartet and 4
trombones (1954)**
R. Tear, Paris InterContemporain Ens, P. Boulez
Concert　　(2/92) (DG) ① **431 751-2GC**
**Introitus in memoriam T. S. Eliot—male
voices and chamber ensemble (1965)**
New London Chmbr Ch, Ens, J. Wood *Concert*
　　　　　(2/92) (HYPE) ① **CDA64410**
**3 Japanese Lyrics—sop & pf/2 fl, 2 cl, pf &
stg qt (1912-13)** (wds. trans A Brandta)
1. Akahito; 2. Mazatsumi; 3. Tsaraiuki.
Y. Furusawa, SRO, E. Ansermet (bp1950) *Concert*
　　　　　(1/01) (CLAV) ① **CD50-8918**
J. Manning, Nash Ens, S. Rattle (r1977) *Concert*
　　　　　(10/91) (CHAN) ① **CHAN6535**
D. Upshaw, Inst Ens *Concert*
　　　　　(11/91) (NONE) ① **7559-79262-2**
P. Bryn-Julson, Paris InterContemporain Ens, P.
Boulez *Concert* (2/92) (DG) ① **431 751-2GC**
**3 Little Songs—voice and piano (c1906 rev
1913)** (wds. trad Russian)
1. The Magpie; 2. The Rook; 3. The Jackdaw.
P. Bryn-Julson, Paris InterContemporain Ens, P.
Boulez *Concert* (2/92) (DG) ① **431 751-2GC**

**Mass—mixed chorus and double wind
quintet (1944-48)**
English Bach Fest Chor, Trinity Boys' Ch, English
Bach Fest Orch, L. Bernstein *Noces.*
　　　　　(6/88) (DG) ① **423 251-2GC**
Westminster Cath Ch, CLS, J. O'Donnell *Concert*
　　　　　(9/91) (HYPE) ① **CDA64437**
Trinity Coll Ch, Cambridge, London Musici, R.
Marlow (r1994) *Concert*
　　　　　(6/95) (CONI) ① **75605 51232-2**
C. Ciesinski, J. Humphries, D. Evitts, M. Wait, St
Luke's Orch, R. Craft *Concert*
　　　　　(10/95) (MUSM) ① **67152-2**
**Pastorale—soprano and piano/chamber
ensemble (1907 instr 1923)**
P. Bryn-Julson, Paris InterContemporain Ens, P.
Boulez *Concert* (2/92) (DG) ① **431 751-2GC**
Pater noster—4vv a capella (1926 rev 1949)
(Wds. Slavonic text, rev Latin)
Lower Rhine Choral Soc, H. Schmitt *Concert*
　　　　　(2/90) (SCHW) ① **313001**
Tallis Scholars, P. Phillips *Concert*
　　　　　(6/91) (GIME) ① **CDGIM002**
Westminster Cath Ch, J. O'Donnell *Concert*
　　　　　(9/91) (HYPE) ① **CDA64437**
Voronezh Chbr Ch (1926 Slavonic vers) *Concert*
　　　　　(2/92) (HYPE) ① **CDA64410**
Trinity Coll Ch, Cambridge, R. Marlow (r1994)
Concert　　(6/95) (CONI) ① **75605 51232-2**
**2 Poems of Konstantin Bal'mont—soprano,
tenor and piano; chamber ensemble (1911
orch 1954)**
1. The flower; 2. The dove.
J. Manning, Robert Russell Bennett (r1977) *Concert*
　　　　　(10/91) (CHAN) ① **CHAN6535**
D. Upshaw, Inst Ens *Concert*
　　　　　(11/91) (NONE) ① **7559-79262-2**
P. Bryn-Julson, Paris InterContemporain Ens, P.
Boulez *Concert* (2/92) (DG) ① **431 751-2GC**
**2 Poems of Paul Verlaine—baritone and
piano, Op. 9 (1910 orch 1910 and 1951)**
1. Sagesse; 2. La bonne chanson.
D. Fischer-Dieskau, Stuttgart RSO, G. Bertini
Concert　　(8/87) (ORFE) ① **C015821A**
J. Shirley-Quirk, Paris InterContemporain Ens, P.
Boulez *Concert* (2/92) (DG) ① **431 751-2GC**
**Pribaoutki—male voice and chamber
ensemble (1914)** (Wds. trad Russian)
1. Kornillo; 2. Natashka; 3. The colonel; 4. The old
man and the hare.
J. Shirley-Quirk, Paris InterContemporain Ens, P.
Boulez *Concert* (2/92) (DG) ① **431 751-2GC**
C. Ciesinski, St Luke's Orch, R. Craft *Concert*
　　　　　(10/95) (MUSM) ① **67152-2**
**Requiem canticles—alto, bass, chorus and
orchestra (1965-66)**
S. Bickley, D. Wilson-Johnson, New London Chbr
Ch, London Sinfonietta, O. Knussen (r1994) *Concert*
　　　　　(10/95) (DG) ① **447 068-2GH**
**4 Russian Peasant Songs—female voices
(1914-17)**
1. On saints' days in Chigisakh (4vv); 2. Ovsen (2vv);
3. The pike (3 solo vv); 4. Master Portly (1 solo v).
Voronezh Chbr Ch, New London Chmbr Ch, Ens, J.
Wood (1954 revision) *Concert*
　　　　　(2/92) (HYPE) ① **CDA64410**
Voronezh Chbr Ch, New London Chmbr Ch, Ens, J.
Wood (1954 revision) *Concert*
　　　　　(2/92) (HYPE) ① **CDA64410**
3 Shakespeare Songs (1953)
1. Musick to heare; 2. Full fathom five; 3. When
daisies pied.
A. Murray, Paris InterContemporain Ens, P. Boulez
Concert　　(2/92) (DG) ① **431 751-2GC**
4 Songs (1953-54) (Wds. cpsr)
1. The Drake; 2. A Russian spiritual; 3. Three geese
and swans; 4. Tilimbom.
P. Bryn-Julson, Paris InterContemporain Ens, P.
Boulez *Concert* (2/92) (DG) ① **431 751-2GC**
1. J. Manning, Robert Russell Bennett (r1977)
Concert　　(10/91) (CHAN) ① **CHAN6535**
**3 Stories for children—voice and piano
(1915-17)** (wds. trad Russian)
1. Tilimbom; 2. Geese, swans; 3. The bear's little
song.
1. P. Bryn-Julson, Paris InterContemporain Ens, P.
Boulez *Concert* (2/92) (DG) ① **431 751-2GC**
1. A. Kipnis, C. Dougherty (r1939) *Concert*
　　　　　(9/92) (RCA) ① **GD60522**
Stravinsky in his own words
I. Stravinsky *Concert*
　　　　　(8/92) (SONY) ① **SM2K46294**
**Symphony of Psalms—chorus and orchestra
(1930 rev 1948)** (Wds. Bible (Vulgate))
Stuttgart Rad Chor, Stuttgart RSO, G. Bertini *Concert*
　　　　　(8/87) (ORFE) ① **C015821A**

Swedish Rad Ch, Swedish RSO, S. Ehrling *Rite of
Spring.*　　(9/88) (BIS) ① **BIS-CD400**
Berlin Deutsche Op Chor, BPO, H. von Karajan
Concert　　(12/88) (DG) ① **423 252-2GC**
FNC, FNO, I. Markevitch (pp1967) *Mahler:
Symphony 1.*　　(4/89) (MONT) ① **TCE8811**
Westminster Cath Ch, CLS, J. O'Donnell *Concert*
　　　　　(9/91) (HYPE) ① **CDA64437**
Atlanta Sym Chor, Atlanta SO, Robert Shaw *Verdi:
Pezzi sacri.*　　(10/92) (TELA) ① **CD80254**
Toronto Fest Sngrs, CBC SO, I. Stravinsky *Concert*
　　　　　(8/92) (SONY) ① **SM2K46294**
Czech Phil Chor, Czech PO, K. Ančerl *Oedipus Rex.*
　　　　　(3/93) (SUPR) ① **11 1947-2**
Vlassof Chor, Walther Straram Orch, I. Stravinsky
(r1931) *Concert* (5/93) (EMI) ① **[2] CDS7 54607-2**
Suisse Romande Chor Ch, Lausanne Pro Arte Ch,
Brassus Choral Soc, SRO, N. Järvi (r1993) *Concert*
　　　　　(2/94) (CHAN) ① **[5] CHAN9240**
Suisse Romande Chbr Ch, Lausanne Pro Arte Ch,
Brassus Choral Soc, SRO, N. Järvi (r1993) *Concert*
　　　　　(2/94) (CHAN) ① **CHAN9239**
LSC, LSO, M. Tilson Thomas (r1991) *Concert*
　　　　　(7/94) (SONY) ① **SK53275**
English Bach Fest Chor, LSO, L. Bernstein (r1972)
Concert　　(11/94) (SONY) ① **SMK47628**
Russian St Acad Ch, Russian St Acad Orch, I.
Markevitch (r1962) *Concert*
　　　　　(2/95) (PHIL) ① **[2] 438 973-2PM2**
Berlin RIAS Chor, Berlin RIAS Children's Chor, Berlin
St Hedwig's Cath Ch, Berlin RIAS Orch, F. Fricsay
(r1957) *Concert*
　　　　　(11/95) (DG) ① **[2] 447 343-2GDB2**
**2 Wolf Songs—mezzo and nine instruments
(1968)**
1. Herr, was trägt der Boden hier; 2. Wunden trägst
du.
A. Murray, Paris InterContemporain Ens, P. Boulez
Concert　　(2/92) (DG) ① **431 751-2GC**

┌─────────────────────────────────┐
│   SECTION V: STAGE WORKS   │
└─────────────────────────────────┘

Agon—ballet (1957—New York)
Cpte Berlin Deutsches SO, Vladimir Ashkenazy
(r1993) *Concert* (12/94) (DECC) ① **443 772-2DH**
Los Angeles Fest SO, I. Stravinsky *Concert*
　　　　　(8/92) (SONY) ① **[3] SM3K46292**
St. Luke's Orch, R. Craft (r1991/2) *Concert*
　　　　　(6/94) (MUSM) ① **67113-2**
Apollo—ballet: 2 scenes (1947) (revision of
Apollon musagète)
BPO, H. von Karajan (r1969) *Rite of Spring.*
　　　　　(9/86) (DG) ① **415 979-2GH**
CBSO, S. Rattle *Rite of Spring.*
　　　　　(11/89) (EMI) ① **CDC7 49636-2**
Columbia SO, I. Stravinsky *Concert*
　　　　　(8/92) (SONY) ① **[3] SM3K46292**
**Apollon musagète—ballet: 2 scenes
(1928—Washington)**
Cpte SRO, N. Järvi (r1993) *Concert*
　　　　　(2/94) (CHAN) ① **[5] CHAN9240**
Cpte SRO, N. Järvi (r1993) *Concert*
　　　　　(2/94) (CHAN) ① **CHAN9237**
Cpte Montreal Sinfonietta, C. Dutoit (r1992) *Concert*
　　　　　(9/94) (DECC) ① **440 327-2DH**
Cpte ASMF, N. Marriner (r1994) *Concert*
　　　　　(4/95) (DECC) ① **443 577-2DCS**
St John's Smith Square Orch, J. Lubbock *Concert*
　　　　　(9/88) (ASV) ① **CDDCA618**
BRSO, I. Stravinsky (pp1951) *Jeu de cartes.*
　　　　　(8/90) (ORFE) ① **C198891A**
LSO, I. Markevitch (r1954) *Concert*
　　　　　(1/94) (PHIL) ① **[2] 438 350-2PM2**
LSO, I. Markevitch (r1963) *Concert*
　　　　　(2/95) (PHIL) ① **[2] 438 973-2PM2**
BPO, H. von Karajan (r1972) *Concert*
　　　　　(5/95) (DG) ① **439 463-2GCL**
Apollo and Terpsichore Boston SO, S.
Koussevitzky (r1928) *Concert*
　　　　　(6/93) (PEAR) ① **GEMMCD9020**
**Le Baiser de la fée, '(The) Fairy's
Kiss'—ballet: 4 scènes (1928 rev
1950—Paris)**
Cpte Milan La Scala PO, R. Muti (1993) *Bartók:
Pictures, Sz46.*　　(9/95) (SONY) ① **SK58949**
SNO, N. Järvi *Tchaikovsky: Sleeping Beauty.*
　　　　　(7/85) (CHAN) ① **CHAN8360**
Columbia SO, I. Stravinsky *Concert*
　　　　　(8/92) (SONY) ① **[3] SM3K46292**
Excs Boston SO, I. Stravinsky (rehearsal) *Concert*
　　　　　(8/92) (ARHI) ① **ADCD110**
**The Firebird—concert suite from ballet
(1911)**
1. Introduction; 2. Kaschei's enchanted garden; 3.
Dance of the Firebird; 4. Supplication of the Firebird;

Cpte P. Donohoe, CBSO, S. Rattle *Symphony in 3 Movements*. (5/88) (EMI) ① **CDC7 49053-2**
Cpte Detroit SO, A. Dorati *Rite of Spring*. (1/89) (DECC) ① **417 758-2DM**
Cpte L. Howard, LSO, C. Abbado (1911 vers) *Mussorgsky: Pictures*. (3/89) (DG) ① **423 901-2GH**
Cpte RPO, Y. Temirkanov (r1988) *Rite of Spring*. (9/90) (RCA) ① **RD87985**
Cpte Baltimore SO, D. Zinman *Concert* (11/91) (TELA) ① **CD80270**
Cpte SO, I. Stravinsky (r1928) *Rite of Spring*. (1/92) (PEAR) ① **GEMMCD9329**
Cpte LPO, B. Haitink (1911 vers) *Rite of Spring*. (8/92) (PHIL) ① **434 147-2PM**
Cpte Columbia SO, I. Stravinsky (1911 vers) *Concert* (8/92) (SONY) ① [3] **SM3K46291**
Cpte Cleveland Orch, P. Boulez *Rite of Spring*. (9/92) (DG) ① **435 769-2GH**
Cpte Czech PO, K. Ančerl *Concert* (3/93) (SUPR) ① **11 1945-2**
Cpte New Philh, C. Mackerras (1911 vers) *Mussorgsky: Pictures*. (4/93) (VANG) ① **08.4065.71**
Cpte Philadelphia, L. Stokowski (r1937) *Concert* (5/93) (DUTT) ① **CDAX8002**
Cpte Philadelphia, L. Stokowski (r1937) *Rite of Spring*. (8/93) (RCA) ① **09026 61394-2**
Cpte LPO, B. Haitink (r1973) *Concert* (1/94) (PHIL) ① [2] **438 350-2PM2**
Cpte Oslo PO, M. Jansons (r1992) *Rite of Spring*. (1/94) (EMI) ① **CDC7 54899-2**
Cpte SRO, N. Järvi (r1993) *Concert* (2/94) (CHAN) ① [5] **CHAN9240**
Cpte SRO, N. Järvi (r1993) *Concert* (2/94) (CHAN) ① **CHAN9237**
Cpte Danish Nat RSO, D. Kitaienko (r1991) *Concert* (7/94) (CHAN) ① **CHAN9198**
Cpte Leningrad PO, E. Mravinsky (bp1946) *Prokofiev: Symphony 6*. (8/94) (MULT) ① **310189-2**
Cpte Boston SO, P. Monteux (r1959) *Concert* (9/94) (RCA) ① [15] **09026 61893-2**
Cpte Berlin RIAS Orch, F. Fricsay (r1953) *Concert* (11/94) (DG) ① **445 405-2GDO**
Cpte Berlin RIAS Orch, F. Fricsay (r1953) *Concert* (11/94) (DG) ① [11] **445 400-2GDO10**
Cpte NYPO, P. Boulez (r1969) *Rite of Spring*. (5/95) (SONY) ① **SMK64109**
Cpte LSO, C. Dutoit (r1975/6: 1911 vers) *Concert* (5/95) (DECC) ① **439 463-2GCL**
Cpte Concertgebouw, R. Chailly (r1992) *Pulcinella*. (6/95) (DECC) ① **443 774-2DH**
Cpte SRO, E. Ansermet (r1957; 1911 version) *Concert* (9/95) (DECC) ① [2] **443 467-2DF2**
Cpte Berlin RIAS Orch, F. Fricsay (r1952) *Concert* (11/95) (DG) ① [2] **447 343-2GDB2**
Philh, E-P. Salonen (r1991) *Orpheus*. (2/94) (SONY) ① **SK53274**
Minneapolis SO, A. Dorati (r1959) *Concert* (3/94) (MERC) ① **434 331-2MM**
1a-d, 4a-g NBC SO, A. Toscanini (bp1940) *Concert* (11/92) (RCA) ① **GD60323**
1d J. Szigeti, N. Magaloff (arr Dushkin & cpsr: r1937) *Concert* (1/90) (BIDD) ① [2] **LAB007/8**
1d, 3a, 4a, 4b, 4e, 4f Boston SO, S. Koussevitzky *Concert* (6/93) (PEAR) ① **GEMMCD9020**
Pulcinella—ballet (1920 (comp 1919-20) (Lib. cpsr)
Cpte Y. Kenny, J. Aler, J. Tomlinson, London Sinfonietta, E-P. Salonen *Concert* (1/92) (SONY) ① **SK45965**
Cpte I. Jordan, G. Shirley, D. Gramm, Columbia SO, I. Stravinsky *Concert* (8/92) (SONY) ① [3] **SM3K46292**
Cpte A. C. Antonacci, P. Ballo, W. Shimell, Concertgebouw, R. Chailly (r1993) *Petrushka*. (6/95) (DECC) ① **443 774-2DH**
A. Murray, A. Rolfe Johnson, S. Estes, FNO, P. Boulez *Chant du rossignol*. (5/86) (ERAT) ① **2292-45382-2**
T. Berganza, R. Davies, J. Shirley-Quirk, LSO, C. Abbado (rev) *Jeu de Cartes*. (1/89) (DG) ① **423 889-2GGA**
S. Graham, Gran Wilson, J. Opalach, Seattle SO, G. Schwarz *Rite of Spring*. (12/92) (DELO) ① **DE3100**
J. Smith, J. Fryatt, M. King, Northern Sinfonia, S. Rattle (r1977/8) *Weill: Sieben Todsünden*. (12/93) (EMI) ① **CDM7 64739-2**
Pulcinella—concert suite from ballet (1922 rev 1949) (1949 version unless indicated)
1. Sinfonia (Overture); 2. Serenata; 3. Scherzino - Allegro - Andantino; 4. Tarantella; 5. Toccata; 6. Gavotta con due variazioni; 7. Duetto (1949: Vivo); 8. Minuetto e Finale.
ECO, A. Gibson (1922 vers) *Danses concertantes*. (2/85) (CHAN) ① **CHAN8325**

VPO, C. Krauss (pp1952) *Concert* (2/92) (DG) ① [12] **435 321-2GWP12**
Limburg SO, S. Mas Conde *R. Strauss: Bourgeois gentilhomme suite*. (10/92) (SCHW) ① **310272**
Atlanta SO, Y. Levi *Rite of Spring*. (12/92) (TELA) ① **CD80266**
N German RSO, G. Wand (pp1991) *Tchaikovsky: Symphony 6*. (4/93) (RCA) ① **09026 61190-2**
NYPO, L. Bernstein (r1960) *Concert* (11/94) (SONY) ① **SMK47628**
ASMF, N. Marriner (r1967) *Concert* (4/95) (DECC) ① **443 577-2DCS**
1, 2. ECO, A. Gibson *Concert* (7/83) (CHAN) ① **CHAN8301**
The **Rake's Progress—opera: 3 acts (1951—Venice)** (Lib. W H Auden & C Kallman)
Cpte P. Langridge, C. Pope, S. Ramey, Sarah Walker, J. Dobson, A. Varnay, S. Dean, M. Best, London Sinfonietta Chor, London Sinfonietta, R. Chailly (2/85) (DECC) ① [2] **411 644-2DH2**
Cpte J. Garrison, J. West, J. Cheek, W. White, M. Lowery, S. Love, A. Woodley, J. Johnson, Gregg Smith Sngrs, St Luke's Orch, R. Craft (r1993) (3/95) (MUSM) ① [2] **67131-2**
Renard—burlesque in song and dance (1922—Paris)
Cpte T. Baker, D. Martin, D. Evitts, W. Pauley, St Luke's Orch, R. Craft (r1991-93) *Concert* (9/94) (MUSM) ① **67110-2**
H. Hetherington, P. Harrhy, P. Donnelly, N. Cavallier, Matrix Ens, R. Ziegler *Concert* (7/91) (ASV) ① **CDDCA758**
J. Aler, N. Robson, J. Tomlinson, D. Wilson-Johnson, London Sinfonietta, E-P. Salonen *Concert* (1/92) (SONY) ① **SK45965**
G. Shirley, L. Driscoll, W. Murphy, D. Gramm, T. Koves, Columbia Chbr Ens, I. Stravinsky *Concert* (8/92) (SONY) ① [3] **SM3K46291**
The **Rite of Spring, '(Le) sacre du printemps'—ballet: pictures from pagan Russia in 2 parts (1913, rev 1947—Paris)** (1947 version unless indicated)
PART 1: 1a. Introduction (Lento); 1b. The Augurs of Spring; 1c. Mock Abduction; 1d. Spring Round Dances; 1e. Games of the Rival Tribes; 1f. Procession of the Wise Elder; 1g. Adoration of the Earth; 1h. Dance of the Earth. PART 2: 2a. Introduction (Largo); 2b. Mystical Circles of the Young Girls; 2c. Glorification of the Chosen Victim; 2d. Summoning of the Ancestors; 2e. Ritual of the Ancestors; 2f. Sacrificial Dance.
Cpte BPO, H. von Karajan (r1975) *Apollo*. (9/86) (DG) ① **415 979-2GH**
Cpte LSO, C. Abbado *Firebird Suite (1919)*. (4/87) (DG) ① **415 854-2GGA**
Cpte Boston SO, P. Monteux (r1951) *Petrushka*. (11/87) (RCA) ① **GD86529**
Cpte D. Achatz (trans pf: Achatz) *Concert* (6/88) (BIS) ① **BIS-CD188**
Cpte Swedish RSO, S. Ehrling *Symphony of Psalms*. (9/88) (BIS) ① **BIS-CD400**
Cpte Detroit SO, A. Dorati *Petrushka*. (1/89) (DECC) ① **417 758-2DM**
Cpte NYO, S. Rattle (r1977) *Firebird*. (10/89) (ASV) ① **CDQS6031**
Cpte CBSO, S. Rattle *Apollo*. (11/89) (EMI) ① **CDC7 49636-2**
Cpte RPO, Y. Temirkanov (r1988) *Petrushka*. (9/90) (RCA) ① **RD87985**
Cpte Paris SO, P. Monteux (r1929) *Petrushka*. (1/92) (PEAR) ① **GEMMCD9329**
Cpte Walther Straram Orch, I. Stravinsky (r1929) *Firebird*. (1/92) (PEAR) ① **GEMMCD9334**
Cpte Philadelphia, L. Stokowski (r1929/30) *Concert* (2/92) (PEAR) ① **GEMMCD9488**
Cpte LPO, K. Nagano *Perséphone*. (2/92) (VIRG) ① [2] **VCK7 59077-2**
Cpte LPO, B. Haitink *Petrushka*. (8/92) (PHIL) ① **434 147-2PM**
Cpte Columbia SO, I. Stravinsky (r1960) *Concert* (8/92) (SONY) ① [3] **SM3K46291**
Cpte Cleveland Orch, P. Boulez *Petrushka*. (9/92) (DG) ① **435 769-2GH**
Cpte SRO, I. Markevitch (pp1982) *Markevitch: Psaume*. (11/92) (CASC) ① **VEL2004**
Cpte Philadelphia, R. Muti *Mussorgsky: Pictures*. (11/92) (EMI) ① **CDM7 64516-2**
Cpte Seattle SO, G. Schwarz *Pulcinella*. (12/92) (DELO) ① **DE3100**
Cpte Atlanta SO, Y. Levi *Pulcinella Suite*. (12/92) (TELA) ① **CD80266**
Cpte St Louis SO, L. Slatkin (r1990) *Concert* (5/93) (RCA) ① **09026 60993-2**
Cpte Philh, E. Inbal (r1989) *Concert* (7/93) (TELD) ① **4509-91449-2**

Cpte Brussels BRT PO, A. Rahbari (r1990) *Jeu de cartes*. (8/93) (NAXO) ① **8 550472**
Cpte Philadelphia, L. Stokowski (r1929/30) *Petrushka*. (8/93) (RCA) ① **09026 61394-2**
Cpte NY Met Op Orch, James Levine (r1992) *Mussorgsky: Pictures*. (11/93) (DG) ① **437 531-2GH**
Cpte LPO, B. Haitink (r1973) *Concert* (1/94) (PHIL) ① [2] **438 350-2PM2**
Cpte Oslo PO, M. Jansons (r1992) *Petrushka*. (1/94) (EMI) ① **CDC7 54899-2**
Cpte Minneapolis SO, A. Dorati (r1959) *Concert* (3/94) (MERC) ① **434 331-2MM**
Cpte Cleveland Orch, L. Maazel (r1980) *Shostakovich: Symphony 5*. (7/94) (TELA) ① **CD82001**
Cpte Boston SO, P. Monteux (r1951) *Concert* (9/94) (RCA) ① [15] **09026 61893-2**
Cpte Paris Cons, P. Monteux (r1956) *Firebird Suite (1911)*. (9/94) (DECC) ① **440 064-2DM**
Cpte Berlin RIAS Orch, F. Fricsay (r1954) *Concert* (11/94) (DG) ① **445 405-2GDO**
Cpte Berlin RIAS Orch, F. Fricsay (r1954) *Concert* (11/94) (DG) ① [11] **445 400-2GDO10**
Cpte LSO, E. Goossens (r1959) *Rachmaninov: Symphonic Dances*. (4/95) (EVER) ① **EVC9002**
Cpte Cleveland Orch, P. Boulez (r1969) *Petrushka*. (5/95) (SONY) ① **SMK64109**
Cpte SRO, E. Ansermet (r1957) *Concert* (9/95) (DECC) ① [2] **443 467-2DF2**
Cpte Berlin RIAS Orch, F. Fricsay (r1953) *Concert* (11/95) (DG) ① [2] **447 343-2GDB2**
2f Hollywood Bowl SO, J. Mauceri (r1993) *Concert* (1/95) (PHIL) ① **442 425-2PH**
Scènes de ballet—ballet (1944—Philadelphia)
CBC SO, I. Stravinsky *Concert* (8/92) (SONY) ① [3] **SM3K46292**
St. Luke's Orch, R. Craft (r1991/2) *Concert* (6/94) (MUSM) ① **67113-2**

SECTION II: CHAMBER

3 Etudes for Violin and Piano (1981)
T. Moore, E. Gilgore (r1990s) *Concert* (2/95) (CENT) ① **CRC2176**
3 Pieces for Violin and Piano (1983)
T. Moore, E. Gilgore (r1990s) *Concert* (2/95) (CENT) ① **CRC2176**
Trio for Violin, Cello and Piano (1985)
T. Moore, C. Pegis, E. Gilgore (r1990s) *Concert* (2/95) (CENT) ① **CRC2176**

SECTION V: STAGE WORKS

Encounters—ballet (1992—Sarasota) (suite of piano pieces reassembled by E. Toussaint)
EXCERPTS: 1. Passacaglia and Marcia (from Character Pieces, 1978); 2. 6 Piano Variations (1968); 3. 3 Preludes and Fugues in Memoriam I. Stravinsky (1982).
E. Gilgore (r1990s) *Concert* (2/95) (CENT) ① **CRC2176**

SECTION IV: VOCAL AND CHORAL

Dreamin' time—song
E. Mason, orch (r1924) *Concert* (8/93) (SYMP) ① **SYMCD1136**
E. Mason, orch, F. Black (1924) *Concert* (8/94) (ROMO) ① **81009-2**
E. Mason, orch, F. Black (r1925) *Concert* (8/94) (ROMO) ① **81009-2**
Mah Lindy Lou—song (1920) (Wds. cpsr)
A. Galli-Curci, orch, R. Bourdon (r1924) *Concert* (8/94) (ROMO) ① [2] **81004-2**

SECTION I: ORCHESTRAL

Concerto for Clarinet and Orchestra (1975)
A.O. Popa, Satu Mare PO, C. Dumbrăveanu *Concert* (9/92) (OLYM) ① **OCD418**

STROGERS, Nicholas (fl 1560–1575) England

SECTION II: CHAMBER

In Nomine Pavan—consort (pub 1599)
J. Bream, J. Bream Consort (r1987; ed Bream)
Concert   (8/93) (RCA) ① **[28] 09026 61583-2(3)**
J. Bream Consort (r1987; ed Bream) Concert
          (9/94) (RCA) ① **09026 61590-2**

STROKINE, Mikhail (Porfirevich) (1832–1887) Russia

SECTION IV: VOCAL AND CHORAL

Now let us depart in peace—song
F. Chaliapin, Paris Russian Met Church Ch, N.
Afonsky (r1932) Concert
          (6/93) (PREI) ① **[2] 89207**

STROMBERG, John (1853–1902) USA

SECTION V: STAGE WORKS

Hurly Burly—Weber & Fields burlesque
(1898—New York)
EXCERPTS: 1. Hypnotic Scene.
1. L. Fields, J. Weber, Broadway Cast (r1912)
Concert
          (5/94) (PEAR) ① **[3] GEMMCDS9050/2(1)**
Pousse Café—Weber & Fields burlesque
(1897—New York)
EXCERPTS: 1. Contract Scene.
1. L. Fields, J. Weber, Broadway Cast (r1912)
Concert
          (5/94) (PEAR) ① **[3] GEMMCDS9050/2(1)**
Twirly-Whirly—Weber & Fields burlesque
(1902—New York)
EXCERPTS: 1. Come Down, Ma Evenin' Star (Lyrics
Smith).
. 1. L. Russell, Broadway Cast (r1912) Concert
          (5/94) (PEAR) ① **[3] GEMMCDS9050/2(1)**
Whirl-i-Gig—Weber & Fields burlesque
(1899)
EXCERPTS: 1. Drinking Scene.
1. L. Fields, J. Weber, Broadway Cast (r1912)
Concert
          (5/94) (PEAR) ① **[3] GEMMCDS9050/2(1)**

STROUSE, Charles (b 1928) USA

SECTION V: STAGE WORKS

Dance a Little Closer—musical show
(?1983—New York) (Book & Lyrics A. J.
Lerner, after Sherwood)
EXCERPTS: 1. Overture; 2. It Never Would've
Worked; 3. Happy New Year; 4. No Man Is Worth It;
5. What Are You Going to do About It?; 6. A Woman
Who Thinks I'm Wonderful; 7. Pas de Deux/There's
Never Been Anything Like Us; 8. Another Life; 9.
Why Can't the World Go and Leave Us Alone?; 10.
He Always Comes Home to Me; 11. I Got a New Girl;
12. Dance a Little Closer; 13. There's Always One
You Can't Forget; 14. Entr'acte/Homesick; 15. Mad;
16. I Don't Know/Anyone Who Loves; 17. Auf
Wiedersehn; 18. I Never Want to See You Again; 19.
On Top of the World; 20. Finale (Dance a Little
Closer).
Cpte L. Cariou, L. Robertson, G. Rose, Orig
Broadway Cast, P. Howard (r1983)
          (7/90) (TER) ① **CDTER1174**

STROZZI, Barbara (1619–1664 or later) Italy

SECTION IV: VOCAL AND CHORAL

Amor, non dormir più (Amor
dormiglione)—arietta: 1v
Musica Secreta (r1992) Concert
          (1/95) (AMON) ① **CD-SAR61**
Anima del mio core (Dialogo in
partenza)—2vv
Musica Secreta (r1992) Concert
          (1/95) (AMON) ① **CD-SAR61**
Ariette a voce sola, Op. 6 (1657)
1. Lilla dici; 2. Miei pensieri; 3. Non ti doler mio cor; 4.
Rissolvetevi pensieri.
3, 4. T. Berganza, Ens, J.E. Dähler (hpd/dir) Concert
          (3/84) (CLAV) ① **CD50-8206**
4. T. Berganza, Ens, J.E. Dähler (hpd/dir) Concert
          (3/84) (CLAV) ① **CD50-8206**

Bella madre d'amore (Le tre
grazie)—madrigal (3vv)
Consort of Musicke, A. Rooley Concert
          (12/91) (DHM) ① **RD77154**
Musica Secreta (r1992) Concert
          (1/95) (AMON) ① **CD-SAR61**
Cantate, ariette e duetti—1-2vv and
continuo, Op. 2 (1651)
1. Soccorete luci avare; 2. Dimmi, ah dimmi.
2. Musica Secreta (r1992) Concert
          (1/95) (AMON) ① **CD-SAR61**
Che dolce udire (Canto di bella
bocca)—madrigal (2vv)
Consort of Musicke, A. Rooley Concert
          (12/91) (DHM) ① **RD77154**
Musica Secreta (r1992) Concert
          (1/95) (AMON) ① **CD-SAR61**
Godere e tacere—2vv
Musica Secreta (r1992) Concert
          (1/95) (AMON) ① **CD-SAR61**
Il Gran Giove (La vittoria)—madrigal (2vv)
Consort of Musicke, A. Rooley Concert
          (12/91) (DHM) ① **RD77154**
Merce di voi (Sonetto proemio
dell'opera)—2vv
Musica Secreta (r1992) Concert
          (1/95) (AMON) ① **CD-SAR61**
Mi ferite oh begli occhi (Begli occhi)—2vv
Musica Secreta (r1992) Concert
          (1/95) (AMON) ① **CD-SAR61**
Mordeva un bianco lino (Dal pianto degli
Amanti scherniti s'imparo a far)—2vv
Musica Secreta (r1992) Concert
          (1/95) (AMON) ① **CD-SAR61**
Non ci lusinghi più (Libertà)—3vv
Musica Secreta (r1992) Concert
          (1/95) (AMON) ① **CD-SAR61**
Gl' occhi superbi—2vv
Musica Secreta (r1992) Concert
          (1/95) (AMON) ① **CD-SAR61**
Oh dolci, oh cari, oh desiati baci! (I
baci)—2vv
Musica Secreta (r1992) Concert
          (1/95) (AMON) ① **CD-SAR61**
Sete pur fastidioso—1vv
Musica Secreta (r1992) Concert
          (1/95) (AMON) ① **CD-SAR61**
Sino alla morte—1v
Musica Secreta (r1992) Concert
          (1/95) (AMON) ① **CD-SAR61**

STROZZI, Gregorio (c1615–after 1687) Italy

SECTION III: INSTRUMENTAL

Corrente terze—keyboard
R. Alessandrini (r1994) Concert
          (4/95) (O111) ① **OPS30-118**

STRUNGK, Delphin (c1601–1694) Germany

SECTION III: INSTRUMENTAL

Lass mich Dein sein, 'Ach Herr, mich armen
Sünder'—organ
G. Leonhardt Concert   (10/94) (SONY) ① **SK53371**
Variations on the Magnificat, 'Meine Sehl
erhebet den Herrn'—organ
G. Leonhardt Concert   (10/94) (SONY) ① **SK53371**

STRUNGK, Nicolaus Adam (1640–1700) Germany

SECTION IV: VOCAL AND CHORAL

Ich ruf zu dir, Herr Jesu Christ—chorale
melody
M. Zedelius, Cologne Musica Antiqua, R. Goebel
(r1985) Concert   (1/93) (ARCH) ① **437 079-2AT**

STUART, Leslie (1864–1928) England

SECTION V: STAGE WORKS

Florodora—musical comedy: 2 acts
(1899—London) (Lib. E. Boyd-Jones & P.
Rubens)
EXCERPTS: 1. Opening Chorus; 2. Tell Me, Pretty
Maiden; 3. I Want to Be a Military Man; 4. Burlesque
on 'Pretty Maiden'; 5. In the Shade of the Palm; 6.
Whistling; 7. Willie Was a Gay Boy; 8. Galloping; 9.
Queen of the Philippine Islands; 10. Tact; 11. I've an
Inkling; 12. He Loves Me, He Loves Me Not; 13.
Phrenology; 14. Come and See Our Island; 15. The

Silver Star of Love; 16. When an Interfering Person;
17. The Millionaire; 18. Jack and Jill (for 1915
Revival).
2. M. Hill Smith, P. Morrison, Chandos Concert Orch,
S. Barry Concert   (2/90) (CHAN) ① **CHAN8759**
2. Broadway Cast (r1902) Concert
          (5/94) (PEAR) ① **[3] GEMMCDS9050/2(1)**

STUBLEY, Simon (d 1754) England

SECTION III: INSTRUMENTAL

Voluntary in C—organ
A. Stringer, N. Rawsthorne (r1974) Concert
          (11/87) (CRD) ① **CRD3308**
J. Bate Concert   (11/91) (UNIC) ① **DKPCD9106**

STURGEON, ? Nicholas (d 1454) England

SECTION IV: VOCAL AND CHORAL

Salve mater domini/Salve templum
domini—isorhythmic motet: 3vv
Gothic Voices, C. Page (lte/dir) Concert
          (9/92) (HYPE) ① **CDA66588**

STYNE, Jule (1905–1994) USA

SECTION V: STAGE WORKS

Funny Girl—musical show (1964—New York)
(Lyrics B. Merrill; Book Lennart)
EXCERPTS: 1. Overture; 2. If a Girl Isn't Pretty; 3.
I'm the Greatest Star; 4. Coronet Man; 5. Who
Taught Her Everything; 6. His Love Makes Me
Beautiful; 7. I Want to Be Seen with You Tonight; 8.
Henry Street; 9. People; 10. You Are Woman; 11.
Don't Rain on My Parade; 12. Sadie, Sadie; 13. Find
Yourself a Man; 14. Rat-Tat-Tat-Tat; 15. Who Are
You Now?; 16. The Music That Makes Me Dance; 17.
Don't Rain on My Parade (reprise).
Cpte B. Streisand, J. Stapleton, S. Chaplin, Orig
Broadway Cast, M. Rosenstock (r1964)
          (11/93) (EMI) ① **ZDM7 64661-2**

SUCHOŇ, Eugen (1908–1993) Slovakia

SECTION I: ORCHESTRAL

Serenade—string orchestra, Op. 5 (1933) (arr
cpsr from Wind Quintet (1932)
Slovak CO, B. Warchal Concert
          (10/89) (OPUS) ① **9350 1773**

SECTION IV: VOCAL AND CHORAL

3 Slovakian Folksongs—male vv
Orphei Drängar Ch, E. Ericson Concert
          (7/88) (BIS) ① **BIS-CD383**

SECTION V: STAGE WORKS

The Whirlpool (Krútňava)—opera: 6 scenes
(1949) (Lib. cpsr & S. Hoza, after M. Urban)
Cpte P. Dvorský, G. Beňačková, O. Malachovský, V.
Kubovčik, A. Michalková, J. Sedlarova, O. Hanakova,
E. Antoličová, L. Barikova, J. Valásková, J. Kundlák,
J. Martvon, P. Mikuláš, S. Benňačka, A. Kubankova,
L. Ludha, A. Martvonova, J. Valentik, Slovak Phil
Chor, Bratislava RSO, O. Lenárd
          (11/90) (CAMP) ① **[2] RR2CD1311/2**

SUDER, Joseph (1892 – 1980) Germany

SECTION V: STAGE WORKS

Kleider machen Leute—opera (cpted 1934:
première 1964) (Lib. cpsr, after Keller)
Cpte K. König, Morris Morgan, P. Coburn, W. Probst,
W. Plate, S. Klare, J-H. Rootering, K. Geber, B.
Nachbaur, B. Lindner, D. Pauli, Bavarian Rad Chor,
Bamberg SO, U. Mund
          (5/92) (ORFE) ① **[2] C124862H**

SUK, Josef (1874–1935) Bohemia

SECTION I: ORCHESTRAL

Asrael—symphony, Op. 27 (1905-06)
Czech PO, V. Neumann (r1983)
          (9/91) (SUPR) ① **11 0715-2**
RLPO, L. Pešek (r1990)
          (9/91) (VIRG) ① **VC7 59638-2**

Czech PO, J. Bělohlávek (r1991)
(5/92) (CHAN) ① CHAN9042
Czech PO, V. Talich (r1952) Dvořák: Stabat mater.
(12/93) (SUPR) ① [2] 11 1902-2
BRSO, R. Kubelík (bp1981)
(1/94) (PANT) ① 81 1101-2
Russian St SO, E. Svetlanov (r1993)
(1/94) (RUSS) ① RDCD11011
Fairy Tale (Podádka)—concert suite from 'Radúz a Mahulena', Op. 16 (1899-1900)
1. Love and sorrow of the royal children; 2. Folkdance (Polka); 3. Funeral music; 4. Queen Runa's curse.
P. Skvor, Czech PO, L. Pešek Praga.
(12/85) (SUPR) ① 10 3389-2
Czech PO, J. Bělohlávek Serenade, Op. 6.
(3/93) (CHAN) ① CHAN9063
2. Chicago SO, F. Stock (r1926) Concert
(2/95) (BIDD) ① [2] WHL021/2
Fantastické scherzo, Op. 25 (1903)
Czech PO, J. Bělohlávek Concert
(1/91) (CHAN) ① CHAN8897
Fantasy—violin and orchestra, Op. 24 (1902-03)
J. Suk, Czech PO, K. Ančerl Dvořák: Violin Concerto.
(12/89) (SUPR) ① 11 0601-2
J. Suk, Czech PO, V. Neumann Dvořák: Violin Concerto.
(5/90) (SUPR) ① 11 0283-2
Filled with longing—orchestra
Czech PO, V. Neumann Concert
(9/90) (ORFE) ① C180891A
Praga—symphonic poem, Op. 26 (1904)
Czech PO, L. Pešek Fairy Tale.
(12/85) (SUPR) ① 10 3389-2
RLPO, L. Pešek (r1992) Ripening.
(1/94) (VIRG) ① VC7 59318-2
Czech PO, L. Pešek (r982) Summer's Tale.
(8/95) (SUPR) ① 11 1984-2
The Ripening—symphonic poem, Op. 34 (1912-17)
Liverpool Phil Ch, RLPO, L. Pešek (r1992) Praga.
(1/94) (VIRG) ① VC7 59318-2
Serenade in E flat—strings, Op. 6 (1892)
Berne Camerata Concert
(1/89) (NOVA) ① 150 022-2
Australian CO, C. Mackerras (r1988) Martinů: Sinfonietta giocosa.
(8/89) (CONI) ① CDCF170
Slovak CO, B. Warchal Dvořák: Serenade, Op.22.
(4/90) (OPUS) ① 9150 1501
Czech PO, V. Talich (r1938) Dvořák: Symphony 6.
(1/92) (KOCH) ① 37060-2
Czech PO, J. Bělohlávek Fairy Tale.
(3/93) (CHAN) ① CHAN9063
Czech PO, V. Talich (r1949) Dvořák: Symphony 9.
(2/94) (SUPR) ① 11 1899-2
Polish Radio CO, A. Duczmal Concert
(3/94) (ASV) ① CDQS6094
London CO, C. Warren-Green (r1989) Dvořák: Serenade, Op. 22.
(11/94) (VIRG) ① CUV5 61144-2
Prague Virtuosi, O. Vlček (r1993-4) Concert
(9/95) (DINT) ① DICD920234
A Summer's Tale—symphonic poem, Op. 29 (1907-9)
Czech PO, L. Pešek (r1984) Praga.
(8/95) (SUPR) ① 11 1984-2
RLPO, L. Pešek (r1994)
(8/95) (VIRG) ① VC5 45057-2

Bagatelle, 'Carrying a bouquet'—flute, violin and piano (1917)
J. Válek, J. Suk, J. Hála (r1990) Concert
(2/94) (SUPR) ① 11 1533-2
Balada in D minor—string quartet (1890)
Suk Qt (r1978) Concert
(2/94) (SUPR) ① 11 1533-2
Suk Qt Concert (11/94) (CRD) ① CRD3472
Balada in D minor—violin and piano (1890)
J. Suk, J. Panenka (r1966) Concert
(2/94) (SUPR) ① 11 1533-2
Ballade in D minor—cello and piano, Op. 3/1 (1890)
M. Jerie, I. Klánský (r1983) Concert
(2/94) (SUPR) ① 11 1533-2
Suk Qt Concert (11/94) (CRD) ① CRD3472
Barcarolle in B flat—string quartet (1888)
(Movt 2 of String Quartet in D minor)
Suk Qt (r1978) Concert
(2/94) (SUPR) ① 11 1533-2
Elegie, Op. 23 (1902)
Suk Trio Dvořák: Piano Trio 4.
(12/85) (SUPR) ① C37-7057
J. Suk, F. Host, R. Kodadová, J. Hála, Suk Qt (r1990; orig vers) Concert (2/94) (SUPR) ① 11 1533-2

Suk Trio (r1967; rev vers) Concert
(2/94) (SUPR) ① 11 1532-2
Meditation on an old Czech hymn, 'St Wenceslas', Op. 35a (1914)
Suk Qt (r1984) Concert
(2/94) (SUPR) ① 11 1531-2
Suk Qt Concert (11/94) (CRD) ① CRD3472
Prague Virtuosi, O. Vlček (r1993-4) Concert
(9/95) (DINT) ① DICD920234
Melodie—two violins (1893)
J. Suk, J. Nováková (r1991) Concert
(2/94) (SUPR) ① 11 1533-2
Minuet—violin and piano (c1919)
J. Suk, J. Hála (r1991) Concert
(2/94) (SUPR) ① 11 1533-2
Piano Quartet in A minor, Op. 1 (1891)
J. Suk, J. Talich, M. Fukačová, J. Panenka (r1992) Concert (2/94) (SUPR) ① 11 1532-2
Piano Quintet in G minor, Op. 8 (1893 rev 1915)
P. Štěpán, Suk Qt (r1978) Concert
(2/94) (SUPR) ① 11 1532-2
Piano Trio in C minor, Op. 2 (1889 rev 1890-91)
Suk Trio (r1991) Concert
(2/94) (SUPR) ① 11 1532-2
4 Pieces—violin and piano, Op. 17 (1900)
1. Quasi ballata; 2. Appassionata; 3. Un poco triste; 4. Burleska.
J. Suk, J. Panenka (r1966) Concert
(2/94) (SUPR) ① 11 1533-2
2, 3. G. Neveu, B. Seidler-Winkler (r1938) Concert
(10/92) (TEST) ① SBT1010
4. R. Ricci, C. Fürstner (two versions: r1938) Concert
(12/91) (BIDD) ① LAB044
4. N. Milstein, A. Balsam (r1940) Concert
(3/93) (BIDD) ① LAB063
4. Chee-Yun, A. Eguchi Concert
(12/93) (DENO) ① CO-75118
Quartet movement in B flat (1915) (alternative finale for String Quartet No 1)
Suk Qt (r1978) Concert
(2/94) (SUPR) ① 11 1531-2
Serenade in A—cello and piano, Op. 3/2 (?1898)
M. Jerie, I. Klánský (r1983) Concert
(2/94) (SUPR) ① 11 1533-2
Sousedská—5 violins, double-bass, cymbals, triangle, timpani (1935)
J. Nováková, L. Vybíralová, M. Kosina, J. Krištůfek, Z. Mann, T. Josífko, J. Fousek, L. Kubánek (r1992) Concert (2/94) (SUPR) ① 11 1533-2
String Quartet No. 1 in B flat, Op. 11 (1896)
Suk Qt (r1979) Concert
(2/94) (SUPR) ① 11 1531-2
Suk Qt Concert (11/94) (CRD) ① CRD3472
String Quartet No. 2, Op. 31 (1911)
Suk Qt (r1984) Concert
(2/94) (SUPR) ① 11 1531-2
Suk Qt Concert (11/94) (CRD) ① CRD3472
Tempo di menuetto (1915)
Suk Qt (r1984) Concert
(2/94) (SUPR) ① 11 1531-2

About Friendship—piano, Op. 36 (1920)
N. Immelman (r ?1994) Concert
(1/95) (MERI) ① CDE84269
About Mother—five pieces: piano, Op. 28 (1907)
1. When Mother was ... 2. Long ago in Spring; 3. Like Mother singing; 4. On Mother's knee; 5. Souvenirs.
M. Fingerhut Concert
(4/93) (CHAN) ① [2] CHAN9026/7
6 Lullabies—piano, Op. 33 (1910-12)
1. Sleeping Children; 2. Song; 3. Sentimental self-parody; 4. On a friend's recovery; 5. Christmas dream; 6. Death, come softly.
M. Fingerhut Concert
(4/93) (CHAN) ① [2] CHAN9026/7
6 Pieces—piano, Op. 7 (1891-93)
1. Love song; 2. Humoreske; 4. Idyll I; 5. Dumka; 6. Idyll II.
1, 2, 4, N. Immelman (r ?1994) Concert
(1/95) (MERI) ① CDE84269
1, 2, 4-6. M. Fingerhut Concert
(4/93) (CHAN) ① [2] CHAN9026/7
Spring—five pieces: piano, Op. 22a (1902)
1. Spring; 2. The breeze; 3. In expectation; 4. Andante; 5. Yearning.
M. Fingerhut Concert
(4/93) (CHAN) ① [2] CHAN9026/7
N. Immelman (r ?1994) Concert
(1/95) (MERI) ① CDE84269

Summer moods—three pieces: piano, Op. 22b (1902)
1. At Midday; 2. Children playing; 3. Evening mood.
M. Fingerhut Concert
(4/93) (CHAN) ① [2] CHAN9026/7
Things lived and dreamt—10 pieces: piano, Op. 30 (1909)
1. Allegretto moderato: With humour and irony; 2. Allegro vivo: Restlessly and shyly, without strong expression; 3. Andante sostenuto: Mysteriously and highly airily; 4. Poco allegretto: Contemplatively then increasingly aggresively; 5. On my son's recovery. Adagio: Calmly, with deep feeling; 6. Moderato quasi Allegretto: With quiet, carefree good humour; 7. Adagio non tanto: Simply, then with shattering power; 8. Vivace: Gently, twittering like a swallow; 9. Poco Andante: Whisperingly and mysteriously; 10. The forgotten graves in the corner of the Křečovice cemetary.
M. Fingerhut Concert
(4/93) (CHAN) ① [2] CHAN9026/7
N. Immelman (r ?1994) Concert
(1/95) (MERI) ① CDE84269

10 Songs—SSA & pf four hands, Op. 15 (1899) (Wds. Slavonic trad)
1. Sorrow; 2. Longing; 3. Single Grave; 4. Shepherds in Spring; 5. Miraculous Water; 6. Fairies; 7. The Shepherd and the Shepherdess; 8. Memories; 9. Yearning for Marriage; 10. If only they knew!.
M. Lapšanský, D. Buranovsky, Prague Chbr Ch, J. Pancik (r1994) Concert
(12/95) (CHAN) ① CHAN9257

SULLIVAN, Sir Arthur (Seymour) (1842-1900) England

Absent-minded Beggar March (1899)
Kneller Hall Band, F. Renton (r1992: arr F Renton) Concert (9/93) (BAND) ① BNA5067
Concerto for Cello and Orchestra in D (1866) (orch score lost: recons Mackie & Mackerras)
J. Lloyd Webber, LSO, C. Mackerras (r1986: recons. Mackerras/Mackie) Concert
(4/95) (EMI) ① CDM7 64726-2
Imperial March—orchestra (1893)
BBC Concert Orch, O. A. Hughes (r1993) Concert
(4/95) (CPO) ① CPO999 171-2
Overture di ballo—orchestra (1870 rev 1889)
D'Oyly Carte Op Orch, J. Pryce-Jones (r1991: orig 1870 version) Gondoliers.
(5/92) (TER) ① [2] CDTER2 1187
D'Oyly Carte Op Orch, J. Pryce-Jones (r1991: orig 1870 version) Concert (5/93) (TER) ① CDVIR8316
ASMF, N. Marriner (r1992) Concert
(6/93) (PHIL) ① 434 916-2PH
Kneller Hall Band, F. Renton (r1992: arr F Renton) Concert (9/93) (BAND) ① BNA5067
RLPO, C. Groves (r1968) Concert
(4/94) (EMI) ① CDM7 64726-2
Overture in C, 'In Memoriam' (1866)
RTE Concert Orch, A. Penny (r1992) Concert
(6/93) (MARC) ① 8 223461
BBC Concert Orch, O. A. Hughes (r1993) Concert
(4/95) (CPO) ① CPO999 171-2
Princess of Wales's March, 'Marche danoise' (1863) (for the marriage of Princess Alexandra of Denmark)
Kneller Hall Band, F. Renton (r1992: arr F Renton) Concert (9/93) (BAND) ① BNA5067
Procession March (1863) (for the marriage of Princess Alexandra of Denmark)
Kneller Hall Band, F. Renton (r1992: arr F Renton) Concert (9/93) (BAND) ① BNA5067
Symphony in E, 'Irish' (1866)
RLPO, C. Groves (r1968) Concert
(4/94) (EMI) ① CDM7 64726-2
BBC Concert Orch, O. A. Hughes (r1993) Concert
(4/95) (CPO) ① CPO999 171-2

Arabian love song (1866) (Wds. P B Shelley)
R. Conrad, W. Merrill (r1993) Concert
(2/95) (PEAR) ① SHECD9636
Coming home—duet: soprano, contralto and piano (pub 1873) (Wds. R. Reece)
F. Lott, A. Murray, G. Johnson (r1991) Concert
(7/92) (EMI) ① CDC7 54411-2
County guy—song (1867) (Wds. W Scott)
R. Conrad, W. Merrill (r1993) Concert
(2/95) (PEAR) ① SHECD9636

Golden days—song (1872) (Wds. L Lewin)
R. Conrad, W. Merrill (r1993) *Concert*
(2/95) (PEAR) ① SHECD9636
The **Golden Legend**—cantata (1886) (Wds J.
Bennett, after Longfellow)
O Gladsome Light; The Night is Calm and
Cloudless; God sent his Messenger, the Rain K.
Flowers, B. Lees, P. Mayes, P. Woods, A. Sutton, M.
Kennedy, S. Dunn, W. Mee, G. Macnevin, W. Ruby,
Britten-Pears Chbr Ch, Ely Cath Ch, D. Price, P.
Trepte (r1992) *Concert*
(9/93) (CNTO) ① CRCD2368
Guinevere!—song (1872) (Wds. L Lewin)
R. Conrad, W. Merrill (r1993) *Concert*
(2/95) (PEAR) ① SHECD9636
I would I were a King—song (1878) (Wds. A.
Cockburn, after V. Hugo)
R. Conrad, W. Merrill (r1993) *Concert*
(2/95) (PEAR) ① SHECD9636
Ich möchte hinaus es jauchzen—song (1859)
(Wds. A. Corrodi)
R. Conrad, W. Merrill (r1993) *Concert*
(2/95) (PEAR) ① SHECD9636
If doughty deeds—song (1866) (Wds. R.
Graham)
R. Conrad, W. Merrill (r1993) *Concert*
(2/95) (PEAR) ① SHECD9636
Lead Kindly Light—hymn (1871) (Wds. J. H.
Newman)
Ely Cath Ch, D. Price, P. Trepte (r1992) *Concert*
(9/93) (CNTO) ① CRCD2368
A life that lives for you—song (1870) (Wds. L
Lewin)
R. Conrad, W. Merrill (r1993) *Concert*
(2/95) (PEAR) ① SHECD9636
The **Light of the World**—oratorio (1873 rev
1890) (Wds. cpsr)
In Rama was there a Voice heard; Yea, though I
walk; The Lord is Risen K. Flowers, Ely Cath Ch, D.
Price, P. Trepte (r1992) *Concert*
(9/93) (CNTO) ① CRCD2368
The **long day closes**—partsong: male vv
(1868) (Wds. H. Chorley)
PCA, M. Brown *Concert* (3/87) (CONI) ① CDCF145
Hilliard Ens, L-L. Kiesel *Concert*
(12/91) (MERI) ① DUOCD89009
The **Lost chord**—song (1877) (Wds. A. A.
Procter)
E. Caruso, orch (r1912) *Concert*
(7/91) (RCA) ① [12] GD60495(4)
E. Caruso, orch (r1912) *Concert*
(10/91) (PEAR) ① [3] EVC3(1)
P. McCann, I. Robertson (r1984: arr P McCann)
Concert (11/92) (CHAN) ① CHAN4501
Kneller Hall Band, F. Renton (r1992: arr F Renton)
Concert (9/93) (BAND) ① BNA5067
Besses o' the Barn Band, Black Dyke Mills Band,
Yorkshire Imperial Band, H. Mortimer (pp1987: arr G
Langford) *Concert* (11/93) (CHAN) ① CHAN4513
Mary Morison—song (1874) (Wds. R. Burns)
R. Conrad, W. Merrill (r1993) *Concert*
(2/95) (PEAR) ① SHECD9636
O Israel—sacred song (pub 1855) (Wds.
Hosea XIV vv 1-2)
Ely Cath Ch, D. Price, P. Trepte (r1992) *Concert*
(9/93) (CNTO) ① CRCD2368
O mistress mine—song (1863-64) (Wds.
Shakespeare)
R. Conrad, W. Merrill (r1993) *Concert*
(2/95) (PEAR) ① SHECD9636
Oh! ma charmante—song (1872) (Wds. V
Hugo)
R. Conrad, W. Merrill (r1993) *Concert*
(2/95) (PEAR) ① SHECD9636
On Shore and Sea—cantata (1871) (Wds. T.
Taylor)
Sink and scatter, Clouds of War B. Lees, P. Mayes,
P. Woods, A. Sutton, M. Kennedy, S. Dunn, W. Mee,
G. Macnevin, W. Ruby, Britten-Pears Chbr Ch, Ely
Cath Ch, D. Price, P. Trepte (r1992) *Concert*
(9/93) (CNTO) ① CRCD2368
Once again—song (1872) (Wds. L Lewin)
R. Conrad, W. Merrill (r1993) *Concert*
(2/95) (PEAR) ① SHECD9636
Onward! Christian soldiers—hymn (1871)
(Wds. S. Baring-Gould: Tune 'St Gertrude')
Kneller Hall Band, F. Renton (r1992: arr D Bartie)
Concert (9/93) (BAND) ① BNA5067
Orpheus with his lute—song (1863-64) (Wds.
Shakespeare)
Sarah Walker, R. Vignoles *Concert*
(10/92) (CRD) ① CRD3473
R. Conrad, W. Merrill (r1993) *Concert*
(2/95) (PEAR) ① SHECD9636

The **Prodigal Sun**—oratorio (1869) (Wds.
cpsr, from Bible)
Thou, O Lord, art our Father Ely Cath Ch, D. Price,
P. Trepte (r1992) *Concert*
(9/93) (CNTO) ① CRCD2368
She is not fair to outward view—song (1866)
(Wds. H. Coleridge)
R. Conrad, W. Merrill (r1993) *Concert*
(2/95) (PEAR) ① SHECD9636
Sigh no more, ladies—song (1863-64) (Wds.
Shakespeare)
R. Conrad, W. Merrill (r1993) *Concert*
(2/95) (PEAR) ① SHECD9636
The **strain upraise in joy and praise**—hymn
(1868) (Wds. trans Neale)
Ely Cath Ch, D. Price, P. Trepte (r1992) *Concert*
(9/93) (CNTO) ① CRCD2368
Sweet day, so cool—song (1864) (Wds. G.
Herbert)
R. Conrad, W. Merrill (r1993) *Concert*
(2/95) (PEAR) ① SHECD9636
Te Deum—a thanksgiving for victory: chorus
and orchestra (1900) (Wds. liturgical)
B. Lees, P. Mayes, P. Woods, A. Sutton, M.
Kennedy, S. Dunn, W. Mee, G. Macnevin, W. Ruby,
Britten-Pears Chbr Ch, D. Price, P. Trepte (r1992)
Concert (9/93) (CNTO) ① CRCD2368
**Te Deum and Domine salvam fac
reginam**—chorus, organ/military
band/orchestra (1872) (Wds. liturgical)
The Glorious Company of the Apostles; When
Thou tookest upon Thee; Vouchsafe, O Lord K.
Flowers, B. Lees, P. Mayes, P. Woods, A. Sutton, M.
Kennedy, S. Dunn, W. Mee, G. Macnevin, W. Ruby,
Britten-Pears Chbr Ch, Ely Cath Ch, D. Price, P.
Trepte (r1992) *Concert*
(9/93) (CNTO) ① CRCD2368
Tears, idle tears—song (Wds. A E Tennyson)
R. Conrad, W. Merrill (r1993) *Concert*
(2/95) (PEAR) ① SHECD9636
Thou art lost to me—song (1865) (Wds.
anon)
R. Conrad, W. Merrill (r1993) *Concert*
(2/95) (PEAR) ① SHECD9636
Thou'rt passing hence—song (pub 1875)
(Wds. F. Hemans)
C. Santley, anon (r1903) *Concert*
(10/92) (SYMP) ① SYMCD1093

SECTION V: STAGE WORKS

The **Gondoliers (or The King of
Barataria)**—comic operetta: 2 acts
(1889—London) (Lib. W. S. Gilbert)
EXCERPTS: 1. Overture. ACT 1: 2a. List and learn;
2b. Good morrow, pretty maids; 2c. For the merriest
fellow; 2d. Buon giorno, signorine; 2e. We're called
gondolieri; 2f. And now to choose our brides; 2g.
Thank you gallant gondolieri; 3. From the sunny
Spanish shore; 4. In enterprise of martial kind; 5. O
rapture; 6. There was a time; 7. I stole the prince; 8.
But, bless my heart consider my position; 9. Try we
lifelong; 10a. Bridegroom and bride; 10b. When a
merry maiden marries; 11a. Kind sir you cannot have
the heart; 11b. Then one of us. ACT 2: 12. Of
happiness the very pith; 13. Rising early in the
morning; 14. Take a pair of sparkling eyes; 15. Here
we are; 16a. Dance a cachucha; 16b. Dance; 17.
There lived a King; 18. In a contemplative fashion;
19. With ducal pomp; 20. On the day; 21a. To help
unhappy commoners; 21b. Small titles and orders;
22. I am a courtier grave and serious; 23. Here is a
case unprecedented; 24a. Now let the loyal lieges;
24b. The Royal Prince; 24c. This statement we
receive; 24d. Once more gondolieri.
Abridged George Baker, William Booth, S. Granville,
D. Oldham, L. Rands, L. Hubbard, S. Robertson,
D'Oyly Carte Op Chor, SO, M. Sargent (r1931)
Patience. (7/89) (ARAB) ① [2] Z8095-2
Cpte T. Round, A. Styler, M. Sansom, J. Wright, J.
Reed, G. Knight, J. Toye, J. Skitch, K. Sandford, J.
Roach, M. Wakeham, J. Riordan, G. Cook, D.
Bradshaw, C. Jones, D. Gill, D'Oyly Carte Op Chor,
New SO, I. Godfrey (with dialogue)
(1/90) (DECC) ① [2] 425 177-2LM2
Cpte D. Fieldsend, A. Oke, L.E. Ross, R. Hanley, R.
Suart, J. Pert, E. Woollett, P. Creasey, J. Rath, C.
Kelly, T. Morgan, D. Cavendish, T. Barrett, G.
Vaughan, Y. Patrick, P. Baxter, E. Elliott, D'Oyly
Carte Op Chor, D'Oyly Carte Op Orch, J. Pryce-
Jones (r1991) *Di Ballo*.
(5/92) (TER) ① [2] CDTER2 1187
1. New Sadler's Wells Op Orch, S. Phipps (r1977)
Concert (5/93) (TER) ① CDVIR8316
1. ASMF, N. Marriner (r1992) *Concert*
(6/93) (PHIL) ① 434 916-2PH

2e, 4, 14, 16a J. Toye, G. Knight, T. Round, A. Styler,
J. Reed, J. Skitch, D'Oyly Carte Op Chor, New SO, I.
Godfrey *Concert* (6/91) (DECC) ① 430 095-2DWO
3, 7, 11b J. Wright, J. Toye, M. Sansom, G. Knight,
T. Round, J. Skitch, J. Reed, K. Sandford, A. Styler,
New SO, I. Godfrey *Concert*
(2/93) (DECC) ① 433 868-2DWO
13, 15. King's Sngrs (r1993; arr Gritton) *Concert*
(5/94) (RCA) ① 09026 61885-2
14. H. Nash, orch (r1926) *Concert*
(8/89) (PEAR) ① GEMMCD9319
18, 24d T. Dahl, M. Forrester, T. Chiles, R. Suart, D.
Grant, D. Morphy, Winnipeg Sngrs, Winnipeg G & S
Soc, Winnipeg SO, B. Tovey (r1994) *Concert*
(6/95) (CBC) ① SMCD5139
Henry VIII—incidental music to
Shakespeare's play (1877—Manchester)
EXCERPTS: 1. March; 2. King Henry's song; 3.
Graceful Dance; 4. Water Music.
1-3. Kneller Hall Band, F. Renton (r1992: arr F
Renton) (9/93) (BAND) ① BNA5067
1-4. RTE Concert Orch, A. Penny (r1992) *Concert*
(6/93) (MARC) ① 8 223461
**HMS Pinafore (or The Lass that Loved a
Sailor)**—comic operetta: 2 acts
(1878—London) (Lib. W. S. Gilbert)
EXCERPTS: 1. Overture. ACT 1: 2. We sail the
ocean blue; 3a. Hail, men-o'-war's men; 3b. I'm
called little Buttercup; 4a. But, tell me; 4b. The
Nightingale; 4c. A maiden fair to see; 5a. My gallant
crew; 5b. I am the Captain of the Pinafore; 6a. Sir
you are sad; 6b. Sorry her lot who loves too well; 7.
Over the bright blue sea; 8a. Sir Joseph's barge is
seen; 8b. Gaily tripping, lightly skipping; 9. I am the
monarch of the sea; 10. When I was a lad I served a
term; 11. A British tar is a soaring soul; 12. Refrain,
audacious tar; 13a. Can I survive this overbearing;
13b. Oh joy, oh rapture unforseen; 13c. Let's give
three cheers for a sailor's bride; 14a. Entr'acte. ACT
2: 14b. Fair moon, to thee I sing; 15. Things are
seldom what they seem; 16. The hours creep on
apace; 17. Never mind the why and wherefore; 18.
Kind Captain, i've important information; 19a.
Carefully on tiptoe stealing; 19b. He is an
Englishman; 19c. Did you hear him?; 20. Farewell my
own; 21. A many years ago; 22. Oh joy, oh rapture
unforseen
Cpte N. Grace, G. Sandison, C. Gillett, E. Ritchie, T.
Lawlor, P. Parfitt, P. Thomson, J. Roebuck, L.
Ormiston, New Sadler's Wells Op Chor, New Sadler's
Wells Op Orch, S. Phipps (ed Russell Hume)
(5/88) (TER) ① [2] CDTER2 1150
Cpte J. Reed, J. Skitch, T. Round, J. Hindmarsh, D.
Adams, G. Cook, E. Wilson Hyde, J. Wright, G.
Knight, D'Oyly Carte Op Chor, New SO, I. Godfrey
(with dialogue)
(1/90) (DECC) ① [2] 414 283-2LM2
Cpte R. Suart, F. Palmer, R. Evans, T. Allen, M.
Schade, D. Adams, V. Seymour, R. Van Allan, J.
King, P. Lloyd-Evans, WNO Chor, WNO Orch, C.
Mackerras (r1994: omits dialogue)
(1/95) (TELA) ① CD80374
1. New Sadler's Wells Op Orch, S. Phipps (r1977)
Concert (5/93) (TER) ① CDVIR8316
1. ASMF, N. Marriner (r1992) *Concert*
(6/93) (PHIL) ① 434 916-2PH
2, 5a, 5b, 13b J. Hindmarsh, G. Knight, T.
Round, J. Skitch, D'Oyly Carte Op Chor, New SO, I.
Godfrey *Concert* (2/93) (DECC) ① 433 868-2DWO
3b, 9, 10, 17. J. Reed, J. Skitch, J. Wright, G. Knight,
J. Hindmarsh, D'Oyly Carte Op Chor, New SO, I.
Godfrey *Concert* (6/91) (DECC) ① 430 095-2DWO
11. King's Sngrs (r1993; arr Gritton) *Concert*
(5/94) (RCA) ① 09026 61885-2
16, 17. T. Dahl, M. Forrester, T. Chiles, R. Suart, D.
Grant, D. Morphy, Winnipeg Sngrs, Winnipeg G & S
Soc, Winnipeg SO, B. Tovey (r1994) *Concert*
(6/95) (CBC) ① SMCD5139
L' ile enchantée—ballet (1864—London)
EXCERPTS: 1. Prelude; 2. Dance of the Nymphs
and Satyrs—pas de Châles; 3. Galop; 4.
Storm—Entrance of the Gnomes—Entrance of Fairy
Queen; 5. Pas de deux; 6a. Mazurka; 6b. Variation;
7. Scène des disparitions; 8a. Tempo di valse; 8b.
Variations for Mlle Carmine; 9. Pas de trois (after Mlle
Carmine's Variation); 10. Scène de jalousie; 11.
untitled; 12. Galop; 13. Finale.
Cpte RTE Concert Orch, A. Penny (r1992) *Thespis*.
(6/93) (MARC) ① 8 223460
Iolanthe (or The Peer and the Peri)—comic
operetta: 2 acts (1882—London) (Lib. W. S.
Gilbert)
EXCERPTS: 1. Overture. ACT 1: 2. Tripping hither
tripping thither; 3. Iolanthe; 4. Good morrow, good
mother; 5. Fare thee well attractive stranger; 6a.
Good morrow, good lover; 6b. None shall part us; 7.

Loudly let the trumpet bray (March of the Peers); 8a. Entrance of Lord Chancellor; 8b. The law is the true embodiment; 9a. My well-loved Lord and Guardian; 9b. Of all the young ladies; 10. Nay tempt me not; 11. Spurn not the nobly born; 12. My Lords it may not be; 13. When I went to the Bar as a very young man; 14a. When darkly looms the day; 14b. In babyhood; 14c. For riches and rank I do not long. ACT 2: 15. When all night long a chap remains; 16. Strephon's a Member of Parliament; 17. When Britain really ruled the waves; 18. In vain to us you plead; 19. Oh foolish fay; 20. Tho' p'r'aps I may incur your blame; 21a. Love, unrequited; 21b. When you're lying awake with a dismal headache; 22. If you go in, you're sure to win; 23. If we're weak enough to tarry; 24a. My Lord, a suppliant at your feet; 24b. He loves if in the bygone years; 25. It may not be; 26. Soon as we may.

Cpte Y. Newman, A. Styler, G. Knight, M. Sansom, J. Reed, D. Adams, T. Round, K. Sandford, J. Toye, P. Wales, D. Bradshaw, D'Oyly Carte Op Chor, Grenadier Guards Band, New SO, I. Godfrey (with dialogue) (1/90) (DECC) ① [2] **414 145-2LM2**

Cpte R. Hanley, Philip Blake Jones, J. Pert, E. Woollett, R. Suart, L. Richard, P. Creasey, J. Rath, Y. Patrick, M. Mitchell, L. Owen, D'Oyly Carte Op Chor, D'Oyly Carte Op Orch, J. Pryce-Jones (omits dialogue) *Thespis.* (5/92) (TER) ① [2] **CDTER2 1188**

1. D'Oyly Carte Op Orch, J. Pryce-Jones (r1991) *Concert* (5/93) (TER) ① **CDVIR8316**

1. ASMF, N. Marriner (r1992) *Concert* (6/93) (PHIL) ① **434 916-2PH**

1. Kneller Hall Band, F. Renton (r1992: arr N Richardson) *Concert* (9/93) (BAND) ① **BNA5067**

1, 19, 21a T. Dahl, M. Forrester, T. Chiles, R. Suart, D. Grant, D. Morphy, Winnipeg Sngrs, Winnipeg G & S Soc, Winnipeg SO, B. Tovey (r1994) *Concert* (6/95) (CBC) ① **SMCD5139**

1, 6b, 7, 10, 11, 13, 14c, 15-17, 19, 21a, 21b, 22, 23, 24a, 24b, 25, 26. E. Shilling, D. Dowling, S. Bevan, Leon Greene, E. Harwood, J. Moyle, H. Begg, P. Kern, E. Robson, C. Morey, Sadlers Wells Op Chor, Sadlers Wells Op Orch, A. Faris (r c1961) *Mikado.* (4/94) (CFP) ① [2] **CD-CFPD4730**

7. Kneller Hall Band, F. Renton (r1992: arr F Renton) *Concert* (9/93) (BAND) ① **BNA5067**

7, 22. T. Round, J. Reed, D. Adams, D'Oyly Carte Op Chor, New SO, I. Godfrey *Concert* (6/91) (DECC) ① **430 095-2DWO**

15. D. Adams, New SO, I. Godfrey *Concert* (2/93) (DECC) ① **433 868-2DWO**

Macbeth—incidental music to Shakespeare's play (1888—London)

EXCERPTS: 1. Overture; 2. Andante espressivo; 3. Introduction, Act 4; 4. Chorus of the Spirits in the Air: 'Black spirits and white'; 5. Chorus of Witches and Spirits: 'Come away, come away'; 6. Prelude, Act 5; 7. Prelude, Act 6.

1. English Northern Philh, D. Lloyd-Jones *Concert* (1/92) (HYPE) ① **CDA66515**

1. ASMF, N. Marriner (r1992) *Concert* (6/93) (PHIL) ① **434 916-2PH**

The **Merchant of Venice—incidental music to Shakespeare's play (1871—Manchester)**

EXCERPTS: 1. Introduction; 2. Barcarole (Sérénade); 3. Introduction and Bourrée; 4. Danse grotesque; 5. À la valse; 6. Melodrama; 7. Finale.

1-7. E. Lawler, RTE Concert Orch, A. Penny (r1992) *Concert* (6/93) (MARC) ① **8 223461**

The **Mikado (or The Town of Titipu)—comic operetta: 2 acts (1885—London)** (Lib. W. S. Gilbert)

EXCERPTS: 1. Overture. ACT 1: 2. If you want to know who we are; 3a. Gentleman, I pray you tell me; 3b. A wandering minstrel I; 4. Our great Mikado; 5. Young men despair; 6a. And have I journey'd for a month; 6b. Behold the Lord High Executioner; 6c. Taken from the county jail; 7. As some day it may happen; 8. Comes a train of little ladies; 9. Three little maids; 10. So please you, sir; 11. Were you not to Ko-Ko plighted?; 12. I am so proud; 13a. With aspect stem; 13b. Your revels cease; 13c. The hour of gladness. ACT 2: 14. Braid the raven hair; 15. The sun, whose rays are all ablaze; 16. Brightly dawns our wedding day; 17. Here's a how-de-do!; 18. Miya sama, miya sama; 19. From every kind of man; 20. A more humane Mikado; 21. The criminal cried; 22. See how the Fates; 23. The flowers that bloom in the spring; 24a. Alone, and yet alive; 24b. Hearts do not break!; 25. On a tree by a river a little tom-tit (Tit Willow); 26. There is beauty in the bellow of the blast; 27. For he's gone and married Yum-Yum.

Cpte J. Ayldon, C. Wright, J. Reed, K. Sandford, M. Rayner, V. Masterson, P.A. Jones, P. Wales, L. Holland, J. Broad, D'Oyly Carte Op Chor, RPO, R. Nash (omits dialogue) (1/90) (LOND) ① [2] **425 190-2LM2**

Cpte M. Ducarel, B. Bottone, E. Roberts, M. Rivers, Gareth Jones, D. Rees, T. Ker, Y. Patrick, S. Gorton, D'Oyly Carte Op Chor, D'Oyly Carte Op Orch, J. Pryce-Jones (omits dialogue) (9/90) (TER) ① [2] **CDTER2 1178**

Cpte D. Adams, A. Rolfe Johnson, R. Suart, R. Van Allan, N. Folwell, M. McLaughlin, A. Howells, J. Watson, F. Palmer, WNO Chor, WNO Orch, C. Mackerras (omits dialogue) (5/92) (TELA) ① **CD80284**

Cpte J. Holmes, J. Wakefield, C. Revill, D. Dowling, J.H. Nash, M. Studholme, P. Kern, D. Nash, J. Allister, Sadlers Wells Op Chor, Sadlers Wells Op Orch, A. Faris (r1962: omits dialogue) *Iolanthe.* (4/94) (CFP) ① [2] **CD-CFPD4730**

1. NYPO, J. Stransky (r1919) *Concert* (4/92) (PEAR) ① [3] **GEMMCDS9922**

1. D'Oyly Carte Op Orch, J. Pryce-Jones (r1990) *Concert* (5/93) (TER) ① **CDVIR8316**

1. ASMF, N. Marriner (r1992) *Concert* (6/93) (PHIL) ① **434 916-2PH**

1, 2, 3a, 3b, 4, 6b, 7, 9, 10, 13a-c(pt), 14, 15, 18-21, 23, 25-27. J. Ayldon, C. Wright, J. Reed, K. Sandford, M. Rayner, J. Broad, V. Masterson, P.A. Jones, P. Wales, L. Holland, D'Oyly Carte Op Chor, RPO, R. Nash (1/92) (DECC) ① **433 618-2DSP**

2, 3b, 4, 5, 6b, 7-11, 13(part), 14, 15, 17, 20, 23, 24a, 25, 26. R. Angas, B. Bottone, E. Idle, R. Van Allan, M. Richardson, L. Garrett, J. Rigby, S. Bullock, F. Palmer, ENO Chor, ENO Orch, Peter Robinson (3/87) (TER) ① **CDTER1121**

3b, 7, 9, 23, 25. V. Masterson, P.A. Jones, P. Wales, C. Wright, J. Reed, D'Oyly Carte Op Chor, RPO, R. Nash *Concert* (6/91) (DECC) ① **430 095-2DWO**

3b, 15-17, 20, 25. King's Sngrs (r1993; arr Gritton, Chilcott & Runswick) *Concert* (5/94) (RCA) ① **09026 61885-2**

6b, 26, 27. P.A. Jones, V. Masterson, P. Wales, L. Holland, C. Wright, J. Reed, K. Sandford, M. Rayner, D'Oyly Carte Op Chor, New SO, R. Nash *Concert* (2/93) (DECC) ① **433 868-2DWO**

7, 9, 23, 24a, 25, 26, 27. T. Dahl, M. Forrester, T. Chiles, R. Suart, D. Grant, D. Morphy, Winnipeg Sngrs, Winnipeg G & S Soc, Winnipeg SO, B. Tovey (r1994) *Concert* (6/95) (CBC) ① **SMCD5139**

9. Kneller Hall Band, F. Renton (r1992: arr P Stredwick) *Concert* (9/93) (BAND) ① **BNA5067**

15. B. Hendricks, Philh, L. Foster (r1992) *Concert* (8/93) (EMI) ① **CDC7 54626-2**

15. L. Garrett, RPO, P. Robinson (r1994) *Concert* (4/95) (SILV) ① **SILKD6004**

Patience (or Bunthorne's Bride)—operetta: 2 acts (1881—London) (Lib. W. S. Gilbert)

EXCERPTS: 1. Overture. ACT 1: 2. Twenty lovesick maidens; 3a. Still brooding on their mad infatuation; 3b. I cannot tell what this love may be; 4a. The Soldiers of our Queen; 4b. If you want a receipt; 5. In a doleful train; 6. When I first put this uniform on; 7a. Am I alone and unobserved?; 7b. If you're anxious for to shine; 8. Long years ago, fourteen maybe; 9. Prithee pretty maiden; 10a. Let the merry cymbals sound; 10b. True love must single-hearted be. ACT 2: 11. On such eyes as maidens cherish; 12a. Sad is that woman's lot; 12b. Silvered is the raven hair; 13. Turn, oh turn in this direction; 14. A magnet hung in a hardware shop; 15. Love is a plaintive song; 16. So go to him and say to him; 17. It's clear that medieval art alone retains its zest; 18. If Saphir I choose to marry; 19. When I go out of door; 20. I'm a Waterloo House young man; 21. After much debate internal.

Cpte W. Lawson, George Baker, L. Rands, N. Briercliffe, R. Mackay, M. Eyre, B. Lewis, D. Fancourt, M. Green, D. Oldham, D'Oyly Carte Op Chor, SO, M. Sargent (r1930: omits dialogue) *Gondoliers.* (7/89) (ARAB) ① [2] **Z8095-2**

Cpte M. Sansom, J. Reed, K. Sandford, Y. Newman, J. Toye, B. Lloyd-Jones, G. Knight, D. Adams, J. Cartier, P. Potter, D'Oyly Carte Op Chor, New SO, I. Godfrey (with dialogue) (1/90) (LOND) ① [2] **425 193-2LM2**

1. D'Oyly Carte Op Orch, J.O. Edwards (r1992) *Concert* (5/93) (TER) ① **CDVIR8316**

1. ASMF, N. Marriner (r1992) *Concert* (6/93) (PHIL) ① **434 916-2PH**

7a, 7b, 16. G. Knight, J. Reed, New SO, I. Godfrey *Concert* (2/93) (DECC) ① **433 868-2DWO**

Pineapple Poll—ballet (1951—London) (compiled & arr. Mackerras)

EXCERPTS: SCENE 1: 1. Opening Dance; 2. Poll's Dance and Pas de deux; 3. Belaye's Solo; 4. Pas de trois; 5. Finale. SCENE 2: 6. Poll's Solo; 7. Jasper's Solo. SCENE 3: 8. Belaye's Solo and Sailors' Dance; 9. Poll's Solo; 10. Entry of Belaye with Blanche as His Bride; 11. Reconciliation; 12. Grand Finale.

12. Besses o' the Barn Band, Black Dyke Mills Band, Yorkshire Imperial Band, H. Mortimer (pp1987) *Concert* (11/93) (CHAN) ① **CHAN4513**

The **Pirates of Penzance (or The Slave of Duty)—operetta: 2 acts (1879—Paignton)** (Lib. W. S. Gilbert)

EXCERPTS: 1. Overture. ACT 1: 2. Pour, o pour the pirate sherry; 3. When Frederic was a little lad; 4. Oh better far to live and die; 5a. O false one; 5b. You told me you were fair; 5c. What shall I do; 6. Climbing over rocky mountains; 7a. Stop ladies pray; 7b. Oh is there not one maiden breast?; 8. Poor wandering one; 9. What ought we to do?; 10. How beautifully blue the sky; 11. Stay, we must not lose our senses; 12a. Hold, monsters; 12b. Here's a first-class opportunity; 13. I am the very model of a modern Major-General; 14. Oh, men of dark and dismal fate. ACT 2: 15. Oh dry the glistening tear; 16a. Now Frederic, let your escort; 16b. When the foeman bares his steel; 17. Now the Pirates' lair; 18. When you had left our pirate fold; 19. Away, away; 20. All is prepared; 21a. Stay, Fredric; 21b. Ah, leave me not; 22a. Now I'll be brave; 22b. When a felon's not engaged; 23. A rollicking band; 24. With cat-like tread; 25a. Hush hush not a word; 25b. Sighing softly; 25c. Now what is this; 25d. We triumph now; 25e. Poor wandering ones.

Cpte P. Dawson, D. Oldham, George Baker, E. Griffin, S. Robertson, L. Sheffield, D. Gill, N. Walker, N. Briercliffe, D'Oyly Carte Op Chor, SO, M. Sargent (r1929: omits dialogue) *Sorcerer.* (11/87) (ARAB) ① [2] **Z8068-2**

Cpte D. Adams, P. Potter, J. Reed, V. Masterson, G. Cook, O. Brannigan, C. Palmer, P. Wales, J. Allister, S. Maisey, D'Oyly Carte Op Chor, RPO, I. Godfrey (with dialogue) (1/90) (LOND) ① [2] **425 196-2LM2**

Cpte M. Rivers, P. Creasey, E. Roberts, M. Hill Smith, Gareth Jones, S. Masterton-Smith, S. Gorton, P. Birchall, P. Cameron, D'Oyly Carte Op Chor, D'Oyly Carte Op Orch, J. Pryce-Jones (omits dialogue) (9/90) (TER) ① [2] **CDTER2 1177**

Cpte D. Adams, J.M. Ainsley, R. Suart, R. Evans, N. Folwell, R. van Allan, G. Knight, J. Williams, J. Gossage, WNO Chor, WNO Orch, C. Mackerras (omits dialogue) (11/93) (TELA) ① **CD80353**

B. Hendricks, Ambrosian Sngrs, Philh, L. Foster (r1992) *Concert* (8/93) (EMI) ① **CDC7 54626-2**

1. D'Oyly Carte Op Orch, J. Pryce-Jones (r1990) *Concert* (5/93) (TER) ① **CDVIR8316**

1. ASMF, N. Marriner (r1992) *Concert* (6/93) (PHIL) ① **434 916-2PH**

4, 21b, 24. King's Sngrs (r1993; arr Chilcott) *Concert* (5/94) (RCA) ① **09026 61885-2**

7a, 7b, 8, 13, 20, 21a T. Dahl, M. Forrester, T. Chiles, R. Suart, D. Grant, D. Morphy, Winnipeg Sngrs, Winnipeg G & S Soc, Winnipeg SO, B. Tovey (r1994) *Concert* (6/95) (CBC) ① **SMCD5139**

8, 13, 16b, 22b V. Masterson, J. Allister, J. Reed, O. Brannigan, D'Oyly Carte Op Chor, RPO, I. Godfrey *Concert* (6/91) (DECC) ① **430 095-2DWO**

24, 25e V. Masterson, P. Wales, C. Palmer, J. Allister, P. Potter, G. Cook, D'Oyly Carte Op Chor, RPO, I. Godfrey *Concert* (2/93) (DECC) ① **433 868-2DWO**

Princess Ida (or Castle Adamant)—operetta: 3 acts (1884—London) (Lib. W. S. Gilbert)

EXCERPTS: 1. Overture. ACT 1: 2. Search throughout the panorama; 3. Now hearken to my strict command; 4a. Today we meet; 4b. Ida was a twelvemonth old; 5. From the distant panorama; 6. We are warriors three; 7. If you give me your attention; 8a. Perhaps, if you address the lady; 8b. Expressive glances; 8c. For a month to dwell. ACT 2: 9. Towards the empyrean heights; 10. Mighty maiden; 11a. Minerva; 11b. Oh goddess wise; 11c. And thus to empyrean height; 12. Come, mighty Must; 13. Gently, gently; 14. I am a maiden, cold and steely; 15. The world is but a broken toy; 16. A lady fair, of lineage high; 17. The woman of the wisest wit; 18. Now would'nt you like to rule; 19. Merrily ring the luncheon bell; 20. Would you like to know the kind of maid; 21a. Oh joy, our chief is saved; 21b. Whom thou hast chained must wear his chain. ACT 3: 22. Death to the invader; 23. When'er I spoke sarcastic joke; 24. I built upon a rock; 25. When anger spreads his wing; 26. This helmet, I suppose; 27. This is our duty plain; 28. With joy abiding.

1. D'Oyly Carte Op Orch, J.O. Edwards (r1992) *Concert* (5/93) (TER) ① **CDVIR8316**

7, 24, 26. E. Harwood, J. Reed, A. Raffell, G. Cook, D'Oyly Carte Op Chor, M. Sargent *Concert* (2/93) (DECC) ① **433 868-2DWO**

Ruddigore (or The Witch's Curse)—operetta: 2 acts (1887—London) (Lib. W. S. Gilbert)
EXCERPTS: 1. Overture (Geoffrey Toye version: 1921). ACT 1: 2. Fair is Rose; 3. Sir Rupert Murgatroyd; 4. If somebody there chanced to be; 5. I know a youth; 6a. From the briny sea; 6b. I shipped, d'ye see; 7a. Hornpipe; 7b. My boy, you may take it from me; 8. The battle's roar is over; 9. If well his suit has sped; 10. In sailing o'er life's ocean wide; 11a. Cheerily carols the lark; 11b. To a garden full of posies; 12. Welcome gentry for your entry; 13. O why am I moody and sad?; 14. You understand?; 15a. Hail the bride of seventeen summers; 15b. When the buds are blossoming; 15c. Hold, bride and bridegroom; 15d. As pure and blameless peasant; 15e. Within this breast; 15f. Farewell; 15g. Dance. ACT 2: 16. I once was as meek; 17. Happily coupled; 18. In bygone days; 19. Painted emblems of a race; 20. When the night wind howls (The Ghosts' High-Noon); 21. He yields! He answers to your call!; 22a. Away, Remorse!; 22b. Ye well-to-do squires; 23. I once was a very abandon'd person; 24. My eyes are fully open; 25. There grew a little flower; 26. On, happy the lily. ADDITIONAL ITEM: 27. Overture (original Hamilton Clarke version: 1887).
1, 27. New Sadler's Wells Op Orch, S. Phipps (1987) *Concert* (3/90) (TER) ① **CDVIR8316**
13. J. Reed, RPO, I. Godfrey *Concert* (2/93) (DECC) ① **433 868-2DWO**
20. King's Sngrs (r1993; arr Runswick) *Concert* (5/94) (RCA) ① **09026 61885-2**

The Sapphire Necklace—opera: 4 acts (1860s) (Lib. H. Chorley)
EXCERPTS: 1. Overture (recons R. Spencer).
1. RTE Concert Orch, A. Penny (r1992) *Concert* (6/93) (MARC) ① **8 223461**

The Sorcerer—operetta: 2 acts (1877—London) (Lib. W. S. Gilbert)
EXCERPTS: 1. Overture. ACT 1: 2. Ring forth ye bells; 3a. Constance, my daughter; 3b. When he is here; 4a. The air is charged; 4b. Time was when Love and I; 5. Sir Marmaduke; 6. With heart and voice; 7a. My kindly friends; 7b. Oh happy young heart; 8. My child; 9. With heart and with voice; 10. Welcome joy; 11. All is prepared; 12. Love feeds on many kinds of food; 13. My name is John Wellington Wells; 14a. Sprites of earth and air; 14b. Let us fly; 15a. Now to the banquet; 15b. Eat, drink and be gay. ACT 2: 16. 'Tis twelve; 17. Dear friends, take pity; 18. Thou hast the power; 19. I rejoice that it's decided; 20. Alexis doubt me not; 21. Hate me!; 22. Oh, my voice is sad and low; 23. Oh, joyous boon!; 24. Prepare for sad surprises; 25. Or he or I must die.
Abridged D. Fancourt, D. Oldham, L. Rands, S. Robertson, George Baker, D. Gill, M. Dickson, A. Bethell, A. Moxon, D'Oyly Carte Op Chor, SO, I. Godfrey (r1933) *Pirates of Penzance.* (11/87) (ARAB) ① [2] **Z8068-2**
13. J. Reed, RPO, I. Godfrey *Concert* (2/93) (DECC) ① **433 868-2DWO**

Thespis (or The Gods Grown Old)—operatic extravaganza: 2 acts (1871—London) (Lib. W S Gilbert: fragments recons 1990)
EXCERPTS—ACT 2: 1. Ballet Music; 1a. Introduction; 1b. Pas de Châles; 1c. Valse; 1d. St George and the Dragon; 2. Galop.
1, 2. D'Oyly Carte Op Orch, J. Pryce-Jones *Iolanthe.* (5/92) (TER) ① [2] **CDTER2 1188**
1, 2. RTE Concert Orch, A. Penny (r1992) *Ile enchantée.* (6/93) (MARC) ① **8 223460**

Trial by Jury—operetta: 1 act (1866—London) (Lib. W. S. Gilbert)
EXCERPTS: 1. Hark the hour; 2a. Is this the Court; 2b. When first my old love I knew; 3. All hail, great Judge; 4. When I, good friends was called to the Bar; 5. Swear thou the Jury; 6. Comes the broken flower; 7. Oh, never since I joined the human race; 8. May it please you my lud; 9. That she is reeling; 10. Oh gentlemen listen; 11. That seems a reasonable proposition; 12. A nice dilemma we have here; 13. I love him, I love him, with fervour unceasing; 14. Oh joy unbounded.
Cpte A. Hood, T. Round, J. Reed, K. Sandford, D. Adams, A. Raffell, ROHO, I. Godfrey *Yeomen of the Guard.* (1/90) (DECC) ① [2] **417 358-2LM2**
14. T. Dahl, M. Forrester, T. Chiles, R. Suart, D. Grant, D. Morphy, Winnipeg Sngrs, Winnipeg G & S Soc, Winnipeg SO, B. Tovey (r1994) *Concert* (6/95) (CBC) ① **SMCD5139**

Victoria and Merrie England—concert suite No. 1 from ballet (1897) (arr cpsr from ballet)
1. March of the Druids; 2. Mistletoe Dance—Dance around the Oak Tree; 3. May Day Festivities.
BBC Concert Orch, O. A. Hughes (r1993) *Concert* (4/95) (CPO) ① **CPO999 171-2**

The Yeomen of the Guard (or The Merryman and his Maid)—operetta: 2 acts (1888—London) (Lib. W. S. Gilbert)
EXCERPTS: 1. Overture. ACT 1: 2. When maiden loves, she sits and sighs; 3. Tower Warders, Under orders; 4. When our gallant Norman foes; 5. Alas! I waver to and fro; 6. Is life a boon?; 7. Here's a man of jollity; 8. I have a song to sing, O!; 9. Here's a man, maiden; 10a. I've jibe and joke and quip and crank; 10b. I've wisdom from the East; 11a. Though I'm a bridel'; 11b. Though tear and long-drawn sigh; 12. Were I thy bride. Finale: 13a. Oh, Sergeant Meryll, is it true; 13b. Didst thou not, oh Leonard Meryll; 13c. To thy fraternal care; 13d. The prisoner comes to meet his doom. ACT 2: 14a. Night has spread her pall once more; 14b. Warders are ye?; 15. Oh! a private buffoon; 16. Herupon we're both agreed; 17. Free from his fetters grim; 18. Strange adventure; 19. Hark! what was that, sir?; 20. A man who would woo a fair maid; 21. When a wooer goes a-wooing; 22. Rapture, rapture; 23. Comes the pretty young bride.
ADDITIONAL EXCERPTS: 24. When jealous torments rack my soul (Act 1); 25. A laughing boy (Act 1); 26. Is life a boon? (original version).
Cpte A. Raffell, P. Potter, D. Adams, D. Palmer, J. Reed, K. Sandford, E. Harwood, A. Hood, G. Knight, M. Eales, D. Palmer, T. Lawlor, D'Oyly Carte Op Chor, RPO, M. Sargent (omits dialogue) *Trial by Jury.* (1/90) (DECC) ① [2] **417 358-2LM2**
Cpte D. Maxwell, D. Fieldsend, T. Sharpe, J. Jenson, F. Gray, G. Montaine, L.E. Ross, J. Roebuck, J. Pert, C. Lesley-Green, D'Oyly Carte Op Chor, D'Oyly Carte Op Orch, J.O. Edwards (r1991: omits dialogue) *Yeomen of the Guard.* (5/93) (TER) ① [2] **CDTER2 1195**
Cpte R. Lloyd, K. Streit, S. Dean, N. Mackie, T. Allen, B. Terfel, S. McNair, J. Rigby, A. Collins, J. Howarth, A. Michaels-Moore, ASMF Chor, ASMF, N. Marriner (r1992: with dialogue) (11/93) (PHIL) ① [2] **438 138-2PH2**
1. D'Oyly Carte Op Orch, J. Pryce-Jones (r1991) *Concert* (5/93) (TER) ① **CDVIR8316**
1. ASMF, N. Marriner (r1992) *Concert* (6/93) (PHIL) ① **434 916-2PH**
1. Kneller Hall Band, F. Renton (r1992: arr W J Duthoit) *Concert* (9/93) (BAND) ① **BNA5067**
1. Besses o' th' Barn Band, Black Dyke Mills Band, Yorkshire Imperial Band, H. Mortimer (pp1987: arr brass band: Sargent) *Concert* (11/93) (CHAN) ① **CHAN4513**
1. Black Dyke Mills Band, R. Newsome (r1977; arr brass band: M. Sargent) *Concert* (1/94) (CHAN) ① **CHAN4528**
2, 3. A. Hood, T. Lawlor, ROHO, I. Godfrey *Concert* (2/93) (DECC) ① **433 868-2DWO**
4, 7. E. Harwood, G. Knight, J. Reed, D'Oyly Carte Op Chor, RPO, M. Sargent *Concert* (6/91) (DECC) ① **430 095-2DWO**
8. T. Dahl, M. Forrester, T. Chiles, R. Suart, D. Grant, D. Morphy, Winnipeg Sngrs, Winnipeg G & S Soc, Winnipeg SO, B. Tovey (r1994) *Concert* (6/95) (CBC) ① **SMCD5139**
24, 25, 26. D. Maxwell, D. Fieldsend, T. Sharpe, J. Jenson, F. Gray, G. Montaine, L.E. Ross, J. Roebuck, J. Pert, C. Lesley-Green, D'Oyly Carte Op Chor, D'Oyly Carte Op Orch, J.O. Edwards (r1991: omits dialogue) *Yeomen of the Guard.* (5/93) (TER) ① [2] **CDTER2 1195**

SULZER, Joseph (1850–1926) Austria

SECTION II: CHAMBER

Sarabande—violin/cello and piano, Op. 8
F. Kreisler, anon (r1904) *Concert* (7/90) (BIDD) ① [2] **LAB009/10**
F. Kreisler, anon (r1904) *Concert* (8/90) (SYMP) ① **SYMCD1071**

SUMERA, Lepo (b 1950) Estonia

SECTION I: ORCHESTRAL

Concerto for Piano and Orchestra (1989)
K. Randalu, Malmö SO, P. Järvi (r1994) *Concert* (9/95) (BIS) ① **BIS-CD690**

Musica tenera—triangle & orchestra (1992)
Malmö SO, P. Järvi (r1994) *Concert* (9/95) (BIS) ① **BIS-CD690**

Symphony No. 1 (1981)
Malmö SO, P. Järvi (r1994) *Concert* (12/94) (BIS) ① **BIS-CD660**

Symphony No. 2 (1984)
Malmö SO, P. Järvi (r1994) *Concert* (12/94) (BIS) ① **BIS-CD660**

Symphony No. 3 (1988)
Malmö SO, P. Järvi (r1993) *Concert* (12/94) (BIS) ① **BIS-CD660**

Symphony No. 4, 'Serena borealis' (1992)
Malmö SO, P. Järvi (r1994) *Concert* (9/95) (BIS) ① **BIS-CD690**

SECTION II: CHAMBER

For B. B. B. and his Friend—flute and guitar (1988)
Tallinn Camerata (r1993) *Concert* (5/95) (FINL) ① **4509-95705-2**

SECTION III: INSTRUMENTAL

Piece from the year 1981—piano (1981)
L. Väinmaa (r1993) *Concert* (7/95) (FINL) ① **4509-95704-2**

SUMSION, Herbert (Whitton) (1899–1995) England

SECTION III: INSTRUMENTAL

Chorale Prelude on 'Down Ampney'—organ (1979)
Don Hunt *Concert* (3/90) (HYPE) ① **CDA66078**
Introduction and Theme—organ (1935)
Don Hunt *Concert* (3/90) (HYPE) ① **CDA66078**

SECTION IV: VOCAL AND CHORAL

Evening Service in A—4vv and organ
Chichester Cath Ch, A. Thurlow, J. Thomas (r1994) *Concert* (5/95) (PRIO) ① **PRCD511**
Evening Service in G (1942)
1. Magnificat; 2. Nunc dimittis.
1, 2. St Paul's Cath Ch, C. Dearnley, John Scott *Concert* (1/89) (HYPE) ① **CDA66305**
Evening Service in G—boys' voices (1942)
Gloucester Cath Ch, J. Sanders, M. Lee (r1994) *Concert* (4/95) (PRIO) ① **PRCD494**
Evening Service in G—full choir (1942)
Gloucester Cath Ch, J. Sanders, M. Lee (r1994) *Concert* (4/95) (PRIO) ① **PRCD494**
Evening Service in G—mens' voices (1942)
Gloucester Cath Ch, J. Sanders, M. Lee (r1994) *Concert* (4/95) (PRIO) ① **PRCD494**
In exile (Wds. Psalm 137 vv1-6)
D. Hunt Sngrs, Don Hunt *Concert* (3/90) (HYPE) ① **CDA66078**
Te Deum laudamus—choir and organ (1935)
Worcester Cath Ch, A. Partington *Concert* (3/90) (HYPE) ① **CDA66078**
Hereford Cath Ch, R. Massey, G. Bowen (r1994) *Concert* (2/95) (PRIO) ① **PRCD507**
There is a green hill—hymn (Wds. Alexander)
St John's Episcopal Cath Ch, D. Pearson *Concert* (10/92) (DELO) ① **DE3125**
They that go down to the sea in ships—choir and organ (1979) (Wds. Psalm 107)
Worcester Cath Ch, A. Partington *Concert* (3/90) (HYPE) ① **CDA66078**

SUPPÉ, Franz (von) (1819–1895) Austria

SECTION I: ORCHESTRAL

Herzeneintracht, 'Harmony of Hearts'—polka
Košice St PO, A. Walter (r1994) *Concert* (12/95) (MARC) ① **8 223683**
Humorous Variations on the popular song, 'What comes there from on high?'—orchestra
Košice St PO, A. Walter (r1994) *Concert* (12/95) (MARC) ① **8 223683**
O du mein Österreich—march
Hungarian St Op Orch, J. Sandor *Concert* (11/90) (LASE) ① **15 611**
Berlin Phil Wind Qnt, H. von Karajan (r1973: arr Preis/Doblinger) *Concert* (5/94) (DG) ① **439 346-2GX2**
Triumph Overture—orchestra
Košice St PO, A. Walter (r1994) *Concert* (12/95) (MARC) ① **8 223683**
Wiener Jubel, 'Vienna Jubilee'—concert overture (pub 1890)
1. Overture.
1. ASMF, N. Marriner *Concert* (10/90) (EMI) ① **CDC7 54056-2**

SECTION IV: VOCAL AND CHORAL

Requiem—SATB, chorus and orchestra (1855)
O. Tchaikovsky, D. Michel, G. Vitale, J-L. Bindi, Lyon Franco-German Ch, Bonn Youth SO, W. Badun
(1/92) (BNL) ① **BNL112774**

SECTION V: STAGE WORKS

Afrikareise—operetta: 3 acts (1883—Vienna) (Lib. M. Wert, Genée & O F Berg)
EXCERPTS: 1. Overture; 2. Titania Waltz.
2. Košice St PO, A. Walter (r1994) *Concert*
(12/95) (MARC) ① **8 223683**

Banditenstreiche, 'The Jolly Robbers'—comic operetta: 1 act (1867—Vienna) (Lib. R Boutonnier)
1. Overture.
1. Montreal SO, C. Dutoit *Concert*
(2/86) (DECC) ① **414 408-2DH**
1. Hungarian St Op Orch, J. Sandor *Concert*
(11/90) (LASE) ① **15 611**
1. BPO, H. von Karajan *Concert*
(8/92) (DG) ① [2] **435 712-2GX2**
1. LSO, C. Mackerras (r1961) *Concert*
(12/95) (MERC) ① **434 352-2MM**

Boccaccio—operetta: 3 acts (1879—Vienna) (Lib. Zell & Genée, after Boccaccio)
EXCERPTS: 1. Overture; 2. Florenz hat schöne Frauen; 3. Hab'ich nur deine Liebe; 4. Mia bella fiorentina; 5. Menuet and Tarantella.
1. Košice St PO, A. Walter (r1993) *Concert*
(6/95) (MARC) ① **8 223648**
1. Košice St PO, A. Walter (r1994) *Concert*
(12/95) (MARC) ① **8 223683**
2, 3. Raphaele Concert Orch, P. Walden (arr Waldenmaier) *Concert*
(5/91) (MOZA) ① **MECD1002**
3. E. Schwarzkopf, Philh, O. Ackermann *Concert*
(1/86) (EMI) ① **CDC7 47284-2**
3. L. Popp, ASMF, N. Marriner *Concert*
(6/88) (EMI) ① **CDC7 49700-2**
3. J. Patzak, Berlin St Op Orch (r1934) *Concert*
(3/90) (PEAR) ① **GEMMCD9383**
3. M. Reining, Berlin Deutsche Op Orch, W. Lutze (r1939) *Concert*
(9/92) (PREI) ① **90083**
3. E. Rethberg, Victor SO, R. Bourdon (r1931) *Concert*
(10/95) (ROMO) ① [2] **81014-2**

Dichter und Bauer, 'Poet and Peasant'—comedy with songs: 3 acts (1846—Vienna) (Lib. F Kaiser)
1. Overture.
1. Montreal SO, C. Dutoit *Concert*
(2/86) (DECC) ① **414 408-2DH**
1. ASMF, N. Marriner *Concert*
(10/90) (EMI) ① **CDC7 54056-2**
1. Hungarian St Op Orch, J. Sandor *Concert*
(11/90) (LASE) ① **15 611**
1. NBC SO, A. Toscanini (bp1943) *Concert*
(1/91) (RCA) ① **GD60308**
1. BPO, H. von Karajan *Concert*
(8/92) (DG) ① [2] **435 712-2GX2**
1. T. Trotter (r1992: trans org: E. Evans) *Concert*
(4/94) (DECC) ① **436 656-2DH**

Donna Juanita—operetta: 3 acts (1880—Vienna) (Lib. R Genée & F Zell)
EXCERPTS: 1. Overture; 2. March.
1. Košice St PO, A. Walter (r1993) *Concert*
(6/95) (MARC) ① **8 223648**

Fatinitza—operetta: 3 acts (1876—Vienna) (Lib. R Genée & F Zell)
1. Overture; 2. March.
1. Montreal SO, C. Dutoit *Concert*
(2/86) (DECC) ① **414 408-2DH**
1. Hungarian St Op Orch, J. Sandor *Concert*
(11/90) (LASE) ① **15 611**
1. Košice St PO, A. Walter (r1994) *Concert*
(12/95) (MARC) ① **8 223683**
2. Košice St PO, A. Walter (r1993) *Concert*
(6/95) (MARC) ① **8 223648**

Die Flotten Burschen—operetta: 1 act (1863—Vienna) (Lib. J Braun)
1. Overture.
1. Hungarian St Op Orch, J. Sandor *Concert*
(11/90) (LASE) ① **15 611**

Franz Schubert—operetta: 1 act (1864—Vienna) (Wds. H Max)
EXCERPTS: 1. Overture.
1. Košice St PO, A. Walter (r1994) *Concert*
(12/95) (MARC) ① **8 223683**

Die Frau Meisterin, 'The Lady Mistress'—magical operetta: 3 acts (1868—Vienna) (Lib. C Costa)
EXCERPTS: 1. Overture.
1. ASMF, N. Marriner *Concert*
(10/90) (EMI) ① **CDC7 54056-2**

Die Heimkehr von der Hochzeit, 'Homecoming from the Wedding'—opera: 3 acts (1853—Vienna) (Lib. Feldman)
EXCERPTS: 1. Overture.
1. Košice St PO, A. Walter (r1994) *Concert*
(12/95) (MARC) ① **8 223683**

Die Irrfahrt um's Glück (Die Jagd nach dem Glück), 'Fortune's Labyrinth'—operetta: 3 acts (1880—Vienna) (Lib. R Genée & F Zell)
EXCERPTS: 1. Overture.
1. ASMF, N. Marriner *Concert*
(10/90) (EMI) ① **CDC7 54056-2**

Isabella—comic operetta: 1 act (1869—Vienna) (Lib. J Wely)
EXCERPTS: 1. Overture.
1. Košice St PO, A. Walter (r1993) *Concert*
(6/95) (MARC) ① **8 223648**

Der Krämer und sein Kommis—farce with songs: 2 acts (1844—Vienna) (Wds. F Kaiser)
EXCERPTS: 1. Overture.
1. Košice St PO, A. Walter (r1993) *Concert*
(6/95) (MARC) ① **8 223648**

Leichte Kavallerie, 'Light Cavalry'—comic operetta: 2 acts (1866—Vienna) (Lib. C Costa)
1. Overture.
1. Montreal SO, C. Dutoit *Concert*
(2/86) (DECC) ① **414 408-2DH**
1. ASMF, N. Marriner *Concert*
(10/90) (EMI) ① **CDC7 54056-2**
1. Hungarian St Op Orch, J. Sandor *Concert*
(11/90) (LASE) ① **15 611**
1. BPO, H. von Karajan *Concert*
(8/92) (DG) ① [2] **435 712-2GX2**
1. Black Dyke Mills Band, P. Parkes (arr brass band: G Langford) *Concert* (9/93) (CHAN) ① **CHAN4514**
1. Košice St PO, A. Walter (r1994) *Concert*
(12/95) (MARC) ① **8 223683**

Das Modell—operetta: 3 acts (1895—Vienna) (Lib. V Léon & L Held)
EXCERPTS: 1. Overture.
1. Košice St PO, A. Walter (r1993) *Concert*
(6/95) (MARC) ① **8 223648**

Ein Morgen, ein Mittag, ein Abend in Wien, 'Morning, Noon and Night in Vienna'—local play with songs: 2 acts (1844—Vienna) (Wds. F X Told)
1. Overture.
1. Montreal SO, C. Dutoit *Concert*
(2/86) (DECC) ① **414 408-2DH**
1. ASMF, N. Marriner *Concert*
(10/90) (EMI) ① **CDC7 54056-2**
1. Hungarian St Op Orch, J. Sandor *Concert*
(11/90) (LASE) ① **15 611**
1. BPO, H. von Karajan *Concert*
(8/92) (DG) ① [2] **435 712-2GX2**
1. LPO, T. Beecham (r1939) *Concert*
(7/93) (DUTT) ① **CDLX7001**

Paragraph drei—opera: 3 acts (1858—Vienna)
EXCERPTS: 1. Overture.
1. Košice St PO, A. Walter (r1990) *Concert*
(6/95) (MARC) ① **8 223648**

Pique Dame, 'Queen of Spades'—comic opera: 2 acts (1864—Vienna) (Lib. T Treumann. Rev from 'Die Kartenschlägerin')
1. Overture.
1. Montreal SO, C. Dutoit *Concert*
(2/86) (DECC) ① **414 408-2DH**
1. ASMF, N. Marriner *Concert*
(10/90) (EMI) ① **CDC7 54056-2**
1. Hungarian St Op Orch, J. Sandor *Concert*
(11/90) (LASE) ① **15 611**
1. Raphaele Concert Orch, P. Walden (arr Waldenmaier) *Concert*
(5/91) (MOZA) ① **MECD1002**
1. BPO, H. von Karajan *Concert*
(8/92) (DG) ① [2] **435 712-2GX2**

Die schöne Galathee, 'Beautiful Galatea'—operetta: 1 act (1865—Berlin) (Lib. P Henrion)
1 Overture.
Trinklied; Was sagst du? Ich lausche L. Schöne, orch (r1925) *Concert* (12/92) (NIMB) ① **NI7833**
1. Montreal SO, C. Dutoit *Concert*
(2/86) (DECC) ① **414 408-2DH**
1. Hungarian St Op Orch, J. Sandor *Concert*
(11/90) (LASE) ① **15 611**
1. BPO, H. von Karajan *Concert*
(8/92) (DG) ① [2] **435 712-2GX2**
1. NYPO, L. Bernstein *Concert*
(11/92) (SONY) ① **SMK47532**
1. Black Dyke Mills Band, D. Hurst (arr brass band: G Langford) *Concert* (9/93) (CHAN) ① **CHAN4514**

1. Košice St PO, A. Walter (r1993) *Concert*
(6/95) (MARC) ① **8 223648**

Tantalusqualen, 'The Torments of Tantalus'—comic opera: 1 act (1868—Vienna) (Lib. cpsr, after L Angely)
1. Overture.
1. ASMF, N. Marriner *Concert*
(10/90) (EMI) ① **CDC7 54056-2**
1. Košice St PO, A. Walter (r1993) *Concert*
(6/95) (MARC) ① **8 223648**

Tricoche und Cacolet—humoresque: 3 acts (1873—Vienna) (Lib. H Meilhac & LHalévy)
EXCERPTS: 1. Overture.
1. Košice St PO, A. Walter (r1994) *Concert*
(12/95) (MARC) ① **8 223683**

SURINACH, Carlos (b 1915) Spain

SECTION II: CHAMBER

String Quartet (1975)
New World Qt (r1978) *Concert*
(10/93) (VOX) ① [2] **115775-2**

SECTION III: INSTRUMENTAL

3 Canciones y Danzas españolas—piano (1951)
A. de Larrocha *Concert*
(9/92) (DECC) ① [2] **433 929-2DM2**

SUSA, Conrad (b 1935) USA

SECTION IV: VOCAL AND CHORAL

A song to the Lamb (Wds. Book of Revelation)
St John's Episcopal Cath Ch, D. Pearson *Concert*
(10/92) (DELO) ① **DE3125**

SUSATO, Tylman (? c1500–1561/4) ? Flanders

SECTION II: CHAMBER

Danserye—dance collection (pub 1551)
1. ALLEMAIGNES: 1a. Untitled; 1b. Den tweeden Allemaigne; 1c. Der Bettler Tanz; 1d. Allemande du Prince; 2. BASSE DANSES: 2a. Untitled; 2b. Mon desir; 2c. Le cuer est bon; 2d. La Mourisque; 2e. Danse du Roy; 2f. Entre du Fol; 2g. Cest une dure despartie; 2h. Cest a grant tort; 3. BERGERETTES: 3a. Untitled; 3b. Sans roch; 3c. Dont vient cela; 3d. La Brosse; 4. BRANLES: 4a. Untitled; 4b. Les quatre Branles; 4c. Fagot; 4d. Den Hoboeckendans; 4e. De Post; 4f. Danse de Hercules oft maticine; 4g. De Matrigale; 5. GAILLARDES: 5a. Untitled; 5b. Mille ducas; 5c. Le Tout; 5d. La dona; 6. PAVANS: 6a. Untitled; 6b. La Bataille; 6c. Mille Regretz; 6d. Si pas souffrir; 7. RONDES: 7a. Untitled; 7b. Mon Amy; 7c. Pour quoy; 7d. Il estoit une filette; 7e. Wo bistu; 7f. Ronde et Saltarelle. MISCELLANEOUS DANCES: 8. Aliud; 9. Passe et medio; 10. Le pingne; 11. Mohrentanz; 12. Tausend Dukaten; 13. Le joly boys. **1a(x7), 2b, 2d, 2e, 2f, 3b, 3c, 3d, 4b, 4c, 4d, 4e, 4f, 4g, 5a(x8), 6b, 6c, 7a(x7), 9.** New London Consort, P. Pickett (r1991) (1/94) (L'OI) ① **436 131-2OH**
7b Ulsamer Collegium, J. Ulsamer *Concert*
(2/86) (ARCH) ① **415 294-2AH**
11. I. Tracey (1990; arr Tracey) *Concert*
(4/91) (MIRA) ① **MRCD901**

SUSO, Foday Musa (b 1950) Gambia

SECTION II: CHAMBER

Tilliboyo (Sunset)—kora and string quartet (1990)
Kronos Qt, F. Musa Suso *Concert*
(11/92) (NONE) ① **7559-79275-2**

SÜSSMAYR, Franz Xaver (1766–1803) Austria

SECTION I: ORCHESTRAL

Concerto movement for Basset Clarinet and Orchestra in D
T. King, ECO, L. Hager *Concert*
(5/93) (HYPE) ① **CDA66504**

SUTTON, Harry O. *(19th–20th Cent) USA*

SECTION IV: VOCAL AND CHORAL

And the World Goes On—song for the play 'Easy Dawson' (1905) (Lyrics Jean Lenox)
R. Hitchcock, Broadway Cast (r1910) *Concert*
(5/94) (PEAR) ① [3] **GEMMCDS9050/2(2)**
I Don't Care—theme song of Eva Tanguay (1905) (Lyrics Jean Lenox)
E. Tanguay (r1922) *Concert*
(5/94) (PEAR) ① [3] **GEMMCDS9053/5**

SVENDSEN, Johann (Severin) *(1840–1911) Norway*

SECTION I: ORCHESTRAL

Carnival in Paris—orchestra, Op. 9 (1872)
Oslo PO, Ø. Fjeldstad *Concert*
(12/89) (NKF) ① **NKFCD50011-2**
Stavanger SO, G. Llewellyn (r1993) *Concert*
(9/94) (CHAT) ① **FCM1002**
Festival Polonaise—orchestra, Op. 12 (1873)
Oslo PO, Ø. Fjeldstad *Concert*
(12/89) (NKF) ① **NKFCD50011-2**
2 Icelandic Melodies—orchestra
Iceland SO, P. Sakari (arr orch) *Concert*
(8/92) (CHAN) ① **CHAN9028**
Norwegian Artists' Carnival—orchestra, Op. 14 (1874)
Bergen SO, K. Andersen *Concert*
(12/89) (NKF) ① **NKFCD50009-2**
Stavanger SO, G. Llewellyn (r1993) *Concert*
(9/94) (CHAT) ① **FCM1002**
Norwegian Rhapsody 1—orchestra, Op. 17 (c1872)
Bergen SO, K. Andersen *Concert*
(12/89) (NKF) ① **NKFCD50009-2**
Norwegian Rhapsody 2—orchestra, Op. 19 (c1872)
Bergen SO, K. Andersen *Concert*
(12/89) (NKF) ① **NKFCD50009-2**
Stavanger SO, G. Llewellyn (r1993) *Concert*
(9/94) (CHAT) ① **FCM1002**
Norwegian Rhapsody 3—orchestra, Op. 21 (c1872)
Bergen SO, K. Andersen *Concert*
(12/89) (NKF) ① **NKFCD50009-2**
Norwegian Rhapsody 4—orchestra, Op. 22 (1878)
Bergen SO, K. Andersen *Concert*
(12/89) (NKF) ① **NKFCD50009-2**
Romance in G—violin and orchestra, Op. 26 (1881)
O.B. Hansen, Oslo PO, Ø. Fjeldstad *Concert*
(12/89) (NKF) ① **NKFCD50011-2**
Malmö SO, J. DePreist *Concert*
(1/93) (BIS) ① **BIS-CD570**
K. Sillito, ASMF Chbr Ens (r1993) *Concert*
(5/94) (CHAN) ① **CHAN9258**
M. Thorsen, Stavanger SO, G. Llewellyn (r1993) *Concert*
(9/94) (CHAT) ① **FCM1002**
Swedish Folk Tunes—string orchestra, Op. 27 (1876)
1. Allt under himmelens fäste: adagio; 2. Du gamla, du friska, du fjellhöga Nord: moderato.
Gothenburg SO, N. Järvi *Concert*
(11/87) (BIS) ① **BIS-CD347**
Symphony No. 1 in D, Op. 4 (1865-66)
Gothenburg SO, N. Järvi *Concert*
(11/87) (BIS) ① **BIS-CD347**
Symphony No. 2 in B flat, Op. 15 (1876)
Gothenburg SO, N. Järvi *Concert*
(11/87) (BIS) ① **BIS-CD347**
Oslo PO, M. Jansons *Symphony 2.*
(11/88) (EMI) ① **CDC7 49769-2**
Symphony No. 2 in B flat, Op. 15 (1876)
Gothenburg SO, N. Järvi *Concert*
(11/87) (BIS) ① **BIS-CD347**
Oslo PO, M. Jansons *Symphony 1.*
(11/88) (EMI) ① **CDC7 49769-2**
Zorahayda—legend for orchestra, Op. 11
Bergen SO, K. Andersen *Concert*
(12/89) (NKF) ① **NKFCD50009-2**

SECTION II: CHAMBER

Octet in A—strings, Op. 3
ASMF Chbr Ens (r1993) *Concert*
(5/94) (CHAN) ① **CHAN9258**

SVIRIDOV, Gyorgy *(b 1915) Russia*

SECTION IV: VOCAL AND CHORAL

3 Choruses from Tsar Feodor Ioannovich—chorus a cappella
1. Rejoice, O Virgin; 2. Sacred love; 3. A hymn of repentance.
Moscow New Ch, E. Rastvorova (r1994) *Concert*
(9/95) (OLYM) ① **OCD541**
4 Choruses, 'Songs of Troubled Times' (1980) (Wds. A Blok)
EXCERPTS; 1. Autumn; 2. The Bright Fields; 3. Spring and the Wizard; 4. The Icon.
Moscow New Ch, E. Rastvorova (r1994) *Concert*
(9/95) (OLYM) ① **OCD541**
Night Clouds—choral cantata (1979) (Wds. A Blok)
EXCERPTS; 1. Night Clouds; 2. On the Green Bank; 3. The Hands of the Clock are Nearing Midnight; 4. Love (An extract from Heine); 5. The Puppet Show.
Moscow New Ch, E. Rastvorova (r1994) *Concert*
(9/95) (OLYM) ① **OCD541**
Oratorio Pathétique—oratorio: two basses, chorus and orchestra (1959) (wds. V. Mayakovsky)
A. Vassilev, Varna Phil Chor, Varna PO (r1989)
Shostakovich: Execution of Stepan Razin.
(3/91) (KOCH) ① **37017-2**
Pushkin's Garland—concerto for chorus (1980) (Wds. A Pushkin)
EXCERPTS; 1. A Winter's Morning; 2. A Ring for my Sweetheart; 3. To Mary; 4. The Echo; 5. The Greek Feast; 6. Camphor and Musk; 7. Reveille is Sounded; 8. Natasha; 9. Arise, O Timid One!; 10. The White-Flanked Magpie.
Moscow New Ch, E. Rastvorova (r1994) *Concert*
(9/95) (OLYM) ① **OCD541**

SWANN, Donald *(1923–1994) England*

SECTION IV: VOCAL AND CHORAL

Ill wind—song after Mozart's Horn Concerto, K495 (?1960s) (Wds. M Flanders)
R. Suart, Scottish CO, C. Mackerras (r1993) *Concert*
(10/94) (TELA) ① **CD80367**

SWAYNE, Giles (Oliver Cairnes) *(b 1946) England*

SECTION IV: VOCAL AND CHORAL

Cry—28 amplified voices with electronic treatment (1978-79)
BBC Sngrs, J. Poole (r1984)
(10/94) (NMC) ① **NMCD016**
Magnificat—double choir
Cambridge Sngrs, J. Rutter *Concert*
(4/92) (CLLE) ① **COLCD116**

SWEELINCK, Jan Pieterszoon *(1562–1621) The Netherlands*

SECTION III: INSTRUMENTAL

Aeolian Echo Fantasia—keyboard
J.D. Christie (r1993) *Concert*
(2/95) (NAXO) ① **8 550904**
Ballo del granduca—keyboard, Sw3/1
B. van Asperen (r1990) *Concert*
(3/91) (SONY) ① **SK46349**
J.D. Christie (r1993) *Concert*
(2/95) (NAXO) ① **8 550904**
Erbarm dich mein, o Herre Gott—keyboard
J.D. Christie (r1993) *Concert*
(2/95) (NAXO) ① **8 550904**
Fantasia—keyboard (unidentified)
G. Gould (pp1959) *Concert*
(9/95) (SONY) ① **SMK53474**
Fantasia B-A-C-H in D minor, 'Aeolian'—keyboard
S. Hussong (accordian) *Bach: Goldberg Variations.*
(5/90) (THOR) ① **CTH2047**
Fantasia chromatica, 'Dorian'—keyboard
B. van Asperen (r1990) *Concert*
(3/91) (SONY) ① **SK46349**
G. Gould (r1964) *Concert*
(11/93) (SONY) ① **SMK52589**
Malle Sijmen—pavan: keyboard, Sw3/5 (St Petersburg MS)
J.D. Christie (r1993) *Concert*
(2/95) (NAXO) ① **8 550904**

Mein junges Leben hat ein End'—song variations: keyboard
Amsterdam Loeki Stardust Qt *Concert*
(10/94) (L'OI) ① **440 207-2OM**
J.D. Christie (r1993) *Concert*
(2/95) (NAXO) ① **8 550904**
Onder een linde groen—song variations: keyboard
J.D. Christie (r1993) *Concert*
(2/95) (NAXO) ① **8 550904**
Pavana Lachrimae—keyboard
B. van Asperen (r1990) *Concert*
(3/91) (SONY) ① **SK46349**
Margaret Phillips (r1989) *Concert*
(4/91) (REGE) ① **REGCD105**
N. O'Neill *Concert*
(11/92) (CNTO) ① **CRCD2366**
Poolsche dans—keyboard
J.D. Christie (r1993) *Concert*
(2/95) (NAXO) ① **8 550904**
Ricercar—keyboard
J.D. Christie (r1993) *Concert*
(2/95) (NAXO) ① **8 550904**
Toccata ex C
J.D. Christie (r1993) *Concert*
(2/95) (NAXO) ① **8 550904**
Toccata in A minor I—keyboard
J.D. Christie (r1993) *Concert*
(2/95) (NAXO) ① **8 550904**

SECTION IV: VOCAL AND CHORAL

De profundis clamavi ad te Domine—motet: 5vv and continuo (pub 1619) (Wds. Psalm 130)
Toulouse Sacqueboutiers, J. Bernfeld, B. Fabre-Garrus (r1993) *Concert* (3/95) (ASTR) ① **E8521**
Donnez au Seigneur gloire—psalm: 5vv (Wds. Psalm 107, trans C Marot)
C. Goudimel Ens, C. Morel (r1994) *Concert*
(9/95) (NAXO) ① **8 553025**
Hodie Christus natus est—motet: 5vv (pub 1619)
Cambridge Sngrs, CLS, J. Rutter *Concert*
(12/89) (CLLE) ① **COLCD111**
M. Petri, Westminster Abbey Ch, National PO, M. Neary *Concert* (12/91) (RCA) ① **RD60060**
Kings College Ch, D. Willcocks *Concert*
(12/91) (EMI) ① **CDM7 64130-2**
Pseaumes des David—Troisième livre—4-8vv (pub 1614) (30 settings)
1. Qui au conseil des malins n'a esté; 2. D'ou vient, Seigneur, que tu nous as espars; 3. A quoy tant de gents; 4. Alors qu'affliction me presse; 5. Or sus serviteurs de Seigneur; 6. Alors que de captivité; 7. Sois moy, Seigneur, ma garde et mon appuy; 8. O combien est plaisant et souhaittable; 9. Les cieux en chacun lieu; 10. Ne sois fasché, si durant ceste; 11. Vous tous qui la terre habitez; 12. O Dieu on mon espoir j'ay mis; 13. Sus, louez Dieu, mon ame en toute chose; 14. Quand je t'invoque, helas escoute; 15. Le Toutpuissant a mon Seigneur et maistre; 16. Jamais ne cesseray; 17. Du Seigneur les bontés sans fin je chanteray; 18. Deba contre mes debatteurs; 19. Bienheureuse est la personne qui vit; 20. Mon Dieu, j'ay toy esperance; 21. Mon ame en Dieu tant deulement; 22. Vous tous les habitans des cieux; 23. Seigneur, je n'ay point la coeur fier; 24. Enfans, qui le seigneur servez; 25. Vouloir m'est due de mettre en escriture; 26. Revenge moy, pren la querelle; 27. Ainsi qu'on oit le cerf bruire; 28. Dieu est assis en l'asemblee; 29. O bienheureux qui juge sagement; 30. Or soit loué l'Eternel.
1, 2, 5, 9-11, 15-17, 20-22, 25, 26, 30. Trinity Coll Ch, Cambridge, R. Marlow (8/92) (CONI) ① **CDCF205**

SYBERG, Franz (Adolf) *(1904–1955) Denmark*

SECTION II: CHAMBER

Allegro Sonatissimo—violin and piano (1926)
S. Elbaek, M. Mogensen (r c1994) *Concert*
(6/95) (KONT) ① **32197**
Scherzando—flute, oboe, piano & cello (1934)
T. S. Hermansen, M. Mogensen, T.L. Christiansen, E. M. Møller (r c1994) *Concert*
(6/95) (KONT) ① **32197**
String Trio (1934)
S. Elbaek, P. Zelazny, T. S. Hermansen (r c1994) *Concert*
(6/95) (KONT) ① **32197**

SZÖLLÖSY, András (b 1921)
Hungary

SECTION III: INSTRUMENTAL
Paesaggio con morti—piano (1988)
P. Frankl (r?1992) *Concert*
    (6/93) (ASV) ① **CDDCA860**

SZULC, Jósef (1875–1956)
Poland

SECTION IV: VOCAL AND CHORAL
Clair de lune—song, Op. 83/1 (Wds. Verlaine)
M. Garden, J. Dansereau (r1929) *Concert*
    (8/94) (ROMO) ① **81008-2**
Hantise d'amour—song (Wds. H. Rey-Roise)
E. Caruso, orch, W.B. Rogers (r1914) *Concert*
    (12/90) (NIMB) ① **NI7809**
E. Caruso, orch, W.B. Rogers (r1914) *Concert*
    (7/91) (RCA) ① [12] **GD60495(5)**
E. Caruso, orch, W.B. Rogers (r1914) *Concert*
    (10/91) (PEAR) ① [3] **EVC3(1)**

SZYMANOWSKI, Karol (Maciej) (1882–1937) Poland

SECTION I: ORCHESTRAL
Concert Overture in E, Op. 12 (1904-05 rev 1912-13)
Polish Nat RSO, J. Kaspszyk (r1981) *Concert*
    (7/94) (EMI) ① **CDM5 65082-2**
Concerto for Violin and Orchestra No. 1, Op. 35 (1916)
C. Edinger, Katowice RSO, K. Penderecki *K.A. Hartmann: Concerto funèbre.*
    (9/90) (THOR) ① **CTH2057**
C. Juillet, Montreal SO, C. Dutoit (r1992) *Concert*
    (10/93) (DECC) ① **436 837-2DH**
R. Zimansky, Janáček PO, D. Burkh (r1992) *Symphony 4.*
    (7/94) (CENT) ① **CRC2153**
Concerto for Violin and Orchestra No. 2, Op. 61 (1933)
C. Juillet, Montreal SO, C. Dutoit (r1992) *Concert*
    (10/93) (DECC) ① **436 837-2DH**
Symphony No. 2 in B flat, Op. 19 (1909-10 rev 1936)
Polish Nat RSO, J. Kaspszyk (r1981) *Concert*
    (7/94) (EMI) ① **CDM5 65082-2**
Symphony No. 3, '(The) song of the night'—ten/sop, chorus and orchestra, Op. 27 (1914-16) (Wds. M. D. Rumi)
S. Woytowicz, Polish Rad & TV Ch, Polish Radio & TV SO, T. Strugała (r1987) *Concert*
    (4/94) (KOCH) ① **312652**
W. Ochman, Polish Rad Chor, Polish Nat RSO, J. Semkow (r1979) *Concert*
    (7/94) (EMI) ① **CDM5 65082-2**
J. Garrison, CBSO Chor, CBSO, S. Rattle (r1993) *Concert*
    (8/94) (EMI) ① **CDC5 55121-2**
BBC Sngrs, BBC Sym Chor, BBC SO, N. Del Mar (pp1983) *Concert*
    (12/95) (BBCR) ① **BBCRD9124**
Symphony No. 4, 'Symphonie Concertante'—piano and orchestra, Op. 60 (1932)
M. Wilson, Janáček PO, D. Burkh (r1992) *Violin Concerto 1.*
    (7/94) (CENT) ① **CRC2153**
Polish Nat RSO, J. Semkow (r1979) *Concert*
    (4/95) (EMI) ① **CDM5 65307-2**
P. Paleczny, BBC SO, M. Elder (pp1983) *Concert*
    (12/95) (BBCR) ① **BBCRD9124**

SECTION II: CHAMBER
Kurpian Song—violin and piano (1928-29) (arr cpsr & P. Kochanski from Choral Songs, Op. 55)
W. Wilkomirska, T. Chmielewski *Concert*
    (7/90) (POLS) ① **PNCD065**
K. Danczowska, K. Zimerman *Concert*
    (8/91) (DG) ① **431 469-2GGA**
Lullaby, '(La) berceuse d'Aïtacho Enia'—violin and piano, Op. 52 (1925)
W. Wilkomirska, T. Chmielewski *Concert*
    (7/90) (POLS) ① **PNCD065**
3 Myths—violin and piano, Op. 30 (1915)
1. La fontaine d'Aréthuse; 2. Narcisse; 3. Dryades et Pan.
K. Kulka, J. Marchwinski *Concert*
    (7/90) (POLS) ① **PNCD065**
L. Mordkovitch, M. Gusak-Grin *Concert*
    (6/91) (CHAN) ① **CHAN8747**
K. Danczowska, K. Zimerman *Concert*
    (8/91) (DG) ① **431 469-2GGA**

---

1. J. Szigeti, N. Magaloff (r1933) *Concert*
    (1/90) (BIDD) ① [2] **LAB007/8**
1. Midori, R. McDonald (r1992) *Concert*
    (6/93) (SONY) ① **SK52568**
1. T. Varga, G. Moore (r1947) *Concert*
    (11/93) (CLAV) ① [4] **CD50-9300/4**
1. T. Varga, G. Moore (r1947) *Concert*
    (11/93) (CLAV) ① **CD50-9314**
1. Chee-Yun, A. Eguchi *Concert*
    (12/93) (DENO) ① **CO-75118**
1. J. Thibaud, T. Janopoulo (r1933) *Concert*
    (12/94) (APRI) ① [2] **APR7028**
Nocturne and Tarantella—violin and piano, Op. 28 (1915)
W. Wilkomirska, T. Chmielewski *Concert*
    (7/90) (POLS) ① **PNCD065**
L. Mordkovitch, M. Gusak-Grin *Concert*
    (6/91) (CHAN) ① **CHAN8747**
Tarantella N. Milstein, L. Mittman (r1938) *Concert*
    (9/95) (BIDD) ① **LAB096**
Romance in D—violin and piano, Op. 23 (1910)
W. Wilkomirska, T. Chmielewski *Concert*
    (7/90) (POLS) ① **PNCD065**
H. Temianka, J. Graudan (r1937) *Concert*
    (2/93) (BIDD) ① [2] **LAB059/60**
Sonata for Violin and Piano in D minor, Op. 9 (1904)
L. Mordkovitch, M. Gusak-Grin *Concert*
    (6/91) (CHAN) ① **CHAN8747**
String Quartet No. 1 in C, Op. 37 (1917)
Varsovia Qt *Concert*
    (6/89) (OLYM) ① **OCD328**
Carmina Qt *Concert*
    (3/92) (DENO) ① **CO-79462**
Maggini Qt (r1993) *Concert*
    (2/95) (ASV) ① **CDDCA908**
String Quartet No. 2, Op. 56 (1927)
Varsovia Qt *Concert*
    (6/89) (OLYM) ① **OCD328**
Wilanów Qt *Concert*
    (7/90) (POLS) ① **PNCD065**
Carmina Qt *Concert*
    (3/92) (DENO) ① **CO-79462**
Maggini Qt (r1993) *Concert*
    (2/95) (ASV) ① **CDDCA908**

SECTION III: INSTRUMENTAL
4 Etudes—piano, Op. 4 (1902)
1. Allegro moderato; 2. Allegro moderato; 3. Andante in modo d'una canzona; 4. Allegro (ma non troppo).
C. Rosenberger *Concert*
    (9/87) (DELO) ① **DE1002**
D. Lee *Concert*
    (7/91) (HYPE) ① **CDA66409**
A. Vernède *Concert*
    (10/92) (CHNN) ① **CG9110**
Martin Jones (r1992/3) *Concert*
    (9/94) (NIMB) ① [2] **NI5405/6**
M. Roscoe (r1994) *Concert*
    (9/95) (NAXO) ① **8 553016**
3. W. Małcużyński *Concert*
    (7/90) (POLS) ① **PNCD066**
12 Etudes—piano, Op. 33 (1916)
C. Rosenberger *Concert*
    (9/87) (DELO) ① **DE1002**
A. Vernède *Concert*
    (10/92) (CHNN) ① **CG9110**
Fantasy—piano, Op. 14 (1905)
D. Lee *Concert*
    (7/91) (HYPE) ① **CDA66409**
Martin Jones (r1992/3) *Concert*
    (9/94) (NIMB) ① [2] **NI5405/6**
Masques—piano, Op. 34 (1916)
1. Shéhéherazade; 2. Tantris the Clown; 3. Don Juan's Serenade.
C. Rosenberger *Concert*
    (9/87) (DELO) ① **DE1002**
A. Stefanski *Concert*
    (7/90) (POLS) ① **PNCD066**
D. Lee *Concert*
    (7/91) (HYPE) ① **CDA66409**
E. Wiedner-Zając (r1993) *Concert*
    (9/95) (DORI) ① **DIS80121**
4. A. Vernède *Concert*
    (10/92) (CHNN) ① **CG9110**
20 Mazurkas—piano, Op. 50 (1924-25)
1. Sostenuto (E flat minor); 2. Moderato (G flat); 3. Moderato (B flat minor); 4. Allegramente risoluto; 7. Poco vivace (Tempo oberka); 11. Allegretto; 13. Moderato; 15. Allegretto dolce; 18. Vivace (Agitato tempo oberka); 19. Poco vivace; 20. Allegramente/brio brio.
Excs F. Blumental (r1974) *Concert*
    (4/95) (EMI) ① **CDM5 65307-2**
1, 2, 3, 4. A. Rubinstein (pp1961) *Concert*
    (10/93) (RCA) ① **09026 61445-2**
1, 2, 3, 7, 11, 15, 18. C. Rosenberger *Concert*
    (9/87) (DELO) ① **DE1002**
1, 2, 4, 7, 13, 15, 18-20. B. Hesse-Bukowska *Concert*
    (7/90) (POLS) ① **PNCD066**
1-4. E. Wiedner-Zając (r1993) *Concert*
    (9/95) (DORI) ① **DIS80121**
1-4. M. Roscoe (r1994) *Concert*
    (9/95) (NAXO) ① **8 553016**
2 Mazurkas—piano, Op. 62 (1933-34)
C. Rosenberger *Concert*
    (9/87) (DELO) ① **DE1002**
A. Vernède *Concert*
    (10/92) (CHNN) ① **CG9110**
Metopes—piano, Op. 29 (1915)
D. Lee *Concert*
    (7/91) (HYPE) ① **CDA66409**

M. Roscoe (r1994) *Concert*
    (9/95) (NAXO) ① **8 553016**
Prelude and Fugue in C sharp minor—piano (1909)
Martin Jones (r1992/3) *Concert*
    (9/94) (NIMB) ① [2] **NI5405/6**
9 Preludes—piano, Op. 1 (1900)
1. Andante ma non troppo; 2. Andante con moto; 3. Andantino; 4. Andantino con moto; 5. Allegro molto, impetuoso; 6. Lento, mesto; 7. Moderato; 8. Andante ma non troppo; 9. Lento, mesto.
Martin Jones (r1992/3) *Concert*
    (9/94) (NIMB) ① [2] **NI5405/6**
1, 2, 5. E. Wiedner-Zając (r1993) *Concert*
    (9/95) (DORI) ① **DIS80121**
Sonata for Piano No. 1 in C minor (1903-04) (Op. 8)
Martin Jones (r1992/3) *Concert*
    (9/94) (NIMB) ① [2] **NI5405/6**
Sonata for Piano No. 2 in A, Op. 21 (1911)
A. Stefanski *Concert*
    (7/90) (POLS) ① **PNCD066**
Martin Jones (r1992/3) *Concert*
    (9/94) (NIMB) ① [2] **NI5405/6**
M. Roscoe (r1994) *Concert*
    (9/95) (NAXO) ① **8 553016**
Variations in B flat minor—piano, Op. 3 (1903)
Martin Jones (r1992/3) *Concert*
    (9/94) (NIMB) ① [2] **NI5405/6**
F. Blumental (r1974) *Concert*
    (4/95) (EMI) ① **CDM5 65307-2**
Variations on a Polish folk theme—piano, Op. 10 (1904)
A. Vernède *Concert*
    (10/92) (CHNN) ① **CG9110**
Martin Jones (r1992/3) *Concert*
    (9/94) (NIMB) ① [2] **NI5405/6**

SECTION IV: VOCAL AND CHORAL
3 Fragments from poems by Jan Kasprowicz—voice and piano/orchestra, Op. 5 (1902)
K. Szostek-Radkowa, Katowice Polish Rad & TV Great SO, J. Maksymiuk (r1976) *Concert*
    (4/94) (KOCH) ① **312652**
4 Gesänge—soprano and piano, Op. 41 (1918) (Wds. R. Tagore)
1. Mein Herz; 2. Der junge Prinz I; 3. Der junge Prinz II; 4. Das letzte Lied.
D. Dorow, R. Jansen *Concert*
    (1/92) (ETCE) ① **KTC1090**
Litany to the Virgin Mary—soprano, female chorus and orchestra, Op. 59 (1930-33) (Wds. J Liebert)
E. Szmytka, CBSO Chor, CBSO, S. Rattle (r1993) *Concert*
    (8/94) (EMI) ① **CDC5 55121-2**
6 Love-songs of Hafiz—voice and piano, Op. 24 (1911) (trans. Bethge)
1. Wishes; 2. The only remedy; 3. The glowing tulips; 4. Dance; 5. The wind in love; 6. A sad spring.
H. Lukomska, J. Sulikowski *Concert*
    (7/90) (POLS) ① **PNCD067**
D. Dorow, R. Jansen *Concert*
    (1/92) (ETCE) ① **KTC1090**
8 Love-Songs of Hafiz, Op. 26 (1914) (Wds trans Bethge (incl Op. 24/1, 4 & 5 orch))
1. Desires; 2. Infatuated East Wind; 3. Dance; 4. Pearls of my soul; 5. To be young when old; 6. Your voice; 7. Drinking song; 8. Hafiz' tomb.
K. Rorbach, Polish Nat Op Orch, R. Satanowski *Concert*
    (12/89) (SCHW) ① **314001**
3 Songs, Op. 5 (1902) (Wds. J. Kasprowicz)
1. Holy Lord; 2. I am here and I am crying; 3. My evening song.
K. Szostek-Radkowa, Polish Nat Op Orch, R. Satanowski *Concert*
    (12/89) (SCHW) ① **314001**
T. Zylis-Gara, J. Marchwinski *Concert*
    (7/90) (POLS) ① **PNCD066**
5 Songs, Op. 13 (1905-07)
Zuleika H. Lukomska, J. Sulikowski *Concert*
    (7/90) (POLS) ① **PNCD067**
7 Songs, Op. 54 (1926) (Wds. J. Joyce)
1. Gentle Lady; 2. Sleep now; 3. Lean out of the window; 4. My dove, my beautiful one; 5. Strings in the Earth; 6. Rain has fallen; 7. Winds of May.
A. Bachlada, J. Marchwinski *Concert*
    (7/90) (POLS) ① **PNCD066**
D. Dorow, R. Jansen *Concert*
    (1/92) (ETCE) ① **KTC1090**
Songs of a fairy-tale princess, Op. 31 (1915) (Wds. Z. Szymanowska)
1. The lonely moon; 2. Nightingale; 3. Golden shoes; 4. Dance; 5. Song about wave; 6. Feast.
I. Kłosińska, Polish Nat Op Orch, R. Satanowski *Concert*
    (12/89) (SCHW) ① **314001**
J. Gadulanka, J. Marchwinski *Concert*
    (7/90) (POLS) ① **PNCD065**

D. Dorow, R. Jansen *Concert*
(1/92) (ETCE) ① **KTC1090**
**Songs of the infatuated muezzin—voice and
piano/orchestra, Op. 42 (1918 orch 1934)**
(Wds. Iwaszkiewicz)
B. Zagórzanka, Polish Nat Op Orch, R. Satanowski
Concert (12/89) (SCHW) ① **314001**
G. Ottenthal, Berlin RSO, G.M. Guida *F. David:
Désert.* (5/92) (CAPR) ① **10 379**
**Stabat Mater—soloists. chorus and
orchestra, Op. 53 (1925-26)**
S. Woytowicz, K. Szostek-Radkowa, A. Hiolski,
Polish Rad & TV Ch, Katowice Polish Rad & TV
Great SO, S. Wislocki (r1974) *Concert*
(4/94) (KOCH) ① **312652**
E. Szmytka, F. Quivar, J. Connell, CBSO Chor,
CBSO, S. Rattle (r1993) *Concert*
(8/94) (EMI) ① **CDC5 55121-2**
C. Goerke, M. Simpson, V. Ledbetter, Atlanta Sym
Chor, Atlanta SO, Robert Shaw (r1993) *Concert*
(5/95) (TELA) ① **CD80362**

SECTION V: STAGE WORKS

**Harnasie—ballet pantomime (3 acts), Op. 46
(1935—Prague)**
J. Stępień, Polish Nat Op Chor, Polish Nat Op Orch,
R. Satanowski *Mandragora.*
(12/91) (SCHW) ① **311064**
Polish Rad Chor, Cracow RSO, A. Wit (r1981)
Concert (4/95) (EMI) ① **CDM5 65307-2**
Dance W. Wilkomirska, T. Chmielewski *Concert*
(7/90) (POLS) ① **PNCD065**
**King Roger—opera: 3 acts, Op. 46
(1926—Warsaw)** (Lib. cpsr and J.
Iwaszkiewicz)
Roxana's Song K. Danczowska, K. Zimerman (arr
vn/pf) *Concert* (8/91) (DG) ① **431 469-2GGA**
Roxana's song H. Temianka, J. Graudan (arr
Kochanski: r1937) *Concert*
(2/93) (BIDD) ① [2] **LAB059/60**
Roxana's Song J. Heifetz (r1935) *Concert*
(11/94) (RCA) ① [65] **09026 61778-2(03)**
**Mandragora—pantomime: 3 scenes, Op. 43
(1920—Warsaw)** (Wds. Boguslawski/Schiller,
after Molière)
P. Raptis, Polish Nat Op Chor, Polish Nat Op Orch,
R. Satanowski *Harnasie.*
(12/91) (SCHW) ① **311064**

SZYMANSKI, Pawel *(b 1954)*
Poland

SECTION II: CHAMBER

5 Pieces—string quartet (1993)
Brodsky Qt (r1994) *Concert*
(10/94) (SILV) ① **SILKD6001**

TAFFANEL, (Claude) Paul
(1844–1908) France

SECTION II: CHAMBER

**Andante pastorale et Scherzettino—flute and
piano**
S. Milan, I. Brown *Concert*
(11/88) (CHAN) ① **CHAN8609**
R. Aitken, R. McCabe *Concert*
(9/89) (BIS) ① **BIS-CD184**
Wind Quintet (c1880)
Aulos Wind Qnt *Concert*
(10/91) (SCHW) ① **310087**

TAGELL, Huguety *(20th Cent)*

SECTION II: CHAMBER

Flamenco—cello and piano
M. Kliegel, B. Glemser (r1993) *Concert*
(1/95) (NAXO) ① **8 550785**

TAGLIAFERRI, Ernesto
(1889–1937) Italy

SECTION IV: VOCAL AND CHORAL

Piscatore 'e Pusilleco—Song (1926) (Wds.
Murolo)
L. Pavarotti, Teatro Communale Orch, A. Guadagno
Concert (8/83) (DECC) ① **410 015-2DH**

TAILLEFERRE, Germaine
(1892–1983) France

SECTION I: ORCHESTRAL

Concertino—harp and orchestra (1927)
G. Benet, Women's PO, J. Falletta *Concert*
(2/93) (KOCH) ① **37169-2**

SECTION II: CHAMBER

Arabesque—clarinet and piano
V. Soames, J. Drake *Concert*
(9/92) (CLRI) ① **CC0001**
Premières Prouesses—piano duet
P. Corre, E. Exerjean *Concert*
(5/94) (PIER) ① **PV786091**
Sonata for Violin and Piano No. 2 (1956)
J. Roche, P. Freed *Concert*
(10/94) (VOX) ① [2] **115845-2**
Suite Burlesque—piano duet
P. Corre, E. Exerjean *Concert*
(5/94) (PIER) ① **PV786091**
2 Waltzes—piano duet (1951)
P. Corre, E. Exerjean *Concert*
(5/94) (PIER) ① **PV786091**

SECTION III: INSTRUMENTAL

Au Pavillon d'Alsace—piano (1937)
B. Lerner *Concert* (1/89) (ETCE) ① **KTC1061**
Sonata—clarinet (1957)
V. Soames *Concert* (9/92) (CLRI) ① **CC0001**

TAÏRA, Yoshihisa *(b 1938) Japan*

SECTION II: CHAMBER

Hiéropfonie V—six percussionists (1974)
Kroumata Perc Ens (pp1983) *Concert*
(1/84) (BIS) ① **BIS-CD232**

TAKEMITSU, Toru *(b 1930)
Japan*

SECTION I: ORCHESTRAL

**Concerto for Viola and Orchestra, '(A) String
around Autumn' (1989)**
N. Imai, Saito Kinen Orch, S. Ozawa *Concert*
(8/92) (PHIL) ① **432 176-2PH**
Dream/Window—orchestra (1985)
Tokyo Metropolitan SO, H. Wakasugi (r1994) *Concert*
(10/95) (DENO) ① **CO-78944**
**Fantasma/Cantos—clarinet and orchestra
(1991)**
R. Stoltzman, BBC Welsh SO, T. Otaka (r1992)
Concert (1/95) (RCA) ① **09026 62537-2**
**Gémeaux—oboes, trombone, 2 orchestras &
conductors (1972-86)**
M. Honma, C. Lindberg, Tokyo Metropolitan SO, H.
Wakasugi, R. Numajiri (r1994) *Concert*
(10/95) (DENO) ① **CO-78944**
November Steps—orchestra (1967)
K. Yokoyama, K. Tsuruta, Saito Kinen Orch, S.
Ozawa *Concert* (8/92) (PHIL) ① **432 176-2PH**
Rain Coming—chamber orchestra (1982)
London Sinfonietta, O. Knussen *Concert*
(9/91) (VIRG) ① **VC7 59020-2**
Riverrun—piano and orchestra (1984)
P. Crossley, London Sinfonietta, O. Knussen *Concert*
(9/91) (VIRG) ① **VC7 59020-2**
Spirit Garden—orchestra (1994)
Tokyo Metropolitan SO, H. Wakasugi (r1994) *Concert*
(10/95) (DENO) ① **CO-78944**
**To the Edge of Dream—guitar and
orchestra**
J. Williams, London Sinfonietta, E-P. Salonen (r1989)
Concert (1/92) (SONY) ① **SK46720**
J. Bream, CBSO, S. Rattle (r1992) *Concert*
(7/93) (EMI) ① **CDC7 54661-2**
Tree Line—chamber orchestra (1988)
London Sinfonietta, O. Knussen *Concert*
(9/91) (VIRG) ① **VC7 59020-2**
**Vers, l'Arc-en-ciel, Palma—guitar, oboe
d'amore and orchestra**
J. Williams, G. Hulse, London Sinfonietta, E-P.
Salonen *Concert* (1/92) (SONY) ① **SK46720**
Visions—orchestra (1989)
1. Mystère; 2. Les yeux clos.
Chicago SO, D. Barenboim (pp1993) *Concert*
(8/95) (TELD) ① **4509-99596-2**

SECTION II: CHAMBER

A Way A Lone—string quartet (1981)
Tokyo Qt (r1992) *Concert*
(2/94) (RCA) ① **09026 61387-2**

**And then I knew 'twas Wind—flute, viola and
harp (1992)**
A. Nicolet, N. Imai, N. Yoshino (r1993) *Concert*
(12/94) (PHIL) ① **442 012-2PH**
Eclipse—shakuhachi and biwa (1966)
K. Yokoyama, K. Tsuruta *Concert*
(8/92) (PHIL) ① **432 176-2PH**
Quatrain II—cl, vn, vc, pf (1975, trans 1977)
(trans cpsr from orchestral work)
Tashi (r1978) *Concert*
(1/95) (RCA) ① **09026 62537-2**
**Rain Spell—flute, clarinet, harp, piano and
vibraphone (1982)**
London Sinfonietta, O. Knussen *Concert*
(9/91) (VIRG) ① **VC7 59020-2**
**Toward the Sea—alto flute and guitar
(1981)**
J. Williams, S. Bell *Concert*
(1/92) (SONY) ① **SK46720**
**Toward the Sea III—flute, viola and harp
(1981, rev 1989)**
A. Nicolet, N. Imai, N. Yoshino (r1993) *Concert*
(12/94) (PHIL) ① **442 012-2PH**
**Water-Ways—cl, vn, vc, pf, 2 hps, 2 vibs
(1978)**
Tashi, B. Allen, N. Allen, D. Frost, R. Fitz (r1978)
Concert (1/95) (RCA) ① **09026 62537-2**
Waves—cl, hn, 2 tbns, perc (1977)
R. Stoltzman, R. Routch, R. Borror, R. Chamberlain,
D. Frost (r1978) *Concert*
(1/95) (RCA) ① **09026 62537-2**

SECTION III: INSTRUMENTAL

All in Twilight—four pieces: guitar (1988)
J. Bream (r1992) *Concert*
(4/94) (EMI) ① **CDC7 54901-2**
Corona—piano (1962)
R. Woodward *Concert* (6/91) (ETCE) ① **KTC1103**
The Crossing—piano (1962)
R. Woodward *Concert* (6/91) (ETCE) ① **KTC1103**
Far away—piano (1973)
R. Woodward *Concert* (6/91) (ETCE) ① **KTC1103**
3 Folios—guitar (1974)
J. Williams (r1989) *Concert*
(1/92) (SONY) ① **SK46720**
Litany—piano (1950-89)
R. Woodward *Concert* (6/91) (ETCE) ① **KTC1103**
Pause uninterrupted—piano (1952-59)
1. Slowly and sadly and as if to converse with; 2.
Quietly and with a cruel reverberation; 3. A song of
love.
R. Woodward *Concert* (6/91) (ETCE) ① **KTC1103**
Piano Distance—piano (1961)
R. Woodward *Concert* (6/91) (ETCE) ① **KTC1103**
Rain tree sketch—piano (1982)
R. Woodward *Concert* (6/91) (ETCE) ① **KTC1103**
12 Songs for Guitar—transcriptions (1977)
1. Here, There and Everywhere (John Lennon & Paul
McCartney); 2. What a Friend (Charles C Converse);
3. Amours perdues (Joseph Kosma); 4. Summertime
('Porgy and Bess': George Gershwin).
1-4. J. Williams (r1989) *Concert*
(1/92) (SONY) ① **SK46720**
Les Yeux clos—piano (1979 & 1989)
R. Woodward *Concert* (6/91) (ETCE) ① **KTC1103**

SECTION IV: VOCAL AND CHORAL

**All that the Man Left Behind When He Died
(Shinda Otoko no Nokoshita Mono
wa)—song: chorus (1960, arr 1984)** (Wds S.
Tanikawa)
Shin-Yu Kai Ch, S. Sekiya (r1992) *Concert*
(8/94) (PHIL) ① **438 135-2PH**
**Cherry Blossoms (Sakura)—folksong
arrangement: chorus (1980)** (Wds
Traditional)
Shin-Yu Kai Ch, S. Sekiya (r1992) *Concert*
(8/94) (PHIL) ① **438 135-2PH**
Sayonara—song: chorus (1954, arr 1983)
(Wds K. Akiyama)
Shin-Yu Kai Ch, S. Sekiya (r1992) *Concert*
(8/94) (PHIL) ① **438 135-2PH**
**A Song of Circles and Triangles (Maru to
Sankaku no Uta)—song from the film 'Furyo
Shonen': chorus (1961, arr 1984)** (Wds cpsr)
Shin-Yu Kai Ch, S. Sekiya (r1992) *Concert*
(8/94) (PHIL) ① **438 135-2PH**
Songs I—song collection: mixed chorus
EXCERPTS: 1. Small Sky (1961, arr 1981); 2. I Just
Sing (1950s, arr 1981); 3. In a Small Room (1955, arr
1981); 4. The Game of Love (from the film Hannyo,
1961 arr 1982); 5. Unseen Child (from the film Kanojo
to Kare, 1963 arr 1982); 6. Will Tomorrow, I Wonder,
Be Cloudy or Clear? (1992).

Cpte Shin-Yu Kai Ch, S. Sekiya (r1992) *Concert*
(8/94) (PHIL) ① **438 135-2PH**
To the Island (Shima e)—chorus (1983) (Wds
M. Izawa)
Shin-Yu Kai Ch, S. Sekiya (r1992) *Concert*
(8/94) (PHIL) ① **438 135-2PH**
**Wings, 'Tsubasa'—song: chorus (1982, arr
1983)** (Wds cpsr)
Shin-Yu Kai Ch, S. Sekiya (r1992) *Concert*
(8/94) (PHIL) ① **438 135-2PH**

TAKTAKISHVILI, Otar
(1924–1989) USSR

SECTION II: CHAMBER

Sonata for Flute and Piano (1968)
M. Wiesler, R. Pöntinen *Concert*
(6/90) (BIS) ① **BIS-CD419**

TALBOT, Howard (1865–1928)
England

SECTION IV: VOCAL AND CHORAL

**O praise God in His Holiness—choir a
cappella** (Wds. Psalm 50)
Lincoln Cath Ch, C. Walsh (r1994) *Concert*
(7/94) (PRIO) ① **PRCD454**

SECTION V: STAGE WORKS

**A Chinese Honeymoon—musical show
(1901—London)** (Book & Lyrics George
Dance)
EXCERPTS: 1. I Want to be a Lidy; 2. The à la Girl;
3. Sweet Little Sing-Sing; 4. Mandie of Ohio; 5. A
Paper Fan; 6. Dolly With the Dimple On Her Chin; 7.
Roses Red and White; 8. Egypt; 9. The Twiddley
Bits; 10. Martha Spanks the Grand Pianner.
1. K. Barry, Broadway Cast (r1904) *Concert*
(5/94) (PEAR) ① [3] **GEMMCDS9050/2(1)**

TALGORN, Frédéric (b 1961)
France

SECTION V: STAGE WORKS

Fortress—film score (1993)
EXCERPTS: 1. Main Title.
1. Prague City PO, W. Motzing (r1993) *Concert*
(8/94) (SILV) ① **FILMCD146**

TALLIS, Thomas (c1505–1585)
England

SECTION II: CHAMBER

Fantasia a 5—consort: 5 parts (attrib)
Fretwork *Concert*   (3/88) (AMON) ① **CD-SAR29**
In Nomine a 4 No. 1—consort: 4 parts
Fretwork *Concert*   (3/88) (AMON) ① **CD-SAR29**
In Nomine a 4 No. 2—consort: 4 parts
Fretwork *Concert*   (3/88) (AMON) ① **CD-SAR29**
Amsterdam Loeki Stardust Qt (r1991) *Concert*
(2/94) (L'OI) ① **436 155-2OH**
Libera nos, salva nos—consort: 5 parts
Fretwork *Concert*   (3/88) (AMON) ① **CD-SAR29**
Solfaing Song a 5—consort: 5 parts (attrib)
C. Wilson, Fretwork *Concert*
(3/88) (AMON) ① **CD-SAR29**

SECTION III: INSTRUMENTAL

Ecce tempus idoneum—keyboard (vespers
hymn, Lent 3)
A. Davis *Concert*   (10/92) (DECC) ① **433 676-2DM**
Clerkes of Oxenford, D. Wulstan (r1973) *Concert*
(3/94) (CFP) ① **CD-CFP4638**
Felix namque I—keyboard (1562)
L.U. Mortensen *Concert*   (12/88) (KONT) ① **32003**
Felix namque II—keyboard (1564)
L.U. Mortensen *Concert*   (12/88) (KONT) ① **32003**
Lesson (Two parts in one)—keyboard (also
attrib Bull)
A. Davis *Concert*   (10/92) (DECC) ① **433 676-2DM**
Veni Redemptor gentium—keyboard (vigil of
Navitity)
A. Davis *Concert*   (10/92) (DECC) ① **433 676-2DM**

SECTION IV: VOCAL AND CHORAL

Absterge Domine—motet: 5vv (pub 1575)
(included in 'Cantiones Sacrae')
New College Ch, E. Higginbottom *Concert*
(4/87) (CRD) ① **CRD3429**
Tallis Scholars, P. Phillips *Concert*
(5/92) (GIME) ① **CDGIM025**

Audivi vocem de caelo—respond: 4vv
New College Ch, E. Higginbottom *Concert*
(4/89) (CRD) ① **CRD3372**
Taverner Consort, A. Parrott *Concert*
(5/89) (EMI) ① **CDC7 49555-2**
Oxford Camerata, J. Summerly (r1992) *Concert*
(11/94) (NAXO) ① **8 550576**
**Blessed are those that be
undefiled—anthem: 5vv** (adapted from 'Mihi
autem nimis')
Tallis Scholars, P. Phillips *Concert*
(12/86) (GIME) ① **CDGIM007**
**Candidi facti sunt Nazarei—respond: 5vv
(pub 1575)**
New College Ch, E. Higginbottom *Concert*
(4/87) (CRD) ① **CRD3429**
Taverner Ch, A. Parrott *Concert*
(5/89) (EMI) ① **CDC7 49555-2**
Christ rising again—anthem: 5vv (attrib)
Tallis Scholars, P. Phillips *Concert*
(12/86) (GIME) ① **CDGIM007**
Derelinquat impius—motet: 5vv (pub 1575)
New College Ch, E. Higginbottom *Concert*
(4/87) (CRD) ① **CRD3429**
Tallis Scholars, P. Phillips *Concert*
(5/92) (GIME) ① **CDGIM025**
King's College Ch, D. Willcocks *Concert*
(10/92) (DECC) ① **433 676-2DM**
**Dum transisset Sabbatum—respond: 5vv
(pub 1575)** (included in 'Cantiones Sacrae')
New College Ch, E. Higginbottom *Concert*
(4/87) (CRD) ① **CRD3429**
Taverner Ch, A. Parrott *Concert*
(5/89) (EMI) ① **CDC7 49555-2**
**Gaude gloriosa Dei mater—votive antiphon:
6vv**
Tallis Scholars, P. Phillips *Concert*
(3/86) (GIME) ① **CDGIM006**
New College Ch, E. Higginbottom *Concert*
(4/87) (CRD) ① **CRD3429**
Tallis Scholars, P. Phillips *Concert*
(1/91) (GIME) ① **CDGIM999**
The Sixteen, H. Christophers *Concert*
(2/91) (CHAN) ① **CHAN0513**
Clerkes of Oxenford, D. Wulstan (r1973) *Concert*
(3/94) (CFP) ① **CD-CFP4638**
Hear the voice and prayer—anthem: 4vv
Tallis Scholars, P. Phillips *Concert*
(12/86) (GIME) ① **CDGIM007**
R. Johnston, Worcester Cath Ch, Don Hunt *Concert*
(5/93) (ABBE) ① **CDCA943**
Hodie nobis caelorum Rex—respond: 4vv
Taverner Consort, A. Parrott *Concert*
(5/89) (EMI) ① **CDC7 49555-2**
Homo quidam fecit coenam—respond: 6vv
Taverner Ch, A. Parrott *Concert*
(5/89) (EMI) ① **CDC7 49555-2**
Honor virtus et potestas—respond: 5vv
(included in 'Cantiones Sacrae')
New College Ch, E. Higginbottom *Concert*
(4/89) (CRD) ① **CRD3372**
Taverner Ch, A. Parrott *Concert*
(5/89) (EMI) ① **CDC7 49555-2**
I call and cry to thee—anthem: 5vv (adapted
from 'O sacrum convivium')
Magdalen Oxford Coll Ch, J. Harper *Concert*
(11/91) (ABBE) ① **CDCA901**
If ye love me—anthem: 4vv
Tallis Scholars, P. Phillips *Concert*
(12/86) (GIME) ① **CDGIM007**
Cambridge Sngrs, J. Rutter *Concert*
(6/88) (CLLE) ① **COLCD107**
R. Johnston, Worcester Cath Ch, Don Hunt *Concert*
(5/93) (ABBE) ① **CDCA943**
In jejunio et fletu—respond: 5vv (pub 1575)
(included in 'Cantiones Sacrae')
New College Ch, E. Higginbottom *Concert*
(4/87) (CRD) ① **CRD3429**
Winchester Cath Ch, D. Hill *Concert*
(5/90) (HYPE) ① **CDA66400**
Tallis Scholars, P. Phillips *Concert*
(5/92) (GIME) ① **CDGIM025**
King's College Ch, D. Willcocks *Concert*
(10/92) (DECC) ① **433 676-2DM**
In manus tuas—respond: 5vv (pub 1575)
(included in 'Cantiones Sacrae')
Winchester Cath Ch, D. Hill *Concert*
(5/90) (HYPE) ① **CDA66400**
Tallis Scholars, P. Phillips *Concert*
(5/92) (GIME) ① **CDGIM025**
King's College Ch, D. Willcocks *Concert*
(10/92) (DECC) ① **433 676-2DM**
Oxford Camerata, J. Summerly (r1992) *Concert*
(11/94) (NAXO) ① **8 550576**

In pace in idipsum—respond: 4vv
Taverner Consort, A. Parrott *Concert*
(5/89) (EMI) ① **CDC7 49555-2**
Jesu salvator seaculi—hymn: 5vv
The Sixteen, H. Christophers *Concert*
(2/91) (CHAN) ① **CHAN0513**
Lamentations of Jeremiah—5vv
PCA, M. Brown *Concert*   (7/86) (CARL) ① **PCD806**
Ars Nova, B. Holten *Concert*
(12/88) (KONT) ① **32003**
Winchester Cath Ch, D. Hill *Concert*
(5/90) (HYPE) ① **CDA66400**
The Sixteen, H. Christophers *Concert*
(2/91) (CHAN) ① **CHAN0513**
Tallis Scholars, P. Phillips *Concert*
(5/92) (GIME) ① **CDGIM025**
Wells Cath Vicars Choral, A. Nethsingha *Concert*
(9/92) (ABBE) ① **CDCA924**
PCA, B. Turner (r1972) *Byrd: Mass for three voices.*
(1/93) (ARCH) ① **437 077-2AT**
Oxford Camerata, J. Summerly *Concert*
(4/93) (NAXO) ① **8 550572**
Loquebantur variis linguis—respond: 7vv
Tallis Scholars, P. Phillips *Concert*
(3/86) (GIME) ① **CDGIM006**
Cambridge Sngrs, J. Rutter *Concert*
(6/88) (CLLE) ① **COLCD107**
Taverner Ch, A. Parrott *Concert*
(5/89) (EMI) ① **CDC7 49555-2**
The Sixteen, H. Christophers *Concert*
(2/91) (CHAN) ① **CHAN0513**
Clerkes of Oxenford, D. Wulstan (r1973) *Concert*
(3/94) (CFP) ① **CD-CFP4638**
Oxford Camerata, J. Summerly (r1992) *Concert*
(11/94) (NAXO) ① **8 550576**
Magnificat and Nunc Dimittis—5vv
New College Ch, E. Higginbottom *Concert*
(4/87) (CRD) ① **CRD3429**
Mass for four voices
Oxford Camerata, J. Summerly (r1992) *Concert*
(11/94) (NAXO) ① **8 550576**
Mass Puer natus est nobis—7vv
1. Gloria; 2. Credo; 3. Sanctus; 4. Agnus Dei.
Clerkes of Oxenford, D. Wulstan (r1977) *Concert*
(11/95) (CALL) ① **CAL6623**
1. Cambridge Taverner Ch, O. Rees (r1993) *Concert*
(12/93) (PAST) ① **3589**
Mass Salve intemerata virgo—5vv
St John's College Ch, I. Shaw, G. Guest *Concert*
(12/89) (ASV) ① **CDGAU114**
Mihi autem nimis—introit: 5vv (pub 1575)
(included in 'Cantiones Sacrae')
Tallis Scholars, P. Phillips *Concert*
(5/92) (GIME) ① **CDGIM025**
Miserere nostri—motet: 7vv (pub 1575)
(included in 'Cantiones Sacrae')
Tallis Scholars, P. Phillips *Concert*
(3/86) (GIME) ① **CDGIM006**
A New commandment—anthem: 4vv
Tallis Scholars, P. Phillips *Concert*
(12/86) (GIME) ① **CDGIM007**
O Lord, give thy Holy Spirit—anthem: 4vv
Tallis Scholars, P. Phillips *Concert*
(12/86) (GIME) ① **CDGIM007**
Magdalen Oxford Coll Ch, J. Harper *Concert*
(11/91) (ABBE) ① **CDCA901**
O Lord, in thee is all my trust—anthem: 4vv
Tallis Scholars, P. Phillips *Concert*
(12/86) (GIME) ① **CDGIM007**
O nata lux de lumine—hymn: 5vv (pub 1575)
(included in 'Cantiones Sacrae')
Ars Nova, B. Holten *Concert*
(12/88) (KONT) ① **32003**
Winchester Cath Ch, D. Hill *Concert*
(5/90) (HYPE) ① **CDA66400**
The Sixteen, H. Christophers *Concert*
(2/91) (CHAN) ① **CHAN0513**
Hilliard Ens *Concert*   (6/91) (HYPE) ① **CDA66370**
Cambridge Sngrs, J. Rutter *Concert*
(4/92) (CLLE) ① **COLCD113**
Tallis Scholars, P. Phillips *Concert*
(5/92) (GIME) ① **CDGIM025**
King's College Ch, D. Willcocks *Concert*
(10/92) (DECC) ① **433 676-2DM**
Clerkes of Oxenford, D. Wulstan (r1973) *Concert*
(3/94) (CFP) ① **CD-CFP4638**
Truro Cath Ch, D. Briggs, S. Morley (r1992) *Concert*
(7/94) (PRIO) ① **PRCD429**
Worcester Cath Ch, Don Hunt, R. Johnston (r1993)
Concert   (2/95) (ABBE) ① **CDCA957**
**O sacrum convivium—antiphon: 5vv (pub
1575)** (included in Cantiones Sacrae')
New College Ch, E. Higginbottom *Concert*
(4/89) (CRD) ① **CRD3372**
Winchester Cath Ch, D. Hill *Concert*
(5/90) (HYPE) ① **CDA66400**

The Sixteen, H. Christophers *Concert*
(2/91) (CHAN) ① **CHAN0513**
Tallis Scholars, P. Phillips *Concert*
(5/92) (GIME) ① **CDGIM025**
Oxford Camerata, J. Summerly (r1992) *Concert*
(11/94) (NAXO) ① **8 550576**

O salutaris hostia—antiphon: 5vv
Winchester Cath Ch, D. Hill *Concert*
(5/90) (HYPE) ① **CDA66400**
Tallis Scholars, P. Phillips *Concert*
(5/92) (GIME) ① **CDGIM025**
Worcester Cath Ch, Don Hunt, R. Johnston (r1993)
Concert (2/95) (ABBE) ① **CDCA957**

O ye tender babes—secular partsong
Theatre Of Voices, P. Hillier (r1992) *Concert*
(9/94) (ECM) ① **439 172-2**

Out from the deep—anthem (spurious:
probably by W. Parsons)
Tallis Scholars, P. Phillips *Concert*
(12/86) (GIME) ① **CDGIM007**

**9 Psalm Tunes for Archbishop Parker's
Psalter—4vv (pub 1567)**
1. Man blest no doubt; 2. Let God arise; 3. Why
fum'th in fight—cf Vaughan Williams: Fantasia; 4. O
come in one to praise the Lord; 5. E'en like the
hunted hind; 6. Expend, O Lord; 7. Why brag'st in
malice high; 8. God grant we grace—Tallis's Canon;
9. Come Holy Ghost.
Tallis Scholars, P. Phillips *Concert*
(12/86) (GIME) ① **CDGIM007**
Tallis Scholars, P. Phillips *Concert*
(1/91) (GIME) ① **CDGIM999**

Purge me, O Lord—anthem: 4vv (secular
version: Fond youth is a bubble)
Tallis Scholars, P. Phillips *Concert*
(12/86) (GIME) ① **CDGIM007**
Magdalen Oxford Coll Ch, J. Harper *Concert*
(11/91) (ABBE) ① **CDCA901**

Remember not, O Lord God—anthem: 4vv
(expanded version)
Tallis Scholars, P. Phillips *Concert*
(12/86) (GIME) ① **CDGIM007**

**Salvator mundi Domine...Adesto nunc
proprius—hymn: 5vv**
Clerkes of Oxenford, D. Wulstan (r1977) *Concert*
(11/95) (CALL) ① **CAL6623**

**Salvator mundi, salva nos I—antiphon: 5vv
(pub 1575)** (included in 'Cantiones Sacrae')
Tallis Scholars, P. Phillips *Concert*
(3/86) (GIME) ① **CDGIM006**
Ars Nova, B. Holten *Concert*
(12/88) (KONT) ① **32003**
New College Ch, E. Higginbottom *Concert*
(4/89) (CRD) ① **CRD3372**
Oxford Christ Church Cath Ch, S. Preston *Concert*
(2/90) (GAMU) ① **GOUPCD153**
Winchester Cath Ch, D. Hill *Concert*
(5/90) (HYPE) ① **CDA66400**
The Sixteen, H. Christophers *Concert*
(2/91) (CHAN) ① **CHAN0513**
King's College Ch, D. Willcocks *Concert*
(10/92) (DECC) ① **433 676-2DM**
R. Johnston, Worcester Cath Ch, Don Hunt *Concert*
(5/93) (ABBE) ① **CDCA943**
Oxford Camerata, J. Summerly (r1992) *Concert*
(11/94) (NAXO) ① **8 550576**

Salvator mundi, salva nos II—antiphon: 5vv
(pub 1575) (included in 'Cantiones Sacrae')
Tallis Scholars, P. Phillips *Concert*
(3/86) (GIME) ① **CDGIM006**
New College Ch, E. Higginbottom *Concert*
(4/87) (CRD) ① **CRD3429**
Winchester Cath Ch, D. Hill *Concert*
(5/90) (HYPE) ① **CDA66400**

Salve intemerata virgo—antiphon: 5vv
Tallis Scholars, P. Phillips *Concert*
(3/86) (GIME) ① **CDGIM006**

**Sancte Deus, sancte fortis—votive antiphon:
4vv**
Tallis Scholars, P. Phillips *Concert*
(3/86) (GIME) ① **CDGIM006**
New College Ch, E. Higginbottom *Concert*
(4/89) (CRD) ① **CRD3372**
King's College Ch, A. Davis, D. Willcocks *Concert*
(10/92) (DECC) ① **433 676-2DM**
Oxford Camerata, J. Summerly (r1992) *Concert*
(11/94) (NAXO) ① **8 550576**

Spem in alium—respond: 40vv
Tallis Scholars, P. Phillips *Concert*
(3/86) (GIME) ① **CDGIM006**
PCA, M. Brown *Concert* (7/86) (CARL) ① **PCD806**
W. Becu, P. Nicholson, A. Wilson, Taverner Consort,
Taverner Ch, A. Parrott *Concert*
(5/89) (EMI) ① **CDC7 49555-2**

Winchester Cath Ch, Winchester Quiristers,
Winchester Vocal Arts, T. Byram-Wigfield, D. Hill
Concert (5/90) (HYPE) ① **CDA66400**
The Sixteen, H. Christophers *Concert*
(2/91) (CHAN) ① **CHAN0513**
Kronos Qt (arr Kronos Qt) *Concert*
(4/91) (NONE) ⑦ **7559-79242-2**
CUMS, King's College Ch, D. Willcocks *Concert*
(10/92) (DECC) ① **433 676-2DM**
E. Futral, J. Malafronte, F. Urrey, W. Pauley, Musica
Sacra, R. Westenburg *Concert*
(1/93) (RCA) ① **09026 60970-2**
Clerkes of Oxenford, D. Wulstan (r1973) *Concert*
(3/94) (CFP) ① **CD-CFP4638**

Suscipe quaeso Dominus—motet: 7vv
Clerkes of Oxenford, D. Wulstan (r1977) *Concert*
(11/95) (CALL) ① **CAL6623**

**Te lucis ante terminum I—hymn: 5vv (pub
1575)** (included in 'Cantiones Sacrae')
Winchester Cath Ch, D. Hill *Concert*
(5/90) (HYPE) ① **CDA66400**
The Sixteen, H. Christophers *Concert*
(2/91) (CHAN) ① **CHAN0513**
King's College Ch, D. Willcocks *Concert*
(10/92) (DECC) ① **433 676-2DM**
Oxford Camerata, J. Summerly (r1992) *Concert*
(11/94) (NAXO) ① **8 550576**

**Te lucis ante terminum II—hymn: 5vv (pub
1575)** (included in 'Cantiones Sacrae')
King's College Ch, D. Willcocks *Concert*
(10/92) (DECC) ① **433 676-2DM**

Verily, verily say I unto you—anthem: 4vv
Tallis Scholars, P. Phillips *Concert*
(12/86) (GIME) ① **CDGIM007**

Videte miraculum—respond: 6vv
The Sixteen, H. Christophers *Concert*
(12/88) (HYPE) ① **CDA66263**
Ars Nova, B. Holten *Concert*
(12/88) (KONT) ① **32003**
Taverner Ch, A. Parrott *Concert*
(5/89) (EMI) ① **CDC7 49555-2**
King's College Ch, A. Davis, D. Willcocks *Concert*
(10/92) (DECC) ① **433 676-2DM**
Cambridge Taverner Ch, O. Rees (r1993) *Concert*
(12/93) (PAST) ① **3589**
Oxford Camerata, J. Summerly (r1992) *Concert*
(11/94) (NAXO) ① **8 550576**

TAMPLINI

SECTION II: CHAMBER

**Fantasia on Themes from Donizetti's 'Don
Pasquale'—bassoon and piano**
K. Walker, J. Drake *Concert*
(10/89) (REGE) ① **REGCD104**

TAMUSUZA, Justinian (b 1951)
Uganda

SECTION II: CHAMBER

**Ekitundu Ekisooka (First movement)—string
quartet (1988)**
Kronos Qt *Concert*
(11/92) (NONE) ⑦ **7559-79275-2**

TAN DUN (b 1957) China/USA

SECTION I: ORCHESTRAL

Death and Fire, 'Dialogue with Paul Klee'
(1992)
BBC Scottish SO, T. Dun (r1992) *Concert*
(4/94) (SCHW) ① **312982**

On Taoism (1985)
BBC Scottish SO, T. Dun (Tan Dun) *Concert*
(4/94) (SCHW) ① **312982**

Orchestral Theatre I (1990)
BBC Scottish SO, T. Dun (r1992) *Concert*
(4/94) (SCHW) ① **312982**

TANAKA, Toshimitsu (b 1927)
Japan

SECTION III: INSTRUMENTAL

2 Movements—marimba
E. Glennie *Concert* (1/92) (RCA) ① **RD60557**

TANEYEV, Alexander
(1850–1918) Russia

SECTION I: CHAMBER

String Quartet No. 1 in G, Op. 25
Talan Qt (r1994) *Concert*
(10/95) (OLYM) ① **OCD543**
String Quartet No. 2 in C, Op. 28
Talan Qt (r1994) *Concert*
(10/95) (OLYM) ① **OCD543**
String Quartet No. 3 in A, Op. 30
Talan Qt (r1994) *Concert*
(10/95) (OLYM) ① **OCD543**

TANEYEV, Sergey Ivanovich
(1856–1915) Russia

SECTION I: ORCHESTRAL

Canzona in F minor—clarinet and strings
(1883)
W. Thomas-Mifune, BRSO, M.H. Tang (arr vc/orch)
Suite de concert, Op. 28. (4/93) (SCHW) ① **311352**
**Overture to Oresteya—orchestra, Op. 6 (pub
1897)**
Philh, N. Järvi *Symphony 4.*
(4/92) (CHAN) ① **CHAN8953**
**Suite de concert—cello and orchestra, Op.
28 (1909)**
W. Thomas-Mifune, BRSO, M.H. Tang *Canzona.*
(4/93) (SCHW) ① **311352**
Symphony No. 4 in C minor, Op. 12 (1898)
Philh, N. Järvi *Oresteya.*
(4/92) (CHAN) ① **CHAN8953**

SECTION II: CHAMBER

Piano Trio in D, Op. 22 (1907)
Borodin Trio (2/89) (CHAN) ① **CHAN8592**

SECTION III: INSTRUMENTAL

Andante semplice—piano (pub 1953)
M. Fingerhut (r1992) *Concert*
(4/94) (CHAN) ① **CHAN9218**
**Prelude and Fugue in G sharp minor—piano,
Op. 29 (1910)**
L. Zilberstein (1992) *Concert*
(8/94) (DG) ① **437 805-2GH**
**Scherzo in E flat minor—piano (1873-74) (pub
1953)**
M. Fingerhut (r1992) *Concert*
(4/94) (CHAN) ① **CHAN9218**

SECTION IV: VOCAL AND CHORAL

Venice at Night—song, Op.9/1 (1899) (Wds.
A. Fet)
A. Rolfe Johnson, G. Johnson, H. d'Alton *Concert*
(3/88) (HYPE) ① **CDA66112**

TANGERINE DREAM (20th Cent)
Germany

synthesiser ensemble

SECTION V: STAGE WORKS

Near Dark—film score (1987)
EXCERPTS: 1. Mae's Theme.
1. OST, Tangerine Dream *Concert*
(5/93) (SILV) ① **SILVAD3003**

TANSMAN, Alexandre
(1897–1986) Poland/France

SECTION I: ORCHESTRAL

4 Movements—orchestra (1968)
Košice St PO, M. Minsky *Concert*
(3/93) (MARC) ① **8 223379**
Symphony No. 5 in D minor (1942)
Košice St PO, M. Minsky *Concert*
(3/93) (MARC) ① **8 223379**

SECTION II: CHAMBER

5 Pieces—violin and piano
EXCERPTS: 3. Mouvement perpétuel.
3. J. Heifetz, E. Bay (r1947) *Concert*
(11/94) (RCA) ① **[65] 09026 61778-2(06)**
String Quartet No. 2 (1922)
Silesian Qt *Concert* (8/92) (ETCE) ① **[2] KTC2017**
String Quartet No. 3 (1925)
Silesian Qt *Concert* (8/92) (ETCE) ① **[2] KTC2017**
String Quartet No. 4 (1935)
Silesian Qt *Concert* (8/92) (ETCE) ① **[2] KTC2017**
String Quartet No. 5 (1940)
Silesian Qt *Concert* (8/92) (ETCE) ① **[2] KTC2017**

String Quartet No. 6 (1944)
  Silesian Qt Concert (8/92) (ETCE) ① [2] **KTC2017**
String Quartet No. 7 (1947)
  Silesian Qt Concert (8/92) (ETCE) ① [2] **KTC2017**
String Quartet No. 8 (1956)
  Silesian Qt Concert (8/92) (ETCE) ① [2] **KTC2017**
Triptyque—string quartet (1930)
  Silesian Qt Concert (8/92) (ETCE) ① [2] **KTC2017**

SECTION III: INSTRUMENTAL

Le Géant—piano
  B. Lerner Concert (1/89) (ETCE) ① **KTC1061**
Pour les enfants—piano
1. Petite rêverie; 2. Cheval mécanique; 3. Disque; 4.
Le petit oiseau; 5. Le petit nègre; 6. Leçon de danse;
7. Parade.
  L. Laskine (r1963; arr hp) Concert
      (12/93) (ERAT) ① **4509-92131-2**
Sonata No. 1, 'Rustica'—piano (1925)
  D. Blumenthal (r1992) Concert
      (9/94) (ETCE) ① [2] **KTC2021**
Sonata No. 2—piano (1929)
  D. Blumenthal (r1992) Concert
      (9/94) (ETCE) ① [2] **KTC2021**
Sonata No. 3—piano (1932)
  D. Blumenthal (r1992) Concert
      (9/94) (ETCE) ① [2] **KTC2021**
Sonata No. 4—piano (1941)
  D. Blumenthal (r1992) Concert
      (9/94) (ETCE) ① [2] **KTC2021**
Sonata No. 5—piano (1954)
  D. Blumenthal (r1992) Concert
      (9/94) (ETCE) ① [2] **KTC2021**
Sonatina No. 1—piano (1923)
  D. Blumenthal (r1992) Concert
      (9/94) (ETCE) ① [2] **KTC2021**
Sonatina No. 2, 'Transatlantique'—piano (1930)
  D. Blumenthal (r1992) Concert
      (9/94) (ETCE) ① [2] **KTC2021**
Sonatina No. 3—piano (1933)
  D. Blumenthal (r1992) Concert
      (9/94) (ETCE) ① [2] **KTC2021**
Suite variée—piano (1962)
1. Invention; 2. Pastorale; 3. Valse; 4. Burlesque; 5.
Berceuse; 6. Fuga; 7. Ostinato ritmico.
  D. Blumenthal (r1992) Concert
      (9/94) (ETCE) ① [2] **KTC2021**
  5. M. Fingerhut Concert
      (9/88) (CHAN) ① **CHAN8578**

SECTION IV: VOCAL AND CHORAL

Stèle, 'in memoriam Stravinsky'—1v and orchestra (1972)
  Košice St PO, M. Minsky Concert
      (3/93) (MARC) ① **8 223379**

TAPISSIER, Johannes (c1370–1410) France

SECTION IV: VOCAL AND CHORAL

Eya dulcis adque vernans rosa/Vale placens peroratrix—isorhythmic motet: 4vv
  Orlando Consort (bp1994) Concert
      (11/95) (METR) ① **METCD1008**

TARRAGÓ, Graciano (1892–?) Spain

SECTION IV: VOCAL AND CHORAL

Parado de Valldemosa—song
  J. Gomez, J. Constable (r1994) Concert
      (9/94) (CONI) ① **CDCF243**

TÁRREGA (Y EIXEA), Francisco (1852–1909) Spain

SECTION III: INSTRUMENTAL

Alborada—capriccio: guitar
  T. Kerstens (r1992-3) Concert
      (9/94) (CONI) ① **CDCF518**
  N. Kraft (r1993) Concert
      (1/95) (NAXO) ① **8 553007**
Capricho árabe—serenade andantino: guitar
  M. Kayath Concert (5/88) (CARL) ① **PCD876**
  S. Isbin Concert (10/90) (VIRG) ① **VC7 59591-2**
  W. Lendle Concert (7/92) (TELD) ① **9031-75864-2**
  T. Kerstens (r1992-3) Concert
      (9/94) (CONI) ① **CDCF518**
20 Estudios—guitar
1. en forma de Minuetto; 2. de Velodidad; 3. G; 4. B
minor; 5. A; 6. A; 7. A; 8. A minor; 9. E; 10. E; 11. D;
12. C; 13. A; 14. La mariposa; 15. sobre un tema de

Wagner; 16. inspirado en J. B. Cramer; 17. sobre un
tema de Mendelssohn; 18. A; 19. E minor; 20.
Estudio Brillante de Alard.
  4. W. Lendle Concert
      (7/92) (TELD) ① **9031-75864-2**
  20. A. Segovia (r1935) Concert
      (5/89) (EMI) ① [2] **CHS7 61047-2**
  20. J. Bream (r1983-90) Concert
      (8/93) (RCA) ① [28] **09026 61583-2(6)**
  20. J. Bream (r1983) Concert
      (8/93) (RCA) ① [28] **09026 61583-2(6)**
  20. J. Bream (r1983) Concert
      (8/93) (RCA) ① **09026 61610-2**
  20. J. Bream (r1983-90) Concert
      (6/94) (RCA) ① **09026 61609-2**
  20. N. Kraft (r1993) Concert
      (1/95) (NAXO) ① **8 553007**
Gran Jota—guitar
  P. Romero (r1993; arr P. Romero) Concert
      (4/95) (PHIL) ① **442 150-2PH**
Gran vals—guitar
  N. Kraft (r1993) Concert
      (1/95) (NAXO) ① **8 553007**
Maria—gavota
  W. Lendle Concert (7/92) (TELD) ① **9031-75864-2**
  N. Kraft (r1993) Concert
      (1/95) (NAXO) ① **8 553007**
4 Mazurkas—guitar
1. G minor, 'Adelita'; 2. Mazurka in G; 3. Marieta; 4.
Sueño.
  N. Kraft (r1993) Concert
      (1/95) (NAXO) ① **8 553007**
  1, 3. W. Lendle Concert
      (7/92) (TELD) ① **9031-75864-2**
  1-3. J. Bream (r1970) Concert
      (8/93) (RCA) ① [28] **09026 61583-2(4)**
  1-3. J. Bream (r1970) Concert
      (6/94) (RCA) ① **09026 61594-2**
  1, 3, 4. T. Kerstens (r1992-3) Concert
      (9/94) (CONI) ① **CDCF518**
  2, 3. J. Bream (r1983-90) Concert
      (8/93) (RCA) ① [28] **09026 61583-2(6)**
  2, 3. J. Bream (r1983-90) Concert
      (6/94) (RCA) ① **09026 61609-2**
Pavana—guitar
  T. Kerstens (r1992-3) Concert
      (9/94) (CONI) ① **CDCF518**
16 Preludios—guitar
1. E; 2. A; 3. A minor; 4. B minor; 5. G; 6. D minor; 7.
G; 8. E (Lágrima); 9. D minor (Endecha); 10. D minor
(Oremus); 11. D; 12. D; 13. E; 14. A minor; 15. A
minor; 16. E.
  1, 8, 9, 11. N. Kraft (r1993) Concert
      (1/95) (NAXO) ① **8 553007**
  8. J. Bream (r1970) Concert
      (8/93) (RCA) ① [28] **09026 61583-2(4)**
  8. J. Bream (r1970) Concert
      (6/94) (RCA) ① **09026 61594-2**
  8-10(Allegro, Andante sostenuto) T. Kerstens
  (r1992-3) Concert (9/94) (CONI) ① **CDCF518**
  15. M. Kayath Concert (5/88) (CARL) ① **PCD876**
  15. J. Bream (r1983-90) Concert
      (8/93) (RCA) ① [28] **09026 61583-2(6)**
  15. J. Bream (r1983) Concert
      (8/93) (RCA) ① [28] **09026 61583-2(6)**
  15. J. Bream (r1983) Concert
      (8/93) (RCA) ① **09026 61610-2**
  15. J. Bream (r1983-90) Concert
      (6/94) (RCA) ① **09026 61609-2**
Recuerdos de la Alhambra—guitar
  M. Kayath Concert (5/88) (CARL) ① **PCD876**
  A. Segovia (r1927) Concert
      (5/89) (EMI) ① [2] **CHS7 61047-2**
  W. Lendle Concert (7/92) (TELD) ① **9031-75864-2**
  A. Gifford (r1990) Concert
      (12/92) (NATI) ① **NTCD001**
  J. Bream (r1983) Concert
      (8/93) (RCA) ① [28] **09026 61583-2(6)**
  J. Bream (r1983) Concert
      (8/93) (RCA) ① **09026 61610-2**
  J. Bream (r1983-90) Concert
      (6/94) (RCA) ① **09026 61609-2**
  N. Kraft (r1993) Concert
      (1/95) (NAXO) ① **8 553007**
Rosita—polka: guitar
  N. Kraft (r1993) Concert
      (1/95) (NAXO) ① **8 553007**
Valse—suite: guitar
1. Paquito; 2. Las dos Hermanitas; 3. Vals in D.
  3. W. Lendle Concert
      (7/92) (TELD) ① **9031-75864-2**

TARTINI, Giuseppe (1692–1770) Italy

SECTION I: ORCHESTRAL

Concertino for Clarinet and Strings (transcr G. Jacob)
  E. Johnson, ECO, Y.P. Tortelier (arr.Jacob) Concert
      (9/87) (ASV) ① **CDDCA585**
Concerto for Cello and Orchestra in D
  M. Rostropovich, St Paul CO, H. Wolff (r1992)
  Concert (1/94) (TELD) ① **9031-77311-2**
Concerto for Cello and Strings in A
  M. Rostropovich, Zurich Collegium Musicum, P.
  Sacher Concert (4/90) (DG) ① **429 098-2GGA**
  M. Rostropovich, Zurich Collegium Musicum, P.
  Sacher Concert (10/94) (DG) ① [2] **437 952-2GX2**
Concerto for Flute and Strings in G
  J. Galway, Solisti Veneti, C. Scimone (r1991) Concert
      (4/94) (RCA) ① **09026 61164-2**
Concerto for Trumpet and Strings in D
  R. Smedvig, Scottish CO, J. Ling Concert
      (8/90) (TELA) ① **CD80232**
  O.E. Antonsen, ECO, J. Tate (r1993) Concert
      (2/94) (EMI) ① **CDC7 54897-2**
  J. Wallace, S. Wright (r1993) Concert
      (11/94) (EMI) ① **CDC5 55086-2**
Concerto for Violin and Strings in A, D94
3. 3rd movt: Allegro.
  3. Solisti Italiani (r1993) Concert
      (12/94) (DENO) ① **CO-78912**
Concerto for Violin and Strings in A, D96
  Adagio J. Szigeti, N. Magaloff (arr vn/pf: r1936)
  Concert (1/90) (BIDD) ① [2] **LAB007/8**
Concerto for Violin and Strings in D minor, D45
  J. Szigeti, Orch, W. Goehr (r1937) Concert
      (11/92) (BIDD) ① **LAB064**

SECTION II: CHAMBER

Sonata for Violin and Continuo in G minor, 'Devil's Trill'
  I. Perlman, J.G. Guggenheim (pp1990) Concert
      (2/91) (EMI) ① **CDC7 54108-2**
  Y. Menuhin, A. Balsam (r1932) Concert
      (12/91) (BIDD) ① **LAB046**
  Locatelli Trio (r1990) Violin Sonatas and Pastorale
  (1734). (4/92) (HYPE) ① **CDA66430**
  N. Milstein, L. Mittman (arr Kreisler: r1938) Concert
      (10/92) (BIDD) ① **LAB055**
  A. Grumiaux, R. Castagnone (r1956; arr Kreisler)
  Concert (11/93) (PHIL) ① [3] **438 516-2PM3**
  A-S. Mutter, VPO, James Levine (1992: arr
  Zandonai) Concert (12/93) (DG) ① **437 544-2GH**
  N. Milstein, L. Pommers (r1959) Concert
      (5/94) (EMI) ① [6] **ZDMF7 64830-2**
Sonata for Violin (and Continuo) in B flat, BB1 (c1745-60) (unpub MS)
  Locatelli Trio Concert
      (11/92) (HYPE) ① **CDA66485**
Sonata for Violin (and Continuo) in D, BD19 (c1745-60) (unpub MS)
  Locatelli Trio Concert
      (11/92) (HYPE) ① **CDA66485**
Sonata in A, 'sopra lo stile che suona il Prette dalla Chitarra Portoghese'—violin and optional continuo, BA4 (c1745-60) (unpub MS)
  Locatelli Trio Concert
      (11/92) (HYPE) ① **CDA66485**
12 Sonatas and Pastorale for Violin, Op. 1 (part) (1734)
1. A; 2. F; 3. C; 4. G; 5. E minor; 6. D; 7. D; 8. C
minor; 9. A; 10. G minor (Didone abbandonata); 11.
E; 12. F; 13. Pastorale in A.
  2, 8, 10, 12, 13. Locatelli Trio (1990) Devil's Trill
  Sonata. (4/92) (HYPE) ① **CDA66430**
12 Sonatas for Violin and Continuo, Op. 2 (part) (1745) (pub as Op. 3 in Paris)
1. D; 2. G; 3. A; 4. B minor; 5. A minor; 6. C; 7. G
minor; 8. D; 9. B flat; 10. F; 11. E minor; 12. G.
  12. J. Szigeti, K. Ruhrseitz (r1927) Concert
      (1/90) (BIDD) ① [2] **LAB005/6**
  12(Adagio) A. Busch, B. Seidler-Winkler (arr Corti:
  r1921) Concert (6/93) (SYMP) ① **SYMCD1109**
6 Sonatas for Violin and Continuo, Op. 5 (pub 1747) (some dubious)
1. A minor; 2. B flat; 3. A; 4. G; 5. F; 6. B flat.
  6. Locatelli Trio Concert
      (11/92) (HYPE) ① **CDA66485**

TATE, Arthur F(rank) *(1880–1950)* England

SECTION IV: VOCAL AND CHORAL

Somewhere a voice is calling o'er land and sea—song (1911) (Wds. E. Newton)
L. Tetrazzini, orch (r1914) *Concert*
(9/92) (EMI) ① [3] **CHS7 63802-2(2)**
M. Garden, J. Dansereau (r1927/9: 2 vers) *Concert*
(8/94) (ROMO) ① **81008-2**

TATE, Phyllis (Margaret) *(1911–1987)* England

SECTION II: CHAMBER

String Quartet in F (1953)
English Qt (r1992) *Concert*
(12/93) (TREM) ① **TREM102-2**

SECTION IV: VOCAL AND CHORAL

Epitaph—song (pub 1948) (Wds Walter Raleigh)
A. Rolfe Johnson, G. Johnson (r1991/3) *Concert*
(8/94) (HYPE) ① **CDA66709**
The lark in the clear air—Irish folksong arrangement (Wds. S. Ferguson)
A. Murray, G. Johnson (r1992) *Concert*
(8/93) (HYPE) ① **CDA66627**
C. Robbin, M. McMahon (r1985) *Concert*
(7/94) (MARQ) ① **ERAD113**

TAUBE, Evert *(1889–1976)* Sweden

SECTION I: ORCHESTRAL

Nocturne—cello, guitar and orchestra
J. Lloyd Webber, S-B. Taube, RPO, N. Cleobury (arr vc) *Concert*
(3/87) (PHIL) ① **416 698-2PH**

TAUBER, Richard *(1891–1948)* Austria/England

SECTION V: STAGE WORKS

Old Chelsea—musical romance: 2 acts (1943—London) (Lib. Tysh and Ellis)
My heart and I P. Morrison, Chandos Concert Orch,
S. Barry *Concert* (6/85) (CHAN) ① **CHAN8362**
My heart and I R. Tauber, orch (r1943) *Concert*
(2/92) (LYRC) ① [2] **SRO830**
Der Singende Traum—operetta (1934—Vienna) (Lib. Marischka)
EXCERPTS: 1. Du bist die Welt für mich.
1. R. Tauber, orch (r1934) *Concert*
(7/89) (EMI) ① **CDM7 69476-2**
1. P. Morrison, Chandos Sngrs, Chandos Concert
Orch, S. Barry (Eng) *Concert*
(2/90) (CHAN) ① **CHAN8759**
1. F. Araiza, Munich RSO, R. Weikert (arr Friebe)
Concert (3/93) (RCA) ① **09026 61163-2**

TAUBERT, Wilhelm *(1811–1891)* Germany

SECTION IV: VOCAL AND CHORAL

Es steht ein Baum in jenem Tal—song
E. Rethberg, anon, stg qt (r1928-9) *Concert*
(2/95) (ROMO) ① [2] **81012-2**

TAUSCH, Franz Wilhelm *(1762–1817)* Germany

SECTION I: ORCHESTRAL

Concertante for Two Clarinets and Orchestra No. 2 in B flat, Op. 26
T. King, N. Bucknall, ECO, L. Hager *Concert*
(5/93) (HYPE) ① **CDA66504**
Concerto for Two Clarinets and Orchestra No. 1 (1797)
T. King, N. Bucknall, ECO, L. Hager *Concert*
(5/93) (HYPE) ① **CDA66504**

TAUSIG, Carl *(1841–1871)* Poland

SECTION III: INSTRUMENTAL

Hungarian Gypsy Airs—rhapsody: piano
M. Setrak, Polish Chmbr PO, W. Rajski (orch Eibenschütz) *Concert*
(11/90) (CHNT) ① **LDC278 962**

Marche militaire (Schubert)—piano
L. Godowsky (r1924) *Concert*
(4/89) (APR) ① [2] **APR7011**
5 Nouvelles soirées de Vienne—valses-caprices d'après Johann Strauss II
1. Nachtfalter, Op. 157; 2. Man lebt nur einmal, Op. 167; 3. Wahlstimmen, Op. 250; 4. E; 5. A.
D. Hennig *Schubert Arrangements.*
(10/90) (ETCE) ① **KTC1086**
2. E. Wild (r1995) *Concert*
(12/95) (SONY) ① **SK62036**
Paraphrases on 'Tristan und Isolde' (Wagner)—piano
D. Hennig *Concert* (5/90) (ETCE) ① **KTC1076**
Schubert Arrangements—piano
1. Rondeau brillant (Divertissement, D823/3); 2. Polonaise mélancholique (Polonaise, D599/2 - trio); 3. Marche militaire (D733/1).
D. Hennig *Nouvelles soirées de Vienne.*
(10/90) (ETCE) ① **KTC1086**
Transcription of Kaisermarsch (Wagner)—piano (1871)
D. Hennig *Concert* (5/90) (ETCE) ① **KTC1076**
Transcriptions from 'Die Walküre' (Wagner)—piano
1. Siegmunds Liebesesang; 2. Der Ritt der Walküren.
D. Hennig *Concert* (5/90) (ETCE) ① **KTC1076**

TAUSKY, Vilem *(b 1910)* Czechoslovakia/England

SECTION I: ORCHESTRAL

Concertino for Harmonica and Orchestra
T. Reilly, ASMF, N. Marriner *Concert*
(10/88) (CHAN) ① **CHAN8617**

TAVENER, John (Kenneth) *(b 1944)* England

SECTION I: ORCHESTRAL

The Protecting Veil—cello and orchestra
S. Isserlis, LSO, G. Rozhdestvensky *Concert*
(3/92) (VIRG) ① **VC7 59052-2**

SECTION II: CHAMBER

The Hidden Treasure—string quartet (1989)
Chilingirian Qt (r1993) *Concert*
(5/94) (VIRG) ① **VC5 45023-2**
The Last Sleep of the Virgin—string quartet and handbells (1991)
Chilingirian Qt (r1993) *Concert*
(5/94) (VIRG) ① **VC5 45023-2**

SECTION III: INSTRUMENTAL

Thrinos—cello
S. Isserlis *Concert* (3/92) (VIRG) ① **VC7 59052-2**

SECTION IV: VOCAL AND CHORAL

The Acclamation—choir (1987)
Oxford Pro Musica Sngrs, M. Smedley (r1993)
Concert (12/94) (PROU) ① **PROUCD136**
Akathist of Thanksgiving—2 altos, organ, chorus and orchestra (1993) (Wds. G. Petrov)
J. Bowman, T. Wilson, M. Baker, Westminster Abbey Ch, BBC Sngrs, BBC SO, M. Neary (pp1994)
(9/94) (SONY) ① **SK64446**
Angels—choir and organ (1985)
Winchester Cath Ch, D. Dunnett, D. Hill (r1994)
Concert (8/94) (VIRG) ① **VC5 45035-2**
The Annunciation—4 soloists and chorus a cappella (1992)
Winchester Cath Ch, D. Hill (r1994) *Concert*
(8/94) (VIRG) ① **VC5 45035-2**
Oxford Pro Musica Sngrs, M. Smedley (r1993)
Concert (12/94) (PROU) ① **PROUCD136**
St Paul's Cath Ch, John Scott, Andrew Lucas (r1994)
Concert (5/95) (HYPE) ① **CDA66758**
Westminster Abbey Ch, M. Neary (r1994) *Concert*
(12/95) (SONY) ① **SK66613**
Eonia (1989)
The Sixteen, H. Christophers (r1993) *Concert*
(6/94) (COLL) ① **Coll1405-2**
BBC Sngrs, S. Joly, C. Bowers-Broadbent (r1994)
Concert (4/95) (UNIT) ① **88023-2**
Tallis Scholars, P. Phillips *Concert*
(6/91) (GIME) ① **CDGIM005**
Kings College Ch, S. Cleobury (r1994) *Concert*
(12/94) (EMI) ① **CDC5 55096-2**
God is with us—Christmas proclamation (1987)
W. Kendall, D. Dunnett, Winchester Cath Ch, D. Hill
(r1994) *Concert* (8/94) (VIRG) ① **VC5 45035-2**

BBC Sngrs, S. Joly, C. Bowers-Broadbent (r1994)
Concert (4/95) (UNIT) ① **88023-2**
Great Canon of St Andrew of Crete—chorus a capella (1981)
Tallis Scholars, P. Phillips *Concert*
(6/91) (GIME) ① **CDGIM002**
He Hath Entered the Heven—choir, with optional handbells (1982)
Oxford Pro Musica Sngrs, M. Smedley (r1993)
Concert (12/94) (PROU) ① **PROUCD136**
Hymn for the Dormition of the Mother of God (1985)
Cambridge Sngrs, J. Rutter *Concert*
(4/92) (CLLE) ① **COLCD113**
The Sixteen, H. Christophers (r1993) *Concert*
(6/94) (COLL) ① **Coll1405-2**
BBC Sngrs, S. Joly, C. Bowers-Broadbent (r1994)
Concert (4/95) (UNIT) ① **88023-2**
Westminster Abbey Ch, M. Neary (r1995) *Concert*
(12/95) (SONY) ① **SK66613**
Hymn to the Holy Spirit (1987) (Wds. various Orthodox services)
Oxford Christ Church Cath Ch, S. Darlington *Concert*
(10/92) (NIMB) ① **NI5328**
Hymn to the Mother of God (1985) (Wds from Liturgy of St. Basil)
Magdalen Oxford Coll Ch, J. Harper *Concert*
(11/91) (ABBE) ① **CDCA915**
Norwich Cath Ch, M. Nicholas, N. Taylor *Concert*
(3/92) (PRIO) ① **PRCD351**
Cambridge Sngrs, J. Rutter *Concert*
(4/92) (CLLE) ① **COLCD113**
St Paul's Cath Ch, John Scott, Adrian Lucas (r1991)
Concert (8/93) (HYPE) ① **CDA66618**
The Sixteen, H. Christophers (r1993) *Concert*
(6/94) (COLL) ① **Coll1405-2**
BBC Sngrs, S. Joly, C. Bowers-Broadbent (r1994)
Concert (4/95) (UNIT) ① **88023-2**
Westminster Abbey Ch, M. Neary (r1995) *Concert*
(12/95) (SONY) ① **SK66613**
Hymns of Paradise—bass, female chorus and six violins (1992) (Wds. St Ephrem the Syrian)
D. Sweeney, vn ens, Winchester Cath Ch, D. Hill
(r1994) *Concert* (8/94) (VIRG) ① **VC5 45035-2**
I will lift up mine eyes—SATBB (1989) (Psalm 121)
St Paul's Cath Ch, John Scott *Concert*
(10/91) (HYPE) ① **CDA66439**
Ikon of Light—double choir and string trio (1984) (Wds. St Simeon the New Theologian)
Tallis Scholars, Chilingirian Qt, P. Phillips *Concert*
(6/91) (GIME) ① **CDGIM005**
The Sixteen, Duke Qt, H. Christophers (r1993)
Concert (6/94) (COLL) ① **Coll1405-2**
Ikon of St Cuthbert of Lindisfarne
Durham Cath Ch, J. Lancelot, I. Shaw *Concert*
(7/91) (PRIO) ① **PRCD296**
Ikon of the Nativity—choir (Wds St Ephrem of Syria)
Oxford Pro Musica Sngrs, M. Smedley (r1993)
Concert (12/94) (PROU) ① **PROUCD136**
Innocence (1995)
P. Rozario, L. Nixon, G. Titus, A. Neary, C. Fullbrook,
M. Baker, Westminster Abbey Ch, M. Neary (r1995)
Concert (12/95) (SONY) ① **SK66613**
The Lamb, 'Little Lamb, who made thee?'—carol (1982) (Wds. W. Blake)
The Sixteen, H. Christophers *Concert*
(12/90) (COLL) ① **Coll1270-2**
Tallis Scholars, J. Tavener *Concert*
(6/91) (GIME) ① **CDGIM005**
King's College Ch *Concert*
(12/91) (COLL) ① **Coll1335-2**
Westminster Cath Ch, J. O'Donnell *Concert*
(3/93) (HYPE) ① **CDA66668**
Trinity Coll Ch, Cambridge, R. Marlow (r1993)
Concert (12/93) (CONI) ① **CDCF517**
Oxford Pro Musica Sngrs, M. Smedley (r1993)
Concert (12/93) (PROU) ① **PROUCD134**
Cambridge Sngrs, CLS, J. Rutter (r1993) *Concert*
(12/93) (CLLE) ① **COLCD121**
The Sixteen, H. Christophers (r1990) *Concert*
(6/94) (COLL) ① **Coll1405-2**
Oxford Pro Musica Sngrs, M. Smedley (r1993)
Concert (12/94) (PROU) ① **PROUCD136**
Ex Cathedra Chbr Ch, J. Skidmore (r c1994) *Concert*
(12/94) (ASV) ① **CDDCA912**
BBC Sngrs, S. Joly, C. Bowers-Broadbent (r1994)
Concert (4/95) (UNIT) ① **88023-2**
Westminster Abbey Ch, M. Neary (r1995) *Concert*
(12/95) (SONY) ① **SK66613**
The Lament of the Mother of God—soprano and chorus a cappella (1990)
S. Kringelborn, Winchester Cath Ch, D. Hill (r1994)
Concert (8/94) (VIRG) ① **VC5 45035-2**

Lamentation, Last Prayer and Exultation—soprano and handbells (1977)
P. Rozario, I. Simcock (r1994) *Concert*
(2/95) (COLL) ℗ Coll1428-2
Little Requiem for Father Malachy Lynch (1972)
Westminster Abbey Ch, ECO, M. Neary (r1994)
Concert (12/95) (SONY) ℗ SK66613
The Lord's Prayer—choir (1982)
Oxford Pro Musica Sngrs, M. Smedley (r1993)
Concert (12/94) (PROU) ℗ PROUCD136
Magnificat (1986)
Kings College Ch, S. Cleobury (r1994) *Concert*
(12/94) (EMI) ℗ CDC5 55096-2
Many Years—choir (1987)
Oxford Pro Musica Sngrs, M. Smedley (r1993)
Concert (12/94) (PROU) ℗ PROUCD136
Melina—soprano (1994) (in memoriam Melina Mercouri)
P. Rozario (r1994) *Concert*
(2/95) (COLL) ℗ Coll1428-2
A Mini Song Cycle for Gina—soprano and piano (1984)
1. When you are old; 2. A cradle song; 3. He reproves the curlew; 4. When you are old.
P. Rozario, J. Tavener (r1994) *Concert*
(2/95) (COLL) ℗ Coll1428-2
A Nativity—female choir (1984) (Wds Yeats)
Elysian Sngrs, M. Greenall *Concert*
(12/91) (CNTI) ℗ CCD1043
Oxford Pro Musica Sngrs, M. Smedley (r1993)
Concert (12/93) (PROU) ℗ PROUCD134
Oxford Pro Musica Sngrs, M. Smedley (r1993)
Concert (12/94) (PROU) ℗ PROUCD136
Nunc dimittis (1986)
Kings College Ch, S. Cleobury (r1994) *Concert*
(12/94) (EMI) ℗ CDC5 55096-2
Responsorium in memoriam Annon Lee Silver—choir & organ (1971)
BBC Sngrs, S. Joly, C. Bowers-Broadbent (r1994)
Concert (4/95) (UNIT) ℗ 88023-2
Song for Athene—choir & organ (1993)
BBC Sngrs, S. Joly, C. Bowers-Broadbent (r1994)
Concert (4/95) (UNIT) ℗ 88023-2
Westminster Abbey Ch, M. Neary (r1994) *Concert*
(12/95) (SONY) ℗ SK66613
Thunder entered Her—chorus a cappella (1990) (Wds. St Ephrem the Syrian)
W. Kendall, I. Simcock, D. Dunnett, Winchester Cath Ch, D. Hill (r1994) *Concert*
(8/94) (VIRG) ℗ VC5 45035-2
BBC Sngrs, S. Joly, C. Bowers-Broadbent (r1994)
Concert (4/95) (UNIT) ℗ 88023-2
The Tiger (1987) (Wds. W. Blake)
The Sixteen, H. Christophers (r1993) *Concert*
(6/94) (COLL) ℗ Coll1405-2
BBC Sngrs, S. Joly, C. Bowers-Broadbent (r1994)
Concert (4/95) (UNIT) ℗ 88023-2
Westminster Abbey Ch, M. Neary (r1995) *Concert*
(12/95) (SONY) ℗ SK66613
To a child dancing in the wind—soprano, flute, viola and harp (1983) (Wds W B Yeats)
1. He wishes for the cloths of Heaven; 2. The old men admiring themselves in the water; 3. To a child dancing in the wind; 4. Two years later; 5. The fiddler of Dooney; 6. A deep-sworn vow; 7. Sweet dancer; 8. The stolen child; 9. He wishes for the cloths of heaven; 10. The Countess Cathleen in paradise.
P. Rozario, K. Lukas, S. Tees, H. Tunstall, I. Simcock, J. Tavener (r1994) *Concert*
(2/95) (COLL) ℗ Coll1428-2
Today the Virgin—carol (1989)
Oxford Pro Musica Sngrs, M. Smedley (r1993)
Concert (12/93) (PROU) ℗ PROUCD134
The Sixteen, H. Christophers (r1993) *Concert*
(6/94) (COLL) ℗ Coll1405-2
Oxford Pro Musica Sngrs, M. Smedley (r1993)
Concert (12/94) (PROU) ℗ PROUCD136
We shall see Him as He is—STT, chorus and orchestra (1922)
P. Rozario, J.M. Ainsley, A. Murgatroyd, Britten Sngrs, Chester Fest Chor, BBC Welsh Sym Chor, BBC Welsh SO, R. Hickox (pp1992)
(1/93) (CHAN) ℗ CHAN9128
Wedding Prayer—choir (1987)
Oxford Pro Musica Sngrs, M. Smedley (r1993)
Concert (12/94) (PROU) ℗ PROUCD136
The Whale—dramatic cantata (1966) (Wds. Bible)
A. Reynolds, R. Herincx, A. Lidell, J. Tavener, London Sinfonietta Chor, London Sinfonietta, D. Atherton (r1970) (6/93) (EMI) ℗ CDSAPCOR15

Mary of Egypt—icon in music and dance: 5 acts (1992—Snape) (Lib. Mother Thekla)
Cpte P. Rozario, C. Goodchild, S. Varcoe, Ely Cath Choristers, Britten-Pears Chbr Ch, Aldeburgh Fest Ens, L. Friend (pp1992)
(5/93) (COLL) ℗ [2] Coll7023-2

TAVERNER, John (c1490–1545) England

In Nomine a 4—consort (4 parts)
Fretwork *Concert* (3/88) (AMON) ℗ CD-SAR29
Amsterdam Loeki Stardust Qt (r1991) *Concert*
(2/94) (L'OI) ℗ 436 155-2OH
Fretwork (r1992) *Concert*
(3/94) (HYPE) ℗ CDA66639
F. Brüggen, Brüggen Consort (r1967/79) *Concert*
(10/95) (TELD) ℗ 4509-97465-2

In Nomine—lute
C. Wilson *Concert* (3/88) (AMON) ℗ CD-SAR29
C. Wilson *Concert* (11/91) (VIRG) ℗ VC7 59034-2
C. Bowers-Broadbent (r1992) *Concert*
(9/94) (ECM) ℗ 439 172-2
Amsterdam Loeki Stardust Qt *Concert*
(10/94) (L'OI) ℗ 440 207-2OM

Alleluia, Veni electa mea—motet: 4vv (for Lady Mass)
The Sixteen, H. Christophers *Concert*
(9/93) (HYPE) ℗ CDA66507
Oxford Christ Church Cath Ch, S. Darlington (r1992)
Concert (10/93) (NIMB) ℗ NI5360
Audivi vocem—motet: 4vv
Oxford Christ Church Cath Ch, S. Darlington (r1992)
Concert (10/93) (NIMB) ℗ NI5360
Ave Dei patris filia—votive antiphon: 5vv
Oxford Christ Church Cath Ch, S. Darlington (r1992)
Concert (10/93) (NIMB) ℗ NI5360
Christe Jesu, pastor bone—votive antiphon: 5vv (later version of O Wilhelme, pastor bone)
Cambridge Sngrs, J. Rutter *Concert*
(4/92) (CLLE) ℗ COLCD113
Dum transisset Sabbatum I—antiphon: 5vv (for Matins, Easter Sunday)
Tallis Scholars, P. Phillips *Concert*
(7/86) (GIME) ℗ CDGIM004
Tallis Scholars, P. Phillips *Concert*
(1/91) (GIME) ℗ CDGIM999
The Sixteen, H. Christophers *Concert*
(3/91) (HYPE) ℗ CDA66325
The Sixteen, H. Christophers (r1990) *Concert*
(4/92) (HYPE) ℗ CDA66427
Oxford Christ Church Cath Ch, S. Darlington (r1992)
Concert (10/93) (NIMB) ℗ NI5360
Truro Cath Ch, D. Briggs, S. Morley (r1992) *Concert*
(7/94) (PRIO) ℗ PRCD429
Worcester Cath Ch, Don Hunt, R. Johnston (r1993)
Concert (2/95) (ABBE) ℗ CDCA957
Tallis Scholars, P. Phillips (r1986) *Concert*
(12/95) (GIME) ℗ CDGIM995
Dum transisset Sabbatum II—antiphon: 5vv
Oxford Christ Church Cath Ch, S. Darlington (r1992)
Concert (10/93) (NIMB) ℗ NI5360
Ex eius tumba—respond: 5vv (also known by titles, 'Sospitati dedit aegros')
The Sixteen, H. Christophers (r1990) *Concert*
(4/92) (HYPE) ℗ CDA66427
Oxford Christ Church Cath Ch, S. Darlington (r1992)
Concert (10/93) (NIMB) ℗ NI5360
Gaude plurimum—votive antiphon: 5vv
The Sixteen, H. Christophers *Concert*
(1/90) (HYPE) ℗ CDA66360
Hodie nobis caelorum Rex—respond: 4vv
The Sixteen, H. Christophers (r1992) *Concert*
(3/94) (HYPE) ℗ CDA66639
In pace in idipsum—respond: 5vv
The Sixteen, H. Christophers *Concert*
(1/90) (HYPE) ℗ CDA66360
Kyrie, 'Leroy'—4vv
Tallis Scholars, P. Phillips *Concert*
(7/86) (GIME) ℗ CDGIM004
The Sixteen, H. Christophers *Concert*
(3/91) (HYPE) ℗ CDA66325
Oxford Christ Church Cath Ch, S. Darlington *Concert*
(10/92) (NIMB) ℗ NI5328
Oxford Christ Church Cath Ch, S. Darlington (r1992)
Concert (10/93) (NIMB) ℗ NI5360
Tallis Scholars, P. Phillips (r1986) *Concert*
(12/95) (GIME) ℗ CDGIM995

Magnificat—5vv
Oxford Christ Church Cath Ch, S. Darlington (r1992)
Concert (10/93) (NIMB) ℗ NI5360
Magnificat sexti toni—4vv
The Sixteen, H. Christophers (r1992) *Concert*
(3/94) (HYPE) ℗ CDA66639
Mass, 'Western Wynde'—4vv
New College Ch, E. Higginbottom *Concert*
(4/89) (CRD) ℗ CRD3372
The Sixteen, H. Christophers *Concert*
(9/93) (HYPE) ℗ CDA66507
Tallis Scholars, P. Phillips *Concert*
(9/93) (GIME) ℗ CDGIM027
Tallis Scholars, P. Phillips (r1993) *Concert*
(12/95) (GIME) ℗ CDGIM995
Mater Christi sanctissima—votive antiphon: 5vv
New College Ch, E. Higginbottom *Concert*
(3/87) (PROU) ℗ PROUCD114
New College Ch, E. Higginbottom *Concert*
(4/89) (CRD) ℗ CRD3372
Oxford Christ Church Cath Ch, S. Darlington *Concert*
(4/90) (NIMB) ℗ NI5218
The Sixteen, H. Christophers (r1992) *Concert*
(3/94) (HYPE) ℗ CDA66639
Missa Corona spinea—6vv
The Sixteen, H. Christophers *Concert*
(1/90) (HYPE) ℗ CDA66360
Oxford Christ Church Cath Ch, F. Grier *O Wilhelme, pastor bone.* (1/90) (ASV) ℗ CDGAU115
Missa Gloria tibi Trinitas—6vv
Tallis Scholars, P. Phillips *Concert*
(7/86) (GIME) ℗ CDGIM004
Tallis Scholars, P. Phillips (r1986) *Concert*
(12/95) (GIME) ℗ CDGIM995
Missa Mater Christi—5vv
Oxford Christ Church Cath Ch, S. Darlington *Concert*
(4/90) (NIMB) ℗ NI5218
The Sixteen, H. Christophers (r1992) *Concert*
(3/94) (HYPE) ℗ CDA66639
Missa O Michael—6vv
The Sixteen, H. Christophers *Concert*
(3/91) (HYPE) ℗ CDA66325
Missa Sancti Wilhelmi—5vv (also known as Missa Small Devotion)
The Sixteen, H. Christophers (r1990) *Concert*
(4/92) (HYPE) ℗ CDA66427
Nesciens mater—antiphon: 4vv
The Sixteen, H. Christophers (r1992) *Concert*
(3/94) (HYPE) ℗ CDA66639
O splendor gloriae—votive antiphon: 5vv
The Sixteen, H. Christophers *Concert*
(9/93) (HYPE) ℗ CDA66507
O Wilhelme, pastor bone—motet: 5vv (original version of Christe Jesu, pastor bone)
Oxford Christ Church Cath Ch, F. Grier *Missa Corona spinea.* (1/90) (ASV) ℗ CDGAU115
Oxford Christ Church Cath Ch, S. Darlington *Concert*
(4/90) (NIMB) ℗ NI5218
The Sixteen, H. Christophers (r1990) *Concert*
(4/92) (HYPE) ℗ CDA66427
Quemadmodum—motet: 6vv
The Sixteen, Fretwork, H. Christophers (r1992)
Concert (3/94) (HYPE) ℗ CDA66639
Te Deum laudamus—motet: 5vv
The Sixteen, H. Christophers *Concert*
(9/93) (HYPE) ℗ CDA66507

TAYLOR, (Joseph) Deems (1885–1966) USA

Fanfare for Russia—brass ensemble (1942)
LPO, J. Mester *Concert* (7/91) (KOCH) ℗ 37012-2

The King's Henchman—opera: 3 acts, Op. 19 (1927—New York) (Lib. Millay)
Nay, Maccus, lay him down L. Tibbett, NY Met Op Orch, NY Met Op Chor, G. Setti (r1928) *Concert*
(4/94) (RCA) ℗ [6] 09026 61580-2(3)
Oh, Caesar, great wert thou!; Nay, Maccus, lay him down L. Tibbett, NY Met Op Chor, NY Met Op Orch, G. Setti (r1928) *Concert*
(3/91) (PEAR) ℗ [2] GEMMCDS9452

TCHAIKOVSKY, Pyotr Il'yich (1840–1893) Russia

SECTION I: ORCHESTRAL

Andante cantabile for cello and strings, Op. 11 (?1886-88) (arr cpsr from String Quartet No. 1)
R. Wallfisch, ECO, G. Simon *Concert*
(2/85) (CHAN) ① **CHAN8347**
LSO, J. Judd *Piano Concerto 1.*
(11/88) (CARL) ① **PCD893**
Scottish CO, J. Serebrier (orch Serebrier) *Concert*
(3/91) (ASV) ① **CDDCA719**
M. Rostropovich (vc/dir), BPO *Concert*
(8/91) (DG) ① **431 475-2GGA**
ECO, J. Judd (r1989) *Concert*
(10/91) (NOVA) ① **150 057-2**
O. Harnoy, LPO, C. Mackerras *Concert*
(10/92) (RCA) ① **RD60758**
Y-Y. Ma, Pittsburgh SO, L. Maazel *Concert*
(11/92) (SONY) ① **SK48382**
Primavera CO, P. Manley *Concert*
(3/93) (UNIC) ① **DKPCD9134**
Philh, P. Kletzki (r1958) *Concert*
(9/93) (EMI) ① [2] **CZS7 67726-2**
M. Rostropovich (vc/dir), BPO *Concert*
(10/94) (DG) ① [2] **437 952-2GX2**
USSR SO, E. Svetlanov (r1989) *Concert*
(12/94) (MELO) ① [6] **74321 17101-2**
USSR SO, E. Svetlanov *Concert*
(12/94) (MELO) ① **74321 17097-2**
BBC PO, M. Bamert (r1994: orch Stokowski) *Concert*
(6/95) (CHAN) ① **CHAN9349**
Andante in B flat and Finale in E flat—piano and orchestra, Op. 79 (1893) (unfinished: cpted & orch Taneyev)
W. Haas, Monte Carlo Nat Op Orch, E. Inbal (r1971) *Concert*
(9/93) (PHIL) ① [2] **438 329-2PM2**
Capriccio Italien, Op. 45 (1880)
Dallas SO, E. Mata *Concert*
(6/83) (RCA) ① **RCD14439**
Cincinnati SO, E. Kunzel *Concert*
(12/83) (TELA) ① **CD80041**
BPO, H. von Karajan *Symphony 3.*
(12/86) (DG) ① **419 178-2GH**
Oslo PO, M. Jansons *Symphony 2.*
(11/87) (CHAN) ① **CHAN8460**
LSO, G. Rozhdestvensky *Symphony 5.*
(1/88) (CARL) ① **PCD875**
Prague SO, J. Bělohlávek *Symphony 6.*
(4/88) (SUPR) ① **2SUP0008**
Oslo PO, M. Jansons *Concert*
(1/89) (CHAN) ① [7] **CHAN8672/8**
ASMF, N. Marriner *Symphony 3.*
(5/93) (CAPR) ① **10 402**
Israel PO, Z. Mehta (r1992) *Concert*
(8/93) (TELD) ① **4509-90201-2**
Philh, P. Domingo (r1993) *Concert*
(4/94) (EMI) ① **CDC5 55018-2**
RPO, Y. Temirkanov (r1990) *Concert*
(5/94) (RCA) ① [6] **09026 61821-2**
Detroit SO, A. Dorati (r1978) *Concert*
(5/94) (DECC) ① [2] **443 003-2DF2**
Concertgebouw, B. Haitink (r1961) *Concert*
(10/94) (PHIL) ① [6] **442 061-2PB6**
USSR SO, E. Svetlanov (r1987) *Concert*
(12/94) (MELO) ① [6] **74321 17101-2**
USSR SO, E. Svetlanov *Concert*
(12/94) (MELO) ① **74321 17095-2**
BBC SO, A. Boult (r1940) *Concert*
(2/95) (BEUL) ① **1PD12**
Kirov Th Orch, V. Gergiev (r1993; includes bonus sampler CD) *Concert* (7/95) (PHIL) ① **442 775-2PH**
NYPO, T. Beecham (r1942) *Concert*
(11/95) (BEEC) ① **BEECHAM6**
Moscow New Russian Orch, C. Païta (r1994) *Concert*
(12/95) (LODI) ① **LO-CD791**
Minneapolis SO, A. Dorati (r1955) *Concert*
(12/95) (MERC) ① **434 360-2MM**
Concert Fantasia in G—piano and orchestra, Op. 56 (1884)
J. Lowenthal, LSO, S. Comissiona *Piano Concerto 1.*
(1/90) (ARAB) ① **Z6611**
M. Pletnev, Philh, V. Fedoseyev *Piano Concerto 1.*
(11/91) (VIRG) ① **VC7 59612-2**
W. Haas, Monte Carlo Nat Op Orch, E. Inbal (r1971) *Concert* (9/93) (PHIL) ① [2] **438 329-2PM2**
Barry Douglas, Philh, L. Slatkin (r1992) *Concert*
(6/94) (RCA) ① [2] **09026 61631-2**
Concerto for Piano and Orchestra No. 1 in B flat minor, Op. 23 (1875, rev 1879 and 1889)
EXCERPTS: 1. Allegro non troppo e molto maestoso; 2. Andantino semplice; 3. Allegro con fuoco.

M. Argerich, RPO, C. Dutoit *Prokofiev: Piano Concerto 3.* (5/85) (DG) ① **415 062-2GH**
I. Pogorelich, LSO, C. Abbado
(6/86) (DG) ① **415 122-2GH**
J.K. Parker, RPO, A. Previn (r1985) *Prokofiev: Piano Concerto 3.* (12/86) (TELA) ① **CD80124**
S. Richter, Vienna SO, H. von Karajan *Rachmaninov: Preludes.* (8/87) (DG) ① **419 068-2GGA**
M. Dichter, Boston SO, E. Leinsdorf *Violin Concerto.*
(11/87) (RCA) ① **GD86526**
L. Berman, Berlin RSO, Y. Temirkanov (orig version)
(8/88) (SCHW) ① **311037**
A. Weissenberg, Paris Orch, H. von Karajan *Mussorgsky: Pictures.* (11/88) (EMI) ① **CDM7 69381-2**
J. Lill, LSO, J. Judd *Andante cantabile, Op.11.*
(11/88) (CARL) ① **PCD893**
Vladimir Ashkenazy, LSO, L. Maazel *Chopin: Piano Concerto 2.* (1/89) (DECC) ① **417 750-2DM**
A. Gavrilov, BPO, Vladimir Ashkenazy (r1988) *Piano Concerto 3.* (11/89) (EMI) ① **CDC7 49632-2**
E. Kissin, BPO, H. von Karajan (pp1988) *Concert*
(1/90) (DG) ① **427 485-2GH**
J. Lowenthal, LSO, S. Comissiona (orig version) *Concert Fantasia.* (1/90) (ARAB) ① **Z6611**
C. Orbelian, Philh, N. Järvi *Suite 4.*
(5/90) (CHAN) ① **CHAN8777**
H. Gutiérrez, Baltimore SO, D. Zinman (r1990) *Rachmaninov: Paganini Rhapsody.*
(10/90) (TELA) ① **CD80193**
V. Horowitz, NBC SO, A. Toscanini (pp1943) *Beethoven: Piano Concerto 5.*
(12/90) (RCA) ① **GD87992**
J. Browning, LSO, S. Ozawa *Violin Concerto.*
(3/91) (RCA) ① **VD60491**
Emil Gilels, NYPO, Z. Mehta *Violin Concerto.*
(3/91) (SONY) ① **SBK46339**
M. Pletnev, Philh, V. Fedoseyev *Concert Fantasia.*
(4/91) (VIRG) ① **VC7 59612-2**
B. Janis, LSO, H. Menges *Concert*
(11/91) (MERC) ① **432 011-2MM**
V. Postnikova, Vienna SO, G. Rozhdestvensky *Violin Concerto.* (12/91) (DECC) ① **430 725-2DM**
V. Horowitz, NBC SO, A. Toscanini (r1941) *Concert*
(1/92) (RCA) ① **GD60449**
M. Rudy, Leningrad PO, M. Jansons *Rachmaninov: Piano Concerto 2.* (4/92) (EMI) ① **CDC7 54232-2**
A. Rubinstein, LSO, J. Barbirolli (r1932) *Brahms: Piano Concerto 2.*
(11/92) (CLAR) ① **CDGSE78-50-41**
A. Gavrilov, Philh, R. Muti (r1979) *Concert*
(11/92) (EMI) ① **CDM7 64329-2**
V. Horowitz, NBC SO, A. Toscanini (pp1943) *Mussorgsky: Pictures.* (9/93) (RCA) ① **GD60321**
V. Horowitz, NBC SO, A. Toscanini (r1941) *Concert*
(9/93) (RCA) ① **GD60319**
W. Haas, Monte Carlo Nat Op Orch, E. Inbal (r1970) *Concert* (9/93) (PHIL) ① [2] **438 329-2PM2**
E. Petri, LPO, W. Goehr (r1937) *Concert*
(11/93) (APR) ① [2] **APR7023**
Emil Gilels, Leningrad PO, E. Mravinsky (pp1971) *Piano Sonata, Op. 80.*
(4/94) (RUSS) ① **RDCD11170**
M. Argerich, RPO, C. Dutoit (r1970) *Violin Concerto.*
(6/94) (DG) ① **439 420-2GCL**
Barry Douglas, LSO, L. Slatkin (r1986) *Concert*
(6/94) (RCA) ① [2] **09026 61631-2**
S. Richter, Leningrad PO, E. Mravinsky (r1959) *Piano Concerto 2.* (9/94) (MELO) ① **74321 17083-2**
N. Demidenko, BBC SO, A. Lazarev (r1993) *Scriabin: Piano Concerto.* (10/94) (HYPE) ① **CDA66680**
P. Jablonski, Philh, P. Maag *Grieg: Piano Concerto.*
(10/94) (DECC) ① **443 174-2DH**
G. Cziffra, Philh, A. Vandernoot (r1958) *Concert*
(3/95) (EMI) ① **CDM5 65252-2**
J. Ogdon, LSO, P. Maag (pp1963) *Concert*
(3/95) (VANG) ① [2] **08.8032.72**
S. Richter, Vienna SO, H. von Karajan (r1962) *Rachmaninov: Piano Concerto 2.*
(7/95) (DG) ① **447 420-2GOR**
M. Argerich, BRSO, K. Kondrashin (pp1980) *Rachmaninov: Piano Concerto 3.*
(8/95) (PHIL) ① **446 673-2PH**
R. O'Hora, RPO, J. Judd (r1994) *Seasons.*
(10/95) (TRIN) ① **TRP023**
A. Watts, Atlanta SO, Y. Levi (r1994) *Saint-Saëns: Piano Concerto 2.* (10/95) (TELA) ① **CD80386**
G. Anda, Philh, A. Galliera (r1953) *Concert*
(10/95) (TEST) ① **SBT1064**
1(pt) Martin Jones (r1989: trans pf: Grainger) *Concert* (7/90) (NIMB) ① **NI5232**
3. V. Horowitz, Danish RSO, N. Malko (bp1934) *Concert* (8/92) (DANA) ① **DACOCD303**

Concerto for Piano and Orchestra No. 2 in G, Op. 44 (1880)

J. Lowenthal, LSO, S. Comissiona (orig vers) *Piano Concerto 3.* (11/88) (ARAB) ① **Z6583**
M. Pletnev, Philh, V. Fedoseyev *Piano Concerto 3.*
(6/91) (VIRG) ① **VC7 59631-2**
E. Leonskaja, Leipzig Gewandhaus, K. Masur *Piano Sonata, Op. 37.* (9/92) (TELD) ① **9031-72296-2**
Emil Gilels, USSR SO, K. Kondrashin (pp1959) *Mozart: Piano Concerto 21.*
(5/93) (MEZH) ① **MK417106**
W. Haas, Monte Carlo Nat Op Orch, E. Inbal (r1971) *Concert* (9/93) (PHIL) ① [2] **438 329-2PM2**
Barry Douglas, Philh, L. Slatkin (r1991) *Concert*
(6/94) (RCA) ① [2] **09026 61631-2**
V. Postnikova, Vienna SO, G. Rozhdestvensky (r1982) *Piano Concerto 3.*
(6/94) (DECC) ① **436 485-2DM**
Emil Gilels, USSR SO, E. Svetlanov (r1972) *Piano Concerto 1.* (9/94) (MELO) ① **74321 17083-2**
Concerto for Piano and Orchestra No. 3 in E flat, Op. 75 (1893)** (unfinished: movt 1 only)
J. Lowenthal, LSO, S. Comissiona *Piano Concerto 2.*
(11/88) (ARAB) ① **Z6583**
A. Gavrilov, BPO, Vladimir Ashkenazy (r1988) *Piano Concerto 1.* (11/89) (EMI) ① **CDC7 49632-2**
M. Pletnev, Philh, V. Fedoseyev *Piano Concerto 2.*
(6/91) (VIRG) ① **VC7 59631-2**
G. Tozer, LPO, N. Järvi (r1991) *Symphony 7.*
(4/93) (CHAN) ① **CHAN9130**
W. Haas, Monte Carlo Nat Op Orch, E. Inbal (r1970) *Concert* (9/93) (PHIL) ① [2] **438 329-2PM2**
V. Postnikova, Vienna SO, G. Rozhdestvensky (r1982) *Piano Concerto 2.*
(6/94) (DECC) ① **436 485-2DM**
Barry Douglas, Philh, L. Slatkin (r1992) *Concert*
(6/94) (RCA) ① [2] **09026 61631-2**
Concerto for Violin and Orchestra in D, Op. 35 (1878)
1. Allegro moderato; 2. Canzonetta: Andante; 3. Allegro vivacissimo.
K-W. Chung, Montreal SO, C. Dutoit (r1981) *Mendelssohn: Violin Concerto, Op. 64.*
(8/83) (DECC) ① **410 011-2DH**
I. Perlman, Philadelphia, E. Ormandy *Sérénade mélancolique.* (4/85) (EMI) ① **CDC7 47106-2**
N. Shkolnikova, Philh, G. Simon *Concert*
(3/87) (CALA) ① [2] **CACD0101**
V. Mullova, Boston SO, S. Ozawa *Sibelius: Violin Concerto.* (5/87) (PHIL) ① **416 821-2PH**
N. Milstein, VPO, C. Abbado *Mendelssohn: Violin Concerto, Op. 64.* (8/87) (DG) ① **419 067-2GGA**
I. Perlman, Boston SO, E. Leinsdorf *Piano Concerto 1.* (11/87) (RCA) ① **GD86526**
F.P. Zimmermann, BPO, L. Maazel *Prokofiev: Violin Concerto 1.* (12/88) (EMI) ① **CDC7 49758-2**
J. Bell, Cleveland Orch, Vladimir Ashkenazy *Wieniawski: Violin Concerto 2.*
(12/88) (DECC) ① **421 716-2DH**
A-S. Mutter, VPO, H. von Karajan (pp1988)
(1/89) (DG) ① **419 241-2GH**
D. Oistrakh, Philadelphia, E. Ormandy *Sibelius: Violin Concerto.* (11/89) (SONY) ① **MPK44854**
Z. Francescatti, NYPO, T. Schippers (r1965) *Mendelssohn: Violin Concerto, op 64.*
(2/90) (SONY) ① **MPK45700**
J-J. Kantorow, LPO, B. Thomson (r1987) *Stravinsky: Violin Concerto.* (9/90) (DENO) ① **CO-73325**
X. Wei, Philh, S. Accardo *Concert*
(9/90) (ASV) ① **CDDCA713**
I. Perlman, Israel PO, Z. Mehta (pp1990) *Concert*
(2/91) (EMI) ① **CDC7 54108-2**
E. Friedman, LSO, S. Ozawa *Piano Concerto 1.*
(3/91) (RCA) ① **VD60491**
D. Oistrakh, Philadelphia, E. Ormandy *Piano Concerto 1.* (3/91) (SONY) ① **SBK46339**
B. Huberman, Berlin St Op Orch, W. Steinberg (r1929) *Concert* (10/91) (EPM) ① **150 032**
K-W. Chung, Montreal SO, C. Dutoit *Piano Concerto 1.* (12/91) (DECC) ① **430 725-2DM**
J. Heifetz, LPO, J. Barbirolli (r1937) *Concert*
(10/92) (DG) ① **CDH7 64030-2**
Vanessa-Mae, LSO, K. Bakels *Beethoven: Violin Concerto.* (11/92) (TRIT) ① **TCMA27103**
N. Milstein, Chicago SO, F. Stock (r1940) *Concert*
(3/93) (BIDD) ① **LAB063**
J. Heifetz, Chicago SO, F. Reiner (r1957) *Brahms: Violin Concerto.* (4/93) (RCA) ① **09026 61495-2**
P. Amoyal, Philh, C. Dutoit *Concert*
(5/93) (ERAT) ① **2292-45971-2**
L. Kogan, Paris Cons, C. Silvestri (r1959) *Concert*
(9/93) (EMI) ① [2] **CZS7 67732-2**
G. Shaham, Philh, G. Sinopoli (r1991) *Sibelius: Violin Concerto.* (9/93) (DG) ① **437 540-2GH**
T. Varga, Vienna Fest Orch, J-M. Auberson (r1965) *Concert* (11/93) (CLAV) ① [4] **CD50-9300/4**

T. Varga, Vienna Fest Orch, J-M. Auberson (r1965)
  Bruch: Violin Concerto 1.
    (11/93) (CLAV) ① CD50-9313
I. Gitlis, Vienna Pro Musica orch, H. Swarowsky
  (1950s) Concert (11/93) (VOX) ① [2] CDX2 5505
K. Takezawa, Moscow RSO, V. Fedoseyev
  Prokofiev: Violin Concerto 2.
    (12/93) (RCA) ① 09026 60759-2
S. Chang, LSO, Colin Davis (r1992) Brahms:
  Hungarian Dances.
    (12/93) (EMI) ① CDC7 54753-2
V. Spivakov, RPO, Y. Temirkanov (r1991) Prokofiev:
  Violin Concerto 1. (12/93) (RCA) ① 09026 60990-2
N. Kennedy, LPO, O. Kamu (r1985) Rococo
  Variations. (12/93) (EMI) ① CDC7 54890-2
I. Perlman, Philadelphia, E. Ormandy (r1978) Concert
    (4/94) (EMI) ① [3] CMS7 64922-2
N. Milstein, Pittsburgh SO, W. Steinberg (r1959)
  Concert (5/94) (EMI) ① [6] ZDMF7 64830-2
N. Milstein, VPO, C. Abbado (r1972) Piano Concerto
  1. (6/94) (DG) ① 439 420-2GCL
A. Grumiaux, New Philh, J. Krenz (r1975) Concert
    (9/94) (PHIL) ① [2] 442 287-2PM2
I. Haendel, RPO, E. Goossens (r1957) Brahms:
  Violin Concerto. (10/94) (TEST) ① SBT1038
Y. Menuhin, Berlin RIAS Orch, F. Fricsay (bp1949)
  Symphony 6. (11/94) (DG) ① 445 409-2GDO
Y. Menuhin, Berlin RIAS Orch, F. Fricsay (bp1949)
  Concert (11/94) (DG) ① [11] 445 400-2GDO10
J. Heifetz, LPO, T. Beecham (r1937) Concert
    (11/94) (RCA) ① [65] 09026 61778-2(18)
J. Heifetz, Philh, W. Susskind (r1950) Concert
    (11/94) (RCA) ① [65] 09026 61778-2(07)
J. Heifetz, Chicago SO, F. Reiner (1957) Concert
    (11/94) (RCA) ① [65] 09026 61778-2(11-15)
K-W. Chung, LSO, A. Previn (r1970) Sibelius: Violin
  Concerto. (5/95) (DECC) ① 425 080-2DCS
D. Oistrakh, Staatskapelle Dresden, F. Konwitschny
  (r1954) Concert
    (6/95) (DG) ① [2] 447 427-2GOR2
I. Perlman, Philadelphia, E. Ormandy Concert
    (6/95) (EMI) ① [20] CZS4 83177-2(1)
J. Rachlin, Moscow RSO, V. Fedoseyev (pp1994)
  Prokofiev: Violin Concerto 1.
    (8/95) (SONY) ① SK66567
A. Campoli, LSO, A. Argenta (r1956) Concert
    (9/95) (BEUL) ① 3PD10
J. Heifetz, LPO, J. Barbirolli (r1937) Concert
    (11/95) (PEAR) ① [2] GEMMCDS9157
M. Vengerov, BPO, C. Abbado (r1995) Glazunov:
  Violin Concerto. (11/95) (TELD) ① 4509-90881-2
2. J. Kubelík, G. Lapierre (r1912) Concert
    (6/91) (BIDD) ① [2] LAB033/4
2. F. Kreisler, C. Lamson (r1924) Concert
    (9/93) (BIDD) ① [2] LAB068/9
2. B. Huberman, P. Frenkel (r1923) Concert
    (3/94) (BIDD) ① [2] LAB077/8
2. J. Heifetz, orch, J. Pasternack (r1920) Concert
    (11/94) (RCA) ① [65] 09026 61778-2(01)

Elegy in G (in honour of Ivan
Samarin)—strings (1884) (used as Act 4
  Ent'acte (Hamlet)
Scottish CO, J. Serebrier Concert
    (3/91) (ASV) ① CDDCA719
Kremlin CO, M. Rachlevsky (r1991) Concert
    (6/93) (CLAV) ① CD50-9116
Serenata of London, B. Wilde (r1994) Concert
    (2/95) (CARL) ① PCD1108

Fate—symphonic poem, Op. 77 (1868)
  (destroyed by cpsr: recons 1896)
St Louis SO, L. Slatkin Concert
    (7/91) (RCA) ① RD60432
RPO, Y. Temirkanov (r1993) Concert
    (5/94) (RCA) ① [6] 09026 61821-2
Washington NSO, A. Dorati (r1975) Concert
    (5/94) (DECC) ① [2] 443 003-2DF2
USSR SO, E. Svetlanov (r1970) Concert
    (12/94) (MELO) ① [6] 74321 17101-2
USSR SO, E. Svetlanov Concert
    (12/94) (MELO) ① 74321 17095-2
Frankfurt RSO, E. Inbal (r1974) Concert
    (5/95) (PHIL) ① [2] 442 586-2PM2

Festival Coronation March in D (1883)
SNO, N. Järvi Concert (2/87) (CHAN) ① CHAN8476
Leipzig Gewandhaus, K. Masur (r1991) Concert
    (5/93) (TELD) ① 9031-76456-2

Festival Overture on the Danish national
hymn in D, Op. 15 (1866)
LSO, G. Simon Concert (7/84) (CHAN) ① [2] CHAN8310/1
LSO, G. Simon (r1981) Concert
    (7/94) (CHAN) ① CHAN9190
USSR SO, E. Svetlanov (r1987) Manfred Symphony.
    (12/94) (MELO) ① 74321 17098-2

Francesca da Rimini—symphonic fantasia
after Dante, Op. 32 (1876)
Oslo PO, M. Jansons Concert
    (1/88) (EMI) ① CDC7 49141-2
NY Stadium SO, L. Stokowski Hamlet.
    (4/88) (DELL) ① CDDA9006
RLPO, S. Edwards Concert
    (12/89) (EMIN) ① CD-EMX2152
Leipzig Gewandhaus, K. Masur (r1989) Symphony 1.
    (6/90) (TELD) ① 2292-44939-2
NYPO, L. Bernstein (pp1989) Symphony 4.
    (4/91) (DG) ① 429 778-2GH
Houston SO, C. Eschenbach Dvořák: Symphony 9.
    (2/92) (VIRG) ① VC7 59053-2
Leningrad PO, E. Mravinsky (pp1981) Concert
    (6/92) (ERAT) ① 2292-45757-2
Leningrad PO, E. Mravinsky (pp1981) Concert
    (6/92) (ERAT) ① [11] 2292-45763-2
Philadelphia, R. Muti Symphony 5.
    (7/92) (EMI) ① CDC7 54338-2
Leipzig Gewandhaus, K. Masur (r1989) Concert
    (5/93) (TELD) ① 9031-76456-2
ASMF, N. Marriner (r1992) Symphony 5.
    (2/94) (CAPR) ① 10 410
RPO, Y. Temirkanov (r1991) Concert
    (5/94) (RCA) ① [6] 09026 61821-2
Washington NSO, A. Dorati (r1973) Concert
    (5/94) (DECC) ① [2] 443 003-2DF2
Polish Nat RSO, A. Wit (r1993) Symphony 6.
    (9/94) (NAXO) ① 8 550782
Concertgebouw, B. Haitink (r1972) Concert
    (10/94) (PHIL) ① [6] 442 061-2PB6
Houston SO, C. Eschenbach (r1990) Dvořák:
  Symphony 9. (11/94) (VIRG) ① CUV5 61124-2
USSR SO, E. Svetlanov (1970) Concert
    (12/94) (MELO) ① [6] 74321 17101-2
USSR SO, E. Svetlanov Symphony 1.
    (12/94) (MELO) ① 74321 17092-2
New Philh, I. Markevitch (r1967) Concert
    (5/95) (PHIL) ① [2] 442 586-2PM2
Baltimore SO, D. Zinman (1992) Concert
    (12/95) (TELA) ① CD80378

Hamlet—fantasy overture after Shakespeare,
Op. 67 (1888)
NY Stadium SO, L. Stokowski Francesca da Rimini.
    (4/88) (DELL) ① CDDA9006
Oregon SO, J. DePreist Concert
    (5/90) (DELO) ① DE3081
VPO, L. Maazel (r1965) Manfred Symphony.
    (11/93) (DECC) ① 425 051-2DM
LSO, A. Coates (r1932) Concert
    (11/93) (BIDD) ① WHL014
Hallé, C. Lambert (r1942) Concert
    (1/94) (DUTT) ① CDLX7006
Washington NSO, A. Dorati (r1974) Concert
    (5/94) (DECC) ① [2] 443 003-2DF2
New Philh, I. Markevitch (r1967) Concert
    (5/95) (PHIL) ① [2] 442 586-2PM2

Legend: Christ had a garden—cello and
orchestra, Op. 54/5 (arr cpsr from song)
R. Wallfisch, ECO, G. Simon Concert
    (2/85) (CHAN) ① CHAN8347

Manfred Symphony, Op. 58 (1885)
Oslo PO, M. Jansons (5/88) (CHAN) ① CHAN8535
Oslo PO, M. Jansons Concert
    (1/89) (CHAN) ① [7] CHAN8672/8
NBC SO, A. Toscanini (r1949) Romeo and Juliet.
    (6/92) (RCA) ① GD60298
Bournemouth SO, A. Litton (r1994)
    (3/93) (VIRG) ① VC7 59230-2
VPO, L. Maazel (r1971) Hamlet.
    (11/93) (DECC) ① 425 051-2DM
ASMF, N. Marriner (r1992) Marche slave.
    (3/94) (CAPR) ① 10 433
Philh, R. Muti (r1981)
    (3/94) (EMI) ① CDM7 64872-2
Concertgebouw, B. Haitink (r1979) Concert
    (10/94) (PHIL) ① [6] 442 061-2PB6
Russian Federation St SO, E. Svetlanov (pp1992)
  Concert (12/94) (CANY) ① [7] EC3630-2
USSR SO, E. Svetlanov (r1960s) Festival Overture.
    (12/94) (MELO) ① 74321 17098-2
Russian Nat Orch, M. Pletnev Tempest.
    (12/94) (DG) ① 439 891-2GH
Philh, P. Kletzki (r1954) Borodin: Symphony 2.
    (3/95) (TEST) ① SBT1048
Movt 2. LSO, A. Coates (r1932) Concert
    (11/93) (BIDD) ① WHL014

Marche slave, 'Slavonic March', Op. 31
(1876)
St. Louis SO, L. Slatkin Concert
    (12/83) (TELA) ① CD80072
LPO, A. Davison Concert
    (11/87) (CFP) ① CD-CFP9000
LSO, G. Rozhdestvensky Symphony 4.
    (12/87) (CARL) ① PCD867

BPO, H. von Karajan (r1966) Symphony 5.
    (4/88) (DG) ① 419 066-2GGA
Cincinnati Pops, E. Kunzel Concert
    (10/89) (TELA) ① CD80170
RLPO, S. Edwards Concert
    (12/89) (EMIN) ① CD-EMX2152
NYPO, W. Mengelberg (r1925) Concert
    (7/90) (SYMP) ① SYMCD1078
Gothenburg SO, N. Järvi Concert
    (3/91) (DG) ① 429 984-2GH
Russian Nat Orch, M. Pletnev (r1991) Symphony 6.
    (1/92) (VIRG) ① VC7 59661-2
LSO, L. Stokowski Concert
    (4/92) (DECC) ① 433 625-2DSP
NYPO, W. Mengelberg (r1926) Concert
    (4/92) (PEAR) ① [3] GEMMCDS9922
RPO, K. Koizumi Symphony 5.
    (7/92) (RPO) ① CDRPO7017
LSO, A. Coates (r1930) Concert
    (12/92) (KOCH) ① 37700-2
Israel PO, Z. Mehta (1992) Concert
    (8/93) (TELD) ① 4509-90201-2
ASMF, N. Marriner (r1991) Manfred Symphony.
    (3/94) (CAPR) ① 10 433
RPO, Y. Temirkanov (r1991) Concert
    (5/94) (RCA) ① [6] 09026 61821-2
Detroit SO, A. Dorati (r1978) Concert
    (5/94) (DECC) ① [2] 443 003-2DF2
Chicago SO, F. Reiner (1959) Concert
    (8/94) (RCA) ① 09026 61958-2
Concertgebouw, B. Haitink (r1972) Concert
    (10/94) (PHIL) ① [6] 442 061-2PB6
Russian St SO, V. Polyansky (r1993) Symphony 6.
    (5/95) (CHAN) ① CHAN9356
National SO, A. Fistoulari (r1944) Concert
    (5/95) (DUTT) ① CDK1200
Kirov Th Orch, V. Gergiev (r1993; includes bonus
  sampler CD) Concert (7/95) (PHIL) ① 442 775-2PH
K. Labèque, M. Labèque (r1994: arr pf duet: Batalin)
  Concert (12/95) (PHIL) ① 442 778-2PH

Nocturne in D minor—cello and orchestra,
Op. 19/4 (c1888) (trans cpsr)
R. Wallfisch, ECO, G. Simon Concert
    (2/85) (CHAN) ① CHAN8347
J. Lloyd Webber, LSO, M. Shostakovich Concert
    (5/92) (PHIL) ① 434 106-2PH
O. Harnoy, LPO, C. Mackerras Concert
    (10/92) (RCA) ① RD60758
M. Maisky, Paris Orch, S. Bychkov Concert
    (10/92) (DG) ① 435 781-2GH
M. Kliegel, Ireland National SO, G. Markson (r1993)
  Concert (11/94) (NAXO) ① 8 550519

Overture in F (1865-66)
Russian Nat Orch, M. Pletnev Concert
    (12/94) (DG) ① 439 892-2GH

Pezzo capriccioso in B minor—cello and
orchestra, Op. 62 (1887)
R. Wallfisch, ECO, G. Simon (orig. version) Concert
    (2/85) (CHAN) ① CHAN8347
O. Harnoy, LPO, C. Mackerras Concert
    (10/92) (RCA) ① RD60758
M. Kliegel, Ireland National SO, G. Markson (r1993)
  Concert (11/94) (NAXO) ① 8 550519

Romeo and Juliet—fantasy overture after
Shakespeare (1869 rev 1879 and 1880) (1880
version unless otherwise stated)
EXCERPTS: 1. Love Theme.
LSO, G. Simon (1869 version) Concert
    (7/84) (CHAN) ① [2] CHAN8310/1
Oslo PO, M. Jansons Concert
    (1/88) (EMI) ① CDC7 49141-2
RPO, T. Beecham (1946/7) Symphony 3.
    (6/89) (BEEC) ① BEECHAM1
RLPO, S. Edwards Concert
    (12/89) (EMIN) ① CD-EMX2152
NYPO, L. Bernstein (pp1989) Symphony 5.
    (2/90) (DG) ① 429 234-2GH
Baltimore SO, D. Zinman (1989) Symphony 4.
    (4/91) (TELA) ① CD80228
Leipzig Gewandhaus, K. Masur Symphony 2.
    (5/91) (TELD) ① 2292-44943-2
Chicago SO, G. Solti Concert
    (8/91) (DECC) ① 430 707-2DM
Philh, R. Muti Concert
    (9/91) (EMI) ① [4] CZS7 67314-2
VPO, L. Maazel Concert
    (4/92) (DECC) ① [4] 430 787-2DC4
USSR Ministry of Culture SO, G. Rozhdestvensky
  Symphony 4. (4/92) (ERAT) ① 2292-45620-2
RPO, K. Koizumi Symphony 6.
    (6/92) (RPO) ① CDRPO7004
NBC SO, A. Toscanini (r1946) Manfred Symphony.
    (6/92) (RCA) ① GD60298
Boston SO, S. Koussevitzky (r1936) Symphony 6.
    (3/93) (RCA) ① GD60920

ASMF, N. Marriner *Symphony 4.*
(5/93) (CAPR) ① **10 401**
Leipzig Gewandhaus, K. Masur (r1990) *Concert*
(5/93) (TELD) ① **9031-76456-2**
Boston SO, C. Munch (r1961) *Symphony 6.*
(8/93) (RCA) ① **09026 61563-2**
LSO, A. Coates (r1928) *Concert*
(11/93) (BIDD) ① **WHL014**
CBO, C. Lambert (r1941) *Concert*
(1/94) (DUTT) ① **CDLX7006**
Philh, P. Domingo (r1993) *Concert*
(4/94) (EMI) ① **CDC5 55018-2**
RPO, Y. Temirkanov (r1989) *Concert*
(5/94) (RCA) ① [6] **09026 61821-2**
Washington NSO, A. Dorati (r1974) *Concert*
(5/94) (DECC) ① [2] **443 003-2DF2**
Cleveland Orch, L. Maazel (r1981) *Symphony 4.*
(7/94) (TELA) ① **CD82002**
LSO, G. Simon (r1981: orig vers) *Hamlet.*
(7/94) (CHAN) ① **CHAN9191**
National SO, A. Coates (r1945) *Symphony 6.*
(7/94) (BEUL) ① **1PD6**
Concertgebouw, B. Haitink (r1964) *Concert*
(10/94) (PHIL) ① [6] **442 061-2PB6**
Concertgebouw, W. Mengelberg (r1930) *Concert*
(10/94) (MUSI) ① [2] **MACD-809**
USSR SO, E. Svetlanov (r1970) *Concert*
(12/94) (MELO) ① [6] **74321 17101-2**
USSR SO, E. Svetlanov *Symphony 3.*
(12/94) (MELO) ① **74321 17094-2**
LSO, P. Monteux (pp1963) *Concert*
(3/95) (VANG) ① [2] **08.8032.72**
Concertgebouw, B. Haitink (r1964) *Concert*
(5/95) (PHIL) ① [2] **442 586-2PM2**
St Louis SO, L. Slatkin (r1993) *Concert*
(11/95) (RCA) ① **09026 68045-2**
Moscow New Russian Orch, C. Païta (r1994) *Concert*
(12/95) (LODI) ① **LO-CD791**
LSO, A. Dorati (r1959) *Symphony 6.*
(12/95) (MERC) ① **434 353-2MM**
Serenade for Nikolay Rubinstein's name day
(1872)
LSO, G. Simon *Concert*
(7/84) (CHAN) ① [2] **CHAN8310/1**
LSO, G. Simon (r1981) *Concert*
(7/94) (CHAN) ① **CHAN9190**
Serenade in C—string orchestra, Op. 48
(1880)
1. Pezzo in forma di Sonatina; 2. Waltz; 3. Elegy; 4.
Finale.
BPO, H. von Karajan *Dvořák: Serenade, Op. 22.*
(3/83) (DG) ① **400 038-2GH**
St Louis SO, L. Slatkin *Concert*
(1/84) (TELA) ① **CD80080**
Orpheus CO *Concert*
(2/88) (DG) ① **423 060-2GH**
BPO, H. von Karajan (r1966) *Concert*
(4/88) (DG) ① **415 855-2GGA**
Norwegian CO, I. Brown *Concert*
(1/89) (SIMA) ① **PSC1035**
Soviet Emigré Orch, L. Gozman *Concert*
(8/89) (OLYM) ① **OCD196**
Orpheus CO *Concert*
(5/90) (DG) ① **429 488-2GDC**
Moscow Sols Ens, Y. Bashmet *Concert*
(3/91) (RCA) ① **RD60368**
Scottish CO, J. Serebrier *Concert*
(3/91) (ASV) ① **CDDCA719**
ECO, J. Judd (r1989) *Concert*
(10/91) (NOVA) ① **150 057-2**
Vienna CO, P. Entremont *Souvenir of Florence.*
(10/91) (NAXO) ① **8 550404**
Philh Hungarica, A. Dorati *Nutcracker.*
(9/92) (MERC) ① [2] **432 750-2MM2**
Auvergne Orch, J-J. Kantorow *Souvenir of Florence.*
(3/93) (DENO) ① **CO-75026**
Kremlin CO, M. Rachlevsky (r1991) *Concert*
(6/93) (CLAV) ① **CD50-9116**
Boston SO, C. Munch (r1957) *Concert*
(9/93) (RCA) ① **09026 61424-2**
Polish Radio CO, A. Duczmal *Concert*
(3/94) (ASV) ① **CDQS6094**
BPO, S. Bychkov *Concert*
(3/94) (PHIL) ① **434 108-2PH**
Saito Kinen Orch, S. Ozawa (r1992) *Concert*
(9/94) (PHIL) ① **438 137-2PH**
Philh, D.V. Yu (r1993) *Souvenir of Florence.*
(11/94) (CARL) ① **MCD89**
USSR SO, E. Svetlanov (r1970) *Concert*
(12/94) (MELO) ① [6] **74321 17101-2**
USSR SO, E. Svetlanov *Symphony 4.*
(12/94) (MELO) ① **74321 17093-2**
Moscow Virtuosi, V. Spivakov (r1992) *Concert*
(12/94) (RCA) ① **09026 61964-2**
BRSO, Colin Davis *Dvořák: Serenade, Op. 22.*
(12/94) (PHIL) ① **442 402-2PM**

BBC SO, A. Boult (r1937) *Concert*
(2/95) (BEUL) ① **1PD12**
2. Concertgebouw, W. Mengelberg (r1928) *Concert*
(10/94) (MUSI) ① [2] **MACD-809**
2. J. Heifetz, orch, J. Pasternack (r1919) *Concert*
(11/94) (RCA) ① [65] **09026 61778-2(01)**
2. J. Heifetz, CO (r1970) *Concert*
(11/94) (RCA) ① [65] **09026 61778-2(11-15)**
Sérénade mélancolique in B minor, Op. 26
(1875)
I. Perlman, Philadelphia, E. Ormandy *Violin*
Concerto. (4/85) (EMI) ① **CDC7 47106-2**
L. Mordkovitch, M. Gusak-Grin (trans cpsr) *Concert*
(3/87) (CHAN) ① **CHAN8500**
X. Wei, Philh, S. Accardo *Concert*
(9/90) (ASV) ① **CDDCA713**
O. Harnoy, LPO, C. Mackerras (arr J. Harnoy)
Concert (10/92) (RCA) ① **RD60758**
P. Amoyal, Philh, C. Dutoit *Concert*
(5/93) (ERAT) ① **2292-45971-2**
L. Kogan, Philh, K. Kondrashin (r1959) *Concert*
(9/93) (EMI) ① [2] **CZS7 67732-2**
J. Heifetz, CO (r1970) *Concert*
(11/94) (RCA) ① [65] **09026 61778-2(11-15)**
J. Heifetz, Los Angeles PO, A. Wallenstein (r1954)
Concert (11/94) (RCA) ① [65] **09026 61778-2(20)**
J. Heifetz, orch, J. Pasternack (r1920) *Concert*
(11/94) (RCA) ① [65] **09026 61778-2(01)**
I. Perlman, Philadelphia, E. Ormandy *Concert*
(6/95) (EMI) ① [20] **CZS4 83177-2(2)**
The Storm—overture to Ostrovsky's play,
Op. 76 (1864)
LSO, G. Rozhdestvensky *Symphony 6.*
(1/88) (CARL) ① **PCD878**
Polish Nat RSO, A. Wit (r1992) *Symphony 5.*
(7/94) (NAXO) ① **8 550716**
Concertgebouw, B. Haitink (r1977) *Concert*
(10/94) (PHIL) ① [6] **442 061-2PB6**
Frankfurt RSO, E. Inbal (r1974) *Concert*
(5/95) (PHIL) ① [2] **442 586-2PM2**
Suite No. 1, Op. 43 (1878/79)
EXCERPTS: 1. Marche miniature.
1. Boston Pops, A. Fiedler (r1958) *Concert*
(1/94) (RCA) ① **09026 61249-2**
1. Chicago SO, F. Reiner (r1959) *Concert*
(1/94) (RCA) ① **09026 61958-2**
Suite No. 3 in G, Op. 55 (1884)
Stuttgart RSO, N. Marriner *Suite 4.*
(5/88) (CAPR) ① **10 200**
Ireland National SO, S. Sanderling (r1992/3) *Suite 4.*
(10/94) (NAXO) ① **8 550728**
Suite No. 4 in G, 'Mozartiana', Op. 61 (1887)
Stuttgart RSO, N. Marriner *Suite 3.*
(5/88) (CAPR) ① **10 200**
Philh, N. Järvi *Piano Concerto 1.*
(5/90) (CHAN) ① **CHAN8777**
Scottish CO, J. Serebrier *Concert*
(3/91) (ASV) ① **CDDCA719**
ECO, J. Judd (r1989) *Concert*
(10/91) (NOVA) ① **150 057-2**
Ireland National SO, S. Sanderling (r1992/3) *Suite 3.*
(10/94) (NAXO) ① **8 550728**
Symphony No. 1 in G minor, 'Winter
Daydreams', Op. 13 (1866 rev 1874)
Oslo PO, M. Jansons (2/86) (CHAN) ① **CHAN8402**
BPO, H. von Karajan *Eugene Onegin.*
(12/86) (DG) ① **419 176-2GH**
Oslo PO, M. Jansons *Concert*
(1/89) (CHAN) ① [7] **CHAN8672/8**
Leipzig Gewandhaus, K. Masur (r1989) *Francesca da*
Rimini. (6/90) (TELD) ① **2292-44939-2**
Bournemouth SO, A. Litton *Symphony 2.*
(12/90) (VIRG) ① **VC7 59588-2**
LSO, I. Markevitch *Concert*
(3/91) (PHIL) ① [4] **426 848-2PB4**
ASMF, N. Marriner *Symphony 2.*
(5/91) (CAPR) ① **10 355**
New Philh, R. Muti *Concert*
(9/91) (EMI) ① [4] **CZS7 67314-2**
VPO, L. Maazel *Concert*
(4/92) (DECC) ① [4] **430 787-2DC4**
RPO, Y. Temirkanov (r1993) *Concert*
(5/94) (RCA) ① [6] **09026 61821-2**
Concertgebouw, B. Haitink (r1979) *Concert*
(10/94) (PHIL) ① [6] **442 061-2PB6**
Russian Federation St SO, E. Svetlanov (pp1990)
Concert (12/94) (CANY) ① [7] **EC3630-2**
USSR SO, E. Svetlanov (r1967) *Concert*
(12/94) (MELO) ① [6] **74321 17101-2**
USSR SO, E. Svetlanov *Francesca da Rimini.*
(12/94) (MELO) ① **74321 17092-2**
Symphony No. 2 in C minor, 'Little Russian',
Op. 17 (1872 rev 1879)
BPO, H. von Karajan *1812.*
(12/86) (DG) ① **419 177-2GH**

Pittsburgh SO, L. Maazel (r1986) *Rimsky-Korsakov:*
Symphony 2. (11/87) (TELA) ① **CD80131**
Oslo PO, M. Jansons *Capriccio italien.*
(11/87) (CHAN) ① **CHAN8460**
Oslo PO, M. Jansons *Concert*
(1/89) (CHAN) ① [7] **CHAN8672/8**
Bournemouth SO, A. Litton *Symphony 1.*
(12/90) (VIRG) ① **VC7 59588-2**
LSO, I. Markevitch *Concert*
(3/91) (PHIL) ① [4] **426 848-2PB4**
Leipzig Gewandhaus, K. Masur *Romeo and Juliet.*
(5/91) (TELD) ① **2292-44943-2**
ASMF, N. Marriner *Symphony 1.*
(5/91) (CAPR) ① **10 355**
New Philh, C. Abbado *Symphony 4.*
(8/91) (DG) ① **429 527-2GR**
Philh, R. Muti *Concert*
(9/91) (EMI) ① [4] **CZS7 67314-2**
VPO, L. Maazel *Concert*
(4/92) (DECC) ① [4] **430 787-2DC4**
Polish Nat RSO, A. Leaper *Symphony 4.*
(5/93) (NAXO) ① **8 550488**
Philh, C.M. Giulini (r1956) *Concert*
(9/93) (EMI) ① [2] **CZS7 67723-2**
RPO, Y. Temirkanov (r1990) *Concert*
(5/94) (RCA) ① [6] **09026 61821-2**
LSO, G. Simon (r1982: orig vers) *Concert*
(7/94) (CHAN) ① **CHAN9190**
Concertgebouw, B. Haitink (r1977) *Concert*
(10/94) (PHIL) ① [6] **442 061-2PB6**
Russian Federation St SO, E. Svetlanov (pp1990)
Concert (12/94) (CANY) ① [7] **EC3630-2**
USSR SO, E. Svetlanov (r1967) *Concert*
(12/94) (MELO) ① [6] **74321 17101-2**
USSR SO, E. Svetlanov *Serenade, Op.48.*
(12/94) (MELO) ① **74321 17093-2**
Cincinnati SO, E. Goossens (r1941) *Symphony 5.*
(5/95) (BEUL) ① **1PD11**
St Louis SO, L. Slatkin (r1993) *Concert*
(11/95) (RCA) ① **09026 68045-2**
Symphony No. 3 in D, 'Polish', Op. 29
(1875)
Oslo PO, M. Jansons (7/86) (CHAN) ① **CHAN8463**
BPO, H. von Karajan *Capriccio italien.*
(12/86) (DG) ① **419 178-2GH**
Oslo PO, M. Jansons *Concert*
(1/89) (CHAN) ① [7] **CHAN8672/8**
RPO, T. Beecham (r1947) *Romeo and Juliet.*
(8/89) (BEEC) ① **BEECHAM1**
LSO, I. Markevitch *Concert*
(3/91) (PHIL) ① [4] **426 848-2PB4**
Philh, R. Muti *Concert*
(9/91) (EMI) ① [4] **CZS7 67314-2**
VPO, L. Maazel *Concert*
(4/92) (DECC) ① [4] **430 787-2DC4**
ASMF, N. Marriner *Capriccio italien.*
(5/93) (CAPR) ① **10 402**
LSO, A. Coates (r1932) *Concert*
(11/93) (BIDD) ① **WHL014**
Polish Nat RSO, A. Wit (r1992) *Tempest.*
(2/94) (NAXO) ① **8 550518**
RPO, Y. Temirkanov (r1991) *Concert*
(5/94) (RCA) ① [6] **09026 61821-2**
Concertgebouw, B. Haitink (r1979) *Concert*
(10/94) (PHIL) ① [6] **442 061-2PB6**
Russian Federation St SO, E. Svetlanov (pp1990)
Concert (12/94) (CANY) ① [7] **EC3630-2**
USSR SO, E. Svetlanov (r1967) *Concert*
(12/94) (MELO) ① [6] **74321 17101-2**
USSR SO, E. Svetlanov *Romeo and Juliet.*
(12/94) (MELO) ① **74321 17094-2**
Symphony No. 4 in F minor, Op. 36 (1877)
1. Andante sostenuto—Moderato con anima; 2.
Andantino in modo di canzone; 3. Scherzo: Pizzicato
ostinato, allegro; 4. Allegro con fuoco.
Oslo PO, M. Jansons (9/85) (CHAN) ① **CHAN8361**
Leningrad PO, E. Mravinsky (r1960) *Concert*
(8/87) (DG) ① [2] **419 745-2GH2**
LSO, G. Rozhdestvensky *Marche slave.*
(12/87) (CARL) ① **PCD867**
Oslo PO, M. Jansons *Concert*
(1/89) (CHAN) ① [7] **CHAN8672/8**
LSO, I. Markevitch *Concert*
(3/91) (PHIL) ① [4] **426 848-2PB4**
Baltimore SO, D. Zinman (r1988) *Romeo and Juliet.*
(4/91) (TELA) ① **CD80228**
NYPO, L. Bernstein (pp1989) *Francesca da Rimini.*
(4/91) (DG) ① **429 778-2GH**
St Louis SO, L. Slatkin *Concert*
(7/91) (RCA) ① **RD60432**
VPO, C. Abbado *Symphony 2.*
(8/91) (DG) ① **429 527-2GR**
Philh, R. Muti *Concert*
(9/91) (EMI) ① [4] **CZS7 67314-2**
VPO, L. Maazel *Concert*
(4/92) (DECC) ① [4] **430 787-2DC4**

USSR Ministry of Culture SO, G. Rozhdestvensky
Romeo and Juliet. (4/92) (ERAT) ① [2] **2292-45620-2**
ASMF, N. Marriner *Romeo and Juliet.*
(5/93) (CAPR) ① **10 401**
Polish Nat RSO, A. Leaper *Symphony 2.*
(5/93) (NAXO) ① **8 550488**
St Petersburg PO, Y. Temirkanov (r1992) *Concert*
(5/93) (RCA) ① [2] **09026 61377-2**
Hallé, C. Lambert (r1942) *Concert*
(1/94) (DUTT) ① **CDLX7006**
LSO, I. Markevitch (r1963) *Concert*
(2/94) (PHIL) ① [2] **438 335-2PM2**
RPO, Y. Temirkanov (r1990) *Concert*
(5/94) (RCA) ① [6] **09026 61821-2**
Cleveland Orch, L. Maazel (r1979) *Romeo and Juliet.*
(7/94) (TELA) ① **CD82002**
Boston SO, P. Monteux (r1959) *Concert*
(9/94) (RCA) ① [15] **09026 61893-2**
Concertgebouw, B. Haitink (r1978) *Concert*
(10/94) (PHIL) ① [6] **442 061-2PB6**
Concertgebouw, W. Mengelberg (r1929) *Concert*
(10/94) (MUSI) ① [2] **MACD-809**
VPO, R. Kubelík (r1960) *Concert*
(11/94) (EMI) ① [2] **CZS5 68223-2**
Russian Federation St SO, E. Svetlanov (pp1990)
Concert (12/94) (CANY) ① [7] **EC3630-2**
USSR SO, E. Svetlanov (r1967) *Concert*
(12/94) (MELO) ① [6] **74321 17101-2**
USSR SO, E. Svetlanov *Concert*
(12/94) (MELO) ① **74321 17095-2**
Leipzig Gewandhaus, K. Masur *Concert*
(1/95) (TELD) ① **4509-95981-2**
Leningrad PO, K. Sanderling (r1956) *Concert*
(6/95) (DG) ① [2] **447 423-2GOR2**
Moscow New Russian Orch, C. Paíta (r1994) *Concert*
Nicholl] *Concert* (9/93) (POLY) ① **QPRL053D**
Symphony No. 5 in E minor, Op. 64 (1888)
1. Andante—Allegro con anima; 2. Andante
cantabile, con alcuna licenza; 3. Valse: Allegro
moderato; 4. Andante maestoso—Allegro vivace.
Philadelphia, E. Ormandy
(10/84) (DELO) ① **DE3015**
Oslo PO, M. Jansons (3/85) (CHAN) ① **CHAN8351**
RPO, A. Previn (r1984) *Rimsky-Korsakov: Tale of
Tsar Saltan.* (5/85) (TELA) ① **CD80107**
Leningrad PO, E. Mravinsky (r1960) *Concert*
(8/87) (DG) ① [2] **419 745-2GH2**
LSO, G. Rozhdestvensky *Capriccio Italien.*
(1/88) (CARL) ① **PCD875**
Moscow PO, L. Leighton Smith *Concert*
(2/88) (SHEF) ① **CD25**
BPO, H. von Karajan (r1975) *Marche slave.*
(4/88) (DG) ① **419 066-2GGA**
Oslo PO, M. Jansons *Concert*
(1/89) (CHAN) ① [7] **CHAN8672/8**
LSO, R. Frühbeck de Burgos *Kodály: Háry János
Suite.* (7/90) (NIMB) ① **NI5194**
NYPO, L. Bernstein (pp1988) *Romeo and Juliet.*
(12/90) (DG) ① **429 234-2GH**
Bournemouth SO, A. Litton *Tempest.*
(2/91) (VIRG) ① **VC7 59598-2**
LSO, I. Markevitch *Concert*
(3/91) (PHIL) ① [4] **426 848-2PB4**
Philh, R. Muti *Concert*
(9/91) (EMI) ① [4] **CZS7 67314-2**
LPO, S. Edwards *Eugene Onegin.*
(1/92) (EMIN) ① **CD-EMX2187**
VPO, L. Maazel (r1963) *Concert*
(4/92) (DECC) ① [4] **430 787-2DC4**
Leningrad PO, E. Mravinsky (pp1983) *Concert*
(6/92) (ERAT) ① [11] **2292-45763-2**
Leningrad PO, E. Mravinsky (pp1983)
(6/92) (ERAT) ① **2292-45755-2**
RPO, K. Koizumi *Marche slave.*
(7/92) (RPO) ① **CDRPO7017**
Philadelphia, R. Muti *Francesca da Rimini.*
(7/92) (EMI) ① **CDC7 54338-2**
St Petersburg PO, Y. Temirkanov (r1992) *Concert*
(5/93) (RCA) ① [2] **09026 61377-2**
VPO, D. Oistrakh (pp1972) *Mozart: Serenade, K525.*
(6/93) (ORFE) ① **C302921B**
New Philh, J. Horenstein (1968) *Swan Lake Suite.*
(8/93) (CHES) ① **Chesky CD94**
LSO, I. Markevitch (r1966) *Concert*
(2/94) (PHIL) ① [2] **438 335-2PM2**
ASMF, N. Marriner (r1992) *Francesca da Rimini.*
(2/94) (CAPR) ① **10 410**
Philh, S. Sinopoli (r1992) *Rimsky-Korsakov: Russian
Easter Festival Ov.* (3/94) (DG) ① **437 542-2GH**
RPO, Y. Temirkanov (r1989) *Concert*
(5/94) (RCA) ① [6] **09026 61821-2**
Polish Nat RSO, A. Wit (r1992) *Storm.*
(7/94) (NAXO) ① **8 550716**

Concertgebouw, W. Mengelberg (pp1939) *Concert*
(7/94) (MUSI) ① [4] **MACD-780**
Boston SO, P. Monteux (r1958) *Concert*
(9/94) (RCA) ① [15] **09026 61893-2**
Concertgebouw, B. Haitink (r1974) *Concert*
(10/94) (PHIL) ① [6] **442 061-2PB6**
Concertgebouw, W. Mengelberg (r1928) *Concert*
(10/94) (MUSI) ① [2] **MACD-809**
Philh, C. Silvestri (r1957) *Concert*
(11/94) (EMI) ① [2] **CZS5 68229-2**
Russian Federation St SO, E. Svetlanov (pp1990)
Concert (12/94) (CANY) ① [7] **EC3630-2**
USSR SO, E. Svetlanov (r1967) *Concert*
(12/94) (MELO) ① [6] **74321 17101-2**
USSR SO, E. Svetlanov *Tempest.*
(12/94) (MELO) ① **74321 17096-2**
Leipzig Gewandhaus, K. Masur *Concert*
(1/95) (TELD) ① **4509-95981-2**
Chicago SO, F. Stock (r1927) *Concert*
(2/95) (BIDD) ① [2] **WHL021/2**
BPO, C. Abbado (rr1994) *Mussorgsky: Songs and
Dances of Death.* (3/95) (SONY) ① **SK66276**
LSO, P. Monteux (pp1963) *Concert*
(3/95) (VANG) ① [2] **08.8032.72**
National SO, Sidney Beer (r1944) *Symphony 2.*
(5/95) (BEUL) ① **1PD11**
N. German RSO, G. Wand (r1956) *Mozart:
Symphony 40.* (6/95) (RCA) ① **09026 68032-2**
Leningrad PO, E. Mravinsky (r1956) *Concert*
(6/95) (DG) ① [2] **447 423-2GOR2**
BPO, S. Ozawa (r1989) *1812.*
(8/95) (DG) ① **429 751-2GH**
Philadelphia, L. Stokowski (r1934) *Concert*
(8/95) (BIDD) ① **WHL015**
**Symphony No. 6 in B minor, 'Pathétique',
Op. 74 (1893)**
1. Adagio—Allegro con troppo; 2. Allegro con grazia;
3. Allegro molto vivace; 4. Adagio lamentoso.
Philadelphia, E. Ormandy
(10/84) (DELO) ① **DE3016**
Oslo PO, M. Jansons (5/87) (CHAN) ① **CHAN8446**
NYPO, L. Bernstein (pp1986)
(5/87) (DG) ① **419 604-2GH**
Leningrad PO, E. Mravinsky (r1960) *Concert*
(8/87) (DG) ① [2] **419 745-2GH2**
Cleveland Orch, C. von Dohnányi (1986) *Eugene
Onegin.* (10/87) (TELA) ① **CD80130**
LSO, G. Rozhdestvensky *Storm.*
(1/88) (CARL) ① **PCD878**
Czech PO, L. von Matačič *Capriccio Italien.*
(4/88) (SUPR) ① **2SUP0008**
Oslo PO, M. Jansons *Concert*
(1/89) (CHAN) ① [7] **CHAN8672/8**
Crommelynck Duo (arr cpsr: pf duet) *Russian Folk
Songs.* (7/89) (CLAV) ① **CD50-8805**
BRSO, F. Fricsay (pp1960) *Bartók: Piano Concerto
3.* (8/90) (ORFE) ① **C200891A**
LSO, I. Markevitch *Concert*
(3/91) (PHIL) ① [4] **426 848-2PB4**
Philadelphia, R. Muti *Scriabin: Poème de l'extase.*
(3/91) (EMI) ① **CDC7 54061-2**
Philadelphia, A. Toscanini (r1942) *Concert*
(6/91) (RCA) ① [4] **GD60328**
Philh, R. Muti *Concert*
(9/91) (EMI) ① [4] **CZS7 67314-2**
Russian Nat Orch, M. Pletnev (r1991) *Marche slave.*
(1/92) (VIRG) ① **VC7 59661-2**
VPO, L. Maazel *Concert*
(4/92) (DECC) ① [4] **430 787-2DC4**
RPO, K. Koizumi *Romeo and Juliet.*
(6/92) (RPO) ① **CDRPO7004**
Frankfurt RSO, E. Inbal *Wagner: Tristan und Isolde.*
(6/92) (DENO) ① **CO-77715**
Vancouver SO, R. Barshai *Mussorgsky: Night on the
bare mountain.* (6/92) (CBC) ① **SMCD5083**
ASMF, N. Marriner *1812.* (6/92) (CAPR) ① **10 385**
Leningrad PO, E. Mravinsky (pp1982)
(6/92) (ERAT) ① [2] **2292-45756-2**
Leningrad PO, E. Mravinsky (pp1982) *Concert*
(6/92) (ERAT) ① [11] **2292-45763-2**
Boston SO, S. Koussevitzky (r1930) *Romeo and
Juliet.* (3/93) (RCA) ① **GD60920**
N German RSO, G. Wand (pp1991) *Stravinsky:
Pulcinella Suite.* (4/93) (RCA) ① **09026 61190-2**
St Petersburg PO, Y. Temirkanov (r1992) *Concert*
(5/93) (RCA) ① [2] **09026 61377-2**
Concertgebouw, W. Mengelberg (r1941) *Concert*
(6/93) (ARHI) ① **ADCD108**
Boston SO, C. Munch (r1962) *Romeo and Juliet.*
(8/93) (RCA) ① **09026 61563-2**
LSO, I. Markevitch *Concert*
(2/94) (PHIL) ① [2] **438 335-2PM2**
Czech PO, V. Talich (r1953) *Mozart: Symphony 39.*
(4/94) (SUPR) ① **11 1908-2**
RPO, Y. Temirkanov (r1990) *Concert*
(5/94) (RCA) ① [6] **09026 61821-2**

BPO, W. Furtwängler (r1938) *Concert*
(7/94) (BIDD) ① [2] **WHL006/7**
National SO, A. Coates (r1945) *Romeo and Juliet.*
(7/94) (BEUL) ① **1PD6**
Boston SO, P. Monteux (r1955) *Concert*
(9/94) (RCA) ① [15] **09026 61893-2**
Polish Nat RSO, A. Wit (r1993) *Francesca da Rimini.*
(9/94) (NAXO) ① **8 550782**
Concertgebouw, B. Haitink (r1978) *Concert*
(10/94) (PHIL) ① [6] **442 061-2PB6**
Concertgebouw, W. Mengelberg (r1941) *1812.*
(10/94) (TELD) ① **4509-93673-2**
Concertgebouw, W. Mengelberg (r1937) *Concert*
(10/94) (MUSI) ① [2] **MACD-809**
BPO, F. Fricsay (r1953) *Violin Concerto.*
(11/94) (DG) ① **445 409-2GDO**
BPO, F. Fricsay (r1953) *Concert*
(11/94) (DG) ① [11] **445 400-2GDO10**
Russian Federation St SO, E. Svetlanov (pp1990)
Concert (12/94) (CANY) ① [7] **EC3630-2**
USSR SO, E. Svetlanov (r1967) *Concert*
(12/94) (MELO) ① [6] **74321 17101-2**
USSR SO, E. Svetlanov *Concert*
(12/94) (MELO) ① **74321 17097-2**
Leipzig Gewandhaus, K. Masur *Concert*
(1/95) (TELD) ① **4509-95981-2**
Russian St SO, V. Polyansky (r1993) *Marche slave.*
(5/95) (CHAN) ① **CHAN9356**
Leningrad PO, E. Mravinsky (r1956) *Concert*
(6/95) (DG) ① [2] **447 423-2GOR2**
LSO, A. Dorati (r1960) *Romeo and Juliet.*
(12/95) (MERC) ① **434 353-2MM**
2. Black Dyke Mills Band, J. Watson (r1992: arr
Barry) *Concert* (9/93) (POLY) ① **QPRL053D**
2, 3. SO, T. Beecham (r1915) *Concert*
(11/91) (SYMP) ① [2] **SYMCD1096/7**
3. Locke Brass Consort, J. Stobart (arr Stobard)
Concert (9/92) (CRD) ① **CRD3402**
Symphony No. 7 in E flat (1882) (sketches
only)
LPO, N. Järvi (1991) *Piano Concerto 3.*
(4/93) (CHAN) ① **CHAN9130**
**The Tempest—symphonic fantasia in F
minor after Shakespeare, Op. 18 (1873)**
LSO, Y. Butt *Liszt: Ce qu'on entend sur la montagne.*
(11/87) (ASV) ① **CDDCA586**
Oregon SO, J. DePreist *Concert*
(5/90) (DELO) ① **DE3081**
Bournemouth SO, A. Litton *Symphony 5.*
(2/91) (VIRG) ① **VC7 59598-2**
Polish Nat RSO, A. Wit (r1992) *Symphony 3.*
(2/94) (NAXO) ① **8 550518**
Washington NSO, A. Dorati (r1975) *Concert*
(5/94) (DECC) ① [2] **443 003-2DF2**
USSR SO, E. Svetlanov (r1970) *Concert*
(12/94) (MELO) ① [6] **74321 17101-2**
USSR SO, E. Svetlanov *Symphony 5.*
(12/94) (MELO) ① **74321 17096-2**
Russian Nat Orch, M. Pletnev *Manfred Symphony.*
(12/94) (DG) ① **439 891-2GH**
Frankfurt RSO, E. Inbal (r1974) *Concert*
(5/95) (PHIL) ① [2] **442 586-2PM2**
**Valse-scherzo in C—violin and orchestra,
Op. 34 (1877)**
X. Wei, Philh, S. Accardo *Concert*
(9/90) (ASV) ① **CDDCA713**
P. Amoyal, Philh, C. Dutoit *Concert*
(5/93) (ERAT) ① **2292-45971-2**
N. Milstein, orch, R. Irving (r1962) *Concert*
(5/94) (EMI) ① [6] **ZDMF7 64830-2**
S. Nakarjakov, A. Markovich (r1994: arr tpt/pf)
Concert (6/95) (TELD) ① **4509-94554-2**
**Variations on a Rococo Theme in A—cello
and orchestra, Op. 33 (1876)**
R. Wallfisch, ECO, G. Simon (orig. version) *Concert*
(2/85) (CHAN) ① **CHAN8347**
O. Harnoy, Victoria SO, P. Freeman *Concert*
(11/86) (RCA) ① **RD71003**
M. Rostropovich, Boston SO, S. Ozawa *Dvořák:
Cello Concerto.* (12/86) (ERAT) ① **2292-45252-2**
J. Starker, LSO, A. Dorati *Concert*
(4/89) (MERC) ① **432 001-2MM**
M. Malsky, Philh, S. Sinopoli *Elgar: Cello Concerto.*
(7/91) (DG) ① **431 685-2GH**
J. Lloyd Webber, LSO, M. Shostakovich *Concert*
(5/92) (PHIL) ① **434 106-2PH**
O. Harnoy, LPO, C. Mackerras *Concert*
(10/92) (RCA) ① **RD60758**
Y-Y. Ma, Pittsburgh SO, L. Maazel *Concert*
(11/92) (SONY) ① **SK48382**
L. Rose, Philadelphia, E. Ormandy (r1962) *Concert*
(5/93) (SONY) ① **SBK48278**
G. Cassadó, Vienna Pro Musica Orch, J. Perlea
(1950s) *Concert* (11/93) (VOX) ① [2] **CDX2 5502**
P. Tortelier, Northern Sinfonia, Y.P. Tortelier (r1973)
Violin Concerto. (12/93) (EMI) ① **CDC7 54890-2**

T. Mørk, Oslo PO, M. Jansons (r1992) *Dvořák: Cello Concerto.*
(1/94) (VIRG) ① **VC7 59325-2**
M. Rostropovich, BPO, H. von Karajan (r1968) *Concert*
(10/94) (DG) ① [2] **437 952-2GX2**
M. Kliegel, Ireland National SO, G. Markson (r1993) *Concert*
(11/94) (NAXO) ① **8 550519**
M. Rostropovich, BPO, H. von Karajan (r1968) *Dvořák: Cello Concerto.*
(5/95) (DG) ① **447 413-2GOR**
P. Tortelier, RPO, N. del Mar (r1948) *Concert*
(12/95) (EMI) ① **CDH5 65502-2**

Voyevoda—symphonic ballad in A minor, Op. 78 (1890-91)
St Louis SO, L. Slatkin *Concert*
(7/91) (RCA) ① **RD60432**
Washington NSO, A. Dorati (r1974) *Concert*
(5/94) (DECC) ① [2] **443 003-2DF2**
USSR SO, E. Svetlanov (r1989) *Concert*
(12/94) (MELO) ① [6] **74321 17101-2**
USSR SO, E. Svetlanov *Concert*
(12/94) (MELO) ① **74321 17097-2**
Frankfurt RSO, E. Inbal (r1974) *Concert*
(5/95) (PHIL) ① [2] **442 586-2PM2**

Was I not a blade of grass—cello and strings (arr of song, Op.47/7 by cpsr)
R. Wallfisch, ECO, G. Simon *Concert*
(2/85) (CHAN) ① **CHAN8347**

1812—Overture, Op. 49 (1880)
Cincinnati SO, E. Kunzel (with cannons and bells) *Concert*
(12/83) (TELA) ① **CD80041**
Philadelphia, R. Muti *Concert*
(3/85) (EMI) ① **CDC7 47022-2**
S. Jaroff Cossack Ch, BPO, H. von Karajan *Symphony 2.*
(12/86) (DG) ① **419 177-2GH**
LPO, C. Mackerras *Concert*
(11/87) (CFP) ① **CD-CFP9000**
Oslo PO, M. Jansons *Concert*
(1/88) (EMI) ① **CDC7 49141-2**
Don Cossack Ch, BPO, H. von Karajan (r1966) *Concert*
(4/88) (DG) ① **415 855-2GGA**
RLPO, S. Edwards *Concert*
(12/89) (EMIN) ① **CD-EMX2152**
Berlin SO, C.P. Flor (pp1988) *Concert*
(4/90) (RCA) ① **RD60119**
Oregon SO, J. DePreist *Concert*
(5/90) (DELO) ① **DE3081**
Gothenburg Sym Chor, Gothenburg Sym Brass, Gothenburg SO, N. Järvi *Concert*
(3/91) (DG) ① **429 984-2GH**
Royal Phil Chor, WNO Chor, RPO, Grenadier Guards Band, L. Stokowski *Concert*
(4/92) (DECC) ① **433 625-2DSP**
ASMF, N. Marriner *Symphony 6.*
(6/92) (CAPR) ① **10 385**
Britannia Building Soc Band, Desford Colliery Caterpillar Band, CWS (Glasgow) Band, IMI Yorkshire Imperial Band, G. Brand (pp1991: arr Z Wright) *Concert*
(8/92) (POLY) ① **QPRL049D**
Israel PO, Z. Mehta (r1992) *Concert*
(8/93) (TELD) ① **4509-90201-2**
Philh, P. Domingo (r1993) *Concert*
(4/94) (EMI) ① **CDC5 55018-2**
Dutch Royal Marine Band, Kirov Th Orch, V. Gergiev (r1993) *Concert*
(4/94) (PHIL) ① **442 011-2PH**
Detroit SO, A. Dorati (r1978) *Concert*
(5/94) (DECC) ① [2] **443 003-2DF2**
Concertgebouw, B. Haitink (r1972) *Concert*
(10/94) (PHIL) ① [6] **442 061-2PB6**
Concertgebouw, W. Mengelberg (r1940) *Symphony 6.*
(10/94) (TELD) ① **4509-93673-2**
Concertgebouw, I. Markevitch (r1964) *Concert*
(5/95) (PHIL) ① [2] **442 586-2PM2**
BPO, S. Ozawa (r1992) *Symphony 6.*
(8/95) (DG) ① **429 751-2GH**
Culver Girls' Acad Ch, St Louis SO, L. Slatkin (r1991; with Carillon of Culver Military Academy) *Concert*
(11/95) (RCA) ① **09026 68045-2**
Philadelphia, L. Stokowski (r1930) *Concert*
(11/95) (BIDD) ① **WHL015**
Minneapolis SO, A. Dorati (r1958) *Concert*
(12/95) (MERC) ① **434 360-2MM**

SECTION II: CHAMBER

Adagio molto in E flat—string quartet and harp (1863-64)
Shostakovich Qt, E. Moskvitina *Concert*
(6/93) (OLYM) ① **OCD522**

Capriccio italien—piano duet, Op. 45 (1880)
K. Labèque, M. Labèque (1994) *Concert*
(12/95) (PHIL) ① **442 778-2PH**

4 Early Pieces—string quartet (1863-64)
1. Allegretto, 6 2. Allegro vivace, B flat; 3. Andante ma non troppo, E minor (Prelude); 4. Andante molto, G.
1-4. St Petersburg Qt (r1993) *Concert*
(1/95) (SONY) ① [2] **SM2K57654**

Festival Overture on the Danish national anthem in D—piano: four hands, Op. 15 (1878) (trans cpsr from orch work)
T. Lønskov, R. Llambias (r1995) *Symphony 6.*
(10/95) (KONT) ① **32204**

Piano Trio in A minor, Op. 50 (1881-82)
Borodin Trio
(2/85) (CHAN) ① **CHAN8348**
Vladimir Ashkenazy, I. Perlman, L. Harrell
(12/87) (EMI) ① **CDC7 47988-2**
Borodin Trio *Alabiev: Piano Trio.*
(10/91) (CHAN) ① **CHAN8975**
Solomon Trio *Arensky: Piano Trio 1.*
(5/93) (CARL) ① **MCD52**
P. Amoyal, F. Lodéon, P. Rogé
(5/93) (ERAT) ① **2292-45972-2**
R. Stamper, C. Jackson, Vovka Ashkenazy (r1990) *Arensky: Piano Trio 1.*
(7/93) (NAXO) ① **8 550467**
Oslo Trio *Concert*
(10/93) (VICT) ① **VCD19079**
C-L. Lin, G. Hoffman, Y. Bronfman (r1992) *Arensky: Piano Trio 1.*
(9/94) (SONY) ① **SK53269**
I. Oistrakh, E. Altman, N. Zertsalova (1984)
(10/94) (MELO) ① **74321 17087-2**
J. Heifetz, G. Piatigorsky, A. Rubinstein (r1950) *Mendelssohn: Piano Trio 1.*
(11/94) (RCA) ① [65] **09026 61778-2(36)**
I. Perlman, L. Harrell, Vladimir Ashkenazy *Concert*
(6/95) (EMI) ① [20] **CZS4 83177-2(2)**

50 Russian Folk Songs—piano 4 hands (1868-69)
EXCERPTS: 1. A long walk; 2. Regrets; 3. Recollections; 4. Jumping fish; 5. Do not overflow, my Danube; 6. Go on spinning; 7. The attic; 8. A swinging pine tree; 9. Flowers will fade; 10. Floating; 11. Green vine branches; 12. Do not howl, impetuous winds; 13. At daybreak; 14. Sadness; 15. Arise, Sun; 16. Sing not, oh Nightingale; 17. Promenading; 18. A duckling; 19. After the feast; 20. I will come near your city; 21. The roaring of the wind has ceased; 22. Down the mountain; 23. A little duckling swimming in the sea; 24. My braids; 25. Green meadows; 26. Country place; 27. On the blue sea; 28. On the green meadows; 29. Wine cellar; 30. I will come near the city; 31. The Abbot; 32. Hailing Vanya; 33. The green; 34. Happy Katya; 35. Heavy heart; 36. My little duck; 37. A young maiden; 38. Play, my bagpipe; 39. My beloved friends; 40. A round dance; 41. The grey cockerel; 42. Under the apple tree; 43. My fields; 44. The princess; 45. Picking raspberries; 46. Playing in the meadows; 47. Vanya; 48. At the gate; 49. Song of the Volga boatman; 50. There was no wind.
Crommelynck Duo *Symphony 6.*
(7/89) (CLAV) ① **CD50-8805**
V. Postnikova, G. Rozhdestvensky (r1992) *Concert*
(7/93) (ERAT) ① [7] **2292-45969-2**

Souvenir de Florence—string sextet, Op. 70 (1890 rev 1891-92)
A. Lysy, M-K. Lee, P. Coletti, N. Chastain, A. Lysy, E. Vassallo *Concert*
(3/87) (CLAV) ① **CD50-8507**
Borodin Qt, Y. Bashmet, N. Gutman *Concert*
(8/88) (EMI) ① [2] **CDS7 49775-2**
Montreal I Musici, Y. Turovsky *Schubert: Minuets and Trios, D89.*
(9/89) (CHAN) ① **CHAN8547**
S. Accardo, M. Batjer, T. Hoffman, S. Gazeau, R. Filippini, G. Hoffman *String Quartet 1.*
(6/91) (NUOV) ① **6866**
Vienna CO, P. Entremont (arr stg orch) *Serenade, Op. 48.*
(10/91) (NAXO) ① **8 550404**
Primavera CO, M. Manley *Concert*
(3/93) (UNIC) ① **DKPCD9134**
Auvergne Orch, J-J. Kantorow *Serenade, Op. 48.*
(3/93) (DENO) ① **CO-75026**
Shostakovich Qt, K. Belotsvetov, A. Kovalyov *Concert*
(7/93) (OLYM) ① **OCD523**
Y. Yurov, M. Milman, Borodin Qt (r1993) *Concert*
(1/94) (TELD) ① [2] **4509-90422-2**
Raphael Ens (r1993) *Arensky: String Quartet 2.*
(2/94) (HYPE) ① **CDA66648**
Kremlin CO, M. Rachlevsky (arr stg orch; r1993) *Concert*
(7/94) (CLAV) ① **CD50-9317**
Keller Qt, K. Kashkashian, M. Perényi (r1993) *String Quartet 3.*
(10/94) (ERAT) ① **4509-94819-2**
Borodin Qt, G. Talalyan, M. Rostropovich (r1980) *Concert*
(10/94) (MELO) ① [2] **74321 18290-2**
Philh, D.V. Yu (1994; arr Yu) *Serenade, Op. 48.*
(11/94) (CARL) ① **MCD89**
J. Heifetz, I. Baker, M. Thomas, P. Rosenthal, G. Piatigorsky, L. Lesser (r1968) *Dvořák: Piano Trio 3.*
(11/94) (RCA) ① [65] **09026 61778-2(39)**

Souvenir d'un lieu cher—violin and piano, Op.42 (1878)
1. Méditation in D minor; 2. Scherzo in C minor; 3. Mélodie in E flat.
L. Mordkovitch, M. Gusak-Grin (trans cpsr) *Concert*
(3/87) (CHAN) ① **CHAN8500**

1. I. Perlman, Israel PO, Z. Mehta (orch. Glazunov) *Khachaturian: Violin Concerto.*
(7/85) (EMI) ① **CDC7 47087-2**
1. K. Takezawa, P. Moll *Concert*
(2/93) (RCA) ① **09026 60704-2**
1. I. Perlman, Israel PO, Z. Mehta (orch Glazunov) *Concert*
(6/95) (EMI) ① [20] **CZS4 83177-2(2)**
1, 2. N. Milstein, orch. R. Irving (r1962: arr Glazunov) *Concert*
(5/94) (EMI) ① [6] **ZDMF7 64830-2**
1, 3. V. Vaidman, E. Krasovsky *Concert*
(6/90) (CARL) ① **PWK1137**
2. Kremlin CO, M. Rachlevsky (r1991; arr Rachlevsky) *Concert*
(6/93) (CLAV) ① **CD50-9116**
2. J. Heifetz, S. Chotzinoff (1919) *Concert*
(11/94) (RCA) ① [65] **09026 61778-2(01)**
2. N. Milstein, L. Mittman (r1938: arr Zimbalist) *Concert*
(9/95) (BIDD) ① **LAB096**
2, 3. M. Vengerov, I. Golan (r1993) *Concert*
(4/94) (TELD) ① **9031-77351-2**
3. L. Auer, anon (arr Wilhelmj: r1920) *Concert*
(8/90) (SYMP) ① **SYMCD1071**
3. X. Wei, Pam Nicholson *Concert*
(9/90) (ASV) ① **CDDCA698**
3. X. Wei, Philh, S. Accardo (orch Glazunov) *Concert*
(9/90) (ASV) ① **CDDCA713**
3. L. Auer, W. Bogutskahein (arr Auer; r1920) *Concert*
(12/91) (APR) ① [2] **APR7015**
3. M. Elman, P. Kahn (r1906) *Concert*
(12/91) (APR) ① [2] **APR7015**
3. C. Pavlík, Dvořák CO, V. Válek *Concert*
(4/92) (SUPR) ① **11 0111-2**
3. J. Hassid, G. Moore (r1940) *Concert*
(10/92) (PEAR) ① **GEMMCD9939**
3. J. Hassid, G. Moore (r1940) *Concert*
(10/92) (TEST) ① **SBT1010**
3. S. Chang, S. Rivers (ed Galamian) *Concert*
(6/93) (EMI) ① **CDC7 54352-2**
3. Midori, R. McDonald (r1992) *Concert*
(6/93) (SONY) ① **SK52568**
3. B. Huberman, P. Frenkel (r1922) *Concert*
(3/94) (BIDD) ① [2] **LAB077/8**
3. B. Huberman, S. Schultze (r1929) *Concert*
(9/94) (BIDD) ① [2] **LAB081/2**
3. J. Heifetz, E. Bay (r1945) *Concert*
(11/94) (RCA) ① [65] **09026 61778-2(19)**
3. V. Spivakov, S. Bezrodny (r1991: orch cpsr) *Concert*
(5/95) (RCA) ① **09026 62524-2**
3. I. Perlman, S. Sanders (arr vn/pf: Fleisch) *Concert*
(6/95) (EMI) ① [20] **CZS4 83177-2(2)**

String Quartet Movement in B flat (1865)
Shostakovich Qt *Concert*
(7/93) (OLYM) ① **OCD523**
Borodin Qt (r1993) *Concert*
(1/94) (TELD) ① [2] **4509-90422-2**
Borodin Qt (r1979) *Concert*
(10/94) (MELO) ① [2] **74321 18290-2**
St Petersburg Qt (r1993) *Concert*
(1/95) (SONY) ① [2] **SM2K57654**

String Quartet No. 1 in D, Op. 11 (1871)
1. Moderato e semplice; 2. Andante cantabile; 3. Scherzo; 4. Allegro giusto.
Talich Qt (r1986) *Borodin: String Quartet 2.*
(5/88) (CALL) ① **CAL6202**
Borodin Qt *Concert*
(8/88) (EMI) ① [2] **CDS7 49775-2**
Gabrieli Qt (5/90) (DECC) ① **425 541-2DM**
S. Accardo, M. Batjer, T. Hoffman, G. Hoffman *Souvenir de Florence.*
(6/91) (NUOV) ① **6866**
Kremlin CO, M. Rachlevsky (r1991; arr Rachlevsky) *Concert*
(6/93) (CLAV) ① **CD50-9116**
Borodin Qt (r1993) *Concert*
(1/94) (TELD) ① [2] **4509-90422-2**
Schubert Qt *String Quartet 3.*
(4/94) (NIMB) ① **NI5380**
Borodin Qt (r1980) *Concert*
(10/94) (MELO) ① [2] **74321 18290-2**
St Petersburg Qt (r1993) *Concert*
(1/95) (SONY) ① [2] **SM2K57654**
Hollywood Qt (r1952) *Concert*
(8/95) (TEST) ① **SBT1061**
2. I. Perlman, J.G. Guggenheim (pp1990: arr Kreisler) *Concert*
(2/91) (EMI) ① **CDC7 54108-2**
2. Elman Qt (r1918) *Concert*
(10/91) (BIDD) ① **LAB039**
2. L. Kaufman, P. Ulanowsky (r1950s: arr Kreisler) *Concert*
(8/92) (CAMB) ① **CD-1063**
2. F. Kreisler, F. Rupp (r1938: arr Kreisler) *Concert*
(12/93) (EMI) ① **CDH7 64701-2**
2. I. Perlman, S. Sanders (arr vn/pf: Kreisler) *Concert*
(6/95) (EMI) ① [20] **CZS4 83177-2(2)**

String Quartet No. 2 in F, Op. 22 (1874)
Borodin Qt *Concert*
(8/88) (EMI) ① [2] **CDS7 49775-2**
Borodin Qt (r1993) *Concert*
(1/94) (TELD) ① [2] **4509-90422-2**

Borodin Qt (r1980) *Concert*
(10/94) (MELO) ① [2] 74321 18290-2
St Petersburg Qt (r1993) *Concert*
(1/95) (SONY) ① [2] SM2K57654
String Quartet No. 3 in E flat minor, Op. 30 (1876)
Borodin Qt *Concert*
(8/88) (EMI) ① [2] CDS7 49775-2
Shostakovich Qt *Concert*
(6/93) (OLYM) ① OCD522
Borodin Qt (r1993) *Concert*
(1/94) (TELD) ① [2] 4509-90422-2
Schubert Qt *String Quartet 1.*
(4/94) (NIMB) ① NI5380
Kremlin CO, M. Rachlevsky (arr Rachlevsky; r1993)
Concert (7/94) (CLAV) ① CD50-9317
Keller Qt (r1992) *Souvenir de Florence.*
(10/94) (ERAT) ① 4509-94819-2
Borodin Qt (r1965) *Concert*
(10/94) (MELO) ① [2] 74321 18290-2
St Petersburg Qt (r1993) *Concert*
(1/95) (SONY) ① [2] SM2K57654
Swan Lake—transcription: two pianos (1880)
1. Danse russe; 2. Danse espagnole; 3. Danse napolitaine.
K. Labèque, M. Labèque (1994: arr Debussy)
Concert (12/95) (PHIL) ① 442 778-2PH
Symphony No. 6 in B minor, 'Pathétique'—piano: four hands, Op. 74 (1893)
T. Lønskov, R. Llambias (1995) *Festival Overture.*
(10/95) (KONT) ① 32204
Valse-scherzo—violin and piano, Op.34 (1877)
L. Mordkovitch, M. Gusak-Grin (trans cpsr) *Concert*
(3/87) (CHAN) ① CHAN8500
M. Vengerov, I. Vinogradova *Concert*
(4/90) (BIDD) ① LAW001
V. Vaidman, E. Krasovsky *Concert*
(6/90) (CARL) ① PWK1137
K. Takezawa, P. Moll *Concert*
(2/93) (RCA) ① 09026 60704-2
V. Spivakov, S. Bezrodny (r1991-2) *Concert*
(5/95) (RCA) ① 09026 62524-2

SECTION III: INSTRUMENTAL

Album for the young, Op. 39 (1878)
1. Morning Prayer; 2. A Winter Morning; 3. The Hobby-Horse; 4. Little Mother; 5. March of the Wooden Soldiers; 6. The Sick Doll; 7. The Doll's Funeral; 8. Waltz; 10. Mazurka; 11. Russian Song; 12. The Peasant plays his Ziehharmonika; 13. Folksong (Kamarinskaya); 14. Polka; 15. Italian Song; 16. Old French Melody; 17. German Song (Ländler); 18. Neapolitan Song; 19. The Old Nurse's Tale; 20. The Witch (Baba-Yaga); 21. Sweet Dreams; 22. Song of the Lark; 23. The Organ-Grinder sings; 24. In Church.
L. Edlina *Album for the Young.*
(11/85) (CHAN) ① CHAN8365
R. Dubinsky, M. Zweig, J. Horner, Y. Turovsky (arr. Dubinsky) *Album for the young.*
(11/85) (CHAN) ① CHAN8365
O. Mustonen *Concert*
(2/93) (DECC) ① 436 255-2DH
V. Postnikova (r1991) *Concert*
(7/93) (ERAT) ① [7] 2292-45969-2
I. Biret (r1993) *Concert*
(10/94) (NAXO) ① 8 550885
Moscow Virtuosi, V. Spivakov (r1992; trans V. Milman & V. Spivakov) *Concert*
(12/94) (RCA) ① 09026 61964-2
4, 8. L. Rév *Concert* (7/87) (HYPE) ① CDA66185
12, 17, 23. G. Tozer *Concert*
(12/92) (TALL) ① TP001
Aveu passioné in E minor—piano (?1892)
V. Postnikova (r1992) *Concert*
(7/93) (ERAT) ① [7] 2292-45969-2
Capriccio in G flat—piano, Op. 8 (1870)
V. Postnikova (r1991-92) *Concert*
(7/93) (ERAT) ① [7] 2292-45969-2
Dumka (Russian rustic scene)—piano, Op. 59 (1886)
V. Horowitz (r1942) *Concert*
(1/93) (RCA) ① GD60526
V. Horowitz (r1929: pf roll) *Concert*
(1/93) (COND) ① 690.07.009
V. Postnikova (r1992) *Concert*
(7/93) (ERAT) ① [7] 2292-45969-2
L. Vogt (r1991) *Concert*
(11/93) (EMI) ① CDC7 54548-2
M. Fingerhut (r1992) *Concert*
(4/94) (CHAN) ① CHAN9218

Impromptu in A flat—piano (1889)
V. Postnikova (r1992) *Concert*
(7/93) (ERAT) ① [7] 2292-45969-2
Impromptu-caprice in G—piano (1884)
V. Postnikova (r1992) *Concert*
(7/93) (ERAT) ① [7] 2292-45969-2
Military March in B flat—piano (1893)
V. Postnikova (r1992) *Concert*
(7/93) (ERAT) ① [7] 2292-45969-2
Momento lirico (Impromptu) in A flat—piano (?1893)
V. Postnikova (r1992) *Concert*
(7/93) (ERAT) ① [7] 2292-45969-2
3 Morceaux—piano, Op. 9 (1870)
1. Rêverie; 2. Polka de salon; 3. Mazurka de salon.
V. Postnikova (r1991-92) *Concert*
(7/93) (ERAT) ① [7] 2292-45969-2
2 Morceaux—piano, Op. 10 (1871)
1. Nocturne, F; 2. Humoresque, E minor.
V. Postnikova (r1991-92) *Concert*
(7/93) (ERAT) ① [7] 2292-45969-2
S. Richter (r1983) *Concert*
(1/94) (OLYM) ① OCD334
2. F. Kreisler, C. Lamson (arr Kreisler: vn/pf; r1926)
Concert (1/90) (PEAR) ① GEMMCD9324
2. S. Rachmaninov (r1923) *Concert*
(3/93) (RCA) ① 09026 61265-2(3)
2. F. Kreisler, C. Lamson (r1926: arr Kreisler)
Concert (12/93) (BIDD) ① LAB075
2. M. Fingerhut (r1992) *Concert*
(4/94) (CHAN) ① CHAN9218
6 Morceaux—piano, Op. 19 (1873)
1. Rêverie du soir, G minor; 2. Scherzo humoristique, D; 3. Feuillet d'album, D; 4. Nocturne, C sharp minor; 5. Capriccioso, B flat; 6. Thème original et variations, F.
V. Postnikova (r1992) *Concert*
(7/93) (ERAT) ① [7] 2292-45969-2
1, 5. S. Richter (r1983) *Concert*
(1/94) (OLYM) ① OCD334
4. M. Maisky, P. Gililov (arr vc/pf) *Concert*
(7/91) (DG) ① 431 544-2GH
4. M. Fingerhut (r1992) *Concert*
(4/94) (CHAN) ① CHAN9218
6. A. Gavrilov (r1977) *Concert*
(11/92) (EMI) ① CDM7 64329-2
12 Morceaux—piano, Op. 40 (1878)
1. Etude, G; 2. Chanson triste, G minor; 3. Marche funèbre, C minor; 4. Mazurka, C; 5. Mazurka, D; 6. Chants sans paroles, A minor; 7. Au village, A minor; 8. Valse, A flat; 9. Valse, F sharp minor; 10. Danse russe, A minor; 11. Scherzo, D minor; 12. Rêverie interrompue, F minor.
V. Postnikova (r1992) *Concert*
(7/93) (ERAT) ① [7] 2292-45969-2
2, 8. S. Richter (r1983) *Concert*
(1/94) (OLYM) ① OCD334
7. M. Fingerhut (r1992) *Concert*
(4/94) (CHAN) ① CHAN9218
7. Philadelphia, L. Stokowski (r1928: arr orch)
Concert (11/93) (BIDD) ① WHL015
8. S. Rachmaninov (r1923) *Concert*
(3/93) (RCA) ① [10] 09026 61265-2(3)
6 Morceaux—piano, Op. 51 (1882)
1. Valse de salon, A flat; 2. Polka peu dansante, B minor; 3. Menuetto scherzoso, E flat; 4a. Natha-valse, A (1878); 4b. Natha-valse, A; 5. Romance, F; 6. Valse sentimentale, F minor.
V. Postnikova (r1992) *Concert*
(7/93) (ERAT) ① [7] 2292-45969-2
O. Yablonskaya (r1994) *Morceaux, Op. 37.*
(10/95) (NAXO) ① 8 553063
1, 3, 5. S. Richter (r1983) *Concert*
(1/94) (OLYM) ① OCD334
5, 6. A. Goldenweiser (r1947) *Concert*
(8/95) (MELO) ① [11] 74321 25172-2(1)
5, 6. A. Goldenweiser (r1947) *Concert*
(8/95) (MELO) ① 74321 25173-2
6. K-W. Chung, P. Moll (arr Press) *Concert*
(9/87) (DECC) ① 417 289-2DH
6. G. Piatigorsky, I. Newton (r1993: arr Piatigorsky)
Concert (10/91) (MUSI) ① MACD-644
6. O. Harnoy, LPO, C. Mackerras (orch J. Harnoy)
Concert (10/92) (RCA) ① RD60758
6. J. Szigeti, H. Kaufman (r1994: arr Grunes) *Concert*
(5/93) (SONY) ① MPK52569
6. J. Bálint, N. Mercz (r1992: arr fl/hp: Mercz) *Concert*
(12/94) (NAXO) ① 8 550741
6. M. Kliegel, B. Glemser (r1993: arr vc/pf: L Rose)
Concert (1/95) (NAXO) ① 8 550785
6. V. Spivakov, S. Bezrodny (r1991-2) *Concert*
(5/95) (RCA) ① 09026 62524-2
18 Morceaux—piano, Op. 72 (1893)
1. Impromptu, F minor; 2. Berceuse, A flat; 3. Tendres reproches, C sharp minor; 4. Danse caractéristique, D; 5. Méditation, D; 6. Mazurque pour

danser, B flat; 7. Polacca de concert, E flat; 8. Dialogue, B; 9. Un poco di Schumann, B; 10. Scherzo-fantaisie, E flat minor; 11. Valse bleuette, E flat; 12. L'espiègle, E; 13. Echo rustique, E flat; 14. Chant élégiaque, D flat; 15. Un poco di Chopin. C sharp minor; 16. Valse à cinq temps, D; 17. Passé lointain, E flat; 18. Scène dansante (invitation au trepak), C.
V. Postnikova (r1992) *Concert*
(7/93) (ERAT) ① [7] 2292-45969-2
5. A. Goldenweiser (r1947) *Concert*
(8/95) (MELO) ① [11] 74321 25172-2(1)
5. A. Goldenweiser (r1947) *Concert*
(8/95) (MELO) ① 74321 25173-2
5, 12, 15. S. Richter (r1983) *Concert*
(1/94) (OLYM) ① OCD334
8. A. Goldenweiser (r1954) *Concert*
(8/95) (MELO) ① 74321 25173-2
8. A. Goldenweiser (r1954) *Concert*
(8/95) (MELO) ① [11] 74321 25172-2(1)
18. J. Lhévinne (r1920) *Concert*
(10/92) (APR) ① [2] APR7013
6 Morceaux composés sur un seul thème—piano, Op. 21 (1873)
1. Prélude, B; 2. Fugue à 4 voix, G sharp minor; 3. Impromptu, C sharp minor; 4. Marche funèbre, A flat minor; 5. Mazurque, A flat minor; 6. Scherzo, A flat.
V. Postnikova (r1992) *Concert*
(7/93) (ERAT) ① [7] 2292-45969-2
M. Pletnev (r1994) *Seasons.*
(12/94) (VIRG) ① VC5 45042-2
2 Pieces—piano, Op. 1 (1867)
1. Scherzo à la russe, B flat; 2. Impromptu, E flat minor.
V. Postnikova (r1991-92) *Concert*
(7/93) (ERAT) ① [7] 2292-45969-2
Potpourri on Themes from the opera 'Voyevoda'—piano (1868)
V. Postnikova (r1992) *Concert*
(7/93) (ERAT) ① [7] 2292-45969-2
Romance in F minor—piano, Op. 5 (1868)
V. Postnikova (r1991-92) *Concert*
(7/93) (ERAT) ① [7] 2292-45969-2
S. Richter (r1983) *Concert*
(1/94) (OLYM) ① OCD334
3 Romances
1. Berceuse; 2. On chante encore; 3. Qu'importe.
V. Postnikova (r1992) *Concert*
(7/93) (ERAT) ① [7] 2292-45969-2
The Seasons—piano, Op. 37b (1875-76)
1. January; 2. February; 3. March; 4. April; 5. May; 6. June; 7. July; 8. August; 9. September; 10. October; 11. November; 12. December.
L. Artymiw (1/85) (CHAN) ① CHAN8349
P. Katin *Piano Sonata, Op.37.*
(2/88) (OLYM) ① OCD192
V. Postnikova *Piano Sonata, Op. 80.*
(6/92) (ERAT) ① 2292-45512-2
V. Postnikova (r1990) *Concert*
(7/93) (ERAT) ① [7] 2292-45969-2
M. Pletnev (r1994) *Morceaux, Op.21.*
(12/94) (VIRG) ① VC5 45042-2
1, 2, 4, 5, 8, 10, 11, 12. R. O'Hora (r1994) *Piano Concerto 1.* (10/95) (TRIN) ① TRP023
1, 5, 6, 11. S. Richter (r1983) *Concert*
(1/94) (OLYM) ① OCD334
6, 10, 11. L. Vogt (r1991) *Concert*
(11/93) (EMI) ① CDC7 54548-2
10. O. Harnoy, LPO, C. Mackerras (orch J. Harnoy)
Concert (10/92) (RCA) ① RD60758
11. M. Levitzki (r1924) *Concert*
(1/93) (APR) ① [2] APR7014
11. S. Rachmaninov (r1928) *Concert*
(3/93) (RCA) ① [10] 09026 61265-2(2)
11. S. Rachmaninov (r1920) *Concert*
(3/93) (RCA) ① [10] 09026 61265-2(3)
Sonata for Piano in C sharp minor, Op. 80 (1865)
V. Postnikova *Seasons.*
(6/92) (ERAT) ① 2292-45512-2
V. Postnikova (r1991) *Concert*
(7/93) (ERAT) ① [7] 2292-45969-2
Emil Gilels (pp1962) *Piano Concerto 1.*
(4/94) (RUSS) ① RDCD11170
Sonata for Piano in G, Op. 37 (1878)
P. Katin *Seasons.* (2/88) (OLYM) ① OCD192
E. Leonskaja *Piano Concerto 2.*
(9/92) (TELD) ① 9031-72296-2
V. Postnikova (r1990) *Concert*
(7/93) (ERAT) ① [7] 2292-45969-2
O. Yablonskaya (r1994) *Morceaux, Op. 51.*
(10/95) (NAXO) ① 8 553063
3 Souvenirs de Hapsal—piano, Op. 2
1. Ruines d'un château; 2. Scherzo; 3. Chant sans paroles.

V. Postnikova (r1991-92) *Concert*
(7/93) (ERAT) ① [7] **2292-45969-2**
3. F. Kreisler, anon (r1904: arr. Kreisler) *Concert*
(7/90) (BIDD) ① [2] **LAB009/10**
3. F. Kreisler, H. Squire (r1911: arr. Kreisler) *Concert*
(7/90) (BIDD) ① [2] **LAB009/10**
3. F. Kreisler, C. Lamson (r1924: arr Kreisler)
Concert (9/93) (BIDD) ① [2] **LAB068/9**
3. I. Perlman, S. Sanders (arr vn/pf: Kreisler) *Concert*
(6/95) (EMI) ① [20] **CZS4 83177-2(2)**
Theme and Variations in A minor—piano
(1863-64)
V. Postnikova (r1992) *Concert*
(7/93) (ERAT) ① [7] **2292-45969-2**
Valse caprice in D—piano, Op. 4 (1886)
V. Postnikova (r1991-92) *Concert*
(7/93) (ERAT) ① [7] **2292-45969-2**
Valse-scherzo (No. 1) in A, Op. 7 (1870)
V. Postnikova (r1991-92) *Concert*
(7/93) (ERAT) ① [7] **2292-45969-2**
S. Richter (r1983) *Concert*
(1/94) (OLYM) ① **OCD334**
Valse-scherzo in A—piano (1889)
V. Postnikova (r1992) *Concert*
(7/93) (ERAT) ① [7] **2292-45969-2**

SECTION IV: VOCAL AND CHORAL
---

16 Children's Songs, Op. 54 (1881-83) (Wds.
Pleshcheyev unless stated)
1. Granny and grandson; 2. The little bird; 3. Spring;
4. My little garden; 5. Legend: When Jesus Christ
was but a child; 6. On the bank; 7. Winter evening; 8.
The cuckoo (wds. after Gellert); 9. Spring: the snow
is already melting; 10. Lullaby in a storm; 11. The
flower (wds. after Ratisbonne); 12. Winter; 13. Spring
song; 14. Autumn; 15. The swallow (wds. Surikov
after Lenartowicz); 16. Child's song (wds. Axakov).
5. K. Vayne, C. Tilney (r1966) *Concert*
(6/95) (PREI) ① **89996**
8, 10, 13. J. Rodgers, R. Vignoles *Concert*
(2/93) (HYPE) ① **CDA66617**
8, 9. E. Söderström, Vladimir Ashkenazy (r1979)
Concert (5/94) (DECC) ① **436 204-2DM**
6 Duets, Op. 46 (1880)
1. Evening (wds. Surikov); 2. Scottish ballad (wds.
Tolstoy); 3. Tears (wds. Tyutchev); 4. In the garden,
near the ford (wds. Surikov after Shevchenko); 5.
Passion spent (wds. Tolstoy); 6. Dawn (wds.
Surikov).
2. V. de los Angeles, D. Fischer-Dieskau, G. Moore
(r1960: Ger) *Concert*
(4/94) (EMI) ① [4] **CMS5 65061-2(2)**
3, 4, 6. E. Söderström, K. Meyer, J. Eyron (r1974)
Concert (9/93) (BIS) ① **BIS-CD017**
I should like in a single word—song (1875)
(Wds. Mey after Heine)
J. Varady, A. Reimann *Concert*
(8/89) (ORFE) ① **C053851A**
D. Hvorostovsky, M. Arkadiov *Concert*
(2/95) (PHIL) ① **442 536-2PH**
Liturgy of St John
Chrysostom—unaccompanied chorus, Op.
41 (1878)
1. Lord, have mercy; 2. Glory be to the Father, the
Son and the Holy Spirit; 3. Come let us worship; 4.
Alleluia; 5. Glory be to Thee; 6. Cherubical hymn; 7.
Lord, have mercy; 8. The Creed; 9. The mercy of
peace; 10. We sing thee; 11. It is meet; 12. Amen.
And with Thy spirit; 13. Our Father; 14. Praise ye the
Lord from the heavens; 15. Blessed be he that
cometh in the name of the Lord.
Excs St Petersburg Glinka Acad Ch, V.
Chernushenko *Concert*
(3/92) (TELD) ① **9031-73241-2**
Mezza notte—song: 1v and piano (c1855-60)
(Wds. anon)
E. Söderström, Vladimir Ashkenazy (r1980) *Concert*
(5/94) (DECC) ① **436 204-2DM**
My genius, my angel, my friend—song: 1v
and piano (c1855-60) (Wds. A. Fet)
E. Söderström, Vladimir Ashkenazy (r1982) *Concert*
(5/94) (DECC) ① **436 204-2DM**
O. Borodina, L. Gergieva (r1993) *Concert*
(6/94) (PHIL) ① [2] **442 013-2PH**
D. Hvorostovsky, M. Arkadiov *Concert*
(2/95) (PHIL) ① **442 536-2PH**
9 Sacred Pieces—unaccompanied mixed
chorus (1884)
1. Cherubim's song, F; 2. Cherubim's song, D; 3.
Cherubim's song, C; 4. We sing to Thee; 5. It is very
meet; 6. Our Father; 7. I. beseech thee once, choose; 8.
Let my prayer ascend; 9. Today the heavenly
powers.
5. Cambridge Sngrs, J. Rutter *Concert*
(4/92) (CLLE) ① **COLCD116**

---

6 Songs, Op. 6 (1869)
1. Do not believe, my friend (wds. Tolstoy); 2. Not a
word, o my friend (wds. Pleshcheyev after
Hartmann); 3. Both painfully and sweetly (wds.
Rostopchina); 4. A tear trembles (wds. Tolstoy); 5.
Why? (wds. Mey after Heine); 6. None but the lonely
heart (wds. Mey after Goethe).
1. E. Söderström, Vladimir Ashkenazy (r1982)
Concert (5/94) (DECC) ① **436 204-2DM**
1, 2, 5, 6. J. Rodgers, R. Vignoles *Concert*
(2/93) (HYPE) ① **CDA66617**
1, 2, 5, 6. O. Borodina, L. Gergieva (r1993) *Concert*
(6/94) (PHIL) ① [2] **442 013-2PH**
1, 5. J. Varady, A. Reimann *Concert*
(8/89) (ORFE) ① **C053851A**
1, 6. M. Price, J. Lockhart (r1973) *Concert*
(11/95) (CFP) ① **CD-CFP4669**
2. D. Hvorostovsky, M. Arkadiov *Concert*
(2/95) (PHIL) ① **442 536-2PH**
3. K. Vayne, C. Tilney (r1966) *Concert*
(6/95) (PREI) ① **89996**
4. N. Shevelev, anon (r1901) *Concert*
(6/93) (PEAR) ① [3] **GEMMCDS9007/9(2)**
4, 6. D. Hvorostovsky, M. Arkadiov *Concert*
(10/91) (PHIL) ① **432 119-2PH**
5. E. Caruso, orch, J. Pasternack (French: r1916)
Concert (7/91) (RCA) ① [12] **GD60495(5)**
5. E. Caruso, orch, J. Pasternack (French: r1916)
Concert (10/91) (PEAR) ① [3] **EVC4(1)**
5. N. Obukhova, M. Sakharov (r1949) *Concert*
(4/92) (EMI) ① [7] **CHS7 69741-2(6)**
5, 6. E. Söderström, Vladimir Ashkenazy (r1979)
Concert (5/94) (DECC) ① **436 204-2DM**
6. I. Stern, Columbia SO, M. Katims (arr Harris)
Concert (7/90) (SONY) ① **SK45816**
6. G. Piatigorsky, K. Szreter (arr Piatigorsky: r c1928)
Concert (3/92) (MUSI) ① **MACD-674**
6. P. Domingo, I. Perlman, NY Studio Orch, J. Tunick
(r1990) *Concert* (3/92) (EMI) ① **CDC7 54266-2**
6. P. McCann, Black Dyke Mills Band, P. Parkes
(r1984: arr G Langford) *Concert*
(11/92) (CHAN) ① **CHAN4501**
6. S. Cherkassky (bp1979; arr Nagel) *Concert*
(6/93) (DECC) ① **433 651-2DH**
6. P. Domingo, O. Harnoy, Philh, R. Behr (r1993)
Concert (4/94) (EMI) ① **CDC5 55018-2**
6. N. Koshetz, Inst Ens (r c1922) *Concert*
(6/94) (MMOI) ① **CDMOIR422**
6. N. Ghiaurov, P. Dokovska (r1993) *Concert*
(1/95) (RCA) ① **09026 62501-2**
6. E. Rethberg, orch (r1925: Ger) *Concert*
(2/95) (ROMO) ① [2] **81012-2**
6. L. Garrett, RPO, P. Robinson (r1994) *Concert*
(4/95) (SILV) ① **SILKD6004**
6. P. Domingo, I. Perlman, NY Studio Orch, J. Tunick
(r1990) *Concert*
(6/95) (EMI) ① [20] **CZS4 83177-2(3)**
6 Songs, Op. 16 (1872)
1. Cradle song (wds. Maykov); 2. Wait (wds. Grekov);
3. Accept just once (wds. Fet); 4. O sing that song
(wds. Pelshcheyev after Hemans); 5. Thy radiant
image (wds. Grekov); 6. In dark Hell (wds. Maykov).
1. Cambridge Clare College Ch, Cambridge Clare
College Orch, J. Rutter (Eng) *Concert*
(12/89) (DECC) ① **425 500-2DM**
1. S. Rachmaninov (r1942: arr Rachmaninov: pf)
Concert (5/90) (RCA) ① **GD87766**
1. H. Shelley (r1991: arr pf: Rachmaninov) *Concert*
(3/92) (HYPE) ① **CDA66486**
1. J. Rodgers, R. Vignoles *Concert*
(2/93) (HYPE) ① **CDA66617**
1. S. Rachmaninov (r1942; arr Rachmaninov: pf)
Concert (3/93) (RCA) ① [10] **09026 61265-2(2)**
1. J. Weber (r1992: arr pf: Rachmaninov) *Concert*
(12/93) (CARL) ① **PCD1051**
1. H. Shelley (r1991: arr pf: Rachmaninov) *Concert*
(3/94) (HYPE) ① [8] **CDS44041/8**
1. E. Söderström, Vladimir Ashkenazy (r1980)
Concert (5/94) (DECC) ① **436 204-2DM**
1. O. Borodina, L. Gergieva (r1993) *Concert*
(6/94) (PHIL) ① [2] **442 013-2PH**
1. N. Lugansky (r1993: arr pf: Rachmaninov) *Concert*
(1/95) (VANG) ① **08.99009**
3. A. Orda, J. Lee (bp1959) *Concert*
(12/89) (SYMP) ① **SYMCD1067**
4. E. Söderström, Vladimir Ashkenazy (r1982)
Concert (5/94) (DECC) ① **436 204-2DM**
6 Songs, Op. 25 (1874-75)
1. Reconciliation (wds. Shcherbina); 2. As o'er the
burning ashes (wds. Tyutchev); 3. Mignon's song
(wds. Tyutchev after Goethe); 4. The canary (wds.
Mey); 5. I never spoke to him (wds. Mey); 6. As they
reiterated, 'Fool' (wds. Mey).
1. D. Hvorostovsky, O. Boshniakovich *Concert*
(10/91) (PHIL) ① **432 119-2PH**

---

1. O. Borodina, L. Gergieva (r1993) *Concert*
(6/94) (PHIL) ① [2] **442 013-2PH**
2. E. Söderström, Vladimir Ashkenazy (r1980)
Concert (5/94) (DECC) ① **436 204-2DM**
4. J. Rodgers, R. Vignoles *Concert*
(2/93) (HYPE) ① **CDA66617**
6. A. Orda, J. Lee (bp1959) *Concert*
(12/89) (SYMP) ① **SYMCD1067**
6 Songs, Op. 27 (1875)
1. At bedtime (wds. Ogaryov); 2. Look, yonder cloud
(wds. Grekov); 3. Do not leave me (wds. Fet); 4.
Evening (wds. Mey after Shevchenko); 5. Was it the
mother who bore me? (wds. Mey after Mickiewicz);
My spoilt darling (wds. Mey after Mickiewicz).
4. E. Söderström, Vladimir Ashkenazy (r1979)
Concert (5/94) (DECC) ① **436 204-2DM**
6 Songs, Op. 28 (1875)
1. No, I shall never tell (wds. Grekov after Musset); 2.
The corals (wds. Mey after Kondratowicz); 3. Why did
I dream of you? (wds. Mey); 4. He loved me so much
(wds. Apukhtin?); 5. No response, or word, or
greeting (wds. Apukhtin); 6. The fearful minute (wds.
cpsr).
3. J. Varady, A. Reimann *Concert*
(8/89) (ORFE) ① **C053851A**
3. E. Söderström, Vladimir Ashkenazy (r1982)
Concert (5/94) (DECC) ① **436 204-2DM**
3, 6. J. Rodgers, R. Vignoles *Concert*
(2/93) (HYPE) ① **CDA66617**
6. D. Hvorostovsky, O. Boshniakovich *Concert*
(10/91) (PHIL) ① **432 119-2PH**
6. E. Söderström, Vladimir Ashkenazy (r1979)
Concert (5/94) (DECC) ① **436 204-2DM**
6. O. Borodina, L. Gergieva (r1993) *Concert*
(6/94) (PHIL) ① [2] **442 013-2PH**
6 Songs, Op. 38 (1878)
1. Don Juan's Serenade (wds. Tolstoy); 2. It was in
the early Spring (wds. Tolstoy); 3. At the ball (wds.
Tolstoy); 4. O if only you could for one moment (wds.
Tolstoy); 5. The love of a dead man (wds.
Lermontov); 6. Pimpinella (wds. Anon).
1. A. Orda, J. Lee (bp1959) *Concert*
(12/89) (SYMP) ① **SYMCD1067**
1. E. Caruso, orch, W.B. Rogers (r1914) *Concert*
(7/91) (RCA) ① [12] **GD60495(5)**
1. E. Caruso, orch, W.B. Rogers (r1914) *Concert*
(10/91) (PEAR) ① [3] **EVC3(1)**
1. D. Hvorostovsky, O. Boshniakovich *Concert*
(10/91) (PHIL) ① **432 119-2PH**
1, 3. N. Ghiaurov, P. Dokovska (r1993) *Concert*
(1/95) (RCA) ① **09026 62501-2**
2. O. Borodina, L. Gergieva (r1993) *Concert*
(6/94) (PHIL) ① [2] **442 013-2PH**
2, 3. J. Rodgers, R. Vignoles *Concert*
(2/93) (HYPE) ① **CDA66617**
2, 3. E. Söderström, Vladimir Ashkenazy (r1982)
Concert (5/94) (DECC) ① **436 204-2DM**
2-5. D. Hvorostovsky, M. Arkadiov *Concert*
(2/95) (PHIL) ① **442 536-2PH**
3. I. Tartakov, anon (r1901) *Concert*
(6/93) (PEAR) ① [3] **GEMMCDS9997/9(1)**
3. L. Sobinov, anon (r1911) *Concert*
(6/94) (MMOI) ① **CDMOIR422**
3. P. Frijsh, E. Nielsen (1933) *Concert*
(4/95) (PEAR) ① [2] **GEMMCDS9095(2)**
3. M. Price, J. Lockhart (r1973) *Concert*
(11/95) (CFP) ① **CD-CFP4669**
3. E. Wild (r1995: trans pf: Wild) *Concert*
(5/95) (SONY) ① **SK62036**
6. E. Schwarzkopf, G. Parsons (r1967) *Concert*
(12/90) (EMI) ① **CDM7 63654-2**
6. E. Caruso, G. Scognamiglio (r1913) *Concert*
(7/91) (RCA) ① [12] **GD60495(5)**
6. E. Caruso, G. Scognamiglio (r1913) *Concert*
(10/91) (PEAR) ① [3] **EVC3(1)**
6. E. Caruso, G. Scognamiglio (r1913) *Concert*
(6/94) (MMOI) ① **CDMOIR422**
7 Songs, Op. 47 (1880)
1. If only I had known (wds. Tolstoy); 2. Softly the
spirit flew up to heaven (wds. Tolstoy); 3. Dusk fell on
the earth (wds. Berg after Mickiewicz); 4. Sleep, poor
friend (wds. Tolstoy); 5. I bless you, forests (wds.
Tolstoy); 6. Does the day reign? (wds. Apukhtin); 7.
Was I not a little blade of grass? (wds. Surikov).
1. E. Söderström, Vladimir Ashkenazy (r1982)
Concert (5/94) (DECC) ① **436 204-2DM**
1, 2. J. Varady, A. Reimann *Concert*
(8/89) (ORFE) ① **C053851A**
1, 6, 7. J. Rodgers, R. Vignoles *Concert*
(2/93) (HYPE) ① **CDA66617**
1, 6, 7. E. Podles, G. Johnson *Concert*
(5/95) (FORL) ① **UCD16683**
1, 7. X. Belmas, A. Kitschin (r1929) *Concert*
(6/94) (MMOI) ① **CDMOIR422**
5. A. Orda, J. Lee (bp1959) *Concert*
(12/89) (SYMP) ① **SYMCD1067**

5. M. Reizen, A. Coates (r1929) *Concert* (4/92) (EMI) ① [7] **CHS7 69741-2(6)**
5. O. Natzke, H. Greenslade (Eng: r1938) *Concert* (12/92) (ODE) ① **CDODE1365**
5. L. Tibbett, orch, N. Shilkret (r1932: Eng) *Concert* (6/94) (MMOI) ① **CDMOIR422**
5. N. Ghiaurov, P. Dokovska (r1993) *Concert* (1/95) (RCA) ① **09026 62501-2**
5, 6. D. Hvorostovsky, M. Arkadiov *Concert* (2/95) (PHIL) ① **442 536-2PH**
6. E. Söderström, Vladimir Ashkenazy (r1979) *Concert* (5/94) (DECC) ① **436 204-2DM**

6 Songs, Op. 57 (1884)
1. Tell me, what in the shade of the branches (wds. Sollogub); 2. On the golden cornfields (wds. Tolstoy); 3. Do not ask (wds. Strugovshchikov after Goethe); 4. Sleep (wds. Merezhkovsky); 5. Death (wds. Merezhkovsky); 6. Only thou alone (Pleshcheyev after Kristen).
2. D. Hvorostovsky, M. Arkadiov *Concert* (2/95) (PHIL) ① **442 536-2PH**

12 Songs, Op. 60 (1886)
1. Last night (wds. Khomyakov); 2. I'll tell you nothing (wds. Fet); 3. O, if only you knew (wds. Pleshcheyev); 4. The nightingale (wds. Pushkin after Stefanovíc Karadzíc); 5. Simple words (wds. cpsr); 6. Frenzied nights (wds. Apukhtin); 7. Gypsy's song (wds. Polonsky); 8. Forgive (wds. Nekrasov); 9. Night (wds. Polonsky); 10. Behind the window in the shadow (wds. Polonsky); 11. Exploit (wds. Khomyakov); 12. The mild stars shone for us (wds. Pleshcheyev).
1, 4, 10. J. Rodgers, R. Vignoles *Concert* (2/93) (HYPE) ① **CDA66617**
1, 4, 5. E. Söderström, Vladimir Ashkenazy (r1979/80) *Concert* (5/94) (DECC) ① **436 204-2DM**
4. F. Chaliapin, anon (r1902) *Concert* (7/93) (SYMP) ① **SYMCD1105**
4. F. Chaliapin, anon (r1921) *Concert* (6/94) (MMOI) ① **CDMOIR422**
4. N. Ghiaurov, P. Dokovska (r1993) *Concert* (1/95) (RCA) ① **09026 62501-2**
4, 11. D. Hvorostovsky, O. Boshniakovich *Concert* (10/91) (PHIL) ① **432 119-2PH**
6, 7, 12. O. Borodina, L. Gergieva (r1993) *Concert* (6/94) (PHIL) ① [2] **442 013-2PH**
9. A. Davidov, anon (r1901) *Concert* (6/93) (PEAR) ① [3] **GEMMCDS9007/9(1)**
10. L. Sobinov, anon (r1901) *Concert* (6/93) (PEAR) ① [3] **GEMMCDS9997/9(1)**

6 Songs, Op. 63 (1887) (Wds. Romanov)
1. I did not love you at first; 2. I opened the window; 3. I do not please you; 4. The first meeting; 5. The fires in the rooms were already out; 6. Serenade: O child beneath thy window.
2. D. Hvorostovsky, O. Boshniakovich *Concert* (10/91) (PHIL) ① **432 119-2PH**
4, 5. O. Borodina, L. Gergieva (r1993) *Concert* (6/94) (PHIL) ① [2] **442 013-2PH**
6. J. Rodgers, R. Vignoles *Concert* (2/93) (HYPE) ① **CDA66617**
6. I. Ershov, anon (r1903) *Concert* (6/93) (PEAR) ① [3] **GEMMCDS9997/9(1)**
6. V. Kastorsky, anon (r1906) *Concert* (6/93) (PEAR) ① [3] **GEMMCDS9001/3(1)**

6 Songs, Op. 65 (1888)
1. Sérénade (wds. Turquéty); 2. Déception (wds. Collin); 3. Sérénade (wds. Collin); 4. Qu'importe que l'hiver (wds. Collin); 5. Les larmes (wds. Blanchecotte); 6. Rondel (wds. Collin).
J. Varady, A. Reimann *Concert* (8/89) (ORFE) ① **C053851A**
1. O. Borodina, L. Gergieva (r1993) *Concert* (6/94) (PHIL) ① [2] **442 013-2PH**
1, 2, 4, 5. E. Söderström, Vladimir Ashkenazy (r1980) *Concert* (5/94) (DECC) ① **436 204-2DM**
2. F. Chaliapin, anon (r1902) *Concert* (7/93) (SYMP) ① **SYMCD1105**

6 Songs, Op. 73 (1893) (Wds. D. Rathaus)
1. We sat together; 2. Night; 3. In this moonlight; 4. The sun has set; 5. 'Mid sombre days; 6. Again, as before, alone.
J. Varady, A. Reimann *Concert* (8/89) (ORFE) ① **C053851A**
1. D. Hvorostovsky, M. Arkadiov *Concert* (2/95) (PHIL) ① **442 536-2PH**
2, 4, 6. O. Borodina, L. Gergieva (r1993) *Concert* (6/94) (PHIL) ① [2] **442 013-2PH**
4. E. Söderström, Vladimir Ashkenazy (r1980) *Concert* (5/94) (DECC) ① **436 204-2DM**
6. D. Hvorostovsky, O. Boshniakovich *Concert* (10/91) (PHIL) ① **432 119-2PH**
6. National PO, L. Stokowski (arr Stokowski) *Concert* (4/92) (EMI) ① **CDM7 64140-2**
6. Philadelphia, L. Stokowski (r1937: arr orch: Stokowski) *Concert* (11/95) (BIDD) ① **WHL015**

Take my heart away—song: 1v and piano (1873) (Wds. A. Fet)
E. Söderström, Vladimir Ashkenazy (r1982) *Concert* (5/94) (DECC) ① **436 204-2DM**
O. Borodina, L. Gergieva (r1993) *Concert* (6/94) (PHIL) ① [2] **442 013-2PH**

To forget so soon—song (1870) (Wds. Apukhtin)
J. Rodgers, R. Vignoles *Concert* (2/93) (HYPE) ① **CDA66617**
E. Söderström, Vladimir Ashkenazy (r1982) *Concert* (5/94) (DECC) ① **436 204-2DM**
K. Vayne, C. Tilney (r1966) *Concert* (6/95) (PREI) ① **89996**

Zemfira's song—1v and piano (c1855-60) (Wds. Tsïgani)
E. Söderström, Vladimir Ashkenazy (r1982) *Concert* (5/94) (DECC) ① **436 204-2DM**
E. Podles, G. Johnson *Concert* (5/95) (FORL) ① **UCD16683**

SECTION V: STAGE WORKS

Cherevichki, '(The) Slippers'—comic-fantastic, Op. 4 (1887—Moscow) (Lib. V Burenin rev cpsr, after S Pushkin)
Couplets of His Highness L. Sibiriakov, anon (r1906) *Concert* (6/93) (PEAR) ① [3] **GEMMCDS9001/3(2)**
Does the maiden hear? A. Bogdanovich, anon (r1905) *Concert* (6/93) (PEAR) ① [3] **GEMMCDS9007/9(1)**

The **Enchantress—opera: 4 acts (1887—St. Petersburg)** (Lib. I Shpazhinsky)
Ah, the image of that enchantress N. Shevelev, anon (r1901) *Concert* (6/93) (PEAR) ① [3] **GEMMCDS9007/9(2)**
Business, official duties D. Hvorostovsky, Rotterdam PO, V. Gergiev *Concert* (7/90) (PHIL) ① **426 740-2PH**
Looking down from Nizhni N. Ermolenko-Yuzhina, orch (r1910) *Concert* (6/93) (PEAR) ① [3] **GEMMCDS9001/3(2)**
The Prince's aria P. Lisitsian, Bolshoi Th Orch, A. Melik-Pashayev (r1960) *Concert* (8/93) (PREI) ① **89061**

Eugene Onegin—opera: 3 acts (1879—Moscow) (Lib. Pushkin)
EXCERPTS: 1. Introduction. ACT 1: 2. Have you not heard (Slikhali i vi za roschei glas nochnai); 3. My swift little feet ache (Bolyat moyi skori nozhenki); 4. One day across the bridge (Uzh kak po mostu, mostochku); 5. How I love to dream (Kak ya lyublyu pod zvuki pesen etikh); 6. 'One day across the bridge' ('Uzk kak po mostu, mostochki'); 7. Well, my frolicsome one (Nu ti, moya vostrushka); 8. Mesdames, I've taken the liberty (Mesdames! Ya na sebya vzyal smyelost); 9. Tell, which is Tatyana? (Skazhi, kororaya Tatyana?); 10. How happy, how happy I am! (Kak shchastliv, kak shchastilv ya!); 11. I love you (Ya lyublyu vas); 12. Ah, there you are! (A, vot i vi!); 13. Well, I've let my tongue run on! (Nu, zaboltalas ya!); 14. Let me perish, but first let me summon (Puskai pogibnu ya, no pryezde); 15. Ah, night is past (Akh, noch minula); 16. Pretty maidens, dear companions (Dyevitsi-krasavsti); 17. He's here! He's here! Yevgeni! (Zdyes on, zdyes on, Yevgeni!); 18. You wrote to me (Kogda bi zhizn domashnim krugom). ACT 2: 19. Waltz; 20. Well, what a surprise (Vot tak syurpriz!); 21. Have I deserved such riducule from you (Uzhel ya zasluzhil ot vas); 22. Please do not interrupt me (A cette fête convié); 23. Ladies and gentlemen (Messieurs, mesdames, mesta zanyat izvolte); 24a. Aren't you dancing, Lenski? (Ti ne tantsuyesh, Lenski?); 24b. Mazurka; 25. In your house! (V vashem dome!); 26. What's this? (Nu, shto zhe?); 27. Faint echo of my youth (Kuda, kuda, kuda vi udalilis—Lenski's aria); 28. Ah, here they are! (A, vot oni!). ACT 3: 29. Polonaise; 30. I'm bored here too (I zdyes mnye skuchno!); 31. Princess Greminia! Look! (Knyaginya Gremina! Smotrite!); 32. Everyone knows love on earth (Lyubvi vsye vozrasti pokorni—Gremin's aria); 33. So come, I'll present (Itak, poidyom, tebya predstavlyu ya); 34. Can this really be the same Tatyana? (Uzhel ta samaya Tatyana); 35. O, how distressed I am! (O! Kak mnye tyazhelo!); 36. Onegin! I was younger then (Onegin! Ya togda molozhe).
Cpte B. Weikl, T. Kubiak, S. Burrows, J. Hamari, N. Ghiaurov, A. Reynolds, E. Hartle, M. Sénéchal, R. Van Allan, W. Mason, John Alldis Ch, ROHO, G. Solti (8/87) (DECC) ① [2] **417 413-2DH2**
Cpte Y. Mazurok, T. Milashkina, V. Atlantov, T. Sinyavskaya, E. Nesterenko, T. Tugarinova, L. Avdeyeva, L. Kuznetsov, V. Yaroslavtsev, A. Yapridze, Bolshoi Th. Chor, Bolshoi Th. Orch, M. Ermler (12/87) (OLYM) ① [2] **OCD115**
Cpte T. Allen, M. Freni, N. Shicoff, A.S. von Otter, P. Burchuladze, R. Lang, R. Engert-Ely, M. Sénéchal, J. Hartfiel, Leipzig Rad Chor, Staatskapelle Dresden, James Levine (r1987) (3/89) (DG) ① [2] **423 959-2GH2**
Cpte Y. Mazurok, A. Tomowa-Sintow, N. Gedda, R. Troeva-Mircheva, N. Ghiuselev, S. Popangelova, M. Lilowa, M. Lecocq, S. Georgiev, D. Stanchev, Sofia National Op Chor, Sofia Fest Orch, E. Tchakarov (3/91) (SONY) ① [2] **S2K45539**
Cpte D. Hvorostovsky, N. Focile, N. Shicoff, O. Borodina, A. Anisimov, Sarah Walker, I. Arkhipova, F. Egerton, H. Hennequin, S. Zadvorny, St Petersburg Chbr Ch, Paris Orch, S. Bychkov (r1990) (12/93) (PHIL) ① [2] **438 235-2PH2**
Cpte P. Nortsov, G. Zhukovskaya, S. Lemeshev, B. Zlatogorova, A. Pirogov, M. Butienina, K. Antarova, I. Kovalenko, A. Yakhontov, Y. Manchavin, Bolshoi Th Chor, Bolshoi Th Orch, V. Nebolsin (r1936) (1/94) (DANT) ① [2] **LYS10/1**
Cpte T. Hampson, K. Te Kanawa, N. Rosenshein, P. Bardon, J. Connell, L. Finnie, E. Bainbridge, N. Gedda, R. Van Allan, WNO Chor, WNO Orch, C. Mackerras (r1992: Eng) (4/94) (EMI) ① [2] **CDS5 55004-2**
Cpte E. Belov, G. Vishnevskaya, S. Lemeshev, L. Avdeyeva, I. Petrov, V. Petrova, E. Verbitskaya, A. Sokolov, I. Mikhailov, G. Pankov, Bolshoi Th Chor, Bolshoi Th Orch, B. Khaikin (r1955) (12/94) (MELO) ① [2] **74321 17090-2**
9. A. Pendachanska, Sofia SO, M. Angelov (r1994) *Concert* (12/95) (CAPR) ① **10 706**
11. D. Smirnov, orch (r1913) *Concert* (6/93) (PEAR) ① [3] **GEMMCDS9004/6(1)**
11. L. Sobinov, orch (r1911) *Concert* (6/94) (MMOI) ① **CDMOIR422**
11, 27 (two vers) L. Sobinov, anon (r1901) *Concert* (6/93) (PEAR) ① [3] **GEMMCDS9997/9(1)**
11, 27. A. Labinsky, orch, B. Seidler-Winkler (r1905) *Concert* (6/93) (PEAR) ① [3] **GEMMCDS9001/3(1)**
14. E. Schwarzkopf, LSO, A. Galliera (Ger) *Concert* (10/88) (EMI) ① **CDM7 69501-2**
14. L. Popp, Munich RO, S. Soltesz (r1987) *Concert* (4/89) (EMI) ① **CDC7 49319-2**
14 (pt) C. Muzio, orch (r1920: Ital) *Concert* (5/90) (BOGR) ① [2] **BIM705-2**
14. E. Hannan, LPO, S. Edwards *Symphony 5.* (1/92) (EMIN) ① **CD-EMX2187**
14(pt) Lotte Lehmann, orch (Ger: r1917) *Concert* (6/92) (PREI) ① [3] **89302**
14. J. Hammond, RLPO, C. Lambert (r1943: Eng) *Concert* (12/92) (TEST) ① **SBT1013**
14(pt) C. Muzio, orch (r1920: Ital) *Concert* (1/94) (ROMO) ① [2] **81005-2**
14 (pt) Lotte Lehmann, orch (r c1917) *Concert* (6/94) (MMOI) ① **CDMOIR422**
18. J. Hynninen, Estonian SO, E. Klas *Concert* (4/90) (ONDI) ① **ODE731-2**
18. H. Schlusnus, Berlin St Op Orch, L. Blech (Ger: r1934) *Concert* (9/90) (PREI) ① **89006**
18. M. Battistini, anon (r1902: Ital) *Concert* (10/92) (NIMB) ① **NI7831**
18 (pt) N. Shevelev, anon (r1901) *Concert* (6/93) (PEAR) ① [3] **GEMMCDS9007/9(2)**
18. P. Lisitsian, Bolshoi Th Orch, A. Melik-Pashayev (r1960) *Concert* (8/93) (PREI) ① **89061**
18. E. Giraldoni, anon (r1906: Ital) *Concert* (4/94) (EMI) ① [3] **CHS7 64860-2(1)**
18. H. Schlusnus, orch (r1925: Ger) *Concert* (12/95) (PREI) ① **89110**
18, 34. D. Hvorostovsky, Rotterdam PO, V. Gergiev *Concert* (7/90) (PHIL) ① **426 740-2PH**
19, 29. BPO, H. von Karajan *Symphony 1.* (12/86) (DG) ① **419 176-2GH**
19, 29. BPO, H. von Karajan (r1966) *Concert* (4/88) (DG) ① **415 855-2GGA**
19, 29. Kirov Th Orch, V. Gergiev (r1993; includes bonus sampler CD) *Concert* (7/95) (PHIL) ① **442 775-2PH**
25. D. Smirnov, orch (r1912) *Concert* (6/93) (PEAR) ① [3] **GEMMCDS9004/6(1)**
25. D. Smirnov, orch (r1912) *Concert* (6/94) (MMOI) ① **CDMOIR422**
27. G. Martinelli, orch, J. Pasternack (r1921: Ital) *Concert* (10/89) (NIMB) ① **NI7804**
27. J. Patzak, orch, M. Gurlitt (Ger: r1929) *Concert* (3/90) (PEAR) ① **GEMMCD9383**
27. F. Marconi, S. Cottone (r1903: Ital) *Concert* (10/90) (SYMP) ① **SYMCD1069**
27. E. Caruso, orch, J. Pasternack (r1916: French) *Concert* (7/91) (RCA) ① [12] **GD60495(5)**
27. E. Caruso, orch, J. Pasternack (French: r1916) *Concert* (10/91) (PEAR) ① [3] **EVC4(1)**
27. R. Tauber, orch, K. Besl (r1923: Ger) *Concert* (3/92) (EMI) ① **CDH7 64029-2**

27. O. Harnoy, LPO, C. Mackerras (arr vc/orch: J Harnoy) *Concert* (10/92) (RCA) ① **RD60758**
27. R. Tauber, orch, K. Besl (r1923: Ger) *Concert* (12/92) (NIMB) ① **NI7830**
27. F. Wunderlich, Bavarian St Op Orch, O. Gerdes (Ger) *Concert* (5/93) (DG) ① **431 110-2GB**
27. D. Yuzhin, anon (r1902) *Concert* (6/93) (PEAR) ① [3] **GEMMCDS9001/3(1)**
27. D. Smirnov, orch (r1909) *Concert* (6/93) (PEAR) ① [3] **GEMMCDS9004/6(1)**
27. A. Bogdanovich, anon (r1903) *Concert* (6/93) (PEAR) ① [3] **GEMMCDS9007/9(1)**
27. I. Alchevsky, anon (r1900s) *Concert* (7/93) (SYMP) ① **SYMCD1105**
27. A. Piccaver, orch (r1920: Ger) *Concert* (8/93) (PREI) ① **89060**
27. C. Kullman, orch (r1935: Ger) *Concert* (11/93) (PREI) ① **89057**
27. F. Wunderlich, Bavarian St Orch, M. von Zallinger (r1962: Ger) *Concert* (12/93) (NIMB) ① **NI7851**
27. G. Martinelli, orch, J. Pasternack (r1921; Ital) *Concert* (4/94) (RCA) ① [6] **09026 61580-2(2)**
27. P. Domingo, Philh, R. Behr (r1993) *Concert* (4/94) (EMI) ① **CDC5 55018-2**
27. C. Kullman, Vienna St Op Orch, H. Reichenberger (pp1934: Ger) *Concert* (7/94) (SCHW) ① [2] **314512**
27. D. Smirnov, orch (r1909) *Concert* (9/94) (NIMB) ① **NI7856**
27. E. Caruso, orch (r1916: French) *Concert* (7/95) (NIMB) ① **NI7866**
29. Cleveland Orch, C. von Dohnányi (r1986) *Symphony 6.* (10/87) (TELA) ① **CD80130**
29. J. Patzak, Berlin St Op Orch, Wolfgang Martin (r1936: Ger) *Concert* (6/94) (MMOI) ① **CDMOIR422**
29. Baltimore SO, D. Zinman (r1990) *Concert* (12/95) (TELA) ① **CD80378**
29. Boston Pops, A. Fiedler (r1959) *Concert* (12/95) (RCA) ① **09026 68132-2**
32. M. Salminen, Lahti SO, E. Klas *Concert* (8/92) (BIS) ① **BIS-CD520**
32. A. Kipnis, Victor SO, N. Berezowski (r1945) *Concert* (9/92) (RCA) ① **GD60522**
32. M. Reizen, Bolshoi Th Orch, A. Melik-Pashayev (r1948) *Concert* (12/92) (PREI) ① **89059**
32. L. Sibiriakov, orch (r1906) *Concert* (6/93) (PEAR) ① [3] **GEMMCDS9001/3(2)**
32. B. Christoff, Philh, W. Schüchter (r1952) *Concert* (6/93) (EMI) ① **CDH7 64252-2**
32. D. Bukhtoyarov, anon (r1901) *Concert* (6/93) (PEAR) ① [3] **GEMMCDS9001/3(1)**
32. K. Borg, Berlin RSO, H. Stein (r1963) *Concert* (12/94) (FINL) ① [3] **4509-95606-2**
32. V. Kastorsky, orch (r1908) *Concert* (3/95) (NIMB) ① **NI7865**
34. G. Baklanoff, orch (r1918) *Concert* (6/94) (MMOI) ① **CDMOIR422**

Hamlet—incidental music, Op. 67a (1891)
EXCERPTS: 1. Overture; 2. Mélodrame (Act 1 Scene 1); 3a. Fanfare (Act 1 Scene 4); 3b. Mélodrame (Act 1 Scene 4); 4. Mélodrame (Act 1 Scene 5); 5. Entr'acte (Act 2); 6. Fanfare (Act 2 Scene 2); 7. Entr'acte (Act 3); 8a. Fanfare (Act 3 Scene 2); 8b. Fanfare (Act 3 Scene 2); 8c. Mélodrame (Act 3 Scene 2); 9. Entr'acte: Elegy (Act 4); 10. Scène d'Ophélie: Mad Scene (Act 4 Scene 5); 11. Second Scène d'Ophélie (Act 4 Scene 5); 12. Entr'acte (Act 5); 13. Chant du Fossoyeur (Act 5 Scene 1); 14. Marche funèbre (Act 5 Scene 1); 15. Fanfare (Act 5 Scene 2); 16. Marche Finale (Act 5 Scene 2).
Cpte J. Kelly, D. Hammond-Stroud, LSO, G. Simon *Concert* (7/84) (CHAN) ① [2] **CHAN8310/1**
Cpte J. Kelly, D. Hammond-Stroud, LSO, G. Simon (r1981) *Romeo and Juliet.* (7/94) (CHAN) ① **CHAN9191**
10, 11. J. Kelly, LSO, G. Simon *Concert* (7/83) (CHAN) ① **CHAN8301**

Iolanta—opera: 1 act (1892—St Petersburg) (Lib. M. Tchaikovsky)
Cpte G. Vishnevskaya, N. Gedda, W. Grönroos, D. Petkov, T. Krause, V. Cortez, J. Anderson, T. Gedda, C. Gaetano, F. Dumont, France Groupe Vocal, Paris Orch, M. Rostropovich (pp1984) (5/86) (ERAT) ① [2] **2292-45973-2**
Duke Robert's aria M. Maksakov, orch (r c1908) *Concert* (6/94) (MMOI) ① **CDMOIR422**
Iolanta's arioso L. Lipkowska, anon (r1912) *Concert* (6/94) (MMOI) ① **CDMOIR422**
O God, if I have sinned L. Sibiriakov, anon (r1906) *Concert* (6/93) (PEAR) ① [3] **GEMMCDS9001/3(2)**
Who can compare with my Mathilde? D. Hvorostovsky, Rotterdam PO, V. Gergiev *Concert* (7/90) (PHIL) ① **426 740-2PH**
Who can compare? V. Kastorsky, orch (r c1910) *Concert* (6/94) (MMOI) ① **CDMOIR422**

The **Maid of Orleans—opera: 4 acts (1881—St Petersburg)** (Lib. cpsr)
EXCERPTS. ACT 1: 1a. Oui, Dieu le veut!; 1b. Adieu, forêts (Joan's aria).
1. O. Ouroussov, Henry Wood (Eng: r1908) *Concert* (10/92) (SYMP) ① **SYMCD1093**
1b B. Fassbaender, Stuttgart RSO, H. Graf *Concert* (11/86) (ORFE) ① **C096841A**
1b S. Jurinac, Philh, L. Collingwood (Ger: r1950) *Concert* (1/90) (EMI) ① **CDH7 63199-2**
1b M. Jeritza, orch (r1926: Fr) *Concert* (4/94) (PREI) ① **89079**
1b M. Jeritza, orch (r1927: Fr) *Concert* (6/94) (MMOI) ① **CDMOIR422**

Mazeppa—opera: 3 acts (1884—Moscow) (Lib. cpsr & V Burenin, after Pushkin)
EXCERPTS: 1. Introduction. ACT ONE: 2a. I weave my fragrant garland; 2b. Greetings Maria, greetings, my beauty; 3a. You love the songs, dear companions; 3b. Maria...Oh! You frightened me!; 4. Well, Vasily, you honour me; 5. There is no bridge here; 6. Hopak (Cossack Dance); 7. That's fine, I like that; 8a. Mazeppa, I'm distressed by what you say; 8b. You crazy old man, tell me; 8c. The shameless, disgraceful old man, how could he?; 8d. Father! O Hetman! Cease your quarrelling; 9. As the storm brings clouds over the sky; 10a. Abandon your grief, Kochubey; 10b. But it is time we gave warning of the hetman's intrigues; 10c. Send me, send me to the Tsar!. ACT TWO: 11a. So this is the reward for my information; 11b. It's you, cruel man; 11c. No, you are not mistaken; 12a. How still is the Ukrainian night; 12b. Well?; 13. O Maria, Maria; 14a. My dearest love; 14b. My dear, you are unjust!; 14c. Would I, at my age; 14d. O my dearest, you will be Tsar of our homeland; 15a. How the stars twinkle in the sky; 15b. You alone can assuage their fury; 16. Will it be soon?; 17a. Hey-ho, fiddle-de-dee; 17b. My friend, Let us offer up for the last time. ACT THREE: 18. The Battle of Poltava; 19a. In bloody battle, on the field of honour; 19b. Here days passed by in happy succession; 20a. I hear in the distance the clatter of horses hooves; 20b. You destroyer of sacred innocence; 21a. Unhappy man!; 21b. Oh hush, hush, hush, my dear; 21c. Let's run away, I hear a noise; 22a. The old man's gone, how my heart beats; 22b. Sleep my baby, my pretty.
Cpte S. Leiferkus, G. Gorchakova, A. Kocherga, L. Dyadkova, S. Larin, M. Pederson, R. Margison, H. Zednik, Stockholm Royal Op Chor, Gothenburg SO, N. Järvi (r1993) (11/94) (DG) ① [3] **439 906-2GH3**
6. Cincinnati SO, E. Kunzel *Concert* (12/83) (TELA) ① **CD80041**
6. Leipzig Gewandhaus, K. Masur (r1991) *Concert* (5/93) (TELD) ① **9031-76456-2**
6. LSO, C. Mackerras (r1961) *Concert* (12/95) (MERC) ① **434 352-2MM**
6, 18. LSO, G. Simon *Concert* (7/84) (CHAN) ① [2] **CHAN8310/1**
6, 18. LSO, G. Simon (r1981) *Concert* (7/94) (CHAN) ① **CHAN9190**
11c A. Ivanov, orch (r1947) *Concert* (4/92) (EMI) ① [7] **CHS7 69741-2(6)**
13. D. Hvorostovsky, Rotterdam PO, V. Gergiev *Concert* (7/90) (PHIL) ① **426 740-2PH**
13. P. Lisitsian, Bolshoi Th Orch, A. Melik-Pashayev (r1960) *Concert* (8/93) (PREI) ① **89061**
22b N. Milstein, G. Pludermacher (pp1986: arr vn/pf) *Concert* (5/95) (TELD) ① **4509-95998-2**

The **Nutcracker—ballet: 2 acts, Op. 71 (1892—St Petersburg)**
EXCERPTS: 1a. Miniature Overture. ACT 1: 1b. Decoration of the Christmas Tree; 2. March; 3. Children's Galop and Entry of the Parents; 4. Arrival of Drosselmayer; 5. The Nutcracker and Grandfather Dance; 6. Departure of the guests - Night; 7. The Battle and Transformation Scene; 8. The forest of fir trees in Winter (Journey through the snow); 9. Waltz of the Snowfalkes. ACT 2: 10. The Enchanted Palace of the Kingdom of Sweets (The magic castle); 11. Arrival of Clara and the Nutcracker; 12. Divertissement: 12a. Chocolate (Spanish Dance); 12b. Coffee (Arab Dance); 12c. Tea (Chinese Dance); 12d. Trepak (Russian Dance); 12e. Dance of the Mirlitons (Flutes); 12f. Mother Gigogne and the Clowns; 13. Waltz of the Flowers; 14a. Pas de deux (The Prince and the Sugar-Plum Fairy); 14b. Variation I (Tarantella); 14c. Variation II (Dance of the Sugar-Plum Fairy); 14d. Coda; 15. Final Waltz and Apotheosis. 16. ADDITIONAL ITEM FOR DIVERTISSEMENT—Gigue (English Dance): orch Lanchbery.
Cpte Staatskapelle Dresden, H. Vonk (12/86) (CAPR) ① [2] **10 071/2**
Cpte St Louis Sym Chor, St Louis SO, L. Slatkin (12/86) (RCA) ① [2] **RD87005**
Cpte Tiffin Boys' Ch, LSO, C. Mackerras (5/87) (TELA) ① [2] **CD80137**
Cpte Halesworth Middle Sch Ch, ROHO, M. Ermler *Arensky: Tchaikovsky Variations.* (12/89) (ROH) ① [2] **ROH304/5**
Cpte Bratislava RSO, O. Lenárd *Chopin: Sylphides.* (9/91) (NAXO) ① [2] **8 550324/5**
Cpte Finchley Children's Music Group, RPO, Vladimir Ashkenazy *Glazunov: Seasons.* (4/92) (DECC) ① [2] **433 000-2DH2**
Cpte American Boychoir, Boston SO, S. Ozawa *Sleeping Beauty.* (6/92) (DG) ① [2] **435 619-2GH2**
Cpte LSO, A. Dorati *Serenade, Op.48.* (9/92) (MERC) ① [2] **432 750-2MM2**
Cpte New London Children's Ch, LPO, M. Jansons (3/93) (EMI) ① [2] **CDS7 54600-2**
Cpte Bonn Klassische PO, H. Beissel (3/93) (SONY) ① **SXK48083**
Cpte Ambrosian Sngrs, LSO, A. Previn (r1972) (3/93) (CFP) ① [2] **CD-CFPD4706**
Cpte Montreal SO, C. Dutoit (r1992) *Sleeping Beauty.* (3/94) (DECC) ① [2] **440 477-2DH2**
Act 2. SNO, N. Järvi (r1988) *Swan Lake.* (3/89) (CHAN) ① **CHAN8556**
1a, 1b LPO, T. Beecham (bp1939) *Concert* (11/91) (SYMP) ① [2] **SYMCD1096/7**
1a, 2, 12b-e, 13, 14c LSO, A. Previn *Concert* (11/92) (EMI) ① **CDM7 64332-2**
1a, 2, 3, 7-9, 12a-f, 13, 14c, 15. Ambrosian Sngrs, LSO, A. Previn *Concert* (3/92) (EMI) ① [2] **CZS7 62816-2**
1a, 2, 6-9, 12a-f, 13, 14a, 14c, 15. Tiffin Boys' Ch, LSO, C. Mackerras (3/89) (TELA) ① **CD80140**
1a, 2, 7-9, 12, 13, 14a, 14c, 15. Halesworth Middle Sch Ch, ROHO, M. Ermler (12/89) (ROH) ① **ROH002**
2. St Louis SO, L. Slatkin *Concert* (6/89) (RCA) ① **RD87716**

The **Nutcracker—concert suite from ballet, Op. 71a (1892)**
1. Miniature Overture; 2. March; 3. Dance of the sugar-plum fairy (Danse de la fée dragée); 4. Trepak (Danse russe); 5. Arab Dance; 6. Chinese Dance; 7. Dance of the reeds (Danse des mirlitons); 8. Waltz of the flowers (Valse des fleurs).
Minnesota Orch, L. Slatkin *Swan Lake.* (12/84) (PRO) ① **CDD121**
BPO, H. von Karajan *Concert* (12/86) (DG) ① **419 175-2GH**
BPO, M. Rostropovich *Concert* (4/90) (DG) ① **429 097-2GGA**
Chicago SO, G. Solti *Concert* (8/91) (DECC) ① **430 707-2DM**
Philadelphia, L. Stokowski (r1926) *Concert* (2/92) (PEAR) ① **GEMMCD9488**
VPO, James Levine *Concert* (11/94) (DG) ① **437 806-2GH**
M. Pletnev (r1978; arr Pletnev) *Concert* (8/95) (MELO) ① **74321 25181-2**
BBC SO, M. Sargent (pp1966) *Concert* (10/95) (BBCR) ① [2] **DMCD98**
1, 7, 8. T. Trotter (r1992: trans org: R Goss-Custard) *Concert* (4/94) (DECC) ① **436 656-2DH**
2-7. C. Cann, A. Cann (r1992: arr Cann) *Concert* (5/93) (PP) ① **PP10393**
8. RPO, Vladimir Ashkenazy (pp1989) *Concert* (5/90) (RPO) ① **CDRPO7014**
9. M. Pletnev (r1978: arr Pletnev) *Concert* (8/95) (MELO) ① [11] **74321 25172-2(2)**

Oprichnik, '(The) Guardsman'—opera: 4 acts (1874—St Petersburg) (Lib. cpsr)
I swear before God N. Figner, anon (r1901) *Concert* (6/93) (PEAR) ① [3] **GEMMCDS9997/9(1)**
Little nightingale N. Ermolenko-Yuzhina, orch (r1911) *Concert* (6/93) (PEAR) ① [3] **GEMMCDS9001/3(2)**
Overture National SO, A. Fistoulari (r1944) *Concert* (5/95) (DUTT) ① **CDK1200**

The **Queen of Spades, 'Pique Dame'—opera: 3 acts (1890—St. Petersburg)** (Lib. cpsr and M. Tchaikovsky)
EXCERPTS: 1. Introduction. ACT 1: 2. Shine, sun, bright!; 3a. How did the play end yesterday; 3b. I do not know her name; 3c. If this is the case, we must get to work!; 4a. At last heaven has sent us a sunny day!; 4b. But are you sure that she's not noticed you?; 4c. Happy day, I bless you; 4d. Tell us, whom are you marrying?; 5. I feel afraid! There again he is; 6a. What an old witch, that Countess; 6b. Once at Versailles; 7. Se non è vero; 8. 'Tis evening...the cloudy spaces darken; 9a. Fascinatingland delightful!; 9b. Yes, that's it...'My darling friends'; 9c. Come on, bright-eyed Mashenka; 10. What a noise

you are making; 11a. It is time now to break up your party; 11b. You need not shut the door, leave it open; 11c. What am I crying for, what is it?; 11d. Stay, I beg of you!; 11e. Forgive me, loveliest of creatures; 11f. Liza! Open the door; 11g. ...he who, impelled by burning passion. ACT 2: 12a. Entr'acte; 12b. In joy and merriment; 13a. The host asks his worthy guests; 13b. I love you beyond all measure; 14. After the performance wait for me in the hall; 15a. In the deep shadows; 15b. Dance of the Shepherds and Shepherdesses; 15c. My tender friend, my darling shepherd; 15d. How sweet you are my beauty!; 16a. 'He who is impelled by burning passion...'; 16b. The Empress! Her Majesty!; 17a. Yes, everything is just as she said; 17b. And how our noble benefactress enjoys herself; 17c. Enough of your flatteries!; 17d. Je crains de lui parles la nuit; 18a. Don't be frightened!; 18b. What is all that noise? ACT 3: 19a. Entr'acte; 19b. I do not believe you intended the Countess's death; 20a. It is terrifying!; 20b. I have come to you against my will; 21a. It is close on midnight already; 21b. Ah! I am weary with sorrow; 22a. Ah, what if midnight chimes answer; 22b. Yes, I have come, my darling; 23a. Drink and make merry!; 23b. Make your bids!; 24a. If darling girls could fly like birds; 24b. When the weather was wet; 25a. And now, gentlemen, to business; 25b. What is our life? A game!; 25c. No more play!; 25d. Prince! Prince! forgive me!; 25e. Lord, pardon him!.

Cpte W. Ochman, S. Evstatieva, P. Dilova, I. Konsulov, Y. Mazurok, Angel Petkov, P. Petrov, M. Popov, S. Georgiev, S. Toczyska, W. Katsarova, R. Bareva, E. Stoyanova, Gouslarche Boys' Ch, Svetoslav Obretenov Nat Chor, Sofia Fest Orch, E. Tchakarov (12/90) (SONY) Ⓓ [3] **S3K45720**

Cpte V. Atlantov, M. Freni, M. Forrester, S. Leiferkus, D. Hvorostovsky, Katherine Ciesinski, E. Gavazzi, J. Rodescu, D. Petersen, R. Clement, J. Chaminé, J. Taylor, D. Labelle, American Boychoir, Tanglewood Fest Chor, Boston SO, S. Ozawa (11/92) (RCA) Ⓓ [3] **09026 60992-2**

Cpte G. Grigorian, M. Gulegina, I. Arkhipova, N. Putilin, V. Chernov, O. Borodina, V. Solodovnikov, S. Alexashkin, E. Boitsov, N. Gassiev, G. Bezebenkov, L. Filatova, T. Filimonova, Kirov Th Chor, Kirov Th Orch, V. Gergiev (r1992) (10/93) (PHIL) Ⓓ [3] **438 141-2PH3**

Cpte V. Atlantov, T. Milashkina, V. Levko, V. Valaitis, A. Fedoseyev, G. Borisova, A. Sokolov, V. Yaroslavtsev, V. Vlasov, K. Baskov, Y. Dementiev, N. Grigorieva, N. Lebedeva, Bolshoi Th Chor, Bolshoi Th Orch, M. Ermler (r1974) (10/94) (MELO) Ⓓ [3] **74321 17091-2**

Cpte N. Khanayev, X. Derzhinskaya, F. Petrova, A. Baturin, P. Selivanov, N. Obukhova, S. Ostroumov, Y. Manchavin, M. Novoyenin, K. Terekin, L. Stavrovskaya, N. Chubienko, Bolshoi Th Chor, Bolshoi Th Orch, S. Samosud (r1937) *Concert* (8/95) (DANT) Ⓓ [3] **LYS013/5**

Excs N. Khanayev, A. Baturin, P. Nortsov, K. Terekin, B. Zlatogorova, X. Derzhinskaya, S. Ostroumov, Y. Manchavin, M. Novoyenin, M. Maksakova, V. Barsova, V. Politkovsky, Bolshoi Th Chor, Bolshoi Th Orch, S. Samosud (r1942) *Concert* (8/95) (DANT) Ⓓ [3] **LYS013/5**

3b, 25b G. Nelepp, Bolshoi Th Chor, Bolshoi Th Orch, S. Samosud (r1940s) *Concert* (8/95) (DANT) Ⓓ [3] **LYS013/5**

6b A. Didur, anon (r1906) *Concert* (4/94) (EMI) Ⓓ [3] **CHS7 64860-2(2)**

6b, 24a A. Didur, anon (r1906: Pol) *Concert* (1/94) (CLUB) Ⓓ **CL99-089**

7(pt) E. Vitting, orch (r1913) *Concert* (3/95) (NIMB) Ⓓ **NI7865**

8, 15c, 21a E. Destinn, M. Duchêne, orch, W.B Rogers (r1915: Ger/Fr) *Concert* (12/94) (SUPR) Ⓓ [12] **11 2136-2(5)**

8, 21a E. Destinn, M. Duchêne, orch, W.B. Rogers (r1915: Ger) *Concert* (11/93) (ROMO) Ⓓ [2] **81002-2**

9b A. Panina, anon (r1907) *Concert* (6/93) (PEAR) Ⓓ [3] **GEMMCDS9001/3(2)**

9b E. Zbrueva, anon (r1907) *Concert* (6/93) (PEAR) Ⓓ [3] **GEMMCDS9004/6(2)**

9b E. Destinn, M. Duchêne, orch, W.B. Rogers (r1915: Fr) *Concert* (11/93) (ROMO) Ⓓ [2] **81002-2**

11b, 25b J. Rogatchewsky, orch (r1928: Fr) *Concert* (6/94) (MMOI) Ⓓ **CDMOIR422**

11e N. Figner, anon (r1901) *Concert* (6/93) (PEAR) Ⓓ [3] **GEMMCDS9997/9(1)**

11e A. Davidov, anon (r1902) *Concert* (6/93) (PEAR) Ⓓ [3] **GEMMCDS9007/9(1)**

11e, 25b D. Smirnov, orch, J. Harrison (r1923) *Concert* (6/93) (PEAR) Ⓓ [3] **GEMMCDS9004/6(2)**

13b J. Hynninen, Estonian SO, E. Klas *Concert* (4/90) (ONDI) Ⓓ **ODE731-2**

13b D. Hvorostovsky, Rotterdam PO, V. Gergiev *Concert* (7/90) (PHIL) Ⓓ **426 740-2PH**

13b H. Schlusnus, Berlin St Op Orch, A. Melichar (r1932: Ger) *Concert* (9/90) (PREI) Ⓓ **89006**

13b N. Shevelev, anon (r1901) *Concert* (6/93) (PEAR) Ⓓ [3] **GEMMCDS9007/9(2)**

13b P. Lisitsian, Bolshoi Th Orch, A. Melik-Pashayev (r1952) *Concert* (8/93) (PREI) Ⓓ **89061**

13b H. Schlusnus, Berlin St Op Orch, A. Melichar (r1932: Ger) *Concert* (6/94) (MMOI) Ⓓ **CDMOIR422**

13b M. Karakash, orch (r1913) *Concert* (3/95) (NIMB) Ⓓ **NI7865**

15c M. Michailova, K. Tugarinova, anon (r c1905) *Concert* (6/94) (MMOI) Ⓓ **CDMOIR422**

15c M. Kovalenko, E. Zbrueva, orch (r1910) *Concert* (3/95) (NIMB) Ⓓ **NI7865**

17d A. Panina, orch (r1907) *Concert* (6/93) (PEAR) Ⓓ [3] **GEMMCDS9001/3(2)**

21a L. Popp, Munich RO, S. Soltesz (r1987) *Concert* (4/89) (EMI) Ⓓ **CDC7 49319-2**

21a S. Jurinac, Philh, L. Collingwood (Ger: r1950) *Concert* (1/90) (EMI) Ⓓ **CDH7 63199-2**

21a S. Jurinac, Philh, L. Collingwood (r1950: Ger) *Concert* (4/92) (EMI) Ⓓ [7] **CHS7 69741-2(4)**

21a X. Belmas, orch, A. Kitschin (r1927) *Concert* (10/92) (PREI) Ⓓ **89047**

21a M. Mei-Figner, anon (r1901) *Concert* (6/93) (PEAR) Ⓓ [3] **GEMMCDS9997/9(1)**

21a E. Destinn, orch, W.B. Rogers (r1915: Ger) *Concert* (4/94) (RCA) Ⓓ [6] **09026 61580-2(2)**

21a E. Destinn, orch, B. Seidler-Winkler (r1909: Ger) *Concert* (5/94) (SUPR) Ⓓ **11 1337-2**

21a X. Belmas, orch, A. Kitschin (r1927) *Concert* (6/94) (MMOI) Ⓓ **CDMOIR422**

21a E. Destinn, orch, B. Seidler-Winkler (r1909: Ger) *Concert* (12/94) (SUPR) Ⓓ [12] **11 2136-2(2)**

21a K. Vayne, orch (bp1958-9) *Concert* (6/95) (PREI) Ⓓ **89996**

24a V. Kastorsky, chor, orch (r1906) *Concert* (6/93) (PEAR) Ⓓ [3] **GEMMCDS9001/3(1)**

24a A. Didur, anon (r1906: Ital) *Concert* (6/94) (MMOI) Ⓓ **CDMOIR422**

25b A. Davidov, anon (r1901) *Concert* (6/93) (PEAR) Ⓓ [3] **GEMMCDS9007/9(1)**

Romeo and Juliet—duet for soprano, tenor and orchestra (1893) (cpted Taneyev. Wds Shakespeare, trans Sokolovsky)

S. Murphy, K. Lewis, SNO, N. Järvi (orch. Taneyev) *Concert* (2/87) (CHAN) Ⓓ **CHAN8476**

The **Sleeping Beauty—ballet: prologue and 3 acts, Op. 66 (1890—St Petersburg)**

EXCERPTS: 1. Introduction. PROLOGUE: 2. Entrance of King and Court; 3. Dance Scene—Entrance of Fairies; 4. Pas de Six—Fairies present gifts; 4a. Intrada; 4b. Adagio (Allegro vivo); 4c. Variation I—Candite; 4d. Variation II—Coulante; 4e. Variation III—Falling crumbs; 4f. Variation IV—Song-bird Fairy; 4g. Variation V—Violente; 4h. Variation VI—Lilac Fairy (Waltz); 4i. Coda; 5. Finale—La Fée des lilas sort. ACT 1: 6. Scene—The Palace Garden; 7. Valse; 8. Scene—The Four Princes; 9. Pas d'action: 9a. Introduction (Andante) and Adagio ('Rose Adagio'); 9b. Dance of Maids of Honour and Pages; 9c. Variation d'Aurore (with vn solo); 9d. Coda; 10. Finale—La Fée des lilas paraît. ACT 2: 11. Entr'acte and Scene; 12. Colin-Maillard—Allegro vivo; 13a. Scene (Moderato); 13b. Danse des duchesses (Minuet); 13c. Danse des baronnes (Gavotte); 13d. Danse des comtesses; 13e. Danse de marquises; 14a. Farandole; 14b. Danse (Tempo di Mazurka); 15. Scene—Arrival of Huntsmen; 16. Coda; 16a. Pas d'action ('Vision' with vc solo); 16b. Variation d'Aurore (Allegro comodo); 17. Scene—Allegro agitato; 18. Panorama (Andantino); 19. Entr'acte (Andante sostenuto); 20a. Entr'acte and Scene—Aurora's sleep; 20b. Finale—Allegro agitato (Breaking of spell). ACT 3: 21. Marche; 22. Polacca (Allegro moderato); 23. Pas de quatre: 23a. Intrada (Allegro non tanto); 23b. Variation I—Valse; 23c. Variation II—Polka (Silver Fairy); 23d. Variation III—Saphir; 23e. Variation IV—Diamant; 23f. Coda; 24. Pas de caractère—Puss in Boots; 25. Pas de quatre: 25a. Adagio (with fl solo); 25b. Variation I—Cinderella and Prince (Waltz); 25c. Variations II—Bluebird and Florisse; 25d. Coda; 26. Pas de caractère (Red Riding Hood); 27a. Pas berrichon (Hop 'o my Thumb); 27b. Cinderella and Prince Fortune (Allegro and Waltz); 28. Pas de deux: 28a. Intrada; 28b. Adagio; 28c. Variation I—Prince; 28d. Variation II (Aurora); 28e. Coda—Allegro vivace (The Three Ivans); 29. Sarabande; 30. Finale: 30a. Allegro brillante (Mazurka); 30b. Apotheosis—Andante molto maestoso.

Cpte Philh, G. Weldon (1/89) (CFP) Ⓓ [2] **CD-CFPD4458**

Cpte National PO, R. Bonynge *Meyerbeer: Patineurs.* (1/90) (DECC) Ⓓ [3] **425 468-2DM3**

Cpte ROHO, M. Ermler (5/90) (ROH) Ⓓ [3] **ROH306/8**

Cpte Košice St PO, A. Mongrelia (4/93) (NAXO) Ⓓ [3] **8 550490/2**

Cpte Kirov Th Orch, V. Gergiev (r1992) (7/93) (PHIL) Ⓓ [3] **434 922-2PH3**

Act 2. Montreal SO, C. Dutoit (r1992) *Nutcracker.* (3/94) (DECC) Ⓓ [2] **440 477-2DH2**

1-3, 4a, 4b, 7, 9a, 9b, 15, 16a, 16b, 17, 18, 24, 26, 29c, 32. ROHO, M. Ermler (5/90) (ROH) Ⓓ **ROH003**

1, 4h, 7, 9a, 18, 24. BPO, H. von Karajan *Concert* (12/86) (DG) Ⓓ **419 175-2GH**

1, 4h, 7, 9a, 18, 24. RPO, C. Mackerras (r1987) *Swan Lake Suite.* (2/88) (TELA) Ⓓ **CD80151**

1, 4h, 7, 9a, 18, 24. BPO, M. Rostropovich *Concert* (4/90) (DG) Ⓓ **429 097-2GGA**

1, 4h, 7, 9a, 18, 24. Bratislava RSO, O. Lenárd *Glazunov: Seasons.* (10/90) (NAXO) Ⓓ **8 550079**

1, 4h, 7, 9a, 18, 24. Boston SO, S. Ozawa *Nutcracker.* (6/92) (DG) Ⓓ [2] **435 619-2GH2**

1, 4h, 7, 9a, 18, 24. BPO, H. von Karajan (r1971) *Concert* (10/94) (DG) Ⓓ [2] **437 404-2GX2**

1, 4, 7, 18, 25. Philadelphia, R. Muti *Swan Lake Suite.* (7/85) (EMI) Ⓓ **CDC7 47075-2**

1, 4, 7, 9a, 9b, 18, 21, 23a, 28a, 30b Philadelphia, E. Ormandy *Rossini: Boutique fantasque.* (3/91) (SONY) Ⓓ **SBK46340**

1, 7, 9a, 18, 24. VPO, James Levine *Concert* (11/94) (DG) Ⓓ **437 806-2GH**

1, 7, 9a, 18, 26. K. Labèque, M. Labèque (r1994: arr pf duet: Rachmaninov) *Concert* (12/95) (PHIL) Ⓓ **442 778-2PH**

1, 7, 9c, 21, 22, 23a, 23b, 23c, 23d, 23e, 25c, 28a, 28b, 28c, 30a, 30b LSO, A. Previn *Concert* (3/92) (EMI) Ⓓ [2] **CZS7 62816-2**

1, 9b, 9c, 13c, 19, 24, 25, 28b, 29, 30. M. Pletnev (arr pf: Pletnev) *Mussorgsky: Pictures.* (4/91) (VIRG) Ⓓ **VC7 59611-2**

6, 19. Scottish CO, J. Serebrier (orch Stravinsky) *Concert* (3/91) (ASV) Ⓓ **CDDCA719**

7. Hallé, M. Sargent (r1941) *Concert* (2/95) (DUTT) Ⓓ **CDAX8010**

7. Boston Pops, A. Fiedler (r1959) *Concert* (12/95) (RCA) Ⓓ **09026 68132-2**

7, 9a, 18, 24, 28a, 28b, 28e, 30. LSO, A. Previn *Concert* (11/92) (EMI) Ⓓ **CDM7 64332-2**

26. SNO, N. Järvi (arr. Stravinsky) *Stravinsky: Baiser de la fée.* (7/85) (CHAN) Ⓓ **CHAN8360**

The **Snow Maiden—incidental music, Op. 12 (1873)** (Wds. Ostrovsky)

EXCERPTS: 1. Introduction; 2. Dance and choirs of the birds; 3. Winter's monologue; 4. Carnival procession; 5. Melodrama; 6. Interlude; 7. Lehl's first song; 8. Lehl's second song; 9. Interlude; 10. Chant of the blind bards; 11. Melodrama; 12. Chorus of the people and the courtiers; 13. Round of the young maidens; 14. Dance of the tumblers; 15. Lehl's third song; 16. Brussils's song; 17. Appearance of the Spirit of the wood; 18. Interlude. The spring Fairy; 19. Tsar Berendey's march and chorus; 20. Final chorus.

Cpte N. Erassova, A. Arkhipov, N. Vassiliev, Russian St Ch, orch, A. Chistiakov (r1993) (3/95) (CDM) Ⓓ **LDC288 090**

Cpte I. Mishura-Lekhtman, V. Grishko, Michigan Univ Mus Soc Chor, Detroit SO, N. Järvi (r1994) (3/95) (CHAN) Ⓓ **CHAN9324**

5. Moscow Virtuosi, V. Spivakov (r1992) *Concert* (12/94) (RCA) Ⓓ **09026 61964-2**

11. Kremlin CO, M. Rachlevsky (r1993) *Concert* (7/94) (CLAV) Ⓓ **CD50-9317**

Swan Lake—ballet: 4 acts, Op. 20 (1877—Moscow) (numbering of excerpts based on cpte score, pub Jurengson)

EXCERPTS: 1. Introduction. ACT 1: 2. Opening Scene (Allegro giusto); 3. Waltz in A flat (Corps de Ballet); 4. Scene—Entrance of Pages (Allegro moderato); 5. Pas de trois: 5a. Intrada (Allegro moderato); 5b. Pas de trois I (Andante sostenuto); 5c. Pas de trois II (Allegro semplice—Presto); 5d. Pas de trois III—Prince (Moderato); 5e. Pas de trois IV (Allegro); 5f. Coda (Allegro vivace); 6. Pas de deux (items comprising this number sometimes appear in Act 3): 6a. Intrada—Waltz in D; 6b. Pas de deux I (Andante, or Adagio); 6c. Pas de deux II—Waltz in B flat; 6d. Coda (Allegro molto vivace); 7. Pas d'action (andantino quasi moderato—Allegro); 8. Scene—Dusk falls; 9. Danse des coupes—Polonaise (Temmpo di polacca); 10. Finale—Swan theme (Andante). ACT 2: 11. Scene—Swan theme (Moderato); 12. Scene—Benno's entry (Allegro moderato—Allegro vivo); 13. Scène (Allegro); 14.

Danses des cygnes; 14a. I—Waltz in A; 14b. II—First
Dance of the Queen (Moderato assai—Molto più
mosso); 14c. III—Danse générale (Waltz in A flat);
14d. IV—Danses des (petites) cynges (Allegro
moderato); 14e. V—Pas d'action: Second Dance of
the Queen (Andante); 14f. Coda (Allegro vivace); 15.
Scene—Swan theme (Moderato). ACT 3: 16.
Scene—Danse de fançailles (Allegro giusto); 17.
Danses du corps de ballet et des nains; 18. Scene:
La sortie des invités (Fanfares) et la valse (A flat); 19.
Scène (Allegro—Allegro giusto); 20. Pas de six: 20a.
Intrada—Moderato assai; 20b. Variation 1 (Allegro);
20c. Variation 2 (Andante con moto); 20d. Variation 3
(Moderato); 20e. Variation 4 (Allegro); 20f. Variation
5 (Moderato—Allegro semplice); 20g. Coda (Allegro
molto vivace); 21a. Pas de deux (supplementary
number); 21b. Danse hongroise (Czárdás); 21c.
Danse russe (supplementary number); 22. Danse
espagnole; 23. Danse napolitaine; 24. Mazurka; 25.
Scene (Allegro—Valse—Allegro vivo). ACT 4: 26.
Entr'acte (Moderato); 27. Scene (Allegro ma non
troppo); 28. Danses des petits cynges (Moderato);
29. Scene (Allegro agitato); 30a. Scene finale
(Andante); 30b. Allegro agitato; 30c. Alla breve
(Moderato e maestoso).
Cpte USSR RSO, V. Fedoseyev (r1985)
    (10/88) (OLYM) ① [2] **OCD210**
Cpte ROHO, M. Ermler (r1989)
    (12/89) (ROH) ① [3] **ROH301/3**
Cpte National PO, R. Bonynge Massenet: Cigale.
    (1/90) (DECC) ① [3] **425 413-2DM3**
Cpte Bratislava RSO, O. Lenárd
    (12/91) (NAXO) ① [2] **8 550246/7**
Cpte LSO, M. Tilson Thomas
    (4/92) (SONY) ① [2] **S2K46592**
Cpte Montreal SO, C. Dutoit
    (2/93) (DECC) ① [2] **436 212-2DH2**
Cpte Philadelphia, W. Sawallisch
    (1/95) (EMI) ① [2] **CDS5 55277-2**
Cpte SRO, E. Ansermet (r1959) Prokofiev: Romeo
and Juliet Suites.
    (9/95) (DECC) ① [2] **440 630-2DF2**
Excs LSO, P. Monteux (r1962) Concert
    (12/94) (PHIL) ① [5] **442 544-2PM5**
1, 3, 5b, 6a, 8, 9, 16, 18, 20b, 20c, 20e, 20f, 22, 23,
28, 29, 30a-c ROHO, M. Ermler (r1989)
    (12/89) (ROH) ① **ROH001**
3, 11, 14a, 14e, 21b, 22-24. SNO, N. Järvi (r1988)
Nutcracker.   (3/89) (CHAN) ① **CHAN8556**
3, 11, 14d, 14e, 21b, 22. LSO, A. Previn Concert
    (12/91) (EMI) ① **CDM7 64332-2**
6a, 9, 14a, 14e, 15, 16, 20a, 20b, 21c, 22, 23, 25, 29,
30a-c LSO, A. Previn Concert
    (3/92) (EMI) ① [2] **CZS7 62816-2**
10, 13, 21a-c, 24-27, 29. Minnesota Orch, L. Slatkin
Nutcracker Suite.   (12/84) (PRO) ① **CDD121**
14d E. Wild (r1995: trans pf: Wild) Concert
    (12/95) (SONY) ① **SK62036**
24. Israel PO, Z. Mehta (r1992) Concert
    (8/93) (TELD) ① **4509-90201-2**
**Swan Lake—concert suite from ballet, Op. 20
(1876)**
1. Scène: 'Swan Theme' (moderato); 2. Valse in A; 3.
Danses des (petits) cynges (Allegro moderato); 4.
Scène (Second Dance of the Queen); 5. Danse
hongroise (Czárdás); 6a. Scène (Allegro agitato); 6b.
Final Scene (Andante—Allegro agitato).
Philadelphia, R. Muti Sleeping Beauty.
    (7/85) (EMI) ① **CDC7 47075-2**
BPO, H. von Karajan Concert
    (12/86) (DG) ① **419 175-2GH**
RPO, C. Mackerras (r1987) Sleeping Beauty.
    (2/88) (TELA) ① **CD80151**
BPO, M. Rostropovich Concert
    (4/90) (DG) ① **429 097-2GGA**
Chicago SO, G. Solti Concert
    (8/91) (DECC) ① **430 707-2DM**
LPO, J. Barbirolli (r1933) Concert
    (3/92) (KOCH) ① **37077-2**
Israel PO, Z. Mehta (r1992) Concert
    (8/93) (TELD) ① **4509-90201-2**
New SO, A. Boult (r1960) Symphony 5.
    (8/93) (CHES) ① **Chesky CD94**
RPO, Y. Temirkanov (r1993) Concert
    (5/94) (RCA) ① [6] **09026 61821-2**
VPO, James Levine Concert
    (11/94) (DG) ① **437 806-2GH**
3. Berlin Ens Concert   (5/91) (ORFE) ① **C126901A**

TCHAIKOWSKY, André
(1935–1982) Poland/England

SECTION II: CHAMBER
String Quartet No. 2 in C, Op. 5
Lindsay Qt (bp1978) Concert
    (1/93) (ASV) ① **CDDCA825**

TCHEREPNIN, Alexander
(Nikolayevich) *(1899–1977)*
Russia/France/USA

SECTION I: ORCHESTRAL
**Concerto for Piano and Orchestra No. 1, Op.
12 (1919-20)**
M. McLachlan, Chetham's SO, J. Clayton (r1995)
Concert   (12/95) (OLYM) ① **OCD440**
**Concerto for Piano and Orchestra No. 2, Op.
26 (1922-23)**
M. McLachlan, Chetham's SO, J. Clayton (r1994)
Concert   (11/94) (OLYM) ① **OCD439**
**Concerto for Piano and Orchestra No. 3, Op.
48 (1931-32)**
M. McLachlan, Chetham's SO, J. Clayton (r1994)
Concert   (11/94) (OLYM) ① **OCD439**
**Concerto for Piano and Orchestra No. 4,
'Fantaisie', Op. 78 (1947)**
M. McLachlan, Chetham's SO, J. Clayton (r1995)
Concert   (12/95) (OLYM) ① **OCD440**
**Concerto for Piano and Orchestra No. 5, Op.
96 (1963)**
M. McLachlan, Chetham's SO, J. Clayton (r1995)
Concert   (12/95) (OLYM) ① **OCD440**
**Concerto for Piano and Orchestra No. 6, Op.
99 (1965)**
M. McLachlan, Chetham's SO, J. Clayton (r1994)
Concert   (11/94) (OLYM) ① **OCD439**
Romantic Overture, Op. 67 (1940s)
Košice St PO, W-S. Yip Concert
    (10/92) (MARC) ① **8 223380**
Russian Dances
Košice St PO, W-S. Yip Concert
    (10/92) (MARC) ① **8 223380**
Suite—orchestra, Op. 87 (1953)
Košice St PO, W-S. Yip Concert
    (10/92) (MARC) ① **8 223380**
Symphony No. 4, Op. 91 (1957)
Košice St PO, W-S. Yip Concert
    (10/92) (MARC) ① **8 223380**

SECTION II: CHAMBER
Ode—cello & piano
J. Starker, G. Moore (r1958) Concert
    (12/95) (EMI) ① [6] **CZS5 68485-2**
String Duo—violin and cello, Op. 49 (1932)
E. Turovsky, Y. Turovsky Concert
    (7/89) (CHAN) ① **CHAN8652**
String Quartet No. 2, Op. 40 (1927)
New World Qt (r1978) Concert
    (10/93) (VOX) ① [2] **115775-2**

SECTION III: INSTRUMENTAL
Autour des montagnes russes—piano
B. Lerner Concert   (1/89) (ETCE) ① **KTC1061**

TCHEREPNIN, Nikolay
(Nikolayevich) *(1873–1945)*
Russia

SECTION V: STAGE WORKS
**Pavillon d'Armide—ballet (1908—St
Petersburg)**
Moscow SO, H. Shek (r1994)
    (12/95) (MARC) ① **8 223779**

TCHESNOKOV, Pavel
(1877–1944) Russia

SECTION IV: VOCAL AND CHORAL
God is with us—tenor and choir
St Petersburg Glinka Acad Ch, V. Chernushenko
Concert   (3/92) (TELD) ① **9031-73241-2**
N. Gedda, Paris Russian Orthodox Cath Ch, E. Evetz
Concert   (1/93) (PHIL) ① **434 174-2PM**
**Let my prayer be set forth before
Thee—contralto and choir**
St Petersburg Glinka Acad Ch, V. Chernushenko
Concert   (3/92) (TELD) ① **9031-73241-2**
Magnificat—soprano and choir
St Petersburg Glinka Acad Ch, V. Chernushenko
Concert   (3/92) (TELD) ① **9031-73241-2**

TEIKE, Carl Albert Hermann
(1864–1922) Germany

SECTION I: ORCHESTRAL
**Alte Kameraden—march, 1900 (Eng. Old
Comrades)**
Berlin Phil Wind Qnt, H. von Karajan (r1973) Concert
    (9/90) (DG) ① **439 346-2GX2**

TEIXEIRA, Antonio *(1707–c1759)*
Portugal

SECTION IV: VOCAL AND CHORAL
Te Deum (1734)
The Sixteen, The Sixteen Orch, H. Christophers
    (11/92) (COLL) ① **Coll1359-2**

TELEMANN, Georg Philipp
(1681–1767) Germany

TWV—Nos from M. Ruhnke,
Telemann—Werkverzeichnis

SECTION I: ORCHESTRAL
**Concerto à 6 in F—recorder, bassoon,
strings & continuo**
F. Brüggen, O. Fleischmann, VCM, N. Harnoncourt
(r1968) Concert   (10/95) (TELD) ① **4509-97472-2**
Concerto for Flute and Strings No. 4 in D
W. Hazelzet, Cologne Musica Antiqua, R. Goebel
Concert   (8/87) (ARCH) ① **419 633-2AH**
**Concerto for Flute, Chalumeau, Oboe, 2
Double Basses, Strings and Continuo in G**
Cologne Stravaganza, A. Manze (r1994) Concert
    (11/95) (DENO) ① **CO-78933**
**Concerto for Flute, Oboe d'amore, Viola
d'amore and Strings in E**
S. Preston, C. Shanks, M. Huggett, AAM, C.
Hogwood (hpd/dir) Concert
    (8/84) (L'OI) ① **411 949-2OH**
S. Francis (ob d'amore/dir), G. Mayger, E. Watson,
London Hpd Ens Concert
    (8/94) (UNIC) ① **DKPCD9131**
Cologne Stravaganza, A. Manze (r1994) Concert
    (11/95) (DENO) ① **CO-78933**
**Concerto for Flute, Strings and Continuo in
D**
K. Kaiser, Cologne Camerata Concert
    (12/91) (DHM) ① **RD77201**
Cologne Stravaganza, A. Manze (r1994) Concert
    (11/95) (DENO) ① **CO-78933**
**Concerto for Flute, Violin and Strings in E
minor**
R. Brown, Collegium Musicum 90, S. Standage
(vn/dir) Concert   (4/92) (CHAN) ① **CHAN0519**
Cologne Stravaganza, A. Manze (r1994) Concert
    (11/95) (DENO) ① **CO-78933**
Concerto for Horn and Orchestra in D
H. Baumann, ASMF, I. Brown Concert
    (6/85) (PHIL) ① **412 226-2PH**
Concerto for Oboe and Strings in C minor
1. Adagio; 2. Adagio; 3. Adagio; 4. Allegro.
London Hpd Ens, S. Francis (ob/dir) Concert
    (4/93) (UNIC) ① **DKPCD9128**
Concerto for Oboe and Strings in E flat
1. Allegro; 2. Largo; 3. Allegro.
London Hpd Ens, S. Francis (ob/dir) Concert
    (4/93) (UNIC) ① **DKPCD9128**
**Concerto for Oboe and Strings No. 2 in C
minor**
H. Holliger, ASMF, I. Brown (vn/dir) Concert
    (2/86) (PHIL) ① **412 879-2PH**
C. Lindberg, New Stockholm CO, O. Kamu (trans
tbn) Concert   (8/88) (BIS) ① **BIS-CD348**
J. Freeman-Attwood, I. Simcock (r1993: arr tpt/org)
Concert   (5/94) (PROU) ① **PROUCD135**
S. Francis (ob/dir), London Hpd Ens Concert
    (8/94) (UNIC) ① **DKPCD9131**
Concerto for Oboe and Strings No. 3 in D
H. Holliger, ASMF, I. Brown (vn/dir) Concert
    (2/86) (PHIL) ① **412 879-2PH**
London Hpd Ens, S. Francis (ob/dir) Concert
    (4/93) (UNIC) ① **DKPCD9128**
**Concerto for Oboe and Strings No. 4 in D
minor**
H. Holliger, ASMF, I. Brown (vn/dir) Concert
    (2/86) (PHIL) ① **412 879-2PH**
P. Goodwin, King's Consort, R. King Concert
    (7/88) (HYPE) ① **CDA66267**
S. Francis (ob/dir), London Hpd Ens Concert
    (8/94) (UNIC) ① **DKPCD9131**

Concerto for Oboe and Strings No. 6 in E minor
H. Holliger, ASMF, I. Brown (vn/dir) *Concert*
(2/86) (PHIL) ① **412 879-2PH**
H-P. Westermann, Cologne Camerata *Concert*
(12/91) (DHM) ① **RD77201**
London Hpd Ens, S. Francis (ob/dir) *Concert*
(4/93) (UNIC) ① **DKPCD9128**

Concerto for Oboe and Strings No. 7 in F minor
London Hpd Ens, S. Francis (ob/dir) *Concert*
(4/93) (UNIC) ① **DKPCD9128**

Concerto for Oboe and Strings No. 8 in F minor
H. Holliger, ASMF, I. Brown (vn/dir) *Concert*
(2/86) (PHIL) ① **412 879-2PH**
S. Francis (ob/dir), London Hpd Ens *Concert*
(8/94) (UNIC) ① **DKPCD9131**

Concerto for Oboe d'amore and Strings in E minor
S. Francis (ob d'amore/dir), London Hpd Ens *Concert*
(8/94) (UNIC) ① **DKPCD9131**

Concerto for Oboe d'amore and Strings No. 1 in G
P. Goodwin, King's Consort, R. King *Concert*
(7/88) (HYPE) ① **CDA66267**
London Hpd Ens, S. Francis (ob/dir) *Concert*
(4/93) (UNIC) ① **DKPCD9128**

Concerto for Oboe d'amore and Strings No. 2 in A
S. Francis (ob d'amore/dir), London Hpd Ens *Concert*
(8/94) (UNIC) ① **DKPCD9131**

Concerto for Oboe, 3 Trumpets, Oboe, Timpani and Strings
M. Bennett, M. Harrison, N. Thompson, P. Goodwin, L. Wood, English Concert, T. Pinnock (hpd/dir)
(r1993) *Concert* (8/94) (ARCH) ① **439 893-2AH**

Concerto for Recorder and Strings No. 1 in C
M. Petri, ASMF, I. Brown *Concert*
(7/83) (PHIL) ① **400 075-2PH**
M. McGraw, Drottningholm Baroque Ens *Concert*
(2/86) (BIS) ① **BIS-CD271**
P. Holtslag, Parley of Instr, P. Holman *Concert*
(10/91) (HYPE) ① **CDA66413**
P. Pickett (rec/dir), New London Consort *Concert*
(11/92) (L'OI) ① **433 043-2OH**
F. Brüggen, VCM, N. Harnoncourt (r1968) *Concert*
(10/95) (TELD) ① **4509-97472-2**

Concerto for Recorder and Strings No. 2 in F
P. Holtslag, Parley of Instr, P. Holman *Concert*
(10/91) (HYPE) ① **CDA66413**
M. Schneider, Cologne Camerata *Concert*
(12/91) (DHM) ① **RD77201**

Concerto for Recorder, Bassoon and Strings in F
M. Petri, K. Thunemann, ASMF, I. Brown *Concert*
(5/84) (PHIL) ① **410 041-2PH**
C. Pehrsson, M. McGraw, Drottningholm Baroque Ens *Concert* (2/86) (BIS) ① **BIS-CD271**
C. Pehrsson, Drottningholm Baroque Ens, M. McCraw (r1984) *Concert*
(7/94) (BIS) ① **BIS-CD617**

Concerto for Recorder, Flute and Strings in E minor
1. Largo; 2. Allegro; 3. Largo; 4. Presto.
M. Petri, W. Bennett, ASMF, I. Brown *Concert*
(5/84) (PHIL) ① **410 041-2PH**
J. Turner, S. Preston, AAM, C. Hogwood (hpd/dir)
Concert (8/84) (L'OI) ① **411 949-2OH**
E. Hering, E-B. Hilse, Berlin Ancient Music Academy *Concert* (7/87) (CAPR) ① **10 134**
F. Immer, M. Schneider, M. Krämer, W. Erhard *Concert* (8/87) (ARCH) ① **419 633-2AH**
P. Evison, C. Pehrsson, Drottningholm Baroque Ens *Concert* (10/88) (BIS) ① **BIS-CD249**
F. Brüggen, F. Vester, Amsterdam CO, A. Rieu (r1967) *Concert* (7/93) (TELD) ① **9031-77620-2**
C. Pehrsson, Drottningholm Baroque Ens, M. McCraw, D. Laurin, O. Larsson, P. Evison (r1983) *Concert* (7/94) (BIS) ① **BIS-CD617**
F. Brüggen, F. Vester, Amsterdam CO, A. Rieu (r c1962) *Concert* (10/95) (TELD) ① **4509-97474-2**

Concerto for Recorder, Viola da gamba and Strings in A minor
M. Schneider, R. Zipperling, Cologne Camerata *Concert* (12/91) (DHM) ① **RD77201**
P. Pickett (rec/dir), M. Levy, New London Consort *Concert* (11/92) (L'OI) ① **433 043-2OH**
M. Verbruggen, S. Cunningham, OAE, M. Huggett (r1992) *Concert* (1/94) (HARM) ① **HMU90 7093**
C. Pehrsson, Drottningholm Baroque Ens, O. Larsson *Concert* (7/94) (BIS) ① **BIS-CD617**

Concerto for Strings and Continuo in E flat
Cologne Stravaganza, A. Manze (r1994) *Concert*
(11/95) (DENO) ① **CO-78933**

Concerto for Trumpet and Strings in D
1. Adagio; 2. Allegro; 3. Grave; 4. Allegro.
G. Schwarz (tpt/dir), NY Y CO *Concert*
(10/84) (DELO) ① **DE3002**
M. André, Philh, R. Muti *Concert*
(1/86) (EMI) ① **CDC7 47311-2**
P. Carrai, F. Immer, Cologne Musica Antiqua, R. Goebel (vn/dir) *Concert*
(8/87) (ARCH) ① **419 633-2AH**
H. Hardenberger, ASMF, I. Brown (r1987; ed Grebe) *Concert* (8/88) (PHIL) ① **420 954-2PH**
M. André, BPO, H. von Karajan (ed Grebe) *Concert*
(2/89) (EMI) ① **CDC7 49237-2**
J. Wallace, English Stg Orch, W. Boughton *Concert*
(12/89) (NIMB) ① **NI5189**

Concerto for Viola and Strings in G
P. Doctor, Concerto Amsterdam, F. Brüggen (r1968) *Concert* (7/93) (TELD) ① **9031-77620-2**

Concerto for Viola da gamba and Strings No. 1 in G
J. Harrington, Cantilena, A. Shepherd *Concert*
(9/84) (CHAN) ① **CHAN8319**
S. Shingles, ASMF, N. Marriner *Concert*
(7/91) (DECC) ① **430 265-2DM**

Concerto for Violin and Strings in A minor
Collegium Musicum 90, S. Standage (vn/dir) *Concert*
(4/92) (CHAN) ① **CHAN0519**

Concerto for Violin and Strings in F sharp minor
Collegium Musicum 90, S. Standage (vn/dir) *Concert*
(4/92) (CHAN) ① **CHAN0512**

Concerto for Violin and Strings No. 3 in E
Collegium Musicum 90, S. Standage (vn/dir) *Concert*
(4/92) (CHAN) ① **CHAN0519**

Concerto for Violin and Strings No. 9 in G
Collegium Musicum 90, S. Standage (vn/dir) *Concert*
(4/92) (CHAN) ① **CHAN0512**

Concerto for Violin, Cello, Trumpet and Strings in D
L. Klevit, R. Goebel (vn/dir), M. Krämer, W. Erhard *Concert* (8/87) (ARCH) ① **419 633-2AH**

Concerto for 2 Chalumeaux and Orchestra No. 1 in D minor
E. Hoeprich, L. Klevit, Cologne Musica Antiqua, R. Goebel *Concert* (8/87) (ARCH) ① **419 633-2AH**

Concerto for 2 Flutes, Violin, Cello and Strings in D
R. Brown, S. Peasgood, J. Coe, Collegium Musicum 90, S. Standage (vn/dir) *Concert*
(4/92) (CHAN) ① **CHAN0512**

Concerto for 2 Horns, 2 Oboes and Strings No. 1 in D
H. Baumann, T. Brown, ASMF, I. Brown *Concert*
(6/85) (PHIL) ① **412 226-2PH**

Concerto for 2 Oboes, Trumpet and Strings No. 1 in D
N. Black, Jeremy Brown, C. Steele-Perkins, ECO, A. Halstead *Concert* (6/86) (CARL) ① **PCD821**
C. Nicklin, T. Miller, H. Hardenberger, ASMF, I. Brown (r1987) *Concert*
(8/88) (PHIL) ① **420 954-2PH**
P. Arden-Taylor, A. Evans, J. Wallace, English Stg Orch, W. Boughton *Concert*
(12/89) (NIMB) ① **NI5189**

Concerto for 2 Oboes, Trumpet and Strings No. 2 in D (ed Grebe from chamber work)
C. Nicklin, T. Miller, H. Hardenberger, ASMF, I. Brown (r1987) *Concert*
(8/88) (PHIL) ① **420 954-2PH**
P. Arden-Taylor, A. Evans, J. Wallace, English Stg Orch, W. Boughton *Concert*
(12/89) (NIMB) ① **NI5189**
M. André, ECO, C. Mackerras *Concert*
(11/90) (EMI) ① **CDM7 63528-2**
C. Steele-Perkins, Tafelmusik, J. Lamon (vn/dir) (r1993) *Concert* (4/95) (SONY) ① **SK53365**

Concerto for 2 Recorders and Strings in A minor
Amsterdam Loeki Stardust Qt, AAM, C. Hogwood (r1992) *Concert* (7/94) (L'OI) ① **436 905-2OH**

Concerto for 2 Recorders and Strings in B flat
Amsterdam Loeki Stardust Qt, AAM, C. Hogwood (r1992) *Concert* (7/94) (L'OI) ① **436 905-2OH**

Concerto for 2 Recorders, 2 Oboes and Strings in A minor
Cologne Musica Antiqua, R. Goebel (r1984) *Concert*
(3/85) (ARCH) ① **413 788-2AH**
C. Pehrsson, Drottningholm Baroque Ens, D. Laurin (r1993) *Concert* (7/94) (BIS) ① **BIS-CD617**

Concerto for 2 Recorders, 2 Oboes, Bassoon and Strings in B flat
Cologne Musica Antiqua, R. Goebel (r1984) *Concert*
(3/85) (ARCH) ① **413 788-2AH**
C. Pehrsson, Drottningholm Baroque Ens, D. Laurin (r1993) *Concert* (7/94) (BIS) ① **BIS-CD617**

Concerto for 2 Recorders, 2 Oboes, Bassoon and Strings in F
Cologne Musica Antiqua, R. Goebel (r1984) *Concert*
(3/85) (ARCH) ① **413 788-2AH**

Concerto for 2 Violins and Strings in E minor
Freiburg Baroque Orch, G. von der Goltz (r1993) *Concert* (1/95) (DHM) ① **05472 77321-2**

Concerto for 2 Violins and Strings in G
M. Comberti, Collegium Musicum 90, S. Standage (vn/dir) *Concert* (4/92) (CHAN) ① **CHAN0512**

Concerto for 2 Violins, 2 Oboes and Strings in D
M. Utiger, H. Bäss, M. McGraw, Cologne Camerata *Concert* (12/91) (DHM) ① **RD77201**

Concerto for 3 Horns, Violin and Orchestra in D
H. Baumann, T. Brown, N. Hill, ASMF, I. Brown *Concert* (6/85) (PHIL) ① **412 226-2PH**
A. Halstead, C. Rutherford, R. Diaz, Collegium Musicum 90, S. Standage (vn/dir) (r1993) *Concert* (7/94) (CHAN) ① **CHAN0547**

Concerto for 3 Oboes, 3 Violins and Strings in B flat (also played on 3 trumpets and 3 violins)
P. Westermann, M. Niesemann, P. Dhont, M. Krämer, W. Erhard, Cologne Musica Antiqua, R. Goebel (vn/dir) *Concert*
(8/87) (ARCH) ① **419 633-2AH**
W. Marsalis, ECO, R. Leppard (trans 3 tpts) *Concert*
(6/88) (SONY) ① **SK42478**

Concerto for 3 Trumpets and Orchestra No. 1 in D
F. Immer, M. Laird, I. Wilson, AAM, C. Hogwood (hpd/dir) *Concert* (8/84) (L'OI) ① **411 949-2OH**
W. Marsalis, ECO, R. Leppard *Concert*
(6/88) (SONY) ① **SK42478**
H. Läubin, W. Läubin, B. Läubin, ECO, S. Preston (hpd/dir) *Concert* (12/91) (DG) ① **431 817-2GH**

Concerto for 3 Trumpets and Orchestra No. 2 in D
H. Hardenberger, M. Laird, W. Houghton, ASMF, I. Brown (r1987) *Concert*
(8/88) (PHIL) ① **420 954-2PH**
J. Wallace, John Miller, W. Stokes, English Stg Orch, W. Boughton *Concert* (12/89) (NIMB) ① **NI5189**
H. Läubin, W. Läubin, B. Läubin, ECO, S. Preston (hpd/dir) *Concert* (12/91) (DG) ① **431 817-2GH**

Concerto for 4 Violins and Strings in A
M. Comberti, M. Golding, A. Manze, Collegium Musicum 90, S. Standage (vn/dir) *Concert*
(4/92) (CHAN) ① **CHAN0519**

Concerto in D—trumpet and strings
O.E. Antonsen, ECO, J. Tate (r1993) *Concert*
(2/94) (EMI) ① **CDC7 54897-2**

Concerto in G, 'Grillen-Symphonie' (mid-late 1730s)
Collegium Musicum 90, S. Standage (vn/dir) (r1993) *Concert* (7/94) (CHAN) ① **CHAN0547**

Concerto in G, 'Polonois'—strings
AAM, C. Hogwood (hpd/dir) *Concert*
(8/84) (L'OI) ① **411 949-2OH**
English Concert, T. Pinnock (hpd/dir) *Concert*
(12/91) (ARCH) ① **435 262-2AH**

5 Concertos—2 flutes, colascione (lute)/bassoon and strings (?1720)
1. A; 2. B minor; 3. D; 4. E minor; 5. G.
Dresden Bar Sols, E. Haupt (fl/dir)
(6/90) (CAPR) ① **10 284**

Musique de table, 'Tafelmusik'—orchestral & chamber works (pub 1733)
PRODUKTION 1: 1a. Ouverture-Suite in E minor (2 flutes & strings); 1b. Quartet in G (flute, oboe, violin, cello & continuo); 1c. Concerto in A (flute, violin & strings); 1d. Trio in E flat (2 violins & continuo); 1e. Solo Sonata in E minor (flute & continuo); 1f. Conclusion in E minor (2 flutes & strings).
PRODUKTION II: 2a. Ouverture in D (oboe, trumpet & strings); 2b. Quartet in D minor (2 flutes, recorder, cello & continuo); 2c. Concerto in F (3 violins & strings); 2d. Trio in E minor (flute, oboe & continuo); 2e. Solo Sonata in A (violin & continuo); 2f. Conclusion in D (oboe, trumpet & strings).
PRODUKTION III: 3a. Ouverture-Suite in B flat (2 oboes & strings); 3b. Quartet in E minor (recorder/flute, violin, cello & continuo); 3c. Concerto in E flat (2 horns & strings); 3d. Trio in D (2 flutes & continuo); 3e. Solo Sonata in G minor (oboe & continuo); 3f. Conclusion in B flat (2 oboes & strings).

TWV41: B 3; 27. Napolitana, B flat (ob d'amore),
TWV41: B 4; 28. Sinfonie à la Françoise (fl), TWV41:
h 2. TWO INSTRUMENTS & CONTINUO: 29. Trio
Sonata, C (2 recs), TWV42: C 1. MISCELLANEOUS
PIECES: 30. Etliche Contrapunctische
Veränderungen; 31. Einige plötzliche Eintritte in
entfernete Accords; 32. Theme zur Fuge, Auflsögen
und Canon perpetuus; 33. Themata zu Fugen.
WORKS BY OTHER COMPOSERS: 34. Anon
(Bonporti?): Bizaria und Giga, A (va & continuo); 35.
Baron: Suite, D (lte); 36. Goerner: Passacaille, B
minor; 37. Goerner: Trouble-Fête (hpd); 38.
Haltmeier: Fantasia, D (hpd); 39. Kreising: Suite, D
(hpd); 40. Kreising: Pièce, C (hpd); 41. Pezold: Suite,
B flat (hpd); 42. Pisendel: Gigue, A minor (va); 43.
Störmer: Sonata, F (va); 44. Weiss: Presto: Presto, G
(lte).
Cpte Cologne Camerata (r1990-1) *Getreue Music-
Meister.* (4/93) (DHM) ① [5] RD77239
12, 19, 20. V. Boeckman, F. Hansen, L.U. Mortensen
Concert (11/89) (KONT) ① 32014
12, 19, 20, 26. F. Brüggen, A. Bylsma, G. Leonhardt
Concert (10/95) (TELD) ① 4509-93688-2
19. E. Talmi, Y. Talmi *Concert*
(6/90) (CARL) ① PWK1133
20. M. Petri, H. Petri, D. Petri *Concert*
(11/88) (RCA) ① RD87749
23. P. Dombrecht, R. Kohnen *Concert*
(2/85) (ACCE) ① ACC48013D
23. C. Lambour *Concert*
(8/90) (ETCE) ① KTC1083
25. M. Zupnik, M. Shuman, R. Leppard *Concert*
(9/89) (ASV) ① CDDCA663

**Kleine Cammer-Music—six partitas:
violin/flute and continuo (pub 1716)**
1. B minor, TWV41: B 1; 2. G, TWV41: G 2; 3. C
minor, TWV41: c 1; 4. G minor, TWV41: g 2; 5. E
minor, TWV41: e 1; 6. E flat, TWV41: Es 1.
2. P. Dombrecht, R. Kohnen *Concert*
(2/85) (ACCE) ① ACC48013D
5. B. Kol, A. Brodo, D. Shemer *Concert*
(6/90) (CARL) ① PWK1138
**Musique héroïque (or 12 Marches)—two
instruments and continuo (1728) (TWV50:
31-42)**
1. La Majesté; 2. La Grâce; 3. La Vaillance; 4. La
Tranquillité; 5. L'Armement; 6. L'Amour; 7. La
Vigilance; 8. La Gaillardise; 9. La Douceur; 10. La
Générosité; 11. L'Espérance; 12. La Réjouissance.
H. Hardenberger, S. Preston *Concert*
(12/92) (PHIL) ① 434 074-2PH
O.E. Antonsen, W. Marshall (r1992: arr tpt/org: Alain)
Concert (10/94) (EMI) ① CDC5 55048-2
Ouverture a 4 in C (r1710) (unidentified)
Parley of Instr, R. Goodman, P. Holman *Concert*
(9/91) (HYPE) ① CDA66074
**Overture-Suite in A, 'Festliche'—2 violins,
cello and continuo (unidentified)**
Seattle NW CO, A. Francis *Concert*
(12/88) (HYPE) ① CDH88028
**6 Paris Quartets, 'Nouveaux quatuors en six
suites'—flute, violin, viola da gamba and
continuo (pub 1738)**
1. D, TWV43: D 3; 2. A minor, TWV43: a 2; 3. G,
TWV43: G 4; 4. B minor, TWV43: h 2; 5. A, TWV43:
A 3; 6. E minor, TWV43: e 4.
M. Arita, Tokyo Baroque Trio (r1992)
(2/94) (DENO) ① [2] CO-75354/5
Amsterdam Qt (r1964) *Concert*
(10/95) (TELD) ① [2] 4509-92177-2
1, 2. Hortus Musicus, A. Mustonen (vn/dir) (r1992)
Concert (5/95) (FINL) ① 4509-95578-2
2, 6. W. Hazelzet, Sonnerie Trio *Paris Quartets
(Quadri).* (3/92) (VIRG) ① VC7 59049-2
3, 4. W. Hazelzet, Sonnerie Trio (1991) *Paris
Quartets (Quadri).* (11/94) (VIRG) ① VC5 45020-2
6. Florilegium Ens (r1992) *Concert*
(10/93) (CHNN) ① CCS5093
**6 Paris Quartets, 'Quadri'—flute, violin, viola
da gamba/cello and continuo (pub 1730)**
1. Concerto primo in G, TWV43: G 1; 2. Concerto
secondo in D, TWV43: D 1; 3. Sonata prima in A,
TWV43: A 1; 4. Sonata seconda in G minor, TWV43:
g 1; 5. Première Suite in E minor, TWV43: e 1; 6.
Deuxième Suite in B minor, TWV43: h 1.
1, 2, 3, 4. American Baroque, S. Schultz
(3/89) (AMON) ① CD-SAR39
1, 3. W. Hazelzet, Sonnerie Trio *Paris Quartets
(Nouveaux quatuors).*
(3/92) (VIRG) ① VC7 59049-2
1-5. Ricercar Qt (3/89) (RICE) ① RIC043020
2. Music's Recreation *Concert*
(6/88) (MERI) ① CDE84114
2, 5. W. Hazelzet, Sonnerie Trio (1991) *Paris
Quartets (Nouveaux quatuors).*
(11/94) (VIRG) ① VC5 45020-2

6. European Baroque Sols *Concert*
(6/92) (DENO) ① CO-77614
**Partie Polonoise in B flat—suite: two lutes,
TWV39: 1**
J. Bream, J. Williams (r1978; ed Bream & Williams)
Concert (11/93) (RCA) ① 09026 61452-2
**Quartet in A minor—recorder, oboe, violin
and continuo, TWV43: a 3 (c1730) (Chamber
Concerto)**
Chandos Baroque Plyrs *Concert*
(7/87) (HYPE) ① CDA66195
Florilegium Ens (r1992) *Concert*
(10/93) (CHNN) ① CCS5093
**Quartet in B flat—2 violins, viola and
continuo, TWV43: B 2**
C. Mackintosh, C. Hirons, T. Jones, T. Mason
Concert (8/84) (L'OI) ① 411 949-2OH
**Quartet in G—recorder, oboe, violin and
continuo, TWV43: G 6**
Chandos Baroque Plyrs *Concert*
(7/87) (HYPE) ① CDA66195
**Quartet in G—flute, 2 viola da gambas and
continuo, TWV43: G 12**
Barthold Kuijken, S. Kuijken, W. Kuijken, R. Kohnen
Concert (3/86) (ACCE) ① ACC58019D
Collegium Musicum 90, S. Standage (vn/dir) *Concert*
(4/93) (CHAN) ① CHAN0525
**Quartet in G minor—oboe, violin, viola da
gamba and continuo, TWV43: g 2**
Chandos Baroque Plyrs *Concert*
(7/87) (HYPE) ① CDA66195
**Quartet in G minor—flute, violin, viola and
continuo, TWV43: g 4 (c1710-15)**
Florilegium Ens (r1992) *Concert*
(10/93) (CHNN) ① CCS5093
**XII Solos for Violin (or Flute) and Continuo
(pub 1734)**
1. F, TWV41: F 3; 2. E minor, TWV41: e 4; 3. A,
TWV41: A 5; 4. C, TWV41: C 4; 5. G minor, TWV41:
g 7; 6. D, TWV41: D 8; 7. D minor, TWV41: d 3; 8. G,
TWV41: G 8; 9. B minor, TWV41: h 5; 10. E, TWV41:
E 6; 11. A minor, TWV41: a 5; 12. F sharp minor,
TWV41: fis 1.
1, 5, 6, 7, 10, 11. M. Miessen, B. van Asperen, G.
Wilson, W. Möller (trans rec)
(10/88) (ETCE) ① KTC2004-2
2, 3, 4, 8, 9, 12. M. Miessen, B. van Asperen, G.
Wilson, W. Möller (trans rec)
(10/88) (ETCE) ① KTC2004-1
**Sonata (Septett) in E minor—2 obs, 2 vns, 2
vas & bc (c1730s) (Unidentified)**
Cologne Musica Antiqua, R. Goebel (r1995) *Concert*
(12/95) (ARCH) ① 445 824-2AH
Sonata in E minor—2 violins (unidentified)
Collegium Musicum 90, S. Standage (vn/dir) *Concert*
(4/93) (CHAN) ① CHAN0525
**Sonata in F minor for Recorder and
Continuo, TWV41: f 2 (Brussels Ms)**
V. Boeckman, F. Hansen, L.U. Mortensen *Concert*
(11/89) (KONT) ① 32014
**12 Sonate metodiche—violin/flute and
continuo (pub 1728 and 1732) (Nos. 1-6 pub
as 'Op. 13')**
1. G minor, TWV41: g 3; 2. A, TWV41: A 3; 3. E
minor, TWV41: e 2; 4. D, TWV41: D 3; 5. A minor,
TWV41: a 2; 6. G, TWV41: G 4; 7. B minor, TWV41:
h 3; 8. C minor, TWV41: c 3; 9. E, TWV41: 41: E 5;
10. B flat, TWV41: B 5; 11. D minor, TWV41: d 2; 12.
C, TWV41: C 3.
1. M. Zupnik, M. Shuman, R. Leppard *Concert*
(9/89) (ASV) ① CDDCA663
3, 4, 5, 6, 7, 10. F. Brüggen, H. de Vries, A. Bylsma,
W. Möller, G. Leonhardt, B. van Asperen, Boston
Museum Trio (r1981-2) (10/89) (RCA) ① GD71957
10. M. Stucki, C. Lambour, D. Munnik *Concert*
(8/90) (ETCE) ① KTC1083
**6 Sonates Corellisantes—2 violins/flutes and
continuo (pub 1735)**
1. F, TWV42: F 2; 2. A, TWV42: A 5; 3. B minor,
TWV42: h 3; 4. E, TWV42: E 3; 5. D minor, TWV42:
g 4; 6. D, TWV42: D 8.
S. Standage, M. Comberti, J. Coe, N. Parle (r1993)
Canons mélodieux, TWV40: 118-123.
(7/94) (CHAN) ① CHAN0549
1. Florilegium Ens (r1992) *Concert*
(10/93) (CHNN) ① CCS5093
**6 Sonates sans Basse—2
flutes/violins/recorders, without continuo,
TWV40: 101-106 (pub 1727)**
1. G; 2. D; 3. A; 4. G; 5. D; 6. E.
M. Petri, E. Selin (4/91) (RCA) ① RD87903
**Trio Sonata in C minor—oboe, violin and
continuo, TWV42: c 5**
P. Bree, H. Dusowa, C. Lambour, D. Munnik *Concert*
(8/90) (ETCE) ① KTC1083

**Trio Sonata in D minor—recorder, violin and
continuo, TWV42: d 10**
Chandos Baroque Plyrs *Concert*
(7/87) (HYPE) ① CDA66195

SECTION III: INSTRUMENTAL

**Bourrée alla Polacca—harpsichord
(unidentified)**
J. Williams (trans J.Williams) *Concert*
(8/88) (SONY) ① SK44518
**12 Fantasies for Flute without Continuo,
TWV40: 2-13 (pub 1732-33)**
1. A; 2. A minor; 3. B minor; 4. B flat; 5. C; 6. D
minor; 7. D; 8. E minor; 9. E; 10. F sharp minor; 11.
G; 12. G minor.
M. Arita (7/91) (DENO) ① CO-76685
P. Gallois (r1992) (6/93) (DG) ① 437 543-2GH
P. Holtslag (r1994; arr rec)
(12/94) (GLOB) ① GLO5117
Barthold Kuijken (9/85) (ACCE) ① ACC57803D
1, 3, 7, 8, 10, 11. F. Brüggen (r1969/70; trans rec)
Concert (10/95) (TELD) ① 4509-93688-2
**12 Fantasies for Violin without Continuo,
TWV40: 14-25 (pub 1735)**
1. B; 2. G; 3. F minor; 4. D; 5. A; 6. E minor; 7. E flat;
8. E; 9. B minor; 10. D; 11. F; 12. A minor.
B.M. Santos (r1992) (8/94) (GALL) ① CD-718
P. Sheppard (8/94) (MERI) ① CDE84266
M. Homburger (r1993) (8/94) (MAYA) ① MCD9302

SECTION IV: VOCAL AND CHORAL

**Ach Herr, strafe mich nicht—psalm (1v, 2
violins and continuo)**
A. Markert, Parnaso Musicale *Concert*
(12/92) (CHRI) ① CHR77119
R. Jacobs, Kuijken Consort *Concert*
(4/88) (ACCE) ① ACC77912D
**Alles redet itzt und singet—cantata (1720)
(Wds. Brockes)**
B. Schlick, S. Varcoe, Kleine Konzert, H. Max
Concert (11/91) (CAPR) ① 10 315
**An den Schlaf—ode (pub 1741) (Wds. von
Hagedorn from '24 Oden')**
R. Jacobs, Berlin Ancient Music Academy *Concert*
(11/92) (CAPR) ① 10 338
**Cantata, 'Herr, strafe mich nicht in Deinem
Trinitatis'—4vv, choir and orchestra, TWV1:
771 (19th Sunday after Trinity)**
B. Schlick, M. Georg, C. Prégardien, G. Schwarz,
Stagione, M. Schneider (r1993) *Schwanengesang,*
Concert (6/94) (CPO) ① CPO999 212-2
**Deus judicium tuum—grand motet: SATB
(Wds. Psalm 71)**
B. Schlick, M. Lins, S. Weisheit, C. Prégardien, S.
Varcoe, H-G. Wimmer, Rheinische Kantorei, Kleine
Konzert, H. Max *Concert* (11/91) (CAPR) ① 10 315
P. Kwella, C. Denley, M. Tucker, S. Roberts, M.
Collegium Musicum 90 Chor, Collegium Musicum 90,
R. Hickox (r1993) *Donner-Ode.*
(8/94) (CHAN) ① CHAN0548
**Die Donner-Ode, 'Thunder Ode'—cantata:
5vv, chor & orchestra, TWV6:3 (1756) (Wds. J
A Cramer)**
P. Kwella, C. Denley, M. Tucker, S. Roberts, M.
George, Collegium Musicum 90 Chor, Collegium
Musicum 90, R. Hickox (r1993) *Deus judicium tuum.*
(8/94) (CHAN) ① CHAN0548
B. Schlick, A. Köhler, W. Jochens, H-G. Wimmer, S.
Schreckenberger, Rheinische Kantorei, Kleine
Konzert, H. Max (r1992) *Herr ist König.*
(11/95) (CAPR) ① 10 556
**Du aber Daniel, gehe hin—funeral cantata:
4vv (Wds. Bible)**
EXCERPTS: 1. Sonata; 2. Du aber Daniel; 3. Mit
Freuden folgt die Seele; 4. Du Aufenhalt der blassen
Sorgen; 5. Mit sehnendem Verlangen; 6. Brecht, ihr
müden Augenlieder; 7. Dir ist, hochsei'ger Mann; 8.
Schlaf wohl, ihr seligen Gebeine.
G. de Reyghere, J. Bowman, G. de Mey, M. van
Egmond, Ricercar Consort *Concert*
(7/91) (RICE) ① RIC079061
5, 6. E. Ameling, Collegium Aureum, R. Pohl (1968)
Concert (3/94) (RCA) ① [4] 74321 26617-2(1)
**Die Einsamkeit—Lied (pub 1733-34) (from
'Singe-, spiel-, oder General bassüburgen')**
R. Jacobs, Berlin Ancient Music Academy *Concert*
(11/92) (CAPR) ① 10 338
**Ergeuss dich zur Salbung—cantata (1v, flute
and continuo) (pub 1725-26) (Wds. Wilkens.
Der Harmonische Gottes-Dienst)**
J. Bowman, Music's Recreation *Concert*
(1/90) (MERI) ① CDE84159

Erscheine, Gott, in deinem Tempel—cantata (1v, flute and continuo) (pub 1725-26) (Wds. Wilkens). Der Harmonische Gottes-Dienst)
J. Bowman, Music's Recreation *Concert*
(1/90) (MERI) ① **CDE84159**

Der **Getreue Music-Meister—Vocal Works—25 Lessons (pub 1728-29)**
1. Aria, 'Sage mir doch' (Emma und Eginhard); 2. Aria, 'Nimm dein Herz' (Emma und Eginhard); 3. Aria, 'Es glänzet die Unschuld' (Sancio); 4. Aria, 'So oft du deinen Schatz' (Sancio); 5. Aria, 'Das Frauenzimmer'; 6. Aria, 'Vergiss dich selbst' (Emma und Eginhard); 7. Aria, 'Süsse Worte' (Sancio); 8. Aria, 'Più del fiume da diletto' (Aesopus); 9. Aria, 'Ergrimmet nicht' (Emma und Eginhard); 10. Aria, 'Glückselig ist' (Die verkehrte Welt); 11. Szene aus Die verkehrte Welt; 12. Fable, 'Die Kuh—doch halt' (Aesopus); 13. Chorus, 'Gedoppelt schön' (Calypso); 14. Aria, 'Gesundheits-Brunnen' (Emma und Eginhard); 15. Aria, 'Bum, bum, bum' (Aesopus); 16. Cantata, 'Ich kann lachen'; 17. Aria, 'Säume nicht'; 18. Aria a 2, 'Ich folge dir' (Emma und Eginhard); 19. Aria, 'Dass ich mich dir ergeben sollte' (Belsazar). MISC WORKS: 20. Bach: Canon, BWV1074 (4vv); 21. Dimslot: Canon (4vv); 22. Fontaines: Air, 'Komm süsser Schalf'; 23. Schmidt: Canon: 'Non nobis Domine' (3vv); 24. Zelenka: Canon, 'Vide Domine'.
Cpte B. Schlick, M. Lins, K. Wessel, M. Post, H-G. Wimmer, Cologne Camerata (r1990-1) *Getreue Music-Meister.* (4/93) (DHM) ① [5] **RD77239**
5, 6. R. Jacobs, Berlin Ancient Music Academy *Concert*
(11/92) (CAPR) ① **10 338**

Der **Herr ist König—cantata: 3vv, chor & orchestra, TWV8:6**
A. Monoyios, W. Jochens, H. van der Kamp, S. Schreckenberger, Rheinische Kantorei, Kleine Konzert, H. Max (r1990) *Donner-Ode.*
(11/95) (CAPR) ① **10 556**

Ihr Völker hört—cantata (1v, flute and continuo) (pub 1725-26) (Wds. Wilkens. Der Harmonische Gottes-Dienst)
J. Baird, Music's Recreation *Concert*
(1/90) (MERI) ① **CDE84159**
R. Jacobs, Parnassus Ens *Concert*
(4/88) (ACCE) ① **ACC77912D**

Ino—cantata: 1v (1765) (Wds. C.W. Ramler).
R. Alexander, VCM, N. Harnoncourt (r1988) *Tag des Gerichts.* (7/93) (TELD) ① [2] **9031-77621-2**

Jauchze, jubilier and singe—oratoria for the Captains' Music, TWV15: 5 (1730)
M. van der Sluis, G. Pushee, W. Jochens, P. Langshaw, H. van der Kamp, Alsfeld Voc Ens, Bremen Baroque Orch, W. Helbich (r1991) *Magnificat, TWV9: 17.*
(6/94) (CPO) ① **CPO999 109-2**

Magnificat in C—SATB, 3 trumpets, timpani, strings and continuo, TWV9: 17 (Wds. Latin)
M. van der Sluis, G. Pushee, W. Jochens, P. Langshaw, H. van der Kamp, Alsfeld Voc Ens, Bremen Baroque Orch, W. Helbich (r1991) *Jauchze, jubilier und singe, TWV15: 5.*
(6/94) (CPO) ① **CPO999 109-2**

Meines Bleibens ist nicht hier—cantata
R. Jacobs, Berlin Ancient Music Academy *Concert*
(11/92) (CAPR) ① **10 338**

Missa brevis—alto, 2 vns and continuo
D. Cordier, Kleine Konzert, H. Max *Concert*
(11/91) (CAPR) ① **10 315**

6 Moralische Cantaten, Volume II—1v, flute/violin and continuo (pub 1736-37)
3. Das mässige Glück (Emma); 3. Zimmermann).
3. Collegium Musicum 90, S. Standage (vn/dir) *Concert* (4/93) (CHAN) ① **CHAN0525**

Nach Finsternis und Todesschatten—Midsummer Eve cantata (pub 1731-32) (Wds. Schubart)
R. Jacobs, Berlin Ancient Music Academy *Concert*
(11/92) (CAPR) ① **10 338**

Packe dich, gelähmter Drache—cantata (1v, violin and continuo) (pub 1725-26) (Wds. Wilkens. Der Harmonische Gottes-Dienst)
J. Baird, Music's Recreation *Concert*
(1/90) (MERI) ① **CDE84159**

Schwanengesang—funeral music for Garlieb Sillem, Mayor of Hamburg, TWV4: 6 (1733)
B. Schlick, M. Georg, C. Prégardien, G. Schwarz, Stagione, M. Schneider (r1993) *Cantata, TWV1: 771.*
(7/94) (CPO) ① **CPO999 212-2**

Seufzen, Kummer, Angst und Tränen—secular cantata: alto and continuo
A. Markert, Parnaso Musicale *Concert*
(12/92) (CHRI) ① **CHR77119**

Singe-, Spiel- und Generalbass-Übungen—exercises: voice, instruments & continuo (pub 1733-34) (Wds. various)
SONGS: 1. Zufriedenheit; 2. Seltenes Glück; 3. Die Einsamkeit; 4. Glück.
1-4. Collegium Musicum 90, S. Standage (vn/dir) *Concert* (4/93) (CHAN) ① **CHAN0525**

St Matthew Passion—6vv, chorus & orchestra (1746)
Cpte B. Schlick, C. Schubert, W. Jochens, S. Dörr, A. Rück, H-G. Wimmer, Siegen Bach Chor Collegium Vocale, Cologne Stravaganza, U. Stötzel (r1994)
(10/95) (HANS) ① [2] **98 960**
M. Zedelius, A. Browner, H-P. Blochwitz, W. Schmidt, A. Scharinger, Darmstadt Chor, Darmstadt CO, W. Seeliger (r1984) (5/95) (CHRI) ① **CHR77149**

Der **Tag des Gerichts—oratorio (1762)** (Lib. C.W. Alers)
Cpte G. Landwehr-Hermann, C. Canne-Meijer, K. Equiluz, M. van Egmond, Vienna Boys' Ch, Hamburg Monteverdi Ch, VCM, N. Harnoncourt (r1966) *Ino.*
(7/93) (TELD) ① [2] **9031-77621-2**
Cpte A. Monoyios, D. Cordier, W. Jochens, S. Schreckenberger, Rheinische Kantorei, Kleine Konzert, H. Max (r1990) (8/93) (CAPR) ① **10 413**

24 Theils ernsthafte, theils scherzende Odes—serious and lighthearted odes (pub 1741)
1. An den Schlaf; 2. Trinklied.
1, 2. Collegium Musicum 90, S. Standage (vn/dir) *Concert* (4/93) (CHAN) ① **CHAN0525**

Tirsis am Scheidewege—cantata (pub ?1731)
R. Jacobs, Berlin Ancient Music Academy *Concert*
(11/92) (CAPR) ① **10 338**
A. Markert, Parnaso Musicale *Concert*
(12/92) (CHRI) ① **CHR77119**

Trauer-Music eines kunsterfahrenen Canarien-Vogels, 'Canary Cantata'—cantata: 1v & continuo (1737)
A.S. von Otter, Drottningholm Baroque Ens, A. Öhrwall *Concert* (10/91) (PROP) ① **PRCD9008**

Weg mit Sodoms gift'gen Fruchten—cantata (1v, violin and continuo) (pub 1725-26) (Wds. Wilkens. Der Harmonische Gottes-Dienst)
J. Bowman, King's Consort, R. King (org/dir) *Concert*
(6/87) (MERI) ① **CDE84138**

Don Quichotte auf der Hochzeit des Comacho—comic opera/serenata (1761) (Lib. D. Schiebeler)
Cpte R. Nolte, M. Schopper, S. Stapf, M. Bach, H. Hallaschka, A. Köhler, K-H. Brandt, Bremen Voc Ens, Stagione, M. Schneider (pp1993)
(9/94) (CPO) ① **CPO999 210-2**

Flavius Bertaridus—opera: 3 acts (1729—Hamburg) (Lib. Wend)
Lieto suono di trombe guerriere J. Kowalski, Berlin CO, M. Pommer *Concert* (9/88) (CAPR) ① **10 113**

Pimpinone—intermezzo: 2 acts (1728—Hamburg) (Lib. J.P. Praetorius, after P. Pariati)
Cpte J. Ostendorf, J. Baird, St Luke's Baroque Orch, R. Palmer (1/92) (NEWP) ① **NCD60117**
Cpte M. Schopper, M. Bach, Stagione, M. Schneider (r1992) (4/94) (DHM) ① **05472 77284-2**

Bach goes to Town—piano (1938)
G. Malcolm (r1962) *Concert*
(11/95) (DECC) ① **444 390-2DWO**

Topsy-Turvy Suite—harpsichord (1938)
Bach Goes to Town B. Harbach *Concert*
(3/89) (KING) ① **KCLCD2005**

Ergodos I—computer sound generation (1963) (for John Cage)
J. Tenney (r1963) *Concert*
(8/94) (KOCH) ① [2] **37238-2**

Sofrir m'estuet et plus non puis durer—virelai
Gothic Voices, C. Page *Concert*
(3/92) (HYPE) ① **CDA66463**

Coridon's Lament (Coridons Klage-Vise)—1v and harpsichord (pub 1648)
R. Covey-Crump, L.U. Mortensen *Concert*
(2/89) (BIS) ① **BIS-CD391**

Daphnis begs his Galathee to remember him (Daphnis beder sin Galathee)—1v and harpsichord (pub 1653)
R. Covey-Crump, L.U. Mortensen *Concert*
(2/89) (BIS) ① **BIS-CD391**

Daphnis' worried thoughts of love (Daphniss bekymrede Kiaerligheds)—1v and harpsichord (pub 1648)
R. Covey-Crump, L.U. Mortensen *Concert*
(2/89) (BIS) ① **BIS-CD391**

A Drinking Song (Druckenskabs oc Vinens)—1v and harpsichord (pub 1654)
R. Covey-Crump, L.U. Mortensen *Concert*
(2/89) (BIS) ① **BIS-CD391**

Hylas does not want to get married (Hylas vill intet giffte sig)—1v and harpsichord (pub 1653)
R. Covey-Crump, L.U. Mortensen *Concert*
(2/89) (BIS) ① **BIS-CD391**

Myrtillo's Lament (Myrtillo Klage-Vise)—lv and harpsichord (pub 1648)
R. Covey-Crump, L.U. Mortensen *Concert*
(2/89) (BIS) ① **BIS-CD391**

To know a faithful heart (Jt trofaste Hierte gaar for Alting)—1v and harpsichord (pub 1654)
R. Covey-Crump, L.U. Mortensen *Concert*
(2/89) (BIS) ① **BIS-CD391**

The very sorrowful Daphnis' heart-rending lament (Dend højestbedrøffeude Daf—1v and harpsichord (pub 1654)
R. Covey-Crump, L.U. Mortensen *Concert*
(2/89) (BIS) ① **BIS-CD391**

La Fiancée du Scaphandrier—operetta: 1 act (1902—?Paris) (Lib. Franc-Nohain)
Cpte L. Dachary, C. Jacquin, G. Friedmann, J. Tharande, M. Hamel, ORTF Lyric Orch, J. Doussard (with dialogue: bp) *Travaux d'Hercule.*
(3/92) (MUSD) ① [2] **20179-2**

Les Travaux d'Hercule—operetta: 3 acts (1901—Paris) (Lib. R. de Flers & G. A. de Caillavet)
Cpte G. Rey, L. Dachary, D. Tirmont, C. Harbell, R. Lenoty, B. Alvi, L. Lovano, M. Fauchey, Lestelly, C. Daguerressar, M. Siderer, H. Hennetier, G. Parat, French Rad Lyric Chor, French Rad Lyric Orch, M. Cariven (with dialogue: bp) *Fiancée du Scaphandrier.*
(3/92) (MUSD) ① [2] **20179-2**

Canzone a otto voci per suonar a 4 liutti overo fantasia
J. Lindberg, R. Meunier, N. North, P. O'Dette *Concert*
(12/86) (BIS) ① **BIS-CD341**

Intavolatura di liuto, Secondo libro (pub 1599)
1. Toccata dell'Autore; 2. Volta quarta Francese; 3. Fantasia in modo in Canzon Francese del Guami.
1, 3. J. Lindberg (r1991) *Concert*
(11/93) (BIS) ① **BIS-CD599**

TESSIER, Guillaume (fl c1582) France

SECTION IV: VOCAL AND CHORAL

In a grove most rich of shade—song (1v and lute) (pub 1610) (Wds. P. Sidney)
E. Van Evera, P. O'Dette *Concert*
(2/88) (HARM) ① HMC90 5192

THALBEN-BALL, Sir George (Thomas) (1896–1987) Australia/England

SECTION III: INSTRUMENTAL

Elegy—organ
I. Tracey *Concert* (1/90) (CFP) ① CD-CFP4558

THALBERG, Sigismond (Fortuné François) (1812–1871) Germany/Austria

SECTION I: ORCHESTRAL

Concerto for Piano and Orchestra in F minor, Op. 5
M. Ponti, Westphalian SO, R. Kapp *Rubinstein: Piano Concerto 4.*
(5/93) (VOX) ① 115711-2

SECTION III: INSTRUMENTAL

Fantasia on 'God save the Queen'—piano, Op. 27
S. Mayer *Concert* (12/92) (ASV) ① CDDCA783
Fantasia on 'La fille du régiment' (Donizetti)—piano, Op. 68
F. Nicolosi (r1991) *Concert*
(7/94) (MARC) ① 8 223365
Fantasia on 'Lucrezia Borgia' (Donizetti)—piano, Op. 50
F. Nicolosi (r1991) *Concert*
(7/94) (MARC) ① 8 223365
Fantasia on the Serenade and Minuet from Mozart's 'Don Giovanni'—piano, Op. 42
C. Katsaris (r1992) *Concert*
(6/93) (SONY) ① SK52551
Fantasia on themes from Rossini's 'Moïse'—piano, Op. 33
S. Mayer *Concert* (12/92) (ASV) ① CDDCA783
Fantasy on themes from Donizetti's 'Don Pasquale'—piano, Op. 67
E. Wild *Concert* (8/92) (VANG) ① 08.4033.71
F. Nicolosi (r1991) *Concert*
(7/94) (MARC) ① 8 223365
Lacrimosa (after Mozart's Requiem Mass, K626)—piano
C. Katsaris (r1992) *Concert*
(6/93) (SONY) ① SK52551
Variations on a theme from 'L'elisir d'amore' (Donizetti)—piano, Op. 66
F. Nicolosi (r1991) *Concert*
(7/94) (MARC) ① 8 223365
Variations on a theme from 'Lucia di Lammermoor' (Donizetti)—piano, Op. 44
F. Nicolosi (r1991) *Concert*
(7/94) (MARC) ① 8 223365

THÄRICHEN, Werner (b 1921) Germany

SECTION I: ORCHESTRAL

Concerto for Timpani, Op. 34 (1954)
W. Thärichen, Berlin RSO, V. Handley *Concert*
(10/88) (SCHW) ① 311052

THEODORAKIS, Mikis (b 1925) Greece

SECTION IV: VOCAL AND CHORAL

A Day in May—song (Wds. Y. Ritsos)
A. Baltsa, K. Papadopoulos, Athens Exp Orch, S. Xarhakos (arr. Xarhakos) *Concert*
(2/87) (DG) ① 419 236-2GH
I gave you rose-water to drink—song (Wds. N. Gatsos)
A. Baltsa, K. Papadopoulos, Athens Exp Orch, S. Xarhakos (arr. Xarhakos) *Concert*
(2/87) (DG) ① 419 236-2GH
The **Train leaves at eight**—song (Wds. M. Eleftheriou)
A. Baltsa, K. Papadopoulos, Athens Exp Orch, S. Xarhakos (arr. Xarhakos) *Concert*
(2/87) (DG) ① 419 236-2GH

THIBAULT DE CHAMPAGNE (1201–1253) France

SECTION IV: VOCAL AND CHORAL

Aussi come unicorne sui—poem
A. Azéma, S. Kammen (r1993) *Concert*
(11/94) (ERAT) ① 4509-94830-2

THIEL, Olof (1892–1976) Sweden

also known as Jacques Armand

SECTION IV: VOCAL AND CHORAL

Was it a dream?—song (Wds. A. Berggren)
J. Björling, orch, S. Waldimir (r1933) *Concert*
(8/92) (BLUE) ① ABCD016

THOMAS, (Charles Louis) Ambroise (1811–1896) France

SECTION II: CHAMBER

String Quartet in E minor
Daniel Qt (r1991) *Concert*
(12/94) (DINT) ① DICD920159

SECTION V: STAGE WORKS

Le Caïd—opera: 2 acts (1849—Paris) (Lib. Sauvage)
Enfant chéri...Le tambour-major E. Pinza, orch, R. Bourdon (r1927) *Concert*
(2/89) (PEAR) ① GEMMCD9306
Enfant chéri...Le tambour-major E. Pinza, orch, R. Bourdon (r1927) *Concert*
(7/91) (MMOI) ① CDMOIR404
Enfant chérie...Le tambour-major P. Plançon, anon (r1903) *Concert* (9/91) (PEAR) ① GEMMCD9497
Enfant chérie...Le tambour-major P. Plançon, orch (r1907) *Concert* (9/91) (PEAR) ① GEMMCD9497
Enfant chéri...Le tambour-major P. Plançon, anon (r1902) *Concert* (3/93) (SYMP) ① SYMCD1100
Enfant chéri...Le Tambour-Major P. Plançon, orch (r1907) *Concert* (1/95) (NIMB) ① NI7860
Enfin chéri...Le tambour-major P. Plançon, orch (r1906/7: 2 vers)
(12/94) (ROMO) ① [2] 82001-2
Enfin chéri...Le tambour-major P. Plançon, anon (r1903) *Concert* (12/94) (ROMO) ① [2] 82001-2
Le tambour-major tout galonné d'or E. Pinza, orch, R. Bourdon (r1927) *Concert* (3/92) (PREI) ① 89050
Le tambour-major tout galonné d'or E. Pinza, orch, R. Bourdon (r1927) *Concert*
(9/93) (RCA) ① 09026 61245-2
Françoise de Rimini—opera: 5 acts (1882—Paris) (Lib. J. Barbier & Carré, after Dante)
Ballet Suite English Concert Orch, R. Bonynge *Concert* (11/90) (DECC) ① [2] 421 818-2DH2
Hamlet—opera: 5 acts (1869—Paris) (Lib. Carré, after Shakespeare)
EXCERPTS: ACT 1: 1. Prelude; 2a. Vains regrets!; 2b. Doute de la lumière; 3. Spectre infernal!. ACT 2: 4a. Se main depuis hier n'a pas touché ma main!; 4b. Adieu, dit-il; 5. Dans son regard; 6. O vin, dissipe la tristesse (Brindisi). ACT 3: 7. Etre ou ne pas être!; 8. Je t'implore, ô mon frère!. ACT 4: 9a. Entr'acte; 9b. Ballet; 10a. A vos jeux (Mad Scene); 10b. Des larmes de la nuit; 10c. Partagez-vous mes fleurs!; 10d. Pâle et blonde. ACT 5: 11. Comme une pâle fleur.
Cpte S. Milnes, J. Sutherland, G. Winbergh, B. Conrad, J. Morris, J. Tomlinson, K. Lewis, A.H. Morgan, P. Gelling, P. Garazzi, J. Rouleau, WNO Chor, WNO Orch, R. Bonynge
(5/93) (DECC) ① [3] 433 857-2DMO3
Cpte T. Hampson, J. Anderson, G. Kunde, D. Graves, S. Ramey, J-P. Courtis, G. Garino, M. Trempont, F. Le Roux, T. Félix, J-P. Furlan, Ambrosian Op Chor, LPO, A. de Almeida (r1993)
(1/94) (EMI) ① CDS7 54820-2
Exc R. Blanchart, anon (r1902) *Concert*
(11/92) (MEMO) ① [2] HR4408/9(1)
2a, 2b M. Journet, F. Heldy, SO (r1930) *Concert*
(1/94) (CLUB) ① CL99-034
4a, 4b E. Norena, orch, P. Coppola (r1932) *Concert*
(3/91) (PREI) ① 89041
6. G. Kaschmann, S. Cottone (Ital: r1903) *Concert*
(3/93) (SYMP) ① SYMCD1065
6. T. Ruffo, orch, C. Sabajno (Ital: r1907) *Concert*
(10/89) (NIMB) ① NI7810
6. M. Battistini, La Scala Chor, orch, C. Sabajno (Ital: r1911) *Concert* (10/92) (NIMB) ① NI7831
6. T. Ruffo, orch (Ital: r1920) *Concert*
(2/93) (PREI) ① [3] 89303(1)

6. E. Badini, orch (r1909: Ital) *Concert*
(12/94) (BONG) ① GB1043-2
6, 11. M. Battistini, orch (r1911: Ital) *Concert*
(2/92) (PREI) ① 89045
7. Vanni-Marcoux, orch (r1931) *Concert*
(1/94) (CLUB) ① CL99-101
10a J. Sutherland, ROHO, F. Molinari-Pradelli *Concert* (1/90) (DECC) ① [2] 425 493-2DM2
10a N. Melba, orch, L. Ronald (r1904) *Concert*
(7/92) (PEAR) ① [3] GEMMCDS9923(1)
10a L. Tetrazzini, orch (Ital: r1911) *Concert*
(9/92) (EMI) ① [3] CHS7 63802-2(1)
10a L. Tetrazzini, orch (Ital: r1911) *Concert*
(9/92) (PEAR) ① GEMMCD9222
10a A. Galli-Curci, orch (r1925: Ital) *Concert*
(8/94) (NIMB) ① NI7852
10a-d M. Callas, Philh Chor, Philh, N. Rescigno *Concert*
(6/86) (EMI) ① CDC7 47283-2
10a-d N. Melba, orch (r1907) *Concert*
(4/94) (RCA) ① [6] 09026 61580-2(1)
10a, 10d N. Melba, orch, W.B. Rogers (r1907) *Concert*
(9/93) (RCA) ① 09026 61412-2
10a, 10d N. Melba, orch, W.B. Rogers (r1907) *Concert*
(5/95) (ROMO) ① [3] 81011-2(1)
10b E. Norena, orch, H. Defosse (r1930) *Concert*
(3/91) (PREI) ① 89041
10b N. Melba, orch, W.B. Rogers (r1910) *Concert*
(5/95) (ROMO) ① [3] 81011-2(2)
10b, 10d N. Melba, orch (r1910) *Concert*
(7/93) (NIMB) ① [2] NI7840/1
10d E. Bronskaya, orch (r1913: Russ) *Concert*
(3/95) (NIMB) ① NI7865
11. M. Renaud, orch (r1908) *Concert*
(12/94) (SYMP) ① [3] GEMMCDS9923(2)
11. G. De Luca, anon (Ital: r1902) *Concert*
(8/93) (SYMP) ① SYMCD1111
Mignon—opera: 3 acts (1866—Paris) (Lib. Carré and Barbier)
EXCERPTS: 1. Overture. ACT 1: 2. Fugitif et tremblant; 3a. Laërte, amis; 3b. O filles de Bohême; 4a. Oui, je veux par le monde; 4b. Si l'amour sur ta route; 5. Connais-tu le pays?; 6. Légères hirondelles (Swallow Duet); 7. Me voici, tu m'as rachetée. ACT 2: 8. Entr'acte; 9. Plus de soucis, Mignon (Trio); 10a. Me voilà seule hélas!; 10b. Je connais un pauvre enfant (Styrienne); 11a. C'est moi; 11b. Me voici dans son boudoir (Gavotte); 12. Adieu, Mignon! Courage!; 13a. Elle est là; 13b. Elle est aimée!; 14. As-tu souffert?; 15a. Oui, pour ce soir; 15b. Je suis Titania (Polonaise). ACT 3: 15c. Ah! Au soufflé léger du vent (Barcarolle); 16. De son coeur, j'ai calmé (Berceuse); 17a. Etrange regard!; 17b. Elle ne croyait pas; 17c. Ah! que ton âme enfin; 18. O Vierge Marie. ALTERNATIVE OPENING TO ACT 2: 19. A merveille!; ALTERNATIVE FINALE TO ACT 3: 20. Dansons, dansons, amis!
1. NBC SO, A. Toscanini (r1952) *Concert*
(11/92) (RCA) ① GD60322
1. Detroit SO, P. Paray (r1960) *Concert*
(8/93) (MERC) ① 434 321-2MM
1. NYPO, L. Bernstein (r1963) *Concert*
(9/93) (SONY) ① SMK47601
1. LSO, C. Mackerras (r1961) *Concert*
(12/95) (MERC) ① 434 352-2MM
4a H. Roswaenge, orch (r1935: Ger) *Concert*
(4/95) (PREI) ① [2] 89209
5. A. Patti, A. Barili (r1906) *Concert*
(4/90) (PEAR) ① GEMMCD9312
5. K. Branzell, orch (r1928) *Concert*
(8/92) (PREI) ① 89039
5. C. Supervia, orch, G. Cloëz (r1931) *Concert*
(3/93) (NIMB) ① [2] NI7836/7
5. E. Destinn, orch (r1914: Ger) *Concert*
(11/93) (ROMO) ① [2] 81002-2
5. E. Destinn, orch (r1914: Ger) *Concert*
(5/94) (SUPR) ① 11 1337-2
5. E. Destinn, orch (r1914: Ger) *Concert*
(12/94) (SUPR) ① [12] 11 2136-2(5)
5. E. Destinn, orch (r1904: Ger) *Concert*
(12/94) (SUPR) ① [12] 11 2136-2(1)
5. C. Muzio, orch (r1917: Ital) *Concert*
(1/95) (ROMO) ① [2] 81010-2
5, 10b X. Belmas, orch, A. Kitschin (r1928) *Concert*
(10/92) (PREI) ① 89047
5, 10b E. Destinn, orch, B. Seidler-Winkler (r1908: Ger) *Concert* (12/94) (SUPR) ① [12] 11 2136-2(1)
5, 10b E. Destinn, orch (r1905: Ger) *Concert*
(12/94) (SUPR) ① [12] 11 2136-2(1)
5, 10b, 13b E. Destinn, orch (r1911: Ger) *Concert*
(12/94) (SUPR) ① [12] 11 2136-2(4)
5, 13a Lotte Lehmann, orch (Ger: r1917) *Concert*
(6/92) (PREI) ① [3] 89302
5(pt), 18. E. Destinn, orch, F. Kark (r1906: Ger) *Concert* (12/94) (SUPR) ① [12] 11 2136-2(1)
5, 6. C. Supervia, V. Bettoni, orch, A. Albergoni (r1929: Ital) *Concert* (9/90) (CLUB) ① CL99-074

6. Lotte Lehmann, H. Schlusnus, orch (Ger: r1920)
Concert (6/92) (PREI) ① [3] 89302
6. G. Farrar, M. Journet, orch (r1910) Concert
(10/94) (NIMB) ① NI7859
6, 14, 16. G. Zinetti, T. Pasero, orch, L. Molajoli (Ital:
r1928) Concert (6/90) (PREI) ① 89010
8. Philadelphia, L. Stokowski (r1930s) Concert
(8/95) (BIDD) ① WHL011
10b E. Stignani, EIAR Orch, U. Tansini (Ital: r1937)
Concert (1/91) (PREI) ① 89014
10b, 13a I. Seefried, Lamoureux Orch, J. Fournet
(r1963: Ger) Concert
(9/93) (DG) ① [2] 437 677-2GDO2
12. T. Schipa, orch (Ital: r1924) Concert
(2/89) (PEAR) ① GEMMCD9322
12. J. Patzak, orch (Ger: r1935) Concert
(3/90) (PEAR) ① GEMMCD9383
12. H.E. Groh, orch, F. Weissmann (Ger: r1931)
Concert (3/92) (PEAR) ① GEMMCD9419
12. G. di Stefano, La Scala Orch, E. Tieri (Ital: r1947)
Concert (4/92) (EMI) ① [7] CHS7 69741-2(7)
12. Ferruccio Tagliavini, EIAR Orch, U. Tansini
(r1943: Ital) Concert (3/94) (CENT) ① CRC2164
12. J. Patzak, orch (r c1934: Ger) Concert
(9/94) (NIMB) ① NI7856
12. W. Ludwig, Berlin City Op Orch, W. Ladwig
(r1932: Ger) Concert (7/95) (PREI) ① 89088
12, 17b B. Gigli, orch, R. Bourdon (Ital: r1928)
Concert (9/88) (PEAR) ① GEMMCD9316
12, 17b D. Borgioli, orch (Ital: r c1923) Concert
(12/90) (CLUB) ① CL99-014
12, 17b R. Tauber, orch, K. Besl (Ger: r1923)
Concert (3/92) (EMI) ① CDH7 64029-2
12, 17b A. Piccaver, orch (r1914: Ger) Concert
(8/93) (PREI) ① 89060
15a-c E. Gruberová, Munich RO, L. Gardelli Concert
(11/86) (ORFE) ① C101841A
15a-c M. Callas, FRNO, G. Prêtre Concert
(2/90) (EMI) ① CDM7 63182-2
15a-c P. Munsel, RCA SO, S. Levin (r1945) Concert
(4/94) (RCA) ① [6] 09026 61580-2(6)
15b M. Callas, FRNO, G. Prêtre Concert
(2/88) (EMI) ① CDC7 49059-2
15b L. Tetrazzini, orch (r1911) Concert
(10/89) (NIMB) ① NI7802
15b T. dal Monte, La Scala Orch, C. Sabajno (r1929:
Ital) Concert (2/90) (PREI) ① 89001
15b A. Galli-Curci, orch, R. Bourdon (Ital: r1919)
Concert (5/90) (NIMB) ① NI7806
15b L. Pons, Columbia SO, A. Kostelanetz (r1949)
Concert (7/90) (SONY) ① MPK45694
15b L. Tetrazzini, orch (Ital: r1911) Concert
(10/90) (NIMB) ① NI7808
15b L. Tetrazzini, orch (Ital: r1911) Concert
(9/92) (EMI) ① [3] CHS7 63802-2(1)
15b L. Tetrazzini, orch, P. Pitt (Ital: r1907) Concert
(9/92) (EMI) ① [3] CHS7 63802-2(1)
15b L. Tetrazzini, orch, P. Pitt (Ital: r1908) Concert
(9/92) (EMI) ① [3] CHS7 63802-2(2)
15b L. Tetrazzini, orch, P. Pitt (Ital: r1907) Concert
(9/92) (PEAR) ① GEMMCD9221
15b L. Tetrazzini, orch (Ital: r1911) Concert
(9/92) (PEAR) ① GEMMCD9222
15b L. Tetrazzini, orch (Ital: r1911) Concert
(9/92) (PEAR) ① GEMMCD9224
15b A. Galli-Curci, orch, J. Pasternack (r1919: Ital)
Concert (3/94) (ROMO) ① [2] 81003-2
15b P. Alarie, Lamoureux Orch, J. Dervaux (r1953)
Concert (11/94) (PHIL) ① [2] 438 953-2PM2
15b E. Steber, orch, G. Goossens (bp1942) Concert
(11/95) (VAI) ① VAIA1072
16. P. Plançon, orch (r1908) Concert
(9/91) (PEAR) ① GEMMCD9497
16. E. Pinza, orch, R. Bourdon (r1927) Concert
(3/92) (PREI) ① 89050
16. A. Didur, orch (r c1918) Concert
(1/94) (CLUB) ① CL99-089
16. G. Hüsch, Berlin St Op Orch, H.U. Müller (r1937:
Ger) Concert (3/94) (PREI) ① 89071
16. P. Plançon, orch (r1908: Ital) Concert
(12/94) (ROMO) ① [2] 82001-2
17b H. Nash, orch (Eng: r1926) Concert
(8/89) (PEAR) ① GEMMCD9319
17b L. Sobinov, orch (r1911: Russ) Concert
(6/93) (PEAR) ① [3] GEMMCDS9997/9(2)
17b A. Bonci, anon (Ital: r1905) Concert
(12/93) (SYMP) ① SYMCD1113
17b T. Schipa, orch (Ital: r1924: Ital) Concert
(12/93) (NIMB) ① NI7851
17b L. David, anon (r1905) Concert
(12/94) (SYMP) ① SYMCD1172
17b G. Anselmi, orch (r1907: Ital) Concert
(7/95) (SYMP) ① SYMCD1170

Raymond—opera: 3 acts (1851—Paris) (Lib.
Rosier and de Leuven)
Overture Montreal SO, C. Dutoit Concert
(6/89) (DECC) ① 421 527-2DH
Overture Detroit SO, P. Paray (r1960) Concert
(8/93) (MERC) ① 434 321-2MM
Le Songe d'une nuit d'été—opera: 3 acts
(1850—Paris) (Lib. J B Rosier & A de Leuven)
EXCERPTS: 1. Malgré l'éclat qui m'environne.
1. S. Jo, ECO, R. Bonynge (r1993) Concert
(9/94) (DECC) ① 440 679-2DH

THOMAS, John (1826–1913)
Wales

SECTION III: INSTRUMENTAL

Echoes of a Waterfall—caprice for harp
S. Drake Concert (9/86) (HYPE) ① CDA66038
Fantasia on 'David of the White
Rock'—harp
S. Drake (r1988) Concert
(2/90) (HYPE) ① CDA66340
Megan's Daughter—air and variations for
harp
S. Drake Concert (9/86) (HYPE) ① CDA66038
Study—harp
S. Drake (r1988) Concert
(2/90) (HYPE) ① CDA66340
Watching the Wheat—air and variations for
harp
S. Drake Concert (9/86) (HYPE) ① CDA66038
T. Owen Concert (3/87) (CARL) ① PCD835

THOMAS, John Rogers
(19th–20th cents)

SECTION IV: VOCAL AND CHORAL

Eileen Allanna—song (1873) (Wds. E S
Marble)
H. Nash, G. Moore (r1931) Concert
(11/95) (PEAR) ① GEMMCD9175

THOMAS, Mansel (1909–1986)
Wales

SECTION IV: VOCAL AND CHORAL

Blest are the pure in heart—anthem (1965)
(Wds. J Keble & others)
Llandaff Cath Ch, M. Smith, M. Hoeg (r1994) Concert
(10/95) (PRIO) ① PRCD510
For thy servant David—anthem (1955) (Wds.
from H Riley and W Morgan)
Llandaff Cath Ch, M. Smith, M. Hoeg (r1994) Concert
(10/95) (PRIO) ① PRCD510

THOMAS, Michael (20th Cent)
England

SECTION II: CHAMBER

Gabo de Gata—string quartet
Brodsky Qt Concert (4/92) (TELD) ① 2292-46015-2
Harold In Islington—string quartet (1993)
Brodsky Qt (r1994) Concert
(10/94) (SILV) ① SILKD6001
Variations on a Theme of Banjo Patterson,
'Waltzing Matilda'—string quartet (1993)
Brodsky Qt (r1994) Concert
(10/94) (SILV) ① SILKD6001

THOMÉ, Francis (1850–1909)
France

SECTION III: INSTRUMENTAL

Simple aveu—piano, Op. 25
A. Etherden Concert
(7/93) (HUNT) ① HMPCD0589

THOMMESEN ?Norway

SECTION IV: VOCAL AND CHORAL

Lille-Barnet, '(The) Little child'—song
K. Flagstad, orch (r1930) Concert
(12/95) (SIMA) ① [3] PSC1821(1)

THOMPSON, Randall (1899–1984)
USA

SECTION I: ORCHESTRAL

Symphony No. 2 (1931)
NZ SO, A. Schenck Symphony 3.
(9/92) (KOCH) ① 37074-2
Symphony No. 3 in A minor (1947-49)
NZ SO, A. Schenck Symphony 2.
(9/92) (KOCH) ① 37074-2

SECTION IV: VOCAL AND CHORAL

Alleluia—4vv (1940)
Roberts Wesleyan Coll Chorale, R. Shewan Concert
(6/90) (BAY) ① BCD-1011
E. Futral, J. Malafronte, F. Urrey, W. Pauley, Musica
Sacra, R. Westenburg Concert
(1/93) (RCA) ① 09026 60970-2
The Best of Rooms—4vv a capella (1964)
(Wds. R. Herrick)
Roberts Wesleyan Coll Chorale, R. Shewan Concert
(6/90) (BAY) ① BCD-1011
A Feast of Praise—cantata: 4vv, brass,
harp/piano (1963)
Roberts Wesleyan Coll Chorale, Roberts Wesleyan
Brass Ens, R. Shewan Concert
(6/90) (BAY) ① BCD-1011
The Last words of David—4vv,
piano/orchestra (1949)
Roberts Wesleyan Coll Chorale, B. Harbach, Roberts
Wesleyan Brass Ens, R. Shewan Concert
(6/90) (BAY) ① BCD-1011
Velvet shoes—song (1927) (Wds. E H Wylie)
P. Frijsh, C. Dougherty (r1940) Concert
(4/95) (PEAR) ① [2] GEMMCDS9095(1)

THOMSEN, Magnus (?–1612)
Denmark

SECTION II: CHAMBER

Toccata I—trumpets and drums (c1600)
Gabrieli Players, P. McCreesh Concert
(5/90) (VIRG) ① VC7 59006-2

THOMSON, Virgil (1896–1989)
USA

SECTION I: ORCHESTRAL

Acadian Songs and Dances (1948) (from film
score 'Louisiana Story')
1. Sadness; 2. Papa's Tune; 3. A Narrative; 4. The
Alligator and the Coon; 5. Super-sadness; 6.
Walking-song; 7. The Squeeze-box.
New London Orch, R. Corp Concert
(8/92) (HYPE) ① CDA66576
Fanfare for France—brass ensemble (1942)
LPO, J. Mester Concert (9/91) (KOCH) ① 37012-2
Fugues and Cantilenas (1959) (from film score
'Power Among Men')
New London Orch, R. Corp Concert
(8/92) (HYPE) ① CDA66576
A Joyful Fugue—orchestra (1962)
Budapest SO, J. Bolle Concert
(4/90) (ALBA) ① TROY017-2
A Solemn Music—orchestra (1949 orch
1961)
Budapest SO, J. Bolle Concert
(4/90) (ALBA) ① TROY017-2
Symphony No. 2 (1930 rev 1941)
Monadnock Fest Orch, J. Bolle Concert
(4/90) (ALBA) ① TROY017-2
Symphony on a Hymn Tune (1928)
Monadnock Fest Orch, J. Bolle Concert
(4/90) (ALBA) ① TROY017-2

SECTION II: CHAMBER

Family Portrait—2 trumpets, horn & 2
trombones (1974)
1. A Fanfare: Robin Smith; 2. At 14: Annie Barnard;
3. A Portrait of Howard Rea; 4. Scherzo: Priscilla
Rea; 5. Man of Iron, Willy Eisenhart.
London Gabrieli Brass Ens, C. Larkin Concert
(5/92) (HYPE) ① CDA66517

SECTION III: INSTRUMENTAL

Portrait (Marya Freund)—piano (1956)
B. Harbach Concert (3/89) (KING) ① KCLCD2005
25 Portraits—piano (1940)
1. Tango Lullaby...Mlle Alvarez de Toledo; 2. With
Tpt and Hn...Louise Ardant; 3. Poltergeist...Hans Arp;
4. Stretching...Jamie Campbell; 5. Cantabile...Nicolas
de Chatelain; 6. Duet...Clarita, Comtesse de
forceville; 7. In a Bird Cage...Lise Deharme; 8. Pf

Sonata no. 4: Guggenheim jeune; 9.
Barcarolle...Georges Hugnet; 10. Aria...Germaine
Hugnet; 11. Invention: Theodate Johnson Busy and
Resting; 12. Fanfare for france...Max Hahn; 13. 5-
finger Exercise...Leon Kochnitzky; 14. Awake or
Asleep...Pierre Mabille; 15. The Bard...Sherry
Mangan; 16. Canons with Cadenza...Andrré Ostier;
17. Bugles and Birds...Pablo Picasso; 18. Dora Maar
or the Presence of Pablo Picasso; 19. Lullaby which
is also a Spinning Song...Howard Putzel; 20. The
dream world of Peter Rose-Pulham; 21.
Fugue...Alexander Smallens; 22. Swiss
Waltz...Sophie Tauber-Arp; 23. Eccentric
Dance...Madame Kristians Tonny; 24.
Pastoral...Tristan Tzara; 25. Toccata...Mary Whitney.
4, 12, 23. B. Harbach *Concert*
(3/89) (KING) ① KCLCD2005
10 Portraits—piano (1983)
1. Mark Beard: Never Alone; 2. Power Boothe: with
Pencil; 3. Charles Fussell: in Meditation; 4. Glynn
Boothe Harte: Reaching; 5. Bennett Lerner: senza
espressione; 6. Peter McWilliams: Thinking
Spontaneous; 7. Malitte Matta: in the Executive Style;
8. Philip Ramey: Thinking Hard; 9. Louis Rispoli: in a
Boat; 10. Vassilis Voglin: on the March.
5, 8. B. Lerner *Concert*
(12/88) (ETCE) ① KTC1019
3 Sentimental Tangos—piano (1923)
B. Lerner *Concert* (12/88) (ETCE) ① KTC1019

SECTION IV: VOCAL AND CHORAL

**5 Blake Songs—baritone and orchestra
(1951)**
1. The Divine Image; 2. Tiger! Tiger!; 3. The Land of
Dreams; 4. The Little Black Boy; 5. And did those
feet.
2. S. Milnes, NY Met Op Orch, J. Conlon (pp1991)
Concert (6/93) (RCA) ① 09026 61509-2
**Shipwreck and Love Scene from Byron's
'Don Juan'—tenor and orchestra (1967)**
M. Hill, Budapest SO, J. Bolle *Concert*
(4/90) (ALBA) ① TROY017-2

SECTION V: STAGE WORKS

Lord Byron—opera: 3 acts (1972—New York)
(Lib. J. Larson)
EXCERPTS: ACT ONE: 1. Byron is dead; 2a. Ay me
that dreerie death; 2b. Spenser, Thomson, Milton,
Chaucer; 2c. We shall all our duty; 2d. Byron is
dead; 2e. Interlude; 2f. I've no great cause. ACT
TWO: 3a. It truly reminds me of him; 3b. Remember,
the poet we knew; 4a. Alas! the love of woman!; 4b.
Mi-lord, we should not pay such attention; 4c. Byron!
Byron!; 4d. They have started the waltz lesson; 4e.
No! I have no desire to spin round and round; 4f. She
referred to my foot; 4g. A wanderer from the British
world of fashion; 4h. You are very bitter; 4i. You are
too late; 4j. Ah! Ah!; 5a. Prelude; 5b. God bless you,
my love (Lady Caroline's Aria); 5c. God! I am more
degenerate; 5d. Ask not for valour; 5e. Seductive
waltz!; 5f. My sister waltzes; 5g. Sweet lady; 6a.
Prelude; 6b. Should auld acquaintance; 6c. I take him
from this day; 6d. I should hate to be a cuckold; 6e.
Let us retire; 6f. Should auld acquaintance. ACT
THREE: 7a. How we two; 7b. My baby Byron!; 7c.
Dear, your house is so charming; 7d. Kisses, give
your baby kisses; 7e. Your being here; 7f. You walk
in beauty; 7g. I did not retire; 7h. I'd sooner burn in
hell; 7i. As once I wept; 7j. 'Tis my nature; 7k. Fare
thee well; 8a. Eventful volume!; 8b. Please! What are
you burning?; 8c. Saviour, breathe an ev'ning
blessing; 8d. Interlude; 8e. They weigh a life; 8f. Ah,
he has outsoared the shadow; 8g. From mighty
wrongs.
Cpte M. Lord, R. Zeller, D. Fortunato, R. Johnson, J.
Ommerlé, G. Mercer, A. Csengery, T. Woodman, S.
Owen, L. Jonason, D. Vanderlinde, M. Dry,
Monadnock Fest Chor, Monadnock Fest Orch, J.
Bolle (pp1991) (5/93) (KOCH) ① [2] 37124-2
4a, 4g, 5g, 7h, 7k M. Hill, Budapest SO, J. Bolle
Concert (4/90) (ALBA) ① TROY017-2
**Louisiana Story—concert suite from film
score (1948)**
New London Orch, R. Corp *Concert*
(8/92) (HYPE) ① CDA66576
**The Mother of us all—opera: 2 acts
(1947—New York)** (Lib. G. Stein)
Cpte M. Dunn, J. Atherton, P. Booth, B. Godfrey, W.
Lewis, L. Maxwell, H. Vanni, D. Perry, A. Putnam, J.
McKee, G. Ives, Santa Fé Op Chor, Santa Fé Op
Orch, R. Leppard (r1976)
(7/90) (NEW) ① [2] NW288/9-2
**The Plow that broke the Plains—film score
(1936)**
1. The old South; 2. Prologue; 4. Industrial expansion
in the Mississippi Valley; 5. Soil erosion and floods; 6.

Finale.
Philh Virtuosi, R. Kapp *River.*
(8/92) (SCHW) ① 311166
New London Orch, R. Corp *Concert*
(8/92) (HYPE) ① CDA66576
The River—film score (1937)
1. Prelude and Fugue; 2. Grass-Pastorale; 3. Cattle;
4. The homesteader; 5. War and the tractor; 6. Blues
(Speculation); 7. Drought; 8. Wind and dust; 9.
Devastation.
Philh Virtuosi, R. Kapp *Plow that broke the Plains.*
(8/92) (SCHW) ① 311166

┌─────────────────────────────────────┐
│ **THORKELL, Sigurbjörnsson** (b   │
│ **1938) Iceland**   │
└─────────────────────────────────────┘

SECTION I: ORCHESTRAL

**Columbine—divertimento: flute and strings
(1982)**
2. Siciliano.
2. Musica Vitae CO, W. Rajski, M. Wiesler *Concert*
(6/90) (BIS) ① BIS-CD461

┌─────────────────────────────────────┐
│ **THORPE DAVIE, Cedric**   │
│ **(1913–1983) Scotland**   │
└─────────────────────────────────────┘

SECTION IV: VOCAL AND CHORAL

Come, Holy Ghost, the Maker—hymn
Dundee Cath Ch, R. Lightband (org/dir) *Concert*
(8/92) (ABBE) ① CDCA926

┌─────────────────────────────────────┐
│ **THRANE, Waldemar (1790–1828)**   │
│ **Norway**   │
└─────────────────────────────────────┘

SECTION IV: VOCAL AND CHORAL

Aagots Fjeldsang—song
K. Flagstad, orch (r1914) *Concert*
(12/95) (SIMA) ① [3] PSC1821(1)

┌─────────────────────────────────────┐
│ **THUILLE, Ludwig (1861–1907)**   │
│ **Austria**   │
└─────────────────────────────────────┘

SECTION II: CHAMBER

**Sextet in B flat—piano and wind quintet, Op.
6 (1886-88)**
D.R. Davies, Stuttgart Wind Qnt *Poulenc: Sextet.*
(11/89) (MDG) ① L3287
**Sonata for Cello and Piano in D minor, Op.
22 (1901-02)**
S. Rolland, M-A. Hamelin (r c1994) *R. Strauss: Cello
Sonata.* (3/95) (ASV) ① CDDCA913

SECTION V: STAGE WORKS

**Lobetanz—opera: 3 acts, Op. 10
(1898—Karlsruhe)** (Lib. O. J. Bierbaum)
An allen Zweigen J. Gadski, orch (r1914) *Concert*
(7/91) (CLUB) ① CL99-109

┌─────────────────────────────────────┐
│ **TIENSUU, Jukka (b 1948)**   │
│ **Finland**   │
└─────────────────────────────────────┘

SECTION I: ORCHESTRAL

**Concerto for Clarinet and Orchestra, 'Puro'
(1989)**
K. Kriikku, Finnish RSO, J-P. Saraste *Concert*
(10/92) (ONDI) ① ODE778-2

┌─────────────────────────────────────┐
│ **TIERNEY, Harry (Austin)**   │
│ **(1890–1965) USA**   │
└─────────────────────────────────────┘

SECTION V: STAGE WORKS

**Irene—musical show (1919, revival
1973—New York)** (Lyrics J. McCarthy;
additional material for revival by Gaynor &
Clements)
EXCERPTS: ACT ONE: 1. Overture; 2. The World
Must Be Bigger Than An Avenue; 3. What Do You
Want to Make Those Eyes At Me For?; 4. The Family
Tree; 5. Alice Blue Gown; 6. They Go Wild, Simply
Wild, Over Me; 7. An Irish Girl; 8. Mother, Angel,
Darling; 9. The Riviera Rage; 10. I'm Always Chasing
Rainbows. ACT TWO: 11. The Last Part of Ev'ry
Party; 12. We're Getting Away With It; 13. Irene; 14.
The Great Lover Tango; 15. You Made Me Love You;
16. You Made Me Love You (reprise); 17. Finale.
ITEMS FROM ORIGINAL PRODUCTION: 18. Castle
of Dreams; 19. To Be Worthy of You; 20. Sky Rocket.
5, 13, 18-20. E. Day, Orig Broadway Cast (r1920)
Concert (5/94) (PEAR) ① [3] GEMMCDS9059/61

┌─────────────────────────────────────┐
│ **TIERSOT, Julien (1857–1936)**   │
│ **France**   │
└─────────────────────────────────────┘

SECTION IV: VOCAL AND CHORAL

En passant par la Lorraine—song
E. Clément, anon (r1910s) *Concert*
(8/95) (PEAR) ① GEMMCD9161

┌─────────────────────────────────────┐
│ **TINCTORIS, Johannes**   │
│ **(c1435–?1511) Flanders**   │
└─────────────────────────────────────┘

SECTION IV: VOCAL AND CHORAL

De tous biens playne—chanson (from
Segovia MS)
Daedalus Ens *Concert*
(12/92) (ACCE) ① ACC9176D

┌─────────────────────────────────────┐
│ **TIOMKIN, Dimitri (1894–1979)**   │
│ **Russia/USA**   │
└─────────────────────────────────────┘

SECTION I: ORCHESTRAL

**A President's Country—orchestral suite
(1966)**
RCM Orch, D. Willcocks *Concert*
(2/86) (UNIC) ① DKPCD9047

SECTION V: STAGE WORKS

The Alamo—film score (1960)
EXCERPTS: 1. Main Theme, 'The Green Leaves of
Summer' (Lyrics P F Webster); 2. Overture; 3.
SUITE: arr C Palmer: 3a. Overture & Prologue; 3b.
Davy Crockett; 3c. Intermezzo I: The Green Leaves
of Summer; 3d. The Battle of the Alamo; 3e.
Intermezzo II: Tennesse Babe; 3f. The Ballad of the
Alamo.
2. Prague City PO, P. Bateman (r1994; arr Palmer)
Concert (11/94) (SILV) ① FILMCD153
Dial M for Murder—film score (1954)
EXCERPTS: 1. Main Title; 2. The Telephone; 3. The
Trap; 4. Finale.
1-4. Prague City PO, P. Bateman (r1993) *Concert*
(3/94) (SILV) ① FILMCD137
**The Fall of the Roman Empire—film score
(1964)**
EXCERPTS: 1. Fanfares & Flourishes; 2. Prelude; 3.
Dawn on the Northern Frontier; 4. Livius' Arrival; 5.
Old Acquaintances; 6. Pax Romana; 7. The Dawn of
Love; 8. Decoy Patrol; 9. The Battle in the
Forest/Reinforcements; 10. The Funeral of Marcus
Aurelius; 11. The Roman Forum/By Jove &
Intermission Title; 12. Intermezzo: Livius & Lucilla;
13. Conflict in the Caverns; 14. Aftermath & The
Journey to Rome; 15. The Army Enters Rome/The
New God/Challenge; 16. Finale.
1-16. OST, D. Tiomkin (r1964)
(4/92) (CLOU) ① ACN7016
1, 2, 4, 5, 8, 9, 12, 15. OST, D. Tiomkin (r1964)
Concert (10/93) (CLOU) ① CNS5006
2, 6. RCM Orch, D. Willcocks *Concert*
(2/86) (UNIC) ① DKPCD9047
The Great Waltz—film score (1938) (arr of
waltzes by J Strauss II)
EXCERPTS: 1. Main Title; 1b. Wiener Blut Waltzes;
2a. Blue Danube; 2b. Final Sequence.
1a, 1b, 2a, 2b Hollywood Bowl SO, J. Mauceri
(r1993; arr Mauceri; restored Palmer) *Concert*
(6/94) (PHIL) ① 438 685-2PH
The Guns of Navarone—film score (1961)
EXCERPTS: 1. Prelude (Legend of Navaronne); 2.
Prologue; 3. Epilogue (Mission Accomplished); 4.
Main Theme.
1. National PO, C. Gerhardt *Concert*
(10/92) (RCA) ① GD82792
1. Prague City PO, P. Bateman (r1994; arr C.
Palmer) *Concert* (11/94) (SILV) ① FILMCD151
1-3. RCM Orch, D. Willcocks *Concert*
(2/86) (UNIC) ① DKPCD9047
The High and the Mighty—film score (1954)
EXCERPTS: 1. Prelude.
1. Prague City PO, P. Bateman (r1994; arr Palmer)
Concert (11/94) (SILV) ① FILMCD153
**The Magnificent Showman, 'Circus
World'—film score (1964)**
EXCERPTS: 1. John Wayne March; 2. Main Title:
Circus World; 3. Buffalo Gal; 4. Toni and Giovanna;
5. In Old Vienna; 6. Exit Music: Circus World
(reprise).
1-6. OST, D. Tiomkin (r1964) *Concert*
(10/93) (CLOU) ① CNS5006
Rhapsody of Steel—film score (1959)
Suite RCM Orch, D. Willcocks *Concert*
(2/86) (UNIC) ① DKPCD9047

Strangers On a Train—film score (1951)
EXCERPTS: 1. Main Title; 2. Approaching the Train;
3. The Tennis Game & The Cigarette Lighter; 4.
Bruno's Death & Finale.
1-4. Prague City PO, P. Bateman *Concert*
(9/95) (SILV) ① **FILMCD159**
The Thing (from Another World)—film score (1951)
EXCERPTS: 1. Prelude; 2. The Flying Saucer under
the Ice; 3. Melting Sequence; 4. The Hand; 5. Plasma
I; 6. Plasma II; 7. The Growing Plants; 8. The Thing
on the Walkway; 9. Electrocution.
Suite National PO, C. Gerhardt *Concert*
(10/92) (RCA) ① **GD82792**
Wild is the Wind—film score (1957)
Main Theme RCM Orch, D. Willcocks *Concert*
(2/86) (UNIC) ① **DKPCD9047**
55 Days At Peking—film score (1963)
EXCERPTS: 1. Overture; 2. Prelude; 3. Murder of
the German Ambassador; 4. The Orphan & the Major
(Moonfire); 5. Attack on the French Legation; 6.
Intermezzo: So Little Time; 7. SUITE, arr C Palmer:
7a. Overture; 7b. Welcome Marines/Tuan's
Procession; 7c. Attack and Explosion; 7d.
Intermezzo: Children's Corner/Peking Theme (So
Little Time); 7e. Chinese Victory Celebration/Hauling
the Gun; 7f. Finale.
1-6. OST, D. Tiomkin (r1963) *Concert*
(10/93) (CLOU) ① **CNS5006**

TIPPETT, Keith (b 1947) England

SECTION IV: VOCAL AND CHORAL

Sun—The Living Son—song (Wds. J.
Tippett)
M. Wiegold, Composers Ens, D. Muldowney *Concert*
(4/92) (NMC) ① **NMCD003**

TIPPETT, Sir Michael (Kemp) (b 1905) England

SECTION I: ORCHESTRAL

Concerto for Double String Orchestra (1938-39)
Moscow CO, R. Barshai (r1962) *Concert*
(12/91) (EMI) ① [2] **CMS7 63522-2**
Concerto for Orchestra (1962-63)
Bournemouth SO, R. Hickox (r1994) *Triple Concerto.*
(8/95) (CHAN) ① **CHAN9384**
Concerto for Piano and Orchestra (1953-55)
J. Ogdon, Philh, Colin Davis (r1963) *Concert*
(12/91) (EMI) ① [2] **CMS7 63522-2**
H. Shelley, Bournemouth SO, R. Hickox (r1994)
Symphony 1. (4/95) (CHAN) ① **CHAN9333**
Concerto for Violin, Viola, Cello and Orchestra (1979)
L. Chilingirian, S. Rowland-Jones, P. de Groote,
Bournemouth SO, R. Hickox (r1994) *Concerto for
orchestra.* (8/95) (CHAN) ① **CHAN9384**
Fanfare for the Four Corners—brass
Wallace Collection, J. Wallace *Concert*
(3/92) (COLL) ① **Coll1229-2**
Fantasia Concertante on a Theme of Corelli—strings (1953)
I. Brown, K. Sillito, D. Vigay, ASMF, N. Marriner
Concert (2/85) (ASV) ① **CDDCA518**
ASMF, K. Sillito *Concert*
(10/91) (COLL) ① **Coll1234-2**
Bath Fest Orch, M. Tippett (r1964) *Concert*
(12/91) (EMI) ① [2] **CMS7 63522-2**
RPO, C. Groves (r1989) *Concert*
(9/92) (CARL) ① **CDRPO5005**
Bournemouth SO, R. Hickox (r1993) *Concert*
(11/93) (CHAN) ① **CHAN9233**
Fantasia on a Theme of Handel—piano and orchestra (1939-41)
H. Shelley, Bournemouth SO, R. Hickox (r1993)
Concert (11/93) (CHAN) ① **CHAN9233**
Festal Brass with Blues—brass band (1984)
London Collegiate Brass, J. Stobart *Concert*
(9/87) (CRD) ① **CRD3444**
Wallace Collection, J. Wallace *Concert*
(3/92) (COLL) ① **Coll1229-2**
Little Music for strings (1946)
Soloists of Australia, R.Thomas (vn/dir) (pp1986)
Concert (4/87) (CHAN) ① **CHAN8498**
Soloists of Australia, R. Thomas (vn/dir) *Concert*
(6/92) (CHAN) ① **CHAN6576**
Praeludium—brass, bells and percussion (1962)
English Northern Philh, M. Tippett *Concert*
(4/90) (NIMB) ① **NI5217**
Bournemouth SO, R. Hickox (r1993) *Symphony 3.*
(6/94) (CHAN) ① **CHAN9276**

Suite in D—a birthday suite for Prince Charles (1948)
English Northern Philh, M. Tippett *Concert*
(4/90) (NIMB) ① **NI5217**
Chicago SO, G. Solti *Concert*
(7/90) (LOND) ① [3] **425 646-2LM3**
Symphony No. 1 (1944-45)
LSO, Colin Davis *Concert*
(7/90) (LOND) ① [3] **425 646-2LM3**
Bournemouth SO, R. Hickox (r1994) *Piano Concerto.*
(4/95) (CHAN) ① **CHAN9333**
Symphony No. 2 (1956-57)
LSO, Colin Davis *Concert*
(7/90) (LOND) ① [3] **425 646-2LM3**
Bournemouth SO, R. Hickox (r1994) *New Year Suite.*
(10/94) (CHAN) ① **CHAN9299**
Symphony No. 3—soprano and orchestra (1970-72) (Wds. cpsr)
H. Harper, LSO, Colin Davis *Concert*
(7/90) (LOND) ① [3] **425 646-2LM3**
F. Robinson, Bournemouth SO, R. Hickox (r1993)
Praeludium. (6/94) (CHAN) ① **CHAN9276**
Symphony No. 4 (1976-77)
Chicago SO, G. Solti *Concert*
(7/90) (LOND) ① [3] **425 646-2LM3**
Chicago SO, G. Solti (r1979) *Byzantium.*
(4/93) (DECC) ① **433 668-2DH**
Bournemouth SO, R. Hickox (r1993) *Concert*
(11/93) (CHAN) ① **CHAN9233**

SECTION II: CHAMBER

Sonata—four horns (1955)
Wallace Collection, J. Wallace *Concert*
(3/92) (COLL) ① **Coll1229-2**
String Quartet No. 1 (1934-35)
Britten Qt *Concert*
(12/91) (COLL) ① [2] **Coll7006-2**
Edinburgh Qt (r1960s) *Concert*
(12/91) (EMI) ① [2] **CMS7 63522-2**
String Quartet No. 2 in F (1941-42)
Britten Qt *Concert*
(12/91) (COLL) ① [2] **Coll7006-2**
String Quartet No. 3 (1945-46)
Britten Qt *Concert*
(12/91) (COLL) ① [2] **Coll7006-2**
String Quartet No. 4 (1978)
Lindsay Qt *Britten: String Quartet 3.*
(5/88) (ASV) ① **CDDCA608**
Britten Qt *Concert*
(12/91) (COLL) ① [2] **Coll7006-2**
String Quartet No. 5 (1990-91)
Lindsay Qt (r1992) *Concert*
(1/94) (ASV) ① **CDDCA879**

SECTION III: INSTRUMENTAL

The Blue guitar (1983)
E. Kotzia *Concert* (6/89) (PEAR) ① **SHECD9609**
N. Kraft *Concert* (1/90) (CHAN) ① **CHAN8784**
C. Ogden (r1994) *Concert* (6/95) (NIMB) ① **NI5390**
Sonata for Piano No. 1 (1934-35 rev 1942)
J. Ogdon (r1966) *Concert*
(12/91) (EMI) ① [2] **CMS7 63522-2**
P. Crossley *Concert*
(6/92) (CRD) ① [2] **CRD3430/1**
Sonata for Piano No. 2 (1941-42)
J. Ogdon (r1963) *Concert*
(12/91) (EMI) ① [2] **CMS7 63522-2**
P. Crossley *Concert*
(6/92) (CRD) ① [2] **CRD3430/1**
Sonata for Piano No. 3 (1972-73)
P. Crossley *Concert*
(6/92) (CRD) ① [2] **CRD3430/1**
Sonata for Piano No. 4 (1984)
P. Crossley *Concert*
(6/92) (CRD) ① [2] **CRD3430/1**

SECTION IV: VOCAL AND CHORAL

Bonny at Morn—unison voices and 3 recorders (1956) (arr of Northumbrian folksong)
Oxford Christ Church Cath Ch, Inst. Ens, S.
Darlington *Concert* (1/91) (NIMB) ① **NI5266**
Boyhood's End—cantata: 1v & piano (1943) (Wds. W H Hudson)
M. Hill, A. Ball (r1994) *Concert*
(4/95) (HYPE) ① **CDA66749**
Byzantium—soprano and orchestra (1989) (Wds. W B Yeats)
F. Robinson, Chicago SO, G. Solti (r1991)
Symphony 4. (4/93) (DECC) ① **433 668-2DH**
A Child of Our Time—oratorio (1939-41) (Wds. cpsr)
Cpte J. Gomez, H. Watts, K. Woollam, J. Shirley-Quirk, BBC Sym Chor, BBC SO, G. Rozhdestvensky
(pp1980) (11/95) (BBCR) ① **BBCRD9130**

J. Norman, J. Baker, R. Cassilly, J. Shirley-Quirk,
BBC Sngrs, BBC Choral Soc, BBC SO, Colin Davis
(r1975) (11/87) (PHIL) ① **420 075-2PH**
F. Robinson, Sarah Walker, J. Garrison, J. Cheek,
CBSO Chor, CBSO, M. Tippett
(9/92) (COLL) ① **Coll1339-2**
C. Haymon, C. Clarey, D. Evans, W. White, LSC,
LSO, R. Hickox (2/93) (CHAN) ① **CHAN9123**
J. Norman, J. Baker, R. Cassilly, J. Shirley-Quirk,
BBC Sngrs, BBC Choral Soc, BBC SO, Colin Davis
(r1975) *Knot Garden.*
(9/95) (PHIL) ① [2] **446 331-2PH2**
Crown of the Year—cantata:female voices and orchestra (1958) (Wds. C. Fry)
Oxford Christ Church Cath Ch, Medici Qt, Inst. Ens,
S. Darlington *Concert* (1/91) (NIMB) ① **NI5266**
Dance, Clarion Air—madrigal: 5vv a capella (1952) (Wds. C. Fry)
Oxford Christ Church Cath Ch, S. Darlington *Concert*
(1/91) (NIMB) ① **NI5266**
Cambridge Univ Chbr Ch, T. Brown *Concert*
(4/92) (GAMU) ① **GAMCD529**
Finzi Sngrs, P. Spicer (r1994) *Concert*
(7/95) (CHAN) ① **CHAN9265**
The Heart's Assurance—song cycle: 1v & piano (1951) (Wds. A Lewis & S Keyes)
1. Song (Lewis); 2. The Heart's Assurance (Keyes);
3. Compassion (Lewis); 4. The Dancer (Lewis); 5.
Remember your lovers (Keyes).
M. Hill, A. Ball (r1994) *Concert*
(4/95) (HYPE) ① **CDA66749**
Lullaby—6vv a capella (1959) (Wds. W B Yeats)
Finzi Sngrs, P. Spicer (r1994) *Concert*
(7/95) (CHAN) ① **CHAN9265**
2 Madrigals—4vv a capella (1942)
1. The Windhover (wds. G M Hopkins); 2. The
Source (wds. E Thomas).
Finzi Sngrs, P. Spicer (r1994) *Concert*
(7/95) (CHAN) ① **CHAN9265**
Magnificat and Nunc dimittis, 'Collegium Sancti Johannis Cantabrigiense'—choir and organ (1962)
Finzi Sngrs, A. Lumsden, P. Spicer (r1994) *Concert*
(7/95) (CHAN) ① **CHAN9265**
A Mask of Time—soloists, chorus and orchestra (1972-84) (Wds. cpsr)
F. Robinson, Sarah Walker, R. Tear, J. Cheek, BBC
Sngrs, BBC Sym Chor, BBC SO, A. Davis (pp1986)
(10/93) (EMI) ① [2] **CMS7 64711-2**
Music—unison voices, strings (ad lib) and piano (1960)
Oxford Christ Church Cath Ch, Martin Jones, S.
Darlington *Concert* (1/91) (NIMB) ① **NI5266**
M. Hill, A. Ball (r1994) *Concert*
(4/95) (HYPE) ① **CDA66749**
5 Negro Spirituals from 'A Child of Our Time' (1958)
1. Steal Away; 2. Nobody Knows; 3. Go Moses
Down; 4. By and By; 5. Deep River.
Oxford Christ Church Cath Ch, S. Darlington *Concert*
(1/91) (NIMB) ① **NI5266**
Finzi Sngrs, P. Spicer (r1994) *Concert*
(7/95) (CHAN) ① **CHAN9265**
Plebs angelica—motet: 8vv a capella (1943)
Oxford Christ Church Cath Ch, S. Darlington *Concert*
(1/91) (NIMB) ① **NI5266**
Finzi Sngrs, P. Spicer (r1994) *Concert*
(7/95) (CHAN) ① **CHAN9265**
Songs for Achilles—song cycle: 1v & guitar (1961) (Wds. cpsr)
1. In the tent; 2. Across the plain; 3. By the sea.
M. Hill, C. Ogden (r1994) *Concert*
(4/95) (HYPE) ① **CDA66749**
Songs for Ariel (1962) (Wds. Shakespeare)
1. Come unto these yellow sands; 2. Full fathom five;
3. Where the bee sucks.
A. Rolfe Johnson, G. Johnson *Concert*
(5/92) (HYPE) ① **CDA66480**
M. Hill, A. Ball (r1994) *Concert*
(4/95) (HYPE) ① **CDA66749**
4 Songs from the British Isles—chorus a cappella (1956)
1. Early one morning; 2. Poortith Cauld; 3. Lilliburleo;
4. Gwenllian.
Finzi Sngrs, P. Spicer (r1994) *Concert*
(7/95) (CHAN) ① **CHAN9265**
The Weeping Babe—motet: soprano and chorus (1944) (Wds. E. Sitwell)
Oxford Christ Church Cath Ch, S. Darlington *Concert*
(1/91) (NIMB) ① **NI5266**
Finzi Sngrs, P. Spicer (r1994) *Concert*
(7/95) (CHAN) ① **CHAN9265**

SECTION V: STAGE WORKS

The **Ice Break—opera: 3 acts
(1977—London)** (Lib. cpsr)
Cpte H. Harper, D. Wilson-Johnson, S. Sylvan, C.
Page, C. Clarey, T. Randle, B. Bottone, D. Maxwell,
C. Robson, Sarah Walker, London Sinfonietta Chor,
London Sinfonietta, D. Atherton
(2/92) (VIRG) ① **VC7 59048-2**

The **Knot Garden—opera: 3 acts
(1970—London)** (Lib. cpsr)
Cpte R. Herincx, Y. Minton, J. Gomez, J. Barstow, T.
Carey, R. Tear, T. Hemsley, ROHO, Colin Davis
(r1973) *Child of Our Time.*
(9/95) (PHIL) ① [2] **446 331-2PH2**

The **Midsummer Marriage—opera: 3 acts
(1955—London)** (Lib. cpsr)
1. Ritual Dances; 2. Sosostris's Dances.
1, 2. R. Cullis, M. Curtis, A. Hodgson, M. Best, Op.
North Chor, English Northern Philh, M. Tippett
Concert (4/90) (NIMB) ① **NI5217**

New Year—concert suite from opera (1990)
1. The Space Ship lands; 2. Prelude; 3. The Shaman
Dance; 4. The Hunt for the Scapegoat; 5. Donny's
Skarade; 6. Donny's Dream; 7. Dream Interlude; 8.
Jo Ann's Dreamsong; 9. Love Scene for Jo Ann and
Pelegrin; 10. Paradise Dance; 11. The Beating-Out of
the Scapegoat; 12. Ringing in the New Year; 13. The
Space Ship takes off again.
Bournemouth SO, R. Hickox (r1994) *Symphony 2.*
(10/94) (CHAN) ① **CHAN9299**

TIRINDELLI, Pietro Adolfo (1858–1937) Italy

SECTION IV: VOCAL AND CHORAL

Mistica—song
F. Corradetti, anon (r1906) *Concert*
(12/94) (BONG) ① **GB1043-2**

Myosotis—song
G. Campanari, orch (r1909) *Concert*
(12/94) (BONG) ① **GB1043-2**

O primavera—song (Wds. Bonetti)
H. Spani, La Scala Orch, C. Sabajno (r1931) *Concert*
(9/90) (CLUB) ① [2] **CL99-509/10**

TISHCHENKO, Boris Ivanovich (b 1939) USSR

SECTION I: ORCHESTRAL

**Concerto for Violin and Orchestra No. 2, Op.
84 (1982)**
S. Stadler, Leningrad PO, V. Sinaisky (r1986)
(12/88) (OLYM) ① **OCD123**

Symphony No. 5
USSR Ministry of Culture SO, G. Rozhdestvensky
(pp1985) (12/88) (OLYM) ① **OCD213**

TISNÉ, Antoine (b 1932) France

SECTION II: CHAMBER

Héraldiques
H. Hardenberger, R. Pöntinen *Concert*
(11/85) (BIS) ① **BIS-CD287**

TITELOUZE, Jehan (1562/3–1633) France

SECTION III: INSTRUMENTAL

Hymnes de l'Eglise—organ (pub 1623)
1. Ad coenam; 2. Veni Creator; 3. Pange lingua; 4. Ut
queant laxis; 5. Ave maris stella; 6. Conditor alme
siderum; 7. A solis ortus; 8. Exultet coelum; 9. Annue
Christe; 10. Sanctorum meritis; 11. Iste confessor;
12. Urbs Hierusalem.
1. J. Payne (r1994) *Concert*
(10/95) (NAXO) ① **8 553215**
2, 3, 5, 8. A. Isoir *Couperin: Messe pour les
couvents.* (6/90) (CALL) ① **CAL9908**

Le **Magnificat—organ (1626)**
1. Tone 1; 2. Tone 2; 3. Tone 3; 4. Tone 4; 5. Tone 5;
6. Tone 6; 7. Tone 7; 8. Tone 8.
5 (3 versets) J. Payne (r1994) *Concert*
(10/95) (NAXO) ① **8 553215**

TITTA, Ettore (1875–1956)

SECTION IV: VOCAL AND CHORAL

E suonan le campane—song
T. Ruffo, orch (r1914) *Concert*
(2/93) (PREI) ① [3] **89303(1)**

Oh che m'importa?—song
T. Ruffo, orch (r1914) *Concert*
(2/93) (PREI) ① [3] **89303(1)**

TJEKNAVORIAN, Loris (b 1937) Iran

SECTION V: STAGE WORKS

Ballet fantastique, Op. 2 (1958)
1. Danse rhythmique; 2. Danse gracieuse; 3. Danse
lyrique; 4. Danse de fête; 5. Danse amoureuse; 6.
Danse élégiaque; 7. Danse d'extase.
Armenian PO, L. Tjeknavorian *Concert*
(3/94) (ASV) ① **CDDCA884**

TOBIAS, Rudolf (1873–1918) Estonia

SECTION I: ORCHESTRAL

Julius Caesar—overture (1896)
SNO, N. Järvi *Concert*
(11/89) (CHAN) ① **CHAN8656**

TOCH, Ernst (1887–1964) USA

SECTION I: ORCHESTRAL

**Jephta—Rhapsodic Poem (Symphony No. 5),
Op. 89 (1963)**
Louisville Orch, R. Whitney *Concert*
(6/90) (ALBA) ① **TROY021-2**

SECTION II: CHAMBER

2 Divertimenti—violin and cello, Op. 37
EXCERPTS: 1. No. 1; 2. No. 2.
2. J. Heifetz, G. Piatigorsky (r1965) *Concert*
(11/94) (RCA) ① [65] **09026 61778-2(35)**

**5 Wind and Percussion pieces, Op. 83
(1959)**
Deutsche Kammerphilharmonie *Concert*
(7/95) (VIRG) ① **VC5 45056-2**

TOLDRÁ, Eduardo (1895–1962) Spain

SECTION IV: VOCAL AND CHORAL

12 Canciones gallagas—1v and piano
As floriñas dos toxos V. de los Angeles, G. Soriano
(r1961/2) *Concert*
(4/94) (EMI) ① [4] **CMS5 65061-2(2)**

4 Cançons—1v and orchestra (Wds. various)
1. Cançó de grumet; 2. Cançó incarta; 3. Maig; 4.
Anacreòntica.
V. de los Angeles, Barcelona Patronato Orch, A.
Ros-Marbà (r1969) *Concert*
(4/94) (EMI) ① [4] **CMS5 65061-2(1)**

TOLLETT, Thomas (?–1696) Ireland

SECTION I: ORCHESTRAL

The **Queen's Farewell—march (1695)** (for the
funeral of Queen Mary)
The Sixteen, The Sixteen Orch, H. Christophers
(r1994) *Concert* (1/95) (COLL) ① **Coll1425-2**
New London Consort, M. Neary (r1994) *Concert*
(3/95) (SONY) ① **SK66243**

TOMASI, Henri (1901–1971) France

SECTION I: ORCHESTRAL

Concerto for Trumpet and Orchestra (1948)
S. Nakarjakov, Lausanne CO, J. López-Cobos
(r1993) *Concert* (9/93) (TELD) ① **4509-90846-2**

SECTION II: CHAMBER

**Concert champêtre—oboe, clarinet and
bassoon (1933)**
London Wind Trio *Concert*
(9/92) (CARL) ① **MCD38**

6 Divertissements—clarinet quartet (1964)
1. Poursuites; 2. Mascarade; 3. Rondes.
Thurston Cl Qt *Concert*
(10/93) (ASV) ① **CDWHL2076**

Printemps—saxophone and wind quintet
M. Preis, Berlin Phil Wind Qnt *Concert*
(4/93) (BIS) ① **BIS-CD536**

Triptyque—ttrumpet and piano
W. Marsalis, J.L. Stillman (r1992) *Concert*
(5/94) (SONY) ① **SK47193**

SECTION IV: VOCAL AND CHORAL

Triomphe de Jeanne—oratorio (1955) (Wds.
P. Soupault)
R. Gorr, J. Doucet, M. Lupovici, French Rad Maîtrise,
French Rad and TV Chor, FNO, H. Tomasi (r1957)
Don Juan de Mañara.
(10/92) (FORL) ① [2] **UCD16652/3**

SECTION V: STAGE WORKS

**Don Juan de Mañara—opera: 4 acts & 6
tableaux (1952—Paris)** (Lib. after Milosz)
Cpte R. Jobin, M. Angelici, A. Vessières, J. Brumaire,
B. Demigny, P. Cabanel, J. Peyron, H. Vermeil,
French Rad Chor, FNO, H. Tomasi (r1952) *Triomphe
de Jeanne.* (10/92) (FORL) ① [2] **UCD16652/3**

TOMKINS, Thomas (1572–1656) Wales

SECTION III: INSTRUMENTAL

Barafostus' Dream—keyboard
S. Yates (r1994) *Concert*
(12/95) (CHAN) ① **CHAN0574**

A Fancy—keyboard
T. Dart (r1957) *Concert* (5/95) (JMS) ① **JMSCD1**

A Fancy for two to play
T. Koopman, T. Mathot *Concert*
(5/91) (CAPR) ① **10 254**

In Nomine—keyboard (1648)
D. Burchell (r1990) *Concert*
(9/94) (CRD) ① **CRD3467**

In Nomine—keyboard (1652)
D. Burchell (r1990) *Concert*
(9/94) (CRD) ① **CRD3467**

Voluntary in A minor—keyboard
D. Burchell (r1990) *Concert*
(9/94) (CRD) ① **CRD3467**

Voluntary in C—keyboard
D. Burchell (r1990) *Concert*
(9/94) (CRD) ① **CRD3467**

Voluntary in G—keyboard
D. Burchell (r1990) *Concert*
(9/94) (CRD) ① **CRD3467**

SECTION IV: VOCAL AND CHORAL

**Above the stars my saviour dwells—verse
anthem: 1/6vv and organ (pub 1668)**
St George's Chapel Ch, R. Judd, C. Robinson
Concert (3/90) (HYPE) ① **CDA66345**

**Adieu, ye city-prisoning towers—madrigal:
5vv (pub 1622)**
Cambridge Sngrs, J. Rutter *Concert*
(11/87) (CLLE) ① **COLCD105**

**Almighty God, the fountain of all
wisdom—full anthem: 5vv and organ (pub
1668)**
St George's Chapel Ch, R. Judd, C. Robinson
Concert (3/90) (HYPE) ① **CDA66345**
Tallis Scholars, P. Phillips *Concert*
(3/92) (GIME) ① **CDGIM024**
R. Johnston, Worcester Cath Ch, Don Hunt *Concert*
(5/93) (ABBE) ① **CDCA943**

**Arise, O Lord, into thy resting
place—anthem: 5vv and organ (1668)**
Trinity Coll Ch, Cambridge, R. Marlow (r1993)
Concert (12/93) (CONI) ① **CDCF216**

**Be strong and of a good courage—anthem:
7vv and organ (pub 1668)**
Tallis Scholars, P. Phillips *Concert*
(3/92) (GIME) ① **CDGIM024**
Trinity Coll Ch, Cambridge, R. Marlow (r1993)
Concert (12/93) (CONI) ① **CDCF216**

**Behold, the hour cometh—verse anthem:
3/4vv and organ (pub 1668)**
St George's Chapel Ch, R. Judd, C. Robinson
Concert (3/90) (HYPE) ① **CDA66345**

**Domine tu eruisti animam—anthem: 5vv and
organ** (Latin ver of 'Why art thou so full of
heaviness')
Trinity Coll Ch, Cambridge, R. Marlow (r1993)
Concert (12/93) (CONI) ① **CDCF216**

**Funeral Sentences—I am the resurrection/I
heard a voice—4vv (1668)**
Trinity Coll Ch, Cambridge, R. Marlow (r1993)
Concert (12/93) (CONI) ① **CDCF216**

**Glory be to God on high—verse anthem:
7/7vv and organ (pub 1668)**
St George's Chapel Ch, R. Judd, C. Robinson
Concert (3/90) (HYPE) ① **CDA66345**

Know you not—verse anthem
New College Ch, E. Higginbottom, D. Burchell
(r1990) *Concert* (9/94) (CRD) ① **CRD3467**

My beloved spake—verse anthem: 4/4vv and organ (pub 1668)
St George's Chapel Ch, R. Judd, C. Robinson
Concert   (3/90) (HYPE) ① **CDA66345**
Worcester Cath Ch, Don Hunt, R. Johnston (r1993)
Concert   (2/95) (ABBE) ① **CDCA957**

My shepherd is the living Lord—verse anthem: 2/4vv and organ (pub 1668)
St George's Chapel Ch, R. Judd, C. Robinson
Concert   (3/90) (HYPE) ① **CDA66345**
Worcester Cath Ch, Don Hunt, R. Johnston (r1993)
Concert   (2/95) (ABBE) ① **CDCA957**

O God, the proud are risen against me—full anthem: 8vv and organ (pub 1668)
St George's Chapel Ch, R. Judd, C. Robinson
Concert   (3/90) (HYPE) ① **CDA66345**
Tallis Scholars, P. Phillips *Concert*
                   (3/92) (GIME) ① **CDGIM024**
Trinity Coll Ch, Cambridge, R. Marlow (r1993)
Concert   (12/93) (CONI) ① **CDCF216**

O Lord, let me know mine end—anthem: 1/5vv, org (pub 1668)
New College Ch, E. Higginbottom, D. Burchell
(r1990) *Concert*   (9/94) (CRD) ① **CRD3467**

O praise the Lord all ye heathen—anthem (1668)
Magdalen Oxford Coll Ch, J. Harper *Concert*
                   (11/91) (ABBE) ① **CDCA912**
Trinity Coll Ch, Cambridge, R. Marlow (r1993)
Concert   (12/93) (CONI) ① **CDCF216**

O sing unto the Lord a new song—full anthem: 7vv and organ (pub 1668)
St George's Chapel Ch, R. Judd, C. Robinson
Concert   (3/90) (HYPE) ① **CDA66345**
Worcester Cath Ch, Don Hunt *Concert*
                   (9/90) (CARL) ① **PCD937**
Tallis Scholars, P. Phillips *Concert*
                   (3/92) (GIME) ① **CDGIM024**
Trinity Coll Ch, Cambridge, R. Marlow (r1993)
Concert   (12/93) (CONI) ① **CDCF216**
Worcester Cath Ch, Don Hunt, R. Johnston (r1993)
Concert   (2/95) (ABBE) ① **CDCA957**

O that the salvation were given—anthem: 4/8vv, org (pub 1668)
New College Ch, E. Higginbottom, D. Burchell
(r1990) *Concert*   (9/94) (CRD) ① **CRD3467**

Oyez! has any found a lad?—madrigal: 4vv (pub 1622)
Amaryllis Consort, C. Brett *Concert*
                   (3/88) (CARL) ① **PCD873**

See, see, the shepherd's Queen—madrigal: 5vv (pub 1622)
Hilliard Ens, P. Hillier *Concert*
                   (2/89) (EMI) ① **CDC7 49197-2**

Sing unto God—verse anthem: 2/5vv and organ (pub 1668)
St George's Chapel Ch, R. Judd, C. Robinson
Concert   (3/90) (HYPE) ① **CDA66345**
Red Byrd, Rose Consort *Concert*
                   (12/91) (AMON) ① **CD-SAR46**

Then David mourned—lament: 5vv and organ (pub 1668)
St George's Chapel Ch, R. Judd, C. Robinson
Concert   (3/90) (HYPE) ① **CDA66345**
Magdalen Oxford Coll Ch, J. Harper *Concert*
                   (11/91) (ABBE) ① **CDCA912**
Tallis Scholars, P. Phillips *Concert*
                   (3/92) (GIME) ① **CDGIM024**
Trinity Coll Ch, Cambridge, R. Marlow (r1993)
Concert   (12/93) (CONI) ① **CDCF216**

Third Service (Great Service)—4/8vv (pub 1668)
1. Te Deum; 2. Jubilate; 3. Magnificat; 4. Nunc dimittis.
Tallis Scholars, P. Phillips *Concert*
                   (3/92) (GIME) ① **CDGIM024**
New College Ch, E. Higginbottom, D. Burchell
(r1990) *Concert*   (9/94) (CRD) ① **CRD3467**
3, 4. St George's Chapel Ch, R. Judd, C. Robinson
Concert   (3/90) (HYPE) ① **CDA66345**

Too much I once lamented—madrigal: 5vv (pub 1622)
Cambridge Sngrs, J. Rutter *Concert*
                   (11/87) (CLLE) ① **COLCD105**

When David heard—lament: 5vv (pub 1622)
Oxford Christ Church Cath Ch, S. Preston *Concert*
                   (2/90) (GAMU) ① **GOUPCD153**
St George's Chapel Ch, C. Robinson *Concert*
                   (3/90) (HYPE) ① **CDA66345**
Tallis Scholars, P. Phillips *Concert*
                   (3/92) (GIME) ① **CDGIM024**
Cambridge Sngrs, J. Rutter *Concert*
                   (4/92) (CLLE) ① **COLCD113**
R. Johnston, Worcester Cath Ch, Don Hunt *Concert*
                   (5/93) (ABBE) ① **CDCA943**

Trinity Coll Ch, Cambridge, R. Marlow (r1993)
Concert   (12/93) (CONI) ① **CDCF216**

Woe is me that I am constrained—anthem: 6vv (pub 1622)
Tallis Scholars, P. Phillips *Concert*
                   (3/92) (GIME) ① **CDGIM024**
Trinity Coll Ch, Cambridge, R. Marlow (r1993)
Concert   (12/93) (CONI) ① **CDCF216**

TOMLINSON, Ernest (b 1927) England

SECTION I: ORCHESTRAL

Comedy Overture (1956)
Slovak RSO, E. Tomlinson (r1992) *Concert*
                   (3/95) (MARC) ① **8 223513**

Cumberland Square (1960)
Slovak RSO, E. Tomlinson (r1992) *Concert*
                   (3/95) (MARC) ① **8 223513**

An English Overture—orchestra
Bratislava RSO, E. Tomlinson *Concert*
                   (12/92) (MARC) ① **8 223413**

First Suite of English Folk-Dances—orchestra (1951)
1. Jenny Pluck Pears; 2. Ten pound lass; 3. Dick's Maggot; 4. Nonesuch; 5. Hunt the Squirrel; 6. Woodicock.
Light Music Soc Orch, V. Dunn *Concert*
                   (12/91) (EMI) ① **CDM7 64131-2**
Slovak RSO, E. Tomlinson (r1992) *Concert*
                   (3/95) (MARC) ① **8 223513**

3 Gaelic Sketches—orchestra
1. Gaelic Lullaby.
1. Bratislava RSO, E. Tomlinson *Concert*
                   (12/92) (MARC) ① **8 223413**

A Georgian Miniature (1962)
Slovak RSO, E. Tomlinson (r1992) *Concert*
                   (3/95) (MARC) ① **8 223513**

Georgian Suite—orchestra (after Arne's '8 Sonatas of lessons for Harpsichord')
1. Gavotte.
1. RTE Concert Orch, E. Tomlinson (r1993) *Concert*
                   (12/95) (MARC) ① **8 223522**

Kielder Water (1983)
Bratislava RSO, E. Tomlinson *Concert*
                   (12/92) (MARC) ① **8 223413**

Light Music Suite (1971)
1. Pizzicato humoresque; 2. Serenade to a Wayward Miss; 3. Waltz for a Princess.
Slovak RSO, E. Tomlinson (r1992) *Concert*
                   (3/95) (MARC) ① **8 223513**

Little Serenade—orchestra (1955)
Bratislava RSO, E. Tomlinson *Concert*
                   (12/92) (MARC) ① **8 223413**

Lyrical Suite—orchestra (1957)
1. Nocturne.
1. Bratislava RSO, E. Tomlinson *Concert*
                   (12/92) (MARC) ① **8 223413**

2 Miniature Dances (1958)
1. Rigadoon.
1. Slovak RSO, E. Tomlinson (r1992) *Concert*
                   (3/95) (MARC) ① **8 223513**

Nautical Interlude—orchestra
Bratislava RSO, E. Tomlinson *Concert*
                   (12/92) (MARC) ① **8 223413**

Passepied (1947)
Slovak RSO, E. Tomlinson (r1992) *Concert*
                   (3/95) (MARC) ① **8 223513**

3 Pastoral Dances—orchestra (1950)
3. Hornpipe.
3. Bratislava RSO, E. Tomlinson *Concert*
                   (12/92) (MARC) ① **8 223413**

Rhapsody and Rondo—horn and piano (1957)
R. Watkins, Slovak RSO, E. Tomlinson (r1992)
Concert   (3/95) (MARC) ① **8 223513**

Second Suite of English Folk-dances—orchestra (1977)
1. Ketteldrum; 2. Chipping Lane; 3. Newcastle; 4. Up goes Ely/The Fits come on me now; 5. Love-in-a-mist; 6. Catch me if you can.
Bratislava RSO, E. Tomlinson *Concert*
                   (12/92) (MARC) ① **8 223413**

Shenandoah (c1949)
Slovak RSO, E. Tomlinson (r1992) *Concert*
                   (3/95) (MARC) ① **8 223513**

Silverthorn Suite—orchestra (1950s)
1. Alla marcia; 2. Canzonet; 3. Concert Jig.
Bratislava RSO, E. Tomlinson *Concert*
                   (12/92) (MARC) ① **8 223413**

Sweet and Dainty—orchestra
                   (12/92) (MARC) ① **8 223413**

SECTION V: STAGE WORKS

Aladdin—ballet: 3 acts (1974—Manchester)
EXCERPTS: ACT 2: 1. Birdcage Dance; 2. Cushion Dance; 3. Belly Dance.
1, 2, 3. Slovak RSO, E. Tomlinson (r1992) *Concert*
                   (3/95) (MARC) ① **8 223513**

The Story of Cinderella—radio musical play (1955) (Book R. Plomley, lyrics H. Ege)
EXCERPTS: 1. Fairy Coach; 2. Cinderella Waltz.
1, 2. Bratislava RSO, E. Tomlinson *Concert*
                   (12/92) (MARC) ① **8 223413**

TOMMASINI, Vincenzo (1878–1950) Italy

SECTION I: ORCHESTRAL

Il Carnevale a Venezia (Variations on a theme of Paganini)—orchestra (1928)
NBC SO, A. Toscanini (bp1941) *Concert*
                   (5/94) (ATS) ① [2] **ATCD100**

SECTION V: STAGE WORKS

The Good-Humoured Ladies—choreographic comedy: 1 act (1917—Rome) (after Goldini: orch of various D Scarlatti sonatas)
Suite English Concert Orch, R. Bonynge *Concert*
                   (11/90) (DECC) ① [2] **421 818-2DH2**
2-5. NBC SO, A. Toscanini (bp1946) *Concert*
                   (5/94) (ATS) ① [2] **ATCD100**

TOPHAM, William (fl 1701–9) England

SECTION II: CHAMBER

6 Sonatas, five in four and a sixth in seven parts, Op. 3
6. Sonata for Two Trumpets and Strings in seven parts.
6. English Tpt Virtuosi, A. Hoskins (tpt/dir) *Concert*
                   (10/95) (MOSC) ① **070979**

TORELLI, Giuseppe (1658–1709) Italy

G numbers in Giegling's catalogue

SECTION I: ORCHESTRAL

Concerti grossi, 'con una pastorale per il SS Natale', Op. 8 (pub 1709)
1. C; 2. A minor; 3. E; 4. B flat; 5. G; 6. G minor (Christmas Concerto); 7. D minor; 8. G minor; 9. E minor; 10. A; 11. F; 12. D.
6. Seattle NW CO, A. Francis *Concert*
                   (12/88) (HYPE) ① **CDH88028**
6. Virtuosi Saxoniae, L. Güttler *Concert*
                   (12/89) (CAPR) ① **10 225**
6. Giardino Armonico Ens *Concert*
                   (12/91) (TELD) ① **2292-46013-2**
6. St James's Baroque Plyrs, I. Bolton (r1988)
Concert   (9/93) (TELD) ① **4509-91192-2**
6. Solisti Italiani (r1993) *Concert*
                   (12/94) (DENO) ① **CO-78912**

12 Concerti musicali, Op. 6 (pub 1698)
1. G; 2. E minor; 3. B minor; 4. D; 5. G minor; 6. C minor; 7. C; 8. F; 9. A minor; 10. D minor; 11. B flat; 12. A.
1. St James's Baroque Plyrs, I. Bolton (r1988)
Concert   (9/93) (TELD) ① **4509-91192-2**
10. ASMF, N. Marriner (r1961) *Concert*
                   (9/93) (DECC) ① **436 224-2DM**
10. Berlin Barock Compagney (r1993) *Concert*
                   (10/95) (CAPR) ① **10 459**

Concerto a due chori con trombe, G32
San Petronio Cappella Musicale Orch, S. Vartolo
(r1993) *Concert* (5/95) (BONG) ① [3] **GB5523/5-2**
Concerto con due trombe e stromenti, G24 (not in Giegling's Catalogue)
St James's Baroque Plyrs, I. Bolton (r1988) *Concert*
                   (9/93) (TELD) ① **4509-91192-2**
San Petronio Cappella Musicale Orch, S. Vartolo
(r1993) *Concert* (5/95) (BONG) ① [3] **GB5523/5-2**
Concerto con trombe, G18
M. André, Philh, R. Muti *Concert*
                   (1/86) (EMI) ① **CDC7 47311-2**
C. Steele-Perkins, ECO, A. Halstead *Concert*
                   (6/86) (CARL) ① **PCD821**
R. Smedvig, Scottish CO, J. Ling *Concert*
                   (8/90) (TELA) ① **CD80232**
G. Touvron, Slovak CO, B. Warchal *Concert*
                   (9/91) (OPUS) ① **9350 1710**
San Petronio Cappella Musicale Orch, S. Vartolo
(r1993) *Concert* (5/95) (BONG) ① [3] **GB5523/5-2**

Concerto con trombe, obois, e violini, G27
San Petronio Cappella Musicale Orch, S. Vartolo
(r1993) *Concert* (5/95) (BONG) ① [3] **GB5523/5-2**
Concerto for 2 Trumpets and Strings in D (pub c1715) (Etienne Roger 188)
St James's Baroque Plyrs, I. Bolton (r1988) *Concert*
(9/93) (TELD) ① **4509-91192-2**
Concerto in E minor—4 violins, strings and continuo
Cologne Musica Antiqua, R. Goebel *Concert*
(9/92) (ARCH) ① **435 393-2AH**
Sinfonia a 4, G33
San Petronio Cappella Musicale Orch, S. Vartolo
(r1993) *Concert* (5/95) (BONG) ① [3] **GB5523/5-2**
Sinfonia a 4 con tromba, e violini unissoni, G4
San Petronio Cappella Musicale Orch, S. Vartolo
(r1993) *Concert* (5/95) (BONG) ① [3] **GB5523/5-2**
Sinfonia con due trombe, G17
San Petronio Cappella Musicale Orch, S. Vartolo
(r1993) *Concert* (5/95) (BONG) ① [3] **GB5523/5-2**
Sinfonia con due trombe, G20
San Petronio Cappella Musicale Orch, S. Vartolo
(r1993) *Concert* (5/95) (BONG) ① [3] **GB5523/5-2**
Sinfonia con due trombe, G23
St James's Baroque Plyrs, I. Bolton (r1988) *Concert*
(9/93) (TELD) ① **4509-91192-2**
San Petronio Cappella Musicale Orch, S. Vartolo
(r1993) *Concert* (5/95) (BONG) ① [3] **GB5523/5-2**
Sinfonia con due trombe e instromenti, G22
San Petronio Cappella Musicale Orch, S. Vartolo
(r1993) *Concert* (5/95) (BONG) ① [3] **GB5523/5-2**
Sinfonia con due trombe e violini unissoni, G19
San Petronio Cappella Musicale Orch, S. Vartolo
(r1993) *Concert* (5/95) (BONG) ① [3] **GB5523/5-2**
Sinfonia con due trombe et altri strumenti, G21
San Petronio Cappella Musicale Orch, S. Vartolo
(r1993) *Concert* (5/95) (BONG) ① [3] **GB5523/5-2**
Sinfonia con obois, trombe e violini, G30
San Petronio Cappella Musicale Orch, S. Vartolo
(r1993) *Concert* (5/95) (BONG) ① [3] **GB5523/5-2**
Sinfonia con tromba, G2
San Petronio Cappella Musicale Orch, S. Vartolo
(r1993) *Concert* (5/95) (BONG) ① [3] **GB5523/5-2**
Sinfonia con tromba, G8
San Petronio Cappella Musicale Orch, S. Vartolo
(r1993) *Concert* (5/95) (BONG) ① [3] **GB5523/5-2**
Sinfonia con tromba, G10
San Petronio Cappella Musicale Orch, S. Vartolo
(r1993) *Concert* (5/95) (BONG) ① [3] **GB5523/5-2**
Sinfonia con tromba, G11
San Petronio Cappella Musicale Orch, S. Vartolo
(r1993) *Concert* (5/95) (BONG) ① [3] **GB5523/5-2**
Sinfonia con tromba, G26
San Petronio Cappella Musicale Orch, S. Vartolo
(r1993) *Concert* (5/95) (BONG) ① [3] **GB5523/5-2**
Sinfonia con tromba e violini unissoni, G9
San Petronio Cappella Musicale Orch, S. Vartolo
(r1993) *Concert* (5/95) (BONG) ① [3] **GB5523/5-2**
Sinfonia con tromba e due obue e quattro violini e viole obligati, G31
San Petronio Cappella Musicale Orch, S. Vartolo
(r1993) *Concert* (5/95) (BONG) ① [3] **GB5523/5-2**
Sinfonia con tromba e violini, G16
San Petronio Cappella Musicale Orch, S. Vartolo
(r1993) *Concert* (5/95) (BONG) ① [3] **GB5523/5-2**
Sinfonia con tromba, obue, e altri strumenti, G29 (1707)
San Petronio Cappella Musicale Orch, S. Vartolo
(r1993) *Concert* (5/95) (BONG) ① [3] **GB5523/5-2**
Sinfonie a 3 e concerti a 4, Op. 5 (pub 1692)
SINFONIE: 1. A minor; 2. C; 3. G minor; 4. A; 5. D; 6. E minor. CONCERTI: 7. D minor; 8. A; 9. D; 10. G minor; 11. F; 12. G.
4. St James's Baroque Plyrs, I. Bolton (r1988) *Concert* (9/93) (TELD) ① **4509-91192-2**
Sonata a 4 con trombe, G25 (not in Giegling's Catalogue)
San Petronio Cappella Musicale Orch, S. Vartolo
(r1993) *Concert* (5/95) (BONG) ① [3] **GB5523/5-2**
Sonata a 5 con tromba, G3
W. Marsalis, ECO, R. Leppard *Concert*
(1/86) (SONY) ① **MK39061**
San Petronio Cappella Musicale Orch, S. Vartolo
(r1993) *Concert* (5/95) (BONG) ① [3] **GB5523/5-2**
Sonata a 5 con tromba, G5
San Petronio Cappella Musicale Orch, S. Vartolo
(r1993) *Concert* (5/95) (BONG) ① [3] **GB5523/5-2**
Sonata a 5 con tromba, G6
San Petronio Cappella Musicale Orch, S. Vartolo
(r1993) *Concert* (5/95) (BONG) ① [3] **GB5523/5-2**
Sonata a 5 con tromba, G7
W. Marsalis, C. Tunnell, ECO, R. Leppard *Concert*
(1/86) (SONY) ① **MK39061**

San Petronio Cappella Musicale Orch, S. Vartolo
(r1993) *Concert* (5/95) (BONG) ① [3] **GB5523/5-2**
H. Hardenberger, I Musici (r1993) *Concert*
(5/95) (PHIL) ① **442 131-2PH**
Sonata a 5 con tromba, G13
San Petronio Cappella Musicale Orch, S. Vartolo
(r1993) *Concert* (5/95) (BONG) ① [3] **GB5523/5-2**
Sonata a 5, due trombe, e violini unisoni, G15
San Petronio Cappella Musicale Orch, S. Vartolo
(r1993) *Concert* (5/95) (BONG) ① [3] **GB5523/5-2**
Suonata con stromenti e tromba, G1 (1690)
G. Schwarz (tpt/dir), NY Y CO *Concert*
(10/84) (DELO) ① **DE3002**
San Petronio Cappella Musicale Orch, S. Vartolo
(r1993) *Concert* (5/95) (BONG) ① [3] **GB5523/5-2**

SECTION II: CHAMBER

10 Sonate a tre, Op. 1 (pub 1686)
1. G; 2. D; 3. B minor; 4. D minor; 5. A; 6. G minor; 7. A minor; 8. C minor; 9. C; 10. F.
1. Berlin Barock Compagney (r1993) *Concert*
(10/95) (CAPR) ① **10 459**

SECTION IV: VOCAL AND CHORAL

Tu lo sai
E. Pinza, F. Kitzinger (r1940) *Concert*
(9/93) (RCA) ① **09026 61245-2**
P. Frijsh, D. Bucktrout (r1932) *Concert*
(4/95) (PEAR) ① [2] **GEMMCDS9095(2)**
P. Frijsh, WNYC Concert Orch, H. Newmann (bp1938) *Concert*
(4/95) (PEAR) ① [2] **GEMMCDS9095(2)**

TORKE, Michael *(b 1961) USA*

SECTION I: ORCHESTRAL

Ash—orchestra/chamber orchestra (1989)
Baltimore SO, D. Zinman *Concert*
(2/92) (ARGO) ① **433 071-2ZH**
Bright Blue Music—orchestra (1985)
Baltimore SO, D. Zinman *Concert*
(2/92) (ARGO) ① **433 071-2ZH**
Concerto for Soprano Saxophone and Orchestra (1993)
J. Harle, Albany SO, D. A. Miller (r1994) *Concert*
(7/95) (ARGO) ① **444 529-2ZH**
Ecstatic Orange—orchestra (1985) (later expanded to include 'Green' and Purple')
Baltimore SO, D. Zinman *Concert*
(2/92) (ARGO) ① **433 071-2ZH**
Green—orchestra (1986) (later incorporated into ballet 'Ecstatic Orange')
Baltimore SO, D. Zinman *Concert*
(2/92) (ARGO) ① **433 071-2ZH**
Purple—orchestra (1987) (later incorporated in ballet 'Ecstatic Orange')
Baltimore SO, D. Zinman *Concert*
(2/92) (ARGO) ① **433 071-2ZH**
Slate—concertante group and orchestra (1989)
M. Torke, Double Edge, J. Pugliese, G. Schall, London Sinfonietta, K. Nagano *Concert*
(12/90) (ARGO) ① **430 209-2ZH**
Vanada—brass, keyboards and percussion (1984)
M. Torke, London Sinfonietta, K. Nagano *Concert*
(12/90) (ARGO) ① **430 209-2ZH**
The Yellow Pages—flute/piccolo, clarinet, violin, cello & piano (1985)
M. Torke, London Sinfonietta, D. Miller *Concert*
(12/90) (ARGO) ① **430 209-2ZH**

SECTION II: CHAMBER

Adjustable wrench—chamber ensemble (1987)
M. Torke, London Sinfonietta, K. Nagano *Concert*
(12/90) (ARGO) ① **430 209-2ZH**
Chalk—string quartet (1992)
Balanescu Qt (r1992) *Concert*
(3/93) (ARGO) ① **436 565-2ZH**
Monday—chamber orchestra (1992)
London Sinfonietta, L. Zagrosek (r1993) *Concert*
(1/95) (ARGO) ① **443 528-2ZH**
Music on the floor—three movement: chamber ensemble (1992)
London Sinfonietta, L. Zagrosek (r1993) *Concert*
(1/95) (ARGO) ① **443 528-2ZH**
Rust—piano and wind instruments (1989)
M. Torke, London Sinfonietta, D. Miller *Concert*
(12/90) (ARGO) ① **430 209-2ZH**
Tuesday—chamber ensemble (1992)
London Sinfonietta, L. Zagrosek (r1993) *Concert*
(1/95) (ARGO) ① **443 528-2ZH**

SECTION IV: VOCAL AND CHORAL

4 Proverbs—female voice and ensemble (1993) (Wds. Book of Proverbs XV)
1. Better a dish of herbs; 2. Drink water from your own cistern; 3. One man pretendeth to be rich; 4. There is joy for a man.
C. Bott, Argo Band, M. Torke (r1993) *Concert*
(1/95) (ARGO) ① **443 528-2ZH**

SECTION V: STAGE WORKS

Black and White—ballet (1988—New York)
EXCERPTS: 7. Charcoal.
7. Baltimore SO, D. Zinman (r1994) *Concert*
(7/95) (ARGO) ① **444 454-2ZH**

TORMIS, Veljo *(b 1930) Estonia*

SECTION I: ORCHESTRAL

Overture No. 2—orchestra (1959)
SNO, N. Järvi *Concert*
(11/89) (CHAN) ① **CHAN8656**

SECTION IV: VOCAL AND CHORAL

Ingrian Evenings—folksongs for mixed choir (1979) (Wds. adapted A. Ambus)
1. Rõntuska I (Dance Song); 2. Rõntushka II; 3. Rõntushka II; 4. Chastuska I (Village Party Songs); 5. Chastuska II; 6. A Roundelay; 7. Rõntushka IV; 8. Rõntushka V; 9. Ending and going home.
Cpte Estonian Phil Chbr Ch, T. Kaljuste *Concert*
(10/92) (ECM) ① [2] **434 275-2**
Izhorian Epic—runic songs for mixed choir (1975) (Wds. adapted A. Laanest)
1. Creation of the World; 2. The call of three cuckoos; 3. The Wedding Song; 4. A Son or a Daughter; 5. Recruitment; 6. Oh, I'm a luckless lad; 7a. My mouth was singing; 7b. My heart was worrying; 8. A Sword from the Sea; 9. Incantation of Snakes; 10. Undarmoi and Kalervoi.
Cpte Estonian Phil Chbr Ch, T. Kaljuste *Concert*
(10/92) (ECM) ① [2] **434 275-2**
Karelian Destiny—runic songs for mixed choir (1989) (Wds. adapted K Laukkanen, V Tedre & J Õispu)
1. A Weeping Maiden; 2. Suitors from the Sea; 3. A thrall in Viru; 4. The Oak Cutter; 5. A lullaby.
Cpte Estonian Phil Chbr Ch, T. Kaljuste *Concert*
(10/92) (ECM) ① [2] **434 275-2**
Livonian Heritage—folksongs for mixed choir (1970) (Wds. adapted H. Tampere)
1. Waking the Birds; 2. Day of a Herdsboy; 3. Shrove Tuesday; 4. Wee Winky Mouse; 5. Sang the Father, Sang his Son.
Cpte Estonian Phil Chbr Ch, T. Kaljuste *Concert*
(10/92) (ECM) ① [2] **434 275-2**
Raua needmine, 'The Curse upon Iron'—ten, bass, mixed choir & shaman drum (1972)
Danish Nat Rad Ch, S. Parkman (r1993) *Concert*
(4/95) (CHAN) ① **CHAN9264**
The Songs of Hamlet—chorus (wds. Rummo)
Orphei Drängar Ch, E. Ericson *Concert*
(7/88) (BIS) ① **BIS-CD383**
Vespian Paths—folksongs for mixed choir (1983) (Wds. adapted M. Joalaid)
1. My Sister, my little cricket; 2. Urging into the boat; 3. Heavenly Suitors; 4. I went to Kikoila; 5. Cuckoo and cuckoo; 6. I went to fetch some water; 7. Pussy-cat, pussy-cat; 8. I'd like to sing you a song; 9. Where did you sleep last night?; 10. What are they doing at your place?; 11. The ox climbed a fir tree; 12. Forced to get married; 13. A Cradle song; 14. The only son; 15. Toot-toot, Herdsboy.
Cpte Estonian Phil Chbr Ch, T. Kaljuste *Concert*
(10/92) (ECM) ① [2] **434 275-2**
Votic Wedding Songs—runic songs for mixed choir (1971) (Wds. adapted E Adler & T Seilenthal)
1. The ritual whisking of the Bridge; 2. The arrival of Wedding Guests; 3. Mockery singing; 4. Distributing the Dowry Chest; 5. Instructing the Newly-Weds; 6. Praising the Cook; 7. When I, Chick, was growing up.
Cpte Estonian Phil Chbr Ch, T. Kaljuste *Concert*
(10/92) (ECM) ① [2] **434 275-2**

TORRE, Francisco de la *(fl 1483–1504) Spain*

SECTION II: CHAMBER

Danza Alta (Cancionero de Palacio)
Hespèrion XX, J. Savall *Concert*
(7/92) (ASTR) ① **E8762**
C. Bott, New London Consort, P. Pickett *Concert*
(7/92) (LINN) ① **CKD007**

SECTION IV: VOCAL AND CHORAL

Dime, triste coraçon (Cancionero de Colombina)
Hespèrion XX, J. Savall *Concert*
(7/92) (ASTR) ① **E8763**

Dime, triste corazón—song
T. Berganza, N. Yepes *Concert*
(12/92) (DG) ① [2] **435 848-2GX2**

Justa fué mi perdición—villancico: 3vv (from Segovia MS)
Daedalus Ens *Concert*
(12/92) (ACCE) ① **ACC9176D**

Pámpano Verde—song
V. de los Angeles, G. Parsons (pp1990) *Concert*
(12/91) (COLL) ① **Coll1247-2**
T. Berganza, F. Lavilla *Concert*
(12/92) (DG) ① [2] **435 848-2GX2**

TORREJÓN Y VELASCO, Tomás de *(1644–1728) Spain/Peru*

SECTION IV: VOCAL AND CHORAL

Invitatorio de difuntos
Cordoba Children's Ch, Elyma Ens, G. Garrido
(r1992) *Concert* (9/93) (K617) ① **K617025**

Magnificat sexti toni—12vv and continuo
Cordoba Children's Ch, Elyma Ens, G. Garrido
(r1992) *Concert* (9/93) (K617) ① **K617025**

TORTELIER, Paul *(1914–1990) France*

SECTION I: ORCHESTRAL

Alla Maud—valse
M. Tortelier, P. Tortelier (vc/dir), ECO *Concert*
(7/88) (VIRG) ① **VC7 59668-2**

SECTION II: CHAMBER

Le Pitre—burlesque: cello & piano
P. Tortelier, G. Moore (r1948) *Concert*
(12/95) (EMI) ① **CDH5 65502-2**

TOSELLI, Enrico *(1883–1926) Italy*

SECTION IV: VOCAL AND CHORAL

Serenade (Serenata)—song (pub 1900) (Wds. A. Silvestri)
B. Gigli, orch, J. Pasternack (r1926) *Concert*
(9/88) (PEAR) ① **GEMMCD9316**
P. Domingo, I. Perlman, NY Studio Orch, J. Tunick
(r1990) *Concert* (3/92) (EMI) ① **CDC7 54266-2**
B. Gigli, orch, J. Pasternack (r1926) *Concert*
(6/93) (MMOI) ① **CDMOIR417**
P. Domingo, I. Perlman, NY Studio Orch, J. Tunick
(r1990) *Concert*
(6/95) (EMI) ① [20] **CZS4 83177-2(3)**

TOSTI, Sir (Francesco) Paolo *(1846–1916) Italy/England*

SECTION IV: VOCAL AND CHORAL

'A Vucchella—song (pub 1903) (Wds. G. d'Annunzio)
L. Pavarotti, Teatro Communale Orch, A. Guadagno
Concert (8/83) (DECC) ① **410 015-2DH**
E. Caruso, orch (r1919) *Concert*
(5/89) (PEAR) ① **GEMMCD9309**
T. Schipa, orch, R. Bourdon (r1927) *Concert*
(12/89) (RCA) ① **GD87969**
L. Pavarotti, National PO, G. Chiaramello (arr Chiarmello)
(7/90) (DECC) ① [2] **425 681-2DM2**
E. Caruso, orch, J. Pasternack (r1919) *Concert*
(7/91) (RCA) ① [12] **GD60495(6)**
E. Caruso, orch, J. Pasternack (r1919) *Concert*
(10/91) (PEAR) ① [3] **EVC4(2)**
G. Valdengo, Kingsway SO, A. Erede (r1949)
Concert (4/92) (EMI) ① [7] **CHS7 69741-2(7)**
T. Schipa, orch, R. Bourdon (r1927) *Concert*
(10/92) (TEST) ① **SBT1005**
T. Gobbi, Orch, A. Erede (r1948) *Concert*
(8/93) (TEST) ① **SBT1019**
R. Ponselle, orch, R. Bourdon (r1926) *Concert*
(11/94) (ROMO) ① [2] **81007-2**
E. Palacio, G. Scabbia, H. Liviabella, B. Giuffredi, M. Rapattoni (r1993; arr M. de Bernart) *Concert*
(1/95) (AKAD) ① **CDAK125**

Addio—song (pub 1880) (Wds. S Rizzelli: Eng wds. G J Whyte-Melville)
R. Tauber, orch, E. Hauke (Ger: r1928) *Concert*
(7/89) (EMI) ① **CDM7 69476-2**

E. Turner, orch (r1926: Eng) *Concert*
(9/89) (EMI) ① **CDH7 69791-2**
E. Caruso, orch (r1910) *Concert*
(3/91) (PEAR) ① [3] **EVC2**
E. Caruso, orch (r1910) *Concert*
(7/91) (RCA) ① [12] **GD60495(3)**
R. Tauber, orch (Eng: r1941) *Concert*
(2/92) (LYRC) ① [2] **SRO830**
E. Mason, orch (r1925) *Concert*
(8/93) (SYMP) ① **SYMCD1136**
R. Ponselle, orch, R. Romani (r1918: Eng) *Concert*
(10/93) (NIMB) ① **NI7846**
E. Eames, anon (r1905: Eng) *Concert*
(11/93) (ROMO) ① [2] **81001-2**
E. Mason, orch, F. Black (r1925) *Concert*
(8/94) (ROMO) ① **81009-2**
E. Mason, orch, F. Black (r1924) *Concert*
(8/94) (ROMO) ① **81009-2**
R. Ponselle, orch, R. Bourdon (r1924: 2 vers: Eng)
Concert (11/94) (ROMO) ① [2] **81006-2**
R. Ponselle, orch, R. Bourdon (r1927: Eng) *Concert*
(11/94) (ROMO) ① [2] **81007-2**
N. Melba, orch, W.B. Rogers (r1907: Eng) *Concert*
(5/95) (ROMO) ① [3] **81011-2(1)**
N. Melba, orch, W.B. Rogers (r1910: Eng) *Concert*
(5/95) (ROMO) ① [3] **81011-2(2)**

L' alba separa dalla luce l'ombra—song (1907) (Wds. G. d'Annunzio)
E. Caruso, orch, J. Pasternack (2 vers: r1917)
Concert (7/91) (RCA) ① [12] **GD60495(6)**
E. Caruso, orch, J. Pasternack (2 vers: r1917)
Concert (10/91) (PEAR) ① [3] **EVC4(1)**
E. Palacio, M. Rapattoni (r1993; arr M. de Bernart)
Concert (1/95) (AKAD) ① **CDAK125**

Ancora!—song (1897)
F. Giraud, anon (r1904) *Concert*
(5/91) (SYMP) ① **SYMCD1077**
M. Battistini, anon (r1902) *Concert*
(10/92) (PEAR) ① **GEMMCD9936**
E. Palacio, B. Giuffredi, C. Passerini, M. Rapattoni (r1993; arr M. de Bernart) *Concert*
(1/95) (AKAD) ① **CDAK125**

Anima mia—song (1915) (Wds. M dei Fiori & G. d'Annunzio)
E. Palacio, H. Liviabella, B. Giuffredi, C. Passerini, M. Decimo, M. Rapattoni (r1993; arr M. de Bernart)
Concert (1/95) (AKAD) ① **CDAK125**

Aprile—song (1882) (Wds. C. Erriso)
L. Tetrazzini, P. Pitt (r1909) *Concert*
(9/92) (EMI) ① [3] **CHS7 63802-2(1)**
L. Tetrazzini, P. Pitt (r1909) *Concert*
(9/92) (PEAR) ① **GEMMCD9221**
E. Palacio, G. Scabbia, B. Giuffredi, C. Passerini, M. Rapattoni (r1993; arr M. de Bernart) *Concert*
(1/95) (AKAD) ① **CDAK125**

Au temps du grand Roi—song
V. Maurel, anon (r1907) *Concert*
(12/94) (SYMP) ① **SYMCD1128**
V. Maurel, orch (r1907) *Concert*
(10/95) (NIMB) ① **NI7867**

Chanson de l'adieu—song (1898) (Wds. E. d'Haraucourt)
R. Tauber, orch (Ger: r1928) *Concert*
(7/89) (PEAR) ① **GEMMCD9327**
E. Pinza, orch, D. Voorhees (bp1947) *Concert*
(7/91) (MMOI) ① **CDMOIR404**

Chitarrata abruzzese—song
T. Ruffo, orch (r1925) *Concert*
(2/93) (PREI) ① [3] **89303(2)**

Donna, vorrei morir—song (1879) (Wds. L. Steccheti)
E. Palacio, M. Rapattoni (r1993; arr M. de Bernart)
Concert (1/95) (AKAD) ① **CDAK125**

Dopo—song
E. Eames, orch (r1911) *Concert*
(7/93) (NIMB) ① [2] **NI7840/1**
E. Carelli, S. Cottone (r1904) *Concert*
(8/93) (SYMP) ① **SYMCD1111**
E. Eames, anon (r1911) *Concert*
(11/93) (ROMO) ① [2] **81001-2**

Ideale—song (1882) (Wds. C. Errico)
P. Domingo, NYPO, Z. Mehta (pp1988) *Concert*
(9/89) (SONY) ① **MK44942**
E. Caruso, orch (r1906) *Concert*
(12/90) (PEAR) ① [3] **EVC1(2)**
A. Garulli, anon (r1902) *Concert*
(5/91) (SYMP) ① **SYMCD1077**
E. Caruso, orch (r1906) *Concert*
(7/91) (RCA) ① [12] **GD60495(2)**
P. Domingo, I. Perlman, NY Studio Orch, J. Tunick
(r1990) *Concert* (3/92) (EMI) ① **CDC7 54266-2**
J. Björling, Stockholm Royal Op Orch, N. Grevillius
(r1937) *Concert* (9/92) (MMOI) ① **CDMOIR409**
J. Björling, orch, N. Grevillius (r1937) *Concert*
(10/93) (NIMB) ① **NI7842**

J. Björling, Stockholm Royal Op Orch, N. Grevillius
(r1937) *Concert* (10/93) (EMI) ① **CDH7 64707-2**
J. Björling, orch, N. Grevillius (r1937) *Concert*
(9/94) (CARL) ① **GLRS103**
G. Lauri-Volpi, orch (r c1923) *Concert*
(9/94) (NIMB) ① **NI7856**
E. Palacio, M. Rapattoni (r1993; arr M. de Bernart)
Concert (1/95) (AKAD) ① **CDAK125**
P. Domingo, I. Perlman, NY Studio Orch, J. Tunick
(r1990) *Concert*
(6/95) (EMI) ① [20] **CZS4 83177-2(3)**

Invano—song
A. Scotti, anon (r1902) *Concert*
(3/93) (SYMP) ① **SYMCD1100**

Luna d'estate—song (Wds. R. Mazzola)
E. Caruso, orch, W.B. Rogers (r1916) *Concert*
(7/91) (RCA) ① [12] **GD60495(5)**
E. Caruso, orch, W.B. Rogers (r1916) *Concert*
(10/91) (PEAR) ① [3] **EVC3(2)**
R. Ponselle, orch, R. Bourdon (r1926) *Concert*
(11/94) (ROMO) ① [2] **81007-2**

Malià—song (1887) (Wds. R. E. Pagliara)
E. Palacio, G. Scabbia, H. Liviabella, C. Passerini, M. Decimo, M. Rapattoni (r1993; arr M. de Bernart)
Concert (1/95) (AKAD) ① **CDAK125**

Marechiare—song (Wds. E. Praga)
L. Pavarotti, Teatro Communale Orch, A. Guadagno
Concert (8/83) (DECC) ① **410 015-2DH**
T. Schipa, orch, R. Bourdon (r1930) *Concert*
(12/89) (RCA) ① **GD87969**
T. Ruffo, orch (r1923) *Concert*
(2/93) (PREI) ① [3] **89303(2)**
T. Gobbi, LSO, A. La Rosa Parodi (r1952) *Concert*
(8/93) (TEST) ① **SBT1019**
V. Maurel, anon (r1905) *Concert*
(12/94) (SYMP) ① **SYMCD1128**

Mattinata, 'Mary, tremando l'ultima stella'—song (1895) (Wds. E. Panzacchi)
E. Palacio, H. Liviabella, C. Passerini, M. Decimo, M. Rapattoni (r1993; arr M. de Bernart) *Concert*
(1/95) (AKAD) ① **CDAK125**
N. Melba (r1907) *Concert*
(5/95) (ROMO) ① [3] **81011-2(1)**

Mattinata, 'Sulla villa solitaria'—song (1903) (Wds. F. Cimmino)
E. Palacio, G. Scabbia, H. Liviabella, B. Giuffredi, M. Rapattoni (r1993; arr M. de Bernart) *Concert*
(1/95) (AKAD) ① **CDAK125**

Mi guitarra dice 'Te amo!'—song (1885) (Wds U. Fleres)
E. Palacio, G. Scabbia, B. Giuffredi, M. Rapattoni (r1993; arr M. de Bernart) *Concert*
(1/95) (AKAD) ① **CDAK125**

La Mia canzone—song (Wds. F. Cimmino)
E. Caruso, S. Cottone (r1902) *Concert*
(5/89) (EMI) ① **CDH7 61046-2**
E. Caruso, S. Cottone (r1902) *Concert*
(12/90) (PEAR) ① [3] **EVC1(1)**
E. Caruso, S. Cottone (r1902) *Concert*
(7/91) (RCA) ① [12] **GD60495(1)**
E. Caruso, orch, W.B. Rogers (r1915) *Concert*
(7/91) (RCA) ① [12] **GD60495(5)**
E. Caruso, orch, W.B. Rogers (r1915) *Concert*
(10/91) (PEAR) ① [3] **EVC3(2)**

Ninon—song (1912) (Wds. A de Musset)
F. Saville, anon (r c1902) *Concert*
(5/91) (SYMP) ① **SYMCD1093**
V. Maurel, anon (r1905) *Concert*
(12/94) (SYMP) ① **SYMCD1128**

Non t'amo più!—song (1884) (Wds. C. Errico)
E. Palacio, H. Liviabella, M. Decimo, M. Rapattoni (r1993; arr M. de Bernart) *Concert*
(1/95) (AKAD) ① **CDAK125**
G. Anselmi, Bettinelli (r1910) *Concert*
(7/95) (SYMP) ① **SYMCD1170**

O falce di luna calante—song (1911) (Wds. G. d'Annunzio)
E. Palacio, M. Rapattoni (r1993; arr M. de Bernart)
Concert (1/95) (AKAD) ① **CDAK125**

Oblio—song
F. Giraud, anon (r1904) *Concert*
(5/91) (SYMP) ① **SYMCD1077**

Parted!—song (Wds. F. E. Weatherley)
E. Caruso, orch (r1914) *Concert*
(5/89) (PEAR) ① **GEMMCD9309**
E. Caruso, orch, W.B. Rogers (r1914) *Concert*
(7/91) (RCA) ① [12] **GD60495(5)**
E. Caruso, orch, W.B. Rogers (r1914) *Concert*
(10/91) (PEAR) ① [3] **EVC3(1)**

Penso—song (1889) (Wds. R. E. Pagliara)
M. Mei-Figner, anon (r1901) *Concert*
(6/93) (PEAR) ① [3] **GEMMCDS9997/9(1)**
E. Palacio, G. Scabbia, H. Liviabella, B. Giuffredi, M. Decimo (r1993; arr M. de Bernart) *Concert*
(1/95) (AKAD) ① **CDAK125**

Il **Pescatore pensa**—song (1910) (Wds. R. Mazzola)
E. Palacio, B. Giuffredi, C. Passerini, M. Decimo, M. Rapattoni (r1993; arr M. de Bernart) *Concert*
(1/95) (AKAD) ① **CDAK125**
Pour un baiser—song (Wds. G. Doncieux)
E. Caruso, orch (r1909) *Concert*
(3/91) (PEAR) ① [3] **EVC2**
E. Caruso, orch, W.B. Rogers (r1909) *Concert*
(7/91) (RCA) ① [12] **GD60495(3)**
Ricordati di me—song (1878) (Wds. G. della Valle)
E. Palacio, M. Rapattoni (r1993; arr M. de Bernart) *Concert* (1/95) (AKAD) ① **CDAK125**
Il **Segreto**—song (1887) (Wds. L. Stecchetti)
A. Davidov, anon (r1901: Russ) *Concert*
(6/93) (PEAR) ① [3] **GEMMCDS9007/9(1)**
E. Palacio, H. Liviabella, M. Decimo, M. Rapattoni (r1993; arr M. de Bernart) *Concert*
(1/95) (AKAD) ① **CDAK125**
La **Serenata**—song (1888) (Wds. G. A. Cesareo)
A. Patti, A. Barili (r1906) *Concert*
(4/90) (PEAR) ① **GEMMCD9312**
L. Tetrazzini, P. Pitt (r1909) *Concert*
(9/92) (EMI) ① [3] **CHS7 63802-2(1)**
L. Tetrazzini, P. Pitt (r1909) *Concert*
(9/92) (PEAR) ① **GEMMCD9222**
A. Nezhdanova, orch (r1913: Russ) *Concert*
(6/93) (PEAR) ① [3] **GEMMCDS9007/9(2)**
E. Mason, orch (r1926) *Concert*
(8/93) (SYMP) ① **SYMCD1136**
E. Mason, Inst Ens (r1925) *Concert*
(8/94) (ROMO) ① **81009-2**
E. Mason, Inst Ens (r1926) *Concert*
(8/94) (ROMO) ① **81009-2**
R. Ponselle, F. Lapitino (r1924: 2 vers: Eng) *Concert*
(11/94) (ROMO) ① [2] **81006-2**
R. Ponselle, F. Lapitino (r1927: Eng) *Concert*
(11/94) (ROMO) ① [2] **81007-2**
E. Palacio, G. Scabbia, B. Giuffredi, M. Rapattoni (r1993; arr M. de Bernart) *Concert*
(1/95) (AKAD) ① **CDAK125**
N. Melba, A. Sassoli (r1907) *Concert*
(5/95) (ROMO) ① [3] **81011-2(1)**
Si tu le voulais—song (wds. H. Vacaresco)
A. Didur, anon (r1900: Pol) *Concert*
(6/93) (PEAR) ① [3] **GEMMCDS9997/9(2)**
A. Didur, orch (r c1916: Pol) *Concert*
(1/95) (CLUB) ① **CL99-089**
Sogno—song (1886) (Wds. L. Stecchetti)
R. Tebaldi, R. Bonynge (1972) *Concert*
(9/94) (DECC) ① **436 202-2DM**
E. Palacio, H. Liviabella, M. Rapattoni (r1993; arr M. de Bernart) *Concert* (1/95) (AKAD) ① **CDAK125**
T'amo ancora—song
P. Aramis, anon (r1905) *Concert*
(12/94) (SYMP) ① **SYMCD1172**
Tristezza—song (1908) (Wds. R. Mazzola)
E. Palacio, M. Decimo, M. Rapattoni (r1993; arr M. de Bernart) *Concert* (1/95) (AKAD) ① **CDAK125**
L' **Ultima canzone**—song (1905) (Wds. F Cimmino)
E. Pinza, orch, R. Bourdon (1927) *Concert*
(3/92) (PREI) ① **89050**
E. Pinza, orch, R. Bourdon (1927) *Concert*
(9/93) (RCA) ① **09026 61245-2**
E. Destinn, orch, W.B. Rogers (r1916) *Concert*
(11/93) (ROMO) ① [2] **81002-2**
E. Destinn, orch, W.B Rogers (r1916) *Concert*
(12/94) (SUPR) ① [12] **11 2136-2(5)**
E. Palacio, H. Liviabella, M. Decimo, M. Rapattoni (r1993; arr M. de Bernart) *Concert*
(1/95) (AKAD) ① **CDAK125**
Vorrei morire—song (1884) (Wds. G. Cognetti)
E. Palacio, H. Liviabella, M. Rapattoni (r1993; arr M. de Bernart) *Concert* (1/95) (AKAD) ① **CDAK125**
G. Anselmi, anon (r1907) *Concert*
(7/95) (SYMP) ① **SYMCD1170**
Vuoi note...o banconote?—song (1882) (Wds. ?cpsr)
E. Palacio, G. Scabbia, H. Liviabella, B. Giuffredi, C. Passerini, M. Decimo, M. Rapattoni (r1993; arr M. de Bernart) *Concert* (1/95) (AKAD) ① **CDAK125**

TOURNEMIRE, Charles (Arnould) (1870–1939) France

SECTION I: ORCHESTRAL

Symphony No. 1 in A, 'Romantique', Op. 18 (1900)
Moscow SO, A. de Almeida (r1994) *Symphony 5.*
(7/95) (MARC) ① **8 223476**

Symphony No. 2 in B flat minor, 'Ouessant', Op. 36 (1908-09)
Moscow SO, A. de Almeida (r1994) *Symphony 4.*
(7/95) (MARC) ① **8 223478**
Symphony No. 4, 'Pages symphoniques', Op. 44 (1912)
Moscow SO, A. de Almeida (r1994) *Symphony 2.*
(7/95) (MARC) ① **8 223478**
Symphony No. 5 in F minor, Op. 47 (1913-14)
Moscow SO, A. de Almeida (r1994) *Symphony 1.*
(7/95) (MARC) ① **8 223476**

SECTION III: INSTRUMENTAL

Cantilène improvisée—organ (improvised 1930) (recons Duruflé)
J. Watts *Concert* (9/90) (PRIO) ① **PRCD286**
Choral-Improvisation sur le Victimae Paschali—organ (improvised 1930) (recons Duruflé)
J. Watts *Concert* (1/92) (PRIO) ① **PRCD294**
7 Chorals-Poèmes pour les Sept Paroles du Christ—organ, Op. 67 (1935)
1. Pater, dimitte illis nesciunt enim quid faciunt; 2. Hodie mecum eris in paradiso; 3. Mulier, ecce filius tuus. Ecce mater tua; 4. Eli, eli, lamma sabacthani; 5. Sitio; 6. Pater, in manus tuas commendo spiritum meum; 7. Consummatum est.
7. T. Mechler *Concert* (9/90) (MOTE) ① **CD10881**
Fantaisie-Improvisation sur l'Ave maris stella—organ (improvised 1930) (recons Duruflé)
J. Watts *Concert* (1/92) (PRIO) ① **PRCD294**
2 Fresques symphoniques sacrées—organ, Opp. 75/76 (1938-39)
M-B. Dufourcet *Concert* (3/92) (PRIO) ① **PRCD328**
Improvisation sur le Te Deum—organ (improvised 1930) (recons Duruflé)
J.S. Whiteley (trans. Duruflé) *Concert*
(7/87) (YORK) ① **CD101**
J. Watts *Concert* (9/90) (PRIO) ① **PRCD286**
Méditation—organ (improvised 1930) (recons Duruflé)
M.H. Long *Concert* (4/91) (KOCH) ① **37008-2**
L' Orgue mystique—Cycle après la Pentecôte—26 Offices for the Liturgical Year, Op. 57 (1927-32)
Each individual work contains the following movements: Prélude à l'Introit; Offertoire; Elévation; Communion; Pièce terminale (indicated in brackets); 1. Sainte-Trinité (Triptyche); 2. Très Saint-Sacrement (Fantaisie-paraphrase); 3. Sacré-Coeur de Jésus (Prélude et Fresque); 4. 4ième dimanche après la Pentecôte (Alleluia No 1); 5. Sième après la Pentecôte (Alleluia No 2); 6. 6ième après la Pentecôte (Alleluia No 3); 7. 7ième après la Pentecôte (Alleluia No 4); 8. 8ième après la Pentecôte (Alleluia No 5); 9. 9ième après la Pentecôte (Supplications et Fugue); 10. Assumption (Paraphrase-carillon); 11. 10ième après la Pentecôte (Choral No 1); 12. 11ième après la Pentecôte (Choral No 2); 13. 12ième après la Pentecôte (Choral No 3); 14. 13ième après la Pentecôte (Choral No 4); 15. 14ième après la Pentecôte (Choral No 5); 16. 15ième après la Pentecôte (Prélude et Fugue); 17. Nativité de la Vierge (Prélude et Louanges); 18. 16ième après la Pentecôte (Choral alleluiatique No 1); 19. 17ième après la Pentecôte (Choral alleluiatique No 2); 20. 18ième la Pentecôte (Choral alleluiatique No 3); 21. 19ième après la Pentecôte (Choral alleluiatique No 4); 22. 20ième après la Pentecôte (Choral alleluiatique No 5); 23. Toussaint (Choral); 24. 21ième après la Pentecôte (Fugue); 25. 22ième après la Pentecôte (Postlude alleluiatique); 26. 23ième après la Pentecôte (Fantaisie sur le Te Deum).
Exc J. Jones *Concert* (8/91) (MOTE) ① **CD11491**
Excs J. Boucher, St John the Baptist Ch Schola, A. Saint-Cyr (with plainchant)
(3/92) (REM) ① **REM311131**
3. N. Hakim *Concert* (10/89) (MOTE) ① **CD40081**
7. D.M. Patrick *Concert* (5/93) (PRIO) ① **PRCD371**
8b, 8e, 24b, 24e, 28b, 29b, 29e, 30e, 36d, 38b, 38d, 41b, 48b, 51e A. Gunning
(6/90) (LIBR) ① **LRCD155**
26. M-B. Dufourcet *Concert*
(3/92) (PRIO) ① **PRCD328**
L' Orgue mystique—Cycle de Noël—11 Offices for the Liturgical Year, Op. 55 (1927-32)
Each individual work contains the following movements: Prélude à l'Introit; Offertoire; Elévation; Communion; Pièce terminale (indicated in brackets); 1. Troisième dimanche de l'avent (Toccata); 2. Immaculé Conception (Postlude); 3. Noël

---

(Paraphrase); 4. Dimanche dans l'Octave de Noël (Postlude-choral); 5. Circoncision (Fantasie et Chorale); 6. Saint Nom de Jésus (Variations); 7. Epiphanie (Fantasie); 8. Premier dimanche après l'Ephiphanie (Fantasia-choral); 9. Deuxième après l'Ephiphanie (Fantasie-choral); 10. Troisième après l'Epiphanie (Postlude et Fugue modale); 11. Purification (Diptyque).
7. M-B. Dufourcet *Concert*
(3/92) (PRIO) ① **PRCD328**
Petite rapsodie improvisée—organ (improvised 1930) (recons Duruflé)
J. Watts *Concert* (9/90) (PRIO) ① **PRCD286**
Suite évocatrice—organ, Op. 74 (1938)
J. Filsell *Concert* (3/92) (HERA) ① **HAVPCD145**
Symphonie-Choral—organ, Op. 69 (1935)
J. Watts *Concert* (1/92) (PRIO) ① **PRCD294**
Triple Choral—organ, Op. 41 (1910)
J. Watts *Concert* (1/92) (PRIO) ① **PRCD294**

TOURNIER, Marcel-Lucien (1879–1951) France

SECTION III: INSTRUMENTAL

Au matin—étude de concert: harp
S. McDonald *Concert* (10/84) (DELO) ① **DE3005**
L. Laskine (r1975) *Concert*
(12/93) (ERAT) ① **4509-92131-2**
Jazz Band—harp
S. McDonald *Concert* (10/84) (DELO) ① **DE3005**

TOWER, Joan (b 1938) USA

SECTION III: INSTRUMENTAL

Clocks—guitar (1985)
S. Isbin (r c1992) *Concert*
(7/94) (VIRG) ① **VC5 45024-2**

TOWNS, Colin (20th cent) England

SECTION I: ORCHESTRAL

Concerto for Trumpet and String Orchestra
G. Ashton, Orch, A. Wilson *Concert*
(9/95) (KOCH) ① **38703-2**
1930 Cityscape—saxophone & orchestra
P. Todd, Orch *Concert* (9/95) (KOCH) ① **38703-2**

SECTION V: STAGE WORKS

The Buccaneers—television score (1995)
EXCERPTS: 1. Allfriars; 2. Lov'd I Not Honour More (Song); 3. The Buccaneers; 4. Nan & Julius; 5. Trevenick Ruins; 6. Newport New Jersey; 7. Birth of an Heir; 8. Waltz of a Lost Room; 9. Capture (Christmas); 10. This is Miss Annabelle; 11. Love Theme; 12. Turn Out Like You; 13. Runnymede; 14. Nothing to Live For But My Passions; 15. Willows Whiten, Aspens Quiver; 16. Card Games & Summer Lawns; 17. The Coreggio Room; 18. Visitors/Guy & Annabel; 19. Lov'd I Not Honour More (reprise).
1-19. OST, M. Simpson, London Filmworks Orch, C. Towns (r1994-5) (9/95) (MERC) ① **526 866-2**
Full Circle: The Haunting of Julia—film score (1978)
EXCERPTS: 1. Theme from Full Circle—The Park; 2. Have You Got a Magnificent Problem?; 3. Pretty Men Are Very Receptive; 4. Kate; 5. Olivia; 6. Love Scene; 7. Magnus—The Unwelcome Intrusion; 8. Full Circle (Everything's Right Now).
1-8. OST, C. Towns (r1978) *Concert*
(9/95) (KOCH) ① **38703-2**
The Wolves of Willoughby Chase—film score (1988)
EXCERPTS: 1. Willoughby House; 2. Main Theme; 3. Rocking Horse; 4. Bonnie collects Sylvia; 5. Playing in the Snow; 6. Simon's Cave; 7. Slighcarp in the Bath; 8. Secret Passage; 9. Journey to Blastburn; 10. Mrs Brisket; 11. Home Thoughts; 12. Cottage; 13. Dangerous Laundry; 14. Quick They've Escaped; 15. The Ski Sledge; 16. Theme; 17. Slighcarp the Witch; 18. The Parents Return; 19. Sufficient for Her Needs; 20. Main Themes.
1-20. OST, Graunke SO, A. Jones (r1988)
(3/90) (TER) ① **CDTER1162**

TOYE, Geoffrey (1889–1942) England

SECTION I: ORCHESTRAL

Haunted Ballroom—concert waltz (1935) (from ballet 'Haunted Ballroom')
RTE Concert Orch, E. Tomlinson (r1993) *Concert*
(12/95) (MARC) ① **8 223522**

TRABACI, Giovanni Maria (c1575–1647) Italy

SECTION III: INSTRUMENTAL

Ancidetemi pur—harp/lute (pub 1615)
A. Lawrence-King *Concert*
(9/87) (HYPE) ① **CDA66229**

Canzone francese—keyboard
3. Terza; 5. Quinta sopra dunque credete ch'io.
3. Amsterdam Loeki Stardust Qt *Concert*
(10/94) (L'OI) ① **440 207-2OM**

Gagliarda quatra, alla Spagnola—harp/lute (pub 1615)
A. Lawrence-King *Concert*
(9/87) (HYPE) ① **CDA66229**

Gagliarda terza a 4. detta la Talianella—harp/lute (pub 1615)
A. Lawrence-King *Concert*
(9/87) (HYPE) ① **CDA66229**

Gagliarda terza a 5, sopra La Mantouana—harp/lute (pub 1615)
A. Lawrence-King *Concert*
(9/87) (HYPE) ① **CDA66229**

Partite sopra Rugiero—keyboard (pub 1615)
R. Alessandrini (r1994) *Concert*
(4/95) (O111) ① **OPS30-118**

Partite sopra Zefiro—harp/lute (pub 1615)
A. Lawrence-King *Concert*
(9/87) (HYPE) ① **CDA66229**

Toccata seconda and Ligature—harp/lute (pub 1615)
A. Lawrence-King *Concert*
(9/87) (HYPE) ① **CDA66229**

TRADITIONAL Including folk music

For Christmas carols see separate section

SECTION I: ORCHESTRAL

Brian Boru's March (Ireland)
R. A. Morgan *Concert* (12/87) (ETCE) ① **KTC1049**

Christmas Fanfare—brass (20th Cent—England) (Music A. Green)
Prince of Wales Brass *Concert*
(12/93) (ASV) ① **CDWHL2083**

Irish Jig
A. Campoli, Orch, W. Goehr *Concert*
(10/91) (PEAR) ① **PASTCD9744**

Irish Reels
A. Campoli, Orch, W. Goehr *Concert*
(10/91) (PEAR) ① **PASTCD9744**

Wedding March from Nordmøre (Norway)
O.E. Antonsen, W. Marshall (1992: arr tpt/org: Antonsen/Marshall) *Concert*
(10/94) (EMI) ① **CDC5 55048-2**

Yankee Doodle—Confederate tune
Boston Pops, A. Fiedler (r1958; arr Gould) *Concert*
(1/94) (RCA) ① **09026 61249-2**

SECTION II: CHAMBER

An dro nevez—bombarde and side drum (Brittany)
R. Canter, J. Wood *Concert*
(4/87) (AMON) ① **CD-SAR22**

Daphne—country dance (16th Cent—England) (arr from ballad)
N. Hadden *Concert* (1/90) (HYPE) ① **CDA66307**

Etenraku—Hichiriki with temple drum and bell (Japan)
R. Canter, J. Wood *Concert*
(4/87) (AMON) ① **CD-SAR22**

Furiant—consort
London Musica Antiqua, M. Uridge (r1980-83) *Concert* (12/93) (SYMP) ① **SYMCD1157**

Grimstock—country dance (16th Cent—England)
Circa 1500, N. Hadden (r1991) *Concert*
(8/93) (CRD) ① **CRD3487**
J. Bream, J. Bream Consort (r1987; ed Tyler)
Concert (8/93) (RCA) ① [28] **09026 61583-2(3)**
J. Bream Consort (r1987; ed Tyler) *Concert*
(9/94) (RCA) ① **09026 61590-2**

Pastorella Sonata (18th Cent—Germany) (Music G. Noëlli)
Pantaleon Ens, K-H. Schickhaus (dulcimer/dir)
(r1991) *Concert* (12/93) (TUDO) ① **Tudor 767**

Pastorellen vor die Weynacht-Zeit (pub 1743—Germany) (Music J.V. Rathgeber)
Pantaleon Ens, K-H. Schickhaus (dulcimer/dir)
(r1991) *Concert* (12/93) (TUDO) ① **Tudor 767**

Robin is to the greenwood gone—country dance (17th Cent—England)
Musicians of Swanne Alley *Concert*
(11/89) (VIRG) ① **VC7 59534-2**

Salvonic Folktunes—consort (16th cent)
1. Folk Tune; 2. Folk Tune; 3. Polka; 4. I cannot forget thee; 5. Walachian dance.
London Musica Antiqua, M. Uridge (r1980-83)
Concert (12/93) (SYMP) ① **SYMCD1157**

Untitled instrumental piece (c1270—England) (source: Bodleian Library MS Douce 139)
Sinfonye, S. Wishart (r1993) *Concert*
(12/93) (HYPE) ① **CDA66685**

Weihnachtslieder aus 'Airs propres pour le Tympanon' (1700-1720) (Music G. Noëlli)
1. Quand Josephe et Pousa Marie; 2. A l'avenue de noël; 3. Or nous ditte Marie.
Pantaleon Ens, K-H. Schickhaus (dulcimer/dir)
(r1991) *Concert* (12/93) (TUDO) ① **Tudor 767**

Wiegenlied für den Christmonat (pub 1759—Germany) (Music J.E. Eberlin)
Pantaleon Ens, K-H. Schickhaus (dulcimer/dir)
(r1991) *Concert* (12/93) (TUDO) ① **Tudor 767**

SECTION III: INSTRUMENTAL

Wayfaring Stranger—folk melody (USA)
Boston Camerata, J. Cohen (r1993) *Concert*
(12/93) (ERAT) ① **4509-92874-2**

SECTION IV: VOCAL AND CHORAL

About a young maiden—folksong (Ukraine)
P. Plishka, T. Hrynkiv (arr Meytus) *Concert*
(11/92) (FORL) ① **UCD16645**

Ach mein herzliebes Jesulein (Germany)
Alberquerque Música Antigua (arr Scheidt) *Concert*
(8/93) (DORI) ① **DIS80104**

Ach, wie ist's möglich dann—Deutsche Volkslied
R. Tauber, M. Spoliansky (r1926) *Concert*
(9/90) (PEAR) ① **GEMMCD9370**

Ack Värmland, du sköma—Swedish song
J. Björling, orch, N. Grevillius (r1936: arr Randel)
Concert (9/92) (MMOI) ① **CDMOIR409**
J. Björling, orch, N. Grevillius (r1936: arr Randel)
Concert (9/94) (CONI) ① **CDHD214**

Adam lay y-bounden—carol (15th Cent—England)
Cambridge Sngrs, J. Rutter (arr Ord) *Concert*
(12/87) (CLLE) ① **COLCD106**
Quink (arr Ord) *Concert*
(12/89) (TELA) ① **CD80202**
Lichfield Cath Ch, J. Rees-Williams (arr Ord) *Concert*
(12/90) (ABBE) ① **CDCA903**
Charterhouse Special Ch, R. Burton, R. Wells (arr Ord) *Concert* (12/91) (HERA) ① **HAVPCD142**
King's College Ch (arr Warlock) *Concert*
(12/91) (COLL) ① **Coll1335-2**
R. Hammersley, Gavin Williams, Guildford Cath Ch, Barry Rose (r1966; arr Ord) *Concert*
(12/91) (EMI) ① **CDM7 64131-2**
King's College Sngrs, E.H. Warrell (arr Ord) *Concert* (12/91) (REGE) ① **REGCD106**
RCS, J. Birch, L. Heltay (pp1991; arr Ord) *Concert*
(12/93) (CARL) ① **PCD1026**
R. Hammersley, Gavin Williams (r1966: arr Warlock) *Concert* (9/94) (EMI) ① **CDM5 65101-2**

Advent Responsory—unaccompanied choir (Music R. Marlow, based on Bach's 'Wachet auf')
Trinity Coll Ch, Cambridge, R. Marlow *Concert*
(12/90) (CONI) ① **CDCF501**

Afton water—folksong (Scotland)
Cambridge Sngrs, CLS, J. Rutter (r1992; arr Rutter)
Concert (11/93) (CLLE) ① **COLCD120**

Ah, little darling—folksong (Russia)
D. Hvorostovsky, Ossipov Russian Folk Orch, N. Kalinin (r1991) *Concert*
(11/92) (PHIL) ① **434 080-2PH**

A-hunting we will go—song (1775—England)
(Wds. H Fielding in 'Don Quixote in England' : 1734)
L. Skeaping, J. Potter, Broadside Band, J. Barlow (r1992; arr J. Barlow) *Concert*
(6/93) (SAYD) ① **CD-SDL400**

All and some—carol (20th Cent) (Music J. Byrt)
Elysian Sngrs, M. Greenall *Concert*
(12/93) (CNTI) ① **CCD1043**

All my heart this night rejoices—carol (Germany) (Music J.G.Ebeling; Wds. Gerhardt trans Winkworth)
Kings College Ch, D. Willcocks *Concert*
(12/91) (CFP) ① **CD-CFP4586**

All through the night, 'Ar hyd y nos'—folksong (Wales)
R. A. Morgan (Welsh) *Concert*
(12/87) (ETCE) ① **KTC1049**
R. Crooks, J. Crawford (r1932: arr Somervell-Hadull)
Concert (9/93) (CLAR) ① **CDGSE78-50-50**

Alleluya: A nywe werk is come on honde—carol (15th Cent—England) (Seldon Manuscript)
Taverner Ch, Taverner Consort, A. Parrott *Concert*
(12/89) (EMI) ① **CDC7 49809-2**
Anon 4 (r1992) *Concert*
(12/93) (HARM) ① **HMU90 7099**

Als Maria übers Gebirge ging (Bavaria) (traditional version of The Magnificat)
Vienna Boys' Ch, U.C. Harrer (arr Harrer) *Concert*
(12/91) (PHIL) ① **426 860-2PH**

Amazing Grace—song
J. Norman, Ambrosian Sngrs, RPO, A. Gibson (arr. Hope) *Concert* (4/83) (PHIL) ① **400 019-2PH**
B. Hendricks, Orphei Drängar, U. Johansson, E. Ericson *Concert* (4/91) (EMI) ① **CDC7 54098-2**
D. Ross, Gumpoldskirchner Kinderchor, Vienna SO, V. Sutej (pp1992; arr Schifrin) *Concert*
(12/93) (SONY) ① **SK53358**

And all in the morning—carol (England)
Kings College Ch, D. Willcocks (arr Vaughan Williams) *Concert* (12/91) (CFP) ① **CD-CFP4586**

Andulko šafářova—folksong (Czechoslovakia)
E. Destinn, F. Kark (r1906) *Concert*
(12/94) (SUPR) ① [12] **11 2136-2(1)**

The Angel Gabriel—carol
King's College Sngrs, E.H. Warrell (arr Pettman)
Concert (12/91) (REGE) ① **REGCD106**

Angeles del zielo—song (17th Cent—Spain)
Alberquerque Música Antigua *Concert*
(8/93) (DORI) ① **DIS80104**

Angels, from the realms of glory, '(Les) Anges dans nos campagnes'—carol (France) (English wds. J.R. Montgomery)
The Sixteen, H. Christophers *Concert*
(12/91) (COLL) ① **Coll1300-2**
K. Te Kanawa, London Voices, Philh, Carl Davis (arr D Cullen) *Concert* (12/91) (DECC) ① **433 010-2DM**
R. Scotto, St Patrick's Cath Ch, St Patrick's Cath Orch, L. Anselmi (r1981; arr Grady) *Concert*
(12/93) (VAI) ① **VAIA1013**

Angels we have heard on high—carol
G. de Chiaro (arr gtr: De Chiaro) *Concert*
(12/91) (CENT) ① **CRC2101**
K. Battle, F. von Stade, Chor, Orch, A. Previn (pp1991) *Concert* (12/92) (SONY) ① **SK48235**
R. Shaw Chbr Sngrs, Robert Shaw (r1993) *Concert*
(12/94) (TELA) ① **CD80377**

Angelus ad virginem—carol (14th Cent)
Tallis Scholars, P. Phillips *Concert*
(12/86) (GIME) ① **CDGIM010**
Trinity Coll Ch, Cambridge, R. Marlow (ed Stevens)
Concert (12/90) (CONI) ① **CDCF501**
Kings College Ch, D. Willcocks *Concert*
(12/91) (EMI) ① **CDM7 64130-2**
Kings College Ch, A. Davis, D. Whittaker, D. Willcocks (arr Poston) *Concert*
(12/91) (EMI) ① **CDM7 64130-2**
A. Doyle, S. Liley, East London Chor, M. Kibblewhite (arr Grainger) *Concert* (12/93) (KOCH) ① **37202-2**

Annie Laurie—Scottish folksong
N. Melba, orch, W.B. Rogers (r1916) *Concert*
(3/89) (LARR) ① **CDLRH221**
M. Garden, J. Dansereau (r1926) *Concert*
(8/94) (ROMO) ① **81008-2**
N. Melba, orch, W.B. Rogers (r1916) *Concert*
(5/95) (ROMO) ① [3] **81011-2(2)**
H. Nash, Male Qt, anon (r1933) *Concert*
(11/95) (PEAR) ① **GEMMCD9175**

Arise, red sun—folksong (Russia)
F. Chaliapin, Afonsky Ch, Balalaika Orch (r1934)
Concert (6/93) (PREI) ① [2] **89207**

A-roving—English folksong
K. Livingstone, N. Mackie, J.J. Blakely (arr Brown)
Concert (2/89) (UNIC) ① **UKCD2009**

As I rode out—carol (16th Cent—England)
Alberquerque Música Antigua *Concert*
(8/93) (DORI) ① **DIS80104**
London Musica Antiqua, M. Uridge (r1980-83)
Concert (12/93) (SYMP) ① **SYMCD1157**

As I sat on a sunny bank—carol (England)
London Musica Antiqua, M. Uridge (r1980-83)
Concert (12/93) (SYMP) ① **SYMCD1157**

As Joseph was a-walking—carol (Music E. Walters; Wds. Anon)
Liverpool Phil Ch, St Ambrose RC Jun Sch Ch, RLPO, E. Walters *Concert*
(12/87) (CHAN) ① **CHAN8436**

As Ola Ola, min eigen Onge, 'Oh Ola, Ola, my own one'—folk song (Norway)
K. Flagstad, orch (r1914) *Concert*
(12/95) (SIMA) ① [3] **PSC1821(1)**

As with gladness men of old—carol (Germany) (Tune: 'Treuer Heiland' abridged C. Kocher)
RCS, J. Birch, L. Heltay (pp1991; arr Willcocks) *Concert* (12/93) (CARL) ① **PCD1026**
Birmingham Bach Ch, M. Shepherd, P. Spicer (r1992; arr Kocher/Gower) *Concert*
(12/93) (BIRM) ① **BBCCD2**
Trinity Coll Ch, Cambridge, P. Rushforth, R. Marlow (r1993) *Concert* (12/93) (CONI) ① **CDCF517**

At the time when the stars—folksong (Russia)
D. Hvorostovsky, Ossipov Russian Folk Orch, N. Kalinin (r1991) *Concert*
(11/92) (PHIL) ① **434 080-2PH**

Au clair de la lune—song
R. Streich, E. Werba (r1957) *Concert*
(10/94) (DG) ① [2] **437 680-2GDO2**

Auld Lang Syne—Scottish song
N. Melba, Coldstream Guards Band, M. Rogan (r1905) *Concert* (3/89) (LARR) ① **CDLRH221**

Ave Maria—carol (15th Cent—England)
Anon 4 (r1992) *Concert*
(12/93) (HARM) ① **HMU90 7099**

Ave Maria, virgo virginum—rondellus (c1250—Anglo-Norman)
Sinfonye, S. Wishart (r1993) *Concert*
(12/93) (HYPE) ① **CDA66685**

Away in a manger—carol
King's College Ch, D. Briggs, S. Cleobury *Concert*
(12/84) (ARGO) ① **414 042-2ZH**
St George's Chapel Ch, J. Porter, C. Robinson (arr Kirkpatrick) *Concert* (12/84) (ABBS) ① **CDMVP287**
Cambridge Sngrs, J. Rutter (arr Kirkpatrick) *Concert*
(12/87) (CLLE) ① **COLCD106**
John Alldis Ch, LSO, Colin Davis (arr Kirkpatrick) *Concert* (12/89) (PHIL) ① **416 249-2PB**
Sheffield Chorale, Sheaf Concert Orch, J. Kirkwood (arr Kirkpatrick) *Concert*
(12/89) (CHOR) ① **EECD109**
Trinity Coll Ch, Cambridge, R. Marlow (arr Kirkpatrick) *Concert* (12/90) (CONI) ① **CDCF501**
King's College Ch, D. Willcocks (arr Kirkpatrick) *Concert* (12/90) (DECC) ① **430 089-2DWO**
Canterbury Cath Ch, D. Flood (arr Jacques) *Concert* (12/90) (YORK) ① **CD109**
Lichfield Cath Ch, J. Rees-Williams *Concert*
(12/90) (ABBE) ① **CDCA903**
The Sixteen, H. Christophers (arr Kirkpatrick) *Concert*
(12/91) (COLL) ① **Coll1300-2**
York Minster Ch *Concert* (12/91) (YORK) ① **CD846**
K. Battle, F. von Stade, Chor, Orch, A. Previn (pp1991) *Concert* (12/92) (SONY) ① **SK48235**
Birmingham Bach Ch, P. Spicer (r1992; arr Willocks/Gower) *Concert*
(12/93) (BIRM) ① **BBCCD2**
St Alban's Abbey Ch, A. Parnell, Barry Rose (r1992; arr Rose) *Concert* (12/93) (LAMM) ① **LAMM081D**
Westminster Cath Ch, J. O'Donnell (arr Moore) *Concert* (12/93) (HYPE) ① **CDA66668**
Prince of Wales Brass (2 vers: arr Kirkpatrick/Green & arr Redhead/Quirk) *Concert*
(12/93) (ASV) ① **CDWHL2083**
Jenkins Family Sngrs, N. Jenkins *Concert*
(12/93) (MAYH) ① **KM93071405410**
Edinburgh Cath Ch, T. Byram-Wigfield (r1993; arr Willcocks) *Concert* (12/93) (HERA) ① **HAVPCD163**
St John's College Ch, G. Guest, S. Cleobury (r c1974: arr Willcocks) *Concert*
(12/93) (BELA) ① **450 111-2**
Ex Cathedra Chbr Ch, J. Skidmore (r c1994: arr Willcocks) *Concert* (12/94) (ASV) ① **CDDCA912**
R. Shaw Chbr Sngrs, Robert Shaw (r1994) [1993] *Concert*
(12/94) (TELA) ① **CD80377**

A babe is born—carol (15th Cent—England)
The Sixteen, H. Christophers (arr Fricker) *Concert*
(12/90) (COLL) ① **Coll1270-2**

A Babe is born I wys—carol (Music E. Bainton)
Kings College Ch, D. Willcocks *Concert*
(12/91) (CFP) ① **CD-CFP4586**

The Babe of Bethlehem—carol (pub 1835—America) (Music W. Walker)
Taverner Ch, Taverner Consort, A. Parrott *Concert*
(12/89) (EMI) ① **CDC7 49809-2**

Balaam de quo vaticinans—motet (13th-14th Cent—England)
Anon 4 (r1992) *Concert*
(12/93) (HARM) ① **HMU90 7099**

Ballad of Dovbush—folksong (Ukraine)
P. Plishka, T. Hrynkiv (arr Zador) *Concert*
(11/92) (FORL) ① **UCD16645**

Balulalow—carol (16th Cent) (Wds. Luther, trans. Wedderburn)
I. Partridge, J. Partridge (arr Warlock) *Concert*
(4/90) (ETCE) ① **KTC1078**
The Sixteen, R. Jeffrey, Margaret Phillips, The Sixteen Orch, H. Christophers (arr Warlock) *Concert* (12/90) (COLL) ① **Coll1270-2**
Cambridge Sngrs, CLS, J. Rutter (r1993) *Concert*
(12/93) (CLLE) ① **COLCD121**
J. Baker, P. Ledger (r1980: arr Warlock) *Concert*
(9/94) (EMI) ① **CDM5 65101-2**

The Banks of Allan Water—song
A. Patti, L. Ronald (r1905) *Concert*
(4/90) (PEAR) ① **GEMMCD9312**

Beautiful is the Blue Sky, 'Deilig er den himmel blaa'—carol (Denmark)
M. Petri, Westminster Abbey Ch, National PO, M. Neary *Concert* (12/91) (RCA) ① **RD60060**

Before the Marvel of this Night—carol (20th Cent—America) (Music C. Schalk; Wds. J. Vajda)
St Alban's Bach Ch, A. Parnell, Barry Rose (r1992) *Concert* (12/93) (LAMM) ① **LAMM081D**

Begone dull care—duet (1793—England)
L. Skeaping, Broadside Band, J. Barlow (r1992; arr J. Barlow) *Concert* (6/93) (SAYD) ① **CD-SDL400**

Behold a lovely vine (USA) (source 'The Christian Harmony')
Boston Camerata, J. Cohen (1993) *Concert*
(12/93) (ERAT) ① **4509-92874-2**

Believe me, if all those endearing young charms—song
S. McDonald (hp) *Concert*
(10/84) (DELO) ① **DE3005**
W. Marsalis, Eastman Wind Ens, D. Hunsberger (arr D Hunsberger) *Concert* (9/87) (SONY) ① **MK42137**
N. Melba (r1909) *Concert*
(3/89) (LARR) ① **CDLRH221**
E. Rethberg, orch (r1926) *Concert*
(2/95) (ROMO) ① [2] **81012-2**
N. Melba (r1909: arr T.Moore) *Concert*
(5/95) (ROMO) ① [3] **81011-2(1)**

Benedicamus Domino—carol: 8vv (1918—England) (Music P. Warlock)
The Sixteen, H. Christophers *Concert*
(12/90) (COLL) ① **Coll1270-2**
York Minster Ch *Concert* (12/91) (YORK) ① **CD846**
Finzi Sngrs, P. Spicer (r1992) *Concert*
(10/93) (CHAN) ① **CHAN9182**
Birmingham Bach Ch, P. Spicer (r1992) *Concert*
(12/93) (BIRM) ① **BBCCD2**
Trinity Coll Ch, Cambridge, R. Marlow (r1993) *Concert* (12/93) (CONI) ① **CDCF517**

Berceuse—carol (Poland)
Quink (arr Serocky) *Concert* (12/89) (TELA) ① **CD80202**

Der Beruhigte—folksong (Bavaria)
E. Schwarzkopf, M. Raucheisen (bp1944) *Concert*
(6/87) (ACAN) ① **43 801**

Bethlehem Down—4vv (1927) (Music P. Warlock; Wds. B. Blunt)
Lichfield Cath Ch, J. Rees-Williams *Concert*
(12/90) (ABBE) ① **CDCA903**
Charterhouse Special Ch, R. Burton, R. Wells *Concert* (12/91) (HERA) ① **HAVPCD142**
Guildford Cath Ch, Barry Rose (r1966) *Concert*
(12/91) (EMI) ① **CDM7 64131-2**
Finzi Sngrs, P. Spicer (r1992) *Concert*
(10/93) (CHAN) ① **CHAN9182**
Westminster Cath Ch, J. O'Donnell *Concert*
(12/93) (HYPE) ① **CDA66668**
Birmingham Bach Ch, P. Spicer (r1992) *Concert*
(12/93) (BIRM) ① **BBCCD2**
Edinburgh Cath Ch, T. Byram-Wigfield (r1993) *Concert* (12/93) (HERA) ① **HAVPCD163**
Guildford Cath Ch, Barry Rose (r1966) *Concert*
(9/94) (EMI) ① **CDM5 65101-2**

Billy boy—folksong (Britain)
O. Natzke, chor, orch (r1943) *Concert*
(12/92) (ODE) ① **CDODE1365**

The Birds, 'When Jesus Christ was four years old'—song
R. Golden, L. Rothfuss *Concert*
(10/92) (KOCH) ① **37118-2**
London Musica Antiqua, M. Uridge (r1980-83) *Concert* (12/93) (SYMP) ① **SYMCD1157**

The Birth—carol (20th Cent—England) (Music J. Coppin)
Coppin ens *Concert* (12/91) (RED) ① **RSKCD111**

Birthday carol—choir, brass, percussion and organ (20th Cent—England) (Wds. & Music D. Willcocks)
Atlanta Choral Guild, W. Noll *Concert*
(12/91) (NEWP) ① **NPD85529**

Blessed be that maid Mary—carol (England)
King's College Ch, D. Willcocks (arr Willcocks) *Concert* (12/89) (DECC) ① **425 499-2DM**
Cambridge Sngrs, CLS, J. Rutter (r1993; arr Willcocks) *Concert* (12/93) (CLLE) ① **COLCD121**

The blessed Son of God—carol
King's College Ch, D. Willcocks, S. Preston *Concert* (12/94) (BELA) ① **450 112-2**

Blow the man down—sea shanty
O. Natzke, chor, orch (r1943) *Concert*
(12/92) (ODE) ① **CDODE1365**

Blow the wind southerly—folksong
L. Finnie, A. Legge (arr. Whittaker) *Concert*
(4/90) (CHAN) ① **CHAN8749**
K. Ferrier (r1949: arr Whittaker) *Concert*
(6/91) (DECC) ① **430 096-2DWO**
V. de los Angeles, G. Parsons (arr Warlock: pp1990) *Concert* (12/91) (COLL) ① **Coll1247-2**
Sarah Walker, J. Constable *Concert*
(4/92) (GAMU) ① **GAMD506**
K. Ferrier (r1949: arr Whittaker) *Concert*
(6/92) (DECC) ① **433 475-2DM**

Blow ye winds in the morning—folksong (England)
K. Livingstone, N. Mackie, J.J. Blakely (arr Brown) *Concert* (2/89) (UNIC) ① **UKCD2009**

The Boar's Head Carol (16th Cent—England)
Liverpool Phil Ch, St Ambrose RC Jun Sch Ch, RLPO, E. Walters (arr Walters) *Concert*
(12/87) (CHAN) ① **CHAN8436**
The Sixteen, H. Christophers *Concert*
(12/88) (HYPE) ① **CDA66263**
Kings College Ch, D. Willcocks (arr Maconchy) *Concert* (12/91) (EMI) ① **CDM7 64130-2**
RCS, J. Birch, L. Heltay (pp1991; arr Sargent) *Concert* (12/93) (CARL) ① **PCD1026**
R. Shaw Chbr Sngrs, Robert Shaw (r1993) *Concert*
(12/94) (TELA) ① **CD80377**

Bobby Shaftoe—folksong (England)
Magdalen (Oxford) Coll Ch, G. Ives *Concert*
(11/92) (CNTO) ① **CRCD2366**

Bohemian Carol
London Musica Antiqua, M. Uridge (r1980-83) *Concert* (12/93) (SYMP) ① **SYMCD1157**

The bold grenadier—folksong (England)
Cambridge Sngrs, CLS, J. Rutter (r1992; arr Rutter) *Concert* (11/93) (CLLE) ① **COLCD120**

Bonny labouring boy—folksong (England)
J. Johnston, W. Reynold Orch, F. Collinson (r1948) *Concert* (4/95) (TEST) ① **SBT1058**

Born is the babe—consort song (16th Cent—England)
A. Tysall, Rose Consort *Concert*
(12/91) (WOOD) ① **WOODM001-2**

5 Bridal folk songs from the Voronezh District
1. Now, my little grey duck; 2. Good day, my fair one; 3. Oh, mother, my little head hurts; 4. Oh, come to me; 5. Indoors, outside.
Voronezh Chbr Ch *Concert*
(2/92) (HYPE) ① **CDA66410**

Bright Bright the Holly Berries—carol (Music A. Burt)
Atlanta Choral Guild, W. Noll *Concert*
(12/91) (NEWP) ① **NPD85529**

Bring us good ale (medieval—England)
London Musica Antiqua, M. Uridge (r1980-83) *Concert* (12/93) (SYMP) ① **SYMCD1157**

Buenos Reyes—carol (Spain)
Liverpool Phil Ch, St Ambrose RC Jun Sch Ch, RLPO, E. Walters (arr. Walters) *Concert*
(12/87) (CHAN) ① **CHAN8436**

Bugeilio'r Gwenith Gwyn, 'Watching the White Wheat'—Welsh folksong
S. Bullock, A. Bryn Parri (r1994; arr Bryn Parri) *Concert* (11/95) (SAIN) ① **SCDC2070**

Burschenlust—folksong (Germany)
R. Tauber, M. Spoliansky (r1926) *Concert*
(9/90) (PEAR) ① **GEMMCD9370**

By the wayside stands a tree—Jewish song
I. Perlman, Israel PO, D. Seltzer (1986: arr vn/orch) *Concert* (6/95) (EMI) ① [20] **CZS4 83177-2(3)**

Calvary—Negro spiritual
J. Norman, chor, orch, James Levine (pp1990) *Concert* (5/91) (DG) ① **429 790-2GH**

The Campden carol (Gloucestershire)
Coppin ens (arr Coppin) *Concert*
(12/91) (RED) ① **RSKCD111**

Cançó de Sega—folksong: 1v and orchestra (Catalonia)
V. de los Angeles, Lamoureux Orch, A. Ros-Marbà (r1969: arr Ros-Marbà) *Concert*
(4/94) (EMI) ① [4] CMS5 65061-2(1)
El Cant del Ocells, '(The) Song of the Birds'—folksong (Catalonia)
V. de los Angeles, Barcelona Patronato Orch, A. Ros-Marbà (r1969: arr Ros-Marbà) *Concert*
(4/94) (EMI) ① [4] CMS5 65061-2(1)
Canto delle risaiole—wordless folk melody
R. Streich, E. Werba (r1957: arr Rasch) *Concert*
(10/94) (DG) ① [2] 437 680-2GDO2
Carmen-Carmela—Spanish-Californian folksong
R. Ponselle, I. Chichagov (r1954) *Concert*
(1/90) (RCA) ① GD87810
The carnal and the crane—carol (medieval—England)
East London Chorale, M. Kibblewhite (arr B. Kelly - Abingdon carols No. 3) *Concert*
(12/93) (KOCH) ① 37202-2
Carnevale di Venezia—song
T. dal Monte, Orch, R. Bourdon (r1926: arr Benedict) *Concert*
(2/90) (PREI) ① 89001
Carol of the Bells (Ukraine)
Sheffield Chorale, Sheaf Concert Orch, J. Kirkwood (arr Clover) *Concert* (12/89) (CHOR) ① EECD109
Atlanta Choral Guild, W. Noll (arr Leontovich & Wilhousky) *Concert* (12/91) (NEWP) ① NPD85529
Toronto Children's Chor, J.A. Bartle (r1992; arr Leontovitch) *Concert* (12/93) (CBC) ① SMCD5119
The Carol singers—song
Liverpool Phil Ch, St Ambrose RC Jun Sch Ch, RLPO, E. Walters (arr Walters; wds. Rhodes) *Concert* (12/87) (CHAN) ① CHAN8436
A Carol-Lullaby (pub 1922) (Wds. & Music P. Meacham)
Lichfield Cath Ch, J. Rees-Williams *Concert*
(12/90) (ABBE) ① CDCA903
Catalan Folk-song (unidentified)
M. Maisky, P. Gililov (arr Casals) *Concert*
(7/91) (DG) ① 431 544-2GH
Cherry Tree Carol—carol (England)
Cambridge Sngrs, J. Rutter (arr. Willcocks) *Concert*
(12/87) (CLLE) ① COLCD106
Quink (arr Willcocks) *Concert*
(12/89) (TELA) ① CD80202
King's College Ch *Concert*
(12/91) (COLL) ① Coll1335-2
Kings College Ch, D. Willcocks (arr Willcocks) *Concert* (12/91) (CFP) ① CD-CFP4586
Salisbury Cath Ch, R. Seal (1983; arr Willcocks) *Concert* (12/93) (MERI) ① CDE84068
R. Shaw Chbr Sngrs, Robert Shaw (r1993) *Concert* (12/94) (TELA) ① CD80377
Child in a manger—carol (Wales) (Eng Wds. J. Rutter)
Cambridge Clare College Ch, Cambridge Clare College Orch, J. Rutter (arr Rutter) *Concert*
(12/89) (DECC) ① 425 500-2DM
Jenkins Family Sngrs, N. Jenkins *Concert*
(12/93) (MAYH) ① KM93071405410
A Child is born in Bethlehem, '(Ein) Kind geborn zu Bethlehem'—carol (17th Cent—Germany)
Kings College Ch, D. Willcocks (arr Scheidt) *Concert* (12/91) (CFP) ① CD-CFP4586
York Minster Ch (arr Scheidt) *Concert*
(12/91) (YORK) ① CD846
Trinity Coll Ch, Cambridge, R. Marlow (r1993) *Concert* (12/93) (CONI) ① CDCF517
The Child of Light—song (1985—England) (Wds. & Music R. Saxton)
Elysian Sngrs, M. Greenall *Concert*
(12/91) (CNTI) ① CCD1043
Child of the Manger—carol (Music S. Lole; Wds. A.J. Lewis)
St Mary Collegiate Church Ch, K. Bowyer, S. Lole (r1992) *Concert* (3/94) (REGE) ① REGCD107
Christ was born on Christmas day—carol (Germany)
R. Shaw Chbr Sngrs, Robert Shaw (r1993) *Concert*
(12/94) (TELA) ① CD80377
Christmas at the Cloisters—song (1966—USA) (Music J. Corigliano; Wds. W.M. Hoffmann)
R. Scotto, St Patrick's Cath Ch, St Patrick's Cath Orch, L. Anselmi (r1981) *Concert*
(12/93) (VAI) ① VAIA1013
A Christmas Carol, 'Little star of Bethlehem' (1894) (Music Charles Ives)
Quink *Concert* (12/89) (TELA) ① CD80202

A Christmas Carol, '(The) Shepherds had an Angel' (Music H. Darke)
Birmingham Bach Ch, M. Shepherd, P. Spicer (r1992) *Concert* (12/93) (BIRM) ① BBCCD2
Christmas Day—carol (Music D. Sanger)
Edinburgh Cath Ch, T. Byram-Wigfield (r1993) *Concert* (12/93) (HERA) ① HAVPCD163
A Christmas Garland—soprano, chorus and string orchestra (1959—England) (Music G. Dyson)
V. Hill, J. Watts, RCM Chbr Ch, RPO, D. Willcocks *Concert* (12/86) (UNIC) ① DKPCD9057
Christmas Hymn, 'Hark! Hark! what news the angels bring' (18th Cent—America)
Boston Camerata, J. Cohen (r1993) *Concert*
(12/93) (ERAT) ① 4509-92874-2
Christmas is coming—round
Jenkins Family Sngrs, N. Jenkins *Concert*
(12/93) (MAYH) ① KM93071405410
Christmas Night—carol (16th Cent—France) (Eng Wds. J. Rutter)
Cambridge Sngrs, CLS, J. Rutter (arr. Rutter) *Concert* (12/87) (CLLE) ① COLCD106
The Christmas Song, 'Chestnuts roasting by an open fire'—song (1946) (Wds. & Music R. Wells & M. Tormé)
K. Battle, W. Marsalis, Jazz Ens (pp1991) *Concert* (12/92) (SONY) ① SK48235
Christmas Spirituals—medley (arr Joseph Jennings)
EXCERPTS: 1. Rise up shepherd and follow; 2. Behold that star; 3. Sweet little Jesus boy; 4. Poor little Jesus; 5. What month was Jesus born in?; 6. Children, go where I send thee; 7. Go tell it on the mountain.
Chanticleer (r1990) *Concert*
(12/94) (CHTI) ① CR-8803
The Christmas Tree with its decorations—carol (20th Cent—Denmark) (Music E. Harder)
M. Petri, Westminster Abbey Ch, National PO, M. Neary (arr Christiansen) *Concert*
(12/91) (RCA) ① RD60060
Christum wir sollen loben schon—carol (16th Cent—Germany) (Music L. Osiander)
Taverner Ch, Taverner Consort, A. Parrott *Concert* (12/89) (EMI) ① CDC7 49800-2
La cloche de Noël—carol (France)
Toronto Children's Chor, Toronto SO, J.A. Bartle (r1992) *Concert* (12/93) (CBC) ① SMCD5119
Come all you worthy Christian friends—carol (Devon/Somerset)
Coppin ens (arr Coppin) *Concert*
(12/91) (RED) ① RSKCD111
Come all you worthy gentlemen—carol (England)
Jenkins Family Sngrs, N. Jenkins *Concert*
(12/93) (MAYH) ① KM93071405410
Comin' thro' the Rye—Folksong
N. Melba, G. Lapierre (r1913) *Concert*
(3/89) (LARR) ① CDLRH221
A. Patti, L. Ronald (r1905) *Concert*
(4/90) (PEAR) ① GEMMCD9312
N. Melba, G. Lapierre (r1913) *Concert*
(9/93) (RCA) ① 09026 61412-2
N. Melba, G. Lapierre (r1913) *Concert*
(5/95) (ROMO) ① [3] 81011-2(2)
El condor pasa, 'If I could'—folksong setting (pub 1933—Bolivia) (based on Peruvian folksong)
V. Taylor, T. Kain (arr Morel) *Concert*
(9/92) (TALL) ① TP003
Convict's Song, 'Why was I born?' (Russia)
L. Sibiriakov, anon (r1910) *Concert*
(6/93) (PEAR) ① GEMMCDS9007/9(2)
A Cornish Christmas Carol—8vv (1918) (Music P. Warlock; Wds. H. Jenner)
Finzi Sngrs, P. Spicer (r1992) *Concert*
(10/93) (CHAN) ① CHAN9182
Cossack's longing—folksong (Ukraine)
P. Plishka, T. Hrynkiv (arr Stetsenko) *Concert*
(11/92) (FORL) ① UCD16645
The Coulin—air (Ireland) (Wds. trad Gaelic)
A. Murray (r1992) *Concert*
(8/93) (HYPE) ① CDA66627
Counting the goats—folk melody
R. A. Morgan (Welsh) *Concert*
(12/87) (ETCE) ① KTC1049

Coventry Carol, 'Lully, lulla, thou little tiny child'—carol (1591—England) (Wds. from Pageant of Shearman & Tailors, Coventry)
Tallis Scholars, P. Phillips *Concert*
(12/86) (GIME) ① CDGIM010
Tallis Scholars, P. Phillips *Concert*
(12/86) (GIME) ① CDGIM010
Gothic Voices, C. Page *Concert*
(11/87) (HYPE) ① CDA66238
The Sixteen, H. Christophers *Concert*
(12/88) (HYPE) ① CDA66263
Cambridge Sngrs, CLS, J. Rutter *Concert*
(12/89) (CLLE) ① COLCD111
John Alldis Ch, LSO, Colin Davis (arr Hope) *Concert* (12/89) (PHIL) ① 416 249-2PB
King's College Ch, D. Willcocks (arr M. Shaw) *Concert* (12/89) (DECC) ① 425 499-2DM
Taverner Ch, Taverner Consort, A. Parrott *Concert* (12/89) (EMI) ① CDC7 49800-2
Quink *Concert* (12/89) (TELA) ① CD80202
Salisbury Cath Ch, R. Seal (arr Leighton) *Concert* (11/90) (MERI) ① CDE84180
Trinity Coll Ch, Cambridge, R. Marlow (arr Shaw) *Concert* (12/90) (CONI) ① CDCF501
The Sixteen, H. Christophers (arr Leighton) *Concert* (12/90) (COLL) ① Coll1270-2
York Minster Ch, F. Jackson *Concert*
(12/91) (CHAN) ① CHAN6520
PCA *Concert* (12/91) (DHM) ① GD77228
The Sixteen, H. Christophers *Concert*
(12/91) (COLL) ① Coll1300-2
St Paul's Cath Ch, John Scott, Adrian Lucas (arr Leighton) *Concert* (12/92) (HYPE) ① CDA66489
Toronto Children's Chor, Toronto SO, J.A. Bartle (r1992; arr Cable) *Concert*
(12/93) (CBC) ① SMCD5119
St Alban's Abbey Ch, A. Parnell, Barry Rose (r1992; arr Leighton) *Concert*
(12/93) (LAMM) ① LAMM081D
Boston Camerata, J. Cohen (r1993) *Concert*
(12/93) (ERAT) ① 4509-92874-2
R. Scotto, St Patrick's Cath Ch, St Patrick's Cath Orch, L. Anselmi (r1981; arr Grady) *Concert* (12/93) (VAI) ① VAIA1013
Trinity Coll Ch, Cambridge, R. Marlow (r1993) *Concert* (12/93) (CONI) ① CDCF517
Oxford Pro Musica Sngrs, M. Smedley (r1993) *Concert* (12/93) (PROU) ① PROUCD134
Cambridge Taverner Ch, O. Rees (r1993) *Concert* (12/93) (PAST) ① 3589
Prince of Wales Brass (arr Warren) *Concert*
(12/93) (ASV) ① CDWHL2083
Edinburgh Cath Ch, T. Byram-Wigfield (r1993; arr Grier) *Concert* (12/93) (HERA) ① HAVPCD163
London Musica Antiqua, M. Uridge (1980-83) *Concert* (12/93) (SYMP) ① SYMCD1157
Jenkins Family Sngrs, N. Jenkins *Concert*
(12/93) (MAYH) ① KM93071405410
R. Shaw Chbr Sngrs, Robert Shaw (r1993) *Concert* (12/94) (TELA) ① CD80377
Cradle Song—carol (20th Cent) (Music A. Porter; Wds. I. Watts)
Cambridge Clare College Ch, Cambridge Clare College Orch, J. Rutter (arr Rutter) *Concert*
(12/89) (DECC) ① 425 500-2DM
Lichfield Cath Ch, J. Rees-Williams *Concert*
(12/90) (ABBE) ① CDCA903
Cradle Song, 'My little sweet darling'—consort song (16th Cent) (Music attrib. Byrd)
Liverpool Phil Ch, St Ambrose RC Jun Sch Ch, RLPO, E. Walters *Concert*
(12/87) (CHAN) ① CHAN8436
The Crown of Roses, 'When Jesus Christ was yet a Child'—carol (Russia) (Music Tchaikovsky; Wds. Plechtcheev trans. Dearmer)
RCS, J. Birch, L. Heltay (pp1991) *Concert*
(12/93) (CARL) ① PCD1026
Ex Cathedra Chbr Ch, J. Skidmore (r c1994) *Concert* (12/94) (ASV) ① CDDCA912
Crucifixion/Hear the lamb's crying—spiritual
M. Anderson, F. Rupp (r1941) *Concert*
(1/90) (RCA) ① GD87911
Plymouth Music Series Ens Sngrs, Plymouth Music Series Chor, Moore by Four Voc Jazz Ens, P. Brunelle (r1994) *Concert*
(9/95) (COLL) ① Coll1449-2
The cuckoo—folksong (England)
Cambridge Sngrs, CLS, J. Rutter (r1992; arr Rutter) *Concert* (11/93) (CLLE) ① COLCD120

La **Dama d'Arago—folksong: 1v and orchestra (Catalonia)**
V. de los Angeles, Barcelona Patronato Orch, A. Ros-Marbà (r1969: arr Nicolau) *Concert* (4/94) (EMI) Ⓓ [4] **CMS5 65061-2(1)**

Dance little goatling—carol (20th Cent—England) (Music G. Walters; Wds. P. Kennerley)
Liverpool Phil Ch, St Ambrose RC Jun Sch Ch, RLPO, E. Walters *Concert* (12/87) (CHAN) Ⓓ **CHAN8436**

Danny Boy—Irish folksong
E. Schwarzkopf, G. Moore (r1958) *Concert* (12/90) (EMI) Ⓓ **CDM7 63654-2**
P. Domingo, I. Perlman, NY Studio Orch, J. Tunick (r1990) *Concert* (3/92) (EMI) Ⓓ **CDC7 54266-2**
A. Murray (r1992) *Concert* (8/93) (HYPE) Ⓓ **CDA66627**
E. Steber, orch, H. Barlow (bp1946) *Concert* (11/95) (VAI) Ⓓ **VAIA1072**

Dark Eyes—folksong (Russia)
D. Hvorostovsky, Ossipov Russian Folk Orch, N. Kalinin (r1991) *Concert* (11/92) (PHIL) Ⓓ **434 080-2PH**
F. Chaliapin, Aristov Ch, Balalaika Orch, A.A. Scriabin (r1927) *Concert* (6/93) (PREI) Ⓓ [2] **89207**

Dark the night—carol (England) (Wds. W. Lloyd)
East London Chor, M. Kibblewhite (arr B. Kelly - Abingdon carols No. 2) *Concert* (12/93) (KOCH) Ⓓ **37202-2**

The **Dark-eyed sailor—song (England)**
J. Johnston, W. Reynold Orch, F. Collinson (r1948) *Concert* (4/95) (TEST) Ⓓ **SBT1058**

David of the White Rock, 'Dafydd y Garreg Wen'—Welsh air (aka The dying bard)
R. A. Morgan (Welsh) *Concert* (12/87) (ETCE) Ⓓ **KTC1049**
Britannia Building Soc Band, Desford Colliery Caterpillar Band, CWS (Glasgow) Band, IMI Yorkshire Imperial Band, G. Brand (pp1991: arr G H Willcocks) *Concert* (8/92) (POLY) Ⓓ **QPRL049D**

De supernis sedibus—rondellus (13th Cent—England)
Anon 4 (r1992) *Concert* (12/93) (HARM) Ⓓ **HMU90 7099**

De Virgin Mary had a baby-boy—spiritual (West Indies)
St Alban's Bach Ch, A. Parnell, Barry Rose (r1992; arr Sargent) *Concert* (12/93) (LAMM) Ⓓ **LAMM081D**
Oxford Pro Musica Sngrs, M. Smedley (r1993; arr Blackwell) *Concert* (12/93) (PROU) Ⓓ **PROUCD134**

Death is going to lay his cold, icy hands on me—Negro spiritual
Plymouth Music Series Ens Sngrs, Plymouth Music Series Chor, Moore by Four Voc Jazz Ens, P. Brunelle (r1994) *Concert* (9/95) (COLL) Ⓓ **Coll1449-2**

Deck the hall—carol (Wales)
Liverpool Phil Ch, St Ambrose RC Jun Sch Ch, RLPO, E. Walters (arr Walters) *Concert* (12/87) (CHAN) Ⓓ **CHAN8436**
John Alldis Ch, LSO, Colin Davis (arr Hope) *Concert* (12/89) (PHIL) Ⓓ **416 249-2PB**
Quink (arr Willcocks) *Concert* (12/89) (TELA) Ⓓ **CD80202**
The Sixteen, H. Christophers *Concert* (12/91) (COLL) Ⓓ **Coll1300-2**
Atlanta Choral Guild, W. Noll (arr Willcocks) *Concert* (12/91) (NEWP) Ⓓ **NPD85529**
Atlanta Choral Guild, W. Noll (arr McKelvy) *Concert* (12/91) (NEWP) Ⓓ **NPD85529**
G. de Chiaro (arr gtr) *Concert* (12/91) (CENT) Ⓓ **CRC2101**
K. Battle, F. von Stade, Chor, Orch, A. Previn (pp1991) *Concert* (12/92) (SONY) Ⓓ **SK48235**
Prince of Wales Brass (arr Warren) *Concert* (12/93) (ASV) Ⓓ **CDWHL2083**
Oxford Pro Musica Sngrs, M. Smedley (r1993; arr Gritton) *Concert* (12/93) (PROU) Ⓓ **PROUCD134**
Jenkins Family Sngrs, N. Jenkins *Concert* (12/93) (MAYH) Ⓓ **KM93071405410**
Cambridge Sngrs, CLS, J. Rutter (r1993; arr Rutter) *Concert* (12/93) (CLLE) Ⓓ **COLCD121**
R. Shaw Chbr Sngrs, Robert Shaw (r1993) *Concert* (12/94) (TELA) Ⓓ **CD80377**

Deep River—spiritual
X. Wei, Pam Nicholson (arr Heifetz) *Concert* (9/90) (ASV) Ⓓ **CDDCA698**
W. White, G. McNaught (arr M Marshall) *Concert* (6/92) (CHAN) Ⓓ **CHAN8960**
D.L. Ragin, M. Hogan (arr Burleigh) *Concert* (8/92) (CHNN) Ⓓ **CCS2991**
J. Heifetz, M. Kaye (r1944) *Concert* (11/94) (RCA) Ⓓ [65] **09026 61778-2(19)**

Descend from heaven—carol (Germany) (Tune 'Susanni'; Eng Wds. G.R. Woodward)
Canterbury Cath Ch, M. Harris, A. Wicks (arr. D.Iliff) *Concert* (12/87) (CONI) Ⓓ **CDCF160**
R. Shaw Chbr Sngrs, Robert Shaw (r1993) *Concert* (12/94) (TELA) Ⓓ **CD80377**

Dezí, flor resplandeçiente—villancicos (c1500—Spain)
Hilliard Ens *Concert* (6/91) (HYPE) Ⓓ **CDA66370**

Dies est leticie—song (c1500—Poland)
Alberquerque Música Antigua *Concert* (8/93) (DORI) Ⓓ **DIS80104**

Ding dong! merrily on high—carol (16th Cent—France) (Eng Wds. G.R. Woodward)
King's College Ch, D. Briggs, S. Cleobury *Concert* (12/84) (ARGO) Ⓓ **414 042-2ZH**
St George's Chapel Ch, J. Porter, C. Robinson (arr. Wood) *Concert* (12/84) (ABBS) Ⓓ **CDMVP827**
Liverpool Phil Ch, St Ambrose RC Jun Sch Ch, RLPO, E. Walters (arr. Walters) *Concert* (12/87) (CHAN) Ⓓ **CHAN8436**
Cambridge Clare College Ch, Cambridge Clare College Orch, J. Rutter (arr Willcocks) *Concert* (12/89) (DECC) Ⓓ **425 500-2DM**
Cambridge Sngrs, CLS, J. Rutter (arr C. Wood) *Concert* (12/89) (CLLE) Ⓓ **COLCD111**
Sheffield Chorale, Sheaf Concert Orch, J. Kirkwood (arr. Willcocks) *Concert* (12/89) (CHOR) Ⓓ **EECD109**
King's College Ch, D. Willcocks (arr C. Wood) *Concert* (12/89) (DECC) Ⓓ **425 499-2DM**
Taverner Plyrs, A. Parrott *Concert* (12/89) (EMI) Ⓓ **CDC7 49809-2**
Trinity Coll Ch, Cambridge, R. Marlow (arr Wood) *Concert* (12/90) (CONI) Ⓓ **CDCF501**
Canterbury Cath Ch, D. Flood (arr Willcocks) *Concert* (12/90) (YORK) Ⓓ **CD109**
King's College Ch, D. Willcocks (arr Wood) *Concert* (12/90) (DECC) Ⓓ **430 089-2DWO**
M. Petri, Westminster Abbey Ch, National PO, M. Neary (arr. D. Willcocks) *Concert* (12/91) (RCA) Ⓓ **RD60060**
York Minster Ch, F. Jackson *Concert* (12/91) (CHAN) Ⓓ **CHAN6520**
Charterhouse Special Ch, R. Burton, R. Wells (arr Wood) *Concert* (12/91) (HERA) Ⓓ **HAVPCD142**
The Sixteen, H. Christophers *Concert* (12/91) (COLL) Ⓓ **Coll1300-2**
T. Hampson, St Paul CO, H. Wolff (arr Pasatieri) *Concert* (12/91) (TELD) Ⓓ **9031-73135-2**
Atlanta Choral Guild, W. Noll (arr Willcocks) *Concert* (12/91) (NEWP) Ⓓ **NPD85529**
Kings College Ch, D. Willcocks (arr Willcocks) *Concert* (12/91) (CFP) Ⓓ **CD-CFP4586**
Westminster Cath Ch, J. O'Donnell *Concert* (12/93) (HYPE) Ⓓ **CDA66668**
Prince of Wales Brass (arr Green) *Concert* (12/93) (ASV) Ⓓ **CDWHL2083**
Oxford Pro Musica Sngrs, M. Smedley (r1993) *Concert* (12/93) (PROU) Ⓓ **PROUCD134**
Edinburgh Cath Ch, T. Byram-Wigfield (r1993; arr Wood) *Concert* (12/93) (HERA) Ⓓ **HAVPCD163**
St John's College Ch, G. Guest, S. Cleobury (r c1974) *Concert* (12/94) (BELA) Ⓓ **450 111-2**

Donkey and ox—carol (Pyrenees)
Canterbury Cath Ch, M. Harris, A. Wicks (arr. J.Barnard) *Concert* (12/87) (CONI) Ⓓ **CDCF160**

Down the Peterskaya road—folk melody (Russia)
F. Chaliapin, Balalaika Orch (r1929) *Concert* (6/93) (PREI) Ⓓ [2] **89207**

Down the Volga—folksong (Russia)
F. Chaliapin, Paris Russian Met Church Ch, N. Afonsky (r1932: arr Alexandrov) *Concert* (6/93) (PREI) Ⓓ [2] **89207**

Doyna—folksong (Romania)
I. Perlman, I. Zohar, Israel PO, D. Seltzer (r1986: arr Seltzer) *Concert* (5/93) (EMI) Ⓓ [4] **CMS7 64617-2**
I. Perlman, Israel PO, D. Seltzer (r1986: arr vn/orch) *Concert* (6/95) (EMI) Ⓓ [20] **CZS4 83177-2(3)**

Drink to me only with thine eyes—song (c1780s—England) (Wds. B. Jonson)
Welbeck Light Qt *Concert* (10/91) (PEAR) Ⓓ **PASTCD9744**
K. Ferrier, P. Spurr (r1951) *Concert* (6/92) (DECC) Ⓓ **433 475-2DM**
D. Bispham, anon (r1902) *Concert* (10/92) (SYMP) Ⓓ **SYMCD1093**
J. Potter, Broadside Band, J. Barlow (r1992; arr J. Barlow) *Concert* (6/93) (SAYD) Ⓓ **CD-SDL400**

Drinking Song—folksong (Ukraine)
P. Plishka, T. Hrynkiv (arr Revutsky) *Concert* (11/92) (FORL) Ⓓ **UCD16645**

The **Drummer Boy—carol (Czechoslovakia)**
London Musica Antiqua, M. Uridge (r1980-83) *Concert* (12/93) (SYMP) Ⓓ **SYMCD1157**

The **Drunken Sailor—song**
O. Natzke, chor, orch (r1943) *Concert* (12/92) (ODE) Ⓓ **CDODE1365**

Du, du liegst mir im Herzen—Deutsche Volkslied
R. Tauber, M. Spoliansky (r1926) *Concert* (9/90) (PEAR) Ⓓ **GEMMCD9370**
E. Schumann-Heink, orch (r1924) *Concert* (2/91) (NIMB) Ⓓ **NI7811**

E la don don—carol (16th Cent—Spain)
Chanticleer (r1990) *Concert* (12/94) (CHTI) Ⓓ **CR-8803**
Ex Cathedra Chbr Ch, J. Skidmore (r c1994: arr Skidmore) *Concert* (12/94) (ASV) Ⓓ **CDDCA912**

Early one morning—folksong (England)
L. Skeaping, Broadside Band, J. Barlow (r1992; setting W. Hawes, 1820) *Concert* (6/93) (SAYD) Ⓓ **CD-SDL400**

Ecce mundi gaudium—rondellus (c1250—Anglo-Norman)
Sinfonye, S. Wishart (r1993) *Concert* (12/93) (HYPE) Ⓓ **CDA66685**

Ecce quod natura—carol (15th Cent)
PCA *Concert* (12/91) (DHM) Ⓓ **GD77228**
Anon 4 (r1992) *Concert* (12/93) (HARM) Ⓓ **HMU90 7099**

The **Echo Carol (17th Cent)**
Lichfield Cath Ch, J. Rees-Williams *Concert* (12/90) (ABBE) Ⓓ **CDCA903**
King's College Sngrs, E.H. Warrell *Concert* (12/91) (REGE) Ⓓ **REGCD106**
Jenkins Family Sngrs, N. Jenkins *Concert* (12/93) (MAYH) Ⓓ **KM93071405410**

Edi beo lhu, hevene quene, 'Blessed Be Thou, Queen of Heaven'—carol (Wds. Anon)
Trinity Coll Ch, Cambridge, R. Marlow (r1993) *Concert* (12/93) (CONI) Ⓓ **CDCF517**

Elijah Rock—Negro spiritual
Plymouth Music Series Ens Sngrs, Plymouth Music Series Chor, Moore by Four Voc Jazz Ens, P. Brunelle (r1994) *Concert* (9/95) (COLL) Ⓓ **Coll1449-2**

Eriksay Love-lilt—Scottish folksong
J. Hislop, P. Kahn (r1926) *Concert* (1/93) (PEAR) Ⓓ **GEMMCD9956**

Es hat sich eröffnet—Nativity hymn (Tyrol)
Vienna Boys' Ch, U.C. Harrer (arr Wawak) *Concert* (12/91) (PHIL) Ⓓ **426 860-2PH**

Es ist ein Ros' entsprungen—song (Germany)
Quink (arr Distler) *Concert* (12/89) (TELA) Ⓓ **CD80202**
Vienna Boys' Ch, U.C. Harrer (arr Harrer) *Concert* (12/91) (PHIL) Ⓓ **426 860-2PH**
Toronto Children's Chor, J.A. Bartle (r1992; arr Praetorius) *Concert* (12/93) (CBC) Ⓓ **SMCD5119**

Es wird schon glei dumpa—lullaby (Tyrol)
Vienna Boys' Ch, Teufel Family, U.C. Harrer (arr Harrer) *Concert* (12/91) (PHIL) Ⓓ **426 860-2PH**

Ev'ry time I feel de spirit—spiritual
W. White, G. McNaught (arr H Johnson) *Concert* (6/92) (CHAN) Ⓓ **CHAN8960**
D.L. Ragin, New World Voc Ens (arr Hogan) *Concert* (8/92) (CHNN) Ⓓ **CCS2991**
Wells Cath Vicars Choral, A. Nethsingha (arr Adelmann) *Concert* (9/92) (ABBE) Ⓓ **CDCA924**

Farewell, happiness—folksong (Russia)
D. Hvorostovsky, Ossipov Russian Folk Orch, N. Kalinin (r1991) *Concert* (11/92) (PHIL) Ⓓ **434 080-2PH**

Fidgety bairn—folksong
K. Ferrier, J. Newmark (r1950) *Concert* (6/92) (DECC) Ⓓ **433 475-2DM**

Les **Filles de la Rochelle—song**
E. Clément, anon (r1910s) *Concert* (8/95) (PEAR) Ⓓ **GEMMCD9161**

The **first good joy that Mary had (Joys Seven)—carol (England)**
King's College Ch, D. Briggs, S. Cleobury (arr Cleobury) *Concert* (12/84) (ARGO) Ⓓ **414 042-2ZH**
King's College Sngrs, E.H. Warrell (arr Cleobury) *Concert* (12/91) (REGE) Ⓓ **REGCD106**

The **First Mercy—song (1927)** (Music P. Warlock; Wds. B. Blunt)
B. Luxon, D. Willison *Concert* (2/89) (CHAN) Ⓓ **CHAN8643**
Sarah Walker, R. Vignoles *Concert* (10/92) (CRD) Ⓓ **CRD3473**
R. Golden, L. Rothfuss *Concert* (10/92) (KOCH) Ⓓ **37118-2**

The **First Nowell—carol (England)**
King's College Ch, D. Briggs, S. Cleobury (arr
Willcocks) *Concert*
(12/84) (ARGO) ① **414 042-2ZH**
P. Rickard, St George's Chapel Ch, J. Porter, C.
Robinson (arr Willcocks) *Concert*
(12/84) (ABBS) ① **CDMVP827**
Winchester Cath Ch, M. Neary (arr Willcocks)
Concert (12/88) (ASV) ① **CDQS6011**
John Alldis Ch, LSO, Colin Davis (arr Hope) *Concert*
(12/89) (PHIL) ① **416 249-2PB**
E. Schwarzkopf, Ambrosian Sngrs, Philh, C.
Mackerras (arr Mackerras) *Concert*
(12/90) (EMI) ① **CDM7 63574-2**
Trinity Coll Ch, Cambridge, G. Jackson, R. Marlow
(arr Willcocks) *Concert*
(12/90) (CONI) ① **CDCF501**
King's College Ch, D. Willcocks (arr Willcocks)
Concert (12/90) (DECC) ① **430 089-2DWO**
York Minster Ch, F. Jackson *Concert*
(12/91) (CHAN) ① **CHAN6520**
The Sixteen, H. Christophers *Concert*
(12/91) (COLL) ① **Coll1300-2**
T. Hampson, St Paul CO, H. Wolff (arr Pasatieri)
Concert (12/91) (TELD) ① **9031-73135-2**
G. de Chiaro (arr gtr) *Concert*
(12/91) (CENT) ① **CRC2101**
K. Battle, F. von Stade, Chor, Orch, A. Previn
(pp1991) *Concert* (12/92) (SONY) ① **SK48235**
RCS, J. Birch, L. Heltay (pp1991) *Concert*
(12/93) (CARL) ① **PCD1026**
St John's College Ch, G. Guest, S. Cleobury (r
c1974: arr Willcocks) *Concert*
(12/94) (BELA) ① **450 111-2**
Un **Flambeau, Jeanette, Isabelle, 'Bring a
torch, Jeanette, Isabelle'—carol (France)**
L. Quilico, Toronto Children's Chor, Toronto SO, J.A.
Bartle (r1992; arr Cable) *Concert*
(12/93) (CBC) ① **SMCD5119**
Cambridge Sngrs, CLS, J. Rutter (r1993; arr Rutter)
Concert (12/93) (CLLE) ① **COLCD121**
R. Shaw Chbr Sngrs, Robert Shaw (r1993) *Concert*
(12/94) (TELA) ① **CD80377**
The **Flowering of the thorn—carol (20th
Cent—England)** (Music J. Coppin in
collaboration with Broomhall)
Coppin ens *Concert* (12/91) (RED) ① **RSKCD111**
The **Foggy, foggy dew—folksong**
J. McCormack, S. Clay (arr Clay: r1913) *Concert*
(5/93) (MMOI) ① **CDMOIR418**
2 Folksongs of Little Russia
A. Didur, orch (r c1921: arr Zimbalist) *Concert*
(1/94) (CLUB) ① **CL99-089**
**Follow that star—carol (Wds. & Music P.
Gritton)**
Oxford Pro Musica Sngrs, M. Smedley (r1993)
Concert (12/93) (PROU) ① **PROUCD134**
**Forest idyll (I skovens dybe stille
ro)—folksong (Denmark)**
M. Hanskov, T. Lønskov *Concert*
(3/92) (DANA) ① **DACOCD378**
**Fortune my foe—folksong (17th
Cent—England)**
E. Van Evera, Musicians of Swanne Alley *Concert*
(11/89) (VIRG) ① **VC7 59534-2**
**From stormy wyndis—carol (15th
Cent—England)** (Music E. Turges)
The Sixteen, H. Christophers *Concert*
(4/92) (COLL) ① **Coll1314-2**
The **Frostbound Wood—song (1929)** (Music
P. Warlock; Wds. B. Blunt)
I. Partridge, J. Partridge *Concert*
(4/90) (ETCE) ① **KTC1078**
R. Golden, L. Rothfuss *Concert*
(10/92) (KOCH) ① **37118-2**
Fum, fum, fum—carol (Spain)
Quink (arr Carreras) *Concert*
(12/89) (TELA) ① **CD80202**
Toronto Children's Chor, Toronto SO, J.A. Bartle
(r1992; arr Cable) *Concert*
(12/93) (CBC) ① **SMCD5119**
R. Shaw Chbr Sngrs, Robert Shaw (r1993) *Concert*
(12/94) (TELA) ① **CD80377**
**Gabriel fram heven-king—carol (14th
Cent—Basque)**
Hilliard Ens (r1984) *Concert*
(3/87) (HARM) ① **HMC90 1154**
Taverner Ch, Taverner Consort, Taverner Plyrs, A.
Parrott *Concert* (12/89) (EMI) ① **CDC7 49809-2**
Sinfonye, S. Wishart (r1993; voc & instr versions)
Concert (12/93) (HYPE) ① **CDA66685**
Anon 4 (r1992) *Concert*
(12/93) (HARM) ① **HMU90 7099**
Trinity Coll Ch, Cambridge, R. Marlow (r1993; arr
Marlow) *Concert* (12/93) (CONI) ① **CDCF517**

Oxford Pro Musica Sngrs, M. Smedley (r1993; arr
Pettman) *Concert* (12/93) (PROU) ① **PROUCD134**
Gabriel's message—carol (Basque) (Wds. S.
Baring-Gould)
St George's Chapel Ch, J. Porter, C. Robinson (arr.
Baring Gould) *Concert*
(12/84) (ABBS) ① **CDMVP827**
Cambridge Clare College Ch, Cambridge Clare
College Orch, J. Rutter (arr Willcocks) *Concert*
(12/89) (DECC) ① **425 500-2DM**
King's College Ch *Concert*
(12/91) (COLL) ① **Coll1335-2**
Westminster Cath Ch, J. O'Donnell (arr Pettman)
Concert (12/93) (HYPE) ① **CDA66668**
RCS, J. Birch, L. Heltay (pp1991; arr Pettman)
Concert (12/93) (CARL) ① **PCD1026**
Salisbury Cath Ch, R. Seal (r1983) *Concert*
(12/93) (MERI) ① **CDE84068**
King's College Ch, D. Willcocks, S. Preston *Concert*
(12/94) (BELA) ① **450 112-2**
**Gaudete, gaudete! Christus est natus—carol
(pub 1582)**
The Sixteen, H. Christophers *Concert*
(12/88) (HYPE) ① **CDA66263**
Taverner Ch, Taverner Consort, Taverner Plyrs, A.
Parrott *Concert* (12/89) (EMI) ① **CDC7 49809-2**
Canterbury Cath Ch, D. Flood (arr Wulston) *Concert*
(12/90) (YORK) ① **CD109**
Oxford Pro Musica Sngrs, M. Smedley (r1993)
Concert (12/93) (PROU) ① **PROUCD134**
**Gegrüsst seist du, Maria—Annunciation
hymn (Austria)**
Vienna Boys' Ch, Teufel Family, U.C. Harrer (arr
Bresgen) *Concert* (12/91) (PHIL) ① **426 860-2PH**
The **Gentle Maiden—Folksong**
J. Heifetz, I. Achron (r1924; arr C. Scott) *Concert*
(11/94) (RCA) ① **[65] 09026 61778-2(01)**
Gesù bambino—carol (Italy)
K. Battle, F. von Stade, Chor, Orch, A. Previn
(pp1991) *Concert* (12/92) (SONY) ① **SK48235**
L. Quilico, Toronto Children's Chor, Toronto SO, J.A.
Bartle (r1992; arr Yon) *Concert*
(12/93) (CBC) ① **SMCD5119**
The **Gift of Love (20th Cent)** (Music P.
Domingo Jr; Wds. M.K. Reilly)
P. Domingo, Gumpoldskirchner Kinderchor, Vienna
SO, V. Sutej (pp1992; arr Schifrin) *Concert*
(12/93) (SONY) ① **SK53358**
Give me Jesus—spiritual
D.L. Ragin, New World Voc Ens (arr Hogan) *Concert*
(8/92) (CHNN) ① **CCS2991**
**Glory to God on high—hymn (18th/19th
Cent—America)** (Music A. Ingalls; Wds. I.
Watts)
Taverner Ch, Taverner Consort, A. Parrott *Concert*
(12/89) (EMI) ① **CDC7 49809-2**
**Gloucestershire Wassail, 'Wassail, wassail
all over the town!'—carol**
Cambridge Sngrs, CLS, J. Rutter (arr Rutter) *Concert*
(12/89) (CLLE) ① **COLCD111**
Coppin ens (arr Coppin) *Concert*
(12/91) (RED) ① **RSKCD111**
Jenkins Family Sngrs, N. Jenkins *Concert*
(12/93) (MAYH) ① **KM93071405410**
Go down, Moses—Negro spiritual
M. Anderson, Orch, Mr Prince (r1924) *Concert*
(1/90) (RCA) ① **GD87911**
W. White, G. McNaught (arr M. Marshall) *Concert*
(6/92) (CHAN) ① **CHAN8960**
Plymouth Music Series Sngrs, Plymouth Music
Series Chor, Moore by Four Voc Jazz Ens, P.
Brunelle (r1994) *Concert*
(9/95) (COLL) ① **Coll1449-2**
Go tell it on the Mountain—Negro spiritual
T. Hampson, St Paul CO, H. Wolff (arr Pasatieri)
Concert (12/91) (TELD) ① **9031-73135-2**
K. Battle, F. von Stade, W. Marsalis, Chor, Orch, A.
Previn (pp1991) *Concert*
(12/92) (SONY) ① **SK48235**
Cambridge Sngrs, CLS, J. Rutter (r1993; arr Rutter)
Concert (12/93) (CLLE) ① **COLCD121**
Plymouth Music Series Sngrs, Plymouth Music
Series Chor, Moore by Four Voc Jazz Ens, P.
Brunelle (r1994) *Concert*
(9/95) (COLL) ① **Coll1449-2**
Go where I send thee—negro spiritual
Plymouth Music Series Sngrs, Plymouth Music
Series Chor, Moore by Four Voc Jazz Ens, P.
Brunelle (r1994) *Concert*
(9/95) (COLL) ① **Coll1449-2**
**God rest you merry, gentlemen—carol
(England)**
King's College Ch, D. Briggs, S. Cleobury (arr.
Willcocks) *Concert*
(12/84) (ARGO) ① **414 042-2ZH**

St George's Chapel Ch, J. Porter, C. Robinson (arr.
Stainer) *Concert* (12/84) (ABBS) ① **CDMVP827**
Canterbury Cath Ch, M. Harris, A. Wicks (arr.
J.Stainer) *Concert* (12/87) (CONI) ① **CDCF160**
Winchester Cath Ch, M. Neary (arr Willcocks)
Concert (12/88) (ASV) ① **CDQS6011**
John Alldis Ch, LSO, Colin Davis (arr Hope) *Concert*
(12/89) (PHIL) ① **416 249-2PB**
Taverner Ch, Taverner Consort, Taverner Plyrs, A.
Parrott *Concert* (12/89) (EMI) ① **CDC7 49809-2**
Canterbury Cath Ch, M. Harris, D. Flood (arr
Willcocks) *Concert* (12/90) (YORK) ① **CD109**
King's College Ch, D. Willcocks *Concert*
(12/90) (DECC) ① **430 089-2DWO**
Lichfield Cath Ch, J. Rees-Williams (arr Willcocks)
Concert (12/90) (ABBE) ① **CDCA903**
York Minster Ch, F. Jackson *Concert*
(12/91) (CHAN) ① **CHAN6520**
King's College Ch *Concert*
(12/91) (COLL) ① **Coll1335-2**
The Sixteen, H. Christophers *Concert*
(12/91) (COLL) ① **Coll1300-2**
Atlanta Choral Guild, W. Noll (arr Pinkham) *Concert*
(12/91) (NEWP) ① **NPD85529**
St Alban's Bach Ch, A. Parnell, Barry Rose (r1992;
arr Willcocks) *Concert*
(12/93) (LAMM) ① **LAMM081D**
RCS, J. Birch, L. Heltay (pp1991) *Concert*
(12/93) (CARL) ① **PCD1026**
Prince of Wales Brass (arr Green) *Concert*
(12/93) (ASV) ① **CDWHL2083**
Salisbury Cath Ch, R. Seal (r1983; arr Willcocks)
Concert (12/93) (MERI) ① **CDE84068**
Edinburgh Cath Ch, T. Byram-Wigfield (r1993; arr
Willcocks) *Concert* (12/93) (HERA) ① **HAVPCD163**
St John's College Ch, G. Guest, S. Cleobury (r
c1974: arr Willcocks) *Concert*
(12/94) (BELA) ① **450 111-2**
R. Shaw Chbr Sngrs, Robert Shaw (r1993) *Concert*
(12/94) (TELA) ① **CD80377**
God's innocent Lamb (Swedish Psalm No.
94)
J. Björling, Inst Ens (r1920) *Concert*
(8/92) (BLUE) ① **ABCD016**
Good Christian men, rejoice—carol
R. Shaw Chbr Sngrs, Robert Shaw (r1993) *Concert*
(12/94) (TELA) ① **CD80377**
**Good King Wenceslas—carol (16th
Cent—Sweden)** (Wds. J.M. Neale)
John Alldis Ch, LSO, Colin Davis (arr Hope) *Concert*
(12/89) (PHIL) ① **416 249-2PB**
Canterbury Cath Ch, M. Harris, D. Flood (arr
Jacques) *Concert* (12/90) (YORK) ① **CD109**
York Minster Ch, F. Jackson *Concert*
(12/91) (CHAN) ① **CHAN6520**
The Sixteen, H. Christophers *Concert*
(12/91) (COLL) ① **Coll1300-2**
J. Sutherland, P. Clark, Ambrosian Sngrs, New Philh,
R. Bonynge (arr Gamley) *Concert*
(12/91) (DECC) ① **433 010-2DM**
St Alban's Abbey Ch, A. Parnell, Barry Rose (r1992)
Concert (12/93) (LAMM) ① **LAMM081D**
Prince of Wales Brass (arr Curnow) *Concert*
(12/93) (ASV) ① **CDWHL2083**
Jenkins Family Sngrs, N. Jenkins *Concert*
(12/93) (MAYH) ① **KM93071405410**
St John's College Ch, G. Guest, S. Cleobury (r
c1974: arr Woodward) *Concert*
(12/94) (BELA) ① **450 111-2**
R. Shaw Chbr Sngrs, Robert Shaw (r1993) *Concert*
(12/94) (TELA) ① **CD80377**
Good News—negro spiritual
K. Battle, M. Garrett (arr Sadin: pp1991) *Concert*
(7/92) (DG) ① **435 440-2GH**
K. Battle, J. Norman, chor, orch, James Levine
(pp1990) *Concert* (5/91) (DG) ① **429 790-2GH**
Goodnight—folksong (Czechoslovakia)
E. Destinn, D. Gilly, orch (r1914: Czech) *Concert*
(11/93) (ROMO) ① **[2] 81002-2**
E. Destinn, D. Gilly, orch (r1914: Czech) *Concert*
(11/94) (SUPR) ① **[12] 11 2136-2(5)**
Gospel train—Negro spiritual
K. Battle, J. Norman, chor, orch, James Levine
(pp1990) *Concert* (5/91) (DG) ① **429 790-2GH**
A **Great and Mighty Wonder—carol
(Germany)**
Trinity Coll Ch, Cambridge, P. Rushforth, R. Marlow
(r1993) *Concert* (12/93) (CONI) ① **CDCF517**
Great day—Negro spiritual
J. Norman, G. Parsons (pp1987) *Concert*
(8/88) (PHIL) ① **422 048-2PH**
K. Battle, J. Norman, chor, orch, James Levine
(pp1990) *Concert* (5/91) (DG) ① **429 790-2GH**
**Greensleeves, 'Alas! my love'—English
folksong (16th Cent-)** (various arrs)
S. McDonald (hp) *Concert*
(10/84) (DELO) ① **DE3005**

834

King's College Ch (arr Sullivan) *Concert*
(12/91) (COLL) ① **Coll1335-2**
Kings College Ch, D. Willcocks (arr Sullivan) *Concert*
(12/91) (CFP) ① **CD-CFP4586**
G. de Chiaro (gtr; arr Willis) *Concert*
(12/91) (CENT) ① **CRC2101**
Ely Cath Ch, D. Price, P. Trepte (r1992; arr Sullivan)
Concert (9/93) (CNTO) ① **CRCD2368**
RCS, J. Birch, L. Heltay (pp1991; arr Sullivan)
Concert (12/93) (CARL) ① **PCD1026**
St Alban's Abbey Ch, A. Parnell, Barry Rose (r1992;
arr Sullivan/Lowman) *Concert*
(12/93) (LAMM) ① **LAMM081D**
It's the most wonderful time of the
year—song (Music E. Pola; Wds. G. Wyle)
D. Ross, Gumpoldskirchner Kinderchor, Vienna SO,
V. Sutej (pp1992; arr Schifrin) *Concert*
(12/93) (SONY) ① **SK53358**
Der Jäger Abshied—Deutsche Volkslied
R. Tauber, M. Spoliansky (r1926) *Concert*
(9/90) (PEAR) ① **GEMMCD9370**
Jägerleben—Deutsche Volkslied
R. Tauber, M. Spoliansky (r1926) *Concert*
(9/90) (PEAR) ① **GEMMCD9370**
J'ai vû le loup—chanson (14-15th cent)
Baltimore Consort (r1992; arr Baltimore Consort)
Concert (4/95) (DORI) ① **DOR90177**
Jeder Bauern Bubi—folksong (Bavaria)
M. Hanskov, T. Lønskov *Concert*
(3/92) (DANA) ① **DACOCD378**
Jesu, Son most sweet and dear—carol
East London Chor, M. Kibblewhite (arr B. Kelly -
Abingdon carols No. 4) *Concert*
(12/93) (KOCH) ① **37202-2**
Jesu, thou the Virgin-born—carol, H82 (Op.
20b/3) (1907—England) (Music G. Holst, Wds
Anon)
Holst Sngrs, S. Layton (r1993) *Concert*
(6/94) (HYPE) ① **CDA66705**
Jesus Christ the Apple Tree—carol (Wds.
Anon)
St George's Chapel Ch, J. Porter, C. Robinson (arr
Poston) *Concert* (12/84) (ABBS) ① **CDMVP827**
Cambridge Sngrs, J. Rutter (arr Poston) *Concert*
(6/88) (CLLE) ① **COLCD107**
Winchester Cath Ch, M. Neary (arr Poston) *Concert*
(12/88) (ASV) ① **CDQS6011**
Cambridge Clare College Ch, Cambridge Clare
College Orch, J. Rutter (arr Poston) *Concert*
(12/89) (DECC) ① **425 500-2DM**
King's College Ch (arr Poston) *Concert*
(12/91) (COLL) ① **Coll1335-2**
Kings College Ch, D. Willcocks (arr Poston) *Concert*
(12/91) (EMI) ① **CDM7 64130-2**
King's College Sngrs, E.H. Warrell (arr Poston)
Concert (12/91) (REGE) ① **REGCD106**
Dundee Cath Ch, R. Lightband (org/dir) (arr Piccolo)
Concert (8/92) (ABBE) ① **CDCA926**
Jesus Christ the Lord is born—carol (15th
Cent) (from 'Piae Cantiones')
Canterbury Cath Ch, M. Harris, A. Wicks (arr Dr. D.Iliff)
Concert (12/87) (CONI) ① **CDCF160**
Jesus, good above all other—carol (14th
Cent—Germany)
St Mary Collegiate Church Ch, K. Bowyer, S. Lole
(r1992; arr Lole) *Concert*
(3/94) (REGE) ① **REGCD107**
Jesus, lover of my soul—Negro spiritual
Plymouth Music Series Ens Sngrs, Plymouth Music
Series Chor, Moore by Four Voc Jazz Ens, P.
Brunelle (r1994) *Concert*
(9/95) (COLL) ① **Coll1449-2**
Jesus the Light of the World (19th
Cent—USA)
Boston Camerata, J. Cohen (r1993) *Concert*
(12/93) (ERAT) ① **4509-92874-2**
Jhesu, fili virginis—carol (mid 15th Cent)
PCA *Concert* (12/91) (DHM) ① **GD77228**
Jingle Bells—song (1857) (Wds. & Music J.S.
Pierpont)
Atlanta Choral Guild, W. Noll *Concert* (arr Willcocks)
(12/91) (NEWP) ① **NPD85529**
Oxford Pro Musica Sngrs, M. Smedley (r1993; arr
Blackwell) *Concert*
(12/93) (PROU) ① **PROUCD134**
D. Ross, J. Carreras, P. Domingo, Gumpoldskirchner
Kinderchor, Vienna SO, V. Sutej (pp1992; arr
Schifrin) *Concert* (12/93) (SONY) ① **SK53358**
Jock O'Hazeldean—song (Scotland)
M. Garden, A. Russell (r1929: 2 vers) *Concert*
(8/94) (ROMO) ① **81008-2**
Jog on—folksong (16th Cent—England)
A. Lawrence-King *Concert*
(1/90) (HYPE) ① **CDA66307**

John Anderson, my Jo—song (Wds. R.
Burns)
M. Garden, orch (r1912) *Concert*
(8/93) (SYMP) ① **SYMCD1136**
Jordanis oras praebia—Advent hymn
King's College Ch, D. Willcocks, S. Preston *Concert*
(12/94) (BELA) ① **450 112-2**
Josep i Maria—Catalan folksong
V. de los Angeles, G. Parsons (arr Morante; pp1990)
Concert (12/91) (COLL) ① **Coll1247-2**
Joseph, lieber Joseph mein—carol
(Germany)
Jenkins Family Sngrs, N. Jenkins *Concert*
(12/93) (MAYH) ① **KM93071405410**
London Musica Antiqua, M. Uridge (r1980-83; 2 vers)
Concert (12/93) (SYMP) ① **SYMCD1157**
The Journey (Music S. Lole; Wds. C.G.
Rossetti)
St Mary Collegiate Church Ch, K. Bowyer, S. Lole
(r1992) *Concert* (3/94) (REGE) ① **REGCD107**
Joy to the World—carol (19th
Cent—America) (Music L. Mason; Wds. I.
Watts)
John Alldis Ch, LSO, Colin Davis (arr Hope) *Concert*
(12/89) (PHIL) ① **416 249-2PB**
Cambridge Sngrs, CLS, J. Rutter (arr Rutter) *Concert*
(12/89) (CLLE) ① **COLCD111**
T. Hampson, St Paul CO, H. Wolff (arr Pasatieri)
Concert (12/91) (TELD) ① **9031-73135-2**
Atlanta Choral Guild, W. Noll (arr Rutter) *Concert*
(12/91) (NEWP) ① **NPD85529**
J. Sutherland, Ambrosian Sngrs, New Philh, R.
Bonynge (arr Gamley) *Concert*
(12/91) (DECC) ① **433 010-2DM**
G. de Chiaro (arr gtr) *Concert*
(12/91) (CENT) ① **CRC2101**
W. Marsalis, Jazz Ens (pp1991) *Concert*
(12/92) (SONY) ① **SK48235**
R. Scotto, St Patrick's Cath Ch, St Patrick's Cath
Orch, L. Anselmi (r1981; arr Grady) *Concert*
(12/93) (VAI) ① **VAIA1013**
Boston Camerata, J. Cohen (r1993) *Concert*
(12/93) (ERAT) ① **4509-92874-2**
Prince of Wales Brass (arr Cumow) *Concert*
(12/93) (ASV) ① **CDWHL2083**
D. Ross, J. Carreras, P. Domingo, Gumpoldskirchner
Kinderchor, Vienna SO, V. Sutej (pp1992; arr
Schifrin) *Concert* (12/93) (SONY) ① **SK53358**
Just another star—carol (20th Cent) (Wds. &
Music K. Jenkins and C. Barratt)
Oxford Pro Musica Sngrs, M. Smedley (r1993; arr
Gritton) *Concert* (12/93) (PROU) ① **PROUCD134**
Kalinka—Russian folksong
A. Kipnis, Berlin St Op Orch, E. Orthmann (r1931)
Concert (12/90) (PREI) ① **89019**
A. Kipnis, Berlin St Op Orch, E. Orthmann (r1931)
Concert (10/91) (PEAR) ① **GEMMCD9451**
Kalitka—Russian folksong
St Petersburg Glinka Acad Ch, V. Chernushenko (arr
Fliarkovsky) *Concert*
(3/92) (TELD) ① **9031-73241-2**
Kamarinskaya—folksong (Russia)
D. Hvorostovsky, Ossipov Russian Folk Orch, N.
Kalinin (r1991) *Concert*
(11/92) (PHIL) ① **434 080-2PH**
Když jsem přišel včera večer k ní—folksong
(Czechoslovakia)
E. Destinn, F. Kark (r1906) *Concert*
(12/94) (SUPR) ① [12] **11 2136-2(1)**
The Keel Row—English folksong
K. Ferrier, P. Spurr (arr W G Whittaker: r1949)
Concert (6/91) (DECC) ① **430 096-2DWO**
K. Ferrier, P. Spurr (r1949) *Concert*
(6/92) (DECC) ① **433 475-2DM**
Cambridge Sngrs, CLS, J. Rutter (r1992; arr Rutter)
Concert (11/93) (CLLE) ① **COLCD120**
Ein Kind ward geboren
wunderschön—Nativity hymn (Lower
Austria)
Vienna Boys' Ch, U.C. Harrer (arr Harrer) *Concert*
(12/91) (PHIL) ① **426 860-2PH**
Ein Kindlein in der Wiegen—carol
(Germany)
Regensburg Cath Ch *Concert*
(12/91) (RCA) ① **RD60736**
King Jesus hath a garden—carol
(Netherlands) (Wds. translated by G.R.
Woodward)
Cambridge Clare College Ch, Cambridge Clare
College Orch, J. Rutter (arr Rutter) *Concert*
(12/89) (DECC) ① **425 500-2DM**
King's College Ch, D. Willcocks (arr Wood) *Concert*
(12/90) (DECC) ① **430 089-2DWO**
Charterhouse Special Ch, R. Burton, R. Wells (arr
Hawes) *Concert* (12/91) (HERA) ① **HAVPCD421**

King's College Ch *Concert*
(12/91) (COLL) ① **Coll1335-2**
King's College Ch, D. Willcocks, S. Preston *Concert*
(12/94) (BELA) ① **450 112-2**
Kitty, my love, will you marry
me?—folksong
L. Finnie, A. Legge (arr. Hughes) *Concert*
(4/90) (CHAN) ① **CHAN8749**
K. Ferrier, F. Stone (arr H Hughes: bp1952) *Concert*
(6/91) (DECC) ① **430 096-2DWO**
K. Ferrier, F. Stone (arr Hughes: bp1952) *Concert*
(7/91) (LOND) ① **430 061-2LM**
K. Ferrier, F. Stone (bp1952) *Concert*
(6/92) (DECC) ① **433 473-2DM**
Kling, Glöckchen, klingelingeling—carol
(Germany)
J. Galway, Regensburg Cath Ch, Munich RO, J.
Georgiadis *Concert* (12/91) (RCA) ① **RD60736**
Kommt a Vogerl geflogen—song (Eng: A bird
came a-flying)
R. Tauber, M. Spoliansky (r1926) *Concert*
(9/92) (MMOI) ① **CDMOIR409**
Komt verwondert u hier, menschen—carol
(19th/20th Cent—Holland) (Music Julius
Röntgen)
Quink *Concert* (12/89) (TELA) ① **CD80202**
Die Könige, '(The) Three Kings'—carol
(1856—Germany) (C.A.P. Cornelius -
Weihnachtslieder, Op. 8/3)
N. Sears, Cambridge Sngrs, J. Rutter (arr Atkins)
Concert (12/87) (CLLE) ① **COLCD106**
Winchester Cath Ch, M. Neary (arr Atkins) *Concert*
(12/88) (ASV) ① **CDQS6011**
Sheffield Chorale, Sheaf Concert Orch, J. Kirkwood
(arr Atkins) *Concert* (12/89) (CHOR) ① **EECD109**
Trinity Coll Ch, Cambridge, R. Marlow (arr Atkins)
Concert (12/90) (CONI) ① **CDCF501**
Canterbury Cath Ch, D. Flood (arr Atkins) *Concert*
(12/90) (YORK) ① **CD109**
Kings College Ch, D. Willcocks (arr Atkins) *Concert*
(12/91) (CFP) ① **CD-CFP4586**
York Minster Ch *Concert* (12/91) (YORK) ① **CD846**
Westminster Cath Ch, J. O'Donnell *Concert*
(12/93) (HYPE) ① **CDA66668**
Oxford Pro Musica Sngrs, M. Smedley (r1993; arr
Atkins) *Concert* (12/93) (PROU) ① **PROUCD134**
Salisbury Cath Ch, R. Seal (r1983; arr Atkins)
Concert (12/93) (MERI) ① **CDE84068**
The Lark in the clear air—folksong
(Ireland)
Cambridge Sngrs, CLS, J. Rutter (r1992; arr Carter)
Concert (11/93) (CLLE) ① **COLCD120**
Leaping and dancing—carol (Catalonia)
London Musica Antiqua, M. Uridge (r1980-83)
Concert (12/93) (SYMP) ① **SYMCD1157**
Lebewohl—Deutsche Volkslied
R. Tauber, M. Spoliansky (r1926) *Concert*
(9/90) (PEAR) ① **GEMMCD9370**
Lift your heart and raise your voice—carol
(20th Cent—England) (Music P. Edwards;
Wds. M. Perry)
Canterbury Cath Ch, M. Harris, A. Wicks *Concert*
(12/87) (CONI) ① **CDCF160**
The Lime tree—folksong (Russia)
D. Hvorostovsky, Ossipov Russian Folk Orch, N.
Kalinin (r1991) *Concert*
(11/92) (PHIL) ① **434 080-2PH**
A Little child on the earth has been
born—carol (Flanders)
Birmingham Bach Ch, Fine Arts Brass Ens, P. Spicer
(r1992; arr Trepte) *Concert*
(12/93) (BIRM) ① **BBCCD2**
A little child there is yborn (Eia
susanni)—carol (19th Cent—Germany) (Wds.
14th Cent)
St Alban's Abbey Ch, Barry Rose (r1992; arr R.R.
Bennett) *Concert* (12/93) (LAMM) ① **LAMM081D**
Little David, play on your harp—spiritual
D.L. Ragin, M. Hogan (arr Burleigh) *Concert*
(8/92) (CONN) ① **CCS2991**
Little donkey—carol (20th Cent—England)
(Music E. Boswell)
Jenkins Family Sngrs, N. Jenkins *Concert*
(12/93) (MAYH) ① **KM93071405410**
The Little drummer boy—carol (1958—USA)
(Wds. & Music K.Davis, H.Onorati &
H.Simone)
Atlanta Choral Guild, W. Noll *Concert*
(12/91) (NEWP) ① **NPD85529**
T. Hampson, St Paul CO, H. Wolff (arr Pasatieri)
Concert (12/91) (TELD) ① **9031-73135-2**
D. Ross, J. Carreras, Gumpoldskirchner Kinderchor,
Vienna SO, V. Sutej (pp1992; arr Schifrin) *Concert*
(12/93) (SONY) ① **SK53358**

Salisbury Cath Ch, R. Seal (r1983; arr Vaughan
Williams) *Concert* (12/93) (MERI) ① **CDE84068**
D. Ross, J. Carreras, P. Domingo, Gumpoldskirchner
Kinderchor, Vienna SO, V. Sutej (pp1992; arr
Schifrin) *Concert* (12/93) (SONY) ① **SK53358**
St John's College Ch, G. Guest, S. Cleobury (r
c1974: arr Vaughan Williams) *Concert*
(12/94) (BELA) ① **450 111-2**
O mountains—folksong (Czechoslovakia)
E. Destinn, orch, J. Pasternack (r1919) *Concert*
(11/93) (ROMO) ① [2] **81002-2**
**O nobilis nativitas—motet (13th-14th
Cent—England)**
Anon 4 (r1992) *Concert*
(12/93) (HARM) ① **HMU90 7099**
**O staris in presepio—3vv (15th
Cent—Poland)**
Alberquerque Música Antigua *Concert*
(8/93) (DORI) ① **DIS80104**
O Tannenbaum—carol (Germany)
Cambridge Sngrs, J. Rutter (arr. Rutter) *Concert*
(12/87) (CLLE) ① **COLCD106**
John Alldis Ch, LSO, Colin Davis (arr Hope) *Concert*
(12/89) (PHIL) ① **416 249-2PB**
Lichfield Cath Ch, J. Rees-Williams (arr Jacques)
Concert (12/90) (ABBE) ① **CDCA903**
Vienna Boys' Ch, U.C. Harrer *Concert*
(12/91) (PHIL) ① **426 860-2PH**
Regensburg Cath Ch *Concert*
(12/91) (RCA) ① **RD60736**
T. Hampson, St Paul CO, H. Wolff (arr Pasatieri)
Concert (12/91) (TELD) ① **9031-73135-2**
J. Loman (r1992; arr Salzedo: hp) *Concert*
(12/93) (CBC) ① **SMCD5119**
D. Ross, J. Carreras, P. Domingo, Gumpoldskirchner
Kinderchor, Vienna SO, V. Sutej (pp1992; arr
Schifrin) *Concert* (12/93) (SONY) ① **SK53358**
R. Shaw Chbr Sngrs, Robert Shaw (r1993) *Concert*
(12/94) (TELA) ① **CD80377**
**Of the Father's heart begotten—carol (pub
1582)** (Wds. Prudentius, trans. R.F. Davis)
Trinity Coll Ch, Cambridge, G. Jackson, R. Marlow
(arr Willcocks) *Concert*
(12/90) (CONI) ① **CDCF501**
Westminster Cath Ch, J. O'Donnell *Concert*
(12/93) (HYPE) ① **CDA66668**
Edinburgh Cath Ch, T. Byram-Wigfield (r1993; arr
Willcocks) *Concert* (12/93) (HERA) ① **HAVPCD163**
Oh, glory—Negro spiritual
K. Battle, H. Laws, chor, orch, James Levine
(pp1990) *Concert* (5/91) (DG) ① **429 790-2GH**
**Oh, if only words could convey—folksong
(Russia)**
D. Hvorostovsky, Ossipov Russian Folk Orch, N.
Kalinin (r1991) *Concert*
(11/92) (PHIL) ① **434 080-2PH**
Oh, no John—folksong (England)
K. Livingstone, N. Mackie, J.J. Blakely (arr Brown)
Concert (2/89) (UNIC) ① **UKCD2009**
Oh, sweet night—folksong (Russia)
D. Hvorostovsky, Ossipov Russian Folk Orch, N.
Kalinin (r1991) *Concert*
(11/92) (PHIL) ① **434 080-2PH**
Oh, the little box is full—folksong (Russia)
D. Hvorostovsky, Ossipov Russian Folk Orch, N.
Kalinin (r1991) *Concert*
(11/92) (PHIL) ① **434 080-2PH**
Oh, what a beautiful city—Negro spiritual
K. Battle, J. Norman, orch, James Levine (pp1990)
Concert (5/91) (DG) ① **429 790-2GH**
D.L. Ragin, M. Hogan (arr Boatner) *Concert*
(8/92) (CHNN) ① **CCS2991**
**Ohie Meneche (La fiera del Mast'
Andrea)—folksong (Naples)** (poss cpsed F.
Giannini)
D. Giannini, orch, G.W. Byng (r1928) *Concert*
(4/93) (PREI) ① **89044**
The Old Chalet—folksong (Switzerland)
Britannia Building Soc Band, H. Snell (r1990; arr
Snell: brass band) *Concert*
(8/92) (DOYE) ① **DOYCD004**
**The Old Rocking Chair—folksong (Shetland
Islands)**
M. Hanskov, T. Lønskov *Concert*
(3/92) (DANA) ① **DACOCD378**
**The Old Year now away is fled—carol (16th
Cent—England)** (Tune 'Greensleeves')
Taverner Ch, Taverner Consort, Taverner Plyrs, A.
Parrott *Concert* (12/89) (EMI) ① **CDC7 49809-2**
An Olde Rhyme (Music P. Gritton)
Oxford Pro Musica Sngrs, M. Smedley (r1993)
Concert (12/93) (PROU) ① **PROUCD134**
Ole time religion—spiritual
D.L. Ragin, New World Voc Ens (arr Hogan) *Concert*
(8/92) (CHNN) ① **CCS2991**

**Omnis mundus jucundetur—hymn (pub
1582—Sweden)** (from Piae Cantiones)
Alberquerque Música Antigua *Concert*
(8/93) (DORI) ① **DIS80104**
**Once, as I remember—carol (17th
Cent—Italy)** (English words by G.R.
Woodward)
Cambridge Sngrs, J. Rutter (arr Wood) *Concert*
(12/87) (CLLE) ① **COLCD106**
M. Petri, Westminster Abbey Ch, National PO, M.
Neary (arr Wood) *Concert*
(12/91) (RCA) ① **RD60060**
Once in Royal David's city—carol (England)
(Music H.J. Gauntlett; Wds. C.F. Alexander)
King's College Ch, D. Briggs, S. Cleobury *Concert*
(12/84) (ARGO) ① **414 042-2ZH**
J. Collin, St George's Chapel Ch, J. Porter, C.
Robinson *Concert* (12/84) (ABBS) ① **CDMVP827**
Canterbury Cath Ch, M. Harris, A. Wicks *Concert*
(12/87) (CONI) ① **CDCF160**
Winchester Cath Ch, M. Neary *Concert*
(12/88) (ASV) ① **CDQS6011**
Canterbury Cath Ch, M. Harris, D. Flood *Concert*
(12/90) (YORK) ① **CD109**
York Minster Ch, F. Jackson *Concert*
(12/91) (CHAN) ① **CHAN6520**
Charterhouse Special Ch, R. Burton, R. Wells (arr
Mann/Wells) *Concert*
(12/91) (HERA) ① **HAVPCD142**
King's College Ch *Concert*
(12/91) (COLL) ① **Coll1335-2**
The Sixteen, H. Christophers *Concert*
(12/91) (COLL) ① **Coll1300-2**
RCS, J. Birch, L. Heltay (pp1991; arr Willcocks)
Concert (12/93) (CARL) ① **PCD1026**
Westminster Cath Ch, I. Simcock, J. O'Donnell
Concert (12/93) (HYPE) ① **CDA66668**
Trinity Coll Ch, Cambridge, S. Standage, R. Marlow
(r1993) *Concert* (12/93) (CONI) ① **CDCF517**
Prince of Wales Brass (arr Himes) *Concert*
(12/93) (ASV) ① **CDWHL2083**
Edinburgh Cath Ch, T. Byram-Wigfield (r1993; arr
Willcocks) *Concert* (12/93) (HERA) ① **HAVPCD163**
**Orto sole serene—motet (13th-14th
Cent—England)**
Anon 4 (r1992) *Concert*
(12/93) (HARM) ① **HMU90 7099**
Outside, how hard it bloweth—carol
King's College Sngrs, E.H. Warrell (arr Schutz)
Concert (12/91) (REGE) ① **REGCD106**
**Over my Head I hear Music—Negro
spiritual**
K. Battle, H. Laws, N. Allen (pp1990) *Concert*
(5/91) (DG) ① **429 790-2GH**
K. Battle, M. Garrett (pp1991) *Concert*
(7/92) (DG) ① **435 440-2GH**
The Oxen—song (20th Cent—England)
(Wds. T. Hardy)
Coppin ens (arr Coppin) *Concert*
(12/91) (RED) ① **RSKCD111**
Past three a clock—carol (England) (Wds.
G.R. Woodward; Refrain Trad)
King's College Ch, D. Willcocks (arr Woodward)
Concert (12/89) (DECC) ① **430 089-2DWO**
Lichfield Cath Ch, J. Rees-Williams (arr Bochmann)
Concert (12/90) (ABBE) ① **CDCA903**
Prince of Wales Brass (arr Green) *Concert*
(12/93) (ASV) ① **CDWHL2083**
Pastorcito Santo—carol (Spain) (Wds. L de
Vega, Music J Rodrigo)
Ex Cathedra Chbr Ch, J. Skidmore (r c1994) *Concert*
(12/94) (ASV) ① **CDDCA912**
People look East—carol
St George's Chapel Ch, J. Porter, C. Robinson (arr.
M. Shaw) *Concert* (12/84) (ABBS) ① **CDMVP827**
Perperit virgo—song (14th Cent—England)
(Wds. R. de Ledrede from 'Red Book of
Ossory')
Anon 4 (r1992) *Concert*
(12/93) (HARM) ① **HMU90 7099**
**Personent hodie—carol (14th
Cent—Germany)** (Wds. from Piae Cantiones,
pub 1582)
Cambridge Sngrs, CLS, J. Rutter (arr Rutter) *Concert*
(12/89) (CLLE) ① **COLCD111**
King's College Ch, S. Preston, D. Willcocks (arr
Holst) *Concert* (12/89) (DECC) ① **425 499-2DM**
Atlanta Choral Guild, W. Noll (arr Holst) *Concert*
(12/91) (NEWP) ① **NPD85529**
Jenkins Family Sngrs, N. Jenkins *Concert*
(12/93) (MAYH) ① **KM93071405410**

Plyaska—dance
D. Hvorostovsky, Ossipov Russian Folk Orch, N.
Kalinin (r1991) *Concert*
(11/92) (PHIL) ① **434 080-2PH**
Powder and Paint—song
N. Plevitskaya, S. Rachmaninov (r1926; arr
Rachmaninov: pf) *Concert*
(3/93) (RCA) ① [10] **09026 61265-2(2)**
**Pretty Home—Shaker spiritual (19th
Cent—USA)**
Boston Camerata, J. Cohen (r1993) *Concert*
(12/93) (ERAT) ① **4509-92874-2**
**Procedenti puero—rondellus (c1250—Anglo-
Norman)**
Sinfonye, S. Wishart (r1993) *Concert*
(12/93) (HYPE) ① **CDA66685**
**Prolis eterne genitor—pes motet (13th-14th
Cent—England)**
Anon 4 (r1992) *Concert*
(12/93) (HARM) ① **HMU90 7099**
**Pršívalo, jen de lilo—folksong
(Czechoslavakia)**
E. Destinn, F. Kark (r1906) *Concert*
(12/94) (SUPR) ① [12] **11 2136-2(1)**
Puellare gremium
East London Chor, M. Kibblewhite (arr Grainger)
Concert (12/93) (KOCH) ① **37202-2**
Anon 4 (r1992) *Concert*
(12/93) (HARM) ① **HMU90 7099**
Puer natus est
Alberquerque Música Antigua (arr Cristobal de
Morales) *Concert* (8/93) (DORI) ① **DIS80104**
Puncha, puncha—sephardic song
E. Lamandier *Concert* (11/86) (ALIE) ① **AL1012**
Quanno nascete ninno—carol (Sicily)
Taverner Plyrs, A. Parrott *Concert*
(12/89) (EMI) ① **CDC7 49809-2**
**Qué bonito niño chiquito!—carol (15th
Cent—Spain)** (from Colombina Song Book)
Alberquerque Música Antigua *Concert*
(8/93) (DORI) ① **DIS80104**
**Quelle est cette odeur agréable? (Whence is
that goodly fragrance flowing?)—carol
(France)** (Eng translation by A.B. Ramsay)
Cambridge Clare College Ch, Cambridge Clare
College Orch, J. Rutter (arr Willcocks) *Concert*
(12/89) (DECC) ① **425 500-2DM**
Quink (arr Willcocks/Quink) *Concert*
(12/89) (TELA) ① **CD80202**
Charterhouse Special Ch, R. Burton, R. Wells (arr
Wells) *Concert* (12/91) (HERA) ① **HAVPCD142**
Cambridge Sngrs, CLS, J. Rutter (r1993; arr Willan)
Concert (12/93) (CLLE) ① **COLCD121**
Jenkins Family Sngrs, N. Jenkins *Concert*
(12/93) (MAYH) ① **KM93071405410**
**Quem pastores laudavere—carol (14th
Cent—Germany)**
The Sixteen, H. Christophers *Concert*
(12/88) (HYPE) ① **CDA66263**
Cambridge Sngrs, CLS, J. Rutter (arr Rutter) *Concert*
(12/89) (CLLE) ① **COLCD111**
Sheffield Chorale, Sheaf Concert Orch, J. Kirkwood
(arr. Rutter) *Concert* (12/89) (CHOR) ① **EECD109**
Taverner Ch, Taverner Consort, Taverner Plyrs, A.
Parrott *Concert* (12/89) (EMI) ① **CDC7 49809-2**
Atlanta Choral Guild, W. Noll (arr Willcocks) *Concert*
(12/91) (NEWP) ① **NPD85529**
**Quittez pasteurs, 'Come Leave Your
Sheep'—carol (France)**
St Alban's Abbey Ch, A. Parnell, Barry Rose (r1992;
arr Leighton) *Concert*
(12/93) (LAMM) ① **LAMM081D**
Cambridge Sngrs, CLS, J. Rutter (r1993; arr Rutter)
Concert (12/93) (CLLE) ① **COLCD121**
**Rannoch Herding Song—Scottish folk
melody**
R. A. Morgan *Concert* (12/87) (ETCE) ① **KTC1049**
**Rejoice with heart and voice—carol (Tune
'Gaudete, gaudete')**
Canterbury Cath Ch, M. Harris, A. Wicks (arr.
J.Barnard) *Concert* (12/87) (CONI) ① **CDCF160**
Trinity Coll Ch, Cambridge, R. Marlow (r1993; arr
Byrd) *Concert* (12/93) (CONI) ① **CDCF517**
**Rejoice, ye shining worlds on high (18th
Cent—America)** (Tune 'Kingsbridge')
Boston Camerata, J. Cohen (r1993) *Concert*
(12/93) (ERAT) ① **4509-92874-2**
Remember, O thou man—carol
King's College Ch, D. Willcocks, S. Preston *Concert*
(12/94) (BELA) ① **450 112-2**
Ride on, King Jesus—Negro spiritual
J. Norman, orch, James Levine (pp1990) *Concert*
(5/91) (DG) ① **429 790-2GH**

Ring out the bells—carol (Tune 'Past three a clock'; Wds. M. Parry)
Canterbury Cath Ch, M. Harris, A. Wicks (arr. D.Iliff) Concert
(12/87) (CONI) ① CDCF160
Rio Grande—song
O. Natzke, chor, orch (r1943) Concert
(12/92) (ODE) ① CDODE1365
Riu, riu, chiu—carol (medieval—Spain)
The Sixteen, H. Christophers Concert
(12/88) (HYPE) ① CDA66263
Taverner Ch, Taverner Consort, A. Parrott Concert
(12/89) (EMI) ① CDC7 49809-2
Oxford Pro Musica Sngrs, M. Smedley (r1993)
Concert (12/93) (PROU) ① PROUCD134
S. Varcoe, Cambridge Sngrs, CLS, J. Rutter (r1993)
Concert (12/93) (CLLE) ① COLCD121
Chanticleer (r1990) Concert
(12/94) (CHTI) ① CR-8803
Ex Cathedra Chbr Ch, J. Skidmore (r c1994) Concert
(12/94) (ASV) ① CDDCA912
Robin Adair—folksong (Wds. attrib Lady Caroline Keppel)
E. Albani, anon (r1904) Concert
(10/92) (SYMP) ① SYMCD1093
Rocking Carol, 'Little Jesu sweetly sleep' (Czechoslovakia) (Wds. trans P. Dearmer)
Quink (arr Willcocks) Concert
(12/89) (TELA) ① CD80202
The Sixteen, H. Christophers Concert
(12/91) (COLL) ① Coll1300-2
London Musica Antiqua, M. Uridge (r1980-83)
Concert (12/93) (SYMP) ① SYMCD1157
El Rossinyol—Catalan folksong
V. de los Angeles, G. Parsons (arr Morante; pp1990)
Concert (12/91) (COLL) ① Coll1247-2
Rumlekvadrillen—folksong (Denmark)
M. Hanskov, T. Lønskov Concert
(3/92) (DANA) ① DACOCD378
Russian Village Wedding Songs
EXCERPTS: 1. Play, Skomoroshek; 2. River; 3. Trumpet; 4. Cosmas and Demian; 5. The Drinker; 6. Green Forest; 7. God Bless, Jesus; 8. My White Peas; 9. Steambath; 10. Berry; 11. Black Beaver; 12. In the House; 13. Bunny with Short Legs; 14. The Bed; 15. Birch Tree.
1-15. Pokrovsky Ens Stravinsky: Noces.
(9/94) (NONE) ① 7559-79335-2
's Schätzli ('Gsätzli)—Swiss folksong
E. Schwarzkopf, M. Raucheisen (bp1944) Concert
(6/87) (ACAN) ① 43 801
E. Schwarzkopf, G. Moore (r1956) Concert
(12/90) (EMI) ① CDM7 63654-2
M. Ivogün, M. Raucheisen (r1932) Concert
(8/92) (NIMB) ① NI7832
R. Streich, E. Werba (r1957) Concert
(10/94) (DG) ① [2] 437 680-2GDO2
Sail on, sail on—song
Sarah Walker, T. Allen, R. Vignoles (arr. Britten)
Concert (11/87) (HYPE) ① CDA66165
Sailor's carol (20th Cent—England) (Music J. Coppin; Wds. Causeley)
Coppin ens Concert (12/91) (RED) ① RSKCD111
Salva nos, stella maris—rondellus (c1250—Anglo-Norman)
Sinfonye, S. Wishart (r1993) Concert
(12/93) (HYPE) ① CDA66685
Salve, Virgo virginum—rondellus (c1250—Anglo-Norman)
Sinfonye, S. Wishart (r1993) Concert
(12/93) (HYPE) ① CDA66685
Sans Day Carol, 'Now the holly bears a berry'—carol (Cornwall)
M. Petri, Westminster Abbey Ch, National PO, M. Neary (arr. J. Rutter) Concert
(12/91) (RCA) ① RD60060
Coppin ens (arr Coppin) Concert
(12/91) (RED) ① RSKCD111
Salisbury Cath Ch, R. Seal (r1983; arr Rutter)
Concert (12/93) (MERI) ① CDE84068
Jenkins Family Sngrs, N. Jenkins Concert
(12/93) (MAYH) ① KM93071405410
Cambridge Sngrs, CLS, J. Rutter (r1993; arr Rutter)
Concert (12/93) (CLLE) ① COLCD121
Santa Claus is coming to Town—song (1934)
(Wds A Music H. Gillespie and F. Coots)
Oxford Pro Musica Sngrs, M. Smedley (r1993; arr Gritton) Concert (12/93) (PROU) ① PROUCD134
Prince of Wales Brass (arr Haines) Concert
(12/93) (ASV) ① CDWHL2083
Scandalize my name—Negro spiritual
K. Battle, J. Norman, S.O. Lee (pp1990) Concert
(5/91) (DG) ① 429 790-2GH

The Scots Musical Museum—folksong collection (pub 1787-1803) (ed James Johnson; several collected by Burns)
EXCERPTS: 3. VOLUME 3, 1790: 3a. Ay Waukin O; 4. VOLUME 4, 1792: 4a. The deuks dang o'er my daddie; 4b. Ae fond kiss; 4c. O Knemure's on and awa, Willie; 4d. There'll never be peace till Jamie comes home; 4e. The Deil's awa wi' th' Exciseman.
3a, 4a-e Scottish Early Music Consort (r1987)
Concert (10/95) (CHAN) ① CHAN0581
See amid the winter's snow—carol (19th Cent—England) (Music J. Goss; Wds. E. Caswall)
King's College Ch, S. Preston, D. Willcocks (arr Willcocks) Concert
(12/89) (DECC) ① 425 499-2DM
King's College Ch, D. Willcocks (arr Willcocks)
Concert (12/90) (DECC) ① 430 089-2DWO
The Sixteen, H. Christophers Concert
(12/91) (COLL) ① Coll1300-2
York Minster Ch Concert (12/91) (YORK) ① CD846
Jenkins Family Sngrs, N. Jenkins Concert
(12/93) (MAYH) ① KM93071405410
Ex Cathedra Chbr Ch, J. Skidmore (r c1994) Concert
(12/94) (ASV) ① CDDCA912
Shaker Chants and Spirituals (composers given where known)
EXCERPTS: 1. Come life, Shaker life (I Bates, 1758-1837); 2. In yonder valley (J Whittaker, 1751-87); 3. Virgins clothed in a clean white garment; 4. Mother (R McNemar, 1770-1839); 5. Father James' Song (J Whittaker); 6. Followers of the Lamb (C Jacobs, 1833-1905); 7. Mother Ann's Song (A Lee, 1736-84); 8. I have a soul to be saved or lost; 9. Heavenly comfort; 10. A companion to stiff; 11. Pinch'd up nip'd up; 12. I will fight and never slack; 13. Celestial choir; 14. Holy angel; 15. The Lark; 16. Nightingale's Song; 17. Holy Order Song; 18. Learned of Angel; 19. Laughing John's Interrogatory; 20. I'll beat my drum as I march along; 21. Mother's warning; 22. The Solemn Bell; 23. Mother's Cup of Tribulation; 24. Encouragement; 26. Verdant valley; 27. In yonder valley (reprise); 28. Solemn Song; 29. Turn to the right; 30. O will you sing another song; 31. The Spiritual sailor (R McNemar); 32. Mother has come (P Springer, 1887); 33. Holy Mother's protecting chain; 34. Simple gifts (J Brackett, 1797-1882).
34. L. Garrett, RPO, P. Robinson (r1994; arr Bateman) Concert (4/95) (SILV) ① SILKD6004
Shenandoah—song
O. Natzke, chor, orch (r1943) Concert
(12/92) (ODE) ① CDODE1365
The Shepherd's Cradle Song—carol (Germany) (Ger title 'Des Hirten Wiegenlied')
Quink (arr Leuner/MacPherson) Concert
(12/89) (TELA) ① CD80202
Lichfield Cath Ch, J. Rees-Williams (arr Somervell)
Concert (12/90) (ABBE) ① CDCA903
M. Petri, Westminster Abbey Ch, National PO, M. Neary (arr Leuner/MacPherson) Concert
(12/91) (RCA) ① RD60060
Trinity Coll Ch, Cambridge, R. Marlow (r1993; arr Macpherson) Concert (12/93) (CONI) ① CDCF517
Shepherds, in the field abiding—carol (France) (Tune 'Angels from the realms'; Wds. Woodward)
King's College Ch, D. Willcocks (arr C. Wood)
Concert (12/89) (DECC) ① 425 499-2DM
Shepherd's rejoice (19th Cent—USA) (Tune 'Auld Lang Syne')
Boston Camerata, J. Cohen (r1993) Concert
(12/93) (ERAT) ① 4509-92874-2
Shepherd's Song, 'Auf, auf ihr Hirten' (Upper Austria)
Vienna Boys' Ch, Teufel Family, U.C. Harrer (arr Harrer) Concert (12/91) (PHIL) ① 426 860-2PH
Shepherd's Song, 'Gehts, Buama, stehts gschwind auf' (Upper Austria)
Vienna Boys' Ch, Teufel Family, U.C. Harrer (arr Bregen) Concert (12/91) (PHIL) ① 426 860-2PH
Shepherd's Song, 'Heissa, Buama' (Austria)
Vienna Boys' Ch, Teufel Family, U.C. Harrer (arr Bregen) Concert (12/91) (PHIL) ① 426 860-2PH
Shepherd's Song, 'Kommet ihr Hirten' (Bohemia)
Vienna Boys' Ch, U.C. Harrer (arr Theimer) Concert
(12/91) (PHIL) ① 426 860-2PH
Shepherd's Song, 'Teut eilands erwachen' (Carinthia)
Vienna Boys' Ch, Teufel Family, U.C. Harrer (arr Froschauer) Concert
(12/91) (PHIL) ① 426 860-2PH

Shepherd's Story—carol (20th Cent) (Music C. Dickinson)
Atlanta Choral Guild, W. Noll Concert
(12/91) (NEWP) ① NPD85529
She's like the swallow—folksong (Newfoundland)
Cambridge Sngrs, CLS, J. Rutter (r1992; arr Chapman) Concert (11/93) (CLLE) ① COLCD120
Siberian Prisoner's Song
B. Christoff, G. Moore (r1951) Concert
(6/93) (EMI) ① CDH7 64252-2
Sing a song of Christmas—carol (20th Cent—USA) (Music Robert A. Harris)
Quink Concert (12/89) (TELA) ① CD80202
Sing lullaby (The Infant King)—noël (Basque) (Wds. S. Baring-Gould)
King's College Ch, D. Briggs, S. Cleobury (arr Willcocks) Concert
(12/84) (ARGO) ① 414 042-2ZH
Liverpool Phil Ch, St Ambrose RC Jun Sch Ch, RLPO, E. Walters (arr. Pettman) Concert
(12/87) (CHAN) ① CHAN8436
Cambridge Sngrs, J. Rutter (arr Howells; wds. Harvey) Concert (6/88) (CLLE) ① COLCD107
Cambridge Sngrs, CLS, J. Rutter (arr Rutter) Concert
(12/89) (CLLE) ① COLCD111
The Sixteen, H. Christophers (arr Howells; wds. Harvey) Concert (12/91) (COLL) ① Coll1270-2
New College Ch, E. Higginbottom (arr Howells; wds. Harvey) Concert (12/91) (CRD) ① CRD3455
Westminster Cath Ch, J. O'Donnell (arr Howells)
Concert (12/93) (HYPE) ① CDA66668
Birmingham Bach Ch, P. Spicer (r1992; arr Willcocks) Concert (12/93) (BIRM) ① BBCCD2
Sinner, please don't let this harvest pass—Negro spiritual
J. Norman, orch, James Levine (pp1990) Concert
(5/91) (DG) ① 429 790-2GH
Sister Mary had but one child—negro spiritual
K. Battle, F. von Stade, Orch, A. Previn (pp1991)
Concert (12/92) (SONY) ① SK482335
Skye Boat Song—folk melody (Scotland)
J. Lloyd Webber, RPO, N. Cleobury (arr vc) Concert
(3/87) (PHIL) ① 416 698-2PH
Sleep Lord Jesus—carol (20th Cent) (Music Cunningham; Dormi Jesu! trans. Perry)
Canterbury Cath Ch, M. Harris, A. Wicks Concert
(12/87) (CONI) ① CDCF160
The Sleigh (Music R. Kountz; Wds. I. Tchervanow)
Toronto Children's Choir, Toronto SO, J.A. Bartle (r1992; arr Cable) Concert
(12/93) (CBC) ① SMCD5119
Slow Traveller—song (19th Cent—USA) (source 'The Christian Harmony')
Boston Camerata, J. Cohen (r1993) Concert
(12/93) (ERAT) ① 4509-92874-2
Small wonder the star—carol (20th Cent—England) (Music P. Edwards; Wds. P. Wigmore)
Canterbury Cath Ch, M. Harris, A. Wicks Concert
(12/87) (CONI) ① CDCF160
St Alban's Abbey Ch, A. Parnell, Barry Rose (r1992)
Concert (12/93) (LAMM) ① LAMM081D
A snowstorm blows—folksong (Russia)
D. Hvorostovsky, Ossipov Russian Folk Orch, N. Kalinin (r1991) Concert
(11/92) (PHIL) ① 434 080-2PH
The snowy-breasted pearl—song (Ireland) (Wds. De Vere)
E. Rethberg, orch (r1928) Concert
(2/95) (ROMO) ① [2] 81012-2
So blest a sight—carol (England)
R. Shaw Chbr Sngrs, Robert Shaw (r1993) Concert
(12/94) (TELA) ① CD80377
Soldier, soldier—folksong (England)
K. Livingstone, N. Mackie, J.J. Blakely (arr Britten)
Concert (2/89) (UNIC) ① UKCD2009
Soldier's Song—Russian folksong
A. Kipnis, Berlin St Op Orch, E. Orthmann (r1931)
Concert (12/90) (PREI) ① 89019
A. Kipnis, Berlin St Op Orch, E. Orthmann (r1931)
Concert (10/91) (PEAR) ① GEMMCD9451
Sometimes I feel like a motherless child—Negro spiritual
W. Marsalis, Eastman Wind Ens, D. Hunsberger (arr D Hunsberger) Concert (9/87) (SONY) ① MK42137
B. Hendricks Concert
(4/91) (EMI) ① CDC7 54098-2
Song for Loders—carol (20th Cent—England) (Music J. Coppin; Wds. Clark)
Coppin ens Concert (12/91) (RED) ① RSKCD111

TRAETTA, Tommaso (Michele Francesco Saverio) (1727–1779) Italy

SECTION V: STAGE WORKS

TRAVERS, John (c1703–1758) England

SECTION III: INSTRUMENTAL

TREBOR (fl 1390–1410) France

SECTION IV: VOCAL AND CHORAL

TRÉMISOT, Edouard (1874–1952) France

SECTION IV: VOCAL AND CHORAL

TRIANA, Juan de (fl 1478–1483) Spain

SECTION IV: VOCAL AND CHORAL

TRIMARCHI, Rocco (1881–?)
Italy

TROMBONCINO, Bartolomeo (c1470–in or after 1535) Italy

TRUNK, Richard (1879–1968)
Germany

TRUSCOTT, Harold (1914–1992)
England

TSITSANIS, Vasilis (b 1915)
Greece

TUBIN, Eduard (1905–1982)
Estonia

Sonata for Violin (1962)
A. Leibur (r1991) *Concert*
    (8/93) (BIS) ① [2] BIS-CD541/2
Sonatina in D minor—piano (1942)
V. Rumessen *Concert*
    (3/89) (BIS) ① [3] BIS-CD414/6
Suite of Estonian Dance Tunes—violin (1979)
1. Bagpipe tune; 2. By the Shepherd's Fire; 3. Slow waltz; 4. Horn tune; 5. Serf's dance.
A. Leibur (r1991) *Concert*
    (8/93) (BIS) ① [2] BIS-CD541/2
Suite on Estonian Shepherd Melodies—piano (1959)
V. Rumessen *Concert*
    (3/89) (BIS) ① [3] BIS-CD414/6
Variations on an Estonian Folk Tune—piano (1945 rev 1981)
V. Rumessen *Concert*
    (3/89) (BIS) ① [3] BIS-CD414/6

SECTION IV: VOCAL AND CHORAL

Requiem for Fallen Soldiers (1979)
K. Lundin, R. Rydell, H. Hardenberger, H. Sitar, P. Wallin, J. Larson, Lund Choral Soc, N. Järvi
Symphony 10.   (9/88) (BIS) ① BIS-CD297

SECTION V: STAGE WORKS

Barbara von Tisenhusen—opera: 3 acts (1968) (Lib. A. Kallas & J. Kross)
Cpte H. Raamat, T. Sild, M. Jõgeva, U. Kreen, I. Kuusk, V. Puura, A. Kollo, H. Millberg, M. Palm, Estonia Op Chor, Estonia Op Orch, P. Lilje
    (4/93) (ONDI) ① [2] ODE776-2

TUDOR, David (b 1926) USA

SECTION II: CHAMBER

Webwork—music for Merce Cunningham's dance 'Shards' (1988)
Exc D. Tudor (r1988) *Concert*
    (8/94) (KOCH) ① [2] 37238-2

TULLY, Richard Walton (19th–20th Cent) USA

SECTION V: STAGE WORKS

The Bird of Paradise—play with traditional Hawaiian music (1912—New York) (trad music arr Tully)
EXCERPTS: 1. Aiaihea: Hula Shouting Song.
1. Hawaiian Qnt, Orig Broadway Cast (r1913)
Concert (9/94) (PEAR) ① [3] GEMMCDS9053/5

TULOU, Jean-Louis (1786–1865) France

SECTION II: CHAMBER

Fantaisie brillant on Halévy's 'La fée aux roses'—flute and piano
S. Preston, L. Carolan *Concert*
    (3/87) (AMON) ① CD-SAR19

TUNDER, Franz (1614–1667) Germany

SECTION IV: VOCAL AND CHORAL

Ach Herr, lass deine liebe Engelein—1v and strings
G. de Reyghere, Ricercar Consort *Concert*
    (1/90) (RICE) ① RIC046023
M. Zedelius, Cologne Musica Antiqua, R. Goebel
(1985) *Concert*   (1/93) (ARCH) ① 437 079-2AT
An Wasserflüssen Babylon—1v and strings
G. de Reyghere, Ricercar Consort *Concert*
    (1/90) (RICE) ① RIC046023
M. Zedelius, Cologne Musica Antiqua, R. Goebel
(1985) *Concert*   (1/93) (ARCH) ① 437 079-2AT
Ein Kleines Kindelein—sacred aria (1v and strings)
G. de Reyghere, Ricercar Consort (r1989) *Concert*
    (5/90) (RICE) ① RIC060048
Wachet auf! ruft uns die Stimme—cantata (1v, strings and continuo)
G. de Reyghere, Ricercar Consort *Concert*
    (1/90) (RICE) ① RIC046023

TURINA, Joaquín (1882–1949) Spain

SECTION I: ORCHESTRAL

Danzas fantásticas—symphonic poem, Op. 22 (1920)
1. Exultación; 2. Ensueño; 3. Orgía.
Paris Cons, R. Frühbeck de Burgos *Concert*
    (7/92) (EMI) ① [2] CZS7 67474-2
Bamberg SO, A. de Almeida *Concert*
    (7/92) (RCA) ① RD60895
Danzas Gitanas Set I—string orchestra, Op. 55 (1930) (arr cpsr from piano work)
1. Zambra; 2. Danza de seducción; 3. Danza ritual; 4. Generalife; 5. Sacro Monte.
Granada City Orch, J. de Udaeta *Concert*
    (12/92) (CLAV) ① CD50-9215
5. Philadelphia, L. Stokowski (r1937) *Concert*
    (10/93) (STOK) ① LSCD20
La Procesión del Rocio—symphonic poem, Op. 9 (1913)
Mexico City PO, E. Bátiz *Concert*
    (9/91) (ASV) ① CDDCA735
Bamberg SO, A. de Almeida *Concert*
    (7/92) (RCA) ① RD60895
Rapsodia sinfónica—piano and orchestra, Op. 66 (1931)
A. de Larrocha, LPO, R. Frühbeck de Burgos *Concert*
    (10/84) (DECC) ① 410 289-2DH
Granada City Orch, J. de Udaeta *Concert*
    (12/92) (CLAV) ① CD50-9215
Ritmos—fantasía coreográfica, Op. 43 (1928)
Bamberg SO, A. de Almeida *Concert*
    (7/92) (RCA) ① RD60895
Sinfonia sevillana, Op. 23 (pub. 1920)
Bamberg SO, A. de Almeida *Concert*
    (7/92) (RCA) ① RD60895

SECTION II: CHAMBER

La Oración del torero—string quartet/string orchestra, Op. 34 (1925)
Mexico City PO, E. Bátiz *Concert*
    (9/91) (ASV) ① CDDCA735
Granada City Orch, J. de Udaeta *Concert*
    (12/92) (CLAV) ① CD50-9215
Hollywood Qt (r1953) *Concert*
    (3/95) (TEST) ① SBT1053
Piano Trio No. 1, Op. 35 (1926)
Borodin Trio *Concert* (7/92) (CHAN) ① CHAN9016
J. Heifetz, G. Piatigorsky, L. Pennario (r1963)
Concert (11/94) (RCA) ① [65] 09026 61778-2(27)
Serenata—string quartet/string orchestra, Op. 87 (1935)
Granada City Orch, J. de Udaeta *Concert*
    (12/92) (CLAV) ① CD50-9215
Tema y variaciones—harp and piano, Op. 100 (1945)
Granada City Orch, J. de Udaeta (arr Frübeck de Burgos) *Concert* (12/92) (CLAV) ① CD50-9215

SECTION III: INSTRUMENTAL

Bailete—piano, Op. 79 (pub 1933)
D. Buechner (r1990) *Concert*
    (10/94) (CONN) ① CD4186
3 Danzas Andaluzas—piano, Op. 8 (1912)
1. Petenera; 2. Tango; 3. Zapateado.
D. Buechner (r1990) *Concert*
    (10/94) (CONN) ① CD4186
3. A. de Larrocha *Concert*
    (7/90) (DECC) ① 417 795-2DM
3. A. de Larrocha *Concert*
    (9/92) (DECC) ① [2] 433 929-2DM2
Danzas Gitanas Set I—piano, Op. 55 (1930)
1. Zambra; 2. Danza de la seducción; 3. Danza ritual; 4. Generalife; 5. Sacro-Monte.
5. A. de Larrocha *Concert*
    (7/90) (DECC) ① 417 795-2DM
5. A. de Larrocha *Concert*
    (9/92) (DECC) ① [2] 433 929-2DM2
Danzas Gitanas, Set II—piano, Op. 84 (1934)
1. Fiesta de las calderas; 2. Circulos ritmicos; 3. Invocación; 4. Danza rítmica; 5. Seguiriya.
1, 5. Empire Brass (r1991) *Concert*
    (11/93) (TELA) ① CD80301
Fandanguillo—guitar, Op. 36 (1926)
A. Segovia (r1927) *Concert*
    (5/89) (EMI) ① [2] CHS7 61047-2
M. Barrueco *Concert*
    (3/93) (EMI) ① CDC7 54382-2
J. Bream (r1983) *Concert*
    (8/93) (RCA) ① [28] 09026 61583-2(6)

J. Bream (r1962) *Concert*
    (8/93) (RCA) ① [28] 09026 61583-2(3)
J. Bream (r1962) *Concert*
    (8/93) (RCA) ① 09026 61591-2
Hommage à Tárrega—guitar, Op. 69 (1935)
1. Garrotin; 2. Soleares.
M. Barrueco *Concert*
    (3/93) (EMI) ① CDC7 54382-2
J. Bream (r1962) *Concert*
    (8/93) (RCA) ① [28] 09026 61583-2(6)
J. Bream (r1962) *Concert*
    (6/94) (RCA) ① 09026 61609-2
La Marchande de Fleurs (la Florista)—piano
Empire Brass (r1991) *Concert*
    (11/93) (TELA) ① CD80301
Mujeres de Sevilla—piano, Op. 89 (pub 1935)
D. Buechner (r1990) *Concert*
    (10/94) (CONN) ① CD4186
Mujeres Españolas—piano, Op. 17 (pub 1917)
D. Buechner (r1990) *Concert*
    (10/94) (CONN) ① CD4186
Mujeres Españolas—piano, Op. 73 (pub 1932)
D. Buechner (r1990) *Concert*
    (10/94) (CONN) ① CD4186
Ráfaga—guitar, Op. 53 (1930)
M. Barrueco *Concert*
    (3/93) (EMI) ① CDC7 54382-2
A-S. Ramírez (r1991) *Concert*
    (2/94) (DENO) ① CO-75357
Sevillana—guitar, Op. 29 (1923)
M. Barrueco *Concert*
    (3/93) (EMI) ① CDC7 54382-2
J. Bream (r1983) *Concert*
    (8/93) (RCA) ① [28] 09026 61583-2(6)
A-S. Ramírez (r1991) *Concert*
    (2/94) (DENO) ① CO-75357
Sonata for Guitar, Op. 61 (1931)
M. Barrueco *Concert*
    (3/93) (EMI) ① CDC7 54382-2
A-S. Ramírez (r1991) *Concert*
    (2/94) (DENO) ① CO-75357
P. Romero (r1993) *Concert*
    (4/95) (PHIL) ① 442 150-2PH

SECTION IV: VOCAL AND CHORAL

Canto a Sevilla—soprano and orchestra, Op. 37 (1927) (wds. San Roman)
1. Preludio; 2. Semana Santa; 3. Las Fuenecitas del Parque; 4. Noche de teria; 5. Fantasma; 6. La Giralda; 7. Ofrenda.
Y. Pappas, Israel SO, G. Stern *Concert*
    (2/88) (MERI) ① CDE84134
V. de los Angeles, LSO, A. Fistoulari (r1952/3)
Concert   (4/92) (EMI) ① CDH7 64028-2
5. T. Berganza, F. Lavilla *Concert*
    (12/92) (DG) ① [2] 435 848-2GX2
Poema en forma de canciones, Op. 19 (1923) (Wds. Campoamor)
1. Dedicator; 2. Nunca Olvida; 3. Cantares; 4. Los dos miedos; 5. Los locas por amor.
M. Bayo, J.A. Alvarez-Parejo (r1992) *Concert*
    (6/93) (CLAV) ① CD50-9205
D. Jones, M. Martineau (r1993) *Concert*
    (9/94) (CHAN) ① CHAN9277
3. V. de los Angeles, Phil, W. Susskind (r1949)
Concert   (4/92) (EMI) ① CDH7 64028-2
3. T. Berganza, F. Lavilla *Concert*
    (12/92) (DG) ① [2] 435 848-2GX2
3. M. Caballé, M. Burgueras (pp1994) *Concert*
    (1/95) (RCA) ① 09026 62547-2
Saeta en forme de Salve a la Virgen de la Esperanza—song, Op. 60 (1930) (Wds. Alvares Quintero)
V. de los Angeles, Phil, W. Susskind (r1949)
Concert   (4/92) (EMI) ① CDH7 64028-2
T. Berganza, F. Lavilla *Concert*
    (12/92) (DG) ① [2] 435 848-2GX2
Tríptico—1v and piano, Op. 45 (1929) (Wds. Campoamor & Rivas)
1. Farruca; 2. Cantilena; 3. Madrigal.
1. V. de los Angeles, G. Soriano (r1961/2) *Concert*
    (4/94) (EMI) ① [4] CMS5 65061-2(2)

TURINI, Francesco (c1589–1656) Italy

SECTION II: CHAMBER

Sonata a tre—2 violins & continuo (pub 1624) (from Madrigals, Book 2)
Palladian Ens (r1993) *Concert*
    (1/95) (LINN) ① CKD015

TURNAGE, Mark-Anthony (b 1960) England

SECTION I: ORCHESTRAL

Drowned Out—large orchestra (1922-93)
CBSO, S. Rattle (r1994) Concert
(9/94) (EMI) ① CDC5 55091-2
Kai—cello and ensemble (1989-90)
U. Heinen, Birmingham Contemp Mus Group, S.
Rattle (r1993) Concert
(9/94) (EMI) ① CDC5 55091-2
Momentum—large orchestra (1990-91)
CBSO, S. Rattle (r1993) Concert
(9/94) (EMI) ① CDC5 55091-2
On All Fours—saxophone, cello and 14 players (1983)
M. Robertson, C. Van Kampen, Nash Ens, O.
Knussen (r1994) Concert
(9/95) (NMC) ① NMCD024M
3 Screaming Popes (after Francis Bacon)—orchestra (1988-98)
CBSO, S. Rattle (r1992) Concert
(9/94) (EMI) ① CDC5 55091-2

SECTION II: CHAMBER

Release—eight players (1988)
M. Robertson, I. Brown, Nash Ens, O. Knussen
(r1994) Concert (9/95) (NMC) ① NMCD024M
Sarabande—soprano saxophone and piano (1985)
F. Kimm, I. Brown, O. Knussen (r1994) Concert
(9/95) (NMC) ① NMCD024M

SECTION IV: VOCAL AND CHORAL

Lament for a Hanging Man—soprano and six players (1985) (Wds. S Plath)
F. Kimm, M. Robertson, Nash Ens, O. Knussen
(r1994) Concert (9/95) (NMC) ① NMCD024M

SECTION V: STAGE WORKS

Greek—opera: 2 acts (1988—Munich) (Lib. S
Berkoff, from stage play)
Cpte Q. Hayes, R. Suart, F. Kimm, H. Charnock,
Ens, R. Bernas (r1992)
(7/94) (ARGO) ① 440 368-2ZHO

TURNER, Dame Eva (1892–1990) England

SECTION IV: VOCAL AND CHORAL

Introductory talk on recording (1988)
E. Turner Concert (9/89) (EMI) ① CDH7 69791-2

TURNER, William (1651–1740) England

SECTION IV: VOCAL AND CHORAL

The King shall rejoice—anthem: 5/4vv, trumpets and strings (1697)
Westminster Abbey Ch, S. Preston (r1986)
Concert (7/95) (ARCH) ① 447 155-2AP
See where she sits—song (Wds Cowley)
Consort of Musicke, A. Rooley (lte/dir) (r1993)
Concert (11/95) (MOSC) ① 070986

TÜÜR, Erkki-Sven (b 1959) Estonia

SECTION I: ORCHESTRAL

Insular Deserta, 'Desert Island' (1989)
Ostrobothnian CO, J. Kangas (r1994) Concert
(4/95) (FINL) ① 4509-97893-2
Searching for Roots (1990)
Helsinki PO, S. Comissiona Concert
(4/92) (ONDI) ① ODE767-2

SECTION II: CHAMBER

String Quartet
Tallinn Qt (r1992) Concert
(1/94) (BIS) ① BIS-CD574

SECTION III: INSTRUMENTAL

Sonata for Piano (1985)
L. Väinmaa (r1993) Concert
(7/95) (FINL) ① 4509-95704-2

TVEITT, Geirr (1908–1981) Norway

SECTION I: ORCHESTRAL

Concerto for Harp and Orchestra No. 2, Op. 170
T. Kniejski, RPO, P. Dreier Concert
(12/94) (SIMA) ① PSC3108
100 Folk Tunes from Hardanger—Suite No. 1—orchestra, Op. 151
1. Welcome with honour; 2. Flute sound; 3. Most
beautiful song on earth; 4. Cloudbeines and
Moorbeines; 5. Stave Church Chant; 6. Please
preserve me from my sweetheart; 7. Consecration of
the new beer; 8. Mournful ballad for an empty brandy
keg; 9. Langeleik Tune; 10. Echo from the mountain
pasture; 11. The hasty wedding; 12. God's goodness
and God's greatness; 13. Wise folks gossip about
certain people; 14. The Boaster's Ballad; 15. Fare
thee well.
RPO, P. Dreier Concert
(12/94) (SIMA) ① PSC3108
Water sprite (Nykken)
RPO, P. Dreier Concert
(12/94) (SIMA) ① PSC3108

TWINING, Toby (b 1958) USA

SECTION IV: VOCAL AND CHORAL

Agnus Dei—4vv (1992)
T. Twining Music (r1993) Concert
(2/95) (CATA) ① 09026 61981-2
Between Stars—4vv (1989)
T. Twining Music (r1993) Concert
(2/95) (CATA) ① 09026 61981-2
Hee-oo-oom-ha—5vv (1987)
T. Twining Music, P. Stewart (r1993) Concert
(2/95) (CATA) ① 09026 61981-2
Hell's Kitchen Hootenanny—4vv (1993)
T. Twining Music (r1993) Concert
(2/95) (CATA) ① 09026 61981-2
Himalaya—4vv (1993)
T. Twining Music (r1993) Concert
(2/95) (CATA) ① 09026 61981-2
Hotel Destiné—4vv (1992)
T. Twining Music (r1993) Concert
(2/95) (CATA) ① 09026 61981-2
Hymn—5vv (1987)
T. Twining Music, P. Stewart (r1993) Concert
(2/95) (CATA) ① 09026 61981-2
Munu Munu—4vv (1992)
T. Twining Music (r1993) Concert
(2/95) (CATA) ① 09026 61981-2
Numa Exotic—5vv (1993)
T. Twining Music, P. Stewart (r1993) Concert
(2/95) (CATA) ① 09026 61981-2
Richi Richi Rubel—4vv (1992)
T. Twining Music (r1993) Concert
(2/95) (CATA) ① 09026 61981-2
Sanctus—4vv (1992)
T. Twining Music (r1993) Concert
(2/95) (CATA) ① 09026 61981-2
Shaman—4vv (1987)
T. Twining Music (r1993) Concert
(2/95) (CATA) ① 09026 61981-2

TYE, Christopher (c1505–?1572) England

SECTION II: CHAMBER

Amavit—consort (5 parts)
Hespèrion XX, J. Savall Concert
(11/89) (ASTR) ① E8708
Christus resurgens—consort (5 parts)
Hespèrion XX, J. Savall Concert
(11/89) (ASTR) ① E8708
4 Dum transissets—consort (5 parts)
Hespèrion XX, J. Savall Concert
(11/89) (ASTR) ① E8708
In Nomine—consort (4 parts)
Hespèrion XX, J. Savall Concert
(11/89) (ASTR) ① E8708
In Nomine—consort (6 parts)
Hespèrion XX, J. Savall Concert
(11/89) (ASTR) ① E8708
19 In Nomines—consort (5 parts)
1. Weepe no more Rachell; 2. Farewell my good 1,
for ever; 3. Rachells weeping; 4. My death; 5.
Blameless; 6. -; 7. Rounde; 8. Follow me; 9. Surrexit
non est hic; 10. Free from all; 11. Trust; 12. Beleve
me; 13. Crye; 14. I come; 15. Re la re; 16. Howld
fast; 17. Saye so; 18. Seldom sene; 19. Reporte.

Hespèrion XX, J. Savall Concert
(11/89) (ASTR) ① E8708
11, 13. Fretwork Concert
(3/88) (AMON) ① CD-SAR29
13. Circa 1500, N. Hadden (r1991) Concert
(8/93) (CRD) ① CRD3487
13. F. Brüggen, Brüggen Consort (r1967/79) Concert
(10/95) (TELD) ① 4509-97465-2
Lawdes Deo—consort (5 parts)
Hespèrion XX, J. Savall Concert
(11/89) (ASTR) ① E8708
O Lux—consort (5 parts)
Hespèrion XX, J. Savall Concert
(11/89) (ASTR) ① E8708
Rubum quem—consort (5 parts)
Hespèrion XX, J. Savall Concert
(11/89) (ASTR) ① E8708
Sit fast—consort (3 parts)
Hespèrion XX, J. Savall Concert
(11/89) (ASTR) ① E8708

SECTION IV: VOCAL AND CHORAL

I will exalt thee—anthem (4vv) (pub 1641)
Magdalen Oxford Coll Ch, J. Harper Concert
(11/91) (ABBE) ① CDCA901
Kyrie, 'Orbis factor'—4vv
Winchester Cath Ch, D. Hill Concert
(1/91) (HYPE) ① CDA66424
Mass, 'Euge Bone'—6vv
Clerkes of Oxenford, D. Wulstan Concert
(5/90) (PROU) ① PROUCD126
Winchester Cath Ch, D. Hill Concert
(1/91) (HYPE) ① CDA66424
Oxford Camerata, J. Summerly (r1993) Concert
(2/95) (NAXO) ① 8 550937
Mass, 'Western Wind'—4vv
Tallis Scholars, P. Phillips Concert
(9/93) (GIME) ① CDGIM027
Miserere mei, Deus—motet (5vv)
Winchester Cath Ch, D. Hill Concert
(1/91) (HYPE) ① CDA66424
Omnes gentes, plaudite—motet (5vv)
Winchester Cath Ch, D. Hill Concert
(1/91) (HYPE) ① CDA66424
Oxford Camerata, J. Summerly (r1993) Concert
(2/95) (NAXO) ① 8 550937
Peccavimus cum patribus—motet (7vv)
Clerkes of Oxenford, D. Wulstan Concert
(5/90) (PROU) ① PROUCD126
Winchester Cath Ch, D. Hill Concert
(1/91) (HYPE) ① CDA66424
Oxford Camerata, J. Summerly (r1993) Concert
(2/95) (NAXO) ① 8 550937
Quaesumus omnipotens—motet (6vv)
Winchester Cath Ch, D. Hill Concert
(1/91) (HYPE) ① CDA66424

TYES, John (fl c1400) England

SECTION IV: VOCAL AND CHORAL

Sanctus and Benedictus—4vv
Westminster Abbey Ch, M. Neary, M. Baker (r1994)
Concert (12/95) (SONY) ① SK66614

UCCELLINI, Marco (c1603–1680) Italy

SECTION II: CHAMBER

Sonatas (Sonate, sinfonie et Correnti)—2-4 instruments and continuo, Op. 2 (pub 1639)
8. Sonata ottava a due violini; 12. Sonata duodecima.
2. Palladian Ens (r1992) Concert
(7/93) (LINN) ① CKD010
8. Arcadian Academy, N. McGegan (hpd/dir) (r1993)
Concert (7/94) (HARM) ① HMU90 7066
Sonatas (Sonate, arie et correnti)—2-3 instruments and continuo, Op. 3 (pub 1642)
4. Sonata quarta detta 'La Trasformata'; 5. Aria
quinta sopra 'La Bergamasca'; 6. Aria sesta sopra un
balletto; 9a. Sonata nona a doi violini detta 'La
Reggiana'; 9b. Aria nona, 'La Emenfrodito'.
4, 5, 6, 9. Arcadian Academy, N. McGegan (hpd/dir)
(r1993) Concert (7/94) (HARM) ① HMU90 7066
Sonatas (Sonate, correnti e arie)—1-3 instruments and continuo, Op. 4 (pub 1645)
2. Sonata seconda detta 'La Lucimínia contenta'; 4.
Sonata quarta a violino solo detta 'La Hortensa
virtuosa'; 11. Aria undecima a doi violini sopra 'Il
Caporal Simon'; 14. Aria decima quarta a doi violini
'La mia Pedrina'; 15. Aria decima quinta sopra 'La
Scatola dagli agghi'; 18. Sonata decima ottava a doi
violini; 20. Sonata vigesima a doi violini; 21. Sonata
vigesima prima a doi violini; 25. Sonata vigesima
quinta; 26. Sonata vigesima sesta sopra 'La
Prosperina'; 27. Sonata vigesima settima.

2, 4, 11, 14, 15, 18, 20, 21, 25, 26, 27. Arcadian
Academy, N. McGegan (hpd/dir) (r1993) Concert
(7/94) (HARM) ① **HMU90 7066**
11, 14, 15. Palladian Ens (r1993) Concert
(1/95) (LINN) ① **CKD015**
**Sonatas (Sonate, over canzoni)—violin and
continuo, Op. 5 (pub 1649)**
4. Sonata quarta; 8. Sonata ottava; 12. Sonata
tredecima 'al riversa'.
4. Palladian Ens (r1993) Concert
(1/95) (LINN) ① **CKD015**
**Sonatas (Sinfonici Concerti brevi e facili)—1-
4 instruments and continuo, Op. 9 (pub
1667)**
1. Sinfonia prima; 2. Primo brando alla francese per
ballare; 9. Sinfonia nona a tre violini; 20. Sinfonia
vigesima.
9. J. Holloway, S. Ritchie, A. Manze, N. North, M.
Springfels, J. Toll (r1993) Concert
(2/94) (HARM) ① **HMU90 7091**
**Sonatas, '(L')Ozio regio'—1-6 instruments
and continuo, Op. 7 (pub 1660)**
1. Toccata prima; 9. Sonata nona.
9. Arcadian Academy, N. McGegan (hpd/dir) (r1993)
Concert (7/94) (HARM) ① **HMU90 7066**

**UGARTE, Floro Manuel
(1884–1975) Argentina**

SECTION IV: VOCAL AND CHORAL

Dia del fiesta—song
H. Spani, orch, G. Nastrucci (r1930) Concert
(9/90) (CLUB) ① [2] **CL99-509/10**
H. Spani, Inst Ens, G. Nastrucci (r1930) Concert
(12/92) (PREI) ① **89037**

**UGOLINI, Vincenzo (c1580–1638)
Italy**

SECTION IV: VOCAL AND CHORAL

Beata es Virgo Maria—motet
King's College Ch, D. Briggs, S. Cleobury Concert
(5/85) (EMI) ① **CDC7 47065-2**

**ULLMANN, Viktor (1898–1944)
Austria/Hungary**

SECTION I: ORCHESTRAL

**Concerto for Piano and Orchestra, Op. 25
(1940)**
Konrad Richter, Brno St PO, I. Yinon (1992) Concert
(10/94) (BAYE) ① **BR100228**
Symphony No. 2 in D (1944, recons 1989)
(recons Wulff from Pf Sonata 7)
Brno St PO, I. Yinon (r1992) Concert
(10/94) (BAYE) ① **BR100228**
**5 Variations and Double Fugue on a Piano
Piece of Arnold Schoenberg (1929)**
Brno St PO, I. Yinon (r1992) Concert
(10/94) (BAYE) ① **BR100228**

SECTION II: CHAMBER

String Quartet No. 3, Op. 43 (1943)
V. Eskin, Hawthorne Qt Concert
(12/91) (CHNN) ① **CCS1691**
Martinů Qt (pp1991) Concert
(8/92) (ROMA) ① [2] **RR1941**
Group for New Music Concert
(10/92) (KOCH) ① **37109-2**

SECTION III: INSTRUMENTAL

Sonata for Piano No. 5, Op. 45
R. Kolben Concert (10/92) (KOCH) ① **37109-2**
Sonata for Piano No. 6, Op. 49 (1943)
E. Leichner Concert (8/92) (ROMA) ① [2] **RR1941**
E. Steiner-Kraus Concert
(10/92) (KOCH) ① **37109-2**
Sonata for Piano No. 7 (1944)
R. Kolben Concert (10/92) (KOCH) ① **37109-2**
**Variationen und Doppelfuge über ein Theme
von Arnold Schoenberg—piano, Op. 3a
(1924, rev 1934)**
G. Herzfeld (r1994) Concert
(11/95) (EDA) ① **EDA008-2**

SECTION IV: VOCAL AND CHORAL

Abendphantasie—song (1943) (Wds.
Hölderlin)
E. Berendsen, D. Bloch Concert
(8/92) (ROMA) ① [2] **RR1941**
M. Shirai, H. Höll Concert
(12/94) (CAPR) ① **10 534**
I. Vermillion, J. Alder (r1993) Concert
(12/94) (DECC) ① **440 854-2DH**

Der **Frühling—song (1943)** (Wds Hölderlin)
M. Shirai, H. Höll Concert
(12/94) (CAPR) ① **10 534**
I. Vermillion, J. Alder (r1993) Concert
(12/94) (DECC) ① **440 854-2DH**
Immer Inmitten—song (Wds. Adler)
E. Berendsen, D. Bloch Concert
(8/92) (ROMA) ① [2] **RR1941**
**3 Jiddische Lieder—voice and piano, Op.
53**
1. Berjoskele; 2. Margaritholech; 3. A Mejdel in die
Jahren.
E. Berendsen, D. Bloch Concert
(8/92) (ROMA) ① [2] **RR1941**
Little Cakewalk—song (Wds. French children's
song)
E. Berendsen, D. Bloch Concert
(8/92) (ROMA) ① [2] **RR1941**
Die **Weise von Liebe und Tod des Cornets
Christoph Rilke—12 pieces for speaker &
piano (1944)** (Wds. Rilke)
G. Westphal, M. Allan (r1994) Concert
(11/95) (EDA) ① **EDA008-2**
Wo bist du?—song (1943) (Wds Hölderlin)
I. Vermillion, J. Alder (r1993) Concert
(12/94) (DECC) ① **440 854-2DH**

SECTION V: STAGE WORKS

Der **Kaiser von Atlantis, oder Die Tod-
Verweigerung—opera: 1 act, Op. 49 (1943)**
(Lib. P Kien)
Cpte M. Kraus, F. Mazura, M. Petzold, C. Oelze, W.
Berry, H. Lippert, I. Vermillion, Leipzig Gewandhaus,
L. Zagrosek (r1993) Concert
(12/94) (DECC) ① **440 854-2DH**

**URBAITIS, Mindaugas (b 1952)
USSR/Lithuania**

SECTION I: ORCHESTRAL

Lithuanian Folk Music (1990)
Ostrobothnian CO, J. Kangas (r1994) Concert
(11/95) (FINL) ① **4509-97893-2**

**URREDA, Johannes (late 15th
Cent) Flanders/Spain**

also known as Juan Urrede

SECTION IV: VOCAL AND CHORAL

Donde estás que non te veo (Cancionero de
Colombina)
Hespèrion XX, J. Savall Concert
(7/92) (ASTR) ① **E8763**
Muy triste sera mi vida—3vv (Cancionero de
Colombina)
Hespèrion XX, J. Savall Concert
(7/92) (ASTR) ① **E8763**
C. Bott, New London Consort, P. Pickett Concert
(7/92) (LINN) ① **CKD007**
Nunca fué pena major—chanson (Cancionero
de Colombina)
Hespèrion XX, J. Savall Concert
(7/92) (ASTR) ① **E8763**
Pange lingua—motet: 4vv (Cancionero de
Segovia)
Daedalus Ens Concert
(12/92) (ACCE) ① **ACC9176D**

**USANDIZAGA, José Maria
(1887–1915) Spain**

SECTION V: STAGE WORKS

**Las Golondrinas—zarzuela: 3 acts
(1914—Madrid)** (Lib. G Martinez Sierra. Rev as
opera: fp 1929)
Cpte J. Cubeiro, I. Rivas, V. Sardinero, R. Alonso,
Madrid Coros Cantores, Spanish Lyric Orch, F.
Moreno Torroba (10/92) (HISP) ① **CDZ7 67453-2**

**USIGLIO, Emilio (1841–1910)
Italy**

SECTION V: STAGE WORKS

**Le Educande di Sorrento—opera: 3 acts
(1868—Florence)**
Ma zitta, giunge alcun...Un bacio rendimi E. Petri,
F. Corradetti, anon (r1906-7) Concert
(6/94) (IRCC) ① **IRCC-CD808**

**USTVOL'SKAYA, Galina Ivanova
(b 1919) USSR**

SECTION II: CHAMBER

**Composition No. 1, 'Dona nobis
pacem'—piccolo, tuba & piano (1970-1)**
Schoenberg Ens, R. de Leeuw (r1993) Concert
(4/95) (PHIL) ① **442 532-2PH**
**Composition No. 2, 'Dies irae'—8 double-
basses, cube & piano (1972-3)**
Schoenberg Ens, R. de Leeuw (r1993) Concert
(4/95) (PHIL) ① **442 532-2PH**
**Composition No. 3, 'Benedictus qui
venit'—4 flutes, 4 bassoons & piano (1974-
5)**
Schoenberg Ens, R. de Leeuw (r1993) Concert
(4/95) (PHIL) ① **442 532-2PH**
Grand Duet—cello and piano (1959)
M. Beiser, C. Oldfather (r c1994) Concert
(11/95) (KOCH) ① **37258-2**

**VACCAI, Nicola (1790–1848)
Italy**

SECTION V: STAGE WORKS

**Giulietta e Romeo—opera: 2 acts
(1825—Milan)** (Lib. F. Romani)
Ah! se tu dormi G. Fabbri, S. Cottone (r1903)
Concert (12/89) (SYMP) ① **SYMCD1065**

**VACHON, Pierre (1731–1803)
France**

SECTION II: CHAMBER

6 String Quartets, Op. 7
2 (Andantino) Rasumovsky Qt Concert
(12/92) (IMPE) ① **RAZCD901**

**VAČKÁŘ, Dalibor (1906–1984)
Bohemia**

SECTION I: ORCHESTRAL

Abend am Meer—Waltz
Czech PO, V. Neumann Concert
(6/87) (ORFE) ① **C107201A**
**Concerto for Trumpet, Piano and Percussion
(1963)**
R. Kvapil, E. Glennie, Wallace Collection, J. Wallace
Concert (7/89) (NIMB) ① **NI5103**
Der **Freier—March**
Czech PO, V. Neumann Concert
(6/87) (ORFE) ① **C107201A**
Weckruf—March
Czech PO, V. Neumann Concert
(6/87) (ORFE) ① **C107201A**

VÄHI, Peeter (b 1955) Estonia

SECTION II: CHAMBER

**To His Highness Salvador D—flute, violin
and guitar (1988)**
Tallinn Camerata (r1993) Concert
(5/95) (FINL) ① **4509-95705-2**

SECTION III: INSTRUMENTAL

Fata Morgana—piano (1975)
L. Väinmaa (r1993) Concert
(7/95) (FINL) ① **4509-95704-2**

**VAINBERG, Moysey Samuilovich
(b 1919) Poland**

SECTION I: ORCHESTRAL

**Concerto for Trumpet and Orchestra in B
flat, Op. 95**
T. Dokshitser, Moscow PO, A. Zhuraitis Symphony 5.
(2/94) (RUSS) ① **RDCD11006**
Symphony No. 5 in F minor, Op. 76 (1962)
Moscow PO, K. Kondrashin Trumpet Concerto.
(2/94) (RUSS) ① **RDCD11006**
**Symphony No. 7—string orchestra and harp,
Op. 81 (1964)**
Moscow CO, R. Barshai (r1967) Symphony 12.
(11/94) (OLYM) ① **OCD472**
**Symphony No. 12, 'In memory of
Shostakovich', Op. 114 (1976)**
USSR TV & Rad SO, M. Shostakovich (r1979)
Symphony 7. (11/94) (OLYM) ① **OCD472**

SECTION II: CHAMBER

Quintet for Piano and Strings, Op. 18 (1944)
M. Vainberg, Borodin Qt (r1963) *String Quartet 12.*
(4/95) (OLYM) ① **OCD474**
String Quartet No. 12, Op. 103 (1970)
Y. Smirnov, A. Kobyhkansky, V. Trushin, A. Vasilieva
(r1970) *Piano Quintet, Op. 18.*
(4/95) (OLYM) ① **OCD474**

SECTION III: INSTRUMENTAL

Sonata for Piano No. 4 in B minor (1955)
Emil Gilels (pp1957) *Concert*
(4/93) (MEZH) ① **MK417072**

SECTION V: STAGE WORKS

The Golden Key—concert suites from ballet, Op. 55 (1955, rev 1964)
EXCERPTS: 1. Suite No. 1; 2. Suite No. 2; 3. Suite
No. 3; 4. Suite No. 4.
1-3, 4(pt) Bolshoi Th Orch, M. Ermler (r1966)
(5/95) (OLYM) ① **OCD473**

VALDERRÁBANO, Enríquez de (c1500–c1556) Spain

SECTION II: CHAMBER

Discantar sobre un punto
Kithara (r1993) *Concert*
(3/95) (CHAN) ① **CHAN0562**

SECTION IV: VOCAL AND CHORAL

De dónde venís, amore?—song
T. Berganza, N. Yepes *Concert*
(12/92) (DG) ① [2] **435 848-2GX2**
J. Gomez, J. Constable (1994; arr Tarragó) *Concert*
(9/94) (CONI) ① **CDCF243**

VALEN, (Olav) Fartein (1887–1952) Norway

SECTION I: ORCHESTRAL

Cantico di ringraziamento, Op. 17/2 (1932-33)
Oslo PO, M. Caridis (r1972) *Concert*
(6/93) (SIMA) ① **PSC3115**
Le cimitière marin, Op. 20 (1933-34)
Oslo PO, M. Caridis (r1972) *Concert*
(6/93) (SIMA) ① **PSC3115**
La isla de las calmas, Op. 21 (1934)
Oslo PO, M. Caridis (r1972) *Concert*
(6/93) (SIMA) ① **PSC3115**
Nenia, Op. 18/1 (1932)
Oslo PO, M. Caridis (r1972) *Concert*
(6/93) (SIMA) ① **PSC3115**
Ode to Solitude, Op. 35 (1939)
Oslo PO, M. Caridis (r1972) *Concert*
(6/93) (SIMA) ① **PSC3115**
Pastorale, Op. 11 (1929-30)
Oslo PO, M. Caridis (r1972) *Concert*
(6/93) (SIMA) ① **PSC3115**
Sonette di Michelangelo, Op. 17/1 (1932)
Oslo PO, M. Caridis (r1972) *Concert*
(6/93) (SIMA) ① **PSC3115**
Symphony No. 1, Op. 30 (1937-39)
Bergen PO, A. Ceccato (1986) *Concert*
(8/93) (SIMA) ① [2] **PSC3101**
Symphony No. 2, Op. 40 (1941-44)
Bergen PO, A. Ceccato (1986) *Concert*
(8/93) (SIMA) ① [2] **PSC3101**
Symphony No. 3, Op. 41 (1944-46)
Bergen PO, A. Ceccato (1986) *Concert*
(8/93) (SIMA) ① [2] **PSC3101**
Symphony No. 4, Op. 43 (1947-49)
Bergen PO, A. Ceccato (1986) *Concert*
(8/93) (SIMA) ① [2] **PSC3101**

SECTION III: INSTRUMENTAL

Sonata No. 2—piano, Op. 38 (1940-41)
G. Gould *Concert* (3/93) (SONY) ① **SMK52677**

SECTION IV: VOCAL AND CHORAL

Ave Maria—song, Op. 4 (1917-21)
D. Dorow, Oslo PO, M. Caridis (r1972) *Concert*
(6/93) (SIMA) ① **PSC3115**
Chinesische Gedichte, Op. 8 (1925-27)
1. In Erwartung des Freundes; 2. Der Abschied des
Freundes.
D. Dorow, Oslo PO, M. Caridis (r1972) *Concert*
(6/93) (SIMA) ① **PSC3115**
Darest Thou now o soul, Op. 9 (1920-28)
D. Dorow, Oslo PO, M. Caridis (r1972) *Concert*
(6/93) (SIMA) ① **PSC3115**

Die **dunkle Nacht die Seele, Op. 32**
D. Dorow, Oslo PO, M. Caridis (r1972) *Concert*
(6/93) (SIMA) ① **PSC3115**

VALENTE, Antonio (c1520–c1580) Italy

SECTION II: CHAMBER

Intavolatura di Cimbalo—dance collection (pub 1576)
1. Gagliarda Lombarda; 2. Ballo Lombardo; 3.
Gagliarda secondo.
1-3. Broadside Band, J. Barlow *Concert*
(3/88) (HYPE) ① **CDA66244**

SECTION III: INSTRUMENTAL

Tenore del passo e mezzo
Kithara (r1993) *Concert*
(3/95) (CHAN) ① **CHAN0562**
R. Alessandrini (r1994) *Concert*
(4/95) (O111) ① **OPS30-118**

VALENTE, Nicola (1881–1946) Italy

SECTION IV: VOCAL AND CHORAL

Torna!—song (1930) (Wds. P. Vento)
T. Gobbi, Orch, A. Erede (r1948) *Concert*
(8/93) (TEST) ① **SBT1019**

VALENTE, Vincenzo (1855–1921) Italy

SECTION IV: VOCAL AND CHORAL

Manella mia—song (wds. F. Russo)
E. Caruso, orch, W.B. Rogers (r1914) *Concert*
(7/91) (RCA) ① [12] **GD60495(5)**
E. Caruso, orch, W.B. Rogers (r1914) *Concert*
(10/91) (PEAR) ① [3] **EVC3(1)**
D. Giannini, orch, G.W. Byng (r1928) *Concert*
(4/93) (PREI) ① **89044**
Nuttata napulitana—song (Wds. Murolo)
L. Tetrazzini, T. Amici (r1922) *Concert*
(9/92) (EMI) ① [3] **CHS7 63802-2(2)**
L. Tetrazzini, orch (r1922) *Concert*
(9/92) (PEAR) ① **GEMMCD9225**
Passione—song (Wds. Bovio & Tagliaferri)
L. Pavarotti, National PO, G. Chiaramello (arr
Chiarmello) *Concert*
(7/90) (DECC) ① [2] **425 681-2DM2**

VALENTINI, Giuseppe (1680–1759) Italy

SECTION I: ORCHESTRAL

12 Concerti grossi—2-4vns, strings and continuo, Op. 7 (pub 1710)
11. A minor.
11. Cologne Musica Antiqua, R. Goebel *Concert*
(9/92) (ARCH) ① **435 393-2AH**

SECTION II: CHAMBER

12 Sinfonie—2 violins, cello and continuo, Op. 1 (pub 1701)
12. Seattle NW CO, J. A. Francis *Concert*
(12/88) (HYPE) ① **CDH88028**

VALLE, Francisco L. (1869–1906) Brazil

also known as Francisco Vale

SECTION III: INSTRUMENTAL

Prelude XV, 'Ao pé da foguiera'—piano
J. Heifetz, E. Bay (r1945) *Concert*
(11/94) (RCA) ① [65] **09026 61778-2(19)**
A. A. Meyers, S. Rivers (r1993; trans Heifetz: vn/pf)
Concert (4/95) (RCA) ① **09026 62546-2**

VALLET, Nicolas (c1583–after 1642) The Netherlands

SECTION II: CHAMBER

Suite for 4 lutes
J. Lindberg, R. Meunier, N. North, P. O'Dette *Concert*
(12/86) (BIS) ① **BIS-CD341**

VALLS, Francisco (1665–1747) Spain

SECTION IV: VOCAL AND CHORAL

En un noble, sagrado firmamento—solo cantata to San Francisco de Borja
Al Ayre Español, E. L. Banzo (r1994) *Concert*
(8/95) (DHM) ① **05472 77325-2**
Missa Scala Aretina—11vv (c1702)
S. Piau, M. van der Sluis, B. Lettinga, D. Cordier, J.
Elwes, H. van der Kamp, Netherlands Bach Soc Ch,
Netherlands Bach Soc Baroque Orch, G. Leonhardt
(r1992) *Biber: Requiem in F minor.*
(9/95) (DHM) ① **05472 77277-2**
London Oratory Ch, Thames CO, J. Hoban (r c1980)
(9/95) (CRD) ① **CRD3371**

VALVERDE, Joaquín (1846–1910) Spain

SECTION IV: VOCAL AND CHORAL

Clavelitos—song
A. Galli-Curci, orch (r1920) *Concert*
(2/89) (PEAR) ① **GEMMCD9308**
V. de los Angeles, G. Parsons (pp1990) *Concert*
(12/91) (COLL) ① **Coll1247-2**
C. Supervia, CO (r1927) *Concert*
(3/93) (NIMB) ① [2] **NI7836/7**
A. Galli-Curci, orch, J. Pasternack (r1920) *Concert*
(3/94) (ROMO) ① [2] **81003-2**

SECTION V: STAGE WORKS

The Land of Joy—musical show (1917—New York)
EXCERPTS: 1. Alegrias.
1. LaCalle's Spanish Orch (r1917) *Concert*
(5/94) (PEAR) ① [3] **GEMMCDS9059/61**

VAN ALSTYNE, Egbert (1882–1951) USA

SECTION IV: VOCAL AND CHORAL

Pretty Baby—song for the show 'Chin-Chin' (1914) (collab with T Jackson)
Six Brown Brothers (r1916) *Concert*
(5/94) (PEAR) ① [3] **GEMMCDS9056/8**

VAN BIENE, August (1850–1913)

SECTION II: CHAMBER

Broken melody—cello and piano
B. Harrison, Margaret Harrison (r1929) *Concert*
(3/93) (CLAR) ① **CDGSE78-50-47**

VAN CLEVE, Nathan (1910–1970) USA

SECTION I: ORCHESTRAL

Paramount Vista Vision Fanfare
Prague City PO, P. Bateman (arr Bateman) *Concert*
(9/95) (SILV) ① **FILMCD159**

VAN DE VATE, Nancy (b 1930) USA

SECTION I: ORCHESTRAL

Chernobyl—orchestra (1987)
Polish Radio & TV SO, S. Kawalla *Concert*
(1/90) (CONI) ① **CDCF168**
Concerto for Violin and Orchestra No. 1 (1986)
J. Miryński, Polish Radio & TV SO, S. Kawalla
Concert (1/90) (CONI) ① **CDCF168**
Concertpiece—cello and small orchestra (1985)
Z. Łapiński, Polish Radio & TV SO, S. Kawalla *Concert*
(10/87) (CONI) ① **CDCF147**
Dark Nebulae—orchestra (1981)
Polish Radio & TV SO, S. Kawalla *Concert*
(10/87) (CONI) ① **CDCF147**
Distant Worlds—violin and orchestra (1985)
J. Miryński, Polish Radio & TV SO, S. Kawalla
Concert (10/87) (CONI) ① **CDCF147**
Journeys—orchestra (1984)
Polish Radio & TV SO, S. Kawalla *Concert*
(10/87) (CONI) ① **CDCF147**

SECTION IV: VOCAL AND CHORAL

Cocaine Lil—mezzo-soprano and four jazz singers
Bel Canto Ens., D. Spohr (r1993) *Concert*
(3/95) (SCHW) ① **314322**

VAN DIEREN, Bernard (1887–1936) England

SECTION II: CHAMBER

Sonata tyroica—violin and piano (1913)
C. Nicholls, J. Ayerst (r1984-92) *Concert*
(2/94) (BRIT) ① **BML001**

SECTION III: INSTRUMENTAL

2 Estemporales—harp (1931)
S. Goossens (r1984-92) *Concert*
(2/94) (BRIT) ① **BML001**
Piccolo pralinudettino fridato—piano
E. Davies (r1984-85) *Concert*
(2/94) (BRIT) ① **BML001**
Sonata for Violin, Op. 5 (1935)
C. Nicholls (r1984-92) *Concert*
(2/94) (BRIT) ① **BML001**

SECTION IV: VOCAL AND CHORAL

Der Asra—1v and piano (Wds. Heine)
L. Andrew, Philip Thomas (r1984-92) *Concert*
(2/94) (BRIT) ① **BML001**
Ich wandelte unter den Bäumen—1v and piano (Wds. Heine)
L. Andrew, Philip Thomas (r1984-92) *Concert*
(2/94) (BRIT) ① **BML001**
Mädchenlied: an einem jungen Rosenblatt—1v and piano (1914) (Wds. Bierbaum)
L. Andrew, Philip Thomas (r1984-92) *Concert*
(2/94) (BRIT) ① **BML001**
Mit deinen blauen Augen—1v and piano (Wds. Heine: unpub)
L. Andrew, Philip Thomas (r1984-92) *Concert*
(2/94) (BRIT) ① **BML001**
Mit träumte von einem Königskind—1v and piano (Wds. Heine: unpub)
L. Andrew, Philip Thomas (r1984-92) *Concert*
(2/94) (BRIT) ① **BML001**
Les Roses étaient toutes rouges—1v and piano (Wds. P. Verlaine)
L. Andrew, Philip Thomas (r1984-92) *Concert*
(2/94) (BRIT) ① **BML001**
2 Songs—1v and string quartet (1917)
1. Song from 'The Cenci' (wds. Shelley); 2. Rapsodia (wds. De Quincey).
L. Andrew, Emperor Qt (r1984-92) *Concert*
(2/94) (BRIT) ① **BML001**
Spring Song of the Birds—1v and piano (Wds. King James I of Scotland)
L. Andrew, Philip Thomas (r1984-92) *Concert*
(2/94) (BRIT) ① **BML001**
Und wüssten's die Blumen—1v and piano (pub 1907-08) (Wds. Heine)
L. Andrew, Philip Thomas (r1984-92) *Concert*
(2/94) (BRIT) ① **BML001**
Wenn ich auf dem Lager liege—1v and piano (pub 1907-08) (Wds. Heine)
L. Andrew, Philip Thomas (r1984-92) *Concert*
(2/94) (BRIT) ① **BML001**
Wer zum erstenmale liebt—1v and piano (pub 1907-08) (Wds. Heine)
L. Andrew, Philip Thomas (r1984-92) *Concert*
(2/94) (BRIT) ① **BML001**

VAN HOOF, Jef (1886–1959) Belgium

SECTION I: ORCHESTRAL

Symphonic Suite No. 1 (1919)
Belgian Rad & TV Orch, A. Rahbari (r1992) *Concert*
(8/94) (DINT) ① **DICD920100**

VAN ZEELAND, Cees (b 1954) The Netherlands

SECTION II: CHAMBER

Initials—two pianos (1989)
Pianoduo *Concert*
(5/93) (CHNN) ① **CCS4592**

VANGELIS (PAPATHANASSIOU), (Odyssey) (20th Cent) Greece

SECTION I: ORCHESTRAL

Un Après-midi—synthesizers and cello
J. Lloyd Webber, Vangelis, RPO, N. Cleobury *Concert*
(3/87) (PHIL) ① **416 698-2PH**

VANHAL, Johann Baptist (1739–1813) Bohemia

SECTION I: ORCHESTRAL

Concerto for 2 Bassoons and Orchestra
A. Wallin, A. Nilsson, Umeå Sinfonietta, J-P. Saraste *Concert*
(5/86) (BIS) ① **BIS-CD288**
Symphony in A minor, Bryan Am2
Umeå Sinfonietta, J-P. Saraste *Concert*
(5/86) (BIS) ① **BIS-CD288**
Symphony in F, Bryan F2
Umeå Sinfonietta, J-P. Saraste *Concert*
(5/86) (BIS) ① **BIS-CD288**

SECTION II: CHAMBER

Sonata for Viola and Keyboard in E flat
A. B. Duetschler, U. Duetschler (r1994) *Concert*
(11/95) (CLAV) ① **CD50-9502**

VANN, Stanley (b 1910) England

SECTION IV: VOCAL AND CHORAL

Evening (Chichester) Service—choir and organ
Chichester Cath Ch, A. Thurlow, J. Thomas (r1994) *Concert*
(5/95) (PRIO) ① **PRCD511**

VANNAH, Kate (1855–1933) USA

also used pseudonym Kate van Twinkle

SECTION IV: VOCAL AND CHORAL

Goodbye, sweet Day—song: 1v and piano (1891) (Wds. L. H. Ross)
S. Mentzer, K. Schmidt (r1991) *Concert*
(12/93) (KOCH) ① **37240-2**

VARÈSE, Edgar (Victor Achille Charles) (1883–1965) France/USA

SECTION I: ORCHESTRAL

Amériques—orchestra (?1918-21)
NYPO, P. Boulez *Concert*
(10/90) (SONY) ① **SMK45844**
FNO, K. Nagano *Concert*
(8/93) (ERAT) ① **4509-92137-2**
Cleveland Orch, C. von Dohnányi *Concert*
(11/94) (DECC) ① **443 172-2DH**
Arcana—orchestra (1925-27)
NYPO, P. Boulez *Concert*
(10/90) (SONY) ① **SMK45844**
FNO, K. Nagano *Concert*
(8/93) (ERAT) ① **4509-92137-2**
Concertgebouw, R. Chailly (r1992) *Concert*
(11/94) (DECC) ① **436 640-2DH**
Ionisation—13 percussion instruments (1929-31)
NYPO, P. Boulez *Concert*
(10/90) (SONY) ① **SMK45844**
Z. Kocsis, Amadinda Perc Group *Concert*
(11/90) (HUNG) ① **HCD12991**

SECTION II: CHAMBER

Hyperprism—9 wind and 7 percussion instruments (1922-23)
FNO, K. Nagano *Concert*
(8/93) (ERAT) ① **4509-92137-2**
Intégrales—11 wind and 4 percussion instruments (1924-25)
Paris InterContemporain Ens, P. Boulez *Concert*
(10/90) (SONY) ① **SMK45844**
Octandre—chamber ensemble (1923)
Chicago Pro Musica *Concert*
(8/89) (REFE) ① **RRCD-29**
Paris InterContemporain Ens, P. Boulez *Concert*
(10/90) (SONY) ① **SMK45844**
FNO, K. Nagano *Concert*
(8/93) (ERAT) ① **4509-92137-2**

SECTION III: INSTRUMENTAL

Density 21.5—solo flute (1936)
L. Beauregard *Concert*
(10/90) (SONY) ① **SMK45844**

SECTION IV: VOCAL AND CHORAL

Offrandes—soprano and small orchestra (1922) (Wds. Huidobro and Tablada)
R. Yakar, Paris InterContemporain Ens, P. Boulez *Concert*
(10/90) (SONY) ① **SMK45844**
P. Bryn-Julson, FNO, K. Nagano *Concert*
(8/93) (ERAT) ① **4509-92137-2**

VARIOUS, (composers)

for works involving a multiplicity of composers

SECTION I: ORCHESTRAL

Variations on a Russian Folk Song—string orchestra
1. Theme; 2. Variation I (N Artcibuscher); 3. Variation II (A Scriabin); 4. Variation III (A Glazunov); 5. Variation IV (N Rimsky-Korsakov); 6. Variation V (A Liadov); 7. Variation VI (J Vihtol); 8. Variation VII (F Blumenthal); 9. Variation VIII (V Evald); 10. Variation IX (A Vinkler); 11. Variation X (N Sokolov).
Amati Ens, A. Balogh (r1994) *Concert*
(11/95) (CALI) ① **CAL50940**

SECTION III: INSTRUMENTAL

The Bauyn Manuscript—collection of French harpsichord works (before 1676) (composer details given in parentheses)
EXCERPTS: 1. Suite in C (J. C. Chambonnières); 2. Suite in G minor (L. Couperin); 3. Pavanne Italiene (Anonymous); 4. Pavanne Angloise (Anonymous); 5. Courante in A minor (member of the Monnard family, early 17th cent); 6. Sarabande in C (Germain Pinel, d 1661); 7. Courante in C (member of the Monnard family); 8. Sarabande in C (member of the Monnard family); 9. Gavotte in C (Anonymous); 10. Sarabande Grave (J-H. D'Anglebert); 11. Sarabande in C (Rene Mezangeot, d c1638); 12. Sarabande in C (R. Mezangeot); 13. Canaries in C (member of the Gautier family, 17th cent); 14. Fanbasia (Lorency, c1567—c1625); 15. Passacaille (L. Rossi); 16. Pavanne (Vincent, fl 1606—1643); 17. Suite in D minor (member of the Richard family, 17th cent); 18. Suite in A minor (member of the Richard family); 19. Suite (member of the La Barre family, 17th cent); 20. Suite in G (Anonyous/Richard); 21. Suite in A minor (L. Couperin); 22. Suite in D minor (L. Couperin); 23. Prélude in C (L. Couperin); 24. Pavanne in F sharp minor (L. Couperin); 25. Suite in A minor (Froberger); 26. Toccata in A minor (Froberger); 27. Suite in G (Froberger); 28. Ricercar in C (Froberger); 29. Capriccio in G (Frescobaldi); 30. Fantasia in E minor (Frescobaldi); 31. Four Pavannes (Anonymous); 32. Suite in D (Jacques Champion Chambonnières, 1601/2-72); 33. Suite in G (J. C. Chambonnières); 34. Suite in D minor (J. C. Chambonnières); 35. Suite in F (J. C. Chambonnières); 36. Suite in D minor (Henry Dumont, 1610-84); 37. Allemande in C (H. Dumont); 38. Allemande in A minor (H. Dumont); 39. Allemande Grave in C (H. Dumont); 40. Allemande in C (H. Dumont); 41. Suite in D minor (member of the Hardel family, 17th cent).
1-20. J. Chapman (r1994)
(3/95) (COLL) ① **Coll1420-2**
21-31. J. Chapman (r1994)
(4/95) (COLL) ① **Coll1421-2**
32-41. J. Chapman (r1994)
(8/95) (COLL) ① **Coll1422-2**

SECTION IV: VOCAL AND CHORAL

Codex Speciálník—choir a cappella (c1500) (Prague manuscript)
1. Exordium/Nate Dei/Concrepet/Verbum Caro (Anon); 2. Tria sunt/Videntes stellam/Reges Tharsis (Anon); 3. In Natali Domini (Anon); 4. Sophia Nascitur/O Quam Pulchra/Magi Videntes (Anon); 5. Congaudemus Pariter/En Lux Immensa (Anon); 6. Magnum Miraculum (Anon); 7. Nobis Est Natus (Anon); 8. Salve Mater Gracie (Anon); 9. Christus Iam/Terra Tremuit/Angelus Domini/Surrexit (Anon); 10. Presulem Ephebeatum (Petrus de Grudencz); 11. Paraneuma Eructemus (Petrus de Grudencz); 12. Presidiorum Erogatrix (Petrus de Grudencz); 13. Pneuma/Veni Vere/Dator Eya/Paraclito (Petrus de Grudencz); 14. Terrigenarum Plasmator (Anon); 15. Pulcherrima Rosa (Anon); 16. Chorus Iste (Johannes Touront); 17. Bud'buchu chvála čest (Gontrášek); 18. O Virens Virginium (Agricola); 19. Missa 'Petite Camusette'; 20. Tota Pulchra Es (Plummer); 21. Ave Pura Tu Puella; 22. Ave Maria (Desprez).

1-22. Hilliard Ens (r1993)
(9/95) (ECM) ① **447 807-2**
Messa per Rossini—soloists, chorus and orchestra (1869: fp—1988)
1. Requiem; Kyrie: Antonio BUZZOLLA (1815—1871); 2. Dies irae: Antonio BAZZINI (1818—1897; 3. Tuba mirum: Carlo PEDROTTI (1817—1893); 4. Quid sum miser: Antonio CAGNONI (1828—1896); 5. Recordare Jesu: Federico RICCI (1809—1877); 6. Ingemisco: Alessandro NINI (1805—1880); 7. Confutatis; Oro supplex: Raimondo BOUCHERON (1800—1876); 8. Lacrimosa; Amen: Carlo COCCIA (1782—1873); 9. Domine Jesu; Quam olim Abrahae; Hostias: Gaetano GASPARI (1808—1881); 10. Sanctus; Hosanna; Benedictus: Pietro PLATANIA (1828—1907); 11. Agnus Dei: Lauro ROSSI (1812—1885); 12. Lux aeterna: Teodulo MABELLINI (1817—1897); 13. Libera me; Dies irae; Requiem aeternam: Giuseppe VERDI (1813—1901).
Cpte G. Beňačková, F. Quivar, J. Wagner, A. Agache, A. Haugland, Stuttgart Gächinger Kantorei, Prague Phil Chor, Stuttgart RSO, H. Rilling
(2/90) (HANS) ① [2] **98 949**
National Anthems (composers and words in brackets)
1. ARGENTINA: Oid mortales ! (Parera/López y Planes); 2. AUSTRALIA: Advance, Australia fair (McCormick); 3. AUSTRIA: Land der Berges(Anon/Preradovic); 4. BELGIUM: La brabançonne (Capenhout/Rogier); 5. BELORUSSIA: A chto tam sidie (Rogowski/Kupala); 6. BRAZIL: Ouviram do Ipiranga (Silva/Estrada); 7. BULGARIA: Gorda Stara Planina (Radoslavov); 8a. CANADA: see Great Britain; 8b. CANADA: O! Canada (Lavallée/Routhier); 9. CHINA: March on, brave people (Erh/collective); 10. CZECHOSLOVAKIA: Kde domov múj? (Skroup/Tyl); 11. DENMARK: Kong Kristian (Anon/Ewald); 12. EGYPT: Walla xaman ya silahi (Attawyl/Shahyn); 13. ESTONIA: Mu isamaa (Pacius/Janssen); 14. ETHIOPIA: March forward, dear Mother Ethiopia (Anon); 15. FINLAND: Maamme (Pacius/Runeberg); 16. FRANCE: La marseillaise (Rouget de Lisle); 17. GERMANY: Einigkeit und Recht und Freiheit (Haydn/Fallersleben); 18. GREAT BRITAIN: God save the King/Queen (Anon); 19. GREECE: Segnorizo apo tin kopsi (Mantzaros/Solomos); 20. HUNGARY: Isten áldd meg amagyart (Erkel/Kölcsey); 21. IRELAND: Amthranna bhFiann (Kearney & Heaney); 22. ISRAEL: Hatiqvah (Trad arr Cohen/Imber); 23. ITALY: Inno di Mameli (Novaro/Mameli); 24. JAPAN: Kimiga yowa Chi yoni (Hayashi/Anon 9th cent); 25. KENYA: Ee Mungu nguvu yeu (Trad arr); 26. LATVIA: Dievs, sveti Latuviju (Baumanis); 27. LITHUANIA: Lietuva (Kudirka); 28. MEXICO: Meicanos al grito (Nunó/Bocanegra); 29. NETHERLANDS: Wilhelmus van Nassouwe (Anon/St Aldegonde); 30. NEW ZEALAND: see Great Britain; 31. NORWAY: Ja, vi elsker dette landet/Nordraak/Bjørnson); 32. POLAND: Mazurek Dabrowskiego (Trad/Wybicki); 33. PORTUGAL: A portugêsa (Keil/Mendonça); 34. SOUTH AFRICA: Die stem van Suid-Afrika (Villiers/Langenhoven); 35. SPAIN: Marcha real (Anon); 36. SWEDEN: Du gamla, du fria (Trad/Dybeck); 37. SWITZERLAND: Trittst im Morgenrot (Zwyssig/Widmer); 38. WALES: Land of My Fathers (Trad/E James).
16. S. McNair, R. Leech, St David's Baltimore Ch, Baltimore Sym Chor, Baltimore SO, D. Zinman (r1987: arr Berlioz) *Concert*
(12/88) (TELA) ① **CD80164**
16. Leeds Fest Chor, Wallace Collection, J. Wallace *Concert* (7/89) (NIMB) ① **NI5175**
16. L. Pons, orch (bp1945) *Concert*
(4/92) (MSOU) ① **DFCDI-111**
16. Paris Orch Chor, Paris Orch, D. Barenboim (arr Berlioz) *Concert*
(7/93) (DG) ① [2] **437 638-2GGA2**
16. Detroit SO, P. Paray (r1959) *Concert*
(11/93) (MERC) ① **434 332-2MM**
18. Three Choirs Fest Chor, LSO, E. Elgar (pp1927; arr Elgar) *Concert*
(6/92) (EMI) ① [3] **CDS7 54560-2**
18. Chor, LSO, E. Elgar (r1928; arr Elgar) *Concert*
(2/93) (EMI) ① [3] **CDS7 54564-2**
18. V. Horowitz (pp1982; arr Horowitz) *Concert*
(5/93) (RCA) ① **09026 61414-2**
18. London Sym Chor, LSO, B. Britten (r1961: arr Britten) *Concert* (6/93) (DECC) ① **436 403-2DWO**
18. L. Skeaping, J. Potter, Broadside Band, J. Barlow (r1992; setting by Arne, 1745) *Concert*
(6/93) (SAYD) ① **CD-SDL400**
18. LPO, G. Solti (r1977: LPO concert ver) *Concert*
(4/94) (DECC) ① **440 317-2DWO**

18. Westminster Abbey Ch, M. Baker, London Brass, M. Neary (r1993/4: arr G Jacob) *Concert*
(9/94) (CNTO) ① **CSACD3050**
38. L. Godowsky (arr Godowsky: r1920) *Concert*
(4/89) (APR) ① [2] **APR7011**
38. S. Rachmaninov (arr Rachmaninov: pf roll) *Concert* (6/90) (DECC) ① **425 964-2DM**
38. NBC SO, A. Toscanini (arr Toscanini: r1942) *Concert* (11/92) (RCA) ① **GD60307**
38. E. Eames, anon (r1905) *Concert*
(11/93) (ROMO) ① [2] **81001-2**
38. Gregg Smith Sngrs, R. Craft (1991/2) *Concert*
(6/94) (MUSM) ① **67113-2**
39. Black Dyke Mills Band, R. Newsome (r1977: arr brass band: G. Langford) *Concert*
(1/94) (CHAN) ① **CHAN4528**
Requiem of Reconciliation—soloists, choruses and orchestra (1995)
1. Prolog (Berio); 2. Introitus and Kyrie (Cerha); 3. Dies irae (Dittrich); 4. Judex ergo (Kopelent); 5. Juste judex (Harbison); 6. Confutatis (Nordheim); 7. Interludium (Rands); 8. Domine Jesu Christe, Rex Gloriae (Dalbavie); 9. Sanctus (Weir); 10. Agnus Dei (Penderecki); 11. Communio I (Rihm); 12. Communio II (Schnittke/Rozhdestvensky); 13. Reponsorium (Yuasa); 14. Epilog (Kurtag).
Cpte T. Janzik, D. Brown, J. Moffat, I. Danz, T. Randle, A. Schmidt, Stuttgart Gächinger Kantorei, Cracow Chbr Ch, Israel PO, H. Rilling (pp1995)
(11/95) (HANS) ① [2] **98 931**
Russian Easter Liturgy, '(The) Luminous Resurrection of Christ'—trad melodies, harmonisations & orig works (Works by Bortnyansky, Balakirev, Kalinnikov etc)
Moscow Liturgic Ch, Father Amvrosy (r1992)
(10/93) (ERAT) ① **4509-91699-2**

La Belle Paree—musical revue (1911—New York)
EXCERPTS: 1. De Devilin' Tune (Tours/Madden); 2. That Lovin' Traumerei (Stauffer).
1. S. Mayhew, Orig Broadway Cast (r1911) *Concert*
(5/94) (PEAR) ① **GEMMCDS9053/5**
2. A. Jolson, Orig Broadway Cast (r1912) *Concert*
(5/94) (PEAR) ① **GEMMCDS9053/5**
Betty—musical show (1916—New York)
EXCERPTS: 1. Sometime (Tierney/Jerome); 2. Here Comes the Groom (Burt).
1, 2. R. Hitchcock, Orig Broadway Cast (r1916) *Concert* (5/94) (PEAR) ① [3] **GEMMCDS9056/8**
Century Girl—musical show (1916—New York)
EXCERPTS: 1. Hawaiian Sunshine (Morgan/Gilbert).
1. Van & Schenck, Orig Broadway Cast (r1916) *Concert* (5/94) (PEAR) ① [3] **GEMMCDS9056/8**
Cohan Revue of 1918—musical revue (1918—New York)
EXCERPTS: 1. The Man Who Put the Germ in Germany (Bayes/Downing/Glatt); 2. Regretful Blues (Hess/Clarke).
1, 2. N. Bayes, Orig Broadway Cast (r1918) *Concert*
(5/94) (PEAR) ① [3] **GEMMCDS9059/61**
Dancing Around—musical show (1914—New York)
EXCERPTS: 1. When the Grown Up Ladies Act Like Babies (Abrahams/Young/Leslie).
1. A. Jolson, Orig Broadway Cast (r1914) *Concert*
(5/94) (PEAR) ① [3] **GEMMCDS9056/8**
Doing Our Bit—musical revue (1917—New York)
EXCERPTS: 1. The Wild Wild Women (Piantadosi/Lewis/Wilson); 2. I'm the Brother of Lily of the Valley (Friedland/Lewis).
1, 2. H. Lewis, Orig Broadway Cast (r1918) *Concert*
(5/94) (PEAR) ① [3] **GEMMCDS9059/61**
L' Eventail de Jeanne—ballet (1 act) (1920—Paris)
1. Fanfare: Maurice RAVEL; 2. Marche: Pierre-Octave FERROUD (1900—1936); 3. Valse: Jacques IBERT (1890—1962); 4. Canarie: Alexis ROLAND-MANUEL (1891—1966); 5. Bourée: Marcel DELANNOY (1898—1962); 6. Sarabande: Albert ROUSSEL; 7. Polka: Darius MILHAUD; 8. Pastourelle: Francis POULENC; 9. Rondeau: Georges AURIC; 10. Kermesse-Valse: Florent SCHMITT.
Philh, G. Simon *Six: Mariés de la Tour Eiffel.*
(4/85) (CHAN) ① **CHAN8356**
Follow Me—musical show (1916—New York)
EXCERPTS: 1. Oh! Johnny Oh! (Olman/Rose); 2. Lily of the Valley (Friedland/Gilbert); 3. What Do You Want to Make Those Eyes at Me For? (Monaco/Johnson); 4. Love is a Wonderful Thing (Friedland/Gilbert); 5. Where the Black Eyed Susans Grow (Whiting/Radford).

1-5. H. Lewis, Orig Broadway Cast (r1917) *Concert*
(5/94) (PEAR) ① [3] **GEMMCDS9056/8**
The Girl On the Film—musical show (1913—New York)
EXCERPTS: 1. Tommy, Won't You Teach Me How to Tango (Penso/Ross).
1. G. Grossmith (r1913) *Concert*
(5/94) (PEAR) ① [3] **GEMMCDS9056/8**
The Grand Vizier—operetta (1895—New York)
EXCERPTS: 1. Who is Egen? (Tracy).
1. T. Q. Seabrooke, Broadway Cast (r1904) *Concert*
(5/94) (PEAR) ① [3] **GEMMCDS9050/2(1)**
Greenwich Village Follies of 1919—musical revue (1919—New York)
EXCERPTS: 1. When My Baby Smiles at Me (Munro/Sterling/Lewis).
1. T. Lewis & His Orch (r1920) *Concert*
(5/94) (PEAR) ① [3] **GEMMCDS9059/61**
The Heart o' th' Heather—operetta (1916—New York)
EXCERPTS: 1. Don't Believe All You Hear in the Moonlight (Lang/MacFarlane/Green); 2. In Scotland (Morse/MacFarlane).
1, 2. G. MacFarlane, Orig Broadway Cast (r1916) *Concert* (5/94) (PEAR) ① [3] **GEMMCDS9056/8**
Hitchy-Koo—musical revue (1917—New York)
EXCERPTS: 1. Six Times Six is Thirty-Six (White/Hanlon); 2. I'd Like to be a Monkey in the Zoo (White/Hanlon).
1, 2. F. White, Orig Broadway Cast (r1917) *Concert*
(5/94) (PEAR) ① [3] **GEMMCDS9059/61**
Honeymoon Express—musical show (1913—New York)
EXCERPTS: 1. You Made Me Love You (I Didn't Want to Do It) (Monaco/McCarthy); 2. My Yellow Jacket Girl (Schwartz/Atteridge); 3. The Spaniard that Blighted My Life (Billy Merson).
1-3. A. Jolson, Orig Broadway Cast (r1913) *Concert*
(5/94) (PEAR) ① [3] **GEMMCDS9056/8**
The Midnight Sons—musical show (1909—New York)
EXCERPTS: 1. Billiken Man (Gideon); 2. I've Got Rings on My Fingers (Scott/Weston/Barnes).
1, 2. B. Ring, Orig Broadway Cast (r1909) *Concert*
(5/94) (PEAR) ① [3] **GEMMCDS9053/5**
Monte Christo, Jr.—musical show (1919—New York)
EXCERPTS: 1. I Always Think I'm Up in Heaven (Abrahams/Lewis); 2. Sahara (Schwartz/Bryan); 3. Who Played Poker With Pocahontas? (Alhert/Lewis/Young).
1-3. E. Walker, F. Watson, Watson Sisters, Orig Broadway Cast (r1919) *Concert*
(5/94) (PEAR) ① [3] **GEMMCDS9059/61**
Mr Hamlet of Broadway—musical show (1908—New York)
EXCERPTS: 1. Goodbye, Molly Brown (Jerome/Madden); 2. The Dusky Salome (Jerome/Madden).
1, 2. M. Raymond, Orig Broadway Cast (r1909) *Concert* (5/94) (PEAR) ① [3] **GEMMCDS9053/5**
Mrs Wilson, That's All—musical show (1906—New York)
EXCERPTS: 1. Mat-ri-mony (McKenna); 2. Moses Andrew Jackson, Goodbye (Snyder/Shields).
1, 2. M. Irwin, Broadway Cast (r1907) *Concert*
(5/94) (PEAR) ① [3] **GEMMCDS9050/2(2)**
My Lady Friends—musical show (1919—New York)
EXCERPTS: 1. I Want to Spread a Little Sunshine (Crawford).
1. J. Norworth, Orig Broadway Cast (r1920) *Concert*
(5/94) (PEAR) ① [3] **GEMMCDS9059/61**
Odds and Ends of 1917—musical revue (1917—New York)
EXCERPTS: 1. Fancy You Fancying Me (Bayes/Norworth); 2. The Further it is from Tipperary (Byrnes/Dudley/Godfrey).
1, 2. J. Norworth, Orig Broadway Cast (r1918) *Concert* (5/94) (PEAR) ① [3] **GEMMCDS9059/61**
Oh, What a Girl!—musical show (1919—New York)
EXCERPTS: 1. Oh, What a Girl! (Jules/Pressburg/Smith).
1. S. Ash, Orig Broadway Cast (r1919) *Concert*
(5/94) (PEAR) ① [3] **GEMMCDS9059/61**
The Passing Show of 1912—musical revue (1912—New York)
EXCERPTS: 1. The Wedding Glide (Hirsch).
1. S. Kellogg (r1913) *Concert*
(5/94) (PEAR) ① [3] **GEMMCDS9053/5**

Tilzer/Brown/Buzzell); 7. Oh, the Last Rose of
Summer (Ruby/Cantor/Ponce); 8. It's Nobody's
Business But My Own (Walker/Skidmore).
1-8. E. Cantor, J. Steel, Van & Schenck, Bert
Williams, Orig Broadway Cast (r1919) *Concert*
(5/94) (PEAR) ① [3] **GEMMCDS9059/61**
**Ziegfeld Midnight Frolic—musical revue
(1917—New York)**
EXCERPTS: 1. M-i-s-s-i-s-s-i-p-p-i
(Tierney/Hanlon/Ryan); 2. Go-Zin-To (Ponce).
1, 2. F. White, Orig Broadway Cast (r1917) *Concert*
(5/94) (PEAR) ① [3] **GEMMCDS9059/61**
1492—musical show (1893—New York)
EXCERPTS: 1. The King's Song (Pfleuger/Barnet).
1. E. M. Favor, Broadway Cast (r ?1893) *Concert*
(5/94) (PEAR) ① [3] **GEMMCDS9050/2(1)**
**2001—A Space Odyssey—music from the
film (1968)** (extracts from works by various
cpsrs)
EXCERPTS: 1. Also sprach Zarathustra—opening
(R. Strauss); 2. The Monolith: Requiem (Ligeti); 3.
The Lunar Landscape: Lux aeterna (Ligeti); 4. The
Space Station: The Blue Danube (J. Strauss II); 5.
The Discovery: Gayaneh—Ballet Suite
(Khachaturian); 6. Beyond the Infinite: Atmosphères
(Ligeti); 7. The Star Child: Also sprach Zarathustra
(R. Strauss); 8. End Titles: The Blue Danube.
1. Rochester Pops, L. Schifrin *Concert*
(5/93) (SILV) ① **SILVAD3002**

VARKONYI, Béla *(1878–1946)*
Hungary

SECTION II: CHAMBER

Leda—Fantasy, Op. 42a (1929)
Shumsky/Reisman Duo Piano Trio, Op.17.
(9/87) (JERU) ① **CATD8701**
Piano Trio in F, Op. 17 (1904)
Seraphim Trio *Leda—Fantasy.*
(9/87) (JERU) ① **CATD8701**

VASKS, Peteris *(b 1946) Latvia*

SECTION I: ORCHESTRAL

Cantabile—string orchestra (1979)
Riga PO, K. Rusmanis *Concert*
(1/95) (CONI) ① **CDCF236**
Ostrobothnian CO, J. Kangas (r1994) *Concert*
(11/95) (FINL) ① **4509-97893-2**
**Concerto for Cor Anglais and Orchestra
(1989)**
N. Schnee, Riga PO, K. Rusmanis *Concert*
(1/95) (CONI) ① **CDCF236**
Lauda—orchestra (1986)
Riga PO, K. Rusmanis *Concert*
(1/95) (CONI) ① **CDCF236**
**Message—strings, two pianos and
percussion (1982)**
Riga PO, K. Rusmanis *Concert*
(1/95) (CONI) ① **CDCF236**
Musica dolorosa—string orchestra (1983)
Riga PO, K. Rusmanis *Concert*
(1/95) (CONI) ① **CDCF236**
Symphony for Strings, 'Stimmen' (1990-91)
Ostrobothnian CO, J. Kangas (r1994) *Concert*
(11/95) (FINL) ① **4509-97892-2**

VASQUEZ, Juan *(c1510–c1560)*
Spain

SECTION IV: VOCAL AND CHORAL

En la fuente del rosel—song
T. Berganza, N. Yepes *Concert*
(12/92) (DG) ① [2] **435 848-2GX2**
Morenica, dame un beso—villancico
J. Gomez, J. Constable (r1994; arr Tarragó) *Concert*
(9/94) (CONI) ① **CDCF243**
Vos me matastes—song
T. Berganza, N. Yepes *Concert*
(12/92) (DG) ① [2] **435 848-2GX2**

VASSAL *(fl 16th cent)*

SECTION IV: VOCAL AND CHORAL

Vray Dieu—chanson
Scholars (r1993) *Concert*
(2/95) (NAXO) ① **8 550880**

VAUGHAN WILLIAMS, Ralph
(1872–1958) England

SECTION I: ORCHESTRAL

Charterhouse Suite—string orchestra (1923)
(arr J Brown and cpsr from piano pieces,
1923)
Israel CO, D. Atlas *Concert*
(3/90) (STRA) ① **SCD8011**
**Concerto for Oboe and Strings in A minor
(1944)**
D. Theodore, LSO, B. Thomson *Symphony 3.*
(8/88) (CHAN) ① **CHAN8594**
J. Girdwood, Consort of London, R. Haydon Clark
Concert (10/91) (COLL) ① **Coll1140-2**
J. Small, RLPO, V. Handley *Concert*
(12/91) (EMIN) ① **CD-EMX2179**
R. Canter, LSO, J. Judd (r1992) *Concert*
(10/93) (CARL) ① **MCD59**
N. Black, ECO, D. Barenboim (r1975) *Concert*
(4/94) (DG) ① **439 529-2GGA**
C. Nicklin, ASMF, N. Marriner (r1977) *Concert*
(4/94) (DECC) ① **440 320-2DWO**
D. Theodore, LSO, B. Thomson (r1988) *Concert*
(8/94) (CHAN) ① [2] **CHAN9262/3**
**Concerto for Piano and Orchestra in C
(1933)**
H. Shelley, LSO, B. Thomson *Symphony 9.*
(7/91) (CHAN) ① **CHAN8941**
H. Shelley, RPO, V. Handley *Foulds: Dynamic
Triptych.* (3/93) (LYRI) ① **SRCD211**
H. Shelley, LSO, B. Thomson (r1990) *Concert*
(8/94) (CHAN) ① [2] **CHAN9262/3**
P. Lane, RLPO, V. Handley (r1994) *Concert*
(11/95) (EMIN) ① **CD-EMX2239**
**Concerto for Tuba and Orchestra in F minor
(1954)**
EXCERPTS: 2. Romanza.
P. Harrild, LSO, B. Thomson *Symphony 6.*
(9/89) (CHAN) ① **CHAN8740**
P. Harrild, LSO, B. Thomson (r1988) *Concert*
(8/94) (CHAN) ① [2] **CHAN9262/3**
2. J. Lloyd Webber, ASMF, N. Marriner (r1994; arr
vc) *Concert* (12/94) (PHIL) ① **442 530-2PH**
**Concerto for Two Pianos and Orchestra
(1946)** (arr cpsr of Piano Concerto: 1931)
Ralph Markham, K. Broadway, RPO, Y. Menuhin
(r1987) *Symphony 5.* (1/89) (VIRG) ① **VJ5 61105-2**
**Concerto for Violin and Orchestra in D
minor, 'Concerto accademico'—violin and
orchestra (1924-25)**
K. Sillito, LSO, B. Thomson *Symphony 4.*
(1/89) (CHAN) ① **CHAN8633**
Z. Schiff, Israel PO, D. Atlas *Concert*
(3/90) (STRA) ① **SCD8011**
J.O. Buswell IV, LSO, A. Previn *Concert*
(3/91) (RCA) ① **GD90501**
L. Kaufman, Winterthur SO, C. Dahinden (r1951)
Concert (1/92) (MUSI) ① **MACD-667**
F. Grinke, Boyd Neel Orch, B. Neel (r1939) *Concert*
(5/94) (DUTT) ① **CDAX8007**
K. Sillito, LSO, B. Thomson (r1988) *Concert*
(8/94) (CHAN) ① [2] **CHAN9262/3**
**Concerto Grosso—string orchestra (3
groups) (1950)**
LSO, B. Thomson *Symphony 2.*
(10/89) (CHAN) ① **CHAN8629**
ASMF, N. Marriner (r1977) *Concert*
(4/94) (DECC) ① **440 320-2DWO**
LSO, B. Thomson (r1988) *Concert*
(8/94) (CHAN) ① [2] **CHAN9262/3**
**English Folk Song Suite—military band
(1923)**
Cleveland Winds, F. Fennell *Concert*
(10/84) (TELA) ① **CD80099**
Coldstream Guards Band, R.A. Ridings *Concert*
(4/87) (BAND) ① **BNA5002**
London Wind Orch, D.Wick *Concert*
(7/88) (ASV) ① **CDQS6021**
ASMF, N. Marriner *Concert*
(5/89) (DECC) ① **417 778-2DM**
Boston Pops, A. Fiedler *Concert*
(6/91) (DECC) ① **430 093-2DWO**
RLPO, V. Handley (orch Jacob) *Concert*
(12/91) (EMIN) ① **CD-EMX2179**
LSO, A. Boult *Concert*
(5/92) (EMI) ① **CDM7 64022-2**
ASMF, N. Marriner (r1980: orch G Jacob) *Concert*
(4/94) (DECC) ① **440 320-2DWO**

**Fantasia on a Theme by Thomas
Tallis—double string orchestra (1910 rev
1919)** (on Tallis's Psalm Tune: 'Why fum'th in
fight')
J. Korman, B. Schiebler, T. Dumm, J. Sant'Ambrogio,
St Louis SO, L. Slatkin *Concert*
(12/83) (TELA) ① **CD80059**
I. Brown, M. Latchem, S. Shingles, D. Vigay, ASMF,
N. Marriner *Concert* (2/85) (ASV) ① **CDDCA518**
ASMF, N. Marriner *Concert*
(9/86) (ARGO) ① **414 595-2ZH**
Allegri Qt, Sinfonia of London, J. Barbirolli *Concert*
(2/87) (EMI) ① **CDC7 47537-2**
LPO, B. Thomson *Concert*
(5/87) (CHAN) ① **CHAN8502**
LPO, B. Haitink (r1986) *Symphony 2.*
(7/88) (EMI) ① **CDC7 49394-2**
ECO, Y. Menuhin *Concert*
(12/88) (ARAB) ① **Z6568**
RPO, A. Previn (r1988) *Symphony 5.*
(5/89) (TELA) ① **CD80158**
LSO, R. Frühbeck de Burgos *Concert*
(1/90) (CARL) ① **PCD930**
Israel PO, D. Atlas *Concert*
(3/90) (STRA) ① **SCD8011**
BBC SO, A. Davis *Concert*
(8/91) (TELD) ① **9031-73127-2**
D. Juritz, Consort of London, R. Haydon Clark
Concert (10/91) (COLL) ① **Coll1140-2**
RLPO, V. Handley *Concert*
(12/91) (EMIN) ① **CD-EMX2179**
London Fest Orch, R. Pople *Concert*
(4/92) (ASV) ① **CDDCA779**
LPO, A. Boult *Symphony 2.*
(5/92) (EMI) ① **CDM7 64017-2**
RPO, C. Groves (r1989) *Concert*
(9/92) (CARL) ① **CDRPO5005**
Philh, L. Slatkin (r1991) *Concert*
(8/93) (RCA) ① **09026 61193-2**
Indianapolis SO, R. Leppard (r1992) *Symphony 7.*
(10/93) (KOSS) ① **KC2214**
CLS, R. Hickox (r1991) *Concert*
(12/93) (EMI) ① **CDC7 54407-2**
ASMF, N. Marriner (r1972) *Concert*
(4/94) (DECC) ① **440 320-2DWO**
NQHO, B. Wordsworth (1992) *Concert*
(5/94) (ARGO) ① **440 116-2ZH**
Boyd Neel Orch, B. Neel (r1936) *Concert*
(5/94) (DUTT) ① **CDAX8007**
NYPO, L. Bernstein (r1976) *Concert*
(7/94) (SONY) ① **SMK47638**
London CO, C. Warren-Green (vn/dir) (r1988)
Concert (11/94) (VIRG) ① **CUV5 61126-2**
New Philh, L. Stokowski (pp1974) *Concert*
(3/95) (BBCR) ① **BBCRD9107**
CBSO, N. del Mar (r1980) *Concert*
(4/95) (EMI) ① **CDM5 65131-2**
ASMF, N. Marriner (r1993) *Concert*
(6/95) (PHIL) ① **442 427-2PH**
Orpheus CO (r1985) *Concert*
(12/95) (DG) ① **445 561-2GMA**
**Fantasia on 'Greensleeves'—flutes, harp
and strings (1934)** (arr R Greaves from opera
'Sir John in Love')
St Louis SO, L. Slatkin *Concert*
(1/84) (TELA) ① **CD80080**
ASMF, N. Marriner *Concert*
(9/86) (ARGO) ① **414 595-2ZH**
Sinfonia of London, J. Barbirolli *Concert*
(2/87) (EMI) ① **CDC7 47537-2**
LSO, G. Simon *Concert*
(3/87) (CALA) ① [2] **CACD0101**
ECO, Y. Menuhin *Concert*
(12/88) (ARAB) ① **Z6568**
ASMF, N. Marriner *Concert*
(5/89) (DECC) ① **417 778-2DM**
LSO, R. Frühbeck de Burgos *Concert*
(1/90) (CARL) ① **PCD930**
LSO, B. Thomson *Concert*
(8/90) (CHAN) ① **CHAN8828**
ASMF, N. Marriner *Concert*
(6/91) (DECC) ① **430 093-2DWO**
D. Juritz, Consort of London, R. Haydon Clark
Concert (10/91) (COLL) ① **Coll1140-2**
RLPO, V. Handley *Concert*
(12/91) (EMIN) ① **CD-EMX2179**
London Fest Orch, R. Pople *Concert*
(4/92) (ASV) ① **CDDCA779**
LSO, A. Boult *Concert*
(5/92) (EMI) ① **CDM7 64022-2**
Queen's Hall Orch, Henry Wood (r1936) *Concert*
(10/93) (DUTT) ① **CDAX8004**
Philh, L. Slatkin (r1992) *Concert*
(11/93) (RCA) ① **09026 61194-2**
ECO, D. Barenboim (r1973) *Concert*
(4/94) (DG) ① **439 529-2GGA**

ASMF, N. Marriner (r1980) *Concert*
(4/94) (DECC) ① **440 320-2DWO**
NQHO, B. Wordsworth (r1992) *Concert*
(5/94) (ARGO) ① **440 116-2ZH**
NYPO, L. Bernstein (r1969) *Concert*
(7/94) (SONY) ① **SMK47638**
Oxford Orch da Camera, G. Vass (r1993) *Concert*
(9/94) (MEDI) ① **MQCD4002**
London CO, C. Warren-Green (vn/dir) (r1988)
Concert (11/94) (VIRG) ① **CUV5 61126-2**
Orpheus CO (r1985) *Concert*
(12/95) (DG) ① **445 561-2GMA**

Fantasia on Sussex Folk Tunes—cello and orchestra (1929)
J. Lloyd Webber, Philh, V. Handley *Concert*
(7/87) (RCA) ① **RD70800**

Flos campi—suite for viola, small chorus and small orchestra (1925)
C. Balmer, Liverpool Phil Ch, RLPO, V. Handley
(r1986) *Symphony 5.*
(3/88) (EMIN) ① **CD-EMX9512**
R. Best, Oxford Christ Church Cath Ch, English Stg Orch, S. Darlington *Concert*
(6/89) (NIMB) ① **NI5166**
N. Imai, Corydon Sngrs, ECO, M. Best *Concert*
(9/90) (HYPE) ① **CDA66420**
F. Riddle, Bournemouth Sinfonietta Ch, Bournemouth Sinfonietta, N. del Mar (r1977) *Concert*
(11/92) (CHAN) ① **CHAN6545**
C. Balmer, RLPO, V. Handley,
A. Barlow
(r1986) *Concert*
(1/95) (EMIN) ① [6] **CDBOX-VW1**
P. Dukes, Northern Sinfonia Chor, Northern Sinfonia, R. Hickox (r1995) *Concert*
(11/95) (CHAN) ① **CHAN9392**

Flourish for Glorious John (Barbirolli)—orchestra (1957) (unpub)
Philh, L. Slatkin (r1991) *Concert*
(8/93) (RCA) ① **09026 61196-2**

Henry V—Overture for brass band (1933)
London Collegiate Brass, J. Stobart *Concert*
(9/86) (CRD) ① **CRD3434**
London Brass Virtuosi, D. Honeyball *Concert*
(11/87) (HYPE) ① **CDA66189**

2 Hymn-Tune Preludes—small orchestra (1936)
Bournemouth Sinfonietta, G. Hurst *Concert*
(8/87) (CHAN) ① **CHAN8432**
LSO, B. Thomson *Concert*
(8/90) (CHAN) ① **CHAN8828**
Bournemouth Sinfonietta, G. Hurst (r1975) *Concert*
(11/92) (CHAN) ① **CHAN6545**
LSO, B. Thomson (r1989) *Concert*
(8/94) (CHAN) ① [2] **CHAN9262/3**

In the Fen Country—symphonic impression (1904-1907 rev 1935)
LPO, B. Thomson *Concert*
(5/87) (CHAN) ① **CHAN8502**
London Fest Orch, R. Pople *Concert*
(4/92) (ASV) ① **CDDCA779**
New Philh, A. Boult *Concert*
(5/92) (EMI) ① **CDM7 64022-2**
NQHO, B. Wordsworth (r1992) *Concert*
(5/94) (ARGO) ① **440 116-2ZH**
BBC SO, C. Groves (pp1969) *Concert*
(5/95) (BBCR) ① **BBCRD9111**
ASMF, N. Marriner (r1993) *Concert*
(6/95) (PHIL) ① **442 427-2PH**

The Lark ascending—romance: violin and orchestra (1914 rev 1920)
I. Brown, ASMF, N. Marriner *Concert*
(2/85) (ASV) ① **CDDCA518**
I. Brown, ASMF, N. Marriner *Concert*
(9/86) (ARGO) ① **414 595-2ZH**
B. Griffiths, RPO, A. Previn *Symphony 2.*
(7/87) (TELA) ① **CD80138**
D. Nolan, LPO, V. Handley *Concert*
(10/87) (EMIN) ① **CD-EMX9508**
M. Davis, LSO, B. Thomson *Symphony 5.*
(1/88) (CHAN) ① **CHAN8554**
J-L. Garcia, ECO, Y. Menuhin *Concert*
(12/88) (ARAB) ① **Z6568**
M. Bochmann, English SO, W. Boughton *Concert*
(2/90) (NIMB) ① **NI5208**
Z. Schiff, Israel PO, D. Atlas *Concert*
(3/90) (STRA) ① **SCD8011**
I. Brown, ASMF, N. Marriner *Concert*
(11/91) (DECC) ① **430 093-2DWO**
T. Little, BBC SO, A. Davis *Concert*
(8/91) (TELD) ① **9031-73127-2**
D. Juritz, Consort of London, R. Haydon Clark *Concert*
(10/91) (COLL) ① **Coll1140-2**
R. Friedman, London Fest Orch, R. Pople *Concert*
(4/92) (ASV) ① **CDDCA779**

H. Bean, New Philh, A. Boult *Concert*
(5/92) (EMI) ① **CDM7 64022-2**
A.A. Meyers, Philh, A. Litton (r1993) *Concert*
(2/94) (RCA) ① **09026 61700-2**
P. Zukerman, ECO, D. Barenboim (r1973) *Concert*
(4/94) (DG) ① **439 529-2GGA**
H. Shaham, NQHO, B. Wordsworth (r1992) *Concert*
(5/94) (ARGO) ① **440 116-2ZH**
M. Davis, LSO, B. Thomson (r1977) *Concert*
(8/94) (CHAN) ① [2] **CHAN9262/3**
London CO, C. Warren-Green (vn/dir) (r1988)
Concert (11/94) (VIRG) ① **CUV5 61126-2**
D. Wise, Liverpool PO, M. Sargent (r1947) *Concert*
(5/95) (DUTT) ① **CDAX8012**
S. Chang, LPO, B. Haitink (r1994) *Concert*
(12/95) (EMI) ① **CDC5 55487-2**

Norfolk Rhapsody No. 1 (1905-06)
LPO, B. Thomson *Concert*
(5/87) (CHAN) ① **CHAN8502**
New Philh, A. Boult *Concert*
(5/92) (EMI) ① **CDM7 64022-2**
Philh, L. Slatkin (r1991) *Concert*
(8/93) (RCA) ① **09026 61193-2**
NQHO, B. Wordsworth (r1992) *Concert*
(5/94) (ARGO) ① **440 116-2ZH**
CBSO, N. del Mar (r1980) *Concert*
(4/95) (EMI) ① **CDM5 65131-2**
ASMF, N. Marriner (r1993) *Concert*
(6/95) (PHIL) ① **442 427-2PH**
LPO, B. Haitink (r1994) *Concert*
(12/95) (EMI) ① **CDC5 55487-2**

Partita for Double String Orchestra (1946-48)
LSO, B. Thomson *Concert*
(8/90) (CHAN) ① **CHAN8828**
RLPO, V. Handley *Concert*
(12/91) (EMIN) ① **CD-EMX2179**
London Fest Orch, R. Pople *Concert*
(4/92) (ASV) ① **CDDCA779**
LSO, B. Thomson (r1989) *Concert*
(8/94) (CHAN) ① [2] **CHAN9262/3**
LPO, A. Boult (r1956) *Symphony 2.*
(12/94) (BELA) ① **461 008-2**

Romance in D flat—harmonica, strings and piano (1951)
T. Reilly, ASMF, N. Marriner *Concert*
(10/88) (CHAN) ① **CHAN8617**
T. Reilly, ASMF, N. Marriner (r1976) *Concert*
(4/94) (DECC) ① **440 320-2DWO**

The Running Set—orchestra (1933)
Bournemouth Sinfonietta, G. Hurst *Concert*
(8/87) (CHAN) ① **CHAN8432**
Bournemouth Sinfonietta, G. Hurst (r1975) *Concert*
(11/92) (CHAN) ① **CHAN6545**

Sea Songs—march: military band (1923)
Cleveland Winds, F. Fennell *Concert*
(10/84) (TELA) ① **CD80099**
Bournemouth Sinfonietta, G. Hurst *Concert*
(8/87) (CHAN) ① **CHAN8432**
Bournemouth Sinfonietta, G. Hurst *Concert*
(10/91) (CHAN) ① **CHAN6538**

Serenade to Music—orchestra (1939) (arr cpsr from vocal work)
LPO, V. Handley *Concert*
(1/85) (CHAN) ① **CHAN8330**
RLPO, V. Handley (r1990) *Concert*
(1/95) (EMIN) ① [6] **CDBOX-VW1**

Suite for Viola and Small Orchestra (1934)
F. Riddle, Bournemouth Sinfonietta, N. del Mar
(r1977) *Concert* (11/92) (CHAN) ① **CHAN6545**

Symphony No. 1, '(A) Sea Symphony'—soprano, baritone, chorus and orchestra (1903-09 rev 1923) (Wds. W. Whitman)
J. Rodgers, W. Shimell, Liverpool Phil Ch, RLPO, V. Handley (2/89) (EMIN) ① **CD-EMX2142**
F. Lott, J. Summers, LP Ch, Cantilena, LPO, B. Haitink (1989) (1/90) (EMI) ① **CDC7 49911-2**
Y. Kenny, B. Rayner Cook, LSC, LSO, B. Thomson
(2/90) (CHAN) ① **CHAN8764**
H. Harper, J. Shirley-Quirk, LSC, LSO, A. Previn
(r1970) (3/91) (RCA) ① **GD90500**
S. Armstrong, J. Carol Case, LP Ch, LPO, A. Boult
(5/92) (EMI) ① **CDM7 64016-2**
B. Valente, T. Allen, Philh Chor, Philh, L. Slatkin
(1992) (2/94) (RCA) ① **09026 61197-2**
I. Baillie, J. Cameron, LP Ch, LPO, A. Boult (r1953)
(7/94) (BELA) ① **450 144-2**
J. Rodgers, W. Shimell, Liverpool Phil Ch, RLPO, V. Handley (r1988) *Concert*
(1/95) (EMIN) ① [6] **CDBOX-VW1**
A. Roocroft, T. Hampson, BBC Sym Chor, BBC SO, A. Davis (r1994) (8/95) (TELD) ① **4509-94550-2**

Symphony No. 2, '(A) London Symphony' (1913 rev 1920 and 1933)
RPO, A. Previn *Lark Ascending.*
(7/87) (TELA) ① **CD80138**
LPO, B. Haitink (r1986) *Tallis Fantasia.*
(7/88) (EMI) ① **CDC7 49394-2**
LSO, B. Thomson *Concerto Grosso.*
(10/89) (CHAN) ① **CHAN8629**
LSO, A. Previn *Concert* (3/91) (RCA) ① **GD90501**
LPO, A. Boult *Tallis Fantasia.*
(5/92) (EMI) ① **CDM7 64017-2**
Hallé, J. Barbirolli (1957) *Symphony 8.*
(6/92) (EMI) ① **CDM7 64197-2**
Philh, L. Slatkin (1991) *Concert*
(8/93) (RCA) ① **09026 61193-2**
RLPO, V. Handley (1992) *Symphony 8.*
(8/93) (EMIN) ① **CD-EMX2209**
Queen's Hall Orch, Henry Wood (1936) *Concert*
(10/93) (DUTT) ① **CDAX8004**
Cincinnati SO, E. Goossens (r1941: 1920 ver)
Concert (12/93) (BIDD) ① **WHL016**
Bournemouth SO, K. Bakels (1993) *Wasps.*
(6/94) (NAXO) ① **8 550734**
Hallé, J. Barbirolli (r1967) *Ireland: London Overture.*
(12/94) (EMI) ① **CDM5 65109-2**
LPO, A. Boult (r1952) *Partita.*
(12/94) (BELA) ① **461 008-2**
RLPO, V. Handley (1992) *Concert*
(1/95) (EMIN) ① [6] **CDBOX-VW1**
BBC SO, A. Davis (r1993) *Symphony 8.*
(2/95) (TELD) ① **4509-90858-2**

Symphony No. 3, '(A) Pastoral Symphony' (1921)
Y. Kenny, LSO, B. Thomson *Oboe Concerto.*
(8/88) (CHAN) ① **CHAN8594**
H. Harper, LSO, A. Previn *Symphony 4.*
(3/91) (RCA) ① **GD90503**
M. Price, New Philh, A. Boult *Symphony 5.*
(5/92) (EMI) ① **CDM7 64018-2**
A. Barlow, RLPO, V. Handley *Symphony 4.*
(11/92) (EMIN) ① **CD-EMX2192**
L. Hohenfeld, Philh, L. Slatkin (1991) *Concert*
(11/93) (RCA) ① **09026 61194-2**
P. Rozario, Bournemouth SO, K. Bakels (1992)
Symphony 6. (12/94) (NAXO) ① **8 550733**
A. Barlow, RLPO, V. Handley (1991) *Concert*
(1/95) (EMIN) ① [6] **CDBOX-VW1**

Symphony No. 4 in F minor (1931-34)
LSO, B. Thomson *Concerto Accademico.*
(1/89) (CHAN) ① **CHAN8633**
LSO, A. Previn *Symphony 3.*
(3/91) (RCA) ① **GD90503**
BBC SO, R. Vaughan Williams (r1937) *Holst: Planets.* (4/91) (KOCH) ① **37018-2**
New Philh, A. Boult *Symphony 6.*
(5/92) (EMI) ① **CDM7 64019-2**
RLPO, V. Handley *Symphony 3.*
(11/92) (EMIN) ① **CD-EMX2192**
Philh, L. Slatkin (1991) *Concert*
(11/93) (RCA) ① **09026 61194-2**
BBC SO, A. Davis (r1992) *Symphony 5.*
(2/94) (TELD) ① **4509-90844-2**
NYPO, L. Bernstein (1965) *Concert*
(7/94) (SONY) ① **SMK47638**
RLPO, V. Handley (1991) *Concert*
(1/95) (EMIN) ① [6] **CDBOX-VW1**
BBC SO, R. Vaughan Williams (r1937) *Symphony 5.*
(6/95) (DUTT) ① **CDAX8011**

Symphony No. 5 in D (1938-43 rev 1951)
LSO, B. Thomson *Lark Ascending.*
(1/88) (CHAN) ① **CHAN8554**
RLPO, V. Handley (r1986) *Flos Campi.*
(3/88) (EMIN) ① **CD-EMX9512**
RPO, A. Previn (1988) *Tallis Fantasia.*
(5/89) (TELA) ① **CD80158**
LSO, A. Previn *England of Elizabeth Suite.*
(3/91) (RCA) ① **GD90506**
ASMF, N. Marriner (1990) *Symphony 6.*
(4/92) (COLL) ① **Coll1202-2**
Philh, L. Slatkin (r1990) *Symphony 6.*
(4/92) (RCA) ① **RD60556**
LPO, A. Boult *Symphony 3.*
(5/92) (EMI) ① **CDM7 64018-2**
RPO, Y. Menuhin (r1987) *2-Piano Concerto.*
(1/94) (VIRG) ① **VJ5 61105-2**
BBC SO, A. Davis (r1992) *Symphony 4.*
(2/94) (TELD) ① **4509-90844-2**
RLPO, V. Handley (r1986) *Concert*
(1/95) (EMIN) ① [6] **CDBOX-VW1**
Philh, J. Barbirolli (1962) *Bax: Tintagel.*
(12/95) (EMI) ① **CDM5 65110-2**
Hallé, J. Barbirolli (r1944) *Symphony 4.*
(6/95) (DUTT) ① **CDAX8011**
BBC SO, G. Rozhdestvensky (pp1980) *Sancta civitas.* (10/95) (BBCR) ① **BBCRD9125**

LPO, B. Haitink (r1994) *Concert*
(12/95) (EMI) ① **CDC5 55487-2**

Symphony No. 6 in E minor (1944-47 rev 1950)
LSO, B. Thomson *Tuba Concerto*.
(9/89) (CHAN) ① **CHAN8740**
LSO, A. Previn *Symphony 9*.
(3/91) (RCA) ① **GD90508**
BBC SO, A. Davis *Concert*
(8/91) (TELD) ① **9031-73127-2**
ASMF, N. Marriner (r1990) *Symphony 5*.
(4/92) (COLL) ① **Coll1202-2**
Philh, L. Slatkin (r1990) *Symphony 5*.
(4/92) (RCA) ① **RD60556**
New Philh, A. Boult *Symphony 4*.
(5/92) (EMI) ① **CDM7 64019-2**
Bournemouth SO, K. Bakels (r1993) *Symphony 3*.
(12/94) (NAXO) ① **8 550733**
RLPO, V. Handley (r1994) *Concert*
(1/95) (EMIN) ① [6] **CDBOX-VW1**
RLPO, V. Handley (r1994) *Symphony 9*.
(1/95) (EMIN) ① **CD-EMX2230**

Symphony No. 7, 'Sinfonia antartica'—soprano, women's chorus and orchestra (1949-52) (based on themes from the film 'Scott of the Antarctic')
S. Armstrong, LP Ch, LPO, B. Haitink
(1/87) (EMI) ① **CDC7 47516-2**
C. Bott, LSC, LSO, B. Thomson *Toward the Unknown Region*. (4/90) (CHAN) ① **CHAN8796**
R. Richardson, H. Harper, Ambrosian Sngrs, LSO, A. Previn *Serenade to Music*. (3/91) (RCA) ① **GD90510**
A. Hargan, Liverpool Phil Ch, RLPO, V. Handley *Serenade to Music*. (9/91) (EMIN) ① **CD-EMX2173**
N. Burrowes, LP Ch, LPO, A. Boult *Wasps*.
(5/92) (EMI) ① **CDM7 64020-2**
D. Labelle, R. Allam, Indianapolis Sym Ch, Indianapolis SO, R. Leppard (r1992) *Tallis Fantasia*.
(10/93) (KOSS) ① **KC2214**
A. Hargan, Liverpool Phil Ch, RLPO, V. Handley (r1990) *Concert*
(1/95) (EMIN) ① [6] **CDBOX-VW1**

Symphony No. 8 in D minor (1956)
LSO, B. Thomson *Concert*
(8/90) (CHAN) ① **CHAN8828**
LSO, A. Previn *Symphony 7*.
(3/91) (RCA) ① **GD90510**
LPO, A. Boult *Symphony 9*.
(5/92) (EMI) ① **CDM7 64021-2**
Hallé, J. Barbirolli (r1956) *Symphony 2*.
(6/92) (EMI) ① **CDM7 64197-2**
Philh, L. Slatkin (r1991) *Concert*
(8/93) (RCA) ① **09026 61196-2**
RLPO, V. Handley (r1992) *Symphony 2*.
(8/93) (EMIN) ① **CD-EMX2209**
RLPO, V. Handley (r1992) *Concert*
(1/95) (EMIN) ① [6] **CDBOX-VW1**
BBC SO, A. Davis (r1993) *Symphony 2*.
(2/95) (TELD) ① **4509-90858-2**

Symphony No. 9 in E minor (1956-57 rev 1958)
LSO, A. Previn *Symphony 6*.
(3/91) (RCA) ① **GD90508**
LSO, B. Thomson *Piano Concerto*.
(7/91) (CHAN) ① **CHAN8941**
LPO, A. Boult *Symphony 8*.
(5/92) (EMI) ① **CDM7 64021-2**
Philh, L. Slatkin (r1991) *Symphony 6*.
(8/93) (RCA) ① **09026 61196-2**
RLPO, V. Handley (r1994) *Symphony 6*.
(1/95) (EMIN) ① **CD-EMX2230**
RLPO, V. Handley (r1994) *Concert*
(1/95) (EMIN) ① [6] **CDBOX-VW1**
LPO, A. Boult (r1958) *Arnold: Symphony 3*.
(4/95) (EVER) ① **EVC9001**

Toccata marziale—military band (1924)
Coldstream Guards Band, R.A. Ridings *Concert*
(4/87) (BAND) ① **BNA5002**
London Wind Orch, D.Wick *Concert*
(7/88) (ASV) ① **CDQS6021**

5 Variants of 'Dives and Lazarus'—string orchestra and harp(s) (1939)
ASMF, N. Marriner *Concert*
(9/86) (ARGO) ① **414 595-2ZH**
LPO, B. Thomson *Concert*
(5/87) (CHAN) ① **CHAN8502**
LPO, V. Handley *Concert*
(10/87) (EMIN) ① **CD-EMX9508**
ECO, Y. Menuhin *Concert*
(12/88) (ARAB) ① **Z6568**
NQHO, B. Wordsworth (r1992) *Concert*
(4/94) (ARGO) ① **440 116-2ZH**
Jacques Orch, D. Willcocks (r1968) *Concert*
(6/94) (EMI) ① **CDM7 64722-2**
Bournemouth Sinfonietta, R. Studt (vn/dir) (r1993) *Concert*
(10/94) (NAXO) ① **8 550823**

CBSO, N. del Mar (r1980) *Concert*
(4/95) (EMI) ① **CDM5 65131-2**
ASMF, N. Marriner (r1993) *Concert*
(6/95) (PHIL) ① **442 427-2PH**

Variations for Brass Band (1957)
Bournemouth SO, R. Hickox (arr G.Jacob) *Job*.
(7/92) (EMI) ① **CDC7 54421-2**
ASMF, N. Marriner (r1993: orch G Jacob) *Concert*
(6/95) (PHIL) ① **442 427-2PH**

SECTION II: CHAMBER

Household Music—3 preludes on Welsh hymn tunes (1941) (exact scoring unspecified)
Northern Sinfonia, R. Hickox (r1995) *Concert*
(11/95) (CHAN) ① **CHAN9392**

Phantasy Quintet—2 violins, 2 violas and cello (1912)
English Qt, N. Blume *Concert*
(12/89) (UNIC) ① **DKPCD9076**
S. Rowland-Jones, Medici Qt *Concert*
(12/89) (NIMB) ① **NI5191**
Music Group of London (1973) *Concert*
(10/94) (EMI) ① **CDM5 65100-2**

Romance—viola and piano
K. Kashkashian, R. Levin *Concert*
(9/86) (ECM) ① **827 744-2**
P. Coletti, L. Howard (r1993) *Concert*
(10/94) (HYPE) ① **CDA66687**

Sonata for Violin and Piano in A minor (1954)
H. Bean, D. Parkhouse (r1973) *Concert*
(10/94) (EMI) ① **CDM5 65100-2**

String Quartet No. 1 in G minor (1908)
English Qt *Concert* (9/89) (UNIC) ① **DKPCD9076**
Medici Qt *Concert* (12/89) (NIMB) ① **NI5191**
Britten Qt *Concert* (2/92) (EMI) ① **CDC7 54346-2**

String Quartet No. 2 in A minor (1943-44)
English Qt *Concert* (9/89) (UNIC) ① **DKPCD9076**
Medici Qt *Concert* (12/89) (NIMB) ① **NI5191**
Music Group of London (1972) *Concert*
(10/94) (EMI) ① **CDM5 65100-2**

6 Studies in English folk song—cello and piano (1926) (also arr for violin/viola/clarinet)
1. Adagio (Lovely on the water); 2. Andante sostenuto (Spurn point); 3. Larghetto (Van Diemen's Land); 4. Lento (She borrowed some of her mother's gold); 5. Andante tranquillo (The lady and the dragoon); 6. Allegro vivace (As I walked over London Bridge).
J. Hilton, K. Swallow *Concert*
(2/89) (CHAN) ① **CHAN8683**
Daniel Smith, R. Vignoles *Concert*
(9/89) (ASV) ① **CDDCA535**
J. Polmear, D. Ambache *Concert*
(9/92) (UNIC) ① **DKPCD9121**
R. Canter, LSO, J. Judd (1992: arr ob/stgs: Canter) *Concert* (10/93) (CARL) ① **MCD59**
E. Johnson, M. Martineau *Concert*
(7/94) (ASV) ① **CDDCA891**
E. Croxford, D. Parkhouse (r1973) *Concert*
(10/94) (EMI) ① **CDM5 65100-2**
J. Cohler, J. Gordon (r1993) *Concert*
(5/95) (CRYS) ① **Crystal CD733**

Suite de ballet—flute and piano (?1913)
M. Cox, N. Clayton *Concert*
(9/90) (KING) ① **KCLCD2013**

SECTION III: INSTRUMENTAL

3 Preludes on Welsh Hymn-Tunes—organ (1920)
1. Bryn Calfaria (melody by W. Owen: 1814—1893); 2. Rhosymedre (melody by J. D. Edwards: 1805—1885); 3. Hyfrydol (melody by R. H. Prichard: 1811—1887).
2. C. Curley (r1991) *Concert*
(4/92) (ARGO) ① **433 450-2ZH**
2. G. Green *Concert* (3/93) (NAXO) ① **8 550582**
2. T. Horton *Concert* (7/93) (CNTO) ① **CRCD2367**

SECTION IV: VOCAL AND CHORAL

Adieu—soprano, baritone and piano (1903) (German folksong trans Ferguson)
R. Golden, T. Woodman, L. Rothfuss (r1992) *Concert*
(5/94) (KOCH) ① **37168-2**

Along the Field—soprano and violin (1927 rev 1954) (Wds. A. E. Housman)
1. We'll to the woods no more; 2. Along the Field; 3. The Half-Moon westers low; 4. In the morning; 5. The sigh that heaves the grasses; 6. Goodbye; 7. Fancy's knell; 8. With rue my heart is laden.
R. Golden, N. Bean (r1992) *Concert*
(5/94) (KOCH) ① **37168-2**

And all in the morning—choir and organ (Wds. and tune trad. Derbyshire)
Guildford Cath Ch, Gavin Williams, Barry Rose (r1966) *Concert* (12/91) (EMI) ① **CDM7 64131-2**

Benedicite—soprano, 4vv chorus and orchestra (1929) (Wds. Bible (Apocrypha) and J. Austin)
Lynda Russell, Waynflete Sngrs, Winchester Cath Ch, Bournemouth SO, D. Hill (r1991) *Concert*
(5/93) (ARGO) ① **436 120-2ZH**
H. Harper, Bach Ch, LSO, D. Willcocks (r1968) *Concert* (6/94) (EMI) ① **CDM7 64722-2**

10 Blake Songs—voice and oboe (1957)
1. Infant Joy; 2. A Poison Tree; 3. The Piper; 4. London; 5. The Lamb; 6. The Shepherd; 7. Ah! Sunflower; 8. Cruelty has a human heart; 9. The Divine Image; 10. Eternity.
J. Bowman, P. Goodwin *Concert*
(3/89) (MERI) ① **CDE84158**

3 Choral Hymns—T/B, chorus & orchestra (1929) (Wds. M. Coverdale)
1. Easter Hymn; 2. Christmas Hymn; 3. Whitsunday Hymn.
J. Bowen, R. Judd, Corydon Sngrs, CLS, M. Best *Concert* (8/92) (HYPE) ① **CDA66569**

Claribel—song (1896) (Wds. A. Tennyson)
R. Golden, L. Rothfuss (r1992) *Concert*
(5/94) (KOCH) ① **37168-2**

Dona nobis pacem—cantata: soprano, baritone, chorus and orchestra (1936) (Wds. various)
1. Agnus Dei (wds. Liturgy); 2. Beat! Beat! Beat! (wds. W. Whitman); 3. Reconciliation (wds. W. Whitman); 4. Dirge for two veterans (wds. W. Whitman); 5a. The Angel of death; 5b. We look for peace; 5c. O man, greatly beloved; 5d. The glory of this latter house; 5e. Nation shall not lift up a sword against nation.
E. Wiens, B. Rayner Cook, LP Ch, LPO, B. Thomson *Mystical Songs*. (3/89) (CHAN) ① **CHAN8590**
R. Flynn, Roy Henderson, BBC Chor, BBC SO, R. Vaughan Williams (bp1936) *Concert*
(12/89) (PEAR) ① **GEMMCD9342**
Y. Kenny, B. Terfel, LSC, LSO, R. Hickox (r1992) *Sancta Civitas*. (12/93) (EMI) ① **CDC7 54788-2**
J. Howarth, T. Allen, Corydon Sngrs, Corydon Orch, M. Best (r1993) *Concert*
(5/94) (HYPE) ① **CDA66655**

Dreamland—song (1898) (Wds. C. Rossetti)
R. Golden, L. Rothfuss (r1992) *Concert*
(5/94) (KOCH) ① **37168-2**

3 Elizabethan Songs—4vv a capella (?1891-96) (Wds. Shakespeare & G. Herbert)
1. Sweet Day; 2. The Willow Song; 3. O Mistress mine.
3. Magdalen (Oxford) Coll Ch, G. Ives *Concert*
(11/92) (CNTO) ① **CRCD2366**

5 English Folksongs—4vv a capella (1913)
1. The dark-eyed sailor; 2. The springtime of the year; 3. Just as the tide was flowing; 4. The love's ghost; 5. Wassail song.
Cpte Cambridge Sngrs, CLS, J. Rutter (r1992) *Concert* (11/93) (CLLE) ① **COLCD120**

The English Hymnal—hymn settings (pub 1906) (tune names in parentheses with EH number)
This listing omits arrangements of works by other composers; 1. Come down, O Love Divine (Down Ampney: 152); 2. Come, let us join the church above (Rodmell: 186); 3. Father hear the prayer we offer (Sussex: 385); 4. For all the Saints (Sine Nomine: 641); 5. From Thee all skill and science flow (Farnham: 525); 6. God be with you till we meet again (Randolph: 524); 7. Hail thee, Festival day (Salve festa dies: 624); 8. Hark! How all the welkin rings (Dent Dale: 23); 9. He who would valiant be (Monk's Gate: 402); 10. I could not do without Thee (Gosterwood: 594); 11. I love to hear the story (Gosterwood: 594); 12. I think when I read that sweet story old (East Horndon: 595); 13. It is a thing most wonderful (Herongate: 597); 14. O God of earth and altar (King's Lynn: 562); 15. O Little Town of Bethlehem (Forest Green: 15); 16. Saints of God! Lo Jesu's people (Sussex: 239); 17. There's a friend for little children (Ingrave: 607); 18. 'Tis winter now: the fallen snow (Danby: 295); 19. When Christ was born in Bethlehem (Rodmell: 611); 20. When spring unlocks the flowers (Gosterwood: 299).
9. St Paul's Cath Ch, C. Dearnley, John Scott *Concert* (7/90) (HYPE) ① **CDH88036**

Epithalamion—cantata: baritone, chorus and small orchestra (1957) (Wds. E. Spenser)
S. Roberts, J. Snowden, H. Shelley, Bach Ch, LPO, D. Willcocks (r1986) *Concert*
(4/94) (EMI) ① **CDM7 64730-2**

E. Connell, L. Kitchen, Anne Dawson, A. Roocroft, Sarah Walker, J. Rigby, D. Montague, C. Wyn-Rogers, J.M. Ainsley, M. Hill, A. Davies, M. Davies, T. Allen, A. Opie, G. Howell, J. Connell, ECO, M. Best *Concert* (9/90) (HYPE) ① **CDA66420**
Liverpool Phil Ch, RLPO, V. Handley *Symphony 7.* (9/91) (EMIN) ① **CD-EMX2173**
N. Burrowes, S. Armstrong, S. Longfield, M. Hayward, A. Hodgson, G. Jennings, S. Minty, M. Dickinson, I. Partridge, B. Dickerson, W. Evans, K. Bowen, R. Angas, J. Carol Case, J. Noble, C. Keyte, LPO, A. Boult *Concert* (5/92) (EMI) ① **CDM7 64022-2**
L. Stiles-Allen, I. Baillie, E. Suddaby, E. Turner, M. Balfour, M. Brunskill, A. Desmond, M. Jarred, Parry Jones, H. Nash, F. Titterton, W. Widdop, Roy Henderson, N. Allin, R. Easton, H. Williams, BBC SO, Henry Wood (r1938) *Concert* (10/93) (DUTT) ① **CDAX8004**
A. Addison, L. Amara, E. Farrell, L. Chookasian, J. Tourel, S. Verrett, C. Bressler, R. Tucker, J. Vickers, G. London, E. Flagello, Donald Bell, NYPO, L. Bernstein (pp1962) *Concert* (7/94) (SONY) ① **SMK47638**

3 Shakespeare Songs—unaccompanied (4vv) (1951)
1. Full fathom five; 2. The Cloud-Capp'd Towers; 3. Over hill, over dale.
Cpte Cambridge Sngrs, J. Rutter *Concert* (4/87) (CLLE) ① **COLCD104**
L. Heather, King's College Ch, D. Willcocks *Concert* (6/91) (DECC) ① **430 093-2DWO**
1. Magdalen (Oxford) Coll Ch, G. Ives *Concert* (11/92) (CNTO) ① **CRCD2366**

Silence and Music—SATB (1953) (Wds. U. Vaughan Williams)
Cambridge Univ Chbr Ch, T. Brown *Concert* (4/92) (GAMU) ① **GAMCD529**

The **Sky above the roof—song (1908)** (Wds. Verlaine, trans M. Dearmer)
J. Bowman, Downshire Players, P. Ash (orch A.Ridout) *Concert* (3/89) (MERI) ① **CDE84158**
R. Golden, L. Rothfuss (r1992) *Concert* (5/94) (KOCH) ① **37168-2**

A **Song of Thanksgiving—soprano, narrator, organ, chorus and orchestra (1944)** (Wds. compiled cpsr)
J. Gielgud, L. Dawson, John Scott, London Oratory Jnr Ch, Corydon Sngrs, CLS, M. Best *Concert* (8/92) (HYPE) ① **CDA66569**

Songs of Travel—songs (1904) (Wds. R.L. Stevenson)
1. The Vagabond; 2. Let Beauty awake; 3. The Roadside fire; 4. Youth and Love; 5. In Dreams; 6. The Infinite Shining Heavens; 7. Whither must I wander?; 8. Bright is the Ring of Words; 9. I have Trod the Upward and the Downward Slope (pub 1960).
B. Luxon, D. Willison *Concert* (6/87) (CHAN) ① **CHAN8475**
T. Allen, CBSO, S. Rattle (r1983) *Concert* (3/94) (EMI) ① **CDM7 64731-2**
B. Terfel, M. Martineau (r1994) *Concert* (8/95) (DG) ① **445 946-2GH**
1. R. Tear, P. Ledger *Concert* (6/91) (DECC) ① **430 093-2DWO**
1. R. Herincx, J. Constable *Concert* (4/92) (GAMU) ① **GAMD506**

Te Deum in G—choir and organ/orchestra (1928)
Corydon Sngrs, M. Best *Concert* (10/87) (HYPE) ① **CDA66076**
Oxford Christ Church Cath Ch, English Stg Orch, S. Darlington *Concert* (6/89) (NIMB) ① **NI5166**
Hereford Cath Ch, R. Massey, G. Bowen (r1994) *Concert* (2/95) (PRIO) ① **PRCD507**

Think of me—soprano, baritone and piano (1903) (German folksong trans Ferguson)
R. Golden, T. Woodman, L. Rothfuss (r1992) *Concert* (5/94) (KOCH) ① **37168-2**

Toward the Unknown Region—chorus and orchestra (1905-06) (Wds. W. Whitman)
LSC, LSO, B. Thomson *Symphony 7.* (4/90) (CHAN) ① **CHAN8796**
Waynflete Sngrs, Winchester Cath Ch, Bournemouth SO, D. Hill (r1991) *Concert* (5/93) (ARGO) ① **436 120-2ZH**
Corydon Sngrs, Corydon Orch, M. Best (r1993) *Concert* (5/94) (HYPE) ① **CDA66655**
LSC, LSO, B. Thomson (r1989) *Concert* (8/94) (CHAN) ① [2] **CHAN9262/3**
CBSO Chor, CBSO, N. del Mar (r1980) *Concert* (4/95) (EMI) ① **CDM5 65131-2**

5 Tudor Portraits—choral suite: mez, bar, chorus & orchestra (1935) (Wds. J. Skelton)
1. The tunning of Elinor Rumming; 2. My pretty Bess; 3. Epitaph on John Jayberd of Diss; 4. Jane Scroop; 5. Jolly Rutterkin.
E. Bainbridge, J. Carol Case, Bach Ch, New Philh, D. Willcocks (r1969) *Concert* (6/94) (EMI) ① **CDM7 64722-2**

Valiant for truth—motet (4vv, optional organ/piano) (1940) (Wds. J. Bunyan)
BBC Sym Chor, S. Jackson (r1994) *Concert* (7/95) (LARG) ① [2] **Largo5130**

A **Vision of Aeroplanes—motet: 4vv amd organ (1956)** (Wds. Book of Ezekiel)
Finzi Sngrs, H. Bicket, P. Spicer *Concert* (5/92) (CHAN) ① **CHAN9019**

3 Vocalises—soprano and clarinet (1958)
E. Johnson, J. Howarth *Concert* (7/94) (ASV) ① **CDDCA891**

Wassail Song—carol: tenor, choir and organ (Wds and tune trad. Yorkshire)
C. Mould, Guildford Cath Ch, Gavin Williams, Barry Rose (r1966) *Concert* (12/91) (EMI) ① **CDM7 64131-2**

Whitsunday Hymn
Magdalen Oxford Coll Ch, G. Webber *Concert* (11/91) (ABBE) ① **CDCA914**

Wither's Rocking Hymn (1928) (Wds. G. Withers)
Southwark Cath Ch, P. Wright, S. Layton (r1992) *Concert* (7/94) (PRIO) ① **PRCD435**

SECTION V: STAGE WORKS

A **Bunyan Sequence—incidental music for radio (1942)**
J. Gielgud, R. Pasco, U. Howells, A. Oliver, Corydon Sngrs, CLS, M. Best (arr Palmer) (8/91) (HYPE) ① **CDA66511**

Coastal Command—film score (1942) (suite arr Mathieson; 'U-Boat Alert' added by C Palmer)
EXCERPTS: 1. Prelude; 2. Hebrides; 3. U-Boat alert; 4. Taking off at night; 5. Hudsons take-off from Iceland; 6. Dawn Patrol; 7. The Battle of the Beauforts; 8. Finale.
Philh, K. Alwyn *Concert* (2/91) (SILV) ① **FILMCD713**
RTE Concert Orch, A. Penny (r1993) *Concert* (10/95) (MARC) ① **8 223665**
6. Philh, K. Alwyn *Concert* (5/93) (SILV) ① **SILVAD3002**

The **England of Elizabeth—concert suite from film score (1955)** (adapted Mathieson)
EXCERPTS; 1. Explorer; 2. Poet; 3. Queen.
RTE Concert Orch, A. Penny (r1993) *Concert* (10/95) (MARC) ① **8 223665**
1-3. LSO, A. Previn *Symphony 5.* (3/91) (RCA) ① **GD90506**

Hugh the Drover—ballad opera: 2 acts (1924—London) (Lib. H Child)
EXCERPTS: ACT 1: 1. Buy, buy, buy! Who'll buy?; 2. Who'll buy my sweet primroses; 3. Cold blows the wind on Cotsall; 4. Ballads! Buy me ballads, pretty ballads!; 5. As I was a-walking on morning in spring; 6. Bless! What's this?; 7. Show me a richer man in all this town; 8. See, see here they come! Way for the morris men!; 9. They're gone!...My husabnd that's to be!; 10. Sweetheart, life must be full of care; 11. Alone I would be as the wind and as free; 12. Hey! She will obey; 13. Sweet little linnet that longs to be free; 14. Horse hoofs, thunder down the valley (Hugh's Song of the Road); 15. Mary, come back I say!; 16. In the night-time I have seen you riding (Love duet); 17. Mary! Mary!; 18. Who'll fight? A fight! Who's for a fight?; 19. Brave English lads, lovers of manly sport; 20. Down, down with John the Butcher!; 21. Alone and friendless, on this foreign ground I am to die; 22. Are you ready? Go!; 23. Hugh the Drover!; 24. Oh, the devil and Bonyparty. ACT 2: 25. Past four o'clock, and dawn is coming; 26. Gaily I go to die; 27. Hugh! My dear one!; 28. Rise up, my Mary; come away; 29. Dear sun, I crave a boon; 30. O I've been rambling all this night; 31. Here, queen uncrowned, in this most royal place; 32. The soldiers!; 33. Dropped from the ranks on a winter night; 34. Now you are mine!; 35. Halloo! Halloo, Mary and Hugh.
Cpte B. Bottone, R. Evans, R. Van Allan, A. Opie, Sarah Walker, N. Jenkins, R. Poulton, K. M. Daymond, H. Nicoll, A. Hutton, J. Gooding, W. Evans, J. Saunders, A. Coote, L. Atkinson, P. Robinson, J. Pearce, P. Im Thurn, New London Children's Ch, Corydon Sngrs, Corydon Orch, M. Best (r1994) (10/94) (HYPE) ① [2] **CDA66901/2**
Cpte R. Tear, S. Armstrong, R. Lloyd, M. Rippon, H. Watts, J. Fryatt, H. Newman, T. Sharpe, L. Fyson, O. Broome, S. Burgess, D. Johnston, L. Richardson, S. Minty, N. Jenkins, B. Ogston, D. Read, S. Davies, St Paul's Cath Ch, Ambrosian Op Chor, RPO, C. Groves (r1978) (10/94) (EMI) ① [2] **CMS5 65224-2**
14. J. Johnston, Philh, J. Robertson (r1950) *Concert* (4/92) (EMI) ① [7] **CHS7 69741-2(2)**
14. J. Johnston, Philh, J. Robertson (r1950) *Concert* (4/95) (TEST) ① **SBT1058**
16. Mary Lewis, T. Davies, orch, M. Sargent (r1924) *Concert* (7/95) (BEUL) ① **1PD13**

Job—masque for dancing (1931—London)
Cpte LPO, A. Boult (r1958) *Concert* (5/95) (EVER) ① **EVC9006**
Bournemouth SO, R. Hickox *Variations for Brass Band.* (7/92) (EMI) ① **CDC7 54421-2**
LPO, V. Handley (3/93) (CFP) ① **CD-CFP4603**

The **Poisoned Kiss—romantic extravaganza: 3 acts (1936—Cambridge)** (Lib. E. Sharp, after R. Garnett)
Overture Bournemouth Sinfonietta, G. Hurst *Concert* (8/87) (CHAN) ① **CHAN8432**
Overture Bournemouth Sinfonietta, G. Hurst (r1975) *Concert* (11/92) (CHAN) ① **CHAN6545**

Riders to the Sea—opera: 1 act (1937—London) (Lib. cpsr, after J.M. Synge)
Cpte N. Burrowes, M. Price, H. Watts, B. Luxon, P. Stevens, Ambrosian Sngrs, London Orch Nova, M. Davies (r1970) *Concert* (4/94) (EMI) ① **CDM7 64730-2**
Cpte I. Attrot, L. Dawson, L. Finnie, K. M. Daymond, P. H. Stephen, Northern Sinfonia, R. Hickox (r1995) *Concert* (11/95) (CHAN) ① **CHAN9392**

Scott of the Antarctic—film score (1948)
EXCERPTS: 1. Prologue; 2. Pony March; 3. Penguins; 4. Climbing the Glacier; 5. Final Music.
1-5. Philh, E. Irving (r1948) *Concert* (9/94) (EMI) ① **CDGO 2059**

The **Shepherds of the Delectable Mountains—pastoral episode: 1 act (1921—London)** (Lib. cpsr, after J Bunyan)
L. Kitchen, J.M. Ainsley, Adrian Thompson, A. Opie, B. Terfel, J. Best, Corydon Sngrs, CLS, M. Best *Concert* (8/92) (HYPE) ① **CDA66569**

The **Story of a Flemish Farm—concert suite from film score (1943, rev 1945)**
EXCERPTS: 1. The Flag Flutters in the Wind; 2. Night By the Sea—Farewell to the Flag; 3. Dawn in the Barn—The Parting of the Lovers; 4. In a Belgian Café; 5. The Major Goes to Face His Fate; 6. The Dead Man's Kit; 7. The Wanderings of the Flag.
RTE Concert Orch, A. Penny (r1993) *Concert* (10/95) (MARC) ① **8 223665**

The **Wasps—Aristophanic Suite (from incidental music) (1909)**
1. Overture; 2. Entr'acte; 3. March past of the Kitchen Utensils; 4. Entr'acte; 5. Ballet and Final Tableau.
Cpte LPO, V. Handley *Concert* (10/87) (EMIN) ① **CD-EMX9508**
Cpte LPO, A. Boult *Symphony 7.* (5/92) (EMI) ① **CDM7 64020-2**
1. LPO, V. Handley *Concert* (1/85) (CHAN) ① **CHAN8330**
1. LSO, A. Previn *Walton: Symphony 1.* (2/89) (RCA) ① **GD87830**
1. English SO, W. Boughton *Concert* (2/90) (NIMB) ① **NI5208**
1. LSO, A. Previn *Concert* (3/91) (RCA) ① **GD90501**
1. Queen's Hall Orch, Henry Wood (r1936) *Concert* (10/93) (DUTT) ① **CDAX8004**
1. Bournemouth SO, K. Bakels (r1993) *Symphony 2.* (6/94) (NAXO) ① **8 550734**
1. LPO, A. Boult (r1958) *Concert* (5/95) (EVER) ① **EVC9006**
1. ASMF, N. Marriner (r1993) *Concert* (6/95) (PHIL) ① **442 427-2PH**

49th Parallel—film score (1940-41)
EXCERPTS: 1. Prelude.
1. RTE Concert Orch, A. Penny (r1993) *Concert* (10/95) (MARC) ① **8 223665**

VAUTOR, Thomas *(fl 1590–1620)* *England*

SECTION IV: VOCAL AND CHORAL

Sweet Suffolk Owl—madrigal (5vv) (pub 1619-20)
Hilliard Ens, P. Hillier *Concert* (2/89) (EMI) ① **CDC7 49197-2**

VECCHI, Orazio (Tiberio) (1550–1605) Italy

SECTION IV: VOCAL AND CHORAL

L' Amfiparnaso—comédie harmonieuse: prologue and 3 acts (1597)
Cpte C. Janequin Ens, D. Visse (r1993) *Convito musicale.* (12/93) (HARM) ① **HMC90 1461**
Il convito musicale—3-8vv (pub 1597)
1. O giardiniero; 2. Lunghi danni; 3. Bando del asino.
1-3. C. Janequin Ens, D. Visse (r1993) *Amfiparnaso.* (12/93) (HARM) ① **HMC90 1461**
So ben, mi, c'ha bon tempo—canzonetta (4vv)
Amaryllis Consort *Concert* (6/86) (CARL) ① **PCD822**
Tiridola, non dormire—madrigal: 6vv (pub 1590)
Consort of Musicke, A. Rooley (lte/dir) *Concert* (2/89) (BIS) ① **BIS-CD392**

VECSEY, Franz von (1893–1935) Hungary

SECTION II: CHAMBER

Caprice No. 1, 'Le vent'—violin and piano
R. Ricci, E. Lush (r1957) *Concert* (5/92) (DECC) ① **433 220-2DWO**
K. Daeshik Kang, M. Rahkonen (1992) *Concert* (9/93) (NIMB) ① **NI5358**

VEDEL, Artemy (1767–1806) Ukraine

SECTION IV: VOCAL AND CHORAL

Open the gates of repentance—song
F. Chaliapin, Paris Russian Met Church Ch, N. Afonsky (r1932) *Concert* (6/93) (PREI) ① [2] **89207**

VEJVANOVSKY, Pavel Josef (?c1633 or c1639–1693) Moravia

SECTION I: ORCHESTRAL

Sonata Natalis
Virtuosi Saxoniae, L. Güttler *Concert* (12/89) (CAPR) ① **10 225**

VELASQUEZ, Glauco (1884–1914) Brazil

SECTION III: INSTRUMENTAL

Brutto sogno—piano (1910)
C. Sverner (r1993) *Concert* (7/95) (MARC) ① **8 223556**
Canzone Strana—piano (1907)
C. Sverner (r1993) *Concert* (7/95) (MARC) ① **8 223556**
Danse de silphes—piano
C. Sverner (r1993) *Concert* (7/95) (MARC) ① **8 223556**
Devaneio—piano (1911)
C. Sverner (r1993) *Concert* (7/95) (MARC) ① **8 223556**
Divertimento No. 2—piano
C. Sverner (r1993) *Concert* (7/95) (MARC) ① **8 223556**
2 Folha d'album—piano (1905)
C. Sverner (r1993) *Concert* (7/95) (MARC) ① **8 223556**
Impromptu—piano (1906)
C. Sverner (r1993) *Concert* (7/95) (MARC) ① **8 223556**
Melancolia—piano (1910)
C. Sverner (r1993) *Concert* (7/95) (MARC) ① **8 223556**
Minuetto e Gavotte Moderni—piano (1910)
C. Sverner (r1993) *Concert* (7/95) (MARC) ① **8 223556**
Petite Suite—piano (1905)
1. Gavotte; 2. Minuetto; 3. Valsa mignonne.
C. Sverner (r1993) *Concert* (7/95) (MARC) ① **8 223556**
Prelúdio e Scherzo—piano (1910)
C. Sverner (r1993) *Concert* (7/95) (MARC) ① **8 223556**
Prelúdio No. 1—piano (1908)
C. Sverner (r1993) *Concert* (7/95) (MARC) ① **8 223556**

Prelúdio No. 2—piano (1908)
C. Sverner (r1993) *Concert* (7/95) (MARC) ① **8 223556**
Rêverie—piano (1906)
C. Sverner (r1993) *Concert* (7/95) (MARC) ① **8 223556**
Valsa lenta—piano (1905)
C. Sverner (r1993) *Concert* (7/95) (MARC) ① **8 223556**
Valsa romântica—piano (1910)
C. Sverner (r1993) *Concert* (7/95) (MARC) ① **8 223556**

VELUT, Gilet (fl early 15th Cent) France

SECTION IV: VOCAL AND CHORAL

Benedicta viscera/Ave mater gratie/Ora pro nobis Deum alleluya—isorhythmic motet: 4vv
Orlando Consort (bp1994) *Concert* (11/95) (METR) ① **METCD1008**
Je voel servir plus c'onques mais—rondeau
Gothic Voices, C. Page *Concert* (3/92) (HYPE) ① **CDA66463**

VENTO, Ivo de (c1543/5–1575) Flanders/Germany

SECTION II: CHAMBER

Die Weiber mit den Flohen—consort
London Musica Antiqua, M. Uridge (r1980-83) *Concert* (12/93) (SYMP) ① **SYMCD1157**

VENZANO, Luigi (1814–1878) Italy

SECTION IV: VOCAL AND CHORAL

O che assorta—song
L. Tetrazzini, orch (r c1912) *Concert* (10/90) (NIMB) ① **NI7808**
L. Tetrazzini, orch (r1912) *Concert* (9/92) (EMI) ① [3] **CHS7 63802-2(2)**
L. Tetrazzini, orch (r1912) *Concert* (9/92) (PEAR) ① **GEMMCD9223**
L. Tetrazzini, orch (r1913) *Concert* (9/92) (PEAR) ① **GEMMCD9224**

VERACINI, Francesco Maria (1690–1768) Italy

SECTION I: ORCHESTRAL

6 Overtures
1. B flat; 2. F; 3. B flat; 4. F; 5. B; 6. B flat.
1, 2, 3, 4, 6. Cologne Musica Antiqua, R. Goebel (12/94) (ARCH) ① **439 937-2AH**

SECTION II: CHAMBER

Capriccio sesto con due soggetti in G minor—violin and bass (unidentified)
F. Biondi, M. Naddeo, R. Alessandrini, P. Monteilhet (r1995) *Violin Sonatas, Op. 2.* (9/95) (O111) ① **OPS30-138**
12 Sonatas—violin/recorder and continuo (pub 1716)
EXCERPTS: 2. G; 6. A minor.
No 1. E. Haupt, C. Schornsheim *Concert* (2/90) (CAPR) ① **10 234**
2, 6. F. Brüggen, A. Bylsma, G. Leonhardt (1967, 1972) *Concert* (7/94) (TELD) ① **4509-93669-2**
12 Sonatas for Violin/Flute and Continuo, Op. 1 (pub 1721)
1. G minor; 2. A minor; 3. B minor; 4. C; 5. D minor; 6. E minor; 7. A; 8. B flat; 9. C; 10. D; 11. E; 12. F.
6. Barthold Kuijken, W. Kuijken, R. Kohnen *Concert* (5/92) (ACCE) ① **ACC9177D**
7. A. Grumiaux, R. Castagnone (r1956; arr Castagnone) *Concert* (11/93) (PHIL) ① [3] **438 516-2PM3**
12 Sonatas, 'Sonate accademiche'—violin and continuo, Op. 2 (pub 1744)
1. D; 2. B flat; 3. G; 4. F; 5. G minor; 6. A; 7. D minor; 8. E minor; 9. A; 10. F; 11. E; 12. D minor.
6(Largo) J. Szigeti, K. Ruhrseltz (r1927) *Concert* (1/90) (BIDD) ① [2] **LAB005/6**
7, 8, 9, 12. F. Biondi, M. Naddeo, R. Alessandrini, P. Monteilhet (r1995) *Capriccio.* (9/95) (O111) ① **OPS30-138**
8(Giga); 11(Minuet & Gavotte) J. Thibaud, T. Janopoulo (r1936: arr Salmon) *Concert* (12/94) (APR) ① **APR7028**

SECTION V: STAGE WORKS

Rosalinda—opera (1744—London) (Lib. Rolli)
Meco verrai L. Tetrazzini, orch (r1914) *Concert* (10/90) (NIMB) ① **NI7808**
Meco verrai L. Tetrazzini, orch (r1914) *Concert* (9/92) (EMI) ① [3] **CHS7 63802-2(2)**
Meco verrai L. Tetrazzini, orch (r1914) *Concert* (9/92) (PEAR) ① **GEMMCD9223**
Meco verrai L. Tetrazzini, orch (r1913) *Concert* (9/92) (PEAR) ① **GEMMCD9224**

VERDELOT, Philippe (?1470/80–1552) France

SECTION IV: VOCAL AND CHORAL

Ave Maria—7vv
Tallis Scholars, P. Phillips *Concert* (12/86) (GIME) ① **CDGIM010**

VERDI, Giuseppe (Fortunino Francesco) (1813–1901) Italy

SECTION II: CHAMBER

String Quartet in E minor (1873)
1. Allegro; 2. Andantino; 3. Prestissimo; 4. Scherzo fuga. Allegro assai mosso.
Nuovo Quartetto *Concert* (11/86) (DENO) ① **CO-1029**
S. Accardo, M. Batjer, T. Hoffman, P. Wiley *Borodin: String Quartet 2.* (5/89) (DYNA) ① **CDS47**
Alberni Qt *Concert* (5/89) (CRD) ① **CRD3366**
Delmé Qt *R. Strauss: String Quartet, Op. 2.* (7/89) (HYPE) ① **CDA66317**
Vogler Qt *Berg: Lyric Suite.* (12/91) (RCA) ① **RD60855**
Hagen Qt (r1993) *Concert* (12/95) (DG) ① **447 069-2GH**
3. Busch Qt (r1922) *Concert* (6/93) (SYMP) ① **SYMCD1109**
3, 4. NBC SO, A. Toscanini (bp1946) *Concert* (5/94) (ATS) ① [2] **ATCD100**

SECTION IV: VOCAL AND CHORAL

Il Brigidino—song (1863) (Wds. dall'Ongaro)
R. Scotto, I. Davis (pp1983) *Concert* (10/86) (ETCE) ① **KTC2002**
L' Esule—canzona (1839) (Wds. Solera)
J. Carreras, Martin Katz *Concert* (9/90) (SONY) ① **SK45863**
Inno delle Nazioni—solo voice, chorus and orchestra (1862) (Wds. A. Boito)
J. Peerce, Westminster Ch, NBC SO, A. Toscanini (bp1943) *Concert* (5/90) (RCA) ① [7] **GD60326**
Messa da Requiem—soloists, chorus and orchestra (1874)
1. Requiem; 2. Dies irae; 3. Tuba mirum; 4. Liber scriptus; 5. Quid sum miser; 6. Rex tremendae; 7. Recordare; 8. Ingemisco; 9. Confutatis; 10. Lacrymosa; 11. Offertorio; 12. Sanctus; 13. Agnus Dei; 14. Lux aeterna; 15. Libera me.
Cpte J. Sutherland, M. Horne, L. Pavarotti, M. Talvela, Vienna St. Op. Chor, VPO, G. Solti (12/84) (DECC) ① [2] **411 944-2DH2**
Cpte A. Tomowa-Sintow, A. Baltsa, J. Carreras, J. Van Dam, Vienna St. Op. Chor, Sofia National Op. Chor, VPO, H. von Karajan (r1984) (5/85) (DG) ① [2] **415 091-2GH2**
Cpte K. Ricciarelli, S. Verrett, P. Domingo, N. Ghiaurov, La Scala Chor, La Scala Orch, C. Abbado (r1980) (10/86) (DG) ① [2] **415 976-2GH2**
Cpte E. Schwarzkopf, C. Ludwig, N. Gedda, N. Ghiaurov, Philh Chor, Philh, C.M. Giulini (r1963/4) *Pezzi sacri.* (4/87) (EMI) ① [2] **CDS7 47257-8**
Cpte C. Studer, D. Zajick, L. Pavarotti, S. Ramey, La Scala Chor, La Scala Orch, R. Muti (pp1987) (11/87) (EMI) ① [2] **CDS7 49390-2**
Cpte S. Dunn, D. Curry, J. Hadley, P. Plishka, Atlanta Sym Chor, Atlanta SO, Robert Shaw *Concert* (3/88) (TELA) ① [2] **CD80152**
Cpte M. Freni, C. Ludwig, C. Cossutta, N. Ghiaurov, Vienna Singverein, BPO, H. von Karajan (r1972) (4/89) (DG) ① [2] **413 215-2GGA2**
Cpte L. Price, R. Elias, J. Björling, G. Tozzi, Vienna Singverein, VPO, F. Reiner *Pezzi sacri.* (8/89) (DECC) ① [2] **421 608-2DM2**
Cpte M. Stader, O. Dominguez, G. Carelli, I. Sardi, Berlin St Hedwig's Cath Ch, Berlin RSO, F. Fricsay (pp1960) *Pezzi sacri.* (11/89) (DG) ① [2] **429 076-2GDO2**
Cpte S. Sweet, F. Quivar, V. Cole, S. Estes, Ernst Senff Chor, BPO, C.M. Giulini (1989) (2/90) (DG) ① [2] **423 674-2GH2**

Cpte H. Nelli, F. Barbieri, G. di Stefano, C. Siepi, R. Shaw Chorale, NBC SO, A. Toscanini (bp1951) *Concert* (5/90) (RCA) ① [7] **GD60326**
Cpte M.L. Fanelli, I. Minghini-Cattaneo, F. Lo Giudice, E. Pinza, La Scala Chor, La Scala Orch, C. Sabajno (r1929) (5/90) (PEAR) ① **GEMMCD9374**
Cpte M. Cunitz, E. Höngen, W. Ludwig, J. Greindl, Bavarian Rad Chor, BRSO, E. Jochum (pp1950) *Bruckner: Te Deum.* (8/90) (ORFE) ① [2] **C195892H**
Cpte M. Caballé, F. Cossotto, J. Vickers, R. Raimondi, New Philh Chor, New Philh, J. Barbirolli *Mozart: Requiem.* (10/90) (EMI) ① [2] **CZS7 62892-2**
Cpte C. Vaness, F. Quivar, D. O'Neill, C. Colombara, Bavarian Rad Chor, BRSO, Colin Davis (1/93) (RCA) ① [2] **09026 60902-2**
Cpte L. Price, J. Baker, V. Luchetti, J. Van Dam, Chicago Sym Chor, Chicago SO, G. Solti (r1977) (9/93) (RCA) ① [2] **09026 61403-2**
Cpte C. Studer, M. Lipovšek, J. Carreras, R. Raimondi, Vienna St Op Concert Ch, VPO, C. Abbado (pp1991) *Pezzi sacri.* (9/93) (DG) ① [2] **435 884-2GH2**
Cpte M. Gauci, G. Alperyn, D. George, P. Mikuláš, Slovak Phil Chor, Slovak Radio New PO, A. Rahbari (r1993) (2/94) (DINT) ① [2] **DICD920105/6**
Cpte A. Marc, W. Meier, P. Domingo, F. Furlanetto, Chicago Sym Chor, Chicago SO, D. Barenboim (r1993) (11/94) (ERAT) ① [2] **4509-96357-2**
Cpte E. Connell, A. Gunson, E. Barham, J. Tomlinson, Brighton Fest Chor, RCS, RPO, O.A. Hughes (pp1994) (11/94) (EMIN) ① [2] **CD-EMXD2503**
Cpte Z. Milanov, B. Castagna, J. Björling, N. Moscona, Westminster Ch, NBC SO, A. Toscanini (pp1940) *Pezzi Sacri.* (3/95) (MUSI) ① [2] **MACD-240**
Cpte M. Caniglia, E. Stignani, B. Gigli, E. Pinza, Rome Op Chor, Rome Op Orch, T. Serafin (r1939) (3/95) (DUTT) ① **CDLX7010**
Cpte M. Stader, O. Dominguez, G. Carelli, I. Sardi, Berlin St Hedwig's Cath Ch, Berlin RIAS Orch, F. Fricsay (pp1960) *Rossini: Stabat Mater.* (4/95) (DG) ① [2] **439 684-2GX2**
Cpte O. Romanko, S. Toczyska, V. Ombuena, F. de Grandis, Bulgarian Nat Ch, Sofia PO, E. Tabakov (r1994) *Pezzi sacri.* (4/95) (CAPR) ① [2] **10 646/7**
Cpte L. Orgonášová, A. S. von Otter, L. Canonici, A. Miles, Monteverdi Ch, ORR, J. E. Gardiner (r1992) *Pezzi sacri.* (4/95) (PHIL) ① [2] **442 142-2PH2**
Cpte M. Caniglia, E. Stignani, B. Gigli, E. Pinza, Rome Op Chor, Rome Op Orch, T. Serafin (r1939) (9/95) (PEAR) ① **GEMMCD9162**
Cpte E. Schwarzkopf, O. Dominguez, G. di Stefano, C. Siepi, La Scala Chor, La Scala Orch, V. de Sabata (r1954) *Concert* (9/95) (EMI) ① [2] **CHS5 65506-2**
8. L. Pavarotti, VPO, G. Solti *Concert* (7/86) (DECC) ① [2] **417 011-2DH2**
8. J. Björling, Hilversum RO, F. Weissmann (pp1939) *Concert* (8/88) (BLUE) ① **ABCD006**
8. J. Björling, Bergen SO, C. Garaguly (pp1954) *Concert* (8/88) (BLUE) ① **ABCD006**
8. N. Gedda, Philh, C.M. Giulini *Concert* (8/89) (CFP) ① **CD-CFP4532**
8. F. Marconi, S. Cottone (r1903) *Concert* (10/90) (SYMP) ① **SYMCD1069**
8. E. Caruso, orch, W.B. Rogers (r1915) *Concert* (7/91) (RCA) ① [12] **GD60495(5)**
8. E. Caruso, orch, W.B. Rogers (r1915) *Concert* (10/91) (PEAR) ① [3] **EVC3(2)**
8. L. Pavarotti, VPO, G. Solti *Concert* (12/91) (DECC) ① **433 710-2DH**
8. J. Björling, orch, N. Grevillius (r1938) *Concert* (1/93) (MMOI) ① **CDMOIR411**
8. J. Björling, orch, N. Grevillius (r1938) *Concert* (10/93) (EMI) ① **CDH7 64707-2**
8. J. Björling, orch, N. Grevillius (r1938) *Concert* (2/94) (MYTO) ① [2] **2MCD90317**
8. G. Zenatello, orch (r1916) *Concert* (5/94) (PEAR) ① [4] **GEMMCDS9074(2)**
8. J. Björling, orch, N. Grevillius (r1938) *Concert* (9/94) (CARL) ① **GLRS103**
8. J. Björling, orch, N. Grevillius (r1938) *Concert* (9/94) (CONI) ① **CDHD214**
8. J. Björling, VPO, F. Reiner (r1959) *Concert* (10/95) (DECC) ① **443 930-2DM**
9. E. Pinza, orch, R. Bourdon (r1929) *Concert* (2/89) (PEAR) ① **GEMMCD9306**
9. E. Pinza, orch, R. Bourdon (r1929) *Concert* (7/91) (MMOI) ① **CDMOIR404**
9. E. Pinza, orch, R. Bourdon (r1929) *Concert* (3/92) (PREI) ① **89050**
9. E. Pinza, La Scala Orch, C. Sabajno (r1929) *Concert* (1/93) (MMOI) ① **CDMOIR411**
9. E. Pinza, orch, R. Bourdon (r1929) *Concert* (9/93) (RCA) ① **09026 61245-2**
9. L. Sibiriakov, orch (r1913) *Concert* (3/95) (NIMB) ① **NI7865**
9. T. Pasero, SO, D. Marzollo (r1944) *Concert* (4/95) (PREI) ① **89074**
12. Chicago Sym Chor, Chicago SO, G. Solti *Concert* (4/91) (DECC) ① **430 226-2DH**
13. M. Caballé, F. Cossotto, New Philh Chor, New Philh, J. Barbirolli *Concert* (8/89) (CFP) ① **CD-CFP4532**
15. E. Schwarzkopf, La Scala Chor, La Scala Orch, V. de Sabata (r1954) *Concert* (12/90) (EMI) ① **CDM7 63657-2**

Pater Noster—5vv a capella (1880)
Lower Rhine Choral Soc, H. Schmitt *Concert* (2/90) (SCHW) ① **313001**

Pietà, Signor—song (1894) (Wds. Boito)
R. Scotto, I. Davis (pp1983) *Concert* (10/86) (ETCE) ① **KTC2002**

Il **Poveretto—canzona (1847)** (Wds. Maggioni)
J. Carreras, Martin Katz *Concert* (9/90) (SONY) ① **SK45863**

La **Preghiera del poeta—song (?1858)** (Wds. Sole)
R. Scotto, I. Davis (pp1983) *Concert* (10/86) (ETCE) ① **KTC2002**

Quattro pezzi sacri—chorus and orchestra (pub 1898)
1. Ave Maria (1889); 2. Stabat mater (1896-97); 3. Laudi alla Vergine Maria (wds. Dante: c1890); 4. Te Deum (1895-96).
Cpte A. Auger, Swedish Rad Ch, Stockholm Chbr Ch, BPO, R. Muti (3/85) (EMI) ① **CDC7 47066-2**
Cpte J. Baker, Philh Chor, Philh, C.M. Giulini (r1962) *Requiem.* (4/87) (EMI) ① [2] **CDS7 47257-8**
Cpte Y. Minton, Los Angeles Master Chorale, Los Angeles PO, Z. Mehta *Requiem.* (8/89) (DECC) ① [2] **421 608-2DM2**
Cpte Berlin St Hedwig's Cath Ch, Berlin RIAS Chbr Ch, Berlin RSO, F. Fricsay (pp1952) *Requiem.* (11/89) (DG) ① [2] **429 076-2GDO2**
Cpte Atlanta Sym Chor, Atlanta SO, Robert Shaw *Stravinsky: Symphony of Psalms.* (10/91) (TELA) ① **CD80254**
Cpte S. Sweet, Ernst Senff Chor, BPO, C.M. Giulini *Vivaldi: Credo, RV591.* (10/91) (SONY) ① **SK46491**
Cpte C. Studer, Vienna St Op Concert Ch, VPO, C. Abbado (r1991) *Requiem.* (9/93) (DG) ① [2] **435 884-2GH2**
Cpte Bulgarian Nat Ch, Sofia PO, E. Tabakov (r1994) *Requiem.* (4/95) (CAPR) ① [2] **10 646/7**
Cpte D. Brown, Monteverdi Ch, ORR, J. E. Gardiner (r1992) *Requiem.* (4/95) (PHIL) ① [2] **442 142-2PH2**
1. Cambridge Sngrs, J. Rutter *Concert* (4/92) (CLLE) ① **COLCD116**
4. Atlanta Sym Chor, Atlanta SO, Robert Shaw *Concert* (9/85) (TELA) ① [2] **CD80109**
4. R. Shaw Chorale, NBC SO, A. Toscanini (bp1954) *Concert* (5/90) (RCA) ① [7] **GD60326**
4. Westminster Ch, NBC SO, A. Toscanini (pp1940) *Requiem.* (3/95) (MUSI) ① [2] **MACD-240**

6 Romanze (1838) (Wds. various)
1. Non t'accostare all'urna (wds. J. Vittorelli); 2. More, Elisa, lo stanco poeta (wds. T. Bianchi); 3. In solitaria stanza (wds. J. Vittorelli); 4. Nell'orror di notte oscura (wds. C. Angiolini); 5. Perduta ho lo pace (wds. J. W. Goethe, trans L. Balestra); 6. Deh pietoso, oh Addolorata (wds. J. W. Goethe, trans L. Balestra).
3. J. Carreras, Martin Katz *Concert* (9/90) (SONY) ① **SK45863**

6 Romanze (1845) (Wds. various)
1. Il tramonto (wds. A. Maffei); 2. La zingara (wds. S. M. Maggioni); 3. Lo spazzacamino (wds. F. Romani); 4. Lo spazzicamino (wds. F. Romani); 5. Il mistero (wds. F. Romani); 6. Brindisi (wds. A. Maffei).
1, 6. J. Carreras, Martin Katz *Concert* (9/90) (SONY) ① **SK45863**
4. E. Schwarzkopf, M. Raucheisen (bp1944) *Concert* (6/87) (ACAN) ① **43 801**

Stornello—canzona (1869) (Wds. Anon)
R. Scotto, I. Davis (pp1983) *Concert* (10/86) (ETCE) ① **KTC2002**

SECTION V: STAGE WORKS

Aida—opera: 4 acts (1871—Cairo) (Lib. A Ghislanzoni, after A Mariette)
EXCERPTS: 1. Prelude. ACT 1: 2. Si, corre voce; 3a. Se quel guerrier; 3b. Celeste Aida; 4a. Quale insolita gioia; 4b. Vieni o diletta; 5a. Alta cagion v'aduna; 5b. Or di vulcano al tempio; 5c. Sul del Nilo; 6a. Ritorna vincitor; 6b. L'insana parola; 6c. I sacri nomi; 7a. Possente Possenta—Immenso Ftha; 7b. Dance of the Priestesses; 7c. Mortal diletto. ACT 2: 8a. Chi mai; 8b. Dance of the Moorish slaves; 9a. Fu la sortè dell' armi; 9b. Amore, amore; 10a. Gloria all' Egitto; 10b. March ('Grand March'); 10c. Ballabile; 10d. Vieni, o guerriero; 10e. Quest'assisa; 11. O Re, pei sacri Numi. ACT 3: 12a. O tu che sei d'Osiride; 12b. Vieni d'Iside; 12c. Qui Radames verrà; 12d. O patria mia; 13. Ciel mio padre; 14a. Pur' ti riveggo; 14b. Fuggiam gli ardor ... Là, tra foreste vergini; 14c. Tu! Amonasro!...Io son disonorato!. ACT 4: 15a. Introduction; 15b. L'abborita rivale; 15c. Già i sacerdoti; 15d. Misero appien mi festi; 16a. Ohimè morir mi sento; 16b. Spirto del nume; 17a. La fatale pietra; 17b. Morir si pura e bella; 18a. Immenso immenso; 18b. O terra addio.
Cpte K. Ricciarelli, E. Obraztsova, P. Domingo, L. Nucci, N. Ghiaurov, R. Raimondi, P. de Palma, L.V. Terrani, La Scala Chor, La Scala Orch, C. Abbado (12/82) (DG) ① [3] **410 092-2GH3**
Cpte M. Caballé, F. Cossotto, P. Domingo, P. Cappuccilli, N. Ghiaurov, L. Roni, N. Martinucci, E. Casas, ROH Chor, New Philh, R. Muti (r1974) (1/87) (EMI) ① [3] **CDS7 47271-8**
Cpte L. Price, R. Gorr, J. Vickers, R. Merrill, G. Tozzi, P. Clabassi, F. Ricciardi, M. Sighele, Rome Op Chor, Rome Op Orch, G. Solti (r1961) (9/87) (DECC) ① [3] **417 416-2DH3**
Cpte M. Callas, F. Barbieri, R. Tucker, T. Gobbi, G. Modesti, N. Zaccaria, F. Ricciardi, E. Galassi, La Scala Chor, La Scala Orch, T. Serafin (r1955) (11/87) (EMI) ① [3] **CDS7 49030-8**
Cpte M. Freni, A. Baltsa, J. Carreras, P. Cappuccilli, R. Raimondi, J. Van Dam, T. Moser, K. Ricciarelli, Vienna St Op Chor, VPO, H. von Karajan (r1979) (4/88) (EMI) ① [3] **CMS7 69300-2**
Cpte L. Price, G. Bumbry, P. Domingo, S. Milnes, R. Raimondi, H. Sotin, B. Brewer, J. Mathis, John Alldis Ch, LSO, E. Leinsdorf (r1970) (8/88) (RCA) ① [3] **RD86198**
Cpte Z. Milanov, F. Barbieri, J. Björling, L. Warren, B. Christoff, P. Clabassi, Mario Carlin, B. Rizzoli, Rome Op Chor, Rome Op Orch, J. Perlea (r1955) (8/88) (RCA) ① [3] **GD86652**
Cpte R. Tebaldi, G. Simionato, C. Bergonzi, C. MacNeil, A. Van Mill, F. Corena, P. de Palma, E. Ratti, Vienna Singverein, VPO, H. von Karajan (1/89) (DECC) ① [3] **414 087-2DM3**
Cpte B. Nilsson, G. Bumbry, F. Corelli, M. Sereni, B. Giaiotti, F. Mazzoli, P. de Palma, M. Fiorentini, Rome Op Chor, Rome Op Orch, Z. Mehta (r1966) (1/90) (EMI) ① [2] **CMS7 63229-2**
Cpte M. Chiara, G. Dimitrova, L. Pavarotti, L. Nucci, P. Burchuladze, L. Roni, E. Gavazzi, M. Renée, La Scala Chor, La Scala Orch, L. Maazel (5/90) (DECC) ① [3] **417 439-2DH3**
Cpte M. Caniglia, E. Stignani, B. Gigli, G. Bechi, T. Pasero, I. Tajo, A. Zagonara, M. Huder, Rome Op Chor, Rome Op Orch, T. Serafin (r1946) (5/90) (EMI) ① [2] **CHS7 63331-2**
Cpte H. Nelli, E. Gustavson, R. Tucker, G. Valdengo, N. Scott, D. Harbour, V. Assandri, T. Stich-Randall, R. Shaw Chorale, NBC SO, A. Toscanini (bp1949) *Concert* (5/90) (RCA) ① [7] **GD60326**
Cpte A. Millo, D. Zajick, P. Domingo, J. Morris, S. Ramey, T. Cook, C. Anthony, H-K. Hong, NY Met Op Chor, NY Met Op Orch, James Levine (5/91) (SONY) ① [3] **S3K45973**
Cpte M. Dragoni, B. Dever, K. Johannsson, M. Rucker, F.E. D'Artegna, R. Ferrari, A. Marceno, M. Trini, RTE Phil Ch, RTE Chbr Ch, Culwick Choral Soc, Bray Choral Soc, Dublin County Ch, Dun Laoghaire Choral Soc, Cantabile Sngrs, Goethe Institut Ch, Musica Sacra Sngrs, Phoenix Sngrs, Irish Army Band, Ireland National SO, R. Saccani (r1994) (10/95) (NAXO) ① [2] **8 660033/4**
Excs J. Björling, M. Németh, K. Thorborg, A. Sved, L. Hofmann, Vienna St Op Chor, Vienna St Op Orch, V. de Sabata (pp1936: Ger/Swed) *Concert* (12/94) (SCHW) ① [2] **314542**
Excs M. Németh, R. Anday, K. von Pataky, A. Sved, N. Zec, C. Bissuti, Vienna St Op Chor, Vienna St Op Orch, V. de Sabata (pp1936: Ger) *Concert* (12/94) (SCHW) ① [2] **314542**
Excs T. Mazaroff, M. Németh, K. Thorborg, A. Sved, H. Alsen, Vienna St Op Chor, Vienna St Op Orch, B. Walter (pp1937: Ger) *Concert* (2/95) (SCHW) ① [2] **314572**
Excs S. Svanholm, D. Ilitsch, H. Hotter, E. Nikolaidi, J. von Manowarda, M. Rus, Vienna St Op Chor, Vienna St Op Orch, V. Gui (pp1941: Ger) *Concert* (4/95) (SCHW) ① [2] **314582**
Excs B. Gigli, M. Németh, R. Anday, N. Zec, A. Sved, A. Kipnis, Vienna St Op Chor, Vienna St Op Orch, K. Alwin (pp1937: Ital/Ger) *Concert* (6/95) (SCHW) ① [2] **314632**

Alzira—opera: prologue & 2 acts (1845—Naples) (Lib. S. Cammarano)

EXCERPTS: 1. Overture. PROLOGUE: 2. Muoia, muoia coverto d'insulti; 3a. Ah! Tu! Fia vero!; 3b. Ed a' nemici ancora; 3c. Una inca...eccesso orribile!; 3d. Risorto fra le tenebre; 3e. Dio della guerra. ACT 1: 4. Giunse or, da lido ispano; 5a. Alta cagion qui v'assembrara; 5b. Eterna la memoria; 5c. Quanto un mortal puo chiedere; 6a. Riposa. Tutte, in suo dolor vegliante; 6b. Da Gusman, su fragil barca; 6c. Nell'astro più che fulgido; 7. Figlia! Padre!; 8a. Anima mia!; 8b. Risorge ne'tuoi lumi; 9a. Qual ardimento! Ola?; 9b. Teco sperai combattare; 9c. Nella polvem, genuflesso; 9d. Qual suon? Che avvenne?; 9e. Trema, trema...a ritorni fra l'armi. ACT 2: 10. Mesci, mesci, Vittoria! Vittoria!; 11a. Guerreri, al nuovi di, fra voi le opime; 11b. Il pianto, il gaudio, la ragion di lena mi priva; 12a. Di prai non più; 12b. Colma di gioia ho l'anima; 13. Amicil Propizio; 14a. Miserandi avanzi; 14b. Irne lunghi ancor dovrei; 14c. Non di codarde lagrime; 15. Tergi del pianto America; 16a. Prodi figli d'Iberia; 16b. E dolce la trombla che suo vittorio; 17a.

La mano e questa che a te si deve; 17b. Altre virtudo, insam.
1. BPO, H. von Karajan *Concert*
(1/95) (DG) ① **439 972-2GGA2**
6a, 6b M. Caballé, RCA Italiana Op Chor, RCA Italiana Op Orch, A. Guadagno *Concert*
(11/92) (RCA) ① [2] **GD60941**

Aroldo—opera: 4 acts (1857—Rimini) (Lib. F. Piave)

EXCERPTS: 1. Overture. ACT 1: 2. Tocchiamo!; 3. Ciel, ch'io respiri!; 4. Salvami to, gran Dio; 5. Egli vieni; 6. Sotto il sol di Siria; 7. Ma lagrima ti grondanol; 8. Ebben, parlatemi; 9. Tosto ei dissel; 10. Dite che il fallo; 11. Ed io pure in faccia; 12. Or meco venite; 13. O Mina, tu mi sfuggi; 14. E'bello di guerra; 15. Eterna vivra in Kenth; 16. Vi fi in Palestina; 17. Oh, qual m'invade; 18. Chi ti salve. ACT 2: 19. Oh cielo! Ove son io?; 20. Ah, dagli scanni; 21. Minal...Voi qui!; 22. Ah, dal sein di quella tomba; 23. Io resto; 24. Ah! Era vero?; 25. Dessa non è; 26. Non punirmi, o Signor. ACT 3: 27. Ei fugge!; 28. Mina, pensa che un angelo; 29. Oh, gioia inesprimibile; 30. L'istante s'avvicina!; 31. Opposto è il calle; 32. Non allo sposo; 33. Ah si, voliamo al tempio. ACT 4: 34. Cade il giorno; 35. Cantan felicil; 36. Angiol di Dio; 37. A lago (Burrasca); 38. Ah! più non reggo; 39. Ah, da me fuggi; 40. Allora che gli anni.

Attila—dramma lirico: prologue, 3 acts (1846—Venice) (Lib. Solera and Piave)

EXCERPTS: 1. Overture. PROLOGUE: 2. Urli, rapine; 3. Eroi, levatevi; 4a. Di vergini straniere; 4b. Santo di patria indefinito amor!; 5. Allor che i forti corrono; 6. Da te questo or m'è concesso; 7. Uldino, a me dinanzi l'inviato; 8. Attila!...Oh, il nobil messol; 9. Trado per gli anni, e tremulo; 10. Vanitosil; 11. Qual notte!; 12. L'alito del mattin...Preghiam!; 13. Quai vocil; 14. Ella in poter del barbarol; 15. Cara patria. ACT 1: 16a. Liberamente or piangi; 16b. Oh! nel fuggente nuvolo; 17. Qual suon di passil; 18a. Si, quell'io son; 18b. Va! Racconta al sacrilego; 18c. Oh! t'inebria nell'amplesso; 19a. Uldino! Uldinil; 19b. Mentre gonfiarsi l'anima; 19c. Oltre a quel limite t'attendo; 20. Parla, imponi...Vieni. Le menti visita; 21. No!...non è sogno. ACT 2: 22a. Tregua è cogl'Unni; 22b. Dagli immortali vertici; 22c. Che vien?...Salute ad Ezio; 22d. È gettata la mia sorte; 23a. Del ciel l'immensa volta; 23b. Ezio, ben vienil; 23c. Chi dona luce al di?...Ah!...Lo spirto de'monti; 23e. L'orrenda procella; 23f. Si riaccendan le quercie; 23g. Oh, miei prodi! ACT 3: 24. Qui del convengo è il loco; 25. Non avrebbe il misero; 26. Che più s'indugia; 27. Cessa, seh, cessa; 28. Te sol, te sol spero l'amplesso; 29. Non involarti, seguimi; 30a. Tu, rea donna; 30b. Nella tenda. ADDITIONAL ITEM: 31. Oh. Dolore.

Un **ballo in maschera, '(A) masked ball'**—opera: 3 acts (1859—Rome) (Lib. Somma)
EXCERPTS: 1. Prelude; ACT 1: 2a. Posa in pace; 2b. Amici miei...soldati; 2c. La rivedrà nell'estasi; 3a. Conte...Oh ciel!; 3b. Alla vita che t'arride; 4a. Il primo giudice; 4b. Volta la terrea; 4c. Sia condonnata; 5a. Zitti...l'incanto non dèssi turbare; 5b. Re dell'abisso; 5c. Arrivo il primo!; 5d. È lui, è lui!; 6. Su, fatemi largo; 7a. Sentite, la mia Signora; 7b. Che v'agita così?; 7c. Della città all'occaso; 8a. Su, profetessa; 8b. Di' tu se fedele; 9. Chi voi siate; 10. È scherzo od è follia; 11a. Finisci il vaticinio; 11b. O figlio d'Inghilterra. ACT 2: 12a. Prelude; 12b. Ecco l'orrido campo; 12c. Ma dall'arido stelo divulsa; 13a. Teco io sto; 13b. M'ami. m'ami; 13c. Oh, qual soave brivido; 14a. Ahimè! S'appressa; 14b. Amico, gelosa; 14c. Odi tu come fremono cupi; 15a. Seguitemi; 15b. Ve', se di notte. ACT 3: 16a. A tal colpa; 16b. Morrò, ma prima in grazia; 17a. Alzati! la tuo figlio; 17b. Eri tu che macchiavi; 18a. Siam soli; 18b. Dunque l'onta; 19a. Il messaggio entri; 19b. Di che fulgor; 20a. Forse la soglia; 20b. Ma se m'è forza perderti; 21a. Fervono amori; 21b. Saper vorreste; 22a. Ah! perchè qui!; 22b. T'amo, sì, t'amo; 23a. E tu ricevi il mio!; 23b. Ah! Morte, infamia; 23c. Ella è pura (Finale).
Cpte M. Price, L. Pavarotti, R. Bruson, K. Battle, C. Ludwig, R. Lloyd, M. King, P. Weber, A. Oliver, P. Hall, London Op Chor, RCM Jnr Chor, National PO, G. Solti (r1982/3)
(9/85) (DECC) ① [2] 410 210-2DH2
Cpte K. Ricciarelli, P. Domingo, R. Bruson, E. Gruberová, E. Obraztsova, R. Raimondi, G. Foiani, L. de Corato, A. Savastano, G. Manganotti, La Scala Chor, La Scala Orch, C. Abbado
(9/86) (DG) ① [2] 415 685-2GH2
Cpte M. Callas, G. di Stefano, T. Gobbi, E. Ratti, F. Barbieri, S. Maionica, N. Zaccaria, E. Giordano, R. Ercolani, La Scala Chor, La Scala Orch, A. Votto (r1956)
(9/87) (EMI) ① [2] CDS7 47498-8
Cpte L. Price, C. Bergonzi, R. Merrill, R. Grist, S. Verrett, E. Flagello, F. Mazzoli, M. Basiola II, P. de Palma, F. Iacopucci, RCA Italiana Op Chor, RCA Italiana Op Orch, E. Leinsdorf
(11/88) (RCA) ① [2] GD86645
Cpte M. Arroyo, P. Domingo, P. Cappuccilli, R. Grist, F. Cossotto, G. Howell, R. Van Allan, G. Giorgetti, K. Collins, D. Barrett, Haberdashers' Aske's Sch Girls' Ch, ROH Chor, Medici Qt, New Philh, R. Muti
(11/88) (EMI) ① [2] CMS7 69576-2
Cpte J. Barstow, P. Domingo, L. Nucci, S. Jo, F. Quivar, K. Rydl, G. Simic, J-L. Chaignaud, W. Witte, A. Tomaschek, Vienna St Op Chor, VPO, H. von Karajan (1989)
(11/89) (DG) ① [2] 427 635-2GH2
Cpte M. Caballé, J. Carreras, I. Wixell, S. Ghazarian, P. Payne, R. Lloyd, G. Howell, J. Summers, R. Leggate, W. Elvin, ROH Chor, ROHO, Colin Davis (1/91) (PHIL) ① [2] 426 560-2PM2
Cpte H. Nelli, J. Peerce, R. Merrill, V. Haskins, C. Turner, N. Moscona, N. Scott, G. Cehanovsky, J.C. Rossi, R. Shaw Chorale, NBC SO, A. Toscanini (bp1954)
(7/91) (RCA) ① [2] GD60301
Cpte Z. Milanov, J. Björling, A. Sved, S. Andreva, B. Castagna, N. Cordon, N. Moscona, A. Kent, J. Carter, L. Oliviero, NY Met Op Chor, NY Met Op Orch, E. Panizza (pp1940) Concert
(2/94) (MYTO) ① [2] 2MCD90317
Cpte R. Tebaldi, L. Pavarotti, S. Milnes, H. Donath, R. Resnik, L. Monreale, N. Christov, J. van Dam, P. Poli, M. Alessandrini, Santa Cecilia Academy Chor, Santa Cecilia Academy Orch, B. Bartoletti (1970)
(5/94) (DECC) ① [2] 440 042-2DMO2
Excs M. Lorenz, M. Ahlersmeyer, H. Konetzni, E. Nikolaidi, A. Noni, S. Roth, M. Rus, F. Wörff, Vienna St Op Chor, Vienna St Op Orch, K. Böhm (pp1942: Ger) Concert
(4/95) (SCHW) ① [2] 314582
Excs P. Gallois, London Fest Orch, R. Pople (r1993: arr fl: Genin/Pierre) Concert
(5/95) (DG) ① 445 822-2GH
1. BPO, H. von Karajan Concert
(10/87) (DG) ① 419 622-2GH
1. BPO, H. von Karajan Concert
(5/90) (DG) ① 429 164-2GR
1. BPO, H. von Karajan Concert
(1/95) (DG) ① 439 972-2GGA2
2a Chicago Sym Chor, Chicago SO, G. Solti Concert
(4/91) (DECC) ① 430 226-2DH
2b, 2c, 10. F. Hempel, M. Duchêne, E. Caruso, L. Rothier, A. de Segurola, NY Met Op Chor, orch, G. Scognamiglio (r1914) Concert
(7/91) (RCA) ① [12] GD60495(5)
2b, 2c, 10. F. Hempel, M. Duchêne, E. Caruso, A. de Segurola, L. Rothier, NY Met Op Chor, orch, G. Scognamiglio (r1914) Concert
(10/91) (PEAR) ① [3] EVC3(1)

2c K. Battle, L. Pavarotti, R. Lloyd, M. King, London Op Chor, National PO, G. Solti Concert
(7/90) (DECC) ① [2] 425 681-2DM2
2c, 8b L. Slezak, orch (Ger: r1907) Concert
(2/91) (PREI) ① 89020
2c, 8b G. Zenatello, anon (r1905) Concert
(12/93) (SYMP) ① SYMCD1138
2c, 8b G. Zenatello, chor, orch (r1908) Concert
(12/93) (SYMP) ① SYMCD1138
2c, 8b G. Zenatello, chor, orch (r1908) Concert
(5/94) (PEAR) ① [4] GEMMCDS9073(2)
2c, 8b G. Zenatello, chor, anon (r1905) Concert
(5/94) (PEAR) ① [4] GEMMCDS9073(1)
3b T. Ruffo, orch (r1912) Concert
(2/93) (PREI) ① [3] 89303(1)
3b M. Ahlersmeyer, Vienna St Op Orch, K. Böhm (pp1942: Ger) Concert (6/94) (SCHW) ① 314502
3b, 17b M. Battistini, orch (r1906) Concert
(2/92) (PREI) ① 89045
3b, 17b M. Battistini, orch, C. Sabajno (r1906) Concert (10/92) (NIMB) ① NI7831
3b, 17b M. Battistini, orch, C. Sabajno (r1906) Concert (10/92) (PEAR) ① GEMMCD9936
3b, 17b P. Lisitsian, Bolshoi Th Orch, O. Bron (r1952: Russ) Concert (8/93) (PREI) ① 89061
4b F. Hempel, orch (r1916) Concert
(3/94) (NIMB) ① NI7849
5b M. Anderson, NY Met Op Chor, NY Met Op Orch, D. Mitropoulos (r1955) Concert
(1/90) (RCA) ① GD87911
5b I. Minghini-Cattaneo, La Scala Orch, C. Sabajno (r1930) Concert (6/90) (PREI) ① 89008
5b E. Stignani, EIAR Orch, A. la Rosa Parodi (1940) Concert (1/91) (PREI) ① 89014
5b K. Branzell, orch (Ger: r1927) Concert
(8/92) (PREI) ① 89039
5b M. Anderson, NY Met Op Orch, D. Mitropoulos (r1955) Concert
(4/94) (RCA) ① [6] 09026 61580-2(6)
5b M. Klose, Berlin St Op Orch, B. Seidler-Winkler (r1936: Ger) Concert (7/95) (PREI) ① 89082
7b G. Zenatello, E. Burzio, E. Petri, anon (r1907) Concert (5/94) (PEAR) ① [4] GEMMCDS9073(1)
8a, 8b, 20a, 20b P. Domingo, R. Grist, ROH Chor, New Philh, R. Muti (r1975) Concert
(6/94) (EMI) ① CDC5 55017-2
8a, 8b, 23c G. Zenatello, S. Marion, A. Boemi, Apollo Chor, orch, R. Bourdon (1930) Concert
(5/94) (PEAR) ① [4] GEMMCDS9074(2)
8b J. Björling, orch, N. Grevillius (r1944) Concert
(10/88) (EMI) ① CDH7 61053-2
8b E. Caruso, orch (r1911) Concert
(5/89) (PEAR) ① GEMMCD9309
8b E. Caruso, NY Met Op Chor, orch (r1911) Concert
(10/89) (NIMB) ① NI7803
8b J. Patzak, orch, M. Gurlitt (Ger: r1929) Concert
(3/90) (PEAR) ① GEMMCD9383
8b E. Caruso, NY Met Op Chor, orch (r1911) Concert
(7/91) (RCA) ① [12] GD60495(4)
8b G. Zenatello, chor, orch (r1916) Concert
(5/94) (PEAR) ① [4] GEMMCDS9074(2)
8b H. Roswaenge, Berlin St Op Orch, B. Seidler-Winkler (r1936: Ger) Concert
(4/95) (PREI) ① 89209
8b J. Björling, MMF Orch, A. Erede (r1959) Concert
(10/95) (DECC) ① 443 930-2DM
8b, 20a, 20b P. Domingo, La Scala Orch, C. Abbado Concert (7/86) (DG) ① 415 366-2GH
8b, 20a, 20b E. Caruso, NY Met Op Chor, orch (r1911) Concert (3/91) (PEAR) ① [3] EVC3
8b, 23b, 23c G. Zenatello, S. Marion, A. Boemi, Apollo Chor, orch, R. Bourdon (1930) Concert
(11/91) (CLUB) ① CL99-025
8b, 23b, 23c G. Zenatello, S. Marion, A. Boemi, Apollo Chor, orch, R. Bourdon (1930) Concert
(11/91) (PREI) ① 89038
12a-c R. Hunter, Tasmanian SO, D. Franks (1989) Concert (10/95) (ABCC) ① 8 7000 10
12b, 12c A. Tomowa-Sintow, Munich RO, P. Sommer (r1986) (ORFE) ① C106841A
12b, 12c M. Callas, Paris Cons, N. Rescigno Concert
(9/87) (EMI) ① CDC7 47730-2
12b, 12c M. Seinemeyer, Berlin St Op Orch, F. Weissmann (Ger: r1929) Concert
(11/90) (PREI) ① 89029
12b, 12c, 13. M. Callas, G. di Stefano, La Scala Chor, La Scala Orch, A. Votto (r1956) Concert
(2/90) (EMI) ① [4] CMS7 63244-2
12b, 12c, 16b R. Tebaldi, New Philh, O. de Fabritiis Concert (8/91) (DECC) ① [2] 430 481-2DX2
12c H. Spani, La Scala Orch, C. Sabajno (r1927) Concert (9/90) (CLUB) ① [2] CL99-509/10
12c J. Gadski, orch (r1914) Concert
(7/91) (CLUB) ① CL99-109
12c C. Boninsegna, orch, C. Sabajno (r1905) Concert (7/92) (PEAR) ① [3] GEMMCDS9924(1)

12c H. Spani, La Scala Orch, C. Sabajno (r1927) Concert (12/92) (PREI) ① 89037
12c C. Muzio, orch (r1918) Concert
(1/95) (ROMO) ① [2] 81010-2
12c E. Rethberg, Victor SO, R. Bourdon (r1929) Concert (10/95) (ROMO) ① [2] 81014-2
12c, 16b G. Arangi-Lombardi, La Scala Orch, L. Molajoli (r1933) Concert (10/90) (PREI) ① 89013
12c, 16b G. Cigna, orch, L. Molajoli (r1932) Concert
(11/90) (PREI) ① 89016
12c, 16b G. Cigna, orch, L. Molajoli (r1932) Concert
(11/90) (LYRC) ① SRO805
12c, 16b M. Németh, orch (Ger) Concert
(1/94) (CLUB) ① CL99-007
13a K. Ricciarelli, P. Domingo, Santa Cecilia Academy Orch, G. Gavazzeni Concert
(12/87) (RCA) ① GD86534
13a, 13b M. Price, L. Pavarotti, National PO, G. Solti Concert (12/91) (DECC) ① 430 724-2DM
13a(pt), 13b G. Zenatello, E. Burzio, anon (r1906) (5/94) (PEAR) ① [4] GEMMCDS9073(1)
13a, 13b, 13c M. Callas, G. di Stefano, La Scala Orch, A. Votto Concert
(10/88) (EMI) ① CDM7 69543-2
13b, 13c G. Zenatello, E. Mazzoleni, orch (r1909) Concert (5/94) (PEAR) ① [4] GEMMCDS9073(2)
13c G. Zenatello, E. Mazzoleni, anon (r1909) Concert
(12/93) (SYMP) ① SYMCD1138
13c G. Zenatello, E. Burzio, anon (r1906) Concert
(12/93) (SYMP) ① SYMCD1138
14a, 14b G. Russ, L. Longobardi, G. Pacini, anon (r1904) Concert (12/93) (SYMP) ① SYMCD1113
15b F. Leider, H. Schlusnus, O. Helgers, M. Abendroth, orch (Ger: r1925) Concert
(5/91) (PREI) ① [3] 89301
16b M. Callas, Paris Cons, N. Rescigno Concert
(9/87) (EMI) ① CDC7 47943-2
16b E. Burzio, orch (r1913) Concert
(1/91) (CLUB) ① [2] CL99-587/8
16b E. Destinn, orch, J. Pasternack (r1921) Concert
(11/93) (ROMO) ① [2] 81002-2
16b K. Ricciarelli, Verona Arena Orch, B. Martinotti (pp) Concert (5/94) (DECC) ① [2] 443 018-2DF2
16b E. Destinn, orch, J. Pasternack (r1921) Concert
(12/94) (SUPR) ① [12] 11 2136-2(5)
16b E. Rethberg, Victor SO, R. Bourdon (r1930) Concert (10/95) (ROMO) ① [2] 81014-2
17. P. Amato, orch (r1914) Concert
(4/94) (RCA) ① [6] 09026 61580-2(2)
17a, 17b T. Gobbi, LSO, W. Braithwaite (r1952) Concert (10/89) (EMI) ① CDM7 63109-2
17a, 17b J. Hynninen, Estonian SO, E. Klas Concert
(4/90) (ONDI) ① ODE731-2
17a, 17b T. Ruffo, orch, W.B. Rogers (r1915) Concert
(11/90) (NIMB) ① NI7810
17a, 17b Bechi, Rome Op Orch, T. Serafin (r1943) Concert (4/94) (EMI) ① [3] CHS7 64864-2(2)
17b L. Tibbett, orch, R. Bourdon (r1929) Concert
(10/89) (NIMB) ① NI7801
17b G. Bechi, La Scala Orch, U. Berrettoni (r1941) Concert (3/90) (PREI) ① 89009
17b L. Tibbett, orch, R. Bourdon (r1930) Concert
(3/90) (RCA) ① GD87808
17b H. Schlusnus, Berlin St Op Orch, L. Blech (Ger: r1935) Concert (3/90) (PREI) ① 89006
17b C. Tagliabue, Turin EIAR Orch, U. Tansini (r1939) Concert (11/90) (PREI) ① 89015
17b L. Tibbett, orch, N. Shilkret (r1929) Concert
(3/91) (PEAR) ① GEMMCDS9452
17b G. De Luca, orch (r1917) Concert
(1/92) (PREI) ① 89036
17b G. Galeffi, La Scala Orch, L. Molajoli (r1926) Concert (11/92) (PREI) ① 89040
17b E. Danise, orch (r1921) Concert
(11/92) (MEMO) ① HR4408/9(2)
17b T. Ruffo, orch (r1915) Concert
(2/93) (PREI) ① [3] 89303(1)
17b G. De Luca, anon (r1902) Concert
(8/93) (SYMP) ① SYMCD1111
17b H. Hüsch, Berlin St Op Orch, H.U. Müller (r1937: Ger) Concert (3/94) (PREI) ① 89071
17b M. Ancona, orch (r1915) Concert
(10/95) (NIMB) ① NI7867
20a, 20b E. Caruso, orch (r1911) Concert
(10/89) (NIMB) ① NI7803
20a, 20b E. Caruso, NY Met Op Chor, orch (r1911) Concert (7/91) (RCA) ① [12] GD60495(4)
20a, 20b E. Caruso, orch (r1911) Concert
(7/91) (MSCM) ① MM30352
20a, 20b P. Domingo, La Scala Orch, C. Abbado Concert (6/94) (BELA) ① 450 121-2
20b H. Roswaenge, Berlin St Op Orch (1935: Ger) Concert (4/95) (PREI) ① 89209
21b L. Tetrazzini, orch (r1911) Concert
(10/89) (NIMB) ① NI7802

21b L. Tetrazzini, orch (r1911) *Concert* (10/90) (NIMB) Ⓓ **NI7808**
21b S. Kurz, orch (r c1909) *Concert* (7/92) (PEAR) Ⓓ [3] **GEMMCDS9924(1)**
21b L. Tetrazzini, orch, P. Pitt (r1909) *Concert* (9/92) (EMI) Ⓓ [3] **CHS7 63802-2(1)**
21b L. Tetrazzini, orch (r1911) *Concert* (9/92) (PEAR) Ⓓ **GEMMCD9223**
21b L. Tetrazzini, orch, P. Pitt (r1909) *Concert* (9/92) (PEAR) Ⓓ **GEMMCD9221**
21b K. Battle, National PO, G. Solti (r1983) *Concert* (10/93) (DECC) Ⓓ **436 461-2DM**

La **battaglia di Legnano, '(The) Battle of Legnano'—opera: 4 acts (1849—Rome)** (Lib. S. Cammarano)
EXCERPTS: 1. Overture. ACT 1: 2. Viva Italia!; 3a. O magnanima e prima; 3b. La pia materna mano; 4a. Viva Italia forte ed una; 4b. Spento tra la fiamme du Susa; 4c. Ah! m'abbraccia; 5. Giulive trombe!; 6. Plaude all'arrivo Milan dei forti; 7a. Voi lo diceste; 7b. Quante volte come un dono; 8. Che...signor!; 9. A frenarti, o cor; 10. Sposa... 11a. È ver? Sei d'altri; 11b. T'amai, t'amai qual angelo. ACT 2: 12a. Udiste?; 12b. Sì, tradi e invano; 13. Invia la baldanzosa Lombarda Lega; 14a. Ah! ben vi scorgo; 14b. Favellaste acerbi detti; 15. A che smarriti e pallidi?; 16. Le mie possenti squadre. ACT 3: 17a. Fra queste dense tenebre; 17b. Campioni della Morte; 18. Giuriam d'Italia; 19. Lida, Lida? Ove corri?; 20. Digli ch'è sangue italico; 21. Tu m'appellavi; 22. Se al nuovo di pugnando; 23. Rolando? M'ascolta; 24a. Regna la notte ancor; 24b. Ah! d'un consorte, o perfidi; 25. Vendetta d'un momento. ACT 4: 26. Deus meus, pone illos ut rotam; 27. Vittoria! Vittoria!; 28. Per la salvata Italia.
Cpte K. Ricciarelli, J. Carreras, M. Manuguerra, N. Ghiuselev, H. Lichtenberger, D. Kavrakos, J. Summers, F. Handlos, A. Murray, Austrian Rad Chor, Austrian RSO, L. Gardelli (r1977) (11/89) (PHIL) Ⓓ [2] **422 435-2PM2**
1. BPO, H. von Karajan *Concert* (10/87) (DG) Ⓓ **419 622-2GH**
1. BPO, H. von Karajan *Concert* (1/95) (DG) Ⓓ **439 972-2GGA2**
18, 26. Slovak Phil Chor, Bratislava RSO, O. Dohnányi *Concert* (4/91) (NAXO) Ⓓ **8 550241**

Il **Corsaro—opera: 3 acts (1848—Trieste)** (Lib. F Piave, after Byron)
EXCERPTS: 1. Prelude. ACT 1: 2. Come liberi volano i venti; 3a. Ah! sì, ben dite; 3b. Tutto parea sorridere; 3c. Della brezza col favore; 4. Si: de' corsari il fulmine; 5a. Egli non riede ancora!; 5b. Non so le tetre immagini; 6a. È pur tristo, o Medora; 6b. No, tu non sai comprendere; 6c. Tornerai, ma forse spenta. ACT 2: 7. Oh qual perenne gaudio t'aspetta; 8a. Nè sulla terra creatura alcuna; 8b. Vola talor dal carcere; 8c. Seide celebra con gioia e festa; 8d. Ah conforto è sol la speme; 9a. Sol grida di festa; 9b. O prodi miei, sorgete; 9c. Salve, Allah!; 10a. Giunge un Dervis; 10b. Di': que' ribaldi tremano; 11a. Resta ancora; 11b. Audace cotanto mostrarti pur sai?; 11c. Signor, trafitti giacciono. ACT 3: 12. Alfin questo corsaro è mio prigione!; 13a. Cento leggiarde vergini; 13b. Ma pria togliam dall'anima; 13c. S'avvicina il tuo momento; 14a. Eccola!...fingasi; 14b. Sia l'istante maledetto; 15. Eccomi progioniero!; 16. Ei dorme?; 17a. Seid la vuole; 17b. Non sai ti che sulla testa; 18. Sul capo mio discenda; 19. La terra, il ciel m'abborrino; 20a. Voi tacete; 20b. Per me felice; 20c. O mio Corrado, appressati.
Cpte J. Carreras, J. Norman, M. Caballé, G-P. Mastromei, J. Noble, C. Grant, A. Oliver, Ambrosian Sngrs, New Philh, L. Gardelli (r1975) (3/90) (PHIL) Ⓓ [2] **426 118-2PM2**
1. BPO, H. von Karajan *Concert* (10/87) (DG) Ⓓ **419 622-2GH**
1. BPO, H. von Karajan *Concert* (1/95) (DG) Ⓓ **439 972-2GGA2**
5a, 5b K. Ricciarelli, Rome PO, G. Gavazzeni *Concert* (12/87) (RCA) Ⓓ **GD86534**
5a, 5b M. Caballé, RCA Italiana Op Orch, A. Guadagno *Concert* (11/92) (RCA) Ⓓ [2] **GD60941**
5a, 5b K. Ricciarelli, Parma Teatro Regio Orch, G. Patanè (pp1976) *Concert* (5/94) (DECC) Ⓓ [2] **443 018-2DF2**
5a, 5b, 8a, 8b M. Callas, Paris Op Orch, N. Rescigno *Concert* (9/87) (EMI) Ⓓ **CDC7 47943-2**

Don Carlo—opera: 5 acts (1867 rev 1884—Paris) (Lib. Méry & du Locle. Italian version of Don Carlos)
EXCERPTS: ACT 1: 1. Su, cacciator; 2a. Fontainebleau! Foresta immensa; 2b. Io la vidi; 3a. Io suon del corno; 3b. Io sono uno stranier; 3c. Che mai fate voi?; 3d. Di qual amor; 4a. Al fedel ch'ora viene; 4b. L'ora fatale; 5. Inni di festa; 6. Il glorioso Re di Francia. ACT 2: 7. Carlo il sommo Imperatore; 8. Al chiostro di San Giusto; 9a. È lui! desso! l'Infante!; 9b. Qual pallor; 9c. Dio, che nell'alma infondere; 10. Sotto ai folti; 11. Nei giardin del bello; 12. La Regina!; 13. Che mai si fa nel suol francese; 14. Carlo ch'è sol il nostro amor; 15a. Io vengo a domandar; 15b. Perduta ben, mio sol tesor; 15c. Qual voce; 16a. Il Re!; 16b. Non pianger, mia compagna; 17a. Restate! Presso alla mia persona; 17b. O Signor, di Fiandre arrivo. ACT 3: 18a. A mezza-notte, ai giardin della Regina; 18b. Sei tu, sei tu; 19. Che disse mai?!; 20. Spuntato ecco il dì d'esultanza; 21. Nel posar sul mio capo la corona; 22. Sire, no, l'ora estrema. ACT 4: 23a. Ella giammai m'amò; 23b. Dormirò sol nel manto mio regal; 24a. Il Grande Inquisitor!...Son io dinanzi al Re?; 24b. Nell'ispano suol mai; 25a. Giustizia! o Sire; 25b. Ah! sii maledetto; 26. Pietà!; 27a. Ah! più non vedrò; 27b. O don fatale; 28a. Son io, mio Carlo; 28b. Convien qui dirci addio!; 28c. Per me giunto; 28d. O Carlo, ascolta; 28e. Io morrò; 29a. Mio Carlo, a te la spada; 29b. Ciel! suona a stormo!. ACT 5: 30. Tu che le vanità; 31a. È dessa!...Un detto, un sol; 31b. Vago sogno m'arrise; 31c. Ma lassù ci vedremo; 31d. Sì, per sempre! ADDITIONAL ARIAS: 32. Io l'ho perduta (for Italian 4-act version: Act 1 Scene 1).
Cpte P. Domingo, M. Caballé, S. Verrett, S. Milnes, R. Raimondi, G. Foiani, S. Estes, D. Wallis, R. Davies, J. Noble, M-R. del Campo, Ambrosian Op Chor, ROHO, C.M. Giulini (7/87) (EMI) Ⓓ [3] **CDS7 47701-8**
Cpte J. Carreras, M. Freni, A. Baltsa, P. Cappuccilli, N. Ghiaurov, R. Raimondi, J. Van Dam, E. Gruberová, H. Nitsche, C. Meletti, B. Hendricks, Berlin Deutsche Op Chor, BPO, H. von Karajan (r1978: 4-act vers) (4/88) (EMI) Ⓓ [3] **CMS7 69304-2**
Cpte F. Labò, A. Stella, F. Cossotto, E. Bastianini, B. Christoff, I. Vinco, A. Maddalena, A. Cattelani, F. Piva, P. de Palma, G. Matteini, La Scala Chor, La Scala Orch, G. Santini (r1961) (9/91) (DG) Ⓓ [3] **437 730-2GX3**
Cpte M. Sylvester, A. Millo, D. Zajick, V. Chernov, F. Furlanetto, S. Ramey, P. Plishka, J. Bunnell, D. Croft, J. H. Murray, K. Battle, NY Met Op Chor, NY Met Op Orch, James Levine (r1992) (4/93) (SONY) Ⓓ [3] **S3K52500**
Cpte M. Filippeschi, A. Stella, E. Nicolai, T. Gobbi, B. Christoff, G. Neri, P. Clabassi, L. di Lelio, P. Caroli, O. Moscucci, Rome Op Chor, Rome Op Orch, G. Santini (r1954: 4-act ver) (4/93) (EMI) Ⓓ [3] **CMS7 64642-2**
Cpte L. Pavarotti, D. Dessì, L. d'Intino, P. Coni, S. Ramey, A. Anisimov, A. Silvestrelli, M. Laurenza, O. Zanetti, M. Bolognesi, N. Focile, La Scala Chor, La Scala Orch, R. Muti (pp1992: 4-act vers) (5/94) (EMI) Ⓓ [3] **CDS7 54867-2**
Cpte E. Fernandi, S. Jurinac, G. Simionato, E. Bastianini, C. Siepi, M. Stefanoni, N. Zaccaria, N. Balatsch, C. Schmidt, N. Foster, A. Rothenberger, Vienna St Op Chor, VPO, H. von Karajan (pp1958: 4-act ver) (9/95) (DG) Ⓓ [3] **447 655-2GX2**
Excs T. Mazaroff, P. Pierotic, M. Reining, P. Tutsek, C. Bissuti, H. Alsen, Vienna St Op Chor, Vienna St Op Orch, B. Walter (pp1937: Ger/Bulg) *Concert* (12/94) (SCHW) Ⓓ [2] **314542**
Excs F. Völker, A. Kipnis, N. Ardelli, A. Jerger, H. Konetzni, E. Nikolaidi, L. Helletsgruber, H. Alsen, Vienna St Op Chor, Vienna St Op Orch, B. Walter (pp1936/7: Ger) *Concert* (3/95) (SCHW) Ⓓ [2] **314602**
Excs F. Völker, J. von Manowarda, E. Schipper, A. Jerger, V. Ursuleac, G. Rünger, Vienna St Op Orch, C. Krauss (pp1933: Ger) *Concert* (9/95) (SCHW) Ⓓ [2] **314662**
1, 2a, 2b P. Domingo, Ambrosian Op Chor, ROHO, C.M. Giulini (r1970) *Concert* (6/94) (EMI) Ⓓ **CDC5 55017-2**
9a-c G. Aragall, E. Tumagian, Bratislava RSO, A. Rahbari (r1992) *Concert* (12/94) (NAXO) Ⓓ **8 550684**
9b(pt), 9c J. Björling, R. Merrill, E. Markow, RCA Victor SO, R. Cellini *Concert* (2/89) (RCA) Ⓓ **GD87799**
9c E. Caruso, A. Scotti, orch, W.B. Rogers (r1912) *Concert* (7/91) (RCA) Ⓓ [12] **GD60495(4)**
9c E. Caruso, A. Scotti, orch, W.B. Rogers (r1912) *Concert* (10/91) (PEAR) Ⓓ [3] **EVC3(1)**
9c T. Mazaroff, P. Pierotic, Vienna St Op Orch, B. Walter (pp1937: Ger) *Concert* (6/94) (SCHW) Ⓓ **314502**
14. G. Kaschmann, S. Cottone (r1903) *Concert* (12/89) (SYMP) Ⓓ **SYMCD1065**
14. G. Kaschmann, S. Cottone (r1903) *Concert* (4/94) (EMI) Ⓓ [3] **CHS7 64860-2(1)**
16b K. Ricciarelli, Rome Polyphonic Chor, Rome PO, G. Gavazzeni *Concert* (12/87) (RCA) Ⓓ **GD86534**
16b, 27b M. Callas, Paris Cons, N. Rescigno *Concert* (9/87) (EMI) Ⓓ **CDC7 47943-2**
20. Atlanta Sym Chor, Atlanta SO, Robert Shaw *Concert* (3/88) (TELA) Ⓓ [2] **CD80152**
20. Chicago Sym Chor, Chicago SO, G. Solti *Concert* (4/91) (DECC) Ⓓ **430 226-2DH**
20. Slovak Phil Chor, Bratislava RSO, O. Dohnányi *Concert* (4/91) (NAXO) Ⓓ **8 550241**
23. R. Raimondi, Ambrosian Op Chor, ROHO, C.M. Giulini *Concert* (10/88) (EMI) Ⓓ **CDM7 69549-2**
23a, 23b T. Pasero, orch, L. Molajoli (r1928) *Concert* (6/90) (PREI) Ⓓ **89010**
23a, 23b A. Kipnis, Berlin St Op Orch, C. Schmalstich (Ger: r1930) *Concert* (12/90) (PREI) Ⓓ **89019**
23a, 23b A. Kipnis, orch (Ger: r1922) *Concert* (10/91) (PEAR) Ⓓ **GEMMCD9451**
23a, 23b N. de Angelis, orch, L. Molajoli (r1927) *Concert* (7/92) (PREI) Ⓓ **89042**
23a, 23b M. Salminen, Lahti SO, E. Klas *Concert* (8/92) (BIS) Ⓓ **BIS-CD520**
23a, 23b J. Van Dam, Loire PO, M. Soustrot (r1992) *Concert* (8/93) (FORL) Ⓓ **UCD16681**
23a, 23b P. Burchuladze, English Concert Orch, E. Downes (r1984) *Concert* (10/93) (DECC) Ⓓ **436 464-2DM**
23a, 23b T. Pasero, orch (r c1938) *Concert* (4/94) (EMI) Ⓓ [3] **CHS7 64864-2(1)**
23a, 23b K. Borg, Bamberg SO, A. Rother (r1957) *Concert* (12/94) (FINL) Ⓓ [3] **4509-95606-2**
23a, 23b M. Reizen, Bolshoi Th Orch, S. Samosud (r1951) *Concert* (2/95) (PREI) Ⓓ **89080**
23b E. Pinza, orch, R. Bourdon (r1927) *Concert* (2/89) (PEAR) Ⓓ **GEMMCD9306**
23b E. Pinza, orch, R. Bourdon (r1927) *Concert* (7/91) (MMOI) Ⓓ **CDMOIR404**
23b E. Pinza, orch, R. Bourdon (r1927) *Concert* (3/92) (PREI) Ⓓ **89050**
23b A. Didur, anon (r1900) *Concert* (6/93) (PEAR) Ⓓ [3] **GEMMCDS9997/9(2)**
24. N. Ghiaurov, R. Raimondi, BPO, H. von Karajan *Concert* (10/88) (EMI) Ⓓ **CDM7 69549-2**
24a, 24b, 25a, 25b, 26, 27a, 27b H. Konetzni, E. Höngen, G. Oeggl, A. Pernerstorfer, A. Welitsch, Vienna St Op Orch, E. Baltzer (pp1950: Ger) *Macbeth.* (5/94) (PREI) Ⓓ [2] **90175**
27b M. Lipovšek, Munich RO, G. Patanè *Concert* (6/90) (ORFE) Ⓓ **C179891A**
27b E. Stignani, EIAR Orch, A. la Rosa Parodi (r1940) *Concert* (1/91) (PREI) Ⓓ **89014**
27b S. Onegin, orch, R. Bourdon (r1929) *Concert* (2/91) (PREI) Ⓓ **89027**
27b F. Leider, orch (Ger: r1926) *Concert* (5/91) (PREI) Ⓓ [3] **89301**
27b M. Callas, Philh, A. Tonini *Concert* (2/93) (EMI) Ⓓ **CDC7 54437-2**
27b G. Bumbry, ROHO, G. Solti (r1965) *Concert* (10/93) (DECC) Ⓓ **436 462-2DM**
27b M. Klose, Berlin St Op Orch, B. Seidler-Winkler (r1936: Ger) *Concert* (7/95) (PREI) Ⓓ **89082**
28a, 28b, 28c, 28d D. Hvorostovsky, Rotterdam PO, V. Gergiev *Concert* (7/90) (PHIL) Ⓓ **426 740-2PH**
28a, 28b, 28c, 28d R. Merrill, RCA SO, R. Cellini (r1950) *Concert* (4/94) (RCA) Ⓓ [6] **09026 61580-2(6)**
28b, 28c T. Gobbi, La Scala Orch, U. Berrettoni (r1942) *Concert* (8/93) (TEST) Ⓓ **SBT1019**
28c E. Giraldoni, anon (r1902) *Concert* (6/90) (SYMP) Ⓓ **SYMCD1073**
28c H. Schlusnus, orch (r1925) *Concert* (12/95) (PREI) Ⓓ **89110**
28c, 28d G. De Luca, orch (r1921) *Concert* (1/92) (PREI) Ⓓ **89036**
28c, 28d M. Battistini, orch, C. Sabajno (r1913) *Concert* (10/92) (NIMB) Ⓓ **NI7831**
28c, 28e J. Hynninen, Estonian SO, E. Klas *Concert* (4/90) (ONDI) Ⓓ **ODE731-2**
28d G. Bechi, Milan SO, A. Quadri (r1949) *Concert* (4/92) (EMI) Ⓓ [7] **CHS7 69741-2(7)**
28d G. De Luca, orch, R. Bourdon (r1929) *Concert* (10/94) (PREI) Ⓓ **89073**
28d, 28e T. Gobbi, La Scala Orch, U. Berrettoni (r1942) *Concert* (10/89) (EMI) Ⓓ **CDM7 63109-2**
28e G. Bechi, Milan SO, A. Quadri (r1949) *Concert* (2/90) (PREI) Ⓓ **89009**
30. K. Te Kanawa, LPO, J. Pritchard *Concert* (5/85) (SONY) Ⓓ **MK37298**
30. M. Callas, Philh, N. Rescigno *Concert* (9/87) (EMI) Ⓓ **CDC7 47730-2**
30. M. Caballé, ROHO, C.M. Giulini *Concert* (10/88) (EMI) Ⓓ **CDM7 69500-2**
30. J. Barstow, ENO Orch, M. Elder *Concert* (1/89) (TER) Ⓓ **CDVIR8307**
30. M. Callas, Philh, N. Rescigno *Concert* (2/90) (EMIN) Ⓓ **CD-EMX2123**

30. M. Seinemeyer, Berlin St Op Orch, F. Weissmann (r1927) *Concert* (11/90) (PREI) Ⓓ **89029**
30. R. Tebaldi, New Philh, O. de Fabritiis *Concert* (8/91) (DECC) Ⓓ [2] **430 481-2DX2**
30. M. Grandi, RPO, A. Erede (r1948) *Concert* (4/92) (EMI) Ⓓ [7] **CHS7 69741-2(7)**
30. M. Teschemacher, Berlin St Op Orch, B. Seidler-Winkler (Ger: r1939) *Concert* (11/92) (PREI) Ⓓ **89049**
30. M. Gauci, Belgian Rad & TV Orch, A. Rahbari *Concert* (11/92) (NAXO) Ⓓ **8 550606**
30. J. Hammond, Philh, V. Tausky (r1952) *Concert* (12/92) (TEST) Ⓓ **SBT1013**

Don Carlos—opera: 5 acts (1867—Paris) (Lib. Méry & du Locle. French version of Don Carlo)
EXCERPTS: ACT 1: 1. Le cerf s'enfuit sous la ramure; 2a. Fontainebleau! Forêt immense; 2b. Je l'ai vue; 3a. Le bruit du cor; 3b. Je suis un étranger; 3c. Que faites-vous donc?; 3d. De quels transport; 4a. A celui qui vous vient; 4b. L'heure fatale est sonnée!; 5. O chants de fête; 6. Le trè-glorieux Roi de France. ACT 2: 7. Charles-Quint, l'auguste Empereur; 8. Au couvent de Saint-Just; 9a. Le voilà! C'est l'Infant!; 9b. Tu pâlis; 9c. Dieu, tu semas dans nos âmes; 10. Sous ces bois; 11. Au palais des fées; 12. La Reine!; 13. Que fait-on à la cour de France; 14. L'Infant Carlos; 15a. Je viens solliciter de la Reine; 15b. O bien perdu; 15c. Par quelle douce voix; 16a. Le Roi!; 16b. O ma chère compagne; 17a. Restez! Auprès de ma personne; 17b. O Roi! J'arrive de Flandre. ACT 3: 18a. Prélude; 18b. À minuit, aux jardins de la Reine; 18c. C'est vous!; 19. Que dit-il? Il est en délire; 20. Ce jour heureux; 21. En plaĉant sur mon front; 22. Sire, la dernière heure. ACT 4: 23a. Elle ne m'aime pas!; 23b. Je dormirai dans mon manteau royal; 24a. Le Grand Inquisiteur!...Suis-je devant le Roi?; 24b. Dans ce beau pays; 25a. Justice! Sire! J'ai foi; 25b. Maudit soit le soupĉon infâme; 26. Pitié!; 27a. Ah! Je ne verrai plus la Reine!; 27b. O don fatal; 28a. C'est moi, Carlos!; 28b. Il faut nous dire adieu!; 28c. Oui, Carlos! C'est mon jour suprême; 28d. Carlos, écoute; 28e. Ah! Je meurs l'âme joyeuse; 29a. Mon fils, reprenez votre épée; 29b. Ciel! Le tocsin. ACT 5: 30. Toi qui sus le néant des grandeurs; 31a. C'est elle!...Un mot; 31b. J'avais fait un beau rêve!; 31c. Au revoir dans un monde; 31d. Oui, pour toujours!. ITEMS OMITTED PRIOR TO PREMIÈRE IN 1867: ACT 1: 32. L'hiver est long! (Prelude and Introduction); ACT 3: Scene 1: 33. Que de fleurs...Viens Eboli; (Introduction and Chorus); ACT 3: Scene 2: 34. Le Ballet de la Reine; ACT 4: Scene 1: 35. J'ai tout compris; ACT 4: Scene 2: 36. Mons fils, reprenez votre épée (Finale: part 1 - reconstructed); ACT 5; 37. Oui, pour toujours! (Finale).
Cpte P. Domingo, K. Ricciarelli, L.V. Terrani, L. Nucci, R. Raimondi, N. Ghiaurov, N. Storozhev, A. Murray, T. Raffalli, A. Savastano, A. Auger, La Scala Chor, La Scala Orch, C. Abbado (includes appendix) (12/85) (DG) Ⓓ [4] **415 316-2GH4**
9a J. Hadley, T. Hampson, WNO Orch, C. Rizzi (r1992) *Concert* (11/93) (TELD) Ⓓ **9031-73283-2**
9a, 9b F. Wunderlich, H. Prey, Munich RO, H. Stein (Ger) *Concert* (5/93) (DG) Ⓓ **431 110-2GB**
23b P. Plançon, orch (r1907) *Concert* (9/91) (PEAR) Ⓓ **GEMMCD9497**
23b P. Plançon, orch (r1907) *Concert* (7/93) (NIMB) Ⓓ [2] **NI7840/1**
23b P. Plançon, orch (r1907) *Concert* (12/94) (ROMO) Ⓓ [2] **82001-2**
30. K. Te Kanawa, ROHO, J. Tate *Concert* (2/90) (EMI) Ⓓ **CDC7 49863-2**
34. NY Met Op Orch, James Levine (r1992) *Concert* (6/94) (SONY) Ⓓ **SK52489**

I due Foscari, '(The) Two Foscaris'—opera: 3 acts (1844—Rome) (Lib. F Piave, after Byron)
EXCERPTS: 1. Prelude. ACT 1: 2. Silenzio; 3a. Qui ti rimani; 3b. Brezza del suol natio; 3c. Dal più remoto esilio; 3d. Odio solo, ed odio atroce; 4a. No...mi lasciate; 4b. Tu al cui sguardo onnipossente; 4c. Che mi rechi?; 5. Tacque il reo!; 6a. Eccomi solo alfine; 6b. O vecchio cor, che batti; 7a. L'illustre dama Foscari; 7b. Tu pur lo sai; 7c. Di sua innocenza dubiti? ACT 2: 8. Prelude; 9a. Notte! perpetua notte; 9b. Non maledirmi, o prode; 10a. Ah, sposo mio!; 10b. No, non morrai; 10c. Tutta è calma la laguna; 10d. Sperenza dolce ancora; 11a. Ah, padre!; 11b. Nel tuo paterno amplesso; 11c. Addio... 12. Ah sì, il tempo; 13. Che più si tarda?; 14a. O patrizi; 14b. Queste innocenti lagrime. ACT 3: 15a. Alla gioia!; 15b. Tace il vento; 16a. Donna infelice; 16b. All'infelice veglio; 17a. Egli ora parte; 17b. Più non vive!; 18a. Signor, chiedon parlarti; 18b. Questa dunque è l'inquia mercede; 18c. Che venga a me, se lice; 18d. Quel bronzo infernale.
Cpte P. Cappuccilli, J. Carreras, K. Ricciarelli, S. Ramey, V. Bello, E. Connell, M. Antoniak, F. Handlos, Austrian Rad Chor, Austrian RSO, L. Gardelli (r1976) (12/89) (PHIL) Ⓓ [2] **422 426-2PM2**
3a, 3c L. Pavarotti, A. Savastano, La Scala Orch, C. Abbado *Concert* (6/87) (SONY) Ⓓ **MK37228**
4a, 4b M. Caballé, M. Sunara, RCA Italiana Op Orch, A. Guadagno *Concert* (11/92) (RCA) Ⓓ [2] **GD60941**
6b P. Amato, orch (r1913) *Concert* (10/95) (NIMB) Ⓓ **NI7867**

Ernani—opera: 4 acts (1844—Venice) (Lib. F Piave)
EXCERPTS: ACT 1: 1. Prelude; 2. Evviva!; 3a. Mercè, dilette amici; 3b. Come rugiada al cespite; 3c. O tu che l'alma adora; 4a. Surta è la notte; 4b. Ernani! Ernani, involami; 4c. Tutto sprezzo che d'Ernani; 5a. Fa che a me venga; 5b. Qui mi trasse amor possente; 5c. Da quel dì che t'ho veduta; 6. Tu se', Ernani!; 7a. Che mai vegg'io!; 7b. Infelice! E tuo credevi; 7c. L'offeso onor, signori; 8. Vedi come il buon vegliardo. ACT 2: 9. Esultiamo; 10. Oro, Quant'oro; 11. Ah, morir; 12. No, vendetta più tremenda; 13a. Cugino, a che munito; 13b. Lo vedremo, veglio audace; 14. Vieni meco, sol di rose. 15. A te, scegli, seguimi!. ACT 3: 16a. Prelude; 16b. È questo il loco; 17a. Gran Dio!; 17b. Oh, de' verd'anni miei; 18a. Un patto!; 18b. Si ridesti; 19. O sommo Carlo. ACT 4: 20. Oh, come felici; 21a. Tutto ora tace intorno; 21b. Solingo, errante e misero.
Cpte P. Domingo, M. Freni, R. Bruson, N. Ghiaurov, J. Michieli, G. Manganotti, A. Giacomotti, La Scala Chor, La Scala Orch, R. Muti (pp1982) (1/84) (EMI) Ⓓ [3] **CDS7 47083-8**
Cpte C. Bergonzi, L. Price, M. Sereni, E. Flagello, J. Hamari, F. Iacopucci, H. Mueller, RCA Italiana Op Chor, RCA Italiana Op Orch, T. Schippers (r1967) (8/88) (RCA) Ⓓ [2] **GD86503**
D'Ernani i fidi...Odi il voto (Act 2) L. Pavarotti, G. Morresi, A. Giacomotti, La Scala Orch, C. Abbado *Concert* (6/87) (SONY) Ⓓ **MK37228**
1. BPO, H. von Karajan *Concert* (10/87) (DG) Ⓓ **419 622-2GH**
1. BPO, H. von Karajan *Concert* (1/95) (DG) Ⓓ **439 972-2GGA2**
3a, 3b G. Martinelli, orch, W.B. Rogers (r1915) *Concert* (10/89) (NIMB) Ⓓ **NI7804**
3a, 3b G. Martinelli, orch, W.B. Rogers (r1915) *Concert* (7/95) (MMOI) Ⓓ **CDMOIR428**
3b L. Slezak, orch (Ger: r1907) *Concert* (2/91) (PREI) Ⓓ **89020**
4a, 4b A. Tomowa-Sintow, Munich RO, P. Sommer *Concert* (11/86) (ORFE) Ⓓ **C106841A**
4a, 4b M. Callas, Philh, N. Rescigno *Concert* (9/87) (EMI) Ⓓ **CDC7 47730-2**
4a, 4b R. Ponselle, orch, R. Bourdon (r1924) *Concert* (10/89) (NIMB) Ⓓ **NI7805**
4a, 4b R. Ponselle, orch, R. Bourdon (r1928) *Concert* (1/90) (RCA) Ⓓ **GD87810**
4a, 4b M. Callas, Philh, N. Rescigno *Concert* (2/90) (EMI) Ⓓ **CDM7 63182-2**
4a, 4b E. Gruberová, Smetana Th Chor, Czech PO, F. Haider *Concert* (5/90) (SONY) Ⓓ **SK45633**
4a, 4b V. de los Angeles, Rome Op Orch, G. Morelli (r1954) *Concert* (8/90) (EMI) Ⓓ **CDH7 63495-2**
4a, 4b F. Hempel, orch (r1915) *Concert* (3/94) (NIMB) Ⓓ **NI7849**
4a, 4b C. Muzio, orch (r1918) *Concert* (1/95) (ROMO) Ⓓ [2] **81010-2**
4b X. Belmas, orch, A. Kitschin (r1928) *Concert* (10/92) (PREI) Ⓓ **89047**
4b M. Korjus, Berlin St Op Orch, B. Seidler-Winkler (Ger: r1936) *Concert* (10/93) (PREI) Ⓓ **89054**
4b R. Raisa, orch (r1923) *Concert* (1/94) (CLUB) Ⓓ **CL99-052**
4b R. Ponselle, orch, R. Bourdon (r1923/4: 2 vers) *Concert* (11/94) (ROMO) Ⓓ [2] **81006-2**
4b R. Ponselle, orch, R. Bourdon (r1927/8 (2 vers) *Concert* (11/94) (ROMO) Ⓓ [2] **81007-2**
4b K. Vayne, anon (r1949) *Concert* (6/95) (PREI) Ⓓ **89996**
4b E. Steber, orch, W. Pelletier (bp1940) *Concert* (11/95) (VAI) Ⓓ **VAIA1072**
4b, 4c R. Ponselle, orch, R. Bourdon (r1928) *Concert* (7/95) (MMOI) Ⓓ **CDMOIR428**
5c G. Arangi-Lombardi, E. Molinari, La Scala Orch, L. Molajoli (r1929) *Concert* (10/90) (PREI) Ⓓ **89013**
5c, 13b, 14, 19. M. Battistini, E. Corsi, A. Sillich, L. Colazza, orch (r1906) *Concert* (2/92) (PREI) Ⓓ **89045**
7a, 7b E. Pinza, orch, R. Bourdon (r1929) *Concert* (2/89) (PEAR) Ⓓ **GEMMCD9306**
7a, 7b E. Pinza, orch, R. Bourdon (r1929) *Concert* (7/91) (MMOI) Ⓓ **CDMOIR404**
7a, 7b E. Pinza, orch, R. Bourdon (r1929) *Concert* (9/93) (RCA) Ⓓ **09026 61245-2**
7b T. Pasero, orch, L. Molajoli (r1927) *Concert* (6/90) (PREI) Ⓓ **89010**
7b E. Pinza, orch, R. Bourdon (r1929) *Concert* (3/92) (PREI) Ⓓ **89050**
7b A. Didur, anon (r1900: Pol) *Concert* (6/93) (PEAR) Ⓓ [3] **GEMMCDS9997/9(2)**
7b E. Pinza, orch, R. Bourdon (r1929) *Concert* (12/93) (NIMB) Ⓓ **NI7851**
13b, 17b T. Ruffo, orch (r1921) *Concert* (2/93) (PREI) Ⓓ [3] **89303(2)**
14, 19. M. Battistini, E. Corsi, L. Colazza, A. Sillich, La Scala Chor, orch, C. Sabajno (r1906) *Concert* (10/92) (NIMB) Ⓓ **NI7831**
17b G. Kaschmann, S. Cottone (r1903) *Concert* (12/89) (SYMP) Ⓓ **SYMCD1065**
17b C. Tagliabue, La Scala Orch, U. Berrettoni (r1946) *Concert* (11/90) (PREI) Ⓓ **89015**
17b G. Kaschmann, anon (r1903) *Concert* (11/92) (MEMO) Ⓓ [2] **HR4408/9(1)**
17b M. Battistini, orch (r1906) *Concert* (7/93) (NIMB) Ⓓ [2] **NI7840/1**
17b M. Battistini, orch, C. Sabajno (r1906) *Concert* (4/94) (EMI) Ⓓ [3] **CHS7 64860-2(1)**
17b G. De Luca, orch (r1916) *Concert* (10/95) (NIMB) Ⓓ **NI7867**
18b Slovak Phil Chor, Bratislava RSO, O. Dohnányi *Concert* (4/91) (NAXO) Ⓓ **8 550241**
19. C. Galeffi, La Scala Orch, L. Molajoli (r1926) *Concert* (2/92) (PREI) Ⓓ **89040**
19. G. De Luca, G. Anthony, A. Tedesco, NY Met Op Chor, NY Met Op Orch, G. Setti (r1928) *Concert* (10/94) (PREI) Ⓓ **89073**
21b L. Signoretti, anon (r1901) *Concert* (12/89) (SYMP) Ⓓ **SYMCD1065**

Falstaff—opera: 3 acts (1893—Milan) (Lib. A Boito, after Shakespeare)
EXCERPTS: ACT 1: 1. Falstaff! Olà!; 2. So che se andiam,la notte; 3. Ma è tempo d'assottigliar l'ingegno; 4a. Ehi! paggio!; 4b. L'Onore! Ladri!; 5. Alice... Meg... Nannetta; 6a. Fulgida Alice! amor t'offro; 6b. Quell'otre! quel tino!; 6c. È un ribaldo, un furbo, un labro; 7. In due parole; 8a. Pst, pst, Nannetta; 8b. Labbro di foco!; 8c. Falstaff m'ha canzonata; 8d. Torno all'assalto; 9. Del tuo barbaro diagnostico. ACT 2: 10a. Siam pentiti e contriti; 10b. Reverenza!; 11a. Alice, è mia!; 11b. Va, vecchio John; 12. Signore, v'assista il cielo!; 13a. C'è Windsor una dama; 13b. V'ascolto; 14a. È sogno? o realtà; 14b. Eccomi qua. Son pronto; 15a. Presenteremo un bill; 15b. Giunta all'Albergo della Giarrettiera; 16a. Fra poco s'incomincia la commedia; 16b. A noi! Tu la parte farai che ti spetta; 17. Alfin t'ho colto; 18a. Quand'ero paggio; 18b. Voi mi celiate; 19a. Mia signora!; 19b. Vien qua; 19c. Al ladro; 20a. C'è. C'è; 20b. Facciamo le viste. ACT 3: 21a. Ehi! Taverniere!; 21b. Mondo ladro; 22a. Reverenza. La bella Alice; 22b. Quando il rintocco; 23. Sarai la Fata Regina delle Fate; 24a. Dal labbro il canto; 24b. Nossignore! Tu indossa; 25a. Una, due, tre, quattro; 25b. Odo un soave passo!; 26a. Ninfe! Elfi! Silfi!; 26b. Sul fil d'un soffio etesio; 27a. Alto là; 27b. Pizzica, pizzica; 28. Ogni sorta di gente dozzinale; 29a. Facciamo il paremtado; 29b. Tutto nel mondo è burla.
Cpte R. Bruson, L. Nucci, K. Ricciarelli, B. Hendricks, D. Gonzalez, L.V. Terrani, B. Boozer, M. Sells, F. Egerton, W. Wilderman, Los Angeles Master Chorale, Los Angeles PO, C.M. Giulini (pp1982) (12/83) (DG) Ⓓ [2] **410 503-2GH2**
Cpte T. Gobbi, R. Panerai, E. Schwarzkopf, A. Moffo, L. Alva, F. Barbieri, N. Merriman, T. Spataro, R. Ercolani, N. Zaccaria, Chor, Philh, H. von Karajan (9/88) (EMI) Ⓓ [2] **CDS7 49668-2**
Cpte G. Evans, R. Merrill, I. Ligabue, M. Freni, Alfredo Kraus, G. Simionato, R. Elias, J. Lanigan, P. de Palma, G. Foiani, RCA Italiana Op Chor, RCA Italiana Op Orch, G. Solti (3/90) (DECC) Ⓓ [2] **417 168-2DM2**
Cpte G. Valdengo, F. Guarrera, H. Nelli, T. Stich-Randall, A. Madasi, C. Elmo, N. Merriman, G. Carelli, J.C. Rossi, N. Scott, R. Shaw Chorale, NBC SO, A. Toscanini (bp1950) *Concert* (5/90) (RCA) Ⓓ [7] **GD60326**
Cpte R. Panerai, A. Titus, S. Sweet, J. Kaufmann, F. Lopardo, M. Horne, S. Quittmeyer, P. de Palma, U. Ress, F.E. d'Artegna, Bavarian Rad Chor, BRSO, Colin Davis (10/92) (RCA) Ⓓ [2] **09026 60705-2**
Cpte J. Pons, R. Frontali, D. Dessì, M. O'Flynn, R. Vargas, B. Manca di Nissa, D. Ziegler, E. Gavazzi, P. Barbacini, L. Roni, La Scala Chor, La Scala Orch, R. Muti (pp1993) (11/94) (SONY) Ⓓ [2] **S2K58961**

Excs A. Jerger, G. Monthy, E. Réthy, D. Komarek, A. Dermota, G. Maikl, O. Levko-Antosch, E. Nikolaidi, W. Wernigk, N. Zec, Vienna St Op Chor, Vienna St Op Orch, W. Loibner (pp1939: Ger) *Concert* (3/95) (SCHW) Ⓓ [2] **314602**

Excs G. Hann, K. Kronenberg, E. Réthy, A. Kern, A. Dermota, J. Witt, M. Bugarinovic, E. Nikolaidi, W. Wernigk, M. Rus, Vienna St Op Chor, Vienna St Op Orch, C. Krauss (pp1941: Ger) *Concert* (4/95) (SCHW) Ⓓ [2] **314582**

4b G. Bechi, Milan SO, A. Quadri (r1951) *Concert* (2/90) (PREI) Ⓓ **89009**

4b M. Stabile, orch (r1926) *Concert* (7/92) (PEAR) Ⓓ [3] **GEMMCDS9926(1)**

4b T. Ruffo, orch (r1921) *Concert* (2/93) (PREI) Ⓓ [3] **89303(2)**

4b T. Ruffo, orch (r1921) *Concert* (10/95) (NIMB) Ⓓ **NI7867**

12. M. Stabile, A. Poli, G. Nessi, L. Donaggio, La Scala Orch, A. Erede (r1942) *Concert* (4/94) (EMI) Ⓓ [3] **CHS7 64864-2(2)**

14a L. Tibbett, Orch, R. Bourdon (r1926) *Concert* (3/90) (RCA) Ⓓ **GD87808**

14a L. Tibbett, orch (pp1935) *Concert* (3/91) (PEAR) Ⓓ [2] **GEMMCDS9452**

18a T. Gobbi, Philh, A. Erede (r1963) *Concert* (10/89) (EMI) Ⓓ **CDM7 63109-2**

18a T. Ruffo, orch, J. Pasternack (r1922) *Concert* (11/90) (NIMB) Ⓓ **NI7810**

18a A. Scotti, anon (r1903) *Concert* (7/92) (PEAR) Ⓓ [3] **GEMMCDS9925(1)**

18a V. Maurel, anon (r1907) *Concert* (7/92) (PEAR) Ⓓ [3] **GEMMCDS9923(1)**

18a D. Bispham, anon (r1902) *Concert* (10/92) (SYMP) Ⓓ **SYMCD1093**

18a V. Maurel, anon (r1907) *Concert* (11/92) (MEMO) Ⓓ [2] **HR4408/9(1)**

18a T. Ruffo, orch (r1922) *Concert* (2/93) (PREI) Ⓓ [3] **89303(2)**

18a A. Scotti, anon (r1902) *Concert* (3/93) (SYMP) Ⓓ **SYMCD1100**

18a V. Maurel, anon (r1907) *Concert* (7/93) (NIMB) Ⓓ [2] **NI7840/1**

18a V. Maurel, anon (r1907) *Concert* (4/94) (EMI) Ⓓ [3] **CHS7 64860-2(1)**

18a V. Maurel, anon (r1907) *Concert* (12/94) (SYMP) Ⓓ **SYMCD1128**

18a A. Magini-Coletti, E. Petri, orch (r1906) *Concert* (10/95) (NIMB) Ⓓ **NI7867**

24a T. Schipa, orch (r1921) *Concert* (4/90) (EMI) Ⓓ **CDH7 63200-2**

24a Ferruccio Tagliavini, EIAR Orch, U. Tansini (r1940) *Concert* (3/94) (CENT) Ⓓ **CRC2164**

26b T. dal Monte, La Scala Orch, C. Sabajno (r1929) *Concert* (2/90) (PREI) Ⓓ **89001**

26b K. Ricciarelli, Parma Teatro Regio Orch, G. Patanè (pp1976) *Concert* (5/94) (DECC) Ⓓ [2] **443 018-2DF2**

La **forza del destino, '(The) force of destiny'—opera: 4 acts (1862—St Petersburg)** (Lib. F. Piave)

EXCERPTS: 1. Overture. ACT 1: 2. Buona notte, mia figlia; 3a. Temea restasse; 3b. Me pellegrina ed orfana; 4a. Ah! per sempre; 4b. Seguirti fino agl'ultimi; 5a. È tardi; 5b. Vil seduttor!. ACT 2: 6a. Holà (Ballabile); 6b. La cena è pronto; 7a. Viva la guerra!; 7b. Al suon del tamburo; 8a. Padre Eterno Signor; 8b. Viva la buona compagnia; 9a. Poich'imberbe è l'incognito; 9b. Son Pereda, son ricco d'onore; 10. Sta bene (Finale); 11a. Son giunta!; 11b. Madre, pietosa Vergine; 12a. Chi siete?; 12b. Chi mi cerca?; 12c. Or siam soli... 12d. Infelice, delusa, reietta; 12e. Sull'alba il piede; 13a. Il santo nome; 13b. La Vergine degli angeli. ACT 3: 14a. Attenti al gioco; 14b. La vita è inferno; 14c. Oh, tu che in seno; 15a. Al tradimento; 15b. Amici in vita, in morte; 15c. All'armi!; 16a. Arde la mischia! (Battle Scene); 16b. Piano, qui posi; 16c. Solenne in quest'ora; 17a. Morir! Tremenda cosa!; 17b. Urna fatale; 17c. Ah! Egli è salvo; 18. Compagni, sostiamo; 19a. Nè gustare m'è dato; 19b. Sleale! Il segreto; 20a. Lorchè pifferi; 20b. Qua, vivandiere, un sorso; 20c. A buon mercato; 20d. Pane, pan per carità; 20e. Che vergogna!; 21a. Nella guerra, è la follia; 21b. Toh, toh! Poffare il mondo; 22a. Lasciatelo ch'ei vada; 22b. Rataplan. ACT 4: 23a. Fate la carità; 23b. Che? Siete all'osteria?; 24a. Auf! Pazienza; 24b. Del mondo i disinganni; 25a. Giunge qualcun; 25b. Siete il portiere?; 25c. Invano Alvaro; 25d. Le minaccie; 26. Pace, pace, mio Dio; 27a. Io muoio! Confessione!; 27b. Non imprecare, umiliata.

Cpte M. Freni, P. Domingo, G. Zancanaro, P. Plishka, D. Zajick, S. Bruscantini, G. Surian, E. Gavazzi, F. Garbi, S. Sammaritano, La Scala Chor, La Scala Orch, R. Muti (r1986) (5/87) (EMI) Ⓓ [3] **CDS7 47485-8**

Cpte R. Plowright, J. Carreras, R. Bruson, P. Burchuladze, A. Baltsa, J. Pons, J. Tomlinson, M. Curtis, J. Rigby, R. Van Allan, P. Salomaa, Ambrosian Op Chor, Philh, G. Sinopoli (5/87) (DG) Ⓓ [3] **419 203-2GH3**

Cpte M. Callas, R. Tucker, C. Tagliabue, N. Rossi-Lemeni, E. Nicolai, R. Capecchi, P. Clabassi, G. del Signore, R. Cavallari, D. Caselli, La Scala Chor, La Scala Orch, T. Serafin (r1954) (10/87) (EMI) Ⓓ [3] **CDS7 47581-8**

Cpte L. Price, P. Domingo, S. Milnes, B. Giaiotti, F. Cossotto, G. Bacquier, K. Moll, M. Sénéchal, G. Knight, M. King, W. Elvin, John Alldis Ch, LSO, James Levine (10/87) (RCA) Ⓓ [3] **RD81864**

Cpte L. Price, R. Tucker, R. Merrill, G. Tozzi, S. Verrett, E. Flagello, G. Foiani, P. de Palma, C. Vozza, R. Bottcher, M. Rinaudo, RCA Italiana Op Chor, RCA Italiana Op Orch, T. Schippers (r1964) (12/88) (RCA) Ⓓ [3] **GD87971**

Cpte R. Tebaldi, M. del Monaco, E. Bastianini, C. Siepi, G. Simionato, F. Corena, S. Maionica, P. de Palma, G. Carturan, E. Giordano, E. Coda, Santa Cecilia Academy Chor, Santa Cecilia Academy Orch, F. Molinari-Pradelli (1/89) (DECC) Ⓓ [3] **421 598-2DM3**

Cpte M. Arroyo, C. Bergonzi, P. Cappuccilli, R. Raimondi, B. Casoni, G. Evans, A. Zerbini, F. Andreolli, M. Cova, V. Carbonari, D. Hammond-Stroud, Ambrosian Op Chor, RPO, L. Gardelli (r1969) (6/93) (EMI) Ⓓ [3] **CMS7 64646-2**

Excs Grimethorpe Colliery Band, E. Howarth (arr Wright) *Concert* (12/92) (DOYE) Ⓓ **DOYCD013**

1. BPO, H. von Karajan *Concert* (10/87) (DG) Ⓓ **419 622-2GH**

1. BPO, H. von Karajan *Concert* (5/90) (DG) Ⓓ **429 164-2GR**

1. Black Dyke Mills Band, P. Parkes (arr brass band: F Wright) *Concert* (9/93) (CHAN) Ⓓ **CHAN4514**

1. I. Seefried, M. Forrester, E. Haefliger, D. Fischer-Dieskau, Berlin St Hedwig's Cath Ch, BPO, F. Fricsay, H. Krebs, T. Varga, Berlin RIAS Chbr Ch, Berlin RIAS Orch, H. Geusser, W. Fugmann, M. Weber, G. Herzog, Berlin RSO, VPO, E. Grümmer, G. Pitzinger, H. Hotter, Y. Menuhin (r1953) *Concert* (11/94) (DG) Ⓓ [11] **445 400-2GDO10**

1. Berlin RIAS Orch, F. Fricsay (r1953) *Concert* (11/94) (DG) Ⓓ **445 406-2GDO**

1. BPO, H. von Karajan *Concert* (1/95) (DG) Ⓓ **439 972-2GGA2**

3b E. Burzio, orch (r1913) *Concert* (1/91) (CLUB) Ⓓ [2] **CL99-587/8**

3b, 11b G. Cigna, orch, L. Molajoli (r1930) *Concert* (11/90) (PREI) Ⓓ **89016**

3b, 11b G. Cigna, orch, L. Molajoli (r1930) *Concert* (11/90) (LYRC) Ⓓ **SRO805**

3b, 26. A. Marc, NZ SO, H. Wallberg *Concert* (6/92) (DELO) Ⓓ **DE3108**

9b, 17a-c C. Tagliabue, Turin EIAR Orch, G. Marinuzzi (r1941) *Concert* (11/90) (PREI) Ⓓ **89015**

11a, 11b, 12a-e, 13a, 13b G. Cigna, G. Vaghi, E. Ghirardini, Rome RAI Chor, Rome RAI Orch, O. de Fabritiis (bp1938) *Trovatore.* (2/94) (LYRC) Ⓓ [2] **LCD173**

11a, 11b, 26. D. Giannini, orch, J. Barbirolli (r1928) *Concert* (4/93) (PREI) Ⓓ **89044**

11b E. Burzio, orch (r c1907) *Concert* (1/91) (CLUB) Ⓓ [2] **CL99-587/8**

12d, 12e, 13b M. Arroyo, R. Raimondi, Ambrosian Op Chor, RPO, L. Gardelli *Concert* (10/88) (EMI) Ⓓ **CDM7 69549-2**

13a I. Andrésen, chor, Berlin St Op Orch, F. Weissmann (Ger: r1927) *Concert* (10/90) (PREI) Ⓓ **89028**

13b R. Ponselle, E. Pinza, NY Met Op Chor, NY Met Op Orch, G. Setti (r1928) *Concert* (10/89) (NIMB) Ⓓ **NI7805**

13b D. Giannini, La Scala Orch, C. Sabajno (r1928) *Concert* (4/93) (PREI) Ⓓ **89044**

13b R. Ponselle, chor, orch, R. Romani (r1918) *Concert* (10/93) (NIMB) Ⓓ **NI7846**

13b R. Ponselle, E. Pinza, NY Met Op Chor, orch, G. Setti (r1928) *Concert* (11/94) (ROMO) Ⓓ [2] **81007-2**

13b E. Destinn, chor, orch (r1912) *Concert* (12/94) (SUPR) Ⓓ [12] **11 2136-2(5)**

13b R. Ponselle, E. Pinza, NY Met Op Chor, NY Met Op Orch, G. Setti (r1928) *Concert* (7/95) (MMOI) Ⓓ **CDMOIR428**

14b F. Merli, orch, L. Molajoli (r1926) *Concert* (1/91) (PREI) Ⓓ **89026**

14b, 14c B. Gigli, La Scala Orch, U. Berrettoni (r1941) *Concert* (5/90) (EMI) Ⓓ **CDH7 61052-2**

14b, 14c G. Martinelli, orch, R. Bourdon (r1927) *Concert* (10/89) (NIMB) Ⓓ **NI7804**

14b, 14c B. Heppner, Munich RO, R. Abbado (r1993/4) *Concert* (11/95) (RCA) Ⓓ **09026 62504-2**

14c E. Caruso, orch (r1909) *Concert* (5/89) (PEAR) Ⓓ **GEMMCD9309**

14c E. Caruso, orch (r1909) *Concert* (10/89) (NIMB) Ⓓ **NI7803**

14c A. Pertile, La Scala Orch, C. Sabajno (r1928) *Concert* (9/90) (PREI) Ⓓ **89007**

14c E. Caruso, orch (r1909) *Concert* (3/91) (PEAR) Ⓓ [3] **EVC2**

14c E. Caruso, orch, W.B. Rogers (r1909) *Concert* (7/91) (RCA) Ⓓ [12] **GD60495(3)**

14c E. Caruso, orch (r1909) *Concert* (7/91) (MSCM) Ⓓ **MM30352**

14c G. Zenatello, orch (r1909) *Concert* (12/93) (SYMP) Ⓓ **SYMCD1138**

14c G. Zenatello, orch (r1909) *Concert* (5/94) (PEAR) Ⓓ [4] **GEMMCDS9073(2)**

14c P. Domingo, La Scala Orch, R. Muti (r1986) *Concert* (6/94) (EMI) Ⓓ **CDC5 55017-2**

14c H. Roswaenge, Berlin St Op Orch (r1935: Ger) *Concert* (4/95) (PREI) Ⓓ [2] **89209**

14c, 25c, 25d G. Martinelli, G. De Luca, orch, R. Bourdon (r1927) *Concert* (3/93) (PREI) Ⓓ **89062**

16c J. Björling, R. Merrill, RCA Victor SO, R. Cellini *Concert* (2/89) (RCA) Ⓓ **GD87799**

16c R. Tauber, B. Ziegler, orch (Ger: r1922) *Concert* (7/89) (PEAR) Ⓓ **GEMMCD9327**

16c H. Roswaenge, G. Hüsch, Berlin St Op Orch, B. Seidler-Winkler (Ger: r1937) *Concert* (5/90) (PEAR) Ⓓ **GEMMCD9394**

16c F. Marconi, N. della Torre, orch (r1908) *Concert* (10/90) (SYMP) Ⓓ **SYMCD1069**

16c E. Caruso, A. Scotti, orch (r1906) *Concert* (12/90) (PEAR) Ⓓ [3] **EVC1(2)**

16c E. Caruso, A. Scotti, orch (r1906) *Concert* (7/91) (RCA) Ⓓ [12] **GD60495(2)**

16c H.E. Groh, G. Hüsch, orch (r1932) *Concert* (3/92) (PEAR) Ⓓ **GEMMCD9419**

16c J. Hislop, A. Granforte, orch, G.W. Byng (r1926) *Concert* (1/93) (PEAR) Ⓓ **GEMMCD9956**

16c T. Ruffo, B. Gigli, orch (r1926) *Concert* (2/93) (PREI) Ⓓ [3] **89303(2)**

16c B. Gigli, G. De Luca, orch, R. Bourdon (r1927) *Concert* (6/93) (MMOI) Ⓓ **CDMOIR417**

16c C. Kullman, W. Grossmann, Berlin St Op Orch, E. Orthmann (Ger: r1931) *Concert* (11/93) (PREI) Ⓓ **89057**

16c E. Garbin, M. Sammarco, anon (r1905) *Concert* (12/93) (SYMP) Ⓓ **SYMCD1113**

16c G. De Luca, B. Gigli, orch, R. Bourdon (r1927) *Concert* (10/94) (PREI) Ⓓ **89073**

16c H. Schlusnus, R. Hutt, orch (r1921: Ger) *Concert* (12/95) (PREI) Ⓓ **89110**

16c, 25c G. Bechi, G. Lauri-Volpi, Rome Op Orch, R. Arduini (r1943) *Concert* (2/90) (PREI) Ⓓ **89009**

16c, 25c, 25d G. Lauri-Volpi, G. Bechi, Rome Op Orch, R. Arduini (r1943) *Concert* (7/94) (NIMB) Ⓓ **NI7853**

16c, 25c, 25d G. Aragall, E. Tumagian, Bratislava RSO, A. Rahbari (r1992) *Concert* (12/94) (NAXO) Ⓓ **8 550684**

17a, 17b E. Bastianini, E. Coda, Santa Cecilia Academy Orch, F. Molinari-Pradelli (r1955) *Concert* (10/93) (DECC) Ⓓ **436 464-2DM**

17b T. Gobbi, Philh, J. Robertson (r1950) *Concert* (10/89) (EMI) Ⓓ **CDM7 63109-2**

17b J. Hynninen, Estonian SO, E. Klas *Concert* (4/90) (ONDI) Ⓓ **ODE731-2**

17b T. Ruffo, orch (r1915) *Concert* (2/93) (PREI) Ⓓ [3] **89303(1)**

17b G. Viviani, orch (r c1924) *Concert* (12/94) (BONG) Ⓓ **GB1043-2**

17c M. Battistini, orch, C. Sabajno (r1921) *Concert* (10/92) (PEAR) Ⓓ **GEMMCD9936**

19. E. Caruso, G. De Luca, orch, J. Pasternack (r1918) *Concert* (7/91) (RCA) Ⓓ [12] **GD60495(6)**

19a, 19b E. Caruso, G. De Luca, orch, J. Pasternack (r1918) *Concert* (10/91) (PEAR) Ⓓ [3] **EVC4(1)**

19a, 25c J. Lotrič, I. Morozov, Slovak RSO, J. Wildner, Slovak Op Chor (r1994) *Concert* (2/95) (NAXO) Ⓓ **8 553030**

22b E. Stignani, EIAR Orch, G. Marinuzzi (r1941) *Concert* (1/91) (PREI) Ⓓ **89014**

22b Slovak Phil Chor, Bratislava RSO, O. Dohnányi *Concert* (4/91) (NAXO) Ⓓ **8 550241**

25c F. Merli, G. Vanelli, orch, L. Molajoli (r1929) *Concert* (1/91) (PREI) Ⓓ **89026**

25c, 25d G. Martinelli, G. De Luca, orch, R. Bourdon (r1928) *Concert* (10/89) (NIMB) Ⓓ **NI7804**

25c, 25d E. Caruso, P. Amato, orch (r1911) *Concert* (3/91) (PEAR) Ⓓ [3] **EVC2**

25c, 25d E. Caruso, P. Amato, orch (r1911) *Concert* (7/91) (RCA) Ⓓ [12] **GD60495(4)**

25d F.M. Bonini, G.M. Patti, anon (r1906) *Concert* (12/94) (BONG) Ⓓ **GB1043-2**

25d L. Montesanto, N. Fusati, orch (r c1918) *Concert* (12/94) (BONG) Ⓓ **GB1043-2**

26. G. Bumbry, Stuttgart RSO, S. Soltesz *Concert* (11/86) (ORFE) Ⓓ **C081841A**
26. M. Caballé, RPO, A. Guadagno *Concert* (10/88) (EMI) Ⓓ **CDM7 69500-2**
26. J. Barstow, ENO Orch, M. Elder *Concert* (1/89) (TER) Ⓓ **CDVIR8307**
26. R. Ponselle, orch, R. Bourdon (r1928) *Concert* (1/90) (RCA) Ⓓ **GD87810**
26. C. Muzio, orch (r1922) *Concert* (5/90) (BOGR) Ⓓ [2] **BIM705-2**
26. K. Te Kanawa, LSO, Myung-Whun Chung *Concert* (11/90) (EMI) Ⓓ **CDC7 54062-2**
26. E. Burzio, orch (r c1908) *Concert* (1/91) (CLUB) Ⓓ [2] **CL99-587/8**
26. C. Muzio, orch, L. Molajoli (r1935) *Concert* (4/91) (NIMB) Ⓓ **NI7814**
26. R. Tebaldi, Santa Cecilia Academy Orch, F. Molinari-Pradelli *Concert* (8/91) (DECC) Ⓓ [2] **430 481-2DX2**
26. R. Ponselle, orch, R. Bourdon (r1928) *Concert* (7/92) (PEAR) Ⓓ [3] **GEMMCDS9926(2)**
26. L. Tetrazzini, orch (r1914) *Concert* (9/92) (EMI) Ⓓ [3] **CHS7 63802-2(2)**
26. L. Tetrazzini, orch (r1914) *Concert* (9/92) (PEAR) Ⓓ **GEMMCD9225**
26. M. Gauci, Belgian Rad & TV Orch, A. Rahbari *Concert* (11/92) (NAXO) Ⓓ **8 550606**
26. C. Muzio, orch (r1922) *Concert* (1/94) (ROMO) Ⓓ [2] **81005-2**
26. R. Ponselle, orch, R. Bourdon (r1924) *Concert* (4/94) (RCA) Ⓓ [6] **09026 61580-2(3)**
26. K. Ricciarelli, Parma Teatro Regio Orch, G. Patanè (pp1976) *Concert* (5/94) (DECC) Ⓓ [2] **443 018-2DF2**
26. R. Ponselle, orch, R. Bourdon (r1923/4: 3 vers) *Concert* (11/94) (ROMO) Ⓓ [2] **81006-2**
26. R. Ponselle, orch, R. Bourdon (r1928 (2 vers) *Concert* (11/94) (ROMO) Ⓓ [2] **81007-2**
26. C. Muzio, orch (r1917) *Concert* (1/95) (ROMO) Ⓓ [2] **81010-2**
26. Leonie Rysanek, Berlin SO, W. Schüchter (r1955: Ger) *Concert* (2/95) (EMI) Ⓓ **CDH5 65201-2**
26. K. Vayne, orch (bp1959) *Concert* (6/95) (PREI) Ⓓ **89996**
26. R. Ponselle, orch, R. Bourdon (r1928) *Concert* (7/95) (MMOI) Ⓓ **CDMOIR428**
26. R. Hunter, Tasmanian SO, D. Franks (r1989) *Concert* (10/95) (ABCC) Ⓓ **8 7000 10**
27a R. Ponselle, G. Martinelli, E. Pinza, NY Met Op Chor, NY Met Op Orch, G. Setti (r1928) *Concert* (10/89) (NIMB) Ⓓ **NI7804**
27a, 27b R. Ponselle, G. Martinelli, E. Pinza, orch, R. Bourdon (r1928) *Concert* (1/90) (RCA) Ⓓ **GD87810**
27a, 27b N. Stemme, P. Domingo, K. Youn, Paris Opéra-Bastille Orch, E. Kohn (pp1992) *Concert* (6/94) (SONY) Ⓓ **SK46691**
27a, 27b R. Ponselle, G. Martinelli, E. Pinza, orch, R. Bourdon (r1928 (2 vers) *Concert* (11/94) (ROMO) Ⓓ [2] **81007-2**
27a, 27b R. Ponselle, G. Martinelli, E. Pinza, orch, R. Bourdon (r1928) *Concert* (7/95) (MMOI) Ⓓ **CDMOIR428**
27b B. Scacciati, F. Merli, T. Pasero, orch, L. Molajoli (r1929) *Concert* (6/90) (PREI) Ⓓ **89010**

Un **giorno di regno, '(A) king for a day'—opera: 2 acts (1840—Milan)** (Lib. F Romani)

EXCERPTS: 1. Overture. ACT 1: 2. Mai no rise un più bel dì; 3. Tesoriere garbatissimo; 4a. Sua Maestà, signori; 4b. Compagnoni di Parigi; 4c. Verrà pur troppo il giorno; 5a. Al doppio matrimonio; 5b. Sire tremante io vengo; 6a. Proverò che degno io sono; 6b. Infiammato da spirito guerriero; 7a. Ah, non m'hanno ingannata!; 7b. Grave a core innamorato; 8a. Sì festevola mattina; 8b. Non san quant'io nel petto; 8c. Non vo' quel vecchio, non son sì sciocca; 9. Ebben, Giuletta mia; 10a. Cara Giulia, alfin ti vedo; 10b. Madamine, il mio scudiere; 11. In te, cugina, io spero; 12. Bella speranza invero; 13. Quanto diceste mostra un gran talento; 14. Diletto genero, a voi ne vengo; 15a. Tesorier! io creder voglio; 15b. In qual punto il Re ci ha colto!; 16a. Olà spiegatemi tosto, o Barone; 16b. Affidate alla mente reale. ACT 2: 17a. Ma la nozze non si fanno?; 17b. Pietoso al lungo pianto; 17c. Deh, lasciate a un'alma amante; 18. Bene, scudiero, vi ritrovo in tempo; 19a. Un mio castello! cinque mila scudi!; 19b. Tutte l'armi si può prendere; 20. Ch'io non posso il ver comprendere?; 21. Nipote, un quest'istante; 22a. Perchè dunque non vien?; 22b. Sì, scordar saprò l'infido; 23a. Oh me felice appieno!; 23b. Ah! non sia, mio ben, fallace; 24a. Sì, caro conte!; 24b. A tal colpo preparata; 25a. Sire, venne in quest'istante; 25b. Eh! facciamo da buoni amici.

Cpte F. Cossotto, J. Norman, J. Carreras, I. Wixell, V. Sardinero, W. Ganzarolli, W. Elvin, R. Cassinelli, Ambrosian Sngrs, RPO, L. Gardelli (r1973) (12/89) (PHIL) Ⓓ [2] **422 429-2PM2**
1. RPO, K.H. Adler (pp1982) *Concert* (8/91) (DECC) Ⓓ **430 716-2DM**
1. BPO, H. von Karajan *Concert* (1/95) (DG) Ⓓ **439 972-2GGA2**
7a, 7b M. Caballé, RCA Italiana Op Orch, A. Guadagno *Concert* (11/92) (RCA) Ⓓ [2] **GD60941**

Giovanna d'Arco, 'Joan of Arc'—dramma lirico: 4 acts (1845—Milan) (Lib. Solera, after Schiller)

EXCERPTS: 1. Overture; 2. Qual v'ha speme?; 3. Il Re!; 4. Sotto una quercia parvemi; 5. V'ha dunque un loco simile; 6. Pondo è letal, martiro; 7. Gelo, terrore m'invade!; 8. O, ben s'addice questo torbido; 9. Sempre all'alba ed alla sera; 10. Paventi, Carlo, tu forse?; 11. Tu sei bella; 12. Pronta sono!...Son guerriera... ACT 1: 13. Ai lari!...Alla patria!; 14. Questa rea che vi percuote; 15. Franco son io, ma in core; 16. So che per via di triboli; 17. Qui! qui...dove più s'apre libero il cielo; 18. O faticida foresta; 19. Ho risolto... 20. T'arretri e palpiti!; 21. Taci!...Le vie traboccano; 22. Vieni al tempio. ACT 2: 23. Dal cielo a noi chi viene; 24. Ecco il luogo....Speme al vecchio era una figlia... 25. Te, Dio, lodiam; 26. Compiuto è il rito!...Non fuggir, donzella!; 27. No! forme d'angelo...L'amaro calice sommessa io bevo; 28. Ti discopla!...Imbianca e tace!. ACT 3: 29. I Franchi!...Oh qual mi scuote rumor di guerra?; 30. A lui pensa!...Amai, ma un solo istante; 31. Tu che all'eletto Sàulo; 32. Or dal padre benedetta; 33. Ecco! Ella vola; 34. Di novel prodigo il ciel ne arrise; 35. Qual più fido amico; 36. Un suon funero; 37. Che mai fu?...S'apre il cielo.

Cpte M. Caballé, P. Domingo, S. Milnes, K. Erwen, R. Lloyd, Ambrosian Op Chor, LSO, James Levine (11/89) (EMI) Ⓓ [2] **CMS7 63226-2**
1. BPO, H. von Karajan *Concert* (1/95) (DG) Ⓓ **439 972-2GGA2**
8, 9. R. Tebaldi, New Philh, O. de Fabritiis *Concert* (8/91) (DECC) Ⓓ [2] **430 481-2DX2**
17, 18. K. Ricciarelli, Rome PO, G. Gavazzeni *Concert* (12/87) (RCA) Ⓓ **GD86534**

Io la vidi—scene: two tenors & orchestra (c1832-35) (Wds. Bassi)

L. Pavarotti, La Scala Orch, C. Abbado *Concert* (6/87) (SONY) Ⓓ **MK37228**

Jérusalem—opera: 4 acts (1847—Paris) (Lib. A. Royer and G. Vaëz)

Ave Maria K. Ricciarelli, Rome PO, G. Gavazzeni *Concert* (12/87) (RCA) Ⓓ **GD86534**
Je veux encore entendre L. Escalais, anon (r1906) *Concert* (12/93) (SYMP) Ⓓ **SYMCD1126**

I **Lombardi alla prima crociata—opera: 4 acts (1843—Milan)** (Lib. Solera)

EXCERPTS: 1. Prelude and Introduction. ACT 1: 2. Oh nobile esempio; 3. A te nell'ora infausta; 4. Sciagurata! hai tu creduto; 5. Tutta tremante ancor; 6a. Te, Vergin santa; 6b. Salve Maria!; 7. Vieni! Già posa Arvino. ACT 2: 8. É dunque vero!; 9a. Oh madre mia; 9b. La mia letizia infondere; 10. Come poteva un angelo; 11. È ancor silenzio; 12. Al tuo guerrier; 13. Sei tu l'uom della caverna?; 14. Stolto Allhà!; 15. La bella straniera; 16a. O madre dal cielo; 16b. Se vano è il pregare. ACT 3: 17. Gerusalem!; 18a. Dove sola m'inoltro; 18b. Teco io fuggo; 19a. Che vid'io mai?; 19b. Sì! del ciel che non punisce; 20a. Qui posa il fianco; 20b. Qual voluttà (Trio). ACT 4: 21. Componi, o cara vergine; 22. In cielo benedetto; 23a. Qual prodigio! (Polonaise); 23b. Non fu sogno; 24. O Signore, del tetto natio (Chorus); 25a. Al Siloè!; 25b. Quali voci!; 26. Guerra! guerra!; 27. Questa è mia tenda; 28. Te lodiamo (Finale).

Cpte C. Deutekom, P. Domingo, R. Raimondi, J. lo Monaco, S. Dean, C. Grant, M. Aparici, K. Erwen, D. Malvisi, Ambrosian Sngrs, RPO, L. Gardelli (r1971) (11/89) (PHIL) Ⓓ [2] **422 420-2PM2**
6a M. Callas, Paris Cons, N. Rescigno *Concert* (2/93) (EMI) Ⓓ **CDC7 54437-2**
6a, 16a G. Arangi-Lombardi, La Scala Orch, L. Molajoli (r1933) *Concert* (10/90) (PREI) Ⓓ **89013**
9a, 9b S. Mazzetti, L. Pavarotti, Rome Op Orch, G. Gavazzeni (pp1969) *Concert* (10/95) (RCA) Ⓓ **09026 68014-2**
9b L. Pavarotti, RPO, K.H. Adler (pp1982) *Concert* (8/91) (DECC) Ⓓ **430 716-2DM**
9b L. Escalais, anon (r1906) *Concert* (12/93) (SYMP) Ⓓ **SYMCD1126**
9b Ferruccio Tagliavini, EIAR Orch, U. Tansini (r1940) *Concert* (3/94) (CENT) Ⓓ **CRC2164**
9b L. Pavarotti, Parma Teatro Regio Orch, G. Patanè (pp1976) *Concert* (5/94) (DECC) Ⓓ [2] **443 018-2DF2**
16. M. Callas, Paris Cons, N. Rescigno *Concert* (9/87) (EMI) Ⓓ **CDC7 47730-2**
16a C. Muzio, orch (r1922) *Concert* (1/94) (ROMO) Ⓓ [2] **81005-2**
16a, 16b C. Muzio, orch (r1922) *Concert* (5/90) (BOGR) Ⓓ [2] **BIM705-2**
16a, 16b L. Price, LSO, E. Downes *Concert* (12/92) (RCA) Ⓓ [4] **09026 61236-2**
17, 24. Chicago Sym Chor, Chicago SO, G. Solti *Concert* (4/91) (DECC) Ⓓ **430 226-2DH**
20a, 20b V. della Chiesa, J. Peerce, N. Moscona, NBC SO, A. Toscanini (bp1943) *Concert* (6/91) (RCA) Ⓓ **GD60276**
20b E. Rethberg, B. Gigli, E. Pinza, orch, R. Bourdon (r1930) *Concert* (5/90) (PEAR) Ⓓ **GEMMCD9367**
20b E. Rethberg, B. Gigli, E. Pinza, orch, R. Bourdon (r1930) *Concert* (10/90) (RCA) Ⓓ **GD87811**
20b F. Alda, E. Caruso, M. Journet, orch, W.B. Rogers (r1912) *Concert* (7/91) (RCA) Ⓓ [12] **GD60495(4)**
20b E. Caruso, M. Journet, F. Alda, orch, W.B. Rogers (r1912) *Concert* (10/91) (PEAR) Ⓓ [3] **EVC3(1)**
20b E. Rethberg, B. Gigli, E. Pinza, Victor SO, R. Bourdon (r1930: 2 takes) *Concert* (10/95) (ROMO) Ⓓ [2] **81014-2**
23a, 23b M. Caballé, RCA Italiana Op Orch, A. Guadagno *Concert* (11/92) (RCA) Ⓓ [2] **GD60941**
24. Berlin Deutsche Op Chor, Berlin Deutsche Op Orch, G. Sinopoli *Concert* (10/85) (DG) Ⓓ **415 283-2GH**

Luisa Miller—opera: 3 acts (1849—Naples) (Lib. S Cammarano)

EXCERPTS: 1. Overture. ACT 1: 2a. Ti desta, Luisa, regina de' cori; 2b. Non temer: più nobil spirto; 2c. Lo vidi, e'l primo palpito; 3a. T'amo d'amor ch'esprimere; 3b. Mia diletta!; 3c. Ferma ed ascolta!; 3d. Sacra la scelta è d'un consorte; 4. Ah! fu giusto il mio sospetto!; 5a. Che mai narrasti!; 5b. Il mio sangue; 5c. Padre...M'abbraccia; 6a. Quale un sorriso d'amica sorte; 6b. Dall'aule raggiante de vano splendor; 6c. Deh! La parola amara; 7a. Sciogliete i levrieri; 7b. Luisa, non temer; 7c. Fra' mortali ancora oppressa; 7d. Ad immagina tua creata. ACT 2: 8a. Ah! Luisa, Luisa, ove sei?; 8b. E segnare questa mano; 8c. Tu puniscimi, o Signore; 9a. Egli delira: sul mattin degli anni; 9b. L'alto retaggio; 9c. O meco incolume sarai; 9d. Vien la Duchessa!; 9e. Presentati alla Duchessa puoi, Luisa; 9f. Come celar la smanie; 10a. Il foglio dunque?; 10b. Oh! fede negar potessi; 10c. Quando le sere al placido; 11a. Di me chiedeste?; 11b. L'ara, o l'avello apprestami. ACT 3: 12a. Come in un giorno solo; 12b. La tombaè un letto; 13a. Ah! l'ultima preghiera; 13b. Ah, piangi! Il tuo dolore; 13c. Avean mio padre i barbari; 13d. Padre, ricevi l'estremo addio.

Cpte K. Ricciarelli, P. Domingo, R. Bruson, G. Howell, E. Obraztsova, W. Ganzarolli, A. Michael, L. de Corato, ROH Chor, ROHO, L. Maazel (r1979) (5/88) (DG) Ⓓ [2] **423 144-2GH2**
Cpte A. Moffo, C. Bergonzi, C. MacNeil, G. Tozzi, S. Verrett, E. Flagello, G. Carturan, P. de Palma, RCA Italiana Op Chor, RCA Italiana Op Orch, F. Cleva (r1964) (10/88) (RCA) Ⓓ [2] **GD86646**
Cpte M. Caballé, L. Pavarotti, S. Milnes, B. Giaiotti, A. Reynolds, R. Van Allan, A. Céline, F. Pavarotti, London Op Chor, National PO, P. Maag (10/88) (DECC) Ⓓ [2] **417 420-2DH2**
Cpte A. Millo, P. Domingo, V. Chernov, J-H. Rootering, F. Quivar, P. Plishka, W. White, J. Bills, NY Met Op Chor, NY Met Op Orch, James Levine (9/92) (SONY) Ⓓ [2] **S2K48073**
1. BPO, H. von Karajan *Concert* (10/87) (DG) Ⓓ **419 622-2GH**
1. BPO, H. von Karajan *Concert* (1/95) (DG) Ⓓ **439 972-2GGA2**
2a, 3a, 4, 5a, 5b, 8a, 9a, 9c, 9e, 9f, 10c Hagen Qt (r1994: arr stg qt: E Muzio) *Concert* (12/95) (DG) Ⓓ **447 069-2GH**
3d D. Hvorostovsky, Rotterdam PO, V. Gergiev *Concert* (7/90) (PHIL) Ⓓ **426 740-2PH**
5b T. Pasero, La Scala Orch, A. Sabino (r1942) *Concert* (4/95) (PREI) Ⓓ **89074**
10b, 10c P. Domingo, ROHO, L. Maazel *Concert* (7/86) (DG) Ⓓ **415 366-2GH**
10b, 10c J. Peerce, NBC SO, A. Toscanini (bp1943) *Concert* (5/90) (RCA) Ⓓ [7] **GD60326**
10b, 10c L. Pavarotti, Vienna Op Orch, E. Downes *Concert* (7/90) (DECC) Ⓓ [2] **425 681-2DM2**
10b, 10c L. Pavarotti, RPO, K.H. Adler (pp1982) *Concert* (8/91) (DECC) Ⓓ **430 716-2DM**
10b, 10c C. Bergonzi, Santa Cecilia Academy Orch, G. Gavazzeni (r1957) *Concert* (10/93) (DECC) Ⓓ **436 463-2DM**
10b, 10c A. Bonci, anon (r1906) *Concert* (9/94) (NIMB) Ⓓ **NI7856**

10b, 10c L. Pavarotti, NYPO, L. Magiera (pp1993)
Concert (2/95) (DECC) ① 444 450-2DH
10b, 10c G. Anselmi, anon (r1907) Concert
(7/95) (SYMP) ① SYMCD1170
10b, 10c L. Pavarotti, Rome SO, N. Bonavolontà
(pp1967) Concert (10/95) (RCA) ① 09026 68014-2
10b, 10c B. Heppner, Munich RO, R. Abbado
(r1993/4) Concert (11/95) (RCA) ① 09026 62504-2
10b, 10c, 13b P. Domingo, K. Ricciarelli, ROHO, L.
Maazel (r1979) Concert
(6/94) (BELA) ① 450 121-2
10c L. Signoretti, anon (r1901) Concert
(12/89) (SYMP) ① SYMCD1065
10c A. Pertile, La Scala Orch, C. Sabajno (r1927)
Concert (9/90) (PREI) ① 89007
10c F. Giraud, anon (r1904) Concert
(5/91) (SYMP) ① SYMCD1077
10c G. Lugo, orch (r1939) Concert
(2/92) (PREI) ① 89034
10c F. Giraud, anon (r1904) Concert
(11/92) (MEMO) ① [2] HR4408/9(1)
10c G. Lauri-Volpi, Rome Op Orch, R. Arduini
(r1943) Concert (7/94) (NIMB) ① NI7853
10c F. de Lucia, anon (r1908) Concert
(1/95) (SYMP) ① SYMCD1149
10c A. Giorgini, orch (r1905) Concert
(4/95) (RECO) ① TRC3

Macbeth—opera: 4 acts (1847—Florence)
(Lib. Piave and Maffei)
EXCERPTS: 1. Prelude. ACT 1: 2. Che faceste? dite
su!; 3a. Giorno non vidi mai; 3b. Due vaticini
compiuto or sono; 4. S'allontanarono!; 5a. Nel di della
vittoria; 5b. Vieni! t'affretta!; 5c. Ambizioso spirto; 5d.
Or tutti sorgete; 6. Oh donna mia!; 7a. Sappia la
sposa mia; 7b. Regna il sonno; 7c. Fatal mia donna!;
8a. Di destarlo per tempo; 8b. Schiudi, inferno, la
bocca. ACT 2: 9a. Perchè mi sfuggi; 9b. La luce
langue; 10. Chi osò mandarvi a noi?; 11a. Studia, il
passo; 11b. Come dal ciel precipita; 12a. Salve, o
Rel; 12b. Si colmi il calice; 12c. Va', spirto d'abisso!.
ACT 3: 13. Tre volte miagola; 14. Ballet Music; 15a.
Finchè appelli; 15b. Fuggi, regal fantasima; 16.
Ondine e Silfidi; 17a. Ove son io?; 17b. Ora di morte.
ACT 4: 18. Patria oppressa!; 19a. O figli, o figli mieil;
19b. Ah, la paterna mano; 20. Dove siam? che bosco
è quello?; 21a. Vegliammo invan due notti; 21b. Una
macchia è qui tuttora; 22a. Perfidi! All'Anglo contro
me v'unite!; 22b. Pietà, rispetto, amore; 23. Ella è
mortal; 24. Vittoria! (Finale). SUPPLEMENTARY
NUMBERS: Act 2: 25. Trionfai. ACT 3: 26. Vada in
fiamme e in polve cada. ACT 4: 27. Mal per me che
m'affidai (Death of Macbeth).
Cpte R. Bruson, M. Zampieri, R. Lloyd, N. Shicoff,
C.H. Ahnsjö, P. Salomaa, M. Nikolič, A. Schmidt, L.
Aliberti, Berlin Deutsche Op Chor, Berlin Deutsche
Op Orch, G. Sinopoli (r1983)
(2/85) (PHIL) ① [2] 412 133-2PH3
Cpte P. Cappuccilli, S. Verrett, N. Ghiaurov, P.
Domingo, A. Savastano, C. Zardo, G. Foiani, S.
Fontana, A. Mariotti, S. Malagù, La Scala Chor, La
Scala Orch, C. Abbado (r1976)
(9/86) (DG) ① [3] 415 688-2GH3
Cpte L. Warren, Leonie Rysanek, J. Hines, C.
Bergonzi, W. Olvis, G. Pechner, H. Sternberg, O.
Hawkins, C. Ordassy, NY Met Op Chor, NY Met Op
Orch, E. Leinsdorf (r1959)
(9/88) (RCA) ① [2] GD84516
Cpte S. Milnes, F. Cossotto, R. Raimondi, J.
Carreras, G. Bernardi, C. del Bosco, L. Fyson, N.
Taylor, J. Noble, M. Borgato, Ambrosian Op Chor,
New Philh, R. Muti (r1976)
(2/93) (EMI) ① [2] CMS7 64339-2
Cpte E. Mascherini, M. Callas, I. Tajo, G. Penno, L.
Della Pergola, D. Caselli, A. Barbesi, I. Vinco, M.
Tommasini, A. Vercelli, La Scala Chor, La Scala
Orch, V. de Sabata (pp1952)
(1/94) (EMI) ① [2] CMS7 64944-2
Cpte M. Ahlersmeyer, M. Callas, I. Tajo, J. Witt,
W. Franter, V. Madin, K. Ettl, E. Boettcher, Vienna St
Op Chor, Vienna St Op Orch, K. Böhm (pp1943: Ger)
Don Carlo. (5/94) (PREI) ① [2] 90175
Cpte D. Fischer-Dieskau, E. Suliotis, N. Ghiaurov, L.
Pavarotti, R. Casainelli, R. Myers, J. Noble, D. Reed,
L. Fyson, H. Lawrence, Ambrosian Op Chor, LPO, L.
Gardelli (r1970)
(7/94) (DECC) ① [2] 440 048-2DMO2
1. BPO, H. von Karajan Concert
(10/87) (DG) ① 419 622-2GH
1. BPO, H. von Karajan Concert
(1/95) (DG) ① 439 972-2GGA2
2. LSC, LSO, R. Hickox Concert
(4/89) (CARL) ① PCD908
5, 9b, 21b M. Callas, Philh, N. Rescigno Concert
(9/87) (EMI) ① CDC7 47730-2
9a, 9b R. Hunter, Tasmanian SO, D. Franks (r1989)
Concert (10/95) (ABCC) ① 8 7000 10

9b M. Callas, Philh, N. Rescigno Concert
(2/90) (EMIN) ① CD-EMX2123
9b L. Price, New Philh, N. Santi (r1977) Concert
(12/92) (RCA) ① [4] 09026 61236-2
9b, 21b J. Barstow, S. Burgess, J. Connell, ENO
Orch, M. Elder Concert
(1/89) (TER) ① CDVIR8307
11. R. Raimondi, New Philh, R. Muti Concert
(10/88) (EMI) ① CDM7 69549-2
11. J. Hines, NY Met Op Orch, E. Leinsdorf (r1959)
Concert (4/94) (RCA) ① [6] 09026 61580-2(6)
11a, 11b I. Andrésen, orch (Ger: r1929) Concert
(10/90) (PREI) ① 89028
11b M. Salminen, Lahti SO, E. Klas Concert
(8/92) (BIS) ① BIS-CD520
13, 18. Chicago Sym Chor, Chicago SO, G. Solti
Concert (4/91) (DECC) ① 430 226-2DH
14. SNO, A. Gibson Concert
(9/85) (CHAN) ① CHAN8379
14. NY Met Op Orch, James Levine (r1992) Concert
(6/94) (SONY) ① SK52489
18. Berlin Deutsche Op Chor, Berlin Deutsche Op
Orch, G. Sinopoli Concert
(10/85) (DG) ① 415 283-2GH
18. Atlanta Sym Chor, Atlanta SO, Robert Shaw
Concert (3/88) (TELA) ① [2] CD80152
18. Slovak Phil Chor, Bratislava RSO, O. Dohnányi
Concert (4/91) (NAXO) ① 8 550241
19. P. Domingo, ROHO, J. Barker (pp1988) Concert
(9/89) (EMI) ① CDC7 49811-2
19a, 19b E. Caruso, orch (r1916) Concert
(7/91) (MSCM) ① MM30352
19a, 19b L. Pavarotti, RPO, K.H. Adler (pp1982)
Concert (8/91) (DECC) ① 430 716-2DM
19a, 19b E. Caruso, orch, W.B. Rogers (r1916)
Concert (10/91) (PEAR) ① [3] EVC3(2)
19a, 19b P. Domingo, La Scala Orch, C. Abbado
Concert (5/93) (DG) ① 431 104-2GB
19a, 19b P. Domingo, La Scala Orch, C. Abbado
(r1976) Concert (6/94) (BELA) ① 450 121-2
19b E. Caruso, orch, W.B Rogers (r1916) Concert
(7/91) (RCA) ① [2] GD60495(5)
19b L. Pavarotti, Parma Teatro Regio Orch, G.
Patanè (pp1988) Concert
(5/94) (DECC) ① [2] 443 018-2DF2
19b E. Caruso, orch (r1916) Concert
(7/95) (NIMB) ① NI7866
21. M. Caballé, E. Bainbridge, T. Allen, RPO, A.
Guadagno Concert
(10/88) (EMI) ① CDM7 69500-2
21. Leonie Rysanek, G. Pechner, C. Ordassy, NY
Met Op Orch, E. Leinsdorf (r1959) Concert
(4/94) (RCA) ① [6] 09026 61580-2(7)
21a, 21b L. Price, C. Vozza, R. El Hage, RCA
Italiana Op Orch, F. Molinari-Pradelli Concert
(12/92) (RCA) ① [4] 09026 61236-2
21b M. Callas, Philh, N. Rescigno Concert
(2/90) (EMI) ① CMS7 63244-2
22. T. Gobbi, Rome Op Orch, O. de Fabritiis (r1955)
Concert (10/89) (EMI) ① CDM7 63109-2
22. D. Hvorostovsky, Rotterdam PO, V. Gergiev
Concert (7/90) (PHIL) ① 426 740-2PH
22. A. Sved, orch (r1940) Concert
(4/94) (EMI) ① [3] CHS7 64864-2(2)
22a, 22b M. Battistini, C. Sabajno (r1912) Concert
(10/92) (NIMB) ① NI7831
22b T. Gobbi, LSO, W. Braithwaite (r1952) Concert
(8/93) (TEST) ① SBT1019
199. C. Bergonzi, NY Met Op Orch, E. Leinsdorf
(r1959) Concert
(4/94) (RCA) ① [6] 09026 61580-2(7)

I Masnadieri—opera: 4 acts (1847—London)
(Lib. Maffei, after Schiller)
EXCERPTS: 1. Prelude. ACT 1: 2a. Quando io leggo
in Plutarco; 2b. O mio castel paterno; 3a. Ecco un
foglio; 3b. Nell'argilla maledetta; 4a. Vecchio! spiccai
da te; 4b. La sua lampada vitale; 5a. Trionfo, trionfo!;
5b. Tremate o miseri; 6a. Venerabile o padre; 6b. Lo
sguardo avea degli angeli; 7a. Mio Carlo; 7b. Carlo!
io muoio; 8a. Un messaggero; 8b. Sul capo mio
colpevole. ACT 2: 9a. Dall'infame banchetto; 9b. Tu
del mio Carlo; 9c. Ah, signora!; 9d. Carlo vive?; 10a.
Perchè fuggisti; 10b. Io t'amo, Amalia; 10c.
Tracotante!; 10d. Ti scosta, o malnato; 11a. Tutto
quest'oggi; 11b. I cittadini correano alla festa; 12a.
Come splendido; 12b. Di ladroni attorniato; 13.
Capitano!. ACT 3: 14. Dio, ti ringrazio; 15a. Qual
mare, qual terra; 15b. Qual nel bosco?; 15c. Lassù
risplendere; 16. Le rube, gli stupri; 17a. Ben giunto, o
Capitano!; 17b. Tutto è buio e silenzio; 17c. Un
ignoto; 17d. Destatevi, o pietrel. ACT 4: 18.
Tradimento!; 19. Pareami che sorto; 20a. M'hai
chiamato; 20b. Precipita dal monte un foribondo; 21.
Francesco! mio figliol; 22. Come il bacio d'un padre;
23. Qui son essi!; 24. Caduto è il reprobo!

Cpte R. Raimondi, C. Bergonzi, P. Cappuccilli, M.
Caballé, J. Sandor, M. Mazzieri, W. Elvin, Ambrosian
Sngrs, New Philh, L. Gardelli (r1974)
(11/89) (PHIL) ① [2] 422 423-2PM2
Cpte J. Sutherland, F. Bonisolli, M. Manuguerra, S.
Ramey, A. Davies, S. Alaimo, J. Harris, WNO Chor,
WNO Orch, R. Bonynge (r1982)
(7/93) (DECC) ① [2] 433 854-2DMO2
1. BPO, H. von Karajan Concert
(10/87) (DG) ① 419 622-2GH
1. BPO, H. von Karajan Concert
(1/95) (DG) ① 439 972-2GGA2
9a, 9b, 9c, 9d K. Ricciarelli, R. Truffelli, Rome PO, G.
Gavazzeni Concert (12/87) (RCA) ① GD86534
16. Chicago Sym Chor, Chicago SO, G. Solti Concert
(4/91) (DECC) ① 430 226-2DH

Nabucco—opera: 4 acts (1842—Milan) (Lib.
Solera)
EXCERPTS: 1. Overture. ACT 1: 2. Gli arredi festivi;
3a. Sperate, o figli!; 3b. D'Egitto la sui lidi; 3c. Come
notte; 4a. Fenena! O mia diletta!; 4b. Io t'amaval; 5.
Prode guerrieri!; 6. Lo vedeste?; 7a. Viva Nabucco!;
7b. Che tenti?; 7c. Tremin gl'insani; 8a. O vinti, il
capo; 8b. Mio furore. ACT 2: 9a. Ben io t'avenni; 9b.
Anch'io dischiuso un giorno; 9c. Salgo già del trono;
10a. Vieni, o Levital; 10b. Tu sul labbro; 11a. Che si
vuol?; 11b. Il maledetto non ha fratelli; 12a. Deh,
fratelli; 12b. S'appressan gl'istanti; 12c. S'oda or me!;
12d. Chi mi toglie il regio scettro?. ACT 3: 13. E
l'Assiria una reina; 14. Eccelsa Donna; 15. Donna,
chi sei?; 16. Oh, di qual'onta aggravisi; 17. Deh,
perdona; 18. Va pensiero, sull'ali dorate; 19a. Oh, chi
piange?; 19b. Del futuro nel buio discerno. ACT 4:
20. Son pur queste mie membra!; 21. Dio di Giuda!;
22. Cadran, cadranno i perfidi; 23a. Marcia funebra;
23b. Va! la palma del martirio; 23c. Oh, dischiuso;
24a. Viva Nabucco!; 24b. Oh! chi veggi'io?; 24c. Su
me...morente.
Cpte P. Cappuccilli, G. Dimitrova, P. Domingo, L.V.
Terrani, E. Nesterenko, K. Rydl, V. Horn, L. Popp,
Berlin Deutsche Op Chor, Berlin Deutsche Op Orch,
G. Sinopoli (5/84) (DG) ① [2] 410 512-2GH2
Cpte T. Gobbi, E. Suliotis, B. Prevedi, D. Carral, C.
Cava, G. Foiani, W. Kräutler, A. d'Auria, Vienna St
Op Chor, Vienna St Op Orch, L. Gardelli
(1/87) (DECC) ① [2] 417 407-2DH2
1. BPO, H. von Karajan Concert
(10/87) (DG) ① 419 622-2GH
1. BPO, H. von Karajan Concert
(5/90) (DG) ① 429 164-2GR
1. Berlin RIAS Orch, F. Fricsay (bp1952) Concert
(11/94) (DG) ① 445 406-2GDO
1. I. Seefried, M. Forrester, E. Haefliger, D. Fischer-
Dieskau, Berlin St Hedwig's Cath Ch, BPO, F.
Fricsay, H. Krebs, T. Varga, Berlin RIAS Chbr Ch,
Berlin RIAS Orch, H. Geusser, W. Fugmann, M.
Weber, G. Herzog, Berlin RSO, VPO, E. Grümmer,
G. Pitzinger, H. Hotter, Y. Menuhin (bp1952) Concert
(11/94) (DG) ① [11] 445 400-2GDO10
1. BPO, H. von Karajan Concert
(1/95) (DG) ① 439 972-2GGA2
2, 18. LSC, LSO, R. Hickox Concert
(4/89) (CARL) ① PCD908
2, 18. Chicago Sym Chor, Chicago SO, G. Solti
Concert (4/91) (DECC) ① 430 226-2DH
2, 18. Slovak Phil Chor, Bratislava RSO, O. Dohnányi
Concert (4/91) (NAXO) ① 8 550241
3a B. Christoff, Rome Op Orch, V. Gui (r1955)
Concert (4/92) (EMI) ① [7] CHS7 69741-2(6)
3a, 10b N. de Angelis, orch, L. Molajoli (1928)
Concert (7/92) (PREI) ① 89042
7b, 7c T. Ruffo, orch, W.B. Rogers (r1914) Concert
(11/90) (NIMB) ① NI7810
7c T. Ruffo, orch (r1914) Concert
(2/93) (PREI) ① [3] 89303(1)
9. M. Callas, Philh, N. Rescigno Concert
(9/87) (EMI) ① CDC7 47730-2
10a, 10b J. Van Dam, Loire PO, M. Soustrot (r1992)
Concert (8/93) (FORL) ① UCD16681
10b T. Pasero, La Scala Orch, A. Sabino (r1942)
Concert (4/95) (PREI) ① 89074
12d, 21. R. Stracciari, orch (r1925) Concert
(2/90) (PREI) ① 89003
18. Berlin Deutsche Op Chor, Berlin Deutsche Op
Orch, G. Sinopoli Concert
(10/85) (DG) ① 415 283-2GH
18. Atlanta Sym Chor, Atlanta SO, Robert Shaw
Concert (3/88) (TELA) ① [2] CD80152
18. ROH Chor, ROHO, B. Haitink Concert
(11/89) (EMI) ① CDC7 49849-2
18. Westminster Ch, NBC SO, A. Toscanini (bp1943)
Concert (5/90) (RCA) ① [7] GD60326
18. ROH Chor, RPO, R. Stapleton Concert
(10/90) (CARL) ① MCD15

18. La Scala Chor, La Scala Orch, V. Veneziani (r1928) *Concert* (4/94) (EMI) Ⓓ [3] **CHS7 64864-2(2)**

20, 21, 22. T. Gobbi, W. Kräutler, Vienna St Op Concert Ch, Vienna Op Orch, L. Gardelli (r1965) *Concert* (10/93) (DECC) Ⓓ **436 464-2DM**

21. T. Gobbi, Rome Op Orch, O. de Fabritiis (r1955) *Concert* (10/89) (EMI) Ⓓ **CDM7 63109-2**

21. C. Galeffi, orch (r1916) *Concert* (4/94) (EMI) Ⓓ [3] **CHS7 64860-2(2)**

Oberto, Conte di San Bonifaco—dramma: 2 acts (1839—Milan) (Lib. Soleva)

EXCERPTS: 1. Overture. ACT 1: 2a. Di vermiglia, amabil luce; 2b. Son fra voi! Già parmi udire il fremito; 3a. Ah, sgombro è il loco alfin; 3b. Sotto il paterno tetto; 3c. Oh, potesi nel mio core; 4. Oh patria terra, alfina io ti rivedo; 5a. Al cader della notte; 5b. Guardami! sul mio ciglio; 5c. Non ti basto il periglio; 5d. Del tuo favour soccorrimi; 5e. Un amplesso riceri, o pentita; 6. Findanzata avventurosa; 7a. Basta, basta, o fedeli!; 7b. Cuniza, ah parmi; 7c. Il pensier d'amore felice; 7d. Fra il timpre è la speme; 8. Alta cagione adunque; 9. A, perchè tanto in petto; 10a. Son io stresso! A te davanti; 10b. Su quella fronte impressa; 11a. A me gli amici! Mira!; 11b. A quell' aspetto un fremito. ACT 2: 12. Infelice! Nel core; 13a. Riccardo! E che gli resta?; 13b. Oh, chi torna l'ardente; 13c. Più che i vezzi e lo splendore; 14. Dov'è l'astro che nel cielo; 15a. Ei tarda ancor!; 15b. L'onor del tradimento; 15c. Ma tu, superbo giovane; 16. Eccolo! è desso! or son tranquillo; 17a. Ferma! Ah troppo in questa terra; 17b. La vergogna ed il dispetto; 17c. Ah Riccardo, se a misera amante; 18. Li vedeste; 19. Ciel, che feci!; 20. Dove son? il cerco invano!; 21a. Vieni, o misera, cresciuta; 21b. Sciagurata! a questa lido; 22. Una messaggio a questa volta?.

Cpte R. Baldani, G. Dimitrova, A. Browner, C. Bergonzi, R. Panerai, Bavarian Rad Chor, Munich RO, L. Gardelli (6/87) (ORFE) Ⓓ [2] **C105842H**

1. BPO, H. von Karajan *Concert* (1/95) (DG) Ⓓ **439 972-2GGA2**

Otello—opera: 4 acts (1887—Milan) (Lib. A Boito, after Shakespeare)

EXCERPTS: ACT 1: 1a. Una vela!; 1b. Esultate!; 2. Roderigo, ebben che pensi?; 3. Fuoco di gioia!; 4a. Roderigo, beviam!; 4b. Inaffia l'ugola! (Brindisi); 5a. Capitano, v'attende; 5b. Abbasso le spade!; 6a. Già nella notte densa (Love Duet); 6b. Venga la morte!. ACT 2: 7a. Non ti crucciar; 7b. Vanne! la tua meta; 7c. Credo in un Dio crudel; 8a. Ciò m'accora... 8b. Dove guardi; 9. D'un uom che geme; 10a. Desdemona rea!... 10b. Tu?! Indietro! fuggi!; 10c. Ora e per sempre; 11. Era la notte (Dream); 12a. Oh! mostruosa colpa!; 12b. Ah! mille vite; 12c. Si, pel ciel (Oath Duet). ACT 3: 13. La vedetta del porto; 14a. Dio ti giocondi; 14b. Esterrefatta fisso; 15. Dio! mi potevi (Monologue); 16a. Vieni; l'aula è deserta; 16b. Questa è una ragna; 17a. Quest'è il segnale; 17b. Come la ucciderò; 18a. Viva! Evviva!; 18b. Eccolo! È lui!; 18c. A terra!; 19. Ballabile. ACT 4: 20a. Era più calmo?; 20b. Mia madre aveva; 20c. Piangea cantando (Willow Song); 21. Ave Maria; 22. Chi è là? (Death of Desdemona); 23. Niun mi tema.

Cpte P. Domingo, R. Scotto, S. Milnes, F. Little, P. Crook, J. Kraft, P. Plishka, M. King, Ambrosian Op Chor, National PO, James Levine (r1978) (3/86) (RCA) Ⓓ [2] **GD82951**

Cpte P. Domingo, K. Ricciarelli, J. Diaz, E. Di Cesare, C. Zaharia, P. Malakova, J. Macurdy, E. Tumagian, G. Pigliucci, La Scala Chor, La Scala Orch, L. Maazel (r1985) (12/86) (EMI) Ⓓ [2] **CDS7 47450-8**

Cpte M. del Monaco, R. Tebaldi, A. Protti, N. Romanato, A. Cesarini, A.R. Satre, F. Corena, T. Krause, L. Arbace, Vienna Children's Ch, Vienna St Op Chor, VPO, H. von Karajan (r1961) (3/87) (DECC) Ⓓ [2] **411 618-2DH2**

Cpte J. Vickers, M. Freni, P. Glossop, A. Bottion, M. Sénéchal, S. Malagù, J. Van Dam, M. Macchì, H. Helm, Berlin Deutsche Op Chor, BPO, H. von Karajan (r1973) (4/88) (EMI) Ⓓ [2] **CMS7 69308-2**

Cpte J. Vickers, Leonie Rysanek, T. Gobbi, F. Andreolli, Mario Carlin, M. Pirazzini, F. Mazzoli, F. Calabrese, R. Kerns, Rome Op Chor, Rome Op Orch, T. Serafin (r1960) (11/88) (RCA) Ⓓ [2] **GD81969**

Cpte G. Martinelli, E. Rethberg, L. Tibbett, N. Massue, T. Votipka, N. Moscona, G. Cehanovsky, NY Met Op Chor, NY Met Op Orch, E. Panizza (pp1938) (9/91) (MUSI) Ⓓ [2] **MACD-645**

Cpte L. Pavarotti, K. Te Kanawa, L. Nucci, A. Rolfe Johnson, J. Keyes, E. Ardam, D. Kavrakos, A. Opie, R. Cohn, NY Met Op Children's Ch, Chicago Sym Chor, Chicago SO, G. Solti (pp1991) (11/91) (DECC) Ⓓ [2] **433 669-2DH2**

Cpte R. Vinay, H. Nelli, G. Valdengo, V. Assandri, L. Chabay, N. Merriman, N. Moscona, A. Newman, Chor, NBC SO, A. Toscanini (r1947) (3/92) (RCA) Ⓓ [2] **GD60302**

Cpte C. Murgu, M. Gulegina, R. Bruson, M. Saltarin, H. Yoshida, G. Pasino, M. Pertusi, G. de Angelis, Tokyo Little Sngrs, Fujiwara Op Chor, Tokyo PO, G Kuhn (pp1991) (6/92) (SCHW) Ⓓ [2] **314074**

Cpte M. del Monaco, R. Tebaldi, A. Protti, P. de Palma, A. Mercuriali, L. Ribacchi, F. Corena, P. L. Latinucci, D. Caselli, Santa Cecilia Academy Chor, Santa Cecilia Academy Orch, A. Erede (r1954) (5/94) (LOND) Ⓓ [2] **440 245-2LF2**

Cpte C. Cossutta, M. Price, G. Bacquier, P. Dvorský, K. Equiluz, J. Berbié, K. Moll, S. Dean, H. Helm, Vienna Boys' Ch, Vienna St Op Chor, VPO, G. Solti (r1977) (5/94) (DECC) Ⓓ [2] **440 045-2DMO2**

Cpte P. Domingo, C. Studer, S. Leiferkus, R. Vargas, M. Schade, D. Graves, I. d'Arcangelo, G. Prestia, P. Duminy, Hauts-de-Seine Maîtrise, Paris Opéra-Bastille Chor, Paris Opéra-Bastille Orch, Myung-Whun Chung (r1993) (12/94) (DG) Ⓓ [2] **439 805-2GH2**

1a, 1b, 6a(pt), 6b, 12c G. Zenatello, A. Granforte, H. Spani, La Scala Chor, La Scala Orch, C. Sabajno (r1926) *Concert* (5/94) (PEAR) Ⓓ [4] **GEMMCDS9074(2)**

1a, 1b, 6b, 12b, 12c G. Zenatello, H. Spani, A. Granforte, La Scala Orch, C. Sabajno (r1926) *Concert* (11/91) (PREI) Ⓓ **89038**

1a, 1b, 12b, 12c G. Zenatello, A. Granforte, La Scala Orch, C. Sabajno (r1926) *Concert* (11/91) (CLUB) Ⓓ **CL99-025**

1b M. del Monaco, Milan SO, A. Quadri (r1951) *Concert* (4/92) (EMI) Ⓓ [7] **CHS7 69741-2(7)**

1b F. Tamagno, anon (r1903) *Concert* (7/92) (PEAR) Ⓓ [3] **GEMMCDS9923(2)**

1b F. Tamagno, anon (r1903) *Concert* (11/92) (MEMO) Ⓓ [2] **HR4408/9(1)**

1b, 6a, 6b, 10c, 12c, 15, 23. G. Lauri-Volpi, M. Caniglia, M. Basiola I, La Scala Orch, G. Marinuzzi (r1941) *Concert* (7/94) (NIMB) Ⓓ **NI7853**

1b, 10c F. Tamagno, anon (r1903) *Concert* (4/94) (EMI) Ⓓ [3] **CHS7 64860-2(1)**

1b, 10c, 23. F. Tamagno, Anon (pf) (r1903-04) *Concert* (2/92) (OPAL) Ⓓ **OPALCD9846**

1b, 23. F. Tamagno, anon (r1903) *Concert* (9/94) (NIMB) Ⓓ **NI7856**

3. Atlanta Sym Chor, Atlanta SO, Robert Shaw *Concert* (3/88) (TELA) Ⓓ [2] **CD80152**

3. ROH Chor, ROHO, B. Haitink *Concert* (12/89) (EMI) Ⓓ **CDC7 49849-2**

3. Chicago Sym Chor, Chicago SO, G. Solti *Concert* (4/91) (DECC) Ⓓ **430 226-2DH**

3. Slovak Phil Chor, Bratislava RSO, O. Dohnányi *Concert* (4/91) (NAXO) Ⓓ **8 550241**

3. Vienna St Op Chor, Vienna St Op Orch, V. de Sabata (pp1935: Ger) *Concert* (7/94) (SCHW) Ⓓ [2] **314512**

4b A. Granforte, P. Girardi, N. Palai, La Scala Orch, C. Sabajno (r1931) *Concert* (12/91) (PREI) Ⓓ **89048**

4b G. Inghilleri, O. Dua, L. Cilla, chor, orch, J. Barbirolli (r1929) *Concert* (7/92) (PEAR) Ⓓ [3] **GEMMCDS9926(1)**

4b, 7c, 11. R. Stracciari, orch (r1925) *Concert* (2/90) (PREI) Ⓓ **89003**

6. C. Studer, P. Domingo, ROHO, J. Barker (pp1988) *Concert* (9/89) (EMI) Ⓓ **CDC7 49811-2**

6. G. Lauri-Volpi, M. Caniglia, Rome Op Orch, D. Olivieri (r1941) *Concert* (4/94) (EMI) Ⓓ [3] **CHS7 64864-2(2)**

6a(pt) H. Spani, G. Zenatello, La Scala Orch, C. Sabajno (r1926) *Concert* (9/90) (CLUB) Ⓓ [2] **CL99-509/10**

6a, 6b M. Seinemeyer, T. Pattiera, Berlin St Op Orch, F. Weissmann (r1928) *Concert* (11/90) (PREI) Ⓓ **89029**

6a, 6b J. Sutherland, K. Te Kanawa, NYC Op Orch, R. Bonynge *Concert* (12/91) (DECC) Ⓓ **430 724-2DM**

6a, 6b G. Zenatello, E. Mazzoleni, orch (r c1910) *Concert* (12/93) (SYMP) Ⓓ **SYMCD1148**

6a, 6b G. Zenatello, L. Pasini-Vitale, orch (r1909) *Concert* (12/93) (SYMP) Ⓓ **SYMCD1148**

6a, 6b M. Price, C. Cossutta, VPO, G. Solti (r1977) *Concert* (12/93) (DECC) Ⓓ **433 439-2DA**

6a, 6b G. Zenatello, L. Pasini-Vitale, orch (r1909) *Concert* (5/94) (PEAR) Ⓓ [4] **GEMMCDS9073(2)**

6a, 6b K. Ricciarelli, L. Pavarotti, Parma Teatro Regio Orch, G. Patanè (pp1976) *Concert* (5/94) (DECC) Ⓓ [2] **443 018-2DF2**

6a, 6b G. Zenatello, E. Mazzoleni, orch (r1911) *Concert* (5/94) (PEAR) Ⓓ [4] **GEMMCDS9074(1)**

6a, 6b N. Stemme, P. Domingo, Paris Opéra-Bastille Orch, E. Kohn (pp1992) *Concert* (6/94) (SONY) Ⓓ **SK46691**

6a, 6b T. Ralf, T. Lemnitz, Berlin St Op Orch, B. Seidler-Winkler (r1939: Ger) *Concert* (10/94) (PREI) Ⓓ **89077**

6a, 6b, 21. K. Ricciarelli, P. Domingo, Santa Cecilia Academy Orch, G. Gavazzeni *Concert* (12/87) (RCA) Ⓓ **GD86534**

6a(pt), 10c, 11. F. Völker, V. Ursuleac, J. von Manowarda, Vienna St Op Orch, C. Krauss (pp1933: Ger) *Concert* (9/95) (SCHW) Ⓓ [2] **314662**

6b C. Muzio, F. Merli, orch, L. Molajoli (r1935) *Concert* (4/91) (NIMB) Ⓓ **NI7814**

7. T. Gobbi, Rome Op Orch, T. Serafin (r1960) *Concert* (4/94) (RCA) Ⓓ [6] **09026 61580-2(6)**

7a-c, 8a, 10b, 10c, 11, 12a-c L. Tibbett, G. Martinelli, A. de Paolis, NY Met Op Orch, E. Panizza (pp1941) *Concert* (3/91) (PEAR) Ⓓ [2] **GEMMCDS9452**

7b, 7c T. Gobbi, Philh, A. Erede (r1963) *Concert* (10/89) (EMI) Ⓓ **CDM7 63109-2**

7b, 7c T. Gobbi, Philh, J. Robertson (r1950) *Concert* (8/93) (TEST) Ⓓ **SBT1019**

7c G. Kaschmann, S. Cottone (r1903) *Concert* (12/89) (SYMP) Ⓓ **SYMCD1065**

7c T. Ruffo, orch, W.B. Rogers (r1914) *Concert* (11/90) (NIMB) Ⓓ **NI7810**

7c C. Tagliabue, Turin EIAR Orch, A. la Rosa Parodi (r1942) *Concert* (11/90) (PREI) Ⓓ **89015**

7c A. Endrèze, orch, G. Cloëz (French: r c1932) *Concert* (11/92) (MSCM) Ⓓ **MM30451**

7c I. Caley, S. Milnes, LPO, S. Varviso (1972) *Concert* (10/93) (DECC) Ⓓ **436 464-2DM**

7c C. Formichi, orch, A. Ketèlbey (r1924) *Concert* (11/94) (PREI) Ⓓ **89055**

7c E. Giraldoni, orch (r1905) *Concert* (10/95) (NIMB) Ⓓ **NI7867**

7c H. Schlusnus, orch (r1921: Ger) *Concert* (12/95) (PREI) Ⓓ **89110**

7c, 11. G. Bechi, Santa Cecilia Academy Orch, A. Votto (r1946) *Concert* (2/90) (PREI) Ⓓ **89009**

7c, 11. P. Schoeffler, LPO, K. Rankl (r1947) *Concert* (1/95) (PREI) Ⓓ **90190**

7c, 12c T. Ruffo, E. Caruso, orch (r1914) *Concert* (2/93) (PREI) Ⓓ [3] **89303(1)**

8a(pt), 10c, 12b, 12c, 15, 16b, 23. G. Zenatello, G. Noto, L. Cilla, E. Cotreil, M. Sampieri, orch, V. Bellezza (pp1926) *Concert* (5/94) (PEAR) Ⓓ [4] **GEMMCDS9074(2)**

10a, 10c, 12c J. Lotrič, I. Morozov, Slovak RSO, J. Wildner (r1994) *Concert* (2/95) (NAXO) Ⓓ **8 553030**

10b, 10c F. Völker, Berlin Staatskapelle, J. Schüler (r1937: Ger) *Concert* (8/94) (PREI) Ⓓ **89070**

10b, 10c, 12c G. Zenatello, P. Amato, orch (r1909) *Concert* (5/94) (PEAR) Ⓓ [4] **GEMMCDS9073(2)**

10c E. Caruso, orch (r1910) *Concert* (5/89) (PEAR) Ⓓ **GEMMCD9309**

10c F. Merli, orch, L. Molajoli (r1927) *Concert* (1/91) (PREI) Ⓓ **89026**

10c E. Caruso, orch (r1910) *Concert* (3/91) (PEAR) Ⓓ [3] **EVC2**

10c E. Caruso, orch (r1910) *Concert* (7/91) (RCA) Ⓓ [12] **GD60495(3)**

10c G. Zenatello, orch, V. Bellezza (pp1926) *Concert* (7/92) (PEAR) Ⓓ [3] **GEMMCDS9925(2)**

10c G.B. de Negri, anon (r1902) *Concert* (11/92) (MEMO) Ⓓ [2] **HR4408/9(1)**

10c A. Paoli, anon (r1907) *Concert* (11/92) (MEMO) Ⓓ [2] **HR4408/9(2)**

10c G. Zenatello, orch (r1909) *Concert* (12/93) (SYMP) Ⓓ **SYMCD1148**

10c E. Caruso, orch (r1910) *Concert* (9/94) (NIMB) Ⓓ **NI7856**

10c L. Escalais, anon (r1906: Fr) *Concert* (12/94) (SYMP) Ⓓ **SYMCD1128**

10c, 23. G.B. de Negri, anon (r1902) *Concert* (12/89) (SYMP) Ⓓ **SYMCD1065**

10c, 23. G.B. De Negri, anon (r1902) *Concert* (4/94) (EMI) Ⓓ [3] **CHS7 64860-2(1)**

11. T. Gobbi, RPO, A. Erede (r1948) *Concert* (10/89) (EMI) Ⓓ **CDM7 63109-2**

11. T. Ruffo, orch, J. Pasternack (r1920) *Concert* (11/90) (NIMB) Ⓓ **NI7810**

11. M. Sammarco, orch (r1908) *Concert* (7/92) (PEAR) Ⓓ [3] **GEMMCDS9924(2)**

11. V. Maurel, anon (r1904) *Concert* (7/92) (PEAR) Ⓓ [3] **GEMMCDS9923(1)**

11. V. Maurel, anon (r1903) *Concert* (10/92) (SYMP) Ⓓ **SYMCD1101**

11. T. Ruffo, orch (r1920) *Concert* (2/93) (PREI) Ⓓ [3] **89303(1)**

11. M. Ancona, orch (r1907) *Concert* (7/93) (NIMB) Ⓓ [2] **NI7840/1**

11. V. Maurel, anon (r1904) *Concert* (4/94) (EMI) Ⓓ [3] **CHS7 64860-2(1)**

17. J. Björling, orch, N. Grevillius (r1936) *Concert* (10/93) (NIMB) ① **NI7842**
17. J. Björling, orch, N. Grevillius (r1936) *Concert* (10/93) (EMI) ① **CDH7 64707-2**
17. Alfredo Kraus, RCA Italiana Op Orch, G. Solti (r1963) *Concert* (4/94) (RCA) ① [6] **09026 61580-2(8)**
17. M. Fleta, orch, C. Sabajno (r1923) *Concert* (4/94) (EMI) ① [3] **CHS7 64864-2(1)**
17. J. Björling, orch, N. Grevillius (r1936) *Concert* (9/94) (CARL) ① **GLRS103**
17. J. Carreras, P. Domingo, L. Pavarotti, Los Angeles Music Center Op Chor, Los Angeles PO, Z. Mehta (pp1994) *Concert* (12/94) (TELD) ① **4509-96200-2**
17. F. de Lucia, anon (r1903) *Concert* (1/95) (SYMP) ① **SYMCD1149**
17. E. Caruso, orch (r1908) *Concert* (7/95) (NIMB) ① **NI7866**
17. R. Alagna, LPO, R. Armstrong *Concert* (12/95) (EMI) ① **CDC5 55540-2**
18b A. Galli-Curci, L. Homer, G. De Luca, B. Gigli, NY Met Op Orch, G. Setti (r1927) *Concert* (9/88) (EMI) ① **CDH7 61051-2**
18b G. De Luca, A. Galli-Curci, B. Gigli, L. Homer, NY Met Op Orch, G. Setti (r1927) *Concert* (9/88) (PEAR) ① **GEMMCD9316**
18b L. Tetrazzini, J. Jacoby, E. Caruso, P. Amato, orch, W.B. Rogers (r1912) *Concert* (7/90) (CLUB) ① **CL99-060**
18b L. Tetrazzini, J. Jacoby, E. Caruso, P. Amato, orch (r1912) *Concert* (10/90) (NIMB) ① **NI7808**
18b M. Sembrich, G. Severina, E. Caruso, A. Scotti, orch, W.B. Rogers (r1908) *Concert* (12/90) (PEAR) ① [3] **EVC1(2)**
18b(2 vers) B. Abott, L. Homer, E. Caruso, A. Scotti, orch (r1907) *Concert* (12/90) (PEAR) ① [3] **EVC1(2)**
18b(opening) E. Caruso, orch, J. Pasternack (r1917) *Concert* (7/91) (RCA) ① [12] **GD60495(6)**
18b L. Tetrazzini, J. Jacoby, E. Caruso, P. Amato, orch, W.B. Rogers (r1912) *Concert* (7/91) (RCA) ① [12] **GD60495(4)**
18b M. Sembrich, G. Severina, E. Caruso, A. Scotti, orch, W.B. Rogers (r1908) *Concert* (7/91) (RCA) ① [12] **GD60495(2)**
18b A. Galli-Curci, F. Perini, E. Caruso, G. De Luca, orch, J. Pasternack (r1917) *Concert* (7/91) (RCA) ① [12] **GD60495(6)**
18b B. Abott, L. Homer, E. Caruso, A. Scotti, orch (r1907) *Concert* (7/91) (RCA) ① [12] **GD60495(2)**
18b A. Galli-Curci, F. Perini, E. Caruso, G. De Luca, orch (r1917) *Concert* (7/91) (MSCM) ① **MM30352**
18b L. Tetrazzini, J. Jacoby, E. Caruso, P. Amato, orch, W.B. Rogers (r1912) *Concert* (10/91) (PEAR) ① [3] **EVC3(1)**
18b(opening) E. Caruso, orch, J. Pasternack (r1917) *Concert* (10/91) (PEAR) ① [3] **EVC4(1)**
18b A. Galli-Curci, F. Perini, E. Caruso, G. De Luca, orch, J. Pasternack (r1917) *Concert* (10/91) (PEAR) ① [3] **EVC4(1)**
18b F. Hüni-Mihacsek, E. Leisner, H. Roswaenge, T. Scheidl, orch (r1928: Ger) *Concert* (2/92) (PREI) ① [2] **89201**
18b L. Tetrazzini, E. Caruso, P. Amato, M. Journet, orch (r1912) *Concert* (9/92) (PEAR) ① **GEMMCD9224**
18b R. Pinkert, G. Lukacewska, A. Bonci, A. Magini-Coletti, anon (r1905) *Concert* (12/93) (SYMP) ① **SYMCD1113**
18b A. Galli-Curci, F. Perini, E. Caruso, G. De Luca, orch, J. Pasternack (r1917) *Concert* (3/94) (ROMO) ① [2] **81003-2**
18b A. Galli-Curci, F. Perini, E. Caruso, G. De Luca, orch, W.B. Rogers (r1917/92) *Concert* (5/94) (CLAR) ① **CDGSE78-50-52**
18b A. Galli-Curci, L. Homer, B. Gigli, G. De Luca, NY Met Op Orch, G. Setti (r1927) *Concert* (8/94) (NIMB) ① **NI7852**
18b H. Roswaenge, P. Yoder, L. Kindermann, H. Reinmar, Berlin St Op Orch, S. Meyrowitz (r1932: Ger) *Concert* (4/95) (PREI) ① [2] **89209**
18b M. Licette, M. Brunskill, H. Nash, D. Noble, orch (r1931: Eng) *Concert* (11/95) (PEAR) ① **GEMMCD9175**
21a-c(pt) G. De Luca, A. Galli-Curci, orch (r1918) *Concert* (1/92) (PREI) ① **89036**

Simon Boccanegra—opera: prologue & 3 acts (1857 rev 1881—Venice) (Lib. F Piave, rev A Boito)

O. PROLOGUE: EXCERPTS: PROLOGUE: 1a. A te l'estremo addio; 1b. Il lacerato spirito; 2. Suona ogni labbro il mio nome; 3. Oh de' Fieschi implacata. ACT 1: 4. Come in quest'ora bruna; 5a. Orfanella il tetto umile; 5b. Figlia! a tal nome io palpito; 6. Plebe! Patrizi!. ACT 2: 7. Quei due vedesti; 8a. O inferno! Amelia qui!; 8b. Sento avvampar nell'anima; 9a. Oh! Amelia, ami un nemico; 9b. Perdon, Amelia. ACT 3: 10a. M'ardon le tempia; 10b. Come un fantasima; 11. Piango, perchè mi parla in te.

Cpte P. Cappuccilli, M. Freni, J. Carreras, N. Ghiaurov, J. Van Dam, G. Foiani, A. Savastano, La Scala Chor, La Scala Orch, C. Abbado (r1977) (9/86) (DG) ① [2] **415 692-2GH2**
Cpte P. Cappuccilli, K. Ricciarelli, P. Domingo, R. Raimondi, G-P. Mastromei, M. Mazzieri, P. de Palma, O. Jachetti, RCA Chor, RCA Orch, G. Gavazzeni (9/87) (RCA) ① [2] **RD70729**
Cpte L. Nucci, K. Te Kanawa, G. Aragall, P. Burchuladze, P. Coni, C. Colombara, E. Gavazzi, A. Zoroberto, La Scala Chor, La Scala Orch, G. Solti (r1988) (12/89) (DECC) ① [2] **425 628-2DH2**
Cpte T. Gobbi, V. de los Angeles, G. Campora, B. Christoff, W. Monachesi, P. Dari, P. Caroli, S. Bertona, Rome Op Chor, Rome Op Orch, G. Santini (r1957) (9/90) (EMI) ① [2] **CMS7 63513-2**
Cpte J. Van Dam, N. Gustafson, A. Cupido, D. Pittsinger, W. Stone, C. Krause, A. Gregoire, Brussels Théâtre de la Monnaie Chor, Brussels Théâtre de la Monnaie Orch, S. Cambreling (pp1990) (1/92) (RICE) ① [2] **RIS093070/1**
Cpte E. Tumagian, M. Gauci, G. Aragall, P. Mikuláš, V. Sardinero, V. de Kanel, G. Tomckowiack, M. Pieck, Brussels BRT Phil Chor, Brussels BRT PO, A. Rahbari (r1994) (2/95) (DINT) ① [2] **DICD920225/6**
Prelude La Scala Orch, C. Abbado *Concert* (6/87) (SONY) ① **MK37228**
1. E. Pinza, orch, C. Sabajno (r1923) *Concert* (2/89) (PEAR) ① **GEMMCD9306**
1. A. Kipnis, Berlin St Op Orch, E. Orthmann (r1931) *Concert* (10/91) (PEAR) ① **GEMMCD9451**
1a T. Pasero, SO, D. Marzollo (r1944) *Concert* (4/95) (PREI) ① **89074**
1a, 1b E. Pinza, NY Met Op Chor, NY Met Op Orch, E. Panizza (bp1939) *Concert* (7/91) (MMOI) ① **CDMOIR404**
1a, 1b E. Pinza, R. Shaw Chorale, RCA Victor Orch, E. Leinsdorf (r1951) *Concert* (9/93) (RCA) ① **09026 61245-2**
1b G. Gravina, anon (r1902) *Concert* (12/89) (SYMP) ① **SYMCD1065**
1b E. Pinza, NY Met Op Orch, F. Cleva (r1946) *Concert* (4/90) (SONY) ① **MPK45693**
1b A. Kipnis, chor, Berlin St Op Orch, E. Orthmann (r1931) *Concert* (12/90) (PREI) ① **89019**
1b M. Salminen, Lahti SO, E. Klas *Concert* (8/92) (BIS) ① **BIS-CD520**
1b V. Arimondi, orch (r1907) *Concert* (11/92) (MEMO) ① [2] **HR4408/9(1)**
1b M. Reizen, Bolshoi Th Orch, V. Nebolsin (r1953: Russ) *Concert* (2/95) (PREI) ① **89080**
2, 3, 6, 10a, 10b L. Tibbett, E. Rethberg, G. Martinelli, L. Warren, E. Pinza, NY Met Op Chor, NY Met Op Orch, E. Panizza (pp1939) *Concert* (3/91) (PEAR) ① [2] **GEMMCDS9452**
4. L. Price, LSO, E. Downes *Concert* (12/92) (RCA) ① [4] **09026 61236-2**
5b L. Tibbett, R. Bampton, Orch, W. Pelletier (r1939) *Concert* (3/90) (RCA) ① **GD87808**
6. T. Gobbi, Philh, A. Erede (r1963) *Concert* (10/89) (EMI) ① **CDM7 63109-2**
6. H. Schlusnus, Berlin St Op Orch, A. Melichar (Ger: r c1931) *Concert* (9/90) (PREI) ① **89006**
8a, 8b G. Aragall, P. Coni, La Scala Orch, G. Solti (r1988) *Concert* (10/93) (DECC) ① **436 463-2DM**
8a, 8b J. Johnston, ROHO, M. Mudie (r1948: Eng) *Concert* (4/95) (TEST) ① **SBT1058**

Stiffelio—opera: 3 acts (1950—Trieste) (Lib. F. Piave)

EXCERPTS: 1. Overture. ACT 1: 2. Oh santo libro; 3. Di qua varcando; 4a. Son quanti giorno?; 4b. Colla cenere disperso; 4c. Viva Stiffelio!; 5a. Non ha per me un accento!; 5b. Vidi dovunque gemere; 5c. Ah! v'appare in fronte scritto; 6. Tosto ei disse!; 7a. Verrà Dovrò risponder!; 7b. Dite che il fallo a tergere; 7c. Ed io pure in faccia agli uomini; 7d. Or meco venite; 8. M'evitan; 9. Plaudiam!; 10. Cugino, pensaste al sermone?; 11. Oh qual m'invade ed agita; 12. Nol volete?. ACT 2: 13a. Oh cielo! dove son io!; 13b. Ah, dagli scanni eterei; 13c. Perder dunque voi volete; 14. Io resto; 15a. Qual rumore!; 15b. Santo è il loco; 15c. Ah no, è impossibile!; 16. Dessa non è. ACT 3: 17a. Ei fugge!; 17b. Lina, pensai che un angelo; 17c. Ah, si finisca; 17d. In questo teto uno di noi morrà; 18. Dite ai fratei che al tempio; 19a. Inevitabil fu questo colloquio; 19b. Opposto è il calle; 19c. Non allo sposo volgomi; 19d. Egli un patto proponeva; 19e. Ah sì, voliamo al tempio; 20. Non punirmi, Signor; 21. Stiffelio! Eccomi.

Cpte J. Carreras, S. Sass, M. Manuguerra, W. Ganzarolli, E. di Cesare, M. Venuti, T. Moser, Austrian Rad Chor, Austrian RSO, L. Gardelli (r1979) (3/90) (PHIL) ① [2] **422 432-2PM2**

La **Traviata—opera: 3 acts (1853—Venice)** (Lib. F Piave, after A Dumas)

EXCERPTS; 1. Prelude. ACT 1: 2. Dell'invito trascora è già l'ora; 3. Libiamo, ne' lieti calci (Brindisi); 4a. Che è ciò?; 4b. Un dì, felice; 5. Si ridesta in ciel; 6a. È strano! È strano!; 6b. Ah, fors'è lui; 6c. Follie! Sempra libera. ACT 2: 7a. Lunge da lei; 7b. De' miei bollenti spiriti; 7c. O mio romorso!; 8a. Madamigella Valery?; 8b. Pura siccome un angelo; 8c. Bella voi siete; 8d. Dite alla giovine; 9a. Morrò! La mia memoria; 9b. Dammi tu forza; 10a. Ah, vive sol quel core; 10b. Di Provenza il mar; 10c. Ne rispondi; 11. Avrem lieta; 12a. Noi siamo zingarelle; 12b. Di Madride noi siam Mattadori; 13. Alfredo! Voi!; 14a. Ogni suo aver tal femmina; 14b. Di Sprezzo degno! ACT 3: 15. Prelude; 16a. Annina? Commandate?; 16b. Teneste la promessa; 16c. Addio del passato; 17. Largo al quadrupede; 18a. Signora, Che t'accade; 18b. Parigi, o cara; 18c. Gran Dio! morir sì giovine; 19. Ah! Violetta.

Cpte I. Cotrubas, P. Domingo, S. Milnes, S. Malagù, H. Jungwirth, W. Gullino, B. Grella, A. Giacomotti, G. Foiani, W. Gullino, P. Winter, P. Friess, Bavarian St Op Chor, Bavarian St Orch, C. Kleiber (r1977) (3/86) (DG) ① [2] **415 132-2GH2**
Cpte R. Scotto, Alfredo Kraus, R. Bruson, Sarah Walker, C. Buchan, S. Mariategui, H. Newman, R. Van Allan, R. Kennedy, M-R. Cosotti, C. Keyte, Ambrosian Op. Chor, Royal Marines Band, Philh, R. Muti (r1980) (11/87) (EMI) ① [2] **CDS7 47538-8**
Cpte M. Callas, Alfredo Kraus, M. Sereni, L. Zannini, M.C. de Castro, P. de Palma, A. Malta, V. Susca, A. Maddalena, M. Leitao, Lisbon San Carlos Nat Th Chor, Lisbon San Carlos Nat Th Orch, F. Ghione (pp1958) (11/87) (EMI) ① [2] **CDS7 49187-8**
Cpte M. Caballé, C. Bergonzi, S. Milnes, D. Krebill, N. Stokes, F. Iacopucci, G. Boucher, T. Jamerson, H. Enns, C. Sforza, F. Ruta, F. Tasin, RCA Italiana Op Chor, RCA Italiana Op Orch, G. Prêtre (r1967) (9/88) (RCA) ① [2] **RD86180**
Cpte R. Ponselle, F. Jagel, L. Tibbett, E. Vettori, H. Wakefield, A. Bada, A. Gandolfi, M. Picco, P. Ananian, NY Met Op Chor, NY Met Op Orch, E. Panizza (pp1935) *Bellini: Norma.* (1/89) (PEAR) ① [2] **GEMMCD9317**
Cpte J. Sutherland, C. Bergonzi, R. Merrill, M.T. Pace, D. Carral, P. de Palma, P. Pedani, S. Maionica, G. Foiani, A. Mercuriali, M. Frosini, MMF Chor, MMF Orch, J. Pritchard (r1962) (2/89) (DECC) ① [2] **411 877-2DM2**
Cpte L. Aliberti, P. Dvorský, R. Bruson, F. Mochiki, S. Sawa, H. Mochiki, H. Okayama, A. Shikano, Y. Yanagisawa, Fujiwara Op Chor, Tokyo PO, R. Paternostro (pp1988) (9/89) (CAPR) ① [2] **10 274/5**
Cpte M. Callas, G. di Stefano, E. Bastianini, S. Zanolli, L. Mandelli, G. Zampieri, A. la Porta, A. Zerbini, S. Maionica, F. Ricciardi, La Scala Chor, La Scala Orch, C.M. Giulini (pp1955) (2/91) (EMI) ① [2] **CMS7 63628-2**
Cpte R. Tebaldi, G. Poggi, A. Protti, A. Vercelli, R. Cavallari, P. de Palma, A. Sacchetti, D. Caselli, I. Sardi, M. Bianchi, L. Mancini, Santa Cecilia Academy Chor, Santa Cecilia Academy Orch, F. Molinari-Pradelli (8/91) (DECC) ① [2] **430 250-2DM2**
Cpte L. Albanese, J. Peerce, R. Merrill, M. Stellman, J. Moreland, J. Garris, G. Cehanovsky, P. Dennis, A. Newman, Chor, NBC SO, A. Toscanini (bp1946) (4/92) (RCA) ① [2] **GD60303**
Cpte C. Studer, L. Pavarotti, J. Pons, W. White, S. Kelly, A. Laciura, B. Pola, J. Wells, J. Robbins, J. Hanriot, M. Sendrowitz, R. Crolius, NY Met Op Chor, NY Met Op Orch, James Levine (11/92) (DG) ① [2] **435 797-2GH2**
Cpte E. Gruberová, N. Shicoff, G. Zancanaro, P. Spence, M. Bacelli, K. Begley, P. Sidhom, D. Barrell, A. Miles, P. Bronder, N. Folwell, F. Visentin, Ambrosian Sngrs, LSO, C. Rizzi (2/93) (TELD) ① [2] **9031-76348-2**
Cpte T. Fabbricini, R. Alagna, P. Coni, N. Curiel, A. Trevisan, E. Cossutta, O. Mori, E. Capuano, F. Musinu, E. Gavazzi, E. Panariello, S. Sammaritano, La Scala Chor, La Scala Orch, R. Muti (pp1992) (10/93) (SONY) ① [2] **S2K52486**
Cpte K. Te Kanawa, Alfredo Kraus, D. Hvorostovsky, S. Mazzoni, O. Borodina, B. Banks, R. Scaltriti, G. Gatti, D. Di Stefano, M. La Guardia, A. Calamai, MMF Chor, MMF Orch, Z. Mehta (r1992) (12/93) (PHIL) ① [2] **438 238-2PH2**

Cpte P. Lorengar, G. Aragall, D. Fischer-Dieskau, S.
Malagù, M. Fiorentino, P. F. Poli, V. Carbonari, S.
Maionica, G. Foiani, A. Losa, Berlin Deutsche Op
Chor, Berlin Deutsche Op Orch, L. Maazel (r1968)
(5/94) (DECC) ① [2] 443 000-2DF2
Cpte M. Callas, F. Albanese, U. Savarese, E.M.
Gandolfo, I. Marietti, M. Caruso, A. Albertini, M.
Zorgniotti, T. Soley, Chor, Turin RAI Orch, G. Santini
(r1953) (2/95) (FONI) ① [2] CDO9
Cpte A. Gheorghiu, F. Lopardo, L. Nucci, L-M. Jones,
G. Knight, R. Leggate, R. Van Allan, R. Earle, M.
Beesley, N. Griffiths, B. Secombe, R. Gibson, ROH
Chor, ROHO, G. Solti (pp1994)
(8/95) (DECC) ① [2] 448 119-2DHO2
Excs Grimethorpe Colliery Band, E. Howarth (arr
Greenwood) Concert
(12/92) (DOYE) ① DOYCD013
Excs P. Gallois, London Fest Orch, R. Pople (r1993:
arr fl: Genin/Guiot) Concert
(5/95) (DG) ① 445 822-2GH
1. BPO, H. von Karajan Concert
(10/87) (DG) ① 419 622-2GH
1. BPO, H. von Karajan Concert
(5/90) (DG) ① 429 164-2GR
1. BPO, H. von Karajan Concert
(1/95) (DG) ① 439 972-2GGA2
1, 15. NYPSO, A. Toscanini (r1929) Concert
(3/90) (PEAR) ① [3] GEMMCDS9373
1, 15. Gothenburg SO, N. Järvi Concert
(6/90) (DG) ① 429 494-2GDC
1, 15. NYPSO, A. Toscanini (r1929) Concert
(11/92) (RCA) ① GD60318
1, 15. Berlin RIAS Orch, F. Fricsay (r1953) Concert
(11/94) (DG) ① 445 406-2GDO
1, 15. I. Seefried, M. Forrester, E. Haefliger, D.
Fischer-Dieskau, Berlin St Hedwig's Cath Ch, BPO,
F. Fricsay, H. Krebs, T. Varga, Berlin RIAS Chbr Ch,
Berlin RIAS Orch, H. Geusser, W. Fugmann, M.
Weber, G. Herzog, Berlin RSO, VPO, E. Grümmer,
G. Pitzinger, H. Hotter, Y. Menuhin (r1953) Concert
(11/94) (DG) ① [11] 445 400-2GDO10
1, 15. Santa Cecilia Academy Orch, V. de Sabata
(r1948) Concert (9/95) (EMI) ① CHS5 65506-2
1, 3, 4b, 6, 7, 8b, 10b, 16b, 16c, 18b, 19. J.
Sutherland, L. Pavarotti, M. Manuguerra, D. Jones,
M. Lambriks, A. Oliver, J. Summers, J. Tomlinson, G.
Tadeo, London Op. Chor, National PO, R. Bonynge
(3/83) (DECC) ① 400 057-2DH
3. C. Studer, P. Domingo, ROHO, J. Barker (pp1988)
Concert (9/89) (EMI) ① CDC7 49811-2
3. A. Gluck, E. Caruso, NY Met Op Chor, NY Met Op
Orch (r1914) Concert
(7/91) (RCA) ① [12] GD60495(5)
3. E. Caruso, A. Gluck, NY Met Op Chor, NY Met Op
Orch (r1914) Concert (7/91) (MSCM) ① MM303052
3. E. Caruso, A. Gluck, NY Met Op Chor, NY Met Op
Orch (r1914) Concert
(10/91) (PEAR) ① [3] EVC3(1)
3. J. Sutherland, L. Pavarotti, National PO, R.
Bonynge Concert (12/91) (DECC) ① 430 724-2DM
3. M. Caniglia, B. Gigli, ROH Chor, LPO, P. Cimara
(pp1939) Concert
(7/92) (PEAR) ① [3] GEMMCDS9926(2)
3. M. Freni, L. Pavarotti, Ater Orch, L. Magiera (pp)
Concert (5/94) (DECC) ① [2] 443 018-2DF2
3. A. Arteta, I. Mula-Tchako, N. Stemme, P.
Domingo, Ivan, Paris Opéra-Bastille Orch, E.
Kohn (pp1992) Concert (6/94) (SONY) ① SK46691
3. J. Carreras, P. Domingo, L. Pavarotti, Los Angeles
Music Center Op Chor, Los Angeles PO, Z. Mehta
(pp1994) Concert (12/94) (TELD) ① 4509-96200-2
3, 18b F. Wunderlich, H. Gueden, Bavarian Rad
Chor, BRSO, B. Bartoletti (Ger) Concert
(5/93) (DG) ① 431 110-2GB
3, 6b, 6c, 18e E. Steber, A. Tokatyan, orch, W.
Pelletier (r1940) Concert
(11/95) (VAI) ① VAIA1072
3, 7a-c P. Domingo, I. Cotrubas, Bavarian St Op
Chor, Bavarian St Orch, C. Kleiber Concert
(5/93) (DG) ① 431 104-2GB
4b A. Galli-Curci, T. Schipa, orch, R. Bourdon (r1928)
Concert (12/89) (RCA) ① GD87969
4b G. Zenatello, anon (r1903) Concert
(6/90) (SYMP) ① SYMCD1073
4b E. Ventura, anon (r1904) Concert
(11/92) (MEMO) ① [2] HR4408/9(1)
4b G. Zenatello, anon (r1903) Concert
(5/94) (PEAR) ① [4] GEMMCDS9073(1)
4b F. de Lucia, anon (r1904) Concert
(1/95) (SYMP) ① SYMCD1149
4b, 7a, 7b, 9b(pt), 18b M. Moralès, L. Simoneau,
Lamoureux Orch, P. Dervaux (r1953) Concert
(11/94) (PHIL) ① [2] 438 953-2PM2
4b, 18b A. Galli-Curci, T. Schipa, orch (r1930)
Concert (2/89) (PEAR) ① GEMMCD9322

4b, 18b F. Hempel, H. Jadlowker, orch (Ger: r1900s)
Concert (12/91) (CLUB) ① CL99-042
4b, 18b J. Sutherland, L. Pavarotti, National PO, R.
Bonynge (r1979) Concert
(12/93) (DECC) ① 433 439-2DA
4b, 18b A. Galli-Curci, T. Schipa, orch (r1924)
Concert (3/94) (CONI) ① CDHD201
4b, 18b A. Galli-Curci, T. Schipa, orch (r1928)
Concert (8/94) (NIMB) ① NI7852
4b, 18b A. Galli-Curci, T. Schipa, orch, R. Bourdon
(r1924) Concert (8/94) (ROMO) ① [2] 81004-2
4b, 18b H. Roswaenge, M. Perras, Berlin St Op
Orch, B. Seidler-Winkler (r1936: Ger) Concert
(4/95) (PREI) ① [2] 89209
4c, 5, 6. M. Callas, Alfredo Kraus, P. de Palma,
Lisbon San Carlos Nat Th Chor, Lisbon San Carlos
Nat Th Orch, F. Ghione (pp1958) Concert
(2/90) (EMI) ① [4] CMS7 63244-2
4, 6. J. Anderson, Alfredo Kraus, Paris Op Orch, M.
Veltri (pp1987) Concert
(12/88) (EMI) ① CDC7 49067-2
5, 12a Slovak Phil Chor, Bratislava RSO, O.
Dohnányi Concert (4/91) (NAXO) ① 8 550241
6. K. Te Kanawa, LPO, J. Pritchard Concert
(5/85) (SONY) ① MK37298
6. A. Galli-Curci, orch (r1919) Concert
(2/89) (PEAR) ① GEMMCD9308
6. M. Freni, Rome Op Orch, F. Ferraris Concert
(10/89) (EMI) ① CDM7 63110-2
6. L. Tetrazzini, orch (r1907/8) Concert
(7/92) (PEAR) ① [3] GEMMCDS9924(2)
6. L. Tetrazzini, orch (r1911) Concert
(9/92) (EMI) ① [3] CHS7 63802-2(1)
6. L. Tetrazzini, orch, P. Pitt (r1907/8) Concert
(9/92) (EMI) ① [3] CHS7 63802-2(1)
6. L. Tetrazzini, orch, P. Pitt (r1907/8) Concert
(8/92) (EMI) ① GEMMCD9221
6a E. Gruberová, L.M. Vodička, Czech PO, F. Haider
Concert (5/90) (SONY) ① SK45633
6a-c J. Sutherland, ROHO, F. Molinari-Pradelli
Concert (1/90) (DECC) ① [2] 425 493-2DM2
6a-c M. Ivogün, orch (r1916: Ger) Concert
(8/92) (NIMB) ① NI7832
6a-c A. Galli-Curci, orch, J. Pasternack (r1919)
Concert (2/94) (ROMO) ① [2] 81003-2
6a, 6b M. Kuznetsova, orch (r1904: Russ) Concert
(6/93) (PEAR) ① [3] GEMMCDS9004/6(1)
6a, 16b A. Pendachanska, Sofia SO, M. Angelov
(r1994) Concert (12/95) (CAPR) ① 10 706
6b G. Bellincioni, S. Cottone (r1903) Concert
(6/90) (SYMP) ① SYMCD1073
6b M. Sembrich, orch (r1908) Concert
(7/92) (PEAR) ① [3] GEMMCDS9923(1)
6b A. Nezhdanova, U. Masetti (r1906: Russ) Concert
(6/93) (PEAR) ① [3] GEMMCDS9007/9(1)
6b M. Kuznetsova, orch (Russ: r1905) Concert
(7/93) (SYMP) ① SYMCD1105
6b M. Garden, orch (r1911: Fr) Concert
(8/93) (SYMP) ① SYMCD1136
6b F. Hempel, orch (r1914) Concert
(3/94) (NIMB) ① NI7849
6b G. Bellincioni, S. Cottone (r1903) Concert
(4/94) (EMI) ① [3] CHS7 64860-2(1)
6b, 6c N. Melba, W.B. Rogers (r1910) Concert
(3/89) (LARR) ① CDLRH221
6b, 6c L. Tetrazzini, orch (r1911) Concert
(9/92) (PEAR) ① GEMMCD9223
6b, 6c L. Tetrazzini, orch (r1911) Concert
(9/92) (PEAR) ① GEMMCD9222
6b, 6c E. Orel, anon (Russ: r c1902) Concert
(7/93) (SYMP) ① SYMCD1105
6b, 6c N. Melba, orch, W.B. Rogers (r1910) Concert
(9/93) (RCA) ① 09026 61412-2
6b, 6c N. Melba, orch, W.B. Rogers (r1907) Concert
(5/95) (ROMO) ① [3] 81011-2(1)
6b, 6c N. Melba, orch, W.B. Rogers (r1910) Concert
(5/95) (ROMO) ① [3] 81011-2(2)
6c A. Galli-Curci, orch, R. Bourdon (r1919) Concert
(2/94) (ROMO) ① [2] 81003-2
6c I. Bohuss, anon (r1902: Pol) Concert
(6/93) (PEAR) ① [3] GEMMCDS9004/6(1)
6c L. Tetrazzini, orch (r1912: Russ) Concert
(6/93) (PEAR) ① [3] GEMMCDS9007/9(1)
6c G. Bréjean-Silver, anon (1905) Concert
(12/94) (SYMP) ① SYMCD1172
6c A. Nezhdanova, orch (r1912: Russ) Concert
(3/95) (NIMB) ① NI7865
7. P. Domingo, Bavarian St Op Chor, C. Kleiber Concert
(7/86) (DG) ① 415 366-2GH
7. B. Gigli, orch, R. Bourdon (r1928) Concert
(8/90) (EMI) ① GEMMCD9316
7. P. Domingo, NYPO, Z. Mehta (pp1988) Concert
(9/89) (SONY) ① MK44942
7. J. McCormack, orch (r1910) Concert
(4/94) (RCA) ① [6] 09026 61580-2(2)

7, Oh, mio rimorso Alfredo Kraus, Philh, R. Muti
Concert (10/89) (EMI) ① CDM7 63104-2
7a-c L. Pavarotti, National PO, R. Bonynge Concert
(7/90) (DECC) ① [2] 425 681-2DM2
7a, 7b G. Martinelli, orch, J. Pasternack (r1917)
Concert (10/89) (NIMB) ① NI7804
7a, 7b G. Aragall, Berlin Deutsche Op Orch, L.
Maazel (r1968) Concert
(10/93) (DECC) ① 436 463-2DM
7a, 7b L. Pavarotti, Parma Teatro Regio Orch, G.
Patanè (pp1976) Concert
(5/94) (DECC) ① [2] 443 018-2DF2
7a, 7b G. Zenatello, orch (r1916) Concert
(5/94) (PEAR) ① [4] GEMMCDS9074(1)
7a, 7b G. Thill, orch, E. Bigot (r1927: Fr) Concert
(8/95) (FORL) ① UCD16727
7a, 7b L. Pavarotti, Modena Teatro Comunale Orch,
L. Magiera (pp1965) Concert
(10/95) (RCA) ① 09026 68014-2
7a, 7b, 14a G. Zenatello, chor, anon (r1906) Concert
(5/94) (PEAR) ① [4] GEMMCDS9073(1)
7a, 7b, 14a G. Zenatello, chor, anon (r1908) Concert
(5/94) (PEAR) ① [4] GEMMCDS9073(1)
7b J. Patzak, orch, M. Gurlitt (Ger: r1929) Concert
(3/90) (PEAR) ① GEMMCD9383
7b D. Smirnov, orch (r1913) Concert
(7/90) (CLUB) ① CL99-031
7b H. Roswaenge, orch (r1928: G· ·) Concert
(2/92) (PREI) ① [2] 89201
7b H. Roswaenge, Berlin St Op Orch, B. Seidler-
Winkler (r1935: Ger) Concert
(10/93) (NIMB) ① NI7848
7b F. de Lucia, anon (r1906) Concert
(1/95) (SYMP) ① SYMCD1149
7b D. Smirnov, orch (r1910: Russ) Concert
(3/95) (NIMB) ① NI7865
7b H. Roswaenge, BPO, E. Orthmann (r1933: Ger)
Concert (4/95) (PREI) ① [2] 89209
7b H. Roswaenge, Berlin St Op Orch, B. Seidler-
Winkler (r1937: Ger) Concert
(4/95) (PREI) ① [2] 89209
7b G. Anselmi, Bettinelli (r1910) Concert
(7/95) (SYMP) ① SYMCD1170
7b, 14a G. Zenatello, chor, orch (r1908) Concert
(12/93) (SYMP) ① SYMCD1138
7b, 14a G. Zenatello, chor, anon (r1906) Concert
(12/93) (SYMP) ① SYMCD1138
8a, 8b M. Battistini, M. Mokrzycka, orch, C. Sabajno
(r1912) Concert (10/92) (NIMB) ① NI7831
8b M. Battistini, M. Mokrzycka, orch, C. Sabajno
(r1912) Concert (7/92) (PEAR) ① GEMMCD9936
8b, 10b P. Lisitsian, E. Shumskaya, Bolshoi Th Orch,
A. Orlov (r1947: Russ) Concert
(8/93) (PREI) ① 89061
8b, 14b L. Warren, E. Steber, A. Tokatyan, chor,
orch, W. Pelletier (r1940) Concert
(8/93) (VAI) ① VAIA1017
8d N. Melba, J. Brownlee, H. Craxton (r1926)
Concert (3/89) (LARR) ① CDLRH221
8d A. Galli-Curci, G. De Luca, orch, R. Bourdon
(r1918) Concert (5/90) (NIMB) ① NI7806
8d A. Granforte, A. Rozsa, La Scala Orch, C.
Sabajno (r1930) Concert (11/91) (PREI) ① 89048
8d A. Galli-Curci, G. De Luca, orch, J. Pasternack
(r1918) Concert (3/94) (ROMO) ① [2] 81003-2
8d G. De Luca, A. Galli-Curci, NY Met Op Orch, G.
Setti (r1927) Concert (3/94) (PREI) ① 89073
9b(pt) C. Muzio, G. Tommasini, orch (r1911) Concert
(1/94) (ROMO) ① [2] 81005-2
10a, 10b G. Aragall, D. Fischer-Dieskau, Berlin
Deutsche Op Orch, L. Maazel (r1968) Concert
(10/93) (DECC) ① 436 464-2DM
10b L. Melchior, Orch (Danish: r1913) Concert
(8/88) (DANA) ① [2] DACOCD311/2
10b J. Hynninen, Estonian SO, E. Klas Concert
(4/90) (ONDI) ① ODE731-2
10b D. Hvorostovsky, Rotterdam PO, V. Gergiev
Concert (7/90) (PHIL) ① 426 740-2PH
10b H. Schlusnus, Berlin St Op Orch, J. Schüler
(Ger: r1937) Concert (9/90) (PREI) ① 89006
10b T. Ruffo, orch, S. Cottone (r1907) Concert
(11/90) (NIMB) ① NI7810
10b M. Battistini, orch (r1911) Concert
(2/91) (PREI) ① 89045
10b M. Battistini, orch, C. Sabajno (r1911) Concert
(7/92) (PEAR) ① [3] GEMMCDS9923(1)
10b R. Stracciari, orch (r1906) Concert
(7/92) (PEAR) ① [3] GEMMCDS9924(1)
10b M. Battistini, orch, C. Sabajno (r1911) Concert
(10/92) (PEAR) ① GEMMCD9936
10b T. Gobbi, Philh, W. Susskind (r1950) Concert
(8/93) (TEST) ① SBT1019
10b G. De Luca, NY Met Op Orch, G. Setti (r1929)
Concert (4/94) (RCA) ① [6] 09026 61580-2(2)
10b R. Stracciari, orch (r1906) Concert
(4/94) (EMI) ① [3] CHS7 64860-2(2)

I **vespri Siciliani, '(The) Sicilian Vespers'—opera: 5 acts (1855—Paris)** (Lib. Scribe and Duveyrier)

EXCERPTS: 1. Overture. ACT 1: 2a. In alto mare e battuto dai venti; 2b. Deh! tu calma, O Dio possente; 3. Arrigo...Non altro? ACT 2: 4a. O patria; 4b. O tu, Palermo. ACT 3: 5. In braccio alle dovizie; 6a. Sogno, o son desto?; 6b. Guardate ei viene. ACT 4: 7. Ballet—'The Four Seasons'; 7a. Winter; 7b. Spring; 7c. Summer; 7d. Autumn. ACT 4: 8a. È di Monforte il cennol; 8b. Giorno di pianto; 9a. O sdegni miei, tacete; 9b. Arrigo! Ah, parli. ACT 5: 10. Si celebri alfine; 11. Mercè, dilette amiche (Bolero); 12. A toi que j'ai chérie (Alternative aria for Act 4).

1. I. Seefried, M. Forrester, E. Haefliger, D. Fischer-
   Dieskau, Berlin St Hedwig's Cath Ch, BPO, F.
   Fricsay, H. Krebs, T. Varga, Berlin RIAS Chbr Ch,
   Berlin RIAS Orch, H. Geusser, W. Fugmann, M.
   Weber, G. Herzog, Berlin RSO, VPO, E. Grümmer,
   G. Pitzinger, H. Hotter, Y. Menuhin (r1952) *Concert*
   (11/94) (DG) ① [11] **445 400-2GDO10**
1. Berlin RIAS Orch, F. Fricsay (r1952) *Concert*
   (11/94) (DG) ① **445 406-2GDO**
1. BPO, H. von Karajan *Concert*
   (1/95) (DG) ① **439 972-2GGA2**
1. NYPO, L. Magiera (pp1993) *Concert*
   (2/95) (DECC) ① **444 450-2DH**
1. Santa Cecilia Academy Orch, V. de Sabata (r1947)
   Concert (9/95) (EMI) ① [2] **CHS5 65506-2**
3, 6b J. Lotrić, I. Morozov, Slovak RSO, J. Wildner
   (r1994) *Concert* (2/95) (NAXO) ① **8 553030**
4a, 4b E. Pinza, orch. R. Bourdon (r1927) *Concert*
   (7/91) (MMOI) ① **CDMOIR404**
4b E. Pinza, orch. R. Bourdon (r1927) *Concert*
   (2/89) (PEAR) ① **GEMMCD9306**
4b E. Pinza, orch. R. Bourdon (r1927) *Concert*
   (3/92) (PREI) ① **89050**
4b M. Reizen, Bolshoi Th Orch, V. Nebolsin (r1951)
   Concert (2/95) (PREI) ① **89080**
5. H. Schlusnus, Berlin St Op Orch, A. Melichar (Ger:
   r c1931) *Concert* (9/90) (PREI) ① **89006**
6a, 6b H. Roswaenge, H. Schlusnus, Berlin St Op
   Orch, A. Melichar (r1933: Ger) *Concert*
   (4/95) (PREI) ① [2] **89209**
7. Cleveland Orch, L. Maazel (r1974) *Concert*
   (11/93) (DECC) ① **425 052-2DM**
7. NY Met Op Orch, James Levine (r1992) *Concert*
   (6/94) (SONY) ① **SK52489**
8b H. Roswaenge, Berlin St Op Orch, F.A. Schmidt
   (r1932: Ger) *Concert* (4/95) (PREI) ① [2] **89209**
9b M. Callas, Paris Cons, N. Rescigno *Concert*
   (9/87) (EMI) ① **CDC7 47730-2**
9b K. Ricciarelli, Rome PO, G. Gavazzeni *Concert*
   (12/87) (RCA) ① **GD86534**
9b M. Callas, Philh, A. Tonini *Concert*
   (2/93) (EMI) ① **CDC7 54437-2**
11. M. Callas, Philh, T. Serafin (r1954) *Concert*
    (11/86) (EMI) ① **CDC7 47282-2**
11. M. Callas, Philh, N. Rescigno (r1954) *Concert*
    (2/90) (EMI) ① [4] **CMS7 63244-2**
11. E. Gruberová, Smetana Th Chor, Czech PO, F.
    Haider *Concert* (5/90) (SONY) ① **SK45633**
11. C. Muzio, orch (r1924) *Concert*
    (5/90) (BOGR) ① [2] **BIM705-2**
11. L. Tetrazzini, orch (r1914) *Concert*
    (10/90) (NIMB) ① **NI7808**
11. L. Tetrazzini, orch, P. Pitt (r1910) *Concert*
    (9/92) (EMI) ① [3] **CHS7 63802-2(1)**
11. L. Tetrazzini, orch, P. Pitt (r1910) *Concert*
    (9/92) (PEAR) ① **GEMMCD9222**
11. L. Tetrazzini, orch (r1914) *Concert*
    (9/92) (PEAR) ① **GEMMCD9225**
11. A. Nezhdanova, orch (r1914: Russ) *Concert*
    (6/93) (PEAR) ① [3] **GEMMCDS9007/9(2)**
11. M. Korjus, Berlin St Op Orch, B. Seidler-Winkler
    (r1935) *Concert* (10/93) (PREI) ① **89054**
11. R. Raisa, orch (r1921) *Concert*
    (1/94) (CLUB) ① **CL99-052**
11. C. Muzio, orch (r1924) *Concert*
    (1/94) (ROMO) ① [2] **81005-2**
11. M. Freni, Ater Orch, L. Magiera (pp) *Concert*
    (5/94) (DECC) ① [2] **443 018-2DF2**
11. C. Muzio, orch (r1918) *Concert*
    (1/95) (ROMO) ① [2] **81010-2**
11. I. Galante, Latvian Nat SO, A. Vilumanis (r1994)
    Concert (11/95) (CAMP) ① **RRCD1335**

VERDONCK, Cornelis
(1563–1625) Flanders

SECTION IV: VOCAL AND CHORAL

Donna bella e gentile—madrigal: 4vv
M. Arruabarrena, K. van Laethem, M. Valenta, J.
Benet, M. van Altena, J. Cabré, T. de Zwart, A. Pols,
R. Van Der Meer, K. Junghänel (lte/dir) *Concert*
(1/92) (ACCE) ① **ACC8864D**

VERESS, Sándor (1907–1992)
Hungary

SECTION I: ORCHESTRAL

Musica Concertante—12 strings (1965-6)
Berne Camerata, H. Holliger (r1993) *Concert*
(9/95) (ECM) ① **447 390-2**
**Passacaglia Concertante—oboe & string
orchestra (1961)**
Berne Camerata, H. Holliger (ob/dir) (r1993) *Concert*
(9/95) (ECM) ① **447 390-2**

SECTION II: CHAMBER

Trio for Strings (1954)
H. Schneeberger, T. Zimmermann, T. Demenga
(r1991) *Concert* (9/93) (ECM) ① **437 440-2**

SECTION III: INSTRUMENTAL

Sonata for Cello (1967)
T. Demenga (r1991) *Concert*
(9/93) (ECM) ① **437 440-2**
Sonata for Violin (1935)
H. Schneeberger (r1991) *Concert*
(9/93) (ECM) ① **437 440-2**

SECTION IV: VOCAL AND CHORAL

**Song of the Seasons—seven madrigals for
mixed choir (1967)** (Wds. C Brennan)
London Voices, T. Edwards (r1992) *Concert*
(9/95) (ECM) ① **447 390-2**

VERMONT LE JEUNE, Pernot
(?–1558) France

Pierre le jeune

SECTION IV: VOCAL AND CHORAL

Ce n'est pas trop—chanson
C. Janequin Ens, D. Visse (r1994) *Concert*
(5/95) (HARM) ① **HMC90 1453**

VERSTOVSKY, Alexey
Nikolayevich (1799–1862)
Russia

SECTION V: STAGE WORKS

**Askold's Grave—opera: 4 acts
(1835—Moscow)** (Lib. Zagoskin)
Drinking Song G. Nelepp, Moscow All-Union Rad
Ch, Moscow All-Union RSO, V. Smirnov (r1952)
Concert (4/92) (EMI) ① [7] **CHS7 69741-2(6)**
In olden days our forefathers lived N. Shevelev,
anon (r1901) *Concert*
(6/93) (PEAR) ① [3] **GEMMCDS9007/9(2)**
In olden days our forefathers lived L. Sibiriakov,
chor, orch (r1910) *Concert*
(6/93) (PEAR) ① [3] **GEMMCDS9007/9(2)**
Near the town of Slavyansk A. Labinsky, anon
(r1905) *Concert* (7/93) (SYMP) ① **SYMCD1105**

VERT, Juan (1890–1931) Spain

SECTION V: STAGE WORKS

**La leyenda del beso—zarzuela: 2 acts
(1924—Madrid)** (Lib. E Reoyo, Paso & S
Arumburu)
Amor mi raza sabe conquistar J. Carreras, I. Rey,
ECO, E. Ricci (r1994) *Concert*
(2/95) (ERAT) ① **4509-95789-2**

VIADANA, Lodovico
(c1560–1627) Italy

SECTION II: CHAMBER

Sinfonie musicali a 8, Op. 18 (1610)
1. La Romana; 2. La Napolitana; 3. La Venetiana; 4.
La Milanese; 5. La Genovese; 6. La Fiorentina; 7. La
Bolognese; 8. La Veronese; 9. La Mantovana; 10. La
Cremonese; 11. La Padovana; 12. La Bergamasca;
13. La Brescia; 14. La Ferrarese; 15. La
Parmigiana; 16. La Piacentina; 17. La Modenese; 18.
La Reggiana.
11, 12. Wallace Collection, S. Wright *Concert*
(11/90) (TELA) ① **CD80204**

VIARDOT-GARCIA, (Michelle
Ferdinande) Pauline (1821–1910)
France

SECTION IV: VOCAL AND CHORAL

Adieu les beaux jours—song (Wds. anon)
K. Ott, C. Keller *Concert*
(12/90) (CPO) ① **CPO999 044-2**
Aime-moi—song (Wds. L. Pomey: based on
Chopin Mazurka, Op 32/2)
K. Ott, C. Keller *Concert*
(12/90) (CPO) ① **CPO999 044-2**
Bonjour mon coeur—song (Wds. Ronsard)
K. Ott, C. Keller *Concert*
(12/90) (CPO) ① **CPO999 044-2**
Chanson de la Pluie—song (Wds. I.
Turgenev)
K. Ott, C. Keller *Concert*
(12/90) (CPO) ① **CPO999 044-2**

La Chêne et la roseau—mélodie (Wds.
anon)
K. Ott, C. Keller *Concert*
(12/90) (CPO) ① **CPO999 044-2**
La Danse—song (Wds. L. Pomey: based on
Chopin Mazurka, Op 50/1)
K. Ott, C. Keller *Concert*
(12/90) (CPO) ① **CPO999 044-2**
Désespoir—song (Wds. L. Pomey)
K. Ott, C. Keller *Concert*
(12/90) (CPO) ① **CPO999 044-2**
L' Enfant et la mère—song (Wds. anon)
K. Ott, C. Keller *Concert*
(12/90) (CPO) ① **CPO999 044-2**
Grands oiseaux blancs—song (Wds. L.
Pomey)
K. Ott, C. Keller *Concert*
(12/90) (CPO) ① **CPO999 044-2**
Havanaise—song (Wds. L. Pomey)
K. Ott, C. Keller *Concert*
(12/90) (CPO) ① **CPO999 044-2**
Madrid—song (Wds. A. de Musset)
K. Ott, C. Keller *Concert*
(12/90) (CPO) ① **CPO999 044-2**
L' Oiselet—song (Wds. L. Pomey: based on
Chopin Mazurka, Op. 68/2)
K. Ott, C. Keller *Concert*
(12/90) (CPO) ① **CPO999 044-2**
La Petite chevrière—song (Wds. anon)
K. Ott, C. Keller *Concert*
(12/90) (CPO) ① **CPO999 044-2**
Scène d'Hermione—song (Wds. J. Racine)
K. Ott, C. Keller *Concert*
(12/90) (CPO) ① **CPO999 044-2**
Seize Ans—song (Wds. L. Pomey: based on
Chopin Mazurka, Op 50/2)
K. Ott, C. Keller *Concert*
(12/90) (CPO) ① **CPO999 044-2**
Sérénade—song (Wds. T. Gautier)
K. Ott, C. Keller *Concert*
(12/90) (CPO) ① **CPO999 044-2**

VICTORIA, Tomás Luis de
(1548–1611) Spain

SECTION IV: VOCAL AND CHORAL

**Alma redemptoris mater—antiphon: 8vv and
organ (pub 1581)**
Mixylodian, P. Schmidt *Concert*
(5/92) (CARL) ① **PCD970**
Westminster Cath Ch, J. O'Donnell (r1994) *Concert*
(3/95) (HYPE) ① **CDA66738**
**Ascendens Christus in altum—motet: 5vv
(pub 1572)**
Westminster Cath Ch, D. Hill *Concert*
(9/87) (HYPE) ① **CDA66190**
**Ave Maria, gratia plena—motet: 4vv
(dubious)**
Tallis Scholars, P. Phillips *Concert*
(12/86) (GIME) ① **CDGIM010**
Westminster Cath Ch, J. O'Donnell, D. Hill *Concert*
(1/89) (HYPE) ① **CDA66129**
Cambridge Sngrs, J. Rutter *Concert*
(4/92) (CLLE) ① **COLCD116**
**Ave Maria, gratia plena—motet: 8vv (pub
1572)**
Tallis Scholars, P. Phillips *Concert*
(12/86) (GIME) ① **CDGIM010**
Cambridge Sngrs, J. Rutter *Concert*
(4/92) (CLLE) ① **COLCD116**
Compañia musical, La Fenice, J. Cabré, Y. Repérant
(r1992) *Concert* (9/93) (K617) ① **K617024**
Ave maris stella—hymn: 4vv (pub 1581)
Westminster Cath Ch, J. O'Donnell, D. Hill *Concert*
(1/89) (HYPE) ① **CDA66129**
**Ave regina coelorum—antiphon: 5vv (pub
1572)**
Westminster Cath Ch, J. O'Donnell (r1994) *Concert*
(3/95) (HYPE) ① **CDA66738**
**Lauda Sion—sequence: 8vv and organ (pub
1585)**
A. Wright, Westminster Cath Ch, S. Cleobury (r1994)
Petti) *Concert* (7/83) (ARGO) ① **410 005-2ZH**
**Magnificat primi toni—8vv and organ (pub
1600)**
Westminster Cath Ch, J. O'Donnell (r1994) *Concert*
(3/95) (HYPE) ① **CDA66738**
**Missa Ascendens Christus in altum—5vv
(pub 1592)**
Westminster Cath Ch, D. Hill *Concert*
(9/87) (HYPE) ① **CDA66190**
Missa Ave maris stella—4vv (pub 1576)
Westminster Cath Ch, D. Hill *Concert*
(6/86) (HYPE) ① **CDA66114**

C. Walsh Duruflé: Suite, Op. 5.
(12/88) (PRIO) ① **PRCD236**
M. Murray (r1992) Symphony 3.
(5/94) (TELA) ① **CD80329**
Final J. Parker-Smith Concert
(3/89) (ASV) ① **CDDCA610**
Final S. Preston Concert
(6/91) (DECC) ① **430 091-2DWO**
Finale P. Hurford (r1987) Concert
(10/95) (DECC) ① **444 567-2DM**
Symphony No. 2 in E minor—organ, Op. 20 (1902-03)
B. van Oosten Concert
(9/87) (MDG) ① [2] **L3211/2**
O. Latry Symphony 3.
(10/90) (BNL) ① **BNL112741**
C. Walsh (r1992) Symphony 3.
(10/94) (PRIO) ① **PRCD446**
Symphony No. 3 in F sharp minor—organ, Op. 28 (1912)
F-H. Houbart Concert
(3/86) (PIER) ① **PV784041**
D. Roth Concert
(2/87) (MOTE) ① **CD10491**
B. van Oosten Concert
(9/87) (MDG) ① [2] **L3211/2**
D. Sanger Symphony 4.
(10/90) (MERI) ① **CDE84176**
O. Latry Symphony 2.
(10/90) (BNL) ① **BNL112741**
J. Filsell Concert
(3/92) (HERA) ① **HAVPCD145**
M. Murray (r1992) Symphony 1.
(5/94) (TELA) ① **CD80329**
C. Walsh (r1992) Symphony 2.
(10/94) (PRIO) ① **PRCD446**
Symphony No. 4 in G minor—organ, Op. 32 (1914)
D. Sanger Symphony 3.
(10/90) (MERI) ① **CDE84176**
Symphony No. 6 in B minor—organ, Op. 59 (1930)
D. Craighead Reger: Organ Sonata, Op. 60.
(7/91) (DELO) ① **DE3096**
Scherzo G. Weir Concert
(12/92) (KOSS) ① **KC1013**
Triptyque—organ, Op. 58 (1929-31)
1. Matines; 2. Communion; 3. Stèle un enfant défunt.
C. Walsh Pièces en stile libre.
(3/92) (PRIO) ① [2] **PRCD319**
3. J. Parker-Smith Concert
(3/89) (ASV) ① **CDDCA610**
3. M.H. Long Concert (4/91) (KOCH) ① **37008-2**

SECTION IV: VOCAL AND CHORAL

Messe solennelle in C sharp minor—4vv and 2 organs, Op. 16 (1900)
Paris Sacre Coeur Ch, Paris St Michael Anglican
Church Ch, Paris American Church Ch, C. Glessner,
F. Gramann, P. Maze Concert
(10/89) (MOTE) ① **CD40081**

VIERNE, René (1878-1918) France

SECTION III: INSTRUMENTAL

Pièces de différents caractères—organ (pub 1914)
1. Prélude (pour une Messe Basse); 2. Intermezzo; 3.
Offertoire; 4. Epithalme; 5. Marche de Procession; 6.
Entrée; 7. Prélude funèbre; 8. Prière; 9. Sortie; 10.
Postlude; 11. Caprice.
6-11. M-B. Dufourcet (r1992) Concert
(6/95) (PRIO) ① **PRCD422**

VIERU, Anatol (b 1926) Romania

SECTION I: ORCHESTRAL

Symphony No. 2 (1973)
Bucharest Nat Rad Orch, L. Bacs (r1975) Concert
(4/95) (OLYM) ① **OCD449**
Symphony No. 4 (1982)
Cluj-Napoca PO, E. Simon (r1983) Concert
(4/95) (OLYM) ① **OCD449**

SECTION IV: VOCAL AND CHORAL

Psalm 1993—chorus and orchestra (1993)
Bucharest Rad CO, L. Bacs (r1993) Concert
(4/95) (OLYM) ① **OCD449**

VIEUXTEMPS, Henry (1820-1881) Belgium

SECTION I: ORCHESTRAL

Concerto for Cello and Orchestra No. 1 in A minor, Op. 46 (1876)
H. Schiff, Stuttgart RSO, N. Marriner (rev.
M.Stegemann) Cello Concerto 2.
(2/88) (EMI) ① **CDC7 47761-2**
Concerto for Cello and Orchestra No. 2 in B minor, Op. 50 (1880)
H. Schiff, Stuttgart RSO, N. Marriner (rev.
M.Stegemann) Cello Concerto 1.
(2/88) (EMI) ① **CDC7 47761-2**
Concerto for Violin and Orchestra No. 4 in D minor, Op. 31 (c1850)
J. Heifetz, LPO, J. Barbirolli (1935) Concert
(1/91) (BIDD) ① **LAB025**
J. Heifetz, LPO, J. Barbirolli (1935) Concert
(5/92) (EMI) ① **CDH7 64251-2**
J. Heifetz, LPO, J. Barbirolli (1935) Concert
(11/94) (RCA) ① [65] **09026 61778-2(03)**
I. Perlman, Paris Orch, D. Barenboim Concert
(6/95) (EMI) ① [20] **CZS4 83177-2(1)**
J. Heifetz, LPO, J. Barbirolli (1935) Concert
(11/95) (PEAR) ① [2] **GEMMCDS9167**
Concerto for Violin and Orchestra No. 5 in A minor, Op. 37 (1861)
V. Mullova, ASMF, N. Marriner Paganini: Violin
Concerto 1. (10/89) (PHIL) ① **422 332-2PH**
S. Mintz, Israel PO, Z. Mehta (pp1988) Concert
(3/92) (DG) ① **427 676-2GH**
J. Heifetz, LSO, M. Sargent (r1947) Concert
(10/94) (EMI) ① **CDH5 65191-2**
J. Heifetz, LSO, M. Sargent (r1947) Concert
(11/94) (RCA) ① [65] **09026 61778-2(06)**
Chee-Yun, LPO, J. López-Cobos (r1994)
Mendelssohn: Violin Concerto, Op. 64.
(1/95) (DENO) ① **CO-78913**
I. Perlman, Paris Orch, D. Barenboim Concert
(6/95) (EMI) ① [20] **CZS4 83177-2(1)**
2. J. Heifetz, New SO, M. Sargent (r1961) Concert
(11/94) (RCA) ① [65] **09026 61778-2(11-15)**

SECTION II: CHAMBER

Ballade and Polonaise—violin and orchestra, Op. 38 (c1860) (also for violin and piano)
B. Huberman, P. Frenkel (r1922) Concert
(3/94) (BIDD) ① [2] **LAB077/8**
Elégie—violin/viola and piano, Op. 30
K. Kashkashian, R. Levin Concert
(9/86) (ECM) ① **827 744-2**
N. Imai, R. Vignoles (r1992) Concert
(9/92) (CHAN) ① **CHAN8873**
3 Morceaux de salon—violin and piano, Op. 32 (pub c1855)
2. Rondino.
2. C. Hansen, B. Zakharoff (r1924) Concert
(12/91) (APR) ① [2] **APR7015**
Sonata in B flat—viola and piano, Op. 36 (pub 1863)
N. Imai, R. Vignoles (r1992) Concert
(9/92) (CHAN) ① **CHAN8873**
Souvenir d'Amérique on 'Yankee Doodle'—violin and piano, Op. 17 (c1845)
I. Perlman, S. Sanders Concert
(6/95) (EMI) ① [20] **CZS4 83177-2(3)**

SECTION III: INSTRUMENTAL

36 Etudes—violin, Op. 48 (pub 1882)
18. Lamento; 24. Cantilena.
24. M. Kliegel, R. Havenith (arr vc/pf) Concert
(9/92) (MARC) ① **8 223403**
6 Morceaux and a capriccio—violin (morceaux); viola (capriccio), Op. 61 (pub 1883)
Capriccio N. Imai (r1992) Concert
(9/92) (CHAN) ① **CHAN8873**

VILBOA, Konstantin Petrovich (1817-1882) Russia

SECTION IV: VOCAL AND CHORAL

The Seafarers—song
I. Ershov, V. Sharonov, anon (r1903) Concert
(6/93) (PEAR) ① [3] **GEMMCDS9997/9(1)**
L. Sibiriakov, E. Witting, orch (r1912) Concert
(6/93) (PEAR) ① [3] **GEMMCDS9007/9(2)**

VILLA-LOBOS, Heitor (1887-1959) Brazil

SECTION I: ORCHESTRAL

Amazonas—symphonic poem (1917)
Bratislava RSO, R. Duarte Concert
(3/92) (MARC) ① **8 223357**
Bachianas Brasileiras No. 2—orchestra (1930)
1. Preludio; 2. Aria; 3. Danza; 4. Toccata: 'The little train of the Caipira'.
RPO, E. Bátiz Concert
(11/87) (EMI) ① [3] **CDS7 47901-8**
FRNO, H. Villa-Lobos (r1956) Concert
(9/88) (EMI) ① **CDH7 61015-2**
4. LSO, E. Goossens (r1959) Concert
(4/95) (EVER) ① **EVC9007**
4. FRNO, H. Villa-Lobos (r1956) Concert
(6/95) (EMI) ① **CDC5 55224-2**
Bachianas Brasileiras No. 3—piano and orchestra (1938)
J.F. Osorio, RPO, E. Bátiz Concert
(11/87) (EMI) ① [3] **CDS7 47901-8**
Bachianas Brasileiras No. 4—orchestra (1930-40)
RPO, E. Bátiz Concert
(11/87) (EMI) ① [3] **CDS7 47901-8**
FRNO, H. Villa-Lobos (r1957) Concert
(6/95) (EMI) ① **CDC5 55224-2**
Bachianas Brasileiras No. 7—orchestra (1942)
RPO, E. Bátiz Concert
(2/87) (EMI) ① **CDC7 47433-2**
RPO, E. Bátiz Concert
(11/87) (EMI) ① [3] **CDS7 47901-8**
Bachianas Brasileiras No. 8—orchestra (1944)
RPO, E. Bátiz Concert
(11/87) (EMI) ① [3] **CDS7 47901-8**
Bachianas Brasileiras No. 9—string orchestra (orchestration of choral version)
RPO, E. Bátiz Concert
(11/87) (EMI) ① [3] **CDS7 47901-8**
FRNO, H. Villa-Lobos (r1956) Concert
(9/88) (EMI) ① **CDH7 61015-2**
Chôros No. 6—orchestra (1926)
World PO, L. Maazel (pp1986) Concert
(7/88) (AUVI) ① **AV6113**
Chôros No.8—2 pianos & orchestra (1925)
Hong Kong PO, K. Schermerhorn Chôro 9.
(2/86) (MARC) ① **8 220322**
Chôros No.9—orchestra (1929)
Hong Kong PO, K. Schermerhorn Chôros 8.
(2/86) (MARC) ① **8 220322**
Concerto for Cello and Orchestra No. 1 (1913)
U. Schmid, NW German PO, D. Roggen Cello
Concerto 2. (11/89) (MDG) ① **L3339**
Concerto for Cello and Orchestra No. 2 (1953)
U. Schmid, NW German PO, D. Roggen Cello
Concerto 1. (11/89) (MDG) ① **L3339**
Concerto for Guitar and Orchestra (1951)
T. Santos, Brazilian CO, B. Bessler Concert
(11/87) (CHNT) ① [2] **LDC278 869/70**
A. Moreno, Mexico City PO, E. Bátiz Concert
(9/88) (EMI) ① [3] **CDS7 47901-8**
R. Dyens, J-W. Audoli Ins Ens, J-W. Audoli Concert
(9/88) (AUVI) ① **AV6114**
G. Söllscher, Orpheus CO Concert
(6/90) (DG) ① **429 232-2GH**
J. Bream, LSO, A. Previn (r1971) Concert
(8/93) (RCA) ① [28] **09026 61583-2(5)**
N. Kraft, Northern CO, N. Ward (r1992) Concert
(4/94) (NAXO) ① **8 550729**
Concerto for Harmonia and Orchestra in A minor (1955-56)
T. Reilly, SW German Rad Orch, E. Smola (r1981)
Concert (5/94) (CHAN) ① **CHAN9248**
Concerto for Piano and Orchestra No. 1 (1945)
C. Ortiz, RPO, M.A. Gómez-Martínez Concert
(5/92) (DECC) ① [2] **430 628-2DH2**
Concerto for Piano and Orchestra No. 2 (1948)
C. Ortiz, RPO, M.A. Gómez-Martínez Concert
(5/92) (DECC) ① [2] **430 628-2DH2**
Concerto for Piano and Orchestra No. 3 (1952-57)
C. Ortiz, RPO, M.A. Gómez-Martínez Concert
(5/92) (DECC) ① [2] **430 628-2DH2**

T. Santos *Concert*
(11/87) (CHNT) ① [2] **LDC278 869/70**
E. Kotzia *Concert* (6/89) (PEAR) ① **SHECD9609**
J. Freire *Concert* (7/92) (LEMA) ① **LC42601**
A. Gifford (r1990) *Concert*
(12/92) (NATI) ① **NTCD001**
J. Bream (r1971) *Concert*
(8/93) (RCA) ① [28] **09026 61583-2(5)**
A-S. Ramírez (r1993) *Concert*
(12/95) (DENO) ① **CO-78931**
E minor J. Bream (r1962) *Concert*
(8/93) (RCA) ① [28] **09026 61583-2(3)**
E minor J. Bream (r1962) *Concert*
(8/93) (RCA) ① **09026 61591-2**
**Prole do bebê, Book I—eight pieces: piano
(1918)**
1. Branquinha; 2. Moreninha; 3. Caboclinha; 4.
Mulatinha; 5. Negrinha; 6. Pobrezinha; 7.
Polichinelle; 8. Bruxa.
M. Bratke (r1994) *Concert*
(2/95) (OLYM) ① **OCD455**
Excs A. Rubinstein (pp1961) *Concert*
(10/93) (RCA) ① **09026 61445-2**
2, 6, 7. L. Rév *Concert*
(7/87) (HYPE) ① **CDA66185**
**Prole do bebê, Book II—10 pieces: piano
(1921)**
1. Baratinha; 2. Gatinha; 3. Camundongo; 4.
Cachorrinho; 5. Cavalinho; 6. Boizinho; 7.
Passarinho; 8. Ursinho; 9. Lobozinho.
2, 6. M. Verzoni *Concert* (4/90) (SCHW) ① **310019**
**Suite populaire brésilienne—guitar (1908-
12)**
1. Mazurka-Chôro; 2. Schottische-Chôro; 3. Valse-
Chôro; 4. Gavotte-Chôro.
T. Santos *Concert*
(11/87) (CHNT) ① [2] **LDC278 869/70**
R. Dyens *Concert* (9/88) (AUVI) ① **AV6114**
J. Bream (r1978) *Concert*
(8/93) (RCA) ① [28] **09026 61583-2(4)**
J. Bream (r1978) *Concert*
(6/94) (RCA) ① **09026 61596-2**
2. J. Bream (r1971) *Concert*
(8/93) (RCA) ① [28] **09026 61583-2(3)**
2. J. Bream (r1971) *Concert*
(8/93) (RCA) ① **09026 61591-2**
Valsa da dor—piano (1932)
A. Petchersky *Concert* (9/88) (ASV) ① **CDDCA607**

SECTION IV: VOCAL AND CHORAL

Ave Maria—5vv (1938) (Wds. Portuguese)
Corydon Sngrs, M. Best (r1992-3) *Concert*
(8/93) (HYPE) ① **CDA66638**
Ave Maria—6vv (1948)
Corydon Sngrs, M. Best (r1992-3) *Concert*
(8/93) (HYPE) ① **CDA66638**
**Bachianas Brasileiras No. 5—soprano, solo
cello and cello ensemble (1938-45)**
EXCERPTS: 1. Aria (Cantilena); 2. Dança (Martelo).
K. Te Kanawa, L. Harrell, Inst. Ens (r1984)
Canteloube: Chants d'Auvergne.
(1/85) (DECC) ① **411 730-2DH**
B. Hendricks, E. Fox, RPO Vc Ens *Concert*
(2/87) (EMI) ① **CDC7 47433-2**
K. Te Kanawa, L. Harrell, Inst. Ens *Concert*
(11/87) (DECC) ① **417 645-2DH**
B. Hendricks, E. Fox, RPO Vc Ens *Concert*
(11/87) (EMI) ① [3] **CDS7 47901-8**
J. Gomez, Pleeth Cello Octet *Concert*
(12/87) (HYPE) ① **CDA66257**
V. de los Angeles, FRNO, H. Villa-Lobos (r1956)
Concert (9/88) (EMI) ① **CDH7 61015-2**
N. Davrath, NYPO, L. Bernstein (r1963) *Concert*
(5/93) (SONY) ① **SMK47544**
V. de los Angeles, FRNO, H. Villa-Lobos (r1956)
Concert (6/95) (EMI) ① **CDC5 55224-2**
I. Galante, Latvian Nat SO, A. Vilumanis (r1994)
Concert (11/95) (CAMP) ① **RRCD1335**
A. Moffo, American SO, L. Stokowski *Concert*
(6/89) (RCA) ① **GD87831**
1. T. Santos, L. Guimaraes (trans sop and gtr)
Concert (11/87) (CHNT) ① [2] **LDC278 869/70**
Bendita sabedoria—6vv (1958) (Wds. Bible)
Corydon Sngrs, M. Best (r1992-3) *Concert*
(8/93) (HYPE) ① **CDA66638**
Canção de cristal—song (1950)
C. Scimone, A. Heller *Concert*
(11/92) (ETCE) ① **KTC1139**
**Cançao do poeta do Século XVIII—song
(1948)** (Wds. Ferreira)
M. Heller, A. Heller *Concert*
(11/92) (ETCE) ① **KTC1139**

**Chôros No. 3, 'Picapau'—male vv, clarinet,
saxophone, bassoon and 3 horns (1925)**
Rio de Janeiro Assoc for Choral Song (male
members), J. Botelho, P. Moura, N. Devos, S. Svab,
T. Tritle, C. Gomes de Oliveira, J. Sadoc *Concert*
(6/87) (CHNT) ① **LDC278 835**
**Chôros No. 10, 'Rasga o coracão'—chorus
and orchestra (1926)**
S. Bolívar Orféon Universitario, S. Bolívar SO, E.
Mata *Estévez: Cantata Criolla.*
(4/93) (DORI) ① **DIS80101**
Jeunesses Musicales Chor, FRNO, H. Villa-Lobos
(r1957) *Concert* (6/95) (EMI) ① **CDC5 55224-2**
Confidencias—song (1908)
M. Heller, A. Heller *Concert*
(11/92) (ETCE) ① **KTC1139**
Cor dulce, cor amabile—4vv (1952)
Corydon Sngrs, M. Best (r1992-3) *Concert*
(8/93) (HYPE) ① **CDA66638**
Duas Paisagens—song (1946)
1. Manha na Praia; 2. Tarda na Gloria.
C. Scimone, A. Heller *Concert*
(11/92) (ETCE) ① **KTC1139**
**8 Epigrammes irónicas e
sentimentais—songs (1921-23)** (Wds.
Carvalho)
VOLUME 1: 1. Eis a Vida!; 2. Inutil Epigramma; 3.
Sonho de uma Noite de Verão; 4. Epigramma.
VOLUME 2: 5. Perversidade; 6. Pudor; 7. Imagem; 8.
Verdade.
C. Scimone, A. Heller *Concert*
(11/92) (ETCE) ① **KTC1139**
Forêts de l'Amazonie—songs (1958)
1. Valeiro; 2. Cair da trade; 3. Canção de amor; 4.
Melodia Sentimental.
4. S. Isbin (arr Barbosa-Lima) *Concert*
(10/90) (VIRG) ① **VC7 59591-2**
Jardim Fanado—song (1955)
C. Scimone, A. Heller *Concert*
(11/92) (ETCE) ① **KTC1139**
**Magnificat alleluia—1v, chorus and
orchestra (1958)**
E. McCormack, Corydon Sngrs, Corydon Orch, M.
Best (r1992-3) *Concert*
(8/93) (HYPE) ① **CDA66638**
6 Miniatures—songs (1907-08)
1. Chromo No. 2 (1916: Wds. Lopes); 2. A Viola
(1916: Wds. Romero); 3. Chromo No. 3 (1916: Wds.
Barreto); 4. Sonho (1916: Wds. A. Guimarães); 5.
Japonezes (1907: Wds. L. Guimarães); 6. Sino da
Aldeia (1917: Wds. de Oliveira).
M. Heller, A. Heller *Concert*
(11/92) (ETCE) ① **KTC1139**
2. F. Fuller, H. Villa-Lobos (r1948) *Concert*
(4/92) (EMI) ① [7] **CHS7 69741-2(2)**
2. F. Fuller, H. Villa-Lobos (r1948) *Concert*
(6/95) (EMI) ① **CDC5 55224-2**
Missa São Sebastião—3vv (1937)
Corydon Sngrs, M. Best (r1992-3) *Concert*
(8/93) (HYPE) ① **CDA66638**
**Modinhas e Cançoes, Series I—songs (1933-
43)**
1. Canção do Marinheiro; 2. Lundú da Marqueza de
Santos; 3. Cantilena; 4. A Gatinha Parda; 5. O
Remeiro de São Francisco; 6. Nhapópé; 7.
Evocaçao.
M. Heller, A. Heller *Concert*
(11/92) (ETCE) ① **KTC1139**
3. F. Fuller, H. Villa-Lobos (r1948) *Concert*
(6/95) (EMI) ① **CDC5 55224-2**
**Modinhas e Cançoes, Series II—children's
songs (1943)**
1. Pobre Peregrino; 2. Vida Formaosa; 3. Nesta Rua;
4. Mando Tiro, Tiro, Lá; 5. João Cambuete; 6. Na
Corda de Viola.
C. Scimone, A. Heller *Concert*
(11/92) (ETCE) ① **KTC1139**
Panis angelicus—4vv (1950)
Corydon Sngrs, M. Best (r1992-3) *Concert*
(8/93) (HYPE) ① **CDA66638**
Pater noster—4vv (1950)
Corydon Sngrs, M. Best (r1992-3) *Concert*
(8/93) (HYPE) ① **CDA66638**
Praesepe—4vv (1952)
Corydon Sngrs, M. Best (r1992-3) *Concert*
(8/93) (HYPE) ① **CDA66638**
Samba-Clássico—song (1950)
M. Heller, A. Heller *Concert*
(11/92) (ETCE) ① **KTC1139**
14 Serestas—songs (1923-43) (Wds.
various)
1. Pobre Cega (wds. A. Moreyra); 2. O Anjo da
Guarda (wds. M. Bandeira); 3. Canção da Folha
Morta (wds. O. Mariano); 4. Saudades da Minha Viola
(wds. D. Milano); 5. Modinha (wds. M. Bandeira); 6.
Na Paz do Outono (wds. R. de Carvalho); 7. Cantiga

do Viúvo (wds. C. D. de Andrade); 8. Canção do
Carreiro (wds. R. Couto); 9. Abril (wds. R. Couto); 10.
Desejo (wds. G. de ALmeida); 11. Redondilha (wds.
D. Milano); 12. Realejo (wds. A. Moreyra); 13.
Serenata (wds. D. Nasser); 14. Vôo (wds. A.
Renault).
8. E. Houston, P. Miguel (r1941) *Concert*
(4/92) (EMI) ① [7] **CHS7 69741-2(1)**
Sête vezes—song (1958)
C. Scimone, A. Heller *Concert*
(11/92) (ETCE) ① **KTC1139**
Sub tuum praesidium—4vv (1952)
Corydon Sngrs, M. Best (r1992-3) *Concert*
(8/93) (HYPE) ① **CDA66638**
Suite for Voice and Violin (1923)
J. Gomez, P. Manning *Concert*
(12/87) (HYPE) ① **CDA66257**
Vira—song (1926)
M. Heller, A. Heller *Concert*
(11/92) (ETCE) ① **KTC1139**

SECTION V: STAGE WORKS

**The Discovery of Brazil—concert suites
from film score (1937)**
Slovak Phil Chor, Slovak RSO, R. Duarte (r1993)
(8/94) (MARC) ① **8 223551**
Gênesis—ballet (1954)
Bratislava RSO, R. Duarte *Concert*
(3/92) (MARC) ① **8 223357**
**Magdalena—musical comedy, 2 acts
(1947—Los Angeles)** (lyrics G. Forrest & R.
Wright)
Cpte J. Kaye, G. Rose, F. Esham, K. Gray, J.
Hadley, K. Curran, C. Damsel, C. Repole, Concora,
New England Orch, E. Haile
(2/91) (SONY) ① **MK44945**
Uirapuru—ballet (1917)
S. Bolívar SO, E. Mata (r1994) *Concert*
(8/95) (DORI) ① **DOR90211**

VILLAMOV ?Russia

SECTION IV: VOCAL AND CHORAL

Pray—romance
L. Sibiriakov, M.T. Manasevich, anon (r1905) *Concert*
(6/93) (PEAR) ① [3] **GEMMCDS9001/3(2)**

**VILLETTE, Pierre (1926–1969)
France**

SECTION IV: VOCAL AND CHORAL

Attende Domine—motet
Rodolfus Ch, R. Allwood (r1993) *Concert*
(9/95) (HERA) ① **HAVPCD176**
Hymne à la Vierge—soprano and choir
P. Stow, Cambridge Clare College Ch, T. Brown
Concert (12/88) (MERI) ① **CDE84153**
Cambridge Sngrs, J. Rutter *Concert*
(4/92) (CLLE) ① **COLCD116**
Westminster Cath Ch, J. O'Donnell (r1993) *Concert*
(3/94) (HYPE) ① **CDA66669**
Rodolfus Ch, R. Allwood (r1993) *Concert*
(9/95) (HERA) ① **HAVPCD176**
O magnum mysterium—motet (1983)
Rodolfus Ch, R. Allwood (r1993) *Concert*
(9/95) (HERA) ① **HAVPCD176**
O sacrum convivium—motet
Rodolfus Ch, R. Allwood (r1993) *Concert*
(9/95) (HERA) ① **HAVPCD176**
Salve Regina—motet
Rodolfus Ch, R. Allwood (r1993) *Concert*
(9/95) (HERA) ① **HAVPCD176**

**VILLOLDO, Angel (20th Cent)
Argentina**

SECTION IV: VOCAL AND CHORAL

El Choclo—tango (Wds. ?Discepolo &
Catan)
Buenos Aires Qnt, RPO, E. Stratta (arr J. Calandrelli)
Concert (1/93) (TELD) ① **9031-76997-2**

**VINCENT, Thomas (c1720–1783)
England**

SECTION II: CHAMBER

**Sonata for Oboe and Continuo No. 2 in A
minor (pub 1748)**
P. Dombrecht, W. Kuijken, R. Kohnen *Concert*
(9/86) (ACCE) ① **ACC57804D**

VINE, Carl (b 1954) Australia

SECTION I: ORCHESTRAL

MicroSymphony (1986)
Sydney SO, S. Challender (r1990) *Concert*
(10/95) (ABCC) ① **8 77000 5**
Symphony No. 2 (1988)
Sydney SO, S. Challender (r1990) *Concert*
(10/95) (ABCC) ① **8 77000 5**
Symphony No. 3 (1990)
Sydney SO, S. Challender (r1990) *Concert*
(10/95) (ABCC) ① **8 77000 5**

SECTION II: CHAMBER

Café Concertino—chamber ensemble (1984)
Australia Ens *Concert*   (7/92) (TALL) ① **TP002**

VINTER, Gilbert (1909–1969) England

SECTION I: ORCHESTRAL

James Cook—Circumnavigator—brass band (1969)
Black Dyke Mills Band, R. Newsome *Concert*
(7/93) (CHAN) ① **CHAN4508**
John O'Gaunt—brass band
Black Dyke Mills Band, P. Parkes (pp1978) *Concert*
(3/94) (CHAN) ① **CHAN4522**
Portuguese Party—orchestra
RTE Concert Orch, E. Tomlinson (r1993) *Concert*
(12/95) (MARC) ① **8 223522**
Triumphant Rhapsody—brass band (1965)
Britannia Building Soc Band, Desford Colliery
Caterpillar Band, CWS (Glasgow) Band, IMI
Yorkshire Imperial Band, G. Brand (pp1991) *Concert*
(8/92) (POLY) ① **QPRL049D**

VIOTTI, Giovanni Battista (1755–1824) Italy

G—Nos. from Giazotto (1956)

SECTION I: ORCHESTRAL

Concerto for Cello and Orchestra in C (c1800)
O. Harnoy, Solisti Veneti, C. Scimone (r1991)
(8/93) (RCA) ① **09026 61228-2**
Concerto for Harp and Orchestra in C minor
Adagio non troppo M. Nordmann, F. Liszt CO, J-P.
Rampal (r1993) *Concert*
(10/95) (SONY) ① **SK58919**
Concerto for Piano and Orchestra No. 3 (with Violin obbligato) (c1783-86) (arr from Violin Concerto, G51)
P. Entremont (pf/dir), O. Rudner, Vienna CO
Mendelssohn: Violin and Piano Concerto.
(6/90) (SCHW) ① **311047**

VISÉE, Robert de (c1660–1725) France

SECTION III: INSTRUMENTAL

Les Baricades Mistérieuses de M. F. Couperin—theorbo transcription
Y. Imamura (r1992) *Concert*
(8/94) (CAPR) ① **10 464**
Logistille de Roland de M. Lully—theorbo transcription (1685) (from Lully's opera)
Y. Imamura (r1992) *Concert*
(8/94) (CAPR) ① **10 464**
La Ménetou de M. F. Couperin—theorbo transcription
Y. Imamura (r1992) *Concert*
(8/94) (CAPR) ① **10 464**
Le Montsermeil—rondeau
K. Junghänel (r1991) *Concert*
(8/93) (DHM) ① **05472 77176-2**
La Muzette de M. Forqueray
B. Mason *Concert*   (10/90) (AMON) ① **CD-SAR45**
Ouverture de la Grotte de Versailles de M. Lully—theorbo transcription (1685) (from Lully's opera)
M. Barrueco (gtr) *Concert*
(2/91) (EMI) ① **CDC7 49980-2**
Y. Imamura (r1992) *Concert*
(8/94) (CAPR) ① **10 464**
Pieces for guitar
Sarabande; Bourée; Menuet A. Segovia (r1939)
Concert   (5/89) (EMI) ① [2] **CHS7 61047-2**

Les Silvains de M. Couperin—lute
K. Junghänel (r1991) *Concert*
(8/93) (DHM) ① **05472 77176-2**
Suite in A—theorbo
Y. Imamura (r1992) *Concert*
(8/94) (CAPR) ① **10 464**
Suite in B minor—guitar (1686)
M. Barrueco (gtr) *Concert*
(2/91) (EMI) ① **CDC7 49980-2**
Suite in C minor—theorbo
Y. Imamura (r1992) *Concert*
(8/94) (CAPR) ① **10 464**
Suite in D minor—guitar (pub 1686) (from 'Livre de Pièces pour la Guitare')
1. Prélude; 2. Allemande; 3. Courante; 4. Sarabande;
5. Gavotte; 6. Bourrée; 7. Passacaille; 8. Gigue; 9.
Menuet.
N. North *Concert*   (6/87) (AMON) ① **CD-SAR18**
J. Lindberg (r1986) *Concert*
(11/87) (BIS) ① **BIS-CD327**
J. Bream (r1966) *Concert*
(8/93) (RCA) ① [28] **09026 61583-2(3)**
J. Bream (r1966) *Concert*   (4/94) (RCA) ① **09026 61592-2**
Suite in E minor—theorbo
Y. Imamura (r1992) *Concert*
(8/94) (CAPR) ① **10 464**
Suite in G—theorbo
Y. Imamura (r1992) *Concert*
(8/94) (CAPR) ① **10 464**
Tombeau de Vieux Gallot—allemande
K. Junghänel (r1991) *Concert*
(8/93) (DHM) ① **05472 77176-2**

VITALI, Giovanni Battista (1632–1692) Italy

SECTION II: CHAMBER

Ciacona in G minor—violin and continuo, Op. 7/3 (pub 1682)
N. Milstein, L. Mittman (arr Charlier: r1935) *Concert*
(10/92) (BIDD) ① **LAB055**
A. Grumiaux, R. Castagnone (r1956; arr Grumiaux)
Concert   (11/93) (PHIL) ① [3] **438 516-2PM3**
J. Thibaud, T. Janopoulo (r1936: arr Charlier)
Concert   (12/94) (APR) ① [2] **APR7028**
Palladian Ens (r1993) *Concert*
(1/95) (LINN) ① **CKD015**
13, 20. J. Heifetz, R. Ellsasser (r1950) *Concert*
(11/94) (RCA) ① [65] **09026 61778-2(24)**

VITALI, Tomaso Antonio (1663–1745) Italy

SECTION II: CHAMBER

Ciacona in G minor—violin and keyboard (probably not by Vitali)
N. Milstein, A. Balsam (r1955) *Concert*
(5/94) (EMI) ① [6] **ZDMF7 64830-2**

VITRÉ, Zacharie de (1659–?) France

SECTION IV: VOCAL AND CHORAL

Comme trois forgerons
A. Azéma (r1994) *Concert*
(11/95) (ERAT) ① **4509-98480-2**

VIVALDI, Antonio (Lucio) (1678–1741) Italy

RV numbers use in P. Ryom's *Verzeichnis der Werke
Antonio Vivaldi*

SECTION I: ORCHESTRAL

6 Concerti for Flute and Strings, Op. 10 (pub c1728)
1. La tempesta di mare, F (RV433); 2. La notte, G
minor (RV439); 3. Il gardellino, D (RV428); 4. G
(RV435); 5. F (RV434); 6. G (RV437).
A. Marion, F Liszt CO, J. Rolla
(9/87) (DENO) ① **CO-1406**
R. Stallman, St John's Smith Square Orch, J.
Lubbock *Concerto, RV441.*
(7/91) (ASV) ① **CDDCA733**
S. Gazzelloni, I. Musici *Concert*
(7/91) (PHIL) ① [19] **426 925-2PM19**
G. Antonini, Giardino Armonico Ens
(4/92) (TELD) ① **9031-73267-2**
J. Stinton, Concertgebouw CO, H. Christophers
Concert   (9/92) (COLL) ① **Coll1324-2**
P. Gallois, Orpheus CO
(5/94) (DG) ① **437 839-2GH**

S. Preston, AAM, C. Hogwood (r1976)
(8/95) (L'OI) ① **444 163-2OM**
1. Montreal I Musici, Y. Turovsky *Concert*
(7/86) (CHAN) ① **CHAN8444**
1, 2. Giardino Armonico Ens (r1990) *Concert*
(7/94) (TELD) ① **4509-91852-2**
1, 2, 5. D. Laurin, Drottningholm Baroque Ens (r1991)
(7/94) (BIS) ① **BIS-CD635**
1, 3. J-P. Rampal, Solisti Veneti, C. Scimone *Concert*
(8/92) (SONY) ① [2] **SK48184**
1, 5, 6. M. Schneider, Cologne Camerata *Concert*
(2/91) (DHM) ① **RD77156**
2. Hanover Band, A. Halstead (r1992) *Concert*
(9/93) (EMIN) ① **CD-EMX2210**
2, 3. K. Smith, London Musici, M. Stephenson
Concert   (5/92) (CONI) ① **CDCF203**
2-4. K. Kaiser, Cologne Camerata *Concert*
(2/91) (DHM) ① **RD77156**
3. J. See, Philh Baroque Orch, N. McGegan *Concert*
(8/88) (HARM) ① **HMC90 5193**
3. G.G. Viscardi, ECCO, E. Aadland *Concert*
(3/92) (CARL) ① **PCD979**
4. Toulon Musica Antiqua, C. Mendoze (rec/dir)
Concert   (10/94) (PIER) ① **PV794033**
6 Concerti for Violin and Strings, Op. 6 (pub c1729-30)
1. G minor (RV324); 2. E flat (RV259); 3. G minor
(RV318); 4. D (RV216); 5. E minor (RV280); 6. D
minor (RV239).
P. Carmirelli, I. Musici *Concert*
(7/91) (PHIL) ① [19] **426 925-2PM19**
6 Concerti for Violin and Strings, Op. 11 (pub c1729-30)
1. D (RV207); 2. Il favorito, E minor (RV277); 3. A
(RV336); 4. D (RV308); 5. C minor (RV202); 6. G
minor (oboe, RV460).
S. Accardo, I. Musici *Concert*
(7/91) (PHIL) ① [19] **426 925-2PM19**
S. Ritchie, F. de Bruine, AAM, C. Hogwood (hpd/dir)
(r1991)   (4/94) (L'OI) ① **436 172-2OH**
2. M. Huggett (vn/dir), London Vivaldi Orch *Concert*
(12/86) (ASV) ① **CDGAU105**
2. J. Van Zweden, Amsterdam Combattimento, J.W.
de Vriend (r1992) *Concert*
(8/93) (SONY) ① **SK53265**
2. M. Sirbu, I Musici (r1993) *Concert*
(7/95) (PHIL) ① **442 145-2PH**
4. Hanover Band, A. Halstead (r1992) *Concert*
(9/93) (EMIN) ① **CD-EMX2210**
5. F. Biondi (vn/dir), Europa Galante *Concert*
(9/91) (O111) ① **OPS30-9004**
6. B. Glaetzner, C. Schornsheim, Leipzig New Bach
Collegium Musicum, M. Pommer *Concert*
(2/90) (CAPR) ① **10 230**
6 Concerti for Violin and Strings, Op. 12 (pub c1729-30)
1. G minor (RV317); 2. D minor (RV244); 3. D
(RV124); 4. C (RV173); 5. B flat (RV379); 6. B flat
(RV361).
S. Accardo, I. Musici *Concert*
(7/91) (PHIL) ① [19] **426 925-2PM19**
12 Concerti for Violin and Strings, '(La) cetra', Op. 9 (pub 1727)
1. C (RV181a); 2. A (RV345); 3. G minor (RV334); 4.
E (RV263a); 5. E minor (RV358); 6. A (RV348); 7. B
flat (RV359); 8. D minor (RV238); 9. B flat (2 violins,
RV530); 10. G (RV300); 11. C minor (RV198a); 12. B
minor (RV391).
S. Standage, AAM, C. Hogwood *Concert*
(4/89) (L'OI) ① [2] **421 366-2OH2**
F. Ayo, I. Musici *Concert*
(7/91) (PHIL) ① [19] **426 925-2PM19**
Solisti Italiani   (9/92) (DENO) ① [2] **CO-79475/6**
12 Concerti for Violin and Strings, '(Il) cimento dell'armonia e dell'inventione', Op. 8 (pub 1725)
1-4—Four Seasons: 1. Spring, E (RV269); 2.
Summer, G minor (RV315); 3. Autumn, F (RV293); 4.
Winter, F minor (RV297); 5. La tempesta di mare, E
flat (RV253); 6. Il piacere, C (RV108); 7. D minor
(RV242); 8. G minor (RV332); 9. D minor (RV236);
arr oboe (RV454); 10. La caccia, B flat (RV362); 11.
D (RV210); 12. C (RV178); arr oboe (RV449).
S. Standage, English Concert, T. Pinnock (hpd/dir)
Concert   (8/88) (CRD) ① [2] **CRD3348/9**
F. Ayo, I. Musici *Concert*
(7/91) (PHIL) ① [19] **426 925-2PM19**
F. Ayo, I Musici (r1959/1961)
(9/93) (PHIL) ① [2] **438 344-2PM2**
P. Toso, Solisti Veneti, C. Scimone (r1971)
(10/93) (ERAT) ① [2] **4509-92189-2**
1-4. S. Standage, English Concert, T. Pinnock
Concert   (3/83) (ARCH) ① **400 045-2AH**
1-4. P. Carmirelli, I Musici
(4/83) (PHIL) ① **410 001-2PH**

Concerto for Bassoon and Strings in C, RV470
Daniel Smith, ECO, P. Ledger *Concert*
(1/88) (ASV) ① **CDDCA571**
Concerto for Bassoon and Strings in C, RV472
Daniel Smith, ECO, P. Ledger *Concert*
(11/89) (ASV) ① **CDDCA662**
Concerto for Bassoon and Strings in C, RV473
Daniel Smith, Zagreb Sols, T. Ninič *Concert*
(4/92) (ASV) ① **CDDCA752**
Concerto for Bassoon and Strings in C, RV474
Daniel Smith, ECO, P. Ledger *Concert*
(1/88) (ASV) ① **CDDCA571**
D. Bond, AAM, C. Hogwood (hpd/dir) (r1992) *Concert*
(4/95) (L'OI) ① **436 867-2OH**
Concerto for Bassoon and Strings in C, RV476
Daniel Smith, ECO, P. Ledger *Concert*
(1/88) (ASV) ① **CDDCA571**
Concerto for Bassoon and Strings in C, RV477
Daniel Smith, ECO, P. Ledger *Concert*
(11/89) (ASV) ① **CDDCA662**
Concerto for Bassoon and Strings in C, RV478
Daniel Smith, Zagreb Sols, T. Ninič *Concert*
(4/92) (ASV) ① **CDDCA752**
Concerto for Bassoon and Strings in C, RV479
Daniel Smith, ECO, P. Ledger *Concert*
(11/89) (ASV) ① **CDDCA662**
Concerto for Bassoon and Strings in C minor, RV480
Daniel Smith, Zagreb Sols, T. Ninič *Concert*
(4/92) (ASV) ① **CDDCA751**
Concerto for Bassoon and Strings in D minor, RV481
Daniel Smith, ECO, P. Ledger *Concert*
(11/89) (ASV) ① **CDDCA662**
Concerto for Bassoon and Strings in E flat, RV483
Daniel Smith, Zagreb Sols, T. Ninič *Concert*
(4/92) (ASV) ① **CDDCA752**
Concerto for Bassoon and Strings in E flat, RV502
M. Alexander, London CO, C. Warren-Green (vn/dir)
Concert (12/90) (VIRG) ① **VC7 59609-2**
Daniel Smith, Zagreb Sols, T. Ninič *Concert*
(4/92) (ASV) ① **CDDCA752**
Concerto for Bassoon and Strings in E minor, RV484
M. Turkovic, English Concert, T. Pinnock *Concert*
(6/87) (ARCH) ① **419 615-2AH**
Daniel Smith, Zagreb Sols, T. Ninič *Concert*
(4/92) (ASV) ① **CDDCA751**
Concerto for Bassoon and Strings in F, RV485
C. Pehrsson, Drottningholm Baroque Ens *Concert*
(2/86) (BIS) ① **BIS-CD271**
Daniel Smith, Zagreb Sols, T. Ninič *Concert*
(4/92) (ASV) ① **CDDCA752**
A. Grazzi, English Concert, T. Pinnock (r1993)
Concert (10/95) (ARCH) ① **445 839-2AH**
Concerto for Bassoon and Strings in F, RV486
Daniel Smith, ECO, P. Ledger *Concert*
(1/88) (ASV) ① **CDDCA565**
Concerto for Bassoon and Strings in F, RV487
Daniel Smith, ECO, P. Ledger *Concert*
(1/88) (ASV) ① **CDDCA571**
M. Wilkie, COE, A. Schneider (pp1988) *Concert*
(11/92) (EMI) ① **CDCOE810**
Concerto for Bassoon and Strings in F, RV488
Daniel Smith, ECO, P. Ledger *Concert*
(11/89) (ASV) ① **CDDCA662**
Concerto for Bassoon and Strings in F, RV489
Daniel Smith, Zagreb Sols, T. Ninič *Concert*
(4/92) (ASV) ① **CDDCA751**
D. Bond, AAM, C. Hogwood (hpd/dir) (r1992) *Concert*
(4/95) (L'OI) ① **436 867-2OH**
Concerto for Bassoon and Strings in F, RV491
Daniel Smith, ECO, P. Ledger *Concert*
(1/88) (ASV) ① **CDDCA565**
Concerto for Bassoon and Strings in G, RV493
Daniel Smith, Zagreb Sols, T. Ninič *Concert*
(4/92) (ASV) ① **CDDCA751**

Concerto for Bassoon and Strings in G, RV494
Daniel Smith, ECO, P. Ledger *Concert*
(1/88) (ASV) ① **CDDCA571**
Concerto for Cello and Strings in A minor, RV418
A. Bylsma, Tafelmusik, J. Lamon *Concert*
(9/92) (SONY) ① **SK48044**
Concerto for Cello and Strings in A minor, RV420
O. Harnoy, Toronto CO, Paul Robinson (r1992)
Concert (1/94) (RCA) ① **09026 61578-2**
Concerto for Cello and Strings in A minor, RV422
O. Harnoy, Toronto CO, Paul Robinson *Concert*
(4/90) (RCA) ① **RD60155**
Concerto for Cello and Strings in B flat, RV423
O. Harnoy, Toronto CO, Paul Robinson *Concert*
(8/88) (RCA) ① **RD87774**
Concerto for Cello and Strings in B minor, RV424
A. Pleeth, English Concert, T. Pinnock (hpd/dir)
Concert (8/88) (CRD) ① [2] **CRD3348/9**
P. Tortelier, LMP, P. Ledger (hpd/dir) (r1979) *Concert*
(3/90) (EMI) ① **CDM7 69835-2**
O. Harnoy, Toronto CO, Paul Robinson *Concert*
(4/90) (RCA) ① **RD60155**
N. Brown, Scottish Ens, J. Rees (r1992) *Concert*
(2/94) (VIRG) ① **VJ5 61103-2**
Concerto for Cello and Strings in C, RV398
M. Rostropovich, Zurich Collegium Musicum, P.
Sacher *Concert* (4/90) (DG) ① **429 098-2GGA**
M. Rostropovich, Zurich Collegium Musicum, P.
Sacher *Concert* (10/94) (DG) ① [2] **437 952-2GX2**
Concerto for Cello and Strings in C, RV399
O. Harnoy, Toronto CO, Paul Robinson *Concert*
(8/88) (RCA) ① **RD87774**
Concerto for Cello and Strings in C, RV400
P. Tortelier, LMP, P. Ledger (hpd/dir) (r1979) *Concert*
(3/90) (EMI) ① **CDM7 69835-2**
Concerto for Cello and Strings in C minor, RV401
B. Schneider, Berne Camerata, T. Füri *Concert*
(2/88) (NOVA) ① **150 016-2**
O. Harnoy, Toronto CO, Paul Robinson *Concert*
(8/88) (RCA) ① **RD87774**
P. Tortelier, LMP, P. Ledger (hpd/dir) (r1979) *Concert*
(3/90) (EMI) ① **CDM7 69835-2**
A. Shulman, London CO, C. Warren-Green (vn/dir)
Concert (12/90) (VIRG) ① **VC7 59609-2**
ASMF, N. Marriner, K. Heath *Concert*
(12/90) (DECC) ① **425 721-2DM**
Concerto for Cello and Strings in C minor, RV402
O. Harnoy, Toronto CO, Paul Robinson *Concert*
(4/90) (RCA) ① **RD60155**
C. Coin, AAM, C. Hogwood *Concert*
(1/92) (L'OI) ① **433 052-2OH**
Concerto for Cello and Strings in D, RV403
O. Harnoy, Toronto CO, Paul Robinson *Concert*
(4/90) (RCA) ① **RD60155**
Concerto for Cello and Strings in D, RV404
O. Harnoy, Toronto CO, Paul Robinson (r1992)
Concert (1/94) (RCA) ① **09026 61578-2**
Concerto for Cello and Strings in D minor, RV405
O. Harnoy, Toronto CO, Paul Robinson *Concert*
(8/88) (RCA) ① **RD87774**
Concerto for Cello and Strings in D minor, RV406
O. Harnoy, Toronto CO, Paul Robinson *Concert*
(4/90) (RCA) ① **RD60155**
C. Coin, AAM, C. Hogwood *Concert*
(1/92) (L'OI) ① **433 052-2OH**
M. Rostropovich, St Paul CO, H. Wolff (r1992)
Concert (1/94) (TELD) ① **9031-77311-2**
Concerto for Cello and Strings in D minor, RV407
O. Harnoy, Toronto CO, Paul Robinson (r1992)
Concert (1/94) (RCA) ① **09026 61578-2**
Concerto for Cello and Strings in E minor, RV409
O. Harnoy, J. McKay, Toronto CO, Paul Robinson
Concert (8/88) (RCA) ① **RD87774**
Concerto for Cello and Strings in F, RV411
O. Harnoy, Toronto CO, Paul Robinson (r1992)
Concert (1/94) (RCA) ① **09026 61578-2**
Concerto for Cello and Strings in F, RV412
O. Harnoy, Toronto CO, Paul Robinson *Concert*
(4/90) (RCA) ① **RD60155**
Concerto for Cello and Strings in G, RV413
M. Rostropovich, Zurich Collegium Musicum, P.
Sacher *Concert* (4/90) (DG) ① **429 098-2GGA**
G. Sollima, ECCO, E. Aadland *Concert*
(3/92) (CARL) ① **PCD979**

A. Bylsma, Tafelmusik, J. Lamon *Concert*
(9/92) (SONY) ① **SK48044**
L. Harrell, ECO, P. Zukerman *Concert*
(11/92) (EMI) ① **CDM7 64326-2**
M. Rostropovich, Zurich Collegium Musicum, P.
Sacher *Concert* (10/94) (DG) ① [2] **437 952-2GX2**
Concerto for Cello and Strings in G, RV414
O. Harnoy, Toronto CO, Paul Robinson *Concert*
(4/90) (RCA) ① **RD60155**
C. Coin, AAM, C. Hogwood *Concert*
(1/92) (L'OI) ① **433 052-2OH**
Concerto for Cello and Strings in G minor, RV417
L. Harrell, ECO, P. Zukerman *Concert*
(11/92) (EMI) ① **CDM7 64326-2**
O. Harnoy, Toronto CO, Paul Robinson (r1992)
Concert (1/94) (RCA) ① **09026 61578-2**
Concerto for Flute and Strings in A minor, RV440
J. See, Philh Baroque Orch, N. McGegan *Concert*
(8/88) (HARM) ① **HMC90 5193**
J. Stinton, Concertgebouw CO, H. Christophers
Concert (9/92) (COLL) ① **Coll1324-2**
Concerto for Flute and Strings in D, RV427
J. See, Philh Baroque Orch, N. McGegan *Concert*
(8/88) (HARM) ① **HMC90 5193**
Concerto for Flute and Strings in D, RV429
S. Preston, English Concert, T. Pinnock (hpd/dir)
Concert (8/88) (CRD) ① [2] **CRD3348/9**
J. See, Philh Baroque Orch, N. McGegan *Concert*
(8/88) (HARM) ① **HMC90 5193**
Concerto for Flute and Strings in G, RV436
L. Beznosiuk, English Concert, T. Pinnock *Concert*
(6/87) (ARCH) ① **419 615-2AH**
J. See, S. Schultz, N. McGegan *Concert*
(8/88) (HARM) ① **HMC90 5193**
Concerto for Flute and Strings in G, RV438
J. See, Philh Baroque Orch, N. McGegan *Concert*
(8/88) (HARM) ① **HMC90 5193**
Concerto for Flute/Recorder and Strings in C minor, RV441
R. Harvey, London Vivaldi Orch, M. Huggett *Concert*
(5/88) (ASV) ① **CDGAU111**
P. Holtslag, Parley of Instr, P. Holman *Concert*
(8/89) (HYPE) ① **CDA66328**
W. Bennett, ECO, G. Malcolm *Concert*
(9/89) (ASV) ① **CDDCA645**
M. Petri, Solisti Veneti, C. Scimone *Concert*
(7/90) (RCA) ① **RD87885**
R. Stallman, St John's Smith Square Orch, J.
Lubbock *Concerti, Op. 10.*
(7/91) (ASV) ① **CDDCA733**
J. Stinton, Concertgebouw CO, H. Christophers
Concert (9/92) (COLL) ① **Coll1324-2**
D. Laurin, Drottningholm Baroque Ens (r1991)
Concert (7/94) (BIS) ① **BIS-CD635**
W. Bennett, ASMF, N. Marriner (r1975) *Concert*
(12/94) (DECC) ① [2] **443 476-2DF2**
F. Brüggen, VCM, N. Harnoncourt (r1969) *Concert*
(10/95) (TELD) ① **4509-97470-2**
Concerto for Mandolin and Strings in C, RV425
Celedonio Romero, ASMF, I. Brown (trans gtr)
Concert (1/86) (PHIL) ① **412 624-2PH**
Parley of Instr, R. Goodman, P. Holman *Concert*
(10/86) (HYPE) ① **CDA66160**
Celedonio Romero, San Antonio SO, V. Alessandro
Concert (3/90) (PHIL) ① **426 076-2PCC**
S. Mayor (arr Mayor: mandolin ens) *Concert*
(3/92) (ACOU) ① **CDACS012**
N. Woodhouse, London Musici, M. Stephenson
Concert (5/92) (CONI) ① **CDCF203**
U. Orlandi, Solisti Veneti, C. Scimone *Concert*
(12/93) (ERAT) ① **4509-92132-2**
C. Parkening, ASMF, I. Brown (1993: arr gtr/orch)
Concert (10/94) (EMI) ① **CDC5 55052-2**
Concerto for Multiple Instruments in A, 'per eco lo lontano'—vns & strings, RV552
C. Coin, Giardino Armonico Ens, G. Antonini (r1994)
Concert (8/95) (TELD) ① **4509-94552-2**
Concerto for Multiple Instruments in C—vn, ob, org ad lib & strings, RV554
R. Studt (vn/dir), S. Francis, J. Bate, Tate Music
Group *Concert* (6/87) (UNIC) ① **DKPCD9050**
Collegium Musicum 90, S. Standage *Concert*
(3/93) (CHAN) ① **CHAN0528**
Concerto for Multiple Instruments in C—2 vns, recs, mands, salmoes, theorbos, vc & str, RV558
S. Standage, M. Comberti, P. Pickett, R. Beckett, C.
Lawson, C. Reoira, J. Tyler, R. Jeffrey, N. North, J.
Lindberg, A. Pleeth, A. Pleeth, T. Pinnock *Concert*
(9/86) (ARCH) ① **415 674-2AH**

Sonata for Cello and Continuo in A minor, RV44 (pub c1740)
Ecole d'Orphée *Concert*
    (12/87) (CRD) ① **CRD3441**
A. Bylsma, J. Ogg, H. Suzuki *Concert*
    (6/90) (DHM) ① **RD77909**
A. Pleeth, R. Woolley, S. Towb *Concert*
    (11/91) (ASV) ① [2] **CDGAD201**
C. Coin, E. Ferré, C. Hogwood *Concert*
    (1/92) (L'OI) ① **433 052-2OH**
J. Berger, S-J. Bleicher *Concert*
    (8/92) (ORFE) ① [2] **C251912H**
P. Wispelwey, Florilegium Ens (r1994) *Concert*
    (11/94) (CHNN) ① **CCS6294**
D. Watkin, H. Gough, D. Miller, R. King (r1993)
Concert   (8/95) (HYPE) ① [2] **CDA66881/2**
**Sonata for Cello and Continuo in B flat, RV45
(pub c1740)** (VI Sonatas No. 4)
Ecole d'Orphée *Concert*
    (12/87) (CRD) ① **CRD3440**
A. Pleeth, R. Woolley, S. Towb *Concert*
    (11/91) (ASV) ① [2] **CDGAD201**
J. Berger, S-J. Bleicher *Concert*
    (8/92) (ORFE) ① [2] **C251912H**
P. Tortelier, R. Veyron-Lacroix *Concert*
    (8/94) (ERAT) ① [2] **4509-95359-2**
P. Wispelwey, Florilegium Ens (r1994) *Concert*
    (11/94) (CHNN) ① **CCS6294**
D. Watkin, H. Gough, D. Miller, R. King (r1993)
Concert   (8/95) (HYPE) ① [2] **CDA66881/2**
**Sonata for Cello and Continuo in B flat, RV46
(pub c1740)** (VI Sonates No. 6)
Ecole d'Orphée *Concert*
    (12/87) (CRD) ① **CRD3441**
A. Pleeth, R. Woolley, S. Towb *Concert*
    (11/91) (ASV) ① [2] **CDGAD201**
J. Berger, S-J. Bleicher *Concert*
    (8/92) (ORFE) ① [2] **C251912H**
P. Tortelier, R. Veyron-Lacroix *Concert*
    (8/94) (ERAT) ① [2] **4509-95359-2**
P. Wispelwey, Florilegium Ens (r1994) *Concert*
    (11/94) (CHNN) ① **CCS6294**
D. Watkin, H. Gough, D. Miller, R. King (r1993)
Concert   (8/95) (HYPE) ① [2] **CDA66881/2**
**Sonata for Cello and Continuo in B flat, RV47
(pub c1740)** (VI Sonates No. 1)
Ecole d'Orphée *Concert*
    (12/87) (CRD) ① **CRD3440**
A. Pleeth, R. Woolley, S. Towb *Concert*
    (11/91) (ASV) ① [2] **CDGAD201**
J. Berger, S-J. Bleicher *Concert*
    (8/92) (ORFE) ① [2] **C251912H**
P. Tortelier, R. Veyron-Lacroix *Concert*
    (8/94) (ERAT) ① [2] **4509-95359-2**
D. Watkin, H. Gough, D. Miller, R. King (r1993)
Concert   (8/95) (HYPE) ① [2] **CDA66881/2**
**Sonata for Cello and Continuo in E flat, RV39
(pub c1740)**
Ecole d'Orphée *Concert*
    (12/87) (CRD) ① **CRD3441**
A. Bylsma, J. Ogg, H. Suzuki *Concert*
    (6/90) (DHM) ① **RD77909**
A. Pleeth, R. Woolley, S. Towb *Concert*
    (11/91) (ASV) ① [2] **CDGAD201**
C. Coin, E. Ferré, C. Hogwood *Concert*
    (1/92) (L'OI) ① **433 052-2OH**
J. Berger, S-J. Bleicher *Concert*
    (8/92) (ORFE) ① [2] **C251912H**
P. Wispelwey, Florilegium Ens (r1994) *Concert*
    (11/94) (CHNN) ① **CCS6294**
D. Watkin, H. Gough, D. Miller, R. King (r1993)
Concert   (8/95) (HYPE) ① [2] **CDA66881/2**
**Sonata for Cello and Continuo in E minor,
RV40 (pub c1740)** (VI Sonatas No. 5)
Ecole d'Orphée *Concert*
    (12/87) (CRD) ① **CRD3441**
A. Bylsma, J. Ogg, H. Suzuki *Concert*
    (6/90) (DHM) ① **RD77909**
A. Pleeth, R. Woolley, S. Towb *Concert*
    (11/91) (ASV) ① [2] **CDGAD201**
J. Berger, S-J. Bleicher *Concert*
    (8/92) (ORFE) ① [2] **C251912H**
P. Tortelier, R. Veyron-Lacroix *Concert*
    (8/94) (ERAT) ① [2] **4509-95359-2**
P. Wispelwey, Florilegium Ens (r1994) *Concert*
    (11/94) (CHNN) ① **CCS6294**
D. Watkin, H. Gough, D. Miller, R. King (r1993)
Concert   (8/95) (HYPE) ① [2] **CDA66881/2**
**Sonata for Cello and Continuo in F, RV41
(pub c1740)** (VI Sonatas No. 2)
Ecole d'Orphée *Concert*
    (12/87) (CRD) ① **CRD3440**
A. Bylsma, J. Ogg, D. Miller, R. King (r1993)
    (6/90) (DHM) ① **RD77909**
A. Pleeth, R. Woolley, S. Towb *Concert*
    (11/91) (ASV) ① [2] **CDGAD201**

J. Berger, S-J. Bleicher *Concert*
    (8/92) (ORFE) ① [2] **C251912H**
P. Tortelier, R. Veyron-Lacroix *Concert*
    (8/94) (ERAT) ① [2] **4509-95359-2**
D. Watkin, H. Gough, D. Miller, R. King (r1993)
Concert   (8/95) (HYPE) ① [2] **CDA66881/2**
**Sonata for Cello and Continuo in G minor,
RV42**
Ecole d'Orphée *Concert*
    (12/87) (CRD) ① **CRD3441**
A. Bylsma, J. Ogg, H. Suzuki *Concert*
    (6/90) (DHM) ① **RD77909**
A. Pleeth, R. Woolley, S. Towb *Concert*
    (11/91) (ASV) ① [2] **CDGAD201**
C. Coin, E. Ferré, C. Hogwood *Concert*
    (1/92) (L'OI) ① **433 052-2OH**
J. Berger, S-J. Bleicher *Concert*
    (8/92) (ORFE) ① [2] **C251912H**
P. Wispelwey, Florilegium Ens (r1994) *Concert*
    (11/94) (CHNN) ① **CCS6294**
D. Watkin, H. Gough, D. Miller, R. King (r1993)
Concert   (8/95) (HYPE) ① [2] **CDA66881/2**
**Sonata for Flute and Continuo in D minor,
RV49**
E. Haupt, C. Schornsheim (arr rec) *Concert*
    (2/90) (CAPR) ① **10 234**
**Sonata for Multiple Instruments in C—vn, ob,
chalumeau & org, RV779**
Cologne Camerata *Concert*
    (2/91) (DHM) ① **RD77156**
P. Goodwin, C. Lawson, J. Holloway, J. Toll (r1992)
Concert   (11/93) (HARM) ① **HMU90 7104**
**Sonata for Oboe and Continuo in C minor,
RV53**
P. Goodwin, S. Sheppard, N. North, J. Toll (r1992)
Concert   (11/93) (HARM) ① **HMU90 7104**
**Sonata for Violin and Continuo, RV35 (Op.
5/16)**
S. Accardo, B. Canino, R. de Saram *Concert*
    (7/91) (PHIL) ① [19] **426 925-2PM19**
**Sonata for Violin and Continuo in A, RV30
(Op. 5/14)**
S. Accardo, B. Canino, R. de Saram *Concert*
    (7/91) (PHIL) ① [19] **426 925-2PM19**
Sonata for Violin and Continuo in A, RV29
Boston Museum Trio *Concert*
    (4/88) (HARM) ① **HMA190 1088**
Purcell Qt *Concert*   (9/90) (CHAN) ① **CHAN0502**
Sonata for Violin and Continuo in C, RV2
Boston Museum Trio *Concert*
    (4/88) (HARM) ① **HMA190 1088**
Purcell Qt *Concert*   (6/91) (CHAN) ① **CHAN0511**
Sonata for Violin and Continuo in D, RV10
N. Milstein, L. Mittman (arr Respighi: r1936) *Concert*
    (10/92) (BIDD) ① **LAB055**
**Sonata for Violin and Continuo in F, RV18
(Op. 5/13)**
S. Accardo, B. Canino, R. de Saram *Concert*
    (7/91) (PHIL) ① [19] **426 925-2PM19**
Sonata for Violin and Continuo in G, RV25
Boston Museum Trio *Concert*
    (4/88) (HARM) ① **HMA190 1088**
**6 Sonatas for Flute and Continuo, '(II) pastor
fido', 'Op. 13' (pub c1737)** (spurious: actually
comp Chédeville)
1. C, RV54; 2. C, RV56; 3. G, RV57; 4. A, RV59; 5.
   C, RV55; 6. G minor, RV58.
4. P. Goodwin, S. Sheppard, N. North, J. Toll (r1992)
   Concert   (11/93) (HARM) ① **HMU90 7104**
5. Barthold Kuijken, W. Kuijken, R. Kohnen *Concert*
    (5/92) (ACCE) ① **ACC9177D**
6. M. Petri, G. Malcolm *Concert*
    (10/86) (PHIL) ① **412 632-2PH**
6. B. Kol, A. Brodo, D. Shemer *Concert*
    (9/90) (CARL) ① **PWK1138**
6. P. Goodwin, S. Sheppard, N. North, J. Toll (r1992)
   Concert   (11/93) (HARM) ① **HMU90 7104**
6. F. Brüggen, A. Bylsma, G. Leonhardt (r1967)
   Concert   (TELD) ① **4509-93669-2**
**12 Sonatas for Violin and Continuo, Op. 2
(pub 1712-13)**
1. G minor, RV27; 2. A, RV31; 3. D minor, RV14; 4.
   F, RV20; 5. B minor, RV36; 6. C, RV1; 7. C minor,
   RV8; 8. G, RV23; 9. E minor, RV10. F minor,
   RV21; 11. D, RV9; 12. A minor, RV32.
S. Accardo, B. Canino, R. de Saram *Concert*
    (7/91) (PHIL) ① [19] **426 925-2PM19**
2. N. Milstein, L. Mittman (arr David: r1936) *Concert*
    (10/92) (BIDD) ① **LAB055**
2. N. Milstein, L. Pommers (r1959) *Concert*
    (5/94) (EMI) ① [6] **ZDMF7 64830-2**
2. J. Heifetz, A. Sándor (r1934) *Concert*
    (9/90) (EMI) ① [65] **09026 61778-2(02)**
4. M. André, BPO, H. von Karajan (arr. tpt & orch.
   Thilde) *Concert*   (2/89) (EMI) ① **CDC7 49237-2**

**12 Sonatas for Violin and Continuo,
'Manchester Sonatas'** (Manchester Central
Library MS)
1. C, RV3; 2. D minor, RV12; 3. G minor, RV757; 4.
   D, RV755; 5. B flat, RV759; 6. A, RV758; 7. C minor,
   RV6; 8. G, RV22; 9. E minor, RV17a; 10. B minor,
   RV760; 11. E flat, RV756; 12. C, RV754.
F. Biondi, M. Naddeo, P. Pandolfo, R. Lislevand, R.
   Alessandrini   (11/92) (ARCA) ① [2] **AR04/05**
Romanesca (r1992)
    (1/94) (HARM) ① [2] **HMU90 7089/90**
6, 12. Purcell Qt *Concert*
    (7/87) (HYPE) ① **CDA66193**
7. Boston Museum Trio *Concert*
    (4/88) (HARM) ① **HMA190 1088**
7. Purcell Qt *Concert*   (6/91) (CHAN) ① **CHAN0511**
**Trio Sonata for Flute, Violin and Continuo in
D, RV84**
M. Verbruggen, J. Holloway, J. Toll, S. Comberti
   Concert   (4/92) (HARM) ① **HMU90 7046**
Palladian Ens (r1993) *Concert*
    (1/95) (LINN) ① **CKD015**
**Trio Sonata for Recorder, Bassoon and
Continuo in A minor, RV86**
Chandos Baroque Plyrs *Concert*
    (4/90) (HYPE) ① **CDA66309**
M. Verbruggen, D. Godburn, J. Toll *Concert*
    (4/92) (HARM) ① **HMU90 7046**
**Trio Sonata for Violin, Lute and Continuo in
C, RV82**
T. Füri (vn/dir), G. Söllscher, Berne Camerata (lte
   part trans gtr) *Concert* (2/86) (DG) ① **415 487-2GH**
J. Lindberg, N-E. Sparf, Drottningholm Baroque Ens
   Concert   (4/86) (BIS) ① **BIS-CD290**
Parley of Instr, R. Goodman, P. Holman *Concert*
    (10/86) (HYPE) ① **CDA66160**
Celedonio Romero, J. Corigliano, D. Saltarelli, M.
   Bella (lte part trans gtr) *Concert*
    (3/90) (PHIL) ① **426 076-2PCC**
J. Rolla (vn/dir), J. Williams, B. Verdery, F. Liszt CO
   Concert   (11/91) (SONY) ① **SK46556**
C. Parkening, I. Brown, L. Handy, J. Constable
   (r1993) *Concert*   (10/94) (EMI) ① **CDC5 55052-2**
**Trio Sonata for Violin, Lute and Continuo in
C, RV82**
J. Bream, G. Malcolm (1974; ed Malcolm) *Concert*
    (8/93) (RCA) ① [28] **09026 61583-2(2)**
**Trio Sonata for Violin, Lute and Continuo in
G minor, RV85**
T. Füri (vn/dir), G. Söllscher, Berne Camerata (trans
   gtr) *Concert*   (2/86) (DG) ① **415 487-2GH**
J. Lindberg, N-E. Sparf, Drottningholm Baroque Ens
   Concert   (4/86) (BIS) ① **BIS-CD290**
Parley of Instr, R. Goodman, P. Holman *Concert*
    (10/86) (HYPE) ① **CDA66160**
J. Bream, G. Malcolm (1974; ed Malcolm) *Concert*
    (8/93) (RCA) ① [28] **09026 61583-2(2)**
J. Bream, G. Malcolm (1974; ed Bream) *Concert*
    (8/93) (RCA) ① **09026 61588-2**
**Trio Sonata for 2 Oboes and Continuo in G
minor, RV81**
P. Goodwin, G. Hennessey, F. Eustace, N. North, J.
   Toll (r1992) *Concert*
    (11/93) (HARM) ① **HMU90 7104**
**Trio Sonata for 2 Violins and Continuo in B
flat, RV76 (Op. 5/17)**
Purcell Qt *Concert*   (9/90) (CHAN) ① **CHAN0502**
S. Accardo, S. Gazeau, B. Canino, R. de Saram
   Concert   (7/91) (PHIL) ① [19] **426 925-2PM19**
**Trio Sonata for 2 Violins and Continuo in B
flat, RV77**
Purcell Qt *Concert*   (6/91) (CHAN) ① **CHAN0511**
Ens 415 (without continuo) *Concert*
    (4/92) (HARM) ① **HMC90 1366**
**Trio Sonata for 2 Violins and Continuo in C,
RV60 (doubtful)**
Purcell Qt *Concert*   (7/87) (HYPE) ① **CDA66193**
**Trio Sonata for 2 Violins and Continuo in F,
RV68**
Purcell Qt *Concert*   (6/91) (CHAN) ① **CHAN0511**
Ens 415 (without continuo) *Concert*
    (4/92) (HARM) ① **HMC90 1366**
**Trio Sonata for 2 Violins and Continuo in F,
RV70**
Purcell Qt *Concert*   (9/90) (CHAN) ① **CHAN0502**
Ens 415 (without continuo) *Concert*
    (4/92) (HARM) ① **HMC90 1366**
**Trio Sonata for 2 Violins and Continuo in G,
RV71**
Purcell Qt *Concert*   (9/90) (CHAN) ① **CHAN0502**
Ens 415 (without continuo) *Concert*
    (4/92) (HARM) ① **HMC90 1366**
**Trio Sonata for 2 Violins and Continuo in G
minor, RV72 (Op. 5/18)**
Purcell Qt *Concert*   (9/90) (CHAN) ① **CHAN0502**

S. Accardo, S. Gazeau, B. Canino, R. de Saram
Concert (7/91) (PHIL) ① [19] **426 925-2PM19**
Trio Sonata for 2 Violins and Continuo in G minor, RV74
Purcell Qt *Concert* (7/87) (HYPE) ① **CDA66193**
12 Trio Sonatas for 2 Violins and Continuo, Op. 1 (pub 1705)
1. G minor, RV73; 2. E minor, RV67; 3. C, RV61; 4. E, RV66; 5. F, RV69; 6. D, RV62; 7. E flat, RV65; 8. D minor, RV64; 9. A flat, RV75; 10. B flat, RV78; 11. B minor, RV79; 12. D minor, variations on 'La Follia', RV63.
S. Accardo, F. Gulli, B. Canino, R. de Saram *Concert*
(7/91) (PHIL) ① [19] **426 925-2PM19**
7, 10. Purcell Qt *Concert*
(9/90) (CHAN) ① **CHAN0502**
8, 12. Ens 415 *Concert*
(4/92) (HARM) ① **HMC90 1366**
8, 9, 11. Purcell Qt *Concert*
(6/91) (CHAN) ① **CHAN0511**
12. Purcell Qt *Concert* (7/87) (HYPE) ① **CDA66193**
12. Giardino Armonico Ens (r1991) *Concert*
(7/94) (TELD) ① **4509-91852-2**

SECTION IV: VOCAL AND CHORAL

Alla caccia, alla caccia—cantata: voice and continuo, RV670
D.L. Ragin, V. de Hoog, C. Farr *Concert*
(10/89) (ETCE) ① **KTC1069**
Amor hai vinto—cantata: 1v, strings and continuo, RV683
R. Jacobs, Complesso Barocco, A. Curtis (hpd/dir)
(r1977) *Concert* (1/93) (ARCH) ① **437 082-2AT**
Beatus vir in B flat, RV598 (Wds. Psalm 112)
M. Marshall, F. Lott, S. Daniel, John Alldis Ch, ECO, V. Negri *Concert* (2/89) (PHIL) ① **420 649-2PM**
Beatus vir in C—two choirs, RV597 (Wds. Psalm 112)
Ex Cathedra Chbr Ch, Ex Cathedra Baroque Orch, J. Skidmore *Concert* (12/92) (ASV) ① **CDGAU137**
J. Smith, I. Buchanan, H. Watts, I. Partridge, J. Shirley-Quirk, King's College Ch, ECO, S. Cleobury (r1984) *Concert*
(12/94) (DECC) ① [2] **443 455-2DF2**
Canta in prato in G—motet (Introduzione al Dixit), RV636
M. Marshall, ECO, V. Negri (ed Giegling) *Concert*
(2/89) (PHIL) ① **420 649-2PM**
Care selve amici prati—cantata: voice and continuo, RV671
D.L. Ragin, V. de Hoog, C. Farr *Concert*
(10/89) (ETCE) ① **KTC1069**
Cessate, omai cessate—cantata: 1v, strings and continuo, RV684
R. Jacobs, Complesso Barocco, A. Curtis (hpd/dir)
(r1977) *Concert* (1/93) (ARCH) ① **437 082-2AT**
Clarae stellae—motet, RV625
R. Stene, Taverner Ch, Taverner Consort, Taverner Plyrs, A. Parrott *Concert*
(8/91) (EMI) ① **CDC7 54117-2**
Credo in E minor, RV591
Ernst Senff Chor, BPO, C.M. Giulini (rev/ed Malipiero) *Verdi: Pezzi sacri.*
(10/91) (SONY) ① **SK46491**
King's Consort Choristers, King's Consort Ch, King's Consort, R. King (r1994) *Concert*
(6/95) (HYPE) ① **CDA66769**
Dixit Dominus in D—two choirs, RV594 (Wds. Psalm 110)
M. Marshall, A. Murray, A. Collins, A. Rolfe Johnson, R. Holl, John Alldis Ch, ECO, V. Negri *Concert*
(2/89) (PHIL) ① **420 649-2PM**
J. Smith, I. Buchanan, H. Watts, I. Partridge, J. Shirley-Quirk, King's College Ch, ECO, S. Cleobury (r1984) *Concert*
(12/94) (DECC) ① [2] **443 455-2DF2**
S. Gritton, L. Milne, C. Denley, L. Atkinson, D. Wilson-Johnson, King's Consort Choristers, King's Consort Ch, King's Consort, R. King (r1994) *Concert* (6/95) (HYPE) ① **CDA66769**
Domine ad adiuvandum me in G—psalm setting, RV593 (Wds. Psalm 60)
Ex Cathedra Chbr Ch, Ex Cathedra Baroque Orch, J. Skidmore *Concert* (12/92) (ASV) ① **CDGAU137**
Filiae mestae in C minor—motet (Miserere), RV638
G. Lesne, Seminario Musicale Ens *Concert*
(3/91) (HRMO) ① **H/CD8720**
Gloria in D, RV588
Lynda Russell, P. Kwella, A. Wilkens, K. Bowen, St John's College Ch, Wren Orch, G. Guest (r1981)
Concert (12/94) (DECC) ① [2] **443 455-2DF2**

Gloria in D, RV589
1. Et in terra pax.
R. Bollen, Berne Chbr Ch, South-West German CO, J.E. Dähler *Galuppi: Magnificat in G.*
(10/86) (CLAV) ① **CD50-0801**
T. Berganza, L.V. Terrani, Philh Chor, Philh, R. Muti (ed.Malipiero) *Magnificat, RV611.*
(5/88) (EMI) ① **CDC7 47990-2**
M. Marshall, A. Murray, B. Finnilä, John Alldis Ch, ECO, V. Negri (ed. Negri) *Concert*
(5/88) (PHIL) ① **420 648-2PM**
N. Argenta, I. Attrot, C. Denley, English Concert Ch, English Concert, T. Pinnock *A. Scarlatti: Dixit Dominus II.* (5/88) (ARCH) ① **423 386-2AH**
E. Vaughan, J. Baker, King's College Ch, ASMF, D. Willcocks *Haydn: Mass 11.*
(2/89) (DECC) ① **421 146-2DM**
D. Upshaw, P. Jensen, M. Simpson, Atlanta Sym Chbr Chor, Atlanta SO, Robert Shaw (r1988) *Bach: Magnificat, BWV243.* (8/89) (TELA) ① **CD80194**
E. Kirkby, T. Bonner, M. Chance, Collegium Musicum 90 Chor, Collegium Musicum 90, R. Hickox *Concert*
(7/91) (CHAN) ① **CHAN0518**
B. Hendricks, A. Murray, ASMF Chor, ASMF, N. Marriner *Bach: Magnificat, BWV243.*
(3/92) (EMI) ① **CDC7 54283-2**
Lynda Russell, G. Fisher, A. Browner, I. Partridge, M. George, The Sixteen, The Sixteen Orch, H. Christophers *Concert*
(12/92) (COLL) ① **Coll1320-2**
J. Smith, W. Staempfli, N. Rossier, H. Schaer, Lausanne Voc Ens, Lausanne Instr Ens, M. Corboz *Concert* (6/93) (ERAT) ① **2292-45923-2**
N. Argenta, J. Smith, C. Wyn-Rogers, English Concert Ch, English Concert, T. Pinnock (r1992) *Concert* (3/94) (ARCH) ① **437 834-2AH**
S. McNair, E. von Magnus, M. Lipovšek, A. Schoenberg Ch, VCM, N. Harnoncourt (r1991) *Pergolesi: Stabat Mater.*
(7/94) (TELD) ⑨ **9031-76989-2**
Lynda Russell, P. Kwella, A. Wilkens, K. Bowen, St John's College Ch, Wren Orch, G. Guest (r1981) *Concert* (12/94) (DECC) ① [2] **443 455-2DF2**
E. Van Evera, A. Place, M. Cable, Taverner Ch, Taverner Plyrs, A. Parrott (r1992) *Concert*
(1/95) (VIRG) ① **VC7 59326-2**
In exitu Israel in C, RV064
Taverner Ch, Taverner Plyrs, A. Parrott (r1992) *Concert* (1/95) (VIRG) ① **VC7 59326-2**
In furore giustissimae in C minor—motet, RV626
K. Eckersley, Fiori Musicali, P. Rapson *Concert*
(10/90) (MERI) ① **CDE84195**
In turbato mare in D—motet, RV627
E. Kirkby, Tafelmusik, J. Lamon *Concert*
(12/87) (HYPE) ① **CDA66247**
Introduzione al Gloria—motet, RV637
G. Lesne, Seminario Musicale (r1991) *Concert*
(6/93) (VIRG) ① **VC7 59232-2**
Introduzione al Miserere—motet, RV641
G. Lesne, Seminario Musicale (r1991) *Concert*
(6/93) (VIRG) ① **VC7 59232-2**
Kyrie in G minor—2 choirs, RV587
Lausanne Voc Ens, Lausanne Instr Ens, M. Corboz *Concert* (6/93) (ERAT) ① **2292-45923-2**
King's Consort Choristers, King's Consort Ch, King's Consort, R. King (r1994) *Concert*
(6/95) (HYPE) ① **CDA66769**
Laetatus sum—chorus and strings, RV607
Taverner Ch, Taverner Plyrs, A. Parrott (r1992) *Concert* (1/95) (VIRG) ① **VC7 59326-2**
Lauda Jerusalem in E minor—2 choirs, RV609 (Wds. Psalm 147)
M. Marshall, A. Murray, John Alldis Ch, ECO, V. Negri *Concert* (5/88) (PHIL) ① **420 648-2PM**
S. Gritton, L. Milne, King's Consort Choristers, King's Consort Ch, King's Consort, R. King (r1994) *Concert* (6/95) (HYPE) ① **CDA66769**
Laudate Dominum in D minor, RV606 (Wds. Psalm 117)
John Alldis Ch, ECO, V. Negri (ed. Giegling) *Concert*
(5/88) (PHIL) ① **420 648-2PM**
Taverner Ch, Taverner Plyrs, A. Parrott (r1992) *Concert* (1/95) (VIRG) ① **VC7 59326-2**
Laudate pueri Dominum in A major—2 choirs, RV602 (Wds. Psalm 113)
M. Marshall, F. Lott, John Alldis Ch, ECO, V. Negri (ed. Giegling) *Concert*
(5/88) (PHIL) ① **420 648-2PM**
Laudate pueri Dominum in G major, RV601 (Wds. Psalm 113)
L. Dawson, King's Consort, R. King *Nisi Dominus.*
(9/87) (MERI) ① **CDE84129**

Lungi dal vago volto—cantata: 1v, violin and continuo, RV680
E. Kirkby, J. Lamon *Concert*
(12/87) (HYPE) ① **CDA66247**
Magnificat in G minor, RV610
Ex Cathedra Chbr Ch, Ex Cathedra Baroque Orch, J. Skidmore *Concert* (12/92) (ASV) ① **CDGAU137**
P. Castle, M. Cockerham, A. King, King's College Ch, ASMF, P. Ledger (r1976) *Concert*
(12/94) (DECC) ① [2] **443 455-2DF2**
Magnificat in G minor—two choirs, RV610a
E. Kirkby, S. Leblanc, D. Forget, R. Cunningham, H. Ingram, Tafelmusik Chbr Ch, Tafelmusik, J. Lamon *Concert* (12/87) (HYPE) ① **CDA66247**
E. Van Evera, N. Argenta, A. Place, C. King, M. Cable, Taverner Ch, Taverner Plyrs, A. Parrott (r1992) *Concert* (1/95) (VIRG) ① **VC7 59326-2**
S. Gritton, L. Milne, C. Denley, L. Atkinson, King's Consort Choristers, King's Consort Ch, King's Consort, R. King (r1994) *Concert*
(6/95) (HYPE) ① **CDA66769**
Magnificat in G minor, RV611
T. Berganza, L.V. Terrani, Philh Chor, Philh, R. Muti *Gloria, RV589.* (5/88) (EMI) ① **CDC7 47990-2**
M. Marshall, F. Lott, S. Burgess, L. Finnie, A. Collins, John Alldis Ch, ECO, V. Negri (ed Negri) *Concert* (2/89) (PHIL) ① **420 649-2PM**
Nisi Dominus in G minor, RV608 (Wds. Psalm 127)
J. Bowman, AAM, C. Hogwood *Concert*
(8/85) (L'OI) ① **414 329-2OH**
C. Robson, King's Consort, R. King *Laudate pueri Dominum, RV601.* (9/87) (MERI) ① **CDE84129**
G. Lesne, Seminario Musicale Ens *Concert*
(3/91) (HRMO) ① **H/CD8720**
C. Brett, Toulon Musica Antiqua, C. Mendoze (rec/dir) *Concert* (10/94) (PIER) ① **PV794033**
O mie porpore più belle—cantata: 1v and continuo, RV685
R. Jacobs, Complesso Barocco, A. Curtis (hpd/dir)
(r1977) *Concert* (1/93) (ARCH) ① **437 082-2AT**
Ostro picta—motet (introduzione al Gloria, RV589), RV642
M. Marshall, ECO, V. Negri (ed. Giegling) *Concert*
(5/88) (PHIL) ① **420 648-2PM**
E. Kirkby, Collegium Musicum 90, R. Hickox *Concert*
(7/91) (CHAN) ① **CHAN0518**
Perfidissimo cor—cantata (1v and continuo), RV674
D.L. Ragin, V. de Hoog, C. Farr *Concert*
(10/89) (ETCE) ① **KTC1069**
Piango, gemo, sospiro—cantata (1v and continuo), RV675
J. Bowman, S. Sempé, J. Bernfeld *Concert*
(9/89) (ARIO) ① **ARN68046**
T. Berganza, ECO, M. Viotti *Concert*
(3/91) (CLAV) ① **CD50-9016**
Pianti, sospiri—cantata: voice and continuo, RV676
D.L. Ragin, V. de Hoog, C. Farr *Concert*
(10/89) (ETCE) ① **KTC1069**
Qual per ignoto—cantata (1v and continuo), RV677
D.L. Ragin, V. de Hoog, C. Farr *Concert*
(10/89) (ETCE) ① **KTC1069**
Salve Regina in C minor—antiphon (2 choirs), RV616
J. Bowman, King's Consort, R. King (org/dir) *Concert*
(6/87) (MERI) ① **CDE84138**
J. Bowman, J-W. Audoli Inst Ens, J-W. Audoli (ed. Negri) *Concert* (12/89) (ARIO) ① **ARN68026**
G. Lesne, Seminario Musicale (r1991) *Concert*
(6/93) (VIRG) ① **VC7 59232-2**
Salve Regina in G minor—antiphon, RV618
G. Lesne, Seminario Musicale (r1991) *Concert*
(6/93) (VIRG) ① **VC7 59232-2**
Sorge vermiglia in ciel—cantata: voice and continuo, RV667
D.L. Ragin, V. de Hoog, C. Farr *Concert*
(10/89) (ETCE) ① **KTC1069**
Sposa son disprezzata—aria (unidentified)
C. Bartoli, G. Fischer *Concert*
(12/92) (DECC) ① **436 267-2DH**
Stabat Mater in F minor—sequence, RV621
J. Bowman, AAM, C. Hogwood *Concert*
(8/85) (L'OI) ① **414 329-2OH**
G. Lesne, Seminario Musicale Ens *Concert*
(3/91) (HRMO) ① **H/CD8720**
N. Stutzmann, Moscow Virtuosi, V. Spivakov *Concert*
(5/91) (RCA) ① **RD60240**
Ex Cathedra Chbr Ch, Ex Cathedra Baroque Orch, J. Skidmore *Concert* (12/92) (ASV) ① **CDGAU137**
C. Brett, Toulon Musica Antiqua, C. Mendoze (rec/dir) *Concert* (10/94) (PIER) ① **PV794033**

Vestro Principi divino—motet, RV633
G. Lesne, Seminario Musicale Ens *Concert*
(3/91) (HRMO) ① **H/CD8720**

SECTION V: STAGE WORKS

L' Atenaide o sia Gli affetti generosi—dramma per musica: 3 acts, RV702 (1728—Florence) (Lib. Zeno)
EXCERPTS: 1. Un certo non so che; 2. Ferma, Teodosio.
2. E. Kirkby, Brandenburg Consort, R. Goodman
(r1994) *Concert* (5/95) (HYPE) ① **CDA66745**
Bajazet (aka Tamerlano)—dramma per musica: 3 acts, RV703 (1735—Verona) (Lib. Piovene)
EXCERPTS: 1. Sinfonia; 2. Sposa son disprezzata.
1. Brandenburg Consort, R. Goodman (r1994)
Concert (5/95) (HYPE) ① **CDA66745**
Catone in Utica—dramma per musica: 3 acts, RV705 (1737—Verona) (Lib Metastasio: Act 1 lost)
EXCERPTS: 1. Se mai senti spirarti sul volto; 2. Se in campo armato.
1, 2. E. Kirkby, Brandenburg Consort, R. Goodman
(r1994) *Concert* (5/95) (HYPE) ① **CDA66745**
Dorilla in Tempe—dramma per musica: 3 acts, RV709 (1726—Venice) (Lib. Lucchini)
Cpte M. C. Kiehr, J. Elwes, P. Cantor, J. Nirouët, C. Caroli, L. Florentin, Nice Op Chor, Nice Baroque Ens, G. Bezzina (r1993) (2/95) (PIER) ① **[2] PV794092**
La Fida ninfa—dramma per musica: 3 acts, RV714 (1732—Verona) (Lib. Maffei)
EXCERPTS: 1. Alma oppressa.
1. K. Eckersley, Fiori Musicali, P. Rapson *Concert*
(10/90) (MERI) ① **CDE84195**
Griselda—dramma per musica: 3 acts, RV718 (1735—Venice) (Lib. Zeno, adapted by C. Goldoni)
EXCERPTS: 1. Sinfonia; 2. Agitata da due venti; 3. Ombre vane, ingiusti orrori.
1-3. E. Kirkby, Brandenburg Consort, R. Goodman
(r1994) *Concert* (5/95) (HYPE) ① **CDA66745**
2. K. Eckersley, Fiori Musicali, P. Rapson *Concert*
(10/90) (MERI) ① **CDE84195**
L' Incoronazione di Dario—dramma per musica: 3 acts, RV719 (1717—Venice) (Lib. Morselli)
EXCERPTS: 1. Sinfonia; 2. Non mi lusinga vana speranza.
1. K. Eckersley, Fiori Musicali, P. Rapson *Concert*
(10/90) (MERI) ① **CDE84195**
2. E. Kirkby, Brandenburg Consort, R. Goodman
(r1994) *Concert* (5/95) (HYPE) ① **CDA66745**
Montezuma—pasticcio by J-C Malgoire after opera seria, RV723 (1733—Venice) (Lib. G. Giusti)
Cpte D. Visse, D. Borst, I. Poulenard, N. Rivenq, B. Balleys, L. Masson, Voc Ens, Grande Ecurie, J-C. Malgoire (pp1992) (4/93) (ASTR) ① **[2] E8501**
L' Olimpiade—dramma per musica: 3 acts (1734—Venice)
EXCERPTS: 1. Overture.
1. Freiburg Baroque Orch, T. Hengelbrock (r1992)
Concert (4/94) (DHM) ① **05472 77289-2**
Orlando (Furioso)—dramma per musica: 3 acts, RV728 (1727—Venice) (Lib. Braccioli)
Cpte M. Horne, V. de los Angeles, L. V. Terrani, C. Gonzales, L. Kozma, S. Bruscantini, N. Zaccaria, Amici della Polifonia Chor, Solisti Veneti, C. Scimone
(4/87) (ERAT) ① **[3] 2292-45147-2**
Sol da te mio dolce amore J. Bowman, King's Consort, R. King *Concert*
(8/88) (CARL) ① **PCD894**
Ottone in Villa—dramma per musica: 3 acts, RV729 (1713—Vicenza) (Lib. Lalli)
EXCERPTS: 1. Sinfonia; 2. Vieni, vieni o mio diletto; 3. Gelosia, tu già rendi l'alma mia; 4. L'ombre, l'aure, e ancora il rio (duet).
1, 3, 4. E. Kirkby, L. Mazzarri, Brandenburg Consort, R. Goodman (r1994) *Concert*
(5/95) (HYPE) ① **CDA66745**
Tito Manlio—pasticcio, RV778 (1720—Rome) (collab with G. Boni & C. Giorgio; Lib della Pace)
EXCERPTS: 1. Non ti lusinghi la crudeltade.
1. E. Kirkby, Brandenburg Consort, R. Goodman
(r1994) *Concert* (5/95) (HYPE) ① **CDA66745**

VIVANCO, Sebastián de (c1551–1622) Spain

SECTION IV: VOCAL AND CHORAL

Magnificat octavi toni
Westminster Cath Ch, D. Hill *Concert*
(3/87) (HYPE) ① **CDA66168**

VIVES, Amadeo (1871–1932) Spain

SECTION V: STAGE WORKS

Bohemios—zarzuela: 1 act (1904) (Lib. G Perrín & M Palacios)
Cpte A.M. Higueras, P. Lavirgen, S. Garcia, P. Farrés, M. del Carmen Ramírez, M. Oran, M. Aragon, L. Frutos, E. Fuentes, Madrid Coros Cantores, Madrid Concerts Orch, P. Sorozábal *Doña Francisquita*. (10/92) (HISP) ① **[2] CZS7 67322-2**
Cpte M. Bayo, L. Lima, S. S. Jerico, C. Alvarez, R. M. Ysas, M. J. Martos, I. Monar, A. Echeverria, E. Sánchez, Laguna Uni Polyphonic Chor, Puerto de la Cruz Ch, Laguna Uni Ch, Tenerife SO, A. R. Marbà
(r1993) (3/95) (AUVI) ① **V4711**
No quiero que sepa que aqui vengo yo I. Rey, ECO, E. Ricci (r1994) *Concert*
(2/95) (ERAT) ① **4509-95789-2**
Doña Francisquita—zarzuela: 3 acts (1923—Madrid) (Lib. after Lope de Vega)
Cpte T. Tourné, M. R. Gabriel, P. Lavirgen, S. Garcia, J. Catania, C. Gimines, L. Frutos, Madrid Coros Cantores, Madrid Concerts Orch, P. Sorozábal *Bohemios*. (10/92) (HISP) ① **[2] CZS7 67322-2**
Cpte M. Bayo, R. Pierotti, Alfredo Kraus, S. S. Jerico, A. Echeverria, R. M. Ysas, I. Pons, Laguna Uni Polyphonic Chor, Tenerife SO, A. R. Marbà (r1993)
(9/94) (AUVI) ① **[2] V4710**
Cpte A. Arteta, P. Domingo, L. Mirabal, E. del Portal, M. Perelstein, C. Alvarez, C. Chausson, Cordoba Grand Th Chor, Seville SO, M. Roa (r1994)
(4/95) (SONY) ① **[2] S2K66563**
Coro de Románticos chor, Madrid SO, E. G. Asensio (pp1991) *Concert*
(11/92) (CARL) ① **MCD45**
Mujer fatal A. Cortis, orch (r1925) *Concert*
(3/94) (NIMB) ① **NI7850**

VIVIANI, Giovanni Buonaventura (1638–1692 or later) Italy

SECTION II: CHAMBER

Capricci armonici da chiesa e da camera—violin or trumpet and continuo (pub 1678)
1. Trumpet Sonata 1; 2. Trumpet Sonata 2; 3. Sinfonia cantabile (vn); 4. Violin Sonata 1.
1. A. Stringer, N. Rawsthorne (r1974) *Concert*
(11/87) (CRD) ① **CRD3308**
1. S. Keavy, Parley of Instr *Concert*
(1/89) (HYPE) ① **CDA66255**
1. J. Freeman-Attwood, I. Simcock (r1993; arr tpt/org)
Concert (5/94) (PROU) ① **PROUCD135**
1. H. Hardenberger, I Musici (r1993) *Concert*
(5/95) (PHIL) ① **442 131-2PH**

VOIGTLÄNDER, Gabriel (1596–1643) Germany

SECTION IV: VOCAL AND CHORAL

Als er guten Bescheid von seiner Damen empfangen—1v and harpsichord (pub 1642)
R. Covey-Crump, L.U. Mortensen *Concert*
(2/89) (BIS) ① **BIS-CD391**
Ein Sommerliedlein—1v and harpsichord (pub 1642)
R. Covey-Crump, L.U. Mortensen *Concert*
(2/89) (BIS) ① **BIS-CD391**

VOLANS, Kevin (b 1949) South Africa

SECTION II: CHAMBER

Kneeling Dance—mutliple pianos
Piano Circus (r1992) *Concert*
(1/94) (ARGO) ① **440 294-2ZH**
Mbira—two harpsichords and percussion (1980)
K. Volans, D. James, R. Schulkowsky (r1984)
Concert (10/91) (LAND) ① **CTLCD111**
Movement for String Quartet (1987)
Duke Qt (r1994) *Concert*
(7/95) (COLL) ① **Coll1417-2**
String Quartet No. 1, 'White Man Sleeps' (1986)
1. Movt 1.
Smith Qt (r1989) *Concert*
(10/91) (LAND) ① **CTLCD111**
Kronos Qt *Concert*
(11/92) (NONE) ① **7559-79275-2**

String Quartet No. 2, 'Hunting: Gathering' (1987)
Balanescu Qt (r1993) *String Quartet 3*.
(8/94) (ARGO) ① **440 687-2ZH**
String Quartet No. 3, '(The) Songlines' (1988)
Balanescu Qt (r1993) *String Quartet 2*.
(8/94) (ARGO) ① **440 687-2ZH**
String Quartet No. 4, 'Ramanujan Notebooks' (1990-4)
Duke Qt (r1994) *Concert*
(7/95) (COLL) ① **Coll1417-2**
String Quartet No. 5, 'Dancers on a Plane' (1993)
Duke Qt (r1994) *Concert*
(7/95) (COLL) ① **Coll1417-2**
White Man Sleeps—two harpsichords, viola da gamba and percussion (1982)
K. Volans, R. Hill, M. Tindemans, R. Schulkowsky
(r1984) *Concert* (10/91) (LAND) ① **CTLCD111**

SECTION III: INSTRUMENTAL

She who sleeps with a small blanket—percussion solo (1985)
R. Schulkowsky (pp1989) *Concert*
(10/91) (LAND) ① **CTLCD111**

VOLLSTEDT, Robert (1854–1919) Germany

pseudonym of Robert Roberti

SECTION IV: VOCAL AND CHORAL

Jolly Brothers—song
A. Campoli, Orch, W. Goehr *Concert*
(10/91) (PEAR) ① **PASTCD9744**

VON TILZER, Harry (1872–1946) USA

SECTION IV: VOCAL AND CHORAL

I wants to be a Actor Lady—song from 'In Dahomey' (W. M. Crook) (1904) (Wds. Bryan)
Cincinnati Uni Sngrs, Cincinnati Uni Th Orch, E. Rivers (r1978) *Concert* (4/94) (NEW) ① **80221-2**
If You Only Knew—song for the show 'The Star Gazer' (1917) (Lyrics Fleeson)
J. C. Thomas, Orig Broadway Cast (r1923) *Concert*
(5/94) (PEAR) ① **[3] GEMMCDS9059/61**

VOŘÍŠEK, Jan Václav Hugo (1791–1825) Bohemia

SECTION I: ORCHESTRAL

Symphony in D, Op. 24
W. German Sinf, D. Joeres (r1990) *Schubert: Symphony 2*. (8/94) (CARL) ① **PCD1052**
Scottish CO, C. Mackerras (r1995) *Concert*
(11/95) (HYPE) ① **CDA66800**

SECTION III: INSTRUMENTAL

Fantasia in C—piano, Op. 12 (pub 1822)
N. Demidenko (pp1993) *Concert*
(1/94) (HYPE) ① **[2] CDA66781/2**
R. Kvapil (r1993) *Concert*
(6/94) (UNIC) ① **DKPCD9145**
A. Pizarro (r1994) *Concert*
(10/95) (COLL) ① **Coll1458-2**
6 Impromptus—piano, Op. 7 (1822)
1. C; 2. G; 3. D; 4. A; 5. E; 6. B.
R. Kvapil (r1993) *Concert*
(6/94) (UNIC) ① **DKPCD9145**
A. Pizarro (r1994) *Concert*
(10/95) (COLL) ① **Coll1458-2**
Sonata for Piano in B flat major, Op. 20 (1820)
R. Kvapil (r1993) *Concert*
(6/94) (UNIC) ① **DKPCD9145**
A. Pizarro (r1994) *Concert*
(10/95) (COLL) ① **Coll1458-2**
Variations in B flat—piano, Op. 19 (1825)
R. Kvapil (r1993) *Concert*
(6/94) (UNIC) ① **DKPCD9145**
A. Pizarro (r1994) *Concert*
(10/95) (COLL) ① **Coll1458-2**

VRÁNA, František (b 1914) Czechoslovakia

SECTION III: INSTRUMENTAL

Concertante Study—organ (1934)
N. Kynaston *Concert* (4/89) (HYPE) ① **CDA66265**

VRANGEL, V.G. (1862–1901)

SECTION IV: VOCAL AND CHORAL

In my soul winter reigns—song
N. Figner, anon (r1901) Concert
(6/93) (PEAR) ① [3] GEMMCDS9997/9(1)

VYCPÁLEK, Ladislav (1882–1969) Czechoslovakia

SECTION IV: VOCAL AND CHORAL

Czech Requiem (Death and
Redemption)—SAB, chorus and orchestra,
Op. 24 (1940) (Wds. Bible)
1. Vanity of vanities; 2. The Day of Wrath; 3. Light in
the darkness; 4. He came to save.
M. Řeháková, M. Mrázová, T. Šrubař, Czech Phil
Chor, Czech PO, K. Ančerl (pp1968) Last things of
Man.   (7/93) (SUPR) ① [2] 11 1933-2
The Last Things of Man—cantata: SB,
chorus and orchestra, Op. 16 (1920-22) (Wds.
Moravian traditional)
D. Tikalová, L. Mráz, Czech Phil Chor, Czech PO, K.
Ančerl (r1957) Czech Requiem.
(7/93) (SUPR) ① [2] 11 1933-2

WAELRANT, Hubert (1516/7–1595) Flanders

SECTION IV: VOCAL AND CHORAL

Als ich u vinde—4vv
J. Lindberg, R. Meunier, N. North, P. O'Dette, E. Van
Evera, M. Nichols, A. King, R. Wistreich Concert
(12/86) (BIS) ① BIS-CD341
Mi voglio fare—madrigal: 6vv
M. Arruabarrena, K. van Laethem, M. Valenta, J.
Benet, M. van Altena, J. Cabré, T. de Zwart, A. Pols,
R. Van Der Meer, K. Junghänel (lte/dir) Concert
(1/92) (ACCE) ① ACC8864D
O villanella—4vv
J. Lindberg, R. Meunier, N. North, P. O'Dette, E. Van
Evera, M. Covey-Crump, A. King, R. Wistreich
Concert   (12/86) (BIS) ① BIS-CD341
Tra romor di tamburi—madrigal: 6vv
M. Arruabarrena, K. van Laethem, M. Valenta, J.
Benet, M. van Altena, J. Cabré, T. de Zwart, A. Pols,
R. Van Der Meer, K. Junghänel (lte/dir) Concert
(1/92) (ACCE) ① ACC8864D
Vorria morire—madrigal: 4vv
M. Arruabarrena, K. van Laethem, M. Valenta, J.
Benet, M. van Altena, J. Cabré, T. de Zwart, A. Pols,
R. Van Der Meer, K. Junghänel (lte/dir) Concert
(1/92) (ACCE) ① ACC8864D
Vorria morire—madrigal: 6vv
M. Arruabarrena, K. van Laethem, M. Valenta, J.
Benet, M. van Altena, J. Cabré, T. de Zwart, A. Pols,
R. Van Der Meer, K. Junghänel (lte/dir) Concert
(1/92) (ACCE) ① ACC8864D

WAGENAAR, Johann (1862–1941) The Netherlands

SECTION I: ORCHESTRAL

Fanfare for Airmen—brass ensemble (1942)
LPO, J. Mester Concert   (7/91) (KOCH) ① 37012-2

WAGNER, J(osef) F(ranz) (1856–1908) Austria

SECTION I: ORCHESTRAL

Tiroler Holzhackerbuab'n—march (Eng:
Tirolean Woodcutter Lads)
Berlin Phil Wind Qnt, H. von Karajan (r1973) Concert
(5/94) (DG) ① 439 346-2GX2
Unter dem Doppeladler—march, Op. 159
(1893) (Eng: Under the Double Eagle)
Berlin Phil Wind Qnt, H. von Karajan (r1973) Concert
(5/94) (DG) ① 439 346-2GX2

WAGNER, (Wilhelm) Richard (1813–1883) Germany

SECTION I: ORCHESTRAL

A Faust Overture—orchestra (1840 rev 1843-
44, 1855)
Philh, F. d'Avalos Concert
(10/90) (ASV) ① CDDCA704
NBC SO, A. Toscanini (r1946) Concert
(11/92) (RCA) ① GD60305

South-West German RSO, J. Horenstein (r1950s)
Concert   (11/93) (VOX) ① [2] CDX2 5504
Seattle SO, G. Schwarz (r1992) Concert
(4/94) (DELO) ① DE3120
LPO, T. Beecham (r1935/6) Concert
(10/94) (DUTT) ① CDLX7009
NYPO, P. Boulez (r1971) Concert
(7/95) (SONY) ① SMK64108
Grosser Festmarsch (1876)
Hong Kong PO, V. Kojian Concert
(8/87) (MARC) ① 8 220114
Kaisermarsch (1871)
Hong Kong PO, V. Kojian Concert
(8/87) (MARC) ① 8 220114
Polonia—Overture (1836)
Hong Kong PO, V. Kojian Concert
(8/87) (MARC) ① 8 220114
Rule Britannia—Overture (1837)
Hong Kong PO, V. Kojian Concert
(8/87) (MARC) ① 8 220114
Siegfried Idyll—chamber orchestra (1870)
COE, J. Judd Concert   (8/85) (CARL) ① PCD805
NYPO, G. Sinopoli Concert
(10/86) (DG) ① 419 169-2GH
VPO, H. von Karajan (pp1987) Concert
(8/88) (DG) ① 423 613-2GH
Berlin St Op Orch, O. Klemperer (r1927) Concert
(2/89) (SYMP) ① SYMCD1042
Linos Ens Brahms: Serenade 2.
(12/89) (SCHW) ① 310000
Philh, O. Klemperer (r1960/1) Mahler: Symphony 9.
(1/90) (EMI) ① [2] CMS7 63277-2
Philh, F. d'Avalos Concert
(3/90) (ASV) ① CDDCA666
NYPSO, A. Toscanini (r1936) Concert
(3/90) (PEAR) ① [3] GEMMCDS9373
Berlin St Op Orch, K. Muck (r1929) Concert
(4/90) (OPAL) ① [2] OPALCDS9843
NBC SO, A. Toscanini (r1952) Concert
(12/91) (RCA) ① GD60264
Sinfonia Varsovia, E. Krivine Concert
(10/92) (DENO) ① CO-79442
NBC SO, A. Toscanini (r1946) Concert
(11/92) (RCA) ① GD60296
NYPO, A. Toscanini (r1936) Concert
(11/92) (RCA) ① GD60317
Philh, G. Cantelli (r1951) Concert
(2/93) (TEST) ① SBT1012
San Francisco SO, H. Blomstedt (r1991) Bruckner:
Symphony 6.   (5/93) (DECC) ① 436 129-2DH
BPO, James Levine (r1991) Concert
(8/93) (DG) ① 435 883-2GH
VPO, B. Walter (r1935) Concert
(8/94) (PREI) ① 90157
BPO, H. von Karajan (r1977) Bruckner: Symphony 8.
(12/94) (DG) ① [2] 439 969-2GGA2
NYPO, J. Barbirolli (pp1938) Concert
(3/95) (DUTT) ① CDSJB1001
NYPO, P. Boulez (r1977) Concert
(7/95) (SONY) ① SMK64108
LCP, R. Norrington (r1994) Concert
(11/95) (EMI) ① CDC5 55479-2
Symphony in C (1832)
Tokyo Metropolitan SO, H. Wakasugi (r1992)
Symphony in E.   (6/93) (DENO) ① CO-75259
Symphony in E (1834)
Tokyo Metropolitan SO, H. Wakasugi (r1992)
Symphony in C.   (6/93) (DENO) ① CO-75259

SECTION II: CHAMBER

Polonaise in D—piano duet, Op. 2 (?1832)
S. Möller, G. Mandozzi Concert
(6/93) (SCHW) ① 313622

SECTION III: INSTRUMENTAL

Albumblatt für Frau Betty Schott—piano
(1875)
S. Möller Concert   (6/93) (SCHW) ① 313622
G. Oppitz (r1993) Concert
(2/95) (RCA) ① 09026 61843-2
Albumblatt in C, 'In das Album der Fürstin
Metternich'—piano (1861)
S. Möller Concert   (6/93) (SCHW) ① 313622
Albumblatt in E—Lied ohne Worte (1840)
(composed for E.B. Kietz)
L. Howard Concert   (12/86) (HYPE) ① CDA66090
L. Mordkovitch (arr Wilhelmj) Concert
(11/90) (CHAN) ① CHAN8748
G. Enescu, E.C. Harris (arr Wilhelmj) r1924) Concert
(8/93) (BIDD) ① LAB066
S. Möller Concert   (6/93) (SCHW) ① 313622
T. Seidel, M. Rabinovitch (r c1941: arr Wilhelmj)
Concert   (7/93) (APR) ① [2] APR7016
Ankunft bei den schwarzen Schwänen in A
flat—piano (1861)
S. Möller Concert   (6/93) (SCHW) ① 313622

G. Oppitz (r1993) Concert
(2/95) (RCA) ① 09026 61843-2
Elegie in A flat—piano (1859-62)
(unpublished)
S. Möller Concert   (6/93) (SCHW) ① 313622
Fantasia in F sharp minor—piano, Op. 3
(1831)
S. Möller Concert   (6/93) (SCHW) ① 313622
Notenbrief für Mathilde Wesendonk—piano
(1857) (unpublished)
S. Möller Concert   (6/93) (SCHW) ① 313622
Polka in G—piano (1853)
S. Möller Concert   (6/93) (SCHW) ① 313622
Polonaise in D—piano (1831-32)
S. Möller Concert   (6/93) (SCHW) ① 313622
Sonata for Piano in A, Op. 4 (1832)
S. Möller Concert   (6/93) (SCHW) ① 313612
Sonata for Piano in B flat, Op. 1 (1831)
S. Möller Concert   (6/93) (SCHW) ① 313612
Eine Sonate für das Album von Frau M.
W.—piano (1853) (composed for Mathilde
Wesendonk)
S. Möller Concert   (6/93) (SCHW) ① 313612
G. Oppitz (r1993) Concert
(2/95) (RCA) ① 09026 61843-2
Züricher Vielliebchen: Walzer, Polka oder
sonst was in E flat—piano (1854)
S. Möller Concert   (6/93) (SCHW) ① 313622

SECTION IV: VOCAL AND CHORAL

Les Deux grenadiers—song (1840) (Wds. H.
Heine, trans F-A. Loeve-Veimar)
T. Hampson, G. Parsons (r1993) Concert
(5/94) (EMI) ① CDC5 55047-2
N. Stutzmann, G. Oppitz (r1993) Concert
(2/95) (RCA) ① 09026 61843-2
7 Faust Lieder—1v and piano, Op. 5 (1831)
(Wds. Goethe)
EXCERPTS: 1. Lied der Soldaten: Burgen mit hohen
Mauern; 2. Bauer unter der Linde: Der Schäfer putzte
sich zum Tanz; 3. Branders Lied: Es war eine Ratt im
Kellernest; 4. Lied des Mephistopheles 1: Es war
einmal ein König; 5. Lied des Mephistopheles 2: Was
machst du mir vor Liebchens Tür; 6. Gretchen am
Spinnrade: Meine Ruh ist hin; 7. Melodram
Gretchens: Ach neige, du Schmerzenreiche.
4, 5. T. Hampson, G. Parsons (r1993) Concert
(5/94) (EMI) ① CDC5 55047-2
3 Mélodies (1839)
1. Dors, mon enfant (wds. V. Hugo); 2. Mignonne
(wds. P. Ronsard); 3. L'attente (wds. V. Hugo).
2. T. Hampson, G. Parsons (r1993) Concert
(5/94) (EMI) ① CDC5 55047-2
2, 3. N. Stutzmann, G. Oppitz (r1993) Concert
(2/95) (RCA) ① 09026 61843-2
3. F. Lott, G. Johnson (r1984) Concert
(5/87) (HARM) ① HMA190 1138
Der Tannenbaum—Lied: 1v and piano (1838)
(Wds. G Scheurlin)
T. Hampson, G. Parsons (r1993) Concert
(5/94) (EMI) ① CDC5 55047-2
Tout n'est qu'images fugitives—song: 1v
and piano (1839) (Wds. J Reboul)
T. Hampson, G. Parsons (r1993) Concert
(5/94) (EMI) ① CDC5 55047-2
N. Stutzmann, G. Oppitz (r1993) Concert
(2/95) (RCA) ① 09026 61843-2
Wesendonk Lieder (1857/8) (Wds.
Wesendonk)
1. Der Engel; 2. Stehe still; 3. Im Treibhaus; 4.
Schmerzen; 5. Träume.
J. Norman, LSO, Colin Davis Tristan und Isolde.
(8/85) (PHIL) ① 412 655-2PH
T. Lemnitz, Berlin Staatskapelle, R. Heger (bp1944)
Schillings: Glockenlieder.   (7/89) (ACAN) ① 43 275
K. Flagstad, G. Moore (r1948) Concert
(8/89) (EMI) ① CDH7 63030-2
W. Meier, Paris Orch, D. Barenboim Concert
(4/90) (ERAT) ① 2292-45417-2
C. Ludwig, Philh, O. Klemperer Concert
(9/92) (EMI) ① [4] CMS7 64074-2(2)
R. Kollo, Berlin Deutsche Op Orch, C. Thielemann
(arr Mottl) Concert   (5/93) (DG) ① CDC7 54776-2
E. Meyer-Topsøe, Copenhagen PO, H.N. Bihlmaier
(r1993) Concert   (1/94) (KONT) ① 32156
T. Lemnitz, M. Raucheisen (r1930s) Concert
(1/94) (CLUB) ① CL99-007
C. Studer, Staatskapelle Dresden, G. Sinopoli
Concert   (7/94) (DG) ① 439 865-2GH
M. Price, G. Johnson (r1993) Concert
(2/95) (FORL) ① UCD16728
K. Flagstad, VPO, H. Knappertsbusch (r1956)
Concert   (12/95) (LOND) ① [5] 440 490-2LM5(1)
K. Flagstad, Vienna SO, H. Knappertsbusch (r1956)
Concert   (12/95) (LOND) ① 440 491-2LM

4. G. Lubin, orch, H. Defosse (French: r1929) *Concert* (5/91) (EPM) Ⓓ **150 052**
4. S. Sedlmair, anon (r1904) *Concert* (7/91) (SYMP) Ⓓ **SYMCD1081**
4. E. Rethberg, Berlin St Op Orch, F. Zweig (r1927) *Concert* (1/92) (EMI) Ⓓ [4] **CMS7 64008-2(1)**
4. G. Jones, Cologne RSO, R. Paternostro *Concert* (2/92) (CHAN) Ⓓ **CHAN8930**
4. H. Traubel, NYPSO, A. Rodzinski (r1945) *Concert* (4/92) (EMI) Ⓓ [7] **CHS7 69741-2(1)**
4. E. Destinn, orch, B. Seidler-Winkler (r1908) *Concert* (7/92) (PEAR) Ⓓ [3] **GEMMCDS9924(1)**
4. H. Spani, La Scala Orch, C. Sabajno (Ital: r1928) *Concert* (12/92) (PREI) Ⓓ **89037**
4. F. Litvinne, anon (r1905: Fr) *Concert* (7/93) (NIMB) Ⓓ [2] **NI7840/1**
4. K. Flagstad, orch, H. Lange (r1935) *Concert* (7/93) (NIMB) Ⓓ **NI7847**
4. R. Pampanini, EIAR Orch, U. Tansini (Ital: r1940) *Concert* (8/93) (PREI) Ⓓ **89063**
4. R. Ponselle, orch, R. Romani (r1923) *Concert* (10/93) (NIMB) Ⓓ **NI7846**
4. J. Norman, Vienna St Op Concert Ch, VPO, G. Solti (r1985) *Concert* (10/93) (DECC) Ⓓ **436 461-2DM**
4. A. Marc, Seattle SO, G. Schwarz (r1992) *Concert* (4/94) (DELO) Ⓓ **DE3120**
4. H. Traubel, RCA SO, B. Reibold (r1940) *Concert* (4/94) (RCA) Ⓓ [6] **09026 61580-2(4)**
4. E. Destinn, orch, B. Seidler-Winkler (r1906) *Concert* (5/94) (SUPR) Ⓓ **11 1337-2**
4. F. Litvinne, anon (r1905: Fr) *Concert* (12/94) (SYMP) Ⓓ **SYMCD1128**
4. E. Destinn, Odeon Orch, A. Pilz (r1908) *Concert* (12/94) (SUPR) Ⓓ [12] **11 2136-2(2)**
4. E. Rethberg, orch (r1928) *Concert* (2/95) (ROMO) Ⓓ [2] **81012-2**
4. E. Rethberg, Berlin SO, F. Zweig (r1927) *Concert* (10/95) (ROMO) Ⓓ [2] **81014-2**
4. K. Flagstad, VPO, H. Knappertsbusch (r1956) *Concert* (12/95) (LOND) Ⓓ [5] **440 490-2LM5(1)**
4. K. Flagstad, VPO, H. Knappertsbusch (r1956) *Concert* (12/95) (LOND) Ⓓ **440 495-2LM**
4. K. Flagstad, orch, H. Lange (r1935) *Concert* (12/95) (SIMA) Ⓓ [3] **PSC1821(1)**
4, 10. T. Lemnitz, Berlin St Op Orch, J. Schüler (r1937) *Concert* (10/90) (PREI) Ⓓ **89025**
4, 10. Lotte Lehmann, orch (r1914) *Concert* (6/92) (PREI) Ⓓ [3] **89302**
4, 10. M. Reining, Berlin Deutsche Op Orch, W. Lutze (r1939) *Concert* (9/92) (PREI) Ⓓ **90083**
4, 10. G. Janowitz, Berlin Deutsche Op Orch, F. Leitner (r1967) *Concert* (12/95) (DG) Ⓓ [2] **447 352-2GDB2**
4(2 vers), 10, 12c E. Destinn, orch, B. Seidler-Winkler (r1906) *Concert* (12/94) (SUPR) Ⓓ [12] **11 2136-2(1)**
4, 19a M. Teschemacher, M. Wittrisch, Berlin St Op Orch, F. Zaun (r1933) *Concert* (11/92) (PREI) Ⓓ **89049**
5b(pt), 13, 18. Bayreuth Fest Chor, Bayreuth Fest Orch, W. Pitz *Concert* (4/90) (DG) Ⓓ **429 169-2GR**
6. A. Pertile, La Scala Chor, La Scala Orch, C. Sabajno (Ital: r1927) *Concert* (1/92) (EMI) Ⓓ [4] **CMS7 64008-2(1)**
6, 19c L. Slezak, orch (r1907) *Concert* (2/91) (PREI) Ⓓ **89020**
6, 21. A. Pertile, La Scala Orch, C. Sabajno (r1927: Ital) *Concert* (10/94) (PREI) Ⓓ **89072**
6(pt), 7, 12c, 15(pt) P. Kötter, M. Teschemacher, H. Alsen, A. Konetzni, Vienna St Op Chor, Vienna St Op Orch, H. Knappertsbusch (pp1936) *Concert* (12/95) (SCHW) Ⓓ [2] **314672**
7, 19a, 19c(pt) E. Destinn, E. Kraus, orch, B. Seidler-Winkler (r1906) *Concert* (12/94) (SUPR) Ⓓ [12] **11 2136-2(1)**
8. G. Hann, Berlin Deutsche Op Orch, A. Rother (r1942) *Concert* (5/94) (PREI) Ⓓ **90168**
8(pt) T. Ralf, L. Helletsgruber, L. Hofmann, E. Schipper, A. Konetzni, Vienna St Op Chor, Vienna St Op Orch, H. Knappertsbusch (pp1936) *Concert* (7/94) (SCHW) Ⓓ [2] **314512**
8, 17, 18, 19a-c, 21, 22. M. Müller, M. Klose, F. Völker, J. Prohaska, J. von Manowarda, Bayreuth Fest Chor, Bayreuth Fest Orch, H. Tietjen (r1936) *Concert* (8/93) (TELD) Ⓓ **9031-76442-2**
9. M. Lawrence, M. Singher, Pasdeloup Orch, P. Coppola (French: r1933) *Concert* (5/90) (PREI) Ⓓ **89011**
9. M. Lawrence, M. Singher, SO, P. Coppola (French: r1933) *Concert* (1/92) (EMI) Ⓓ [4] **CMS7 64008-2(1)**
10. H. Spani, La Scala Orch, C. Sabajno (Ital: r1927) *Concert* (9/90) (CLUB) Ⓓ [2] **CL99-509/10**
10. J. Gadski, orch (r1914) *Concert* (7/91) (CLUB) Ⓓ **CL99-109**
10. H. Spani, La Scala Orch, C. Sabajno (Ital: r1927) *Concert* (1/92) (EMI) Ⓓ [4] **CMS7 64008-2(1)**
10. Lotte Lehmann, orch, F. Weissmann (r1930) *Concert* (1/92) (EMI) Ⓓ [4] **CMS7 64008-2(1)**
10. F. Saville, anon (r c1902) *Concert* (10/92) (SYMP) Ⓓ **SYMCD1093**
10. H. Spani, La Scala Orch, C. Sabajno (Ital: r1927) *Concert* (12/92) (PREI) Ⓓ **89037**
10. K. Flagstad, Philadelphia, E. Ormandy (r1937) *Concert* (7/93) (NIMB) Ⓓ **NI7847**
10. M. Jeritza, orch (r1922) *Concert* (4/94) (PREI) Ⓓ **89079**
10. E. Destinn, orch, F. Kark (r1906) *Concert* (12/94) (SUPR) Ⓓ [12] **11 2136-2(1)**
10. E. Rethberg, orch (r1927) *Concert* (2/95) (ROMO) Ⓓ [2] **81012-2**
10. K. Flagstad, Philadelphia, E. Ormandy (r1937) *Concert* (12/95) (SIMA) Ⓓ [3] **PSC1821(2)**
10, 12a-c E. Schwarzkopf, C. Ludwig, Philh, H. Wallberg *Concert* (10/88) (EMI) Ⓓ **CDM7 69501-2**
10, 12c E. Destinn, orch (r1911) *Concert* (12/94) (SUPR) Ⓓ [12] **11 2136-2(4)**
11. C. Studer, W. Meier, BPO, C. Abbado (pp1993) *Concert* (5/94) (DG) Ⓓ **439 768-2GH**
11. K. Thorborg, E. Rethberg, J. Huehn, NY Met Op Orch, E. Leinsdorf (bp1940) *Concert* (4/95) (PREI) Ⓓ **89084**
11, 12a-c M. Lawrence, Y. Brothier, Pasdeloup Orch, P. Coppola (French: r1933) *Concert* (5/90) (PREI) Ⓓ **89011**
11, 12a-c T. Lemnitz, M. Klose, Berlin St Op Orch, J. Schüler (r1948) *Concert* (1/92) (EMI) Ⓓ [4] **CMS7 64008-2(1)**
12a, 12b M. Klose, M. Müller, Vienna St Op Orch, H. Tietjen (pp1938) *Concert* (6/94) (SCHW) Ⓓ **314502**
12c C. Ferrani, E. Ceresoli, anon (Ital: r1902) *Concert* (5/91) (SYMP) Ⓓ **SYMCD1077**
12c Lotte Lehmann, orch (r1916) *Concert* (6/92) (PREI) Ⓓ [3] **89302**
12c E. Eames, L. Homer, orch (r1908) *Concert* (11/93) (ROMO) Ⓓ [2] **81001-2**
12c E. Eames, L. Homer, orch (r1908) *Concert* (1/95) (NIMB) Ⓓ **NI7860**
17. LPO, C. Mackerras *Concert* (11/87) (CFP) Ⓓ **CD-CFP9000**
17. Oslo PO, M. Jansons *Concert* (12/92) (EMI) Ⓓ **CDC7 54583-2**
17. NY Met Op Orch, James Levine (r1991) *Concert* (10/93) (DG) Ⓓ **435 874-2GH**
17. LPO, T. Beecham (r1935) *Concert* (6/94) (DUTT) Ⓓ **CDLX7007**
17. RCA Victor Orch, F. Reiner (r1950) *Concert* (8/94) (RCA) Ⓓ **09026 61792-2**
17. LCP, R. Norrington (r1994) *Concert* (11/95) (EMI) Ⓓ **CDC5 55479-2**
18. ROH Chor, ROHO, B. Haitink *Concert* (12/89) (EMI) Ⓓ **CDC7 49849-2**
18. S. Cleobury (r1979: arr C Wood) *Concert* (6/93) (DECC) Ⓓ **436 402-2DWO**
18. G. Thalben-Ball (r c1931: arr org) *Concert* (9/94) (BEUL) Ⓓ **1PD5**
19a S. Sedlmair, E. Schmedes, anon (r1904) *Concert* (7/91) (SYMP) Ⓓ **SYMCD1081**
19a T. Lemnitz, T. Ralf, Berlin Staatskapelle, L. Blech (r1939) *Concert* (7/92) (PEAR) Ⓓ [3] **GEMMCDS9926(2)**
19a T. Ralf, T. Lemnitz, Berlin St Op Orch, B. Seidler-Winkler (r1939) *Concert* (10/94) (PREI) Ⓓ **89077**
19a A. Pertile, I.A. Tellini, M.L. Fanelli, La Scala Orch, C. Sabajno (r1927/8: Ital) *Concert* (10/94) (PREI) Ⓓ **89072**
19a-c E. Bettendorf, L. Melchior, orch, F. Weissmann (r1926) *Concert* (8/88) (DANA) Ⓓ [2] **DACOCD313/4**
19a-c W. Widdop, G. Ljungberg, LSO, L. Collingwood (r1930) *Concert* (11/92) (CLAR) Ⓓ **CDGSE78-50-46**
19b F. Völker, Berlin St Op Orch, M. Gurlitt (r1928) *Concert* (2/90) (PREI) Ⓓ **89005**
19b, 19c F. Ansseau, orch (Fr: r1924) *Concert* (1/91) (PREI) Ⓓ **89022**
19c L. Melchior, Berlin St Op Orch, L. Blech (r1928) *Concert* (10/89) (EMI) Ⓓ **CDH7 69789-2**
19c F. Merli, orch, L. Molajoli (Ital: r1926) *Concert* (1/91) (PREI) Ⓓ **89026**
19c H. Winkelmann, anon (r1904) *Concert* (7/91) (SYMP) Ⓓ **SYMCD1081**
19c T. Ralf, M. Hussa, Vienna St Op Orch, J. Krips (pp1936) *Concert* (7/94) (SCHW) Ⓓ [2] **314512**
19c, 21, 22. F. Völker, Berlin St Op Orch, J. Heidenreich (r1927) *Concert* (2/90) (PREI) Ⓓ **89005**
19c, 22. L. Melchior, Berlin St Op Orch, L. Blech (r1928) *Concert* (8/88) (DANA) Ⓓ [2] **DACOCD315/6**
21. L. Melchior, Orch (Danish: r c1920) *Concert* (8/88) (DANA) Ⓓ [2] **DACOCD311/2**
21. M. Wittrisch, Berlin St Op Orch, F. Zaun (r1933) *Concert* (1/92) (EMI) Ⓓ [4] **CMS7 64008-2(1)**
21. R. Tauber, orch, N. Treep (bp1939) *Concert* (2/92) (LYRC) Ⓓ [2] **SRO830**
21. F. Viñas, S. Cottone (Ital: r1903) *Concert* (7/92) (PEAR) Ⓓ [3] **GEMMCDS9923(1)**
21. J. Hislop, orch, J. Barbirolli (Eng: r1929) *Concert* (1/93) (PEAR) Ⓓ **GEMMCD9956**
21. P. Anders, Cologne RSO, R. Kraus (bp1951) *Concert* (8/93) (ACAN) Ⓓ **43 268**
21. C. Kullman, orch, W. Goehr (r1938) *Concert* (11/93) (PREI) Ⓓ **89057**
21. L. Suthaus, orch *Concert* (3/94) (MYTO) Ⓓ [3] **3MCD93381**
21. S. Kónya, Boston SO, E. Leinsdorf (r1965) *Concert* (4/94) (RCA) Ⓓ [6] **09026 61580-2(7)**
21. F. Viñas, S. Cottone (r1903: Ital) *Concert* (4/94) (EMI) Ⓓ [3] **CHS7 64860-2(1)**
21. W. Widdop, orch, L. Collingwood (r1926: Eng) *Concert* (5/94) (CLAR) Ⓓ **CDGSE78-50-52**
21. G. Thill, orch, E. Bigot (r1930: Fr) *Concert* (8/95) (FORL) Ⓓ **UCD16727**
22. H. Roswaenge, VPO, R. Moralt (r1942) *Concert* (1/92) (EMI) Ⓓ [4] **CMS7 64008-2(1)**
22. L. Melchior, Philadelphia, E. Ormandy (r1938) *Concert* (10/92) (TEST) Ⓓ **SBT1005**
22. L. Sobinov, orch (r1910: Russ) *Concert* (6/93) (PEAR) Ⓓ [3] **GEMMCDS9997/9(2)**
22. G. Borgatti, orch (r1919: Ital) *Concert* (4/94) (EMI) Ⓓ [3] **CHS7 64860-2(1)**

Die **Meistersinger von Nürnberg, '(The) Mastersingers of Nuremburg'—opera: 3 acts (1868—Munich)** (Lib. cpsr)

EXCERPTS: 1. Prelude. ACT 1: 2. Da zu dir der Heiland kam; 3. Verweilt! Ein Wort! ein einzig Wort!; 4. Da bin ich! Wer ruft?; 5. David! Was stehst?; 6. Mein Herr! Der Singer Meisterschlag; 7. Der Meister Tön' und Weisen; 8. Damit, Herr Ritter, ist's so bewandt!; 9. So bleibt mir einzig der Meister-Lohn!; 10. Seid meiner Treue wohl versehen; 11a. Gott grüsst Euch, Meister; 11b. Zu einer Freiung und Zunftberatung; 12. Das schöne Fest, Johannistag (Pogner's address); 13. Vielleicht schon ginget ihr zu weit; 14a. Wohl, Meister, zur Tagesordnung kehrt; 14b. Dacht' ich mir's doch!; 15. Am stillen Herd; 16. Nun, Meister! Wenn's gefällt; 17. Was euch zum Liede Richt' und Schnur; 18. 'Fanget an'—So rief der Lenz (Trial Song); 19. Seid Ihr nun fertig?; 20. Halt! Meister! Nicht so geeilt! ACT 2: 21. Johannistag!; 22. Lass seh'n, ob Meister Sachs zu Haus?; 23a. Zeig' her, 's ist gut. Dort an die Tür'; 23b. Was duftet doch der Flieder (Fliedermonolog); 24. Gut'n Abend, Meister!; 25. Das dacht' ich wohl; 26. Da ist er!...Ja, ihr seid es; 27a. Geliebter, spare den Zorn; 27b. Hört, ihr Leut, und lasst euch sagen; 27c. Uble Dinge, die ich da merk; 28a. Tu's nicht!—Doch horch!; 28b. Jerum! Jerum!; 29a. Das Fenster geht auf; 29b. Freund Sachs! So hört doch nur ein Wort!; 30. Den Tag seh' ich erscheinen (Beckmesser's Serenade); 31. Mit den Schuhen ward ich fertig schier; 32. Zum Teufel mit dir, verdammter Kerl! ACT 3: 33. Prelude; 34. Gleich, Meister! Hier!; 35. Am Jordan Sankt Johannes stand; 36. Wahn! Wahn! Überall Wahn! (Wahnmonolog); 37. Grüss Gott, mein Junker!; 38. Mein Freund! In holder Jugendzeit; 39. Morgenlich leuchtend (Prize song rehearsal); 40. Abendlich glühend; 41. Ein Werbelied! Von Sachs!; 42. Das Gedicht! hier liess ich's; 43a. So ganz boshaft doch keinen ich fand; 43b. Sieh Ev'chen!...Grüss Gott, mein Ev'chen; 44. Hat man mit dem Schuhwerk; 45. O Sachs! Mein Freund!; 46a. Mein Kind, von Tristan und Isolde; 46b. Aha! Da streicht die Lene; 46c. Ein Kind ward hier geboren; 47. Selig wie die Sonne (Quintet); 48. Sankt Krispin, lobet ihn! (Guild Choruses); 49. Ihr tanzt? (Dance of the Apprentices); 50. Entry of the Masters; 51. Wach auf! es nahet gen den Tag; 52. Euch macht ihr's leicht; 53. Nun denn, wenn's Meistern und Volk beliebt; 54. Morgen ich leuchte (Beckmesser); 55. Das Lied, für wahr, ist nicht von mir; 56. Morgenlich leuchtend (Prize Song); 57. Verachtet mir die Meister nicht (Sachs' Panegyric); 58. Ehrt eure deutche

Cpte D. Fischer-Dieskau, P. Domingo, C. Ligendza, P. Lagger, R. Hermann, H. Laubenthal, C. Ludwig, G. Feldhoff, P. Maus, R. Bañuelas, L. Driscoll, K-E. Mercker, M. Vantin, K. Lang, I. Sardi, M. Nikolič, V. von Halem, Berlin Deutsche Op Chor, Berlin Deutsche Op Orch, E. Jochum (r1976) (10/85) (DG) Ⓓ [4] **415 278-2GH4**

Cpte N. Bailey, R. Kollo, H. Bode, K. Moll, B. Weikl, A. Dallapozza, J. Hamari, G. Nienstedt, Adalbert Kraus, M. Egel, M. Schomberg, W. Appel, M. Sénéchal, H. Berger-Tuna, K. Rydl, R. Hartmann, W. Klumlikboldt, Gumpoldskirchner Spatzen, Vienna St Op Chor, VPO, G. Solti (r1975/6) (7/87) (DECC) Ⓓ [4] **417 497-2DH4**

Cpte T. Adam, R. Kollo, H. Donath, K. Ridderbusch, G. Evans, P. Schreier, R. Hesse, Z. Kélémen, E. Büchner, H. Lunow, H.J. Rotzsch, P. Bindszus, H. Hiestermann, H.C. Polster, H. Reeh, S. Vogel, K. Moll, Dresden St Op Chor, Leipzig Rad Chor, Staatskapelle Dresden, H. von Karajan (r1970) (7/88) (EMI) Ⓓ [4] **CDS7 49683-2**

Cpte O. Wiener, Jess Thomas, C. Watson, H. Hotter, B. Kusche, F. Lenz, L. Benningsen, J. Metternich, D. Thaw, C. Hoppe, W. Carnuth, F. Klarwein, K. Ostertag, A. Keil, G. Wieter, M. Proebstl, H.B. Ernst, Bavarian St Op Chor, Bavarian St Op Orch, J. Keilberth (pp1963) (4/90) (EURO) Ⓓ [4] **GD69008**

Cpte O. Edelmann, H. Hopf, E. Schwarzkopf, F. Dalberg, E. Kunz, G. Unger, I. Malaniuk, H. Pflanzl, E. Majkut, H. Berg, J. Janko, K. Mikorey, G. Stolze, H. Tandler, H. Borst, A. Van Mill, W. Faulhaber, Bayreuth Fest Chor, Bayreuth Fest Orch, H. von Karajan (pp1951) (9/90) (EMI) Ⓓ [4] **CHS7 63500-2**

Cpte K. Ridderbusch, J. Cox, H. Bode, H. Sotin, K. Hirte, F. Stricker, A. Reynolds, G. Nienstedt, H. Steinbach, J. Dene, R. Licha, W. Appel, N. Orth, H. Feldhoff, H. Bauer, N. Hillebrand, B. Weikl, Bayreuth Fest Chor, Bayreuth Fest Orch, S. Varviso (pp1974) (10/92) (PHIL) Ⓓ [4] **434 611-2PH4**

Cpte F. Frantz, R. Schock, E. Grümmer, G. Frick, B. Kusche, G. Unger, M. Höffgen, G. Neidlinger, H. Wilhelm, W. Stoll, M. Schmidt, L. Clam, Herold Kraus, R. Koffmane, A. Metternich, H. Pick, H. Prey, Berlin St Hedwig's Cath Ch, Berlin Deutsche Op Chor, Berlin St Op Chor, BPO, R. Kempe (r1956) (2/93) (EMI) Ⓓ [4] **CMS7 64154-2**

Cpte P. Schoeffler, L. Suthaus, H. Scheppan, F. Dalberg, E. Kunz, E. Witte, C. Kallab, F. Krenn, B. Arnold, H. Fehn, G. Witting, G. Rödin, K. Krollmann, H. Gosebruch, F. Sauer, A. Dome, E. Pina, Bayreuth Fest Chor, Bayreuth Fest Orch, H. Abendroth (pp1943) (2/94) (PREI) Ⓓ [4] **90174**

Cpte B. Weikl, B. Heppner, C. Studer, K. Moll, S. Lorenz, D. van der Walt, C. Kallisch, H-J. Ketelsen, M. Schade, H. Wilbrink, U. Ress, H. Sapell, R. Wagenführer, R. Büse, G. Götzen, F. Kunder, R. Pape, Bavarian St Op Chor, Bavarian St Orch, W. Sawallisch (r1993) (8/94) (EMI) Ⓓ [4] **CDS5 55142-2**

Cpte P. Schoeffler, G. Treptow, H. Gueden, O. Edelmann, K. Dönch, A. Dermota, E. Schürhoff, A. Poell, H. Meyer-Welfing, W. Felden, E. Majkut, W. Wernigk, H. Gallos, H. Pröglhöf, F. Bierbach, L. Pantscheff, Vienna St Op Chor, VPO, H. Knappertsbusch (r1950/1) (10/94) (DECC) Ⓓ [4] **440 057-2DMO4**

Cpte P. Schoeffler, A. Seider, I. Seefried, H. Alsen, E. Kunz, P. Klein, E. Schürhoff, F. Krenn, A. Dermota, V. Madin, G. Maikl, J. Witt, W. Wernigk, A. Muzzarelli, A. Jerger, M. Rus, Vienna St Op Chor, VPO, K. Böhm (pp1944) (6/95) (PREI) Ⓓ [4] **90234**

Act 2. G. Hann, H. Noort, T. Kempf, W. Schirp, E. Kunz, K. Wessely, M-L. Schilp, H. Heinz Nissen, A. Fügel, L. Windisch, H. Florian, W. Ulbricht, E. Schneider, E. Heyer, W. Lang, A. Will, Berlin Rad Chor, Berlin RO, A. Rother (bp1942) *Concert* (5/94) (PREI) Ⓓ **90168**

Exc A. Pinto, orch (r1914: Ital) *Concert* (11/92) (MEMO) Ⓓ [2] **HR4408/9(2)**

Excs J. Prohaska, C. Reich, J. Kalenberg, H. Wiedemann, Vienna St Op Orch, J. Krips (pp1937) *Concert* (11/94) (SCHW) Ⓓ [2] **314532**

Excs M. Lorenz, V. Ursuleac, A. Jerger, E. Zimmermann, B. Paalen, N. Zec, H. Gallos, H. Duhan, H. Wiedemann, V. Madin, A. Arnold, Wolken, W. Wernigk, A. Muzzarelli, H. Reich, K. Ettl, Vienna St Op Chor, Vienna St Op Orch, C. Krauss (pp1933) *Concert* (1/95) (SCHW) Ⓓ [2] **314562**

Excs L. Hofmann, H. Alsen, G. Maikl, G. Monthy, H. Wiedemann, V. Madin, A. Arnold, E. Fritsch, R. Tomek, A. Muzzarelli, H. Reich, K. Ettl, J. Kalenberg, R. Sallaba, V. Mansinger, K. Thorborg, Vienna St Op Chor, Vienna St Op Orch, H. Knappertsbusch (pp1936) *Concert* (3/95) (SCHW) Ⓓ [2] **314602**

Excs A. Jerger, V. Ursuleac, F. Völker, E. Zimmermann, E. Szánthó, Vienna St Op Chor, Vienna St Op Orch, C. Krauss (pp1934) *Concert* (3/95) (SCHW) Ⓓ [2] **314602**

Excs R. Bockelmann, N. Zec, G. Maikl, H. Duhan, H. Wiedemann, V. Madin, A. Arnold, Wolken, R. Tomek, A. Muzzarelli, H. Reich, K. Ettl, E. Schipper, E. Zimmermann, V. Ursuleac, G. Rünger, Vienna St Op Chor, Vienna St Op Orch, C. Krauss (pp1933) *Concert* (8/95) (SCHW) Ⓓ [2] **314642**

1. NYPO, G. Sinopoli *Concert* (10/86) (DG) Ⓓ **419 169-2GH**

1. T. Trotter (arr Lemare) *Concert* (11/87) (HYPE) Ⓓ **CDA66216**

1. LSO, W. Morris *Concert* (12/87) (CIRR) Ⓓ **CICD1005**

1. Columbia SO, B. Walter (r1959) *Concert* (2/90) (SONY) Ⓓ **MPK45701**

1. Philh, F. d'Avalos *Concert* (3/90) (ASV) Ⓓ **CDDCA666**

1. Chicago SO, G. Solti *Concert* (5/91) (DECC) Ⓓ **430 448-2DM**

1. VPO, R. Strauss (pp1944) *Concert* (2/92) (DG) Ⓓ **435 333-2GWP**

1. VPO, R. Strauss (pp1944) *Concert* (2/92) (DG) Ⓓ [12] **435 321-2GWP12**

1. NBC SO, A. Toscanini (r1946) *Concert* (11/92) (RCA) Ⓓ **GD60305**

1. Cleveland Orch, G. Szell *Concert* (11/92) (SONY) Ⓓ **SBK48175**

1. Oslo PO, M. Jansons *Concert* (12/92) (EMI) Ⓓ **CDC7 54583-2**

1. NY Met Op Orch, James Levine (r1991) *Concert* (10/93) (DG) Ⓓ **435 874-2GH**

1. Minnesota Orch, N. Marriner (r1983) *Concert* (2/94) (TELA) Ⓓ **CD82005**

1. Leningrad PO, E. Mravinsky (pp1967) *Concert* (3/94) (RUSS) Ⓓ **RDCD11166**

1. LPO, T. Beecham (r1936) *Concert* (6/94) (DUTT) Ⓓ **CDLX7007**

1. Vienna St Op Orch, F. Weingartner (pp1935) *Concert* (7/94) (SCHW) Ⓓ [2] **314512**

1. Chicago SO, F. Stock (r1926) *Concert* (2/95) (BIDD) Ⓓ [2] **WHL021/2**

1. NQHO, B. Wordsworth (r1995) *Concert* (6/95) (EYE) Ⓓ [2] **EOS5001**

1. NYPO, P. Boulez (r1972) *Concert* (7/95) (SONY) Ⓓ **SMK64108**

1. LCP, R. Norrington (r1994) *Concert* (11/95) (EMI) Ⓓ **CDC5 55479-2**

1. Solti Orchestral Project, G. Solti (pp1994) *Concert* (12/95) (DECC) Ⓓ **444 458-2DH**

1, 2, 20, 23b, 24, 28b, 29b(pt), 31(pt), 33, 36-38, 45, 46b, 46c, 47, 51, 52(pt), 55, 57, 58. R. Bockelmann, J. von Manowarda, J. Katona, E. Bürger, E. Fuchs, G. Hann, G. Heckel, K. Mikorey, J. Brombacher, W. Markgraf, A. von Diehl, H. Krenn, E. Laholm, E. Zimmermann, T. Lemnitz, R. Berglund, Vienna St Op Chor, Nuremberg Op Chor, Vienna St Op Orch, W. Furtwängler (pp1938) *Parsifal.* (8/94) (SCHW) Ⓓ [2] **314522**

1, 23b B. Terfel, BPO, C. Abbado (pp1993) *Concert* (5/94) (DG) Ⓓ **439 768-2GH**

1, 33, 49. VPO, W. Furtwängler (r1949/50) *Concert* (4/94) (EMI) Ⓓ [2] **CHS7 64935-2**

1, 33, 49, 50. Chicago SO, F. Reiner (r1959) *Concert* (8/94) (RCA) Ⓓ **09026 61792-2**

1, 49. LPO, K.A. Rickenbacher *Concert* (11/87) (CFP) Ⓓ **CD-CFP9008**

1, 49. Philh, O. Klemperer (r1960) *Concert* (11/90) (EMI) Ⓓ **CDM7 63618-2**

2, 51, 56. T. Lemnitz, T. Ralf, ROH Chor, LPO, T. Beecham (pp1936) *Concert* (6/94) (DUTT) Ⓓ **CDLX7007**

12. I. Andrésen, orch (r1929) *Concert* (10/90) (PREI) Ⓓ **89028**

12. A. Kipnis, Berlin St Op Orch, E. Orthmann (r1931) *Concert* (12/90) (PREI) Ⓓ **89019**

12. A. Kipnis, Berlin St Op Orch, E. Orthmann (r1931) *Concert* (7/92) (PEAR) Ⓓ [3] **GEMMCDS9926(1)**

12. W. Hesch, orch (r1906) *Concert* (7/93) (NIMB) Ⓓ [2] **NI7840/1**

15. L. Melchior, LSO, L. Collingwood (r1931) *Concert* (8/88) (DANA) Ⓓ [2] **DACOCD315/6**

15. L. Melchior, LSO, L. Collingwood (r1931) *Concert* (10/89) (EMI) Ⓓ **CDH7 69789-2**

15. F. Völker, Berlin St Op Orch, J. Heidenreich (r1928) *Concert* (2/90) (PREI) Ⓓ **89005**

15. G. Zenatello, anon (r1903: Ital) *Concert* (6/90) (SYMP) Ⓓ **SYMCD1073**

15. L. Melchior, LSO, L. Collingwood (r1931) *Concert* (10/92) (TEST) Ⓓ **SBT1005**

15. R. Tauber, Berlin St Op Orch, G. Szell (r1927) *Concert* (12/92) (NIMB) Ⓓ **NI7830**

15. M. Lorenz, Berlin St Op Orch, C. Schmalstich (r1930) *Concert* (10/93) (NIMB) Ⓓ **NI7848**

15. G. Zenatello, orch (r1911: Ital) *Concert* (5/94) (SYMP) Ⓓ **SYMCD1168**

15. G. Zenatello, orch (r1911: Ital) *Concert* (5/94) (PEAR) Ⓓ [4] **GEMMCDS9073(2)**

15. G. Zenatello, anon (r1903: Ital) *Concert* (5/94) (PEAR) Ⓓ [4] **GEMMCDS9073(1)**

15, 18. F. Giraud, anon (r1904: Ital) *Concert* (5/91) (SYMP) Ⓓ **SYMCD1077**

15, 18. P. Anders, H. Hotter, B. Kusche, ROHO, T. Beecham (bp1951) *Concert* (8/93) (ACAN) Ⓓ **43 268**

15, 56. R. Tauber, orch (r1927) *Concert* (7/89) (PEAR) Ⓓ **GEMMCD9327**

15, 56. R. Tauber, Berlin St Op Orch, G. Szell (r1927) *Concert* (3/92) (EMI) Ⓓ **CDH7 64029-2**

15, 56. H. Roswaenge, Berlin St Op Orch, F.A. Schmidt (r1932) *Concert* (4/95) (PREI) Ⓓ [2] **89209**

18. G. Zenatello, orch (r1910: Ital) *Concert* (5/94) (SYMP) Ⓓ **SYMCD1168**

18. G. Zenatello, orch (r1910: Ital) *Concert* (5/94) (PEAR) Ⓓ [4] **GEMMCDS9073(2)**

18. T. Ralf, Berlin St Op Orch, H.U. Müller (r1941) *Concert* (10/94) (PREI) Ⓓ **89077**

18, 56. F. Völker, Berlin St Op Orch, M. Gurlitt (r1928) *Concert* (2/90) (PREI) Ⓓ **89005**

23b F. Schorr, LSO, A. Coates (r1930) *Concert* (1/92) (EMI) Ⓓ [4] **CMS7 64008-2(1)**

23b P. Schoeffler, Zurich Tonhalle Orch, H. Knappertsbusch (r1947) *Concert* (1/95) (PREI) Ⓓ **90190**

23b, 36. B. Weikl, Munich RO, H. Wallberg *Concert* (3/89) (ACAN) Ⓓ **43 266**

23b, 36. M. Schenk, Nuremberg SO, K. Seibel *Concert* (12/91) (COLO) Ⓓ **COL34 9004**

23b, 57. H. Hermann Nissen, Berlin SO, F. Zweig (r1929) *Concert* (12/95) (PREI) Ⓓ **89090**

24. Lotte Lehmann, M. Bohnen, orch (r1916) *Concert* (6/92) (PREI) Ⓓ [3] **89302**

24. M. Reining, P. Schoeffler, Zurich Tonhalle Orch, H. Knappertsbusch (r1949) *Concert* (9/92) (PREI) Ⓓ **90083**

24. P. Schoeffler, M. Reining, Zurich Tonhalle Orch, H. Knappertsbusch (r1949) *Concert* (1/95) (PREI) Ⓓ **90190**

26. G. Thill, G. Martinelli, orch, E. Bigot (French: r1935) *Concert* (1/92) (EMI) Ⓓ [4] **CMS7 64008-2(1)**

28b F. Schorr, LSO, A. Coates (r1930) *Concert* (9/91) (PEAR) Ⓓ **GEMMCD9398**

28b R. Bockelmann, Berlin St Op Orch, C. Schmalstich (r1930) *Concert* (1/92) (EMI) Ⓓ [4] **CMS7 64008-2(1)**

28b R. Bockelmann, Berlin St Op Orch, C. Schmalstich (r1930) *Concert* (7/92) (PEAR) Ⓓ [3] **GEMMCDS9926(2)**

28b A. Van Rooy, anon (r1902) *Concert* (3/93) (SYMP) Ⓓ **SYMCD1100**

28b, 47. L. Hofmann, Lotte Lehmann, K. Thorborg, E. Laholm, W. Wernigk, H. Wiedemann, Vienna St Op Orch, F. Weingartner (pp1935) *Concert* (11/95) (SCHW) Ⓓ [2] **314622**

33. NBC SO, A. Toscanini (r1951) *Concert* (11/92) (RCA) Ⓓ **GD60305**

33. Vienna St Op Orch, F. Weingartner (pp1934) *Concert* (7/94) (SCHW) Ⓓ [2] **314512**

33, 49, 50. Seattle SO, G. Schwarz *Concert* (3/87) (DELO) Ⓓ **DE3040**

33, 49, 50. NYPO, J. Barbirolli (pp1938) *Concert* (3/95) (DUTT) Ⓓ **CDSJB1001**

36. F. Schorr, Berlin St Op Orch, L. Blech (r1929) *Concert* (1/92) (EMI) Ⓓ [4] **CMS7 64008-2(1)**

36. C. Whitehill, orch, P. Pitt (r1922) *Concert* (7/92) (PEAR) Ⓓ [3] **GEMMCDS9924(1)**

36. P. Schoeffler, National SO, K. Rankl (r1946) *Concert* (1/95) (PREI) Ⓓ **90190**

36. H. Hermann Nissen, Berlin SO, F. Zweig (r1927) *Concert* (12/95) (PREI) Ⓓ **89090**

36, 37, 40. C. Doig, D. McIntyre, NZ SO, H. Wallberg *Concert* (11/92) (ODE) Ⓓ **CDMANU1317**

40. L. Melchior, F. Schorr, LSO, R. Heger (r1931) *Concert* (8/88) (DANA) Ⓓ [2] **DACOCD315/6**

43b, 44. E. Rethberg, F. Schorr, Victor SO, R. Bourdon (r1929) *Concert* (10/95) (ROMO) Ⓓ [2] **81014-2**

43b, 44, 45. E. Rethberg, F. Schorr, orch, R. Bourdon (r1929) *Concert* (4/94) (RCA) Ⓓ [6] **09026 61580-2(3)**

45. Lotte Lehmann, orch (r1921) *Concert* (6/92) (PREI) Ⓓ [3] **89302**

47. E. Schumann, G. Parr, L. Melchior, B. Williams, F. Schorr, LSO, J. Barbirolli (r1931) *Concert* (8/88) (DANA) Ⓓ [2] **DACOCD315/6**

47. E. Schumann, G. Parr, L. Melchior, B. Williams, F. Schorr, LSO, J. Barbirolli (r1931) *Concert* (1/92) (EMI) Ⓓ [4] **CMS7 64008-2(1)**

47. H. Roswaenge, P. Yoder, L. Kindermann, H. Reinmar, M. Kuttner, Berlin St Op Orch, S. Meyrowitz (r1932) *Concert* (4/95) (PREI) Ⓓ [2] **89209**

50, 51. Bayreuth Fest Chor, Bayreuth Fest Orch, W. Pitz *Concert* (4/90) (DG) Ⓓ **429 169-2GR**
51. Vienna St Op Chor, Vienna St Op Orch, W. Furtwängler (pp1938) *Concert* (6/94) (SCHW) Ⓓ **314502**
56. L. Melchior, O. Helgers (r1926) *Concert* (8/88) (DANA) Ⓓ [2] **DACOCD315/6**
56. L. Melchior, LSO, J. Barbirolli (r1931) *Concert* (8/88) (DANA) Ⓓ [2] **DACOCD315/6**
56. L. Melchior, orch (r1923) *Concert* (8/88) (DANA) Ⓓ [2] **DACOCD313/4**
56. L. Melchior, LSO, J. Barbirolli (r1931) *Concert* (10/89) (EMI) Ⓓ **CDH7 69789-2**
56. F. Kreisler, H. Kreisler, C. Keith (r1923: arr Kreisler) *Concert* (7/90) (BIDD) Ⓓ [2] **LAB009/10**
56(pt) H. Winkelmann, anon (r1904) *Concert* (7/91) (SYMP) Ⓓ **SYMCD1081**
56. P. Casals, N. Mednikoff (r1926: arr vc/pf) *Concert* (10/91) (BIDD) Ⓓ **LAB017**
56. T. Lemnitz, T. Ralf, R. Bockelmann, ROH Chor, LPO, T. Beecham (pp1936) *Concert* (1/92) (EMI) Ⓓ [4] **CMS7 64008-2(1)**
56. H.E. Groh, orch (r1933) *Concert* (3/92) (PEAR) Ⓓ **GEMMCD9419**
56. J. Hislop, orch, J. Barbirolli (r1929: Eng) *Concert* (1/93) (PEAR) Ⓓ **GEMMCD9956**
56. B. Harrison, C. Salzedo, orch (r1915: arr vc/orch) *Concert* (3/93) (CLAR) Ⓓ **CDGSE78-50-47**
56. P. Domingo, D. Fischer-Dieskau, P. Lagger, C. Ligendza, Berlin Deutsche Op Chor, Berlin Deutsche Op Orch, E. Jochum *Concert* (5/93) (DG) Ⓓ **431 104-2GB**
56. C. Kullman, orch, W. Goehr (r1938) *Concert* (11/93) (PREI) Ⓓ **89057**
56. S. Svanholm, RCA SO, F. Weissmann (r1947) *Concert* (4/94) (RCA) Ⓓ [6] **09026 61580-2(6)**
56. R. Crooks, orch, R. Bourdon (r1928) *Concert* (5/94) (CLAR) Ⓓ **CDGSE78-50-52**
56. P. Domingo, D. Fischer-Dieskau, P. Lagger, C. Ligendza, Berlin Deutsche Op Chor, Berlin Deutsche Op Orch, E. Jochum *Concert* (6/94) (BELA) Ⓓ **450 121-2**
56. R. Tauber, orch (r1927) *Concert* (12/94) (MMOI) Ⓓ **CDMOIR425**
56. J. Johnston, ROHO, M. Mudie (r1948: Eng) *Concert* (4/95) (TEST) Ⓓ **SBT1058**
57. A. Kipnis, Berlin St Op Orch, L. Blech (r1926) *Concert* (10/91) (PEAR) Ⓓ **GEMMCD9451**

Parsifal—opera: 3 acts (1882—Bayreuth) (Lib. cpsr)

1. Prelude. ACT 1: 2. He! Ho! Waldhüter ihr; 3. Hei! Wie fliegen der Teufelsmähre; 4. Recht so! - Habt Dank!; 5. Wann alles ratlos steht; 6. Das ist ein and'res; 7. Titurel, der fromme Held; 8. Weh! Weh! Hoho! Auf!; 9. Unerhörtes Werk; 10. Den Vaterlosen gebar die Mutter; 11. So recht! So nach des Grales Gnade; 12a. Vom Bade kehrt der König heim; 12b. Transformation Scene; 13. Nun achte wohl....Zum letzten Liebesmahle; 14a. Mein Sohn Amfortas; 14b. Nein! Lasst ihn unenthüllt; 14c. Wehvolles Erbe; 15. 'Durch Mitleid wissend....'. ACT 2: 16. Prelude; 17. Die Zeit ist da; 18. Ach! Tiefe Nacht...Furchtbare Not!; 19. Hier war das Tosen!; 20. Komm; Komm; holder Knabe!; 21. Dies alles - hab' ich nun geträumt?; 22. Ich sah das Kind (Herzeleide); 23. Wehe! Wehe! Was tat ich?; 24. Amfortas! Die wunde!; 25. Grausamer! Fühlst du im Herzen; 26. Auf Ewigkeit. ACT 3: 27. Prelude; 28. Von dorther kam; 29. Heil dir, mein Gast!; 30. Zu ihm, des tiefe Klagen; 31. O Gnade! Höchstes Heil!; 32. Du wuchest mir die Füsse (Good Friday music); 33a. Transformation Scene; 33b. Geleiten wir im bergenden Schrein; 34. Ja, Wehe! Wehe! Weh' über mich!; 35. Nur eine Waffe taugt. 36. Good Friday music (concert version).

Cpte P. Hofmann, J. Van Dam, K. Moll, D. Vejzovic, S. Nimsgern, V. von Halem, C.H. Ahnsjö, K. Rydl, M. Lambriks, A. Gjevang, H. Hopfner, G. Tichy, B. Hendricks, J. Perry, D. Soffel, I. Nielsen, A. Michael, R. Yachmi-Caucig, H. Schwarz, Berlin Deutsche Op Chor, BPO, H. von Karajan (r1979/80) (10/84) (DG) Ⓓ [4] **413 347-2GH4**
Cpte Jess Thomas, G. London, H. Hotter, I. Dalis, G. Neidlinger, M. Talvela, N. Møller, G. Nienstedt, Š. Červená, U. Boese, G. Stolze, G. Paskuda, G. Janowitz, A. Silja, E-M. Gardelli, D. Siebert, R. Bartos, Š. Červená, Bayreuth Fest Chor, Bayreuth Fest Orch, H. Knappertsbusch (pp1962) (6/86) (PHIL) Ⓓ [4] **416 390-2PH4**
Cpte R. Kollo, D. Fischer-Dieskau, G. Frick, C. Ludwig, Z. Kélémen, H. Hotter, R. Tear, H. Lackner, R. Hansmann, M. Schiml, H. Zednik, E. Aichberger, L. Popp, A. Hargan, A. Howells, K. Te Kanawa, G. Knight, M. Lilowa, B. Finnilä, Vienna Boys' Ch, Vienna St Op Chor, VPO, G. Solti (r1971/2) (9/86) (DECC) Ⓓ [4] **417 143-2DH4**
Cpte S. Jerusalem, J. Van Dam, M. Hölle, W. Meier, G. von Kannen, J. Tomlinson, K. Schreibmayer, C. Hauptmann, M. Rørholm, A. Küttenbaum, H. Pampuch, P. Maus, E. Wiens, C. Hauman, D. Bechly, H. Leidland, P. Coburn, S. Burgess, W. Meier, Berlin St Op Chor, BPO, D. Barenboim (10/91) (TELD) Ⓓ [4] **9031-74448-2**
Cpte R. Goldberg, W. Schöne, R. Lloyd, Y. Minton, A. Haugland, H. Tschammer, P. Frey, G. Cachemaille, T. Herz, H. Schaer, C. Bladin, M. Roider, B-M. Aruhn, E. Saurova, G. Oertel, J. Chamonin, Prague Phil Chor, Monte Carlo Op Orch, A. Jordan (9/92) (ERAT) Ⓓ [4] **2292-45662-2**
Cpte J. King, T. Stewart, F. Crass, G. Jones, D. McIntyre, K. Ridderbusch, H. Esser, B. Rundgren, E. Schwarzenberg, S. Wagner, D. Slembeck, H. Zednik, H. Bode, M. Kyriaki, I. Paustian, D. Siebert, W. Fine, Bayreuth Fest Chor, Bayreuth Fest Orch, P. Boulez (pp1970) (9/92) (DG) Ⓓ [3] **435 718-2GX3**
Cpte P. Hofmann, S. Estes, H. Sotin, W. Meier, F. Mazura, M. Salminen, M. Pabst, M. Hölle, R. Engert-Ely, S. Fues, H. Pampuch, P. Maus, D. Sasson, S. Roberts, M. Schmitt, A. Browner, H. Leidland, M. Neubauer, Bayreuth Fest Chor, Bayreuth Fest Orch, James Levine (pp1985) (10/92) (PHIL) Ⓓ [4] **434 616-2PH4**
Cpte W. Windgassen, G. London, L. Weber, M. Mödl, H. Uhde, A. Van Mill, W. Fritz, W. Faulhaber, H. Ludwig, E. Wild, G. Baldauf, G. Stolze, H. Schünemann, E. Zimmermann, P. Brivkalne, M. Lacorn, R. Siewert, Bayreuth Fest Chor, Bayreuth Fest Orch, H. Knappertsbusch (pp1951) (8/93) (TELD) Ⓓ [4] **9031-76047-2**
Cpte R. Kollo, T. Adam, U. Cold, G. Schröter, R. Bunger, F. Teschler, H. Gebhardt, H.C. Polster, E. Breul, G. Pohl, H-J. Wachsmuth, R. Werner, H. Ambros, H. Terner, I. Ludwig-Jahns, I. Springer, Leipzig Rad Chor, Berlin Rad Chor, Leipzig St Thomas Church Ch, Leipzig RSO, H. Kegel (pp1975) (1/94) (SCHW) Ⓓ [4] **313482**
Cpte P. Domingo, J. Morris, K. Moll, J. Norman, E. Wlaschiha, J-H. Rootering, A. Glassman, J. Robbins, H.G. Murphy, J. Bunnell, P. Groves, A. Laciura, K. Erickson, K. Uecker, J. Guyer, W. White, H. Katagiri, NY Met Op Chor, NY Met Op Orch, James Levine (r1991/2) (11/94) (DG) Ⓓ [4] **437 501-2GH4**
Act 3 (abridged) G. Pistor, C. Bronsgeest, L. Hofmann, Berlin St Op Chor, Berlin St Op Orch, K. Muck (r1928) *Concert* (4/90) (OPAL) Ⓓ [2] **OPALCDS9843**
Excs M. Lorenz, H. Braun, Vienna St Op Chor, Vienna St Op Orch, H. Knappertsbusch (pp1942) *Concert* (1/95) (SCHW) Ⓓ [2] **314562**
Excs M. Lorenz, P. Schoeffler, S. Roth, H. Braun, Adolf Vogel, Vienna St Op Chor, Vienna St Op Orch, L. Reichwein (pp1942) *Concert* (1/95) (SCHW) Ⓓ [2] **314562**
Excs H. Alsen, N. Zec, F. Destal, E. Nikolaidi, Vienna St Op Chor, Vienna St Op Orch, H. Knappertsbusch (pp1937) *Concert* (6/95) (SCHW) Ⓓ [2] **314632**
Excs G. Graarud, J. von Manowarda, E. Schipper, G. Rünger, H. Wiedemann, Vienna St Op Chor, Vienna St Op Orch, C. Krauss (pp1933) *Concert* (8/95) (SCHW) Ⓓ [2] **314642**
Symphonic synthesis from Act 3. Philadelphia, L. Stokowski (arr Stokowski: r1934) *Concert* (2/91) (PEAR) Ⓓ **GEMMCD9448**
1. BPO, W. Furtwängler (r1938) *Concert* (2/89) (ACAN) Ⓓ **43 121**
1. Berlin St Op Orch, K. Muck (r1927) *Concert* (4/90) (OPAL) Ⓓ [2] **OPALCDS9843**
1. Philh, O. Klemperer (r1961) *Concert* (11/90) (EMI) Ⓓ **CDM7 63618-2**
1. Philh, Y. Simonov *Concert* (10/91) (COLL) Ⓓ **Coll1207-2**
1. NYPSO, F. Reiner (r1938) *Concert* (4/92) (PEAR) Ⓓ [3] **GEMMCDS9922**
1. NQHO, B. Wordsworth (r1995) *Concert* (6/95) (EYE) Ⓓ [2] **EOS5001**
1. LCP, R. Norrington (r1994) *Concert* (11/95) (EMI) Ⓓ **CDC5 55479-2**
1, 13, 16, 19, 20, 24, 26(pt), 27, 32(pt), 33a, 33b, 35(pt) H. Grahl, H. Alsen, A. Konetzni, H. Wiedemann, Vienna St Op Chor, Vienna St Op Orch, H. Knappertsbusch (pp1939) *Meistersinger.* (8/94) (SCHW) Ⓓ [2] **314522**
1, 36. Philadelphia, L. Stokowski (r1936) *Concert* (2/91) (PEAR) Ⓓ **GEMMCD9448**
1, 36. NBC SO, A. Toscanini (r1949) *Concert* (11/92) (RCA) Ⓓ **GD60305**
1, 36. BPO, W. Furtwängler (r1938) *Concert* (4/94) (EMI) Ⓓ [2] **CHS7 64935-2**
1, 36. BPO, W. Furtwängler (r1938) *Concert* (7/94) (BIDD) Ⓓ [2] **WHL006/7**
7, 32. I. Andrésen, Berlin St Op Orch, L. Blech (r1927) *Concert* (10/90) (PREI) Ⓓ **89028**
12b, 15, 19. Bayreuth Fest Chor, Bayreuth Fest Orch, K. Muck (r1927) *Concert* (4/90) (OPAL) Ⓓ [2] **OPALCDS9843**
13. J. Greindl, Bayreuth Fest Chor, Bayreuth Fest Orch, W. Pitz *Concert* (4/90) (DG) Ⓓ **429 169-2GR**
14a C. Whitehill, orch, T. Levy (r1914) *Concert* (4/94) (RCA) Ⓓ [6] **09026 61580-2(2)**
14b, 14c H. Hermann Nissen, Berlin SO, F. Zweig (r1928) *Concert* (12/95) (PREI) Ⓓ **89090**
21, 22. K. Flagstad, L. Melchior, RCA Victor SO, E. MacArthur (r1940) *Concert* (10/90) (RCA) Ⓓ **GD87915**
22. F. Leider, LSO, J. Barbirolli (r1931) *Concert* (11/89) (PEAR) Ⓓ **GEMMCD9331**
22. F. Leider, LSO, J. Barbirolli (r1931) *Concert* (2/90) (PREI) Ⓓ **89004**
22. F. Leider, orch (r1925) *Concert* (5/91) (PREI) Ⓓ [3] **89301**
22. F. Leider, LSO, J. Barbirolli (r1931) *Concert* (1/92) (EMI) Ⓓ [4] **CMS7 64008-2(2)**
22. F. Leider, LSO, J. Barbirolli (r1931) *Concert* (2/92) (MMOI) Ⓓ **CDMOIR408**
22. K. Thorborg, RCA SO, K. Riedel (r1940) *Concert* (4/95) (PREI) Ⓓ **89084**
22. K. Flagstad, VPO, H. Knappertsbusch (r1956) *Concert* (12/95) (LOND) Ⓓ [5] **440 490-2LM5(1)**
22. K. Flagstad, VPO, H. Knappertsbusch (r1956) *Concert* (12/95) (LOND) Ⓓ **440 495-2LM**
22. K. Flagstad, RCA Victor SO, E. McArthur (r1941) *Concert* (12/95) (SIMA) Ⓓ [3] **PSC1821(2)**
24. L. Melchior, orch, P. Breisach (r1925) *Concert* (8/88) (DANA) Ⓓ [2] **DACOCD313/4**
25(pt) K. Thorborg, Vienna St Op Orch, F. Weingartner (pp1936) *Concert* (7/94) (SCHW) Ⓓ [2] **314512**
31(pt), 32(pt) C. Doig, D. McIntyre, NZ SO, H. Wallberg *Concert* (11/92) (ODE) Ⓓ **CDMANU1317**
32. F. Wolff, A. Kipnis, Bayreuth Fest Orch, S. Wagner (r1927) *Concert* (1/92) (EMI) Ⓓ [4] **CMS7 64008-2(2)**
35. L. Melchior, orch, P. Breisach (r1924) *Concert* (8/88) (DANA) Ⓓ [2] **DACOCD313/4**

Rienzi—opera: 5 acts (1842—Dresden) (Libr. cpsr)

ACT 1: 1. Overture; 2. Erstehe, hohe Roma, neu; 3. Ihr Römer, hort die Kunde; 4. Gerechter Gott...In seiner Blüthe; 5. Allmächt'ger Vater (Rienzi's prayer).

Cpte R. Kollo, S. Wennberg, N. Hillebrand, J. Martin, T. Adam, S. Vogel, P. Schreier, G. Leib, I. Springer, Leipzig Rad Chor, Dresden St Op Chor, Staatskapelle Dresden, H. Hollreiser (2/92) (EMI) Ⓓ [3] **CMS7 63980-2**
Excs F. Völker, R. Anday, H. Gallos, K. Ettl, Vienna St Op Chor, Vienna St Op Orch, J. Krips (pp1933) *Concert* (9/95) (SCHW) Ⓓ [2] **314662**
1. Philh, F. d'Avalos *Concert* (10/90) (ASV) Ⓓ **CDDCA704**
1. Philh, O. Klemperer *Concert* (11/90) (EMI) Ⓓ **CDM7 63617-2**
1. Oslo PO, M. Jansons *Concert* (12/92) (EMI) Ⓓ **CDC7 54583-2**
1. NY Met Op Orch, James Levine (r1991) *Concert* (10/93) (DG) Ⓓ **435 874-2GH**
1. Minnesota Orch, N. Marriner (r1983) *Concert* (2/94) (TELA) Ⓓ **CD82005**
1. NYPO, J. Barbirolli (pp1938) *Concert* (3/95) (DUTT) Ⓓ **CDSJB1001**
1. NQHO, B. Wordsworth (r1995) *Concert* (6/95) (EYE) Ⓓ [2] **EOS5001**
1. LCP, R. Norrington (r1994) *Concert* (11/95) (EMI) Ⓓ **CDC5 55479-2**
2. F. Völker, Berlin St Op Orch, A. Melichar (r1933) *Concert* (2/90) (PREI) Ⓓ **89005**
2. F. Völker, Vienna St Op Chor, Vienna St Op Orch, J. Krips (pp1933) *Concert* (6/94) (SCHW) Ⓓ **314502**
4. E. Schumann-Heink, orch (r1908) *Concert* (2/91) (NIMB) Ⓓ **NI7811**
4. F. Leider, orch (r1922) *Concert* (5/91) (PREI) Ⓓ [3] **89301**
4. G. Janowitz, Berlin Deutsche Op Orch, F. Leitner (r1967) *Concert* (12/95) (DG) Ⓓ [2] **447 352-2GDB2**
5. L. Melchior, orch (r1923) *Concert* (8/88) (DANA) Ⓓ [2] **DACOCD313/4**
5. L. Melchior, LSO, J. Barbirolli (r1930) *Concert* (8/88) (DANA) Ⓓ [2] **DACOCD315/6**
5. L. Melchior, LSO, J. Barbirolli (r1930) *Concert* (10/89) (EMI) Ⓓ **CDH7 69789-2**
5. F. Völker, Berlin St Op Orch, H. Weigert (r1930) *Concert* (2/90) (PREI) Ⓓ **89005**
5. P. Domingo, National PO, E. Kohn *Concert* (11/90) (EMI) Ⓓ **CDC7 54053-2**
5. F. Völker, Berlin Staatskapelle, A. Melichar (r1930) *Concert* (10/93) (NIMB) Ⓓ **NI7848**

5. F. Völker, Berlin Staatskapelle, G. Steeger (r1941) *Concert* (8/94) (PREI) ① **89070**

Der **Ring des Nibelungen—explanation and analysis of Leitmotifs**

D. Cooke, Sols, VPO, G. Solti (r1958-67) (5/95) (DECC) ① [2] **443 581-2DCS2**

Der **Ring des Nibelungen: Part 1, '(Das) Rheingold'—opera: 4 scenes (1869—Munich)** (Lib. cpsr)

EXCERPTS. SCENE 1; 1. Prelude; 2. Weia! Waga! Woge, du Welle; 3. He he! Ihr Nicker!; 4. Garstig glatter glitschriger Glimmer!; 5. Lugt, Schwestern; 6a. Der Welt Erbe; 6b. Spottet nur zu!; 7. orchestral interlude. SCENE 2: 8. Wotan! Gemahl! erwache!; 9. So schirme sie jetzt; 10. Sanft schloss Schlaf dein Aug'; 11. Du da, folge uns; 12. Endlich Loge!; 13. Immer ist Undank Loges Lohn; 14. Hör Wotan, der Harrenden Wort!; 15a. Schwester! Brüder! Rettet! Helft!; 15b. Uber stock und Stein; 16. Jetzt fand ich's; 17. Wotan, Gemahl, unsel'ger Mann!; 18a. Auf Loge hinab mit mir!; 18b. Nach! Nibelheim fahren wir nieder; 19. orchestral interlude (descent into Nibelheim). SCENE 3: 20. Hehe! hehe!; 21. Nibelheim hier; 22. Mit eurem Gefrage; 23. Was wollt ihr hier?; 24. Die in linder Lüfte Wehn da oben ihr lebt; 25. Riesenwurm winde sich ringeland!. SCENE 4: 26. Da, Vetter, sitze du fest!; 27. Wohlan, die Nibelheim rief ich mir nah; 28. Bin ich nun frei? (Alberich's curse); 29. Lauschtest du seinem Liebesgruss?; 30. Halt! Nicht sie berührt; 31. Nich so leicht und locker gefügt; 32. Freia, die Schöne; 33. Weiche, Wotan, weiche! (Erda's warning); 34. Hört, ihr Riesen!; 35. Halt, du Gieriger!; 36. Was gelicht, Wotan; 37. Schwüles Gedünst schwebt in der Luft; 38. Zur Burg führt die Brücke; 39. Abendlich strahlt; 40. Ihrem Ende; 41. Rheingold! Rheingold!; 42. Entrance of the Gods into Valhalla (orchestral version).

Cpte G. London, K. Flagstad, S. Svanholm, P. Kuen, G. Neidlinger, C. Watson, W. Kmentt, E. Waechter, J. Madeira, W. Kreppel, K. Böhme, O. Balsborg, H. Plümacher, I. Malaniuk, VPO, G. Solti (r1958) (10/84) (DECC) ① [3] **414 101-2DH3**

Cpte T. Adam, Y. Minton, P. Schreier, C. Vogel, S. Nimsgern, M. Napier, E. Büchner, K-H. Stryczek, O. Wenkel, R. Bracht, M. Salminen, L. Popp, U. Priew, H. Schwarz, Staatskapelle Dresden, M. Janowski (10/84) (EURM) ① [2] **GD69004**

Cpte T. Adam, A. Burmeister, W. Windgassen, E. Wohlfahrt, G. Neidlinger, A. Silja, H. Esser, G. Nienstedt, V. Soukupová, M. Talvela, K. Böhme, D. Siebert, H. Dernesch, R. Hesse, Bayreuth Fest Orch, K. Böhm (pp1967) (7/85) (PHIL) ① [2] **412 475-2PH2**

Cpte D. Fischer-Dieskau, J. Veasey, G. Stolze, E. Wohlfahrt, Z. Kélémen, S. Mangelsdorff, D. Grobe, R. Kerns, O. Dominguez, M. Talvela, K. Ridderbusch, H. Donath, E. Moser, A. Reynolds, BPO, H. von Karajan (r1967) (7/85) (DG) ① [3] **415 141-2GH3**

Cpte H. Hotter, I. Malaniuk, E. Witte, P. Kuen, G. Neidlinger, B. Falcon, G. Stolze, H. Uhde, M. von Ilosvay, L. Weber, J. Greindl, E. Zimmermann, H. Plümacher, G. Litz, Bayreuth Fest Orch, C. Krauss (pp1953) *Concert* (6/88) (FOYE) ① [15] **15-CF2011**

Cpte H. Hotter, I. Malaniuk, E. Witte, P. Kuen, G. Neidlinger, B. Falcon, G. Stolze, H. Uhde, M. von Ilosvay, L. Weber, J. Greindl, E. Zimmermann, H. Plümacher, G. Litz, Bayreuth Fest Orch, C. Krauss (pp1953) (6/88) (FOYE) ① [3] **3-CF2007**

Cpte H. Hotter, H. Uhde, G. Stolze, E. Witte, G. Neidlinger, P. Kuen, L. Weber, J. Greindl, I. Malaniuk, B. Falcon, M. von Ilosvay, E. Zimmermann, H. Plümacher, G. Litz, Bayreuth Fest Orch, C. Krauss (pp1953) (6/88) (LAUD) ① [3] **LCD3 4002**

Cpte G. London, K. Flagstad, S. Svanholm, P. Kuen, G. Neidlinger, C. Watson, W. Kmentt, E. Waechter, J. Madeira, W. Kreppel, K. Böhme, O. Balsborg, H. Plümacher, I. Malaniuk, VPO, G. Solti (r1958) *Concert* (3/89) (DECC) ① [15] **414 100-2DM15**

Cpte J. Morris, M. Lipovšek, H. Zednik, P. Haage, T. Adam, E. Johansson, P. Seiffert, A. Schmidt, J. Rappé, H. Tschammer, K. Rydl, J. Kaufman, S. Herman, S. Quittmeyer, BRSO, B. Haitink (r1988) (12/89) (EMI) ① [2] **CDS7 49853-2**

Cpte F. Frantz, I. Malaniuk, W. Windgassen, J. Patzak, G. Neidlinger, E. Grümmer, L. Fehenberger, A. Poell, R. Siewert, J. Greindl, G. Frick, S. Jurinac, M. Gabory, H. Rössl-Majdan, Rome RAI Orch, W. Furtwängler (bp1953) *Concert* (2/91) (EMI) ① [13] **CZS7 67123-2**

Cpte D. Fischer-Dieskau, J. Veasey, G. Stolze, E. Wohlfahrt, Z. Kélémen, S. Mangelsdorff, D. Grobe, R. Kerns, O. Dominguez, M. Talvela, K. Ridderbusch, H. Donath, E. Moser, A. Reynolds, BPO, H. von Karajan *Concert* (4/92) (DG) ① [15] **435 211-2GX15**

Cpte N. Bailey, K. Pring, E. Belcourt, G. Dempsey, D. Hammond-Stroud, L. McDonall, R. Ferguson, N. Welsby, A. Collins, R. Lloyd, C. Grant, V. Masterson, S. Squires, H. Attfield, ENO Orch, R. Goodall (Eng: pp1975) (4/92) (EMI) ① [3] **CMS7 64110-2**

Cpte D. McIntyre, H. Schwarz, H. Zednik, H. Pampuch, H. Becht, C. Reppel, S. Jerusalem, M. Egel, O. Wenkel, M. Salminen, F. Hübner, N. Sharp, I. Gramatzki, M. Schiml, Bayreuth Fest Orch, P. Boulez (pp1980) (10/92) (PHIL) ① [2] **434 421-2PH2**

Cpte J. Tomlinson, L. Finnie, G. Clark, H. Pampuch, G. von Kannen, E. Johansson, K. Schreibmayer, B. Brinkmann, B. Svendén, M. Hölle, P. Kang, H. Leidland, A. Küttenbaum, J. Turner, Bayreuth Fest Orch, D. Barenboim (pp1991) (10/93) (TELD) ① [2] **4509-91185-2**

Cpte J. Morris, C. Ludwig, S. Jerusalem, H. Zednik, E. Wlaschiha, M.A. Häggander, M. Baker, S. Lorenz, B. Svendén, K. Moll, J-H. Rootering, H-K. Hong, D. Kesling, M. Parsons, NY Met Op Orch, James Levine (r1988) *Concert* (10/94) (DG) ① [14] **445 354-2GX14**

Cpte T. Adam, A. Burmeister, W. Windgassen, E. Wohlfahrt, G. Neidlinger, A. Silja, H. Esser, G. Nienstedt, V. Soukupová, M. Talvela, K. Böhme, D. Siebert, H. Dernesch, R. Hesse, Bayreuth Fest Orch, K. Böhm (pp1966) *Concert* (10/94) (PHIL) ① [14] **446 057-2PB14**

Cpte R. Hale, H. Schwarz, K. Begley, P. Schreier, F-J. Kapellmann, N. Gustafson, T. Sunnegårdh, E. W. Schulte, E. Zaremba, J-H. Rootering, W. Fink, G. Fontana, I. Komlósi, M. Hintermeier, Cleveland Orch, C. von Dohnányi (r1993) (11/95) (DECC) ① [2] **443 690-2DHO2**

Excs BPO, L. Maazel (without voices) *Concert* (10/88) (TELA) ① **CD80154**

Excs J. Prohaska, N. Zec, H. Alsen, A. Konetzni, Vienna St Op Orch, J. Krips (pp1937) *Concert* (8/95) (SCHW) ① [2] **314592**

Excs J. von Manowarda, B. Paalen, V. Ursuleac, G. Graarud, V. Madin, J. Kalenberg, E. Zimmermann, H. Wiedemann, F. Markhoff, L. Helletsgruber, D. With, E. Szánthó, Vienna St Op Orch, C. Krauss (pp1933) *Concert* (8/95) (SCHW) ① [2] **314642**

Leitmotifs LSO, L. Collingwood (r1931) *Concert* (4/95) (PEAR) ① [7] **GEMMCDS9137**

1, 42. SO, A. Coates (r1926) *Concert* (11/91) (CLAR) ① [2] **CDGSE78-50-35/6**

1-5, 6a, 6b, 28-41. L. Otto, M. Muszely, S. Wagner, B. Kusche, R. Siewert, F. Frantz, J. Blatter, H. Melchert, J. Metternich, R. Schock, Berlin Staatskapelle, R. Kempe (r1959) *Concert* (10/94) (EMI) ① [4] **CMS5 65212-2**

1, 6b, 17. L. Trenton, E. Suddaby, N. Walker, W. Widdop, K. McKenna, H. Fry, A. Fear, LSO, A. Coates (r1926/8) *Concert* (4/95) (PEAR) ① [7] **GEMMCDS9137**

1, 7, 19, 42. Netherlands Rad PO, E. de Waart (r1992; arr Vlieger) *Concert* (9/93) (FIDE) ① **9201**

5, 38. Z. Kélémen, D. Grobe, D. Fischer-Dieskau, J. Veasey, G. Stolze, BPO, H. von Karajan (r1967) *Concert* (3/94) (DG) ① **439 423-2GCL**

6b, 7, 17, 18a, 18b, 19. L. Trenton, E. Suddaby, N. Walker, W. Widdop, K. McKenna, H. Fry, A. Fear, LSO, A. Coates (r1928) *Concert* (11/91) (CLAR) ① [2] **CDGSE78-50-35/6**

13(pt) O. Briesemeister, anon (r1904) *Concert* (7/91) (SYMP) ① **SYMCD1081**

21(pt) H. Breuer, anon (r1904) *Concert* (7/91) (SYMP) ① **SYMCD1081**

33. E. Schumann-Heink, H. Witherspoon, orch (r1907) *Concert* (2/91) (NIMB) ① **NI7811**

33. E. Schumann-Heink, orch, R. Bourdon (r1919) *Concert* (2/91) (NIMB) ① **NI7811**

33. E. Schumann-Heink, H. Witherspoon, orch (r1907) *Concert* (7/92) (PEAR) ① [3] **GEMMCDS9923(1)**

33. K. Branzell, orch (r1928) *Concert* (8/92) (PREI) ① **89039**

33. E. Feinhals, orch (r1908) *Concert* (12/93) (SYMP) ① **SYMCD1113**

33. K. Thorborg, RCA SO, K. Riedel (r1940) *Concert* (4/95) (PREI) ① **89084**

38. G. Guszalewicz, W. Henke, F. Schorr, Berlin St Op Orch, L. Blech (r1927) *Concert* (4/95) (PEAR) ① [7] **GEMMCDS9137**

38-41. D. Grobe, D. Fischer-Dieskau, J. Veasey, G. Stolze, H. Donath, E. Moser, A. Reynolds, BPO, H. von Karajan *Concert* (4/90) (DG) ① **429 168-2GR**

39. T. Bertram, anon (r1904) *Concert* (7/91) (SYMP) ① **SYMCD1081**

39. F. Schorr, Berlin St Op Orch, L. Blech (r1927) *Concert* (1/92) (EMI) ① [4] **CMS7 64008-2(2)**

39. T. Bertram, B. Seidler-Winkler (r1904) *Concert* (7/92) (PEAR) ① [3] **GEMMCDS9923(2)**

39. A. Van Rooy, anon (r1902) *Concert* (3/93) (SYMP) ① **SYMCD1100**

42. VPO, G. Solti *Concert* (11/83) (DECC) ① **410 137-2DH**

42. Seattle SO, G. Schwarz *Concert* (3/87) (DELO) ① **DE3040**

42. Philh, O. Klemperer (r1961) *Concert* (11/90) (EMI) ① **CDM7 63618-2**

42. Cleveland Orch, G. Szell *Concert* (11/92) (SONY) ① **SBK48175**

42. LSO, A. Coates (r1926) *Concert* (4/93) (KOCH) ① [2] **37704-2**

Der **Ring des Nibelungen: Part 2, '(Die) Walküre'—opera: 3 acts (1850—Weimar)** (Lib. cpsr)

EXCERPTS. ACT 1: 1. Prelude; 2. Wes Herd dies auch sei; 3. Müd am Herd fand ich den Mann; 4. Friedmund darf ich nicht heissen; 5. Ich weiss ein wildes Geschlecht; 6. Ein Schwert verheiss mir der Vater; 7. Schläfst du, Gast?; 8. Der Männer Sippe; 9. Winterstürme wichen dem Wonnemond; 10. Du bist der Lenz; 11. War Wälse dein Vater; 12. Siegmund heiss ich. ACT 2: 13. Prelude; 14. Nun zäume dein Ross; 15a. Hojotoho!; 15b. Dir rat ich, Vater; 16. Der alte Sturm; 17. So ist es denn aus; 18. Was verlangst du?; 19. Deiner ew'gen Gattin heilige Ehre; 20. Schimm, fürcht ich; 21. Als junger Liebe; 22. Ein andres ist's; 23a. Ihrem Willen muss ich gewähren; 23b. So nimmst du von Siegmund; 24. So sah ich Siegvater nie; 25. Raste nun hier; 26. Siegmund! Sieh auf mich! (Todesverkundigung); 27. Du sahest der Walküre; 28. Zauberfest bezähmt ein Schlaf; 29a. Der dort mich ruft; 29b. Kehrte der Vater nur heim!; 30a. Zu Ross, dass ich dich rette!; 30b. Geh hin, Knecht! ACT 3: 31. Hojotoho! (Ride of the Valkyries); 32. Schützt mich und helft; 33. Nicht sehre dich Sorgen; 34. Wo ist Brünnhild'; 35. Hier bin ich, Vater; 36. War es so schmählich; 37. Weil für dich im Auge; 38. So tatest du; 39a. Und das ich ihm in Stücken; 39b. Nicht streb, o Maid; 40. Leb wohl (Wotan's Farewell); 41. Der Augen leuchtendes Paar; 42. Loge, hör!; 43. Magic Fire Music; 44. Ride of the Valkyries (concert version).

Cpte S. Jerusalem, J. Norman, J. Altmeyer, T. Adam, Y. Minton, K. Moll, E-M. Bundschuh, R. Falcon, C. Studer, O. Wenkel, U. Priew, C. Borchers, K. Kuhlmann, A. Gjevang, Staatskapelle Dresden, M. Janowski (10/84) (EURO) ① [4] **GD69005**

Cpte J. King, Leonie Rysanek, B. Nilsson, T. Adam, A. Burmeister, G. Nienstedt, D. Mastilovic, L. Synek, H. Dernesch, G. Hopf, Š. Červená, E. Schärtel, S. Wagner, Bayreuth Fest Orch, K. Böhm (pp1967) (2/85) (PHIL) ① [4] **412 478-2PH4**

Cpte J. King, R. Crespin, B. Nilsson, H. Hotter, C. Ludwig, G. Frick, V. Schlosser, B. Lindholm, H. Dernesch, B. Fassbaender, C. Hellmann, V. Little, M. Tyler, H. Watts, VPO, G. Solti (r1965) (4/85) (DECC) ① [4] **414 105-2DH4**

Cpte J. Vickers, G. Janowitz, R. Crespin, T. Stewart, J. Veasey, M. Talvela, L. Rebmann, D. Mastilovic, C. Ordassy, I. Steger, H. Jenckel, B. Ericson, C. Ahlin, L. Brockhaus, BPO, H. von Karajan (r1966) (7/85) (DG) ① [4] **415 145-2GH4**

Cpte R. Vinay, R. Resnik, A. Varnay, H. Hotter, I. Malaniuk, J. Greindl, B. Friedland, L. Thomamüller, B. Falcon, L. Sorrell, E. Schubert, G. Litz, S. Plate, M. von Ilosvay, Bayreuth Fest Orch, C. Krauss (pp1953) *Concert* (6/88) (FOYE) ① [15] **15-CF2011**

Cpte R. Vinay, R. Resnik, A. Varnay, H. Hotter, I. Malaniuk, J. Greindl, B. Friedland, L. Thomamüller, B. Falcon, L. Sorrell, E. Schubert, G. Litz, S. Plate, M. von Ilosvay, Bayreuth Fest Orch, C. Krauss (pp1953) (6/88) (FOYE) ① [4] **4-CF2008**

Cpte R. Vinay, R. Resnik, A. Varnay, H. Hotter, J. Greindl, I. Malaniuk, B. Friedland, B. Falcon, L. Sorrell, M. von Ilosvay, L. Thomamüller, G. Litz, S. Plate, E. Schubert, Bayreuth Fest Orch, C. Krauss (pp1953) (6/88) (LAUD) ① [4] **LCD4 4003**

Cpte G. Lakes, J. Norman, H. Behrens, J. Morris, C. Ludwig, K. Moll, M. Napier, L. Kelm, M. Mims, R. Runkel, A. Wilkens, D. Kesling, M. Parsons, R. Engert-Ely, NY Met Op Orch, James Levine (11/88) (DG) ① [4] **423 389-2GH4**

Cpte R. Goldberg, C. Studer, E. Marton, J. Morris, W. Meier, M. Salminen, A. Soldh, R. Falcon, S. Herman, U. Walther, M. Lilowa, M. Hintermeier, C. Watkinson, U. Kunz, BRSO, B. Haitink (r1988) (12/88) (EMI) ① [4] **CDS7 49534-2**

Cpte J. King, R. Crespin, B. Nilsson, H. Hotter, C. Ludwig, G. Frick, V. Schlosser, B. Lindholm, H. Dernesch, B. Fassbaender, C. Hellmann, V. Little, M. Tyler, H. Watts, VPO, G. Solti (r1965) *Concert* (3/89) (DECC) ① [15] **414 100-2DM15**

Cpte L. Suthaus, Leonie Rysanek, M. Mödl, F.
Frantz, M. Klose, G. Frick, G. Schreyer, E. Köth, J.
Hellwig, D. Schmedes, D. Hermann, H. Töpper, J.
Blatter, R. Siewert, VPO, W. Furtwängler (r1954)
　(7/89) (EMI) ① [3] CHS7 63045-2
Cpte W. Windgassen, H. Konetzni, M. Mödl, F.
Frantz, E. Cavelti, G. Frick, G. Scheyrer, J. Hellwig,
M. Gabory, D. Schmedes, I. Malaniuk, O. Bennings,
E. Cavelti, H. Rössl-Majdan, Rome RAI Orch, W.
Furtwängler (bp1953) Concert
　(2/91) (EMI) ① [13] CZS7 67123-2
Cpte A. Remedios, M. Curphey, R. Hunter, N. Bailey,
A. Howard, C. Grant, K. Clarke, Anne Evans, A.
Conoley, E. Connell, A. Collins, Sarah Walker, S.
Squires, H. Attfield, ENO Orch, R. Goodall (Eng:
pp1975)　(7/91) (EMI) ① [4] CMS7 63918-2
Cpte J. Vickers, G. Janowitz, R. Crespin, T. Stewart,
J. Veasey, M. Talvela, L. Rebmann, D. Mastilovic, C.
Ordassy, I. Steger, H. Jenckel, B. Ericson, C. Ahlin,
L. Brockhaus, BPO, H. von Karajan Concert
　(4/92) (DG) ① [15] 435 211-2GX15
Cpte J. Vickers, G. Brouwenstijn, B. Nilsson, G.
London, R. Gorr, D. Ward, M. Collier, Judith Pierce,
J. Malyon, M. Elkins, J. Veasey, N. Berry, M. Guy, J.
Edwards, LSO, E. Leinsdorf (r1961)
　(5/92) (DECC) ① [3] 430 391-2DM3
Cpte P. Hofmann, J. Altmeyer, G. Jones, D.
McIntyre, H. Schwarz, M. Salminen, C. Reppel, K.
Clarke, K. Middleton, G. Schnaut, E. Glauser, M.
Schiml, I. Gramatzki, G. Killebrew, Bayreuth Fest
Orch, P. Boulez (pp1980)
　(10/92) (PHIL) ① [3] 434 422-2PH3
Cpte P. Elming, N. Secunde, Anne Evans, J.
Tomlinson, L. Finnie, M. Hölle, E. Johansson, E-M.
Bundschuh, R. Floeren, S. Close, H. Dijkstra, S.
Close, B. Svendén, H. Katagiri, Bayreuth Fest Orch,
D. Barenboim (pp1992)
　(10/93) (TELD) ① [4] 4509-91186-2
Cpte L. Suthaus, M. Müller, P. Buchner, J.
Herrmann, M. Klose, J. Greindl, I. Grunow, F. Fleig,
C. Breske, F. Schmalz, E. Hufnagel, H. Grohmann,
E. Hagemann, C. Schäblen, Berlin City Op Orch, F.
Fricsay (pp1951) Concert
　(3/94) (MYTO) ① [3] 3MCD93381
Cpte G. Lakes, J. Norman, H. Behrens, J. Morris, C.
Ludwig, K. Moll, M. Napier, L. Kelm, M. Mims, R.
Runkel, A. Wilkens, D. Kesling, M. Parsons, R.
Engert-Ely, NY Met Op Orch, James Levine (r1987)
Concert　(10/94) (DG) ① [14] 445 354-2GX14
Cpte J. King, Leonie Rysanek, B. Nilsson, T. Adam,
A. Burmeister, G. Nienstedt, D. Mastilovic, L. Synek,
H. Dernesch, G. Hopf, Š. Červená, E. Schärtel, S.
Wagner, Bayreuth Fest Orch, K. Böhm (pp1967)
Concert　(10/94) (PHIL) ① [14] 446 057-2PB14
Act 1. Lotte Lehmann, L. Melchior, E. List, VPO, B.
Walter (r1935)　(10/88) (EMI) ① CDH7 61020-2
Act 1. M. Lorenz, M. Teschemacher, K. Böhme,
Saxon St Orch, K. Elmendorff (bp1944)
　(4/91) (PREI) ① 90015
Act 1. K. König, S. Dunn, P. Meven, Pittsburgh SO,
L. Maazel　(7/91) (TELA) ① CD80258
Act 1. M. Reining, F. Krauss, J. von Manowarda,
Stuttgart RSO, C. Leonhardt (bp1938) Tristan und
Isolde.　(11/93) (PREI) ① 90151
Act 1. H. Dernesch, W. Cochran, H. Sotin, New
Philh, O. Klemperer (r1969/70) Concert
　(10/94) (EMI) ① [4] CMS5 65212-2
Act 1. J. King, Leonie Rysanek, G. Nienstedt,
Bayreuth Fest Orch, K. Böhm (pp1967)
　(7/95) (PHIL) ① 442 640-2PM
Act 2. L. Melchior, Lotte Lehmann, M. Fuchs, E.
Flesch, H. Hotter, A. Jerger, M. Klose, E. List, VPO,
B. Walter, Berlin St Op Orch, B. Seidler-Winkler
(r1935/8)　(5/92) (EMI) ① CDH7 64255-2
Act 3. A. Varnay, S. Björling, Leonie Rysanek, B.
Friedland, L. Thomamüller, E. Wild, R. Siewert, E.
Lausch, H. Töpper, I. Malaniuk, H. Ludwig, Bayreuth
Fest Orch, H. von Karajan (pp1951)
　(10/93) (EMI) ① CDH7 64704-2
Excs BPO, L. Maazel (without voices) Concert
　(10/88) (TELA) ① CD80154
Excs G. Ljungberg, L. Trenton, F. Austral, F. Leider,
W. Widdop, H. Fry, F. Schorr, LSO, A. Coates, SO, L.
Collingwood, Berlin St Op Orch, L. Blech (r1926/7)
Concert　(11/91) (CLAR) ① [2] CDGSE78-50-35/6
Excs Grimethorpe Colliery Band, E. Howarth (arr
Owen) Concert　(12/92) (DOYE) ① DOYCD013
Excs L. Hofmann, F. Völker, H. Konetzni, R. Merker,
H. Alsen, K. Thorborg, L. Helletsgruber, E. Flesch, M.
Bokor, D. With, A. Michalsky, F. Stroinigg, B. Paalen,
E. Weichert, Vienna St Op Orch, B. Walter (pp1936)
Concert　(8/95) (SCHW) ① [2] 314592

Excs F. Schorr, M. Jeritza, F. Hüni-Mihacsek, F.
Völker, R. Mayr, L. Helletsgruber, E. Hadrabová, M.
Bokor, R. Anday, A. Michalsky, D. With, B. Paalen, E.
Szánthó, Vienna St Op Orch, C. Krauss (pp1933)
　(8/95) (SCHW) ① [2] 314642
Excs G. Rünger, H. Konetzni, Vienna St Op Orch, H.
Knappertsbusch (pp1938) Concert
　(9/95) (SCHW) ① [2] 314662
Excs F. Schorr, F. Völker, Lotte Lehmann, M. Jeritza,
L. Helletsgruber, E. Hadrabová, M. Bokor, R. Anday,
A. Michalsky, D. With, B. Paalen, E. Szánthó, Vienna
St Op Orch, C. Krauss (pp1933) Concert
　(11/95) (SCHW) ① [2] 314622
Leitmotifs LSO, L. Collingwood (r1931) Concert
　(4/95) (PEAR) ① [7] GEMMCDS9137
1, 2, 6-9, 12, 25, 26, 28, 30b G. Ljungberg, W.
Widdop, F. Austral, L. Trenton, H. Fry, LSO, A.
Coates (r1927) Concert
　(4/95) (PEAR) ① [7] GEMMCDS9137
3(pt), 9. F. Völker, V. Ursuleac, R. Mayr, Vienna St
Op Orch, C. Krauss (pp1933) Concert
　(9/95) (SCHW) ① [2] 314662
4, 6. L. Melchior, orch (r1923) Concert
　(8/88) (DANA) ① [2] DACOCD313/4
6. L. Melchior, Berlin St Op Orch, L. Blech (r1929)
Concert　(8/88) (DANA) ① [2] DACOCD315/6
6. L. Melchior, Berlin St Op Orch, L. Blech (r1928)
Concert　(8/88) (DANA) ① [2] DACOCD315/6
6. L. Melchior, Berlin St Op Orch, L. Blech (r1929)
Concert　(7/92) (PEAR) ① [3] GEMMCDS9925(2)
6, 12. L. Melchior, Berlin St Op Orch, L. Blech (r1929)
Concert　(10/89) (EMI) ① CDH7 69789-2
6-12. H. Traubel, L. Melchior, NBC SO, A. Toscanini
(bp1941) Concert　(12/91) (RCA) ① GD60264
6, 31, 40-43. J. Vickers, T. Stewart, BPO, H. von
Karajan Concert　(4/90) (DG) ① 429 168-2GR
6, 7, 8, 9. R. Kollo, I. Haubold, Berlin Deutsche Op
Orch, C. Thielemann Concert
　(5/93) (EMI) ① CDC7 54776-2
6, 9. F. Völker, Berlin Staatskapelle, J. Schüler
(r1937) Concert　(8/94) (PREI) ① 89070
8. G. Lubin, orch, H. Defosse (French: r1929)
Concert　(5/91) (CLUB) ① CL99-022
8. Lotte Lehmann, orch (r1921) Concert
　(6/92) (PREI) ① [3] 89302
8. M. Kurt, orch (r1911) Concert
　(7/92) (PEAR) ① [3] GEMMCDS9924(2)
8, 10. M. Seinemeyer, Berlin Staatskapelle, F.
Weissmann (r1929) Concert
　(1/92) (EMI) ① CMS7 64008-2(2)
8, 10. K. Flagstad, VPO, H. Knappertsbusch (r1956)
Concert　(12/95) (LOND) ① 440 495-2LM
8, 10. K. Flagstad, VPO, H. Knappertsbusch (r1956)
Concert　(12/95) (LOND) ① [5] 440 490-2LM5(1)
8, 12. G. Lubin, R. Verdière, orch, H. Defosse
(French: r1929) Concert　(5/91) (EPM) ① 150 052
8, 31, 41, 42. G. Janowitz, T. Stewart, BPO, H. von
Karajan (r1966) Concert
　(3/94) (DG) ① 439 423-2GCL
8(pt), 9, 10, 44. W. Meier, S. Jerusalem, BPO, C.
Abbado (pp1993) Concert
　(5/94) (DG) ① 439 768-2GH
8(pt), 9-12. W. Widdop, G. Ljungberg, LSO, A.
Coates, Orch, L. Collingwood (r1926/7) Concert
　(11/92) (CLAR) ① CDGSE78-50-46
9. L. Melchior, O. Helgers (r1926) Concert
　(8/88) (DANA) ① [2] DACOCD315/6
9. L. Melchior, LSO, J. Barbirolli (1931) Concert
　(8/88) (DANA) ① [2] DACOCD315/6
9. L. Melchior, orch, P. Breisach (r1924) Concert
　(8/88) (DANA) ① [2] DACOCD313/4
9. L. Melchior, Orch (Danish: r c1921) Concert
　(8/88) (DANA) ① [2] DACOCD311/2
9. L. Melchior, LSO, J. Barbirolli (1931) Concert
　(10/89) (EMI) ① CDH7 69789-2
9. M. Lorenz, Berlin St Op Orch, E. Viebig (r1927)
Concert　(1/92) (EMI) ① [4] CMS7 64008-2(2)
9. W. Widdop, LSO, A. Coates (r1927) Concert
　(7/92) (PEAR) ① [3] GEMMCDS9926(1)
9. W. Hyde, orch, G.W. Byng (Eng: r1921) Concert
　(7/92) (PEAR) ① [3] GEMMCDS9924(2)
9. P. Cornelius, orch (Danish: r1909) Concert
　(7/92) (PEAR) ① [3] GEMMCDS9924(2)
9. G. Borgatti, orch (Ital: r1919) Concert
　(11/92) (MEMO) ① [2] HR4408/9(2)
9. R. Tauber, orch (r1920) Concert
　(12/92) (NIMB) ① NI7830
9. G. Morskoi, anon (r1901: Russ) Concert
　(6/93) (PEAR) ① [3] GEMMCDS9001/3(1)
9. J. Vickers, LSO, E. Leinsdorf (r1962) Concert
　(12/93) (RCA) ① 09026 61236-2
9. S. Svanholm, Vienna St Op Orch, H.
Knappertsbusch (pp1941) Concert
　(6/94) (SCHW) ① 314502
9. L. Melchior, LSO, J. Barbirolli (1931) Concert
　(9/94) (NIMB) ① NI7856

9. T. Ralf, Berlin St Op Orch, H.U. Müller (r1941)
Concert　(10/94) (PREI) ① 89077
9. E. Van Dyck, anon (r1905: Fr) Concert
　(12/94) (SYMP) ① SYMCD1172
9. T. Hampson, Munich RO, F. Luisi (r1994) Concert
　(9/95) (EMI) ① CDC5 55233-2
9, 10, 12. M. Müller, F. Völker, Bayreuth Fest Orch,
H. Tietjen (r1936) Concert
　(8/93) (TELD) ① 9031-76442-2
9, 12. A. von Bary, anon (r1904) Concert
　(7/91) (SYMP) ① SYMCD1081
10. K. Flagstad, Philadelphia, E. Ormandy (r1937)
Concert　(10/90) (RCA) ① GD87915
10. Lotte Lehmann, orch (r1917) Concert
　(6/92) (PREI) ① [3] 89302
10. G. Ljungberg, orch, L. Collingwood (r1926)
Concert　(7/92) (PEAR) ① [3] GEMMCDS9925(2)
10. L. Price, E. Downes Concert
　(12/92) (RCA) ① [4] 09026 61236-2
10. K. Flagstad, Philadelphia, E. Ormandy (r1937)
Concert　(7/93) (NIMB) ① NI7847
10. Lotte Lehmann, VPO, B. Walter (r1935) Concert
　(12/93) (NIMB) ① NI7851
10. M. Jeritza, orch (r1922) Concert
　(4/94) (PREI) ① 89079
10. G. Ljungberg, W. Widdop, LSO, L. Collingwood
(r1926) Concert
　(4/95) (PEAR) ① [7] GEMMCDS9137
10. K. Flagstad, Philadelphia, E. Ormandy (r1937)
Concert　(12/95) (SIMA) ① [3] PSC1821(2)
10-12. F. Leider, L. Melchior, orch (r1923) Concert
　(8/88) (DANA) ① [2] DACOCD313/4
10-12. F. Leider, L. Melchior, orch (r1923) Concert
　(5/91) (PREI) ① [3] 89301
10, 33(pt) J. Gadski, orch (r1913) Concert
　(7/91) (CLUB) ① CL99-109
12. L. Melchior, Berlin St Op Orch, L. Blech (r1929)
Concert　(8/88) (DANA) ① [2] DACOCD315/6
12. G. Guszalewicz, L. Melchior, Berlin St Op Orch,
L. Blech (r1928) Concert
　(8/88) (DANA) ① [2] DACOCD315/6
12, 28. F. Völker, V. Ursuleac, Vienna St Op Orch, C.
Krauss (pp1934) Concert
　(9/95) (SCHW) ① [2] 314662
13, 14, 15a W. Grossmann, A. Konetzni, Vienna St
Op Orch, W. Furtwängler (pp1936) Concert
　(6/94) (SCHW) ① 314502
13-15. M. Lawrence, J. Claverie, Pasdeloup Orch, P.
Coppola (French: r1933) Concert
　(5/90) (PREI) ① 89011
14, 15a L. Hofmann, A. Konetzni, Vienna St Op Orch,
H. Knappertsbusch (pp1937) Concert
　(1/95) (SCHW) ① [2] 314562
14, 15a, 20(pt), 23b(pt), 31, 34, 36, 40-42. F. Leider,
E. Leisner, F. Schorr, G. Ljungberg, G. Guszalewicz,
E. Marherr-Wagner, L. Kindermann, Berlin St Op
Orch, L. Blech (r1927) Concert
　(4/95) (PEAR) ① [7] GEMMCDS9137
15a K. Flagstad, orch, H. Lange (r1935) Concert
　(10/90) (RCA) ① GD87915
15a S. Sedlmair, anon (r1904) Concert
　(7/91) (SYMP) ① SYMCD1081
15a F. Litvinne, A. Cortot (r1902) Concert
　(10/92) (SYMP) ① SYMCD1101
15a F. Litvinne, anon (r1903) Concert
　(10/92) (SYMP) ① SYMCD1101
15a K. Flagstad, orch, H. Lange (r1935) Concert
　(7/93) (NIMB) ① NI7847
15a K. Flagstad, orch, H. Lange (r1935) Concert
　(12/95) (SIMA) ① [3] PSC1821(1)
16-18. E. Leisner, F. Schorr, LSO, J. Barbirolli
(r1932) Concert
　(4/95) (PEAR) ① [7] GEMMCDS9137
17. K. Thorborg, RCA SO, K. Riedel (r1940) Concert
　(4/94) (RCA) ① [6] 09026 61580-2(4)
17. K. Thorborg, RCA SO, K. Riedel (r1940) Concert
　(4/95) (PREI) ① 89084
17. M. Klose, Berlin St Op Orch, B. Seidler-Winkler
(r1939) Concert　(7/95) (PREI) ① 89082
26. F. Leider, F. Soot, orch (r1925) Concert
　(5/91) (PREI) ① [3] 89301
26. M. Kurt, J. Urlus, orch (r1910) Concert
　(7/92) (PEAR) ① [3] GEMMCDS9925(2)
26. K. Flagstad, S. Svanholm, Philh, K. Böhm (r1949)
Concert　(7/93) (TEST) ① SBT1018
26, 27. K. Flagstad, S. Svanholm, Philh, K. Böhm
(r1949) Concert
　(10/94) (EMI) ① [4] CMS5 65212-2
26-28. K. Flagstad, S. Svanholm, VPO, G. Solti
(r1957) Concert
　(12/95) (LOND) ① [5] 440 490-2LM5(1)
26-28. K. Flagstad, S. Svanholm, VPO, G. Solti
(r1957) Concert　(12/95) (LOND) ① 440 495-2LM
31, 43. Cleveland Orch, G. Szell Concert
　(11/92) (SONY) ① SBK48175

31, 43. Netherlands Rad PO, E. de Waart (r1992; arr Vlieger) *Concert* (9/93) (FIDE) Ⓓ **9201**
36. M. Lawrence, Pasdeloup Orch, P. Coppola (French: r1933) *Concert* (5/90) (PREI) Ⓓ **89011**
36. F. Leider, orch (r1925) *Concert* (5/91) (PREI) Ⓓ [3] **89301**
36. J. Gadski, orch (r1910) *Concert* (7/91) (CLUB) Ⓓ **CL99-109**
36. M. Lawrence, Pasdeloup Orch, P. Coppola (French: r1933) *Concert* (1/92) (EMI) Ⓓ [4] **CMS7 64008-2(2)**
36. F. Leider, Berlin St Op Orch, L. Blech (r1927) *Concert* (7/92) (PEAR) Ⓓ [3] **GEMMCDS9925(2)**
36-38, 39a, 39b, 40-43. B. Nilsson, H. Hotter, Philh, L. Ludwig (r1957) *Concert* (10/94) (EMI) Ⓓ [4] **CMS5 65212-2**
40. M. Schenk, Nuremberg SO, K. Seibel *Concert* (12/91) (COLO) Ⓓ **COL34 9004**
40. R. Bockelmann, Berlin St Op Orch, C. Schmalstich (r1930) *Concert* (1/92) (EMI) Ⓓ [4] **CMS7 64008-2(2)**
40. M. Journet, SO, P. Coppola (French: r1928) *Concert* (1/92) (EMI) Ⓓ [4] **CMS7 64008-2(2)**
40. N. de Angelis, orch, L. Molajoli (Ital: r1929) *Concert* (7/92) (PREI) Ⓓ **89042**
40. F. Schorr, Berlin St Op Orch, L. Blech (r1927) *Concert* (7/92) (PEAR) Ⓓ [3] **GEMMCDS9925(2)**
40. A. Van Rooy, anon (r1902) *Concert* (7/92) (PEAR) Ⓓ [3] **GEMMCDS9923(2)**
40(pt) C. Formichi, orch (Ital: r1920) *Concert* (11/92) (MEMO) Ⓓ [2] **HR4408/9(2)**
40. A. Van Rooy, anon (r1902) *Concert* (3/93) (SYMP) Ⓓ **SYMCD1100**
40. V. Sharonov, anon (Russ: r1903) *Concert* (7/93) (SYMP) Ⓓ **SYMCD1105**
40. M. Journet, SO, P. Coppola (r1928: French) *Concert* (1/94) (CLUB) Ⓓ **CL99-034**
40. G. Hann, Berlin Deutsche Op Orch, H. Steinkopf (bp1942) *Concert* (5/94) (PREI) Ⓓ **90168**
40. C. Formichi, orch (r1920: Ital) *Concert* (11/94) (PREI) Ⓓ **89055**
40. J-F. Delmas, anon (r1905: Fr) *Concert* (12/94) (SYMP) Ⓓ **SYMCD1172**
40. H. Hermann Nissen, Berlin SO, F. Zweig (r1927) *Concert* (12/95) (PREI) Ⓓ **89090**
40, 42. A. Kipnis, Berlin St Op Orch, L. Blech (r1926) *Concert* (10/91) (PEAR) Ⓓ **GEMMCD9451**
40, 43. L. Tibbett, Philadelphia, L. Stokowski (r1934: arr Stokowski) *Concert* (3/90) (RCA) Ⓓ **GD87808**
40-43. N. Bailey, New Philh, O. Klemperer *Concert* (10/91) (EMI) Ⓓ [2] **CMS7 63835-2**
40, 43. Seattle SO, G. Schwarz (r1992) *Concert* (4/94) (DELO) Ⓓ **DE3120**
40-43. D. Fischer-Dieskau, BRSO, R. Kubelík (r1977) *Concert* (10/94) (EMI) Ⓓ [4] **CMS5 65212-2**
40-43. P. Schoeffler, LSO, K. Rankl (r1946) *Concert* (1/95) (PREI) Ⓓ **90190**
40-43. M. Reizen, Bolshoi Th Orch, V. Nebolsin (r1950) *Concert* (2/95) (PREI) Ⓓ **89080**
40, 43, 44. VPO, G. Solti *Concert* (11/83) (DECC) Ⓓ **410 137-2DH**
40, 43, 44. J. Tomlinson, Philh, F. d'Avalos *Concert* (3/90) (ASV) Ⓓ **CDDCA666**
43. LSO, A. Coates (r1926) *Concert* (4/93) (KOCH) Ⓓ [2] **37704-2**
44. Los Angeles PO, E. Leinsdorf *Concert* (8/87) (SHEF) Ⓓ **CD-7/8**
44. LPO, K.A. Rickenbacher *Concert* (11/87) (CFP) Ⓓ **CD-CFP9008**
44. LPO, W. Furtwängler (pp1937) *Concert* (2/89) (ACAN) Ⓓ **43 121**
44. Cincinnati Pops, E. Kunzel *Concert* (10/89) (TELA) Ⓓ **CD80170**
44. RPO, R. Stapleton *Concert* (10/90) (CARL) Ⓓ **MCD15**
44. Philh, O. Klemperer (r1960) *Concert* (11/90) (EMI) Ⓓ **CDM7 63618-2**
44. Philh, Y. Simonov *Concert* (10/91) (COLL) Ⓓ **Coll1207-2**
44. NBC SO, A. Toscanini (r1952) *Concert* (12/91) (RCA) Ⓓ **GD60264**
44. NYPO, W. Mengelberg (r1926) *Concert* (4/92) (PEAR) Ⓓ [3] **GEMMCDS9922**
44. Leningrad PO, E. Mravinsky (pp1978) *Concert* (6/92) (ERAT) Ⓓ [11] **2292-45763-2**
44. Leningrad PO, E. Mravinsky (pp1978) *Concert* (6/92) (ERAT) Ⓓ **2292-45762-2**
44. Oslo PO, M. Jansons *Concert* (12/92) (EMI) Ⓓ **CDC7 54583-2**
44. Leningrad PO, E. Mravinsky (pp1967) *Concert* (3/94) (RUSS) Ⓓ **RDCD11166**
44. VPO, W. Furtwängler (r1949) *Concert* (4/94) (EMI) Ⓓ [2] **CHS7 64935-2**
44. T. Trotter (r1992: trans org: E Lemare) *Concert* (4/94) (DECC) Ⓓ **436 656-2DH**
44. Queen's Hall Orch, Henry Wood (r1935) *Concert* (9/94) (DUTT) Ⓓ **CDAX8008**

Der **Ring des Nibelungen: Part 3, 'Siegfried'—opera: 3 acts (1876—Bayreuth)** (Lib. cpsr)

EXCERPTS. ACT 1: 1. Prelude; 2. Zwangvolle Plage!; 3. Hoiho! Hoiho! Hau ein!; 4. Als zullendes Kind; 5. Vieles lehrtest du, Mime; 6. Einst lag wimmernd ein Weib; 7. Soll ich der Kunde glauben; 8. Heil dir, weiser Schmied!; 9. Hier sitz' ich am Herd; 10. Auf wolkigen Höhn; 11. Was zu wissen dir frommt; 12. Verfluchtes Licht; 13. Bist du es, Kind?; 14. Fühltest du nie im finstren Wald; 15. Her mit den Stücken; 16. Nothung! Neidliches Schwert! (Forging Song); 17a. Hoho! Hoho! Haheil; 17b. Schmiede, mein Hammer; 18. Den der Bruder schuf. ACT 2: 19. Prelude; 20. In Wald und Nacht; 21a. Wer naht dort schimmernd; 21b. Zur Neidhöhle fuhr ich; 22. Fafner, Fafner! Erwache, Wurm!; 23a. Ich lieg' und besitz; 23b. Nun, Alberich, das schlug fehl; 24. Wir sind zur Stelle!; 25a. Dass der mein Vater nicht ist (Forest murmurs); 25b. Forest murmurs (concert version); 26a. Meine Mutter, ein Menschenweib!; 26b. Du holdes Vöglein!; 27. Siegfried's horn-call; 28. Haha! Da hätte mein Lied; 29a. Da lieg, neidischer Kerl; 29b. Wer bist du, Kühner Knabe; 30. Zur Kunde taugt kein Toter; 31. Wohin schleichst du?; 32. Wilkommen, Siegfried!; 33. Neides Zoll zahlt Nothung; 34. Da lieg auch du, dunkler Wurm; 35. Freundliches Vöglein; 36a. Nun sing! Ich lausche; 36b. Hei! Siegfried erschlug nun den schlimmen Zwerg. ACT 3: 37. Prelude; 38. Wache, Wala! Erwach!; 39. Stark ruft das Lied; 40a. Weisst du, was Wotan will?; 40b. Dir Unweisen ruf' ich; 41. Dort seh' ich Siegfried nahn; 42. Mein Vöglein schwebte mir fort!; 43. Kenntest du mich, kühner Spross; 44. orchestral interlude. Scene 3: 45a. Selig Öde auf sonniger Höh!; 45b. Was ruht dort schlummernd; 46a. Dass ist kein Mann!; 46b. Brennender Zauber; 47. Heil dir, Sonne!; 48. O Siegfried! Seliger Held!; 49. Dort seh' ich Grane; 50. Ewig war ich, ewig bin ich.

Cpte R. Kollo, T. Adam, J. Altmeyer, P. Schreier, S. Nimsgern, O. Wenkel, M. Salminen, N. Sharp, Staatskapelle Dresden, M. Janowski (10/84) (EURO) Ⓓ [4] **GD69006**
Cpte W. Windgassen, H. Hotter, B. Nilsson, G. Stolze, G. Neidlinger, M. Höffgen, K. Böhme, J. Sutherland, VPO, G. Solti (r1962) (12/84) (DECC) Ⓓ [4] **414 110-2DH4**
Cpte Jess Thomas, T. Stewart, H. Dernesch, G. Stolze, Z. Kélémen, O. Dominguez, K. Ridderbusch, C. Gayer, BPO, H. von Karajan (r1968/9) (7/85) (DG) Ⓓ [4] **415 150-2GH4**
Cpte W. Windgassen, T. Adam, B. Nilsson, E. Wohlfahrt, G. Neidlinger, V. Soukupová, K. Böhme, E. Köth, Bayreuth Fest Orch, K. Böhm (pp1967) (8/85) (PHIL) Ⓓ [4] **412 483-2PH4**
Cpte W. Windgassen, H. Hotter, A. Varnay, P. Kuen, G. Neidlinger, M. von Ilosvay, J. Greindl, R. Streich, Bayreuth Fest Orch, C. Krauss (pp1953) (6/88) (FOYE) Ⓓ [4] **4-CF2009**
Cpte W. Windgassen, H. Hotter, A. Varnay, P. Kuen, G. Neidlinger, M. von Ilosvay, J. Greindl, R. Streich, Bayreuth Fest Orch, C. Krauss (pp1953) *Concert* (6/88) (FOYE) Ⓓ [15] **15-CF2011**
Cpte W. Windgassen, P. Kuen, H. Hotter, G. Neidlinger, A. Varnay, M. von Ilosvay, J. Greindl, R. Streich, Bayreuth Fest Orch, C. Krauss (pp1953) (6/88) (LAUD) Ⓓ [4] **LCD4 4004**
Cpte W. Windgassen, H. Hotter, B. Nilsson, G. Stolze, G. Neidlinger, M. Höffgen, K. Böhme, J. Sutherland, VPO, G. Solti (r1962) *Concert* (3/89) (DECC) Ⓓ [15] **414 100-2DM15**
Cpte L. Suthaus, F. Frantz, M. Mödl, J. Patzak, A. Pernerstorfer, M. Klose, J. Greindl, R. Streich, Rome RAI Orch, W. Furtwängler (bp1953) *Concert* (2/91) (EMI) Ⓓ [13] **CZS7 67123-2**
Cpte A. Remedios, N. Bailey, R. Hunter, G. Dempsey, D. Hammond-Stroud, A. Collins, C. Grant, M. London, Sadler's Wells Op Orch, R. Goodall (Eng: pp1973) (3/91) (EMI) Ⓓ [4] **CMS7 63595-2**
Cpte S. Jerusalem, J. Morris, E. Marton, P. Haage, T. Adam, J. Rappé, K. Rydl, K. Te Kanawa, BRSO, B. Haitink (r1990) (11/91) (EMI) Ⓓ [4] **CDS7 54290-2**
Cpte R. Goldberg, J. Morris, H. Behrens, H. Zednik, E. Wlaschiha, B. Svendén, K. Moll, K. Battle, NY Met Op Orch, James Levine (r1988) (3/92) (DG) Ⓓ [4] **429 407-2GH4**
Cpte Jess Thomas, T. Stewart, H. Dernesch, G. Stolze, Z. Kélémen, O. Dominguez, K. Ridderbusch, C. Gayer, BPO, H. von Karajan *Concert* (4/92) (DG) Ⓓ [15] **435 211-2GX15**
Cpte L. Melchior, F. Schorr, K. Flagstad, K. Laufkötter, E. Habich, K. Thorborg, E. List, S. Andreva, NY Met Op Orch, A. Bodanzky (pp1937) (7/92) (MUSI) Ⓓ [3] **MACD-696**
Cpte M. Jung, D. McIntyre, G. Jones, H. Zednik, H. Becht, O. Wenkel, F. Hübner, N. Sharp, Bayreuth Fest Orch, P. Boulez (pp1980) (10/92) (PHIL) Ⓓ [3] **434 423-2PH3**
Cpte R. Goldberg, C. Ludwig, H. Behrens, H. Zednik, E. Wlaschiha, B. Svendén, K. Moll, K. Battle, NY Met Op Orch, James Levine (r1988) *Concert* (10/94) (DG) Ⓓ [14] **445 354-2GX14**
Cpte S. Jerusalem, J. Tomlinson, Anne Evans, G. Clark, G. von Kannen, B. Svendén, P. Kang, H. Leidland, Bayreuth Fest Orch, D. Barenboim (pp1992) (10/94) (TELD) Ⓓ [4] **4509-94193-2**
Cpte W. Windgassen, T. Adam, B. Nilsson, E. Wohlfahrt, G. Neidlinger, V. Soukupová, M. Talvela, E. Köth, Bayreuth Fest Orch, K. Böhm (pp1966) *Concert* (10/94) (PHIL) Ⓓ [14] **446 057-2PB14**
Excs BPO, L. Maazel (without voices) *Concert* (10/88) (TELA) Ⓓ **CD80154**
Excs M. Lorenz, J. Prohaska, R. Anday, W. Wernigk, L. Helletsgruber, Vienna St Op Orch, J. Krips (pp1937) *Concert* (11/94) (SCHW) Ⓓ [2] **314532**
Excs L. Hofmann, M. Lorenz, W. Wernigk, E. Szánthó, Vienna St Op Orch, H. Knappertsbusch (pp1937) *Concert* (3/95) (SCHW) Ⓓ [2] **314602**
Excs R. Schubert, G. Kappel, E. Zimmermann, Vienna St Op Orch, R. Heger (pp1933) *Concert* (8/95) (SCHW) Ⓓ [2] **314592**
Leitmotifs LSO, L. Collingwood (r1931) *Concert* (4/95) (PEAR) Ⓓ [7] **GEMMCDS9137**
1-4, 7, 8, 20, 21b, 28, 31, 45a, 46a L. Melchior, H. Tessmer, F. Schorr, E. Habich, LSO, R. Heger (r1930/1) *Concert* (4/95) (PEAR) Ⓓ [7] **GEMMCDS9137**
4. H. Breuer, anon (r1904) *Concert* (7/91) (SYMP) Ⓓ **SYMCD1081**
10. H. Hermann Nissen, Berlin St Op Orch, B. Seidler-Winkler (r1939) *Concert* (1/92) (EMI) Ⓓ [4] **CMS7 64008-2(2)**
14. L. Melchior, A. Reiss, LSO, A. Coates (r1929) *Concert* (7/90) (CLAR) Ⓓ **CDGSE78-50-33**
14, 16, 17a, 25a, 26b, 34, 36b, 43, 44. L. Melchior, A. Reiss, N. Gruhn, R. Bockelmann, LSO, A. Coates (r1929) *Concert* (4/95) (PEAR) Ⓓ [7] **GEMMCDS9137**
16. L. Melchior, A. Reiss, LSO, A. Coates (r1929) *Concert* (10/89) (EMI) Ⓓ **CDH7 69789-2**
16. I. Ershov, anon (r1903: Russ) *Concert* (6/93) (PEAR) Ⓓ [3] **GEMMCDS9997/9(1)**
16, 17a, 17b L. Melchior, orch (r1923) *Concert* (8/88) (DANA) Ⓓ [2] **DACOCD313/4**
16, 17a, 17b, 47. Jess Thomas, G. Stolze, H. Dernesch, BPO, H. von Karajan *Concert* (4/90) (DG) Ⓓ **429 168-2GR**
16, 17a, 17b L. Melchior, LSO, A. Coates (r1929) *Concert* (7/90) (CLAR) Ⓓ **CDGSE78-50-33**
16, 17b, 25a M. Lorenz, E. Zimmermann, Bayreuth Fest Orch, H. Tietjen (r1936) *Concert* (8/93) (TELD) Ⓓ **9031-76442-2**
16, 25a, 47, 50. F. Leider, R. Laubenthal, Berlin St Op Orch, L. Blech (r1927/8) *Concert* (4/95) (PEAR) Ⓓ [7] **GEMMCDS9137**
25a L. Melchior, orch, F. Weissmann (r1925) *Concert* (8/88) (DANA) Ⓓ [2] **DACOCD313/4**
25a L. Melchior, LSO, A. Coates (r1929) *Concert* (10/89) (EMI) Ⓓ **CDH7 69789-2**
25a L. Melchior, LSO, A. Coates (r1929) *Concert* (7/90) (CLAR) Ⓓ **CDGSE78-50-33**
25a Cleveland Orch, G. Szell *Concert* (11/92) (SONY) Ⓓ **SBK48175**
25a, 36a, 47. Jess Thomas, C. Gayer, H. Dernesch, BPO, H. von Karajan (r1968/9) *Concert* (3/94) (DG) Ⓓ **439 423-2GCL**
25a, 37, 44. Netherlands Rad PO, E. de Waart (r1992; arr Vlieger) *Concert* (9/93) (FIDE) Ⓓ **9201**
25b VPO, G. Solti *Concert* (11/83) (DECC) Ⓓ **410 137-2DH**
25b Los Angeles PO, E. Leinsdorf *Concert* (8/87) (SHEF) Ⓓ **CD-7/8**
25b Columbia SO, B. Walter (r1959) *Concert* (2/90) (SONY) Ⓓ **MPK45701**
25b Philh, O. Klemperer (r1961) *Concert* (11/90) (EMI) Ⓓ **CDM7 63618-2**
25b Philh, Y. Simonov *Concert* (10/91) (COLL) Ⓓ **Coll1207-2**
25b Leningrad PO, E. Mravinsky (pp1967) *Concert* (3/94) (RUSS) Ⓓ **RDCD11166**
25b Seattle SO, G. Schwarz (r1992) *Concert* (4/94) (DELO) Ⓓ **DE3120**
27. D. Brain (r1947) *Concert* (2/93) (TEST) Ⓓ **SBT1012**
30(pt) E. Feuge, anon (r1904) *Concert* (7/91) (SYMP) Ⓓ **SYMCD1081**

34. L. Melchior, N. Gruhn, LSO, A. Coates (r1929) *Concert* (10/89) (EMI) ① **CDH7 69789-2**
34, 35, 36a, 36b L. Melchior, N. Gruhn, LSO, A. Coates (r1929) *Concert* (7/90) (CLAR) ① **CDGSE78-50-33**
37-39, 40b M. Olczewska, E. Schipper, Vienna St Op Orch, K. Alwin (r1928) *Concert* (4/95) (PEAR) ① **[7] GEMMCDS9137**
39. M. Olczewska, E. Schipper, Vienna St Op Orch, K. Alwin (r1928) *Concert* (1/92) (EMI) ① **[4] CMS7 64008-2(2)**
43. L. Melchior, R. Bockelmann, LSO, A. Coates (r1929) *Concert* (7/90) (CLAR) ① **CDGSE78-50-33**
44. Rome RAI Orch, W. Furtwängler (bp1953) *Concert* (2/89) (ACAN) ① **43 121**
47. F. Leider, F. Soot, orch (r1925) *Concert* (5/91) (PREI) ① **[3] 89301**
47, 48(pt), 50. J. Kalenberg, A. Konetzni, Vienna St Op Orch, H. Knappertsbusch (pp1936) *Concert* (1/95) (SCHW) ① **[2] 314562**
47, 48, 50. F. Easton, L. Melchior, orch, R. Heger (r1932) *Concert* (4/95) (PEAR) ① **[7] GEMMCDS9137**
47-50. F. Leider, R. Laubenthal, Berlin St Op Orch, L. Blech (r1927) *Concert* (2/90) (PREI) ① **89004**
47, 50. F. Leider, R. Laubenthal, Berlin St Op Orch, L. Blech (r1927) *Concert* (1/92) (EMI) ① **[4] CMS7 64008-2(2)**
47-50. K. Flagstad, S. Svanholm, Philh, G. Sébastian (r1951) *Concert* (10/94) (EMI) ① **[4] CMS5 65212-2**
50. K. Flagstad, S. Svanholm, Philh, G. Sébastian (r1951) *Concert* (8/89) (EMI) ① **CDH7 63030-2**
50. G. Lubin, orch, H. Defosse (French: r1929) *Concert* (5/91) (CLUB) ① **CL99-022**
50. G. Lubin, orch (French: r1929) *Concert* (5/91) (EPM) ① **150 052**
50. F. Leider, F. Soot, orch (r1925) *Concert* (5/91) (PREI) ① **[3] 89301**
50. J. Gadski, orch (r1910) *Concert* (7/91) (CLUB) ① **CL99-109**
50. G. Lubin, orch, H. Defosse (French: r1930) *Concert* (1/92) (EMI) ① **[4] CMS7 64008-2(2)**

Der Ring des Nibelungen: Part 4, 'Götterdämmerung'—opera: prologue & 3 acts (1876—Bayreuth) (Lib. cpsr)
EXCERPTS. PROLOGUE: 1a. Introduction; 1b. Welch Licht leuchtet dort?; 2. orchestral interlude (Dawn); 3. Zu neuen Taten; 4. O heilige Götter!; 5. orchestral interlude (Siegfried's Rhine Journey). ACT 1: 6. Nun hör, Hagen; 7a. Was weckst du Zweifel und Zwist!; 7b. Brächte Siegfried die Braut; 8a. Heil! Siegfried, teurer Held!; 8b. Wer ist Gibichs, Sohn?; 9. Begrüsse froh o Held; 10. Willkommen, Gast, in Gibichs Haus!; 11. Hast du, Gunther, ein Weib?; 12a. Blut-Brüderschaft schwöre ein Eid!; 12b. Blühenden Lebens labendes Blut; 13. Hier sitz' ich zur Wacht (Hagen's Watch); 14. orchestral interlude; 15. Altgewohntes Geräusch; 16a. Höre mit Sinn (Waltraute's Narration); 16b. Seit er von dir geschieden; 17. Da sann ich nach; 18. Welch banger Träume Mären; 19. Brünnhild! Ein Freier kam. ACT 2: 20. Prelude; 21. Schläfst du, Hagen, mein Sohn; 22. orchestral interlude; 23. Hoiho, Hagen! Müder Mann!; 24. Hoiho! Ihr Gibichsmannen; 25. Heil dir, Gunther; 26. Brünnhild', die hehrste Frau; 27a. Was ist ihr? Ist sie entrückt?; 27b. Was müht Brünnhildes Blick?; 28. Helle Wehr! Heilige Waffe!; 29. Welches Unholds List liegt hier verholnen?; 30. Dir hilft kein Hirn. ACT 3: 31. Prelude; 32. Frau Sonne sendet lichte Strahlen; 33. Hoiho!; 34. Trink, Gunther, trink; 35. Mime heiss ein mürrischer Zwerg (Siegfried's Narration); 36. Brünnhilde, heilige Braut!; 37. Siegfried's funeral march; 38. War das sein Horn?; 39. Schweigt eures Jammers; 40. Starke Scheite (Brünnhildes's Immolation); 41. Mein Erbe nun nehm' ich zu eigen; 42. Fliegt heim, ihr Raben!; 43. Zurück vom Ring (orchestral finale); 44. Dawn and Siegfried's Rhine Journey (concert version).
Cpte J. Altmeyer, R. Kollo, M. Salminen, S. Nimsgern, H.G. Nöcker, N. Sharp, O. Wenkel, L. Popp, U. Priew, H. Schwarz, A. Gjevang, D. Evangelatos, R. Falcon, Leipzig Rad Chor, Dresden St Op Chor, Staatskapelle Dresden, M. Janowski (10/84) (EURO) ① **[4] GD69007**
Cpte B. Nilsson, W. Windgassen, J. Greindl, G. Neidlinger, T. Stewart, L. Dvořáková, M. Mödl, D. Siebert, H. Dernesch, S. Wagner, M. Höffgen, A. Burmeister, A. Silja, Bayreuth Fest Chor, Bayreuth Fest Orch, K. Böhm (pp1967) (5/85) (PHIL) ① **[4] 412 488-2PH4**
Cpte B. Nilsson, W. Windgassen, G. Frick, G. Neidlinger, D. Fischer-Dieskau, C. Watson, C. Ludwig, L. Popp, G. Jones, M. Guy, H. Watts, G. Hoffman, A. Välkki, Vienna St Op Chor, VPO, G. Solti (r1964) (5/85) (DECC) ① **[4] 414 115-2DH4**

Cpte H. Dernesch, H. Brilioth, K. Ridderbusch, Z. Kélémen, T. Stewart, G. Janowitz, C. Ludwig, L. Rebmann, E. Moser, A. Reynolds, L. Chookasian, C. Ligendza, Berlin Deutsche Op Chor, BPO, H. von Karajan (r1969/70) (7/85) (DG) ① **[4] 415 155-2GH4**
Cpte A. Varnay, W. Windgassen, J. Greindl, G. Neidlinger, H. Uhde, N. Hinsch-Gröndahl, I. Malaniuk, E. Zimmermann, H. Plümacher, G. Litz, M. von Ilosvay, R. Resnik, Bayreuth Fest Chor, Bayreuth Fest Orch, C. Krauss (pp1953) *Concert* (6/88) (FOYE) ① **[15] 15-CF2011**
Cpte A. Varnay, W. Windgassen, J. Greindl, G. Neidlinger, H. Uhde, N. Hinsch-Gröndahl, I. Malaniuk, E. Zimmermann, H. Plümacher, G. Litz, M. von Ilosvay, R. Resnik, Bayreuth Fest Chor, Bayreuth Fest Orch, C. Krauss (pp1953) *Concert* (6/88) (FOYE) ① **[4] 4-CF2010**
Cpte A. Varnay, W. Windgassen, J. Greindl, G. Neidlinger, H. Uhde, N. Hinsch-Gröndahl, I. Malaniuk, E. Zimmermann, H. Plümacher, G. Litz, M. von Ilosvay, R. Resnik, Bayreuth Fest Chor, Bayreuth Fest Orch, C. Krauss (pp1953) (6/88) (LAUD) ① **[4] LCD4 4005**
Cpte B. Nilsson, W. Windgassen, G. Frick, G. Neidlinger, D. Fischer-Dieskau, C. Watson, C. Ludwig, L. Popp, G. Jones, M. Guy, H. Watts, G. Hoffman, A. Välkki, Vienna St Op Chor, VPO, G. Solti (r1964) *Concert* (3/89) (DECC) ① **[15] 414 100-2DM15**
Cpte M. Mödl, L. Suthaus, J. Greindl, A. Pernerstorfer, A. Poell, S. Jurinac, M. Klose, M. Gabory, H. Rössl-Majdan, Rome RAI Chor, Rome RAI Orch, W. Furtwängler (bp1953) *Concert* (2/91) (EMI) ① **[13] CZS7 67123-2**
Cpte H. Behrens, R. Goldberg, M. Salminen, E. Wlaschiha, B. Weikl, C. Studer, H. Schwarz, H-K. Hong, D. Kesling, M. Parsons, H. Dernesch, T. Troyanos, A. Gruber, NY Met Op Chor, NY Met Op Orch, James Levine (8/91) (DG) ① **[4] 429 385-2GH4**
Cpte H. Dernesch, H. Brilioth, K. Ridderbusch, Z. Kélémen, T. Stewart, G. Janowitz, C. Ludwig, L. Rebmann, E. Moser, A. Reynolds, L. Chookasian, C. Ligendza, Berlin Deutsche Op Chor, BPO, H. von Karajan (4/92) (DG) ① **[15] 435 211-2GX15**
Cpte E. Marton, S. Jerusalem, J. Tomlinson, T. Adam, T. Hampson, E-M. Bundschuh, M. Lipovšek, J. Kaufman, S. Herman, C. Hagen, J. van Nes, A.S. von Otter, J. Eaglen, Bavarian Rad Chor, BRSO, B. Haitink (r1991) (9/92) (EMI) ① **[4] CDS7 54485-2**
Cpte G. Jones, M. Jung, F. Hübner, H. Becht, F. Mazura, J. Altmeyer, G. Killebrew, N. Sharp, I. Gramatzki, M. Schiml, O. Wenkel, G. Schnaut, K. Clarke, Bayreuth Fest Chor, Bayreuth Fest Orch, P. Boulez (pp1979) (10/92) (PHIL) ① **[4] 434 424-2PH4**
Cpte R. Hunter, A. Remedios, A. Haugland, D. Hammond-Stroud, N. Welsby, M. Curphey, K. Pring, V. Masterson, S. Squires, H. Attfield, A. Collins, G. Knight, Anne Evans, ENO Chor, ENO Orch, R. Goodall (Eng: pp1977) (11/92) (EMI) ① **[5] CMS7 64244-2**
Cpte M. Fuchs, S. Svanholm, F. Dalberg, R. Burg, E. Koch, E. Fischer, C. Kallab, H. Scheppan, I. Langhammer, M. Booth, H. Jachnow, C. Siewart, Bayreuth Fest Chor, Bayreuth Fest Orch, L. Elmendorff (pp1942) (1/94) (PREI) ① **[4] 90164**
Cpte H. Behrens, R. Goldberg, M. Salminen, E. Wlaschiha, B. Weikl, C. Studer, H. Schwarz, H-K. Hong, D. Kesling, M. Parsons, H. Dernesch, T. Troyanos, A. Gruber, NY Met Op Chor, NY Met Op Orch, James Levine (r1989) *Concert* (10/94) (DG) ① **[14] 445 354-2GX14**
Cpte Anne Evans, S. Jerusalem, P. Kang, G. von Kannen, B. Brinkmann, E-M. Bundschuh, W. Meier, H. Leidland, A. Küttenbaum, J. Turner, B. Svendén, L. Finnie, U. Priew, Bayreuth Fest Chor, Bayreuth Fest Orch, D. Barenboim (pp1991) (10/94) (TELD) ① **[4] 4509-94194-2**
Cpte B. Nilsson, W. Windgassen, J. Greindl, G. Neidlinger, T. Stewart, L. Dvořáková, M. Mödl, D. Siebert, H. Dernesch, S. Wagner, M. Höffgen, A. Burmeister, A. Silja, Bayreuth Fest Chor, Bayreuth Fest Orch, K. Böhm (pp1967) *Concert* (4/95) (PHIL) ① **[14] 446 057-2PB14**
Act 2, Sc 4/5. F. Leider, A. von Stosch, L. Melchior, H. Janssen, W. Schirp, ROH Chor, ROHO, W. Furtwängler (pp1938) *Concert* (11/89) (PEAR) ① **GEMMCD9331**
Act 3, Sc 2/3. R. Hunter, A. Remedios, C. Grant, N. Bailey, M. Curphey, Sadler's Wells Op Chor, Sadler's Wells Op Orch, R. Goodall (r1972; Eng) (11/93) (CHAN) ① **CHAN6593**

Excs BPO, L. Maazel (without voices) *Concert* (10/88) (TELA) ① **CD80154**
Excs W. Widdop, R. Laubenthal, A. Fear, D. Zádor, F. Collier, I. Andrésen, E. List, F. Austral, G. Ljungberg, M. Offers, G. Palmer, E. Arden, N. Eadie, T. de Garmo, L. Kindermann, E. Marherr-Wagner, Berlin St Op Chor, LSO, A. Coates, SO, Berlin St Op Orch, L. Collingwood, L. Blech (r1926/8) (11/91) (CLAR) ① **[2] CDGSE78-50-37/8**
Excs J. Kalenberg, H. Trundt, E. Schipper, E. Schipper, Vienna St Op Chor, Vienna St Op Orch, Vienna St Op Orch, J. Krips (pp1933) *Concert* (11/94) (SCHW) ① **[2] 314532**
Excs M. Bugarinovic, D. With, E. Réthy, Vienna St Op Orch, H. Knappertsbusch (pp1938) *Concert* (3/95) (SCHW) ① **[2] 314602**
Excs G. Kappel, J. Kalenberg, E. Schipper, W. Achsel, R. Anday, J. von Manowarda, G. Rünger, B. Paalen, E. Szánthó, Vienna St Op Orch, R. Heger (pp1933) (8/95) (SCHW) ① **[2] 314592**
Excs J. Kalenberg, H. Trundt, R. Anday, J. von Manowarda, E. Schipper, E. Szánthó, R. Anday, E. Hadrabová, Vienna St Op Orch, C. Krauss (pp1933) (8/95) (SCHW) ① **[2] 314642**
Excs J. von Manowarda, E. Schipper, E. Szánthó, R. Anday, G. Rünger, Vienna St Op Chor, Vienna St Op Orch, C. Krauss (pp1934) *Concert* (9/95) (SCHW) ① **[2] 314662**
Excs J. Pölzer, A. Konetzni, J. von Manowarda, E. Schipper, E. Szánthó, R. Anday, G. Rünger, Vienna St Op Orch, J. Krips (pp1933) *Concert* (9/95) (SCHW) ① **[2] 314662**
Leitmotifs LSO, L. Collingwood (r1931) *Concert* (4/95) (PEAR) ① **[7] GEMMCDS9137**
1b, 2, 3, 5, 9, 16b, 28, 29, 37, 43. N. Eadie, E. Arden, G. Palmer, F. Austral, W. Widdop, A. Fear, F. Collier, G. Ljungberg, M. Offers, chor, LSO, A. Coates (r1926/9) (4/95) (PEAR) ① **[7] GEMMCDS9137**
1b(pt), 3, 23. A. Konetzni, S. Svanholm, M. Alsen, D. Söderqvist, E. Schürhoff, P. Tutsek, H. Konetzni, Vienna St Op Chor, H. Knappertsbusch (pp1943) *Concert* (12/95) (SCHW) ① **[2] 314672**
2, 36, 37, 40. Seattle SO, G. Schwarz *Concert* (3/87) (DELO) ① **DE3040**
2, 5, 35, 37, 40. Netherlands Rad PO, E. de Waart (r1992; arr Vlieger) *Concert* (9/93) (FIDE) ① **9201**
3. F. Leider, F. Soot, orch (r1925) *Concert* (6/90) (LYRC) ① **[2] LCD146**
3. K. Flagstad, L. Melchior, San Francisco Op Orch, E. MacArthur (r1939) *Concert* (10/90) (RCA) ① **GD87915**
3. F. Leider, F. Soot, orch (r1925) *Concert* (5/91) (PREI) ① **[3] 89301**
3. J. Gadski, orch (r1912) *Concert* (7/91) (CLUB) ① **CL99-109**
3. F. Austral, W. Widdop, LSO, A. Coates (1928) *Concert* (1/92) (EMI) ① **[4] CMS7 64008-2(2)**
3. F. Austral, W. Widdop, LSO, A. Coates (1928) *Concert* (7/92) (PEAR) ① **GEMMCDS9925(1)**
3. W. Widdop, F. Austral, LSO, A. Coates (1928) *Concert* (11/92) (CLAR) ① **CDGSE78-50-46**
3. G. Rünger, J. Pölzer, Vienna St Op Orch, H. Knappertsbusch (pp1938) *Concert* (9/95) (SCHW) ① **[2] 314662**
3. K. Flagstad, L. Melchior, San Francisco SO, E. McArthur (r1939) *Concert* (12/95) (SIMA) ① **[3] PSC1821(2)**
3(pt), 28. L. Melchior, A. Konetzni, J. von Manowarda, Vienna St Op Chor, Vienna St Op Orch, F. Weingartner (pp1934) *Concert* (7/94) (SCHW) ① **[2] 314512**
3, 4. K. Flagstad, S. Svanholm, Philh, G. Sébastian (r1951) *Concert* (10/94) (EMI) ① **[4] CMS5 65212-2**
3, 40, 44. Anne Evans, Philh, F. d'Avalos *Tannhäuser.* (2/88) (ASV) ① **CDDCA595**
5. LSO, W. Morris *Concert* (12/87) (CIRR) ① **CICD1005**
5. La Scala Orch, W. Furtwängler (pp1950) *Concert* (2/89) (ACAN) ① **43 121**
5. Philh, O. Klemperer (r1961) *Concert* (11/90) (EMI) ① **CDM7 63618-2**
5. Minnesota Orch, N. Marriner (r1983) *Concert* (2/94) (TELA) ① **CD82005**
5. Vienna St Op Orch, C. Krauss (pp1933) *Concert* (6/94) (SCHW) ① **314502**
5. National SO, Sidney Beer (r1944) *Concert* (5/95) (DUTT) ① **CDK1200**
5, 37. Philh, Y. Simonov *Concert* (10/91) (COLL) ① **Coll1207-2**
5, 37. LSO, A. Coates (1926) *Concert* (4/93) (KOCH) ① **[2] 37704-2**
5, 37. VPO, W. Furtwängler (r1954) *Concert* (4/94) (EMI) ① **[2] CHS7 64935-2**

5, 37. Chicago SO, F. Reiner (r1959) *Concert*
(8/94) (RCA) ① **09026 61792-2**
5, 37. Philh, W. Sawallisch (r1958) *Concert*
(10/94) (EMI) ① [4] **CMS5 65212-2**
5, 37. Berlin St Op Orch, K. Muck (r1927) *Concert*
(4/95) (PEAR) ① [7] **GEMMCDS9137**
5, 37, 44. Cleveland Orch, G. Szell *Concert*
(11/92) (SONY) ① **SBK48175**
11. L. Melchior, F. Schorr, L. Topas, R. Watzke,
Berlin St Op Orch, L. Blech (r1929) *Concert*
(8/88) (DANA) ① [2] **DACOCD315/6**
13-15, 16a, 16b, 17-19, 23-26, 27a, 27b, 28-30. F.
Leider, L. Melchior, K. Thorborg, L. Weber, H.
Janssen, M. Nedzadel, ROH Chor, LPO, T. Beecham
(pp1936) *Concert* (6/90) (LYRC) ① [2] **LCD146**
13, 24. H. Janssen, L. Weber, ROH Chor, LPO, T.
Beecham (pp1936) *Concert*
(6/94) (DUTT) ① **CDLX7007**
13, 24. G. Frick, Berlin Deutsche Op Chor, Berlin
Deutsche Op Orch, F. Konwitschny (r1959) *Concert*
(10/94) (EMI) ① [4] **CMS5 65212-2**
13, 24, 32, 35, 36. I. Andrésen, R. Laubenthal, T. de
Garmo, L. Kindermann, E. Marherr-Wagner, D.
Zádor, E. List, Berlin St Op Chor, Berlin St Op Orch,
L. Blech (r1928) *Concert*
(4/95) (PEAR) ① [7] **GEMMCDS9137**
16a E. Schumann-Heink, orch, R. Bourdon (r1919)
Concert (2/91) (NIMB) ① **NI7811**
16a C. Ludwig, VPO, G. Solti (r1964) *Concert*
(10/93) (DECC) ① **436 462-2DM**
16a, 16b B. Fassbaender, Stuttgart RSO, H. Graf
Concert (11/86) (ORFE) ① **C096841A**
16b R. Anday, Berlin St Op Orch, J. Prüwer (r1928)
Concert (5/92) (PREI) ① **89046**
16b K. Thorborg, RCA SO, K. Riedel (r1940) *Concert*
(4/95) (PREI) ① **89084**
18(pt) S. Sedlmair, anon (r1904) *Concert*
(7/91) (SYMP) ① **SYMCD1081**
23. E. List, Berlin Staatskapelle Chor, Berlin
Staatskapelle, E. Mörike (r1928) *Concert*
(1/92) (EMI) ① [4] **CMS7 64008-2(2)**
24. Bayreuth Fest Chor, Bayreuth Fest Orch, W. Pitz
Concert (4/90) (DG) ① **429 169-2GR**
24. I. Andrésen, Berlin St Op Orch, L. Blech (r1927)
Concert (10/90) (PREI) ① **89028**
24(pt)-26. L. Weber, H. Janssen, ROH Chor, LPO, T.
Beecham (pp1936) *Concert*
(1/92) (EMI) ① [4] **CMS7 64008-2(2)**
28. K. Flagstad, S. Svanholm, Philh, H. Weigert
(r1951) *Concert*
(10/94) (EMI) ① [4] **CMS5 65212-2**
35, 36. Orch, LSO (r1930) *Concert*
(8/88) (DANA) ① [2] **DACOCD315/6**
35(pt), 36. M. Lorenz, P. Schoeffler, J. von
Manowarda, Vienna St Op Orch, J. Reichwein
(pp1942) *Concert* (1/95) (SCHW) ① [2] **314562**
36. L. Melchior, LSO, R. Heger (r1930) *Concert*
(10/89) (EMI) ① **CDH7 69789-2**
36, 37. H. Brilioth, BPO, H. von Karajan *Concert*
(4/90) (DG) ① **429 168-2GR**
37. Los Angeles PO, E. Leinsdorf *Concert*
(8/87) (SHEF) ① **CD-7/8**
37. orch, A. Coates (r1926) *Concert*
(7/90) (CLAR) ① **CDGSE78-50-33**
37. Philh, O. Klemperer (r1960) *Concert*
(11/90) (EMI) ① **CDM7 63618-2**
37. BPO, W. Furtwängler (r1933) *Concert*
(4/92) (KOCH) ① [2] **37073-2**
37. Leningrad PO, E. Mravinsky (pp1968) *Concert*
(6/92) (ERAT) ① [11] **2292-45763-2**
37. Leningrad PO, E. Mravinsky (pp1968) *Concert*
(6/92) (ERAT) ① **2292-45762-2**
37. Oslo PO, M. Jansons *Concert*
(12/92) (EMI) ① **CDC7 54583-2**
37. Leningrad PO, E. Mravinsky (pp1967) *Concert*
(3/94) (RUSS) ① **RDCD11166**
37, 39, 40. F. Austral, LSO, L. Collingwood (r1927)
Concert (4/95) (PEAR) ① [7] **GEMMCDS9137**
37, 42, 43. H. Dernesch, K. Ridderbusch, BPO, H.
von Karajan (r1969/70) *Concert*
(3/94) (DG) ① **439 423-2GCL**
37, 43. VPO, G. Solti *Concert*
(11/83) (DECC) ① **410 137-2DH**
37, 44. LPO, K.A. Rickenbacher *Concert*
(11/87) (CFP) ① **CD-CFP9008**
39-43. F. Leider, E. Marherr-Wagner, Berlin St Op
Orch, L. Blech (r1928) *Concert*
(11/89) (PEAR) ① **GEMMCDS9331**
39-43. F. Leider, E. Marherr-Wagner, Berlin St Op
Orch, L. Blech (r1928) *Concert*
(6/90) (LYRC) ① [2] **LCD146**
40. K. Flagstad, San Francisco Op Orch, E. McArthur
(r1939) *Concert* (7/93) (NIMB) ① **NI7847**
40-42. K. Flagstad, Vienna St Op Orch, F.
Weingartner (pp1936) *Concert*
(7/94) (SCHW) ① [2] **314512**

40-42. K. Flagstad, Oslo PO, Norwegian Rad Orch, Ø.
Fjeldstad (r1956) *Concert*
(12/95) (LOND) ① **440 495-2LM**
40-42. K. Flagstad, VPO, Oslo PO, A. Boult (r1956)
Concert (12/95) (LOND) ① [5] **440 490-2LM5(1)**
40-43. J. Norman, LPO, K. Tennstedt *Concert*
(11/88) (EMI) ① **CDC7 49759-2**
40-43. K. Flagstad, Philh, W. Furtwängler (r1948)
Concert (8/89) (EMI) ① **CDH7 63030-2**
40-43. M. Lawrence, Pasdeloup Orch, P. Coppola
(French: r1933) *Concert* (5/90) (PREI) ① **89011**
40-43. G. Lubin, orch, H. Defosse (French: r1929)
Concert (5/91) (EPM) ① **150 052**
40-43. M. Lawrence, Pasdeloup Orch, P. Coppola
(French: r1933) *Concert*
(1/92) (EMI) ① [4] **CMS7 64008-2(2)**
40-43. G. Jones, Cologne RSO, R. Paternostro
Concert (2/92) (CHAN) ① **CHAN8930**
40-43. K. Flagstad, Philh, W. Furtwängler (r1948)
Concert (4/94) (EMI) ① [2] **CHS7 64935-2**
40-43. K. Flagstad, Philh, W. Furtwängler (r1948)
Concert (10/94) (EMI) ① [4] **CMS5 65212-2**
41. M. Saltzmann-Stevens, orch, P. Pitt (Eng: r1909)
Concert (7/92) (PEAR) ① [3] **GEMMCDS9924(2)**
41-43. K. Flagstad, San Francisco Op Orch, E.
MacArthur (r1939) *Concert*
(10/90) (RCA) ① **GD87915**
44. NYPSO, A. Toscanini (1936) *Concert*
(3/90) (PEAR) ① [3] **GEMMCDS9373**
44. NBC SO, A. Toscanini (r1941) *Concert*
(11/92) (RCA) ① **GD60296**
44. NYPO, A. Toscanini (1936) *Concert*
(11/92) (RCA) ① **GD60318**

Tannhäuser—opera: 3 acts (1845—Dresden)
(Lib. cpsr)
ACT 1: 1. Overture; 2. Venusberg Music; 3.
Geliebter, sag, wo weilt dein Sinn?; 4. Dir töne Lob;
5. Geliebter, komm! Sieh dort die Grotte; 6. Stets soll
nur dir, nur dir mein Lied ertönen!; 7. Frau Holda kam
aus dem Berg hervor; 8. Zu dir wall ich; 9. Als du in
kuhnem Sange. ACT 2: 10. Dich teure Halle
(Elisabeth's Greeting); 11. O Fürstin! Gott! Stehet
auf!; 12. Entry of the Guests (Grand March); 13.
Freudig begrüssen; 14. Gar viel und schön
(Landgrave's address); 15. Blick ich umher; 16.
Heraus zum kampfe mit uns allen; 17. O Himmel!
Lass dich jetzt; 18. Zurück; 19. Ein Engel; 20. Ein
furchbares Verbrechen. ACT 3: 21. Prelude; 22. Wohl
wüsst ich hier sie im Gebet zu finden; 23. Beglückt
darf nun (Pilgrims' Chorus); 24. Allmächt'ge Jungfrau
(Elisabeth's Prayer); 25a. Wie Todesahnung; 25b. O
du mein holder Abendstern; 26. Ich hörte
Harfenschlag; 27. Inbrunst im Herzen (Rome
Narration). 28. Willkommen, ungetreuer Mann!
Cpte K. König, L. Popp, B. Weikl, W. Meier, K. Moll,
S. Jerusalem, W. Grönroos, D. Litaker, R. Scholze,
G. Sima, Bavarian Rad Chor, BRSO, B. Haitink
(2/86) (EMI) ① [3] **CDS7 47296-8**
Cpte R. Kollo, H. Dernesch, V. Braun, C. Ludwig, H.
Sotin, W. Hollweg, M. Jungwirth, K. Equiluz, N.
Bailey, Vienna Boys' Ch, Vienna St Op Chor, VPO,
G. Solti (Paris vers)
(2/86) (DECC) ① [3] **414 581-2DH3**
Cpte P. Domingo, C. Studer, A. Schmidt, A. Baltsa,
M. Salminen, W. Pell, K. Rydl, C. Biber, O.
Hillebrandt, B. Bonney, ROH Chor, Philh, G. Sinopoli
(Paris vers) (9/89) (DG) ① [3] **427 625-2GH3**
Cpte H. Hopf, E. Grümmer, D. Fischer-Dieskau, M.
Schech, G. Frick, F. Wunderlich, R. Gonszar, G.
Unger, R. Süss, L. Otto, Berlin St Op Chor, Berlin St
Op Orch, F. Konwitschny
(10/90) (EMI) ① [3] **CMS7 63214-2**
Cpte W. Windgassen, A. Silja, E. Waechter, G.
Bumbry, J. Greindl, G. Stolze, F. Crass, G. Paskuda,
G. Nienstedt, E-M. Gardelli, Bayreuth Fest Chor,
Bayreuth Fest Orch, W. Sawallisch (pp1962)
(10/92) (PHIL) ① [3] **434 607-2PH3**
Excs Lotte Lehmann, J. Kalenberg, R. Mayr, F.
Schorr, G. Maikl, F. Markhoff, W. Wernigk, K. Ettl,
Vienna St Op Chor, Vienna St Op Orch, R. Heger
(pp1933) *Concert* (11/95) (SCHW) ① [2] **314622**
Symphonic synthesis Pittsburgh Mendelssohn Ch,
Pittsburgh SO, L. Maazel (arr Maazel)
(4/92) (SONY) ① **SK47178**
1. LSO, W. Morris *Concert*
(12/87) (CIRR) ① **CICD1005**
1. VPO, H. von Karajan (r1987) *Concert*
(8/88) (DG) ① **423 613-2GH**
1. VPO, W. Furtwängler (r1952) *Concert*
(2/89) (ACAN) ① **43 121**
1. Philh, O. Klemperer *Concert*
(11/90) (EMI) ① **CDM7 63617-2**
1. Chicago SO, G. Solti *Concert*
(5/91) (DECC) ① **430 448-2DM**
1. Leningrad PO, E. Mravinsky (pp1973) *Concert*
(6/92) (ERAT) ① **2292-45762-2**

1. Oslo PO, M. Jansons *Concert*
(12/92) (EMI) ① **CDC7 54583-2**
1. Leningrad PO, E. Mravinsky (pp1967) *Concert*
(3/94) (RUSS) ① **RDCD11166**
1. VPO, W. Furtwängler (r1952) *Concert*
(4/94) (EMI) ① [2] **CHS7 64935-2**
1. Concertgebouw, W. Mengelberg (pp1940) *Concert*
(7/94) (MUSI) ① [4] **MACD-780**
1. SO, A. Coates (r1926) *Concert*
(2/95) (CLAR) ① **CDGSE78-50-54**
1. NQHO, B. Wordsworth (r1995) *Concert*
(6/95) (EYE) ① [2] **EOS5001**
1. NYPO, P. Boulez (r1973) *Concert*
(7/95) (SONY) ① **SMK64108**
1, 10, 25a, 25b C. Studer, B. Terfel, BPO, C. Abbado
(pp1993) *Concert* (5/94) (DG) ① **439 768-2GH**
1, 12. LPO, T. Beecham (r1937/8) *Concert*
(6/94) (DUTT) ① **CDLX7007**
1, 2. Seattle SO, G. Schwarz *Concert*
(3/87) (DELO) ① **DE3040**
1, 2. Philh, F. d'Avalos *Götterdämmerung.*
(2/88) (ASV) ① **CDDCA595**
1, 2. Occidental Coll Concert Ch, Columbia SO, B.
Walter (r1959) *Concert*
(2/90) (SONY) ① **MPK45701**
1, 2. Philadelphia, L. Stokowski (1937) *Concert*
(2/91) (PEAR) ① **GEMMCD9448**
1, 2. NY Met Op Orch, James Levine (r1991) *Concert*
(10/93) (DG) ① **435 874-2GH**
1, 2. Chor, Sym of the Air, L. Stokowski (r1961)
Concert (3/94) (RCA) ① **09026 61503-2**
1, 2. BBC Chor, RPO, T. Beecham (pp1954) *Concert*
(10/95) (BBCR) ① [2] **DMCD98**
2. NYPO, J. Barbirolli (pp1938) *Concert*
(3/95) (DUTT) ① **CDSJB1001**
2, 12. chor, SO, A. Coates (r1925: Eng) *Concert*
(2/95) (CLAR) ① **CDGSE78-50-54**
4. L. Melchior, LSO, J. Barbirolli (r1930) *Concert*
(8/88) (DANA) ① [2] **DACOCD315/6**
4. L. Melchior, LSO, J. Barbirolli (r1930) *Concert*
(10/89) (EMI) ① **CDH7 69789-2**
4. F. Giraud, anon (Ital: r1904) *Concert*
(5/91) (SYMP) ① **SYMCD1077**
4. L. Melchior, RCA SO, E. McArthur (r1940) *Concert*
(4/94) (RCA) ① [6] **09026 61580-2(3)**
6. H. Winkelmann, anon (r1904) *Concert*
(7/91) (SYMP) ① **SYMCD1081**
8, 23. B. Jones, W. Widdop, E. Halland, chor, SO, A.
Coates (r1925: Eng) *Concert*
(2/95) (CLAR) ① **CDGSE78-50-54**
9. F. Schorr, New SO, A. Coates (r c1930) *Concert*
(9/91) (PEAR) ① **GEMMCD9398**
9. D. Bispham, anon (r1903) *Concert*
(10/92) (SYMP) ① **SYMCD1093**
9(pt), 10, 18(pt), 19(pt), 20(pt), 27(pt) M. Lorenz, M.
Reining, A. Konetzni, H. Alsen, A. Schellenberg, G.
Maikl, V. Madin, H. Gallos, K. Ettl, Vienna St Op
Chor, Vienna St Op Orch, H. Knappertsbusch
(pp1937) *Concert* (12/95) (SCHW) ① [2] **314672**
9, 15. F. Schorr, New SO, A. Coates (r1930) *Concert*
(2/95) (CLAR) ① **CDGSE78-50-54**
9, 22, 25b A. Sved, Vienna St Op Orch, W.
Furtwängler (pp1935) *Concert*
(12/94) (EMI) ① [2] **314542**
10. A. Tomowa-Sintow, Munich RO, P. Sommer
Concert (11/86) (ORFE) ① **C106841A**
10. E. Turner, orch, J. Batten (r1933: Eng) *Concert*
(9/89) (EMI) ① **CDH7 69791-2**
10. V. de los Angeles, Philh, A. Fistoulari (r1950)
Concert (8/90) (EMI) ① **CDH7 63495-2**
10. G. Lubin, orch, H. Defosse (French: r1929)
Concert (5/91) (CLUB) ① **CL99-022**
10. G. Lubin, orch, H. Defosse (French: r1929)
Concert (5/91) (EPM) ① **150 052**
10. F. Leider, orch (r1921) *Concert*
(5/91) (PREI) ① [3] **89301**
10. F. Leider, orch (r1926) *Concert*
(5/91) (PREI) ① [3] **89301**
10. M. Müller, Bayreuth Fest Orch, K. Elmendorff
(r1930) *Concert*
(1/92) (EMI) ① [4] **CMS7 64008-2(1)**
10. Lotte Lehmann, Berlin St Op Chor, F. Weissmann
(r1930) *Concert* (2/92) (MMOI) ① **CDMOIR408**
10. A. Varnay, Philh, G. Sébastian (r1951) *Concert*
(4/94) (EMI) ① [7] **CHS7 69741-2(1)**
10. A. Marc, NZ SO, H. Wallberg *Concert*
(6/92) (DELO) ① **DE3108**
10. K. Fleischer-Edel, orch (r1908) *Concert*
(7/92) (PEAR) ① [3] **GEMMCDS9924(2)**
10. A. Marc, NZ SO, H. Wallberg *Concert*
(11/92) (ODE) ① **CDMANU1317**
10. L. Price, New Philh, N. Santi (r1977) *Concert*
(12/92) (RCA) ① **09026 61236-2**
10. T. Lemnitz, Berlin St Op Orch, L. Blech (r1934)
Concert (10/93) (NIMB) ① **NI7848**

10. E. Destinn, orch, B. Seidler-Winkler (r1909) *Concert* (5/94) (SUPR) Ⓓ **11 1337-2**
10. E. Destinn, orch, B. Seidler-Winkler (r1908) *Concert* (12/94) (SUPR) Ⓓ [12] **11 2136-2(1)**
10. E. Destinn, orch, B. Seidler-Winkler (r1909) *Concert* (12/94) (SUPR) Ⓓ [12] **11 2136-2(2)**
10. E. Rethberg, orch (r1927) *Concert* (2/95) (ROMO) Ⓓ [2] **81012-2**
10. E. Rethberg, Berlin SO, F. Zweig (r1927) *Concert* (10/95) (ROMO) Ⓓ [2] **81014-2**
10. E. Rethberg, K. Ruhrseitz (r1932) *Concert* (10/95) (ROMO) Ⓓ [2] **81014-2**
10, 18(pt) S. Sedlmair, anon (r1904) *Concert* (7/91) (SYMP) Ⓓ **SYMCD1081**
10, 24. E. Schwarzkopf, Philh, W. Susskind *Concert* (10/88) (EMI) Ⓓ **CDM7 69501-2**
10, 24. J. Norman, LPO, K. Tennstedt *Concert* (11/88) (EMI) Ⓓ **CDC7 49759-2**
10, 24. T. Lemnitz, Berlin St Op Orch, L. Blech (r1934) *Concert* (10/90) (PREI) Ⓓ **89025**
10, 24. G. Jones, Cologne RSO, R. Paternostro *Concert* (2/92) (CHAN) Ⓓ **CHAN8930**
10, 24. Lotte Lehmann, orch (r1916) *Concert* (6/92) (PREI) Ⓓ [3] **89302**
10, 24. M. Reining, Zurich Tonhalle Orch, H. Knappertsbusch (r1949) *Concert* (9/92) (PREI) Ⓓ **90083**
10, 24. K. Flagstad, orch, H. Lange (r1935) *Concert* (7/93) (NIMB) Ⓓ **NI7847**
10, 24. E. Destinn, orch, F. Kark (r1906) *Concert* (12/94) (SUPR) Ⓓ [12] **11 2136-2(1)**
10, 24. E. Destinn, orch, B. Seidler-Winkler (r1906) *Concert* (12/94) (SUPR) Ⓓ [12] **11 2136-2(1)**
10, 24. H. Konetzni, Berlin Deutsche Op Orch, H. Schmidt-Isserstedt (r1937) *Concert* (1/95) (PREI) Ⓓ **90078**
10, 24. G. Janowitz, Berlin Deutsche Op Orch, F. Leitner (r1967) *Concert* (12/95) (DG) Ⓓ [2] **447 352-2GDB2**
10, 24. K. Flagstad, orch, H. Lange (r1935) *Concert* (12/95) (SIMA) Ⓓ [3] **PSC1821(1)**
11. L. Melchior, E. Bettendorf, orch, P. Breisach (r1925) *Concert* (8/88) (DANA) Ⓓ [2] **DACOCD313/4**
11(pt) S. Sedlmair, L. Slezak, anon (r1904) *Concert* (7/91) (SYMP) Ⓓ **SYMCD1081**
11. M. Reining, M. Lorenz, VPO, R. Moralt (r1942) *Concert* (1/92) (EMI) Ⓓ [4] **CMS7 64008-2(1)**
11. M. Reining, M. Lorenz, VPO, R. Moralt (r1942) *Concert* (9/94) (PREI) Ⓓ **89065**
11(pt) E. Destinn, K. Jörn, orch, B. Seidler-Winkler (r1908) *Concert* (12/94) (SUPR) Ⓓ [12] **11 2136-2(2)**
12. LPO, T. Beecham (bp1939) *Concert* (11/91) (SYMP) Ⓓ [2] **SYMCD1096/7**
12. Grimethorpe Colliery Band, E. Howarth (arr Greenwood) *Concert* (12/92) (DOYE) Ⓓ **DOYCD013**
12. RCA Victor Orch, F. Reiner (r1950) *Concert* (8/94) (RCA) Ⓓ **09026 61792-2**
13. Berlin Deutsche Op Chor, Berlin Deutsche Op Orch, G. Sinopoli *Concert* (10/85) (DG) Ⓓ **415 283-2GH**
13, 23, 27(pt) E. Schärtel, Bayreuth Fest Chor, Bayreuth Fest Orch, W. Pitz *Concert* (4/90) (DG) Ⓓ **429 169-2GR**
14. I. Andrésen, Berlin St Op Orch, F. Zweig (r1928) *Concert* (10/90) (PREI) Ⓓ **89028**
14. M. Schenk, Nuremberg SO, K. Seibel *Concert* (12/91) (COLO) Ⓓ **COL34 9004**
14. L. Weber, Philh, I. Dobroven (r1951) *Concert* (4/92) (EMI) Ⓓ [7] **CHS7 69741-2(4)**
14. L. Hofmann, Vienna St Op Orch, W. Furtwängler (pp1935) *Concert* (3/95) (SCHW) Ⓓ [2] **314602**
14, 20. W. Schirp, Vienna St Op Orch, L. Reichwein (pp1939) *Concert* (6/95) (SCHW) Ⓓ [2] **314632**
15. F. Schorr, LSO, A. Coates (r1930) *Concert* (9/91) (PEAR) Ⓓ **GEMMCD9398**
15. H. Janssen, Bayreuth Fest Orch, K. Elmendorff (r1930) *Concert* (1/92) (EMI) Ⓓ [4] **CMS7 64008-2(1)**
15. J. Berglund, orch, L. Blech (r c1946) *Concert* (4/92) (EMI) Ⓓ [7] **CHS7 69741-2(5)**
15. H. Janssen, Bayreuth Fest Orch, K. Elmendorff (r1930) *Concert* (7/92) (PEAR) Ⓓ [3] **GEMMCDS9926(1)**
15. M. Battistini, anon (Ital: r1911) *Concert* (10/92) (PEAR) Ⓓ **GEMMCD9936**
15. A. Endrèze, orch, F. Ruhlmann (French: r c1932) *Concert* (11/92) (MSCM) Ⓓ **MM30451**
15. A. Van Rooy, anon (r1902) *Concert* (3/93) (SYMP) Ⓓ **SYMCD1100**
15, 25a, 25b B. Weikl, Munich RO, H. Wallberg *Concert* (3/89) (ACAN) Ⓓ **43 266**
15, 25a, 25b H. Schlusnus, Berlin St Op Orch, L. Blech (r1935) *Concert* (9/90) (PREI) Ⓓ **89006**
15, 25b G. Hüsch, Berlin St Op Orch, H.U. Müller (r1936) *Concert* (3/94) (PREI) Ⓓ **89071**
18(pt) E. Destinn, orch (r1910) *Concert* (12/94) (SUPR) Ⓓ [12] **11 2136-2(4)**
20. I. Andrésen, orch (r1929) *Concert* (10/90) (PREI) Ⓓ **89028**
21. Philadelphia, L. Stokowski (arr Stokowski: r1936) *Concert* (2/91) (PEAR) Ⓓ **GEMMCD9448**
21. SO, A. Coates (r1925) *Concert* (2/95) (CLAR) Ⓓ **CDGSE78-50-54**
22. C. Whitehill, anon (r1904) *Concert* (7/91) (SYMP) Ⓓ **SYMCD1081**
22, 25a, 25b G. Hüsch, Berlin St Op Orch, H.U. Müller (r1936) *Concert* (1/92) (EMI) Ⓓ [4] **CMS7 64008-2(1)**
23. S. Preston (trans org: arr. Lemare) *Concert* (6/91) (DECC) Ⓓ **430 091-2DWO**
23. T. Trotter (r1992: trans org: E Lemare) *Concert* (4/94) (DECC) Ⓓ **436 656-2DH**
23(pt), 25a, 25b, 27(pt), 28(pt) J. Kalenberg, R. Bockelmann, G. Rünger, Vienna St Op Chor, Vienna St Op Orch, R. Heger (pp1933) *Concert* (7/94) (SCHW) Ⓓ [2] **314512**
24. K. Flagstad, Philh, I. Dobroven (r1948) *Concert* (8/89) (EMI) Ⓓ **CDH7 63030-2**
24. J. Gadski, orch (r1906) *Concert* (7/91) (CLUB) Ⓓ **CL99-109**
24. K. Flagstad, Philh, I. Dobroven (r1948) *Concert* (1/92) (EMI) Ⓓ [4] **CMS7 64008-2(1)**
24. E. Destinn, orch (r1914) *Concert* (11/93) (ROMO) Ⓓ [2] **81002-2**
24. M. Reining, Berlin RSO, A. Rother (bp1943) *Concert* (9/94) (PREI) Ⓓ **89065**
24. E. Destinn, orch, W.B Rogers (r1914) *Concert* (12/94) (SUPR) Ⓓ [12] **11 2136-2(5)**
24. E. Rethberg, orch (r1928) *Concert* (2/95) (ROMO) Ⓓ [2] **81012-2**
25a, 25b L. Tibbett, orch, N. Shilkret (r1934) *Concert* (3/91) (PEAR) Ⓓ [2] **GEMMCDS9452**
25a, 25b T. Hampson, Munich RO, F. Luisi (r1994) *Concert* (9/95) (EMI) Ⓓ **CDC5 55233-2**
25b R. Stracciari, orch (r1925: Ital) *Concert* (2/90) (PREI) Ⓓ **89003**
25b E. Giraldoni, anon (Ital: r1902) *Concert* (6/90) (SYMP) Ⓓ **SYMCD1073**
25b C. Tagliabue, orch, U. Berrettoni (Ital: r1946) *Concert* (11/90) (PREI) Ⓓ **89015**
25b F. Schorr, Berlin St Op Orch, L. Blech (r c1928) *Concert* (9/91) (PEAR) Ⓓ **GEMMCD9398**
25b P. Casals, N. Mednikoff (arr vc/pf: r1926) *Concert* (10/91) (BIDD) Ⓓ **LAB017**
25b A. Granforte, La Scala Orch, C. Sabajno (Ital: r1928) *Concert* (12/91) (PREI) Ⓓ **89048**
25b M. Renaud, anon (r1902) *Concert* (3/93) (SYMP) Ⓓ **SYMCD1100**
25b J. Schwarz, orch (r c1918) *Concert* (10/95) (NIMB) Ⓓ **NI7867**
27. L. Melchior, LSO, A. Coates (r1929) *Concert* (8/88) (DANA) Ⓓ [2] **DACOCD315/6**
27. L. Melchior, orch (r1923-26) *Concert* (8/88) (DANA) Ⓓ [2] **DACOCD313/4**
27. L. Melchior, LSO, A. Coates (r1929) *Concert* (10/89) (EMI) Ⓓ **CDH7 69789-2**
27. L. Melchior, LSO, A. Coates (r1929) *Concert* (7/90) (CLAR) Ⓓ **CDGSE78-50-33**
27. L. Melchior, LSO, A. Coates (r1929) *Concert* (7/92) (PEAR) Ⓓ [3] **GEMMCDS9926(1)**
27. L. Melchior, LSO, A. Coates (r1929) *Concert* (10/93) (NIMB) Ⓓ **NI7848**
27. L. Suthaus, orch *Concert* (3/94) (MYTO) Ⓓ [3] **3MCD93381**
27. F. Völker, Berlin Staatskapelle, A. Melichar (r1933) *Concert* (8/94) (PREI) Ⓓ **89070**
27. L. Melchior, LSO, A. Coates (r1929) *Concert* (2/95) (CLAR) Ⓓ **CDGSE78-50-54**

Tristan und Isolde—music drama: 3 acts (1865—Munich) (Lib. cpsr)

ACT 1; 1. Prelude; 2. Hab acht, Tristan; 3. Doch nun von Tristan!; 4. Wie lachend sie (Isolde's Narrative and Curse); 5. So reihte sie die Mutter; 6. Begehrt, Herrin. ACT 2: 7. Prelude; 8a. Isolde! Geliebte! Tristan! Geliebter!; 8b. O sink hernieder, Nacht der Liebe; 8c. O sink hernieder; 9a. Einsam wachend (Brangäne's Warning); 9b. Lausch Geliebter!; 9c. So starben wir; 9d. Lass' mich sterben!; 10. Tatest du's wirklich? (King Marke's monologue); 11. O König...Wohin nun Tristan scheidet. ACT 3: 12. Prelude; 13. Die alte Weise; 14. Dünkt dich das?; 15. Wie sie selig; 16. O diese Sonne!; 17. Ha! Ich bin's, ich bin's; 18. Mild und leise (Liebestod). 19. Prelude and Liebestod (concert version: arr. Humperdinck).

Cpte L. Suthaus, K. Flagstad, B. Thebom, J. Greindl, D. Fischer-Dieskau, E. Evans, R. Schock, R. Davies, ROH Chor, Philh, W. Furtwängler (r1952) (5/86) (EMI) Ⓓ [4] **CDS7 47322-8**
Cpte R. Kollo, M. Price, B. Fassbaender, K. Moll, D. Fischer-Dieskau, W. Götz, A. Dermota, Wolfgang Hellmich, E. Büchner, Leipzig Rad Chor, Staatskapelle Dresden, C. Kleiber (11/86) (DG) Ⓓ [4] **413 315-2GH4**
Cpte J. Vickers, H. Dernesch, C. Ludwig, K. Ridderbusch, W. Berry, B. Weikl, P. Schreier, M. Vantin, P. Schreier, Berlin Deutsche Op Chor, BPO, H. von Karajan (r1971/2) (7/88) (EMI) Ⓓ [4] **CMS7 69319-2**
Cpte L. Melchior, K. Flagstad, K. Thorborg, E. List, J. Huehn, G. Cehanovsky, D. Beattie, A. Marlowe, NY Met Op Chor, NY Met Op Orch, E. Leinsdorf (pp1940) (7/91) (MUSI) Ⓓ [3] **MACD-647**
Cpte L. Melchior, K. Flagstad, M. Klose, S. Kalter, S. Nilsson, E. List, H. Janssen, B. Hitchin, F. Sale, O. Dua, L. Horsman, Parry Jones, R. Devereux, ROH Chor, LPO, F. Reiner, T. Beecham (pp1936/7) (1/92) (EMI) Ⓓ [3] **CHS7 64037-2**
Cpte W. Windgassen, B. Nilsson, C. Ludwig, M. Talvela, E. Waechter, C. Heater, E. Wohlfahrt, G. Nienstedt, P. Schreier, Bayreuth Fest Chor, Bayreuth Fest Orch, K. Böhm (pp1966) (10/92) (PHIL) Ⓓ [3] **434 425-2PH3**
Cpte L. Melchior, K. Flagstad, S. Kalter, E. List, H. Janssen, F. Sale, O. Dua, L. Horsman, R. Devereux, ROH Chor, LPO, F. Reiner (pp1936) (1/93) (VAI) Ⓓ [3] **VAIA1004**
Cpte G. Treptow, H. Braun, M. Klose, F. Frantz, P. Schoeffler, A. Peter, P. Kuen, F.R. Bender, Bavarian St Op Chor, Bavarian St Orch, H. Knappertsbusch (pp1950) (5/95) (ORFE) Ⓓ [3] **C355943D**
Cpte J. Mitchinson, L. E. Gray, A. Wilkens, G. Howell, P. Joll, N. Folwell, A. Davies, G. Moses, J. Harris, WNO Chor, WNO Orch, R. Goodall (r1980/1) (5/95) (DECC) Ⓓ [4] **443 682-2DMO4**
Cpte M. Lorenz, P. Buchner, M. Klose, L. Hofmann, J. Prohaska, E. Fuchs, E. Zimmermann, F. Fleischer, B. Arnold, Berlin St Op Chor, Berlin Staatskapelle, R. Heger (bp1943) (9/95) (PREI) Ⓓ [3] **90243**
Cpte S. Jerusalem, W. Meier, M. Lipovšek, M. Salminen, F. Struckmann, J. Botha, P. Maus, R. Trekel, U. Heilmann, Berlin St Op Chor, BPO, D. Barenboim (r1994) (9/95) (TELD) Ⓓ [4] **4509-94568-2**
Act 3 (abridged) W. Widdop, G. Ljungberg, G. Guszalewicz, I. Andrésen, H. Fry, C. Victor, E. Habich, M. Noe, K. McKenna, SO, LSO, Berlin St Op Orch, A. Coates, L. Blech, L. Collingwood (r1926/7) *Concert* (7/89) (CLAR) Ⓓ **CDGSE78-50-26**
Dein werk J. Gadski, orch (r1909) *Concert* (7/91) (CLUB) Ⓓ **CL99-109**
Dein Werk? O thör'ge Maid! N. Larsen-Todsen, A. Helm, Bayreuth Fest Orch, K. Elmendorff (r1928) *Concert* (1/92) (EMI) Ⓓ [4] **CMS7 64008-2(2)**
Excs M. Lorenz, A. Konetzni, M. Klose, H. Alsen, P. Schoeffler, G. Monthy, H. Gallos, K. Ettl, W. Franter, Vienna St Op Chor, Vienna St Op Orch, W. Furtwängler (pp1941/3) (5/95) (SCHW) Ⓓ [2] **314612**
1. Los Angeles PO, E. Leinsdorf *Concert* (8/87) (SHEF) Ⓓ **CD-7/8**
1. BPO, W. Furtwängler (r1938) *Concert* (2/89) (ACAN) Ⓓ **43 121**
1. SO, A. Coates (r1926) *Concert* (7/89) (CLAR) Ⓓ **CDGSE78-50-26**
1. I. Paderewski (arr Schelling: r1930) *Concert* (3/93) (RCA) Ⓓ **GD60923**
1. I. Paderewski (arr Schelling: r1930) *Concert* (3/93) (PEAR) Ⓓ **GEMMCD9943**
1, 18. J. Norman, LSO, Colin Davis *Wesendonk Lieder.* (8/85) (PHIL) Ⓓ **412 655-2PH**
1, 18. J. Norman, VPO, H. von Karajan (pp1987) *Concert* (8/88) (DG) Ⓓ **423 613-2GH**
1, 18. J. Norman, LPO, K. Tennstedt *Concert* (11/88) (EMI) Ⓓ **CDC7 49759-2**
1, 18. G. Jones, Cologne RSO, R. Paternostro *Concert* (2/92) (CHAN) Ⓓ **CHAN8930**
1, 18. C. Studer, Staatskapelle Dresden, G. Sinopoli *Concert* (7/94) (DG) Ⓓ **439 865-2GH**
1, 18. J. Eaglen, LCP, R. Norrington (r1994) *Concert* (11/95) (EMI) Ⓓ **CDC5 55479-2**
1, 9a, 12, 18. A. Marc, Seattle SO, G. Schwarz (r1992) *Concert* (4/94) (DELO) Ⓓ **DE3120**
3. F. Leider, E. Marherr-Wagner, Berlin St Op Orch, L. Blech (r1928) *Concert* (1/92) (EMI) Ⓓ [4] **CMS7 64008-2(2)**
3. F. Leider, E. Marherr-Wagner, Berlin St Op Orch, L. Blech (r1928) *Concert* (10/93) (NIMB) Ⓓ **NI7848**
3, 4. K. Flagstad, E. Höngen, Philh, I. Dobroven (r1948) *Concert* (8/89) (EMI) Ⓓ **CDH7 63030-2**
3, 8a-c, 9b-d, 18. M. Mödl, J. Blatter, W. Windgassen, Berlin City Op Orch, A. Rother (r1952/4) (5/95) (TELD) Ⓓ **4509-95516-2**

4. F. Leider, E. Marherr-Wagner, Berlin St Op Orch, L. Blech (r1928) *Concert*
(11/89) (PEAR) ① **GEMMCD9331**
4. F. Leider, E. Marherr-Wagner, Berlin St Op Orch, L. Blech (r1928) *Concert*
(6/90) (LYRC) ① [2] **LCD146**
6(pt) E. Ferrari-Fontana, orch (r1915: Ital) *Concert*
(4/94) (EMI) ① [3] **CHS7 64860-2(2)**
8. F. Leider, L. Melchior, Berlin St Op Orch, A. Coates (r1929) *Concert*
(8/88) (DANA) ① [2] **DACOCD315/6**
8. L. Melchior, F. Leider, Berlin St Op Orch, LSO, A. Coates (r1929) *Concert*
(7/89) (CLAR) ① **CDGSE78-50-26**
8. F. Leider, L. Melchior, LSO, Berlin St Op Orch, A. Coates (r1929) *Concert*
(6/90) (LYRC) ① [2] **LCD146**
8a F. Leider, L. Melchior, Berlin St Op Orch, A. Coates (r1929) *Concert*
(1/92) (EMI) ① [4] **CMS7 64008-2(2)**
8a-c F. Leider, L. Melchior, Berlin St Op Orch, LSO, A. Coates (r1929) *Concert*   (2/90) (PREI) ① **89004**
8a, 8c F. Leider, H. Soot, orch (r1925) *Concert*
(5/91) (PREI) ① [3] **89301**
8c S. Sedlmair, E. Schmedes, anon (r1904) *Concert*
(7/91) (SYMP) ① **SYMCD1081**
8c F. Leider, L. Melchior, LSO, A. Coates (r1929) *Concert*   (1/92) (EMI) ① [4] **CMS7 64008-2(2)**
8c K. Flagstad, C. Shacklock, S. Svanholm, Philh, K. Böhm (r1949) *Concert*   (7/93) (TEST) ① **SBT1018**
8c K. Flagstad, L. Melchior, San Francisco SO, E. McArthur (r1939) *Concert*
(12/95) (SIMA) ① [3] **PSC1821(2)**
8c, 9a, 9c M. Lorenz, A. Konetzni, M. Klose, Vienna St Op Orch, W. Furtwängler (pp1941) *Concert*
(1/95) (SCHW) ① [2] **314562**
9a R. Anday, orch (r1926) *Concert*
(5/92) (PREI) ① **89046**
9a K. Thorborg, RCA SO, K. Riedel (r1940) *Concert*
(4/95) (PREI) ① **89084**
10. A. Kipnis, orch (r c1916) *Concert*
(10/91) (PEAR) ① **GEMMCD9451**
10. M. Schenk, Nuremberg SO, K. Seibel *Concert*
(12/91) (COLO) ① **COL34 9004**
10. J. von Manowarda, J. Sattler, Vienna SO, H. Weisbach (pp1940) *Walküre.*
(11/93) (PREI) ① **90151**
11, 15. L. Melchior, LSO, R. Heger (r1930) *Concert*
(8/88) (DANA) ① [2] **DACOCD315/6**
11, 15. L. Melchior, LSO, R. Heger (r1930) *Concert*
(10/89) (EMI) ① **CDH7 69789-2**
11, 15. L. Melchior, LSO, R. Heger (r1930) *Concert*
(1/92) (EMI) ① [4] **CMS7 64008-2(2)**
12. Berlin St Op Orch, W. Furtwängler (pp1947) *Concert*   (2/89) (ACAN) ① **43 121**
12. Sym of the Air, L. Stokowski (r1961) *Concert*
(4/94) (RCA) ① **09026 61503-2**
12. NQHO, B. Wordsworth (r1995) *Concert*
(6/95) (EYE) ① [2] **EOS5001**
14. R. Kollo, Berlin Deutsche Op Orch, C. Thielemann *Concert* (5/93) (EMI) ① **CDC7 54776-2**
15, 16. W. Widdop, G. Ljungberg, C. Victor, LSO, A. Coates (r1927) *Concert*
(11/92) (CLAR) ① **CDGSE78-50-46**
18. G. Saba (trs. Moszkowski) *Concert*
(10/87) (CARL) ① **PCD858**
18. K. Flagstad, Philh, I. Dobroven (r1948) *Concert*
(8/89) (EMI) ① **CDH7 63030-2**
18. F. Leider, LSO, J. Barbirolli (r1931) *Concert*
(11/89) (PEAR) ① **GEMMCD9331**
18. F. Leider, LSO, J. Barbirolli (r1931) *Concert*
(2/90) (PREI) ① **89004**
18. F. Leider, LSO, J. Barbirolli (r1931) *Concert*
(6/90) (LYRC) ① [2] **LCD146**
18. K. Flagstad, San Francisco Op Orch, E. MacArthur (r1939) *Concert*
(10/90) (RCA) ① **GD87915**
18. C. Curley (arr Curley) *Concert*
(2/91) (ARGO) ① **430 200-2ZH**
18. G. Lubin, orch, H. Defosse (French: r1930) *Concert*   (5/91) (CLUB) ① **CL99-022**
18. G. Lubin, orch, H. Defosse (French: r1930) *Concert*   (5/91) (EPM) ① **150 052**
18. F. Leider, orch (r1921) *Concert*
(5/91) (PREI) ① [3] **89301**
18. M. Seinemeyer, Berlin St Op Orch, F. Weissmann (r1928) *Concert*
(1/92) (EMI) ① [4] **CMS7 64008-2(2)**
18. G. Lubin, Paris Cons, P. Gaubert (French: r1938) *Concert*   (1/92) (EMI) ① [4] **CMS7 64008-2(2)**
18. O. Fremstad, orch (r1913) *Concert*
(7/92) (EMI) ① [3] **GEMMCDS9923(2)**
18. K. Flagstad, orch, H. Lange (r1935) *Concert*
(7/92) (EMI) ① [3] **GEMMCDS9926(2)**
18. C. Ludwig, Philh, O. Klemperer *Concert*
(9/92) (EMI) ① [4] **CMS7 64074-2(2)**

18. F. Litvinne, anon (Fr: r1903) *Concert*
(10/92) (SYMP) ① **SYMCD1101**
18. F. Litvinne, A. Cortot (Fr: r1902) *Concert*
(10/92) (SYMP) ① **SYMCD1101**
18. L. Price, Philh, H. Lewis (r1979) *Concert*
(12/92) (RCA) ① [4] **09026 61236-2**
18. K. Flagstad, orch, H. Lange (r1935) *Concert*
(7/93) (NIMB) ① **NI7847**
18. K. Flagstad, orch, H. Lange (r1935) *Concert*
(12/93) (NIMB) ① **NI7851**
18. M. Jeritza, orch (r1927) *Concert*
(4/94) (PREI) ① **89079**
18. K. Flagstad, orch, H. Lange (r1936) *Concert*
(4/94) (RCA) ① [6] **09026 61580-2(4)**
18. E. Destinn, orch (r1910) *Concert*
(12/94) (SUPR) ① [12] **11 2136-2(4)**
18. E. Destinn, orch (r1911) *Concert*
(12/94) (SUPR) ① [12] **11 2136-2(4)**
18. K. Flagstad, orch, H. Lange (r1935) *Concert*
(12/95) (SIMA) ① [3] **PSC1821(1)**
19. LSO, W. Morris *Concert*
(12/87) (CIRR) ① **CICD1005**
19. Philh, O. Klemperer *Concert*
(11/90) (EMI) ① **CDM7 63617-2**
19. Chicago SO, G. Solti *Concert*
(5/91) (DECC) ① **430 448-2DM**
19. Philh, Y. Simonov *Concert*
(10/91) (COLL) ① **Coll1207-2**
19. NBC SO, A. Toscanini (r1952) *Concert*
(12/91) (RCA) ① **GD60264**
19. BPO, W. Furtwängler (r1930) *Concert*
(4/92) (KOCH) ① [2] **37073-2**
19. Frankfurt RSO, E. Inbal *Tchaikovsky: Symphony 6.*   (6/92) (DENO) ① **CO-77715**
19. Leningrad PO, E. Mravinsky (pp1978) *Concert*
(6/92) (ERAT) ① **2292-45762-2**
19. Leningrad PO, E. Mravinsky (pp1978) *Concert*
(6/92) (ERAT) ① [11] **2292-45763-2**
19. BPO, V. de Sabata (r1939) *Concert*
(11/92) (KOCH) ① **37126-2**
19. Cleveland Orch, G. Szell *Concert*
(11/92) (SONY) ① **SBK48175**
19. Oslo PO, M. Jansons *Concert*
(12/92) (EMI) ① **CDC7 54583-2**
19. Leningrad PO, E. Mravinsky (pp1967) *Concert*
(3/94) (RUSS) ① **RDCD11166**
19. BPO, W. Furtwängler (r1938) *Concert*
(4/94) (EMI) ① [2] **CHS7 64935-2**
19. BPO, W. Furtwängler (r1938) *Concert*
(7/94) (BIDD) ① [2] **WHL006/7**
19. NYPO, J. Barbirolli (pp1938) *Concert*
(3/95) (DUTT) ① **CDSJB1001**
19. BPO, W. Furtwängler (pp1942) *Concert*
(3/95) (TAHR) ① [4] **FURT1004/7**
19. NYPO, P. Boulez (r1973) *Concert*
(7/95) (SONY) ① **SMK64108**

WAGNER, Siegfried (Helferich Richard) (1869–1930) Germany

SECTION I: ORCHESTRAL

Sehnsucht—symphonic poem (after Schiller) (pub. 1895)
Thüringen SO, K. Bach (r1993/4) *Concert*
(2/95) (MARC) ① **8 223660**

SECTION V: STAGE WORKS

Der Bärenhäuter—opera: 3 acts, Op. 1 (1899) (Lib. cpsr)
EXCERPTS: 1. Overture. ACT 3: 2. Introduction; 3. Devil's Waltz (concert vers of Act 1 Finale).
Cpte V. Horn, H. Kiichli, K. Lukic, T. Koon, B. Johanning, L. Hübel, A. Feilhaber, K. Quandt, N. Barowski, R. Hartmann, A. Wenhold, A. Waller, Thüringian Landestheater Chor, Thüringian SO, K. Bach (1993)   (6/95) (MARC) ① [2] **8 223713/4**
Schwarzschwanenreich, 'Kingdom of the Black Swan'—opera: 3 acts, Op. 7 (1918—Karlsruhe) (Lib. cpsr)
Cpte B. Johanning, W. Raffeiner, K. Quandt, A. Wenhold, J. M. Schmitz, R. Hartmann, L. Chioreanu, K. Lukic, Thüringian Landestheater Chor, Thüringian SO, K. Bach (pp1994)
(11/95) (MARC) ① [2] **8 223777/8**

WAGNES, Eduard (1863–1936) Austria

SECTION I: ORCHESTRAL

Die Bosniaken kommen—march (c1894) (Eng: The Bosnians are coming)
Berlin Phil Wind Qnt, H. von Karajan (r1973) *Concert*
(5/94) (DG) ① **439 346-2GX2**

WAINWRIGHT, John (1723–1768) England

SECTION IV: VOCAL AND CHORAL

Christians awake—hymn tune (Stockport) (Wds. Bryom)
York Minster Ch, F. Jackson *Concert*
(12/91) (CHAN) ① **CHAN6520**

WALCH, Johann Heinrich (1776–1855) Germany

SECTION I: ORCHESTRAL

Pariser Einzugsmarsch—wind band (Eng: The entry into Paris)
Berlin Phil Wind Qnt, H. von Karajan (r1973) *Concert*
(5/94) (DG) ① **439 346-2GX2**

WALDTEUFEL, (Charles) Emile (1837–1915) France

NB: Opus nos in brackets are not those of the composer

SECTION I: ORCHESTRAL

Acclamations—waltz, (Op. 223) (1888)
Monte Carlo PO, W. Boskovsky *Concert*
(12/89) (EMI) ① **CDM7 63136-2**
Ange d'amour—waltz, (Op. 241) (1889)
Košice St PO, A. Walter (r1991) *Concert*
(2/94) (MARC) ① **8 223438**
Bien aimés, 'Well loved'—waltz, (Op. 143) (1875)
Košice St PO, A. Walter (r1991) *Concert*
(2/94) (MARC) ① **8 223438**
Les bohémiens, 'The Bohemians'—polka, (Op. 216) (1887)
Košice St PO, A. Walter (r1991) *Concert*
(2/94) (MARC) ① **8 223438**
Camarade, 'Comrade'—polka, (Op. 197) (1884)
Košice St PO, A. Walter (r1991) *Concert*
(2/94) (MARC) ① **8 223433**
Chantilly—waltz, (Op. 171) (1879)
Košice St PO, A. Walter (r1991) *Concert*
(2/94) (MARC) ① **8 223433**
Dans les bois, 'In the woods'—polka-mazurka, (Op. 119) (1866)
Košice St PO, A. Walter (r1991) *Concert*
(2/94) (MARC) ① **8 223433**
Dans tes yeux, 'In your eyes'—waltz, (Op. 227) (1888)
Košice St PO, A. Walter (r1991) *Concert*
(2/94) (MARC) ① **8 223438**
España—waltz, (Op. 236) (1886) (after Chabrier)
Monte Carlo PO, W. Boskovsky *Concert*
(12/89) (EMI) ① **CDM7 63136-2**
Košice St PO, A. Walter (r1991) *Concert*
(2/94) (MARC) ① **8 223438**
L' esprit français, 'French spirit'—polka, (Op. 182) (1882)
Košice St PO, A. Walter (r1991) *Concert*
(2/94) (MARC) ① **8 223433**
Estudiantina—waltz, (Op. 191) (1883)
Monte Carlo PO, W. Boskovsky *Concert*
(12/89) (EMI) ① **CDM7 63136-2**
Košice St PO, A. Walter (r1991) *Concert*
(2/94) (MARC) ① **8 223433**
Fleurs et baisers, 'Flowers and Kisses'—waltz (1904)
Košice St PO, A. Walter (r1991) *Concert*
(2/94) (MARC) ① **8 223450**
Les Fleurs, '(The) Flowers'—waltz, (Op. 190) (1883)
Košice St PO, A. Walter (r1991) *Concert*
(2/94) (MARC) ① **8 223450**
Fontaine lumineuse, 'Bright Fountain'—waltz, (Op. 247) (1891)
Košice St PO, A. Walter (r1991) *Concert*
(2/94) (MARC) ① **8 223438**
Hébé—waltz, (Op. 228) (1888)
Košice St PO, A. Walter (r1991) *Concert*
(2/94) (MARC) ① **8 223450**
Hommage aux dames, 'Hommage to the Ladies'—waltz, (Op. 153) (1878)
Košice St PO, A. Walter (r1991) *Concert*
(2/94) (MARC) ① **8 223433**
Invitation à la gavotte, 'Invitation to the Gavotte', (Op. 246) (1891)
Košice St PO, A. Walter (r1991) *Concert*
(2/94) (MARC) ① **8 223441**

Je t'aime, 'I love you'—waltz, (Op. 177) (1882)
Košice St PO, A. Walter (r1991) *Concert*
(2/94) (MARC) ① **8 223438**

Jeu d'Esprit, 'Witticism'—polka, (Op. 196) (1884)
Košice St PO, A. Walter (r1991) *Concert*
(2/94) (MARC) ① **8 223433**

Joyeux Paris, 'Merry Paris'—polka, (Op. 215) (1886) (orig called 'La Cinquantaine')
Košice St PO, A. Walter (r1991) *Concert*
(2/94) (MARC) ① **8 223441**

Ma Voisine, 'My Neighbour'—polka, (Op. 206) (1886)
Košice St PO, A. Walter (r1991) *Concert*
(2/94) (MARC) ① **8 223441**

Par-ci, par-là—polka, (Op. 239) (1883)
Košice St PO, A. Walter (r1991) *Concert*
(2/94) (MARC) ① **8 223450**

Les Patineurs, '(The) Skaters Waltz', (Op. 183) (1882)
Monte Carlo PO, W. Boskovsky *Concert*
(12/89) (EMI) ① **CDM7 63136-2**
NBC SO, A. Toscanini (r1945) *Concert*
(1/91) (RCA) ① **GD60308**
Košice St PO, A. Walter (r1991) *Concert*
(2/94) (MARC) ① **8 223433**

Pluie de diamants—waltz, (Op. 160) (1879)
Košice St PO, A. Walter (r1991) *Concert*
(2/94) (MARC) ① **8 223441**

Retour des champs, 'Return from the Fields'—polka, (Op. 203) (1885)
Košice St PO, A. Walter (r1991) *Concert*
(2/94) (MARC) ① **8 223438**

Sans les nuages, 'In the Clouds'—waltz, (Op. 200) (1886)
Košice St PO, A. Walter (r1991) *Concert*
(2/94) (MARC) ① **8 223438**

Les Sirènes, '(The) Sirens'—waltz, (Op. 154) (1878)
Košice St PO, A. Walter (r1991) *Concert*
(2/94) (MARC) ① **8 223441**

Soirée d'été, 'Summer Evening'—waltz, (Op. 188) (1883)
Košice St PO, A. Walter (r1991) *Concert*
(2/94) (MARC) ① **8 223441**

Solitude—waltz, (Op. 174) (1881)
Košice St PO, A. Walter (r1991) *Concert*
(2/94) (MARC) ① **8 223450**

Les Sourires, '(The) Smiles'—waltz, (Op. 187) (1883)
Košice St PO, A. Walter (r1991) *Concert*
(2/94) (MARC) ① **8 223450**

Toujours fidèle—waltz, (Op. 169) (1879)
Košice St PO, A. Walter (r1991) *Concert*
(2/94) (MARC) ① **8 223450**

Toujours ou jamais, 'Always or never'—waltz, (Op. 156) (1877)
Košice St PO, A. Walter (r1991) *Concert*
(2/94) (MARC) ① **8 223450**

Tout en rose, 'Through Rose-Coloured Spectacles'—waltz, (Op. 200) (1885)
Košice St PO, A. Walter (r1991) *Concert*
(2/94) (MARC) ① **8 223441**

Tout ou rien, 'All or nothing'—polka, (Op. 219) (1887)
Košice St PO, A. Walter (r1991) *Concert*
(2/94) (MARC) ① **8 223438**

Tout-Paris, 'Fashionable Paris'—waltz, (Op. 240) (1889)
Košice St PO, A. Walter (r1991) *Concert*
(2/94) (MARC) ① **8 223438**

Très jolie, 'Very Pretty'—waltz, (Op. 159) (1878)
Košice St PO, A. Walter (r1991) *Concert*
(2/94) (MARC) ① **8 223441**

Zig-zag—polka, (Op. 248) (1891)
Košice St PO, A. Walter (r1991) *Concert*
(2/94) (MARC) ① **8 223450**

WALKER, Ernest (1870–1949) England

SECTION IV: VOCAL AND CHORAL

I will lift up mine eyes—anthem, Op. 16/1 (1899 rev 1947)
Guildford Cath Ch, A. Millington, P. Wright *Concert*
(5/89) (PRIO) ① **PRCD257**

WALKER, George (b 1922) USA

SECTION I: ORCHESTRAL

Concerto for Trombone and Orchestra (1957)
C. Lindberg, Malmö SO, J. DePreist (r1993) *Concert*
(9/94) (BIS) ① **BIS-CD628**

WALLACE, (William) Vincent (1812–1865) Ireland

SECTION V: STAGE WORKS

Maritana—opera: 3 acts (1845—London) (Lib. Fitzball)
EXCERPTS: 1. Overture. ACT 1: 3. 'Tis the harp in the air; 4. The Angelus; 5. Of fairy wand had I the power; 7. Pretty Gitana. ACT 2: 9. Alas! Those chimes; 11. Turn on, old time; 12. Yes, let me like a soldier fall; 13. In happy moments day by day; 17. Hear me, gentle Maritana; 18. There is a flower that bloometh; 19. What mystery? (Finale). ACT 3: 21. Scenes that are brightest; 22. I am the King of Spain; 24. Oh Maritana!; 25. Sainted Mother.
12. H. Nash, orch (r1931) *Concert*
(8/89) (PEAR) ① **GEMMCD9319**
12. W. Widdop, Orch, L. Collingwood (r1930) *Concert*
(11/92) (CLAR) ① **CDGSE78-50-46**

WALLEN, Errolyn (20th Cent) England

SECTION IV: VOCAL AND CHORAL

It all depends on you (1989) (Wds. P. Larkin)
Lontano, O. de la Martinez *Concert*
(9/92) (LORE) ① **LNT101**

WALLER, 'Fats' (Thomas Wright) (1904–1943) USA

SECTION II: CHAMBER

Squeeze Me—jazz combo (1939)
A. Feinberg (r1994; arr Willie Smith, trans Riccardo Scivales) *Concert* (11/95) (ARGO) ① **444 457-2ZH**

SECTION III: INSTRUMENTAL

Ain't Misbehavin'—piano (1929)
A. Feinberg (r1994; trans Jed Distler) *Concert*
(11/95) (ARGO) ① **444 457-2ZH**

SECTION V: STAGE WORKS

Ain't Misbehavin'—musical revue (1978—New York) (Book Horwitz & Maltby Jr; Lyrics various.)
EXCERPTS: Music by Waller unless indicated; 1. Ain't Misbehavin' (Waller/Brooks); 2. Lookin' Good but Feelin' Bad; 3. 'T Ain't Nobody's Biz-Ness If I Do (Grainger/Robbins); 4. Honeysuckle Rose; 5. Squeeze Me; 6. Handful of Keys; 7. I've Got a Feeling I'm Falling; 8. How Ya Baby; 9. The Jitterbug Waltz; 10. The Ladies Who Sing With the Band; 11. Yacht Club Swing (Waller/Autrey); 12. When the Nylons Bloom Again; 13. Cash for Your Trash; 14. Off-Time (Waller/Brooks); 15. The Joint is Jumpin' (McHugh); 16. Entr'acte; 17. Spreadin' Rhythm Around (McHugh); 18. Lounging at the Waldorf; 19. The Viper's Drag—The Reefer's Song (Traditional); 20. Mean to Me (Turk); 21. Your Feet's too Big (Benson); 22. That Ain't Right (Cole); 23. Keepin' Out of Mischief Now; 24. Find Out What They Like; 25. Fat and Greasy (Grainger); 26. Black and Blue; 27. Finale (medley).
9. M. Patinkin, Orch, E. Stern (r1993; orch Troob, arr Ford) *Concert* (11/94) (NONE) ⑦ **7559-79330-2**

WALMISLEY, Thomas Attwood (1814–1856) England

SECTION II: CHAMBER

Sonatina No.2 in G—oboe and piano
R. Canter, R. Burnett *Concert*
(4/87) (AMON) ① **CD-SAR22**

SECTION IV: VOCAL AND CHORAL

Bless the Lord, o my soul (Psalm 104)—psalm of David (Wds. Bible)
Durham Cath Ch, J. Lancelot, I. Shaw *Concert*
(7/91) (PRIO) ① **PRCD296**

Evening Service in D minor (1855)
1. Magnificat. 2. Nunc dimittis.
1, 2. St Paul's Cath Ch, C. Dearnley, John Scott *Concert* (3/88) (HYPE) ① **CDA66249**

Music, all powerful—glee (Wds. H. K. White)
Hilliard Ens, L-L. Kiesel *Concert*
(12/91) (MERI) ① **DUOCD89009**

Remember, O Lord, what is come upon us—anthem (5/4vv, organ) (?1838)
Dundee Cath Ch, R. Lightband (org/dir) *Concert*
(8/92) (ABBE) ① **CDCA926**
Llandaff Cath Ch, M. Smith, M. Hoeg (r1994) *Concert*
(10/95) (PRIO) ① **PRCD510**

WALOND, William (c1725–1770) England

SECTION III: INSTRUMENTAL

6 Voluntaries—organ/harpsichord, Op. 1 (c1752)
2. G; 3. D minor; 5. G; 6. A minor.
2. J. Bate *Concert* (5/91) (UNIC) ① **DKPCD9101**
5. D. Burchell *Concert*
(10/89) (MERI) ① **CDE84151**
5. Margaret Phillips *Concert*
(5/91) (GAMU) ① **GAMCD514**
5. J. Bate *Concert* (7/91) (UNIC) ① **DKPCD9105**
6. J. Bate *Concert* (2/91) (UNIC) ① **DKPCD9096**

10 Voluntaries—organ/harpsichord, Op. 2 (pub 1758)
2. B minor.
No 3. T. Koopman *Concert*
(5/91) (CAPR) ① **10 254**
2. Margaret Phillips *Concert*
(5/91) (GAMU) ① **GAMCD514**
2. J. Bate *Concert* (5/91) (UNIC) ① **DKPCD9099**

WALTER, Johann (1496–1570) Germany

SECTION IV: VOCAL AND CHORAL

Der Junge Ehemann—Lied (Wds. Eichendorff)
D. Fischer-Dieskau, W. Sawallisch (pp1975) *Concert*
(1/90) (ORFE) ① **C185891A**
Der Soldat—Lied (Wds. Eichendorff)
D. Fischer-Dieskau, W. Sawallisch (pp1975) *Concert*
(1/90) (ORFE) ① **C185891A**

WALTHER, Johann Gottfried (1684–1748) Germany

SECTION III: INSTRUMENTAL

Concerti del Signor Telemann—organ
1. C minor; 2. G (per la chiesa).
1, 2. S. Farr *Concert* (8/92) (MERI) ① **CDE84213**
Concerti del Signor Torelli—organ
1. D minor; 2. A minor.
1(Allegro) S. Farr *Concert*
(8/92) (MERI) ① **CDE84213**
Concerto del Signor Meck (or Vivaldi?) in B minor—organ
Margaret Phillips (r1989) *Concert*
(4/91) (REGE) ① **REGCD105**
S. Farr *Concert* (8/92) (MERI) ① **CDE84213**
Concerto del Signor Taglietti in B flat—organ
S. Farr *Concert* (8/92) (MERI) ① **CDE84213**
Es ist das Heil uns kommen her—chorale prelude: organ
S. Farr *Concert* (8/92) (MERI) ① **CDE84213**
Herr Gott, nun schleuss der Himmel auf—chorale prelude: organ
S. Farr *Concert* (8/92) (MERI) ① **CDE84213**
Herr Jesu Christ, ich weiss gar wohl—chorale prelude: organ
S. Farr *Concert* (8/92) (MERI) ① **CDE84213**
Hilf mir Gott, das mir's gelinge—chorale prelude: organ
S. Farr *Concert* (8/92) (MERI) ① **CDE84213**
Jesu meine Freude—partita: organ
S. Farr *Concert* (8/92) (MERI) ① **CDE84213**
Schmücke dich—chorale prelude: organ
S. Farr *Concert* (8/92) (MERI) ① **CDE84213**

WALTON, Sir William (Turner) (1902–1983) England

SECTION I: ORCHESTRAL

5 Bagatelles—guitar and orchestra (arr from Varii capricci & Bagatelles: P Russ: 1991)
C. Parkening, RPO, A. Litton (r1992) *Concert*
(9/93) (EMI) ① **CDC7 54665-2**
Capriccio Burlesco (1968)
RLPO, C. Groves (r1969) *Concert*
(7/90) (EMI) ① **CDM7 63369-2**

LPO, B. Thomson *Concert*
(11/91) (CHAN) ① **CHAN8968**
LSO, W. Walton *Concert*
(7/92) (LYRI) ① **SRCD224**
Florida PO, J. Judd *Concert*
(11/92) (HARM) ① **HMU90 7070**
Concerto for Cello and Orchestra (1955-56 rev 1974)
Y.-Y. Ma, LSO, A. Previn *Elgar: Cello Concerto.*
(8/85) (SONY) ① **SK39541**
R. Wallfisch, LPO, B. Thomson *Concert*
(9/91) (CHAN) ① **CHAN8959**
R. Kirshbaum, SNO, A. Gibson *Concert*
(11/92) (CHAN) ① **CHAN6547**
L. Harrell, CBSO, S. Rattle (r1991) *Symphony 1.*
(12/92) (EMI) ① **CDC7 54572-2**
G. Piatigorsky, Boston SO, C. Munch (r1957) *Dvořák: Cello Concerto.*
(4/93) (RCA) ① **09026 61498-2**
R. Cohen, Bournemouth SO, A. Litton (r1995)
Symphony 1.
(10/95) (LOND) ① **443 450-2LH**
Concerto for Viola and Orchestra in A minor (1928-29, rev 1936 & 1961)
N. Kennedy, RPO, A. Previn *Violin Concerto.*
(4/88) (EMI) ① **CDC7 49628-2**
N. Imai, LPO, J.L. Koenig *Concert*
(4/93) (CHAN) ① **CHAN9106**
F. Riddle, LSO, W. Walton (r1937) *Concert*
(12/93) (DUTT) ① **CDAX8003**
Y. Menuhin, New Philh, W. Walton (r1968) *Concert*
(11/94) (EMI) ① [4] **CHS5 65003-2**
Concerto for Violin and Orchestra in B minor (1938-39 rev 1943)
N. Kennedy, RPO, A. Previn *Viola Concerto.*
(4/88) (EMI) ① **CDC7 49628-2**
S. Accardo, LSO, R. Hickox *Elgar: Violin Concerto.*
(7/92) (COLL) ① **Coll1338-2**
L. Mordkovitch, LPO, J. Latham-König (r1991)
Concert
(10/92) (CHAN) ① **CHAN9073**
A. Rosand, Florida PO, J. Judd *Concert*
(11/92) (HARM) ① **HMU90 7070**
J. Heifetz, Cincinnati SO, E. Goossens (r1941: orig ver) *Concert*
(12/93) (BIDD) ① **WHL016**
Y. Menuhin, LSO, W. Walton (r1969) *Concert*
(11/94) (EMI) ① [4] **CHS5 65003-2**
J. Heifetz, Philh, W. Walton (r1950) *Gruenberg: Violin Concerto.*
(11/94) (RCA) ① [65] **09026 61778-2(23)**
T. Little, Bournemouth SO, A. Litton (r1995) *Concert*
(10/95) (LOND) ① **444 114-2LH**
J. Heifetz, Cincinnati SO, E. Goossens (r1941)
Concert (11/95) (PEAR) ① [2] **GEMMCDS9167**
2. J. Heifetz, Cincinnati SO, E. Goossens (r1941)
Concert (11/94) (RCA) ① [65] **09026 61778-2(05)**
Crown Imperial—Coronation March (1937)
RPO, A. Previn (r1985) *Concert*
(8/87) (TELA) ① **CD80125**
I. Tracey (arr Tracey) *Concert*
(1/90) (CFP) ① **CD-CFP4558**
RLPO, C. Groves (r1969) *Concert*
(7/90) (EMI) ① **CDM7 63369-2**
S. Preston (trans org: arr. Murrill) *Concert*
(6/91) (DECC) ① **430 091-2DWO**
Eastman Wind Ens, F. Fennell *Concert*
(12/91) (MERC) ① **432 009-2MM**
S. Preston (r1964) *Concert*
(6/93) (DECC) ① **436 403-2DWO**
London Brass, M. Baker, M. Neary (r1993/4: arr C Palmer) *Concert* (9/94) (CNTO) ① **CSACD3050**
Philh, W. Walton (r1953) *Concert*
(11/94) (EMI) ① [4] **CHS5 65003-2**
Bournemouth SO, A. Litton (r1995) *Concert*
(10/95) (LOND) ① **448 134-2LH**
Façade—suites for orchestra (1926, 1938)
1. SUITE NO. 1: 1a. Polka; 1b. Valse; 1c. Swiss Yodelling Song; 1d. Tango-Pasodoble; 1e. Tarantelle Sevillana; 2. SUITE NO. 2: 2a. Fanfare; 2b. Scotch Rhapsody; 2c. Country Dance; 2d. Noche espagnole; 2e. Popular Song; 2f. Old Sir Faulk; 3. SUITE NO. 3 (arr/orch C. Palmer): 3a. Hornpipe; 3b. Through gilded terraces; 3c. The Wind's Tambourine (Something lies beyond the scene).
1, 2. English Northern Philh, D. Lloyd-Jones *Concert*
(3/91) (HYPE) ① **CDA66436**
1, 2. Philh, W. Walton (r1955/7) *Concert*
(11/94) (EMI) ① [4] **CHS5 65003-2**
1, 2a, 2e, 3a, 3c, Tetra (r1989-91: arr Goss: gtr qt)
(11/93) (CONI) ① **CDCF903**
1-3. LPO, J. Latham-König (r1991/2) *Concert*
(1/94) (CHAN) ① **CHAN9148**
The First Shoot—brass ensemble (1936 trans 1979-80) (arr of ballet for revue 'Follow the Sun')
London Collegiate Brass, J. Stobart *Concert*
(8/87) (CRD) ① **CRD3444**
LPO, B. Thomson (orch C. Palmer) *Concert*
(11/91) (CHAN) ① **CHAN8968**

Galop Final (c1940)
LPO, B. Thomson (orch C. Palmer) *Concert*
(11/91) (CHAN) ① **CHAN8968**
Granada Prelude—orchestra (1962)
LPO, B. Thomson *Concert*
(11/91) (CHAN) ① **CHAN8968**
Improvisations on an Impromptu of Benjamin Britten—orchestra (1968-69)
LPO, B. Thomson *Concert*
(9/91) (CHAN) ① **CHAN8959**
LSO, A. Previn (r1972) *Concert*
(10/93) (EMI) ① **CDM7 64723-2**
Johannesburg Festival Overture (1956)
RLPO, C. Groves (r1969) *Concert*
(7/90) (EMI) ① **CDM7 63369-2**
LPO, B. Thomson *Concert*
(11/91) (CHAN) ① **CHAN8968**
Philh, W. Walton (r1957) *Concert*
(11/94) (EMI) ① [4] **CHS5 65003-2**
Music for Children (1940) (orch version of 'Duets for Children')
LPO, B. Thomson *Concert*
(11/91) (CHAN) ① **CHAN8968**
LPO, W. Walton *Concert*
(7/92) (LYRI) ① **SRCD224**
Orb and Sceptre—Coronation March (1952-53)
RPO, A. Previn (r1985) *Concert*
(8/87) (TELA) ① **CD80125**
RLPO, C. Groves (r1969) *Concert*
(7/90) (EMI) ① **CDM7 63369-2**
Bournemouth SO, D. Hill (r1991) *Concert*
(5/93) (ARGO) ① **436 120-2ZH**
Bournemouth SO, D. Hill (r1991) *Concert*
(6/93) (DECC) ① **436 403-2DWO**
M. Baker (r1993/4: trans org: McKie) *Concert*
(9/94) (CNTO) ① **CSACD3050**
Philh, W. Walton (r1953) *Concert*
(11/94) (EMI) ① [4] **CHS5 65003-2**
Partita—orchestra (1957)
LPO, B. Thomson *Concert*
(9/91) (CHAN) ① **CHAN8959**
Cleveland Orch, G. Szell *Concert*
(12/91) (SONY) ① **MPK46732**
Philh, W. Walton (r1959) *Concert*
(11/94) (EMI) ① [4] **CHS5 65003-2**
Portsmouth Point—overture (1924-25)
LPO, A. Boult (r1954) *Concert*
(9/90) (LOND) ① **425 661-2LM**
LPO, B. Thomson *Concert*
(11/91) (CHAN) ① **CHAN8968**
LPO, W. Walton *Concert*
(7/92) (LYRI) ① **SRCD224**
LSO, A. Previn (r1973) *Concert*
(10/93) (EMI) ① **CDM7 64723-2**
LPO, J. Latham-König (r1991: arr C Lambert)
Concert (1/94) (CHAN) ① **CHAN9148**
LPO, L. Slatkin (r1987) *Symphony 1.*
(11/94) (VIRG) ① **CUV5 61146-2**
Philh, W. Walton (r1953) *Concert*
(11/94) (EMI) ① [4] **CHS5 65003-2**
Prologo e Fantasia—orchestra (1981-82)
LPO, B. Thomson *Concert*
(11/91) (CHAN) ① **CHAN8968**
Scapino—comedy overture (1940 rev 1950)
RLPO, C. Groves (r1969) *Concert*
(7/90) (EMI) ① **CDM7 63369-2**
LPO, A. Boult (r1954) *Concert*
(9/90) (LOND) ① **425 661-2LM**
LPO, B. Thomson *Concert*
(11/91) (CHAN) ① **CHAN8968**
LSO, W. Walton *Concert*
(7/92) (LYRI) ① **SRCD224**
LSO, A. Previn (r1973) *Concert*
(10/93) (EMI) ① **CDM7 64723-2**
Chicago SO, F. Stock (r1941: orig vers) *Concert*
(2/95) (BIDD) ① [2] **WHL021/2**
Bournemouth SO, A. Litton (r1995) *Concert*
(10/95) (LOND) ① **444 114-2LH**
Siesta—small orchestra (1926 rev 1962)
LPO, A. Boult (r1954) *Concert*
(9/90) (LOND) ① **425 661-2LM**
LPO, B. Thomson *Concert*
(7/92) (LYRI) ① **SRCD224**
LPO, J. Latham-König *Concert*
(1/94) (CHAN) ① **CHAN9148**
Sinfonia Concertante—orchestra with piano obbligato (1926-27 rev 1943)
K. Stott, RPO, V. Handley (orig version) *Concert*
(1/90) (CONI) ① **CDCF175**
P. Katin, LSO, W. Walton *Concert*
(7/92) (LYRI) ① **SRCD224**
E. Parkin, LPO, J. Latham-König (r1992: orig version)
Concert (1/94) (CHAN) ① **CHAN9148**

Sonata for strings (1971) (tran from String Quartet in A)
LPO, J.L. Koenig *Concert*
(4/93) (CHAN) ① **CHAN9106**
CLS, R. Hickox (r1991) *Concert*
(12/93) (EMI) ① **CDC7 54407-2**
Spitfire Prelude and Fugue (1942) (from film score 'The First of the Few')
RLPO, C. Groves (r1969) *Concert*
(7/90) (EMI) ① **CDM7 63369-2**
ASMF, N. Marriner *Concert*
(12/90) (CHAN) ① **CHAN8870**
Florida PO, J. Judd *Concert*
(11/92) (HARM) ① **HMU90 7070**
ECO, S. Bedford *Symphony 1.*
(1/94) (ASV) ① **CDQS6093**
Philh, W. Walton (r1963) *Concert*
(11/94) (EMI) ① [4] **CHS5 65003-2**
Symphony No. 1 in B flat minor (1931-35)
RPO, A. Previn (r1985) *Concert*
(8/87) (TELA) ① **CD80125**
LSO, A. Previn (r1966) *Vaughan Williams: Wasps.*
(2/89) (RCA) ① **GD87830**
LPO, C. Mackerras (r1989) *Symphony 2.*
(12/89) (EMIN) ① **CD-EMX2206**
LPO, B. Thomson (r1990) *Varii caprici.*
(7/91) (CHAN) ① **CHAN8862**
CBSO, S. Rattle (r1990) *Cello Concerto.*
(12/92) (EMI) ① **CDC7 54572-2**
LSO, H. Harty (r1935) *Concert*
(12/93) (DUTT) ① **CDAX8003**
RLPO, V. Handley (r1978) *Spitfire Prelude and Fugue.*
(1/94) (ASV) ① **CDQS6093**
SNO, A. Gibson (r1983) *Elgar: Cockaigne.*
(5/94) (CHAN) ① **CHAN6570**
LPO, L. Slatkin (r1987) *Portsmouth Point.*
(11/94) (VIRG) ① **CUV5 61146-2**
Philh, W. Walton (r1951) *Concert*
(11/94) (EMI) ① [4] **CHS5 65003-2**
Bournemouth SO, A. Litton (r1995) *Cello Concerto.*
(10/95) (LOND) ① **443 450-2LH**
Symphony No. 2 (1957-60)
LSO, C. Mackerras (r1989) *Symphony 1.*
(12/89) (EMIN) ① **CD-EMX2206**
LPO, B. Thomson *Troilus and Cressida Suite.*
(7/90) (CHAN) ① **CHAN8772**
RPO, Vladimir Ashkenazy (pp1989) *Concert*
(1/91) (RPO) ① **CDRPO7015**
Cleveland Orch, G. Szell *Concert*
(12/91) (SONY) ① **MPK46732**
Bournemouth SO, A. Litton (r1995) *Concert*
(10/95) (LOND) ① **444 114-2LH**
Variations on a Theme by Hindemith—orchestra (1962-63)
Cleveland Orch, G. Szell *Concert*
(12/91) (SONY) ① **MPK46732**
LPO, J.L. Koenig *Concert*
(4/93) (CHAN) ① **CHAN9106**
Cleveland Orch, G. Szell (r1964) *Concert*
(4/94) (SONY) ① **SBK53258**
Varii capricci—orchestra (1975-77) (free trans of 5 Bagatelles for gtr)
LPO, B. Thomson (r1990) *Symphony 1.*
(7/91) (CHAN) ① **CHAN8862**
A Wartime Sketchbook—orchestra (compiled/arr C Palmer)
1. Prologue (Went the Day Well; Next of Kin); 2. Bicycle-chase (Next of Kin; The Foreman went to France); 3. Refugees (The Foreman went to France); 4. Scherzo—Gay Berlin (The Battle of Britain); 5. Foxtrots (Next of Kin); 6. Lovers (Next of Kin); 7. Striptease; 8. Epilogue (The Foreman went to France).
ASMF, N. Marriner *Concert*
(12/90) (CHAN) ① **CHAN8870**

SECTION II: CHAMBER

10 Duets for children—piano duets (1940)
1. The Music Lesson; 2. The Three-Legged Race; 3. The Silent Lake; 4. Pony trap; 5. Ghosts; 6. Hop-Scotch; 7. Swing-Boats; 8. Song at Dusk; 9. Puppet's Dance; 10. Trumpet Tune; 11. Galop (arr P Lane).
H. Milne, B. Dowdeswell (r1992) *Concert*
(10/94) (CHAN) ① **CHAN9292**
2 Pieces—violin and piano (1951)
1. Canzonetta; 2. Scherzetto.
L. Mordkovitch, LPO, J. Latham-König (r1992: orch C Palmer) *Concert* (10/92) (CHAN) ① **CHAN9073**
K. Sillito, H. Milne (r1991) *Concert*
(10/94) (CHAN) ① **CHAN9292**
Quartet for Piano and Strings (1918-21 rev 1973-74)
J. McCabe, English Qt *String Quartet.*
(10/87) (MERI) ① **CDE84139**
K. Sillito, R. Smissen, S. Orton, H. Milne *Violin Sonata.* (3/92) (CHAN) ① **CHAN8999**

A **Song for the Lord Mayor's Table**—soprano and piano/orchestra (1962) (Wds. various)
1. The Lord Mayor's Table; 2. Glide gently; 3. Wapping Old Stairs; 4. Holy Thursday; 5. The Contrast; 6. Rhyme.
J. Gomez, CLS, R. Hickox *Concert*
(12/90) (CHAN) ① **CHAN8824**
3. Sarah Walker, R. Vignoles *Concert*
(11/87) (HYPE) ① **CDA66165**
Through gilded trellises—song (1931-32) (Wds. E. Sitwell)
J. Gomez, CLS, R. Hickox *Concert*
(12/90) (CHAN) ① **CHAN8824**
D. Stevens, H. Foss (r1940) *Concert*
(12/93) (DUTT) ① **CDAX8003**
J. Gomez, J. Constable (r1994) *Concert*
(9/94) (CONI) ① **CDCF243**
Tritons—song: 1v and piano (1920) (Wds. Drummond)
J. M. Ainsley, H. Milne (r1993) *Concert*
(10/94) (CHAN) ① **CHAN9292**
The **Twelve**—anthem: chorus and organ (1964-65) (Wds. W. H. Auden)
Trinity Coll Ch, Cambridge, G. Jackson, R. Marlow *Concert*
(5/89) (CONI) ① **CDCF164**
P. Forbes, R. Gleave, S. Gay, J. Oxley, P. Harvey, Westminster Sngrs, CLS, R. Hickox *Concert*
(12/90) (CHAN) ① **CHAN8824**
Finzi Sngrs, A. Lumsden, P. Spicer *Concert*
(12/93) (CHAN) ① **CHAN9222**
Oxford Christ Church Cath Ch, S. Darlington (r1992) *Concert*
(3/94) (NIMB) ① **NI5364**
What cheer?—unaccompanied carol (4vv) (1961) (Wds. 16th Cent anon)
Cambridge Sngrs, J. Rutter *Concert*
(6/88) (CLLE) ① **COLCD107**
Trinity Coll Ch, Cambridge, R. Marlow *Concert*
(5/89) (CONI) ① **CDCF164**
Quink *Concert*
(12/89) (TELA) ① **CD80202**
Trinity Coll Ch, Cambridge, R. Marlow *Concert*
(12/90) (CONI) ① **CDCF501**
Oxford Christ Church Cath Ch, S. Darlington (r1992) *Concert*
(3/94) (NIMB) ① **NI5364**
Where does the uttered music go?—unaccompanied choir (1946) (Wds. J. Masefield)
Trinity Coll Ch, Cambridge, R. Marlow *Concert*
(5/89) (CONI) ① **CDCF164**
Finzi Sngrs, A. Lumsden, P. Spicer *Concert*
(12/93) (CHAN) ① **CHAN9222**
Oxford Christ Church Cath Ch, S. Darlington (r1992) *Concert*
(3/94) (NIMB) ① **NI5364**
Winds—1v and piano (1918) (Wds. Swiburne)
J. M. Ainsley, H. Milne (r1993) *Concert*
(10/94) (CHAN) ① **CHAN9292**

SECTION V: STAGE WORKS

As You Like It—film score (1936)
Suite C. Bott, ASMF, N. Marriner (arr Palmer) *Hamlet.*
(6/90) (CHAN) ① **CHAN8842**
The **Battle of Britain**—concert suite from film (1969) (arr/ed. C Matthews)
EXCERPTS: 1. Spitfire Music; 2. Battle in the Air; 3. March Introduction; 4. March; 5. Siegfried Music.
1-5. ASMF, N. Marriner *Concert*
(12/90) (CHAN) ① **CHAN8870**
The **Bear**—extravaganza: 1 act (1967—Aldeburgh) (Lib. I P Dehn, after Chekhov)
Cpte D. Jones, A. Opie, J. Shirley-Quirk, Northern Sinfonia, R. Hickox (r1993)
(1/94) (CHAN) ① **CHAN9245**
Christopher Columbus—suite: mez, ten, chorus and orchestra (1942) (arr C Palmer from inc music radio play)
EXCERPTS -; 1. Fiesta; 2. Romanza (Beatriz' song); 3. Gloria.
L. Finnie, A. Davies, Westminster Sngrs, CLS, R. Hickox *Concert* (12/90) (CHAN) ① **CHAN8824**
Escape me never—film score (1934)
Suite ASMF, N. Marriner (arr Palmer) *Concert*
(12/90) (CHAN) ① **CHAN8870**
Hamlet—film score (1947)
EXCERPTS (as arranged by C. Palmer): 1. Prelude; 2. Fanfare and Soliloquy; 3. Hamlet and Ophelia; 4. The Question—'To be or not to be'; 6. The Mousetrap; 7. Ophelia's Death; 8. Retribution and Threnody; 9. Finale (Funeral March).
Suite J. Gielgud, ASMF, N. Marriner (arr Palmer) *As You Like It.* (6/90) (CHAN) ① **CHAN8842**
9. RLPO, C. Groves (r1983: arr Mathieson) *Concert*
(7/90) (EMI) ① **CDM7 63369-2**
9. Philh, W. Walton (r1963: arr Mathieson) *Concert*
(11/94) (EMI) ① [4] **CHS5 65003-2**

Henry V—film score (1943-44)
EXCERPTS: 1. London 1600; 2. Duke of Burgundy's Speech.
Cpte film score Westminster Cath Ch, ASMF Chor, ASMF, N. Marriner, C. Plummer (arr Palmer) *Concert*
(4/91) (CHAN) ① **CHAN8892**
Scenes from the film L. Olivier, chor, Philh, W. Walton, R. Douglas (r1946) *Concert*
(11/94) (EMI) ① [4] **CHS5 65003-2**
1, 2. National PO, C. Gerhardt (arr Gerhardt) *Concert*
(6/90) (VARE) ① **VSD5207**
Henry V—concert suite from film score (adapted Mathieson)
EXCERPTS: 1. Overture: The Globe Playhouse; 2. Passacaglia: The Death of Falstaff; 3. Charge and Battle of Agincourt; 4. Touch Her Soft Lips and Part; 5. Agincourt Song.
RPO, A. Previn *Belshazzar's Feast.*
(6/86) (RPO) ① **CDRPO7013**
National PO, C. Gerhardt (arr Gerhardt) *Concert*
(6/90) (VARE) ① **VSD5207**
Florida PO, J. Judd *Concert*
(11/92) (HARM) ① **HMU90 7070**
Philh, W. Walton (r1963) *Concert*
(11/94) (EMI) ① [4] **CHS5 65003-2**
Bournemouth SO, A. Litton (r1995) *Concert*
(10/95) (LOND) ① **448 134-2LH**
1, 3, 5. L. Olivier, chor, Philh, W. Walton, R. Douglas (r1946) *Concert*
(11/94) (EMI) ① [4] **CHS5 65003-2**
2, 4. ASMF, K. Sillito *Concert*
(10/91) (COLL) ① **Coll1234-2**
2, 4. LPO, L. Slatkin (r1989) *Concert*
(9/92) (RCA) ① **RD60813**
2, 4. ECO, D. Barenboim (r1973) *Concert*
(4/94) (DG) ① **439 529-2GGA**
2, 4. Bournemouth Sinfonietta, R. Studt (vn/dir) (r1993) *Concert* (10/94) (NAXO) ① **8 550979**
Macbeth—music for Shakespeare's play (1941)
EXCERPTS—; 1. Banquet Music; 2. March of the Eight Kings.
1, 2. ASMF, N. Marriner, J. Gielgud (arr Palmer as 'Fanfare and March') *Concert*
(5/91) (CHAN) ① **CHAN8841**
Major Barbara—film score (1941)
EXCERPTS—; 1. A Shavian Sequence for Orchestra (arr C. Palmer).
1. ASMF, N. Marriner, J. Gielgud *Concert*
(5/91) (CHAN) ① **CHAN8841**
The **Quest**—ballet: 1 act (1943—London)
Cpte LPO, B. Thomson (r1990: ed Palmer) *Wise Virgins.* (4/91) (CHAN) ① **CHAN8871**
Suite LSO, W. Walton *Concert*
(7/92) (LYRI) ① **SRCD224**
Richard III—film score (1955)
1. Prelude (arr Mathieson); 2. A Shakespeare Suite (arr Mathieson); 2a. Fanfare: Music plays; 2b. The Princes in the Tower; 2c. With Drum and Colours; 2d. I would I knew thy heart; 2e. Trumpets sound; 3. Shakespeare Scenario (arr C Palmer).
1, 2. RLPO, C. Groves (r1983) *Concert*
(7/90) (EMI) ① **CDM7 63369-2**
1, 2. Philh, W. Walton (r1963) *Concert*
(11/94) (EMI) ① [4] **CHS5 65003-2**
3. I. Watson, ASMF, N. Marriner, J. Gielgud (arr Palmer) *Concert* (5/91) (CHAN) ① **CHAN8841**
The **Three Sisters**—film score (1970)
ASMF, N. Marriner (ed Palmer) *Concert*
(12/90) (CHAN) ① **CHAN8870**
Troilus and Cressida—opera: 3 acts (1954—London) (Lib. C Hassall, after G Chaucer: rev 1976)
EXCERPTS: ACT 1: 1. Is Cressida a slave?; 2. Slowly it all comes back. ACT 2: 3. How can I sleep?; 4. Is anyone there?; 5. If one last doubt; 6. Now close your arms; 7. Interlude; 8. From isle to isle chill waters. ACT 3: 9. All's well; 10. Diomede!...Father!.
Cpte A. Davies, J. Howarth, N. Robson, Y. Howard, J. Thornton, C. Bayley, D. Owen-Lewis, A. Opie, P. Bodenham, K. Mills, B. Budd, S. Dowson, B. Cookson, Op North Chor, English Northern Philh, R. Hickox (r1995) (5/95) (CHAN) ① [2] **CHAN9370/1**
Cpte R. Cassilly, J. Baker, G. English, E. Bainbridge, M. Rivers, R. Van Allan, R. Lloyd, B. Luxon, G. Macpherson, G. Sullivan, H. Thomas, Alan James II, D. McCoshan, ROH Chor, ROHO, L. Foster (pp1976) (7/95) (EMI) ① [2] **CMS5 65550-2**
1-3, 5-10. E. Schwarzkopf, M. Sinclair, Richard Lewis, L. Thomas, G. Walls, J. Hauxvell, Philh, W. Walton (r1955) *Troilus and Cressida.*
(1/94) (EMI) ① **CDM7 64199-2**
4. M. Collier, P. Pears, ROHO, W. Walton (r1968) *Troilus and Cressida.*
(1/94) (EMI) ① **CDM7 64199-2**

Troilus and Cressida—concert suite from opera (1987) (arr C. Palmer)
1. Prelude and Seascape; 2. Scherzo; 3. The Lovers; 4. Finale.
LPO, B. Thomson *Symphony 2.*
(7/90) (CHAN) ① **CHAN8772**
The **Wise Virgins**—ballet (1943—London)
EXCERPTS: 1. What God hath done is rightly done (Cantata 199); 2. Lord, hear my longing (Chorale-Prelude, 'Herzlich tut mich'); 3. See what his love can do (Cantata 85); 4. Ah! how ephemeral (Cantata 26); 5. Sheep may safely graze (Cantata 208); 6. Praise be to God (Cantata 129).
1-6. LPO, B. Thomson (r1990) *Quest.*
(4/91) (CHAN) ① **CHAN8871**
1-6. Sadlers Wells Orch, W. Walton (r1940) *Concert*
(11/94) (EMI) ① [4] **CHS5 65003-2**
5. Philh, W. Walton (r1953) *Concert*
(11/94) (EMI) ① [4] **CHS5 65003-2**

WANNBERG, Ken (20th Cent) USA

SECTION V: STAGE WORKS

The **Philadelphia Experiment**—film score (1984)
EXCERPTS: 1. Main Theme; 2. The Experiment Begins/Time Slip; 3. The 'Eldridge' Remains; 4. David Confronts His Past; 5. The Navire Sucks/David's Escape; 6. A Tender Moment; 7. The Doctor Reflects; 8. The Chase; 9. Fugitives in Love; 10. Storming the Compound; 11. David's Father; 12. David's Decision/Fate of the Vortex; 13. David's Choice/End Title.
1. Prague City PO, W. Motzing (r1993) *Concert*
(8/94) (SILV) ① **FILMCD146**

WARD, John (1571–1638) England

SECTION II: CHAMBER

Fantasia on In Nomine a 6 No. 2 in C minor—viol consort
Consort of Musicke, A. Rooley (r1984) *Concert*
(7/95) (MOSC) ① **070981**
7 Fantasias a 6—viol consort
EXCERPTS: 1. A minor; 2. F; 3. A minor; 4. G minor; 7. C minor.
1-4, 7. Consort of Musicke, A. Rooley (r1984) *Concert* (7/95) (MOSC) ① **070981**
In Nomine a 6 No. 1 in G minor—viol consort
Consort of Musicke, A. Rooley (r1984) *Concert*
(7/95) (MOSC) ① **070981**

SECTION IV: VOCAL AND CHORAL

Come, sable night—madrigal: 6vv (pub 1613)
Consort of Musicke, A. Rooley *Concert*
(3/88) (HYPE) ① **CDA66256**
Amaryllis Consort, C. Brett *Concert*
(3/88) (CARL) ① **PCD873**
Hilliard Ens, P. Hillier *Concert*
(2/89) (EMI) ① **CDC7 49197-2**
Cor mio, deh non languire—madrigal: 5vv (pub 1613) (Wds Guarini)
Consort of Musicke, A. Rooley (r1984) *Concert*
(7/95) (MOSC) ① **070981**
Cruel unkind—madrigal: 5vv
Consort of Musicke, A. Rooley *Concert*
(3/88) (HYPE) ① **CDA66256**
Consort of Musicke, A. Rooley (r1984) *Concert*
(7/95) (MOSC) ① **070981**
Die not, fond man—madrigal: 6vv (pub 1613)
Consort of Musicke, A. Rooley *Concert*
(3/88) (HYPE) ① **CDA66256**
Down caitive wretch/Prayer is an endless chain—anthem: 5vv
Consort of Musicke, A. Rooley (r1988) *Concert*
(7/95) (MOSC) ① **070982**
Down in a dale—madrigal: 5vv (pub 1613)
Consort of Musicke, A. Rooley (r1984) *Concert*
(7/95) (MOSC) ① **070981**
Have mercy upon me—Psalm 51: 3vv
Consort of Musicke, A. Rooley (r1988) *Concert*
(7/95) (MOSC) ① **070982**
Hope of my heart—madrigal: 5vv (pub 1613)
Consort of Musicke, A. Rooley *Concert*
(3/88) (HYPE) ① **CDA66256**

How long wilt thou forget me—Psalm 13: 5vv
Consort of Musicke, A. Rooley (r1988) *Concert*
(7/95) (MOSC) ① **070982**

I have entreated—madrigal: 6vv (pub 1613)
Consort of Musicke, A. Rooley *Concert*
(3/88) (HYPE) ① **CDA66256**

I will praise the Lord—anthem (Psalm 9)
Consort of Musicke, A. Rooley (r1988) *Concert*
(7/95) (MOSC) ① **070982**

If Heaven's just wrath—madrigal: 5vv
Consort of Musicke, A. Rooley (r1988) *Concert*
(3/88) (HYPE) ① **CDA66256**
Consort of Musicke, A. Rooley (r1984) *Concert*
(7/95) (MOSC) ① **070981**

If the deep sighs—madrigal: 6vv (pub 1613)
Consort of Musicke, A. Rooley *Concert*
(3/88) (HYPE) ① **CDA66256**

Let God arise—Psalm 68
Consort of Musicke, A. Rooley (r1988) *Concert*
(7/95) (MOSC) ① **070982**

My breast I'll set upon a silver stream—madrigal: 5vv (pub 1613)
Consort of Musicke, A. Rooley *Concert*
(3/88) (HYPE) ① **CDA66256**
Consort of Musicke, A. Rooley (r1984) *Concert*
(7/95) (MOSC) ① **070981**

No object dearer—madrigal: 6vv (pub 1613)
Consort of Musicke, A. Rooley (r1984) *Concert*
(7/95) (MOSC) ① **070981**

O let me tread in the right path—anthem: 4vv (pub 1614)
Consort of Musicke, A. Rooley (r1988) *Concert*
(7/95) (MOSC) ① **070982**

O Lord consider my great moans—anthem: 5vv (pub 1614)
Consort of Musicke, A. Rooley (r1988) *Concert*
(7/95) (MOSC) ① **070982**

Oft have I tendered—madrigal: 6vv (pub 1613)
Consort of Musicke, A. Rooley *Concert*
(3/88) (HYPE) ① **CDA66256**

Out from the vale—madrigal: 6vv (pub 1613)
Consort of Musicke, A. Rooley (r1988) *Concert*
(3/88) (HYPE) ① **CDA66256**

Praise the Lord, O my soul—Psalm 103: 3vv
Consort of Musicke, A. Rooley (r1988) *Concert*
(7/95) (MOSC) ① **070982**

Praise the Lord, O my soul—Psalm 104: 6vv
Consort of Musicke, A. Rooley (r1988) *Concert*
(7/95) (MOSC) ① **070982**

Retire, my troubled soul—madrigal: 6vv (pub 1613)
Amaryllis Consort, C. Brett *Concert*
(3/88) (CARL) ① **PCD873**
Consort of Musicke, A. Rooley *Concert*
(3/88) (HYPE) ① **CDA66256**

Sweet Philomel—madrigal: 5vv (pub 1613)
Consort of Musicke, A. Rooley *Concert*
(3/88) (HYPE) ① **CDA66256**

This is a Joyful, Happy, Holy Day—anthem: 6vv
Consort of Musicke, A. Rooley (r1984) *Concert*
(7/95) (MOSC) ① **070982**

Well-sounding pipes—madrigal: 6vv (pub 1613)
Consort of Musicke, A. Rooley (r1984) *Concert*
(7/95) (MOSC) ① **070981**

WARD, Robert (b 1917) USA

SECTION I: ORCHESTRAL

Concerto for Saxophone and Orchestra (1983) (version for wind band arr Leist, 1984)
J. Houlik, North Carolina SO, G. Zimmermann *Concert*
(9/89) (ALBA) ① **AR001**

Jubilation—overture (1945)
North Carolina SO, G. Zimmermann *Concert*
(9/89) (ALBA) ① **AR001**

Sonic Structure—orchestra (1980)
North Carolina SO, G. Zimmermann *Concert*
(9/89) (ALBA) ① **AR001**

Symphony No. 4 (1958)
North Carolina SO, G. Zimmermann *Concert*
(9/89) (ALBA) ① **AR001**

SECTION V: STAGE WORKS

The Crucible—opera: 4 acts (1961—New York) (Lib. B. Stambler, after A. Miller)
Cpte J. Ebert, N. Kelly, G. Wynder, P. Brooks, N. Farr, P. Ukena, E. Alberts, S. Malas, M. Stern, C. Ludgin, J. Macurdy, F. Bible, N. Foster, R. Krause, J. DeLon, L. Ceniceros, H. Guile, M. Kova, E. Schwering, B. Evans, NYC Op Orch, E. Buckley
(6/90) (ALBA) ① [2] **TROY025/6-2**

WARD, Samuel Augustus (19th Cent) USA

SECTION IV: VOCAL AND CHORAL

America the Beautiful—patriotic song (1895) (Wds. K.L. Bates)
L. Price, NY Met Op Orch, J. Conlon (pp1991) *Concert*
(6/93) (RCA) ① **09026 61509-2**

WARLOCK, Peter (1894–1930) England

pseudonym of Philip Arnold Heseltine

SECTION I: ORCHESTRAL

Capriol Suite—string orchestra (1926) (arr orch: 1928)
1. Basse-danse; 2. Pavane; 3. Tordion; 4. Bransles; 5. Pieds-en-l'air; 6. Mattachins (Sword Dance).
Bournemouth Sinfonietta, G. Hurst *Concert*
(8/85) (CHAN) ① **CHAN8375**
ASMF, N. Marriner *Concert*
(5/89) (DECC) ① **417 778-2DM**
ASMF, N. Marriner *Concert*
(8/89) (LOND) ① **421 391-2LM**
Ulster Orch, V. Handley *Concert*
(3/91) (CHAN) ① **CHAN8808**
Britannia CO, D. Falkowski *Concert*
(6/92) (ENGL) ① **ERC5001**
English Sinfonia, N. Dilkes (r1971: orch vers) *Concert*
(9/94) (EMI) ① **CDM5 65101-2**
C. Parkening, ASMF, I. Brown (r1993: arr gtr/orch) *Concert*
(10/94) (EMI) ① **CDC5 55052-2**
Bournemouth Sinfonietta, R. Studt (vn/dir) *Concert*
(10/94) (NAXO) ① **8 550823**
English Sinfonia, C. Groves (r1988) *Concert*
(10/95) (CARL) ① **PCD2017**

Basse-danse; Pavane; Mattachins J. Szigeti, N. Magaloff (arr Szigeti: r1936) *Concert*
(1/90) (BIDD) ① [2] **LAB007/8**

Serenade—string orchestra (1921-23) (for Frederick Delius on his 60th birthday)
Ulster Orch, V. Handley *Concert*
(3/91) (CHAN) ① **CHAN8808**
Britannia CO, D. Falkowski *Concert*
(6/92) (ENGL) ① **ERC5001**
Oxford Orch da Camera, G. Vass (r1993) *Concert*
(9/94) (MEDI) ① **MQCD4002**
Bournemouth Sinfonietta, N. Del Mar (r1967) *Concert*
(9/94) (EMI) ① **CDM5 65101-2**

SECTION IV: VOCAL AND CHORAL

After two years—song: 1v and piano (1930) (Wds. R. Adlington)
I. Partridge, J. Partridge *Concert*
(4/90) (ETCE) ① **KTC1078**

All the flowers of the Spring—8vv (1923) (Wds. J Webster)
Finzi Sngrs, P. Spicer (r1992) *Concert*
(10/93) (CHAN) ① **CHAN9182**

As dew in Aprylle—7vv (1918) (Wds. 15th cent anon)
Finzi Sngrs, P. Spicer (r1992) *Concert*
(10/93) (CHAN) ① **CHAN9182**

As ever I saw—song: 1v and piano (1918) (Wds. 16th cent anon)
B. Luxon, D. Willison *Concert*
(2/89) (CHAN) ① **CHAN8643**
J. M. Ainsley, R. Vignoles (r1994) *Concert*
(1/95) (HYPE) ① **CDA66736**

Autumn Twilight—song: 1v and piano (1922) (Wds. A. Symons)
B. Luxon, D. Willison *Concert*
(2/89) (CHAN) ① **CHAN8643**
F. Harvey, G. Moore (r1966) *Concert*
(9/94) (EMI) ① **CDM5 65101-2**
J. M. Ainsley, R. Vignoles (r1994) *Concert*
(1/95) (HYPE) ① **CDA66736**

Away to Twiver—song: 1v and piano (1926) (Wds from 'The Famous History of Friar Bacon')
I. Partridge, J. Partridge *Concert*
(4/90) (ETCE) ① **KTC1078**

S. Austin, May Harrison, H. Gaskell, C. Lynch (arr van Dieren: bp1936) *Concert*
(12/90) (SYMP) ① **SYMCD1075**

The Bachelor—song: 1v and piano (1922) (Wds. 15th cent anon)
B. Luxon, D. Willison *Concert*
(2/89) (CHAN) ① **CHAN8643**

The Bayly berith the bell away—song: 1v and piano (1918) (Wds. 16th cent anon)
B. Luxon, D. Willison *Concert*
(2/89) (CHAN) ① **CHAN8643**
J. M. Ainsley, R. Vignoles (r1994) *Concert*
(1/95) (HYPE) ① **CDA66736**

The Birds—song: 1v and piano (1926) (Wds. H Belloc)
C. Robbin, M. McMahon (r1985) *Concert*
(7/94) (MARQ) ① **ERAD113**

Captain Stratton's Fancy—song: 1v and piano (1920) (Wds. J. Masefield)
B. Luxon, D. Willison *Concert*
(2/89) (CHAN) ① **CHAN8643**
R. Lloyd, N. Walker (r1976) *Concert*
(9/94) (EMI) ① **CDM5 65101-2**

The Cloths of Heaven—song: 1v and piano (1916) (Wds. W B Yeats)
R. Golden, L. Rothfuss *Concert*
(10/92) (KOCH) ① **37118-2**

Consider—song: 1v and piano (1923) (Wds. F. Maddox Ford)
S. Leonard, M. Martineau (r1993) *Concert*
(3/95) (UNIT) ① **88016-2**

The Contented Lover—song: 1v and piano (1929) (Wds J. Mabbe)
J. M. Ainsley, R. Vignoles (r1994) *Concert*
(1/95) (HYPE) ① **CDA66736**

A Cornish Carol (Kanow Kernow)—6vv (1918)
Finzi Sngrs, P. Spicer (r1992) *Concert*
(10/93) (CHAN) ① **CHAN9182**

Corpus Christi—contralto, tenor and 8vv (1918)
Finzi Sngrs, P. Spicer (r1992) *Concert*
(10/93) (CHAN) ① **CHAN9182**

Cradle Song—song: 1v and piano (1927) (Wds. J. Philip)
R. Golden, L. Rothfuss *Concert*
(10/92) (KOCH) ① **37118-2**
J. M. Ainsley, R. Vignoles (r1994) *Concert*
(1/95) (HYPE) ① **CDA66736**

The Curlew—song cycle: ten, fl, cor ang & string quartet (1920-22) (Wds. W.B. Yeats)
1. The Curlew, cry no more; 2. Pale brows, still hands; 3. I cried when the moon; 4. I wander by the edge.
I. Partridge, D. Butt, J. Craxton, H. Bean, F. Mason, C. Wellington, E. Croxford (r1973) *Concert*
(9/94) (EMI) ① **CDM5 65101-2**

Fair and True—song: 1v and piano (1926) (Wds. N. Breton)
J. M. Ainsley, R. Vignoles (r1994) *Concert*
(1/95) (HYPE) ① **CDA66736**

The First Mercy—song: 1v and piano (1927) (Wds B. Blunt)
J. M. Ainsley, R. Vignoles (r1994) *Concert*
(1/95) (HYPE) ① **CDA66736**

The Fox—song: 1v and piano (1930) (Wds. B. Blunt)
B. Luxon, D. Willison *Concert*
(2/89) (CHAN) ① **CHAN8643**
Sarah Walker, R. Vignoles *Concert*
(10/92) (CRD) ① **CRD3473**
J. M. Ainsley, R. Vignoles (r1994) *Concert*
(1/95) (HYPE) ① **CDA66736**

The full heart—soprano and 8vv (1916 rev 1921) (Wds. R Nicholls)
Finzi Sngrs, P. Spicer (r1992) *Concert*
(10/93) (CHAN) ① **CHAN9182**

Ha'nacker Mill—song: 1v and piano (1926) (Wds. H. Belloc)
B. Luxon, D. Willison *Concert*
(2/89) (CHAN) ① **CHAN8643**
S. Austin, May Harrison, H. Gaskell, C. Lynch (arr van Dieren: bp1936) *Concert*
(12/90) (SYMP) ① **SYMCD1075**
R. Golden, L. Rothfuss *Concert*
(10/92) (KOCH) ① **37118-2**
J. M. Ainsley, R. Vignoles (r1994) *Concert*
(1/95) (HYPE) ① **CDA66736**

Hey troly loly lo—song: 1v and piano (1922) (Wds. 16th cent anon)
B. Luxon, D. Willison *Concert*
(2/89) (CHAN) ① **CHAN8643**

I have a garden—song: 1v and piano (1910) (Wds. Moore)
R. Golden, L. Rothfuss *Concert*
(10/92) (KOCH) ① **37118-2**

I held love's head—song: 1v and piano
(1923) (Wds. R. Herrick)
B. Luxon, D. Willison Concert
(2/89) (CHAN) ① CHAN8643
J. M. Ainsley, R. Vignoles (r1994) Concert
(1/95) (HYPE) ① CDA66736
S. Leonard, M. Martineau (r1993) Concert
(3/95) (UNIT) ① 88016-2
I saw a fair maiden—5vv (1927) (Wds. anon)
Finzi Sngrs, P. Spicer (r1992) Concert
(10/93) (CHAN) ① CHAN9182
St Alban's Abbey Ch, A. Parnell, Barry Rose (r1992)
Concert (12/93) (LAMM) LAMM081D
Cambridge Sngrs, CLS, J. Rutter (r1993) Concert
(12/93) (CLLE) ① COLCD121
In an arbour green—song: 1v and piano
(1922) (Wds R. Wever)
J. M. Ainsley, R. Vignoles (r1994) Concert
(1/95) (HYPE) ① CDA66736
Jillian of Berry—song: 1v and piano (1926)
(Wds. H Beaumont & J Fletcher)
I. Partridge, J. Partridge Concert
(4/90) (ETCE) ① KTC1078
Sarah Walker, R. Vignoles Concert
(10/92) (CRD) ① CRD3473
J. M. Ainsley, R. Vignoles (r1994) Concert
(1/95) (HYPE) ① CDA66736
The Jolly Shepherd—song: 1v and piano
(1927) (Wds. anon)
B. Luxon, D. Willison Concert
(2/89) (CHAN) ① CHAN8643
The lady's birthday—male vv and piano
(1925) (Wds. anon)
Baccholian Sngrs, J. Partridge (r1976) Concert
(9/94) (EMI) ① CDM5 65101-2
Late summer—song: 1v and piano (1919)
(Wds. E. Shanks)
B. Luxon, D. Willison Concert
(2/89) (CHAN) ① CHAN8643
R. Golden, L. Rothfuss Concert
(10/92) (KOCH) ① 37118-2
J. M. Ainsley, R. Vignoles (r1994) Concert
(1/95) (HYPE) ① CDA66736
Lillygay—song cycle: 1v and piano (1922)
(Wds. Neuberg)
1. The Distracted Maid; 2. Johnny wi' the Tye; 3. The
Shoemaker; 4. Burd Ellen and Young Tamlane; 5.
Rantum Tantum.
R. Golden, L. Rothfuss Concert
(10/92) (KOCH) ① 37118-2
Love for love—song: 1v and piano (1919)
(Wds. attrib Henry VIII)
J. Bowman, Downshire Players, P. Ash (orch.
A.Ridout) Concert (3/89) (MERI) ① CDE84158
The Lover's Maze—song: 1v and piano
(1927) (Wds attrib T. Campion)
J. M. Ainsley, R. Vignoles (r1994) Concert
(1/95) (HYPE) ① CDA66736
Lullaby—song: 1v and piano (1918) (Wds. T.
Dekker)
B. Luxon, D. Willison Concert
(2/89) (CHAN) ① CHAN8643
R. Golden, L. Rothfuss Concert
(10/92) (KOCH) ① 37118-2
J. M. Ainsley, R. Vignoles (r1994) Concert
(1/95) (HYPE) ① CDA66736
Milkmaids—song: 1v and piano (1923) (Wds.
J. Smith)
B. Luxon, D. Willison Concert
(2/89) (CHAN) ① CHAN8643
Mourn no moe—song: 1v and piano (1919
rev 1927) (Wds. J. Fletcher)
B. Luxon, D. Willison Concert
(2/89) (CHAN) ① CHAN8643
Mr Belloc's Fancy—song (1921) (Wds. J. C.
Squire)
B. Luxon, D. Willison Concert
(2/89) (CHAN) ① CHAN8643
My ghostly Fader—song: 1v and piano
(1918) (Wds. C. d'Orléans)
B. Luxon, D. Willison Concert
(2/89) (CHAN) ① CHAN8643
My Own Country—song: 1v and piano (1926)
(Wds. H Belloc)
B. Luxon, D. Willison Concert
(2/89) (CHAN) ① CHAN8643
J. Bowman, Downshire Players, P. Ash (orch.
A.Ridout) Concert (3/89) (MERI) ① CDE84158
I. Partridge, J. Partridge Concert
(4/90) (ETCE) ① KTC1078
F. Lott, G. Johnson Concert
(7/90) (CHAN) ① CHAN8722
R. Golden, L. Rothfuss Concert
(10/92) (KOCH) ① 37118-2
J. M. Ainsley, R. Vignoles (r1994) Concert
(1/95) (HYPE) ① CDA66736

The Night—song: 1v and piano (1926) (Wds.
H Belloc)
B. Luxon, D. Willison Concert
(2/89) (CHAN) ① CHAN8643
Sarah Walker, R. Vignoles Concert
(10/92) (CRD) ① CRD3473
R. Golden, L. Rothfuss Concert
(10/92) (KOCH) ① 37118-2
J. M. Ainsley, R. Vignoles (r1994) Concert
(1/95) (HYPE) ① CDA66736
Passing by—song: 1v and piano (1928)
(Wds. 16th cent anon)
B. Luxon, D. Willison Concert
(2/89) (CHAN) ① CHAN8643
I. Partridge, J. Partridge Concert
(4/90) (ETCE) ① KTC1078
J. M. Ainsley, R. Vignoles (r1994) Concert
(1/95) (HYPE) ① CDA66736
Piggesnie—song: 1v and piano (1922) (Wds.
16th cent anon)
B. Luxon, D. Willison Concert
(2/89) (CHAN) ① CHAN8643
Play acting—song: 1v and piano (1920)
(Wds. anon)
B. Luxon, D. Willison Concert
(2/89) (CHAN) ① CHAN8643
A Prayer to St Anthony of Padua—song: 1v
and piano (1925) (Wds A. Symons)
J. M. Ainsley, R. Vignoles (r1994) Concert
(1/95) (HYPE) ① CDA66736
Pretty Ring Time—song: 1v and piano (1918)
(Wds. Shakespeare)
I. Partridge, J. Partridge Concert
(4/90) (ETCE) ① KTC1078
K. Ferrier, F. Stone (bp1952) Concert
(7/91) (LOND) ① 430 061-2LM
K. Ferrier, F. Stone (bp1952) Concert
(6/92) (DECC) ① 433 473-2DM
R. Golden, L. Rothfuss Concert
(10/92) (KOCH) ① 37118-2
J. Baker, G. Moore (1967) Concert
(9/94) (EMI) ① CDM5 65101-2
J. Baker, G. Moore (1967) Concert
(11/94) (EMI) ① CDM5 65009-2
J. M. Ainsley, R. Vignoles (r1994) Concert
(1/95) (HYPE) ① CDA66736
Rest, sweet nymphs—song: 1v and piano
(1922) (Wds. 17th cent anon)
B. Luxon, D. Willison Concert
(2/89) (CHAN) ① CHAN8643
I. Partridge, J. Partridge Concert
(4/90) (ETCE) ① KTC1078
J. M. Ainsley, R. Vignoles (r1994) Concert
(1/95) (HYPE) ① CDA66736
The rich cavalcade—4vv (1928) (Wds. F.
Kendon)
Finzi Sngrs, P. Spicer (r1992) Concert
(10/93) (CHAN) ① CHAN9182
Robin Goodfellow—song: 1v and piano
(1926)
J. M. Ainsley, R. Vignoles (r1994) Concert
(1/95) (HYPE) ① CDA66736
Rutterkin—song: 1v and piano (1922) (Wds. J
Skelton)
S. Leonard, M. Martineau (r1993) Concert
(3/95) (UNIT) ① 88016-2
A Sad Song—1v and piano (1922) (Wds J.
Fletcher)
J. M. Ainsley, R. Vignoles (r1994) Concert
(1/95) (HYPE) ① CDA66736
S. Leonard, M. Martineau (r1993) Concert
(3/95) (UNIT) ① 88016-2
The Shrouding of the Duchess of
Malfi—male vv (1925) (Wds. J Webster)
Baccholian Sngrs (r1976) Concert
(9/94) (EMI) ① CDM5 65101-2
The Sick Heart—song: 1v and piano (1925)
(Wds A. Symons)
J. M. Ainsley, R. Vignoles (r1994) Concert
(1/95) (HYPE) ① CDA66736
Sigh no more, ladies—song: 1v and piano
(1927) (Wds. Shakespeare)
J. M. Ainsley, R. Vignoles (r1994) Concert
(1/95) (HYPE) ① CDA66736
The Singer—song: 1v and piano (1919) (Wds
E. Shanks)
J. M. Ainsley, R. Vignoles (r1994) Concert
(1/95) (HYPE) ① CDA66736
S. Leonard, M. Martineau (r1993) Concert
(3/95) (UNIT) ① 88016-2
Sleep—song: 1v and piano (1922) (Wds. J
Fletcher)
B. Luxon, D. Willison Concert
(2/89) (CHAN) ① CHAN8643
J. Bowman, Downshire Players, P. Ash (orch.
A.Ridout) Concert (3/89) (MERI) ① CDE84158

I. Partridge, J. Partridge Concert
(4/90) (ETCE) ① KTC1078
K. Ferrier, F. Stone (bp1952) Concert
(7/91) (LOND) ① 430 061-2LM
K. Ferrier, F. Stone (bp1952) Concert
(6/92) (DECC) ① 433 473-2DM
R. Golden, L. Rothfuss Concert
(10/92) (KOCH) ① 37118-2
J. M. Ainsley, R. Vignoles (r1994) Concert
(1/95) (HYPE) ① CDA66736
Sweet and twenty—song: 1v and piano
(1924) (Wds. Shakespeare)
I. Partridge, J. Partridge Concert
(4/90) (ETCE) ① KTC1078
Sweet content—song: 1v and piano (1919)
(Wds. T Dekker)
B. Luxon, D. Willison Concert
(2/89) (CHAN) ① CHAN8643
R. Golden, L. Rothfuss Concert
(10/92) (KOCH) ① 37118-2
J. M. Ainsley, R. Vignoles (r1994) Concert
(1/95) (HYPE) ① CDA66736
Take, o take those lips away (second
setting)—song: 1v and piano (1918) (Wds.
Shakespeare)
B. Luxon, D. Willison (first version) Concert
(2/89) (CHAN) ① CHAN8643
J. M. Ainsley, R. Vignoles (r1994) Concert
(1/95) (HYPE) ① CDA66736
There is a lady sweet and kind—song: 1v
and piano (1919) (from Ford's 'Musicke of
Sundrie Kindes')
B. Luxon, D. Willison Concert
(2/89) (CHAN) ① CHAN8643
J. M. Ainsley, R. Vignoles (r1994) Concert
(1/95) (HYPE) ① CDA66736
Thou gav'st me leave to kiss—song: 1v and
piano (1923) (Wds. R. Herrick)
B. Luxon, D. Willison Concert
(2/89) (CHAN) ① CHAN8643
J. M. Ainsley, R. Vignoles (r1994) Concert
(1/95) (HYPE) ① CDA66736
S. Leonard, M. Martineau (r1993) Concert
(3/95) (UNIT) ① 88016-2
To the Memory of a Great Singer—song: 1v
and piano (1928) (Wds. R. L. Stevenson)
R. Golden, L. Rothfuss Concert
(10/92) (KOCH) ① 37118-2
J. M. Ainsley, R. Vignoles (r1994) Concert
(1/95) (HYPE) ① CDA66736
Walking the Woods—song: 1v and piano
(1927) (Wds. 16th cent anon)
B. Luxon, D. Willison Concert
(2/89) (CHAN) ① CHAN8643
Whenas the rye—song: 1v and piano (1918)
(Wds. G. Peele)
B. Luxon, D. Willison Concert
(2/89) (CHAN) ① CHAN8643
Where riches is everlasting—unison vv and
organ (1927) (Wds. medival anon)
King's College Ch, D. Willcocks (r1965) Concert
(9/94) (EMI) ① CDM5 65101-2
The Wind from the West—song: 1v and
piano (1911) (Wds. E. Young)
B. Luxon, D. Willison Concert
(2/89) (CHAN) ① CHAN8643
J. M. Ainsley, R. Vignoles (r1994) Concert
(1/95) (HYPE) ① CDA66736
Yarmouth Fair—song: 1v and piano (1924)
(Wds. H Collins)
B. Luxon, D. Willison Concert
(2/89) (CHAN) ① CHAN8643
I. Partridge, J. Partridge Concert
(4/90) (ETCE) ① KTC1078
O. Brannigan, E. Lush (r1960) Concert
(9/94) (EMI) ① CDM5 65101-2
J. M. Ainsley, R. Vignoles (r1994) Concert
(1/95) (HYPE) ① CDA66736

WARNER, Ken (1902–1988)
England

full name: Onslow Boyden Waldo Warner

SECTION I: ORCHESTRAL

Scrub, brother, scrub—strings & piano; wind
& percussion added (1941 rev 1945)
RTE Concert Orch, E. Tomlinson (r1993) Concert
(12/95) (MARC) ① 8 223522

WARREN, Harry (Salvatore) (1893–1981) USA

SECTION V: STAGE WORKS

Billy Rose's Diamond Horseshoe—songs for the film (1945)
EXCERPTS: 1. I Wish I Knew (lyrics Mack Gordon).
1. M. Patinkin, Orch, E. Stern (r1993; orch Troob, arr Ford) *Concert*   (11/94) (NONE) ① **7559-79330-2**

Dames—musical film (1934) (Lyrics Al Dubin)
EXCERPTS: 1. I Only Have Eyes for You; 2. Dames; 3. The Girl at the Ironing Board.
2. D. Shapiro Gravitte, J. Sylvester, B. Barrett, G. Stroman, S. Chandler, L. Raben, J. McGlinn, D. Engel, London Sinfonietta Chor, London Sinfonietta, J. McGlinn (r1993; orig Heindorf orchestration) *Concert*   (12/94) (EMI) ① **CDC5 55189-2**

Gold Diggers of 1933—musical film (1933) (Lyrics Al Dubin)
EXCERPTS: 1. We're in the Money (The Gold Diggers' Song); 2. I've Got to Sing a Torch Song; 3. Remember My Forgotten Man; 4. Shadow Waltz; 5. Pettin' in the Park.
1, 3, 5. J. Blazer, D. Shapiro Gravitte, A. Morrison, B. Barrett, G. Stroman, S. Chandler, L. Raben, London Sinfonietta Chor, London Sinfonietta, J. McGlinn (r1993; orig Heindorf orchestration) *Concert*
  (12/94) (EMI) ① **CDC5 55189-2**

Gold Diggers of 1935—musical film (1935) (Lyrics Al Dubin)
EXCERPTS: 1. Lullaby of Broadway; 2. I'm Going Shopping With You; 3. The Words Are in My Heart.
1, 2. D. Shapiro Gravitte, A. Morrison, N. Long, B. Barrett, S. Chandler, L. Raben, D. Engel, London Sinfonietta Chor, London Sinfonietta, J. McGlinn (r1993; orig Heindorf orchestration) *Concert*
  (12/94) (EMI) ① **CDC5 55189-2**

42nd Street—musical film (1933) (Lyrics Al Dubin)
EXCERPTS—; 1. Forty-Second Street; 2. Shuffle off to Buffalo; 3. You're Getting to be a Habit With Me; 4. Young and Healthy.
1–4. J. Blazer, D. Shapiro Gravitte, A. Morrison, B. Barrett, G. Stroman, London Sinfonietta Chor, London Sinfonietta, J. McGlinn (r1993; orig Heindorf orchestration) *Concert*
  (12/94) (EMI) ① **CDC5 55189-2**

WASSENAER, Unico Wilhelm, Graf van (1692–1766) The Netherlands

SECTION II: CHAMBER

Concerti Armonici—4vn, va, vc & bc (pub 1740) (previously attrib. Pergolesi)
1. G; 2. B flat; 3. A; 4. G; 5. F minor; 6. E flat.
Montreal I Musici, Y. Turovsky
  (3/87) (CHAN) ① **CHAN8481**
Brandenburg Consort, R. Goodman (r1993)
  (4/94) (HYPE) ① **CDA66670**

WATERSON, James (1834–1893) England

SECTION II: CHAMBER

Morceau de concert—clarinet and piano (1888)
C. Bradbury, O. Davies *Concert*
  (6/90) (ASV) ① **CDDCA701**

WATKINS, David (b 1939) England

SECTION III: INSTRUMENTAL

Petite Suite—harp (1961)
EXCERPTS: 1. Prelude; 2. Nocturne; 3. Fire Dance.
3. S. McDonald *Concert*   (10/84) (DELO) ① **DE3005**

WATLING

SECTION III: INSTRUMENTAL

Cantilène in B minor—organ
R. Goss-Custard (r c1927) *Concert*
  (9/94) (BEUL) ① **1PD5**

WATSON, Anthony (1933–1973) New Zealand

SECTION I: ORCHESTRAL

Prelude and Allegro—string orchestra (1960)
New Zealand CO (r1993) *Concert*
  (9/95) (KOCH) ① **37260-2**

WATSON, Sydney (b 1903) England

SECTION IV: VOCAL AND CHORAL

Evening Service in E—choir and organ (1936)
Lichfield Cath Ch, A. Lumsden, N. Potts (r1994) *Concert*   (10/95) (PRIO) ① **PRCD505**

WATSON, William Michael (1840–1889) England

SECTION III: INSTRUMENTAL

The Fairies' Gathering—piano
A. Etherden *Concert*
  (7/93) (HUNT) ① **HMPCD0589**

WAXMAN, Franz (1906–1967) Germany/USA

SECTION I: ORCHESTRAL

Athaneal the Trumpeter—concert overture from film 'The Horn Blows' (1949)
Queensland SO, R. Mills *Concert*
  (10/90) (VARE) ① **VSD5242**

Carmen Fantasia—violin and orchestra (1946) (on themes from the opera by Bizet)
J. Heifetz, RCA Victor SO, D. Voorhees (r1946) *Concert*   (4/89) (RCA) ① **GD87963**
M. Vengerov, I. Vinogradova *Concert*
  (4/90) (BIDD) ① **LAW001**
M. Vengerov, Israel PO, Z. Mehta *Concert*
  (5/92) (TELD) ① **9031-73266-2**
J. Heifetz, RCA Victor SO, D. Voorhees (r1946) *Concert*   (11/94) (RCA) ① [65] **09026 61778-2(21)**
S. Nakarjakov, A. Markovich *Concert*
  (6/95) (TELD) ① **4509-94554-2**

Dusk: A Setting for Orchestra—concert work from film 'Night Unto Night' (1949)
Queensland SO, R. Mills (r1990) *Concert*
  (11/94) (VARE) ① **VSD5480**

Metro-Goldwyn-Mayer Fanfare—orchestra (1936)
National PO, C. Gerhardt (r1974) *Concert*
  (11/91) (RCA) ① **GD80708**
National PO, C. Gerhardt *Concert*
  (10/92) (RCA) ① **GD82792**

Nightride for Orchestra—concert work from film 'Night & the City' (1950)
Queensland SO, R. Mills (r1990) *Concert*
  (11/94) (VARE) ① **VSD5480**

3 Reminiscences for Orchestra—concert work from film 'Come Back, Little Sheba' (1952)
Queensland SO, R. Mills *Concert*
  (10/90) (VARE) ① **VSD5242**

Sinfonietta—string orchestra and timpani (1955)
Berlin SO, I. Jackson (r1992) *Concert*
  (7/93) (KOCH) ① **37152-2**

SECTION III: INSTRUMENTAL

The Charm Bracelet—piano (1949)
E. Parkin *Concert*   (1/89) (PREA) ① **PRCD1776**

SECTION V: STAGE WORKS

The Bride of Frankenstein—film score (1935)
EXCERPTS. 1. Main Title; 2. Prologue. Menuetto and Storm; 3. Monster Entrance; 4. Processional March; 5a. A Strange Apparition; 5b. Pretorius' Entrance; 5c. You will need a Coat; 6. Battle Sequence; 7a. Female Monster Music; 7b. Pastoral/Village/Chase; 8. Crucifixion/Monster breaks out; 9. Fire in the Hut/Graveyard; 10. Dance Macabre; 11. The Creation of the Female Monster; 12. The Tower explodes and Finale.
1-4, 5a-c, 6, 7a, 7b, 8-12. Westminster PO, K. Alwyn (r1993) *Invisible Ray Suite.*
  (3/94) (SILV) ① **FILMCD135**
11. National PO, C. Gerhardt (r1974) *Concert*
  (11/91) (RCA) ① **GD80708**

Demetrius and the Gladiators—film score (1954)
EXCERPTS: 1. Prelude; 2. Lucia, Messalina and Demetrius; 3. The Marriage of Life and Death; 4. Return to Faith.
1. Queensland SO, R. Mills *Concert*
  (10/90) (VARE) ① **VSD5242**

Destination Tokyo—film score (1944)
EXCERPTS: 1. Main Title; 2. Thinking of Home; 3. Sea Power; 4. Montage; 5. Finale.
1-5. Queensland SO, R. Mills (r1990; arr Palmer, 'Montage for Orch') *Concert*
  (11/94) (VARE) ① **VSD5480**

Dr Jekyll and Mr Hyde—film score (1941)
Suite Los Angeles Master Chorale, Hollywood Bowl SO, J. Mauceri (r1993; arr Palmer) *Concert*
  (1/95) (PHIL) ① **442 425-2PH**

Elephant Walk—film score (1954)
EXCERPTS: 1. Prelude; 2. The Plantation; 3. Appeal for Help; 4. Cylon Romance; 5. Elephant Stampede; 6. Finale.
1-6. Queensland SO, R. Mills (r1990; arr Palmer) *Concert*   (11/94) (VARE) ① **VSD5480**

The Furies—concert suite from film score (1950)
EXCERPTS: 1. Prelude; 2. Juan and Vance; 3. The Mark of the Furies; 4. The Romance Revived; 5. The King of the Furies.
1-5. Queensland SO, R. Mills (r1990) *Concert*
  (11/94) (VARE) ① **VSD5480**

Hotel Berlin—film score (1945)
EXCERPTS: 1. Café Waltzes.
1. Hollywood Bowl SO, J. Mauceri (r1993; arr Freed/Mauceri) *Concert*
  (6/94) (PHIL) ① **438 685-2PH**
1. Queensland SO, R. Mills (r1990) *Concert*
  (11/94) (VARE) ① **VSD5480**

The Invisible Ray—concert suite from film score (1936) (arr & orch S. Bernstein)
Westminster PO, K. Alwyn (r1993) *Bride of Frankenstein.*   (3/94) (SILV) ① **FILMCD135**

Mr Skeffington—film score (1944)
EXCERPTS: 1. Forsaken; 2. Finale.
1. National PO, C. Gerhardt *Concert*
  (3/90) (RCA) ① **GD80183**
1, 2. Queensland SO, R. Mills (r1990) *Concert*
  (11/94) (VARE) ① **VSD5480**

The Nun's Story—film score (1959)
EXCERPTS: 1a. Main Title; 1b. Gaby and her Father; 2. Leaving; 3. Gaby enters the Convent; 4. Goodbye; 5. New home; 6a. First Day; 6b. Mother Superior; 7. Sister Luke; 8. I accuse myself; 9a. Haircutting; 9b. Gran Coro; 10. Penance; 11. Angel Gabriel; 12. Departure and the Congo; 13. European Hospital; 14. Bad accident; 15. Killing of Aurelie; 16. Sister Luke bids farewell; 17. Return to Belgium; 18a. Letter from Dr Fortunati; 18b. Convent life; 18c. War; 19. Underground; 20. News of Father's death; 21. Leaving the Convent; 22. Finale.
1a, 1b, 2-5, 6a, 6b, 7, 8, 9a, 9b, 10-17, 18a-c, 19-22. OST, F. Waxman (r1958)
  (11/91) (STAN) ① **STZ114**

Objective, Burma!—film score (1945)
EXCERPTS: 1. Prelude; 2. Take-Off; 3. In the Plane; 4. Parachute Drop; 5. The Petrol; 6. Stop Firing; 7. No Landing; 8. Up the Hill; 9. Invasion; 10. Retreat; 11. Finale.
1-11. Queensland SO, R. Mills *Concert*
  (10/90) (VARE) ① **VSD5242**
4. National PO, C. Gerhardt *Concert*
  (11/91) (RCA) ① **GD80912**
4. National PO, C. Gerhardt *Concert*
  (10/92) (RCA) ① **GD82792**

Old Acquaintance—film score (1943)
1. Elegy for Strings (orig. Kit and Preston).
1. National PO, C. Gerhardt (r1974) *Concert*
  (11/91) (RCA) ① **GD80708**

The Paradine Case—film score (1947)
EXCERPTS: 1. Rhapsody for Piano and Orchestra.
1. Queensland SO, R. Mills *Concert*
  (10/90) (VARE) ① **VSD5242**

Peyton Place—film score (1957)
EXCERPTS: 1. Prelude (Main Title); 2. Entering Peyton Place; 3. Going to School; 4. Swimming; 5. The Hilltop.
1. National PO, C. Gerhardt *Concert*
  (10/92) (RCA) ① **GD82792**
1-5. Queensland SO, R. Mills *Concert*
  (10/90) (VARE) ① **VSD5242**

The Philadelphia Story—film score (1940)
EXCERPTS: 1. Main Title; 2. True Love.
1, 2. National PO, C. Gerhardt (r1974) *Concert*
  (11/91) (RCA) ① **GD80708**

A Place in the Sun—concert suite from film score (1951)
EXCERPTS: 1. Prelude; 2. Angela; 3. Loon Lake; 4. Farewell & Frenzy; 5. The Farewell.
1-5. Hollywood Bowl SO, J. Mauceri (r1991) *Concert*
(9/91) (PHIL) ① **432 109-2PH**
1-5. National PO, C. Gerhardt (r1974) *Concert*
(11/91) (RCA) ① **GD80708**
Prince Valiant—film score (1954)
EXCERPTS: 1. Prelude; 2. King Aguar's Escape; 3. The Fens; 4. The First Chase; 5. The Tournament; 6. Sir Brack's Death; 7. Finale.
1-7. National PO, C. Gerhardt (r1974) *Concert*
(11/91) (RCA) ① **GD80708**
Rear Window—film score (1954)
EXCERPTS: 1. Prelude; 2. Rhumba; 3. Ballet; 4. Finale; 5. Lisa (Intermezzo).
1-4. San Diego SO, L. Schifrin (r1990) *Concert*
(11/91) (PRO) ① **CDS524**
5. Prague City PO, P. Bateman *Concert*
(9/95) (SILV) ① **FILMCD159**
Rebecca—film score (1940)
EXCERPTS: 1a. Introduction; 1b. Foreword; 1c. Opening Scene; 2. Hotel Lobby (Waltz); 3a. Terrace Scene; 3b. Tennis Montage I; 3c. Tennis Montage II; 4a. Proposal Scene; 4b. Marriage; 4c. Arrival at Manderley; 5a. Entrance Hall; 5b. Mrs Danvers; 6. Morning Room; 7. Beatrice; 8a. Bridge Sequence; 8b. Walk to the Beach; 8c. The Boathouse; 8d. Coming Back from the Boathouse; 9. The New Dress; 10a. Rebecca's Room; 10b. The New Mrs de Winter; 11. Sketching Scene; 12. Manderley Ball; 13a. After the Ball; 13b. The Rockets; 13c. At Dawn; 14a. Confession Scene; 14b. Telephone Rings; 15a. Fireplace Tableau; 15b. The Fire; 15c. Epilogue.
1a-c, 2, 3a-c, 4a-c, 5a, 5b, 6, 7, 8a-d, 9, 10a, 10b, 11, 12, 13a-c, 14a, 14b, 15a-c Bratislava RSO, Adriano (r1990) *Alf Newman: Selznick International Pictures Fanfare.* (10/92) (MARC) ① **8 223399**
Rebecca—concert suite from film score (1940)
EXCERPTS: 1. Prelude; 2. After the Ball; 3. Mrs Danvers; 4. Confession Scene; 5. Manderley in flames.
San Diego SO, L. Schifrin (r1990) *Concert*
(11/91) (PRO) ① **CDS524**
National PO, C. Gerhardt (r1974) *Concert*
(11/91) (RCA) ① **GD80708**
Prague City PO, P. Bateman (r1993) *Concert*
(3/94) (SILV) ① **FILMCD137**
The Silver Chalice—film score (1955)
EXCERPTS: 1. Prelude; 2. The Chase; 3. Simon the Magician; 4. Fight for the Cup; 5. Finale.
1-5. Queensland SO, R. Mills (r1990) *Concert*
(11/94) (VARE) ① **VSD5480**
Sorry, Wrong Number—film score (1948)
EXCERPTS: 1. Passacaglia.
1. Queensland SO, R. Mills *Concert*
(10/90) (VARE) ① **VSD5242**
The Spirit of St Louis—film score (1956)
EXCERPTS: 1. Prelude: Main Title; 2. Building the Spirit; 3. First Test Flight; 4. Flight to St Louis; 5. St Christopher; 6. New York to Cape Cod; 7. Nova Scotia; 8. St John's; 9. Barnstorming; 10. Fishing Boats; 11. The Old Jenny; 12. The Spirit of St Louis; 13. Rolling Out; 14. Asleep; 15. Ireland; 16. Plymouth; 17. Le Bourget/End Title.
1-17. OST, F. Waxman (r1956)
(6/90) (VARE) ① **VSD5212**
Sunset Boulevard—film score (1950)
EXCERPTS: 1. Main Title; 2. Norma Desmond; 3. The Studio Stroll; 4. The Comeback; 5. Norma as Salome.
1. Queensland SO, R. Mills *Concert*
(10/90) (VARE) ① **VSD5242**
Sonata for Orchestra Hollywood Bowl SO, J. Mauceri (r1993; arr Mauceri) *Concert*
(1/95) (PHIL) ① **442 425-2PH**
1-5. National PO, C. Gerhardt (r1974) *Concert*
(11/91) (RCA) ① **GD80708**
Suspicion—film score (1941)
EXCERPTS: 1. Prelude; 2. Sunday Morning.
1, 2. Prague City PO, P. Bateman (r1993) *Concert*
(3/94) (SILV) ① **FILMCD137**
Taras Bulba—film score (1962)
EXCERPTS: 1. The Ride to Dubno (Ride of the Cossacks).
1. National PO, C. Gerhardt (r1974) *Concert*
(11/91) (RCA) ① **GD80708**
Task Force—film score (1949)
EXCERPTS: 1. Liberty Fanfares.
1. Queensland SO, R. Mills *Concert*
(10/90) (VARE) ① **VSD5242**
To Have and Have Not—film score (1944)
EXCERPTS: 1. Main Title; 2. Martinique.
1, 2. National PO, C. Gerhardt *Concert*
(10/90) (RCA) ① **GD80422**

The Two Mrs Carrolls—film score (1947)
EXCERPTS: 1. Main Title; 2. The Storm; 4. The Poisoned Milk; 5. The Window; 6. Geoffrey's Madness; 7. Finale.
1-7. National PO, C. Gerhardt *Concert*
(10/90) (RCA) ① **GD80422**

WEAVER, John (b 1937) USA

SECTION III: INSTRUMENTAL

Passacaglia on a Theme by Dunstable—organ (1978) (based on the Agincourt Hymn—attrib Dunstable)
C. Herrick *Concert* (5/89) (HYPE) ① **CDA66258**

SECTION IV: VOCAL AND CHORAL

Epiphany alleluias—chorus (Wds. from Epiphany Mass Propers)
St John's Episcopal Cath Ch, D. Pearson *Concert*
(10/92) (DELO) ① **DE3125**

WEBBE I, Samuel (1740–1816) England

SECTION IV: VOCAL AND CHORAL

Discord, dire sister—glee
Hilliard Ens, L-L. Kiesel *Concert*
(12/91) (MERI) ① **DUOCD89009**

WEBBE II, Samuel (c1770–1843) England

SECTION III: INSTRUMENTAL

Funeral march in honour of Beethoven—piano (1828)
T. Roberts (r1994) *Concert*
(3/95) (HYPE) ① **CDA66740**

SECTION IV: VOCAL AND CHORAL

The death of the common soldier—ballad: 1v & piano (1797) (Wds Southey, after Joan of Arc)
Invocation (r1994) *Concert*
(3/95) (HYPE) ① **CDA66740**
Love wakes and weeps—serenade: 1v & piano (1821)
Invocation (r1994) *Concert*
(3/95) (HYPE) ① **CDA66740**

WEBER, Carl Maria (Friedrich Ernst) von (1786–1826) Germany

J numbers used in F. W. Jahn's thematic catalogue

SECTION I: ORCHESTRAL

Andante e Rondo ungarese in C minor—bassoon and orchestra, J158 (Op. 35) (1813) (rev from J79)
K. Thunemann, ASMF, N. Marriner *Concert*
(5/91) (PHIL) ① **432 081-2PH**
Der Beherrscher der Geister—overture, J122 (Op. 27) (1811)
BPO, H. von Karajan *Concert*
(6/88) (DG) ① **419 070-2GGA**
Hanover Band, R. Goodman *Concert*
(6/89) (NIMB) ① **NI5154**
Philh, W. Sawallisch *Concert*
(1/90) (EMI) ① **CDM7 69572-2**
Philh, N. Järvi *Concert*
(1/90) (CHAN) ① **CHAN8766**
Philh, N. Järvi *Concert*
(4/93) (CHAN) ① **CHAN9066**
Concertino for Clarinet and Orchestra in E flat, J109 (Op. 26) (1811)
J. Hilton, CBSO, N. Järvi (r1982) *Concert*
(3/84) (CHAN) ① **CHAN8305**
E. Brunner, Bamberg SO, O. Caetani *Concert*
(4/84) (ORFE) ① **C067831A**
E. Johnson, ECO, W. Groves *Concert*
(11/86) (ASV) ① **CDDCA559**
S. Meyer, Staatskapelle Dresden, H. Blomstedt *Concert* (4/87) (EMI) ① **CDC7 47351-2**
A. Pay (cl/dir), OAE *Concert*
(10/88) (VIRG) ① **VC7 59002-2**
R. Kell, orch, W. Goehr (r1939) *Concert*
(6/91) (TEST) ① **SBT1002**
E. Ottersamer, Košice St PO, J. Wildner *Concert*
(7/91) (NAXO) ① **8 550378**
E. Johnson, ECO, W. Groves *Concert*
(7/91) (ASV) ① **CDDCA747**
J. Campbell, Canadian Nat Arts Centre Orch, F-P. Decker *Concert* (9/92) (CBC) ① **SMCD5096**

P. Meyer, RPO, G. Herbig *Concert*
(10/92) (DENO) ① **CO-79551**
abridged C. Draper, wind band (rc1906) *Concert*
(2/94) (CLRI) ① **CC0005**
Concertino for Horn and Orchestra in E minor, J188 (Op. 45) (1809 rev 1815)
H. Baumann, Leipzig Gewandhaus, K. Masur *Concert* (6/85) (PHIL) ① **412 237-2PH**
Concerto for Bassoon and Orchestra in F, J127 (Op. 75) (1811 rev 1822)
K. Thunemann, ASMF, N. Marriner (1811 vers) *Concert* (5/91) (PHIL) ① **432 081-2PH**
G. Brooke, RLPO, M. Sargent (r1947) *Concert*
(10/92) (TEST) ① **SBT1009**
Concerto for Clarinet and Orchestra No. 1 in F minor, J114 (Op. 73) (1811)
1. Allegro; 2. Adagio ma non troppo; 3. Rondo (Allegretto).
J. Hilton, CBSO, N. Järvi (r1982) *Concert*
(3/84) (CHAN) ① **CHAN8305**
E. Brunner, Bamberg SO, O. Caetani *Concert*
(4/84) (ORFE) ① **C067831A**
S. Meyer, Staatskapelle Dresden, H. Blomstedt *Concert* (4/87) (EMI) ① **CDC7 47351-2**
E. Johnson, ECO, Y.P. Tortelier *Concert*
(9/87) (ASV) ① **CDDCA585**
A. Pay (cl/dir), OAE *Concert*
(10/88) (VIRG) ① **VC7 59002-2**
E. Ottersamer, Košice St PO, J. Wildner *Concert*
(7/91) (NAXO) ① **8 550378**
E. Johnson, ECO, Y.P. Tortelier *Concert*
(7/91) (ASV) ① **CDDCA747**
A. Marriner, ASMF, N. Marriner *Clarinet Concerto 1.*
(9/92) (PHIL) ① **432 146-2PH**
P. Meyer, RPO, G. Herbig *Concert*
(10/92) (DENO) ① **CO-79551**
S. Dangain, Luxembourg Rad & TV SO, L. de Froment *Concert* (11/94) (FORL) ① **FF009**
Abridged C. Esberger, wind band (r1907) *Concert*
(2/94) (CLRI) ① **CC0005**
3. J. Hilton, CBSO, N. Järvi *Concert*
(7/83) (CHAN) ① **CHAN8301**
Concerto for Clarinet and Orchestra No. 2 in E flat, J118 (Op. 74) (1811)
J. Hilton, CBSO, N. Järvi (r1982) *Concert*
(3/84) (CHAN) ① **CHAN8305**
E. Brunner, Bamberg SO, O. Caetani *Concert*
(4/84) (ORFE) ① **C067831A**
T. King, LSO, A. Francis *Crusell: Clarinet Concerto 2.*
(8/85) (HYPE) ① **CDA66088**
S. Meyer, Staatskapelle Dresden, H. Blomstedt *Concert* (4/87) (EMI) ① **CDC7 47351-2**
A. Pay (cl/dir), OAE *Concert*
(10/88) (VIRG) ① **VC7 59002-2**
E. Johnson, ECO, G. Schwarz *Concert*
(11/89) (ASV) ① **CDDCA659**
E. Ottersamer, Košice St PO, J. Wildner *Concert*
(7/91) (NAXO) ① **8 550378**
E. Johnson, ECO, G. Schwarz *Concert*
(7/91) (ASV) ① **CDDCA747**
A. Marriner, ASMF, N. Marriner *Clarinet Concerto 1.*
(9/92) (PHIL) ① **432 146-2PH**
P. Meyer, RPO, G. Herbig *Concert*
(10/92) (DENO) ① **CO-79551**
G. de Peyer, LSO, Colin Davis *Concert*
(7/93) (DECC) ① **433 727-2DM**
E. Ottersamer, VPO, Colin Davis *Concert*
(6/94) (PHIL) ① **438 868-2PH**
S. Dangain, Luxembourg Rad & TV SO, L. de Froment *Concert* (11/94) (FORL) ① **FF009**
Concerto for Piano and Orchestra No. 1 in C, J98 (Op. 11) (1810)
M. Drewnowski, Polish Nat RSO, A. Wit *Concert*
(5/92) (EURM) ① **350238**
N. Demidenko, Scottish CO, C. Mackerras (r1994) *Concert* (6/95) (HYPE) ① **CDA66729**
Concerto for Piano and Orchestra No. 2 in E flat, J155 (Op. 32) (1812)
M. Drewnowski, Polish Nat RSO, A. Wit *Concert*
(5/92) (EURM) ① **350238**
N. Demidenko, Scottish CO, C. Mackerras (r1994) *Concert* (6/95) (HYPE) ① **CDA66729**
Invitation to the Dance, 'Aufforderung zum Tanze'—Rondo brillant in D flat, J260 (Op. 65) (1819) (orch Berlioz from piano work: 1841)
BPO, H. von Karajan *Concert*
(6/88) (DG) ① **419 070-2GGA**
Hanover Band, R. Goodman *Concert*
(6/89) (NIMB) ① **NI5154**
NBC SO, A. Toscanini (r1951) *Concert*
(1/91) (RCA) ① **GD60308**
BPO, W. Furtwängler (r1932) *Concert*
(4/92) (KOCH) ① [2] **37073-2**
Chicago SO, F. Reiner (r1957) *Concert*
(4/93) (RCA) ① **09026 61250-2**

BPO, E. Kleiber (r1932) *Concert*
(5/94) (ARCI) ① **ARC102**
BBC SO, A. Toscanini (r1938) *Concert*
(5/94) (BIDD) ① [2] **WHL008/9**
LSO, C. Mackerras (r1961) *Concert*
(12/95) (MERC) ① **434 352-2MM**
Jubel-Ouverture in E, J245 (Op. 59) (1818)
T. Trotter (arr.Best) *Concert*
(11/87) (HYPE) ① **CDA66216**
Philh, W. Sawallisch *Concert*
(1/90) (EMI) ① **CDM7 69572-2**
Philh, N. Järvi *Concert*
(4/93) (CHAN) ① **CHAN9066**
Konzertstück for piano and orchestra in F minor, J282 (Op. 79) (1821)
A. Brendel, LSO, C. Abbado *Schumann: Piano Concerto.*
(3/86) (PHIL) ① **412 251-2PH**
M. Drewnowski, Polish Nat RSO, A. Wit *Concert*
(5/92) (EURM) ① **350238**
N. Demidenko, Scottish CO, C. Mackerras (r1994) *Concert*
(6/95) (HYPE) ① **CDA66729**
M. Tan, LCP, R. Norrington (r1994) *Concert*
(9/95) (EMI) ① **CDC5 55348-2**
Andantino E. Feuermann, G. Moore (arr vc/pf: r1936) *Concert*
(10/91) (PEAR) ① **GEMMCD9446**
Symphony No. 1 in C, J50 (Op. 19) (1807)
ASMF, N. Marriner *Symphony 2.*
(2/85) (ASV) ① **CDDCA515**
Queensland PO, J. Georgiadis (r1994) *Concert*
(2/95) (NAXO) ① **8 550928**
LCP, R. Norrington (r1994) *Concert*
(9/95) (EMI) ① **CDC5 55348-2**
Philh, C. P. Flor (r1991) *Concert*
(11/95) (RCA) ① **09026 62712-2**
Symphony No. 2 in C, J51 (1807)
ASMF, N. Marriner *Symphony 1.*
(2/85) (ASV) ① **CDDCA515**
Queensland PO, J. Georgiadis (r1994) *Concert*
(2/95) (NAXO) ① **8 550928**
LCP, R. Norrington (r1994) *Concert*
(9/95) (EMI) ① **CDC5 55348-2**
Philh, C. P. Flor (r1991) *Concert*
(11/95) (RCA) ① **09026 62712-2**

SECTION II: CHAMBER

Clarinet Quintet in B flat, J182 (Op. 34) (1815)
J. Hilton, Lindsay Qt *Concert*
(11/85) (CHAN) ① **CHAN8366**
Nash Ens *Flute Trio, J259.*
(3/89) (CRD) ① **CRD3398**
E. Daniels, Composers Qt *Brahms: Clarinet Quintet.*
(12/91) (REFE) ① **RRCD-40**
V. Soames, Duke Qt (r1990s) *Concert*
(8/93) (CLRI) ① **CC0003**
AAM Chbr Ens (r1990) *Beethoven: Septet, Op. 20.*
(7/94) (L'OI) ① **433 044-2OH**
R. Stoltzman, Tokyo Qt (r1993) *Brahms: Clarinet Quintet.*
(8/95) (RCA) ① **09026 68033-2**
C. Neidich, Archibudelli (r1993) *Concert*
(9/95) (SONY) ① **SK57968**
Grand duo concertant—clarinet and piano, J204 (Op. 48) (1815-16)
J. Hilton, K. Swallow *Concert*
(11/85) (CHAN) ① **CHAN8366**
H-R. Stalder, Z. Sirokay *Concert*
(11/87) (JECK) ① **JD536-2**
E. Johnson, G. Back *Concert*
(5/91) (ASV) ① **CDDCA732**
E. Johnson, G. Back *Concert*
(7/91) (ASV) ① **CDDCA747**
M. Collins, K. Stott *Concert*
(9/92) (EMI) ① **CDC7 54419-2**
J. Cohler, J. Gordon (1992) *Concert*
(11/94) (ONGA) ① **024-101**
C. Neidich, R. Levin (1993) *Concert*
(9/95) (SONY) ① **SK64302**
Melody in F—clarinet and piano, J119 (1811)
(pf accomp by Jähns: 1872)
V. Soames, J. Drake (r1990s; arr Weston) *Concert*
(8/93) (CLRI) ① **CC0003**
Romance
C. Lindberg, R. Pöntinen *Concert*
(9/85) (BIS) ① **BIS-CD298**
6 Sonatas—violin/flute and piano, J99-104 (1810)
1. F, J99; 2. G, J100; 3. D minor, J101; 4. E flat, J102; 5. A, J103; 6. C, J104.
A. Nicolet, B. Canino (r1990: arr fl/pf) *Flute Trio, J259.*
(7/91) (NOVA) ① **150 065-2**
1(Romance) F. Kreisler, M. Raucheisen (r1930: arr Kreisler) *Concert* (12/93) (EMI) ① **CDH7 64701-2**
2(Movt 2); 3(Movt 3) G. Piatigorsky, I. Newton (arr Piatigorgky: r1934) *Concert*
(10/91) (MUSI) ① **MACD-644**

3 (Thème russe; Rondo) J. Szigeti, N. Magaloff (arr Szigeti: r1936) *Concert*
(1/90) (BIDD) ① [2] **LAB007/8**
5. G. Piatigorsky, I. Newton (arr Piatigorsky: r1934) *Concert*
(10/91) (PEAR) ① **GEMMCD9447**
5. G. Piatigorsky, I. Newton (arr Piatigorsky: r1933/4) *Concert*
(10/91) (MUSI) ① **MACD-644**
Trio for Flute, Cello and Piano, J259 (Op. 63) (1819)
Nash Ens *Clarinet Quintet, J182.*
(3/89) (CRD) ① **CRD3398**
A. Nicolet, R. Filippini, B. Canino (r1990) *Violin Sonatas, J99-104.*
(7/91) (NOVA) ① **150 065-2**
7 Variations on a theme from 'Silvana'—clarinet and piano, J128 (Op. 33) (1811)
J. Hilton, K. Swallow *Concert*
(11/85) (CHAN) ① **CHAN8366**
G. de Peyer, G. Pryor *Concert*
(4/87) (CHAN) ① **CHAN8506**
H-R. Stalder, Z. Sirokay *Concert*
(11/87) (JECK) ① **JD536-2**
C. Bradbury, O. Davies *Concert*
(6/90) (ASV) ① **CDDCA701**
E. Johnson, G. Back *Concert*
(5/91) (ASV) ① **CDDCA732**
V. Soames, J. Drake (r1990s) *Concert*
(8/93) (CLRI) ① **CC0003**

SECTION III: INSTRUMENTAL

Adagio Patetico in C sharp minor—keyboard (1826)
I. Hobson *Concert*
(3/89) (ARAB) ① **Z6595**
Adieux—piano, Op. posth
A. Paley (r1994) *Concert*
(2/95) (NAXO) ① **8 553006**
Grande Polonaise in E flat—piano, J59 (Op. 21) (1808)
J. Martin (r1979) *Concert*
(4/94) (ARIO) ① [2] **ARN268240**
A. Paley (r1994) *Concert*
(2/95) (NAXO) ① **8 550989**
Invitation to the Dance (Aufforderung zum Tanze)—Rondo brillante in D flat, J260 (Op. 65) (1819)
G. Ohlsson *Concert* (3/89) (ARAB) ① [2] **Z6584-2**
P. Fowke (arr Tausig: pf) *Concert*
(8/89) (CRD) ① **CRD3396**
B. Moiseiwitsch (r1939) *Concert*
(9/90) (APR) ① [2] **APR7005**
R. de Waal (arr Godowsky) *Concert*
(3/92) (HYPE) ① **CDA66496**
A. Cortot (r1926) *Concert* (6/92) (BIDD) ① **LHW002**
H. Milne *Concert* (9/92) (CRD) ① **CRD3485**
J. Martin (r1979) *Concert*
(4/94) (ARIO) ① [2] **ARN268240**
A. Cortot (r1923) *Concert*
(10/94) (BIDD) ① **LHW014/5**
A. Paley (r1994) *Concert*
(2/95) (NAXO) ① **8 550988**
Momento Capriccioso in B flat—piano, J56 (Op. 12) (1808)
G. Ohlsson *Concert* (3/89) (ARAB) ① [2] **Z6584-2**
A. Paley (r1994) *Concert*
(2/95) (NAXO) ① **8 550990**
Polacca brillante in E, ('L') hilarité—piano, J268 (Op. 72) (1819)
H. Milne *Concert* (11/92) (CRD) ① **CRD3486**
J. Martin (r1979) *Concert*
(4/94) (ARIO) ① [2] **ARN268240**
A. Paley (r1994) *Concert*
(2/95) (NAXO) ① **8 553006**
Rondo brillante in E flat, 'La gaîté'—piano, J252 (Op. 62) (1819)
G. Ohlsson *Concert* (3/89) (ARAB) ① [2] **Z6584-2**
H. Milne *Concert* (9/92) (CRD) ① **CRD3485**
J. Martin (r1979) *Concert*
(4/94) (ARIO) ① [2] **ARN268240**
A. Paley (r1994) *Concert*
(2/95) (NAXO) ① **8 553006**
Sonata for Piano No. 1 in C, J138 (Op. 24) (1812)
1. Allegro; 2. Adagio; 3. Menuetto; 4. Rondo (presto), 'Perpetuum mobile'.
G. Ohlsson *Concert* (3/89) (ARAB) ① [2] **Z6584-2**
H. Milne *Concert* (9/92) (CRD) ① **CRD3485**
Martin Jones *Piano Sonata 2.*
(9/92) (PP) ① **PP20792**
J. Martin (r1979) *Concert*
(4/94) (ARIO) ① [2] **ARN268240**
A. Paley (r1994) *Concert*
(2/95) (NAXO) ① **8 550988**
4. B. Moiseiwitsch (r1922) *Concert*
(4/89) (OPAL) ① **OPALCD9839**
4. S. Barere (pp1949) *Concert*
(11/89) (APR) ① **APR7008**

4. B. Moiseiwitsch (r1950) *Concert*
(9/90) (APR) ① [2] **APR7005**
4. S. Barere (pp1946) *Concert*
(5/91) (APR) ① [2] **APR7009**
4. A. Friedheim (r1911) *Concert*
(8/93) (PEAR) ① **GEMMCD9993**
4. A. Brailowsky (r c1928) *Concert*
(2/95) (PEAR) ① **GEMMCD9132**
4. A. Brailowsky (r1928) *Concert*
(11/95) (DANA) ① [2] **DACOCD338/9**
Sonata for Piano No. 2 in A flat, J199 (Op. 39) (1816)
G. Ohlsson *Concert* (3/89) (ARAB) ① [2] **Z6584-2**
A. Brendel *Brahms: Ballades.*
(6/91) (PHIL) ① **426 439-2PH**
A. Cortot (r1939) *Concert*
(6/92) (MUSI) ① **MACD-662**
A. Cortot (r1939) *Concert* (6/92) (BIDD) ① **LHW002**
Martin Jones *Piano Sonata 1.*
(9/92) (PP) ① **PP20792**
H. Milne *Concert* (9/92) (CRD) ① **CRD3485**
Emil Gilels (bp1968) *Concert*
(9/93) (PRAG) ① **PR250 039**
J. Martin (r1979) *Concert*
(4/94) (ARIO) ① [2] **ARN268240**
A. Paley (r1994) *Concert*
(2/95) (NAXO) ① **8 550989**
Emil Gilels (pp1968) *Concert*
(8/95) (MELO) ① **74321 25179-2**
Emil Gilels (r1968) *Concert*
(8/95) (MELO) ① [1] **74321 25172-2(1)**
Sonata for Piano No. 3 in D minor, J206 (Op. 49) (1816)
G. Ohlsson *Concert* (3/89) (ARAB) ① [2] **Z6584-2**
H. Milne *Concert* (11/92) (CRD) ① **CRD3486**
J. Martin (r1979) *Concert*
(4/94) (ARIO) ① [2] **ARN268240**
S. Richter *Concert*
(8/94) (PHIL) ① [2] **438 617-2PH2**
A. Paley (r1994) *Concert*
(2/95) (NAXO) ① **8 550990**
Sonata for Piano No. 4 in E minor, J287 (Op. 70) (1819-22)
G. Ohlsson *Concert* (3/89) (ARAB) ① [2] **Z6584-2**
H. Milne *Concert* (11/92) (CRD) ① **CRD3486**
J. Martin (r1979) *Concert*
(4/94) (ARIO) ① [2] **ARN268240**
A. Paley (r1994) *Concert*
(2/95) (NAXO) ① **8 553006**
7 Variationen über an ein Zigeunerlied—piano, J219 (Op. 55) (1817)
A. Paley (r1994) *Concert*
(2/95) (NAXO) ① **8 550989**
7 Variations on 'A peine au sortir de l'enfance from Méhul's 'Joseph'—piano, J141 (Op. 28) (1812)
A. Paley (r1994) *Concert*
(2/95) (NAXO) ① **8 553006**
9 Variations on a Russian Theme, 'Schöne Minka'—piano, J179 (Op. 40)
A. Paley (r1994) *Concert*
(2/95) (NAXO) ① **8 550988**
6 Variations on an original theme—piano, J7 (Op. 2) (1800)
A. Paley (r1994) *Concert*
(2/95) (NAXO) ① **8 550989**
7 Variations on an original theme—piano, J55 (Op. 9) (1808)
A. Paley (r1994) *Concert*
(2/95) (NAXO) ① **8 550990**
8 Variations sur l'air de ballet de Castor et Pollux (Vogler)—piano, J40 (Op. 5) (1804)
A. Paley (r1994) *Concert*
(2/95) (NAXO) ① **8 550990**
6 Variations sur 'A peine au sortir' from Naga (from Vogler's opera 'Samori')—piano, J43 (Op. 6) (1804)
J. Martin (r1979) *Concert*
(4/94) (ARIO) ① [2] **ARN268240**
A. Paley (r1994) *Concert*
(2/95) (NAXO) ① **8 550989**
7 Variations sur l'air vien quà, Dorina bella (Bianchi)—piano, J53 (Op. 7) (1807)
A. Paley (r1994) *Concert*
(2/95) (NAXO) ① **8 550990**

SECTION IV: VOCAL AND CHORAL

Abendsegen—Lied, J255 (Op. 54/5) (1819)
(Wds. trad)
T. Hampson, G. Parsons *Concert*
(10/90) (TELD) ① **2292-44923-2**
3 Canzonettas—songs with guitar/piano (1811) (Wds. anon)
1. Ah, dove siete (J108); 2. Ch'io mai vi possa (J120); 3. Ninfe se liete (J124).
P. Schreier, K. Ragossnig (Ger) *Concert*
(10/89) (NOVA) ① **150 039-2**

SECTION V: STAGE WORKS

12a M. Jeritza, orch (r1926) *Concert*
(4/94) (PREI) ① **89079**
12a-c T. Lemnitz, Berlin St Op Orch, B. Seidler-
Winkler (r1939) *Concert* (10/90) (PREI) ① **89025**
12a-c E. Destinn, orch (r1912) *Concert*
(12/94) (SUPR) ① [12] **11 2136-2(4)**
12a-c, 16. I. Seefried, BRSO, E. Jochum (r1959)
Concert (9/93) (DG) ① [2] **437 677-2GDO2**
12a, 12b H. Konetzni, Berlin Deutsche Op Orch, H.
Schmidt-Isserstedt (r1937) *Concert*
(1/95) (PREI) ① **90078**
12a, 12b E. Rethberg, orch (r1929) *Concert*
(2/95) (ROMO) ① [2] **81012-2**
12a, 12b, 16. E. Destinn, orch, F. Kark (r1908)
Concert (12/94) (SUPR) ① [12] **11 2136-2(2)**
12a, 12b, 16. G. Janowitz, Berlin Deutsche Op Orch,
F. Leitner (r1967) *Concert*
(12/95) (DG) ① [2] **447 352-2GDB2**
12a, 16. E. Destinn, orch (r1910) *Concert*
(12/94) (SUPR) ① [12] **11 2136-2(4)**
12c Lotte Lehmann, orch (r1916) *Concert*
(6/92) (PREI) ① [3] **89302**
12c(pt) E. Destinn, orch, F. Kark (r1908) *Concert*
(5/94) (SUPR) ① **11 1337-2**
12, 12b L. Price, RCA Italiana Op Orch, F. Molinari-
Pradelli *Concert*
(12/92) (RCA) ① [4] **09026 61236-2**
12, 16. E. Schwarzkopf, Philh, W. Susskind *Concert*
(10/88) (EMI) ① **CDM7 69501-2**
16. A. Tomowa-Sintow, Munich RO, P. Sommer
Concert (6/91) (ORFE) ① **C106841A**
16. T. Lemnitz, Berlin St Op Orch, L. Blech (r1935)
Concert (10/90) (PREI) ① **89025**
16. Lotte Lehmann, orch (r1921) *Concert*
(6/92) (PREI) ① [3] **89302**
16. M. Teschemacher, Berlin City Op Orch, H.U.
Müller (r1934) *Concert* (11/92) (PREI) ① **89049**
19. Berlin Deutsche Op Choir, Berlin Deutsche Op
Orch, G. Sinopoli *Concert*
(10/85) (DG) ① **415 283-2GH**
19. ROH Chor, ROHO, B. Haitink *Concert*
(12/89) (EMI) ① **CDC7 49849-2**
21. F. Schorr, New SO, A. Coates (r1930) *Concert*
(2/95) (CLAR) ① **CDGSE78-50-54**
Oberon—romantic opera: 3 acts, J306
(1826—London) (Lib. Planché)
1. Overture. ACT 1: 2. Von Jugend auf schon in
Kampfgefild. ACT 2: 7. Arabiens einsam Kind; 9.
Über die blauen Wogen; 11. O wie wogt es sich
schön; 13. Vater! Hör mich flehn ACT 3: 16. Ozean
du Ungheuer! ACT 3: 16. Arabien, mein Heimatland;
17. Traure, mein Herz; 18. An der Strande der
Garonne; 20. March.
Cpte D. Grobe, B. Nilsson, P. Domingo, H. Prey, J.
Hamari, M. Schiml, A. Auger, Bavarian Rad Chor,
BRSO, R. Kubelik (with dialogue)
(12/91) (DG) ① [2] **419 038-2GX2**
Cpte G. Lakes, D. Voigt, B. Heppner, D. Croft, D.
Ziegler, V. Livengood, M. Obata, Cologne Op Chor,
Cologne Gürzenich Orch, J. Conlon (r1992: with
narration) (6/93) (EMI) ① [2] **CDS7 54739-2**
1. BPO, H. von Karajan *Concert*
(6/88) (DG) ① **419 070-2GGA**
1. Hanover Band, R. Goodman *Concert*
(6/89) (NIMB) ① **NI5154**
1. Philh, W. Sawallisch *Concert*
(1/90) (EMI) ① **CDM7 69501-2**
1. Philh, N. Järvi *Concert*
(1/90) (CHAN) ① **CHAN8766**
1. NYPO, W. Mengelberg (r1923) *Concert*
(7/90) (SYMP) ① **SYMCD1078**
1(pt) SO, T. Beecham (r1912) *Concert*
(11/91) (SYMP) ① [2] **SYMCD1096/7**
1. Philh, N. Järvi *Concert*
(4/93) (CHAN) ① **CHAN9066**
1. LSO, A. Coates (r1926) *Concert*
(4/93) (KOCH) ① [2] **37704-2**
1. Black Dyke Mills Band, P. Parkes (arr brass band:
P Parkes) *Concert* (9/93) (CHAN) ① **CHAN4514**
1. NYPO, L. Bernstein (r1968) *Concert*
(9/93) (SONY) ① **SMK47601**
1. LPO, T. Beecham (r1938) *Concert*
(10/94) (DUTT) ① **CDLX7009**
1. Luxembourg Rad & TV SO, L. de Froment *Concert*
(11/94) (FORL) ① **FF009**
1. NBC SO, B. Walter (pp1939) *Concert*
(2/95) (PEAR) ① **GEMMCD9131**
2. H. Roswaenge, Berlin St Op Orch, B. Seidler-
Winkler (r1936) *Concert* (5/90) (PREI) ① **89018**
2, 13. P. Domingo, BRSO, R. Kubelik *Concert*
(6/94) (BELA) ① **450 121-2**
2, 13. H. Roswaenge, Berlin St Op Orch, B. Seidler-
Winkler (r1936) *Concert*
(4/95) (PREI) ① [2] **89209**
14. F. Loider, orch (r1021) *Concert*
(5/91) (PREI) ① [3] **89301**

14. M. Teschemacher, Stuttgart Op Orch, G. Görlich
(bp1936) *Concert* (2/92) (MMOI) ① **CDMOIR408**
14. Lotte Lehmann, orch (r1919) *Concert*
(6/92) (PREI) ① [3] **89302**
14. M. Teschemacher, Berlin St Op Orch, B. Seidler-
Winkler (r1937) *Concert* (11/92) (PREI) ① **89049**
14. L. Price, Philh, H. Lewis (r1979) *Concert*
(12/92) (RCA) ① [4] **09026 61236-2**
14. M. Callas, Philh, A. Tonini (Eng) *Concert*
(12/93) (EMI) ① **CDC7 54437-2**
14. K. Flagstad, Philadelphia, E. Ormandy (r1937)
Concert (7/93) (NIMB) ① **NI7847**
14. M. Németh, orch (r1920s) *Concert*
(1/94) (CLUB) ① **CL99-007**
14. H. Konetzni, Vienna SO, L. Ludwig Beethoven:
Fidelio. (8/94) (PREI) ① [2] **90195**
14. K. Flagstad, Philadelphia, E. Ormandy (r1937)
Concert (12/95) (SIMA) ① **PSC1821(2)**
14, 17. G. Janowitz, Berlin Deutsche Op Orch, F.
Leitner (r1967) *Concert*
(12/95) (DG) ① [2] **447 352-2GDB2**
Peter Schmoll und seine Nachbarn—opera:
2 acts, J8 (1803—Augsburg) (Lib. J. Türk(e),
after C. G. Crämer)
Cpte R. Busching, J. Schmidt, A. Pfeffer, S. Basa, H.
J. Porcher, H-J. Schöpflin, Hage PO, G. Markson
(r1993) (4/94) (MARC) ① [2] **8 223592/3**
Overture BPO, H. von Karajan *Concert*
(6/88) (DG) ① **419 070-2GGA**
Overture Hanover Band, R. Goodman *Concert*
(6/89) (NIMB) ① **NI5154**
Overture Philh, N. Järvi *Concert*
(4/93) (CHAN) ① **CHAN9066**
Preciosa—incidental music to Wolff's play,
J279 (1821—Berlin)
Overture Philh, W. Sawallisch *Concert*
(1/90) (EMI) ① **CDM7 69501-2**
Overture Philh, N. Järvi *Concert*
(4/93) (CHAN) ① **CHAN9066**
Silvana—opera: 3 acts, J87
(1810—Frankfurt-am-Main) (Lib. F C Hiemer,
after 'Das Waldmädchen' text)
EXCERPTS: 1. Overture; 2. Tanz der Edelknaben;
3. Fackel Tanz.
Soll denn dies Herz wie Liebe finden A. Piccaver,
orch (r1920) *Concert* (8/93) (PREI) ① **89060**
1. Philh, N. Järvi *Concert*
(4/93) (CHAN) ① **CHAN9066**
2, 3. Queensland PO, J. Georgiadis (r1994) *Concert*
(2/95) (NAXO) ① **8 550928**
Turandot, Prinzessin von China—incidental
music, J75 (1809—Stuttgart)
Queensland PO, J. Georgiadis (r1994) *Concert*
(2/95) (NAXO) ① **8 550928**
Overture Philh, N. Järvi *Concert*
(4/93) (CHAN) ① **CHAN9066**
Overture; March Philh, N. Järvi *Concert*
(1/90) (CHAN) ① **CHAN8766**

WEBER, Frederick Dionysus
(1766–1842) Germany

SECTION I: ORCHESTRAL

Variations in F—Trumpet and Orchestra
J. Wallace, Philh, C. Warren-Green (r1986) *Concert*
(2/95) (NIMB) ① **NI7016**

WEBERN, Anton (Friedrich
Wilhelm von) (1883–1945)
Austria

SECTION I: ORCHESTRAL

Passacaglia—large orchestra, Op. 1 (1908)
BPO, H. von Karajan *Concert*
(7/88) (DG) ① **423 254-2GC**
SNO, M. Bamert Schoenberg: Pelleas und
Melisande. (10/88) (CHAN) ① **CHAN8619**
BPO, H. von Karajan *Concert*
(9/89) (DG) ① [3] **427 424-2GC3**
LSO, P. Boulez (r1969) *Concert*
(6/91) (SONY) ① [3] **SM3K45845**
VPO, C. Abbado (r1990) *Concert*
(5/93) (DG) ① **431 774-2GH**
5 Pieces—strings, Op. 5 (1928 rev 1929) (arr
cpsr from String Quartet, Op 5)
BPO, H. von Karajan *Concert*
(7/88) (DG) ① **423 254-2GC**
BPO, H. von Karajan *Concert*
(9/89) (DG) ① [3] **427 424-2GC3**
LSO, P. Boulez (r1969) *Concert*
(6/91) (SONY) ① [3] **SM3K45845**
6 Pieces—large orchestra, Op. 6 (1909)
BPO, James Levine *Concert*
(8/87) (DG) ① **419 781-2GH**

BPO, H. von Karajan *Concert*
(7/88) (DG) ① **423 254-2GC**
BPO, H. von Karajan *Concert*
(9/89) (DG) ① [3] **427 424-2GC3**
CBSO, S. Rattle (r1987/8) *Concert*
(11/89) (EMI) ① **CDC7 49857-2**
LSO, P. Boulez (r1969) *Concert*
(6/91) (SONY) ① [3] **SM3K45845**
VPO, C. Abbado (r1990) *Concert*
(5/93) (DG) ① **431 774-2GH**
5 Pieces—small orchestra, Op. 10 (1911-13)
LSO, A. Dorati *Concert*
(3/91) (MERC) ① **432 006-2MM**
LSO, P. Boulez (r1969) *Concert*
(6/91) (SONY) ① [3] **SM3K45845**
N German RSO, G. Wand (pp1984) *Concert*
(1/92) (RCA) ① **RD60827**
VPO, C. Abbado (r1990) *Concert*
(5/93) (DG) ① **431 774-2GH**
Paris InterContemporain Ens, P. Boulez (r1992)
Concert (3/95) (DG) ① **437 786-2GH**
Symphony, Op. 21 (1928)
BPO, H. von Karajan *Concert*
(7/88) (DG) ① **423 254-2GC**
BPO, H. von Karajan *Concert*
(9/89) (DG) ① [3] **427 424-2GC3**
LSO, P. Boulez (r1969) *Concert*
(6/91) (SONY) ① [3] **SM3K45845**
Variations—orchestra, Op. 30 (1940)
LSO, P. Boulez (r1969) *Concert*
(6/91) (SONY) ① [3] **SM3K45845**
VPO, C. Abbado (r1992) *Concert*
(5/93) (DG) ① **431 774-2GH**

SECTION II: CHAMBER

6 Bagatelles—string quartet, Op. 9 (1911-
13)
LaSalle Qt *Concert*
(4/88) (DG) ① [4] **419 994-2GCM4**
Juilliard Qt (r1970) *Concert*
(6/91) (SONY) ① [3] **SM3K45845**
Arditti Qt *Concert* (12/91) (MONT) ① **789008**
Artis Qt *Concert* (7/92) (SONY) ① **SK48059**
Emerson Qt (r1992) *Concert*
(5/95) (DG) ① **445 828-2GH**
Concerto for Nine Instruments—fl, ob, cl, hn,
tpt, tbn, pf, vn and va, Op. 24 (1931-34)
LSO, P. Boulez (r1969) *Concert*
(6/91) (SONY) ① [3] **SM3K45845**
Nash Ens, S. Rattle (r1977) Schoenberg: Pierrot
Lunaire. (8/92) (CHAN) ① **CHAN6534**
P-L. Aimard, Paris InterContemporain Ens, P. Boulez
(r1992) *Concert* (3/95) (DG) ① **437 786-2GH**
3 Little Pieces—1v and string quartet (1913)
1. Mässig (also Op. 9/1); 2. Schmerz immer blick
nach oben (wds. cpsr); 3. Fliessend (also Op. 9/6).
D. Dorow, Schoenberg Ens, R. de Leeuw (r1986)
Concert (5/90) (SCHW) ① **314005**
M.A. McCormick, Emerson Qt (r1994) *Concert*
(5/95) (DG) ① **445 828-2GH**
3 Little Pieces—cello and piano, Op. 11
(1914)
1. Mässige Achtel; 2. Sehr bewegt; 3. Äussert ruhig.
G. Piatigorsky, C. Rosen (r1972) *Concert*
(6/91) (SONY) ① [3] **SM3K45845**
W. Conway, Peter Evans (r1992) *Concert*
(10/93) (LINN) ① **CKD009**
Movement (Sehr lebhaft)—string trio (1927)
(originally intended for String Trio, op.20)
Arditti Qt *Concert* (12/91) (MONT) ① **789008**
Emerson Qt (r1994) *Concert*
(5/95) (DG) ① **445 828-2GH**
5 Movements—string quartet, Op. 5 (1909)
LaSalle Qt *Concert*
(4/88) (DG) ① [4] **419 994-2GCM4**
Juilliard Qt (r1970) *Concert*
(6/91) (SONY) ① [3] **SM3K45845**
Arditti Qt *Concert* (12/91) (MONT) ① **789008**
Artis Qt *Concert* (7/92) (SONY) ① **SK48059**
Emerson Qt (r1994) *Concert*
(5/95) (DG) ① **445 828-2GH**
Brindisi Qt (r1994) *Concert*
(6/95) (METR) ① **METCD1007**
4 Pieces—violin and piano, Op. 7 (1910)
I. Stern, C. Rosen (r1971) *Concert*
(6/91) (SONY) ① [3] **SM3K45845**
N. Gotkovsky, I. Gotkovsky *Concert*
(9/91) (PYRA) ① **PYR13496**
Quartet—clarinet, tenor saxophone, piano
and violin, Op. 22 (1930)
C. Rosen, D. Majeske, John Aldis Ch, R. Marcellus
(r1970) *Concert* (6/91) (SONY) ① [3] **SM3K45845**
P-L. Aimard, Paris InterContemporain Ens, P. Boulez
(r1992) *Concert* (3/95) (DG) ① **437 786-2GH**

WECKERLIN, Jean-Baptiste (Théodore) *(1821–1910) France*

SECTION IV: VOCAL AND CHORAL

Romances et Chansons du XVIII siècle—song collection (1860s)
1. Menuet d'Exaudet; 2. Que ne suis-je la fougère; 3. Bergère légère; 4. Jeunes fillettes; 5. Non, je n'irai plus au bois; 6. Maman, dites-moi; 7. Ô ma tendre musette; 8. Aminte; 9. Venez, agréable printemps; 10. Phillis plus avare que tendre; 11. Je connais un berger discret; 12. La mère Bontemps; 13. Chaque chose a son temps; 14. Non, je ne crois pas; 15. Lison dormait; 16. Ronde villageoise; 17. Chassant dans nos forêts; 18. La batelière; 19. Ah! mon berger!; 20. Les belles manières; 21. Menuet tendre; 22. Paris est au Roi; 23. Il pleut bergère (harm G. van Parys).
  3. E. Clément, F. La Forge (r1911) *Concert*
        (8/95) (ROMO) ① **82002-2**
  3. E. Clément, F. La Forge (r1911) *Concert*
        (8/95) (PEAR) ① **GEMMCD9161**
  9, 16. E. Clément, anon (r1910s) *Concert*
        (8/95) (PEAR) ① **GEMMCD9161**

WECKMANN, Matthias *(1619 or earlier–1674) Germany*

SECTION II: CHAMBER

Sonata a 4—organ and brass ensemble
A. Ross, His Majesties Sagbutts and Cornetts
  Concert   (9/87) (MERI) ① **CDE84096**
Sonata II à 4—vn, cornettino, tbe, dulcian & continuo (Lüneberg MS)
Musica Fiata, R. Wilson (r1991) *Concert*
        (8/93) (DHM) ① **05472 77183-2**
Sonata IX à 4—violin, cornettino, trombone, dulcian & continuo (Lüneburg MS)
Musica Fiata, R. Wilson (r1991) *Concert*
        (8/93) (DHM) ① **05472 77183-2**

SECTION III: INSTRUMENTAL

Canzon in C minor—organ
G. Leonhardt *Concert*   (10/94) (SONY) ① **SK53371**
Lucidor, einst hüt't der Schaf—organ
G. Leonhardt *Concert*   (10/94) (SONY) ① **SK53371**

SECTION IV: VOCAL AND CHORAL

Angelicus coeli chorus—2vv and 2 violins (1665)
G. de Reyghere, M. van Egmond, Ricercar Consort
  Concert   (4/93) (RICE) ① [2] **RIC109097/8**
Dialogo von Tobias and Raguel, 'Wo willen wir ein Kehren'—3vv and 2 violins (1665)
J. Bowman, I. Honeyman, M. van Egmond, Ricercar Consort *Concert* (4/93) (RICE) ① [2] **RIC109097/8**
Es erhub sich ein streit—5/4vv and instruments
G. de Reyghere, J. Feldman, J. Bowman, G. de Mey, M. van Egmond, Capella Sancti Michaelis Voc Ens, E. van Nevel, Ricercar Consort *Concert*
        (4/93) (RICE) ① [2] **RIC109097/8**
Gegrüsset seist du, Holdselige—dialogus: 2vv and instruments
G. de Reyghere, G. de Mey, Ricercar Consort
  (r1989) *Concert*   (5/90) (RICE) ① **RIC060048**
G. de Reyghere, I. Honeyman, Ricercar Consort
  Concert   (4/93) (RICE) ① [2] **RIC109097/8**
Herr, wenn ich nur dich habe—3vv and strings (1663)
J. Bowman, I. Honeyman, M. van Egmond, Ricercar Consort *Concert* (4/93) (RICE) ① [2] **RIC109097/8**
Kommet her zu mir alle—1v and strings (1664)
M. van Egmond, Ricercar Consort *Concert*
        (4/93) (RICE) ① [2] **RIC109097/8**
Rex virtutum—1v and 2 violins (1665)
M. van Egmond, Ricercar Consort *Concert*
        (4/93) (RICE) ① [2] **RIC109097/8**
Der Tod ist verschlungen—3vv and strings
G. de Reyghere, I. Honeyman, M. van Egmond, Ricercar Consort *Concert*
        (4/93) (RICE) ① [2] **RIC109097/8**
Weine nicht, es hat über wunden—3vv and strings (1664)
J. Bowman, I. Honeyman, M. van Egmond, Ricercar Consort *Concert* (4/93) (RICE) ① [2] **RIC109097/8**
Wenn der Herr die Gefangen zu Zion erlösen wird—cantata: 4vv, strings and continuo
G. de Reyghere, J. Bowman, I. Honeyman, M. van Egmond, Ricercar Consort *Concert*
        (4/93) (RICE) ① [2] **RIC109097/8**

Wie liegt die Stadt so wuste (1663)
M. Zedelius, Cologne Musica Antiqua, R. Goebel
  (r1985) *Concert* (1/93) (ARCH) ① **437 079-2AT**
G. de Reyghere, M. van Egmond, Ricercar Consort
  Concert   (4/93) (RICE) ① [2] **RIC109097/8**
Zion spricht, der Herr hat mich verlassen—3vv and strings (1663)
J. Bowman, I. Honeyman, M. van Egmond, Ricercar Consort *Concert* (4/93) (RICE) ① [2] **RIC109097/8**

WEELKES, Thomas *(1576–1623) England*

SECTION III: INSTRUMENTAL

Pavane—keyboard
T. Byram-Wigfield *Concert*
        (10/92) (HYPE) ① **CDA66477**
2 Voluntaries—keyboard
T. Byram-Wigfield *Concert*
        (10/92) (HYPE) ① **CDA66477**

SECTION IV: VOCAL AND CHORAL

All laud and praise—anthem: 4vv and organ
Winchester Cath Ch, D. Hill, T. Byram-Wigfield
  Concert   (10/92) (HYPE) ① **CDA66477**
All people clap your hands—anthem: 5vv
Trinity Coll Ch, Cambridge, R. Marlow (r1993)
  Concert   (12/93) (CONI) ① **CDCF216**
Alleluia, I heard a voice—full anthem: 5vv and organ
Oxford Christ Church Cath Ch, S. Darlington *Concert*
        (3/89) (NIMB) ① **NI5125**
Salisbury Cath Ch, R. Seal *Concert*
        (11/90) (MERI) ① **CDE84180**
Winchester Cath Ch, D. Hill, T. Byram-Wigfield
  Concert   (10/92) (HYPE) ① **CDA66477**
Ayres or Phantasticke Spirites for Three Voices—catches (pub 1608)
1. Alas tarry but one halfe houre; 2. As deadly serpents lurking; 3. Aye me alas hey hoe; 4. Come come, lets begin; 5. Come sirrah Jacke hoe; 6. Death hath deprived me (A remembrance of my friend T. Morley); 7. Donna il vostro bel viso; 8. Fa la la, O now weepe; 9. Fowre armes two neckes; 10. Ha ha this world doth passe; 11. I bei ligustri e rose; 12. Jockey thine home pipes dull; 13. Late in my rash accounting; 14. Lord when I thinke; 15. No, no though I shrinke still; 16. Say wanton will you love me; 17. Since Robin Hood; 18. Some men desire spouses; 19. Strike it up tabor; 20. Tan ta ra ran tant, cryes Mars; 21. The ape, the monkey; 22. The gods have heard my vows; 23. The nightingale the organ of delight; 24. Though my carriage be but carelesse; 25. To morrow is the marriage day; 26. Upon a hill, the bonny boy.
  6. Cambridge Sngrs, J. Rutter *Concert*
        (11/87) (CLLE) ① **COLCD105**
  11. Cambridge Sngrs, J. Rutter *Concert*
        (11/87) (CLLE) ① **COLCD105**
  16, 18. Hilliard Ens, P. Hillier *Concert*
        (2/89) (EMI) ① **CDC7 49197-2**
Balletts and Madrigals to Five Voyces, with One to six (pub 1598)
1. All at once well met faire ladies; 2. Cease now delight: An elogie in remembrance of Lord Borough (6vv); 3. Come clap thy hands; 4. Farewell my joy adue my love; 5. Give me my hart; 6. Harke all ye lovely saints above (wds. ?B. Barnes); 7. I love, and have my love regarded; 8. In prime of May; 9. Ladie, your eye my love enforced; 10. Now is my Cloris fresh as May; 11. Now is the bridalls of faire Choralis; 12. On the plaines Fairie traines (wds. B. Barnes); 13. Phillis goe take thy pleasure; 14. Say daintie dames shall wee goe play; 15. Sing shepherds after mee; 16. Sing wee at pleasure; 17. Sweet hart arise; 18. Sweete love, I will no more sorrow; 19. To shorten winters sadnesse; 20. Unto our flockes sweet Corolus; 21. Wee shepherds sing; 22. Welcome sweet pleasure; 23. Whilst youthful sports.
  6. Cambridge Sngrs, J. Rutter *Concert*
        (11/87) (CLLE) ① **COLCD105**
  12. Amaryllis Consort, C. Brett *Concert*
        (3/88) (CARL) ① **PCD873**
Cries of London—5vv
Red Byrd, Circa 1500, N. Hadden (r1991) *Concert*
        (8/93) (CRD) ① **CRD3487**
Give ear, O Lord—verse anthem: 6/5vv and organ
Oxford Christ Church Cath Ch, S. Darlington *Concert*
        (3/89) (NIMB) ① **NI5125**
Give the king thy judgements—verse anthem: 3/6vv and organ
Oxford Christ Church Cath Ch, S. Darlington *Concert*
        (3/89) (NIMB) ① **NI5125**

Winchester Cath Ch, D. Hill, T. Byram-Wigfield
  Concert   (10/92) (HYPE) ① **CDA66477**
Gloria in excelsis Deo (Sing my soul to God)—full anthem: 6vv
Oxford Christ Church Cath Ch, S. Darlington *Concert*
        (3/89) (NIMB) ① **NI5125**
King's College Sngrs, E.H. Warrell *Concert*
        (12/91) (REGE) ① **REGCD106**
Kings College Ch, D. Willcocks *Concert*
        (12/91) (EMI) ① **CDM7 64130-2**
Winchester Cath Ch, D. Hill, T. Byram-Wigfield
  Concert   (10/92) (HYPE) ① **CDA66477**
R. Johnston, Worcester Cath Ch, Don Hunt *Concert*
        (5/93) (ABBE) ① **CDCA943**
Trinity Coll Ch, Cambridge, R. Marlow (r1993)
  Concert   (12/93) (CONI) ① **CDCF216**
Hosanna to the Son of David—full anthem: 6vv
Oxford Christ Church Cath Ch, S. Darlington *Concert*
        (3/89) (NIMB) ① **NI5125**
Oxford Christ Church Cath Ch, S. Preston *Concert*
        (2/90) (GAMU) ① **GOUPCD153**
Salisbury Cath Ch, R. Seal *Concert*
        (11/90) (MERI) ① **CDE84180**
Magdalen Oxford Coll Ch, J. Harper *Concert*
        (11/91) (ABBE) ① **CDCA912**
Kings College Ch, D. Willcocks *Concert*
        (12/91) (EMI) ① **CDM7 64130-2**
Winchester Cath Ch, D. Hill, T. Byram-Wigfield
  Concert   (10/92) (HYPE) ① **CDA66477**
R. Johnston, Worcester Cath Ch, Don Hunt *Concert*
        (5/93) (ABBE) ① **CDCA943**
Trinity Coll Ch, Cambridge, R. Marlow (r1993)
  Concert   (12/93) (CONI) ① **CDCF216**
Truro Cath Ch, D. Briggs, S. Morley (r1992) *Concert*
        (7/94) (PRIO) ① **PRCD429**
If King Manasses—anthem: 6vv and organ
Winchester Cath Ch, D. Hill, T. Byram-Wigfield
  Concert   (10/92) (HYPE) ① **CDA66477**
Laboravi in gemitu meo—motet: 6vv (incomplete)
Winchester Cath Ch, D. Hill, T. Byram-Wigfield
  Concert   (10/92) (HYPE) ① **CDA66477**
Trinity Coll Ch, Cambridge, R. Marlow (r1993)
  Concert   (12/93) (CONI) ① **CDCF216**
Madrigals of Five and Six Parts—viols or voices (pub 1600)
1. A sparrow-hauck proud (6vv); 2. As wanton birds (5vv); 3. Cold winter ice is fled (5vv); 4. Lady the birds right fairley (5vv); 5. Like two proud armies (6vv); 6. Mars in a furie (6vv); 7. Noell, adew thou courtsdelight (6vv); 8. Now let us make a merry greeting (5vv); 9. O care thou wilt dispatch mee (5vv); 10. See where the maides are singing (5vv); 11. Take heere my heart (5vv); 12. Three times a day (5vv); 13. Thule the period of cosmographie (6vv); 14. What have the gods (6vv); 15. When Thoralis delights to walke (6vv); 16. Why are you ladies staying (5vv).
  9, 13. Hilliard Ens, P. Hillier *Concert*
        (2/89) (EMI) ① **CDC7 49197-2**
O happy he—anthem: 5vv
Trinity Coll Ch, Cambridge, R. Marlow (r1993)
  Concert   (12/93) (CONI) ① **CDCF216**
O how amiable are thy dwellings—full anthem: 5vv
Winchester Cath Ch, D. Hill, T. Byram-Wigfield
  Concert   (10/92) (HYPE) ① **CDA66477**
Trinity Coll Ch, Cambridge, R. Marlow (r1993)
  Concert   (12/93) (CONI) ① **CDCF216**
O Jonathan, woe is me—sacred madrigal: 6vv
Winchester Cath Ch, D. Hill, T. Byram-Wigfield
  Concert   (10/92) (HYPE) ① **CDA66477**
Trinity Coll Ch, Cambridge, R. Marlow (r1993)
  Concert   (12/93) (CONI) ① **CDCF216**
O Lord, arise—full anthem: 7vv
Magdalen Oxford Coll Ch, J. Harper *Concert*
        (11/91) (ABBE) ① **CDCA912**
Winchester Cath Ch, D. Hill, T. Byram-Wigfield
  Concert   (10/92) (HYPE) ① **CDA66477**
Trinity Coll Ch, Cambridge, R. Marlow (r1993)
  Concert   (12/93) (CONI) ① **CDCF216**
Llandaff Cath Ch, M. Smith, M. Hoeg (r1994) *Concert*
        (10/95) (PRIO) ① **PRCD510**
O Lord, grant the king a long life—full anthem: 7vv
Oxford Christ Church Cath Ch, S. Darlington *Concert*
        (3/89) (NIMB) ① **NI5125**
Trinity Coll Ch, Cambridge, R. Marlow (r1993)
  Concert   (12/93) (CONI) ① **CDCF216**
Evening Service—5vv
1. Te Deum; 2. Jubilate Deo; 3. Magnificat; 4. Nunc dimittis.
Oxford Christ Church Cath Ch, S. Darlington (ed Wulstan) *Concert* (3/89) (NIMB) ① **NI5125**

Evening **Service for Trebles—5/5vv**
　1. Te Deum; 2. Magnificat; 3. Nunc dimittis.
2, 3. Winchester Cath Ch, D. Hill, T. Byram-Wigfield
　Concert　　　　　　　(10/92) (HYPE) ① **CDA66477**
Evening **Service No. 1—choir and organ**
　Chichester Cath Ch, A. Thurlow, J. Thomas (r1994)
　Concert　　　　　　　(5/95) (PRIO) ① **PRCD511**
Evening **Service No. 6—choir and organ**
　Chichester Cath Ch, A. Thurlow, J. Thomas (r1994)
　Concert　　　　　　　(5/95) (PRIO) ① **PRCD511**
Evening **Service No. 9—7vv**
　1. Magnificat; 2. Nunc dimittis.
　Oxford Christ Church Cath Ch, S. Darlington (ed
　　Wulstan) Concert　　　　　　(3/89) (NIMB) ① **NI5125**
When David heard—sacred madrigal: 6vv
　Oxford Christ Church Cath Ch, S. Darlington Concert
　　　　　　　　　　　　(3/89) (NIMB) ① **NI5125**
　Oxford Christ Church Cath Ch, S. Preston Concert
　　　　　　　　　　　　(2/90) (GAMU) ① **GOUPCD153**
　Winchester Cath Ch, D. Hill, T. Byram-Wigfield
　Concert　・　　　　　(10/92) (HYPE) ① **CDA66477**
　R. Johnston, Worcester Cath Ch, Don Hunt Concert
　　　　　　　　　　　　(5/93) (ABBE) ① **CDCA943**
　Trinity Coll Ch, Cambridge, R. Marlow (r1993)
　Concert　　　　　　　(12/93) (CONI) ① **CDCF216**

WEIGL, Karl (1881–1949)
Austria

SECTION IV: VOCAL AND CHORAL

7 Gesänge—1v and piano, Op. 1
　EXCERPTS: 1. Hiob XIV; 2. Der Einsamste (Wds
　Nietzsche); 3. Der Tag klingt ab (Wds Nietzsche); 4.
　Fragen (Wds Heine); 5. Wanderers Nachtlied (Wds
　Goethe); 6. Ein Gleiches (Wds Goethe); 7. Schmied
　Schmerz (Wds Bierbaum).
　Cpte S. Kimbrough, D. Baldwin (r1990) Concert
　　　　　　　　　　　　(2/95) (SCHW) ① **310942**
Liebeslied—1v and piano (1936) (Wds
　Schell)
　S. Kimbrough, D. Baldwin (r1990) Concert
　　　　　　　　　　　　(2/95) (SCHW) ① **310942**

WEILL, Kurt (Julian) (1900–1950)
Germany/USA

SECTION I: ORCHESTRAL

Concerto for Violin and Wind Orchestra, Op.
12 (1924)
　R. Pellerin, Amor Artis Orch, J. Somary Concert
　　　　　　　　　　　　(12/91) (NEWP) ① **NCD60098**
　W. Wächter, Leipzig RSO, M. Pommer Concert
　　　　　　　　　　　　(8/92) (ONDI) ① **ODE771-2**
　E. Glab, Musique Oblique Ens, P. Herreweghe
　(r1992) Concert　　　(8/93) (HARM) ① **HMC90 1422**
　E. Aadland, Norwegian Wind Ens, O.K. Ruud (r1991)
　Berg: Chamber Concerto.
　　　　　　　　　　　　(8/93) (SIMA) ① **PSC1090**
　St Luke's Orch, J. Rudel, N. Tanaka Kleine
　Dreigroschenmusik.　　(2/94) (MUSM) ① **67007-2**
　C. Tetzlaff, Deutsche Kammerphilharmonie Concert
　　　　　　　　　　　　(7/95) (VIRG) ① **VC5 45056-2**
Kleine Dreigroschenmusik—concert suite
from opera: wind instruments (1928-29)
　1. Overture; 2. Die Moritat von Mackie Messer; 3.
　Anstatt-dass-Song; 4. Die Ballade vom angenehmen
　Leben; 5. Polly Lied; 6. Tango-Ballade; 7. Kanonen-
　Lied; 8. Dreigroschen-Finale.
　Berlin St Op Orch, O. Klemperer (r1931) Concert
　　　　　　　　　　　　(2/89) (SYMP) ① **SYMCD1042**
　LSO, M. Tilson Thomas Sieben Todsünden.
　　　　　　　　　　　　(3/89) (SONY) ① **MK44529**
　Chicago Pro Musica Concert
　　　　　　　　　　　　(8/89) (REFE) ① **RRCD-29**
　Amor Artis Orch, J. Somary Concert
　　　　　　　　　　　　(12/91) (NEWP) ① **NCD60098**
　Leipzig RSO, M. Pommer Concert
　　　　　　　　　　　　(8/92) (ONDI) ① **ODE771-2**
　St Luke's Orch, J. Rudel Violin Concerto.
　　　　　　　　　　　　(2/94) (MUSM) ① **67007-2**
2, 4, 6, 7. Berlin St Op Orch, O. Klemperer (r1931)
　　　　　　　　　　　　(11/91) (KOCH) ① **37053-2**
Symphony No. 1 (1921)
　Cracow PO, R. Bader Symphony 2.
　　　　　　　　　　　　(10/91) (SCHW) ① **311147**
Symphony No. 2 (1933-34)
　Cracow PO, R. Bader Symphony 1.
　　　　　　　　　　　　(10/91) (SCHW) ① **311147**

SECTION II: CHAMBER

String Quartet (1923)
　Brandis Qt (r1992) Concert
　　　　　　　　　　　　(3/95) (NIMB) ① **NI5410**

SECTION IV: VOCAL AND CHORAL

Der **Abschiedsbrief—song (1933)** (Wds. E.
　Kästner)
　A.S. von Otter, B. Forsberg Concert
　　　　　　　　　　　　(12/94) (DG) ① **439 894-2GH**
At **Potsdam—song (1927)** (Wds. Brecht)
　Düsseldorf Evangelist Church Students' Ch, Helmut
　Schmidt (pp1990) Concert
　　　　　　　　　　　　(4/92) (SCHW) ① **314050**
Berlin im Licht—song: voice and piano
(1928) (Wds. cpsr: also march for military
　band)
　A. Réaux, R. Kapilow Concert
　　　　　　　　　　　　(6/92) (KOCH) ① [2] **37087-2**
　W. Sharp, S. Blier (r1991) Concert
　　　　　　　　　　　　(7/93) (KOCH) ① **37086-2**
　B. Fassbaender, C. Garben (r1993) Concert
　　　　　　　　　　　　(12/93) (HARM) ① **HMC90 1420**
Das **Berliner Requiem—tenor, baritone,**
male chorus and wind orchestra (1928)
　1. Grosser Dankchoral: Lobet die Nacht (chorus); 2.
　Ballade vom ertrunkenen Mädchen (trio/chorus); 3.
　Marterl: Hier ruht die Jungfrau Johanna Back (tenor,
　chorus); 3a. Grabschrift 1919 (tenor, chorus:
　alternative to No 3); 4. Erster Bericht: Wir kamen von
　den Gebirgen (tenor, chorus); 5. Zweiter Bericht:
　Alles, was ich euch sagte (baritone, chorus); 6. Zu
　Potsdam unter den Eichen (trio); 7. Können einem
　toten Mann nicht helfen (trio).
　J. Wagner, W. Holzmair, Lower Rhine Community
　Ch, R. Schumann CO, Düsseldorf SO Wind Ens,
　Helmut Schmidt (pp1990) Concert
　　　　　　　　　　　　(4/92) (SCHW) ① **314050**
　A. Laiter, P. Kooy, Paris Chapelle Royale Chor,
　Musique Oblique Ens, P. Herreweghe (r1992)
　Concert　　　　　　　(8/93) (HARM) ① **HMC90 1422**
2, 6. G. May, W. Eberhardt, H. Dittmann, W. Dersch,
　M. Schmieder, G. Sonsalla, S. Lotz, Studio Orch, H.
　Krtschil Concert　　　(8/89) (CAPR) ① **10 180**
3. C. Farley, R. Vignoles Concert
　　　　　　　　　　　　(6/92) (ASV) ① **CDDCA790**
3. A. Réaux, R. Kapilow Concert
　　　　　　　　　　　　(6/92) (KOCH) ① [2] **37087-2**
6. U. Lemper, Berlin Rad Ens, J. Mauceri (arr. Hazell)
　Concert　　　　　　　(3/89) (DECC) ① **425 204-2DNL**
Come up from the fields, Father—song:
voice and piano (1947) (Wds. W. Whitman)
　S. Kimbrough, D. Baldwin Concert
　　　　　　　　　　　　(11/88) (ARAB) ① **Z6579**
Complainte de la Seine—song (1934) (Wds.
　M. Magre)
　B. Fassbaender, C. Garben (r1993) Concert
　　　　　　　　　　　　(12/93) (HARM) ① **HMC90 1420**
Divertimento—small orchestra with male
chorus, Op. 5 (1921-2)
　1. Fantasia; 2. (Ostinato); 3. Aria; 4. (Waltz); 5.
　Scherzo; 6. Chorale-Fantasy: Herr Gott dein Zorn tu
　um uns wenden.
　6. Poznań Op Chor, Poznań PO, A. Borejko (r1994)
　Concert　　　　(7/95) (LARG) ① [2] **Largo5130**
Es regnet—song (1933) (Wds. after J.
　Cocteau)
　B. Fassbaender, C. Garben (r1993) Concert
　　　　　　　　　　　　(12/93) (HARM) ① **HMC90 1420**
Im Volkston, '(Das) Scheiden, ach das
Scheiden'—song: voice and piano (1916)
　(Wds. A. Holz)
　S. Kimbrough, D. Baldwin Concert
　　　　　　　　　　　　(11/88) (ARAB) ① **Z6579**
Je ne t'aime pas—song: voice and piano
(1934) (Wds. M. Magre)
　U. Lemper, K. Rautenberg Concert
　　　　　　　　　　　　(3/89) (DECC) ① **425 204-2DNL**
　A. Réaux, R. Kapilow Concert
　　　　　　　　　　　　(6/92) (KOCH) ① [2] **37087-2**
　A.S. von Otter, B. Forsberg Concert
　　　　　　　　　　　　(12/94) (DG) ① **439 894-2GH**
Kiddush—Hebrew prayer (T, SATB and
organ) (1946)
　G. Hirst, Amor Artis Chorale, R. Pellerin, J. Somary
　Concert　　　　　　　(12/91) (NEWP) ① **NCD60098**
　J. Wagner, Lower Rhine Community Ch, A. Ruus, M-
　A. Schlingensiepen (pp1990) Concert
　　　　　　　　　　　　(4/92) (SCHW) ① **314050**
Die **Legende vom toten Soldaten—chorus**
(1929) (Wds. B. Brecht)
　Lower Rhine Community Ch, Helmut Schmidt
　(pp1990) Concert　　(4/92) (SCHW) ① **314050**
Nannas Lied, 'Meine Herren, mit Siebzehn
Jahren'—song: voice and piano (1939) (Wds.
　B. Brecht)
　U. Lemper, K. Rautenberg Concert
　　　　　　　　　　　　(3/89) (DECC) ① **425 204-2DNL**

　A. Réaux, R. Kapilow Concert
　　　　　　　　　　　　(6/92) (KOCH) ① [2] **37087-2**
　B. Fassbaender, C. Garben (r1993) Concert
　　　　　　　　　　　　(12/93) (HARM) ① **HMC90 1420**
　A.S. von Otter, B. Forsberg Concert
　　　　　　　　　　　　(12/94) (DG) ① **439 894-2GH**
Ofrah's Lieder—song cycle: 1v and piano
(1916) (Wds. J. Halevi, trans modern German)
　1. In meinem Garten steh'n zwei Rosen; 2. Nichts ist
　die Welt mir'; 3. Er sah mir liebend in die Augen; 4.
　Denkst du des kühnen Flugs der Nacht; 5. Nur dir,
　fürwahr, mein stolzer Aar.
　Cpte C. Sieden, S. Blier (r1991) Concert
　　　　　　　　　　　　(7/93) (KOCH) ① **37086-2**
9 Propaganda Songs (1942) (Wds. various)
　1. Song of the Free (wds. A. McLeish); 2.
　Schickelgruber (wds. H. Dietz); 3. On Morning in
　Spring (wds. St. Clair McKelway: now lost); 4. The
　Good Earth (wds. O. Hammerstein); 5. Buddy on the
　Nightshift (wds. L. Allan); 7. We don't feel
　surrendering today (wds. M. Anderson); 8. On Uncle
　Samuel (wds. M. Anderson: melody by Henry C.
　Work); 9. Toughen up, buckle down, carry on (wds.
　D. Fields).
　1. S. Kimbrough, D. Baldwin Concert
　　　　　　　　　　　　(11/88) (ARAB) ① **Z6579**
　2, 5. A.S. von Otter, B. Forsberg Concert
　　　　　　　　　　　　(12/94) (DG) ① **439 894-2GH**
Recordare—4-part chorus, children's chorus
(a capella), Op. 11 (1923) (Wds. Bible:
　Lamentations of Jeremiah)
　Lower Rhine Community Ch, Hanover Girls' Ch,
　Helmut Schmidt (pp1990) Concert
　　　　　　　　　　　　(4/92) (SCHW) ① **314050**
Reiterlied—Lied (1914) (Wds. H. Löns)
　C. Farley, R. Vignoles Concert
　　　　　　　　　　　　(6/92) (ASV) ① **CDDCA790**
Das **Schöne Kind—song: voice and piano**
(1917) (Wds. Anon)
　S. Kimbrough, D. Baldwin Concert
　　　　　　　　　　　　(11/88) (ARAB) ① **Z6579**
　C. Farley, R. Vignoles Concert
　　　　　　　　　　　　(6/92) (ASV) ① **CDDCA790**
Stundenbuch—song cycle: baritone and
orchestra, Op. 13 (1923-24) (Wds. R. M.
　Rilke)
　1. Vielleicht, dass ich durche schwere; 2. Mach mich
　zum Wächter deiner Weiten; 3. Manchmal steht ein
　Mann steht beim Abendrot; 4. Bei Tag bist du das
　Hörensagen; 5. Lösch mir die Augen aus; 6. In
　deinem Dorfe steht das letzte Haus.
　1, 2, 6. S. Kimbrough, D. Baldwin Concert
　　　　　　　　　　　　(11/88) (ARAB) ① **Z6579**
Vom Tod im Wald—bass and 10 wind
instruments, Op. 23 (1927) (Wds. B. Brecht)
　W. Wächter, Leipzig RSO, M. Pommer Concert
　　　　　　　　　　　　(8/92) (ONDI) ① **ODE771-2**
　P. Kooy, Musique Oblique Ens, P. Herreweghe
　(r1992) Concert　　　(8/93) (HARM) ① **HMC90 1422**
4 Walt Whitman Songs—voice and
piano/orchestra (1942) (Wds. W. Whitman)
　1. Oh! Captain, My Captain; 2. Beat! Beat! Drums; 3.
　Dirge for Two Veterans; 4. Come up from the fields
　father.
　Cpte S. Kimbrough, D. Baldwin Concert
　　　　　　　　　　　　(11/88) (ARAB) ① **Z6579**
　W. Holzmair, R. Schumann CO, M-A.
　Schlingensiepen (pp1990) Concert
　　　　　　　　　　　　(4/92) (SCHW) ① **314050**
Wie lange noch?—song: voice and piano
(1944) (Wds. W. Mehring)
　B. Fassbaender, C. Garben (r1993) Concert
　　　　　　　　　　　　(12/93) (HARM) ① **HMC90 1420**
Workers' Choruses—4vv a cappella (1929)
　1. Zu Potsdam unter den Eichen (Wds. Brecht; arr
　from Berliner Requiem); 2. Die Legende vom toten
　Soldaten.
　1. BBC Sym Chor, S. Jackson (r1994) Concert
　　　　　　　　　　　　(7/95) (LARG) ① [2] **Largo5130**
Youkali—vocal version of Tango from 'Marie
Galante' (1934 pub 1946) (Wds. Fernay)
　A. Réaux, R. Kapilow Concert
　　　　　　　　　　　　(6/92) (KOCH) ① [2] **37087-2**
　U. Lemper, Berlin RIAS Sinfonietta, J. Mauceri
　(r1991-2; orch Hazell) Concert
　　　　　　　　　　　　(7/93) (DECC) ① **436 417-2DH**
　B. Fassbaender, C. Garben (r1993) Concert
　　　　　　　　　　　　(12/93) (HARM) ① **HMC90 1420**

SECTION V: STAGE WORKS

Aufstieg und Fall der Stadt Mahagonny, 'Rise and Fall of the City of Mahagonny'—opera: 3 acts (1930—Leipzig) (Lib. B Brecht & cpsr)

1a. Prelude. ACT 1: 1b. Melodrama (Fatty, Moses, Begbick); 1c. Darum lasst uns hier eine Stadt gründen (Begbick); 1d. Sie soll sein wie ein Netz (Begbick); 1e. Aber dieses ganze Mahgonny (Begbick, Fatty, Moses); 2. Alabama Song (Jenny, girls); 3a. Wir wohnen in den Städchen (chorus); 3b. Fern vom Getriebe der Welt (Fatty, Moses); 4. Auf nach Mahagonny (Jim, Jack, Bill, Joe); 5a. Wenn man an einem fremden Strand kommt (Jim, Jack, Bill, Joe); 5b. Ach, meine Herren, willkommen zu Hause (Begbick); 5c. Heraus, ihr Schönen von Mahagonny (Jim, Jack, Bill, Joe, Jenny, girls); 5d. Ach bedenken Sie, Herr Jack O'Brien (Jenny); 5e. Ich kenn' die Jimmys aus Alaska schon (Jenny, Jim, ensemble); 6a. Ich habe gelernt (jenny, Jim); 6b. Bitte, Jenny (Jenny, Jim); 7a. Ach deises ganze Mahagonny (Begbick, Fatty, Moses); 7b. Auch ich bein einmal Mauer gestanden (Begbick); 8a. Melodrama (Jim, Jack, Bill, Joe); 8b. Wunderbar ist das Heraufkommen des Abends (Jack, Bill, Joe); 8c. Ich glaube, ich will meinen Hut aufess'n (Jim); 9a. The Maiden's Prayer (piano solo); 9b. Tief in Alaskas schneeweissen Wäldern (Jim); 9c. Sieben Jahre (Jim, full ensemble); 10a. Fugato (orchestra); 10b. Oh furchtbares Ereignis (ensemble, chorus); 10c. Ach mit eurem ganzen Mahagonny (Jim); 11a. Haltet euch aufrecht (male chorus); 11b. On Moon of Alabama (Jenny, girls): Es nutzt nichts (Jake); 11c. Siehst du, so ist die Welt (Jim); 11d. Wenn es etwas gibt, das du haben kannst für Geld (Jim); 11e. Zerstört ist Pensacola (Fatty, Begbick, Jim, ensemble); 11f. Denn wie man sich bettet, so liegt man (Jim, full ensemble).

Cpte A. Silja, W. Neumann, K. Hirte, A. Schlemm, T. Lehrberger, F. Mayer, H. Franzen, P. Wolfrum, F. Mayer, Cologne Pro Musica, Cologne RSO, J. Latham-König (8/88) (CAPR) Ⓓ [2] **10 160/1**

Cpte L. Lenya, H. Sauerbaum, H. Günter, G. Litz, P. Markwort, F. Göllnitz, S. Roth, G. Mund, F. Göllnitz, NW German Rad Chor, NW German RO, W. Brückner-Rüggeberg (8/88) (SONY) Ⓓ [2] **M2K77341**

2. A. Réaux, R. Kapilow *Concert* (6/92) (KOCH) Ⓓ [2] **37087-2**

2, 19l U. Lemper, Berlin Rad Ens, J. Mauceri *Concert* (3/89) (DECC) Ⓓ **425 204-2DNL**

2, 5a-e, 11f G. May, Studio Orch, H. Krtschil *Concert* (8/89) (CAPR) Ⓓ **10 180**

2, 5d, 11f C. Farley, R. Vignoles *Concert* (6/92) (ASV) Ⓓ **CDDCA790**

Down in the Valley—folk opera: 1 act (1948—Indiana) (Lib. A. Sundgaard)

Cpte I. Davidson, M. Acito, D. Collup, J. Mabry, D.P. Lang, Fredonia Chbr Sngrs, Dortmund Univ Chbr Ch, Buffalo College Wind Plyrs, Westphalia CO, W. Gundlach *Jasager.* (4/92) (CAPR) Ⓓ **60 020-1**

Der **Dreigroschenoper, '(The) Threepenny Opera'—play with music: 3 acts (1928—Berlin)** (Lib. B. Brecht, after Gay's 'The Beggars's Opera')

EXCERPTS: 1. Overture. PROLOGUE: 2. Moritat vom Mackie Messer (Eng: Ballad of Mack the Knife). ACT 1: 3. Morgenchoral des Peachum; 4. Anstatt-dass-Song (Mr and Mrs Peachum); 5. Hochzeitslied (chorus); 6. Seeräuberjenny (Polly); 7. Kanonen Song (Macheath, Brown); 8. Liebeslied (Polly, Macheath); 9. Barbara Song (Polly); 10. Erste Dreigroschenfinale (Polly, Peachum, Mrs Peachum). ACT 2: 11a. Hübsch als es wärhte—Melodrama (Macheath); 11b. Polly's Lied; 12. Ballade von der sexuellen Hörigkeit (Mrs Peachum); 13. Zuhälterballade (Macheath, Jenny); 14. Ballade vom angenehmen Leben (Macheath); 15. Eifersuchtsduett (Lucy, Polly); 16. Zweite Dreigroschenfinale (Macheath. Mrs Peachum and chorus). ACT 3: 17. Lied von der Unzulänglichkeit menschlichen Strebens; 18. Salomon Song (Jenny); 19. Ruf aus der Gruft (Macheath); 20a. Grabschrift (Macheath); 20b. Gang zum Galgen (orchestra); 21. Dritte Dreigroschenoperfinale.

Cpte L. Lenya, E. Schellow, W. Trenk-Trebitsch, T. Hesterburg, J. von Kóczián, W. Grunert, I. Wolffberg, W. Neuss, K. Hellwig, P-O. Kuster, J. Hausmann, M. Hoeppner, Günther Arndt Ch, Radio Free Berlin Dance Orch, W. Brückner-Rüggeberg (r1958) (3/89) (SONY) Ⓓ **MK42637**

Cpte R. Kollo, U. Lemper, Milva, M. Adorf, H. Dernesch, W. Reichmann, S. Tremper, R. Boysen, Berlin RIAS Chbr Ch, Berlin RIAS Sinfonietta, J. Mauceri (3/90) (DECC) Ⓓ **430 075-2DH**

Cpte A. Shoumanova, M. Jung, H. Becht, A. Herrmann, S. Myszak, E. Demerdjiev, N. Afeyan, W. Kmentt, Bulgarian TV & Rad Mixed Chor, Bulgarian TV & Rad SO, V.C. Symonette (2/91) (KOCH) Ⓓ **37006-2**

1, 12, 18. U. Lemper, W. Meyer, Berlin Rad Ens, J. Mauceri *Concert* (3/89) (DECC) Ⓓ **425 204-2DNL**

1, 2, 4, 7, 11b, 13, 14. Tetra (r1989-91; arr Goss: gtr qt) *Concert* (11/93) (CONI) Ⓓ **CDCF903**

2. J. Heifetz, E. Bay (r1945) *Concert* (11/94) (RCA) Ⓓ [65] **09026 61778-2(19)**

2, 6, 9, 12, 17, 18. G. May, M. Samko, Studio Orch, H. Krtschil *Concert* (8/89) (CAPR) Ⓓ **10 180**

9, 18. A. Réaux, R. Kapilow *Concert* (6/92) (KOCH) Ⓓ [2] **37087-2**

11a, 12. C. Farley, R. Vignoles *Concert* (6/92) (ASV) Ⓓ **CDDCA790**

12. C. Berberian, Juilliard Ens, L. Berio (r1968; arr Berio) *Concert* (7/95) (RCA) Ⓓ **09026 62540-2**

Firebrand of Florence—operetta: 2 acts (1945—Boston) (Book E J Mayer, lyrics I Gershwin)

1. Prelude. ACT 1: 2. The bell of doom is clanging (Hangman, assistants); 2b. Come to Florence (Hangman, chorus); 2c. Life, Love, and Laughter (Cellini, chorus); 3. Our Master is Free Again (Emilia, Ascanio); 4. I had just been pardoned (Cellini); 5. You're far too near me (Cellini, Angela); 6. Alessandro the Wise (Duke, chorus); 7. Finaletto (Angela, Emilia, Ottavino, Cellini, Duke, chorus); 8. Duchess's Entrance (Blackamoor); 9. Sing Me Not a Ballad (Duchess, courtiers); 10. When the Duchess is Away (Captain of the Guard, Duke, Emilia, chorus); 11. Life, Love, and Laughter (Angela, Cellini); 12. The Nozy Cook (Angela, Duke, Cellini); 13. Finale alla Tarantella (Emilia, Angela, Duke, Duchess, Cellini); 14. The Duchess's Letter (Cellini); 15. The Little Naked Boy (Angela and models); 16. We're Soldiers of the Duchy (Just in Case—March chorus); 17. A Rhyme for Angela (Duke, Poets, Ladies-in-Waiting); 18. Procession; 19. Love is my Enemy (Cellini, Angela); 19a. Hear Ye! Hear Ye! (Clerk); 19b. The World is Full of Villains (three judges); 19c. You Have to Do What You Do Do (Cellini, Duke, chorus); 19d. How wonderfully fortunate (Angela); 19e. Love is my Enemy (Cellini, Angela); 20. Come to Paris (Marquis, two girls, chorus); 21. Finale; 21a. Sarabande (orch version of 19e); 21b. Come to Florence (full company).

9. A. Réaux, R. Kapilow *Concert* (6/92) (KOCH) Ⓓ [2] **37087-2**

Happy End—comedy with music: 3 acts (1929—Berlin) (Book E Hauptmann, wds. B Brecht)

1. Bilbao Song (Bill); 2. Der kleine Leutnant des lieben Gottes (Lilian); 3. Heilsarmeelied I (Lilian, Salvationists); 4. Matrosen-Tango (Lilian); 5. Heilsarmeelied II—Bruder, gib dir einem Stoss; 6. Heilsarmeelied III—Fürchte dich nicht; 7. Heilsarmeelied IV—In der Jugend gold'nem Schimmer; 8. Das Lied vom Branntweinhändler (Hannibal Jackson); 9. Mandelay Song (Sam Worlitzer); 10. Surabaya-Johnny (Lilian); 11. Das Lied von der harten Nuss (Bill); 12. Die Ballade von der Höllen-Lili (Lady in Grey); 13. Hosianna Rockefeller (full cast).

Cpte W. Raffeiner, S. Kimbrough, G. Ramm, K. Ploog, Cologne Pro Musica, König Ens, J. Latham-König (9/90) (CAPR) Ⓓ **60 015-1**

Cpte L. Lenya, chor, orch, W. Brückner-Rüggeberg *Sieben Todsünden.* (4/91) (SONY) Ⓓ **MPK45886**

1, 10, 11. A.S. von Otter, N German RSO, J.E. Gardiner *Concert* (12/94) (DG) Ⓓ **439 894-2GH**

1, 4, 8, 9, 10. U. Lemper, J. Cohen, Berlin RIAS Sinfonietta, J. Mauceri (r1991-2) *Concert* (7/93) (DECC) Ⓓ **436 417-2DH**

1, 4, 9, 10, 11, 12. G. May, Studio Orch, H. Krtschil *Concert* (8/89) (CAPR) Ⓓ **10 180**

4, 6, 7, 12. C. Farley, R. Vignoles *Concert* (6/92) (ASV) Ⓓ **CDDCA790**

10. C. Berberian, B. Canino *Concert* (7/89) (WERG) Ⓓ **WER60054-50**

10. C. Berberian, Juilliard Ens, L. Berio (r1968; arr Berio) *Concert* (7/95) (RCA) Ⓓ **09026 62540-2**

10, 11. A. Réaux, R. Kapilow *Concert* (6/92) (KOCH) Ⓓ [2] **37087-2**

Huckleberry Finn—musical play (unfinished) (1950) (Books and lyrics M. Anderson, after M. Twain)

1. River Chantry; 2. Come, in Morning (Come in, Sun); 3. Apple Jack; 4. This time next year; 5. Catfish Song.

1. S. Kimbrough, D. Baldwin *Concert* (11/88) (ARAB) Ⓓ **Z6579**

4. C. Farley, R. Vignoles *Concert* (6/92) (ASV) Ⓓ **CDDCA790**

Der **Jasager—school opera: 2 acts (1930—Berlin)** (Lib. B. Brecht)

Cpte T. Schmeisser, H. Helling, U. Schütte, T. Bräutigam, T. Fischer, M. Knöppel, Fredonia Chbr Sngrs, Dortmund Univ Chbr Ch, Buffalo College Wind Plyrs, Westphalia CO, W. Gundlach *Down in the Valley.* (4/92) (CAPR) Ⓓ **60 020-1**

Knickerbocker Holiday—musical play: 2 acts (1938—New York) (Book and lyrics M. Anderson)

6. It never was you (Brom, Tina); 15. September Song (Stuyvesant).

2. K. Colson, London Sinfonietta, J. McGlinn *Concert* (8/93) (EMI) Ⓓ **CDC7 54586-2**

6. J. Gomez, J. Constable *Concert* (6/88) (UNIC) Ⓓ **DKPCD9055**

6. A. Réaux, R. Kapilow *Concert* (6/92) (KOCH) Ⓓ [2] **37087-2**

15. J. Norman, J.T. Williams (r1987) *Concert* (4/92) (PHIL) Ⓓ **422 401-2PH**

15. R. Merrill, NY Met Op Orch, J. Conlon (pp1991) *Concert* (6/93) (RCA) Ⓓ **09026 61509-2**

15. E. Pinza, Johnny Green Orch, J. Green (r1950) *Concert* (9/93) (RCA) Ⓓ **09026 61245-2**

Konjunktur—music for Leo Lania's play (1928—Berlin) (song texts F. Gasbarra)

1. Anfang (opening); 2. Landungsbrücke (Jetty); 3. Kleiner Marsch; 4. Oelblase (oil bubble); 5. Petroleum-musik; 6. Arbeitsrhythmus (work rhythm); 7. Arbeiterlied: first version (Work song); 8. Arbeiterlied: second version (Work song); 9. Die Muschel von Margate (Mussel song).

9. C. Sieden, S. Blier (r1991) *Concert* (7/93) (KOCH) Ⓓ **37086-2**

Der **Kuhhandel—operetta: 2 acts (1934)** (Lib. R Vambery: incomplete)

Excs L. Peacock, E. Büchner, C. Schotenröhr, W. Raffeiner, U. Holdorf, O. Hillebrandt, D. Niemirowicz, I. Most, F. Mayer, R. Zimmermann, R. Röttger, F. Gerihsen, H. Heidbüchel, J. Wagner, Cologne Rad Chor, Cologne RSO, J. Latham-König (1/93) (CAPR) Ⓓ **60 013**

Lady in the Dark—musical play: 2 acts (1940—Boston) (Book M. Hart, lyrics I. Gershwin)

3. One Life to Live (Liza, Beckmann); 13. The Saga of Jenny (Liza); 17. My Ship.

3, 13, 17. U. Lemper, J. Cohen, London Voices, Berlin RIAS Sinfonietta, J. Mauceri (r1991-2) *Concert* (7/93) (DECC) Ⓓ **436 417-2DH**

3, 17. A.S. von Otter, N German RSO, J.E. Gardiner *Concert* (12/94) (DG) Ⓓ **439 894-2GH**

13. C. Farley, R. Vignoles *Concert* (6/92) (ASV) Ⓓ **CDDCA790**

13. K. Criswell, Ambrosian Sngrs, London Sinfonietta, J. McGlinn (r1992) *Concert* (4/94) (EMI) Ⓓ **CDC7 54802-2**

13, 17. D. Upshaw, orch, E. Stern (r1993: orch L Wilcox & D Troob arr E Stern) *Concert* (12/94) (NONE) Ⓓ **7559-79345-2**

17. J. Gomez, J. Constable *Concert* (6/88) (UNIC) Ⓓ **DKPCD9055**

17. J. Norman, J.T. Williams (r1987) *Concert* (4/92) (PHIL) Ⓓ **422 401-2PH**

17. A. Réaux, R. Kapilow *Concert* (6/92) (KOCH) Ⓓ [2] **37087-2**

Lost in the Stars—musical tragedy (1949—New York) (Book and lyrics M. Anderson)

EXCERPTS: 1. The Hills of Ixopo; 2. Thousand of Miles; 2a. The Little Tin God (replaced in final version); 3. Train to Johannesburg; 4. The Search; 5. The Little Gray House; 6. Who'll buy?; 7. Gold; 8. Trouble Man (Irina); 9. Murder in Parkworld; 10. Fear!; 11. The Shadowy Glass; 12. Lost in the Stars (Stephen, chorus); 13. Entr'acte; 14. The Wild Justice; 15. O Trixo, Help Me; 16. Stay Well; 17. Cry the Beloved Country; 18. Big Mole; 19. A Bird of Passage; 20. Four o'clock; 21. Finale: Thousands of Miles (reprise).

Cpte G. Hopkins, A. Woodley, R. Pindell, C. Clarey, C. Woods, J. Howard, R. Vogt, NY Concert Chorale, St Luke's Orch, J. Rudel (r1992) (11/93) (MUSM) Ⓓ **67100-2**

16. D. Upshaw, orch, E. Stern (r1993: orch L Wilcox) *Concert* (12/94) (NONE) Ⓓ **7559-79345-2**

Love Life—vaudeville: 2 parts (1948—Boston) (Book & lyrics A J Lerner)

7b. Green-up Time (Susan, women); 22. Is it him or is it me? (Susan); 25. This is the life.

22. C. Farley, R. Vignoles *Concert* (6/92) (ASV) Ⓓ **CDDCA790**

22. A. Réaux, R. Kapilow *Concert* (6/92) (KOCH) Ⓓ [2] **37087-2**

25. S. Kimbrough, D. Baldwin *Concert* (11/88) (ARAB) Ⓓ **Z6579**

Mahagonny-Gesänge—Songspiel: 3 parts (1927—Baden-Baden) (Lib. B Brecht)
1. Auf nach Mahagonny; 2. Kleiner Marsch (orchestra); 3. Alabama Song; 4. Vivace (orchestra); 5. Wer in Mahagonny blieb; 6. Vivace assai (orchestra); 7. Benares Song; 8. Choral (orchestra); 9. Gott in Mahagonny; 10. Finale: Dieses ganze Mahagonny.
Cpte U. Lemper, H. Wildhaber, P. Haage, T. Mohr, M. Jungwirth, S. Tremper, Berlin RIAS Sinfonietta, J. Mauceri (r1989) *Sieben Todsünden.*
(4/91) (DECC) ① **430 168-2DH**
Cpte T. Schmidt, G. Ramm, H. Hiestermann, P.N. Kante, W. Raffeiner, H. Franzen, König Ens, J. Latham-König (r1991) *Sieben Todsünden.*
(12/93) (CAPR) ① **60 028**
Marie Galante—incidental music to Deval's play (1934—Paris)
1. Introduction; 2a. Les filles de Bordeaux (Mamouille); 2b. Les filles de Bordeaux (chorus); 3a. Intermezzo (orchestra); 3b. Je ne suis pas un ange (male chorus); 4. Marche de l'armée panaméenne; 5a. Introduction, Scène 3 (orchestra); 5b. Scéne au Dancing (orchestra); 6. Tango (orchestra); 7. J'attends un navire (Josiah, Marie); 8a. Complainte (orchestra); 8b. L'arreglo religioso (Mercédès, Soledad); 9. Tengo quantince ce años (Soleadad); 10. Le roi d'Aquitaine (Marie); 11. Choeur nègre (chorus); 12. Train du ciel (chorus); 13. Yo le dije al caporal (Staub); 14. Le Grand Lustucru (Maria); 15. Reprise of No. 7.
2a, 7, 10, 12, 14. U. Lemper, J. Cohen, Berlin RIAS Sinfonietta, J. Mauceri (r1991-2) *Concert*
(7/93) (DECC) ① **436 417-2DH**
2a, 7, 10, 14. J. Gomez, J. Constable *Concert*
(6/88) (UNIC) ① **DKPCD9055**
7, 12. A. Réaux, R. Kapilow *Concert*
(6/92) (KOCH) ① [2] **37087-2**
14. C. Berberian, Juilliard Ens, L. Berio (r1968; arr Berio) *Concert* (7/95) (RCA) ① **09026 62540-2**
One Touch of Venus—musical comedy: 2 acts (1943—Boston) (Book S. J. Perelman and O. Nash: lyrics Nash)
1. Overture. ACT 1: 5. I'm a stranger here myself (Venus); 7. West Wind (Savory); 9. Foolish Heart (Venus); 11. Speak Low (Venus, Rodney); 17. That's him (Venus).
5, 17. A. Réaux, R. Kapilow *Concert*
(6/92) (KOCH) ① [2] **37087-2**
5, 7, 11. U. Lemper, Berlin Rad Ens, J. Mauceri *Concert* (3/89) (DECC) ① **425 204-2DNL**
5, 9, 11. A.S. von Otter, N German RSO, J.E. Gardiner *Concert* (12/94) (DG) ① **439 894-2GH**
9, 11, 17. C. Farley, R. Vignoles *Concert*
(6/92) (ASV) ① **CDDCA790**
11. J. Norman, J.T. Williams (r1987) *Concert*
(4/92) (PHIL) ① **422 401-2PH**
17. D. Upshaw, E. Stern (r1993: orch E Stern) *Concert* (1/94) (NONE) ① **7559-79345-2**
Die Sieben Todsünden, '(The) Seven Deadly Sins'—spectacle: 9 scenes (1933—Paris) (Wds. B. Brecht)
1a. Introduction: Meine Schwester und ich stammen aus Louisiana; 1b. Faulheit (Sloth): Müssiggang ist aller Laster Anfang; 2. Stolz (Pride): Als wir aber ausgestattet waren; 3. Zorn (Anger): Das gebt nicht vorwärts; 4. Völlerei (Gluttony): Das ist ein Brief aus Philadelphia; 5. Unzucht (Lechery): Und wir fanden einen Mann; 6. Habsucht (Avarice): Wie hier in der Zeitung steht; 7a. Neid (Envy): Und die letzte Stadt; 7b. Finaletto: Darauf kehrten wir zurück nach Louisiana.
Cpte J. Migenes, R. Tear, S. Kale, A. Opie, R. Kennedy, LSO, M. Tilson Thomas (arr Brückner-Rüggeberg) *Kleine Dreigroschenmusik.*
(3/89) (SONY) ① **MK44529**
Cpte L. Lenya, male qt, orch, W. Brückner-Rüggeberg (r1956) *Happy End.*
(4/91) (SONY) ① **MPK45886**
Cpte U. Lemper, H. Wildhaber, P. Haage, T. Mohr, M. Jungwirth, Berlin RIAS Sinfonietta, J. Mauceri (r1989) *Mahagonny-Gesänge.*
(4/91) (DECC) ① **430 168-2DH**
Cpte B. Fassbaender, K-H. Brandt, H. Sojer, H. Komatsu, I. Urbas, Hanover Rad PO, C. Garben (r1992) *Concert* (12/93) (HARM) ① **HMC90 1420**
Cpte D. Bierett, D. Ellenbeck, K. Markus, C. Feller, M. Smith, Cologne RSO, L. Zagrosek (r1978) *Mahagonny-Gesänge.* (12/93) (CAPR) ① **60 028**
Cpte A. Réaux, Hudson Shad, NYPO, K. Masur *Berg: Lulu—Symphonie.*
(12/94) (TELD) ① **4509-95029-2**
Cpte A.S. von Otter, N German RSO, J.E. Gardiner *Concert* (12/94) (DG) ① **439 894-2GH**

E. Ross, A. Rolfe Johnson, I. Caley, M. Rippon, J. Tomlinson, CBSO, S. Rattle (r1982) *Stravinsky: Pulcinella.* (12/93) (EMI) ① **CDM7 64739-2**
Der Silbersee—musical play: 3 acts (1933—Leipzig, Magdeburg, Erfurt)
6. Was zahlen Sie für einen Rat? (Lottery Agent); 8. Ich bin eine arme Verwandte (Fennimore's Song); 9. Rom hiess eine Stadt (Ballad of Caesar's Death—Fennimore).
Cpte W. Schmidt, H. Heichele, H. Korte, E. Tamassy, U. Holdorf, F. Mayer, Cologne Pro Musica, Cologne RSO, J. Latham-König
(8/90) (CAPR) ① [2] **60 011-2**
6, 8, 9. U. Lemper, Berlin Rad Ens, J. Mauceri *Concert* (3/89) (DECC) ① **425 204-2DNL**
8. A. Réaux, R. Kapilow *Concert*
(6/92) (KOCH) ① [2] **37087-2**
9. W. Sharp, S. Blier (r1991) *Concert*
(7/93) (KOCH) ① **37086-2**
Street Scene—American opera: 2 acts (1946—Philadelphia) (Book E. Rice, lyrics L. Hughes)
ACT 1: 7. Ice-Cream Sextet; 10. Lonely house (Sam); 12. What good would the moon be? (Rose). ACT 2: 14. Remember that I care (Sam and Rose); 17. A Boy Like You (Mrs Maurrant).
7. M. O'Flynn, P. Pancella, J. Hadley, P. Groves, Daniel Smith, J. Mattsey, NY Met Op Orch, J. Conlon (pp1991) *Concert* (6/93) (RCA) ① **09026 61509-2**
10. J. Gomez, J. Constable *Concert*
(6/88) (UNIC) ① **DKPCD9055**
10, 14. A. Réaux, R. Kapilow *Concert*
(6/92) (KOCH) ① [2] **37087-2**
Zar lässt sich Photographieren—opera buffa: 1 act, Op. 21 (1928—Leipzig) (Lib. G. Kaiser)
Cpte B. McDaniel, C. Pohl, T. Lehrberger, U. Tocha, M. Napier, H. Kruse, H. Helling, M. Brell, H. Franzen, Cologne Rad Chor, Cologne RSO, J. Latham-König (5/90) (CAPR) ① **10 147**

SECTION I: ORCHESTRAL

Under the Spreading Chestnut Tree (Variations and Fugue on an old English Tune)—orchestra (1939)
LPO, C. Lambert (r1939) *Concert*
(11/93) (DUTT) ① **CDAX8005**

SECTION V: STAGE WORKS

Schwanda the Bagpiper—folk opera: 2 acts (1927—Prague) (Lib. Brod and Kareš)
1. Polka; 2. Fugue.
1, 2. Cincinnati Pops, E. Kunzel *Concert*
(9/86) (TELA) ① **CD80115**
1, 2. Chicago SO, F. Reiner (r1956) *Concert*
(8/95) (RCA) ① **09026 62587-2**

SECTION I: ORCHESTRAL

Suite on Hungarian Folk Tunes, Op. 18 (1931)
Philh, N. Järvi *Bartók: Miraculous Mandarin.*
(3/92) (CHAN) ① **CHAN9029**

SECTION II: CHAMBER

Sonata for Violin and Piano No. 1 in D, Op. 9 (1911)
O. Shumsky, S. Lipkin (r1993) *Concert*
(6/95) (BIDD) ① **LAW015**
Sonata for Violin and Piano No. 2 in F sharp minor, Op. 11 (1918)
O. Shumsky, S. Lipkin (r1993) *Concert*
(6/95) (BIDD) ① **LAW015**

SECTION III: INSTRUMENTAL

3 Hungarian Rural Dances—piano (trans cpsr from Divertimento, Op. 20)
1. Fox Dance; 2. Ronde of Marosszek; 3. Peasant's Dance.
P. Frankl (r?1992) *Concert*
(6/93) (ASV) ① **CDDCA860**

SECTION V: STAGE WORKS

Prinz Csonger und die Kobolde—concert suite from ballet, Op. 10b (1927)
1. Introduction; 2. Scherzo.
1, 2. Chicago SO, G. Solti (pp1993) *Concert*
(1/95) (DECC) ① **443 444-2DH**

SECTION I: ORCHESTRAL

Concerto for Viola and Orchestra, Op. 78 (1977)
S. Weiner, Hilversum Radio Chbr Orch, J. Stulen *Violin Concerto 4.* (1/90) (SCHW) ① **311022**
Concerto for Violin and Orchestra No. 4, Op. 54 (1974)
S. Weiner, Hilversum Radio Chbr Orch, J. Stulen *Viola Concerto.* (1/90) (SCHW) ① **311022**

SECTION IV: VOCAL AND CHORAL

Liebesfeier—song, Op. 16/2 (Wds. N. Lenau)
L. Melchior, orch (r1923) *Concert*
(8/88) (DANA) ① [2] **DACOCD313/4**
H. Schlusnus, Berlin St Op Orch, A. Melichar (r1932) *Concert* (1/94) (PREI) ① [2] **89205**

SECTION II: CHAMBER

Ardnamurchan Point—two pianos (1990)
W. Howard, P. Casén (r1995) *Concert*
(12/95) (COLL) ① **Coll1453-2**
The Bagpiper's String Trio—violin, viola & cello (1985)
Domus (r1995) *Concert*
(12/95) (COLL) ① **Coll1453-2**
Distance and Enchantment—violin, viola, cello and piano (1989)
Domus (r1995) *Concert*
(12/95) (COLL) ① **Coll1453-2**
I Broke off a Golden Branch—violin, viola, cello, double bass & piano
Schubert Ens of London (1995) *Concert*
(12/95) (COLL) ① **Coll1453-2**
El Rey de Francia—violin, viola, cello, doublebass & piano (1993)
Schubert Ens of London (1995) *Concert*
(12/95) (COLL) ① **Coll1453-2**

SECTION III: INSTRUMENTAL

The Art of Touching the Keyboard—piano (1983)
W. Howard (r1995) *Concert*
(12/95) (COLL) ① **Coll1453-2**
The King of France—piano (1993)
S. Tomes (r1995) *Concert*
(12/95) (COLL) ① **Coll1453-2**

SECTION IV: VOCAL AND CHORAL

Ascending into Heaven (Me receptet Sion illa)—anthem (1983) (Wds. Hildebert of Lavardin, trans cpsr)
King's College Ch, S. Cleobury (r1991) *Concert*
(6/93) (EMI) ① **CDC7 54418-2**
Don't let that horse—song: 1v and horn (1990) (Wds. L. Ferlinghetti)
J. Manning, Jane's Minstrels (r1993) *Concert*
(10/95) (NMC) ① **NMCD025**
Illuminare, Jerusalem (1985) (Wds. 15th Cent. Scottish)
Elysian Sngrs, M. Greenall *Concert*
(12/91) (CNTI) ① **CCD1043**
Truro Cath Ch, D. Briggs, S. Morley (r1992) *Concert*
(7/94) (PRIO) ① **PRCD429**
Missa del Cid—SAAATTTBBB and speaker (1988)
N. Herrett, Combattimento, D. Mason (r1988) *Concert* (3/90) (NOVE) ① **NVLCD109**
The Romance of Count Arnaldos—song (Wds. Spanish anon 15th-16th cent)
M. Wiegold, Composers Ens, D. Muldowney *Concert* (4/92) (NMC) ① **NMCD003**
Songs from the Exotic (on the rocks)—1v, clarinet & piano (1989) (clarinet part added by Michael Finnissy)
EXCERPTS: 1. Sevdalino, my little one (Serbian folksong); 2. In the lovely village of Nevesinje (Serbian epic); 3. The Romance of Count Arnaldos (15-16th Century Spanish); 4. Song of a girl ravished away by the fairies in South Uist (Scottish).
Tapestry (r1994) *Concert*
(12/95) (BRIT) ① **BML012**

SECTION V: STAGE WORKS

**Blond Eckbert—opera: 2 acts
(1994—London)** (Lib. cpsr)
Cpte N. Jones, A-M. Owens, C. Ventris, N. Folwell,
ENO Chor, ENO Orch, S. Edwards (pp1994)
(7/95) (COLL) ① **Coll1461-2**
The **Consolations of Scholarship—Chinese
Yüan drama (1985—Durham)** (based on 13th-
14th Cent texts)
EXCERPTS: 1. Lamento.
L. Hirst, Lontano, O. de la Martinez (r1989) Concert
(3/90) (NOVE) ① **NVLCD109**
**King Harald's Saga—'grand opera': 2 acts
(1979—Dumfries)** (after 'Heimskoingla Saga')
J. Manning (r1989) Concert
(3/90) (NOVE) ① **NVLCD109**

WEISS, Silvius Leopold (1686–1750) Germany

SECTION III: INSTRUMENTAL

Fantasie
J. Williams (trans J.Williams) Concert
(8/88) (SONY) ① **SK44518**
J. Bream (r1966) Concert
(8/93) (RCA) ① [28] **09026 61583-2(3)**
J. Bream (r1966) Concert
(6/94) (RCA) ① **09026 61592-2**
Passacaglia—lute
J. Williams (trans J.Williams) Concert
(8/88) (SONY) ① **SK44518**
J. Bream (r1966) Concert
(8/93) (RCA) ① [28] **09026 61583-2(3)**
J. Bream (r1966) Concert
(6/94) (RCA) ① **09026 61592-2**
Prelude and Fugue in C—lute
K. Junghänel Concert
(1/87) (ACCE) ① **ACC67910D**
Prelude and Fugue in D minor—lute
K. Junghänel (r1985) Concert
(5/87) (HARM) ① **HMA190 1183**
Prelude, Fantasia and Fugue in C—lute
N. North Concert (12/92) (LINN) ① **CKD006**
**Sonata in A minor, '(L')infidele'—lute
(1719)**
1. Entrée; 2. Courante; 3. Sarabande; 4. Menuet; 5.
Musette; 6. Paysanne.
E.M. Dombois Concert (10/89) (RCA) ① **GD71958**
N. North Concert (12/92) (LINN) ① **CKD006**
Suite I in C minor—lute
1. Ouverture; 2. Allemande; 3. Courante; 4. Gavotte;
5. Sarabande; 6. Menuet; 7. Gigue.
K. Junghänel Concert
(1/87) (ACCE) ① **ACC67910D**
Suite I in D—lute
1. Prelude; 2. Allemande; 3. Courante; 4. Angloise; 5.
Sarabande; 6. Menuet; 7. Passacaille.
K. Heindel (lute-hpd) Concert
(2/91) (KING) ① **KCLCD2020**
Suite I in G minor—lute
1. Prélude; 2. Allemande; 3. Courante; 4. Bourrée; 5.
Sarabande; 6. Menuets I & II; 7. Paysanne; 8. Gigue.
K. Junghänel Concert
(1/87) (ACCE) ① **ACC67910D**
Suite II in F—lute (comp Lindberg from Brit Lib
& Dresden MSS)
1. Prelude; 2. Allemande; 3. Courante; 4. Bourrée; 5.
Sarabande; 6. Menuet I and II; 7. Gigue.
J. Lindberg (r1986) Concert
(11/87) (BIS) ① **BIS-CD327**
Suite in D minor—lute (compiled Stubbs from
Moscow MS)
1. Vivace (Partitta Signor Veis); 2. Courante; 3.
Andante; 4. Menuet; 5. Presto.
S. Stubbs Concert (3/93) (EMI) ① **CDC7 54519-2**
Suite No. 3 in C—lute (c1725-34) (Dresden
MS)
1. Entré; 2. Courante; 3. Patisane (Paysane); 4.
Sarabande; 5. Menuet; 6. Allegro.
S. Stubbs Concert (3/93) (EMI) ① **CDC7 54519-2**
**Tombeau sur la mort de M. Cajetan (Baron
d'Hartig)—lute**
J. Williams (trans J.Williams) Concert
(8/88) (SONY) ① **SK44518**
Tombeau sur la mort de M. Comte de Logy
J. Lindberg (r1986) Concert
(11/87) (BIS) ① **BIS-CD327**
L. Kirchhof Concert (11/92) (SONY) ① **SK48068**
N. North Concert (12/92) (LINN) ① **CKD006**
J. Bream (r1966) Concert
(8/93) (RCA) ① [28] **09026 61583-2(3)**
J. Bream (r1966) Concert
(6/94) (RCA) ① **09026 61592-2**

WEISS, Willoughby Hunter (19th Cent) USA

SECTION IV: VOCAL AND CHORAL

The **Village Blacksmith—song (1857)** (Wds.
H W Longfellow)
O. Natzke, orch, H. Geehl (r1938) Concert
(12/92) (ODE) ① **CDODE1365**

WELDON, John (1676–1736) England

SECTION IV: VOCAL AND CHORAL

O Lord, rebuke me not
EXCERPTS: 1. Alleluia.
1. A. Rolfe Johnson, G. Johnson (r1995; arr Britten)
Concert (11/95) (HYPE) ① [2] **CDA67061/2**
Reason, what art thou?—song (c1700) (Wds.
J. Lawrance)
C. Bott, D. Roblou, M. Levy (1990) Concert
(2/93) (L'OI) ① **433 187-2OH**
The **wakeful nightingale—song: 1v**
E. Tubb, F. Kelly (1992) Concert
(9/93) (MOSC) ① **070987**

SECTION V: STAGE WORKS

The **Judgment of Paris—incidental music
(1701—London)** (Wds. Congreve)
EXCERPTS: 1. This way mortal bend thy eyes; 2.
Hark the glorious voice of war.
1, 2. E. Tubb, English Tpt Virtuosi, A. Hoskins
(tpt/dir), M. Hoskins (tpt/dir) (r1994) Concert
(10/95) (MOSC) ① **070979**
The **Tempest—incidental music to
Shakespeare's play (c1712—London)**
EXCERPTS: 1. Dry those eyes; 2. Halcyon days; 3.
Arise ye subterranean winds.
3. M. George, King's Consort, R. King Concert
(8/88) (CARL) ① **PCD894**

WENNERBERG, Gunnar (1817–1901) Sweden

SECTION IV: VOCAL AND CHORAL

The **Girls (Flickorna)—duet**
E. Söderström, K. Meyer, J. Eyron (r1974) Concert
(9/93) (BIS) ① **BIS-CD017**
Gluntarne—vocal duets (pub 1849-51)
1. Uppsala is best; 2. The lecture; 3. Sundown in
Eklundshof; 4. A march by night; 5. The morning
after; 6. The unlucky serenade; 7. The castle bell; 8.
Parting at Flottsund.
1-8. L. Melchior, H. Hansen, Anon (pf) (r1920)
Concert (8/88) (DANA) ① [2] **DACOCD311/2**
Psalm 4, 'Hear me'
J. Björling, Inst Ens (r1920) Concert
(8/92) (BLUE) ① **ABCD016**
The **Sutlers (Marketenterskorna)—duet**
E. Söderström, K. Meyer, J. Eyron (r1974) Concert
(9/93) (BIS) ① **BIS-CD017**

WERNICK, Richard (b 1934) USA

SECTION II: CHAMBER

String Quartet No. 4
Emerson Qt (r1991) Concert
(11/93) (DG) ① **437 537-2GH**

SECTION III: INSTRUMENTAL

Piano Sonata (1982)
L. Orkis Crumb: Little Suite for Christmas, AD1979.
(3/87) (BRID) ① **BCD9003**

WERT, Giaches de (1535–1596) The Netherlands/Italy

SECTION IV: VOCAL AND CHORAL

Adesti dolori meo—motet (5vv) (pub 1566)
Ars Nova, B. Holten Concert
(11/87) (KONT) ① **32001**
**Amen, amen dico vobis—motet (5vv) (pub
1581)**
Ars Nova, B. Holten Concert
(11/87) (KONT) ① **32001**
**Ascendente Jesu in naviculam—motet (6vv)
(pub 1581)**
Ars Nova, B. Holten Concert
(11/87) (KONT) ① **32001**
Egressus Jesus—motet (7vv) (pub 1581)
Ars Nova, B. Holten Concert
(11/87) (KONT) ① **32001**

Vezzosi augelli—madrigal (5vv) (pub 1586)
(Wds. Tasso)
Amaryllis Consort Concert
(6/86) (CARL) ① **PCD822**
**Vox in Rama audita est—motet (5vv) (pub
1581)**
Ars Nova, B. Holten Concert
(11/87) (KONT) ① **32001**

WESLEY, Samuel (1766–1837) England

SECTION I: ORCHESTRAL

Symphony in B flat (1802)
Milton Keynes CO, H.D. Wetton Concert
(10/91) (UNIC) ① **DKPCD9098**
Symphony in D (1784)
Milton Keynes CO, H.D. Wetton Concert
(10/91) (UNIC) ① **DKPCD9098**
Symphony in E flat (1784)
Milton Keynes CO, H.D. Wetton Concert
(10/91) (UNIC) ① **DKPCD9098**
Symphony No. 5 in A (1784)
ECCO, J. Faerber Concert
(10/86) (HYPE) ① **CDA66156**
Milton Keynes CO, H.D. Wetton Concert
(10/91) (UNIC) ① **DKPCD9098**

SECTION III: INSTRUMENTAL

Duet for organ
H. Fagius, D. Sanger Concert
(10/85) (BIS) ① **BIS-CD273**
**God rest you merry, gentlemen—rondo:
piano (1815)**
I. Hobson Concert (3/89) (ARAB) ① **Z6594**
**12 Short Pieces with a Voluntary
added—keyboard (pub 1816)**
6. A minor; 7. A minor; 8. Gavotte in F; 9. Air in F; 12.
D.
6, 8. J. Bate Concert (5/91) (UNIC) ① **DKPCD9101**
7, 12. J. Bate Concert
(2/91) (UNIC) ① **DKPCD9096**
8, 9. C. Curley (r1991) Concert
(4/92) (ARGO) ① **433 450-2ZH**
9. J. Bate Concert (5/91) (UNIC) ① **DKPCD9099**
12 Voluntaries—organ, Op. 6 (1802-08)
BOOK 1: 1. D; 2. C; 3. C minor; 4. G; 5. D; 6. C.
BOOK 2: 7. E flat; 8. D; 9. G; 10. F; 11. A; 12. F.
1. J. Bate Concert (2/91) (UNIC) ① **DKPCD9096**
1. Margaret Phillips Concert
(7/91) (GAMU) ① **GAMCD522**
3. J. Bate Concert (5/91) (UNIC) ① **DKPCD9099**
5. J. Bate Concert (5/91) (UNIC) ① **DKPCD9101**
7. J. Bate Concert (11/91) (UNIC) ① **DKPCD9106**
9. J. Bate Concert (7/91) (UNIC) ① **DKPCD9104**
10. J. Bate Concert (7/91) (UNIC) ① **DKPCD9105**
Voluntary in B flat—organ (1829)
J. Bate Concert (11/91) (UNIC) ① **DKPCD9106**

SECTION IV: VOCAL AND CHORAL

**In exitu Israel—anthem: 8vv and organ
(1810)**
St Paul's Cath Ch, John Scott, Adrian Lucas (r1991)
Concert (8/93) (HYPE) ① **CDA66618**
**O sing unto me roundelaie—madrigal: 5vv
(1811)** (Wds Chatterton)
Invocation (r1994) Concert
(3/95) (HYPE) ① **CDA66740**

WESLEY, Samuel Sebastian (1810–1876) England

SECTION III: INSTRUMENTAL

Air and Gavotte—organ
John Scott Concert (12/87) (CIRR) ① **CICD1007**
**An Air with Variations (composed for
Holsworthy Church Bells)—organ (c1874)**
G. Thalben-Ball (r c1931) Concert
(9/94) (BEUL) ① **1PD5**
Andante in E minor—organ (pub 1877)
E. Higginbottom Concert
(10/91) (CRD) ① **CRD3463**
Larghetto in F minor—organ (c1835)
E. Higginbottom Concert
(10/91) (CRD) ① **CRD3463**
March and Rondo—piano (1842)
I. Hobson Concert (3/89) (ARAB) ① **Z6596**
**3 Pieces for a Chamber Organ—Set
1—organ**
1. Andante in E flat; 2. Andante in F; 3. Choral Song
and Fugue.
3. E. Higginbottom Concert
(10/91) (CRD) ① **CRD3463**
3. C. Curley (r1991) Concert
(4/92) (ARGO) ① **433 450-2ZH**

WESLEY *(continued)*

SECTION IV: VOCAL AND CHORAL

Ascribe unto the Lord—anthem (7/4vv, organ) (1849-53)
Guildford Cath Ch, A. Millington, P. Wright *Concert*
(5/89) (PRIO) ① **PRCD257**
New College Ch, E. Higginbottom (org/dir) *Concert*
(10/91) (CRD) ① **CRD3463**
Worcester Cath Ch, A. Partington, Don Hunt *Concert*
(10/91) (HYPE) ① **CDA66446**

Blessed be the God and Father—anthem: 1- 5vv and organ (1833-35)·
Salisbury Cath Ch, C. Walsh, R. Seal *Concert*
(9/87) (MERI) ① **CDE84025**
St Paul's Cath Ch, Andrew Lucas, John Scott
Concert (9/90) (HYPE) ① **CDA66374**
New College Ch, E. Higginbottom (org/dir) *Concert*
(10/91) (CRD) ① **CRD3463**
Worcester Cath Ch, A. Partington, Don Hunt *Concert*
(10/91) (HYPE) ① **CDA66446**
Magdalen Oxford Coll Ch, J. Harper *Concert*
(11/91) (ABBE) ① **CDCA913**
Southwark Cath Ch, P. Wright, S. Layton (r1992)
Concert (7/94) (PRIO) ① **PRCD435**

Burial Service, 'Man that is born of a woman'—choir (c1842-49)
Worcester Cath Ch, A. Partington, Don Hunt *Concert*
(10/91) (HYPE) ① **CDA66469**

Cast me not away from Thy presence—anthem: 6vv and organ (1848)
New College Ch, E. Higginbottom (org/dir) *Concert*
(10/91) (CRD) ① **CRD3463**
Worcester Cath Ch, A. Partington, Don Hunt *Concert*
(10/91) (HYPE) ① **CDA66446**

Evening Service in E (1841-45)
1. Magnificat; 2. Te Deum.
Gloucester Cath Ch, J. Sanders, M. Lee (r1994)
Concert (4/95) (PRIO) ① **PRCD494**

The face of the Lord—anthem
Worcester Cath Ch, A. Partington, Don Hunt *Concert*
(10/91) (HYPE) ① **CDA66469**

Let us lift up our heart—anthem (5-8vv, organ) (pub 1853)
Worcester Cath Ch, A. Partington, Don Hunt *Concert*
(10/91) (HYPE) ① **CDA66446**

Morning and Evening Service in E—canticles and responses (pub 1845)
EXCERPTS: MORNING: 1a. Te Deum; 1b. Jubilate
Deo. COMMUNION: 2a. Kyrie 1; 2b. Kyrie 2; 2c.
Credo. EVENING: 3a. Magnificat; 3b. Nunc Dimittis.
1a, 1b New College Ch, M. Nicholas, N. Taylor
(r1993) *Concert* (10/94) (PRIO) ① **PRCD470**
3a, 3b St Paul's Cath Ch, C. Dearnley, John Scott
Concert (3/88) (HYPE) ① **CDA66249**

O give thanks unto the Lord—anthem
Worcester Cath Ch, A. Partington, Don Hunt *Concert*
(10/91) (HYPE) ① **CDA66469**

O Lord, thou art my God—anthem (1839)
Worcester Cath Ch, A. Partington, Don Hunt *Concert*
(10/91) (HYPE) ① **CDA66469**

Praise the Lord, O my soul—anthem (1861)
Worcester Cath Ch, A. Partington, Don Hunt *Concert*
(10/91) (HYPE) ① **CDA66469**

Solomon's Prayer, 'O Lord, my God'—anthem: 4vv & organ (pub 1853)
Worcester Cath Ch, A. Partington, Don Hunt *Concert*
(10/91) (HYPE) ① **CDA66469**

Thou wilt keep him in perfect peace—anthem: 5vv (pub 1853)
Guildford Cath Ch, A. Millington, P. Wright *Concert*
(5/89) (PRIO) ① **PRCD257**
Westminster Abbey Ch, I. Simcock, M. Neary
Concert (10/89) (CARL) ① **PCD919**
Truro Cath Ch, D. Briggs, H. Doughty *Concert*
(7/91) (PRIO) ① **PRCD322**
New College Ch, E. Higginbottom (org/dir) *Concert*
(10/91) (CRD) ① **CRD3463**
Worcester Cath Ch, A. Partington, Don Hunt *Concert*
(10/91) (HYPE) ① **CDA66446**
Westminster Abbey Ch, M. Baker, M. Neary (r1993/4)
Concert (9/94) (CNTO) ① **CSACD3050**
St Paul's Cath Ch, John Scott, Andrew Lucas (r1994)
Concert (5/95) (HYPE) ① **CDA66758**

Wash me throughly from my wickedness—anthem (pub 1853)
Westminster Abbey Ch, I. Simcock, M. Neary
Concert (10/89) (CARL) ① **PCD919**
New College Ch, E. Higginbottom (org/dir) *Concert*
(10/91) (CRD) ① **CRD3463**
Worcester Cath Ch, A. Partington, Don Hunt *Concert*
(10/91) (HYPE) ① **CDA66469**

The Wilderness and the solitary place—anthem (1832)
New College Ch, E. Higginbottom (org/dir) *Concert*
(10/91) (CRD) ① **CRD3463**

Worcester Cath Ch, A. Partington, Don Hunt *Concert*
(10/91) (HYPE) ① **CDA66446**
Magdalen Oxford Coll Ch, J. Harper *Concert*
(11/91) (ABBE) ① **CDCA913**

WESLEY-SMITH, Martin *(b 1945)* Australia

SECTION II: CHAMBER

White Knight and Beaver—marimba, xylophone and tape (1984)
Australia Ens *Concert* (7/92) (TALL) ① **TP002**

WESTBROOK, Mike *(b 1936)* England

SECTION I: ORCHESTRAL

Bean Rows and Blues Shots—saxophone and orchestra
J. Harle, Bournemouth Sinfonietta, I. Bolton *Concert*
(7/92) (ARGO) ① **433 847-2ZH**

WESTERHOUT, Nicola van *(1857–1898) Italy*

SECTION IV: VOCAL AND CHORAL

Ovunque tu—song
A. Garulli, anon (r1902) *Concert*
(5/91) (SYMP) ① **SYMCD1077**

WESTHOFF, Johann Paul von *(1656–1705) Germany*

SECTION II: CHAMBER

Sonata in A, '(La) guerra'—violin and piano (pub 1682)
Cologne Musica Antiqua, R. Goebel (r1980) *Concert*
(1/93) (ARCH) ① **437 089-2AT**

WESTLAKE, Nigel *(b 1958)* Australia

SECTION I: ORCHESTRAL

Antartica—suite: guitar and orchestra (1992)
1. The last place on earth; 2. Wooden ships; 3.
Penguin ballet; 4. The ice core—Finale.
J. Williams, LSO, P. Daniel (r1994) *Concert*
(5/95) (SONY) ① **SK53361**

SECTION II: CHAMBER

Refractions at Summer Cloud Bay—chamber ensemble (1989)
Australia Ens *Concert* (7/92) (TALL) ① **TP002**

WETZEL, Justus Hermann *(1879–1973) Germany*

SECTION IV: VOCAL AND CHORAL

In Danzig—Lied (Wds. Eichendorff)
H. Schlusnus, F. Rupp (r1933) *Concert*
(1/94) (PREI) ① [2] **89205**

WETZGER

SECTION II: CHAMBER

By the brook—flute and piano
J. Lemmoné, N. Melba (r1910) *Concert*
(3/89) (LARR) ① **CDLRH221**
J. Lemmoné, N. Melba (r1910) *Concert*
(5/95) (ROMO) ① [3] **81011-2(2)**

WEYSE, Christoph Ernst Friedrich *(1774–1842) Denmark*

SECTION IV: VOCAL AND CHORAL

The Blessed Day—song (Wds. N. F. S. Grundtvig)
L. Melchior, Brass Ens (r1915) *Concert*
(8/88) (DANA) ① [2] **DACOCD311/2**

Ever dauntless, as you move—song (Wds. C. Richardt)
L. Melchior, Brass Ens (r1915) *Concert*
(8/88) (DANA) ① [2] **DACOCD311/2**

WHITAKER, David *(20th cent)* England

SECTION V: STAGE WORKS

Vampire Circus—film score (1971)
EXCERPTS: 1. Prologue.
1. Philh, N. Richardson *Concert*
(10/93) (SILV) ① **FILMCD127**

WHITE, Charles Albert *(1832–1891) USA*

SECTION IV: VOCAL AND CHORAL

Trusting—song (?1873)
K. Battle, C. Rayam, L. Skrobacs (r1977) *Concert*
(2/94) (NEW) ① **80220-2**

WHITE, Clarence Cameron *(1880–1960) USA*

SECTION II: CHAMBER

Levee Dance, Op. 27/2 (based on 'Go down Moses')
J. Heifetz, M. Kaye (r1944) *Concert*
(11/94) (RCA) ① [65] **09026 61778-2(19)**

WHITE, Edward *(1910–1994)* England
aka Teddy White

SECTION I: ORCHESTRAL

Puffin' Billy—orchestra (1940s) (theme for BBC Radio series 'Children's Choice')
RTE Concert Orch, E. Tomlinson (r1993) *Concert*
(12/95) (MARC) ① **8 223522**

WHITE, L.J. *(20th Cent) England*

SECTION IV: VOCAL AND CHORAL

A Prayer of St Richard of Chichester—anthem: boys' vv (c1919)
Wellington College Chs, T. Byram-Wigfield, S.
Anderson *Concert* (10/92) (HERA) ① **HAVPCD153**

WHITE, Maude Valerie *(1855–1937) England*

SECTION IV: VOCAL AND CHORAL

Chantez, chantez, jeune inspirée—song (Wds. Hugo)
F. Lott, G. Johnson (r1984) *Concert*
(5/87) (HARM) ① **HMA190 1138**

The Devout Lover—song (1882) (Wds Pollock)
A. Rolfe Johnson, G. Johnson (r1991/3) *Concert*
(8/94) (HYPE) ① **CDA66709**

Ici bas—song: 1v and piano
S. Mentzer, K. Schmidt (r1991) *Concert*
(12/93) (KOCH) ① **37240-2**

John Anderson, my Jo—song (Wds. R. Burns)
N. Melba, G. Lapierre (r1913) *Concert*
(3/89) (LARR) ① **CDLRH221**
N. Melba, G. Lapierre (r1913) *Concert*
(9/93) (RCA) ① **09026 61412-2**
N. Melba, G. Lapierre (r1913) *Concert*
(5/95) (ROMO) ① [3] **81011-2(2)**

My soul is an enchanted boat—song (Wds Shelley)
A. Rolfe Johnson, G. Johnson (r1991/3) *Concert*
(8/94) (HYPE) ① **CDA66709**

So we'll go no more a-roving—song (1920s) (Wds. cpsr)
F. Lott, G. Johnson *Concert*
(7/90) (CHAN) ① **CHAN8722**
A. Rolfe Johnson, G. Johnson (r1991/3) *Concert*
(8/94) (HYPE) ① **CDA66709**

The Throstle—song: 1v and piano
S.J. Langton, K. Schmidt (r1991) *Concert*
(12/93) (KOCH) ① **37240-2**
A. Rolfe Johnson, G. Johnson (r1991/3) *Concert*
(8/94) (HYPE) ① **CDA66709**

To Mary—song
H. Nash, anon (r1933) *Concert*
(9/91) (PEAR) ① **GEMMCD9473**
P. Jeffes, J. Constable *Concert*
(4/92) (GAMU) ① **GAMD506**

WHITE, Robert (c1538–1574) England

SECTION II: CHAMBER

6 Fantasias a 4—consort
3. Fantasia III; 4. Fantasia IV.
3, 4. Amsterdam Loeki Stardust Qt (r1991) *Concert*
(2/94) (L'OI) ① **436 155-2OH**

SECTION IV: VOCAL AND CHORAL

O praise God in his holiness—double choir
(attrib)
Worcester Cath Ch, Don Hunt, R. Johnston (r1993)
Concert (2/95) (ABBE) ① **CDCA957**

WHITEHEAD, Gillian (b 1941) New Zealand

SECTION II: CHAMBER

Manutaki—chamber ensemble (1986)
Australia Ens *Concert* (7/92) (TALL) ① **TP002**

WHITLOCK, Percy (William) (1903–1946) England

SECTION III: INSTRUMENTAL

4 Extemporizations—organ (1935)
1. Carol; 2. Divertimento; 3. Fidelis; 4. Fanfare.
4. C. Herrick *Concert* (7/86) (HYPE) ① **CDA66121**
6 Hymn Preludes—organ
1. Darwall's 148th; 2. Song 13; 3. Deo Gracias; 4. St
Denio; 5. Werde Munter; 6. King's Lynn.
1, 2. G. Green *Concert* (3/93) (NAXO) ① **8 550582**
5 Pieces for organ (1930)
1. Allegretto; 2. Folk Tune; 3. Andante tranquillo; 4.
Scherzo; 5. Paean.
2. C. Curley (r1991) *Concert*
(4/92) (ARGO) ① **433 450-2ZH**
4. G. Weir *Concert* (12/92) (KOSS) ① **KC1013**
5. C. Herrick *Concert* (10/92) (HYPE) ① **CDA66605**

SECTION IV: VOCAL AND CHORAL

Be still, my soul—motet
Dundee Cath Ch, R. Lightband (org/dir) *Concert*
(8/92) (ABBE) ① **CDCA926**
Glorious in heaven—anthem (pub 1927)
Jesus College Ch, D. Phillips, T. Horton *Concert*
(7/93) (CNTO) ① **CRCD2367**

WHYTE, Robert (c1538–1574) England

SECTION IV: VOCAL AND CHORAL

Christe, qui lux es et dies—compline hymn: 4vv
Tallis Scholars, P. Phillips *Concert*
(6/95) (GIME) ① **CDGIM030**
Clerkes of Oxenford, D. Wulstan (r1977) *Concert*
(6/95) (GIME) ① **CAL6623**
Westminster Abbey Ch, M. Neary, M. Baker (r1994)
Concert (12/95) (SONY) ① **SK66614**
Christe, qui lux es et dies—compline hymn: 4vv
Tallis Scholars, P. Phillips *Concert*
(6/95) (GIME) ① **CDGIM030**
Domine quis habitavit—motet
Clerkes of Oxenford, D. Wulstan (r1977) *Concert*
(11/95) (CALL) ① **CAL6623**
Exaudiat te Dominus—psalm-motet: 5vv
(Wds. Psalm 20)
Tallis Scholars, P. Phillips *Concert*
(6/95) (GIME) ① **CDGIM030**
Lamentations a Jeremiah—5vv
Oxford Camerata, J. Summerly *Concert*
(4/93) (NAXO) ① **8 550572**
Tallis Scholars, P. Phillips *Concert*
(6/95) (GIME) ① **CDGIM030**
Magnificat—6vv
Tallis Scholars, P. Phillips *Concert*
(6/95) (GIME) ① **CDGIM030**
Portio mea Domine—psalm-motet: 5vv (Wds.
Psalm 119)
Tallis Scholars, P. Phillips *Concert*
(6/95) (GIME) ① **CDGIM030**
Clerkes of Oxenford, D. Wulstan (r1977) *Concert*
(11/95) (CALL) ① **CAL6623**
Regina coeli—votive antiphon: 5vv
Tallis Scholars, P. Phillips *Concert*
(6/95) (GIME) ① **CDGIM030**
Clerkes of Oxenford, D. Wulstan (r1977) *Concert*
(11/95) (CALL) ① **CAL6623**

WHYTHORNE, Thomas (1528–1596) England

SECTION IV: VOCAL AND CHORAL

Buy new broom—1v and viols (pub 1571)
A. Deller, SCB, A. Wenzinger (r1956: arr P Warlock)
Concert (4/95) (VANG) ① **08.5068.71**

WIDMANN, Erasmus (1572–1634) Germany

SECTION II: CHAMBER

Musicalischer Tugendtspiegel—dances (pub 1613)
Excs London Musica Antiqua, M. Uridge (r1980-83)
Concert (12/93) (SYMP) ① **SYMCD1157**

WIDOR, Charles-Marie(-Jean-Albert) (1844–1937) France

SECTION II: CHAMBER

Piano Quintet No. 1 in D minor, Op. 7 (c1890)
I. Prunyi, New Budapest Qt (r1988) *Piano Trio.*
(11/89) (MARC) ① **8 223193**
Piano Trio in B flat, Op. 19 (1875)
I. Prunyi, New Budapest Qt (r1988) *Piano Quintet 1.*
(11/89) (MARC) ① **8 223193**
4 Pièces en Trio—violin, cello and piano (1890)
Göbel Trio, Berlin *Concert*
(7/88) (THOR) ① **CTH2002**
Suite—flute and piano, Op. 34 (1898)
R. Aitken, R. McCabe *Concert*
(9/89) (BIS) ① **BIS-CD184**

SECTION III: INSTRUMENTAL

Fugue, 'Hommage à Haydn'—piano (1930)
M. Fingerhut *Concert* (9/88) (CHAN) ① **CHAN8578**
3 Nouvelles pièces—organ, Op. 87 (1934)
T. Trotter *Concert* (10/92) (ARGO) ① **433 152-2ZH**
D.M. Patrick *Concert* (5/93) (PRIO) ① **PRCD371**
2. D. Hill *Concert* (10/87) (HYPE) ① **CDA66181**
Symphonie gothique—organ, Op. 70 (pub 1895)
EXCERPTS: 1. Moderato; 2. Andante sostenuto; 4.
Moderato—Variations.
1, 2, 4. C-M. Widor (r1932) *Concert*
(5/94) (EMI) ① **CDC5 55037-2**
Symphony No. 1 in C minor—organ, Op. 13/1 (1876)
1. Prélude; 2. Allegretto; 3. Intermezzo; 4. Adagio; 5.
Marche pontificale; 6. Méditation; 7. Finale.
G. Kaunzinger (r1990) *Symphony 2.*
(3/92) (NOVA) ① **150 073-2**
5. J. Parker-Smith *Concert*
(4/86) (ASV) ① **CDDCA539**
5. D. Hill *Concert* (10/87) (HYPE) ① **CDA66181**
5. M. Harris *Concert* (3/92) (YORK) ① **CD112**
Symphony No. 2—organ, Op. 13/2 (1876)
1. Praeludium circulaire; 2. Pastorale; 3. Andante; 4.
Salve Regina; 5. Adagio; 6. Finale.
M-A. Morisset-Balier *Vierne: Messe basse, Op. 62.*
(7/89) (MOTE) ① **CD11231**
G. Kaunzinger (r1990) *Symphony 1.*
(3/92) (NOVA) ① **150 073-2**
Symphony No. 4 in F minor—organ, Op. 13/4 (1876)
1. Toccata; 2. Fugue; 3. Andante cantabile; 4.
Scherzo; 5. Adagio; 6. Finale.
2, 3. J. Parker-Smith *Concert*
(3/89) (ASV) ① **CDDCA610**
Symphony No. 5 in F minor—organ, Op. 42/1 (1880)
1. Allegro vivace; 2. Allegro cantabile; 3. Andantino
quasi allegretto; 4. Adagio; 5. Toccata.
S. Preston (r1983) *Vierne: Suite 3.*
(11/84) (DG) ① **413 438-2GH**
D. Hill *Concert* (10/87) (HYPE) ① **CDA66181**
G. Kaunzinger *Symphony 6.*
(6/89) (NOVA) ① **150 015-2**
H. Musch *Concert* (7/91) (CHRI) ① **CD74606**
I. Tracey (r1993) *Concert*
(11/94) (CHAN) ① **CHAN9271**
4, 5. T. Trotter *Concert*
(10/92) (ARGO) ① **433 152-2ZH**
5. P-Y. Asselin *Mussorgsky: Pictures.*
(3/87) (DENO) ① **CO-1028**
5. C. Herrick *Concert* (3/89) (MERI) ① **CDE84148**
5. M. Neary *Concert* (10/89) (CARL) ① **PCD919**
5. I. Tracey *Concert* (1/90) (CFP) ① **CD-CFP4558**
5. S. Preston *Concert*
(6/91) (DECC) ① **430 091-2DWO**

5. J-G. Proulx *Concert*
(8/91) (REM) ① **REM311078**
5. P. Hurford *Concert*
(8/91) (DECC) ① **430 710-2DM**
5. S. Lindley *Concert* (3/93) (NAXO) ① **8 550581**
5. P. Hurford (r1982) *Concert*
(6/93) (DECC) ① **436 402-2DWO**
5. C-M. Widor (r1932) *Concert*
(5/94) (EMI) ① **CDC5 55037-2**
5. P. Hurford (r1982) *Concert*
(10/95) (DECC) ① **444 567-2DM**
Symphony No. 6 in C minor—organ, Op. 42/2 (?1880)
1. Allegro; 2. Adagio; 3. Intermezzo: Allegro; 4.
Cantabile; 5. Finale: Allegro.
G. Kaunzinger *Symphony 5.*
(6/89) (NOVA) ① **150 015-2**
1. R. Noehren *Concert* (11/87) (DELO) ① **DE3045**
1. C. Walsh *Concert* (3/90) (PRIO) ① **PRCD281**
1. P. Hurford *Concert*
(8/91) (DECC) ① **430 710-2DM**
1. T. Trotter *Concert*
(10/92) (ARGO) ① **433 152-2ZH**
1. C. Herrick *Concert* (10/92) (HYPE) ① **CDA66605**
1. P. Hurford (r1987) *Concert*
(10/95) (DECC) ① **444 567-2DM**
3. G. Weir *Concert* (12/92) (KOSS) ① **KC1013**
5. M. Murray *Concert* (3/89) (TELA) ① **CD80169**
Symphony No. 7—organ, Op. 42/3 (1887 rev 1887, 1901, 1918 and 1927)
1. Moderato; 2. Choral; 3. Andante; 4. Allegro ma non
troppo; 5. Lento; 6. Finale.
1, 4. T. Trotter *Concert*
(10/92) (ARGO) ① **433 152-2ZH**
6. C. Herrick *Concert* (7/86) (HYPE) ① **CDA66121**
Symphony No. 8—organ, Op. 42/4 (1887 rev 1901)
1. Allegro risoluto; 2. Moderato cantabile; 3. Allegro;
4a. Prélude; 4b. Variations; 5. Adagio; 6. Finale.
6. G.D. Cunningham (r c1930) *Concert*
(9/94) (BEUL) ① **1PD5**
Symphony No. 9 in C minor, 'Gothic'—organ, Op. 70 (1895)
1. Moderato; 2. Andante sostenuto; 3. Allegro; 4.
Moderato—Variations.
M-A. Morisset-Balier *Vierne: Messe basse, Op. 30.*
(2/87) (MOTE) ① **CD10411**
G. Kaunzinger *Symphony 9.*
(10/90) (NOVA) ① **150 038-2**
J. Filsell *Concert* (3/92) (HERA) ① **HAVPCD145**
T. Trotter *Concert* (10/92) (ARGO) ① **433 152-2ZH**
2. J. Parker-Smith *Concert*
(4/86) (ASV) ① **CDDCA539**
Symphony No. 10, 'Roman'—organ, Op. 73 (1900)
1. Moderato; 2. Choral—Adagio; 3. Cantilene—Lento;
4. Final—Allegro.
G. Kaunzinger *Symphony 9.*
(10/90) (NOVA) ① **150 038-2**

SECTION IV: VOCAL AND CHORAL

6 Mélodies, Op. 43
2. La vase brisé (wds. Prudhomme); 3.
Contemplation (wds. Hugo); 6. La vieille chanson du
jeune temps (wds. Hugo).
6. L. Fugère, anon (r1929) *Concert*
(6/93) (SYMP) ① **SYMCD1125**

WIEDERMANN, Bedřich (1993–1951) Czechoslovakia

SECTION III: INSTRUMENTAL

Impetuoso—organ
N. Kynaston *Concert* (4/89) (HYPE) ① **CDA66265**
Notturno in C sharp minor—organ (1942)
N. Kynaston *Concert* (4/89) (HYPE) ① **CDA66265**

WIENIAWSKI, Henryk (1835–1880) Poland

SECTION I: ORCHESTRAL

Concerto for Violin and Orchestra No. 1 in F sharp minor, Op. 14 (1853)
G. Shaham, LSO, L. Foster *Concert*
(12/91) (DG) ① **431 815-2GH**
I. Perlman, LPO, S. Ozawa (r1971) *Concert*
(5/93) (EMI) ① **[4] CMS7 64617-2**
I. Perlman, LPO, S. Ozawa *Concert*
(6/95) (EMI) ① **[20] CZS4 83177-2(1)**
Concerto for Violin and Orchestra No. 2 in D minor, Op. 22 (1862)
I. Perlman, Paris Orch, D. Barenboim *Saint-Saëns: Violin Concerto 3.* (3/84) (DG) ① **410 526-2GH**

J. Bell, Cleveland Orch, Vladimir Ashkenazy
Tchaikovsky: Violin Concerto.
(12/88) (DECC) ① **421 716-2DH**
M. Kaplan, LSO, M. Miller (r1988) Paganini: Violin
Concerto 1.   (7/89) (ARAB) ① **Z6597**
G. Shaham, LSO, L. Foster Concert
(12/91) (DG) ① **431 815-2GH**
J. Heifetz, LPO, J. Barbirolli (r1935) Concert
(5/92) (EMI) ① **CDH7 64251-2**
J. Rachlin, Israel PO, Z. Mehta Saint-Saëns: Violin
Concerto 3.   (12/92) (SONY) ① **SK48373**
J. Heifetz, LPO, J. Barbirolli (r1935) Concert
(11/94) (RCA) ① **[65] 09026 61778-2(03)**
J. Heifetz, RCA Victor SO, I. Solomon (r1954)
Concert   (11/94) (RCA) ① **[65] 09026 61778-2(20)**
I. Perlman, LPO, S. Ozawa Concert
(6/95) (EMI) ① **[20] CZS4 83177-2(1)**
J. Heifetz, LPO, J. Barbirolli (r1935) Concert
(11/95) (PEAR) ① **[2] GEMMCDS9167**
Movt 2. J. Heifetz, A. Benoist (r1918) Concert
(1/91) (BIDD) ① **LAB015**
Movt 2. N. Milstein, L. Mittman (r1937) Concert
(7/93) (APR) ① **[2] APR7016**
Movt 2. B. Huberman, P. Frenkel (r1923) Concert
(3/94) (BIDD) ① **[2] LAB077/8**
Movt 2. J. Heifetz, A. Benoist (r1918) Concert
(11/94) (RCA) ① **[65] 09026 61778-2(01)**
Movt 2. N. Milstein, L. Mittman (r1937) Concert
(9/95) (BIDD) ① **LAB096**
Movt 3. J. Kubelík, G. Lapierre (r1913) Concert
(6/91) (BIDD) ① **[2] LAB033/4**
Fantaisie brillante on themes from Gounod's
'Faust'—violin and piano, Op. 20 (pub
1868)
Garden scene J. Kubelík, anon (r1902) Concert
(6/91) (BIDD) ① **[2] LAB033/4**
Mephisto variations J. Kubelík, anon (r1905)
Concert   (6/91) (BIDD) ① **[2] LAB033/4**
Légende—violin and orchestra, Op. 17 (pub.
c1860)
G. Shaham, LSO, L. Foster Concert
(12/91) (DG) ① **431 815-2GH**
R. Ricci, J. Gruenberg Concert
(6/92) (UNIC) ① **UKCD2048**
E. Friedman, LSO, M. Sargent Concert
(8/93) (RCA) ① **09026 61210-2**
A-S. Mutter, VPO, James Levine (r1992) Concert
(12/93) (DG) ① **437 544-2GH**
Polonaise No. 1 in D—violin and orchestra,
Op. 4 (pub 1853)
N. Milstein, L. Mittman (r1937) Concert
(7/93) (APR) ① **[2] APR7016**
I. Perlman, S. Sanders (r1972) Concert
(6/95) (EMI) ① **[20] CZS4 83177-2(1)**
Polonaise No. 2 in A—violin and orchestra,
Op. 21 (pub 1870)
R. Ricci, J. Gruenberg Concert
(6/92) (UNIC) ① **UKCD2048**
H. Temianka, J. Graudan (r1935) Concert
(2/93) (BIDD) ① **[2] LAB059/60**
H. Temianka, V. Topilin (r1935) Concert
(2/93) (BIDD) ① **[2] LAB059/60**
I. Perlman, S. Sanders Concert
(6/95) (EMI) ① **[20] CZS4 83177-2(1)**
Souvenir de Moscou—violin and orchestra,
Op. 6 (1853)
Y. Menuhin, M. Gazelle (r1935) Concert
(9/91) (TEST) ① **SBT1003**
M. Elman, P. Kahn (r1906) Concert
(12/91) (APR) ① **APR7015**
R. Ricci, J. Gruenberg Concert
(6/92) (UNIC) ① **UKCD2048**

SECTION II: CHAMBER

Adagio élégiaque—violin and piano, Op. 5
(1853)
S. Lupu, P. Pettinger Concert
(7/90) (CNTI) ① **CCD1017**
Capriccio-Valse—violin and piano, Op. 7
(1852)
X. Wei, Pam Nicholson Concert
(9/90) (ASV) ① **CDDCA698**
R. Ricci, J. Gruenberg Concert
(6/92) (UNIC) ① **UKCD2048**
B. Huberman, P. Frenkel (r1923) Concert
(3/94) (BIDD) ① **[2] LAB077/8**
M. Bisengaliev, J. Lenehan (r1992) Concert
(10/94) (NAXO) ① **8 550744**
J. Heifetz, B. Smith (r1937) Concert
(11/94) (RCA) ① **[65] 09026 61778-2(31)**
8 Etudes-Caprices, Op. 18
1. G minor; 2. E flat; 3. D; 4. A minor; 5. E flat; 6. D;
7. C minor; 8. F.
4. K-W. Chung, P. Moll Concert
(9/87) (DECC) ① **417 289-2DH**

4. I. Perlman, J.G. Guggenheim (arr Kreisler:
pp1990) Concert   (2/91) (EMI) ① **CDC7 54108-2**
4. I. Perlman, S. Sanders Concert
(6/95) (EMI) ① **[20] CZS4 83177-2(1)**
Fantasie orientale—violin and piano, Op. 24
S. Lupu, P. Pettinger Concert
(7/90) (CNTI) ① **CCD1017**
Gigue in E minor—violin and piano, Op. 27
(pub posth)
M. Bisengaliev, J. Lenehan (r1992) Concert
(10/94) (NAXO) ① **8 550744**
Grand caprice fantastique—violin and piano,
Op. 1 (1847)
S. Lupu, P. Pettinger Concert
(7/90) (CNTI) ① **CCD1017**
Kujawiak in A minor—violin and piano
(1853)
C. Hansen, B. Zakharoff (r1925) Concert
(12/91) (APR) ① **[2] APR7015**
R. Ricci, J. Gruenberg Concert
(6/92) (UNIC) ① **UKCD2048**
M. Bisengaliev, J. Lenehan (r1992) Concert
(10/94) (NAXO) ① **8 550744**
Légende—violin and piano, Op. 17
M. Vengerov, I. Golan (r1993) Concert
(4/94) (TELD) ① **9031-77351-2**
M. Bisengaliev, J. Lenehan (r1992) Concert
(10/94) (NAXO) ① **8 550744**
2 Mazurkas—violin and piano, Op. 12
1. D (Sielanka); 2. G minor (La Ménetrier).
2. M. Bisengaliev, J. Lenehan (r1992) Concert
(10/94) (NAXO) ① **8 550744**
2 Mazurkas—violin and piano, Op. 19
(c1860)
1. G (Obertass); 2. D (Dudziarz).
M. Bisengaliev, J. Lenehan (r1992) Concert
(10/94) (NAXO) ① **8 550744**
1. E. Ysaÿe, C. DeCreus (r1912) Concert
(8/90) (SYMP) ① **SYMCD1071**
1. K. Gregorowicz, anon (r1909) Concert
(8/90) (SYMP) ① **SYMCD1071**
1. R. Ricci, J. Gruenberg Concert
(6/92) (UNIC) ① **UKCD2048**
1. I. Perlman, S. Sanders Concert
(6/95) (EMI) ① **[20] CZS4 83177-2(1)**
2. J. Kubelík, anon (r1911) Concert
(6/91) (BIDD) ① **[2] LAB033/4**
2. B. Huberman, P. Frenkel (r1922) Concert
(3/94) (BIDD) ① **[2] LAB077/8**
Polonaise No. 1 in D—violin and piano, Op. 4
(1853)
R. Ricci, J. Gruenberg Concert
(6/92) (UNIC) ① **UKCD2048**
M. Vengerov, I. Golan (r1993) Concert
(4/94) (TELD) ① **9031-77351-2**
M. Bisengaliev, J. Lenehan (r1992) Concert
(10/94) (NAXO) ① **8 550744**
J. Heifetz, E. Bay (r1950) Concert
(11/94) (RCA) ① **[65] 09026 61778-2(08)**
J. Heifetz, E. Bay (r1937) Concert
(11/94) (RCA) ① **[65] 09026 61778-2(03)**
N. Milstein, L. Mittman (r1936) Concert
(9/95) (BIDD) ① **LAB096**
Russian Carnival—violin and piano, Op. 11
(1854)
S. Lupu, P. Pettinger Concert
(7/90) (CNTI) ① **CCD1017**
M. Bisengaliev, J. Lenehan (r1992) Concert
(10/94) (NAXO) ① **8 550744**
Saltarello—two violins (unidentified)
M. Bisengaliev, J. Lenehan (r1992) Concert
(10/94) (NAXO) ① **8 550744**
Scherzo-tarantelle in G minor—violin and
piano, Op. 16 (1856)
K-W. Chung, P. Moll (arr. Francescatti) Concert
(9/87) (DECC) ① **417 289-2DH**
J. Heifetz, A. Benoist (r1917) Concert
(1/91) (BIDD) ① **LAB015**
J. Kubelík, anon (r1906) Concert
(6/91) (BIDD) ① **[2] LAB033/4**
J. Heifetz, A. Benoist (r1917) Concert
(12/91) (APR) ① **[2] APR7015**
Y. Menuhin, A. Balsam (r1932) Concert
(12/91) (BIDD) ① **LAB046**
A. Campoli, D. Ibbott (r1979) Concert
(5/92) (DECC) ① **433 220-2DWO**
R. Ricci, J. Gruenberg Concert
(6/92) (UNIC) ① **UKCD2048**
H. Temianka, J. Graudan (r1936) Concert
(2/93) (BIDD) ① **[2] LAB059/60**
N. Milstein, L. Pommers (r1957) Concert
(5/94) (EMI) ① **[6] ZDMF7 64830-2**
M. Bisengaliev, J. Lenehan (r1992) Concert
(10/94) (NAXO) ① **8 550744**
J. Heifetz, E. Bay (r1950) Concert
(11/94) (RCA) ① **[65] 09026 61778-2(40)**

J. Heifetz, A. Sándor (r1934) Concert
(11/94) (RCA) ① **[65] 09026 61778-2(02)**
I. Perlman, S. Sanders (r1972) Concert
(6/95) (EMI) ① **[20] CZS4 83177-2(1)**
J. Heifetz, A. Sándor (r1934) Concert
(11/95) (PEAR) ① **[2] GEMMCDS9157**
Movt 2. J. Heifetz, A. Benoist (r1917) Concert
(11/94) (RCA) ① **[65] 09026 61778-2(01)**
Souvenir de Moscou—violin and piano, Op.
6 (1853)
M. Bisengaliev, J. Lenehan (r1992) Concert
(10/94) (NAXO) ① **8 550744**
Variations on an Original Theme—violin and
piano, Op. 15 (1854)
R. Ricci, J. Gruenberg Concert
(6/92) (UNIC) ① **UKCD2048**
M. Bisengaliev, J. Lenehan (r1992) Concert
(10/94) (NAXO) ① **8 550744**

WIENIAWSKI, Józef (1837–1912)
Poland

SECTION I: ORCHESTRAL

Concerto for Piano and Orchestra in G
minor, Op. 20 (1859)
M. Setrak, Baltic Phil SO, W. Rajski Chopin: Piano
Concerto 1.   (11/90) (CHNT) ① **LDC278 902**

WIKANDER, David (1884–1955)
Sweden

SECTION IV: VOCAL AND CHORAL

King Lily of the Valley—chorus (Wds.
Fröding)
Orphei Drängar Ch, E. Ericson Concert
(7/88) (BIS) ① **BIS-CD383**

WIKMANSON, Johan (1753–1800)
Sweden

SECTION II: CHAMBER

String Quartet No. 2 in E minor, Op. 1/2 (pub
1801)
Chilingirian Qt Concert
(8/89) (CRD) ① **[2] CRD3312/3**
Chilingirian Qt (r1979) F. Berwald: String Quartet 1.
(3/95) (CRD) ① **CRD3361**

WILBY, Philip (20th Cent)
England

SECTION IV: VOCAL AND CHORAL

Easter Wings—song (Wds. G. Herbert)
M. Wiegold, Composers Ens, D. Muldowney Concert
(4/92) (NMC) ① **NMCD003**

WILBYE, John (1574–1638)
England

SECTION IV: VOCAL AND CHORAL

The First Set of English Madrigals—3-6vv
(pub 1598)
1. Adew, sweet Amarillis (4vv); 2. Alas, what a
wretched life is this (5vv); 3. Alas, what hope of
speeding (4vv); 4. Away, thou shalt not love me
(3vv); 5. Ay mee, can every rumour (3vv); 6. Cruell,
behold my heavie ending (4vv); 7. Deere pitie, how?
ah how? (3vv); 8. Dye hapless man (5vv); 9. Flora
gave mee fairest flowers (4vv); 10. Fly love sixth to
heaven (3vv); 11. I alwaies beg (5vv); 12. I fall, I fall,
O stay mee (5vv); 13. I soung sometimes my
thoughts and fancies pleasure (5vv); 14. Lady, when I
beehold (4vv); 15. Lady, when I beehold (6vv); 16.
Lady, your words doe spight mee (4vv); 17. Of joys
and pleasing pains I late went singing (6vv); 18.
Sweet love, if thou wilt gaine a monarches glory
(6vv); 19. Thou art but young thou sayst (6vv); 20.
This saith my Cloris bright (4vv); 21. Unkind, O stay
thy flying (5vv); 22. Weepe, O mine eies (3vv); 23.
What needeth all this travaile (4vv); 24. When shall
my wretched life give place to death? (6vv); 25. Why
dost thou shoot (6vv); 26. Yee restlesse thoughts
(3vv).
1. Amaryllis Consort, C. Brett Concert
(3/88) (CARL) ① **PCD873**
1. Hilliard Ens, P. Hillier Concert
(2/89) (EMI) ① **CDC7 49197-2**
1, 9. Cambridge Sngrs, J. Rutter Concert
(11/87) (CLLE) ① **COLCD105**
Homo natus de muliere—motet: 6vv
Worcester Cath Ch, Don Hunt, R. Johnston (r1993)
Concert   (2/95) (ABBE) ① **CDCA957**

The **Second Set of Madrigals**—3-6vv (pub 1609)
1. Ah, cannot sighes, nor teares (6vv); 2. Ah, cruell Amarillis (3vv); 3. All pleasure is of this condition (5vv); 4. As fayre as morne (3vv); 5. A silly silvan (5vv); 6. As matchlesse beauty (4vv); 7. Change me O heavens (4vv); 8. Come shepheard swaynes (3vv); 9. Downe in a valley (5vv); 10. Draw on sweet night (6vv); 11. Flourish yee hillocks (3vv); 12. Fly not so swift (4vv); 13. Happy, O happy he (4vv); 14. Happy streams whose trembling fall (4vv); 15. I live, and yet me thinks (3vv); 16. I love alas, yet am not loved (4vv); 17. Long have I made these hills (6vv); 18. Love not me for comely grace (4vv); 19. Oft have I vowde (4vv); 20. O what shall I doe (3vv); 21. O wretched man (6vv); 22. Softly, softly drop mine eyes (6vv); 23. So light is love (3vv); 24. Stay Coridon thou swaine (6vv); 25. Sweet hony sucking bees (5vv); 26. There is a jewell (3vv); 27. There where I saw (5vv); 28. Weepe, mine eyes (5vv); 29. When Cloris heard of her Amintas dying (4vv); 30. Where most my thoughts (6vv); 31. Yee that doe love (5vv).
10, 25. Hilliard Ens, P. Hillier *Concert*
(2/89) (EMI) ① CDC7 49197-2
10, 28. Cambridge Sngrs, J. Rutter *Concert*
(11/87) (CLLE) ① COLCD105
10, 28. Amaryllis Consort, C. Brett *Concert*
(3/88) (CARL) ① PCD873

WILD, Earl (b 1915) USA

SECTION III: INSTRUMENTAL

Hommage à Poulenc—piano
E. Wild (r1995) *Concert*
(12/95) (SONY) ① SK62036
Improvisation in the form of a Theme and Variations on Gershwin's 'Someone to watch over me'—piano (1989)
E. Wild *Concert* (10/90) (CHES) ① Chesky CD32
Improvisation on 'Après un rêve' (Fauré)—piano
E. Wild (r1995) *Concert*
(12/95) (SONY) ① SK62036
Reminiscences of 'Snow White and the Seven Dwarfs' (Churchill)—piano
E. Wild (r1995) *Concert*
(12/95) (SONY) ① SK62036
7 Virtuoso Etudes after Gershwin—piano (1950s rev 1976)
1. I got rhythm; 2. Oh, lady, be good!; 3. Liza; 4. Embraceable you; 5. Somebody loves me; 6. Fascinatin' rhythm; 7. The man I love.
E. Wild *Concert* (10/90) (CHES) ① Chesky CD32

WILDER, Alec (1907–1978) USA

SECTION I: ORCHESTRAL

Concerto for Oboe, Orchestra and Percussion
H. Lucarelli, Brooklyn PO, M. Barrett (r1993) *Concert*
(7/94) (KOCH) ① 37187-2

SECTION II: CHAMBER

Piece for Oboe and Improvisatory Percussion
H. Lucarelli, M. Wood (r1993) *Concert*
(7/94) (KOCH) ① 37187-2

WILDER, Philip van (c1500–1553) Flanders/Britain

SECTION III: INSTRUMENTAL

Arthur's Dump—lute (doubtful)
C. Wilson *Concert* (11/91) (VIRG) ① VC7 59034-2

SECTION IV: VOCAL AND CHORAL

Blessed art thou—anthem
Magdalen Oxford Coll Ch, J. Harper *Concert*
(11/91) (ABBE) ① CDCA901

WILKINSON, Robert (c1450–1515 or later) England

may be spelt Wylkynson

SECTION IV: VOCAL AND CHORAL

Credi in Deum/Jesus autem—13vv (from 'Eton Choirbook')
The Sixteen, H. Christophers *Concert*
(7/93) (COLL) ① Coll1342-2
Salve regina—motet: 9vv (from Eton Choirbook)
The Sixteen, H. Christophers *Concert*
(11/89) (MERI) ① CDE84175

The Sixteen, H. Christophers *Concert*
(7/93) (COLL) ① Coll1342-2

WILLAERT, Adrian (c1490–1562) Flanders

SECTION II: CHAMBER

O dolce vita mia—lirone, Italian harp and chitarrone
Tragicomedia *Concert*
(9/92) (EMI) ① CDC7 54191-2

SECTION IV: VOCAL AND CHORAL

A quand'haveva—chanson (pub 1545) (from 'Canzone Villanesche all Napolitana')
Kithara (r1993) *Concert*
(3/95) (CHAN) ① CHAN0562
Ave virgo sponsa Dei
King's Sngrs *Concert*
(9/92) (EMI) ① CDC7 54191-2
Dessus le marché d'Arras—chanson: 4vv (c1528)
C. Janequin Ens, D. Visse (r1994) *Concert*
(5/95) (HARM) ① HMC90 1453
O bene mio—chanson (pub 1545) (from 'Canzone Villanesche')
Kithara (r1993) *Concert*
(3/95) (CHAN) ① CHAN0562
O dolce vita mia
King's Sngrs, Tragicomedia *Concert*
(9/92) (EMI) ① CDC7 54191-2
Qual dolcezza giamai
King's Sngrs *Concert*
(9/92) (EMI) ① CDC7 54191-2
Vecchie letrose
King's Sngrs, Tragicomedia *Concert*
(9/92) (EMI) ① CDC7 54191-2

WILLAN, (James) Healey (1880–1968) England/Canada

B-Numbers used in G. Bryant, 1972

SECTION III: INSTRUMENTAL

Introduction, Passacaglia and Fugue—organ, B149 (1916)
A. Fletcher *Concert* (11/91) (MIRA) ① MRCD903

WILLE, Rudolf (fl 1939) Austria

SECTION V: STAGE WORKS

Königsballade—operetta
Euren König will ich preisen; Ewig muss ich dein gedenken H. Roswaenge, Berlin St Op Orch, B. Seidler-Winkler (r1938) *Concert*
(5/90) (PREI) ① 89018

WILLIAMS, Bert (1874–1922) West Indies/USA

SECTION IV: VOCAL AND CHORAL

I'm Tired of Eating in the Restaurants—song for W M Cook's show 'Bandanna Land' (1908—New York)
Bert Williams, Orig Broadway Cast (r1906) *Concert*
(5/94) (PEAR) ① [3] GEMMCDS9053/5
Moriah: A Scotch Medley—song for the show 'The Old Town' (1910)
Montgomery & Stone, Orig Broadway Cast (r1911) *Concert* (5/94) (PEAR) ① [3] GEMMCDS9053/5

SECTION V: STAGE WORKS

In Abyssinia—musical show (1906—New York)
EXCERPTS: 1. Nobody (Lyrics Rogers); 2. Let it Alone (Lyrics Rogers); 3. Here it Comes Again; 4. Pretty Desdemone (Music & Lyrics Wildman).
1-4. Bert Williams, Broadway Cast (r1906) *Concert*
(5/94) (PEAR) ① [3] GEMMCDS9050/2(2)
Sons of Ham—songs for the vaudeville show (1902)
EXCERPTS: 1. All Goin Out and Nothing Coming In (Lyrics George Walker); 2. The Phrenologist Coon (Accooe & Hogan); 3. My Little Zule Babe (Potter).
1-3. Bert Williams, Broadway Cast (r1901) *Concert*
(5/94) (PEAR) ① [3] GEMMCDS9050/2(1)

WILLIAMS, Charles (1893–1978) England

SECTION V: STAGE WORKS

The Lady Vanishes—film score (1938) (collab with Louis Levy)
EXCERPTS: 1. Prelude.
1. Prague City PO, P. Bateman (recons & orch Philip Lane) *Concert* (9/95) (SILV) ① FILMCD159
The Night Has Eyes—film score (1946)
EXCERPTS: 1. Theme.
1. QHLO, C. Williams (r1946) *Concert*
(9/94) (EMI) ① CDGO 2059

WILLIAMS, Clifton (1923–1976) USA

SECTION I: ORCHESTRAL

Fanfare and Allegro—wind orchestra (1956)
Eastman Wind Ens, F. Fennell *Concert*
(12/91) (MERC) ① 432 009-2MM

WILLIAMS, Grace (Mary) (1906–1977) Wales

SECTION I: ORCHESTRAL

Carillons—oboe and orchestra (1965 rev 1973)
A. Camden, LSO, C. Groves (r1973) *Concert*
(6/95) (LYRI) ① SRCD323
Concerto for Trumpet and Orchestra (1973)
H. Snell, LSO, C. Groves (r1973) *Concert*
(6/95) (LYRI) ① SRCD323
Fantasia on Welsh Nursery Tunes—orchestra (1940)
LSO, C. Groves (r1973) *Concert*
(6/95) (LYRI) ① SRCD323
Penillion—orchestra (1955)
R. Allan, RPO, C. Groves (r1971) *Concert*
(6/95) (LYRI) ① SRCD323
Sea Sketches—string orchestra (1944)
ECO, D. Atherton (r1970) *Concert*
(6/95) (LYRI) ① SRCD323

WILLIAMS, Graham (b 1940) England

SECTION II: CHAMBER

The song within—clarinet, cello and piano (1980)
Mühlfeld Ens (r1993) *Concert*
(10/94) (CLRI) ① CC0007

WILLIAMS, John (Towner) (b 1932) USA

SECTION V: STAGE WORKS

Born on the Fourth of July—film score (1989)
EXCERPTS: 2. End Credits.
2. Prague City PO, P. Bateman (r c1994: arr P Bateman) *Concert* (9/95) (SILV) ① FILMCD160
The Cowboys—concert suite from film score
Prague City PO, P. Bateman (r1994) *Concert*
(11/94) (SILV) ① FILMCD153
Prague City PO, P. Bateman (r c1994) *Concert*
(9/95) (SILV) ① FILMCD160
Dracula—film score (1979)
EXCERPTS: 1. Main Title and Storm Sequence; 2. The Night Visitor; 3. To Scarborough; 4. The Abduction of Lucy; 5. Night Journeys; 6. The Love Scene; 7. Meeting in the Cave; 8. The Bat Attack; 9. For Mina; 10. Dracula's Death; 11. End Titles.
5. Hollywood Bowl SO, J. Mauceri (r1993) *Concert*
(1/95) (PHIL) ① 442 425-2PH
E. T. (The Extra Terrestrial)—film score (1982)
EXCERPTS: 1. Three Million Light Years From Home; 2. Abandoned and Pursued; 3. E.T. and Me; 4. E.T.'s Halloween; 5. Flying Theme; 6. E.T. Phone Home; 7. Over the Moon; 8. Adventures on Earth; 8a. The Bicycle Chase; 8b. The Departure.
5. Hollywood Bowl SO, J. Mauceri (r1991) *Concert*
(9/91) (PHIL) ① 432 109-2PH
Family Plot—film score (1976)
EXCERPTS: 1. Finale.
1. Prague City PO, P. Bateman (orch Kevin Townend) *Concert* (9/95) (SILV) ① FILMCD159
1. Prague City PO, P. Bateman (r c1994: arr K Townend) *Concert* (9/95) (SILV) ① FILMCD160

Far and Away—film score (1992)
EXCERPTS: 1. County Galway, June 1892; 2. The Fighting Donnellys; 3. Joe Sr.'s Passing & The Duel Scene; 4. Leaving Home; 5. Burning the Manor House; 6. Blowing Off Steam; 7. Fighting for Dough; 8. Am I Beautiful?; 9. The Big Match; 10. Inside the Mansion; 11. Shannon is Shot; 12. Joseph's Dream; 13. The Reunion; 14. Oklahoma Territory; 15. The Land Race; 16. Settling with Steven & The Race to the River; 17. Joseph and Shannon; 18. End Credits; 19. SONG: Book of Days (comp & perf Enya).
18. Prague City PO, P. Bateman (r c1994: arr P Bateman) *Concert*   (9/95) (SILV) ① FILMCD160

Home Alone—film score (1990) (song cpsrs given in parentheses)
EXCERPTS: 1. Main Title: Somewhere In My Memory (Wds Bricusse); 2. Holiday Flight; 3. The House; 4. Star of Bethlehem (orchestral vers); 5. Man of the House; 6. Scammed by a Kindergartner; 7. Follow That Kid!; 8. Making the Plane; 9. Star of Bethlehem (Wds Bricusse); 10. Setting the Trap; 11. Somewhere In My Memory (Wds Bricusse); 12. The Attack on the House; 13. Mom Returns & Finale; 14. We Wish You a Merry Christmas (Trad arr Williams) & End Title; 15. SONG: White Christmas (I. Berlin); 16. SONG: Please Come Home for Christmas (Brown/Redd); 17. SONG: O Holy Night (Adam, trans Dwight); 18. SONG: Carol of the Bells (Wilhousky); 19. SONG: Have Yourself a Merry Little Christmas (Martin/Blane).
1-19. OST, J.T. Williams (r1990)
   (5/91) (SONY) ① MK46595

Indiana Jones and the Last Crusade—film score (1988)
EXCERPTS: 1. Indy's Very First Adventure; 2. X Marks the Spot; 3. Scherzo for Motorcycle and Orchestra; 4. Ah, Rats!; 5. Escape from Venice; 6. No Ticket; 7. The Keeper of the Grail; 8. Keeping Up With the Joneses; 9. Brother of the Cruciform Sword; 10. Belly of the Steel Beast; 11. The Canyon of the Crescent Moon; 12. The Penitent Man Will Pass; 13. End Credits (Raiders March).
13. Prague City PO, P. Bateman (r c1994) *Concert*
   (9/95) (SILV) ① FILMCD160

Indiana Jones and the Temple of Doom—film score (1984)
EXCERPTS: 1. Anything Goes (Cole Porter, arr Williams); 2. Fast Streets of Shanghai; 3. Nocturnal Activities; 4. Shortround's Theme; 5. Children in Chains; 6. Slalom on Mount Humol; 7. The Temple of Doom; 8. Bug Tunnel and Death Trap; 9a. Slave Children's Crusade; 9b. Parade of the Slave Children (concert arr of 9a); 10. The Mine Car Chase; 11. Finale and End Credits.
3. Prague City PO, P. Bateman (r c1994) *Concert*
   (9/95) (SILV) ① FILMCD160

Jane Eyre—film score (1970)
EXCERPTS: 1. Jane Eyre Theme; 2. Overture; 3. Lowood; 4. To Thornfield; 5. String Quartet—Festivity at Thornfield; 6. Grace Poole and Mason's Arrival; 7. Trio—The Meeting; 8. Thwarted Wedding; 9. Across the Moors; 10. Restoration; 11. Reunion.
4. National PO, C. Gerhardt *Concert*
   (6/90) (VARE) ① VSD5207

Jaws—film score (1975)
EXCERPTS: 1. Main Theme; 2. Chrissie's Death; 3. Promenade (Tourists on the Menu); 4. Out to Sea; 5. The Indianapolis Story; 6. Sea Attack Number One; 7. One Barrel Chase; 8. Preparing the Cage (concert arr as 'The Shark Cage Fugue'); 9. Night Search; 10. The Underwater Siege; 11. Hand to Hand Combat; 12. End Title.
1. Prague City PO, P. Bateman (r c1994: arr P Smith) *Concert*   (9/95) (SILV) ① FILMCD160

Jurassic Park—film score (1993)
EXCERPTS: 1. Opening Titles; 2. Theme from Jurassic Park; 3. Incident at Isla Nublar; 4. Journey to the Island; 5. The Raptor Attack; 6. Hatching Baby Raptor; 7. Welcome to Jurassic Park; 8. My Friend, the Brachiosaurus; 9. Dennis steals the Embryo; 10. A Tree for My Bed; 11. High-Wire Stunts; 12. Remembering Petticoat Lane; 13. Jurassic Gate; 14. Eye to Eye; 15. T-Rex Rescue and Finale; 16. End Credits.
Main Themes Prague City PO, P. Bateman (r c1994) *Concert*   (9/95) (SILV) ① FILMCD160
2. Los Angeles Master Chorale, Hollywood Bowl SO, J. Mauceri (r1993) *Concert*
   (1/95) (PHIL) ① 442 425-2PH

Midway—film score (1976)
EXCERPTS: 1. March.
1. Prague City PO, P. Bateman (r1994; arr J. Bell) *Concert*   (11/94) (SILV) ① FILMCD151

Presumed Innocent—film score (1990)
EXCERPTS: 1. Presumed Innocent; 2. Remembering Carolyn; 3. Family Life; 4. Love Scene;

5. The B File; 6. The Bedroom Scene; 7. Carolyn's Office; 8. 'Leon Talks'; 9. Rusty Accused; 10. Case Dismissed; 11. The Boat Scene; 12. The Basement Scene; 13. Barbara's Confession; 14. End Title.
14. Prague City PO, P. Bateman (r c1994) *Concert*   (9/95) (SILV) ① FILMCD160

Raiders of the Lost Ark—film score (1981)
EXCERPTS: 1. Flight From Peru; 2. The Map Room; 3. Dawn; 4. The Basket Game; 5. The Well of Souls; 6. Desert Chase; 7. Marion's Theme; 8. The Miracle of the Ark; 9. The Raiders March.
9. San Diego SO, L. Schifrin *Concert*
   (5/93) (SILV) ① SILVAD3001

The Reivers—film score (1969)
EXCERPTS: 1. Main Title/First Instruction/The Winton Flyer; 2. Family Funeral/Lucius' First Drive; 3. The Road to Memphis; 4. Corrie's Entrance/The Picture; 5. Reflections; 6. The Sheriff Departs/The Bad News/Ned's Secret; 7. Memphis; 8. Ned's Trde; 9. The People Protest; 10. Prayers at Bedtime; 11. Lucius Runs to Corrie/Back Home; 12. Finale.
Suite National PO, C. Gerhardt (arr Gerhardt) *Concert*   (6/90) (VARE) ① VSD5207
1-12. OST, J. T. Williams (r1969)
   (9/95) (COLU) ① CK66130

Schindler's List—film score (1993)
EXCERPTS: 1. Theme from Schindler's List; 2. Jewish Town (Krakow Ghetto—Winter '41); 3. Immolation (With Our Lives, We Give Life); 4. Remembrance; 5. Schindler's Workforce; 6. OYF'N Pripteshok (comp Mark Warschafsky) and Nacht Aktion; 7. I Could Have Done More; 8. Auschwitz-Birkenau; 9. Stolen Memories; 10. Making the List; 11. Give Me Your Names; 12. Yeroushalaim Chel Zahav (Jerusalem of Gold; comp Naomi Shemer); 13. Remembrances (with violin solo); 14. Theme from Schindler's List (reprise).
1. Prague City PO, P. Bateman (r c1994) *Concert*   (9/95) (SILV) ① FILMCD160
1-14. OST, I. Perlman, Li-Ron Herzeliya Children's Ch, Ramat Gan Chbr Ch, Boston SO, J.T. Williams (r1993)   (8/94) (MCA) ① MCD10969

Star Wars: Episode IV, '(A) New Hope'—film score (1977) (some items arr as concert versions)
EXCERPTS: 1. Main Title; 2. Imperial Attack; 3. Princess Leia's Theme (concert arr); 4. The Little People Work; 5a. The Desert; 5b. The Robot Auction; 6. The Princess Appears; 7. The Land of the Sandpeople; 8. The Return Home; 9. A Hive of Villainy; 10. Inner City; 11a. Cantina Band; 11b. Cantina Band 2; 12a. Mouse Robot; 12b. Blasting Off; 13. Destruction of Alderaan; 14. Rescue of the Princess; 15. The Walls Converge; 16a. Ben's Death; 16b. TIE Fighter Attack (concert arr as 'Here They Come!'); 17. Standing By; 18. The Last Battle; 19a. The Throne Room; 19b. End Title.
Suite Rochester Pops, L. Schifrin *Concert*
   (5/93) (SILV) ① SILVAD3002
1. National PO, C. Gerhardt *Concert*
   (10/92) (RCA) ① GD82792
1. Prague City PO, P. Bateman (r c1994) *Concert*
   (9/95) (SILV) ① FILMCD160
1-4, 5a, 5b, 6-10, 11a, 11b, 12a, 12b, 13-15, 16a, 16b, 17, 18, 19a, 19b OST, LSO, J. T. Williams (r1977)   (11/94) (FOX) ① [4] 07822 11012-2

Star Wars: Episode V, '(The) Empire Strikes Back'—film score (1980) (some items arr as concert versions)
EXCERPTS: 1a. Main Title; 1b. The Imperial Probe; 2. Luke's Escape; 3. Luke's Rescue; 4. The Imperial March: Darth Vader's Theme (concert arr); 5a. Drawing the Battle Lines; 5b. Leia's First Instructions; 6. The Battle in the Snow; 7. Luke's First Crash; 8. The Rebels Escape Again; 9. The Asteroid Field; 10. Crash Landing; 11. Yoda's Theme (concert arr); 12. Han Solo and the Princess; 13. The Training of a Jedi Knight; 14. The Magic Tree; 15. Attack Position; 16. Yoda and the Force; 17. City in the Clouds; 18. Lando's Palace; 19a. Carbon Freeze; 19b. Luke Pursues the Captives; 19c. Departure of Boba Fett; 20. The Duel; 21. Losing a Hand; 22. Hyperspace; 23a. Finale; 23b. End Credits.
1a, 1b, 2a, 4, 5a, 5b, 6-18, 19a-c, 20-22, 23a, 23b OST, LSO, J. T. Williams (r1980) *Concert*   (11/94) (FOX) ① [4] 07822 11012-2
4. St Louis SO, L. Slatkin *Concert*
   (6/89) (RCA) ① RD87716
4. San Diego SO, L. Schifrin *Concert*
   (5/93) (SILV) ① SILVAD3003
12. Prague City PO, P. Bateman (r c1994) *Concert*   (9/95) (SILV) ① FILMCD160

Star Wars: Episode VI, 'Return of the Jedi'—film score (1983) (some items arr as concert versions)
EXCERPTS: 1a. Main Title; 1b. Approaching the Death Star; 2a. Han Solo Returns: At the Court of Jabba the Hut; 2b. Jabba the Hut (concert arr); 3. Lapti Nek: Jabba's Palace Band; 4. Fight in the Dungeon; 5a. The Return of the Jedi (original version); 5b. The Return of the Jedi (film version); 6. The Emperor Arrives; 7. The Death of Yoda; 8. Faking the Code; 9. Parade of the Ewoks (concert arr); 10a. The Fleet Goes into Hyperspace; 10b. Heroic Ewok; 11a. Brother and Sister; 11b. Luke & Leia (concert arr of 'Brother & Sister'); 12. The Emperor Confronts Luke; 13. Into the Trap; 14a. First Ewok Battle; 14b. Fight With the Fighters; 15a. The Ewok Battle; 15b. The Forest Battle (concert arr of 'Ewok Battle'); 16a. Leia is Wounded; 16b. Luke and Vader Duel; 17a. Final Duel; 17b. Into the Death Star; 18. The Emperor's Death (aka 'The Emperor'); 19. Darth Vader's Death; 20. Through the Flames; 21a. Leia Breaks the News; 21b. Funeral Pyre for a Jedi (aka 'Rebel Briefing'); 22a. Ewok Celebration; 22b. Finale.
1a, 1b, 2a, 3, 4, 5a, 5b, 6-9, 10a, 10b, 11a, 11b, 12, 13, 14a, 14b, 15a, 15b, 16a, 16b, 17a, 17b, 18-20, 21a, 21b, 22a, 22b OST, LSO, J. T. Williams (r1983) *Concert*   (11/94) (FOX) ① [4] 07822 11012-2
15b Prague City PO, P. Bateman (r c1994) *Concert*   (9/95) (SILV) ① FILMCD160

Superman—film score (1978)
EXCERPTS: 1. Main Theme (Superman March); 2. Love Theme; 3. The Planet Krypton; 4. Destruction of Krypton; 5. The Trip to Earth; 6. Leaving Home; 7. The Fortress of Solitude; 8. The Flying Sequence & Can You Read My Mind (Lyrics L Bricusse); 9. Super Rescues; 10. Superfeats; 11. The March of the Villains; 12. Chasing Rockets; 13. Turning Back the World; 14. End Title.
1. San Diego SO, L. Schifrin *Concert*
   (5/93) (SILV) ① SILVAD3003

1941—film score (1979)
EXCERPTS: 1. March; 2. The Invasion; 3. The Sentries; 4. Riot at the U. S. O. 5. To Hollywood and Glory; 6. Swing, Swing, Swing; 7. The Battle of Hollywood; 8. The Ferris Wheel sequence; 9. Finale.
1. Prague City PO, P. Bateman (r1994; arr B. Rogers) *Concert*   (11/94) (SILV) ① FILMCD151
1. Prague City PO, P. Bateman (r c1994: arr B Rogers) *Concert*   (9/95) (SILV) ① FILMCD160

WILLIAMS, Meiron (1901-1976)
Wales

SECTION IV: VOCAL AND CHORAL

Adlewych, 'Reflection'—song cycle
1. Y Cymro (The Welshman); 2. Aberdaron; 3. Y Môr Enaid (The soul of the sea); 4. Rhos y Pererinion (Moor of the Pilgrims); 5. Yr Hwyr (Evening); 6. Ffarwel y Bardd (The poet's farewell).
Cpte B. Terfel, A. Bryn Parri (r1992-3) *Concert*
   (8/93) (SAIN) ① SCDC2013

Aros Mae'r Mynyddau Mawr, '(The) Mountains Remain'—song (Wds. Ceiriog)
B. Terfel, A. Bryn Parri (r1992-3) *Concert*
   (8/93) (SAIN) ① SCDC2013

Awelon y Mynydd, 'Mountain Breezes'—song (Wds. J. Evans)
B. Terfel, A. Bryn Parri (r1992-3) *Concert*
   (8/93) (SAIN) ① SCDC2013

Cloch y Llan, '(The) Church Bell'—song (Wds. Crwys)
B. Terfel, A. Bryn Parri (r1992-3) *Concert*
   (8/93) (SAIN) ① SCDC2013

Ffarwel Iti, Cymru, 'Farewell, fair Wales'—song (Wds. Ceiriog)
B. Terfel, A. Bryn Parri (r1992-3) *Concert*
   (8/93) (SAIN) ① SCDC2013

Gwynfyd, 'Paradise'—song (Wds. Crwys)
B. Terfel, A. Bryn Parri (r1992-3) *Concert*
   (8/93) (SAIN) ① SCDC2013

O Fab y Dyn, 'O! Son of Man'—song (Wds. G. Rees)
B. Terfel, A. Bryn Parri (r1992-3) *Concert*
   (8/93) (SAIN) ① SCDC2013

Ora Pro Nobis, 'Pray for Us'—song (Wds. Eifion Wyn)
B. Terfel, A. Bryn Parri (r1992-3) *Concert*
   (8/93) (SAIN) ① SCDC2013

Pan Ddaw'r Nos, 'When Night Comes'—song (Wds. Elfed)
B. Terfel, A. Bryn Parri (r1992-3) *Concert*
   (8/93) (SAIN) ① SCDC2013

Rhosyn yr Haf, 'Summer Rose'—song (Wds. Ceiriog)
B. Terfel, A. Bryn Parri (r1992-3) Concert
(8/93) (SAIN) ① SCDC2013
Y Llyn, '(The) Lake'—song (Wds. Caradog Prichard)
B. Terfel, A. Bryn Parri (r1992-3) Concert
(8/93) (SAIN) ① SCDC2013

WILLIAMSON, Roy (20th cent)
Scotland

SECTION IV: VOCAL AND CHORAL

Flower of Scotland—song
Glasgow CWS Band, H. Snell (arr Ferney) Concert
(9/92) (DOYE) ① DOYCD005

WILLSON, Meredith (1902–1984)
USA

SECTION V: STAGE WORKS

The Music Man—musical show (1957—New York) (Book and lyrics cpsr)
EXCERPTS: 1. Overture; 2. Rock Island; 3. Iowa Stubborn; 4. Ya Got Trouble; 5. Piano Lesson; 6. Goodnight My Someone; 7. Seventy-Six Trombones; 8. Sincere; 9. The Sadder-But-Wiser Girl For Me; 10. Pick-a-Little, Talk-a-Little; 11. Goodnight Ladies; 12. Marian the Librarian; 13. My White Knight; 14. Wells Fargo Wagon; 15. It's You; 16. Shipoopi; 17. Lida Rose; 18. Will I Ever Tell You; 19. Gary, Indiana; 20. Till There Was You; 21. Finale.
Cpte B. Cook, R. Preston, Orig Broadway Cast, H. Greene (r1957)   (11/93) (EMI) ① ZDM7 64663-2
20. V. Masterson, T. Allen, Philh, J.O. Edwards (r1990) Concert   (5/94) (TER) ① CDVIR8317
The Unsinkable Molly Brown—musical show (1960—New York) (Lyrics cpsr)
Cpte T. Grimes, H. Presnell, Orig Broadway Cast, H. Greene (r1960)   (11/93) (EMI) ① ZDM7 64761-2

WILSON, Al H. (19th–20th Cent)
USA

SECTION IV: VOCAL AND CHORAL

In Tyrol—song from the show 'The Watch On the Rhine' (1905)
A. H. Wilson, Broadway Cast (r1906) Concert
(5/94) (PEAR) ① [3] GEMMCDS9050/2(2)

SECTION V: STAGE WORKS

A Prince of Tatters—songs from the show (1902)
EXCERPTS: 1. The Winding of the Yarn; 2. Whispering Breezes.
1, 2. A. H. Wilson, Broadway Cast (r1906-7) Concert
(5/94) (PEAR) ① [3] GEMMCDS9050/2(1)

WILSON, G.D. (19th Cent)

SECTION III: INSTRUMENTAL

The Shepherd Boy—piano
A. Etherden Concert
(7/93) (HUNT) ① HMPCD0589

WILSON, Ian (b 1964) Ireland

SECTION II: CHAMBER

Winter's Edge—string quartet (1990s)
Vanbrugh Qt (r1993) Concert
(10/94) (CHAN) ① CHAN9295

WILSON, Sandy (Alexander Galbraith) (b 1924) England

SECTION V: STAGE WORKS

The Boy Friend—musical show (1954—London) (Book & Lyrics cpsr)
EXCERPTS: 1. Overture; 2. Perfect Young Ladies; 3. The Boy Friend; 4. Won't You Charleston With Me; 5. Fancy Forgetting; 6. I Could Be Happy With You; 7. Sur la Plage; 8. A Room in Bloomsbury; 9. It's Nicer in Nice; 10. The You-Don't-Want-to-Play-With-Me Blues; 11. Safety in Numbers; 12. The Riviera; 13. It's Never too Late to Fall in Love; 14. Poor Little Pierrette; 15. Finale.
Cpte London Cast, C. Walker (r1984; 30th anniversary cast)   (3/87) (TER) ① CDTER1095

WILSON, Stanley (20th Cent)
England

SECTION IV: VOCAL AND CHORAL

Gibberish—part-song, Op. 55 (Wds. M. Coleridge)
King's Sngrs Concert
(6/88) (EMI) ① CDC7 49765-2
To a Lady seen from the train—part-song, Op. 42/2 (Wds. Cornford)
King's Sngrs Concert
(6/88) (EMI) ① CDC7 49765-2

WILSON, Thomas (b 1927)
USA/Scotland

SECTION I: ORCHESTRAL

Concerto for Piano and Orchestra (1984)
D. Wilde, SNO, B. Thomson Introit.
(10/88) (CHAN) ① CHAN8626
Introit, 'Towards the Light...'—orchestra (1982)
SNO, B. Thomson Piano Concerto.
(10/88) (CHAN) ① CHAN8626

WINTER, Peter (1754–1825)
Germany

SECTION I: ORCHESTRAL

Concerto for Oboe and Orchestra in F
P.W. Feit, Württemberg CO, J. Faerber Neuner:
Oboe Concerto.   (10/89) (SCHW) ① 311027

SECTION V: STAGE WORKS

Maometto II—opera: 2 acts (1817—Milan) (Lib. F. Romani)
Del che plangendo imploro B. Mills, A. Mason, C. du Plessis, Philh, D. Parry Concert
(10/90) (OPRA) ① [3] ORCH103

WINTERNITZ, Felix (1872–1948)

SECTION II: CHAMBER

Dance of the marionettes—violin and piano
F. Kreisler, C. Lamson (r1928) Concert
(12/93) (BIDD) ① LAB080

WIRÉN, Dag (Ivar) (1905–1986)
Sweden

SECTION I: ORCHESTRAL

Concerto for Violin and Orchestra (1945-46)
N-E. Sparf, Stockholm PO, S. Comissiona Concert
(4/92) (CPRI) ① CAP21326
Serenade—string orchestra, Op. 11 (1937)
1. Allegro molto; 2. Andante espressivo; 3. Scherzo; 4. Marcia.
Stockholm Sinfonietta, E-P. Salonen Concert
(4/85) (BIS) ① BIS-CD285
Scottish Baroque Ens, Lionel Friedman Concert
(10/87) (CRD) ① CRD3342
Triptych—small orchestra, Op. 33 (1958)
Stockholm Sinfonietta, J-O. Wedin Concert
(4/92) (CPRI) ① CAP21326

SECTION II: CHAMBER

Piano Trio No. 1, Op. 6 (1933)
Stockholm Arts Trio (r1992) Concert
(2/94) (BIS) ① BIS-CD582
Piano Trio No. 2, Op. 36 (1961)
Stockholm Arts Trio (r1992) Concert
(2/94) (BIS) ① BIS-CD582
Sonatina for Cello and Piano, Op. 1 (1931)
T. Thedéen, S. Bojsten (r1992) Concert
(2/94) (BIS) ① BIS-CD582
Sonatina for Violin and Piano, Op. 15 (1940)
D. Almgren, S. Bojsten (r1992) Concert
(2/94) (BIS) ① BIS-CD582
String Quartet No. 3, Op. 18 (1941-45)
Lindsay Qt (bp1987) Concert
(1/93) (ASV) ① CDDCA825
String Quartet No. 5, Op. 41 (1968-70)
Saulesco Qt Concert   (4/92) (CPRI) ① CAP21326
Wind Quintet—flute, oboe, clarinet, horn and bassoon, Op. 42 (1971)
Stockholm Wind Qnt Concert
(4/92) (CPRI) ① CAP21326

SECTION III: INSTRUMENTAL

5 Ironical Miniatures—piano, Op. 19 (1942-45)
S. Bojsten (r1992) Concert
(2/94) (BIS) ① BIS-CD582

WISE, Michael (c1647–1687)
England

SECTION IV: VOCAL AND CHORAL

The Ways of Zion do mourn—verse anthem
New College Ch, E. Higginbottom Concert
(3/90) (PROU) ① PROUCD125
J. Budd, St Paul's Cath Ch, Adrian Lucas, John Scott Concert   (10/91) (HYPE) ① CDA66439

WISEMAN, Debbie (20th Cent)
England

SECTION V: STAGE WORKS

Tom and Viv—film score (1993)
EXCERPTS: 1. Opening Titles; 2. Maurice's Farewell; 3. Hospital Scene; 4. Tom & Viv's Dance; 5. The Honeymoon; 6. Tom & Bertie; 7. Bertie & Viv's Pianola Rag; 8. The Road to Garsington; 9. Viv & Maurice; 10. Viv Becomes Ill; 11. Tom Wants Nothing; 12. Love Theme; 13. The Harvard Letter; 14. Church Scene; 15. Viv & Louise; 16. The Poetry Reading; 17. The Wibbly Wobbly Walk (comp Long & Pelham); 18. The Print Room; 19. Viv Is Excluded; 20. Viv Explains; 21. Viv Is Committed; 22. End Titles.
1-22. OST, D. Wiseman, Palm Court Th Orch, D. Wiseman (r1993)   (11/94) (SONY) ① SK64381

WISHART, Peter Charles Arthur (1921–1984) England

SECTION II: CHAMBER

String Quartet No. 3 in A (1953)
English Qt (r1992) Concert
(12/93) (TREM) ① TREM102-2

SECTION IV: VOCAL AND CHORAL

Jesu, dulcis memoria—anthem
King's College Sngrs, E.H. Warrell Concert
(12/91) (REGE) ① REGCD106

WITMARK, Isidore (?1871–1941)
USA

SECTION V: STAGE WORKS

The Chaperons—musical show (1902—New York) (Lyrics Ranken)
EXCERPTS: 1. It Seems Like Yesterday.
1. L. Gunning, Broadway Cast (r1901) Concert
(5/94) (PEAR) ① [3] GEMMCDS9050/2(1)

WITT, Friedrich (1771–1837)
Germany

SECTION II: CHAMBER

Septet in F
Charis Ens Kreutzer: Grand Septet, Op. 62.
(11/87) (MDG) ① L3232

WOLF, Hugo (Filipp Jakob) (1860–1903) Austria

SECTION I: ORCHESTRAL

Italian Serenade—small orchestra (1892) (arr of string quartet)
COE, A. Schneider (pp1988) Concert
(4/89) (ASV) ① CDCOE810
BPO, S. Bychkov Concert
(3/94) (PHIL) ① 434 108-2PH

SECTION II: CHAMBER

Italian Serenade—string quartet (1887)
Hagen Qt Concert   (1/90) (DG) ① 427 669-2GH
Budapest Qt (r1932) Concert
(4/95) (BIDD) ① LAB098
String Quartet in D minor (1878-84)
LaSalle Qt Concert
(2/93) (DG) ① [2] 437 128-2GX2

11, 23, 24, 26. A. Trianti, C. Van Bos (r1932) *Concert*
(6/94) (PEAR) ① [2] **GEMMCDS9075**
12. M. Shirai, Berlin RSO, D. Shallon (orch cpsr)
Concert (10/92) (CAPR) ① **10 335**
12, 15-17, 21, 31, 34, 41, 44. M. Shirai, J. Protschka,
H. Höll *Manuel Venegas*. (5/91) (CAPR) ① **10 362**
12, 36. C. Ludwig, C. Spencer (pp1994) *Concert*
(3/95) (RCA) ① **09026 62652-2**
14, 15. G. Hüsch, H.U. Müller (r1935) *Concert*
(6/94) (PEAR) ① [2] **GEMMCDS9085**
16. E. Schwarzkopf, G. Moore (r1965) *Concert*
(12/90) (EMI) ① **CDM7 63653-2**
21, 30. K. Erb, G. Moore (r1937) *Concert*
(6/94) (PEAR) ① [2] **GEMMCDS9085**
29, 38. R. Ginster, G. Moore (r1935) *Concert*
(6/94) (PEAR) ① [2] **GEMMCDS9085**
31-34. H. Janssen, G. Moore (r1937) *Concert*
(6/94) (PEAR) ① [2] **GEMMCDS9085**
44. L. Price, D. Garvey (r1959) *Concert*
(5/93) (RCA) ① **09026 61499-2**

**Ständchen (Alles endet, was
entstehet)**—Lied, UP30 (1877) (Wds. T.
Körner)
D. Fischer-Dieskau, Munich RO, S. Soltesz *Concert*
(10/92) (ORFE) ① **C219911A**
Über Nacht—Lied, UP48 (1878) (Wds. J.
Sturm)
R. Tauber, Orch, F. Weissmann (r1932) *Concert*
(4/90) (EMI) ① **GEMMCD9381**
Wiegenlied—Lied (1878) (Wds. A. Wette-
Humperdinck)
R. Streich, E. Werba (1957: arr Humperdinck)
Concert (10/94) (DG) ① [2] **437 680-2GDO2**
Wohin mit der Freud?—Lied, UP89 (1882)
(Wds. R. Reinick)
R. Streich, E. Werba (r1957) *Concert*
(10/94) (DG) ① [2] **437 680-2GDO2**

SECTION V: STAGE WORKS

Der Corregidor—opera: 4 acts
(1896—Mannheim) (Lib. Mayreder, after
Alarcon)
Cpte W. Hollweg, H. Donath, D. Fischer-Dieskau, D.
Soffel, K. Moll, V. von Halem, H. Berger-Tuna, P.
Maus, G. Schreckenbach, Berlin RIAS Chbr Ch,
Berlin RSO, G. Albrecht (r1985)
(12/87) (SCHW) ① [2] **314010**
Manuel Venegas—opera: 3 acts
(1903—Mannheim) (Lib. M Hoernes, after
Alarcon. 5 scenes only cpted)
M. Shirai, J. Protschka, C. Hauptmann, C. Späth, O.
Widmer, K-J. Dusseljee, Württemberg Chbr Ch, H.
Höll *Spanisches Liederbuch*.
(5/91) (CAPR) ① **10 362**

WOLFE, Julia (b 1958) USA

SECTION II: CHAMBER
---

my lips from speaking—five pianos,
prepared piano and typewriter (1990s)
Piano Circus (r1992-93) *Concert*
(2/95) (ARGO) ① **443 527-2ZH**

**WOLFF, Christian (b 1934)
France/USA**

SECTION III: INSTRUMENTAL
---

6 Melodies Variation for Solo Violin (1993) (in
memoriam John Cage)
R. Zahab (r1993) *Concert*
(8/94) (KOCH) ① [2] **37238-2**

**WOLF-FERRARI, Ermanno
(1876—1948) Italy**

SECTION I: ORCHESTRAL

**Suite-Concertino in F—bassoon and
orchestra, Op. 16 (pub 1933)**
K. Walker, LMP, J. Glover *Concert*
(8/89) (GALL) ① **CD-499**

SECTION II: CHAMBER

Piano Trio in D, Op. 5 (1896)
Raphael Trio (r1994) *Piano Trio, Op. 7*.
(11/95) (ASV) ① **CDDCA935**
Piano Trio in F sharp, Op. 7 (1900)
Raphael Trio (r1994) *Piano Trio, Op. 5*.
(11/95) (ASV) ① **CDDCA935**

SECTION IV: VOCAL AND CHORAL
---

44 Canzoniere, Op. 17 (1936) (wds trad
Tuscan)
Part 1: 1. La vedovella; 2. M'à statto reglato tre viole;
3. Giovanottino, il bello andar che hai; 4. Tutte le notti

---

in sogno mi venite; 5. La luna s'è venuta a lamentare;
6. Rama d'olivo e preziosa palma; 7. Ninna-nanna la
malcontenta; 8. S'io non son bella al vostro
paragone; 9. Io vado a letto con una croce in pelto;
10. Se gli alberi potessin invellare; 11. Vedo la casa e
non vedo il bel viso; 12. Mamma, no mi mandate fuori
sola; 13. Dimmelo, Nino mio, come facesti; 14. Come
tu mi fal rabbia quando passi; 15. Si dà principio a
questa serenata; 16. Alza le trecce bionde e non
dormire; 17. O tu che dormi e riposata stai; 18. Il letto
ti sia fatto di viole; 19. E giacchè vedo qui l'alba
apparire. Part 2: 20. M'è stato detto che te ne vuoi
ire; 21. Vai in buon ora, o viso delicato; 22. E questa
valle mi par rabbuiata; 23. O miei sospiri andate ove
vi mando; 24. L'è rivenuto il fior di primavera; 25. Io
mi credeva che tu fossi morto; 26. Giovanottino che
passi per via; 27. Vo' fa' 'na palazzina alla marina;
28. Dio ti facesse star tanta digiuno; 29. Dimmi,
bellino, com'io ho da fare; 30. Quando a letto vo la
sera; 31. Quando sarà quel benedetto giorno; 32. Ero
nel mezzo al mare e mi fu ditto; 33. La casa del mio
amor vuola 'n profondo; 34. Non posso più di notte
camminare; 35. Avevo una campagna sola sola; 36.
Oggi sposa il mio ben che amavo tanto!; 37. Bella,
che censessanta ne chiaimate; 38. Dov'è la voce
mia, ch'era sì bella; 39. 'N del mezzo al mare che c'è
un uccellino; 40. Io ho una spada che taglieria il ferro;
41. Vado di notte, come fa la luna; 42. Giovanetti,
cantate ora che siete; 43. Lunga e distesa mi pongo
nel letto; 44. Spirito Santo, entrate nel mio cuore.
1-3, 7-9, 12-14, 20-31, 35, 36, 41, 43, 44. M. de
Francesca-Cavazza, H. Göbel *Edelwild*.
(4/90) (SCHW) ① **314004**
26-30, 41, 42. E. Schwarzkopf, G. Moore (r1965)
Concert (12/90) (EMI) ① **CDM7 63654-2**
Edelwild—song cycle (1893) (Wds. T. Resa)
Cpte M. de Francesca-Cavazza, H. Göbel
Canzoniere. (4/90) (SCHW) ① **314004**

SECTION V: STAGE WORKS

L' Amore medico, 'Doctor Love'—opera: 2
acts (1913—Dresden) (cl)
EXCERPTS: 1. Overture; 2. Intermezzo.
1. RPO, J. Serebrier *Concert*
(9/93) (ASV) ① **CDDCA861**
1, 2. ASMF, N. Marriner *Concert*
(3/93) (EMI) ① **CDC7 54585-2**
Il Campiello—comic opera: 3 acts
(1936—Milan) (Lib. Ghisalberti, after de Vega)
EXCERPTS: 1. Introduzione. ACT 1: 2. Ancuo zé
una zornada cuzzi bela; 3. Anzoleto, mio Anzoleto; 4.
Vàrdelo qua?; 5. Aghi de fiandra!; 6. Oe, Lucieta?; 7.
Via, l'amante è partito; 8. No son più una putela; 9.
Vôi scoar sto campielo; 10. Voria, mi sposarme; 11.
Anca mi, se ò da dir la verità; 12. Io per tutte le donne
ho daltri il rispetto; 13. Gnese, quel fior m'àstu donà
tì?; 14. Che 'l diga quel che 'l vuol; 15. Brava in ogni
maniera; 16. Intermezzo. ACT 2: 17. I muci i vôi far
mil; 18. Ma cos'e stato?; 19. Volemo i rissi co la
castradina; 20. Ve femo reverenza; 21. A tola! A tola!
Dài!... 22. Balletto: 22a. Le tose; 22b. I Peociosi; 22c.
Serenata de Peociosi; 22d. La Polenta; 23. Uff! Non
ne posso più... 24. Signor; 25. Soldi...Soldi!; 26. Ma
cozza zé zto ztrepito; 27. El Cavalier Aztolfi?; 28. Sol
sol sol sol; 29. Ritornello. ACT 3: 30. E ze la caza
non me piaze a mi?; 31. Bravi! Pulitol; 32. Fai
massaria?; 33. Ah! parcossa me dàlo; 34. Baron, me
vustu ben?; 35. Coss'è ste baronae?; 36. Se lo
saveva avanti; 37. Oh! per Dio! La finite?; 38. Cara la
mia Venezia.
16, 29. ASMF, N. Marriner *Concert*
(3/93) (EMI) ① **CDC7 54585-2**
16, 29. RPO, J. Serebrier *Concert*
(9/93) (ASV) ① **CDDCA861**
29. La Scala Orch, G. Marinuzzi (r1936) *Concert*
(4/94) (EMI) ① [3] **CHS7 64864-2(2)**
La Dama boba—opera: 3 acts (1939—Milan)
(Lib. Ghisalberti, after de Vega)
EXCERPTS: 1. Overture.
1. ASMF, N. Marriner *Concert*
(3/93) (EMI) ① **CDC7 54585-2**
1. RPO, J. Serebrier *Concert*
(9/93) (ASV) ① **CDDCA861**
Le Donne Curiose—opera: 3 acts
(1906—Munich) (Lib Sugana, after Goldini)
Rimprovera la mia curiosita...Tutta per te G.
Farrar, orch (r1912) *Concert*
(10/94) (NIMB) ① **NI7857**
Se in vol cotanto...Io cor nel contento G. Farrar, H.
Jadlowker, orch (r1912) *Concert*
(4/94) (RCA) ① [6] **09026 61580-2(2)**
I **Gioielli della Madonna, '(The) Jewels of
the Madonna'**—opera: 3 acts (1911—Berlin)
(Lib. Golisicani and Zangarini)
1. Festa popolare; 2. Intermezzo, Act 2; 3. Serenata;
4. Danza napolitana.

Aprila, o bella G. De Luca, NY Met Op Orch, G. Setti
(r1929) *Concert* (10/94) (PREI) ① **89073**
Excs N. Ardelli, M. Bokor, A. Jerger, G. Maikl, K. Ettl,
Vienna St Op Chor, Vienna St Op Orch, H.
Knappertsbusch (pp1937: Ger) *Concert*
(12/95) (SCHW) ① [2] **314672**
Intermezzo, Act 1; 2. National SO, B. Neel (r1944)
Concert (5/95) (DUTT) ① **CDK1200**
1, 2, 3, 4. RPO, J. Serebrier *Concert*
(9/93) (ASV) ① **CDDCA861**
1-4. ASMF, N. Marriner *Concert*
(3/93) (EMI) ① **CDC7 54585-2**
2. BPO, H. von Karajan *Concert*
(10/87) (DG) ① [3] **419 257-2GH3**
2. Gothenburg SO, N. Järvi *Concert*
(6/90) (DG) ① **429 494-2GDC**
3. T. Gobbi, Rome Op Orch, O. de Fabritiis (r1955)
Concert (10/89) (EMI) ① **CDM7 63109-2**
I **Quattro Rusteghi, '(The) Four
Ruffians'**—opera: 3 acts (1906—Munich) (Lib.
L Sugana & G Pizzolato, after Goldoni)
EXCERPTS: 1. Overture; 2. Intermezzo.
Luceta xe un bel nome Ferruccio Tagliavini, EIAR
Orch, U. Tansini (r1940) *Concert*
(3/94) (CENT) ① **CRC2164**
1, 2. ASMF, N. Marriner *Concert*
(3/93) (EMI) ① **CDC7 54585-2**
1, 2. RPO, J. Serebrier *Concert*
(9/93) (ASV) ① **CDDCA861**
2. Santa Cecilia Academy Orch, V. de Sabata (1948)
Concert (4/94) (EMI) ① [2] **CHS5 65506-2**
Il **Segreto di Susanna, 'Susanna's
Secret'**—opera: 1 act (1909—Munich) (Lib.
Golisicani)
O gioia, la nube leggera G. Farrar, orch (r1913)
Concert (10/94) (NIMB) ① **NI7857**
O gioia, la nube leggera C. Muzio, orch (r1917)
Concert (5/95) (ROMO) ① [2] **81010-2**
Overture La Scala Orch, A. Toscanini (r1921)
Concert (11/92) (RCA) ① **GD60315**
Overture RPO, J. Serebrier *Concert*
(9/93) (ASV) ① **CDDCA861**
Overture NBC SO, A. Toscanini (bp1946) *Concert*
(5/94) (ATS) ① [2] **ATCD100**
Overture Santa Cecilia Academy Orch, V. de Sabata
(r1948) *Concert* (9/95) (EMI) ① [2] **CHS5 65506-2**
Overture; Intermezzo ASMF, N. Marriner *Concert*
(3/93) (EMI) ① **CDC7 54585-2**

**WÖLFL, Joseph (1773—1812)
Austria**

SECTION II: CHAMBER

**Sextet in D—2 oboes, 2 bassoons, 2 horns
and double-bass (1800)**
Consortium Classicum *Concert*
(9/90) (SCHW) ① **310002**

**WOLPE, Stefan (1902—1972)
Germany/USA**

SECTION II: CHAMBER

**In 2 Parts—clarinet,trumpet,violin,cello,harp
& piano (1962)**
Parnassus, A. Korf *Concert*
(12/92) (KOCH) ① **37141-2**
Piece for Trumpet and 7 instruments (1971)
R. Mase, Parnassus, A. Korf *Concert*
(12/92) (KOCH) ① **37141-2**
**Piece for 2 instrumental units—fl, ob, vn, vc,
bass, perc and piano (1962)**
Parnassus, A. Korf *Concert*
(12/92) (KOCH) ① **37141-2**
**Quartet for Oboe, Cello, Percussion and
Piano (1955)**
S. Taylor, F. Sherry, D. Kennedy, A. Karis (r1991)
Concert (2/94) (KOCH) ① **37112-2**
**Quartet for Tenor Saxophone, Trumpet,
Percussion and Piano (1950)**
Parnassus, A. Korf *Concert*
(12/92) (KOCH) ① **37141-2**
Sonata for Violin and Piano (1949)
J. Fleezanis, G. Ohlsson (r1991) *Concert*
(2/94) (KOCH) ① **37112-2**
**Trio in Two Parts—flute, cello and piano
(1963-64)**
H. Solberger, F. Sherry, C. Wuorinen (1991) *Concert*
(2/94) (KOCH) ① **37112-2**

SECTION III: INSTRUMENTAL
---

4 Adagios—piano (1920)
1. Gesang, weil ich etwas Teures verlassen muss.
1. G.D. Madge *Concert*
(3/90) (CPO) ① **CPO999 055-2**

5 Characteristic Marches—piano, Op. 10 (1929-34)
1. Energico ed animato.
1. G.D. Madge *Concert*
(3/90) (CPO) ① **CPO999 055-2**

Dance in the form of a Chaconne—piano (1938)
G.D. Madge *Concert*
(3/90) (CPO) ① **CPO999 055-2**

Displaced Spaces, Shocks, Negations,a New Sort of Relationship in Space, Pattern, Tempo—piano (1946)
G.D. Madge *Concert*
(3/90) (CPO) ① **CPO999 055-2**

Encouragements—piano (1943-47)
1. The Good Spirit of a Right Cause; 2. Battle Piece.
2. G.D. Madge *Concert*
(3/90) (CPO) ① **CPO999 055-2**

Form IV: Broken Sequences—piano (1969)
P. Serkin *Concert* (4/87) (NEW) ① **NW344-2**
G.D. Madge *Concert*
(3/90) (CPO) ① **CPO999 055-2**

Pastorale—piano (1939)
P. Serkin *Concert* (4/87) (NEW) ① **NW344-2**

Rag-Caprice—piano (1927)
G.D. Madge *Concert*
(3/90) (CPO) ① **CPO999 055-2**

Solo Piece for Trumpet (1966)
R. Mase *Concert* (12/92) (KOCH) ① **37141-2**
R. Friedrich (r1992) *Concert*
(6/93) (CAPR) ① **10 439**

Stehende Musik—piano (1925)
G.D. Madge *Concert*
(3/90) (CPO) ① **CPO999 055-2**

4 Studies on Basic Rows—piano (1936)
1. On Tritones; 2. On Minor Thirds; 3. Presto furioso; 4. Passacaglia.
4. P. Serkin *Concert* (4/87) (NEW) ① **NW344-2**
4. G.D. Madge (rev 1971) *Concert*
(3/90) (CPO) ① **CPO999 055-2**

Tango—piano (1927)
G.D. Madge *Concert*
(3/90) (CPO) ① **CPO999 055-2**

Toccata in Three Parts—piano (1941)
G.D. Madge *Concert*
(3/90) (CPO) ① **CPO999 055-2**

SECTION IV: VOCAL AND CHORAL
---

3 Lieder—contralto and piano (1943) (Wds. B. Brecht)
1. Ballade von den Osseger Witwen; 2. Der Gott sei bei uns; 3. Keiner oder aller.
J. Castle, Parnassus, A. Korf *Concert*
(12/92) (KOCH) ① **37141-2**

To the Dancemaster—song (1938)
J. Castle, Parnassus, A. Korf *Concert*
(12/92) (KOCH) ① **37141-2**

SECTION V: STAGE WORKS

Hamlet—incidental music (1929) (Play by W. Shakespeare)
Parnassus, A. Korf *Concert*
(12/92) (KOCH) ① **37141-2**

WOOD, Charles (1866–1926) Ireland

SECTION II: CHAMBER

String Quartet in A minor—string quartet (1911-12)
Lindsay Qt (r1992) *Concert*
(1/94) (ASV) ① **CDDCA879**

SECTION III: INSTRUMENTAL

Nunc dimittis—chorale prelude: organ (1912)
J. Parker-Smith *Concert*
(9/90) (ASV) ① **CDDCA702**

SECTION IV: VOCAL AND CHORAL

Evening Service in F, 'Collegium Regale'—8vv & organ
1. Magnificat; 2. Nunc dimittis.
1, 2. St Paul's Cath Ch, C. Dearnley, John Scott *Concert* (3/88) (HYPE) ① **CDA66249**

Expectans expectavi—anthem
Magdalen Oxford Coll Ch, J. Harper *Concert*
(11/91) (ABBE) ① **CDCA913**
St Paul's Cath Ch, John Scott, Andrew Lucas (r1991) *Concert* (8/93) (HYPE) ① **CDA66618**
Truro Cath Ch, D. Briggs, S. Morley (r1992) *Concert*
(7/94) (PRIO) ① **PRCD429**

Glory and Honour and Laud—anthem: 8vv (pub. 1925) (Wds. Theodulph of Orleans, trans Neale)
St Paul's Cath Ch, John Scott, Andrew Lucas (r1994) *Concert* (5/95) (HYPE) ① **CDA66758**

Great Lord of Lords—anthem: men's vv (Wds. H. R. Bramley)
Norwich Cath Ch, M. Nicholas, N. Taylor *Concert*
(3/92) (PRIO) ① **PRCD351**

Hail, gladdening light—anthem (Wds. anon 3rd-cent Greek, trans J Keble)
St Paul's Cath Ch, Andrew Lucas, John Scott *Concert* (9/90) (HYPE) ① **CDA66374**
King's College Ch, D. Willcocks *Concert*
(1/91) (CFP) ① **CD-CFP4570**
Magdalen Oxford Coll Ch, J. Harper *Concert*
(11/91) (ABBE) ① **CDCA913**
Cambridge Sngrs, J. Rutter *Concert*
(4/92) (CLLE) ① **COLCD113**
King's College Ch, S. Cleobury (r1991) *Concert*
(6/93) (EMI) ① **CDC7 54418-2**
Trinity Coll Ch, Cambridge, R. Marlow (r1993) *Concert* (2/94) (CONI) ① **CDCF219**
Southwark Cath Ch, P. Wright, S. Layton (r1992) *Concert* (7/94) (PRIO) ① **PRCD435**

O thou, the central orb
Guildford Cath Ch, A. Millington, P. Wright *Concert*
(5/89) (PRIO) ① **PRCD257**
Magdalen Oxford Coll Ch, J. Harper *Concert*
(11/91) (ABBE) ① **CDCA913**
St Paul's Cath Ch, John Scott, Andrew Lucas (r1993) *Concert* (6/94) (HYPE) ① **CDA66678**

St Mark Passion (1921)
W. Kendall, P. Harvey, Gonville & Caius College Ch, G. Webber, R. Hill *Holloway: Since I believe.*
(5/93) (ASV) ① **CDDCA854**

There comes a new moon—part-song (Wds. Dickens)
King's Sngrs *Concert*
(6/88) (EMI) ① **CDC7 49765-2**

This joyful Easter-tide—carol
Cambridge Sngrs, J. Rutter *Concert*
(6/88) (CLLE) ① **COLCD107**

When winds that move not—part-song (Wds. Shelley)
King's Sngrs *Concert*
(6/88) (EMI) ① **CDC7 49765-2**

WOOD, Gareth (b 1950) Wales

SECTION I: ORCHESTRAL

Scherzino—tenor horn and brass band
S. Smith, N. Law, P. Parkes (r1989) *Concert*
(10/94) (CHAN) ① **CHAN4523**

WOOD, Haydn (1882–1959) England

SECTION I: ORCHESTRAL

Apollo—overture (1934-35)
Bratislava RSO, A. Leaper *Concert*
(8/92) (MARC) ① **8 223402**

A Brown Bird Singing—paraphrase for orchestra
Bratislava RSO, A. Leaper *Concert*
(8/92) (MARC) ① **8 223402**

London Cameos (c1942)
1. Miniature Overture—The City; 2. Intermission—St James's Park in Spring; 3. Finale—A State Ball at Buckingham Palace.
Bratislava RSO, A. Leaper *Concert*
(8/92) (MARC) ① **8 223402**

Mannin Veen, 'Dear Isle of Man'—Manx tone poem (1932-33)
Bratislava RSO, A. Leaper *Concert*
(8/92) (MARC) ① **8 223402**

Moods—suite for orchestra (1932)
1. Prelude: Dignity; 2. Novelette: Allurement; 3. Caprice: Coquetry; 4. Romance: Pensiveness; 5. Felicity: Spring Song; 6. Concert Waltz: Joyousness.
6. Bratislava RSO, A. Leaper *Concert*
(8/92) (MARC) ① **8 223402**

Mylecharane—rhapsody for orchestra
Bratislava RSO, A. Leaper *Concert*
(8/92) (MARC) ① **8 223402**

Paris—orchestral suite (1944)
1. Monmartre—march.
1. Southern Fest Orch, R. White *Concert*
(5/93) (CHAN) ① **CHAN9110**

The Seafarer—nautical rhapsody (1940)
Bratislava RSO, A. Leaper *Concert*
(8/92) (MARC) ① **8 223402**

Serenade to Youth (1952)
Bratislava RSO, A. Leaper *Concert*
(8/92) (MARC) ① **8 223402**

Sketch of a Dandy (1950)
Bratislava RSO, A. Leaper *Concert*
(8/92) (MARC) ① **8 223402**

WOOD, Sir Henry J(oseph) (1869–1944) England

SECTION I: ORCHESTRAL

Fantasia on British Sea Songs (1905)
I. Tracey (r1990; arr Tracey) *Concert*
(4/91) (MIRA) ① **MRCD901**
LSO, Henry Wood (r1939) *Concert*
(9/94) (DUTT) ① **CDAX8008**
BBC SO, A. Davis (r1994) *Concert*
(2/95) (TELD) ① **4509-97868-2**

WOOD, Hugh (b 1932) England

SECTION II: CHAMBER

String Quartet No. 1 (1962)
Chilingirian Qt (r1994) *Concert*
(6/95) (CONI) ① **75605 51239-2**

String Quartet No. 2 (1969-70)
Chilingirian Qt (r1994) *Concert*
(6/95) (CONI) ① **75605 51239-2**

String Quartet No. 3, Op. 20 (1978)
Lindsay Qt (bp1980) *Concert*
(1/93) (ASV) ① **CDDCA825**
Chilingirian Qt (r1994) *Concert*
(6/95) (CONI) ① **75605 51239-2**

String Quartet No. 4 (1992-93)
Chilingirian Qt (r1994) *Concert*
(6/95) (CONI) ① **75605 51239-2**

SECTION IV: VOCAL AND CHORAL

The Kingdom of God—anthem: 12vv, Op. 38 (Wds. F Thompson)
St Paul's Cath Ch, John Scott, Andrew Lucas (r1994) *Concert* (5/95) (HYPE) ① **CDA66758**

WOOD, Mary Knight (1857–1944) USA

SECTION IV: VOCAL AND CHORAL

Ah love but a day—song: 1v and piano
S. Mentzer, K. Schmidt (r1991) *Concert*
(12/93) (KOCH) ① **37240-2**

Ashes and Roses—song: 1v and piano (Wds. Schirmer)
S. Mentzer, K. Schmidt (r1991) *Concert*
(12/93) (KOCH) ① **37240-2**

WOODBURY, Isaac Baker (1819–1858) USA

SECTION IV: VOCAL AND CHORAL

Heavenly Voices, 'We are happy now, dear mother'—song (1853)
Harmoneion Sngrs, N. Bruce, L. Skrobacs (1977) *Concert* (2/94) (NEW) ① **80220-2**

WOODCOCK, Clement (fl c1575) England

SECTION II: CHAMBER

Browning my dere—consort (5 parts)
Musicians of Swanne Alley *Concert*
(11/89) (VIRG) ① **VC7 59534-2**
Circa 1500, N. Hadden (r1991) *Concert*
(8/93) (CRD) ① **CRD3487**

Hackney—consort (5 parts)
Musicians of Swanne Alley *Concert*
(11/89) (VIRG) ① **VC7 59534-2**

WOODCOCK, Robert (1690–1728) England

SECTION I: ORCHESTRAL

Concerto for Flute and Strings in D (pub 1727-30)
W. Bennett, Thames CO, M. Dobson *Concert*
(6/87) (CRD) ① **CRD3331**

Concerto for Oboe and Strings in E flat
N. Black, Thames CO, M. Dobson *Concert*
(6/87) (CRD) ① **CRD3331**

YIM, Jay Alan (20th Cent) USA

SECTION II: CHAMBER

Autumn Rhythm—string quartet (1984-85)
Arditti Qt (r1991-92) *Concert*
(12/93) (MONT) ① **782010**

YOCOH, Yuquijiro (b 1929) Japan

SECTION III: INSTRUMENTAL

Sakura—Variations on a Japanese folksong—guitar
J. Williams (r1992) *Concert*
(1/94) (SONY) ① **SK53359**

YON, Pietro (1886-1943) Italy

SECTION III: INSTRUMENTAL

Humoresque, '(L')organo primitivo'—organ (1946) (also know as 'Toccatina for the flute')
I. Tracey *Concert* (1/90) (CFP) ① **CD-CFP4558**
G. Weir *Concert* (12/92) (KOSS) ① **KC1013**

SECTION IV: VOCAL AND CHORAL

Gesù Bambino—Song
J. Norman, Ambrosian Sngrs, RPO, A. Gibson (Eng)
Concert (4/83) (PHIL) ① **400 019-2PH**
L. Pavarotti, National PO, K.H. Adler *Concert*
(12/91) (DECC) ① **433 710-2DH**
L. Pavarotti, National PO, K.H. Adler *Concert*
(12/91) (DECC) ① **433 010-2DM**
G. de Chiaro (arr gtr: De Chiaro) *Concert*
(12/91) (CENT) ① **CRC2101**

YOON, Young-Ha (20th cent) Korea

SECTION IV: VOCAL AND CHORAL

Barley Field—popular Korean song
S. Jo, Monte Carlo PO, P. Olmi (r1994: arr M Constant) *Concert* (6/95) (ERAT) ① **4509-97239-2**

YORK, Andrew (20th Cent) USA

SECTION II: CHAMBER

Rosetta—guitar trio (1992)
Pro Arte Gtr Trio *Concert*
(1/94) (ASV) ① **CDWHL2079**

SECTION III: INSTRUMENTAL

Lullaby—guitar
J. Williams *Concert* (8/89) (SONY) ① **SK44898**
Sunburst—guitar
J. Williams *Concert* (8/89) (SONY) ① **SK44898**

YORKE, Peter (1902-1966) England

SECTION I: ORCHESTRAL

The Shipbuilders—suite: brass band
1. Web of Steel; 2. The Launching; 3. All Hands at Work; 4. Maiden Voyage.
Black Dyke Mills Band, G. Brand *Concert*
(9/93) (RSR) ① **RSRD1002**

YOUMANS, Vincent (1898-1946) USA

SECTION V: STAGE WORKS

No, No, Nanette—musical show (1925—New York) (Lyrics I. Caesar & O. Harbach; Book O. Harbach)
EXCERPTS: 1. Overture; 2. Too many rings around Rosie; 3. I've confessed to the breeze; 4. Call of the sea; 5. I want to be happy; 6. You can dance with any girl; 7. Non, No, Nanette; 8. Tea for two; 9. I want to be happy; 10. Telephone girlie; 11. Finaletto, Act 2; 12. 'Where-has-my-hubby-gone' Blues; 13. Waiting for you; 14. Take a little one-step; 15. Finale.
8. R. Luker, D. Dvorsky, Ambrosian Sngrs, London Sinfonietta, J. McGlinn *Concert*
(8/93) (EMI) ① **CDC7 54586-2**

YOUNG, Christopher (20th Cent) USA

SECTION V: STAGE WORKS

Haunted Summer—film score
EXCERPTS: 1. Haunted Summer; 2. Menage; 3. Villa Diodati; 4. The Night Was Made for Loving; 5. Polidori's Potions; 6. Ariel; 7. Confreres; 8. Geneva; 9. Alby; 10. An Unquiet Dream; 11. Hauntings: 11a. Hotel d'Angleterre; 11b. In the Caves of Chillon; 11c. Incubus; 11d. Mont Blanc.
1-11. OST, M. Zimoski (r1988)
(11/89) (SILV) ① **FILMCD037**
Hellraiser—film score (1987)
EXCERPTS: 1. Resurrection; 2. Hellbound Heart; 3. The Lament Configuration; 4. Reunion; 5. A Quick Death; 6. Seduction & Pursuit; 7. In Love's Name; 8. Cenobites; 9. The Rat Slice Quartet; 10. Re-Resurrection; 11. Uncle Frank; 12. Brought On By Night; 13. Another Puzzle.
1. OST *Concert* (5/93) (SILV) ① **SILVAD3003**

YOUNG, La Monte (b 1935) USA

SECTION II: CHAMBER

On remembering a naiad—five small pieces: string quartet (1956)
1. A wisp; 2. A gnarl; 3. A leaf; 4. A twig; 5. A tooth.
Arditti Qt (r1991-92) *Concert*
(12/93) (MONT) ① **782010**

YOUNG, Victor (1900-1956) USA

SECTION IV: VOCAL AND CHORAL

Sweet Sue—song (1928) (wds. W. J. Harris)
Harvey and the Wallbangers, London Sinfonietta, S. Rattle *Concert* (12/87) (EMI) ① **CDC7 47991-2**

SECTION V: STAGE WORKS

For whom the bell tolls—film score (1943)
Warner Bros Studio Orch, R. Heindorf (1958)
Concert (11/91) (STAN) ① **STZ112**
The Left Hand of God—film score (1955)
EXCERPTS: 1. Main Title; 2. Love Theme.
2. National PO, C. Gerhardt *Concert*
(10/90) (RCA) ① **GD80422**
The Quiet Man—concert suite from film score (1952)
EXCERPTS: 1. Danaher's House; 2. My Mother (Sean and Kate); 3. The Big Fight; 4. Forlorn (Mary Kate's Lament); 5. I'll Take You Home Again Kathleen (Composed by Thomas P. Westendorf); 6. St Patrick's Day.
1, 2, 6. Prague City PO, P. Bateman (r1994: arr Townend) *Concert* (11/94) (SILV) ① **FILMCD153**
1-6. Orch, V. Young *Samson and Delilah Suite*.
(11/94) (VARE) ① **VSD5497**
Samson and Delilah—concert suite from film score (1949)
EXCERPTS: 1. Samson's Call; 2. Miriam and the Dance Dragon; 3. The Valley of Zorah; 4. The Feather Dance; 5. Delilah's Remorse; 6. The Feast Dance; 7. Bacchanale; 8. Delilah's Harp; 9. Samson and Delilah.
1-9. Paramount SO, V. Young *Quiet Man Suite*.
(11/94) (VARE) ① **VSD5497**

YRADIER, Sebastián de (1809-1865) Spain

SECTION IV: VOCAL AND CHORAL

La Calasera—song
A. Patti, A. Barili (r1906) *Concert*
(10/89) (NIMB) ① **NI7802**
A. Patti, A. Barili (r1906) *Concert*
(4/90) (PEAR) ① **GEMMCD9312**
A. Patti, A. Barili (r1906) *Concert*
(7/93) (NIMB) ① [2] **NI7840/1**
La Paloma—song
V. de los Angeles, Sinfonia of London, R. Frühbeck de Burgos (orch Gamley) *Concert*
(10/88) (EMI) ① **CDM7 69502-2**
J. Schmidt, orch (r1930s) *Concert*
(4/90) (EMI) ① **CDM7 69478-2**
B. Gigli, orch (r1939) *Concert*
(9/92) (MMOI) ① **CDMOIR409**
C. Supervia, orch, A. Capdevila (r1930) *Concert*
(3/93) (NIMB) ① [2] **NI7836/7**
A. Galli-Curci, H. Samuels (r1928) *Concert*
(3/94) (CONI) ① **CDHD201**

YSAŸE, Eugène (Auguste) (1858-1931) Belgium

SECTION I: ORCHESTRAL

Caprice d'après l'Étude en forme de valse de Saint-Saëns—violin and orchestra
J. Bell, RPO, A. Litton *Concert*
(1/92) (DECC) ① **433 519-2DH**

SECTION II: CHAMBER

Rêve d'enfant—violin and piano, Op. 14 (c1902)
R. Ricci, C. Fürstner (r1938) *Concert*
(12/91) (BIDD) ① **LAB044**
Midori, R. McDonald (r1992) *Concert*
(6/93) (SONY) ① **SK52568**

SECTION III: INSTRUMENTAL

6 Sonatas for Solo Violin, Op. 27 (1923)
1. G minor; 2. A minor; 3. D minor (Ballade); 4. E minor; 5. G; 6. E.
L. Mordkovitch (5/88) (CHAN) ① **CHAN8599**
V. Szabadi (5/93) (HUNG) ① **HCD31476**
3. R. Ricci *Concert* (9/86) (ETCE) ① **KTC1038**
3. M. Vengerov *Concert* (4/90) (BIDD) ① **LAW001**
5. J. Kang (r1994) *Concert*
(8/95) (DINT) ① **DICD920241**

YUASA, Joji (b 1929) Japan

SECTION I: ORCHESTRAL

The Midnight Sun (1990)
Helsinki PO, S. Comissiona *Concert*
(4/92) (ONDI) ① **ODE767-2**

YUN, Isang (b 1917) Korea

SECTION I: ORCHESTRAL

Symphony No. 5—baritone & orchestra (1987) (Wds N. Sachs)
EXCERPTS: 1. Erinnerung; 2. Wir Geretteten; 3. Aufruf; 4. Ihr Zuschauenden; 5. Frieden.
R. Salter, Pomeranian PO, T. Ukigaya (r1993)
(12/94) (CPO) ① **CPO999 148-2**

SECTION II: CHAMBER

Quintet—clarinet and string quartet
S. Meyer, Vienna Stg Sextet *Brahms: Clarinet Quintet*. (11/91) (EMI) ① **CDC7 54304-2**

YVAIN, Maurice (1891-1965) France

SECTION V: STAGE WORKS

Ta bouche—musical comedy (1922—Paris)
Valse B. Hendricks, G. Quilico, Lyon Op Orch, L. Foster (r1993) *Concert*
(6/95) (EMI) ① **CDC5 55151-2**

ZABEL, Albert (1834-1910) Germany

SECTION III: INSTRUMENTAL

La Source—harp, Op. 23
S. McDonald (arr. McDonald) *Concert*
(10/84) (DELO) ① **DE3005**
Valse Caprice—harp, Op. 37
S. Drake (r1988) *Concert*
(2/90) (HYPE) ① **CDA66340**

ZACHARIA DE TERANO, Antonio (14th Cent) Italy

SECTION IV: VOCAL AND CHORAL

Un for gentil—ballata
Newberry Consort, M. Springfels (r1990) *Concert*
(7/93) (HARM) ① **HMU90 7038**
Rosetta—ballata
Newberry Consort, M. Springfels (r1990) *Concert*
(7/93) (HARM) ① **HMU90 7038**

ZACHARIAS, Nicola (14th/15th Cent) Italy

SECTION IV: VOCAL AND CHORAL

Gia per gran nobelta—ballata: 2vv
Orlando Consort (bp1994) *Concert*
(11/95) (METR) ① **METCD1008**

P. Gailhard, anon (r1904) *Concert*
(12/94) (SYMP) ① **SYMCD1172**

Sumite, karissimi—ballade: 3vv
P. Memelsdorff, K. Boeke, S. Fomina, C. Deslignes,
K-E. Schröder, J. Feldman, H. Rodriguez (r1993)
Concert (4/95) (ARCA) ① **A21**

ZAHAB, Roger (b 1957) USA

SECTION II: CHAMBER

Verging Lightfall—violin & piano (1992)
1. Librias ikon: path; 2. Moetnas frond; 3. Wintered
stars, the slow fire.
R. Zahab, E. Moe (r1994) *Concert*
(11/95) (KOCH) ① **37130-2**

ZANDONAI, Riccardo
(1883–1944) Italy

SECTION IV: VOCAL AND CHORAL

L' assiuolo—song: 1v and piano
R. Tebaldi, R. Bonynge (r1972) *Concert*
(9/94) (DECC) ① **436 202-2DM**

SECTION V: STAGE WORKS

Francesca da Rimini—opera: 4 acts
(1914—Turin) (Lib. d'Annunzio, arr T. Ricordi)
EXCERPTS: ACT 1: 1. Allegretto mosso; 2.
Adonella, Adonella; 3. Meravigliosamente... 4. So le
storie; 5. Come Morgana; 6. Or venuta che fue; 7.
Che fai qui manigoldo; 8. Egli era si povero in arnese;
9. Allegretto mosso (Oimè, Oimè); 10. Francesca,
dove andrai; 11. Verrà in breve anche il tuo giorno;
12. Madonna Francesca!; 13. O dattero fronzuto; 14.
Portami nella stanza; 15. Largo (Per la terra di
maggio). ACT 2: 16. Grave e pesante (È ancora
sgombro il campo del comune?); 17. Paolo!
Francesca!; 18. Ecco l'elmetto ch'io vi dono; 19.
Questo cimento; 20. Ah non mi muoiol; 21. Viva, viva
Giovanni Malatesta; 22. Orsù bisogna manganare
una botte grande; 23. O sciagura, sciagura!; 24. La
botte! La botte! ACT 3: 25. Allegro non troppo; 26. E
Galeotto dice... 27. 'Nova in calen di marzo'; 28.
Smaragdi, non torna?; 29. O dama, non ti disperare!;
30. Marzo è giunto; 31. Agitato e più mosso; 32.
Benvenuto, signore mio cognato; 33. Paolo, datemi
pace!; 34. Inghirlandata di violette; 35. Nemica ebbi
la luce; 36. E Galeotto dice... ACT 4: 37. Agitato
(Perchè tanto sei strano?); 38. Mia cara donna; 39.
Torna Malatestino; 40. Era teco la tua moglie; 41. E
se il fratello vede; 42. Allegretto triste; 43. L'ha colta il
sonno, Dorme; 44. Oh! No, no! Non son io!; 45. O
Biancofiore, piccola tu sei!; 46. Smaragdi! Smaragdi!;
47. Vieni, vieni, Francesca.
16, 17, 18, 19, 20, 31, 32, 33, 34, 35, 36, 45, 46, 47.
M. Olivero, M. del Monaco, V. Carbonari, A.
Gasparini, A. Cesarini, Monte Carlo Nat Op Orch, N.
Rescigno *Giordano: Fedora.*
(3/92) (DECC) ① [2] **433 033-2DM2**
33. M. Freni, Venice La Fenice Orch, R. Abbado
Concert (9/92) (DECC) ① **433 316-2DH**
33. L. Price, RCA Italiana Op Orch, F. Molinari-
Pradelli *Concert*
(12/92) (RCA) ① [4] **09026 61236-2**
34, 35, 36. R. Tebaldi, F. Corelli, Leman Chor, SRO,
A. Guadagno (r1972) *Concert*
(10/93) (DECC) ① **436 301-2DA**
Giuliano—opera: prologue, 2 acts & epilogue
(1928—Naples) (Lib. A Rosato, after J da
Varagine)
La dolce nenia del vago usignolo R. Pampanini,
orch, L. Molajoli (1928) *Concert*
(8/93) (PREI) ① **89063**
Giulietta e Romeo—opera: 3 acts
(1922—Rome) (Lib. A. Rossato, after da Porto
& Shakespeare)
Giulietta! son io! M. Fleta, orch (r1922) *Concert*
(2/90) (PREI) ① **89002**

ZANETTI, Gasparo (fl 1626–1645)
Italy

SECTION II: CHAMBER

Intrada de Marchese di Caravazzo (pub
1645)
G. Laurens, T. Malakate, J. Aymonino, K.
Paliatsaras, Capriccio Stravagante, S. Sempé
(hpd/dir) *Concert* (2/94) (DHM) ① **05472 77190-2**

ZANGIUS, Nicolaus
(c1570–c1620) Germany

SECTION IV: VOCAL AND CHORAL

Ade meins Herzens krönlein—Lied: 1v
A. Köhler, Lautten Compagney (r1990/1) *Concert*
(6/93) (CAPR) ① **10 431**
Fahr hin all Freud—Lied: 1v
A. Köhler, Lautten Compagney (r1990/1) *Concert*
(6/93) (CAPR) ① **10 431**
Jungfrau ich sag es euch gut deutsch—Lied:
1v
A. Köhler, Lautten Compagney (r1990/1) *Concert*
(6/93) (CAPR) ① **10 431**
Zu Dienst will ich ihr singen—Lied: 1v
A. Köhler, Lautten Compagney (r1990/1) *Concert*
(6/93) (CAPR) ① **10 431**

ZARDO, Redento (19th/20th Cent)
Italy

SECTION IV: VOCAL AND CHORAL

Luna fedel—song (Wds. A. Boito)
E. Caruso, S. Cottone (r1902) *Concert*
(5/89) (EMI) ① **CDH7 61046-2**
E. Caruso, S. Cottone (r1902) *Concert*
(12/90) (PEAR) ① [3] **EVC1(1)**
E. Caruso, anon (r1903) *Concert*
(12/90) (PEAR) ① [3] **EVC1(1)**
E. Caruso, S. Cottone (r1902) *Concert*
(7/91) (RCA) ① [12] **GD60495(1)**
E. Caruso, anon (r1903) *Concert*
(7/91) (RCA) ① [12] **GD60495(1)**

ZARĘBSKI, Juliusz (1854–1885)
Poland

SECTION III: INSTRUMENTAL

Berceuse—piano, Op. 22 (pub 1884)
E. Wiedner-Zając (r1993) *Concert*
(9/95) (DORI) ① **DIS80121**
Grande polonaise in F sharp—piano, Op. 6
(pub 1881)
E. Wiedner-Zając (r1993) *Concert*
(9/95) (DORI) ① **DIS80121**
Tarantelle—piano, Op. 25 (?1885)
E. Wiedner-Zając (r1993) *Concert*
(9/95) (DORI) ① **DIS80121**

ZARZYCKI, Aleksander
(1834–1895) Poland

SECTION II: CHAMBER

Mazurka in G—violin and piano, Op. 26
O. Renardy, W. Robert (r1940) *Concert*
(12/92) (BIDD) ① [2] **LAB061/2**
B. Huberman, P. Frenkel (r1922) *Concert*
(3/94) (BIDD) ① [2] **LAB077/8**
B. Huberman, S. Schultze (r1929) *Concert*
(4/94) (BIDD) ① [2] **LAB081/2**

SECTION IV: VOCAL AND CHORAL

Sad song
J. Korolewicz-Wayda, anon (r1901) *Concert*
(6/93) (PEAR) ① [3] **GEMMCDS9004/6(1)**

ZECKWER, Camille (1875–1924)
USA

SECTION III: INSTRUMENTAL

In a boat—piano
L. Godowsky (r1925) *Concert*
(4/96) (APR) ① [2] **APR7011**

ZELENKA, Jan Dismas
(1679–1745) Bohemia

SECTION I: ORCHESTRAL

Capriccio I in D—orchestra (1729)
Berne Camerata, A. van Wijnkoop *Concert*
(1/89) (ARCH) ① [3] **423 703-2AX3**
Capriccio II in G—orchestra (1729)
Berne Camerata, A. van Wijnkoop *Concert*
(1/89) (ARCH) ① [3] **423 703-2AX3**
Capriccio III in F—orchestra (1729)
Berne Camerata, A. van Wijnkoop *Concert*
(1/89) (ARCH) ① [3] **423 703-2AX3**
Capriccio IV in A—orchestra (1729)
Berne Camerata, A. van Wijnkoop *Concert*
(1/89) (ARCH) ① [3] **423 703-2AX3**

Capriccio V in G—orchestra (1729)
Berne Camerata, A. van Wijnkoop *Concert*
(1/89) (ARCH) ① [3] **423 703-2AX3**
Concerto a 8 in G
Berne Camerata, A. van Wijnkoop *Concert*
(1/89) (ARCH) ① [3] **423 703-2AX3**
Freiburg Baroque Orch, G. von der Goltz (r1994)
Concert (10/95) (DHM) ① **05472 77339-2**
Hipocondrie a 7 in A—orchestra, ZMV187
(1723)
Berne Camerata, A. van Wijnkoop *Concert*
(1/89) (ARCH) ① [3] **423 703-2AX3**
Freiburg Baroque Orch, G. von der Goltz (r1994)
Concert (10/95) (DHM) ① **05472 77339-2**
Overture a 7 in F—orchestra, ZWV188
(1723)
Berne Camerata, A. van Wijnkoop *Concert*
(1/89) (ARCH) ① [3] **423 703-2AX3**
Sinfonia a 8 in A minor, ZWV189 (1723)
Berne Camerata, A. van Wijnkoop *Concert*
(1/89) (ARCH) ① [3] **423 703-2AX3**
Freiburg Baroque Orch, G. von der Goltz (r1994)
Concert (10/95) (DHM) ① **05472 77339-2**

SECTION II: CHAMBER

6 Trio Sonatas—2 oboes, bassoon and
continuo (1715-16)
H. Holliger, M. Bourgue, K. Thunemann, S. Gawriloff,
L. Buccarella, C. Jaccottet
(1/89) (ARCH) ① [2] **423 937-2AX2**
P. Dombrecht, M. Ponseele, K. Ebbinge, D. Bond, C.
Banchini, R. van der Meer, R. Kohnen
(3/89) (ACCE) ① [2] **ACC8848D**
2, 5, 6. Zefiro Ens (r1993) (6/94) (ASTR) ① **E8511**

SECTION IV: VOCAL AND CHORAL

The Lamentations of Jeremiah—ATB and
orchestra (1732)
M. Chance, J.M. Ainsley, M. George, Chandos
Baroque Plyrs (7/91) (HYPE) ① **CDA66426**
Litanie lauretenae (Salus
infirmorum)—soloists, chorus and
orchestra, ZWV152 (1741-44)
N. Argenta, M. Chance, C. Prégardien, Gordon
Jones, Stuttgart Chbr Ch, Tafelmusik, F. Bernius
Missa dei fili, ZWV20. (10/90) (DHM) ① **RD77922**
Miserere in C minor—soprano, SATB, 2
oboes, strings & organ, ZWV57 (1738)
A. Hlavenková, Czech Chbr Ch, Baroque 1994 Ens,
R. Válek (r1994) *Requiem, ZWV48.*
(12/95) (SUPR) ① **SU0052-2**
Missa dei fili (Missa ultimarum
secundat)—soloists, chorus and orchestra,
ZWV20 (1740-41)
N. Argenta, M. Chance, C. Prégardien, Gordon
Jones, Stuttgart Chbr Ch, Tafelmusik, F. Bernius
Litanie lauretanae, ZWV152.
(10/90) (DHM) ① **RD77922**
Missa Promissae gloriae (Missa Gratias
agimus tibi)—SATB, choir and orchestra
(1730)
J. Jonášová, M. Mrázová, V. Doležal, P. Mikuláš,
Czech Phil Chor, Czech PO, J. Bělohlávek *Concert*
(5/92) (SUPR) ① **11 0816-2**
Requiem in C
B. Fournier, B. Balleys, K. Ishii, N. Tüller, Berne Chbr
Ch, Berne CO, J.E. Dähler
(9/86) (CLAV) ① **CD50-8501**
Requiem in D minor—soloists, SATB &
orchestra, ZWV48 (?1721) (composed for
Anniversary of Joseph I)
H. Pellarová, M. Kožená, L. Richter, M. Pospíšil,
Czech Chbr Ch, Baroque 1994 Ens, R. Válek (r1994)
Miserere, ZWV57. (12/95) (SUPR) ① **SU0052-2**
Responsoria pro Hebdomada Sancta (1732)
Czech Phil Chor, L. Mátl *Concert*
(5/92) (SUPR) ① **11 0816-2**
Su tuum praesidium No. 3 in D—marian
antiphon: 4vv, strings and organ (1729-34)
Czech Phil Chor, L. Mátl *Concert*
(5/92) (SUPR) ① **11 0816-2**

ZELEŃSKI, Władysław
(1837–1921) Poland

SECTION IV: VOCAL AND CHORAL

Black skirt—song
I. Bohuss, anon (r1902) *Concert*
(6/93) (PEAR) ① [3] **GEMMCDS9004/6(1)**

ZELLER, Carl (Johann Adam) (1842–1898) Austria

SECTION V: STAGE WORKS

Der **Obersteiger**, '(The) Master Miner'—operetta: 3 acts (1894—Vienna) (Lib. West & Held)
EXCERPTS: 1a. Wo sie war die Müllerin; 1b. 'Sei nicht bös, es kann nicht sein'; 2. Ja dort in den Bergen.
1a, 1b M. Hill Smith, Chandos Concert Orch, S. Barry (Eng) Concert   (6/85) (CHAN) ① **CHAN8362**
1a, 1b E. Schwarzkopf, Philh, O. Ackermann Concert
(1/86) (EMI) ① **CDC7 47284-2**
1a, 1b L. Popp, ASMF, N. Marriner Concert
(6/88) (EMI) ① **CDC7 49700-2**
2. L. Schöne, orch (r1925) Concert
(12/92) (NIMB) ① **NI7833**
Der **Vogelhändler**, '(The) Bird Catcher'—operetta: 3 acts (1891—Vienna) (Lib. West and Held)
EXCERPTS: 1a. Prelude. ACT 1: 1b. Introduction; 2. Grüss euch Gott, alle miteinander; 3. Als dir die Welt voll Rosen ning (Duet); 4. Fröhlich Pfalz; 5. Ich bin die Christel von der Post; 6. Ach, ihre Reputation; 7c. Schenkt man sich Rosen in Tirol; ACT 2: 8. Introduction; 9. Ich bin der Prodekan; 10. Bescheiden, mit verschämten Wangen; 11. Mir scheint, ich kenn' dich, spröde Feel; 12b. Wie mein Ahn'l zwanzig Jahr, 'Nightingale song'; 12c. Also fangt's an, Gott'snam'l; ACT 3: 13. Introduction; 14. Als geblüht der Kirschenbaum; 15. Kämpfeine mit Frau'n.
Cpte A. Rothenberger, G. Litz, W. Berry, G. Unger, J. Förster, K. Dönch, A. Dallapozza, R. Holm, W. Anheisser, Vienna St Op Chor, Vienna SO, W. Boskovsky   (7/89) (EMI) ① [2] **CMS7 69357-2**
Excs E. Köth, R. Holm, R. Schock, K-E. Mercker, K. Herford, R. Glawitsch, E. Pauly, Günther Arndt Ch, Berlin SO, F. Fox   (2/91) (EURO) ① **GD69026**
Hast du schon einmal zu gleich H.E. Groh, orch (r1932) Concert   (3/92) (PEAR) ① **GEMMCD9419**
5. L. Schöne, orch (r1925) Concert
(12/92) (NIMB) ① **NI7833**
5, 7c E. Schwarzkopf, Philh, O. Ackermann Concert
(1/86) (EMI) ① **CDC7 47284-2**
7c P. Domingo, ECO, J. Rudel Concert
(2/87) (EMI) ① **CDC7 47398-2**
7c Raphaele Concert Orch, P. Walden (arr Waldenmaier) Concert
(5/91) (MOZA) ① **MECD1002**
7c H.E. Groh, E. Bettendorf, orch (r1931) Concert
(3/92) (PEAR) ① **GEMMCD9419**
7c B. Hendricks, Philh, L. Foster (r1992) Concert
(8/93) (EMI) ① **CDC7 54626-2**
12b R. Tauber, Orch, E. Hauke (r1928) Concert
(12/89) (EMI) ① **CDH7 69787-2**
12b E. Kunz, VPO, O. Ackermann (r1951) Concert
(9/95) (TEST) ① **SBT1059**

ZELTER, Carl Friedrich (1758–1832) Germany

SECTION IV: VOCAL AND CHORAL

Abschied—Lied
D. Fischer-Dieskau, A. Reimann Concert
(3/88) (ORFE) ① **C097841A**
An die Entferne—Lied
D. Fischer-Dieskau, A. Reimann Concert
(3/88) (ORFE) ① **C097841A**
Berglied—Lied
D. Fischer-Dieskau, A. Reimann Concert
(3/88) (ORFE) ① **C097841A**
Einsamkeit (Harfenspieler I)—Lied
D. Fischer-Dieskau, A. Reimann Concert
(3/88) (ORFE) ① **C097841A**
Erster Verlust—Lied
D. Fischer-Dieskau, A. Reimann Concert
(3/88) (ORFE) ① **C097841A**
Gesang und Kuss—Lied
D. Fischer-Dieskau, A. Reimann Concert
(3/88) (ORFE) ① **C097841A**
Harfenspieler II—Lied
D. Fischer-Dieskau, A. Reimann Concert
(3/88) (ORFE) ① **C097841A**
Klage—Lied
1. Harfenspieler III:1; 2. Harfenspieler III:2.
D. Fischer-Dieskau, A. Reimann Concert
(3/88) (ORFE) ① **C097841A**
Rastlose Liebe—Lied
D. Fischer-Dieskau, A. Reimann Concert
(3/88) (ORFE) ① **C097841A**

Ruhe (Wand'rers Nachtlied)—Lied
D. Fischer-Dieskau, A. Reimann Concert
(3/88) (ORFE) ① **C097841A**
Die **Sänger der Vorwelt**—Lied
D. Fischer-Dieskau, A. Reimann Concert
(3/88) (ORFE) ① **C097841A**
Selige Sehnsucht—Lied
D. Fischer-Dieskau, A. Reimann Concert
(3/88) (ORFE) ① **C097841A**
Uber allen Gipfeln—Lied
D. Fischer-Dieskau, A. Reimann Concert
(3/88) (ORFE) ① **C097841A**
Um Mitternacht—Lied
D. Fischer-Dieskau, A. Reimann Concert
(3/88) (ORFE) ① **C097841A**
Wand'rers Nachtlied—Lied
D. Fischer-Dieskau, A. Reimann Concert
(3/88) (ORFE) ① **C097841A**
Wo geht's Liebchen, 'Mailied'—Lied
D. Fischer-Dieskau, A. Reimann Concert
(3/88) (ORFE) ① **C097841A**
Wonne der Wehmut—Lied
D. Fischer-Dieskau, A. Reimann Concert
(3/88) (ORFE) ① **C097841A**

ZEMLINSKY, Alexander von (1871–1942) Austria

SECTION I: ORCHESTRAL

3 Ballettstücke (1903) (arr cpsr from 'Triumph der Zeit')
Hamburg PO, G. Albrecht (r1992) Concert
(3/94) (CAPR) ① **10 448**
Sinfonietta—orchestra, Op. 23 (1934)
Berlin RSO, B. Klee Concert
(7/90) (SCHW) ① **311122**
Symphony No. 1 in D minor—orchestra (1892)
Bratislava RSO, L. Rajter Gläserne Herz Suite.
(12/91) (MARC) ① **8 223166**

SECTION II: CHAMBER

String Quartet No. 1 in A, Op. 4
LaSalle Qt Concert
(8/89) (DG) ① [2] **427 421-2GC2**
String Quartet No. 2, Op. 15
LaSalle Qt Concert
(8/89) (DG) ① [2] **427 421-2GC2**
Artis Qt Schoenberg: String Quartet.
(7/90) (ORFE) ① **C194901A**
Schoenberg Qt String Quartet 3.
(3/92) (SCHW) ① **310118**
String Quartet No. 3, Op. 19
LaSalle Qt Concert
(8/89) (DG) ① [2] **427 421-2GC2**
Schoenberg Qt String Quartet 2.
(3/92) (SCHW) ① **310118**
String Quartet No. 4, Op. 25
LaSalle Qt Concert
(8/89) (DG) ① [2] **427 421-2GC2**
Trio for Clarinet/Viola, Cello and Piano in D minor, Op. 3 (1896)
Beaux Arts Trio Korngold: Piano Trio, Op. 1.
(6/94) (PHIL) ① **434 072-2PH**

SECTION III: INSTRUMENTAL

Albumblatt—piano (1895)
S. Mauser (r1993) Concert
(9/95) (VIRG) ① **VC5 45125-2**
Balladen—piano (1892)
S. Mauser (r1993) Concert
(9/95) (VIRG) ① **VC5 45125-2**
Fantasien über Gedichte von Richard Dehmel—piano solo, Op. 9 (c1900)
S. Mauser (r1993) Concert
(9/95) (VIRG) ① **VC5 45125-2**
Fuge in G minor—piano
S. Mauser (r1993) Concert
(9/95) (VIRG) ① **VC5 45125-2**
Ländliche Tänze—piano solo, Op. 1 (1892)
S. Mauser (r1993) Concert
(9/95) (VIRG) ① **VC5 45125-2**
Skizze—piano (1896)
S. Mauser (r1993) Concert
(9/95) (VIRG) ① **VC5 45125-2**

SECTION IV: VOCAL AND CHORAL

Ahnung Beatricens—Lied (Wds. F. Werfel)
B. Bonney, C. Garben Concert
(10/89) (DG) ① [2] **427 348-2GH2**
2 Balladen (1907)
1. Jane Grey (wds. H Amann); 2. Der verlorene Haufen (wds. V Klemperer).
A. Schmidt, C. Garben (r1993) Concert
(6/95) (SONY) ① **SK57960**

2 Brettl-Lieder (1901)
1. In der Sonnengasse (wds. A Holz); 2. Herr Bombardil (wds. R A Schröder).
I. Vermillion, C. Garben (r1993) Concert
(6/95) (SONY) ① **SK57960**
Das **Bucklichte Männlein**—Lied (1934) (Wds. Des knaben Wunderhorn)
T. Hampson, G. Parsons Concert
(10/90) (TELD) ① **2292-44923-2**
Gesänge, Op. 5:Bk 1 (c1896)
1. Schlaf nur ein! (wds. Heyse); 2. Hütet euch! (wds. Heyse); 3. O Blätter, dürre Blätter (wds. Pfau); 4. O Sterne, goldene Sterne (wds. Pfau).
1. H-P. Blochwitz, C. Garben Concert
(10/89) (DG) ① [2] **427 348-2GH2**
2. B. Bonney, C. Garben Concert
(10/89) (DG) ① [2] **427 348-2GH2**
3. A.S. von Otter, C. Garben Concert
(10/89) (DG) ① [2] **427 348-2GH2**
4. A. Schmidt, C. Garben Concert
(10/89) (DG) ① [2] **427 348-2GH2**
Gesänge, Op. 5:Bk 2 (c1896)
1. Unter blühenden Bäumen (wds. Gensichen); 2. Tiefe Sehnsucht (wds. von Liliencron); 3. Nach dem Gewitter (wds. Evers); 4. Im Korn (wds. Evers).
1-3. A. Schmidt, C. Garben Concert
(10/89) (DG) ① [2] **427 348-2GH2**
4. H-P. Blochwitz, C. Garben Concert
(10/89) (DG) ① [2] **427 348-2GH2**
6 Gesänge—waltz-songs on Tuscan folk-lyrics, Op. 6 (1898) (Wds. F. Gregorovius)
1. Liebe Schwalbe; 2. Klagen ist der Mond gekommen; 3. Fensterlein, nachts bist du zu; 4. Ich gehe des Nachts; 5. Blaues Sternlein; 6. Briefchen schrieb ich.
1, 3, 5, 6. B. Bonney, C. Garben Concert
(10/89) (DG) ① [2] **427 348-2GH2**
2, 4. A.S. von Otter, C. Garben Concert
(10/89) (DG) ① [2] **427 348-2GH2**
5 Gesänge, Op. 7 (c1899)
1. Da waren zwei Kinder (wds. Morgenstern); 2. Entbietung (wds. Dehmel); 3. Meeraugen (wds. Dehmel); 4. Irmelin Rose (wds. Jacobsen); 5. Sonntag (wds. Wertheimer?).
1. A.S. von Otter, C. Garben Concert
(10/89) (DG) ① [2] **427 348-2GH2**
2. A. Schmidt, C. Garben Concert
(10/89) (DG) ① [2] **427 348-2GH2**
3, 5. B. Bonney, C. Garben Concert
(10/89) (DG) ① [2] **427 348-2GH2**
4. H-P. Blochwitz, C. Garben Concert
(10/89) (DG) ① [2] **427 348-2GH2**
4 Gesänge, Op. 8 (c1899)
1. Turmwächterlied (wds. Jacobsen); 2. Und hat der Tag all seine Qual (wds. Jabobsen); 3. Mit Trommeln und Pfeifen (wds. von Liliencros); 4. Tod in Ähren (wds. von Liliencros).
1, 3, 4. A. Schmidt, C. Garben Concert
(10/89) (DG) ① [2] **427 348-2GH2**
2. A.S. von Otter, C. Garben Concert
(10/89) (DG) ① [2] **427 348-2GH2**
6 Gesänge, Op. 10 (c1900)
1. Ehetanzlied (wds. Bierbaum); 2. Selige Stunde (wds. Wertheimer?); 3. Vöglein Schwermut (wds. Morgenstern); 4. Meine Braut führ ich heim (wds. Jacobsen); 5. Klopfet, so ward euch aufgetan (wds. Lingen); 6. Kirchweih (wds. Busse).
1, 3, 6. H-P. Blochwitz, C. Garben Concert
(10/89) (DG) ① [2] **427 348-2GH2**
2, 4. A. Schmidt, C. Garben Concert
(10/89) (DG) ① [2] **427 348-2GH2**
5. B. Bonney, C. Garben Concert
(10/89) (DG) ① [2] **427 348-2GH2**
6 Gesänge, Op. 13 (1910-13) (Wds. Maeterlinck)
Cpte A.S. von Otter, C. Garben Concert
(10/89) (DG) ① [2] **427 348-2GH2**
D. Dorow, M. Damerini (pp1980) Concert
(8/89) (ETCE) ① **KTC1044**
6 Gesänge nach Maeterlinck—mezzo/baritone and piano/orchestra, Op. 13 (1910-13)
H. Fassbender, Czech PO, V. Neumann (pp1992) Reger: Hiller Variations.
(7/93) (SUPR) ① **11 1811-2**
Lieder, Op. 2:Bk 1 (1896)
1. Heilige Nacht (wds. Fel); 2. Der Himmel hat keine Sterne (wds. Heyse); 3. Geflüster der Nacht (wds. Storm); 6. Um Mitternacht (wds. Rodenberg); 7. Vor der Stadt (wds. Eichendorff).
1, 7. A. Schmidt, C. Garben Concert
(10/89) (DG) ① [2] **427 348-2GH2**
2, 6. B. Bonney, C. Garben Concert
(10/89) (DG) ① [2] **427 348-2GH2**
3. A.S. von Otter, C. Garben Concert
(10/89) (DG) ① [2] **427 348-2GH2**

Lieder, Op. 2:Bk 2 (1896)
1. Frühlingstag (wds. Siebel); 2. Altdeutsches Minnelied (wds. 'Des Knaben Wunderhorn'); 3. Der Traum (wds. von Blüthgen); 4. Im Lenz (wds. Heyse); 5. Das verlassene Mädchen (wds. von Leixner); 6. Empfängnis (wds. Wertheimer).
1, 3, 5. A.S. von Otter, C. Garben *Concert*
　　　　(10/89) (DG) ① [2] **427 348-2GH2**
2, 4. A. Schmidt, C. Garben *Concert*
　　　　(10/89) (DG) ① [2] **427 348-2GH2**
6. B. Bonney, C. Garben *Concert*
　　　　(10/89) (DG) ① [2] **427 348-2GH2**
6 Lieder, Op. 22 (1934)
1. Auf braunen Sammetschuhen (wds. Morgenstern); 2. Abendkelch voll Sonnenlicht (wds. Morgenstern); 3. Feiger Gedanken bängliches Schwanken (wds. wds. Goethe); 4. Elfenlied (wds. Goethe); 5. Volkslied (wds. Morgenstern); 6. Das bucklichte Männlein (wds. 'Des knaben Wunderhorn'); 6a. Auf dem Meere meiner Seele (wds. Morgenstern).
1. A.S. von Otter, C. Garben *Concert*
　　　　(10/89) (DG) ① [2] **427 348-2GH2**
2, 3, 5. H-P. Blochwitz, C. Garben *Concert*
　　　　(10/89) (DG) ① [2] **427 348-2GH2**
4, 6. B. Bonney, C. Garben *Concert*
　　　　(10/89) (DG) ① [2] **427 348-2GH2**
6. C. Sieden, S. Blier (r1991) *Concert*
　　　　(7/93) (KOCH) ① **37086-2**
6a A. Schmidt, C. Garben *Concert*
　　　　(10/89) (DG) ① [2] **427 348-2GH2**
12 Lieder, Op. 27 (c1936) (Wds. George, Kalidasa, Goethe)
1. Entführung (wds. George); 2. Sommer (wds. Kalidasa); 3. Frühling (wds. Kalidasa); 4. Jetzt ist die Zeit (wds. Kalidasa); 5. Die Verschmähte (wds. Amara); 6. Der Wind des Herbstes (wds. Kalidasa); 7. Misery (wds. Hughes); 8. Harlem Tänzerin (wds. McKay); 9. Afrikanischer Tanz (wds. Hughes); 10. Gib ein Lied mir wieder (wds. George); 11. Regenzeit (wds. Kalidasa); 12. Wandrers Nachtlied (wds. Goethe).
1-3, 6, 8, 12. H-P. Blochwitz, C. Garben *Concert*
　　　　(10/89) (DG) ① [2] **427 348-2GH2**
4, 5, 7, 11. B. Bonney, C. Garben *Concert*
　　　　(10/89) (DG) ① [2] **427 348-2GH2**
7. C. Sieden, S. Blier (r1991) *Concert*
　　　　(7/93) (KOCH) ① **37086-2**
8, 9. J. Gomez, J. Constable *Concert*
　　　　(6/88) (UNIC) ① **DKPCD9055**
9. A. Schmidt, C. Garben *Concert*
　　　　(10/89) (DG) ① [2] **427 348-2GH2**
10. A.S. von Otter, C. Garben *Concert*
　　　　(10/89) (DG) ① [2] **427 348-2GH2**
6 Lieder (1889-90) (Wds. various)
1. Die schlanke Wasserlilie (wds. H. Heine); 2. Gute Nacht (wds. J von Eichendorff); 3. Liebe und Frühling (wds. H. von Fallersleben); 4. Ich sah mein eigen Angesicht); 5. In der Ferne (wds. R Prutz); 6. Waldgespräch (wds. J von Eichendorff).
R. Ziesak, I. Vermillion, H-P. Blochwitz, A. Schmidt, C. Garben (r1993) *Concert*
　　　　(6/95) (SONY) ① **SK57960**
2 Lieder (1890)
1. Das Rosenband (wds. F Klopstock); 2. Abendstern (wds. J Mayrhofer).
I. Vermillion, H-P. Blochwitz, C. Garben (r1993) *Concert* (6/95) (SONY) ① **SK57960**
4 Lieder (1895-96)
1. Orientalisches Sonett (wds. H Grasberger); 2. Süsse, süsse Sommemacht (wds. A Lynx); 3. Herbsten (wds. P Wertheimer); 4. Nun schwillt der See so band (wds. P Wertheimer).
R. Ziesak, I. Vermillion, H-P. Blochwitz, C. Garben (r1993) *Concert* (6/95) (SONY) ① **SK57960**
3 Lieder (1903-05)
1. Es war ein alter König (wds. H Heine); 2. Über eine Wiege (wds. D von Liliencron); 3. Mädel, kommst du mit zum Tanz? (wds. L Feld).
I. Vermillion, H-P. Blochwitz, C. Garben (r1993) *Concert* (6/95) (SONY) ① **SK57960**
4 Lieder (1916)
1. Noch spür ich ihren Atem (wds. H von Hofmannsthal); 2. Hörtest du denn nicht hinein (wds. H von Hofmannsthal); 3. Die Beiden (wds. H von Hofmannsthal); 4. Harmonie des Abends (wds. C Baudelaire).
R. Ziesak, C. Garben (r1993) *Concert*
　　　　(6/95) (SONY) ① **SK57960**
5 Lieder auf Gedichte von Richard Dehmel (1907)
1. Stromüber; 2. Ansturm; 3. Vorspiel; 4. Letzte Bitte; 5. Auf See.
2, 3, 5. H-P. Blochwitz, C. Garben (r1993) *Concert* (6/95) (SONY) ① **SK57960**

Ein **Lyrische Symphonie**—soprano, baritone, chorus and orchestra, Op. 18 (1923)
K. Armstrong, I. Kusnjer, Czech PO, B. Gregor
　　　　(10/91) (SUPR) ① **11 0395-2**
A. Marc, H. Hagegård, Concertgebouw, R. Chailly (r1993) *Symphonische Gesänge, Op. 20.*
　　　　(12/94) (DECC) ① **443 569-2DH**
2 Preislieder (1891-92) (Wds. V Zusner)
1. Das Mädchens Klage; 2. Der Morgenstern.
R. Ziesak, C. Garben (r1993) *Concert*
　　　　(6/95) (SONY) ① **SK57960**
Schlummerlied—Lied (Wds. R. Beer-Hofmann)
B. Bonney, C. Garben (r1993) *Concert*
　　　　(10/89) (DG) ① [2] **427 348-2GH2**
Symphonische Gesänge—1v and orchestra, Op. 20 (1929) (Wds. various)
1. Lied aus Dixieland; 2. Lied der Baumwollpflücker; 3. Totes braunes; 4. Ütler Bursche; 5. Erkenntnis; 6. Afrikanischer Tanz; 7. Arabeske.
F. Grundheber, Hamburg PO, G. Albrecht (r1992) *Concert* (3/94) (CAPR) ① **10 448**
W. White, Concertgebouw, R. Chailly (r1993) *Lyrische Symphonie.*
　　　　(12/94) (DECC) ① **443 569-2DH**
Und Einmal gehst du
A. Schmidt, C. Garben (r1993) *Concert*
　　　　(6/95) (SONY) ① **SK57960**
Wandl' ich im Wald des Abends—Lied (1892) (Wds. H Heine)
A. Schmidt, C. Garben (r1993) *Concert*
　　　　(6/95) (SONY) ① **SK57960**

SECTION V: STAGE WORKS

Es war einmal—opera: prologue & 3 acts (1900—Vienna) (Lib. M Singer, after H Drachmann)
Cpte E. Johansson, K. Westi, P-A. Wahlgren, A. Haugland, O. Hedegaard, G. Paevatalu, C. Christiansen, S. Lillesøe, Danish Nat Rad Chor, Danish Nat RSO, H. Graf
　　　　(5/91) (CAPR) ① [2] **60 019-2**
Eine **Florentinische Tragödie**—opera: 1 act, Op. 16 (1917—Stuttgart) (Lib. Wilde trans Meyerfeld)
D. Soffel, K. Riegel, G. Sarabia, Berlin RSO, G. Albrecht (12/85) (SCHW) ① **314012**
Der **Geburtstag der Infantin (aka 'Der Zwerg')**—opera, Op. 17 (1922—Cologne) (Lib. Klaren, after Klaren)
cpte I. Nielsen, K. Riegel, B. Haldas, D. Weller, C. Studer, O. Fredricks, M. Hirsti, Berlin RSO, G. Albrecht (4/86) (SCHW) ① **314013**
Gläserne Herz—concert suite from ballet (1903)
Bratislava RSO, L. Rajter *Symphony 1.*
　　　　(12/91) (MARC) ① **8 223166**
Kleider machen Leute—comic opera: 2 acts (1910—Vienna) (Lib. Feld, after Keller)
Cpte H. Winkler, E. Mathis, W. Slabbert, H. Franzen, S. Kaluza, V. Vogel, U. Hunziker, B. Jensson, U.S. Eggimann, R. Hartmann, P. Keller, R. Rohner, J. Will, R. Scholze, R. Lenhart, K. Justus, S. Salminen, C. Otelli, U. Peter, Zurich Op Hse Chor, Zurich Op Orch, R. Weikert (pp1990) (1/92) (SCHW) ① [2] **314069**
Der **König Kandaules**—opera: 3 acts (1935-36) (Lib. Gide: orch unfinished)
EXCERPTS: ACT 3: 1. Prelude; 2. Gyges's monologue.
1, 2. F. Grundheber, Hamburg PO, G. Albrecht (r1992: orch Beaumont) *Concert*
　　　　(3/94) (CAPR) ① **10 448**
Der **Kreidekreis**—opera: 3 acts (1933—Zurich) (Lib. Klabund (Alfred Henschke)
Cpte R. Behle, G. Schreckenbach, R. Hermann, S. Lorenz, R. Goldberg, U. Peter, H. Helm, G. Ottenthal, K. Borris, G. Saks, C. Lindsley, Berlin RSO, S. Soltesz (1/92) (CAPR) ① [2] **60 016-2**
Die **Traumgörge**—opera: 2 acts & epilogue (1904-06) (Lib. L. Feld)
Cpte J. Martin, J. Protschka, P. Coburn, H. Welker, M. Blasius, P. Haage, V. von Halem, H. Kruse, B. Calm, G.M. Ronge, Hesse Rad Ch, Frankfurt RSO, G. Albrecht (3/89) (CAPR) ① [2] **10 241/2**

ZIEGLER, Pablo *(20th Cent)*
Argentina

SECTION III: INSTRUMENTAL

Milonga en el viento—tango milonga
Buenos Aires Qnt, RPO, E. Stratta (arr J. Calandrelli) *Concert* (1/93) (TELD) ① **9031-76997-2**

ZIEHRER, C(arl) M(ichael) *(1843–1922) Austria*

SECTION I: ORCHESTRAL

Busserl—polka mazur, Op. 389 (1887)
LSO, J. Georgiadis *Concert*
　　　　(4/89) (CARL) ① **PCD902**
Casimir—waltz, Op. 511 (1913) (based on melodies from 'Fürst Casimir')
London Viennese Orch, J. Rothstein *Concert*
　　　　(5/93) (CHAN) ① **CHAN9127**
Die **Lustigmacherin**—polka schnell (c1863) (Eng: Dancing temptress)
London Viennese Orch, J. Rothstein *Concert*
　　　　(5/93) (CHAN) ① **CHAN9127**
Nachtschwalbe—polka française, Op. 417 (1890)
Košice St PO, M. Eichenholz (r1992) *Concert*
　　　　(2/94) (MARC) ① **8 223471**
Weana Mad'ln—waltz, Op. 388 (c1887) (Eng: Viennese maidens)
VPO, C. Krauss (r1931) *Concert*
　　　　(11/92) (PREI) ① **90112**

SECTION V: STAGE WORKS

Die **Drei Wünsche**—operetta: prelude and 3 acts (1901—Vienna) (Lib. L. Krenn and C. Lindau)
Dünn, dünn ist die Leopoldin' P. Morrison, Chandos Concert Orch, S. Barry (Eng) *Concert*
　　　　(2/90) (CHAN) ① **CHAN8759**
Der **Fremdenführer**—operette: prelude & 3 acts (1902—Vienna) (Lib. L. Krenn and C. Lindau)
Military Life! P. Morrison, Chandos Concert Orch, S. Barry *Concert* (7/88) (CHAN) ① **CHAN8561**
Die **Schätzmeister, '(The) Pawnbroker's Valuer'**—operette: 3 acts (1904—Vienna) (Lib. Engel & Horst)
(ACT 1); 1. Do re mi fa sol la si.
O let me hold your tiny little hand M. Hill Smith, P. Morrison, Chandos Concert Orch, S. Barry *Concert*
　　　　(7/88) (CHAN) ① **CHAN8561**
1. M. Hill Smith, Chandos Concert Orch, S. Barry (Eng: arr. F. Bauer) *Concert*
　　　　(6/85) (CHAN) ① **CHAN8362**

ZILCHER, Hermann *(1881–1948) Germany*

SECTION IV: VOCAL AND CHORAL

Ein gar alt fröhlich, auch andächtig Weihnachtsliedlein—Lied
K. Erb, B. Seidler-Winkler (r1935) *Concert*
　　　　(6/94) (PREI) ① [2] **89208**
Rococo Suite—voice, violin, cello and piano, Op. 65 (Wds. various)
1. An der Menschen (wds. J.W.L. Gleim); 2. Der Frühling (wds. J. N. Götz); 3. Abendständchen (wds. C. von Brentano); 4. Die Nacht (wds. F. von Hagedorn); 5. Die Alte (wds. F. von Hagedorn); 6. Mailied (wds. J. W. Goethe); 7. An den Menschen (wds. J.W.L. Gleim).
E. Schwarzkopf, P. Richartz, A. Steiner, M. Raucheisen (bp1944) *Concert*
　　　　(6/87) (ACAN) ① **43 801**

ZILLNER *(19th–20th cents) Austria*

SECTION IV: VOCAL AND CHORAL

Es steht ein alter Nussbaum—Viennese song
E. Kunz, Kemmeter-Faltl Schrammel Ens (r1949) *Concert* (9/95) (TEST) ① **SBT1059**

ZIMBALIST, Efrem *(1889–1985) Russia*

SECTION II: CHAMBER

3 Slavonic dances—violin and piano
1. Russian dance; 2. Hebrew melody and dance; 3. Polish dance.
2. E. Zimbalist, anon (r1911) *Concert*
　　　　(7/93) (APR) ① [2] **APR7016**
3. E. Zimbalist, orch (r1916) *Concert*
　　　　(7/93) (APR) ① [2] **APR7016**

ZIMMER, Hans (20th Cent) Germany/USA

SECTION V: STAGE WORKS
Pacific Heights—film score (1990)
OST, H. Zimmer (r1990)
(5/91) (VARE) ① **VSD5286**

ZIMMERMAN, Charles A. (1861–1916) USA

SECTION I: ORCHESTRAL
Anchors aweigh—march (1907)
Cleveland Winds, F. Fennell Concert
(10/84) (TELA) ① **CD80099**

ZIMMERMANN, Bernd Alois (1918–1970) Germany

SECTION I: ORCHESTRAL
Concerto for Trumpet and Orchestra in C, 'Nobody knows the trouble I see' (1954)
R. Friedrich, Frankfurt RSO, D. Kitaienko (r1991-2)
Concert
(6/93) (CAPR) ① **10 482**

SECTION II: CHAMBER
Intercomunicazione—cello and piano (1967)
M. Bach, B. Wambach (r1992) Concert
(8/94) (CPO) ① **CPO999 198-2**

SECTION III: INSTRUMENTAL
Enchiridion—small pieces: piano (1949-52)
B. Wambach (r1992) Concert
(8/94) (CPO) ① **CPO999 198-2**
4 Short Studies—cello (1970)
M. Bach (r1992) Concert
(8/94) (CPO) ① **CPO999 198-2**
Sonata—cello (1930)
M. Bach (r1992) Concert
(8/94) (CPO) ① **CPO999 198-2**

SECTION IV: VOCAL AND CHORAL
Requiem für einen jungen Dichter—lingual for spkrs, sngrs, choirs & instruments (1967-9) (Wds. Various)
Cpte V. Orsanic, J. Johnson, M. Rotschopf, B. Schir,
C. Grund, A. von Schlippenbach Jazz Band, Cologne
Rad Chor, Stuttgart Rad Chor, Edinburgh Fest Chor,
Bratislava Slovak Chor, Bratislava City Chor, South-
West German RSO, M. Gielen (r1995)
(12/95) (SONY) ① **SK61995**

SECTION V: STAGE WORKS
Die Soldaten—opera: 4 acts (1958-60 rev 1963-64—Cologne) (Lib. cpsr, after Lenz)
Cpte M. Munkittrick, N. Shade, M. Vargas, G.
Hoffman, M. Ebbecke, E. Maurer, A. Treml, W.
Cochran, G. Renard, K-F. Dürr, K. Hirte, R.
Wolansky, J. Eidloth, R. Wörle, H. Holzapfel, U.
Koszut, J. van der Schaaf, K-H. Eichler, J. Bolle, J.
Geiger, P. Flottau, H. Tübinger, U. Rohde, Stuttgart
Op Chor, Stuttgart St Orch, B. Kontarsky
(7/91) (TELD) ① [2] **9031-72775-2**

ZIMMERMANN, Udo (b 1943) Germany

SECTION V: STAGE WORKS
Weisse Rose—opera: 8 scenes (1967-68) (Lib. I. Zimmermann)
Cpte G. Fontana, L-M. Harder, Inst. Ens, U.
Zimmermann
(9/88) (ORFE) ① **C162871A**

ZIPOLI, Domenico (1688–1726) Italy

SECTION IV: VOCAL AND CHORAL
Missa San Ignacio—Mass Ordinary (Chiquitos Mission Archive)
Cordoba Children's Ch, Elyma Ens, G. Garrido
(r1992) Concert
(9/93) (K617) ① **K617025**
Vespers for San Ignacio—reconstruction (MSS in Chiquitos & San Ignacio de Mojos archives)
1. Deus in adjutorium; 2. Domine ad adjuvandum (arr
anon from keyboard work); 3a. Antiphon: Domine
quinque; 3b. Psalm: Dixit Dominus; 4a. Antiphon:
Euge serve; 4b. Confitebor tibi Domine; 5a. Antiphon:
Fidelis servus; 5b. Psalm: Beatus vir; 6a. Antiphon:
Beatuus ille servus; 6b. Psalm: Laudate pueri (anon:
attrib Zipoli); 7a. Antiphon: Serve bone; 7b. Psalm:
Laudate Dominum (attrib M Schmid); 8. Hymn: Iste
confessor (attrib M Schmid); 9a. Antiphon: Hic vir
(plainchant); 9b. Magnificat (plainchant); 10.
Pastoreta ichepe flauta (attrib M Schmid); 11. Te
Deum laudamus.
Cordoba Children's Ch, Elyma Ens, G. Garrido
(r1992) Concert
(9/93) (K617) ① **K617027**

ZORZI, Juan Carlos (b 1936) Argentina

SECTION II: CHAMBER
Adagio elegíaco—strings (1964)
Camerata Bariloche (r1994) Concert
(11/95) (DORI) ① **DOR90202**

ZUMAYA, Manuel de (c1678–1756) Mexico

SECTION IV: VOCAL AND CHORAL
Celebren, publiquen—double choir
Chanticleer, Chanticleer Sinfonia, J. Jennings (r1993)
Concert
(12/94) (TELD) ① **4509-93333-2**
Hieremiae Prophetae Lamentationes—Lamentations of Jeremiah (1717)
Chanticleer (r1993) Concert
(12/94) (TELD) ① **4509-93333-2**
Laetatus sum (Wds. Psalm 121)
Compañia musical, Maîtrise Nationale Ch, Grande
Ecurie, J-C. Malgoire (r1992) Concert
(9/93) (K617) ① **K617026**
Lauda Jerusalem—8vv and instruments (Wds. Psalm 126)
Compañia musical, Maîtrise Nationale Ch, Grande
Ecurie, J-C. Malgoire (r1992) Concert
(9/93) (K617) ① **K617026**
Sol-fa de Pedro—solfeggio piece (1715)
Chanticleer, Chanticleer Sinfonia, J. Jennings (r1993)
Concert
(12/94) (TELD) ① **4509-93333-2**

ZWILICH, Ellen Taaffe (b 1939) USA

SECTION I: ORCHESTRAL
Celebration—orchestra (1984)
Indianapolis SO, J. Nelson Concert
(6/87) (NEW) ① **NW336-2**
Concerto for Oboe and Orchestra (1990)
J. Sedares, Louisville Orch (r1994) Concert
(12/95) (KOCH) ① **37278-2**
Concerto for Tenor Trombone and Orchestra (1988)
C. Lindberg, Malmö SO, J. DePreist (r1993) Concert
(9/94) (BIS) ① **BIS-CD628**
Concerto Grosso 1985—orchestra (1985)
J. Sedares, Louisville Orch (r1994) Concert
(12/95) (KOCH) ① **37278-2**
Prologue and Variations—orchestra (1983-84)
Indianapolis SO, J. Nelson Concert
(6/87) (NEW) ① **NW336-2**
Symphony No. 1—3 movements for orchestra (1981-82)
Indianapolis SO, J. Nelson Concert
(6/87) (NEW) ① **NW336-2**
Symphony No. 3 (1992)
J. Sedares, Louisville Orch (r1994) Concert
(12/95) (KOCH) ① **37278-2**

Artist index

(DECC) 443 009-2DF2 Mozart—Choral Works
(EMI) CDC7 49283-2 Mozart Sacred Works

ACADEMY OF ST MARTIN IN THE FIELDS
Handel: Concerti grossi, Op. 6 (exc)
see CONCERT INDEX under:
(CFP) CD-CFP4570 Choral Favourites
(CHAN) CHAN8841 Walton—Film Music, Vol 4
(CHAN) CHAN8840 Walton—Film Music, Vol 3
(COLL) Coll1234-2 English Music for Strings
(DECC) 425 721-2DM Vivaldi: Concertos
(PHIL) 412 226-2PH Telemann: Horn Concertos
(PHIL) 412 879-2PH Telemann: Oboe Concertos
(PHIL) 422 508-2PME4 The Complete Mozart Edition
Vol 8
(PHIL) 422 545-2PME3 The Complete Mozart Edition
Vol.45
  cond I. BROWN
Geminiani: Concerti Grossi, Op. 7
Poulenc: Organ Concerto
see CONCERT INDEX under:
(DECC) 425 627-2DM Poulenc: Choral and Orchestral
Works
(DECC) 425 723-2DM Harp Concertos
(EMI) CDC5 55052-2
Praetorius/Vivaldi/Warlock—Works arr guitar
(EMI) CDC7 54842-2 Stamitz—Clarinet Concertos
(PHIL) 400 075-2PH Recorder Concertos
(PHIL) 410 041-2PH Telemann: Recorder works
(PHIL) 412 226-2PH Telemann: Horn Concertos
(PHIL) 412 624-2PH Vivaldi: Guitar Concertos
(PHIL) 412 851-2PH Bach—Oboe Concertos
(PHIL) 420 954-2PH Telemann—Trumpet Concertos
  cond COLIN DAVIS
Mozart: Entführung (Cpte)
  cond G. GUEST
Haydn: Mass 9, Mass 10, Mass 13, Mass 14
see CONCERT INDEX under:
(DECC) 430 159-2DM Haydn, M.Haydn & Mozart:
Sacred Choral Works
(DECC) 430 160-2DM Haydn: Masses & Keyboard
Concerto
(DECC) 430 360-2DWO Faure/Poulenc—Sacred Choral
Works
(DECC) 436 486-2DF2
Durufle/Fauré/Poulenc—Choral Works
  cond P. LEDGER
M-A. Charpentier: Te Deum H146
see CONCERT INDEX under:
(DECC) 443 455-2DF2 Vivaldi—Sacred Choral Works
  cond N. MARRINER
Avison: Concerti after D. Scarlatti
Bach: Art of Fugue, Brandenburg Concertos (exc),
Magnificat, BWV243, Mass in B minor, BWV232
(Cpte), Musikalisches Opfer, BWV1079, Suites,
BWV1066-9
Beethoven: Piano Concerto 2, Piano Concerto 3,
Romances, Violin Concerto
Bizet: Arlésienne Suites, Symphony
Bruch: Violin Concerto 1
Corelli: Concerti grossi, Op. 6
Dvořák: Serenade, Op. 22, Serenade, Op. 44
Elgar: In the South, Serenade, Symphony 1
Falla: Nights in the Gardens of Spain, Sombrero de
tres picos (Cpte)
Grieg: Peer Gynt (exc)
Handel: Concerti grossi, Op. 3, Concerto grosso:
Alexander's Feast, Coronation Anthem, Fireworks
Music, Judas Maccabaeus (exc), Messiah (Cpte),
Water Music
Haydn: Cello Concerto in C, Cello Concerto in D,
Jahreszeiten (Cpte), Schöpfung (Cpte)
M-A. Charpentier: Magnificat, H74, Te Deum, H146
Mendelssohn: Elijah (Cpte), Symphony 3, Symphony
4, Violin Concerto, Op. 64, Violin Concerto (1822)
Mozart: Ave verum corpus, K618, Clarinet Concerto,
K622, Così fan tutte (Cpte), Don Giovanni (Cpte),
Horn Concerti, Mass, K427, Nozze di Figaro (Cpte),
Oboe Concerto, K314, Piano Concerto 15, Piano
Concerto 21, Piano Concerto 23, Piano Concerto 27,
Requiem, Rè Pastore (Cpte), Rondo, K371,
Serenade, K361, Zauberflöte (Cpte)
Paganini: Violin Concerto 1
Rossini: Barbiere di Siviglia (Cpte), Cenerentola
(Cpte), Messa di gloria, Turco in Italia (Cpte)
Sullivan: Yeomen of the Guard (Cpte)
Tchaikovsky: Capriccio italien, Francesca da Rimini,
Manfred Symphony, Marche slave, Romeo and Juliet,
Symphony 1, Symphony 2, Symphony 3, Symphony
4, Symphony 5, Symphony 6, 1812
Vaughan Williams: Symphony 5, Symphony 6
Vieuxtemps: Violin Concerto 5
Vivaldi: Concerti, Op. 8 (exc), Gloria, RV589
Walton: As You Like It (exc), Hamlet (exc)
Weber: Clarinet Concerto 1, Clarinet Concerto 2,
Symphony 1, Symphony 2
see CONCERT INDEX under:
(ARGO) 410 552-2ZH Fauré: Orchestral Works
(ARGO) 414 595-2ZH Vaughan Williams—Orchestral
Works
(ARGO) 417 818-2ZH American Music
(ASV) CDDCA517 The French Connection
(ASV) CDDCA518 The English Connection
(CAPR) 10 436 Classical Trumpet Concertos
(CAPR) 10 501 Elgar—Orchestral Works
(CAPR) 10 532 Kowalski sings Bach and Handel
Sacred Arias
(CFP) CD-CFP4557 Baroque Favourites
(CHAN) CHAN8617 Works for Harmonica and
Orchestra

(CHAN) CHAN8870 Sir William Walton's Film Music
Vol. 2
(DECC) 417 715-2DM Bach—Orchestral Works
(DECC) 417 778-2DM English Orchestral Music
(DECC) 425 721-2DM Vivaldi: Concertos
(DECC) 430 093-2DWO The World of Vaughan
Williams
(DECC) 430 094-2DWO The World of Elgar
(DECC) 430 160-2DM Haydn: Masses & Keyboard
Concerto
(DECC) 430 260-2DM Bach—Cantatas
(DECC) 430 261-2DM Handel—Orchestral Works
(DECC) 430 265-2DM Telemann—Orchestral works
(DECC) 430 268-2DM Mozart—Symphonies
(DECC) 430 498-2DWO The World of Mozart
(DECC) 430 499-2DWO World of Bach
(DECC) 430 500-2DWO World of Handel
(DECC) 430 633-2DM Haydn—Concertos
(DECC) 433 729-2DM Mendelssohn—Orchestral
Works
(DECC) 436 224-2DM Italian Concertos
(DECC) 440 033-2DM Harpsichord Concertos
(DECC) 440 037-2DM Bach—Concertos
(DECC) 440 317-2DWO World of British Classics,
Volume I
(DECC) 440 320-2DWO World of British Classics,
Volume IV
(DECC) 440 323-2DWO World of British Classics,
Volume V
(DECC) 443 009-2DF2 Mozart—Choral Works
(DECC) 443 476-2DF2 Vivaldi—L'estro armonico, Op
3
(DECC) 443 577-2DCS Stravinsky—Orchestral Works
(DECC) 443 838-2DF2 Italian Orchestral Works
(DECC) 443 847-2DF2 Bach—Concertos
(EMI) CDC5 55396-2 Mozart & his Contemporaries
(EMI) CDC7 47014-2 Mozart: Opera Overtures
(EMI) CDC7 49155-2 Rossini: Overtures
(EMI) CDC7 49179-2 Handel—Arias
(EMI) CDC7 49283-2 Mozart Sacred Arias
(EMI) CDC7 49700-2 Lucia Popp sings Viennese
Operetta
(EMI) CDC7 54056-2 Suppé—Overtures
(EMI) CDC7 54301-2 Saxophone Concertos
(EMI) CDC7 54302-2 Mozart—Concertos
(EMI) CDC7 54438-2 Cherubini—Overtures
(EMI) CDC7 54585-2 Wolf-Ferrari—Overtures &
Intermezzi
(EMI) CDM7 64326-2 Haydn/Vivaldi—Cello Concertos
(EMI) CDM7 69569-2 Mozart—Horn Concertos, etc
(EMI) CZS7 67564-2 Mozart—Symphonies
(EMIL) CDZ114 Best of Baroque
(HANS) 98 995 Grieg—Orchestral Works
(LOND) 421 390-2LM Delius: Orchestral Works
(LOND) 421 391-2LM British Music
(PHIL) 412 176-2PH6 Schubert: Complete
Symphonies
(PHIL) 412 727-2PH Grieg and Sibelius: Orchestral
works
(PHIL) 412 892-2PH Vivaldi: Double Concertos
(PHIL) 416 386-2PH Classical Academy
(PHIL) 420 203-2PH Classical Trumpet Concertos
(PHIL) 422 501-2PME6 The Complete Mozart Edition
Vol 1
(PHIL) 422 502-2PME6 The Complete Mozart Edition
Vol 2
(PHIL) 422 503-2PME7 The Complete Mozart Edition
Vol 3
(PHIL) 422 507-2PME12 The Complete Mozart Edition
Vol 7
(PHIL) 422 509-2PME5 The Complete Mozart Edition
Vol 9
(PHIL) 422 545-2PME3 The Complete Mozart Edition
Vol.45
(PHIL) 426 462-2PBQ2 Bach—Orchestral Works
(PHIL) 432 081-2PH Hummel & Weber—Bassoon
Concertos
(PHIL) 432 828-2PM Splendour of Spain, Vol.8 -
Rodrigo
(PHIL) 434 016-2PM3 Rossini—Overtures
(PHIL) 434 105-2PH
Martin/Honegger/Martinů—Concertos and Chamber
Music
(PHIL) 434 173-2PM Arie Amorose
(PHIL) 434 916-2PH Gilbert & Sullivan—Overtures
(PHIL) 438 016-2PH Rodrigo—Guitar Works
(PHIL) 438 706-2PM2 Beethoven—Overtures;
Minuets; Dances
(PHIL) 442 269-2PM2 Mozart—The Great Piano
Concertos, Volume 1
(PHIL) 442 410-2PM Queen of the Night—Cheryl
Studer sings Mozart
(PHIL) 442 427-2PH Vaughan Williams—Orch Works
(PHIL) 442 530-2PH English Idylls
(PHIL) 442 571-2PM2 Mozart—The Great Piano
Concertos, Volume II
(PHIL) 446 196-2PM Rossini—Overtures
(SONY) MK42401 Mendelssohn—Piano Works
(SONY) SMK64251 Mozart—Piano Concertos
  cond K. SILLITO
Cimarosa: Flute and Oboe Concertante in G
see CONCERT INDEX under:
(CAPR) 10 420 Handel—Overtures
(CAPR) 10 523 Jochen Kowalski sings Bach Cantatas
  cond D. WILLCOCKS
Handel: Messiah (Cpte)
Vivaldi: Gloria, RV589
see CONCERT INDEX under:
(CFP) CD-CFP4532 Sacred Arias
(CFP) CD-CFP4570 Choral Favourites
(DECC) 436 256-2DM Handel/Blow—Anthems

(DECC) 436 259-2DM Handel/Blow—Choral Works
(DECC) 443 868-2DF2 Italian Baroque Sacred
Works

ACCADEMIA BIZANTINA
see CONCERT INDEX under:
(DENO) CO-75448 Berio—Duets for Two Violins,
Volume 1
(DENO) CO-78916 20th Century Italian Orchestral
Works
  cond C. CHIARAPPA
see CONCERT INDEX under:
(DENO) CO-78904 Pergolesi/Feo—Sacred Vocal
Works

ACCARDO, Salvatore (cond)
see ECO

ACCARDO, Salvatore (vn)
Beethoven: Romances, String Quintet, Op. 29, Violin
Concerto
Borodin: String Quartet 2
Dvořák: Piano Quintet, Op.81, Romantic Pieces,
String Quintet, Op.77, Terzetto, Op.74, Violin
Concerto
Elgar: Violin Concerto
Mendelssohn: String Quintet 2
Mozart: String Quintet, K174, String Quintet, K406,
String Quintet, K515, String Quintet, K516, String
Quintet, K593, String Quintet, K614
Paganini: Caprices, Op. 1, Violin Concerto 1, Violin
Concerto 2
Penderecki: Violin Concerto (1976)
Sibelius: Violin Concerto
Tchaikovsky: Souvenir de Florence, String Quartet 1
Verdi: String Quartet
Walton: Violin Concerto
see CONCERT INDEX under:
(ASV) CDDCA713 Tchaikovsky—Works for Violin and
Orchestra
(DG) 423 578-2GH Paganini: Works for Violin and
Orchestra
(DG) 423 717-2GH Paganini: Works for Violin and
Orchestra
(DG) 427 314-2GH Ravel: Orchestral & Vocal Works
(DG) 439 414-2GCL Ravel—Vocal and Orchestral
Works
(DG) 439 981-2GGA Paganini—Violin Works
(EMI) CDC7 47005-2 Bach—Violin Concertos
(NUOV) 6742 Mozart—Violin Sonatas, Vol.3
(NUOV) 6743 Mozart—Violin Sonatas, Vol.4
(NUOV) 6802 Mozart—Chamber Works
(PHIL) 426 925-2PM19 The Complete Vivaldi Edition
(PHIL) 432 282-2PSL3 Bruch—Works for Violin and
Orchestra
(PHIL) 442 302-2PM2 The Best of Mendelssohn

ACCARDO, Salvatore (vn/dir)
Mozart: Concertone, K190, Sinfonia Concertante,
K364, Violin Concerto, K207, Violin Concerto, K211,
Violin Concerto, K216, Violin Concerto, K218
see CONCERT INDEX under:
(PHIL) 422 065-2PH Vivaldi: Violin Concertos
(PHIL) 438 797-2PM2 Haydn—Concertos

ACÉL, Ervin (cond)
see Oradea PO

ACERBI, Giuseppe (ten)
see CONCERT INDEX under:
(CLUB) CL99-587/8 Eugenia Burzio (1872-1922)

ACHATZ, Dag (pf)
Pierné: Piano Concerto
see CONCERT INDEX under:
(BIS) BIS-CD188 Stravinsky. Piano Works
(BIS) BIS-CD352 Bernstein: Piano Arrangements
(BIS) BIS-CD404 Gershwin: Piano Works
(BIS) BIS-CD489 Ravel: Arrangements for two
Pianos

ACHRON, Isidor (pf)
see CONCERT INDEX under:
(RCA) 09026 61778-2(01) The Heifetz Collection,
Vol.1 - 1917-24
(RCA) 09026 61778-2(02) The Heifetz Collection,
Vol.2 - 1925-34

ACHSEL, Wanda (sop)
see CONCERT INDEX under:
(SCHW) 314592 Vienna State Opera Live, Vol.9
(SCHW) 314602 Vienna State Opera Live, Vol.10
(SCHW) 314662 Vienna State Opera Live, Vol.16

ACHUCCARO, Joaquin (pf)
see CONCERT INDEX under:
(RCA) GD80707 Citizen Kane—Classic Film Scores
of Bernard Herrmann

ACITO, Marc (ten)
Weill: Down in the Valley (Cpte)

ACKERMAN, Mary (gtr)
see CONCERT INDEX under:
(TELA) CD80340 Schubert—Songs for Male Chorus

ACKERMANN, Otto (cond)
see Philh

ACKTÉ, Aino (sop)
see CONCERT INDEX under:
(SIMA) PSC1810(1) Grieg—Songs (historical
recordings, pt 1)

ACOSTA, Ana Caridad (contr)
C.H. Graun: Montezuma (Cpte)

ADAM, Claus (vc)
Schumann: Piano Quartet, Op. 47

ADAM, Gunter (bass)
R. Strauss: Ariadne auf Naxos (Cpte)

ADAM, Theo (bass-bar)
Bach: St. Matthew Passion, BWV244 (Cpte)
Beethoven: Fidelio (Cpte)
Einem: Dantons Tod (Cpte)
Handel: Messias, K572 (Cpte)
Mendelssohn: Elias (Cpte), Paulus (Cpte)
Mozart: Clemenza di Tito (Cpte), Requiem,
Zauberflöte (Cpte)
R. Strauss: Ariadne auf Naxos (Cpte), Rosenkavalier
(Cpte)
Schoeck: Penthesilea (Cpte)
Wagner: Götterdämmerung (Cpte), Meistersinger
(Cpte), Parsifal (Cpte), Rheingold (Cpte), Rienzi
(Cpte), Siegfried (Cpte), Walküre (Cpte)
Weber: Freischütz (Cpte)
see CONCERT INDEX under:
(ARCH) **439 369-2AX4** Bach—Cantatas, Vol.1
(ARCH) **439 374-2AX5** Bach—Cantatas, Volume 2 -
Easter
(ARCH) **439 394-2AX5** Bach—Cantatas, Volume 5
(PHIL) **446 057-2PB14** Wagner—The Ring Cycle -
Bayreuth Festival 1967

ADAMOPOULOS, Tasso (va)
see CONCERT INDEX under:
(SONY) **SK47230** Mozart—Chamber Works

ADAMS, Donald (bass)
Sullivan: HMS Pinafore (Cpte), Iolanthe (Cpte),
Mikado (Cpte), Patience (Cpte), Pirates of Penzance
(Cpte), Trial by Jury (Cpte), Yeomen of the Guard
(Cpte)
see CONCERT INDEX under:
(DECC) **430 095-2DWO** The World of Gilbert &
Sullivan, Vol.1
(DECC) **433 868-2DWO** The World of Gilbert &
Sullivan - Volume 2

ADAMS, John (cond)
see London Sinfonietta

ADAMS, John (bar)
Massenet: Cid (Cpte)
see CONCERT INDEX under:
(NONE) **7559-79311-2** John Adams—Hoodoo
Zephyr

ADAMS, John (synth)
J. Adams: Light over Water
see CONCERT INDEX under:
(NONE) **7559-79311-2** John Adams—Hoodoo
Zephyr

ADAMS, Suzanne (sop)
see CONCERT INDEX under:
(SYMP) **SYMCD1100** Harold Wayne Collection,
Vol.8

ADANI, Mariella (sop)
Puccini: Bohème (Cpte)

ADDISON, Adele (sop)
see CONCERT INDEX under:
(SONY) **SMK47638** Vaughan Williams—Orchestral
Works

ADDISON, John (cond)
see PAO

ADDY, Obo (perc)
see CONCERT INDEX under:
(NONE) **7559-79275-2** Pieces of Africa

ADE-JESEMANN, Ingrid (sop)
Nono: Prometeo (Cpte)
see CONCERT INDEX under:
(SONY) **SK53978** Prometheus

ADELBRECHT, Henry (tpt)
see CONCERT INDEX under:
(PHIL) **426 086-2PBQ** Vivaldi—Double Concertos

ADELMANN, Stefan (db)
Pergolesi: Orfeo, Stabat Mater

ADENEY, Richard (fl)
Bach: Triple Concerto, BWV1044

(LES) ADIEUX
Mozart: Flute Quartets, Oboe Quartet, K370
Reicha: Flute Quartets, Op.98 (exc), Oboe Quintet,
Op.107
see CONCERT INDEX under:
(DHM) **RD77250** Bach's Sons—Chamber Music

ADINI, Ada (sop)
see CONCERT INDEX under:
(SYMP) **SYMCD1172** The Harold Wayne Collection,
Vol.21

ADLER, Charles F. (cond)
see Vienna Concert Orch

ADLER, Clarence (pf)
see CONCERT INDEX under:
(APR) **APR7016** The Auer Legacy, Vol.2

ADLER, Kurt Herbert (cond)
see National PO

ADLER, Kurt Theo (cl)
see CONCERT INDEX under:
(ORFE) **C015821A** Stravinsky: Choral and Vocal
Works

ADLER, Peter Herman (cond)
see New Philh

ADLER, Samuel (cond)
see Berlin SO

ADLER, Stephen (bar)
G. Lloyd: John Socman (exc)

ADORF, Mario (bar)
Weill: Dreigroschenoper (Cpte)

ADORJÁN, András (fl)
see CONCERT INDEX under:
(ORFE) **C003812H** Danzi: Flute Concertos

ADORNI, Claudio (ten)
Donizetti: Don Pasquale (Cpte)

ADRIANO, M. (cond)
see Bratislava RSO

AEOLIAN QUARTET
Mozart: Clarinet Quintet, K581, Divertimenti, K136-8
(exc)
Schubert: String Quintet

AESCHBACHER, Adrian (pf)
see CONCERT INDEX under:
(TAHR) **FURT1004/7** Furtwängler conducts the Berlin
Philharmonic

AESCHBACHER, Matthias (cond)
see Lausanne CO

AFANASSIEV, Valery (pf)
Schubert: Piano Sonata, D894, Schwanengesang,
D957 (Cpte)
Schumann: Kreisleriana, Waldszenen
see CONCERT INDEX under:
(DENO) **CO-75090** Brahms—Piano Works
(DENO) **CO-78906** Brahms—Piano Works
(DG) **431 654-2GH** Schubert—Works for Violin and
Piano

AFEYAN, Natalia (sngr)
Weill: Dreigroschenoper (Cpte)

AFFRE, Augustarello (ten)
see CONCERT INDEX under:
(IRCC) **IRCC-CD800** Souvenirs from Meyerbeer
Operas
(IRCC) **IRCC-CD802** Souvenirs of Rare French
Opera

AFONSKY, Nicolai (cond)
see Paris Russian Met Church Ch

AFONSKY CHOIR
see CONCERT INDEX under:
(PREI) **89207** Feodor Chaliapin Song
Book—Electrical Recordings

AFONSO, Helena (sop)
Monteverdi: Orfeo (Cpte)

AGACHE, Alexander (bar)
Bretan: Arald (Cpte), Golem (Cpte)
Donizetti: Lucia di Lammermoor (Cpte)
Gounod: Faust (Cpte)
Various: Messa per Rossini (Cpte)
Verdi: Rigoletto (Cpte)

AGE OF ENLIGHTENMENT CHOIR
cond G. LEONHARDT
Bach: Cantata 11, Cantata 211, Cantata 213, Easter
Oratorio, BWV249 (Cpte)
see CONCERT INDEX under:
(VIRG) **VC7 59243-2** Purcell—Odes for Queen Mary

AGGESEN, Niels Erik (organ)
see CONCERT INDEX under:
(DANA) **DACOCD378** Mette Hanskov plays music for
Double Bass

AGHOVA, Livia (sop)
Dvořák: Dimitrij (Cpte), Spectre's Bride, Stabat
Mater

AGNETTI, Mario (ten)
Shostakovich: Lady Macbeth of Mtsensk (Cpte)

AGNEW, Paul (ten)
Blow: Venus and Adonis (Cpte)
Monteverdi: Madrigals, Bk 8 (exc), Scherzi musicali
(1632) (exc)
Purcell: Dioclesian, Z627 (Cpte), Timon of Athens,
Z632 (Cpte)
see CONCERT INDEX under:
(ERAT) **4509-96967-2** Rameau—Les Grands Motets
(HARM) **HMC90 1462** Purcell—Funeral Music for
Queen Mary; Te Deum; Anthems
(HARM) **HMX290 1528/33(1)** A Purcell Companion (pt
1)
(HYPE) **CDA66663** Purcell—Complete Anthems &
Services, Vol.6
(VIRG) **VC7 59606-2** Monteverdi—Madrigals, Book 8

AGOSTINI, Federico (vn)
Vivaldi: Concerti, Op.8 (exc)

AGUILAR, Silvia (narr)
Falla: Amor Brujo (Cpte)

AHLÉN, Ulrika (sop)
see CONCERT INDEX under:
(BIS) **BIS-CD438** Stenhammar: Vocal and Orchestral
Works

AHLERSMEYER, Mathieu (bar)
Mozart: Nozze di Figaro (Cpte)
Verdi: Macbeth (Cpte)
see CONCERT INDEX under:
(SCHW) **314502** Vienna State Opera—Live
Recordings (sampler)
(SCHW) **314562** Vienna State Opera Live, Vol.6
(SCHW) **314582** Vienna State Opera Live, Vol.8
(SCHW) **314602** Vienna State Opera Live, Vol.10

AHLIN, Cvetka (mez)
Mozart: Zauberflöte (Cpte)
R. Strauss: Elektra (Cpte), Rosenkavalier (Cpte)
Wagner: Walküre (Cpte)
see CONCERT INDEX under:
(DG) **435 211-2GX15** Wagner—Der Ring des
Nibelungen

AHLSTEDT, Douglas (ten)
Mysliveček: Bellerofonte (Cpte)

AHMAS, Harri (bn)
see CONCERT INDEX under:
(BIS) **BIS-CD636** Gubaidulina—Bassoon and Cello
Works

AHNSJÖ, Claes Hakon (ten)
Alfvén: Symphony 4
Bach: St. John Passion, BWV245 (Cpte), St Matthew
Passion, BWV244 (Cpte)
Gluck: Rencontre imprévue (Cpte)
Haydn: Armida (Cpte), Infedelta Delusa (Cpte),
Orlando Paladino (Cpte), Vera Costanza (Cpte)
Massenet: Chérubin (Cpte)
Mozart: Nozze di Figaro (Cpte), Rè Pastore (Cpte),
Sogno di Scipione (Cpte)
Puccini: Turandot (Cpte)
Verdi: Macbeth (Cpte)
Wagner: Parsifal (Cpte)
see CONCERT INDEX under:
(PHIL) **432 416-2PH3** Haydn—L'incontro
improvviso/Arias

AHRONOVITCH, Yuri (cond)
see LSO

AICHBERGER, Ewald (ten)
R. Strauss: Frau ohne Schatten (Cpte),
Rosenkavalier (Cpte)
Wagner: Parsifal (Cpte)

AIMARD, Pierre-Laurent (pf)
R. Strauss: Cello Sonata
Rachmaninov: Cello Sonata
see CONCERT INDEX under:
(AUVI) **V4748** Kodaly/Janáček/Liszt—Works for Cello
and Piano
(DG) **437 786-2GH** Webern—Orchestral, Vocal &
Chamber Works
(DG) **439 808-2GH** Boulez conducts Ligeti
(DG) **445 833-2GH** Boulez conducts Boulez

AINLEY, Henry (narr)
see CONCERT INDEX under:
(PEAR) **GEMMCDS9951/5** The Elgar
Edition—Acoustic Recordings 1914-25

AINSLEY, John Mark (ten)
B. Goldschmidt: Mediterranean Songs (Cpte)
Bach: Mass in B minor, BWV232 (Cpte)
Berlioz: Troyens (Cpte)
Blow: Venus and Adonis (Cpte)
Britten: Gloriana (Cpte)
Bruckner: Mass in F minor, Psalm 150
F. Loewe: Brigadoon (Cpte)
Handel: Acis and Galatea (Cpte), Joshua (Cpte),
Look down, harmonious saint, Messiah (exc),
Occasional Oratorio (Cpte), Saul (Cpte)
Howells: Hymnus Paradisi
Mendelssohn: Elias (Cpte)
Monteverdi: Orfeo (Cpte), Vespers
Mozart: Don Giovanni (Cpte), Mass, K427
Porter: Kiss Me, Kate (Cpte)
Purcell: Birthday Ode, Z342, Dido (Cpte), Dioclesian,
Z627 (Cpte), Fairy Queen, Z629 (Cpte), St Cecilia's
Day Ode, Z328, Timon of Athens, Z632 (exc)
Stravinsky: Oedipus Rex (Cpte)
Sullivan: Pirates of Penzance (Cpte)
Tavener: We shall see Him as He is
Zelenka: Lamentations of Jeremiah
see CONCERT INDEX under:
(ARCH) **423 594-2AH** Handel—Vocal Works
(ASV) **CDDCA881** English Church Music, Vol.3
(CARL) **PCD894** Great Baroque Arias, Part I
(CHAN) **CHAN0518** Vivaldi & Bach—Choral Works
(CHAN) **CHAN9185/6** Howells—Songs
(CHAN) **CHAN9292** Walton—Chamber Music
(EMI) **CDC7 49849-2** Famous Opera Choruses
(EMI) **CDC7 54525-2** Mozart—Sacred Works
(HYPE) **CDA66314** Purcell—Complete Odes &
Welcome Songs, Vol.1
(HYPE) **CDA66315** Handel: Music for Royal
Occasions
(HYPE) **CDA66398** Schutz—Christmas Story;
Gabrieli—Motets
(HYPE) **CDA66420** Vaughan Williams: Vocal Works
(HYPE) **CDA66437** Stravinsky—Sacred Choral
Works
(HYPE) **CDA66476** Purcell—Complete Odes &
Welcome Songs, Vol.5
(HYPE) **CDA66569** Vaughan Williams—Choral Works
(HYPE) **CDA66598** Purcell—Complete Odes &
Welcome Songs, Vol.8
(HYPE) **CDA66646** Blow—Fairest work of happy
Nature
(HYPE) **CDA66655** Vaughan Williams—Choral Works
(HYPE) **CDA66736** Warlock—Songs
(HYPE) **CDA67061/2** Britten—Purcell Realizations
(HYPE) **CDJ33012** Schubert—Complete Lieder,
Vol.12
(HYPE) **CDJ33020** Schubert—Complete Lieder,
Vol.20
(HYPE) **CDJ33022** Schubert—Complete Lieder,
Vol.22

(L'OI) **433 848-2OH** Schubert—Chamber and Vocal
Works
(L'OI) **436 460-2OH** Biber—Requiem; Chamber
Works
(L'OI) **436 585-2OH** Mozart—Sacred Choral Works
(L'OI) **440 637-2OH** Monteverdi—Ballets
(UNIT) **88002-2** My Beloved Spake
(VIRG) **VC5 45159-2** Purcell—Come ye sons of art

AINSLIE MURRAY, J. (cond)
see New Light SO

AIRINEN, Kai (ten)
Madetoja: Juha (Cpte)

AITKEN, Robert (fl)
see CONCERT INDEX under:
(BIS) **BIS-CD184** French Flute Music

AIX-EN-PROVENCE FESTIVAL CHORUS
cond A. CLUYTENS
Gounod: Mireille (Cpte)

AKADEMIA
cond F. LASSERRE
see CONCERT INDEX under:
(PIER) **PV794041** Palestrina—Motets and Madrigals

AKAHOSHI, Akira (db)
see CONCERT INDEX under:
(SCHW) **311122** Early Twentieth Century Music

ÅKERLUND, Lina (sop)
A. Scarlatti: Giardino d'amore
see CONCERT INDEX under:
(DENO) **CO-78904** Pergolesi/Feo—Sacred Vocal
Works

AKINS, Thomas (timp)
see CONCERT INDEX under:
(HARM) **HMU90 7106** Kraft—Orchestral Works

AKYAL, Gürer (cond)
see LPO

AL AYRE ESPAÑOL
cond E. L. BANZO
see CONCERT INDEX under:
(DHM) **05472 77325-2** Spanish Baroque, Volume 1

ALABAMA SYMPHONY ORCHESTRA
cond P. POLIVNICK
see CONCERT INDEX under:
(HARM) **HMU90 7106** Kraft—Orchestral Works

ALAGNA, Roberto (ten)
Donizetti: Elisir d'amore (Cpte)
Verdi: Rigoletto (Cpte), Traviata (Cpte)
see CONCERT INDEX under:
(DECC) **436 261-2DHO3** Puccini—Il Trittico
(EMI) **CDC5 55540-2** Roberto Alagna sings Operatic
Arias

ALAIMO, Simone (bar)
Bellini: Zaira (Cpte)
Donizetti: Maria Stuarda (Cpte)
Mozart: Don Giovanni (Cpte)
Rossini: Barbiere di Siviglia (Cpte), Cenerentola
(Cpte), Turco in Italia (Cpte)
Verdi: Masnadieri (Cpte)

ALAIMO, Vincenzo (sngr)
Donizetti: Maria di Rohan (Cpte)

ALAIN, Marie-Claire (organ)
see CONCERT INDEX under:
(ERAT) **2292-45664-2** Bach—Organ Works
(ERAT) **2292-45922-2** Bach—Organ Works
(ERAT) **2292-45943-2** French Works for Organ &
Orchestra
(ERAT) **4509-91702-2** Bach—Complete Organ Works,
Vol.8
(ERAT) **4509-95362-2** Mozart—Sacred Choral
Works

ALAIN, Olivier (organ)
see CONCERT INDEX under:
(ERAT) **4509-95362-2** Mozart—Sacred Choral
Works

ALAN, Hervey (bass)
Purcell: King Arthur, Z628 (Cpte)
Rossini: Cenerentola (Cpte)
see CONCERT INDEX under:
(DECC) **425 499-2DM** On Christmas night
(DECC) **430 093-2DWO** The World of Vaughan
Williams

ALANKO, Petri (alto fl)
see CONCERT INDEX under:
(ONDI) **ODE804-2** Saariaho—Orchestral and
Chamber Works

ALANKO, Petri (fl)
see CONCERT INDEX under:
(ONDI) **ODE802-2** Ibert/Jolivet/Nielsen—Flute
Concertos

ALARIE, Pierrette (sop)
Bizet: Pêcheurs de Perles (Cpte)
Gluck: Orphée (Cpte)
R. Strauss: Schweigsame Frau (Cpte)
see CONCERT INDEX under:
(PHIL) **438 953-2PM2** Alarie/Simoneau - Arias &
Duets
(PHIL) **438 970-2PM2** Camille Maurane

ALBAN BERG QUARTET
Berg: Lyric Suite, String Quartet
Berio: Notturno
Brahms: Piano Quintet, String Sextet 1, String Sextet
2 (exc)

Debussy: String Quartet
Dvořák: Piano Quintet, Op.81 (exc), String Quartet
12
Haydn: String Quartets, Op.77
Janáček: String Quartet 1, String Quartet 2
Mozart: String Quartet, K387, String Quartet, K421,
String Quartet, K428, String Quartet, K458, String
Quartet, K464, String Quartet, K465, String Quartet,
K499, String Quartet, K575, String Quartet, K589,
String Quartet, K590, String Quintet, K515, String
Quintet, K516
Ravel: String Quartet
Rihm: String Quartet 4
Schnittke: String Quartet 4
Schubert: String Quartet, D804, String Quartet, D810,
String Quartet, D887, String Quintet, Trout Quintet,
D667
Smetana: String Quartet 1
see CONCERT INDEX under:
(EMI) **CDC7 54881-2** Viennese Dance Music
(EMI) **CDS7 47127-8** Beethoven: Early String
Quartets
(EMI) **CDS7 47131-8** Beethoven: Middle Quartets
(EMI) **CDS7 47135-8** Beethoven: Late Quartets
(EMI) **CDS7 47720-8** Bartók—String Quartets
(EMI) **CDS7 54587-2** Beethoven—String Quartets,
Vol.1
(EMI) **CDS7 54592-2** Beethoven—String Quartets,
Vol.2
(EMI) **CDS7 54829-2** Brahms—String Quartets
(TELD) **4509-95503-2** Brahms/Dvořák—String
Quartets

ALBANESE, Francesco (ten)
Verdi: Traviata (Cpte)

ALBANESE, Licia (sop)
Bizet: Carmen (Cpte)
Puccini: Bohème (Cpte), Manon Lescaut (Cpte)
Verdi: Traviata (Cpte)
see CONCERT INDEX under:
(EMI) **CHS7 64864-2(2)** La Scala Edition - Vol.2,
1915-46 (pt 2)
(RCA) **GD87799** The Pearl Fishers Duet plus Duets
and Scenes
(RCA) **09026 61580-2(5)** RCA/Met 100 Singers, 100
Years (pt 5)

ALBANI, Emma (sop)
see CONCERT INDEX under:
(SYMP) **SYMCD1093** The Harold Wayne Collection,
Vol.7

ALBANY SYMPHONY ORCHESTRA
cond J. HEYGI
Chadwick: Symphony 2
H. Parker: Northern Ballad
cond G. LLOYD
G. Lloyd: Symphony 1, Symphony 4, Symphony 11,
Symphony 12
cond D. A. MILLER
see CONCERT INDEX under:
(ARGO) **443 529-2ZH** Sax Drive

ALBERGONI, Angelo (cond)
see orch

ALBERMAN, David (vn)
see CONCERT INDEX under:
(AUVI) **MO782025** Schoenberg—Chamber Music,
Vol. 3

ALBERNI QUARTET
Brahms: String Sextet 1, String Sextet 2
Britten: String Quartet 1, String Quartet 2, String
Quartet 3
Bruckner: Intermezzo and Trio, String Quintet
Mendelssohn: String Quartet 5
Schubert: String Quartet, D703, String Quartet, D810,
String Quintet, Trout Quintet, D667
Schumann: Piano Quintet, Op. 44, Piano Quintet, Op.
44, String Quartet 1, String Quartet 2, String Quartet
3
Shostakovich: Piano Quintet, Op.57
see CONCERT INDEX under:
(CRD) **CRD3366** Italian String Quartets
(CRD) **CRD3457** Dvořák—Hausmusik
(NIMB) **NI5140** Mendelssohn and Shostakovich
Octets

ALBERQUERQUE MÚSICA ANTIGUA
see CONCERT INDEX under:
(DORI) **DIS80104** A Rose of Swych Virtu

ALBERS, Henri (bar)
see CONCERT INDEX under:
(IRCC) **IRCC-CD802** Souvenirs of Rare French
Opera

ALBERT, Donnie Ray (bar)
Gershwin: Porgy and Bess (Cpte)

ALBERT, Laurence (bass)
Handel: Messiah (Cpte)

ALBERT, Thomas (cond)
see Fiori Musicali

ALBERT, Werner Andreas (cond)
see Bamberg SO

ALBERTINI, Alberto (bar)
Verdi: Traviata (Cpte)

ALBERTS, Eunice (contr)
R. Ward: Crucible (Cpte)
see CONCERT INDEX under:
(VANG) **08.4016.71** Music of Samuel Barber

ALBION ENSEMBLE
Beethoven: Piano and Wind Quintet, Op.16
Mozart: Piano and Wind Quintet, K452, Serenade,
K361, Serenade, K375, Serenade, K388

ALBRECHT, George Alexander (cond)
see Philh Hungarica

ALBRECHT, Gerd (cond)
see Austrian RSO

ALBRECHT, Kenneth (hn)
see CONCERT INDEX under:
(ALBA) **TROY024-2** American Orchestral Works

ALBRO, Arthur (sngr)
see CONCERT INDEX under:
(PEAR) **GEMMCDS9053/5** Music from the New York
Stage, Vol. 2: 1908-1913

ALCANTARA, Lynette (sop)
Lehár: Lustige Witwe (Cpte)

ALCHEVSKY, Ivan (ten)
see CONCERT INDEX under:
(SYMP) **SYMCD1105** The Harold Wayne Collection,
Vol.10

ALDA, Catarina (mez)
Verdi: Rigoletto (Cpte)

ALDA, Frances (sop)
see CONCERT INDEX under:
(BIDD) **LAB039** Elman—Victor Records with Caruso,
Alda & Str Quartet
(CLUB) **CL99-060** Enrico Caruso—Opera & Song
Recital
(PEAR) **EVC2** The Caruso Edition, Vol.2—1908-12
(PEAR) **EVC3(1)** The Caruso Edition, Vol.3 (pt 1)
(PEAR) **GEMMCD9309** Enrico Caruso - Opera and
Song Recital
(RCA) **GD60495(3)** The Complete Caruso Collection
(pt 3)
(RCA) **GD60495(4)** The Complete Caruso Collection
(pt 4)
(RCA) **GD60495(5)** The Complete Caruso Collection
(pt 5)
(RCA) **09026 61580-2(2)** RCA/Met 100 Singers, 100
Years (pt 2)

ALDEBURGH FESTIVAL CHOIR
cond S. BEDFORD
Gay: Beggar's Opera (Cpte)
cond B. BRITTEN
Britten: St Nicolas

ALDEBURGH FESTIVAL ENSEMBLE
cond S. BEDFORD
Britten: Turn of the Screw (Cpte)
cond L. FRIEND
Tavener: Mary of Egypt (Cpte)

ALDEBURGH FESTIVAL ORCHESTRA
cond S. BEDFORD
Gay: Beggar's Opera (Cpte)
cond B. BRITTEN
Britten: St Nicolas

ALDEBURGH FESTIVAL SINGERS
cond B. BRITTEN
Schumann: Szenen aus Goethes Faust (Cpte)

ALDER, Jonathan (pf)
see CONCERT INDEX under:
(DECC) **440 854-2DH** Ullmann—Der Kaiser von
Atlantis

ALDER, Stephen (bar)
Bach: Cantata 211, Cantata 212

ALDWINCKLE, Robert (hpd)
see CONCERT INDEX under:
(CARL) **PCD817** Bach: Keyboard Works
(CARL) **PCD850** Harpsichord recital
(CARL) **PCD873** English Madrigals

ALEKSANDROVICH, Aleksandr (ten)
see CONCERT INDEX under:
(PEAR) **GEMMCDS9007/9(2)** Singers of Imperial
Russia, Vol.4 (pt 2)

ALEKSASHKIN, Sergei (bass)
Shostakovich: Symphony 13

ALER, John (ten)
Bach: Mass in B minor, BWV232 (Cpte)
Bartók: Cantata profana
Beethoven: Missa solemnis
Berlioz: Enfance du Christ (Cpte)
Bizet: Pêcheurs de Perles (Cpte)
Gazzaniga: Don Giovanni (Cpte)
Gluck: Iphigénie en Aulide (Cpte), Iphigénie en
Tauride (Cpte)
Gounod: Mors et Vita (Cpte)
Handel: Joshua (Cpte), Semele (Cpte), Sosarme
(Cpte)
Haydn: Jahreszeiten (Cpte)
Lehár: Lustige Witwe (Cpte)
M-A. Charpentier: Magnificat, H74, Te Deum, H146
Mozart: Così fan tutte (Cpte), Mass, K427
Offenbach: Belle Hélène (Cpte)
Orff: Carmina Burana
Rossini: Comte Ory (Cpte)
see CONCERT INDEX under:
(ARAB) **Z6623** Rossini—Songs
(DG) **435 860-2GH2** Berlioz—Mélodies
(SONY) **SK45965** Esa-Pekka Salonen conducts
Stravinsky
(SONY) **SK46667** Stravinsky—Miscellaneous Works
(TELA) **CD80109** Berlioz: Requiem, etc

ALESSANDRINI, Mario (ten)
Verdi: Ballo in maschera (Cpte)

ALESSANDRINI, Rinaldo (cond)
see Concerto Italiano

ALESSANDRINI, Rinaldo (organ)
Frescobaldi: Fiori musicali (Cpte)

ALESSANDRINI, Rinaldo (hpd)
G. Böhm: Chorale Partite and Variations, Keyboard
Suites (exc)
Veracini: Capriccio, Violin Sonatas, Op. 2 (exc)
Vivaldi: Manchester Sonatas
see CONCERT INDEX under:
(0111) OPS30-118   150 Years of Italian Music,
Volume 1

ALESSANDRO, Victor (cond)
see San Antonio SO

ALEXANDER, Carlos (bar)
Orff: Antigonae (Cpte)

ALEXANDER, Chris (sngr)
see CONCERT INDEX under:
(SONY) SM3K47154   Bernstein—Theatre Works
Volume 1

ALEXANDER, Jason (sngr)
Gershwin: Lady, be Good! (Cpte)

ALEXANDER, John (ten)
Bellini: Norma (exc)

ALEXANDER, Juraj (vc)
Bach: Trio Sonatas, BWV1030-5
Gluck: Trio Sonatas (1746)
Grechaninov: Piano Trio 1, Piano Trio 2
Hummel: Cello Sonata, Op.104

ALEXANDER, Meyrick (bn)
Mozart: Sinfonia Concertante, K297b
see CONCERT INDEX under:
(CONI) CDCF173   Prokofiev: Orchestral & Chamber
Works
(EMI) CDC5 55086-2   Trumpet Recital
(VIRG) VC7 59609-2   Vivaldi—Concertos

ALEXANDER, Peter (bar)
Benatzky: Im weissen Rössl (exc)
Offenbach: Vie Parisienne (exc)

ALEXANDER, Roberta (sop)
B. Goldschmidt: Gewaltige Hahnrei (Cpte)
Bach: Mass in B minor, BWV232 (Cpte)
Beethoven: Symphony 9
Gluck: Paride ed Elena (Cpte)
Handel: Samson (Cpte), Theodora (Cpte)
Mozart: Don Giovanni (Cpte), Idomeneo (Cpte)
Telemann: Ino
see CONCERT INDEX under:
(ETCE) KTC1028   R. Strauss: Lieder
(ETCE) KTC1035   Mozart: Lieder
(ETCE) KTC1037   Bernstein: Songs
(ETCE) KTC1050   Puccini: Songs and Rare Pieces
(ETCE) KTC1055   Barber. Songs
(ETCE) KTC1068   Charles Ives: Songs, Vol. 2
(ETCE) KTC1100   Copland—Songs
(ETCE) KTC1114   Barber—Scenes and Arias
(ETCE) KTC1150   Castelnuovo-Tedesco—Vocal and
Guitar Works
(SONY) S2K66836   Goldschmidt—Beatrice Cenci, etc

ALEXANDER, Stephen (treb)
Britten: Noye's Fludde (Cpte)
see CONCERT INDEX under:
(DECC) 436 990-2DWO   The World of Benjamin
Britten

ALEXANDERSSON, Sven-Erik (ten)
Haeffner: Electra (Cpte)

ALEXANDRIDIS, Michal (treb)
Krása: Brundibár (Cpte)

ALEXANDROVA, Olga (mez)
Mahler: Symphony 3

ALEXASHKIN, Sergei (bass)
Prokofiev: War and Peace (Cpte)
Rimsky-Korsakov: Sadko (Cpte)
Tchaikovsky: Queen of Spades (Cpte)

ALEXEEV, Dmitri (pf)
Grieg: Piano Concerto
Medtner: Piano Concerto 1, Piano Quintet
Schumann: Piano Concerto
see CONCERT INDEX under:
(CFP) CD-CFP4547   Shostakovich: Piano Concertos
(EMI) CDS7 54251-2   Scriabin—Symphonies and Tone
Poems
(HYPE) CDA66654   Medtner/Rachmaninov—Music for
Two Pianos
(OLYM) OCD165   Glazunov: Concertos
(RCA) 09026 62710-2   Rachmaninov—Orchestral
Works
(VIRG) VCD7 59289-2   Rachmaninov—Piano Works

ALEXEEV, Valery (bar)
Mussorgsky: Khovanshchina (Cpte)

ALFÖLDI, Zsuzsa (sop)
Schoeck: Venus (Cpte)

ALGOS, Angelo (bass)
see CONCERT INDEX under:
(SYMP) SYMCD1126   The Harold Wayne Collection,
Vol.14

ALIBERTI, Lucia (sop)
Verdi: Macbeth (Cpte), Traviata (Cpte)
see CONCERT INDEX under:
(CAPR) 10 247   The Art of Bel Canto
(ORFE) C119841A   Lucia Aliberti: Famous Opera
Arias

ALICIA, Marthe (sngr)
Hahn: Mozart (Cpte)

ALKAN TRIO
see CONCERT INDEX under:
(MARC) 8 223383   Alkan—Chamber Works

ALL SAINTS MARGARET STREET CHURCH CHOIR
cond B. BRITTEN
see CONCERT INDEX under:
(LOND) 436 394-2LM   Britten—Vocal & Choral
Works

ALLA FRANCESCA
see CONCERT INDEX under:
(0111) OPS30-101   Ciconia—Vocal Works
(0111) OPS30-131   Llibre vermell de Montserrat

ALLAIN-DUPRÉ, Philippe (fl)
Blavet: Flute Sonatas, Op. 2 (exc), Flute Sonatas, Op.
3 (exc)
see CONCERT INDEX under:
(PIER) PV786101   Campra—French Cantatas

ALLAM, Roger (narr)
Vaughan Williams: Symphony 7

ALLAN, Michael (pf)
see CONCERT INDEX under:
(EDA) EDA008-2   Works by Ullmann and Schoenberg

ALLAN, Raymond (tpt)
(LYRI) SRCD323   Grace Williams—Orchestral Works

ALLANSON, Peter (bass)
(SYMP) SYMCD1075   May Harrison—Violinist and
Composer

(JOHN) ALLDIS CHOIR
Beethoven: Choral Fantasia
Berlioz: Béatrice et Bénédict (Cpte), Enfance du
Christ (Cpte), Symphonie funèbre et triomphale
Bizet: Carmen (Cpte)
Giordano: Andrea Chénier (Cpte)
Handel: Messiah (Cpte)
Massenet: Esclarmonde (Cpte)
Mozart: Così fan tutte (Cpte), Entführung (Cpte),
Mass, K427, Nozze di Figaro (Cpte), Requiem
Puccini: Bohème (Cpte), Tosca (Cpte), Turandot
(Cpte)
Tchaikovsky: Eugene Onegin (Cpte)
Verdi: Aida (Cpte), Forza del destino (Cpte), Vespri
Siciliani (Cpte)
see CONCERT INDEX under:
(DECC) 425 681-2DM2   Tutto Pavarotti
(EMI) CMS7 63360-2   Beethoven: Complete Piano
Concertos
(PHIL) 416 249-2PB   A Festival of Christmas Carols
(PHIL) 416 431-2PH   Works by Berlioz
(PHIL) 420 648-2PM   Vivaldi: Sacred Choral Music,
Vol.1
(PHIL) 420 649-2PM   Vivaldi: Sacred Choral Music,
Vol.2
(PHIL) 438 800-2PM2   Mozart—Choral Works
(PHIL) 442 290-2PM2   Berlioz—Great Orchestral
Works
(SONY) SM3K45845   Webern—Complete Works
cond P. BOULEZ
see CONCERT INDEX under:
(SONY) SM3K45845   Webern—Complete Works

ALLEGRI, Maria Garcia (contr)
see CONCERT INDEX under:
(DG) 419 257-2GH3   'Cav' and 'Pag', etc

ALLEGRI QUARTET
Brahms: Clarinet Quintet, Piano Quintet
Schubert: String Quartet, D353, String Quartet,
D887
see CONCERT INDEX under:
(CALA) CACD1018   French Chamber Music for
Woodwinds, Volume 2
(CALA) CACD1019   Sirmen—String Quartets
(HYPE) CDA66077   Crusell: Clarinet Quartets Nos 1-
3
cond J. BARBIROLLI
see CONCERT INDEX under:
(EMI) CDC7 47537-2   English String Music

ALLEMANO, Carlo (ten)
Gazzaniga: Don Giovanni (Cpte)
Mozart: Nozze di Figaro (Cpte)

ALLEN, Barbara (hp)
see CONCERT INDEX under:
(RCA) 09026 62537-2   Takemitsu—Cantos

ALLEN, Betty (mez)
Joplin: Treemonisha (Cpte)

ALLEN, Gregory (pf)
see CONCERT INDEX under:
(BRID) BCD9027   Rodrigo—Piano Works

ALLEN, Martin (perc)
see CONCERT INDEX under:
(CNTI) CCD1008   Anderson: Mask and other works
(ECM) 847 537-2   Gavin Bryars—After the Requiem
(SONY) SM3K46291   Stravinsky—Ballets, Vol.1

ALLEN, Nancy (hp)
see CONCERT INDEX under:
(ASV) CDDCA654   Ginastera—Orchestral Works
(DG) 427 677-2GH   Mozart—Concertos
(DG) 429 790-2GH   Spirituals in Concert
(DG) 431 665-2GX3   Mozart—Wind Concertos
(EMI) CZS7 67435-2   Rodrigo—Orchestral Works
(RCA) 09026 62537-2   Takemitsu—Cantos

ALLEN, Thomas (bar)
Berlioz: Béatrice et Bénédict (Cpte), Enfance du
Christ (Cpte)
Bizet: Carmen (Cpte)
Brahms: Deutsches Requiem, Op. 45 (Cpte)
Britten: Peter Grimes (Cpte), War Requiem
Donizetti: Don Pasquale (Cpte)
Duruflé: Requiem
Gluck: Iphigénie en Tauride (Cpte)
Gounod: Faust (Cpte)
Janáček: Cunning Little Vixen (Cpte)
Leoncavallo: Pagliacci (Cpte)
Mahler: Klagende Lied, Symphony 8
Massenet: Werther (Cpte)
Mendelssohn: Elijah (Cpte)
Mozart: Così fan tutte (Cpte), Don Giovanni (Cpte),
Nozze di Figaro (Cpte), Zauberflöte (Cpte)
Orff: Carmina Burana
Purcell: Birthday Ode, Z323, Dido (Cpte)
Rossini: Barbiere di Siviglia (Cpte)
Sullivan: HMS Pinafore (Cpte), Yeomen of the Guard
(Cpte)
Tchaikovsky: Eugene Onegin (Cpte)
Vaughan Williams: Symphony 1
Wolf: Goethe Lieder (exc), Mörike Lieder (exc)
see CONCERT INDEX under:
(COLL) Coll7039-2   Britten—The Folk Songs
(CRD) CRD3437   Poulenc: Chamber & Vocal Works
(DG) 435 860-2GH2   Berlioz—Mélodies
(EMI) CDC7 49811-2   Covent Garden Gala Concert
(EMI) CDH5 65072-2   Glyndebourne Recorded - 1934-
1994
(EMI) CDM7 64731-2   Vaughan
Williams/Elgar/Butterworth—Songs
(EMI) CDM7 69500-2   Montserrat Caballé sings Bellini
& Verdi Arias
(EMIL) CDZ7 67015-2   Mozart—Opera Arias
(ERAT) 4509-96371-2   Gardiner—The Purcell
Collection
(GAMU) GAMD506   An Anthology Of English Song
(HYPE) CDA66165   The Sea
(HYPE) CDA66323   Duparc: Mélodies
(HYPE) CDA66420   Vaughan Williams: Vocal Works
(HYPE) CDA66655   Vaughan Williams—Choral Works
(HYPE) CDJ33016   Schubert—Complete Lieder,
Vol.16
(RCA) RD60813   Walton—Belshazzar's Feast
(TER) CDVIR8317   If I Loved You - Love Duets from
the Musicals
(UNIC) DKPCD9063   Delius—Choral & Orchestral
Works
(UNIC) UKCD2073   The Delius Collection, Volume 3
(VIRG) VC5 45033-2   Barber—Vocal and Chamber
Works
(VIRG) VC5 45053-2
Fauré/Ravel/Poulenc—Mélodies
(VIRG) VC7 59057-2   Schoenberg—Miscellaneous
Works

ALLERS, Franz (cond)
see Berlin SO

ALLEY, John (pf)
Britten: St Nicolas
see CONCERT INDEX under:
(CONI) CDCF167   Dickinson—Vocal Works
(EMI) CDC5 55085-2   Flute Recital
(EMI) CDC5 55398-2   Britten—Chamber Works

ALLEYN'S SCHOOL CHOIR
cond B. BRITTEN
see CONCERT INDEX under:
(LOND) 436 393-2LM   Britten—The Little Sweep, etc

ALLIN, Norman (bass)
see CONCERT INDEX under:
(DUTT) CDAX8004   Sir Henry Wood conducts
Vaughan Williams
(PEAR) GEMMCDS9925(1)   Covent Garden on
Record—Vol.3 (pt 1)
(PEAR) GEMMCD9342   Vaughan Williams: Vocal
Works

ALLIOT-LUGAZ, Colette (sop)
Berlioz: Nuits d'été
Chausson: Poème de l'amour et de la mer
Debussy: Pelléas et Mélisande (Cpte)
Fauré: Pénélope (Cpte)
Gluck: Iphigénie en Tauride (Cpte)
Lully: Alceste (Cpte)
Massenet: Manon (Cpte)
Offenbach: Belle Hélène (Cpte), Brigands (Cpte)
see CONCERT INDEX under:
(DECC) 440 333-2DH   Ravel—Vocal Works
(REM) REM311086   French Duets

ALLISTER, Jean (mez)
Cavalli: Ormindo (Cpte)
Sullivan: Mikado (Cpte), Pirates of Penzance (Cpte)
see CONCERT INDEX under:
(DECC) 430 095-2DWO   The World of Gilbert &
Sullivan, Vol.1
(DECC) 433 868-2DWO   The World of Gilbert &
Sullivan - Volume 2

AMBROS, Hermi (sop)
R. Strauss: Elektra (Cpte)
Wagner: Parsifal (Cpte)

AMBROSIAN CHORUS
 cond J.O. EDWARDS
Forrest/Wright: Kismet (Cpte), Song of Norway (Cpte), Timbuktu (exc)
Romberg: Student Prince (Cpte)
 cond J. MCGLINN
Berlin: Annie Get Your Gun (Cpte)
F. Loewe: Brigadoon (Cpte)
Kern: Show Boat (Cpte)
Porter: Anything Goes (Cpte), Kiss Me, Kate (Cpte)
 see CONCERT INDEX under:
(EMI) **CDC7 54071-2** Frederica von Stade sings Rodgers & Hart
 cond R. MUTI
Prokofiev: Ivan the Terrible

AMBROSIAN OPERA CHORUS
 cond C. ABBADO
Rossini: Barbiere di Siviglia (Cpte)
 cond A. DE ALMEIDA
A. Thomas: Hamlet (Cpte)
Halévy: Juive (Cpte)
 cond R. BONYNGE
Gounod: Faust (Cpte)
Rossini: Semiramide (Cpte)
Verdi: Rigoletto (Cpte)
 see CONCERT INDEX under:
(DECC) **433 706-2DMO3** Bellini—Beatrice di Tenda; Operatic Arias
 cond B. BRITTEN
Purcell: Fairy Queen, Z629 (Cpte)
 see CONCERT INDEX under:
(DECC) **436 990-2DWO** The World of Benjamin Britten
 cond B. CAMPANELLA
 see CONCERT INDEX under:
(DG) **435 866-2GH** Kathleen Battle sings Italian Opera Arias
 cond R. CHAILLY
Rossini: Guillaume Tell (Cpte), Turco in Italia (Cpte)
 cond C.F. CILLARIO
Bellini: Norma (Cpte)
 see CONCERT INDEX under:
(RCA) **GD60941** Rarities - Montserrat Caballé
 cond L. GARDELLI
Rossini: Guillaume Tell (Cpte)
Verdi: Forza del destino (Cpte), Macbeth (Cpte)
(EMI) **CDM7 69549-2** Ruggero Raimondi: Italian Opera Arias
 cond A. GIBSON
(EMI) **CDM7 69544-2** Berlioz: Vocal Works
 cond C.M. GIULINI
Verdi: Don Carlo (Cpte)
 see CONCERT INDEX under:
(EMI) **CDC5 55017-2** Domingo Opera Classics
(EMI) **CDM7 69549-2** Ruggero Raimondi: Italian Opera Arias
 cond C. GROVES
Vaughan Williams: Hugh the Drover (Cpte)
 cond A. GUADAGNO
 see CONCERT INDEX under:
(RCA) **GD60818** Great Operatic Duets
 cond JAMES LEVINE
Bellini: Norma (Cpte)
Cilea: Adriana Lecouvreur (Cpte)
Puccini: Tosca (Cpte)
Verdi: Giovanna d'Arco (Cpte), Otello (Cpte)
 cond E. KOHN
 see CONCERT INDEX under:
(EMI) **CDC7 54053-2** Roman Heroes
 cond E. LEINSDORF
Mozart: Così fan tutte (Cpte)
(RCA) **GD86722** R.Strauss: Orchestral and Vocal Works
 cond H. LEWIS
Meyerbeer: Prophète (Cpte)
 see CONCERT INDEX under:
(RCA) **09026 61236-2** Leontyne Price - Prima Donna Collection
 cond J. LÓPEZ-COBOS
Rossini: Otello (Cpte)
 cond L. MAAZEL
Puccini: Madama Butterfly (Cpte), Rondine (Cpte), Villi (Cpte)
 see CONCERT INDEX under:
(SONY) **M3K79312** Puccini: Il Trittico
 cond I. MARIN
Donizetti: Lucia di Lammermoor (Cpte)
Rossini: Semiramide (Cpte)
 cond N. MARRINER
Mozart: Così fan tutte (Cpte), Don Giovanni (Cpte), Nozze di Figaro (Cpte), Zauberflöte (Cpte)
Rossini: Barbiere di Siviglia (Cpte), Cenerentola (Cpte), Turco in Italia (Cpte)
 see CONCERT INDEX under:
(EMI) **CDC7 49700-2** Lucia Popp sings Viennese Operetta
 cond Z. MEHTA
Verdi: Trovatore (Cpte)
 cond R. MUTI
Donizetti: Don Pasquale (Cpte)
Gluck: Orfeo ed Euridice (Cpte)
Leoncavallo: Pagliacci (Cpte)
Mascagni: Cavalleria rusticana (Cpte)

Verdi: Macbeth (Cpte), Traviata (Cpte)
 see CONCERT INDEX under:
(EMI) **CDM7 63104-2** Alfredo Krauss - Opera Recital
 cond G. NAVARRO
Falla: Vida breve (Cpte)
 cond J. NELSON
Handel: Semele (Cpte)
 cond G. PRÊTRE
G. Charpentier: Louise (Cpte)
 cond N. RESCIGNO
Donizetti: Lucia di Lammermoor (Cpte)
 cond M. ROSTROPOVICH
Shostakovich: Lady Macbeth of Mtsensk (Cpte)
 cond J. RUDEL
Massenet: Cendrillon (Cpte)
 cond N. SANTI
 see CONCERT INDEX under:
(RCA) **09026 61236-2** Leontyne Price - Prima Donna Collection
 cond T. SCHIPPERS
Rossini: Siège de Corinthe (Cpte)
 cond C. SCIMONE
Rossini: Armida (Cpte), Maometto II (Cpte), Mosè in Egitto (exc)
 cond G. SINOPOLI
Puccini: Madama Butterfly (Cpte)
Verdi: Forza del destino (Cpte)
 cond K. TENNSTEDT
 see CONCERT INDEX under:
(EMI) **CDC7 49759-2** Wagner: Opera Scenes and Arias

AMBROSIAN SINGERS
Monteverdi: Ballo delle ingrate
 see CONCERT INDEX under:
(LOND) **425 159-2LM** Salute to Percy Grainger
 cond C. ABBADO
Bizet: Carmen (Cpte)
 see CONCERT INDEX under:
(DG) **431 104-2GB** Great Voices - Plácido Domingo
(DG) **445 501-2GMA** Bartók/Janáček—Orchestral Works
 cond J. BARBIROLLI
Elgar: Dream of Gerontius (Cpte)
 see CONCERT INDEX under:
(EMI) **CMS5 65119-2** Delius—Orchestral Works
 cond S. BARRY
 see CONCERT INDEX under:
(CHAN) **CHAN8561** Treasures of Operetta, Vol. 2
 cond S. BEDFORD
(LOND) **425 159-2LM** Salute to Percy Grainger
 cond E. BERNSTEIN
(MILA) **74321 14081-2** Bernard Herrmann—Film Scores
 cond R. BONYNGE
Donizetti: Elisir d'amore (Cpte), Lucia di Lammermoor (Cpte)
 see CONCERT INDEX under:
(DECC) **433 010-2DM** Christmas Stars
 cond B. BRITTEN
 see CONCERT INDEX under:
(LOND) **425 159-2LM** Salute to Percy Grainger
 cond COLIN DAVIS
Berlioz: Damnation de Faust (Cpte)
 cond M. DAVIES
 see CONCERT INDEX under:
(EMI) **CDM7 64730-2** Vaughan Williams—Riders to the Sea; Epithalamion, etc
 cond A. DELLER
Monteverdi: Ballo delle ingrate
 see CONCERT INDEX under:
(PHIL) **400 011-2PH** Ketèlbey: Orchestral Works
 cond E. FENBY
 see CONCERT INDEX under:
(UNIC) **DKPCD9063** Delius—Choral & Orchestral Works
(UNIC) **UKCD2071** The Delius Collection, Volume 1
(UNIC) **UKCD2073** The Delius Collection, Volume 3
 cond G. FISCHER
 see CONCERT INDEX under:
(EMI) **CDM7 69546-2** Lucia Popp
 cond L. FOSTER
 see CONCERT INDEX under:
(EMI) **CDC7 54626-2** Operetta Arias
 cond L. GARDELLI
Verdi: Attila (Cpte), Corsaro (Cpte), Giorno di Regno (Cpte), Lombardi (Cpte), Masnadieri (Cpte)
 cond P. GEMIGNANI
Forrest/Wright: Kismet (Cpte)
 cond C. GERHARDT
 see CONCERT INDEX under:
(RCA) **GD80136** Now Voyager—Classic Film Scores of Max Steiner
(RCA) **GD80911** Spellbound—Classic Film Scores of Miklos Rozsa
 cond A. GIBSON
 see CONCERT INDEX under:
(PHIL) **400 019-2PH** Popular Sacred Songs
 cond A. GUADAGNO
 see CONCERT INDEX under:
(DECC) **433 010-2DM** Christmas Stars
 cond V. HANDLEY
Holst: Planets
 cond J. HORENSTEIN
Mahler: Symphony 3
 cond I. KERTÉSZ
 see CONCERT INDEX under:
(DECC) **421 810-2DM2** Dvořák & Kodály: Vocal Works

 cond J. LANCHBERY
 see CONCERT INDEX under:
(CFP) **CD-CFP4637** Ketèlbey/Luigini—Orchestral Music
 cond P. LEDGER
 see CONCERT INDEX under:
(LYRI) **SRCD225** Bliss—Orchestral Works
 cond L. MAAZEL
 see CONCERT INDEX under:
(DECC) **417 252-2DH** Scriabin: Orchestral Works
 cond C. MACKERRAS
Handel: Messiah (Cpte)
Purcell: St Cecilia's Day Ode, Z328
 see CONCERT INDEX under:
(EMI) **CDM7 63574-2** Elisabeth Schwarzkopf Christmas Album
 cond L. MAGIERA
 see CONCERT INDEX under:
(DECC) **425 681-2DM2** Tutto Pavarotti
 cond I. MARIN
 see CONCERT INDEX under:
(DG) **435 387-2GH** Cheryl Studer sings Sacred Arias
 cond N. MARRINER
Grieg: Peer Gynt (exc)
 see CONCERT INDEX under:
(PHIL) **422 503-2PME7** The Complete Mozart Edition Vol 3
(PHIL) **434 016-2PM3** Rossini—Overtures
 cond G-F. MASINI
Rossini: Elisabetta (Cpte)
 cond J. MCCARTHY
 see CONCERT INDEX under:
(ARAB) **Z6582** The Rossini Tenor
 cond J. MCGLINN
(EMI) **CDC7 54586-2** Broadway Showstoppers
(EMI) **CDC7 54802-2** The Lorelei
 cond R. MUTI
Cherubini: Symphony 2
 cond K. NAGANO
Puccini: Bohème (Cpte)
 cond A. PREVIN
Beethoven: Symphony 9
Holst: Planets
Ravel: Enfant et les sortilèges (Cpte)
Tchaikovsky: Nutcracker (Cpte)
Vaughan Williams: Symphony 7
 see CONCERT INDEX under:
(EMI) **CZS7 62816-2** Tchaikovsky—Ballet Music
 cond G. PRÊTRE
(EMI) **CZS7 62690-2** Poulenc—Orchestral and Ballet Works
 cond S. RATTLE
Holst: Planets
 cond C. RIZZI
Verdi: Traviata (Cpte)
 cond J. RUDEL
 see CONCERT INDEX under:
(EMI) **CDC7 47398-2** Placido Domingo: Vienna, City of My Dreams
 cond W. SAWALLISCH
Brahms: Schicksalslied, Op. 54
 cond C. SCIMONE
Handel: Messiah (Cpte)
Rossini: Petite messe solennelle, Zelmira (Cpte)
 see CONCERT INDEX under:
(SONY) **MK76404** Beethoven: Choral Works
 cond M. TILSON THOMAS
 see CONCERT INDEX under:
(ARAB) **Z6612** Rossini: Opera Arias

AMELING, Elly (sop)
Bach: Mass in B minor, BWV232 (Cpte)
Berlioz: Nuits dété
Cimarosa: Requiem in G minor
Handel: Messiah (Cpte)
Haydn: Orlando Paladino (Cpte)
Martin: Mystère de la Nativité
Mendelssohn: Elias (Cpte)
Wolf: Mörike Lieder (exc), Spanisches Liederbuch (exc)
 see CONCERT INDEX under:
(DECC) **433 175-2DM** Bach—Sacred Choral Works
(DG) **435 596-2GGA2** Schubert—Duets, Trios & Quartets
(DHM) **GD77085** Schubert & Schumann—Lieder
(DHM) **GD77151** Bach—Secular Cantatas
(DHM) **74321 26617-2(1)** Elly Ameling - The Early Recorings, Vols. 1-3
(DHM) **74321 26617-2(2)** Elly Ameling - The Early Years, Vol. 4
(EMI) **CDC5 55000-2** Bach—Cantata Arias
(EMI) **CMS7 64079-2(1)** Fauré—Complete Songs (pt 1)
(EMI) **CMS7 64079-2(2)** Fauré—Complete Songs (pt 2)
(EMI) **CMS7 64095-2** Debussy—Mélodies
(HYPE) **CDA46444** Brahms: Lieder
(HYPE) **CDJ33007** Schubert—Complete Lieder, Vol. 7
(JECK) **JD563-2** Frank Martin interprets Frank Martin
(PHIL) **438 528-2PM4(1)** Schubert—Lieder (pt 1)
(PHIL) **438 528-2PM4(2)** Schubert—Lieder (pt 2)
(PHIL) **442 050-2PB10** Schubert—Complete Symphonies
(PHIL) **442 744-2PM2** Wolf/R.Strauss—Lieder

AMENGUAL, Ana Maria (sngr)
Bretón: Verbena de La Paloma (Cpte)

AMERICAN BACH SOLOISTS
cond J. THOMAS
Bach: Mass in B minor, BWV232 (Cpte)
see CONCERT INDEX under:
(KOCH) **37138-2** Bach—Solo Cantatas
(KOCH) **37164-2** Bach—Cantatas, Vol.3

AMERICAN BAROQUE
Telemann: Quartets, Bk 4
see CONCERT INDEX under:
(KOCH) **37096-2** 18th Century French Cantatas
cond S. SCHULTZ
Telemann: Paris Quartets (Quadri) (exc)

AMERICAN BOYCHOIR
cond S. OZAWA
Mahler: Symphony 3
Tchaikovsky: Nutcracker (Cpte), Queen of Spades
(Cpte)

AMERICAN CHAMBER PLAYERS
see CONCERT INDEX under:
(KOCH) **37027-2** American Chamber Works

AMERICAN COMPOSERS ORCHESTRA
cond D. R. DAVIES
see CONCERT INDEX under:
(ARGO) **440 337-2ZH** Beaser—Orchestral and Vocal
Works
(MUSM) **7021-2** Hovhaness/Harrison—Orchestral
Works
cond C. WUORINEN
Babbitt: Piano Concerto

AMERICAN GAMELAN
cond J. BERGAMO
see CONCERT INDEX under:
(NALB) **NA015CD** Lou Harrison: Various Works
cond P. BRETT
see CONCERT INDEX under:
(NALB) **NA015CD** Lou Harrison: Various Works

AMERICAN OPERA SOCIETY CHORUS
cond N. RESCIGNO
Bellini: Pirata (Cpte)

AMERICAN OPERA SOCIETY ORCHESTRA
cond N. RESCIGNO
Bellini: Pirata (Cpte)

AMERICAN QUARTET
Prokofiev: String Quartet 1, String Quartet 2

AMERICAN SYMPHONY ORCHESTRA
cond L. STOKOWSKI
see CONCERT INDEX under:
(RCA) **GD87831** Moffo & Stokowski
(SONY) **MPK46726** Ives—Orchestral and Vocal
Works
(SONY) **SM3K52632** Beethoven—Piano Concertos

AMERICAN THEATRE ORCHESTRA
cond P. GEMIGNANI
see CONCERT INDEX under:
(RCA) **09026 62681-2** Mr Jerry Hadley—Golden Days

AMICI, Toto (gtr)
see CONCERT INDEX under:
(EMI) **CHS7 63802-2(2)** Tetrazzini—The London
Records (pt 2)

AMICI DELLA POLIFONIA CHORUS
cond C. SCIMONE
Vivaldi: Orlando Furioso (Cpte)

AMICI QUARTET
Herrmann: Echoes

AMICO, Midela d' (sop)
Donizetti: Fille du Régiment (Cpte)

AMIEL, Henry (ten)
Offenbach: Orphée aux enfers (Cpte), Périchole
(Cpte)

AMINI, Nancy (sop)
Bach: Cantata 21

AMIS, John (ten)
Herrmann: Fantasticks

AMIT, Sheila (sop)
Britten: Albert Herring (Cpte)

AMLIN, Martin (pf)
see CONCERT INDEX under:
(HYPE) **CDA66414** Koechlin—Flute Works

AMOR ARTIS CHORALE
cond J. SOMARY
Handel: Judas Maccabaeus (Cpte), Theodora (Cpte)
see CONCERT INDEX under:
(NEWP) **NCD60098** Weill—Vocal & Instrumental
Works

AMOR ARTIS ORCHESTRA
cond J. SOMARY
Handel: Sosarme (Cpte)
see CONCERT INDEX under:
(NEWP) **NCD60098** Weill—Vocal & Instrumental
Works

AMORETTI, Ruben (ten)
Gounod: Requiem

AMOS, David (cond)
see Cracow PO

AMOYAL, Pierre (vn)
Dutilleux: Violin Concerto
Tchaikovsky: Piano Trio, Op. 50
see CONCERT INDEX under:

(DECC) **436 866-2DH** Fauré—Violin and Piano
Works
(DECC) **443 324-2DH** Respighi/Saint-Saëns—Violin
Concertos
(ERAT) **2292-45971-2** Tchaikovsky—Orchestral
Works
(RCA) **09026 61778-2(25)** The Heifetz Collection, Vol.
25

AMPLEFORTH ABBEY MONASTIC CHOIR
see CONCERT INDEX under:
(CFM) **CFMCD1783** Vision of Peace

AMPS, Kym (sop)
see CONCERT INDEX under:
(CHAN) **CHAN9363** Adams/Lang—Wind Music

AMSTERDAM BACH SOLOISTS
Bach: Art of Fugue (exc), Cantata 35, Cantata 170
see CONCERT INDEX under:
(OLYM) **OCD428** Haydn—Violin Concertos
cond J.W. DE VRIEND
see CONCERT INDEX under:
(ETCE) **KTC1064** Baroque Opera Arias

AMSTERDAM BAROQUE CHOIR
cond T. KOOPMAN
Bach: Mass in B Minor, BWV232 (Cpte)
Biber: Requiem in A, Vesperae
Purcell: Fairy Queen, Z629
see CONCERT INDEX under:
(ERAT) **4509-98536-2** Bach—Complete Cantatas,
Volume 1

AMSTERDAM BAROQUE ORCHESTRA
Biber: Requiem in A, Vesperae
see CONCERT INDEX under:
(PHIL) **422 507-2PME12** The Complete Mozart Edition
Vol 7
cond T. KOOPMAN
Bach: Mass in B Minor, BWV232 (Cpte), St Matthew
Passion, BWV244 (Cpte), Suites, BWV1066-9
Handel: Messiah (Cpte), Resurrezione (Cpte), Water
Music
Mozart: Divertimenti, K136-8, Divertimento, K251,
March, K249, Requiem, Serenade, K250
Purcell: Fairy Queen, Z629
see CONCERT INDEX under:
(ERAT) **2292-45431-2** Mozart—Symphonies
(ERAT) **2292-45807-2** Haydn—Symphonies
(ERAT) **2292-45822-2** M-A.Charpentier—Motets
(ERAT) **2292-45857-2** Mozart—Symphonies
(ERAT) **4509-98536-2** Bach—Complete Cantatas,
Volume 1

AMSTERDAM CHAMBER ORCHESTRA
cond A. RIEU
see CONCERT INDEX under:
(TELD) **4509-97474-2** F. Brüggen Edition Vol.
12—Recorder Sonatas & Concertos
(TELD) **9031-77620-2** Telemann—Orchestral Works

AMSTERDAM COMBATTIMENTO CONSORT
cond J.W. DE VRIEND
see CONCERT INDEX under:
(SONY) **SK53265** Vivaldi—Violin Concertos

AMSTERDAM LOEKI STARDUST QUARTET
see CONCERT INDEX under:
(L'OI) **436 155-2OH** A Concorde of Sweete Sounde
(L'OI) **440 207-2OM** Capriccio di Flauti
cond C. HOGWOOD
(L'OI) **436 905-2OH** Recorder Concertos

AMSTERDAM NIEUW SINFONIETTA
cond R. DE LEEUW
Martin: Cornet
cond L. MARKIZ
see CONCERT INDEX under:
(BIS) **BIS-CD518** Denisov—Orchestral & Chamber
Works
(BIS) **BIS-CD643** Mendelssohn—String Symphonies,
Vol.1
(BIS) **BIS-CD683** Mendelssohn—String Symphonies,
Vol. 2

AMSTERDAM QUARTET
see CONCERT INDEX under:
(TELD) **4509-92177-2** Telemann—Paris Quartets;
Suites

AMSTERDAM STEM DES VOLKS CHOIR
cond B. HAITINK
see CONCERT INDEX under:
(PHIL) **442 050-2PB10** Mahler—Complete
Symphonies

AMSTERDAM TOONKUNST CHOIR
cond B. HAITINK
see CONCERT INDEX under:
(PHIL) **442 050-2PB10** Mahler—Complete
Symphonies
cond O. KLEMPERER
Mahler: Symphony 2
cond W. MENGELBERG
Beethoven: Symphony 9

(FATHER) AMVROSY (cond)
see Moscow Liturgic Ch

ANANIAN, Paolo (bass)
Verdi: Traviata (Cpte)

ANČERL, Karel (cond)
see Berlin RSO

ANCONA, Mario (bar)
see CONCERT INDEX under:

(IRCC) **IRCC-CD800** Souvenirs from Meyerbeer
Operas
(NIMB) **NI7840/1** The Era of Adelina Patti
(NIMB) **NI7859** Caruso, Farrar & Journet in French
Opera
(NIMB) **NI7867** Legendary Baritones
(PEAR) **EVC1(2)** The Caruso Edition, Vol.1 (pt 2)
(PEAR) **GEMMCDS9923(1)** Covent Garden on
Record, Vol.1 (pt 1)
(PEAR) **GEMMCDS9923(2)** Covent Garden on
Record, Vol.1 (pt 2)
(RCA) **GD60495(2)** The Complete Caruso Collection
(pt 2)

ANDA, Géza (pf)
Bartók: For Children (1908-09), Piano Concerto 3
Beethoven: Triple Concerto
Grieg: Piano Concerto
Schumann: Piano Concerto
see CONCERT INDEX under:
(DG) **413 158-2GW2** Grieg/Sibelius—Orchestral
Works
(DG) **427 410-2GDO2** Bartók—Orchestral Works
(DG) **447 399-2GOR** Bartók—Piano Concertos
(TEST) **SBT1064** Géza Anda plays Tchaikovsky &
Rachmaninov
(TEST) **SBT1066** Chopin—Piano Works
(TEST) **SBT1067** Géza Anda plays Liszt, Bartók &
Dohnányi

ANDA, Géza (pf/dir)
see CONCERT INDEX under:
(DG) **429 001-2GX10** Mozart: Complete Solo Piano
Concertos
(RCA) **74321 17888-2** Mozart—Orchestral Works

ANDAY, Rosette (contr)
Beethoven: Symphony 9
R. Strauss: Arabella (Cpte)
see CONCERT INDEX under:
(DG) **435 321-2GWP12** 150 Years - Vienna
Philharmonic
(PREI) **89046** Rosette Anday (1903-1977)
(SCHW) **314532** Vienna State Opera Live, Vol.3
(SCHW) **314542** Vienna State Opera Live, Vol.4
(SCHW) **314592** Vienna State Opera Live, Vol.9
(SCHW) **314622** Vienna State Opera Live, Vol.12
(SCHW) **314632** Vienna State Opera Live, Vol.13
(SCHW) **314642** Vienna State Opera Live, Vol.14
(SCHW) **314662** Vienna State Opera Live, Vol.16

ANDERS, Peter (ten)
Beethoven: Symphony 9
Schillings: Glockenlieder (exc)
see CONCERT INDEX under:
(ACAN) **43 268** Peter Anders sings German Opera
Arias
(ACAN) **44 2114-2** Schubert—Song Cycles
(ARAB) **Z6082** R. Strauss: Orchestral & Vocal
Works
(EMI) **CHS7 69741-2(4)** Record of Singing,
Vol.4—German School
(TAHR) **FURT1004/7** Furtwängler conducts the Berlin
Philharmonic

ANDERSEN, Georg Svendsen (va)
Kuhlau: Flute Quintets, Op. 51

ANDERSEN, Karsten (cond)
see Bergen SO

ANDERSEN, Stig Fogh (ten)
Mussorgsky: Boris Godunov (Cpte)
Nørgård: Siddhartha (Cpte)

ANDERSON, Barry (ten)
Mascagni: Rantzau (Cpte)

ANDERSON, Cynthia (contr)
Schoenberg: Moses und Aron (Cpte)

ANDERSON, Dean (perc)
see CONCERT INDEX under:
(BRID) **BCD9031** J. Harvey—Miscellaneous Works

ANDERSON, Elizabeth (vc)
see CONCERT INDEX under:
(RCA) **09026 60237-2** Giuliani—Chamber Works with
guitar

ANDERSON, James (bass)
Tchaikovsky: Iolanta (Cpte)

ANDERSON, John (ob)
Mozart: Sinfonia concertante, K297b
see CONCERT INDEX under:
(NIMB) **NI5330** Oboe Concertos

ANDERSON, John (ob d'amore)
see CONCERT INDEX under:
(NIMB) **NI5121** Virtuoso Trumpet Concertos
(NIMB) **NI7016** Classical Trumpet Concertos

ANDERSON, June (sop)
A. Thomas: Hamlet (Cpte)
Albinoni: Nascimento dell'Aurora (Cpte)
Beethoven: Christus am Oelberge, Op. 85, Symphony
9
Bernstein: Candide (1988) (Cpte)
Bizet: Jolie fille de Perth (Cpte)
Halévy: Juive (Cpte)
Massenet: Chérubin (Cpte)
Mozart: Zauberflöte (Cpte)
Orff: Carmina burana
Rossini: Donna del lago (Cpte), Maometto II (Cpte),
Mosè in Egitto (Cpte), Soirées musicales
Verdi: Rigoletto (Cpte)
see CONCERT INDEX under:

(DECC) **436 209-2DH** Pergolesi & A Scarlatti—Choral Works
(EMI) **CDC7 49067-2** Opera Arias and Duets

ANDERSON, Lane (vc)
see CONCERT INDEX under:
(ERAT) **2292-45368-2** Chausson: Songs

ANDERSON, Lorna (sop)
Britten: Folk Songs (exc)
Purcell: Fairy Queen, Z629 (Cpte)
T. Linley II: Shakespeare Ode
see CONCERT INDEX under:
(HYPE) **CDJ33022** Schubert—Complete Lieder, Vol.22

ANDERSON, Marian (contr)
see CONCERT INDEX under:
(NIMB) **NI7801** Great Singers, Vol.1
(RCA) **GD87911** Marian Anderson - Opera, Oratorio & Song Recital
(RCA) **09026 61580-2(6)** RCA/Met 100 Singers, 100 Years (pt 6)
(RCA) **09026 61893-2** Pierre Monteux Edition

ANDERSON, Mark (pf)
Brahms: Piano Concerto 1
Dohnányi: Nursery Variations
see CONCERT INDEX under:
(NIMB) **NI5422** Brahms/Liszt/Schumann—Piano Works

ANDERSON, Norman (bass)
Bach: Cantata 21

ANDERSON, Ruth (sop)
MacMillan: Búsqueda (Cpte)

ANDERSSON, Karin (organ)
see CONCERT INDEX under:
(BIS) **BIS-CD510** Organ Music from the USA

ANDERSSON, Per Åke (cond)
see Norwegian Nat Op Orch

ANDONIAN, Andrea (sop)
see CONCERT INDEX under:
(EMI) **CZS7 67819-2** Brahms/Schumann—Requiems

ANDOR, Eva (sop)
Kodály: Budavári Te Deum

ANDRADE, Francesco d' (bar)
see CONCERT INDEX under:
(PEAR) **GEMMCDS9923(1)** Covent Garden on Record, Vol.1 (pt 1)

ANDRASSY, Anni (sop)
see CONCERT INDEX under:
(PEAR) **GEMMCDS9925(2)** Covent Garden on Record—Vol.3 (pt 2)

ANDRÉ, Maurice (tpt)
see CONCERT INDEX under:
(EMI) **CDC5 55231-2** Trumpet Concertos
(EMI) **CDC7 47311-2** Maurice André plays Trumpet Concertos
(EMI) **CDC7 49219-2** Operas Arias for Trumpet
(EMI) **CDC7 49237-2** Trumpet Concertos
(EMI) **CDC7 54086-2** Classical Trumpet Concertos
(EMI) **CDC7 54330-2** Arrangements for Trumpet and Organ
(EMI) **CDM7 63528-2** Trumpet Concertos

ANDREAE, Volkmar (cond)
see VPO

ANDRÉASON, Lotte (vn)
see CONCERT INDEX under:
(CPRI) **CAP21510** Rosenberg plays Rosenberg

ANDREESCU, Horia (cond)
see Romanian Nat Rad Orch

ANDRÉN, Sven-Gunnar (pf)
see CONCERT INDEX under:
(EMI) **CHS5 69741-2(5)** Record of Singing, Vol.4—Scandinavian School

ANDREOLLI, Florindo (ten)
Cilea: Adriana Lecouvreur (Cpte)
Giordano: Andrea Chénier (Cpte)
Leoncavallo: Pagliacci (Cpte)
Puccini: Fanciulla del West (Cpte), Madama Butterfly (Cpte)
Verdi: Forza del destino (Cpte), Otello (Cpte)
see CONCERT INDEX under:
(SONY) **M3K79312** Puccini: Il Trittico

ANDRÉSEN, Ivar (bass)
Wagner: Götterdämmerung (exc)
see CONCERT INDEX under:
(CLAR) **CDGSE78-50-26** Wagner: Tristan und Isolde excerpts
(EMI) **GEMMCDS9137** Wagner—Der Ring des Nibelungen
(PEAR) **GEMMCDS9926(2)** Covent Garden on Record—Vol.4 (pt 2)
(PREI) **89028** Ivar Andresen (1896-1940)

ANDREVA, Stella (sop)
Wagner: Siegfried (Cpte)
see CONCERT INDEX under:
(DUTT) **CDLX7012** The Incomparable Heddle Nash
(LYRC) **SRO830** Smetana—The Bartered Bride, etc
(MYTO) **2MCD90317** Verdi—Un Ballo in maschera
(PEAR) **GEMMCDS9926(2)** Covent Garden on Record—Vol.4 (pt 2)
(PEAR) **GEMMCD9473** Heddle Nash—Vol.2

ANDREW, Ludmilla (sop)
see CONCERT INDEX under:

(BRIT) **BML001** Bernard van Dieren Collection
(CHAN) **CHAN9327** Medtner—Songs
(OPRA) **ORC003** Donizetti—Gabriella di Vergy

ANDREW, Mark (organ)
see CONCERT INDEX under:
(CLAR) **CDGSE78-50-50** Richard Crooks sings Ballads & Sacred Songs

ANDREWS, Julie (bn)
see CONCERT INDEX under:
(EMIN) **CD-EMX2238** R. Strauss—Orchestral Works

ANDREWS, Julie (sop)
Rodgers: King and I (Cpte)
Sondheim: Putting It Together (Cpte)
Various: Star! (Cpte)
see CONCERT INDEX under:
(PHIL) **442 603-2PH** Julie Andrews sings Richard Rodgers

ANDSNES, Leif Ove (pf)
see CONCERT INDEX under:
(BIS) **BIS-CD428** Nielsen—Wind Chamber Music
(SIMA) **PSC1063** Chopin/Schumann—Cello and Piano Works
(VIRG) **VCK7 59072-2** Chopin—Piano Works
(VIRG) **VC5 45122-2** 20th Century Violin Sonatas
(VIRG) **VC7 59300-2** Grieg—Piano Works
(VIRG) **VC7 59309-2** Brahms/Schumann—Viola Sonatas
(VIRG) **VC7 59613-2** Grieg/Liszt—Piano Works
(VIRG) **VC7 59639-2** Janáček—Piano Works

ANGADI, Darien (treb)
Britten: Noye's Fludde (Cpte)
see CONCERT INDEX under:
(DECC) **436 990-2DWO** The World of Benjamin Britten

ANGAS, Richard (bass)
Schoenberg: Moses und Aron (Cpte)
Sondheim: Pacific Overtures (Cpte)
Sullivan: Mikado (exc)
see CONCERT INDEX under:
(EMI) **CDM7 64022-2** Vaughan Williams—Orchestral Works

ANGEL, Michael (ten)
Nyman: Prospero's Books

ANGELES, Victoria de los (sop)
Berlioz: Nuits d'été
Bizet: Carmen (Cpte)
Debussy: Pelléas et Mélisande (Cpte)
Gounod: Faust (Cpte)
Leoncavallo: Pagliacci (Cpte)
Mascagni: Cavalleria Rusticana (Cpte)
Massenet: Werther (Cpte)
Offenbach: Contes d'Hoffmann (Cpte)
Puccini: Bohème (Cpte), Madama Butterfly (Cpte)
Rossini: Barbiere di Siviglia (Cpte)
Verdi: Simon Boccanegra (Cpte)
Vivaldi: Orlando Furioso (Cpte)
see CONCERT INDEX under:
(CFP) **CD-CFP4532** Sacred Arias
(COLL) **Coll1247-2** An Evening with Victoria De Los Angeles
(EMI) **CDC5 55224-2** Villa-Lobos conducts Villa-Lobos
(EMI) **CDH5 65072-2** Glyndebourne Recorded - 1934-1994
(EMI) **CDH7 61015-2** De los Angeles sings Villa-Lobos
(EMI) **CDH7 63495-2** Victoria de los Angeles—Early Recordings
(EMI) **CDH7 64028-2** Victoria de los Angeles sings Spanish Songs
(EMI) **CDM7 64365-2** Chausson—Chamber, Orchestra & Vocal Works
(EMI) **CDM7 69502-2** On Wings of Song
(EMI) **CHS7 69741-2(3)** Record of Singing, Vol.4—French School
(EMI) **CMS5 65061-2(1)** The Fabulous Victoria de los Angeles (pt 1)
(EMI) **CMS5 65061-2(2)** The Fabulous Victoria de los Angeles (pt 2)
(EMI) **CMS7 64165-2** Puccini—Trittico
(HARM) **HMC90 1432** Falla—Vocal & Orchestral Works

ANGELICI, Martha (sop)
Bizet: Carmen (Cpte), Pêcheurs de Perles (Cpte)
Gounod: Faust (Cpte)
Ravel: Enfant et les sortilèges (Cpte)
Tomasi: Don Juan de Mañara (Cpte)
see CONCERT INDEX under:
(EMI) **CHS7 69741-2(3)** Record of Singing, Vol.4—French School

ANGELIS, Giovanni de (bass)
Puccini: Bohème (Cpte), Fanciulla del West (Cpte)
Verdi: Otello (Cpte)

ANGELIS, Nazzareno De (bass)
see CONCERT INDEX under:
(EMI) **CHS7 64864-2(1)** La Scala Edition - Vol.2, 1915-46 (pt 1)
(IRCC) **IRCC-CD800** Souvenirs from Meyerbeer Operas
(PREI) **89042** Nazzareno de Angelis (1881-1962)
(SYMP) **SYMCD1113** The Harold Wayne Collection, Vol.13

ANGELO, Gianna d' (sop)
Offenbach: Contes d'Hoffmann (Cpte)
Puccini: Bohème (Cpte)

ANGELOV, Mihail (cond)
see Sofia SO

ANGERER, Margit (sop)
see CONCERT INDEX under:
(SCHW) **314532** Vienna State Opera Live, Vol.3

ANGERER, Paul (cond)
see South-West German CO

ANGERS CATHEDRAL CHOIR
see CONCERT INDEX under:
(STUD) **SM1220.02** Immortel Grégorien

ANGERVO, Heljä (contr)
R.Strauss: Salome (Cpte)

ANGERVO, Ilari (va)
see CONCERT INDEX under:
(ONDI) **ODE826-2** Sibelius—Early Chamber Music, Vol. 1

ANGSTER, Armand (cl)
see CONCERT INDEX under:
(ETCE) **KTC1070** Ferneyhough: Various Works

ANGUELOV, Ivan (cond)
see Rencontres Musicales Orch

ANGULO, Manuel (ob)
Falla: Harpsichord Concerto

ANGUS, Andrew (bass)
see CONCERT INDEX under:
(UNIT) **88033-2** Howells/F. Martin—Choral Works

ANHEISSER, Wolfgang (bar)
Zeller: Vogelhändler (Cpte)

ANHORN, Carmen (sop)
R. Strauss: Elektra (Cpte)

ANIMA ETERNA ORCHESTRA
Mozart: Piano Concerto 5, Piano Concerto 6, Piano Concerto 9, Piano Concerto 15, Piano Concerto 16, Piano Concerto 17, Piano Concerto 18, Piano Concerto 19, Piano Concerto 22, Piano Concerto 23, Piano Concerto 24, Piano Concerto 25, Piano Concerto 26, Piano Concerto 27
(CHNN) **CCS0690** Mozart—Keyboard Concertos Vol 2
(CHNN) **CCS0990** Mozart—Keyboard Concertos Vol 3
cond J. VAN IMMERSEEL
Mendelssohn: Hochzeit des Camacho (Cpte)
Schubert: Rosamunde (exc), Symphony 5
see CONCERT INDEX under:
(CHNN) **CCS7895** Buxtehude—Cantatas

ANISIMOV, Alexander (bass)
Tchaikovsky: Eugene Onegin (Cpte)
Verdi: Don Carlo (Cpte)

ANJOU VOCAL ENSEMBLE
cond D. DEBART
Xenakis: Orestia (Cpte)

ANKERSEN, Heidrun (contr)
Humperdinck: Königskinder (Cpte)

ANNEAR, Gwenyth (sop)
Delibes: Lakmé (Cpte)
Mahler: Symphony 8

ANONYMOUS BOY ALTO (boy alto)
see CONCERT INDEX under:
(TELD) **4509-91756-2** Bach—Cantatas, Vol.2
(TELD) **4509-91759-2** Bach—Cantatas, Vol.5

ANONYMOUS CONDUCTOR (cond)
see Gaumont British Orch

ANONYMOUS HARMONIUM PERFORMERS (harm)
see CONCERT INDEX under:
(DANA) **DACOCD311/2** Lauritz Melchior Anthology - Vol.1

ANONYMOUS HARP PERFORMERS (hp)
see CONCERT INDEX under:
(EMI) **CDH7 61052-2** Beniamino Gigli—Arias and Duets (1932-1949)
(ROMO) **81012-2** Elisabeth Rethberg - Brunswick Recordings 1924-1929
(TEST) **SBT1008** Viva Rossini

ANONYMOUS ORGAN PERFORMERS (organ)
see CONCERT INDEX under:
(DANA) **DACOCD311/2** Lauritz Melchior Anthology - Vol.1
(EMI) **CDH7 69791-2** Dame Eva Turner sings Opera Arias and Songs
(PHIL) **438 528-2PM4(1)** Schubert—Lieder (pt 1)

ANONYMOUS PIANIST(S) (pf)
see CONCERT INDEX under:
(APR) **APR7015** The Auer Legacy, Vol.1
(APR) **APR7016** The Auer Legacy, Vol.2
(BIDD) **LAB009/10** The Kreisler Collection
(BIDD) **LAB033/4** Jan Kubelik—The Acoustic Recordings (1902-13)
(BIDD) **LAB081/2** Huberman—Columbia recordings with piano
(BOGR) **BIM705-2** Muzio—The Published Edisons, 1920-25
(BONG) **GB1043-2** Italian Baritones of the Acoustic Era
(CLAR) **CDGSE78-50-44** Walter Widdop (1892-1949)
(CLAR) **CDGSE78-50-57** Lotte Lehmann sings Lieder
(CLRI) **CC0005** The Clarinet - Historical Recordings, Vol.1

(EPM) **150 122** Milhaud—Historic Recordings 1928-1948

ANZELLOTTI, Alba (sop)
see CONCERT INDEX under:
(EMI) **CHS7 69741-2(7)** Record of Singing, Vol.4—Italian School

ANZELLOTTI, Teodoro (accordion)
Holliger: Beiseit

APAP, Gilles (vn)
see CONCERT INDEX under:
(SONY) **SK47184** Glenn Gould—The Composer

APARICI, Montserrat (sop)
Verdi: Lombardi (Cpte)

APOLLO CHORUS
cond R. BOURDON
see CONCERT INDEX under:
(CLUB) **CL99-025** Giovanni Zenatello (1876-1949)
(PEAR) **GEMMCDS9074(2)** Giovanni Zenatello, Vol.2 (pt 2)
(PREI) **89038** Giovanni Zenatello (1876-1949)

APOLLO SAXOPHONE QUARTET
see CONCERT INDEX under:
(ARGO) **443 903-2ZH** First & Foremost

APOLLONI, Anita (sop)
see CONCERT INDEX under:
(PREI) **89023** Conchita Supervia (1895-1936)

APOSTOLU, Giovanni (ten)
see CONCERT INDEX under:
(SYMP) **SYMCD1077** The Harold Wayne Collection, Vol.4

APPEL, Wolfgang (ten)
Wagner: Meistersinger (Cpte)

APPELGREN, Curt (bass)
Lidholm: Dream Play (Cpte)

APPELT, Hans-Dieter (bass)
Puccini: Bohème (Cpte)

APPLETON, Colin (ten)
Shostakovich: Lady Macbeth of Mtsensk (Cpte)

APPÓNYI QUARTET
Haydn: String Quartets, Op. 33

APREA, Tito (pf)
see CONCERT INDEX under:
(TEST) **SBT1024** Brahms—Violin Sonatas

APTER, David (pf)
see CONCERT INDEX under:
(MARC) **8 223298** Enescu & Villa-Lobos: Cello Works

AQUARIUS
cond N. CLEOBURY
Falla: Amor brujo (Cpte), Corregidor y la Molinera (Cpte)

ARA, Augustín Léo (vn)
see CONCERT INDEX under:
(EMI) **CZS7 67435-2** Rodrigo—Orchestral Works
(PHIL) **438 016-2PH** Rodrigo—Guitar Works

ARAGALL, Giacomo (ten)
Donizetti: Lucrezia Borgia (Cpte)
Gounod: Faust (Cpte)
Mascagni: Cavalleria Rusticana (Cpte)
Massenet: Esclarmonde (Cpte)
Puccini: Bohème (Cpte), Tosca (Cpte)
Verdi: Rigoletto (Cpte), Simon Boccanegra (Cpte), Traviata (Cpte)
see CONCERT INDEX under:
(DECC) **430 724-2DM** Great Operatic Duets
(DECC) **436 463-2DM** Ten Top Tenors
(DECC) **436 464-2DM** Ten Top Baritones & Basses
(NAXO) **8 550684** Duets and Arias from Italian Operas

ARAGON, Maria (sngr)
Vives: Bohemios (Cpte)

ARAIZA, Francisco (ten)
Berlioz: Te Deum
Catalani: Wally (Cpte)
Donizetti: Maria Stuarda (Cpte)
Gounod: Faust (Cpte)
Haydn: Schöpfung (Cpte)
Mahler: Lied von der Erde
Mozart: Così fan tutte (Cpte), Don Giovanni (Cpte), Entführung (Cpte), Idomeneo (Cpte), Requiem, Zauberflöte (Cpte)
Puccini: Bohème (Cpte), Turandot (Cpte)
Rossini: Barbiere di Siviglia (Cpte), Cenerentola (Cpte), Italiana in Algeri (Cpte), Messa di gloria, Viaggio a Reims (Cpte)
Spontini: Vestale (Cpte)
see CONCERT INDEX under:
(DG) **437 244-2GGA2** Berlioz/Franck—Vocal & Orchestral Works
(EMI) **CDM7 69223-2** Schubert—Choral Works
(EMI) **CMS7 64778-2** Schubert—Sacred Works, Vol.1
(EMI) **CMS7 64783-2** Schubert—Sacred Works, Vol.2
(EMIL) **CDZ7 67015-2** Mozart—Opera Arias
(RCA) **09026 61163-2** The Romantic Tenor

ARAMBURO, Antonio (ten)
see CONCERT INDEX under:
(MEMO) **HR4408/9(1)** Singers in Genoa, Vol.1 (disc 1)

ARAMIS, Pericles (bar)
see CONCERT INDEX under:
(SYMP) **SYMCD1172** The Harold Wayne Collection, Vol.21

ARANGI-LOMBARDI, Giannina (sop)
see CONCERT INDEX under:
(EMI) **CHS7 64864-2(1)** La Scala Edition - Vol.2, 1915-46 (pt 1)
(PREI) **89013** Giannina Arangi-Lombardi (1890-1951)
(PREI) **89026** Francesco Merli (1887-1976) - I
(PREI) **89040** Carlo Galeffi (1884-1961)

ARANYI, Jelly d' (vn)
see CONCERT INDEX under:
(APR) **APR7012** Myra Hess—A vignette

ARAPIAN, Armand (ten)
Massenet: Chérubin (Cpte)

ARÁVALO, Carlos (voc)
M. Monk: Atlas (Cpte)

ARBACE, Libero (bass)
Puccini: Tosca (Cpte)
Verdi: Otello (Cpte)

ARCADIAN ACADEMY
see CONCERT INDEX under:
(HARM) **HMU90 7066** Uccellini—Chamber Works
(HARM) **HMU90 7067** Nicola Matteis—Ayres for the Violin

ARCANGELO, Ildebrando d' (bass)
Mozart: Don Giovanni (Cpte), Nozze di Figaro (Cpte)
Rossini: Armida (Cpte)
Verdi: Otello (Cpte)

ARCHE COMMUNITY CHOIR
see CONCERT INDEX under:
(STUD) **SM1220.02** Immortel Grégorien

ARCHER, Malcolm (cond)
see Bristol Cath Ch

ARCHER, Malcolm (organ)
see CONCERT INDEX under:
(MERI) **CDE84168** Elgar: Choral Music

ARCHER, Neill (ten)
Bach: St John Passion, BWV245 (Cpte)
Howells: Stabat mater
Mayr: Medea (Cpte)

(L') ARCHIBUDELLI
Beethoven: Serenade, Op. 8, String Trio, Op. 3, String Trios, Op. 9
Gade: Octet, Op. 17
Mendelssohn: Octet, Op. 20
Mozart: String Quintet, K515, String Quintet, K516
Reicha: Cello and Viola Quintets (exc), Cello Quintet (1807)
see CONCERT INDEX under:
(SONY) **SK46631** Mozart—Chamber Works
(SONY) **SK46702** Mozart—Chamber Works
(SONY) **SK53366** Mozart—Chamber Music for Clarinet
(SONY) **SK53370** Spohr—Chamber Works
(SONY) **SK53980** Franchomme/Chopin—Grand Duo Concertante
(SONY) **SK53987** Michael Haydn—String Quintets
(SONY) **SK57968** Weber/Hummel/Reicha—Works for Clarinet
(SONY) **SK66251** Bruckner—Chamber Works
cond B. WEIL
(SONY) **SK53368** Haydn—Sacred Music

ARCO, Annie d' (pf)
see CONCERT INDEX under:
(CALL) **CAL9828** Chabrier: Piano Works

ARCY, Michael d' (vn)
see CONCERT INDEX under:
(NMC) **NMCD022** Gerald Barry—Instrumental & Chamber Works

ARDAM, Elzbieta (mez)
R. Strauss: Frau ohne Schatten (Cpte)
Verdi: Otello (Cpte)

ARDAŠEV, Igor (pf)
see CONCERT INDEX under:
(SUPR) **11 1878-2** The Unknown Janáček

ARDELEANU, Mircea (perc)
Henze: Cimarrón

ARDELLI, Norbert (bar)
see CONCERT INDEX under:
(SCHW) **314602** Vienna State Opera Live, Vol.10
(SCHW) **314672** Vienna State Opera Live, Vol.17

ARDEN, Evelyn (mez)
Wagner: Götterdämmerung (exc)
see CONCERT INDEX under:
(PEAR) **GEMMCDS9137** Wagner—Der Ring des Nibelungen

ARDEN-TAYLOR, Paul (ob)
see CONCERT INDEX under:
(NIMB) **NI5189** Telemann: Trumpet Concertos

ARDITTI, Irvine (vn)
see CONCERT INDEX under:
(AUVI) **MO782025** Schoenberg—Chamber Music, Vol. 3
(ETCE) **KTC1070** Ferneyhough: Various Works

ARDITTI QUARTET
Berg: Lyric Suite, String Quartet
Cage: Music for Four, Pieces for String Quartet, String Quartet
Carter: String Quartet 1, String Quartet 4
Ligeti: String Quartet 1, String Quartet 2
see CONCERT INDEX under:
(AUVI) **MO782024** Schoenberg—String Quartets
(AUVI) **MO782025** Schoenberg—Chamber Music, Vol. 3
(BRID) **BCD9045** Benedict Mason—Chamber and Orchestral Works
(ETCE) **KTC1066** Carter—String Quartets
(GVIS) **GV79439-2** Modern String Quartets
(GVIS) **GV79440-2** Works for String Quartet
(MARC) **DCCD9003** Rasmussen/Sorensen—String Quartets
(MONT) **782002** Compositions for String Quartet and Percussion Trio
(MONT) **782010** U.S.A.
(MONT) **789006** Spanish Chamber Music
(MONT) **789007** Modern String Quartets
(MONT) **789008** Webern—The School of Vienna Volume 3
(SALA) **SCD8904/5** Scelsi—Chamber Works
(WERG) **WER60114/5-50** Henze: String Quartets
cond A. BRIZZI
see CONCERT INDEX under:
(SALA) **SCD8904/5** Scelsi—Chamber Works
cond A. MINCK
(MONT) **782002** Compositions for String Quartet and Percussion Trio

ARDUINI, Remo (cond)
see Rome Op Orch

ARDWYN SINGERS
cond G. KAPLAN
Mahler: Symphony 2

ARÉVALO, Octavio (ten)
Rossini: Semiramide (Cpte), Signor Bruschino (Cpte)

ARGENTA, Ataulfo (cond)
see LSO

ARGENTA, Nancy (sop)
A. Scarlatti: Dixit Dominus II
Bach: Christmas Oratorio, BWV248 (Cpte), Magnificat, BWV243, Mass in B minor, BWV232 (Cpte), St John Passion, BWV245 (Cpte)
Blow: Venus and Adonis (Cpte)
Gluck: Iphigénie en Tauride (Cpte), Orfeo ed Euridice (Cpte)
Handel: Floridante (exc), Israel in Egypt (Cpte), Resurrezione (Cpte), Solomon (Cpte)
Monteverdi: Orfeo (Cpte)
Mozart: Così fan tutte (Cpte), Don Giovanni (Cpte), Nozze di Figaro (Cpte), Zauberflöte (Cpte)
Purcell: Dioclesian, Z627 (Cpte), Fairy Queen, Z629 (Cpte), King Arthur, Z628 (Cpte), Timon of Athens, Z632 (Cpte)
Vivaldi: Gloria, RV589
Zelenka: Litanie lauretanae, ZWV152, Missa dei fili, ZWV20
see CONCERT INDEX under:
(ACCE) **ACC9395D** Bach—Cantatas
(ARCH) **429 782-2AH** Bach—Cantatas Nos 106, 118b & 198
(ARCH) **437 327-2AH** Bach—Cantatas
(ARCH) **437 834-2AH** Christmas in Rome - Gloria
(COLL) **Coll7016-2** Handel—Alexander's Feast
(DHM) **05472 77295-2** Handel/Purcell—Works
(EMI) **CDC7 54525-2** Mozart—Sacred Works
(HYPE) **DJ33012** Schubert—Complete Lieder, Vol.12
(VIRG) **VC5 45038-2** Bach—Cantatas
(VIRG) **VC5 45059-2** Bach—Cantatas
(VIRG) **VC7 59324-2** Purcell—O Solitude - Songs and Airs
(VIRG) **VC7 59326-2** Vivaldi—Sacred Choral Works

ARGENTEUIL VITTORIA CHOIR
Fauré: Requiem (Cpte)

ARGERICH, Martha (pf)
Bach: Viola da gamba Sonatas, BWV1027-9
Beethoven: Piano Concerto 1, Piano Concerto 2, Violin Sonata 4, Violin Sonata 5
Chopin: Piano Concerto 1
Haydn: Keyboard Concerto, HobXVIII:11
Liszt: Piano Concerto 1
Mendelssohn: Violin and Piano Concerto
Messiaen: Visions de l'Amen
Prokofiev: Piano Concerto 3
Rachmaninov: Piano Concerto 3
Ravel: Gaspard de la Nuit, Piano Concerto
Schumann: Fantasie, Fantasiestücke, Op. 12, Kinderszenen, Kreisleriana, Piano Concerto, Violin Concerto, Violin Sonata 1, Violin Sonata 2
Shostakovich: Piano Concerto 1
Stravinsky: Noces
Tchaikovsky: Piano Concerto 1
see CONCERT INDEX under:
(DG) **415 138-2GH** Beethoven: Violin Sonatas, Vol. 1
(DG) **415 836-2GGA** Chopin: Piano works
(DG) **423 665-2GH** Ravel: Orchestral Works
(DG) **423 880-2GGA** Bach—Keyboard Works
(DG) **427 351-2GH** 20th-Century Violin and Piano Works
(DG) **431 801-2GH** Beethoven—Cello Sonatas, etc

(DG) 431 803-2GH   Prokofiev—Violin and Piano Works
(DG) 437 252-2GGA   Liszt/Schumann/Brahms—Piano Works
(DG) 437 514-2GH   Beethoven—Cello Sonatas, etc
(DG) 439 409-2GCL   Liszt—Piano Works
(DG) 439 413-2GCL   Prokofiev—Orchestral Works
(DG) 439 867-2GH   Bartók/Ravel—Works for 2 Pianos
(DG) 439 934-2GH2   Beethoven—Cello Sonatas, etc
(DG) 445 652-2GH   Beethoven—Violin Sonatas
(DG) 447 430-2GOR   Martha Argerich—Début Recital
(DG) 447 438-2GOR   Prokofiev/Ravel—Piano Concertos
(EMI) CDM7 63577-2   Franck & Debussy: Cello Sonatas, etc
(ETCE) KTC1038   Violin and piano recital
(PHIL) 412 230-2PH   Works for Cello and Piano
(SONY) SK52565   New Year's Eve Concert 1992
(SONY) SK53978   Prometheus
(TELD) 4509-91378-2   Mozart—Sonatas for 2 pianos & for piano 4 hands
(TELD) 4509-92257-2   Brahms—Piano Works
(TELD) 9031-74717-2   Rachmaninov—Works for Two Pianos

ARGIROS, Marios (ob)
see CONCERT INDEX under:
(KING) KCLCD2027   South American Flute Music

ARGO BAND
cond M. TORKE
see CONCERT INDEX under:
(ARGO) 443 528-2ZH   Torke—Music on the Floor

ARGO CHAMBER ORCHESTRA
cond G. GUEST
see CONCERT INDEX under:
(DECC) 443 868-2DF2   Italian Baroque Sacred Works
cond L. HELTAY
Haydn: Salve Regina, HobXXIIIb/1, Stabat Mater

ARGO SYMPHONY ORCHESTRA
cond J. JUDD
see CONCERT INDEX under:
(ARGO) 443 529-2ZH   Sax Drive

ARGÜELLES, Julian (sax)
see CONCERT INDEX under:
(ECM) 847 537-2   Gavin Bryars—After the Requiem

ARICO, Fortunato (vc)
see CONCERT INDEX under:
(ASV) CDGAU104   Haydn—Baryton Trios

ARIÉ, Raffaele (bass)
Donizetti: Lucia di Lammermoor (Cpte)
see CONCERT INDEX under:
(EMI) CHS7 69741-2(7)   Record of Singing, Vol.4—Italian School
(EMI) CHS7 63244-2   The Art of Maria Callas

ARIEL QUARTET
Herrmann: Souvenirs de voyage

ARIEL WIND QUINTET
cond D. TEETERS
see CONCERT INDEX under:
(KOCH) 37180-2   Pinkham—Cantatas & Chamber Works

ARIMONDI, Vittorio (bass)
see CONCERT INDEX under:
(MEMO) HR4408/9(1)   Singers in Genoa, Vol.1 (disc 1)
(PEAR) GEMMCDS9924(1)   Covent Garden on Record, Vol.2 (pt 1)

ARION TRIO
see CONCERT INDEX under:
(BIS) BIS-CD513/4   Mozart—Chamber Works

(D.I.) ARISTOV CHOIR
cond A.A. SCRIABIN
see CONCERT INDEX under:
(PREI) 89207   Feodor Chaliapin Song Book—Electrical Recordings

ARITA, Chiyoko (hpd)
Blavet: Flute Sonatas, Op.2 (exc), Flute Sonatas, Op.3 (exc)
Rameau: Pièces de clavecin en concerts
see CONCERT INDEX under:
(DENO) CO-73868/9   Bach: Flute Works

ARITA, Masahiro (fl)
Blavet: Flute Sonatas, Op.2 (exc), Flute Sonatas, Op.3 (exc)
Mozart: Flute Quartets
Rameau: Pièces de clavecin en concerts
Telemann: Fantaisies, TWV40: 2-13, Paris Quartets (Nouvoaux quatuors)
see CONCERT INDEX under:
(DENO) CO-73868/9   Bach: Flute Works

ARIZMENDI, Elena (sop)
see CONCERT INDEX under:
(EMI) CHS7 69741-2(7)   Record of Singing, Vol.4—Italian School

ARIZONA STATE UNIVERSITY CONCERT CHOIR
cond J. SEDARES
E. Bernstein: Hallelujah Trail Overture

ARKADIEV, O.I. (cond)
see orch

ARKADIOV, Mikhail (pf)
see CONCERT INDEX under:
(PHIL) 442 536-2PH   My Restless Soul

ARKEL, Teresa (sop)
see CONCERT INDEX under:
(EMI) CHS7 64860-2(1)   La Scala Edition - Vol.1, 1878-1914 (pt 1)
(MEMO) HR4408/9(1)   Singers in Genoa, Vol.1 (disc 1)

ARKHIPOV, Alexander (ten)
Rachmaninov: Miserly knight (Cpte)
Shostakovich: Gamblers (Cpte)
Tchaikovsky: Snow Maiden (Cpte)

ARKHIPOVA, Irina (mez)
Prokofiev: Ivan the Terrible
Tchaikovsky: Eugene Onegin (Cpte), Queen of Spades (Cpte)

ARKIN, Adam (sngr)
Gershwin: Oh, Kay! (Cpte)

ARKOR, André d' (ten)
see CONCERT INDEX under:
(TEST) SBT1008   Viva Rossini

ARMAN, Howard (cond)
see Halle Op House Handel Fest Orch

ARMANINI, Giuseppe (ten)
see CONCERT INDEX under:
(SYMP) SYMCD1113   The Harold Wayne Collection, Vol.13

ARMENGAUD, Jean-Pierre (pf)
see CONCERT INDEX under:
(ACCO) 20202-2   Poulenc—Chamber Works

ARMENIAN PHILHARMONIC ORCHESTRA
cond L. TJEKNAVORIAN
Khachaturian: Battle for Stalingrad Suite, Symphony 1, Symphony 2, Symphony 3
see CONCERT INDEX under:
(ASV) CDDCA772   Rimsky-Korsakov—Orchestral Works
(ASV) CDDCA773   Russian Orchestral and Ballet Music
(ASV) CDDCA884   Khachaturian/Tjeknavorian—Orchestral Works

ARMENIAN STATE CHAMBER ENSEMBLE
Shchedrin: Carmen Ballet

ARMENIAN STATE PERCUSSION ENSEMBLE
cond V. SPIVAKOV
Shchedrin: Carmen Ballet

ARMENTIA, Alicia (sngr)
Bretón: Verbena de la Paloma (Cpte)

ARMITSTEAD, Melanie (sop)
Fénelon: Chevalier Imaginaire (Cpte)

ARMSTRONG, Karan (sop)
Henze: Bassariden (Cpte)
Zemlinsky: Lyrische Symphonie
see CONCERT INDEX under:
(ETCE) KTC1045   Menotti: Chamber and Vocal Works

ARMSTRONG, Nancy (sop)
Mozart: Mass, K427

ARMSTRONG, Richard (cond)
see LPO

ARMSTRONG, Rosalie (hpd)
see CONCERT INDEX under:
(NIMB) NI5357   Hoddinott—Orchestral Works

ARMSTRONG, Sheila (sop)
Britten: Spring Symphony
Mahler: Symphony 2
Mozart: Requiem
Orff: Carmina Burana
Purcell: Dido (Cpte)
Rachmaninov: Bells
Vaughan Williams: Hugh the Drover (Cpte), Symphony 1, Symphony 7
see CONCERT INDEX under:
(ARCH) 439 369-2AX4   Bach—Cantatas, Vol.1
(EMI) CDM7 64022-2   Vaughan Williams—Orchestral Works
(EMI) CDM7 64364-2   Fauré/Bach—Choral Works
(EMI) CES5 68519-2   Beethoven—Symphonies
(ERAT) 4509-96961-2   Schubert—Stabat Mater; Offertorium; Magnificat

ARMYTAGE, Christopher Green (pf)
Simpson: Horn Quartet, Horn Trio, Violin Sonata (1984)

(GÜNTHER) ARNDT CH
cond W. BRÜCKNER-RÜGGEBERG
Weill: Dreigroschenoper (Cpte)
cond F. FOX
Fall: Rose von Stambul (exc)
Millöcker: Dubarry (exc)
Zeller: Vogelhändler (exc)
cond W. SCHMIDT-BOELCKE
Abraham: Blume von Hawaii (exc), Viktoria und ihr Husar (exc)
cond R. STOLZ
Lehár: Land des Lächelns (exc)
see CONCERT INDEX under:
(EURO) GD69022   Oscar Straus: Operetta excerpts

ARNELL, Johann (cond)
see Berlin RSO

ARNELL, Richard (cond)
see PAO

ARNESEN, Bodil (sop)
Beethoven: Joseph II Cantata, Leopold II Cantata

ARNHEIM, Avigail (cl)
see CONCERT INDEX under:
(CARL) PWK1141   French Impressions

ARNHEM PHILHARMONIC ORCHESTRA
cond R. BENZI
Bruch: Violin Concerto 1
Mahler: Knaben Wunderhorn (exc)
cond Y. MENUHIN
Elgar: Violin Concerto

ARNOLD, Anton (ten)
see CONCERT INDEX under:
(SCHW) 314562   Vienna State Opera Live, Vol.6
(SCHW) 314572   Vienna State Opera Live, Vol.7
(SCHW) 314602   Vienna State Opera Live, Vol.10
(SCHW) 314642   Vienna State Opera Live, Vol.14

ARNOLD, Benno (ten)
Wagner: Meistersinger (Cpte), Tristan und Isolde (Cpte)

ARNOLD, David (bar)
Beethoven: Symphony 9
Mozart: Requiem

ARNOLD, Sir Malcolm (cond)
see BBC SO

ARNOLDSON, Sigrid (sop)
see CONCERT INDEX under:
(PEAR) GEMMCDS9923(1)   Covent Garden on Record, Vol.1 (pt 1)

ARNONE, Francesca (sop)
Paisiello: Don Chisciotte (Cpte)

ARNOULT, Louis (ten)
Ravel: Heure espagnole (Cpte)

ARONOV, Arkady (pf)
see CONCERT INDEX under:
(CHAN) CHAN8509   Prokofiev: Songs

ARONOWITZ, Cecil (va)
Brahms: String Sextet 1, String Sextet 2
see CONCERT INDEX under:
(DG) 419 875-2GCM3   Brahms. Quintets and Sextets.
(DG) 431 149-2GCM3   Mozart: String Quintets
(EMI) CDM5 65079-2
Schoenberg/Bartók/Hindemith—Orchestral Works
(LYRI) SRCD223   Holst—Orchestral Works

ARP, Klaus (cond)
see Kaiserslautern Rad Orch

ARPINO, André (perc)
see CONCERT INDEX under:
(DECC) 436 798-2DH   Loussier—Concertos

ARRAU, Claudio (pf)
Beethoven: Piano Concerto 5, Triple Concerto
Chopin: Etudes (exc), Nocturnes, Piano Concerto 1, Piano Concerto 2, Polonaises (exc), Scherzos
Liszt: Études d'exécution, S139, Piano Concerto 2
see CONCERT INDEX under:
(EMI) CZS7 67379-2   Beethoven Edition - Arrau
(MUSI) MACD-643   Mozart & Schumann—Chamber Works
(PEAR) GEMMCD9928   The Young Claudio Arrau
(PHIL) 422 149-2PH3   Beethoven: Complete Piano Concertos
(PHIL) 432 173-2PH2   Claudio Arrau—The Final Sessions
(PHIL) 432 301-2PM11   Beethoven—Piano Works
(PHIL) 432 304-2PM2   Debussy—Piano Works
(PHIL) 432 306-2PM7   Claudio Arrau plays Mozart
(PHIL) 442 580-2PM2   Beethoven—Concertos, Volume 2
(RCA) GD87841   Claudio Arrau plays Bach

ARRIAGA QUARTET
Milhaud: String Quartet 1, String Quartet 2

ARRIGNON, Michel (cl)
see CONCERT INDEX under:
(DG) 447 405-2GOR   Berg/Stravinsky—Chamber Works
(TIMP) 1C1010   Honegger—Chamber Works, Vol.3
(TIMP) 4C1012   Honegger—Chamber Works

ARROYO, Martina (sop)
Beethoven: Fidelio (exc), Missa Solemnis, Symphony 9
Mozart: Don Giovanni (Cpte)
Verdi: Ballo in maschera (Cpte), Forza del destino (Cpte), Vespri Siciliani (Cpte)
see CONCERT INDEX under:
(DG) 429 042-2GX10   Mahler: Complete Symphonies
(EMI) CDM7 69549-2   Ruggero Raimondi: Italian Opera Arias
(SONY) MPK46727   Barber—Vocal Works

ARRUABARRENA, Maite (sop)
see CONCERT INDEX under:
(ACCE) ACC8864D   Symphonia Angelica

ARS LAETA CHOIR
cond F. MARTIN
Martin: Requiem

ARS NOVA
cond B. HOLTEN
see CONCERT INDEX under:
(KONT) 32001   La Rue/Wert—Sacred Choral Works
(KONT) 32003   Tallis—Choral & Instrumental Works
(KONT) 32008   Gombert/La Rue—Sacred Choral Works

(KONT) **32038** Gombert—Sacred Choral Works
cond O. SCHMIDT
Schmidt/Jansson: Öresund Symphony

ARS REDIVIVA
cond M. MUNCLINGER
see CONCERT INDEX under:
(SONY) **SK48184** Rampal plays Great Flute
Concertos

ARSEGUET, Lise (sngr)
Audran: Miss Helyett (Cpte)

ARSHAVSKAYA, Ludmilla (cond)
see Cantus Sacred Music Ens

ARTARIA QUARTET
Boccherini: Guitar Quintets, G445-453 (exc)
Giuliani: Gran Quintetto, Op. 65

ARTEGNA, Francesco Ellero d' (bass)
Bellini: Puritani (Cpte)
Catalani: Wally (Cpte)
Cilea: Adriana Lecouvreur (Cpte)
Donizetti: Maria Stuarda (Cpte)
Puccini: Bohème (Cpte), Fanciulla del West (Cpte)
Verdi: Aida (Cpte), Falstaff (Cpte), Trovatore (Cpte)

ARTETA, Ainhoa (sop)
Vives: Doña Francisquita (Cpte)
see CONCERT INDEX under:
(SONY) **SK46691** The First Placido Domingo
International Voice Competition

ARTHUR, (ten)
Donizetti: Ugo, Conte di Parigi (Cpte)
Offenbach: Christopher Columbus (Cpte)
see CONCERT INDEX under:
(OPRA) **ORC003** Donizetti—Gabriella di Vergy

ARTIS QUARTET
Brahms: Piano Quintet
Magnard: String Quartet
Mozart: String Quintet, K515, String Quintet, K516
Schoenberg: String Quartet
Schubert: String Quartet, D32, String Quartet, D810
Schumann: Piano Quintet, Op. 44
Zemlinsky: String Quartet 2
see CONCERT INDEX under:
(ACCO) **20034-2** Mendelssohn: Works for String
Quartet
(ACCO) **20067-2** Mendelssohn: String Quartets
(ACCO) **20068-2** Mendelssohn: Works for String
Quartet
(SONY) **SK48059** Webern/Gielen—Works for String
Quartet

(LES) ARTS FLORISSANTS CHORUS
cond W. CHRISTIE
Campra: Idoménée (Cpte)
Handel: Messiah (Cpte)
Lully: Atys (Cpte)
M-A. Charpentier: Médée (Cpte)
Montéclair: Jephté (Cpte)
Mozart: Ave verum corpus, K618, Requiem
Purcell: Fairy Queen, Z629 (Cpte), King Arthur, Z628
(Cpte)
Rameau: Castor et Pollux (Cpte), Indes galantes
(Cpte), Nélée et Myrthis (Cpte), Pygmalion (Cpte)
see CONCERT INDEX under:
(ERAT) **4509-96967-2** Rameau—Les Grands Motets
(HARM) **HMC90 1351** Delalande—Sacred Choral
Works
(HARM) **HMC90 1416** Delalande—Petits Motets
(HARM) **HMC90 1426** Monteverdi—Il combattimento
di Tancredi e Clorinda
(HARM) **HMC90 1471** Bouzignac—Te Deum; Motets

**(LES) ARTS FLORISSANTS INSTRUMENTAL
ENSEMBLE**
cond W. CHRISTIE
M-A. Charpentier: Arts Florissants (Cpte), In
nativitatem Domini canticum, H416, Pastorale, H482, Pastorale,
H483
Monteverdi: Ballo delle ingrate, Madrigals, Bk.6
(exc)
Purcell: Dido (Cpte)
Rameau: Anacréon (Cpte)
see CONCERT INDEX under:
(HARM) **HMA190 1068** Monteverdi—Monteverdi
(HARM) **HMC90 066** M-A. Charpentier—Sacred
Choral Works
(HARM) **HMC90 1250** Monteverdi—Selve Morale
(HARM) **HMC90 1268** Gesualdo—Madrigals
(HARM) **HMC90 1274** Lully—Petits Motets
(HARM) **HMC90 1280** Montéclair—Cantatas
(HARM) **HMC90 1298** M-A. Charpentier—Sacred
Works
(HARM) **HMC90 1471** Bouzignac—Te Deum; Motets
(HARM) **HMX290 1528/33(1)** A Purcell Companion (pt
1)

(LES) ARTS FLORISSANTS ORCHESTRA
cond W. CHRISTIE
Campra: Idoménée (Cpte)
Handel: Concerti Grossi, Op. 6 (exc), Messiah
(Cpte)
Lully: Atys (Cpte)
M-A. Charpentier: Malade Imaginaire, Médée (Cpte)
Montéclair: Jephté (Cpte)
Mozart: Ave verum corpus, K618, Requiem
Purcell: Fairy Queen, Z629 (Cpte), King Arthur, Z628
(Cpte)
Rameau: Castor et Pollux (Cpte), Indes galantes
(Cpte), Nélée et Myrthis (Cpte), Pygmalion (Cpte)
see CONCERT INDEX under:

(ERAT) **4509-96967-2** Rameau—Les Grands Motets
(HARM) **HMC90 1351** Delalande—Sacred Choral
Works
(HARM) **HMC90 1416** Delalande—Petits Motets
(HARM) **HMC90 1426** Monteverdi—Il combattimento
di Tancredi e Clorinda

(LES) ARTS FLORISSANTS VOCAL ENSEMBLE
see CONCERT INDEX under:
(HARM) **HMA190 1238** Campra—French Cantatas
cond W. CHRISTIE
M-A. Charpentier: Arts Florissants (Cpte), In
nativitatem Domini canticum, H414, In nativitatem
Domini canticum, H416, Malade Imaginaire,
Pastorale, H482, Pastorale, H483
Monteverdi: Ballo delle ingrate, Madrigals, Bk.6
(exc)
Purcell: Dido (Cpte)
Rameau: Anacréon (Cpte)
see CONCERT INDEX under:
(HARM) **HMA190 1068** Monteverdi—Monteverdi
(HARM) **HMC90 066** M-A. Charpentier—Sacred
Choral Works
(HARM) **HMC90 1250** Monteverdi—Selve Morale
(HARM) **HMC90 1268** Gesualdo—Madrigals
(HARM) **HMC90 1298** M-A. Charpentier—Sacred
Works
(HARM) **HMX290 1528/33(1)** A Purcell Companion (pt
1)

ARTY, Mady (contr)
see CONCERT INDEX under:
(MSCM) **MM30451** Mascagni—Cavalleria Rusticana,
etc

ARTYMIW, Lydia (pf)
Tchaikovsky: Seasons

ARTYSZ, Jerzy (bar)
see CONCERT INDEX under:
(HARM) **HMC90 1482** Mompou—Vocal and
Orchestral Works

ARUHN, Britt-Marie (sop)
Mozart: Lucio Silla (Cpte)
Nørgård: Gilgamesh (Cpte)
Wagner: Parsifal (Cpte)

ASAWA, Brian (alto)
Handel: Judas Maccabaeus (Cpte)

ASCOLI, Bernard d' (pf)
see CONCERT INDEX under:
(NIMB) **NI5249** Chopin: Piano Works

ASENSIO, Enrique Garcia (cond)
see Madrid SO

ASH, Peter (cond)
see Downshire Players

ASH, Sam (sngr)
see CONCERT INDEX under:
(PEAR) **GEMMCDS9056/8** Music from the New York
Stage, Vol. 3: 1913-17
(PEAR) **GEMMCDS9059/61** Music from the New York
Stage, Vol. 4: 1917-20

ASHE, Rosemary (sop)
Coward: Bitter Sweet (Cpte)
Forrest/Wright: Kismet (Cpte), Timbuktu (exc)
Offenbach: Christopher Columbus (Cpte)
Romberg: Student Prince (Cpte)
see CONCERT INDEX under:
(EMI) **CDC7 54071-2** Frederica von Stade sings
Rodgers & Hart

ASHKENAZY, Dmitri (cl)
see CONCERT INDEX under:
(DECC) **436 415-2DH** R. Strauss—Orchestral Works
(DECC) **440 229-2DH** Stravinsky—Works for Piano
and Orchestra

ASHKENAZY, Vladimir (cond)
see Berlin Deutsches SO

ASHKENAZY, Vladimir (pf)
Beethoven: Allegretto, Hess48, Piano Concerto 3,
Piano Concerto 4, Piano Concerto 5, Piano Trios
(exc), Violin Sonata 5, Violin Sonata 9
Brahms: Piano Concerto 1, Piano Concerto 2
Chopin: Ballades, Etudes (exc), Mazurkas (exc),
Nocturnes (exc), Piano Concerto 2, Scherzos,
Waltzes (exc)
Mussorgsky: Pictures
Rachmaninov: Corelli Variations, Etudes-tableaux,
Op. 39, Paganini Rhapsody, Piano Concerto 1, Piano
Concerto 2, Piano Concerto 3, Piano Concerto 4,
Piano Sonata 2, Preludes
Tchaikovsky: Piano Concerto 1, Piano Trio, Op. 50
see CONCERT INDEX under:
(DECC) **410 180-2DH** Chopin: Favourite Piano Works
(DECC) **410 260-2DH** Beethoven—Piano Sonatas
Nos 8, 14 & 23
(DECC) **417 252-2DH** Scriabin: Orchestral Works
(DECC) **417 476-2DH** Chopin: Preludes & Impromptus
(DECC) **417 732-2DH** Beethoven—Piano Sonatas
(DECC) **417 798-2DM** Ashkenazy plays Chopin
Favourites
(DECC) **421 010-2DH** Schumann—Piano Works,
Vol.2
(DECC) **421 290-2DH** Schumann—Piano Works,
Vol.3
(DECC) **421 453-2DM4** Beethoven: Complete Violin
Sonatas
(DECC) **421 590-2DH2** Rachmaninov: Complete
Piano Concertos

(DECC) **425 031-2DM** Mozart—Piano Works
(DECC) **425 044-2DM** Mozart—Works for Piano and
Orchestra
(DECC) **425 081-2DM**
Debussy/Ravel/Scriabin—Piano Works
(DECC) **425 097-2DM** Mozart—Piano Concertos, Vol.
10
(DECC) **425 109-2DH** Schumann—Piano Works,
Vol.4
(DECC) **425 570-2DM2** Prokofiev: Complete Piano
Concertos
(DECC) **425 579-2DM2** Scriabin: Complete Piano
Sonatas
(DECC) **425 838-2DH** Beethoven: Piano Sonatas
(DECC) **425 940-2DH** Schumann—Piano Works,
Vol.5
(DECC) **430 149-2DH** Brahms/Schumann—Works for
Clarinet
(DECC) **430 370-2DH** R. Strauss—Works for Horn
(DECC) **430 759-2DM** Piano Favourites
(DECC) **433 070-2DWO** World of Chopin
(DECC) **433 695-2DM** Chamber Works
(DECC) **433 829-2DH** Stravinsky—Works for Two
Pianos
(DECC) **436 076-2DM** Beethoven—Piano Sonatas
(DECC) **436 204-2DM** Tchaikovsky—Songs
(DECC) **436 471-2DM** Beethoven—Piano Works
(DECC) **436 920-2DM** Rachmaninov—Complete
Songs
(DECC) **443 322-2DH** Schumann—Piano Works,
Vol.6
(DECC) **443 576-2DCS** Mozart—Piano Concertos, etc
(DECC) **443 579-2DCS** Schubert—Piano Works
(DECC) **444 318-2DH** Ravel/Debussy—Chamber
Music
(DECC) **444 389-2DWO** The World of Borodin
(DECC) **444 408-2DH** Prokofiev—Piano Sonatas Nos
6-8
(EMI) **CDC7 47403-2** Brahms—Violin Sonatas
(EMI) **CDS7 54725-2** Brahms—Piano Trios
(EMI) **CMS7 64617-2** The art of Itzhak Perlman
(EMI) **CZS4 83177-2(1)** Itzhak Perlman Edition (pt 1)
(EMI) **CZS4 83177-2(2)** Itzhak Perlman Edition (pt 2)
(LOND) **443 727-2LC10** Mozart—The Piano
Concertos
(RCA) **09026 61454-2** Perlman plays Prokofiev
(RUSS) **RDCD11208** Vladimir Ashkenazy Piano
Recital - 1963

ASHKENAZY, Vladimir (pf/dir)
Beethoven: Choral Fantasia, Piano Concerto 1, Piano
Concerto 2, Piano Concerto 3, Piano Concerto 4,
Piano Concerto 5
Mozart: Piano Concerto 20, Piano Concerto 22
see CONCERT INDEX under:
(DECC) **421 718-2DH3** Beethoven—Piano Concertos
(DECC) **425 044-2DM** Mozart—Works for Piano and
Orchestra
(DECC) **425 088-2DM** Mozart—Piano Concertos, Vol.
1
(DECC) **425 089-2DM** Mozart—Piano Concertos, Vol.
2
(DECC) **425 090-2DM** Mozart—Piano Concertos, Vol.
3
(DECC) **425 091-2DM** Mozart—Piano Concertos, Vol.
4
(DECC) **425 092-2DM** Mozart—Piano Concertos, Vol.
5
(DECC) **425 093-2DM** Mozart—Piano Concertos, Vol.
6
(DECC) **425 095-2DM** Mozart—Piano Concertos, Vol.
8
(DECC) **425 096-2DM** Mozart—Piano Concertos, Vol.
9
(DECC) **425 097-2DM** Mozart—Piano Concertos, Vol.
10
(DECC) **430 498-2DWO** The World of Mozart
(LOND) **443 727-2LC10** Mozart—The Piano
Concertos
(RPO) **CDRPO7014** Ashkenazy Live in Moscow

ASHKENAZY, Vovka (pf)
Arensky: Piano Trio 1
Tchaikovsky: Piano Trio, Op. 50

ASHLEY, Robert (synths)
see CONCERT INDEX under:
(KOCH) **37238-2** A Chance Operation - John Cage
Tribute

ASHMAN, David (bar)
see CONCERT INDEX under:
(OPRA) **ORCH104** A Hundred Years of Italian Opera:
1820-1830

ASHTON, Caroline (sop)
Purcell: Dido (Cpte)
Rutter: Requiem
see CONCERT INDEX under:
(ABBE) **CDCA954** Dvořák/Elgar—Sacred Choral
Works
(CLLE) **COLCD109** Fauré: Sacred Choral Works
(MERI) **CDE84153** French Choral Music

ASHTON, Graham (tpt)
see CONCERT INDEX under:
(CLAV) **CD50-9017** Respighi—Works for Violin and
Orchestra
(KOCH) **38703-2** Full Circle—Original Soundtrack,
etc
(VIRG) **VC5 45003-2** Contemporary Trumpet Music
(VIRG) **VC7 59609-2** Vivaldi—Concertos

ASIKAINEN, Seppo (perc)
Crumb: Madrigals, Music for a Summer Evening

ASKELAND, Reidun (pf)
see CONCERT INDEX under:
(VICT) **VCD19006** Norwegian Chamber Works
(VICT) **VCD19071** Grieg—Chamber Works, Vol.1

ASKO ENSEMBLE
Messiaen: Canyons aux étoiles
cond P. EÖTVÖS
Maderna: Hyperion (Cpte)
cond R. DE LEEUW
L. Andriessen: De Stijl

ASMUS, Rudolf (narr)
R. Strauss: Ariadne auf Naxos (Cpte)

ASPEN WIND QUINTET
see CONCERT INDEX under:
(CATA) **09026 61979-2** Memento Bittersweet

ASPEREN, Bob van (organ)
Bach: Viola da gamba Sonatas, BWV1027-9
J. C. F. Bach: Cello Sonata in A
Telemann: Solos (1734) (exc)
see CONCERT INDEX under:
(TELD) **4509-97466-2** Frans Brüggen Edition Vol.
4—Early Baroque Recorder Music

ASPEREN, Bob van (fp)
see CONCERT INDEX under:
(SONY) **SK53362** Boccherini—Cello Sonatas

ASPEREN, Bob van (hpd)
D. Scarlatti: Keyboard Sonatas (exc)
Soler: Keyboard Sonatas I (exc), Keyboard Sonatas II
(exc)
Telemann: Sonate Metodiche (exc)
see CONCERT INDEX under:
(ASTR) **E8768** Soler—Harpsichord Works, Vol.1
(ASTR) **E8769** Soler—Harpsichord Works, Vol. 2
(ASTR) **E8770** Soler—Harpsichord Works, Vol.3
(ASTR) **E8771** Soler—Harpsichord Works, Vol.4
(DHM) **GD77013** Bach—Keyboard Works
(EMI) **CDC7 54478-2** Bach—Harpsichord Concertos -
Volume 1
(SONY) **SK46349** The Harpsichord in the
Netherlands
(SONY) **S2K53964** C. P. E. Bach—Flute Sonatas
(TELD) **4509-95532-2** Bull—Harpsichord Music
(TELD) **4509-97465-2** Franz Brüggen Edition Vol.
3—English Ensemble Music
(TELD) **4509-97466-2** Frans Brüggen Edition Vol.
4—Early Baroque Recorder Music
(TELD) **4509-97467-2** Frans Brüggen Edition Vol.
5—Late Baroque Chamber Music
(TELD) **9031-77623-2** C.P.E. Bach—Keyboard
Sonatas

ASPEREN, Bob van (hpd/dir)
Bach: 2-Harpsichord Concerti

ASSAD, Odair (gtr)
see CONCERT INDEX under:
(NONE) **7559-79292-2** Baroque Guitar Transcriptions

ASSAD, Sérgio (gtr)
see CONCERT INDEX under:
(NONE) **7559-79292-2** Baroque Guitar Transcriptions

ASSANDRI, Virginio (ten)
Verdi: Otello (Cpte)
see CONCERT INDEX under:
(RCA) **GD60326** Verdi—Operas & Choral Works

ASSELIN, Pierre-Yves (organ)
Mussorgsky: Pictures
Widor: Symphony 5 (exc)

ASSENHEIMER, Isolde (contr)
Killmayer: Yolimba (Cpte)

**ASSOCIAZIONE TEATRI EMILIA ROMAGNA
ORCHESTRA**
cond L. MAGIERA
see CONCERT INDEX under:
(DECC) **443 018-2DF2**
Pavarotti/Freni/Ricciarelli—Live

ASTON MAGNA
see CONCERT INDEX under:
(HARM) **HMU90 7059** Mozart—Quintets

ASTRUC, Yvonne (vn)
see CONCERT INDEX under:
(EPM) **150 122** Milhaud—Historic Recordings 1928-
1948

ATAMIAN, Dickran (pf)
Khachaturian: Piano Concerto
Prokofiev: Piano Concerto 3

ATANASOVA, Rosiza (contr)
Pfitzner: Herz (Cpte)

ATGER, Marie (sop)
see CONCERT INDEX under:
(AUVI) **V4644** Debussy/Ravel—Orchestral Songs

ATHENA ENSEMBLE
Mozart: Don Giovanni (exc)
see CONCERT INDEX under:
(CHAN) **CHAN6536** Milhaud—Music for Wind
Instruments
(CHAN) **CHAN6553** Elgar—Wind Quintet Works,
Vol.1
(CHAN) **CHAN6554** Elgar—Wind Quintet Works,
Vol.2
(CHAN) **CHAN8385** Debussy—Chamber Works
(CHAN) **CHAN6680** Nielsen—Music for Wind
Instruments

ATHENAEUM-ENESCU QUARTET
Chausson: String Quartet, Op. 35
Franck: Piano Quintet

ATHENS EXPERIMENTAL ORCHESTRA
cond S. XARHAKOS
see CONCERT INDEX under:
(DG) **419 236-2GH** Songs my country taught me

ATHERHOLT, Robert (ob)
see CONCERT INDEX under:
(CARL) **TCD77** Mozart—Wind Concertos
(VIRG) **VC7 59007-2** Picker—Orchestral Works

ATHERTON, David (cond)
see ECO

ATHERTON, David (tape op)
see CONCERT INDEX under:
(BRID) **BCD9031** J. Harvey—Miscellaneous Works

ATHERTON, James (ten)
R. Strauss: Rosenkavalier (Cpte)
V. Thomson: Mother of us all (Cpte)

ATKINS, Jane (va)
see CONCERT INDEX under:
(ASV) **CDDCA898** Damase—Music for Flute, Harp
and Strings

ATKINSON, Lynton (ten)
Vaughan Williams: Hugh the Drover (Cpte)
see CONCERT INDEX under:
(COLL) **Coll1349-2** Respighi—Vocal and Orchestral
Works
(HYPE) **CDA66769** Vivaldi—Sacred Music, Volume
1
(MERI) **DUOCD89003** Haydn & Schubert: Masses, etc

ATKINSON, Lynton (treb)
Liszt: Missa choralis, S10
see CONCERT INDEX under:
(DECC) **430 263-2DM** Purcell—Sacred choral works

ATLAN, Françoise (mez)
Ohana: Cantigas

ATLANTA BOY CHOIR
cond ROBERT SHAW
Britten: War Requiem
Mahler: Symphony 8

ATLANTA CHORAL GUILD
cond W. NOLL
see CONCERT INDEX under:
(NEWP) **NPD85529** A Christmas Potpourri

ATLANTA SYMPHONY CHAMBER CHORUS
cond ROBERT SHAW
Bach: Magnificat, BWV243, Mass in B minor,
BWV232 (Cpte)
Handel: Messiah (Cpte)
Haydn: Creation (Cpte)
Schubert: Mass, D167, Mass, D950
Vivaldi: Gloria, RV589

ATLANTA SYMPHONY CHORUS
cond Y. LEVI
Ravel: Daphnis et Chloé (Cpte)
cond ROBERT SHAW
Beethoven: Missa Solemnis
Brahms: Deutsches Requiem, Op. 45 (Cpte)
Britten: War Requiem
Duruflé: Requiem
Dvořák: Te Deum
Fauré: Requiem (Cpte)
Glass: Itaipu
Hindemith: Requiem
Janáček: Glagolitic Mass (Cpte)
Mahler: Symphony 8
Mozart: Mass, K427, Requiem
Orff: Carmina Burana
Schubert: Mass, D167, Mass, D950
Stravinsky: Symphony of Psalms
Verdi: Pezzi sacri (Cpte)
see CONCERT INDEX under:
(TELA) **CD80109** Berlioz: Requiem, etc
(TELA) **CD80152** Verdi: Requiem & Opera Choruses
(TELA) **CD80176** Brahms: Choral Works
(TELA) **CD80181** Walton & Bernstein: Choral Works
(TELA) **CD80248** Beethoven: Choral Works
(TELA) **CD80362** Poulenc/Szymanowski—Stabat
Mater

ATLANTA SYMPHONY ORCHESTRA
cond L. LANE
see CONCERT INDEX under:
(TELA) **CD80078** Copland: Orchestral Works
(TELA) **CD80085** Respighi: Tone poems
cond Y. LEVI
Brahms: Haydn Variations, Serenade 2
Copland: Music for the Theatre, Symphony 3
Mendelssohn: Midsummer Night's Dream (exc),
Symphony 4
Prokofiev: Symphony 1, Symphony 5
Ravel: Daphnis et Chloé (Cpte), Pavane
Saint-Saëns: Piano Concerto 2
Schoenberg: Pelleas und Melisande, Verklärte
Nacht
Shostakovich: Symphony 5, Symphony 8, Symphony
9, Symphony 10
Sibelius: Symphony 1, Symphony 5
Stravinsky: Pulcinella Suite, Rite of Spring (Cpte)
Tchaikovsky: Piano Concerto 1
see CONCERT INDEX under:
(TELA) **CD80195** Hindemith: Orchestral Works
(TELA) **CD80250** Barber—Popular Orchestral Works
(TELA) **CD80296** Mussorgsky—Orchestral Works

(TELA) **CD80320** Sibelius—Tone Poems and
Incidental Music
(TELA) **CD80334** Rossini—Overtures
cond ROBERT SHAW
Bach: Magnificat, BWV243, Mass in B minor,
BWV232 (Cpte)
Beethoven: Missa Solemnis
Berlioz: Nuits dété
Brahms: Deutsches Requiem, Op. 45 (Cpte)
Britten: War Requiem
Duruflé: Requiem
Dvořák: Te Deum
Fauré: Pelléas et Mélisande Suite (exc), Requiem
(Cpte)
Glass: Canyon, Itaipu
Handel: Messiah (Cpte)
Haydn: Creation (Cpte)
Hindemith: Requiem
Janáček: Glagolitic Mass (Cpte)
Mahler: Symphony 8
Mozart: Mass, K427, Requiem
Orff: Carmina Burana
Schubert: Mass, D167, Mass, D950
Stravinsky: Symphony of Psalms
Verdi: Pezzi sacri (Cpte)
Vivaldi: Gloria, RV589
see CONCERT INDEX under:
(TELA) **CD80109** Berlioz: Requiem, etc
(TELA) **CD80152** Verdi: Requiem & Opera Choruses
(TELA) **CD80176** Brahms: Choral Works
(TELA) **CD80181** Walton & Bernstein: Choral Works
(TELA) **CD80248** Beethoven: Choral Works
(TELA) **CD80362** Poulenc/Szymanowski—Stabat
Mater

ATLANTIC SINFONIETTA
cond A. SCHENCK
Barber: Medea
Copland: Appalachian Spring Suite
see CONCERT INDEX under:
(KOCH) **37051-2** More Music for Martha Graham
cond E. TCHIVZHEL
see CONCERT INDEX under:
(KOCH) **37167-2** Music for Martha Graham, Volume 3

ATLANTIS ENSEMBLE
Schubert: Octet, D803

ATLANTOV, Vladimir (ten)
Mussorgsky: Khovanshchina (Cpte)
Tchaikovsky: Eugene Onegin (Cpte), Queen of
Spades (Cpte)

ATLAS, Dalia (cond)
see Israel CO

ATMACAYAN, Garbis (vc)
F. X. Scharwenka: Piano Quartet, Op. 37, Piano Trio,
Op. 45

ATRI, Gloria d' (pf)
see CONCERT INDEX under:
(CARL) **PCD964** Piano Concertos

ATTFIELD, Helen (sop)
Wagner: Götterdämmerung (Cpte), Rheingold (Cpte),
Walküre (Cpte)

ATTROT, Ingrid (sop)
Handel: Floridante (exc)
Vivaldi: Gloria, RV589
see CONCERT INDEX under:
(CHAN) **CHAN9392** Vaughan Williams—Riders to the
Sea etc.

ATWELL, Roy (sngr)
see CONCERT INDEX under:
(PEAR) **GEMMCDS9056/8** Music from the New York
Stage, Vol. 3: 1913-17

ATZMON, Moshe (cond)
see Malmö SO

AUBER, Stefan (vc)
Schoenberg: Pierrot Lunaire

AUBERSON, Jean-Marie (cond)
see Vienna Fest Orch

AUBERT, J. (bar)
Ravel: Heure espagnole (Cpte)

AUBERT, Roger (pf)
see CONCERT INDEX under:
(DECC) **443 467-2DF2** Stravinsky—Ballet Music

AUBIN, Alain (alto)
see CONCERT INDEX under:
(PIER) **PV790013** A. Scarlatti—Cantatas

AUBIN, Tony (cond)
see French Rad Lyric Orch

AUBUT, Alain (vc)
see CONCERT INDEX under:
(CHAN) **CHAN8651** Vivaldi: Concertos

AUDOLI, Jean-Philippe (vn)
Fauré: Messe des Pêcheurs de Villerville
see CONCERT INDEX under:
(TIMP) **1C1009** Honegger—Chamber Works, Vol.2
(TIMP) **4C1012** Honegger—Chamber Works

AUDOLI, Jean-Walter (cond)
see J-W. Audoli Inst Ens

**(JEAN-WALTER) AUDOLI INSTRUMENTAL
ENSEMBLE**
cond J-W. AUDOLI
see CONCERT INDEX under:
(ARIO) **ARN68026** Baroque Choral and String Works

(ARIO) **ARN68035** Britten—Vocal and String works
(ARIO) **ARN68071** Sauget—Vocal and orchestral works
(AUVI) **AV6114** Guitar Works

AUDUBON QUARTET
see CONCERT INDEX *under:*
(TELA) **CD80205** Oboe Music by English Composers

AUER, Gerhard (bass)
Mozart: Nozze di Figaro (Cpte)
Puccini: Gianni Schicchi (Cpte)
Verdi: Rigoletto (Cpte)
see CONCERT INDEX *under:*
(EURO) **GD69043** Puccini: Il Trittico

AUER, Leopold (vn)
see CONCERT INDEX *under:*
(APR) **APR7015** The Auer Legacy, Vol.1
(SYMP) **SYMCD1071** Great Violinists, Vol.1

AUGER, Arleen (sop)
Bach: Cantata 21, Cantata 28, Cantata 31, Cantata 36, Cantata 63, Cantata 93, Cantata 198, Christmas Oratorio, BWV248 (Cpte), Easter Oratorio, BWV249 (Cpte), Mass in B minor, BWV232 (Cpte)
Beethoven: Symphony 9
Brahms: Deutsches Requiem, Op. 45 (Cpte)
Canteloube: Chants d'Auvergne (exc)
Cimarosa: Matrimonio segreto (Cpte)
Handel: Alcina (Cpte), Belshazzar (Cpte), Messiah (Cpte), Orlando (Cpte)
Haydn: Creation (Cpte), Jahreszeiten (Cpte), Orlando Paladino (Cpte), Salve Regina, HobXXIIIb/1, Stabat Mater
Mahler: Symphony 2, Symphony 8
Mozart: Apollo et Hyacinthus (Cpte), Ascanio in Alba (Cpte), Don Giovanni (Cpte), Entführung (Cpte), Lucio Silla (Cpte), Mass, K427, Mitridate (Cpte), Nozze di Figaro (Cpte), Requiem, Schauspieldirektor (Cpte)
Orff: Carmina Burana
R. Strauss: Capriccio (Cpte), Rosenkavalier (Cpte), Vier letzte Lieder
Ravel: Enfant et les sortilèges (Cpte)
Verdi: Don Carlos (Cpte), Pezzi sacri (Cpte)
Weber: Oberon (Cpte)
Wolf: Goethe Lieder (exc), Mörike Lieder (exc)
see CONCERT INDEX *under:*
(ARAB) **Z6623** Rossini—Songs
(ARCH) **423 594-2AH** Handel—Vocal Works
(DECC) **430 804-2DC10** Mahler—Complete Symphonies
(DECC) **433 437-2DA** Pavarotti—King of the High Cs
(DELO) **DE3026** A. Auger - Bach and Handel arias
(DG) **431 791-2GH** Mozart—Sacred Choral Works
(EMI) **CDC7 49857-2** Second Viennese School
(HANS) **98 802** Bach—Cantatas, Vol.40
(HANS) **98 803** Bach—Cantatas, Vol.41
(HANS) **98 805** Bach—Cantatas, Vol.42
(HANS) **98 805** Bach—Cantatas, Vol.43
(HANS) **98 807** Bach—Cantatas, Vol.45
(HANS) **98 808** Bach—Cantatas, Vol.46
(HANS) **98 809** Bach—Cantatas, Vol.47
(HANS) **98 810** Bach—Cantatas, Vol.48
(HANS) **98 812** Bach—Cantatas, Vol.50
(HANS) **98 813** Bach—Cantatas, Vol.51
(HANS) **98 815** Bach—Cantatas, Vol.53
(HANS) **98 816** Bach—Cantatas, Vol.54
(HANS) **98 817** Bach—Cantatas, Vol.55
(HANS) **98 818** Bach—Cantatas, Vol.56
(HANS) **98 819** Bach—Cantatas, Vol.57
(HANS) **98 820** Bach—Cantatas, Vol.58
(HANS) **98 821** Bach—Cantatas, Vol.59
(HANS) **98 822** Bach—Cantatas, Vol.60
(HANS) **98 824** Bach—Cantatas, Vol.62
(HANS) **98 825** Bach—Cantatas, Vol.63
(HANS) **98 826** Bach—Cantatas, Vol.64
(HANS) **98 828** Bach—Cantatas, Vol.66
(HANS) **98 829** Bach—Cantatas, Vol.67
(HANS) **98 855** Bach—Cantatas, Vol.4
(HANS) **98 857** Bach—Cantatas, Vol.6
(HANS) **98 858** Bach—Cantatas, Vol.7
(HANS) **98 861** Bach—Cantatas, Vol.10
(HANS) **98 863** Bach—Cantatas, Vol.12
(HANS) **98 864** Bach—Cantatas, Vol.13
(HANS) **98 866** Bach—Cantatas, Vol.15
(HANS) **98 868** Bach—Cantatas, Vol.17
(HANS) **98 869** Bach—Cantatas, Vol.18
(HANS) **98 871** Bach—Cantatas, Vol.20
(HANS) **98 872** Bach—Cantatas, Vol.21
(HANS) **98 873** Bach—Cantatas, Vol.22
(HANS) **98 874** Bach—Cantatas, Vol.23
(HANS) **98 875** Bach—Cantatas, Vol.24
(HANS) **98 876** Bach—Cantatas, Vol.25
(HANS) **98 877** Bach—Cantatas, Vol.26
(HANS) **98 878** Bach—Cantatas, Vol.27
(HANS) **98 879** Bach—Cantatas, Vol.28
(HANS) **98 882** Bach—Cantatas, Vol.31
(HANS) **98 885** Bach—Cantatas, Vol.34
(HANS) **98 886** Bach—Cantatas, Vol.35
(HANS) **98 887** Bach—Cantatas, Vol.36
(HANS) **98 890** Bach—Cantatas, Vol.37
(HANS) **98 891** Bach—Cantatas, Vol.38
(HYPE) **CDJ33009** Schubert: Complete Lieder, Vol.9
(KOCH) **37248-2** The Art of Arleen Auger
(NOVA) **150 029-2** Bach—Cantatas
(PHIL) **432 420-2PH3** Haydn—Il mondo della luna/Arias
(VIRG) **VC7 59630-2** Schubert—Lieder

AUGSBURG CATHEDRAL BOYS' CHOIR
cond R. ABBADO
Puccini: Turandot (Cpte)

cond R. KAMMLER
Bach: Motets (Cpte)

AUGSBURG EARLY MUSIC ENSEMBLE
see CONCERT INDEX *under:*
(CHRI) **CHR74584** Sacred Music of the 12th Century

AULOS WIND QUINTET
see CONCERT INDEX *under:*
(SCHW) **310011** Cambini; Danzi; Reicha—Wind Quintets
(SCHW) **310022** Français—Chamber Works
(SCHW) **310051** Works for Wind Instruments
(SCHW) **310087** Music for Wind Ensemble

AUREL, Geneviève (sngr)
Lecocq: Jour et la Nuit (Cpte)
see CONCERT INDEX *under:*
(MUSD) **20239-2** Delibes—Opéras-Comiques

AURÉOLE
see CONCERT INDEX *under:*
(KOCH) **37102-2** Aureole

AURIA, Anna d' (sop)
Verdi: Nabucco (Cpte)

AURIA, Diego d' (ten)
Rossini: Bianca e Falliero (Cpte)

AURORA ENSEMBLE
A. Scarlatti: Lamentazioni (Cpte)

AURORA QUARTET
see CONCERT INDEX *under:*
(NAXO) **8 550861** Mendelssohn—String Quartets, Volume 1
(NAXO) **8 550862** Mendelssohn—String Quartets, Volume 2
(NAXO) **8 550863** Mendelssohn—String Quartets, Volume 3
(NAXO) **8 553136** Prokofiev—Chamber Works

AUSENSI, Manuel (bar)
Rossini: Barbiere di Siviglia (Cpte)

AUSTBØ, Haakon (pf)
Messiaen: Vingt regards
see CONCERT INDEX *under:*
(SIMA) **PSC1055** Scriabin—Piano Sonatas, Vol. 1

AUSTIN, Charles (bass-bar)
Puccini: Tosca (Cpte)

AUSTIN, Ivy (sngr)
Gershwin: Lady, be Good! (Cpte)

AUSTIN, Michael (ten)
Hammerstein: Carmen Jones (Cpte)

AUSTIN, Richard (cond)
see Bournemouth Municipal Orch

AUSTIN, Sumner (bar)
see CONCERT INDEX *under:*
(SYMP) **SYMCD1075** May Harrison—Violinist and Composer

AUSTRAL, Florence (sop)
Wagner: Götterdämmerung (exc)
see CONCERT INDEX *under:*
(CLAR) **CDGSE78-50-35/6** Wagner—Historical recordings
(CLAR) **CDGSE78-50-46** Walter Widdop (1892-1949)
(EMI) **CMS7 64008-2(2)** Wagner Singing on Record (pt 2)
(MMOI) **CDMOIR411** Sacred Songs and Arias
(PEAR) **GEMMCDS9137** Wagner—Der Ring des Nibelungen
(PEAR) **GEMMCDS9925(1)** Covent Garden on Record—Vol.3 (pt 1)
(PREI) **89002** Miguel Fleta (1893-1938)
(TEST) **SBT1008** Viva Rossini

AUSTRALIA ENSEMBLE
Mozart: Flute Quartets, Oboe Quartet, K370
Schubert: Hirt auf dem Felsen, D965, String Quintet
see CONCERT INDEX *under:*
(TALL) **TP002** Café Concertino

AUSTRALIAN CHAMBER ORCHESTRA
cond R. HICKOX
see CONCERT INDEX *under:*
(SONY) **SK53351** From Australia
cond S. KOVACEVICH
Beethoven: Grosse Fuge
cond C. MACKERRAS
Haydn: Symphony 80, Symphony 81
Martinů: Sinfonietta giocosa
Suk: Serenade, Op. 6
see CONCERT INDEX *under:*
(CONI) **CDCF210** Martinu—Orchestral Works

AUSTRIAN RADIO CHORUS
see CONCERT INDEX *under:*
(DG) **431 476-2GGA2** Schubert: Lieder
cond G. ALBRECHT
Schoeck: Penthesilea (Cpte)
cond L. GARDELLI
Berlioz: Roméo et Juliette (Cpte)
Verdi: Battaglia di Legnano (Cpte), Due Foscari (Cpte), Stiffelio (Cpte)
cond E. HOWARTH
Ligeti: Grand Macabre (Cpte)
cond E. INBAL
Berlioz: Grande Messe des Morts (Cpte)
cond L. MAAZEL
see CONCERT INDEX *under:*
(SONY) **SX14K48198** Mahler—Complete Symphonies, etc

cond C. MACKERRAS
Handel: Messias, K572 (Cpte)
cond L. ZAGROSEK
Einem: Dantons Tod (Cpte)

AUSTRIAN RADIO SYMPHONY ORCHESTRA
cond G. ALBRECHT
Schoeck: Penthesilea (Cpte)
cond L. GARDELLI
Berlioz: Roméo et Juliette (Cpte)
Verdi: Battaglia di Legnano (Cpte), Due Foscari (Cpte), Stiffelio (Cpte)
cond P. GUTH
see CONCERT INDEX *under:*
(MARC) **8 223226** Johann Strauss II Edition, Vol.26
(MARC) **8 223227** Johann Strauss II Edition, Vol.27
cond E. HOWARTH
Ligeti: Grand Macabre (Cpte)
cond C. MACKERRAS
Delius: Village Romeo and Juliet (Cpte)
Handel: Messias, K572 (Cpte)
cond M. SCHÖNHERR
see CONCERT INDEX *under:*
(CAMB) **CD1066** Korngold in Vienna
cond P. STEINBERG
Bellini: Beatrice di Tenda (Cpte)
Wagner: Fliegende Holländer (Cpte)
see CONCERT INDEX *under:*
(RCA) **09026 68008-2** Kasarova sings Berlioz,Ravel and Chausson
cond L. ZAGROSEK
Einem: Dantons Tod (Cpte)
Martin: Cornet
Schmidt: Buch mit Sieben Siegeln

AUSTRIAN STATE RADIO ORCHESTRA
cond G. KASSOWITZ
see CONCERT INDEX *under:*
(CAMB) **CD-1032** From the Operas of Erich Wolfgang Korngold
cond E. KORNGOLD
see CONCERT INDEX *under:*
(CAMB) **CD-1032** From the Operas of Erich Wolfgang Korngold
cond W. LOIBNER
see CONCERT INDEX *under:*
(CAMB) **CD-1032** From the Operas of Erich Wolfgang Korngold
cond J. STROBL
see CONCERT INDEX *under:*
(CAMB) **CD-1032** From the Operas of Erich Wolfgang Korngold

AUSTRO-HUNGARIAN HAYDN ORCHESTRA
cond A. FISCHER
see CONCERT INDEX *under:*
(NIMB) **NI5179** Haydn—Symphonies
(NIMB) **NI5200/4** Haydn: London Symphonies
(NIMB) **NI5240** Haydn: Symphonies Nos. 6-8
(NIMB) **NI5331** Haydn—Symphonies Nos 14-17
(NIMB) **NI5341** Haydn—Orchestral Works
(NIMB) **NI5392** J & M Haydn—Orchestral Works
(NIMB) **NI5419/20** Haydn—'Paris' Symphonies

AUTENRIETH, Claire (sop)
R. Strauss: Elektra (Cpte)

AUTRAN, Victor (bar)
Gounod: Faust (Cpte)

AUVERGNE ORCHESTRA
Paganini: Violin Concerto 1, Violin Concerto 2
cond L. HAGER
Mozart: Cassation, K63, Serenade, K185, Serenade, K203, Serenade, K204, Serenade, K250
cond J-J. KANTOROW
Canteloube: Chants d'Auvergne (exc)
Tchaikovsky: Serenade, Op. 48, Souvenir de Florence

AVALOS, Francesco d' (cond)
see Hungarian St SO

AVANTI CHAMBER ORCHESTRA
cond J-P. SARASTE
see CONCERT INDEX *under:*
(ONDI) **ODE778-2** Works for Clarinet and Orchestra
(ONDI) **ODE802-2** Ibert/Jolivet/Nielsen—Flute Concertos
cond L. SEGERSTAM
Segerstam: Waiting for ...

AVANTI! QUARTET
see CONCERT INDEX *under:*
(ONDI) **ODE727-2** Crusell: Clarinet Quartets

AVDEYEVA, Larissa (mez)
Tchaikovsky: Eugene Onegin (Cpte)

AVELING, Valda (pf)
see CONCERT INDEX *under:*
(RCA) **09026 61357-2** Leontyne Price Sings Mozart

AVIS, Marjorie (sop)
Delius: Village Romeo and Juliet (Cpte)

AVON COMEDY FOUR
see CONCERT INDEX *under:*
(PEAR) **GEMMCDS9059/61** Music from the New York Stage, Vol. 4: 1917-20

AX, Emanuel (pf)
Beethoven: Cello Sonata 1, Cello Sonata 2, Piano Concerto 4, Piano Concerto 5, Piano Quartet, Op. 16
Chopin: Piano Concerto 1, Piano Concerto 2
Dvořák: Piano Trio 3, Piano Trio 4
Fauré: Piano Quartet 1, Piano Quartet 2

BALDWIN, Dalton (pf)
see CONCERT INDEX under:
(ARAB) **Z6579** Kurt Weill: Songs
(ARAB) **Z6623** Rossini—Songs
(ARCO) **AAOC93232** Mélodies Françaises
(DECC) **440 065-2DM** Schubert/Schumann—Lieder
(EMI) **CDM5 65161-2** Duparc/Chausson—Mélodies
(EMI) **CMS7 64079-2(1)** Fauré—Complete Songs (pt 1)
(EMI) **CMS7 64079-2(2)** Fauré—Complete Songs (pt 2)
(EMI) **CMS7 64095-2** Debussy—Mélodies
(ERAT) **2292-45583-2** Mendelssohn: Lieder
(PHIL) **416 445-2PH** French songs
(PHIL) **438 511-2PM4** Schubert—Lieder
(PHIL) **438 528-2PM4(1)** Schubert—Lieder (pt 1)
(PHIL) **438 528-2PM4(2)** Schubert—Lieder (pt 2)
(PHIL) **438 964-2PM4(1)** Souzay sings French Songs (pt 1)
(PHIL) **438 964-2PM4(2)** Souzay sings French Songs (pt 2)
(PHIL) **442 272-2PM2** The Best of Bizet
(PHIL) **442 744-2PM2** Wolf/R.Strauss—Lieder
(SCHW) **310942** Steven Kimbrough—Lieder Recital

BALDWIN, Marcia (mez)
Bizet: Carmen (Cpte)

BALDY, Colin (bar)
Lampe: Pyramus and Thisbe (Cpte)

BALET, Bernard (perc)
see CONCERT INDEX under:
(ERAT) **4509-91721-2** Dutilleux—Piano Works and Chamber Music

BALEY, Virko (cond)
see Young Russia State SO

BALFOUR, Margaret (contr)
see CONCERT INDEX under:
(DUTT) **CDAX8004** Sir Henry Wood conducts Vaughan Williams
(EMI) **CDS7 54560-2** The Elgar Edition, Vol.1
(EMI) **CDS7 54564-2** The Elgar Edition, Vol.2
(PEAR) **GEMMCD9342** Vaughan Williams: Vocal Works

BÁLINT, János (fl)
see CONCERT INDEX under:
(NAXO) **8 550741** Romantic Music for Flute and Harp

BALL, Andrew (pf)
see CONCERT INDEX under:
(HYPE) **CDA66749** Tippett—Songs and Purcell Realisations
(MARC) **8 223514** Mayerl—Orchestral Works

BALL, Michael (sngr)
Bernstein: West Side Story (Cpte)

BALLARD, Jeremy (vn)
see CONCERT INDEX under:
(HYPE) **CDA66271/2** Elgar:The Complete Choral Songs

BALLER, Adolf (pf)
see CONCERT INDEX under:
(EMI) **CHS7 64741-2(2)** Record of Singing, Vol.4—Anglo-American School (pt 2)

BALLEYS, Brigitte (contr)
Berlioz: Nuits d'été
Janáček: Diary of One who Disappeared
Massenet: Chérubin (Cpte)
Schubert: Fierrabras (Cpte)
Vivaldi: Montezuma (Cpte)
Zelenka: Requiem in C
see CONCERT INDEX under:
(DECC) **436 567-2DH** Berg—Orchestral and Vocal Works
(DG) **423 103-2GH** Debussy: Vocal & Orchestral Works
(ERAT) **4509-95307-2** Schubert/Schumann—Sacred Choral Works

BALLI, Heinz (organ)
see CONCERT INDEX under:
(DENO) **C37-7068** Organ Concert at St. Nikolaus Church, Frauenfeld, Switzerland

BALLISTA, Antonio (pf)
Liszt: Symphony 9 (Beethoven), S657

BALLO, Pietro (ten)
Stravinsky: Pulcinella (Cpte)

BALMAIN, Ian (tpt)
Haydn: Trumpet Concerto

BALMER, Christopher (va)
Vaughan Williams: Flos Campi
see CONCERT INDEX under:
(EMIN) **CDBOX-VW1** Vaughan Williams—Symphonies Nos 1-9, etc

BALOGH, Attila (cond)
see Amati Ens

BALOGH, Ferenc (vn)
Bartók: Duos, Sz298
Sterndale Bennett: Piano Sextet, Op. 8
see CONCERT INDEX under:
(MARC) **8 223405** Atterberg—Chamber Works

BALOGH, József (basset-hn)
see CONCERT INDEX under:
(NAXO) **8 550390** Mozart—Chamber Works for Clarinet

BALOGH, József (cl)
Brahms: Clarinet Quintet, Clarinet Trio
see CONCERT INDEX under:
(NAXO) **8 550390** Mozart—Chamber Works for Clarinet
(NAXO) **8 550439** Mozart—Works for Clarinet
(NAXO) **8 553090** Beethoven—Chamber Works

BALSAM, Artur (pf)
Dvořák: Slavonic Dances
see CONCERT INDEX under:
(BIDD) **LAB046** The Young Yehudi Menuhin
(BIDD) **LAB063** Nathan Milstein - American Columbia Recordings
(EMI) **ZDMF7 64830-2** The Art of Nathan Milstein
(MUSI) **MACD-620** 20th Century French Violin Works
(RCA) **GD60325** Brahms: Symphonies & Other Works
(TEST) **SBT1003** The Young Menuhin—Encores, Vol.1

BALSBORG, Oda (sop)
Wagner: Rheingold (Cpte)
see CONCERT INDEX under:
(DECC) **414 100-2DM15** Wagner: Der Ring des Nibelungen

BALSLEV, Lisbeth (sop)
Wagner: Fliegende Holländer (Cpte)

BALTHROP, Carmen (voc)
Joplin: Treemonisha (Cpte)

BALTIC PHILHARMONIC SYMPHONY ORCHESTRA
cond W. RAJSKI
Chopin: Piano Concerto 1
J. Wieniawski: Piano Concerto, Op. 20

(THE) BALTIMORE CONSORT
see CONCERT INDEX under:
(DORI) **DOR90177** La Rocque 'n' Roll

BALTIMORE SYMPHONY CHORUS
cond D. ZINMAN
see CONCERT INDEX under:
(TELA) **CD80164** Berlioz—Orchestral Works

BALTIMORE SYMPHONY ORCHESTRA
cond D. ZINMAN
Elgar: Pomp and Circumstance Marches (exc), Symphony 1
Rachmaninov: Paganini Rhapsody, Songs, Op.34 (exc), Symphonic Dances, Symphony 2, Symphony 3
Schumann: Symphony 1, Symphony 2, Symphony 3, Symphony 4
Tchaikovsky: Piano Concerto 1, Romeo and Juliet, Symphony 4
see CONCERT INDEX under:
(ARGO) **433 071-2ZH** Michael Torke—Orchestral Works
(ARGO) **436 288-2ZH** Barber—Orchestral Works
(ARGO) **440 639-2ZH** Copland—Orchestral Works
(ARGO) **440 454-2ZH** Dance Mix
(SONY) **SK57961** The New York Album
(TELA) **CD80164** Berlioz—Orchestral Works
(TELA) **CD80192** Elgar: Orchestral Works
(TELA) **CD80204** Stravinsky—Ballet Music
(TELA) **CD80271** Berlioz—Orchestral Works
(TELA) **CD80378** Russian Sketches

BALTSA, Agnes (mez)
Beethoven: Missa Solemnis, Symphony 9
Bellini: Capuleti (Cpte)
Bizet: Carmen (exc)
Donizetti: Campanello di notte (Cpte), Maria Stuarda (Cpte)
Gluck: Orfeo ed Euridice (Cpte)
J. Strauss II: Fledermaus (Cpte)
Mahler: Lied von der Erde, Symphony 8
Mascagni: Cavalleria rusticana (Cpte)
Mozart: Ascanio in Alba (Cpte), Don Giovanni (Cpte), Idomeneo (Cpte), Mass, K317, Minuets (Cpte), Nozze di Figaro (Cpte), Requiem, Zauberflöte (exc)
Ponchielli: Gioconda (Cpte)
R. Strauss: Ariadne auf Naxos (Cpte), Rosenkavalier (exc), Salome (Cpte)
Rossini: Barbiere di Siviglia (Cpte), Cenerentola (Cpte), Italiana in Algeri (Cpte), Stabat Mater
Saint-Saëns: Samson et Dalila (Cpte)
Verdi: Aida (Cpte), Don Carlo (Cpte), Forza del destino (Cpte), Requiem (Cpte)
Wagner: Tannhäuser (Cpte)
see CONCERT INDEX under:
(DECC) **430 724-2DM** Great Operatic Duets
(DECC) **436 462-2DM** Ten Top Mezzos
(DG) **419 236-2GH** Songs my country taught me
(DG) **435 162-2GX13** Mahler—Complete Symphonies
(EMIL) **CDZ7 67015-2** Mozart—Opera Arias
(SONY) **SX14K48198** Mahler—Complete Symphonies, etc

BALTZER, Erwin (cond)
see Vienna St Op Orch

BAMBER, Peter (ten)
G. Charpentier: Louise (Cpte)
see CONCERT INDEX under:
(L'OI) **425 893-2OM6(1)** Purcell—Theatre Music (Part 1)
(L'OI) **425 893-2OM6(2)** Purcell—Theatre Music (Part 2)

BAMBERG QUARTET
Pergolesi: Orfeo, Stabat Mater

BAMBERG SYMPHONY CHORUS
cond C.P. FLOR
Mendelssohn: Midsummer Night's Dream (exc), Symphony 2
cond M.A. GÓMEZ-MARTÍNEZ
Donizetti: Messa da Requiem
cond G. KUHN
Schumann: Paradies und die Peri (Cpte)

BAMBERG SYMPHONY ORCHESTRA
cond R. ABBADO
see CONCERT INDEX under:
(RCA) **RD60953** Liszt—Works for Piano and Orchestra
cond W.A. ALBERT
see CONCERT INDEX under:
(CPO) **CPO999 079-2** Pfitzner—Violin Concerto, etc
(CPO) **CPO999 080-2** Pfitzner—Symphonies, etc
(CPO) **CPO999 135-2** Pfitzner—Cello Concertos
(CPO) **CPO999 136-2** Pfitzner—Orchestral Works
cond A. DE ALMEIDA
see CONCERT INDEX under:
(RCA) **RD60895** Turina—Orchestral Works
cond O. CAETANI
Rachmaninov: Symphony 3
see CONCERT INDEX under:
(ORFE) **C067831A** Weber: Music for Clarinet and Orchestra
cond D. R. DAVIES
Hindemith: Cello Concerto
Schumann: Cello Concerto
cond C.P. FLOR
Mendelssohn: Midsummer Night's Dream (exc), Symphony 2, Violin Concerto, Op. 64, Violin Concerto (1822)
Mozart: Piano Concerto 20, Piano Concerto 21, Piano Concerto 22, Piano Concerto 23, Piano Concerto 24, Piano Concerto 27
see CONCERT INDEX under:
(RCA) **RD87905** Mendelssohn—Overtures
(RCA) **RD87988** Mendelssohn: Works for Piano & Orchestra
cond H. GIERSTER
see CONCERT INDEX under:
(DG) **431 110-2GB** Great Voices - Fritz Wunderlich
cond M.A. GÓMEZ-MARTÍNEZ
Donizetti: Messa da Requiem
cond T. GUSCHLBAUER
see CONCERT INDEX under:
(ERAT) **2292-45937-2** Mozart—Wind Concertos
(ERAT) **4509-95361-2** Mozart—Wind Concertos
cond J. HORENSTEIN
Mahler: Kindertotenlieder
cond N. JÄRVI
Dvořák: Legends
Glazunov: Concert Waltz 1, Concert Waltz 2, Lyric Poem, Op.12, Symphony 2, Symphony 3, Symphony 4, Symphony 6, Symphony 7
Janáček: Sinfonietta
Martinů: Symphony 1, Symphony 2, Symphony 3, Symphony 4, Symphony 5, Symphony 6
Tubin: Kratt, Symphony 5
see CONCERT INDEX under:
(BIS) **BIS-CD434** Pärt: Orchestral Works
cond E. JOCHUM
Mozart: Maurerische Trauermusik, K477, Symphony 39, Symphony 40, Symphony 41
see CONCERT INDEX under:
(RCA) **74321 17888-2** Mozart—Orchestral Works
cond O. KAMU
see CONCERT INDEX under:
(DG) **413 844-2GW2** 19th Century Violin Works
cond R. KRAUS
see CONCERT INDEX under:
(DG) **413 158-2GW2** Grieg/Sibelius—Orchestral Works
cond G. KUHN
Schumann: Paradies und die Peri (Cpte)
cond F. LEITNER
Mozart: Piano Concerto 23, Piano Concerto 24
see CONCERT INDEX under:
(DG) **439 699-2GX2** Mozart—Piano Concertos
cond I. METZMACHER
Ives: Robert Browning Overture
K. A. Hartmann: Symphony 3
cond U. MUND
Suder: Kleider machen Leute (Cpte)
cond J. PERLEA
see CONCERT INDEX under:
(VOX) **CDX2 5502** Cassadó performs Cello Masterpieces
cond F. PROHASKA
see CONCERT INDEX under:
(DG) **413 850-2GW2** Rachmaninov/Liszt—Piano Concertos
cond K.A. RICKENBACHER
(SCHW) **311972** Humperdinck—Orchestral Works
(SCHW) **312952** Hartmann—Orchestral and Vocal Works
(VIRG) **CUV5 61128-2** Humperdinck—Fairy-tale Music
cond A. ROTHER
see CONCERT INDEX under:
(FINL) **4509-95606-2** Kim Borg - Songs and Arias
cond H. STEIN
R. Strauss: Alpensinfonie
Reger: Ballettsuite, Hiller Variations, Konzert im alten Stil, Sinfonietta, Op. 90
cond C. STEPP
see CONCERT INDEX under:

(DG) **437 677-2GDO2** Irmgard Seefried - Opera
Recital
  cond H. WALLBERG
Brahms: Double Concerto
  cond L. ZAGROSEK
Bruckner: String Quintet
Schoenberg: Verklärte Nacht
  see CONCERT INDEX *under:*
(SCHW) **311065** Double Concertos

BAMBINI DI PRAGA
  cond M. KLEMENS
  see CONCERT INDEX *under:*
(ROMA) **RR1941** Terezín - The Music 1941-44

BAMERT, Matthias (cond)
  see BBC PO

BAMPTON, Rose (sop)
Beethoven: Fidelio (Cpte)
  see CONCERT INDEX *under:*
(EMI) **CHS7 69741-2(1)** Record of Singing,
Vol.4—Anglo-American School (pt 1)
(RCA) **GD87808** Lawrence Tibbett sings Opera
Arias
(RCA) **09026 61580-2(4)** RCA/Met 100 Singers, 100
Years (pt 4)
(VAI) **VAIA1017** Leonard Warren—Early Recordings

BANAUDI, Antonella (sop)
Verdi: Trovatore (Cpte)

BANCHETTO MUSICALE CHORUS
Haydn: Mass 11

BANCHETTO MUSICALE ORCHESTRA
Haydn: Mass 11

BANCHINI, Chiara (cond)
  see Ens 415

BANCHINI, Chiara (vn)
Corelli: Sonatas, Op. 5 (exc)
Leclair: Violin Sonatas, Op. 3
Telemann: Musique de Table (exc)
Zelenka: Trio Sonatas
  see CONCERT INDEX *under:*
(HARM) **HMC90 1466/7** Mozart—Violin Sonatas,
Vol.1: Palatine Sonatas
(HARM) **HMC90 1468/9** Mozart—Violin Sonatas,
Vol.2
(HARM) **HMC90 1470** Mozart—Violin Sonatas, Vol.3

BANCHINI, Chiara (vn/dir)
Corelli: Concerti Grossi, Op.6
  see CONCERT INDEX *under:*
(HARM) **HMA190 1245** G.B. & G.
Sammartini—Concerti & Sinfonie

BANCROFT SCHOOL BOYS' CHOIR
  cond H. VON KARAJAN
R. Strauss: Rosenkavalier (Cpte)

BANCROFT'S SCHOOL CHORUS
  cond H. VON KARAJAN
Humperdinck: Hänsel und Gretel (Cpte)

BAND OF THE BLUES AND ROYALS
  cond E. W. JEANES
  see CONCERT INDEX *under:*
(CHAN) **CHAN6517** Invincible Eagle—Famous Sousa
Marches

BANDERA, Claudia Nicole (mez)
Puccini: Manon Lescaut (Cpte)

BANDITELLI, Gloria (contr)
A. Scarlatti: Maddalena (Cpte)
Handel: Agrippina (Cpte), Poro (Cpte)
Mozart: Betulia Liberata (Cpte)
Rossini: Barbiere di Siviglia (Cpte), Cenerentola
(Cpte)
Verdi: Vespri siciliani (Cpte)

BÁNFALVI, Béla (vn)
Boëllmann: Piano Quartet, Op. 10, Piano Trio, Op.
19
Pierné: Piano Trio, Op.45

BANFIELD, Volker (pf)
Busoni: Piano Concerto, Op.39

BANIA, Maria (fl)
  see CONCERT INDEX *under:*
(CHAN) **CHAN0535** Baroque Flute Concertos

BANIEWICZ, Wiera (contr)
Mascagni: Cavalleria rusticana (Cpte)
Mussorgsky: Boris Godunov (Cpte)
Puccini: Gianni Schicchi (Cpte)
  see CONCERT INDEX *under:*
(EURO) **GD69043** Puccini: Il Trittico

BANKS, Anna Victoria (mez)
Paisiello: Serva Padrona (Cpte)

BANKS, Barry (ten)
Cavalli: Calisto (Cpte)
Puccini: Bohème (Cpte)
Verdi: Rigoletto (Cpte), Traviata (Cpte)

BANKS-MARTIN, George (bass)
Purcell: Fairy Queen, Z629 (Cpte)

BANNATYNE-SCOTT, Brian (bass)
Purcell: Dioclesian, Z627 (Cpte), King Arthur, Z628
(Cpte), Timon of Athens, Z632 (Cpte)
Smyth: Wreckers (Cpte)

BANOWETZ, Joseph (pf)
Balakirev: Mazurkas, Scherzi
Liszt: Piano Concerto 1

Rubinstein: Caprice russe, Op. 102, Piano Concerto
1, Piano Concerto 2, Piano Concerto 5, Soirées
musicales

BANSE, Juliane (sop)
  see CONCERT INDEX *under:*
(JECK) **JD677-2** Schoeck—Complete Lieder, Vol.7
(SCHW) **312592** Dvořák/Brahms/Reger—Duets

BANTZER, Christoph (narr)
Mendelssohn: Midsummer Night's Dream (exc)

BAÑUELAS, Roberto (bar)
Beethoven: Symphony 9

BAÑUELAS, Roberto (ten)
Wagner: Meistersinger (Cpte)

BANZO, Eduardo Lopez (cond)
  see Al Ayre Español

BAQUERIZO, Enrique (bass)
Bretón: Verbena de La Paloma (Cpte)

BÄR, Olaf (bar)
Bach: Christmas Oratorio, BWV248 (Cpte), St
Matthew Passion, BWV244 (Cpte)
Brahms: Deutsches Requiem, Op.45 (Cpte)
Duruflé: Requiem
Fauré: Requiem (Cpte)
J. Strauss II: Fledermaus (Cpte)
Mozart: Zauberflöte (Cpte)
R. Strauss: Ariadne auf Naxos (Cpte)
Schubert: Schöne Müllerin (Cpte), Winterreise
(Cpte)
Schumann: Dichterliebe, Op. 48 (Cpte), Gedichte,
Op. 35 (Cpte), Liederkreis, Op. 24 (Cpte), Liederkreis,
Op. 39 (Cpte)
Wolf: Spanisches Liederbuch (Cpte)
  see CONCERT INDEX *under:*
(ARCH) **437 327-2AH** Bach—Cantatas
(EMI) **CDC5 55345-2** Liebeslieder
(EMI) **CDC5 55430-2** Brahms/Schumann—Lieder
(EMI) **CDC7 49997-2** Schubert—Lieder
(EMI) **CDC7 54453-2** Bach—Cantatas
(EMI) **CDC7 54879-2** Beethoven—Lieder
(PHIL) **438 873-2PH2** Bach—Magnificat and Masses

BARABAS, Sari (sop)
Rossini: Comte Ory (Cpte)
  see CONCERT INDEX *under:*
(EMI) **CDH5 65072-2** Glyndebourne Recorded - 1934-
1994

BARABINI, Olga (pf)
  see CONCERT INDEX *under:*
(BIDD) **WHL012** Stokowski conducts French Music,
Vol.2

BARACCHI, Aristide (bar)
Puccini: Bohème (Cpte)
  see CONCERT INDEX *under:*
(EMI) **CHS7 64864-2(1)** La Scala Edition - Vol.2,
1915-46 (pt 1)
(PREI) **89023** Conchita Supervia (1895-1936)

BARANTSCHIK, Alexander (vn)
  see CONCERT INDEX *under:*
(EMI) **CDC5 55398-2** Britten—Chamber Works
(EMI) **CDC5 55399-2** Delius—Chamber Works

BÁRÁNY, Pál László (bar)
Respighi: Belfagor (Cpte)

BARANYI, László (bn)
  see CONCERT INDEX *under:*
(DECC) **425 935-2DM4** Haydn—Symphonies, Vol.8
(DECC) **430 100-2DM32(2)** Haydn—Complete
Symphonies (Volumes 5-8)

BARATTI, Giuseppe (ten)
Bellini: Pirata (Cpte)
Donizetti: Lucrezia Borgia (Cpte)
  see CONCERT INDEX *under:*
(EMI) **CDM7 69500-2** Montserrat Caballé sings Bellini
& Verdi Arias

BARATTI, Walter (treb)
Puccini: Tosca (Cpte)

BARBACINI, Paolo (ten)
Donizetti: Ajo nell'imbarazzo (Cpte)
Paisiello: Don Chisciotte (Cpte)
Rossini: Barbiere di Siviglia (Cpte), Pietra del
paragone (Cpte), Turco in Italia (Cpte)
Verdi: Falstaff (Cpte), Vespri siciliani (Cpte)

BARBAGALLO, James (pf)
  see CONCERT INDEX *under:*
(MARC) **8 223631** Macdowell—Piano Works, Vol.1

BARBAUX, Christine (sop)
Bizet: Carmen (Cpte)
Debussy: Pelléas et Mélisande (Cpte)
Fauré: Pénélope (Cpte)
Honegger: Aventures du Roi Pausole (Cpte)
Massenet: Werther (Cpte)
Mozart: Clemenza di Tito (Cpte), Lucio Silla (Cpte),
Nozze di Figaro (Cpte)
  see CONCERT INDEX *under:*
(EMI) **CDM7 64687-2** French Works inspired by Edgar
Allan Poe

BARBER, Graham (organ)
  see CONCERT INDEX *under:*
(ASV) **CDGAU120** Bach—Early Organ Works, Vol 1
(ASV) **CDGAU123** Bach—Early Organ Works, Vol 2
(ASV) **CDGAU125** Krebs—Organ works in the style of
Bach
(PRIO) **PRCD269** Great European Organs, No. 13
(PRIO) **PRCD297** Great European Organs, Vol.20

(PRIO) **PRCD314** Great European Organs No 23
(PRIO) **PRCD315** Great European Organs No 30
(PRIO) **PRCD373** Great European Organs No 25
(PRIO) **PRCD391** Great European Organs, No 27

BARBER, Kimberley (sop)
Delius: Village Romeo and Juliet (Cpte)

BARBER, Sally (sop)
  see CONCERT INDEX *under:*
(UNIT) **88003-2** Howells/F. Martin—Choral Works

BARBER, Samuel (pf)
  see CONCERT INDEX *under:*
(RCA) **09026 61983-2** Leontyne Price sings Barber
(SONY) **MPK46727** Barber—Vocal Works
(SONY) **SM3K46291** Stravinsky—Ballets, Vol.1

BARBER, Timothy (treb)
  see CONCERT INDEX *under:*
(ARGO) **430 836-2ZH** English Sacred Choral Music

BARBESI, Attilio (bass)
Verdi: Macbeth (Cpte)

BARBICAN PIANO TRIO
  see CONCERT INDEX *under:*
(ASV) **CDDCA899** Lalo—Piano Trios

BARBIER, Jean-Claude (bar)
Massenet: Don Quichotte (Cpte)

BARBIERI, Fedora (mez)
Donizetti: Linda di Chamounix (Cpte)
Mascagni: Cavalleria Rusticana (Cpte)
Verdi: Aida (Cpte), Ballo in maschera (Cpte), Falstaff
(Cpte), Trovatore (Cpte)
  see CONCERT INDEX *under:*
(EMI) **CHS7 69741-2(7)** Record of Singing,
Vol.4—Italian School
(EMI) **CMS7 64165-2** Puccini—Trittico
(RCA) **GD60326** Verdi—Operas & Choral Works

BARBIROLLI, Sir John (cond)
  see Barbirolli CO

BARBIROLLI CHAMBER ORCHESTRA
  cond J. BARBIROLLI
  see CONCERT INDEX *under:*
(KOCH) **37077-2** The Young John Barbirolli

BARBIROLLI SYMPHONY ORCHESTRA
  cond J. BARBIROLLI
  see CONCERT INDEX *under:*
(KOCH) **37077-2** The Young John Barbirolli

BARBIZET, Pierre (pf)
Brahms: Violin Sonata 1
  see CONCERT INDEX *under:*
(EMI) **CDM7 64365-2** Chausson—Chamber,
Orchestra & Vocal Works

BARBOSA, Airton (bn)
  see CONCERT INDEX *under:*
(CHNT) **LDC278 835** Villa-Lobos—Chôros for
Chamber Ensembles

BĂRBUCEANU, Valeriu (cl)
Enescu: Wind Decet, Op. 14

BARCELONA PATRONATO ORCHESTRA
  cond A. ROS-MARBÀ
  see CONCERT INDEX *under:*
(EMI) **CMS5 65061-2(1)** The Fabulous Victoria de los
Angeles (pt 1)

BARCELONA PAU CASALS ORCHESTRA
  cond A. CORTOT
  see CONCERT INDEX *under:*
(EMI) **CHS7 64057-2** Cortot-Thibaud-Casals
Trio—Historic Recordings
(KOCH) **37705-2** Alfred Cortot as Conductor

BARCELONA TRIO
Beethoven: Piano Trios (exc)
Dvořák: Piano Trio 3, Piano Trio 4
  cond E. COLOMER
Beethoven: Triple Concerto

BARCLAY, Yvonne (sop)
  see CONCERT INDEX *under:*
(HYPE) **CDA66608** Dibdin—Three Operas

BARDACH, Nicholas (timp)
  see CONCERT INDEX *under:*
(SCHW) **311052** Virtuoso Kettledrum Concertos

BARDON, Claude (cond)
  see Monte Carlo PO

BARDON, Patricia (mez)
Tchaikovsky: Eugene Onegin (Cpte)
Verdi: Rigoletto (Cpte)
  see CONCERT INDEX *under:*
(ASV) **CDDCA758** Falla, Milhaud &
Stravinsky—Operas

BARDON, Pierre (organ)
Daquin: Nouveau livre de Noëls
  see CONCERT INDEX *under:*
(PIER) **PV79801** Vivaldi—Organ Concertos
(PIER) **PV784011** Organists of the Sun King
(PIER) **PV785051/2** French 17th and 18th Century
Organ Works

BARDOT, Francis (ten)
Haydn: Mass 11

BARENBOIM, Daniel (cond)
  see Bayreuth Fest Orch

BARENBOIM, Daniel (pf)
Bach: Goldberg Variations

Beethoven: Allegretto, Hess48, Choral Fantasia,
Diabelli Variations, Piano and Wind Quintet, Op. 16,
Piano Trios (exc)
Brahms: Piano Concerto 1, Violin Sonata 1
Chopin: Cello Sonata, Nocturnes (exc)
Franck: Violin Sonata
Liszt: Années de pèlerinage 2 (exc)
Mozart: Piano and Wind Quintet, K452, Violin Sonata,
K526, Violin Sonata, K547
Schubert: Impromptus (exc), Piano Sonata, D960,
Winterreise (Cpte)
see CONCERT INDEX under:
(DECC) **425 088-2DM** Mozart—Piano Concertos, Vol.
1
(DECC) **425 090-2DM** Mozart—Piano Concertos, Vol.
3
(DECC) **430 232-2DH** Mozart: Piano Concertos
(DG) **413 311-2GH** Brahms: Lieder
(DG) **413 759-2GX6** Beethoven: Piano Sonatas, Vol.1
(DG) **413 766-2GX6** Beethoven: Piano Sonatas, Vol.2
(DG) **415 118-2GH** Romantic piano works
(DG) **419 602-2GH** Beethoven—Piano Sonatas 8, 14
& 23
(DG) **427 803-2GDC** Beethoven: Piano Sonatas
(DG) **431 167-2GR** Schumann—Piano Works
(DG) **431 784-2GX4** Mozart—Violin Sonatas
(DG) **435 072-2GGA** Schubert—Piano Works
(DG) **435 591-2GGA** Liszt—Piano Works
(DG) **437 248-2GGA** Brahms—Viola Sonatas
(DG) **437 470-2GX2** Mendelssohn—Songs without
words
(DG) **439 975-2GGA2** Wolf—Lieder
(DG) **447 405-2GOR** Berg/Stravinsky—Chamber
Works
(EMI) **CDC7 47657-2** Mahler—Lieder
(EMI) **CDM7 63537-2** Brahms: Orchestral Works
(EMI) **CDM7 64626-2** Schumann—Concertos, etc
(EMI) **CDM7 64631-2** Beethoven—Violin Sonatas
(EMI) **CDS7 54362-2** Mozart—Complete Variations for
Piano Solo
(EMI) **CMS7 63015-2** Beethoven—Cello Sonatas, etc
(EMI) **CMS7 63360-2** Beethoven: Complete Piano
Concertos
(EMI) **CMS7 69707-2** Impressions of Jacqueline du
Pré
(EMI) **CZS5 68132-2** Les introuvables de Jacqueline
du Pré
(EMI) **CZS7 62863-2** Beethoven—Piano Sonatas
(EMI) **CZS7 67294-2** Mozart—Piano Concertos
(EMI) **CZS7 67521-2** Schumann—Concertos
(SONY) **SK45819** Brahms: Violin Sonatas
(SONY) **SMK48466** Boulez conducts
Schoenberg—Volume 3
(TELD) **4509-98256-2** Schoenberg—Piano and
Orchestral Pieces

BARENBOIM, Daniel (pf/dir)
Beethoven: Choral Fantasia, Piano Concerto, Op.61,
Triple Concerto
Mozart: Piano Concerto 9, Piano Concerto 17, Piano
Concerto 20, Piano Concerto 21, Piano Concerto 22,
Piano Concerto 23, Piano Concerto 24, Piano
Concerto 27
see CONCERT INDEX under:
(DECC) **425 044-2DM** Mozart—Works for Piano and
Orchestra
(EMI) **CDM7 69124-2** Mozart—Piano Concertos
(EMI) **CDS7 47974-8** Beethoven—Piano Concertos
(EMI) **CZS7 62825-2** Mozart—Complete Piano
Concertos
(LOND) **443 727-2LC10** Mozart—The Piano
Concertos
(TELD) **4509-90674-2** Mozart—Piano Concertos, etc

BARERE, Simon (pf)
see CONCERT INDEX under:
(APR) **APR7001** Simon Barere—Complete HMV
Recordings, 1934-36
(APR) **APR7007** Simon Barere at Carnegie Hall,
Vol.1
(APR) **APR7008** Simon Barere at Carnegie Hall,
Vol.2
(APR) **APR7009** Simon Barere at Carnegie Hall,
Vol.3
(APR) **APR7014** Romantic Piano Rarities, Vol.2

BAREVA, Rumiana (sop)
Tchaikovsky: Queen of Spades (Cpte)

BARFORD, Imogen (hp)
see CONCERT INDEX under:
(HYPE) **CDA66144** The Garden of Zephirus

BARHAM, Edmund (ten)
Forrest/Wright: Kismet (Cpte), Timbuktu (exc)
Mozart: Zauberflöte (Cpte)
Rossini: Petite Messe Solennelle
Verdi: Requiem (Cpte)
see CONCERT INDEX under:
(CARL) **MCD15** Opera Spectacular

BARIKOVA, L'uba (contr)
Suchoň: Whirlpool (Cpte)

BARILE, Claudio (fl)
see CONCERT INDEX under:
(DORI) **DOR90202** Impressions—Camerata
Bariloche

BARILI, Alfredo (pf)
see CONCERT INDEX under:
(EMI) **CHS7 64860-2(1)** La Scala Edition - Vol.1,
1878-1914 (pt 1)
(NIMB) **NI7802** Divas 1906-1935
(NIMB) **NI7840/1** The Era of Adelina Patti

(PEAR) **GEMMCDS9923(1)** Covent Garden on
Record, Vol.1 (pt 1)
(PEAR) **GEMMCD9312** Adelina Patti

BARIONI, Daniele (ten)
Puccini: Rondine (Cpte)
see CONCERT INDEX under:
(RCA) **09026 61236-2** Leontyne Price - Prima Donna
Collection

BARKEL, Charles (vn)
see CONCERT INDEX under:
(CPRI) **CAP21510** Rosenberg plays Rosenberg

BARKER, Edwin (db)
see CONCERT INDEX under:
(NORT) **NR248-CD** Silenced Voices - Victims of the
Holocaust

BARKER, John (cond)
see ROHO

BARLEY, Peter (organ)
see CONCERT INDEX under:
(ARGO) **430 205-2ZH** Howells—Sacred Choral Works
(ARGO) **433 215-2ZH** Britten—Christmas Music

BARLOW, Alison (sop)
Vaughan Williams: Symphony 3
see CONCERT INDEX under:
(EMIN) **CDBOX-VW1** Vaughan
Williams—Symphonies Nos 1-9, etc

BARLOW, Howard (cond)
see orch

BARLOW, Jeremy (cond)
see Broadside Band

BARNABEE, Henry Clay (sngr)
see CONCERT INDEX under:
(PEAR) **GEMMCDS9050/2(1)** Music from the New
York Stage, Vol. 1 (part 1)

BARNES, Rosemary (pf)
see CONCERT INDEX under:
(CNTI) **CCD1046** Bax—Songs

BARNETT, Christopher (cond)
see Wenhaston Boys' Ch

BARONE, Clement (fl)
see CONCERT INDEX under:
(SUPR) **11 2136-2(5)** Emmy Destinn—Complete
Edition, Discs 11 & 12

BARONI, Enrico (ten)
see CONCERT INDEX under:
(PEAR) **GEMMCDS9074/2(2)** Giovanni Zenatello, Vol.2
(pt 2)

BARONTI, Duilio (bass)
Puccini: Bohème (Cpte)

BAROQUE BRASS OF LONDON
cond D. HILL
see CONCERT INDEX under:
(ARGO) **436 833-2ZH** Purcell—Music for the Funeral
of Queen Mary

BAROQUE INSTRUMENTAL ENSEMBLE
cond F. BRÜGGEN
Bach: Cantata 56, Cantata 82
see CONCERT INDEX under:
(TELD) **9031-77608-2** Purcell—Anthems,Instrumental
Music & Songs

BAROQUE PLAYERS
see CONCERT INDEX under:
(VANG) **08.2003.72** Purcell—Celebrated
Songs,Sacred Airs and Concert Pieces

BAROQUE 1994 ENSEMBLE
cond R. VÁLEK
Zelenka: Miserere, ZWV57, Requiem, ZWV48

BAROVÁ, Anna (contr)
Dvořák: Kate and the Devil (Cpte)
Fibich: Šárka (Cpte)
Janáček: Jenufa (Cpte)
Martinů: Miracles of Mary (Cpte)
see CONCERT INDEX under:
(SUPR) **11 1878-2** The Unknown Janáček

BAROWSKI, Nikolai (sngr)
S. Wagner: Bärenhäuter (Cpte)

BARRA, Donald (cond)
see Moscow PO

BARRARD, Marc (bar)
Gounod: Faust (Cpte)
Ravel: Enfant et les sortilèges (Cpte)

BARRATT, Harry (bar)
see CONCERT INDEX under:
(PEAR) **GEMMCDS9951/5** The Elgar
Edition—Acoustic Recordings 1914-25

BARRATT DUE, Mary (pf)
see CONCERT INDEX under:
(SIMA) **PSC1809(2)** Grieg—Historical Piano
Recordings (pt 2)

BARRAULT, Jean-Louis (narr)
see CONCERT INDEX under:
(SONY) **SM3K64103** Berlioz—Orchestral and Vocal
Works

BARRELL, David (bar)
Verdi: Traviata (Cpte)

BARRETT, Brent (sngr)
F. Loewe: Brigadoon (Cpte)

Gershwin: Strike Up the Band I (Cpte), Strike Up the
Band II
see CONCERT INDEX under:
(EMI) **CDC5 55189-2** The Busby Berkeley Album
(EMI) **CDC7 54586-2** Broadway Showstoppers

BARRETT, David (bar)
Verdi: Ballo in maschera (Cpte)

BARRETT, Michael (cond)
see Brooklyn PO

BARRETT, Michael (pf)
see CONCERT INDEX under:
(KOCH) **37000-2** Bernstein—Songs & Duets

BARRETT, Toby (bass)
Sullivan: Gondoliers (Cpte)

BARRICK, David (bass)
see CONCERT INDEX under:
(PHIL) **442 534-2PH** Janáček—Choral Works

BARRIENTOS, Maria (sop)
see CONCERT INDEX under:
(EMI) **CDC7 54836-2** Granados/Falla/Mompou/Nin
(MEMO) **HR4408/9(2)** Singers in Genoa, Vol.1 (disc
2)
(PEAR) **GEMMCDS9073(1)** Giovanni Zenatello, Vol.1
(pt 1)
(SIMA) **PSC1810(1)** Grieg—Songs (historical
recordings, pt 1)
(SYMP) **SYMCD1113** The Harold Wayne Collection,
Vol.13
(SYMP) **SYMCD1168** The Harold Wayne Collection,
Vol.19
(TEST) **SBT1008** Viva Rossini

BARRIO, Amalia (sngr)
Penella: Gato Montés (Cpte)

BARRITT, Paul (vn)
see CONCERT INDEX under:
(DELO) **DE3186** Heigh Ho! Mozart
(HYPE) **CDA66665** Howells—Music for Violin and
Piano
(MERI) **CDE84169** Mozart: Clarinet Works

BARROW, John (bar)
see CONCERT INDEX under:
(EMI) **CDM7 64131-2** Orchestral Music for Christmas

BARROWS, Robert (organ)
see CONCERT INDEX under:
(NEWP) **NC60021** Praetorius—Chorale Settings

BARRUECO, Manuel (gtr)
see CONCERT INDEX under:
(EMI) **CDC7 49980-2** Manuel Barrueco plays Bach
and De Visée
(EMI) **CDC7 54382-2** Albéniz/Turina—Works for
Guitar

BARRY, Elaine (sop)
see CONCERT INDEX under:
(UNIC) **UKCD2010** Knussen—Orchestral & Vocal
Works

BARRY, John (cond)
see OST

BARRY, Katie (sngr)
see CONCERT INDEX under:
(PEAR) **GEMMCDS9050/2(1)** Music from the New
York Stage, Vol. 1 (part 1)

BARRY, Stuart (cond)
see Chandos Concert Orch

BARSCHA, Monique (sop)
Honegger: Aventures du Roi Pausole (Cpte)

BARSHAI, Rudolf (cond)
see COE

BARSHAI, Rudolf (va)
see CONCERT INDEX under:
(EMIL) **CDZ7 67005-2** Mozart—Violin Concertos, etc

BARSÓNY, László (va)
see CONCERT INDEX under:
(MARC) **8 223727** Truscott—Chamber Music

BÁRSONY, László (va)
Sterndale Bennett: Piano Sextet, Op. 8

BARSOVA, Valeria (sop)
see CONCERT INDEX under:
(DANT) **LYS013/5** Tchaikovsky—The Queen of
Spades

BARSTOW, Dame Josephine (sop)
Britten: Gloriana (Cpte)
Porter: Kiss Me, Kate (Cpte)
Tippett: Knot Garden (Cpte)
Verdi: Ballo in maschera (Cpte)
see CONCERT INDEX under:
(CHAN) **CHAN8712/7** Beethoven: Complete
Symphonies
(TER) **CDVIR8307** Josephine Barstow sings Verdi
Arias

BÁRTA, Aleš (harm)
(SUPR) **11 1878-2** The Unknown Janáček

BARTELLONI, Anne (mez)
see CONCERT INDEX under:
(ERAT) **4509-95362-2** Mozart—Sacred Choral
Works

BARTH, Irmgard (mez)
R. Strauss: Salome (Cpte)

BARTHOLDY PIANO QUARTET
Mendelssohn: Piano Quartet 1, Piano Quartet 2, Piano Quartet 3, Sextet, Op.110

BARTHOLDY QUARTET
see CONCERT INDEX under:
(ACAN) **43 075** Mendelssohn—String Quartets

BARTHOLOMÉE, Pierre (cond)
see Liège PO

BARTLE, Jean Ashworth (cond)
see Toronto Children's Chor

BARTLER, Annika (mez)
Nørgård: Gilgamesh (Cpte)

BARTLETT, Peta (sngr)
Berlin: Annie Get Your Gun (Cpte)
G. Charpentier: Louise (Cpte)
see CONCERT INDEX under:
(EMI) **CDC7 54071-2** Frederica von Stade sings Rodgers & Hart

BARTO, Tzimon (pf)
Bartók: Piano Concerto 2
Falla: Nights in the Gardens of Spain
Rachmaninov: Piano Concerto 3
Schumann: Kreisleriana, Symphonic Studies
see CONCERT INDEX under:
(EMI) **CDC7 49495-2** Works for Piano & Orchestra
(EMI) **CDC7 49566-2** Liszt: Piano Works
(EMI) **CDC7 54367-2** Chopin—Piano Works

BARTÓK, Bela (pf)
(BIDD) **LAB007/8** The Art of Joseph Szigeti, Vol.2
(BIDD) **LAB070/1** Szigeti recordings with Bartók and Foldes
(EMI) **CDC5 55031-2** Bartók/Dohnányi—Play their own works
(SONY) **MK42227** Benny Goodman Collector's Edition

BARTÓK CHORUS
cond T. PÁL
Górecki: Beatus vir, Op. 38, Symphony 2

BARTÓK QUARTET
see CONCERT INDEX under:
(CANY) **EC3698-2** Bartók—String Quartets

BARTOLETTI, Bruno (cond)
see BRSO

BARTOLI, Cecilia (mez)
Mozart: Clemenza di Tito (Cpte), Così fan tutte (Cpte), Lucio Silla (Cpte), Nozze di Figaro (Cpte), Requiem
Puccini: Manon Lescaut (Cpte)
Rossini: Barbiere di Siviglia (Cpte), Cenerentola (Cpte)
see CONCERT INDEX under:
(DECC) **425 430-2DH** Cecilia Bartoli sings Rossini Arias
(DECC) **430 513-2DH** Mozart—Arias
(DECC) **430 518-2DH** Cecilia Bartoli—Rossini Recital
(DECC) **436 075-2DH** Rossini Heroines
(DECC) **436 209-2DH** Pergolesi & A Scarlatti—Choral Works
(DECC) **436 267-2DH** Arie Antiche—Bartoli
(DECC) **436 462-2DM** Ten Top Mezzos
(DECC) **440 297-2DH** Italian Songs
(DECC) **443 452-2DH** Mozart Portraits—Bartoli

BARTOLI, Sandro Ivo (pf)
see CONCERT INDEX under:
(ASV) **CDDCA929** Malipiero—Piano Music

BARTOLINI, Lando (ten)
Respighi: Semirama (Cpte)

BARTOLOMEY, Franz (vc)
R. Strauss: Don Quixote

(THE) BARTON WORKSHOP
see CONCERT INDEX under:
(ETCE) **KTC3002** The Barton Workshop plays John Cage

BARTOS, Rita (sop)
Wagner: Parsifal (Cpte)

BÄRTSCHI, Werner (pf)
Onslow: Septet

BARWAHSER, Hubert (fl)
see CONCERT INDEX under:
(PHIL) **442 299-2PM2** Mozart—Complete Flute Works

BARY, Alfred von (ten)
see CONCERT INDEX under:
(SYMP) **SYMCD1081** The Harold Wayne Collection, Vol.5

BASA, Sibrand (ten)
Weber: Peter Schmoll (Cpte)

BASCH, Wolfgang (picc tpt)
see CONCERT INDEX under:
(ARGO) **440 212-2ZH** Schoenfield—Orchestral Works

BASCH, Wolfgang (tpt)
see CONCERT INDEX under:
(SCHW) **311071** Trumpet Concertos

BASH ENSEMBLE
see CONCERT INDEX under:
(ARGO) **440 216-2ZH** Fitkin—Chamber Works

BASHKIROVA, Elena (pf)
Schumann: Dichterliebe, Op. 48 (Cpte), Liederkreis, Op. 39 (Cpte)
see CONCERT INDEX under:
(ORFE) **C248921A** Mozart/Strauss—Lieder

BASHMET, Yuri (cond)
see Moscow Sols Ens

BASHMET, Yuri (va)
Berlioz: Harold in Italy
Schnittke: Viola Concerto
see CONCERT INDEX under:
(EMI) **CDS7 49775-2** Tchaikovsky—Chamber Works
(RCA) **RD60112** Yuri Bashmet—Recital
(RCA) **09026 61273-2** Russian Viola Sonatas

BASHMET, Yuri (va)
see CONCERT INDEX under:
(RCA) **74321 24894-2** Homage to Schnittke
(RCA) **RD60464** Yuri Bashmet—Recital
(RCA) **74321 24894-2** Homage to Schnittke

BASILE, Arturo (cond)
see RCA SO

BASILIDES, Maria (mez)
see CONCERT INDEX under:
(BIDD) **LAB045** Hubay & Flesch —HMV Recordings
(EMI) **CDC5 55031-2** Bartók/Dohnányi—Play their own works

BASIOLA I, Mario (bar)
Verdi: Trovatore (Cpte)
see CONCERT INDEX under:
(NIMB) **NI7853** Lauri-Volpi sings Verdi

BASIOLA II, Mario (bar)
Puccini: Bohème (Cpte), Rondine (Cpte)
Verdi: Ballo in maschera (Cpte)

BASKERVILLE, Priscilla (sop)
A. Davis: X (Cpte)

BASKIN, Theodore (ob)
see CONCERT INDEX under:
(CHAN) **CHAN8651** Vivaldi: Concertos

BASKOV, Konstantin (ten)
Tchaikovsky: Queen of Spades (Cpte)

BASLE BOYS' CHOIR
cond M. VENZAGO
Schoeck: Venus (Cpte)

BASLE MADRIGALISTS
cond M. VENZAGO
Honegger: Aventures du Roi Pausole (Cpte)
Schumann: Manfred (Cpte)

BASLE RADIO SYMPHONY ORCHESTRA
cond C. DUMONT
(CHAN) **CHAN9248** Harmonica Concertos
cond A. FRANCIS
(CPO) **CPO999 166-2** Milhaud—Symphonies

BASLE SYMPHONY ORCHESTRA
cond F. TRAVIS
Holliger: Siebengesang
cond H. ZENDER
Holliger: Magische Tänzer (Cpte)

BASLE THEATRE CHOIR
cond H. ZENDER
Holliger: Magische Tänzer (Cpte)

BASLER, Susanne (vc)
Brahms: Double Concerto

BÄSS, Hajo (pf)
see CONCERT INDEX under:
(DHM) **RD77201** Telemann—Wind Concertos

BASS, Robert (cond)
see Collegiate Orch

BASSANO, Peter (cond)
see His Majesties Sagbutts and Cornetts

BASSE-NORMANDIE ENSEMBLE
cond D. DEBART
Nyman: Noises, Sounds and Sweet Airs (Cpte)
Xenakis: Orestia (Cpte)

BASSI, James (sngr)
Forrest/Wright: Kismet (Cpte)

(IL) BASSO INSTRUMENTAL ENSEMBLE
cond R. OTTO
Monteverdi: Vespers

BASTIAN, Gert (bar)
Nielsen: Maskarade (Cpte)

BASTIAN, William (ten)
Mozart: Kleine Freimaurer-Kantate, K623, Requiem

BASTIANINI, Ettore (bar)
J. Strauss II: Fledermaus (Cpte)
Ponchielli: Gioconda (Cpte)
Puccini: Bohème (Cpte)
Verdi: Don Carlo (Cpte), Forza del Destino (Cpte), Traviata (Cpte), Trovatore (Cpte)
see CONCERT INDEX under:
(DECC) **436 464-2DM** Ten Top Baritones & Basses

BASTIN, Jules (bass)
Auber: Fra Diavolo (Cpte)
Berg: Lulu (Cpte)
Berlioz: Benvenuto Cellini (Cpte), Béatrice et Bénédict (Cpte), Damnation de Faust (Cpte), Enfance du Christ (Cpte)

Debussy: Rodrigue et Chimène (Cpte)
Lekeu: Andromède
Massenet: Cendrillon (Cpte), Werther (Cpte)
Meyerbeer: Prophète (Cpte)
Mozart: Nozze di Figaro (Cpte)
Offenbach: Périchole (Cpte)
Prokofiev: Love for 3 Oranges (Cpte)
R. Strauss: Rosenkavalier (Cpte), Salome (Cpte), Salomé (Cpte)
Ravel: Enfant et les sortilèges (Cpte)
Verdi: Attila (Cpte)
see CONCERT INDEX under:
(DG) **437 244-2GGA2** Berlioz/Franck—Vocal & Orchestral Works

BASTIN, Jules (spkr)
Stravinsky: Oedipus Rex (Cpte)

BATE, Jennifer (organ)
Messiaen: Banquet céleste, Corps glorieux, Diptyque, Livre du Saint Sacrement, Nativité du Seigneur
see CONCERT INDEX under:
(ASV) **CDQS6127** Liszt/Schumann—Organ Works
(UNIC) **DKPCD9014** Franck—Organ Works Vol. II
(UNIC) **DKPCD9024/5** Messiaen—Organ Works
(UNIC) **DKPCD9028** Messiaen—Organ Works
(UNIC) **DKPCD9030** Franck—Organ Works Vol. III
(UNIC) **DKPCD9050** Vivaldi—Concertos
(UNIC) **DKPCD9096** From Stanley to Wesley, Vol. 1
(UNIC) **DKPCD9099** From Stanley to Wesley Vol 2
(UNIC) **DKPCD9101** From Stanley to Wesley Vol 3
(UNIC) **DKPCD9104** From Stanley to Wesley Vol 4
(UNIC) **DKPCD9105** From Stanley to Wesley Vol 5
(UNIC) **DKPCD9106** From Stanley to Wesley Vol 6

BATEMAN, Paul (cond)
see Prague City PO

BATER, Glenn (bass)
Verdi: Trovatore (Cpte)

BATES, Jennifer (sop)
Schubert: Hirt auf dem Felsen, D965

BATH FESTIVAL CHAMBER ORCHESTRA
cond Y. MENUHIN
(CFP) **CD-CFP4557** Baroque Favourites

BATH FESTIVAL CHORUS
cond R. HICKOX
Mahler: Klagende Lied (Cpte)

BATH FESTIVAL ENSEMBLE
see CONCERT INDEX under:
(CFP) **CD-CFP4557** Baroque Favourites

BATH FESTIVAL ORCHESTRA
cond Y. MENUHIN
Bach: Brandenburg Concertos
see CONCERT INDEX under:
(EMI) **CES5 68517-2** Bach—Orchestral Works
cond M. TIPPETT
(EMI) **CMS7 63522-2** Tippett—Chamber & Orchestral Works

BATHORI, Jane (mez)
see CONCERT INDEX under:
(EPM) **150 122** Milhaud—Historic Recordings 1928-1948

BÁTIZ, Enrique (cond)
see LPO

BATJER, Margaret (vn)
Beethoven: String Quintet, Op. 29
Borodin: String Quartet 2
Dvořák: Piano Quintet, Op.81, String Quintet, Op.77, Terzetto, Op.74
Mendelssohn: String Quintet 2
Mozart: Concertone, K190, String Quintet, K174, String Quintet, K406, String Quintet, K515, String Quintet, K516, String Quintet, K593, String Quintet, K614
Tchaikovsky: Souvenir de Florence, String Quartet 1
Verdi: String Quartet
see CONCERT INDEX under:
(NUOV) **6802** Mozart—Chamber Works

BÁTOR, Tamás (bass)
Giordano: Andrea Chénier (Cpte)

BATTEN, Joseph (cond)
see orch

BATTERSBY, Edmund (pf)
Rachmaninov: Etudes-tableaux, Op. 39 (exc), Preludes (exc)

BATTISTINI, Mattia (bar)
see CONCERT INDEX under:
(EMI) **CHS7 64860-2(1)** La Scala Edition - Vol.1, 1878-1914 (pt 1)
(NIMB) **NI7831** Mattia Battistini (1856-1928)
(NIMB) **NI7840/1** The Era of Adelina Patti
(NIMB) **NI7867** Legendary Dancers
(PEAR) **GEMMCDS9923(1)** Covent Garden on Record, Vol.1 (pt 1)
(PEAR) **GEMMCDS9924(1)** Covent Garden on Record, Vol.2 (pt 1)
(PEAR) **GEMMCD9936** Mattia Battistini, Vol.1
(PREI) **89045** Mattia Battistini (1856-1928)

BATTLE, Kathleen (sop)
Donizetti: Elisir d'amore (Cpte)
Fauré: Requiem (Cpte)
Handel: Semele (Cpte)
Haydn: Schöpfung (Cpte)
Mahler: Symphony 2

Wagner: Götterdämmerung (Cpte), Rheingold (Cpte),
Siegfried (Cpte), Tannhäuser (Cpte), Walküre (Cpte)
see CONCERT INDEX under:
(ORFE) C025821A   Brahms Choral Songs
   cond R. HEGER
see CONCERT INDEX under:
(SCHW) 310045   Hindemith: Works for Viola and
Orchestra
   cond L. HERBIG
Busoni: Piano Concerto, Op.39
   cond P. HINDEMITH
see CONCERT INDEX under:
(ORFE) C197891A   Hindemith & Berg: Orchestral
Works
   cond N. JÄRVI
Glazunov: Symphony 1, Symphony 5
see CONCERT INDEX under:
(ORFE) C093201A   Glazunov: Orchestral works
   cond E. JOCHUM
Bruckner: Te Deum
Mozart: Entführung (Cpte), Mass, K317, Requiem,
Vespers, K339
Verdi: Requiem (Cpte)
Weber: Freischütz (Cpte)
see CONCERT INDEX under:
(DG) 423 127-2GX4   Bruckner: Sacred Works for
Chorus
(DG) 429 079-2GX9   Bruckner: Complete Symphonies
(DG) 437 677-2GDO2   Irmgard Seefried - Opera
Recital
(DG) 447 409-2GOR2   Bruckner—The Masses
   cond R. KEMPE
Haydn: Sinfonia concertante
R. Strauss: Don Quixote
   cond B. KLEE
Mendelssohn: Hochzeit des Camacho (Cpte)
   cond O. KLEMPERER
Bach: Suites, BWV1066-9 (exc)
Brahms: Symphony 4
   cond K. KONDRASHIN
Tchaikovsky: Piano Concerto 1
   cond C. KRAUSS
see CONCERT INDEX under:
(ORFE) C196891A   Krauss conducts Haydn, Ravel &
Strauss
   cond R. KUBELÍK
Beethoven: Symphony 9
Bruckner: Symphony 8
Dvořák: Scherzo Capriccioso, Stabat Mater
Haydn: Schöpfung (Cpte)
Hindemith: Mathis der Maler (Cpte)
Janáček: Glagolitic Mass (Cpte), Taras Bulba
Pfitzner: Palestrina (Cpte)
Schumann: Symphony 1, Symphony 2
Suk: Asrael
Weber: Freischütz (Cpte), Oberon (Cpte)
see CONCERT INDEX under:
(BELA) 450 121-2   Plácido Domingo
(DG) 415 191-2GH   Mahler: Lieder
(DG) 423 120-2GX6   Dvořák: Complete Symphonies
(DG) 429 042-2GX10   Mahler: Complete Symphonies
(DG) 435 074-2GGA2   Dvořák—Orchestral Works
(DG) 437 254-2GGA   Smetana/Janáček—Orchestral
Works
(DG) 439 411-2GCL   Mendelssohn—Orchestral
Works
(DG) 439 476-2GCL   Schumann—Piano Works
(EMI) CMS5 65212-2   Wagner—Les introuvables du
Ring
(PANT) 81 1264-2   Kubelík conducts Kubelík
(SCHW) 310045   Hindemith: Works for Viola and
Orchestra
(SONY) SBK48270   Schumann—Orchestral Works
(WERG) WER60187-50   Hartmann: Symphonies
   cond F. LEITNER
Busoni: Doktor Faust (Cpte)
Orff: Antigonae (Cpte)
see CONCERT INDEX under:
(WERG) WER60187-50   Hartmann: Symphonies
   cond L. MAAZEL
see CONCERT INDEX under:
(RCA) 09026 68225-2   R. Strauss—Orchestral Works
   cond Z. MACAL
see CONCERT INDEX under:
(WERG) WER60187-50   Hartmann: Symphonies
   cond D. MITROPOULOS
Prokofiev: Symphony 5
Schoenberg: Violin Concerto
   cond E. ORMANDY
see CONCERT INDEX under:
(ORFE) C199891A   Ormandy conducts the BRSO,
1959
   cond K.A. RICKENBACHER
Grieg: Symphony
R.Strauss: Symphony in D minor
Spohr: Symphony 6, Symphony 9
see CONCERT INDEX under:
(SCHW) 311232   Messiaen—Works for Piano and
Orchestra
   cond F. RIEGER
see CONCERT INDEX under:
(WERG) WER60187-50   Hartmann: Symphonies
   cond D. RUNNICLES
Humperdinck: Hänsel und Gretel (Cpte)
   cond W. SAWALLISCH
Brahms: Deutsches Requiem, Op. 45 (Cpte)
R. Strauss: Elektra (Cpte), Frau ohne Schatten
(Cpte), Intermezzo (Cpte)
see CONCERT INDEX under:
(EMI) CDC7 47407-2   Schubert: Sacred Choral works
(EMI) CDM7 69223-2   Schubert—Choral Works

(EMI) CMS7 64778-2   Schubert—Sacred Works,
Vol.1
(EMI) CMS7 64783-2   Schubert—Sacred Works,
Vol.2
   cond P. SCHNEIDER
Killmayer: Yolimba (Cpte)
   cond D. SHALLON
Bartók: Viola Concerto
Hindemith: Schwanendreher
   cond M. SHOSTAKOVICH
Shostakovich: Cello Concerto 1, Cello Concerto 2
   cond L. SLATKIN
R. Strauss: Don Quixote, Till Eulenspiegel
   cond S. SOLTESZ
Mendelssohn: Oedipus (Cpte)
   cond G. SOLTI
R. Strauss: Don Quixote, Till Eulenspiegel
see CONCERT INDEX under:
(DECC) 440 618-2DF2   R. Strauss—Tone Poems
   cond I. STRAVINSKY
Stravinsky: Apollon musagète, Jeu de cartes
   cond M.H. TANG
Taneyev: Canzona, Suite de concert, Op. 28
   cond J. TATE
Humperdinck: Hänsel und Gretel (Cpte)

BAVARIAN STATE OPERA CHORUS
   cond F. FRICSAY
Beethoven: Fidelio (Cpte)
   cond R. HEGER
Flotow: Martha (Cpte)
Nicolai: Lustigen Weiber von Windsor (Cpte)
   cond E. JOCHUM
Mozart: Entführung (Cpte)
   cond J. KEILBERTH
Janáček: Excursions of Mr Brouček (Cpte)
R. Strauss: Arabella (Cpte)
Wagner: Meistersinger (Cpte)
   cond C. KLEIBER
Verdi: Traviata (Cpte)
see CONCERT INDEX under:
(DG) 431 104-2GB   Great Voices - Plácido Domingo
   cond H. KNAPPERTSBUSCH
Wagner: Tristan und Isolde (Cpte)
   cond W. SAWALLISCH
Mozart: Zauberflöte (Cpte)
R.Strauss: Arabella (Cpte)
Wagner: Meistersinger (Cpte)
   cond P. STEINBERG
Massenet: Chérubin (Cpte)
   cond H. WALLBERG
Millöcker: Gasparone (Cpte)

BAVARIAN STATE OPERA ORCHESTRA
   cond O. GERDES
see CONCERT INDEX under:
(DG) 431 110-2GB   Great Voices - Fritz Wunderlich
   cond J. KEILBERTH
Wagner: Meistersinger (Cpte)
   cond W. SAWALLISCH
Mozart: Zauberflöte (Cpte)
see CONCERT INDEX under:
(EMIL) CDZ7 67015-2   Mozart—Opera Arias

BAVARIAN STATE ORCHESTRA
Janáček: Excursions of Mr Brouček (Cpte)
   cond W. EGK
Egk: Verlobung in San Domingo (Cpte)
   cond F. FRICSAY
Beethoven: Fidelio (Cpte)
see CONCERT INDEX under:
(DG) 437 677-2GDO2   Irmgard Seefried - Opera
Recital
   cond R. HEGER
Flotow: Martha (Cpte)
Nicolai: Lustigen Weiber von Windsor (Cpte)
   cond E. JOCHUM
see CONCERT INDEX under:
(DG) 431 110-2GB   Great Voices - Fritz Wunderlich
   cond J. KEILBERTH
R. Strauss: Arabella (Cpte), Salome (Cpte)
   cond C. KLEIBER
Beethoven: Symphony 4
Dvořák: Piano Concerto
Verdi: Traviata (Cpte)
see CONCERT INDEX under:
(DG) 415 366-2GH   Placido Domingo Recital
(DG) 431 104-2GB   Great Voices - Plácido Domingo
   cond H. KNAPPERTSBUSCH
Wagner: Tristan und Isolde (Cpte)
   cond W. SAWALLISCH
Bartók: Duke Bluebeard's Castle (Cpte)
Bruckner: Symphony 1, Symphony 6, Symphony 9
R.Strauss: Arabella (Cpte)
Wagner: Meistersinger (Cpte)
   cond R. STRAUSS
R. Strauss: Alpensinfonie
see CONCERT INDEX under:
(PREI) 90205   Strauss conducts Strauss, Vol.1
   cond M. VON ZALLINGER
(NIMB) NI7851   Legendary Voices

BÄVERSTAM, Åsa (sop)
see CONCERT INDEX under:
(SONY) SK53276   Nielsen—Orchestral Works

BAX, Sir Arnold (pf)
see CONCERT INDEX under:
(CLAR) CDGSE78-50-47   The Harrison Sisters—An
English Musical Heritage
(SYMP) SYMCD1075   May Harrison—Vioinist and
Composer
(SYMP) SYMCD1140   The Harrison Sisters

BAXTER, Pamela (mez)
Sullivan: Gondoliers (Cpte)

BAXTRESSER, Jeanne (fl)
see CONCERT INDEX under:
(EMI) CDC5 55400-2   Barber—Chamber and
Instrumental Works

BAY, Emanuel (pf)
see CONCERT INDEX under:
(APR) APR7015   The Auer Legacy, Vol.1
(APR) APR7016   The Auer Legacy, Vol.2
(BIDD) LAB011   Brahms—Historic Chamber Music
Recordings
(RCA) GD87704   Beethoven: Violin Sonatas, Vol.1
(RCA) GD87705   Beethoven: Violin Sonatas, Vol.2
(RCA) GD87706   Beethoven: Violin Sonatas, Vol.3
(RCA) GD87871   Jascha Heifetz Collection
(RCA) 09026 61778-2(03)   The Heifetz Collection, Vol.
3
(RCA) 09026 61778-2(04)   The Heifetz Collection, Vol.
4
(RCA) 09026 61778-2(05)   The Heifetz Collection, Vol.
5
(RCA) 09026 61778-2(06)   The Heifetz Collection, Vol.
6
(RCA) 09026 61778-2(07)   The Heifetz Collection, Vol.
7
(RCA) 09026 61778-2(08)   The Heifetz Collection, Vol.
8
(RCA) 09026 61778-2(09)   The Heifetz Collection, Vol.
9
(RCA) 09026 61778-2(10)   The Heifetz Collection, Vol.
10
(RCA) 09026 61778-2(16)   The Heifetz Collection, Vol.
16
(RCA) 09026 61778-2(19)   The Heifetz Collection, Vol.
19
(RCA) 09026 61778-2(31)   The Heifetz Collection, Vol.
31
(RCA) 09026 61778-2(35)   The Heifetz Collection, Vol.
35
(RCA) 09026 61778-2(40)   The Heifetz Collection, Vol.
40
(RCA) 09026 61778-2(44)   The Heifetz Collection, Vol.
44

BAYES, Nora (sngr)
see CONCERT INDEX under:
(PEAR) GEMMCDS9053/5   Music from the New York
Stage, Vol. 2: 1908—1913
(PEAR) GEMMCDS9059/61   Music from the New York
Stage, Vol. 4: 1917-20

BAYLEY, Clive (bar)
Bernstein: Candide (1988) (Cpte)
M. Berkeley: Baa Baa Black Sheep (Cpte)
Walton: Troilus and Cressida (Cpte)

BAYLEY, Clive (bass)
see CONCERT INDEX under:
(OPRA) ORCH104   A Hundred Years of Italian Opera:
1820-1830

BAYO, Maria (sop)
Bretón: Verbena de La Paloma (Cpte)
Cavalli: Calisto (Cpte)
Falla: Atlántida (Cpte)
Rossini: Occasione fa il ladro (Cpte)
Vives: Bohemios (Cpte), Doña Francisquita (Cpte)
see CONCERT INDEX under:
(CLAV) CD50-9205   Canciones Españolas

BAYOD, Antonio Perez (sngr)
Bretón: Verbena de La Paloma (Cpte)

BAYREUTH FESTIVAL CHORUS
   cond H. ABENDROTH
Wagner: Meistersinger (Cpte)
   cond D. BARENBOIM
Wagner: Götterdämmerung (Cpte)
   cond P. BOULEZ
Wagner: Parsifal (Cpte), Parsifal (Cpte)
   cond K. BÖHM
Wagner: Fliegende Holländer (Cpte),
Götterdämmerung (Cpte), Tristan und Isolde (Cpte)
see CONCERT INDEX under:
(PHIL) 446 057-2PB14   Wagner—The Ring Cycle -
Bayreuth Festival 1967
   cond K. ELMENDORFF
Wagner: Götterdämmerung (Cpte)
   cond JAMES LEVINE
Wagner: Parsifal (Cpte)
   cond H. VON KARAJAN
Wagner: Meistersinger (Cpte)
   cond J. KEILBERTH
Wagner: Lohengrin (Cpte)
   cond H. KNAPPERTSBUSCH
Wagner: Parsifal (Cpte)
   cond C. KRAUSS
Wagner: Götterdämmerung (Cpte)
see CONCERT INDEX under:
(FOYE) 15-CF2011   Wagner—Der Ring de Nibelungen
   cond K. MUCK
see CONCERT INDEX under:
(OPAL) OPALCDS9843   Karl Muck conducts Wagner
   cond W. NELSSON
Wagner: Fliegende Holländer (Cpte)
   cond W. PITZ
(DG) 429 169-2GR   Wagner—Choruses
   cond W. SAWALLISCH
Wagner: Fliegende Holländer (Cpte), Lohengrin
(Cpte), Tannhäuser (Cpte)

cond P. SCHNEIDER
Wagner: Lohengrin (Cpte)
cond H. TIETJEN
see CONCERT INDEX under:
(TELD) **9031-76442-2** Wagner—Excerpts from the
1936 Bayreuth Festival
cond S. VARVISO
Wagner: Meistersinger (Cpte)

BAYREUTH FESTIVAL ORCHESTRA
cond H. ABENDROTH
Wagner: Meistersinger (Cpte)
cond D. BARENBOIM
Wagner: Götterdämmerung (Cpte), Rheingold (Cpte),
Siegfried (Cpte), Walküre (Cpte)
cond P. BOULEZ
Wagner: Götterdämmerung (Cpte), Parsifal (Cpte),
Rheingold (Cpte), Siegfried (Cpte), Walküre (Cpte)
cond K. BÖHM
Wagner: Fliegende Holländer (Cpte),
Götterdämmerung (Cpte), Rheingold (Cpte), Siegfried
(Cpte), Tristan und Isolde (Cpte), Walküre (Cpte)
(PHIL) **446 057-2PB14** Wagner—The Ring Cycle -
Bayreuth Festival 1967
cond K. ELMENDORFF
Wagner: Götterdämmerung (Cpte)
see CONCERT INDEX under:
(EMI) **CMS7 64008-2(1)** Wagner Singing on Record
(pt 1)
(EMI) **CMS7 64008-2(2)** Wagner Singing on Record
(pt 2)
(PEAR) **GEMMCDS9926(1)** Covent Garden on
Record—Vol.4 (pt 1)
cond JAMES LEVINE
Wagner: Parsifal (Cpte)
cond H. VON KARAJAN
Wagner: Meistersinger (Cpte), Walküre (exc)
cond J. KEILBERTH
Wagner: Lohengrin (Cpte)
cond H. KNAPPERTSBUSCH
Wagner: Parsifal (Cpte)
cond C. KRAUSS
Wagner: Götterdämmerung (Cpte), Rheingold (Cpte),
Siegfried (Cpte), Walküre (Cpte)
see CONCERT INDEX under:
(FOYE) **15-CF2011** Wagner—Der Ring de Nibelungen
cond K. MUCK
(OPAL) **OPALCDS9843** Karl Muck conducts Wagner
cond W. NELSSON
Wagner: Fliegende Holländer (Cpte)
cond W. PITZ
see CONCERT INDEX under:
(DG) **429 169-2GR** Wagner—Choruses
cond W. SAWALLISCH
Wagner: Fliegende Holländer (Cpte), Lohengrin
(Cpte), Tannhäuser (Cpte)
cond P. SCHNEIDER
Wagner: Lohengrin (Cpte)
cond H. TIETJEN
see CONCERT INDEX under:
(TELD) **9031-76442-2** Wagner—Excerpts from the
1936 Bayreuth Festival
cond S. VARVISO
Wagner: Meistersinger (Cpte)
cond S. WAGNER
see CONCERT INDEX under:
(EMI) **CMS7 64008-2(2)** Wagner Singing on Record
(pt 2)

BAZEMORE, Raymond (voc)
A. Davis: X (Cpte)
Joplin: Treemonisha (Cpte)

BAZILEVSKY, Jean (pf)
see CONCERT INDEX under:
(PREI) **89207** Feodor Chaliapin Song
Book—Electrical Recordings

BAZOLA-MINORI, François (bar)
Handel: Teseo (Cpte)
Montéclair: Jephté (Cpte)
Purcell: Fairy Queen, Z629 (Cpte), King Arthur, Z628
(Cpte)

BAZSINKA, Zsuzsanna (sop)
Mascagni: Lodoletta (Cpte)

BBC CHOIR
cond T. BEECHAM
Gounod: Faust (Cpte)
Handel: Messiah (Cpte)

BBC CHORAL SOCIETY
cond P. BOULEZ
Schoenberg: Gurrelieder
cond COLIN DAVIS
Tippett: Child of Our Time

BBC CHORUS
cond O. ACKERMANN
Lehár: Land des Lächelns (Cpte), Lustige Witwe
(Cpte)
cond T. BEECHAM
Schumann: Manfred (Cpte)
(BBCR) **DMCD98** BBC Proms - The Centenary: 1895-
1995
(DUTT) **CDLX7011** Beecham conducts Delius
(PEAR) **GEMMCD9473** Heddle Nash—Vol.2
(SONY) **SMK58934** Delius—Orchestral Works
cond P. BOULEZ
see CONCERT INDEX under:

(EMI) **CDM7 63948-2** 20th Century French Orchestral
Works
(SONY) **SM2K44571** Schoenberg: Choral Works
cond A. BOULT
Holst: Hymn of Jesus
cond COLIN DAVIS
Mozart: Nozze di Figaro (Cpte)
cond O. KLEMPERER
Bach: Mass in B minor, BWV232 (Cpte)
cond I. STRAVINSKY
see CONCERT INDEX under:
(EMI) **CDS7 54607-2** Stravinsky plays and conducts
Stravinsky
cond R. VAUGHAN WILLIAMS
see CONCERT INDEX under:
(PEAR) **GEMMCD9342** Vaughan Williams: Vocal
Works

BBC CONCERT ORCHESTRA
cond K. ALWYN
see CONCERT INDEX under:
(MARC) **8 223732** Addinsell—British Light Music
cond A. BOULT
see CONCERT INDEX under:
(BBCR) **BBCRD9106** The Music of Eric Coates
cond O. A. HUGHES
see CONCERT INDEX under:
(CPO) **CPO999 171-2** Sullivan—Orchestral Works
cond G. LLOYD
G. Lloyd: Iernin
cond B. WORDSWORTH
see CONCERT INDEX under:
(ARGO) **443 529-2ZH** Sax Drive

BBC NATIONAL ORCHESTRA OF WALES
cond G. LLEWELLYN
see CONCERT INDEX under:
(BIS) **BIS-CD658** British Trombone Concertos
cond T. OTAKA
Firsova: Cassandra, Op. 60
Franck: Chasseur maudit, Psyché
Gubaidulina: Pro et contra
Rachmaninov: Piano Concerto 3

BBC NORTHERN SINGERS
cond G. THORNE
Liszt: Missa choralis, S10, Via Crucis, S53

BBC NORTHERN SYMPHONY ORCHESTRA
cond N. DEL MAR
see CONCERT INDEX under:
(BBCR) **BBCRD9129** Bridge/Britten/Pärt—Orchestral
Works
cond R. LEPPARD
Mahler: Lied von der Erde

BBC PHILHARMONIC BRASS
cond G. LLOYD
see CONCERT INDEX under:
(ALBA) **TROY015-2** G. Lloyd—Orchestral Works

BBC PHILHARMONIC ORCHESTRA
cond M. BAMERT
Korngold: Sinfonietta, Sursum corda, Op. 13
(CHAN) **CHAN9259** Stokowski's Symphonic Bach
(CHAN) **CHAN9349** Stokowski Encores
cond E. DOWNES
Elgar: Cello Concerto, Enigma Variations, Symphony
2
Glière: Bronze Horseman Suite, Horn Concerto, Op.
91, Red Poppy Suite, Symphony 1, Symphony 2,
Symphony 3, Zaporozhy Cossacks
Korngold: Abschiedslieder, Op. 14 (exc), Symphony,
Op. 40
Miaskovsky: Symphony 5, Symphony 9
Respighi: Concerto in modo misolidio, Piano
Concerto in A minor, Sinfonia Drammatica
Stevens: Cello Concerto, Symphony of Liberation,
Symphony 2, Violin Concerto
see CONCERT INDEX under:
(CHAN) **CHAN9232** Respighi—Orchestral Works
(CHAN) **CHAN9311** Respighi—Orchestral Works
(CONI) **CDCF187** Elgar: Orchestral Works
cond F. GLUSHCHENKO
see CONCERT INDEX under:
(CHAN) **CHAN9321** Khachaturian/Ippolitov-
Ivanov—Orchestral Works
cond S. GUNZENHAUSER
(NAXO) **8 550600** Dvořák—Overtures
cond G. HERBIG
Brahms: Academic Festival Overture, Symphony 1
cond E. HOWARTH
see CONCERT INDEX under:
(PHIL) **432 075-2PH** Contemporary English Trumpet
Concertos
cond G. HURST
Elgar: Imperial March, Symphony 1
cond G. LLOYD
G. Lloyd: Piano Concerto 3, Symphony 2, Symphony
5, Symphony 7, Symphony 9
see CONCERT INDEX under:
(ALBA) **TROY015-2** G. Lloyd—Orchestral Works
cond O. DE LA MARTINEZ
Smyth: Wreckers (Cpte)
cond P. MAXWELL DAVIES
Maxwell Davies: Black Pentecost, Lighthouse (Cpte),
Resurrection (Cpte), Stone Litany, Symphony 1,
Symphony 2, Symphony 3
see CONCERT INDEX under:
(COLL) **Coll1308-2** Maxwell Davies—Orchestral
Works

(COLL) **Coll1390-2** Maxwell Davies—Orchestral
Works
(COLL) **Coll1460-2** Maxwell Davies—Symphony No 5
etc
cond Y. P. TORTELIER
Dukas: Polyeucte, Symphony
Dutilleux: Symphony 1, Symphony 2
Hindemith: Cello Concerto, Four Temperaments,
Harmonie der Welt, Symphonia serena
Poulenc: Gloria, Stabat mater
see CONCERT INDEX under:
(CHAN) **CHAN9060** Hindemith—Orchestral Works
(CHAN) **CHAN9271** Poulenc/Guilmant/Widor—Organ
Works
(CHAN) **CHAN9325** Gershwin—Orchestral Works
cond G. VARGA
see CONCERT INDEX under:
(ASV) **CDDCA867** French Cello Works

BBC SCOTTISH SYMPHONY ORCHESTRA
cond R. BERNAS
Goehr: Symphony Op. 29
cond M. BRABBINS
see CONCERT INDEX under:
(HYPE) **CDA66717** Alkan/Henselt—Piano Concertos
(HYPE) **CDA66764** Alexander Mackenzie—Orchestral
Music
cond T. DUN
(SCHW) **312982** Tan Dun—Orchestral Works
cond A. FRANCIS
Albert: Piano Concerto 1, Piano Concerto 2
Pettersson: Symphonic Movement, Symphony 2,
Symphony 13
cond L. FRIEND
see CONCERT INDEX under:
(MARC) **8 223479** Brian—Orchestral Works
cond F. GLUSHCHENKO
Dohnányi: Piano Concerto 1, Piano Concerto 2
cond J. MAKSYMIUK
MacMillan: Confession of Isobel Gowdie, Tryst
Medtner: Piano Concerto 2, Piano Concerto 3
Mendelssohn: 2-Piano Concerto in A flat, 2-Piano
Concerto in E
Moszkowski: Piano Concerto
Paderewski: Piano Concerto
see CONCERT INDEX under:
(HYPE) **CDA66624** Romantic Piano Concerto -
Volume 4
(NAXO) **8 550864** Grieg—Orchestral Works
cond J. Y. OSSONCE
Chabrier: Briséis (Cpte)

BBC SINGERS
cond P. BOULEZ
Schoenberg: Gurrelieder, Moses und Aron (Cpte)
Stravinsky: Nightingale (Cpte)
(DG) **437 786-2GH** Webern—Orchestral, Vocal &
Chamber Works
(ERAT) **2292-45494-2** Boulez—Cantatas and
Orchestral Works
(SONY) **SMK48462** Boulez conducts Schoenberg
(SONY) **SMK48464** Boulez conducts Schoenberg -
Volume 2
(SONY) **SM2K44571** Schoenberg: Choral Works
cond COLIN DAVIS
Tippett: Child of Our Time
cond A. DAVIS
Tippett: Mask of Time
see CONCERT INDEX under:
(TELD) **4509-97868-2** The Last Night of the Proms
1994
cond N. DEL MAR
see CONCERT INDEX under:
(BBCR) **BBCRD9124**
Szymanowski/Panufnik—Symphonies
cond J. GLOVER
Mozart: Requiem
cond S. JOLY
see CONCERT INDEX under:
(COLL) **Coll7039-2** Britten—The Folk Songs
(UNIT) **88023-2** Tavener—Ikons
cond G. LLOYD
G. Lloyd: Iernin
cond M. NEARY
Tavener: Akathist of Thanksgiving
cond J. POOLE
Swayne: Cry
see CONCERT INDEX under:
(COLL) **Coll1283-2** Saxton—Orchestral & Vocal
Works
cond G. ROZHDESTVENSKY
Vaughan Williams: Sancta civitas
cond Y. P. TORTELIER
Poulenc: Gloria, Stabat mater

BBC SYMPHONY CHORUS
cond A. DAVIS
Tippett: Mask of Time
Vaughan Williams: Symphony 1
see CONCERT INDEX under:
(TELD) **4509-92374-2** Elgar—The Music Makers;
String Pieces
(TELD) **4509-97868-2** The Last Night of the Proms
1994
cond N. DEL MAR
see CONCERT INDEX under:
(BBCR) **BBCRD9124**
Szymanowski/Panufnik—Symphonies
cond S. JACKSON
see CONCERT INDEX under:

(ASV) **CDDCA900**   Daniel-Lesur—Choral and Organ works
(LARG) **Largo5130**   Testimonies of War
cond G. ROZHDESTVENSKY
Tippett: Child of Our Time (Cpte)
Vaughan Williams: Sancta civitas
cond G. SIMON
see CONCERT INDEX *under:*
(CALA) **CACD1011**   Borodin—Orchestral Works
cond K. TENNSTEDT
see CONCERT INDEX *under:*
(EMI) **CZS7 67819-2**   Brahms/Schumann—Requiems

BBC SYMPHONY CHORUS (WOMEN'S VOICES)
cond A. DAVIS
Holst: Planets

BBC SYMPHONY ORCHESTRA
cond M. ARNOLD
see CONCERT INDEX *under:*
(BBCR) **BBCRD9111**   Elgar—Cello Concerto etc
cond S. BAINBRIDGE
see CONCERT INDEX *under:*
(CNTI) **CCD1020**   Simon Bainbridge—Orchestral Works
cond M. BAMERT
see CONCERT INDEX *under:*
(COLL) **Coll1283-2**   Saxton—Orchestral & Vocal Works
cond T. BEECHAM
see CONCERT INDEX *under:*
(EMI) **CDM7 63397-2**   Sibelius: Orchestral Works
cond L. BERNSTEIN
see CONCERT INDEX *under:*
(DG) **413 490-2GH**   Elgar: Orchestral Works
cond P. BOULEZ
Bartók: Duke Bluebeard's Castle (Cpte)
Berg: Violin Concerto
Boulez: Pli selon pli, Rituel in memoriam Maderna
Schoenberg: Gurrelieder, Lieder, Op. 22, Moses und Aron (Cpte)
Stravinsky: Nightingale (Cpte)
see CONCERT INDEX *under:*
(EMI) **CDM7 63948-2**   20th Century French Orchestral Works
(EMI) **CDM7 63985-2**   Bartók—Violin and Viola Works
(ERAT) **2292-45494-2**   Boulez—Cantatas and Orchestral Works
(SONY) **SMK48462**   Boulez conducts Schoenberg
(SONY) **SMK48464**   Boulez conducts Schoenberg - Volume 2
(SONY) **SMK48466**   Boulez conducts Schoenberg—Volume 3
(SONY) **SMK64107**   Ravel/Roussel—Vocal & Orchestral Works
(SONY) **SM2K44571**   Schoenberg: Choral Works
(SONY) **SM2K64100**   Bartók/Scriabin—Orchestral Works
(SONY) **SM3K64103**   Berlioz—Orchestral and Vocal Works
cond A. BOULT
Beethoven: Piano Concerto 3
Brahms: Piano Concerto 2
Holst: Hymn of Jesus
see CONCERT INDEX *under:*
(BBCR) **BBCRD9114**   Beethoven—Orchestral Works
(BBCR) **DMCD98**   BBC Proms - The Centenary: 1895-1995
(BEUL) **1PD12**   Boult's BBC Years
(BIDD) **LHW017**   Backhaus plays Brahms, Volume 1
(EMI) **CDH7 63498-2**   Pablo Casals plays Cello Concertos
(EMI) **CHS5 65503-2**   Beethoven—Piano Concertos, etc
cond COLIN DAVIS
Beethoven: Piano Concerto 3, Piano Concerto 4
Berlioz: Benvenuto Cellini (Cpte)
Mozart: Nozze di Figaro (Cpte), Requiem
Tippett: Child of Our Time
see CONCERT INDEX *under:*
(PHIL) **426 660-2PSL**   Bartók—Piano Concertos
(PHIL) **438 380-2PM2**   Best of Grieg
(PHIL) **438 800-2PM2**   Mozart—Choral Works
(PHIL) **438 812-2PM2**   Bartók—Orchestral Works
(PHIL) **442 302-2PM2**   The Best of Mendelssohn
(PHIL) **442 577-2PM2**   Beethoven—Concertos, Volume 1
cond P. DANIEL
see CONCERT INDEX *under:*
(COLL) **Coll1414-2**   Birtwistle—Orchestral Works
cond A. DAVIS
Elgar: In the South, Pomp and Circumstance Marches (exc), Symphony 1, Symphony 2
Holst: Egdon Heath, Planets
Shostakovich: Violin Concerto 2, Violin Concerto 2
Tippett: Mask of Time
Vaughan Williams: Symphony 1, Symphony 2, Symphony 4, Symphony 5, Symphony 8
see CONCERT INDEX *under:*
(TELD) **4509-90845-2**   Delius—Orchestral Works
(TELD) **4509-92374-2**   Elgar—The Music Makers; String Pieces
(TELD) **4509-97868-2**   The Last Night of the Proms 1994
(TELD) **9031-73126-2**   Britten—Orchestral Works
(TELD) **9031-73127-2**   Vaughan Williams—Orchestral Works
(TELD) **9031-73279-2**   Elgar—Orchestral Works
(VIRG) **VC7 59618-2**   Nielsen—Orchestral Works
cond N. DEL MAR
see CONCERT INDEX *under:*

(BBCR) **BBCRD9124**   Szymanowski/Panufnik—Symphonies
cond A. DORATI
see CONCERT INDEX *under:*
(EMI) **CDM7 63948-2**   20th Century French Orchestral Works
cond M. ELDER
Buller: Proença, Theatre of Memory
see CONCERT INDEX *under:*
(BBCR) **BBCRD9124**   Szymanowski/Panufnik—Symphonies
cond E. ELGAR
see CONCERT INDEX *under:*
(EMI) **CDS7 54568-2**   The Elgar Edition, Vol.3
cond L. FRIEND
Brian: Symphony 3
cond C. GROVES
see CONCERT INDEX *under:*
(BBCR) **BBCRD9111**   Elgar—Cello Concerto etc
cond HENRY WOOD
see CONCERT INDEX *under:*
(DUTT) **CDAX8004**   Sir Henry Wood conducts Vaughan Williams
(PEAR) **GEMMCD9342**   Vaughan Williams: Vocal Works
cond R. KEMPE
see CONCERT INDEX *under:*
(BBCR) **DMCD98**   BBC Proms - The Centenary: 1895-1995
cond O. KNUSSEN
Holloway: Second Concerto, Op. 40
cond S. KOUSSEVITZKY
see CONCERT INDEX *under:*
(PEAR) **GEMMCDS9408**   Koussevitsky conducts Sibelius
cond A. LAZAREV
Medtner: Piano Concerto 1
Scriabin: Piano Concerto
Tchaikovsky: Piano Concerto 1
cond W. LUTOSŁAWSKI
see CONCERT INDEX *under:*
(DG) **423 696-2GH**   Lutosławski/Stravinsky—Concerted Works
(DG) **431 664-2GH**   Lutosławski—Orchestral Works
(DG) **445 487-2GX3**   Mutter plays Modern Works
cond W. MENGELBERG
see CONCERT INDEX *under:*
(ARHI) **ADCD111**   Mengelberg Edition - Volume 5
cond M. NEARY
Tavener: Akathist of Thanksgiving
see CONCERT INDEX *under:*
(BBCR) **BBCRD9124**
Szymanowski/Panufnik—Symphonies
cond J. PRITCHARD
see CONCERT INDEX *under:*
(BBCR) **DMCD98**   BBC Proms - The Centenary: 1895-1995
cond G. ROZHDESTVENSKY
Prokofiev: Violin Concerto 1, Violin Concerto 2
Tippett: Child of Our Time (Cpte)
Vaughan Williams: Sancta civitas, Symphony 5
see CONCERT INDEX *under:*
(BBCR) **BBCRD9129**   Bridge/Britten/Pärt—Orchestral Works
(BBCR) **DMCD98**   BBC Proms - The Centenary: 1895-1995
(EMI) **CZS4 83177-2(2)**   Itzhak Perlman Edition (pt 2)
cond M. SARGENT
Elgar: Cello Concerto, Enigma Variations
Holst: Planets
see CONCERT INDEX *under:*
(BBCR) **DMCD98**   BBC Proms - The Centenary: 1895-1995
cond G. SCHURMANN
see CONCERT INDEX *under:*
(CHAN) **CHAN8301**   The Special Sound of Chandos
cond A. TAMAYO
Dillon: German Triptych (exc), Ignis noster
see CONCERT INDEX *under:*
cond A. TOSCANINI
see CONCERT INDEX *under:*
(BIDD) **WHL008/9**   Toscanini conducts the BBC Symphony Orchestra
(TEST) **SBT1015**   Toscanini—Unpublished HMV Recordings, 1935/38
cond R. VAUGHAN WILLIAMS
Vaughan Williams: Symphony 4
see CONCERT INDEX *under:*
(PEAR) **GEMMCD9342**   Vaughan Williams: Vocal Works
cond A. WALTER
Furtwängler: Symphony 2
cond B. WALTER
Brahms: Symphony 4
cond A. WEBERN
Berg: Violin Concerto

BBC SYMPHONY ORCHESTRA CELLOS
cond G. SIMON
see CONCERT INDEX *under:*
(CALA) **CACD0104**   The London Cello Sound

BBC THEATRE CHORUS
cond R. GOODALL
see CONCERT INDEX *under:*
(EMI) **CMS7 64727-2**   Britten—Opera excerpts and Folksongs

BBC WELSH CHORUS
cond A. KAPLAN
Mahler: Symphony 2
cond T. OTAKÁ
Franck: Psyché

BBC WELSH SYMPHONY CHORUS
cond R. HICKOX
Tavener: We shall see Him as He is

BBC WELSH SYMPHONY ORCHESTRA
cond R. HICKOX
Tavener: We shall see Him as He is
cond W. MATHIAS
Mathias: Symphony 1, Symphony 2
cond T. OTAKA
Rachmaninov: Isle of the Dead, Symphony 2, Symphony 3, Vocalise
see CONCERT INDEX *under:*
(NIMB) **NI5235**   R. Strauss: Orchestral Works
(NIMB) **NI5357**   Hoddinott—Orchestral Works
(RCA) **09026 62537-2**   Takemitsu—Cantos

BEAN, Hugh (vn)
Elgar: Violin Concerto, Violin Sonata
see CONCERT INDEX *under:*
(BBCR) **BBCRD9114**   Beethoven—Orchestral Works
(EMI) **CDM5 65100-2**   Vaughan Williams—Chamber Works
(EMI) **CDM5 65101-2**   A Warlock Centenary Album
(EMI) **CDM7 64022-2**   Vaughan Williams—Orchestral Works

BEAN, Nancy (vn)
see CONCERT INDEX *under:*
(KOCH) **37168-2**   Silent Noon—Songs of Vaughan Williams

BEASLEY-MURRAY, Timothy (treb)
see CONCERT INDEX *under:*
(EMI) **CDC7 47065-2**   Music of Sixteenth-Century Works

BEATON, Morag (sop)
Herrmann: Wuthering Heights (Cpte)

BEATTIE, Douglas (bar)
Wagner: Tristan und Isolde (Cpte)

BEATTIE, Eileen (pf)
see CONCERT INDEX *under:*
(APR) **APR7015**   The Auer Legacy, Vol.1

BEATTIE, Herbert (bass)
Beethoven: Christus am Oelberge, Op. 85

BEAUMONT, Kevin (organ)
see CONCERT INDEX *under:*
(ABBE) **CDCA954**   Dvořák/Elgar—Sacred Choral Works

BEAUNE BASILICA CHOIR
see CONCERT INDEX *under:*
(STUD) **SM1220.02**   Immortel Grégorien

BEAUPRÉ, Odette (mez)
see CONCERT INDEX *under:*
(DECC) **440 333-2DH**   Ravel—Vocal Works

BEAUREGARD, Lawrence (fl)
see CONCERT INDEX *under:*
(SONY) **SMK45844**   Varèse: Orchestral, Chamber and Vocal Works

BEAUX ARTS TRIO
Arensky: Piano Trio 1, Piano Trio 2
Beethoven: Piano Trios (exc)
Chausson: Piano Trio
Dvořák: Piano Trio 3, Piano Trio 4
Korngold: Piano Trio, Op. 1
Mozart: Piano Quartet, K478, Piano Quartet, K493
Ravel: Piano Trio
Schubert: Piano Trio, D28, Piano Trio 2
Schumann: Piano Quartet, Op. 47, Piano Quintet, Op. 44
Shostakovich: Piano Quintet, Op. 57, Piano Trio 2
Zemlinsky: Trio, Op. 3
see CONCERT INDEX *under:*
(PHIL) **412 620-2PH2**   Schubert: Music for piano trio
(PHIL) **416 838-2PH2**   Brahms: Piano Trios
(PHIL) **420 790-2PH**   Haydn: Piano Trios
(PHIL) **422 079-2PH3**   Mozart: Piano Trios
(PHIL) **422 514-2PME5**   The Complete Mozart Edition Vol 14
(PHIL) **432 061-2PM9**   Haydn—The 43 Piano Trios
(PHIL) **432 165-2PH2**   Schumann—Piano Trios
(PHIL) **438 365-2PM2**   Brahms—Complete Trios
(PHIL) **438 700-2PM2**   Schubert—Complete Trios
(PHIL) **446 154-2PM2**   The Complete Piano Trios
cond K. MASUR
Beethoven: Triple Concerto

BEAVAN, David (bass)
Puccini: Rondine (Cpte)
Shostakovich: Lady Macbeth of Mtsensk (Cpte)

BEAVAN, Nigel (bass)
Giordano: Andrea Chénier (Cpte)
see CONCERT INDEX *under:*
(HARM) **HMX290 1528/33(2)**   A Purcell Companion (pt 2)

BEAVER, Martin (vn)
F. Fossa: Guitar Trios, Op. 18 (exc)
Messiaen: Quatuor

BECCLES SIR JOHN LEMAN SCHOOL CHOIR
cond B. BRITTEN
Britten: St Nicolas

BECERRA, Flavio (ten)
Beethoven: Symphony 9

BEC-HELLOUIN ABBEY CHOIR
see CONCERT INDEX *under:*

(STUD) **SM1220.02** Immortel Grégorien
cond P. ZOBEL
Anon: Bec-Hellouin Abbey

BECHI, Gino (bar)
Verdi: Aida (Cpte)
see CONCERT INDEX *under:*
(EMI) **CHS7 64864-2(2)** La Scala Edition - Vol.2, 1915-46 (pt 2)
(EMI) **CHS7 69741-2(7)** Record of Singing, Vol.4—Italian School
(NIMB) **NI7853** Lauri-Volpi sings Verdi
(PREI) **89009** Gino Bechi (b. 1913)
(PREI) **89074** Tancredi Pasero (1893-1983) - II

BECHLY, Daniela (sop)
Wagner: Parsifal (Cpte)

BECHT, Hermann (bar)
R.Strauss: Arabella (Cpte)
Schoenberg: Gurrelieder
Wagner: Götterdämmerung (Cpte), Rheingold (Cpte), Siegfried (Cpte)
Weill: Dreigroschenoper (Cpte)

BECK, Gustaf (pf)
see CONCERT INDEX *under:*
(EMI) **CDH7 63493-2** Ginette Neveu—Recital
(TEST) **SBT1010** Ginette Neveu & Josef Hassid

BECKER, Josef (bass)
Hindemith: Nusch-Nuschi (Cpte)
Mendelssohn: Hochzeit des Camacho (Cpte)
Schreker: Gezeichneten (Cpte)
Spontini: Olimpie (Cpte)

BECKER, Peter (alto)
see CONCERT INDEX *under:*
(NEWP) **NC60021** Praetorius—Chorale Settings

BECKERBAUER, Stefan (treb)
Gluck: Orfeo ed Euridice (Cpte)

BECKER-FOSS, Hans Christoph (organ)
see CONCERT INDEX *under:*
(ROSE) **3221** Schumann—Miscellaneous Works

BECKETT, Edward (fl)
see CONCERT INDEX *under:*
(HYPE) **CDA66332** Malcolm Arnold—Orchestral Works

BECKLEY, Lisa (sop)
see CONCERT INDEX *under:*
(NAXO) **8 550765** Fauré—Choral Works

BECKMANN, Friedel (mez)
Bach: St Matthew Passion, BWV244 (exc)
see CONCERT INDEX *under:*
(EMI) **CHS7 69741-2(4)** Record of Singing, Vol.4—German School
(EMI) **CMS7 64008-2(1)** Wagner Singing on Record (pt 1)
(PREI) **89077** Torsten Ralf (1901-1954)

BECKMANN, Judith (sop)
Bach: Cantata 194
see CONCERT INDEX *under:*
(HANS) **98 890** Bach—Cantatas, Vol.37

BECQUET, Michel (tbn)
see CONCERT INDEX *under:*
(TIMP) **1C1010** Honegger—Chamber Works, Vol.3
(TIMP) **4C1012** Honegger—Chamber Works

BECU, Wim (bass sackbut)
see CONCERT INDEX *under:*
(EMI) **CDC7 49555-2** Tallis: Sacred Choral Works

BEDEX, Henri (sngr)
Lecocq: Jour et la Nuit (Cpte)
Messager: Monsieur Beaucaire (Cpte)

BEDFORD, Peter (bass)
G. Charpentier: Louise (Cpte)

BEDFORD, Steuart (cond)
see Aldeburgh Fest Ens

BEDNÁŘ, Vaclav (bass)
Martinů: Julietta (Cpte)
Smetana: Devil's Wall (Cpte)

BEECHAM, Sir Thomas (cond)
see BBC SO

BEECHAM, Sir Thomas (pf)
see CONCERT INDEX *under:*
(DUTT) **CDLX7011** Beecham conducts Delius

BEECHAM CHORAL SOCIETY
cond T. BEECHAM
Borodin: Prince Igor (exc)
see CONCERT INDEX *under:*
(EMI) **CDS7 47509-8** Beecham conducts Delius
(EMI) **CHS7 63715-2** Mozart: Die Entführung, etc

BEEDIE, Norman (pf)
see CONCERT INDEX *under:*
(BMS) **BMS416CD** Berkeley—Music for Solo Piano and Piano Duets

BEEGLE, Raymond (cond)
see NY Voc Arts Ens

BEENHOUWER, Josef de (pf)
see CONCERT INDEX *under:*
(PART) **Part9293-2** Clara Schumann—Works for Piano

BEER, Sidney (cond)
see National SO

BEESLEY, Mark (bar)
Verdi: Traviata (Cpte)

BEESLEY, Shauna (mez)
Purcell: Dido (Cpte)

BEETHOVEN ACADEMY
cond J. CAEYERS
see CONCERT INDEX *under:*
(HARM) **HMC90 1489** Nielsen—Orchestral Works

BEETHOVEN BROADWOOD TRIO
Spohr: Piano Trio 1, Piano Trio 2

BEGDE, Dietrich (vc)
see CONCERT INDEX *under:*
(ASV) **CDDCA645** Vivaldi—Concertos

BEGG, Heather (mez)
Berlioz: Troyens (Cpte)
Britten: Little Sweep (Cpte)
Sullivan: Iolanthe (exc)

BEGLEY, Kim (ten)
Bellini: Norma (Cpte)
Mendelssohn: Elijah (Cpte)
R. Strauss: Salome (Cpte)
Verdi: Traviata (Cpte)
Wagner: Rheingold (Cpte)

BÉGUELIN, Jean-Noël (bass)
see CONCERT INDEX *under:*
(EMI) **CDM7 63104-2** Alfredo Krauss - Opera Recital

BEHLE, Renate (sop)
Schumann: Genoveva (Cpte)
Spohr: Jessonda (Cpte)
Zemlinsky: Kreidekreis (Cpte)

BEHR, Randall (cond)
see Philh

BEHREND, Jeanne (pf)
see CONCERT INDEX *under:*
(STOK) **LSCD20** Stokowski conducts Philadelphia Rarities

BEHRENS, Hildegard (sop)
Berg: Wozzeck (Cpte)
Humperdinck: Hänsel und Gretel (Cpte)
R. Strauss: Elektra (Cpte), Frau ohne Schatten (Cpte), Salome (Cpte)
Wagner: Fliegende Holländer (Cpte), Götterdämmerung (Cpte), Siegfried (Cpte), Walküre (Cpte)
Weber: Freischütz (Cpte)
see CONCERT INDEX *under:*
(DG) **445 354-2GX14** Wagner—Der Ring des Nibelungen

BEHRINGER, Michael (organ)
see CONCERT INDEX *under:*
(ASTR) **E8724** Jenkins—Consort Music for Viols

BEILKE, Irma (sop)
Mozart: Zauberflöte (Cpte)
see CONCERT INDEX *under:*
(PREI) **89049** Margarete Teschemacher (1903-1959)

BEINUM, Eduard van (cond)
see Concertgebouw

BEISER, Maya (vc)
see CONCERT INDEX *under:*
(KOCH) **37258-2** Gubaidulina/Ustvolskaya—Works for Cello

BEISSEL, Heribert (cond)
see Bonn Klassische PO

BEKE, R.O. von (vc)
see CONCERT INDEX *under:*
(PEAR) **GEMMCDS9004/6(2)** Singers of Imperial Russia, Vol.3 (pt 2)

(THE) BEKOVA SISTERS
Schubert: Notturno, D897, Piano Trio 2

BEKOVA TRIO
Brahms: Piano Trio 1, Piano Trio 2
Rachmaninov: Trio élégiaque, Op. 9, Trio élégiaque (1892)

BEL CANTO ENSEMBLE
cond D. SPOHR
see CONCERT INDEX *under:*
(SCHW) **314322** Ensemble Belcanto—Lieder Recital

BELA, Dajos (cond)
see orch

BELAMARIC, Neven (sngr)
Schreker: Irrelohe (Cpte)

BELANOVÁ, Kvĕta (sop)
Janáček: Jenufa (Cpte)

BELARSKY, Sidor (bass)
Beethoven: Fidelio (Cpte)

BELAZA-LEOZ, Fernando (bar)
Martín y Soler: Cosa Rara (Cpte)

BELCOURT, Emile (ten)
Delibes: Lakmé (Cpte)
Nyman: Man Who Mistook His Wife for a Hat (Cpte)
Wagner: Rheingold (Cpte)

BELFAST PHILHARMONIC SOCIETY
cond Y. P. TORTELIER
Ravel: Daphnis et Chloé (Cpte)

BELGIAN NATIONAL ORCHESTRA
cond A. CLUYTENS
see CONCERT INDEX *under:*
(EMI) **CZS5 68220-2** André Cluytens—A profile

BELGIAN RADIO AND TELEVISION CHORUS
cond P. STRAUSS
Franck: Psyché

BELGIAN RADIO AND TELEVISION ORCHESTRA
cond F. DEVREESE
see CONCERT INDEX *under:*
(MARC) **8 223505** Devreese—Piano Concertos
(MARC) **8 223680** Devreese—Orchestral Works
(MARC) **8 223681** Devreese—Film music
cond A. RAHBARI
Brahms: Haydn Variations, Symphony 1
see CONCERT INDEX *under:*
(DINT) **DICD920100** Salve Antverpia
(DINT) **DICD920101** Flemish Rhapsodies
(NAXO) **8 550281** Brahms: Orchestral Works
(NAXO) **8 550505** Debussy—Orchestral Works
(NAXO) **8 550606** Soprano Arias from Italian Operas

BELKIN, Boris (vn)
Brahms: Violin Concerto
Bruch: Violin Concerto 1
Prokofiev: Violin Concerto 1, Violin Concerto 2
Shostakovich: Violin Concerto 1
Sibelius: Violin Concerto
see CONCERT INDEX *under:*
(DECC) **436 415-2DH** R. Strauss—Orchestral Works
(DENO) **CO-78918** Mozart—Orchestral Works

BELL, Catriona (mez)
Janáček: Fate (Cpte)

BELL, David (organ)
see CONCERT INDEX *under:*
(EMI) **CDC7 54205-2** Vivaldi—Double Concertos

BELL, Donald (bar)
see CONCERT INDEX *under:*
(EMI) **CHS5 65003-2** Walton conducts Walton
(SONY) **SMK47638** Vaughan Williams—Orchestral Works

BELL, Donaldson (bar)
Herrmann: Wuthering Heights (Cpte)
Massenet: Werther (Cpte)

BELL, Galloway (sngr)
Saxton: Caritas (Cpte)

BELL, Joshua (vn)
Bruch: Violin Concerto 1
Mendelssohn: Violin Concerto, Op.64
Tchaikovsky: Violin Concerto
Wieniawski: Violin Concerto 2
see CONCERT INDEX *under:*
(DECC) **433 519-2DH** Works for Violin and Orchestra
(DECC) **436 376-2DH** Mozart—Works for Violin and Orchestra
(DECC) **440 331-2DH** Prokofiev—Orchestral Works
(DECC) **440 926-2DH** Prokofiev—Works for Violin and Piano

BELL, Sebastian (alto fl)
see CONCERT INDEX *under:*
(SONY) **SK46720** John Williams plays music of Takemitsu

BELL, Sebastian (fl)
see CONCERT INDEX *under:*
(NONE) **7559-79362-2** Górecki—Orchestral and Vocal Works

BELL, Susan (bn)
see CONCERT INDEX *under:*
(EMI) **CDS7 47901-8** Villa-Lobos: Orchestral and Chamber Works
(NIMB) **NI5167** Benjamin—Antara; J. Harvey—Song Offerings; Boulez—Orch music

BELLA, Benito di (bar)
Mascagni: Amico Fritz (Cpte)

BELLA, Margaret (vc)
see CONCERT INDEX *under:*
(PHIL) **426 076-2PCC** Vivaldi: Concertos

BELLAMY, Marcia (mez)
Busoni: Arlecchino (Cpte)

BELLANTONI, Giuseppe (bar)
see CONCERT INDEX *under:*
(BONG) **GB1043-2** Italian Baritones of the Acoustic Era
(MEMO) **HR4408/9(2)** Singers in Genoa, Vol.1 (disc 2)

BELLEAU, Marc (bass)
Berlioz: Troyens (Cpte)

BELLERI, L. M. (sop)
see CONCERT INDEX *under:*
(RCA) **GD87808** Lawrence Tibbett sings Opera Arias

BELLEZZA, Vincenzo (cond)
see orch

BELLEZZA, Vincenzo (pf)
see CONCERT INDEX *under:*
(CLUB) **CL99-060** Enrico Caruso—Opera & Song Recital
(PEAR) **EVC4(1)** The Caruso Edition, Vol.4 (pt 1)
(RCA) **GD60495(6)** The Complete Caruso Collection (pt 6)

BELLINCIONI, Gemma (sop)
see CONCERT INDEX *under:*
(EMI) **CHS7 64860-2(1)** La Scala Edition - Vol.1, 1878-1914 (pt 1)

(WERG) **WER60054-50** Magnificathy—the many voices of Cathy Berberian

BERBIÉ, Guy (ten)
Bizet: Carmen (Cpte)

BERBIÉ, Jane (mez)
Auber: Fra Diavolo (Cpte)
Berlioz: Benvenuto Cellini (Cpte)
Bizet: Carmen (Cpte)
Boïeldieu: Dame blanche (Cpte)
Cavalli: Ormindo (Cpte)
Delibes: Lakmé (Cpte)
G. Charpentier: Louise (Cpte)
Massenet: Cendrillon (Cpte)
Mozart: Nozze di Figaro (Cpte)
Offenbach: Orphée aux enfers (Cpte)
Ravel: Enfant et les Sortilèges (Cpte), Heure espagnole (Cpte)
Rossini: Turco in Italia (Cpte)
Roussel: Padmâvatî (Cpte)
Verdi: Otello (Cpte)
see CONCERT INDEX under:
(EMI) **CDM7 63182-2** The Incomparable Callas

BERENDSEN, Emilie (mez)
see CONCERT INDEX under:
(ROMA) **RR1941** Terezín - The Music 1941-44

BEREZOVSKY, Boris (pf)
Chopin: Etudes
Rachmaninov: Chopin Variations, Op. 22, Piano Concerto 3, Piano Sonata 1, Preludes (exc)
see CONCERT INDEX under:
(TELD) **4509-94539-2** Ravel—Piano Works
(TELD) **9031-77476-2** Schumann—Piano Works

BEREZOWSKI, Nicolai (cond)
see RCA SO

BERG, Hans (cond)
Wagner: Meistersinger (Cpte)

BERG, Jacob (fl)
Bolcom: Sessions I

BERG, Nathan (bass)
Handel: Messiah (Cpte)
Mozart: Requiem
Purcell: Dido (Cpte), Dioclesian, Z627 (exc)

BERGAMO, John (cond)
see American Gamelan

BERGAMO HOUSE ORCHESTRA
cond T. BRICCETTI
Mayr: Rosa Bianca (Cpte)

BERGANZA, Teresa (mez)
Bizet: Carmen (Cpte)
Duruflé: Requiem
Falla: Atlántida (Cpte), Vida breve (Cpte)
J. Strauss II: Fledermaus (Cpte)
Massenet: Don Quichotte (Cpte)
Mozart: Clemenza di Tito (Cpte), Don Giovanni (Cpte), Finta semplice (Cpte), Nozze di Figaro (Cpte)
Offenbach: Périchole (Cpte)
Penella: Gato Montés (Cpte)
Puccini: Madama Butterfly (Cpte)
Rossini: Barbiere di Siviglia (Cpte), Italiana in Algeri (Cpte)
Stravinsky: Pulcinella
Vivaldi: Gloria, RV589, Magnificat, RV611
see CONCERT INDEX under:
(CLAV) **CD50-8206** Venetian Music for Voice and Instruments
(CLAV) **CD50-9016** Teresa Berganza—Recital
(DECC) **417 771-2DM** de Falla: Orchestral & Stage Works
(DECC) **421 899-2DA** Teresa Berganza - Mozart Arias
(DECC) **433 908-2DM2** Falla—Orchestral Music
(DECC) **436 462-2DM** Ten Top Mezzos
(DG) **431 104-2GB** Great Voices - Plácido Domingo
(DG) **435 848-2GX2** Spanish Songs - Berganza

BERGASA, Carlos (bar)
Puccini: Bohème (Cpte)

BERGASA, Carlos (sngr)
Penella: Gato Montés (Cpte)

BERGEL, Erich (cond)
see Budapest PO

BERGEN CATHEDRAL CHOIR
cond M. MANGERSNES
see CONCERT INDEX under:
(AURO) **ACD4971** Nystedt—Chamber and Vocal Works

BERGEN PHILHARMONIC ORCHESTRA
cond A. CECCATO
Schumann: Symphony 1, Symphony 2
see CONCERT INDEX under:
(SIMA) **PSC3101** Valen—Complete Symphonies
cond C. EGGEN
Hvoslef: Violin Concerto
cond N. JÄRVI
Hvoslef: Antigone
see CONCERT INDEX under:
(BIS) **BIS-CD420** Britten—Orchestral Works
cond D. KITAIENKO
Grieg: Symphonic Dances, Symphony
Hvoslef: Antigone
see CONCERT INDEX under:
(CHAN) **CHAN9178** Rimsky-Korsakov—Orchestral Works
(VIRG) **VC7 59613-2** Grieg/Liszt—Piano Works

(VIRG) **VJ7 59659-2** The Sorcerer's Apprentice

BERGEN SYMPHONY ORCHESTRA
see CONCERT INDEX under:
(BIS) **BIS-CD227** Tubin: Orchestral Works
cond K. ANDERSEN
see CONCERT INDEX under:
(NKF) **NKFCD50009-2** Svendsen—Orchestral Works
cond C. GARAGULY
see CONCERT INDEX under:
(BLUE) **ABCD006** Jussi Björling Live - Holland 1939, Norway 1954
cond D. KITAIENKO
see CONCERT INDEX under:
(CHAN) **CHAN9229** Rimsky-Korsakov—Orchestral Works

BERGEN WIND QUINTET
see CONCERT INDEX under:
(BIS) **BIS-CD291** 20th-Century Music for Wind Quintet
(BIS) **BIS-CD428** Nielsen—Wind Chamber Music

BERGER, Angelica (hp)
see CONCERT INDEX under:
(CAPR) **10 805** Mozart: Wind Concertos

BERGER, Erna (sop)
Mozart: Don Giovanni (Cpte), Zauberflöte (Cpte)
see CONCERT INDEX under:
(ACAN) **43 268** Peter Anders sings German Opera Arias
(NIMB) **NI7848** Great Singers at the Berlin State Opera
(PREI) **89035** Erna Berger (1900-1990) - I
(PREI) **89057** Charles Kullmann (1903-1982)
(RCA) **09026 61580-2(5)** RCA/Met 100 Singers, 100 Years (pt 5)
(SCHW) **314672** Vienna State Opera Live, Vol.17

BERGER, Julius (pf)
see South-West German RSO

BERGER, Julius (vc)
Dittersdorf: String Quintets (1789) (exc)
Hindemith: Cello Pieces, op 8, Cello Sonata, op 11/3
see CONCERT INDEX under:
(CPO) **CPO999 020-2** Wilhelm Killmayer: Chamber Works
(CPO) **CPO999 077-2** Korngold—Orchestral Works Vol.3
(CPO) **CPO999 079-2** Pfitzner—Violin Concerto, etc
(EBS) **EBS6058** Boccherini—Cello Concerti
(ORFE) **C251912H** Vivaldi—Cello Sonatas
(SONY) **SK64301** Beethoven—Songs from the British Isles
(WERG) **WER60145-50** Hindemith: Cello & Piano Works, Vol.2

BERGER, Kurt (bass cl)
see CONCERT INDEX under:
(SCHW) **310501** Works for Wind Instruments

BERGER, Kurt (cl)
see CONCERT INDEX under:
(ORFE) **C015821A** Stravinsky: Choral and Vocal Works

BERGER, Leon (bar)
Sondheim: Pacific Overtures (exc)

BERGER, Rudolf (ten)
see CONCERT INDEX under:
(SUPR) **11 2136-2(3)** Emmy Destinn—Complete Edition, Discs 5 to 8

BERGERICH, Martha (pf)
see CONCERT INDEX under:
(ROSE) **3221** Schumann—Miscellaneous Works

BERGER-TUNA, Helmut (bass)
Einem: Dantons Tod (Cpte)
K. A. Hartmann: Simplicius Simplicissimus (Cpte)
Puccini: Fanciulla del West (Cpte)
Wagner: Meistersinger (Cpte)
Wolf: Corregidor (Cpte)

BERGGOLD, Christiane (mez)
B. Goldschmidt: Gewaltige Hahnrei (Cpte)
Gurlitt: Wozzeck (Cpte)
Schreker: Gezeichneten (Cpte)

BERGIUS, Alan (treb)
see CONCERT INDEX under:
(TELD) **2292-42615-2** Bach—Cantatas, Volume 31
(TELD) **2292-42617-2** Bach—Cantatas, Volume 32
(TELD) **2292-42631-2** Bach—Cantatas, Volume 35
(TELD) **2292-42632-2** Bach—Cantatas, Volume 37
(TELD) **2292-42635-2** Bach—Cantatas, Volume 40
(TELD) **4509-91761-2** Bach—Cantatas, Vol.7
(TELD) **4509-91762-2** Bach—Cantatas, Vol.8
(TELD) **4509-91763-2** Bach—Cantatas, Vol.9
(TELD) **9031-74798-2** Bach—Arias and Duets

BERGLUND, Joel (bar)
see CONCERT INDEX under:
(EMI) **CHS7 69741-2(5)** Record of Singing, Vol.4—Scandinavian School
(SCHW) **314622** Vienna State Opera Live, Vol.12

BERGLUND, Paavo (cond)
see COE

BERGLUND, Rut (contr)
Mozart: Zauberflöte (Cpte)
Wagner: Meistersinger (exc)

BERGMAN, Marcel (vc)
Beethoven: Piano Trios (exc)
Brahms: Clarinet Trio

BERGMAN, Marit (vn)
see CONCERT INDEX under:
(BIS) **BIS-CD403** Handel: Vocal and Chamber Works

BERGMANN, Ludwig (pf)
see CONCERT INDEX under:
(EMI) **CHS7 69741-2(3)** Record of Singing, Vol.4—French School

BERGMANN, Walter (hpd)
see CONCERT INDEX under:
(VANG) **08.2003.72** Purcell—Celebrated Songs,Sacred Airs and Concert Pieces
(VANG) **08.5060.71** Purcell—Choice

BERGONZI, Carlo (ten)
Cilea: Adriana Lecouvreur (Cpte)
Donizetti: Lucia di Lammermoor (Cpte)
Puccini: Bohème (Cpte), Edgar (Cpte), Madama Butterfly (Cpte), Tosca (Cpte)
Verdi: Aida (Cpte), Attila (Cpte), Ballo in maschera (Cpte), Ernani (Cpte), Forza del destino (Cpte), Luisa Miller (Cpte), Macbeth (Cpte), Masnadieri (Cpte), Oberto (Cpte), Rigoletto (Cpte), Traviata (Cpte)
see CONCERT INDEX under:
(DECC) **417 686-2DC** Puccini—Operatic Arias
(DECC) **430 481-2DX2** Renata Tebaldi sings Opera Arias
(DECC) **436 463-2DM** Ten Top Tenors
(DG) **419 257-2GH3** 'Cav' and 'Pag', etc
(RCA) **09026 61580-2(7)** RCA/Met 100 Singers, 100 Years (pt 7)

BERGQUIST, Eleanor (sop)
Massenet: Cid (Cpte)

BERGQVIST, Christian (vn)
see CONCERT INDEX under:
(BIS) **BIS-CD364** The Russian Violin
(BIS) **BIS-CD377** Schnittke: Concertos
(BIS) **BIS-CD537** Schnittke Edition, Volume 12

BERGSTRÖM, Anders (bar)
Lidholm: Dream Play (Cpte)

BERIO, Daniel (vn)
see CONCERT INDEX under:
(DENO) **CO-75448** Berio—Duets for Two Violins, Volume 1

BERIO, Luciano (cond)
see Cologne RSO

BERKELEY, Sir Lennox (cond)
see LPO

BERKELEY, Michael (spkr)
see CONCERT INDEX under:
(DG) **447 068-2GH** Stravinsky—The Flood, etc

BERKELEY SYMPHONY ORCHESTRA
cond K. NAGANO
see CONCERT INDEX under:
(HARM) **HMU90 7106** Kraft—Orchestral Works

BERKELEY (CALIFORNIA) UNIVERSITY CHAMBER CHORUS
cond P. BRETT
M. Feldman: Rothko Chapel
see CONCERT INDEX under:
(NALB) **NA015CD** Lou Harrison: Various Works
cond N. MCGEGAN
Handel: Judas Maccabaeus (Cpte), Messiah (Cpte), Susanna (Cpte), Theodora (Cpte)

BERKELEY (CALIFORNIA) UNIVERSITY CHORUS
cond P. BRETT
see CONCERT INDEX under:
(NALB) **NA015CD** Lou Harrison: Various Works

BERKELEY-STEELE, Richard (ten)
Henze: English Cat (Cpte)

BERKES, Kálmán (cl)
see CONCERT INDEX under:
(NAXO) **8 550749** Bartók—Violin Sonatas; Contrasts

BERKES, Kálmán (cl/dir)
see CONCERT INDEX under:
(NAXO) **8 553178** Krommer—Clarinet Concertos

BERKI, Sándor (hn)
see CONCERT INDEX under:
(NAXO) **8 553090** Beethoven—Chamber Works

BERKMAN, Louis (bar)
Bloch: Sacred Service

BERKOWITZ, Paul (pf)
Rossini: Petite messe solennelle
Schubert: Piano Sonata, D784, Piano Sonata, D894, Piano Sonata, D959, Piano Sonata, D960, Waltzes, D365
see CONCERT INDEX under:
(MERI) **CDE84102** Schubert—Piano Works

BERKSHIRE BOY CHOIR
cond L. BERNSTEIN
Bernstein: Mass (Cpte)

BERKSHIRE FESTIVAL CHORUS
cond P. MONTEUX
see CONCERT INDEX under:
(RCA) **09026 61893-2** Pierre Monteux Edition

BERLIN, Irving (sngr)
see CONCERT INDEX under:
(PEAR) **GEMMCDS9056/8** Music from the New York Stage, Vol. 3: 1913-17

BERLIN ANCIENT MUSIC ACADEMY
see CONCERT INDEX under:
(CAPR) **10 134** Flute and Recorder Concertos

(CAPR) 10 338   Telemann—Cantatas and Odes
cond M. CREED
Hasse: Conversione di Sant' Agostino (Cpte)

BERLIN ARS-NOVA ENSEMBLE
cond P. SCHWARZ
see CONCERT INDEX *under:*
(LARG) **Largo 5115**   Goldschmidt—Letzte Kapitel

BERLIN ART SCHOOL CHAMBER CHOIR
cond M. ATZMON
Haydn: Schöpfung (Cpte)

BERLIN BAROCK COMPAGNEY
see CONCERT INDEX *under:*
(CAPR) 10 459   Music from Charlottenburg Castle

BERLIN CATHEDRAL BOYS' CHOIR
cond R. CHAILLY
Orff: Carmina Burana
cond H. VON KARAJAN
Bach: St Matthew Passion, BWV244 (Cpte)
cond S. OZAWA
Orff: Carmina burana

BERLIN CHAMBER ORCHESTRA
cond M. POMMER
see CONCERT INDEX *under:*
(CAPR) 10 069   C.P.E. Bach—Oboe Concertos
(CAPR) 10 113   Berlin Opera Composers
cond P. WOHLERT
Bach: Brandenburg Concertos (exc), Harpsichord
Concerto, BWV1054
Dvořák: Serenade, Op. 22, Slavonic Dances (exc)
see CONCERT INDEX *under:*
(CAPR) 10 801   Mozart—Serenades & Divertimenti

**BERLIN CHARLOTTENBURG STÄDTISCHEN OPER
ORCHESTRA**
cond J. HEIDENREICH
see CONCERT INDEX *under:*
(PEAR) **GEMMCD9451**   Alexander Kipnis

BERLIN CITY OPERA ORCHESTRA
cond F. FRICSAY
see CONCERT INDEX *under:*
(MYTO) **3MCD93381**   Wagner—Die Walküre, etc
cond W. LADWIG
see CONCERT INDEX *under:*
(PREI) 89088   Walther Ludwig (1902-1981)
cond H.U. MÜLLER
see CONCERT INDEX *under:*
(PREI) 89049   Margarete Teschemacher (1903-
1959)
cond W.F. REUSS
see CONCERT INDEX *under:*
(PREI) 89035   Erna Berger (1900-1990) - I
cond A. ROTHER
Wagner: Tristan und Isolde (exc)
cond A. VON ZEMLINSKY
see CONCERT INDEX *under:*
(PREI) 89057   Charles Kullmann (1903-1982)
(PREI) 89071   Gerhard Hüsch (1901-1984) - II
cond F. ZWEIG
see CONCERT INDEX *under:*
(PREI) 89057   Charles Kullmann (1903-1982)

BERLIN COURT OPERA CHORUS
cond A. PILZ
see CONCERT INDEX *under:*
(SUPR) 11 2136-2(3)   Emmy Destinn—Complete
Edition, Discs 5 to 8
cond B. SEIDLER-WINKLER
see CONCERT INDEX *under:*
(SUPR) 11 2136-2(3)   Emmy Destinn—Complete
Edition, Discs 5 to 8

BERLIN DEUTSCHE OPER CHORUS
Beethoven: Choral Fantasia
cond G. ALBRECHT
Spontini: Olimpie (Cpte)
cond F. ALLERS
Offenbach: Vie Parisienne (exc)
cond K. BÖHM
Berg: Wozzeck (Cpte)
Mozart: Nozze di Figaro (Cpte)
cond C. VON DOHNÁNYI
Henze: Jungе Lord (Cpte)
cond E. JOCHUM
Orff: Carmina Burana
Wagner: Meistersinger (Cpte)
see CONCERT INDEX *under:*
(BELA) 450 121-2   Plácido Domingo
(DG) 423 127-2GX4   Bruckner: Sacred Works for
Chorus
(DG) 431 104-2GB   Great Voices - Plácido Domingo
cond H. VON KARAJAN
Bach: St Matthew Passion, BWV244 (Cpte)
Beethoven: Fidelio (Cpte)
Debussy: Pelléas et Mélisande (Cpte)
Haydn: Jahreszeiten (exc)
Lehár: Lustige Witwe (exc)
Mendelssohn: Symphony 2
Mozart: Don Giovanni (Cpte), Zauberflöte (Cpte)
Puccini: Bohème (Cpte), Tosca (Cpte)
Verdi: Don Carlo (Cpte), Otello (Cpte), Trovatore
(Cpte)
Wagner: Götterdämmerung (Cpte), Lohengrin (Cpte),
Parsifal (Cpte), Tristan und Isolde (Cpte)
see CONCERT INDEX *under:*
(DG) 423 252-2GC   Stravinsky—Orchestral Works
(DG) 429 664-2GSE3   Mendelssohn—Complete
Symphonies
(DG) 435 211-2GX15   Wagner—Der Ring des
Nibelungen

(DG) 435 712-2GX2   Lehár—The Merry Widow.
Suppé—Overtures
cond J. KEILBERTH
Weber: Freischütz (Cpte)
cond R. KEMPE
Wagner: Meistersinger (Cpte)
cond F. KONWITSCHNY
Wagner: Fliegende Holländer (Cpte)
see CONCERT INDEX *under:*
(EMI) **CMS5 65212-2**   Wagner—Les introuvables du
Ring
cond L. MAAZEL
Verdi: Traviata (Cpte)
cond L. VON MATAČIĆ
Weber: Freischütz (Cpte)
cond W. SCHMIDT-BOELCKE
Raymond: Maske in Blau (exc)
cond W. SCHÜCHTER
see CONCERT INDEX *under:*
(EMI) **CDH5 65201-2**   Leonie Rysanek - Operatic
Recital
(EMI) **CHS7 69741-2(4)**   Record of Singing,
Vol.4—German School
cond G. SINOPOLI
Verdi: Macbeth (Cpte), Nabucco (Cpte)
see CONCERT INDEX *under:*
(DG) 415 283-2GH   Opera Choruses

BERLIN DEUTSCHE OPER ORCHESTRA
cond K. BÖHM
Berg: Lulu (Cpte), Wozzeck (Cpte)
Mozart: Nozze di Figaro (Cpte)
cond C. VON DOHNÁNYI
Henze: Junge Lord (Cpte)
cond A. GRÜBER
see CONCERT INDEX *under:*
(ACAN) 43 268   Peter Anders sings German Opera
Arias
cond E. JOCHUM
Orff: Carmina Burana
Wagner: Meistersinger (Cpte)
see CONCERT INDEX *under:*
(BELA) 450 121-2   Plácido Domingo
(DG) 431 104-2GB   Great Voices - Plácido Domingo
cond F. KONWITSCHNY
Wagner: Fliegende Holländer (Cpte)
(EMI) **CMS5 65212-2**   Wagner—Les introuvables du
Ring
cond F. LEITNER
see CONCERT INDEX *under:*
(DG) 447 352-2GDB2   Gundula Janowitz - A Portrait
cond W. LUTZE
(PREI) 90083   Maria Reining
cond L. MAAZEL
Verdi: Traviata (Cpte)
cond L. VON MATAČIĆ
Weber: Freischütz (Cpte)
cond A. ROTHER
see CONCERT INDEX *under:*
(EMI) **CHS7 69741-2(4)**   Record of Singing,
Vol.4—German School
(PREI) 90168   Wagner—Die Meistersinger, Act 2, etc
cond H. SCHMIDT-ISSERSTEDT
(PREI) 90078   Hilde Konetzni
cond W. SCHÜCHTER
(EMI) **CHS7 69741-2(4)**   Record of Singing,
Vol.4—German School
cond G. SINOPOLI
R. Strauss: Salome (Cpte)
Verdi: Macbeth (Cpte), Nabucco (Cpte)
see CONCERT INDEX *under:*
(DG) 415 283-2GH   Opera Choruses
cond G. STEEGER
(PREI) 89082   Margarete Klose (1902-1968)
cond H. STEINKOPF
(PREI) 90168   Wagner—Die Meistersinger, Act 2, etc
cond C. THIELEMANN
see CONCERT INDEX *under:*
(EMI) **CDC7 54776-2**   René Kollo sings Wagner and
Strauss

BERLIN DEUTSCHES SYMPHONY ORCHESTRA
cond G. ALBRECHT
Gurlitt: Wozzeck (Cpte)
cond R. CHAILLY
(DECC) 425 790-2DH   Mahler—Lieder
cond A. FRANCIS
Pettersson: Symphony 9
cond VLADIMIR ASHKENAZY
Mendelssohn: Midsummer Night's Dream (exc),
Octet, Op. 20, Symphony 1, Symphony 5
(DECC) 440 229-2DH   Stravinsky—Works for Piano
and Orchestra
(DECC) 443 772-2DH   Stravinsky—Ballet Music
cond L. ZAGROSEK
B. Goldschmidt: Gewaltige Hahnrei (Cpte)
Schreker: Gezeichneten (Cpte)
see CONCERT INDEX *under:*
(SONY) **S2K66836**   Goldschmidt—Beatrice Cenci, etc

BERLIN DOCTORS' CHOIR
cond K. SINGER
see CONCERT INDEX *under:*
(PREI) 89027   Sigrid Onegin (1889-1943)

BERLIN ENSEMBLE
Avison: Concerti after D. Scarlatti (exc)
see CONCERT INDEX *under:*
(ORFE) **C126901A**   Salonmusik

BERLIN FESTIVAL ORCHESTRA
cond V. PETROSCHOFF
see CONCERT INDEX *under:*
(ROSE) 3221   Schumann—Miscellaneous Works

BERLIN GÖBEL TRIO
Schumann: Fantasiestücke, Op. 88, Piano Trio 1,
Piano Trio 2, Piano Trio 3
cond T. UKIGAYA
see CONCERT INDEX *under:*
(THOR) **CTH2013**   Martinů—Orchestral Works

BERLIN KÜNSTLERTHEATER ORCHESTRA
cond E. HAUKE
see CONCERT INDEX *under:*
(EMI) **CDH7 69787-2**   Richard Tauber sings Operetta
Arias
(MMOI) **CDMOIR425**   Three Tenors, Volume 2
(NIMB) **NI7833**   Schöne & Tauber in Operetta
(PEAR) **GEMMCD9381**   Richard Tauber sings Lieder

BERLIN MOTET CHOIR
cond F. FRICSAY
Gluck: Orfeo ed Euridice (Cpte)

BERLIN PHILHARMONIA ENSEMBLE
Schubert: Octet, D803
see CONCERT INDEX *under:*
(DENO) **CO-2199**   Boccherini: String Quintets

BERLIN PHILHARMONIA QUARTET
see CONCERT INDEX *under:*
(DENO) **C37-7034**   Mozart Music for oboe and cor
anglais

BERLIN PHILHARMONIC CHORUS
cond L. SEGERSTAM
Mahler: Symphony 8

BERLIN PHILHARMONIC OCTET
Beethoven: Septet, Op.20, Sextet, Op.81b
Brahms: String Quintet 1, String Quintet 2
see CONCERT INDEX *under:*
(PHIL) **446 172-2PM2**   Brahms—Complete Quintets

BERLIN PHILHARMONIC ORCHESTRA
Mozart: Piano Concerto 9, Piano Concerto 17, Piano
Concerto 22, Piano Concerto 23
Vivaldi: Concerti Grossi, Op.3
(DG) **445 400-2GDO10**   Ferenc Fricsay - A Portrait
cond C. ABBADO
Brahms: Alto Rhapsody, Op. 53, Deutsches Requiem,
Op.45 (Cpte), Gesang der Parzen, Op. 89, Piano
Concerto 1, Piano Concerto 2, Symphony 1,
Symphony 2, Violin Concerto
Dvořák: Noon Witch, Symphony 8
Glazunov: Violin Concerto
Janáček: Diary of One who Disappeared, Sinfonietta
Mahler: Symphony 1, Symphony 5, Symphony 8
Mozart: Mass, K427
Mussorgsky: Boris Godunov (Cpte), Songs and
Dances of Death
Prokofiev: Piano Concerto 1, Piano Concerto 3
Rachmaninov: Piano Concerto 2, Piano Concerto 3
Ravel: Piano Concerto
Rossini: Viaggio a Reims (Cpte)
Schoenberg: Piano Concerto
Schumann: Piano Concerto, Szenen aus Goethes
Faust (Cpte)
Tchaikovsky: Symphony 5, Violin Concerto
see CONCERT INDEX *under:*
(DG) 429 765-2GH   Brahms—Orchestral & Choral
Works
(DG) 435 349-2GH   Brahms—Orchestral and Choral
Works
(DG) 435 617-2GH   Beethoven in Berlin—New Year's
Eve Concert
(DG) 439 413-2GCL   Prokofiev—Orchestral Works
(DG) 439 768-2GH   Wagner-Gala - New Year's Eve
Concert 1993
(DG) 439 770-2GH3   Beethoven—Piano Concertos
(DG) 445 238-2GH   Mussorgsky—Orchestral and
Choral Works
(DG) 445 501-2GMA   Bartók/Janáček—Orchestral
Works
(DG) 445 522-2GMA   Schumann—Piano Works
(DG) 447 023-2GX12   Mahler—The Symphonies
(DG) 447 389-2GH   Hindemith—Orchestral Works
(DG) 447 438-2GOR   Prokofiev/Ravel—Piano
Concertos
(SONY) **SK48063**   Mozart—Symphonies
(SONY) **SK48385**   Mozart—Symphonies
(SONY) **SK52565**   New Year's Eve Concert 1992
(SONY) **SK53277**   Mozart—Orchestral Works
(SONY) **SK53360**   Mahler/Nono—Vocal Works
(SONY) **SK53978**   Composers Inspired by the Poet
Friedrich Hölderlin
(SONY) **SK53978**   Prometheus
cond H. ABENDROTH
see CONCERT INDEX *under:*
(TAHR) **TAH102**   Hermann Abendroth - 1927-1941
Recordings
cond J. BARBIROLLI
Mahler: Symphony 9

cond D. BARENBOIM
Beethoven: Romances, Violin Concerto
Berlioz: Symphonie fantastique
Brahms: Violin Concerto
Bruckner: Symphony 4, Symphony 5, Symphony 6,
Symphony 7, Symphony 9
Liszt: Dante Symphony
Mahler: Knaben Wunderhorn (exc), Lieder eines
fahrenden Gesellen
Mozart: Così fan tutte (Cpte), Don Giovanni (Cpte),
Nozze di Figaro (Cpte)
Wagner: Parsifal (Cpte), Tristan and Isolde (Cpte)
see CONCERT INDEX under:
(EMI) CZS4 83177-2(1)   Itzhak Perlman Edition (pt 1)
cond T. BEECHAM
Mozart: Zauberflöte (Cpte)
see CONCERT INDEX under:
(DUTT) CDLX7009   Beecham conducts Favourite
Overtures, Volume 2
(MMOI) CDMOIR408   Great Sopranos
(PREI) 89025   Tiana Lemnitz (b. 1897)
cond L. BERNSTEIN
Mahler: Symphony 9
cond L. BLECH
see CONCERT INDEX under:
(KOCH) 37072-2   Leo Blech conducts
cond P. BOULEZ
Ravel: Daphnis et Chloé (Cpte), La Valse
see CONCERT INDEX under:
(DG) 439 859-2GH   Ravel—Orchestral Works
cond K. BÖHM
Mozart: Serenade, K320, Zauberflöte (Cpte)
see CONCERT INDEX under:
(DG) 413 424-2GW2   Brahms—Orchestral Works
(DG) 415 191-2GH   Mahler: Lieder
(DG) 419 318-2GH4   Schubert: Complete Symphonies
(DG) 427 210-2GR   Mozart—Symphonies
(DG) 427 241-2GX12   Mozart: Complete Symphonies
(DG) 431 110-2GB   Great Voices - Fritz Wunderlich
(DG) 439 419-2GCL   R. Strauss—Tone Poems
(DG) 447 416-2GOR2   Mozart—Symphonies
cond S. BYCHKOV
Mozart: 2-Piano Concerto, K365
see CONCERT INDEX under:
(PHIL) 434 108-2PH   Serenades for Strings
cond A. CLUYTENS
see CONCERT INDEX under:
(EMI) CZS5 68220-2   André Cluytens—A profile
cond A. EREDE
see CONCERT INDEX under:
(TEST) SBT1036   Lisa Della Casa sings Richard
Strauss
cond K. FORSTER
Bruckner: Te Deum
cond F. FRICSAY
Beethoven: Leonore (exc), Symphony 9
Tchaikovsky: Symphony 6
see CONCERT INDEX under:
(DG) 445 400-2GDO10   Ferenc Fricsay - A Portrait
(DG) 445 402-2GDO   Bartók—Orchestral Works
(DG) 445 403-2GDO   R. Strauss—Orchestral Works
cond O. FRIED
see CONCERT INDEX under:
(KOCH) 37146-2   Oskar Fried conducts the BPO
cond W. FURTWÄNGLER
Beethoven: Symphony 9
Bruckner: Symphony 8
Haydn: Symphony 88
Mendelssohn: Violin Concerto, Op.64
Schubert: Symphony 9
Schumann: Piano Concerto
Sibelius: Violin Concerto
see CONCERT INDEX under:
(ACAN) 43 121   Wagner: Orchestral Works
(ARAB) Z6082   R. Strauss: Orchestral & Vocal
Works
(BIDD) WHL006/7   Furtwängler—Pre-war HMV
Recordings
(EMI) CHS7 64935-2   Wagner—Opera Excerpts
(KOCH) 37059-2   Furtwängler—The Early
Recordings
(KOCH) 37073-2   Furtwängler—Early Recordings
1926-1937
(MUSI) MACD-824   Beethoven—Symphonies
(TAHR) FURT1004/7   Furtwängler conducts the Berlin
Philharmonic
(TAHR) FURT1008/11   A Tribute to Wilhelm
Furtwängler
cond C.M. GIULINI
Beethoven: Symphony 9
Franck: Psyché (exc), Symphony
Mahler: Lied von der Erde
Mozart: Symphony 40, Symphony 41
Mussorgsky: Pictures
Verdi: Pezzi sacri (Cpte), Requiem (Cpte)
Vivaldi: Credo, RV591
cond B. HAITINK
Mahler: Lieder eines Fahrenden Gesellen, Symphony
1, Symphony 2, Symphony 3, Symphony 4,
Symphony 5, Symphony 6, Symphony 7, Symphony
10 (exc)
cond H.W. HENZE
see CONCERT INDEX under:
(DG) 429 854-2GC2   Henze—Symphonies
cond P. HINDEMITH
see CONCERT INDEX under:
(SCHW) 311342   Hindemith plays and conducts
cond J. HORENSTEIN
Bruckner: Symphony 7
cond JAMES LEVINE
Debussy: Images

Dukas: Apprenti sorcier
Dvořák: Violin Concerto
Elgar: Enigma Variations
Haydn: Mass 10, Schöpfung (Cpte)
Mendelssohn: Symphony 3, Symphony 4
Mozart: Mass, K317
Saint-Saëns: Symphony 3
Schumann: Symphony 2, Symphony 3
Sibelius: Symphony 4, Symphony 5, Violin Concerto
see CONCERT INDEX under:
(DG) 419 781-2GH   Modern Viennese School
(DG) 419 783-2GH2   Berlioz—Requiem, etc
(DG) 429 750-2GH   Oboe Concertos
(DG) 435 856-2GH   Schumann—Orchestral Works
(DG) 435 883-2GH   German Orchestral Works
(DG) 437 828-2GH   Sibelius—Orchestral Works
cond M. JANSONS
Shostakovich: Piano Concerto 1, Symphony 1
cond E. JOCHUM
Beethoven: Violin Concerto
Brahms: Piano Concerto 1, Piano Concerto 2
Bruckner: Symphony 4
see CONCERT INDEX under:
(DG) 413 145-2GW2   Beethoven—Orchestral Works
(DG) 419 158-2GH2   Brahms: Piano Works
(DG) 423 127-2GX4   Bruckner: Sacred Works for
Chorus
(DG) 429 079-2GX9   Bruckner: Complete Symphonies
(DG) 437 677-2GDO2   Irmgard Seefried - Opera
Recital
cond H. VON KARAJAN
Bach: Brandenburg Concertos, Mass in B minor,
BWV232 (Cpte), St Matthew Passion, BWV244
(Cpte)
Bartók: Music for Strings, Percussion and Celesta
Beethoven: Coriolan, Fidelio (Cpte), Leonore (exc),
Missa Solemnis, Symphony 2, Symphony 3,
Symphony 5, Symphony 6, Symphony 7, Symphony
9, Triple Concerto, Violin Concerto
Berlioz: Damnation de Faust (exc), Symphonie
fantastique
Bizet: Carmen (exc)
Borodin: Prince Igor (exc)
Brahms: Deutsches Requiem, Op. 45 (Cpte), Haydn
Variations, Symphony 1, Symphony 2, Symphony 3,
Symphony 4, Tragic Overture, Violin Concerto
Bruch: Violin Concerto 1
Bruckner: Symphony 2, Symphony 4, Symphony 7,
Symphony 8
Debussy: Pelléas et Mélisande (Cpte)
Dvořák: Cello Concerto, Serenade, Op. 22, Slavonic
Dances (exc), Symphony 9
Handel: Concerti grossi, Op.6
Haydn: Jahreszeiten (exc), Schöpfung (Cpte)
Hindemith: Mathis der Maler
Honegger: Symphony 2, Symphony 3
Lehár: Lustige Witwe (exc)
Mahler: Kindertotenlieder, Lied von der Erde, Rückert
Lieder, Symphony 4, Symphony 5, Symphony 6
Mendelssohn: Symphony 3, Symphony 3,
Symphony 4, Violin Concerto, Op.64
Mozart: Don Giovanni (exc), Mass, K317, Requiem,
Symphony 40, Symphony 41, Violin Concerto, K216,
Violin Concerto, K219, Zauberflöte (Cpte)
Nielsen: Symphony 4
Prokofiev: Symphony 1, Symphony 5
Puccini: Bohème (Cpte), Tosca (Cpte)
R. Strauss: Alpensinfonie, Don Quixote,
Metamorphosen, Till Eulenspiegel, Tod und
Verklärung
Rimsky-Korsakov: Scheherazade
Schoenberg: Variations, Op. 31, Verklärte Nacht
Schubert: Rosamunde (exc), Symphony 8, Symphony
9
Schumann: Overture, Scherzo and Finale, Symphony
1, Symphony 2
Shostakovich: Symphony 10
Sibelius: Symphony 2, Tapiola
Stravinsky: Apollo, Rite of Spring (exc)
Tchaikovsky: Capriccio italien, Eugene Onegin (exc),
Marche slave, Rococo Variations, Serenade, Op. 48,
Symphony 1, Symphony 2, Symphony 3, Symphony
5, 1812
Verdi: Don Carlo (Cpte), Otello (exc), Requiem
(Cpte), Trovatore (Cpte)
Wagner: Fliegende Holländer (Cpte),
Götterdämmerung (Cpte), Lohengrin (Cpte), Parsifal
(Cpte), Rheingold (Cpte), Siegfried (Cpte), Siegfried
Idyll, Tristan und Isolde (Cpte), Walküre (Cpte)
see CONCERT INDEX under:
(DECC) 417 011-2DH2   Pavarotti's Greatest Hits
(DECC) 425 681-2DM2   Tutto Pavarotti
(DECC) 433 437-2DA   Pavarotti—King of the High Cs
(DECC) 433 439-2DA   Great Love Duets
(DECC) 436 461-2DM   Ten Top Sopranos
(DECC) 436 463-2DM   Ten Top Tenors
(DG) 400 044-2GH   Offenbach: Overtures
(DG) 413 158-2GW2   Grieg/Sibelius—Orchestral
Works
(DG) 413 432-2GW2   J. Strauss II—Overtures, Polkas
& Waltzes
(DG) 413 822-2GH   Respighi: Orchestral works
(DG) 413 844-2GW2   19th Century Violin Works
(DG) 415 276-2GH   Beethoven—Orchestral Works
(DG) 415 301-2GH   Italian Baroque Concertos
(DG) 415 565-2GX4   Great Violin Concertos
(DG) 415 833-2GGA   Beethoven—Orchestral Works
(DG) 415 853-2GGA   R. Strauss: Orchestral Works
(DG) 415 855-2GGA   Tchaikovsky: Orchestral works
(DG) 415 967-2GGA   Liszt—Orchestral Works
(DG) 419 046-2GGA   Baroque Orchestral Favourites

(DG) 419 048-2GGA   Beethoven: Orchestral Works
(DG) 419 051-2GGA   Beethoven: Orchestral Works
(DG) 419 070-2GGA   Weber: Orchestral Works
(DG) 419 175-2GH   Tchaikovsky: Orchestral Works
(DG) 419 257-2GH3   'Cav' and 'Pag', etc
(DG) 419 474-2GGA   Grieg: Orchestral Works
(DG) 419 622-2GH   Verdi: Overtures & Preludes
(DG) 419 624-2GH   Beethoven: Vocal, Orchestral &
Wind Music
(DG) 419 871-2GGA   Sibelius—Orchestral Works
(DG) 423 252-2GC   Stravinsky—Orchestral Works
(DG) 423 254-2GC   Webern: Orchestral Works
(DG) 423 888-2GGA   R. Strauss—Orchestral & Vocal
Works
(DG) 427 250-2GGA   French Orchestral Works
(DG) 427 424-2GC3   Second Viennese School
(DG) 427 485-2GH   Kissin plays Tchaikovsky &
Scriabin
(DG) 427 602-2GH3   Brahms: Symphonies, etc
(DG) 429 036-2GX5   Beethoven: Complete
Symphonies
(DG) 429 156-2GR   Liszt & Brahms: Hungarian Works
(DG) 429 163-2GR   Ballet Scores
(DG) 429 164-2GR   Rossini & Verdi: Overtures &
Preludes
(DG) 429 168-2GR   Wagner: Excerpts from Der Ring
(DG) 429 644-2GSE3   Brahms: Symphonies
(DG) 429 648-2GSE9   Bruckner: Symphonies
(DG) 429 664-2GSE3   Mendelssohn—Complete
Symphonies
(DG) 429 672-2GSE2   Schumann: Symphonies
(DG) 431 160-2GR   Bizet & Offenbach—Orchestral
Works
(DG) 435 070-2GGA   Mozart—Symphonies
(DG) 435 211-2GX15   Wagner—Der Ring des
Nibelungen
(DG) 435 712-2GX2   Lehár—The Merry Widow.
Suppé—Overtures
(DG) 437 255-2GGA   Strauss family—Waltzes &
Polkas
(DG) 437 404-2GX2   Famous Ballet Works
(DG) 437 952-2GX2   Great Cello Works
(DG) 439 346-2GX2   Prussian and Austrian Marches
(DG) 439 418-2GCL   Sibelius—Orchestral Works
(DG) 439 422-2GCL   Vivaldi—Concertos
(DG) 439 423-2GCL   Wagner—Der Ring des
Nibelungen (highlights)
(DG) 439 463-2GCL   Stravinsky—Ballet Music
(DG) 439 467-2GCL   R. Strauss—Vocal and
Orchestral Works
(DG) 439 527-2GGA   Sibelius—Orchestral Works
(DG) 439 678-2GX2   Mahler—Symphony No 9;
Lieder
(DG) 439 972-2GGA2   Verdi—Overtures & Preludes
(DG) 439 982-2GGA   Sibelius—Orchestral Works
(DG) 445 532-2GMA2   Haydn—Paris Symphonies
(DG) 447 426-2GOR
Debussy/Mussorgsky/Ravel—Orchestral Works
(DG) 447 435-2GOR   Honegger—Symphonies;
Stravinsky—Concerto
(EMI) CDC7 49237-2   Trumpet Concertos
(EMI) CDM7 64331-2   Sibelius—Orchestral Works
(EMI) CDM7 64357-2   Debussy/Ravel—Orchestral
Works
(EMI) CDM7 64747-2   Franck—Orchestral Works
(EMI) CDM7 69018-2   J. Strauss II—Waltzes
(EMI) CDM7 69549-2   Ruggero Raimondi: Italian
Opera Arias
(EMI) CMS7 69884-2   Schubert—The Complete
Symphonies
cond J. KEILBERTH
Bruch: Violin Concerto 1
Weber: Freischütz (Cpte)
cond R. KEMPE
Brahms: Deutsches Requiem, Op.45 (Cpte)
Mozart: Requiem
Wagner: Meistersinger (Cpte)
see CONCERT INDEX under:
(EMI) CDC7 47657-2   Mahler—Lieder
(EMI) CESS 68518-2   Beethoven—Orchestral Works
(EMI) CESS 68525-2   Berlioz/Saint-Saëns—Orchestral
Works
(EMI) CZS7 67310-2   Menuhin plays Popular Violin
Concertos
(TEST) SBT3054   Brahms—Symphonies, etc
cond P. VAN KEMPEN
see CONCERT INDEX under:
(PHIL) 438 533-2PM2   Beethoven—Orchestral Works
cond E. KLEIBER
see CONCERT INDEX under:
(ARCI) ARC102   Kleiber conducts Waltzes and
Overtures
cond H. KNAPPERTSBUSCH
Beethoven: Symphony 9
Brahms: Symphony 3
Bruckner: Symphony 4
Haydn: Symphony 94
Liszt: Préludes
cond R. KUBELÍK
Dvořák: Symphony 9
Grieg: Piano Concerto
Schumann: Piano Concerto
see CONCERT INDEX under:
(DG) 413 158-2GW2   Grieg/Sibelius—Orchestral
Works
(DG) 120-2GX6   Dvořák: Complete Symphonies
cond J. KULKA
Chopin: Piano Concerto 2

cond F. LEITNER
Beethoven: Piano Concerto 1, Piano Concerto 2,
Piano Concerto 4, Piano Concerto 5
see CONCERT INDEX *under:*
(DG) 427 237-2GX3   Beethoven: Complete Piano
Concertos, etc
(DG) 439 699-2GX2   Mozart—Piano Concertos
cond W. LUTOSŁAWSKI
Lutosławski: Espaces du sommeil, Symphony 3
cond L. MAAZEL
Bartók: Concerto for Orchestra
Dvořák: Slavonic Dances
Prokofiev: Violin Concerto 1
Rachmaninov: Isle of the Dead, Symphony 2
Tchaikovsky: Violin Concerto
see CONCERT INDEX *under:*
(BELA) 450 129-2   Images of Spain
(DG) 413 424-2GW2   Brahms—Orchestral Works
(DG) 435 594-2GGA   Rachmaninov—Orchestral
Works
(SONY) SK42206   Dvořák—Works for cello and
orchestra
(TELA) CD80154   Wagner: The 'Ring' without Words
cond F. MARTIN
see CONCERT INDEX *under:*
(JECK) JD645-2   Frank Martin conducts Frank Martin
cond Z. MEHTA
Bartók: Violin Concerto 1, Violin Concerto 2
Mozart: Serenade, K361
cond K. MUTI
Handel: Water Music
Mozart: Ave verum corpus, K618, Requiem
Verdi: Pezzi sacri (Cpte)
cond E. ORTHMANN
see CONCERT INDEX *under:*
(PREI) 89209   Helge Roswaenge (1897-1972) - II
cond S. OZAWA
Bartók: Music for Strings, Percussion and Celesta,
Viola Concerto
Orff: Carmina burana
Prokofiev: Lt. Kijé suite, Symphony 1, Symphony 2,
Symphony 3, Symphony 4, Symphony 5, Symphony
6, Symphony 7
Tchaikovsky: Symphony 5, 1812
cond H. PFITZNER
see CONCERT INDEX *under:*
(PREI) 90029   Hans Pfitzner Accompanies &
Conducts
cond J. PRÜWER
see CONCERT INDEX *under:*
(DANA) DACOCD336/7   Brailowsky—The Berlin
Recordings, Vol. 1
(DANA) DACOCD338/9   Brailowsky—The Berlin
Recordings, Vol. 2
cond S. RATTLE
Liszt: Faust Symphony
cond M. ROSTROPOVICH
see CONCERT INDEX *under:*
(DG) 429 097-2GGA   Tchaikovsky: Ballet Suites
cond V. DE SABATA
(KOCH) 37126-2   Victor de Sabata conducts the BPO
cond E-P. SALONEN
Prokofiev: Romeo and Juliet (exc)
cond W. SAWALLISCH
Mendelssohn: Symphony 2
cond F.A. SCHMIDT
see CONCERT INDEX *under:*
(PREI) 89209   Helge Roswaenge (1897-1972) - II
cond H. SCHMIDT-ISSERSTEDT
Beethoven: Violin Concerto
Mendelssohn: Violin Concerto, Op.64
Schumann: Violin Concerto
cond W. SCHÜCHTER
see CONCERT INDEX *under:*
(EMI) CDH5 65201-2   Leonie Rysanek - Operatic
Recital
cond B. SEIDLER-WINKLER
see CONCERT INDEX *under:*
(PREI) 89025   Tiana Lemnitz (b. 1897)
cond J. SEMKOW
Chopin: Piano Concerto 1
cond G. SOLTI
Beethoven: Missa solemnis (Cpte)
cond L. STOKOWSKI
Stravinsky: Firebird Suite (1919) (exc)
cond G. SZELL
Dvořák: Cello Concerto
see CONCERT INDEX *under:*
(DG) 429 155-2GR   Works for Cello & Orchestra
cond J. TATE
Grieg: Peer Gynt (exc)
cond K. TENNSTEDT
see CONCERT INDEX *under:*
(EMI) CZS7 67521-2   Schumann—Concertos
cond P. VAN KEMPEN
(DG) 435 744-2GDO3   Beethoven—Piano Concertos,
etc
cond VLADIMIR ASHKENAZY
Tchaikovsky: Piano Concerto 1, Piano Concerto 3
cond A. WALLENSTEIN
Elgar: Cello Concerto
see CONCERT INDEX *under:*
(DG) 429 155-2GR   Works for Cello & Orchestra

BERLIN PHILHARMONIC WIND QUINTET
Danzi: Wind Quintet, Op.41, Wind Quintets, Op.56
see CONCERT INDEX *under:*
(BIS) BIS-CD536   French Works for Wind Quintet
(ORFE) C152861A   Mozart: Divertimento for 6 Wind
Instruments

cond H. VON KARAJAN
see CONCERT INDEX *under:*
(DG) 439 346-2GX2   Prussian and Austrian Marches
cond H. PRIEM-BERGRATH
see CONCERT INDEX *under:*
(DG) 419 624-2GH   Beethoven: Vocal, Orchestral &
Wind Music

BERLIN RADIO CHAMBER CHOIR
cond G. ALBRECHT
Henze: Bassariden (Cpte)
Hindemith: Cardillac (Cpte)
cond D. ZINMAN
see CONCERT INDEX *under:*
(RCA) 09026 61955-2   Koechlin—The Jungle Book

BERLIN RADIO CHILDREN'S CHOIR
cond G. ALBRECHT
Gurlitt: Wozzeck (Cpte)
cond B. KLEE
Lortzing: Wildschütz (Cpte)

BERLIN RADIO CHORUS
cond C. ABBADO
Brahms: Gesang der Parzen, Op. 89
Mahler: Symphony 8
Mozart: Mass, K427
Mussorgsky: Boris Godunov (Cpte)
Rossini: Viaggio a Reims (Cpte)
see CONCERT INDEX *under:*
(DG) 435 349-2GH   Brahms—Orchestral and Choral
Works
(DG) 447 023-2GX12   Mahler—The Symphonies
(SONY) SK53360   Mahler/Nono—Vocal Works
cond G. ALBRECHT
Schreker: Ferne Klang (Cpte)
cond L. BERNSTEIN
Beethoven: Symphony 9
cond P. BOULEZ
Ravel: Daphnis et Chloé (Cpte)
cond C.P. FLOR
Cherubini: Requiem 1
cond R. GRITTON
Rachmaninov: Vespers, Op. 37 (Cpte)
cond HANS HAENCHEN
Gluck: Orfeo ed Euridice (Cpte)
cond E. INBAL
Liszt: Faust Symphony
cond M. JANOWSKI
Weber: Freischütz (Cpte)
cond H. KEGEL
Wagner: Parsifal (Cpte)
see CONCERT INDEX *under:*
(CAPR) 10 451/5   Beethoven—Symphonies 1-9
cond B. KLEE
Lortzing: Wildschütz (Cpte)
cond J. MAUCERI
Korngold: Wunder der Heliane (Cpte)
cond R. REUTER
see CONCERT INDEX *under:*
(CPO) CPO999 158-2   Pfitzner—Das dunkle Reich
cond A. ROTHER
see CONCERT INDEX *under:*
(PREI) 90168   Wagner—Die Meistersinger, Act 2, etc
cond M. SCHÖNWANDT
Schumann: Manfred (Cpte)
cond S. SOLTESZ
Mendelssohn: Antigone (Cpte), Oedipus (Cpte)
cond G. SOLTI
Beethoven: Missa solemnis (Cpte)
cond VLADIMIR ASHKENAZY
Mendelssohn: Midsummer Night's Dream (exc)
cond M. YUROVSKY
Shostakovich: King Lear, Op. 58a
cond L. ZAGROSEK
B. Goldschmidt: Gewaltige Hahnrei (Cpte)
Schreker: Gezeichneten (Cpte)
see CONCERT INDEX *under:*
(SONY) S2K66836   Goldschmidt—Beatrice Cenci, etc

BERLIN RADIO ENSEMBLE
cond J. MAUCERI
see CONCERT INDEX *under:*
(DECC) 425 204-2DNL   Ute Lemper sings Kurt Weill

BERLIN RADIO ORCHESTRA
cond M. JANOWSKI
Weber: Freischütz (Cpte)
cond W. MENGELBERG
see CONCERT INDEX *under:*
(ARHI) ADCD111   Mengelberg Edition - Volume 5
cond J. MÜLLER
see CONCERT INDEX *under:*
(PREI) 89054   Miliza Korjus (1912-1980)
cond A. ROTHER
Beethoven: Piano Concerto 5
see CONCERT INDEX *under:*
(PREI) 90168   Wagner—Die Meistersinger, Act 2, etc

BERLIN RADIO SYMPHONY CHORUS
cond R. CHAILLY
Mahler: Klagende Lied
Orff: Carmina burana
cond K. A. RICKENBACHER
Beethoven: Joseph II Cantata, Leopold II Cantata

BERLIN RADIO SYMPHONY ORCHESTRA
cond G. ALBRECHT
Busoni: Arlecchino (Cpte), Turandot (Cpte)
Henze: Bassariden (Cpte)
Hindemith: Cardillac (Cpte), Dämon (Cpte), Gesänge,
Op. 9, Junge Magd, Lustige Sinfonietta, Mörder,
Hoffnung der Frauen (Cpte), Nusch-Nuschi (Cpte),
Rag Time, Sancta Susanna (Cpte), Todes Tod
Korngold: Sinfonietta

Meyerbeer: Amori di Teolinda
Reger: Romantische Suite, Symphonic Poems,
Op.128
Schreker: Ferne Klang (Cpte)
Spontini: Olimpie (Cpte)
Wolf: Corregidor (Cpte)
Zemlinsky: Florentinische Tragödie, Geburtstag der
Infantin (Cpte)
see CONCERT INDEX *under:*
(CAPR) 10 479   Busoni—Orchestral Works
(SCHW) 311088   Spohr—Instrumental Works
cond K. ANCERL
Dvořák: Slavonic Dances
Haydn: Symphony 93
Rimsky-Korsakov: Scheherazade
Schubert: Symphony 9
cond J. ARNELL
Pettersson: Symphony 14
cond R. BADER
Donizetti: Messa di Gloria e Credo
E.T.A. Hoffmann: Undine (Cpte)
cond M. BAMERT
see CONCERT INDEX *under:*
(SCHW) 311135   Schubertiana
cond K. BÖHM
see CONCERT INDEX *under:*
(DG) 437 677-2GDO2   Irmgard Seefried - Opera
Recital
cond R. CHAILLY
Bruckner: Overture in G minor, Symphony 0
Mahler: Klagende Lied
Orff: Carmina Burana
Rachmaninov: Piano Concerto 3
Schoenberg: Gurrelieder
see CONCERT INDEX *under:*
(DECC) 436 483-2DM   French Orchestral Works
cond M. CREED
see CONCERT INDEX *under:*
(CAPR) 10 169   Mozart: Choral Works
(CAPR) 10 244   Schubert: Choral Music
cond C.P. FLOR
Cherubini: Requiem 1
cond H. FRICKE
Chopin: Sylphides
Delibes: Coppélia (exc)
see CONCERT INDEX *under:*
(CAPR) 10 416   Jochen Kowalski sings Opera Arias
(LASE) 15 616   French Ballet Music
cond F. FRICSAY
Bartók: Duke Bluebeard's Castle (Cpte)
Beethoven: Triple Concerto
Brahms: Double Concerto
Gluck: Orfeo ed Euridice (Cpte)
Mozart: Adagio and Fugue, K546, Don Giovanni
(Cpte), Exsultate, jubilate, K165, Nozze di Figaro
(Cpte)
Stravinsky: Oedipus Rex (Cpte)
Verdi: Pezzi sacri (Cpte), Requiem (Cpte)
see CONCERT INDEX *under:*
(DG) 413 432-2GW2   J. Strauss II—Overtures, Polkas
& Waltzes
(DG) 437 677-2GDO7   Irmgard Seefried - Opera
Recital
(DG) 445 400-2GDO10   Ferenc Fricsay - A Portrait
(DG) 445 404-2GDO
Liebermann/Blacher/Egk/Einem—Orchestral Works
(DG) 445 405-2GDO   Stravinsky—Orchestral Works
(DG) 445 407-2GDO   Brahms—Orchestral Works
(DG) 445 410-2GDO   Kodály—Orchestral Works
(DG) 447 343-2GDB2   Stravinsky—Orchestral &
Choral Works
(DG) 447 399-2GOR   Bartók—Piano Concertos
cond C. GARBEN
see CONCERT INDEX *under:*
(RCA) 09026 61184-2   Mahler (orch Berio)/R.
Strauss—Lieder
cond M. GIELEN
see CONCERT INDEX *under:*
(SCHW) 311078   Schrecker: Orchestral Works
cond B. GOLDSCHMIDT
see CONCERT INDEX *under:*
(LARG) Largo5130   Testimonies of War
cond G.M. GUIDA
F. David: Désert
Szymanowski: Songs, Op.42
cond P. GÜLKE
Schumann: Carnaval
cond V. HANDLEY
(SCHW) 311052   Virtuoso Kettledrum Concertos
cond E. INBAL
Liszt: Faust Symphony
cond JOHN SCOTT
Korngold: Anthony Adverse
cond M. JUROWSKI
Kancheli: Symphony 2, Symphony 7
cond W. KAMIRSKI
Górecki: Symphony 3
cond B. KLEE
see CONCERT INDEX *under:*
(SCHW) 311122   Early Twentieth Century Music
cond U. LAJOVIC
see CONCERT INDEX *under:*
(SCHW) 311122   Early Twentieth Century Music
cond J. LÓPEZ-COBOS
(SCHW) 311045   Romantic Clarinet Concertos
cond L. LUDWIG
Hindemith: Mathis der Maler (exc)
Weber: Abu Hassan (Cpte)

cond L. MAAZEL
see CONCERT INDEX under:
(DG) **447 414-2GOR** Falla/Stravinsky—Ballet Music
cond J. MAUCERI
Korngold: Wunder der Heliane (Cpte)
cond R. PATERNOSTRO
see CONCERT INDEX under:
(CAPR) **10 247** The Art of Bel Canto
cond C. PERICK
Schmidt: Notre Dame (Cpte)
cond R. REUTER
see CONCERT INDEX under:
(CPO) **CPO999 158-2** Pfitzner—Das dunkle Reich
cond K. A. RICKENBACHER
Beethoven: Joseph II Cantata, Leopold II Cantata
see CONCERT INDEX under:
(SCHW) **311078** Schrecker: Orchestral Works
(SCHW) **311232** Messiaen—Works for Piano and
Orchestra
cond A. ROTHER
Wagner: Fliegende Holländer (exc)
see CONCERT INDEX under:
(ACAN) **43 268** Peter Anders sings German Opera
Arias
(PREI) **89065** Maria Reining (1903-1991)
(PREI) **90222** Maria Cebotari sings Richard Strauss
cond P. RUZICKA
Pettersson: Symphony 15
Ruzicka: Orchestral Sketches
cond T. SANDERLING
Pettersson: Symphony 8
cond A. SCHMÖHE
Burgmüller: Symphony 2
Schumann: Symphony 4
cond H.M. SCHNEIDT
Ravel: Shéhérazade
Rimsky-Korsakov: Scheherazade
see CONCERT INDEX under:
(CAPR) **10 380** Breezes from the Orient, Vol.2
cond D. SHALLON
(CAPR) **10 335** Wolf—Lieder with Orchestra
cond N. SHERIFF
(LARG) **Largo5130** Testimonies of War
cond S. SOLTESZ
Mendelssohn: Antigone (Cpte)
Zemlinsky: Kreidekreis (Cpte)
cond H. STEIN
see CONCERT INDEX under:
(FINL) **4509-95606-2** Kim Borg - Songs and Arias
cond G. SZELL
see CONCERT INDEX under:
(EMI) **CDC7 47276-2** R. Strauss: Lieder with
Orchestra
cond Y. TEMIRKANOV
Tchaikovsky: Piano Concerto 1
cond M. VIOTTI
see CONCERT INDEX under:
(ORFE) **C323941A** Puccini—Famous Opera Arias
cond VLADIMIR ASHKENAZY
(DECC) **430 843-2DH** Scriabin—Orchestral Works
(DECC) **436 415-2DH** R. Strauss—Orchestral Works
cond M. YUROVSKY
Shostakovich: King Lear, Op. 58a, King Lear, Op.
137
cond D. ZINMAN
see CONCERT INDEX under:
(RCA) **09026 61955-2** Koechlin—The Jungle Book

BERLIN RADIO WOMEN'S CHORUS
cond D. BARENBOIM
Liszt: Dante Symphony

BERLIN RIAS CHAMBER CHOIR
see CONCERT INDEX under:
(DG) **435 596-2GGA2** Schubert—Duets, Trios &
Quartets
cond C. ABBADO
Janáček: Diary of One who Disappeared
see CONCERT INDEX under:
(DG) **435 617-2GH** Beethoven in Berlin—New Year's
Eve Concert
cond G. ALBRECHT
Busoni: Turandot (Cpte)
Gurlitt: Wozzeck (Cpte)
Hindemith: Mörder, Hoffnung der Frauen (Cpte),
Sancta Susanna (Cpte)
Meyerbeer: Amori di Teolinda
Schreker: Ferne Klang (Cpte)
Spontini: Olimpie (Cpte)
Wolf: Corregidor (Cpte)
cond D. BARENBOIM
Mozart: Così fan tutte (Cpte), Don Giovanni (Cpte),
Nozze di Figaro (Cpte)
cond K. BÖHM
Mozart: Zauberflöte (Cpte)
cond M. CREED
Hasse: Conversione di Sant' Agostino (Cpte)
Krenek: Lamentatio Jeremiae prophetae
see CONCERT INDEX under:
(CAPR) **10 169** Mozart: Choral Works
(CAPR) **10 244** Schubert: Choral Music
cond F. FRICSAY
Gluck: Orfeo ed Euridice (Cpte)
Mozart: Don Giovanni (Cpte), Entführung (Cpte),
Nozze di Figaro (Cpte), Requiem, Zauberflöte (Cpte)
Stravinsky: Oedipus Rex (Cpte)
Verdi: Pezzi sacri (Cpte)
see CONCERT INDEX under:
(DG) **445 400-2GDO10** Ferenc Fricsay - A Portrait

(DG) **445 402-2GDO** Bartók—Orchestral Works
(DG) **445 407-2GDO** Brahms—Orchestral Works
cond E. INBAL
Berlioz: Roméo et Juliette (Cpte)
Mahler: Symphony 8
cond JAMES LEVINE
Haydn: Mass 10
Mozart: Mass, K317
cond B. KLEE
Mendelssohn: Hochzeit des Camacho (Cpte)
cond J. MAUCERI
Weill: Dreigroschenoper (Cpte)
cond C. PERICK
Schmidt: Notre Dame (Cpte)
cond W. SCHMIDT-BOELCKE
Jessel: Schwarzwaldmädel (exc)
cond P. SCHREIER
see CONCERT INDEX under:
(PHIL) **438 873-2PH2** Bach—Magnificat and Masses

BERLIN RIAS CHILDREN'S CHORUS
cond F. FRICSAY
see CONCERT INDEX under:
(DG) **447 343-2GDB2** Stravinsky—Orchestral &
Choral Works

BERLIN RIAS CHORUS
cond F. FRICSAY
see CONCERT INDEX under:
(DG) **447 343-2GDB2** Stravinsky—Orchestral &
Choral Works

BERLIN RIAS ORCHESTRA
cond F. FRICSAY
Mozart: Entführung (Cpte), Requiem, Zauberflöte
(Cpte)
Rossini: Stabat Mater
Tchaikovsky: Violin Concerto
Verdi: Requiem (Cpte)
see CONCERT INDEX under:
(DG) **427 410-2GDO2** Bartók—Orchestral Works
(DG) **445 400-2GDO10** Ferenc Fricsay - A Portrait
(DG) **445 402-2GDO** Bartók—Orchestral Works
(DG) **445 403-2GDO** R. Strauss—Orchestral Works
(DG) **445 404-2GDO**
Liebermann/Blacher/Egk/Einem—Orchestral Works
(DG) **445 405-2GDO** Stravinsky—Orchestral Works
(DG) **445 406-2GDO** Rossini/Verdi—Overtures and
Preludes
(DG) **445 410-2GDO** Kodály—Orchestral Works
(DG) **447 343-2GDB2** Stravinsky—Orchestral &
Choral Works
cond H. VON KARAJAN
Donizetti: Lucia di Lammermoor (Cpte)

BERLIN RIAS SINFONIETTA
cond J. MAUCERI
Weill: Dreigroschenoper (Cpte), Mahagonny-Gesänge
(Cpte), Sieben Todsünden (Cpte)
see CONCERT INDEX under:
(DECC) **436 417-2DH** Ute Lemper sings Kurt Weill,
Vol.2
cond J. VELAZCO
see CONCERT INDEX under:
(SCHW) **311035** Stravinsky—Choral Works

BERLIN SCHAROUN ENSEMBLE
Brahms: Serenade 1

BERLIN SCHAUSPIELHAUS ORCHESTRA
cond E. HAUKE
see CONCERT INDEX under:
(NIMB) **NI7830** Richard Tauber in Opera
(NIMB) **NI7833** Schöne & Tauber in Operetta
(PEAR) **GEMMCD9381** Richard Tauber sings Lieder

BERLIN SINGAKADEMIE
cond C. ABBADO
see CONCERT INDEX under:
(SONY) **SK53978** Prometheus

BERLIN SOLOISTS
Beethoven: Septet, Op. 20
Brahms: Clarinet Quintet
Mozart: Clarinet Quintet, K581, Horn Quintet, K407
Schubert: Octet, D803
see CONCERT INDEX under:
(TELD) **9031-73400-2** Prokofiev/Hindemith—Chamber
Works

BERLIN STAATSKAPELLE
cond D. BARENBOIM
Beethoven: Symphony 9
cond L. BLECH
see CONCERT INDEX under:
(PEAR) **GEMMCDS9926(2)** Covent Garden on
Record—Vol.4 (pt 2)
cond E. HAUKE
see CONCERT INDEX under:
(EMI) **CDH7 64029-2** Richard Tauber - Opera Recital
(EMI) **CDH7 69787-2** Richard Tauber sings Operetta
Arias
(MMOI) **CDMOIR425** Three Tenors, Volume 2
(NIMB) **NI7830** Richard Tauber in Opera
(PEAR) **GEMMCD9381** Richard Tauber sings Lieder
cond R. HEGER
Schillings: Glockenlieder (exc)
Wagner: Tristan und Isolde (Cpte), Wesendonk
Lieder
see CONCERT INDEX under:
(ACAN) **43 268** Peter Anders sings German Opera
Arias
cond R. KEMPE
see CONCERT INDEX under:
(EMI) **CMS5 65212-2** Wagner—Les introuvables du
Ring

cond B. KLEE
Lortzing: Wildschütz (Cpte)
Mozart: Zaïde (Cpte)
cond F. LEHÁR
(EMI) **CDC7 54838-2** Franz Lehár
(EMI) **CDH7 69787-2** Richard Tauber sings Operetta
Arias
(NIMB) **NI7833** Schöne & Tauber in Operetta
cond A. MELICHAR
see CONCERT INDEX under:
(NIMB) **NI7848** Great Singers at the Berlin State
Opera
(PREI) **89070** Franz Völker (1899-1965) - II
cond E. MÖRIKE
see CONCERT INDEX under:
(EMI) **CMS7 64008-2(2)** Wagner Singing on Record
(pt 2)
cond F.A. SCHMIDT
see CONCERT INDEX under:
(PREI) **89070** Franz Völker (1899-1965) - II
cond K. SCHMIDT
see CONCERT INDEX under:
(ACAN) **43 268** Peter Anders sings German Opera
Arias
cond J. SCHÜLER
see CONCERT INDEX under:
(NIMB) **NI7848** Great Singers at the Berlin State
Opera
(PREI) **89070** Franz Völker (1899-1965) - II
cond G. STEEGER
see CONCERT INDEX under:
(PREI) **89070** Franz Völker (1899-1965) - II
cond O. SUITNER
Brahms: Hungarian Dances
Schubert: Symphony 3, Symphony 6
Schumann: Symphony 1, Symphony 2, Symphony 3,
Symphony 4
cond F. WEISSMANN
see CONCERT INDEX under:
(EMI) **CDH7 69787-2** Richard Tauber sings Operetta
Arias
(EMI) **CDM7 69478-2** A Portrait of Joseph Schmidt
(EMI) **CMS7 64008-2(2)** Wagner Singing on Record
(pt 2)

BERLIN STAATSKAPELLE CHORUS
cond E. MÖRIKE
see CONCERT INDEX under:
(EMI) **CMS7 64008-2(2)** Wagner Singing on Record
(pt 2)

BERLIN STATE BOY'S CHOIR
cond H. VON KARAJAN
Bach: St Matthew Passion, BWV244 (Cpte)

BERLIN STATE OPERA CHORUS
see CONCERT INDEX under:
(NIMB) **NI7830** Richard Tauber in Opera
cond D. BARENBOIM
Beethoven: Symphony 9
Wagner: Parsifal (Cpte), Tristan und Isolde (Cpte)
cond L. BLECH
(PEAR) **GEMMCDS9137** Wagner—Der Ring des
Nibelungen
cond A. COATES
Wagner: Götterdämmerung (exc)
cond R. HEGER
Wagner: Lohengrin (Cpte), Tristan und Isolde (Cpte)
cond R. KEMPE
Wagner: Meistersinger (Cpte)
cond F. KONWITSCHNY
Wagner: Tannhäuser (Cpte)
cond K. MUCK
(OPAL) **OPALCDS9843** Karl Muck conducts Wagner
cond J. PRÜWER
(PEAR) **GEMMCD9383** Julius Patzak—Opera &
Operetta Recital
cond B. SEIDLER-WINKLER
see CONCERT INDEX under:
(MMOI) **CDMOIR411** Sacred Songs and Arias
(TEST) **SBT1005** Ten Top Tenors

BERLIN STATE OPERA ORCHESTRA
see CONCERT INDEX under:
(CLAR) **CDGSE78-50-26** Wagner: Tristan und Isolde
excerpts
(PREI) **89004** Frida Leider (1888-1975) - I
cond K. BESL
see CONCERT INDEX under:
(PREI) **89302** The Young Lotte Lehmann
cond L. BLECH
(BIDD) **LAB049/50** Kreisler - The Berlin HMV
Recordings (1926-7)
(CLUB) **CL99-020** Maria Ivogün & Lotte
Schöne—Lieder
(DANA) **DACOCD315/6** Lauritz Melchior Anthology -
Vol. 3
(EMI) **CDH7 69789-2** Melchior sings Wagner
(EMI) **CMS7 64008-2(1)** Wagner Singing on Record
(pt 1)
(EMI) **CMS7 64008-2(2)** Wagner Singing on Record
(pt 2)
(KOCH) **37072-2** Leo Blech conducts
(LYRC) **LCD146** Frida Leider sings Wagner
(NIMB) **NI7832** Maria Ivogün (1891-1987)
(NIMB) **NI7848** Great Singers at the Berlin State
Opera

(PEAR) **GEMMCDS9137** Wagner—Der Ring des Nibelungen
(PEAR) **GEMMCDS9925(2)** Covent Garden on Record—Vol.3 (pt 2)
(PEAR) **GEMMCDS9996** Kreisler - Violin Concertos
(PEAR) **GEMMCD9331** Frida Leider sings Wagner
(PEAR) **GEMMCD9398** Friedrich Schorr
(PEAR) **GEMMCD9451** Alexander Kipnis
(PREI) **89004** Frida Leider (1888-1975) - I
(PREI) **89006** Heinrich Schlusnus (1888-1952) - I
(PREI) **89025** Tiana Lemnitz (b. 1897)
(PREI) **89027** Sigrid Onegin (1889-1943)
(PREI) **89028** Ivar Andresen (1896-1940)
(PREI) **89035** Erna Berger (1900-1990) - I
  cond F. BUSCH
  see CONCERT INDEX *under:*
(PEAR) **GEMMCDS9365** R. Strauss: Der Rosenkavalier (abridged), etc
  cond A. COATES
  see CONCERT INDEX *under:*
(CLAR) **CDGSE78-50-26** Wagner: Tristan und Isolde excerpts
(DANA) **DACOCD315/6** Lauritz Melchior Anthology - Vol. 3
(EMI) **CMS7 64008-2(2)** Wagner Singing on Record (pt 2)
(LYRC) **LCD146** Frida Leider sings Wagner
  cond O. DOBRINDT
  see CONCERT INDEX *under:*
(PREI) **89005** Franz Völker (1899-1965) - I
  cond W. FURTWÄNGLER
  see CONCERT INDEX *under:*
(ACAN) **43 121** Wagner: Orchestral Works
  cond M. GURLITT
  see CONCERT INDEX *under:*
(PEAR) **GEMMCD9394** Helge Roswaenge—Operatic Recital
(PREI) **89005** Franz Völker (1899-1965) - I
  cond R. HEGER
Wagner: Lohengrin (Cpte)
  cond J. HEIDENREICH
  see CONCERT INDEX *under:*
(PREI) **89005** Franz Völker (1899-1965) - I
  cond E. KLEIBER
  see CONCERT INDEX *under:*
(ARCI) **ARC102** Kleiber conducts Waltzes and Overtures
(KOCH) **37011-2** Legendary Conductors
  cond O. KLEMPERER
  see CONCERT INDEX *under:*
(KOCH) **37053-2** The Young Otto Klemperer
(SYMP) **SYMCD1042** Otto Klemperer and the Kroll Years
  cond H. KNAPPERTSBUSCH
  see CONCERT INDEX *under:*
(PREI) **90951** Mozart—Symphonies
  cond F. KONWITSCHNY
Wagner: Tannhäuser (Cpte)
  cond C. KRAUSS
  see CONCERT INDEX *under:*
(NIMB) **NI7848** Great Singers at the Berlin State Opera
(PREI) **89035** Erna Berger (1900-1990) - I
  cond E. KÜNNEKE
  see CONCERT INDEX *under:*
(PREI) **89209** Helge Roswaenge (1897-1972) - II
  cond F. LEHÁR
  see CONCERT INDEX *under:*
(EMI) **CDM7 69476-2** Richard Tauber - A Portrait
(PEAR) **GEMMCD9310** Franz Lehár conducts Richard Tauber
  cond A. MELICHAR
  see CONCERT INDEX *under:*
(MMOI) **CDMOIR411** Sacred Songs and Arias
(MMOI) **CDMOIR422** Great Voices in Tchaikovsky
(PEAR) **GEMMCD9383** Julius Patzak—Opera & Operetta Recital
(PREI) **89005** Franz Völker (1899-1965) - I
(PREI) **89006** Heinrich Schlusnus (1888-1952) - I
(PREI) **89035** Erna Berger (1900-1990) - I
(PREI) **89205** Heinrich Schlusnus Lieder Album, Vol.1
(PREI) **89209** Helge Roswaenge (1897-1972) - II
  cond S. MEYROWITZ
  see CONCERT INDEX *under:*
(PREI) **89209** Helge Roswaenge (1897-1972) - II
  cond K. MUCK
  see CONCERT INDEX *under:*
(OPAL) **OPALCDS9843** Karl Muck conducts Wagner
(PEAR) **GEMMCDS9137** Wagner—Der Ring des Nibelungen
  cond H.U. MÜLLER
  see CONCERT INDEX *under:*
(EMI) **CMS7 64008-2(1)** Wagner Singing on Record (pt 1)
(NIMB) **NI7848** Great Singers at the Berlin State Opera
(PREI) **89071** Gerhard Hüsch (1901-1984) - II
(PREI) **89077** Torsten Ralf (1901-1954)
  cond E. NICK
  see CONCERT INDEX *under:*
(PREI) **89054** Miliza Korjus (1912-1980)
  cond E. ORTHMANN
  see CONCERT INDEX *under:*
(CLUB) **CL99-020** Maria Ivogün & Lotte Schöne—Opera Recital
(NIMB) **NI7848** Great Singers at the Berlin State Opera
(NIMB) **NI7851** Legendary Voices
(PEAR) **GEMMCDS9926(1)** Covent Garden on Record—Vol.4 (pt 1)

(PEAR) **GEMMCD9451** Alexander Kipnis
(PREI) **89019** Alexander Kipnis (1891-1978)
(PREI) **89057** Charles Kullmann (1903-1982)
  cond H. PFITZNER
Schumann: Symphony 2, Symphony 4
  see CONCERT INDEX *under:*
(EMI) **CDC5 55225-2** Pfitzner plays and conducts Pfitzner
(PREI) **90029** Hans Pfitzner Accompanies & Conducts
  cond J. PRÜWER
  see CONCERT INDEX *under:*
(PEAR) **GEMMCD9383** Julius Patzak—Opera & Operetta Recital
(PREI) **89005** Franz Völker (1899-1965) - I
(PREI) **89046** Rosette Anday (1903-1977)
  cond H. ROSBAUD
  see CONCERT INDEX *under:*
(APR) **APR5511** Gieseking—First Concerto Recordings, Vol.1
  cond A. ROTHER
  see CONCERT INDEX *under:*
(EMI) **CHS7 69741-2(4)** Record of Singing, Vol.4—German School
  cond C. SCHMALSTICH
  see CONCERT INDEX *under:*
(CLAR) **CDGSE78-50-52** Three Tenors
(EMI) **CDM7 69478-2** A Portrait of Joseph Schmidt
(EMI) **CMS7 64008-2(1)** Wagner Singing on Record (pt 1)
(EMI) **CMS7 64008-2(2)** Wagner Singing on Record (pt 2)
(NIMB) **NI7848** Great Singers at the Berlin State Opera
(PREI) **89019** Alexander Kipnis (1891-1978)
(PREI) **89035** Erna Berger (1900-1990) - I
(PREI) **89044** Dusolina Giannini (1902-1986)
(PREI) **89057** Charles Kullmann (1903-1982)
  cond F.A. SCHMIDT
  see CONCERT INDEX *under:*
(PREI) **89025** Tiana Lemnitz (b. 1897)
(PREI) **89082** Margarete Klose (1902-1968)
(PREI) **89209** Helge Roswaenge (1897-1972) - II
  cond H. SCHMIDT-ISSERSTEDT
  see CONCERT INDEX *under:*
(PREI) **89078** Hilde Konetzni
  cond F. SCHÖNBAUMSFELD
  see CONCERT INDEX *under:*
(PREI) **89054** Miliza Korjus (1912-1980)
  cond J. SCHÜLER
  see CONCERT INDEX *under:*
(ACAN) **43 268** Peter Anders sings German Opera Arias
(EMI) **CMS7 64008-2(1)** Wagner Singing on Record (pt 1)
(PREI) **89006** Heinrich Schlusnus (1888-1952) - I
(PREI) **89025** Tiana Lemnitz (b. 1897)
(PREI) **89035** Erna Berger (1900-1990) - I
  cond W. SCHÜTZE
  see CONCERT INDEX *under:*
(PREI) **89035** Erna Berger (1900-1990) - I
  cond B. SEIDLER-WINKLER
  see CONCERT INDEX *under:*
(EMI) **CHS7 69741-2(4)** Record of Singing, Vol.4—German School
(EMI) **CMS7 64008-2(1)** Wagner Singing on Record (pt 1)
(EMI) **CMS7 64008-2(2)** Wagner Singing on Record (pt 2)
(MMOI) **CDMOIR411** Sacred Songs and Arias
(NIMB) **NI7848** Great Singers at the Berlin State Opera
(PEAR) **GEMMCDS9926(2)** Covent Garden on Record—Vol.4 (pt 2)
(PEAR) **GEMMCD9394** Helge Rosvaenge—Operatic Recital
(PREI) **89018** Helge Rosvaenge (1897-1972)
(PREI) **89025** Tiana Lemnitz (b. 1897)
(PREI) **89049** Margarete Teschemacher (1903-1959)
(PREI) **89054** Miliza Korjus (1912-1980)
(PREI) **89077** Torsten Ralf (1901-1954)
(PREI) **89082** Margarete Klose (1902-1968)
(PREI) **89088** Walther Ludwig (1902-1981)
(PREI) **89209** Helge Roswaenge (1897-1972) - II
  cond K. SINGER
  see CONCERT INDEX *under:*
(PREI) **89027** Sigrid Onegin (1889-1943)
  cond G. STEEGER
  see CONCERT INDEX *under:*
(PREI) **89006** Heinrich Schlusnus (1888-1952) - I
(PREI) **89088** Walther Ludwig (1902-1981)
  cond W. STEINBERG
  see CONCERT INDEX *under:*
(EPM) **150 032** The Romantic Violin
  cond R. STRAUSS
Beethoven: Symphony 5, Symphony 7
  see CONCERT INDEX *under:*
(KOCH) **37076-2** Richard Strauss conducts Mozart
(PEAR) **GEMMCD9366** Strauss conducts Strauss
  cond G. SZELL
  see CONCERT INDEX *under:*
(EMI) **CDH7 64029-2** Richard Tauber - Opera Recital
(NIMB) **NI7830** Richard Tauber in Opera
(PREI) **89302** The Young Lotte Lehmann
  cond E. VIEBIG
  see CONCERT INDEX *under:*

(EMI) **CMS7 64008-2(2)** Wagner Singing on Record (pt 2)
  cond H. WEIGERT
  see CONCERT INDEX *under:*
(NIMB) **NI7833** Schöne & Tauber in Operetta
(PEAR) **GEMMCD9383** Julius Patzak—Opera & Operetta Recital
(PREI) **89005** Franz Völker (1899-1965) - I
(PREI) **89205** Heinrich Schlusnus Lieder Album, Vol.1
(PREI) **89209** Helge Roswaenge (1897-1972) - II
(PREI) **89302** The Young Lotte Lehmann
  cond F. WEISSMANN
  see CONCERT INDEX *under:*
(CLAR) **CDGSE78-50-57** Lotte Lehmann sings Lieder
(EMI) **CDM7 69478-2** A Portrait of Joseph Schmidt
(EMI) **CHS7 64487-2** R. Strauss—Der Rosenkavalier & Lieder
(EMI) **CMS7 64008-2(2)** Wagner Singing on Record (pt 2)
(MMOI) **CDMOIR408** Great Sopranos
(NIMB) **NI7867** Legendary Baritones
(PEAR) **GEMMCDS9925(2)** Covent Garden on Record—Vol.3 (pt 2)
(PEAR) **GEMMCD9394** Helge Roswaenge—Operatic Recital
(PREI) **89028** Ivar Andresen (1896-1940)
(PREI) **89029** Meta Seinemeyer (1895-1929)
(PREI) **89084** Kerstin Thorborg (1896-1970)
  cond WOLFGANG MARTIN
  see CONCERT INDEX *under:*
(MMOI) **CDMOIR422** Great Voices in Tchaikovsky
  cond F. ZAUN
  see CONCERT INDEX *under:*
(EMI) **CMS7 64008-2(1)** Wagner Singing on Record (pt 1)
(PREI) **89049** Margarete Teschemacher (1903-1959)
(PREI) **89088** Walther Ludwig (1902-1981)
  cond F. ZWEIG
  see CONCERT INDEX *under:*
(CLUB) **CL99-020** Maria Ivogün & Lotte Schöne—Opera Recital
(EMI) **CMS7 64008-2(1)** Wagner Singing on Record (pt 1)
(MMOI) **CDMOIR408** Great Sopranos
(NIMB) **NI7848** Great Singers at the Berlin State Opera
(NIMB) **NI7853** Lauri-Volpi sings Verdi
(PEAR) **GEMMCDS9926(1)** Covent Garden on Record—Vol.4 (pt 1)
(PREI) **89028** Ivar Andresen (1896-1940)
(PREI) **89035** Erna Berger (1900-1990) - I
(PREI) **89082** Margarete Klose (1902-1968)
(PREI) **90034** Maria Cebotari (1910-49)

BERLIN SYMPHONY ORCHESTRA
  cond S. ADLER
Gershwin: Piano Concerto
  cond F. ALLERS
Offenbach: Vie Parisienne (exc)
  cond J. FAERBER
Sinding: Piano Concerto
  see CONCERT INDEX *under:*
(VOX) **115708-2** Mosonyi/Raff/Stavenhaegn—Piano Concertos
  cond C.P. FLOR
Martinů: Symphony 1, Symphony 2
  see CONCERT INDEX *under:*
(CAPR) **10 281** Romantic Oboe Concertos
(RCA) **RD60119** Nineteenth Century Orchestral Works
  cond K. FORSTER
  see CONCERT INDEX *under:*
(EMI) **CMS7 64074-2(2)** Christa Ludwig—Recital (pt 2)
  cond F. FOX
Fall: Rose von Stambul (exc)
Millöcker: Dubarry (exc)
Zeller: Vogelhändler (exc)
  cond I. JACKSON
  see CONCERT INDEX *under:*
(KOCH) **37152-2** Works for String Orchestra
(KOCH) **37154-2** Still—Miscellaneous Works
  cond F. LEHÁR
  see CONCERT INDEX *under:*
(PEAR) **GEMMCD9310** Franz Lehár conducts Richard Tauber
  cond W. SCHMIDT-BOELCKE
Abraham: Blume von Hawaii (exc), Viktoria und ihr Husar (exc)
Jessel: Schwarzwaldmädel (exc)
Künneke: Vetter aus Dingsda (exc)
Lehár: Friederike (exc), Schön ist die Welt (exc)
Raymond: Maske in Blau (exc)
  cond V. SCHMIDT-GERTENBACH
(VOX) **115712-2** Hiller/Litolff/Moscheles—Piano Concertos
(VOX) **115713-2** Mendelssohn/Reinecke/Rheinberger—Piano Concertos
(VOX) **115717-2** Chopin/Henselt/Hiller—Piano Concertos
  cond M. SCHÖNWANDT
Schumann: Manfred (Cpte)
  cond W. SCHÜCHTER
  see CONCERT INDEX *under:*
(EMI) **CDH5 65201-2** Leonie Rysanek - Operatic Recital
(EMI) **CHS7 69741-2(4)** Record of Singing, Vol.4—German School

BERTON, Liliane (sop)
  Gounod: Faust (Cpte)
  Lecocq: Jour et la Nuit (Cpte)
  Poulenc: Dialogues des Carmélites (Cpte)
  see CONCERT INDEX under:
  (EMI) **CZS7 67515-2** Offenbach—Operetta highlights

BERTONA, Sylvia (sop)
  Puccini: Madama Butterfly (Cpte)
  Verdi: Simon Boccanegra (Cpte)
  see CONCERT INDEX under:
  (EMI) **CMS7 64165-2** Puccini—Trittico

BERTRAM, Theodor (bar)
  see CONCERT INDEX under:
  (PEAR) **GEMMCDS9923(2)** Covent Garden on
  Record, Vol.1 (pt 2)
  (SYMP) **SYMCD1081** The Harold Wayne Collection,
  Vol.5

BERTSCH, Rolf (pf)
  R. Strauss: Bourgeois Gentilhomme Suite

BERWALD QUARTET
  see CONCERT INDEX under:
  (MSVE) **MSCD521** Berwald—Chamber Works

BESANÇON, Aimé (ten)
  Offenbach: Périchole (Cpte)

BESANÇON, Maurice (bass)
  Bizet: Carmen (Cpte)

BESL, Karl (cond)
  see Berlin St Op Orch

BESSES O' THE BARN BAND
  see CONCERT INDEX under:
  (CHAN) **CHAN4513** British Bandsman Centenary
  Concert
  cond R. NEWSOME
  see CONCERT INDEX under:
  (CHAN) **CHAN4513** British Bandsman Centenary
  Concert

BESSLER, Bernardo (cond)
  see Brazilian CO

BESSLER-REIS QUARTET
  see CONCERT INDEX under:
  (CHNT) **LDC278 901** Villa-Lobos: String Quartets

BEST, Jonathan (bass)
  Maxwell Davies: Resurrection (Cpte)
  Purcell: King Arthur, Z628 (Cpte)
  Saxton: Caritas (Cpte)
  see CONCERT INDEX under:
  (HYPE) **CDA66076** British Choral Works
  (HYPE) **CDA66569** Vaughan Williams—Choral Works
  (OPRA) **ORCH103** Italian Opera—1810-20

BEST, Matthew (cond)
  see CLS

BEST, Matthew (bass)
  Rossini: Barbiere di Siviglia (Cpte)
  Stravinsky: Rake's Progress (Cpte)
  (ASV) **CDDCA758** Falla, Milhaud &
  Stravinsky—Operas
  (NIMB) **NI5217** Tippett conducts Tippett

BEST, Roger (va)
  Brahms: String Sextet 1, String Sextet 2
  see CONCERT INDEX under:
  (ASV) **CDQS6140** Haydn/Stamitz—Sinfonie
  Concertanti
  (CRD) **CRD3457** Dvořák—Hausmusik
  (NIMB) **NI5166** Vaughan Williams: Choral Works

BEST, Roger (vn)
  see CONCERT INDEX under:
  (CRD) **CRD3457** Dvořák—Hausmusik

BETHELL, Anna (mez)
  Sullivan: Sorcerer (Cpte)

BETHS, Gijs (va)
  see CONCERT INDEX under:
  (CHNN) **CCS1491** Beethoven—Songs
  (SONY) **SK46631** Mozart—Chamber Works

BETHS, Vera (vn)
  Schubert: Rondo, D438, String Quintet
  see CONCERT INDEX under:
  (BAYE) **BR100009** Ravel—Vocal & Chamber Works
  (CHNN) **CCS1491** Beethoven—Songs
  (SONY) **SK46631** Mozart—Chamber Works
  (SONY) **SK53120** Haydn—Piano Trios
  (SONY) **SK64307** Dotzauer—Chamber Works

BETTELHEIM, Dorf (vn)
  Schumann: Piano Quintet, Op. 44

BETTENDORF, Emmy (sop)
  see CONCERT INDEX under:
  (DANA) **DACOCD313/4** Lauritz Melchior Anthology -
  Vol. 2
  (NIMB) **NI7830** Richard Tauber in Opera
  (PEAR) **GEMMCD9398** Friedrich Schorr
  (PEAR) **GEMMCD9419** Herbert Ernst Groh—Opera
  Recital

BETTERIDGE, Stephen (pf)
  see CONCERT INDEX under:
  (SYMP) **SYMCD1075** May Harrison—Violinist and
  Composer

BETTI, Freda (contr)
  Lecocq: Jour et la Nuit (Cpte)
  Offenbach: Chanson de Fortunio (Cpte)

Planquette: Rip van Winkle (Cpte)
  see CONCERT INDEX under:
  (EMI) **CZS7 67515-2** Offenbach—Operetta highlights
  (MONT) **TCE8790** Debussy: Orchestral and Dramatic
  Works

BETTINA, Judith (sop)
  Babbitt: Head of the Bed

BETTINELLI (pf)
  see CONCERT INDEX under:
  (SYMP) **SYMCD1170** The Harold Wayne Collection,
  Vol.20

BETTONI, Vincenzo (bass)
  see CONCERT INDEX under:
  (CLUB) **CL99-074** Conchita Supervia (1895-1936)
  (MEMO) **HR4408/9(2)** Singers in Genoa, Vol.1 (disc
  2)

BEUACHEMIN, Michel (bass)
  Berlioz: Troyens (Cpte)

BEUDERT, Mark (ten)
  Bernstein: Candide (1988) (exc)

BEUERLE, Hans Michael (cond)
  see Frankfurt Chbr Ch

BEVAN, Maurice (bar)
  Monteverdi: L'Arianna (exc)
  Purcell: Dido (Cpte), Indian Queen, Z630 (Cpte)
  see CONCERT INDEX under:
  (HARM) **HMA190 201** Blow—Vocal Works
  (HARM) **HMX290 1528/33(2)** A Purcell Companion (pt
  2)
  (VANG) **08.2003.72** Purcell—Celebrated
  Songs,Sacred Airs and Concert Pieces

BEVAN, Rachel (sop)
  Purcell: Dido (Cpte)
  see CONCERT INDEX under:
  (PAUL) **PACD56** Nielsen: Songs

BEVAN, Rosalind (pf)
  Stockhausen: Mantra

BEVAN, Stanley (ten)
  Sullivan: Iolanthe (exc)

BEYER, Achim (va)
  see CONCERT INDEX under:
  (CAPR) **10 234** Italian Recorder Works

BEYER, Bernd (ten)
  R. Strauss: Rosenkavalier (Cpte)

BEYER, Franz (va)
  Mozart: String Quintet, K515, String Quintet, K516

BEYER, Isabel (pf)
  Schubert: Divertissement, D823, Polonaises, D824
  see CONCERT INDEX under:
  (FOUR) **FHMD891** Schubert: Piano Duets, Vol.1
  (FOUR) **FHMD892** Schubert—Piano Duets, Vol.2
  (FOUR) **FHMD893** Schubert—Piano Duets, Volume
  3
  (FOUR) **FHMD894** Schubert—Piano Duets, Volume
  4
  (FOUR) **FHMD9111** Mozart—Works for Piano Duet
  (FOUR) **FHMD9212** Piano Duets - Children's Games

BEYER, Reinhard (bass)
  Schreker: Gezeichneten (Cpte)
  see CONCERT INDEX under:
  (SONY) **S2K66836** Goldschmidt—Beatrice Cenci, etc

BEYERLE, Hatto (va)
  see CONCERT INDEX under:
  (SCHW) **311088** Spohr—Instrumental Works

BEYLE, Léon (ten)
  see CONCERT INDEX under:
  (IRCC) **IRCC-CD802** Souvenirs of Rare French
  Opera

BEZKORVANY, Sergei (vn)
  J. Gibbs: Solos, Op.1

BEZNOSIUK, Lisa (fl)
  Bach: Triple Concerto, BWV1044
  see CONCERT INDEX under:
  (ARCH) **413 731-2AH** Bach: Concerti
  (ARCH) **419 615-2AH** Vivaldi: Concertos
  (L'OI) **417 622-2OH** Mozart—Wind Concertos
  (MERI) **ECD84080** Haydn: Vocal works

BEZNOSIUK, Pavlo (vn)
  see CONCERT INDEX under:
  (HYPE) **CDA66739** The Spirits of England and France

BEZRODNY, Sergei (hpd)
  see CONCERT INDEX under:
  (RCA) **RD87991** Bach: Concerti

BEZRODNY, Sergei (pf)
  see CONCERT INDEX under:
  (RCA) **09026 62524-2** It's Peaceful Here
  (RCA) **74321 24894-2** Homage to Schnittke

BEZUBENKOV, Gennadi (bass)
  Rimsky-Korsakov: Sadko (Cpte)
  Tchaikovsky: Queen of Spades (Cpte)

BEZZINA, Gilbert (cond)
  see Nice Baroque Ens

BHATT, Krishna (tabala)
  see CONCERT INDEX under:
  (NONE) **7559-79310-2** Short Stories

BIANCHI, Bonifacio (mndl)
  see CONCERT INDEX under:
  (ERAT) **4509-92132-2** The Magic of the Mandolin

BIANCHI, Chiara (vn)
  see CONCERT INDEX under:
  (HARM) **HMA190 5137** Arias and Cantatas for
  Soprano and Trumpet

BIANCHI, Luigi Alberto (vn)
  Paganini: Lucca Sonatas

BIANCHI, Mario (ten)
  Verdi: Traviata (Cpte)

BIANCHINI, Giovanni (treb)
  Puccini: Tosca (Cpte)

BIANCO, René (bar)
  Bizet: Pêcheurs de Perles (Cpte)
  Poulenc: Dialogues des Carmélites (Cpte)
  see CONCERT INDEX under:
  (PHIL) **442 272-2PM2** The Best of Bizet

BIANCONI, P (pf)
  Schubert: Winterreise (Cpte)

BIBER, Clemens (ten)
  Wagner: Tannhäuser (Cpte)

BIBLE, Frances (mez)
  P. Paray: Joan of Arc Mass
  R. Ward: Crucible (Cpte)

BICKET, Harry (organ)
  see CONCERT INDEX under:
  (CHAN) **CHAN8936** Finzi—Choral works
  (CHAN) **CHAN9019** Howells & Vaughan
  Williams—Choral Works

BICKLEY, Susan (mez)
  Purcell: Dido (Cpte), Fairy Queen, Z629 (Cpte)
  see CONCERT INDEX under:
  (ASV) **CDDCA758** Falla, Milhaud &
  Stravinsky—Operas
  (ECM) **831 959-2** Pärt—Arbos
  (OPRA) **ORCH103** Italian Opera—1810-20

BICKLEY, Susan (sop)
  see CONCERT INDEX under:
  (DG) **447 068-2GH** Stravinsky—The Flood, etc

BIEBER, Clemens (ten)
  Mendelssohn: Hochzeit des Camacho (Cpte)
  Mozart: Zauberflöte (Cpte)
  R. Strauss: Salome (Cpte)

BIELBY, Jonathan (organ)
  see CONCERT INDEX under:
  (PRIO) **PRCD298** Great European Organs, Vol.21

BIELECKI, André (ten)
  Mussorgsky: Boris Godunov (Cpte)

BIELEFELD OPERA CHORUS
  cond G. MOULL
  Spohr: Faust (Cpte)

BIELEFELD PHILHARMONIC ORCHESTRA
  cond G. MOULL
  Spohr: Faust (Cpte)

BIENVENU, Lily (pf)
  see CONCERT INDEX under:
  (EMI) **CHS7 69741-2(3)** Record of Singing,
  Vol.4—French School
  (PHIL) **438 970-2PM2** Camille Maurane

BIERBACH, Franz (bass)
  Beethoven: Fidelio (Cpte)
  R. Strauss: Rosenkavalier (Cpte)
  Wagner: Meistersinger (Cpte)
  see CONCERT INDEX under:
  (DECC) **425 959-2DM** Lisa della Casa sings R.
  Strauss

BIERETT, Doris (sop)
  Weill: Sieben Todsünden (Cpte)

BIERMANN, Barbara (hp)
  Saint-Saëns: Oratorio de Noël, Op. 12

BIGLEY, Roger (va)
  Simpson: String Quintet

BIGOT, Eugène (cond)
  see Lamoureux Orch

BIHLMAIER, Hans Norbert (cond)
  see Copenhagen PO

BILANDZIJA, Beate (sop)
  Delius: Village Romeo and Juliet (Cpte)
  Schillings: Mona Lisa (Cpte)

BILBAO CHORAL SOCIETY
  cond J.L. OCEJO
  see CONCERT INDEX under:
  (PHIL) **420 955-2PH** Ramirez: Choral Works
  cond D. SANCHEZ
  see CONCERT INDEX under:
  (PHIL) **420 955-2PH** Ramirez: Choral Works

BÍLEK, Zdenek (cond)
  see Slovak PO

BILGRAM, Hedwig (organ)
  see CONCERT INDEX under:
  (DG) **423 127-2GX4** Bruckner: Sacred Works for
  Chorus
  (EMI) **CDC7 54330-2** Arrangements for Trumpet and
  Organ

BILLINGS, James (bar)
  Bernstein: Candide (1982) (Cpte)

BILLS, John (ten)
  Verdi: Luisa Miller (Cpte)

(DECC) 443 476-2DF2 Vivaldi—L'estro armonico, Op 3
(DG) 439 529-2GGA Delius/Vaughan Williams/Walton—Orchestral Works
(EMI) CDC7 49862-2 Bach: Concertos
(EMI) CDC7 54205-2 Vivaldi—Double Concertos
(HYPE) CDA66295 Villa-Lobos: Chamber Works
(NOVA) 150 017-2 Bach—Violin Concertos
(PHIL) 422 509-2PME5 The Complete Mozart Edition Vol 9
(PHIL) 422 545-2PME3 The Complete Mozart Edition Vol.45
(PHIL) 422 833-2PC Mozart—Chamber Works
(VIRG) VJ7 59656-2 Italian Baroque Concertos

BLACK, Robert (cond)
see Speculum Musicae

BLACK, Robert (db)
see CONCERT INDEX under:
(KOCH) 37238-2 A Chance Operation - John Cage Tribute

BLACK, Stanley (cond)
see London Fest Orch

BLACK, Stanley (pf/dir)
see CONCERT INDEX under:
(DECC) 433 616-2DSP
Addinsell/Gershwin—Orchestral Works

BLACK, Virginia (harm)
see CONCERT INDEX under:
(CRD) CRD3457 Dvořák—Hausmusik

BLACK, Virginia (hpd)
D. Scarlatti: Keyboard Sonatas (exc)
J. C. Bach: Keyboard Sonatas, Op. 5 (exc), Keyboard Sonatas, Op. 17 (exc)
Soler: Keyboard Sonatas I (exc), Keyboard Sonatas II (exc)
see CONCERT INDEX under:
(ARGO) 440 282-2ZH Nyman—Time Will Pronounce
(COLL) Coll5024-2 The Essential Harpsichord
(CRD) CRD3435 Mozart—Violin Sonatas
(UNIT) 88005-2 D. Scarlatti/Soler—Music from the Courts of Europe: Madrid

BLACK, William (pf)
Rachmaninov: Piano Concerto 4

BLACK DYKE MILLS BAND
see CONCERT INDEX under:
(CHAN) CHAN4513 British Bandsman Centenary Concert
cond G. BRAND
see CONCERT INDEX under:
(CHAN) CHAN6539 Classic Brass
(RSR) RSRD1002 Black Dyke Mills Band, Vol.2 - Sovereign Heritage
cond D. BROADBENT
see CONCERT INDEX under:
(CHAN) CHAN4506 Life Divine—4 Famous Test-Pieces
cond W. HALLIWELL
see CONCERT INDEX under:
(BEUL) 1PD2 Crystal Palace Champions
cond D. HURST
see CONCERT INDEX under:
(CHAN) CHAN4514 Black Dyke Mills Band play Overtures
cond R. NEWSOME
see CONCERT INDEX under:
(CHAN) CHAN4508 Epic Brass—British Music for Brass Band
(CHAN) CHAN4528 The Lion and the Eagle
(CHAN) CHAN6539 Classic Brass
(RSR) RSRD1002 Black Dyke Mills Band, Vol.2 - Sovereign Heritage
cond P. PARKES
see CONCERT INDEX under:
(CHAN) CHAN4501 The World's Most Beautiful Melodies
(CHAN) CHAN4505 Black Dyke plays Rossini
(CHAN) CHAN4506 Life Divine—4 Famous Test-Pieces
(CHAN) CHAN4507 A Tribute to Elgar, Delius and Vaughan Williams
(CHAN) CHAN4513 British Bandsman Centenary Concert
(CHAN) CHAN4514 Black Dyke Mills Band play Overtures
(CHAN) CHAN4522 'Volcano'—live at the Royal Albert Hall, London
(CHAN) CHAN4523 Concerto
(RSR) RSRD1002 Black Dyke Mills Band, Vol.2 - Sovereign Heritage
cond T. WALMSLEY
see CONCERT INDEX under:
(CHAN) CHAN4505 Black Dyke plays Rossini
cond J. WATSON
see CONCERT INDEX under:
(POLY) QPRL053D Slavonic Brass

BLACKBURN, Harold (bass)
Britten: Curlew River (Cpte)

BLACKBURN, Olivia (sop)
MacMillan: Visitatio Sepulchri (Cpte)
see CONCERT INDEX under:
(ASV) CDDCA902 Ginastera—Piano Works, Volume 3

BLACKWELL, Derek (ten)
Berlioz: Benvenuto Cellini (Cpte)

BLACKWELL, Harolyn (sop)
Gershwin: Porgy and Bess (Cpte)

BLACKWOOD, Easley (pf)
Blackwood: Cello Sonata
Bridge: Cello Sonata

BLADIN, Christer (ten)
Braunfels: Verkündigung (Cpte)
Wagner: Parsifal (Cpte)

BLAGOVEST CHOIR
cond V. PONKIN
see CONCERT INDEX under:
(CDM) LDC288 027/8 Prokofiev—Film and Stage Music

BLÁHA, Milan (accordion)
see CONCERT INDEX under:
(SUPR) 11 0767-2 Martinů—Cantatas

BLAIR, James (cond)
see Scottish CO

BLAKE, Howard (cond)
see ECO

BLAKE, Lowri (vc)
see CONCERT INDEX under:
(ETCE) KTC1111 Saint-Saëns—Works for Cello and Piano
(ETCE) KTC1153 Fauré—Works for Cello & Piano

BLAKE, Rockwell (ten)
Rossini: Donna del lago (Cpte)
see CONCERT INDEX under:
(ARAB) Z6543 The Rossini Tenor
(ARAB) Z6598 Rockwell Blake, the Mozart Tenor
(ARAB) Z6612 Rossini: Opera Arias
(EMI) CDC7 54643-2 Rossini—Bicentenary Gala Concert

BLAKELY, John J (pf)
Beethoven: Violin Sonata 5, Violin Sonata 9
see CONCERT INDEX under:
(CNTI) CCD1022 Bridge/Britten—Works for Violin and Piano
(MERI) CDE84259 Fauré—Works for Violin and Piano
(MERI) DUOCD89002 German Lieder sung in English
(UNIC) UKCD2009 A-Courting we will go

BLANC, Ernst (bar)
Bizet: Carmen (Cpte), Pêcheurs de perles (Cpte)
Gounod: Faust (Cpte)
Offenbach: Contes d'Hoffmann (Cpte)
Saint-Saëns: Samson et Dalila (Cpte)

BLANC, Frédéric (organ)
Blanc: Genesis Meditations, Messe Improvisée

BLANCAS, Angeles (treb)
Penella: Gato Montés (Cpte)

(ROGER) BLANCHARD VOCAL ENSEMBLE
cond H. ROSBAUD
Gluck: Orphée (Cpte)

BLANCHART, Ramon (bar)
see CONCERT INDEX under:
(MEMO) HR4408/9(1) Singers in Genoa, Vol.1 (disc 1)

BLAND, Elsa (sop)
see CONCERT INDEX under:
(PREI) 89020 Leo Slezak (1873-1946)

BLANKENBURG, Elke Mascha (cond)
see Cologne Kurrende Orch

BLANKENHEIM, Toni (bar)
Berg: Lulu (Cpte)

BLANKESTIJN, Marieke (vn)
(ASV) CDCOE803 Chamber Concertos
(DG) 435 383-2GH Martin—Chamber Orchestral Works
(DG) 435 873-2GH Vivaldi—Oboe Concertos

BLANKESTIJN, Marieke (vn/dir)
Vivaldi: Concerti, Op. 8 (exc)

BLANZAT, Anne-Marie (sop)
Dukas: Ariane et Barbe-Bleue (Cpte)

BLASI, Angela Maria (sop)
Brahms: Deutsches Requiem, Op.45 (Cpte)
Handel: Samson (Cpte)
Mahler: Symphony 8
Mozart: Litanies, K243, Mass, K257, Requiem, Rè Pastore (Cpte)
Puccini: Bohème (Cpte)

BLASIUS, Martin (bass)
Kreutzer: Nachtlager in Granada (Cpte)
Zemlinsky: Traumgörge (Cpte)

BLATTER, Johanna (mez)
Wagner: Tristan und Isolde (exc), Walküre (Cpte)
see CONCERT INDEX under:
(EMI) CMS5 65212-2 Wagner—Les introuvables du Ring

BLAUMER, Stephan (va)
see CONCERT INDEX under:
(ETCE) KTC1045 Menotti: Chamber and Vocal Works

BLAYDEN, Alastair (vc)
see CONCERT INDEX under:
(CLRI) CC0006 Clarinet Virtuosi of the Past—Hermstedt

BLAZER, Judith (sop)
Gershwin: Girl crazy (Cpte)
see CONCERT INDEX under:
(EMI) CDC5 55189-2 The Busby Berkeley Album

BLAZHKOV, Igor (cond)
see Leningrad PO

BLECH, Harry (cond)
see LMP

BLECH, Leo (cond)
see Berlin St Op Orch

BLECH QUARTET
see CONCERT INDEX under:
(EMI) CHS5 65198-2 Maggie Teyte sings French Songs

BLEEKE, Mark (ten)
see CONCERT INDEX under:
(NEWP) NC60021 Praetorius—Chorale Settings

BLEGEN, Judith (sop)
Fauré: Requiem (Cpte)
Haydn: Mass 14, Schöpfung (Cpte)
Mahler: Symphony 8
Mozart: Nozze di Figaro (Cpte), Zaïde (Cpte)
Orff: Carmina Burana
Poulenc: Gloria
Puccini: Bohème (Cpte)
see CONCERT INDEX under:
(DG) 435 162-2GX13 Mahler—Complete Symphonies
(SONY) SMK45838 Berg: Vocal & Orchestral Works
(SONY) SM2K47563 Haydn—Choral & Orchestral Works

BLEICHER, Stefan-Johannes (organ)
see CONCERT INDEX under:
(EBS) EBS6065 Brixi—Organ Concertos
(ORFE) C251912H Vivaldi—Cello Sonatas

BLESSED, Brian (narr)
see CONCERT INDEX under:
(CALA) CACD1010 Bliss—Choral and Orchestral Works

BLIER, Steven (pf)
see CONCERT INDEX under:
(KOCH) 37000-2 Bernstein—Songs & Duets
(KOCH) 37028-2 Gershwin—Songs & Duets
(KOCH) 37050-2 Blitzstein—Songs
(KOCH) 37086-2 Unquiet Peace—The Lied Between the Wars

BLISS, Sir Arthur (cond)
see LPO

BLOCH, David (pf)
see CONCERT INDEX under:
(ROMA) RR1941 Terezín - The Music 1941-44

BLOCH, Kalman (cl)
Schoenberg: Pierrot Lunaire

BLOCHWITZ, Hans-Peter (ten)
Bach: Christmas Oratorio, BWV248 (Cpte), Mass in B minor, BWV232 (Cpte), St Matthew Passion, BWV244 (Cpte)
Beethoven: Fidelio (Cpte), Missa Solemnis
Handel: Theodora (Cpte)
Haydn: Mass 10, Mass 13
Mahler: Klagende Lied (Cpte), Lied von der Erde
Mendelssohn: Paulus (Cpte)
Mozart: Don Giovanni (Cpte), Finta semplice (Cpte), Mass, K317, Mass, K427, Requiem, Zauberflöte (Cpte)
Schubert: Winterreise (Cpte)
Schumann: Szenen aus Goethes Faust (Cpte)
Telemann: St Matthew Passion (1746)
see CONCERT INDEX under:
(DG) 415 353-2GH4 Mendelssohn—Complete Symphonies, etc
(DG) 427 348-2GH2 Zemlinsky: Lieder
(PHIL) 422 522-2PME6 The Complete Mozart Edition Vol 22
(PHIL) 426 275-2PH Mozart—Sacred Choral Works
(PHIL) 438 932-2PH Schubert—Lieder
(SONY) SK57960 Zemlinsky—Posthumous Songs

BLOKKER, Kees (tbn)
see CONCERT INDEX under:
(DECC) 444 455-2DH Martin—Ballades; Concerto for 7 Wind Instruments

BLOM, Inger (contr)
Scriabin: Symphony 1
see CONCERT INDEX under:
(BIS) BIS-CD437 Schnittke: Orchestral & Vocal Works

BLOMSTEDT, Herbert (cond)
see Danish RSO

BLUM, Eberhard (fl)
Cage: Atlas Eclipticalis
M. Feldman: For Christian Wolff, For Philip Guston

BLUM, Robert (cond)
see orch

BLUME, Karl (bass)
Pärt: Berliner Messe

BLUME, Norbert (va)
see CONCERT INDEX under:
(MERI) CDE84236 Hummel—Chamber Music - Volume 2
(UNIC) DKPCD9076 Vaughan Williams—Chamber Music

BLUME, Norbert (va d'amore)
see CONCERT INDEX under:
(DECC) 433 816-2DH2   Hindemith—Kammermusik
(SONY) SK46556   Vivaldi—Concertos

BLUMENSTOCK, Elizabeth (vn)
see CONCERT INDEX under:
(HARM) HMU90 7084/5   Bach—Violin Sonatas

BLUMENTAL, Felicja (pf)
see CONCERT INDEX under:
(EMI) CDM5 65307-2   Szymanowski—Orchestral and Piano Works

BLUMENTHAL, Daniel (pf)
Czerny: Andante and Polacca, Schubert Fantasies, Op. 339
Fuchs: Piano Sonata 1, Piano Sonata 2
see CONCERT INDEX under:
(ASV) CDDCA716   Koechlin—Works for Horn & Piano
(CFP) CD-CFP9012   Gershwin. Works for Piano and Orchestra
(ETCE) KTC1135   French Music for Horn
(ETCE) KTC2018   The Classical Sonatina
(ETCE) KTC2021   Tansman—Piano Sonatas and Sonatinas
(MARC) 8 223421   Bülow—Piano Transcriptions
(MARC) 8 223423   Fuchs—Works for Cello & Piano
(MARC) 8 223424   Stanchinsky—Piano Works
(MARC) 8 223474   Fuchs—Piano Sonatas, Vol.2
(MARC) 8 223505   Devreese—Piano Concertos
(MARC) 8 223656   Blumenfeld—Piano Etudes

BLYTH, Alan (spkr)
Horenstein: Blyth Interview

BNFL BAND
cond R. EVANS
see CONCERT INDEX under:
(POLY) QPRL062D   Masterworks for Brass Band - Volume 2 - Partita

BOANTĂ, Mircea (cl)
Enescu: Wind Decet, Op. 14

BOATWRIGHT, McHenry (bar)
Gershwin: Porgy and Bess (Cpte)

BOBILLIER, Gisèle (sop)
see CONCERT INDEX under:
(DECC) 433 400-2DM2   Ravel & Debussy—Stage Works

BOCCHERINI QUARTET TOKYO
Mozart: Flute Quartets

BOCHMANN, Michael (vn)
see CONCERT INDEX under:
(NIMB) NI5208   Delius & Vaughan Williams—Orchestral Works

BOCKELMANN, Rudolf (bass-bar)
Wagner: Meistersinger (exc)
see CONCERT INDEX under:
(CLAR) CDGSE78-50-33   Lauritz Melchior & Albert Coates
(EMI) CMS7 64008-2(1)   Wagner Singing on Record (pt 1)
(EMI) CMS7 64008-2(2)   Wagner Singing on Record (pt 2)
(PEAR) GEMMCDS9137   Wagner—Der Ring des Nibelungen
(PEAR) GEMMCDS9926(2)   Covent Garden on Record—Vol.4 (pt 2)
(SCHW) 314512   Vienna State Opera Live, Vol.1
(SCHW) 314642   Vienna State Opera Live, Vol.14

BODANZKY, Artur (cond)
see NY Met Op Orch

BODE, Hannelore (sop)
Wagner: Meistersinger (Cpte), Parsifal (Cpte)

BODENHAM, Peter (ten)
Walton: Troilus and Cressida (Cpte)

BODENSTEIN, Christoph (ten)
R. Strauss: Rosenkavalier (Cpte)

BODINI, Maria Rosa (pf)
see CONCERT INDEX under:
(NUOV) 6809   Falla: Vocal & Instrumental Works

BODRA SMYANA CHILDREN'S CHOIR
cond E. TCHAKAROV
Mussorgsky: Boris Godunov (Cpte)

BODY, Marcus (treb)
see CONCERT INDEX under:
(ARGO) 433 215-2ZH   Britten—Christmas Music

BOECKMAN, Vicki (rec)
see CONCERT INDEX under:
(KONT) 32014   Telemann—Recorder Sonatas

BOEHM, Mary Louise (pf)
Beach: Piano Concerto

BOEKE, Kees (fl/vielle)
see CONCERT INDEX under:
(ARCA) A21   Ars Subtilis Ytalica

BOEKE, Kees (rec)
see CONCERT INDEX under:
(TELD) 4509-97465-2   Franz Brüggen Edition Vol. 3—English Ensemble Music
(TELD) 4509-97466-2   Frans Brüggen Edition Vol. 4—Early Baroque Recorder Music
(TELD) 4509-97467-2   Frans Brüggen Edition Vol. 5—Late Baroque Chamber Music
(TELD) 4509-97468-2   Frans Brüggen Edition Vol.6—French Recorder Suites

(TELD) 4509-97469-2   Frans Brüggen Edition Vol. 7—French Recorder Sonatas

BOEMI, A. (bar)
see CONCERT INDEX under:
(CLUB) CL99-025   Giovanni Zenatello (1876-1949)
(PEAR) GEMMCDS9074(2)   Giovanni Zenatello, Vol.2 (pt 2)
(PREI) 89038   Giovanni Zenatello (1876-1949)

BOER, Harmen de (cl)
see CONCERT INDEX under:
(CHAN) CHAN9210   Twentieth-Century American Music

BOESCH, Christian (bar)
J. Strauss II: Fledermaus (exc)
Mozart: Zauberflöte (Cpte)

BOESE, Ursula (mez)
Berg: Lulu (Cpte)
R. Strauss: Salome (Cpte)
Wagner: Parsifal (Cpte)

BOETTCHER, Else (mez)
Verdi: Macbeth (Cpte)
see CONCERT INDEX under:
(SCHW) 314552   Vienna State Opera Live, Vol.5

BOETTCHER, Wilfried (cond)
see Vienna SO

BOETTCHER, Wolfgang (vc)
Schubert: String Quintet

BOETTGER, Andreas (perc)
Stockhausen: Michaels Reise

BOEYKENS, Walter (cl)
Mozart: Clarinet Quintet, K581, Piano Trio, K498
see CONCERT INDEX under:
(HARM) HMC90 1489   Nielsen—Orchestral Works

(WALTER) BOEYKENS ENSEMBLE
Beethoven: Piano Trios (exc), Septet, Op. 20
Messiaen: Quatuor
Mozart: Clarinet Quintet, K581, Piano Trio, K498
Schubert: Octet, D803
see CONCERT INDEX under:
(HARM) HMC90 1419   Prokofiev/Khachaturian/Kókai

BOFFARD, Florent (pf)
see CONCERT INDEX under:
(DG) 445 833-2GH   Boulez conducts Boulez

BOGACHEV, Vladimir (ten)
Shostakovich: Gamblers (Cpte)
see CONCERT INDEX under:
(CHAN) CHAN9149   Rimsky-Korsakov/Glinka—Vocal Works

BOGARDE, Sir Dirk (narr)
Lehár: Lustige Witwe (Cpte)

BOGARDUS, Stephen (voc)
Bernstein: West Side Story (Cpte)

BOGART, John (alto)
see CONCERT INDEX under:
(SONY) SM3K47162   Bernstein plays and conducts Bernstein Volume III

BOGART, John Paul (bass)
Bizet: Carmen (exc)
Donizetti: Messa da Requiem
Puccini: Turandot (Cpte)

BOGATIN, Barbara (baroque vc)
Bach: Flute Sonatas, BWV1030-5

BOGDAN, Thomas (ten)
M. Monk: Atlas (Cpte)

BOGDANOVA, A. (sop)
see CONCERT INDEX under:
(OLYM) OCD194   Shostakovich: Vocal & Orchestral Works

BOGDANOVICH, Aleksandr (ten)
see CONCERT INDEX under:
(PEAR) GEMMCDS9007/9(1)   Singers of Imperial Russia, Vol.4 (pt 1)

BOGINO, Konstantin (pf)
see CONCERT INDEX under:
(CONI) CDCF199   Brahms/Joachim—Viola Works

BOGUET, Jean (pf)
see CONCERT INDEX under:
(MSCM) MM30373   Gounod—Mélodies

BOGUNIA, Stanislav (pf)
see CONCERT INDEX under:
(CALL) CAL9628   Mozart—Chamber Works
(SUPR) CO-72646   Dvořák: Moravian Duets
(SUPR) 11 0751-2   Martinů—Choral Works
(SUPR) 11 0752-2   Martinů—Spalíček, etc
(SUPR) 11 0767-2   Martinů—Cantatas

BOGUTSKAHEIN, W. (pf)
see CONCERT INDEX under:
(APR) APR7015   The Auer Legacy, Vol.1

BOHÁČOVÁ, Marta (sop)
Janáček: Jenufa (Cpte)

BOHÉE, Philippe (bar)
Saint-Saëns: Henry VIII (Cpte)

BÖHEIM, Franz (buffo)
J.Strauss II: Fledermaus (Cpte)
Lehár: Lustige Witwe (Cpte)

BÖHM, Karl (cond)
see Bayreuth Fest Orch

BÖHM, Karl-Walter (ten)
R.Strauss: Salome (Cpte)

BÖHM, Regine (mez)
see CONCERT INDEX under:
(BAYE) BR100041   Choral and Vocal Works

BÖHME, Kurt (bass)
Janáček: Excursions of Mr Brouček (Cpte)
Mozart: Don Giovanni (Cpte), Entführung (Cpte), Nozze di Figaro (Cpte)
Offenbach: Vie Parisienne (exc)
Orff: Kluge (Cpte)
Wagner: Rheingold (Cpte), Siegfried (Cpte), Walküre (exc)
Weber: Freischütz (Cpte)
see CONCERT INDEX under:
(ACAN) 43 267   Fritz Wunderlich sings Opera Arias
(DECC) 414 100-2DM15   Wagner: Der Ring des Nibelungen
(DG) 437 677-2GDO2   Irmgard Seefried - Opera Recital
(PHIL) 446 057-2PB14   Wagner—The Ring Cycle - Bayreuth Festival 1967

BOHN, James (bar)
Britten: Paul Bunyan (Cpte)
Copland: Tender Land (Cpte)
see CONCERT INDEX under:
(VIRG) VC7 59022-2   Smyth—Vocal and Orchestral Works

BOHNEN, Michael (bass)
Weber: Abu Hassan (Cpte)
see CONCERT INDEX under:
(PREI) 89302   The Young Lotte Lehmann
(SCHW) 314672   Vienna State Opera Live, Vol.17

BOHUSS, Irena (sop)
see CONCERT INDEX under:
(PEAR) GEMMCDS9004/6(1)   Singers of Imperial Russia, Vol.3 (pt 1)

BOITSOV, Evgeni (ten)
Tchaikovsky: Queen of Spades (Cpte)

BOITSOV, Yevgeny (ten)
Rimsky-Korsakov: Sadko (Cpte)

BOJSTEN, Stefan (pf)
see CONCERT INDEX under:
(BIS) BIS-CD582   Wirén—Chamber Works

BOKATTI, Aron (sngr)
Giordano: Fedora (Cpte)

BOKOR, Margit (sop)
see CONCERT INDEX under:
(SCHW) 314542   Vienna State Opera Live, Vol.4
(SCHW) 314552   Vienna State Opera Live, Vol.5
(SCHW) 314572   Vienna State Opera Live, Vol.7
(SCHW) 314592   Vienna State Opera Live, Vol.9
(SCHW) 314622   Vienna State Opera Live, Vol.12
(SCHW) 314642   Vienna State Opera Live, Vol.14
(SCHW) 314652   Vienna State Opera Live, Vol.15
(SCHW) 314672   Vienna State Opera Live, Vol.17

BOKY, Colette (sop)
Bizet: Carmen (Cpte)
Falla: Sombrero de tres picos (Cpte)

BOLDIN, Leonid (bar)
Kabalevsky: Colas Breugnon (Cpte)

BOLDRINI, Giancarlo (bass)
Mascagni: Rantzau (Cpte)

BOLET, Jorge (pf)
Liszt: Années de pèlerinage 1, Années de pèlerinage 2, Études d'exécution, S139
see CONCERT INDEX under:
(DECC) 410 115-2DH   Liszt: Piano Works, Vol.3
(DECC) 410 257-2DH   Liszt: Piano Works, Vol. 1
(DECC) 411 803-2DH   Liszt: Piano Works, Vol.6
(DECC) 414 575-2DH   Liszt: Piano Works, Vol.2
(DECC) 417 523-2DH   Liszt: Piano Works, Vol.8
(DECC) 425 689-2DX   Jorge Bolet plays Liszt
(DECC) 430 726-2DM   Popular Works for Piano and Orchestra
(DECC) 433 070-2DWO   World of Chopin
(DECC) 436 648-2DH   Franck/Liszt/Mendelssohn—Piano Works

BOLGAN, Marina (sop)
Paisiello: Nina (Cpte)

(SIMÓN) BOLÍVAR ORFEÓN UNIVERSITARIO
cond E. MATA
Villa-Lobos: Chôros 10

(SIMÓN) BOLÍVAR SYMPHONY ORCHESTRA, VENEZUELA
cond E. MATA
Villa-Lobos: Chôros 10
see CONCERT INDEX under:
(DORI) DOR90210   Falla—Vocal Works
(DORI) DOR90211   Latin American Ballets

BOLLE, James (cond)
see Budapest SO

BOLLE, Jürgen (spkr)
B.A. Zimmermann: Soldaten (Cpte)

BOLLEN, Ria (contr)
Galuppi: Magnificat in G
Handel: Alessandro (Cpte)
Martin: Requiem
Vivaldi: Gloria, RV589
see CONCERT INDEX under:
(HANS) 98 812   Bach—Cantatas, Vol.50

BOLLER, Bettina (vn)
Schoeck: Violin Concerto

BOLLHAMMER, Karl (ten)
see CONCERT INDEX under:
(SCHW) 314602 Vienna State Opera Live, Vol.10

BOLLMAN, Hans Heinz (ten)
see CONCERT INDEX under:
(PEAR) GEMMCD9310 Franz Lehár conducts Richard
Tauber

BOLLONGINO, Ellen (sop)
Schreker: Gezeichneten (Cpte)

BOLOGNA TEATRO COMUNALE CHORUS
cond R. BONYNGE
Donizetti: Favorita (Cpte), Maria Stuarda (Cpte)
cond B. CAMPANELLA
Donizetti: Fille du Régiment (Cpte)
cond R. CHAILLY
Puccini: Manon Lescaut (Cpte)
Rossini: Cenerentola (Cpte), Petite messe solennelle
(Cpte)
Verdi: Rigoletto (Cpte)
cond D. GATTI
Rossini: Armida (Cpte)
cond G. PATANÈ
Rossini: Barbiere di Siviglia (Cpte)

BOLOGNA TEATRO COMUNALE ORCHESTRA
cond R. BONYNGE
Donizetti: Favorita (Cpte), Maria Stuarda (Cpte)
see CONCERT INDEX under:
(DECC) 417 011-2DH2 Pavarotti's Greatest Hits
(DECC) 430 462-2DM Ten Top Mezzos
cond B. CAMPANELLA
Donizetti: Fille du Régiment (Cpte)
cond R. CHAILLY
Puccini: Manon Lescaut (Cpte)
Rossini: Cenerentola (Cpte), Petite messe solennelle
(Cpte)
Verdi: Rigoletto (Cpte)
see CONCERT INDEX under:
(DECC) 430 724-2DM Great Operatic Duets
(DECC) 436 463-2DM Ten Top Tenors
(DECC) 436 832-2DH Rossini—String Sonatas,
Volume 2
cond D. GATTI
Rossini: Armida (Cpte)
cond A. GUADAGNO
see CONCERT INDEX under:
(DECC) 417 011-2DH2 Pavarotti's Greatest Hits
cond G. PATANÈ
Rossini: Barbiere di Siviglia (Cpte)
see CONCERT INDEX under:
(DECC) 436 462-2DM Ten Top Mezzos
(DECC) 436 464-2DM Ten Top Baritones & Basses

BOLOGNESI, Mario (ten)
Monteverdi: Orfeo (Cpte)
Paisiello: Don Chisciotte (Cpte)
Puccini: Manon Lescaut (Cpte), Tosca (Cpte)
Verdi: Don Carlo (Cpte)

BOLSHOI SYMPHONY ORCHESTRA
cond A. LAZAREV
Rachmaninov: Symphony 2, Vocalise
see CONCERT INDEX under:
(ERAT) 4509-91723-2 Russian Opera Choruses
(ERAT) 4509-94808-2 Rimsky-Korsakov—Orchestral
Works

BOLSHOI THEATRE BRASS ENSEMBLE
cond E. SVETLANOV
Shostakovich: Festive Overture

BOLSHOI THEATRE CHILDREN'S CHOIR
cond A. ZABORONOK
(COLL) Coll1443-2 Kastalsky—Liturgy of St John
Chrysostom

BOLSHOI THEATRE CHORUS
cond M. ERMLER
Tchaikovsky: Eugene Onegin (Cpte), Queen of
Spades (Cpte)
cond B. KHAIKIN
Tchaikovsky: Eugene Onegin (Cpte)
cond A. LAZAREV
see CONCERT INDEX under:
(ERAT) 4509-91723-2 Russian Opera Choruses
cond V. NEBOLSIN
Tchaikovsky: Eugene Onegin (Cpte)
cond S. SAMOSUD
see CONCERT INDEX under:
(DANT) LYS013/5 Tchaikovsky—The Queen of
Spades

BOLSHOI THEATRE ORCHESTRA
cond O. BRON
see CONCERT INDEX under:
(PREI) 89061 Pavel Lisitian (born 1911)
cond A. CHISTIAKOV
Rachmaninov: Miserly knight (Cpte)
Rimsky-Korsakov: Tsar's Bride (Cpte)
cond M. ERMLER
Rimsky-Korsakov: Mozart and Salieri (Cpte)
Tchaikovsky: Eugene Onegin (Cpte), Queen of
Spades (Cpte)
Vainberg: Golden Key Suites (exc)
cond R. GLIÈRE
Glière: Khrizis (exc)
cond N. GOLOVANOV
see CONCERT INDEX under:

(EMI) CHS7 69741-2(6) Record of Singing,
Vol.4—Russian & Slavonic Schools
(PREI) 89059 Mark Reizen (1895-1992) - I
(PREI) 89061 Pavel Lisitian (born 1911)
(PREI) 89080 Mark Reizen (1895-1992) - II
cond B. KHAIKIN
Tchaikovsky: Eugene Onegin (Cpte)
cond A. MELIK-PASHAYEV
see CONCERT INDEX under:
(PREI) 89059 Mark Reizen (1895-1992) - I
(PREI) 89061 Pavel Lisitian (born 1911)
cond V. NEBOLSIN
Tchaikovsky: Eugene Onegin (Cpte)
see CONCERT INDEX under:
(PREI) 89059 Mark Reizen (1895-1992) - I
(PREI) 89061 Pavel Lisitian (born 1911)
(PREI) 89080 Mark Reizen (1895-1992) - II
cond A. ORLOV
see CONCERT INDEX under:
(EMI) CHS7 69741-2(6) Record of Singing,
Vol.4—Russian & Slavonic Schools
(PREI) 89061 Pavel Lisitian (born 1911)
cond V. PIRADOV
see CONCERT INDEX under:
(PREI) 89061 Pavel Lisitian (born 1911)
cond G. ROZHDESTVENSKY
Shostakovich: Symphony 4
cond S. SAMOSUD
(DANT) LYS013/5 Tchaikovsky—The Queen of
Spades
(EMI) CHS7 69741-2(6) Record of Singing,
Vol.4—Russian & Slavonic Schools
(PREI) 89059 Mark Reizen (1895-1992) - I
(PREI) 89061 Pavel Lisitian (born 1911)
(PREI) 89080 Mark Reizen (1895-1992) - II
cond A. ZIURAITIS
Prokofiev: Romeo and Juliet (Cpte)

BOLSHOI THEATRE SOLOISTS ENSEMBLE
cond A. LAZAREV
Shchedrin: Frescoes of Dionysius

BOLTON, Andrea (sop)
see CONCERT INDEX under:
(OPRA) ORCH103 Italian Opera—1810-20

BOLTON, Ivor (cond)
see Bournemouth Sinfonietta

BOLTON, Ivor (hpd)
Bach: Concertos, BWV972-987 (exc)

BOLTON, Ivor (hpd/dir)
see CONCERT INDEX under:
(CARL) PCD864 Bach: Harpsichord Concertos

BÖMCHES, Helge Von (bass)
Mozart: Zauberflöte (Cpte)
R.Strauss: Salome (Cpte)

BOMFIM, Marcelo (fl)
see CONCERT INDEX under:
(CHNT) LDC278 869/70 Villa-Lobos—Guitar Works

BON, Maarten (pf)
see CONCERT INDEX under:
(PHIL) 442 534-2PH Janáček—Choral Works

BON, Marja (pf)
Messiaen: Canyons aux étoiles

BONA, Jacques (bar)
Lully: Atys (Cpte)
M-A. Charpentier: Médée (Cpte)
Montéclair: Jephté (Cpte)
Rameau: Zoroastre (Cpte)
see CONCERT INDEX under:
(RICE) RIC037011 Charpentier—Cantatas and Airs
(VIRG) VC7 59295-2 M-A. Charpentier—Tenebrae
Lessons for Good Friday

BONATTA, Andrea (pf)
see CONCERT INDEX under:
(ASTR) E8752 Brahms—Piano Works

BONAVERA, Alfredo (cond)
see ECO

BONAVOLONTÀ, Nino (cond)
see Rome SO

BONAZZI, Elaine (mez)
Rossini: Pietra del Paragone (Cpte)

BONCI, Alessandro (ten)
see CONCERT INDEX under:
(EMI) CHS7 64860-2(1) La Scala Edition - Vol.1,
1878-1914 (pt 1)
(MEMO) HR4408/9(1) Singers in Genoa, Vol.1 (disc
1)
(NIMB) NI7856 Legendary Tenors
(PEAR) GEMMCDS9923(2) Covent Garden on
Record, Vol.1 (pt 2)
(PEAR) GEMMCDS9924(2) Covent Garden on
Record, Vol.2 (pt 2)
(SYMP) SYMCD1113 The Harold Wayne Collection,
Vol.13

BONCOMPAGNI, Elio (cond)
see Turin RAI Orch

BOND, Danny (bn)
Devienne: Bassoon Sonatas, Op. 24
Zelenka: Trio Sonatas
see CONCERT INDEX under:
(L'OI) 417 622-2OH Mozart—Wind Concertos
(L'OI) 436 867-2OH Vivaldi—Bassoon Concertos

BOND, Dorothy (sop)
Delius: Village Romeo and Juliet (Cpte)

BOND, Jonathon (treb)
see CONCERT INDEX under:
(DECC) 430 360-2DM Fauré/Poulenc—Sacred Choral
Works
(DECC) 436 486-2DF2
Duruflé/Fauré/Poulenc—Choral Works

BONDE-HANSEN, Henriette (sop)
Mahler: Symphony 8
see CONCERT INDEX under:
(KONT) 32188 Nielsen—Vocal Works

BONELL, Carlos (gtr)
see CONCERT INDEX under:
(CHAN) CHAN9292 Walton—Chamber Music
(DECC) 430 703-2DM Spanish Orchestral Works

BONGERS, Els (sop)
Biber: Requiem in A, Vesperae

BONIFACCIO, Maddalena (sop)
Pergolesi: Serva Padrona

BONIME, Joseph (pf)
see CONCERT INDEX under:
(APR) APR7015 The Auer Legacy, Vol.1
(APR) APR7016 The Auer Legacy, Vol.2

BONINI, Francesco Maria (bar)
see CONCERT INDEX under:
(BONG) GB1043-2 Italian Baritones of the Acoustic
Era

BONINSEGNA, Celestina (sop)
see CONCERT INDEX under:
(EMI) CHS7 64860-2(2) La Scala Edition - Vol.1,
1878-1914 (pt 2)
(IRCC) IRCC-CD808 Souvenirs of 19th Century Italian
Opera
(PEAR) GEMMCDS9924(1) Covent Garden on
Record, Vol.2 (pt 1)
(SYMP) SYMCD1149 Fernando De Lucia
(TEST) SBT1008 Viva Rossini

BONISOLLI, Franco (ten)
Bizet: Djamileh (Cpte)
Gluck: Iphigénie en Tauride (Cpte)
Leoncavallo: Bohème (Cpte)
Verdi: Masnadieri (Cpte), Trovatore (Cpte)
see CONCERT INDEX under:
(ACAN) 49 384 Puccini: Opera Arias and Duets

BONITZ, Birgit (sop)
R. Strauss: Rosenkavalier (Cpte)

BONN BEETHOVENHALLE ORCHESTRA
cond D.R. DAVIES
Kancheli: Vom Winde beweint
see CONCERT INDEX under:
(ECM) 847 539-2 Pärt—Miserere; Festina lente;
Sarah was ninety-years old
(SCHW) 311116 Dvořák—Bagatelles, Op. 47;
Serenade, Op. 44

BONN KLASSISCHE PHILHARMONIE TELECOM
cond H. BEISSEL
Tchaikovsky: Nutcracker (Cpte)

BONN YOUTH SYMPHONY ORCHESTRA
cond W. BADUN
Suppé: Requiem

BONNAFOUS, Jean-Claude (cond)
Offenbach: Orphée aux enfers (Cpte)

BONNEAU, Jacqueline (pf)
see CONCERT INDEX under:
(DECC) 425 975-2DM Gerard Souzay—Song Recital
(DECC) 440 065-2DM Schubert/Schumann—Lieder
(EMI) CHS7 69741-2(3) Record of Singing,
Vol.4—French School

BONNELL, Carlos (gtr)
see CONCERT INDEX under:
(COLL) Coll7039-2 Britten—The Folk Songs

BONNEMA, Albert (sngr)
Schillings: Mona Lisa (Cpte)

BONNER, Tessa (sop)
Monteverdi: Orfeo (Cpte), Vespers
Mozart: Zauberflöte (Cpte)
Purcell: Birthday Ode, Z342, Dido (Cpte), Indian
Queen, Z630 (Cpte)
see CONCERT INDEX under:
(CHAN) CHAN0518 Vivaldi & Bach—Choral Works
(EMI) CDC7 47998-2 Una Stravaganza dei Medici -
Florentine Intermedi (ed. Keyte)
(HARM) HMC90 1462 Purcell—Funeral Music for
Queen Mary; Te Deum; Anthems
(HARM) HMX290 1528/33(1) A Purcell Companion (pt
1)
(HYPE) CDA66314 Purcell—Complete Odes &
Welcome Songs, Vol.1
(HYPE) CDA66412 Purcell—Complete Odes &
Welcome Songs, Vol.3
(HYPE) CDA66456 Purcell—Complete Odes &
Welcome Songs, Vol.4
(HYPE) CDA66598 Purcell—Complete Odes &
Welcome Songs, Vol.8
(L'OI) 436 460-2OH Biber—Requiem; Chamber
Works
(L'OI) 440 637-2OH Monteverdi—Ballets
(NAXO) 8 550603 Gibbons—Consort and Keyboard
Music, Songs and Anthems
(NAXO) 8 550604 Byrd—Music for Viols, Voices and
Keyboard

BONNEVIE, Robert (hn)
see CONCERT INDEX *under:*
(DELO) **DE3084** Schumann: Orchestral Works

BONNEY, Barbara (sop)
Bach: Cantata 211, Cantata 213, St Matthew
Passion, BWV244 (Cpte)
Beethoven: Fidelio (Cpte)
Bernstein: West Side Story (Cpte)
Grieg: Peer Gynt (Cpte)
Haydn: Jahreszeiten (Cpte), Mass 11, Stabat Mater
Humperdinck: Hänsel und Gretel (Cpte)
J. Strauss II: Fledermaus (exc)
Lehár: Lustige Witwe (Cpte)
Mozart: Clemenza di Tito (Cpte), Don Giovanni
(Cpte), Mass, K427, Nozze di Figaro (Cpte),
Requiem, Zauberflöte (Cpte)
Orff: Carmina burana
R. Strauss: Ariadne auf Naxos (Cpte)
Schoenberg: Moses und Aron (Cpte)
Schumann: Szenen aus Goethes Faust (Cpte)
Wagner: Tannhäuser (Cpte)
Wolf: Italienisches Liederbuch (Cpte)
see CONCERT INDEX *under:*
(ARCH) **445 353-2AH** Mozart—Sacred Choral Works
(DG) **427 348-2GH2** Zemlinsky: Lieder
(DG) **435 486-2GH** Schubert/Schumann—Sacred
Choral Works
(DG) **437 519-2GH** Grieg—Orchestral Songs
(EMI) **CDC5 55430-2** Brahms/Schumann—Lieder
(HYPE) **CDA66710** Purcell—Secular Solo Songs,
Volume 1
(HYPE) **CDA66720** Purcell—Secular Solo Songs,
Volume 2
(HYPE) **CDA66730** Purcell—Secular Solo Songs, Vol.
3
(PHIL) **438 873-2PH2** Bach—Magnificat and Masses
(SONY) **SK53360** Mahler/Nono—Vocal Works
(TELD) **2292-44194-2** Bach—Cantatas, Volume 45
(TELD) **2292-44946-2** Mendelssohn—Lieder
(TELD) **4509-90874-2** Schubert—Lieder
(TELD) **4509-91764-2** Bach—Cantatas, Vol.10

BONTE, Raymond (ten)
Mussorgsky: Boris Godunov (Cpte)

BONUCCI, Rodolfo (vn)
see CONCERT INDEX *under:*
(ASV) **CDDCA686** Fauré—Orchestral Works

BONYNGE, Richard (cond)
see Bologna Teatro Comunale Orch

BONYNGE, Richard (pf)
see CONCERT INDEX *under:*
(DECC) **436 202-2DM** Italian Songs

BOON, Saskia (vc)
Schnittke: Concerto grosso 4

BOOTH, Colin (hpd)
D. Scarlatti: Keyboard Sonatas (exc)
see CONCERT INDEX *under:*
(OLYM) **OCD433** C.P.E. Bach—Harpsichord Sonatas
(OLYM) **OCD437** J. S. Bach ... By Arrangement

BOOTH, Juliet (sop)
Bruckner: Mass in F minor, Psalm 150

BOOTH, Margery (mez)
Wagner: Götterdämmerung (Cpte)

BOOTH, Philip (bass)
V. Thomson: Mother of us all (Cpte)

BOOTH, Thomas (ten)
G. Lloyd: John Socman (exc)

BOOTH, Webster (ten)
see CONCERT INDEX *under:*
(DUTT) **CDAX8012** Malcolm Sargent conducts
English Music
(EMI) **CHS7 69741-2(2)** Record of Singing,
Vol.4—Anglo-American School (pt 2)

BOOTH, William (ten)
Sullivan: Gondoliers (Cpte)

BOOTHBY, Richard (lyra viol)
see CONCERT INDEX *under:*
(VIRG) **VC5 45147-2** Lawes—Concord is Conquer'd

BOOTHBY, Richard (va da gamba)
Corelli: Trio Sonatas, Op. 3 (exc), Trio Sonatas, Op. 4
(exc)
see CONCERT INDEX *under:*
(HYPE) **CDA66239** C.P.E. Bach: Chamber Works
(VIRG) **VC7 59324-2** Purcell—O Solitude - Songs and
Airs

BOOTH-JONES, Christopher (bar)
Handel: Giulio Cesare (Cpte)
Sondheim: Pacific Overtures (exc)

BOOZER, Brenda (mez)
Verdi: Falstaff (Cpte)

BORCHERS, Christel (contr)
Wagner: Walküre (Cpte)

BORCIANI, Mario (pf)
Martucci: Piano Quintet, Op. 45, Piano Trio, Op. 59

BORDEAUX AQUITAINE ORCHESTRA
cond A. LOMBARD
Bizet: Carmen (Cpte)
Mahler: Symphony 5
Ravel: Enfant et les sortilèges (Cpte)

BORDEAUX CNR CHILDREN'S CHOIR
cond A. LOMBARD
Bizet: Carmen (Cpte)

BORDEAUX THEATRE CHORUS
cond A. LOMBARD
Bizet: Carmen (Cpte)
Ravel: Enfant et les sortilèges (Cpte)

BORDEN, Barbara (sop)
Purcell: Dido (Cpte)
see CONCERT INDEX *under:*
(HARM) **HMX290 1528/33(1)** A Purcell Companion (pt
1)
(PHIL) **442 534-2PH** Janáček—Choral Works
(TELD) **4509-90798-2** Monteverdi—Il Ballo delle
ingrate
(TELD) **4509-95068-2** Purcell—Songs of Welcome &
Farewell

BOREALIS ENSEMBLE
cond C. EGGEN
Rypdal: Largo, Op.55, Q.E.D.
see CONCERT INDEX *under:*
(AURO) **ACD4973** Borealis

BOREJKO, Andrzej (cond)
see Poznań PO

BORELIUS, Torkel (bass)
Schnittke: Symphony 2

BORELLI, Giannella (mez)
see CONCERT INDEX *under:*
(EMI) **CDH7 63495-2** Victoria de los Angeles—Early
Recordings

BORG, Kim (bass)
Bruckner: Te Deum
Dvořák: Requiem, Stabat Mater
Elgar: Dream of Gerontius (Cpte)
Mozart: Requiem, Zauberflöte (Cpte)
Mussorgsky: Boris Godunov (Cpte)
Orff: Antigonae (Cpte)
Rossini: Stabat Mater
see CONCERT INDEX *under:*
(DG) **423 127-2GX4** Bruckner: Sacred Works for
Chorus
(DG) **447 409-2GOR2** Bruckner—The Masses
(EMI) **CHS7 69741-2(5)** Record of Singing,
Vol.4—Scandinavian School
(FINL) **4509-95606-2** Kim Borg - Songs and Arias
(SONY) **SM2K47522** Beethoven & Haydn—Choral
Works

BORG, Siv (spkr)
Grieg: Peer Gynt (exc)

BORGATO, Maria (mez)
Verdi: Macbeth (Cpte)

BORGATTI, Giuseppe (ten)
see CONCERT INDEX *under:*
(EMI) **CHS7 64860-2(1)** La Scala Edition - Vol.1,
1878-1914 (pt 1)
(MEMO) **HR4408/9(2)** Singers in Genoa, Vol.1 (disc
2)

BORGHESE, Simone (mez)
Offenbach: Contes d'Hoffmann (Cpte)

BORGIOLI, Dino (ten)
see CONCERT INDEX *under:*
(CLUB) **CL99-014** Dino Borgioli (1891-1960)
(EMI) **CHS7 64864-2(1)** La Scala Edition - Vol.2,
1915-46 (pt 1)
(PEAR) **GEMMCDS9925(2)** Covent Garden on
Record—Vol.3 (pt 2)
(PEAR) **GEMMCDS9926(1)** Covent Garden on
Record—Vol.4 (pt 1)
(PREI) **89063** Rosetta Pampanini (1896-1973)
(TEST) **SBT1008** Viva Rossini

BORGONOVO, Luigi (bar)
see CONCERT INDEX *under:*
(NIMB) **NI7845** Giacomo Lauri-Volpi (1892-1979)
(PREI) **89012** Giacomo Lauri-Volpi (1894-1979)

BORGOVONO, Pietro (ob)
see CONCERT INDEX *under:*
(EDEL) **ED1012** Schumann: Chamber Music with
Piano

BORI, Lucrezia (sop)
see CONCERT INDEX *under:*
(MMOI) **CDMOIR418** Great Voices of the
Century—John McCormack
(PREI) **89002** Miguel Fleta (1893-1938)
(PREI) **89036** Giuseppe de Luca (1876-1950) - I
(RCA) **GD87811** Beniamino Gigli—Operatic Arias
(RCA) **09026 61580-2(2)** RCA/Met 100 Singers, 100
Years (pt 2)

BORISKIN, Michael (pf)
see CONCERT INDEX *under:*
(HARM) **HMU90 7124** Perle/Danielpour—Piano
Works

BORISOVA, Galina (mez)
Rachmaninov: Aleko (Cpte)
Tchaikovsky: Queen of Spades (Cpte)

BORK, Hanneke van (sop)
Cavalli: Ormindo (Cpte)
see CONCERT INDEX *under:*
(DECC) **433 175-2DM** Bach—Sacred Choral Works
(PHIL) **442 050-2PB10** Mahler—Complete
Symphonies

BORKH, Inge (sop)
Orff: Antigonae (Cpte)
Puccini: Turandot (Cpte)
R. Strauss: Elektra (Cpte), Salome (Cpte)
see CONCERT INDEX *under:*
(EMI) **CHS7 69741-2(4)** Record of Singing,
Vol.4—German School
(RCA) **GD60874** R. Strauss—Scenes from Elektra &
Salome

BORMIDA, Ida (mez)
Mascagni: Cavalleria Rusticana (Cpte)
see CONCERT INDEX *under:*
(DECC) **425 681-2DM2** Tutto Pavarotti

BORODIN QUARTET
Borodin: String Quartet 1, String Quartet 2
Brahms: Piano Quintet, String Quartet 1, String
Quartet 2, String Quartet 3
Haydn: String Quartet, Op. 51
Schubert: String Quintet
Shostakovich: String Quartet 5, String Quartet 15
Vainberg: Piano Quintet, Op. 18
see CONCERT INDEX *under:*
(DECC) **425 541-2DM** Russian String Quartets
(DECC) **444 389-2DWO** The World of Borodin
(EMI) **CDC7 47507-2** Shostakovich—Chamber
Works
(EMI) **CDC7 49268-2** Shostakovich: String Quartets
(EMI) **CDC7 49269-2** Shostakovich—Chamber Works
(EMI) **CDS7 49775-2** Tchaikovsky—Chamber Works
(MELO) **74321 18290-2** Tchaikovsky—Chamber
Works
(PHIL) **438 624-2PH2** Richter—The Authorised
Recordings: Beethoven
(RUSS) **RDCD11087**
Shostakovich/Beethoven—Works for String Quartet
(TELD) **4509-90422-2** Tchaikovsky—Chamber Works
(VIRG) **VC7 59040-2** Schnittke—Chamber Works
(VIRG) **VC7 59041-2** Shostakovich—String Quartets

BORODIN TRIO
Alabiev: Piano Trio
Bax: Piano Trio in B flat
Beethoven: Piano Trios
Bridge: Piano Trio
Dvořák: Piano Trio 1, Piano Trio 2, Piano Trio 3
Mendelssohn: Piano Trio 1, Piano Trio 2
Rachmaninov: Trio élégiaque, Op. 9, Trio élégiaque
(1892)
Schubert: Piano Trio 1, Piano Trio 2
Shostakovich: Piano Quintet, Op. 57, Piano Trio 2
Spohr: Piano Trio 3, Piano Trio 4
Taneyev: Piano Trio
Tchaikovsky: Piano Trio, Op. 50
see CONCERT INDEX *under:*
(CHAN) **CHAN8334/5** Brahms—Piano Trios
(CHAN) **CHAN8458** Debussy & Ravel: Chamber
Works
(CHAN) **CHAN8536/7** Mozart—Piano Trios
(CHAN) **CHAN8655** Haydn, Mozart & Beethoven:
Chamber Works
(CHAN) **CHAN8809/10** Brahms: Piano Quartets
(CHAN) **CHAN8832/3** Schumann: Chamber Works
(CHAN) **CHAN6924** Russian Vocal and Chamber
works
(CHAN) **CHAN9016** Works for Piano Trio

BORODINA, Olga (mez)
Borodin: Prince Igor (Cpte)
Mussorgsky: Khovanshchina (Cpte)
Prokofiev: War and Peace (Cpte)
Rachmaninov: Vespers, Op. 37 (Cpte)
Tchaikovsky: Eugene Onegin (Cpte), Queen of
Spades (Cpte)
Verdi: Traviata (Cpte)
see CONCERT INDEX *under:*
(PHIL) **442 013-2PH** Tchaikovsky—Romances
(PHIL) **442 780-2PH** Songs of Desire

BORONAT, Olimpia (sop)
see CONCERT INDEX *under:*
(NIMB) **NI7865** Great Singers at the Mariinsky
Theatre

BOROWSKA, Joanna (sop)
Mozart: Così fan tutte (Cpte)
Mussorgsky: Khovanshchina (Cpte)

BOROWSKI, Nikolai (bar)
Pfitzner: Herz (Cpte)

BORRIELLO, Mario (bar)
Mozart: Così fan tutte (Cpte)
Puccini: Madama Butterfly (Cpte), Manon Lescaut
(Cpte), Turandot (Cpte)

BORRIS, Kaja (mez)
Schmidt: Notre Dame (Cpte)
Schreker: Gezeichneten (Cpte)
Wagner: Fliegende Holländer (Cpte)
Zemlinsky: Kreidekreis (Cpte)

BORROR, Ronald (tbn)
see CONCERT INDEX *under:*
(RCA) **09026 62537-2** Takemitsu—Cantos

BORSKÝ, Miroslav (bar)
Hába: Mother (Cpte)

BORST, Danielle (sop)
Fauré: Pénélope (Cpte)
Monteverdi: Incoronazione di Poppea (Cpte)
Vivaldi: Montezuma (Cpte)
see CONCERT INDEX *under:*
(NAXO) **8 553176** Poulenc—Choral Works
(REM) **REM311049** Duparc: Mélodies

BORST, Heinz (bass)
Wagner: Meistersinger (Cpte)

BORST, Martina (mez)
Pergolesi: Stabat Mater
Spohr: Faust (Cpte)

BORTHAYRE, Jean (bass)
Gounod: Faust (Cpte)

BORTOLI, Carlo de (bass)
Verdi: Rigoletto (Cpte)

BOSCHI, Hélène (pf)
see CONCERT INDEX under:
(CALL) CAL9211   Clara Schumann: Piano Works
(CHNT) LDC278 1068   Chabrier—Une Education
Manquée/Mélodies

BOSCHKOWÁ, Nelly (mez)
Dvořák: Stabat mater
Puccini: Madama Butterfly (Cpte)

BOSCO, Carlo del (bass)
Verdi: Macbeth (Cpte)
see CONCERT INDEX under:
(SONY) M3K79312   Puccini: Il Trittico

BOSHNIAKOVICH, Oleg (pf)
see CONCERT INDEX under:
(PHIL) 432 119-2PH   Russian Romances

BOSI, Carlo (ten)
Mascagni: Rantzau (Cpte)
Paisiello: Nina (Cpte)
Puccini: Fanciulla del West (Cpte)
Rossini: Armida (Cpte)

BOSKOVSKY, Alfred (cl)
see CONCERT INDEX under:
(DECC) 417 643-2DM   Chamber Works for Clarinet &
Strings

BOSKOVSKY, Willi (cond)
see LPO

BOSKOVSKY, Willi (vn/dir)
see CONCERT INDEX under:
(DECC) 433 220-2DWO   The World of the Violin

BOSTON BAROQUE
cond M. PEARLMAN
Handel: Concerti Grossi, Op.6 (exc), Messiah (Cpte)
Mozart: Requiem

BOSTON BAROQUE CHORUS
cond M. PEARLMAN
Handel: Messiah (Cpte)

BOSTON BOY CHOIR
cond S. OZAWA
Berlioz: Damnation de Faust (Cpte)

BOSTON CAMERATA
cond J. COHEN
see CONCERT INDEX under:
(ERAT) 4509-92874-2   An American Christmas
(ERAT) 4509-98480-2   Lamentations - Holy Week in
Provence

BOSTON CECILIA
cond D. TEETERS
see CONCERT INDEX under:
(KOCH) 37180-2   Pinkham—Cantatas & Chamber
Works

BOSTON COMPOSERS QUARTET
see CONCERT INDEX under:
(KOCH) 37180-2   Pinkham—Cantatas & Chamber
Works

BOSTON EARLY MUSIC FESTIVAL CHORUS
cond A. PARROTT
Mozart: Kleine Freimaurer-Kantate, K623, Requiem

BOSTON EARLY MUSIC FESTIVAL ORCHESTRA
cond A. PARROTT
Bach: Suites, BWV1066-9, Triple Concerto,
BWV1044
Mozart: Church Sonatas (exc), Kleine Freimaurer-
Kantate, K623, Mass, K427, Requiem

BOSTON EARLY MUSIC SOLOISTS
cond W. MALLOCH
Bach: Suites, BWV1066-9

BOSTON MUSEUM TRIO
Marais: La gamme (exc)
Telemann: Sonate Metodiche (exc)
see CONCERT INDEX under:
(HARM) HMA190 1088   Vivaldi—Violin Sonatas

BOSTON PHILHARMONIC ORCHESTRA
cond B. ZANDER
Beethoven: Symphony 9

BOSTON POPS ORCHESTRA
cond A. FIEDLER
Offenbach: Gaîté Parisienne (Cpte)
Rachmaninov: Paganini Rhapsody
Rossini: Boutique fantasque
see CONCERT INDEX under:
(BELA) 450 129-2   Images of Spain
(DECC) 430 093-2DWO   The World of Vaughan
Williams
(RCA) GD86519   Gershwin—Orchestral Works
(RCA) 09026 61249-2   Marches in Hi-Fi
(RCA) 09026 61429-2   Offenbach in America
(RCA) 09026 68131-2   Classics for Children—Boston
Pops
(RCA) 09026 68132-2   Pops Caviar—Russian
Orchestral Fireworks

BOSTON PRO MUSICA CHORUS
cond B. ZANDER
Beethoven: Symphony 9

BOSTON SCHOLA CANTORUM
cond J. COHEN
see CONCERT INDEX under:
(ERAT) 4509-98480-2   Lamentations - Holy Week in
Provence

BOSTON SYMPHONY CHAMBER PLAYERS
Brahms: Clarinet Quintet
Mozart: Clarinet Quintet, K581

BOSTON SYMPHONY ORCHESTRA
cond L. BERNSTEIN
Beethoven: Symphony 7
Britten: Sea Interludes, Op. 33a
Liszt: Faust Symphony
see CONCERT INDEX under:
(PHIL) 416 600-2PH4   Sibelius—Symphonies & Tone
Poems
(PHIL) 442 302-2PM2   The Best of Mendelssohn
(PHIL) 442 389-2PM   Sibelius—Orchestral Works
cond C. DUTOIT
Gubaidulina: Offertorium
cond B. HAITINK
Brahms: Alto Rhapsody, Op. 53, Haydn Variations,
Symphony 2, Symphony 3, Symphony 4, Tragic
Overture
cond S. KOUSSEVITZKY
Brahms: Violin Concerto
Tchaikovsky: Romeo and Juliet, Symphony 6
see CONCERT INDEX under:
(BIDD) WHL019   Koussevitzky—Double-bass
Recordings & Early Boston SO
(BIDD) WHL028   Koussevitzky conducts Berlioz
(EMI) CHS7 69741-2(1)   Record of Singing,
Vol.4—Anglo-American School (pt 1)
(PEAR) GEMMCDS9167   Jascha Heifetz Concerto
Recordings, Volume 2
(PEAR) GEMMCDS9408   Koussevitsky conducts
Sibelius
(PEAR) GEMMCD9020   Koussevitsky conducts
Stravinsky and Mussorgsky
(PEAR) GEMMCD9037   Koussevitsky conducts
American Music
(PEAR) GEMMCD9492   Koussevitsky conducts
American Music
(RCA) GD60921   Legendary Performers - William
Kapell
(RCA) 09026 60929-2   R.Strauss—Tone Poems
(RCA) 09026 61657-2   Prokofiev—Orchestral Works
(RCA) 09026 61778-2(04)   The Heifetz Collection, Vol.
4
(RCA) 09026 61879-2   Grieg—Historic Recordings
cond R. KUBELÍK
Bartók: Concerto for Orchestra
Smetana: Má Vlast
cond E. LEINSDORF
Tchaikovsky: Piano Concerto 1, Violin Concerto
see CONCERT INDEX under:
(RCA) GD60396   Leontyne Price sings Strauss arias
(RCA) 07863 56520-2   Works for Violin and
Orchestra
(RCA) 09026 61454-2   Perlman plays Prokofiev
(RCA) 09026 61580-2(7)   RCA/Met 100 Singers, 100
Years (pt 7)
cond P. MONTEUX
Stravinsky: Petrushka (Cpte), Rite of Spring (Cpte)
see CONCERT INDEX under:
(RCA) 09026 61893-2   Pierre Monteux Edition
cond C. MUNCH
Berlioz: Enfance du Christ (Cpte), Grande messe des
morts (Cpte), Harold in Italy, Nuits d'été, Roméo et
Juliette (Cpte), Symphonie fantastique
Dvořák: Cello Concerto
Indy: Symphonie, Op.25
R. Strauss: Don Quixote
Ravel: Daphnis et Chloé (exc)
Roussel: Bacchus et Ariane Suites (exc)
Tchaikovsky: Romeo and Juliet, Symphony 6
Walton: Cello Concerto
see CONCERT INDEX under:
(RCA) GD86719   Debussy: Orchestral Works
(RCA) GD86805   Orchestral Works
(RCA) VD60478   Berlioz: Orchestral Works
(RCA) 09026 61400-2   Berlioz/Saint-
Saëns—Orchestral Works
(RCA) 09026 61424-2   Orchestral Works
(RCA) 09026 61500-2   Munch conducts French
Orchestral Works
(RCA) 09026 61778-2(11-15)   The Heifetz Collection,
Vols. 11-15
(RCA) 09026 61956-2   Debussy/Ravel—Orchestral
Works
cond S. OZAWA
Bartók: Concerto for Orchestra, Miraculous Mandarin
(Cpte), Music for Strings, Percussion and Celesta,
Violin Concerto 2
Beethoven: Choral Fantasia, Piano Concerto 3, Piano
Concerto 5
Berg: Violin Concerto
Berlioz: Damnation de Faust (Cpte), Grande messe
des morts (Cpte), Roméo et Juliette (exc), Symphonie
fantastique
Franck: Symphony
Lieberson: Piano Concerto
Mahler: Symphony 3, Symphony 6
Mendelssohn: Midsummer Night's Dream (exc)
Moret: En rêve
Orff: Carmina Burana

Panufnik: Sinfonia Votiva
Poulenc: Gloria (Cpte), Organ Concerto, Stabat
mater
Prokofiev: Romeo and Juliet (Cpte)
R. Strauss: Elektra (Cpte)
Ravel: Daphnis et Chloé (Cpte), Valses Nobles et
Sentimentales
Schoenberg: Gurrelieder
Schumann: Violin Concerto, Op.129
Sessions: Concerto for Orchestra, When Lilacs last
Bloom'd
Shostakovich: Cello Concerto 2, Violin Concerto 2
Sibelius: Violin Concerto
Stravinsky: Violin Concerto
Tchaikovsky: Nutcracker (Cpte), Queen of Spades
(Cpte), Sleeping Beauty (exc), Violin Concerto
see CONCERT INDEX under:
(BELA) 450 129-2   Images of Spain
(DG) 413 145-2GW2   Beethoven—Orchestral Works
(DG) 415 845-2GGA   Ravel—Orchestral Works
(DG) 423 089-2GH   Fauré: Orchestral Works
(DG) 423 243-2GC   Ives: Orchestral Works
(DG) 423 571-2GH   Liszt: Works for Piano and
Orchestra
(DG) 427 213-2GR   French Orchestral Works
(DG) 431 475-2GGA   Russian Orchestral Works
(DG) 437 952-2GX2   Great Cello Works
(DG) 445 487-2GX3   Mutter plays Modern Works
(EMI) CDC5 55360-2   The American Album
(NEW) NW273-2   Griffes: Vocal & Instrumental Works
(PHIL) 426 284-2PH   French Works for Two Pianos
(RCA) 09026 61548-2   Rachmaninov—Piano Concerto
No 3, etc
(SONY) SK47188   Works for Piano Left-Hand and
Orchestra
(TELA) CD80061   Beethoven: Piano Concertos
cond W. STEINBERG
Holst: Planets
cond I. STRAVINSKY
see CONCERT INDEX under:
(ARHI) ADCD110   Mengelberg Edition - Volume 4
cond M. TILSON THOMAS
see CONCERT INDEX under:
(DG) 423 243-2GC   Ives: Orchestral Works
(DG) 427 213-2GR   French Orchestral Works
cond VLADIMIR ASHKENAZY
see CONCERT INDEX under:
(DECC) 436 566-2DH   Sibelius—Orchestral Works
cond J.T. WILLIAMS
J. T. Williams: Schindler's List (exc)

BOSTRIDGE, Ian (ten)
Nyman: Noises, Sounds and Sweet Airs (Cpte)
Purcell: Dioclesian, Z627 (exc), Timon of Athens,
Z632 (exc)
see CONCERT INDEX under:
(HYPE) CDA67061/2   Britten—Purcell Realizations
(HYPE) CDJ33020   Schubert—Complete Lieder,
Vol.20
(SONY) S2K66243   Music for Queen Mary
(SONY) S2K66836   Goldschmidt—Beatrice Cenci, etc

BOSTRÖM, Erik (organ)
see CONCERT INDEX under:
(PROP) PRCD9010   Messiaen—Complete Organ
Works II

BOTÁR, Ecaterina (hpd)
see CONCERT INDEX under:
(OLYM) OCD406   M. Haydn: Concertos

BOTELHO, José (cl)
see CONCERT INDEX under:
(CHNT) LDC278 835   Villa-Lobos—Chôros for
Chamber Ensembles

BOTHA, Johan (ten)
Wagner: Tristan und Isolde (Cpte)
see CONCERT INDEX under:
(RCA) 09026 61955-2   Koechlin—The Jungle Book

BOTHWELL, Malcolm (va da gamba)
see CONCERT INDEX under:
(PIER) PV790013   A. Scarlatti—Cantatas

BOTSTEIN, Leon (cond)
see LPO

BOTT, Catherine (sop)
Blow: Venus and Adonis (Cpte)
Monteverdi: Orfeo (Cpte), Vespers
Nielsen: Symphony 3
Nyman: Noises, Sounds and Sweet Airs (Cpte)
Purcell: Dido (Cpte), Fairy Queen, Z629, Indian
Queen, Z630 (Cpte)
Stradella: San Giovanni Battista (Cpte)
Vaughan Williams: Symphony 7
Walton: As You Like It (exc)
see CONCERT INDEX under:
(ARGO) 443 528-2ZH   Torke—Music on the Floor
(LINN) CKD007   Music from the time of Columbus
(LINN) CKD011   Elizabethan & Jacobean Consort
Music
(L'OI) 433 187-2OH   Mad Songs
(L'OI) 436 460-2OH   Biber—Requiem; Chamber
Works
(L'OI) 440 637-2OH   Instrumental—Ballets
(MERI) ECD84080   Haydn: Vocal works
(PHIL) 438 149-2PH   French Choral Works
(VIRG) VC5 45147-2   Lawes—Concord is Conquer'd

BÖTTCHER, Else (sop)
see CONCERT INDEX under:
(SCHW) 314532   Vienna State Opera Live, Vol.3

BOTTCHER, Ron (bar)
Verdi: Forza del destino (Cpte)

BOTTINI, Giuseppe (treb)
Puccini: Tosca (Cpte)

BOTTION, Aldo (ten)
Puccini: Fanciulla del West (Cpte)
Verdi: Otello (Cpte)

BOTTONE, Bonaventura (ten)
Bernstein: Candide (1988) (exc)
Donizetti: Lucia di Lammermoor (Cpte)
Forrest/Wright: Kismet (Cpte), Timbuktu (exc)
Romberg: Student Prince (Cpte)
Sullivan: Mikado (exc)
Tippett: Ice Break (Cpte)
Vaughan Williams: Hugh the Drover (Cpte)

BOTVAY, Károly (vc)
Boëllmann: Piano Quartet, Op. 10, Piano Trio, Op.
19
Sterndale Bennett: Piano Sextet, Op. 8

BOUANICHE, Frédéric (cond)
see J-J. Wiederker CO

BOUCHER, Gene (bar)
Verdi: Traviata (Cpte)

BOUCHER, Jacques (organ)
Tournemire: Orgue mystique, Op. 57 (exc)

BOUÉ, Géori (sop)
Hahn: Mozart (Cpte)
Offenbach: Contes d'Hoffmann (Cpte)
  see CONCERT INDEX under:
(EMI) CHS7 69741-2(3)   Record of Singing,
Vol.4—French School

BOUGHTON, Ian (bar)
Boughton: Bethlehem (Cpte)
  see CONCERT INDEX under:
(CALA) CACD1011   Borodin—Orchestral Works

BOUGHTON, William (cond)
see English SO

BOULANGER, Nadia (cond)
see Boulanger Ens

BOULANGER, Nadia (pf)
  see CONCERT INDEX under:
(EMI) CDH7 63038-2   Dinu Lipatti - Piano Recital

BOULANGER ENSEMBLE
cond N. BOULANGER
  see CONCERT INDEX under:
(EMI) CDH7 61025-2   Fauré & Monteverdi Vocal
Works

BOULAY, Laurence (hpd)
  see CONCERT INDEX under:
(ERAT) 2292-45012-2   Couperin—Sacred Choral
Works

BOULEYN, Kathryn (sop)
Rossini: Soirées musicales

BOULEZ, Pierre (cond)
see Bayreuth Fest Orch

BOULIER, Christophe (vn)
Franck: Violin Sonata
Lekeu: Violin Sonata in G

BOULIN, Sophie (sop)
Handel: Alessandro (Cpte)
M-A. Charpentier: Médée (Cpte)
Marais: Alcyone (Cpte)

BOULT, Sir Adrian (cond)
see BBC Concert Orch

BOULTON, Sophie (mez)
Gluck: Iphigénie en Tauride (Cpte)

BOUR, Ernest (cond)
see FRNO

BOURBON, Maurice (bass)
Haydn: Mass 11

(ALIX) BOURBON VOCAL ENSEMBLE
cond M. PLASSON
  see CONCERT INDEX under:
(EMI) CDC7 47939-2   Fauré—Orchestral Works

BOURDIN, Roger (bar)
Hahn: Mozart (Cpte)
Offenbach: Contes d'Hoffmann (Cpte)

BOURDON, Rosario (cond)
see orch

BOURDON, Rosario (vc)
  see CONCERT INDEX under:
(SUPR) 11 2136-2(5)   Emmy Destinn—Complete
Edition, Discs 11 & 12

BOURGUE, Daniel (hn)
  see CONCERT INDEX under:
(FORL) UCD16567   Haydn: Orchestral Works

BOURGUE, Maurice (ob)
Albinoni: Concerti, Op.7, Sinfonie, Op.2 (exc)
Zelenka: Trio Sonatas
  see CONCERT INDEX under:
(DECC) 421 581-2DH   Poulenc—Chamber Works
(EMI) CZS7 62736-2   Poulenc—Chamber Works
(EMI) CZS7 67306-2   Mozart—Works featuring Wind
Instruments
(ERAT) 4509-91721-2   Dutilleux—Piano Works and
Chamber Music

BOURNE, Una (pf)
  see CONCERT INDEX under:
(SIMA) PSC1809(2)   Grieg—Historical Piano
Recordings (pt 2)

BOURNEMOUTH MUNICIPAL ORCHESTRA
cond R. AUSTIN
  see CONCERT INDEX under:
(SYMP) SYMCD1075   May Harrison—Violinist and
Composer

BOURNEMOUTH SINFONIETTA
Boyce: Symphonies (exc)
Vivaldi: Concerti, Op 8 (exc)
  see CONCERT INDEX under:
(CHAN) CHAN8859   Martinů—Orchestral Works
(EMIN) CD-EMX2221   Pärt—Chamber Works
(NAXO) 8 550823   English String Music
(NAXO) 8 550979   20th Century String Music
cond I. BOLTON
  see CONCERT INDEX under:
(ARGO) 433 847-2ZH   Works for Saxophone and
Orchestra
cond N. DEL MAR
  see CONCERT INDEX under:
(EMI) CDM5 65101-2   A Warlock Centenary Album
cond H. FARBERMAN
  see CONCERT INDEX under:
(CRD) CRD3449   Jonathan Haas - Virtuoso
Timpanist
cond G. HURST
Elgar: King Arthur (exc), Starlight Express (exc)
  see CONCERT INDEX under:
(CHAN) CHAN6538   Seascapes
(CHAN) CHAN6544   Elgar—Orchestral Favourites
(CHAN) CHAN6545   Vaughan Williams—Orchestral
Works
(CHAN) CHAN8375   English music for strings
(CHAN) CHAN8432   Elgar/Vaughan
Williams—Orchestral Works
Elgar: Scenes from the Bavarian Highlands, Op.27
Moeran: Cello Concerto, Sinfonietta
Stanford: Symphony 3
  see CONCERT INDEX under:
(CHAN) CHAN6502   Delius: Orchestral Works
(CHAN) CHAN6544   Elgar—Orchestral Favourites
(CHAN) CHAN6545   Vaughan Williams—Orchestral
Works
(EMI) CDM5 65131-2   Vaughan Williams—Choral and
Orchestral Works
cond K. MONTGOMERY
  see CONCERT INDEX under:
(CHAN) CHAN6542   Grainger—Famous Folk-settings
cond H-H. SCHÖNZELER
  see CONCERT INDEX under:
(CHAN) CHAN6599   Rubbra—Orchestral works
cond R. THOMAS
Haydn: Symphony 87, Symphony 88, Symphony 103,
Symphony 104
  see CONCERT INDEX under:
(CHAN) CHAN6592   Britten—Orchestral Works
cond T. VÁSÁRY
  see CONCERT INDEX under:
(CHAN) CHAN8913   Respighi—Vocal and Orchestral
Works
(CHAN) CHAN8993   Honegger—Orchestral Works

BOURNEMOUTH SINFONIETTA CHOIR
cond N. DEL MAR
  see CONCERT INDEX under:
(CHAN) CHAN6545   Vaughan Williams—Orchestral
Works

BOURNEMOUTH SYMPHONY CHORUS
cond R. HICKOX
  see CONCERT INDEX under:
(CHAN) CHAN9214   Delius—Choral Works
cond A. LITTON
  see CONCERT INDEX under:
(LOND) 448 134-2LH   Walton—Belshazzar's Feast,
etc
Elgar: Scenes from the Bavarian Highlands, Op.27
  see CONCERT INDEX under:
(EMI) CDM5 65131-2   Vaughan Williams—Choral and
Orchestral Works

BOURNEMOUTH SYMPHONY ORCHESTRA
cond M. ARNOLD
  see CONCERT INDEX under:
(EMI) CDM7 64044-2   Arnold—Orchestral Works
cond K. BAKELS
Vaughan Williams: Symphony 2, Symphony 3,
Symphony 6, Wasps (exc)
cond H. FARBERMAN
Farberman: Jazz Drum Concerto
cond J. FARRER
  see CONCERT INDEX under:
(CARL) MCD75   Copland/Gershwin—Orchestral
Works
cond C. GROVES
  see CONCERT INDEX under:
(EMI) CDM7 63368-2   Malcolm Arnold—Orchestral
Works
cond V. HANDLEY
Simpson: Symphony 2, Symphony 9
cond R. HICKOX
Mahler: Klagende Lied (Cpte)
Tippett: Concerto for orchestra, New Year Suite,
Piano Concerto, Praeludium, Symphony 1, Symphony
2, Symphony 3, Triple Concerto

Vaughan Williams: Job, Variations for Brass Band
  see CONCERT INDEX under:
(CHAN) CHAN9214   Delius—Choral Works
(CHAN) CHAN9221   Britten—Orchestral Works
(CHAN) CHAN9233   Tippett—Orchestral Works
(CHAN) CHAN9355   Delius—Orchestral Works
cond D. HILL
  see CONCERT INDEX under:
(ARGO) 430 836-2ZH   English Sacred Choral Music
(ARGO) 436 120-2ZH   Vaughan
Williams/Walton—Choral & Orchestral Works
(DECC) 436 403-2DWO   The World of Royal Music
cond M. LAUS
  see CONCERT INDEX under:
(UNIC) DKPCD9150   Camilleri—Piano Concertos
cond A. LITTON
Tchaikovsky: Manfred Symphony, Symphony 1,
Symphony 2, Symphony 5, Tempest
Walton: Cello Concerto, Symphony 1
  see CONCERT INDEX under:
(LOND) 444 114-2LH   Walton—Orchestral Works
(LOND) 448 134-2LH   Walton—Belshazzar's Feast,
etc
(VIRG) CUV5 61119-2   Bernstein—Orchestral Works
cond G. LLOYD
G. Lloyd: Symphonic Mass
cond S. RATTLE
Mahler: Symphony 10
cond C. SILVESTRI
  see CONCERT INDEX under:
(EMI) CZS5 68229-2   Constantin Silvestri—A profile

BOURSIN, Denise (sop)
Boïeldieu: Voitures Versées (Cpte)

BOURVIL (ten)
Offenbach: Contes d'Hoffmann (Cpte)
  see CONCERT INDEX under:
(CHAN) CHAN9380   Martin—Ballades

BOUSFIELD, Ian (tbn)
  see CONCERT INDEX under:
(CHAN) CHAN9380   Martin—Ballades

BOUSQUET, Eugène (bass)
Mussorgsky: Boris Godunov (Cpte)

BOUTARD, André (cl)
  see CONCERT INDEX under:
(SUPR) 2SUP0023   Debussy: Orchestral Works

BOUTET, Benoît (ten)
Donizetti: Roberto Devereux (Cpte)

BOUTON, William (vn)
  see CONCERT INDEX under:
(CARL) DPCD1039   Elgar—Violin & Piano Works

BOUVARD, Michel (organ)
Couperin: Messe pour les couvents

BOUVET, Maximilien-Nicolas (bar)
(SYMP) SYMCD1089   Historic Baritones of the French
School

BOUVIER, Hélène (mez)
Saint-Saëns: Samson et Dalila (Cpte)
  see CONCERT INDEX under:
(EMI) CHS7 69741-2(3)   Record of Singing,
Vol.4—French School
(ERAT) 4509-96952-2   Duruflé—Requiem; Organ
Works

BOVET, Martina (sop)
Monteverdi: Incoronazione di Poppea (Cpte), Ritorno
d'Ulisse in patria (Cpte)

BOVINO, Maria (sop)
Britten: Peter Grimes (Cpte)
(OPRA) ORCH103   Italian Opera—1810-20

BOVY, Vina (sop)
Offenbach: Contes d'Hoffmann (Cpte)

BOWDEN, Pamela (contr)
Herrmann: Wuthering Heights (Cpte)

BOWEN, Geraint (organ)
  see CONCERT INDEX under:
(PRIO) PRCD507   Te Deum and Jubilate, Volume 3

BOWEN, John (ten)
Boughton: Bethlehem (Cpte)
  see CONCERT INDEX under:
(CHAN) CHAN9980   Bliss—Choral Works
(HERI) HRCD901   By Royal Command
(HYPE) CDA66569   Vaughan Williams—Choral Works

BOWEN, Kenneth (ten)
Britten: Death in Venice (Cpte)
Schoenberg: Gurrelieder
  see CONCERT INDEX under:
(DECC) 436 407-2DWO   The World of Schubert
(DECC) 443 455-2DF2   Vivaldi—Sacred Choral Works
(EMI) CDM7 64022-2   Vaughan Williams—Orchestral
Works
(LYRI) SRCD324   Mathias—Choral Works
(SONY) SMK48462   Boulez conducts Schoenberg

BOWERS-BROADBENT, Christopher (organ)
MacMillan: Cantos Sagrados
Pärt: Passio
  see CONCERT INDEX under:
(DECC) 433 080-2DM   Kodály—Choral Works
(ECM) 437 956-2   20th Century works for Organ and
Soprano
(ECM) 439 172-2   Byrd—Motets and Mass for Four
Voices
(ECM) 831 959-2   Pärt—Arbos
(UNIT) 88023-2   Tavener—Ikons

BOWES, Thomas (vn)
see CONCERT INDEX under:
(VIRG) **VC7 59609-2**   Vivaldi—Concertos

BOWLES, Anthony (cond)
see Orig London Cast

BOWLES, David (vc)
Bach: Anna Magdalena Notenbuch (1725) (exc)

BOWMAN, David (bar)
see CONCERT INDEX under:
(DECC) **436 990-2DWO**   The World of Benjamin Britten

BOWMAN, James (alto)
Bach: Mass in B minor, BWV232 (Cpte), St. John Passion, BWV245 (Cpte), St Matthew Passion, BWV244 (Cpte)
Britten: Death in Venice (Cpte), Midsummer Night's Dream (Cpte), Rejoice in the Lamb
Gluck: Orfeo ed Euridice (Cpte)
Handel: Ariodante (Cpte), Athalia (Cpte), Belshazzar (Cpte), Deborah (Cpte), Giulio Cesare (Cpte), Joshua (Cpte), Judas Maccabaeus (Cpte), Messiah (Cpte), Occasional Oratorio (Cpte), Orlando (Cpte), Ottone (Cpte)
M-A. Charpentier: Messe de minuit, H9
Orff: Carmina Burana
Pergolesi: Stabat mater
Purcell: Birthday Ode, Z342, Dioclesian, Z627 (exc), Fairy Queen, Z629 (Cpte), St Cecilia's Day Ode, Z328, Timon of Athens, Z632 (exc)
Schütz: Symphoniae sacrae, Op. 10 (Cpte)
Tavener: Akathist of Thanksgiving
see CONCERT INDEX under:
(ARGO) **440 282-2ZH**   Nyman—Time Will Pronounce
(ARIO) **ARN68026**   Baroque Choral and String Works
(ARIO) **ARN68046**   Italian Airs & Cantatas
(CARL) **PCD894**   Great Baroque Arias, Part I
(CHAN) **CHAN0505**   Handel—Chandos Anthems Vol. 3
(DECC) **430 263-2DM**   Purcell—Sacred choral works
(HYPE) **CDA66253**   Blow & Purcell: Countertenor Works
(HYPE) **CDA66288**   'Mr Henry Purcell's Most Admirable Composure's'
(HYPE) **CDA66314**   Purcell—Complete Odes & Welcome Songs, Vol.1
(HYPE) **CDA66315**   Handel: Music for Royal Occasions
(HYPE) **CDA66326**   Bach—Solo Cantatas
(HYPE) **CDA66412**   Purcell—Complete Odes & Welcome Songs, Vol.3
(HYPE) **CDA66440**   Handel—Italian Duets
(HYPE) **CDA66456**   Purcell—Complete Odes & Welcome Songs, Vol.4
(HYPE) **CDA66474**   Couperin—Vocal Works
(HYPE) **CDA66476**   Purcell—Complete Odes & Welcome Songs, Vol.5
(HYPE) **CDA66483**   Handel—Heroic Arias
(HYPE) **CDA66494**   Purcell—Complete Odes & Welcome Songs, Vol.6
(HYPE) **CDA66585**   Purcell—Complete Anthems & Services, Vol.1
(HYPE) **CDA66587**   Purcell—Complete Odes & Welcome Songs, Vol.7
(HYPE) **CDA66598**   Purcell—Complete Odes & Welcome Songs, Vol.8
(HYPE) **CDA66609**   Purcell—Complete Anthems & Services, Vol.2
(HYPE) **CDA66623**   Purcell—Complete Anthems & Services, Vol.3
(HYPE) **CDA66644**   Purcell—Complete Anthems & Services, Vol.4
(HYPE) **CDA66656**   Purcell—Complete Anthems & Services, Vol.5
(HYPE) **CDA66663**   Purcell—Complete Anthems & Services, Vol.6
(HYPE) **CDA66677**   Purcell—Anthems & Services, Vol.7
(HYPE) **CDA66686**   Purcell—Complete Anthems & Services, Vol.8
(HYPE) **CDA66693**   Purcell—Complete Anthems and Services, Volume 9
(HYPE) **CDA66707**   Purcell—Complete Anthems & Services, Vol. 10
(HYPE) **CDA66710**   Purcell—Secular Solo Songs, Volume 1
(HYPE) **CDA66716**   Purcell—Complete Anthems and Services, Volume 11
(HYPE) **CDA66720**   Purcell—Secular Solo Songs, Volume 2
(HYPE) **CDA66730**   Purcell—Secular Solo Songs, Vol. 3
(HYPE) **CDA67061/2**   Britten—Purcell Realizations
(L'OI) **414 329-2OH**   Vivaldi—Vocal and Instrumental Works
(L'OI) **421 654-2OH**   Handel & Haydn: Choral works
(L'OI) **425 893-2OM6(1)**   Purcell—Theatre Music (Part 1)
(L'OI) **425 893-2OM6(2)**   Purcell—Theatre Music (Part 2)
(LOND) **425 716-2LM**   Britten: Canticles
(MERI) **CDE84126**   James Bowman recital
(MERI) **CDE84138**   Sacred Baroque Vocal Works
(MERI) **CDE84158**   English Songs
(MERI) **CDE84169**   Telemann: Cantatas
(RICE) **RIC004035/7**   German Baroque Cantatas, Vol.4 - Bruhns
(RICE) **RIC079061**   German Baroque Cantatas, Vol.6 - Funeral Cantatas

(RICE) **RIC109097/8**   German Baroque Cantatas, Vol.9 - Weckmann
(TELD) **9031-77608-2**   Purcell—Anthems,Instrumental Music & Songs
(UNIT) **88002-2**   My Beloved Spake
(VIRG) **VC7 59243-2**   Purcell—Odes for Queen Mary

BOWMAN, Peter (ob)
Bolcom: Sessions I

BOWMAN, Robin (pf)
see CONCERT INDEX under:
(UNIC) **DKPCD9111**   Ives—Songs Volume 1
(UNIC) **DKPCD9112**   Ives—Songs, Vol.2

BOWYER, Kevin (organ)
Messiaen: Nativité du Seigneur
Reubke: Organ Sonata
Schumann: B-A-C-H Fugues, Op.60
Sorabji: Organ Symphony 1
see CONCERT INDEX under:
(NIMB) **NI5089**   Alkan: Organ Music
(NIMB) **NI5262**   Brahms: Organ Works
(NIMB) **NI5280**   Bach—Organ Works, Vol.1
(NIMB) **NI5289**   Bach—Organ Works, Vol.2
(NIMB) **NI5290**   Bach—Organ Works, Vol.3
(NIMB) **NI5377**   Bach—Organ Works, Vol.4
(NIMB) **NI5408**   Langlais—Works for Organ
(NIMB) **NI5411**   Hindemith/Schoenberg/Pepping—Organ Works
(NIMB) **NI5423**   Bach—Organ Works, Volume 6
(REGE) **REGCD107**   Lole—Choral Works
(UNIC) **DKPCD9151**   Camilleri—Organ Music

BOYD, Douglas (ob)
Mozart: Oboe Concerto, K314, Oboe Quartet, K370
R. Strauss: Oboe Concerto
see CONCERT INDEX under:
(ASV) **CDCOE803**   Chamber Concertos
(ASV) **CDCOE810**   Orchestral Works
(ASV) **CDCOE814**   Mozart—Wind Concertos
(DG) **435 873-2GH**   Vivaldi—Oboe Concertos
(DG) **439 889-2GH**   Schumann—Music for Oboe and Piano
(EMI) **CMS5 65115-2**   Britten—Chamber Works

BOYD, Douglas (ob/dir)
see CONCERT INDEX under:
(DG) **429 225-2GH**   Bach: Oboe Concertos

BOYD, James (va)
see CONCERT INDEX under:
(EMIN) **CD-EMX2229**   Elgar—Chamber Works

BOYER, Antonio (bar)
Alfano: Risurrezione (Cpte)

BOYER, Jean (organ)
see CONCERT INDEX under:
(FNAC) **592316**   Clérambault—Chants & Motets for the Royal House of Saint-Louis

BOYER, Marie (mez)
Campra: Idoménée (Cpte)

BOYK, James (pf)
Mussorgsky: Pictures

BOYLAN, Patricia (sop)
Cresswell: Modern Ecstasy

BOYSEN, Rolf (spkr)
Mozart: Entführung (Cpte)
Weber: Freischütz (Cpte)
Weill: Dreigroschenoper (Cpte)

BRAATEN, Geir Henning (pf)
Grieg: Lyric Pieces, Op. 71, Peasant dances, Op. 72
see CONCERT INDEX under:
(VICT) **VCD19025**   Grieg—Piano Works, Vol.1
(VICT) **VCD19026**   Grieg—Piano Works, Vol.2
(VICT) **VCD19027**   Grieg—Piano Works, Vol.3
(VICT) **VCD19028**   Grieg—Piano Works, Vol.4
(VICT) **VCD19031**   Grieg—Complete Piano Music - Volume VII
(VICT) **VCD19032**   Grieg—Complete Piano Music - Volume VIII
(VICT) **VCD19035**   Grieg—Complete Piano Music, Volume XI

BRABBINS, Martyn (cond)
see BBC Scottish SO

BRACHET, Huguette (mez)
Honegger: Jeanne d'Arc (Cpte)

BRACHT, Roland (bass)
Gluck: Alceste (1776) (Cpte)
Mozart: Entführung (Cpte), Zauberflöte (Cpte)
Wagner: Rheingold (Cpte)

BRADBURG, John (cl)
Danzi: Sextet

BRADBURY, Colin (cl)
see CONCERT INDEX under:
(ASV) **CDDCA701**   The Virtuoso Clarinettist
(SONY) **SM3K45845**   Webern—Complete Works

BRADBURY, John (cl)
see CONCERT INDEX under:
(BIDD) **LAW013**   Dodgson—Orchestral & Vocal Works

BRADBURY, Paula (sop)
Verdi: Rigoletto (Cpte)

BRADLEY, Gwendolyn (sop)
R.Strauss: Arabella (Cpte)

BRADSHAW, Dawn (sop)
Sullivan: Gondoliers (Cpte), Iolanthe (Cpte)

BRADSHAW, Sally (sop)
Handel: Agrippina (Cpte)

BRADSHAW, Susan (pf)
Holst: Planets

BRAGA, Rannveig (mez)
R. Strauss: Salome (Cpte)

BRAHAM, Jean (sop)
Schoenberg: Moses und Aron (Cpte)

BRAILOWSKY, Alexander (pf)
see CONCERT INDEX under:
(APR) **APR5501**   Alexander Brailowsky
(DANA) **DACOCD336/7**   Brailowsky—The Berlin Recordings, Vol. 1
(DANA) **DACOCD338/9**   Brailowsky—The Berlin Recordings, Vol. 2
(PEAR) **GEMMCD9132**   Alexander Brailowsky

BRAIN, Aubrey (hn)
Brahms: Horn Trio

BRAIN, Dennis (hn)
Mozart: Horn Concerti
see CONCERT INDEX under:
(DECC) **425 960-2DM**   Mozart—Chamber Works
(DECC) **425 996-2DM**   Britten—Vocal Works
(DUTT) **CDAX8014**   British Gramophone Premieres
(EMI) **CDC7 47834-2**   R. Strauss/Hindemith—Horn Concertos
(EMI) **CDS5 55032-2**   Hindemith—Plays and conducts his own works
(PEAR) **GEMMCD9177**   Britten—Vocal Works
(TEST) **SBT1009**   R. Strauss/Weber—Wind Concertos
(TEST) **SBT1012**   Cantelli conducts Wagner & Brahms
(TEST) **SBT1022**   Brain,Kell & Goossens play Schumann & Beethoven

BRAIN, Gary (cond)
see Ireland National SO

BRAININ, Norbert (vn)
Mozart: Concertone, K190, Sinfonia Concertante, K364
Schubert: Trout Quintet, D667

BRAITHWAITE, Nicholas (cond)
see LPO

BRAITHWAITE, Warwick (cond)
see Hallé

BRAMALL, Anthony (cond)
see Slovak PO

BRAMANTE, Aldo (bass)
Cherubini: Lodoïska (Cpte)
Puccini: Fanciulla del West (Cpte), Manon Lescaut (Cpte)
Spontini: Vestale (Cpte)

BRAMBILLA, Hugues (ten)
Offenbach: Orphée aux enfers (Cpte), Périchole (Cpte)

BRAMMA, Harry (organ)
see CONCERT INDEX under:
(CHAN) **CHAN6601**   Elgar—Choral Works

BRAMMER, Philipp (spkr)
R. Strauss: Intermezzo (Cpte)

BRAND, Adrian (ten)
Rameau: Castor et Pollux (Cpte)

BRAND, Geoffrey (cond)
see Black Dyke Mills Band

(THE) BRANDENBURG CONSORT
Handel: Concerti grossi, Op. 3
cond S. CLEOBURY
Handel: Messiah (Cpte)
cond R. GOODMAN
Avison: Concerti after D. Scarlatti
Bach: Brandenburg Concertos
Corelli: Concerti grossi, Op. 6
Wassenaer: Concerti Armonici
see CONCERT INDEX under:
(HYPE) **CDA66501**   Bach—Orchestral Suites
(HYPE) **CDA66745**   Vivaldi—Opera Arias and Sinfonias
cond D. HILL
Handel: Blessed are they that considereth the poor, Coronation Anthems
see CONCERT INDEX under:
(ARGO) **436 832-2ZH**   Purcell— Music for the Funeral of Queen Mary

BRANDENBURG ORCHESTRA
cond D. HILL
Haydn: Mass 7, Mass 14

BRANDES, Christine (sop)
Purcell: Dido (Cpte)
see CONCERT INDEX under:
(KOCH) **37164-2**   Bach—Cantatas, Vol.3

BRANDIS, Thomas (vn)
see CONCERT INDEX under:
(DG) **439 422-2GCL**   Vivaldi—Concertos

BRANDIS, Thomas (vn/dir)
Vivaldi: Concerti Grossi, Op.3

BRANDIS QUARTET
Beethoven: String Quartet 1, String Quartet 2, String Quartet 3, String Quartet 8, String Quartet 11, String Quartet 16
Schubert: String Quartet, D804, String Quartet, D810, String Quintet
see CONCERT INDEX under:

(NIMB) **NI5353** Beethoven—String Quartets, Op 18 Nos 4,5 and 6
(NIMB) **NI5410** Hindemith/Schulhoff/Weill—String Quartets
    cond J. CONLON
    see CONCERT INDEX *under:*
(ERAT) **2292-45499-2** Martinů—Orchestral Works

BRANDT, Karl-Heinz (ten)
Telemann: Don Quichotte (Cpte)
    see CONCERT INDEX *under:*
(HARM) **HMC90 1420** Weill—The Seven Deadly Sins; Songs

BRANISTEANU, Horiana (sop)
Haydn: Schöpfung (Cpte)

BRANNIGAN, Owen (bass)
Britten: Albert Herring (Cpte), Midsummer Night's Dream (Cpte), Noye's Fludde (Cpte), Peter Grimes (Cpte)
Purcell: Fairy Queen, Z629 (Cpte)
Sullivan: Pirates of Penzance (Cpte)
    see CONCERT INDEX *under:*
(DECC) **430 095-2DWO** The World of Gilbert & Sullivan, Vol.1
(DECC) **436 990-2DWO** The World of Benjamin Britten
(EMI) **CDM5 65101-2** A Warlock Centenary Album
(LOND) **436 396-2LM** Britten—Spring Symphony, etc

BRANS, Werner (bar)
Puccini: Bohème (Cpte)

BRANZELL, Karin (contr)
    see CONCERT INDEX *under:*
(EMI) **CDH7 69787-2** Richard Tauber sings Operetta Arias
(PREI) **89039** Karin Branzell (1891-1974)

BRASS ENSEMBLE
    cond K. NYSTEDT
    see CONCERT INDEX *under:*
(AURO) **ACD4971** Nystedt—Chamber and Vocal Works

(ELISABETH) BRASSEUR CHOIR
    cond J. FOURNET
Bizet: Pêcheurs de Perles (Cpte)
    see CONCERT INDEX *under:*
(PHIL) **438 970-2PM2** Camille Maurane
    cond I. MARKEVITCH
Mozart: Mass, K317

(ELISABETH) BRASSEUR CHORALE
    cond S. BAUDO
Honegger: Roi David (Cpte)
    cond I. MARKEVITCH
    see CONCERT INDEX *under:*
(EMI) **CDM7 64281-2** Boulanger—Vocal & Chamber Works

BRASSUS CHORAL SOCIETY
    cond N. JÄRVI
Stravinsky: Oedipus Rex (Cpte)
    see CONCERT INDEX *under:*
(CHAN) **CHAN9239** Stravinsky—Orchestral Works
(CHAN) **CHAN9240** Stravinsky—Choral and Orchestral Works

BRASSUS CHORALE
    cond A. CHARLET
Gounod: Mass 2

BRATHWAITE, Maureen (mez)
Gershwin: Porgy and Bess (Cpte)

BRATISLAVA CHAMBER ENSEMBLE
    cond V. HORÁK
    see CONCERT INDEX *under:*
(CAMP) **RRCD1317** Martinů/Kobayashi—Orchestral Works

BRATISLAVA CHILDREN'S CHOIR
    cond W. HUMBURG
Puccini: Bohème (Cpte)
    cond O. LENÁRD
Puccini: Bohème (Cpte)
    cond C. MACKERRAS
Janáček: Cunning Little Vixen (Cpte)

BRATISLAVA CITY CHOIR
    cond O. LENÁRD
Brian: Symphony 1

BRATISLAVA CITY CHORUS
    cond M. GIELEN
B. A. Zimmermann: Requiem (Cpte)
    cond J. WILDNER
J. Strauss II: Fledermaus (Cpte)

BRATISLAVA NATIONAL OPERA CHORUS
    cond O. LENÁRD
Puccini: Bohème (Cpte)
    cond L. SLOVÁK
Janáček: Glagolitic Mass (Cpte)
    cond R. STANKOVSKY
Miaskovsky: Symphony 6

BRATISLAVA PHILHARMONIC CHOIR
    cond M. GIELEN
    see CONCERT INDEX *under:*
(WERG) **WER60185-50** Schoenberg: Choral & Orchestral Works

BRATISLAVA RADIO SYMPHONY ORCHESTRA
    see CONCERT INDEX *under:*
(OPUS) **9156 1824** Dvorský sings Operatic Arias

    cond ADRIANO
Alf Newman: Selznick International Pictures Fanfare
Honegger: Misérables (Cpte)
Respighi: Primavera
Waxman: Rebecca (exc)
    see CONCERT INDEX *under:*
(MARC) **8 223134** Honegger—Film Music
(MARC) **8 223287** Ibert: Film Music
(MARC) **8 223315** Bliss—Film Music
(MARC) **8 223346** Respighi—Ballets
(MARC) **8 223347** Respighi—Cantatas
(MARC) **8 223348** Respighi—Orchestral Works
(MARC) **8 223466** Honegger—Film Music
    cond F. BAUER-THEUSSL
    see CONCERT INDEX *under:*
(MARC) **8 223240** Johann Strauss II Edition, Vol.40
    cond H. BEISSEL
    see CONCERT INDEX *under:*
(MARC) **8 223162** Pfitzner: Orchestral Works
    cond R. BERNAS
Cresswell: Cello Concerto, Modern Ecstasy
    cond G. CARPENTER
    see CONCERT INDEX *under:*
(MARC) **8 223514** Mayerl—Orchestral Works
    cond K. CLARK
Glière: Symphony 2, Zaporozhy Cossacks
    cond M. DITTRICH
    see CONCERT INDEX *under:*
(MARC) **8 223234** Johann Strauss II Edition, Vol.34
(MARC) **8 223241** Johann Struss II Edition, Vol.41
(MARC) **8 223381** Salieri—Overtures
    cond O. DOHNÁNYI
Liszt: Piano Concerto 1
    see CONCERT INDEX *under:*
(NAXO) **8 550241** Verdi—Opera Choruses
    cond R. DUARTE
    see CONCERT INDEX *under:*
(MARC) **8 223357** Villa-Lobos—Orchestral Works
(MARC) **8 223552** Villa-Lobos—Orchestral Works
    cond A. ESCHWÉ
    see CONCERT INDEX *under:*
(MARC) **8 223217** Johann Strauss II Edition, Vol.17
    cond S. GUNZENHAUSER
Orff: Carmina burana
    see CONCERT INDEX *under:*
(NAXO) **8 550238** Borodin—Symphonies
    cond W. HUMBURG
Puccini: Bohème (Cpte)
    see CONCERT INDEX *under:*
(NAXO) **8 550605** Favourite Soprano Arias
    cond D. JOHANOS
    see CONCERT INDEX *under:*
(MARC) **8 223629** Ippolitov-Ivanov—Orchestral Works
(NAXO) **8 550486** Rimsky-Korsakov—Orchestral Works
    cond A. LEAPER
Brian: Symphony 4, Symphony 12
Holst: Planets, Suite de ballet
    see CONCERT INDEX *under:*
(MARC) **8 223401** Farnon—Popular Orchestral Works
(MARC) **8 223402** Haydn Wood—Popular Orchestral Works
(MARC) **8 223419** Edward German—Orchestral Works
(MARC) **8 223425** Frederic Curzon—Orchestral Works
(MARC) **8 223442** Ketèlbey—British Light Music
(MARC) **8 223444** Quilter—Orchestral Works
(MARC) **8 223445** Coates—Orchestral Works
(MARC) **8 223446** Holbrooke—Orchestral Works
(NAXO) **8 550229** English Festival
    cond O. LENÁRD
Bellini: Sonnambula (Cpte)
Chopin: Sylphides
Glazunov: Seasons
Puccini: Bohème (Cpte)
Suchoň: Whirlpool (Cpte)
Tchaikovsky: Nutcracker (Cpte), Sleeping Beauty (exc), Swan Lake (Cpte)
    see CONCERT INDEX *under:*
(NAXO) **8 550098** Rimsky-Korsakov—Orchestral Works
(NAXO) **8 550343** Russian and French Opera Arias
(NAXO) **8 550411** Janacek—Orchestral works
(OPUS) **9350 2012** Cikker—Orchestral Works
    cond A. RAHBARI
Brahms: Deutsches Requiem, Op.45 (Cpte)
Leoncavallo: Pagliacci (Cpte)
Mascagni: Cavalleria Rusticana (Cpte)
Puccini: Madama Butterfly (Cpte), Tosca (Cpte)
Verdi: Rigoletto (Cpte)
    see CONCERT INDEX *under:*
(NAXO) **8 550684** Duets and Arias from Italian Operas
    cond L. RAJTER
Schmidt: Symphony 1, Symphony 2, Symphony 3, Symphony 4
Zemlinsky: Gläserne Herz Suite, Symphony 1
    see CONCERT INDEX *under:*
(OPUS) **9350 1851/4** Schmidt: Symphonies
    cond L. SLOVÁK
Shostakovich: Symphony 1, Symphony 2, Symphony 3, Symphony 4, Symphony 5, Symphony 6, Symphony 7, Symphony 8, Symphony 9, Symphony 10, Symphony 11, Symphony 12, Symphony 13, Symphony 14, Symphony 15
    cond R. STANKOVSKY
Miaskovsky: Silence, Op. 9, Symphony 6, Symphony 12
Mosonyi: Symphony 1

Rubinstein: Caprice russe, Op. 102, Eroica Fantasia, Op. 110, Piano Concerto 5, Symphony 3
    cond P. STEINBERG
Berlioz: Symphonie fantastique
    cond E. TOMLINSON
    see CONCERT INDEX *under:*
(MARC) **8 223413** British Light Music—Ernest Tomlinson
(MARC) **8 223515** Binge—Orchestral Works
    cond G. TRACK
    see CONCERT INDEX *under:*
(MARC) **8 223250** J.Strauss—Works for Male Chorus and Orchestra
    cond J. WILDNER
J. Strauss II: Fledermaus (Cpte)
    see CONCERT INDEX *under:*
(MARC) **8 223215** Johann Strauss II Edition, Vol.15
(MARC) **8 223250** J.Strauss—Works for Male Chorus and Orchestra
(NAXO) **8 550688** Spohr—Clarinet Works

BRATISLAVA SLOVAK CHORUS
    cond M. GIELEN
B. A. Zimmermann: Requiem (Cpte)

BRATKE, Marcelo (pf)
    see CONCERT INDEX *under:*
(OLYM) **OCD427** Brazilian Piano Music
(OLYM) **OCD431** Berg/Webern/Krenek—Piano Works
(OLYM) **OCD455** Villa-Lobos—Piano Works

BRATLIE, Jens Harald (pf)
Grieg: Cello Sonata
    see CONCERT INDEX *under:*
(SIMA) **PSC1014** Shostakovich—Chamber Works

BRATOEV, Bojidar (cond)
    see Toulouse Nat CO

BRATSCHKE, Detlef (treb)
    see CONCERT INDEX *under:*
(TELD) **2292-42576-2** Bach—Cantatas, Volume 20
(TELD) **2292-42582-2** Bach—Cantatas, Volume 23
(TELD) **2292-42584-2** Bach—Cantatas, Volume 25
(TELD) **2292-42606-2** Bach—Cantatas, Volume 28
(TELD) **4509-91758-2** Bach—Cantatas, Vol.4
(TELD) **4509-91759-2** Bach—Cantatas, Vol.5
(TELD) **4509-91760-2** Bach—Cantatas, Vol.6

BRAUN, Hans (bar)
Bach: Cantata 4, Cantata 78, Cantata 106, Cantata 140
Beethoven: Fidelio (Cpte)
R. Strauss: Daphne (Cpte)
Wagner: Lohengrin (Cpte)

BRAUN, Helena (sop)
Wagner: Tristan und Isolde (Cpte)
    see CONCERT INDEX *under:*
(SCHW) **314502** Vienna State Opera—Live Recordings (sampler)
(SCHW) **314562** Vienna State Opera Live, Vol.6

BRAUN, Mei (bar)
Handel: Floridante (exc)

BRAUN, Victor (bar)
Wagner: Tannhäuser (Cpte)

BRAUNSTEIN, Mark (va)
Elgar: Cello Concerto

BRAUTIGAM, Ronald (hpd)
    see CONCERT INDEX *under:*
(PHIL) **422 515-2PME7** The Complete Mozart Edition Vol 15

BRAUTIGAM, Ronald (pf)
(DECC) **433 702-2DH** Shostakovich—Orchestral Works
(DECC) **433 816-2DH2** Hindemith—Kammermusik
(DECC) **444 455-2DH** Martin—Ballades; Concerto for 7 Wind Instruments
(ETCE) **KTC1059** Prokofiev. Cello Music
(OLYM) **OCD436** Schumann—Piano Works
(PHIL) **422 515-2PME7** The Complete Mozart Edition Vol 15
(SCHW) **315272** Debussy/Fauré/Poulenc—Violin Sonatas

BRAUTIGAM, Ronald (pf/hpd)
Schnittke: Concerto grosso 3

BRÄUTIGAM, Thomas (ten)
Weill: Jasager (Cpte)

BRAVO, Carmen (pf)
    see CONCERT INDEX *under:*
(EMI) **CDM7 64470-2** Mompou—Piano Works

BRAY CHORAL SOCIETY
    cond R. SACCANI
Verdi: Aida (Cpte)

BRAYNE, Christopher (organ)
    see CONCERT INDEX *under:*
(PRIO) **PRCD337** Psalms of David, Volume 2

BRÁZDA, Milan (tbn)
    see CONCERT INDEX *under:*
(SUPR) **11 1878-2** The Unknown Janáček

BRAZILIAN CHAMBER ORCHESTRA
    cond B. BESSLER
    see CONCERT INDEX *under:*
(CHNT) **LDC278 869/70** Villa-Lobos—Guitar Works

BREAM, Julian (gtr)
    see CONCERT INDEX *under:*

(EMI) **CDC5 55123-2** Julian Bream plays Bach
(EMI) **CDC7 54661-2** Guitar Concertos
(EMI) **CDC7 54901-2** Nocturnal - 20th Century Guitar Music
(EMI) **CDM7 63574-2** Elisabeth Schwarzkopf Christmas Album
(RCA) **09026 61450-2** Together - Julian Bream & John Williams
(RCA) **09026 61452-2** Together Again - Julian Bream & John Williams
(RCA) **09026 61583-2(3)** Julian Bream Edition (pt 3)
(RCA) **09026 61583-2(4)** Julian Bream Edition (pt 4)
(RCA) **09026 61583-2(5)** Julian Bream Edition (pt 5)
(RCA) **09026 61583-2(6)** Julian Bream Edition (pt 6)
(RCA) **09026 61591-2** J. Bream Edition, Vol.8: Pop Classics for Spanish Gtr
(RCA) **09026 61592-2** J. Bream Edition, Vol.9: Baroque Gtr
(RCA) **09026 61593-2** J. Bream Edition, Vol.10: Classic Gtr
(RCA) **09026 61594-2** J. Bream Edition, Vol.11: Romantic Gtr
(RCA) **09026 61595-2** J. Bream Edition, Vol.12: 20th-Century Guitar I
(RCA) **09026 61596-2** J. Bream Edition, Vol.13: 20th-Century Guitar II
(RCA) **09026 61597-2** J. Bream Edition, Vol.14: Dedication
(RCA) **09026 61598-2** J. Bream Edition, Vol.15: Guitar Concertos
(RCA) **09026 61599-2** J. Bream Edition, Vol.16: Julian Bream & His Friends
(RCA) **09026 61601-2** J. Bream Edition, Vol.18: Music for Voice & Gtr
(RCA) **09026 61605-2** J. Bream Edition, Vol.22: Gtr Concertos
(RCA) **09026 61607-2** J. Bream Edition, Vol.24: Music of Spain
(RCA) **09026 61608-2** J. Bream Edition, Vol.25: Music of Spain
(RCA) **09026 61609-2** J. Bream Edition, Vol.26: Music of Spain
(RCA) **09026 61610-2** J. Bream Edition, Vol.27: Music of Spain—Guitarra
(RCA) **09026 61611-2** J. Bream Edition, Vol.28: Music of Spain—Rodrigo

BREAM, Julian (lte)
Monteverdi: Ballo delle ingrate
see CONCERT INDEX under:
(RCA) **09026 61583-2(1)** Juliam Bream Edition (pt 1)
(RCA) **09026 61583-2(2)** Julian Bream Edition (pt 2)
(RCA) **09026 61583-2(3)** Julian Bream Edition (pt 3)
(RCA) **09026 61583-2(4)** Julian Bream Edition (pt 4)
(RCA) **09026 61583-2(5)** Julian Bream Edition (pt 5)
(RCA) **09026 61584-2** J. Bream Edition, Vol.1: Golden Age of Eng Lte Mus
(RCA) **09026 61585-2** J. Bream Edition, Vol.2: Lte Music from Royal Courts of Europe
(RCA) **09026 61586-2** J. Bream Edition. Vol.3: Dances of Dowland
(RCA) **09026 61587-2** J. Bream Edition, Vol.4: The Woods So Wild
(RCA) **09026 61588-2** J. Bream Edition, Vol.5: Concertos & Sonatas for Lte
(RCA) **09026 61602-2** J. Bream Edition, Vol.19: Elizabethan Lte Songs
(RCA) **09026 61603-2** J. Bream Edition, Vol.20: Bach
(RCA) **09026 61606-2** J. Bream Edition, Vol.23: Music of Spain

(JULIAN) BREAM CONSORT
see CONCERT INDEX under:
(RCA) **09026 61583-2(2)** Julian Bream Edition (pt 2)
(RCA) **09026 61583-2(3)** Julian Bream Edition (pt 3)
(RCA) **09026 61589-2** J. Bream Edition, Vol.6: Julian Bream Consort
(RCA) **09026 61590-2** J. Bream Edition, Vol.7: Fantasies, Ayres & Dances

BREBION, Jean (cond)
see French Rad Lyric Orch

BRECKNOCK, John (ten)
Offenbach: Robinson Crusoé (Cpte)
see CONCERT INDEX under:
(MERI) **CDE84173** Elgar: Songs & Part-songs

BREDA SACRAMENTS CHOIR
cond T. KOOPMAN
Bach: St Matthew Passion, BWV244 (Cpte)

BREDY, Rosine (sngr)
Offenbach: Madame l'Archiduc (Cpte)

BREE, Peter (cor ang)
see CONCERT INDEX under:
(ETCE) **KTC1074** Works for Oboe & Piano

BREE, Peter (ob)
Devienne: Oboe Sonatas, Op. 71, Sonatas, Op. 23 (exc)
see CONCERT INDEX under:
(ETCE) **KTC1074** Works for Oboe & Piano
(ETCE) **KTC1083** Telemann: Sonatas

BREGA, Marthe (sop)
see CONCERT INDEX under:
(EPM) **150 122** Milhaud—Historic Recordings 1928-1948

BREGONZI, Alec (ten)
Offenbach: Christopher Columbus (Cpte)

BREISACH, Paul (cond)
see orch

BREITMAN, David (fp)
Schubert: Schöne Müllerin (Cpte)

BRÉJEAN-SILVER, Georgette (sop)
see CONCERT INDEX under:
(PEAR) **GEMMCDS9923(2)** Covent Garden on Record, Vol.1 (pt 2)
(SYMP) **SYMCD1113** The Harold Wayne Collection, Vol.13
(SYMP) **SYMCD1172** The Harold Wayne Collection, Vol.21

BREKKE, Ingeborg Marie (contr)
Braein: Anne Pedersdotter (Cpte)

BRELL, Mario (ten)
Weill: Zar lässt sich Photographieren (Cpte)

BREMAR, Jacquelin (sop)
Henze: English Cat (Cpte)

BREMBECK, Christian (cond)
see Capella Istropolitana

BREMEN BAROQUE ORCHESTRA
cond W. HELBICH
Handel: Queen Caroline Te Deum, Ways of Zion do mourn
Telemann: Jauchze, jubilier und singe, TWV15: 5, Magnificat, TWV9: 17

BREMEN STEINTOR BAROCK
cond W. HELBICH
see CONCERT INDEX under:
(CPO) **CPO999 139-2** The Apocryphal Bach Cantatas

BREMEN VOCAL ENSEMBLE FOR ANCIENT MUSIC
cond T. ALBERT
Bach: Cantata 56
Keiser: Masagniello furioso (Cpte)
cond M. SCHNEIDER
Telemann: Don Quichotte (Cpte)

BREMER, Jetse (ten)
see CONCERT INDEX under:
(PHIL) **442 534-2PH** Janáček—Choral Works

BREMNER, Tony (cond)
see Philh

BREMS, Elsa (mez)
see CONCERT INDEX under:
(SCHW) **314572** Vienna State Opera Live, Vol.7

BRENDEL, Alfred (pf)
Beethoven: Choral Fantasia, Diabelli Variations, Piano Concerto 1, Piano Concerto 2, Piano Concerto 3, Piano Concerto 4, Piano Concerto 5
Brahms: Ballades, Piano Concerto 1, Piano Concerto 2
Liszt: Csárdás, S225 (exc), Hungarian Rhapsodies, S244 (exc)
Mozart: Piano Concerto 15, Piano Concerto 21, Piano Concerto 23, Piano Concerto 27
Schubert: Fantasy, D760, Impromptus (exc), Moments musicaux, D780, Piano Sonata, D537, Piano Sonata, D664, Piano Sonata, D784, Piano Sonata, D840, Piano Sonata, D845, Piano Sonata, D850, Piano Sonata, D894, Piano Sonata, D958, Piano Sonata, D960, Winterreise (Cpte)
Schumann: Piano Concerto
Weber: Konzertstück, Piano Sonata 2
see CONCERT INDEX under:
(EMI) **CDH7 63702-2** Mozart: Lieder & Concert Arias
(PHIL) **412 227-2PH** Beethoven: Diabelli work
(PHIL) **412 228-2PH** Haydn: Keyboard works
(PHIL) **412 575-2PH11** Beethoven—Complete Piano Sonatas
(PHIL) **416 365-2PH** Haydn: Piano Sonatas
(PHIL) **416 643-2PH4** Haydn—Complete Piano Sonatas
(PHIL) **422 229-2PH** Schubert—Piano Works
(PHIL) **422 507-2PME12** The Complete Mozart Edition Vol 7
(PHIL) **422 514-2PME5** The Complete Mozart Edition Vol 14
(PHIL) **426 386-2PC** Schumann—Oboe Works
(PHIL) **426 637-2PSL** Liszt—Works for Piano and Orchestra
(PHIL) **434 663-2PH** Mozart—Piano Sonatas
(PHIL) **434 732-2PM** Alfred Brendel plays Schumann
(PHIL) **438 134-2PH** Beethoven—Piano Sonatas, Op.31
(PHIL) **438 374-2PM2** Beethoven—Piano Sonatas
(PHIL) **438 472-2PM** Beethoven—Piano Sonatas, etc
(PHIL) **438 703-2PM2** Schubert—Piano Works
(PHIL) **438 730-2PM2** Beethoven—Favourite Piano Sonatas
(PHIL) **438 863-2PH** Beethoven—Piano Sonatas
(PHIL) **442 124-2PH** Beethoven—Piano Sonatas
(PHIL) **442 269-2PM2** Mozart—The Great Piano Concertos, Volume 1
(PHIL) **442 571-2PM2** Mozart—The Great Piano Concertos, Volume II
(PHIL) **442 787-2PH** Beethoven—Piano Sonatas
(VANG) **08.4025.71** Mozart—Piano Works
(VANG) **08.4026.71** Schubert—Piano Works
(VOX) **115772-2** Beethoven—Piano Sonatas, Vol.3

BRENDEL, Wolfgang (bar)
Brahms: Deutsches Requiem, Op. 45 (Cpte)
J. Strauss II: Fledermaus, Die (Cpte)
Mozart: Zauberflöte (Cpte)
Weber: Freischütz (Cpte)
see CONCERT INDEX under:
(DG) **435 066-2GGA** Brahms—Choral Works

BRENDSTRUP, Henrik (vc)
see CONCERT INDEX under:
(BIS) **BIS-CD710** Gubaidulina—Chamber Works

BRENNER, Janis (voc)
M. Monk: Atlas (Cpte)

BRENNER, Roger (tbn)
see CONCERT INDEX under:
(HYPE) **CDA66177** Bruckner—Sacred Choral Works
(HYPE) **CDA66245** Bruckner—Choral Works

BRESCIA MANDOLIN AND GUITAR ORCHESTRA
cond C. MANDONICO
see CONCERT INDEX under:
(FONE) **91F02** Calace—Works for Mandolins

BRESKE, Claire (sop)
see CONCERT INDEX under:
(MYTO) **3MCD93381** Wagner—Die Walküre, etc

BRESSLER, Charles (ten)
Liszt: Faust Symphony
see CONCERT INDEX under:
(SONY) **SMK47638** Vaughan Williams—Orchestral Works

BRETT, Charles (cond)
see Amaryllis Consort

BRETT, Charles (alto)
Bach: Cantata 78, Cantata 198, Magnificat, BWV243, Mass in B minor, BWV232 (Cpte)
Handel: Blessed are they that considereth the poor, Messiah (Cpte), St John Passion (Cpte), Triumph of Time and Truth (Cpte), Ways of Zion do mourn
Holloway: Sea-Surface Full of Clouds
M-A. Charpentier: Te Deum H146
Purcell: Birthday Ode, Z323, Fairy Queen, Z629 (Cpte)
see CONCERT INDEX under:
(ARGO) **417 468-2ZH** G. Gabrieli: Choral and Instrumental Works
(CHAN) **CHAN0517** Handel—Sacred Choral works
(DECC) **430 263-2DM** Purcell—Sacred choral works
(ERAT) **4509-96371-2** Gardiner—The Purcell Collection
(PIER) **PV794033** Vivaldi—Vocal and Wind Music

BRETT, Jonathan (cond)
see English Classical Players

BRETT, Philip (cond)
see American Gamelan

BREUER, Hans (ten)
see CONCERT INDEX under:
(SYMP) **SYMCD1081** The Harold Wayne Collection, Vol.5

BREUL, Elisabeth (sop)
Wagner: Parsifal (Cpte)

BREWER, Aline (hp)
see CONCERT INDEX under:
(COLL) **Coll1297-2** A Contemporary Collection
(CONI) **CDCF905** Karen Jones—The Flute Album
(REFE) **RRCD-47** Robert Farnon—Concert Works

BREWER, Bruce (ten)
Henze: Boulevard Solitude (Cpte)
Offenbach: Orphée aux enfers (Cpte)
Verdi: Aida (Cpte)

BREWER, Christine (sop)
Dvořák: Te Deum
Janáček: Glagolitic Mass (Cpte)

BREWER CHAMBER CHORUS
cond R. PALMER
Handel: Imeneo (Cpte)

BREWER CHAMBER ORCHESTRA
cond R. PALMER
A. Scarlatti: Flute Sonatas (exc), Ishmael
Handel: Imeneo (Cpte), Joshua (Cpte), Siroe, Rè di Persia (Cpte)
see CONCERT INDEX under:
(NEWP) **NPD85540** Handel/Bononcini—Muzio Scevola

BREY, Carter (vc)
Beach—Cabildo; Six Short Pieces
(DELO) **DE3170** Beach—Cabildo; Six Short Pieces
(RCA) **09026 68181-2** French Chamber Works

BREZINA, Alexander (cond)
see Munich Wind Academy

BRIC, Ion (bass)
Spohr: Faust (Cpte)

BRICCETTI, Thomas (cond)
see Bergamo House Orch

BRICE, Carol (mez)
Gershwin: Porgy and Bess (Cpte)

BRICE, Elizabeth (sngr)
see CONCERT INDEX under:
(PEAR) **GEMMCDS9053/5** Music from the New York Stage, Vol. 2: 1908—1913
(PEAR) **GEMMCDS9056/8** Music from the New York Stage, Vol. 3: 1913-17

BRICE, Fanny (sngr)
see CONCERT INDEX under:
(PEAR) **GEMMCDS9059/61** Music from the New York Stage, Vol. 4: 1917-20

BRIEFF, Frank (cond)
see Columbia SO

BROADWAY, Kenneth (pf)
Vaughan Williams: 2-Piano Concerto

BROADWAY CAST
see CONCERT INDEX under:
(PEAR) GEMMCDS9050/2(1) Music from the New
York Stage, Vol. 1 (part 1)
(PEAR) GEMMCDS9050/2(2) Music from the New
York Stage, Vol. 1 (part 2)
cond EDWARD STRAUSS
F. Loesser: Guys and Dolls (Cpte)
cond M. LEVINE
Gershwin: Of Thee I Sing (Cpte)
cond M. METH
Rodgers: Pal Joey (Cpte)

BROADWAY CHORUS
cond L. BERNSTEIN
Bernstein: West Side Story (Cpte)

BROADWAY ORCHESTRA
cond L. BERNSTEIN
Bernstein: West Side Story (Cpte)

BRÖCHELER, John (bass)
Braunfels: Verkündigung (Cpte)
Donizetti: Lucrezia Borgia (Cpte)
Mahler: Knaben Wunderhorn (exc)
Schumann: Paradies und die Peri (Cpte)
see CONCERT INDEX under:
(HANS) 98 805 Bach—Cantatas, Vol.43
(HANS) 98 809 Bach—Cantatas, Vol.47
(HANS) 98 813 Bach—Cantatas, Vol.51
(SCHW) 312632 Mahler/Busoni—Vocal/Orchestral
Works

BROCKHAUS, Lilo (mez)
Wagner: Walküre (Cpte)
see CONCERT INDEX under:
(DG) 435 211-2GX15 Wagner—Der Ring des
Nibelungen

BROCKMAN, David (cond)
see orch

BRODARD, Michel (bar)
Bach: Mass, BWV236
Beethoven: Christus am Oelberge, Op. 85, Mass in
C
Debussy: Pelléas et Mélisande (Cpte)
Haydn: Mass 10
Rossini: Péchés de vieillesse II (Cpte), Péchés de
vieillesse III (exc)
see CONCERT INDEX under:
(ERAT) 4509-95307-2 Schubert/Schumann—Sacred
Choral Works

BRODERSEN, Edith (sop)
Nielsen: Maskarade (Cpte)

BRODIE, Gary (chalumeau)
see CONCERT INDEX under:
(CLRI) CC0004 The Early Clarinet Family

BRODIE, Gary (cl)
see CONCERT INDEX under:
(CLRI) CC0004 The Early Clarinet Family

BRODO, Amy (vc)
see CONCERT INDEX under:
(CARL) PWK1138 Baroque Favourites

BRODSKY QUARTET
Beethoven: String Quartet 10
Crumb: Black Angels
Delius: String Quartet (1916)
Elgar: String Quartet
Schubert: String Quartet, D804, String Quartet,
D810
see CONCERT INDEX under:
(SILV) SILKD6001 Lament—The Brodsky Quartet
(TELD) 2292-44919-2 Shostakovich: String Quartets
(TELD) 2292-46015-2 Brodsky Unlimited - Encores
(TELD) 9031-71702-2 Shostakovich—The String
Quartets

BROGLIA, Lauren (sop)
Puccini: Bohème (Cpte)

BROHM, Sabine (sop)
R. Strauss: Rosenkavalier (Cpte)

BROISSIN, Nicole (sop)
Ganne: Hans (Cpte)
Messager: Monsieur Beaucaire (Cpte)

BROITMAN, Ruben (ten)
R. Strauss: Friedenstag (Cpte)

BROKMEIER, Willi (ten)
Korngold: Tote Stadt (Cpte)
Millöcker: Gasparone (Cpte)
Mozart: Nozze di Figaro (Cpte), Zauberflöte (Cpte)

BROMBACHER, Julius (bass)
Wagner: Meistersinger (exc)

BRON, Onissim (cond)
see Bolshoi Th Orch

BRONDER, Peter (ten)
Beethoven: Symphony 9
Cilea: Adriana Lecouvreur (Cpte)
Janáček: Fate (Cpte)
Rossini: Turco in Italia (Cpte)
Verdi: Traviata (Cpte)
see CONCERT INDEX under:
(ARAB) Z6612 Rossini: Opera Arias

BRONFMAN, Yefim (pf)
Arensky: Piano Trio 1

Rachmaninov: Piano Concerto 2, Piano Concerto 3
Tchaikovsky: Piano Trio, Op. 50
see CONCERT INDEX under:
(DG) 445 557-2GMA Prokofiev/Ravel—Violin Works
(SONY) SK52483 Prokofiev—Piano Concertos
(SONY) SK52484 Prokofiev—Piano Sonatas
(SONY) SK53107 Brahms—Violin Sonatas
(SONY) SK53972 Mozart—Keyboard and Violin
Sonatas
(SONY) SK58966 Prokofiev—Piano Concertos, etc
(SONY) SK64309 Mozart—Violin Sonatas

BRØNNUM, Otta (sop)
see CONCERT INDEX under:
(SIMA) PSC1810(1) Grieg—Songs (historical
recordings, pt 1)

BRONGEEST, Cornelius (bar)
see CONCERT INDEX under:
(OPAL) OPALCDS9843 Karl Muck conducts Wagner

BRONSKAYA, Eugenia (sop)
see CONCERT INDEX under:
(NIMB) NI7865 Great Singers at the Mariinsky
Theatre

BROOK, Mathew (bass)
Purcell: Dioclesian, Z627 (exc)

BROOKE, Gwydion (bn)
see CONCERT INDEX under:
(TEST) SBT1009 R. Strauss/Weber—Wind Concertos

BROOKES, Oliver (bass viol)
see CONCERT INDEX under:
(DECC) 440 079-2DM The Amorous Flute

BROOKES, Oliver (vc)
see CONCERT INDEX under:
(DECC) 440 079-2DM The Amorous Flute

BROOKLYN BOYS' CHORUS
cond L. BERNSTEIN
Mahler: Symphony 3
see CONCERT INDEX under:
(DG) 435 162-2GX13 Mahler—Complete
Symphonies

BROOKLYN PHILHARMONIC ORCHESTRA
cond M. BARRETT
see CONCERT INDEX under:
(KOCH) 37187-2 20th-Century American Oboe
Works
cond D.R. DAVIES
Glass: Low Symphony
cond L. FOSS
see CONCERT INDEX under:
(NEW) NW375-2 Lukas Foss: Orchestral Works

BROOKS, Brian (vn)
see CONCERT INDEX under:
(HYPE) CDA66112 Souvenirs de Venise

BROOKS, Hilary (vc)
see CONCERT INDEX under:
(ARGO) 436 833-2ZH Purcell—Music for the Funeral
of Queen Mary

BROOKS, Patricia (sop)
R. Ward: Crucible (Cpte)

BROOME, Oliver (bass)
G. Charpentier: Louise (Cpte)
Puccini: Rondine (Cpte)
Shostakovich: Lady Macbeth of Mtsensk (Cpte)
Vaughan Williams: Hugh the Drover (Cpte)

BROSA, Antonio (vn)
see CONCERT INDEX under:
(CLUB) CL99-014 Dino Borgioli (1891-1960)

BROSSE, Jean-Patrice (organ)
see CONCERT INDEX under:
(ARIO) ARN68071 Sauget—Vocal and orchestral
works
(PIER) PV789104 Bach—Organ Works
(PIER) PV794034 Dandrieu—Mass and Vespers for
Easter Sunday

BROTHIER, Yvonne (mez)
see CONCERT INDEX under:
(DANT) LYS003/4 Charles Panzéra - Song Recital
(PREI) 89011 Marjorie Lawrence (1909-1979)

BROUGHTON, Bruce (cond)
see Sinfonia of London

BROUWENSTIJN, Gré (sop)
Wagner: Walküre (Cpte)
see CONCERT INDEX under:
(EMI) CHS7 69741-2(4) Record of Singing,
Vol.4—German School

BROUWER, Leo (cond)
see RCA Victor CO

BROWDER, Risa (va)
see CONCERT INDEX under:
(CHAN) CHAN8663 Purcell: Chamber Works

BROWDER, Risa (vn)
see CONCERT INDEX under:
(CHAN) CHAN8591 Purcell—Chamber Works
(CHAN) CHAN8663 Purcell: Chamber Works

BROWN, Donna (sop)
Berlioz: Messe Solennelle (Cpte)
Brahms: Deutsches Requiem, Op. 45 (Cpte)
Debussy: Rodrigue et Chimène (Cpte)
Handel: Alexander's Feast (Cpte), Messias, K572
(Cpte), Saul (Cpte)
Various: Requiem of Reconciliation (Cpte)

Verdi: Pezzi sacri (Cpte)
see CONCERT INDEX under:
(HARM) HMC90 1167 Lully—Grands Motets

BROWN, Earle (tpt)
see CONCERT INDEX under:
(KOCH) 37238-2 A Chance Operation - John Cage
Tribute

BROWN, Eddy (vn)
see CONCERT INDEX under:
(APR) APR7016 The Auer Legacy, Vol.2

BROWN, Elizabeth (fl)
see CONCERT INDEX under:
(SCHW) 310832 Frank Martin—Orchestral Works

BROWN, Ian (celesta)
see CONCERT INDEX under:
(VIRG) VC7 59604-2 Debussy—Chamber Works

BROWN, Ian (pf)
Britten: Cello Sonata
Fauré: Piano Trio
Schubert: Hirt auf dem Felsen, D965
see CONCERT INDEX under:
(CHAN) CHAN8609 Flute Fantasie—Virtuoso French
Flute Repertoire
(CHAN) CHAN8981/2 Gaubert—Works for Flute and
Piano
(CHAN) CHAN9108 Beethoven—Chamber Works
(CHAN) CHAN9377/8 Ireland—Chamber Works
(CRD) CRD3411 Mozart & Schumann: Chamber
Works
(CRD) CRD3446 Ravel: Chamber works
(EMI) CDC7 54787-2 Janáček—Chamber Works
(ETCE) KTC2006 Britten—Works for Cello
(HYPE) CDA66171 Malcolm Arnold: Chamber Works,
Vol. 1
(HYPE) CDA66172 Malcolm Arnold: Chamber Works,
Vol. 2
(HYPE) CDA66173 Malcolm Arnold: Chamber Works,
Vol. 3
(HYPE) CDA66754 Constant Lambert—Mr Bear
Squash-you-all-flat
(NMC) NMCD024M Turnage—Vocal and Chamber
Works
(VIRG) VC7 59604-2 Debussy—Chamber Works

BROWN, Iona (cond)
see ASMF

BROWN, Iona (vn)
Avison: Concerti after D. Scarlatti
see CONCERT INDEX under:
(ARGO) 414 595-2ZH Vaughan Williams—Orchestral
Works
(ASV) CDDCA518 The English Connection
(DECC) 430 093-2DWO The World of Vaughan
Williams
(DECC) 433 220-2DWO The World of the Violin
(DECC) 443 476-2DF2 Vivaldi—L'estro armonico, Op
3
(EMI) CDC5 55052-2
Praetorius/Vivaldi/Warlock—Works arr guitar
(PHIL) 412 892-2PH Vivaldi: Double Concertos
(PHIL) 422 503-2PME7 The Complete Mozart Edition
Vol 3

BROWN, Iona (vn/dir)
Handel: Concerti grossi, Op. 6 (exc)
see CONCERT INDEX under:
(PHIL) 412 226-2PH Telemann: Horn Concertos
(PHIL) 412 879-2PH Telemann: Oboe Concertos
(PHIL) 422 508-2PME4 The Complete Mozart Edition
Vol 8

BROWN, Jeremy (pf)
see CONCERT INDEX under:
(CARL) PCD821 Trumpet Concertos
(CHAN) CHAN8519 Poulenc: Piano Duo Works
(CHAN) CHAN8603 Bax: Works for Piano Duet

BROWN, Joanna (sop)
Britten: Noye's Fludde (Cpte)
G. Charpentier: Louise (Cpte)

BROWN, Justin (cond)
see Scottish Op Orch

BROWN, Mark (cond)
see PCA

BROWN, Mark (bar)
G. Charpentier: Louise (Cpte)
(SONY) SM3K47154 Bernstein—Theatre Works
Volume 1

BROWN, Niall (vc)
see CONCERT INDEX under:
(VIRG) VJ5 61103-2 Vivaldi—Concertos

BROWN, Phillip (tbn)
see CONCERT INDEX under:
(HYPE) CDA66177 Bruckner—Sacred Choral Works
(HYPE) CDA66245 Bruckner—Choral Works

BROWN, Rachel (fl)
Lampe: Cuckoo Concerto
see CONCERT INDEX under:
(CHAN) CHAN0512 Telemann, Vol.2—Ouverture
burlesque
(CHAN) CHAN0519 Telemann—La Changeante
(CHAN) CHAN0541 Music from the Court of Frederick
the Great
(CHAN) CHAN0544 French Baroque Flute Music
(CHAN) CHAN0564 Leclair—Violin Concertos,
Volume 2

BROWN, Rodne (sngr)
Forrest/Wright: Kismet (Cpte)

BROWN, Timothy (cond)
see Cambridge Clare College Ch

BROWN, Timothy (hn)
see CONCERT INDEX under:
(DECC) 443 476-2DF2   Vivaldi—L'estro armonico, Op 3
(PHIL) 412 226-2PH   Telemann: Horn Concertos
(PHIL) 412 892-2PH   Vivaldi: Double Concertos
(PHIL) 412 545-2PME3   The Complete Mozart Edition Vol.45
(PHIL) 422 833-2PC   Mozart—Chamber Works
(VIRG) VC7 59558-2   Mozart—Works for Horn & Orchestra

BROWN, Wendy (sop)
Hammerstein: Carmen Jones (Cpte)

BROWN, Wilfred (ten)
Haydn: Mass 11
Purcell: Indian Queen, Z630 (exc), King Arthur, Z628 (Cpte)

BROWN, William (ten)
Gershwin: Porgy and Bess (Cpte)
Orff: Carmina Burana

BROWNE, Geoffrey (cor ang)
see CONCERT INDEX under:
(COLL) Coll1210-2   Twentieth-Century Flute Concertos
(LYRI) SRCD230   Alwyn—Orchestral Works

BROWNE, Laidman (spkr)
Schumann: Manfred (Cpte)

BROWNE, Sandra (mez)
Albinoni: Nascimento dell'Aurora (Cpte)
Offenbach: Robinson Crusoé (Cpte)
Rossini: Mosè in Egitto (Cpte)

BROWNER, Alison (mez)
Bach: St Matthew Passion, BWV244 (Cpte)
Telemann: St Matthew Passion (1746)
Verdi: Oberto (Cpte)
Wagner: Parsifal (Cpte)
see CONCERT INDEX under:
(COLL) Coll1320-2   Baroque Choral Works

BROWNING, John (pf)
Liszt: Années de pèlerinage 2 (exc), Piano Sonata, S178
Tchaikovsky: Piano Concerto 1
see CONCERT INDEX under:
(DELO) DE3044   Rachmaninov—Piano Works
(DG) 435 867-2GH2   Barber—The Songs
(RCA) RD60732   Barber—Orchestral Works

BROWNING, Lucielle (mez)
see CONCERT INDEX under:
(VAI) VAIA1017   Leonard Warren—Early Recordings

BROWNLEE, John (bar)
Mozart: Così fan tutte (Cpte), Don Giovanni (Cpte)
see CONCERT INDEX under:
(BEEC) BEECHAM3   Delius—Vocal & Orchestral Works
(DUTT) CDLX7012   The Incomparable Heddle Nash
(EMI) CDH5 65072-2   Glyndebourne Recorded - 1934-1994
(LARR) CDLRH221   Dame Nellie Melba - Opera and Song Recital
(PEAR) GEMMCDS9925(2)   Covent Garden on Record—Vol.3 (pt 2)
(PEAR) GEMMCDS9926(2)   Covent Garden on Record—Vol.4 (pt 2)
(PEAR) GEMMCD9473   Heddle Nash—Vol.2

BROWNRIDGE, Angela (pf)
see CONCERT INDEX under:
(HYPE) CDH88045   Fascinating Rhythm—Gershwin Solo Piano Music

BRUA, Claire (sop)
Jommelli: Armida abbandonata (Cpte)
M-A. Charpentier: Malade Imaginaire
Montéclair: Jephté (Cpte)
Purcell: Dido (Cpte)
Rameau: Castor et Pollux (Cpte)

BRUBAKER, Scott (hn)
see CONCERT INDEX under:
(MUSI) MACD-691   Dvorak & Friends - Czech Wind Music

BRUCE, Neely (cond)
see Harmoneion Sngrs

BRUCK, Charles (cond)
see Netherlands Op Orch

BRÜCKNER-RÜGGEBERG, Wilhelm (cond)
see NW German RO

BRUGES COLLEGIUM INSTRUMENTALE
cond F. NUYTS
see CONCERT INDEX under:
(ETCE) KTC1085   Marimba Concertos

BRÜGGEMANN, Christian (sngr)
Braunfels: Verkündigung (Cpte)

BRÜGGEN, Frans (cond)
see Baroque Instr Ens

BRÜGGEN, Frans (fl)
Rameau: Pièces de clavecin en concerts
Telemann: Sonate Metodiche (exc)
see CONCERT INDEX under:

(RCA) GD71964   Bach: Flute Works
(TELD) 4509-97473-2   F. Brüggen Edition Vol.
11—Bach Chbr & Orch Works
(TELD) 4509-97474-2   F. Brüggen Edition Vol.
12—Recorder Sonatas & Concertos

BRÜGGEN, Frans (rec)
Handel: Recorder Sonatas, Trio Sonatas, Op. 2 (exc)
see CONCERT INDEX under:
(RCA) GD71964   Bach: Flute Works
(TELD) 4509-92180-2   Leclair/Naudot—Concertos
(TELD) 4509-93669-2   Brüggen Edition Vol.2 —Italian Recorder Sonatas
(TELD) 4509-93688-2   Brüggen Edition Vol.1-Telemann Recorder Sonatas
(TELD) 4509-97465-2   Franz Brüggen Edition Vol. 3—English Ensemble Music
(TELD) 4509-97466-2   Frans Brüggen Edition Vol. 4—Early Baroque Recorder Music
(TELD) 4509-97467-2   Frans Brüggen Edition Vol. 5—Late Baroque Chamber Music
(TELD) 4509-97468-2   Frans Brüggen Edition Vol.6—French Recorder Suites
(TELD) 4509-97469-2   Frans Brüggen Edition Vol. 7—French Recorder Sonatas
(TELD) 4509-97470-2   Frans Brüggen Edition Vol. 8—Vivaldi—Chamber Concertos
(TELD) 4509-97472-2   Frans Brüggen Edition Vol. 10—Telemann—Orchestral Works
(TELD) 4509-97474-2   F. Brüggen Edition Vol. 12—Recorder Sonatas & Concertos
(TELD) 9031-77620-2   Telemann—Orchestral Works

BRÜGGEN CONSORT
see CONCERT INDEX under:
(TELD) 4509-97465-2   Franz Brüggen Edition Vol. 3—English Ensemble Music

BRUINE, Frank de (ob)
Vivaldi: Concerti, Op. 11
see CONCERT INDEX under:
(L'OI) 433 674-2OH   Vivaldi—Oboe Concertos

BRUMAIRE, Jacqueline (sop)
Honegger: Roi David (Cpte)
Tomasi: Don Juan de Mañara (Cpte)

BRUN, Jean (bar)
Gounod: Faust (Cpte)

BRUN-BARAŃSKA, Bożena (contr)
Mussorgsky: Boris Godunov (Cpte)

BRUNEAU, Alfred (cond)
see orch

BRUNELLE, Philip (cond)
see Moore by Four Voc Jazz Ens

BRUNET, Sylvie (mez)
Gluck: Iphigénie en Tauride (Cpte)

BRUNETTI, Vito Maria (bass)
Donizetti: Lucrezia Borgia (Cpte), Pazzi per progetto (Cpte)

BRUNI, Paola (pf)
see CONCERT INDEX under:
(CARL) PCD964   Piano Concertos

BRUNNER, Eduard (cl)
Gubaidulina: Hommage
Messiaen: Quatuor
see CONCERT INDEX under:
(ORFE) C060831A   Milhaud: Works for wind and piano
(ORFE) C067831A   Weber: Music for Clarinet and Orchestra
(PHIL) 422 514-2PME5   The Complete Mozart Edition Vol 14
(SCHW) 311065   Double Concertos

BRUNNER, Evelyn (sop)
see CONCERT INDEX under:
(ERAT) 2292-45926-2   Charpentier—Sacred Choral Works

BRUNNER, Richard (ten)
Mozart: Nozze di Figaro (Cpte)

BRÜNNER, Richard (ten)
Mozart: Don Giovanni (exc)

BRUNNER, Wolfgang (cond)
see Salzburg Hofmusik

BRUNNERT, Christian (va)
see CONCERT INDEX under:
(SCHW) 311116   Dvořák—Bagatelles, Op. 47; Serenade, Op. 44

BRUNNSBO CHILDREN'S CHOIR
cond N. JÄRVI
Mahler: Symphony 8

BRUNO, Antonio (sax)
see CONCERT INDEX under:
(CHNT) LDC278 869/70   Villa-Lobos—Guitar Works

BRUNO, Elisa (mez)
see CONCERT INDEX under:
(EMI) CHS7 64860-2(2)   La Scala Edition - Vol.1, 1878-1914 (pt 2)
(PEAR) GEMMCDS9073(2)   Giovanni Zenatello, Vol.1 (pt 2)
(PEAR) GEMMCDS9074(1)   Giovanni Zenatello, Vol.2 (pt 1)
(SYMP) SYMCD1138   The Harold Wayne Collection, Vol.16
(SYMP) SYMCD1148   The Harold Wayne Collection, Vol.17

BRUNO KITTEL CHOIR
cond W. FURTWÄNGLER
Beethoven: Symphony 9
see CONCERT INDEX under:
(TAHR) FURT1004/7   Furtwängler conducts the Berlin Philharmonic

BRUNS, Barbara (pf)
see CONCERT INDEX under:
(KOCH) 37180-2   Pinkham—Cantatas & Chamber Works

BRUNS, Sigurd (organ)
see CONCERT INDEX under:
(CPO) CPO999 158-2   Pfitzner—Das dunkle Reich

BRUNSKILL, Muriel (contr)
Gounod: Faust (Cpte)
Handel: Messiah (Cpte)
see CONCERT INDEX under:
(DUTT) CDAX8004   Sir Henry Wood conducts Vaughan Williams
(PEAR) GEMMCD9175   Heddle Nash - Serenade
(PEAR) GEMMCD9342   Vaughan Williams: Vocal Works

BRUNSSEN, Karen (contr)
Schoenberg: Moses and Aron (Cpte)

BRUNT, Andrew (treb)
see CONCERT INDEX under:
(DECC) 430 360-2DM   Faure/Poulenc—Sacred Choral Works
(DECC) 436 486-2DF2   Duruflé/Fauré/Poulenc—Choral Works

BRUSCANTINI, Sesto (bar)
Donizetti: Don Pasquale (Cpte), Emilia di Liverpool (Cpte), Eremitaggio di Liverpool (Cpte)
Mozart: Così fan tutte (Cpte), Nozze di Figaro (Cpte)
Rossini: Barbiere di Siviglia (Cpte), Cenerentola (Cpte)
Verdi: Forza del destino (Cpte)
Vivaldi: Orlando Furioso (Cpte)
see CONCERT INDEX under:
(EMI) CDH5 65072-2   Glyndebourne Recorded - 1934-1994

BRUSON, Renato (bar)
Donizetti: Don Pasquale (Cpte), Lucia di Lammermoor (Cpte), Martyrs (Cpte), Poliuto (Cpte)
Franchetti: Cristoforo Colombo (Cpte)
Haydn: Isola Disabitata (Cpte)
Mascagni: Cavalleria Rusticana (Cpte)
Mozart: Don Giovanni (Cpte)
Puccini: Manon Lescaut (Cpte), Tosca (Cpte)
Saint-Saëns: Samson et Dalila (Cpte)
Verdi: Ballo in Maschera (Cpte), Ernani (Cpte), Falstaff (Cpte), Forza del destino (Cpte), Luisa Miller (Cpte), Macbeth (Cpte), Otello (Cpte), Rigoletto (Cpte), Traviata (Cpte)
see CONCERT INDEX under:
(CAPR) 10 247   The Art of Bel Canto
(CAPR) 10 348   Mozart Gala—Suntory Hall, Tokyo

BRUSSELS BELGIAN RADIO & TV PHILHARMONIC CHORUS
cond A. RAHBARI
Puccini: Bohème (Cpte), Manon Lescaut (Cpte), Tabarro (Cpte)
Verdi: Simon Boccanegra (Cpte)

BRUSSELS BELGIAN RADIO & TV PHILHARMONIC ORCHESTRA
cond A. RAHBARI
Brahms: Piano Concerto 2, Serenade 1, Serenade 2, Symphony 2, Symphony 3
Dvořák: Symphony 7, Symphony 8, Symphony 9
Puccini: Bohème (Cpte), Gianni Schicchi (Cpte), Manon Lescaut (Cpte), Suor Angelica (Cpte), Tabarro (Cpte)
Schumann: Introduction and Allegro, Op.92
Shostakovich: Symphony 5, Symphony 9
Stravinsky: Jeu de cartes, Rite of Spring (Cpte)
Verdi: Simon Boccanegra (Cpte)
see CONCERT INDEX under:
(DINT) DICD920212   Liszt—Piano Works

BRUSSELS ENSEMBLE DE CUIVRE ANCIENS 'LUDI MUSICI'
cond O. SCHNEEBELI
see CONCERT INDEX under:
(AUVI) AV6108   Bouzignac—Sacred choral music

BRUSSELS NATIONAL OPERA CHORUS
cond S. CAMBRELING
Offenbach: Contes d'Hoffmann (Cpte)

BRUSSELS NATIONAL OPERA ORCHESTRA
cond S. CAMBRELING
Offenbach: Contes d'Hoffmann (Cpte)

BRUSSELS THÉÂTRE DE LA MONNAIE STRING QUARTET
Mozart: Lucio Silla (Cpte)
Verdi: Simon Boccanegra (Cpte)
cond S. CAMBRELING
Mendelssohn: Elias (Cpte)
cond S. CAMBRELING
Mozart: Finta giardiniera (Cpte), Lucio Silla (Cpte)
Verdi: Simon Boccanegra (Cpte)
cond A. PAPPANO
Mendelssohn: Elias (Cpte)

BRUSSELS VIRTUOSI
Mozart: Adagio and Rondo, K617, Flute Quartets

BRUTSCHER, Markus (ten)
Bach: Motets (Cpte)

BRUYÈRE, Jules (bass)
Donizetti: Fille du régiment (Cpte)

BRYAN, Julie (sngr)
see CONCERT INDEX under:
(EMI) **CDANGEL 5** Norton—Chu Chin Chow

BRYAN, Richard (alto)
Boughton: Bethlehem (Cpte)

BRYANT, Dinah (sop)
Lekeu: Andromède
Offenbach: Contes d'Hoffmann (Cpte)
R. Strauss: Aegyptische Helena (Cpte)

BRYANT, Jeffrey (hn)
see CONCERT INDEX under:
(RPO) **CDRPO7015** Ashkenazy in Moscow and
London

BRYANT, Jim (sngr)
Bernstein: West Side Story (Cpte)

BRYARS, Gavin (db)
see CONCERT INDEX under:
(ECM) **847 537-2** Gavin Bryars—After the Requiem

BRYARS, Orlanda (vc)
Bryars: Sinking of the Titanic

BRYARS, Ziella (vc)
Bryars: Sinking of the Titanic

(GAVIN) BRYARS ENSEMBLE
Bryars: Sinking of the Titanic
see CONCERT INDEX under:
(ECM) **445 351-2** Gavin Bryars—Vita Nova

BRYDEN, Jane (sop)
Mozart: Kleine Freimaurer-Kantate, K623, Requiem

BRYHN, Borghild (sop)
see CONCERT INDEX under:
(SIMA) **PSC1810(1)** Grieg—Songs (historical
recordings, pt 1)

BRYMER, Jack (cl)
Mozart: Clarinet Concerto, K622, Clarinet Quintet,
K581
see CONCERT INDEX under:
(CFP) **CD-CFP4669** Margaret Price sings Romantic
Songs
(PHIL) **422 509-2PME5** The Complete Mozart Edition
Vol 9
(PHIL) **422 514-2PME5** The Complete Mozart Edition
Vol 14
(PHIL) **446 154-2PM2** Mozart—The Complete Piano
Trios

BRYMER, Jack (sax)
see CONCERT INDEX under:
(CFP) **CD-CFPD4456** Music by Eric Coates

BRYN PARRI, Annette (pf)
see CONCERT INDEX under:
(SAIN) **SCDC2013** Meirion Williams—Songs
(SAIN) **SCDC2070** Susan Bullock
(SAIN) **SCDC2085** Arthur Davies

BRYNILDSEN, Lars Kristian Holm (cl)
see CONCERT INDEX under:
(BIS) **BIS-CD428** Nielsen—Wind Chamber Music

BRYN-JULSON, Phyllis (sop)
Birtwistle: Punch and Judy (Cpte)
Boulez: Pli selon pli
Stravinsky: Nightingale (Cpte)
see CONCERT INDEX under:
(CHAN) **CHAN6586** Sibelius—Orchestral & Vocal
Works
(CHAN) **CHAN8395/6** Sibelius: Tone Poems
(COLL) **Coll1192-2** Britten/Shostakovich—Orchestral
Works
(COLL) **Coll7037-2** Britten—Orchestral Song Cycles
(DG) **431 751-2GC** Stravinsky—Songs
(EMI) **CDC5 55212-2** Schoenberg—Orchestral Works
(ERAT) **2292-45494-2** Boulez—Cantatas and
Orchestral Works
(ERAT) **4509-92137-2** Varese—Orchestral Works,
Vol. 1
(KOCH) **37272-2** Music of Charles Wuorinen
(MUSI) **MACD-650** Schoenberg—Song Cycles
(NEW) **NW273-2** Griffes: Vocal & Instrumental Works

BRYNNER, Yul (sngr)
Rodgers: King and I (film) (Cpte)

BRYSON, Peabo (sngr)
Rodgers: King and I (Cpte)

BRYSON, Roger (bar)
Boughton: Bethlehem (Cpte), Immortal Hour (Cpte)
Britten: Midsummer Night's Dream (Cpte)
Gay: Beggar's Opera (Cpte)
MacMillan: Visitatio Sepulchri (Cpte)
Saxton: Caritas (Cpte)

BUADES, Aurora (mez)
see CONCERT INDEX under:
(PREI) **89007** Aureliano Pertile (1885-1952) - I

BUBBLES, John W. (ten)
Gershwin: Porgy and Bess (exc)

BUCALO, Emanuele (bar)
see CONCERT INDEX under:
(IRCC) **IRCC-CD808** Souvenirs of 19th Century Italian
Opera

BUCCARELLA, Lucio (db)
Zelenka: Trio Sonatas

BUCHAN, Cynthia (mez)
Rameau: Castor et Pollux (Cpte)
Verdi: Traviata (Cpte)

BUCHANAN, Isobel (sop)
Bellini: Sonnambula (Cpte)
Massenet: Werther (Cpte)
see CONCERT INDEX under:
(DECC) **443 455-2DF2** Vivaldi—Sacred Choral Works

BUCHAREST NATIONAL RADIO ORCHESTRA
cond L. BACS
see CONCERT INDEX under:
(OLYM) **OCD449** Vieru—Orchestral Works

BUCHAREST RADIO CHAMBER ORCHESTRA
cond L. BACS
see CONCERT INDEX under:
(OLYM) **OCD449** Vieru—Orchestral Works

BUCHBAUER, Alois (bass)
R. Strauss: Rosenkavalier (Cpte)

BUCHBERGER QUARTET
see CONCERT INDEX under:
(WERG) **WER6173-2** T.W.Adorno—Chamber &
Choral Works

BUCHBINDER, Rudolf (pf)
see CONCERT INDEX under:
(RCA) **09026 61562-2** Brahms/Schumann—Cello
Works

BÜCHNER, Eberhard (ten)
Bach: Christmas Oratorio, BWV248 (Cpte), St.
Matthew Passion, BWV244 (Cpte)
K. A. Hartmann: Simplicius Simplicissimus (Cpte)
Mozart: Idomeneo (Cpte)
Schumann: Paradies und die Peri (Cpte)
Wagner: Meistersinger (Cpte), Rheingold (Cpte),
Tristan und Isolde (Cpte)
Weill: Kuhhandel (exc)
see CONCERT INDEX under:
(CAPR) **10 451/5** Beethoven—Symphonies 1-9

BÜCHNER, Paula (sop)
Wagner: Tristan und Isolde (Cpte)
see CONCERT INDEX under:
(MYTO) **3MCD93381** Wagner—Die Walküre, etc
(PREI) **90222** Maria Cebotari sings Richard Strauss

BÜCHSEL, Walter (fl)
see CONCERT INDEX under:
(CPO) **CPO999 142-2** Hindemith—Complete Wind
Concertos

BUCHTA, Hubert (ten)
Mozart: Nozze di Figaro (Cpte)
Orff: Mond (Cpte)

BUCK, John (sngr)
Gershwin: Porgy and Bess (Cpte)

BUCKEL, Ursula (sop)
see CONCERT INDEX under:
(ARCH) **439 380-2AX6** Bach—Cantatas, Volume 3 -
Ascension Day; Whitsun; Trinity
(ARCH) **439 387-2AX6** Bach Cantatas, Volume 4
(ARCH) **439 394-2AX5** Bach—Cantatas, Volume 5

BUCKFIELD, Clare (sngr)
Berlin: Annie Get Your Gun (Cpte)

BUCKLEY, Emerson (cond)
see NYC Op Orch

BUCKNALL, Nicholas (cl)
see CONCERT INDEX under:
(HYPE) **CDA66504** Süssmayr/Tausch—Works for
Clarinet

BUCKOKE, Peter (db)
see CONCERT INDEX under:
(HYPE) **CDA66679** Dvořák—Chamber Works

BUCKTROUT, Daisy (pf)
see CONCERT INDEX under:
(PEAR) **GEMMCDS9095(2)** Povla Frijsh (pt 2)

BUCQUET, Marie-Françoise (pf)
see CONCERT INDEX under:
(PHIL) **442 272-2PM2** The Best of Bizet

BUDA, Mauro (bass)
Rossini: Torvaldo e Dorliska (Cpte)

BUDAI, Livia (mez)
Mahler: Symphony 8

BUDAPEST CAMERATA
cond H. GMÜR
J. C. Bach: Symphonies, Op. 3, Symphonies, Op. 6
see CONCERT INDEX under:
(NAXO) **8 553085** J. C. Bach—Sinfonias, Vol. 3
cond M. HALÁSZ
Pergolesi: Orfeo, Stabat Mater
cond L. KOVÁCS
see CONCERT INDEX under:
(MARC) **8 223701** Donizetti—Instrumental
Concertos

BUDAPEST CHAMBER ENSEMBLE
cond A. MIHÁLY
see CONCERT INDEX under:
(HUNG) **HCD11385** 20th Century Vocal Works

BUDAPEST CHORUS
cond A. DORATI
Kodály: Psalmus Hungaricus

BUDAPEST CONSERVATORY ORCHESTRA
cond MR ZSOLT
see CONCERT INDEX under:
(BIDD) **LAB045** Hubay & Flesch —HMV Recordings
(SYMP) **SYMCD1071** Great Violinists, Vol.1

BUDAPEST FAILONI CHAMBER ORCHESTRA
cond M. ANTAL
Bach: Cantata 51, Cantata 80, Cantata 147, Cantata
208, Cantata 211, Cantata 212
cond W. HUMBURG
Rossini: Barbiere di Siviglia (Cpte)
cond G. OBERFRANK
Bach: Christmas Oratorio, BWV248 (Cpte)

BUDAPEST FAILONI ORCHESTRA
cond M. HALÁSZ
Mozart: Zauberflöte (Cpte)
Schubert: Sonata, D812, Symphony 1, Symphony 2,
Symphony 3, Symphony 4, Symphony 6, Symphony
9

BUDAPEST FESTIVAL ORCHESTRA
cond I. FISCHER
see CONCERT INDEX under:
(PHIL) **416 831-2PH3** Bartok: Works for Piano &
Orchestra
(PHIL) **446 366-2PH** Bartók—Piano Concertos

BUDAPEST OPERA ORCHESTRA
Shore: M. Butterfly (exc)

BUDAPEST PHILHARMONIC ORCHESTRA
Bruch: Violin Concerto 1
see CONCERT INDEX under:
(LASE) **15 606** Gershwin: Orchestral Works
(LASE) **15 616** French Ballet Music
(LASE) **15 617** Grieg: Orchestral Works
cond E. BERGEL
Chopin: Piano Concerto 1, Piano Concerto 2
cond J. SÁNDOR
Bizet: Arlésienne Suites, Carmen Suites (exc)

BUDAPEST QUARTET
Beethoven: String Quartet 7, String Quartet 8
Brahms: Clarinet Quintet, String Quartet 3
Debussy: string quartet
Ravel: string quartet
Schubert: String Quartet, D804, String Quartet, D810,
Trout Quintet, D667
see CONCERT INDEX under:
(BIDD) **LAB098** Wolf/Grieg/Sibelius—String Quartets
(CLRI) **CC0005** The Clarinet - Historical Recordings,
Vol.1
(MUSI) **MACD-643** Mozart & Schumann—Chamber
Works
(RCA) **09026 61879-2** Grieg—Historic Recordings
(SONY) **MPK52531** Beethoven—Early String Quartets
(SONY) **SM3K46527** Mozart—Legendary
Interpretations, IV

BUDAPEST ROSSINI ENSEMBLE
Donizetti: Sinfonia in C
Rossini: Sonate a quattro (exc)

BUDAPEST SCHUBERT ENSEMBLE
Schubert: Octet, D72, Octet, D803

BUDAPEST STRAUSS SYMPHONY ORCHESTRA
cond A. WALTER
see CONCERT INDEX under:
(MARC) **8 223561** Josef Strauss—Edition, Volume 1

BUDAPEST SYMPHONY ORCHESTRA
Rachmaninov: Paganini Rhapsody
cond J. BOLLE
see CONCERT INDEX under:
(ALBA) **TROY017-2** Virgil Thomson—Vocal and
Orchestral Works
cond A. JOÓ
Mendelssohn: Violin Concerto, Op. 64
cond G. LEHEL
Liszt: Hungarian Coronation Mass, S11
Rachmaninov: Piano Concerto 2
see CONCERT INDEX under:
(APR) **APR7021** Cziffra—Hungaroton Recordings
1954-1956
cond A. LIGETI
see CONCERT INDEX under:
(CONI) **CDCF189** Works for Viola and Orchestra
(NAXO) **8 550771** Bartók—Piano Concertos
cond G. NÉMETH
Chopin: Piano Concerto 1, Piano Concerto 2

BUDAPEST WIND ENSEMBLE
cond Z. KOCSIS
Mozart: Serenade, K361, Serenade, K388

BUDD, Bruce (bass-bar)
Saxton: Caritas (Cpte)
Walton: Troilus and Cressida (Cpte)

BUDD, Jeremy (treb)
Mendelssohn: Elijah (Cpte)
see CONCERT INDEX under:
(HYPE) **CDA66439** Hear my Prayer
(VIRG) **VCS 45007-2** A Play of Passion

BUECHNER, David (pf)
see CONCERT INDEX under:
(CONN) **CD4186** Turina—Piano Works

BUENOS AIRES QUINTET
cond E. STRATTA
see CONCERT INDEX under:
(TELD) **9031-76997-2** Symphonic Tango

BUESST, Aylmer (cond)
see BNOC Orch

BUFFALO COLLEGE WIND PLAYERS (NEW YORK)
cond W. GUNDLACH
Weill: Down in the Valley (Cpte), Jasager (Cpte)

BUFFONI, Eva (sop)
Gounod: Requiem

BUGAJ, Tomasz (cond)
see Warsaw Chbr Op Orch

BUGARINOVIC, Mela (mez)
see CONCERT INDEX under:
(SCHW) 314532   Vienna State Opera Live, Vol.3
(SCHW) 314582   Vienna State Opera Live, Vol.8
(SCHW) 314602   Vienna State Opera Live, Vol.10
(SCHW) 314652   Vienna State Opera Live, Vol.15

BUKETOFF, Igor (cond)
see Iceland SO

BUKHTOYAROV, Dmitri (bass)
see CONCERT INDEX under:
(PEAR) GEMMCDS9001/3(1)   Singers of Imperial
Russia, Vol.2 (pt 1)

BULDROVÁ, Helena (sop)
Janáček: Cunning Little Vixen (Cpte)

BULGARIAN NATIONAL CHOIR
cond E. TABAKOV
Verdi: Pezzi sacri (Cpte), Requiem (Cpte)

BULGARIAN RADIO SYMPHONY ORCHESTRA
cond V. KAZANDJIEV
MacDowell: Piano Concerto 1, Piano Concerto 2
Shostakovich: Violin Concerto 1, Violin Concerto 2

BULGARIAN TV AND RADIO MIXED CHORUS
cond V.C. SYMONETTE
Weill: Dreigroschenoper (Cpte)

**BULGARIAN TV AND RADIO SYMPHONY
ORCHESTRA**
cond V.C. SYMONETTE
Weill: Dreigroschenoper (Cpte)

BULLER, James (sngr)
Kern: Show Boat (Cpte)

BULLOCK, Sir Ernest (cond)
see Coronation Orch

BULLOCK, Susan (sop)
Sullivan: Mikado (exc)
see CONCERT INDEX under:
(SAIN) SCDC2070   Susan Bullock
(SAIN) SCDC2085   Arthur Davies

BUMANN, Oswald (bass)
Holliger: Alb-Chehr

BUMBRY, Grace (mez)
Massenet: Cid (Cpte)
Verdi: Aida (Cpte)
Wagner: Tannhäuser (Cpte)
see CONCERT INDEX under:
(DECC) 436 462-2DM   Ten Top Mezzos
(DG) 447 414-2GOR   Falla/Stravinsky—Ballet Music
(ORFE) C081841A   Grace Bumbry: Famous Opera
Arias
(RCA) 09026 61580-2(7)   RCA/Met 100 Singers, 100
Years (pt 7)

BUNDSCHUH, Eva-Maria (sop)
Wagner: Götterdämmerung (Cpte), Walküre (Cpte)

BUNGARTEN, Frank (gtr)
Bach: Solo Violin Partitas and Sonatas (exc)

BUNGER, Reid (bar)
Wagner: Parsifal (Cpte)
see CONCERT INDEX under:
(DECC) 433 437-2DA   Pavarotti—King of the High Cs

BUNNELL, Jane (mez)
Verdi: Don Carlo (Cpte)
Wagner: Parsifal (Cpte)
(DELO) DE3078   Barber, Bernstein and Gershwin

BUNNING, Christine (mez)
MacMillan: Visitatio Sepulchri (Cpte)

BUNSE, Rüdiger (bass)
Schreker: Ferne Klang (Cpte)

BÜNTEN, Wolfgang (treb)
Mozart: Zauberflöte (exc)
Puccini: Tosca (Cpte)

BUONOCORE, William (mndl)
see CONCERT INDEX under:
(KOCH) 37180-2   Pinkham—Cantatas & Chamber
Works

BURANDT, Gisela (sop)
Cherubini: Mass in D minor

BURANOVSKY, Daniel (pf)
see CONCERT INDEX under:
(CHAN) CHAN9257   Czech Choral Music

BURCHELL, David (organ)
see CONCERT INDEX under:
(CRD) CRD3451   Gibbons: Sacred Choral Works
(CRD) CRD3454   Howells—Choral & Organ Music,
Vol 1
(CRD) CRD3467   Tomkins—The Third Service and
Anthems
(MERI) CDE84151   Georgian Anthem

BURCHULADZE, Paata (bass)
Mozart: Don Giovanni (Cpte)
Mussorgsky: Khovanshchina (Cpte)
Puccini: Bohème (Cpte)

Rossini: Barbiere di Siviglia (Cpte)
Saint-Saëns: Samson et Dalila (Cpte)
Tchaikovsky: Eugene Onegin (Cpte)
Verdi: Aida (Cpte), Forza del destino (Cpte), Rigoletto
(Cpte), Simon Boccanegra (Cpte)
see CONCERT INDEX under:
(DECC) 436 464-2DM   Ten Top Baritones & Basses

BURFIN, Jean-Marc (cond)
see Württemberg PO

BURG, Robert (bar)
Wagner: Götterdämmerung (Cpte)
see CONCERT INDEX under:
(SIMA) PSC1810(2)   Grieg—Songs (historical
recordings, pt 2)

BURG, Susanna von der (sop)
Corghi: Divara (Cpte)

BÜRGENER, Monika (mez)
see CONCERT INDEX under:
(ERAT) 4509-95362-2   Mozart—Sacred Choral
Works

BÜRGER, Erich (bass)
Wagner: Meistersinger (exc)

BURGESS, Russell (ten)
Bach: St John Passion, BWV245 (Cpte)

BURGESS, Sally (mez)
Bernstein: West Side Story (Cpte)
Kern: Show Boat (Cpte)
Rossini: Barbiere di Siviglia (Cpte)
Vaughan Williams: Hugh the Drover (Cpte)
Wagner: Parsifal (Cpte)
see CONCERT INDEX under:
(CALA) CACD1004   Ravel—Orchestral Works, Vol.1
(CHAN) CHAN9214   Delius—Choral Works
(HYPE) CDA66565   Constant Lambert—Vocal &
Orchestral Works
(PHIL) 420 649-2PM   Vivaldi: Sacred Choral Music,
Vol.2
(TER) CDVIR8307   Josephine Barstow sings Verdi
Arias

BURGON, Geoffrey (cond)
see OST

**BURGOS SANTO DOMINGO DE SILOS MONASTERY
CHOIR**
see CONCERT INDEX under:
(JADE) JADC131   The Spirit of Gregorian Chant

BURGSTHALER-SCHUSTER, Gertrud (contr)
J.Strauss II: Zigeunerbaron (Cpte)

BURGUERAS, Manuel (pf)
see CONCERT INDEX under:
(RCA) 09026 62547-2   Divas in Song—Marilyn Horne's
60th Birthday

BURKH, Dennis (cond)
see Janáček PO

BURLES, Charles (ten)
Berlioz: Lélio (Cpte)
Delibes: Lakmé (Cpte)
Gounod: Roméo et Juliette (Cpte)
Massenet: Manon (Cpte)
Offenbach: Belle Hélène (Cpte), Orphée aux enfers
(Cpte)
Rossini: Guillaume Tell (Cpte)
Roussel: Padmâvatî (Cpte)
see CONCERT INDEX under:
(EMI) CDS7 49361-2   Offenbach: Operettas

BURLEY, Elizabeth (pf)
see CONCERT INDEX under:
(UNIC) DKPCD9158   Chabrier—Piano Works

BURMEISTER, Annelies (mez)
Beethoven: Symphony 9
Mendelssohn: Elias (Cpte)
Mozart: Nozze di Figaro (Cpte)
R. Strauss: Ariadne auf Naxos (Cpte)
Wagner: Götterdämmerung (Cpte), Rheingold (Cpte),
Walküre (Cpte)
see CONCERT INDEX under:
(PHIL) 446 057-2PB14   Wagner—The Ring Cycle -
Bayreuth Festival 1967

BURMESTER, Willy (vn)
see CONCERT INDEX under:
(SYMP) SYMCD1071   Great Violinists, Vol.1

BURNETT, Richard (fp)
Beethoven: Violin Sonata 5, Violin Sonata 7
Mozart: Piano Quartet, K478, Piano Quartet, K493
Schubert: Winterreise (Cpte)
see CONCERT INDEX under:
(AMON) CD-SAR7   The Romantic Fortepiano
(AMON) CD-SAR12   Hummel—Works for Violin &
Piano
(AMON) CD-SAR22   Oboe Collection
(AMON) CD-SAR38   Mendelssohn—Chamber Works
(AMON) CD-SAR48   Field—Chamber Works
(AMON) CD-SAR53   Music for Mandolin

BURNETT, Richard (pf)
see CONCERT INDEX under:
(AMON) CD-SAR32   Gottschalk—Piano Works
(AMON) CD-SAR37   Brahms—Chamber Works
(AMON) CD-SAR38   Mendelssohn—Chamber Works

BURNS, Karla (mez)
Kern: Show Boat (Cpte)
Porter: Kiss Me, Kate (Cpte)

BURNS, Nancy (sop)
see CONCERT INDEX under:
(HANS) 98 807   Bach—Cantatas, Vol.45

BURNS, Stephen (tpt)
see CONCERT INDEX under:
(DELO) DE3021   20th-century Russian music

BURNSIDE, Iain (sop)
see CONCERT INDEX under:
(HYPE) CDA66385   Settings of A. E. Housman

BURROWES, Connor (treb)
see CONCERT INDEX under:
(HYPE) CDA66693   Purcell—Complete Anthems and
Services, Volume 9

BURROWES, Norma (sop)
Bizet: Carmen (Cpte)
Handel: Acis and Galatea (Cpte), Ariodante (Cpte),
Semele (Cpte), Ways of Zion do mourn
Haydn: Armida (Cpte), Schöpfung (exc)
Mozart: Entführung (Cpte)
Orff: Carmina Burana
Purcell: Fairy Queen, Z629 (Cpte)
R. Strauss: Ariadne auf Naxos (Cpte)
Vaughan Williams: Symphony 7
Verdi: Trovatore (Cpte)
see CONCERT INDEX under:
(EMI) CDM7 64022-2   Vaughan Williams—Orchestral
Works
(EMI) CDM7 64730-2   Vaughan Williams—Riders to
the Sea: Epithalamion, etc
(EMI) CDM7 69644-2   Poulenc—Choral, Piano and
Orchestral Works

BURROWS, Stuart (ten)
Beethoven: Symphony 9
Berlioz: Damnation de Faust (Cpte)
Handel: Messiah (Cpte)
Mozart: Clemenza di Tito (Cpte), Don Giovanni
(Cpte), Entführung (Cpte)
Tchaikovsky: Eugene Onegin (Cpte)
see CONCERT INDEX under:
(DECC) 430 792-2DC6   Beethoven—Complete
Symphonies, etc
(GAMU) GAMD506   An Anthology Of English Song
(SONY) SM2K47526   Berlioz—Vocal and Orchestral
Works
(SONY) SM3K64103   Berlioz—Orchestral and Vocal
Works

BURT, Michael (bass)
Henze: Bassariden (Cpte)

BURTON, Amy (sop)
see CONCERT INDEX under:
(EMI) CDC7 54851-2   Gershwin—Blue Monday, etc

BURTON, Miriam (mez)
Gershwin: Porgy and Bess (exc)

BURTON, Russell (cond)
see Charterhouse Special Ch

BURTSCHER, Renata (sop)
Haydn: Seven Last Words, HobXX/2

BURY, Alison (vn)
Vivaldi: Concerti, Op. 8 (exc)
see CONCERT INDEX under:
(MERI) ECD84080   Haydn: Vocal works

BURZIO, Eugenia (sop)
see CONCERT INDEX under:
(CLUB) CL99-587/8   Eugenia Burzio (1872-1922)
(EMI) CHS7 64860-2(2)   La Scala Edition - Vol.1,
1878-1914 (pt 2)
(PEAR) GEMMCDS9073(1)   Giovanni Zenatello, Vol.1
(pt 1)
(SIMA) PSC1810(2)   Grieg—Songs (historical
recordings, pt 2)
(SYMP) SYMCD1138   The Harold Wayne Collection,
Vol.16

BUSCH, Adolf (cond)
see A. Busch Chbr Plyrs

BUSCH, Adolf (vn)
Beethoven: Piano Trios (exc)
Brahms: Horn Trio, Piano Trio 2
Schubert: Fantasie, D934, Piano Trio 2
see CONCERT INDEX under:
(EMI) CDH7 63494-2   Beethoven & Bach: Chamber
Works
(EMI) CHS5 65308-2
Beethoven/Schubert/Mendelssohn—Chamber
Works
(PEAR) GEMMCDS9141   The Busch Quartet -
Complete Schubert Recordings
(PEAR) GEMMCD9942   Adolf Busch and Rudolf
Serkin
(SYMP) SYMCD1109   Great Violinists, Vol.5 - Adolf
Busch

BUSCH, David (alto)
see CONCERT INDEX under:
(PHIL) 422 527-2PME   The Complete Mozart Edition
Vol 27

BUSCH, Fritz (cond)
see Berlin St Op Orch

BUSCH, Hermann (vc)
Beethoven: Piano Trios (exc)
Brahms: Piano Trio 2
Schubert: Piano Trio 2
see CONCERT INDEX under:

Chausson: Roi Arthus (Cpte)
Debussy: Pelléas et Mélisande (Cpte)
Fauré: Requiem (Cpte)
Franck: Béatitudes (Cpte)
Gluck: Iphigénie en Aulide (Cpte), Rencontre imprévue (Cpte)
Gounod: Faust (Cpte)
Mangold: Abraham
Mozart: Clemenza di Tito (Cpte), Così fan tutte (Cpte), Don Giovanni (Cpte), Zauberflöte (Cpte)
R.Strauss: Arabella (Cpte)
Rossini: Comte Ory (Cpte)
Wagner: Parsifal (Cpte)
 see CONCERT INDEX under:
(ARCH) 439 900-2AH5   Beethoven—Symphonies
(DECC) 436 991-2DH   Poulenc—Mélodies
(ERAT) 2292-45517-2   Berlioz—Songs
(ERAT) 4509-91721-2   Dutilleux—Piano Works and Chamber Music
(PHIL) 438 149-2PH   French Choral Works
(TELD) 4509-90494-2   Mozart—Sacred Choral Works

CADDY, Ian (bass)
Gay: Beggar's Opera (Cpte)
Rameau: Naïs (Cpte)
 see CONCERT INDEX under:
(ARGO) 417 468-2ZH   G. Gabrieli: Choral and Instrumental Works
(MERI) CDE84183   Donizetti: Songs

ČADIKOVIČOVÁ, Milada (contr)
Martinů: Julietta (Cpte)

CADONI, Fernanda (mez)
Cilea: Adriana Lecouvreur (Cpte)
Rossini: Cenerentola (Cpte)

CAECILIA CHORALE
 cond M. TANG
 see CONCERT INDEX under:
(WERG) WER6275-2   Orff—Trionfi

CAENS, Thierry (tpt)
 see CONCERT INDEX under:
(TIMP) 1C1016   Honegger—Chamber Works, Vol.3
(TIMP) 4C1012   Honegger—Chamber Works

CAETANI, Oleg (cond)
 see Bamberg SO

CAEYERS, Jan (cond)
 see Beethoven Academy

CAFORIO, Armando (bass)
Bellini: Bianca e Fernando (Cpte)
Rossini: Adelaide di Borgogna (Cpte)

CAGE, John (voc)
 see CONCERT INDEX under:
(MODE) Mode 28/9   Cage—Roaratorio. Laughtears etc

CAHIER, Sarah (contr)
 see CONCERT INDEX under:
(IRCC) IRCC-CD800   Souvenirs from Meyerbeer Operas

CAHILL, Marie (sngr)
 see CONCERT INDEX under:
(PEAR) GEMMCDS9050/2(1)   Music from the New York Stage, Vol. 1 (part 1)

CAHILL, Teresa (sop)
Britten: Peter Grimes (Cpte)
Elgar: Coronation Ode (Cpte), Spirit of England
Mahler: Symphony 8
Massenet: Cendrillon (Cpte)
 see CONCERT INDEX under:
(CHAN) CHAN8830   Bush—A Little Love Music
(PEAR) SHECD9602   Elgar: War Music

CAHUZAC, Louis (cl)
 see CONCERT INDEX under:
(CLRI) CC0002   Nielsen—Orchestral and Chamber Works
(EMI) CDS5 55032-2   Hindemith—Plays and conducts his own works

(PHILIPPE) CAILLARD CHORALE
 cond M. DURUFLÉ
 see CONCERT INDEX under:
(ERAT) 4509-96952-2   Duruflé—Requiem; Organ Works
 cond T. GUSCHLBAUER
 see CONCERT INDEX under:
(ERAT) 4509-95362-2   Mozart—Sacred Choral Works

(STÉPHANE) CAILLAT CHORALE
 cond M. DURUFLÉ
 see CONCERT INDEX under:
(ERAT) 4509-96952-2   Duruflé—Requiem; Organ Works

CAINE, Daniel (synths)
 see CONCERT INDEX under:
(SILV) SILVAD3001   At the Movies 1: Heroes & Tough Guys
(SILV) SILVAD3003   At the Movies 3: Horror & Fantasy

CAINE, Rebecca (sop)
Porter: Anything Goes (Cpte)

CAIRE, Patrice (organ)
 see CONCERT INDEX under:
(REM) REM311053   Boëllmann: Organ Works

CAIRNS, Christine (mez)
Mendelssohn: Erste Walpurgisnacht
Prokofiev: Alexander Nevsky

ČAKRTOVÁ, Agáta (contr)
 see CONCERT INDEX under:
(SUPR) 11 0767-2   Martinů—Cantatas

(THE) CAL ARTS PERCUSSION ENSEMBLE
 cond J. BERGAMO
 see CONCERT INDEX under:
(ETCE) KTC1071   L.Harrison—Music For Guitar And Percussion

CALABRESE, Franco (bass)
Mozart: Nozze di Figaro (Cpte)
Puccini: Manon Lescaut (Cpte), Tosca (Cpte)
Rossini: Turco in Italia (Cpte)
Verdi: Otello (Cpte)
 see CONCERT INDEX under:
(EMI) CDH5 65072-2   Glyndebourne Recorded - 1934-1994
(EMI) CMS7 63244-2   The Art of Maria Callas

(RAFFAELE) CALACE QUINTET
 see CONCERT INDEX under:
(FONE) 91F02   Calace—Works for Mandolins

CALAMAI, Alessandro (bar)
Verdi: Traviata (Cpte)

CALAMINUS, Joachim (ten)
Fux: Death of John the Baptist (Cpte)

CALDER, David (sngr)
Gay: Beggar's Opera (Cpte)

CALE, John (tape op)
 see CONCERT INDEX under:
(KOCH) 37238-2   A Chance Operation - John Cage Tribute

CALÈS, Claude (bar)
Bizet: Carmen (Cpte)
Delibes: Lakmé (exc)

CALEY, Ian (ten)
Donizetti: Maria Padilla (Cpte)
Massenet: Esclarmonde (Cpte)
Meyerbeer: Dinorah (Cpte)
Rameau: Naïs (Cpte)
Stravinsky: Nightingale (Cpte)
Weill: Sieben Todsünden (Cpte)
 see CONCERT INDEX under:
(DECC) 433 080-2DM   Kodály—Choral Works
(DECC) 436 464-2DM   Ten Top Baritones & Basses

CALGARY PHILHARMONIC ORCHESTRA
 cond M. BERNARDI
 see CONCERT INDEX under:
(CBC) SMCD5125   Glitter and Be Gay—Coloratura Soprano Arias

CALIFORNIA BOYS' CHOIR
 cond Z. MEHTA
Mahler: Symphony 3

CALIFORNIA EAR UNIT
M. Feldman: Why Patterns

CALIX, Ariane (sop)
J. Strauss II: Fledermaus (Cpte)

CALLANWOLDE YOUNG SINGERS
 see CONCERT INDEX under:
(TELA) CD80109   Berlioz: Requiem, etc

CALLAS, Maria (sop)
Beethoven: Ah! perfido, Op.65
Bellini: Norma (Cpte), Pirata (exc), Puritani (Cpte), Sonnambula (Cpte)
Bizet: Carmen (Cpte)
Cherubini: Medea (Cpte)
Donizetti: Anna Bolena (Cpte), Lucia di Lammermoor (Cpte)
Leoncavallo: Pagliacci (Cpte)
Mascagni: Cavalleria Rusticana (Cpte)
Ponchielli: Gioconda (Cpte)
Puccini: Bohème (Cpte), Madama Butterfly (Cpte), Manon Lescaut (Cpte), Tosca (Cpte), Turandot (Cpte)
Rossini: Barbiere di Siviglia (Cpte), Turco in Italia (Cpte)
Verdi: Aida (Cpte), Ballo in maschera (Cpte), Forza del destino (Cpte), Macbeth (Cpte), Rigoletto (Cpte), Traviata (Cpte), Trovatore (Cpte)
 see CONCERT INDEX under:
(EMI) CDC7 47282-2   Maria Callas - Operatic Recital
(EMI) CDC7 47283-2   Maria Callas - Mad Scenes & Bel Canto Arias
(EMI) CDC7 47730-2   Maria Callas sings Verdi Arias, Vol.1
(EMI) CDC7 47943-2   Maria Callas sings Verdi Arias, Vol.2
(EMI) CDC7 47966-2   Puccini and Bellini Arias
(EMI) CDC7 49059-2   Callas à Paris
(EMI) CDC7 54437-2   Callas Rarities
(EMI) CDM7 63182-2   The Incomparable Callas
(EMI) CDM7 69543-2   Maria Callas and Giuseppe Di Stefano - Duets
(EMI) CHS7 69741-2(7)   Record of Singing, Vol.4—Italian School
(EMI) CMS7 63244-2   The Art of Maria Callas
(EMIN) CD-EMX2123   Maria Callas sings Operatic Arias

CALLAWAY, Paul (cond)
 see Washington Cath Ch

CALLEGARI, Giordano (bass)
 see CONCERT INDEX under:

(MSCM) MM30231   Don Pasquale & Tito Schipa Recital

CALLEJA, Icilio (ten)
 see CONCERT INDEX under:
(MEMO) HR4408/9(2)   Singers in Genoa, Vol.1 (disc 2)
(SYMP) SYMCD1113   The Harold Wayne Collection, Vol.13

CALLOW, Colin (vn)
Dvořák: Terzetto, op 74

CALLOW, Simon (narr)
 see CONCERT INDEX under:
(KOCH) 37263-2   Schoenberg—A Survivor from Warsaw, etc

CALLOWAY, Cab (ten)
Various: Stormy Weather (Cpte)

CALM, Birgit (mez)
Catalani: Wally (Cpte)
R. Strauss: Elektra (Cpte)
Zemlinsky: Traumgörge (Cpte)
 see CONCERT INDEX under:
(EURO) GD69043   Puccini: Il Trittico

CALUSIO, Ferruccio (cond)
 see NY Met Op Orch

CALVÉ, Emma (sop)
 see CONCERT INDEX under:
(NIMB) NI7840/1   The Era of Adelina Patti
(PEAR) GEMMCDS9923(1)   Covent Garden on Record, Vol.1 (pt 1)
(PEAR) GEMMCDS9924(1)   Covent Garden on Record, Vol.2 (pt 1)
(RCA) 09026 61580-2(1)   RCA/Met 110 Singers, 100 Years (pt 1)
(SYMP) SYMCD1100   Harold Wayne Collection, Vol.8

CALVERT, Stuart (cond)
 see London Cast

CALVET QUARTET
 see CONCERT INDEX under:
(EMI) CDC7 54840-2   Composers in Person—Roussel & Schmitt

CALVI, Caterina (sop)
Handel: Rinaldo (Cpte)

CAMARATA, Salvador (cond) (cond)
 see orch

CAMARGUE PHILHARMONIC ORCHESTRA
 cond REINHARDT WAGNER
 see CONCERT INDEX under:
(HARM) HMC90 1552   The Three Countertenors

CAMBIATA, Remo (bar)
 see CONCERT INDEX under:
(DECC) 436 301-2DA   Renata Tebaldi & Franco Corelli—Arias & Duets

CAMBON, Charles (bass)
Gounod: Roméo et Juliette (Cpte)
Offenbach: Contes d'Hoffmann (Cpte)
Saint-Saëns: Samson et Dalila (Cpte)

CAMBRELING, Frédérique (hp)
 see CONCERT INDEX under:
(EMI) CDM7 64687-2   French Works inspired by Edgar Allan Poe
(ERAT) 2292-45820-2   Milhaud—Orchestral Works

CAMBRELING, Sylvain (cond)
 see Brussels Nat Op Orch

CAMBRIDGE CLARE COLLEGE ORCHESTRA
 cond J. RUTTER
 see CONCERT INDEX under:
(DECC) 425 500-2DM   The Holly and the Ivy

CAMBRIDGE CLASSICAL PLAYERS
 cond S. CLEOBURY
 see CONCERT INDEX under:
(EMI) CDC7 49672-2   Mozart: Sacred Choral Works

CAMBRIDGE GONVILLE & CAIUS COLLEGE CHOIR
 cond G. WEBBER
Wood: St Mark Passion
 see CONCERT INDEX under:
(ASV) CDDCA881   English Church Music, Vol.3
(ASV) CDDCA914   Puccini and Janáček Sacred Choral Music

CAMBRIDGE JESUS COLLEGE CHOIR
 cond D. PHILLIPS
 see CONCERT INDEX under:
(CNTO) CRCD2367   For All the Saints

CAMBRIDGE KING'S COLLEGE CHOIR (MENS' VOICES)
 cond N. HARNONCOURT
Bach: St Matthew Passion, BWV244 (Cpte)

CAMBRIDGE SINGERS
 cond J. RUTTER
Palestrina: Motets, Bk 4 (1584) (Cpte)
 see CONCERT INDEX under:
(CLLE) COLCD100   Rutter: Sacred Music
(CLLE) COLCD104   English Partsongs
(CLLE) COLCD105   Flora Gave Me Fairest Flowers - English Madrigals
(CLLE) COLCD106   Christmas Night
(CLLE) COLCD107   Faire is the Heaven
(CLLE) COLCD108   Poulenc: Sacred Choral Works
(CLLE) COLCD109   Fauré: Sacred Choral Works
(CLLE) COLCD110   Byrd: Sacred Choral Works

(CLLE) **COLCD111** Christmas with the Cambridge Singers
(CLLE) **COLCD113** Hail, gladdening Light
(CLLE) **COLCD114** Rutter—Sacred Choral Works
(CLLE) **COLCD115** Three Musical Fables
(CLLE) **COLCD116** Ave Gracia Plena
(CLLE) **COLCD117** Rutter—Fancies
(CLLE) **COLCD118** I Will lift up mine eyes
(CLLE) **COLCD119** A Cappella
(CLLE) **COLCD120** The Lark in the Clear Air
(CLLE) **COLCD121** Christmas Day in the Morning

CAMBRIDGE TAVERNER CHOIR
cond O. REES
see CONCERT INDEX under:
(PAST) **3589** Music for a Tudor Christmas

CAMBRIDGE UNIVERSITY CHAMBER CHOIR
cond T. BROWN
see CONCERT INDEX under:
(GAMU) **GAMCD529** A Garland for the Queen
(GAMU) **GAMCD535** Barber—Choral Music

CAMBRIDGE UNIVERSITY LADIES CHOIR
cond S. CLEOBURY
see CONCERT INDEX under:
(ARGO) **433 215-2ZH** Britten—Christmas Music

CAMBRIDGE UNIVERSITY MUSICAL SOCIETY CHORUS
see CONCERT INDEX under:
(CFP) **CD-CFP4570** Choral Favourites
cond S. CLEOBURY
Goehr: Death of Moses
cond P. LEDGER
Elgar: Coronation Ode (Cpte)
cond D. WILLCOCKS
see CONCERT INDEX under:
(DECC) **433 676-2DM** Tallis—Choral Works

CAMBRIDGESHIRE CHILDREN'S CHOIR
cond S. CLEOBURY
Goehr: Death of Moses

CAMDEN, Anthony (ob)
Albinoni: Concerti, Op. 9 (exc)
see CONCERT INDEX under:
(LYRI) **SRCD323** Grace Williams—Orchestral Works

(LA) CAMERATA
cond E. MATA
see CONCERT INDEX under:
(DORI) **DOR90215** Chavez—Chamber Works

CAMERATA BARILOCHE
see CONCERT INDEX under:
(DORI) **DOR90202** Impressions—Camerata Bariloche

CAMERATA CASSOVIA
cond J. WILDNER
see CONCERT INDEX under:
(NAXO) **8 550495** Mozart—Sacred Choral Works

CAMERATA CHAMBER CHOIR
cond P. ENEVOLD
see CONCERT INDEX under:
(BIS) **BIS-CD078** Holmboe—Miscellaneous Works
(BIS) **BIS-CD131** Nielsen: Organ Works & Motets

CAMERATA DE PROVENCE CHORUS
Boïeldieu: Calife de Bagdad (Cpte)

CAMERATA DE PROVENCE ORCHESTRA
cond A. DE ALMEIDA
Boïeldieu: Calife de Bagdad (Cpte)

CAMERATA MEDITERRANEA
cond J. COHEN
see CONCERT INDEX under:
(ERAT) **4509-94825-2** Ventadorn—Le Fou sur le Pont (Troubadour Songs)

CAMERATA MUSICALE ORCHESTRA
cond C. DESDERI
Rossini: Pietra del paragone (Cpte)

CAMERATA SINGERS
cond L. BERNSTEIN
see CONCERT INDEX under:
(SONY) **SM3K47162** Bernstein plays and conducts Bernstein Volume III
cond P. BOULEZ
see CONCERT INDEX under:
(SONY) **SM3K45842** Ravel—Orchestral Works

CAMERATA VISTULA
see CONCERT INDEX under:
(OLYM) **OCD343** Polish and Russian Chamber Music

CAMERON, Basil (cond)
see CBO

CAMERON, Grace (sngr)
see CONCERT INDEX under:
(PEAR) **GEMMCDS9050/2(1)** Music from the New York Stage, Vol. 1 (part 1)
(PEAR) **GEMMCDS9053/5** Music from the New York Stage, Vol. 2: 1908—1913

CAMERON, John (bar)
Purcell: King Arthur, Z628 (Cpte)
Vaughan Williams: Symphony 1
see CONCERT INDEX under:
(DECC) **443 461-2DF2** Berlioz—L'Enfance du Christ, etc
(EMI) **CDS7 47509-8** Beecham conducts Delius

CAMERON, Patricia (sop)
Sullivan: Pirates of Penzance (Cpte)

CAMINADA, Anita (mez)
Bellini: Puritani (Cpte)

CAMOSI, Jean (perc)
see CONCERT INDEX under:
(ERAT) **2292-45499-2** Martinů—Orchestral Works

CAMPANARI, Giuseppe (bar)
see CONCERT INDEX under:
(BONG) **GB1043-2** Italian Baritones of the Acoustic Era
(RCA) **09026 61580-2(1)** RCA/Met 110 Singers, 100 Years (pt 1)

CAMPANELLA, Bruno (cond)
see Bologna Teatro Comunale Orch

CAMPANELLA, Michele (pf)
Liszt: Hungarian Rhapsodies, S244
see CONCERT INDEX under:
(NUOV) **6826** Mussorgsky/Balakirev—Piano works

CAMPANINO, Mino (cond)
see orch

CAMPBELL, Colin (bar)
Boughton: Bethlehem (Cpte)
see CONCERT INDEX under:
(HYPE) **CDA66707** Purcell—Complete Anthems & Services, Vol. 10

CAMPBELL, Craig (sngr)
see CONCERT INDEX under:
(PEAR) **GEMMCDS9053/5** Music from the New York Stage, Vol. 2: 1908—1913

CAMPBELL, David (cl)
Krause: Quatuor pour la Naissance
Messiaen: Quatuor
Mozart: Clarinet Concerto, K622
see CONCERT INDEX under:
(CALA) **CACD1017** French Chamber Music for Woodwinds, Volume 1
(CALA) **CACD1018** French Chamber Music for Woodwinds, Volume 2

CAMPBELL, James (cl)
Brahms: Clarinet Quintet, Clarinet Sonata 1, Clarinet Trio
see CONCERT INDEX under:
(CALA) **CACD1001** Debussy—Orchestral Works, Vol.1
(CALA) **CACD1017** French Chamber Music for Woodwinds, Volume 1
(CALA) **CACD1018** French Chamber Music for Woodwinds, Volume 2
(CBC) **SMCD5096** Mozart/Copland/Weber—Clarinet Concertos
(CHAN) **CHAN8655** Haydn, Mozart & Beethoven: Chamber Works
(CHAN) **CHAN8924** Russian Vocal and Chamber works

CAMPBELL, Richard (va da gamba)
see CONCERT INDEX under:
(HYPE) **CDA66226** Corelli: La Folia and other Sonatas
(L'OI) **417 123-2OH** Purcell: Songs and Airs

CAMPI, Enrico (bass)
Puccini: Madama Butterfly (Cpte), Manon Lescaut (Cpte)
Rossini: Italiana in Algeri (Cpte)
see CONCERT INDEX under:
(RCA) **09026 61580-2(5)** RCA/Met 100 Singers, 100 Years (pt 5)

CAMPO, Giuseppe del (cond)
see Vienna St Op Orch

CAMPO, José Antonio (ten)
see CONCERT INDEX under:
(STUD) **SM1223.27** Rossini—Complete unpublished Sacred Works

CAMPO, Maria-Rosa del (sop)
Verdi: Don Carlo (Cpte)

CAMPOLI, Alfredo (vn)
Beethoven: Violin Concerto
Bruch: Scottish Fantasy
Elgar: Violin Concerto
Mendelssohn: Violin Concerto, Op. 64
see CONCERT INDEX under:
(BEUL) **3PD10** Bliss & Tchaikovsky—Violin Concertos
(DECC) **433 220-2DWO** The World of the Violin
(PEAR) **GEMMCD9151** Alfredo Campoli
(PEAR) **PASTCD9744** Campoli's Choice

CAMPORA, Giuseppe (ten)
Verdi: Simon Boccanegra (Cpte)
see CONCERT INDEX under:
(CFP) **CD-CFP4569** Puccini: Arias

CAMPORELLI, Maria (sop)
see CONCERT INDEX under:
(SYMP) **SYMCD1113** The Harold Wayne Collection, Vol.13

CAMPOS, Rafael (sngr)
Moreno Torroba: Luisa Fernanda (Cpte)

CANADIAN NATIONAL ARTS CENTRE ORCHESTRA
cond F-P. DECKER
see CONCERT INDEX under:
(CBC) **SMCD5096** Mozart/Copland/Weber—Clarinet Concertos

CANALI, Anna Maria (mez)
Donizetti: Lucia di Lammermoor (Cpte)

Mascagni: Cavalleria Rusticana (Cpte)
see CONCERT INDEX under:
(EMI) **CMS7 63244-2** The Art of Maria Callas
(EMI) **CMS7 64165-2** Puccini—Trittico

CANCELA, José Luis (sngr)
Bretón: Verbena de la Paloma (Cpte)

CANDIA, Roberto de (sngr)
Bellini: Zaira (Cpte)

CANIGLIA, Maria (sop)
Verdi: Aida (Cpte), Requiem (Cpte)
see CONCERT INDEX under:
(EMI) **CDH7 61051-2** Beniamino Gigli - Operatic Arias
(EMI) **CHS7 64864-2(2)** La Scala Edition - Vol.2, 1915-46 (pt 2)
(NIMB) **NI7853** Lauri-Volpi sings Verdi
(PEAR) **GEMMCDS9926(2)** Covent Garden on Record—Vol.4 (pt 2)

CANIHAC, Jean-Pierre (cornet)
see CONCERT INDEX under:
(ASTR) **E8503** Merula—Arie e Capricci

CANINO, Bruno (hpd)
see CONCERT INDEX under:
(PHIL) **426 925-2PM19** The Complete Vivaldi Edition
(PHIL) **438 797-2PM2** Haydn—Concertos
(WERG) **WER60054-50** Magnificathy—the many voices of Cathy Berberian

CANINO, Bruno (pf)
Bach: Violin Sonatas, BWV1014-19 (exc)
C.P.E. Bach: Sonata, H514
Dvořák: Piano Quintet, Op.81, Romantic Pieces
Liszt: Symphony 9 (Beethoven), S657
Weber: Flute Trio, J259, Violin Sonatas, J99-104
see CONCERT INDEX under:
(ARAB) **Z6649** Bartok—Violin Works
(DECC) **443 894-2DH** Bartók—Chamber Works
(EMI) **CMS7 64617-2** The art of Itzhak Perlman
(EMI) **CZS4 83177-2(2)** Itzhak Perlman Edition (pt 2)
(NOVA) **150 047-2** Haydn: Chamber Works for Flute
(NUOV) **6742** Mozart—Violin Sonatas, Vol.3
(NUOV) **6743** Mozart—Violin Sonatas, Vol.4
(NUOV) **7109** Dallapiccola—Orchestral Works
(PHIL) **442 795-2PH** Skalkottas—Cycle Concert
(WERG) **WER60054-50** Magnificathy—the many voices of Cathy Berberian

CANN, Antoinette (pf)
see CONCERT INDEX under:
(PP) **PP10393** Works for Two Pianos/Piano Duet

CANN, Claire (pf)
see CONCERT INDEX under:
(PP) **PP10393** Works for Two Pianos/Piano Duet

CANNAN, Phyllis (mez)
Britten: Turn of the Screw (Cpte)
Verdi: Trovatore (Cpte)

CANNE-MEIJER, Cora (mez)
Rossini: Comte Ory (Cpte)
Telemann: Tag des Gerichts (Cpte)
see CONCERT INDEX under:
(EMI) **CDH5 65072-2** Glyndebourne Recorded - 1934-1994

CANNETTI, Linda (sop)
(PEAR) **GEMMCDS9073(2)** Giovanni Zenatello, Vol.1 (pt 2)
(SYMP) **SYMCD1138** The Harold Wayne Collection, Vol.16
(SYMP) **SYMCD1158** The Harold Wayne Collection, Vol.18

CANONICI, Luca (ten)
Donizetti: Don Pasquale (Cpte)
Mayr: Rosa Bianca (Cpte)
Rossini: Signor Bruschino (Cpte)
Verdi: Requiem (Cpte)

CANTABILE SINGERS
cond R. SACCANI
Verdi: Aida (Cpte)

CANTELLI, Guido (cond)
see NBC SO

CANTELO, April (sop)
Britten: Albert Herring (Cpte)
Haydn: Mass 9, Mass 10, Mass 13
M-A. Charpentier: Messe de minuit, H9
Monteverdi: Ballo delle ingrate
Purcell: Indian Queen, Z630 (exc)
see CONCERT INDEX under:
(DECC) **436 259-2DM** Handel/Blow—Choral Works
(LOND) **436 393-2LM** Britten—The Little Sweep, etc
(VANG) **08.2003.72** Purcell—Celebrated Songs,Sacred Airs and Concert Pieces

CANTEMUS
cond M. DE BERNART
Rossini: Torvaldo e Dorliska (Cpte)

CANTER, Robin (ob)
see CONCERT INDEX under:
(AMON) **CD-SAR22** Oboe Collection
(AMON) **CD-SAR34** Mozart—Chamber Works
(CARL) **MCD59** Vaughan Williams/R. Strauss—Oboe Works

CANTERBURY CATHEDRAL CHOIR
cond D. FLOOD
see CONCERT INDEX under:

(DECC) **430 093-2DWO** The World of Vaughan Williams
(DECC) **430 094-2DWO** The World of Elgar
(METR) **METCD1003** Gregorian Chant from Canterbury Cathedral
(YORK) **CD109** Canterbury Carols
cond A. WICKS
see CONCERT INDEX under:
(CONI) **CDCF160** Carols for today

CANTICA NOVA CHAMBER CHOIR
cond J. GORITZKI
C.H. Graun: Montezuma (Cpte)

CANTILENA
Vaughan Williams: Symphony 1
cond A. SHEPHERD
Abel: Symphonies, Op. 7
Arne: Favourite Concertos
Boyce: Overtures (exc)
Dittersdorf: Symphonies after Ovid
Hebden: Concerti for strings
see CONCERT INDEX under:
(CHAN) **CHAN6541** Boyce—Concerti Grossi and Overtures
(CHAN) **CHAN8301** The Special Sound of Chandos
(CHAN) **CHAN8319** Encore! An Hour with Cantilena
(CHAN) **CHAN8448/9** Music from the Court of Salzburg
(CHAN) **CHAN8813** Haydn—Symphonies

CANTIN, Catherine (fl)
see CONCERT INDEX under:
(DG) **445 947-2GH** Messiaen—Orchestral Works

CANTOR, Eddie (sngr)
see CONCERT INDEX under:
(PEAR) **GEMMCDS9059/61** Music from the New York Stage, Vol. 4: 1917-20

CANTOR, Philippe (ten)
M-A. Charpentier: Arts Florissants (Cpte), Médée (Cpte)
Monteverdi: Vespers
Purcell: Dido (Cpte)
Rameau: Zoroastre (Cpte)
Vivaldi: Dorilla in Tempe (Cpte)
see CONCERT INDEX under:
(HARM) **HMX290 1528/33(1)** A Purcell Companion (pt 1)

CANTORIA CHILDREN'S CHOIR
cond E. COHEN
Massenet: Werther (Cpte)

CANTUS CHOIR
cond A. LEAPER
Brian: Symphony 4

CANTUS CÖLLN
H. Albert: Arien, Musicalische Kürbs-Hütte
see CONCERT INDEX under:
(DHM) **RD77088** Schein—Vocal Works
(DHM) **RD77182** Lechner: Sacred & Secular Songs
(DHM) **05472 77181-2** Rosenmuller—Italian Cantatas
(DHM) **05472 77282-2** Monteverdi—Madrigali Amorosi
(DHM) **05472 77304-2** Lassus—Prophetiae Sibyllarum
(DHM) **05472 77305-2** Pachelbel/J. Christoph & J. M. Bach—Motets
(DHM) **05472 77322-2** Carissimi/Marazzoli—Oratorios

CANTUS SACRED MUSIC ENSEMBLE
cond L. ARSHAVSKAYA
Grechaninov: Liturgy, Op. 13, Liturgy, Op.177

CANZONE CHOIR
cond F. RASMUSSEN
Gade: Comala

CAO, Pierre (cond)
see Luxembourg Rad & TV SO

CAO, Pierre (narr)
Goetz: Piano Concerto 2
see CONCERT INDEX under:
(VOX) **115708-2** Mosonyi/Raff/Stavenhaegn—Piano Concertos
(VOX) **115709-2** D'Albert/Bronsart/Liszt—Piano Concertos
(VOX) **115713-2** Mendelssohn/Reinecke/Rheinberger—Piano Concertos
(VOX) **115714-2** Balakirev/Lyapunov/Medtner—Piano Concertos
(VOX) **115717-2** Chopin/Henselt/Hiller—Piano Concertos

CAPDEVILA, Antonio (cond)
see orch

CAPE TOWN MELODIC CHOIR
cond A. COATES
see CONCERT INDEX under:
(CLAR) **CDGSE78-50-54** Coates conducts Wagner, Weber & Mendelssohn

CAPE TOWN SYMPHONY ORCHESTRA
cond A. COATES
see CONCERT INDEX under:
(CLAR) **CDGSE78-50-54** Coates conducts Wagner, Weber & Mendelssohn

CAPECCHI, Renato (bar)
Donizetti: Don Pasquale (Cpte), Elisir d'amore (Cpte), Linda di Chamounix (Cpte)
Mozart: Idomeneo (Cpte), Nozze di Figaro (Cpte)

Puccini: Bohème (Cpte), Gianni Schicchi (Cpte), Tosca (Cpte)
Verdi: Forza del destino (Cpte)
see CONCERT INDEX under:
(DECC) **433 706-2DMO3** Bellini—Beatrice di Tenda; Operatic Arias

CAPELLA ALAMIRE
cond P. URQUHART
see CONCERT INDEX under:
(DORI) **DIS80131** The Early Josquin

CAPELLA BAVARIAE
see CONCERT INDEX under:
(EMI) **CDC7 47407-2** Schubert: Sacred Choral works
(EMI) **CMS7 64783-2** Schubert—Sacred Works, Vol.2
cond W. SAWALLISCH
see CONCERT INDEX under:
(EMI) **CDC7 47407-2** Schubert: Sacred Choral works
(EMI) **CMS7 64783-2** Schubert—Sacred Works, Vol.2

CAPELLA BRUGENSIS
Rossini: Tancredi (Cpte)

CAPELLA CLEMENTINA
cond H. MÜLLER-BRÜHL
Hasse: Piramo e Tisbe (Cpte)

CAPELLA CRACOVIENSIS
cond K.A. RICKENBACHER
see CONCERT INDEX under:
(SCHW) **311382** Milhaud—Orchestral Works
(SCHW) **311392** Milhaud—Little Symphonies and Little Operas

(LA) CAPELLA DUCALE
cond ROLAND WILSON
Monteverdi: Selva morale e spirituale (exc)
cond R. WILSON
see CONCERT INDEX under:
(DHM) **05472 77298-2** Schelle—Baroque Christmas Music

CAPELLA ISTROPOLITANA
cond C. BREMBECK
Bach: Mass in B minor, BWV232 (Cpte)
see CONCERT INDEX under:
(NAXO) **8 550431** Bach—Soprano Cantatas
cond S. GUNZENHAUSER
Mozart: Sinfonia Concertante, K364, Violin Concerto, K216, Violin Concerto, K218, Violin Concerto, K219
cond J. KRECHEK
see CONCERT INDEX under:
(NAXO) **8 550877** Italian Concerti Grossi
cond H. NERAT
Mozart: Divertimento, K131, Divertimento, K287
cond F. VAJNAR
see CONCERT INDEX under:
(NAXO) **8 550459** Czech Horn Concertos
cond B. WARCHAL
Bach: Brandenburg Concertos (exc)
cond J. WILDNER
Mozart: Cosi fan tutte (Cpte)
see CONCERT INDEX under:
(NAXO) **8 550383** Mozart—Tenor Arias
(NAXO) **8 550414** Mozart & Saint-Saëns: Violin Works
(NAXO) **8 550435** Mozart—Arias and Duets
cond B. WORDSWORTH
Beethoven: Piano Concerto 1, Piano Concerto 2, Piano Concerto 3, Piano Concerto 4, Piano Concerto 5, Rondo, WoO6
Mozart: Symphony 40, Symphony 41
see CONCERT INDEX under:
(NAXO) **8 550113** Mozart—Symphonies
(NAXO) **8 550119** Mozart—Symphonies
(NAXO) **8 550164** Mozart—Symphonies
(NAXO) **8 550186** Mozart—Symphonies
(NAXO) **8 550264** Mozart—Symphonies
(NAXO) **8 550382** Haydn—Symphonies Nos 45,48 and 102

(LA) CAPELLA REIAL INSTRUMENTAL ENSEMBLE
cond J. SAVALL
Bach: Brandenburg Concertos
Cererols: Missa de batalla, Missa pro defunctis a 7
see CONCERT INDEX under:
(ASTR) **E8532** Arriaga—Orchestral Works

(LA) CAPELLA REIAL VOCAL ENSEMBLE
see CONCERT INDEX under:
(ASTR) **E8766** Guerrero—Sacrae Cantiones
cond J. SAVALL
Cererols: Missa de batalla, Missa pro defunctis a 7
Mozart: Requiem

CAPELLA RICERCAR
see CONCERT INDEX under:
(RICE) **RIC060048** German Baroque Cantatas, Vol. 5
cond J. LÉJEUNE
see CONCERT INDEX under:
(RICE) **RIC052034** Charpentier—Sacred Choral Works

CAPELLA SANCTI MICHAELIS INSTRUMENTAL ENSEMBLE
cond E. VAN NEVEL
see CONCERT INDEX under:
(RICE) **RIC062026** Concerto in forma di una messa

CAPELLA SANCTI MICHAELIS VOCAL ENSEMBLE
cond E. VAN NEVEL
see CONCERT INDEX under:
(RICE) **RIC062026** Concerto in forma di una messa

(RICE) **RIC109097/8** German Baroque Cantatas, Vol.9 - Weckmann

CAPELLA SAVARIA
see CONCERT INDEX under:
(HARM) **HMA190 3010** Bach—Wedding Cantatas, BWV202, 209 and 210
(QUIN) **QUI90 3010** Bach—Wedding Cantatas
cond N. MCGEGAN
Handel: Agrippina (Cpte), Floridante (Cpte)
cond P. NÉMETH
Handel: St John Passion (Cpte)

CAPELLE, Mireille (sop)
Rossini: Petite messe solennelle

CAPELLE, Pierre (ten)
Stravinsky: Noces

CAPELLI, Norberto (pf)
see CONCERT INDEX under:
(MARC) **8 223462** Guastavino—Piano Works

CAPET QUARTET
Beethoven: String Quartet 14, String Quartet 15
see CONCERT INDEX under:
(BIDD) **LAB097** Capet Quartet plays Haydn,Mozart & Beethoven

CAPEZZALI, Jean-Louis (ob)
see CONCERT INDEX under:
(ACCO) **20202-2** Poulenc—Chamber Works

CAPITAL VIRTUOSI
(SPRO) **SPCV1001** Capital Virtuosi

CAPONE, Gloria (sop)
see CONCERT INDEX under:
(ALBA) **TROY021-2** American Choral & Orchestral Works

CAPOUL, Victor (ten)
see CONCERT INDEX under:
(SYMP) **SYMCD1172** The Harold Wayne Collection, Vol.21

CÁPOVÁ, Silvia (pf)
see CONCERT INDEX under:
(MARC) **8 223315** Bliss—Film Music
(MARC) **8 223425** Frederic Curzon—Orchestral Works
(MARC) **8 223515** Binge—Orchestral Works

CAPPELLA COLONIENSIS
cond W. CHRISTIE
Dauvergne: Concerts de Simphonies, Op. 3 (exc), Troqueurs (Cpte)
Hasse: Cleofide (Cpte)
cond G. FERRO
Rossini: Cenerentola (Cpte), Italiana in Algeri (Cpte)

CAPPELLA NOVA
cond R. TARUSKIN
Lupi: Ergone conticuit
Ockeghem: Missa prolationum
cond A. TAVENER
Anon: Feast Days (exc), Saints' Days (exc)
Carver: Mass for 5 voices, Mass for 6 voices, Missa L'homme armé, Missa Pater creator omnium
see CONCERT INDEX under:
(ASV) **CDGAU124** Carver—Scottish Renaissance Polyphony Vol 1

CAPPELLETTI, Andrea (vn)
Respighi: Concerto all'antica, Gregorian Concerto
see CONCERT INDEX under:
(DYNA) **DC-U25** Haydn: Violin Concertos
(SCHW) **311164** Mozart—Violin Concertos

CAPPELLINO, Lucia (sop)
Giordano: Fedora (Cpte)

CAPPONE, Giusto (va)
R. Strauss: Don Quixote

CAPPUCCILLI, Piero (bar)
Bellini: Pirata (Cpte), Puritani (Cpte)
Catalani: Wally (Cpte)
Donizetti: Lucia di Lammermoor (Cpte)
Mascagni: Cavalleria Rusticana (Cpte)
Mozart: Don Giovanni (Cpte), Nozze di Figaro (Cpte)
Ponchielli: Gioconda (Cpte)
Verdi: Aida (Cpte), Ballo in maschera (Cpte), Don Carlo (Cpte), Due Foscari (Cpte), Forza del destino (Cpte), Macbeth (Cpte), Masnadieri (Cpte), Nabucco (Cpte), Rigoletto (Cpte), Simon Boccanegra (Cpte), Trovatore (Cpte)

CAPRICCIO STRAVAGANTE
see CONCERT INDEX under:
(DHM) **RD77218** Lully—Divertissements
(DHM) **RD77220** Monteverdi e il suo Tempo
(DHM) **RD77252** Purcell—Airs and Instrumental Music
(DHM) **05472 77190-2**
Monteverdi—Combattimento/Lamento d'Arianna
(DHM) **05472-77300-2** Buxtehude—Abendmusik

CAPRICORN
Glinka: Sextet in E flat
Hummel: Septet, Op.74, Septet, Op.114
Parry: Nonet
Rimsky-Korsakov: Piano and Wind Quintet
Stanford: Serenade
see CONCERT INDEX under:
(BRID) **BCD9037** Ruders—Chamber Works
cond E. HIGGINBOTTOM
Duruflé: Requiem

Fauré: Requiem (Cpte)
cond O. KNUSSEN
see CONCERT INDEX under:
(BRID) BCD9037   Ruders—Chamber Works

CAPUANA, Franco (cond)
see Santa Cecilia Academy Orch

CAPUANO, Enzo (bass)
Cherubini: Lodoïska (Cpte)
Verdi: Traviata (Cpte), Vespri siciliani (Cpte)

CARACCIOLO, Franco (cond)
see Naples Rossini Orch

CARAMIELLO, Francesco (pf)
Martucci: Piano Concerto 1
see CONCERT INDEX under:
(ASV) CDDCA691   Martucci—Complete Orchestral
Music, Vol. 4

CARBONARI, Virgilio (bass)
Giordano: Fedora (Cpte)
Puccini: Madama Butterfly (Cpte)
Verdi: Forza del destino (Cpte), Rigoletto (Cpte),
Traviata (Cpte)
Zandonai: Francesca da Rimini (exc)

CARCIA, Gerald (gtr)
Haydn: Quatuor, HobII/G4
Schubert: Trio, D96
see CONCERT INDEX under:
(BIS) BIS-CD337   Tubin: Orchestral Works

CARDEW, Cornelius (tape op)
see CONCERT INDEX under:
(WERG) WER60161-50   Ligeti: Instrumental Works

CARDIFF POLYPHONIC CHOIR
cond G. KAPLAN
Mahler: Symphony 2

CARDIN, Catherine (mez)
Fauré: Messe basse

(THE) CARDINALL'S MUSICK
cond A. CARWOOD
Ludford: Ave cuius conceptio, Magnificat Benedicta,
Missa Benedicta, Missa Videte miraculum
see CONCERT INDEX under:
(ASV) CDGAU133   Nicholas Ludford, Volume 3
(ASV) CDGAU140   The Music of Nicholas Ludford,
Volume 4
(ASV) CDGAU142   Fayrfax—Complete Works, Vol. 1

CAREAU, Suzanne (va)
see CONCERT INDEX under:
(CHAN) CHAN8817   Britten: Orchestral Works

CARECCIA, Franco (ten)
Puccini: Gianni Schicchi (Cpte)

CARELLI, Emma (sop)
see CONCERT INDEX under:
(EMI) CHS7 64860-2(1)   La Scala Edition - Vol.1,
1878-1914 (pt 1)
(MEMO) HR4408/9(2)   Singers in Genoa, Vol.1 (disc
2)
(SYMP) SYMCD1111   The Harold Wayne Collection,
Vol.11

CARELLI, Gabor (ten)
Haydn: Orlando Paladino (Cpte)
Verdi: Requiem (Cpte)
see CONCERT INDEX under:
(RCA) GD60326   Verdi—Operas & Choral Works

CAREWE, John (cond)
see Nice PO

CAREWE, Mary (sngr)
Bernstein: West Side Story (Cpte)

CAREY, Colm (organ)
see CONCERT INDEX under:
(NAXO) 8 550765   Fauré—Choral Works

CAREY, Michel (bar)
Couperin: Messe à l'usage ordinaire des paroisses,
Messe pour les couvents
see CONCERT INDEX under:
(AUVI) MO782025   Schoenberg—Chamber Music,
Vol. 3

CAREY, Thomas (bar)
Tippett: Knot Garden (Cpte)

CAREY, Timothy (pf)
see CONCERT INDEX under:
(CHAN) CHAN8993   Honegger—Orchestral Works

CARIDIS, Miltiades (cond)
see Danish RSO

CARIOU, Len (sngr)
Strouse: Dance a Little Closer (Cpte)

CARIVEN, Marcel (cond)
see French Rad Lyric Orch

CARL PHILIP EMANUEL BACH ORCHESTRA
cond HANS HAENCHEN
C. P. E. Bach: Flute Concerto, H435, Flute Concerto,
H445, Sinfonias, H657-62, Sinfonias, H663-6
Gluck: Orfeo ed Euridice (Cpte)
see CONCERT INDEX under:
(CAPR) 10 103   C.P.E. Bach: Sinfonias
(CAPR) 10 104   C.P.E. Bach: Flute Concertos
(CAPR) 10 135   C.P.E. Bach: Organ Works
(CAPR) 10 805   Mozart: Wind Concertos
cond HARTMUT HAENCHEN
see CONCERT INDEX under:
(CAPR) 10 213   Handel and Mozart Arias for
Countertenor

---

cond P. SCHREIER
Mozart: Finta semplice (Cpte), Oca del Cairo (Cpte)
see CONCERT INDEX under:
(EMI) CDC7 49843-2   Bach—Cantatas
(PHIL) 434 918-2PH2   Bach—Concertos

CARLIN, Mario (ten)
Donizetti: Lucia di Lammermoor (Cpte)
Puccini: Madama Butterfly (Cpte), Manon Lescaut
(Cpte), Tosca (Cpte), Turandot (Cpte)
Rossini: Barbiere di Siviglia (Cpte)
Verdi: Aida (Cpte), Otello (Cpte)

CARLO, John Del (bass)
Ponchielli: Gioconda (Cpte)
Rossini: Cenerentola (Cpte)

CARLSEN, Svein (bass)
Braein: Anne Pedersdotter (Cpte)

CARLSEN, Torli (sop)
Grieg: Peer Gynt (Cpte)

CARLSON, Claudine (mez)
Berlioz: Troyens (Cpte)
Debussy: Pelléas et Mélisande (Cpte)
see CONCERT INDEX under:
(CARL) GLRS101   Mahler plays Mahler
(DECC) 440 333-2DH   Ravel—Vocal Works

CARLYLE, Joan (sop)
see CONCERT INDEX under:
(DG) 419 257-2GH3   'Cav' and 'Pag', etc

CARLYSS, Earl (vn)
Rorem: Night Music

CARMASSI, Bruno (bass)
see CONCERT INDEX under:
(EMI) CDH7 69791-2   Dame Eva Turner sings Opera
Arias and Songs

CARME
cond L. IZQUIERDO
see CONCERT INDEX under:
(NUOV) 6809   Falla: Vocal & Instrumental Works

CARMEN ANDRES, Maria del (sngr)
Bretón: Verbena de la Paloma (Cpte)

CARMEN RAMIREZ, Maria del (sngr)
Vives: Bohemios (Cpte)

CARMINA QUARTET
Brahms: String Quartet 1, String Quartet 2
Debussy: String Quartet
Haydn: String Quartets, Op. 76 (exc)
Mendelssohn: String Quartet 2, String Quartet 6
Ravel: String Quartet
see CONCERT INDEX under:
(DENO) CO-79462   Szymanowski/Webern—Works for
String Quartet

CARMIRELLI, Pina (vn)
Vivaldi: Concerti, Op. 8 (exc)
see CONCERT INDEX under:
(PHIL) 426 925-2PM19   The Complete Vivaldi Edition

CARNEIRO, Gonzaga (cl)
see CONCERT INDEX under:
(CHNT) LDC278 835   Villa-Lobos—Chôros for
Chamber Ensembles

CARNOVICH, Daniele (bass)
Monteverdi: Vespers

CARNUTH, Walter (ten)
Wagner: Meistersinger (Cpte)

CAROL CASE, John (bar)
Fauré: Requiem (Cpte)
Vaughan Williams: Symphony 1
see CONCERT INDEX under:
(EMI) CDM7 64022-2   Vaughan Williams—Orchestral
Works
(EMI) CDM7 64722-2   Vaughan Williams—Choral &
Orchestral Works

CAROLAN, Lucy (kybds)
see CONCERT INDEX under:
(AMON) CD-SAR19   Flute Recital

CAROLI, Consuelo (mez)
Prokofiev: Love for 3 Oranges (Cpte)
Vivaldi: Dorilla in Tempe (Cpte)

CAROLI, Paolo (ten)
Bellini: Norma (Cpte)
Puccini: Madama Butterfly (Cpte)
Verdi: Don Carlo (Cpte), Simon Boccanegra (Cpte)

CAROLIS, Natale De (bass-bar)
Handel: Rinaldo (Cpte)
Mozart: Don Giovanni (Cpte)
Puccini: Manon Lescaut (Cpte)
Rossini: Inganno felice (Cpte), Occasione fa il ladro
(Cpte), Scala di Seta (Cpte), Signor Bruschino
(Cpte)
Verdi: Rigoletto (Cpte)

CARON, Leslie (narr)
Debussy: Martyre de St Sébastien (Cpte)

CARON, Rose (sop)
see CONCERT INDEX under:
(IRCC) IRCC-CD802   Souvenirs of Rare French
Opera
(SYMP) SYMCD1172   The Harold Wayne Collection,
Vol.21

CARONNA, Ernesto (bar)
see CONCERT INDEX under:
(IRCC) IRCC-CD808   Souvenirs of 19th Century Italian
Opera

CAROSI, Ubaldo (bass)
Puccini: Tosca (Cpte)

CAROSIO, Margherita (sop)
see CONCERT INDEX under:
(EMI) CHS7 64864-2(2)   La Scala Edition - Vol.2,
1915-46 (pt 2)
(EMI) CHS7 69741-2(7)   Record of Singing,
Vol.4—Italian School
(IRCC) IRCC-CD808   Souvenirs of 19th Century Italian
Opera

CARPENTER, Gary (cond)
see Bratislava RSO

CARPENTER, Nicholas (cl)
see CONCERT INDEX under:
(HERA) HAVPCD152   Music for Clarinet and Piano

CARPIO, Selica Perez (sngr)
Sorozábal: Katiuska (Cpte)

CARR, Colin (vc)
Brahms: Piano Trio 1
Mendelssohn: Piano Trio 1, Piano Trio 2
see CONCERT INDEX under:
(ARAB) Z6580-2   Schubert: Complete Works for Piano
Trio
(ARAB) Z6608   Brahms—Trios, Vol.2
(COLL) Coll1448-2   Scharwenka—Chamber Works,
Volume 2

CARR, Robert (bass)
Gounod: Faust (Cpte)

CARRAI, Phoebe (vc)
see CONCERT INDEX under:
(ARCH) 419 633-2AH   Telemann: Wind Concertos
(DHM) RD77188   C.P.E. Bach—Vocal & Chamber
Works

CARRAL, Dora (sop)
Cilea: Adriana Lecouvreur (Cpte)
Verdi: Nabucco (Cpte), Traviata (Cpte)
see CONCERT INDEX under:
(DECC) 411 665-2DM3   Puccini: Il trittico

CARRÉ, Marguerite (sop)
see CONCERT INDEX under:
(IRCC) IRCC-CD802   Souvenirs of Rare French
Opera

CARRERAS, José (ten)
Bernstein: West Side Story (Cpte)
Bizet: Carmen (exc)
Donizetti: Elisir d'amore (Cpte), Poliuto (Cpte)
Falla: Vida breve (Cpte)
Giordano: Andrea Chénier (Cpte)
Halévy: Juive (Cpte)
Leoncavallo: Pagliacci (Cpte)
Mascagni: Cavalleria rusticana (Cpte)
Massenet: Werther (Cpte)
Offenbach: Périchole (Cpte)
Puccini: Bohème (Cpte), Madama Butterfly (Cpte),
Manon Lescaut (Cpte), Tosca (Cpte), Turandot
(Cpte)
R. Strauss: Rosenkavalier (Cpte)
Rossini: Elisabetta (Cpte), Otello (Cpte), Petite messe
solennelle, Pietra del Paragone (Cpte)
Saint-Saëns: Samson et Dalila (Cpte)
Verdi: Aida (Cpte), Ballo in maschera (Cpte),
Battaglia di Legnano (Cpte), Corsaro (Cpte), Don
Carlo (Cpte), Due Foscari (Cpte), Forza del destino
(Cpte), Giorno di Regno (Cpte), Macbeth (Cpte),
Requiem (Cpte), Simon Boccanegra (Cpte), Stiffelio
(Cpte), Trovatore (Cpte)
see CONCERT INDEX under:
(DECC) 430 433-2DH   Carreras, Domingo and
Pavarotti in Concert
(DECC) 430 724-2DM   Great Operatic Duets
(DECC) 436 463-2DM   Ten Top Tenors
(EMI) CDM7 69549-2   Ruggero Raimondi: Italian
Opera Arias
(ERAT) 4509-95789-2   Zarzuelas-The Passion of
Spain
(PHIL) 420 955-2PH   Ramirez: Choral Works
(PHIL) 434 926-2PH   The Pleasure of Love
(PHIL) 442 272-2PM2   The Best of Bizet
(SONY) MK39097   Puccini Heroines
(SONY) SK45863   Italian Opera Composers' Songs
(SONY) SK53358   Christmas in Vienna
(TELD) 4509-96200-2   The Three Tenors 1994

CARRERAS, Nicole (sop)
Offenbach: Belle Hélène (Cpte)

CARRINGTON, Simon (cond)
see CONCERT INDEX under:
(CLLE) COLCD115   Three Musical Fables
(EMI) CDC7 54191-2   La Dolce Vita

CARRINGTON, Simon (db)
see CONCERT INDEX under:
(DECC) 440 032-2DM   Monteverdi/Gesualdo—Motets
and Madrigals

CARROLI, Silvano (bar)
Puccini: Tosca (Cpte)

CARROLL, David (sngr)
Gershwin: Girl crazy (Cpte)

CARROLL, Diahann (sngr)
Rodgers: No Strings (Cpte)

CARROLL, Edward (tpt)
see CONCERT INDEX under:
(DELO) DE3002   The Sound of Trumpets

CHABRIER, Nadyne (spkr)
Massenet: Amadis (Cpte)

CHADUNELI, Giya (va)
Kancheli: Symphony 6

CHAFFIN, Philip A. (sngr)
Gershwin: Pardon My English (Cpte)

CHAGALL TRIO
see CONCERT INDEX under:
(MERI) **CDE84286** Ethel Smyth—Impressions that Remain

CHAGNON, Pierre (cond)
see orch

CHAIGNAUD, Jean-Luc (bar)
Gazzaniga: Don Giovanni (Cpte)
Verdi: Ballo in maschera (Cpte)

CHAILLY, Riccardo (cond)
see Berlin Deutsches SO

CHALABALA, Zdeněk (cond)
see Czech PO

CHALIAPIN, Feodor (bass)
see CONCERT INDEX under:
(EMI) **CDH7 61009-2** Chaliapin sings Russian Opera Arias
(EMI) **CHS7 64860-2(2)** La Scala Edition - Vol.1, 1878-1914 (pt 2)
(MMOI) **CDMOIR411** Sacred Songs and Arias
(MMOI) **CDMOIR422** Great Voices in Tchaikovsky
(PEAR) **GEMMCDS9925(2)** Covent Garden on Record—Vol.3 (pt 2)
(PEAR) **GEMMCDS9926(1)** Covent Garden on Record—Vol.4 (pt 1)
(PEAR) **GEMMCD9314** Feodor Chaliapin - Aria and Song Recital
(PREI) **89207** Feodor Chaliapin Song Book—Electrical Recordings
(SIMA) **PSC1810(2)** Grieg—Songs (historical recordings, pt 2)
(SYMP) **SYMCD1105** The Harold Wayne Collection, Vol.10

CHALLAN, Annie (hp)
see CONCERT INDEX under:
(EMI) **CMS5 65061-2(2)** The Fabulous Victoria de los Angeles (pt 2)
(EMI) **CZS5 68220-2** André Cluytens—A profile

CHALLENDER, Stuart (cond)
see Sydney SO

CHALMERS, David (organ)
see CONCERT INDEX under:
(GLOR) **GDCD016** Leo Sowerby—American Master of Sacred Song

CHALMERS, Thomas (bar)
see CONCERT INDEX under:
(PEAR) **GEMMCDS9074(2)** Giovanni Zenatello, Vol.2 (pt 2)

CHALUDE, Jacques (bass)
Milhaud: Christophe Colomb (Cpte)

CHAMBER ENSEMBLE
see CONCERT INDEX under:
(ECM) **445 351-2** Gavin Bryars—Vita Nova
(SONY) **SK53981** Purcell—Anthems and Hymns
(SUPR) **11 1491-2** Jarmila Novotna sings Czech Songs and Arias
cond **ADRIANO**
Respighi: Primavera
cond **P. BOULEZ**
(SONY) **SM3K45845** Webern—Complete Works
cond **B. BRITTEN**
(LOND) **436 393-2LM** Britten—The Little Sweep, etc
cond **R. GOTHÓNI**
Gothóni: Ochs und sein Hirte

CHAMBER MUSIC NORTHWEST
Bartók: Contrasts
Brahms: Clarinet Quintet, String Quintet 2
Messiaen: Quatuor
Mozart: Clarinet Quintet, K581
see CONCERT INDEX under:
(DELO) **DE3136** Nielsen/Loeffler/Prokofiev—Chamber Works

CHAMBER ORCHESTRA
cond **E. FENBY**
see CONCERT INDEX under:
(TEST) **SBT1014** Delius—Orchestral Works
cond **W. GOEHR**
see CONCERT INDEX under:
(BIDD) **LAB088** Primrose plays Handel, Mozart and Beethoven
(PEAR) **GEMMCD9045** William Primrose and Albert Spalding
cond **M. WILCOX**
see CONCERT INDEX under:
(RCA) **GD87989** Works for Oboe

CHAMBER ORCHESTRA OF EUROPE
Vivaldi: Concerti, Op. 8 (exc)
see CONCERT INDEX under:
(RCA) **RD87173** Debussy: Orchestral works
cond **C. ABBADO**
Haydn: Symphony 93, Symphony 101
Rossini: Barbiere di Siviglia (Cpte), Viaggio a Reims (Cpte)

Schubert: Fierrabras (Cpte), Symphony 1, Symphony 2, Symphony 3, Symphony 4, Symphony 5, Symphony 6
Vivaldi: Concerti, Op. 8 (exc), Concerto, RV577
see CONCERT INDEX under:
(DG) **423 651-2GH5** Schubert: Complete Symphonies
(DG) **429 396-2GH** Prokofiev—Orchestral Works
(DG) **431 653-2GH** Rossini—Overtures
(DG) **435 486-2GH** Schubert/Schumann—Sacred Choral Works
(DG) **439 932-2GH** Haydn—Symphonies, etc
cond **R. BARSHAI**
Shostakovich: Chamber Symphony, Op.83a, Chamber Symphony, Op.110a, Symphony for Strings, Symphony, Op.73a
cond **P. BERGLUND**
Mozart: Oboe Concerto, K314
R. Strauss: Oboe Concerto
see CONCERT INDEX under:
(ASV) **CDCOE814** Mozart—Wind Concertos
cond **C. ESCHENBACH**
(TELD) **4509-94540-2** Schnittke—Violin Works
cond **T. FISCHER**
(ASV) **CDCOE811** Works for Clarinet and Orchestra
(DG) **435 383-2GH** Martin—Chamber Orchestral Works
cond **J. GALWAY**
see CONCERT INDEX under:
(RCA) **RD87861** Mozart—Works for Flute & Orchestra
cond **J.E. GARDINER**
see CONCERT INDEX under:
(RCA) **09026 61583-2(6)** Julian Bream Edition (pt 6)
(RCA) **09026 61611-2** J. Bream Edition, Vol.28: Music of Spain—Rodrigo
cond **N. HARNONCOURT**
Beethoven: Fidelio (Cpte), Missa Solemnis, Romances, Violin Concerto
Mendelssohn: Erste Walpurgisnacht, Midsummer Night's Dream (exc), Symphony 3, Symphony 4
Schumann: Piano Concerto, Symphony 3, Symphony 4, Violin Concerto
see CONCERT INDEX under:
(TELD) **2292-46452-2** Beethoven—Complete Symphonies
(TELD) **9031-72302-2** Mozart—Concert Arias
(TELD) **9031-74858-2** Mozart—Symphonies
cond **H. HOLLIGER**
(TELD) **9031-77314-2** Schoenberg—Orchestral Works
cond **J. JUDD**
(CARL) **PCD805** Music of the Masters
cond **E. LEINSDORF**
R.Strauss: Bourgeois gentilhomme suite, Divertimento, Op.86
cond **M. POLLINI**
Rossini: Donna del lago (Cpte)
cond **H. SCHIFF**
(DG) **445 520-2GMA** Schnittke—Chamber Works
cond **A. SCHNEIDER**
Dvořák: Serenade, Op. 22, Serenade, Op. 44
Mozart: Horn Concerti, Serenade, K361, Serenade, K375, Serenade, K388, Symphony 38, Symphony 39
see CONCERT INDEX under:
(ASV) **CDCOE803** Chamber Concertos
(ASV) **CDCOE810** Orchestral Works
(ASV) **CDCOE811** Works for Clarinet and Orchestra
(ASV) **CDCOE814** Mozart—Wind Concertos
cond **G. SOLTI**
see CONCERT INDEX under:
(DECC) **430 498-2DWO** The World of Mozart
cond **S. VÉGH**
(ASV) **CDCOE813** Mozart—Wind Concertos

CHAMBER ORCHESTRA OF EUROPE WIND SOLOISTS
see CONCERT INDEX under:
(ASV) **CDCOE807** Beethoven—Music for Wind Instruments
(ASV) **CDCOE812** Music for Wind Instruments
cond **H. HOLLIGER**
(PHIL) **438 933-2PH** R. Strauss—Wind Music

CHAMBERLAIN, Richard (tbn)
see CONCERT INDEX under:
(RCA) **09026 62537-2** Takemitsu—Cantos

CHAMBERS, Celia (fl)
see CONCERT INDEX under:
(CHAN) **CHAN9380** Martin—Ballades

CHAMBON, Jacques (ob)
Albinoni: Concerti, Op. 9 (exc)

CHAMBOUX, Jean (drums)
see CONCERT INDEX under:
(ASTR) **E8521** Helfer—Requiem for the Dukes of Lorraine

CHAMINÉ, Jorge (bar)
Tchaikovsky: Queen of Spades (Cpte)

CHAMONIN, Jocelyne (mez)
Dukas: Ariane et Barbe-bleue (Cpte)
Wagner: Parsifal (Cpte)

CHAMORRO, Adrian (cond)
see Ricercar Consort

CHAMORRO, Adrian (vn)
see CONCERT INDEX under:
(O111) **OPS30-9004** Vivaldi—String Concertos

CHANCE, Michael (alto)
Bach: Cantata 140, Cantata 147, Cantata 206, Cantata 207a, Christmas Oratorio, BWV248 (Cpte), Mass in B minor, BWV232 (Cpte), St John Passion, BWV245 (Cpte), St Matthew Passion, BWV244 (Cpte)
Gluck: Orfeo ed Euridice (Cpte)
Goehr: Death of Moses
Handel: Giustino (Cpte), Israel in Egypt (Cpte), Jephtha (Cpte), Messiah (Cpte), Semele (Cpte)
Landi: Mort d'Orfeo (Cpte)
Monteverdi: Orfeo (Cpte), Vespers
Mozart: Ascanio in Alba (Cpte), Requiem
Orff: Carmina Burana
Purcell: Dido (Cpte), Fairy Queen, Z629 (Cpte), St Cecilia's Day Ode, Z339
Zelenka: Lamentations of Jeremiah, Litanie lauretanae, ZWV152, Missa dei filii, ZWV20
see CONCERT INDEX under:
(ARCH) **423 405-2AH** Schütz—Sacred Choral Works
(ARCH) **429 782-2AH** Bach—Cantatas Nos 106, 118b & 198
(CHAN) **CHAN0518** Vivaldi & Bach—Choral Works
(CHAN) **CHAN0538** Elizabethan Lute Songs
(DHM) **05472 77295-2** Handel/Purcell—Works
(HYPE) **CDA66076** British Choral Works
(HYPE) **CDA66126** Britten: Choral Works
(HYPE) **CDA66253** Blow & Purcell: Countertenor Works
(HYPE) **CDA66294** Pergolesi—Sacred Choral Works
(HYPE) **CDA66314** Purcell—Complete Odes & Welcome Songs, Vol.1
(HYPE) **CDA66335** A Musicall Dreame
(HYPE) **CDA66474** Couperin—Vocal Works
(HYPE) **CDA66498** Britten—Canticles
(HYPE) **CDA66598** Purcell—Complete Odes & Welcome Songs, Vol.8
(SONY) **SK66243** Music for Queen Mary
(VIRG) **VC5 45007-2** A Play of Passion
(VIRG) **VC7 59586-2** Goe Nightly Cares

CHANDLER, Stan (sngr)
see CONCERT INDEX under:
(EMI) **CDC5 55189-2** The Busby Berkeley Album

CHANDOS BAROQUE PLAYERS
Zelenka: Lamentations of Jeremiah
see CONCERT INDEX under:
(HYPE) **CDA66195** Telemann—Chamber Works
(HYPE) **CDA66309** Vivaldi—La Pastourella

CHANDOS CONCERT ORCHESTRA
cond **S. BARRY**
(CHAN) **CHAN8362** Treasures of Operetta
(CHAN) **CHAN8561** Treasures of Operetta, Vol. 2
(CHAN) **CHAN8759** Treasures of Operetta III
(CHAN) **CHAN8978** Marilyn Hill Smith sings Kálmán & Lehár
(CHAN) **CHAN9142** Marilyn Hill Smith sings Ivor Novello

CHANDOS SINGERS
cond **S. BARRY**
see CONCERT INDEX under:
(CHAN) **CHAN8759** Treasures of Operetta III

CHANG, Choong-Jin (va)
Rorem: Eleven Studies

CHANG, Lynn (vn)
see CONCERT INDEX under:
(NORT) **NR227-CD** American Chamber Music with Flute
(SONY) **SK53126** Made in America

CHANG, Sarah (vn)
Brahms: Hungarian Dances (exc)
Tchaikovsky: Violin Concerto
see CONCERT INDEX under:
(EMI) **CDC5 55026-2** Paganini/Saint-Saëns—Violin Works
(EMI) **CDC5 55487-2** Vaughan Williams—Orchestral Works
(EMI) **CDC7 54352-2** Sarah Chang - Debut

CHANNING, Carol (sngr)
J. Herman: Jerry's Girls (Cpte)

CHANNING, Simon (treb)
Britten: Rejoice in the Lamb

CHANT SCHOOL
cond **J. CABRÉ**
Frescobaldi: Fiori musicali (Cpte)

CHANTICLEER
see CONCERT INDEX under:
(CHTI) **CR-8803** Our Heart's Joy—A Chanticleer Christmas
(CHTI) **CR-8805** Brumel/Josquin Desprez—Choral Works
(CHTI) **CR-8808** Josquin Desprez/Agricola—Masses and Motets
(TELD) **4509-93333-2** Mexican Baroque
(TELD) **4509-94561-2** Palestrina—Vocal Works
cond **J. JENNINGS**
see CONCERT INDEX under:
(TELD) **4509-93333-2** Mexican Baroque

CHANTICLEER SINFONIA
cond **J. JENNINGS**
see CONCERT INDEX under:

cond F. REINER
Beethoven: Symphony 9
see CONCERT INDEX under:
(RCA) GD60176 Prokofiev: Vocal & Orchestral Works
cond A. SCHENCK
Barber: Lovers, Prayers of Kierkegaard
cond G. SOLTI
Bach: Mass in B minor, BWV232 (Cpte), St Matthew
Passion, BWV244 (Cpte)
Beethoven: Fidelio (Cpte), Symphony 9
Berlioz: Damnation de Faust (Cpte)
Handel: Messiah (Cpte)
Haydn: Jahreszeiten (Cpte), Schöpfung (Cpte)
Schoenberg: Moses und Aron (Cpte)
Shostakovich: Symphony 13
Verdi: Otello (Cpte), Requiem (Cpte)
see CONCERT INDEX under:
(DECC) 417 645-2DH Kiri - Portrait
(DECC) 430 226-2DH Verdi—Choruses
(DECC) 430 792-2DC6 Beethoven—Complete
Symphonies, etc
(DECC) 430 804-2DC10 Mahler—Complete
Symphonies
(DECC) 436 468-2DH Debussy—Orchestral Works
cond M. TILSON THOMAS
see CONCERT INDEX under:
(SONY) SK42381 Ives: Orchestral Works

CHICAGO SYMPHONY ORCHESTRA
Holst: Planets
cond C. ABBADO
Bartók: Piano Concerto 1, Piano Concerto 2
Berlioz: Symphonie fantastique
Chopin: Piano Concerto 2
Mahler: Rückert Lieder, Symphony 6, Symphony 7
Prokofiev: Lt Kijé Suite, Violin Concerto 1, Violin
Concerto 2
see CONCERT INDEX under:
(DG) 419 629-2GH Violin Works
(DG) 439 413-2GCL Prokofiev—Orchestral Works
(DG) 447 023-2GX12 Mahler—The Symphonies
(DG) 447 419-2GOR Prokofiev—Alexander
Nevsky;Lieutenant Kijé etc
cond D. BARENBOIM
Beethoven: Missa solemnis
Brahms: Academic Festival Overture, Deutsches
Requiem, Op. 45 (Cpte), Haydn Variations,
Symphony 1, Symphony 2, Symphony 3, Symphony
4, Tragic Overture
Bruckner: Symphony 1, Te Deum
Corigliano: Symphony 1
Dvořák: Cello Concerto
Lutosławski: Concerto for Orchestra (1954),
Symphony 3
Mahler: Lied von der Erde
Mendelssohn: Violin Concerto, Op.64
Prokofiev: Violin Concerto 2
R. Strauss: Alpensinfonie, Frau ohne schatten
Fantasy, Heldenleben, Till Eulenspiegel
Rimsky-Korsakov: Scheherazade, Tale of Tsar Saltan
(exc)
Verdi: Requiem (Cpte)
see CONCERT INDEX under:
(DG) 415 841-2GGA Saint-Saëns—Orchestral
Works
(DG) 429 025-2GX10 Bruckner—Complete
Symphonies, etc
(DG) 437 250-2GGA Bruckner—Orchestral & Vocal
Works
(DG) 437 641-2GGA2 Schumann—Symphonies, etc
(EMI) CZS5 68132-2 Les introuvables de Jacqueline
du Pré
(ERAT) 2292-45766-2 Ravel—Orchestral Works
(ERAT) 4509-94817-2 Brahms—Orchestral Works
(TELD) 4509-98256-2 Schoenberg—Piano and
Orchestral Pieces
(TELD) 4509-99596-2
Carter/Berio/Takemitsu—Orchestral Works
cond L. BERNSTEIN
Shostakovich: Symphony 1, Symphony 7
cond P. BOULEZ
Bartók: Cantata profana, Concerto for Orchestra,
Pieces, Sz51, Wooden Prince
Schoenberg: Pelleas und Melisande, Variations, Op.
31
see CONCERT INDEX under:
(DG) 437 850-2GH Stravinsky—Orchestral Works
(DG) 445 825-2GH Bartók—Orchestral Works
cond C.M. GIULINI
Brahms: Violin Concerto
Dvořák: Symphony 9
Mahler: Symphony 9
Schubert: Symphony 8
see CONCERT INDEX under:
(DG) 415 844-2GGA Ravel/Mussorgsky—Orchestral
Works
(DG) 423 239-2GC Britten: Vocal & Orchestral
Works
(EMI) CMS7 64922-2 Perlman plays Romantic Violin
Concertos
(EMI) CZS4 83177-2(1) Itzhak Perlman Edition (pt 1)
(RCA) RD86255 Schumann & Liszt Piano Works
cond W. HENDL
see CONCERT INDEX under:
(RCA) 09026 61210-2 Violin Showpieces
(RCA) 09026 61778-2(11-15) The Heifetz Collection,
Vols. 11-15
cond JAMES LEVINE
Berg: Violin Concerto
Orff: Carmina burana
Prokofiev: Symphony 1, Symphony 5
Rihm: Gesungene Zeit

Stravinsky: Oedipus Rex (Cpte)
see CONCERT INDEX under:
(DG) 427 323-2GH Works for Cello and Orchestra
(DG) 431 625-2GH Gershwin—Orchestral works
(DG) 431 698-2GH American Orchestral Works
(DG) 445 447-2GX3 Mutter plays Modern Works
cond N. JÄRVI
Hindemith: Concerto for Orchestra
Mussorgsky: Pictures
Schmidt: Symphony 2, Symphony 3
Scriabin: Poème de l'extase
see CONCERT INDEX under:
cond P. MONTEUX
see CONCERT INDEX under:
(RCA) GD86805 Orchestral Works
(RCA) 09026 61893-2 Pierre Monteux Edition
cond M. PENDOWSKI
Lavagnino: Orson Welles' Othello (exc)
cond F. REINER
Bartók: Concerto for Orchestra, Music for Strings,
Percussion and Celesta
Beethoven: Symphony 9
Berlioz: Nuits d'été
Brahms: Violin Concerto
Mahler: Lied von der Erde
R. Strauss: Also sprach Zarathustra, Burleske, Don
Quixote, Heldenleben, Sinfonia domestica
Tchaikovsky: Violin Concerto
see CONCERT INDEX under:
(RCA) GD60176 Prokofiev: Vocal & Orchestral Works
(RCA) GD60177 Strauss Family: Waltzes
(RCA) GD60179 Debussy & Ravel: Orchestral Works
(RCA) GD60387 Rossini—Overtures
(RCA) GD60874 R. Strauss—Scenes from Elektra &
Salome
(RCA) GD86722 R.Strauss: Orchestral and Vocal
Works
(RCA) 09026 60729-2 Haydn—Symphonies
(RCA) 09026 60930-2 R. Strauss—Orchestral Works
(RCA) 09026 60962-2 Beethoven—Orchestral Works
(RCA) 09026 61250-2 The Reiner Sound
(RCA) 09026 61263-2 Rubinstein plays Brahms
(RCA) 09026 61401-2
Mussorgsky/Respighi—Orchestral Works
(RCA) 09026 61504-2 Bartók—Orchestral Works
(RCA) 09026 61778-2(11-15) The Heifetz Collection,
Vols. 11-15
(RCA) 09026 61792-2 Reiner conducts Wagner &
Humperdinck
(RCA) 09026 61793-2
Brahms/Schubert/Mendelssohn—Orchestral Works
(RCA) 09026 61957-2
Hovhaness/Prokofiev/Stravinsky—Orchestral
Works
(RCA) 09026 61958-2 Russian Showpieces
(RCA) 09026 62587-2
Dvořák/Smetana/Weinberger—Orchestral Works
(RCA) 09026 68079-2 Respighi/Debussy—Orchestral
Works
cond A. SCHENCK
Barber: Lovers, Prayers of Kierkegaard
cond L. SLATKIN
Bruch: Scottish Fantasy, Violin Concerto 1
cond G. SOLTI
Bach: Mass in B minor, BWV232 (Cpte), St Matthew
Passion, BWV244 (Cpte)
Bartók: Violin Concerto 1
Beethoven: Fidelio (Cpte), Piano Concerto 3, Piano
Concerto 4, Symphony 9
Berlioz: Damnation de Faust (Cpte)
Bruckner: Symphony 2, Symphony 3, Symphony 8
Handel: Messiah (Cpte)
Haydn: Jahreszeiten (Cpte), Schöpfung (Cpte)
Mahler: Symphony 4, Symphony 5, Symphony 8
Prokofiev: Romeo and Juliet (exc), Symphony 1
Schoenberg: Moses und Aron (Cpte)
Shostakovich: Symphony 13
Tippett: Byzantium, Symphony 4
Verdi: Otello (Cpte), Requiem (Cpte)
see CONCERT INDEX under:
(DECC) 417 645-2DH Kiri - Portrait
(DECC) 417 719-2DM Elgar: Orchestral Works
(DECC) 430 226-2DH Verdi—Choruses
(DECC) 430 352-2DH Bartók: Orchestral Works
(DECC) 430 448-2DM The Solti Collection—Wagner
Overtures
(DECC) 430 707-2DM Tchaikovsky—Ballet Music
(DECC) 430 792-2DC6 Beethoven—Complete
Symphonies, etc
(DECC) 430 799-2DC4 Brahms—Complete
Symphonies, etc
(DECC) 430 804-2DC10 Mahler—Complete
Symphonies
(DECC) 436 468-2DH Debussy—Orchestral Works
(DECC) 440 618-2DF2 R. Strauss—Tone Poems
(DECC) 443 444-2DH Hungarian Connections
(LOND) 425 646-2LM3 Tippett Symphonies
cond F. STOCK
see CONCERT INDEX under:
(BIDD) LAB063 Nathan Milstein - American Columbia
Recordings
(BIDD) WHL016 British Music from America
(BIDD) WHL021/2 Frederick Stock and the Chicago
Symphony Orchestra
(RCA) 09026 60929-2 R.Strauss—Tone Poems
cond I. STRAVINSKY
see CONCERT INDEX under:
(SONY) SM3K46292 Stravinsky—Ballets, Vol.2
cond K. TENNSTEDT
Mahler: Symphony 1

cond M. TILSON THOMAS
Ives: Symphony 1, Symphony 4
see CONCERT INDEX under:
(SONY) SK42381 Ives: Orchestral Works
cond G. WAND
Brahms: Symphony 1

CHICHAGOV, Igor (pf)
see CONCERT INDEX under:
(RCA) GD87810 Rosa Ponselle - Opera & Song
Recital

CHICHESTER CATHEDRAL CHOIR
cond J. BIRCH
see CONCERT INDEX under:
(EMI) CDM7 64716-2 Ireland—Piano Concerto, etc
cond G. SOLTI
see CONCERT INDEX under:
(DECC) 436 403-2DWO The World of Royal Music
cond A. THURLOW
see CONCERT INDEX under:
(PRIO) PRCD312 Stanford: Choral Works
(PRIO) PRCD511 Magnificat and Nunc Dimittis,
Volume 2

CHICHESTER CONCERT
cond I. GRAHAM-JONES
see CONCERT INDEX under:
(OLYM) OCD400 John Marsh: Five Symphonies

CHIDELL, Tony (hn)
see CONCERT INDEX under:
(ASV) CDDCA645 Vivaldi—Concertos

CHIESA, Vivian della (sop)
see CONCERT INDEX under:
(RCA) GD60276 Toscanini conducts Boito & Verdi

CHIFFOLEAU, Yvan (vc)
(TIMP) 1C1013 Alkan—Chamber Music

CHILCOTT, Robert (treb)
Fauré: Requiem (Cpte)

CHILDREN'S CHOIR
cond L. BERNSTEIN
Puccini: Bohème (Cpte)

CHILDREN'S CHOIR
cond I. ANGUELOV
Henze: Boulevard Solitude (Cpte)
cond W. SAWALLISCH
Orff: Mond (Cpte)

CHILDS, Lucinda (narr)
Glass: Einstein on the Beach (Cpte)

CHILDS, Nicholas (euphonium)
see CONCERT INDEX under:
(CHAN) CHAN4513 British Bandsman Centenary
Concert
(DOYE) DOYCD002 Euphonium Music
(POLY) QPRL049D Boosey & Hawkes National Brass
Band Gala Concert 1991

CHILDS, Robert (euphonium)
see CONCERT INDEX under:
(CHAN) CHAN4513 British Bandsman Centenary
Concert
(CHAN) CHAN4523 Concerto
(DOYE) DOYCD002 Euphonium Music
(POLY) QPRL049D Boosey & Hawkes National Brass
Band Gala Concert 1991

CHILES, Torin (ten)
see CONCERT INDEX under:
(CBC) SMCD5139 A Gilbert & Sullivan Gala

CHILINGIRIAN, Levon (vn)
F. X. Scharwenka: Piano Quartet, Op. 37, Piano Trio,
Op. 45
Tippett: Triple Concerto
see CONCERT INDEX under:
(CHAN) CHAN9108 Beethoven—Chamber Works
(HYPE) CDA66192 Ferguson & Finzi: Chamber
Works

CHILINGIRIAN QUARTET
Bartók: Piano Quintet, String Quartet 1, String Quartet
2, String Quartet 6
Dvořák: Cypresses, String Quartet 7, String Quartet
8, String Quartet 9, String Quartet 10, String Quartet
11, String Quartet 12, String Quartet 14
Elgar: Piano Quintet, String Quartet
F. Berwald: String Quartet 1
Haydn: String Quartets, Op. 71 (exc)
Mozart: Flute Quartets, String Quartet, K387, String
Quartet, K421, String Quartet, K428, String Quartet,
K458, String Quartet, K464, String Quartet, K465,
String Quartet, K499, String Quartet, K575, String
Quartet, K589, String Quartet, K590
Prokofiev: String Quartet 1, String Quartet 2
Wikmanson: String Quartet 2
see CONCERT INDEX under:
(CHAN) CHAN6535 Stravinsky—Symphonies of Wind
Instruments
(CHAN) CHAN7013/4 Bartók—String Quartets Nos 1-
6
(CHAN) CHAN8634 Bartók: String Quartets
(CHAN) CHAN8894 Dvořák—Chamber Works
(CHAN) CHAN9046 Dvořák—Chamber Works
(CHAN) CHAN9173 Dvořák—Chamber Works
(CONI) CDCF218 Panufnik—String Quartets
(CONI) 75605 51239-2 Hugh Wood—String Quartets
Nos 1-4
(CRD) CRD3312/3 Arriaga & Wikmanson: String
Quartets

(VIRG) **VC5 45023-2** Pärt/Tavener—Works for String Quartet
  cond P. PHILLIPS
  see CONCERT INDEX under:
(GIME) **CDGIM005** Tavener: Choral Works

CHINCHILLA
  cond L. ZAGROSEK
Krenek: Jonny spielt auf (Cpte)

CHINGARI, Mario (bar)
Puccini: Fanciulla del West (Cpte)
Verdi: Vespri siciliani (Cpte)

CHIOREANU, Lucian (ten)
Pfitzner: Herz (Cpte)
S. Wagner: Schwarzschwanenreich (Cpte)

CHISSARI, Santa (sop)
  see CONCERT INDEX under:
(EMI) **CMS7 64165-2** Puccini—Trittico

CHISTIAKOV, Andrey (cond)
see Bolshoi Th Orch

CHIU, Frederic (pf)
  see CONCERT INDEX under:
(HARM) **HMU90 7086/8** Prokofiev—Piano Sonatas
(HARM) **HMU90 7117** Mendelssohn—Piano Sonatas
(HARM) **HMU90 7150** Prokofiev—Piano Works, Vol. 4

CHMIELEWSKI, Tadeusz (pf)
  see CONCERT INDEX under:
(DANA) **DACOCD405** Langgaard—Complete Symphonies, Vol.2
(POLS) **PNCD065** Szymanowski: Chamber Works

CHMURA, Gabriel (cond)
see Stuttgart RSO

CHOEUR CONTEMPORAIN
  cond R. HAYRABEDIAN
Ohana: Cantigas
Stravinsky: Noces

CHOEURS RUSSES DE PARIS
  cond I. DOBROVEN
Mussorgsky: Boris Godunov (Cpte)

CHOJNACKA, Elisabeth (hpd)
  see CONCERT INDEX under:
(ERAT) **2292-45030-2** Xenakis: Miscellaneous Works
(NONE) **7559-79362-2** Górecki—Orchestral and Vocal Works

CHOLETTE, Daniel (pf)
  see CONCERT INDEX under:
(ACCO) **20123-2** Koechlin—Vocal and Chamber Works
(CLAV) **CD50-9003** Jolivet & Koechlin—Chamber Works

CHOLETTE, Daniel (pf/hpd)
  see CONCERT INDEX under:
(ACCO) **20123-2** Koechlin—Vocal and Chamber Works

CHOOKASIAN, Lilli (mez)
Prokofiev: Alexander Nevsky
Wagner: Götterdämmerung (Cpte)
  see CONCERT INDEX under:
(DG) **435 211-2GX15** Wagner—Der Ring des Nibelungen
(SONY) **SMK47638** Vaughan Williams—Orchestral Works

CHORAFAS, Dimitri (cond)
see Luxembourg Rad & TV SO

CHORALE EXPÉRIMENTALE
  cond L. BERIO
Berio: Laborintus II

CHORUS
  see CONCERT INDEX under:
(EMI) **CHS7 63802-2(1)** Tetrazzini—The London Records (pt 1)
(EMI) **CHS7 64860-2(2)** La Scala Edition - Vol.1, 1878-1914 (pt 2)
(HYPE) **CDJ33006** Schubert—Complete Lieder, Vol 6
(HYPE) **CDJ33008** Schubert—Complete Lieder, Vol 8
(HYPE) **CDJ33013** Schubert—Complete Lieder, Vol.13
(IRCC) **IRCC-CD800** Souvenirs from Meyerbeer Operas
(ODE) **CDODE1365** Oscar Natzke - A Legend in His Time
(PEAR) **GEMMCDS9001/3(1)** Singers of Imperial Russia, Vol.2 (pt 1)
(PEAR) **GEMMCDS9004/6(2)** Singers of Imperial Russia, Vol.3 (pt 2)
(PEAR) **GEMMCDS9007/9(1)** Singers of Imperial Russia, Vol.4 (pt 1)
(PEAR) **GEMMCDS9007/9(2)** Singers of Imperial Russia, Vol.4 (pt 2)
(PEAR) **GEMMCDS9073(1)** Giovanni Zenatello, Vol.1 (pt 1)
(PEAR) **GEMMCDS9073(2)** Giovanni Zenatello, Vol.1 (pt 2)
(PEAR) **GEMMCDS9074(1)** Giovanni Zenatello, Vol.2 (pt 1)
(PEAR) **GEMMCDS9074(2)** Giovanni Zenatello, Vol.2 (pt 2)
(PEAR) **GEMMCDS9923(2)** Covent Garden on Record, Vol.1 (pt 2)
(PEAR) **GEMMCDS9925(1)** Covent Garden on Record—Vol.3 (pt 1)
(PEAR) **GEMMCD9175** Heddle Nash - Serenade
(PEAR) **GEMMCD9222** Luisa Tetrazzini—Vol.2

(PHIL) **438 528-2PM4(1)** Schubert—Lieder (pt 1)
(SUPR) **11 1491-2** Jarmila Novotna sings Czech Songs and Arias
(SUPR) **11 2136-2(5)** Emmy Destinn—Complete Edition, Discs 11 & 12
(SYMP) **SYMCD1138** The Harold Wayne Collection, Vol.16
(TEST) **SBT1008** Viva Rossini
  cond O. ACKERMANN
J. Strauss II: Nacht in Venedig (Cpte), Zigeunerbaron (Cpte)
  see CONCERT INDEX under:
(EMI) **CDC7 47284-2** Elisabeth Schwarzkopf sings Operetta
  cond E. G. ASENSIO
  see CONCERT INDEX under:
(CARL) **MCD45** Spanish Royal Gala
  cond J. BARBIROLLI
  see CONCERT INDEX under:
(PEAR) **GEMMCDS9926(1)** Covent Garden on Record—Vol.4 (pt 1)
  cond T. BEECHAM
Delius: Sea Drift, Village Romeo and Juliet (Cpte)
  cond L. BERNSTEIN
  see CONCERT INDEX under:
(SONY) **SM3K47154** Bernstein—Theatre Works Volume 1
  cond R. BLUM
(SUPR) **11 1491-2** Jarmila Novotna sings Czech Songs and Arias
  cond N. BOULANGER
  see CONCERT INDEX under:
(EMI) **CDH7 61025-2** Fauré & Monteverdi Vocal Works
  cond R. BOURDON
  see CONCERT INDEX under:
(NIMB) **NI7846** Rosa Ponselle, Vol.2
(PEAR) **GEMMCDS9074(2)** Giovanni Zenatello, Vol.2 (pt 2)
(ROMO) **81007-2** Rosa Ponselle—Victor Recordings 1926-1929
  cond W. BRAITHWAITE
  see CONCERT INDEX under:
(ODE) **CDODE1365** Oscar Natzke - A Legend in His Time
  cond W. BRÜCKNER-RÜGGEBERG
Weill: Happy End (Cpte)
  cond H. BUSSER
Gounod: Faust (Cpte)
  cond G. CLOËZ
  see CONCERT INDEX under:
(MSCM) **MM30451** Mascagni—Cavalleria Rusticana, etc
  cond A. COATES
  see CONCERT INDEX under:
(CLAR) **CDGSE78-50-54** Coates conducts Wagner, Weber & Mendelssohn
(PEAR) **GEMMCDS9137** Wagner—Der Ring des Nibelungen
  cond M. CORBOZ
Duruflé: Requiem
  cond P. DERVAUX
Ganne: Saltimbanques (exc)
  cond J.O. EDWARDS
Bernstein: West Side Story (Cpte)
Kern: Show Boat (Cpte)
  cond E. ELGAR
  see CONCERT INDEX under:
(EMI) **CDS7 54564-2** The Elgar Edition, Vol.2
  cond J. FEHRING
Benatzky: Im weissen Rössl (exc)
  cond A. GALLIERA
Rossini: Barbiere di Siviglia (Cpte)
  cond P. GAUBERT
  see CONCERT INDEX under:
(PEAR) **GEMMCDS9926(1)** Covent Garden on Record—Vol.4 (pt 1)
  cond G. GELMETTI
Rossini: Barbiere di Siviglia (Cpte)
  cond R. GOEBEL
  see CONCERT INDEX under:
(ARCH) **439 866-2AH** Handel—Marian Cantatas and Arias
  cond W. GOEHR
  see CONCERT INDEX under:
(EMI) **CDM7 69478-2** A Portrait of Joseph Schmidt
  cond E. HAUKE
  see CONCERT INDEX under:
(EMI) **CDH7 64029-2** Richard Tauber - Opera Recital
(NIMB) **NI7830** Richard Tauber in Opera
  cond P. HERREWEGHE
Dusapin: Medeamaterial (Cpte)
  cond J. HOLLINGSWORTH
(EMI) **CDANGEL 5** Norton—Chu Chin Chow
  cond R. JACOBS
(HARM) **HMC90 1310** Schütz—The Nativity
  cond JAMES LEVINE
(DG) **429 790-2GH** Spirituals in Concert
  cond H. VON KARAJAN
J.Strauss II: Fledermaus (exc)
Mozart: Così fan tutte (Cpte)
Verdi: Falstaff (Cpte)
  cond C. KEENE
Puccini: Turandot (exc)
  cond E. KHACHATURIAN
Karetnikov: Till Eulenspiegel (Cpte)

  cond P. LEDGER
Berlioz: Enfance du Christ (Cpte)
  cond R. LEPPARD
Purcell: Dido (Cpte)
  cond L. LUDWIG
Weber: Abu Hassan (Cpte)
  cond C. MANDEAL
Bretan: Golem (Cpte)
  cond N. DEL MAR
Britten: Noye's Fludde (Cpte)
  cond N. MARRINER
  see CONCERT INDEX under:
(ARGO) **410 552-2ZH** Fauré: Orchestral Works
  cond J. MAUCERI
Gershwin: Girl crazy (Cpte), Strike Up the Band I (Cpte), Strike Up the Band II
  cond C. MEDLAM
Blow: Venus and Adonis (Cpte)
  cond A. MELICHAR
  see CONCERT INDEX under:
(PREI) **89070** Franz Völker (1899-1965) - II
  cond F. MOLINARI-PRADELLI
  see CONCERT INDEX under:
(RCA) **09026 68014-2** Pavarotti - The Early Years, Vol.2
  cond R. MUTI
  see CONCERT INDEX under:
(RCA) **09026 68014-2** Pavarotti - The Early Years, Vol.2
  cond E. ORTHMANN
  see CONCERT INDEX under:
(PREI) **89019** Alexander Kipnis (1891-1978)
  cond W. PELLETIER
(VAI) **VAIA1017** Leonard Warren—Early Recordings
  cond P. PICKETT
(L'OI) **440 637-2OH** Monteverdi—Ballets
  cond A. PREVIN
  see CONCERT INDEX under:
(SONY) **SK48235** A Carnegie Hall Christmas Concert
  cond M. RIESMAN
Bryars: Jesus' Blood
Glass: Einstein on the Beach (Cpte)
  cond S. ROBINSON
(EMI) **CDH7 61052-2** Beniamino Gigli—Arias and Duets (1932-1949)
  cond W.B ROGERS
(SUPR) **11 2136-2(5)** Emmy Destinn—Complete Edition, Discs 11 & 12
  cond R. ROMANI
  see CONCERT INDEX under:
(NIMB) **NI7846** Rosa Ponselle, Vol.2
  cond C. SABAJNO
  see CONCERT INDEX under:
(EMI) **CHS7 64864-2(1)** La Scala Edition - Vol.2, 1915-46 (pt 1)
(PEAR) **GEMMCDS9925(1)** Covent Garden on Record—Vol.3 (pt 1)
(PEAR) **GEMMCD9306** Ezio Pinza—Opera Recital
  cond G. SANTINI
Verdi: Traviata (Cpte)
  see CONCERT INDEX under:
(EMI) **CHS7 64864-2(1)** La Scala Edition - Vol.2, 1915-46 (pt 1)
  cond C. SCHMALSTICH
  see CONCERT INDEX under:
(PREI) **89019** Alexander Kipnis (1891-1978)
  cond G. SETTI
(NIMB) **NI7804** Giovanni Martinelli—Opera Recital
  cond E. STERN
Gershwin: Lady, be Good! (Cpte), Oh, Kay! (Cpte), Pardon My English (Cpte)
  cond L. STOKOWSKI
  see CONCERT INDEX under:
(RCA) **09026 61503-2** Stokowski Favourites
  cond A. TOSCANINI
Beethoven: Fidelio (Cpte)
Puccini: Bohème (Cpte)
Verdi: Otello (Cpte), Traviata (Cpte)
  see CONCERT INDEX under:
(DELL) **DA9020** Toscanini conducts music by his contemporaries
(RCA) **GD60325** Brahms: Symphonies & Other Works
  cond T. VETÖ
Nørgård: Gilgamesh (Cpte)
  cond W. WALTON
  see CONCERT INDEX under:
(EMI) **CHS5 65003-2** Walton conducts Walton
  cond F. WEISSMANN
  see CONCERT INDEX under:
(EMI) **CDH7 69787-2** Richard Tauber sings Operetta Arias
(PREI) **89028** Ivar Andresen (1896-1940)
  cond F. ZWEIG
  see CONCERT INDEX under:
(PREI) **89028** Ivar Andresen (1896-1940)

CHORUS MUSICUS
Rossini: Péchés de vieillesse II (Cpte), Péchés de vieillesse III (exc)
  cond C. SPERING
Bach: St Matthew Passion, BWV244 (Cpte)
Le Suer: Coronation Oratorios

CHORUS VIENNENSIS
  see CONCERT INDEX under:
(DG) **439 778-2GH** Britten—Choral Works

(NOVA) 150 081-2 Mozart—The Freemason Music
cond H. GILLESBERGER
see CONCERT INDEX under:
(RCA) GD86535 Mozart: Requiem, etc
cond N. HARNONCOURT
Bach: Christmas Oratorio, BWV248 (Cpte)
see CONCERT INDEX under:
(TELD) 2292-42497-2 Bach—Cantatas, Volume 1
(TELD) 2292-42498-2 Bach—Cantatas, Volume 2
(TELD) 2292-42499-2 Bach—Cantatas, Volume 3
(TELD) 2292-42501-2 Bach—Cantatas, Volume 5
(TELD) 2292-42502-2 Bach—Cantatas, Volume 6
(TELD) 2292-42503-2 Bach—Cantatas, Volume 7
(TELD) 2292-42504-2 Bach—Cantatas, Volume 8
(TELD) 2292-42505-2 Bach—Cantatas, Volume 9
(TELD) 2292-42506-2 Bach—Cantatas, Volume 10
(TELD) 2292-42556-2 Bach—Cantatas, Volume 11
(TELD) 2292-42559-2 Bach—Cantatas, Volume 12
(TELD) 2292-42560-2 Bach—Cantatas, Volume 13
(TELD) 2292-42577-2 Bach—Cantatas, Volume 21
(TELD) 4509-91755-2 Bach—Cantatas, Vol.1
(TELD) 4509-91756-2 Bach—Cantatas, Vol.2
(TELD) 4509-91757-2 Bach—Cantatas, Vol.3
(TELD) 4509-91759-2 Bach—Cantatas, Vol.5
cond M. HASELBÖCK
see CONCERT INDEX under:
(NOVA) 150 081-2 Mozart—The Freemason Music
cond E. INBAL
Shostakovich: Symphony 2

CHORZEMPA, Daniel (organ)
Saint-Saëns: Symphony 3
see CONCERT INDEX under:
(PHIL) 422 521-2PME2 The Complete Mozart Edition
Vol 21

CHOTZINOFF, Samuel (pf)
see CONCERT INDEX under:
(APR) APR7016 The Auer Legacy, Vol.2
(RCA) 09026 61778-2(01) The Heifetz Collection,
Vol.1 - 1917-24

CHRIST, Rudolf (ten)
J.Strauss II: Fledermaus (Cpte)
Orff: Kluge (Cpte), Mond (Cpte)
R. Strauss: Capriccio (Cpte)
see CONCERT INDEX under:
(CAMB) CD-1032 From the Operas of Erich Wolfgang
Korngold

CHRIST, Wolfram (va)
Bartók: Viola Concerto
R. Strauss: Don Quixote
Schubert: Guitar Quartet, D96, Trout Quintet, D667
see CONCERT INDEX under:
(DG) 413 311-2GH Brahms: Lieder
(DG) 429 738-2GH Debussy & Ravel: Chamber
Works
(DG) 431 782-2GH Mozart—Chamber Works

CHRISTENSEN, Blanche (sop)
Milhaud: Homme et son désir

CHRISTENSEN, Jacob (gtr)
Telemann: Essercizii musici (exc)

CHRISTENSEN, Jesper (hpd)
Corelli: Concerti Grossi, Op.6, Sonatas, Op. 5 (exc)

CHRISTENSEN, Ronald (ten)
Milhaud: Homme et son désir

CHRISTIAN, Lesley (mez)
see CONCERT INDEX under:
(SILV) FILMCD127 Vampire Circus—The Essential
Vampire Theme Collection

CHRISTIANSEN, Christian (bass)
Heise: Drot og Marsk (Cpte)
Nielsen: Saul and David (Cpte)
Nørgård: Siddhartha (Cpte)
Schumann: Rose Pilgerfahrt (Cpte)
Zemlinsky: Es war einmal (Cpte)

CHRISTIANSEN, Toke Lund (fl)
see CONCERT INDEX under:
(KONT) 32197 Syberg—Chamber Music, Vol. 2
(KONT) 32202 Ibert—Chamber Music with Flute

CHRISTIE, Gordon (ten)
Sondheim: Pacific Overtures (Cpte)

CHRISTIE, James (organ)
Mozart: Church Sonatas (exc), Mass, K427
see CONCERT INDEX under:
(KOCH) 37180-2 Pinkham—Cantatas & Chamber
Works

CHRISTIE, James David (organ)
see CONCERT INDEX under:
(KOCH) 37179-2 Pinkham—Orchestral Works
(NAXO) 8 550904 Sweelinck—Organ Works

CHRISTIE, William (cond)
see Arts Florissants Chor

CHRISTIE, William (hpd)
Boccherini: Duets, G76, String Quintets, G340-5
(exc)
Couperin: Livre de clavecin II
Fischer: Parnasse Musical (exc), Pièces de clavessin
(exc)
Rameau: Pièces de clavecin (exc)
see CONCERT INDEX under:
(HARM) HMC90 1269 Couperin—Works for Two
Harpsichords
(HARM) HMX290 1528/33(2) A Purcell Companion (pt
2)

CHRISTOFF, Boris (bass)
Gounod: Faust (Cpte)
Mussorgsky: Boris Godunov (Cpte)
Verdi: Aida (Cpte), Don Carlo (Cpte), Simon
Boccanegra (Cpte)
see CONCERT INDEX under:
(EMI) CDH7 64252-2 Christoff sings Russian Arias &
Songs
(EMI) CHS7 63025-2 Mussorgsky—Songs
(EMI) CHS7 69741-2(6) Record of Singing,
Vol.4—Russian & Slavonic Schools
(EMI) CMS7 63386-2 Borodin—Prince Igor &
Complete Solo Songs

CHRISTOPH, Ingo (ten)
Pfitzner: Herz (Cpte)

CHRISTOPHER, Russell (ten)
Bizet: Carmen (Cpte)

CHRISTOPHERS, Harry (cond)
see Concertgebouw CO

CHRISTOPHERS, Harry (ten)
Handel: Dettingen Te Deum

CHRISTOV, Nicolaï (bass)
Rossini: Guillaume Tell (Cpte)
Verdi: Ballo in maschera (Cpte)

CHRYST, Dorethea (sop)
Offenbach: Vie Parisienne (exc)

CHUBIENKO, Nadezhda (sop)
see CONCERT INDEX under:
(DANT) LYS013/5 Tchaikovsky—The Queen of
Spades

CHUCHRO, Josef (vc)
Dvořák: String Sextet

CHUMACHENCO, Nicolas (va)
see CONCERT INDEX under:
(EDEL) ED1012 Schumann: Chamber Music with
Piano

CHUMACHENCO, Ana (vn)
see CONCERT INDEX under:
(ONDI) ODE746-2 Schubert—Violin & Piano Works

CHUNG, Kyung-Wha (vn)
Bartók: Violin Concerto 1, Violin Concerto 2
Beethoven: Violin Concerto
Brahms: Piano Trio 1
Bruch: Violin Concerto
Dvořák: Romance, Op.11, Violin Concerto
Elgar: Violin Concerto
Mendelssohn: Piano Trio 1, Violin Concerto, Op. 64
R. Strauss: Violin Sonata
Respighi: Violin Sonata
Sibelius: Violin Concerto
Tchaikovsky: Violin Concerto
see CONCERT INDEX under:
(DECC) 417 289-2DH Con amore
(DECC) 421 154-2DM French Chamber Works
(DECC) 425 003-2DM Prokofiev & Stravinsky: Violin
Concertos
(DECC) 430 094-2DWO The World of Elgar
(DECC) 433 220-2DWO The World of the Violin
(DECC) 436 483-2DM French Orchestral Works
(EMI) CDC7 54211-2 Bartók—Works for Violin &
Orchestra
(LOND) 421 388-2LM Elgar: Violin Concerto, etc
(RCA) GD86517 Galway plays Bach

CHUNG, Mia (pf)
see CONCERT INDEX under:
(CHNN) CCS7195 Beethoven—Sonatas &
Bagatelles

CHUNG, Myung-Wha (vc)
Brahms: Piano Trio 1
Mendelssohn: Piano Trio 1

CHUNG, Myung-Whun (cond)
see Concertgebouw

CHUNG, Myung-Whun (pf)
Brahms: Piano Trio 1
Mendelssohn: Piano Trio 1

CHUNG TRIO
Beethoven: Piano Trios (exc)

CIACCI, Diego Dini (ob)
see CONCERT INDEX under:
(CARL) PCD979 Vivaldi—Concertos

CIANI, Dino (pf)
see CONCERT INDEX under:
(DYNA) CDS55 Dino Ciani - Piano Recital

CIAPARELLI-VIAFORA, Gina (mez)
see CONCERT INDEX under:
(NIMB) NI7857 Farrar in Italian Opera
(PEAR) EVC1(2) The Caruso Edition, Vol.1 (pt 2)
(RCA) GD60495(2) The Complete Caruso Collection
(pt 2)

CIBELLI, Signor (mndl)
see CONCERT INDEX under:
(PEAR) GEMMCD9306 Ezio Pinza—Opera Recital
(RCA) 09026 61580-2(3) RCA/Met 100 Singers, 100
Years (pt 3)

CICCOLINI, Aldo (pf)
Albéniz: Iberia
Castillon: Piano Concerto in D
Chopin: Cello Sonata
Debussy: Boîte à joujoux, Préludes (exc)
Granados: Goyescas

Indy: Symphonie, Op. 25
Rachmaninov: Cello Sonata
see CONCERT INDEX under:
(EMI) CDC7 49702-2 Satie: Piano Works, Vol.1
(EMI) CDC7 49703-2 Satie: Piano Works, Vol.2
(EMI) CDC7 49713-2 Satie: Piano Works, Vol.3
(EMI) CDC7 49714-2 Satie: Piano Works, Vol.4
(EMI) CDC7 49760-2 Satie: Piano Works, Vol.5
(EMI) CDC7 54447-2 Debussy—Piano Works, Vol.1
(EMI) CDC7 54449-2 Debussy—Piano Works, Vol.3
(EMI) CDC7 54450-2 Debussy—Piano Works, Vol.4
(EMI) CDC7 54451-2 Debussy—Piano Works, Vol.5
(EMI) CDM7 69112-2 Best of Saint-Saëns
(EMI) CMS7 69443-2 Saint-Saëns—Complete Piano
Concertos
(NUOV) 6797/8 Beethoven: Late Piano Sonatas

CICHOWICZ, Vincent (cond)
see Millar Brass Ens

CICOGNA, Adriana (mez)
Donizetti: Pazzi per progetto (Cpte)

CID, Manuel (ten)
Falla: Vida breve (Cpte)

CIDONI, Mary (sngr)
Rorem: Childhood Miracle (Cpte)

CIESINSKI, Catherine (mez)
see CONCERT INDEX under:
(MUSM) 67152-2 Stravinsky—The Composer,
Volume VII

CIESINSKI, Katherine (mez)
Dukas: Ariane et Barbe-Bleue (Cpte)
Prokofiev: War and Peace (Cpte)
Tchaikovsky: Queen of Spades (Cpte)
see CONCERT INDEX under:
(BRID) BCD9014 Elliott Carter: Vocal Works

CIESINSKI, Kristine (sop)
Shostakovich: Lady Macbeth of Mtsensk (Cpte)

CIESLEWICZ, Phillipe (treb)
Mozart: Apollo et Hyacinthus (Cpte)

CIGNA, Gina (sop)
Verdi: Forza del destino (exc), Trovatore (Cpte)
see CONCERT INDEX under:
(EMI) CHS7 64864-2(2) La Scala Edition - Vol.2,
1915-46 (pt 2)
(LYRC) SRO805 Gina Cigna—Opera Recital
(PREI) 89010 Tancredi Pasero (1893-1983) - I
(PREI) 89014 Ebe Stignani (1903-1974)
(PREI) 89016 Gina Cigna (b. 1900)
(PREI) 89042 Nazzareno de Angelis (1881-1962)

CIKADA QUARTET
see CONCERT INDEX under:
(CALA) CACD77001 Black Angels

CILEA, Francesco (pf)
see CONCERT INDEX under:
(EMI) CDH7 61046-2 Enrico Caruso: Opera Arias and
Songs - 1902-1904
(RCA) GD60495(1) The Complete Caruso Collection
(pt 1)
(SYMP) SYMCD1111 The Harold Wayne Collection,
Vol.11

CILIENTO, Nicoletta (mez)
Rossini: Torvaldo e Dorliska (Cpte)

CILLA, Luigi (bass)
see CONCERT INDEX under:
(PEAR) GEMMCDS9926(1) Covent Garden on
Record—Vol.4 (pt 1)

CILLA, Luigi (ten)
see CONCERT INDEX under:
(PEAR) GEMMCDS9074(2) Giovanni Zenatello, Vol.2
(pt 2)

CILLARIO, Carlo Felice (cond)
see LPO

CIMARA, Pietro (cond)
see Columbia SO

CIMARELLA, Maria (contr)
R. Strauss: Aegyptische Helena (Cpte)

CINCA, Dan (hn)
Enescu: Wind Decet, Op. 14

CINCINATTI CONSERVATORY ORCHESTRA
cond A. VON KREISLER
see CONCERT INDEX under:
(PEAR) GEMMCD9933 Grieg and his Circle play
Grieg

CINCINNATI JAZZ ORCHESTRA
cond E. KUNZEL
see CONCERT INDEX under:
(TELA) CD80166 Gershwin: Orchestral Works

CINCINNATI PHILHARMONIA
cond J. VAN
(CENT) CRC2205 Ives—Orchestral Works
cond G. SAMUEL
Rott: Symphony

CINCINNATI POPS CHORALE
cond E. KUNZEL
see CONCERT INDEX under:
(TELA) CD80314 Ein Straussfest II

CINCINNATI POPS ORCHESTRA
cond E. KUNZEL
Gershwin: Catfish Row
Grofé: Grand Canyon Suite

Beethoven: Leonore (exc), Symphony 1, Symphony 2, Symphony 3, Symphony 4, Symphony 5, Symphony 6, Symphony 7, Symphony 8, Symphony 9
Brahms: Violin Concerto
Bruckner: Symphony 6
Busoni: Piano Concerto, Op. 39
Dvořák: Slavonic Dances, Symphony 7, Symphony 8
Mendelssohn: Erste Walpurgisnacht, Symphony 3
Mussorgsky: Night on the bare mountain, Pictures
Schubert: Symphony 8, Symphony 9
Tchaikovsky: Eugene Onegin (exc), Symphony 6
Wagner: Rheingold (Cpte)
　　see CONCERT INDEX under:
(DECC) 443 172-2DH　Ives/Varèse—Orchestral Works
(DECC) 443 173-2DH
Bartók/Martinů/Janáček—Orchestral Works
(DECC) 443 175-2DH　Mozart—Orchestral Works
(DECC) 443 776-2DH
Ives/Ruggles/Seeger—Orchestral Works
　　cond O. KNUSSEN
　　see CONCERT INDEX under:
(ARGO) 443 203-2ZH　Copland—Ballet Music
　　cond Y. LEVI
Prokofiev: Romeo and Juliet Suites (exc)
　　cond L. MAAZEL
Berlioz: Carnaval Romain, Symphonie fantastique
Elgar: Cello Concerto
Gershwin: Porgy and Bess (Cpte)
Mussorgsky: Night on the bare mountain, Pictures
Prokofiev: Romeo and Juliet (Cpte)
Rimsky-Korsakov: Russian Easter Festival Ov, Scheherazade
Shostakovich: Symphony 5
Stravinsky: Rite of Spring (Cpte)
Tchaikovsky: Romeo and Juliet, Symphony 4
　　see CONCERT INDEX under:
(DECC) 417 252-2DH　Scriabin: Orchestral Works
(DECC) 425 052-2DM　Respighi & Verdi—Orchestral Works
(DECC) 433 616-2DSP
Addinsell/Gershwin—Orchestral Works
　　cond N. MARRINER
Schumann: Cello Concerto
　　cond I. STRAVINSKY
　　see CONCERT INDEX under:
(SONY) SM3K46292　Stravinsky—Ballets, Vol.2
　　cond G. SZELL
Beethoven: Piano Concerto 5, Symphony 3, Symphony 8
Brahms: Double Concerto, Piano Concerto 2
Bruckner: Symphony 3, Symphony 8
Dvořák: Slavonic Dances
Grieg: piano concerto
Mendelssohn: Violin Concerto, op 64
Schumann: piano concerto
　　see CONCERT INDEX under:
(SONY) MPK46732　Walton—Orchestral Works
(SONY) SBK46330　Brahms: Orchestral Works
(SONY) SBK46332　Haydn: Symphonies
(SONY) SBK46333　Mozart: Symphonies
(SONY) SBK48175　George Szell conducts Wagner
(SONY) SBK48272　R. Strauss—Orchestral Works
(SONY) SBK48279
Offenbach/Rachmaninov/Smetana—Orchestral Works
(SONY) SBK53258　Hindemith/Walton—Orchestral Works
(SONY) SM3K46519　Mozart—Legendary Interpretations
　　cond VLADIMIR ASHKENAZY
Brahms: Handel Variations, Symphony 4
Prokofiev: Cinderella (Cpte), Symphony 6, Symphony 7
Rachmaninov: Paganini Rhapsody, Piano Concerto 1, Piano Concerto 2, Piano Concerto 3
Tchaikovsky: Violin Concerto
Wieniawski: Violin Concerto 2
　　see CONCERT INDEX under:
(DECC) 430 732-2DM　Debussy—Orchestral Works
CLEVELAND ORCHESTRA CHILDREN'S CHORUS
　　cond L. MAAZEL
Gershwin: Porgy and Bess (Cpte)
CLEVELAND ORCHESTRA CHORUS
Beethoven: Choral Fantasia
　　see CONCERT INDEX under:
(DECC) 421 718-2DH3　Beethoven—Piano Concertos
　　cond P. BOULEZ
　　see CONCERT INDEX under:
(DG) 439 896-2GH　Debussy—Orchestral Works
　　cond C. VON DOHNÁNYI
Beethoven: Symphony 9
Busoni: Piano Concerto, Op. 39
Mendelssohn: Erste Walpurgisnacht
　　see CONCERT INDEX under:
(DECC) 443 776-2DH
Ives/Ruggles/Seeger—Orchestral Works
　　cond L. MAAZEL
Gershwin: Porgy and Bess (Cpte)
　　cond VLADIMIR ASHKENAZY
　　see CONCERT INDEX under:
(DECC) 430 732-2DM　Debussy—Orchestral Works
CLEVELAND QUARTET
Beethoven: String Quartet 6, String Quartet 7, String Quartet 8, String Quartet 9, String Quartet 10, String Quartet 11
Borodin: String Quartet 2
Brahms: String Quartet 1, String Quartet 2

Debussy: String Quartet
Dvo-r7-a1k: String Quartet 12, String Quartet 14
Mendelssohn: Octet, Op.20, String Quartet 2
Mozart: String Quartet, K387, String Quartet, K421
Ravel: String Quartet
Smetana: String Quartet 1
　　see CONCERT INDEX under:
(TELA) CD80382　Beethoven—String Quartets
CLEVELAND WINDS
　　cond F. FENNELL
　　see CONCERT INDEX under:
(TELA) CD80038　Music for Wind Band
(TELA) CD80099　Stars and Stripes Forever
CLEVENGER, Dale (hn)
Beethoven: Piano and Wind Quintet, Op. 16
Mozart: Piano and Wind Quintet, K452
　　see CONCERT INDEX under:
(DG) 423 239-2GC　Britten: Vocal & Orchestral Works
CLIBURN, Van (pf)
Brahms: Piano Concerto 2
Rachmaninov: Paganini Rhapsody
　　see CONCERT INDEX under:
(RCA) GD60415　Van Cliburn plays Mozart, Debussy & Barber
(RCA) GD87834　Romantic Piano Concertos
CLIDAT, France (pf)
Rachmaninov: Piano Concerto 3
　　see CONCERT INDEX under:
(FORL) FF007　Liszt—Piano Concertos Nos 1 and 2; Hungarian Rhapsodies
(FORL) UCD16516　Liszt: Orchestral works
CLIFFORD, Grahame (bass)
　　see CONCERT INDEX under:
(LYRC) SRO830　Smetana—The Bartered Bride, etc
CLIFT, Karen (sop)
Handel: Messiah (Cpte)
CLINTON, Gordon (bar)
Delius: Sea Drift, Village Romeo and Juliet (Cpte)
CLIS, Watson (vc)
　　see CONCERT INDEX under:
(CHNT) LDC278 835　Villa-Lobos—Chôros for Chamber Ensembles
CLOAD, Julia (pf)
(MERI) CDE84155　Haydn: Keyboard Sonatas
(MERI) CDE84210　Haydn—Keyboard Sonatas
(MERI) ECD84083　Haydn: Keyboard Sonatas
CLOËZ, Gustav (cond)
　　see orch
CLOSE, Shirley (mez)
R. Strauss: Elektra (Cpte)
Wagner: Walküre (Cpte)
CLOSEL, Amaury du (cond)
　　see Versailles Camerata
CLOUGH, John (euphonium)
　　see CONCERT INDEX under:
(CHAN) CHAN4505　Black Dyke plays Rossini
CLUJ-NAPOCA PHILHARMONIC ORCHESTRA
　　cond E. SIMON
　　see CONCERT INDEX under:
(OLYM) OCD449　Vieru—Orchestral Works
CLUYTENS, André (cond)
　　see Belgian Nat Orch
COADOU, Luc (bass)
Lully: Armide
COADOU, Luc (ten)
Rameau: Hippolyte et Aricie (Cpte)
COATES, Albert (cond)
　　see Berlin St Op Orch
COATES, Albert (pf)
　　see CONCERT INDEX under:
(EMI) CHS7 69741-2(6)　Record of Singing, Vol.4—Russian & Slavonic Schools
COATES, Edith (mez)
Donizetti: Fille du régiment (Cpte)
COATES, John (ten)
　　see CONCERT INDEX under:
(SYMP) SYMCD1130　Joseph Holbrooke—Historic Recordings
COBELLI, Giuseppina (sop)
　　see CONCERT INDEX under:
(EMI) CHS7 64864-2(1)　La Scala Edition - Vol.2, 1915-46 (pt 1)
COBERT, Robert (cond)
　　see OST
COBURN, Pamela (sop)
Beethoven: Fidelio (Cpte), Missa solemnis
Cherubini: Mass in D minor
Gazzaniga: Don Giovanni (Cpte)
Gounod: Faust (Cpte)
J. Strauss II: Zigeunerbaron (Cpte)
Mendelssohn: Midsummer Night's Dream (exc)
Mozart: Oca del Cairo (Cpte), Zauberflöte (Cpte)
Suder: Kleider machen Leute (Cpte)
Wagner: Parsifal (Cpte)
Zemlinsky: Traumgörge (Cpte)
　　see CONCERT INDEX under:
(SONY) SX14K48198　Mahler—Complete Symphonies, etc

COCHRAN, William (ten)
B.A. Zimmermann: Soldaten (Cpte)
Beethoven: Missa Solemnis
Busoni: Doktor Faust (Cpte)
Hindemith: Mathis der Maler (Cpte)
Schreker: Gezeichneten (Cpte)
　　see CONCERT INDEX under:
(EMI) CMS5 65212-2　Wagner—Les introuvables du Ring
(PHIL) 442 050-2PB10　Mahler—Complete Symphonies
COCHRANE, Frank (sngr)
　　see CONCERT INDEX under:
(EMI) CDANGEL 5　Norton—Chu Chin Chow
COCKERHAM, Michael (alto)
　　see CONCERT INDEX under:
(DECC) 443 455-2DF2　Vivaldi—Sacred Choral Works
COCKERILL, John (hp)
　　see CONCERT INDEX under:
(EMI) CHS7 69741-2(2)　Record of Singing, Vol.4—Anglo-American School (pt 2)
COCTEAU, Jean (narr)
　　see CONCERT INDEX under:
(PHIL) 438 973-2PM2　Igor Markevitch conducts Stravinsky
CODA, Eraldo (bar)
Puccini: Bohème (Cpte)
Verdi: Forza del Destino (Cpte)
　　see CONCERT INDEX under:
(DECC) 436 464-2DM　Ten Top Baritones & Basses
COE, Jane (vc)
Telemann: Sonates Corellisantes
　　see CONCERT INDEX under:
(ARCH) 445 839-2AH　Vivaldi—Woodwind Concertos
(CHAN) CHAN0512　Telemann, Vol.2—Ouverture burlesque
(CHAN) CHAN0541　Music from the Court of Frederick the Great
COERTSE, Mimi (sop)
R. Strauss: Arabella (Cpte), Ariadne auf Naxos (Cpte)
　　see CONCERT INDEX under:
(VANG) 08.2010.71　Bach—Choral Works
COGEN, Pierre (organ)
　　see CONCERT INDEX under:
(CYBE) CY867　Langlais—Organ Works
COHAN, George M. (sngr)
　　see CONCERT INDEX under:
(PEAR) GEMMCDS9050/2(1)　Music from the New York Stage, Vol. 1 (part 1)
(PEAR) GEMMCDS9050/2(2)　Music from the New York Stage, Vol.1 (part 2)
(PEAR) GEMMCDS9053/5　Music from the New York Stage, Vol. 2: 1908–1913
COHEN, Elie (cond)
　　see orch
COHEN, Franklin (cl)
　　see CONCERT INDEX under:
(DECC) 430 149-2DH　Brahms/Schumann—Works for Clarinet
(DG) 439 896-2GH　Debussy—Orchestral Works
COHEN, Harriet (pf)
Bach: Wohltemperierte Klavier (exc)
(DUTT) CDLX7004　Elgar—Chamber Works
(PEAR) GEMMCD9453　William Primrose—Viola Recital
COHEN, Isidore (vn)
Mozart: Clarinet Quintet, K581
COHEN, Jeff (pf)
(DECC) 436 417-2DH　Ute Lemper sings Kurt Weill, Vol.2
(REM) REM311049　Duparc—Mélodies
(REM) REM311069　Hahn—Mélodies
(REM) REM311086　French Duets
(REM) REM311175　Fauré—Mélodies, Vol.1
COHEN, Joel (cond)
　　see Boston Camerata
COHEN, Pablo (gtr)
(DORI) DOR90202　Impressions—Camerata Bariloche
COHEN, Patrick (fp)
Mozart: Piano Trio, K498
　　see CONCERT INDEX under:
(HARM) HMC90 1514　Haydn—Keyboard Trios, Volume 4
COHEN, Patrick (pf)
Beethoven: Piano Trios (exc)
Boccherini: Piano Quintets, G407-12 (exc), Piano Quintets, G413-8 (exc)
　　see CONCERT INDEX under:
(HARM) HMC90 1314　Haydn—Piano Trios, Vol.2
(HARM) HMC90 1400　Haydn—Piano Trios
COHEN, Raymond (vn)
　　see CONCERT INDEX under:
(MERI) DUOCD89019/21　Beethoven—Sonatas for Violin and Piano
(REFE) RRCD-47　Robert Farnon—Concert Works

COHEN, Robert (vc)
Schubert: String Quintet
Walton: Cello Concerto
see CONCERT INDEX under:
(ARGO) 436 545-2ZH Elgar—Orchestral Works
(ARGO) 443 170-2ZH Bliss—Orchestral Works
(CFP) CD-CFP9003 Elgar: Orchestral Works
(CRD) CRD3391 Works for Cello
(EMI) CZS7 67435-2 Rodrigo—Orchestral Works

COHEN, Susanna (bn)
see CONCERT INDEX under:
(ASV) CDDCA922 Arnold—Clarinet Concertos

COHLER, Jonathan (cl)
see CONCERT INDEX under:
(CRYS) Crystal CD733 Moonflowers, Baby!—Clarinet
& Piano Works
(ONGA) 024-101 Cohler on Clarinet
(ONGA) 024-102 More Cohler on Clarinet

COHN, Richard (bar)
Schoenberg: Moses and Aron (Cpte)
Verdi: Otello (Cpte)

COIFFIER, Marthe (sop)
Gounod: Faust (Cpte)

COIN, Christophe (cond)
see Limoges Baroque Ens

COIN, Christophe (va da gamba)
Forqueray: Pièces de viole (exc)

COIN, Christophe (vc)
Beethoven: Piano Trios (exc), In Nomine
(exc)
Gibbons: Fantasias Royals a 3 (exc), In Nomine
(exc)
Haydn: Cello Concerto in C, Cello Concerto in D
Purcell: Sonatas, Z802-11
see CONCERT INDEX under:
(HARM) HMC90 1314 Haydn—Piano Trios, Vol.2
(HARM) HMC90 1400 Haydn—Piano Trios
(HARM) HMC90 1514 Haydn—Keyboard Trios,
Volume 4
(L'OI) 433 052-2OH Vivaldi—Works for Cello
(TELD) 4509-94552-2 Vivaldi—Double and Triple
Concertos

COIN, Christophe (vc/dir)
see CONCERT INDEX under:
(ASTR) E8517 Boccherini—Cello Concertos, etc
(ASTR) E8530 Bach—Cantatas
(ASTR) E8544 Bach—Cantatas

COLAFELICE, Giacomo (bass)
Donizetti: Maria di Rohan (Cpte)

COLAIANNI, Domenico (sngr)
Mascagni: Rantzau (Cpte)

COLAN, Ruxandra (vn)
see CONCERT INDEX under:
(ALTA) AIR-CD-9011 Philip Martin—Chamber & Vocal
Works
(DYNA) CDS21/2 Franck—Chamber works

COLAS, Sylvie (sop)
Montéclair: Jephté (Cpte)

COLAZZA, Luigi (ten)
(IRCC) IRCC-CD808 Souvenirs of 19th Century Italian
Opera
(NIMB) NI7831 Mattia Battistini (1856-1928)
(PREI) 89045 Mattia Battistini (1856-1928)

COLD, Ulrik (bass)
Bach: St Matthew Passion, BWV244 (Cpte)
Janáček: Glagolitic Mass (Cpte)
Mendelssohn: Hochzeit des Camacho (Cpte)
Wagner: Parsifal (Cpte)
see CONCERT INDEX under:
(BIS) BIS-CD437 Schnittke: Orchestral & Vocal Works
(CHAN) CHAN9223 R. Strauss—A cappella choral
works

COLDSTREAM GUARDS BAND
cond R.A. RIDINGS
see CONCERT INDEX under:
(BAND) BNA5002 Masterpieces for Band
cond M. ROGAN
see CONCERT INDEX under:
(LARR) CDLRH221 Dame Nellie Melba - Opera and
Song Recital

COLE, Gary (cond)
see Regent Chbr Ch

COLE, Graham (timp)
see CONCERT INDEX under:
(CONI) CDCF217 Panufnik—Orchestral Works

COLE, Maggie (hpd)
see CONCERT INDEX under:
(VIRG) VC7 59015-2 Boccherini—Cello Concertos
and Sonatas

COLE, Maggie (kybds)
D. Scarlatti: Keyboard Sonatas (exc)
see CONCERT INDEX under:
(AMON) CD-SAR18 Guitar Collection

COLE, Steven (ten)
Floyd: Susannah (Cpte)

COLE, Vinson (ten)
Beethoven: Missa solemnis (Cpte)
Berlioz: Grande messe des morts (Cpte), Roméo et
Juliette (Cpte)
Haydn: Schöpfung (Cpte)

Mozart: Requiem
R. Strauss: Rosenkavalier (Cpte)
Stravinsky: Oedipus Rex (Cpte)
Verdi: Requiem (Cpte)
see CONCERT INDEX under:
(SONY) SK45855 Mozart: Bastien und Bastienne

COLEMAN, Anna (vn)
see CONCERT INDEX under:
(CLRI) CC0006 Clarinet Virtuosi of the
Past—Hermstedt

COLEMAN, Barrington (ten)
Gershwin: Porgy and Bess (Cpte)

COLEMAN-WRIGHT, Peter (bar)
Stravinsky: Oedipus Rex (Cpte)

COLES, Mark (bass)
Corghi: Divara (Cpte)
Henze: Englisch Cat (Cpte)

COLES, Priti (sop)
Mozart: Così fan tutte (Cpte)
see CONCERT INDEX under:
(NAXO) 8 550495 Mozart—Sacred Choral Works

COLES, Samuel (fl)
see CONCERT INDEX under:
(VIRG) VJ5 61108-2 Mozart—Concertos

COLETTI, Paul (va)
Maw: Flute Quartet
see CONCERT INDEX under:
(CLAV) CD50-8507 Chamber recital
(HYPE) CDA66683 Liszt—Piano Works, Vol.23
(HYPE) CDA66687 English Viola Music

COLICOS, Nicolas (sngr)
Romberg: Student Prince (Cpte)

COLLABORATIVE ARTS CHAMBER ORCHESTRA
cond J. MEENA
see CONCERT INDEX under:
(KOCH) 37186-2 French Clarinet Music

COLLARD, André (pf)
see CONCERT INDEX under:
(EMI) CHS7 69741-2(3) Record of Singing,
Vol.4—French School

COLLARD, Catherine (pf)
Indy: Symphonie, Op. 25
see CONCERT INDEX under:
(RCA) RD60899 Ravel/Debussy—Mélodies
(RCA) 09026 61187-2 Nathalie Stutzmann sings
Schumann, Vol.1
(RCA) 09026 61439-2 Fauré—Mélodies
(RCA) 09026 61728-2 Schumann—Lieder, Volume 2
(VIRG) VC7 59296-2 Satie—Piano Works, Vol.3

COLLARD, Jeannine (mez)
Debussy: Pelléas et Mélisande (Cpte)
Offenbach: Contes d'Hoffmann (Cpte)
Ravel: Enfant et les Sortilèges (Cpte)

COLLARD, Jean-Philippe (pf)
Bach: 3-Harpsichord Concerti (exc), 4-Harpsichord
Concerto
Brahms: Hungarian Dances, Waltzes, Op. 39
Chopin: Cello Sonata
Rachmaninov: Cello Sonata
Saint-Saëns: Piano Concerto 2, Piano Concerto 3,
Piano Concerto 4, Piano Concerto 5
Schubert: Piano Trio 2, Sonata, D574
see CONCERT INDEX under:
(DECC) 443 968-2DH Poulenc—Chamber Works
(EMI) CDC7 47939-2 Fauré—Orchestral Works
(EMI) CDC7 49165-2 Schubert: Works for Piano Trio
(EMI) CDC7 49288-2 José van Dam sings French
Songs
(EMI) CDC7 54818-2 Mélodies, Volume 2
(EMI) CMS7 62548-2 Fauré—Chamber Works, Vol.2
(EMI) CZS7 62687-2 Fauré—Piano Works
(EMI) CZS7 62745-2 Rachmaninov—Piano Works

COLLART, Claudine (sop)
Audran: Miss Helyett (Cpte)
Bazin: Voyage en Chine (Cpte)
Boïeldieu: Voitures Versées (Cpte)
Gounod: Roméo et Juliette (Cpte)
Messager: Coups de Roulis (Cpte), Passionément
(Cpte), P'tites Michu (exc)
Planquette: Rip van Winkle (Cpte)
see CONCERT INDEX under:
(CHNT) LDC278 1068 Chabrier—Une Education
Manquée/Mélodies
(EMI) CZS7 67515-2 Offenbach—Operetta highlights

COLLEAUX, Paul (cond)
see Nantes Instr Ens

COLLEGIATE CHORALE
cond R. BASS
R. Strauss: Friedenstag (Cpte)
cond J. CONLON
(RCA) 09026 61509-2 A Salute to American Music

COLLEGIATE ORCHESTRA
cond R. BASS
R. Strauss: Friedenstag (Cpte)

COLLEGIUM AUREUM
Bach: Brandenburg Concertos, Suites, BWV1066-9
Handel: Concerti Grossi, Op.6, Organ Concertos
Mozart: Serenade, K361
Pergolesi: Serva Padrona
see CONCERT INDEX under:
(DHM) GD77151 Bach—Secular Cantatas

(DHM) 74321 26617-2(1) Elly Ameling - The Early
Recorings, Vols. 1-3
cond G. LEONHARDT
Rameau: Indes galantes (exc)
cond R. PETERS
Rameau: Dardanus (exc)
cond R. POHL
see CONCERT INDEX under:
(DHM) 74321 26617-2(1) Elly Ameling - The Early
Recorings, Vols. 1-3
cond G. SCHMIDT-GADEN
see CONCERT INDEX under:
(DHM) 74321 26617-2(1) Elly Ameling - The Early
Recorings, Vols. 1-3
cond I. SEGARRA
Anon: Missa Salisburgensis, Plaudite tympana

COLLEGIUM CARTUSIANUM
cond P. NEUMANN
Mozart: Ave verum corpus, K618, Kyrie, K341, Mass,
K427, Requiem
see CONCERT INDEX under:
(EMI) CDC7 54037-2 Mozart—Masses and Church
Sonatas

COLLEGIUM INSTRUMENTALE BRUGENSE
cond A. ZEDDA
Rossini: Tancredi (Cpte)

COLLEGIUM MUSICUM
cond P. SACHER
see CONCERT INDEX under:
(ERAT) 2292-45626-2 Dutilleux—Orchestral Works
cond M. SCHØNWANDT
Mozart: Piano Concerto 20, Piano Concerto 23

COLLEGIUM MUSICUM AMSTELODAMENSE
cond B. HAITINK
see CONCERT INDEX under:
(PHIL) 442 050-2PB10 Mahler—Complete
Symphonies

COLLEGIUM MUSICUM SOLOISTS
see CONCERT INDEX under:
(KONT) 32202 Ibert—Chamber Music with Flute

COLLEGIUM MUSICUM 90
A. Marcello: Concerto in B flat, Oboe Concerti, 'La
Cetra'
Albinoni: Concerti, Op. 7 (exc), Concerti, Op. 9 (exc)
Leclair: Concertos, Op. 7 (exc), Concertos, Op. 10
(exc)
see CONCERT INDEX under:
(CHAN) CHAN0512 Telemann, Vol.2—Ouverture
burlesque
(CHAN) CHAN0519 Telemann—La Changeante
(CHAN) CHAN0525 Telemann—Domestic Music,
Vol.3
(CHAN) CHAN0528 Vivaldi—Double Concertos
(CHAN) CHAN0547 Telemann—Orchestral Works
cond R. HICKOX
Bach: Mass in B minor, BWV232 (Cpte)
Handel: Messiah (Cpte)
Purcell: Dioclesian, Z627 (Cpte), Timon of Athens,
Z632 (exc)
Telemann: Deus judicium tuum, Donner-Ode
see CONCERT INDEX under:
(CHAN) CHAN0518 Vivaldi & Bach—Choral Works
cond S. STANDAGE
see CONCERT INDEX under:
(CHAN) CHAN0564 Leclair—Violin Concertos,
Volume 2

COLLEGIUM MUSICUM 90 CHORUS
cond R. HICKOX
Bach: Mass in B minor, BWV232 (Cpte)
Handel: Messiah (Cpte)
Purcell: Dioclesian, Z627 (Cpte)
Telemann: Deus judicium tuum, Donner-Ode
see CONCERT INDEX under:
(CHAN) CHAN0518 Vivaldi & Bach—Choral Works

COLLEGIUM VOCALE
cond N. HARNONCOURT
Mozart: Thamos, K345 (Cpte)
cond P. HERREWEGHE
Bach: Cantata 66, Easter Oratorio, BWV249
Beethoven: Missa solemnis
C.P.E. Bach: Auferstehung und Himmelfahrt Jesu
(Cpte)
Dusapin: Medeamaterial (Cpte)
Lully: Armide
Mendelssohn: Elias (Cpte), Midsummer Night's
Dream (Cpte)
Mozart: Mass, K427, Meistermusik, K477
see CONCERT INDEX under:
(ASTR) E7780 Lassus—5 Part Motets
(HARM) HMC90 1462 Purcell—Funeral Music for
Queen Mary; Te Deum; Anthems
(HARM) HMC90 1479 Bach—Cantatas
(HARM) HMX290 1528/33(1) A Purcell Companion (pt
1)
(VIRG) VC7 59320-2 Bach—Cantatas
cond J. VAN IMMERSEEL
see CONCERT INDEX under:
(CHNN) CCS7895 Buxtehude—Cantatas

COLLETT, Barry (cond)
see Rutland Sinfonia

COLLIER, Frederick (bass)
Wagner: Götterdämmerung (exc)
see CONCERT INDEX under:
(PEAR) GEMMCDS9137 Wagner—Der Ring des
Nibelungen

Stravinsky: Firebird Suite (1919)
see CONCERT INDEX under:
(SONY) **SK66832** Debussy/Ravel—Orchestral
Works
  cond B. HAITINK
Beethoven: Piano Concerto 1, Piano Concerto 2,
Piano Concerto 3, Romances, Symphony 5,
Symphony 6, Violin Concerto
Brahms: Double Concerto, Piano Concerto 1,
Symphony 2, Symphony 3, Tragic Overture, Violin
Concerto
Bruch: Violin Concerto 1
Martin: Cello Concerto, Four Elements
Mendelssohn: Violin Concerto, Op. 64
R. Strauss: Alpensinfonie
Rachmaninov: Piano Concerto 1, Piano Concerto 2,
Piano Concerto 3, Piano Concerto 4
Shostakovich: Jewish Folk Poetry, Op 79, Marina
Tsvetaeva Poems, Symphony 5, Symphony 6,
Symphony 8, Symphony 11, Symphony 12,
Symphony 13, Symphony 14
  see CONCERT INDEX under:
(DECC) **421 590-2DH2** Rachmaninov: Complete
Piano Concertos
(EMI) **CMS7 64922-2** Perlman plays Romantic Violin
Concertos
(EMI) **CZS4 83177-2(1)** Itzhak Perlman Edition (pt 1)
(ETCE) **KTC1156** Delden—Orchestral Works
(PHIL) **438 437-2PH** French orchestral works
(PHIL) **438 742-2PM2** Debussy—Orchestral Music
(PHIL) **438 812-2PM2** Bartók—Orchestral Works
(PHIL) **442 040-2PB9** Bruckner—Complete
Symphonies
(PHIL) **442 050-2PB10** Mahler—Complete
Symphonies
(PHIL) **442 061-2PB6** Tchaikovsky—Complete
Symphonies, etc
(PHIL) **442 068-2PB4** Brahms—Complete
Symphonies, etc
(PHIL) **442 073-2PB5** Beethoven—Complete
Symphonies, etc
(PHIL) **442 079-2PB2** Schumann—Complete
Symphonies, etc
(PHIL) **442 287-2PM2** Favourite Violin Concertos
(PHIL) **442 577-2PM2** Beethoven—Concertos,
Volume 1
(PHIL) **442 580-2PM2** Beethoven—Concertos,
Volume 2
(PHIL) **442 586-2PM2** Tchaikovsky—Complete Tone
Poems
  cond N. HARNONCOURT
Bruckner: Symphony 3
J. Strauss II: Fledermaus (exc)
Mozart: Così fan tutte (Cpte), Don Giovanni (Cpte),
Nozze di Figaro (Cpte), Piano Concerto 23, Piano
Concerto 26, Schauspieldirektor (exc), Symphony
38, Symphony 39, Thamos, K345 (Cpte)
Schubert: Symphony 2, Symphony 6, Symphony 9
  see CONCERT INDEX under:
(TELD) **4509-91184-2** Schubert—Symphonies
(TELD) **4509-91187-2** Mozart—Symphonies
(TELD) **4509-91189-2** Mozart—Symphonies
(TELD) **4509-91190-2** Mozart—Symphonies
(TELD) **4509-92628-2** Haydn—'London' Symphonies,
etc
(TELD) **4509-97509-2** Schubert—Symphonies Nos 1
and 4
(TELD) **4509-97511-2** Schubert—Symphonies Nos 3,
5 and 8
(TELD) **9031-74786-2** Johann Strauss II—Orchestral
Works
(TELD) **9031-74859-2** Haydn—Symphonies
  cond E. INBAL
see CONCERT INDEX under:
(BELA) **450 145-2** Debussy—Orchestral Works
  cond M. JANSONS
Berlioz: Carnaval Romain, Symphonie fantastique
  cond N. JÄRVI
Prokofiev: Piano Concerto 2, Piano Concerto 3
Reger: Hiller Variations, Symphonic Poems, Op.128
Stravinsky: Jeu de cartes, Orpheus (Cpte)
  see CONCERT INDEX under:
(CHAN) **CHAN8791** Prokofiev: Piano Concertos
  cond E. JOCHUM
see CONCERT INDEX under:
(ETCE) **KTC1156** Delden—Orchestral Works
  cond O. KLEMPERER
Mahler: Symphony 2
  see CONCERT INDEX under:
(ARCI) **ARC109** Klemperer conducts the
Concertgebouw, Vol.2
(DECC) **425 995-2DM** Brahms/Mahler—Lieder
  cond K. KONDRASHIN
Hindemith: Cello Concerto, Clarinet Concerto
Scriabin: Symphony 3
  see CONCERT INDEX under:
(PHIL) **442 643-2PM** Rimsky-Korsakov—Orchestral
Works
  cond I. MARKEVITCH
see CONCERT INDEX under:
(PHIL) **442 586-2PM2** Tchaikovsky—Complete Tone
Poems
  cond W. MENGELBERG
Beethoven: Symphony 9
R. Strauss: Don Juan, Heldenleben
Tchaikovsky: Symphony 6, 1812
  see CONCERT INDEX under:
(ARHI) **ADCD107** Mengelberg Edition—Volume 1
(ARHI) **ADCD108** Mengelberg Edition, Vol.2
(ARHI) **ADCD110** Mengelberg Edition - Volume 4
(ARHI) **ADCD111** Mengelberg Edition - Volume 5

(ARHI) **ADCD112** The Mengelberg Edition, Volume
6
(KOCH) **37011-2** Legendary Conductors
(MUSI) **MACD-780** The Mengelberg Legacy
(MUSI) **MACD-809** Mengelberg conducts Tchaikovsky
(SYMP) **SYMCD1078** Willem Mengelberg conducts
  cond P. MONTEUX
see CONCERT INDEX under:
(PHIL) **442 544-2PM5** Pierre Monteux
  cond MYUNG-WHUN CHUNG
Prokofiev: Romeo and Juliet Suites (exc)
  cond N. RESCIGNO
Bellini: Pirata (exc)
  cond W. SAWALLISCH
Beethoven: Symphony 1, Symphony 2, Symphony 3,
Symphony 4, Symphony 5, Symphony 6, Symphony
7, Symphony 8, Symphony 9
  cond G. SZELL
see CONCERT INDEX under:
(ETCE) **KTC1156** Delden—Orchestral Works
(PHIL) **442 727-2PM4** George Szell - The Early
Years
  cond K. TENNSTEDT
Beethoven: Violin Concerto
  cond M. TILSON THOMAS
Ives: Symphony 2, Symphony 3
  cond VLADIMIR ASHKENAZY
Rachmaninov: Bells, Isle of the Dead, Russian
Songs, Op.41, Symphonic Dances, Symphony in D
minor, Symphony 1, Symphony 2, Symphony 3
  cond D. ZINMAN
see CONCERT INDEX under:
(PHIL) **442 299-2PM2** Mozart—Complete Flute Works

CONCERTO AMSTERDAM
see CONCERT INDEX under:
(TELD) **4509-92180-2** Leclair/Naudot—Concertos
  cond F. BRÜGGEN
Telemann: Musique de table (Cpte)
  see CONCERT INDEX under:
(TELD) **4509-92177-2** Telemann—Paris Quartets;
Suites
(TELD) **9031-77620-2** Telemann—Orchestral Works
  cond J. JÜRGENS
see CONCERT INDEX under:
(TELD) **4509-93687-2** Bach—Cantatas
  cond J. SCHRÖDER
see CONCERT INDEX under:
(TELD) **9031-77624-2** Boccherini—Cello Concertos

CONCERTO ARMONICO
  cond J. GRIMBERT
Mozart: Ascanio in Alba (Cpte)

CONCERTO COLOGNE
  cond F. BERNIUS
Bach: Cantata 206, Cantata 207a

CONCERTO COPENHAGEN
(CHAN) **CHAN0550** Scheibe—Sinfonias
  cond A. MANZE
see CONCERT INDEX under:
(CHAN) **CHAN0535** Baroque Flute Concertos

CONCERTO ITALIANO
  cond R. ALESSANDRINI
Marenzio: Madrigals (4vv), Bk 1 (Cpte)
Monteverdi: Madrigals, Bk 2, Madrigals, Bk.4 (Cpte)
  see CONCERT INDEX under:
(O111) **OPS30-94** Lassus—Libro de
villanelle,moresche,et altre canzoni

CONCERTO ITALIANO VOCAL ENSEMBLE
  cond R. ALESSANDRINI
Monteverdi: Madrigals, Bk.6 (Cpte)

CONCERTO PALATINO
(DHM) **05472 77326-2** Sacred Choral Works

CONCERTO ROCOCO
Balbastre: Sonates en quatuor, Op. 3
Schobert: Quartets, Op. 7 (exc), Sonatas, Op. 14
(exc), Sonatas, Op. 16
Soler: Quintets (exc)

CONCERTO VOCALE
see CONCERT INDEX under:
(ASTR) **E8530** Bach—Cantatas
(ASTR) **E8544** Bach—Cantatas
(HARM) **HMA190 1084** Monteverdi—Madrigals
(HARM) **HMC90 1133** Clarke & Couperin—Sacred
music
  cond R. JACOBS
Cavalli: Calisto (Cpte)
Monteverdi: Incoronazion di Poppea (Cpte), Orfeo
(Cpte), Ritorno d'Ulisse in patria (Cpte)
Schütz: Auferstehungs Histoire, SWV50, Primo libro
de madrigali (exc)

CONCORDIA
  cond M. ALSOP
see CONCERT INDEX under:
(EMI) **CDC7 54851-2** Gershwin—Blue Monday, etc

CONDE, Carlos (sngr)
Schuman: Mighty Casey (Cpte)

CONDÒ, Nucci (mez)
Alfano: Risurrezione (Cpte)
Boito: Mefistofele (Cpte)
Rossini: Otello (Cpte)

CONGIU, Francesca (sop)
Almeida: Giuditta (Cpte)

CONI, Paolo (bar)
Donizetti: Favorita (Cpte), Maria di Rohan (Cpte)
Leoncavallo: Pagliacci (Cpte)
Puccini: Manon Lescaut (Cpte)
Verdi: Don Carlo (Cpte), Simon Boccanegra (Cpte),
Traviata (Cpte)
  see CONCERT INDEX under:
(DECC) **436 463-2DM** Ten Top Tenors

CONLEY, Eugene (ten)
Beethoven: Missa Solemnis

CONLON, James (cond)
see Cologne Gürzenich Orch

CONN, Michael (gtr)
Arnold: Guitar Concerto, Op.67
Rodrigo: Concierto de Aranjuez

CONNELL, Elizabeth (sop)
Donizetti: Poliuto (Cpte)
Mahler: Symphony 8
Rossini: Guillaume Tell (Cpte)
Schoenberg: Gurrelieder
Schreker: Gezeichneten (Cpte)
Verdi: Due Foscari (Cpte), Requiem (Cpte)
Wagner: Walküre (Cpte)
  see CONCERT INDEX under:
(DG) **415 353-2GH4** Mendelssohn—Complete
Symphonies, etc
(EMI) **CMS7 64476-2** Mahler—Symphonies, Vol.2
(HYPE) **CDA66420** Vaughan Williams: Vocal Works
(HYPE) **CDJ33005** Schubert—Complete Lieder, Vol.
5

CONNELL, John (bass)
Mendelssohn: Elijah (Cpte)
Tchaikovsky: Eugene Onegin (Cpte)
  see CONCERT INDEX under:
(EMI) **CDC5 55121-2** Szymanowski—Choral Works
(HYPE) **CDA66420** Vaughan Williams: Vocal Works
(TER) **CDVIR8307** Josephine Barstow sings Verdi
Arias

CONNORS, Ursula (sop)
G. Charpentier: Louise (Cpte)
Puccini: Rondine (Cpte)
  see CONCERT INDEX under:
(EMI) **CDANGEL 5** Norton—Chu Chin Chow
(SONY) **M3K79312** Puccini: Il Trittico

CONOLEY, Ann (sop)
Wagner: Walküre (Cpte)

CONQUER, Jeanne-Marie (vn)
see CONCERT INDEX under:
(ERAT) **2292-45772-2** Saint-Saëns—Works for
Chamber Ensemble

CONRAD, Andreas (ten)
R. Strauss: Ariadne auf Naxos (Cpte)

CONRAD, Barbara (mez)
A. Thomas: Hamlet (Cpte)
Gershwin: Porgy and Bess (Cpte)

CONRAD, Doda (bass)
see CONCERT INDEX under:
(EMI) **CDH7 61025-2** Fauré & Monteverdi Vocal
Works

CONRAD, Richard (bar)
see CONCERT INDEX under:
(PEAR) **SHECD9636** Sullivan—Guinevere and other
Ballads

CONSORT OF LONDON
  cond R. HAYDON CLARK
Bizet: Arlésienne (Cpte), Jeux d'enfants
Schubert: Octet, D803
  see CONCERT INDEX under:
(COLL) **Coll11140-2** Vaughan Williams—Orchestral
works

CONSORT OF MUSICKE
Dowland: Third and Last Booke of Songs (exc)
Monteverdi: Madrigals, Bk 2 (Cpte), Madrigals, Bk.3
(Cpte), Madrigals, Bk 8 (exc), Scherzi musicali (1632)
(exc)
  see CONCERT INDEX under:
(BIS) **BIS-CD392** Music from the time of Christian IV,
Vol. 4
(MOSC) **070986** The Mistress—Settings of Abraham
Cowley's Poems
(MOSC) **070995** Monteverdi—Erotic Madrigals & their
Sacred Contrafacta
(VIRG) **VC7 59035-2** T. Ravenscroft—Songs, Rounds
& Catches
  cond A. ROOLEY
Dowland: First Book of Songs (exc), Second Booke of
Songs (Cpte)
Marini: Concerto terzo (Cpte)
Monteverdi: Madrigals, Bk.4 (Cpte), Madrigals, Bk.6
(Cpte), Madrigals, Bk 8 (exc)
Notari: Prime musiche nuove (Cpte)
Purcell: Don Quixote: The Musical (Cpte)
  see CONCERT INDEX under:
(CARL) **PCD881** Monteverdi—Solos and Duets
(DHM) **RD77154** Concerto Delle Donne
(HYPE) **CDA66135** H. Lawes: Psalms, Ayres and
Dialogues
(HYPE) **CDA66227** Emma Kirkby Collection
(HYPE) **CDA66256** Ward: Madrigals
(L'OI) **421 480-2OH** Monteverdi: Madrigali Erotici
(MOSC) **070981** John Ward—Madrigals and
Fantasias
(MOSC) **070982** John Ward—Psalms and Anthems

(EMI) CDC7 54437-2   Callas Rarities
(RCA) 09026 61580-2(7)   RCA/Met 100 Singers, 100 Years (pt 7)

CORENA, Fernando (bass)
Cimarosa: Maestro di cappella (Cpte)
Donizetti: Don Pasquale (Cpte), Elisir d'amore (Cpte)
J. Strauss II: Fledermaus (Cpte)
Mozart: Don Giovanni (Cpte), Nozze di Figaro (Cpte)
Puccini: Bohème (Cpte), Madama Butterfly (Cpte), Manon Lescaut (Cpte), Tosca (Cpte), Turandot (Cpte)
Rossini: Barbiere di Siviglia (Cpte), Italiana in Algeri (Cpte)
Verdi: Aida (Cpte), Forza del Destino (Cpte), Otello (Cpte), Rigoletto (Cpte)
see CONCERT INDEX under:
(DECC) 411 665-2DM3   Puccini: Il trittico
(DECC) 433 706-2DMO3   Bellini—Beatrice di Tenda; Operatic Arias
(DECC) 436 464-2DM   Ten Top Baritones & Basses

CORIGLIANO, John (vn)
see CONCERT INDEX under:
(PHIL) 426 076-2PCC   Vivaldi: Concertos

CORKHILL, David (perc)
Britten: Rejoice in the Lamb

CORMAN, David (sngr)
Schuman: Mighty Casey (Cpte), Question of Taste (Cpte)

CORNELIUS, Peter (ten)
see CONCERT INDEX under:
(PEAR) GEMMCDS9924(2)   Covent Garden on Record, Vol.2 (pt 2)
(SIMA) PSC1810(2)   Grieg—Songs (historical recordings, pt 2)

CORNOLDI, Claudio (ten)
see CONCERT INDEX under:
(EMI) CMS7 64165-2   Puccini—Trittico

CORNWELL, Joseph (ten)
Handel: Messiah (Cpte)
Rossini: Petite messe solennelle
see CONCERT INDEX under:
(EMI) CDS7 49749-2   Handel—Music for the Carmelite Vespers

CORONATION CHOIR
cond E. BULLOCK
see CONCERT INDEX under:
(PEAR) GEMMCD9342   Vaughan Williams: Vocal Works

CORONATION ORCHESTRA
cond E. BULLOCK
see CONCERT INDEX under:
(PEAR) GEMMCD9342   Vaughan Williams: Vocal Works

CORP, Ronald (cond)
see New London Orch

CORRADETTI, Ferrucio (bar)
see CONCERT INDEX under:
(BONG) GB1043-2   Italian Baritones of the Acoustic Era
(IRCC) IRCC-CD808   Souvenirs of 19th Century Italian Opera
(SYMP) SYMCD1113   The Harold Wayne Collection, Vol.13
(SYMP) SYMCD1126   The Harold Wayne Collection, Vol.14

CORRE, Philippe (pf)
see CONCERT INDEX under:
(PIER) PV786091   Le Groupe des Six: Piano Duets

CORRÉAS, Jérôme (bass)
Campra: Idoménée (Cpte)
Purcell: Fairy Queen, Z629 (Cpte)
Rameau: Castor et Pollux (Cpte), Indes galantes (Cpte), Nélée et Myrthis (Cpte)
see CONCERT INDEX under:
(HARM) HMC90 1351   Delalande—Sacred Choral Works

CORSI, Emilia (sop)
see CONCERT INDEX under:
(MEMO) HR4408/9(1)   Singers in Genoa, Vol.1 (disc 1)
(NIMB) NI7831   Mattia Battistini (1856-1928)
(PEAR) GEMMCDS9924(1)   Covent Garden on Record, Vol.2 (pt 1)
(PREI) 89045   Mattia Battistini (1856-1928)

CORSI, Rina (sop)
Donizetti: Linda di Chamounix (Cpte)
see CONCERT INDEX under:
(DECC) 443 930-2DM   Jussi Björling sings Opera Arias

CORTESE, Luigi (pf)
see CONCERT INDEX under:
(EMI) CHS7 69741-2(7)   Record of Singing, Vol.4—Italian School

CORTESE, Paul (va)
see CONCERT INDEX under:
(ASV) CDDCA931   Hindemith—Works for Viola, Volume 1

CORTET, Roger (fl)
see CONCERT INDEX under:
(BIDD) LAB028   Jacques Thibaud & Alfred Cortot

CORTEZ, Viorica (mez)
Tchaikovsky: Iolanta (Cpte)

CORTIS, Antonio (ten)
see CONCERT INDEX under:
(NIMB) NI7850   Antonio Cortis (1891-1952)
(PEAR) GEMMCDS9926(2)   Covent Garden on Record—Vol.4 (pt 2)
(PREI) 89043   Antonio Cortis (1891-1952)

CORTIS, Marcello (bar)
Gounod: Mireille (Cpte)
Rossini: Italiana in Algeri (Cpte)

CORTOT, Alfred (cond)
see Barcelona Casals Orch

CORTOT, Alfred (pf)
Beethoven: Piano Trios (exc)
Schubert: Piano Trio 1
see CONCERT INDEX under:
(APR) APR7028   Jacques Thibaud—Complete Solo Recordings 1929-36
(BIDD) LAB028   Jacques Thibaud & Alfred Cortot
(BIDD) LAB029   French Chamber works
(BIDD) LHW001   Alfred Cortot plays Chopin
(BIDD) LHW002   Alfred Cortot plays Weber and Mendelssohn
(BIDD) LHW003   Alfred Cortot plays Schumann, Vol. 1
(BIDD) LHW004   Alfred Cortot plays Schumann, Vol. 2
(BIDD) LHW005   Alfred Cortot plays Schumann, Vol. 3
(BIDD) LHW006   Alfred Cortot plays Debussy & Ravel
(BIDD) LHW014/5   Cortot—The Acoustic Victor Recordings
(BIDD) LHW020   Cortot plays Short Works
(DANT) HPC003   Cortot plays Chopin
(DANT) HPC004/5   Alfred Cortot plays Romantic Piano
(EMI) CDH7 61050-2   Alfred Cortot plays Chopin
(EMI) CDH7 63032-2   French Violin Sonatas
(EMI) CHS7 61038-2   Debussy—Pelléas et Mélisande, etc
(EMI) CHS7 64057-2   Cortot-Thibaud-Casals Trio—Historic Recordings
(EMI) CZS7 67359-2   Cortot plays Chopin
(MSCM) MM30321   Jacques Thibaud—Violin Recital
(MUSI) MACD-317   Cortot plays Chopin
(MUSI) MACD-662   Cortot plays Weber and Liszt
(PEAR) GEMMCD9134   Maggie Teyte - Chansons
(PEAR) GEMMCD9348   Debussy: Orchestral & Chamber Works
(PEAR) GEMMCD9919   Panzéra sings Fauré,Duparc & Schumann
(PEAR) GEMMCD9931   Cortot plays Schumann, Vol.1
(PEAR) GEMMCD9932   Cortot plays Schumann, Vol.2
(SYMP) SYMCD1101   The Harold Wayne Collection, Vol.9

CORTOT, Alfred (pf/dir)
see CONCERT INDEX under:
(MSCM) MM30321   Jacques Thibaud—Violin Recital

CORVER, Ellen (pf)
see CONCERT INDEX under:
(CHAN) CHAN9363   Adams/Lang—Wind Music

CORYDON ORCHESTRA
Bruckner: Mass in D minor, Te Deum
cond M. BEST
Berlioz: Enfance du Christ (Cpte)
Bruckner: Mass in F minor, Psalm 150
Vaughan Williams: Hugh the Drover (Cpte)
see CONCERT INDEX under:
(HYPE) CDA66638   Villa-Lobos—Sacred Choral Music
(HYPE) CDA66655   Vaughan Williams—Choral Works

CORYDON SINGERS
cond M. BEST
Berlioz: Enfance du Christ (Cpte)
Britten: Hymn to St Cecilia, St Nicolas
Bruckner: Mass in D minor, Mass in F minor, Psalm 150, Te Deum
Duruflé: Motets, Op. 10, Requiem
Rachmaninov: Liturgy, Op.37, Vespers, Op.37 (Cpte)
Vaughan Williams: Bunyan Sequence, Hugh the Drover (Cpte)
see CONCERT INDEX under:
(HYPE) CDA66062   Bruckner—Motets
(HYPE) CDA66076   British Choral Works
(HYPE) CDA66126   Britten: Choral Works
(HYPE) CDA66177   Bruckner—Sacred Choral Works
(HYPE) CDA66219   American Choral Works
(HYPE) CDA66245   Bruckner—Choral Works
(HYPE) CDA66359   Fauré: Sacred Choral Works
(HYPE) CDA66359   Mendelssohn—Choral Works
(HYPE) CDA66420   Vaughan Williams: Vocal Works
(HYPE) CDA66569   Vaughan Williams—Choral Works
(HYPE) CDA66638   Villa-Lobos—Sacred Choral Music
(HYPE) CDA66655   Vaughan Williams—Choral Works

CORYN, Franck (db)
Rossini: Tancredi (Cpte)

COSOTTI, Max-René (ten)
Verdi: Traviata (Cpte)

COSSA, Dominic (bar)
Donizetti: Elisir d'amore (Cpte)
Sessions: When Lilacs last Bloom'd

COSSINS, James (sngr)
Gay: Beggar's Opera (Cpte)

COSSOTTO, Fiorenza (mez)
Bellini: Norma (Cpte), Sonnambula (Cpte)
Donizetti: Favorita (Cpte)
Mozart: Nozze di Figaro (Cpte)
Ponchielli: Gioconda (Cpte)
Puccini: Madama Butterfly (Cpte), Manon Lescaut (Cpte)
Verdi: Aida (Cpte), Ballo in maschera (Cpte), Don Carlo (Cpte), Forza del destino (Cpte), Giorno di Regno (Cpte), Macbeth (Cpte), Requiem (Cpte), Rigoletto (Cpte), Trovatore (Cpte)
see CONCERT INDEX under:
(CFP) CD-CFP4532   Sacred Arias
(DECC) 436 462-2DM   Ten Top Mezzos
(DG) 419 257-2GH3   'Cav' and 'Pag', etc
(EMIL) CDZ7 67015-2   Mozart—Opera Arias
(RCA) 09026 61580-2(8)   RCA/Met 100 Singers, 100 Years (pt 8)

COSSUTTA, Carlo (ten)
Verdi: Otello (Cpte), Requiem (Cpte)
see CONCERT INDEX under:
(DECC) 433 439-2DA   Great Love Duets

COSSUTTA, Enrico (ten)
Puccini: Manon Lescaut (Cpte)
Verdi: Traviata (Cpte)

COSTA, Albert da (ten)
Beethoven: Symphony 9

COSTA, Fernanda (sop)
Rossini: Cenerentola (Cpte)

COSTA, Jean-Claude (ten)
Shostakovich: Lady Macbeth of Mtsensk (Cpte)

COSTA, Paolo (alto)
Monteverdi: Vespers

COSTA, Sequeira (pf)
Rachmaninov: Piano Concerto 2, Piano Concerto 4

COSTANTINO, Antonio (ten)
Puccini: Fanciulla del West (Cpte)

COSTARIOL, Giuseppe (bar)
Puccini: Fanciulla del West (Cpte)

COSTE, Sharon (sop)
Gounod: Sapho (Cpte)
see CONCERT INDEX under:
(HARM) HMC90 1417   Caplet—Orchestral and Vocal Works
(MARC) 8 223755   Prix de Rome Cantatas

COSTELLO, Elvis (sngr)
see CONCERT INDEX under:
(SILV) SILKD6001   Lament—The Brodsky Quartet

COSTELLO, Marilyn (hp)
Mozart: Flute and Harp Concerto, K299

COTOGNI, Antonio (bar)
see CONCERT INDEX under:
(MEMO) HR4408/9(1)   Singers in Genoa, Vol.1 (disc 1)
(SYMP) SYMCD1069   The Harold Wayne Collection, Vol.2

COTREIL, Eduard (bass)
see CONCERT INDEX under:
(PEAR) GEMMCDS9074(2)   Giovanni Zenatello, Vol.2 (pt 2)
(PEAR) GEMMCDS9926(1)   Covent Garden on Record—Vol.4 (pt 1)

COTRUBAS, Ileana (sop)
Bizet: Carmen (Cpte), Pêcheurs de Perles (Cpte)
Donizetti: Elisir d'amore (Cpte), Favorita (Cpte)
G. Charpentier: Louise (Cpte)
Haydn: Fedeltà Premiata (Cpte)
Humperdinck: Hänsel und Gretel (Cpte)
Mahler: Symphony 2
Massenet: Manon (Cpte)
Mozart: Cosi fan tutte (Cpte), Finta Giardiniera (Cpte), Mass, K427, Mitridate (Cpte), Nozze di Figaro (Cpte), Schauspieldirektor (Cpte), Sposo deluso (Cpte), Zauberflöte (Cpte)
Verdi: Rigoletto (Cpte), Traviata (Cpte)
see CONCERT INDEX under:
(BELA) 450 121-2   Plácido Domingo
(DECC) 443 009-2DF2   Mozart—Choral Works
(DG) 431 104-2GB   Great Voices - Plácido Domingo
(PHIL) 422 522-2PME6   The Complete Mozart Edition Vol 22
(PHIL) 442 050-2PB10   Mahler—Complete Symphonies
(SONY) MK39097   Puccini Heroines
(SONY) M3K79312   Puccini: Il Trittico

COTTONE, Salvatore (pf)
see CONCERT INDEX under:
(CLUB) CL99-060   Enrico Caruso—Opera & Song Recital
(EMI) CDH7 61046-2   Enrico Caruso: Opera Arias and Songs - 1902-1904
(EMI) CHS7 64860-2(1)   La Scala Edition - Vol.1, 1878-1914 (pt 1)
(EMI) CHS7 64860-2(2)   La Scala Edition - Vol.1, 1878-1914 (pt 2)
(PEAR) EVC1(1)   The Caruso Edition, Vol.1 (pt 1)
(PEAR) GEMMCDS9923(1)   Covent Garden on Record, Vol.1 (pt 1)
(PEAR) GEMMCDS9997/9(2)   Singers of Imperial Russia, Vol.1 (pt 2)
(RCA) GD60495(1)   The Complete Caruso Collection (pt 1)

(SYMP) **SYMCD1065** The Harold Wayne Collection, Vol.1
(SYMP) **SYMCD1069** The Harold Wayne Collection, Vol.2
(SYMP) **SYMCD1073** The Harold Wayne Collection, Vol.3
(SYMP) **SYMCD1111** The Harold Wayne Collection, Vol.11

COUDERC, Florence (sngr)
Lully: Phaëton (Cpte)

COUDURIER, Bernard (organ)
see CONCERT INDEX under:
(BNL) **BNL112753** Lübeck: Organ Works
(BNL) **BNL112754** Bruhns & Hanff: Organ Works

COULL QUARTET
Simpson: String Quartet 10, String Quartet 11, String Quartet 12, String Quintet
see CONCERT INDEX under:
(ASV) **CDDCA613** Chamber Works for Bassoon
(ASV) **CDDCA631** Shostakovich—String Quartets
(HYPE) **CDA66397** Mendelssohn—String Quartets
(HYPE) **CDA66573** Prokofiev—Chamber Works
(HYPE) **CDA66579** Mendelssohn—String Quartets
(HYPE) **CDA66615** Mendelssohn—String Quartets
(HYPE) **CDA66679** Dvořák—Chamber Works
(HYPE) **CDA66718** Bridge/Elgar/Wlaton—Chamber Works
(HYPE) **CDS44051/3** Mendelssohn—Complete String Quartets
(MERI) **CDE84185** Settings from A. E. Housman's 'A Shropshire Lad'

COUPE, Robert (ten)
see CONCERT INDEX under:
(PHIL) **442 534-2PH** Janáček—Choral Works

COURAUD, Marcel (cond)
see French Rad Chor Sols

COURT, Carol (sop)
Henze: English Cat (Cpte)

COURTIS, Jean-Philippe (bass)
A. Thomas: Hamlet (Cpte)
Berlioz: Troyens (Cpte)
Bizet: Carmen (Cpte), Pêcheurs de Perles (Cpte)
Debussy: Pelléas and Mélisande (Cpte)
Haydn: Applausus (Cpte)
Massenet: Grisélidis (Cpte)
Messiaen: Saint François d'Assise (Cpte)
Rameau: Dardanus (Cpte)
Saint-Saëns: Samson et Dalila (Cpte)

COURTNEY, James (bass)
Puccini: Manon Lescaut (Cpte)

COUSINS, Michael (ten)
see CONCERT INDEX under:
(ERAT) **4509-95362-2** Mozart—Sacred Choral Works

COUSU, Philippe (ob)
see CONCERT INDEX under:
(MARC) **8 223659** d'Indy—Orchestral Works

COUTURE, Michelle (sop)
Rorem: Childhood Miracle (Cpte)
Shore: M. Butterfly (exc)

COUTURIER, François (pf)
see CONCERT INDEX under:
(HARM) **HMC90 1552** The Three Countertenors

COVA, Mila (mez)
Verdi: Forza del destino (Cpte)

COVENT GARDEN SINGERS
cond M. PLASSON
Massenet: Werther (Cpte)

COVEY-CRUMP, Rogers (ten)
Bach: Cantata 211, Mass in B minor, BWV232 (Cpte)
Blow: Venus and Adonis (Cpte)
Dowland: First Book of Songs (Cpte)
Handel: Acis and Galatea (Cpte)
Monteverdi: Orfeo (Cpte), Selva morale e spirituale (exc)
Mozart: Mass, K317
Pärt: Passio
Purcell: Birthday Ode, Z342, Dioclesian, Z627 (exc), Indian Queen, Z630 (Cpte), St Cecilia's Day Ode, Z328, Timon of Athens, Z632 (Cpte)
see CONCERT INDEX under:
(BIS) **BIS-CD341** Music for lutes
(BIS) **BIS-CD391** Music from the time of Christian IV, Vol. 3
(DECC) **430 359-2DM** Baroque Church Music
(ECM) **831 959-2** Pärt—Arbos
(EMI) **CDC7 49672-2** Mozart: Sacred Choral Works
(ERAT) **4509-96371-2** Gardiner—The Purcell Collection
(HARM) **HMU90 7053** Humfrey—Verse Anthems
(HYPE) **CDA66228** Ancient Airs and Dances
(HYPE) **CDA66359** Mendelssohn—Choral Works
(HYPE) **CDA66412** Purcell—Complete Odes & Welcome Songs, Vol.3
(HYPE) **CDA66456** Purcell—Complete Odes & Welcome Songs, Vol.4
(HYPE) **CDA66476** Purcell—Complete Odes & Welcome Songs, Vol.5
(HYPE) **CDA66578** Odes on the Death of Henry Purcell
(HYPE) **CDA66587** Purcell—Complete Odes & Welcome Songs, Vol.7

(HYPE) **CDA66609** Purcell—Complete Anthems & Services, Vol.2
(HYPE) **CDA66644** Purcell—Complete Anthems & Services, Vol.4
(HYPE) **CDA66656** Purcell—Complete Anthems & Services, Vol.5
(HYPE) **CDA66663** Purcell—Complete Anthems & Services, Vol.6
(HYPE) **CDA66677** Purcell—Anthems & Services, Vol.7
(HYPE) **CDA66686** Purcell—Complete Anthems & Services, Vol.8
(HYPE) **CDA66693** Purcell—Complete Anthems and Services, Volume 9
(HYPE) **CDA66707** Purcell—Complete Anthems & Services, Vol. 10
(HYPE) **CDA66710** Purcell—Secular Solo Songs, Volume 1
(HYPE) **CDA66716** Purcell—Complete Anthems and Services, Volume 11
(HYPE) **CDA66720** Purcell—Secular Solo Songs, Volume 2
(HYPE) **CDA66730** Purcell—Secular Solo Songs, Vol. 3
(L'OI) **421 478-2OH** Haydn—Masses
(L'OI) **425 893-2OM6(1)** Purcell—Theatre Music (Part 1)
(L'OI) **425 893-2OM6(2)** Purcell—Theatre Music (Part 2)

COVIELLO, Roberto (bar)
Bellini: Adelson e Salvini (Cpte)
Rossini: Gazza ladra (Cpte)

COWAN, Richard (bar)
Puccini: Bohème (Cpte)

COWAN, Sigmund (bar)
Schreker: Gezeichneten (Cpte)

COWLES, Eugene (sngr)
see CONCERT INDEX under:
(PEAR) **GEMMCDS9050/2(1)** Music from the New York Stage, Vol. 1 (part 1)

COWLEY, David (ob)
see CONCERT INDEX under:
(NIMB) **NI5357** Hoddinott—Orchestral Works

COX, Jean (ten)
Wagner: Meistersinger (Cpte)

COX, Kenneth (bass)
Mahler: Symphony 8

COX, Michael (fl)
see CONCERT INDEX under:
(KING) **KCLCD2013** Twentieth Century Flute Music

COXWELL, Janet (sop)
see CONCERT INDEX under:
(HYPE) **CDA66076** British Choral Works
(HYPE) **CDA66126** Britten: Choral Works
(HYPE) **CDA66292** Fauré: Sacred Choral Works

COZETTE, Michel (bar)
Gounod: Faust (Cpte)
see CONCERT INDEX under:
(CLUB) **CL99-034** Marcel Journet (1867-1933)
(CLUB) **CL99-101** Vanni Marcoux (1877-1962)
(PEAR) **GEMMCD9314** Feodor Chaliapin - Aria and Song Recital

CPE BACH CHAMBER ORCHESTRA
cond P. SCHREIER
see CONCERT INDEX under:
(DG) **439 895-2GH** Flute Concertos of the Sans-Souci
(PHIL) **438 873-2PH2** Bach—Magnificat and Masses

CRABTREE, Libby (sop)
Blow: Venus and Adonis (Cpte)
Handel: Blessed are they that considereth the poor

CRACOW BOYS' CHOIR
cond W. MICHNIEWSKI
Preisner: Secret Garden (exc)
cond J. SEMKOW
Mussorgsky: Boris Godunov (Cpte)

CRACOW CHAMBER CHOIR
cond H. RILLING
Various: Requiem of Reconciliation (Cpte)

CRACOW PHILHARMONIC CHORUS
cond K. PENDERECKI
see CONCERT INDEX under:
(EMI) **CDM5 65077-2** Penderecki—Orchestral and Vocal Works

CRACOW PHILHARMONIC ORCHESTRA
cond D. AMOS
see CONCERT INDEX under:
(KOCH) **37036-2** Creston—Orchestral Works
cond R. BADER
Bacewicz: String Orchestra Concerto, Symphony 3
Lyatoshynsky: Symphony 4, Symphony 2
Weill: Symphony 1, Symphony 2
see CONCERT INDEX under:
(SCHW) **310412** Górecki—Orchestral Works
cond G. LEVINE
see CONCERT INDEX under:
(ARAB) **Z6610** Shostakovich: Orchestral Works

CRACOW POLISH RADIO CHORUS
cond J. KRENZ
see CONCERT INDEX under:
(POLS) **PNCD041** Lutosławski: Choral & Orchestral Works

cond J. SEMKOW
Mussorgsky: Boris Godunov (Cpte)
see CONCERT INDEX under:
(EMI) **CDM5 65082-2** Szymanowski—Orchestral Works
cond A. WIT
see CONCERT INDEX under:
(EMI) **CDM5 65307-2** Szymanowski—Orchestral and Piano Works

CRACOW RADIO AND TELEVISION CHORUS
see CONCERT INDEX under:
(ACCO) **20061-2** Scelsi: Choral & Orchestral Works
cond A. WIT
Mahler: Symphony 2

CRACOW RADIO AND TELEVISION ORCHESTRA
see CONCERT INDEX under:
(ACCO) **20061-2** Scelsi: Choral & Orchestral Works

CRACOW RADIO SYMPHONY ORCHESTRA
cond S. HEINRICH
Honegger: Jeanne d'Arc (Cpte)
cond J. SEMKOW
Mussorgsky: Boris Godunov (Cpte)
cond A. WIT
see CONCERT INDEX under:
(EMI) **CDM5 65307-2** Szymanowski—Orchestral and Piano Works

CRAFT, Robert (cond)
see CBC SO

CRAIG, Charles (ten)
see CONCERT INDEX under:
(CFP) **CD-CFP4569** Puccini: Arias

CRAIGHEAD, David (organ)
Reger: Organ Sonata, Op. 60
Vierne: Symphony 6

CRAKER, Christopher (cl)
see CONCERT INDEX under:
(ASV) **CDDCA684** Schubert—Lieder & Chamber Works

CRASS, Franz (bass)
Bach: Christmas Oratorio, BWV248 (Cpte), Mass in B minor, BWV232 (Cpte)
Janáček: Glagolitic Mass (Cpte)
Mozart: Don Giovanni (Cpte), Requiem, Zauberflöte (Cpte)
Orff: Mond (Cpte)
Wagner: Fliegende Holländer (Cpte), Lohengrin (Cpte), Parsifal (Cpte), Tannhäuser (Cpte)
Weber: Freischütz (Cpte)
see CONCERT INDEX under:
(DG) **429 042-2GX10** Mahler: Complete Symphonies
(PHIL) **438 760-2PM2** Brahms—Choral Works and Overtures

CRAVEN, Leslie (cl)
see CONCERT INDEX under:
(KING) **KCLCD2027** South American Flute Music

CRAWFORD, Clifton (sngr)
see CONCERT INDEX under:
(PEAR) **GEMMCDS9053/5** Music from the New York Stage, Vol. 2: 1908—1913

CRAWFORD, Jesse (organ)
see CONCERT INDEX under:
(CLAR) **CDGSE78-50-50** Richard Crooks sings Ballads & Sacred Songs

CRAWFORD, Joe (sngr)
Hammerstein: Carmen Jones (Cpte)

CRAWFORD, Thomas (cond)
see Fairfield Orch

CRAWFORD PIANO TRIO
see CONCERT INDEX under:
(ALTA) **AIR-CD-9011** Philip Martin—Chamber & Vocal Works

CRAXTON, Harold (pf)
see CONCERT INDEX under:
(CLAR) **CDGSE78-50-47** The Harrison Sisters—An English Musical Heritage
(LARR) **CDLRH221** Dame Nellie Melba - Opera and Song Recital
(SYMP) **SYMCD1140** The Harrison Sisters

CRAXTON, Janet (cor ang)
see CONCERT INDEX under:
(EMI) **CDM5 65101-2** A Warlock Centenary Album

CRAYFORD, Marcia (vn)
Fauré: Piano Trio
see CONCERT INDEX under:
(CRD) **CRD3446** Ravel: Chamber works
(HYPE) **CDA66171** Malcolm Arnold: Chamber Works, Vol. 1
(HYPE) **CDA66173** Malcolm Arnold: Chamber Works, Vol. 3
(VIRG) **VC5 45016-2** Ravel—Chamber & Vocal Works
(VIRG) **VC7 59604-2** Debussy—Chamber Works

CRAYFORD, Marcia (vn/va)
Goehr: Sing, Ariel, Op. 51

CREASEY, Philip (ten)
Sullivan: Gondoliers (Cpte), Iolanthe (Cpte), Pirates of Penzance (Cpte)

CREDICO, Oslavio di (ten)
Donizetti: Martyrs (Cpte)
Rossini: Donna del Lago (Cpte), Gazza ladra (Cpte)

CREECH, Philip (ten)
Orff: Carmina burana

CULWICK CHORAL SOCIETY
cond R. SACCANI
Verdi: Aida (Cpte)

CUMMINGS, Claudia (sop)
Glass: Satyagraha (Cpte)

CUMMINGS, Diana (vn)
Dvořák: Terzetto, op 74

CUMMINGS, Douglas (vc)
Schubert: String Quintet

CUMMINGS, Laurence (organ)
see CONCERT INDEX under:
(COLL) Coll1360-2 Sacred Music from Venice and Rome
(NAXO) 8 553129 Purcell—Choral and Organ Music

CUMMINGS, Laurence (hpd)
see CONCERT INDEX under:
(NAXO) 8 550922 L. Couperin—Harpsichord Works

CUMMINGS TRIO
Beethoven: Piano Quartets, WoO36
Mozart: Trio, K563

CUNDARI, Emilia (sop)
Beethoven: Symphony 9
Rossini: Inganno felice (Cpte)

CUNILL, Odilon (cond)
see Montserrat Abbey Ch

CUNITZ, Maud (sop)
Verdi: Requiem (Cpte)
Wagner: Lohengrin (Cpte)

CUNNINGHAM, G(eorge) D(orrington) (organ)
see CONCERT INDEX under:
(BEUL) 1PD5 Historic Organs, Volume 1

CUNNINGHAM, Richard (alto)
see CONCERT INDEX under:
(HYPE) CDA66247 Vivaldi: Vocal and Orchestral Works

CUNNINGHAM, Roberta (sop)
Pfitzner: Herz (Cpte)

CUNNINGHAM, Sarah (va da gamba)
Bach: Flute Sonatas, BWV1030-5 (exc), Violin Sonatas, BWV1020-25 (exc)
see CONCERT INDEX under:
(ARCA) A02 Purcell—Ayres and Songs from Orpheus Britannicus
(ASV) CDGAU112 Marais—Pièces de Violes
(HARM) HMU90 7093 Telemann—Concertos and Suites
(MERI) CDE84112 Purcell: Sacred Choral Works
(TELD) 4509-90841-2 A Gift of Nature - 17th Century English Chamber Music

CUPIDO, Alberto (ten)
Berlioz: Roméo et Juliette (Cpte)
Verdi: Simon Boccanegra (Cpte)

CURIEL, Glauco (cond)
see Philh

CURIEL, Nicoletta (mez)
Mozart: Nozze di Figaro (Cpte)
Pergolesi: Frate 'nnamorato (Cpte)
Verdi: Rigoletto (Cpte), Traviata (Cpte)
see CONCERT INDEX under:
(DECC) 436 261-2DHO3 Puccini—Il Trittico

CURLEY, Carlo (organ)
see CONCERT INDEX under:
(ARGO) 430 200-2ZH The Emperor's Fanfare
(ARGO) 433 450-2ZH Organ Imperial—Works by British composers
(DECC) 436 403-2DWO The World of Royal Music

CURPHEY, Margaret (sop)
Wagner: Götterdämmerung (exc), Walküre (Cpte)

CURRENDE INSTRUMENTAL ENSEMBLE
cond E. VAN NEVEL
D. Scarlatti: Stabat mater
Esteves: Mass for eight voices

CURRENDE VOCAL ENSEMBLE
Landi: Mort d'Orfeo (Cpte)
cond E. VAN NEVEL
D. Scarlatti: Stabat mater
Esteves: Mass for eight voices
Schütz: Cantiones sacrae (exc)

CURROS, Abelardo (sngr)
Moreno Torroba: Luisa Fernanda (Cpte)

CURRY, Diane (contr)
see CONCERT INDEX under:
(TELA) CD80152 Verdi: Requiem & Opera Choruses

CURRY, William Henry (cond)
see St. Luke's Orch

CURTIN, Phyllis (sop)
Beethoven: Symphony 9

CURTIS, Alan (cond)
see Teatro la Fenice Orch

CURTIS, Alan (hpd)
see CONCERT INDEX under:
(TELD) 4509-97452-2 Bach—Harpsichord Concertos

CURTIS, Alan (hpd/dir)
Handel: Floridante (exc)
see CONCERT INDEX under:
(ARCH) 437 082-2AT Collectio Argentea 12: Vivaldi/Bononcini—Cantatas

CURTIS, John (gtr)
see CONCERT INDEX under:
(KOCH) 37180-2 Pinkham—Cantatas & Chamber Works

CURTIS, Mark (ten)
Lehár: Lustige Witwe (exc)
Puccini: Madama Butterfly (Cpte), Manon Lescaut (Cpte)
Verdi: Forza del destino (Cpte)
see CONCERT INDEX under:
(NIMB) NI5217 Tippett conducts Tippett

CURTIS INSTITUTE STUDENT ORCHESTRA
cond I. HILSBERG
see CONCERT INDEX under:
(VAI) VAIA1020 Josef Hofmann, Vol.2
cond A. PREVIN
Rorem: Left Hand Concerto
cond F. REINER
see CONCERT INDEX under:
(VAI) VAIA1020 Josef Hofmann, Vol.2

CURZON, Sir Clifford (pf)
Mozart: Piano Concerto 20, Piano Concerto 27
Schubert: Trout Quintet, D667
see CONCERT INDEX under:
(DECC) 425 082-2DCS Brahms/Franck/Litolff—Piano Works
(DECC) 425 960-2DM Mozart—Chamber Works
(DECC) 425 995-2DM Brahms/Mahler—Lieder
(DECC) 433 628-2DSP Franck/Grieg/Schumann—Piano & Orchestral Works
(DECC) 436 407-2DWO The World of Schubert
(DECC) 443 570-2DCS Schubert—Piano Works
(EMI) CDM7 64281-2 Boulanger—Vocal & Chamber Works
(MUSI) MACD-643 Mozart & Schumann—Chamber Works
(PEAR) GEMMCD9177 Britten—Vocal Works

CUSACK, Niamh (narr)
Prokofiev: Eugene Onegin (Cpte)

CUSICK, Russell (sngr)
Schuman: Mighty Casey (Cpte)

CVEJIC, Biserka (contr)
Mussorgsky: Boris Godunov (Cpte)

CWS (GLASGOW) BAND
see CONCERT INDEX under:
(POLY) QPRL049D Boosey & Hawkes National Brass Band Gala Concert 1991

(LES) CYCLOPES
Pachelbel: Musicalische Ergötzung

CZAKOVÁ, Anna (mez)
Janáček: Makropulos Affair (Cpte)

CZAKOVÁ, Ivana (sngr)
Mysliveček: Abraham and Isaac

CZARNECKI, Vladislav (cond)
see Pforzheim SW German CO

CZECH CHAMBER CHOIR
cond R. VÁLEK
Zelenka: Miserere, ZWV57, Requiem, ZWV48

CZECH CHAMBER ORCHESTRA
cond J. VLACH
Mozart: Adagio and Fugue, K546
see CONCERT INDEX under:
(SUPR) 2SUP0027 Mozart: Orchestral Works

CZECH PHILHARMONIC CHAMBER ENSEMBLE
see CONCERT INDEX under:
(SUPR) 11 0768-2 Janáček—Chamber and Vocal Works with Piano
cond J. VESELKA
see CONCERT INDEX under:
(SUPR) 11 0768-2 Janáček—Chamber and Vocal Works with Piano

CZECH PHILHARMONIC CHORUS
cond G. ALBRECHT
Dvořák: Dimitrij (Cpte)
Schumann: Paradies und die Peri (Cpte)
Dvořák: Requiem
Janáček: Glagolitic Mass (Cpte)
Martinů: Bouquet
Stravinsky: Oedipus Rex (Cpte), Symphony of Psalms
Vycpálek: Czech Requiem, Last things of Man
see CONCERT INDEX under:
(SUPR) 11 1930-2 Janáček/Kabeláč—Choral and Orchestral Works
cond S. BAUDO
Honegger: Cantate de Noël, Jeanne d'Arc (Cpte), Roi David (Cpte)
cond J. BĚLOHLÁVEK
see CONCERT INDEX under:
(CHAN) CHAN9138 Martinů—Orchestral and Choral Works
(SUPR) 11 0816-2 Zelenka—Choral Works
cond F. JÍLEK
Janáček: Excursions of Mr Brouček (Cpte)
cond P. KLETZKI
Beethoven: Symphony 9
cond Z. KOŠLER
Smetana: Bartered Bride (Cpte)
cond C. MACKERRAS
Janáček: Amarus, Glagolitic Mass (Cpte)
Martinů: Field Mass, Greek Passion (Cpte)

cond L. MÁTL
see CONCERT INDEX under:
(SUPR) 11 0816-2 Zelenka—Choral Works
cond V. NEUMANN
Beethoven: Symphony 9
Janáček: Cunning Little Vixen (Cpte), From the House of the Dead (Cpte)
cond Z. PEŠKÓ
Mysliveček: Bellerofonte (Cpte)
cond V. SMETÁČEK
see CONCERT INDEX under:
(SUPR) 2SUP0025 Orff: Choral Works
cond V. TALICH
Dvořák: Stabat mater
cond J. VESELKA
see CONCERT INDEX under:
(SUPR) 11 0768-2 Janáček—Chamber and Vocal Works with Piano

CZECH PHILHARMONIC ORCHESTRA
cond G. ALBRECHT
Dvořák: Dimitrij (Cpte)
Liszt: Dante Symphony
Schumann: Paradies und die Peri (Cpte)
see CONCERT INDEX under:
(SUPR) 11 1830-2 Brahms/Dvořák—Orchestral Works
cond K. ANČERL
Bartók: Concerto for Orchestra
Dvořák: Requiem, Violin Concerto
Janáček: Glagolitic Mass (Cpte), Sinfonietta, Taras Bulba
Martinů: Bouquet, Symphony 6
Shostakovich: Cello Concerto 1, Symphony 5
Smetana: Má Vlast
Stravinsky: Oedipus Rex (Cpte), Symphony of Psalms
Suk: Fantasy
Vycpálek: Czech Requiem, Last things of Man
see CONCERT INDEX under:
(PRAG) PR254 002/3 Ančerl Edition, Vol.2 - Shostakovich
(SUPR) 11 0582-2 David Oistrakh plays Beethoven & Mozart
(SUPR) 11 1930-2 Janáček/Kabeláč—Choral and Orchestral Works
(SUPR) 11 1931-2 Martinů—Orchestral Works
(SUPR) 11 1945-2 Orchestral Works
cond S. BAUDO
Honegger: Jeanne d'Arc (Cpte), Roi David (Cpte)
see CONCERT INDEX under:
(SUPR) 2SUP0023 Debussy: Orchestral Works
cond J. BĚLOHLÁVEK
Brahms: Symphony 1
Dvořák: Carnival, Golden spinning-wheel, Piano Concerto, Psalm 149, Stabat Mater, Symphony 6, Symphony 8, Symphony 9, Wild dove
Martinů: Double Concerto, Symphony 1
Smetana: Má vlast
Suk: Asrael, Fairy Tale, Serenade, Op. 6
see CONCERT INDEX under:
(CHAN) CHAN8897 Czech Orchestral Works
(CHAN) CHAN9015 Martinů—Works for Cello and Orchestra
(CHAN) CHAN9080 Janáček—Orchestral Works
(CHAN) CHAN9138 Martinů—Orchestral and Choral Works
(SUPR) 10 4140-2 Martinů—Orchestral Works
(SUPR) 11 0816-2 Zelenka—Choral Works
cond Z. CHALABALA
Dvořák: Water Goblin
cond A. COPLAND
(ROMA) RR1973 An American in Prague
cond C. ESCHENBACH
Berlioz: Mort de Cléopâtre, Symphonie funèbre et triomphale
cond I. FERENCSIK
Bartók: Violin Concerto 1
cond D. FISCHER-DIESKAU
Berlioz: Harold in Italy
cond B. GREGOR
Zemlinsky: Lyrische Symphonie
see CONCERT INDEX under:
(SUPR) 11 0378-2 Dvořák—Orchestral Works
(SUPR) 11 0526-2 Dvořák—Symphonic Poems and Concert Overtures
cond F. HAIDER
see CONCERT INDEX under:
(SONY) SK45633 Edita Gruberová—Opera Arias
cond F. JÍLEK
Janáček: Excursions of Mr Brouček (Cpte)
see CONCERT INDEX under:
(SUPR) C37-7303 Janáček: Operatic Orchestral Suites
cond P. KLETZKI
Beethoven: Symphony 9
cond Z. KOŠLER
Chausson: Symphony, Op. 20
Dvořák: Symphony 7
R. Strauss: Alpensinfonie
Roussel: Festin de l'araignée
Smetana: Bartered Bride (Cpte), Má Vlast
cond R. KUBELÍK
Dvořák: Symphony 9
Mozart: Symphony 38
Smetana: Má Vlast
cond P. MAAG
see CONCERT INDEX under:
(DG) 413 844-2GW2 19th Century Violin Works
cond C. MACKERRAS
Janáček: Amarus, Glagolitic Mass (Cpte)

Martinů: Field Mass
  cond I. MARKEVITCH
Gounod: St Cecilia Mass
  cond K. MASUR
Beethoven: Triple Concerto
  cond L. VON MATAČIC
Bruckner: Symphony 5, Symphony 7, Symphony 9
Tchaikovsky: Symphony 6
  cond E. MRAVINSKY
Khachaturian: Piano Concerto
  cond J. NELSON
see CONCERT INDEX under:
(ARGO) **436 835-2ZH** Gorecki—Choral and
Orchestral Works
  cond V. NEUMANN
Beethoven: Symphony 9
Berg: Violin Concerto
Dvořák: Symphony 4, Symphony 6, Symphony 7,
Symphony 8, Symphony 9, Violin Concerto
Janáček: Cunning Little Vixen (Cpte), From the
House of the Dead (Cpte), Sinfonietta, Taras Bulba
Mahler: Symphony 9
Martinů: Ariane (Cpte), Symphony 3, Symphony 4
Reger: Hiller Variations
Suk: Asrael, Fantasy
Zemlinsky: Maeterlinck Songs, Op.13
see CONCERT INDEX under:
(ORFE) **C107101A** K. u. K. Festkonzert, Vol. 1
(ORFE) **C107201A** K. u. K. Festkonzert, Vol. 2
(ORFE) **C147861A** Fučík: Orchestral works
(ORFE) **C180891A** Popular Czech Music
(PHIL) **422 387-2PH** Dvořák—Orchestral Works
(SUPR) **C37-7230** Dvořák—Orchestral Works
(SUPR) **11 0382-2** Martinů—Complete Symphonies
(SUPR) **11 0559-2** Dvořák—Symphonies
(SUPR) **11 0714-2** Dvořák—Orchestral Works
(SUPR) **11 0717-2** Janáček—Orchestral Works
(SUPR) **11 1005-2** Dvořák—Symphonies
(SUPR) **11 1969-2** Martinů—Violin and Viola
Concertos
  cond L. PEŠEK
Debussy: Images, La mer
Dvořák: Czech Suite, B93, In Nature's Realm,
Othello, Symphony 4, Symphony 5, Symphony 6,
Violin Concerto
Lalo: Symphonie Espagnole
Suk: Fairy Tale, Praga, Summer's Tale
see CONCERT INDEX under:
(RCA) **09026 61934-2** Martinů—Piano Concertos
(SUPR) **CO-2047** Scriabin: Orchestral Works
  cond G. ROZHDESTVENSKY
Shostakovich: Bolt Suite (exc)
  cond K. SANDERLING
see CONCERT INDEX under:
(MULT) **310106-2** Beethoven—Prague Radio
Recordings (1958)
  cond H. SCHERCHEN
see CONCERT INDEX under:
(MULT) **310078-2** Mozart—Orchestral Works
  cond K. SEJNA
see CONCERT INDEX under:
(SUPR) **11 0682-2** Novak—Orchestral Works
  cond G. SINOPOLI
Brahms: Deutsches Requiem, Op. 45 (Cpte)
see CONCERT INDEX under:
(DG) **435 066-2GGA** Brahms—Choral Works
  cond V. SMETÁČEK
Dvořák: Stabat Mater
Foerster: Cyrano, Op. 55
Smetana: Má Vlast
see CONCERT INDEX under:
(SUPR) **2SUP0025** Orff: Choral Works
  cond G. SZELL
see CONCERT INDEX under:
(EMI) **CDH7 63498-2** Pablo Casals plays Cello
Concertos
(PEAR) **GEMMCD9349** Casals plays Works for Cello
and Orchestra
  cond V. TALICH
Dvořák: Carnival, Cello Concerto, Piano Concerto,
Slavonic Dances, Stabat mater, Symphony 6,
Symphony 39
Mozart: Symphony 39
Smetana: Má Vlast
Suk: Asrael, Serenade, Op.6
Tchaikovsky: Symphony 6
see CONCERT INDEX under:
(MULT) **310078-2** Talich conducts Mozart
(SUPR) **11 1905-2** Czech Orchestral Works
  cond J. WILDNER
Schumann: Symphony 2, Symphony 4
  cond C. ZECCHI
Berlioz: Symphonie fantastique

CZECH PHILHARMONIC WIND ENSEMBLE
see CONCERT INDEX under:
(SUPR) **11 0768-2** Janáček—Chamber and Vocal
Works with Piano

CZECH PIANO TRIO
Beethoven: Piano Trios (exc)

CZECH RADIO CHORUS
  cond E. BRIZIO
see CONCERT INDEX under:
(STUD) **SM12 2389** Paisiello—Music for Napoleon
Bonaparte's Chapel

CZECH RADIO SYMPHONY ORCHESTRA
Brian: Symphony 1
  cond S. GUNZENHAUSER
Dvořák: Legends (exc)

---

  cond D. JOHANOS
Glière: Symphony 3
  cond O. LENÁRD
see CONCERT INDEX under:
(OPUS) **9156 1824** Dvorský sings Operatic Arias
  cond R. STANKOVSKY
Miaskovsky: Symphony 8

CZECH SINGERS CHORUS
  cond K. BÖHM
Mozart: Don Giovanni (Cpte)
  cond I. MARKEVITCH
Gounod: St Cecilia Mass
  cond V. SMETÁČEK
Dvořák: Stabat Mater

CZECH STRING TRIO
see CONCERT INDEX under:
(ROMA) **RR1941** Terezín - The Music 1941-44

CZECH SYMPHONY ORCHESTRA
  cond D. WADSWORTH
see CONCERT INDEX under:
(SILV) **FILMCD129** Rota—The Symphonic
Fellini/Rota

CZERNY, Henrik (sngr)
Schreker: Gezeichneten (Cpte)

CZERNY, Werner (bass)
R. Strauss: Rosenkavalier (Cpte)

CZERWENKA, Oscar (bass)
Mozart: Nozze di Figaro (Cpte)
R. Strauss: Ariadne auf Naxos (Cpte)

CZIFFRA, György (pf)
Liszt: Hungarian Rhapsodies, S244 (exc), Rhapsodie
Espagnole, S254
see CONCERT INDEX under:
(APR) **APR7021** Cziffra—Hungaroton Recordings
1954-1956
(EMI) **CDM5 55250-2** Cziffra Edition, Volume 1
(EMI) **CDM5 55251-2** Cziffra Edition, Volume 2
(EMI) **CDM5 55252-2** Cziffra Edition, Volume 3
(EMI) **CDM5 55253-2** Cziffra Edition, Volume 4
(EMI) **CDM5 55254-2** Cziffra Edition, Volume 5
(EMI) **CDM5 55255-2** Cziffra Edition, Volume 6
(EMI) **CMS7 64882-2** Liszt—Piano Works

CZIFFRA JNR, György (cond)
see Paris Orch

DABBY, Diana (elec kybd)
see CONCERT INDEX under:
(BRID) **BCD9031** J. Harvey—Miscellaneous Works

DACEY, Richard (organ)
see CONCERT INDEX under:
(BIRM) **BBCD2** There shall a star

DACHARY, Lina (sop)
Audran: Miss Helyett (Cpte)
Bazin: Voyage en Chine (Cpte)
Boïeldieu: Voitures Versées (Cpte)
Hahn: O mon bel inconnu (Cpte)
Lecocq: Jour et la Nuit (Cpte), Rose Mousse (Cpte)
Messager: Coups de Roulis (Cpte), Monsieur
Beaucaire (Cpte), Passionément (Cpte)
Offenbach: Chanson de Fortunio (Cpte), Madame
l'Archiduc (Cpte)
Planquette: Rip van Winkle (Cpte)
Terrasse: Fiancée du Scaphandrier (Cpte), Travaux
d'Hercule (Cpte)
see CONCERT INDEX under:
(EMI) **CZS7 67515-2** Offenbach—Operetta highlights
(MUSD) **20239-2** Delibes—Opéras-Comiques

DADDI, Francesco (ten)
see CONCERT INDEX under:
(PEAR) **EVC1(2)** The Caruso Edition, Vol.1 (pt 2)
(RCA) **GD60495(2)** The Complete Caruso Collection
(pt 2)

DAEDALUS ENSEMBLE
see CONCERT INDEX under:
(ACCE) **ACC9176D** El Cancionero de la Catedral de
Segovia
(ACCE) **ACC9289D** 15-16th Century Laudi from
Venice & Florence

DAEL, Lucy van (va)
see CONCERT INDEX under:
(RCA) **GD71964** Bach: Flute Works

DAEL, Lucy van (vn)
see CONCERT INDEX under:
(RCA) **GD71964** Bach: Flute Works
(TELD) **4509-97465-2** Franz Brüggen Edition Vol.
3—English Ensemble Music

DAESHIK KANG, Kimon (vn)
see CONCERT INDEX under:
(NIMB) **NI5358** The Virtuoso Violin

DAGUERRESSAR, Charles (bar)
Messager: Coups de Roulis (Cpte)
Planquette: Rip van Winkle (Cpte)
Terrasse: Travaux d'Hercule (Cpte)

DAGUL, Harvey (pf)
Schubert: Divertissement, D823, Polonaises, D824
see CONCERT INDEX under:
(FOUR) **FHMD891** Schubert: Piano Duets, Vol.1
(FOUR) **FHMD892** Schubert—Piano Duets, Vol.2
(FOUR) **FHMD893** Schubert—Piano Duets, Volume
3
(FOUR) **FHMD894** Schubert—Piano Duets, Volume
4
(FOUR) **FHMD9111** Mozart—Works for Piano Duet

(FOUR) **FHMD9212** Piano Duets - Children's Games

DAHINDEN, Clemens (cond)
see Winterthur SO

DAHL, Anne Margrethe (sop)
Gade: Comala

DAHL, Tim (ten)
Britten: Paul Bunyan (Cpte)

DAHL, Tracy (sop)
see CONCERT INDEX under:
(CBC) **SMCD5125** Glitter and Be Gay—Coloratura
Soprano Arias
(CBC) **SMCD5139** A Gilbert & Sullivan Gala

DAHLBERG, Stefan (ten)
Busoni: Arlecchino (Cpte), Turandot (Cpte)
Nørholm: Symphony 4

DÄHLER, Jörg Ewald (cond)
see Berne CO

DÄHLER, Jörg Ewald (fp)
Schubert: Impromptus (exc), Schöne Müllerin (Cpte),
Schwanengesang, D957 (Cpte), Winterreise (Cpte)
see CONCERT INDEX under:
(CLAV) **CD50-8611** Schubert—Lieder

DÄHLER, Jörg Ewald (hpd/dir)
see CONCERT INDEX under:
(CLAV) **CD50-8206** Venetian Music for Voice and
Instruments

DÄHLER, Jörg Ewald (square pf)
Schubert: Moments musicaux, D780, Piano Sonata,
D960

DAHLMAN, Barbro (pf)
Crumb: Madrigals, Music for a Summer Evening

DAHN, Felix (bar)
see CONCERT INDEX under:
(SUPR) **11 2136-2(3)** Emmy Destinn—Complete
Edition, Discs 5 to 8

DAKIN, Richard (treb)
Britten: Midsummer Night's Dream (Cpte)

DALBERG, Frederick (bass)
Wagner: Götterdämmerung (Cpte), Meistersinger
(Cpte)

DALBERTO, Michel (pf)
Liszt: Années de pèlerinage 2, Beethoven
Symphonies, S464 (exc), Funeral Odes (exc)
Schumann: Maria Stuart Lieder, Op. 135 (Cpte),
Myrthen, Op. 25 (Cpte)
see CONCERT INDEX under:
(DENO) **CO-73787** Schubert—Piano Works, Vol.1
(DENO) **CO-74499** Schubert—Piano Works, Vol.2
(DENO) **CO-75071** Schubert—Piano Works, Vol.6
(DENO) **CO-75258** Grieg/Franck/R.Strauss—Piano
Works
(DENO) **CO-75757** Schubert—Piano Works, Vol.7
(DENO) **CO-75859** Schumann—Works for Piano &
Orchestra
(DENO) **CO-76330** Schubert: Piano Works, Vol.3
(DENO) **CO-78909** Mozart—Variations for Piano, Vol.
2
(DENO) **CO-78914** Schubert—Piano Sonatas,
Volume 8
(DENO) **CO-78955** Schubert—Piano Works, Volume
9
(DENO) **CO-79477** Mozart—Piano Variations
(EMI) **CDC7 49841-2** Fauré—Mélodies
(ERAT) **2292-45368-2** Chausson: Songs

DALE, Clamma (sop)
Bernstein: Songfest
Gershwin: Porgy and Bess (Cpte)
see CONCERT INDEX under:
(VIRG) **VJ7 59641-2** J.S. & C.P.E. Bach—Violin &
Cello Concertos
(VIRG) **VJ7 59652-2** Popular Baroque Works

DALE, Laurence (ten)
Auber: Gustav III (Cpte)
Boïeldieu: Calife de Bagdad (Cpte)
Debussy: Rodrigue et Chimène (Cpte)
Gounod: St Cecilia Mass
Honegger: Roi David (Cpte)
Monteverdi: Orfeo (Cpte)
Rossini: Maometto II (Cpte)
Roussel: Padmâvatî (Cpte)
see CONCERT INDEX under:
(PHIL) **400 011-2PH** Ketèlbey: Orchestral Works

DALES, Ellen (sop)
Purcell: Dido (Cpte)

DALIS, Irene (mez)
Wagner: Parsifal (Cpte)

DALLAPICCOLA ENSEMBLE
  cond L. SUVINI
see CONCERT INDEX under:
(NUOV) **7109** Dallapiccola—Orchestral Works

DALLAPOZZA, Adolf (ten)
Beethoven: Fidelio (Cpte)
Humperdinck: Königskinder (Cpte)
J.Strauss II: Fledermaus (Cpte)
Lehár: Friederike (Cpte)
R.Strauss: Arabella (Cpte), Intermezzo (Cpte)
Wagner: Meistersinger (Cpte)
Zeller: Vogelhändler (Cpte)
see CONCERT INDEX under:
(EMI) **CDC7 47407-2** Schubert: Sacred Choral works
(EMI) **CDM7 69223-2** Schubert—Choral Works

(EMI) CMS7 64778-2　Schubert—Sacred Works, Vol.1
(EMI) CMS7 64783-2　Schubert—Sacred Works, Vol.2

DALLAS SYMPHONY ORCHESTRA
　cond A. DORATI
　　see CONCERT INDEX under:
(RCA) GD60921　Legendary Performers - William Kapell
　cond W. HENDL
　　see CONCERT INDEX under:
(RCA) GD87963　Heifetz plays Korngold, Rózsa & Waxman
(RCA) 09026 61778-2(21)　The Heifetz Collection, Vol. 21
　cond E. MATA
　Albéniz: Iberia
　Falla: Sombrero de tres picos (Cpte)
　　see CONCERT INDEX under:
(RCA) RCD14439　Orchestral Works
(RCA) VD60485　Ravel: Orchestral Works

DALLESSIO, Richard (ob)
　　see CONCERT INDEX under:
(CATA) CD87963　Memento Bittersweet

DALMORES, Charles (ten)
　　see CONCERT INDEX under:
(PEAR) GEMMCDS9924(1)　Covent Garden on Record, Vol.2 (pt 1)
(ROMO) 81001-2　Emma Eames (1865-1952)
(ROMO) 82001-2　Pol Plançon—Complete Victor Recordings

DALTON, Andrew (alto)
　　see CONCERT INDEX under:
(ETCE) KTC1030　Dowland: Songs and Lute Works

DALY, Tyne (sngr)
　Bernstein: On the Town (Cpte)

DAMERINI, Massimiliano (pf)
　　see CONCERT INDEX under:
(ETCE) KTC1044　German Lieder Recital
(ETCE) KTC1118　Glazunov—Piano Works
(ETCE) KTC1119　Bartók—Works for Violin and Piano

DAMIANO, Daniele (bn)
　Beethoven: Piano and Wind Quintet, Op. 16
　Mozart: Piano and Wind Quintet, K452

DAMM, Peter (hn)
　　see CONCERT INDEX under:
(CAMP) RRCD1313　Britten—Vocal and Orchestral Works
(EMI) CDM7 69661-2　R. Strauss—Wind Concertos
(EMI) CMS7 64342-2　R. Strauss—Orchestral Works, Vol.1
(PHIL) 422 509-2PME5　The Complete Mozart Edition Vol 9

DAMONTE, Magali (mez)
　Ravel: Enfant et les sortilèges (Cpte)

DAN, Robert (ten)
　　see CONCERT INDEX under:
(CPO) CPO999 221-2　Frankel—Music for Strings

DANBY, Nicholas (organ)
　　see CONCERT INDEX under:
(CRD) CRD3404　Brahms—Organ Works
(SONY) SMK64239　Bach—Organ Works
(VIRG) VC7 59212-2　Buxtehude—Organ Works
(VIRG) VC7 59277-2　C.P.E. Bach—Organ Works

DANCILA, Mihail (vc)
　　see CONCERT INDEX under:
(DYNA) CDS21/2　Franck—Chamber works

DANCO, Suzanne (sop)
　Gluck: Orphée (Cpte)
　Mozart: Don Giovanni (Cpte), Nozze di Figaro (Cpte)
　Rossini: Album de Musique (Cpte)
　　see CONCERT INDEX under:
(BELA) 450 131-2　Fauré—Requiem
(CASC) VEL2003　Memories of the Suisse Romande - Ansermet conducts Berg
(CASC) VEL2010　Memories of the Suisse Romande - Suzanne Danco
(DECC) 433 400-2DM2　Ravel & Debussy—Stage Works
(EMI) CHS7 69741-2(3)　Record of Singing, Vol.4—French School

DANCZOWSKA, Kaja (vn)
　　see CONCERT INDEX under:
(DG) 431 469-2GGA　Works for Violin and Piano

DANEMAN, Sophie (sop)
　Montéclair: Jephté (Cpte)
　Purcell: Dido (Cpte)
　Rameau: Castor et Pollux (Cpte)
　　see CONCERT INDEX under:
(ERAT) 4509-96967-2　Rameau—Les Grands Motets

DANGAIN, Guy (cl)
　　see CONCERT INDEX under:
(ERAT) 2292-45772-2　Saint-Saëns—Works for Chamber Ensemble

DANGAIN, Serge (cl)
　　see CONCERT INDEX under:
(FORL) FF009　Weber—Clarinet Concertos Nos 1 and 2; Oberon Overture

DANI, Lucia (mez)
　　see CONCERT INDEX under:

(DECC) 443 930-2DM　Jussi Björling sings Opera Arias

DANIECKI, John (ten)
　A. Davis: X (Cpte)
　Orff: Carmina Burana

DANIEL, Nicholas (cor ang)
　　see CONCERT INDEX under:
(CALA) CACD1017　French Chamber Music for Woodwinds, Volume 1
(CHAN) CHAN9065　Alwyn—Orchestral Works
(METR) METCD1005　D. Matthews—Chamber Works

DANIEL, Nicholas (ob)
　　see CONCERT INDEX under:
(CALA) CACD1017　French Chamber Music for Woodwinds, Volume 1
(CALA) CACD1017　French Chamber Music for Woodwinds, Volume 2
(CHAN) CHAN8866　Alwyn—Concertos
(CHAN) CHAN9152　Alwyn—Chamber Works - Volume 1
(CHAN) CHAN9197　Alwyn—Chamber Music, Volume 2
(CNTI) CCD1020　Simon Bainbridge—Orchestral Works
(LEMA) LC44801　Works for Oboe and Piano
(METR) METCD1005　D. Matthews—Chamber Works
(VIRG) CUV5 61141-2　French Oboe Sonatas

DANIEL, Nicholas (ob/dir)
　　see CONCERT INDEX under:
(CHAN) CHAN9152　Alwyn—Chamber Works - Volume 1
(HYPE) CDH88014　Italian Oboe Concertos

DANIEL, Paul (cond)
　　see BBC SO

DANIEL, Susan (mez)
　Bizet: Carmen (Cpte)
　　see CONCERT INDEX under:
(PHIL) 420 649-2PM　Vivaldi: Sacred Choral Music, Vol.2

DANIEL QUARTET
　　see CONCERT INDEX under:
(DINT) DICD920159　Thomas/Gounod/Lalo—String Quartets

DANIELI, Lucia (mez)
　Boito: Mefistofele (Cpte)
　Puccini: Madama Butterfly (Cpte)
　Rossini: Mosè (Cpte)
　　see CONCERT INDEX under:
(DECC) 411 665-2DM3　Puccini: Il trittico

DANIELS, Barbara (sop)
　Puccini: Bohème (Cpte)
　Rodgers: Sound of Music (Cpte)
　Schumann: Szenen aus Goethes Faust (Cpte)

DANIELS, Charles (ten)
　Bach: Cantata 4, Easter Oratorio, BWV249
　Blow: Venus and Adonis (Cpte)
　Gay: Beggar's Opera (Cpte)
　Purcell: Fairy Queen, Z629 (Cpte)
　Schütz: Symphoniae sacrae, Op. 10 (Cpte)
　　see CONCERT INDEX under:
(HYPE) CDA66269　Mondonville: Motets
(HYPE) CDA66314　Purcell—Complete Odes & Welcome Songs, Vol.1
(HYPE) CDA66456　Purcell—Complete Odes & Welcome Songs, Vol.4
(HYPE) CDA66578　Odes on the Death of Henry Purcell
(HYPE) CDA66585　Purcell—Complete Anthems & Services, Vol.1
(HYPE) CDA66587　Purcell—Complete Odes & Welcome Songs, Vol.7
(HYPE) CDA66623　Purcell—Complete Anthems & Services, Vol.3
(HYPE) CDA66644　Purcell—Complete Anthems & Services, Vol.4
(HYPE) CDA66656　Purcell—Complete Anthems & Services, Vol.5
(HYPE) CDA66663　Purcell—Complete Anthems & Services, Vol.6
(HYPE) CDA66677　Purcell—Anthems & Services, Vol.7
(HYPE) CDA66686　Purcell—Complete Anthems & Services, Vol.8
(HYPE) CDA66693　Purcell—Complete Anthems and Services, Volume 9
(HYPE) CDA66707　Purcell—Complete Anthems & Services, Vol. 10
(HYPE) CDA66710　Purcell—Secular Solo Songs, Volume 1
(HYPE) CDA66716　Purcell—Complete Anthems and Services, Volume 11
(HYPE) CDA66720　Purcell—Secular Solo Songs, Volume 2
(HYPE) CDA66730　Purcell—Secular Solo Songs, Vol. 3
(VIRG) VC5 45159-2　Purcell—Come ye sons of art

DANIELS, Claire (sop)
　　see CONCERT INDEX under:
(OPRA) ORCH104　A Hundred Years of Italian Opera: 1820-1830

DANIELS, Eddie (cl)
　Brahms: Clarinet Quintet
　Weber: Clarinet Quintet, J182

DANIELS, Kieran (sngr)
　Bernstein: West Side Story (Cpte)

DANIELSON, Glen (hn)
　　see CONCERT INDEX under:
(DELO) DE3126　The Incredible Walter Piston

DANISE, Giuseppe (bar)
　　see CONCERT INDEX under:
(MEMO) HR4408/9(2)　Singers in Genoa, Vol.1 (disc 2)

DANISH NATIONAL RADIO CHAMBER CHOIR
　cond S. PARKMAN
　　see CONCERT INDEX under:
(CHAN) CHAN8963　Masters of 20th Century A Cappella
(CHAN) CHAN8964　Pizzetti—Choral Works
(CHAN) CHAN9075　Gade—Choral and Orchestral Works

DANISH NATIONAL RADIO CHILDREN'S CHOIR
　cond J. LATHAM-KÖNIG
　Nørgård: Siddhartha (Cpte)

DANISH NATIONAL RADIO CHOIR
　cond D. KITAIENKO
　Prokofiev: Alexander Nevsky
　Rachmaninov: Bells, Spring, Op.20
　　see CONCERT INDEX under:
(CHAN) CHAN9075　Gade—Choral and Orchestral Works
　cond G. KUHN
　Schumann: Rose Pilgerfahrt (Cpte)
　cond J. LATHAM-KÖNIG
　Nørgård: Siddhartha (Cpte)
　cond C. MACKERRAS
　Janáček: Glagolitic Mass (Cpte)
　Kodály: Psalmus Hungaricus
　cond S. PARKMAN
　Pepping: Matthew Passion (Cpte)
　Reger: Geistliche Gesänge, Op. 110, Gesänge, Op. 39
　Schnittke: Concerto, Minnesang
　　see CONCERT INDEX under:
(CHAN) CHAN8853　Nielsen: Choral Works
(CHAN) CHAN9223　R. Strauss—A cappella choral works
(CHAN) CHAN9264　Scandinavian Contemporary a Cappella
　cond M. SCHØNWANDT
　Heise: Drot og Marsk (Cpte)
　cond L. SEGERSTAM
　Mahler: Symphony 8
　　see CONCERT INDEX under:
(CHAN) CHAN8853　Nielsen: Choral Works
　cond E. SEROV
　Nørholm: Symphony 4

DANISH NATIONAL RADIO CHORUS
　cond H. GRAF
　Zemlinsky: Es war einmal (Cpte)
　cond N. JÄRVI
　Nielsen: Saul and David (Cpte)
　cond L. SEGERSTAM
　Beethoven: String Quartet 11 (exc)
　Mahler: Symphony 2, Symphony 3

DANISH NATIONAL RADIO SYMPHONY ORCHESTRA
　cond J. FERENCSIK
　　see CONCERT INDEX under:
(BIS) BIS-CD278　Holmboe—Miscellaneous Works
　cond H. GRAF
　Holten: Sinfonia concertante
　Zemlinsky: Es war einmal (Cpte)
　cond N. JÄRVI
　Arensky: Suite, Op. 23
　Nielsen: Saul and David (Cpte)
　Scriabin: Symphony 3
　　see CONCERT INDEX under:
(CHAN) CHAN9064　Langgaard—Symphonies
(CHAN) CHAN9176　Honneger—Orchestral Works
　cond D. KITAIENKO
　Prokofiev: Alexander Nevsky, Romeo and Juliet (Cpte), Scythian Suite
　Rachmaninov: Bells, Spring, Op.20
　Stravinsky: Chant du rossignol, Firebird (Cpte)
　　see CONCERT INDEX under:
(CHAN) CHAN9075　Gade—Choral and Orchestral Works
(CHAN) CHAN9198　Stravinsky—Orchestral Works
　cond G. KUHN
　Schumann: Rose Pilgerfahrt (Cpte)
　cond J. LATHAM-KÖNIG
　Nørgård: For a Change, Siddhartha (Cpte)
　cond C. MACKERRAS
　Janáček: Glagolitic Mass (Cpte)
　Kodály: Psalmus Hungaricus
　cond J. PANULA
　Holten: Clarinet Concerto
　Nørgård: Between, Remembering Child
　cond G. ROZHDESTVENSKY
　Nielsen: Aladdin (Cpte)
　　see CONCERT INDEX under:
(CHAN) CHAN9209　Lumbye—Waltzes, Galops & Polkas
(CHAN) CHAN9287　Nielsen—Orchestral Works
　cond M. SCHØNWANDT
　Heise: Drot og Marsk (Cpte)
　Schoenberg: Piano Concerto
　Schumann: Piano Concerto
　　see CONCERT INDEX under:
(CHAN) CHAN8894　Nielsen—Concertos
　cond L. SEGERSTAM
　Beethoven: String Quartet 11 (exc)

Mahler: Blumine, Symphony 1, Symphony 2,
Symphony 3, Symphony 6, Symphony 7, Symphony
8, Symphony 9, Symphony 10 (exc)
Sibelius: Finlandia, In Memoriam, Symphony 1,
Symphony 2, Symphony 4, Tempest Suites (exc)
　see CONCERT INDEX *under:*
(BIS) **BIS-CD507**　Schnittke—Cello Works
(CHAN) **CHAN8853**　Nielsen: Choral Works
(CHAN) **CHAN8965**　Sibelius—Orchestral Works
(CHAN) **CHAN9055**　Sibelius—Orchestral Works
(CHAN) **CHAN9179**　Ruders—Orchestral Works

DANISH QUARTET
Debussy: String Quartet
Ravel: String Quartet
　see CONCERT INDEX *under:*
(KONT) **32033/4**　Brahms—Complete String Quartets
(KONT) **32049**　Nørholm—String Quartets
(KONT) **32150/1**　Nielsen—Chamber Works

DANISH RADIO CHAMBER CHOIR
　cond G. ROZHDESTVENSKY
Nielsen: Aladdin (Cpte)

DANISH RADIO CHORUS
　cond J. FRANDSEN
Nielsen: Maskarade (Cpte)
　see CONCERT INDEX *under:*
(DANA) **DACOCD340/1**　Langgaard—Symphonies Nos
4 and 6.Music of the Spheres

DANISH RADIO SYMPHONY ORCHESTRA
　cond H. BLOMSTEDT
Nielsen: Symphonies, etc
(EMI) **CDM5 65415-2**　Nielsen—Symphonies, etc
　cond F. BUSCH
　see CONCERT INDEX *under:*
(DANA) **DACOCD303**　Great Musicians in
Copenhagen
　cond M. CARIDIS
Skalkottas: Odysseus Symphony
　cond J. FRANDSEN
Nielsen: Maskarade (Cpte)
　see CONCERT INDEX *under:*
(DANA) **DACOCD340/1**　Langgaard—Symphonies Nos
4 and 6.Music of the Spheres
　cond L. GRØNDAHL
　see CONCERT INDEX *under:*
(DANA) **DACOCD351/3**　Nielsen—Complete
Symphonies
　cond J. HORENSTEIN
Brahms: Symphony 2
　cond T. JENSEN
　see CONCERT INDEX *under:*
(DANA) **DACOCD351/3**　Nielsen—Complete
Symphonies
　cond O. KNUSSEN
Nørgård: Voyage into the Golden Screen
　cond R. KUBELÍK
(EMI) **CDM5 65182-2**　Nielsen/Sibelius—Orchestral
Works
　cond N. MALKO
　see CONCERT INDEX *under:*
(DANA) **DACOCD303**　Great Musicians in
Copenhagen
　cond J. PANULA
　see CONCERT INDEX *under:*
(BIS) **BIS-CD256**　Works for percussion
　cond E. TUXEN
　see CONCERT INDEX *under:*
(DANA) **DACOCD351/3**　Nielsen—Complete
Symphonies

DANISH STATE RADIO SYMPHONY ORCHESTRA
　cond T. JENSEN
　see CONCERT INDEX *under:*
(DUTT) **CDLXT2502**　Thomas Jensen conducts
Nielsen, Vol.1
　cond E. TUXEN
　see CONCERT INDEX *under:*
(DUTT) **CDLXT2502**　Thomas Jensen conducts
Nielsen, Vol.1
　cond M. WÖLDIKE
Nielsen: Violin Concerto

DANKWORTH, Alec (db)
Ellington: Mainly Black

DANN, Steven (va)
Schubert: Rondo, D438, String Quintet

DANSEREAU, Jean (pf)
　see CONCERT INDEX *under:*
(ROMO) **81008-2**　Mary Garden (1874-1967)
(SYMP) **SYMCD1136**　Opera in Chicago, Vol.1

DANUBE SOUNDS CHOIR
　cond A. NAYDENOV
Prokofiev: Ivan the Terrible

DANUBIUS QUARTET
Boccherini: Guitar Quintets, G445-453 (exc)
Brahms: Clarinet Quintet
Villa-Lobos: String Quartet 2, String Quartet 7
(MARC) **8 223389**　Villa-Lobos—String Quartets
(MARC) **8 223390**　Villa-Lobos—String Quartets
(MARC) **8 223391**　Villa-Lobos—String Quartets
(NAXO) **8 550390**　Mozart—Chamber Works for
Clarinet
(NAXO) **8 550439**　Mozart—Works for Clarinet

DANZ, Ingeborg (mez)
Bach: Mass, BWV235, Mass, BWV236, St Matthew
Passion, BWV244
Beethoven: Mass in C

Franck: Béatitudes (Cpte)
Haydn: Mass 10
Mendelssohn: Midsummer Night's Dream (exc)
Various: Requiem of Reconciliation (Cpte)
　see CONCERT INDEX *under:*
(HANS) **98 979**　Mozart—Sacred Choral Works

DARA, Enzo (bar)
Donizetti: Ajo nell'imbarazzo (Cpte), Campanello di
notte (Cpte), Don Pasquale (Cpte), Elisir d'amore
(Cpte), Fille du Régiment (Cpte)
Giordano: Andrea Chénier (Cpte)
Rossini: Barbiere di Siviglia (Cpte), Cenerentola
(Cpte), Italiana in Algeri (Cpte), Turco in Italia (Cpte),
Viaggio a Reims (Cpte)

DARCLÉE, Hericlea (sop)
　see CONCERT INDEX *under:*
(MEMO) **HR4408/9(1)**　Singers in Genoa, Vol.1 (disc
1)

DARI, Paolo (bar)
Verdi: Simon Boccanegra (Cpte)

DARLING, Edward (sngr)
　see CONCERT INDEX *under:*
(EMI) **CDANGEL 5**　Norton—Chu Chin Chow

DARLINGTON, Stephen (cond)
　see English Stg Orch

DARLOW, Denys (cond)
　see London Handel Orch

DARMSTADT CHAMBER ORCHESTRA
　cond W. SEELIGER
Telemann: St Matthew Passion (1746)

DARMSTADT CHORUS
　cond W. SEELIGER
Mangold: Abraham
Telemann: St Matthew Passion (1746)

DARMSTADT PHILHARMONIC ORCHESTRA
　cond W. SEELIGER
Mangold: Abraham

DARÓCZI, Tamás (ten)
Bretan: Golem (Cpte)

DARRAS, Vincent (alto)
Bach: Motets (Cpte)
Monteverdi: Vespers

DART, Thurston (cond)
　see Philh

DART, Thurston (organ)
　see CONCERT INDEX *under:*
(JMS) **JMSCD1**　Thurston Dart plays English Organ
Music

DARTINGTON ENSEMBLE
　see CONCERT INDEX *under:*
(HYPE) **CDA66133**　Martinů: Chamber Works

DARTINGTON TRIO
C. Schumann: Piano Trio
Mendelssohn-Hensel: Piano Trio
　see CONCERT INDEX *under:*
(HYPE) **CDA66279**　Bridge—Chamber Works

DARZINS, Andra (va)
Mendelssohn: Sextet, Op.110

DASSY, Déva (sop)
　see CONCERT INDEX *under:*
(EMI) **CZS7 67515-2**　Offenbach—Operetta highlights

DATZ, Güsti (narr)
Lehár: Friederike (Cpte)

DAUCHA, Wolfgang (ten)
R. Strauss: Rosenkavalier (Cpte)

DAVENPORT, Glyn (bass-bar)
Henze: English Cat (Cpte)

DAVIÀ, Federico (bass)
Cavalli: Ormindo (Cpte)
Mozart: Nozze di Figaro (Cpte)
Puccini: Bohème (Cpte), Manon Lescaut (Cpte)

DAVID, Imke (va da gamba)
Telemann: Essercizii musici (exc)

DAVID, Léon (ten)
　see CONCERT INDEX *under:*
(SYMP) **SYMCD1172**　The Harold Wayne Collection,
Vol.21

DAVIDOV, Aleksandr (ten)
　see CONCERT INDEX *under:*
(PEAR) **GEMMCDS9007/9(1)**　Singers of Imperial
Russia, Vol.4 (pt 1)

DAVIDOVICH, Bella (pf)
　see CONCERT INDEX *under:*
(DELO) **DE3146**　The Schumann Edition
(ORFE) **C047831A**　Grieg—Violin Sonatas

DAVIDOVICI, Robert (vn)
Conyngham: Monuments, Southern Cross
　see CONCERT INDEX *under:*
(NEW) **NW334-2**　American Violin and Piano Works

DAVIDSON, Beverley (vn)
　see CONCERT INDEX *under:*
(VIRG) **VC7 59609-2**　Vivaldi—Concertos

DAVIDSON, Ilana (sop)
Weill: Down in the Valley (Cpte)

DAVIDSSON, Christian (bn)
　see CONCERT INDEX *under:*
(BIS) **BIS-CD507**　Schnittke—Cello Works

DAVIES, Arthur (ten)
Delius: Village Romeo and Juliet (Cpte)
Elgar: Caractacus (Cpte), Light of Life (Cpte)
Martinů: Greek Passion (Cpte)
Mendelssohn: Elijah (Cpte)
Parry: Invocation to Music
Rossini: Stabat Mater
Verdi: Masnadieri (Cpte)
Wagner: Tristan und Isolde (Cpte)
Walton: Troilus and Cressida (Cpte)
　see CONCERT INDEX *under:*
(CHAN) **CHAN8641/2**　Elgar—Dream of Gerontius.
Parry—Choral Works
(CHAN) **CHAN8788/9**　Elgar—The Kingdom;
Orchestral Works
(CHAN) **CHAN8824**　Walton: Vocal Works
(HYPE) **CDA66420**　Vaughan Williams: Vocal Works
(SAIN) **SCDC2070**　Susan Bullock
(SAIN) **SCDC2085**　Arthur Davies

DAVIES, Dennis Russell (cond)
　see American Cpsrs Orch

DAVIES, Dennis Russell (harm)
　see CONCERT INDEX *under:*
(SCHW) **311116**　Dvořák—Bagatelles, Op. 47;
Serenade, Op. 44

DAVIES, Dennis Russell (pf)
L. Harrison: Grand Duo

DAVIES, Eiluned (pf)
　see CONCERT INDEX *under:*
(BRIT) **BML001**　Bernard van Dieren Collection

DAVIES, Eirian (sop)
Ligeti: Grand Macabre (Cpte)
Saxton: Caritas (Cpte)

DAVIES, Fanny (pf)
　see CONCERT INDEX *under:*
(PEAR) **GEMMCD9291**　Fanny Davies plays
Schumann

DAVIES, Iestyn (treb)
Purcell: Timon of Athens, Z632 (exc)

DAVIES, Iona (vn)
　see CONCERT INDEX *under:*
(MOSC) **070978**　Maurice Greene—Songs and
Keyboard Works

DAVIES, Joan (mez)
Donizetti: Maria Padilla (Cpte)
　see CONCERT INDEX *under:*
(OPRA) **ORC003**　Donizetti—Gabriella di Vergy

DAVIES, Lynne (sop)
　see CONCERT INDEX *under:*
(OPRA) **ORCH104**　A Hundred Years of Italian Opera:
1820-1830

DAVIES, Maldwyn (ten)
Boughton: Immortal Hour (Cpte)
Handel: Alcina (Cpte), Allegro, il penseroso ed il
moderato (Cpte), Messiah (Cpte), Semele (Cpte)
Haydn: Mass 11
Mozart: Requiem
Stainer: Crucifixion
　see CONCERT INDEX *under:*
(HYPE) **CDA66245**　Bruckner—Choral Works
(HYPE) **CDA66420**　Vaughan Williams: Vocal Works

DAVIES, Marion (sop)
Delius: Village Romeo and Juliet (Cpte)

DAVIES, Mary (sop)
Janáček: Fate (Cpte)

DAVIES, Menai (contr)
Fénelon: Chevalier Imaginaire (Cpte)

DAVIES, Meredith (cond)
　see London Orch Nova

DAVIES, Oliver (pf)
　see CONCERT INDEX *under:*
(ASV) **CDDCA701**　The Virtuoso Clarinettist

DAVIES, Paul Edmund (fl)
　see CONCERT INDEX *under:*
(EMI) **CDC5 55085-2**　Flute Recital

DAVIES, Philippa (fl)
Mozart: Flute and Harp Concerto, K299
　see CONCERT INDEX *under:*
(ASV) **CDDCA795**　Mozart—Wind Concertos
(CARL) **PCD835**　The Romance of the Flute and Harp
(VIRG) **VC7 59604-2**　Debussy—Chamber Works

DAVIES, Rhoderick (bar)
Wagner: Tristan and Isolde (Cpte)

DAVIES, Ryland (ten)
Berlioz: Troyens (Cpte)
Cimarosa: Matrimonio segreto (Cpte)
Donizetti: Lucia di Lammermoor (Cpte)
Massenet: Esclarmonde (Cpte)
Mozart: Nozze di Figaro (Cpte), Requiem
Stravinsky: Pulcinella
Verdi: Don Carlo (Cpte), Trovatore (Cpte)
　see CONCERT INDEX *under:*
(PHIL) **412 873-2PH**　Mozart—Sacred Music
(PHIL) **438 800-2PM2**　Mozart—Choral Works

DAVIES, Simon (ten)
Bach: Cantata 208
Biber: Requiem in A, Vesperae

DAVIES, Steve (bass)
Vaughan Williams: Hugh the Drover (Cpte)

DAVIES, Tudor (ten)
see CONCERT INDEX under:
(BEUL) **1PD13** Sir Malcolm Sargent conducts British Music
(EMI) **CDS7 54560-2** The Elgar Edition, Vol.1

DAVIN, Patrick (cond)
see Rhineland-Pfalz State PO

DAVIS, Andrew (cond)
see BBC SO

DAVIS, Andrew (organ)
see CONCERT INDEX under:
(DECC) **433 676-2DM** Tallis—Choral Works
(DECC) **440 032-2DM** Monteverdi/Gesualdo—Motets and Madrigals
(EMI) **CDM7 64130-2** Christmas Music from King's

DAVIS, Barry (ob)
see CONCERT INDEX under:
(PHIL) **412 892-2PH** Vivaldi: Double Concertos

DAVIS, Carl (cond)
see City Lights Orch

DAVIS, Sir Colin (cond)
see ASMF

DAVIS, Howard (vn)
see CONCERT INDEX under:
(CRD) **CRD3435** Mozart—Violin Sonatas
(CRD) **CRD3457** Dvořák—Hausmusik

DAVIS, Ivan (pf)
see CONCERT INDEX under:
(ETCE) **KTC2002** Renata Scotto: Aria and song recital
(MUSM) **67094-2** Antheil—Ballet Mécanique

DAVIS, Jessie Bartlett (sngr)
see CONCERT INDEX under:
(PEAR) **GEMMCDS9050/2(1)** Music from the New York Stage, Vol. 1 (part 1)

DAVIS, Michael (vn)
Vaughan Williams: Lark Ascending
see CONCERT INDEX under:
(CHAN) **CHAN9262/3** Vaughan Williams—Orchestral Works

DAVIS, Robin (hn)
see CONCERT INDEX under:
(DECC) **443 476-2DF2** Vivaldi—L'estro armonico, Op 3

DAVISLIM, Steve (ten)
Schumann: Manfred (Cpte)

DAVISON, Arthur (cond)
see LPO

DAVRATH, Netania (sop)
see CONCERT INDEX under:
(SONY) **SMK47544** Latin-American Orchestral Works
(VANG) **08.8002.72** Canteloube: Songs of the Auvergne

DAVY, Jean (narr)
Milhaud: Christophe Colomb (Cpte)

DAWSON, Alan (ten)
see CONCERT INDEX under:
(DECC) **430 263-2DM** Purcell—Sacred choral works

DAWSON, Anna (sop)
Offenbach: Christopher Columbus (Cpte)

DAWSON, Anne (sop)
Boughton: Immortal Hour (Cpte)
Gay: Beggar's Opera (Cpte)
Mendelssohn: Elijah (Cpte)
Mozart: Nozze di Figaro (Cpte)
Parry: Invocation to Music
see CONCERT INDEX under:
(CHAN) **CHAN9082** Ferguson—Choral and Orchestral Works
(HYPE) **CDA66359** Mendelssohn—Choral Works
(HYPE) **CDA66420** Vaughan Williams: Vocal Works

DAWSON, Herbert (organ)
see CONCERT INDEX under:
(CLAR) **CDGSE78-50-50** Richard Crooks sings Ballads & Sacred Songs
(PREI) **89046** Rosette Anday (1903-1977)

DAWSON, John (treb)
Mozart: Zauberflöte (Cpte)

DAWSON, Julian (hpd)
J. Gibbs: Solos, Op.1

DAWSON, Lynne (sop)
Bach: Cantata 211, Cantata 212, Mass in B minor, BWV232 (Cpte)
Blow: Venus and Adonis (Cpte)
Brahms: Deutsches Requiem, Op.45 (Cpte)
Gluck: Iphigénie en Aulide (Cpte), Orfeo ed Euridice (Cpte), Rencontre imprévue (Cpte)
Handel: Chandos Anthem 10, Chandos Anthem 11, Jephtha (Cpte), Messiah (Cpte), Messias, K572 (Cpte), Saul (Cpte)
Haydn: Schöpfung (Cpte)
Holst: Choral Fantasia, Choral Symphony
Mendelssohn: Midsummer Night's Dream (exc)
Monteverdi: Orfeo (Cpte)
Mozart: Don Giovanni (Cpte), Mass, K427, Requiem
Orff: Carmina Burana
Pärt: Passio
Purcell: Dioclesian, Z627 (exc), Fairy Queen, Z629 (Cpte), Timon of Athens, Z632 (Cpte)

Vivaldi: Laudate pueri Dominum, RV601
see CONCERT INDEX under:
(ARCH) **423 594-2AH** Handel—Vocal Works
(CHAN) **CHAN9004** Handel—Chandos Anthems Vol. 2
(CHAN) **CHAN0517** Handel—Sacred Choral works
(CHAN) **CHAN9185/6** Howells—Songs
(CHAN) **CHAN9307** Schumann—Lieder
(CHAN) **CHAN9392** Vaughan Williams—Riders to the Sea etc.
(ECM) **831 959-2** Pärt—Arbos
(EMI) **CDC7 49672-2** Mozart: Sacred Choral Works
(ERAT) **4509-96371-2** Gardiner—The Purcell Collection
(HYPE) **CDA66254** A. Scarlatti: Cantatas & La Folia
(HYPE) **CDA66569** Vaughan Williams—Choral Works
(HYPE) **CDA66623** Purcell—Complete Anthems & Services, Vol.3

DAWSON, Peter (bass-bar)
Sullivan: Pirates of Penzance (Cpte)
see CONCERT INDEX under:
(MMOI) **CDMOIR411** Sacred Songs and Arias

DAY, Edith (sngr)
see CONCERT INDEX under:
(PEAR) **GEMMCDS9059/61** Music from the New York Stage, Vol. 4: 1917-20

DAYMOND, Karl Morgan (bar)
Vaughan Williams: Hugh the Drover (Cpte)
see CONCERT INDEX under:
(CHAN) **CHAN9392** Vaughan Williams—Riders to the Sea etc.
(OPRA) **ORCH104** A Hundred Years of Italian Opera: 1820-1830

DAZELEY, William (bar)
M. Berkeley: Baa Baa Black Sheep (Cpte)

DEAKIN PIANO TRIO
Parry: Piano Quartet, Piano Trio 1, Piano Trio 2, Piano Trio 3

DEAM, Donna (sop)
Handel: Israel in Egypt (Cpte)
Purcell: Dido (Cpte)
Rutter: Requiem
see CONCERT INDEX under:
(CLLE) **COLCD108** Poulenc: Sacred Choral Works

DEAN, Donna (sop)
see CONCERT INDEX under:
(HARM) **HMU90 7053** Humfrey—Verse Anthems

DEAN, Michael (bass-bar)
Handel: Agrippina (Cpte), Ottone (Cpte), Radamisto (Cpte)
Purcell: Dido (Cpte)

DEAN, Stafford (bass)
Britten: Burning Fiery Furnace (Cpte), Peter Grimes (Cpte)
Delius: Village Romeo and Juliet (Cpte)
Gay: Beggar's Opera (Cpte)
Stravinsky: Rake's Progress (Cpte)
Sullivan: Yeomen of the Guard (Cpte)
Verdi: Lombardi (Cpte), Otello (Cpte)
see CONCERT INDEX under:
(DECC) **430 263-2DM** Purcell—Sacred choral works
(DECC) **436 403-2DWO** The World of Royal Music
(PHIL) **438 800-2PM2** Mozart—Choral Works

DEANE, Christopher (bar)
Gershwin: Porgy and Bess (Cpte)

DEANS, Brian (tbn)
see CONCERT INDEX under:
(DOYE) **DOYCD005** Flower of Scotland

DEARDEN, Ian (perc)
see CONCERT INDEX under:
(CNTI) **CCD1008** Anderson: Mask and other works

DEARDEN, Ian (sound proj)
see CONCERT INDEX under:
(CNTI) **CCD1008** Anderson: Mask and other works

DEARDEN, Ian (tape op)
see CONCERT INDEX under:
(CNTI) **CCD1009** Music of Barry Anderson

DEARNLEY, Caroline (vc)
Brahms: Cello Sonata in D, Cello Sonata 2
Simpson: Horn Quartet
see CONCERT INDEX under:
(CHAN) **CHAN9152** Alwyn—Chamber Works - Volume 1

DEARNLEY, Christopher (organ)
see CONCERT INDEX under:
(HYPE) **CDA66249** My soul doth magnify the Lord—Anglican Evening Service
(HYPE) **CDA66260** Howells—Choral & Organ Works
(HYPE) **CDA66305** My Spirit Hath Rejoiced—Settings of Magnificat & Nunc Dimittis
(HYPE) **CDA66394** Howells—Organ Works
(HYPE) **CDH88036** Praise to the Lord

DEBART, Dominique (cond)
see Basse-Normandie Ens

DEBIČKA, Hedwig von (sop)
see CONCERT INDEX under:
(PEAR) **GEMMCD9394** Helge Roswaenge—Operatic Recital
(PREI) **89201** Helge Roswaenge (1897-1972) - I
(PREI) **89209** Helge Roswaenge (1897-1972) - II

DEBOST, Michel (fl)
see CONCERT INDEX under:

(EMI) **CDM7 63986-2** French Chamber Works
(EMI) **CDM7 69112-2** Best of Saint-Saëns
(EMI) **CZS7 62736-2** Poulenc—Chamber Works
(EMI) **CZS7 67306-2** Mozart—Works featuring Wind Instruments
(SONY) **SMK48466** Boulez conducts Schoenberg—Volume 3

DEBUSSY, Claude (pf)
see CONCERT INDEX under:
(EMI) **CHS7 61038-2** Debussy—Pelléas et Mélisande, etc
(SYMP) **SYMCD1093** The Harold Wayne Collection, Vol.7
(SYMP) **SYMCD1136** Opera in Chicago, Vol.1

DECHENNE, Danielle (pf)
see CONCERT INDEX under:
(LASE) **15 522** Schubert: Chamber Works

DECHORGNAT, Patrick (pf)
see CONCERT INDEX under:
(SCHW) **310652** Fumet/d'Indy/Honegger—Chamber Works

DECIMO, Marco (vc)
see CONCERT INDEX under:
(AKAD) **CDAK125** Tosti—Romanze

DECKER, Franz-Paul (cond)
see Canadian Nat Arts Centre Orch

DECKER, Richard (ten)
Mozart: Così fan tutte (Cpte)

DECORMIER, Robert (cond)
see R. DeCormier Sngrs

(ROBERT) DECORMIER CHORALE
cond V. GOLSCHMANN
see CONCERT INDEX under:
(VANG) **08.4016.71** Music of Samuel Barber

(ROBERT) DECORMIER SINGERS
cond R. DECORMIER
see CONCERT INDEX under:
(ARAB) **Z6622** Dowland—Vocal Works

DECREUS, Camille (pf)
see CONCERT INDEX under:
(SYMP) **SYMCD1071** Great Violinists, Vol.1

DECROOS, Jean (vc)
Martin: Cello Concerto
see CONCERT INDEX under:
(LASE) **15 522** Schubert: Chamber Works
(PHIL) **422 514-2PME5** The Complete Mozart Edition Vol 14

DEDIEU-VIDAL, Marcelle (pf)
Franck: Violin Sonata
Lekeu: Violin Sonata in G

DEE, Kiki (sngr)
Willy Russell: Blood Brothers (Cpte)

DEEKS, Stuart (vn)
see CONCERT INDEX under:
(PIER) **PV790013** A. Scarlatti—Cantatas

DEFERNE, Sylviane (pf)
see CONCERT INDEX under:
(DECC) **436 546-2DH** Poulenc—Concertos

DEFOSSE, Henri (cond)
see orch

DEGAETANI, Jan (mez)
Birtwistle: Punch and Judy (Cpte)
see CONCERT INDEX under:
(ARAB) **Z6141** Brahms: Lieder

DEGELIN, Bernadette (sop)
Puccini: Suor Angelica (Cpte)
see CONCERT INDEX under:
(ERAT) **2292-45202-2** M-A. Charpentier: Sacred Works

DEGENNE, Pierre (vc)
see CONCERT INDEX under:
(CALL) **CAL9893** Debussy & Ravel: String Quartets
(PHIL) **438 964-2PM4(1)** Souzay sings French Songs (pt 1)

DEGLER, Christa (sop)
Diabelli: Pastoral Mass, op 147

DEGUY, Sylvie (mez)
see CONCERT INDEX under:
(HARM) **HMC90 1417** Caplet—Orchestral and Vocal Works

DEINZER, Hans (cl)
see CONCERT INDEX under:
(DHM) **GD77085** Schubert & Schumann—Lieder
(DHM) **74321 26617-2(1)** Elly Ameling - The Early Recorings, Vols. 1-3

DEKOV, Emil (vn)
see CONCERT INDEX under:
(BIS) **BIS-CD026** Shostakovich—Chamber Works

DELAHAYE, Hélène (sop)
Offenbach: Contes d'Hoffmann (Cpte)

DELANGE, Pierrette (sop)
Offenbach: Périchole (Cpte)

DELAVAIVRE, Madeleine (sngr)
Hahn: Mozart (Cpte)

DELBOS, Raphaël (tbn)
see CONCERT INDEX under:
(EMI) **CDS7 54607-2** Stravinsky plays and conducts Stravinsky

DELEITO, Carmen (pf)
see CONCERT INDEX under:
(CHNT) **LDC278 1064/5** Brahms—Complete Piano Variations

DELERUE, Georges (cond)
see Orch

DELESCLUSE, Jean (sngr)
Debussy: Rodrigue et Chimène (Cpte)

DELÉTRÉ, Bernard (bass)
Brossard: Dialogus, Elévations (1698)
Campra: Idoménée (Cpte)
Gluck: Iphigénie en Aulide (Cpte)
Lully: Armide, Atys (Cpte)
M-A. Charpentier: Médée (Cpte)
Marais: Alcyone (Cpte)
Purcell: Fairy Queen, Z629 (Cpte)
Rameau: Indes galantes (Cpte), Platée (Cpte)

DELFS, Andreas (cond)
see Deutsche Kammerphilharmonie

DELILLE, Jany (sop)
Gluck: Orphée (exc)

DELL, Patti (sop)
R. Strauss: Aegyptische Helena (Cpte)

DELLAL, Pamela (mez)
Haydn: Mass 11

DELLER, Alfred (cond)
see Deller Consort

DELLER, Alfred (alto)
Britten: Midsummer Night's Dream (Cpte)
Monteverdi: Ballo delle ingrate
Purcell: Indian Queen, Z630 (Cpte)
see CONCERT INDEX under:
(EMI) **CHS7 69741-2(2)** Record of Singing, Vol.4—Anglo-American School (pt 2)
(HARM) **HMX290 1528/33(2)** A Purcell Companion (pt 2)
(VANG) **08.2003.72** Purcell—Celebrated Songs,Sacred Airs and Concert Pieces
(VANG) **08.5068.71** William Byrd and his Age
(VANG) **08.5069.71** Bach—Cantatas; Handel—Airs

DELLER, Alfred (alto/dir)
Monteverdi: Ballo delle ingrate, L'Arianna (exc)
see CONCERT INDEX under:
(HARM) **HMA190 201** Blow—Vocal Works
(VANG) **08.5060.71** Purcell—Odes

DELLER, Mark (alto)
Purcell: Indian Queen, Z630 (Cpte)
see CONCERT INDEX under:
(HARM) **HMA190 201** Blow—Vocal Works
(HARM) **HMX290 1528/33(2)** A Purcell Companion (pt 2)

DELLER CHOIR
cond A. DELLER
Purcell: Indian Queen, Z630 (Cpte)
see CONCERT INDEX under:
(HARM) **HMX290 1528/33(2)** A Purcell Companion (pt 2)

DELLER CONSORT
Monteverdi: L'Arianna (exc)
see CONCERT INDEX under:
(HARM) **HMA190 201** Blow—Vocal Works
(VANG) **08.5060.71** Purcell—Odes
cond A. DELLER
see CONCERT INDEX under:
(HARM) **HMC90 242** Purcell: Songs

DELLMANN, Diethard (cond)
see Mainz Bach Orch

DELMAN, Jacqueline (sop)
Messiaen: Poèmes pour Mi (exc)
see CONCERT INDEX under:
(BIS) **BIS-CD026** Shostakovich—Chamber Works

DELMAS, Jean-François (bass-bar)
see CONCERT INDEX under:
(IRCC) **IRCC-CD800** Souvenirs from Meyerbeer Operas
(SYMP) **SYMCD1172** The Harold Wayne Collection, Vol.21

DELMÉ QUARTET
Bliss: String Quartet 1, String Quartet 2
Brahms: Clarinet Quintet
Dvořák: String Quartet 12
Haydn: String Quartet, Op. 51
Hummel: String Quartets, Op.30
R. Strauss: String Quartet, Op. 2
Simpson: String Quartet 1, String Quartet 2, String Quartet 4, String Quartet 5, String Quartet 7, String Quartet 8, String Quartet 9
Verdi: String Quartet
see CONCERT INDEX under:
(CHAN) **CHAN8426** Bridge: Music for String Quartet
(HYPE) **CDA66376** Simpson: Chamber Works
(HYPE) **CDA66385** Settings of A. E. Housman
(UNIC) **DKPCD9097** Bernard Stevens—Chamber Works

DELNA, Marie (mez)
see CONCERT INDEX under:
(PEAR) **GEMMCDS9923(1)** Covent Garden on Record, Vol.1 (pt 1)

DELON, Jack (ten)
R. Ward: Crucible (Cpte)

DELONY, Willis (pf)
Barber: Piano Sonata, Op. 26
Prokofiev: Piano Sonata 6

DELUISE, Dom (sngr)
Forrest/Wright: Kismet (Cpte)

DELUNSCH, Mireille (sop)
Berlioz: Herminie

DEMAIFFE, Victor (bass)
see CONCERT INDEX under:
(RICE) **RIC060048** German Baroque Cantatas, Vol. 5

DEMAIN, John (cond)
see Houston Grand Op Orch

DEMANT, Leo (pf)
see CONCERT INDEX under:
(EMI) **CHS7 69741-2(5)** Record of Singing, Vol.4—Scandinavian School

DEMENGA, Catrin (vn)
Kancheli: Exil

DEMENGA, Patrick (vc)
see CONCERT INDEX under:
(ACCO) **20062-2** Scelsi—Chamber Works
(ACCO) **20093-2** Janáček—Chamber Works
(ECM) **445 234-2** 12 Hommages à Paul Sacher

DEMENGA, Thomas (vc)
Magnard: Piano Trio
see CONCERT INDEX under:
(DG) **415 487-2GH** Vivaldi: Guitar Concertos
(ECM) **437 440-2** Bach/Veress—Chamber Works
(ECM) **445 234-2** 12 Hommages à Paul Sacher
(ECM) **831 959-2** Pärt—Arbos
(ECM) **839 617-2** Bach & Carter—Instrumental & Chamber Works
(NOVA) **150 016-2** Vivaldi—Concertos
(PHIL) **434 076-2PH** Heinz Holliger and Friends

DEMENTIEV, Yuri (bass)
Tchaikovsky: Queen of Spades (Cpte)

DEMERDJIEV, Eugene (sngr)
Weill: Dreigroschenoper (Cpte)

DEMERS, Robert Lucien (bar)
Delius: Village Romeo and Juliet (Cpte)

DEMESSE, Magali (va)
see CONCERT INDEX under:
(MARC) **8 223636** In Memoriam Lili Boulanger

DEMETRIADES, Dimitri (cond)
see ECCO

DEMEYERE, Ewald (hpd)
Rossini: Tancredi (Cpte)

DEMIDENKO, Nikolai (pf)
Chopin: Ballades, Piano Concerto 1, Piano Concerto 2, Piano Sonata 3
Medtner: Piano Concerto 2, Piano Concerto 3
Scriabin: Piano Concerto
Tchaikovsky: Piano Concerto 1
see CONCERT INDEX under:
(CONI) **CDCF204** Prokofiev & Scriabin—Piano Works
(HYPE) **CDA66514** Chopin—Scherzi & other piano works
(HYPE) **CDA66597** Chopin—Piano Works
(HYPE) **CDA66616** Liszt—Piano Works
(HYPE) **CDA66636** Medtner—Piano Works
(HYPE) **CDA66654** Medtner/Rachmaninov—Music for Two Pianos
(HYPE) **CDA66713** Rachmaninov—Piano Works
(HYPE) **CDA66729** Weber—Piano Concertos
(HYPE) **CDA66781/2** Demidenko Live at Wigmore Hall
(HYPE) **CDA66808** Clementi—Piano Sonatas

DEMIGNY, Bernard (bass)
Bizet: Carmen (Cpte)
Boïeldieu: Voitures Versées (Cpte)
Tomasi: Don Juan de Mañara (Cpte)
see CONCERT INDEX under:
(EMI) **CZS7 67515-2** Offenbach—Operetta highlights

(LES) DEMOISELLES DE SAINT-CYR
cond E. MANDRIN
Couperin: Messe pour les couvents
see CONCERT INDEX under:
(FNAC) **592316** Clérambault—Chants & Motets for the Royal House of Saint-Louis

DEMPSEY, Gregory (ten)
Wagner: Rheingold (Cpte), Siegfried (Cpte)
see CONCERT INDEX under:
(DECC) **436 990-2DWO** The World of Benjamin Britten

DEMUS, Jörg (pf)
Dvořák: Biblical Songs (exc)
Schubert: Schöne Müllerin (Cpte), Winterreise (Cpte)
Wolf: Italienisches Liederbuch (Cpte)
see CONCERT INDEX under:
(AUVI) **V4622** Schubert: Works for Piano Duet
(DG) **415 189-2GH** Beethoven & Brahms: Lieder
(DHM) **GD77085** Schubert & Schumann—Lieder
(DHM) **74321 26617-2(1)** Elly Ameling - The Early Recorings, Vols. 1-3
(DHM) **74321 26617-2(2)** Elly Ameling - The Early Years, Vol. 4
(PHIL) **422 516-2PME2** The Complete Mozart Edition Vol 16

DEMUTH, Leopold (bar)
see CONCERT INDEX under:
(PREI) **89020** Leo Slezak (1873-1946)

DENBESTE, LeaAnne (sop)
L. Harrison: St Anthony Mass
Pärt: Berliner Messe

DENCH, Dame Judi (narr)
Mendelssohn: Midsummer Night's Dream (exc)

DENE, József (bass)
Wagner: Meistersinger (Cpte)

DENEUVE, Catherine (narr)
see CONCERT INDEX under:
(DG) **429 738-2GH** Debussy & Ravel: Chamber Works

DENEVE, Leo (va)
see CONCERT INDEX under:
(MARC) **8 223741** Maes—Orchestral Works

DENIZE, Nadine (mez)
Berlioz: Roméo et Juliette (Cpte)
Debussy: Pelléas et Mélisande (Cpte)
Gounod: Faust (Cpte), Mors et Vita (Cpte)
Mahler: Symphony 8
see CONCERT INDEX under:
(EMI) **CMS7 64476-2** Mahler—Symphonies, Vol.2

DENLEY, Catherine (mez)
Bach: Mass in B minor, BWV232 (Cpte)
Handel: Coronation Anthems, Deborah (Cpte), Hercules (Cpte), Judas Maccabaeus (Cpte), Messiah (Cpte), Ottone (Cpte), Semele (Cpte)
Haydn: Schöpfung (Cpte)
Monteverdi: Orfeo (Cpte)
Mozart: Zauberflöte (Cpte)
Telemann: Deus judicium tuum, Donner-Ode
Vivaldi: Gloria, RV589
see CONCERT INDEX under:
(HYPE) **CDA66219** American Choral Works
(HYPE) **CDA66245** Bruckner—Choral Works
(HYPE) **CDA66769** Vivaldi—Sacred Music, Volume 1
(HYPE) **CDJ33020** Schubert—Complete Lieder, Vol.20
(HYPE) **CDJ33022** Schubert—Complete Lieder, Vol.22

DENMAN, Mark (vn)
see CONCERT INDEX under:
(KING) **KCLCD2027** South American Flute Music

DENNINGHAM, Claudia (sngr)
Grieg: Peer Gynt (exc)

DENNIS, Paul (bass)
Verdi: Traviata (Cpte)

DENNY, Martin (treb)
see CONCERT INDEX under:
(ABBS) **CDMVP827** 20 Christmas Carols from St George's Chapel, Windsor Castle

DENS, Michel (bar)
Bizet: Carmen (Cpte), Pêcheurs de Perles (Cpte)
Ganne: Hans (Cpte)
Gounod: Mireille (Cpte)
Lully: Alceste (Cpte)

DENT, Karl (ten)
Janáček: Glagolitic Mass (Cpte)
Rachmaninov: Vespers, Op. 37 (Cpte)
see CONCERT INDEX under:
(TELA) **CD80340** Schubert—Songs for Male Chorus

DENT, Susan (hn)
see CONCERT INDEX under:
(CLRI) **CC0004** The Early Clarinet Family

DEPASQUALE, Joseph (va)
see CONCERT INDEX under:
(BIDD) **LAB044** Ruggiero Ricci—1938 Electrola Recordings

DEPLUS, Guy (cl)
Messiaen: Quatuor

DĚPOLTOVÁ, Eva (sop)
Fibich: Šárka (Cpte)
Martinů: Gilgamesh, Miracles of Mary (Cpte)
Smetana: Kiss (Cpte), Libuše (Cpte)

DEPRAZ, Xavier (bass)
Bizet: Carmen (Cpte), Pêcheurs de Perles (Cpte)
Milhaud: Christophe Colomb (Cpte)
Poulenc: Dialogues des Carmélites (Cpte)
see CONCERT INDEX under:
(CHNT) **LDC278 1068** Chabrier—Une Education Manquée/Mélodies
(ERAT) **4509-96952-2** Duruflé—Requiem; Organ Works

DEPREIST, James (cond)
see Helsinki PO

DEQUEKER, Eric (rec)
Telemann: Musique de Table (exc)

DERENNE, Paul (ten)
see CONCERT INDEX under:
(DECC) **433 400-2DM2** Ravel & Debussy—Stage Works

DERICK, Peter van der (bar)
R. Strauss: Friedenstag (Cpte)

DERMOTA, Anton (ten)
Bach: Cantata 78, Cantata 106, St Matthew Passion, BWV244 (exc)
Beethoven: Fidelio (Cpte), Symphony 9

Mozart: Così fan tutte (Cpte), Don Giovanni (Cpte),
Zauberflöte (Cpte)
R. Strauss: Arabella (Cpte), Rosenkavalier (Cpte)
Wagner: Meistersinger (Cpte), Tristan und Isolde
(Cpte)
see CONCERT INDEX under:
(CAMB) CD-1032 From the Operas of Erich Wolfgang
Korngold
(DG) 435 321-2GWP12 150 Years - Vienna
Philharmonic
(EMI) CHS7 69741-2(4) Record of Singing,
Vol.4—German School
(PREI) 90237 R Strauss—Daphne
(PREI) 93261 Richard Strauss accompanies
(PREI) 93262 R.Strauss accompanies
Reining,Dermota and Piltti
(SCHW) 314532 Vienna State Opera Live, Vol.3
(SCHW) 314552 Vienna State Opera Live, Vol.5
(SCHW) 314572 Vienna State Opera Live, Vol.7
(SCHW) 314582 Vienna State Opera Live, Vol.8
(SCHW) 314602 Vienna State Opera Live, Vol.10
(SCHW) 314652 Vienna State Opera Live, Vol.15
(VANG) 08.2010.71 Bach—Choral Works

DERNESCH, Helga (sop/mez)
Beethoven: Fidelio (Cpte)
R.Strauss: Arabella (Cpte)
Schoeck: Penthesilea (Cpte)
Wagner: Götterdämmerung (Cpte), Rheingold (Cpte),
Siegfried (Cpte), Tannhäuser (Cpte), Tristan und
Isolde (Cpte), Walküre (Cpte)
Weill: Dreigroschenoper (Cpte)
see CONCERT INDEX under:
(DECC) 414 100-2DM15 Wagner: Der Ring des
Nibelungen
(DECC) 430 804-2DC10 Mahler—Complete
Symphonies
(DG) 429 168-2GR Wagner: Excerpts from Der Ring
(DG) 435 211-2GX15 Wagner—Der Ring des
Nibelungen
(DG) 439 423-2GCL Wagner—Der Ring des
Nibelungen (highlights)
(DG) 445 354-2GX14 Wagner—Der Ring des
Nibelungen
(EMI) CMS5 65212-2 Wagner—Les introuvables du
Ring
(PHIL) 446 057-2PB14 Wagner—The Ring Cycle -
Bayreuth Festival 1967

DEROO, Lieven (bass)
Landi: Mort d'Orfeo (Cpte)

DERSCH, Wolfgang (bass)
see CONCERT INDEX under:
(CAPR) 10 180 Gisela May sings Weill

DERVAUX, Pierre (cond)
see Lamoureux Orch

DERWINGER, Love (pf)
Danzi: Wind Quintet, Op.41
Scriabin: Prometheus
see CONCERT INDEX under:
(BIS) BIS-CD550 Stenhammer—Vocal and Orchestral
Works
(BIS) BIS-CD574 Chamber Music from Estonia
(BIS) BIS-CD593 Poulenc—Music for Two Pianos
(BIS) BIS-CD619 Grieg—Piano Concerto (original
vers), etc
(BIS) BIS-CD620 Grieg—Piano Works, Vol.12
(BIS) BIS-CD637 Grieg—Songs, Volume 1
(BIS) BIS-CD657 Sibelius—Songs, Volume 2

DERZHINSKAYA, Xenia (sop)
see CONCERT INDEX under:
(DANT) LYS013/5 Tchaikovsky—The Queen of
Spades

DESAILLY, Jean (narr)
Stravinsky: Oedipus Rex (Cpte)

DESANA, Tina (sop)
see CONCERT INDEX under:
(IRCC) IRCC-CD808 Souvenirs of 19th Century Italian
Opera

DESARZENS, Victor (cond)
see Winterthur St Orch

DESBOROUGH SCHOOL CHOIR
cond C. ABBADO
Berlioz: Te Deum
cond L. MAAZEL
see CONCERT INDEX under:
(SONY) M3K79312 Puccini: Il Trittico

DESCHAMPS, Anne-Marie (cond)
see Venance Fortunat Ens

DESCOMBES, Paul (spkr)
Massenet: Amadis (Cpte)

DESDERI, Claudio (cond)
see Camerata Musicale Orch

DESDERI, Claudio (bar)
Mozart: Così fan tutte (Cpte), Nozze di Figaro (Cpte)
Rossini: Signor Bruschino (Cpte)
see CONCERT INDEX under:
(EMI) CDH5 65072-2 Glyndebourne Recorded - 1934-
1994
(EMIL) CDZ7 67015-2 Mozart—Opera Arias

DESFORD COLLIERY CATERPILLAR BAND
see CONCERT INDEX under:
(POLY) QPRL049D Boosey & Hawkes National Brass
Band Gala Concert 1991
cond E. GREGSON
see CONCERT INDEX under:

(DOYE) DOYCD017 Gregson—Brass Music - Volume
1
cond J. WATSON
see CONCERT INDEX under:
(HYPE) CDA66449 Simpson—Brass Band Music
(POLY) QPRL049D Boosey & Hawkes National Brass
Band Gala Concert 1991

DESGRAUPES, Bernard (cond)
see Erwartung Ens

DESLIGNES, Christophe (organ)
see CONCERT INDEX under:
(ARCA) A21 Ars Subtilis Ytalica

DESMOND, Astra (contr)
see CONCERT INDEX under:
(DUTT) CDAX8004 Sir Henry Wood conducts
Vaughan Williams
(PEAR) GEMMCD9342 Vaughan Williams: Vocal
Works

DESMOUTIERS, Gisèle (sop)
Poulenc: Dialogues des Carmélites (Cpte)

DESNOUES, Brigitte (sop)
Massenet: Grisélidis (Cpte)
see CONCERT INDEX under:
(MARC) 8 223755 Prix de Rome Cantatas

DESORMIÈRE, Roger (cond)
see FRNO

(ROGER) DESORMIÈRE ENSEMBLE
cond D. MILHAUD
see CONCERT INDEX under:
(EPM) 150 122 Milhaud—Historic Recordings 1928-
1948

DESROCHERS, Isabelle (sop)
Lully: Atys (Cpte)
Purcell: Fairy Queen, Z629 (Cpte)
see CONCERT INDEX under:
(FNAC) 592096 Rameau—Grand Motets
(FNAC) 592308 Lully—Grand Motets, Volume 1

DESROCHES, Gérard (ten)
Offenbach: Belle Hélène (Cpte)

DESSÌ, Daniella (sop)
Leoncavallo: Pagliacci (Cpte)
Rossini: Petite messe solennelle (Cpte)
Verdi: Don Carlo (Cpte), Falstaff (Cpte), Rigoletto
(Cpte)

DESTAIN, R. (sngr)
Offenbach: Chanson de Fortunio (Cpte)

DESTAL, Fred (bar)
see CONCERT INDEX under:
(SCHW) 314572 Vienna State Opera Live, Vol.7
(SCHW) 314632 Vienna State Opera Live, Vol.13

DESTINN, Emmy (sop)
see CONCERT INDEX under:
(PEAR) EVC3(1) The Caruso Edition, Vol.3 (pt 1)
(PEAR) GEMMCDS9074(1) Giovanni Zenatello, Vol.2
(pt 1)
(PEAR) GEMMCDS9924(1) Covent Garden on
Record, Vol.2 (pt 1)
(PEAR) GEMMCDS9924(2) Covent Garden on
Record, Vol.2 (pt 2)
(RCA) GD60495(5) The Complete Caruso Collection
(pt 5)
(RCA) 09026 61580-2(2) RCA/Met 100 Singers, 100
Years (pt 2)
(ROMO) 81002-2 Emmy Destinn (1878-1930)
(SIMA) PSC1810(1) Grieg—Songs (historical
recordings, pt 1)
(SUPR) 11 1337-2 Emmy Destinn (1878-1930)
(SUPR) 11 2136-2(1) Emmy Destinn—Complete
Edition, Discs 1 & 2
(SUPR) 11 2136-2(2) Emmy Destinn—Complete
Edition, Discs 3 & 4
(SUPR) 11 2136-2(3) Emmy Destinn—Complete
Edition, Discs 5 to 8
(SUPR) 11 2136-2(4) Emmy Destinn—Complete
Edition, Discs 9 & 10
(SUPR) 11 2136-2(5) Emmy Destinn—Complete
Edition, Discs 11 & 12

DESURMONT, Claude (cl)
Messiaen: Quatuor

DETROIT MARINER'S CHURCH CHOIR
see CONCERT INDEX under:
(DELO) DE3045 Organ Recital

DETROIT SYMPHONY ORCHESTRA
cond A. DORATI
Gershwin: Porgy and Bess Suite
Grofé: Grand Canyon Suite
R. Strauss: Aegyptische Helena (Cpte)
Stravinsky: Petrushka (Cpte), Rite of Spring (Cpte)
see CONCERT INDEX under:
(DECC) 430 705-2DM Copland—Orchestral Works
(DECC) 443 003-2DF2 Tchaikovsky—Orchestral
Works
cond N. JÄRVI
Chadwick: Symphonic Sketches, Symphony 2
Creston: Symphony 2
Ellington: River Suite
Fibich: Symphony 1, Symphony 2, Symphony 3
Ives: Symphony 2
Smetana: Má vlast
Tchaikovsky: Snow Maiden (Cpte)
W. G. Still: Symphony 1
see CONCERT INDEX under:
(CHAN) CHAN8958 Barber/Beach—Orchestral works

(CHAN) CHAN8996 Ravel & Roussel—Orchestral
works
(CHAN) CHAN9053 Ives/Barber—Orchestral Works
(CHAN) CHAN9072 French Orchestral Works
(CHAN) CHAN9169 Barber/Bristow—Orchestral
Works
(CHAN) CHAN9226
Still/Dawson/Ellington—Orchestral Works
(CHAN) CHAN9227 Encore!
(CHAN) CHAN9253 Chadwick/Barber—Orchestral
Works
(CHAN) CHAN9261 Rachmaninov—Orchestral
transcriptions
cond P. PARAY
Dvořák: Symphony 9
P. Paray: Joan of Arc Mass
Saint-Saëns: Symphony 3
Sibelius: Symphony 2
see CONCERT INDEX under:
(MERC) 432 003-2MM Ravel & Ibert: Orchestral
Works
(MERC) 434 321-2MM Bizet/Thomas—Orchestral
Works
(MERC) 434 328-2MM Berlioz—Orchestral Works
(MERC) 434 332-2MM French Marches & Overtures
(MERC) 434 343-2MM Debussy/Ravel—Orchestral
Works

DEUBNER, Maacha (sop)
Kancheli: Exil

DEUTEKOM, Cristina (sop)
Verdi: Attila (Cpte), Lombardi (Cpte)

DEUTSCH, Ernst (spkr)
Stravinsky: Oedipus Rex (Cpte)

DEUTSCH, Helmut (pf)
Schubert: Schöne Müllerin (Cpte), Winterreise
(Cpte)
Schumann: Dichterliebe, Op. 48 (Cpte), Liederkreis,
Op.39 (Cpte)
see CONCERT INDEX under:
(CAPR) 10 363 Mendelssohn—Lieder, Vol.2
(CAPR) 10 366 Mendelssohn—Lieder, Vol.1
(CAPR) 10 446/7 Mozart—Lieder
(EMI) CDC5 55430-2 Brahms/Schumann—Lieder
(SONY) SK57969 Wolf/Korngold—Eichendorff
Lieder
(SONY) SK64301 Beethoven—Songs from the British
Isles
(SONY) SK66835 Schubert—Schwanengesang and
Lieder

DEUTSCHE KAMMERPHILHARMONIE
see CONCERT INDEX under:
(TELD) 4509-97449-2
Berg/Hartmann/Janáček—Violin Concertos
cond A. DELFS
see CONCERT INDEX under:
(DECC) 444 819-2DH Schulhoff—Concertos and
Piano Music

DEVALLIER, Lucienne (contr)
see CONCERT INDEX under:
(DECC) 443 467-2DF2 Stravinsky—Ballet Music

DEVER, Barbara (mez)
Verdi: Aida (Cpte)

DEVEREUX, Roy (ten)
Wagner: Tristan und Isolde (Cpte)

DEVIA, Mariella (sop)
Bellini: Puritani (Cpte)
Cherubini: Lodoïska (Cpte)
Donizetti: Elisir d'amore (Cpte)
Rossini: Adelaide di Borgogna (Cpte)
see CONCERT INDEX under:
(BONG) GB2513-2 Mariella Devia—Opera Arias

DEVLIN, Michael (bass-bar)
Haydn: Infedelta Delusa (Cpte)
Rameau: Dardanus (Cpte)
see CONCERT INDEX under:
(PHIL) 432 416-2PH3 Haydn—L'incontro
improvviso/Arias
(SONY) SM2K47563 Haydn—Choral & Orchestral
Works

DEVOL, Luana (sop)
Schreker: Irrelohe (Cpte)

DEVOS, Claude (ten)
Messager: P'tites Michu (exc)
see CONCERT INDEX under:
(EMI) CZS7 67515-2 Offenbach—Operetta highlights

DEVOS, Louis (cond)
see Musica Polyphonica

DEVOS, Louis (ten)
Martin: Mystère de la Nativité
Orff: Carmina Burana
Rameau: Indes Galantes (Cpte)
see CONCERT INDEX under:
(BIS) BIS-CD437 Schnittke: Orchestral & Vocal Works
(EMI) CDM7 63948-2 20th Century French Orchestral
Works
(POLS) PNCD042 Lutosławski: Vocal and Orchestral
Works

DEVOS, Luc (fp)
see CONCERT INDEX under:
(ACCE) ACC9292D Mozart—Sonatas for Keyboard
and Violin, Vol.2

DEVOS, Luc (pf)
see CONCERT INDEX under:

(OLYM) **OCD355** Prokofiev/Janacek—Violin
Sonatas
(RICE) **RIC105081** Mozart—Keyboard Works

DEVOS, Noël (bn)
see CONCERT INDEX under:
(CHNT) **LDC278 835** Villa-Lobos—Chôros for
Chamber Ensembles
(CHNT) **LDC278 869/70** Villa-Lobos—Guitar Works

DEVOYON, Pascal (celesta)
see CONCERT INDEX under:
(TIMP) **1C1010** Honegger—Chamber Works, Vol.3
(TIMP) **4C1012** Honegger—Chamber Works

DEVOYON, Pascal (pf)
Grieg: Piano Concerto
Schumann: Piano Concerto
see CONCERT INDEX under:
(ERAT) **4509-92871-2** Franck—Orchestral Works
(HYPE) **CDA66235** Fauré—Works for Cello and Piano
(NAXO) **8 550276** French Violin Sonatas
(RCA) **09026 61678-2** Concerto! Steven Isserlis plays
Saint-Saëns
(RCA) **09026 68049-2** Fauré—Complete Works for
Cello
(TIMP) **1C1008** Honegger—Chamber Works, Vol.1
(TIMP) **1C1009** Honegger—Chamber Works, Vol.2
(TIMP) **1C1010** Honegger—Chamber Works, Vol.3
(TIMP) **4C1012** Honegger—Chamber Works

DEVREESE, Frédéric (cond)
see Belgian Rad & TV Orch

DEVRIÈS, David (ten)
see CONCERT INDEX under:
(NIMB) **NI7856** Legendary Tenors

DEWALD, Thomas (ten)
Rossini: Petite messe solennelle (Cpte)
see CONCERT INDEX under:
(WERG) **WER6275-2** Orff—Trionfi

DEWEY, Thomas (pf)
see CONCERT INDEX under:
(FORL) **UCD16711** Schumann—Lieder

DEYCK, Lucienne van (mez)
Puccini: Tabarro (Cpte)

DHERAN, Bernard (sngr)
Hahn: Mozart (Cpte)

DHÉRIN, Gustave (bn)
see CONCERT INDEX under:
(EMI) **CDC5 55036-2** Honegger/Poulenc—Perform
their own works
(EMI) **CDS7 54607-2** Stravinsky plays and conducts
Stravinsky
(PEAR) **GEMMCD9311** Poulenc d'après Poulenc

DHONT, Piet (ob)
see CONCERT INDEX under:
(ARCH) **419 633-2AH** Telemann: Wind Concertos

DIACONESCU, Florin (ten)
J. Perrin: De Profundis, Op. 26

DIAKOV, Anton (bass)
Bach: St Matthew Passion, BWV244 (Cpte)
Mussorgsky: Boris Godunov (Cpte)
Saint-Saëns: Samson et Dalila (Cpte)

DIAKOV, Vera (contr)
Martin: Vin herbé

DIAZ, Alirio (gtr)
see CONCERT INDEX under:
(EMI) **CZS7 67474-2** Viva España!

DIAZ, Justino (bass)
Catalani: Wally (Cpte)
Offenbach: Contes d'Hoffmann (Cpte)
Rossini: Pietra del Paragone (Cpte), Siège de
Corinthe (Cpte)
Verdi: Otello (Cpte)
see CONCERT INDEX under:
(SONY) **SK44981** Puccini: Songs

DIAZ, Raul (hn)
see CONCERT INDEX under:
(AMON) **CD-SAR34** Mozart—Chamber Works
(CHAN) **CHAN0547** Telemann—Orchestral Works

DIBNER, Steven (bn)
Mozart: Sinfonia Concertante, K297b
see CONCERT INDEX under:
(CATA) **09026 61979-2** Memento Bittersweet
(DG) **431 665-2GX3** Mozart—Wind Concertos

DICHTER, Mischa (pf)
Tchaikovsky: Piano Concerto 1
see CONCERT INDEX under:
(PHIL) **411 123-2PH** Popular works for piano and
orchestra

DICKEL, Werner (va)
Boccherini: String Sextets, G454-9 (exc)

DICKENSON, Jean (sop)
see CONCERT INDEX under:
(VAI) **VAIA1017** Leonard Warren—Early Recordings

DICKERSON, Bernard (ten)
see CONCERT INDEX under:
(EMI) **CDM7 64022-2** Vaughan Williams—Orchestral
Works

DICKEY, Bruce (cornett)
see CONCERT INDEX under:
(ACCE) **ACC9173D** Quel Lascivissimo Cornetto -
Virtuoso solo music for Cornett

DICKIE, John (ten)
J. Strauss II: Fledermaus (Cpte)
Mozart: Così fan tutte (Cpte)
see CONCERT INDEX under:
(NAXO) **8 550383** Mozart—Tenor Arias
(NAXO) **8 550495** Mozart—Sacred Choral Works

DICKIE, Murray (ten)
Lehár: Giuditta (exc)
Mozart: Nozze di Figaro (Cpte)
R. Strauss: Ariadne auf Naxos (Cpte), Frau ohne
Schatten (Cpte), Rosenkavalier (Cpte)
see CONCERT INDEX under:
(EMI) **CZS7 62707-2** Mahler—Vocal Works

DICKIE, William (bar)
Verdi: Rigoletto (Cpte)

DICKINSON, Meriel (mez)
G. Charpentier: Louise (Cpte)
Herrmann: Fantasticks
Schumann: Szenen aus Goethes Faust (Cpte)
see CONCERT INDEX under:
(CONI) **CDCF167** Dickinson—Vocal Works
(EMI) **CDM7 64022-2** Vaughan Williams—Orchestral
Works

DICKINSON, Peter (pf)
see CONCERT INDEX under:
(CONI) **CDCF512** The Erik Satie Show

DICKS, Wilhelm Walter (bar)
Berg: Lulu (Cpte)
Weber: Freischütz (Cpte)

DICKSON, Muriel (sop)
Sullivan: Sorcerer (Cpte)

DICTEROW, Glenn (vn)
Korngold: Piano Trio, Op.1, Violin Sonata, Op.6

DIDIER GAMBARDELLA, Laura (mez)
Mascagni: Amico Fritz (Cpte)

DIDUR, Adam (bass)
see CONCERT INDEX under:
(CLUB) **CL99-089** Adamo Didur (1874-1946)
(EMI) **CHS7 64860-2(2)** La Scala Edition - Vol.1,
1878-1914 (pt 2)
(MMOI) **CDMOIR422** Great Voices in Tchaikovsky
(PEAR) **GEMMCDS9073(1)** Giovanni Zenatello, Vol.1
(pt 1)
(PEAR) **GEMMCDS9925(1)** Covent Garden on
Record—Vol.3 (pt 1)
(PEAR) **GEMMCDS9997/9(2)** Singers of Imperial
Russia, Vol.1 (pt 2)
(SYMP) **SYMCD1168** The Harold Wayne Collection,
Vol.19
(TEST) **SBT1008** Viva Rossini

DIEBERITZ, Gerd W. (narr)
Millöcker: Gasparone (Cpte)

DIEDRICH, Michael (treb)
Mozart: Zauberflöte (Cpte)

DIEHL, André von (bass)
Wagner: Meistersinger (exc)

DIEKEN, Joseph (spkr)
Nono: Intolleranza 1960 (Cpte)

DIELEMAN, Marianne (contr)
see CONCERT INDEX under:
(PHIL) **442 050-2PB10** Mahler—Complete
Symphonies

DIELEMAN, Marianne (sop)
R. Strauss: Rosenkavalier (Cpte)

DIELTIENS, Roel (vc)
Bach: Solo Cello Suites

DIELTIENS, Roel (vn)
Telemann: Musique de Table (exc)
see CONCERT INDEX under:
(ACCE) **ACC28967D** Martinů—Cello Sonatas

DIETRICH, Marie (sop)
(SUPR) **11 2136-2(3)** Emmy Destinn—Complete
Edition, Discs 5 to 8

DIETSCHY, Véronique (sop)
Rameau: Dardanus (Cpte)
see CONCERT INDEX under:
(ADES) **20217-2** A. Scarlatti—Duo Cantatas, Vol.1

DIEZ, Hugo (pf)
see CONCERT INDEX under:
(EMI) **CHS7 69741-2(4)** Record of Singing,
Vol.4—German School

DIEZ, Ramon (sngr)
Chapí: Revoltosa (Cpte)

DIGIORGIO, Arturo (bar)
see CONCERT INDEX under:
(IRCC) **IRCC-CD808** Souvenirs of 19th Century Italian
Opera

DIJKSTRA, Hebe (mez)
Wagner: Walküre (Cpte)

DIKOV, Anton (pf)
see CONCERT INDEX under:
(LASE) **15 523** Beethoven: Orchestral Works

DILBÈR (sop)
see CONCERT INDEX under:
(ONDI) **ODE768-2** Dilbèr sings Coloratura Arias

DILKES, Neville (cond)
see English Sinfonia

DILOVA, Penka (mez)
Mussorgsky: Boris Godunov (Cpte)
Tchaikovsky: Queen of Spades (Cpte)

DIMCHEWSKA, Martya (sop)
Mussorgsky: Khovanshchina (Cpte)

DIMITRIEDI, Odissely (cond)
see USSR RSO

DIMITROVA, Ghena (sop)
Puccini: Turandot (Cpte)
Verdi: Aida (Cpte), Nabucco (Cpte), Oberto (Cpte)

DING, Lucy (cond)
see Lira Chbr Chor

DINITZEN, Kim Bak (vc)
see CONCERT INDEX under:
(KONT) **32101/2** Britten—Works for Cello

DINKIN, Alvin (va)
Schoenberg: Verklärte Nacht

D'INTINO, Luciana (mez)
Verdi: Don Carlo (Cpte)

DIRKS, Math (bar)
Schreker: Gezeichneten (Cpte)

DISCANTUS
Anon: Codex Las Huelgas (exc)
cond B. LESNE
see CONCERT INDEX under:
(O111) **OPS30-102** Campus Stellae - 12th Century
Pilgrims' Songs

DISMAN RADIO CHILDREN'S CHOIR
cond J. KARAS
Domažlický: Czech Songs
Krása: Brundibár (Cpte)

DISMAN RADIO CHILDREN'S ORCHESTRA
cond J. KARAS
Krása: Brundibár (Cpte)

DISNEY, Agnes (mez)
Delibes: Lakmé (Cpte)

DITLEVSEN, Jørgen (bass)
see CONCERT INDEX under:
(CHAN) **CHAN8853** Nielsen: Choral Works

DITTMANN, Friedwart (vc)
see CONCERT INDEX under:
(CAPR) **10 367** Mendelssohn—Motets

DITTMANN, Horst (bar)
see CONCERT INDEX under:
(CAPR) **10 180** Gisela May sings Weill

DITTRICH, Michael (cond)
see Bratislava RSO

DIVERTIMENTI
Bargiel: Octet
Dyson: Rhapsodies
Howells: String Quartet (1923)
Mendelssohn: Octet, Op.20
cond P. DANIEL
(MERI) **CDE84169** Mozart: Clarinet Works

DIVERTIMENTO ENSEMBLE
cond S. GORLI
Maderna: Satyricon (Cpte)

DIVES, Tamsin (mez)
MacMillan: Visitatio Sepulchri (Cpte)
Maxwell Davies: Martyrdom of St Magnus (Cpte)

DIVOKÝ, Zdeněk (hn)
see CONCERT INDEX under:
(OPUS) **9150 1473** L.Mozart & Telemann: Orchestral
Works

DIXEY, Amilia (mez)
Offenbach: Christopher Columbus (Cpte)

DIXON, Peter (vc)
see CONCERT INDEX under:
(CHAN) **CHAN9380** Martin—Ballades

DMITRIEV, Alexander (cond)
see St Petersburg Philh

DOANE, Steven (vc)
see CONCERT INDEX under:
(SONY) **SK64307** Dotzauer—Chamber Works

DOBEY, Robert Benjamin (organ)
Howells: Organ Sonata 2, Pieces

DOBIÁŠOVÁ, Marica (hpd)
Gluck: Trio Sonatas (1746)

DOBIE, Elizabeth (sop)
Delius: Village Romeo and Juliet (Cpte)

DOBING, Duke (fl)
see CONCERT INDEX under:
(CHAN) **CHAN9270** Holst—Orchestral Works
(CLLE) **COLCD117** Rutter—Fancies

DOBMEIER, Christoph (bass)
Bach: St Matthew Passion, BWV244 (Cpte)

DOBRÉE, Georgina (cl)
see CONCERT INDEX under:
(HYPE) **CDA66022** The Clarinet in Concert
(HYPE) **CDA66300** The Clarinet in Concert—Vol 2

DOBRIANOVA, Nadezhda (sop)
Mussorgsky: Boris Godunov (Cpte)

DOBRINDT, Otto (cond)
see Berlin St Op Orch

DOBROVEN, Issay (cond)
see FRNO

DOBSON, John (ten)
Britten: Peter Grimes (Cpte)
Janáček: Cunning Little Vixen (Cpte)
Menotti: Amahl and the Night Visitors (Cpte)
Puccini: Fanciulla del West (Cpte)
Stravinsky: Rake's Progress (Cpte)

DOBSON, Michael (cond)
see Thames CO

DOBSZAY, László (cond)
see Schola Hungarica

DOCKER, Robert (pf)
Slade: Salad Days (Cpte)

DOCTOR, Paul (va)
see CONCERT INDEX under:
(TELD) 9031-77620-2 Telemann—Orchestral Works

DOGHAN, Phillip (ten)
Fénelon: Chevalier Imaginaire (Cpte)
see CONCERT INDEX under:
(OPRA) ORCH103 Italian Opera—1810-20

DOHMEN, Albert (bar)
Mozart: Così fan tutte (Cpte), Don Giovanni (Cpte)
R. Strauss: Frau ohne Schatten (Cpte)

DOHNÁNYI, Christoph von (cond)
see Berlin Deutsche Op Orch

DOHNÁNYI, Ernö (cond)
see LSO

DOHNÁNYI, Ernö (pf)
see CONCERT INDEX under:
(EMI) CDC5 55031-2 Bartók/Dohnányi—Play their
own works
(SCHW) 311136 Dohnanyi plays and conducts

DOHNÁNYI, Ernö (pf/dir)
see CONCERT INDEX under:
(SCHW) 311136 Dohnanyi plays and conducts

DOHNÁNYI, Oliver (cond)
see Bratislava RSO

DOIG, Christopher (ten)
Einem: Dantons Tod (Cpte)
see CONCERT INDEX under:
(ODE) CDMANU1317 Wagner—Opera Excerpts

DOIKOV, Roumen (ten)
Mussorgsky: Khovanshchina (Cpte)

DOKOUPIL, Hans (pf)
(PREI) 93390 Hans Hotter Lieder recital

DOKOVSKA, Pavlina (pf)
(RCA) 09026 62501-2 Russian Romances

DOKSHITSER, Timofei (tpt)
Vainberg: Trumpet Concerto

DOLBASHIAN, Gregory (narr)
Glass: Einstein on the Beach (Cpte)

DOLBERG, Kirsten (mez)
Beethoven: String Quartet 11 (exc)
Haydn: Applausus (Cpte)
Mahler: Symphony 2, Symphony 8

DOLEŽAL, Vladimír (ten)
Brian: Symphony 1
Martinů: Ariane (Cpte)
Mysliveček: Abraham and Isaac
Orff: Carmina burana
see CONCERT INDEX under:
(STUD) SM1223.27 Rossini—Complete unpublished
Sacred Works
(SUPR) 11 0751-2 Martinů—Choral Works
(SUPR) 11 0767-2 Martinů—Cantatas
(SUPR) 11 0816-2 Zelenka—Choral Works
(SUPR) 11 1878-2 The Unknown Janáček

DOLEŽAL QUARTET
Janáček: String Quartet 1

DOLTON, Geoffrey (bar)
Donizetti: Emilia di Liverpool (Cpte), Eremitaggio di
Liverpool (Cpte)
see CONCERT INDEX under:
(OPRA) ORCH103 Italian Opera—1810-20
(OPRA) ORCH104 A Hundred Years of Italian Opera:
1820-1830

DOLUKHANOVA, Zara (mez)
see CONCERT INDEX under:
(EMI) CHS7 69741-2(6) Record of Singing,
Vol.4—Russian & Slavonic Schools

DOMANÍNSKÁ, Libuše (sop)
Janáček: Cunning Little Vixen (Cpte), Glagolitic Mass
(Cpte), Jenůfa (Cpte)
Martinů: Bouquet
Smetana: Devil's Wall (Cpte)
see CONCERT INDEX under:
(SUPR) 11 1930-2 Janáček/Kabeláč—Choral and
Orchestral Works

DOMARKAS, Juozas (cond)
see Slovak PO

DOMBOIS, Eugen M. (lte)
(RCA) GD71958 The Baroque Lute

DOMBRECHT, Paul (cond)
see Fondamento Ens

DOMBRECHT, Paul (ob)
Telemann: Musique de Table (exc)
Zelenka: Trio Sonatas
see CONCERT INDEX under:
(ACCE) ACC8537D French Oboe Music
(ACCE) ACC48013D Telemann—Works for Oboe &
continuo
(ACCE) ACC57804D Works for oboe

DOMBRECHT, Piet (hn)
Telemann: Musique de Table (exc)

DOME, Alfred (bass)
Wagner: Meistersinger (Cpte)

DOMGRAF-FASSBAENDER, Willi (bar)
Mozart: Così fan tutte (Cpte)
see CONCERT INDEX under:
(EMI) CDH5 65072-2 Glyndebourne Recorded - 1934-
1994
(NIMB) NI7848 Great Singers at the Berlin State
Opera
(PREI) 89047 Xenia Belmas (1890-1981)

DOMINANTE CHOIR
cond U. SÖDERBLOM
Bergman: Singing Tree (Cpte)

DOMINGO, Alvaro (treb)
see CONCERT INDEX under:
(SONY) M3K79312 Puccini: Il Trittico

DOMINGO, Plácido (cond)
see Munich RO

DOMINGO, Plácido (ten)
Beethoven: Missa Solemnis, Symphony 9
Bellini: Norma (Cpte)
Bizet: Carmen (Cpte)
Boito: Mefistofele (Cpte)
Bretón: Verbena de la Paloma (Cpte)
Cilea: Adriana Lecouvreur (Cpte)
Donizetti: Elisir d'amore (Cpte), Lucia di Lammermoor
(Cpte)
G. Charpentier: Louise (Cpte)
Giordano: Andrea Chénier (Cpte)
Gounod: Faust (Cpte)
J. Strauss II: Fledermaus (Cpte)
Leoncavallo: Pagliacci (Cpte)
Mascagni: Cavalleria Rusticana (Cpte), Iris (Cpte)
Massenet: Cid (Cpte)
Offenbach: Contes d'Hoffmann (Cpte)
Penella: Gato Montés (Cpte)
Puccini: Bohème (Cpte), Fanciulla del West (Cpte),
Madama Butterfly (Cpte), Manon Lescaut (Cpte),
Rondine (Cpte), Tosca (Cpte), Turandot (Cpte), Villi
(Cpte)
R. Strauss: Frau ohne Schatten (Cpte),
Rosenkavalier (Cpte)
Rossini: Barbiere di Siviglia (Cpte)
Saint-Saëns: Samson et Dalila (Cpte)
Verdi: Aida (Cpte), Ballo in Maschera (Cpte), Don
Carlo (Cpte), Don Carlos (Cpte), Emani (Cpte), Forza
del destino (Cpte), Giovanna d'Arco (Cpte), Lombardi
(Cpte), Luisa Miller (Cpte), Macbeth (Cpte), Nabucco
(Cpte), Otello (Cpte), Requiem (Cpte), Rigoletto
(Cpte), Simon Boccanegra (Cpte), Traviata (Cpte),
Trovatore (Cpte), Vespri Siciliani (Cpte)
Vives: Doña Francisquita (Cpte)
Wagner: Lohengrin (Cpte), Meistersinger (Cpte),
Parsifal (Cpte), Tannhäuser (Cpte)
Weber: Oberon (Cpte)
see CONCERT INDEX under:
(BELA) 450 121-2 Plácido Domingo
(CARL) MCD45 Spanish Royal Gala
(DECC) 430 433-2DH Carreras, Domingo and
Pavarotti in Concert
(DECC) 436 463-2DM Ten Top Tenors
(DG) 415 366-2GH Placido Domingo Recital
(DG) 431 103-2GB Great Voices—Montserrat Caballé
(DG) 431 104-2GB Great Voices - Plácido Domingo
(DG) 437 638-2GGA2 Berlioz—Vocal & Orchestral
Works
(EMI) CDC5 55017-2 Domingo Opera Classics
(EMI) CDC5 55018-2 Domingo sings and conducts
Tchaikovsky
(EMI) CDC7 47398-2 Placido Domingo: Vienna, City
of My Dreams
(EMI) CDC7 49148-2 Romanzas de Zarzuelas
(EMI) CDC7 49811-2 Covent Garden Gala Concert
(EMI) CDC7 54053-2 Roman Heroes
(EMI) CDC7 54266-2 Domingo and
Perlman—Together
(EMI) CDC7 54337-2 Domingo sings Mozart Arias
(EMI) CZS4 83177-2(3) Itzhak Perlman Edition (pt 3)
(RCA) GD86534 Verdi Arias and Duets
(RCA) 09026 61580-2(7) RCA/Met 100 Singers, 100
Years (pt 7)
(RCA) 09026 61580-2(8) RCA/Met 100 Singers, 100
Years (pt 8)
(SONY) MK44942 Domingo at the Philharmonic
(SONY) M3K79312 Puccini: Il Trittico
(SONY) SK44981 Puccini: Songs
(SONY) SK46691 The First Placido Domingo
International Voice Competition
(SONY) SK53358 Christmas in Vienna
(TELD) 4509-96200-2 The Three Tenors 1994

DOMINGO JNR, Plácido (ten)
see CONCERT INDEX under:
(EMI) CDC7 54053-2 Roman Heroes

DOMINGUEZ, Oralia (mez)
Beethoven: Symphony 9
Mozart: Mass, K317, Requiem

Verdi: Requiem (Cpte)
Wagner: Rheingold (Cpte), Siegfried (Cpte)
see CONCERT INDEX under:
(DG) 435 211-2GX15 Wagner—Der Ring des
Nibelungen
(EMI) CDM7 64281-2 Boulanger—Vocal & Chamber
Works
(EMI) CHS5 65506-2 Victor de Sabata conducts
(EMI) CZS7 67474-2 Viva España!

DOMINICI, Ernesto (bass)
see CONCERT INDEX under:
(PREI) 89040 Carlo Galeffi (1884-1961)

DOMINIQUE, Carl-Axel (pf)
Messiaen: Harawi
Schnittke: Symphony 1
see CONCERT INDEX under:
(BIS) BIS-CD594/6 Messiaen—Complete Bird Music
for Piano Solo

DOMMER, Barbara (spkr)
Braunfels: Verkündigung (Cpte)

DOMONKOS, Judit Kis (vc)
see CONCERT INDEX under:
(MARC) 8 223727 Truscott—Chamber Music

DOMUS
Brahms: Piano Quartet 1, Piano Quartet 2, Piano
Quartet 3
Dvořák: Piano Quartet 1, Piano Quartet 2
Fauré: Piano Quartet 1, Piano Quartet 2, Piano
Quintet 1, Piano Quintet 2
Mahler: Piano Quartet Movement
Schubert: Adagio and Rondo Concertante, D487,
Trout Quintet, D667
see CONCERT INDEX under:
(COLL) Coll1453-2 Distance &
Enchantment—Chamber Works by Judith Weir
(SCHW) 310632 Globokar—Chamber Works
(VIRG) CUV5 61203-2 Mendelssohn—Piano
Quartets

DON COSSACK CHOIR
cond H. VON KARAJAN
see CONCERT INDEX under:
(DG) 415 855-2GGA Tchaikovsky: Orchestral works

DONAGGIO, Luciano (bass)
see CONCERT INDEX under:
(EMI) CHS7 64864-2(2) La Scala Edition - Vol.2,
1915-46 (pt 2)

DONALD HUNT SINGERS
see CONCERT INDEX under:
(HYPE) CDA66271/2 Elgar:The Complete Choral
Songs
cond DON HUNT
(HYPE) CDA66078 Cathedral & Organ Music

DONANDT, Volker (db)
see CONCERT INDEX under:
(SCHW) 312322 Schulhoff—Chamber Music with
wind instruments

DONAT, Zdisława (sop)
Mozart: Zauberflöte (Cpte)

DONATH, Helen (sop)
Bach: Cantata 146, Christmas Oratorio, BWV248
(Cpte)
Beethoven: Fidelio (Cpte), Symphony 9
Gluck: Orfeo ed Euridice (Cpte)
Handel: Messiah (Cpte)
Haydn: Anima del filosofo (Cpte), Vera Costanza
(Cpte)
Hindemith: Sancta Susanna (Cpte)
Humperdinck: Königskinder (Cpte)
K. A. Hartmann: Simplicius Simplicissimus (Cpte)
Lehár: Friederike (Cpte)
Mahler: Symphony 2, Symphony 4
Mendelssohn: Elias (Cpte)
Mozart: Finta Giardiniera (Cpte), Finta semplice
(Cpte), Lucio Silla (Cpte), Nozze di Figaro (Cpte),
Requiem
Pfitzner: Palestrina (Cpte)
Puccini: Gianni Schicchi (Cpte)
R.Strauss: Arabella (Cpte), Rosenkavalier (Cpte)
Verdi: Ballo in maschera (Cpte)
Wagner: Meistersinger (Cpte), Rheingold (Cpte)
Weber: Freischütz (Cpte)
Wolf: Corregidor (Cpte)
see CONCERT INDEX under:
(DG) 429 168-2GR Wagner: Excerpts from Der Ring
(DG) 435 211-2GX15 Wagner—Der Ring des
Nibelungen
(EMI) CDM7 69223-2 Schubert—Choral Works
(EMI) CMS7 64778-2 Schubert—Sacred Works,
Vol.1
(EMI) CMS7 64783-2 Schubert—Sacred Works,
Vol.2
(EMI) CZS7 67819-2 Brahms/Schumann—Requiems
(EMI) CDZ7 67015-2 Mozart—Opera Arias
(EURO) GD69043 Puccini: Il Trittico
(HANS) 98 808 Bach—Cantatas,Vol.46
(HANS) 98 809 Bach—Cantatas,Vol.47
(HANS) 98 814 Bach—Cantatas,Vol.52
(HANS) 98 822 Bach—Cantatas,Vol.60
(HANS) 98 826 Bach—Cantatas,Vol.64
(HANS) 98 829 Bach—Cantatas,Vol.67
(HANS) 98 835 Bach—Cantatas,Vol.69
(HANS) 98 863 Bach—Cantatas,Vol.12
(HANS) 98 867 Bach—Cantatas,Vol.16
(HANS) 98 870 Bach—Cantatas,Vol.19
(HANS) 98 887 Bach—Cantatas,Vol.36

(HYPE) **CDA66340** Romantic Harp Music of the 19th Century, Vol. 3
(OPRA) **ORCH103** Italian Opera—1810-20

DRAKE, Victoria (hp)
see CONCERT INDEX *under:*
(SCHW) **310832** Frank Martin—Orchestral Works

DRAN, Thierry (ten)
Auber: Fra Diavolo (Cpte)
Chausson: Roi Arthus (Cpte)
Offenbach: Brigands (Cpte)

DRAPAL, Otto (treb)
see CONCERT INDEX *under:*
(SCHW) **314602** Vienna State Opera Live, Vol.10

DRAPER, Charles (cl)
see CONCERT INDEX *under:*
(CLRI) **CC0005** The Clarinet - Historical Recordings, Vol.1
(DUTT) **CDLX7013** The Unforgettable Isobel Baillie

DRAPER, Haydn P (cl)
see CONCERT INDEX *under:*
(CLRI) **CC0005** The Clarinet - Historical Recordings, Vol.1

DRAUGSVOLL, Geir (accordion)
see CONCERT INDEX *under:*
(BIS) **BIS-CD710** Gubaidulina—Chamber Works

DRAXINGER, Franz (hn)
see CONCERT INDEX *under:*
(TROU) **TRO-CD01405** Ethel Smyth—Chamber Works & Songs, Vol.3

DREIER, Per (cond)
see LSO

DRENIKOV, Ivan (pf)
Rachmaninov: Preludes (exc)

DRESDEN BAROQUE SOLOISTS
Telemann: 2-Flute concerti

DRESDEN KREUZCHOR
cond M. FLÄMIG
Mendelssohn: Vom Himmel hoch
Saint-Saëns: Oratorio de Noël, Op. 12
see CONCERT INDEX *under:*
(CAPR) **10 367** Mendelssohn—Motets

DRESDEN KREUZCHOR CHILDREN'S VOICES
cond B. HAITINK
R. Strauss: Rosenkavalier (Cpte)

DRESDEN PHILHARMONIC CHORUS (CHILDREN'S VOICES)
cond L. BERNSTEIN
Beethoven: Symphony 9

DRESDEN PHILHARMONIC ORCHESTRA
cond M. FLÄMIG
Mendelssohn: Vom Himmel hoch
Saint-Saëns: Oratorio de Noël, Op. 12
cond H. KEGEL
Beethoven: Choral Fantasia, Triple Concerto
see CONCERT INDEX *under:*
(CAPR) **10 451/5** Beethoven—Symphonies 1-9
(LASE) **15 523** Beethoven: Orchestral Works
cond J-P. WEIGLE
Reger: Mozart Variations, Op.132, Symphonic Poems, Op.128
see CONCERT INDEX *under:*
(CAPR) **10 805** Mozart: Wind Concertos

DRESDEN STATE OPERA CHORUS
Beethoven: Fidelio (Cpte)
R. Strauss: Elektra (Cpte), Rosenkavalier (Cpte)
Schumann: Paradies und die Peri (Cpte)
Wagner: Götterdämmerung (Cpte), Meistersinger (Cpte), Rienzi (Cpte)
see CONCERT INDEX *under:*
(DG) **437 677-2GDO2** Irmgard Seefried - Opera Recital
(PHIL) **446 067-2PH6** Beethoven—Complete Symphonies

DRESDEN STATE OPERA ORCHESTRA
cond K. BÖHM
see CONCERT INDEX *under:*
(PREI) **90237** R Strauss—Daphne

DRESDNER KAPELLKNABEN
Bach: St. Matthew Passion, BWV244 (Cpte)

DRESSEL, Heinz (cond)
see Folkwang CO

DRESSEN, Dan (ten)
Britten: Paul Bunyan (Cpte)
Copland: Tender Land (Cpte)
see CONCERT INDEX *under:*
(VIRG) **VC7 59022-2** Smyth—Vocal and Orchestral Works

DRESSLER, Robert (spkr)
Pfitzner: Herz (Cpte)

DREWNOWSKI, Marek (pf)
see CONCERT INDEX *under:*
(EURM) **350238** Weber—Works for Piano & Orchestra
(POLS) **PNCD045** Lutosławski: Selected Works

DREYER, Annemarie (vn)
see CONCERT INDEX *under:*
(ECM) **445 351-2** Gavin Bryars—Vita Nova

DREYER, Derek (sngr)
Schuman: Mighty Casey (Cpte)

DREYER, Jelle (bar)
Keiser: Masagniello furioso (Cpte)

DREYFUS, Huguette (hpd)
Bach: Concertos, BWV972-987, Goldberg Variations
W.F. Bach: Fantasias, F14-23 (exc)
see CONCERT INDEX *under:*
(ERAT) **4509-91721-2** Dutilleux—Piano Works and Chamber Music

DREYFUS, Laurence (va da gamba)
Rameau: Pièces de clavecin en concerts

DRIEHUYS, Leo (ob)
(PHIL) **426 075-2PCC** Bach: Concertos
(PHIL) **426 086-2PBQ** Vivaldi—Double Concertos

DRISCOLL, Loren (ten)
Berg: Lulu (Cpte)
Henze: Junge Lord (Cpte)
Wagner: Meistersinger (Cpte)
see CONCERT INDEX *under:*
(SONY) **SM3K46291** Stravinsky—Ballets, Vol.1

DROBINSKY, Mark (vc)
see CONCERT INDEX *under:*
(MARC) **8 223423** Fuchs—Works for Cello & Piano

DROBKOVÁ, Drahomira (contr)
Dvořák: Dimitrij (Cpte), St Ludmilla (Cpte)
Janáček: Glagolitic Mass (Cpte)
see CONCERT INDEX *under:*
(STUD) **SM1223.27** Rossini—Complete unpublished Sacred Works
(SUPR) **11 0751-2** Martinů—Choral Works

DROFOVÁ, Barbora (sop)
Krása: Brundibár (Cpte)

DROLC, Eduard (vn)
see CONCERT INDEX *under:*
(DG) **437 131-2GX2** Brahms—Chamber Works

DROTTNINGHOLM BAROQUE ENSEMBLE
see CONCERT INDEX *under:*
(BIS) **BIS-CD617** Telemann—Recorder Concertos
cond A. ÖHRWALL
Handel: Concerti grossi, Op. 6 (exc), Dixit Dominus
Roman: Swedish Mass
see CONCERT INDEX *under:*
(PROP) **PRCD9008** Anne Sofie Von Otter — Recital
cond T. SCHUBACK
Haeffner: Electra (Cpte)

DROTTNINGHOLM COURT THEATRE CHORUS
cond A. ÖSTMAN
Mozart: Nozze di Figaro (Cpte), Zauberflöte (Cpte)

DROTTNINGHOLM COURT THEATRE ORCHESTRA
cond A. ÖSTMAN
Mozart: Don Giovanni (Cpte)
cond A. ÖSTMAN
Mozart: Don Giovanni (Cpte), Nozze di Figaro (Cpte), Zauberflöte (Cpte)

DROUET, Jean-Pierre (perc)
Bartók: Sonata for 2 Pianos and Percussion, 2-Piano Concerto
Bernstein: West Side Story Symphonic Dances
see CONCERT INDEX *under:*
(SCHW) **310632** Globokar—Chamber Works

DRUCKER, Eugene (vn)
Bartók: Duos, Sz98
Fuchs: Duos, Op. 55
Shostakovich: Piano Quintet, Op. 57
see CONCERT INDEX *under:*
(DG) **431 772-2GH** Prokofiev—Chamber Works

DRUCKER, Stanley (cl)
Corigliano: Clarinet Concerto
see CONCERT INDEX *under:*
(DG) **431 672-2GH** Copland—Orchestral Works
(EMI) **CDC5 55400-2** Barber—Chamber and Instrumental Works
(SONY) **SMK47545** Debussy/Ravel—Orchestral Works
(SONY) **SMK47599** Hindemith/Nielsen—Concertos

DRUCKMAN, Daniel (marimba)
see CONCERT INDEX *under:*
(ARGO) **444 457-2ZH** Fascinatin' Rhythm

DRUIETT, Michael (bass)
Floyd: Susannah (Cpte)

DRURY, Stephen (pf)
(CATA) **09026 61980-2** John Cage—In a Landscape
(NORT) **NR228-CD** Youthful Rapture—Chamber Music of Percy Grainger

DRUYNIN, Feodor (va)
see CONCERT INDEX *under:*
(CHNT) **LDC278 1018/9** Shostakovich: Chamber Works

DRY, Marion (mez)
V. Thomson: Lord Byron (Cpte)

DU PRÉ, Jacqueline (vc)
Beethoven: Allegretto, Hess48, Cello Sonata 3, Cello Sonata 5, Piano Trios (exc)
Boccherini: Cello Concerto, G482
Chopin: Cello Sonata
Dvořák: Cello Concerto
Elgar: Cello Concerto
Franck: Violin Sonata
Haydn: Cello Concerto in C, Cello Concerto in D
Lalo: Cello Concerto

R. Strauss: Don Quixote
see CONCERT INDEX *under:*
(EMI) **CDC5 55529-2** Delius—Cello Concerto, etc
(EMI) **CDM7 63165-2** Jacqueline Du Pré—Early BBC Recordings, Vol.1
(EMI) **CDM7 63166-2** Jacqueline Du Pré—Early BBC Recordings, Vol.2
(EMI) **CDM7 64626-2** Schumann—Concertos, etc
(EMI) **CMS7 63015-2** Beethoven—Cello Sonatas, etc
(EMI) **CMS7 69707-2** Impressions of Jacqueline du Pré
(EMI) **CZS5 68132-2** Les introuvables de Jacqueline du Pré

DUA, Octave (ten)
Verdi: Trovatore (Cpte)
Wagner: Tristan und Isolde (Cpte)
see CONCERT INDEX *under:*
(PEAR) **GEMMCDS9926(1)** Covent Garden on Record—Vol.4 (pt 1)

DUARTE, Roberto (cond)
see Bratislava RSO

DUBERNET, Gilles (bar)
Auber: Gustav III (Cpte)

DUBINSKY, Rostislav (vn)
Brahms: Horn Trio
Dvořák: Piano Trio 4
Smetana: Piano Trio in G minor
Tchaikovsky: Album for the Young
see CONCERT INDEX *under:*
(CHAN) **CHAN8343** Shostakovich & Schnittke—Violin and Piano Works
(CHAN) **CHAN8458** Debussy & Ravel: Chamber Works

DUBLIN COUNTY CHOIR
cond R. SACCANI
Verdi: Aida (Cpte)

DUBOSC, Catherine (sop)
Bach: Mass in B minor, BWV232 (Cpte)
Berlioz: Troyens (Cpte)
Gluck: Rencontre imprévue (Cpte)
Mussorgsky: Boris Godunov (Cpte)
Poulenc: Dialogues des Carmélites (Cpte)
Prokofiev: Love for 3 Oranges (Cpte)
see CONCERT INDEX *under:*
(DECC) **436 991-2DH** Poulenc—Mélodies
(DECC) **440 333-2DH** Ravel—Vocal Works
(VIRG) **VC7 59286-2** Poulenc—Sacred Vocal Works

DUBREUIL, Pascal (hpd)
Handel: Water Music

DUCAREL, Michael (bar)
Sullivan: Mikado (Cpte)

DUCHÂBLE, François-René (pf)
Chopin: Etudes (exc)
Grieg: Piano Concerto
Rachmaninov: Piano Concerto 2
see CONCERT INDEX *under:*
(EMI) **CDC5 55166-2**
Schubert/Beethoven/Reinecke—Viola Works
(ERAT) **4509-92403-2** Chopin—Piano Works
(ERAT) **4509-92406-2** Liszt—Piano Concertos

DUCHÊNE, Maria (mez)
see CONCERT INDEX *under:*
(PEAR) **EVC3(1)** The Caruso Edition, Vol.3 (pt 1)
(RCA) **GD60495(5)** The Complete Caruso Collection (pt 5)
(ROMO) **81002-2** Emmy Destinn (1878-1930)
(SUPR) **11 2136-2(5)** Emmy Destinn—Complete Edition, Discs 11 & 12

DUCHESNEAU, Claire (sop)
Schumann: Manfred (Cpte)

DUCKENS, Dorceal (voc)
Joplin: Treemonisha (Cpte)

DUCKETT, Catherine (bn)
Pärt: Passio

(RENÉ) DUCLOS CHOIR
cond A. CLUYTENS
Offenbach: Contes d'Hoffmann (Cpte)
see CONCERT INDEX *under:*
(EMI) **CZS5 68220-2** André Cluytens—A profile
cond G. PRÊTRE
Bizet: Carmen (Cpte)
Saint-Saëns: Samson et Dalila (Cpte)
see CONCERT INDEX *under:*
(EMI) **CDC7 47723-2** Poulenc: Choral and Organ works
(EMIN) **CD-EMX2123** Maria Callas sings Operatic Arias

DUCZMAL, Agnieszka (cond)
see Amadeus CO

DUDA, Petr (hn)
see CONCERT INDEX *under:*
(SUPR) **11 0767-2** Martinů—Cantatas

DUDAREV, Georgy (bass)
Kabalevsky: Colas Breugnon (Cpte)

DUDAROVA, Veronika (cond)
see Anima Chbr Ch

DUDZIAK, Francis (ten)
Berg: Lulu (Cpte)
Gluck: Rencontre imprévue (Cpte)
Offenbach: Brigands (Cpte)
Rossini: Comte Ory (Cpte)

DUESING, Dale (bar)
Barber: Lovers
Mozart: Così fan tutte (Cpte)
Offenbach: Contes d'Hoffmann (Cpte)
see CONCERT INDEX under:
(DELO) **DE3078**   Barber, Bernstein and Gershwin

DUETSCHLER, Anna Barbara (va)
see CONCERT INDEX under:
(CLAV) **CD50-9502**   Baroque Viola Sonatas

DUETSCHLER, Ursula (fp)
see CONCERT INDEX under:
(CLAV) **CD50-9502**   Baroque Viola Sonatas

DUETSCHLER, Ursula (hpd)
see CONCERT INDEX under:
(CLAV) **CD50-9001**   Byrd—Keyboard Works
(RCA) **09026 60900-2**   Galway plays Bach

DUFALLO, Richard (cond)
see Netherlands Wind Ens

(THE) DUFAY COLLECTIVE
see CONCERT INDEX under:
(CNTI) **CCD1042**   Medieval Dance Music

DUFOURCET, Marie-Bernadette (organ)
see CONCERT INDEX under:
(PRIO) **PRCD328**   Tournemire—Organ Music
(PRIO) **PRCD422**   Great European Organs No. 36

DUFRANNE, Hector (bass)
Ravel: Heure espagnole (Cpte)

DUFTSCHMID, Lorentz (violine)
Kapsperger: Chitarrone Book I (exc), Chitarrone Book IV

DUFTSCHMID, Lorenz (vn)
D. Ortiz: Trattado de glosas
see CONCERT INDEX under:
(ASTR) **E8503**   Merula—Arie e Capricci

DUGARDIN, Steve (alto)
see CONCERT INDEX under:
(TELD) **4509-95068-2**   Purcell—Songs of Welcome & Farewell

DUGAS, Sylvie (pf)
see CONCERT INDEX under:
(NAXO) **8 553080**   Chabrier—Piano Works, Volume 3

DUGAY, Richard (ten)
Campra: Idoménée (Cpte)

DUGUAY, Marc (ten)
see CONCERT INDEX under:
(MARC) **8 223755**   Prix de Rome Cantatas

DUGUAY, Richard (alto)
see CONCERT INDEX under:
(FNAC) **592308**   Lully—Grand Motets, Volume 1

DUHAN, Hans (cond)
see Vienna St Op Orch

DUHAN, Hans (bar)
Lehár: Giuditta (exc), Lustige Witwe (exc)
see CONCERT INDEX under:
(SCHW) **314562**   Vienna State Opera Live, Vol.6
(SCHW) **314642**   Vienna State Opera Live, Vol.14

DUHEM, Jacques (vn)
see CONCERT INDEX under:
(ERAT) **2292-45772-2**   Saint-Saëns—Works for Chamber Ensemble

DUIS, Thomas (pf)
see CONCERT INDEX under:
(CAPR) **10 439**   Modern Trumpet
(CAPR) **10 482**   Nobody knows de trouble I see

DUKE QUARTET
see CONCERT INDEX under:
(CLRI) **CC0003**   Clarinet Virtuosi of the Past: Heinrich Baermann
(COLL) **Coll1386-2**   Barber/Dvořák/Glass—String Quartets
(COLL) **Coll1417-2**   Volans—String Quartets
cond H. CHRISTOPHERS
see CONCERT INDEX under:
(COLL) **Coll1405-2**   Tavener—Choral Works

DUKEL, Franciska (mez)
see CONCERT INDEX under:
(CHNN) **CCS7895**   Buxtehude—Cantatas

DUKES, Philip (va)
see CONCERT INDEX under:
(CHAN) **CHAN9380**   Martin—Ballades
(CHAN) **CHAN9392**   Vaughan Williams—Riders to the Sea etc.
(GAMC) **GAMCD537**   Works for Viola and Piano

DULGUEROV, Kiril (ten)
see CONCERT INDEX under:
(EMI) **CMS7 63386-2**   Borodin—Prince Igor & Complete Solo Songs

DULLAERT, Hans (hn)
Messiaen: Canyons aux étoiles

DUMAINE, Olympe (sop)
see CONCERT INDEX under:
(EMI) **CDS7 49361-2**   Offenbach: Operettas

DUMAY, Augustin (vn)
Lalo: Symphonie espagnole, Violin Concerto
Mozart: Trio, K563
Schubert: Piano Trio 2, Sonata, D574
see CONCERT INDEX under:
(DG) **431 771-2GH**   Mozart—Violin Sonatas

(DG) **435 800-2GH**   Brahms—Violin Sonatas
(DG) **437 525-2GH**   Grieg—Violin Sonatas
(DG) **445 880-2GH**   Franck/Debussy/Ravel—Violin Works
(EMI) **CDC7 47544-2**   French music for violin and orchestra
(EMI) **CDC7 49160-2**   Mozart: Works for Violin and Orchestra
(EMI) **CDC7 49165-2**   Schubert: Works for Piano Trio
(EMI) **CMS7 62548-2**   Fauré—Chamber Works, Vol.2

DUMBARTON OAKS CHAMBER ORCHESTRA
cond W. STRICKLAND
see CONCERT INDEX under:
(SONY) **MPK46727**   Barber—Vocal Works

DUMBRĂVEANU, Corneliu (cond)
see Satu Mare PO

DUMINY, Philippe (bass)
Shostakovich: Lady Macbeth of Mtsensk (Cpte)
Verdi: Otello (Cpte)

DUMM, Thomas (va)
Bolcom: Sessions I
see CONCERT INDEX under:
(TELA) **CD80059**   Popular Orchestral Works

DUMONT, Cedric (cond)
see Basle RSO

DUMONT, Fernand (bar)
R. Strauss: Salomé (Cpte)
Tchaikovsky: Iolanta (Cpte)

DUN, Tan (cond)
see BBC Scottish SO

DUN LAOGHAIRE CHORAL SOCIETY
cond R. SACCANI
Verdi: Aida (Cpte)

(THE) DUNCAN SISTERS (sngrs)
see CONCERT INDEX under:
(PEAR) **GEMMCDS9059/61**   Music from the New York Stage, Vol. 4: 1917-20

DUNDEE ST PAUL'S CATHEDRAL CHOIR
see CONCERT INDEX under:
(ABBE) **CDCA926**   Choral Music from Dundee

DUNE, Catherine (sop)
M-A. Charpentier: In honorem sancti Xaverii canticum, H355

DUNKEL, Paul (fl)
see CONCERT INDEX under:
(SONY) **SK64133**   The Essential Philip Glass

DÜNKI, Jean-Jacques (pf)
Reger: Violin Sonata 6, Violin Sonata 7
see CONCERT INDEX under:
(CLAV) **CD50-8808**   Grieg—Violin Sonatas

DUNN, Darcy (sngr)
Rorem: Childhood Miracle (Cpte)

DUNN, John (vn)
see CONCERT INDEX under:
(SYMP) **SYMCD1071**   Great Violinists, Vol.1

DUNN, Mignon (mez)
G. Charpentier: Louise (Cpte)
R. Strauss: Salome (Cpte)
V. Thomson: Mother of us all (Cpte)

DUNN, Stuart (tbn)
see CONCERT INDEX under:
(CNTO) **CRCD2368**   Sullivan—That Glorious Song of Old

DUNN, Susan (sop)
Mahler: Klagende Lied
Schoenberg: Gurrelieder
Wagner: Walküre (exc)
(TELA) **CD80152**   Verdi: Requiem & Opera Choruses

DUNN, Sir Vivian (cond)
see Light Music Soc Orch

DUNNETT, David (organ)
see CONCERT INDEX under:
(ARGO) **436 833-2ZH**   Purcell— Music for the Funeral of Queen Mary
(VIRG) **VC5 45035-2**   Tavener—Thunder entered Her

DUPHIL, Monique (pf)
Villa-Lobos: Cello Sonata 2, Piano Trio 1, Piano Trio 2, Piano Trio 3

DUPOUY, Jean (ten)
Meyerbeer: Prophète (Cpte)
R. Strauss: Salomé (Cpte)

DUPOUY, Jean (va)
see CONCERT INDEX under:
(ERAT) **2292-45772-2**   Saint-Saëns—Works for Chamber Ensemble

DUPRÉ, Desmond (va da gamba)
Monteverdi: Ballo delle ingrate
see CONCERT INDEX under:
(VANG) **08.2003.72**   Purcell—Celebrated Songs,Sacred Airs and Concert Pieces

DUPRÉ, Lily (sngr)
see CONCERT INDEX under:
(IRCC) **IRCC-CD802**   Souvenirs of Rare French Opera

DUPRÉ, Marcel (organ)
Saint-Saëns: Symphony 3
see CONCERT INDEX under:
(BEUL) **1PD5**   Historic Organs, Volume 1

(EMI) **CDC5 55037-2**   French Organists play their own works

DUPUY, Martine (mez)
Poulenc: Dialogues des Carmélites (Cpte)
Rossini: Adelaide di Borgogna (Cpte), Donna del lago (Cpte)

DUPUY, Véronique (sop)
Argento: Virginia Woolf
Benson: End of the World

DURAN, Elena (fl)
see CONCERT INDEX under:
(RCA) **RD87991**   Bach: Concerti

DURAND, Georges (cor ang)
see CONCERT INDEX under:
(EMI) **CDS7 54607-2**   Stravinsky plays and conducts Stravinsky

DURCO, Jan (bass)
Puccini: Tosca (Cpte)

DURDEN, Richard (spkr)
Gay: Beggar's Opera (Cpte)

DUREAU, Aude Perin (vn)
see CONCERT INDEX under:
(MARC) **8 223636**   In Memoriam Lili Boulanger

DURHAM CATHEDRAL CHOIR
cond J. LANCELOT
Stanford: Services, Op. 12, Services, Op. 81
see CONCERT INDEX under:
(PRIO) **PRCD296**   Evensong For St Cuthbert's Day
(PRIO) **PRCD343**   Psalms of David, Vol.3
(PRIO) **PRCD437**   Stanford—Complete Morning & Evening Services, Vol.1

DÜRMÜLLER, Jörg (ten)
Monteverdi: Ritorno d'Ulisse in patria (Cpte)

DÜRR, Karl-Friedrich (bar)
B.A. Zimmermann: Soldaten (Cpte)

DURUFLÉ, Maurice (cond)
see ORTF Nat Orch

DURUFLÉ, Maurice (organ)
see CONCERT INDEX under:
(EMI) **CDC7 47723-2**   Poulenc: Choral and Organ works
(ERAT) **4509-96952-2**   Duruflé—Requiem; Organ Works

DURUFLÉ-CHEVALIER, Marie-Madeleine (organ)
see CONCERT INDEX under:
(ERAT) **4509-96952-2**   Duruflé—Requiem; Organ Works
(ERAT) **4509-98526-2**   Duruflé—Vocal & Organ Works

DUSHKIN, Samuel (vn)
see CONCERT INDEX under:
(EMI) **CDS7 54607-2**   Stravinsky plays and conducts Stravinsky

DUSOWA, Hans (va)
Haydn: Sonatas, HobVI:1-6
see CONCERT INDEX under:
(ETCE) **KTC1083**   Telemann: Sonatas

DUSSAUT, Catherine (sop)
M-A. Charpentier: Arts Florissants (Cpte)

DUSSEK, Michael (pf)
see CONCERT INDEX under:
(CHAN) **CHAN8840**   La flûte enchantée
(MERI) **CDE84227/8**   Brahms—Chamber Works

DUSSEK PIANO TRIO
see CONCERT INDEX under:
(MERI) **CDE84227/8**   Brahms—Chamber Works

DÜSSELDORF EVANGELIST CHURCH STUDENTS' CHOIR
see CONCERT INDEX under:
(SCHW) **314050**   Weill—Vocal and Choral Works

DÜSSELDORF MUSIKVEREIN CHORUS
cond R. CHAILLY
Schoenberg: Gurrelieder
cond H. HOLLREISER
Pfitzner: Von deutscher Seele (Cpte)
cond B. KLEE
Schumann: Szenen aus Goethes Faust (Cpte)
see CONCERT INDEX under:
(EMI) **CZS7 67819-2**   Brahms/Schumann—Requiems
cond W. SAWALLISCH
Beethoven: Symphony 9
Mendelssohn: Symphony 2
cond D. SHALLON
Shostakovich: Symphony 13

DÜSSELDORF SYMPHONY ORCHESTRA WIND ENSEMBLE
see CONCERT INDEX under:
(SCHW) **314050**   Weill—Vocal and Choral Works

DÜSSELDORF SYMPHONY ORCHESTRA
cond H. HOLLREISER
Pfitzner: Von deutscher Seele (Cpte)
cond B. KLEE
Schumann: Szenen aus Goethes Faust (Cpte)
see CONCERT INDEX under:
(EMI) **CZS7 67819-2**   Brahms/Schumann—Requiems
cond D. SHALLON
Shostakovich: Symphony 13

DUSSELJEE, Kor-Jan (ten)
Wolf: Manuel Venegas

EDA-PIERRE, Christiane (sop)
Beethoven: Mass in C
Berlioz: Benvenuto Cellini (Cpte), Béatrice et
  Bénédict (Cpte)
Honegger: Roi David (Cpte)
Messiaen: Saint François d'Assise (Cpte)
Mozart: Entführung (Cpte)
Rameau: Dardanus (Cpte)
see CONCERT INDEX under:
(ARIO) **ARN68035** Britten—Vocal and String works

EDEIKEN, Louise (sop)
Bernstein: West Side Story (Cpte)

EDELMAN, Sergei (pf)
see CONCERT INDEX under:
(RCA) **RD60173** R.Strauss—Orchestral Works
(RCA) **RD87988** Mendelssohn: Works for Piano &
  Orchestra

EDELMANN, Otto (bass)
Bach: St Matthew Passion, BWV244 (exc)
Beethoven: Fidelio (Cpte), Symphony 9
Mozart: Don Giovanni (Cpte)
R. Strauss: Arabella (Cpte), Rosenkavalier (Cpte)
Wagner: Meistersinger (Cpte)
see CONCERT INDEX under:
(EMI) **CMS7 63310-2** Beethoven: Complete
  Symphonies

EDEN, Bracha (pf)
Brahms: Symphony 3, Variations, Op.23
Schubert: Divertissement à la Hongroise, D818,
  Divertissement, D823
see CONCERT INDEX under:
(CARL) **PWK1134** Dances Round the World
(CRD) **CRD3413** Brahms—Works for two pianos &
  one piano, four hands
(CRD) **CRD3424** Ravel—Works for Piano Duet

EDER, Claudia (mez)
Offenbach: Contes d'Hoffmann (Cpte)

EDER, Gerhard (bass)
see CONCERT INDEX under:
(RCA) **GD86535** Mozart: Requiem, etc

EDER QUARTET
Haydn: String Quartets, Op.76 (exc)
Mozart: Divertimenti, K136-8, String Quartet, K465
see CONCERT INDEX under:
(NAXO) **8 550544** Mozart—String Quartets, Vol.5
(NAXO) **8 550545** Mozart—String Quartets, Volume
  6
(NAXO) **8 550546** Mozart—String Quartets, Volume
  7
(NAXO) **8 550547** Mozart—String Quartets, Volume
  8
(NAXO) **8 550973** Shostakovich—String Quartets,
  Volume 2
(NAXO) **8 553103** Mozart—String Quintets, Volume
  1

EDGAR-WILSON, Richard (ten)
Monteverdi: Madrigals, Bk 8 (exc)
Purcell: Dioclesian, Z627 (Cpte)
Stradella: San Giovanni Battista (Cpte)

EDGE, Kenneth (sax)
see CONCERT INDEX under:
(MARC) **8 223515** Binge—Orchestral Works

EDINBURGH CATHEDRAL CHOIR
cond T. BYRAM-WIGFIELD
see CONCERT INDEX under:
(HERA) **HAVPCD163** In the Bleak Midwinter

EDINBURGH FESTIVAL CHORUS
see CONCERT INDEX under:
(DECC) **425 722-2DM** Mozart—Masonic Music
  cond D. BARENBOIM
see CONCERT INDEX under:
(EMI) **CDM7 64634-2** Fauré/Bach—Choral Works
  cond L. BERNSTEIN
Mahler: Symphony 2
  cond J.E. GARDINER
Berlioz: Damnation de Faust (Cpte)
  cond M. GIELEN
B. A. Zimmermann: Requiem (Cpte)
  cond I. KERTÉSZ
see CONCERT INDEX under:
(DECC) **425 722-2DM** Mozart—Masonic Music
(DECC) **443 488-2DF2** Kodály—Háry János; Psalmus
  Hungaricus etc
  cond C. MACKERRAS
Mozart: Così fan tutte (Cpte)

EDINBURGH QUARTET
see CONCERT INDEX under:
(EMI) **CMS7 63522-2** Tippett—Chamber & Orchestral
  Works
(REDC) **RR007** Music by Priaulx Rainier

EDINGER, Christiane (vn)
Busoni: Violin Sonata 1, Violin Sonata 2
K.A. Hartmann: Concerto funèbre
Penderecki: Violin Concerto (1976)
Szymanowski: Violin Concerto 1
see CONCERT INDEX under:
(ASV) **CDDCA905** Blake—Orchestral Works

EDLINA, Luba (pf)
Brahms: Clarinet Trio, Horn Trio
Dvořák: Piano Trio 4
Mendelssohn: Songs without Words
Miaskovsky: Cello Sonata 2
Prokofiev: Cello Sonata, Op. 119
Rachmaninov: Cello Sonata

Shostakovich: Cello Sonata, Op. 40
Smetana: Piano Trio in G minor
Tchaikovsky: Album for the young
see CONCERT INDEX under:
(CHAN) **CHAN8343** Shostakovich & Schnittke—Violin
  and Piano Works
(CHAN) **CHAN8458** Debussy & Ravel: Chamber
  Works
(CHAN) **CHAN8467** Brahms—Intermezzos

EDLINGER, Richard (cond)
see Košice St PO

EDMEADS, Adrian (sngr)
Bernstein: West Side Story (Cpte)

EDVALDSDÓTTIR, Sigrún (vn)
see CONCERT INDEX under:
(CHAN) **CHAN9180** Icelandic Orchestral Works

EDVINA, Louise (sop)
see CONCERT INDEX under:
(PEAR) **GEMMCDS9925(1)** Covent Garden on
  Record—Vol.3 (pt 1)

EDWARDS, Catherine (pf)
Britten: St Nicolas
see CONCERT INDEX under:
(CONI) **CDCF905** Karen Jones—The Flute Album
(HYPE) **CDA66665** Howells—Music for Violin and
  Piano

EDWARDS, Cheryl (sop)
Janáček: Fate (Cpte)

EDWARDS, Jack (spkr)
Lampe: Pyramus and Thisbe (Cpte)

EDWARDS, Joan (contr)
Wagner: Walküre (Cpte)

EDWARDS, John Owen (cond)
see D'Oyly Carte Op Orch

EDWARDS, Rod (cond)
see London Cast

EDWARDS, Ronald (ten)
A. Davis: X (Cpte)

EDWARDS, Sian (cond)
see ENO Orch

EDWARDS, Terry (cond)
see London Sinfonietta

EDWARDS, Terry (bass)
Monteverdi: Orfeo (Cpte)

EEN, Robert (voc)
M. Monk: Atlas (Cpte)

EFFENBERKOVÁ, Božena (sop)
Fibich: Šárka (Cpte)
Janáček: Cunning Little Vixen (Cpte), Jenufa (Cpte)
Smetana: Kiss (Cpte)

EGAN, Daniel (sngr)
Forrest/Wright: Kismet (Cpte)

EGARR, Richard (organ)
see CONCERT INDEX under:
(HARM) **HMC90 1410** CPE Bach—Sonatas
(MERI) **CDE84153** French Choral Music

EGARR, Richard (hpd)
see CONCERT INDEX under:
(CHNN) **CCS5894** Pandolfi—Violin Sonatas

EGEA, Antonio Belda (narr)
Falla: Amor Brujo (Cpte)

EGEL, Martin (bass)
Verdi: Trovatore (Cpte)
Wagner: Meistersinger (Cpte), Rheingold (Cpte)

EGELER, Andrea (sop)
Bach: Motets (Cpte)

EGENER, Minnie (mez)
see CONCERT INDEX under:
(MSCM) **MM30352** Caruso—Italian Opera Arias
(PEAR) **EVC4(1)** The Caruso Edition, Vol.4 (pt 1)
(RCA) **GD60495(6)** The Complete Caruso Collection
  (pt 6)
(ROMO) **81003-2** Galli-Curci—Acoustic Recordings,
  Vol.1

EGERTON, Francis (ten)
Mozart: Nozze di Figaro (Cpte)
Puccini: Bohème (Cpte), Fanciulla del West (Cpte),
  Tosca (Cpte)
Tchaikovsky: Eugene Onegin (Cpte)
Verdi: Falstaff (Cpte)

EGGARS, Walter (sngr)
R. Strauss: Rosenkavalier (Cpte)

EGGEBRECHT-KUPSA (VN), Renate (vn)
see CONCERT INDEX under:
(TROU) **TRO-CD03** Ethel Smyth—Chamber Works,
  Vols.1 & 2
(TROU) **TRO-CD01405** Ethel Smyth—Chamber
  Works & Songs, Vol.3

EGGEN, Christian (cond)
see Bergen PO

EGGER, Georg (vn)
see CONCERT INDEX under:
(BAYE) **BR100058** Serenada Hungaria

EGGIMANN, Ulrich Simon (sngr)
Zemlinsky: Kleider machen Leute (Cpte)

EGK, Werner (cond)
see Bavarian St Orch

EGMOND, Max van (bass)
Bach: Cantata 56, Cantata 82, Mass in B Minor,
  BWV232 (Cpte), St John Passion, BWV245 (Cpte), St
  Matthew Passion, BWV244 (Cpte)
Monteverdi: Orfeo (Cpte)
Schubert: Winterreise (Cpte)
Telemann: Tag des Gerichts (Cpte)
see CONCERT INDEX under:
(ETCE) **KTC1056** Italian Airs and Harpsichord
  Works
(RICE) **RIC041016** German Baroque Cantatas, Vol.2 -
  Buxtehude
(RICE) **RIC048035/7** German Baroque Cantatas,
  Vol.4 - Bruhns
(RICE) **RIC061041** Bach—Cantatas
(RICE) **RIC079061** German Baroque Cantatas, Vol.6 -
  Funeral Cantatas
(RICE) **RIC109077/8** German Baroque Cantatas,
  Vol.9 - Weckmann
(TELD) **2292-42428-2** Bach—Cantatas, Volume 41
(TELD) **2292-42497-2** Bach—Cantatas, Volume 1
(TELD) **2292-42498-2** Bach—Cantatas, Volume 2
(TELD) **2292-42499-2** Bach—Cantatas, Volume 3
(TELD) **2292-42500-2** Bach—Cantatas, Volume 4
(TELD) **2292-42501-2** Bach—Cantatas, Volume 5
(TELD) **2292-42502-2** Bach—Cantatas, Volume 6
(TELD) **2292-42503-2** Bach—Cantatas, Volume 7
(TELD) **2292-42504-2** Bach—Cantatas, Volume 8
(TELD) **2292-42505-2** Bach—Cantatas, Volume 9
(TELD) **2292-42556-2** Bach—Cantatas, Volume 11
(TELD) **2292-42571-2** Bach—Cantatas, Volume 17
(TELD) **2292-42573-2** Bach—Cantatas, Volume 19
(TELD) **2292-42576-2** Bach—Cantatas, Volume 20
(TELD) **2292-42577-2** Bach—Cantatas, Volume 21
(TELD) **2292-42578-2** Bach—Cantatas, Volume 22
(TELD) **2292-42582-2** Bach—Cantatas, Volume 23
(TELD) **2292-42583-2** Bach—Cantatas, Volume 24
(TELD) **2292-42584-2** Bach—Cantatas, Volume 25
(TELD) **2292-42602-2** Bach—Cantatas, Volume 26
(TELD) **2292-42603-2** Bach—Cantatas, Volume 27
(TELD) **2292-42606-2** Bach—Cantatas, Volume 28
(TELD) **2292-42608-2** Bach—Cantatas, Volume 29
(TELD) **2292-42615-2** Bach—Cantatas, Volume 31
(TELD) **2292-42617-2** Bach—Cantatas, Volume 32
(TELD) **2292-42618-2** Bach—Cantatas, Volume 33
(TELD) **2292-42631-2** Bach—Cantatas, Volume 36
(TELD) **2292-42633-2** Bach—Cantatas, Volume 38
(TELD) **2292-42634-2** Bach—Cantatas, Volume 39
(TELD) **2292-42635-2** Bach—Cantatas, Volume 40
(TELD) **2292-42738-2** Bach—Cantatas, Volume 42
(TELD) **2292-44179-2** Bach—Cantatas, Volume 43
(TELD) **4509-91755-2** Bach—Cantatas, Vol.1
(TELD) **4509-91756-2** Bach—Cantatas, Vol.2
(TELD) **4509-91757-2** Bach—Cantatas, Vol.3
(TELD) **4509-91758-2** Bach—Cantatas, Vol.4
(TELD) **4509-91759-2** Bach—Cantatas, Vol.5
(TELD) **4509-91760-2** Bach—Cantatas, Vol.6
(TELD) **4509-91761-2** Bach—Cantatas, Vol.7
(TELD) **4509-91762-2** Bach—Cantatas, Vol.8
(TELD) **4509-91763-2** Bach—Cantatas, Vol.9
(TELD) **4509-91764-2** Bach—Cantatas, Vol.10
(TELD) **4509-93687-2** Bach—Cantatas
(TELD) **9031-77608-2** Purcell—Anthems,Instrumental
  Music & Songs

EGO, Constantin (bar)
Bellini: Pirata (Cpte)

EGUCHI, Akira (pf)
see CONCERT INDEX under:
(DENO) **CO-75118** Violin Show Pieces
(DENO) **CO-75625** French Violin Sonatas

EGUEZ, Eduardo (gtr)
Kapsperger: Chitarrone Book I (exc), Chitarrone Book
  IV

EHRÉN, Håkan (db)
see CONCERT INDEX under:
(BIS) **BIS-CD337** Tubin: Orchestral Works

EHRET, Ernst (cond)
see Munich St. Michael Orch

EHRLING, Sixten (cond)
see Gothenburg SO

EHRSTEDT, Caj (ten)
Braein: Anne Pedersdotter (Cpte)

EIAR ORCHESTRA
cond V. GUI
see CONCERT INDEX under:
(PREI) **89014** Ebe Stignani (1903-1974)
  cond G. MARINUZZI
see CONCERT INDEX under:
(PREI) **89014** Ebe Stignani (1903-1974)
  cond A. LA ROSA PARODI
see CONCERT INDEX under:
(PREI) **89014** Ebe Stignani (1903-1974)
  cond U. TANSINI
see CONCERT INDEX under:
(CENT) **CRC2164** Ferruccio Tagliavini—Early
  Operatic Recordings
(PREI) **89014** Ebe Stignani (1903-1974)
(PREI) **89016** Gina Cigna (b. 1900)
(PREI) **89063** Rosetta Pampanini (1896-1973)
(PREI) **89074** Tancredi Pasero (1893-1983) - II

EICHELBERGER, Freddy (organ)
see CONCERT INDEX under:
(ERAT) **2292-45825-2** LeJeune—Sacred Works

EICHENHOLZ, Mika (cond)
see Košice St PO

EICHHORN, Klaus (organ)
see CONCERT INDEX under:
(THOR) CTH2035 Scheidemann/Scheidt—Organ Works

EICHHORN, Kurt (cond)
see Cologne RSO

EICHLER, Karl-Heinz (spkr)
B.A. Zimmermann: Soldaten (Cpte)

EICHWALDER, Martin (bass)
Spohr: Faust (Cpte)

EIDE, Kaia (sop)
see CONCERT INDEX under:
(SIMA) PSC1810(1) Grieg—Songs (historical recordings, pt 1)

EIDELMAN, Cliff (cond)
see OST

EIDI, Billy (pf)
see CONCERT INDEX under:
(DINT) DICD920167 Milhaud—Piano Works

EIDLOTH, Johannes (ten)
B.A. Zimmermann: Soldaten (Cpte)

EINARSON, Monica (sop)
see CONCERT INDEX under:
(BIS) BIS-CD384 Sibelius: Orchestral Works

EIPPERLE, Trude (sop)
Haydn: Jahreszeiten (Cpte)
see CONCERT INDEX under:
(ACAN) 43 268 Peter Anders sings German Opera Arias
(DG) 435 321-2GWP12 150 Years - Vienna Philharmonic

EISDELL, Hubert (ten)
Handel: Messiah (Cpte)

EISEN, Artur (bass)
Shostakovich: Symphony 13
see CONCERT INDEX under:
(CHNT) LDC278 1007/8 Shostakovich: Symphonies, Vol.4
(OLYM) OCD194 Shostakovich: Vocal & Orchestral Works

EISENBERGER, Severin (pf)
see CONCERT INDEX under:
(PEAR) GEMMCD9933 Grieg and his Circle play Grieg

EISENHARDT, Lex (gtr)
see CONCERT INDEX under:
(ETCE) KTC1025 Sor: Guitar Works

EISENLOHR, Ulrich (pf)
Wolf: Goethe Lieder (exc), Italienisches Liederbuch (Cpte), Mörike Lieder (exc)

EISINGER, Irene (sop)
Mozart: Così fan tutte (Cpte)

EISLER, David (ten)
Bernstein: Candide (1982) (Cpte)

EIWANGER, Tobias (treb)
(TELD) 2292-42633-2 Bach—Cantatas, Volume 38
(TELD) 2292-42634-2 Bach—Cantatas, Volume 39
(TELD) 4509-91762-2 Bach—Cantatas, Vol.8
(TELD) 4509-91763-2 Bach—Cantatas, Vol.9

EJE, Niels (ob)
see CONCERT INDEX under:
(KONT) 32032 Wind Chamber Music

EJSING, Mette (contr)
Nielsen: Aladdin (Cpte)
see CONCERT INDEX under:
(ROND) RCD8329 Nielsen: Songs, Vol.5

EK, Harald (ten)
Wagner: Fliegende Holländer (Cpte)

EK, Kerstin (cond)
see Orpheus Chbr Ens

EKDAHL, Linnéa (sop)
see CONCERT INDEX under:
(SONY) SK53276 Nielsen—Orchestral Works

EKEBERG, Kjersti (sop)
Braein: Anne Pedersdotter (Cpte)

EKER, Annika Finnilä (contr)
Schnittke: Requiem

EKERT, Alice (sop)
Kodály: Missa Brevis

EKLÖF, Marianne (mez)
Grieg: Peer Gynt (exc)
Marschner: Hans Heiling (Cpte)

EL DIN, Hamza (tar)
see CONCERT INDEX under:
(NONE) 7559-79275-2 Pieces of Africa

EL HAGE, Robert (bass)
Donizetti: Lucrezia Borgia (Cpte)
Puccini: Rondine (Cpte)
see CONCERT INDEX under:
(RCA) 09026 61236-2 Leontyne Price - Prima Donna Collection

ELBAEK, Søren (vn)
see CONCERT INDEX under:
(KONT) 32098 Gade—Violin Sonatas
(KONT) 32164 Gade—Works for Violin and Piano
(KONT) 32197 Syberg—Chamber Music, Vol. 2

(KONT) 32200 Nielsen—Works for Violin

ELBERT, Hartmut (bass)
Bach: Mass in B minor, BWV232 (Cpte)
Keiser: St. Mark Passion

ELBERT, Jochen (ten)
Keiser: St. Mark Passion

ELDER, Mark (cond)
see BBC SO

ELECTRIC PHOENIX
see CONCERT INDEX under:
(DECC) 425 832-2DH Berio—Vocal & Orchestral Works

ELENKOV, Stefan (bass)
see CONCERT INDEX under:
(EMI) CDM7 63104-2 Alfredo Krauss - Opera Recital

ELGAR, Anne (sop)
Rossini: Pietra del Paragone (Cpte)

ELGAR, Sir Edward (cond)
see BBC SO

ELGAR, Sir Edward (pf)
see CONCERT INDEX under:
(EMI) CDS7 54568-2 The Elgar Edition, Vol.3

ELHORST, Hans (ob)
Albinoni: Concerti, Op. 7 (exc)

ELIAS, Joanna (contr)
see CONCERT INDEX under:
(CALA) CACD1018 French Chamber Music for Woodwinds, Volume 2

ELIAS, Jonathan (cond)
see OST

ELIAS, Rosalind (mez)
Barber: Vanessa (Cpte)
Bernstein: Songfest
Puccini: Madama Butterfly (Cpte)
Verdi: Falstaff (Cpte), Requiem (Cpte), Rigoletto (Cpte)
see CONCERT INDEX under:
(RCA) GD60176 Prokofiev: Vocal & Orchestral Works
(RCA) 09026 61580-2(5) RCA/Met 100 Singers, 100 Years (pt 5)
(SONY) SM2K47522 Beethoven & Haydn—Choral Works

ELIASSON, Göran (ten)
Schnittke: Symphony 2

ELIZABETHAN SINGERS
cond B. HERRMANN
Herrmann: Wuthering Heights (Cpte)
cond V. TUNNARD
see CONCERT INDEX under:
(DECC) 436 407-2DWO The World of Schubert

ELIZZA, Elisa (sop)
see CONCERT INDEX under:
(SIMA) PSC1810(1) Grieg—Songs (historical recordings, pt 1)

ELKINS, Margreta (mez)
Donizetti: Lucia di Lammermoor (Cpte), Maria Stuarda (Cpte)
Gounod: Faust (Cpte)
Wagner: Walküre (Cpte)
see CONCERT INDEX under:
(DECC) 433 706-2DMO3 Bellini—Beatrice di Tenda; Operatic Arias
(EMI) CDM7 63182-2 The Incomparable Callas
(OPRA) ORC004 Donizetti—Ne m'oubliez pas; Arias
(RCA) GD60941 Rarities - Montserrat Caballé

ELKROG, Arne (ten)
see CONCERT INDEX under:
(CHAN) CHAN8853 Nielsen: Choral Works

ELLENBECK, Dieter (ten)
R.Strauss: Salome (Cpte)
Weill: Sieben Todsünden (Cpte)

ELLIOTT, Elizabeth (sop)
Sullivan: Gondoliers (Cpte)

ELLIOTT, Martin (cond)
see Wren Baroque Sols

ELLIOTT, Paul (ten)
C. P. E. Bach: Gott hat den Herrn auferwecket, H803
Handel: Alceste (Cpte), Esther (Cpte), Messiah (Cpte)
Purcell: Dido (Cpte), Dioclesian, Z627 (exc), Indian Queen, Z630 (Cpte), King Arthur, Z628 (Cpte), St Cecilia's Day Ode, Z328, Timon of Athens, Z632 (Cpte)
see CONCERT INDEX under:
(ARCH) 437 090-2AT Collectio Argentea 20: Bach Family before J.S.
(BIS) BIS-CD341 Music for lutes
(ERAT) 4509-96371-2 Gardiner—The Purcell Collection
(HARM) HMX290 1528/33(2) A Purcell Companion (pt 2)
(L'OI) 421 480-2OH Monteverdi: Madrigali Erotici
(L'OI) 425 893-2OM6(1) Purcell—Theatre Music (Part 1)
(L'OI) 425 893-2OM6(2) Purcell—Theatre Music (Part 2)

ELLIS, David (vc)
see CONCERT INDEX under:
(CHAN) CHAN8817 Britten: Orchestral Works

ELLIS, Melville (pf)
see CONCERT INDEX under:
(PEAR) GEMMCDS9053/5 Music from the New York Stage, Vol. 2: 1908–1913

ELLIS, Osian (hp)
see CONCERT INDEX under:
(ASV) CDDCA517 The French Connection
(CFP) CD-CFP4570 Choral Favourites
(COLL) Coll7039-2 Britten—The Folk Songs
(DECC) 421 154-2DM French Chamber Music
(EMI) CDC5 55529-2 Delius—Cello Concerto, etc
(LOND) 425 716-2LM Britten: Canticles
(LYRI) SRCD230 Alwyn—Orchestral Works
(LYRI) SRCD325 Mathias—Concertos
(MERI) CDE84119 Britten: Songs and Instrumental Works
(PHIL) 442 299-2PM2 Mozart—Complete Flute Works
(UNIC) DKPCD9046 Holst—Choral Works

ELLIS, Philip (cond)
see RPO

ELLIS, Roger (cond)
see French Rad Lyric Orch

ELLSASSER, Richard (organ)
see CONCERT INDEX under:
(RCA) 09026 61778-2(24) The Heifetz Collection, Vol. 24

(GLEN) ELLYN CHILDREN'S CHORUS
cond JAMES LEVINE
Orff: Carmina burana
cond G. SOLTI
Bach: St Matthew Passion, BWV244 (Cpte)
Schoenberg: Moses und Aron (Cpte)
see CONCERT INDEX under:
(DECC) 430 804-2DC10 Mahler—Complete Symphonies

ELMAN, Mischa (vn)
see CONCERT INDEX under:
(APR) APR7015 The Auer Legacy, Vol.1
(BIDD) LAB039 Elman—Victor Records with Caruso, Alda & Str Quartet
(CLAR) CDGSE78-50-52 Three Tenors
(NIMB) NI7805 Rosa Ponselle—Opera & Song Recital
(PEAR) EVC3(1) The Caruso Edition, Vol.3 (pt 1)
(PEAR) EVC3(2) The Caruso Edition, Vol.3 (pt 2)
(RCA) GD60495(4) The Complete Caruso Collection (pt 4)
(RCA) GD60495(5) The Complete Caruso Collection (pt 5)
(RCA) 09026 61879-2 Grieg—Historic Recordings

ELMAN QUARTET
see CONCERT INDEX under:
(BIDD) LAB039 Elman—Victor Records with Caruso, Alda & Str Quartet

ELMENDORFF, Karl (cond)
see Bayreuth Fest Orch

ELMING, Poul (ten)
Heise: Drot og Marsk (Cpte)
Nørgård: Siddhartha (Cpte)
Wagner: Walküre (Cpte)
see CONCERT INDEX under:
(CHAN) CHAN8853 Nielsen: Choral Works
(CHAN) CHAN9075 Gade—Choral and Orchestral Works

ELMO, Cloe (mez)
see CONCERT INDEX under:
(EMI) CDH7 61052-2 Beniamino Gigli—Arias and Duets (1932-1949)
(EMI) CHS7 69741-2(7) Record of Singing, Vol.4—Italian School
(LYRC) SRO805 Gina Cigna—Opera Recital
(PREI) 89016 Gina Cigna (b. 1900)
(RCA) GD60326 Verdi—Operas & Choral Works

ELMS, Lauris (mez)
Britten: Peter Grimes (Cpte)

ELMS, Roderick (hpd)
see CONCERT INDEX under:
(CHAN) CHAN9380 Martin—Ballades

ELMS, Roderick (pf)
see CONCERT INDEX under:
(CHAN) CHAN9380 Martin—Ballades
(MARC) 8 223732 Addinsell—British Light Music

EL-TOUR, Anna (sop)
see CONCERT INDEX under:
(PEAR) GEMMCDS9004/6(1) Singers of Imperial Russia, Vol.3 (pt 1)

ELVIN, William (bar)
Puccini: Bohème (Cpte), Fanciulla del West (Cpte), Tosca (Cpte)
Verdi: Ballo in maschera (Cpte), Forza del destino (Cpte), Giorno di Regno (Cpte), Masnadieri (Cpte)

ELWES, Gervase (ten)
see CONCERT INDEX under:
(SIMA) PSC1810(1) Grieg—Songs (historical recordings, pt 2)

ELWES, John (ten)
Bach: Mass in B minor, BWV232 (Cpte), St Matthew Passion, BWV244 (Cpte)
Biber: Requiem in F minor
Campra: Messe de Requiem
Dowland: First Book of Songs (Cpte)
Handel: Blessed are they that considereth the poor

Landi: Mort d'Orfeo (Cpte)
M-A. Charpentier: Judicium Salomonis, H422
Monteverdi: Vespers
Purcell: Indian Queen, Z630 (Cpte), Tempest, Z631 (Cpte)
Rameau: Indes Galantes (Cpte), Pygmalion (Cpte), Zoroastre (Cpte)
Schumann: Szenen aus Goethes Faust (Cpte)
Valls: Missa Scala Aretina
Vivaldi: Dorilla in Tempe (Cpte)
  see CONCERT INDEX *under:*
(ERAT) **4509-96371-2** Gardiner—The Purcell Collection
(PIER) **PV787092** Airs and Dances of Shakespeare's Time
(SONY) **SK53981** Purcell—Anthems and Hymns
(TELD) **2292-44193-2** Bach—Cantatas, Volume 44
(TELD) **2292-44194-2** Bach—Cantatas, Volume 45
(TELD) **4509-91764-2** Bach—Cantatas, Vol.10

ELY, Dean (sngr)
Handel: Giustino (Cpte)

ELY CATHEDRAL CHOIR
  cond P. HOLMAN
  see CONCERT INDEX *under:*
(HYPE) **CDA66768** John Amner—Cathedral Music
  cond P. TREPTE
  see CONCERT INDEX *under:*
(CNTO) **CRCD2368** Sullivan—That Glorious Song of Old
(GAMU) **GAMCD527** Canticles from Ely
(HYPE) **CDA66768** John Amner—Cathedral Music
(PRIO) **PRCD460** Psalms of David, Vol.8
  cond A. WILLS
  see CONCERT INDEX *under:*
(SAGA) **EC3379-2** Boyce—Anthems and Voluntaries

ELY CATHEDRAL CHORISTERS
  cond L. FRIEND
Tavener: Mary of Egypt (Cpte)

ELYMA ENSEMBLE
  cond G. GARRIDO
Zipoli: San Ignacio Vespers
  see CONCERT INDEX *under:*
(K617) **K617025** Les Chemins du Baroque, Vol.1

ELYSIAN SINGERS OF LONDON
  cond M. GREENALL
  see CONCERT INDEX *under:*
(CNTI) **CCD1043** Music for Christmas

ELYSIAN WIND QUINTET
  see CONCERT INDEX *under:*
(CHAN) **CHAN9077** Holst & Jacob—Chamber Works

EMANUEL SCHOOL BOYS' CHOIR
  cond B. BRITTEN
Britten: Midsummer Night's Dream (Cpte)
  see CONCERT INDEX *under:*
(LOND) **436 396-2LM** Britten—Spring Symphony, etc

EMERSON, Dina (voc)
M. Monk: Atlas (Cpte)

EMERSON QUARTET
Beethoven: String Quartet 11
Brahms: String Quartet 1
Debussy: String Quartet
Dvořák: Piano Quartet 2, Piano Quintet, Op.81
Mozart: Flute Quartets, Piano Sonata, K533 (exc)
Ravel: String Quartet
Schubert: String Quartet, D810, String Quintet
Schumann: String Quartet 3
  see CONCERT INDEX *under:*
(DG) **423 657-2GH2** Bartók—Complete String Quartets
(DG) **427 657-2GH** Mozart & Haydn: String Quartets
(DG) **431 772-2GH** Prokofiev—Chamber Works
(DG) **435 864-2GH** Barber/Ives—String Quartets
(DG) **435 867-2GH2** Barber—The Songs
(DG) **437 537-2GH** American Chamber Works
(DG) **439 914-2GH** Mozart—String Quartets
(DG) **445 828-2GH** Webern—String Quartets and Trios

EMILI, Romano (ten)
  see CONCERT INDEX *under:*
(DECC) **436 261-2DHO3** Puccini—Il Trittico

EMILIA ROMAGNA 'TOSCANINI' SYMPHONY ORCHESTRA
  cond J. R. ENCINAR
  see CONCERT INDEX *under:*
(ETCE) **KTC1148** Jonathan Harvey—Works for Cello
  cond B. RIGACCI
Donizetti: Pazzi per progetto (Cpte)

EMMANUEL, Jane (sop)
Rózsa: Julius Caesar (exc)

EMMANUEL MUSIC CHORUS
  cond C. SMITH
Schütz: Geistliche Chormusik, SWV369-97 (exc), Ich weiss, das mein Erlöser lebet, SWV457
  see CONCERT INDEX *under:*
(KOCH) **37085-2** Schütz—Motets

EMMERMANN, Michael (treb)
  see CONCERT INDEX *under:*
(TELD) **2292-44179-2** Bach—Cantatas, Volume 43
(TELD) **4509-91764-2** Bach—Cantatas, Vol.10

EMMERSON, Steven (bass)
Shostakovich: Lady Macbeth of Mtsensk (Cpte)

EMPEROR STRING QUARTET
  see CONCERT INDEX *under:*
(BRIT) **BML001** Bernard van Dieren Collection

EMPIRE BRASS
  see CONCERT INDEX *under:*
(TELA) **CD80301** Romantic Brass - Music of France & Spain
(TELA) **CD80305** Classical Brass II - On the Edge

EN-CALCAT ABBEY CHOIR
  see CONCERT INDEX *under:*
(STUD) **SM1220.02** Immortel Grégorien

ENCINAR, Jose Roman (cond)
  see Toscanini SO

ENDELLION QUARTET
Haydn: String Quartets, Op. 74
  see CONCERT INDEX *under:*
(ASV) **CDDCA932** Beach/R. Clarke—Chamber Works
(EMI) **CDM7 64730-2** Vaughan Williams—Riders to the Sea; Epithalamion, etc
(EMI) **CMS5 65115-2** Britten—Chamber Works
(PEAR) **SHECD9564** Foulds—Chamber Works
(VIRG) **VC5 45033-2** Barber—Vocal and Chamber Works

ENDERS, David (spkr)
Schumann: Manfred (Cpte)

ENDO, Akira (cond)
  see Louisville Orch

ENDRES, Michael (pf)
Schubert: Piano Sonata, D845, Piano Sonata, D850
  see CONCERT INDEX *under:*
(CAPR) **10 553** Schubert—Piano Sonatas

ENDRÈZE, Arthur (bar)
Puccini: Tosca (exc)
  see CONCERT INDEX *under:*
(EMI) **CMS7 64008-2(1)** Wagner Singing on Record (pt 1)
(MSCM) **MM30451** Mascagni—Cavalleria Rusticana, etc

ENDYMION ENSEMBLE
  cond J. WHITFIELD
  see CONCERT INDEX *under:*
(EMI) **CDM5 65114-2** Britten—Vocal Works

ENESCU, George (cond)
  see Paris SO

ENESCU, George (vn)
  see CONCERT INDEX *under:*
(BIDD) **LAB066** Enescu—Violinist & Composer
(EMI) **CDH7 61018-2** Yehudi Menuhin plays Bach Violin Works
(MSCM) **MM30322** Enescu - Columbia Recordings 1920s-30s

ENEVOLD, Peter (cond)
  see Camerata Chbr Ch

ENGEGARD, Arvid (vn)
  see CONCERT INDEX *under:*
(DECC) **443 893-2DH** Bartók—Violin Works

ENGEL, David (sngr)
Gershwin: Pardon My English (Cpte)
  see CONCERT INDEX *under:*
(EMI) **CDC5 55189-2** The Busby Berkeley Album

ENGEL, Karl (pf)
  see CONCERT INDEX *under:*
(DECC) **436 407-2DWO** The World of Schubert
(DG) **423 133-2GH** Brahms: Vocal Works
(EMI) **CDM7 63569-2** Pfitzner: Lieder
(EMI) **CMS7 63566-2** Schubert—Lieder
(NOVA) **150 010-2** Mozart—Lieder
(NOVA) **150 026-2** Schubert—Lieder

ENGEL, Max (vc)
Biber: Mystery Sonatas

ENGEN, Kieth (bass)
Beethoven: Fidelio (Cpte)
Janáček: Excursions of Mr Brouček (Cpte)
Nicolai: Lustigen Weiber von Windsor (Cpte)
Orff: Antigonae (Cpte)
Stravinsky: Oedipus Rex (Cpte)
  see CONCERT INDEX *under:*
(ARCH) **439 380-2AX6** Bach—Cantatas, Volume 3 - Ascension Day; Whitsun; Trinity
(ARCH) **439 393-2AX4** Bach—Cantatas, Volume 4
(ARCH) **439 394-2AX5** Bach—Cantatas, Volume 5
(TELD) **9031-77614-2** Bach—Cantatas

ENGERER, Brigitte (pf)
Chopin: Nocturnes
  see CONCERT INDEX *under:*
(HARM) **HMC90 1266** Mussorgsky—Piano Works
(HARM) **HMC90 1301/2** Rachmaninov—Works for 2 Pianos & Piano Duet
(HARM) **HMC90 1364** Ravel—Works for Violin and Piano
(HARM) **HMC90 1405** Schumann—Violin Sonatas
(HARM) **HMC90 1492** Grieg—Violin Sonatas

ENGERT-ELY, Ruthild (mez)
Prokofiev: Fiery Angel (Cpte)
Tchaikovsky: Eugene Onegin (Cpte)
Wagner: Parsifal (Cpte), Walküre (Cpte)
  see CONCERT INDEX *under:*
(DG) **445 354-2GX14** Wagner—Der Ring des Nibelungen

ENGL, István (ob)
  see CONCERT INDEX *under:*

(DECC) **425 935-2DM4** Haydn—Symphonies, Vol.8
(DECC) **430 100-2DM32(2)** Haydn—Complete Symphonies (Volumes 5-8)

ENGLICHOVA, Katerina (hp)
Rorem: Eleven Studies

ENGLISH, Gerald (ten)
Orff: Carmina Burana
Walton: Troilus and Cressida (Cpte)
  see CONCERT INDEX *under:*
(CFP) **CD-CFP4557** Baroque Favourites
(DHM) **GD77151** Bach—Secular Cantatas
(TALL) **TP025** Cage—Vocal & Prepared Piano works

ENGLISH BACH FESTIVAL BAROQUE ORCHESTRA
  cond C. FARNCOMBE
Rameau: Castor et Pollux (Cpte)

ENGLISH BACH FESTIVAL CHORUS
  cond L. BERNSTEIN
Stravinsky: Mass, Noces
  see CONCERT INDEX *under:*
(SONY) **SMK47628** Stravinsky—Choral and Orchestral Works
  cond C. FARNCOMBE
Rameau: Castor et Pollux (Cpte)
  cond N. MCGEGAN
Rameau: Naïs (Cpte)

ENGLISH BACH FESTIVAL ORCHESTRA
  cond L. BERNSTEIN
Stravinsky: Mass
  cond N. MCGEGAN
Rameau: Naïs (Cpte)

ENGLISH BACH FESTIVAL PERCUSSION ENSEMBLE
  cond L. BERNSTEIN
Stravinsky: Noces

ENGLISH BAROQUE ENSEMBLE
  cond J.E. GARDINER
Bach: Cantata 51, Magnificat, BWV243

ENGLISH BAROQUE SOLOISTS
Monteverdi: Orfeo (Cpte)
  see CONCERT INDEX *under:*
(ARCH) **423 405-2AH** Schütz—Sacred Choral Works
  cond J.E. GARDINER
Bach: Cantata 140, Cantata 147, Christmas Oratorio, BWV248 (Cpte), Mass in B minor, BWV232 (Cpte), St John Passion, BWV245 (Cpte), St Matthew Passion, BWV244 (Cpte)
Beethoven: Missa Solemnis
Gluck: Orfeo ed Euridice (Cpte)
Handel: Acis and Galatea (Cpte), Alexander's Feast (Cpte), Allegro, il penseroso ed il moderato (Cpte), Concerto grosso: Alexander's Feast, Coronation Anthems (exc), Hercules (Cpte), Israel in Egypt (Cpte), Jephtha (Cpte), Messiah (exc), Saul (Cpte), Semele (Cpte), Solomon (Cpte), Water Music (Cpte)
Haydn: Jahreszeiten (Cpte)
Monteverdi: Vespers
Mozart: Clemenza di Tito (Cpte), Così fan tutte (Cpte), Don Giovanni (Cpte), Entführung (Cpte), Idomeneo (Cpte), Kyrie, K341, Mass, K427, Nozze di Figaro (Cpte), Piano Concerto 20, Piano Concerto 21, Requiem, Symphony 38, Symphony 39, Symphony 40, Symphony 41, Thamos, K345 (Cpte)
Purcell: Dido (Cpte), Dioclesian, Z627 (exc), Fairy Queen, Z629 (Cpte), Indian Queen, Z630 (Cpte), King Arthur, Z628 (Cpte), St Cecilia's Day Ode, Z328, St Cecilia's Day Ode, Z339, Timon of Athens, Z632 (Cpte)
  see CONCERT INDEX *under:*
(ARCH) **429 782-2AH** Bach—Cantatas Nos 106, 118b & 198
(ARCH) **437 327-2AH** Bach—Cantatas
(ARCH) **447 291-2AMA** Mozart—Works for Piano and Orchestra
(ERAT) **2292-45219-2** Sacred Choral Works
(ERAT) **2292-45466-2** Carissimi—Jonas
(ERAT) **4509-96371-2** Gardiner—The Purcell Collection
(PHIL) **434 154-2PM** Handel—Orchestral Works
(PHIL) **434 920-2PH** Handel/Bach—Solo Motets
(PHIL) **442 604-2PH5** Mozart—The Great Symphonies

ENGLISH BRASS ENSEMBLE
  see CONCERT INDEX *under:*
(HYPE) **CDH88036** Praise to the Lord

ENGLISH CHAMBER ORCHESTRA
Mozart: Flute and Harp Concerto, K299
  see CONCERT INDEX *under:*
(ARAB) **Z6563** Elgar—Orchestral Works
(CLAV) **CD50-8602** Kramár—Clarinet Concertos
(DECC) **430 263-2DM** Purcell—Sacred choral works
(DECC) **436 256-2DM** Handel/Blow—Anthems
(DG) **431 817-2GH** Baroque Trumpet Concertos
(SONY) **SK66614** Westminster Abbey Choir - Millennium
(VIRG) **VJ7 59656-2** Italian Baroque Concertos
  cond S. ACCARDO
  see CONCERT INDEX *under:*
(EMI) **CDC7 47005-2** Bach—Violin Concertos
  cond D. ATHERTON
  see CONCERT INDEX *under:*
(LYRI) **SRCD323** Grace Williams—Orchestral Works
  cond D. BARENBOIM
Boccherini: Cello Concerto, G482
Cimarosa: Matrimonio segreto (Cpte)
Haydn: Cello Concerto in C

Mozart: Nozze di Figaro (Cpte), Requiem
see CONCERT INDEX under:
(DG) **439 529-2GGA** Delius/Vaughan
Williams/Walton—Orchestral Works
(EMI) **CDC7 47856-2** Bach: Violin Concertos
(EMI) **CDM5 65079-2**
Schoenberg/Bartók/Hindemith—Orchestral Works
(EMI) **CMS7 69707-2** Impressions of Jacqueline du
Pré
(EMI) **CZS4 83177-2(1)** Itzhak Perlman Edition (pt 1)
(EMI) **CZS5 68132-2** Les introuvables de Jacqueline
du Pré
(EMI) **CZS7 67306-2** Mozart—Works featuring Wind
Instruments
(EMIL) **CDZ7 67011-2** Mozart: Symphonies
(EMIL) **CDZ7 67015-2** Mozart—Opera Arias
cond BARRY ROSE
see CONCERT INDEX under:
(PHIL) **412 629-2PH** Sacred Evergreens
cond S. BEDFORD
Britten: Cello Symphony, Death in Venice (Cpte),
Death in Venice Suite (Cpte), Phaedra, Piano
Concerto, Violin Concerto
Walton: Spitfire Prelude and Fugue
see CONCERT INDEX under:
(ASV) **CDDCA652** Celebration for Flute & Orchestra
(CFP) **CD-CFP9012** Gershwin: Works for Piano and
Orchestra
(COLL) **Coll1102-2** Britten & Saxton: Orchestral
Works
(COLL) **Coll1123-2** Britten & L. Berkeley: Orchestral
Works
(COLL) **Coll1192-2** Britten/Shostakovich—Orchestral
Works
(COLL) **Coll7037-2** Britten—Orchestral Song Cycles
(LOND) **425 159-2LM** Salute to Percy Grainger
cond M. BEST
Britten: St Nicolas
Duruflé: Motets, Op. 10, Requiem
see CONCERT INDEX under:
(HYPE) **CDA66245** Bruckner—Choral Works
(HYPE) **CDA66292** Fauré: Sacred Choral Works
(HYPE) **CDA66359** Mendelssohn—Choral Works
(HYPE) **CDA66420** Vaughan Williams: Vocal Works
cond H. BLAKE
see CONCERT INDEX under:
(HYPE) **CDA66215** Works for Clarinet and Orchestra
cond I. BOLTON
see CONCERT INDEX under:
(ASV) **CDDCA922** Arnold—Clarinet Concertos
cond A. BONAVERA
see CONCERT INDEX under:
(HYPE) **CDA66290** Italian Vocal Music
cond R. BONYNGE
Adam: Corsaire (Cpte)
Donizetti: Elisir d'amore (Cpte)
Minkus: Bayadère (Cpte)
see CONCERT INDEX under:
(DECC) **417 011-2DH2** Pavarotti's Greatest Hits
(DECC) **425 681-2DM2** Tutto Pavarotti
(DECC) **440 679-2DH** Carnaval!
cond B. BRITTEN
Bach: St John Passion, BWV245 (Cpte)
Britten: Albert Herring (Cpte), Piano Concerto, Rape
of Lucretia (Cpte), Violin Concerto
Mozart: Piano Concerto 20, Piano Concerto 27
Purcell: Fairy Queen, Z629 (Cpte)
Schumann: Szenen aus Goethes Faust (Cpte)
see CONCERT INDEX under:
(DECC) **430 094-2DWO** The World of Elgar
(DECC) **430 633-2DM** Haydn—Concertos
(DECC) **436 407-2DWO** The World of Schubert
(DECC) **436 990-2DWO** The World of Benjamin
Britten
(DECC) **443 847-2DF2** Bach—Concertos
(DECC) **444 323-2DF2** Mozart—Symphonies Nos 25,
29, 38 & 40; Serenata notturna
(LOND) **425 100-2LM** Britten: Orchestral & Vocal
Works
(LOND) **425 159-2LM** Salute to Percy Grainger
(LOND) **433 200-2LHO2** Britten—Owen Wingrave,
etc.
(LOND) **436 395-2LM** Britten—Vocal Works
cond N. CLEOBURY
see CONCERT INDEX under:
(PHIL) **412 231-2PH** Travels with my Cello
cond S. CLEOBURY
Duruflé: Requiem
Fauré: Requiem (Cpte)
Mozart: Mass, K317
see CONCERT INDEX under:
(DECC) **443 455-2DF2** Vivaldi—Sacred Choral Works
cond COLIN DAVIS
Berlioz: Nuits d'été
Britten: Illuminations
Mozart: Piano Concerto 9, Piano Concerto 21, Piano
Concerto 22, Piano Concerto 23, Piano Concerto 24,
Piano Concerto 26
see CONCERT INDEX under:
(DECC) **443 461-2DF2** Berlioz—L'Enfance du Christ,
etc
cond E. COLOMER
Beethoven: Triple Concerto
cond A. DAVIS
see CONCERT INDEX under:
(DG) **439 529-2GGA** Cello Concertos
cond G. FISCHER
see CONCERT INDEX under:
(CFP) **CD-CFP4532** Sacred Arias
(EMI) **CDM7 69546-2** Lucia Popp

cond A. FRANCIS
Mozart: Clarinet Concerto, K622
Spohr: Clarinet Concerto 4
cond D. FRASER
see CONCERT INDEX under:
(DELO) **DE3186** Heigh Ho! Mozart
cond J-L. GARCIA
see CONCERT INDEX under:
(SONY) **MK39310** Haydn Concertos
cond D. GARFORTH
see CONCERT INDEX under:
(CHAN) **CHAN8390** Orchestral works by Ireland and
Bridge
cond A. GIBSON
Mozart: Concertone, K190, Sinfonia Concertante,
K364
Stravinsky: Danses concertantes, Pulcinella Suite
see CONCERT INDEX under:
(CFP) **CD-CFP4598** Britten—Orchestral Works
(CHAN) **CHAN8301** The Special Sound of Chandos
cond S. GONLEY
see CONCERT INDEX under:
(ASV) **CDDCA872** Paisiello—Piano Concertos, Vol.1
(ASV) **CDDCA873** Paisiello—Piano Concertos,
Volume 2
cond P-L. GRAF
(CLAV) **CD50-8203** Krommer—Flute & Oboe
Concertos
cond H. GRIFFITHS
see CONCERT INDEX under:
(NOVA) **150 031-2** Stalder & Reindl: Orchestral
Works
(NOVA) **150 070-2** Schoeck—Orchestral Works
cond C. GROVES
see CONCERT INDEX under:
(ASV) **CDDCA559** Works for clarinet and orchestra
(ASV) **CDDCA747** Emma Johnson plays Weber
cond G. GUEST
Mozart: Requiem
see CONCERT INDEX under:
(DECC) **436 403-2DWO** The World of Royal Music
cond L. HAGER
see CONCERT INDEX under:
(HYPE) **CDA66504** Süssmayr/Tausch—Works for
Clarinet
(NOVA) **150 043-2** Mozart—Works for Oboe and
Orchestra
(NOVA) **150 053-2** Mozart—Symphonies
cond A. HALSTEAD
see CONCERT INDEX under:
(CARL) **PCD821** Trumpet Concertos
cond E. HEATH
Beethoven: Triple Concerto
Boccherini: Cello Concerto, G480
cond H. HOLLIGER
see CONCERT INDEX under:
(CLAV) **CD50-8203** Krommer—Flute & Oboe
Concertos
cond I. HOLST
see CONCERT INDEX under:
(LYRI) **SRCD223** Holst—Orchestral works
cond I. JACKSON
Ginastera: Harp Concerto
Mathias: Harp Concerto, Op. 50
cond J. JUDD
see CONCERT INDEX under:
(HYPE) **CDA66300** The Clarinet in Concert—Vol 2
(NOVA) **150 057-2** Tchaikovsky—Chamber Orchestral
Works
cond R. KUBELÍK
Dvořák: Legends
cond P. LEDGER
Bach: Brandenburg Concertos (exc), Suites,
BWV1066-9 (exc)
Berlioz: Enfance du Christ (Cpte)
see CONCERT INDEX under:
(ASV) **CDDCA565** Vivaldi—Bassoon Concertos, Vol
1
(ASV) **CDDCA571** Vivaldi—Bassoon Concertos, Vol.
2
(ASV) **CDDCA662** Vivaldi—Bassoon Concertos, Vol.
3
cond R. LEPPARD
Bach: Brandenburg Concertos (exc)
Handel: Ariodante (Cpte)
Monteverdi: Madrigals, Bk 8 (Cpte), Scherzi musicali
(1632) (exc)
Mozart: Concertone, K190, Sinfonia concertante,
K364
Purcell: Dido (Cpte)
see CONCERT INDEX under:
(CHAN) **CHAN8613** Mozart: Works for Flute and
Orchestra
(CLAV) **CD50-8505** Mozart—Works for Flute and
Orchestra
(PHIL) **426 082-2PBQ** Handel—Orchestral Works
(PHIL) **426 977-2PCC** Works for Violin and
Orchestra
(PHIL) **438 380-2PM2** Best of Grieg
(PHIL) **442 386-2PM** Bach—Brandenburg Concertos
Nos 1-3
(PHIL) **442 592-2PM2** C P E Bach—Concertos
(SONY) **MK39061** Let the best Seraphim
(SONY) **SK42478** Baroque Music for Trumpets
(SONY) **SK57497** Wynton Marsalis—The London
Concert
cond G. LEVINE
see CONCERT INDEX under:
(ARAB) **Z6603** Britten: Vocal and Orchestral Works

cond A. LEWIS
Purcell: Dido (Cpte)
see CONCERT INDEX under:
(DECC) **436 462-2DM** Ten Top Mezzos
cond A. LITTON
(ASV) **CDDCA563** Works by Bottesini
(HYPE) **CDA66215** Works for Clarinet and Orchestra
(HYPE) **CDA66300** The Clarinet in Concert—Vol 2
cond J. LOCKHART
see CONCERT INDEX under:
(RCA) **09026 61635-2** Margaret Price sings Mozart
cond P. MAAG
see CONCERT INDEX under:
(DECC) **436 376-2DH** Mozart—Works for Violin and
Orchestra
cond C. MACKERRAS
Beethoven: Piano Concerto 2, Piano Concerto 4
Handel: Israel in Egypt (Cpte), Messiah (Cpte)
Purcell: Indian Queen, Z630 (exc), St Cecilia's Day
Ode, Z328
(EMI) **CDM7 63528-2** Trumpet Concertos
(EMIN) **CD-EMX2232** Dvořák—Orchestral Works
cond J. MAKSYMIUK
(CFP) **CD-CFP4547** Shostakovich: Piano Concertos
cond G. MALCOLM
Boccherini: Cello Concerto, G480
Handel: Water Music
Haydn: Cello Concerto in C
see CONCERT INDEX under:
(ASV) **CDDCA645** Vivaldi—Concertos
(DENO) **C37-7236** Bach: Keyboard Concertos
cond N. DEL MAR
see CONCERT INDEX under:
(DECC) **436 990-2DWO** The World of Benjamin
Britten
cond I. MARIN
Rossini: Signor Bruschino (Cpte)
cond A. MELVILLE
Boughton: Immortal Hour (Cpte)
cond Y. MENUHIN
see CONCERT INDEX under:
(ARAB) **Z6568** Vaughan Williams: Orchestral Works
(EMIN) **CD-EMX2227** Holst—Orchestral Works
(VIRG) **VJ5 61108-2** Mozart—Concertos
cond G. NAVARRO
Rodrigo: Fantasía
cond M. NEARY
see CONCERT INDEX under:
(CNTO) **CSACD3050** Music from the Coronation of H.
M. Queen Elizabeth II
(SONY) **SK66613** Tavener—Innocence
cond V. NEGRI
see CONCERT INDEX under:
(PHIL) **420 648-2PM** Vivaldi: Sacred Choral Music,
Vol.1
(PHIL) **420 649-2PM** Vivaldi: Sacred Choral Music,
Vol.2
cond J. NELSON
Handel: Semele (Cpte)
cond A. PAY
see CONCERT INDEX under:
(CLAV) **CD50-8602** Kramár—Clarinet Concertos
cond J-P. RAMPAL
see CONCERT INDEX under:
(ERAT) **2292-45937-2** Mozart—Wind Concertos
(ERAT) **4509-95361-2** Mozart—Wind Concertos
cond E. RICCI
see CONCERT INDEX under:
(ERAT) **4509-95789-2** Zarzuelas-The Passion of
Spain
cond M. ROSTROPOVICH
see CONCERT INDEX under:
(SONY) **SK53271** Schnittke—Orchestral and
Chamber Works
cond J. RUDEL
see CONCERT INDEX under:
(EMI) **CDC7 47398-2** Placido Domingo: Vienna, City
of My Dreams
cond G. SCHWARZ
see CONCERT INDEX under:
(ASV) **CDDCA659** The Romantic Clarinet
(ASV) **CDDCA747** Emma Johnson plays Weber
cond G. SIMON
Barber: Cello Concerto
Shostakovich: Cello Concerto 1
see CONCERT INDEX under:
(CAPR) **10 805** Mozart: Wind Concertos
(CHAN) **CHAN8347** Tchaikovsky—Works for Cello
and Orchestra
(CHAN) **CHAN9278** The Edge of Space
cond J. SOMARY
Handel: Judas Maccabaeus (Cpte), Theodora (Cpte)
see CONCERT INDEX under:
(CBC) **PSCD2002** Maureen Forrester sings Handel
Arias
cond V. SUTEJ
see CONCERT INDEX under:
(PHIL) **434 926-2PH** The Pleasure of Love
cond J. TATE
Beethoven: Missa Solemnis, Romances, Violin
Concerto
Canteloube: Chants d'Auvergne (exc)

ENOT, Marcel (sngr)
Ganne: Hans (Cpte)
Messager: Monsieur Beaucaire (Cpte)

ENS, Phillip (bass)
Debussy: Pelléas et Mélisande (Cpte)

(ANONYMOUS) ENSEMBLE
see CONCERT INDEX under:
(CLAV) **CD50-8206** Venetian Music for Voice and Instruments
(RCA) **RD60557** Evelyn Glennie - Light in Darkness
(UNIC) **DKPCD9138** Britten/Cole Porter—Blues & Cabaret Songs
cond R. BERNAS
Turnage: Greek (Cpte)
cond S. CLEOBURY
Goehr: Death of Moses
cond R. GOODMAN
see CONCERT INDEX under:
(BIS) **BIS-CD341** Music for lutes
cond J. WOOD
see CONCERT INDEX under:
(HYPE) **CDA66410** Stravinsky—Choral Works

(L') ENSEMBLE DE LA PAIX
Anon: Melchite Sacred Chant, Traditional Maronite Chants

ENSEMBLE MUSIQUE NOUVELLE
cond G-E. OCTORS
Boesmans: Attitudes

ENSEMBLE 415
Boccherini: Stabat Mater (1781), String Quartets, G220-5 (exc), String Quintets, G325-30 (exc), String Quintets, G337-9, String Quintets, G391-6 (exc), String Quintets, G397-402 (exc), String Sextets, G454-9 (exc)
Corelli: Concerti Grossi, Op.6
Mozart: String Quintet, K515, String Quintet, K516
see CONCERT INDEX under:
(HARM) **HMA190 1245** G.B. & G. Sammartini—Concerti & Sinfonie
(HARM) **HMC90 1366** Vivaldi—Sonate a tre
cond C. BANCHINI
see CONCERT INDEX under:
(HARM) **HMC90 1273** Bach—Cantatas for Alto
(HARM) **HMC90 1291** Boccherini—Symphonies
cond R. JACOBS
Handel: Flavio (Cpte)

ENTREMONT, Philippe (cond)
see Vienna CO

ENTREMONT, Philippe (pf)
see CONCERT INDEX under:
(ERAT) **4509-92871-2** Franck—Orchestral Works
(SONY) **SM2K47511** Bartók—Concertos
(SONY) **SM3K45842** Ravel—Orchestral Works
(SONY) **SM3K47162** Bernstein plays and conducts Bernstein Volume III

ENTREMONT, Philippe (pf/dir)
Viotti: Piano Concerto 3

EÖTVÖS, Peter (cond)
see Asko Ens

EPISTEME
cond W.H. CURRY
A. Davis: X (Cpte)

EPPERSON, Bryan (vc)
F. Fossa: Guitar Trios, Op. 18 (exc)

EPSTEIN, David (cond)
see MIT SO

EQUALE BRASS
cond J.E. GARDINER
Purcell: Birthday Ode, Z323, Funeral Sentences
see CONCERT INDEX under:
(ERAT) **4509-96371-2** Gardiner—The Purcell Collection

EQUILUZ, Kurt (ten)
Bach: Cantata 4, Cantata 140, Cantata 146, Christmas Oratorio, BWV248 (Cpte), Mass in B Minor, BWV232 (Cpte), St Matthew Passion, BWV244 (Cpte)
Lehár: Giuditta (exc), Lustige Witwe (exc)
Monteverdi: Combattimento di Tancredi e Clorinda, Madrigals, Bk 8 (exc), Orfeo (Cpte)
Mozart: Idomeneo (Cpte), Nozze di Figaro (Cpte), Requiem
R. Strauss: Ariadne auf Naxos (Cpte), Daphne (Cpte), Rosenkavalier (Cpte)
Telemann: Tag des Gerichts (Cpte)
Verdi: Otello (Cpte), Trovatore (Cpte)
Wagner: Tannhäuser (Cpte)
(HANS) **98 805** Bach—Cantatas, Vol.43
(HANS) **98 806** Bach—Cantatas, Vol.44
(HANS) **98 808** Bach—Cantatas, Vol.46
(HANS) **98 809** Bach—Cantatas, Vol.47
(HANS) **98 814** Bach—Cantatas, Vol.52
(HANS) **98 816** Bach—Cantatas, Vol.54
(HANS) **98 818** Bach—Cantatas, Vol.56
(HANS) **98 822** Bach—Cantatas, Vol.60
(HANS) **98 863** Bach—Cantatas, Vol.12
(HANS) **98 870** Bach—Cantatas, Vol.19
(HANS) **98 875** Bach—Cantatas, Vol.24
(HANS) **98 876** Bach—Cantatas, Vol.25
(HANS) **98 878** Bach—Cantatas, Vol.27
(HANS) **98 891** Bach—Cantatas, Vol.38
(RCA) **GD66535** Mozart: Requiem, etc
(TELD) **2292-42422-2** Bach—Cantatas, Volume 14

(TELD) **2292-42423-2** Bach—Cantatas, Volume 15
(TELD) **2292-42428-2** Bach—Cantatas, Volume 41
(TELD) **2292-42497-2** Bach—Cantatas, Volume 2
(TELD) **2292-42498-2** Bach—Cantatas, Volume 2
(TELD) **2292-42499-2** Bach—Cantatas, Volume 3
(TELD) **2292-42500-2** Bach—Cantatas, Volume 4
(TELD) **2292-42501-2** Bach—Cantatas, Volume 5
(TELD) **2292-42502-2** Bach—Cantatas, Volume 6
(TELD) **2292-42503-2** Bach—Cantatas, Volume 7
(TELD) **2292-42504-2** Bach—Cantatas, Volume 8
(TELD) **2292-42505-2** Bach—Cantatas, Volume 9
(TELD) **2292-42506-2** Bach—Cantatas, Volume 10
(TELD) **2292-42556-2** Bach—Cantatas, Volume 11
(TELD) **2292-42559-2** Bach—Cantatas, Volume 12
(TELD) **2292-42560-2** Bach—Cantatas, Volume 13
(TELD) **2292-42565-2** Bach—Cantatas, Volume 16
(TELD) **2292-42571-2** Bach—Cantatas, Volume 17
(TELD) **2292-42572-2** Bach—Cantatas, Volume 18
(TELD) **2292-42573-2** Bach—Cantatas, Volume 19
(TELD) **2292-42576-2** Bach—Cantatas, Volume 20
(TELD) **2292-42577-2** Bach—Cantatas, Volume 21
(TELD) **2292-42578-2** Bach—Cantatas, Volume 22
(TELD) **2292-42582-2** Bach—Cantatas, Volume 23
(TELD) **2292-42583-2** Bach—Cantatas, Volume 24
(TELD) **2292-42584-2** Bach—Cantatas, Volume 25
(TELD) **2292-42602-2** Bach—Cantatas, Volume 26
(TELD) **2292-42606-2** Bach—Cantatas, Volume 27
(TELD) **2292-42608-2** Bach—Cantatas, Volume 28
(TELD) **2292-42609-2** Bach—Cantatas, Volume 29
(TELD) **2292-42615-2** Bach—Cantatas, Volume 30
(TELD) **2292-42617-2** Bach—Cantatas, Volume 31
(TELD) **2292-42631-2** Bach—Cantatas, Volume 32
(TELD) **2292-42632-2** Bach—Cantatas, Volume 36
(TELD) **2292-42633-2** Bach—Cantatas, Volume 37
(TELD) **2292-42634-2** Bach—Cantatas, Volume 38
(TELD) **2292-42635-2** Bach—Cantatas, Volume 39
(TELD) **2292-42738-2** Bach—Cantatas, Volume 40
(TELD) **2292-44179-2** Bach—Cantatas, Volume 42
(TELD) **2292-44193-2** Bach—Cantatas, Volume 43
(TELD) **2292-44194-2** Bach—Cantatas, Volume 44
(TELD) **4509-91755-2** Bach—Cantatas, Volume 45
(TELD) **4509-91756-2** Bach—Cantatas, Vol.1
(TELD) **4509-91757-2** Bach—Cantatas, Vol.2
(TELD) **4509-91758-2** Bach—Cantatas, Vol.3
(TELD) **4509-91759-2** Bach—Cantatas, Vol.4
(TELD) **4509-91760-2** Bach—Cantatas, Vol.5
(TELD) **4509-91761-2** Bach—Cantatas, Vol.6
(TELD) **4509-91762-2** Bach—Cantatas, Vol.7
(TELD) **4509-91763-2** Bach—Cantatas, Vol.8
(TELD) **4509-91764-2** Bach—Cantatas, Vol.9
(TELD) **4509-93687-2** Bach—Cantatas, Vol.10
(TELD) **9031-74798-2** Bach—Arias and Duets

ERASSOVA, Natalia (sop)
Rachmaninov: Aleko (Cpte)
Tchaikovsky: Snow Maiden (Cpte)

ERB, Karl (ten)
Bach: St Matthew Passion, BWV244 (exc)
see CONCERT INDEX under:
(CLUB) **CL99-020** Maria Ivogün & Lotte Schöne—Opera Recital
(PEAR) **GEMMCDS9085** Hugo Wolf Society, Volume II
(PREI) **89208** Karl Erb Lieder Album

ERBEN, Valentin (vc)
see CONCERT INDEX under:
(AUVI) **MO782025** Schoenberg—Chamber Music, Vol. 3

ERBLICH, Ferdinand (va)
see CONCERT INDEX under:
(LASE) **15 522** Schubert: Chamber Works

ERBNER, Fritz (bass)
R. Strauss: Rosenkavalier (Cpte)

ERCOLANI, Renato (ten)
Mozart: Nozze di Figaro (Cpte)
Ponchielli: Gioconda (Cpte)
Puccini: Fanciulla del West (Cpte), Madama Butterfly (Cpte), Tosca (Cpte), Turandot (Cpte)
Verdi: Ballo in maschera (Cpte), Falstaff (Cpte), Rigoletto (Cpte), Trovatore (Cpte)
see CONCERT INDEX under:
(DECC) **411 665-2DM3** Puccini: Il trittico
(EMI) **CDM7 69543-2** Maria Callas and Giuseppe Di Stefano - Duets

ERDÉLYI, Csaba (va)
see CONCERT INDEX under:
(PHIL) **416 298-2PH** Richard Strauss: Lieder

EREDE, Alberto (cond)
see BPO

ERHARD, Werner (vn)
see CONCERT INDEX under:
(ARCH) **419 633-2AH** Telemann: Wind Concertos

ERICKSON, Kaaren (sop)
Getty: White Election
Gluck: Cinesi (Cpte)
Handel: Messiah (Cpte)
Wagner: Parsifal (Cpte)

ERICKSON, Raymond (organ)
see CONCERT INDEX under:
(ALBA) **TROY127-2** Purcell—From Rosy Bow'rs

ERICKSON, Raymond (hpd)
see CONCERT INDEX under:
(ALBA) **TROY127-2** Purcell—From Rosy Bow'rs

ERICSON, Barbro (mez)
Verdi: Rigoletto (Cpte)

Wagner: Walküre (Cpte)
see CONCERT INDEX under:
(DG) **435 211-2GX15** Wagner—Der Ring des Nibelungen

ERICSON, Eric (cond)
see Inst Ens

(ERIC) ERICSON CHAMBER CHOIR
cond C. ABBADO
Brahms: Deutsches Requiem, Op.45 (Cpte)
cond E. ERICSON
see CONCERT INDEX under:
(EMI) **CDC7 54098-2** Sacred Songs
cond JAMES LEVINE
Beethoven: Missa Solemnis
cond E-P. SALONEN
Stravinsky: Oedipus Rex (Cpte)

ERICSSON, Hans-Ola (organ)
Aho: Symphony 8
Messiaen: Livre du Saint Sacrement, Méditations, Nativité du Seigneur
see CONCERT INDEX under:
(BIS) **BIS-CD409** Messiaen: Organ Works, Vol 1
(BIS) **BIS-CD510** Organ Music from the USA

ERIKSEN, Olaf (bar)
see CONCERT INDEX under:
(AURO) **ACD4971** Nystedt—Chamber and Vocal Works

ERIKSEN, Randi (contr)
Braein: Anne Pedersdotter (Cpte)

ERIKSSON, Birger (bass)
Nørgård: Gilgamesh (Cpte)

ERISMAN, Hans (cond)
see orch

ERKKILÄ, Eero (ten)
Madetoja: Juha (Cpte)

ERLER, Jörg (treb)
see CONCERT INDEX under:
(TELD) **2292-42573-2** Bach—Cantatas, Volume 19
(TELD) **4509-91758-2** Bach—Cantatas, Vol.4

ERMLER, Mark (cond)
see Bolshoi Th. Orch

ERMOLENKO-YUZHINA, Natalia (sop)
see CONCERT INDEX under:
(PEAR) **GEMMCDS9001/3(2)** Singers of Imperial Russia, Vol.2 (pt 2)

ERMOLLI, Francesca Russo (sop)
Traetta: Buovo d'Antona (Cpte)

ERNMAN, Malena (alto)
Schnittke: Symphony 2

ERNST, Hans Bruno (bass)
Handel: Giulio Cesare (Cpte)
Wagner: Meistersinger (Cpte)

ERNST SENFF CHORUS
cond C. ABBADO
Brahms: Alto Rhapsody, Op. 53
see CONCERT INDEX under:
(DG) **429 765-2GH** Brahms—Orchestral & Choral Works
cond C.M. GIULINI
Beethoven: Symphony 9
Verdi: Pezzi sacri (Cpte), Requiem (Cpte)
Vivaldi: Credo, RV591
cond B. HAITINK
Mahler: Symphony 2
cond JAMES LEVINE
see CONCERT INDEX under:
(DG) **429 724-2GH2** Berlioz—Requiem, etc
cond S. RATTLE
Liszt: Faust Symphony
cond J. TATE
Grieg: Peer Gynt (exc)
cond L. ZAGROSEK
Eisler: Deutsche Sinfonie

ERNSTER, Dezsö (bass)
Mozart: Don Giovanni (Cpte)

ERÖS, Peter (cond)
see Stockholm PO

ERRANTE, Valerie (sop)
Puccini: Gianni Schicchi (Cpte)
(EURO) **GD69043** Puccini: Il Trittico

ERSHOV, Ivan (ten)
see CONCERT INDEX under:
(PEAR) **GEMMCDS9997/9(1)** Singers of Imperial Russia, Vol.1 (pt 1)

ERWARTUNG ENSEMBLE
cond B. DESGRAUPES
see CONCERT INDEX under:
(FNAC) **592292** Satie—Orchestral & Vocal Works

ERWEN, Keith (ten)
Verdi: Giovanna d'Arco (Cpte), Lombardi (Cpte)
see CONCERT INDEX under:
(EMI) **CDM7 69544-2** Berlioz: Vocal Works

ERXLEBEN, Michael (vn/dir)
Boccherini: Symphonies, G515-8 (exc)
see CONCERT INDEX under:
(CAPR) **10 458** Boccherini Edition, Vol.4

ESBERGER, Carl (cl)
see CONCERT INDEX under:

(CLRI) **CC0005** The Clarinet - Historical Recordings, Vol.1

ESCALAIS, Léon (ten)
see CONCERT INDEX under:
(EMI) **CHS7 64860-2(1)** La Scala Edition - Vol.1, 1878-1914 (pt 1)
(IRCC) **IRCC-CD802** Souvenirs of Rare French Opera
(SYMP) **SYMCD1126** The Harold Wayne Collection, Vol.14
(SYMP) **SYMCD1128** The Harold Wayne Collection, Vol.15

ESCHENBACH, Christoph (cond)
see COE

ESCHENBACH, Christoph (pf)
Beethoven: Piano and Wind Quintet, Op. 16
Brahms: Cello Sonata 1, Cello Sonata 2
Mozart: Piano and Wind Quintet, K452
see CONCERT INDEX under:
(DG) **413 145-2GW2** Beethoven—Orchestral Works
(DG) **415 190-2GH** Schumann: Lieder
(DG) **415 655-2GH** Bach: Harpsichord Concertos
(DG) **419 445-2GX5** Mozart—Piano Sonatas
(DG) **419 875-2GCM3** Brahms. Quintets and Sextets.
(DG) **435 042-2GX2** Mozart— Piano Duet Works
(DG) **437 131-2GX2** Brahms—Chamber Works
(DG) **439 417-2GCL** Schumann—Lieder
(TELD) **2292-46154-2** Schumann—Lieder
(TELD) **4509-94540-2** Schnittke—Violin Works
(VIRG) **VC7 59007-2** Picker—Orchestral Works

ESCHENBRENNER, Isabelle (sop)
Gluck: Iphigénie en Aulide (Cpte)

ESCHENBURG, Hans-Jakob (vc)
see CONCERT INDEX under:
(CAPR) **10 539** Schulhoff—Chamber Works

ESCHENBURG, Ulrike (vn)
see CONCERT INDEX under:
(PHIL) **434 918-2PH2** Bach—Concertos

ESCHRIG, Ralph (ten)
see CONCERT INDEX under:
(CAPR) **10 367** Mendelssohn—Motets

ESCHWÉ, Alfred (cond)
see Bratislava RSO

ESCOTT, Harry (treb)
see CONCERT INDEX under:
(CARL) **PCD896** Fauré: Sacred Choral Works

ESCOURROU, Pierre-Marie (spkr)
Honegger: Jeanne d'Arc (Cpte)

ESHAM, Faith (sop)
Bizet: Carmen (exc)
Mozart: Nozze di Figaro (Cpte)

ESKIN, Jules (vc)
see CONCERT INDEX under:
(DG) **423 089-2GH** Fauré: Orchestral Works
(NORT) **NR206-CD** Arthur Foote—Chamber Works

ESKIN, Virginia (pf)
see CONCERT INDEX under:
(CHNN) **CCS1691** Chamber music from Theresienstadt 1941-45
(KOCH) **37056-2** Coleridge-Taylor—Chamber Works
(NORT) **NR206-CD** Arthur Foote—Chamber Works
(NORT) **NR248-CD** Silenced Voices - Victims of the Holocaust
(NORT) **NR9004-CD** Dark Garden

ESPAILLAT, Ulises (ten)
see CONCERT INDEX under:
(NALB) **NA058CD** Guastavino—Canciones Argentinas

ESPINASSE, François (organ)
Guilain: Pièces d'orgue (exc)
Marchand: Pièces choisies pour l'orgue

ESPOO CHAMBER ORCHESTRA
cond J. LAMMINMÄKI
see CONCERT INDEX under:
(FINL) **4509-95859-2** Sibelius—Orchestral Works

ESPOSITO, Andrée (sop)
see CONCERT INDEX under:
(EMI) **CDM7 64365-2** Chausson—Chamber, Orchestra & Vocal Works

ESPOSITO, Valeria (sop)
Verdi: Rigoletto (Cpte)
(DECC) **436 261-2DHO3** Puccini—Il Trittico

ESSEN SCHOLA CANTORUM
cond G. JOPPICH
Anon: Deus, Deus meus - Gregorian Chant

ESSER, Hermin (ten)
Wagner: Fliegende Holländer (Cpte), Parsifal (Cpte), Rheingold (Cpte)
see CONCERT INDEX under:
(PHIL) **446 057-2PB14** Wagner—The Ring Cycle - Bayreuth Festival 1967

ESSEX, Kenneth (va)
see CONCERT INDEX under:
(UNIC) **UKCD2060** Britten—Early Chamber Music

ESSEX, Violet (sop)
see CONCERT INDEX under:
(EMI) **CDANGEL 5** Norton—Chu Chin Chow

ESSMANN, Thomas (ten)
Mangold: Abraham

ESSWOOD, Paul (alto)
Bach: Christmas Oratorio, BWV248 (Cpte), St Matthew Passion, BWV244 (Cpte)
Glass: Akhnaten (Cpte)
Handel: Israel in Egypt (Cpte), Messiah (Cpte)
Purcell: Dido (Cpte), St Cecilia's Day Ode, Z328
see CONCERT INDEX under:
(CARL) **MCD57** Britten—Songs
(DECC) **430 263-2DM** Purcell—Sacred choral works
(DECC) **436 403-2DWO** The World of Royal Music
(DECC) **443 868-2DF2** Italian Baroque Sacred Works
(HYPE) **CDA66070** Purcell: Songs
(SONY) **SK64133** The Essential Philip Glass
(TELD) **2292-42422-2** Bach—Cantatas, Volume 14
(TELD) **2292-42423-2** Bach—Cantatas, Volume 15
(TELD) **2292-42497-2** Bach—Cantatas, Volume 1
(TELD) **2292-42498-2** Bach—Cantatas, Volume 2
(TELD) **2292-42499-2** Bach—Cantatas, Volume 3
(TELD) **2292-42500-2** Bach—Cantatas, Volume 4
(TELD) **2292-42501-2** Bach—Cantatas, Volume 5
(TELD) **2292-42502-2** Bach—Cantatas, Volume 6
(TELD) **2292-42503-2** Bach—Cantatas, Volume 7
(TELD) **2292-42504-2** Bach—Cantatas, Volume 8
(TELD) **2292-42505-2** Bach—Cantatas, Volume 9
(TELD) **2292-42506-2** Bach—Cantatas, Volume 10
(TELD) **2292-42556-2** Bach—Cantatas, Volume 11
(TELD) **2292-42559-2** Bach—Cantatas, Volume 12
(TELD) **2292-42560-2** Bach—Cantatas, Volume 13
(TELD) **2292-42565-2** Bach—Cantatas, Volume 16
(TELD) **2292-42571-2** Bach—Cantatas, Volume 17
(TELD) **2292-42572-2** Bach—Cantatas, Volume 18
(TELD) **2292-42573-2** Bach—Cantatas, Volume 19
(TELD) **2292-42575-2** Bach—Cantatas, Volume 20
(TELD) **2292-42577-2** Bach—Cantatas, Volume 21
(TELD) **2292-42578-2** Bach—Cantatas, Volume 22
(TELD) **2292-42582-2** Bach—Cantatas, Volume 23
(TELD) **2292-42583-2** Bach—Cantatas, Volume 24
(TELD) **2292-42584-2** Bach—Cantatas, Volume 25
(TELD) **2292-42602-2** Bach—Cantatas, Volume 26
(TELD) **2292-42603-2** Bach—Cantatas, Volume 27
(TELD) **2292-42606-2** Bach—Cantatas, Volume 28
(TELD) **2292-42608-2** Bach—Cantatas, Volume 29
(TELD) **2292-42609-2** Bach—Cantatas, Volume 30
(TELD) **2292-42615-2** Bach—Cantatas, Volume 31
(TELD) **2292-42617-2** Bach—Cantatas, Volume 32
(TELD) **2292-42631-2** Bach—Cantatas, Volume 36
(TELD) **2292-42632-2** Bach—Cantatas, Volume 37
(TELD) **2292-42633-2** Bach—Cantatas, Volume 38
(TELD) **2292-42634-2** Bach—Cantatas, Volume 39
(TELD) **2292-42635-2** Bach—Cantatas, Volume 40
(TELD) **2292-42738-2** Bach—Cantatas, Volume 42
(TELD) **2292-44179-2** Bach—Cantatas, Volume 43
(TELD) **4509-91755-2** Bach—Cantatas, Vol.1
(TELD) **4509-91756-2** Bach—Cantatas, Vol.2
(TELD) **4509-91757-2** Bach—Cantatas, Vol.3
(TELD) **4509-91758-2** Bach—Cantatas, Vol.4
(TELD) **4509-91759-2** Bach—Cantatas, Vol.5
(TELD) **4509-91760-2** Bach—Cantatas, Vol.6
(TELD) **4509-91761-2** Bach—Cantatas, Vol.7
(TELD) **4509-91762-2** Bach—Cantatas, Vol.8
(TELD) **4509-91763-2** Bach—Cantatas, Vol.9
(TELD) **4509-91764-2** Bach—Cantatas, Vol.10

ESTAMPIE
cond M. POPP
Anon: Play of Daniel (Cpte)

ESTEP, Craig (ten)
see CONCERT INDEX under:
(EMI) **CDC7 54643-2** Rossini—Bicentenary Gala Concert

ESTERHÁZY QUARTET
Boccherini: String Quartets, G201-6
Haydn: String Quartets, Op.20 (exc)

(NICOLAUS) ESTERHÁZY SINFONIA
see CONCERT INDEX under:
(NAXO) **8 553178** Krommer—Clarinet Concertos
cond B. DRAHOS
Haydn: Symphony 97, Symphony 98
see CONCERT INDEX under:
(NAXO) **8 550768** Haydn—Symphonies, Vol.11
(NAXO) **8 550770** Haydn—Symphonies
(NAXO) **8 550797** Haydn—Symphonies, Volume 15

ESTES, Simon (bass)
Beethoven: Symphony 9
Bizet: Carmen (Cpte)
Falla: Atlántida (Cpte)
Haydn: Mass 14
Mozart: Idomeneo (Cpte), Requiem
Saint-Saëns: Samson et Dalila (Cpte)
Stravinsky: Oedipus Rex (Cpte), Pulcinella
Verdi: Don Carlo (Cpte), Requiem (Cpte)
Wagner: Fliegende Holländer (Cpte), Parsifal (Cpte)
see CONCERT INDEX under:
(SONY) **SM2K47563** Haydn—Choral & Orchestral Works
(SONY) **SX14K48198** Mahler—Complete Symphonies, etc
(SONY) **S2K66836** Goldschmidt—Beatrice Cenci, etc

ESTEVAN, Pedro (perc)
Kapsperger: Chitarrone Book I (exc), Chitarrone Book IV

ESTONIA NATIONAL MALE CHOIR
cond S. SONDECKIS
Shostakovich: Symphony 13

ESTONIA OPERA CHORUS
cond P. LILJE
Tubin: Barbara von Tisenhusen (Cpte)

ESTONIA OPERA ORCHESTRA
cond E. KLAS
see CONCERT INDEX under:
(ONDI) **ODE768-2** Dilbèr sings Coloratura Arias
cond P. LILJE
Tubin: Barbara von Tisenhusen (Cpte)

ESTONIAN BOYS' CHOIR
cond N. JÄRVI
Mahler: Symphony 8

ESTONIAN PHILHARMONIC CHAMBER CHOIR
cond T. KALJUSTE
see CONCERT INDEX under:
(ECM) **434 275-2** Tormis—Forgotten Peoples
(ECM) **439 162-2** Pärt—Choral Works

ESTONIAN STATE ACADEMIC MALE CHOIR
cond P. BERGLUND
Sibelius: Kullervo

ESTONIAN SYMPHONY ORCHESTRA
cond E. KLAS
see CONCERT INDEX under:
(ONDI) **ODE731-2** Jorma Hynninen sings Opera Arias
cond P. LILJE
Englund: Symphony 1, Symphony 2

ESTOURELLE, Catherine (sop)
Berg: Lulu (Cpte)

ESTOURNET, Jean (vn)
see CONCERT INDEX under:
(REM) **REM311175** Fauré—Mélodies, Vol.1

ESTRADA, Father Gregori (cond)
see Montserrat Abbey Ch

(L') ESTRO ARMONICO
cond D. SOLOMONS
see CONCERT INDEX under:
(SONY) **SMK66929** Haydn—Symphonies

ESZTÉNYI, Szabolcs (pf)
see CONCERT INDEX under:
(POLS) **PNCD045** Lutosławski: Selected Works

ETCHEVERRY, Henri (bar)
see CONCERT INDEX under:
(EMI) **CHS7 61038-2** Debussy—Pelléas et Mélisande, etc

ETELÄVUORI, Paula (contr)
Sallinen: Kullervo (Cpte)

ETESON, Richard (treb)
Fauré: Requiem (Cpte)

ETHERDEN, Alan (pf)
(HUNT) **HMPCD0589** Enchanting Melodies

ETHERIDGE, Brian (bass)
Anon: Missa Salisburgensis, Plaudite tympana

ETHERINGTON, Carleton (organ)
(REGE) **REGSB701CD** I saw the Lord

ETON COLLEGE CHAPEL CHOIR
cond R. ALLWOOD
see CONCERT INDEX under:
(FUTU) **FCM1004** Music from the Eton Choirbook

ETTL, Karl (bass)
Verdi: Macbeth (Cpte)
Wagner: Tristan und Isolde (exc)
see CONCERT INDEX under:
(EMI) **CHS7 64487-2** R. Strauss—Der Rosenkavalier & Lieder
(PEAR) **GEMMCDS9365** R. Strauss: Der Rosenkavalier (abridged), etc
(SCHW) **314541** Vienna State Opera Live, Vol.3
(SCHW) **314542** Vienna State Opera Live, Vol.4
(SCHW) **314562** Vienna State Opera Live, Vol.6
(SCHW) **314572** Vienna State Opera Live, Vol.7
(SCHW) **314602** Vienna State Opera Live, Vol.10
(SCHW) **314622** Vienna State Opera Live, Vol.12
(SCHW) **314632** Vienna State Opera Live, Vol.13
(SCHW) **314642** Vienna State Opera Live, Vol.14
(SCHW) **314662** Vienna State Opera Live, Vol.16
(SCHW) **314672** Vienna State Opera Live, Vol.17

EUBA, Wolf (sngr)
Killmayer: Yolimba (Cpte)

EUBA, Wolf (spkr)
K. A. Hartmann: Simplicius Simplicissimus (Cpte)

(L')EUROPA GALANTE
see CONCERT INDEX under:
(O111) **OPS30-88** Leo/Pergolesi—Salve Reginas
(O111) **OPS56-9120** Vivaldi—The Four Seasons (Manchester Version)
cond F. BIONDI
A. Scarlatti: Maddalena (Cpte)
Handel: Poro (Cpte)

(L') EUROPA GALANTE TRIO
Boccherini: String Trios, G107-12

EUROPEAN BAROQUE SOLOISTS
see CONCERT INDEX under:
(DENO) **CO-77614** Telemann—Flute and Oboe Works

EUROPEAN CHAMBER OPERA CHORUS
cond D. HINNELLS
Verdi: Trovatore (Cpte)

EUROPEAN CHAMBER OPERA ORCHESTRA
cond D. HINNELLS
Verdi: Trovatore (Cpte)

EUROPEAN CHAMBER ORCHESTRA PER MUSICA
cond J. REYNOLDS
see CONCERT INDEX *under:*
(ETCE) **KTC1040** Ravel orchestrations

EUROPEAN COMMUNITY CHAMBER ORCHESTRA
cond E. AADLAND
see CONCERT INDEX *under:*
(ASV) **CDDCA766** Handel—Works for Soprano and
Orchestra
(CARL) **PCD964** Piano Concertos
(CARL) **PCD978** Haydn—Symphonies
(CARL) **PCD979** Vivaldi—Concertos
(CARL) **PCD1054** Mozart—Wind Concertos
(SCHW) **311164** Mozart—Violin Concertos
cond D. DEMETRIADES
see CONCERT INDEX *under:*
(HYPE) **CDH88015** The Concerto in Europe
cond J. FAERBER
see CONCERT INDEX *under:*
(HYPE) **CDA66156** The Symphony in Europe

EUROPEAN COMMUNITY YOUTH ORCHESTRA
cond C. ABBADO
Berlioz: Te Deum
cond J. JUDD
R. Strauss: Alpensinfonie

EUROPEAN MASTER ORCHESTRA
cond P. SCHMELZER
see CONCERT INDEX *under:*
(SCHW) **312362** Spanish Guitar Concertos

EUROPEAN SYMPHONY ORCHESTRA
cond A. DORATI
Beethoven: Missa Solemnis

EUROPÉEN VOCAL ENSEMBLE
cond P. HERREWEGHE
Lassus: Lagrime di San Pietro (Cpte)

EUSTACE, Frances (bn)
see CONCERT INDEX *under:*
(HARM) **HMU90 7104** Vivaldi/Chedéville—Oboe
Sonatas

EUSTIS, E. (sop)
see CONCERT INDEX *under:*
(RCA) **GD60328** Toscanini conducts the Philadelphia
Orch

EUSTRATI, Diana (contr)
Mozart: Zauberflöte (Cpte)

EVANGELATOS, Daphne (contr)
R. Strauss: Elektra (Cpte)
Wagner: Götterdämmerung (Cpte)

EVANS, Anna (ob)
see CONCERT INDEX *under:*
(NIMB) **NI5189** Telemann: Trumpet Concertos

EVANS, Anne (sop)
Wagner: Götterdämmerung (exc), Siegfried (Cpte),
Walküre (Cpte)

EVANS, Beverly (sop)
R. Ward: Crucible (Cpte)

EVANS, Damon (ten)
Gershwin: Porgy and Bess (Cpte)
Hammerstein: Carmen Jones (Cpte)
Porter: Kiss Me, Kate (Cpte)
Tippett: Child of Our Time

EVANS, Edgar (ten)
Britten: Albert Herring (Cpte)
Wagner: Tristan und Isolde (Cpte)

EVANS, Sir Geraint (bar)
Britten: Peter Grimes (Cpte)
Donizetti: Elisir d'amore (Cpte)
Mahler: Knaben Wunderhorn (exc)
Mozart: Così fan tutte (Cpte), Nozze di Figaro (Cpte)
Verdi: Falstaff (Cpte), Forza del destino (Cpte)
Wagner: Meistersinger (Cpte)
see CONCERT INDEX *under:*
(LYRI) **SRCD324** Mathias—Choral Works

EVANS, Greek (sngr)
see CONCERT INDEX *under:*
(PEAR) **GEMMCDS9059/61** Music from the New York
Stage, Vol. 4: 1917-20

EVANS, Julian (pf)
see CONCERT INDEX *under:*
(HYPE) **CDA66347** Poulenc & Hahn—Balletic Works

EVANS, Michael (vc)
Bach: Flute Sonatas, BWV1030-5

EVANS, Nancy (contr)
(EMI) **CMS7 64727-2** Britten—Opera excerpts and
Folksongs
(LOND) **436 393-2LM** Britten—The Little Sweep, etc

EVANS, Peter (pf)
see CONCERT INDEX *under:*
(CATA) **09026 61916-2** MacMillan—Veni, Veni
Emmanuel & Other Percussion Works

EVANS, Peter (pf)
Brahms: Cello Sonata 1, Cello Sonata 2
see CONCERT INDEX *under:*

(HYPE) **CDA66296** Martinů—Cello Sonatas
(LINN) **CKD002** French works for cello and piano
(LINN) **CKD009**
Lutoslawski/Rachmaninov/Webern—Cello Works

EVANS, Peter (ten)
Berlioz: Enfance du Christ (Cpte)

EVANS, Ralph (vn)
see CONCERT INDEX *under:*
(HYPE) **CDA66585** Purcell—Complete Anthems &
Services, Vol.1

EVANS, Rebecca (sop)
Mozart: Nozze di Figaro (Cpte)
Sullivan: HMS Pinafore (Cpte), Pirates of Penzance
(Cpte)
Vaughan Williams: Hugh the Drover (Cpte)
Verdi: Rigoletto (Cpte)

EVANS, Richard (cond)
see BNFL Band

EVANS, Robert (bass)
Boughton: Bethlehem (Cpte)
Monteverdi: Orfeo (Cpte)
see CONCERT INDEX *under:*
(HYPE) **CDA66494** Purcell—Complete Odes &
Welcome Songs, Vol.6
(HYPE) **CDA66587** Purcell—Complete Odes &
Welcome Songs, Vol.7
(HYPE) **CDA66598** Purcell—Complete Odes &
Welcome Songs, Vol.8
(HYPE) **CDA66623** Purcell—Complete Anthems &
Services, Vol.3
(HYPE) **CDA66644** Purcell—Complete Anthems &
Services, Vol.4
(HYPE) **CDA66656** Purcell—Complete Anthems &
Services, Vol.5
(HYPE) **CDA66677** Purcell—Anthems & Services,
Vol.7

EVANS, Scott (perc)
see CONCERT INDEX *under:*
(NALB) **NA035CD** Singing Through

EVANS, Wynford (ten)
Bach: Mass in B minor, BWV232 (Cpte)
Mozart: Litanies, K243, Vespers, K321
Puccini: Rondine (Cpte)
Purcell: Fairy Queen, Z629 (Cpte)
Vaughan Williams: Hugh the Drover (Cpte)
Verdi: Trovatore (Cpte)
see CONCERT INDEX *under:*
(DECC) **436 407-2DWO** The World of Schubert
(EMI) **CDM7 64022-2** Vaughan Williams—Orchestral
Works

EVERS, Reinbert (gtr)
Henze: Cimarrón

EVETZ, Eugen (cond)
see Paris Russian Orthodox Cath Ch

EVISON, Penelope (fl)
see CONCERT INDEX *under:*
(BIS) **BIS-CD249** Works for Baroque Flute and
Recorders
(BIS) **BIS-CD617** Telemann—Recorder Concertos

EVITTS, David (bar)
see CONCERT INDEX *under:*
(MUSM) **67152-2** Stravinsky—The Composer,
Volume VII

EVITTS, David (bass)
see CONCERT INDEX *under:*
(MUSM) **67110-2** Stravinsky—The Composer,
Volume V

EVSTATIEVA, Stefka (sop)
Borodin: Prince Igor (Cpte)
Mascagni: Cavalleria Rusticana (Cpte)
Tchaikovsky: Queen of Spades (Cpte)

EVSTIGNEEV, Mikhail (ob)
see CONCERT INDEX *under:*
(RCA) **RD60240** Vivaldi—Orchestral and Choral
works

EWELER, Grete (vn)
see CONCERT INDEX *under:*
(PEAR) **GEMMCD9310** Franz Lehár conducts Richard
Tauber

EWER, Graeme (ten)
Donizetti: Lucrezia Borgia (Cpte)

EWERHART, Rudolf (organ)
Handel: Organ Concertos

EWERHART, Rudolf (org/dir)
see CONCERT INDEX *under:*
(FSM) **FCD91220** French Baroque Christmas Music

EWING, Alan (bass)
Monteverdi: Madrigals, Bk 8 (exc)
Puccini: Bohème (Cpte)
see CONCERT INDEX *under:*
(VIRG) **VC7 59606-2** Monteverdi—Madrigals, Book 8

EWING, Maria (sop)
Berlioz: Damnation de Faust (Cpte)
Debussy: Pelléas et Mélisande (Cpte)
Giordano: Andrea Chénier (Cpte)
Mozart: Don Giovanni (Cpte), Requiem
Shostakovich: Lady Macbeth of Mtsensk (Cpte)
Verdi: Vespri Siciliani (Cpte)
see CONCERT INDEX *under:*
(DG) **423 103-2GH** Debussy: Vocal & Orchestral
Works

(EMI) **CDC7 54204-2** Ravel—Orchestral Works
(EMI) **CDZ7 67015-2** Mozart—Opera Arias

EX CATHEDRA BAROQUE ORCHESTRA
cond J. SKIDMORE
see CONCERT INDEX *under:*
(ASV) **CDGAU137** Vivaldi—Choral Works
(ASV) **CDGAU141** Delalande—Choral Works

EX CATHEDRA CHAMBER CHOIR
cond J. SKIDMORE
see CONCERT INDEX *under:*
(ASV) **CDDCA912** Sir Christèmas - Carols Old and
New
(ASV) **CDGAU137** Vivaldi—Choral Works
(ASV) **CDGAU141** Delalande—Choral Works

EXERJEAN, Edouard (pf)
see CONCERT INDEX *under:*
(PIER) **PV786091** Le Groupe des Six: Piano Duets

EXPOSÉ ENSEMBLE
see CONCERT INDEX *under:*
(ETCE) **KTC1096** Finnissy—Chamber Works

EXTEMPORE STRING ENSEMBLE
see CONCERT INDEX *under:*
(HYPE) **CDA66327** Spanish Music of the Golden Age

EYRE, Emily (voc)
M. Monk: Atlas Songs

EYRE, Marjorie (mez)
Sullivan: Patience (Cpte)

EYRON, Jan (pf)
see CONCERT INDEX *under:*
(BIS) **BIS-CD017** Söderström and Meyer sing Duets

FABBRI, Guerrina (contr)
see CONCERT INDEX *under:*
(SYMP) **SYMCD1065** The Harold Wayne Collection,
Vol.1

FABBRICINI, Tiziana (sop)
Verdi: Traviata (Cpte)

FABBRIS, Guido (ten)
Donizetti: Don Pasquale (Cpte)

FABBRY, Ernst (ten)
Mozart: Zauberflöte (Cpte)

FABRE-GARRUS, Bernard (cond)
see A Sei Voci

FABRITIIS, Oliviero De (cond)
see La Scala Orch

FABRY, Rachel (mez)
Puccini: Gianni Schicchi (Cpte), Suor Angelica
(Cpte)

FABUEL, Gloria (sop)
Martín y Soler: Cosa Rara (Cpte)

FACINI, Enrico (sngr)
Mayr: Rosa Bianca (Cpte)

FACINI, Enrico (ten)
Verdi: Trovatore (Cpte)

FACINI, Francesco (bass)
Rossini: Cambiale di Matrimonio (Cpte), Siège de
Corinthe (Cpte)

FADLE, Jorg (cl)
Meyerbeer: Amori di Teolinda

FAERBER, Jörg (cond)
see Berlin SO

FAGÉUS, Kjäll (cl)
see CONCERT INDEX *under:*
(CPRI) **CAP21415** Works for Wind Orchestra

FAGIUS, Hans (organ)
Bach: Chorales, BWV651-668 (exc)
see CONCERT INDEX *under:*
(BIS) **BIS-CD273** Organ Works
(BIS) **BIS-CD343/4** Bach: Organ Works, Vol.4
(BIS) **BIS-CD439/40** Bach: Organ Works, Vol.7
(BIS) **BIS-CD445** Bach—Organ Works, Vol.9
(BIS) **BIS-CD555** Saint-Saëns—Orchestral Works
(BIS) **BIS-CD556** Saint-Saëns—Organ Works

FAGOTTO, Gianpaolo (ten)
A. Scarlatti: Lamentazioni (Cpte)
Handel: Flavio (Cpte)
Monteverdi: Vespers
Traetta: Buovo d'Antona (Cpte)

FAHBERG, Antonia (sop)
Janáček: Excursions of Mr Brouček (Cpte)
Mozart: Zauberflöte (Cpte)
see CONCERT INDEX *under:*
(TELD) **9031-77614-2** Bach—Cantatas

FAIRFIELD ORCHESTRA
cond T. CRAWFORD
see CONCERT INDEX *under:*
(ECM) **445 350-2** Jarrett—Bridge of Light

FAIRHURST, Robin (treb)
see CONCERT INDEX *under:*
(LOND) **436 393-2LM** Britten—The Little Sweep, etc

FAISANDIER, Gérard (bn)
see CONCERT INDEX *under:*
(EMI) **CZS7 62736-2** Poulenc—Chamber Works

FALCO, Giuseppe (ob)
see CONCERT INDEX *under:*
(CARL) **PCD979** Vivaldi—Concertos

FALCO, Mario (hp)
see CONCERT INDEX *under:*

(ARGO) **436 128–2ZH** Moran—Vocal and Chamber Works

FALCON, André (narr)
see CONCERT INDEX *under:*
(MONT) **TCE8790** Debussy: Orchestral and Dramatic Works

FALCON, Bruni (sop)
Wagner: Rheingold (Cpte), Walküre (Cpte)
see CONCERT INDEX *under:*
(FOYE) **15-CF2011** Wagner—Der Ring de Nibelungen

FALCON, Ruth (sop)
Beethoven: Symphony 9
Wagner: Götterdämmerung (Cpte), Walküre (Cpte)

FALEWICZ, Magdalena (sop)
Gluck: Orfeo ed Euridice (Cpte)

FALK, Juliana (contr)
see CONCERT INDEX *under:*
(EMI) **CDC7 47407-2** Schubert: Sacred Choral works

FALK, Juliana (mez)
see CONCERT INDEX *under:*
(EMI) **CMS7 64783-2** Schubert—Sacred Works, Vol.2

FALKMAN, Carl-Johan (bar)
Henze: Boulevard Solitude (Cpte)

FALKOWSKI, Damien (cond)
see Britannia CO

FALLA, Manuel de (hpd)
see CONCERT INDEX *under:*
(EMI) **CDC7 54836-2** Granados/Falla/Mompou/Nin

FALLA, Manuel de (pf)
see CONCERT INDEX *under:*
(EMI) **CDC7 54836-2** Granados/Falla/Mompou/Nin

FALLETTA, JoAnn (cond)
see LSO

FALLISI, Guiseppe (sngr)
Rossini: Adelaide di Borgogna (Cpte)

FALVAY, Sándor (pf)
see CONCERT INDEX *under:*
(MARC) **8 223404** Atterberg—Chamber Music, Vol.1

FANCOURT, Darrell (bass)
Sullivan: Patience (Cpte), Sorcerer (Cpte)

FANELLI, Gaetano (ten)
Puccini: Turandot (Cpte)

FANELLI, Maria Luisa (sop)
Verdi: Requiem (Cpte)
see CONCERT INDEX *under:*
(PREI) **89072** Aureliano Pertile (1885-1952) - II

FANNY MENDELSSOHN QUARTET
see CONCERT INDEX *under:*
(TROU) **TRO-CD03** Ethel Smyth—Chamber Works, Vols.1 & 2

(THE) FARBER SISTERS (sngrs)
see CONCERT INDEX *under:*
(PEAR) **GEMMCDS9059/61** Music from the New York Stage, Vol. 4: 1917-20

FARBERMAN, Harold (cond)
see Bournemouth Sinfonietta

FARDILHA, José (bass)
Rossini: Barbiere di Siviglia (Cpte)

FARELL, Marita (sop)
Beethoven: Fidelio (Cpte)

FARINELLI, Hanna (sngr)
Killmayer: Yolimba (Cpte)

FARIS, Alexander (cond)
see London Prom

FARKAS, Andor (pseudonym of Andor Foldes) (pf)
see CONCERT INDEX *under:*
(SONY) **MPK52569** Joseph Szigeti Recital

FARKAS, Evá (contr)
Boito: Mefistofele (Cpte)
Giordano: Andrea Chénier (Cpte)

FARKAS, Katalin (sop)
Handel: Floridante (Cpte)

FARKAS, Lajos (vn)
see CONCERT INDEX *under:*
(CPO) **CPO999 037-2** Korngold—Orchestral Works Vol.1

FARKOA, Maurice (sngr)
see CONCERT INDEX *under:*
(PEAR) **GEMMCDS9050/2(1)** Music from the New York Stage, Vol. 1 (part 1)

FARLEY, Carole (sop)
see CONCERT INDEX *under:*
(ASV) **CDDCA669** Prokofiev—Songs
(ASV) **CDDCA760** Prokofiev—Vocal and Orchestral Works
(ASV) **CDDCA790** Weill—Songs
(ASV) **CDDCA810** Milhaud—Vocal Works
(CHAN) **CHAN8509** Prokofiev: Songs

FARNCOMBE, Charles (cond)
see English Bach Fest Baroque Orch

FARNES, Richard (organ)
see CONCERT INDEX *under:*
(ARGO) **417 468–2ZH** G. Gabrieli: Choral and Instrumental Works

---

(DECC) **436 402–2DWO** The World of Wedding Music

FARNETI, Maria (sop)
see CONCERT INDEX *under:*
(MEMO) **HR4408/9(1)** Singers in Genoa, Vol.1 (disc 1)

FARNON, Robert (cond)
see Munich RO

FARON, Christine (fp)
see CONCERT INDEX *under:*
(SCHW) **310094** Haydn—Keyboard Sonatas

FARR, Chris (hpd)
see CONCERT INDEX *under:*
(ETCE) **KTC1056** Italian Airs and Harpsichord Works
(ETCE) **KTC1069** Vivaldi: Cantatas

FARR, Naomi (sop)
R. Ward: Crucible (Cpte)

FARR, Stephen (organ)
(HYPE) **CDA66725** Masters of the Chapel Royal, Lisbon
(MERI) **CDE84213** Walther—Organ Works

FARRALL, Joy (cl)
see CONCERT INDEX *under:*
(CHAN) **CHAN9152** Alwyn—Chamber Works - Volume 1
(CHAN) **CHAN9197** Alwyn—Chamber Music, Volume 2
(EMIN) **CD-EMX2238** R. Strauss—Orchestral Works
(HYPE) **CDA66626** Simpson—Chamber Works

FARRAR, Geraldine (sop)
see CONCERT INDEX *under:*
(CLUB) **CL99-060** Enrico Caruso—Opera & Song Recital
(NIMB) **NI7857** Farrar in Italian Opera
(NIMB) **NI7859** Caruso, Farrar & Journet in French Opera
(PEAR) **EVC1(2)** The Caruso Edition, Vol.1 (pt 2)
(PEAR) **EVC2** The Caruso Edition, Vol.2—1908-12
(PEAR) **EVC3(1)** The Caruso Edition, Vol.3 (pt 1)
(PEAR) **GEMMCD9161** Edmond Clément (1867-1928)
(RCA) **GD60495(2)** The Complete Caruso Collection (pt 2)
(RCA) **GD60495(3)** The Complete Caruso Collection (pt 3)
(RCA) **GD60495(4)** The Complete Caruso Collection (pt 4)
(RCA) **09026 61580-2(2)** RCA/Met 100 Singers, 100 Years (pt 2)
(RCA) **09026 68131-2** Grieg—Historic Recordings
(ROMO) **82002-2** Edmond Clément (1867-1928)
(SIMA) **PSC1810(2)** Grieg—Songs (historical recordings, pt 2)

FARRELL, Eileen (sop)
Rodgers: Sound of Music (Cpte)
see CONCERT INDEX *under:*
(RCA) **GD60324** Beethoven—Complete Symphonies
(RCA) **09026 68131-2** Classics for Children—Boston Pops
(SONY) **SMK47638** Vaughan Williams—Orchestral Works
(SONY) **SM2K47522** Beethoven & Haydn—Choral Works

FARRELL, Joy (basset cl)
see CONCERT INDEX *under:*
(MERI) **CDE84169** Mozart: Clarinet Works

FARRELL, Joy (cl)
see CONCERT INDEX *under:*
(MERI) **CDE84169** Mozart: Clarinet Works

FARRELL, Julian (basset-hn)
(PHIL) **422 545-2PME3** The Complete Mozart Edition Vol.45

FARRELL, Marguerite (sngr)
(PEAR) **GEMMCDS9056/8** Music from the New York Stage, Vol. 3: 1913-17

FARRER, John (cond)
see Bournemouth SO

FARRÉS, Pedro (bar)
Penella: Gato Montés (Cpte)
Vives: Bohemios (Cpte)

FARRUGGIA, Michele (ten)
Donizetti: Favorita (Cpte)
Rossini: Adelaide di Borgogna (Cpte)

FASANO, Renato (cond)
see Virtuosi di Roma

FASSBAENDER, Brigitte (mez)
Beethoven: Symphony 9
Berg: Lulu (Cpte)
Berlioz: Roméo et Juliette (Cpte)
Brahms: Romanzen, Op. 33 (Cpte)
Flotow: Martha (Cpte)
Gounod: Faust (Cpte)
Handel: Messiah (Cpte)
Hindemith: Requiem
J.Strauss II: Fledermaus (Cpte)
Mahler: Klagende Lied, Lied von der Erde
Mozart: Così fan tutte (Cpte), Finta Giardiniera (Cpte), Zauberflöte (Cpte)

Mussorgsky: Songs and Dances of Death
Pfitzner: Palestrina (Cpte)
Puccini: Manon Lescaut (Cpte)
Schoenberg: Gurrelieder
Schubert: Schöne Müllerin (Cpte), Winterreise (Cpte)
Verdi: Rigoletto (Cpte), Trovatore (Cpte)
Wagner: Tristan und Isolde (Cpte), Walküre (Cpte)
Wolf: Mörike Lieder (exc)
see CONCERT INDEX *under:*
(ACAN) **43 507** Brahms—Lieder
(ACAN) **43 579** Songs by Berg, Mahler & Ogermann
(DECC) **414 100-2DM15** Wagner: Der Ring des Nibelungen
(DECC) **425 790-2DH** Mahler—Lieder
(DECC) **430 498-2DWO** The World of Mozart
(DECC) **430 512-2DH** Liszt—Lieder - Fassbaender
(DG) **415 519-2GH** Schumann: Lieder recital
(DG) **423 133-2GH** Brahms: Vocal Works
(DG) **429 766-2GH** Schubert—Lieder
(DG) **435 066-2GGA** Brahms—Choral Works
(DG) **439 417-2GCL** Schumann—Lieder
(EMI) **CDM7 69223-2** Schubert—Choral Works
(EMI) **CMS7 64778-2** Schubert—Sacred Works, Vol.1
(EMI) **CMS7 64783-2** Schubert—Sacred Works, Vol.2
(HARM) **HMC91 1420** Weill—The Seven Deadly Sins; Songs
(HARM) **HMC90 5210** Duos Romantiques
(HYPE) **CDJ33011** Schubert—Complete Lieder, Vol.11
(ORFE) **C096841A** Famous Opera Arias
(SCHW) **312592** Dvořák/Brahms/Reger—Duets
(SONY) **SX14K48198** Mahler—Complete Symphonies, etc
(TELD) **9031-74872-2** Schumann/Brahms—Lieder

FASSBAENDER, Brigitte (narr)
Brahms: Romanzen, Op. 33 (Cpte)

FASSBENDER, Hedwig (mez)
Schoeck: Venus (Cpte)
Zemlinsky: Maeterlinck Songs, Op.13

FAUCHÉ, François (bass)
Rameau: Zoroastre (Cpte)

FAUCHEY, Michel (sngr)
Messager: Coups de Roulis (Cpte)
Offenbach: Madame l'Archiduc (Cpte)
Terrasse: Travaux d'Hercule (Cpte)

FAULHABER, Werner (bass)
Wagner: Meistersinger (Cpte), Parsifal (Cpte)

FAULKNER, Julie (sop)
Mozart: Zauberflöte (Cpte)
Pergolesi: Orfeo, Stabat Mater
R. Strauss: Elektra (Cpte), Rosenkavalier (Cpte)
Rossini: Semiramide (Cpte)
Schumann: Genoveva (Cpte), Paradies und die Peri (Cpte)

FAULL, Ellen (sop)
D. Moore: Carry Nation (Cpte)

FAUQUEUR, Alain (treb)
see CONCERT INDEX *under:*
(EMI) **CDM7 64281-2** Boulanger—Vocal & Chamber Works

FAURÉ, Jean Baptiste (bar)
see CONCERT INDEX *under:*
(SYMP) **SYMCD1089** Historic Baritones of the French School

FAURÉ, Maurice (pf)
see CONCERT INDEX *under:*
(EMI) **CHS7 69741-2(3)** Record of Singing, Vol.4—French School

FAURE, Renée (mez)
Offenbach: Contes d'Hoffmann (Cpte)

FAURY, Eric (ten)
Gounod: Sapho (Cpte)

FAUST, Georg (vc)
Schubert: Guitar Quartet, D96, Trout Quintet, D667
see CONCERT INDEX *under:*
(DG) **429 738-2GH** Debussy & Ravel: Chamber Works
(DG) **431 782-2GH** Mozart—Chamber Works

FAUST, Michael (fl)
Henze: Cimarrón
see CONCERT INDEX *under:*
(CAPR) **10 495** Flute Concertos - Michael Faust

FAVARETTO, Giorgio (pf)
see CONCERT INDEX *under:*
(EMI) **CHS7 69741-2(7)** Record of Singing, Vol.4—Italian School

FAVAT, Dominique (mez)
see CONCERT INDEX *under:*
(FNAC) **592308** Lully—Grand Motets, Volume 1

FAVERO, Mafalda (sop)
see CONCERT INDEX *under:*
(EMI) **CDH7 63200-2** Tito Schipa—Recital
(EMI) **CHS7 64864-2(2)** La Scala Edition - Vol.2, 1915-46 (pt 2)
(NIMB) **NI7801** Great Singers, Vol.1

FAVOR, Edward M. (sngr)
see CONCERT INDEX *under:*
(PEAR) **GEMMCDS9050/2(1)** Music from the New York Stage, Vol. 1 (part 1)

FAVRE, Christian (pf)
Schumann: Kinderszenen, Piano Sonata 3

FAVRES SOLISTEN VEREINIGUNG
cond T. BEECHAM
Mozart: Zauberflöte (Cpte)

FAYT, Marie-Paul (sop)
Schmitt: Salomé (Cpte)

FEAR, Arthur (bass)
Wagner: Götterdämmerung (exc)
see CONCERT INDEX under:
(CLAR) CDGSE78-50-35/6   Wagner—Historical
recordings
(PEAR) GEMMCDS9137   Wagner—Der Ring des
Nibelungen

FEDERICI, Francesco (bar)
see CONCERT INDEX under:
(RECO) TRC3   The Art of Aristodemo Giorgini

FEDERICI, Franco (bass)
Bellini: Puritani (Cpte)
Donizetti: Poliuto (Cpte)
Giordano: Andrea Chénier (Cpte)
Puccini: Gianni Schicchi (Cpte), Tosca (Cpte)
see CONCERT INDEX under:
(EURO) GD69043   Puccini: Il Trittico

FEDIN, Alexander (ten)
Mussorgsky: Boris Godunov (Cpte)
Rimsky-Korsakov: Mozart and Salieri (Cpte)
see CONCERT INDEX under:
(RCA) 74321 20297-2   Scriabin—Symphonies, etc

FEDOSEYEV, Andrei (bar)
Tchaikovsky: Queen of Spades (Cpte)

FEDOSEYEV, Vladimir (cond)
see Moscow RSO

FEEHAN, Brian (chitarrone)
Kapsperger: Chitarrone Book I (exc), Chitarrone Book
IV

FEEHAN, Brian (theorbo)
Chambonnières: Harpsichord Suites

FEHENBERGER, Lorenz (ten)
Bruckner: Te Deum
Janáček: Excursions of Mr Brouček (Cpte)
Mozart: Requiem
R. Strauss: Salome (Cpte)
see CONCERT INDEX under:
(EMI) CZS7 67123-2   Wagner: Der Ring des
Nibelungen

FEHER, Viorica (bn)
Enescu: Wind Decet, Op. 14

FEHÉRVÁRI, János (va)
(NAXO) 8 553103   Mozart—String Quintets, Volume
1

FEHLANDT, Stefan (va)
see CONCERT INDEX under:
(EDA) EDA008-2   Works by Ullmann and Schoenberg

FEHN, Helmut (bass)
Wagner: Meistersinger (Cpte)

FEHRING, Johannes (cond)
see SO

FEIDMAN, Giora (cl)
see CONCERT INDEX under:
(SONY) SK58966   Prokofiev—Piano Concertos, etc

FEIGHAN, Thérèse (sop)
Rameau: Hippolyte et Aricie (Cpte)

FEIGHIN, Grigory (vn)
see CONCERT INDEX under:
(CHNT) LDC278 1018/9   Shostakovich: Chamber
Works

FEIGHIN, Valentin (vc)
see CONCERT INDEX under:
(CHNT) LDC278 1018/9   Shostakovich: Chamber
Works

FEILHABER, Alfred (ten)
S. Wagner: Bärenhäuter (Cpte)

FEINBERG, Alan (pf)
Babbitt: Piano Concerto
see CONCERT INDEX under:
(ARGO) 444 457-2ZH   Fascinatin' Rhythm

FEINBERG, Samuel (pf)
see CONCERT INDEX under:
(MELO) 74321 25172-2(1)   Russian Piano School (pt 1
- Vols.1 - 8)
(MELO) 74321 25175-2   Russian Piano School, Vol.
3

FEINHALS, Elise (mez)
see CONCERT INDEX under:
(SYMP) SYMCD1113   The Harold Wayne Collection,
Vol.13

FEINSTEIN, Michael (bar)
see CONCERT INDEX under:
(NONE) 7559-79285-2   The Burton Lane Songbook,
Vol.2

FEIT, Pierre W (ob)
Neuner: Oboe Concerto
Winter: Oboe Concerto

FEJÉRVÁRI, János (va)
Boëllmann: Piano Quartet, Op. 10

FELBERMAYER, Anny (sop)
Humperdinck: Hänsel und Gretel (Cpte)
Mozart: Nozze di Figaro (Cpte)
R. Strauss: Rosenkavalier (Cpte)
see CONCERT INDEX under:
(EMI) CDH7 61001-2   R. Strauss—Lieder & Arias
(VANG) 08.2010.71   Bach—Choral Works
(VANG) 08.2028.71   Bach—Cantatas

FELDEN, Wilhelm (bass)
Wagner: Meistersinger (Cpte)

FELDER, Linda (sop)
Bazin: Maître Pathelin (Cpte)

FELDHOFF, Gerd (bass)
Berg: Lulu (Cpte)
Hindemith: Mathis der Maler (Cpte)
Wagner: Meistersinger (Cpte)

FELDHOFF, Heinz (bass)
Wagner: Meistersinger (Cpte)

FELDMAN, Jill (sop)
Handel: Clori, Tirsi e Fileno (Cpte), Susanna (Cpte)
M.-A. Charpentier: Arts Florissants (Cpte), Médée
(Cpte)
Mozart: Ascanio in Alba (Cpte)
Purcell: Dido (Cpte)
Rameau: Anacréon (Cpte)
see CONCERT INDEX under:
(ARCA) A02   Purcell—Ayres and Songs from Orpheus
Britannicus
(ARCA) A21   Ars Subtilis Ytalica
(EMI) CDS7 49749-2   Handel—Music for the Carmelite
Vespers
(HARM) HMA190 1150   Couperin—Motets
(HARM) HMA190 1238   Campra—French Cantatas
(HARM) HMX290 1528/33(1)   A Purcell Companion (pt
1)
(RICE) RIC048035/7   German Baroque Cantatas,
Vol.4 - Bruhns
(RICE) RIC052034   Charpentier—Sacred Choral
Works
(RICE) RIC109097/8   German Baroque Cantatas,
Vol.9 - Weckmann

FELDMAN, Jonathan (pf)
Brahms: Hungarian Dances (exc)

FÉLIX, Thierry (bar)
A. Thomas: Hamlet (Cpte)
see CONCERT INDEX under:
(ARCA) A37   Schubert—Goethe Lieder

FELLE, Amelia (sop)
Pergolesi: Frate 'nnamorato (Cpte)
Rossini: Barbiere di Siviglia (Cpte), Inganno felice
(Cpte)

FELLEGI, Ádám (pf)
see CONCERT INDEX under:
(MARC) 8 223371   Medtner—Piano Sonatas
(MARC) 8 223372   Medtner—Piano Works

FELLER, Carlos (bass)
Mozart: Così fan tutte (Cpte), Nozze di Figaro (Cpte)
R. Strauss: Rosenkavalier (Cpte)
Weill: Sieben Todsünden (Cpte)

FELLNER, Till (pf)
Beethoven: Piano Concerto 2, Piano Concerto 3
see CONCERT INDEX under:
(CLAV) CD50-9328   Mozart/Beethoven—Piano
Works

FELS, Elaine (sop)
see CONCERT INDEX under:
(EPM) 150 122   Milhaud—Historic Recordings 1928-
1948

FELTSMAN, Vladimir (pf)
see CONCERT INDEX under:
(MUSM) 67098-2   Beethoven—Piano Sonatas
(SONY) MK44818   Prokofiev—Piano Works

FELUMB, Sven (cond)
see Tivoli Concert Orch

FELUMB, Svend Christian (ob)
see CONCERT INDEX under:
(CLRI) CC0002   Nielsen—Orchestral and Chamber
Works

FENBY, Eric (cond)
see CO

FENBY, Eric (pf)
see CONCERT INDEX under:
(UNIC) UKCD2074   The Delius Collection, Volume 4

(LA) FENICE
cond J. CABRÉ
see CONCERT INDEX under:
(K617) K617024   Les Chemins du Baroque, Vol.3
cond M. LAPLÉNIE
Colin: Missa pro defunctis
Helfer: Missa pro defunctis

FENNELL, Frederick (cond)
see Cleveland Winds

FENOYER, Marinette (mez)
Massenet: Manon (Cpte)

FENTON, George (cond)
see LSO

FENYŐ, Gusztáv (pf)
see CONCERT INDEX under:
(ASV) CDDCA852   Bartók—Violin Works, Vol.1

**(ASV) CDDCA883   Bartók—Music for Violin and
Piano, Volume 2**

FENYVES, Lorand (vn)
see CONCERT INDEX under:
(DECC) 443 893-2DH   Bartók—Violin Works
(DECC) 443 894-2DH   Bartók—Chamber Works

FÉRALDY, Germaine (sop)
Gluck: Orphée (exc)
Massenet: Manon (exc), Werther (Cpte)
see CONCERT INDEX under:
(EMI) CDM7 69548-2   Georges Thill sings French
Opera Arias
(IRCC) IRCC-CD802   Souvenirs of Rare French
Opera

FERBER, Albert (pf)
see CONCERT INDEX under:
(SAGA) EC3397-2   Fauré—Piano Works, Vol.2

FERCHEN, Timothy (perc)
see CONCERT INDEX under:
(ONDI) ODE802-2   Ibert/Jolivet/Nielsen—Flute
Concertos

FERENC, Tibor (cond)
see Hungarian Nat PO

FERENCSIK, János (cond)
see Czech PO

FERENZ, Willy (bass)
J.Strauss II: Zigeunerbaron (Cpte)

FERGUSON, Robert (ten)
Wagner: Rheingold (Cpte)

FERGUS-THOMPSON, Gordon (pf)
Debussy: Etudes, Pour le piano, Préludes (exc), Suite
bergamasque
Rachmaninov: Etudes-tableaux, Op. 33, Etudes-
tableaux, Op. 39, Piano Sonata 1, Piano Sonata 2
see CONCERT INDEX under:
(ASV) CDDCA695   Debussy—Piano Works, Vol. 1
(ASV) CDDCA711   Debussy—Piano Works, Vol. 3
(ASV) CDDCA720   Debussy—Piano Works, Vol. 4
(ASV) CDDCA759   Transcriptions of Bach's Chaconne
(ASV) CDDCA776   Scriabin—Piano Works, Vol.1
(ASV) CDDCA805   Ravel—Piano Works, Vol.1
(ASV) CDDCA809   Ravel—Piano Music, Vol.2
(ASV) CDDCA882   Scriabin—Piano Music, Volume 2
(ASV) CDDCA919   Scriabin—Piano Music, Volume 3
(ASV) CDWHL2066   Rêverie
(KING) KCLCD2001   Gordon Fergus-Thompson plays
Scriabin and Balakirev

FERNANDEZ, Ana Maria (sngr)
Sorozábal: Katiuska (Cpte)

FERNANDEZ, Anita (sngr)
Bretón: Verbena de la Paloma (Cpte)
Moreno Torroba: Luisa Fernanda (Cpte)

FERNANDEZ, Huguette (vn)
Messiaen: Quatuor

FERNANDEZ, Wilhelmenia (sop)
Hammerstein: Carmen Jones (Cpte)
see CONCERT INDEX under:
(SILV) SILKD6001   Lament—The Brodsky Quartet

FERNÁNDEZ DOVAL, Maria Del Mar (sop)
(HYPE) CDA66327   Spanish Music of the Golden Age

FERNANDI, Eugenio (ten)
Puccini: Turandot (Cpte)
Verdi: Don Carlo (Cpte)

FERRAN, Dominique (organ)
see CONCERT INDEX under:
(ARIO) ARN68015   Charpentier—Sacred Choral works
(ASTR) E8524   Allegri—Miserere, Mass & Motets

FERRANDIS, Jean (fl)
see CONCERT INDEX under:
(AUVI) V4644   Debussy/Ravel—Orchestral Songs
(SCHW) 310652   Fumet/d'Indy/Honegger—Chamber
Works

FERRANI, Cesira (sop)
(MEMO) HR4408/9(1)   Singers in Genoa, Vol.1 (disc
1)
(SYMP) SYMCD1077   The Harold Wayne Collection,
Vol.4

FERRANTI, Nick (sngr)
Bernstein: West Side Story (Cpte)

FERRARI, Riccardo (bass)
Verdi: Aida (Cpte)

FERRARI-FONTANA, Edoardo (ten)
see CONCERT INDEX under:
(EMI) CHS7 64860-2(2)   La Scala Edition - Vol.1,
1878-1914 (pt 2)

FERRARINI, Allda (sop)
Verdi: Rigoletto (Cpte)

FERRARIS, Franco (cond)
see Orch

FERRARIS, Ines Maria (sop)
see CONCERT INDEX under:
(CLUB) CL99-074   Conchita Supervia (1895-1936)
(EMI) CHS7 64864-2(1)   La Scala Edition - Vol.2,
1915-46 (pt 1)
(PREI) 89023   Conchita Supervia (1895-1936)

FISCHER-DIESKAU, Manuel (vc)
Messiaen: Quatuor

FISCHER-KUNZ, Annemarie (contr)
Mendelssohn-Hensel: Oratorium nach Bildern der Bibel

FISELIER, Frans (ten)
R. Strauss: Rosenkavalier (Cpte)

FISER, Lee (vc)
Schoenberg: String Trio

FISH, Matthew Adam (treb)
Mussorgsky: Boris Godunov (Cpte)

FISHER, Gillian (sop)
Handel: Aminta e Fillide, Blessed are they that considereth the poor, Triumph of Time and Truth (Cpte)
Monteverdi: Vespers
Purcell: Birthday Ode, Z342, Dioclesian, Z627 (exc), Fairy Queen, Z629 (Cpte), Indian Queen, Z630 (Cpte), King Arthur, Z628 (Cpte), St Cecilia's Day Ode, Z328, Timon of Athens, Z632 (Cpte)
Rameau: Castor et Pollux (Cpte)
see CONCERT INDEX under:
(CARL) PCD894   Great Baroque Arias, Part I
(COLL) Coll1320-2 Baroque Choral Works
(ERAT) 4509-96371-2 Gardiner—The Purcell Collection
(HYPE) CDA66269   Mondonville: Motets
(HYPE) CDA66294   Pergolesi—Sacred Choral Works
(HYPE) CDA66314   Purcell—Complete Odes & Welcome Songs, Vol.1

FISHER, John (cond)
see Venice La Fenice Orch

FISHER, Sylvia (sop)
Britten: Albert Herring (Cpte)
see CONCERT INDEX under:
(LOND) 433 200-2LHO2 Britten—Owen Wingrave, etc

FISICHELLA, Salvatore (ten)
Rossini: Mosè in Egitto (Cpte), Otello (Cpte)

FISKUM, Bjarne (cond)
see Trondheim Sols

FISSORE, Enrico (bar)
Donizetti: Gianni di Parigi (Cpte)
Rossini: Barbiere di Siviglia (Cpte), Turco in Italia (Cpte)

FISSORE, Enrico (bass)
Donizetti: Pazzi per progetto (Cpte)
see CONCERT INDEX under:
(DECC) 436 261-2DHO3 Puccini—Il Trittico

FISTOULARI, Anatole (cond)
see LSO

FITELBERG, Grzegorz (cond)
see Katowice RSO

FITKIN, Graham (cond)
see J. Harle Band

FITZ, Heinz (spkr)
Corghi: Divara (Cpte)

FITZ, Richard (vib)
see CONCERT INDEX under:
(RCA) 09026 62537-2 Takemitsu—Cantos

FITZPATRICK, Frank (cond)
see Orch

FITZWILLIAM ENSEMBLE
Marais: Pièces de viole IV/II (exc), Pièces en trio (exc)

FITZWILLIAM QUARTET
see CONCERT INDEX under:
(DECC) 433 078-2DM6 Shostakovich—String Quartets

FIZDALE, Robert (pf)
see CONCERT INDEX under:
(SONY) SMK47518 Poulenc/Shostakovich—Piano Concertos
(SONY) SM2K47511 Bartók—Concertos

FJELDSTAD, Lise (narr)
see CONCERT INDEX under:
(VIRG) VC5 45051-2 Grieg—Choral Works

FJELDSTAD, Øivin (cond)
see LSO

FLAGELLO, Ezio (bass)
Donizetti: Lucia di Lammermoor (Cpte), Lucrezia Borgia (Cpte)
Mozart: Così fan tutte (Cpte), Don Giovanni (Cpte)
Verdi: Ballo in maschera (Cpte), Ernani (Cpte), Forza del destino (Cpte), Luisa Miller (Cpte), Rigoletto (Cpte)
see CONCERT INDEX under:
(DECC) 433 706-2DMO3 Bellini—Beatrice di Tenda, Operatic Arias
(SONY) SMK47638 Vaughan Williams—Orchestral Works

FLAGSTAD, Kirsten (sop)
Beethoven: Fidelio (Cpte)
Wagner: Rheingold (Cpte), Siegfried (Cpte), Tristan und Isolde (Cpte)
see CONCERT INDEX under:
(DECC) 414 100-2DM15 Wagner: Der Ring des Nibelungen
(EMI) CDH7 63030-2 Kirsten Flagstad - Wagner Opera Arias
(EMI) CHS7 64935-2 Wagner—Opera Excerpts
(EMI) CHS7 69741-2(5) Record of Singing, Vol.4—Scandinavian School
(EMI) CMS5 65212-2 Wagner—Les introuvables du Ring
(EMI) CMS7 64008-2(1) Wagner Singing on Record (pt 1)
(LOND) 440 490-2LM5(1) Kirsten Flagstad Edition (pt 1)
(LOND) 440 490-2LM5(2) Kirsten Flagstad Edition (pt 2)
(LOND) 440 491-2LM Kirsten Flagstad Edition, Vol. 1
(LOND) 440 492-2LM Kirsten Flagstad Edition, Vol. 2
(LOND) 440 493-2LM Kirsten Flagstad Edition, Vol. 3

FLAGSTAD, Maja (pf)
see CONCERT INDEX under:
(SIMA) PSC1821(1) Kirsten Flagstad, Vol.1 (pt 1)

FLAKE, Uta-Maria (sop)
R. Strauss: Daphne (Cpte)

FLÄMIG, Martin (cond)
see Dresden Kreuzchor

FLAMM, Carol (sngr)
Rorem: Three Sisters Who Are Not Sisters (Cpte)

FLAMMER, Amy (vn)
see CONCERT INDEX under:
(ERAT) 2292-45772-2 Saint-Saëns—Works for Chamber Ensemble

FLANIGAN, Lauren (sop)
see CONCERT INDEX under:
(DELO) DE3170 Beach—Cabildo; Six Short Pieces

FLECHTER, Guy (ten)
Gluck: Rencontre imprévue (Cpte)
Handel: Scipione (Cpte)

FLECK, Ludwig (ten)
R. Strauss: Rosenkavalier (Cpte)

FLECKENSTEIN, Barbara (sop)
Monteverdi: Vespers

FLEET, Edgar (ten)
G. Charpentier: Louise (Cpte)
Handel: Theodora (Cpte)
Shostakovich: Lady Macbeth of Mtsensk (Cpte)
see CONCERT INDEX under:
(DECC) 443 461-2DF2 Berlioz—L'Enfance du Christ, etc

FLEEZANIS, Jorja (vn)
see CONCERT INDEX under:
(KOCH) 37112-2 Wolpe—Chamber Works

FLEGL, Jan (treb)
Krása: Brundibár (Cpte)

FLEIG, Fia (sop)
see CONCERT INDEX under:
(MYTO) 3MCD93381 Wagner—Die Walküre, etc

FLEISCHER, Felix (bar)
Wagner: Tristan und Isolde (Cpte)

FLEISCHER-EDEL, Katharina (sop)
see CONCERT INDEX under:
(PEAR) GEMMCDS9924(2) Covent Garden on Record, Vol.2 (pt 2)

FLEISCHMANN, Christine (hp)
Gounod: Requiem

FLEISCHMANN, Otto (bn)
see CONCERT INDEX under:
(TELD) 4509-97472-2 Frans Brüggen Edition Vol. 10—Telemann—Orchestral Works

FLEISHER, Leon (pf)
Beethoven: Piano Concerto 5
Grieg: piano concerto
Schumann: piano concerto
see CONCERT INDEX under:
(SONY) SK47188 Works for Piano Left-Hand and Orchestra

FLEITMANN, Martin (ten)
Delius: Village Romeo and Juliet (Cpte)

FLEMING, Amaryllis (vc)
see CONCERT INDEX under:
(EMI) CMS7 64074-2(2) Christa Ludwig—Recital (pt 2)

FLEMING, Claude (bar)
see CONCERT INDEX under:
(CHAN) CHAN8321 Harty—Orchestral Works

FLEMING, Renée (sop)
Rossini: Armida (Cpte)
see CONCERT INDEX under:
(RCA) 09026 61509-2 A Salute to American Music
(RCA) 09026 62547-2 Divas in Song—Marilyn Horne's 60th Birthday
(SONY) SK52565 New Year's Eve Concert 1992

FLEMSTRÖM, Per (fl)
see CONCERT INDEX under:
(SONY) SK53276 Nielsen—Orchestral Works

FLESCH, Carl (vn)
see CONCERT INDEX under:
(BIDD) LAB045 Hubay & Flesch—HMV Recordings
(SYMP) SYMCD1071 Great Violinists, Vol.1

FLESCH, Ella (sop)
Wagner: Walküre (exc)
see CONCERT INDEX under:
(SCHW) 314592　Vienna State Opera Live, Vol.9
(SCHW) 314672　Vienna State Opera Live, Vol.17

FLETA, Miguel (ten)
see CONCERT INDEX under:
(EMI) CHS7 64864-2(1)　La Scala Edition - Vol.2, 1915-46 (pt 1)
(PEAR) GEMMCDS9925(1)　Covent Garden on Record—Vol.3 (pt 1)
(PREI) 89002　Miguel Fleta (1893-1938)
(RCA) 09026 61580-2(2)　RCA/Met 100 Singers, 100 Years (pt 2)

FLETCHER, Andrew (organ)
see CONCERT INDEX under:
(MIRA) MRCD903　Late Romantic Organ Works

FLETCHER, Dexter (spkr)
Britten: Midsummer Night's Dream (Cpte)

FLETCHER, Graham (sngr)
Sondheim: Pacific Overtures (exc)

FLETCHER, Lyn (vn)
see CONCERT INDEX under:
(CONI) CDCF172　Malcolm Arnold: Concertos
(CONI) CDCF203　Vivaldi—Concertos

FLETCHER, Percy (cond)
see Orig London Cast

FLIEGER, Jiří (bn)
Magnard: Piano and Wind Quintet

FLIEGNER, Christian (treb)
Bach: St Matthew Passion, BWV244 (Cpte)
Gluck: Orfeo ed Euridice (Cpte)
Mozart: Apollo et Hyacinthus (Cpte), Zauberflöte (Cpte)

FLIMM, Jürgen (bass)
J. Strauss II: Zigeunerbaron (Cpte)

FLIPSE, Marinus (pf)
see CONCERT INDEX under:
(ARHI) ADCD112　The Mengelberg Edition, Volume 6

FLOEREN, Ruth (sop)
Wagner: Walküre (exc)

FLONZALEY QUARTET
see CONCERT INDEX under:
(BIDD) LAB089/90　Haydn/Mozart/Beethoven—String Quartets

FLOOD, David (cond)
see Canterbury Cath Ch

FLOOD, David (organ)
see CONCERT INDEX under:
(YORK) CD108　Organ of Canterbury Cathedral

FLOR, Claus Peter (cond)
see Bamberg SO

FLORENTIN, Laure (sop)
Vivaldi: Dorilla in Tempe (Cpte)

FLORIAN, Hans (ten)
see CONCERT INDEX under:
(PREI) 90168　Wagner—Die Meistersinger, Act 2, etc

FLORIANSCHÜTZ, Robert (bass)
Beethoven: Fidelio (Cpte)
J. Strauss II: Zigeunerbaron (Cpte)

FLORIDA ORCHESTRA
cond J. LING
see CONCERT INDEX under:
(CNTI) CCD1061　Montague—Orchestral and Chamber Music

FLORIDA PHILHARMONIC ORCHESTRA
cond J. JUDD
Mahler: Blumine, Symphony 1
see CONCERT INDEX under:
(HARM) HMU90 7070　Walton—Orchestral Works

FLORILEGIUM ENSEMBLE
see CONCERT INDEX under:
(CHNN) CCS5093　Telemann—Chamber Music
(CHNN) CCS6294　Vivaldi—Cello Sonatas
(CHNN) CCS7395　Haydn—Works for Cello and Orchestra
(CHNN) CCS7595　Music for the King's Pleasure

FLORIMO, Enzo (bass)
Mozart: Nozze di Figaro (Cpte)

FLOSSMANN, Gildis (sop)
see CONCERT INDEX under:
(DECC) 425 681-2DM2　Tutto Pavarotti
(DECC) 433 437-2DA　Pavarotti—King of the High Cs

FLOTTAU, Peter (spkr)
B.A. Zimmermann: Soldaten (Cpte)

FLOWER, Edward (gtr)
see CONCERT INDEX under:
(TELA) CD80301　Romantic Brass - Music of France & Spain

FLOWERS, Kate (sop)
see CONCERT INDEX under:
(CNTO) CRCD2368　Sullivan—That Glorious Song of Old

FLUSIN, Olivier (ten)
see CONCERT INDEX under:
(AUVI) AV6108　Bouzignac—Sacred choral music

FLUTTER, Alistair (treb)
see CONCERT INDEX under:
(CHAN) CHAN8658　Poulenc & Charpentier: Sacred Choral Works

FLYNN, Renée (sop)
see CONCERT INDEX under:
(PEAR) GEMMCD9342　Vaughan Williams: Vocal Works

FOCCROULLE, Bernard (organ)
Correa de Arauxo: Libro de Tientos y Discursos (exc)
see CONCERT INDEX under:
(RICE) RIC048035/7　German Baroque Cantatas, Vol.4 - Bruhns
(RICE) RIC052034　Charpentier—Sacred Choral Works
(RICE) RIC064042　Bach—Organ Works, Vol.5
(RICE) RIC085068　Bach—Organ Works, Vol.6
(RICE) RIC086069　Bach—Organ Works, Vol.7
(RICE) RIC105081　Mozart—Keyboard Works

FOCCROULLE, Geneviève (pf)
Boesmans: Extase

FOCILE, Nuccia (sop)
Donizetti: Assedio di Calais (Cpte)
Mozart: Così fan tutte (Cpte), Nozze di Figaro (Cpte)
Pergolesi: Frate 'nnamorato (Cpte)
Tchaikovsky: Eugene Onegin (Cpte)
Verdi: Don Carlo (Cpte)
see CONCERT INDEX under:
(OPRA) ORCH104　A Hundred Years of Italian Opera: 1820-1830

FOCKENOY, Michel (ten)
Berlioz: Enfance du Christ (Cpte)
Offenbach: Brigands (Cpte)

FODENS MOTOR WORKS BAND
cond F. MORTIMER
see CONCERT INDEX under:
(BEUL) 1PD2　Crystal Palace Champions

FOGGI, Ettore (ten)
see CONCERT INDEX under:
(IRCC) IRCC-CD808　Souvenirs of 19th Century Italian Opera

FOIANI, Giovanni (bass)
Cilea: Adriana Lecouvreur (Cpte)
Verdi: Ballo in Maschera (Cpte), Don Carlo (Cpte), Falstaff (Cpte), Forza del destino (Cpte), Macbeth (Cpte), Nabucco (Cpte), Simon Boccanegra (Cpte), Traviata (Cpte)
see CONCERT INDEX under:
(DECC) 411 665-2DM3　Puccini: Il trittico

FOIX, Georges (sngr)
Messager: Monsieur Beaucaire (Cpte)

FOLDES, Andor (pf)
Bartók: Piano Concerto 2, Rhapsody 1, Sz87
see CONCERT INDEX under:
(BIDD) LAB070/1　Szigeti recordings with Bartók and Foldes
(SONY) MPK52569　Joseph Szigeti Recital

FOLDI, Andrew (bass-bar)
Rossini: Pietra del Paragone (Cpte)

FOLEY, Madeline (vc)
Brahms: String Sextet 1

FOLKWANG CHAMBER ORCHESTRA
cond H. DRESSEL
see CONCERT INDEX under:
(PHIL) 442 580-2PM2　Beethoven—Concertos, Volume 2

FOLSTAD, Astrid (narr)
see CONCERT INDEX under:
(VICT) VCD19035　Grieg—Complete Piano Music, Volume XI

FOLWELL, Nicholas (bar)
Janáček: Cunning Little Vixen (Cpte)
Puccini: Tosca (Cpte)
Sullivan: Mikado (Cpte), Pirates of Penzance (Cpte)
Verdi: Traviata (Cpte)
Wagner: Tristan und Isolde (Cpte)
Weir: Blond Eckbert (Cpte)

FOMINA, Svetlana (vielle)
see CONCERT INDEX under:
(ARCA) A21　Ars Subtilis Ytalica

FONDA, Henry (narr)
see CONCERT INDEX under:
(SONY) SM3K46559　Copland Collection—1936-1948

(IL) FONDAMENTO CHOIR
Hasse: Miserere in E minor, Requiem in C

(IL) FONDAMENTO ENSEMBLE
cond P. DOMBRECHT
Telemann: Musique de Table (exc)

FONDARY, Alain (bar)
Massenet: Don Quichotte (Cpte)
Puccini: Fanciulla del West (Cpte)
Saint-Saëns: Samson et Dalila (Cpte)

FONTAINE, Robert (cl)
see CONCERT INDEX under:
(ACCO) 20202-2　Poulenc—Chamber Works
(ERAT) 2292-45772-2　Saint-Saëns—Works for Chamber Ensemble

FONTANA, Gabriele (sop)
J. Strauss II: Fledermaus (Cpte)
R.Strauss: Arabella (Cpte)
U. Zimmermann: Weisse Rose (Cpte)
Wagner: Rheingold (Cpte)

FONTANA, Sergio (bass)
Verdi: Macbeth (Cpte)

FONTANAROSA, Patrice (vn)
see CONCERT INDEX under:
(EMI) CDC7 54913-2　Saint-Saëns—La muse et le poète

FONTENAY TRIO
Beethoven: Piano Trios (exc)
Mendelssohn: Piano Trio 1, Piano Trio 2
Messiaen: Quatuor
Schumann: Piano Trio 2, Piano Trio 3
see CONCERT INDEX under:
(TELD) 2292-44937-2　French Piano Trios
(TELD) 9031-76036-2　Brahms—Piano Trios
cond E. INBAL
Beethoven: Triple Concerto

FORBES, Patricia (sop)
see CONCERT INDEX under:
(CHAN) CHAN8824　Walton: Vocal Works
(CLLE) COLCD114　Rutter—Sacred Choral Works

FORBES, Rupert Oliver (sngr)
MacMillan: Visitatio Sepulchri (Cpte)

FORD, Alpha (sngr)
Gershwin: Porgy and Bess (Cpte)

FORD, Bruce (ten)
Handel: Messiah (Cpte)
Mayr: Medea (Cpte)
Meyerbeer: Crociato in Egitto (Cpte)
Rossini: Armida (Cpte), Barbiere di Siviglia (Cpte)
see CONCERT INDEX under:
(OPRA) ORCH104　A Hundred Years of Italian Opera: 1820-1830

FORDHAM, Cato (treb)
Britten: Little Sweep (Cpte)

FOREL, Michel (ten)
Poulenc: Dialogues des Carmélites (Cpte)

FOREST SCHOOL CHOIR, WINNERSH (BERKSHIRE)
cond C. ABBADO
Berlioz: Te Deum

FORGET, Danièle (sop)
see CONCERT INDEX under:
(HYPE) CDA66247　Vivaldi: Vocal and Orchestral Works

FORMÁČEK, Antonín (vn)
see CONCERT INDEX under:
(SUPR) 11 1878-2　The Unknown Janáček

FORMICHI, Cesare (bar)
(MEMO) HR4408/9(2)　Singers in Genoa, Vol.1 (disc 2)
(PREI) 89055　Cesare Formichi (1883-1949)

FORMICHINI, Dino (ten)
Puccini: Fanciulla del West (Cpte), Manon Lescaut (Cpte)

FORREST, Michael (ten)
Mozart: Nozze di Figaro (Cpte)

FORRESTER, Maureen (contr)
Beethoven: Missa Solemnis, Symphony 9
Gluck: Orfeo ed Euridice (Cpte)
Handel: Theodora (Cpte)
Mahler: Lied von der Erde, Symphony 2, Symphony 3
Rachmaninov: Vespers, Op. 37 (Cpte)
Tchaikovsky: Queen of Spades (Cpte)
(CBC) PSCD2002　Maureen Forrester sings Handel Arias
(CBC) SMCD5139　A Gilbert & Sullivan Gala
(DG) 445 400-2GDO10　Ferenc Fricsay - A Portrait
(DG) 445 407-2GDO　Brahms—Orchestral Works
(EMI) CDS7 47509-8　Beecham conducts Delius
(PHIL) 442 050-2PB10　Mahler—Complete Symphonies

FORSBERG, Bengt (pf)
see CONCERT INDEX under:
(BIS) BIS-CD457　Sibelius: Songs, Vol.1
(BIS) BIS-CD525　Sibelius—Complete Music for Violin and Piano, Vol.1
(BIS) BIS-CD625　Sibelius—Music for Violin and Piano, Volume 2
(DG) 429 727-2GH　Brahms—Lieder
(DG) 437 515-2GH　Berg/Korngold/R. Strauss—Lieder
(DG) 437 521-2GH　Grieg—Songs
(DG) 439 894-2GH　Speak Low - Songs by Kurt Weill
(DG) 445 881-2GH　Schumann—Lieder
(EMI) CDC5 55430-2　Brahms/Schumann—Lieder
(MSVE) MSCD623　Stenhammar: Songs

FORSBERG, Charlotte (mez)
see CONCERT INDEX under:
(BIS) BIS-CD384　Sibelius: Orchestral Works

FORSELL, John (bar)
see CONCERT INDEX under:
(SIMA) PSC1810(1)　Grieg—Songs (historical recordings, pt 1)

FORSÉN, Christa (sop)
Delius: Village Romeo and Juliet (Cpte)

FÖRSTER, Jürgen (ten)
J.Strauss II: Fledermaus (Cpte)
Zeller: Vogelhändler (Cpte)

FORSTER, Karl (cond)
see Berlin SO

FORSTER, Markus (alto)
Biber: Arminio (Cpte)

FORTE, Cinzia (sop)
Sacchini: Contadina in Corte (Cpte)

FÖRTER-BARTH, Hans-Jürgen (bar)
Delius: Village Romeo and Juliet (Cpte)

FORTHINGHAM, George (sngr)
see CONCERT INDEX under:
(PEAR) GEMMCDS9050/2(1) Music from the New
York Stage, Vol. 1 (part 1)

FORTI, Carlo (bass)
Bellini: Puritani (Cpte)
Ponchielli: Gioconda (Cpte)
Puccini: Bohème (Cpte), Fanciulla del West (Cpte),
Manon Lescaut (Cpte)
Verdi: Rigoletto (Cpte)
see CONCERT INDEX under:
(EMI) CDM7 69543-2 Maria Callas and Giuseppe Di
Stefano - Duets
(EMI) CMS7 63244-2 The Art of Maria Callas

FORTUNA, Maria (sop)
see CONCERT INDEX under:
(EMI) CDC7 54643-2 Rossini—Bicentenary Gala
Concert

FORTUNATO, D'Anna (contr)
A. Scarlatti: Ishmael
Beethoven: Symphony 9
Handel: Imeneo (Cpte), Joshua (Cpte), Siroe, Rè di
Persia (Cpte), Sosarme (Cpte)
V. Thomson: Lord Byron (Cpte)
see CONCERT INDEX under:
(NEWP) NPD85540 Handel/Bononcini—Muzio
Scevola
(NORT) NR9004-CD Dark Garden

FORTUNATO, D'Anna (mez)
see CONCERT INDEX under:
(BRID) BCD9055 The Great Regondi, Vol.2

FORTUNATO, Scilly (sop)
see CONCERT INDEX under:
(SONY) M3K79312 Puccini: Il Trittico

FORTUNE, George (bass)
Spontini: Olimpie (Cpte)

FOSS, Hubert (pf)
see CONCERT INDEX under:
(DUTT) CDAX8003 Walton—Gramophone premières

FOSS, Lukas (cond)
see Brooklyn PO

FOSS, Lukas (pf)
see CONCERT INDEX under:
(SONY) SM3K46291 Stravinsky—Ballets, Vol.1

FOSTER, Christopher (bass)
Purcell: Timon of Athens, Z632 (Cpte)

FOSTER, Lawrence (cond)
see CBSO

FOSTER, Nancy (sop)
R. Ward: Crucible (Cpte)

FOSTER, Norman (bass)
Mahler: Kindertotenlieder
Verdi: Don Carlo (Cpte)
see CONCERT INDEX under:
(VANG) 08.2010.71 Bach—Choral Works

FOTI, Clara (mez)
Rossini: Italiana in Algeri (Cpte)

FOUCHÉCOURT, Jean-Paul (ten)
Brossard: Dialogus, Elévations (1698)
Campra: Idoménée (Cpte)
Debussy: Rodrigue et Chimène (Cpte)
Lully: Atys (Cpte), Phaëton (Cpte)
Marais: Alcyone (Cpte)
Mondonville: Titon et l'Aurore (Cpte)
Mouret: Amours de Ragonde (Cpte)
Purcell: Dido (Cpte), Fairy Queen, Z629 (Cpte)
Rameau: Hippolyte et Aricie (Cpte), Indes galantes
(Cpte), Pygmalion (Cpte)
see CONCERT INDEX under:
(FNAC) 592096 Rameau—Grand Motets
(FNAC) 592292 Satie—Orchestral & Vocal Works
(HARM) HMC90 1280 Montéclair—Cantatas
(HARM) HMC90 1351 Delalande—Sacred Choral
Works
(SONY) SK47184 Glenn Gould—The Composer

FOUCHER, Patrick (ten)
Auber: Gustav III (Cpte)
Montéclair: Jephté (Cpte)

FOULKES, Stephen (bar)
see CONCERT INDEX under:
(MERI) CDE84168 Elgar: Choral Music

FOURCADE, Philippe (bass)
Gounod: Faust (Cpte)

FOURESTIER, Louis (cond)
see Paris Op Orch

FOURNET, Anne (narr)
Stravinsky: Perséphone (Cpte)

FOURNET, Jean (cond)
see Concertgebouw

FOURNIÉ, Nicole (sop)
Rameau: Pygmalion (Cpte)

FOURNIER, Brigitte (sop)
Gluck: Orphée (Cpte)
Honegger: Aventures du Roi Pausole (Cpte)
Poulenc: Dialogues des Carmélites (Cpte)
Prokofiev: Love for 3 Oranges (Cpte)
Zelenka: Requiem in C
see CONCERT INDEX under:
(ERAT) 2292-45517-2 Berlioz—Songs

FOURNIER, Carmen (vn)
see CONCERT INDEX under:
(ACCO) 20061-2 Scelsi: Choral & Orchestral Works

FOURNIER, Pierre (vc)
Bach: Solo Cello Suites
Beethoven: Piano Trios (exc), Triple Concerto
Brahms: Piano Trio 1, Piano Trio 2
Dvořák: Cello Concerto
Elgar: Cello Concerto
R. Strauss: Don Quixote
Schubert: Piano Trio 1
Schumann: Piano Trio 1
see CONCERT INDEX under:
(CASC) VEL2001 Martin—Orchestral Works
(CASC) VEL2009 Cello Concertos
(DG) 429 155-2GR Works for Cello & Orchestra
(DG) 437 352-2GDO2 Beethoven—Cello Sonatas
(DG) 437 371-2GX2 Bizet/Lalo—Orchestral Works
(EMI) CZS7 62736-2 Poulenc—Chamber Works
(TAHR) FURT1008/11 A Tribute to Wilhelm
Furtwängler
(TEST) SBT1016 Pierre Fournier - recital

FOURNILLIER, Patrick (cond)
see Budapest F. Liszt SO

FOURRIER, Janine (sop)
Poulenc: Dialogues des Carmélites (Cpte)

(THE) FOURSOME
cond J. MCGLINN
see CONCERT INDEX under:
(EMI) CDC7 47454-2 Kiri sings Gershwin

FOUSEK, Josef (perc)
see CONCERT INDEX under:
(SUPR) 11 1533-2 Suk—Chamber Works, Volume 3

FOVEAU, Eugène (tpt)
see CONCERT INDEX under:
(EMI) CDS7 54607-2 Stravinsky plays and conducts
Stravinsky

FOWKE, Philip (pf)
Bliss: Piano Concerto
Finzi: Grand Fantasia
Rachmaninov: Paganini Rhapsody, Piano Concerto
2
see CONCERT INDEX under:
(CFP) CD-CFP4667 Ravel—Orchestral Works
(CHAN) CHAN8979 Bliss—Piano Works
(CRD) CRD3396 Virtuoso Transcriptions for Piano
(EMI) CDC7 54420-2 Horn Recital
(EMI) CDS7 54270-2 Rattle Conducts Britten
(UNIC) DKPCD9108 Delius—Orchestral Works
(UNIC) UKCD2072 The Delius Collection, Volume 2

FOWLER, Bernard (voc)
see CONCERT INDEX under:
(SONY) SK64133 The Essential Philip Glass

FOWLER, Beth (sngr)
Gershwin: Strike Up the Band I (Cpte), Strike Up the
Band II

FOWLER, Bruce (ten)
Handel: Messiah (Cpte)
Rossini: Armida (Cpte)

FOX, Eldon (vc)
see CONCERT INDEX under:
(EMI) CDC7 47433-2 Villa-Lobos: Bachianas
Brasileiras
(EMI) CDS7 47901-8 Villa-Lobos: Orchestral and
Chamber Works

FOX, Frank (cond)
see Berlin SO

FOX, Harry (sngr)
see CONCERT INDEX under:
(PEAR) GEMMCDS9059/61 Music from the New York
Stage, Vol. 4: 1917-20

FRACKER, Richard (ten)
Glass: Hydrogen Jukebox (Cpte)

FRADKIN, Frederic (vn)
see CONCERT INDEX under:
(ROMO) 81012-2 Elisabeth Rethberg — Brunswick
Recordings 1924-1929

FRAGER, Malcolm (pf)
Beethoven: Violin Sonata 5, Violin Sonata 9
see CONCERT INDEX under:
(DECC) 425 031-2DM Mozart—Piano Works
(EMI) CMS7 64342-2 R. Strauss—Orchestral Works,
Vol.1
(TELA) CD80280 Malcolm Frager plays Chopin

FRAME, Pamela (vc)
see CONCERT INDEX under:
(KOCH) 37281-2 Amy Beach/Rebecca Clarke—Cello
Works

FRANC, Tugomir (bass)
R. Strauss: Elektra (Cpte)

(MARTINA) FRANCA FESTIVAL ORCHESTRA
cond A. ZEDDA
Rossini: Adelaide di Borgogna (Cpte)

FRANÇAIX, Claude (pf)
see CONCERT INDEX under:
(WERG) WER6087-2 Françaix plays Françaix

FRANÇAIX, Jean (pf)
see CONCERT INDEX under:
(WERG) WER6087-2 Françaix plays Françaix
(WERG) WER60143-50 Françaix: Music for Wind
Ensemble

FRANCESCA-CAVAZZA, Maria de (sop)
Wolf-Ferrari: Canzoniere (exc), Edelweide (Cpte)

FRANCESCATTI, Zino (vn)
Brahms: Violin Concerto
Mendelssohn: Violin Concerto, op 64
Paganini: Violin Concerto 1
Saint-Saëns: Violin Concerto 3
Sibelius: Violin Concerto
Tchaikovsky: Violin Concerto
see CONCERT INDEX under:
(SONY) SBK46342 Beethoven: Violin Sonatas
(SONY) SMK47548 French Orchestral Works
(SONY) SMK64468 Mozart—Orchestral Works
(SONY) SM3K47162 Bernstein plays and conducts
Bernstein Volume III

FRANCESCH, Homero (pf)
Mozart: Piano Concerto 21, Piano Concerto 22
Stravinsky: Noces
see CONCERT INDEX under:
(ETCE) KTC1045 Menotti: Chamber and Vocal
Works

FRANCESCHETTO, Romano (sngr)
Paisiello: Don Chisciotte (Cpte)

FRANCI, Benvenuto (bar)
see CONCERT INDEX under:
(CLUB) CL99-014 Dino Borgioli (1891-1960)
(EMI) CHS7 64864-2(1) La Scala Edition - Vol.2,
1915-46 (pt 1)
(PEAR) GEMMCDS9925(2) Covent Garden on
Record—Vol.3 (pt 2)
(PREI) 89007 Aureliano Pertile (1885-1952) - I

FRANCI, Carlo (cond)
see Naples RAI Orch

FRANCI, Francesca (mez)
Donizetti: Maria di Rohan (Cpte)
Verdi: Rigoletto (Cpte)

FRANCIS, Alun (cond)
see Basle RSO

FRANCIS, David (hpd)
see CONCERT INDEX under:
(MERI) CDE84177 Haydn: Concertos

FRANCIS, Hannah (sop)
Rossini: Tancredi (Cpte)
see CONCERT INDEX under:
(DECC) 433 080-2DM Kodály—Choral Works

FRANCIS, Jeffrey (ten)
Rossini: Armida (Cpte)

FRANCIS, Sarah (ob)
Albinoni: Concerti, Op.7 (exc), Concerti, Op.9 (exc)
Boughton: Oboe Concerto 1
see CONCERT INDEX under:
(CHAN) CHAN8392 English Chamber Music
(HYPE) CDA66411 Mozart & Kramar—Oboe
Concertos
(UNIC) DKPCD9050 Vivaldi—Concertos

FRANCIS, Sarah (ob d'amore/dir)
see CONCERT INDEX under:
(UNIC) DKPCD9131 Telemann—Oboe Concertos -
Volume 2

FRANCIS, Sarah (ob/dir)
see CONCERT INDEX under:
(UNIC) DKPCD9071 Vivaldi—Chamber Concertos
(UNIC) DKPCD9128 Telemann—Six Oboe Concertos
- Volume 1
(UNIC) DKPCD9131 Telemann—Oboe Concertos
Volume 2
(UNIC) DKPCD9153 Handel—Oboe Concertos and
Sonatas

FRANCK, Hannerle (sop)
Mozart: Nozze di Figaro (Cpte)

FRANCK, Joseph (ten)
Mussorgsky: Boris Godunov (Cpte)

FRANCK, Walter (spkr)
Mozart: Entführung (Cpte)

FRANCKE, Donald (bass)
Britten: Rejoice in the Lamb

FRANÇOIS, Samson (pf)
see CONCERT INDEX under:
(EMI) CDC7 47368-2 Ravel: Works for piano

FRÂNCU, Virgil (fl)
Enescu: Wind Decet, Op. 14

FRANDSEN, John (cond)
see Copenhagen Op Orch

FRANGOULIS, Stefan (treb)
see CONCERT INDEX under:
(TELD) 2292-42603-2 Bach—Cantatas, Volume 27

(TELD) **4509-91760-2** Bach—Cantatas, Vol.6

FRANK, Pamela (vn)
see CONCERT INDEX under:
(SONY) **SK53112** Chopin—Chamber Works

FRANKE, Paul (ten)
Leoncavallo: Pagliacci (Cpte)
Verdi: Trovatore (Cpte)

FRANKENLAND STATE SYMPHONY ORCHESTRA
cond M. RÓZSA
Rózsa: Background to Violence (exc), Lust for Life (exc)

FRANKFURT CHAMBER CHOIR
cond H.M. BEUERLE
see CONCERT INDEX under:
(WERG) **WER6173-2** T.W.Adorno—Chamber & Choral Works

FRANKFURT CHILDREN'S CHOIR
cond M. TANG
see CONCERT INDEX under:
(WERG) **WER6275-2** Orff—Trionfi

FRANKFURT KANTOREI
cond H. RILLING
see CONCERT INDEX under:
(HANS) **98 801** Bach—Cantatas, Vol.39
(HANS) **98 804** Bach—Cantatas, Vol.42
(HANS) **98 807** Bach—Cantatas, Vol.45
(HANS) **98 810** Bach—Cantatas, Vol.48
(HANS) **98 812** Bach—Cantatas, Vol.50
(HANS) **98 814** Bach—Cantatas, Vol.52
(HANS) **98 816** Bach—Cantatas, Vol.54
(HANS) **98 822** Bach—Cantatas, Vol.60
(HANS) **98 825** Bach—Cantatas, Vol.63
(HANS) **98 826** Bach—Cantatas, Vol.64
(HANS) **98 863** Bach—Cantatas, Vol.12
(HANS) **98 864** Bach—Cantatas, Vol.13
(HANS) **98 870** Bach—Cantatas, Vol.19
(HANS) **98 891** Bach—Cantatas, Vol.38
cond W. SCHÄFER
Orff: Catulli Carmina
Stravinsky: Noces
see CONCERT INDEX under:
(WERG) **WER6275-2** Orff—Trionfi
cond M. TANG
see CONCERT INDEX under:
(WERG) **WER6275-2** Orff—Trionfi

FRANKFURT KANTOREI WOMENS' CHORUS
cond E. INBAL
Mahler: Symphony 3

FRANKFURT NEEBER-SCHULER CHOIR
cond S. HEINRICH
Honegger: Jeanne d'Arc (Cpte)

FRANKFURT OPERA CHORUS
cond E. INBAL
Schoenberg: Gurrelieder

FRANKFURT OPERA ORCHESTRA
cond G. BERTINI
see CONCERT INDEX under:
(WERG) **WER6173-2** T.W.Adorno—Chamber & Choral Works

FRANKFURT PHILHARMONIC ORCHESTRA (ODER)
cond A. WALTER
see CONCERT INDEX under:
(MARC) **8 223546** Furtwängler—Lieder and Choral Works

FRANKFURT RADIO ORCHESTRA
cond A. WEBERN
see CONCERT INDEX under:
(SONY) **SM3K45845** Webern—Complete Works

FRANKFURT RADIO SYMPHONY ORCHESTRA
cond W.A. ALBERT
Hindemith: Four Temperaments, Piano Concerto
see CONCERT INDEX under:
(CPO) **CPO999 142-2** Hindemith—Complete Wind Concertos
cond G. ALBRECHT
Zemlinsky: Traumgörge (Cpte)
cond E. INBAL
Bartók: Duke Bluebeard's castle (Cpte)
Berlioz: Damnation de Faust (Cpte), Grande Messe des Morts (Cpte), Harold in Italy, Roméo et Juliette (Cpte), Symphonie fantastique
Bruckner: Symphony 3, Symphony 4, Symphony 7, Symphony 9
Dvořák: Symphony 9, Wild Dove
Mahler: Lied von der Erde, Symphony 1, Symphony 2, Symphony 3, Symphony 4, Symphony 5, Symphony 6, Symphony 7, Symphony 8, Symphony 9, Symphony 10 (exc)
Puccini: Messa di Gloria
Schoenberg: Gurrelieder
Shostakovich: Symphony 5
Smetana: Má Vlast
Tchaikovsky: Symphony 6
Wagner: Tristan und Isolde (exc)
see CONCERT INDEX under:
(PHIL) **442 586-2PM2** Tchaikovsky—Complete Tone Poems
cond D. KITAIENKO
see CONCERT INDEX under:
(CAPR) **10 482** Nobody knows de trouble I see
(RCA) **74321 20297-2** Scriabin—Symphonies, etc
(TELD) **9031-73257-2** Prokofiev—Piano Concertos
cond M. VIOTTI
Franchetti: Cristoforo Colombo (Cpte)
Puccini: Fanciulla del West (Cpte)

FRANKFURT SINGAKADEMIE

FRANKFURT SINGAKADEMIE (ODER)
cond M. TANG
see CONCERT INDEX under:
(WERG) **WER6275-2** Orff—Trionfi
cond A. WALTER
see CONCERT INDEX under:
(MARC) **8 223546** Furtwängler—Lieder and Choral Works

FRANKFURT VOCAL ENSEMBLE
cond R. OTTO
Bach: Christmas Oratorio, BWV248 (Cpte)
Martin: Mass
Monteverdi: Vespers
Reger: Geistliche Gesänge, op 138

FRANKL, Peter (pf)
Brahms: Piano Quintet
Dvořák: Piano Quintet, Op.81
Martinů: Piano Quintet 1
Schumann: Piano Quintet, Op.44
see CONCERT INDEX under:
(ASV) **CDDCA687** Bartók—Piano Works
(ASV) **CDDCA764** Mozart—Piano Concertos K413-415
(ASV) **CDDCA781** Chopin—Piano Works
(ASV) **CDDCA792** Mozart—Piano Duets, Vol.1
(ASV) **CDDCA799** Mozart—Piano Duets, Vol.2
(ASV) **CDDCA860** The Hungarian Anthology

FRANKLIN, David (bass)
Mozart: Don Giovanni (Cpte)

FRANKLIN, Irene (sngr)
see CONCERT INDEX under:
(PEAR) **GEMMCDS9053/5** Music from the New York Stage, Vol. 2: 1908—1913
(PEAR) **GEMMCDS9059/61** Music from the New York Stage, Vol. 4: 1917-20

FRANKS, Dobbs (cond)
see Tasmanian SO

FRANKS, Peter (tpt)
Maxwell Davies: Strathclyde Concerto 3

FRÁNOVA, Tatiana (pf)
see CONCERT INDEX under:
(MARC) **8 223151** Glazunov—Piano Music, Vol.1
(MARC) **8 223153** Glazunov—Piano Works, Vol.3

FRANSOO, Sylvain (perc)
see CONCERT INDEX under:
(DINT) **DICD920125** Walton—Façade

FRANTER, Willy (ten)
Verdi: Macbeth (Cpte)
Wagner: Tristan und Isolde (exc)
see CONCERT INDEX under:
(SCHW) **314652** Vienna State Opera Live, Vol.15
(SCHW) **314672** Vienna State Opera Live, Vol.17

FRANTZ, Ferdinand (bass-bar)
Wagner: Meistersinger (Cpte), Tristan und Isolde (Cpte), Walküre (Cpte)
see CONCERT INDEX under:
(EMI) **CMS5 65212-2** Wagner—Les introuvables du Ring
(EMI) **CZS7 67123-2** Wagner: Der Ring des Nibelungen

FRANTZ, Justus (pf)
Dvořák: Piano Concerto
Mozart: Piano Concerto 20, Piano Concerto 21, Piano Concerto 22, Piano Concerto 23, Piano Concerto 24, Piano Concerto 27
see CONCERT INDEX under:
(DG) **415 655-2GH** Bach: Harpsichord Concertos
(DG) **423 099-2GH3** Schumann: Symphonies & Concertos
(DG) **435 042-2GX2** Mozart— Piano Duet Works

FRANZ, Paul (ten)
see CONCERT INDEX under:
(PEAR) **GEMMCDS9925(1)** Covent Garden on Record—Vol.3 (pt 1)

FRANZ LISZT SYMPHONY ORCHESTRA, BUDAPEST
cond P. FOURNILLIER
Massenet: Grisélidis (Cpte)

FRANZEN, Hans (bass)
E.T.A. Hoffmann: Undine (Cpte)
Monteverdi: Madrigals, Bk 8 (exc)
Mozart: Zauberflöte (Cpte)
R. Strauss: Frau ohne Schatten (Cpte)
Weill: Mahagonny (Cpte), Mahagonny-Gesänge (Cpte), Zar lässt sich Photographieren (Cpte)
Zemlinsky: Kleider machen Leuto (Cpto)

FRANZETTI, Giulio (vn)
Vivaldi: Concerti, Op. 8 (exc)

FRASCA-COLOMBIER, Monique (vn)
Vivaldi: Concerti, Op.8 (exc)

FRASCANI, Nini (mez)
see CONCERT INDEX under:
(PEAR) **GEMMCDS9073(1)** Giovanni Zenatello, Vol.1 (pt 1)
(SYMP) **SYMCD1138** The Harold Wayne Collection, Vol.16

FRASCATI, Tommaso (ten)
Puccini: Turandot (Cpte)
see CONCERT INDEX under:

(RCA) **GD87799** The Pearl Fishers Duet plus Duets and Scenes

FRASER, Donald (cond)
see ECO

FRASER, Ian (cond)
see London Musicians Orch

FRATE, Ines de (sop)
see CONCERT INDEX under:
(MEMO) **HR4408/9(1)** Singers in Genoa, Vol.1 (disc 1)

FRATI, Dorina (mndl)
see CONCERT INDEX under:
(ERAT) **4509-92132-2** The Magic of the Mandolin

FRECCIA, Massimo (cond)
see RCA Victor SO

FREDLUND, Ingegerd (hp)
see CONCERT INDEX under:
(BIS) **BIS-CD507** Schnittke—Cello Works

FREDMAN, Myer (cond)
see LPO

FREDONIA CHAMBER SINGERS
cond W. GUNDLACH
Weill: Down in the Valley (Cpte), Jasager (Cpte)

FREDRICKS, Helena (sngr)
see CONCERT INDEX under:
(PEAR) **GEMMCDS9050/2(1)** Music from the New York Stage, Vol. 1 (part 1)

FREDRICKS, Olive (sop)
Ligeti: Grand Macabre (Cpte)
Verdi: Rigoletto (Cpte)
Zemlinsky: Geburtstag der Infantin (Cpte)

(ADOLF) FREDRIKS BACH CHOIR
cond A. ÖHRWALL
Roman: Swedish Mass

FREDRIKSSON, Karl-Magnus (bar)
Lehár: Lustige Witwe (Cpte)
Nielsen: Symphony 3

FREED, Paul (pf)
see CONCERT INDEX under:
(VOX) **115845-2** Chamber Works by Women Composers

FREEMAN, Coleton (ten)
Gershwin: Porgy and Bess (Cpte)

FREEMAN, Paul (cond)
see LPO

FREEMAN-ATTWOOD, Jonathan (tpt)
see CONCERT INDEX under:
(PROU) **PROUCD135** Music for Trumpet and Organ

FREI, Rudolf (db)
Onslow: Septet

FREIBURG BAROQUE ORCHESTRA
Handel: Radamisto (Cpte)
cond G. VON DER GOLTZ
see CONCERT INDEX under:
(DHM) **05472 77295-2** Handel/Purcell—Works
(DHM) **05472 77321-2** Telemann—Concerto & Overtures
(DHM) **05472 77339-2** Zelenka/J G.Pisendel—Concerti etc
cond T. HENGELBROCK
see CONCERT INDEX under:
(DHM) **RD77187** C.P.E. Bach: Sinfonias & Concertos
(DHM) **RD77231** Purcell—Instrumental Music
(DHM) **05472 77289-2** Bach/Vivaldi—Orchestral Works
cond N. MCGEGAN
Handel: Giustino (Cpte), Ottone (Cpte)

FREIBURG BAROQUE ORCHESTRA CONSORT
Biber: Sonatas (exc)
Georg Muffat: Armonico tributo sonatas (exc)

FREIBURG SOLOISTS CHOIR
cond C. ABBADO
see CONCERT INDEX under:
(SONY) **SK53978** Prometheus
cond I. METZMACHER
Nono: Prometeo (Cpte)

FREIBURG VOCAL ENSEMBLE
cond M. GIELEN
Busoni: Piano Concerto, Op. 39

FREIRE, Joaquim (gtr)
see CONCERT INDEX under:
(LEMA) **LC42601** Guitar Works

FREIRE, Nelson (pf)
see CONCERT INDEX under:
(DG) **439 867-2GH** Bartók/Ravel—Works for 2 Pianos

FREITAS BRANCO, Pedro de (cond)
see SO

FRELLESVIG, Anne (sngr)
Nørgård: Siddhartha (Cpte)

FRÉMAUX, Louis (cond)
see CBSO

FRÉMEAU, Jean-Marie (bar)
Gounod: Roméo et Juliette (Cpte)
Massenet: Don Quichotte (Cpte), Manon (Cpte)
see CONCERT INDEX under:
(EMI) **CDS7 49361-2** Offenbach: Operettas

FREMSTAD, Olive (mez)
see CONCERT INDEX *under:*
(PEAR) **GEMMCDS9923(2)** Covent Garden on
Record, Vol.1 (pt 2)

FREMY, Gérard (pf)
Cage: Sonatas and Interludes (1946-48)

FRENCH ARMY CHORUS
cond J. MERCIER
Schmitt: Salammbô Suites (exc)
cond M. PLASSON
Gounod: Faust (Cpte)

FRENCH LYRIQUE ORCHESTRA
cond A. GUINGAL
Saint-Saëns: Henry VIII (Cpte)
cond M. SWIERCZEWSKI
Auber: Gustav III (Cpte)

FRENCH NATIONAL CHORUS
cond L. BERNSTEIN
see CONCERT INDEX *under:*
(SONY) **SM2K47526** Berlioz—Vocal and Orchestral
Works
cond E. INBAL
Ravel: Daphnis et Chloé (Cpte)
cond I. MARKEVITCH
Stravinsky: Symphony of Psalms

FRENCH NATIONAL ORCHESTRA
cond L. BERNSTEIN
Franck: Symphony
Ravel: Shéhérazade
Roussel: Symphony 3
see CONCERT INDEX *under:*
(DG) **431 103-2GB** Great Voices—Montserrat Caballé
(EMI) **CDC7 47845-2** Milhaud—Orchestral Works
(EMI) **CDM7 64630-2** Berlioz—Orchestral Works
(SONY) **SMK47603** Ravel—Orchestral Works
(SONY) **SM2K47526** Berlioz—Vocal and Orchestral
Works
cond P. BOULEZ
Berio: Eindrücke, Sinfonia
Stravinsky: Chant du rossignol, Pulcinella
cond J. CONLON
Puccini: Bohème (Cpte)
see CONCERT INDEX *under:*
(ERAT) **2292-45499-2** Martinů—Orchestral Works
(ERAT) **2292-45794-2** Martinů—Works for Piano and
Orchestra
cond A. COPLAND
see CONCERT INDEX *under:*
(ETCE) **KTC1098** Copland—Orchestral Works
cond C. DUTOIT
Dutilleux: Cello Concerto, Violin Concerto
see CONCERT INDEX *under:*
(DECC) **443 324-2DH** Respighi/Saint-Saëns—Violin
Concertos
cond E. INBAL
Ravel: Daphnis et Chloé (Cpte)
see CONCERT INDEX *under:*
(DENO) **CO-1797** Ravel: Orchestral Works, Vol.2
(DENO) **CO-71799** Ravel: Orchestral Works, Vol.4
cond D-E. INGHELBRECHT
Debussy: Nocturnes, Pelléas et Mélisande (Cpte)
see CONCERT INDEX *under:*
(MONT) **TCE8790** Debussy: Orchestral and Dramatic
Works
cond J. KRIPS
Brahms: Symphony 4
Mozart: Symphony 40
cond L. MAAZEL
Bizet: Carmen (Cpte)
cond I. MARKEVITCH
Mahler: Symphony 1
Stravinsky: Symphony of Psalms
cond C. MUNCH
Brahms: Symphony 2
Schumann: Symphony 4
see CONCERT INDEX *under:*
(MONT) **MUN2011** Berlioz—Symphonie fantastique;
Overtures
(MONT) **MUN2031** Charles Munch Conducts
(MONT) **MUN2041** Roussel: Orchestral Works
(MONT) **MUN2051** Honegger: Orchestral Works
cond K. NAGANO
(ERAT) **4509-92137-2** Varese—Orchestral Works,
Vol. 1
cond S. OZAWA
Bizet: Carmen (Cpte)
Honegger: Jeanne d'Arc (Cpte)
Lalo: Symphonie espagnole
Offenbach: Contes d'Hoffmann (Cpte)
Sarasate: Zigeunerweisen
cond G. PRÊTRE
Poulenc: Gloria (Cpte), Stabat Mater
cond D. ROBERTSON
see CONCERT INDEX *under:*
(ERAT) **2292-45992-2** Milhaud—Works for Piano &
Orchestra
cond M. ROSTROPOVICH
Prokofiev: War and Peace (Cpte)
see CONCERT INDEX *under:*
(ERAT) **2292-45626-2** Dutilleux—Orchestral Works
cond G. ROZHDESTVENSKY
Busoni: Piano Concerto, Op. 39
cond C. SCHURICHT
Beethoven: Symphony 1, Symphony 3
cond J. TATE
Berg: Lulu (Cpte)

cond H. TOMASI
Tomasi: Don Juan de Mañara (Cpte), Triomphe de
Jeanne
cond G. TZIPINE
Prokofiev: Violin Concerto 1
cond B. WALTER
Brahms: Symphony 2
Mozart: Symphony 38

**FRENCH RADIO AND TELEVISION SYMPHONY
ORCHESTRA**
cond B. PRIESTMAN
see CONCERT INDEX *under:*
(SCHW) **315012** Jongen—Orchestral Works

FRENCH RADIO AND TV CHORUS
cond H. TOMASI
Tomasi: Triomphe de Jeanne

FRENCH RADIO AND TV ORCHESTRA
cond J.M. LECONTE
see CONCERT INDEX *under:*
(CAMB) **CD-1063** Louis Kaufman - Violin Works

FRENCH RADIO CHORUS
cond T. BEECHAM
Bizet: Carmen (Cpte)
cond J. GRESSIER
Ganne: Hans (Cpte)
cond A. JORDAN
Chausson: Roi Arthus (Cpte)
Dukas: Ariane et Barbe-Bleue (Cpte)
cond L. MAAZEL
Bizet: Carmen (exc)
Ravel: Enfant et les Sortilèges (Cpte)
cond S. OZAWA
Bizet: Carmen (Cpte)
Honegger: Jeanne d'Arc (Cpte)
Offenbach: Contes d'Hoffmann (Cpte)
cond G. PRÊTRE
Bizet: Jolie fille de Perth (Cpte)
Poulenc: Gloria (Cpte), Stabat Mater
see CONCERT INDEX *under:*
(EMI) **CDC7 47723-2** Poulenc: Choral and Organ
works
cond M. ROSENTHAL
Milhaud: Christophe Colomb (Cpte)
cond M. ROSTROPOVICH
Prokofiev: War and Peace (Cpte)
cond G. ROZHDESTVENSKY
Busoni: Piano Concerto, Op. 39
cond H. TOMASI
Tomasi: Don Juan de Mañara (Cpte)

FRENCH RADIO CHORUS SOLOISTS
cond M. COURAUD
Messiaen: Rechants

FRENCH RADIO LYRIC CHORUS
cond T. AUBIN
Messager: Basoche (Cpte)
cond J. BREBION
Bazin: Maître Pathelin (Cpte)
Audran: Poupée (exc)
Bazin: Voyage en Chine (Cpte)
Planquette: Rip van Winkle (Cpte)
Terrasse: Travaux d'Hercule (Cpte)
cond A. GIRARD
see CONCERT INDEX *under:*
(MUSD) **20239-2** Delibes—Opéras-Comiques
cond J. GRESSIER
Messager: Monsieur Beaucaire (Cpte)

FRENCH RADIO LYRIC ORCHESTRA
cond T. AUBIN
Messager: Basoche (Cpte)
cond J. BREBION
Bazin: Maître Pathelin (Cpte)
Boïeldieu: Voitures Versées (Cpte)
Hahn: O mon bel inconnu (Cpte)
cond M. CARIVEN
Audran: Poupée (exc)
Bazin: Voyage en Chine (Cpte)
Planquette: Rip van Winkle (Cpte)
Terrasse: Travaux d'Hercule (Cpte)
cond R. ELLIS
Lecocq: Jour et la Nuit (Cpte)
Messager: P'tites Michu (exc)
cond H. GALLOIS
Gounod: Philémon et Baucis (Cpte)
cond A. GIRARD
see CONCERT INDEX *under:*
(MUSD) **20239-2** Delibes—Opéras-Comiques
cond J. GRESSIER
Ganne: Hans (Cpte)
Messager: Monsieur Beaucaire (Cpte)
cond P-M. LECONTE
Hahn: Mozart (Cpte)
cond M. ROSENTHAL
Milhaud: Christophe Colomb (Cpte)

FRENCH RADIO NATIONAL CHORUS
cond E. BOUR
Ravel: Enfant et les sortilèges (Cpte)
cond J. CONLON
Puccini: Bohème (Cpte)
cond D-E. INGHELBRECHT
Debussy: Nocturnes, Pelléas et Mélisande (Cpte)
cond J. MARTINON
Berlioz: Lélio (Cpte)
cond G. PRÊTRE
Gounod: St Cecilia Mass
cond G. TZIPINE
Bizet: Ivan IV (exc)

FRENCH RADIO NATIONAL MAÎTRISE
cond J. CONLON
Puccini: Bohème (Cpte)

FRENCH RADIO NATIONAL ORCHESTRA
cond T. BEECHAM
Bizet: Carmen (Cpte), Symphony
Franck: Symphony
Lalo: Symphony in G minor
see CONCERT INDEX *under:*
(EMI) **CDM7 63379-2** Beecham conducts French
Orchestral Works
(EMI) **CDM7 63401-2** French Favourites
cond E. BOUR
Ravel: Enfant et les sortilèges (Cpte)
cond A. CLUYTENS
Debussy: Pelléas et Mélisande (Cpte)
see CONCERT INDEX *under:*
(EMI) **CDC7 54606-2** Shostakovich plays
Shostakovich
cond R. DESORMIÈRE
see CONCERT INDEX *under:*
(EPM) **150 122** Milhaud—Historic Recordings 1928-
1948
cond I. DOBROVEN
Mussorgsky: Boris Godunov (Cpte)
cond O. KLEMPERER
Brahms: Violin Concerto
cond J.M. LECONTE
see CONCERT INDEX *under:*
(MUSI) **MACD-620** 20th Century French Violin
Works
cond L. MAAZEL
Ravel: Enfant et les sortilèges (Cpte), Heure
espagnole (Cpte)
see CONCERT INDEX *under:*
(DG) **423 239-2GC** Britten: Vocal & Orchestral Works
cond J. MARTINON
Berlioz: Lélio (Cpte), Symphonie fantastique
see CONCERT INDEX *under:*
(DG) **437 371-2GX2** Bizet/Lalo—Orchestral Works
(EMI) **CDM7 63160-2** Dukas: Orchestral works
(EMI) **CDM7 69587-2** Debussy: Orchestral Works,
Vol.1
(EMI) **CDM7 69589-2** Debussy: Orchestral Works,
Vol.3
(EMI) **CZS7 62643-2** Saint-Saëns: Complete
Symphonies
(ERAT) **2292-45943-2** French Works for Organ &
Orchestra
(ERAT) **4509-92871-2** Franck—Orchestral Works
cond D. MILHAUD
Milhaud: Symphony 4, Symphony 8
see CONCERT INDEX *under:*
(EPM) **150 122** Milhaud—Historic Recordings 1928-
1948
(MUSI) **MACD-620** 20th Century French Violin
Works
cond G. PRÊTRE
see CONCERT INDEX *under:*
(EMI) **CDC7 47723-2** Poulenc: Choral and Organ
works
(EMI) **CDC7 49059-2** Callas à Paris
(EMI) **CDM7 63182-2** The Incomparable Callas
(EMIN) **CD-EMX2123** Maria Callas sings Operatic
Arias
cond L. STOKOWSKI
see CONCERT INDEX *under:*
(MUSI) **MACD-778** Stokowski conducts French Music
cond G. TZIPINE
Bizet: Ivan IV (exc)
see CONCERT INDEX *under:*
(EMI) **CHST 63025-2** Mussorgsky—Songs
cond H. VILLA-LOBOS
see CONCERT INDEX *under:*
(EMI) **CDC5 55224-2** Villa-Lobos conducts Villa-
Lobos
(EMI) **CDH7 61015-2** De los Angeles sings Villa-
Lobos

FRENCH RADIO NEW PHILHARMONIC ORCHESTRA
cond M. CONSTANT
see CONCERT INDEX *under:*
(ERAT) **4509-91707-2** Messiaen—Works for 2 Pianos
& Orchestra
cond A. JORDAN
Chausson: Roi Arthus (Cpte)
cond G. PRÊTRE
Bizet: Jolie fille de Perth (Cpte)
see CONCERT INDEX *under:*
(EMI) **CDM7 63104-2** Alfredo Krauss - Opera Recital

FRENCH RADIO PHILHARMONIC ORCHESTRA
cond M. JANOWSKI
Indy: Jour d'été, Op. 61, Symphonie, Op. 25
see CONCERT INDEX *under:*
(RCA) **09026 61520-2**
Messiaen/Lutoslawski—Orchestral Works

FRENCH STRING TRIO
see CONCERT INDEX *under:*
(EMI) **CMS5 65061-2(2)** The Fabulous Victoria de los
Angeles (pt 2)

FRENI, Mirella (sop)
Bizet: Carmen (Cpte)
Boito: Mefistofele (Cpte)
Donizetti: Don Pasquale (Cpte)
Gounod: Faust (Cpte)
Leoncavallo: Pagliacci (Cpte)
Mascagni: Amico Fritz (Cpte)
Mozart: Don Giovanni (Cpte), Nozze di Figaro
(Cpte)

Puccini: Bohème (Cpte), Madama Butterfly (Cpte), Manon Lescaut (Cpte), Tosca (Cpte), Turandot (Cpte)
Rossini: Guillaume Tell (Cpte), Petite messe solennelle
Tchaikovsky: Eugene Onegin (Cpte), Queen of Spades (Cpte)
Verdi: Aida (Cpte), Don Carlo (Cpte), Ernani (Cpte), Falstaff (Cpte), Forza del destino (Cpte), Otello (Cpte), Requiem (Cpte), Simon Boccanegra (Cpte)
see CONCERT INDEX *under:*
(ACAN) **49 384** Puccini: Opera Arias and Duets
(CFP) **CD-CFP4569** Puccini: Arias
(DECC) **433 316-2DH** Verismo Arias - Mirella Freni
(DECC) **433 439-2DA** Great Love Duets
(DECC) **436 261-2DHO3** Puccini—Il Trittico
(DECC) **436 461-2DM** Ten Top Sopranos
(DECC) **443 018-2DF2** Pavarotti/Freni/Ricciarelli—Live
(EMI) **CDM7 63110-2** Mirella Freni: Opera Recital
(RCA) **09026 61580-2(8)** RCA/Met 100 Singers, 100 Years (pt 8)
(RCA) **09026 62541-2** Pavarotti - The Early Years, Vol.1
(RCA) **09026 68014-2** Pavarotti - The Early Years, Vol.2

FRENKEL, Paul (pf)
see CONCERT INDEX *under:*
(BIDD) **LAB077/8** Huberman—Complete Brunwick Recordings

FRESÁN, Iñaki (sngr)
Falla: Retablo de Maese Pedro (Cpte)
Martín y Soler: Cosa Rara (Cpte)

FRESCHI, Ledo (bass)
Puccini: Manon Lescaut (Cpte)

FRESE, Siegfried Rudolf (bass)
Beethoven: Fidelio (Cpte)
Mussorgsky: Boris Godunov (Cpte)
Puccini: Madama Butterfly (Cpte)
R. Strauss: Rosenkavalier (Cpte)
Verdi: Trovatore (Cpte)

FRETWORK
Dowland: Lachrimae
see CONCERT INDEX *under:*
(AMON) **CD-SAR29** In Nomine: English Consort Works
(ARGO) **440 282-2ZH** Nyman—Time Will Pronounce
(CHAN) **CHAN0578** The Early Byrd
(HYPE) **CDA66639** Taverner—Choral Works
(VIRG) **VC5 45007-2** A Play of Passion
(VIRG) **VC5 45062-2** Purcell—Fantasias
(VIRG) **VC5 45147-2** Lawes—Concord is Conquer'd
(VIRG) **VC7 59021-2** Lawes—For ye Violls
(VIRG) **VC7 59539-2** Nights' Black Bird
(VIRG) **VC7 59586-2** Goe Nightly Cares
cond H. CHRISTOPHERS
(HYPE) **CDA66639** Taverner—Choral Works
cond R. MARLOW
see CONCERT INDEX *under:*
(CONI) **75605 51231-2** O.Gibbons—Hosanna to the Son of David

FREUND, Pia (sop)
Melartin: Symphony 4

FREY, Dorothea (sop)
Gluck: Paride ed Elena (Cpte)

FREY, Paul (ten)
R. Strauss: Ariadne auf Naxos (Cpte), Frau ohne Schatten (Cpte)
Schoenberg: Gurrelieder
Wagner: Lohengrin (Cpte), Parsifal (Cpte)
see CONCERT INDEX *under:*
(PHIL) **446 067-2PH6** Beethoven—Complete Symphonies

FREYER, Renate (mez)
Korngold: Violanta (Cpte)
Pfitzner: Palestrina (Cpte)
Verdi: Rigoletto (Cpte)

FRICK, Gottlob (bass)
Beethoven: Fidelio (Cpte)
Bruckner: Te Deum
Mozart: Don Giovanni (Cpte), Entführung (Cpte), Requiem
Nicolai: Lustigen Weiber von Windsor (Cpte)
Orff: Kluge (Cpte)
Wagner: Fliegende Holländer (Cpte), Götterdämmerung (Cpte), Lohengrin (Cpte), Meistersinger (Cpte), Parsifal (Cpte), Tannhäuser (Cpte), Walküre (Cpte)
Weber: Freischütz (Cpte)
see CONCERT INDEX *under:*
(DECC) **414 100-2DM15** Wagner: Der Ring des Nibelungen
(EMI) **CHS7 63715-2** Die Entführung, etc
(EMI) **CHS7 69741-2(4)** Record of Singing, Vol.4—German School
(EMI) **CMS5 65212-2** Wagner—Les introuvables du Ring
(EMI) **CZS7 67123-2** Wagner: Der Ring des Nibelungen
(EMIL) **CDZ7 67015-2** Mozart—Opera Arias

FRICKE, Heinz (cond)
see Berlin RSO

FRICSAY, Ferenc (cond)
see Bavarian St Orch

FRICSAY SYMPHONIC ORCHESTRA
cond T. PÁL
Górecki: Beatus vir, Op. 38, Symphony 2

FRIED, Gerald (cond)
see OST

FRIED, Miriam (vn)
see CONCERT INDEX *under:*
(FINL) **4509-95856-2** Sibelius: Orchestral Works

FRIED, Oskar (cond)
see BPO

FRIEDAUER, Harry (ten)
Lehár: Land des Lächelns (Cpte)

FRIEDEK, Christine (sop)
see CONCERT INDEX *under:*
(BAYE) **BR100041** Choral and Vocal Works

FRIEDHEIM, Arthur (pf)
see CONCERT INDEX *under:*
(PEAR) **GEMMCD9993** Arthur Friedheim—complete recordings, etc

FRIEDHOFER, Hugo (cond)
see OST

FRIEDLAND, Brünnhilde (sop)
Wagner: Walküre (Cpte)
see CONCERT INDEX *under:*
(FOYE) **15-CF2011** Wagner—Der Ring de Nibelungen

FRIEDLANDER, Erik (vc)
see CONCERT INDEX *under:*
(CATA) **09026 61979-2** Memento Bittersweet

FRIEDLI, Irène (mez)
Gounod: Requiem

FRIEDLI, Thomas (cl)
Mozart: Clarinet Concerto, K622
see CONCERT INDEX *under:*
(CLAV) **CD50-0813** Clarinet Concertos
(CLAV) **CD50-8602** Kramár—Clarinet Concertos
(CLAV) **CD50-9010** R. Strauss—Wind Concertos

FRIEDMAN, Erick (vn)
Tchaikovsky: Violin Concerto
see CONCERT INDEX *under:*
(RCA) **09026 61210-2** Violin Showpieces
(RCA) **09026 61778-2(11-15)** The Heifetz Collection, Vols. 11-15

FRIEDMAN, Ignaz (pf)
see CONCERT INDEX *under:*
(APR) **APR7014** Romantic Piano Rarities, Vol.2
(BIDD) **LAB081/2** Huberman—Columbia recordings with piano
(OPAL) **OPALCD9839** Pupils of Theodore Leschetizky

FRIEDMAN, Lionel (cond)
see Scottish Baroque Ens

FRIEDMAN, Maria (sngr)
Romberg: Student Prince (Cpte)

FRIEDMAN, Richard (vn)
see CONCERT INDEX *under:*
(ASV) **CDDCA769** Franck—Miscellaneous Works
(ASV) **CDDCA779** Vaughan Williams—Orchestral Works
(ASV) **CDDCA898** Damase—Music for Flute, Harp and Strings
(ASV) **CDQS6140** Haydn/Stamitz—Sinfonie Concertanti
(KING) **KCLCD2027** South American Flute Music

FRIEDMAN, Stephanie (mez)
J. Adams: Death of Klinghoffer (Cpte)
Raff: Symphony 1

FRIEDMANN, Gérard (ten)
Bazin: Maître Pathelin (Cpte)
Chausson: Roi Arthus (Cpte)
Fauré: Pénélope (Cpte)
Messager: Passionément (Cpte)
Offenbach: Contes d'Hoffmann (Cpte), Périchole (Cpte)
Saint-Saëns: Samson et Dalila (Cpte)
Terrasse: Fiancée du Scaphandrier (Cpte)

FRIEDMANN, Samuel (cond)
see Rhineland-Pfalz State PO

FRIEDRICH, Fritz (bass)
R. Strauss: Salome (Cpte)

FRIEDRICH, Heinz (bar)
Orff: Kluge (Cpte), Mond (Cpte)
see CONCERT INDEX *under:*
(CAPR) **10 805** Mozart: Wind Concertos

FRIEDRICH, Karl (ten)
R. Strauss: Rosenkavalier (Cpte)
see CONCERT INDEX *under:*
(PREI) **90237** R Strauss—Daphne
(SCHW) **314572** Vienna State Opera Live, Vol.7

FRIEDRICH, Reinhold (tpt)
see CONCERT INDEX *under:*
(CAPR) **10 436** Classical Trumpet Concertos
(CAPR) **10 439** Modern Trumpet
(CAPR) **10 482** Nobody knows of trouble I see
(CPO) **CPO999 142-2** Hindemith—Complete Wind Concertos

FRIEDRICH, Wolf Matthias (bar)
Kreutzer: Nachtlager in Granada (Cpte)

FRIEND, Lionel (cond)
see Aldeburgh Fest Ens

FRIEND, Lionel (pf)
see CONCERT INDEX *under:*
(REDC) **RR008** Music by Alan Bush

FRIESENHAUSEN, Maria (sop)
Lully: Bourgeois Gentilhomme
see CONCERT INDEX *under:*
(HANS) **98 806** Bach—Cantatas, Vol.44

FRIESS, Paul (bass)
Schreker: Ferne Klang (Cpte)
Verdi: Traviata (Cpte)

FRIGARA, Maurice (cond)
see Orch

FRIJSH, Povla (sop)
see CONCERT INDEX *under:*
(PEAR) **GEMMCDS9095(1)** Povla Frijsh (pt 1)
(PEAR) **GEMMCDS9095(2)** Povla Frijsh (pt 2)
(RCA) **09026 61879-2** Grieg—Historic Recordings

FRIMMER, Monika (sop)
Bach: Cantata 11, Easter Oratorio, BWV249 (Cpte)
Handel: Radamisto (Cpte)
Mangold: Abraham
Mozart: Mass, K427
see CONCERT INDEX *under:*
(PHIL) **422 545-2PME3** The Complete Mozart Edition Vol.45

FRISELL, Bill (elec gtr)
see CONCERT INDEX *under:*
(ECM) **847 537-2** Gavin Bryars—After the Requiem

FRISTAD, Merle (bass)
Britten: Paul Bunyan (Cpte)
Copland: Tender Land (Cpte)

FRITH, Benjamin (pf)
Schumann: Davidsbündlertänze, Fantasiestücke, Op. 12
see CONCERT INDEX *under:*
(KOCH) **37162-2** Arnold—Piano Works
(NAXO) **8 550681** Mendelssohn—Works for Piano & Orchestra
(NAXO) **8 550939** Mendelssohn—Piano Music, Vol. 1
(UNIC) **DKPCD9144** Messiaen—Piano Works

FRITSCH, Eduard (ten)
see CONCERT INDEX *under:*
(SCHW) **314602** Vienna State Opera Live, Vol.10

FRITTOLI, Barbara (sop)
Rossini: Barbiere di Siviglia (Cpte)
Verdi: Trovatore (Cpte)
see CONCERT INDEX *under:*
(DECC) **436 261-2DHO3** Puccini—Il Trittico

FRITZ, Walther (ten)
Wagner: Parsifal (Cpte)

FROMANGER, Benoît (fl)
see CONCERT INDEX *under:*
(EMI) **CDC7 54884-2** French Harp Chamber Music

FROMENT, Louis de (cond)
see Luxembourg Rad & TV SO

FRONTALI, Roberto (bar)
Verdi: Falstaff (Cpte)

FRONTALINI, Silvano (cond)
see Minsk PO

FROSCHAUER, Helmuth (cond)
see Cologne RSO

FROSINI, Mario (bass)
Verdi: Traviata (Cpte)

FROST, David (perc)
see CONCERT INDEX *under:*
(RCA) **09026 62537-2** Takemitsu—Cantos

FROST, David (vib)
see CONCERT INDEX *under:*
(RCA) **09026 62537-2** Takemitsu—Cantos

FROST, John (bass)
see CONCERT INDEX *under:*
(DECC) **443 461-2DF2** Berlioz—L'Enfance du Christ, etc

FRÖST, Martin (cl)
see CONCERT INDEX *under:*
(BIS) **BIS-CD652** Penderecki—Chamber Works

FROUMENTY, Pierre (bass)
Debussy: Pelléas et Mélisande (Cpte)
see CONCERT INDEX *under:*
(EPM) **150 122** Milhaud—Historic Recordings 1928-1948

FRÜHBECK DE BURGOS, Rafael (cond)
see LPO

FRUTOS, Luis (bass)
Barbieri: Barberillo de Lavapiès (Cpte)
Vives: Bohemios (Cpte), Doña Francisquita (Cpte)

FRUTSCHNIGG, Melanie (contr)
R. Strauss: Ariadne auf Naxos (Cpte)
see CONCERT INDEX *under:*
(PREI) **90237** R Strauss—Daphne
(SCHW) **314552** Vienna State Opera Live, Vol.5

FRY, Howard (bar)
see CONCERT INDEX *under:*
(CLAR) **CDGSE78-50-26** Wagner: Tristan und Isolde excerpts
(CLAR) **CDGSE78-50-35/6** Wagner—Historical recordings

(PEAR) **GEMMCDS9137** Wagner—Der Ring des Nibelungen

FRY, Tristan (perc)
Britten: Little Sweep (Cpte)
Maxwell Davies: Sinfonia concertante
see CONCERT INDEX *under:*
(LDR) **LDRCD1001** British Masters

FRYATT, John (ten)
Mozart: Nozze di Figaro (Cpte)
Puccini: Manon Lescaut (Cpte)
Stravinsky: Pulcinella
Vaughan Williams: Hugh the Drover (Cpte)

FRYDÉN, Lars (baroque vn)
Rameau: Pièces de clavecin en concerts

FRYDLEWICZ, Miroslav (ten)
Janáček: Cunning Little Vixen (Cpte)

FRYE, Michael (perc)
see CONCERT INDEX *under:*
(UNIC) **UKCD2020** Panufnik—Orchestral Works

FRYER, Sarah (mez)
Rachmaninov: Vespers, Op.37 (Cpte)

FRYKBERG, Sten (cond)
see Swedish RSO

FU, Haijing (bar)
Bellini: Bianca e Fernando (Cpte)

FUCHS, Daniel (organ)
Fauré: Requiem (Cpte)
see CONCERT INDEX *under:*
(PREL) **PRL2153/4** Alain—Piano Works

FUCHS, Eugen (bar)
Wagner: Meistersinger (exc), Tristan und Isolde (Cpte)

FUCHS, Eugen (bass)
see CONCERT INDEX *under:*
(PREI) **89057** Charles Kullmann (1903-1982)
(PREI) **89071** Gerhard Hüsch (1901-1984) - II

FUCHS, Gabriele (sop)
Korngold: Tote Stadt (Cpte)
Lehár: Friederike (Cpte)
Millöcker: Gasparone (Cpte)
R. Strauss: Intermezzo (Cpte)
see CONCERT INDEX *under:*
(PHIL) **422 522-2PME6** The Complete Mozart Edition Vol 22

FUCHS, Joseph (vn)
Beethoven: Piano Trios (exc)
Hindemith: Violin Concerto
see CONCERT INDEX *under:*
(SONY) **SMK58991** Pablo Casals plays Beethoven at Prades and Perpignan, 1951 & 1953

FUCHS, Marta (sop)
Wagner: Götterdämmerung (Cpte), Walküre (exc)
see CONCERT INDEX *under:*
(ACAN) **43 268** Peter Anders sings German Opera Arias
(EMI) **CMS7 64008-2(1)** Wagner Singing on Record (pt 1)
(PEAR) **GEMMCDS9085** Hugo Wolf Society, Volume II

FUENTE, Herrera de la (cond)
see Minería SO

FUENTES, Eduardo (sngr)
Vives: Bohemios (Cpte)

FUES, Sabine (sop)
Wagner: Parsifal (Cpte)

FÜGEL, Alfons (ten)
see CONCERT INDEX *under:*
(PREI) **90168** Wagner—Die Meistersinger, Act 2, etc

FUGÈRE, Lucien (bar)
see CONCERT INDEX *under:*
(IRCC) **IRCC-CD800** Souvenirs from Meyerbeer Operas
(NIMB) **NI7840/1** The Era of Adelina Patti
(NIMB) **NI7867** Legendary Baritones
(SYMP) **SYMCD1089** Historic Baritones of the French School
(SYMP) **SYMCD1125** Lucien Fugère—Opera & Song Recital

FUGMANN, Willi (bn)
see CONCERT INDEX *under:*
(DG) **445 400-2GDO10** Ferenc Fricsay - A Portrait
(DG) **445 403-2GDO** R. Strauss—Orchestral Works

FUJIKAWA, Mayumi (vn)
see CONCERT INDEX *under:*
(ASV) **CDDCA667** Prokofiev—Works for Violin & Piano
(ASV) **CDDCA705** Fauré—Works for Violin
(DECC) **440 621-2DF2** Mozart—Violin Concertos, etc

FUJIWARA, Mari (vc)
Beethoven: Triple Concerto
R. Strauss: Romanze, AV75
see CONCERT INDEX *under:*
(DENO) **C37-7505** Mozart: The complete works for violin and orchestra, Vol. 2

FUJIWARA OPERA CHORUS
cond G KUHN
Verdi: Otello (Cpte)
cond R. PATERNOSTRO
Verdi: Traviata (Cpte)

FUKAČOVÁ, Michaela (vc)
see CONCERT INDEX *under:*
(SUPR) **11 1532-2** Suk—Chamber Works, Volume 2

FULFORD, Lorna (pf)
see CONCERT INDEX *under:*
(AMON) **CD-SAR48** Field—Piano Works

FULKERSON, Gregory (vn)
Glass: Einstein on the Beach (Cpte)
see CONCERT INDEX *under:*
(ALBA) **AR012** Roy Harris—Orchestral Works

FULLBROOK, Charles (bells)
see CONCERT INDEX *under:*
(SONY) **SK66613** Tavener—Innocence

FULLER, Frederick (bar)
see CONCERT INDEX *under:*
(EMI) **CDC5 55224-2** Villa-Lobos conducts Villa-Lobos
(EMI) **CHS7 69741-2(2)** Record of Singing, Vol.4—Anglo-American School (pt 2)

FULLER, Richard (hpd)
see CONCERT INDEX *under:*
(NOVA) **150 025-2** C.P.E.Bach—Keyboard Works

FULTON, Cheryl Ann (hp)
see CONCERT INDEX *under:*
(ERAT) **4509-94830-2** The Unicorn—Medieval French Songs

FUNEN ACADEMY CHILDREN'S CHOIR
cond T. VETÖ
see CONCERT INDEX *under:*
(KONT) **32188** Nielsen—Vocal Works

FUNKE, Christian (vn)
Beethoven: Triple Concerto

FÜRI, Thomas (cond)
see Berne Camerata

FÜRI, Thomas (vn/dir)
Dvořák: Serenade, Op. 22, String Sextet
Mozart: Horn Concerti
Rossini: Sonate a quattro (exc)
see CONCERT INDEX *under:*
(DG) **415 487-2GH** Vivaldi: Guitar Concertos
(NOVA) **150 016-2** Vivaldi—Concertos
(NOVA) **150 049-2** Vivaldi—Violin Concertos

FURIC, Herve (narr)
Six: Mariés de la Tour Eiffel (Cpte)

FURLAN, Jean-Pierre (ten)
A. Thomas: Hamlet (Cpte)

FURLANETTO, Ferruccio (bass)
Donizetti: Martyrs (Cpte)
Gazzaniga: Don Giovanni (Cpte)
Halévy: Juive (Cpte)
Mozart: Cosi fan tutte (Cpte), Don Giovanni (Cpte), Nozze di Figaro (Cpte)
Rossini: Armida (Cpte), Gazza ladra (Cpte)
Verdi: Don Carlo (Cpte), Requiem (Cpte), Vespri siciliani (Cpte)
see CONCERT INDEX *under:*
(SONY) **SK47192** Ferruccio Furlanetto sings Mozart

FURNISS, Rosemary (vn)
see CONCERT INDEX *under:*
(VIRG) **VC7 59609-2** Vivaldi—Concertos

FÜRSTNER, Carl (pf)
see CONCERT INDEX *under:*
(BIDD) **LAB044** Ruggiero Ricci—1938 Electrola Recordings

FURTWÄNGLER, Wilhelm (cond)
see Berlin St Op Orch

FURUSAWA, Yoshiko (sop)
see CONCERT INDEX *under:*
(CLAV) **CD50-8918** Ansermet conducts Stravinsky
(MONT) **TCE8790** Debussy: Orchestral and Dramatic Works

FUSATI, Nicola (ten)
see CONCERT INDEX *under:*
(BONG) **GB1043-2** Italian Baritones of the Acoustic Era

FUSCO, Elisabetta (sop)
Mozart: Nozze di Figaro (Cpte)

FÜSSEL, Uwe (bass tbn)
see CONCERT INDEX *under:*
(CAPR) **10 482** Nobody knows de trouble I see

FUTER, Arkady (vn)
see CONCERT INDEX *under:*
(CIRR) **CICD1004** Bach: Violin Concertos
(RCA) **RD60240** Vivaldi—Orchestral and Choral works
(RCA) **RD87991** Bach: Concerti

FUTRAL, Elizabeth (sop)
Glass: Hydrogen Jukebox (Cpte)
see CONCERT INDEX *under:*
(RCA) **09026 60970-2** Motets

FYSON, Leslie (bar)
Puccini: Bohème (Cpte)

FYSON, Leslie (sop)
G. Charpentier: Louise (Cpte)
Rossini: Semiramide (exc), Zelmira (Cpte)
Shostakovich: Lady Macbeth of Mtsensk (Cpte)
Vaughan Williams: Hugh the Drover (Cpte)
Verdi: Macbeth (Cpte)

GABAI, Maurice (cl)
see CONCERT INDEX *under:*
(EMI) **CDC7 54884-2** French Harp Chamber Music
(EMI) **CZS7 62736-2** Poulenc—Chamber Works

GABARAIN, Marina de (mez)
Rossini: Cenerentola (Cpte)
see CONCERT INDEX *under:*
(DECC) **433 908-2DM2** Falla—Orchestral Music
(EMI) **CDH5 65072-2** Glyndebourne Recorded - 1934-1994

GABARD, Patrick (vc)
see CONCERT INDEX *under:*
(REM) **REM311175** Fauré—Mélodies, Vol.1

GABARRO, Francisco (vc)
see CONCERT INDEX *under:*
(RCA) **GD80185** Classic Film Scores of Korngold

GABBA, Armando (bar)
Verdi: Rigoletto (Cpte)

GABDULLIN, Rustem (db)
see CONCERT INDEX *under:*
(OLYM) **OCD523** Shostakovich Quartet - Volume 3

GABOR, Arnold (bar)
Beethoven: Fidelio (Cpte)

GABORY, Magda (sop)
see CONCERT INDEX *under:*
(EMI) **CZS7 67123-2** Wagner: Der Ring des Nibelungen

GABRIEL, Alain (ten)
Saint-Saëns: Henry VIII (Cpte)

GABRIEL, Andrée (mez)
R. Strauss: Salomé (Cpte)

GABRIEL, Maria Reyes (sngr)
Chapí: Revoltosa (Cpte)
Vives: Doña Francisquita (Cpte)

GABRIELI CONSORT
cond P. MCCREESH
M. Praetorius: Lutheran Christmas Mass
Victoria: Missa pro defunctis
see CONCERT INDEX *under:*
(ARCH) **437 552-2AH2** Venetian Vespers
(ARCH) **437 833-2AH** Christmas Mass in Rome
(ARCH) **445 829-2AH** Purcell—Harmonia Sacra
(ARCH) **445 882-2AH** Purcell—Ode on St Cecilia's Day; Anthems
(VIRG) **VC7 59006-2** Gabrieli—A Venetian Coronation,1595

GABRIELI PLAYERS
cond P. MCCREESH
M. Praetorius: Lutheran Christmas Mass
see CONCERT INDEX *under:*
(ARCH) **437 552-2AH2** Venetian Vespers
(ARCH) **437 833-2AH** Christmas Mass in Rome
(ARCH) **445 829-2AH** Purcell—Harmonia Sacra
(ARCH) **445 882-2AH** Purcell—Ode on St Cecilia's Day; Anthems
(VIRG) **VC7 59006-2** Gabrieli—A Venetian Coronation,1595

GABRIELI QUARTET
Brahms: Clarinet Quintet, String Quartet 1, String Quartet 2
Dohnányi: Piano Quintet 1, String Quartet 2
Elgar: String Quartet
Haydn: String Quartets, Op. 54 (exc), String Quartets, Op. 64 (exc)
Mendelssohn: String Quartet 1, String Quartet 2
Mozart: Clarinet Quintet, K581, Oboe Quartet, K370
Sibelius: Piano Quintet (1889), String Quartet, Op.56
Walton: String Quartet, String Quartet (1919)
see CONCERT INDEX *under:*
(DECC) **425 541-2DM** Russian String Quartets
(DECC) **430 295-2DM** Janáček/Smetana—String Quartets
(UNIC) **UKCD2060** Britten—Early Chamber Music

GABRILOWITSCH, Ossip (pf)
see CONCERT INDEX *under:*
(OPAL) **OPALCD9839** Pupils of Theodore Leschetizky

GADD, Stephen (bass)
Purcell: Dioclesian, Z627 (Cpte)
see CONCERT INDEX *under:*
(ARCH) **445 353-2AH** Mozart—Sacred Choral Works

GADJEV, Zdravko (ten)
Mussorgsky: Khovanshchina (Cpte)

GADSKI, Johanna (sop)
see CONCERT INDEX *under:*
(CLUB) **CL99-109** Johanna Gadski (1871-1932)
(MSCM) **MM30352** Caruso—Italian Opera Arias
(PEAR) **EVC2** The Caruso Edition, Vol.2—1908-12
(PEAR) **GEMMCDS9923(2)** Covent Garden on Record, Vol.1 (pt 2)
(RCA) **GD60495(3)** The Complete Caruso Collection (pt 3)
(RCA) **09026 61580-2(1)** RCA/Met 110 Singers, 100 Years (pt 1)

GADULANKA, Jadwiga (sop)
see CONCERT INDEX *under:*
(POLS) **PNCD067** Szymanowski: Songs

GADZINA, Tadeusz (vn)
see CONCERT INDEX *under:*
(ACCO) **201142** Lutosławski—Chamber Works

GAEDE TRIO
see CONCERT INDEX under:
(LARG) **Largo 5128** Goldschmidt—Retrospectrum

GAETANI, Jan de (mez)
Hindemith: Requiem
see CONCERT INDEX under:
(NEW) **NW357-2** Crumb. Madrigals and Chamber works

GAETANO, Colleen (mez)
Tchaikovsky: Iolanta (Cpte)

GÁFFOROVÁ, Helena (pf)
Hummel: Viola Sonata, Op.5/3

GAFORIO, Armando (bass)
Rossini: Siège de Corinthe (Cpte)

GAGE, Irwin (pf)
Hindemith: Marienleben (Cpte)
Wolf: Goethe Lieder (exc), Mörike Lieder (exc)
see CONCERT INDEX under:
(ACAN) **43 507** Brahms—Lieder
(DG) **415 519-2GH** Schumann: Lieder recital
(DG) **431 476-2GGA2** Schumann: Lieder
(DG) **437 784-2GH** Cheryl Studer—Salzburg Recital
(DG) **437 943-2GX2** Schubert—Lieder
(DG) **439 417-2GCL** Schumann—Lieder
(DG) **447 352-2GDB2** Gundula Janowitz - A Portrait
(JECK) **JD561-2** Early Songs by Berg, Schönberg and Schreker
(ORFE) **C305931A** Debussy/Schoenberg/R. Strauss—Lieder
(RCA) **RD60950** Lucia Popp - Jugendstil-Lieder

GAGELMANN, Jens (perc)
see CONCERT INDEX under:
(LARG) **Largo 5127** Igor Markevitch—Chamber Works

GAGLIANO TRIO
see CONCERT INDEX under:
(ETCE) **KTC1096** Finnissy—Chamber Works

GAHMLICH, Wilfried (ten)
Einem: Dantons Tod (Cpte)
Hindemith: Mörder, Hoffnung der Frauen (Cpte), Nusch-Nuschi (Cpte)
Mozart: Zauberflöte (Cpte)
Mussorgsky: Khovanshchina (Cpte)
R. Strauss: Frau ohne Schatten (Cpte)

GAIFA, Carlo (ten)
Donizetti: Campanello di notte (Cpte)
Puccini: Manon Lescaut (Cpte)

GAILHARD, Pedro (Pierre) (bass)
see CONCERT INDEX under:
(PEAR) **GEMMCDS9923(1)** Covent Garden on Record, Vol.1 (pt 1)
(SYMP) **SYMCD1172** The Harold Wayne Collection, Vol.21

GAILLARD, Annie (rec)
Honegger: Roi David (Cpte)

GAINES, David (sngr)
Porter: Kiss Me, Kate (Cpte)
see CONCERT INDEX under:
(EMI) **CDC7 54586-2** Broadway Showstoppers

GAJDOŠOVÁ, Marie (vn)
see CONCERT INDEX under:
(SUPR) **11 1878-2** The Unknown Janáček

GÁL, Hans (pf)
see CONCERT INDEX under:
(DECC) **425 995-2DM** Brahms/Mahler—Lieder

GAL, Zehava (contr)
Rossini: Mosè in Egitto (Cpte)
see CONCERT INDEX under:
(RCA) **09026 61354-2** Mussorgsky—Orchestral & Choral Works

GALANTE, Inessa (sop)
see CONCERT INDEX under:
(CAMP) **RRCD1335** Inese Galante - Début Recital

GALASSI, Elvira (mez)
Cherubini: Medea (Cpte)
Verdi: Aida (Cpte), Rigoletto (Cpte)

GALDUF, Manuel (cond)
see Valencia Orch

GALE, Elizabeth (sop)
Gluck: Orfeo ed Euridice (Cpte)
Handel: Messiah (Cpte)
Mozart: Don Giovanni (Cpte), Nozze di Figaro (Cpte)
Puccini: Rondine (Cpte)
Purcell: Dido (Cpte)
see CONCERT INDEX under:
(CHAN) **CHAN8855** Britten—Choral Works
(DECC) **433 080-2DM** Kodály—Choral Works
(EMI) **CDH5 65072-2** Glyndebourne Recorded - 1934-1994
(HYPE) **CDA66137** Bliss: Vocal and Chamber Works

GALEFFI, Carlo (bar)
see CONCERT INDEX under:
(EMI) **CHS7 64860-2(2)** La Scala Edition - Vol.1, 1878-1914 (pt 2)
(NIMB) **NI7867** Legendary Baritones
(PREI) **89040** Carlo Galeffi (1884-1961)

GALGANI, Ilaria (sop)
Mozart: Don Giovanni (Cpte)

GALIMIR QUARTET
Berg: Lyric Suite

GALINDO, Miguel López (bar)
Penella: Gato Montés (Cpte)

GALL, Axelie (sop)
Mascagni: Cavalleria Rusticana (Cpte)

GALL, Emmanuelle (sop)
see CONCERT INDEX under:
(ERAT) **4509-91722-2** Charpentier/Grigny/Lully—Sacred Choral and Organ works

GALL, Jeffrey (alto)
Handel: Flavio (Cpte), Teseo (Cpte)

GALLA, Ján (bass)
Bellini: Sonnambula (Cpte)

GALLACHER, Andrew (bass)
Britten: Midsummer Night's Dream (Cpte)

GALLAGHER, Maureen (va)
Mozart: Sinfonia Concertante, K364

GALLAGHER, Peter (sngr)
F. Loesser: Guys and Dolls (Cpte)

GALLIARD, Peter (ten)
Dessau: Hagadah Shel Pessach
Schreker: Schatzgräber (Cpte)
Spohr: Jessonda (Cpte)

GALLI-CURCI, Amelita (sop)
see CONCERT INDEX under:
(CLAR) **CDGSE78-50-52** Three Tenors
(CONI) **CDHD201** Galli-Curci in Opera and Song
(EMI) **CDH7 61051-2** Beniamino Gigli - Operatic Arias
(MSCM) **MM30231** Don Pasquale & Tito Schipa Recital
(MSCM) **MM30352** Caruso—Italian Opera Arias
(NIMB) **NI7801** Great Singers, Vol.1
(NIMB) **NI7802** Divas 1906-1935
(NIMB) **NI7806** Galli-Curci—Opera & Song Recital
(NIMB) **NI7852** Galli-Curci, Vol.2
(PEAR) **EVC4(1)** The Caruso Edition, Vol.4 (pt 1)
(PEAR) **GEMMCD9308** Amelita Galli-Curci - Aria and Song Recital
(PEAR) **GEMMCD9316** Beniamino Gigli
(PEAR) **GEMMCD9322** Tito Schipa sings Opera Arias and Songs
(PEAR) **GEMMCD9367** Gigli—Arias and Duets
(PREI) **89036** Giuseppe de Luca (1876-1950) - I
(PREI) **89073** Giuseppe de Luca (1876-1950) - II
(RCA) **GD60495(6)** The Complete Caruso Collection (pt 6)
(RCA) **GD87969** Tito Schipa - Opera & Song Recital
(RCA) **09026 61580-2(3)** RCA/Met 100 Singers, 100 Years (pt 3)
(RCA) **09026 61879-2** Grieg—Historic Recordings
(ROMO) **81003-2** Galli-Curci—Acoustic Recordings, Vol.1
(ROMO) **81004-2** Galli-Curci—Acoustic Recordings, Vol.2
(SIMA) **PSC1810(2)** Grieg—Songs (historical recordings, pt 2)

GALLIERA, Alceo (cond)
see LSO

GALLIFANT, Alexander (treb)
Britten: Noye's Fludde (Cpte)

GALLIVER, David (ten)
Purcell: King Arthur, Z628 (Cpte)

GALLO, Lucio (bar)
Mozart: Nozze di Figaro (Cpte)
Rossini: Barbiere di Siviglia (Cpte), Viaggio a Reims (Cpte)
Verdi: Rigoletto (Cpte)

GALLOIS, Henri (cond)
see French Rad Lyric Orch

GALLOIS, Patrick (fl)
Khachaturian: Violin Concerto
Paganini: Caprices, Op.1
Rodrigo: Concierto pastoral
Telemann: Fantaisies, TWV40: 2-13
Vivaldi: Concerti, Op.10
see CONCERT INDEX under:
(BIS) **BIS-CD454** Nielsen—Orchestral Works
(BIS) **BIS-CD614/6** Nielsen—Symphonies and Concertos
(BIS) **BIS-CD616** Nielsen—Concertos
(DECC) **421 581-2DH** Poulenc—Chamber Works
(DG) **439 895-2GH** Flute Concertos of the Sans-Souci
(DG) **445 822-2GH** Une flûte à l'opéra

GALLOIS-MONTBRUN, Raymond (vn)
see CONCERT INDEX under:
(ERAT) **4509-96953-2** Fauré—Chamber Works

GALLOS, Hermann (ten)
Beethoven: Fidelio (Cpte)
Wagner: Meistersinger (Cpte), Tristan und Isolde (exc)
see CONCERT INDEX under:
(EMI) **CHS7 64487-2** R. Strauss—Der Rosenkavalier & Lieder
(PEAR) **GEMMCDS9365** R. Strauss: Der Rosenkavalier (abridged), etc
(SCHW) **314512** Vienna State Opera Live, Vol.1
(SCHW) **314562** Vienna State Opera Live, Vol.6
(SCHW) **314632** Vienna State Opera Live, Vol.13
(SCHW) **314652** Vienna State Opera Live, Vol.15

(SCHW) **314662** Vienna State Opera Live, Vol.16
(SCHW) **314672** Vienna State Opera Live, Vol.17

GALUSIN, Vladimir (ten)
Mussorgsky: Khovanshchina (Cpte)
Rimsky-Korsakov: Sadko (Cpte)

GALVANY, Maria (sop)
see CONCERT INDEX under:
(SYMP) **SYMCD1069** The Harold Wayne Collection, Vol.2
(SYMP) **SYMCD1149** Fernando De Lucia

GALVEZ-VALLEJO, Daniel (ten)
Saint-Saëns: Samson et Dalila (Cpte)

GALWAY, James (cond)
see COE
Bach: Flute Sonatas, BWV1030-5 (exc), Violin Sonatas, BWV1020-25 (exc)
Mozart: Flute Quartets, Oboe Quartet, K370
see CONCERT INDEX under:
(RCA) **GD86517** Galway plays Bach
(RCA) **RD60244** C.P.E. Bach: Flute Concertos
(RCA) **RD60247** Quantz—Flute Concertos
(RCA) **RD60736** Christmas with James Galway
(RCA) **RD87756** Beethoven: Chamber Works for Flute
(RCA) **09026 60237-2** Giuliani—Chamber Works with guitar
(RCA) **09026 60900-2** Galway plays Bach
(RCA) **09026 61164-2** Italian Flute Concertos
(RCA) **09026 61447-2** Mercadante—Flute Concertos
(RCA) **09026 61677-2** Concerto! with Dudley Moore
(RCA) **09026 61789-2** Concerto! Galway & Robles play Mozart
(RCA) **09026 61976-2** Danzi—Flute & Clarinet Works
(RCA) **09026 62552-2** Debussy/Ravel—Chamber Works

GALWAY, James (fl/dir)
see CONCERT INDEX under:
(RCA) **GD86517** Galway plays Bach
(RCA) **RD87173** Debussy: Orchestral works
(RCA) **RD87861** Mozart—Works for Flute & Orchestra

GALYNIN, Dmitri (pf)
see CONCERT INDEX under:
(MEZH) **MK417109** Medtner—Works for Violin and Piano

GAMBA, Piero (cond)
see LSO

GAMBILL, Robert (ten)
Gluck: Alceste (1776) (Cpte), Rencontre imprévue (Cpte)
Handel: Messiah (Cpte)
Mozart: Entführung (Cpte)
Offenbach: Contes d'Hoffmann (Cpte)
Puccini: Manon Lescaut (Cpte)
R. Strauss: Frau ohne Schatten (Cpte)
Rossini: Stabat Mater
Schubert: Fierrabras (Cpte)
see CONCERT INDEX under:
(CFP) **CD-CFP4532** Sacred Arias

GAMBOLD, Geoffrey (bn)
Mozart: Sinfonia concertante, K297b

GAMLEY, Douglas (cond)
see RPO

GAMLICH, Wilfried (ten)
Mozart: Entführung (Cpte)

GAMO-YAMAMOTO, Nobuko (sop)
see CONCERT INDEX under:
(HANS) **98 825** Bach—Cantatas, Vol.63
(HANS) **98 867** Bach—Cantatas, Vol.16

GAMPERT, Walter (treb)
Mozart: Zauberflöte (Cpte)
see CONCERT INDEX under:
(TELD) **2292-42502-2** Bach—Cantatas, Volume 4
(TELD) **2292-42502-2** Bach—Cantatas, Volume 6
(TELD) **2292-42505-2** Bach—Cantatas, Volume 9
(TELD) **4509-91755-2** Bach—Cantatas, Vol.1
(TELD) **4509-91756-2** Bach—Cantatas, Vol.2

GANASSI, Sonia (mez)
Rossini: Barbiere di Siviglia (Cpte)

GANDOLFI, Alfredo (bar)
Verdi: Traviata (Cpte)

GANDOLFO, Ede Marietti (mez)
Verdi: Traviata (Cpte)

GANNINGER, Kerstin (sop)
Gluck: Paride ed Elena (Cpte)

GANTNER, Martin (ten)
R. Strauss: Salome (Cpte)

GANZ, Brian (pf)
see CONCERT INDEX under:
(DG) **435 617-2GH** Beethoven in Berlin—New Year's Eve Concert

GANZ, Bruno (spkr)
Maderna: Hyperion (Cpte)
see CONCERT INDEX under:
(SONY) **SK53360** Mahler/Nono—Vocal Works

GANZ, Heidrun (vn)
see CONCERT INDEX under:
(SCHW) **311088** Spohr—Instrumental Works

GANZ, Rudolf (pf)
see CONCERT INDEX under:
(SIMA) **PSC1809(2)**   Grieg—Historical Piano Recordings (pt 2)

GANZAROLLI, Wladimiro (bar)
Haydn: Vera Costanza (Cpte)
Mozart: Così fan tutte (Cpte), Don Giovanni (Cpte), Nozze di Figaro (Cpte)
Rossini: Italiana in Algeri (Cpte)
Verdi: Giorno di Regno (Cpte), Luisa Miller (Cpte), Stiffelio (Cpte)

GAPONOVA, Nina (sop)
Scriabin: Symphony 1

GARAGULY, Carl (cond)
see Bergen SO

GARATTI, Maria Teresa (organ)
see CONCERT INDEX under:
(PHIL) **426 086-2PBQ**   Vivaldi—Double Concertos

GARATTI, Maria Teresa (hpd)
see CONCERT INDEX under:
(PHIL) **426 086-2PBQ**   Vivaldi—Double Concertos

GARAVENTA, Ottavio (ten)
Donizetti: Martyrs (Cpte)
Mascagni: Rantzau (Cpte)

GARAZZI, Peyo (ten)
A. Thomas: Hamlet (Cpte)
Massenet: Don Quichotte (Cpte)

GARBAREK, Jan (sax)
see CONCERT INDEX under:
(ECM) **445 369-2**   Officium

GARBEN, Cord (cond)
see Berlin RSO

GARBEN, Cord (pf)
Godowsky: Impressions
Schubert: Winterreise (Cpte)
see CONCERT INDEX under:
(ACAN) **44 2093-2**   Brahms—Lieder
(CPO) **CPO999 262-2**   Romantic Duets
(DG) **427 348-2GH2**   Zemlinsky: Lieder
(DG) **435 860-2GH2**   Berlioz—Mélodies
(HARM) **HMC90 1420**   Weill—The Seven Deadly Sins; Songs
(HARM) **HMC90 5210**   Duos Romantiques
(ORFE) **C021821A**   Schubert: Lieder
(SCHW) **312592**   Dvořák/Brahms/Reger—Duets
(SONY) **SK57960**   Zemlinsky—Posthumous Songs

GARBI, Francesca (mez)
Verdi: Forza del destino (Cpte)

GARBIN, Edoardo (ten)
see CONCERT INDEX under:
(EMI) **CHS7 64860-2(1)**   La Scala Edition - Vol.1, 1878-1914 (pt 1)
(MEMO) **HR4408/9(1)**   Singers in Genoa, Vol.1 (disc 1)
(PEAR) **GEMMCDS9924(2)**   Covent Garden on Record, Vol.2 (pt 2)
(SYMP) **SYMCD1113**   The Harold Wayne Collection, Vol.13

GARCIA, Emilia (sngr)
Bretón: Verbena de la Paloma (Cpte)

GARCIA, José (bass)
Hammerstein: Carmen Jones (Cpte)
Rossini: Zelmira (Cpte)

GARCIA, José-Luis (cond)
see ECO

GARCIA, José-Luis (vn)
Bach: Triple Concerto, BWV1044
see CONCERT INDEX under:
(ARAB) **Z6568**   Vaughan Williams: Orchestral Works
(ASV) **CDDCA563**   Works by Bottesini
(EMI) **CDC7 47122-2**   Mozart: Concert and Operatic Arias
(NOVA) **150 017-2**   Bach—Violin Concertos
(NOVA) **150 031-2**   Stalder & Reindl: Orchestral Works
(RCA) **RD60718**   Bach—Violin Concertos
(VIRG) **VC7 59668-2**   French Impressions
(VIRG) **VJ7 59656-2**   Italian Baroque Concertos

GARCIA, Segundo (ten)
Chapí: Revoltosa (Cpte)
Vives: Bohemios (Cpte), Doña Francisquita (Cpte)

GARCIA-ASENSIO, Enrique (cond)
see Claremont Stg Orch

GARCIN, Antoine (bar)
Massenet: Amadis (Cpte)

GARCISANZ, Isabel (mez)
Cavalli: Ormindo (Cpte)

GÅRD, Lars (perc)
see CONCERT INDEX under:
(BIS) **BIS-CD501**   Martinů—Orchestral Works

GARDEIL, Jean-François (bar)
Lully: Alceste (Cpte), Atys (Cpte)
M-A. Charpentier: Malade Imaginaire (Cpte)
see CONCERT INDEX under:
(HARM) **HMA190 1238**   Campra—French Cantatas
(HARM) **HMC90 1280**   Montéclair—Cantatas

GARDELLI, Elsa-Margrete (mez)
Wagner: Parsifal (Cpte), Tannhäuser (Cpte)

GARDELLI, Lamberto (cond)
see Austrian RSO

GARDEN, Mary (sop)
see CONCERT INDEX under:
(EMI) **CHS7 61038-2**   Debussy—Pelléas et Mélisande, etc
(ROMO) **81008-2**   Mary Garden (1874-1967)
(SYMP) **SYMCD1093**   The Harold Wayne Collection, Vol.7
(SYMP) **SYMCD1136**   Opera in Chicago, Vol.1

GARDINER, David (pf)
see CONCERT INDEX under:
(PAUL) **PACD46**   Rachmaninov: Complete Works for Two Pianos and Piano Four and Six
(PAUL) **PACD51**   Ravel: Works for Two Pianos and Piano Duet

GARDINER, John Eliot (cond)
see COE

GARDINO, Jolanda (mez)
Rossini: Turco in Italia (Cpte)

GARDNER, Guy (bar)
Orff: Carmina Burana

GARDNER, Jake (bar)
Massenet: Cid (Cpte)

GARDON, Olivier (pf)
see CONCERT INDEX under:
(TIMP) **1C1013**   Alkan—Chamber Music

GARDOW, Helrun (mez)
see CONCERT INDEX under:
(HANS) **98 803**   Bach—Cantatas, Vol.41
(HANS) **98 824**   Bach—Cantatas, Vol.62
(HANS) **98 835**   Bach—Cantatas, Vol.69
(HANS) **98 863**   Bach—Cantatas, Vol.12

GARETTI, Hélène (sop)
Massenet: Chérubin (Cpte)
Rameau: Dardanus (Cpte)

GARFORTH, David (cond)
see ECO

GARI, Suzanne (sop)
Hasse: Piramo e Tisbe (Cpte)

GARIBAY, Minerva (gtr)
see CONCERT INDEX under:
(EMI) **CZS7 67435-2**   Rodrigo—Orchestral Works

GARIN, Remi (ten)
Rossini: Petite Messe Solennelle

GARINO, Gérard (ten)
A. Thomas: Hamlet (Cpte)
Bizet: Carmen (Cpte)
see CONCERT INDEX under:
(DENO) **CO-72886**   Berlioz: Choral Works

GARLITSKI, Boris (vn)
Mozart: Concertone, K190
see CONCERT INDEX under:
(RCA) **RD87991**   Bach: Concerti

GARMO, Tilly de (sop)
Wagner: Götterdämmerung (exc)
see CONCERT INDEX under:
(PEAR) **GEMMCDS9137**   Wagner—Der Ring des Nibelungen
(PREI) **89201**   Helge Roswaenge (1897-1972) - I

GARRETT, David (vn)
see CONCERT INDEX under:
(DG) **445 657-2GH**   Bach/Beethoven/Mozart—Works for Violin and Piano

GARRETT, Eric (bar)
Donizetti: Fille du régiment (Cpte)
Puccini: Fanciulla del West (Cpte)
see CONCERT INDEX under:
(DECC) **417 011-2DH2**   Pavarotti's Greatest Hits
(DECC) **433 437-2DA**   Pavarotti—King of the High Cs

GARRETT, Lesley (sop)
Sullivan: Mikado (exc)
see CONCERT INDEX under:
(SILV) **FILMCD117**   The Television Scores of Geoffrey Burgon
(SILV) **FILMCD127**   Vampire Circus—The Essential Vampire Theme Collection
(SILV) **SILKD6004**   Simple Gifts—Lesley Garrett
(SILV) **SONGCD903**   Diva! A Soprano at the Movies

GARRETT, Margo (pf)
see CONCERT INDEX under:
(DG) **435 440-2GH**   Kathleen Battle at Carnegie Hall
(SONY) **SK53106**   Kathleen Battle & Jean-Pierre Rampal in Concert

GARRIDO, Gabriel (cond)
see Elyma Ens

GARRIGOSA, Francesc (ten)
Martín y Soler: Cosa Rara (Cpte)

GARRIS, John (ten)
Verdi: Traviata (Cpte)

GARRISON, David (sngr)
Berlin: Annie Get Your Gun (Cpte)
Bernstein: On the Town (Cpte)
Gershwin: Girl crazy (Cpte)
Kern: Show Boat (Cpte)
Porter: Kiss Me, Kate (Cpte)

GARRISON, Jon (ten)
Mendelssohn: Erste Walpurgisnacht
Stravinsky: Rake's Progress (Cpte)

Tippett: Child of our Time
see CONCERT INDEX under:
(BRID) **BCD9014**   Elliott Carter: Vocal Works
(EMI) **CDC5 55121-2**   Szymanowski—Choral Works

GARRISON, Kenneth (ten)
R.Strauss: Frau ohne Schatten (Cpte)

GARSIDE, Gwladys (mez)
Delius: Village Romeo and Juliet (Cpte)

GÄRTNER, Bernhard (ten)
Mangold: Abraham
see CONCERT INDEX under:
(BAYE) **BR100041**   Choral and Vocal Works

GARTSIDE, Joyce (sop)
see CONCERT INDEX under:
(TEST) **SBT1058**   James Johnston - Opera Arias and Songs

GARULLI, Alfonso (ten)
see CONCERT INDEX under:
(SYMP) **SYMCD1077**   The Harold Wayne Collection, Vol.4

GARVEY, David (pf)
Argento: Virginia Woolf
see CONCERT INDEX under:
(RCA) **09026 61499-2**   Leontyne Price Recital

GAS, Manuel (sngr)
Sorozábal: Katiuska (Cpte)

GASDIA, Cecilia (sop)
Gounod: Faust (Cpte)
Handel: Rinaldo (Cpte)
Puccini: Turandot (Cpte)
Rossini: Armida (Cpte), Viaggio a Reims (Cpte), Zelmira (Cpte)

GASKELL, Elizabeth (sop)
Janáček: Fate (Cpte)

GASKELL, Helen (ob)
see CONCERT INDEX under:
(SYMP) **SYMCD1075**   May Harrison—Vioinist and Composer

GASPARINI, Annamaria (mez)
Zandonai: Francesca da Rimini (exc)

GASSENHUBER, Angela (pf)
see CONCERT INDEX under:
(TROU) **TRO-CD01405**   Ethel Smyth—Chamber Works & Songs, Vol.3

GASSIEV, Nikolai (ten)
Borodin: Prince Igor (Cpte)
Mussorgsky: Khovanshchina (Cpte)
Rimsky-Korsakov: Sadko (Cpte)
Tchaikovsky: Queen of Spades (Cpte)

GASSNER, Albert (ten)
see CONCERT INDEX under:
(EMI) **CMS7 64783-2**   Schubert—Sacred Works, Vol.2

GASTINEL, Anne (vc)
R. Strauss: Cello Sonata
Rachmaninov: Cello Sonata
see CONCERT INDEX under:
(AUVI) **V4748**   Kodaly/Janáček/Liszt—Works for Cello and Piano

GASZTECKI, Marek (bass)
Schillings: Mona Lisa (Cpte)

GATES, Lucy (sop)
see CONCERT INDEX under:
(SIMA) **PSC1810(2)**   Grieg—Songs (historical recordings, pt 2)

GÁTI, Istvan (bar)
Bach: Cantata 80, Cantata 147, Cantata 208, Cantata 211, Cantata 212, St Matthew Passion, BWV244 (Cpte)
Handel: Floridante (Cpte), St John Passion (Cpte)
Mozart: Nozze di Figaro (Cpte)
Puccini: Tosca (Cpte)

GATT, Martin (bn)
see CONCERT INDEX under:
(CONI) **CDCF173**   Prokofiev: Orchestral & Chamber Works
(DECC) **443 476-2DF2**   Vivaldi—L'estro armonico, Op 3
(EMI) **CZS7 67306-2**   Mozart—Works featuring Wind Instruments

GATTA, Dora (sop)
Mozart: Nozze di Figaro (Cpte)

GATTI, Daniele (cond)
see Bologna Teatro Comunale Orch

GATTI, Enrico (vn)
see CONCERT INDEX under:
(HARM) **HMA190 5137**   Arias and Cantatas for Soprano and Trumpet

GATTI, Gabriella (sop)
see CONCERT INDEX under:
(EMI) **CHS7 69741-2(7)**   Record of Singing, Vol.4—Italian School

GATTI, Giorgio (bar)
Sacchini: Contadina in Corte (Cpte)
Verdi: Traviata (Cpte)

GATTI, Giovanni (fl)
see CONCERT INDEX under:
(PHIL) **426 086-2PBQ**   Vivaldi—Double Concertos

Rameau: Castor et Pollux (Cpte), Hippolyte et Aricie (Cpte), Platée (Cpte)
  see CONCERT INDEX *under:*
(FNAC) **592096**   Rameau—Grand Motets
(HARM) **HMC90 1351**   Delalande—Sacred Choral Works
(HARM) **HMC90 1416**   Delalande—Petits Motets
(VIRG) **VC5 45103-2**   Alessandro Scarlatti—Motets

GENT, Willemijn van (sop)
Purcell: Fairy Queen, Z629 (Cpte)

GENTILE, Maria (sop)
  see CONCERT INDEX *under:*
(PREI) **89040**   Carlo Galeffi (1884-1961)

GENTLEMEN OF THE CHAPPELL
  cond P. BASSANO
  see CONCERT INDEX *under:*
(ASV) **CDGAU122**   Venice Preserved

GEORG, Mechthild (contr)
Mangold: Abraham

GEORG, Mechthild (mez)
A.J. Romberg: Lied von der Glocke
Bach: Cantata 30
Hasse: Conversione di Sant' Agostino (Cpte)
Mendelssohn: Paulus (Cpte)
Puccini: Gianni Schicchi (Cpte)
Rossini: Péchés de vieillesse II (Cpte), Péchés de vieillesse III (exc)
Telemann: Cantata, TWV1: 771, Schwanengesang, TWV4: 6
  see CONCERT INDEX *under:*
(EMI) **CZS7 67819-2**   Brahms/Schumann—Requiems
(EURO) **GD69043**   Puccini: Il Trittico
(HANS) **98 815**   Bach—Cantatas, Vol.53
(HANS) **98 828**   Bach—Cantatas, Vol.66
(HANS) **98 856**   Bach—Cantatas, Vol.5
(HANS) **98 858**   Bach—Cantatas, Vol.7
(NOVA) **150 028-2**   Bach—Cantatas

GEORGE, Donald (ten)
Mendelssohn: Elias (Cpte)
Puccini: Manon Lescaut (Cpte)
Verdi: Requiem (Cpte)

GEORGE, Michael (bass)
Bach: Cantata 208, Christmas Oratorio, BWV248 (Cpte), Mass in B minor, BWV232 (Cpte)
Beethoven: Missa Solemnis
Blow: Venus and Adonis (Cpte)
Chabrier: Briséis (Cpte)
Elgar: Dream of Gerontius (Cpte)
G. Lloyd: John Socman (exc)
Handel: Acis and Galatea (Cpte), Deborah (Cpte), Joshua (Cpte), Judas Maccabaeus (Cpte), Messiah (Cpte), Occasional Oratorio (Cpte), Ottone (Cpte), Resurrezione (Cpte)
Haydn: Creation (Cpte), Mass 7, Mass 14
Monteverdi: Orfeo (Cpte), Vespers
Pärt: Passio
Purcell: Birthday Ode, Z342, Dioclesian, Z627 (exc), Fairy Queen, Z629 (Cpte), St Cecilia's Day Ode, Z328, Timon of Athens, Z632 (Cpte)
Stravinsky: Nightingale (Cpte)
Telemann: Donner-Ode
Zelenka: Lamentations of Jeremiah
  see CONCERT INDEX *under:*
(BIDD) **LAW013**   Dodgson—Orchestral & Vocal Works
(CARL) **PCD894**   Great Baroque Arias, Part I
(CHAN) **CHAN0505**   Handel—Chandos Anthems Vol. 3
(CHAN) **CHAN0517**   Handel—Sacred Choral works
(COLL) **Coll1320-2**   Baroque Choral Works
(COLL) **Coll7016-2**   Handel—Alexander's Feast
(ERAT) **4509-96371-2**   Gardiner—The Purcell Collection
(HYPE) **CDA66245**   Bruckner—Choral Works
(HYPE) **CDA66261/2**   War's Embers
(HYPE) **CDA66292**   Fauré: Sacred Choral Works
(HYPE) **CDA66314**   Purcell—Complete Odes & Welcome Songs, Vol.1
(HYPE) **CDA66315**   Handel: Music for Royal Occasions
(HYPE) **CDA66398**   Schutz—Christmas Story; Gabrieli—Motets
(HYPE) **CDA66412**   Purcell—Complete Odes & Welcome Songs, Vol.3
(HYPE) **CDA66456**   Purcell—Complete Odes & Welcome Songs, Vol.4
(HYPE) **CDA66476**   Purcell—Complete Odes & Welcome Songs, Vol.5
(HYPE) **CDA66494**   Purcell—Complete Odes & Welcome Songs, Vol.6
(HYPE) **CDA66585**   Purcell—Complete Anthems & Services, Vol.1
(HYPE) **CDA66587**   Purcell—Complete Odes & Welcome Songs, Vol.7
(HYPE) **CDA66598**   Purcell—Complete Odes & Welcome Songs, Vol.8
(HYPE) **CDA66609**   Purcell—Complete Anthems & Services, Vol.2
(HYPE) **CDA66623**   Purcell—Complete Anthems & Services, Vol.3
(HYPE) **CDA66644**   Purcell—Complete Anthems & Services, Vol.4
(HYPE) **CDA66656**   Purcell—Complete Anthems & Services, Vol.5
(HYPE) **CDA66663**   Purcell—Complete Anthems & Services, Vol.6
(HYPE) **CDA66677**   Purcell—Anthems & Services, Vol.7

(HYPE) **CDA66686**   Purcell—Complete Anthems & Services, Vol.8
(HYPE) **CDA66693**   Purcell—Complete Anthems and Services, Volume 9
(HYPE) **CDA66707**   Purcell—Complete Anthems & Services, Vol. 10
(HYPE) **CDA66710**   Purcell—Secular Solo Songs, Volume 1
(HYPE) **CDA66716**   Purcell—Complete Anthems and Services, Volume 11
(HYPE) **CDA66720**   Purcell—Secular Solo Songs, Volume 2
(HYPE) **CDA66730**   Purcell—Secular Solo Songs, Vol. 3
(HYPE) **CDJ33020**   Schubert—Complete Lieder, Vol.20
(HYPE) **CDJ33022**   Schubert—Complete Lieder, Vol.22
(LINN) **CKD011**   Elizabethan & Jacobean Consort Music
(L'OI) **436 460-2OH**   Biber—Requiem; Chamber Works
(L'OI) **436 585-2OH**   Mozart—Sacred Choral Works
(L'OI) **440 637-2OH**   Monteverdi—Ballets
(NIMB) **NI5144/8**   Beethoven: Symphonies Nos 1-9
(UNIT) **88002-2**   My Beloved Spake
(VIRG) **VC7 59243-2**   Purcell—Odes for Queen Mary

GEORGEL, Jean-Louis (ten)
Rameau: Hippolyte et Aricie (Cpte)

GEORGES, Philippe (ten)
Gounod: Sapho (Cpte)
Massenet: Cléopâtre (Cpte)

GEORGIA STATE SYMPHONY ORCHESTRA
  cond D. KAKHIDZE
Kancheli: Symphony 3, Symphony 4, Symphony 5, Symphony 6

GEORGIADIS, John (cond)
  see London Virtuosi

GEORGIADIS, John (vn)
  see CONCERT INDEX *under:*
(CARL) **PCD902**   An Evening in Vienna

GEORGIAN, Karine (vc)
Brahms: Clarinet Trio
  see CONCERT INDEX *under:*
(BIDD) **LAW014**   Brahms—Cello Sonatas
(CHAN) **CHAN9377/8**   Ireland—Chamber Works

GEORGIEV, Georgi (va)
  see CONCERT INDEX *under:*
(TROU) **TRO-CD01405**   Ethel Smyth—Chamber Works & Songs, Vol.3

GEORGIEV, Stoil (bar)
Borodin: Prince Igor (Cpte)
Glinka: Life for the Tsar (Cpte)
Mussorgsky: Khovanshchina (Cpte)
Tchaikovsky: Eugene Onegin (Cpte), Queen of Spades (Cpte)

GERAERTS, Harry (ten)
Bach: Cantata 56
  see CONCERT INDEX *under:*
(CPO) **CPO999 139-2**   The Apocryphal Bach Cantatas

GÉRARD, Jean-Claude (fl)
Mozart: Flute Quartets
  see CONCERT INDEX *under:*
(CAPR) **10 479**   Busoni—Orchestral Works
(EMI) **CMS5 65061-2(2)**   The Fabulous Victoria de los Angeles (pt 2)

GERASSIMOVA, Natalia (sop)
  see CONCERT INDEX *under:*
(CDM) **LDC288 038/40**   Rimsky-Korsakov—Complete Songs

GERBINO, Giuse (mez)
Verdi: Rigoletto (Cpte)
  see CONCERT INDEX *under:*
(EMI) **CDM7 69543-2**   Maria Callas and Giuseppe Di Stefano - Duets

GERDES, Otto (cond)
  see Bavarian St Op Orch

GERDESITS, Ferenc (ten)
Puccini: Tosca (Cpte)

GERECZ, Arpad (cond)
  see Solistes Romands

GERELO, Vassili (bar)
Mussorgsky: Khovanshchina (Cpte)
Prokofiev: War and Peace (Cpte)

GERGALOV, Alexander (bar)
Prokofiev: War and Peace (Cpte)
Rimsky-Korsakov: Sadko (Cpte)

GERGIEV, Valery (cond)
  see Kirov Th Orch

GERGIEVA, Larissa (pf)
  see CONCERT INDEX *under:*
(PHIL) **442 013-2PH**   Tchaikovsky—Romances
(PHIL) **442 780-2PH**   Songs of Desire

GERHARD, Maria (sop)
  see CONCERT INDEX *under:*
(SCHW) **314502**   Vienna State Opera—Live Recordings (sampler)

GERHARDT, Charles (cond)
  see Munich RO

GERHARDT, Elena (mez)
  see CONCERT INDEX *under:*
(PEAR) **GEMMCDS9075**   Hugo Wolf Society, Volume I
(SIMA) **PSC1810(2)**   Grieg—Songs (historical recordings, pt 2)

GERHART, Maria (sop)
  see CONCERT INDEX *under:*
(SCHW) **314512**   Vienna State Opera Live, Vol.1

GERIHSEN, Franz (bar)
Weill: Kuhhandel (exc)
  see CONCERT INDEX *under:*
(HANS) **98 802**   Bach—Cantatas, Vol.40

GÉRIMON, Paul (bass)
Monteverdi: Orfeo (Cpte)

GERINGAS, David (vc)
Beethoven: Piano Trios (exc), Serenade, Op. 8
Gubaidulina: Hommage
Schubert: Notturno, D897, Piano Trio 1, Piano Trio 2
  see CONCERT INDEX *under:*
(CLAV) **CD50-8814/6**   Boccherini—Cello Concertos
(CPO) **CPO999 135-2**   Pfitzner—Cello Concertos
(CPO) **CPO999 277-2**   Berthold Goldschmidt—Orchestral Works
(ERAT) **4509-91721-2**   Dutilleux—Piano Works and Chamber Music
(SONY) **SK52490**   Brahms—Lieder

GERIOVÁ, Beata (mez)
Respighi: Liriche (1921)

GERMAIN, Pierre (vc)
Milhaud: Christophe Colomb (Cpte)

GERMAN, Timothy (ten)
Balfe: Bohemian Girl (Cpte)
Janáček: Fate (Cpte)

GERMAN BACH SOLOISTS
  cond H. WINSCHERMANN
  see CONCERT INDEX *under:*
(LASE) **15 525**   Mozart—Violin Concertos
(PHIL) **422 521-2PME2**   The Complete Mozart Edition Vol 21

GERMAN BAROQUE SOLOISTS
  see CONCERT INDEX *under:*
(FSM) **FCD91220**   French Baroque Christmas Music

GERMAN PHILHARMONIC WIND ENSEMBLE
  cond F. BERNIUS
  see CONCERT INDEX *under:*
(SONY) **SK48037**   Bruckner—Choral Works

GERRARD, M. (vn)
  see CONCERT INDEX *under:*
(MERI) **CDE84169**   Mozart: Clarinet Works

GERSHWIN, George (pf)
  see CONCERT INDEX *under:*
(HALC) **DHDL101**   Two Sides of George Gershwin
(NONE) **7559-79287-2**   Gershwin—Piano Rolls

GERSON, Therese (sop)
  see CONCERT INDEX *under:*
(PREI) **89082**   Margarete Klose (1902-1968)

GERTSCHEN, Sabine (dulcimer)
Holliger: Alb-Chehr

GESSENDORF, Mechtild (sop)
Busoni: Turandot (Cpte)
Schoeck: Penthesilea (Cpte)

GESTER, Martin (cond)
  see Parlement de Musique

GESTER, Martin (hpd/dir)
  see CONCERT INDEX *under:*
(O111) **OPS55-9119**   M-A. Charpentier—Office de Ténèbres

GESTER, Martin (org/dir)
  see CONCERT INDEX *under:*
(O111) **OPS30-100**   Hasse—Motets

GESZTY, Sylvia (sop)
Lehár: Schön ist die Welt (exc)
R. Strauss: Ariadne auf Naxos (Cpte)

GEUSSER, Heinrich (cl)
  see CONCERT INDEX *under:*
(DG) **437 680-2GDO2**   Rita Streich - Lieder Recital
(DG) **445 400-2GDO10**   Ferenc Fricsay - A Portrait
(DG) **445 403-2GDO**   R. Strauss—Orchestral Works

GHASNE, Alexis (bar)
  see CONCERT INDEX *under:*
(IRCC) **IRCC-CD802**   Souvenirs of Rare French Opera
(SYMP) **SYMCD1089**   Historic Baritones of the French School

GHAZARIAN, Sona (sop)
Beethoven: Fidelio (Cpte)
Mozart: Don Giovanni (Cpte)
Verdi: Ballo in maschera (Cpte)
  see CONCERT INDEX *under:*
(CAPR) **10 348**   Mozart Gala—Suntory Hall, Tokyo

GHENT CANTABILE
  see CONCERT INDEX *under:*
(ERAT) **2292-45202-2**   M-A. Charpentier: Sacred Works

GHENT COLLEGIUM VOCALE
cond P. HERREWEGHE
Bach: Cantata 21, Cantata 42, Cantata 80, Christmas Oratorio, BWV248 (Cpte), Magnificat, BWV243, Mass, BWV233, Mass, BWV236, Mass in B minor, BWV232 (Cpte), Motets (Cpte), St John Passion, BWV245 (Cpte), St Matthew Passion, BWV244 (Cpte)
Gilles: Requiem
Monteverdi: Vespers
see CONCERT INDEX *under:*
(HARM) HMC90 1122 Brahms—Motets
(HARM) HMC90 1272 Mendelssohn—Psalms; Ave Maria
(HARM) HMC90 1322 Bruckner—Choral Works
(VIRG) VC7 59237-2 Bach—Cantatas
(VIRG) VC7 59587-2 Bach—Masses etc
cond S. KUIJKEN
Gluck: Orfeo ed Euridice (Cpte)
Haydn: Schöpfung (Cpte)
Rameau: Zoroastre (Cpte)
cond G. LEONHARDT
see CONCERT INDEX *under:*
(TELD) 2292-42428-2 Bach—Cantatas, Volume 41
(TELD) 2292-42571-2 Bach—Cantatas, Volume 17
(TELD) 2292-42573-2 Bach—Cantatas, Volume 19
(TELD) 2292-42576-2 Bach—Cantatas, Volume 20
(TELD) 2292-42578-2 Bach—Cantatas, Volume 22
(TELD) 2292-42582-2 Bach—Cantatas, Volume 23
(TELD) 2292-42583-2 Bach—Cantatas, Volume 24
(TELD) 2292-42585-2 Bach—Cantatas, Volume 25
(TELD) 2292-42602-2 Bach—Cantatas, Volume 26
(TELD) 2292-42605-2 Bach—Cantatas, Volume 27
(TELD) 2292-42606-2 Bach—Cantatas, Volume 28
(TELD) 2292-42608-2 Bach—Cantatas, Volume 29
(TELD) 2292-42615-2 Bach—Cantatas, Volume 31
(TELD) 2292-42617-2 Bach—Cantatas, Volume 32
(TELD) 2292-42618-2 Bach—Cantatas, Volume 33
(TELD) 2292-42631-2 Bach—Cantatas, Volume 36
(TELD) 2292-42633-2 Bach—Cantatas, Volume 38
(TELD) 2292-42634-2 Bach—Cantatas, Volume 39
(TELD) 2292-42635-2 Bach—Cantatas, Volume 40
(TELD) 2292-42738-2 Bach—Cantatas, Volume 42
(TELD) 2292-44179-2 Bach—Cantatas, Volume 43
(TELD) 2292-44193-2 Bach—Cantatas, Volume 44
(TELD) 2292-44194-2 Bach—Cantatas, Volume 45
(TELD) 4509-91758-2 Bach—Cantatas, Vol.4
(TELD) 4509-91759-2 Bach—Cantatas, Vol.5
(TELD) 4509-91760-2 Bach—Cantatas, Vol.6
(TELD) 4509-91761-2 Bach—Cantatas, Vol.7
(TELD) 4509-91762-2 Bach—Cantatas, Vol.8
(TELD) 4509-91763-2 Bach—Cantatas, Vol.9
(TELD) 4509-91764-2 Bach—Cantatas, Vol.10

GHENT COLLEGIUM VOCALE ORCHESTRA
cond P. HERREWEGHE
Bach: Christmas Oratorio, BWV248 (Cpte), Mass, BWV233, Mass, BWV236, Mass in B minor, BWV232 (Cpte)
see CONCERT INDEX *under:*
(VIRG) VC7 59237-2 Bach—Cantatas
(VIRG) VC7 59587-2 Bach—Masses etc

GHENT MADRIGAL CHOIR
see CONCERT INDEX *under:*
(ERAT) 2292-45202-2 M-A. Charpentier: Sacred Works

GHEORGHIU, Angela (sop)
Verdi: Traviata (Cpte)

GHIAUROV, Nicolai (bass)
Bellini: Puritani (Cpte), Sonnambula (Cpte)
Boito: Mefistofele (Cpte)
Borodin: Prince Igor (Cpte)
Donizetti: Favorita (Cpte), Lucia di Lammermoor (Cpte)
Gounod: Faust (Cpte)
Massenet: Don Quichotte (Cpte), Roi de Lahore (Cpte)
Mozart: Don Giovanni (Cpte)
Mussorgsky: Boris Godunov (Cpte), Khovanshchina (Cpte)
Ponchielli: Gioconda (Cpte)
Puccini: Bohème (Cpte), Turandot (Cpte)
Rossini: Barbiere di Siviglia (Cpte), Guillaume Tell (Cpte)
Tchaikovsky: Eugene Onegin (Cpte)
Verdi: Aida (Cpte), Don Carlo (Cpte), Don Carlos (Cpte), Ernani (Cpte), Macbeth (Cpte), Requiem (Cpte), Rigoletto (Cpte), Simon Boccanegra (Cpte), Trovatore (Cpte)
see CONCERT INDEX *under:*
(DECC) 417 011-2DH2 Pavarotti's Greatest Hits
(DECC) 433 439-2DA Great Love Duets
(DECC) 436 464-2DM Ten Top Baritones & Basses
(DECC) 444 389-2DWO The World of Borodin
(EMI) CDM7 69549-2 Ruggero Raimondi: Italian Opera Arias
(RCA) 09026 62501-2 Russian Romances

GHIAUROV, Zlatina (pf)
see CONCERT INDEX *under:*
(DECC) 444 389-2DWO The World of Borodin

GHIELMI, Lorenzo (organ)
see CONCERT INDEX *under:*
(DHM) 05472 77278-2 Bach—Organ Works, Vol.3
(DHM) 05472 77312-2 Bach—Organ Works, Volume 5

GHIONE, Franco (cond)
see La Scala Orch

GHIRARDINI, Emilio (bar)
Verdi: Forza del destino (exc)

GHIUSELEV, Nikola (bass)
Borodin: Prince Igor (Cpte)
Mozart: Don Giovanni (Cpte)
Mussorgsky: Boris Godunov (Cpte), Khovanshchina (Cpte)
Offenbach: Contes d'Hoffmann (Cpte)
Prokofiev: War and Peace (Cpte)
Tchaikovsky: Eugene Onegin (Cpte)
Verdi: Battaglia di Legnano (Cpte)

GIACOMINI, Giuseppe (ten)
Bellini: Norma (Cpte)
Mascagni: Cavalleria Rusticana (Cpte)
Puccini: Tosca (Cpte)
see CONCERT INDEX *under:*
(DECC) 436 261-2DHO3 Puccini—Il Trittico

GIACOMOTTI, Alfredo (bass)
Cherubini: Medea (Cpte)
Donizetti: Don Pasquale (Cpte)
Puccini: Turandot (Cpte)
Verdi: Ernani (Cpte), Rigoletto (Cpte), Traviata (Cpte), Trovatore (Cpte)
see CONCERT INDEX *under:*
(RCA) 09026 68014-2 Pavarotti - The Early Years, Vol.2
(SONY) MK37228 Pavarotti sings Verdi

GIAIOTTI, Bonaldo (bass)
Mascagni: Iris (Cpte)
Puccini: Madama Butterfly (Cpte)
Verdi: Aida (Cpte), Forza del destino (Cpte), Luisa Miller (Cpte), Trovatore (Cpte)
see CONCERT INDEX *under:*
(RCA) 09026 68014-2 Pavarotti - The Early Years, Vol.2

GIAMMATEO, Anthony (cl)
see CONCERT INDEX *under:*
(CLRI) CC0005 The Clarinet - Historical Recordings, Vol.1

GIANNINI, Dusolina (sop)
see CONCERT INDEX *under:*
(EMI) CDH7 63702-2 Beniamino Gigli and Arias and Duets (1932-1949)
(MMOI) CDMOIR417 Great Voices of the Century—Beniamino Gigli
(PREI) 89044 Dusolina Giannini (1902-1986)

GIANNOTTI, Pierre (ten)
G. Charpentier: Louise (Cpte)

GIARDELLI, Claire (vc)
Telemann: Musique de Table (exc)

(IL) GIARDINO ARMONICO ENSEMBLE
Vivaldi: Concerti, Op. 8 (exc), Concerti, Op. 10
see CONCERT INDEX *under:*
(TELD) 2292-46013-2 Christmas Concertos
(TELD) 4509-91852-2 Vivaldi—Concertos
(TELD) 4509-93157-2 Musica da Camera a Napoli
cond G. ANTONINI
see CONCERT INDEX *under:*
(TELD) 4509-94552-2 Vivaldi—Double and Triple Concertos

GIBAND, Félix (bass)
Gounod: Philémon et Baucis (Cpte)

GIBAULT, Claire (cond)
see RPO

GIBBONS, Jack (pf)
see CONCERT INDEX *under:*
(ASV) CDDCS227 Alkan—Piano Works
(ASV) CDWHL2074 The Authentic George Gershwin, Vol. 1
(ASV) CDWHL2077 The Authentic Gershwin, Vol.2
(ASV) CDWHL2082 The Authentic Gershwin, Volume 3
(HYPE) CDA66565 Constant Lambert—Vocal & Orchestral Works
(HYPE) CDA66594 Milhaud—Orchestral Works

GIBBONS, John (hpd)
Bach: Triple Concerto, BWV1044

(ORLANDO) GIBBONS VIOL ENSEMBLE
cond W. CHRISTIE
see CONCERT INDEX *under:*
(HARM) HMC90 1471 Bouzignac—Te Deum; Motets

GIBBS, John (bar)
Gay: Beggar's Opera (Cpte)
Puccini: Tosca (Cpte)
Verdi: Rigoletto (Cpte)

GIBBS, Peter (vn)
see CONCERT INDEX *under:*
(VANG) 08.2003.72 Purcell—Celebrated Songs, Sacred Airs and Concert Pieces

GIBBS, Raymond (bar)
Bizet: Carmen (Cpte)

GIBIN, João (ten)
Puccini: Fanciulla del West (Cpte)

GIBSON, Sir Alexander (cond)
see ECO

GIBSON, Jon (sax)
see CONCERT INDEX *under:*
(PNT) 434 873-2PTH Jon Gibson—In Good Company

GIBSON, Lee (sngr)
Bernstein: West Side Story (Cpte)

GIBSON, Mr (cond)
see LSO

GIBSON, Rodney (ten)
Verdi: Traviata (Cpte)

GIEBEL, Agnes (sop)
Bach: Mass in B minor, BWV232 (Cpte)
Bruckner: Te Deum

GIELEN, Michael (cond)
see Berlin RSO

GIELGUD, Sir John (narr)
Prokofiev: Peter and the Wolf
Vaughan Williams: Bunyan Sequence
Walton: Hamlet (exc)
see CONCERT INDEX *under:*
(HYPE) CDA66569 Vaughan Williams—Choral Works
(TRIN) TRP046 Prokofiev—Peter and the Wolf etc
(VIRG) VC7 59007-2 Picker—Orchestral Works

GIENGER, Stefan (treb)
Mozart: Zauberflöte (Cpte)
see CONCERT INDEX *under:*
(TELD) 2292-42635-2 Bach—Cantatas, Volume 40
(TELD) 2292-44193-2 Bach—Cantatas, Volume 44
(TELD) 4509-91763-2 Bach—Cantatas, Vol.9
(TELD) 4509-91764-2 Bach—Cantatas, Vol.10
(TELD) 9031-74798-2 Bach—Arias and Duets

GIEPEL, Dorothea (sop)
R. Strauss: Elektra (Cpte)

GIERSTER, Hans (cond)
see Bamberg SO

GIESEKING, Walter (pf)
Beethoven: Piano Concerto 5
Debussy: Préludes
Schumann: Piano Concerto
see CONCERT INDEX *under:*
(APR) APR5511 Gieseking—First Concerto Recordings, Vol.1
(EMI) CDH7 63702-2 Mozart: Lieder & Concert Arias
(EMI) CDH7 63655-2 Schwarzkopf—The previously unpublished recordings
(MUSI) MACD-612 Walter Gieseking—Historical Broadcasts, 1944-50
(MUSI) MACD-780 The Mengelberg Legacy
(PEAR) GEMMCD9038 Walter Gieseking, Vol.3
(PEAR) GEMMCD9449 Walter Gieseking—Debussy & Ravel
(PEAR) GEMMCD9933 Grieg and his Circle play Grieg
(SIMA) PSC1809(2) Grieg—Historical Piano Recordings (pt 2)

GIESEN, Hubert (pf)
see CONCERT INDEX *under:*
(BIDD) LAB032 The young Yehudi Menuhin, Vol.2
(DG) 423 956-2GDO Schubert: Lieder
(DG) 429 933-2GDO Fritz Wunderlich—Lieder Recital
(DG) 431 110-2GB Great Voices - Fritz Wunderlich
(TEST) SBT1003 The Young Menuhin—Encores, Vol.1

GIFFORD, Anthea (gtr)
see CONCERT INDEX *under:*
(BIDD) LAW013 Dodgson—Orchestral & Vocal Works
(NATI) NTCD001 Anthea Gifford at Coughton Court

GIFFORD, Clemence (sop)
see CONCERT INDEX *under:*
(ARCI) ARC103/4 Schoenberg—String Quartets

GIFFORD, Gerald (hpd)
see CONCERT INDEX *under:*
(LIBR) LRCD156 Georgian Harpsichord Music

GIFFORD, Gerald (org/dir)
Stanley: Organ Concertos, Op. 10 (exc)

GIGER, Paul (vn)
Giger: Chartres

GIGLI, Beniamino (ten)
Puccini: Bohème (Cpte)
Verdi: Aida (Cpte), Requiem (Cpte)
see CONCERT INDEX *under:*
(EMI) CDH7 61051-2 Beniamino Gigli - Operatic Arias
(EMI) CDH7 61052-2 Beniamino Gigli—Arias and Duets (1932-1949)
(EMI) CHS7 64864-2(1) La Scala Edition - Vol.2, 1915-46 (pt 1)
(EMI) CHS7 64864-2(2) La Scala Edition - Vol.2, 1915-46 (pt 2)
(EMI) CHS7 69741-2(7) Record of Singing, Vol.4—Italian School
(MMOI) CDMOIR409 Three Tenors—Björling, Gigli & Tauber
(MMOI) CDMOIR411 Sacred Songs and Arias
(MMOI) CDMOIR417 Great Voices of the Century—Beniamino Gigli
(MMOI) CDMOIR425 Three Tenors, Volume 2
(NIMB) NI7801 Great Singers, Vol.1
(NIMB) NI7807 Beniamino Gigli—Vol. 1: 1918-24
(NIMB) NI7810 Titta Ruffo—Opera Recital
(NIMB) NI7852 Galli-Curci, Vol.2
(NIMB) NI7852 Legendary Tenors
(PEAR) GEMMCDS9926(2) Covent Garden on Record—Vol.4 (pt 2)
(PEAR) GEMMCD9316 Beniamino Gigli
(PEAR) GEMMCD9367 Gigli—Arias and Duets

GILGI, Giuseppe de Luca (1876-1950) - II
(PREI) 89073   Giuseppe de Luca (1876-1950) - II
(PREI) 89303(2)   Titta Ruffo Edition (pt 2)
(RCA) GD87811   Beniamino Gigli—Operatic Arias
(RCA) 09026 61580-2(3)   RCA/Met 100 Singers, 100
  Years (pt 3)
(ROMO) 81014-2   Elisabeth Rethberg (1894-1976)
(SCHW) 314632   Vienna State Opera Live, Vol.13
(TEST) SBT1005   Ten Top Tenors

GILBERT, Daniel (cl)
  see CONCERT INDEX under:
(CATA) 09026 61979-2   Memento Bittersweet

GILBERT, Herschel Burke (cond)
  see Orig Film Cast

GILBERT, Kenneth (hpd)
Bach: Art of Fugue, Goldberg Variations, Viola da
  gamba Sonatas, BWV1027-9, Wohltemperierte
  Klavier, 3-Harpsichord Concerti (exc), 4-Harpsichord
  Concerto
Couperin: Art de toucher le clavecin, Livre de clavecin
  I, Livre de clavecin II, Livre de clavecin III, Livre de
  clavecin IV
Handel: Keyboard Suites, Set I
Rameau: Pièces de clavecin
  see CONCERT INDEX under:
(ARCH) 437 555-2AH   Bach—Harpsichord Works
(HARM) HMA190 1278   Bach—Harpsichord Works
(HARM) HMC90 1496   Purcell—Harpsichord Suites
(NOVA) 150 018-2   Harpsichord Recital

GILBERT, Max (va)
  see CONCERT INDEX under:
(DECC) 425 960-2DM   Mozart—Chamber Works
(DECC) 433 477-2DM   Ferrier Edition - Volume 10

GILELS, Emil (pf)
Beethoven: Piano Sonata 15, Piano Sonata 17, Piano
  Sonata 29, Piano Sonata 30, Piano Sonata 31
Brahms: Ballades, Piano Concerto 1, Piano Concerto
  2, Piano Pieces, Op.116, Piano Quartet 1
Chopin: Piano Concerto 1
Liszt: Piano Sonata, S178
Mozart: Piano Concerto 21
Schubert: Piano Sonata, D850, Trout Quintet, D667
Tchaikovsky: Piano Concerto 1, Piano Concerto 2,
  Piano Sonata, Op. 80
  see CONCERT INDEX under:
(DG) 400 036-2GH   Beethoven: Piano Sonatas
(DG) 419 158-2GH2   Brahms: Piano Works
(DG) 419 162-2GH   Beethoven: Piano Sonatas
(DG) 419 172-2GH   Beethoven: Piano Sonatas
(DG) 419 749-2GH   Grieg: Lyric Pieces
(DG) 423 136-2GH   Beethoven: Piano Works
(MELO) 74321 25172-2(1)   Russian Piano School (pt 1
  - Vols.1 - 8)
(MELO) 74321 25179-2   Russian Piano School, Vol.
  7
(MEZH) MK417072   Emil Gilels—Piano Recital
(MULT) 310106-2   Beethoven—Prague Radio
  Recordings (1958)
(OLYM) OCD269   Kabalevsky—Volume 4
(ORFE) C332931B   Liszt/Schubert—Piano Recital
(PRAG) PR250 039   Brahms/Weber—Piano Works
(TEST) SBT1029   Gilels plays Saint-Saëns and
  Rachmaninov

GILES, Alice (hp)
  see CONCERT INDEX under:
(CARL) PWK1141   French Impressions

GILES, Andrew (alto)
Dvořák: Mass in D

GILFORD, Jack (ten)
Porter: Anything Goes (Cpte)

GILFRY, Rodney (bar)
Brahms: Deutsches Requiem, Op. 45 (Cpte)
Mozart: Così fan tutte (Cpte), Don Giovanni (Cpte),
  Nozze di Figaro (Cpte)

GILGORE, Elisha (pf)
  see CONCERT INDEX under:
(CENT) CRC2176   Works by Soulima Stravinsky

GILHOFER, Eva (contr)
Holliger: Magische Tänzer (Cpte)

GILIBERT, Charles (bar)
  see CONCERT INDEX under:
(ROMO) 81011-2(1)   Dame Nellie Melba (pt 1)

GILIBERT, Gabrielle (mez)
  see CONCERT INDEX under:
(PEAR) EVC2   The Caruso Edition, Vol.2—1908-12

GILILOV, Pavel (pf)
  see CONCERT INDEX under:
(BIDD) LAW014   Brahms—Cello Sonatas
(DG) 431 544-2GH   Meditation
(VIRG) VC5 45002-2   20th Century Violin Sonatas
(VIRG) VC5 45074-2   Prokofiev—Violin Works

GILISSEN, Thérèse-Marie (va)
  see CONCERT INDEX under:
(SCHW) 315012   Jongen—Orchestral Works

GILJE, Tor (ten)
Braein: Anne Pedersdotter (Cpte)

GILL, Dorothy (contr)
Sullivan: Gondoliers (Cpte), Pirates of Penzance
  (Cpte), Sorcerer (Cpte)

GILL, Tim (vc)
  see CONCERT INDEX under:
(MERI) CDE84286   Ethel Smyth—Impressions that
  Remain

GILLES, Henri (pf)
  see CONCERT INDEX under:
(ROMO) 81001-2   Emma Eames (1865-1952)

GILLES, Jean Villard (narr)
  see CONCERT INDEX under:
(CLAV) CD50-8918   Ansermet conducts Stravinsky

GILLES, Raoul (ten)
Ravel: Heure espagnole (Cpte)

GILLESBERGER, Hans (cond)
  see Vienna CO

GILLETT, Christopher (ten)
Gay: Beggar's Opera (Cpte)
Maxwell Davies: Martyrdom of St Magnus (Cpte)
Sullivan: HMS Pinafore (Cpte)

GILLY, Dinh (bar)
  see CONCERT INDEX under:
(PEAR) GEMMCDS9925(1)   Covent Garden on
  Record—Vol.3 (pt 1)
(PEAR) GEMMCD9956   Joseph Hislop (1884-1977)
(ROMO) 81002-2   Emmy Destinn (1878-1930)
(SUPR) 11 2136-2(4)   Emmy Destinn—Complete
  Edition, Discs 9 & 10
(SUPR) 11 2136-2(5)   Emmy Destinn—Complete
  Edition, Discs 11 & 12

GILMA, Sylvaine (sop)
Ravel: Enfant et les Sortilèges (Cpte)

GILMORE, Peter (sngr)
Gay: Beggar's Opera (Cpte)

GIMENEZ, Edoardo (ten)
Mozart: Nozze di Figaro (Cpte)
Rossini: Viaggio a Reims (Cpte)

GIMÉNEZ, Raúl (ten)
Mayr: Medea (Cpte)
Myslivecek: Bellerofonte (Cpte)
Rossini: Barbiere di Siviglia (Cpte), Cenerentola
  (Cpte), Messa di gloria, Soirées musicales, Turco in
  Italia (Cpte), Viaggio a Reims (Cpte)
(NIMB) NI5106   Rossini—Opera Arias
(NIMB) NI5224   Bellini & Donizetti: Arias

GIMENEZ, Charito (mez)
Vives: Doña Francisquita (Cpte)

GIMSE, Håvard (pf)
  see CONCERT INDEX under:
(NAXO) 8 550878   Grieg—Piano & Chamber Works

GINGOLD, Josef (vn)
  see CONCERT INDEX under:
(DELO) DE1015   Janos Starker plays Kodály

GINN, Michael (treb)
Handel: Allegro, il penseroso ed il moderato (Cpte)

GINOT, Eugéne (va)
  see CONCERT INDEX under:
(PEAR) GEMMCD9348   Debussy: Orchestral &
  Chamber Works

GINROD, Friedrich (bar)
  see CONCERT INDEX under:
(SCHW) 314542   Vienna State Opera Live, Vol.4

GINSBERG, Allen (narr)
Glass: Hydrogen Jukebox (Cpte)

GINSBERG, Ernst (spkr)
Weber: Freischütz (Cpte)

GINSBURG, Grigori (pf)
  see CONCERT INDEX under:
(MELO) 74321 25172-2(1)   Russian Piano School (pt 1
  - Vols.1 - 8)
(MELO) 74321 25173-2   Russian Piano School, Vol.
  1

GINSTER, Ria (sop)
  see CONCERT INDEX under:
(PEAR) GEMMCDS9085   Hugo Wolf Society, Volume
  II

GINZEL, Reinhard (ten)
Gurlitt: Wozzeck (Cpte)
Schreker: Gezeichneten (Cpte)

GINZER, Frances (sop)
Cilea: Adriana Lecouvreur (Cpte)

GIOMBI, Claudio (bar)
Puccini: Bohème (Cpte), Fanciulla del West (Cpte)

GIORDANO, Ezio (bass)
Puccini: Turandot (Cpte)
Verdi: Ballo in maschera (Cpte), Forza del Destino
  (Cpte)

GIORDANO, Umberto (pf)
  see CONCERT INDEX under:
(EMI) CDH7 61046-2   Enrico Caruso: Opera Arias and
  Songs - 1902-1904
(PEAR) EVC1(1)   The Caruso Edition, Vol.1 (pt 1)
(RCA) GD60495(1)   The Complete Caruso Collection
  (pt 1)

GIORGETTI, Giorgio (bar)
Ponchielli: Gioconda (Cpte)
Verdi: Ballo in maschera (Cpte)
  see CONCERT INDEX under:
(DECC) 436 261-2DHO3   Puccini—Il Trittico

GIORGINI, Aristodemo (ten)
Puccini: Bohème (Cpte)
  see CONCERT INDEX under:
(RECO) TRC3   The Art of Aristodemo Giorgini

GIOVANE QUARTETTO ITALIANO
Martucci: Piano Quintet, Op. 45, Piano Trio, Op. 59

GIOVANINETTI, Reynald (cond)
  see New Philh

GIOVANNETTI, Julien (bar)
Planquette: Rip van Winkle (Cpte)

GIPON, Jean-Paul (cond)
  see J-P. Gipon Voc Ens

(JEAN-PAUL) GIPON VOCAL ENSEMBLE
  cond J-P. GIPON
  see CONCERT INDEX under:
(JADE) JADC102   Lassus—Tenebrae Office &
  Lamentations of Jeremiah

GIPPO, Jan (picc)
Bolcom: Sessions I

GIRALDONI, Eugenio (bar)
  see CONCERT INDEX under:
(EMI) CHS7 64860-2(1)   La Scala Edition - Vol.1,
  1878-1914 (pt 1)
(EMI) CHS7 64860-2(2)   La Scala Edition - Vol.1,
  1878-1914 (pt 2)
(MEMO) HR4408/9(2)   Singers in Genoa, Vol.1 (disc
  2)
(NIMB) NI7867   Legendary Baritones
(PEAR) GEMMCDS9073(1)   Giovanni Zenatello, Vol.1
  (pt 1)
(SYMP) SYMCD1073   The Harold Wayne Collection,
  Vol.3
(SYMP) SYMCD1168   The Harold Wayne Collection,
  Vol.19

GIRARD, André (cond)
  see French Rad Lyric Orch

GIRARDI, Piero (ten)
  see CONCERT INDEX under:
(PREI) 89048   Apollo Granforte (1886-1975) - I

GIRAUD, Fiorello (ten)
(MEMO) HR4408/9(1)   Singers in Genoa, Vol.1 (disc
  1)
(SYMP) SYMCD1073   The Harold Wayne Collection,
  Vol.3
(SYMP) SYMCD1077   The Harold Wayne Collection,
  Vol.4

GIRAUDEAU, Jean (ten)
Milhaud: Christophe Colomb (Cpte)
Poulenc: Mamelles de Tirésias (Cpte)
Ravel: Heure espagnole (Cpte)

GIRDWOOD, Julia (ob)
Albinoni: Concerti, Op. 9 (exc)
(COLL) Coll1140-2   Vaughan Williams—Orchestral
  works

GIROD, Marie-Catherine (pf)
  see CONCERT INDEX under:
(3DCL) 3D8012   York Bowen—Piano Works

GISH, Lillian (sngr)
Kern: Show Boat (Cpte)

GISMONDO, Giuseppe (ten)
Alfano: Risurrezione (Cpte)

GITLIS, Ivry (vn)
  see CONCERT INDEX under:
(VOX) CDX2 5505   The Art of Ivry Gitlis

GIUFFREDI, Bruno (gtr)
  see CONCERT INDEX under:
(AKAD) CDAK125   Tosti—Romanze

GIULINI, Carlo Maria (cond)
  see BPO

GIURANNA, Bruno (cond)
  see Padua CO

GIURANNA, Bruno (va)
Mozart: Piano Quartet, K478, Piano Quartet, K493
  see CONCERT INDEX under:
(DG) 427 687-2GH2   Beethoven: String Trios
(EMI) CDC7 54302-2   Mozart—Concertos
(PHIL) 422 514-2PME5   The Complete Mozart Edition
  Vol 14

GIUSEPPINI, Giorgio (bass)
Verdi: Rigoletto (Cpte)

GJEVANG, Anne (mez)
Beethoven: Symphony 9
Handel: Messiah (Cpte)
Mahler: Symphony 3, Symphony 8
Nielsen: Saul and David (Cpte)
Schumann: Paradies und die Peri (Cpte)
Wagner: Götterdämmerung (Cpte), Parsifal (Cpte),
  Walküre (Cpte)
  see CONCERT INDEX under:
(CHAN) CHAN9075   Gade—Choral and Orchestral
  Works
(DG) 437 523-2GH   Grieg—Dramatic Works with
  Orchestra
(VICT) VCD19007   Anne Gjevang in Recital

GJEZI, Antony (vn)
  see CONCERT INDEX under:
(DENO) CO-75448   Berio—Duets for Two Violins,
  Volume 1

GLAB, Elisabeth (vn)
  see CONCERT INDEX under:
(HARM) HMC90 1422   Weill—Orchestral and Choral
  Works

GLACKIN, Paddy (vn)
see CONCERT INDEX *under:*
(MODE) Mode 28/9   Cage—Roaratorio. Laughtears etc

GLAETZNER, Burkhard (ob)
see CONCERT INDEX *under:*
(CAPR) 10 069   C.P.E. Bach—Oboe Concertos
(CAPR) 10 230   Vivaldi: Oboe Concertos
(CAPR) 10 281   Romantic Oboe Concertos
(CAPR) 10 805   Mozart: Wind Concertos

GLANVILLE, Mark (bass)
see CONCERT INDEX *under:*
(MERI) DUOCD89003   Haydn & Schubert: Masses, etc
(OPRA) ORCH104   A Hundred Years of Italian Opera: 1820-1830

GLASGOW CWS BAND
cond H. SNELL
see CONCERT INDEX *under:*
(DOYE) DOYCD005   Flower of Scotland
cond R. TENNANT
see CONCERT INDEX *under:*
(DOYE) DOYCD005   Flower of Scotland

GLASHOF, Wolfgang (bar)
(CAPR) 10 380   Breezes from the Orient, Vol.2

GLASL, Georg (zither)
see CONCERT INDEX *under:*
(SONY) SK45808   New Year's Day Concert 1990

GLASS, Philip (pf)
Glass: Hydrogen Jukebox (Cpte)
see CONCERT INDEX *under:*
(SONY) MK45576   Philip Glass: Piano Works
(SONY) SK64133   The Essential Philip Glass

(PHILIP) GLASS ENSEMBLE
(SONY) SK64133   The Essential Philip Glass
cond M. RIESMAN
Glass: Dance, Einstein on the Beach (Cpte)

GLASSMAN, Allan (ten)
Wagner: Parsifal (Cpte)

GLATARD, Raymond (va)
see CONCERT INDEX *under:*
(ERAT) 2292-45772-2   Saint-Saëns—Works for Chamber Ensemble

GLATT, Adelheid (va da gamba)
see CONCERT INDEX *under:*
(RCA) GD71964   Bach: Flute Works

GLAUSER, Elisabeth (contr)
E.T.A. Hoffmann: Undine (Cpte)
Wagner: Walküre (Cpte)

GLAWITSCH, Rupert (ten)
Zeller: Vogelhändler (exc)

GLAZENER, Janet (cond)
see Orig Cast

GLAZER, David (cl)
see CONCERT INDEX *under:*
(CAPR) 10 805   Mozart: Wind Concertos

GLAZER, Robert (va)
see CONCERT INDEX *under:*
(ALBA) TROY013/4-2   Morton Gould—Orchestral Works

GLAZUNOV, Alexander (cond)
see orch

GLAZUNOV QUARTET
Kabalevsky: String Quartet 1, String Quartet 2

GLEAVE, Ruth (mez)
see CONCERT INDEX *under:*
(CHAN) CHAN8824   Walton: Vocal Works

GLEGHORN, Arthur (fl)
see CONCERT INDEX *under:*
(TEST) SBT1053   Chamber Works

GLEISSNER, Rudolf (vc)
see CONCERT INDEX *under:*
(CAPR) 10 309   Haydn: Concertos

GLEIZES, Mireille (pf)
see CONCERT INDEX *under:*
(TELA) CD80387   Pärt—Fratres

GLEMSER, Bernd (pf)
see CONCERT INDEX *under:*
(NAXO) 8 550715   Schumann—Piano Works
(NAXO) 8 550785   Le Grand Tango

GLENNIE, Evelyn (perc)
see CONCERT INDEX *under:*
(CATA) 09026 61916-2   MacMillan—Veni, Veni Emmanuel & Other Percussion Works
(NIMB) NI5103   Music for Brass, Piano and Percussion
(RCA) RD60557   Evelyn Glennie - Light in Darkness
(RCA) 09026 61277-2   Rebounds - Evelyn Glennie
(TELD) 4509-97868-2   The Last Night of the Proms 1994

GLENNON, Jean (sngr)
Floyd: Susannah (Cpte)

GLESSNER, Connie (organ)
see CONCERT INDEX *under:*
(MOTE) CD40081   French Choral and Organ Works

GLICK, David (treb)
Britten: Little Sweep (Cpte)

GLIÈRE, Reinhold (cond)
see Bolshoi Th Orch

GLISE, Anthony (gtr)
Diabelli: Guitar Sonatas, Op. 29

GLORIAE DEI BRASS ENSEMBLE
see CONCERT INDEX *under:*
(GLOR) GDCD016   Leo Sowerby—American Master of Sacred Song

GLORIAE DEI CANTORES
cond E. C. PATTERSON
see CONCERT INDEX *under:*
(GLOR) GDCD016   Leo Sowerby—American Master of Sacred Song

GLOSSOP, Peter (bar)
Berlioz: Troyens (Cpte)
Verdi: Otello (Cpte)
see CONCERT INDEX *under:*
(DECC) 436 990-2DWO   The World of Benjamin Britten

GLOUCESTER CATHEDRAL CHOIR
cond J. SANDERS
see CONCERT INDEX *under:*
(PRIO) PRCD387   Psalms of David, Vol.5
(PRIO) PRCD494   Magnificat and Nunc Dimittis

GLOVER, Cynthia (sop)
Elgar: King Arthur (exc), Starlight Express (exc)

GLOVER, Jane (cond)
see LMP

GLUBOKY, Pyotr (bass)
Karetnikov: Till Eulenspiegel (Cpte)
Rachmaninov: Miserly knight (Cpte)
Rimsky-Korsakov: Tsar's Bride (Cpte)

GLUCK, Alma (sop)
see CONCERT INDEX *under:*
(MSCM) MM30352   Caruso—Italian Opera Arias
(PEAR) EVC3(1)   The Caruso Edition, Vol.3 (pt 1)
(RCA) GD60495(5)   The Complete Caruso Collection (pt 5)
(RCA) 09026 61580-2(2)   RCA/Met 100 Singers, 100 Years (pt 2)

GLUSHCHENKO, Fedor (cond)
see BBC PO

GLYNDEBOURNE FESTIVAL CHORUS
cond F. BUSCH
Mozart: Così fan tutte (Cpte), Don Giovanni (Cpte)
see CONCERT INDEX *under:*
(EMI) CDH5 65072-2   Glyndebourne Recorded - 1934-1994
cond V. GUI
Mozart: Nozze di Figaro (Cpte)
Rossini: Barbiere di Siviglia (Cpte), Cenerentola (Cpte), Comte Ory (Cpte)
see CONCERT INDEX *under:*
(EMI) CDH5 65072-2   Glyndebourne Recorded - 1934-1994
cond B. HAITINK
Mozart: Così fan tutte (Cpte), Don Giovanni (Cpte), Nozze di Figaro (Cpte)
cond R. LEPPARD
Gluck: Orfeo ed Euridice (Cpte)
Monteverdi: Madrigals, Bk 8 (Cpte), Scherzi musicali (1632) (exc)
cond S. RATTLE
Gershwin: Porgy and Bess (Cpte)
cond F. STIEDRY
Gluck: Orfeo ed Euridice (exc)
cond F. WELSER-MÖST
Lehár: Lustige Witwe (Cpte)

GLYNDEBOURNE FESTIVAL ORCHESTRA
cond F. BUSCH
Mozart: Così fan tutte (Cpte), Don Giovanni (Cpte)
see CONCERT INDEX *under:*
(DUTT) CDLX7012   The Incomparable Heddle Nash
(EMI) CDH5 65072-2   Glyndebourne Recorded - 1934-1994
(EMI) CDH7 63199-2   Sena Jurinac—Opera and Song Recital
cond V. GUI
Mozart: Nozze di Figaro (Cpte)
Rossini: Cenerentola (Cpte), Comte Ory (Cpte)
see CONCERT INDEX *under:*
(EMI) CDH5 65072-2   Glyndebourne Recorded - 1934-1994
cond J. PRITCHARD
see CONCERT INDEX *under:*
(EMI) CDH5 65072-2   Glyndebourne Recorded - 1934-1994

GMELIN, Bernhard (vc)
see CONCERT INDEX *under:*
(SCHW) 311672   Schulhoff—Chamber Music for Violin, Cello and Piano

GMÜR, Hanspeter (cond)
see Budapest Camerata

GMYRYA, Boris (bass)
see CONCERT INDEX *under:*
(EMI) CHS7 69741-2(6)   Record of Singing, Vol.4—Russian & Slavonic Schools

GNEDASH, Vladimir (cond)
see Ukrainian Rad & TV SO

GNEUER, Herbert (ten)
R. Strauss: Rosenkavalier (Cpte)

GOBBI, Antonio de (bass)
Verdi: Rigoletto (Cpte)

GOBBI, Tito (bar)
Donizetti: Lucia di Lammermoor (Cpte)
Giordano: Fedora (Cpte)
Leoncavallo: Pagliacci (Cpte)
Puccini: Tosca (Cpte), Villi (Cpte)
Rossini: Barbiere di Siviglia (Cpte)
Verdi: Aida (Cpte), Ballo in maschera (Cpte), Don Carlo (Cpte), Falstaff (Cpte), Nabucco (Cpte), Otello (Cpte), Rigoletto (Cpte), Simon Boccanegra (Cpte)
see CONCERT INDEX *under:*
(DECC) 436 464-2DM   Ten Top Baritones & Basses
(EMI) CDM7 63109-2   Tito Gobbi - Opera Aria Recital
(EMI) CHS7 64864-2(2)   La Scala Edition - Vol.2, 1915-46 (pt 2)
(EMI) CHS7 69741-2(7)   Record of Singing, Vol.4—Italian School
(EMI) CMS7 64165-2   Puccini—Trittico
(NIMB) NI7851   Legendary Voices
(RCA) 09026 61580-2(6)   RCA/Met 100 Singers, 100 Years (pt 6)
(SONY) M3K79312   Puccini: Il Trittico
(TEST) SBT1019   Tito Gobbi - Opera Arias & Songs

GOBBI, Vito (ten)
Donizetti: Ajo nell'imbarazzo (Cpte)

GÖBEL, Horst (pf)
Reger: Piano Trio, op 2
Wolf-Ferrari: Canzoniere (exc), Edelwild (Cpte)
see CONCERT INDEX *under:*
(THOR) CTH2012   Copland—Chamber Works

GÖBEL TRIO, BERLIN
Reger: Piano Trio, op 102
see CONCERT INDEX *under:*
(THOR) CTH2002   Piano Trios
(THOR) CTH2012   Copland—Chamber Works

GOBERMAN, Max (cond)
see Orch

GOBLE, Theresa (mez)
see CONCERT INDEX *under:*
(OPRA) ORCH104   A Hundred Years of Italian Opera: 1820 1830

GODBURN, Dennis (bn)
Schubert: Octet, D803
see CONCERT INDEX *under:*
(HARM) HMU90 7046   Vivaldi—Chamber Concertos
(RCA) 09026 68181-2   French Chamber Works

GODDING, Emile (bass)
Schreker: Gezeichneten (Cpte)

GODEAU, Emile (cl)
see CONCERT INDEX *under:*
(EMI) CDS7 54607-2   Stravinsky plays and conducts Stravinsky

GODES, Pacual (cond)
see orch

GODFREY, Batyah (contr)
V. Thomson: Mother of us all (Cpte)

GODFREY, Isidore (cond)
see New SO

GODHOFF, Burkhard (vn)
see CONCERT INDEX *under:*
(MARC) 8 223334   Schnittke—Works for Cello

GODIN, Emmerich (ten)
see CONCERT INDEX *under:*
(SCHW) 314602   Vienna State Opera Live, Vol.10

GODOWSKY, Leopold (pf)
see CONCERT INDEX *under:*
(APR) APR7010   Godowsky—UK Columbia Recordings, 1928-30
(APR) APR7011   Godowsky—American Recordings, 1913-26
(APR) APR7013   Romantic Piano Rarities, Vol.1
(PEAR) GEMMCD9933   Grieg and his Circle play Grieg

GODOWSKY, Leopold Jnr (pf)
see CONCERT INDEX *under:*
(APR) APR7011   Godowsky—American Recordings, 1913-26

GODWARD, Stephen (bar)
see CONCERT INDEX *under:*
(PEAR) SHECD9602   Elgar: War Music

GOEBEL, Reinhard (cond)
see Cologne Musica Antiqua

GOEBEL, Reinhard (vn)
Biber: Sonata violino solo

GOEBEL, Reinhard (vn/dir)
Bach: Triple Concerto, BWV1044
see CONCERT INDEX *under:*
(ARCH) 419 633-2AH   Telemann: Wind Concertos

GOEDHARDT, Wouter (vn)
R. Strauss: Rosenkavalier (Cpte)

GOEDICKE, Kurt-Hans (timp)
see CONCERT INDEX *under:*
(CHAN) CHAN8855   Britten—Choral Works
(UNIC) UKCD2020   Panufnik—Orchestral Works

GOEHR, Walter (cond)
see CO

GOEKE, Leo (ten)
Verdi: Vespri Siciliani (Cpte)

GOERKE, Christine (sop)
see CONCERT INDEX under:
(TELA) **CD80362** Poulenc/Szymanowski—Stabat
Mater

GOETHE INSTITUT CHOIR
cond R. SACCANI
Verdi: Aida (Cpte)

GOETHEGYMNASIUMS CHILDREN'S CHOIR
cond M. TANG
see CONCERT INDEX under:
(WERG) **WER6275-2** Orff—Trionfi

GOFF, Charles (sngr)
Gershwin: Strike Up the Band I (Cpte), Strike Up the
Band II

GOFF, Scott (fl)
see CONCERT INDEX under:
(DELO) **DE3114** Creston—Orchestral Works
(DELO) **DE3126** The Incredible Walter Piston

GOGORZA, Emilio de (bar)
see CONCERT INDEX under:
(NIMB) **NI7860** Emma Eames & Pol Plançon
(PEAR) **EVC4(1)** The Caruso Edition, Vol.4 (pt 1)
(RCA) **GD60495(6)** The Complete Caruso Collection
(pt 6)
(ROMO) **81001-2** Emma Eames (1865-1952)

GOHL, Kathy (vc)
Corelli: Sonatas, Op. 5 (exc)

GOHL, Kathy (vn)
Handel: German Airs
see CONCERT INDEX under:
(HARM) **HMA190 5137** Arias and Cantatas for
Soprano and Trumpet

GOHL, Verena (contr)
see CONCERT INDEX under:
(HANS) **98 801** Bach—Cantatas, Vol.39
(HANS) **98 804** Bach—Cantatas, Vol.42
(HANS) **98 807** Bach—Cantatas, Vol.45
(HANS) **98 824** Bach—Cantatas, Vol.62
(HANS) **98 866** Bach—Cantatas, Vol.15
(HANS) **98 891** Bach—Cantatas, Vol.38

GOLABEK, Mona (pf)
see CONCERT INDEX under:
(HARM) **HMU90 7106** Kraft—Orchestral Works

GOLAN, Itamar (pf)
see CONCERT INDEX under:
(TELD) **9031-76349-2** Classical Violin Sonatas
(TELD) **9031-77351-2** Virtuoso Works for Violin

GOLANI, Rivka (va)
Rubbra: Viola Concerto
see CONCERT INDEX under:
(CHAN) **CHAN8809/10** Brahms: Piano Quartets
(CHAN) **CHAN8817** Britten: Orchestral Works
(CHAN) **CHAN8924** Russian Vocal and Chamber
works
(CONI) **CDCF171** Elgar/Bax—Works for Viola &
Orchestra
(CONI) **CDCF189** Works for Viola and Orchestra
(CONI) **CDCF199** Brahms/Joachim—Viola Works
(CONI) **CDCF210** Martinu—Orchestral Works

GOLD, Ananda (contr)
see CONCERT INDEX under:
(PHIL) **442 534-2PH** Janáček—Choral Works

GOLD, Arthur (pf)
see CONCERT INDEX under:
(SONY) **SMK47618** Poulenc/Shostakovich—Piano
Concertos
(SONY) **SM2K47511** Bartók—Concertos

GOLD, Ernest (cond)
see OST

GOLDBERG, Daniel (cl)
see CONCERT INDEX under:
(SCHW) **310832** Frank Martin—Orchestral Works

GOLDBERG, Reiner (ten)
Beethoven: Fidelio (Cpte)
Mahler: Klagende Lied
Mozart: Zauberflöte (Cpte)
R. Strauss: Daphne (Cpte)
Wagner: Götterdämmerung (Cpte), Parsifal (Cpte),
Siegfried (Cpte), Walküre (Cpte)
Zemlinsky: Kreidekreis (Cpte)
see CONCERT INDEX under:
(DG) **445 354-2GX14** Wagner—Der Ring des
Nibelungen

GOLDBERG, Szymon (vn)
see CONCERT INDEX under:
(EMI) **CDH7 64250-2** Emmanuel Feuermann -
Recital
(EMI) **CDS5 55032-2** Hindemith—Plays and conducts
his own works
(MUSI) **MACD-665** The Goldberg/Kraus Duo plays
Mozart and Beethoven
(PEAR) **GEMMCD9443** Feuermann—The Columbia
Records, Vol.2
(PEAR) **GEMMCD9446** Feuermann—The Columbia
Records, Vol.3
(SCHW) **311342** Hindemith plays and conducts
(TEST) **SBT1028** Mozart—Violin Concertos

GOLDBERG ENSEMBLE
Schubert: German Dances and Trios, D90, String
Quartet, D810
see CONCERT INDEX under:
(MERI) **CDE84177** Haydn: Concertos

cond M. LAYFIELD
see CONCERT INDEX under:
(MERI) **CDE84177** Haydn: Concertos
(MERI) **CDE84193** Mendelssohn—String
Symphonies, etc

GOLDEN, Ruth (sop)
see CONCERT INDEX under:
(KOCH) **37043-2** Songs of Frederick Delius
(KOCH) **37118-2** My Own Country - Songs of Peter
Warlock
(KOCH) **37168-2** Silent Noon—Songs of Vaughan
Williams

GOLDENWEISER, Alexander (pf)
see CONCERT INDEX under:
(MELO) **74321 25172-2(1)** Russian Piano School (pt 1
- Vols.1 - 8)
(MELO) **74321 25173-2** Russian Piano School, Vol.
1

GOLDERS ORKEST
cond Y. TALMI
see CONCERT INDEX under:
(OTTA) **OTRC98402** Works by Brahms and Mahler

GOLDING, Miles (vn)
see CONCERT INDEX under:
(CHAN) **CHAN0519** Telemann—La Changeante

GOLDRAY, Martin (kybd)
Glass: Hydrogen Jukebox (Cpte)

GOLDRAY, Martin (pf)
see CONCERT INDEX under:
(PNT) **434 873-2PTH** Jon Gibson—In Good
Company

GOLDSACK, Christopher (treb)
R. Strauss: Salomé (Cpte)

GOLDSBROUGH ORCHESTRA
cond COLIN DAVIS
see CONCERT INDEX under:
(DECC) **443 461-2DF2** Berlioz—L'Enfance du Christ,
etc

GOLDSCHMIDT, Berthold (cond)
see Berlin RSO

GOLDSCHMIDT, Berthold (pf)
see CONCERT INDEX under:
(SONY) **S2K65836** Goldschmidt—Beatrice Cenci, etc

GOLDSMITH, Jerry (cond)
see Hungarian St Op Orch

GOLDSMITH, Kenneth (vn)
see CONCERT INDEX under:
(MUSI) **MACD-635** American Chamber Works

GOLDSMITH'S CHORAL UNION
cond P. BOULEZ
Schoenberg: Gurrelieder

GOLDSTONE, Anthony (pf)
Beethoven: Piano Quartets, WoO36
Sibelius: Piano Quintet (1889)
see CONCERT INDEX under:
(CHAN) **CHAN9077** Holst & Jacob—Chamber Works
(CHAN) **CHAN9382** Holst/Lambert—Piano Works
(GAMU) **GAMCD526** The Britten Connection
(MERI) **CDE84229** Mendelssohn—Piano Sonatas
(MERI) **CDE84237** Romantic Sonatas for Piano Duet
(SYMP) **SYMCD1037** Virtuoso Variations for Piano
Duet

GOLFIER, Françoise (sop)
Debussy: Pelléas et Mélisande (Cpte)

GÖLLNITZ, Fritz (ten)
R. Strauss: Elektra (Cpte)
Weill: Mahagonny (Cpte)

GOLOVANOV, Nikolai (cond)
see Bolshoi Th Orch

GOLOVSHIN, Igor (cond)
see Moscow St SO

GOLSCHMANN, Vladimir (cond)
see Columbia SO

GOLTZ, Gottfried von der (cond)
see Freiburg Baroque Orch

GOLUB, David (pf)
Brahms: Horn Trio, Piano Trio 1
Mendelssohn: Piano Trio 1, Piano Trio 2
see CONCERT INDEX under:
(ARAB) **Z6580-2** Schubert: Complete Works for Piano
Trio
(ARAB) **Z6608** Brahms—Trios, Vol.2

GOLUB, Ludmila (organ)
Grechaninov: Liturgy, Op. 79 (Cpte)
see CONCERT INDEX under:
(CDM) **LDC288 062** Contemporary
Listening—Ekimovski

GOLUB KAPLAN CARR TRIO
see CONCERT INDEX under:
(ARAB) **Z6643** French Piano Trios

GOLUSES, Nicholas (gtr)
Bach: Solo Violin Partitas and Sonatas (exc)
see CONCERT INDEX under:
(CATA) **09026 61979-2** Memento Bittersweet

GOLVEN, Alain (bass)
Rossini: Petite Messe Solennelle

GOMES DE OLIVEIRA, Carlos (hn)
see CONCERT INDEX under:

(CHNT) **LDC278 835** Villa-Lobos—Chôros for
Chamber Ensembles

GOMEZ, Jill (sop)
Alwyn: Invocations, Miss Julie (Cpte)
Britten: Midsummer Night's Dream (Cpte)
Canteloube: Chants d'Auvergne (exc)
Falla: Amor brujo (Cpte), Corregidor y la Molinera
(Cpte), Sombrero de tres picos (Cpte)
Tippett: Child of Our Time (Cpte), Knot Garden
(Cpte)
see CONCERT INDEX under:
(CHAN) **CHAN8824** Walton: Vocal Works
(CONI) **CDCF243** A Spanish Songbook
(EMI) **CDM5 65114-2** Britten—Vocal Works
(EMI) **CDS7 54270-2** Rattle Conducts Britten
(HYPE) **CDA66257** Villa-Lobos: Works for Voice and
Strings
(SONY) **SMK64107** Ravel/Roussel—Vocal &
Orchestral Works
(UNIC) **DKPCD9055** Cabaret Classics
(UNIC) **DKPCD9138** Britten/Cole Porter—Blues &
Cabaret Songs
(VIRG) **VC7 59520-2** American Orchestral Works

GOMEZ, Manuel (cl)
see CONCERT INDEX under:
(CLRI) **CC0005** The Clarinet - Historical Recordings,
Vol.1

GÓMEZ-MARTÍNEZ, Miguel Angel (cond)
see Bamberg SO

GONASHVILI, Gamlet (ten)
Kancheli: Symphony 3

GONDA, Anna (mez)
Berg: Wozzeck (Cpte)
Mozart: Zauberflöte (Cpte)
Pergolesi: Stabat Mater
Rossini: Italiana in Algeri (Cpte)

GONDEK, Juliana (sop)
Handel: Giustino (Cpte), Ottone (Cpte), Radamisto
(Cpte)

GONELLA, Claudio (bn)
see CONCERT INDEX under:
(CARL) **PCD979** Vivaldi—Concertos

GONLEY, Stephanie (cond)
see ECO

GONLEY, Stephanie (vn)
see CONCERT INDEX under:
(EMIN) **CD-EMX2232** Dvořák—Orchestral Works

GÖNNENWEIN, Wolfgang (cond)
see Consortium Musicum

GONSZAR, Rudolph (bass)
Wagner: Tannhäuser (Cpte)

GONZALES, Carmen (mez)
Mascagni: Cavalleria Rusticana (Cpte)
Puccini: Bohème (Cpte)
Vivaldi: Orlando Furioso (Cpte)

(JEAN-FRANÇOIS) GONZALES ORCHESTRA
cond B. LALLEMENT
Haydn: Mass 11

GONZALEZ, Ching (voc)
M. Monk: Atlas (Cpte)

GONZALEZ, Dalmacio (ten)
Halévy: Juive (Cpte)
Rossini: Donna del Lago (Cpte), Stabat Mater
Verdi: Falstaff (Cpte)

GONZALEZ, Guillermo (pf)
see CONCERT INDEX under:
(ETCE) **KTC1095** Spanish Orchestral works

GONZALEZ, Irma (sop)
Beethoven: Symphony 9

GOODALL, David (gtr)
see CONCERT INDEX under:
(NIMB) **NI5106** Rossini—Opera Arias

GOODALL, Sir Reginald (cond)
see ENO Orch

GOODCHILD, Chloe (contr)
Tavener: Mary of Egypt (Cpte)

GOODE, David (organ)
see CONCERT INDEX under:
(EMI) **CDC5 55096-2** Ikos

GOODE, Richard (pf)
Brahms: Clarinet Sonata 1, Clarinet Sonata 2
see CONCERT INDEX under:
(NONE) **7559-79212-2** Beethoven: Piano Sonatas,
Op.31
(NONE) **7559-79213-2** Beethoven—Piano Sonatas
(NONE) **7559-79317-2** Goethe Lieder
(NONE) **7559-79328-2** Beethoven—Complete Piano
Sonatas
(RCA) **RD60170** Twentieth Century Chamber Works

GOODING, Julia (sop)
Blow: Venus and Adonis (Cpte)
Handel: Belshazzar (Cpte), Teseo (Cpte)
Monteverdi: Orfeo (Cpte)
Purcell: King Arthur, Z628 (Cpte)
T. Linley II: Shakespeare Ode
Vaughan Williams: Hugh the Drover (Cpte)
see CONCERT INDEX under:
(VIRG) **VC7 59243-2** Purcell—Odes for Queen Mary

GOODMAN, Benny (cl)
see CONCERT INDEX under:

GOTKOVSKY, Ivar (pf)
see CONCERT INDEX under:
(PYRA) **PYR13485** Beethoven: Violin Sonatas
(PYRA) **PYR13487** Brahms: Violin Sonatas
(PYRA) **PYR13496** Works for Violin and Piano

GOTKOVSKY, Neli (vn)
Bartók: Violin Concerto 1, Violin Concerto 2
Shostakovich: Violin Concerto 1, Violin Concerto 2
see CONCERT INDEX under:
(PYRA) **PYR13485** Beethoven: Violin Sonatas
(PYRA) **PYR13487** Brahms: Violin Sonatas
(PYRA) **PYR13496** Works for Violin and Piano

GOTOWTSCHIKOW, Alexander (perc)
see CONCERT INDEX under:
(TROU) **TRO-CD01405** Ethel Smyth—Chamber
Works & Songs, Vol.3

GOTTHELF, Claude (pf)
see CONCERT INDEX under:
(RCA) **09026 61879-2** Grieg—Historic Recordings

GOTTLIEB, Elizabeth (mez)
Schoenberg: Moses and Aron (Cpte)

GOTTLIEB, Gordon (timp)
see CONCERT INDEX under:
(NEW) **NW357-2** Crumb. Madrigals and Chamber
works

GOTTLIEB, Henriette (sop)
see CONCERT INDEX under:
(NIMB) **NI7848** Great Singers at the Berlin State
Opera

GOTTLIEB, Karen (hp)
see CONCERT INDEX under:
(NALB) **NA015CD** Lou Harrison: Various Works

GÖTTLING, Karin (sop)
J. Strauss II: Fledermaus (Cpte)

GOTTSCHICK, Jörg (bass)
Gurlitt: Wozzeck (Cpte)
Schreker: Gezeichneten (Cpte)

GOTTWALD, Clytus (cond)
see Stuttgart Schola Cantorum

GÖTZ, Werner (ten)
Wagner: Tristan und Isolde (Cpte)

GÖTZE, Marie (contr)
see CONCERT INDEX under:
(SUPR) **11 2136-2(3)** Emmy Destinn—Complete
Edition, Discs 5 to 8

GÖTZEN, Guido (bass)
Wagner: Meistersinger (Cpte)

GOUDSWAARD, Jan (gtr)
see CONCERT INDEX under:
(OLYM) **OCD459** Roussel—Chamber Music, Vol. 2

GOUDSWAARD, Willy (perc)
see CONCERT INDEX under:
(ETCE) **KTC1051** Berg. Schoenberg. Webern. Songs

GOUGH, Helen (vc)
see CONCERT INDEX under:
(HYPE) **CDA66881/2** Vivaldi—Cello Sonatas
(MOSC) **070978** Maurice Greene—Songs and
Keyboard Works

GOUGH, Rachel (bn)
see CONCERT INDEX under:
(CALA) **CACD1017** French Chamber Music for
Woodwinds, Volume 1
(CALA) **CACD1018** French Chamber Music for
Woodwinds, Volume 2

GOULD, Clio (vn)
see CONCERT INDEX under:
(REDC) **RR008** Music by Alan Bush

GOULD, Glenn (pf)
Bach: French Overture, BWV831, French Suites,
BWV812-17, Goldberg Variations, Wohltemperierte
Klavier (exc), 2-Part Inventions, BWV772-86, 3-Part
Inventions, BWV787-801
Beethoven: Piano Sonata 24, Piano Sonata 29
Brahms: Piano Quintet
Liszt: Beethoven Symphonies, S464 (exc)
Prokofiev: Piano Sonata 7
Schumann: Piano Quartet, Op. 47
Shostakovich: Piano Quintet, Op.57
see CONCERT INDEX under:
(CBC) **PSCD2004** Glenn Gould broadcast
performances
(CBC) **PSCD2005** Glenn Gould broadcast
performances
(SONY) **SMK52589**
Byrd/Gibbons/Sweelinck—Keyboard Works
(SONY) **SMK52670** Hindemith—Piano Sonatas
(SONY) **SMK52677** Glenn Gould and Contemporary
Music
(SONY) **SMK52688** Gould meets Menuhin
(SONY) **SMK53474** Glenn Gould—Salzburg Recital
1959
(SONY) **SM2K52597** Bach—Keyboard Works
(SONY) **SM2K52612** Bach—Toccatas, BWV910-916
(SONY) **SM2K52623** Haydn—Keyboard Sonatas
(SONY) **SM2K52646** Beethoven—Piano Works
(SONY) **SM2K52654** Grieg/Bizet/Sibelius—Piano
Works
(SONY) **SM2K52657** Strauss—Lieder and Piano
Works
(SONY) **SM2K52664** Schoenberg—Piano Works
(SONY) **SM2K52671** Hindemith—Chamber Works

(SONY) **SM3K52632** Beethoven—Piano Concertos

GOULD, Morton (cond)
see Columbia Jazz Combo

GOURGUES, Raoul (ten)
see CONCERT INDEX under:
(EPM) **150 122** Milhaud—Historic Recordings 1928-
1948

GOUSLARCHE BOYS' CHOIR
cond E. TCHAKAROV
Tchaikovsky: Queen of Spades (Cpte)

GOVIER, Geoffrey (fp)
see CONCERT INDEX under:
(OLYM) **OCD430** Dussek—Keyboard Works

GOWMAN, Richard (organ)
see CONCERT INDEX under:
(DECC) **430 359-2DM** Baroque Church Music

GOZMAN, Lazar (cond)
see Soviet Emigré Orch

GRAAE, Jason (sngr)
Berlin: Annie Get Your Gun (Cpte)
Gershwin: Strike Up the Band I (Cpte), Strike Up the
Band II

GRAAF, Henk de (cl)
see CONCERT INDEX under:
(CHNN) **CG9107** Music for Clarinet, Piano & Viola

GRAARUD, Gunnar (ten)
see CONCERT INDEX under:
(SCHW) **314622** Vienna State Opera Live, Vol.12
(SCHW) **314642** Vienna State Opera Live, Vol.14
(SIMA) **PSC1810(2)** Grieg—Songs (historical
recordings, pt 2)

GRABENHORST, Helene (sop)
Lehár: Friederike (Cpte)

GRABOIS, Daniel (hn)
see CONCERT INDEX under:
(CATA) **09026 61979-2** Memento Bittersweet

GRACE, Nickolas (bar)
Bernstein: Candide (1988) (exc)
Sullivan: HMS Pinafore (Cpte)

GRACIS, Ettore (cond)
see Philh

GRADUS AD PARNASSUM
cond K. JUNGHÄNEL
see CONCERT INDEX under:
(DHM) **05472 77326-2** Sacred Choral Works

GRAEME, James (sngr)
Bernstein: West Side Story (Cpte)

GRAEME, Peter (cor ang)
see CONCERT INDEX under:
(LYRI) **SRCD223** Holst—Orchestral Works

GRAEME, Peter (ob)
see CONCERT INDEX under:
(EMI) **CZS7 67306-2** Mozart—Works featuring Wind
Instruments

GRAF, Anna-Katharina (fl)
Magnard: Piano and Wind Quintet

GRAF, Elisabeth (contr)
see CONCERT INDEX under:
(EMI) **CDC7 54037-2** Mozart—Masses and Church
Sonatas
(HANS) **98 857** Bach—Cantatas, Vol.6
(HANS) **98 859** Bach—Cantatas, Vol.8

GRAF, Hans (cond)
see Danish Nat RSO

GRAF, Hans-Peter (ten)
Handel: Messias, K572 (Cpte)

GRAF, Kathrin (sop)
Haydn: Mass 11
see CONCERT INDEX under:
(ACCO) **20123-2** Koechlin—Vocal and Chamber
Works
(HANS) **98 803** Bach—Cantatas, Vol.41
(HANS) **98 824** Bach—Cantatas, Vol.62
(HANS) **98 863** Bach—Cantatas, Vol.12
(HANS) **98 868** Bach—Cantatas, Vol.17

GRAF, Maria (hp)
see CONCERT INDEX under:
(PHIL) **422 509-2PME5** The Complete Mozart Edition
Vol 9
(SCHW) **311065** Double Concertos

GRAF, Peter-Lukas (cond)
see ECO

GRAF, Peter-Lukas (fl)
Reger: Flute Serenade, Op. 77a, Flute Serenade, Op.
141a
see CONCERT INDEX under:
(CLAV) **CD50-8203** Krommer—Flute & Oboe
(CLAV) **CD50-8505** Mozart—Works for Flute and
Orchestra
(JECK) **JD506-2** Flute Concertos

GRAF, Peter-Lukas (fl/dir)
Mozart: Flute and Harp Concerto, K299

GRAFENAUER, Irena (fl)
see CONCERT INDEX under:
(PHIL) **422 509-2PME5** The Complete Mozart Edition
Vol 9
(PHIL) **434 918-2PH2** Bach—Concertos

GRAFFMAN, Gary (pf)
Rorem: Left Hand Concerto
see CONCERT INDEX under:
(SONY) **SMK47571** Liszt/Rachmaninov/Ravel—Piano
Concertos

GRAHAM, Janice (vn)
see CONCERT INDEX under:
(EMI) **CDC5 55399-2** Delius—Chamber Works

GRAHAM, Robin (hn)
Beethoven: Piano and wind quintet, op 16
Mozart: Piano and wind quintet, K452
see CONCERT INDEX under:
(NUOV) **6802** Mozart—Chamber Works

GRAHAM, Susan (sop)
Berlioz: Béatrice et Bénédict (Cpte), Damnation de
Faust (Cpte)
Schumann: Szenen aus Goethes Faust (Cpte)
Stravinsky: Pulcinella

GRAHAM-CAMPBELL, Robert (cantor)
see CONCERT INDEX under:
(EMI) **CDC7 47771-2** Byrd—Choral Works

GRAHAM-HALL, John (ten)
Britten: Midsummer Night's Dream (Cpte)
Orff: Carmina Burana
see CONCERT INDEX under:
(ASV) **CDDCA584** W.S. Lloyd Webber—Various
Works

GRAHAM-JONES, Ian (cond)
see Chichester Concert

GRAHL, Hans (ten)
Wagner: Parsifal (exc)

GRAINGER, Percy (pf)
see CONCERT INDEX under:
(BIDD) **LHW008** Percy Grainger—Recital
(BIDD) **LHW010** Grainger plays Bach and Chopin
(PEAR) **GEMMCD9933** Grieg and his Circle play
Grieg
(SIMA) **PSC1809(1)** Grieg—Historical Piano
Recordings (pt 1)
(SYMP) **SYMCD1145** Busoni, Grainger & Petri

GRAMANN, Fred (organ)
see CONCERT INDEX under:
(MOTE) **CD40081** French Choral and Organ Works

GRAMATZKI, Ilse (mez)
Mozart: Zauberflöte (Cpte)
Schumann: Szenen aus Goethes Faust (Cpte)
Wagner: Götterdämmerung (Cpte), Rheingold (Cpte),
Walküre (exc)

GRAML, Helmut (bar)
Orff: Mond (Cpte)

GRAMM, Donald (bass)
Beethoven: Symphony 9
Bernstein: Songfest
Bizet: Carmen (Cpte)
see CONCERT INDEX under:
(SONY) **SM3K46291** Stravinsky—Ballets, Vol.1
(SONY) **SM3K46292** Stravinsky—Ballets, Vol.2

GRANADA CITY ORCHESTRA
cond J. DE UDAETA
see CONCERT INDEX under:
(CLAV) **CD50-9215** Turina—Orchestral Works

GRANADOS, Enrique (pf)
see CONCERT INDEX under:
(EMI) **CDC7 54836-2** Granados/Falla/Mompou/Nin

GRANCHER, Micheline (sop)
Debussy: Pelléas et Mélisande (Cpte)

(LA) GRANDE ECURIE ET LA CHAMBRE DU ROY
Lully: Alceste (Cpte)
cond J-C. MALGOIRE
Gluck: Orfeo ed Euridice (Cpte)
Handel: Messias, K572 (Cpte)
Pergolesi: Pro Jesu dum vivo, Stabat Mater
Vivaldi: Montezuma (Cpte)
(K617) **K617026** Les Chemins du Baroque, Vol.2

GRANDI, Margherita (sop)
see CONCERT INDEX under:
(EMI) **CHS7 69741-2(7)** Record of Singing,
Vol.4—Italian School

GRANDIS, Franco de (bass)
Mozart: Don Giovanni (Cpte)
Rossini: Barbiere di Siviglia (Cpte)
Spontini: Vestale (Cpte)
Verdi: Requiem (Cpte)
see CONCERT INDEX under:
(DECC) **436 261-2DHO3** Puccini—Il Trittico

GRANDJEAN, Andrée (mez)
see CONCERT INDEX under:
(EMI) **CZS7 67515-2** Offenbach—Operetta highlights

GRANDMAISON, Gabriel (bn)
see CONCERT INDEX under:
(EMI) **CDS7 54607-2** Stravinsky plays and conducts
Stravinsky

GRANFORTE, Apollo (bar)
Puccini: Tosca (Cpte)
see CONCERT INDEX under:
(CLUB) **CL99-025** Giovanni Zenatello (1876-1949)
(CLUB) **CL99-509/10** Hina Spani (1896-1969)
(PEAR) **GEMMCDS9074(2)** Giovanni Zenatello, Vol.2
(pt 2)

(PEAR) **GEMMCD9956** Joseph Hislop (1884-1977)
(PREI) **89008** Irene Minghini-Cattaneo (1892-1944)
(PREI) **89037** Hina Spani (1896-1969)
(PREI) **89038** Giovanni Zenatello (1876-1949)
(PREI) **89048** Apollo Granforte (1886-1975) - I
(PREI) **89072** Aureliano Pertile (1885-1952) - II

GRANT, Clifford (bass)
Massenet: Esclarmonde (Cpte)
Mozart: Nozze di Figaro (Cpte), Schauspieldirektor
(Cpte), Sposo deluso (Cpte)
Puccini: Tosca (Cpte)
Verdi: Corsaro (Cpte), Lombardi (Cpte), Rigoletto
(Cpte)
Wagner: Götterdämmerung (exc), Rheingold (Cpte),
Siegfried (Cpte), Walküre (Cpte)

GRANT, Donnalynn (mez)
see CONCERT INDEX under:
(CBC) **SMCD5139** A Gilbert & Sullivan Gala

GRANT, Simon (bass)
Blow: Venus and Adonis (Cpte)
Monteverdi: Orfeo (Cpte), Vespers
see CONCERT INDEX under:
(L'OI) **436 460-2OH** Biber—Requiem; Chamber
Works
(TELD) **4509-95068-2** Purcell—Songs of Welcome &
Farewell

GRANT-MURPHY, Heidi (sop)
Haydn: Creation (Cpte)
Mahler: Symphony 8
Mozart: Nozze di Figaro (Cpte)

GRANVILLE, Sydney (bar)
Sullivan: Gondoliers (Cpte)

GRASSI, Rinaldo (ten)
see CONCERT INDEX under:
(EMI) **CHS7 64860-2(2)** La Scala Edition - Vol.1,
1878-1914 (pt 2)

GRAUDAN, Joanna (pf)
see CONCERT INDEX under:
(BIDD) **LAB059/60** Henri Temianka—Recital

GRAUNKE, Kurt (cond)
see Graunke SO

GRAUNKE SYMPHONY ORCHESTRA
cond F. ALLERS
Millöcker: Bettelstudent (Cpte)
cond H. CARSTE
see CONCERT INDEX under:
(DG) **431 110-2GB** Great Voices - Fritz Wunderlich
cond K. GRAUNKE
Friedhofer: Private Parts (exc), Richthofen and Brown
(exc)
cond A. JONES
Towns: Wolves of Willoughby Chase (exc)
cond W. MATTES
Lehár: Land des Lächelns (Cpte)

GRAUWELS, Marc (fl)
Mozart: Adagio and Rondo, K617, Flute Quartets
see CONCERT INDEX under:
(HYPE) **CDA66391** Mozart: Sonatas for Keyboard and
Flute
(HYPE) **CDA66393** Mozart: Complete Original Music
for Flute - 3
(HYPE) **CDH88015** The Concerto in Europe

GRAVES, Denyce (mez)
A. Thomas: Hamlet (Cpte)
Spontini: Vestale (Cpte)
Verdi: Otello (Cpte)

GRAVILL, Alan (pf)
see CONCERT INDEX under:
(GAMU) **GAMCD516** The Piano Music of Ivor Gurney
and Edward Elgar

GRAVINA, Giovanni (bass)
see CONCERT INDEX under:
(SYMP) **SYMCD1065** The Harold Wayne Collection,
Vol.1

GRAY, Fenton (bar)
Sullivan: Yeomen of the Guard (Cpte)

GRAY, Linda Esther (sop)
Wagner: Tristan und Isolde (Cpte)

GRAY, Lissa (sop)
Offenbach: Christopher Columbus (Cpte)

GRAZZI, Alberto (bn)
see CONCERT INDEX under:
(ARCH) **445 839-2AH** Vivaldi—Woodwind Concertos

GRAZZI, Paolo (ob)
Vivaldi: Concerti, Op. 8 (exc)

GREAGER, Richard (ten)
see CONCERT INDEX under:
(CNTI) **CCD1046** Bax—Songs

GREBANIER, Michael (vc)
see CONCERT INDEX under:
(NAXO) **8 553136** Prokofiev—Chamber Works

GRECO, Norina (sop)
see CONCERT INDEX under:
(MYTO) **2MCD90317** Verdi—Un Ballo in maschera

GREEF, Arthur de (pf)
see CONCERT INDEX under:
(APR) **APR7015** The Auer Legacy, Vol.1
(BIDD) **LAB076** Menges plays Beethoven and
Brahms

(PEAR) **GEMMCD9933** Grieg and his Circle play
Grieg
(SIMA) **PSC1809(1)** Grieg—Historical Piano
Recordings (pt 1)

GREEN, Adolf (sngr)
Bernstein: Candide (1988) (Cpte)
see CONCERT INDEX under:
(SONY) **SM3K47154** Bernstein—Theatre Works
Volume 1

GREEN, Eugène (spkr)
see CONCERT INDEX under:
(ASTR) **E8521** Helfer—Requiem for the Dukes of
Lorraine

GREEN, Gareth (organ)
see CONCERT INDEX under:
(NAXO) **8 550582** English Organ Music

GREEN, Johnny (cond)
see Johnny Green Orch

GREEN, Judy (sngr)
Porter: Anything Goes (Cpte)

GREEN, Martyn (bar)
Sullivan: Patience (Cpte)

GREEN, Nancy (vc)
Brahms: Hungarian Dances
Schmidt: Phantasiestücke
see CONCERT INDEX under:
(BIDD) **LAW005** Fuchs—Works for Cello and Piano

GREEN, Philip (cond)
see Orch

GREEN, Simon (sngr)
Berlin: Annie Get Your Gun (Cpte)
Kern: Show Boat (Cpte)
Porter: Anything Goes (Cpte)
Romberg: Student Prince (Cpte)

GREENALL, Matthew (cond)
see Elysian Sngrs

GREENBERG, Sylvia (sop)
Haydn: Anima del filosofo (Cpte), Schöpfung (exc)
Mahler: Symphony 2
Orff: Carmina Burana
Poulenc: Gloria
Schmidt: Buch mit Sieben Siegeln
see CONCERT INDEX under:
(DECC) **425 627-2DM** Poulenc: Choral and Orchestral
Works

GREENE, Brian (sngr)
Kern: Show Boat (Cpte)

GREENE, Eric (ten)
Bach: St Matthew Passion, BWV244 (exc)

GREENE, Herbert (cond)
see Orig Broadway Cast

GREENE, Leon (bass)
Romberg: Student Prince (Cpte)
Sullivan: Iolanthe (exc)

GREENE, Patrick (sngr)
Rorem: Childhood Miracle (Cpte)

GREENSLADE, Hubert (pf)
see CONCERT INDEX under:
(CLAV) **CD50-9300/4** Hommage à Tibor Varga
(CLAV) **CD50-9314** Hommage à Tibor Varga, Volume
4
(ODE) **CDODE1365** Oscar Natzke - A Legend in His
Time

GREENWOOD, Anthony (cond)
see Philh

GREER, Lowell (hn)
Schubert: Octet, D803
see CONCERT INDEX under:
(HARM) **HMU90 7012** Mozart—Horn Concertos, etc
(HARM) **HMU90 7037**
Beethoven/Brahms/Krufft—Works for Horn

GREEVY, Bernadette (mez)
Elgar: Sea Pictures
Victory: Ultima Rerum (Cpte)
see CONCERT INDEX under:
(CHAN) **CHAN8735** Berlioz & Duparc: Songs
(DECC) **430 159-2DM** Haydn, M.Haydn & Mozart:
Sacred Choral Works
(EMI) **CDM7 69544-2** Berlioz: Vocal Works

GREGER, Emmy (mez)
see CONCERT INDEX under:
(EMI) **CDS7 49361-2** Offenbach: Operettas

GREGG SMITH SINGERS
cond R. CRAFT
Stravinsky: Rake's Progress (Cpte)
see CONCERT INDEX under:
(MUSM) **67113-2** Stravinsky—The Composer -
Volume IV

(JAAK) GREGGOOR CHORUS
cond A. RAHBARI
Puccini: Suor Angelica (Cpte)

GREGOIRE, André (ten)
Verdi: Simon Boccanegra (Cpte)

GREGOIRE, Soazig (contr)
Rossini: Petite Messe Solennelle

(JACK) GREGOOR CHOIR
cond A. RAHBARI
Puccini: Manon Lescaut (Cpte), Tabarro (Cpte)

GREGOR, Bohumil (cond)
see Czech PO

GREGOR, József (bass)
Giordano: Andrea Chénier (Cpte)
Kodály: Budavári Te Deum, Missa Brevis
Puccini: Tosca (Cpte)

GREGORIAN, Gegam (ten)
Prokofiev: War and Peace (Cpte)

GREGORIG, Anna (sop)
see CONCERT INDEX under:
(SCHW) **314572** Vienna State Opera Live, Vol.7

GREGOROWICZ, Karol (vn)
see CONCERT INDEX under:
(SYMP) **SYMCD1071** Great Violinists, Vol.1

GREGOR-SMITH, Bernard (vc)
see CONCERT INDEX under:
(ASV) **CDDCA796** Cello Sonatas
(ASV) **CDDCA896** Bax—Complete works for Cello
and Piano

GREGORY, Will (sax)
see CONCERT INDEX under:
(ARGO) **443 903-2ZH** First & Foremost

GREGSON, Edward (cond)
see Desford Colliery Caterpillar Band

GREIF, Haridas (pf)
see CONCERT INDEX under:
(AUVI) **V4679** Schmitt—Chamber Works

GREINDL, Josef (bass)
Beethoven: Fidelio (Cpte)
Berg: Lulu (Cpte)
Mozart: Entführung (Cpte), Zauberflöte (Cpte)
Verdi: Requiem (Cpte)
Wagner: Fliegende Holländer (exc),
Götterdämmerung (exc), Lohengrin (Cpte),
Rheingold (Cpte), Siegfried (Cpte), Tannhäuser
(Cpte), Tristan und Isolde (Cpte), Walküre (Cpte)
(ACAN) **43 128** Elisabeth Schwarzkopf—Vol. 2
(DG) **429 169-2GR** Wagner—Choruses
(EMI) **CZS7 67123-2** Wagner: Der Ring des
Nibelungen
(FOYE) **15-CF2011** Wagner—Der Ring de Nibelungen
(MYTO) **3MCD93381** Wagner—Die Walküre, etc
(PHIL) **446 057-2PB14** Wagner—The Ring Cycle -
Bayreuth Festival 1967

GREINDL-ROSNER, Gudrun (contr)
Lehár: Friederike (Cpte)

GREINDL-ROSNER, Gudrun (sop)
R. Strauss: Intermezzo (Cpte)

GRELLA, Bruno (bar)
Verdi: Traviata (Cpte)

GRENADIER GUARDS BAND
Sullivan: Iolanthe (Cpte)
cond L. STOKOWSKI
see CONCERT INDEX under:
(DECC) **433 625-2DSP** Stokowski conducts Famous
Russian Works

GRESSE, André (bass)
see CONCERT INDEX under:
(IRCC) **IRCC-CD800** Souvenirs from Meyerbeer
Operas

GRESSIER, Jules (cond)
see French Rad Lyric Orch

GREUILLET, Catherine (sop)
see CONCERT INDEX under:
(VIRG) **VC5 45107-2** Charpentier—Leçons de
ténèbres, Vol. 3

GREUTTER, Roland (vn)
Mozart: Serenade, K250

GREVELLE, Sarian (mez)
Verdi: Trovatore (Cpte)

GREVILLIUS, Nils (cond)
see orch

GREY, Geoffrey (vn)
see CONCERT INDEX under:
(CNTI) **CCD1008** Anderson: Mask and other works

GRICOLO, Vittorio (alto)
Puccini: Tosca (Cpte)

GRIEG, Edvard (pf)
see CONCERT INDEX under:
(PEAR) **GEMMCD9933** Grieg and his Circle play
Grieg
(SIMA) **PSC1809(1)** Grieg—Historical Piano
Recordings (pt 1)

GRIEG, Nina Hagerup (sop)
see CONCERT INDEX under:
(SIMA) **PSC1810(1)** Grieg—Songs (historical
recordings, pt 1)

GRIENDL-ROSNER, Gudrun (contr)
see CONCERT INDEX under:
(EMI) **CDC7 47407-2** Schubert: Sacred Choral works

GRIER, Francis (cond)
see Oxford Christ Church Cath Ch

GRIER, Francis (organ)
Grier: Sequence for the Ascension
see CONCERT INDEX under:
(RCA) **09026 61678-2** Concerto! Steven Isserlis plays
Saint-Saëns

Wagner: Parsifal (Cpte)
see CONCERT INDEX *under:*
(DELO) **DE3170** Beach—Cabildo; Six Short Pieces
(RCA) **09026 61509-2** A Salute to American Music

GROVES, Travis Paul (sngr)
Schuman: Question of Taste (Cpte)

GRUBER, Andrea (sop)
Wagner: Götterdämmerung (Cpte)
see CONCERT INDEX *under:*
(DG) **445 354-2GX14** Wagner—Der Ring des Nibelungen

GRÜBER, Arthur (cond)
see Berlin Deutsche Op Orch

GRUBER, Ferry (ten)
Abraham: Blume von Hawaii (exc), Viktoria und ihr Husar (exc)
J. Strauss II: Wiener Blut (exc)
Lehár: Land des Lächelns (exc)
Offenbach: Vie Parisienne (exc)
Orff: Kluge (Cpte), Mond (Cpte)
R. Strauss: Rosenkavalier (Cpte)
see CONCERT INDEX *under:*
(EURO) **GD69022** Oscar Straus: Operetta excerpts

GRUBER, Heinz Karl (cond)
see London Sinfonietta

GRUBER, Heinz Karl (bar)
Cerha: Art Chansons (exc)

GRUBER, Herbert (cl)
see CONCERT INDEX *under:*
(ORFE) **C015821A** Stravinsky: Choral and Vocal Works

GRUBEROVÁ, Edita (sop)
Bellini: Beatrice di Tenda (Cpte), Capuleti (Cpte), Puritani (Cpte)
Donizetti: Linda di Chamounix (Cpte), Lucia di Lammermoor (Cpte), Maria Stuarda (Cpte), Roberto Devereux (Cpte)
Gluck: Orfeo ed Euridice (Cpte)
Humperdinck: Hänsel und Gretel (Cpte)
J. Strauss II: Fledermaus (exc)
Mahler: Symphony 4
Mozart: Don Giovanni (Cpte), Entführung (Cpte), Finta Giardiniera (Cpte), Idomeneo (Cpte), Lucio Silla (Cpte), Mitridate (Cpte), Sogno di Scipione (Cpte), Zauberflöte (exc)
Offenbach: Contes d'Hoffmann (Cpte)
Orff: Carmina burana
R. Strauss: Ariadne auf Naxos (Cpte)
Verdi: Ballo in Maschera (Cpte), Don Carlo (Cpte), Rigoletto (Cpte), Traviata (Cpte)
see CONCERT INDEX *under:*
(ORFE) **C101841A** Famous Operatic Arias
(SONY) **MK39061** Let the bright Seraphim
(SONY) **SK45633** Edita Gruberová—Opera Arias
(SONY) **SK45855** Mozart: Bastien und Bastienne
(SONY) **SK48242** R. Strauss—Orchestral Lieder
(TELD) **2292-44922-2** R. Strauss—Lieder
(TELD) **9031-72302-2** Mozart—Concert Arias

GRUBERT, Naum (pf)
Schubert: Piano Sonata, D784, Piano Sonata, D960
see CONCERT INDEX *under:*
(EMER) **EC3993-2** Mussorgsky/Rachmaninov—Piano Works
(OTTA) **OTRC38611** Liszt—Piano Works

**GRUDGIONZ FESTIVAL CHORUS
cond G-F. MASINI**
see CONCERT INDEX *under:*
(RCA) **09026 68014-2** Pavarotti - The Early Years, Vol.2

**GRUDGIONZ FESTIVAL ORCHESTRA
cond G-F. MASINI**
see CONCERT INDEX *under:*
(RCA) **09026 68014-2** Pavarotti - The Early Years, Vol.2

GRUENBERG, Erich (vn)
Bax: Violin Sonata 1, Violin Sonata 2
Holloway: Romanza, Op. 31
Messiaen: Quatuor
see CONCERT INDEX *under:*
(CNTI) **CCD1024** Reizenstein—Chamber works
(CRD) **CRD3417** Beethoven—Violin Sonatas, Vol.3
(HYPE) **CDA66157** Parry: Chamber Music

GRUENBERG, Joanna (pf)
see CONCERT INDEX *under:*
(UNIC) **UKCD2048** Wieniawski—Virtuoso Showpieces

GRUHN, Nora (sop)
see CONCERT INDEX *under:*
(CLAR) **CDGSE78-50-33** Lauritz Melchior & Albert Coates
(EMI) **CDH7 69789-2** Melchior sings Wagner
(PEAR) **GEMMCDS9137** Wagner—Der Ring des Nibelungen

GRUMBACH, Raimund (bass)
Leoncavallo: Bohème (Cpte)
Orff: Mond (Cpte)
R. Strauss: Intermezzo (Cpte)
Weber: Freischütz (Cpte)

GRUMIAUX, Arthur (vn)
Bach: Solo Violin Partitas and Sonatas
Beethoven: Romances, Violin Concerto
see CONCERT INDEX *under:*
(PHIL) **420 700-2PSL** Bach: Violin Concertos

(PHIL) **422 140-2PLC3** Beethoven: Complete Violin Sonatas
(PHIL) **422 515-2PME7** The Complete Mozart Edition Vol 15
(PHIL) **426 384-2PC** Fauré & Franck—Violin Sonatas
(PHIL) **426 977-2PCC** Works for Violin and Orchestra
(PHIL) **438 323-2PM2** Mozart—Violin Concertos
(PHIL) **438 365-2PM2** Brahms—Complete Trios
(PHIL) **438 516-2PM3** Arthur Grumiaux—Early Recordings
(PHIL) **442 287-2PM2** Favourite Violin Concertos
(PHIL) **442 386-2PM2** Bach—Brandenburg Concertos Nos 1-3
(PHIL) **442 577-2PM2** Beethoven—Concertos, Volume 1
(PHIL) **442 625-2PM5** Clara Haskil—The Legacy Volume 1: Chamber Music
(PHIL) **442 685-2PM12** Clara Haskil - The Legacy

GRUMIAUX ENSEMBLE
see CONCERT INDEX *under:*
(PHIL) **422 511-2PME3** The Complete Mozart Edition Vol 11

(ARTHUR) GRUMIAUX PIANO TRIO
Arensky: Piano Trio 1
Smetana: Piano Trio in G minor

GRUMIAUX TRIO
see CONCERT INDEX *under:*
(PHIL) **422 510-2PME3** The Complete Mozart Edition Vol 10
(PHIL) **422 838-2PC** Schubert: Chamber Works
(PHIL) **438 700-2PM2** Schubert—Complete Trios
(PHIL) **442 299-2PM2** Mozart—Complete Flute Works

GRÜMMER, Elisabeth (sop)
Bach: St Matthew Passion, BWV244 (exc)
Brahms: Deutsches Requiem, Op.45 (exc)
Humperdinck: Hänsel und Gretel (Cpte)
Mozart: Don Giovanni (Cpte), Idomeneo (Cpte), Requiem
Wagner: Lohengrin (Cpte), Meistersinger (Cpte), Tannhäuser (Cpte)
Weber: Freischütz (Cpte)
see CONCERT INDEX *under:*
(DG) **445 400-2GDO10** Ferenc Fricsay - A Portrait
(EMI) **CDH5 65201-2** Leonie Rysanek - Operatic Recital
(EMI) **CDM7 63657-2** Schwarzkopf sings Opera Arias
(EMI) **CHS7 69741-2(4)** Record of Singing, Vol.4—German School
(EMI) **CZS7 67123-2** Wagner: Der Ring des Nibelungen

GRUNBERG, Tina (vn)
see CONCERT INDEX *under:*
(MERI) **CDE84158** English Songs

GRUND, Christoph (organ)
B. A. Zimmermann: Requiem (Cpte)

GRUNDBERG, Per (organ)
see CONCERT INDEX *under:*
(BIS) **BIS-CD510** Organ Music from the USA

GRUNDEN, Per (ten)
Lehár: Lustige Witwe (exc)

GRUNDHEBER, Franz (bar)
Berg: Wozzeck (Cpte)
Busoni: Doktor Faust (Cpte)
Hindemith: Mörder, Hoffnung der Frauen (Cpte)
Humperdinck: Hänsel und Gretel (Cpte)
R.Strauss: Arabella (Cpte), Rosenkavalier (Cpte), Salome (Cpte)
Stravinsky: Oedipus Rex (Cpte)
see CONCERT INDEX *under:*
(CAPR) **10 448** Zemlinsky—Orchestral Works and Songs
(CHAN) **CHAN9240** Stravinsky—Choral and Orchestral Works
(PHIL) **446 067-2PH6** Beethoven—Complete Symphonies

GRUNENWALD, Jean-Jacques (organ)
see CONCERT INDEX *under:*
(EMI) **CDM7 64281-2** Boulanger—Vocal & Chamber Works

GRÜNER-HEGGE, Odd (cond)
see Oslo PO

GRUNERT, Wolfgang (voc)
Weill: Dreigroschenoper (Cpte)

GRÜNFARB, Josef (vn)
Pettersson: 2-Violin Sonatas

GRUNOW, Irina (sop)
see CONCERT INDEX *under:*
(MYTO) **3MCD93381** Wagner—Die Walküre, etc

GRUPPMAN, Igor (vn)
see CONCERT INDEX *under:*
(KOCH) **37134-2** Arnold—Orchestral Works
(KOCH) **37215-2** Italian Orchestral Music

GRUPPMAN, Vesna (vn)
see CONCERT INDEX *under:*
(KOCH) **37134-2** Arnold—Orchestral Works

GRYCHTOLOWNA, Lidia (pf)
see CONCERT INDEX *under:*
(PHIL) **442 580-2PM2** Beethoven—Concertos, Volume 2

GUADAGNO, Anton (cond)
see Bologna Teatro Comunale Orch

GUALDA, Silvio (perc)
Bartók: Sonata for 2 Pianos and Percussion, 2-Piano Concerto
Bernstein: West Side Story Symphonic Dances
Xenakis: Orestia (Cpte)
see CONCERT INDEX *under:*
(ERAT) **2292-45030-2** Xenakis: Miscellaneous Works

GUARENTE, Gitta (sop)
Offenbach: Vie Parisienne (exc)

GUARNERI QUARTET
Brahms: Piano Quartet 1, Piano Quartet 3
Mozart: Piano Quartet, K478, Piano Quartet, K493
see CONCERT INDEX *under:*
(PHIL) **434 115-2PH3** Beethoven—String Quartets, Op. 18
(RCA) **GD60457** Beethoven—Middle String Quartets

GUARNERI TRIO
see CONCERT INDEX *under:*
(OTTA) **OTRC29134** Brahms—Piano Trios

GUARNIERI, Antonio (cond)
see La Scala Orch

GUARRERA, Frank (bar)
see CONCERT INDEX *under:*
(RCA) **GD60326** Verdi—Operas & Choral Works

GUBAIDULINA, Sofia (tape op)
Nono: Lontananza nostalgica

GUDZUHN, Jörg (narr)
Schumann: Manfred (Cpte)

GUEDEN, Hilde (sop)
Donizetti: Elisir d'amore (Cpte)
J. Strauss II: Fledermaus (Cpte), Wiener Blut (exc)
Lehár: Giuditta (exc), Graf von Luxemburg (exc), Lustige Witwe (exc), Zarewitsch (exc)
Mahler: Symphony 4
Mozart: Don Giovanni (Cpte), Nozze di Figaro (Cpte)
R. Strauss: Arabella (Cpte), Ariadne auf Naxos (Cpte), Daphne (Cpte), Rosenkavalier (Cpte), Schweigsame Frau (Cpte)
Verdi: Rigoletto (Cpte)
Wagner: Meistersinger (Cpte)
see CONCERT INDEX *under:*
(DECC) **425 959-2DM** Lisa della Casa sings R. Strauss
(DG) **431 110-2GB** Great Voices - Fritz Wunderlich
(DG) **435 321-2GWP12** 150 Years - Vienna Philharmonic

GUELFI, Giangiacomo (bar)
see CONCERT INDEX *under:*
(DG) **419 257-2GH3** 'Cav' and 'Pag', etc

GUÉNEUX, Georges (fl)
see CONCERT INDEX *under:*
(JECK) **JD506-2** Flute Concertos

GUÉNOT, L. (bass)
Massenet: Manon (Cpte), Werther (Cpte)

(JEAN-CLAUDE) GUÉRINOT CHOIR
Liszt: Via crucis, S53

GUERRINI, Barbara (mez)
see CONCERT INDEX *under:*
(DECC) **436 261-2DHO3** Puccini—Il Trittico

GUERRINI, Virginia (mez)
see CONCERT INDEX *under:*
(EMI) **CHS7 64860-2(2)** La Scala Edition - Vol.1, 1878-1914 (pt 2)
(MEMO) **HR4408/9(2)** Singers in Genoa, Vol.1 (disc 2)

GUEST, Douglas (cond)
see Westminster Abbey Ch

GUEST, George (cond)
see Argo CO

GUGGEIS, Edgar (perc)
see CONCERT INDEX *under:*
(DG) **439 867-2GH** Bartók/Ravel—Works for 2 Pianos

GUGGENHEIM, Janet (pf)
see CONCERT INDEX *under:*
(NAXO) **8 553136** Prokofiev—Chamber Works

GUGGENHEIM, Janet Goodman (pf)
see CONCERT INDEX *under:*
(EMI) **CDC7 54108-2** Tchaikovsky—Violin Works

GUGGIA, Mario (ten)
Donizetti: Martyrs (Cpte)
R. Strauss: Rosenkavalier (Cpte)

GUGLIELMO, Giovanni (vn)
Vivaldi: Concerti, Op. 8 (Cpte)

GUI, Vittorio (cond)
see EIAR Orch

GUIDA, Guido Maria (cond)
see Berlin RSO

GUIDO D'AREZZO CHOIR
Salieri: Axur (Cpte)

GUIGUE, Paul (bar)
Fauré: Pénélope (Cpte)
Offenbach: Périchole (Cpte)

**GUILDFORD CATHEDRAL CHOIR
cond BARRY ROSE**
see CONCERT INDEX *under:*
(EMI) **CDM5 65101-2** A Warlock Centenary Album

(EMI) **CDM7 64131-2** Orchestral Music for Christmas
cond A. MILLINGTON
see CONCERT INDEX under:
(PRIO) **PRCD257** Great Cathedral Anthems
(PRIO) **PRCD416** Psalms of David, Vol.6

GUILDFORD CHORAL SOCIETY
cond H.D. WETTON
Holst: Choral Fantasia, Choral Symphony

GUILDHALL STRING ENSEMBLE
see CONCERT INDEX under:
(RCA) **RD60224** Baroque Oboe Concerti
(RCA) **09026 61275-2** Strings! The Definitive
Collection
cond G. MALCOLM
Vivaldi: Concerti, Op. 8 (exc), Concerto, RV443

GUILE, Helen (contr)
R. Ward: Crucible (Cpte)

GUILLAMAT, Ginette (sop)
see CONCERT INDEX under:
(EMI) **CHS7 69741-2(3)** Record of Singing,
Vol.4—French School

GUILLAUME, Edith (mez)
Nørgård: Siddhartha (Cpte)
see CONCERT INDEX under:
(DANA) **DACOCD340/1** Langgaard—Symphonies Nos
4 and 6.Music of the Spheres

GUILLEAUME, Margot (sop)
Mozart: Zauberflöte (Cpte)

GUILLOT, Pierre (organ)
see CONCERT INDEX under:
(SCAL) **ARI139** Bach & Busoni: Organ Works

GUIMARÃES, Maria Inês (pf)
see CONCERT INDEX under:
(MARC) **8 223548** Nepomuceno—Piano Music

GUIMARAES, Leila (sop)
see CONCERT INDEX under:
(CHNT) **LDC278 869/70** Villa-Lobos—Guitar Works

GUINGAL, Alain (cond)
see French Lyrique Orch

GUIOMAR, Julien (narr)
Bizet: Carmen (Cpte)

GUIOT, Andréa (sop)
Bizet: Carmen (Cpte)

GUIOVART, Albert (pf)
see CONCERT INDEX under:
(HARM) **HMI98 7007** Albéniz—Piano Sonatas

GUITTART, Henk (va)
see CONCERT INDEX under:
(OLYM) **OCD460** Roussel—Chamber Music, Vol. 3

GUITTON, Lyliane (mez)
G. Charpentier: Louise (Cpte)

GULBRANSON, Ellen (sop)
see CONCERT INDEX under:
(SIMA) **PSC1810(2)** Grieg—Songs (historical
recordings, pt 2)

GULDA, Friedrich (pf)
Mozart: Piano Concerto 20, Piano Concerto 21, Piano
Concerto 23, Piano Concerto 26
see CONCERT INDEX under:
(DECC) **433 628-2DSP**
Franck/Grieg/Schumann—Piano & Orchestral
Works
(DG) **437 352-2GDO2** Beethoven—Cello Sonatas

GULDA, Paul (pf)
Brahms: Piano Quintet
Schoenberg: Chamber Symphony 1
see CONCERT INDEX under:
(NAXO) **8 550401** Schumann—Piano Works

GULDBAEK, Ruth (sop)
Nielsen: Symphony 3

GULEGINA, Maria (sop)
Tchaikovsky: Queen of Spades (Cpte)
Verdi: Otello (Cpte)

GÜLKE, Peter (cond)
see Berlin RSO

GULLI, Franco (vn)
see CONCERT INDEX under:
(CLAV) **CD50-8913/4** Mozart—Violin Concertos, etc
(PHIL) **426 925-2PM19** The Complete Vivaldi Edition

GULLINO, Walter (ten)
Verdi: Rigoletto (Cpte), Traviata (Cpte), Trovatore
(exc)

GULYÁS, Dénes (ten)
Berlioz: Damnation de Faust (Cpte)
Liszt: Hungarian Coronation Mass, S11

GUMPOLDSKIRCHNER KINDERCHOR
cond V. SUTEJ
see CONCERT INDEX under:
(SONY) **SK53358** Christmas in Vienna

GUMPOLDSKIRCHNER SPATZEN
Ligeti: Grand Macabre (Cpte)
cond E. HOWARTH
Wagner: Meistersinger (Cpte)
cond G. SOLTI

GUNDLACH, Willi (cond)
see Westphalia CO

GÜNES, Rusen (va)
Saygun: Viola Concerto

GUNNING, Adrian (organ)
Tournemire: Orgue mystique, Op. 57 (exc)

GUNNING, Louise (sngr)
see CONCERT INDEX under:
(PEAR) **GEMMCDS9050/2(1)** Music from the New
York Stage, Vol. 1 (part 1)

GUNSON, Ameral (mez)
Britten: Rape of Lucretia (Cpte)
Janáček: Glagolitic Mass (Cpte)
Verdi: Requiem (Cpte)
see CONCERT INDEX under:
(CHAN) **CHAN8760** Walton—Choral Works
(SONY) **M3K79312** Puccini: Il Trittico

GÜNTER, Horst (bar)
R. Strauss: Arabella (Cpte)
Wagner: Lohengrin (Cpte)
Weill: Mahagonny (Cpte)
see CONCERT INDEX under:
(DECC) **425 995-2DM** Brahms/Mahler—Lieder

GÜNTHER, Carl (ten)
Mozart: Apollo et Hyacinthus (Cpte), Zauberflöte
(Cpte)
see CONCERT INDEX under:
(PREI) **89301** The Art of Frida Leider

GÜNTHER, Felix (cond)
see orch

GUNZENHAUSER, Stephen (cond)
see BBC PO

GURA, Hedy (mez)
R. Strauss: Elektra (Cpte)

GURLITT, Manfred (cond)
see Berlin St Op Orch

GURTNER, Heinrich (organ)
Mendelssohn: Organ Sonatas

GURTU, Trilok (perc)
Bernstein: West Side Story Symphonic Dances

GUS BAND
cond G. BRAND
see CONCERT INDEX under:
(EMI) **CDM7 64716-2** Ireland—Piano Concerto, etc

GUSAK-GRIN, Marina (pf)
see CONCERT INDEX under:
(CHAN) **CHAN8500** Russian Music for Violin and
Piano
(CHAN) **CHAN8747** Szymanowski—Violin & Piano
Works
(CHAN) **CHAN8748** Poème—Works for Violin and
Piano
(CHAN) **CHAN9109** Franck/Messiaen/Saint-
Saëns—Violin & Piano Works

GUSCHLBAUER, Theodore (cond)
see Bamberg SO

GUSTAFSON, Nancy (sop)
Mahler: Symphony 2
Puccini: Bohème (Cpte)
Verdi: Simon Boccanegra (Cpte)
Wagner: Rheingold (Cpte)

GUSTAFSSON, Jan-Erik (vc)
see CONCERT INDEX under:
(ONDI) **ODE826-2** Sibelius—Early Chamber Music,
Vol. 1

GUSTAFSSON, Ulla (sop)
Mahler: Symphony 8

GUSTAVSON, Eva (mez)
see CONCERT INDEX under:
(RCA) **GD60326** Verdi—Operas & Choral Works

GUSZALEWICZ, Genia (sop)
see CONCERT INDEX under:
(CLAR) **CDGSE78-50-26** Wagner: Tristan und Isolde
excerpts
(DANA) **DACOCD315/6** Lauritz Melchior Anthology -
Vol. 3
(PEAR) **GEMMCDS9137** Wagner—Der Ring des
Nibelungen

GUTER, Jacky (sop)
see CONCERT INDEX under:
(CALA) **CACD1018** French Chamber Music for
Woodwinds, Volume 2

GUTH, Peter (cond)
see Austrian RSO

GUTH, Peter (vn/dir)
see CONCERT INDEX under:
(UNIC) **DKPCD9089** Lumbye—Polkas, Mazurkas &
Waltzes

GUTHRIE, Frederick (bass)
see CONCERT INDEX under:
(VANG) **08.2010.71** Bach—Choral Works

GUTIÉRREZ, Horacio (pf)
Brahms: Piano Concerto 1, Piano Concerto 2
Prokofiev: Piano Concerto 2, Piano Concerto 3
Rachmaninov: Paganini Rhapsody
Tchaikovsky: Piano Concerto 1

GUTMAN, Natalia (vc)
Dvořák: Cello Concerto
Schnittke: Cello Concerto 1
Schumann: Cello Concerto
Shostakovich: Cello Concerto 1, Cello Concerto 2
see CONCERT INDEX under:
(EMI) **CDS7 49775-2** Tchaikovsky—Chamber Works

(EMI) **CMS7 64812-2** Dvořák—Orchestral Works

GUTOROVICH, Nikolai (ten)
Kabalevsky: Colas Breugnon (Cpte)

GÜTSCHOW, Gert (spkr)
Eisler: Deutsche Sinfonie

GUTSTEIN, Ernst (bar)
Berg: Lulu (Cpte)
Nicolai: Lustigen Weiber von Windsor (Cpte)
R.Strauss: Arabella (Cpte), Rosenkavalier (Cpte)

GUTTENBERG, Enoch zu (cond)
see Munich Bach Collegium

GÜTTLER, Ludwig (cond)
see Virtuosi Saxoniae

GÜTTLER, Ludwig (tpt)
see CONCERT INDEX under:
(CAPR) **10 051** Classical Trumpet Concertos

(LUDWIG) GÜTTLER BRASS ENSEMBLE
Bach: Christmas Oratorio, BWV248 (Cpte)

GUTTMAN, Michael (vn)
see CONCERT INDEX under:
(ASV) **CDDCA785** Bloch/Serebrier—Works for Violin
and Orchestra
(ASV) **CDDCA855** Four Seasons

GUTTRY, Paul (bass)
see CONCERT INDEX under:
(ERAT) **4509-98480-2** Lamentations - Holy Week in
Provence

GUTU, Alexandra (vc)
J. Perrin: Cello Concerto

GUY, Barry (db)
Lumsdaine: Aria

GUY, Hélène (cond)
see Provence Voc Ens

GUY, Maureen (mez)
Wagner: Götterdämmerung (Cpte), Walküre (Cpte)
see CONCERT INDEX under:
(DECC) **414 100-2DM15** Wagner: Der Ring des
Nibelungen

GUY-BROMLEY, Phillip (bass)
see CONCERT INDEX under:
(OPRA) **ORCH103** Italian Opera—1810-20

GUYER, Joyce (sop)
Wagner: Parsifal (Cpte)

GUZELIMIAN, Armen (pf)
Getty: White Election
see CONCERT INDEX under:
(TELD) **9031-72168-2** German Songs by American
Composers

GUZMÁN, Enrique Pérez de (pf)
Albéniz: Concierto fantástico, op.78

GUZMAN, Josie de (sngr)
F. Loesser: Guys and Dolls (Cpte)

GWYNNE, David (bass)
Martinů: Greek Passion (Cpte)
Saxton: Caritas (Cpte)

GYÖRIVÁNYI-RÁTH, György (cond)
see Hungarian St. Orch

GYR, Suzanne (pf)
see CONCERT INDEX under:
(SYMP) **SYMCD1098/9** Marko Rothmüller—Lieder
Recital

GYTON, Paul (ten)
see CONCERT INDEX under:
(PHIL) **442 785-2PH** The Incomparable Alfredo
Kraus

HAAGE, Peter (ten)
Ligeti: Grand Macabre (Cpte)
Schoenberg: Gurrelieder
Schreker: Schatzgräber (Cpte)
Spohr: Jessonda (Cpte)
Wagner: Rheingold (Cpte), Siegfried (Cpte)
Weill: Mahagonny-Gesänge (Cpte), Sieben
Todsünden (Cpte)
Zemlinsky: Traumgörge (Cpte)

HAAN, John David de (ten)
Korngold: Wunder der Heliane (Cpte)
see CONCERT INDEX under:
(SONY) **S2K66836** Goldschmidt—Beatrice Cenci, etc

HAAN, Richard (bar)
Respighi: Primavera

HAARLEM, Renée van (sop)
R. Strauss: Rosenkavalier (Cpte)

HAARTTI, Kristina (mez)
Madetoja: Juha (Cpte)

HAAS, Jonathan (timp)
see CONCERT INDEX under:
(CRD) **CRD3449** Jonathan Haas - Virtuoso
Timpanist

HAAS, Monique (pf)
see CONCERT INDEX under:
(DG) **447 343-2GDB2** Stravinsky—Orchestral &
Choral Works

HAAS, Werner (pf)
see CONCERT INDEX under:
(PHIL) **438 329-2PM2** Tchaikovsky—Works for Piano
and Orchestra
(PHIL) **438 353-2PM2** Ravel—Piano Works

(PHIL) **438 718-2PM2** Debussy—Complete Piano Music, Vol.1
(PHIL) **438 721-2PM2** Debussy—Complete Piano Music, Vol.2
(PHIL) **442 302-2PM2** The Best of Mendelssohn
(PHIL) **446 172-2PM2** Brahms—Complete Quintets

HAASS, Philipp (va)
  see CONCERT INDEX *under:*
(PREI) **90205** Strauss conducts Strauss, Vol.1

HABERDASHERS' ASKE'S SCHOOL CHOIR
  cond C. ABBADO
  Berlioz: Te Deum
  cond B. HAITINK
  see CONCERT INDEX *under:*
(EMI) **CDC7 49849-2** Famous Opera Choruses
  cond H. LEWIS
  Meyerbeer: Prophète (Cpte)
  cond G. SOLTI
  Bizet: Carmen (Cpte)

HABERDASHERS' ASKE'S SCHOOL GIRLS CHOIR
  cond R. MUTI
  Verdi: Ballo in maschera (Cpte)

HABEREDER, Agnes (sop)
  Pfitzner: Von deutscher Seele (Cpte)

HABICH, Eduard (bass)
  Wagner: Siegfried (Cpte)
  see CONCERT INDEX *under:*
(CLAR) **CDGSE78-50-26** Wagner: Tristan und Isolde excerpts
(PEAR) **GEMMCDS9137** Wagner—Der Ring des Nibelungen
(PREI) **89028** Ivar Andresen (1896-1940)

HACKER, Alan (cl)
  Mozart: Sinfonia concertante, K297b
  see CONCERT INDEX *under:*
(AMON) **CD-SAR37** Brahms—Chamber Works
(AMON) **CD-SAR38** Mendelssohn—Chamber Works
(NIMB) **NI5101** Finzi: Orchestral Works

HACQUARD, Mario (bar)
  Massenet: Cléopâtre (Cpte), Vierge (Cpte)

HADDEN, Nancy (cond)
  see Circa 1500

HADDEN, Nancy (fl)
  Mozart: Flute Quartets, Zauberflöte (exc)
  see CONCERT INDEX *under:*
(CRD) **CRD3488** Hasse—Cantatas, Ballads and Sonatas
(HYPE) **CDA66307** My Mind to me a kingdom is

HADJIEVA, Ludmila (sop)
  Mussorgsky: Boris Godunov (Cpte)

HADLEY, Jerry (ten)
  Bernstein: Candide (1988) (Cpte)
  Floyd: Susannah (Cpte)
  Forrest/Wright: Kismet (Cpte)
  Gounod: Faust (Cpte)
  Handel: Messiah (Cpte)
  Kern: Show Boat (Cpte)
  Mozart: Così fan tutte (Cpte), Requiem, Rè Pastore (Cpte), Zauberflöte (Cpte)
  Puccini: Bohème (Cpte)
  Rossini: Barbiere di Siviglia (Cpte)
  Schubert: Mass, D950
  see CONCERT INDEX *under:*
(NIMB) **NI5234** Britten: Vocal Works
(RCA) **09026 61509-2** A Salute to American Music
(RCA) **09026 62681-2** Mr Jerry Hadley—Golden Days
(TELA) **CD80152** Verdi: Requiem & Opera Choruses
(TELD) **9031-73283-2** Hampson and Hadley

HADRABOVÁ, Eva (mez)
  see CONCERT INDEX *under:*
(SCHW) **314502** Vienna State Opera—Live Recordings (sampler)
(SCHW) **314512** Vienna State Opera Live, Vol.1
(SCHW) **314622** Vienna State Opera Live, Vol.12
(SCHW) **314642** Vienna State Opera Live, Vol.14

HAEBLER, Ingrid (fp)
  see CONCERT INDEX *under:*
(PHIL) **422 507-2PME12** The Complete Mozart Edition Vol 7

HAEBLER, Ingrid (pf)
  Mozart: Piano Sonata, K332, Piano Sonata, K333
  see CONCERT INDEX *under:*
(DENO) **CO-1517** Mozart: Piano Sonatas
(DENO) **CO-2195** Mozart: Piano Sonatas, Vol.3
(DENO) **CO-73087** Mozart: Piano Sonatas, Vol.4
(PHIL) **422 516-2PME2** The Complete Mozart Edition Vol 16
(PHIL) **422 518-2PME5** The Complete Mozart Edition Vol 18
(PHIL) **422 838-2PC** Schubert: Chamber Works

HAEFLIGER, Andreas (pf)
  see CONCERT INDEX *under:*
(SONY) **SK46748** Mozart—Piano Works
(SONY) **SK48036** Schumann—Piano Works
(SONY) **SK53960** Gubaidulina—Piano Works

HAEFLIGER, Ernst (ten)
  Beethoven: Fidelio (Cpte), Symphony 9
  Dvořák: Requiem
  Haydn: Mass 11
  Janáček: Glagolitic Mass (Cpte)
  Mozart: Don Giovanni (Cpte), Entführung (Cpte), Idomeneo (Cpte), Mass, K317, Zauberflöte (Cpte)
  Orff: Antigonae (Cpte)

Rossini: Stabat Mater
Schubert: Schöne Müllerin (Cpte), Schwanengesang, D957 (Cpte), Winterreise (Cpte)
Stravinsky: Oedipus Rex (Cpte)
  see CONCERT INDEX *under:*
(ARCH) **439 369-2AX4** Bach—Cantatas, Vol.1
(ARCH) **439 374-2AX5** Bach—Cantatas, Volume 2 - Easter
(ARCH) **439 380-2AX6** Bach—Cantatas, Volume 3 - Ascension Day; Whitsun; Trinity
(ARCH) **439 387-2AX6** Bach Cantatas, Volume 4
(ARCH) **439 394-2AX5** Bach—Cantatas, Volume 5
(CLAV) **CD50-8611** Schubert—Lieder
(DG) **423 127-2GX4** Bruckner: Sacred Works for Chorus
(DG) **437 677-2GDO2** Irmgard Seefried - Opera Recital
(DG) **445 400-2GDO10** Ferenc Fricsay - A Portrait
(DG) **445 410-2GDO** Kodály—Orchestral Works
(DG) **447 409-2GOR2** Bruckner—The Masses
(EMI) **CMS7 63310-2** Beethoven: Complete Symphonies

HAEGER, Raphael (perc)
  see CONCERT INDEX *under:*
(LARG) **Largo 5127** Igor Markevitch—Chamber Works

HAEGGANDER, Mari-Anne (sop)
  Grieg: Peer Gynt (exc)

HAEMERS, Rudy (sax)
  see CONCERT INDEX *under:*
(DINT) **DICD920125** Walton—Façade

HAENCHEN, Hans (cond)
  see CPE Bach Orch

HAENCHEN, Hartmut (cond)
  see CPE Bach Orch

HAENDEL, Ida (vn)
  Brahms: Violin Concerto
  Tchaikovsky: Violin Concerto
  see CONCERT INDEX *under:*
(PEAR) **GEMMCD9939** Josef Hassid & Ida Haendel - 1940-42 Recordings

HAENGEL, Aracelly (mez)
  Donizetti: Ajo nell'imbarazzo (Cpte)

HAGAN, Samuel (ten)
  Gershwin: Porgy and Bess (Cpte)

HAGEGÅRD, Erland (ten)
  Sibelius: Maiden in the Tower (Cpte)

HAGEGÅRD, Håkan (bar)
  Diepenbrock: Im grossen Schweigen
  Grieg: Psalms, Op.74
  Haydn: Jahreszeiten (Cpte)
  Lidholm: Dream Play (Cpte)
  Mahler: Lieder eines fahrenden gesellen
  Mozart: Don Giovanni (Cpte), Nozze di Figaro (Cpte), Zauberflöte (Cpte)
  Orff: Carmina Burana
  Puccini: Bohème (Cpte)
  Rodgers: Sound of Music (Cpte)
  Rosenberg: Symphony 4
  Rossini: Barbiere di Siviglia (Cpte)
  Schubert: Schöne Müllerin (Cpte)
  Wolf: Italienisches Liederbuch (Cpte)
  Zemlinsky: Lyrische Symphonie
  see CONCERT INDEX *under:*
(ALBA) **TROY036-2** S.Paulus—Songs
(BIS) **BIS-CD054** Lieder Recital
(DG) **437 519-2GH** Grieg—Orchestral Songs
(DG) **437 523-2GH** Grieg—Dramatic Works with Orchestra
(MSVE) **MSCD623** Stenhammar: Songs
(RCA) **09026 61518-2** Grieg—Songs, Vol.1
(RCA) **09026 61629-2** Grieg—Songs, Vol.2

HAGEMANN, Emmi (mez)
  see CONCERT INDEX *under:*
(MYTO) **3MCD93381** Wagner—Die Walküre, etc

HAGEN, Christine (mez)
  Wagner: Götterdämmerung (Cpte)

HAGEN, Reinhard (bass)
  Franck: Béatitudes (Cpte)

HAGEN OPERA CHORUS
  cond M. HALÁSZ
  Schreker: Ferne Klang (Cpte)

HAGEN PHILHARMONIC ORCHESTRA
  cond M. HALÁSZ
  Schreker: Ferne Klang (Cpte)
  cond G. MARKSON
  Weber: Peter Schmoll (Cpte)

HAGEN QUARTET
  Beethoven: Grosse Fuge, String Quartet 16
  Brahms: Piano Quintet
  Haydn: String Quartets, Op.20
  Mozart: Divertimento, K136-8, Serenade, K525
  Schoenberg: Chamber Symphony 1
  Schubert: String Quartet, D810, String Quintet, Trout Quintet, D667
  see CONCERT INDEX *under:*
(DG) **419 601-2GH** Dvořák & Kodály—String Quartets; Dvořák—Cypresses
(DG) **423 622-2GH** Haydn: String Quartets
(DG) **427 669-2GH** Janáček & Wolf: Chamber Works
(DG) **431 645-2GH3** Mozart—Early String Quartets
(DG) **431 686-2GH** 20th Century String Quartets

(DG) **437 836-2GH** Debussy/Ravel/Webern—String Quartets
(DG) **445 864-2GH** Shostakovich—String Quartets
(DG) **447 069-2GH** Verdi/Puccini/Muzio—Works for String Quartet

HAGEN-GROLL, Walter (cond)
  see Vienna St Op Chor

HAGER, Clyde (bass)
  Orff: Carmina Burana

HÅGER, Klaus (bass)
  Lortzing: Undine (Cpte)

HAGER, Leopold (cond)
  see Auvergne Orch

HAGER, Robert (bar)
  R. Strauss: Elektra (Cpte)

HAGERMAN, Karen (contr)
  Bach: Cantata 21

HÄGGANDER, Mari Anne (sop)
  Brahms: Deutsches Requiem, Op. 45 (Cpte)
  Mahler: Symphony 8
  Sibelius: Maiden in the Tower (Cpte)
  see CONCERT INDEX *under:*
(BIS) **BIS-CD270** Sibelius: Songs with orchestra
(DG) **445 354-2GX14** Wagner—Der Ring des Nibelungen

HAGGENMÜLLER, Heinz (bass)
  Anon: Missa Salisburgensis, Plaudite tympana

HÄGGSTAM, Alf (bass)
  Haeffner: Electra (Cpte)

HAGLEY, Alison (sop)
  Mendelssohn: Symphony 2
  Mozart: Nozze di Figaro (Cpte)
  see CONCERT INDEX *under:*
(ARGO) **433 214-2ZH** Elgar—Music inspired by children

HAGOPIAN, Robert (pf)
  see CONCERT INDEX *under:*
(ETCE) **KTC1012** Bartók: Piano Works

(THE) HAGUE PERCUSSION ENSEMBLE
  see CONCERT INDEX *under:*
(ETCE) **KTC1130** Birtwistle—Works for Wind and Percussion
  cond R. DE LEEUW
  L. Andriessen: De Tijd
  Messiaen: Canyons aux étoiles
  cond J. WOOD
  see CONCERT INDEX *under:*
(ETCE) **KTC1130** Birtwistle—Works for Wind and Percussion

(THE) HAGUE PHILHARMONIC ORCHESTRA
  cond W. VAN OTTERLOO
  see CONCERT INDEX *under:*
(PHIL) **442 631-2PM4** Clara Haskil—The Legacy Volume 2: Concertos
(PHIL) **442 685-2PM12** Clara Haskil - The Legacy
  cond H. VONK
  see CONCERT INDEX *under:*
(CHAN) **CHAN8821** Diepenbrock: Orchestral Works
(CHAN) **CHAN8878** Diepenbrock: Symphonic Songs

HAHESSY, John (alto)
  see CONCERT INDEX *under:*
(LOND) **425 716-2LM** Britten: Canticles

HAHN, Josef (tbn)
  see CONCERT INDEX *under:*
(DG) **423 127-2GX4** Bruckner: Sacred Works for Chorus

HAHN, Werner (bar)
  Schreker: Ferne Klang (Cpte)

HAIDER, Friederich (cond)
  see Czech PO

HAIDER, Friederich (cond)
  see CONCERT INDEX *under:*
(TELD) **2292-44922-2** R. Strauss—Lieder

HAIMOVITZ, Matt (vc)
  see CONCERT INDEX *under:*
(DG) **427 323-2GH** Works for Cello and Orchestra
(DG) **429 219-2GH** Cello Concertos
(DG) **431 813-2GH** Modern Cello Solos
(DG) **445 834-2GH** The 20th-Century Cello

HAITINK, Bernard (cond)
  see Boston SO

HAJOS, Mizzi (sngr)
  see CONCERT INDEX *under:*
(PEAR) **GEMMCDS9056/8** Music from the New York Stage, Vol. 3: 1913-17

HAJÓSSYOVÁ, Magdaléna (sop)
  Beethoven: Mass in C
  Dvořák: Dimitrij (Cpte)
  Janáček: Cunning Little Vixen (Cpte), Glagolitic Mass (Cpte)
  Marschner: Hans Heiling (Cpte)
  Shostakovich: Symphony 14
  see CONCERT INDEX *under:*
(OPUS) **9156 1824** Dvorsky sings Operatic Arias
(OPUS) **9352 1887** Gustav and Alma Mahler—Lieder

HAKEN, Eduard (bass)
  Janáček: Glagolitic Mass (Cpte)
  Smetana: Brandenburgers in Bohemia (Cpte), Kiss (Cpte)

Stravinsky: Oedipus Rex (Cpte)
see CONCERT INDEX *under:*
(SUPR) **11 1930-2** Janáček/Kabeláč—Choral and
Orchestral Works

HAKIM, Naji (organ)
see CONCERT INDEX *under:*
(MOTE) **CD40081** French Choral and Organ Works
(PRIO) **PRCD327** Great European Organs Volume 22

HAKKILA, Tuija (fp)
see CONCERT INDEX *under:*
(FINL) **4509-95584-2** Beethoven—Cello Sonatas,
Vol.1

HAKMOUN, Hassan (voc/sintar)
see CONCERT INDEX *under:*
(NONE) **7559-79275-2** Pieces of Africa

HAKMOUN, Saïd (bandar)
see CONCERT INDEX *under:*
(NONE) **7559-79275-2** Pieces of Africa

HÁLA, Josef (harm)
see CONCERT INDEX *under:*
(SUPR) **11 1533-2** Suk—Chamber Works, Volume 3

HÁLA, Josef (pf)
Chausson: Concert, Op 21
Fauré: Violin Sonata 2
see CONCERT INDEX *under:*
(DINT) **DICD920306** Franck/Fauré/Ravel—Violin
Works
(SUPR) **11 0099-2** Martinů: Works for Violin and
Piano
(SUPR) **11 0710-2** Violin Sonatas
(SUPR) **11 1533-2** Suk—Chamber Works, Volume 3

HALÁSZ, Michael (cond)
see Budapest Camerata

HALBAN, Desi (sop)
Mahler: Lieder und Gesänge (exc), Symphony 4

HALDAS, Béatrice (sop)
Hindemith: Mörder, Hoffnung der Frauen (Cpte)
Zemlinsky: Geburtstag der Infantin (Cpte)

HALE, Robert (bass-bar)
Handel: Messiah (exc)
Schumann: Paradies und die Peri (Cpte)
Wagner: Fliegende Holländer (Cpte), Rheingold
(Cpte)

HALEM, Victor von (bass)
Beethoven: Christus am Oelberge, Op. 85
Hindemith: Mathis der Maler (Cpte), Mörder, Hoffnung
der Frauen (Cpte), Nusch-Nuschi (Cpte)
Mozart: Zauberflöte (Cpte)
Pfitzner: Palestrina (Cpte), Von deutscher Seele
(Cpte)
Puccini: Tosca (Cpte)
R. Strauss: Rosenkavalier (Cpte)
Schreker: Ferne Klang (Cpte)
Wagner: Meistersinger (Cpte), Parsifal (Cpte)
Wolf: Corregidor (Cpte)
Zemlinsky: Traumgörge (Cpte)

HALESWORTH MIDDLE SCHOOL CHOIR
cond M. ERMLER
Tchaikovsky: Nutcracker (Cpte)

HALGRIMSON, Amanda (sop)
Mozart: Don Giovanni (Cpte)

HALÍŘ, Václav (bass)
Janáček: Jenufa (Cpte)

HALJÁKOVÁ, Sidónia (sop)
Puccini: Bohème (Cpte)
see CONCERT INDEX *under:*
(OPUS) **9156 1824** Dvorský sings Operatic Arias

HALL, Berniece (sop)
Gershwin: Porgy and Bess (exc)

HALL, Carol (sop)
Bach: Mass in B minor, BWV232 (Cpte)
Purcell: Tempest, Z631 (Cpte)
see CONCERT INDEX *under:*
(ERAT) **4509-96371-2** Gardiner—The Purcell
Collection

HALL, Jim (gtr)
see CONCERT INDEX *under:*
(EMI) **CMS7 64617-2** The art of Itzhak Perlman
(EMI) **CZS4 83177-2(3)** Itzhak Perlman Edition (pt 3)

HALL, Judith (fl)
Mozart: Flute Concerto, K313, Flute Concerto, K314

HALL, Leonore (pf)
see CONCERT INDEX *under:*
(CARL) **DPCD1039** Elgar—Violin & Piano Works

HALL, Lucia (vn)
see CONCERT INDEX *under:*
(CHAN) **CHAN8651** Vivaldi: Concertos

HALL, Marie (vn)
see CONCERT INDEX *under:*
(PEAR) **GEMMCDS9951/5** The Elgar
Edition—Acoustic Recordings 1914-25

HALL, Meredith (sop)
Rameau: Hippolyte et Aricie (Cpte)

HALL, Nicola (gtr)
see CONCERT INDEX *under:*
(DECC) **430 839-2DH** Virtuoso Guitar Transcriptions
(DECC) **440 293-2DH** Works for Guitar and
Orchestra

HALL, Peter (ten)
Nono: Prometeo (Cpte)
Orff: Carmina Burana
Verdi: Ballo in maschera (Cpte)
see CONCERT INDEX *under:*
(ARGO) **417 468-2ZH** G. Gabrieli: Choral and
Instrumental Works
(SONY) **SK53978** Prometheus

HALL, Peter (ten/spkr)
see CONCERT INDEX *under:*
(DG) **447 068-2GH** Stravinsky—The Flood, etc

HALLACKER, Klaus-Peter (bar)
Delius: Village Romeo and Juliet (Cpte)

HALLAND, Edward (bass)
see CONCERT INDEX *under:*
(CLAR) **CDGSE78-50-54** Coates conducts Wagner,
Weber & Mendelssohn

HALLASCHKA, Heike (sop)
Telemann: Don Quichotte (Cpte)

HALLAWELL, Rachael (mez)
Henze: English Cat (Cpte)

HALLCHURCH, Philip (treb)
see CONCERT INDEX *under:*
(HYPE) **CDA66585** Purcell—Complete Anthems &
Services, Vol.1
(HYPE) **CDA66644** Purcell—Complete Anthems &
Services, Vol.4
(HYPE) **CDA66656** Purcell—Complete Anthems &
Services, Vol.5

HALLE CANTAMUS CHAMBER CHOIR
cond N. MCGEGAN
Handel: Giustino (Cpte)

HALLÉ CHOIR
cond J. BARBIROLLI
Elgar: Dream of Gerontius (Cpte)
cond M. HANDFORD
Orff: Carmina Burana
cond J. LOUGHRAN
Holst: Planets

**HALLE OPERA HOUSE HANDEL FESTIVAL
ORCHESTRA**
cond H. ARMAN
see CONCERT INDEX *under:*
(CAPR) **10 547** Handel—Arias

HALLÉ ORCHESTRA
cond J. BARBIROLLI
Elgar: Dream of Gerontius (Cpte), Falstaff
Vaughan Williams: Symphony 2, Symphony 5,
Symphony 8
see CONCERT INDEX *under:*
(BBCR) **DMCD98** BBC Proms - The Centenary: 1895-
1995
(DUTT) **CDSJB1002** Barbirolli conducts French
Music
(EMI) **CDC7 47793-2** Mahler—Song-cycles
(EMI) **CDM7 64193-2** Dvořák—Orchestral Works
(EMI) **CDM7 64716-2** Ireland—Piano Concerto, etc
(EMI) **CDM7 64724-2** Elgar—Orchestral Works
(EMI) **CMS5 65119-2** Delius—Orchestral Works
(EMI) **CZS7 62707-2** Mahler—Vocal Works
(EMIN) **CD-EMX2198** A Delius Festival
cond A. BOULT
see CONCERT INDEX *under:*
(DUTT) **CDAX8010** Hallé Orchestra Wartime
Recordings
cond W. BRAITHWAITE
see CONCERT INDEX *under:*
(DUTT) **CDLX7013** The Unforgettable Isobel Baillie
cond M. HANDFORD
Orff: Carmina Burana
cond V. HANDLEY
see CONCERT INDEX *under:*
(CFP) **CD-CFP4568** Delius: Orchestral Works
cond L. HEWARD
Ireland: Piano Concerto
Moeran: Symphony
see CONCERT INDEX *under:*
(APR) **APR7012** Myra Hess—A vignette
(DUTT) **CDAX8010** Hallé Orchestra Wartime
Recordings
(DUTT) **CDLX7013** The Unforgettable Isobel Baillie
(MMOI) **CDMOIR411** Sacred Songs and Arias
(TEST) **SBT1013** Dame Joan Hammond—A
Celebration
cond J. JUDD
Elgar: Symphony 1
cond C. LAMBERT
see CONCERT INDEX *under:*
(DUTT) **CDAX8010** Hallé Orchestra Wartime
Recordings
(DUTT) **CDLX7006** Tchaikovsky—Orchestral Works
(TEST) **SBT1014** Delius—Orchestral Works
cond J. LOUGHRAN
Elgar: Symphony 1, Symphony 2
Holst: Planets
see CONCERT INDEX *under:*
(CFP) **CD-CFP9011** Popular Orchestral Works
cond M. SARGENT
see CONCERT INDEX *under:*
(DUTT) **CDAX8010** Hallé Orchestra Wartime
Recordings
cond S. SKROWACZEWSKI
Brahms: Academic Festival Overture, Haydn
Variations, Symphony 1, Symphony 2, Symphony 3,
Tragic Overture
Mahler: Symphony 4

Shostakovich: Symphony 5, Symphony 10
cond B. THOMSON
Mozart: Piano Concerto 9, Piano Concerto 21
see CONCERT INDEX *under:*
(CFP) **CD-CFP9015** Waltzes by Johann Strauss II
cond B. TOVEY
see CONCERT INDEX *under:*
(CFP) **CD-CFP4577** A Viennese Evening

HALLER, Andreas (bass-bar)
Schreker: Ferne Klang (Cpte)

HALLETT, Alfred (ten)
Bizet: Carmen (Cpte)

HALLGRIMSSON, Haflidi (vc)
see CONCERT INDEX *under:*
(CARL) **PCD809** Vivaldi: Violin Concertos

HALLIN, Margareta (sop)
Verdi: Rigoletto (Cpte)

HALLING, Elizabeth (mez)
Gade: Comala
Schumann: Rose Pilgerfahrt (Cpte)

HALLIWELL, William (cond)
see Black Dyke Mills Band

HALLMAN, Milton (pf)
see CONCERT INDEX *under:*
(CENT) **CRC2025** Dohnányi: Piano Works

HALLON, Ladislav (ten)
Puccini: Bohème (Cpte)

HALLSTEIN, Ingeborg (sop)
Benatzky: Im weissen Rössl (exc)
Offenbach: Vie Parisienne (exc)
see CONCERT INDEX *under:*
(DG) **431 110-2GB** Great Voices - Fritz Wunderlich

HALSEY, Louis (cond)
see L. Halsey Sngrs

HALSEY, Simon (cond)
see CBSO Chor

(LOUIS) HALSEY SINGERS
cond L. HALSEY
see CONCERT INDEX *under:*
(DECC) **430 094-2DWO** The World of Elgar

HALSTEAD, Anthony (cond)
see ECO

HALSTEAD, Anthony (hn)
Beethoven: Piano and Wind Quintet, Op. 16
Mozart: Horn Concerti, Horn Concerto,
KAnh98a/K494a, Piano and Wind Quintet, K452
see CONCERT INDEX *under:*
(AMON) **CD-SAR34** Mozart—Chamber Works
(CHAN) **CHAN0547** Telemann—Orchestral Works
(CONI) **CDCF220** Michael Haydn—Masses and
Vespers
(L'OI) **443 216-2OH** Mozart—Horn Concertos
(MERI) **CDE84145** Beethoven: Chamber Music on
Period Instruments
(MERI) **CDE84183** Donizetti: Songs
(NIMB) **NI5190** Orchestral Works by the Haydn
Brothers
(NIMB) **NI5234** Britten: Vocal Works
(PHIL) **432 152-2PH** Brahms—Choral Works

HALSTEAD, Anthony (hpd/dir)
Bach: Brandenburg Concertos (exc)

HALSTEAD, Patrick (bass)
G. Charpentier: Louise (Cpte)

HAMARI, Júlia (mez)
Bach: Cantata 63, Christmas Oratorio, BWV248
(Cpte), Easter Oratorio, BWV249 (Cpte)
Beethoven: Mass in C
Cimarosa: Matrimonio segreto (Cpte)
J. Strauss II: Zigeunerbaron (Cpte)
Mascagni: Cavalleria rusticana (Cpte)
Mozart: Mass, K317, Requiem, Vespers, K339
R. Strauss: Salome (Cpte)
Tchaikovsky: Eugene Onegin (Cpte)
Verdi: Ernani (Cpte)
Wagner: Meistersinger (Cpte)
Weber: Oberon (Cpte)
see CONCERT INDEX *under:*
(ARCH) **439 387-2AX6** Bach Cantatas, Volume 4
(DG) **429 042-2GX10** Mahler: Complete Symphonies
(HANS) **98 803** Bach—Cantatas, Vol.41
(HANS) **98 804** Bach—Cantatas, Vol.42
(HANS) **98 805** Bach—Cantatas, Vol.43
(HANS) **98 807** Bach—Cantatas, Vol.45
(HANS) **98 809** Bach—Cantatas, Vol.47
(HANS) **98 811** Bach—Cantatas, Vol.49
(HANS) **98 814** Bach—Cantatas, Vol.52
(HANS) **98 817** Bach—Cantatas, Vol.55
(HANS) **98 829** Bach—Cantatas, Vol.67
(HANS) **98 856** Bach—Cantatas, Vol.5
(HANS) **98 858** Bach—Cantatas, Vol.7
(HANS) **98 866** Bach—Cantatas, Vol.15
(HANS) **98 871** Bach—Cantatas, Vol.20
(HANS) **98 876** Bach—Cantatas, Vol.25
(HANS) **98 879** Bach—Cantatas, Vol.28
(HANS) **98 882** Bach—Cantatas, Vol.31
(HANS) **98 885** Bach—Cantatas, Vol.34
(HANS) **98 887** Bach—Cantatas, Vol.36
(HANS) **98 891** Bach—Cantatas, Vol.38
(HUNG) **HCD31535** Bartók—Songs

HAMBERGER, Thomas (bass)
Bach: St Matthew Passion, BWV244 (Cpte)

HAMBITZER, Gerald (hpd)
see CONCERT INDEX under:
(CAPR) 10 378   Musica Napoletana

HAMBOURG, Mark (pf)
see CONCERT INDEX under:
(OPAL) OPALCD9839   Pupils of Theodore Leschetizky
(PEAR) GEMMCD9147   Mark Hambourg (1879-1960)

HAMBOURG, Michal (pf)
see CONCERT INDEX under:
(PEAR) GEMMCD9147   Mark Hambourg (1879-1960)

HAMBURG MONTEVERDI CHOIR
cond G. ALBRECHT
see CONCERT INDEX under:
(ORFE) C209901A   Reger: Orchestral Songs
cond N. HARNONCOURT
Telemann: Tag des Gerichts (Cpte)
cond C. MACKERRAS
Purcell: Dido (Cpte)

HAMBURG NDR CHAMBER ORCHESTRA
cond C. MACKERRAS
Purcell: Dido (Cpte)

HAMBURG PHILHARMONIC ORCHESTRA
cond G. ALBRECHT
Dessau: Hagadah Shel Pessach
Dvořák: Spectre's Bride
Pettersson: Symphony 7
Schumann: Genoveva (Cpte)
Spohr: Jessonda (Cpte)
see CONCERT INDEX under:
(CAPR) 10 448   Zemlinsky—Orchestral Works and Songs
(CAPR) 10 449   Felix/Fanny Mendelssohn—Orchestral/Vocal Works
(ORFE) C209901A   Reger: Orchestral Songs
cond E. JOCHUM
Bruckner: Symphony 4
R. Strauss: Elektra (Cpte)
cond L. MAGIERA
see CONCERT INDEX under:
(ACAN) 49 384   Puccini: Opera Arias and Duets

HAMBURG RADIO SYMPHONY ORCHESTRA
cond W. SCHÜCHTER
Wagner: Lohengrin (Cpte)
cond G. WAND
Mozart: Symphony 39, Symphony 41

HAMBURG ST MICHAELIS CHOIR
cond G. ALBRECHT
see CONCERT INDEX under:
(ORFE) C209901A   Reger: Orchestral Songs

HAMBURG STATE OPERA CHORUS
cond G. ALBRECHT
Schreker: Schatzgräber (Cpte)
Schumann: Genoveva (Cpte)
Spohr: Jessonda (Cpte)
cond E. JOCHUM
R. Strauss: Elektra (Cpte)
cond G. WAND
see CONCERT INDEX under:
(RCA) 74321 20277-2   Beethoven—Complete Symphonies

HAMBURG STATE OPERA ORCHESTRA
cond G. ALBRECHT
Schreker: Schatzgräber (Cpte)
cond K. BÖHM
R. Strauss: Salome (Cpte)

HAMBURG SYMPHONY ORCHESTRA
cond H. BEISSEL
Hummel: Piano Concerto, Op.110
Kalkbrenner: Piano Concerto 1
cond R. KAPP
F. X. Scharwenka: Piano Concerto, Op.56
see CONCERT INDEX under:
(VOX) 115708-2   Mosonyi/Raff/Stavenhaegn—Piano Concertos

HAMBURG WIND ENSEMBLE FOR EARLY MUSIC
Schütz: Psalmen Davids, SWV22-47 (exc)
cond B. TURNER
see CONCERT INDEX under:
(ARCH) 437 072-2AT   Collectio Argentea 2: Palestrina, Lassus

HAMEL, Michel (ten)
Auber: Fra Diavolo (Cpte)
Audran: Miss Helyett (Cpte)
Bazin: Maître Pathelin (Cpte)
Bizet: Carmen (Cpte)
Hahn: O mon bel inconnu (Cpte)
Lecocq: Jour et la Nuit (Cpte)
Offenbach: Chanson de Fortunio (Cpte)
Terrasse: Fiancée du Scaphandrier (Cpte)
see CONCERT INDEX under:
(DECC) 433 400-2DM2   Ravel & Debussy—Stage Works
(EMI) CDS7 49361-2   Offenbach: Operettas
(EMI) CZS7 67515-2   Offenbach—Operetta highlights
(MUSD) 20239-2   Delibes—Opéras-Comiques

HAMELIN, Gaston (cl)
see CONCERT INDEX under:
(CLRI) CC0005   The Clarinet - Historical Recordings, Vol.1

HAMELIN, Marc-André (pf)
Alkan: Etudes, Op.39 (exc)
Ives: Concord Sonata
M. Wright: Piano Sonata (1982)

R. Strauss: Cello Sonata
Thuille: Cello Sonata, Op. 22
see CONCERT INDEX under:
(ALTA) AIR-CD-9052   Eckhardt-Gramatté—Piano Sonatas
(HYPE) CDA66717   Alkan/Henselt—Piano Concertos
(HYPE) CDA66765   Marc-André Hamelin live at the Wigmore Hall
(HYPE) CDA66794   Alkan—Piano Works

HAMER, Ralph (bass)
Giordano: Andrea Chénier (Cpte)

HÄMER, Therese (spkr)
Mendelssohn: Antigone (Cpte), Oedipus (Cpte)

HAMILTON, Katherine Mary (sop)
see CONCERT INDEX under:
(GLOR) GCDC016   Leo Sowerby—American Master of Sacred Song

HAMILTON, Susan (sop)
see CONCERT INDEX under:
(HYPE) CDA66587   Purcell—Complete Odes & Welcome Songs, Vol.7

HAMMAR, Jan (ten)
Honegger: Jeanne d'Arc (Cpte)

HAMMER, Gusta (mez)
R. Strauss: Elektra (Cpte)

HAMMER, Moshe (vn)
Paganini: Centone di sonate (exc)

HAMMER, Stephen (ob)
see CONCERT INDEX under:
(L'OI) 421 500-2OH   Bach: Double Concertos
(L'OI) 433 674-2OH   Vivaldi—Oboe Concertos

HAMMERSLEY, Robert (ten)
see CONCERT INDEX under:
(EMI) CDM5 65101-2   A Warlock Centenary Album
(EMI) CDM7 64131-2   Orchestral Music for Christmas

HAMMES, Karl (bar)
see CONCERT INDEX under:
(SCHW) 314662   Vienna State Opera Live, Vol.16

HAMMOND, Arthur (cond)
see orch

HAMMOND, Dame Joan (sop)
see CONCERT INDEX under:
(EMI) CHS7 69741-2(1)   Record of Singing, Vol.4—Anglo-American School (pt 1)
(TEST) SBT1013   Dame Joan Hammond—A Celebration

HAMMOND-STROUD, Derek (bar)
R. Strauss: Rosenkavalier (Cpte)
Tchaikovsky: Hamlet (Cpte)
Verdi: Forza del destino (Cpte)
Wagner: Götterdämmerung (Cpte), Rheingold (Cpte), Siegfried (Cpte)
see CONCERT INDEX under:
(CHAN) CHAN8310/1   Tchaikovsky—Orchestral Works
(SYMP) SYMCD1064   Schubert & Wolf—Lieder

HAMMONS, Thomas (bar)
J. Adams: Death of Klinghoffer (Cpte)

HAMNETT, Mike (perc)
see CONCERT INDEX under:
(ARGO) 443 903-2ZH   First & Foremost

HAMNØY, Kari (sop)
Schmidt/Jansson: Oresund Symphony

HAMPE, Christiane (sop)
Lortzing: Undine (Cpte)
see CONCERT INDEX under:
(BAYE) BR100095   Chaconne

HAMPEL, Alfréd (ten)
Smetana: Bartered Bride (Cpte), Two Widows (Cpte)

HAMPSON, Thomas (bar)
A. Thomas: Hamlet (Cpte)
Berlin: Annie Get Your Gun (Cpte)
Bernstein: On the Town (Cpte)
Brahms: Deutsches Requiem, Op. 45 (Cpte)
Delius: Village Romeo and Juliet (Cpte)
Gounod: Faust (Cpte)
Lehár: Lustige Witwe (Cpte)
Mahler: Kindertotenlieder, Knaben Wunderhorn
Mendelssohn: Erste Walpurgisnacht
Mozart: Così fan tutte (Cpte), Don Giovanni (Cpte), Nozze di Figaro (Cpte), Schauspieldirektor (Cpte), Zauberflöte (Cpte)
Orff: Carmina burana
Porter: Kiss Me, Kate (Cpte)
Puccini: Bohème (Cpte)
Rossini: Barbiere di Siviglia (Cpte)
Schubert: Fierrabras (Cpte)
Tchaikovsky: Eugene Onegin (Cpte)
Vaughan Williams: Symphony 1
Wagner: Götterdämmerung (Cpte)
see CONCERT INDEX under:
(DG) 431 682-2GH   Mahler—Lieder
(DG) 435 867-2GH2   Barber—The Songs
(EMI) CDC5 55047-2   Liszt/Wagner/Berlioz—Romantic Songs
(EMI) CDC5 55147-2   Thomas Hampson Lieder Recital
(EMI) CDC5 55233-2   German Opera Arias
(EMI) CDC7 54203-2   Porter—Night and Day
(EMI) CDC7 54242-2   Meyerbeer/Rossini—Songs
(EMI) CDC7 54643-2   Rossini—Bicentenary Gala Concert

(EMI) CDC7 54883-2   Jerome Kern Treasury
(HYPE) CDJ33013   Schubert—Complete Lieder, Vol.13
(HYPE) CDJ33014   Schubert—Complete Lieder, Vol.14
(TELD) 2292-42631-2   Bach—Cantatas, Volume 36
(TELD) 2292-42632-2   Bach—Cantatas, Volume 37
(TELD) 2292-42738-2   Bach—Cantatas, Volume 42
(TELD) 2292-44179-2   Bach—Cantatas, Volume 43
(TELD) 2292-44193-2   Bach—Cantatas, Volume 44
(TELD) 2292-44194-2   Bach—Cantatas, Volume 45
(TELD) 2292-44923-2   Lieder aus Des Knaben Wunderhorn
(TELD) 2292-44935-2   Schumann—Lieder
(TELD) 4509-91762-2   Bach—Cantatas, Vol.8
(TELD) 4509-91764-2   Bach—Cantatas, Vol.10
(TELD) 9031-72168-2   German Songs by American Composers
(TELD) 9031-73135-2   Christmas with Thomas Hampson
(TELD) 9031-73283-2   Hampson and Hadley
(TELD) 9031-74002-2   Mahler (orch Berio)—Lieder
(TELD) 9031-74798-2   Bach—Arias and Duets

HAMPSTEAD CHURCH BOYS' CHOIR
cond O. KLEMPERER
Bach: St Matthew Passion, BWV244 (exc)

HAMPTON QUARTET
cond M. RIESMAN
Bryars: Jesus' Blood

HANAKOVA, Olga (contr)
Suchoň: Whirlpool (Cpte)

HANAN, Stephen Mo (spkr)
see CONCERT INDEX under:
(DELO) DE3170   Beach—Cabildo; Six Short Pieces

HANANI, Yehuda (vc)
see CONCERT INDEX under:
(KOCH) 37070-2   Barber/Foss/Ornstein—Cello Works

HANCHARD, Dana (sop)
Handel: Radamisto (Cpte)
M. Monk: Atlas (Cpte)

HANCOCK, Gerre (cond)
see St Thomas Ch

HANCOCK, John (bar)
Lully: Armide

HANCOCK-CHILD, Nik (bar)
see CONCERT INDEX under:
(MARC) 8 223458   Gibbs—Songs

HANCOCK-CHILD, Rosemary (pf)
see CONCERT INDEX under:
(MARC) 8 223458   Gibbs—Songs

HANCORN, John (bar)
Rameau: Castor et Pollux (Cpte)

HANDEL AND HAYDN SOCIETY CHORUS
cond A. PARROTT
Mozart: Mass, K427

HANDEL AND HAYDN SOCIETY ORCHESTRA
cond C. HOGWOOD
Handel: Concerti Grossi, Op. 3, Concerti grossi, Op. 6

HANDEL FESTIVAL ORCHESTRA
cond A. LEWIS
see CONCERT INDEX under:
(VANG) 08.5069.71   Bach—Cantatas; Handel—Airs

HANDEL OPERA CHORUS
cond C. FARNCOMBE
see CONCERT INDEX under:
(DECC) 430 500-2DWO   World of Handel

HANDFORD, Maurice (cond)
see Hallé

HANDL, Herma (sop)
R. Strauss: Arabella (Cpte)

HANDLEY, Vernon (cond)
see Berlin RSO

HANDLOS, Franz (bass)
Verdi: Battaglia di Legnano (Cpte), Due Foscari (Cpte)

HANDY, Lionel (vc)
see CONCERT INDEX under:
(EMI) CDC5 55052-2   Praetorius/Vivaldi/Warlock—Works arr guitar

HANIČINEC, Petr (spkr)
see CONCERT INDEX under:
(SUPR) 11 0751-2   Martinů—Choral Works
(SUPR) 11 0767-2   Martinů—Cantatas

HANKIN, Wayne (cond)
see Orch

HANLEY, Regina (contr)
Sullivan: Gondoliers (Cpte), Iolanthe (Cpte)

HANN, Georg (bass)
Haydn: Jahreszeiten (Cpte)
R. Strauss: Arabella (Cpte)
Wagner: Meistersinger (exc)
see CONCERT INDEX under:
(ACAN) 43 268   Peter Anders sings German Opera Arias
(DG) 435 321-2GWP12   150 Years - Vienna Philharmonic
(PREI) 90168   Wagner—Die Meistersinger, Act 2, etc
(SCHW) 314582   Vienna State Opera Live, Vol.8

HARTFIEL, Jurgen (ten)
Tchaikovsky: Eugene Onegin (Cpte)

HARTINGER, Albert (bass)
see CONCERT INDEX *under:*
(TELD) 4509-91761-2 Bach—Cantatas, Vol.7

HARTLE, Enid (mez)
Massenet: Cigale
Offenbach: Robinson Crusoé (Cpte)
R. Strauss: Ariadne auf Naxos (Cpte)
Tchaikovsky: Eugene Onegin (Cpte)

HARTLEY PIANO TRIO
see CONCERT INDEX *under:*
(GAMU) GAMCD518 British Piano Trios
(GAMU) GAMCD536 American Piano Trios

HÄRTLING, Peter (narr)
Schubert: Winterreise (Cpte)

HARTMAN, Paul (sngr)
Gershwin: Of Thee I Sing (Cpte)

HARTMAN, Vernon (bar)
see CONCERT INDEX *under:*
(RCA) 09026 61581-2 Bernstein—Orchestral & Vocal
Works

HARTMANN, Arno (organ)
Schubert: Deutsche messe

HARTMANN, Gerda (sop)
Rameau: Indes Galantes (Cpte)

HARTMANN, Roland (bar)
S. Wagner: Bärenhäuter (Cpte),
Schwarzschwanenreich (Cpte)

HARTMANN, Rudolf (bass)
Monteverdi: Madrigals, Bk 8 (exc)
Wagner: Meistersinger (Cpte)
Zemlinsky: Kleider machen Leute (Cpte)

HARTMANN, Willy (ten)
R. Strauss: Salome (Cpte)

HARTMANN-CLAVERIE, Valerie (ondes martenot)
see CONCERT INDEX *under:*
(RCA) 09026 61520-2
Messiaen/Lutoslawski—Orchestral Works

HARTNETT, Michael (treb)
Britten: Rejoice in the Lamb

HARTOG, Bernhard (vn)
see CONCERT INDEX *under:*
(SCHW) 311122 Early Twentieth Century Music

HARTWIG, Hildegard (contr)
see CONCERT INDEX *under:*
(RCA) 74321 20277-2 Beethoven—Complete
Symphonies

HARTY, Sir Hamilton (cond)
see LPO

HARTY, Sir Hamilton (pf)
see CONCERT INDEX *under:*
(APR) APR7015 The Auer Legacy, Vol.1
(PEAR) GEMMCD9462 Dame Myra Hess—Vol.1

HARVARD GLEE CLUB
cond P. GEMIGNANI
see CONCERT INDEX *under:*
(RCA) 09026 62681-2 Mr Jerry Hadley—Golden Days
cond C. MUNCH
Berlioz: Roméo et Juliette (Cpte)

HARVEY, Brian (bass)
Saint-Saëns: Mass, Op. 4

HARVEY, Frederick (bar)
see CONCERT INDEX *under:*
(EMI) CDM5 65101-2 A Warlock Centenary Album

HARVEY, Jonathan (elec)
see CONCERT INDEX *under:*
(ETCE) KTC1148 Jonathan Harvey—Works for Cello

HARVEY, Peter (bass)
Bach: Cantata 21
C.P.E. Bach: Auferstehung und Himmelfahrt Jesu
(Cpte)
Delalande: Dies irae, S31, Miserere mei Deus
secundum, S27
Galuppi: Confitebor tibi, Domini
Purcell: Dido (Cpte), Indian Queen, Z630 (Cpte)
Wood: St Mark Passion
see CONCERT INDEX *under:*
(CHAN) CHAN8824 Walton: Vocal Works
(FNAC) 592096 Rameau—Grand Motets
(FNAC) 592308 Lully—Grand Motets, Volume 1
(VIRG) VC5 45075-2 Charpentier—Leçons de
ténèbres, Vol. 2

HARVEY, Richard (rec)
see CONCERT INDEX *under:*
(ASV) CDGAU111 Italian Recorder Concertos

HARVEY AND THE WALLBANGERS
cond S. RATTLE
see CONCERT INDEX *under:*
(EMI) CDC7 47991-2 The Simon Rattle Jazz Album

HARWOOD, Elizabeth (sop)
Britten: Midsummer Night's Dream (Cpte)
Handel: Messiah (Cpte)
Lehár: Lustige Witwe (exc)
Puccini: Bohème (Cpte)
Schumann: Szenen aus Goethes Faust (Cpte)
Sullivan: Iolanthe (exc), Yeomen of the Guard (Cpte)
see CONCERT INDEX *under:*

(DECC) 430 095-2DWO The World of Gilbert &
Sullivan, Vol.1
(DECC) 433 868-2DWO The World of Gilbert &
Sullivan - Volume 2
(DECC) 443 868-2DF2 Italian Baroque Sacred
Works
(DG) 435 712-2GX2 Lehár—The Merry Widow.
Suppé—Overtures

HASEL, Michael (bass fl)
see CONCERT INDEX *under:*
(SONY) SK53978 Prometheus

HASELBÖCK, Martin (cond)
see Vienna Academy Orch

HASELBÖCK, Martin (organ)
Berlioz: Te Deum
Schmidt: Buch mit Sieben Siegeln
see CONCERT INDEX *under:*
(NOVA) 150 054-2 Mozart—Organ Works
(NOVA) 150 081-2 Mozart—The Freemason Music
(SCHW) 317003 Mozart—Organ Works

HASELBÖCK, Martin (fp)
see CONCERT INDEX *under:*
(NOVA) 150 081-2 Mozart—The Freemason Music

HASELBÖCK, Martin (hpd/dir)
see CONCERT INDEX *under:*
(NOVA) 150 025-2 C.P.E.Bach—Keyboard Works

HASELBÖCK, Martin (org/dir)
see CONCERT INDEX *under:*
(NOVA) 150 025-2 C.P.E.Bach—Keyboard Works

HASKIL, Clara (pf)
see CONCERT INDEX *under:*
(ORFE) C197891A Hindemith & Berg: Orchestral
Works
(PHIL) 422 140-2PLC3 Beethoven: Complete Violin
Sonatas
(PHIL) 442 625-2PM5 Clara Haskil—The Legacy
Volume 1: Chamber Music
(PHIL) 442 631-2PM4 Clara Haskil—The Legacy
Volume 2: Concertos
(PHIL) 442 635-2PM3 Clara Haskil—The Legacy
Volume 3: Solo Repertoire
(PHIL) 442 685-2PM12 Clara Haskil - The Legacy
(SONY) SMK58982 Pablo Casals conducts Bach at
Prades, June 1950

HASKINS, Virginia (sop)
Verdi: Ballo in maschera (Cpte)

HASLAM, David (fl)
Bliss: Pastoral

HASS, Sabine (sop)
Hindemith: Mathis der Maler (Cpte)
see CONCERT INDEX *under:*
(DG) 437 719-2GC Berg—Vocal Works

HASSID, Josef (vn)
see CONCERT INDEX *under:*
(DUTT) CDLX7004 Elgar—Chamber Works
(PEAR) GEMMCD9939 Josef Hassid & Ida Haendel -
1940-42 Recordings
(TEST) SBT1010 Ginette Neveu & Josef Hassid

HASSLO, Hugo (bar)
Verdi: Rigoletto (Cpte)
see CONCERT INDEX *under:*
(BLUE) ABCD028 Jussi Björling live at the Stockholm
Opera
(EMI) CHS7 69741-2(5) Record of Singing,
Vol.4—Scandinavian School

HASSON, Maurice (vn)
see CONCERT INDEX *under:*
(PHIL) 426 462-2PBQ2 Bach—Orchestral Works

HASTINGS, Harold (cond)
see Orig Broadway Cast

HATANO, Hitoshi (ten)
Mendelssohn-Hensel: Oratorium nach Bildern der
Bibel

HATTEY, Philip (bass-bar)
Delius: Village Romeo and Juliet (Cpte)

HATTON, Jean-François (harm)
Rossini: Petite Messe Solennelle

HAUBOLD, Bernd (db)
see CONCERT INDEX *under:*
(CAPR) 10 367 Mendelssohn—Motets

HAUBOLD, Ingrid (sop)
Penderecki: Polish Requiem
Wagner: Fliegende Holländer (Cpte)
see CONCERT INDEX *under:*
(EMI) CDC7 54776-2 René Kollo sings Wagner and
Strauss

HAUGAN, Björn (ten)
Nørgård: Gilgamesh (Cpte)

HAUGLAND, Aage (bass)
Berg: Wozzeck (Cpte)
Heise: Drot og Marsk (Cpte)
Mozart: Zauberflöte (Cpte)
Mussorgsky: Boris Godunov (Cpte), Khovanshchina
(Cpte)
Nielsen: Maskarade (Cpte), Saul and David (Cpte)
Nørgård: Siddhartha (Cpte)
Schoenberg: Moses and Aron (Cpte)
Shostakovich: Lady Macbeth of Mtsensk (Cpte)
Various: Messa per Rossini (Cpte)
Wagner: Götterdämmerung (Cpte), Parsifal (Cpte)

Zemlinsky: Es war einmal (Cpte)
see CONCERT INDEX *under:*
(CHAN) CHAN9336/8 Mussorgsky—Songs

HAUGSAND, Ketil (hpd)
Bach: Partitas, BWV825-30
Rameau: Pièces de clavecin en concerts
see CONCERT INDEX *under:*
(SIMA) PSC1032 Bach—Keyboard Works

HAUKE, Ernst (cond)
see Berlin Künstlertheater Orch

HAUMAN, Constance (sop)
Wagner: Parsifal (Cpte)

HAUPT, Eckart (fl)
Boccherini: Sextets, G461-6 (exc)
C. P. E. Bach: Flute Concerto, H435, Flute Concerto,
H445
Mozart: Flute Quartets
see CONCERT INDEX *under:*
(CAPR) 10 101 C.P.E. Bach: Flute Works
(CAPR) 10 104 C.P.E. Bach: Flute Concertos

HAUPT, Eckart (fl/dir)
Telemann: 2-Flute concerti

HAUPT, Eckart (rec)
see CONCERT INDEX *under:*
(CAPR) 10 234 Italian Recorder Works

HAUPTMANN, Cornelius (bass)
Bach: St John Passion, BWV245 (Cpte), St Matthew
Passion, BWV244 (Cpte)
Beethoven: Missa solemnis
Glass: Akhnaten (Cpte)
Haydn: Stabat Mater
Kreutzer: Nachtlager in Granada (Cpte)
Mozart: Clemenza di Tito (Cpte), Entführung (Cpte),
Idomeneo (Cpte), Mass, K427, Requiem, Zauberflöte
(Cpte)
Wagner: Parsifal (Cpte)
Wolf: Manuel Venegas
see CONCERT INDEX *under:*
(BAYE) BR100038 Loewe—Lieder and Ballads
(DG) 431 791-2GH Mozart—Sacred Choral Works

HAUPTMANN, Norbert (hn)
see CONCERT INDEX *under:*
(EMI) CZS7 67521-2 Schumann—Concertos

HÄUSLER, Regula (vc)
Reger: Piano Trio, Op. 102
see CONCERT INDEX *under:*
(DG) 415 487-2GH Vivaldi: Guitar Concertos

HAUSLER, Robert (cl)
see CONCERT INDEX *under:*
(LARG) Largo 5117 Goldschmidt—Chamber Works

HAUSMANN, Josef (voc)
Weill: Dreigroschenoper (Cpte)

HAUSMUSIK
Beethoven: Septet, Op.20, String Quintet, Op.29
Mendelssohn: Octet, Op.20, String Quartet 2, String
Quintet 1, String Quintet 2
Schubert: Octet, D803

HAUTERMANN, Karin (mez)
Korngold: Violanta (Cpte)
Verdi: Rigoletto (Cpte)
see CONCERT INDEX *under:*
(EURO) GD69043 Puccini: Il Trittico

HAUTERMANN, Karin (spkr)
R. Strauss: Intermezzo (Cpte)

HAUTS-DE-SEINE MAÎTRISE
cond P. FOURNILLIER
Massenet: Amadis (Cpte)
cond MYUNG-WHUN CHUNG
Verdi: Otello (Cpte)

HAUWE, Walter van (rec)
see CONCERT INDEX *under:*
(TELD) 4509-97465-2 Franz Brüggen Edition Vol.
3—English Ensemble Music
(TELD) 4509-97466-2 Frans Brüggen Edition Vol.
4—Early Baroque Recorder Music
(TELD) 4509-97467-2 Frans Brüggen Edition Vol.
5—Late Baroque Chamber Music
(TELD) 4509-97469-2 Frans Brüggen Edition Vol.
7—French Recorder Sonatas

HAUXVELL, John (bar)
Walton: Troilus and Cressida (exc)

HAVENITH, Raimund (pf)
see CONCERT INDEX *under:*
(MARC) 8 223334 Schnittke—Works for Cello
(MARC) 8 223403 Virtuoso Cello Encores

HAVERINEN, Margareta (sop)
Madetoja: Juha (Cpte)

HAVLÁK, Lubomír (ten)
Hába: Mother (Cpte)
Martinů: Bouquet

HAVLIKOVA, Klara (pf)
see CONCERT INDEX *under:*
(CAMP) RRCD1321 Martinů—Keyboard Concertos,
etc

HAWAIIAN QUINTET
see CONCERT INDEX *under:*
(PEAR) GEMMCDS9053/5 Music from the New York
Stage, Vol. 2: 1908—1913

HAWKINS, Ossie (bar)
Bizet: Carmen (Cpte)

Verdi: Macbeth (Cpte)

HAWLATA, Franz (bass)
Puccini: Fanciulla del West (Cpte)
Spohr: Faust (Cpte)

HAWTHORNE, Nigel (narr)
see CONCERT INDEX under:
(HYPE) **CDA66754** Constant Lambert—Mr Bear
Squash-you-all-flat

HAWTHORNE QUARTET
see CONCERT INDEX under:
(CHNN) **CCS1691** Chamber music from
Theresienstadt 1941-45
(DECC) **440 853-2DH** Haas/Krása—String Quartets
(KOCH) **37056-2** Coleridge-Taylor—Chamber Works
(NORT) **NR248-CD** Silenced Voices - Victims of the
Holocaust
cond A. DELFS
see CONCERT INDEX under:
(DECC) **444 819-2DH** Schulhoff—Concertos and
Piano Music

HAY, Rosemary (sop)
see CONCERT INDEX under:
(CHAN) **CHAN8980** Bliss—Choral Works

HAYDEN, Carl (sngr)
see CONCERT INDEX under:
(PEAR) **GEMMCDS9053/5** Music from the New York
Stage, Vol. 2: 1908—1913

HAYDN SOCIETY CHORUS
cond D. MCCALDIN
see CONCERT INDEX under:
(MERI) **DUOCD89003** Haydn & Schubert: Masses, etc

HAYDN SOCIETY ORCHESTRA
cond D. MCCALDIN
see CONCERT INDEX under:
(MERI) **DUOCD89003** Haydn & Schubert: Masses, etc

HAYDN VOCAL ENSEMBLE
cond P. FOURNILLIER
Haydn: Applausus (Cpte)

HAYDON CLARK, Robert (cond)
see Consort of London

HAYES, Marvin (sngr)
Hammerstein: Carmen Jones (Cpte)

HAYES, Quentin (bass)
Turnage: Greek (Cpte)
see CONCERT INDEX under:
(HYPE) **CDA66126** Britten: Choral Works

HAYMON, Cynthia (sop)
Gershwin: Porgy and Bess (Cpte)
Mendelssohn: Symphony 2
R. Strauss: Elektra (Cpte)
Tippett: Child of Our Time
see CONCERT INDEX under:
(EMI) **CDH5 65072-2** Glyndebourne Recorded - 1934-
1994

HAYNES, Bruce (ob)
Handel: Oboe Concertos (exc)

HAYRABEDIAN, Roland (cond)
see Strasbourg Percussions

HAYS, Marian Rian (hp)
see CONCERT INDEX under:
(KOCH) **37215-2** Italian Orchestral Music

HAYTON, Lennie (cond)
see Orig Film Cast

HAYWARD, Marie (vn)
see CONCERT INDEX under:
(EMI) **CDM7 64022-2** Vaughan Williams—Orchestral
Works
(PEAR) **GEMMCD9956** Joseph Hislop (1884-1977)

HAYWARD, Robert (bar)
Mahler: Klagende Lied (Cpte)

HAYWOOD, Lorna (sop)
Britten: War Requiem
Menotti: Amahl and the Night Visitors (Cpte)
see CONCERT INDEX under:
(SONY) **MK76404** Beethoven: Choral Works

HAZA, Luis (cond)
see LSO

HAZART, Jean (bass)
see CONCERT INDEX under:
(EPM) **150 122** Milhaud—Historic Recordings 1928-
1948

HAZELL, Hy (sngr)
Gay: Beggar's Opera (Cpte)

HAZELL, Richard (bass)
Puccini: Bohème (Cpte)

HAZELWOOD, Donald (vn)
see CONCERT INDEX under:
(ABCC) **8 77000 2** Sculthorpe—Orchestral Works

HAZELZET, Wilbert (fl)
Bach: Triple Concerto, BWV1044
Telemann: Paris Quartets (Nouveaux quatuors) (exc),
Paris Quartets (Quadri) (exc)
see CONCERT INDEX under:
(ARCH) **419 633-2AH** Telemann: Wind Concertos
(DHM) **05472 77176-2** Music at the Court of Louis XIV

HEADINGTON, Christopher (pf)
see CONCERT INDEX under:
(KING) **KCLCD2012** Lennox Berkeley—Piano Music

(KING) **KCLCD2017** Twentieth Century British Piano
Music

HEADLEY, Erin (va da gamba)
see CONCERT INDEX under:
(CRD) **CRD3488** Hasse—Cantatas, Ballads and
Sonatas

HEADLEY, Erin (vielle)
see CONCERT INDEX under:
(ECM) **837 360-2** Proensa—Songs of the
Troubadours
(HYPE) **CDA66335** A Musicall Dreame

HEALD-SMITH, Geoffrey (cond)
see Hull Youth SO

HEALY, David (sngr)
Berlin: Annie Get Your Gun (Cpte)

HEANEY, Joe (sngr)
see CONCERT INDEX under:
(MODE) **Mode 28/9** Cage—Roaratorio. Laughtears
etc

HEATER, Claude (ten)
Wagner: Tristan und Isolde (Cpte)

HEATH, Edward (cond)
see ECO

HEATHER, Lindsay (bar)
see CONCERT INDEX under:
(DECC) **430 093-2DWO** The World of Vaughan
Williams

HEATON, Roger (bass cl)

HEATON, Roger (basset-hn)
see CONCERT INDEX under:
(ECM) **847 537-2** Gavin Bryars—After the Requiem
(CLRI) **CC0003** Clarinet Virtuosi of the Past: Heinrich
Baermann

HEATON, Roger (cl)
see CONCERT INDEX under:
(ECM) **847 537-2** Gavin Bryars—After the Requiem

HECKEL, Georg (ten)
Wagner: Meistersinger (exc)

HEDEGAARD, Ole (ten)
Heise: Drot og Marsk (Cpte)
Zemlinsky: Es war einmal (Cpte)

HEDEMARK, Hans (ten)
see CONCERT INDEX under:
(SIMA) **PSC1810(1)** Grieg—Songs (historical
recordings, pt 1)

HEDLUND, Klas (ten)
Donizetti: Linda di Chamounix (Cpte)
Haeffner: Electra (Cpte)

HEENAN, Ashley (cond)
see NZ SO

HEERMANN, Hugo (vn)
see CONCERT INDEX under:
(SYMP) **SYMCD1071** Great Violinists, Vol.1

HEES, Christian (ten)
Honegger: Jeanne d'Arc (Cpte)

HEGEDÜS, Endre (pf)
Miaskovsky: Piano Sonata 1, Piano Sonata 4
see CONCERT INDEX under:
(MARC) **8 223156** Miaskovsky: Piano Sonatas, Vol.1
(MARC) **8 223178** Miaskovsky: Piano Sonatas, Vol.2

HEGEDUS, Olga (vc)
Mozart: Concertone, K190
see CONCERT INDEX under:
(ASV) **CDDCA645** Vivaldi—Concertos

HEGER, Robert (cond)
see Bavarian St Orch

HEGNER, Louis (db)
see CONCERT INDEX under:
(CLRI) **CC0002** Nielsen—Orchestral and Chamber
Works

HEGYI, Ildikó (vn)
see CONCERT INDEX under:
(NAXO) **8 553090** Beethoven—Chamber Works

HEICHELE, Hildegard (sop)
Mahler: Symphony 8
Weill: Silbersee (Cpte)

HEIDBÜCHEL, Heinz (ten)
Weill: Kuhhandel (exc)

HEIDELBERG CHAMBER CHOIR
cond M. VENZAGO
Schoeck: Venus (Cpte)

HEIDELBERG MADRIGAL CHOIR
cond G. KEGELMANN
see CONCERT INDEX under:
(BAYE) **BR100041** Choral and Vocal Works

HEIDENREICH, Johannes (cond)
see Berlin Charlottenburg Op Orch

HEIDER, Klaus (ten)
Lully: Bourgeois Gentilhomme

HEIFETZ, Jascha (vn)
Bach: Solo Violin Partitas and Sonatas
Beethoven: Piano Trios (exc), Violin Concerto
Brahms: Double Concerto, Piano Trio 2, Violin
Concerto
Dvořák: Piano Trio 3
Gruenberg: Violin Concerto
Mendelssohn: Piano Trio 1

Schubert: Piano Trio 1, Piano Trio 2
Tchaikovsky: Piano Trio, Op. 50, Souvenir de
Florence, Violin Concerto
Walton: Violin Concerto
see CONCERT INDEX under:
(APR) **APR7015** The Auer Legacy, Vol.1
(BIDD) **LAB011** Brahms—Historic Chamber Music
Recordings
(BIDD) **LAB015** Heifetz—Early Victor Recordings,
1917-18
(BIDD) **LAB025** Jascha Heifetz plays
(BIDD) **WHL016** British Music from America
(EMI) **CDH5 65191-2** Heifetz plays
Mozart/Mendelssohn/Vieuxtemps
(EMI) **CDH7 64030-2** Heifetz plays Violin Concertos
(EMI) **CDH7 64251-2** Jascha Heifetz - Violin Works
(EMI) **CDH7 64494-2** Heifetz plays Bach
(PEAR) **GEMMCDS9157** Jascha Heifetz - Concerto
Recordings, Volume 1
(PEAR) **GEMMCDS9167** Jascha Heifetz Concerto
Recordings, Volume 2
(RCA) **GD87704** Beethoven: Violin Sonatas, Vol.1
(RCA) **GD87705** Beethoven: Violin Sonatas, Vol.2
(RCA) **GD87706** Beethoven: Violin Sonatas, Vol.3
(RCA) **GD87871** Jascha Heifetz Collection
(RCA) **GD87872** Jascha Heifetz Collection
(RCA) **GD87873** Beethoven, Brahms & Schubert:
Chamber Works
(RCA) **GD87963** Heifetz plays Korngold, Rózsa &
Waxman
(RCA) **GD87965** Dvořák & Brahms: Chamber Works
(RCA) **09026 61778-2(01)** The Heifetz Collection,
Vol.1 - 1917-24
(RCA) **09026 61778-2(02)** The Heifetz Collection,
Vol.2 - 1925-34
(RCA) **09026 61778-2(03)** The Heifetz Collection, Vol.
3
(RCA) **09026 61778-2(04)** The Heifetz Collection, Vol.
4
(RCA) **09026 61778-2(05)** The Heifetz Collection, Vol.
5
(RCA) **09026 61778-2(06)** The Heifetz Collection, Vol.
6
(RCA) **09026 61778-2(07)** The Heifetz Collection, Vol.
7
(RCA) **09026 61778-2(08)** The Heifetz Collection, Vol.
8
(RCA) **09026 61778-2(09)** The Heifetz Collection, Vol.
9
(RCA) **09026 61778-2(10)** The Heifetz Collection, Vol.
10
(RCA) **09026 61778-2(11-15)** The Heifetz Collection,
Vols. 11-15
(RCA) **09026 61778-2(16)** The Heifetz Collection, Vol.
16
(RCA) **09026 61778-2(18)** The Heifetz Collection, Vol.
18
(RCA) **09026 61778-2(19)** The Heifetz Collection, Vol.
19
(RCA) **09026 61778-2(20)** The Heifetz Collection, Vol.
20
(RCA) **09026 61778-2(21)** The Heifetz Collection, Vol.
21
(RCA) **09026 61778-2(22)** The Heifetz Collection, Vol.
22
(RCA) **09026 61778-2(24)** The Heifetz Collection, Vol.
24
(RCA) **09026 61778-2(25)** The Heifetz Collection, Vol.
25
(RCA) **09026 61778-2(26)** The Heifetz Collection, Vol.
26
(RCA) **09026 61778-2(27)** The Heifetz Collection, Vol.
27
(RCA) **09026 61778-2(28)** The Heifetz Collection, Vol.
28
(RCA) **09026 61778-2(30)** The Heifetz Collection, Vol.
30
(RCA) **09026 61778-2(31)** The Heifetz Collection, Vol.
31
(RCA) **09026 61778-2(32)** The Heifetz Collection, Vol.
32
(RCA) **09026 61778-2(33)** The Heifetz Collection, Vol.
33
(RCA) **09026 61778-2(34)** The Heifetz Collection, Vol.
34
(RCA) **09026 61778-2(35)** The Heifetz Collection, Vol.
35
(RCA) **09026 61778-2(37)** The Heifetz Collection, Vol.
37
(RCA) **09026 61778-2(40)** The Heifetz Collection, Vol.
40
(RCA) **09026 61778-2(41)** The Heifetz Collection, Vol.
41
(RCA) **09026 61778-2(42)** The Heifetz Collection, Vol.
42
(RCA) **09026 61778-2(43)** The Heifetz Collection, Vol.
43
(RCA) **09026 61778-2(44)** The Heifetz Collection, Vol.
44
(RCA) **09026 61778-2(45)** The Heifetz Collection, Vol.
45
(RCA) **09026 61778-2(46)** The Heifetz Collection,
Vol.46 - The final recital

HEIGL, Michael (ten)
R. Strauss: Rosenkavalier (Cpte)

HEILBRONN HEINRICH SCHÜTZ CHOIR
cond F. WERNER
see CONCERT INDEX under:
(ERAT) **4509-98525-2** Bach—Cantatas

HEILBRONN HEINRICH SCHÜTZ CHOIR
cond F. WERNER
see CONCERT INDEX under:
(ERAT) 4509-97407-2 Bach—Cantatas

HEILLER, Anton (cond)
see Vienna St Op Orch

HEILMANN, Uwe (ten)
Bach: Magnificat, BWV243
Beethoven: Fidelio (Cpte), Missa solemnis
Haydn: Jahreszeiten (Cpte)
Mendelssohn: Erste Walpurgisnacht
Mozart: Clemenza di Tito (Cpte), Don Giovanni
(Cpte), Finta Giardiniera (Cpte), Idomeneo (Cpte),
Mass, K427, Requiem, Zauberflöte (Cpte)
Schubert: Schöne Müllerin (Cpte)
Wagner: Fliegende Holländer (Cpte), Tristan und
Isolde (Cpte)
see CONCERT INDEX under:
(DECC) 440 680-2DH Great Sacred Arias
(PHIL) 426 290-2PH5 Beethoven—Complete
Symphonies
(TELD) 4509-90494-2 Mozart—Sacred Choral Works

HEIM, Melitta (sop)
see CONCERT INDEX under:
(SIMA) PSC1810(2) Grieg—Songs (historical
recordings, pt 2)

HEIMBERG, Liliana (spkr)
Schumann: Manfred (Cpte)

HEINDEL, Kim (lte-hpd)
see CONCERT INDEX under:
(KING) KLCD2020 The Art of the Lute-Harpsichord

HEINDORF, Ray (cond)
see Warner Bros Studio Orch

HEINEN, Ulrich (vc)
see CONCERT INDEX under:
(EMI) CDC5 55091-2 Turnage—Orchestral Works

HEINIKARI, Matti (ten)
Sallinen: Kullervo (Cpte)

HEINRICH, Siegfried (cond)
see Cracow RSO

HEINZMANN, Hans-Udo (fl)
see CONCERT INDEX under:
(SCHW) 312322 Schulhoff—Chamber Music with
wind instruments

HEISSER, Jean-François (pf)
Bartók: Sonata for 2 pianos and percussion, Suite for
two pianos
Brahms: Piano Sonata 3, Schumann Variations
Granados: Danzas españolas, Escenas románticas
Liszt: Harold in Italy (Berlioz)
Schumann: Märchenbilder
see CONCERT INDEX under:
(ERAT) 2292-45481-2 Falla—Piano Works
(ERAT) 2292-45499-2 Martinů—Orchestral Works
(ERAT) 2292-45772-2 Saint-Saëns—Works for
Chamber Ensemble
(ERAT) 2292-45794-2 Martinů—Works for Piano and
Orchestra

HÉJA, Benedek (treb)
Puccini: Tosca (Cpte)

HELASVUO, Mikael (fl)
see CONCERT INDEX under:
(BIS) BIS-CD368 Mozart: Works for Flute and
Orchestra
(BIS) BIS-CD411 Giuliani: Works for Flute and Guitar,
Vol. 1
(BIS) BIS-CD412 Giuliani: Works for Flute and Guitar,
Vol. 2
(BIS) BIS-CD413 Giuliani: Works for Flute and Guitar,
Vol. 3
(ONDI) ODE781-2 Piazzolla—Works for Flute and
Guitar

HELBICH, Wolfgang (cond)
see Alsfeld Voc Ens

HELDWEIN, Walter (bass)
Bach: Cantata 6, Cantata 28, Cantata 36, Cantata 63,
Cantata 93, Cantata 112, Cantata 194
see CONCERT INDEX under:
(HANS) 98 801 Bach—Cantatas, Vol.39
(HANS) 98 803 Bach—Cantatas, Vol.41
(HANS) 98 807 Bach—Cantatas, Vol.45
(HANS) 98 811 Bach—Cantatas, Vol.49
(HANS) 98 812 Bach—Cantatas, Vol.50
(HANS) 98 813 Bach—Cantatas, Vol.51
(HANS) 98 816 Bach—Cantatas, Vol.54
(HANS) 98 817 Bach—Cantatas, Vol.55
(HANS) 98 825 Bach—Cantatas, Vol.1
(HANS) 98 861 Bach—Cantatas, Vol.10
(HANS) 98 864 Bach—Cantatas, Vol.13
(HANS) 98 868 Bach—Cantatas, Vol.17
(HANS) 98 871 Bach—Cantatas, Vol.20
(HANS) 98 872 Bach—Cantatas, Vol.21
(HANS) 98 873 Bach—Cantatas, Vol.22
(HANS) 98 874 Bach—Cantatas, Vol.23
(HANS) 98 875 Bach—Cantatas, Vol.24
(HANS) 98 882 Bach—Cantatas, Vol.31
(HANS) 98 883 Bach—Cantatas, Vol.32
(HANS) 98 885 Bach—Cantatas, Vol.34
(HANS) 98 887 Bach—Cantatas, Vol.36
(TELD) 2292-42617-2 Bach—Cantatas, Volume 32
(TELD) 4509-91761-2 Bach—Cantatas, Vol.7

HELDY, Fanny (sop)
see CONCERT INDEX under:

(CLUB) CL99-034 Marcel Journet (1867-1933)
(PEAR) GEMMCDS9926(1) Covent Garden on
Record—Vol.4 (pt 1)
(PREI) 89022 Fernand Ansseau (1890-1972)

HELFFER, Claude (pf)
see CONCERT INDEX under:
(ASTR) E7716 Pierre Boulez: Piano Sonatas
(ERAT) 2292-45992-2 Milhaud—Works for Piano &
Orchestra

HELFRICH, Christine (sop)
see CONCERT INDEX under:
(GLOR) GDCD016 Leo Sowerby—American Master
of Sacred Song

HELGERS, Otto (bass)
see CONCERT INDEX under:
(DANA) DACOCD315/6 Lauritz Melchior Anthology -
Vol. 3
(PREI) 89301 The Art of Frida Leider

HELGESON, Edward (ten)
see CONCERT INDEX under:
(MERI) CDE84153 French Choral Music

HÉLIOS QUARTET
see CONCERT INDEX under:
(WERG) WER6203-2 Cage—Chamber Works

HELLEKANT, Charlotta (contr)
Bergman: Singing Tree (Cpte)

HELLEKANT, Charlotte (mez)
Mahler: Symphony 2
(DELO) DE3170 Beach—Cabildo; Six Short Pieces

HELLELAND, Arild (ten)
Braein: Anne Pedersdotter (Cpte)
Lidholm: Dream Play (Cpte)

HELLER, Alfred (pf)
see CONCERT INDEX under:
(ETCE) KTC1139 Villa-Lobos—Songs, Vol.1

HELLER, Camilla (vc)
see CONCERT INDEX under:
(VOX) 115845-2 Chamber Works by Women
Composers

HELLER, Helmut (vn)
see CONCERT INDEX under:
(PEAR) GEMMCD9367 Gigli—Arias and Duets

HELLER, Marc (ten)
see CONCERT INDEX under:
(ETCE) KTC1139 Villa-Lobos—Songs, Vol.1

HELLER-REICHENBACH, Barbara (pf)
see CONCERT INDEX under:
(CPO) CPO999 018-2 A. Mahler—Complete Songs

HELLETSGRUBER, Luise (sop)
Beethoven: Symphony 9
Mozart: Cosi fan tutte (Cpte), Don Giovanni (Cpte)
see CONCERT INDEX under:
(EMI) CDH5 65072-2 Glyndebourne Recorded - 1934-
1994
(SCHW) 314512 Vienna State Opera Live, Vol.1
(SCHW) 314532 Vienna State Opera Live, Vol.3
(SCHW) 314592 Vienna State Opera Live, Vol.9
(SCHW) 314602 Vienna State Opera Live, Vol.10
(SCHW) 314622 Vienna State Opera Live, Vol.12
(SCHW) 314642 Vienna State Opera Live, Vol.14

HELLING, Hilke (contr)
Fux: Death of John the Baptist (Cpte)
Weill: Jasager (Cpte), Zar lässt sich Photographieren
(Cpte)
see CONCERT INDEX under:
(CAPR) 10 208 C.P.E. Bach: Sacred Choral Works

HELLMANN, Claudia (mez)
Orff: Antigonae (Cpte)
Wagner: Walküre (Cpte)
see CONCERT INDEX under:
(DECC) 414 100-2DM15 Wagner: Der Ring des
Nibelungen
(DG) 423 127-2GX4 Bruckner: Sacred Works for
Chorus
(DG) 447 409-2GOR2 Bruckner—The Masses
(ERAT) 4509-97407-2 Bach—Cantatas

HELLMANN, Klaus (bn)
see CONCERT INDEX under:
(CAPR) 10 805 Mozart: Wind Concertos

HELLMICH, Wolfgang (bar)
Wagner: Tristan und Isolde (Cpte)

HELLWIG, Judith (sop)
R. Strauss: Elektra (Cpte), Rosenkavalier (Cpte)
Wagner: Walküre (Cpte)
see CONCERT INDEX under:
(EMI) CZS7 67123-2 Wagner: Der Ring des
Nibelungen

HELLWIG, Kurt (voc)
Weill: Dreigroschenoper (Cpte)

HELM, Anny (sop)
see CONCERT INDEX under:
(EMI) CMS7 64008-2(2) Wagner Singing on Record
(pt 2)

HELM, Hans (bar)
Puccini: Madama Butterfly (Cpte)
R. Strauss: Frau ohne Schatten (Cpte)
Schmidt: Notre Dame (Cpte)
Schreker: Ferne Klang (Cpte), Schatzgräber (Cpte)
Verdi: Otello (Cpte)

Zemlinsky: Kreidekreis (Cpte)

HELMANN, Ferdinand (vn)
see CONCERT INDEX under:
(ARHI) ADCD110 Mengelberg Edition - Volume 4

HELMERSON, Frans (vc)
Dvořák: Cello Concerto, Silent woods
see CONCERT INDEX under:
(BIS) BIS-CD026 Shostakovich—Chamber Works
(BIS) BIS-CD434 Pärt: Orchestral Works

HELSINGBORG SYMPHONY ORCHESTRA
cond H. FARBERMAN
Shchedrin: Carmen Ballet
cond O. KAMU
(ONDI) ODE825-2 Britten—Orchestral Works

HELSINKI GARRISON BAND
cond E. JUURI
see CONCERT INDEX under:
(FINL) 4509-95849-2 Sibelius: Choral Works

(EAST) HELSINKI MUSIC INSITUTE CHOIR
cond O. KAMU
Sallinen: Iron Age Suite

HELSINKI PHILHARMONIC ORCHESTRA
cond P. BERGLUND
Sibelius: Kullervo
cond S. COMISSIONA
see CONCERT INDEX under:
(ONDI) ODE767-2 Homage to Sibelius
cond J. DEPREIST
Shostakovich: Chamber Symphony, Op. 110a,
Festive Overture, Symphony 5, Symphony 8,
Symphony 10, Symphony 11
cond R. KAJANUS
see CONCERT INDEX under:
(KOCH) 37133-2 Kajanus conducts Sibelius, Vol.3
cond O. KAMU
Sallinen: Iron Age Suite, Songs of Life and Death
see CONCERT INDEX under:
(FINL) 4509-95856-2 Sibelius: Orchestral Works
cond M. POMMER
Rautavaara: Cello Concerto, Symphony 6

HELSINKI RADIO SYMPHONY ORCHESTRA
cond O. KAMU
(DG) 413 158-2GW2 Grieg/Sibelius—Orchestral
Works

HELSINKI UNIVERSITY CHORUS
cond M. HYÖKKI
Rautavaara: Myth of Sampo
cond E-P. SALONEN
Sibelius: Kullervo

HELSINKI UNIVERSITY MALE CHOIR
cond P. BERGLUND
Sibelius: Kullervo
cond M. HYÖKKI
see CONCERT INDEX under:
(FINL) 4509-95849-2 Sibelius: Choral Works
cond E. JUURI
see CONCERT INDEX under:
(FINL) 4509-95849-2 Sibelius: Choral Works

HELTAU, Michael (spkr)
Mozart: Entführung (Cpte)

HELTAY, Laszlo (cond)
see Argo CO

HEMINGTON-JONES, Susan (sop)
see CONCERT INDEX under:
(ASV) CDGAU122 Venice Preserved

HEMMINGS, David (treb)
Britten: St Nicolas, Turn of the Screw (Cpte)
see CONCERT INDEX under:
(LOND) 436 393-2LM Britten—The Little Sweep, etc

HEMPEL, Francis (bass)
(GLOR) GDCD016 Leo Sowerby—American Master
of Sacred Song

HEMPEL, Frieda (sop)
see CONCERT INDEX under:
(CLUB) CL99-042 Frieda Hempel (1885-1955) &
Hermann Jadlowker (1877-1953)
(IRCC) IRCC-CD800 Souvenirs from Meyerbeer
Operas
(NIMB) NI7802 Divas 1906-1935
(NIMB) NI7849 Frieda Hempel (1885-1955)
(PEAR) EVC3(1) The Caruso Edition, Vol.3 (pt 1)
(RCA) GD60495(5) The Complete Caruso Collection
(pt 5)
(SIMA) PSC1810(2) Grieg—Songs (historical
recordings, pt 2)

HEMPEL, Jurjen (cond)
see Volharding Orch

HEMPFLING, Volker (cond)
see Cologne Gürzenich Orch

HEMSLEY, Thomas (bar)
Britten: Midsummer Night's Dream (Cpte)
Tippett: Knot Garden (Cpte)
see CONCERT INDEX under:
(EMI) CDM7 64634-2 Fauré/Bach—Choral Works

HENA, Alice (mez)
see CONCERT INDEX under:
(MSCM) MM30451 Mascagni—Cavalleria Rusticana,
etc

HENCHE, José Ramon (sngr)
Bretón: Verbena de la Paloma (Cpte)
Moreno Torroba: Luisa Fernanda (Cpte)

HENCK, Herbert (pf)
Cage: Music of Changes (1951)
Mompou: Musica callada

HENCKEL, Christoph (vc)
Brahms: Cello Sonata 1, Cello Sonata 2
Devienne: Bassoon Quartets, Op.73, Duos
concertants, Op.34 (exc)

HENDERSON, Guy (ob)
see CONCERT INDEX under:
(ABCC) 8 77000 2 Sculthorpe—Orchestral Works

HENDERSON, Roald (ten)
Schoenberg: Moses und Aron (Cpte)

HENDERSON, Roy (cond)
see Boyd Neel Orch

HENDERSON, Roy (bar)
Mozart: Don Giovanni (Cpte)
see CONCERT INDEX under:
(DUTT) CDAX8004 Sir Henry Wood conducts
Vaughan Williams
(EMI) CDH5 65072-2 Glyndebourne Recorded - 1934-
1994
(EMI) CDS7 54607-2 Stravinsky plays and conducts
Stravinsky
(PEAR) GEMMCD9342 Vaughan Williams: Vocal
Works

HENDERSON, Skitch (cond)
see RCA Victor Orch

HENDL, Walter (cond)
see Chicago SO

HENDRICKS, Barbara (sop)
Bach: Magnificat, BWV243
Berlioz: Nuits d'été
Bizet: Pêcheurs de Perles (Cpte)
Britten: Illuminations
Donizetti: Don Pasquale (Cpte)
Fauré: Requiem (Cpte)
Gershwin: Porgy and Bess (Cpte)
Gluck: Orphée (Cpte)
Gounod: Mors et Vita (Cpte), St Cecilia Mass
Grieg: Peer Gynt (exc)
Handel: Solomon (Cpte)
Haydn: Infedeltà Delusa (Cpte), Mass 7, Mass 13,
Ritorno di Tobia (Cpte)
Humperdinck: Hänsel und Gretel (Cpte)
Mahler: Symphony 2, Symphony 4
Mozart: Finta semplice (Cpte), Idomeneo (Cpte),
Nozze di Figaro (Cpte), Zauberflöte (Cpte)
Orff: Carmina Burana
Poulenc: Gloria (Cpte), Stabat Mater
Puccini: Bohème (Cpte), Turandot (Cpte)
R. Strauss: Aegyptische Helena (Cpte),
Rosenkavalier (Cpte)
Verdi: Don Carlo (Cpte), Falstaff (Cpte)
Vivaldi: Gloria, RV589
Wagner: Parsifal (Cpte)
see CONCERT INDEX under:
(DG) 435 162-2GX13 Mahler—Complete
Symphonies
(EMI) CDC5 55151-2 Operetta Duets
(EMI) CDC5 55358-2 Barbara Hendricks sings Barber
& Copland
(EMI) CDC7 47122-2 Mozart: Concert and Operatic
Arias
(EMI) CDC7 47433-2 Villa-Lobos: Bachianas
Brasileiras
(EMI) CDC7 47549-2 Schubert—Lieder Recital
(EMI) CDC7 49283-2 Mozart Sacred Arias
(EMI) CDC7 49689-2 Duparc/Ravel—Vocal Works
(EMI) CDC7 49841-2 Fauré—Mélodies
(EMI) CDC7 49843-2 Bach—Cantatas
(EMI) CDC7 54004-2 Chabrier: Vocal & Orchestral
Works
(EMI) CDC7 54007-2 Mozart—Lieder
(EMI) CDC7 54098-2 Sacred Songs
(EMI) CDC7 54239-2 Schubert—Lieder
(EMI) CDC7 54381-2 R. Strauss—Lieder
(EMI) CDC7 54626-2 Operetta Arias
(EMI) CDS7 47901-8 Villa-Lobos: Orchestral and
Chamber Works
(PHIL) 416 460-2PH Barbara Hendricks sings
Gershwin
(PHIL) 422 545-2PME3 The Complete Mozart Edition
Vol.45

HENDRIKS, Alwin (ten)
Beethoven: Fidelio (Cpte)

HENDRIKX, Louis (bass)
Rossini: Guillaume Tell (Cpte)

HENDRIX, Lois (sop)
see CONCERT INDEX under:
(BAY) BCD-1011 American Choral Music

HENDRY, Linn (pf)
see CONCERT INDEX under:
(ASV) CDDCA868 Schnittke—Chamber Music,
Volume 1

HENGELBROCK, Thomas (cond)
see Freiburg Baroque Orch

HENKE, Waldemar (ten)
see CONCERT INDEX under:
(PEAR) GEMMCDS9137 Wagner—Der Ring des
Nibelungen

HENKEL, Klaus (bass)
Bach: St. Matthew Passion, BWV244 (Cpte)

HENKING, Monika (organ)
see CONCERT INDEX under:
(ARIO) ARN68047 The organs of Malaga Cathedral

HENNEBERG, Matthias (bar)
R. Strauss: Salome (Cpte)

HENNEQUIN, Hervé (bass-bar)
Berg: Lulu (Cpte)
Tchaikovsky: Eugene Onegin (Cpte)

HENNESSEY, Gail (ob)
see CONCERT INDEX under:
(HARM) HMU90 7104 Vivaldi/Chedeville—Oboe
Sonatas

HENNETIER, Huguette (mez)
Audran: Poupée (exc)
Boïeldieu: Voitures Versées (Cpte)
Hahn: Mozart (Cpte)
Terrasse: Travaux d'Hercule (Cpte)

HENNIG, Dennis (pf)
Martinů: Sinfonietta giocosa
Tausig: Nouvelles soirées de Vienne, Schubert
Arrangements
see CONCERT INDEX under:
(CONI) CDCF210 Martinu—Orchestral Works
(ETCE) KTC1076 Tausig: Wagner Transcriptions and
Paraphrases
(ETCE) KTC1132 Cyril Scott—Piano Works

HENNIG, Sebastian (treb)
see CONCERT INDEX under:
(TELD) 2292-42606-2 Bach—Cantatas, Volume 28
(TELD) 2292-42615-2 Bach—Cantatas, Volume 31
(TELD) 2292-42617-2 Bach—Cantatas, Volume 32
(TELD) 2292-42618-2 Bach—Cantatas, Volume 33
(TELD) 2292-42631-2 Bach—Cantatas, Volume 36
(TELD) 4509-91760-2 Bach—Cantatas, Vol.6
(TELD) 4509-91761-2 Bach—Cantatas, Vol.7
(TELD) 4509-91762-2 Bach—Cantatas, Vol.8

HENRIKSEN, Uffe (narr)
Norholm: Symphony 6

HENRIOT-SCHWEITZER, Nicole (pf)
Indy: Symphonie, Op.25
see CONCERT INDEX under:
(RCA) GD86805 Orchestral Works

HENRY, Claire (mez)
see CONCERT INDEX under:
(MILA) 74321 14081-2 Bernard Herrmann—Film
Scores

HENRY, Claire (sop)
see CONCERT INDEX under:
(EMI) CDC7 54626-2 Operetta Arias

HENRY, Didier (bar)
Debussy: Pelléas et Mélisande (Cpte)
Massenet: Amadis (Cpte), Cléopâtre (Cpte), Grisélidis
(Cpte)
Prokofiev: Love for 3 Oranges (Cpte)
see CONCERT INDEX under:
(DECC) 440 333-2DH Ravel—Vocal Works
(NAXO) 8 553196 Duruflé—Sacred Choral and Organ
Works, Volume 1
(NAXO) 8 553197 Duruflé—Sacred Choral and Organ
Works, Volume 2
(REM) REM311105 Poulenc—Melodies

HENRY, Frederick (bar)
see CONCERT INDEX under:
(PEAR) GEMMCDS9951/5 The Elgar
Edition—Acoustic Recordings 1914-25

HENRY, John (hpd)
see CONCERT INDEX under:
(VICT) VCD19013 The Harpsichord 1689-1789

HENRY TRIO
see CONCERT INDEX under:
(PIER) PV794031 Lalo—Piano Trios

HENSCHEL, Dieter (ten)
see CONCERT INDEX under:
(JECK) JD677-2 Schoeck—Complete Lieder, Vol.7

HENSCHEL, Dietrich (bar)
Delius: Village Romeo and Juliet (Cpte)

HENSCHEL, Jane (contr)
Mahler: Symphony 8

HENSON, Leslie (sngr)
see CONCERT INDEX under:
(PEAR) GEMMCDS9056/8 Music from the New York
Stage, Vol. 3: 1913-17

HENSON, Robert (ten)
Gershwin: Porgy and Bess (exc)

HENZE, Hans Werner (cond)
see BPO

HEPBURN, Audrey (sngr)
F. Loewe: My Fair Lady (film) (Cpte)

HEPBURN, Katharine (narr)
see CONCERT INDEX under:
(TELA) CD80117 Copland—Orchestral Works

HEPPE, Leo (ten)
R. Strauss: Elektra (Cpte), Rosenkavalier (Cpte)

HEPPNER, Ben (ten)
Puccini: Turandot (Cpte)
Wagner: Lohengrin (Cpte), Meistersinger (Cpte)

Weber: Oberon (Cpte)
see CONCERT INDEX under:
(CBC) SMCD5142 Ben Heppner sings Richard
Strauss
(RCA) 09026 62504-2 Great Tenor Arias - Ben
Heppner

HÉRAL, Pierre (bass)
Boïeldieu: Dame blanche (Cpte)

HERBER, Sue (mez)
Britten: Paul Bunyan (Cpte)
Copland: Tender Land (Cpte)

HERBERICH, Thomas (bass)
Bach: Motets (Cpte)

HERBERT, Giselle (hp)
see CONCERT INDEX under:
(HYPE) CDA66393 Mozart: Complete Original Music
for Flute - 3

HERBERT, Victor (cond)
see Orig Broadway Cast

HERBIG, Günther (cond)
see BBC PO

HERBIG, Lutz (cond)
see BRSO

HERBILLON, Jacques (bar)
see CONCERT INDEX under:
(CALL) CAL9841 Fauré: Mélodies
(CALL) CAL9893 Debussy & Ravel: String Quartets

HERDENBERG, Sven (bar)
Puccini: Bohème (exc)

HERDER, Hermann (bn)
see CONCERT INDEX under:
(CAPR) 10 309 Haydn: Concertos

HEREFORD CATHEDRAL CHOIR
cond R. MASSEY
see CONCERT INDEX under:
(PRIO) PRCD507 Te Deum and Jubilate, Volume 3

HÉRENT, René (ten)
Ravel: Heure espagnole (Cpte)

HERFORD, Henry (bar)
Britten: Midsummer Night's Dream (Cpte)
G. Lloyd: Iernin
Handel: Messiah (exc)
Maxwell Davies: Resurrection (Cpte)
Rameau: Castor et Pollux (Cpte)
see CONCERT INDEX under:
(ASV) CDDCB1101 Michael Berkeley—Clarinet
Concerto, etc
(EMI) CDC7 54552-2 A Portrait of Charles Ives
(UNIC) DKPCD9111 Ives—Songs Volume 1
(UNIC) DKPCD9112 Ives—Songs, Vol.2

HERFORD, Karl (ten)
Zeller: Vogelhändler (exc)

HERIBAN, Josef (bass)
Smetana: Bartered Bride (Cpte)

HERINCX, Raimund (bass)
Berlioz: Benvenuto Cellini (Cpte), Enfance du Christ
(Cpte), Troyens (Cpte)
Handel: Messiah (Cpte)
Purcell: Dido (Cpte)
Tavener: Whale
Tippett: Knot Garden (Cpte)
see CONCERT INDEX under:
(GAMU) GAMD506 An Anthology Of English Song

HERING, Ekkehard (rec)
see CONCERT INDEX under:
(CAPR) 10 134 Flute and Recorder Concertos

HERING, Jörg (ten)
Haydn: Schöpfung (Cpte)
Schubert: Mass, D678, Mass, D950 (Cpte)
Wagner: Fliegende Holländer (Cpte)

HERITAGE SINGERS
see CONCERT INDEX under:
(HERI) HRCD901 By Royal Command

HERMAN, Benjamin (perc)
see CONCERT INDEX under:
(NEW) NW357-2 Crumb. Madrigals and Chamber
works

HERMAN, František (bn)
see CONCERT INDEX under:
(SUPR) 11 1445-2 Reicha/Beethoven—Compositions
for Wind

HERMAN, Silvia (sop)
Wagner: Götterdämmerung (Cpte), Rheingold (Cpte),
Walküre (Cpte)

HERMANN, Dagmar (mez)
Bach: Cantata 78, Cantata 106
Mozart: Cosi fan tutte (Cpte)
Wagner: Walküre (Cpte)

HERMANN, Roland (bar)
E.T.A. Hoffmann: Undine (Cpte)
Egk: Peer Gynt (Cpte)
Gurlitt: Wozzeck (Cpte)
Hindemith: Mathis der Maler (Cpte)
Loewe: Gregor auf dem Stein, Op.38, Kaiser Karl V,
Op.99
Mahler: Lieder eines fahrenden Gesellen
Schoeck: Massimilla Doni (Cpte)
Schoenberg: Moses und Aron (Cpte)
Schreker: Ferne Klang (Cpte)
Wagner: Meistersinger (Cpte)

Zemlinsky: Kreidekreis (Cpte)
  see CONCERT INDEX *under:*
(RCA) **74321 20277-2** Beethoven—Complete
  Symphonies
HERMANN, Roland (spkr)
  see CONCERT INDEX *under:*
(EDA) **EDA008-2** Works by Ullmann and Schoenberg
HERMANN, Walter (cl)
  see CONCERT INDEX *under:*
(SCHW) **312322** Schulhoff—Chamber Music with
  wind instruments
HERMANSEN, Troels Svane (vc)
  see CONCERT INDEX *under:*
(KONT) **32197** Syberg—Chamber Music, Vol. 2
HERMINGMAN, Jacob (lte)
  see CONCERT INDEX *under:*
(AMON) **CD-SAR55** Dowland—Lachrimae
HERNANDEZ, Marta (sngr)
  Chapí: Revoltosa (Cpte)
HERNDL, Johanna (contr)
  R. Strauss: Rosenkavalier (Cpte)
HEROLD, Vilhelm (ten)
  see CONCERT INDEX *under:*
(SIMA) **PSC1810(1)** Grieg—Songs (historical
  recordings, pt 1)
HERR, Barbara (cor ang)
  Bolcom: Sessions I
(FRANÇOISE) HERR VOCAL ENSEMBLE
  cond M. MINKOWSKI
  Mondonville: Titon et l'Aurore (Cpte)
  Rameau: Platée (Cpte)
HERRETT, Nick (spkr)
  see CONCERT INDEX *under:*
(NOVE) **NVLCD109** Weir—Mini-Operas
HERREWEGHE, Philippe (cond)
  see Chapelle Royale Orch
HERRFURTH, Annelis (sop)
  Jessel: Schwarzwaldmädel (exc)
HERRICK, Christopher (organ)
  Bach: Orgel-Büchlein, BWV599-644, Trio Sonatas,
  BWV525-530
  Daquin: Nouveau livre de noëls
  see CONCERT INDEX *under:*
(HYPE) **CDA66121** Organ Fireworks Vol 1
(HYPE) **CDA66258** Organ Fireworks Vol 2
(HYPE) **CDA66434** Bach—Organ Works
(HYPE) **CDA66455** Bach—Partitas for Organ
(HYPE) **CDA66457** Organ Fireworks III
(HYPE) **CDA66605** Organ Fireworks, Vol.4
(HYPE) **CDA66676** Organ Fireworks, Volume 5
(HYPE) **CDA66791/2** Bach—Organ Works
(MERI) **CDE84148** Popular Organ Music from
  Westminster Abbey
HERRMANN, Anita (sngr)
  Weill: Dreigroschenoper (Cpte)
HERRMANN, Bernard (cond)
  see Columbia SO
HERRMANN, Bernard (narr)
  see CONCERT INDEX *under:*
(MILA) **74321 14081-2** Bernard Herrmann—Film
  Scores
HERRMANN, Josef (bar)
  see CONCERT INDEX *under:*
(EMI) **CHS7 69741-2(4)** Record of Singing,
  Vol.4—German School
(MYTO) **3MCD93381** Wagner—Die Walküre, etc
(PREI) **89077** Torsten Ralf (1901-1954)
(SCHW) **314552** Vienna State Opera Live, Vol.5
HERRMANN, Regine (sngr)
  Killmayer: Yolimba (Cpte)
HERRMANN, Theo (bar)
  see CONCERT INDEX *under:*
(EMI) **CHS7 69741-2(4)** Record of Singing,
  Vol.4—German School
HERSCH, Fred (pf)
  see CONCERT INDEX *under:*
(CATA) **09026 61979-2** Memento Bittersweet
HERSETH, Adolph (tpt)
  see CONCERT INDEX *under:*
(SONY) **SK42381** Ives: Orchestral Works
HERSFELD CHILDREN'S CHOIR
  cond S. HEINRICH
  Honegger: Jeanne d'Arc (Cpte)
HERSFELD FESTIVAL CHORUS
  cond S. HEINRICH
  Honegger: Jeanne d'Arc (Cpte)
HERY, Luc (vn)
  see CONCERT INDEX *under:*
(ERAT) **2292-45772-2** Saint-Saëns—Works for
  Chamber Ensemble
HERZ, Ottó (pf)
  see CONCERT INDEX *under:*
(BIDD) **LAB045** Hubay & Flesch —HMV Recordings
HERZ, Ralph C. (sngr)
  see CONCERT INDEX *under:*
(PEAR) **GEMMCDS9050/2(2)** Music from the New
  York Stage, Vol. 1 (part 2)

HERZ, Tamara (sop)
  Wagner: Parsifal (Cpte)
HERZFELD, Günther (pf)
  see CONCERT INDEX *under:*
(EDA) **EDA008-2** Works by Ullmann and Schoenberg
HERZOG, Colette (sop)
  Ravel: Enfant et les Sortilèges (Cpte)
HERZOG, Gerty (pf)
  see CONCERT INDEX *under:*
(DG) **445 400-2GDO10** Ferenc Fricsay - A Portrait
(DG) **445 404-2GDO**
  Liebermann/Blacher/Egk/Einem—Orchestral Works
HESCH, Wilhelm (bass)
  see CONCERT INDEX *under:*
(NIMB) **NI7840/1** The Era of Adelina Patti
(PREI) **89020** Leo Slezak (1873-1946)
HESPÈRION XX
  see CONCERT INDEX *under:*
(ASTR) **E8724** Jenkins—Consort Music for Viols
(ASTR) **E8766** Guerrero—Sacrae Cantiones
  cond J. SAVALL
  Bach: Art of Fugue
  Couperin: Nations (exc)
  Dowland: Lachrimae
  Du Caurroy: Fantasies (exc)
  Morales: Missa pro defunctis a 5, Officium
  defunctorum
  see CONCERT INDEX *under:*
(ASTR) **E8508** Strele do dia - Cantigas de Santa
  Maria
(ASTR) **E8707** Encina—Romances and Villancicos
(ASTR) **E8708** Tye: Consort Music
(ASTR) **E8729** Intermedios del Barroco Hispanico
(ASTR) **E8762** El Cancionero Palacio
(ASTR) **E8763** El Cancionero de la Colombina
(ASTR) **E8764** El Cancionero de Medinaceli
HESS, Dame Myra (pf)
  Brahms: Piano Trio 1
  see CONCERT INDEX *under:*
(APR) **APR7012** Myra Hess—A vignette
(BIDD) **LHW024** Myra Hess - The complete solo
  American Columbia recordings
(DUTT) **CDLX7005** Dame Myra Hess
(EMI) **CDH7 64250-2** Emmanuel Feuermann -
  Recital
(PEAR) **GEMMCD9446** Feuermann—The Columbia
  Records, Vol.3
(PEAR) **GEMMCD9462** Dame Myra Hess—Vol.1
HESS, Nigel (cond)
  see London Symphonic Wind Orch
HESSE, Ruth (mez)
  Henze: Junge Lord (Cpte)
  Korngold: Violanta (Cpte)
  R. Strauss: Frau ohne Schatten (Cpte)
  Wagner: Meistersinger (Cpte), Rheingold (Cpte)
  see CONCERT INDEX *under:*
(PHIL) **446 057-2PB14** Wagner—The Ring Cycle -
  Bayreuth Festival 1967
HESSE RADIO CHILDREN'S CHOIR
  cond E. INBAL
  Mahler: Symphony 8
HESSE RADIO CHOIR
  cond G. ALBRECHT
  Zemlinsky: Traumgörge (Cpte)
  cond C. SCHURICHT
  Brahms: Deutsches Requiem, Op. 45 (Cpte)
HESSE-BUKOWSKA, Barbara (pf)
  see CONCERT INDEX *under:*
(POLS) **PNCD066** Szymanowski: Piano Works
HESSIAN RADIO ORCHESTRA, FRANKFURT
  cond L. STOKOWSKI
  see CONCERT INDEX *under:*
(MUSI) **MACD-778** Stokowski conducts French Music
HESTER, Timothy (pf)
  see CONCERT INDEX *under:*
(MMAS) **MMD 60195A** American Flute Works
HESTERBURG, Trude (voc)
  Weill: Dreigroschenoper (Cpte)
HET GROOT OMROEPKOOR
  cond R. CHAILLY
  Ravel: Daphnis et Chloé (Cpte)
HETHERINGTON, Hugh (ten)
  see CONCERT INDEX *under:*
(ASV) **CDDCA758** Falla, Milhaud &
  Stravinsky—Operas
HETZEL, Gerhard (vn)
  Bartók: Violin Concerto 1, Violin Concerto 2
  Schubert: Trout Quintet, D667
  see CONCERT INDEX *under:*
(DG) **429 738-2GH** Debussy & Ravel: Chamber
  Works
(NIMB) **NI5362/3** Bartók—Orchestral Works
HEUMANN, Friederike (va da gamba)
  see CONCERT INDEX *under:*
(HARM) **HMC90 1505** German Baroque Songs
HEURTEUR, Fernand (cond)
  see orch
HEUVEL, Jacques (cond)
  see orch

HEWARD, Leslie (cond)
  see CBO
HEWARD, Leslie (pf)
  see CONCERT INDEX *under:*
(EMI) **CDS7 54607-2** Stravinsky plays and conducts
  Stravinsky
HEWETSON, Polly (sop)
  Britten: Noye's Fludde (Cpte)
HEWITT, Angela (pf)
  Granados: Danzas españolas, Goyescas (exc)
  see CONCERT INDEX *under:*
(HYPE) **CDA66746** Bach—Keyboard Works
HEWITT, Peter (pf)
  see CONCERT INDEX *under:*
(TREM) **TREM101-2** Walter Leigh—Piano Music and
  Songs
HEYER, Edwin (bass)
  see CONCERT INDEX *under:*
(PREI) **90168** Wagner—Die Meistersinger, Act 2, etc
HEYGI, Julius (cond)
  see Albany SO
HEYNER, Hubert (bar)
  see CONCERT INDEX *under:*
(EMI) **CDS7 54560-2** The Elgar Edition, Vol.1
HEYNIS, Aafje (contr)
  Martin: Mystère de la Nativité
  see CONCERT INDEX *under:*
(PHIL) **438 760-2PM2** Brahms—Choral Works and
  Overtures
(PHIL) **442 050-2PB10** Mahler—Complete
  Symphonies
HIBBERD, Linda (sngr)
  Saxton: Caritas (Cpte)
HICKOX, Richard (cond)
  see Australian CO
(RICHARD) HICKOX SINGERS
  cond R. HICKOX
  Holloway: Sea-Surface Full of Clouds
  Holst: Sávitri (Cpte)
  see CONCERT INDEX *under:*
(ASV) **CDDCA584** W.S. Lloyd Webber—Various
  Works
(CHAN) **CHAN8865** Rossini: Opera Arias
(COLL) **Coll1349-2** Respighi—Vocal and Orchestral
  Works
HICKS, Kenneth (voc)
  Joplin: Treemonisha (Cpte)
HICKS, Malcolm (celesta)
  Buller: Theatre of Memory
HIDALGO, Elvira de (sop)
  see CONCERT INDEX *under:*
(EMI) **CHS7 64864-2(1)** La Scala Edition - Vol.2,
  1915-46 (pt 1)
HIELSCHER, Ulrich (bass)
  Hindemith: Mathis der Maler (Cpte)
HIERONIMUS (sngr)
  Messager: Passionêment (Cpte)
HIESTERMANN, Horst (ten)
  Einem: Dantons Tod (Cpte)
  Mozart: Zauberflöte (Cpte)
  R. Strauss: Salome (Cpte)
  Schoeck: Penthesilea (Cpte)
  Wagner: Meistersinger (Cpte)
  Weill: Mahagonny-Gesänge (Cpte)
HIGGINBOTTOM, Edward (cond)
  see Capricorn
HIGGINBOTTOM, Edward (organ)
  see CONCERT INDEX *under:*
(CRD) **CRD3454** Howells—Choral & Organ Music,
  Vol 1
(CRD) **CRD3455** Howells—Choral & Organ Music,
  Vol.2
(CRD) **CRD3463** S.S. Wesley—Anthems and Organ
  Works
HIGGINBOTTOM, Edward (org/dir)
  see CONCERT INDEX *under:*
(CRD) **CRD3463** S.S. Wesley—Anthems and Organ
  Works
(HYPE) **CDA66387** LeJeune—Masses
HIGH WYCOMBE PARISH CHURCH CHOIR
  cond C. ABBADO
  Berlioz: Te Deum
HIGHGATE SCHOOL CHOIR
  cond L. BERNSTEIN
  Mahler: Symphony 8
  cond B. BRITTEN
  Britten: War Requiem
  see CONCERT INDEX *under:*
(DECC) **436 990-2DWO** The World of Benjamin
  Britten
HIGUERAS, Ana Maria (sop)
  Chapí: Revoltosa (Cpte)
  Vives: Bohemios (Cpte)
HILDMANN, Hanslutz (spkr)
  Corghi: Divara (Cpte)
HILL, David (cond)
  see Bournemouth SO

HILL, David (organ)
Anon: Divine Office: Vespers
see CONCERT INDEX under:
(ARGO) 436 833-2ZH   Purcell— Music for the Funeral
of Queen Mary
(CARL) PCD823   Organ Spectacular

HILL, Jenny (sop)
Bach: St John Passion, BWV245 (Cpte)
Britten: Rape of Lucretia (Cpte)
Schumann: Szenen aus Goethes Faust (Cpte)

HILL, Kate (fl)
see CONCERT INDEX under:
(CHAN) CHAN9152   Alwyn—Chamber Works -
Volume 1
(CHAN) CHAN9197   Alwyn—Chamber Music, Volume 2

HILL, Martyn (ten)
Almeida: Giuditta (Cpte)
Britten: Serenade
G. Charpentier: Louise (Cpte)
Gilles: Requiem
Handel: Acis and Galatea (Cpte), Allegro, il
penseroso ed il moderato (Cpte), Partenope (Cpte),
Ways of Zion do mourn
Haydn: Mass 3
Holloway: Sea-Surface Full of Clouds
Howells: Missa Sabrinensis (Cpte)
Maxwell Davies: Resurrection (Cpte)
Monteverdi: Ritorno d'Ulisse in patria (Cpte)
Mozart: Requiem
Purcell: Fairy Queen, Z629 (Cpte), Indian Queen,
Z630 (Cpte)
Shostakovich: Lady Macbeth of Mtsensk (Cpte)
see CONCERT INDEX under:
(ALBA) TROY017-2   Virgil Thomson—Vocal and
Orchestral Works
(CHAN) CHAN8625   Bax: Choral Works
(CHAN) CHAN8628   Bax—Symphony No 7; Songs
(CHAN) CHAN8824   Walton: Vocal Works
(CHAN) CHAN8855   Britten—Choral Works
(CHAN) CHAN8983/4   Britten—Choral and Orchestral
Works
(ERAT) 4509-96371-2   Gardiner—The Purcell
Collection
(HYPE) CDA66045   Hahn: Songs
(HYPE) CDA66161/2   Finzi Song Cycles to words by
Thomas Hardy
(HYPE) CDA66175   Music by Bliss, Britten and Holst
(HYPE) CDA66261/2   War's Embers
(HYPE) CDA66420   Vaughan Williams: Vocal Works
(HYPE) CDA66749   Tippett—Songs and Purcell
Realisations
(HYPE) CDJ33010   Schubert—Complete Lieder, Vol
10
(L'OI) 421 476-2OH   Haydn—Masses
(L'OI) 421 654-2OH   Handel & Haydn: Choral works
(L'OI) 425 893-2OM6(1)   Purcell—Theatre Music (Part
1)
(L'OI) 425 893-2OM6(2)   Purcell—Theatre Music (Part
2)
(RPO) CDRPO7015   Ashkenazy in Moscow and
London

HILL, Nicholas (hn)
see CONCERT INDEX under:
(PHIL) 412 226-2PH   Telemann: Horn Concertos
(PHIL) 412 892-2PH   Vivaldi: Double Concertos

HILL, Peter (pf)
Beethoven: Diabelli Variations
Messiaen: Catalogue d'oiseaux (exc), Fauvette des
jardins, Vingt regards
see CONCERT INDEX under:
(UNIC) DKPCD9078   Messiaen—Piano Works
(UNIC) DKPCD9144   Messiaen—Piano Works

HILL, Richard (organ)
Wood: St Mark Passion
see CONCERT INDEX under:
(ASV) CDDCA881   English Church Music, Vol.3

HILL, Robert (cl)
Danzi: Sextet
Herrmann: Souvenirs de voyage

HILL, Robert (hpd)
see CONCERT INDEX under:
(LAND) CTLCD111   Cover him with grass
(OLYM) OCD428   Haydn—Violin Concertos

HILL, Valery (sop)
Boughton: Immortal Hour (Cpte)
see CONCERT INDEX under:
(UNIC) DKPCD9057   A Christmas Garland

HILL, Wendy (sop)
Handel: Agrippina (Cpte)
M. Monk: Atlas (Cpte)

HILL SMITH, Marilyn (sop)
Bernstein: Candide (1988) (exc)
G. Lloyd: Iernin
Meyerbeer: Dinorah (Cpte)
Offenbach: Christopher Columbus (Cpte), Robinson
Crusoé (Cpte)
Romberg: Student Prince (Cpte)
Sullivan: Pirates of Penzance (Cpte)
(CHAN) CHAN8362   Treasures of Operetta
(CHAN) CHAN8381   Vienna Première
(CHAN) CHAN8561   Treasures of Operetta, Vol. 2
(CHAN) CHAN8759   Treasures of Operetta III

(CHAN) CHAN8978   Marilyn Hill Smith sings Kálmán &
Lehár
(CHAN) CHAN9110   Edwardian Echoes
(CHAN) CHAN9142   Marilyn Hill Smith sings Ivor
Novello
(OPRA) ORCH103   Italian Opera—1810-20
(OPRA) ORCH104   A Hundred Years of Italian Opera:
1820-1830
(TER) CDVIR8314   Is it really me?

HILLARY, Sir Edmund (narr)
see CONCERT INDEX under:
(KOCH) 37260-2   Lilburn/Watson/Pruden—String
Works

HILLEBRAND, Nikolaus (bass)
Wagner: Meistersinger (Cpte), Rienzi (Cpte)

HILLEBRANDT, Oskar (bass)
Wagner: Tannhäuser (Cpte)
Weill: Kuhhandel (exc)

HILLEBRECHT, Hildegard (sop)
Busoni: Doktor Faust (Cpte)
Mozart: Zauberflöte (Cpte)
see CONCERT INDEX under:
(CAMB) CD-1032   From the Operas of Erich Wolfgang
Korngold

HILLHOUSE, Wendy (mez)
R. Strauss: Elektra (Cpte)

HILLIARD ENSEMBLE
Anon: Old Hall Manuscript
Gesualdo: Responsoria (Cpte)
Various: Codex Speciálník (exc)
see CONCERT INDEX under:
(ECM) 437 684-2   Walter Frye—Vocal Works
(ECM) 445 351-2   Gavin Bryars—Vita Nova
(ECM) 445 369-2   Officium
(ECM) 831 959-2   Pärt—Arbos
(HARM) HMA190 1106   Medieval English Music
(HARM) HMC90 1154   Sumer is icumen in
(HYPE) CDA66370   Sacred and Secular Music from
six centuries
(MERI) DUOCD89009   The Romantic Englishman
see CONCERT INDEX under:
(ECM) 445 941-2   Kancheli—Abii ne Viderem
cond D. R. DAVIES
(ECM) 445 941-2   Kancheli—Abii ne Viderem
cond P. HILLIER
see CONCERT INDEX under:
(BIS) BIS-CD389   Music from the time of Christian IV,
Vol. 1
(ECM) 837 751-2   Perotin—Sacred Choral Works
(ECM) 847 539-2   Pärt—Miserere; Festina lente;
Sarah was ninety-years old
(EMI) CDC7 49197-2   Draw on sweet night - English
Madrigals
(EMI) CDC7 49209-2   Josquin Desprez—Motets and
Chansons
(HYPE) CDA66358   Machaut—Choral Works

HILLIER, Paul (cond)
see Hilliard Ens

HILLIER, Paul (bass)
see CONCERT INDEX under:
(ECM) 837 360-2   Proensa—Songs of the
Troubadours

HILLYER, Raphael (va)
Schumann: Piano Quartet, Op. 47
see CONCERT INDEX under:
(SCHW) 311612
Bartók/Shostakovich/Stravinsky—Chamber Works

HILSBERG, Ignace (cond)
see Curtis Inst Student Orch

HILSE, Ernst-Burghard (fl)
see CONCERT INDEX under:
(CAPR) 10 134   Flute and Recorder Concertos

HILTON, Janet (cl)
Stanford: Clarinet Concerto
see CONCERT INDEX under:
(CHAN) CHAN8301   The Special Sound of Chandos
(CHAN) CHAN8305   Weber—Clarinet Concertos
(CHAN) CHAN8366   Weber—Chamber Music for
Clarinet
(CHAN) CHAN8618   Works for Clarinet and
Orchestra
(CHAN) CHAN8683   English Chamber Music
(CHAN) CHAN8776   Bruch, Mozart & Schumann:
Chamber Works
(CHAN) CHAN9132   Leighton—Chamber Works

HILVERSUM RADIO CHAMBER ORCHESTRA
cond J. STULEN
S. Weiner: Viola Concerto, Violin Concerto 4

HILVERSUM RADIO ORCHESTRA
cond P. VAN KEMPEN
see CONCERT INDEX under:
(EMI) CHS7 69741-2(4)   Record of Singing,
Vol.4—German School
cond F. WEISSMANN
see CONCERT INDEX under:
(BLUE) ABCD006   Jussi Björling Live - Holland 1939,
Norway 1954

HIMMELHEBER, Liat (mez)
see CONCERT INDEX under:
(WERG) WER60183-50   Reimann—Vocal Works

HIND, Rolf (pf)
see CONCERT INDEX under:
(UNIT) 88019-2   Messiaen—Piano Works

HINDAR QUARTET
see CONCERT INDEX under:
(CHAN) CHAN8802   Works for Harmonica

HINDART, Kerstin (pf)
see CONCERT INDEX under:
(BIS) BIS-CD234   Martinu—Chamber Works

HINDEMITH, Paul (cond)
see BPO

HINDEMITH, Paul (pf)
see CONCERT INDEX under:
(BIDD) LAB087   Hindemith plays Hindemith

HINDEMITH, Paul (va)
see CONCERT INDEX under:
(BIDD) LAB087   Hindemith plays Hindemith
(EMI) CDH7 64250-2   Emmanuel Feuermann -
Recital
(EMI) CDS5 55032-2   Hindemith—Plays and conducts
his own works
(MUSI) MACD-665   The Goldberg/Kraus Duo plays
Mozart and Beethoven
(PEAR) GEMMCD9443   Feuermann—The Columbia
Records, Vol.2
(PEAR) GEMMCD9446   Feuermann—The Columbia
Records, Vol.3
(SCHW) 311342   Hindemith plays and conducts

HINDMARSH, Jean (sop)
Sullivan: HMS Pinafore (Cpte)
see CONCERT INDEX under:
(DECC) 430 095-2DWO   The World of Gilbert &
Sullivan, Vol.1
(DECC) 433 868-2DWO   The World of Gilbert &
Sullivan - Volume 2

HINDS, Esther (sop)
Sessions: When Lilacs last Bloom'd

HINES, Jerome (bass)
Beethoven: Missa Solemnis
Handel: Messiah (Cpte)
Meyerbeer: Prophète (Cpte)
Verdi: Macbeth (Cpte)
see CONCERT INDEX under:
(RCA) 09026 61580-2(6)   RCA/Met 100 Singers, 100
Years (pt 6)

HINNELLS, Duncan (cond)
see European Chbr Op Chor

HINNIGAN, Anthony (vc)
see CONCERT INDEX under:
(ECM) 847 537-2   Gavin Bryars—After the Requiem

HINSCH-GRÖNDAHL, Natalie (sop)
Wagner: Götterdämmerung (Cpte)
see CONCERT INDEX under:
(FOYE) 15-CF2011   Wagner—Der Ring de Nibelungen

HINTERMEIER, Margaretha (contr)
Beethoven: Symphony 9
Haydn: Seven Last Words, HobXX/2
R. Strauss: Rosenkavalier (Cpte)
Wagner: Rheingold (Cpte), Walküre (Cpte)
see CONCERT INDEX under:
(DG) 435 486-2GH   Schubert/Schumann—Sacred
Choral Works

HINTERREITER, Peter (treb)
Mozart: Zauberflöte (Cpte)
see CONCERT INDEX under:
(TELD) 2292-42500-2   Bach—Cantatas, Volume 4
(TELD) 4509-91755-2   Bach—Cantatas, Vol.1

HINTON, Oliver (treb)
see CONCERT INDEX under:
(ABBS) CDMVP827   20 Christmas Carols from St
George's Chapel, Windsor Castle

HINZ, Helle (sop)
Haeffner: Electra (Cpte)
Schumann: Rose Pilgerfahrt (Cpte)

HINZE, Gerhardt (bass)
see CONCERT INDEX under:
(LYRC) SRO830   Smetana—The Bartered Bride, etc

HIOLSKI, Andrzej (bar)
Mussorgsky: Boris Godunov (Cpte)
see CONCERT INDEX under:
(KOCH) 312652   Szymanowski—Orchestral and
Choral Works

HIRAYAMA, Michiko (sop)
see CONCERT INDEX under:
(SALA) SCD8904/5   Scelsi—Chamber Works

HIROKAMI, Jun'ichi (cond)
see Norrköping SO

HIRONS, Christopher (vn)
Vivaldi: Concerti, Op. 8 (exc)
see CONCERT INDEX under:
(L'OI) 400 080-2OH   Bach—Violin Concertos
(L'OI) 411 949-2OH   Telemann: Double & Triple
Concertos
(L'OI) 421 500-2OH   Bach: Double Concertos
(L'OI) 433 052-2OH   Bach/Vivaldi—Orchestral Works

HIRSCH, Hans Ludwig (hpd)
see CONCERT INDEX under:
(JECK) JD5004-2   Carissimi: Cantatas

HIRSCH, Rebecca (vn)
Ruders: Violin Concerto 2
see CONCERT INDEX under:
(UNIC) DKPCD9114   Ruders—Orchestral Works

HIRST, Grayson (ten)
Janáček: Diary of one who disappeared
see CONCERT INDEX under:
(NEWP) **NCD60098** Weill—Vocal & Instrumental
Works

HIRST, Linda (sop)
see CONCERT INDEX under:
(NOVE) **NVLCD109** Weir—Mini-Operas
(UNIC) **UKCD2010** Knussen—Orchestral & Vocal
Works

HIRSTI, Marianne (sop)
Beethoven: Missa Solemnis
Zemlinsky: Geburtstag der Infantin (Cpte)
see CONCERT INDEX under:
(VICT) **VCD19018** Grieg—Songs with Orchestra
(VICT) **VCD19040** Grieg—Complete Songs - Volume
III
(VICT) **VCD19041** Grieg—Songs, Vol.4

HIRTE, Klaus (bar)
B.A. Zimmermann: Soldaten (Cpte)
Lehár: Giuditta (Cpte)
Mozart: Nozze di Figaro (Cpte)
R. Strauss: Intermezzo (Cpte), Rosenkavalier (Cpte)
Wagner: Meistersinger (Cpte)
Weill: Mahagonny (Cpte)

HIRTREITER, Bernhard (ten)
Keiser: St. Mark Passion

HIS MAJESTIES CLERKES
cond P. HILLIER
see CONCERT INDEX under:
(HARM) **HMU90 7048** Billings—Anthems and Fuguing
Tunes

HIS MAJESTIES SAGBUTTS AND CORNETTS
see CONCERT INDEX under:
(HYPE) **CDA66688** Festal Sacred Music of Bavaria
(MERI) **CDE84096** Seventeenth-Century German
Works
cond P. BASSANO
see CONCERT INDEX under:
(ASV) **CDGAU122** Venice Preserved
cond J. O'DONNELL
(HYPE) **CDA66688** Festal Sacred Music of Bavaria
cond J.E. GARDINER
Monteverdi: Orfeo (Cpte), Vespers
see CONCERT INDEX under:
(ARCH) **423 405-2AH** Schütz—Sacred Choral Works
(ERAT) **2292-45466-2** Carissimi—Jonas
cond R. MARLOW
Schütz: Psalmen Davids, SWV22-47 (exc)

HISLOP, Joseph (ten)
see CONCERT INDEX under:
(PEAR) **GEMMCDS9925(1)** Covent Garden on
Record—Vol.3 (pt 1)
(PEAR) **GEMMCDS9926(1)** Covent Garden on
Record—Vol.4 (pt 1)
(PEAR) **GEMMCD9956** Joseph Hislop (1884-1977)

HISPAVOX LYRIC CHORUS
cond F. MORENO TORROBA
Moreno Torroba: Luisa Fernanda (Cpte)

HITCHCOCK, Raymond (sngr)
see CONCERT INDEX under:
(PEAR) **GEMMCDS9050/2(2)** Music from the New
York Stage, Vol. 1 (part 2)
(PEAR) **GEMMCDS9056/8** Music from the New York
Stage, Vol. 3: 1913-17

HITCHIN, Booth (ten)
Wagner: Tristan und Isolde (Cpte)

HITE, William (ten)
Mozart: Kleine Freimaurer-Kantate, K623, Requiem
see CONCERT INDEX under:
(ERAT) **4509-98480-2** Lamentations - Holy Week in
Provence

HIVERT, Jacques (sngr)
Poulenc: Mamelles de Tirésias (Cpte)

HJELSET, Sigmund (pf)
see CONCERT INDEX under:
(SIMA) **PSC1051** Schumann & Wolf—Lieder Recital
(SIMA) **PSC1071** Schubert—Lieder

HLADÍK, Jan (bass)
Dvořák: Kate and the Devil (Cpte)

HLAVÁČEK, Libor (cond)
see Musici de Praga

HLAVENKOVÁ, Anna (sop)
Zelenka: Miserere, ZWV57

HLOBILOVÁ, Eva (mez)
Janáček: Jenufa (Cpte), Káťa Kabanová (Cpte)

HM ROYAL MARINES BAND, PORTSMOUTH
cond J.R. MASON
see CONCERT INDEX under:
(CHAN) **CHAN6584** The Music of Kenneth Alford

HOARE, Peter (ten)
Britten: Gloriana (Cpte)

HOBAN, John (cond)
see Thames CO

HOBARTH, Elfriede (sop)
J.C. Bach: Amadis de Gaule (Cpte)
R.Strauss: Arabella (Cpte)
see CONCERT INDEX under:
(HARM) **HMC90 1314** Haydn—Piano Trios, Vol.2

HÖBARTH, Erich (va)
Mozart: Piano Quartet, K478, Piano Quartet, K493

HÖBARTH, Erich (vn)
Beethoven: Piano Trios (exc)
see CONCERT INDEX under:
(HARM) **HMC90 1400** Haydn—Piano Trios
(HARM) **HMC90 1514** Haydn—Keyboard Trios,
Volume 4

HOBSON, Claude (pf)
see CONCERT INDEX under:
(ARAB) **Z6569** Milhaud—Jazz Works
(ARAB) **Z6570** Saint-Saëns—Chamber Orchestral
Works

HOBSON, Ian (cond)
see Sinfonia da Camera

HOBSON, Ian (pf)
Godowsky: Studies on Chopin Etudes (exc)
Hummel: Piano Sonata 3, Piano Sonata 4
Rachmaninov: Etudes-tableaux, Op.33, Etudes-
tableaux, Op.39, Preludes
see CONCERT INDEX under:
(ARAB) **Z6541** Saint-Saëns/Françaix—Piano
Concertos
(ARAB) **Z6567** R.Strauss: Orchestral Works
(ARAB) **Z6569** Milhaud—Jazz Works
(ARAB) **Z6570** Saint-Saëns—Chamber Orchestral
Works
(ARAB) **Z6594** The London Piano School, Vol.1:
Georgian Classicists
(ARAB) **Z6595** The London Piano School, Vol.2:
Romantic Pioneers
(ARAB) **Z6596** The London Piano School, Vol.3: Early
Victorian Masters
(ARAB) **Z6621/2** Schumann—Piano Works
(ARAB) **Z6637** Beethoven—Piano Sonatas, Vol.1
(CATA) **09026 61979-2** Memento Bittersweet

HOBSON, Ian (pf/dir)
see CONCERT INDEX under:
(ARAB) **Z6570** Saint-Saëns—Chamber Orchestral
Works

HOCA, Claudia (pf)
see CONCERT INDEX under:
(SCHW) **310832** Frank Martin—Orchestral Works

HOCH, Beverley (sop)
Handel: Imeneo (Cpte)
Mozart: Zauberflöte (Cpte)
see CONCERT INDEX under:
(CARL) **PCD827** The Art of the Coloratura

HOCHSTÄTTER, Elfriede (mez)
R. Strauss: Rosenkavalier (Cpte)

HOCKINGS, David (perc)
see CONCERT INDEX under:
(NONE) **7559-79362-2** Górecki—Orchestral and Vocal
Works

HODGES, Theodore (bass)
Massenet: Cid (Cpte)

HODGKINSON, Randall (pf)
see CONCERT INDEX under:
(MUSM) **67094-2** Antheil—Ballet Mécanique
(NORT) **NR227-CD** American Chamber Music with
Flute
(ONGA) **024-102** More Cohler on Clarinet

HODGSON, Alfreda (contr)
Bach: St John Passion, BWV245 (Cpte), St Matthew
Passion, BWV244 (Cpte)
Elgar: Apostles (Cpte), Coronation Ode (Cpte),
Dream of Gerontius (Cpte)
Handel: Messiah (Cpte)
Haydn: Salve Regina, HobXXIIIb/1, Stabat Mater
Ponchielli: Gioconda (Cpte)
Purcell: Dido (Cpte), Fairy Queen, Z629 (Cpte)
Schumann: Szenen aus Goethes Faust (Cpte)
see CONCERT INDEX under:
(CFP) **CD-CFP4570** Choral Favourites
(CHAN) **CHAN8855** Britten—Choral Works
(DECC) **433 080-2DM** Kodály—Choral Works
(DECC) **443 868-2DF2** Italian Baroque Sacred
Works
(EMI) **CDM7 64022-2** Vaughan Williams—Orchestral
Works
(NIMB) **NI5217** Tippett conducts Tippett
(ORFE) **C025821A** Brahms Choral Songs

HOEG, Michael (organ)
see CONCERT INDEX under:
(PRIO) **PRCD510** Great Cathedral Anthems, Volume
VI

HOELSCHER, Ludwig (vc)
see CONCERT INDEX under:
(EMI) **CDC5 55225-2** Pfitzner plays and conducts
Pfitzner
(PREI) **90029** Hans Pfitzner Accompanies &
Conducts

HOELSCHER, Ulf (vn)
Beethoven: Romances, Triple Concerto
see CONCERT INDEX under:
(EMI) **CMS7 64346-2** R. Strauss—Orchestral Works,
Vol.2
(EMI) **CMS7 64790-2** Saint-Saëns—Complete Works
for Violin and Orchestra
(NOVA) **150 070-2** Schoeck—Orchestral Works

HOENING, Christian (spkr)
Nono: Intolleranza 1960 (Cpte)

HOEPPNER, Martin (voc)
Weill: Dreigroschenoper (Cpte)

HOEPRICH, Eric (basset cl)
see CONCERT INDEX under:
(ARCH) **419 633-2AH** Telemann: Wind Concertos
(L'OI) **433 674-2OH** Vivaldi—Oboe Concertos

HOEPRICH, Eric (cl)
Schubert: Octet, D803

HOFER, Pierre (vn)
Bartók: Violin Concerto 2
Prokofiev: Violin Concerto 1

HOFF, Brynjar (ob)
see CONCERT INDEX under:
(SIMA) **PSC1049** Italian Oboe Concertos

HÖFFGEN, Marga (contr)
Bach: Cantata 146, St Matthew Passion, BWV244
(exc)
Beethoven: Missa Solemnis
Bruckner: Te Deum
Mozart: Requiem
Wagner: Götterdämmerung (Cpte), Meistersinger
(Cpte), Siegfried (Cpte)
see CONCERT INDEX under:
(DECC) **414 100-2DM15** Wagner: Der Ring des
Nibelungen
(HANS) **98 814** Bach—Cantatas, Vol.52
(HANS) **98 870** Bach—Cantatas, Vol.19
(HANS) **98 876** Bach—Cantatas, Vol.25
(PHIL) **446 057-2PB14** Wagner—The Ring Cycle -
Bayreuth Festival 1967

HOFFMANN, Gary (vc)
Arensky: Piano Trio 1
Beethoven: String Quintet, Op. 29
Chopin: Cello Sonata
Debussy: Piano Trio
Mendelssohn: String Quintet 2
Mozart: Trio, K563
Rachmaninov: Cello Sonata
Ravel: Piano Trio
Schumann: Piano Quartet, Op.47, Piano Quartet
(1829)
Tchaikovsky: Piano Trio, Op. 50, Souvenir de
Florence, String Quartet 1
see CONCERT INDEX under:
(EMI) **CDC7 54913-2** Saint-Saëns—La muse et le
poète

HOFFMANN, Grace (mez)
B.A. Zimmermann: Soldaten (Cpte)
Handel: Messiah (Cpte)
R. Strauss: Salome (Cpte)
Wagner: Götterdämmerung (Cpte)
see CONCERT INDEX under:
(DECC) **414 100-2DM15** Wagner: Der Ring des
Nibelungen

HOFFMAN, Toby (va)
Beethoven: String Quintet, Op. 29
Borodin: String Quartet 2
Dvořák: Piano Quintet, Op.81, String Quintet, Op.77,
Terzetto, Op.74
Mendelssohn: String Quintet 2
Mozart: Sinfonia Concertante, K364, String Quintet,
K174, String Quintet, K406, String Quintet, K515,
String Quintet, K516, String Quintet, K593, String
Quintet, K614
Tchaikovsky: Souvenir de Florence, String Quartet 1
Verdi: String Quartet
see CONCERT INDEX under:
(NUOV) **6802** Mozart—Chamber Works
(RCA) **09026 68181-2** French Chamber Works

HOFFMANN, Bruno (glass harmonica)
see CONCERT INDEX under:
(PHIL) **422 514-2PME5** The Complete Mozart Edition
Vol 14

HOFFMANN, Hans (bar)
Delius: Village Romeo and Juliet (Cpte)
Messager: Coups de Roulis (Cpte)

HOFFMANN, Jean (sngr)
Messager: Coups de Roulis (Cpte)

HOFFMANN, Ludwig (pf)
see CONCERT INDEX under:
(PHIL) **422 516-2PME2** The Complete Mozart Edition
Vol 16

HOFFMANN, Rainer (pf)
Orff: Catulli Carmina
Stravinsky: Noces

HOFFMANN, Rosmarie (sop)
Mendelssohn: Hochzeit des Camacho (Cpte)

HOFMANN, Josef (pf)
Chopin: Piano Concerto 1, Piano Concerto 2
see CONCERT INDEX under:
(APR) **APR7013** Romantic Piano Rarities, Vol.1
(NIMB) **NI7811** Ernestine Schumann-Heink—Opera &
Song Recital
(NIMB) **NI8803** Chopin—Grand Piano Project
(SIMA) **PSC1809(1)** Grieg—Historical Piano
Recordings (pt 1)
(VAI) **VAIA1020** Josef Hofmann, Vol.2

HOFMANN, Ludwig (bass)
Wagner: Lohengrin (Cpte), Tristan und Isolde (Cpte)
see CONCERT INDEX under:
(OPAL) **OPALCDS9843** Karl Muck conducts Wagner
(SCHW) **314512** Vienna State Opera Live, Vol.1
(SCHW) **314542** Vienna State Opera Live, Vol.4
(SCHW) **314562** Vienna State Opera Live, Vol.6

(SCHW) **314592** Vienna State Opera Live, Vol.9
(SCHW) **314602** Vienna State Opera Live, Vol.10
(SCHW) **314622** Vienna State Opera Live, Vol.12

HOFMANN, Peter (ten)
Beethoven: Fidelio (Cpte)
Mozart: Zauberflöte (exc)
Wagner: Fliegende Holländer (Cpte), Parsifal (Cpte),
Walküre (Cpte)

HOFMANN, Rosmarie (sop)
see CONCERT INDEX under:
(DHM) **RD77188** C.P.E. Bach—Vocal & Chamber
Works

HOGAN, George (bass)
see CONCERT INDEX under:
(EMI) **CDC7 54643-2** Rossini—Bicentenary Gala
Concert

HOGAN, Moses (pf)
see CONCERT INDEX under:
(CHNN) **CCS2991** Ev'ry Time I Feel the Spirit

HÖGMAN, Christina (sop)
Alfvén: Symphony 4
Haeffner: Electra (Cpte)
Handel: Flavio (Cpte)
Monteverdi: Incoronazione di Poppea (Cpte), Ritorno
d'Ulisse in patria (Cpte)
see CONCERT INDEX under:
(BIS) **BIS-CD403** Handel: Vocal and Chamber Works
(BIS) **BIS-CD435** Britten—Orchestral & Vocal Works
(BIS) **BIS-CD703** Schoenberg—Music for Strings

HÖGMAN, Nils (ten)
Schnittke: Requiem

HÖGNER, Günter (hn)
see CONCERT INDEX under:
(DG) **427 639-2GH** Poulenc: Chamber Works

HOGWOOD, Christopher (cond)
see AAM

HOGWOOD, Christopher (fp)
see CONCERT INDEX under:
(L'OI) **443 196-2OM** Schubert/Mendelssohn—Violin
Sonatas

HOGWOOD, Christopher (hpd)
see CONCERT INDEX under:
(DECC) **440 079-2DM** The Amorous Flute
(L'OI) **411 811-2OH2** Bach: Keyboard works

HOGWOOD, Christopher (hpd/dir)
Bach: Cantata 211, Cantata 212
Haydn: Cello Concerto in C, Cello Concerto in D
Mozart: Clarinet Concerto, K622, Oboe Concerto,
K314
Vivaldi: Concerti grossi, Op. 3, Concerti, Op. 4,
Concerti, Op.9, Concerti, Op. 11
see CONCERT INDEX under:
(L'OI) **411 949-2OH** Telemann: Double & Triple
Concertos
(L'OI) **421 500-2OH** Bach: Double Concertos
(L'OI) **433 053-2OH** Bach/Vivaldi—Orchestral Works
(L'OI) **433 674-2OH** Vivaldi—Oboe Concertos
(L'OI) **436 867-2OH** Vivaldi—Bassoon Concertos

HOGWOOD, Christopher (hpd/org)
see CONCERT INDEX under:
(L'OI) **433 052-2OH** Vivaldi—Works for Cello

HOGWOOD, Christopher (spinet/org)
Purcell: Sonatas, Z802-11
see CONCERT INDEX under:
(L'OI) **417 123-2OH** Purcell: Songs and Airs

HOHENFELD, Linda (sop)
see CONCERT INDEX under:
(RCA) **09026 61194-2** Vaughan Williams—Orchestral
Works
(RCA) **09026 61581-2** Bernstein—Orchestral & Vocal
Works

HÖHER, Frank (treb)
Mozart: Zauberflöte (Cpte)

HOKANSON, Leonard (pf)
see CONCERT INDEX under:
(BAYE) **BR100035** Brahms—Piano Works
(DENO) **CO-1254** Lieder recital
(DENO) **C37-7720** Schumann: Lieder
(NORT) **NR232-CD** Piston—Piano and Chamber
Works
(NORT) **NR233-CD** The Young Schubert

HOLBROOKE, Joseph (cond)
see orch

HOLBROOKE, Joseph (pf)
see CONCERT INDEX under:
(SYMP) **SYMCD1130** Joseph Holbrooke—Historic
Recordings

HOLCK, Ingrid (fl)
see CONCERT INDEX under:
(KONT) **32032** Wind Chamber Music

HOLDAR, Anders (perc)
see CONCERT INDEX under:
(BIS) **BIS-CD507** Schnittke—Cello Works

HOLDEN, Poppy (sop)
see CONCERT INDEX under:
(AMON) **CD-SAR53** Music for Mandolin
(L'OI) **421 480-2OH** Monteverdi: Madrigali Erotici

HOLDORF, Udo (ten)
Weill: Kuhhandel (exc), Silbersee (Cpte)

HOLDRIDGE, Lee (cond)
see LSO

HOLEČEK, Alfred (pf)
see CONCERT INDEX under:
(SUPR) **11 0703-2** Dvořák: Violin & Piano Works

HOLECEK, Heinz (bass)
R. Strauss: Salome (Cpte)

HOLECEK, Sebastian (sngr)
Schreker: Irrelohe (Cpte)

HOLEŇA, Jiří (pf)
see CONCERT INDEX under:
(SUPR) **11 1878-2** The Unknown Janáček

HÖLL, Hartmut (pf)
Schoeck: Stille Leuchten, Unter Sternen
Schubert: Winterreise (Cpte)
Wolf: Manuel Venegas, Spanisches Liederbuch
(exc)
see CONCERT INDEX under:
(BAYE) **BR100006** Brahms—Lieder
(BAYE) **BR100041** Choral and Vocal Works
(CAPR) **10 098** Mozart: Lieder recital
(CAPR) **10 099** Schumann: Lieder Recital
(CAPR) **10 171** Schubert: Lieder
(CAPR) **10 204** Brahms: Lieder
(CAPR) **10 419** Berg—Lieder
(CAPR) **10 445** Schumann—Lieder
(CAPR) **10 446/7** Mozart—Lieder
(CAPR) **10 462** Songs with Viola
(CAPR) **10 497** R. Strauss—Lieder
(CAPR) **10 514** Schoenberg—Songs
(CAPR) **10 534** Hölderlin Songs
(CLAV) **CD50-9118** Weber—Lieder
(EMI) **CDC7 49736-2** Clarinet Music by Bruch, Mozart
& Schumann
(EMI) **CDC7 54394-2** Modern Viola Works
(ERAT) **4509-98492-2** Schumann—Lieder
(ERAT) **4509-98493-2** Schubert—Lieder Recital
(ORFE) **C103841A** Spohr: Lieder
(ORFE) **C153861A** Romantic Lieder
(TELD) **4509-97457-2** French Romantic Songs
(TELD) **4509-97458-2** Loewe—Lieder and Balladen

HOLL, Robert (bass)
Bach: Christmas Oratorio, BWV248 (Cpte), St.
Matthew Passion, BWV244 (Cpte)
Beethoven: Missa solemnis
Handel: Messiah (Cpte)
Haydn: Mass 10, Seven Last Words, HobXX/2
Mozart: Don Giovanni (Cpte), Finta semplice (Cpte),
Mass, K427, Requiem, Zaide (Cpte)
Schmidt: Buch mit Sieben Siegeln
Schubert: Fierrabras (Cpte), Mass, D950, Winterreise
(Cpte)
Shostakovich: Symphony 13
see CONCERT INDEX under:
(CHAN) **CHAN8878** Diepenbrock: Symphonic Songs
(DECC) **436 123-2DH** Schumann—Lieder
(OTTA) **OTRC98402** Works by Brahms and Mahler
(PHIL) **420 649-2PM** Vivaldi: Sacred Choral Music,
Vol.2
(PHIL) **442 073-2PB5** Beethoven—Complete
Symphonies, etc
(PREI) **93331** Pfitzner: Lieder
(TELD) **2292-42428-2** Bach—Cantatas, Volume 41
(TELD) **2292-42608-2** Bach—Cantatas, Volume 29
(TELD) **2292-42609-2** Bach—Cantatas, Volume 30
(TELD) **2292-42617-2** Bach—Cantatas, Volume 32
(TELD) **2292-42633-2** Bach—Cantatas, Volume 38
(TELD) **2292-42634-2** Bach—Cantatas, Volume 39
(TELD) **2292-42635-2** Bach—Cantatas, Volume 40
(TELD) **2292-42738-2** Bach—Cantatas, Volume 43
(TELD) **2292-44179-2** Bach—Cantatas, Volume 43
(TELD) **2292-46452-2** Beethoven—Complete
Symphonies
(TELD) **4509-91761-2** Bach—Cantatas, Vol.7
(TELD) **4509-91762-2** Bach—Cantatas, Vol.8
(TELD) **4509-91763-2** Bach—Cantatas, Vol.9
(TELD) **4509-91764-2** Bach—Cantatas, Vol.10

HOLLAND, Charles (ten)
Blitzstein: Airborne Symphony

HOLLAND, James (perc)
Cerha: Art Chansons (exc)
see CONCERT INDEX under:
(CONI) **CDCF167** Dickinson—Vocal Works

HOLLAND, James (vib)
see CONCERT INDEX under:
(UNIC) **DKPCD9102** Goehr—Orchestral and Vocal
Works

HOLLAND, Lyndsie (contr)
Sullivan: Mikado (Cpte)
see CONCERT INDEX under:
(DECC) **433 868-2DWO** The World of Gilbert &
Sullivan - Volume 2

HOLLAND, Mark (bar)
Janáček: Fate (Cpte)
M. Berkeley: Baa Baa Black Sheep (Cpte)

**HOLLAND ITALIAN OPERA CHORUS
cond P. MASCAGNI**
Mascagni: Cavalleria rusticana (Cpte)

**HOLLAND ITALIAN OPERA ORCHESTRA
cond P. MASCAGNI**
Mascagni: Cavalleria rusticana (Cpte)

HOLLANDER, Adrian E. (sngr)
J. Strauss II: Fledermaus (Cpte)

HÖLLE, Matthias (bass)
Dessau: Hagadah Shel Pessach
Haydn: Mass 13
Mozart: Requiem
R. Strauss: Daphne (Cpte)
Wagner: Parsifal (Cpte), Rheingold (Cpte), Walküre
(Cpte)
Weber: Freischütz (Cpte)

HOLLEQUE, Elizabeth (sop)
Shostakovich: Symphony 14

HOLLIGER, Heinz (cond)
see Berne Camerata

HOLLIGER, Heinz (cor ang)
see CONCERT INDEX under:
(PHIL) **434 105-2PH** Martin/Honegger/Martinů—Concertos and Chamber
Music

HOLLIGER, Heinz (ob)
Albinoni: Concerti, Op. 7 (exc), Sinfonie, Op.2 (exc)
Cimarosa: Flute and Oboe Concertante in G
Holliger: Siebengesang
Mozart: Piano and Wind Quintet, K452
Zelenka: Trio Sonatas
see CONCERT INDEX under:
(CLAV) **CD50-8203** Krommer—Flute & Oboe
Concertos
(DG) **445 947-2GH** Messiaen—Orchestral Works
(ORFE) **C06083ta** Milhaud: Works for wind and piano
(PHIL) **412 851-2PH** Bach—Oboe Concertos
(PHIL) **412 879-2PH** Telemann: Oboe Concertos
(PHIL) **420 189-2PH** Baroque Oboe Concertos
(PHIL) **420 700-2PSL** Bach: Violin Concertos
(PHIL) **422 509-2PME5** The Complete Mozart Edition
Vol 9
(PHIL) **422 514-2PME5** The Complete Mozart Edition
Vol 14
(PHIL) **426 082-2PBQ** Handel—Orchestral Works
(PHIL) **426 386-2PC** Schumann—Oboe Works
(PHIL) **426 925-2PM19** The Complete Vivaldi Edition
(PHIL) **434 076-2PH** Heinz Holliger and Friends
(PHIL) **434 105-2PH** Martin/Honegger/Martinů—Concertos and Chamber
Music
(PHIL) **438 733-2PM2** R. Strauss—Music for Wind
(PHIL) **442 015-2PH** Maderna—Oboe Concertos
(PHIL) **442 592-2PM2** C P E Bach—Concertos
(PHIL) **442 795-2PH** Skalkottas—Cycle Concert
(POLS) **PNCD045** Lutosławski: Selected Works
(SCHW) **310632** Globokar—Chamber Works

HOLLIGER, Heinz (ob d'amore)
see CONCERT INDEX under:
(PHIL) **420 189-2PH** Baroque Oboe Concertos
(PHIL) **426 386-2PC** Schumann—Oboe Works

HOLLIGER, Heinz (ob/dir)
see CONCERT INDEX under:
(ECM) **447 390-2** Sandor Veress
(PHIL) **422 509-2PME5** The Complete Mozart Edition
Vol 9
(PHIL) **426 462-2PBQ2** Bach—Orchestral Works

HOLLIGER, Ursula (hp)
Mozart: Flute and Harp Concerto, K299
Spohr: Violin and Harp Concerto 1
see CONCERT INDEX under:
(PHIL) **434 105-2PH** Martin/Honegger/Martinů—Concertos and Chamber
Music
(PHIL) **442 592-2PM2** C P E Bach—Concertos

HOLLINGSWORTH, John (cond)
see Sinfonia of London

HOLLMAN, Josef (vc)
see CONCERT INDEX under:
(ROMO) **81001-2** Emma Eames (1865-1952)

HOLLOWAY, John (vn)
Bach: Musikalisches Opfer, BWV1079
Biber: Mystery Sonatas
Leclair: Violin Sonatas, Op. 3
Vivaldi: Concerti, Op. 8 (exc)
see CONCERT INDEX under:
(HARM) **HMU90 7046** Vivaldi—Chamber Concertos
(HARM) **HMU90 7091** Three Parts upon a Ground
(HARM) **HMU90 7104** Vivaldi/Chedeville—Oboe
Sonatas
(HYPE) **CDA66228** Ancient Airs and Dances
(L'OI) **410 553-2OH** 18th Century Orchestral Works
(L'OI) **433 053-2OH** Bach/Vivaldi—Orchestral Works

HOLLOWAY, Stanley (sngr)
F. Loewe: My Fair Lady (film) (Cpte)

HOLLREISER, Heinrich (cond)
see Düsseldorf SO

HOLLWEG, Ilse (sop)
see CONCERT INDEX under:
(EMI) **CHS7 63715-2** Mozart: Die Entführung, etc
(EMIL) **CDZ7 67015-2** Mozart—Opera Arias

HOLLWEG, Werner (ten)
Beethoven: Fidelio (Cpte)
Einem: Dantons Tod (Cpte)
Handel: Messiah (Cpte)
Haydn: Jahreszeiten (exc), Schöpfung (Cpte)
J. Strauss II: Fledermaus (exc)
Lehár: Lustige Witwe (exc)
Mahler: Klagende Lied
Mendelssohn: Symphony 2
Monteverdi: Combattimento di Tancredi e Clorinda,
Madrigals, Bk 8 (exc)

Mozart: Finta Giardiniera (Cpte), Idomeneo (Cpte),
Mitridate (Cpte), Nozze di Figaro (Cpte), Zaïde
(Cpte)
Puccini: Messa di Gloria
Schubert: Lazarus, D689
Wagner: Tannhäuser (Cpte)
Wolf: Corregidor (Cpte)
see CONCERT INDEX under:
(CAPR) 10 169 Mozart: Choral Works
(CAPR) 10 244 Schubert: Choral Music
(DG) 429 664-2GSE3 Mendelssohn—Complete
Symphonies
(DG) 435 712-2GX2 Lehár—The Merry Widow.
Suppé—Overtures

HOLLYWOOD BOWL ORCHESTRA
cond J. MAUCERI
Rodgers: King and I (Cpte)
see CONCERT INDEX under:
(PHIL) 446 406-2PH Berlin—Heat Wave
cond L. STOKOWSKI
Rachmaninov: Symphony 2

HOLLYWOOD BOWL SYMPHONY ORCHESTRA
cond J. MAUCERI
see CONCERT INDEX under:
(PHIL) 432 109-2PH Hollywood Dreams
(PHIL) 434 127-2PH Rodgers &
Hammerstein—Complete Overtures
(PHIL) 438 685-2PH The Great Waltz
(PHIL) 442 425-2PH Hollywood Nightmares

HOLLYWOOD QUARTET
Schoenberg: Verklärte Nacht
Schubert: String Quintet
see CONCERT INDEX under:
(TEST) SBT1052 Prokofiev/Hindemith/Walton—String
Quartets
(TEST) SBT1053 Chamber Works
(TEST) SBT1061
Borodin/Glazunov/Tchaikovsky—Chamber Works

HOLM, Michael (spkr)
Corghi: Divara (Cpte)

HOLM, Renate (sop)
J.Strauss II: Fledermaus (Cpte)
Künneke: Vetter aus Dingsda (exc)
Lehár: Land des Lächelns (Cpte)
Millöcker: Bettelstudent (Cpte)
Zeller: Vogelhändler (Cpte)

HOLM, Richard (ten)
Egk: Verlobung in San Domingo (Cpte)
Weber: Freischütz (Cpte)
see CONCERT INDEX under:
(DG) 423 127-2GX4 Bruckner: Sacred Works for
Chorus

HOLMAN, Peter (cond)
see Opera Restor'd

HOLMES, James (cond)
see ENO Orch

HOLMES, John (bass)
Sullivan: Mikado (Cpte)

HOLMES, Ralph (vn)
Beethoven: Violin Sonata 5, Violin Sonata 7
Harty: Variations on a Dublin Air, Violin Concerto
see CONCERT INDEX under:
(AMON) CD-SAR12 Hummel—Works for Violin &
Piano
(DECC) 433 220-2DWO The World of the Violin
(UNIC) DKPCD9040 Delius—Works for Violin &
Orchestra
(UNIC) UKCD2072 The Delius Collection, Volume 2
(UNIC) UKCD2074 The Delius Collection, Volume 4

HOLMGREN, Carl Gustaf (bar)
Grieg: Peer Gynt (Cpte)
Prokofiev: Fiery Angel (Cpte)

HOLROYD, Anna (mez)
see CONCERT INDEX under:
(AUVI) AV6110 Vocal & Orchestral Works

HOLST, Grace (sop)
see CONCERT INDEX under:
(PREI) 89055 Cesare Formichi (1883-1949)

HOLST, Gustav (cond)
see LSO

HOLST, Henry (vn)
Beethoven: Piano Trios (exc)
see CONCERT INDEX under:
(APR) APR5503 Solomon—The First HMV
Recordings 1942-3
(TEST) SBT1014 Delius—Orchestral Works

HOLST, Imogen (cond)
see ECO

HOLST ORCHESTRA
cond H.D. WETTON
see CONCERT INDEX under:
(HYPE) CDA66175 Music by Bliss, Britten and Holst
(HYPE) CDA66329 Holst—Choral Works

HOLST SINGERS
cond S. LAYTON
see CONCERT INDEX under:
(HYPE) CDA66705 Holst—Partsongs
cond A. MELVILLE
Boughton: Bethlehem (Cpte)
cond H.D. WETTON
see CONCERT INDEX under:
(HYPE) CDA66175 Music by Bliss, Britten and Holst

(HYPE) CDA66329 Holst—Choral Works

HOLT, Anthony (bar)
see CONCERT INDEX under:
(CLLE) COLCD115 Three Musical Fables

HOLT, Gertrude (sop)
Schumann: Manfred (Cpte)

HOLT, Rebecca (pf)
see CONCERT INDEX under:
(CARL) PCD991 French Flute Music

HOLTEN, Bo (cond)
see Ars Nova

HOLTON, Ruth (sop)
Bach: Cantata 140, Cantata 147, St John Passion,
BWV245 (Cpte)
Handel: Israel in Egypt (Cpte), Jephtha (Cpte),
Messiah (Cpte)
Purcell: Dido (Cpte), St Cecilia's Day Ode, Z339
see CONCERT INDEX under:
(CHAN) CHAN9363 Adams/Lang—Wind Music
(HYPE) CDA66398 Schutz—Christmas Story;
Gabrieli—Motets
(HYPE) CDA66578 Odes on the Death of Henry
Purcell

HOLTSLAG, Peter (rec)
Telemann: Fantaisies, TWV40: 2-13
see CONCERT INDEX under:
(ARCH) 445 839-2AH Vivaldi—Woodwind Concertos
(HYPE) CDA66328 Vivaldi—Recorder Concertos
(HYPE) CDA66413 Telemann—Recorder Works

HOLVIK, Karen (sop)
see CONCERT INDEX under:
(KOCH) 37050-2 Blitzstein—Songs
(RCA) 09026 61509-2 A Salute to American Music

HOLZAPFEL, Helmut (ten)
B.A. Zimmermann: Soldaten (Cpte)
Glass: Akhnaten (Cpte)

HOLZER, Robert (spkr)
Mozart: Zauberflöte (Cpte)

HOLZHERR, Wolfgang (ten)
R. Strauss: Rosenkavalier (Cpte)

HOLZMAIR, Wolfgang (bar)
Brahms: Deutsches Requiem, Op. 45 (Cpte)
Busoni: Arlecchino (Cpte), Turandot (Cpte)
J. Strauss II: Zigeunerbaron (Cpte)
Schubert: Schöne Müllerin (Cpte)
Wolf: Goethe Lieder (exc)
see CONCERT INDEX under:
(PHIL) 442 460-2PH Schubert—Lieder
(PHIL) 446 086-2PH Schumann—Lieder
(PREI) 93368 Mendelssohn—Lieder
(SCHW) 314050 Weill—Vocal and Choral Works

HOMBERGER, Christophe (ten)
Monteverdi: Incoronazione di Poppea (Cpte)
see CONCERT INDEX under:
(CHAN) CHAN8878 Diepenbrock: Symphonic Songs
(ERAT) 4509-95307-2 Schubert/Schumann—Sacred
Choral Works

HOMBERGH, Antoinette (vn)
see CONCERT INDEX under:
(TELD) 4509-97455-2 Franz Brüggen Edition Vol.
3—English Ensemble Music

HOMBURGER, Maya (vn)
Telemann: Fantaisies, TWV40: 14-25

HOMER, Louise (contr)
see CONCERT INDEX under:
(CLUB) CL99-060 Enrico Caruso—Opera & Song
Recital
(EMI) CDH7 61051-2 Beniamino Gigli - Operatic
Arias
(IRCC) IRCC-CD800 Souvenirs from Meyerbeer
Operas
(MSCM) MM30352 Caruso—Italian Opera Arias
(NIMB) NI7852 Galli-Curci, Vol.2
(NIMB) NI7860 Emma Eames & Pol Plançon
(PEAR) EVC1(2) The Caruso Edition, Vol.1 (pt 2)
(PEAR) EVC2 The Caruso Edition, Vol.2—1908-12
(PEAR) EVC4(2) The Caruso Edition, Vol.4 (pt 2)
(PEAR) GEMMCDS9923(2) Covent Garden on
Record, Vol.1 (pt 2)
(PEAR) GEMMCD9316 Beniamino Gigli
(PEAR) GEMMCD9367 Gigli—Arias and Duets
(RCA) GD60495(2) The Complete Caruso Collection
(pt 2)
(RCA) GD60495(3) The Complete Caruso Collection
(pt 3)
(RCA) GD60495(4) The Complete Caruso Collection
(pt 4)
(RCA) GD60495(6) The Complete Caruso Collection
(pt 6)
(RCA) 09026 61580-2(1) RCA/Met 110 Singers, 100
Years (pt 1)
(ROMO) 81001-2 Emma Eames (1865-1952)

HONECK, Manfred (cond)
see Hungarian St Orch

HONEGGER, Arthur (cond)
see Odeon Grand Orch

HONEGGER, Henri (vc)
see CONCERT INDEX under:
(JECK) JD563-2 Frank Martin interprets Frank
Martin

HONEYBALL, David (cond)
see London Brass Virtuosi

HONEYMAN, Ian (ten)
Brossard: Dialogus, Elévations (1698)
Gay: Beggar's Opera (Cpte)
Hasse: Requiem in C
see CONCERT INDEX under:
(RICE) RIC048035/7 German Baroque Cantatas,
Vol.4 - Bruhns
(RICE) RIC109097/8 German Baroque Cantatas,
Vol.9 - Weckmann
(VIRG) VC5 45075-2 Charpentier—Leçons de
ténèbres, Vol. 2
(VIRG) VC7 59295-2 M-A. Charpentier—Tenebrae
Lessons for Good Friday

HONG, Hei-Kyung (sop)
Verdi: Aida (Cpte)
Wagner: Götterdämmerung (Cpte)
see CONCERT INDEX under:
(DG) 445 354-2GX14 Wagner—Der Ring des
Nibelungen

HONG KONG PHILHARMONIC ORCHESTRA
cond K. JEAN
see CONCERT INDEX under:
(MARC) 8 223354 Massenet—Orchestral Suites
cond V. KOJIAN
see CONCERT INDEX under:
(MARC) 8 220114 Wagner: Overtures and Marches
Villa-Lobos: Chôro 9, Chôros 8
cond K. SCHERMERHORN
see CONCERT INDEX under:
(CARL) PCD827 The Art of the Coloratura
(MARC) 8 220308 Cui: Orchestral Works
(MARC) 8 220309 Glazunov: Orchestral Works

HÖNGEN, Elisabeth (contr)
Beethoven: Symphony 9
Verdi: Don Carlo (exc), Macbeth (Cpte), Requiem
(Cpte)
see CONCERT INDEX under:
(EMI) CDH7 63030-2 Kirsten Flagstad - Wagner
Opera Arias
(EMI) CHS7 69741-2(4) Record of Singing,
Vol.4—German School
(EMI) CMS7 63310-2 Beethoven: Complete
Symphonies
(SCHW) 314552 Vienna State Opera Live, Vol.5
(TAHR) FURT1004/7 Furtwängler conducts the Berlin
Philharmonic

HONGNE, Paul (bn)
see CONCERT INDEX under:
(ERAT) 2292-45937-2 Mozart—Wind Concertos
(ERAT) 4509-95361-2 Mozart—Wind Concertos

HONMA, Masashi (ob)
see CONCERT INDEX under:
(DENO) CO-78944 Takemitsu—Orchestral Works

HOOD, Ann (sop)
Sullivan: Trial by Jury (Cpte), Yeomen of the Guard
(Cpte)
see CONCERT INDEX under:
(DECC) 433 868-2DWO The World of Gilbert &
Sullivan - Volume 2

HOOD, Dorothy (sop)
Janáček: Fate (Cpte)

HOOG, Viola de (vc)
see CONCERT INDEX under:
(ETCE) KTC1069 Vivaldi: Cantatas
(OLYM) OCD460 Roussel—Chamber Music, Vol. 3

HOOGEVEEN, Dick (gtr)
see CONCERT INDEX under:
(ETCE) KTC1150 Castelnuovo-Tedesco—Vocal and
Guitar Works

HOOGLAND, Stanley (fp)
see CONCERT INDEX under:
(CHNN) CCS1491 Beethoven—Songs

HOOKER, Christopher (ob)
see CONCERT INDEX under:
(CHAN) CHAN9270 Holst—Orchestral Works

HOOPER, James (bar)
see CONCERT INDEX under:
(PHIL) 432 416-2PH3 Haydn—L'incontro
improvviso/Arias

HOOPER, Nicholas (gtr)
Bach: Cantata 147 (exc), Solo Cello Suites (exc)

HOOS, Barbara (sngr)
Grieg: Peer Gynt (exc)

HOPF, Gertraud (mez)
Wagner: Walküre (exc)
see CONCERT INDEX under:
(PHIL) 446 057-2PB14 Wagner—The Ring Cycle -
Bayreuth Festival 1967

HOPF, Hans (ten)
Egk: Peer Gynt (Cpte)
Wagner: Meistersinger (Cpte), Tannhäuser (Cpte)

HOPFERWIESER, Josef (ten)
J. Strauss II: Fledermaus (Cpte)

HOPFNER, Heiner (ten)
Egk: Peer Gynt (Cpte)
Mozart: Zauberflöte (Cpte)
Wagner: Parsifal (Cpte)

HOPKINS, Sir Anthony (narr)
Shostakovich: Symphony 13

HOPKINS, Gregory (ten)
Weill: Lost in the Stars (Cpte)
see CONCERT INDEX under:
(EMI) CDC7 54851-2   Gershwin—Blue Monday, etc

HOPKINS, Jamie (treb)
Mendelssohn: Elijah (Cpte)

HOPKINS, John (cond)
see Melbourne SO

HOPPE, Carl (bass)
Nicolai: Lustigen Weiber von Windsor (Cpte)
R. Strauss: Arabella (Cpte), Salome (Cpte)
Wagner: Meistersinger (Cpte)

HOPPE, Fritz (bar)
Henze: Junge Lord (Cpte)

HOPPE, Fritz (narr)
Weber: Freischütz (Cpte)

HOPPE, Heinz (ten)
see CONCERT INDEX under:
(CAMB) CD-1032   From the Operas of Erich Wolfgang
Korngold

HOPPE, Leo (bass)
R. Strauss: Rosenkavalier (Cpte)

HOPPER, DeWolf (sngr)
see CONCERT INDEX under:
(PEAR) GEMMCDS9050/2(1)   Music from the New
York Stage, Vol. 1 (part 1)

HÖPS, Berthold (hpd/org)
Pergolesi: Orfeo, Stabat Mater

HORA, Jan (organ)
Brixi: Organ Concertos (exc)
Saint-Saëns: Symphony 3
see CONCERT INDEX under:
(SUPR) 11 0751-2   Martinů—Choral Works

HORÁČEK, Jaroslav (bass)
Dvořák: Kate and the Devil (Cpte)
Fibich: Bride of Messina (Cpte)
Janáček: From the House of the Dead (Cpte)
Martinů: Julietta (Cpte)
Smetana: Bartered Bride (Cpte), Two Widows
(Cpte)

HORÁČEK, Pavel (bass)
see CONCERT INDEX under:
(SONY) SK45633   Edita Gruberová—Opera Arias

HORÁČKOVÁ, Dora (sop)
Krása: Brundibár (Cpte)

HORÁK, Vilém (bn)
see CONCERT INDEX under:
(SUPR) 11 1445-2   Reicha/Beethoven—Compositions
for Wind

HORÁK, Vlastimil (cond)
see Bratislava Chbr Ens

HORDERN, Michael (spkr)
Gay: Beggar's Opera (Cpte)

HORENSTEIN, Jascha (cond)
see Bamberg SO

HORENSTEIN, Jascha (spkr)
Horenstein: Blyth Interview

HORN, Robert (ten)
Britten: Midsummer Night's Dream (Cpte)

HORN, Volker (ten)
Mendelssohn: Hochzeit des Camacho (Cpte)
Mozart: Zauberflöte (Cpte)
Pfitzner: Herz (Cpte)
S. Wagner: Bärenhäuter (Cpte)
Verdi: Nabucco (Cpte)

HORNE, Marilyn (mez)
Beethoven: Symphony 9
Bellini: Norma (exc)
Bernstein: West Side Story (Cpte)
Bizet: Carmen (Cpte)
Donizetti: Lucrezia Borgia (Cpte)
Gluck: Orfeo ed Euridice (Cpte)
Hammerstein: Carmen Jones (Cpte)
Handel: Rinaldo (Cpte), Semele (Cpte)
Meyerbeer: Prophète (Cpte)
Ravel: Shéhérazade
Rodgers: King and I (Cpte)
Rossini: Barbiere di Siviglia (Cpte), Bianca e Falliero
(Cpte), Italiana in Algeri (Cpte), Semiramide (exc),
Tancredi (Cpte)
Roussel: Padmâvatî (Cpte)
Verdi: Falstaff (Cpte), Requiem (Cpte), Trovatore
(Cpte)
Vivaldi: Orlando Furioso (Cpte)
see CONCERT INDEX under:
(DECC) 430 500-2DWO   World of Handel
(DECC) 436 462-2DM   Ten Top Mezzos
(EMI) CDC7 54643-2   Rossini—Bicentenary Gala
Concert
(RCA) RD60811   Marilyn Horne sings Rossini
(RCA) 09026 61276-2   Brahms—Viola Sonatas; Songs
(RCA) 09026 61509-2   A Salute to American Music
(RCA) 09026 61580-2(8)   RCA/Met 100 Singers, 100
Years (pt 8)
(RCA) 09026 61681-2
Dvořák/Saint-Saëns/Mendelssohn—Lieder
(RCA) 09026 62547-2   Divas in Song—Marilyn Horne's
60th Birthday
(SONY) M3K79312   Puccini: Il Trittico
(TELA) CD80176   Brahms: Choral Works

HORNEFFER, Jacques (pf)
see CONCERT INDEX under:
(DECC) 443 467-2DF2   Stravinsky—Ballet Music

HORNER, James (cond)
see LSO

HORNER, Jerry (va)
Shostakovich: Piano Quintet, Op. 57
Tchaikovsky: Album for the Young

HORNIK, Gottfried (bar)
Lortzing: Wildschütz (Cpte)
Mozart: Zauberflöte (exc)
Puccini: Tosca (Cpte), Turandot (Cpte)
R. Strauss: Frau ohne Schatten (Cpte),
Rosenkavalier (Cpte)
see CONCERT INDEX under:
(NOVA) 150 081-2   Mozart—The Freemason Music

HORNIK, Gottfried (narr)
see CONCERT INDEX under:
(DG) 431 774-2GH   Schoenberg/Webern—Orchestral
Works

HOROWITZ, Vladimir (pf)
Beethoven: Piano Concerto 5
Brahms: Piano Concerto 2
D. Scarlatti: Keyboard Sonatas (exc)
Mozart: Piano Concerto 23, Piano Sonata, K333
Mussorgsky: Pictures
Rachmaninov: Piano Concerto 3
Schubert: Piano Sonata, D960
Schumann: Kinderszenen
Tchaikovsky: Piano Concerto 1
see CONCERT INDEX under:
(APR) APR7014   Romantic Piano Rarities, Vol.2
(COND) 690.07.009   Horowitz—Piano Roll
Recordings
(DANA) DACOCD303   Great Musicians in
Copenhagen
(DG) 419 045-2GH   Vladimir Horowitz—Piano Recital
(DG) 419 217-2GH   Vladimir Horowitz—Piano Recital
(DG) 419 499-2GH   Horowitz in Moscow
(DG) 427 772-2GH   Horowitz At Home
(DG) 445 517-2GMA   Mozart—Piano Works
(EMI) CHS7 63538-2   Horowitz—The HMV
Recordings, 1930-51
(RCA) GD60375   Horowitz plays Beethoven Sonatas
(RCA) GD60376   Horowitz plays Chopin—Vol.2
(RCA) GD60377   Vladimir Horowitz—Piano recital
(RCA) GD60449   Vladimir Horowitz plays Russian
Works
(RCA) GD60451   Horowitz—Piano Recital
(RCA) GD60463   Vladimir Horowitz - Piano Recital
(RCA) GD60523   Horowitz plays Brahms, Liszt &
Schubert
(RCA) GD60526   Russian Favourites - Horowitz
(RCA) GD86215   Scriabin—Piano Works
(RCA) GD86680   Horowitz plays Schumann
(RCA) GD87752   Horowitz plays Chopin, Vol.1
(RCA) GD87753   Horowitz plays Clementi
(RCA) 09026 60986-2   Piano Recital - Horowitz
(RCA) 09026 60987-2   Horowitz plays Chopin, Vol.3
(RCA) 09026 61414-2   Horowitz in London
(RCA) 09026 61415-2   Liszt—Piano Works
(RCA) 09026 61416-2   Horowitz at the Met
(SONY) SK45818   Horowitz—His Last Recordings
(SONY) SK48093   The Lost Recording—Horowitz
(SONY) SK53465   Horowitz—The Complete
Masterworks Recordings, 1962-73, Vol 4
(SONY) SK53466   Horowitz—The Complete
Masterworks Recordings, 1962-73: Vol 5
(SONY) SK53467   Horowitz—The Complete
Masterworks Recordings, 1962-73: Vol 6
(SONY) SK53471   Horowitz—The Complete
Masterworks Recordings, 1926—73, Vol 8
(SONY) SK53472   Horowitz—The Complete
Masterworks Recordings, 1962-75: Vol 9
(SONY) S2K53457   Horowitz—The Complete
Masterworks Recordings, 1962-73, Vol 1
(SONY) S2K53468   Horowitz—The Complete
Masterworks Recordings, 1962-73, Vol 7
(SONY) S3K53461   Horowitz—The Complete
Masterworks Recordings, 1962-73, Vol 3

HORREAUX, Jean (gtr)
see CONCERT INDEX under:
(CALL) CAL9204   Granados: Transcriptions for Guitar
Duo

HORSLEY, Colin (pf)
see CONCERT INDEX under:
(EMI) CDM7 64716-2   Ireland—Piano Concerto, etc
(SYMP) SYMCD1068   Schubert: Works for Violin and
Piano
(SYMP) SYMCD1076   Violin & Piano Works

HORSMAN, Leslie (bar)
Verdi: Trovatore (Cpte)
Wagner: Tristan und Isolde (Cpte)

HORSZOWSKI, Mieczyslaw (pf)
Beethoven: Diabelli Variations, Piano Sonata 26,
Piano Sonata 28, Piano Sonata 29
Busoni: Violin Sonata 2
Schubert: Piano Trio 2, Trout Quintet, D667
see CONCERT INDEX under:
(EMI) CHS5 65185-2   Beethoven/Brahms—Cello
Sonatas
(LYRN) LYRCD070   Horszowski at Prades
(NONE) 7559-79261-2   Horszowski— A Portrait
(NONE) 7559-79264-2   Mieczyslaw Horszowski 100th
Birthday Recording

(PEAR) GEMMCDS9138   Mozart—Piano Concertos,
Volume 1
(PEAR) GEMMCDS9979   Horszowski—A Centenary
Celebration
(RELI) CR911022   Beethoven—Piano Sonatas
(RELI) CR911023   Horszowski plays Chopin
(SONY) MPK52569   Joseph Szigeti Recital
(SONY) SMK58984   Pablo Casals conducts Mozart at
Perpignan, 1951
(SONY) SMK58993   Pablo Casals plays Schumann at
Prades, 1952 & 1953
(SONY) SM3K46527   Mozart—Legendary
Interpretations, IV
(VOX) CDX2 5500   Beethoven—Piano Sonatas

HORTIZ, Joseph (sngr)
see CONCERT INDEX under:
(PEAR) GEMMCDS9050/2(2)   Music from the New
York Stage, Vol. 1 (part 2)

HÖRTNAGEL, Georg (db)
Schubert: Trout Quintet, D667

HORTON, John (narr)
see CONCERT INDEX under:
(SONY) SM2K52664   Schoenberg—Piano Works

HORTON, Timothy (organ)
see CONCERT INDEX under:
(CNTO) CRCD2367   For All the Saints

HORTUS MUSICUS
see CONCERT INDEX under:
(FINL) 4509-95578-2   Telemann—Quartets

HOSFORD, Richard (basset cl)
see CONCERT INDEX under:
(ASV) CDCOE811   Works for Clarinet and Orchestra
(ASV) CDCOE814   Mozart—Wind Concertos

HOSFORD, Richard (cl)
see CONCERT INDEX under:
(ASV) CDCOE811   Works for Clarinet and Orchestra
(ASV) CDCOE814   Mozart—Wind Concertos

HOSKINS, Andrew (tpt/dir)
see CONCERT INDEX under:
(MOSC) 070979   Sound the Trumpets from Shore to
Shore

HOSKINS, Bob (spkr)
Gay: Beggar's Opera (Cpte)

HOSKINS, Mark (tpt/dir)
see CONCERT INDEX under:
(MOSC) 070979   Sound the Trumpets from Shore to
Shore

HOST, František (vc)
see CONCERT INDEX under:
(SUPR) 11 1533-2   Suk—Chamber Works, Volume 3

HOTTER, Hans (bass-bar)
Beethoven: Symphony 9
Berg: Lulu (Cpte)
Brahms: Deutsches Requiem, Op. 45 (Cpte)
Mozart: Requiem, Zauberflöte (Cpte)
Orff: Mond (Cpte)
R. Strauss: Arabella (Cpte), Capriccio (Cpte), Salome
(Cpte), Schweigsame Frau (Cpte)
Schubert: Winterreise (Cpte)
Wagner: Meistersinger (Cpte), Parsifal (Cpte),
Rheingold (Cpte), Siegfried (Cpte), Walküre (exc)
see CONCERT INDEX under:
(ACAN) 43 268   Peter Anders sings German Opera
Arias
(ACAN) 44 2114-2   Schubert—Song Cycles
(DECC) 414 100-2DM15   Wagner: Der Ring des
Nibelungen
(DG) 445 400-2GDO10   Ferenc Fricsay - A Portrait
(EMI) CDH5 65196-2   Schubert—Lieder
(EMI) CDH7 63198-2   Hans Hotter sings Bach &
Brahms
(EMI) CHS7 69741-2(4)   Record of Singing,
Vol.4—German School
(EMI) CMS5 65212-2   Wagner—Les introuvables du
Ring
(EMI) CMS7 64008-2(1)   Wagner Singing on Record
(pt 1)
(FOYE) 15-CF2011   Wagner—Der Ring de Nibelungen
(PREI) 90222   Maria Cebotari sings Richard Strauss
(PREI) 93145   Hans Hotter sings Schubert and
Schumann Lieder
(PREI) 93390   Hans Hotter Lieder recital
(SCHW) 314502   Vienna State Opera—Live
Recordings (sampler)
(SCHW) 314532   Vienna State Opera Live, Vol.3
(SCHW) 314582   Vienna State Opera Live, Vol.8
(SCHW) 314652   Vienna State Opera Live, Vol.15

HOTTER, Hans (narr)
Schoenberg: Gurrelieder

HOUBART, François-Henri (organ)
Vierne: Suite 2 (exc), Symphony 1
see CONCERT INDEX under:
(PIER) PV784041   Vierne/Houbart—Organ Works
(PIER) PV784041   Mozart—Organ Works
(PIER) PV785031   Franck—Organ Works

HOUGH, Stephen (pf)
F. X. Scharwenka: Piano Concerto 4
Hummel: Piano Concerto in A minor, Piano Concerto
in B minor
Mozart: Piano Concerto 9, Piano Concerto 21
Sauer: Piano Concerto 1
see CONCERT INDEX under:
(PHIL) 442 425-2PH   Hollywood Nightmares
(VIRG) CUV5 61129-2   Liszt—Piano Works

(VIRG) **VC7 59222-2** Liszt—An Italian Recital
(VIRG) **VC7 59509-2** The Piano Album, Vol.1

HOUGHTON, William (tpt)
Buller: Theatre of Memory
see CONCERT INDEX under:
(PHIL) **412 892-2PH** Vivaldi: Double Concertos
(PHIL) **420 954-2PH** Telemann—Trumpet Concertos

HOULIK, James (sax)
see CONCERT INDEX under:
(ALBA) **AR001** R. Ward—Orchestral Works

HOÚSKA, Eva Novšak (mez)
Dvořák: Stabat mater

HOUSTON, Elsie (sop)
see CONCERT INDEX under:
(EMI) **CHS7 69741-2(1)** Record of Singing,
Vol.4—Anglo-American School (pt 1)

HOUSTON CHORALE
cond L. STOKOWSKI
Orff: Carmina Burana

HOUSTON GRAND OPERA CHORUS
cond J. DEMAIN
Gershwin: Porgy and Bess (Cpte)
cond G. SCHULLER
Joplin: Treemonisha (Cpte)

HOUSTON GRAND OPERA ORCHESTRA
cond J. DEMAIN
Gershwin: Porgy and Bess (Cpte)
cond G. SCHULLER
Joplin: Treemonisha (Cpte)

HOUSTON SYMPHONY ORCHESTRA
cond C. ESCHENBACH
Dvořák: Symphony 9
Tchaikovsky: Francesca da Rimini
see CONCERT INDEX under:
(CARL) **TCD77** Mozart—Wind Concertos
(VIRG) **VC7 59007-2** Picker—Orchestral Works
cond L. STOKOWSKI
Bartók: Concerto for Orchestra
Glière: Symphony 3
Orff: Carmina Burana
see CONCERT INDEX under:
(EVER) **EVC9004** R. Strauss/Canning—Orchestral
Works

HOUSTON YOUTH SYMPHONY BOYS' CHOIR
cond L. STOKOWSKI
Orff: Carmina Burana

HOUTE DE LANGE, Michiel ten (ten)
Bach: Cantata 56

HOUTMANN, Jacques (cond)
see Lorraine PO

HOVHANESS, Alan (cond)
see N. Jersey Wind SO

HOVORA, Daria (pf)
see CONCERT INDEX under:
(DG) **439 863-2GH** Cellissimo

HOWARD, Ann (contr)
Bernstein: Candide (1988) (exc)
Wagner: Walküre (Cpte)
see CONCERT INDEX under:
(SONY) **M3K79312** Puccini: Il Trittico

HOWARD, Christopher (sngr)
Bernstein: West Side Story (Cpte)

HOWARD, Douglas (marimba)
Benson: End of the World

HOWARD, Jamal (treb)
Weill: Lost in the Stars (Cpte)

HOWARD, Jason (bar)
Forrest/Wright: Song of Norway (Cpte)
Kern: Show Boat (Cpte)
Romberg: Student Prince (Cpte)

HOWARD, Kathleen (mez)
see CONCERT INDEX under:
(ROMO) **81010-2** Claudia Muzio—Complete Pathé
Recordings, 1917-8

HOWARD, Leslie (pf)
Liszt: Beethoven Symphonies, S464, Bunte Reihe,
S484, Grandes Études, S137, Hungarian themes and
rhapsodies, S242, Morceau de salon, S142
Rubinstein: Piano Sonata 1, Piano Sonata 2, Piano
Sonata 3, Piano Sonata 4
Stravinsky: Petrushka (Cpte)
see CONCERT INDEX under:
(HYPE) **CDA66090** Rare piano encores
(HYPE) **CDA66201** Liszt—Piano Works, Vol.1
(HYPE) **CDA66301** Liszt—Piano Works, Vol.2
(HYPE) **CDA66302** Liszt—Piano Works, Vol.3
(HYPE) **CDA66346** Liszt—Piano Works, Vol.5
(HYPE) **CDA66357** Liszt—Piano Works, Vol.6
(HYPE) **CDA66371/2** Liszt—Piano Works, Vol.6
(HYPE) **CDA66421/2** Liszt—Piano Works, Vol.7
(HYPE) **CDA66438** Liszt—Piano Works, Vol.13
(HYPE) **CDA66481/2** Liszt—Piano Works, Vol.15
(HYPE) **CDA66575** Liszt—Piano Works, Vol.18
(HYPE) **CDA66661/2** Liszt—Piano Works, Vol.21
(HYPE) **CDA66683** Liszt—Piano Works, Vol.23
(HYPE) **CDA66687** English Viola Music
(HYPE) **CDA66694** Liszt—Piano Works, Vol.25
(HYPE) **CDA66771/2** Liszt—Piano Works, Vol.26
(HYPE) **CDA66787** Liszt—Piano Works, Vol.27
(HYPE) **CDA66811/2** Liszt—Piano Works, Vol.28
(HYPE) **CDA66861/2** Liszt—Piano Works, Vol.30

(HYPE) **CDA66951/3** Liszt—Piano Works, Vol.31
(HYPE) **CDA66954/6** Liszt—Solo Piano Music,
Vol.32
(HYPE) **CDA66957/9** Liszt—Solo Piano Music,
Vol.33
(PEAR) **SHECD9538** Glazunov—Piano Works

HOWARD, Michael (organ)
see CONCERT INDEX under:
(HERA) **HAVPCD125** Franck: Organ Works

HOWARD, Peter (cond)
see Orig Broadway Cast

HOWARD, William (pf)
Fibich: Moods, Op. 41, Part 1 (exc), Moods, Op. 41,
Part 2 (exc)
see CONCERT INDEX under:
(CHAN) **CHAN9044** Dvořák—Piano Works
(COLL) **Coll1453-2** Distance &
Enchantment—Chamber Works by Judith Weir

HOWARD, Yvonne (mez)
Walton: Troilus and Cressida (Cpte)

HOWARD JONES, Evlyn (pf)
Bach: Wohltemperierte Klavier (exc)
see CONCERT INDEX under:
(DUTT) **CDAX8006** The Delius Collection

HOWARTH, Elgar (cond)
see Austrian RSO

HOWARTH, Judith (sop)
Elgar: Caractacus (Cpte), Light of Life (Cpte)
Mendelssohn: Midsummer Night's Dream (exc)
Mozart: Requiem
Smyth: Wreckers (Cpte)
Sullivan: Yeomen of the Guard (Cpte)
Walton: Troilus and Cressida (Cpte)
see CONCERT INDEX under:
(ASV) **CDDCA891** Pastoral - British Clarinet Music
(HYPE) **CDA66655** Vaughan Williams—Choral Works

HOWELL, Gwynne (bass)
Bach: Mass in B minor, BWV232 (Cpte), St John
Passion, BWV245 (Cpte)
Beethoven: Fidelio (Cpte)
Bellini: Capuleti (Cpte)
Berlioz: Enfance du Christ (Cpte)
Bruckner: Mass in F minor, Psalm 150
Elgar: Coronation Ode (Cpte)
Handel: Messiah (Cpte)
Haydn: Salve Regina, HobXXIIIb/1, Schöpfung
(Cpte), Stabat Mater
Janáček: Cunning Little Vixen (Cpte)
Puccini: Fanciulla del West (Cpte)
Rossini: Guillaume Tell (Cpte), Siège de Corinthe
(Cpte), Stabat Mater
Verdi: Ballo in maschera (Cpte), Luisa Miller (Cpte)
Wagner: Tristan und Isolde (Cpte)
see CONCERT INDEX under:
(CHAN) **CHAN8641/2** Elgar—Dream of Gerontius.
Parry—Choral Works
(CHAN) **CHAN8760** Walton—Choral Works
(EMI) **CDM7 69544-2** Berlioz: Vocal Works
(HYPE) **CDA66420** Vaughan Williams: Vocal Works
(PHIL) **412 873-2PH** Mozart—Sacred Music

HOWELLS, Anne (mez)
Berlioz: Troyens (Cpte)
Cavalli: Ormindo (Cpte)
Floyd: Susannah (Cpte)
Haydn: Mass 11
R. Strauss: Rosenkavalier (Cpte)
Sullivan: Mikado (Cpte)
Wagner: Parsifal (Cpte)

HOWELLS, Ursula (narr)
Vaughan Williams: Bunyan Sequence

HOWITT, Barbara (sop)
Falla: Sombrero de tres picos (Cpte)

HOWLETT, Neil (bar)
Giordano: Andrea Chénier (Cpte)
R. Strauss: Salome (Cpte)
Stravinsky: Nightingale (Cpte)

HOYDE, Christopher de la (treb)
Purcell: Timon of Athens, Z632 (exc)

HOYER, Per (bar)
Nørholm: Symphony 4, Symphony 6, Symphony 8
see CONCERT INDEX under:
(CHAN) **CHAN8853** Nielsen: Choral Works
(SONY) **SK53276** Nielsen—Orchestral Works

HRNČÍŘ, Josef (cond)
see Prague SO

HRUBA-FREIBERGER, Venceslava (sop)
see CONCERT INDEX under:
(CAPR) **10 151** Bach: Cantatas

HRYNKIV, Thomas (pf)
see CONCERT INDEX under:
(FORL) **UCD16645** Paul Plishka sings Ukranian
Songs

HSU, John (baryton)
see CONCERT INDEX under:
(ASV) **CDGAU104** Haydn—Baryton Trios

HU, Nai-Yuan (vn)
Bruch: Violin Concerto 2
Goldmark: Violin Concerto 1

HUANG, Si-Jing (vn)
see CONCERT INDEX under:

HUARTE, Julian (pf)
see CONCERT INDEX under:
(RCA) **GD87969** Tito Schipa - Opera & Song Recital

HUBAY, Jenö (vn)
see CONCERT INDEX under:
(BIDD) **LAB045** Hubay & Flesch —HMV Recordings
(SYMP) **SYMCD1071** Great Violinists, Vol.1

HUBBARD, Bruce (bar)
Forrest/Wright: Kismet (Cpte), Timbuktu (exc)
Gershwin: Porgy and Bess (Cpte)
Kern: Show Boat (Cpte)
Porter: Anything Goes (Cpte)

HUBBARD, Leonard (ten)
Sullivan: Gondoliers (Cpte)

HUBEAU, Jean (pf)
see CONCERT INDEX under:
(ERAT) **4509-96953-2** Fauré—Chamber Works

HÜBEL, Lars (bass)
Pfitzner: Herz (Cpte)
S. Wagner: Bärenhäuter (Cpte)

HUBER, Gerhard (perc)
see CONCERT INDEX under:
(ECM) **839 617-2** Bach & Carter—Instrumental &
Chamber Works

HUBER, Marcus (treb)
Mozart: Zauberflöte (Cpte)
Saint-Saëns: Samson et Dalila (Cpte)
see CONCERT INDEX under:
(TELD) **2292-42606-2** Bach—Cantatas, Volume 28
(TELD) **2292-42608-2** Bach—Cantatas, Volume 29
(TELD) **2292-42609-2** Bach—Cantatas, Volume 30
(TELD) **4509-91760-2** Bach—Cantatas, Vol.6
(TELD) **4509-91761-2** Bach—Cantatas, Vol.7

HUBERMAN, Bronislaw (vn)
see CONCERT INDEX under:
(BIDD) **LAB077/8** Huberman—Complete Brunwick
Recordings
(BIDD) **LAB081/2** Huberman—Columbia recordings
with piano
(EPM) **150 032** The Romantic Violin
(PEAR) **GEMMCD9341** Bach & Mozart: Violin
Concertos

HÜBNER, Fritz (bass)
Wagner: Götterdämmerung (Cpte), Rheingold (Cpte),
Siegfried (Cpte)

HUDD, Roy (spkr/bar)
Purcell: Don Quixote: The Musical (Cpte)

HUDDERSFIELD CHORAL SOCIETY
cond V. HANDLEY
Elgar: Dream of Gerontius (Cpte)
cond O. DE LA MARTINEZ
Smyth: Wreckers (Cpte)
cond W. MORRIS
see CONCERT INDEX under:
(DECC) **436 402-2DWO** The World of Wedding
Music
cond M. SARGENT
Elgar: Dream of Gerontius (Cpte)
Handel: Messiah (exc), Messias, K572 (Cpte)
see CONCERT INDEX under:
(DUTT) **CDAX8012** Malcolm Sargent conducts
English Music

HUDER, Maria (mez)
Verdi: Aida (Cpte), Trovatore (Cpte)
see CONCERT INDEX under:
(CENT) **CRC2164** Ferruccio Tagliavini—Early
Operatic Recordings
(EMI) **CMS7 64165-2** Puccini—Trittico

HUDSON, Benjamin (vn)
see CONCERT INDEX under:
(KOCH) **37110-2** Wuorinen—Orchestral & Chamber
Works
(KOCH) **37242-2** Wuorinen—Chamber Works
(NIMB) **NI5158** Mendelssohn: Orchestral Works

HUDSON, Paul (bass)
Cilea: Adriana Lecouvreur (Cpte)
Mozart: Nozze di Figaro (Cpte)
Puccini: Fanciulla del West (Cpte), Tosca (Cpte)
Stravinsky: Noces
see CONCERT INDEX under:
(SONY) **SMK48462** Boulez conducts Schoenberg
(SONY) **SM2K47522** Beethoven & Haydn—Choral
Works

HUDSON SHAD
cond K. MASUR
Weill: Sieben Todsünden (Cpte)

HUEHN, Julius (bar)
Wagner: Tristan und Isolde (Cpte)
see CONCERT INDEX under:
(PREI) **89084** Kerstin Thorborg (1896-1970)

HUEHNS, Colin (treb)
Britten: Little Sweep (Cpte)

HUELGAS ENSEMBLE
cond P. VAN NEVEL
Anon: Homme armé Masses
Brumel: Missa Et ecce terrae motus, Missa pro
defunctis (exc)
see CONCERT INDEX under:
(SONY) **SK46699** Las Ensaladas - Burlesques of the
Spanish Renaissance

HUARTE, Julian (pf) (top right column, also listed)

(NORT) **NR248-CD** Silenced Voices - Victims of the
Holocaust

(SONY) **SK48195** Febus Avant!
(SONY) **SK48249** Gombert—Music from the Court of Charles V
(SONY) **SK53116** Festa—Sacred Vocal Works
(SONY) **SK53976** Music from the Court of King Janus at Nicosia (1374-1432)
  cond P. VAN NEVEL
  Lassus: Lagrime di San Pietro

HUEY, Choo (cond)
  see Singapore SO

HUFF, Harry (organ)
  see CONCERT INDEX under:
(CATA) **09026 61979-2** Memento Bittersweet

HUFFSTODT, Karen (sop)
  R. Strauss: Salomé (Cpte)
  Spontini: Vestale (Cpte)

HUFNAGEL, Elisabeth (mez)
  see CONCERT INDEX under:
(MYTO) **3MCD93381** Wagner—Die Walküre, etc

HUFNAGEL, Wilhelm (bass)
  Benatzky: Im weissen Rössl (exc)

HUGGETT, Monica (cond)
  see Hanover Band

HUGGETT, Monica (va d'amore)
  see CONCERT INDEX under:
(BIS) **BIS-CD290** Vivaldi: works for lute

HUGGETT, Monica (vn)
  Beethoven: Violin Concerto
  Mendelssohn: Violin Concerto, Op.64
  Purcell: Sonatas, Z802-11
  Vivaldi: Concerti, Op. 4
  see CONCERT INDEX under:
(BIS) **BIS-CD290** Vivaldi: works for lute
(HARM) **HMU90 7116** Giuliani/Paganini—Violin and Guitar Works
(L'OI) **410 553-2OH** 18th Century Orchestral Works
(L'OI) **433 053-2OH** Bach/Vivaldi—Orchestral Works
(TELD) **4509-90841-2** A Gift of Nature - 17th Century English Chamber Music

HUGGETT, Monica (vn/dir)
  see CONCERT INDEX under:
(ASV) **CDGAU105** Vivaldi—Violin Concertos
(VIRG) **VC5 45010-2** Mozart—Violin Concertos, Volume 1
(VIRG) **VC5 45060-2** Mozart—Violin Concertos, Volume 2

HUGH, Timothy (vc)
  see CONCERT INDEX under:
(ASV) **CDDCA868** Schnittke—Chamber Music, Volume 1
(CARL) **MCD72** Grieg/Rachmaninov—Cello and Piano Works
(CARL) **MCD80** Beethoven—Sonatas for Cello and Piano
(HYPE) **CDA66274** Britten—Cello Works

HUGHES, Christopher (organ)
  see CONCERT INDEX under:
(ARGO) **433 452-2ZH** Brahms/Mendelssohn—Sacred Choral Works
(EMI) **CDC7 54412-2** Choral Evensong from King's College, Cambridge
(EMI) **CDC7 54418-2** English Anthems
(HERA) **HAVPCD176** Bax/Villette—Choral Music

HUGHES, Owain Arwel (cond)
  see Aarhus SO

HUGUET, Giuseppina (sop)
  see CONCERT INDEX under:
(IRCC) **IRCC-CD800** Souvenirs from Meyerbeer Operas
(TEST) **SBT1008** Viva Rossini

HUGUET, Josefina (sop)
  see CONCERT INDEX under:
(NIMB) **NI7840/1** The Era of Adelina Patti
(SYMP) **SYMCD1149** Fernando De Lucia

HUISMAN, Wilhelm (bass)
  R. Strauss: Rosenkavalier (Cpte)

HULL YOUTH SYMPHONY ORCHESTRA
  cond G. HEALD-SMITH
  see CONCERT INDEX under:
(CAMP) **RR2CD1331/2** Havergal Brian—Orchestral Works

HULSE, Eileen (sop)
  Britten: Turn of the Screw (Cpte)
  Goehr: Sing, Ariel, Op. 51
  M. Berkeley: Baa Baa Black Sheep (Cpte)
  R. Strauss: Lieder, Op. 68
  see CONCERT INDEX under:
(CHAN) **CHAN9094** Glière/Ginastera—Concertos
(KOCH) **37263-2** Schoenberg—A Survivor from Warsaw, etc

HULSE, Gareth (ob)
  see CONCERT INDEX under:
(HYPE) **CDA66172** Malcolm Arnold: Chamber Works, Vol. 2
(HYPE) **CDA66173** Malcolm Arnold: Chamber Works, Vol. 3

HULSE, Gareth (ob d'amore)
  see CONCERT INDEX under:
(SONY) **SK46720** John Williams plays music of Takemitsu

HULTGREN, Clara (sop)
  see CONCERT INDEX under:
(SIMA) **PSC1810(1)** Grieg—Songs (historical recordings, pt 1)

HUMBURG, Will (cond)
  see Bratislava RSO

HUME, Alastair (alto)
  see CONCERT INDEX under:
(CLLE) **COLCD115** Three Musical Fables

HUME, Michael (sngr)
  Forrest/Wright: Kismet (Cpte)

HUMESTON, Jay (vc)
  Villa-Lobos: Piano Trio 1, Piano Trio 2, Piano Trio 3

HUMMEL, Martin (ten)
  see CONCERT INDEX under:
(HARM) **HMC90 1310** Schütz—The Nativity

HUMPHREY, Jon (ten)
  Handel: Messiah (Cpte)
  Haydn: Creation (Cpte)
  Schubert: Mass, D950
  see CONCERT INDEX under:
(TELA) **CD80248** Beethoven: Choral Works

HUMPHREYS, Gillian (sop)
  Herrmann: Fantasticks

HUMPHREYS, Sydney (vn)
  see CONCERT INDEX under:
(CFP) **CD-CFP4557** Baroque Favourites

HUMPHRIES, Jon (ten)
  see CONCERT INDEX under:
(MUSM) **67152-2** Stravinsky—The Composer, Volume VII

HUMPHRIES, Linda (sop)
  Massenet: Werther (Cpte)

HUMPHRIS, Ian (sngr)
  see CONCERT INDEX under:
(EMI) **CDANGEL 5** Norton—Chu Chin Chow

HUNGARIAN CHAMBER ORCHESTRA
  cond V. TÁTRAI
  see CONCERT INDEX under:
(LASE) **15 511** Mozart: Symphonies and Overtures

HUNGARIAN FESTIVAL CHORUS
  cond M. HALÁSZ
  Mozart: Zauberflöte (Cpte)
  cond G. OBERFRANK
  Bach: St Matthew Passion, BWV244 (Cpte)

HUNGARIAN NATIONAL PHILHARMONIC ORCHESTRA
  cond T. FERENC
  see CONCERT INDEX under:
(CARL) **PCD1013** Bartók—Orchestral Works
(CARL) **PCD1021** Bartók—Orchestral Works

HUNGARIAN RADIO AND TELEVISION CHILDREN'S CHORUS

HUNGARIAN RADIO AND TELEVISION CHORUS
  cond A. DORATI
  Kodály: Psalmus Hungaricus
  cond L. GARDELLI
  Respighi: Belfagor (Cpte), Semirama (Cpte)
  cond G. LEHEL
  Liszt: Hungarian Coronation Mass, S11
  cond G. PATANÈ
  Giordano: Andrea Chénier (Cpte)
  cond C. ROSEKRANS
  Mascagni: Lodoletta (Cpte)
  cond M. TILSON THOMAS
  Puccini: Tosca (Cpte)

HUNGARIAN RADIO AND TELEVISION ORCHESTRA
  cond J. FERENCSIK
  Kodály: Budavári Te Deum, Missa Brevis

HUNGARIAN RADIO CHILDREN'S CHOIR
  cond G. OBERFRANK
  Bach: St Matthew Passion, BWV244 (Cpte)

HUNGARIAN RADIO CHORUS
  cond M. ANTAL
  Bach: Cantata 80, Cantata 147, Cantata 208
  cond F. D'AVALOS
  Liszt: Faust Symphony
  cond J. FERENCSIK
  Kodály: Budavári Te Deum, Missa Brevis
  cond W. HUMBURG
  Rossini: Barbiere di Siviglia (Cpte)
  cond G. OBERFRANK
  Bach: Christmas Oratorio, BWV248 (Cpte)
  cond M. VIOTTI
  Franchetti: Cristoforo Colombo (Cpte)
  Puccini: Fanciulla del West (Cpte)

HUNGARIAN STATE CHOIR
  cond A. LIGETI
  Liszt: Faust Symphony

HUNGARIAN STATE OPERA CHILDREN'S CHORUS
  cond C. ROSEKRANS
  Mascagni: Lodoletta (Cpte)

HUNGARIAN STATE OPERA ORCHESTRA
  see CONCERT INDEX under:
(LASE) **15 611** Suppé—Overtures
  cond J. GOLDSMITH
  Goldsmith: King Solomon's Mines (exc)

HUNGARIAN STATE ORCHESTRA
  cond A. DORATI
  Kodály: Peacock Variations, Psalmus Hungaricus

  cond A. FISCHER
  Bartók: Concerto for Orchestra, Duke Bluebeard's Castle (Cpte), Miraculous Mandarin (exc)
  cond L. GARDELLI
  Respighi: Belfagor (Cpte), Semirama (Cpte)
  cond G. GYÖRIVÁNYI-RÁTH
  see CONCERT INDEX under:
(LASE) **15 515** Beethoven: Orchestral Works
  cond M. HONECK
  Bruch: Russian Suite, Symphony 3
  cond J. KOVÁCS
  see CONCERT INDEX under:
(HUNG) **HCD31535** Bartók—Songs
  cond G. PATANÈ
  Boito: Mefistofele (Cpte)
  Giordano: Andrea Chénier (Cpte)
  cond T. PÁL
  see CONCERT INDEX under:
(LASE) **15 517** Dvořák: Orchestral Works
  cond C. ROSEKRANS
  Mascagni: Lodoletta (Cpte)
  cond Z. ROZSNYAI
  see CONCERT INDEX under:
(APR) **APR7021** Cziffra—Hungaroton Recordings 1954-1956
  cond J. SÁNDOR
  Rimsky-Korsakov: Capriccio Espagnol, Scheherazade
  cond M. TILSON THOMAS
  Puccini: Tosca (Cpte)

HUNGARIAN STATE PHILHARMONIC ORCHESTRA
  cond G. OBERFRANK
  Bach: St Matthew Passion, BWV244 (Cpte)

HUNGARIAN STATE SYMPHONY ORCHESTRA
  cond F. D'AVALOS
  Liszt: Faust Symphony
  cond A. FISCHER
  Bartók: Violin Concerto 1, Violin Concerto 2
  Brahms: Piano Concerto 1
  Dohnányi: Nursery Variations
  see CONCERT INDEX under:
(NIMB) **NI5362/3** Bartók—Orchestral Works

HUNGAROTON OPERA CHORUS
  cond G. PATANÈ
  Boito: Mefistofele (Cpte)

HÜNI-MIHACSEK, Felicie (sop)
  see CONCERT INDEX under:
(PREI) **89201** Helge Roswaenge (1897-1972) - I
(SCHW) **314642** Vienna State Opera Live, Vol.14

HUNSBERGER, Donald (cond)
  see Eastman Wind Ens

HUNT, Donald (cond)
  see D. Hunt Sngrs

HUNT, Donald (organ)
  see CONCERT INDEX under:
(CARL) **PCD937** Tapestry of English Cathedral Music
(HYPE) **CDA66078** Cathedral & Organ Music
(HYPE) **CDA66271/2** Elgar:The Complete Choral Songs

HUNT, Gordon (ob)
  Mozart: Sinfonia Concertante, K297b
  see CONCERT INDEX under:
(CRD) **CRD3449** Jonathan Haas - Virtuoso Timpanist
(DECC) **436 415-2DH** R. Strauss—Orchestral Works
(VIRG) **VC7 59609-2** Vivaldi—Concertos

HUNT, Lorraine (sop)
  Bach: Anna Magdalena Notenbuch (1725) (exc)
  Handel: Clori, Tirsi e Fileno (Cpte), Messiah (Cpte), Susanna (Cpte), Theodora (Cpte)
  M-A. Charpentier: Médée (Cpte)
  Monteverdi: Ritorno d'Ulisse in patria (Cpte)
  Purcell: Dido (Cpte), Fairy Queen, Z629 (Cpte)
  see CONCERT INDEX under:
(DG) **423 089-2GH** Fauré: Orchestral Works
(HARM) **HMU90 7056** Handel—Arias for Durastanti

HUNTER, Desmond (organ)
  see CONCERT INDEX under:
(PRIO) **PRCD445** Stanford—Complete Organ Sonatas

HUNTER, Pamela (narr)
  see CONCERT INDEX under:
(DINT) **DICD920125** Walton—Façade

HUNTER, Rita (sop)
  Wagner: Götterdämmerung (Cpte), Siegfried (Cpte), Walküre (Cpte)
  see CONCERT INDEX under:
(ABCC) **8 7000 10** Rita Hunter—Opera Arias

HUNTGEBURTH, Christoph (fl)
  see CONCERT INDEX under:
(DHM) **RD77188** C.P.E. Bach—Vocal & Chamber Works

HUNTLEY, G. P. (sngr)
  see CONCERT INDEX under:
(PEAR) **GEMMCDS9050/2(1)** Music from the New York Stage, Vol. 1 (part 1)

HUNZIKER, Ueli (sngr)
  Zemlinsky: Kleider machen Leute (Cpte)

HURFORD, Peter (organ)
  Saint-Saëns: Symphony 3
  see CONCERT INDEX under:
(ARGO) **433 451-2ZH** Trumpet Voluntary—Music for Organ and Brass

(DECC) 421 337-2DM3 Bach: Organ Works, Vol.1
(DECC) 430 499-2DWO World of Bach
(DECC) 430 710-2DM Organ Spectacular
(DECC) 436 402-2DWO The World of Wedding
Music
(DECC) 436 546-2DH Poulenc—Concertos
(DECC) 443 485-2DF2 Bach—Great Organ Works
(DECC) 444 567-2DM Organ Masterpieces I
(DECC) 444 568-2DM Organ Masterpieces II
(DECC) 444 569-2DM Organ Masterpieces III
(DECC) 444 570-2DM Organ Masterpieces IV
(EMIN) CD-EMX2218 Bach—Organ Works, Vol.1
(EMIN) CD-EMX2226 Bach—Organ Works, Vol 2
(REGE) REGCD105 From Chamber to Chantry

HURST, David (cond)
see Black Dyke Mills Band

HURST, George (cond)
see BBC PO

HURTEAU, Jean-Pierre (bass)
Saint-Saëns: Samson et Dalila (Cpte)

HURTUBISE, Benoît (vc)
see CONCERT INDEX under:
(CHAN) CHAN8651 Vivaldi: Concertos

HURWITZ, Emanuel (vn)
see CONCERT INDEX under:
(LYRI) SRCD223 Holst—Orchestral Works

HÜSCH, Gerhard (bar)
Bach: St Matthew Passion, BWV244 (exc)
Mozart: Zauberflöte (Cpte)
see CONCERT INDEX under:
(EMI) CDC5 55225-2 Pfitzner plays and conducts
Pfitzner
(EMI) CMS7 64008-2(1) Wagner Singing on Record
(pt 1)
(NIMB) NI7848 Great Singers at the Berlin State
Opera
(NIMB) NI7867 Legendary Baritones
(PEAR) GEMMCDS9075 Hugo Wolf Society, Volume I
(PEAR) GEMMCDS9085 Hugo Wolf Society, Volume
II
(PEAR) GEMMCD9119 Schumann—Legendary Song
Cycles
(PEAR) GEMMCD9394 Helge Roswaenge—Operatic
Recital
(PEAR) GEMMCD9419 Herbert Ernst Groh—Opera
Recital
(PREI) 89017 Gerhard Hüsch (1901-1984) sings
Schubert
(PREI) 89071 Gerhard Hüsch (1901-1984) - II
(PREI) 89088 Walther Ludwig (1902-1981)
(PREI) 89202 Gerhard Hüsch Sings
(PREI) 90029 Hans Pfitzner Accompanies &
Conducts

HUSMANN, Mathias (cond)
see Magdeburg PO

HUSS, Manfred (cond)
see Vienna Haydn Sinf

HUSSA, Maria (sop)
see CONCERT INDEX under:
(SCHW) 314512 Vienna State Opera Live, Vol.1

HUSSONG, Stefan (accordion)
Bach: Goldberg Variations
Sweelinck: BACH Fantasia

HUTCHERSON, LeVern (sngr)
Hammerstein: Carmen Jones (Cpte)

HUTCHINS, Timothy (fl)
see CONCERT INDEX under:
(CHAN) CHAN8632 Honneger: Orchestral Works
(DECC) 440 332-2DH Ibert—Orchestral Works

HUTT, Robert (ten)
see CONCERT INDEX under:
(PEAR) GEMMCDS9365 R. Strauss: Der
Rosenkavalier (abridged), etc
(PREI) 89110 Heinrich Schlusnus (1888-1952) - II
(PREI) 89301 The Art of Frida Leider
(PREI) 89302 The Young Lotte Lehmann

HUTTENLOCHER, Philippe (bar)
Bach: Cantata 30, Cantata 66, Cantata 108, Cantata
182, Cantata 198, Easter Oratorio, BWV249 (Cpte)
Busoni: Arlecchino (Cpte)
Debussy: Pelléas et Mélisande (Cpte)
Fauré: Pénélope (Cpte)
Gounod: Faust (Cpte)
Haydn: Schöpfung (Cpte)
Lekeu: Andromède
Lully: Phaëton (Cpte)
Marais: Alcyone (Cpte)
Mondonville: Titon et l'Aurore (Cpte)
Rameau: Castor et Pollux (Cpte), Indes Galantes
(Cpte)
Ravel: Enfant et les sortilèges (Cpte)
Stradella: San Giovanni Battista (Cpte)
see CONCERT INDEX under:
(ERAT) 2292-45926-2 Charpentier—Sacred Choral
Works
(ERAT) 2292-45942-2 Puccini—Choral & Orchestral
Works
(ERAT) 4509-96961-2 Schubert—Stabat Mater;
Offertorium; Magnificat
(HANS) 98 802 Bach—Cantatas, Vol.40
(HANS) 98 804 Bach—Cantatas, Vol.42
(HANS) 98 805 Bach—Cantatas, Vol.44
(HANS) 98 807 Bach—Cantatas, Vol.45
(HANS) 98 810 Bach—Cantatas, Vol.48

(HANS) 98 811 Bach—Cantatas, Vol.49
(HANS) 98 812 Bach—Cantatas, Vol.50
(HANS) 98 813 Bach—Cantatas, Vol.51
(HANS) 98 815 Bach—Cantatas, Vol.53
(HANS) 98 817 Bach—Cantatas, Vol.55
(HANS) 98 818 Bach—Cantatas, Vol.56
(HANS) 98 819 Bach—Cantatas, Vol.57
(HANS) 98 820 Bach—Cantatas, Vol.58
(HANS) 98 821 Bach—Cantatas, Vol.59
(HANS) 98 822 Bach—Cantatas, Vol.60
(HANS) 98 825 Bach—Cantatas, Vol.63
(HANS) 98 826 Bach—Cantatas, Vol.64
(HANS) 98 828 Bach—Cantatas, Vol.66
(HANS) 98 835 Bach—Cantatas, Vol.69
(HANS) 98 857 Bach—Cantatas, Vol.6
(HANS) 98 858 Bach—Cantatas, Vol.7
(HANS) 98 859 Bach—Cantatas, Vol.8
(HANS) 98 861 Bach—Cantatas, Vol.10
(HANS) 98 863 Bach—Cantatas, Vol.12
(HANS) 98 866 Bach—Cantatas, Vol.15
(HANS) 98 867 Bach—Cantatas, Vol.16
(HANS) 98 871 Bach—Cantatas, Vol.20
(HANS) 98 872 Bach—Cantatas, Vol.21
(HANS) 98 873 Bach—Cantatas, Vol.22
(HANS) 98 874 Bach—Cantatas, Vol.23
(HANS) 98 879 Bach—Cantatas, Vol.28
(HANS) 98 882 Bach—Cantatas, Vol.31
(HANS) 98 885 Bach—Cantatas, Vol.34
(HANS) 98 886 Bach—Cantatas, Vol.35
(HANS) 98 887 Bach—Cantatas, Vol.36
(HANS) 98 890 Bach—Cantatas, Vol.37
(HANS) 98 891 Bach—Cantatas, Vol.38
(NOVA) 150 029-2 Bach—Cantatas
(TELD) 2292-42577-2 Bach—Cantatas, Volume 21
(TELD) 2292-42582-2 Bach—Cantatas, Volume 23
(TELD) 2292-42583-2 Bach—Cantatas, Volume 24
(TELD) 2292-42584-2 Bach—Cantatas, Volume 25
(TELD) 2292-42602-2 Bach—Cantatas, Volume 26
(TELD) 2292-42608-2 Bach—Cantatas, Volume 29
(TELD) 2292-42609-2 Bach—Cantatas, Volume 30
(TELD) 4509-91759-2 Bach—Cantatas, Vol.5
(TELD) 4509-91760-2 Bach—Cantatas, Vol.6
(TELD) 4509-91761-2 Bach—Cantatas, Vol.7

HUTTON, Adrian (bass)
Vaughan Williams: Hugh the Drover (Cpte)

HUVÉ, Cyril (pf)
Brahms: Horn Trio
Ligeti: Horn Trio

HUYBRECHTS, François (cond)
see LPO

HVIID, Jørgen (ten)
Nørgård: Gilgamesh (Cpte)

HVOROSTOVSKY, Dmitri (bar)
Mascagni: Cavalleria Rusticana (Cpte)
Tchaikovsky: Eugene Onegin (Cpte), Queen of
Spades (Cpte)
Verdi: Traviata (Cpte)
see CONCERT INDEX under:
(PHIL) 426 740-2PH Dmitri Hvorostovsky sings
Tchaikovsky & Verdi Arias
(PHIL) 432 119-2PH Russian Romances
(PHIL) 434 080-2PH Dmitri Hvorostovsky - Russian
Folk Songs
(PHIL) 434 912-2PH Bel Canto Arias
(PHIL) 438 872-2PH Songs and Dances of Death
(PHIL) 442 536-2PH My Restless Soul

HYDE, Philippa (sop)
Lampe: Pyramus and Thisbe (Cpte)

HYDE, Walter (ten)
see CONCERT INDEX under:
(PEAR) GEMMCDS9924(2) Covent Garden on
Record, Vol.2 (pt 2)

HYDE-WHITE, Wilfrid (sngr)
F. Loewe: My Fair Lady (film) (Cpte)

HYLDGAARD, Tove (sop)
Nielsen: Maskarade (Cpte)

HYNNINEN, Jorma (bar)
Bach: Magnificat, BWV243
Brahms: Ernste Gesänge, Op. 121 (Cpte)
Gothóni: Ochs und sein Hirte
Madetoja: Juha (Cpte)
Mahler: Symphony 8
R. Strauss: Elektra (Cpte)
Rachmaninov: Bells, Spring, Op.20
Sallinen: Kullervo (Cpte), Songs of Life and Death
Schumann: Dichterliebe, Op. 48 (Cpte)
Sibelius: Kullervo, Maiden in the Tower (Cpte)
see CONCERT INDEX under:
(BIS) BIS-CD270 Sibelius: Songs with orchestra
(DG) 437 507-2GH3 Nielsen—Complete Symphonies
(EMI) CMS7 64476-2 Mahler—Symphonies, Vol.2
(EMI) CZS7 67819-2 Brahms/Schumann—Requiems
(ONDI) ODE731-2 Jorma Hynninen sings Opera
Arias
(ONDI) ODE772-2 Kilpinen—Songs

HYÖKKI, Matti (cond)
see Helsinki Univ Chor

I FAGIOLINI
see CONCERT INDEX under:
(CHAN) CHAN0578 The Early Byrd

I MUSICI
Albinoni: Concerti, Op.7, Sinfonie, Op.2 (exc)
Corelli: Concerti grossi, Op.6
Rossini: Sonate a quattro

Vivaldi: Concerti Grossi, Op. 3, Concerti, Op. 8 (exc)
see CONCERT INDEX under:
(PHIL) 410 606-2PH Popular Baroque Music
(PHIL) 420 189-2PH Baroque Oboe Concertos
(PHIL) 426 075-2PCC Bach: Concertos
(PHIL) 426 086-2PBQ Vivaldi—Double Concertos
(PHIL) 426 925-2PM19 The Complete Vivaldi Edition
(PHIL) 438 876-2PH Vivaldi—Concertos for Strings
(PHIL) 442 131-2PH Baroque Trumpet Concertos
(PHIL) 442 145-2PH Vivaldi—Violin Concertos
(PHIL) 442 154-2PH Rolla—Viola Concertos
(PHIL) 442 396-2PM Baroque Favourites

IACIU, Fernand (vn)
Milhaud: Boeuf sur le toit

IACOPUCCI, Fernando (ten)
Donizetti: Lucrezia Borgia (Cpte)
Puccini: Rondine (Cpte)
Verdi: Ballo in maschera (Cpte), Ernani (Cpte),
Traviata (Cpte)

IAŞI MOLDOVA PHILHARMONIC ORCHESTRA
cond P. POPESCU
see CONCERT INDEX under:
(OLYM) OCD418 Aurelian Octav Popa plays Clarinet
Concertos

IBBOTT, Daphne (pf)
see CONCERT INDEX under:
(DECC) 433 220-2DWO The World of the Violin

IBERT, Jacques (cond)
see orch

ICEBREAKER
see CONCERT INDEX under:
(ARGO) 440 216-2ZH Fitkin—Chamber Works

ICELAND SYMPHONY ORCHESTRA
cond I. BUKETOFF
Rachmaninov: Monna Vanna (exc), Piano Concerto
4
cond P. SAKARI
Madetoja: Symphony 1, Symphony 2
see CONCERT INDEX under:
(CHAN) CHAN9028 Grieg and Svendsen—Orchestral
Works
(CHAN) CHAN9036 Madetoja—Orchestral Works
(CHAN) CHAN9158 Sibelius—Orchestral Works
(CHAN) CHAN9180 Icelandic Orchestral Works
(CHAN) CHAN9268 Klami—Orchestral Works
(CHAN) CHAN9313 Alfvén—Orchestral Works

ICELANDIC OPERA CHORUS
cond I. BUKETOFF
Rachmaninov: Monna Vanna (exc)

ICKSTADT, Alois (cond)
see CONCERT INDEX under:
(WERG) WER6275-2 Orff—Trionfi

ICONOMOU, Panito (boy alto)
Bach: Mass in B minor, BWV232 (Cpte)
see CONCERT INDEX under:
(TELD) 2292-42428-2 Bach—Cantatas, Volume 41
(TELD) 2292-42633-2 Bach—Cantatas, Volume 39
(TELD) 2292-42634-2 Bach—Cantatas, Volume 39
(TELD) 2292-42635-2 Bach—Cantatas, Volume 40
(TELD) 4509-91763-2 Bach—Cantatas, Vol.9

IDLE, Eric (bar)
Sullivan: Mikado (exc)

IGLOI, Thomas (vc)
see CONCERT INDEX under:
(CRD) CRD3316 Fauré—Works for Cello and Piano

IGNAL, Madeleine (sop)
Gounod: Mireille (Cpte)

IGNATOWICZ, Ewa (sop)
Gluck: Danza (Cpte)

IHLE, Andrea (sop)
Bach: Christmas Oratorio, BWV248 (Cpte), St.
Matthew Passion, BWV244 (Cpte)

IHLOFF, Jutta-Renate (sop)
Mozart: Finta Giardiniera (Cpte), Finta semplice
(Cpte)

IHUD CHOIR
cond Z. MEHTA
Mahler: Symphony 2

IIYAMA, Emiko (sop)
Bach: Mass in B Minor, BWV232 (Cpte)

ILE DE FRANCE NATIONAL ORCHESTRA
cond J. MERCIER
Schmitt: Salammbô Suites (exc)

ILE DE FRANCE VITTORIA REGIONAL CHOIR
cond M. PIQUEMAL
see CONCERT INDEX under:
(NAXO) 8 553176 Poulenc—Choral Works

ILES, John Henry (cond)
see Massed Brass Bands

ILITSCH, Daniza (sop)
see CONCERT INDEX under:
(SCHW) 314514 Vienna State Opera Live, Vol.6
(SCHW) 314582 Vienna State Opera Live, Vol.8

ILLE, Georghe (vn)
see CONCERT INDEX under:
(OLYM) OCD406 M. Haydn: Concertos

ILLES BALEARS UNIVERSITY CHORUS
cond E. COLOMER
Falla: Atlántida (Cpte)

ILOSFALVY, Robert (ten)
see CONCERT INDEX under:
(DECC) 421 810-2DM2   Dvořák & Kodály: Vocal Works

ILOSVAY, Maria von (mez)
Humperdinck: Hänsel und Gretel (Cpte)
R. Strauss: Elektra (Cpte)
Wagner: Götterdämmerung (Cpte), Rheingold (Cpte), Siegfried (Cpte), Walküre (Cpte)
see CONCERT INDEX under:
(FOYE) 15-CF2011   Wagner—Der Ring de Nibelungen

IM THURN, Paul (bar)
Vaughan Williams: Hugh the Drover (Cpte)

IMAI, Nobuko (va)
Beethoven: Notturno, Op.42
Brahms: Lieder, Op.91
Mozart: String Quintet, K174, String Quintet, K406, String Quintet, K515, String Quintet, K516, String Quintet, K593, String Quintet, K614
Pettersson: Viola Concerto
Schnittke: Viola Concerto
Schubert: Arpeggione Sonata, D821
see CONCERT INDEX under:
(BIS) BIS-CD358   The Russian Viola
(BIS) BIS-CD501   Martinů—Orchestral Works
(BIS) BIS-CD518   Denisov—Orchestral & Chamber Works
(BIS) BIS-CD571   Hindemith—Sonatas for Solo Viola
(BIS) BIS-CD651   Hindemith—Sonatas for Viola and Piano
(BIS) BIS-CD682   Nystroem—Orchestral Works
(CHAN) CHAN8550   Brahms & Schumann: Viola & Piano Works
(CHAN) CHAN8776   Bruch, Mozart & Schumann: Chamber Works
(CHAN) CHAN8873   Franck/Vieuxtemps—Works for Viola
(CHAN) CHAN9106   Walton—Orchestral Works
(HYPE) CDA66022   The Clarinet in Concert
(HYPE) CDA66420   Vaughan Williams: Vocal Works
(PHIL) 416 431-2PH   Works by Berlioz
(PHIL) 422 508-2PME4   The Complete Mozart Edition Vol 8
(PHIL) 432 176-2PH   Takemitsu—Orchestral Works
(PHIL) 442 012-2PH   20th Century Wind Music
(PHIL) 442 290-2PM2   Berlioz—Great Orchestral Works

IMAMURA, Yasunori (lte)
see CONCERT INDEX under:
(CLAV) CD50-8206   Venetian Music for Voice and Instruments
(ETCE) KTC1030   Dowland: Songs and Lute Works

IMAMURA, Yasunori (theorbo)
see CONCERT INDEX under:
(CAPR) 10 464   Visée—Pieces for Theorbo

IMBERT, M. (sngr)
see CONCERT INDEX under:
(IRCC) IRCC-CD802   Souvenirs of Rare French Opera

IMBODEM, Stephan (bass)
see CONCERT INDEX under:
(FNAC) 592096   Rameau—Grand Motets

IMI YORKSHIRE IMPERIAL BAND
cond G. BRAND
see CONCERT INDEX under:
(POLY) QPRL049D   Boosey & Hawkes National Brass Band Gala Concert 1991

IMMELMAN, Niel (pf)
see CONCERT INDEX under:
(ETCE) KTC1112   Bloch—Music For Viola and Piano
(MERI) CDE84269   Suk—Piano Works, Volume 1

IMMER, Friedemann (tpt)
see CONCERT INDEX under:
(ARCH) 419 633-2AH   Telemann: Wind Concertos
(L'OI) 411 949-2OH   Telemann: Double & Triple Concertos
(TELD) 9031-77603-2   Works by Leopold and Wolfgang Amadeus Mozart

IMMERSEEL, Jos van (cond)
see Anima Eterna

IMMERSEEL, Jos van (fp)
Haydn: Seven Last Words

IMMERSEEL, Jos van (fp/dir)
Mozart: Piano Concerto 5, Piano Concerto 6, Piano Concerto 9, Piano Concerto 15, Piano Concerto 16, Piano Concerto 17, Piano Concerto 18, Piano Concerto 19, Piano Concerto 20, Piano Concerto 21, Piano Concerto 22, Piano Concerto 23, Piano Concerto 24, Piano Concerto 25, Piano Concerto 26, Piano Concerto 27
see CONCERT INDEX under:
(CHNN) CCSBOX10   Mozart—Piano Concertos
(CHNN) CCS0690   Mozart—Keyboard Concertos Vol 2
(CHNN) CCS0990   Mozart—Keyboard Concertos Vol 3

IMMERSEEL, Jos van (pf)
Debussy: Images oubliées, Préludes (exc)
Rossini: Petite messe solennelle
Schubert: Winterreise (Cpte)
see CONCERT INDEX under:
(ACCE) ACC58018D   Mozart: Piano Works
(ACCE) ACC67911D   Clementi: Keyboard Sonatas
(ACCE) ACC78332D   Beethoven: Piano Works

IMMLER, Christian (alto)
Bach: Mass in B minor, BWV232 (Cpte)
see CONCERT INDEX under:
(TELD) 2292-42634-2   Bach—Cantatas, Volume 39
(TELD) 2292-42635-2   Bach—Cantatas, Volume 40
(TELD) 4509-91763-2   Bach—Cantatas, Vol.9

INBAL, Eliahu (cond)
see Berlin RSO

INDERMÜHLE, Thomas (ob)
see CONCERT INDEX under:
(NOVA) 150 043-2   Mozart—Works for Oboe and Orchestra

INDIANA UNIVERSITY CHAMBER SINGERS
cond H. RILLING
Bach: Cantata 21, Cantata 31

INDIANAPOLIS SYMPHONY CHOIR
cond R. LEPPARD
Vaughan Williams: Symphony 7

INDIANAPOLIS SYMPHONY ORCHESTRA
cond R. LEPPARD
Vaughan Williams: Symphony 7, Tallis Fantasia
cond J. NELSON
Loeffler: Irish Fantasies, Mort de Tintagiles
see CONCERT INDEX under:
(NEW) NW336-2   Zwilich—Orchestral Works

INDJIC, Eugen (pf)
Chopin: Mazurkas (exc)

INFANTINO, Luigi (ten)
see CONCERT INDEX under:
(EMI) CHS7 69741-2(7)   Record of Singing, Vol.4—Italian School

INGEBRETSEN, Kjell (cond)
see Stockholm Royal Orch

INGHELBRECHT, Désiré-Emile (cond)
see FNO

INGHILLERI, Giovanni (bar)
see CONCERT INDEX under:
(PEAR) GEMMCDS9926(1)   Covent Garden on Record—Vol.4 (pt 1)

INGRAM, Clinton (ten)
Massenet: Cid (Cpte)

INGRAM, Henry (ten)
see CONCERT INDEX under:
(HYPE) CDA66247   Vivaldi: Vocal and Orchestral Works

INGRAM, Michael (treb)
see CONCERT INDEX under:
(LOND) 436 393-2LM   Britten—The Little Sweep, etc

INGRAM, Paula (mez)
Gershwin: Porgy and Bess (Cpte)

IÑIGO, Paloma Perez (sop)
Falla: Vida breve (Cpte)

INNOCENTI, Angelo dell' (sngr)
Donizetti: Poliuto (Cpte)

INNSBRUCK CONSERVATORIUM CHOIR
cond ROBERT WAGNER
see CONCERT INDEX under:
(ROSE) 3221   Schumann—Miscellaneous Works

INOUE, Yuko (va)
Mozart: Sinfonia Concertante, K364
Parry: Piano Quartet

INOU-HELLER, Shihomi (sop)
see CONCERT INDEX under:
(HANS) 98 859   Bach—Cantatas, Vol.8

INSTRUMENTAL ENSEMBLE
Cocteau: Bel indifférent
Kagel: Tactil
Nyman: Man Who Mistook His Wife for a Hat (Cpte)
Villa-Lobos: Bachianas Brasileiras 5
see CONCERT INDEX under:
(ACAN) 43 128   Elisabeth Schwarzkopf—Vol. 2
(BLUE) ABCD016   Jussi Björling—Rare Records & Alternative Takes
(DECC) 417 645-2DH   Kiri - Portrait
(DECC) 443 930-2DM   Jussi Björling sings Opera Arias
(EMI) CDC7 54836-2   Granados/Falla/Mompou/Nin
(EMI) CDH7 63201-2   Elisabeth Schwarzkopf—Early Recordings
(EMI) CHS7 63802-2(2)   Tetrazzini—The London Records (pt 2)
(MMOI) CDMOIR422   Great Voices in Tchaikovsky
(NONE) 7559-79262-2   Dawn Upshaw-The girl with orange lips
(PEAR) GEMMCD9223   Luisa Tetrazzini—Vol.3
(ROMO) 81009-2   Edith Mason—Complete Recordings 1924-1926
(TEST) SBT1019   Tito Gobbi - Opera Arias & Songs
cond S. DARLINGTON
see CONCERT INDEX under:
(NIMB) NI5266   Tippett—Choral Works
cond E. ERICSON
see CONCERT INDEX under:
(EMI) CDC7 54098-2   Sacred Songs
cond R. JACOBS
see CONCERT INDEX under:
(HARM) HMC90 1310   Schütz—The Nativity
cond J. JÜRGENS
see CONCERT INDEX under:
(ARCH) 437 075-2AT   Collectio Argentea 5: Canti Amorosi

cond M. KAGEL
Kagel: Exotica
cond R. KUBELÍK
see CONCERT INDEX under:
(PANT) 81 1264-2   Kubelík conducts Kubelík
cond I. MARKEVITCH
see CONCERT INDEX under:
(PHIL) 438 973-2PM2   Igor Markevitch conducts Stravinsky
cond G. NASTRUCCI
see CONCERT INDEX under:
(PREI) 89037   Hina Spani (1896-1969)
cond J.L. OCEJO
see CONCERT INDEX under:
(PHIL) 420 955-2PH   Ramirez: Choral Works
cond H. OPPENHEIM
see CONCERT INDEX under:
(ARCH) 447 156-2AP   Purcell—Fantasias and Vocal Works
cond T. REISER
Keetman: Weihnachtslieder (exc)
Orff: Weihnachtsgeschichte
cond H. RILLING
Bach: Cantata 106
see CONCERT INDEX under:
(HANS) 98 826   Bach—Cantatas, Vol.64
(HANS) 98 835   Bach—Cantatas, Vol.69
(HANS) 98 877   Bach—Cantatas, Vol.26
(HANS) 98 882   Bach—Cantatas, Vol.31
cond D. SANCHEZ
see CONCERT INDEX under:
(PHIL) 420 955-2PH   Ramirez: Choral Works
cond V. SMETÁCEK
see CONCERT INDEX under:
(SUPR) 2SUP0025   Orff: Choral Works
cond I. STRAVINSKY
see CONCERT INDEX under:
(EMI) CDS7 54607-2   Stravinsky plays and conducts Stravinsky
cond F. WEISSMANN
see CONCERT INDEX under:
(PEAR) GEMMCD9119   Schumann—Legendary Song Cycles
cond U. ZIMMERMANN
U. Zimmermann: Weisse Rose (Cpte)

INTERMEZZO VOCAL ENSEMBLE
cond M. SWIERCZEWSKI
Auber: Gustav III (Cpte)

INTERNATIONAL CAST
cond M. KOCH
C-M. Schönberg: Misérables (Cpte)

INTERNATIONAL MUSICIANS SEMINAR SOLOISTS
cond S. VÉGH
Beethoven: Grosse Fuge, String Quartet 14

INTERNATIONAL QUARTET
see CONCERT INDEX under:
(BIDD) LAB029   French Chamber works

INTINO, Luciana d' (sop)
Pergolesi: Frate 'nnamorato (Cpte)
Rossini: Gazza ladra (Cpte)

INTRUMENTAL ENSEMBLE OF FRANCE
cond J-P. WALLEZ
Haydn: Cello Concerto in C, Cello Concerto in D

(L')INVITI
cond A. LITTON
see CONCERT INDEX under:
(LOND) 448 134-2LH   Walton—Belshazzar's Feast, etc

INVOCATION
see CONCERT INDEX under:
(HYPE) CDA66698   Enchanting Harmonist—A soirée with the Linleys of Bath
(HYPE) CDA66740   The Romantic Muse—English Music in the Time of Beethoven

IONITA, Alexandru (ten)
R.Strauss: Arabella (Cpte)
Verdi: Rigoletto (Cpte)

IONOAIA, Florin (cor ang)
Enescu: Wind Decet, Op. 14

IORIO, Luciano (va)
Dvořák: Terzetto, op 74

IPSWICH SCHOOL PREPARATORY DEPARTMENT CHOIR
cond B. BRITTEN
Britten: St Nicolas

IRELAND, Patrick (va)
Mozart: String Quintet, K516
see CONCERT INDEX under:
(ASV) CDDCA806   The Bohemians, Volume 5
(HYPE) CDA66279   Bridge—Chamber Works
(PHIL) 422 514-2PME5   The Complete Mozart Edition Vol 14
(PHIL) 446 154-2PM2   Mozart—The Complete Piano Trios

IRELAND, Robin (harm)
see CONCERT INDEX under:
(ASV) CDDCA806   The Bohemians, Volume 5

IRELAND NATIONAL CHAMBER CHOIR
cond C. PEARCE
Victory: Ultima Rerum (Cpte)

IRELAND NATIONAL SYMPHONY ORCHESTRA
cond A. DE ALMEIDA
see CONCERT INDEX under:

(NAXO) **8 550754** French Music for Piano and
Orchestra
  cond R. BONYNGE
Balfe: Bohemian Girl (Cpte)
  cond G. BRAIN
see CONCERT INDEX under:
(MARC) **8 223674** Truscott—Orchestral Works
  cond A. CONSTANTINE
Brahms: Double Concerto
Schumann: Cello Concerto
  cond S. GUNZENHAUSER
see CONCERT INDEX under:
(NAXO) **8 550745** Goldmark—Orchestral Works
  cond M. HALÁSZ
Mahler: Lied von der Erde
  cond A. LEAPER
Nielsen: Symphony 1, Symphony 2, Symphony 3,
Symphony 4, Symphony 5, Symphony 6
see CONCERT INDEX under:
(MARC) **8 223480** Bernard Stevens—Orchestral
Works
(MARC) **8 223481** Brian—Orchestral Works
  cond G. MARKSON
see CONCERT INDEX under:
(NAXO) **8 550519** Bloch/Bruch/Tchaikovsky—Cello
Works
  cond C. PEARCE
Victory: Ultima Rerum (Cpte)
  cond A. PENNY
C. A. Gibbs: Symphony 1, Symphony 3
  cond R. SACCANI
Verdi: Aida (Cpte)
  cond S. SANDERLING
Tchaikovsky: Suite 3, Suite 4

IRISH ARMY BAND
Verdi: Aida (Cpte)

IRVING, Ernest (cond)
see Philh

IRVING, Robert (cond)
see orch

IRWIN, May (sngr)
see CONCERT INDEX under:
(PEAR) **GEMMCDS9050/2(1)** Music from the New
York Stage, Vol. 1 (part 1)
(PEAR) **GEMMCDS9050/2(2)** Music from the New
York Stage, Vol. 1 (part 2)

IRWIN, Robert (bar)
see CONCERT INDEX under:
(EMI) **CHS7 69741-2(2)** Record of Singing,
Vol.4—Anglo-American School (pt 2)

ISAACS, Harry (pf)
see CONCERT INDEX under:
(PEAR) **GEMMCD9453** William Primrose—Viola
Recital

ISAKADZE, Ilana (vn)
Schoenberg: Violin Concerto

ISAKOVA, N. (sop)
Kabalevsky: Colas Breugnon (Cpte)

ISBIN, Sharon (gtr)
see CONCERT INDEX under:
(VIRG) **VC5 45024-2** Nightshade Rounds
(VIRG) **VC7 59024-2** Works for Guitar and Orchestra
(VIRG) **VC7 59503-2** Bach—Lute Suites
(VIRG) **VC7 59591-2** Guitar Works

ISEPP, Martin (hpd)
see CONCERT INDEX under:
(SAGA) **EC3361-2** Janet Baker—Lieder Recital

ISEPP, Martin (pf)
see CONCERT INDEX under:
(NIMB) **NI5231** Debussy: Mélodies

ISHERWOOD, Nicholas (bass)
Handel: Agrippina (Cpte)

ISHII, Kenzo (ten)
Zelenka: Requiem in C

ISHIKAWA, Shizuka (vn)
Bruch: Violin Concerto 1
Sibelius: Violin Concerto

ISLANDI, Stefan (ten)
see CONCERT INDEX under:
(EMI) **CHS7 69741-2(5)** Record of Singing,
Vol.4—Scandinavian School

ISOIR, André (organ)
Bach: Orgel-Büchlein, BWV599-644 (exc)
Couperin: Messe pour les couvents
Grigny: Premier livre d'orgue (exc)
Titelouze: Hymnes de l'Église (exc)
see CONCERT INDEX under:
(CALL) **CAL9703/17(1)** Bach—Complete Organ
Works (pt 1)
(CALL) **CAL9703/17(2)** Bach—Complete Organ
Works (pt 2)
(CALL) **CAL9703/17(4)** Bach—Complete Organ
Works (pt 4)
(CALL) **CAL9703/17(5)** Bach—Complete Organ
Works (pt 5)
(CALL) **CAL9710** Bach—Complete Works for Organ
Vol 8
(CALL) **CAL9907** Organ Works
(CALL) **CAL9916** 17th Century French Noëls and
Suites
(ERAT) **4509-91722-2**
Charpentier/Grigny/Lully—Sacred Choral and Organ
works

ISOKOSKI, Soile (sop)
Gothóni: Ochs und sein Hirte
Mendelssohn: Elias (Cpte), Paulus (Cpte), Symphony
2
Mozart: Così fan tutte (Cpte)
see CONCERT INDEX under:
(BIS) **BIS-CD508** Kokkonen—Complete Orchestral
Music, Vol.4
(DG) **437 507-2GH3** Nielsen—Complete Symphonies

ISON, Daniel (treb)
Mozart: Zauberflöte (Cpte)

ISON, G. (pf)
see CONCERT INDEX under:
(DUTT) **CDLX7013** The Unforgettable Isobel Baillie

ISRAEL CHAMBER ORCHESTRA
  cond D. ATLAS
see CONCERT INDEX under:
(STRA) **SCD8011** Vaughan Williams: Orchestral
Works
  cond Y. TALMI
see CONCERT INDEX under:
(CHAN) **CHAN8593** Works for String Orchestra

ISRAEL FLUTE ENSEMBLE
see CONCERT INDEX under:
(CARL) **PWK1139** Flute Serenade

ISRAEL NATIONAL CHOIR, RINAT
  cond Z. MEHTA
Mahler: Symphony 2

ISRAEL PHILHARMONIC ORCHESTRA
  cond D. ATLAS
see CONCERT INDEX under:
(STRA) **SCD8011** Vaughan Williams: Orchestral
Works
  cond L. BERNSTEIN
Bernstein: Chichester Psalms, On the Waterfront
Suite
Bloch: Schelomo
Dvořák: Cello Concerto, Slavonic Dances (exc),
Symphony 9
see CONCERT INDEX under:
(DG) **429 231-2GH** Modern Orchestral Works
(DG) **429 404-2GH** Hindemith: Orchestral Works
(DG) **437 952-2GX2** Great Cello Works
(DG) **439 411-2GCL** Mendelssohn—Orchestral
Works
  cond K. MASUR
Mendelssohn: Elias (Cpte)
  cond Z. MEHTA
Ben Haim: Violin Concerto
Bruch: Scottish Fantasy, Violin Concerto 2
Castelnuovo-Tedesco: Violin Concerto 2
Chopin: Piano Concerto 1, Piano Concerto 2
Glazunov: Violin Concerto
Khachaturian: Violin Concerto
Mahler: Symphony 1, Symphony 2
Mozart: Concertone, K190, Sinfonia Concertante,
K364
Saint-Saëns: Violin Concerto 3
Shostakovich: Violin Concerto 1
Sibelius: Violin Concerto
Smetana: Má vlast
Tchaikovsky: Souvenir d'un lieu cher, Op. 42 (exc)
Vivaldi: Concerti, Op. 8 (exc)
Wieniawski: Violin Concerto 2
see CONCERT INDEX under:
(DG) **427 676-2GH** French Works for Violin and
Orchestra
(EMI) **CDC7 54108-2** Tchaikovsky—Violin Works
(EMI) **CMS7 64617-2** The art of Itzhak Perlman
(EMI) **CZS4 83177-2(1)** Itzhak Perlman Edition (pt 1)
(EMI) **CZS4 83177-2(2)** Itzhak Perlman Edition (pt 2)
(SONY) **SK48184** Rampal plays Great Flute
Concertos
(SONY) **SK52483** Prokofiev—Piano Concertos
(SONY) **SK58966** Prokofiev—Piano Concertos, etc
(TELD) **4509-90201-2** Tchaikovsky—Orchestral
Works
(TELD) **9031-73266-2** Works for Violin and Orchestra
  cond H. RILLING
Various: Requiem of Reconciliation (Cpte)
  cond D. SELTZER
see CONCERT INDEX under:
(EMI) **CMS7 64617-2** The art of Itzhak Perlman
(EMI) **CZS4 83177-2(3)** Itzhak Perlman Edition (pt 3)
  cond W. WELLER
Smetana: Má Vlast

ISRAEL PIANO TRIO
Brahms: Piano Trio 1, Piano Trio 2, Piano Trio 3
Mendelssohn: Piano Trio 1, Piano Trio 2
Schubert: Piano Trio 1
Schumann: Piano Trio 1
see CONCERT INDEX under:
(CRD) **CRD3458** Schumann: Chamber Works

ISRAEL SYMPHONY ORCHESTRA
  cond G. STERN
see CONCERT INDEX under:
(MERI) **CDE84134** Canciones Españolas

ISSERLIS, Rachel (va)
see CONCERT INDEX under:
(MERI) **CDE84169** Mozart: Clarinet Works

ISSERLIS, Steven (vc)
Bloch: Schelomo
Brahms: Cello Sonata 1, Cello Sonata 2
Bridge: Oration
Britten: Cello Symphony

Elgar: Cello Concerto
see CONCERT INDEX under:
(HYPE) **CDA66235** Fauré—Works for Cello and Piano
(HYPE) **CDA66296** Martinů—Cello Sonatas
(RCA) **09026 61677-2** Concerto! with Dudley Moore
(RCA) **09026 61678-2** Concerto! Steven Isserlis plays
Saint-Saëns
(RCA) **09026 62553-2** Mendelssohn—Works for Cello
& Piano
(RCA) **09026 68049-2** Fauré—Complete Works for
Cello
(VIRG) **VC7 59015-2** Boccherini—Cello Concertos
and Sonatas
(VIRG) **VC7 59052-2** Britten/Tavener—Works for
Cello

ISTOMIN, Eugene (pf)
Beethoven: Piano Trios (exc), Triple Concerto
Schubert: Piano Trio 1
see CONCERT INDEX under:
(SONY) **SMK58984** Pablo Casals conducts Mozart at
Perpignan, 1951
(SONY) **SMK58991** Pablo Casals plays Beethoven at
Prades and Perpignan, 1951 & 1953

ITALIAN INTERNATIONAL OPERA ORCHESTRA
  cond M. DE BERNART
Donizetti: Maria di Rohan (Cpte)

ITALIAN INTERNATIONAL ORCHESTRA
  cond F. LUISI
Donizetti: Favorita (Cpte)
  cond C. PIANTINI
Bizet: Pêcheurs de Perles (Cpte)

ITALIAN YOUTH ORCHESTRA
  cond K. PENDERECKI
Penderecki: Violin Concerto (1976)
Shostakovich: Symphony 6

ITHACA COLLEGE CONCERT CHOIR
  cond L. STOKOWSKI
see CONCERT INDEX under:
(SONY) **MPK46726** Ives—Orchestral and Vocal
Works

ITUS, Alan (bass)
Beethoven: Joseph II Cantata, Leopold II Cantata

IVALDI, Jean-Marc (bar)
Massenet: Chérubin (Cpte)
Puccini: Fanciulla del West (Cpte)

IVANOV, Andrei (bar)
see CONCERT INDEX under:
(EMI) **CHS7 69741-2(6)** Record of Singing,
Vol.4—Russian & Slavonic Schools

IVES, Gene (bar)
V. Thomson: Mother of us all (Cpte)

IVES, George (vc)
see CONCERT INDEX under:
(ASV) **CDDCA689** Martucci—Complete Orchestral
Music, Vol. 2

IVES, Grayston (Bill) (cond)
see Magdalen (Oxford) Coll Ch

IVES, Grayston (Bill) (ten)
see CONCERT INDEX under:
(CLLE) **COLCD115** Three Musical Fables

IVESON, John (tbn)
see CONCERT INDEX under:
(DECC) **430 359-2DM** Baroque Church Music
(EMI) **CZS7 62736-2** Poulenc—Chamber Works

IVOGÜN, Maria (sop)
see CONCERT INDEX under:
(CLUB) **CL99-020** Maria Ivogün & Lotte
Schöne—Opera Recital
(NIMB) **NI7832** Maria Ivogün (1891-1987)
(PEAR) **GEMMCDS9925(2)** Covent Garden on
Record—Vol.3 (pt 2)
(PEAR) **GEMMCDS9926(1)** Covent Garden on
Record—Vol.4 (pt 1)

IZQUIERDO, Luis (cond)
see Carme

JABLONSKI, Peter (pf)
Grieg: Piano Concerto
Tchaikovsky: Piano Concerto 1
see CONCERT INDEX under:
(DECC) **430 542-2DH** 20th Century American Works
(DECC) **436 239-2DH** Works for piano and orchestra
(DECC) **440 281-2DH**
Rachmaninov/Scriabin/Prokofiev—Piano Sonatas

JABLOŃSKI, Roman (vc)
Cresswell: Cello Concerto
see CONCERT INDEX under:
(POLS) **PNCD042** Lutosławski: Vocal and Orchestral
Works
(POLS) **PNCD045** Lutosławski: Selected Works

JACCOTTET, Christiane (clav)
see CONCERT INDEX under:
(CAPR) **10 102** C.P.E. Bach: Viola da gamba Works

JACCOTTET, Christiane (fp)
see CONCERT INDEX under:
(CAPR) **10 102** C.P.E. Bach: Viola da gamba Works

JACCOTTET, Christiane (hpd)
Zelenka: Trio Sonatas
see CONCERT INDEX under:
(JECK) **JD529-2** Martin: Concertos

JACHETTI, Ornella (sop)
Verdi: Simon Boccanegra (Cpte)

(NAXO) **8 550511** Mozart/Beethoven—Quintets for Piano and Wind etc
(NAXO) **8 550555** Schubert—Piano Works for Four Hands
(NAXO) **8 550657** Haydn—Keyboard Sonatas, Vol.1
(NAXO) **8 550676** Beethoven—Piano Variations
(NAXO) **8 550749** Bartók—Violin Sonatas: Contrasts
(NAXO) **8 550771** Bartók—Piano Concertos
(NAXO) **8 550783** Schumann—Piano Works, Volume 1
(NAXO) **8 550784** Schumann—Piano Works, Volume 2
(NAXO) **8 550845** Haydn—Piano Sonatas, Volume 3
(NAXO) **8 550846** Schubert—Piano Works
(NAXO) **8 550886** Bartók—Chamber Works
(NAXO) **8 553127** Haydn—Keyboard Sonatas, Volume 4
(NAXO) **8 553128** Haydn—Keyboard Sonatas, Volume 5

JANE'S MINSTRELS
see CONCERT INDEX under:
(NMC) **NMCD011** Lutyens—Vocal and Chamber Works
(NMC) **NMCD025** Artists' Series - Jane Manning
cond R. MONTGOMERY
see CONCERT INDEX under:
(NMC) **NMCD011** Lutyens—Vocal and Chamber Works
(NMC) **NMCD025** Artists' Series - Jane Manning

JÄNICKE, Yvi (contr)
Dessau: Hagadah Shel Pessach
see CONCERT INDEX under:
(CPO) **CPO999 158-2** Pfitzner—Das dunkle Reich

JANIGRO, Antonio (cond)
see Saarbrücken Rad CO

JANIGRO, Antonio (vc)
R. Strauss: Don Quixote
see CONCERT INDEX under:
(ARCI) **ARC112/3** Dinu Lipatti—Les Inédits

JANIS, Byron (pf)
R. Strauss: Burleske
see CONCERT INDEX under:
(MERC) **432 002-2MM** Byron Janis
(MERC) **432 011-2MM** Works for Piano and Orchestra
(MERC) **432 759-2MM** Rachmaninov—Piano Concertos, etc
(RCA) **09026 61250-2** The Reiner Sound

JANIS, Elsie (sngr)
see CONCERT INDEX under:
(PEAR) **GEMMCDS9053/5** Music from the New York Stage, Vol. 2: 1908–1913

JANKEN, Kim (sngr)
Nørgård: Siddhartha (Cpte)

JANKO, Josef (ten)
Wagner: Meistersinger (Cpte)

JANKOBSKÝ, Zdeněk (ten)
Honegger: Jeanne d'Arc (Cpte)
Smetana: Kiss (Cpte)

JANKOVIC, Eleonora (mez)
Bellini: Adelson e Salvini (Cpte), Puritani (Cpte)

JANOPOULO, Tasso (pf)
see CONCERT INDEX under:
(APR) **APR7028** Jacques Thibaud—Complete Solo Recordings 1929-36
(EMI) **CDH7 63032-2** French Violin Sonatas
(EMI) **CHS7 69741-2(3)** Record of Singing, Vol.4—French School
(MSCM) **MM30321** Jacques Thibaud—Violin Recital

JÁNOSKA, Aladár (cl)
Schmidt: Clarinet and Piano Quintet 2
see CONCERT INDEX under:
(MARC) **8 223415** Schmidt—Chamber Works

JANOUŠEK, Jiří (ten)
Hába: Mother (Cpte)

JANOWITZ, Gundula (sop)
Bach: Christmas Oratorio, BWV248 (Cpte), Mass in B minor, BWV232 (Cpte), St Matthew Passion, BWV244 (Cpte)
Beethoven: Fidelio (Cpte), Mass in C, Missa Solemnis, Symphony 9
Haydn: Jahreszeiten (Cpte), Schöpfung (Cpte)
Hindemith: Marienleben (Cpte)
Mendelssohn: Paulus (Cpte)
Mozart: Così fan tutte (Cpte), Mass, K139, Nozze di Figaro (Cpte), Requiem
Orff: Carmina Burana
R. Strauss: Ariadne auf Naxos (Cpte), Capriccio (Cpte)
Wagner: Götterdämmerung (Cpte), Parsifal (Cpte), Walküre (Cpte)
Weber: Freischütz (Cpte)
see CONCERT INDEX under:
(CAMB) **CD-1032** From the Operas of Erich Wolfgang Korngold
(DG) **419 624-2GH** Beethoven: Vocal, Orchestral & Wind Music
(DG) **423 888-2GGA** R. Strauss—Orchestral & Vocal Works
(DG) **429 036-2GX5** Beethoven: Complete Symphonies
(DG) **435 211-2GX15** Wagner—Der Ring des Nibelungen
(DG) **437 943-2GX2** Schubert—Lieder

(DG) **439 423-2GCL** Wagner—Der Ring des Nibelungen (highlights)
(DG) **439 467-2GCL** R. Strauss—Vocal and Orchestral Works
(DG) **447 352-2GDB2** Gundula Janowitz - A Portrait
(VIRG) **VC7 59538-2** R. Strauss—Lieder & Metamorphosen

JANOWSKI, Marek (cond)
see Berlin RO

JANOWSKI, Piotr (vn)
see CONCERT INDEX under:
(OLYM) **OCD392** Bacewicz—Orchestral and Chamber Works

JANSEN, Hans Hermann (ten)
Bach: Motets (Cpte)

JANSEN, Jacques (bar)
Debussy: Pelléas et Mélisande (Cpte)
see CONCERT INDEX under:
(EMI) **CHS7 61038-2** Debussy—Pelléas et Mélisande, etc

JANSEN, Lieve (sop)
see CONCERT INDEX under:
(ERAT) **2292-45202-2** M-A. Charpentier: Sacred Works

JANSEN, Peter (db)
(LASE) **15 522** Schubert: Chamber Works

JANSEN, Rudolf (pf)
Schubert: Schöne Müllerin (Cpte), Winterreise (Cpte)
Wolf: Italienisches Liederbuch (Cpte), Mörike Lieder (exc), Spanisches Liederbuch (exc)
see CONCERT INDEX under:
(CBC) **MVCD1053** Schubert—Lieder
(DG) **437 536-2GH** Schubert—Lieder
(DG) **439 943-2GH** Schumann—Lieder
(ETCE) **KTC1051** Berg. Schoenberg. Webern. Songs
(ETCE) **KTC1090** Szymanowski—Songs
(ETCE) **KTC2008** Webern: Songs
(HYPE) **CDA66444** Brahms: Lieder
(PHIL) **422 522-2PME6** The Complete Mozart Edition Vol 22
(PHIL) **438 528-2PM4(2)** Schubert—Lieder (pt 2)
(PHIL) **438 932-2PH** Schubert—Lieder
(TROU) **TRO-CD01409** Milhaud—Early Works, Vol. 1
(VICT) **VCD19039** Grieg—Songs, Vol.2
(VICT) **VCD19040** Grieg—Complete Songs - Volume III
(VICT) **VCD19041** Grieg—Songs, Vol.4

JANSEN, Willem (organ)
see CONCERT INDEX under:
(HARM) **HMC90 1255** Schütz—Sacred Choral Works

JANSKÁ, Jaroslava (sop)
Fibich: Šárka (Cpte)
Janáček: Jenůfa (Cpte)
see CONCERT INDEX under:
(DECC) **430 375-2DH2** Janáček—Operatic and Orchestral Works
(SUPR) **11 1878-2** The Unknown Janáček

JANSONS, Mariss (cond)
see BPO

JANSSEN, Herbert (bar)
Beethoven: Fidelio (Cpte)
Wagner: Tristan und Isolde (Cpte)
see CONCERT INDEX under:
(DUTT) **CDLX7007** Beecham conducts Wagner
(EMI) **CMS7 64008-2(1)** Wagner Singing on Record (pt 1)
(EMI) **CMS7 64008-2(2)** Wagner Singing on Record (pt 2)
(LYRC) **LCD146** Frida Leider sings Wagner
(PEAR) **GEMMCDS9075** Hugo Wolf Society, Volume I
(PEAR) **GEMMCDS9085** Hugo Wolf Society, Volume II
(PEAR) **GEMMCDS9926(1)** Covent Garden on Record—Vol.4 (pt 1)
(PEAR) **GEMMCD9331** Frida Leider sings Wagner

JANSSEN, John (bar)
Lortzing: Undine (Cpte)

JANSSON, Karl Magnus (organ)
see CONCERT INDEX under:
(BIS) **BIS-CD510** Organ Music from the USA

JANZIK, Tobias (treb)
Various: Requiem of Reconciliation (Cpte)

JARESCH, August (ten)
R. Strauss: Ariadne auf Naxos (Cpte), Rosenkavalier (Cpte)

(SERGE) JAROFF COSSACK CHOIR
cond H. VON KARAJAN
Tchaikovsky: 1812

JARRE, Maurice (cond)
see Munich Studio Orch

JARRED, Mary (contr)
see CONCERT INDEX under:
(DUTT) **CDAX8004** Sir Henry Wood conducts Vaughan Williams
(LYRC) **SRO830** Smetana—The Bartered Bride, etc
(PEAR) **GEMMCD9342** Vaughan Williams: Vocal Works

JARRETT, Keith (hpd)
Bach: Flute Sonatas, BWV1030-5, French Suites, BWV812-17, Goldberg Variations, Viola da gamba Sonatas, BWV1027-9, Wohltemperierte Klavier (exc)
Handel: Recorder Sonatas

JARRETT, Keith (pf)
Bach: Wohltemperierte Klavier (exc)
Shostakovich: Preludes and Fugues, Op.87
see CONCERT INDEX under:
(ECM) **445 350-2** Jarrett—Bridge of Light
(MUSM) **7021-2** Hovhaness/Harrison—Orchestral Works

JARRY, Michel (sngr)
Bazin: Maître Pathelin (Cpte)

JÄRVI, Neeme (cond)
see Bamberg SO

JÄRVI, Paavo (cond)
see L. Borealis Ens

JÄRVIÖ, Päivi (mez)
see CONCERT INDEX under:
(TELD) **4509-90798-2** Monteverdi—Il Ballo delle ingrate

JARVIS, Joyce (sop)
G. Charpentier: Louise (Cpte)

JASPER, Bella (sop)
Henze: Junge Lord (Cpte)

JASZKOWSKI, Bogumit (bass)
Rossini: Signor Bruschino (Cpte)

JAUMILLOT, Irene (sngr)
Messager: Basoche (Cpte)

JAUSLIN, Regina (vc)
(MARC) **8 223237** Johann Strauss II Edition, Vol.37

JAZZ ENSEMBLE
see CONCERT INDEX under:
(SONY) **SK48235** A Carnegie Hall Christmas Concert

JBARA, Gregory (sngr)
Berlin: Annie Get Your Gun (Cpte)

JEAN, Christian (ten)
Offenbach: Brigands (Cpte)

JEAN, Kenneth (cond)
see Hong Kong PO

JEANES, E.W. (cond)
see Blues and Royals Band

JEANTET, Robert (bar)
Gounod: Faust (Cpte)
Poulenc: Mamelles de Tirésias (Cpte)

JEBELEANU, Simon (hn)
Enescu: Wind Decet, Op. 14

JEDENÁCTÍK, Vladimír (bass)
Hába: Mother (Cpte)
Martinů: Julietta (Cpte)

JEDLIČKA, Dalibor (bass)
Janáček: Cunning Little Vixen (Cpte), Jenůfa (Cpte), Makropulos Affair (Cpte)
Martinů: Julietta (Cpte), Miracles of Mary (Cpte)
Smetana: Two Widows (Cpte)
see CONCERT INDEX under:
(DECC) **421 852-2DH2** Janáček: Operatic & Chamber Works
(DECC) **430 375-2DH2** Janáček—Operatic and Orchestral Works

JEDLIČKA, Rudolf (bar)
Janáček: Káťa Kabanová (Cpte)

JEFFES, Peter (ten)
Rameau: Castor et Pollux (Cpte)
Rossini: Tancredi (Cpte)
see CONCERT INDEX under:
(ARAB) **Z6612** Rossini: Opera Arias
(GAMU) **GAMD506** An Anthology Of English Song

JEFFREY, Robin (lte)
see CONCERT INDEX under:
(COLL) **Coll1270-2** 20th Century Christmas Music

JEFFREY, Robin (theorbo)
see CONCERT INDEX under:
(COLL) **Coll1360-2** Sacred Music from Venice and Rome

JELINEK, Friedrich (ten)
R. Strauss: Ariadne auf Naxos (Cpte)
see CONCERT INDEX under:
(SCHW) **314652** Vienna State Opera Live, Vol.15

JELÍNKOVÁ, Štěpánka (sngr)
Martinů: Julietta (Cpte)

JELLINEK, Hubert (hp)
Mozart: Flute and Harp Concerto, K299

JELOSITS, Peter (ten)
Mozart: Nozze di Figaro (Cpte), Zauberflöte (Cpte)
see CONCERT INDEX under:
(TELD) **2292-42423-2** Bach—Cantatas, Volume 15
(TELD) **2292-42565-2** Bach—Cantatas, Volume 16
(TELD) **2292-42571-2** Bach—Cantatas, Volume 17
(TELD) **4509-91757-2** Bach—Cantatas, Vol.3

JELOSITS, Peter (treb)
see CONCERT INDEX under:
(TELD) **2292-42559-2** Bach—Cantatas, Volume 12
(TELD) **2292-42560-2** Bach—Cantatas, Volume 13

(TELD) 4509-91758-2 Bach—Cantatas, Vol.4

JENCKEL, Helga (mez)
Wagner: Walküre (Cpte)
see CONCERT INDEX under:
(DG) 435 211-2GX15 Wagner—Der Ring des
Nibelungen

JENEY, Gabriel (vn/pf)
see CONCERT INDEX under:
(LOND) 436 393-2LM Britten—The Little Sweep, etc

JENEY, Zoltán (fl/pf)
see CONCERT INDEX under:
(LOND) 436 393-2LM Britten—The Little Sweep, etc

JENIS, Dalibor (bar)
Franchetti: Cristoforo Colombo (Cpte)
see CONCERT INDEX under:
(DECC) 436 261-2DHO3 Puccini—Il Trittico

JENISOVÁ, Eva (sop)
Brian: Symphony 1
Orff: Carmina burana

JENKIN, Nicola (sop)
Purcell: Dido (Cpte), St Cecilia's Day Ode, Z339
see CONCERT INDEX under:
(HYPE) CDA66311/2 Monteverdi: St Barbara
Vespers

JENKINS, Gordon (cond)
see OST

JENKINS, Neil (ten)
Bach: St Matthew Passion, BWV244 (Cpte)
Bernstein: Candide (1988) (Cpte)
Britten: Peter Grimes (Cpte)
G. Charpentier: Louise (Cpte)
Maxwell Davies: Resurrection (Cpte)
Mozart: Nozze di Figaro (Cpte)
Ponchielli: Gioconda (Cpte)
Romberg: Student Prince (Cpte)
Rossini: Elisabetta (Cpte)
Schumann: Szenen aus Goethes Faust (Cpte)
Vaughan Williams: Hugh the Drover (Cpte)

JENKINS, Newell (cond)
see Clarion Concerts Orch

JENKINS, Philip (pf)
see CONCERT INDEX under:
(CHAN) CHAN9079 British Music for Clarinet and
Piano

JENKINS, Terry (ten)
Sondheim: Pacific Overtures (exc)

JENKINS, Timothy (ten)
Mozart: Idomeneo (Cpte)
Sondheim: Pacific Overtures (Cpte)

JENKINS FAMILY SINGERS
cond N. JENKINS
see CONCERT INDEX under:
(MAYH) KM93071405410 Christmas is Coming

JENNINGS, Anthony (bass cl)
Buller: Theatre of Memory

JENNINGS, Diane (mez)
Spohr: Faust (Cpte)
see CONCERT INDEX under:
(EURO) GD69043 Puccini: Il Trittico

JENNINGS, Gloria (mez)
G. Charpentier: Louise (Cpte)
see CONCERT INDEX under:
(EMI) CDM7 64022-2 Vaughan Williams—Orchestral
Works
(SONY) M3K79312 Puccini: Il Trittico

JENNINGS, Joseph (cond)
see Chanticleer Sinfonia

JENNINGS, Patricia (Prattis) (pf)
Saint-Saëns: Carnaval des animaux

JENSEN, Dag (bn)
see CONCERT INDEX under:
(LARG) Largo 5127 Igor Markevitch—Chamber
Works

JENSEN, Folmer (pf)
see CONCERT INDEX under:
(EMI) CHS7 69741-2(5) Record of Singing,
Vol.4—Scandinavian School

JENSEN, Gert Henning (ten)
see CONCERT INDEX under:
(CHAN) CHAN9223 R. Strauss—A cappella choral
works

JENSEN, John (pf)
Ives: Concord Sonata, Piano Sonata 1
see CONCERT INDEX under:
(BAY) BCD-1014 Classical Hollywood

JENSEN, Louis (vc)
see CONCERT INDEX under:
(CLRI) CC0002 Nielsen—Orchestral and Chamber
Works

JENSEN, Penelope (sop)
Bach: Magnificat, BWV243
Vivaldi: Gloria, RV589

JENSEN, Thomas (cond)
see Danish RSO

JENSON, Julian (ten)
Sullivan: Yeomen of the Guard (Cpte)

JENSSON, Björn (sngr)
Zemlinsky: Kleider machen Leute (Cpte)

JEPSON, Helen (sop)
see CONCERT INDEX under:
(RCA) 09026 61580-2(4) RCA/Met 100 Singers, 100
Years (pt 4)

JERANJE, Tatiana (contr)
see CONCERT INDEX under:
(CHAN) CHAN9397 Grechaninov—Choral &
Orchestral Works

JERGER, Alfred (bass-bar)
R. Strauss: Rosenkavalier (Cpte)
Wagner: Meistersinger (Cpte), Walküre (exc)
see CONCERT INDEX under:
(SCHW) 314502 Vienna State Opera—Live
Recordings (sampler)
(SCHW) 314542 Vienna State Opera Live, Vol.4
(SCHW) 314552 Vienna State Opera Live, Vol.5
(SCHW) 314562 Vienna State Opera Live, Vol.6
(SCHW) 314572 Vienna State Opera Live, Vol.7
(SCHW) 314602 Vienna State Opera Live, Vol.10
(SCHW) 314632 Vienna State Opera Live, Vol.13
(SCHW) 314652 Vienna State Opera Live, Vol.15
(SCHW) 314662 Vienna State Opera Live, Vol.16
(SCHW) 314672 Vienna State Opera Live, Vol.17

JERIĆ, Ana Pusar (sop)
Dvořák: Stabat mater

JERICO, Santiago S. (bar)
Vives: Bohemios (Cpte), Doña Francisquita (Cpte)

JERIE, Marek (vc)
see CONCERT INDEX under:
(SUPR) 11 1533-2 Suk—Chamber Works, Volume 3

JERITZA, Maria (sop)
see CONCERT INDEX under:
(MMOI) CDMOIR422 Great Voices in Tchaikovsky
(PEAR) GEMMCDS9925(2) Covent Garden on
Record—Vol.3 (pt 2)
(PREI) 89079 Maria Jeritza (1887-1982)
(RCA) 09026 61580-2(3) RCA/Met 100 Singers, 100
Years (pt 3)
(SCHW) 314502 Vienna State Opera—Live
Recordings (sampler)
(SCHW) 314622 Vienna State Opera Live, Vol.12
(SCHW) 314642 Vienna State Opera Live, Vol.14

JEROME, Marcus (ten)
Mercadante: Orazi e Curiazi (Cpte)

JERUSALEM, Siegfried (ten)
Beethoven: Symphony 9
Flotow: Martha (Cpte)
Haydn: Jahreszeiten (Cpte)
Korngold: Violanta (Cpte)
Mahler: Lied von der Erde
Mozart: Zauberflöte (exc)
Schoenberg: Gurrelieder
Schumann: Dichterliebe, Op. 48 (Cpte), Liederkreis,
Op. 39 (Cpte)
Wagner: Götterdämmerung (Cpte), Lohengrin (Cpte),
Parsifal (Cpte), Rheingold (Cpte), Siegfried (Cpte),
Tannhäuser (Cpte), Tristan und Isolde (Cpte),
Walküre (Cpte)
see CONCERT INDEX under:
(DG) 439 768-2GH Wagner—Gala - New Year's Eve
Concert 1993
(DG) 445 354-2GX14 Wagner—Der Ring des
Nibelungen

JERUSALEM STRING TRIO
Beethoven: Piano Quartet, op 16, Serenade, op 8
see CONCERT INDEX under:
(CARL) PWK1141 French Impressions

JERUSALEM SYMPHONY ORCHESTRA
cond D. SHALLON
see CONCERT INDEX under:
(EMI) CDC5 55107-2 Schnittke/Kopytman—Viola
Concertos

JESPERSEN, Holger Gilbert (fl)
see CONCERT INDEX under:
(CLRI) CC0002 Nielsen—Orchestral and Chamber
Works

JESSERER, Gertraud (narr)
Mozart: Zauberflöte (Cpte)

JESSON, Roy (organ)
see CONCERT INDEX under:
(EMI) CDC5 55529-2 Delius—Cello Concerto, etc

JETTE, Maria (sop)
Britten: Paul Bunyan (Cpte)
Copland: Tender Land (Cpte)

JETTER, Margret (contr)
see CONCERT INDEX under:
(HANS) 98 835 Bach—Cantatas, Vol.69

JEUNES DE L'EGLISE CHOIR
cond E. ANSERMET
Martin: Mystère de la Nativité

JEUNES SOLOISTS VOCAL ENSEMBLE
cond P. EÖTVÖS
Maderna: Hyperion (Cpte)

JEUNESSES MUSICALES CHORUS
cond H. VILLA-LOBOS
see CONCERT INDEX under:
(EMI) CDC5 55224-2 Villa-Lobos conducts Villa-
Lobos

(KENNETH) JEWELL CHORALE
cond A. DORATI
R. Strauss: Aegyptische Helena (Cpte)

JEŽIL, Miloš (ten)
Dvořák: Kate and the Devil (Cpte)

JÍLEK, František (cond)
see Brno Janáček Op Orch

JINDRÁK, Jindřich (bar)
Honegger: Cantate de Noël
Janáček: From the House of the Dead (Cpte), Jenufa
(Cpte)
Martinů: Julietta (Cpte), Miracles of Mary (Cpte)
Smetana: Bartered Bride (Cpte), Brandenburgers in
Bohemia (Cpte)

JIRGLOVÁ, Milada (sop)
Janáček: From the House of the Dead (Cpte)

JIROUŠ, Jiří (cond)
see Prague Nat Th Orch

JIROUŠEK, Zdeněk (vn)
Domažlický: Czech Songs

JISKROVÁ, Jana (sop)
see CONCERT INDEX under:
(SUPR) 11 1878-2 The Unknown Janáček

JO, Sumi (sop)
Mahler: Symphony 8
Mozart: Zauberflöte (Cpte)
Orff: Carmina Burana
R. Strauss: Frau ohne Schatten (Cpte)
Rossini: Comte Ory (Cpte), Messa di gloria, Tancredi
(Cpte), Turco in Italia (Cpte)
Verdi: Ballo in maschera (Cpte)
see CONCERT INDEX under:
(DECC) 440 679-2DH Carnaval!
(ERAT) 4509-97239-2 Virtuoso Arias

JOACHIM, Iréne (sop)
see CONCERT INDEX under:
(EMI) CHS7 61038-2 Debussy—Pelléas et Mélisande,
etc
(EMI) CHS7 69741-2(3) Record of Singing,
Vol.4—French School

JOACHIM, Joseph (vn)
see CONCERT INDEX under:
(SYMP) SYMCD1071 Great Violinists, Vol.1

JOACHIM TRIO
Saint-Saëns: Piano Trio 1, Piano Trio 2
see CONCERT INDEX under:
(NAXO) 8 550934 French Piano Trios, Volume 1

JOBIN, Raoul (ten)
Bizet: Carmen (Cpte)
Gounod: Roméo et Juliette (Cpte)
Offenbach: Contes d'Hoffmann (Cpte)
Tomasi: Don Juan de Mañara (Cpte)
see CONCERT INDEX under:
(EMI) CHS7 69741-2(3) Record of Singing,
Vol.4—French School

JOCHENS, Wilfried (ten)
Bach: St Matthew Passion, BWV244 (Cpte)
Handel: Acis and Galatea, K566 (Cpte), Ode for St.
Cecilia's Day (Cpte)
Keiser: Masagniello furioso (Cpte)
Landi: Mort d'Orfeo (Cpte)
Telemann: Donner-Ode, Herr ist König, Jauchze,
jubilier und singe, TWV15: 5, Magnificat, TWV9: 17,
St Matthew Passion (1746) (Cpte), Tag des Gerichts
(Cpte)
W. F. Bach: Es ist eine Stimme, F89, Lasset uns
ablegen, F80
see CONCERT INDEX under:
(CAPR) 10 208 C.P.E. Bach: Sacred Choral Works
(CAPR) 10 426 W. F. Bach—Cantatas, Vol.2

JOCHUM, Eugen (cond)
see Bamberg SO

JODRY, Annie (vn)
see CONCERT INDEX under:
(CALL) CAL9211 Clara Schumann: Piano Works

JODRY, Frederick (alto)
see CONCERT INDEX under:
(ERAT) 4509-98480-2 Lamentations - Holy Week in
Provence

JOERES, Dirk (cond)
see W. German Sinf

JOFFE, Dina (pf)
Chopin: Preludes

JÕGEVA, Mare (mez)
Tubin: Barbara von Tisenhusen (Cpte)

JOHANN STRAUSS ORCHESTRA, LONDON
cond J. ROTHSTEIN
see CONCERT INDEX under:
(CHAN) CHAN8301 The Special Sound of Chandos
(CHAN) CHAN8381 Vienna Première

JOHANN STRAUSS ORCHESTRA OF VIENNA
cond W. BOSKOVSKY
see CONCERT INDEX under:
(EMI) CDC7 47020-2 Lehár: Waltzes
(EMI) CDC7 47052-2 Famous Strauss Waltzes, Vol.1
(EMI) CZS7 62751-2 The Strausses of Vienna

JOHANNES ENSEMBLE
Gade: Sextet, Op. 44, String Quintet 1

JÓHANNESSON, Einar (cl)
see CONCERT INDEX under:
(CHAN) CHAN9079 British Music for Clarinet and
Piano

JOHANNING, Beth (sop)
Pfitzner: Herz (Cpte)
S. Wagner: Bärenhäuter (Cpte),
Schwarzschwanenreich (Cpte)

JOHANNSSON, Kristjan (ten)
Verdi: Aida (Cpte)

JOHANOS, Donald (cond)
see Bratislava RSO

JOHANSEN, Lars Holm (vc)
Kuhlau: Flute Quintets, Op. 51

JOHANSEN, Ronnie (bass)
Heise: Drot og Marsk (Cpte)

JOHANSSON, Eva (sop)
Heise: Drot og Marsk (Cpte)
Wagner: Rheingold (Cpte), Walküre (Cpte)
Zemlinsky: Es war einmal (Cpte)
see CONCERT INDEX under:
(CHAN) CHAN9075 Gade—Choral and Orchestral
Works

JOHANSSON, Jan (db)
see CONCERT INDEX under:
(BIS) BIS-CD503/4 Nielsen—Chamber Works

JOHANSSON, Kerstin (organ)
see CONCERT INDEX under:
(BIS) BIS-CD510 Organ Music from the USA

JOHANSSON, Ulf (pf)
see CONCERT INDEX under:
(EMI) CDC7 54098-2 Sacred Songs

JOHN, Keith (organ)
Alain: Danses (1937/9)
Mussorgsky: Pictures
see CONCERT INDEX under:
(PRIO) PRCD235 Great European Organs No. 6
(PRIO) PRCD264 Bach & Reubke: Organ Works
(PRIO) PRCD370 Great European Organs, No 26

JOHN, Kevin (ten)
see CONCERT INDEX under:
(OPRA) ORCH103 Italian Opera—1810-20

JOHNNY GREEN ORCHESTRA
cond J. GREEN
see CONCERT INDEX under:
(RCA) 09026 61245-2 Ezio Pinza - Recital

JOHNS, Stratford (sngr)
Bricusse: Scrooge (Cpte)

JOHNS, William (ten)
see CONCERT INDEX under:
(ERAT) 2292-45942-2 Puccini—Choral & Orchestral
Works

JOHNSEN, Ivar (pf)
see CONCERT INDEX under:
(SIMA) PSC1809(2) Grieg—Historical Piano
Recordings (pt 2)

JOHNSON, Camelia (mez)
Britten: Noye's Fludde (Cpte)
Gershwin: Porgy and Bess (Cpte)

JOHNSON, Cora (voc)
Joplin: Treemonisha (Cpte)

JOHNSON, David (bar)
Bernstein: Dybbuk (Cpte)
Mozart: Oca del Cairo (Cpte)

JOHNSON, David (perc)
see CONCERT INDEX under:
(CONI) CDCF167 Dickinson—Vocal Works

JOHNSON, Douglas (ten)
Gazzaniga: Don Giovanni (Cpte)
Haydn: Applausus (Cpte)
Mozart: Finta semplice (Cpte)

JOHNSON, Edward (ten)
see CONCERT INDEX under:
(RCA) 09026 61580-2(3) RCA/Met 100 Singers, 100
Years (pt 3)

JOHNSON, Emma (cl)
see CONCERT INDEX under:
(ASV) CDDCA559 Works for clarinet and orchestra
(ASV) CDDCA563 Works by Bottesini
(ASV) CDDCA585 Works for Clarinet and Orchestra
(ASV) CDDCA621 La Clarinette Française
(ASV) CDDCA659 The Romantic Clarinet
(ASV) CDDCA732 Clarinet Celebration
(ASV) CDDCA747 Emma Johnson plays Weber
(ASV) CDDCA763 Emma Johnson plays Clarinet
Concertos
(ASV) CDDCA787 Finzi/Stanford—Clarinet
Concertos, etc
(ASV) CDDCA891 Pastoral - British Clarinet Music
(ASV) CDDCA922 Arnold—Clarinet Concertos
(ASV) CDDCB1101 Michael Berkeley—Clarinet
Concerto, etc

JOHNSON, Evan (vn)
Biber: Mystery Sonatas (exc)

JOHNSON, Gilbert (tpt)
see CONCERT INDEX under:
(SONY) SM2K52671 Hindemith—Chamber Works

JOHNSON, Graham (pf)
Alwyn: Leave-taking
Schumann: Gedichte, Op.35 (Cpte), Liederkreis,
Op.39 (Cpte)
Wolf: Italienisches Liederbuch (Cpte)
see CONCERT INDEX under:

(CARL) MCD22 Schumann—Lieder
(CARL) PCD2016 Schubert—Lieder
(CHAN) CHAN8722 Felicity Lott sings English Songs
(COLL) Coll7039-2 Britten—The Folk Songs
(EMI) CDC7 49930-2 Sweet Power of Song
(EMI) CDC7 54411-2 On Wings of Song
(ETCE) KTC1099 Glenda Maurice at Wigmore Hall
(FORL) UCD16683 Russian Songs
(FORL) UCD16698 Schubert—Lieder
(FORL) UCD16728 The Romantic Lied
(FORL) UCD16730 Poulenc—Mélodies
(HARM) HMA190 1138 Melodies of the poems of
Victor Hugo
(HYPE) CDA66045 Hahn: Songs
(HYPE) CDA66112 Souvenirs de Venise
(HYPE) CDA66209 Britten: Songs
(HYPE) CDA66248 La Procession - Eighty Years of
French Song
(HYPE) CDA66471/2 A Shropshire Lad
(HYPE) CDA66480 Songs to Shakespeare
(HYPE) CDA66627 The Last Rose of Summer
(HYPE) CDA66659 R. Strauss—Lieder
(HYPE) CDA66666 Mendelssohn—Lieder
(HYPE) CDA66709 In Praise of Woman
(HYPE) CDA66801/2 Gounod—Songs
(HYPE) CDA67061/2 Britten—Purcell Realizations
(HYPE) CDJ33001 Schubert—Complete Lieder, Vol.
1
(HYPE) CDJ33002 Schubert—Complete Lieder, Vol.
2
(HYPE) CDJ33003 Schubert—Complete Lieder, Vol.
3
(HYPE) CDJ33004 Schubert—Complete Lieder, Vol.
4
(HYPE) CDJ33005 Schubert—Complete Lieder, Vol.
5
(HYPE) CDJ33006 Schubert—Complete Lieder, Vol 6
(HYPE) CDJ33007 Schubert—Complete Lieder, Vol
7
(HYPE) CDJ33008 Schubert—Complete Lieder, Vol 8
(HYPE) CDJ33009 Schubert: Complete Lieder, Vol.9
(HYPE) CDJ33010 Schubert—Complete Lieder, Vol
10
(HYPE) CDJ33011 Schubert—Complete Lieder,
Vol.11
(HYPE) CDJ33012 Schubert—Complete Lieder,
Vol.12
(HYPE) CDJ33013 Schubert—Complete Lieder,
Vol.13
(HYPE) CDJ33014 Schubert—Complete Lieder,
Vol.14
(HYPE) CDJ33015 Schubert—Complete Lieder,
Vol.15
(HYPE) CDJ33016 Schubert—Complete Lieder,
Vol.16
(HYPE) CDJ33017 Schubert—Complete Lieder,
Vol.17
(HYPE) CDJ33018 Schubert—Complete Lieder,
Vol.18
(HYPE) CDJ33019 Schubert—Complete Lieder,
Vol.19
(HYPE) CDJ33020 Schubert—Complete Lieder,
Vol.20
(HYPE) CDJ33021 Schubert—Complete Lieder,
Vol.21
(HYPE) CDJ33022 Schubert—Complete Lieder,
Vol.22
(HYPE) CDJ33023 Schubert—Complete Lieder,
Vol.23
(MERI) CDE84169 Mozart: Clarinet Works
(RCA) 09026 60901-2 Brahms—Lieder
(SONY) SK57972 Schumann—Lieder

JOHNSON, James (bar)
B. A. Zimmermann: Requiem (Cpte)

JOHNSON, Jeffrey (ten)
Stravinsky: Rake's Progress (Cpte)

JOHNSON, Laurie (cond)
see London Studio SO

JOHNSON, Marc (vc)
Messiaen: Quatuor

JOHNSON, Patricia (mez)
Berg: Lulu (Cpte)
Henze: Junge Lord (Cpte)
Mozart: Nozze di Figaro (Cpte)
Purcell: Dido (Cpte)

JOHNSON, Richard (bass)
V. Thomson: Lord Byron (Cpte)

JOHNSON, Robert (ten)
Beethoven: Fidelio (Cpte)

JOHNSON, Ron (marimba)
see CONCERT INDEX under:
(DELO) DE3168 Hovhaness—The Rubaiyat

JOHNSON, Samuel (narr)
Glass: Einstein on the Beach (Cpte)

JOHNSON, William (bar)
Gershwin: Porgy and Bess (Cpte)

JOHNSTON, David (ten)
Vaughan Williams: Hugh the Drover (Cpte)

JOHNSTON, James (ten)
see CONCERT INDEX under:
(EMI) CHS7 69741-2(2) Record of Singing,
Vol.4—Anglo-American School (pt 2)
(TEST) SBT1058 James Johnston - Opera Arias and
Songs

JOHNSTON, Oliver (treb)
see CONCERT INDEX under:
(PROU) PROUCD125 Rejoice in the Lamb

JOHNSTON, Raymond (organ)
see CONCERT INDEX under:
(ABBE) CDCA943 Tudor Church Music, Vol.1
(ABBE) CDCA957 Tudor Church Music, Volume 2

JOHNSTON, Robert (cantor)
see CONCERT INDEX under:
(ARGO) 433 215-2ZH Britten—Christmas Music

JOHNSTONE, James (hpd)
see CONCERT INDEX under:
(CHAN) CHAN0544 French Baroque Flute Music

JOHNSTONE, Mark (ten)
see CONCERT INDEX under:
(UNIT) 88033-2 Howells/F. Martin—Choral Works

JOITOIU, Dan (vc)
Enescu: String Octet

JOLL, Phillip (bass-bar)
Martinů: Greek Passion (Cpte)
Wagner: Tristan und Isolde (Cpte)

JOLLEY, David (hn)
Brahms: Horn Trio
Mozart: Horn Concerti (exc)
see CONCERT INDEX under:
(DG) 431 665-2GX3 Mozart—Wind Concertos

JOLSON, Al (sngr)
see CONCERT INDEX under:
(PEAR) GEMMCDS9053/5 Music from the New York
Stage, Vol. 2: 1908—1913
(PEAR) GEMMCDS9056/8 Music from the New York
Stage, Vol. 3: 1913-17
(PEAR) GEMMCDS9059/61 Music from the New York
Stage, Vol. 4: 1917-20

JOLY, Catherine (pf)
Hahn: Premières Valses, Rossignol éperdu

JOLY, Simon (cond)
see BBC Sngrs

JONAS, Dorothy (pf)
Mozart: Sinfonia Concertante, K297b
see CONCERT INDEX under:
(KOCH) 37002-2 American Works for 2 Pianos &
Orchestra

JONASON, Louisa (sop)
V. Thomson: Lord Byron (Cpte)

JONÁŠOVÁ, Jana (sop)
Janáček: Excursions of Mr Brouček (Cpte), Jenufa
(Cpte)
Martinů: Greek Passion (Cpte)
Smetana: Bartered Bride (Cpte), Two Widows
(Cpte)
see CONCERT INDEX under:
(SUPR) 11 0816-2 Zelenka—Choral Works

JONELLI, Hans (ten)
Martin: Vin herbé

JONES, Alan (ten)
Donizetti: Fille du régiment (Cpte)
Walton: Troilus and Cressida (Cpte)

JONES, Aled (treb)
Bernstein: Chichester Psalms
Fauré: Requiem (Cpte)
Handel: Athalia (Cpte)

JONES, Allan (cont)
see Graunke SO

JONES, Alonzo (ten)
Gershwin: Porgy and Bess (exc)

JONES, Bessie (sop)
see CONCERT INDEX under:
(CLAR) CDGSE78-50-54 Coates conducts Wagner,
Weber & Mendelssohn

JONES, Ceinwen (mez)
Sullivan: Gondoliers (Cpte)

JONES, Della (mez)
Alwyn: Miss Julie (Cpte)
Beethoven: Symphony 9
Bellini: Sonnambula (Cpte)
Bernstein: Candide (1988) (Cpte)
Bliss: Pastoral
Boito: Mefistofele (Cpte)
Britten: Gloriana (Cpte), Midsummer Night's Dream
(Cpte)
Donizetti: Assedio di Calais (Cpte), Maria Padilla
(Cpte), Ugo, Conte di Parigi (Cpte)
Elgar: Sea Pictures
Floyd: Susannah (Cpte)
Handel: Alcina (Cpte), Giulio Cesare (Cpte), Messiah
(Cpte), Semele (Cpte), Solomon (Cpte), Teseo
(Cpte)
Haydn: Ritorno di Tobia (Cpte)
Holst: Cloud Messenger
Howells: Missa Sabrinensis (Cpte)
Maxwell Davies: Black Pentecost, Resurrection
(Cpte), Stone Litany
Meyerbeer: Crociato in Egitto (Cpte), Dinorah (Cpte)
Mozart: Clemenza di Tito (Cpte), Don Giovanni
(Cpte), Nozze di Figaro (Cpte)
Parry: Lotos Eaters, Soul's Ransom
Purcell: Dido (Cpte)
Rossini: Barbiere di Siviglia (Cpte), Guillaume Tell
(Cpte), Stabat Mater

Verdi: Traviata (exc)
Walton: Bear (Cpte)
see CONCERT INDEX *under:*
(CHAN) **CHAN8865** Rossini: Opera Arias
(CHAN) **CHAN9147** French Songs
(CHAN) **CHAN9277** Spanish Songs
(OPRA) **ORCH103** Italian Opera—1810-20
(OPRA) **ORCH104** A Hundred Years of Italian Opera:
1820-1830
(OPRA) **ORC003** Donizetti—Gabriella di Vergy
(PHIL) **432 416-2PH3** Haydn—L'incontro
improvviso/Arias
(SONY) **M3K79312** Puccini: Il Trittico
(SONY) **S2K66836** Goldschmidt—Beatrice Cenci, etc

JONES, Gareth (bar)
Sullivan: Mikado (Cpte), Pirates of Penzance (Cpte)

JONES, Geraint (cond)
see G. Jones Orch

JONES, Gordon (bass)
Blow: Venus and Adonis (Cpte)
Pärt: Passio
Zelenka: Litanie lauretanae, ZWV152, Missa dei fili,
ZWV20

JONES, Granville (vn)
see CONCERT INDEX *under:*
(VANG) **08.2003.72** Purcell—Celebrated
Songs,Sacred Airs and Concert Pieces

JONES, Dame Gwyneth (sop)
Humperdinck: Hänsel und Gretel (Cpte)
Mahler: Symphony 8
Puccini: Fanciulla del West (Cpte)
R. Strauss: Aegyptische Helena (Cpte),
Rosenkavalier (Cpte), Salome (Cpte)
Schmidt: Notre Dame (Cpte)
Wagner: Fliegende Holländer (Cpte),
Götterdämmerung (Cpte), Parsifal (Cpte), Siegfried
(Cpte), Walküre (Cpte)
see CONCERT INDEX *under:*
(CHAN) **CHAN8930** Wagner—Arias
(DECC) **414 100-2DM15** Wagner: Der Ring des
Nibelungen
(DG) **423 481-2GX6** Beethoven: Complete
Symphonies
(DG) **437 368-2GX2** Beethoven—Orchestral Works
(EMI) **CDM5 65182-2** Nielsen/Sibelius—Orchestral
Works
(SCHW) **314081** R. Strauss—Lieder

JONES, Ieuan (hp)
see CONCERT INDEX *under:*
(CALA) **CACD1017** French Chamber Music for
Woodwinds, Volume 1
(CALA) **CACD1018** French Chamber Music for
Woodwinds, Volume 2
(CHAN) **CHAN9152** Alwyn—Chamber Works -
Volume 1
(CHAN) **CHAN9197** Alwyn—Chamber Music, Volume
2

JONES, Isola (mez)
Gershwin: Porgy and Bess (Cpte)

JONES, James Earl (narr)
see CONCERT INDEX *under:*
(DELO) **DE3140** Portraits of Freedom
(DELO) **DE3160** Hanson—The Mystic Trumpeter

JONES, Joela (pf)
Gershwin: Porgy and Bess (Cpte)

JONES, Joyce (organ)
see CONCERT INDEX *under:*
(MOTE) **CD11491** Organ works

JONES, Karen (fl)
(ASV) **CDDCA918** Jolivet—Vocal and Chamber
Works
(CONI) **CDCF172** Malcolm Arnold: Concertos
(CONI) **CDCF182** Panufnik: Orchestral Works
(CONI) **CDCF217** Panufnik—Orchestral Works
(CONI) **CDCF228** Arnold—Concertos
(CONI) **CDCF905** Karen Jones—The Flute Album

JONES, Leah-Marian (mez)
Verdi: Traviata (Cpte)

JONES, Leslie (cond)
see London Little Orch

JONES, Louise (vn)
see CONCERT INDEX *under:*
(MERI) **CDE84298/9** Delius—The Complete Works for
Violin and Piano

JONES, Martin (pf)
Cerha: Art Chansons (exc)
Debussy: Préludes
Weber: Piano Sonata 1, Piano Sonata 2
see CONCERT INDEX *under:*
(NIMB) **NI5160** Debussy: Piano Works, Vol.1
(NIMB) **NI5161** Debussy: Piano Works, Vol.2
(NIMB) **NI5163** Debussy—Piano Music, Vol. 4 - Ballet
Transcriptions
(NIMB) **NI5164** Debussy: Piano Works, Vol.5
(NIMB) **NI5220** Grainger: Original Works for Piano
(NIMB) **NI5232** Grainger—Piano Works, Vol.1
(NIMB) **NI5244** Grainger—Piano Works, Vol.3
(NIMB) **NI5255** Grainger—Dished up for Piano, Vol.
4
(NIMB) **NI5266** Tippett—Choral Works
(NIMB) **NI5366** 20th Century British Orchestral Works
(NIMB) **NI5369** Hoddinott—Piano Sonatas
(NIMB) **NI5370** Hoddinott—Piano Sonatas

(NIMB) **NI5405/6** Szymanowski—Piano Music,
Volume 1
(UNIC) **DKPCD9138** Britten/Cole Porter—Blues or
Cabaret Songs

JONES, Mason (hn)
see CONCERT INDEX *under:*
(SONY) **SM2K52671** Hindemith—Chamber Works

JONES, Maureen (pf)
Czerny: Variations, Op.73

JONES, Nerys (sop)
Weir: Blond Eckbert (Cpte)

JONES, Parry (ten)
Wagner: Tristan and Isolde (Cpte)
see CONCERT INDEX *under:*
(DUTT) **CDAX8004** Sir Henry Wood conducts
Vaughan Williams
(EMI) **CDS7 54607-2** Stravinsky plays and conducts
Stravinsky
(PEAR) **GEMMCD9342** Vaughan Williams: Vocal
Works

JONES, Peggy Ann (mez)
Sullivan: Mikado (Cpte)
(DECC) **430 095-2DWO** The World of Gilbert or
Sullivan, Vol.1
(DECC) **433 868-2DWO** The World of Gilbert or
Sullivan - Volume 2

JONES, Philip (tpt)
(CFP) **CDCF4547** Shostakovich: Piano Concertos

JONES, Philip Blake (ten)
Sullivan: Iolanthe (Cpte)

JONES, Robert (cond)
see St Bride's Ch, Fleet St

JONES, Shirley (sngr)
Rodgers: Carousel (film) (Cpte), Oklahoma (film)
(Cpte)

JONES, Susan Hemington (sop)
see CONCERT INDEX *under:*
(ERAT) **2292-45466-2** Carissimi—Jonas

JONES, Trevor (va)
see CONCERT INDEX *under:*
(L'OI) **411 949-2OH** Telemann: Double or Triple
Concertos

JONES, Warren (pf)
(ALBA) **TROY036-2** S.Paulus—Songs
(RCA) **09026 61518-2** Grieg—Songs, Vol.1
(RCA) **09026 61629-2** Grieg—Songs, Vol.2
(RCA) **09026 62547-2** Divas in Song—Marilyn Horne's
60th Birthday

JONES, Yolande (sop)
Janáček: Fate (Cpte)

(PHILIP) JONES BRASS ENSEMBLE
see CONCERT INDEX *under:*
(CFP) **CD-CFP4570** Choral Favourites
(CHAN) **CHAN8490** PJBE Finale
(DECC) **436 403-2DWO** The World of Royal Music
cond S. CLEOBURY
(ARGO) **417 468-2ZH** G. Gabrieli: Choral and
Instrumental Works
cond D. FLOOD
(DECC) **430 093-2DWO** The World of Vaughan
Williams
cond J. RUTTER
see CONCERT INDEX *under:*
(CLLE) **COLCD100** Rutter: Sacred Music

(GERAINT) JONES ORCHESTRA
cond GERAINT JONES
see CONCERT INDEX *under:*
(CFP) **CD-CFP4532** Sacred Arias

JOÓ, Árpád (cond)
see Budapest SO

JOPPICH, Father Godehard (cond)
see Essen Schola Cantorum

JORAN, Jiří (bass)
Janáček: Makropulos Affair (Cpte)
Smetana: Brandenburgers in Bohemia (Cpte)

JORAND, Marcel (perc)
Rossini: Péchés de vieillesse II (Cpte), Péchés de
vieillesse III (exc)

JORDA, Enrique (cond)
see LSO

JORDAN, Armin (cond)
see French Rad New PO

JORDAN, Irene (sop)
see CONCERT INDEX *under:*
(SONY) **SM3K46292** Stravinsky—Ballets, Vol.2

JORDAN, James E. Jr (organ)
see CONCERT INDEX *under:*
(GLOR) **GDCD016** Leo Sowerby—American Master
of Sacred Song

JORDANIA, Vakhtang (cond)
see KBS SO

JORDANS, Wyneke (pf)
Dvořák: Legends, Op. 59

Rossini: Petite messe solennelle
see CONCERT INDEX *under:*
(ETCE) **KTC1054** Ravel: Music for Piano, Four
Hands

JORDIS, Eelco von (bass)
Spohr: Faust (Cpte)

JORGENSON, Phil (ten)
Britten: Paul Bunyan (Cpte)

JORIS, Jan (bar)
Puccini: Bohème (Cpte), Gianni Schicchi (Cpte)

JÖRN, Karl (ten)
see CONCERT INDEX *under:*
(SUPR) **11 2136-2(2)** Emmy Destinn—Complete
Edition, Discs 3 or 4
(SUPR) **11 2136-2(3)** Emmy Destinn—Complete
Edition, Discs 5 to 8

JOSE, Richard (sngr)
see CONCERT INDEX *under:*
(PEAR) **GEMMCD9050/2(1)** Music from the New
York Stage, Vol. 1 (part 1)

JOSELSON, Tedd (pf)
(ASV) **CDDCA534** Barber—Orchestral Works
(OLYM) **OCD453** Prokofiev—Piano Works

JOSHUA, Rosemary (sop)
Humperdinck: Hänsel und Gretel (Cpte)

JOSÍFKO, Tomáš (db)
see CONCERT INDEX *under:*
(SUPR) **11 1533-2** Suk—Chamber Works, Volume 3

JOSSOUD, Hélène (mez)
Debussy: Rodrigue et Chimène (Cpte)
R. Strauss: Salomé (Cpte)

JOULAIN, Haervé (bn)
see CONCERT INDEX *under:*
(ACCO) **20202-2** Poulenc—Chamber Works

JOURNET, Marcel (bass)
Gounod: Faust (Cpte)
see CONCERT INDEX *under:*
(CLUB) **CL99-034** Marcel Journet (1867-1933)
(EMI) **CHS7 64864-2(1)** La Scala Edition - Vol.2,
1915-46 (pt 1)
(EMI) **CMS7 64008-2(2)** Wagner Singing on Record
(pt 2)
(IRCC) **IRCC-CD800** Souvenirs from Meyerbeer
Operas
(MMOI) **CDMOIR411** Sacred Songs and Arias
(MSCM) **MM30352** Caruso—Italian Opera Arias
(NIMB) **NI7859** Caruso, Farrar or Journet in French
Opera
(PEAR) **EVC1(2)** The Caruso Edition, Vol.1 (pt 2)
(PEAR) **EVC2** The Caruso Edition, Vol.2—1908-12
(PEAR) **EVC3(1)** The Caruso Edition, Vol.3 (pt 1)
(PEAR) **EVC4(1)** The Caruso Edition, Vol.4 (pt 1)
(PEAR) **EVC4(2)** The Caruso Edition, Vol.4 (pt 2)
(PEAR) **GEMMCDS9923(2)** Covent Garden on
Record, Vol.1 (pt 2)
(PEAR) **GEMMCDS9924(2)** Covent Garden on
Record, Vol.2 (pt 2)
(PEAR) **GEMMCD9161** Edmond Clément (1867-
1928)
(PEAR) **GEMMCD9224** Luisa Tetrazzini—Vol.4
(RCA) **GD60495(2)** The Complete Caruso Collection
(pt 2)
(RCA) **GD60495(3)** The Complete Caruso Collection
(pt 3)
(RCA) **GD60495(4)** The Complete Caruso Collection
(pt 4)
(RCA) **GD60495(6)** The Complete Caruso Collection
(pt 6)
(RCA) **09026 61580-2(1)** RCA/Met 110 Singers, 100
Years (pt 1)
(ROMO) **81003-2** Galli-Curci—Acoustic Recordings,
Vol.1
(ROMO) **82002-2** Edmond Clément (1867-1928)

JOUVE, André (cond)
see Lamoureux Orch

JOY, Geneviève (pf)
see CONCERT INDEX *under:*
(ERAT) **4509-91721-2** Dutilleux—Piano Works and
Chamber Music

JOYCE, Donald (organ)
see CONCERT INDEX *under:*
(CATA) **09026 61825-2** Glass—Organ Works

JOYCE, Eileen (pf)
Ireland: Piano Concerto
(BIDD) **LAB059/60** Henri Temianka—Recital
(DUTT) **CDAX8010** Hallé Orchestra Wartime
Recordings
(DUTT) **CDLXT2501** Bliss conducts Bliss
(PEAR) **GEMMCD9022** Eileen Joyce
(SIMA) **PSC1809(2)** Grieg—Historical Piano
Recordings (pt 2)

JOYFUL COMPANY OF SINGERS
cond P. BROADBENT
see CONCERT INDEX *under:*
(ASV) **CDDCA917** Jonathan Harvey—Choral Music
(UNIC) **DKPCD9091** Camilleri—Choral Music

JUAN, Santiago (vn)
Falla: Harpsichord Concerto

JUCKER, Rama (vc)
see CONCERT INDEX *under:*

(PHIL) 442 592-2PM2   C P E Bach—Concertos

JUDA, Iris (vn)
Boccherini: String Sextets, G454-9 (exc)

JUDD, James (cond)
see Argo SO

JUDD, Roger (organ)
see CONCERT INDEX under:
(HYPE) **CDA66273**   Parry—Cathedral Music
(HYPE) **CDA66345**   Tomkins—Cathedral Music
(HYPE) **CDA66569**   Vaughan Williams—Choral Works

JUDIYABA (vc)
J. Adams: Shaker Loops

JUFFINGER, Andreas (organ)
see CONCERT INDEX under:
(CAPR) **10 261**   Schmidt: Organ Works, Vol. 1
(CAPR) **10 262**   Schmidt: Organ Works, Vol. 2
(CAPR) **10 263**   Schmidt: Organ Works, Vol 3
(CAPR) **10 264**   Schmidt: Organ Works, Vol 4

JUILLET, Chantal (vn)
R. Strauss: Bourgeois Gentilhomme Suite
see CONCERT INDEX under:
(DECC) **436 837-2DH**
Stravinsky/Szymanowski—Violin Concertos
(DECC) **443 968-2DH**   Poulenc—Chamber Works

JUILLIARD CHORUS
cond L. BERNSTEIN
Beethoven: Fidelio (exc), Symphony 9

JUILLIARD ENSEMBLE
cond L. BERIO
see CONCERT INDEX under:
(RCA) **09026 62540-2**   Cathy Berberian sings Berio &
Weill

JUILLIARD OPERA CENTER
cond G. SCHWARZ
Schuman: Mighty Casey (Cpte), Question of Taste
(Cpte)

JUILLIARD ORCHESTRA
see CONCERT INDEX under:
(NEW) **80396-2**
Babbitt/Diamond/Persichetti—Orchestral Works
cond J. DEPREIST
see CONCERT INDEX under:
(NEW) **80396-2**
Babbitt/Diamond/Persichetti—Orchestral Works
cond C. KEENE
see CONCERT INDEX under:
(NEW) **80396-2**
Babbitt/Diamond/Persichetti—Orchestral Works
cond G. SCHWARZ
Schuman: Mighty Casey (Cpte), Question of Taste
(Cpte)

JUILLIARD QUARTET
Bach: Art of Fugue
Schoenberg: String Trio, Verklärte Nacht
see CONCERT INDEX under:
(SONY) **MPK46727**   Barber—Vocal Works
(SONY) **SK52554**   Debussy/Ravel/Dutilleux—String
Quartets
(SONY) **SK58966**   Prokofiev—Piano Concertos, etc
(SONY) **SM2K52664**   Schoenberg—Piano Works
(SONY) **SM3K45845**   Webern—Complete Works
(SONY) **S2K47229**   Carter—Chamber Works
(SONY) **S2K66285**   Brahms—String Quartets; Clarinet
Quintet
cond G. SCHWARZ
see CONCERT INDEX under:
(DELO) **DE3126**   The Incredible Walter Piston

JULER, Pauline (cl)
see CONCERT INDEX under:
(DUTT) **CDAX8014**   British Gramophone Premieres

JULES, Danny John (ten)
Hammerstein: Carmen Jones (Cpte)

JULIAN, Conchita (sop)
C.H. Graun: Montezuma (Cpte)

JULIEN-LAFERRIERE, Julien (vn)
see CONCERT INDEX under:
(PIER) **PV790013**   A. Scarlatti—Cantatas

JULLIA, Gilbert (sngr)
Poulenc: Mamelles de Tirésias (Cpte)

JULLIOT, Marguerite (mez)
Massenet: Manon (Cpte)

JUNG, Helene (mez)
see CONCERT INDEX under:
(PREI) **89029**   Meta Seinemeyer (1895-1929)

JUNG, Jürgen (narr)
Lehár: Giuditta (Cpte)

JUNG, Manfred (ten)
Wagner: Götterdämmerung (Cpte), Siegfried (Cpte)
Weill: Dreigroschenoper (Cpte)

JUNGE DEUTSCHE PHILHARMONIE
Shostakovich: Symphony 7
cond H. HOLLIGER
see CONCERT INDEX under:
(POLS) **PNCD043**   Lutosławski: Orchestral Works
(POLS) **PNCD044**   Lutosławski—Chamber and
Orchestral Works

JUNGHÄNEL, Konrad (cond)
see Gradus ad Parnassum

JUNGHÄNEL, Konrad (lte)
Reusner: Neue Lauten-Früchte
see CONCERT INDEX under:
(ACCE) **ACC67910D**   Weiss—Lute works
(DHM) **05472 77176-2**   Music at the Court of Louis XIV
(HARM) **HMA190 1183**   Works for Lute and Voice
(HARM) **HMC90 1255**   Schütz—Sacred Choral
Works

JUNGHÄNEL, Konrad (lte/dlr)
H. Albert: Arien, Musicalische Kürbs-Hütte
see CONCERT INDEX under:
(ACCE) **ACC8864D**   Symphonia Angelica
(DHM) **RD77088**   Schein—Vocal Works
(DHM) **RD77182**   Lechner: Sacred & Secular Songs
(DHM) **05472 77181-2**   Rosenmuller—Italian
Cantatas
(DHM) **05472 77282-2**   Monteverdi—Madrigali
Amorosi
(DHM) **05472 77304-2**   Lassus—Prophetiae
Sibyllarum
(DHM) **05472 77305-2**   Pachelbel/J. Christoph & J. M.
Bach—Motets

JUNGHÄNEL, Konrad (theorbo)
Biber: Mystery Sonatas
see CONCERT INDEX under:
(ACCE) **ACC57802D**   Purcell: Songs and Elegies
(CHNN) **CCS4792**   Henry Purcell & His Time

JUNGHANNS, Egbert (bar)
Mendelssohn: Vom Himmel hoch
Saint-Saëns: Oratorio de Noël, Op. 12
see CONCERT INDEX under:
(CAPR) **10 367**   Mendelssohn—Motets

JUNGHANNS, Rolf (kybd)
see CONCERT INDEX under:
(DHM) **RD77188**   C.P.E. Bach—Vocal & Chamber
Works

JUNGMANN, Dorothea (sop)
Lully: Bourgeois Gentilhomme

JUNGWIRTH, Helena (sop)
Saint-Saëns: Oratorio de Noël, Op. 12
Verdi: Rigoletto (Cpte), Traviata (Cpte)

JUNGWIRTH, Manfred (bass)
Beethoven: Fidelio (Cpte)
R. Strauss: Ariadne auf Naxos (Cpte), Rosenkavalier
(Cpte)
Wagner: Tannhäuser (Cpte)
Weill: Mahagonny-Gesänge (Cpte), Sieben
Todsünden (Cpte)

JUON, Julia (mez)
Schreker: Ferne Klang (Cpte)

JURANEK, Lidia (sop)
Gluck: Corona (Cpte)

JUREČKA, Antonín (ten)
Janáček: Šárka (Cpte)

JÜRGENS, Curd (narr)
Mozart: Entführung (Cpte)

JÜRGENS, Jürgen (cond)
see Concerto Amsterdam

JURINAC, Sena (sop)
Beethoven: Fidelio (Cpte)
Gluck: Orfeo ed Euridice (Cpte)
Mozart: Così fan tutte (exc), Don Giovanni (Cpte),
Nozze di Figaro (Cpte), Zauberflöte (Cpte)
R. Strauss: Ariadne auf Naxos (Cpte), Rosenkavalier
(Cpte)
Verdi: Don Carlo (Cpte)
see CONCERT INDEX under:
(EMI) **CDH5 65072-2**   Glyndebourne Recorded - 1934-
1994
(EMI) **CDH7 63199-2**   Sena Jurinac—Opera and Song
Recital
(EMI) **CHS7 69741-2(4)**   Record of Singing,
Vol.4—German School
(EMI) **CZS7 67123-2**   Wagner: Der Ring des
Nibelungen

JURITZ, David (vn)
see CONCERT INDEX under:
(COLL) **Coll1140-2**   Vaughan Williams—Orchestral
works

JURKOVIČ, Miloš (fl)
Bach: Flute Sonatas, BWV1030-5
see CONCERT INDEX under:
(OPUS) **9351 1894**   French Chamber Works

JUROWSKI, Michail (cond)
see Berlin RSO

JUSTAFRÉ, Jean-Jacques (hn)
see CONCERT INDEX under:
(ACCO) **20202-2**   Poulenc—Chamber Works

JUSTEN, Felix (gtr)
see CONCERT INDEX under:
(SCHW) **314063**   Songs with Guitar

JUSTUS, Kimberly (sngr)
Zemlinsky: Kleider machen Leute (Cpte)

JUTLAND OPERA CHOIR
cond O.A. HUGHES
Holmboe: Symphony 4

JUURI, Esko (cond)
see Helsinki Garrison Band

JUYOL, Suzanne (mez)
see CONCERT INDEX under:

(EMI) **CHS7 69741-2(3)**   Record of Singing,
Vol.4—French School

KAASCH, Donald (ten)
Rossini: Armida (Cpte)
Stravinsky: Oedipus Rex (Cpte)

KABAIVANSKA, Raina (sop)
Puccini: Tosca (Cpte)

KABALEVSKY, Dmitry (cond)
see Leningrad PO

KACHLÍKOVÁ, Kateřina (contr)
Martinů: Echec au Roi

KAGAN, Oleg (vn)
Bach: Solo Violin Partitas and Sonatas
see CONCERT INDEX under:
(EMI) **CMS7 64429-2**   Sviatoslav Richter—Un Portrait

KAGAN, Susan (pf)
Rudolph of Austria: Variations in F, Violin Sonata

KAGEL, Mauricio (cond)
see Inst Ens

KAHANE, Jeffrey (pf)
see CONCERT INDEX under:
(ARGO) **440 212-2ZH**   Schoenfield—Orchestral
Works
(RCA) **RD87962**   Schubert—Violin Sonatas, Vol 2
(SONY) **SK53126**   Made in America
(TELA) **CD80371**   R. Strauss—Der Rosenkavalier
Suite, etc
(VIRG) **CUV5 61119-2**   Bernstein—Orchestral Works

KAHN, Eric Itor (pf)
see CONCERT INDEX under:
(CLUB) **CL99-022**   Germaine Lubin (1891-1979)
(EPM) **150 052**   Germaine Lubin—Opera & Song
Recital

KAHN, Joseph (pf)
see CONCERT INDEX under:
(RCA) **GD60325**   Brahms: Symphonies & Other
Works

KAHN, Percy (pf)
see CONCERT INDEX under:
(APR) **APR7015**   The Auer Legacy, Vol.1
(BIDD) **LAB039**   Elman—Victor Records with Caruso,
Alda & Str Quartet
(CLAR) **CDGSE78-50-52**   Three Tenors
(EMI) **CDM7 69476-2**   Richard Tauber - A Portrait
(LYRC) **SRO830**   Smetana—The Bartered Bride, etc
(PEAR) **EVC3(1)**   The Caruso Edition, Vol.3 (pt 1)
(PEAR) **GEMMCD9370**   Richard Tauber sings Lieder
(PEAR) **GEMMCD9956**   Joseph Hislop (1884-1977)
(RCA) **GD60495(4)**   The Complete Caruso Collection
(pt 4)

KAIDANOV, K.E. (bass)
see CONCERT INDEX under:
(PEAR) **GEMMCDS9004/6(2)**   Singers of Imperial
Russia, Vol.3 (pt 2)

KAIN, Timothy (gtr)
see CONCERT INDEX under:
(TALL) **TP003**   Works for Flute and Guitar

KAINE, Carmel (vn)
see CONCERT INDEX under:
(DECC) **417 715-2DM**   Bach—Orchestral Works
(DECC) **440 037-2DM**   Bach—Concertos
(DECC) **443 847-2DF2**   Bach—Concertos

KAISER, Karl (fl)
(DHM) **RD77156**   Vivaldi: Concertos
(DHM) **RD77201**   Telemann—Wind Concertos

KAISERSLAUTERN RADIO ORCHESTRA
cond K. ARP
Spohr: Faust (Cpte)

KAJANUS, Robert (cond)
see Helsinki PO

KAJIYAMA, Akemi (sngr)
Braunfels: Verkündigung (Cpte)

KAKHIDZE, Dzansug (cond)
see Georgia St SO

KAKHIDZE, Jansug (cond)
see Tbilisi SO

KAKUSKA, Thomas (va)
see CONCERT INDEX under:
(AUVI) **MO782025**   Schoenberg—Chamber Music,
Vol. 3
(VANG) **08.7001.71**   Mozart: Concertante Works

KALAFUSZ, Hans (vn)
see CONCERT INDEX under:
(CAPR) **10 309**   Haydn: Concertos

KALAŠ, Karel (bass)
Dvořák: Stabat mater
Martinů: Julietta (Cpte)
Smetana: Bartered Bride (Cpte), Brandenburgers in
Bohemia (Cpte)

KALE, Christopher (ten)
see CONCERT INDEX under:
(ERAT) **4509-98480-2**   Lamentations - Holy Week in
Provence

KALE, Stuart (ten)
Berg: Lulu (Cpte)
Britten: Peter Grimes (Cpte)
Floyd: Susannah (Cpte)
Janáček: Fate (Cpte)

Weill: Sieben Todsünden (Cpte)

KALENBERG, Harry (narr)
Lehár: Friederike (Cpte)

KALENBERG, Josef (ten)
see CONCERT INDEX under:
(SCHW) 314512 Vienna State Opera Live, Vol.1
(SCHW) 314532 Vienna State Opera Live, Vol.3
(SCHW) 314542 Vienna State Opera Live, Vol.4
(SCHW) 314562 Vienna State Opera Live, Vol.6
(SCHW) 314592 Vienna State Opera Live, Vol.9
(SCHW) 314602 Vienna State Opera Live, Vol.10
(SCHW) 314622 Vienna State Opera Live, Vol.12
(SCHW) 314642 Vienna State Opera Live, Vol.14

KALENDOCSKY, Jiří (bass)
Smetana: Dalibor (Cpte)
see CONCERT INDEX under:
(STUD) SM1223.27 Rossini—Complete unpublished
Sacred Works

KALER, Ilya (vn)
Brahms: Double Concerto
Paganini: Caprices, Op. 1, Violin Concerto 1, Violin
Concerto 2
see CONCERT INDEX under:
(NAXO) 8 550758 Glazunov/Dvořák—Violin
Concertos
(NAXO) 8 550870 Schumann—Violin Works

KALES, Elisabeth (sop)
Mozart: Zauberflöte (Cpte)

KALICHSTEIN, Joseph (pf)
see CONCERT INDEX under:
(NIMB) NI5112 Mendelssohn: Orchestral Works

KALICHSTEIN/LAREDO/ROBINSON TRIO
Beethoven: Piano Trios (exc)

KALININ, Nikolai (cond)
see Ossipov Russian Folk Orch

KALISH, Gilbert (amplified pf)
see CONCERT INDEX under:
(ARAB) Z6141 Brahms: Lieder

KALISH, Gilbert (pf)
see CONCERT INDEX under:
(DG) 439 869-2GH Ives—Orchestral Works
(SONY) SK53126 Made in America

KALITZKE, Johannes (cond)
see Musikfabrik NRW

KALJUSTE, Tõnu (cond)
see Estonian Phil Chbr Ch

KALLAB, Camilla (mez)
Wagner: Götterdämmerung (Cpte), Meistersinger
(Cpte)

KÁLLAY, Gábor (ten)
Handel: St John Passion (Cpte)

KALLENBERG, Ben (v)
Schnittke: Symphony 1

KALLISCH, Cornelia (contr)
Cherubini: Mass in D minor
Franck: Béatitudes (Cpte)
Handel: Messias, K572 (Cpte)
Mendelssohn: Elias (Cpte)
Mozart: Nozze di Figaro (Cpte)
Stravinsky: Noces
Wagner: Meistersinger (Cpte)

KALM, Stephen (voc)
M. Monk: Atlas (Cpte)

KÁLMÁNDI, Mihály (bar)
Mascagni: Lodoletta (Cpte)

KALMAR, Magda (sop)
Respighi: Belfagor (Cpte)

KALMAR CHAMBER ORCHESTRA OF LONDON
see CONCERT INDEX under:
(VANG) 08.5060.71 Purcell—Odes

KALMUS, Kurt (ob)
Haydn: Sinfonia concertante

KALTENBACH, Jérome (cond)
see Nancy SO

KALTER, Sabine (contr)
Wagner: Tristan und Isolde (Cpte)
see CONCERT INDEX under:
(LYRC) SRO830 Smetana—The Bartered Bride, etc

KALUDOV, Kaludi (ten)
Borodin: Prince Igor (Cpte)
Janáček: Glagolitic Mass (Cpte)
Mussorgsky: Khovanshchina (Cpte)
Puccini: Manon Lescaut (Cpte)
see CONCERT INDEX under:
(DECC) 440 355-2DH Rachmaninov—Choral Works

KALUZA, Stefania (mez)
Zemlinsky: Kleider machen Leute (Cpte)

KALVELAGE, Elzbieta (sop)
Rossini: Petite messe solennelle (Cpte), Péchés de
vieillesse II (Cpte), Péchés de vieillesse III (exc)

KAM, Sharon (cl)
see CONCERT INDEX under:
(TELD) 4509-90873-2 Schubert—Lieder

KAMANN, Karl (bass)
see CONCERT INDEX under:
(SCHW) 314652 Vienna State Opera Live, Vol.15

KAMAS, Pavel (bass)
Dvořák: Kate and the Devil (Cpte)

KAMASA, Stefan (va)
see CONCERT INDEX under:
(POLS) PNCD020 Penderecki: Orchestral Works

KAMEDA, Mayumi (hpd)
see CONCERT INDEX under:
(BIS) BIS-CD507 Schnittke—Cello Works

KAMINKOVSKY, Rimma (vn)
see CONCERT INDEX under:
(CARL) PWK1141 French Impressions

KAMINKOVSKY, Yuval (va)
see CONCERT INDEX under:
(CARL) PWK1141 French Impressions

KAMINS, Benjamin (bn)
see CONCERT INDEX under:
(CARL) TCD77 Mozart—Wind Concertos

KAMIONSKY, Oskar (bar)
see CONCERT INDEX under:
(PEAR) GEMMCDS9001/3(1) Singers of Imperial
Russia, Vol.2 (pt 1)

KAMIRSKI, Włodzimierz (cond)
see Berlin RSO

KAMISHOV, V. (pf)
see CONCERT INDEX under:
(OLYM) OCD124 Glinka: Piano Works

KAMMEN, Shira (vielle)
see CONCERT INDEX under:
(NALB) NA068CD Machaut—Remede de Fortune

KAMMEN, Shira (vielle/rebec/hp)
see CONCERT INDEX under:
(ERAT) 4509-94830-2 The Unicorn—Medieval French
Songs

KAMMLER, Reinhard (cond)
see Augsburg Cath Boys' Ch

KAMNITZER, Peter (va)
Schoenberg: String Trio

KAMP, Harry van der (bass)
Bach: Cantata 56, Cantata 82, Mass in B minor,
BWV232 (Cpte), St John Passion, BWV245 (Cpte)
Biber: Requiem in F minor
Frescobaldi: Primo libro di Capricci (exc)
Handel: Queen Caroline Te Deum, Ways of Zion do
mourn
Haydn: Schöpfung (Cpte)
Keiser: Masagniello furioso (Cpte)
Landi: Mort d'Orfeo (Cpte)
Mozart: Requiem, Schauspieldirektor (Cpte), Thamos,
K345 (Cpte)
Schubert: Mass, D678, Mass, D950 (Cpte)
Telemann: Herr ist König, Jauchze, jubilier und singe,
TWV15: 5, Magnificat, TWV9: 17
Valls: Missa Scala Aretina
see CONCERT INDEX under:
(CAPR) 10 303 J. C. F. Bach: Secular Cantatas
(SONY) SK47184 Glenn Gould—The Composer
(SONY) SK53981 Purcell—Anthems and Hymns
(TELD) 2292-44193-2 Bach—Cantatas, Volume 44
(TELD) 2292-44194-2 Bach—Cantatas, Volume 45
(TELD) 4509-90798-2 Monteverdi—Il Ballo delle
ingrate
(TELD) 4509-91764-2 Bach—Cantatas, Vol.10
(TELD) 4509-95068-2 Purcell—Songs of Welcome &
Farewell

KAMPEN, Katherine van (sop)
Beethoven: Mass in C

KAMU, Okku (cond)
see Bamberg SO

KAN, Vassili (tpt)
see CONCERT INDEX under:
(RCA) RD87947 Shostakovich: Orchestral Works

KANDBLINDER, Roland (ten)
Puccini: Fanciulla del West (Cpte)

KANDINSKY QUARTET
Brahms: Piano Quartet 1, Piano Quartet 3

KANEL, Vladimir de (bass-bar)
Prokofiev: War and Peace (Cpte)
Verdi: Simon Boccanegra (Cpte)

KANG, Dong-Suk (vn)
Nielsen: Violin Concerto
see CONCERT INDEX under:
(BIS) BIS-CD472 Sibelius: Orchestral Works
(BIS) BIS-CD614/6 Nielsen—Symphonies and
Concertos
(BIS) BIS-CD616 Nielsen—Concertos
(BIS) BIS-CD647 Grieg—Violin Sonatas
(NAXO) 8 550276 French Violin Sonatas
(NAXO) 8 550276 Saint-Saëns—Orchestral Works
(TIMP) 1C1008 Honegger—Chamber Works, Vol.1
(TIMP) 1C1009 Honegger—Chamber Works, Vol.2
(TIMP) 1C1010 Honegger—Chamber Works, Vol.3
(TIMP) 1C1013 Alkan—Chamber Music
(TIMP) 4C1012 Honegger—Chamber Works

KANG, Juliette (vn)
see CONCERT INDEX under:
(DINT) DICD920241 Juliette Kang—Debut Recording

KANG, Philip (bar)
Wagner: Götterdämmerung (Cpte), Rheingold (Cpte),
Siegfried (Cpte)

KANGA, Skaila (hp)
see CONCERT INDEX under:
(CHAN) CHAN8391 Bax—Chamber Works
(CHAN) CHAN8621 French Chamber Music
(CHAN) CHAN8802 Works for Harmonica
(CHAN) CHAN9051 Mozart/Salieri—Concertos

KANGAS, Juha (cond)
see Ostrobothnian CO

KAŇKA, Michal (vc)
see CONCERT INDEX under:
(SUPR) 11 1461-2 Dvořák—Chamber Works -
Volume 11

KANN, Hans (pf)
Hummel: Piano Concerto, Op.110
Kalkbrenner: Piano Concerto 1

KANNEN, Günter von (bar)
Gazzaniga: Don Giovanni (Cpte)
Mozart: Nozze di Figaro (Cpte)
Stravinsky: Oedipus Rex (Cpte)
Wagner: Götterdämmerung (Cpte), Parsifal (Cpte),
Rheingold (Cpte), Siegfried (Cpte)
see CONCERT INDEX under:
(CHAN) CHAN9240 Stravinsky—Choral and
Orchestral Works

KANSAS CITY SYMPHONY ORCHESTRA
cond W. MCGLAUGHLIN
see CONCERT INDEX under:
(CATA) 09026 61979-2 Memento Bittersweet

KANTE, Peter Nikolaus (ten)
Schreker: Ferne Klang (Cpte)
Weill: Mahagonny-Gesänge (Cpte)

KANTILÉNA CHILDREN'S CHORUS
cond F. JÍLEK
see CONCERT INDEX under:
(SUPR) 11 0752-2 Martinů—Spaliček, etc
cond J. PINKAS
Dvořák: Jacobin (Cpte)

KANTOR, František (picc)
see CONCERT INDEX under:
(SUPR) 11 1878-2 The Unknown Janáček

KANTOROW, Jean-Jacques (cond)
see Auvergne Orch

KANTOROW, Jean-Jacques (vn)
Beethoven: Romances (exc), Triple Concerto, Violin
Concerto
Mozart: Cassation, K63, Serenade, K185, Serenade,
K203, Serenade, K204, Serenade, K250, Violin
Concerto, K216, Violin Concerto, K219, Violin
Concerto, K268, Violin Concerto, K271a
Paganini: Violin Concerto 1, Violin Concerto 2
Saint-Saëns: Violin Sonata 1, Violin Sonata 2
Stravinsky: Violin Concerto
Tchaikovsky: Violin Concerto
see CONCERT INDEX under:
(BIDD) LAW013 Dodgson—Orchestral & Vocal
Works
(DENO) CO-1666 Schubert & Schumann: Works for
Violin and Orchestra
(DENO) CO-72508 French Piano Trios
(DENO) CO-72718 French Violin Sonatas
(DENO) C37-7505 Mozart: The complete works for
violin and orchestra, Vol. 2
(DENO) C37-7506 Mozart—Works for Violin &
Orchestra, Vol.3
(OLYM) OCD459 Roussel—Chamber Music, Vol. 2

KANTOROW, Jean-Jacques (vn/dir)
Paganini: Violin Concerto 1, Violin Concerto 2

KANUNNIKOVA, Ludmila (contr)
Prokofiev: War and Peace (Cpte)

KAPELL, William (pf)
Prokofiev: Piano Concerto 3
see CONCERT INDEX under:
(RCA) GD60921 Legendary Performers - William
Kapell
(RCA) 09026 61778-2(08) The Heifetz Collection, Vol.
8
(VAI) VAIA1048 William Kapell broadcasts, Vol.2

KAPELLMANN, Franz-Josef (bass)
B. Goldschmidt: Gewaltige Hahnrei (Cpte)
Wagner: Rheingold (Cpte)

KAPER, Bronisław (pf)
see CONCERT INDEX under:
(FACE) FE8101 Bronislaw Kaper plays his Famous
Film Themes

KAPILOW, Robert (pf)
see CONCERT INDEX under:
(KOCH) 37087-2 Songs of Kurt Weill

KAPLAN, Gilbert (cond)
see LSO

KAPLAN, Mark (vn)
Brahms: Horn Trio, Piano Trio 1
Mendelssohn: Piano Trio 1, Piano Trio 2
Paganini: Violin Concerto 1
Wieniawski: Violin Concerto 2
see CONCERT INDEX under:
(ARAB) Z6580-2 Schubert: Complete Works for Piano
Trio
(ARAB) Z6608 Brahms—Trios, Vol.2
(ARAB) Z6649 Bartok—Violin Works

KAPP, Richard (cond)
see Hamburg SO

KAPPAUN, Lothar (bar)
Delius: Village Romeo and Juliet (Cpte)

KAPPEL, Gertrude (sop)
see CONCERT INDEX under:
(SCHW) 314592   Vienna State Opera Live, Vol.9

KAPTAIN, Laurence (cimbalom)
see CONCERT INDEX under:
(DECC) 443 444-2DH   Hungarian Connections

KARADJIAN, Michaela (mez)
Puccini: Suor Angelica (Cpte)

KARAJAN, Herbert von (cond)
see Bayreuth Fest Orch

KARAKASH, Mikhail (bar)
see CONCERT INDEX under:
(NIMB) NI7865   Great Singers at the Mariinsky
Theatre

KARAS, Joža (cond)
see Disman Rad Children's Orch

KÄRCHER, Klaus (ob)
see CONCERT INDEX under:
(SCHW) 311071   Trumpet Concertos

KARCZYKOWSKI, Ryszard (ten)
Rachmaninov: Bells
Shostakovich: Jewish Folk Poetry, Op 79

KARIS, Aleck (pf)
see CONCERT INDEX under:
(BRID) BCD9001   Aleck Karis piano recital
(BRID) BCD9051   Stravinsky—Piano Works
(KOCH) 37112-2   Wolpe—Chamber Works

KARIUS, Wolfgang (organ)
see CONCERT INDEX under:
(SCHW) 311052   Virtuoso Kettledrum Concertos

KARK, Friedrich (cond)
see orch

KARK, Friedrich (pf)
see CONCERT INDEX under:
(SUPR) 11 2136-2(1)   Emmy Destinn—Complete
Edition, Discs 1 & 2

KARLSSON, Ola (vc)
see CONCERT INDEX under:
(MSVE) MSCD521   Berwald—Chamber Works

KAROLIDIS, Paul (bass)
Mussorgsky: Boris Godunov (Cpte)

KAROUSATOS, Nickolas (bass)
Rachmaninov: Monna Vanna (exc)

KARPÍŠEK, Milan (spkr)
Martinů: Gilgamesh

KARPÍŠEK, Milan (ten)
Janáček: From the House of the Dead (Cpte),
Makropulos Affair (Cpte)

KARR, Gary (db)
see CONCERT INDEX under:
(CALA) CACD0101   Orchestral works

KARR, Isidore (cond)
see SRO

KARTTUNEN, Anssi (vc)
see CONCERT INDEX under:
(FINL) 4509-95584-2   Beethoven—Cello Sonatas,
Vol.1
(ONDI) ODE804-2   Saariaho—Orchestral and
Chamber Works

KARWAUTZ, Brigitte (sop)
J. Strauss II: Fledermaus (Cpte)

KASAROVA, Vesselina (mez)
Bellini: Beatrice di Tenda (Cpte)
see CONCERT INDEX under:
(RCA) 09026 68008-2   Kasarova sings Berlioz,Ravel
and Chausson

KASCHMANN, Giuseppe (bar)
see CONCERT INDEX under:
(EMI) CHS7 64860-2(1)   La Scala Edition - Vol.1,
1878-1914 (pt 1)
(MEMO) HR4408/9(1)   Singers in Genoa, Vol.1 (disc
1)
(SYMP) SYMCD1065   The Harold Wayne Collection,
Vol.1

KASEMANN, Franz (ten)
R. Strauss: Rosenkavalier (Cpte)

KASHKASHIAN, Kim (va)
Bach: Viola da gamba Sonatas, BWV1027-9
Kancheli: Vom Winde beweint
Mendelssohn: String Quintet 1, String Quintet 2
Schnittke: Viola Concerto
Tchaikovsky: Souvenir de Florence
see CONCERT INDEX under:
(DECC) 433 816-2DH2   Hindemith—Kammermusik
(ECM) 439 611-2   Works for Viola & Orchestra
(ECM) 445 941-2   Kancheli—Abii ne Viderem
(ECM) 827 744-2   Kashkashian/Levin—Elegies
(ECM) 833 309-2   Hindemith—Viola Sonatas

KASPSZYK, Jacek (cond)
see Polish Nat RSO

KASRASHUBILI, Makuara (sop)
Shostakovich: Symphony 14

KASSAI, István (pf)
Mosonyi: Hungarian Children's World, Hungarian
Development Studies
see CONCERT INDEX under:
(MARC) 8 223288   Bloch: Piano Works, Vol.1
(MARC) 8 223289   Bloch: Piano Works, Vol.2
(MARC) 8 223558   Mosonyi—Piano Music for Four
Hands

KASSOWITZ, Gottfried (cond)
see Austrian St Rad Orch

KASTORSKY, Vladimir (bass)
see CONCERT INDEX under:
(MMOI) CDMOIR422   Great Voices in Tchaikovsky
(NIMB) NI7865   Great Singers at the Mariinsky
Theatre
(PEAR) GEMMCDS9001/3(1)   Singers of Imperial
Russia, Vol.2 (pt 1)
(PEAR) GEMMCDS9007/9(1)   Singers of Imperial
Russia, Vol.4 (pt 1)

KASTU, Matti (ten)
R. Strauss: Aegyptische Helena (Cpte)

KATAGIRI, Hitomi (mez)
Gade: Comala
Wagner: Parsifal (Cpte), Walküre (Cpte)

KATAHN, Enid (pf)
see CONCERT INDEX under:
(KING) KCLCD2019   Nielsen: Piano Works

KATANOSAKA, Eiko (sop)
Monteverdi: Orfeo (Cpte)

KATCHEN, Julius (pf)
Brahms: Piano Trio 1, Piano Trio 2
Stravinsky: Firebird Suite (1911)
see CONCERT INDEX under:
(DECC) 421 092-2DM   Brahms: Violin Sonatas
(DECC) 430 053-2DM6   Brahms—Piano Works
(DECC) 433 070-2DWO   World of Chopin
(DECC) 440 612-2DF2   Brahms—Piano Concertos, etc
(DECC) 440 839-2DF2   Beethoven—Piano Concertos,
etc

KATIMS, Milton (va)
Brahms: String Sextet 1
Schubert: String Quintet
see CONCERT INDEX under:
(APR) APR7016   The Auer Legacy, Vol.2
(SONY) SK45816   Humoresque—Favourite Violin
Encores

KATIN, Peter (fp)
Schubert: Impromptus (exc)

KATIN, Peter (pf)
Chopin: Fantasie, Op.49, Polonaises, Scherzos,
Waltzes
Rachmaninov: Preludes
Schubert: Piano Sonata, D537, Piano Sonata, D960
Tchaikovsky: Piano Sonata, Op.37, Seasons
see CONCERT INDEX under:
(ATHN) ATHCD4   Clementi—Keyboard Sonatas
(LYRI) SRCD224   Walton—Orchestral Works
(LYRI) SRCD325   Mathias—Concertos
(OLYM) OCD186   Chopin—Piano Works
(OLYM) OCD193   Peter Katin plays Chopin, Vol.2
(OLYM) OCD197   Grieg: Piano Works
(OLYM) OCD199   Liszt: Piano Works
(OLYM) OCD218   Schumann: Piano Works
(OLYM) OCD230   Mozart: Piano Sonatas, Vol.1
(OLYM) OCD231   Mozart: Piano Sonatas, Vol.2
(OLYM) OCD232   Mozart: Piano Sonatas, Vol.3
(OLYM) OCD233   Mozart: Piano Sonatas, Vol.4
(OLYM) OCD234   Mozart: Piano Sonatas, Vol.5
(OLYM) OCD254   Chopin: Nocturnes & Impromptus
(OLYM) OCD263   Brahms—Piano Works
(SIMA) PSC1067   Children's Corner - Katin
(UNIC) UKCD2033   Grieg—Lyric Pieces Vol. I
(UNIC) UKCD2034   Grieg—Lyric Pieces Vol. II
(UNIC) UKCD2035   Grieg—Lyric Pieces Vol. III

KATLEWICZ, Jerzy (cond)
see Polish Nat RSO

KATONA, Julius (ten)
Wagner: Meistersinger (exc)

**KATOWICE POLISH RAD & TV GREAT SYMPHONY
ORCHESTRA**
cond J. MAKSYMIUK
see CONCERT INDEX under:
(KOCH) 312652   Szymanowski—Orchestral and
Choral Works
cond S. WISLOCKI
see CONCERT INDEX under:
(KOCH) 312652   Szymanowski—Orchestral and
Choral Works

KATOWICE RADIO SYMPHONY ORCHESTRA
cond G. FITELBERG
see CONCERT INDEX under:
(OLYM) OCD386   Moniuszko—Overtures
cond J. KRENZ
see CONCERT INDEX under:
(OLYM) OCD386   Moniuszko—Overtures
(POLS) PNCD040   Lutosławski: Vocal and Orchestral
Works
(POLS) PNCD041   Lutosławski: Choral & Orchestral
Works
(POLS) PNCD042   Lutosławski: Vocal and Orchestral
Works
cond W. LUTOSŁAWSKI
see CONCERT INDEX under:

(POLS) PNCD040   Lutosławski: Vocal and Orchestral
Works
(POLS) PNCD042   Lutosławski: Vocal and Orchestral
Works
(POLS) PNCD044   Lutosławski: Chamber and
Orchestral Works
cond K. PENDERECKI
K.A. Hartmann: Concerto funèbre
Penderecki: Violin Concerto (1976)
Szymanowski: Violin Concerto 1
cond A. WIT
Górecki: Olden Style Pieces, Symphony 3
Messiaen: Éclairs sur l'Au-Delà
see CONCERT INDEX under:
(NAXO) 8 550752   Saint-Saëns—Orchestral Works
(POLS) PNCD044   Lutosławski: Chamber and
Orchestral Works

KATSARIS, Cyprien (pf)
Brahms: Piano Concerto 2
Chopin: Cello Sonata, Waltzes
Franck: Violin Sonata
Liszt: Beethoven Symphonies, S464 (exc)
Stravinsky: Noces
see CONCERT INDEX under:
(SONY) SK48483   Chopin—Piano Sonatas
(SONY) SK52551   Mozartiana
(SONY) SK53355   Chopin—Piano Works
(SONY) S2K53967   Chopin—Polonaises
(TELD) 4509-92147-2   Grieg—Piano Works
(TELD) 4509-95499-2   Chopin—Piano Works
(TELD) 9031-75860-2   Mendelssohn—Piano
Concertos
(TELD) 9031-75863-2   Schumann—Piano Works

KATSAROVA, Wesselina (mez)
Tchaikovsky: Queen of Spades (Cpte)

KATT, William (sngr)
Gershwin: Pardon My English (Cpte)

KATULSKAYA, Elena (sop)
see CONCERT INDEX under:
(NIMB) NI7865   Great Singers at the Mariinsky
Theatre

KATZ, Eberhard (ten)
Hindemith: Cardillac (Cpte)

KATZ, Florence (sop)
Rameau: Hippolyte et Aricie (Cpte)

KATZ, Martin (pf)
see CONCERT INDEX under:
(RCA) RD60811   Marilyn Horne sings Rossini
(RCA) 09026 61276-2   Brahms—Viola Sonatas; Songs
(RCA) 09026 61681-2
Dvořák/Schumann/Mendelssohn—Lieder
(RCA) 09026 62547-2   Divas in Song—Marilyn Horne's
60th Birthday
(SONY) SK45863   Italian Opera Composers' Songs

KATZ, Shelley (pf)
see CONCERT INDEX under:
(CAPR) 10 359   Jochen Kowalski—Lieder Recital

KAUFMAN, Harry (pf)
see CONCERT INDEX under:
(APR) APR7016   The Auer Legacy, Vol.2
(SONY) MPK52569   Joseph Szigeti Recital

KAUFMAN, Jolanta (sop)
Catalani: Wally (Cpte)
Gazzaniga: Don Giovanni (Cpte)
Gluck: Rencontre imprévue (Cpte)
R. Strauss: Ariadne auf Naxos (Cpte), Frau ohne
Schatten (Cpte)
Wagner: Götterdämmerung (Cpte), Rheingold
(Cpte)

KAUFMAN, Louis (vn)
see CONCERT INDEX under:
(CAMB) CD-1063   Louis Kaufman - Violin Works
(MUSI) MACD-620   20th Century French Violin
Works
(MUSI) MACD-667   Louis Kaufman plays 20th Century
Concertos

KAUFMAN, Richard (cond)
see Nuremberg SO

KAUFMANN, Erich (bass)
see CONCERT INDEX under:
(SCHW) 314572   Vienna State Opera Live, Vol.7

KAUFMANN, Julie (sop)
Mendelssohn: Symphony 2
Schumann: Paradies und die Peri (Cpte)
Verdi: Falstaff (Cpte)
see CONCERT INDEX under:
(ORFE) C305931A   Debussy/Schoenberg/R.
Strauss—Lieder

KAUFMANN, Klaus (pf)
see CONCERT INDEX under:
(SCHW) 310035   Gottschalk—Piano Works

KAUNZINGER, Günter (organ)
Widor: Symphony 1, Symphony 2, Symphony 5,
Symphony 6, Symphony 9, Symphony 10
see CONCERT INDEX under:
(NOVA) 150 069-2   Liszt—Organ Works

KAVACOS, Leonidas (vn)
Paganini: Caprices, Op. 1
Sibelius: Violin Concerto
see CONCERT INDEX under:
(FINL) 4509-95859-2   Sibelius—Orchestral Works

KENLEY, Mack (tbn)
J. Adams: Light over Water

KENNARD, Julie (sop)
Howells: Hyrnnus Paradisi

KENNARD, Robin (bn)
see CONCERT INDEX under:
(CALA) **CACD1017** French Chamber Music for
Woodwinds, Volume 1

KENNEDY, Daniel (perc)
see CONCERT INDEX under:
(KOCH) **37112-2** Wolpe—Chamber Works

KENNEDY, Louisa (sop)
Henze: English Cat (Cpte)

KENNEDY, Mark (treb)
see CONCERT INDEX under:
(HYPE) **CDA66623** Purcell—Complete Anthems &
Services, Vol.3
(HYPE) **CDA66644** Purcell—Complete Anthems &
Services, Vol.4
(HYPE) **CDA66656** Purcell—Complete Anthems &
Services, Vol.5
(HYPE) **CDA66663** Purcell—Complete Anthems &
Services, Vol.6
(HYPE) **CDA66664** Poulenc—Choral Works
(HYPE) **CDA66677** Purcell—Anthems & Services,
Vol.7
(HYPE) **CDA66686** Purcell—Complete Anthems &
Services, Vol.8
(HYPE) **CDA66693** Purcell—Complete Anthems and
Services, Volume 9
(HYPE) **CDA66707** Purcell—Complete Anthems &
Services, Vol. 10
(HYPE) **CDA66716** Purcell—Complete Anthems and
Services, Volume 11

KENNEDY, Martin (tbn)
see CONCERT INDEX under:
(CNTO) **CRCD2368** Sullivan—That Glorious Song of
Old

KENNEDY, Nigel (va)
Walton: Viola Concerto

KENNEDY, Nigel (vn)
Bach: Solo Violin Partitas and Sonatas (exc)
Bartók: Solo Violin Sonata
Beethoven: Violin Concerto
Brahms: Violin Concerto
Ellington: Mainly Black
Massenet: Thaïs (exc)
Sibelius: Violin Concerto
Tchaikovsky: Violin Concerto
Walton: Violin Concerto
see CONCERT INDEX under:
(CHAN) **CHAN8380** Elgar—Music for Violin and
Piano
(DECC) **433 220-2DWO** The World of the Violin
(EMI) **CDC7 49663-2** Works for Violin & Orchestra

KENNEDY, Nigel (vn/dir)
Vivaldi: Concerti, Op.8 (exc)

KENNEDY, Roderick (bass)
Boughton: Immortal Hour (Cpte)
Donizetti: Maria Padilla (Cpte)
Handel: Messiah (Cpte)
Offenbach: Robinson Crusoé (Cpte)
Verdi: Traviata (Cpte)
Weill: Sieben Todsünden (Cpte)

KENNEDY SCOTT, Charles (cond)
see Oriana Madrigal Soc

KENNELLY, Don (tbn)
J. Adams: Light over Water

KENNY, Jonathan Peter (alto)
Purcell: Dido (Cpte)
see CONCERT INDEX under:
(CHNN) **CCS7895** Buxtehude—Cantatas
(HYPE) **CDA66412** Purcell—Complete Odes &
Welcome Songs, Vol.3

KENNY, Jonathan Peter (alto)
Handel: Israel in Egypt (Cpte)

KENNY, Liz (lte)
see CONCERT INDEX under:
(CNTO) **CRCD2366** Music for a May Morning

KENNY, Yvonne (sop)
Beethoven: Symphony 9
Bizet: Carmen (Cpte)
Britten: Gloriana (Cpte)
Donizetti: Emilia di Liverpool (Cpte), Eremitaggio di
Liverpool (Cpte), Ugo, Conte di Parigi (Cpte)
Gay: Beggar's Opera (Cpte)
Handel: Deborah (Cpte)
Mayr: Medea (Cpte)
Mendelssohn: Elijah (Cpte)
Meyerbeer: Crociato in Egitto (Cpte)
Mozart: Entführung (Cpte), Lucio Silla (Cpte), Nozze
di Figaro (Cpte), Requiem, Zauberflöte (Cpte)
Offenbach: Robinson Crusoé (Cpte)
Vaughan Williams: Dona nobis pacem, Symphony 1,
Symphony 3
see CONCERT INDEX under:
(CARL) **GLRS101** Mahler plays Mahler
(ETCE) **KTC1029** Yvonne Kenny at the Wigmore
Hall
(ETCE) **KTC1046** Songs by Britten
(OPRA) **ORCH103** Italian Opera—1810-20
(OPRA) **ORCH104** A Hundred Years of Italian Opera:
1820-1830

(SONY) **SK45965** Esa-Pekka Salonen conducts
Stravinsky
(SONY) **SK46667** Stravinsky—Miscellaneous Works

KENT, Arthur (bar)
see CONCERT INDEX under:
(MYTO) **2MCD90317** Verdi—Un Ballo in maschera

KENTNER, Louis (pf)
see CONCERT INDEX under:
(EMI) **CDM7 63986-2** French Chamber Works
(EMI) **CDM7 63988-2** Schubert, Mendelssohn &
Brahms—Chamber Works
(TEST) **SBT1002** Reginald Kell—Clarinet Works
(TEST) **SBT1007** Kell plays Mozart Clarinet Works
(VOX) **CDX2 5503** Liszt—Piano Works

KENTON, Peter (sngr)
Gay: Beggar's Opera (Cpte)

KENYON, Paul (bar)
see CONCERT INDEX under:
(PEAR) **SHECD9602** Elgar: War Music

KENYON, Philip (organ)
see CONCERT INDEX under:
(HERA) **HAVPCD115** Howells: Organ Works

KER, Thora (mez)
Sullivan: Mikado (Cpte)

KERGONAN ABBEY CHOIR
see CONCERT INDEX under:
(STUD) **SM1220.02** Immortel Grégorien

KERN, Adele (sop)
see CONCERT INDEX under:
(SCHW) **314582** Vienna State Opera Live, Vol.8
(SCHW) **314652** Vienna State Opera Live, Vol.15

KERN, Patricia (mez)
Purcell: Dido (Cpte)
Sullivan: Iolanthe (exc), Mikado (Cpte)

KERNIC, Beatrice (sop)
see CONCERT INDEX under:
(SIMA) **PSC1810(1)** Grieg—Songs (historical
recordings, pt 1)

KERNS, Robert (bar)
Bach: Mass in B minor, BWV232 (Cpte)
Puccini: Madama Butterfly (Cpte), Turandot (Cpte)
Verdi: Otello (Cpte), Rigoletto (Cpte)
Wagner: Lohengrin (Cpte), Rheingold (Cpte)
see CONCERT INDEX under:
(DG) **435 211-2GX15** Wagner—Der Ring des
Nibelungen

KERR, Virginia (sop)
Victory: Ultima Rerum (Cpte)

KERRYSON, Paul (cond)
see Leicester Haymarket Th Cast

KERSTENS, Huub (cond)
see Xenakis Ens

KERSTENS, Tom (gtr)
see CONCERT INDEX under:
(CONI) **CDCF509** Fandango - Spanish Dances for
Guitar
(CONI) **CDCF518** Serenade

KERTESI, Ingrid (sop)
Bach: Cantata 51, Cantata 80, Cantata 147, Cantata
211, Cantata 212, Christmas Oratorio, BWV248
(Cpte)
Mozart: Nozze di Figaro (Cpte)
Rossini: Barbiere di Siviglia (Cpte)

KERTÉSZ, György (vc)
Sterndale Bennett: Sonata Duo, Op. 32
see CONCERT INDEX under:
(MARC) **8 223404** Atterberg—Chamber Music, Vol.1
(MARC) **8 223405** Atterberg—Chamber Works
(MARC) **8 223430** Berwald—Piano Trios, Vol.2

KERTÉSZ, István (cond)
see LSC

KESLING, Diane (mez)
R. Strauss: Elektra (Cpte)
Wagner: Götterdämmerung (Cpte), Walküre (Cpte)
see CONCERT INDEX under:
(DG) **445 354-2GX14** Wagner—Der Ring des
Nibelungen

KESSLER, Martha (mez)
see CONCERT INDEX under:
(HANS) **98 801** Bach—Cantatas, Vol.39

KESTEREN, John van (ten)
Orff: Carmina Burana, Mond (Cpte)
Pfitzner: Palestrina (Cpte)
see CONCERT INDEX under:
(ARCH) **439 380-2AX6** Bach—Cantatas, Volume 3 -
Ascension Day; Whitsun; Trinity
(ARCH) **439 387-2AX6** Bach Cantatas, Volume 4

KETÉLBEY, Albert (cond)
see orch

KETELSEN, Hans-Joachim (bar)
Wagner: Meistersinger (Cpte)

KETTEL, Gary (perc)
see CONCERT INDEX under:
(HYPE) **CDA66219** American Choral Works

KEULEN, Isabelle van (va)
Schnittke: Viola Concerto

KEULEN, Isabelle van (vn)
Gubaidulina: Hommage

Lutosławski: Chain 2
see CONCERT INDEX under:
(PHIL) **422 515-2PME7** The Complete Mozart Edition
Vol 15
(SCHW) **315272** Debussy/Fauré/Poulenc—Violin
Sonatas

KEUSCHNIG, Rainer (pf)
Schnittke: Concerto Grosso 5

KEVEHÁZI, János (hn)
see CONCERT INDEX under:
(NAXO) **8 553090** Beethoven—Chamber Works

KEVEHÁZI, Jenö (hn)
see CONCERT INDEX under:
(NAXO) **8 550511** Mozart/Beethoven—Quintets for
Piano and Wind etc
(NAXO) **8 553090** Beethoven—Chamber Works

KEVOIAN, Peter (sngr)
Gershwin: Pardon My English (Cpte)

KEYES, John (ten)
Verdi: Otello (Cpte)

KEYROUZ SBC, Sr Marie (sop)
Anon: Byzantine Holy Week Chants, Melchite Sacred
Chant, Traditional Maronite Chants

KEYTE, Christopher (bass)
Handel: Israel in Egypt (Cpte)
Haydn: Mass 9
M-A. Charpentier: Messe de minuit, H9
Maxwell Davies: Lighthouse (Cpte)
Puccini: Madama Butterfly (Cpte)
Purcell: Indian Queen, Z630 (exc)
Verdi: Traviata (Cpte)
see CONCERT INDEX under:
(ARCH) **437 075-2AT** Collectio Argentea 5: Canti
Amorosi
(CNTI) **CCD1046** Bax—Songs
(DECC) **436 486-2DF2**
Duruflé/Fauré/Poulenc—Choral Works
(DECC) **443 868-2DF2** Italian Baroque Sacred
Works
(EMI) **CDM7 64022-2** Vaughan Williams—Orchestral
Works
(L'OI) **425 893-2OM6(1)** Purcell—Theatre Music (Part
1)

KHACHATURIAN, Aram (cond)
see Philh

KHACHATURIAN, Emin (cond)
see Soviet Cinema Orch

KHAIKIN, Boris (cond)
see Bolshoi Th Orch

KHANAYEV, Nikhandr (ten)
see CONCERT INDEX under:
(DANT) **LYS013/5** Tchaikovsky—The Queen of
Spades

KHANIN, Michail Mordukhovich (tpt)
see CONCERT INDEX under:
(KOCH) **37159-2** Schnittke/Shostakovich—Piano
Concertos

KHARA, Joan (contr)
R. Strauss: Elektra (Cpte)

KHARADZE, Archil (va)
Kancheli: Symphony 6

KHARITONOV, Dimitri (bass)
see CONCERT INDEX under:
(UNIT) **88001-2** Shostakovich—Orchestral Works &
Songs

KHOURI, Murray (bass cl)
see CONCERT INDEX under:
(CNTI) **CCD1008** Anderson: Mask and other works
(CNTI) **CCD1027** Brahms/Gal—Clarinet Sonatas
(CNTI) **CCD1038** Works for Clarinet and Piano

KHRULEV, Vladimir (bar)
Mussorgsky: Marriage (Cpte)

KIBBLEWHITE, Michael (cond)
see East London Chor

KIBERG, Tina (sop)
Beethoven: Missa solemnis
Janáček: Glagolitic Mass (Cpte)
Nielsen: Saul and David (Cpte)
Nørgård: Siddhartha (Cpte)
see CONCERT INDEX under:
(CHAN) **CHAN9223** R. Strauss—A cappella choral
works

KIEFER, Günter (bar)
Corghi: Divara (Cpte)

KIEHR, Maria Cristina (sop)
Monteverdi: Incoronazione di Poppea (Cpte),
Vespers
Schütz: Symphoniae sacrae, Op. 10 (exc)
Vivaldi: Dorilla in Tempe (Cpte)
see CONCERT INDEX under:
(ADES) **20271-2** Handel—Roman Cantatas

KIEK, Mara (sop)
see CONCERT INDEX under:
(HYPE) **CDA66283** Bella Domna

KIEL OPERA CHORUS
cond K. SEIBEL
Delius: Village Romeo and Juliet (Cpte)
Schillings: Mona Lisa (Cpte)

KIEL PHILHARMONIC ORCHESTRA
cond K. SEIBEL
Delius: Village Romeo and Juliet (Cpte)
Schillings: Mona Lisa (Cpte)

KIELLAND, Olav (cond)
see RPO

KIENER, Maximilian (treb)
Bach: St Matthew Passion, BWV244 (Cpte)
see CONCERT INDEX under:
(WERG) WER6173-2 T.W.Adorno—Chamber &
Choral Works

KIEPURA, Jan (ten)
see CONCERT INDEX under:
(SCHW) 314602 Vienna State Opera Live, Vol.10

KIERKEGAARD, Ingegerd (va)
see CONCERT INDEX under:
(BIS) BIS-CD652 Penderecki—Chamber Works

KIESEL, Lena-Luis (organ)
see CONCERT INDEX under:
(MERI) DUOCD89009 The Romantic Englishman

KIEZLICH, Ivo (timp)
see CONCERT INDEX under:
(SUPR) 11 0751-2 Martinů—Choral Works

KIICHLI, Henry (bass)
S. Wagner: Bärenhäuter (Cpte)
see CONCERT INDEX under:
(MARC) 8 223287 Ibert: Film Music

KILANOWICZ, Zofia (sop)
Górecki: Symphony 3

KILAR, Wojciech (cond)
see Polish SO

KILBERG, Tina (sop)
Beethoven: String Quartet 11 (exc)
Mahler: Symphony 2

KILBEY, Reginald (cond)
see CBSO

KILEY, Richard (sngr)
Rodgers: No Strings (Cpte)

KILIAN, Michael (boy alto)
Bach: Mass in B minor, BWV232 (Cpte)

KILLEBREW, Gwendoline (mez)
Giordano: Andrea Chénier (Cpte)
Haydn: Orlando Paladino (Cpte)
Puccini: Edgar (Cpte)
Wagner: Götterdämmerung (Cpte), Walküre (Cpte)
see CONCERT INDEX under:
(SONY) SM2K47563 Haydn—Choral & Orchestral
Works

KILLIUS, Ruth (va)
Kancheli: Exil

KIM, Ettore (bar)
Bellini: Puritani (Cpte)
*Donizetti: Linda di Chamounix (Cpte), Roberto
Devereux (Cpte)*

KIM, Hye Jin (sop)
Mysliveček: Abraham and Isaac

KIM, Young Uck (vn)
Dvořák: Piano Trio 3, Piano Trio 4
*Schumann: Piano Quartet, Op.47, Piano Quartet
(1829)*
see CONCERT INDEX under:
(DG) 413 844-2GW2 19th Century Violin Works

KIMBROUGH, Steven (bar)
Weill: Happy End (Cpte)
see CONCERT INDEX under:
(ARAB) Z6579 Kurt Weill: Songs
(ARAB) Z6623 Rossini—Songs
(SCHW) 310942 Steven Kimbrough—Lieder Recital

KIMM, Fiona (mez)
Berlioz: Enfance du Christ (Cpte)
M. Berkeley: Baa Baa Black Sheep (Cpte)
Turnage: Greek (Cpte)
see CONCERT INDEX under:
(NMC) NMCD008 Simon Holt—Chamber Works
(NMC) NMCD024M Turnage—Vocal and Chamber
Works
(OPRA) ORCH104 A Hundred Years of Italian Opera:
1820-1830
(SONY) S2K66836 Goldschmidt—Beatrice Cenci, etc

KIMSTEDT, Rainer Johannes (va)
see CONCERT INDEX under:
(CAPR) 10 539 Schulhoff—Chamber Works

KINASZ, Bożena (mez)
Mussorgsky: Boris Godunov (Cpte)

KINCSES, Veronika (sop)
Liszt: Hungarian Coronation Mass, S11
Puccini: Bohème (Cpte)
Respighi: Semirama (Cpte)
see CONCERT INDEX under:
(OPUS) 9156 1824 Dvorský sings Operatic Arias

KINDERMAN, William (pf)
Beethoven: Diabelli Variations

KINDERMANN, Lydia (mez)
Wagner: Götterdämmerung (exc)
see CONCERT INDEX under:
(PEAR) GEMMCDS9137 Wagner—Der Ring des
Nibelungen
(PREI) 89209 Helge Roswaenge (1897-1972) - II

KING, Andrew (ten)
Blow: Venus and Adonis (Cpte)
Handel: Esther (Cpte)
*Monteverdi: Madrigals, Bk 8 (exc), Orfeo (Cpte),
Scherzi musicali (1632) (exc), Vespers*
see CONCERT INDEX under:
(BIS) BIS-CD341 Music for lutes
(DECC) 443 455-2DF2 Vivaldi—Sacred Choral Works
(L'OI) 421 480-2OH Monteverdi: Madrigali Erotici
(L'OI) 440 637-2OH Monteverdi—Ballets
(VIRG) VC7 59606-2 Monteverdi—Madrigals, Book 8

KING, Catherine (mez)
see CONCERT INDEX under:
(VIRG) VC7 59326-2 Vivaldi—Sacred Choral Works

KING, Charles (sngr)
see CONCERT INDEX under:
(PEAR) GEMMCDS9053/5 Music from the New York
Stage, Vol. 2: 1908–1913
(PEAR) GEMMCDS9056/8 Music from the New York
Stage, Vol. 3: 1913-17

KING, Christopher (cl)
see CONCERT INDEX under:
(CHAN) CHAN8972 Debussy & Ravel—Orchestral
works

KING, Gibner (pf)
see CONCERT INDEX under:
(SUPR) 11 1491-2 Jarmila Novotna sings Czech
Songs and Arias

KING, James (ten)
Beethoven: Symphony 9
Hindemith: Mathis der Maler (Cpte)
Mozart: Zauberflöte (Cpte)
*R. Strauss: Ariadne auf Naxos (Cpte), Daphne (Cpte),
Frau ohne Schatten (Cpte), Salome (Cpte)*
Schmidt: Notre Dame (Cpte)
Wagner: Parsifal (Cpte), Walküre (exc)
see CONCERT INDEX under:
(DECC) 414 100-2DM15 Wagner: Der Ring des
Nibelungen
(PHIL) 446 057-2PB14 Wagner—The Ring Cycle -
Bayreuth Festival 1967

KING, John (sngr)
Sullivan: HMS Pinafore (Cpte)

KING, Malcolm (bass)
Berlioz: Damnation de Faust (Cpte)
Giordano: Andrea Chénier (Cpte)
Janáček: Glagolitic Mass (Cpte)
Massenet: Werther (Cpte)
Mozart: Don Giovanni (Cpte)
*Puccini: Fanciulla del West (Cpte), Madama Butterfly
(Cpte), Tosca (Cpte)*
Stravinsky: Pulcinella
*Verdi: Ballo in maschera (Cpte), Forza del destino
(Cpte), Otello (Cpte)*
see CONCERT INDEX under:
(DECC) 425 681-2DM2 Tutto Pavarotti

KING, Mary (mez)
Janáček: Cunning Little Vixen (Cpte)
see CONCERT INDEX under:
(EMI) CDS7 54270-2 Rattle Conducts Britten
(NMC) NMCD009 Birtwistle—Choral and Orchestral
Works

KING, Peter (organ)
see CONCERT INDEX under:
(CONI) CDCF192 Bruckner: Sacred Choral Works

KING, Peter (harm)
Rossini: Petite Messe Solennelle

KING, Robert (cond)
see King's Consort

KING, Robert (organ)
see CONCERT INDEX under:
(HYPE) CDA66474 Couperin—Vocal Works

KING, Robert (hpd/dir)
see CONCERT INDEX under:
(HYPE) CDA66440 Handel—Italian Duets

KING, Robert (org/dir)
see CONCERT INDEX under:
(MERI) CDE84138 Sacred Baroque Vocal Works

KING, Robert (org/hpd)
see CONCERT INDEX under:
(HYPE) CDA66710 Purcell—Secular Solo Songs,
Volume 1
(HYPE) CDA66730 Purcell—Secular Solo Songs, Vol.
3
(HYPE) CDA66881/2 Vivaldi—Cello Sonatas

KING, Robert (treb)
see CONCERT INDEX under:
(DECC) 430 263-2DM Purcell—Sacred choral works
(DECC) 436 486-2DF2
Duruflé/Fauré/Poulenc—Choral Works

KING, Terry (vc)
see CONCERT INDEX under:
(MUSI) MACD-635 American Chamber Works

KING, Thea (basset cl)
see CONCERT INDEX under:
(HYPE) CDA66504 Süssmayr/Tausch—Works for
Clarinet

KING, Thea (cl)
Beethoven: Piano and Wind Quintet, Op. 16
*Brahms: Clarinet Quintet, Clarinet Sonata 1, Clarinet
Sonata 2, Clarinet Trio*
Crusell: Clarinet Concerto 2
Finzi: Clarinet Concerto
*Mozart: Clarinet Concerto, K622, Clarinet Quintet,
K581, Piano and Wind Quintet, K452*
Spohr: Clarinet Concerto 4
Stanford: Clarinet Concerto
Weber: Clarinet Concerto 2
see CONCERT INDEX under:
(EMI) CZS7 67306-2 Mozart—Works featuring Wind
Instruments
(HYPE) CDA66014 Music for clarinet and piano, Vol.
1
(HYPE) CDA66022 The Clarinet in Concert
(HYPE) CDA66044 English Music for Clarinet and
Piano
(HYPE) CDA66077 Crusell: Clarinet Quartets Nos 1-
3
(HYPE) CDA66215 Works for Clarinet and Orchestra
(HYPE) CDA66295 Villa-Lobos: Chamber Works
(HYPE) CDA66300 The Clarinet in Concert—Vol 2
(HYPE) CDA66479 Clarinet Quintets
(HYPE) CDA66504 Süssmayr/Tausch—Works for
Clarinet
(HYPE) CDA66634
Arnold/Britten/Maconchy—Clarinet Concertos
(HYPE) CDJ33009 Schubert: Complete Lieder, Vol.9
(PHIL) 422 545-2PME3 The Complete Mozart Edition
Vol.45

KINGELHOFER, William (hn)
J. Adams: Light over Water

KING'S COLLEGE CHOIR, CAMBRIDGE
see CONCERT INDEX under:
(CFP) CD-CFP4570 Choral Favourites
(COLL) Coll1335-2 Carols from King's
cond B. BRITTEN
Elgar: Dream of Gerontius (Cpte)
see CONCERT INDEX under:
(DECC) 430 094-2DWO The World of Elgar
cond S. CLEOBURY
Duruflé: Requiem
Fauré: Requiem (Cpte)
Handel: Messiah (Cpte)
Mozart: Mass, K317
see CONCERT INDEX under:
(ARGO) 414 042-2ZH Christmas Carols at King's
College, Cambridge
(ARGO) 417 468-2ZH G. Gabrieli: Choral and
Instrumental Works
(ARGO) 430 205-2ZH Howells—Sacred Choral Works
(ARGO) 433 215-2ZH Britten—Christmas Music
(ARGO) 433 452-2ZH Brahms/Mendelssohn—Sacred
Choral Works
(DECC) 436 402-2DWO The World of Wedding
Music
(DECC) 443 455-2DF2 Vivaldi—Sacred Choral Works
(EMI) CDC5 55096-2 Ikos
(EMI) CDC7 47065-2 Music of Sixteenth-Century
Rome
(EMI) CDC7 47771-2 Byrd—Choral Works
(EMI) CDC7 49672-2 Mozart: Sacred Choral Works
(EMI) CDC7 54412-2 Choral Evensong from King's
College, Cambridge
(EMI) CDC7 54418-2 English Anthems
cond J. JUDD
Holst: Planets
cond P. LEDGER
Britten: Little Sweep (Cpte), Rejoice in the Lamb
Elgar: Coronation Ode (Cpte)
M-A. Charpentier: Te Deum H146
see CONCERT INDEX under:
(CFP) CD-CFP4570 Choral Favourites
(DECC) 443 455-2DF2 Vivaldi—Sacred Choral Works
(EMIN) CD-EMX2198 A Delius Festival
cond G. LEONHARDT
see CONCERT INDEX under:
(TELD) 2292-42498-2 Bach—Cantatas, Volume 2
(TELD) 2292-42499-2 Bach—Cantatas, Volume 3
(TELD) 2292-42500-2 Bach—Cantatas, Volume 4
(TELD) 2292-42502-2 Bach—Cantatas, Volume 5
(TELD) 4509-91755-2 Bach—Cantatas, Vol.1
(TELD) 4509-91756-2 Bach—Cantatas, Vol.2
cond B. ORD
see CONCERT INDEX under:
(DECC) 433 677-2DM Gibbons—Sacred Works
cond D. WILLCOCKS
Fauré: Requiem (Cpte)
Handel: Messiah (Cpte)
Haydn: Mass 11
M-A. Charpentier: Messe de minuit, H9
Vivaldi: Gloria, RV589
see CONCERT INDEX under:
(BELA) 450 112-2 Carols for Advent—A Procession
With Carols on Advent Sunday
(CFP) CD-CFP4570 Choral Favourites
(CFP) CD-CFP4586 Carols from King's
(DECC) 421 147-2DM Allegri & Palestrina: Sacred
Choral Works
(DECC) 425 499-2DM On Christmas night
(DECC) 430 089-2DWO King's World of Christmas
(DECC) 430 093-2DWO The World of Vaughan
Williams
(DECC) 430 500-2DWO World of Handel
(DECC) 433 675-2DM Byrd—Three Masses
(DECC) 433 676-2DM Tallis—Choral Works
(DECC) 433 677-2DM Gibbons—Sacred Works
(DECC) 436 256-2DM Handel/Blow—Anthems
(DECC) 436 259-2DM Handel/Blow—Choral Works
(DECC) 436 403-2DWO The World of Royal Music
(DECC) 443 868-2DF2 Italian Baroque Sacred
Works

(EMI) **CDM5 65101-2** A Warlock Centenary Album
(EMI) **CDM7 64130-2** Christmas Music from King's
(TELD) **9031-77608-2** Purcell—Anthems,Instrumental
Music & Songs

KING'S CONSORT
   see CONCERT INDEX under:
(HYPE) **CDA66440** Handel—Italian Duets
(HYPE) **CDA66447** Awake, Sweet Love
(HYPE) **CDA66686** Purcell—Complete Anthems &
Services, Vol.8
(HYPE) **CDA66720** Purcell—Secular Solo Songs,
Volume 2
(MERI) **CDE84138** Sacred Baroque Vocal Works
   cond R. KING
Handel: Acis and Galatea (Cpte), Coronation
Anthems, Deborah (Cpte), Fireworks Music, Joshua
(Cpte), Judas Maccabaeus (Cpte), Look down,
harmonious saint, Occasional Oratorio (Cpte), Ottone
(Cpte)
Purcell: Birthday Ode, Z342, St Cecilia's Day Ode,
Z328
Telemann: Musique de Table (exc)
Vivaldi: Laudate pueri Dominum, RV601, Nisi
Dominus
   see CONCERT INDEX under:
(CARL) **PCD894** Great Baroque Arias, Part I
(HYPE) **CDA66253** Blow & Purcell: Countertenor
Works
(HYPE) **CDA66267** Bach & Telemann—Oboe
Concertos
(HYPE) **CDA66288** 'Mr Henry Purcell's Most
Admirable Composure's'
(HYPE) **CDA66294** Pergolesi—Sacred Choral Works
(HYPE) **CDA66314** Purcell—Complete Odes &
Welcome Songs, Vol.1
(HYPE) **CDA66315** Handel: Music for Royal
Occasions
(HYPE) **CDA66326** Bach—Solo Cantatas
(HYPE) **CDA66380** Bach—Violin Concertos
(HYPE) **CDA66383** Albinoni & Vivaldi—Wind
Concertos
(HYPE) **CDA66398** Schutz—Christmas Story;
Gabrieli—Motets
(HYPE) **CDA66412** Purcell—Complete Odes &
Welcome Songs, Vol.3
(HYPE) **CDA66456** Purcell—Complete Odes &
Welcome Songs, Vol.4
(HYPE) **CDA66476** Purcell—Complete Odes &
Welcome Songs, Vol.5
(HYPE) **CDA66483** Handel—Heroic Arias
(HYPE) **CDA66494** Purcell—Complete Odes &
Welcome Songs, Vol.6
(HYPE) **CDA66585** Purcell—Complete Anthems &
Services, Vol.1
(HYPE) **CDA66587** Purcell—Complete Odes &
Welcome Songs, Vol.7
(HYPE) **CDA66598** Purcell—Complete Odes &
Welcome Songs, Vol.8
(HYPE) **CDA66609** Purcell—Complete Anthems &
Services, Vol.2
(HYPE) **CDA66623** Purcell—Complete Anthems &
Services, Vol.3
(HYPE) **CDA66644** Purcell—Complete Anthems &
Services, Vol.4
(HYPE) **CDA66656** Purcell—Complete Anthems &
Services, Vol.5
(HYPE) **CDA66663** Purcell—Complete Anthems &
Services, Vol.6
(HYPE) **CDA66677** Purcell—Anthems & Services,
Vol.7
(HYPE) **CDA66686** Purcell—Complete Anthems &
Services, Vol.8
(HYPE) **CDA66693** Purcell—Complete Anthems and
Services, Volume 9
(HYPE) **CDA66707** Purcell—Complete Anthems and
Services, Vol. 10
(HYPE) **CDA66716** Purcell—Complete Anthems and
Services, Volume 11
(HYPE) **CDA66769** Vivaldi—Sacred Music, Volume
1
(MERI) **CDE84126** James Bowman recital

KING'S CONSORT CHOIR
   see CONCERT INDEX under:
(HYPE) **CDA66686** Purcell—Complete Anthems &
Services, Vol.8
   cond R. KING
Handel: Occasional Oratorio (Cpte)
   see CONCERT INDEX under:
(HYPE) **CDA66398** Schutz—Christmas Story;
Gabrieli—Motets
(HYPE) **CDA66623** Purcell—Complete Anthems &
Services, Vol.3
(HYPE) **CDA66656** Purcell—Complete Anthems &
Services, Vol.5
(HYPE) **CDA66677** Purcell—Anthems & Services,
Vol.7
(HYPE) **CDA66686** Purcell—Complete Anthems &
Services, Vol.8
(HYPE) **CDA66693** Purcell—Complete Anthems and
Services, Volume 9
(HYPE) **CDA66707** Purcell—Complete Anthems and
Services, Vol. 10
(HYPE) **CDA66716** Purcell—Complete Anthems and
Services, Volume 11
(HYPE) **CDA66769** Vivaldi—Sacred Music, Volume
1
(UNIT) **88002-2** My Beloved Spake

KING'S CONSORT CHORISTERS
   cond R. KING
Handel: Occasional Oratorio (Cpte)
   see CONCERT INDEX under:
(HYPE) **CDA66769** Vivaldi—Sacred Music, Volume
1

KING'S CONSORT CLASSICAL ORCHESTRA
   cond R. KING
Mozart: Church Sonatas

(THE) KING'S MUSICK
   cond A. DELLER
Purcell: Indian Queen, Z630 (Cpte)
   see CONCERT INDEX under:
(HARM) **HMX290 1528/33(2)** A Purcell Companion (pt
2)

KING'S SINGERS
   see CONCERT INDEX under:
(EMI) **CDC7 49765-2** My Spirit Sang All Day
(EMI) **CDC7 54191-2** La Dolce Vita
(RCA) **09026 61885-2** Here's A Howdy Do—A Gilbert
& Sullivan Festival
   cond R. HICKOX
   see CONCERT INDEX under:
(CLLE) **COLCD115** Three Musical Fables

KINGSLEY, Ben (sngr)
Rodgers: King and I (Cpte)

KINGSLEY, Gershon (cond)
   see orch

KINGSWAY SYMPHONY ORCHESTRA
   cond A. EREDE
   see CONCERT INDEX under:
(EMI) **CHS7 69741-2(7)** Record of Singing,
Vol.4—Italian School

KINZEL, Margit (sop)
Gazzaniga: Don Giovanni (Cpte)
Killmayer: Yolimba (Cpte)

KIPNIS, Alexander (bass)
(EMI) **CMS7 64008-2(2)** Wagner Singing on Record
(pt 2)
(NIMB) **NI7848** Great Singers at the Berlin State
Opera
(NIMB) **NI7851** Legendary Voices
(PEAR) **GEMMCDS9075** Hugo Wolf Society, Volume I
(PEAR) **GEMMCDS9085** Hugo Wolf Society, Volume
II
(PEAR) **GEMMCDS9926(1)** Covent Garden on
Record—Vol.4 (pt 1)
(PEAR) **GEMMCD9451** Alexander Kipnis
(PREI) **89019** Alexander Kipnis (1891-1978)
(RCA) **GD60522** Alexander Kipnis—Opera & Song
Recital
(RCA) **09026 61580-2(5)** RCA/Met 100 Singers, 100
Years (pt 5)
(SCHW) **314542** Vienna State Opera Live, Vol.4
(SCHW) **314602** Vienna State Opera Live, Vol.10
(SCHW) **314632** Vienna State Opera Live, Vol.13

KIPNIS, Igor (clav)
   see CONCERT INDEX under:
(ARAB) **Z6577** Bach: Keyboard Works

KIPNIS, Igor (hpd)
Bach: Flute Sonatas, BWV1030-5
   see CONCERT INDEX under:
(ARAB) **Z6577** Bach: Keyboard Works

KIRCHEIS, Friedrich (hpd)
   see CONCERT INDEX under:
(CAPR) **10 051** Classical Trumpet Concertos

KIRCHHOF, Lutz (lte)
   see CONCERT INDEX under:
(SONY) **SK48068** The Lute in Dance and Dream
(SONY) **S2K45858** Bach: Lute Works

KIRCHOFF, Patrice (fl)
   see CONCERT INDEX under:
(AUVI) **V4644** Debussy/Ravel—Orchestral Songs

KIRK, F. (sop)
   see CONCERT INDEX under:
(RCA) **GD60328** Toscanini conducts the Philadelphia
Orch

KIRK, Lisa (sngr)
Porter: Kiss me Kate (Cpte)

KIRKBY, Emma (sop)
Bach: Cantata 51, Cantata 202, Cantata 208, Cantata
211, Cantata 212, Mass in B minor, BWV232 (Cpte)
Handel: Alceste (Cpte), Athalia (Cpte), Esther (Cpte),
Joshua (Cpte), Judas Maccabaeus (Cpte), Messiah
(Cpte), Orlando (Cpte), Triumph of Time and Truth
(Cpte)
Hasse: Cleofide (Cpte)
Haydn: Creation (Cpte)
Monteverdi: Madrigals, Bk 8 (exc), Orfeo (Cpte),
Selva morale e spirituale (exc)
Mozart: Requiem
Pergolesi: Salve Regina in C minor, Stabat mater
Purcell: Dido (Cpte), Don Quixote: The Musical
(Cpte)
Schütz: Symphoniae sacrae, Op. 10 (Cpte)
   see CONCERT INDEX under:
(CARL) **PCD881** Monteverdi—Solos and Duets
(CHAN) **CHAN0518** Vivaldi & Bach—Choral Works
(EMI) **CDC7 47633-2** Praetorius & Schütz: Sacred
Choral Works
(EMI) **CDC7 47998-2** Una Stravaganza dei Medici -
Florentine Intermedi (ed. Keyte)

(EMI) **CDS7 49749-2** Handel—Music for the Carmelite
Vespers
(HYPE) **CDA66021** Monteverdi: Sacred vocal works
(HYPE) **CDA66039** A Feather on the Breath of God
(HYPE) **CDA66056** Purcell: Songs and Dialogues
(HYPE) **CDA66106** Olympia's Lament
(HYPE) **CDA66186** Time Stands Still
(HYPE) **CDA66227** Emma Kirkby Collection
(HYPE) **CDA66237** Dr Arne at Vauxhall Gardens
(HYPE) **CDA66247** Vivaldi: Vocal and Orchestral
Works
(HYPE) **CDA66497** O Tuneful Voice
(HYPE) **CDA66649** Benda—Lieder & Fortepiano
Music
(HYPE) **CDA66745** Vivaldi—Opera Arias and
Sinfonias
(L'OI) **411 832-2OH** Mozart: Choral Works
(L'OI) **414 473-2OH** Handel: Italian Cantatas
(L'OI) **417 123-2OH** Purcell: Songs and Airs
(L'OI) **421 480-2OH** Monteverdi: Madrigali Erotici
(L'OI) **421 654-2OH** Handel & Haydn: Choral works
(L'OI) **425 835-2OH** Mozart—Concert and Opera
Arias
(L'OI) **425 892-2OH** Elizabethan Songs: The Lady
Musick
(L'OI) **425 893-2OM6(1)** Purcell—Theatre Music (Part
1)
(L'OI) **425 893-2OM6(2)** Purcell—Theatre Music (Part
2)
(L'OI) **436 132-2OH** Emma Kirkby sings Mrs Arne
(L'OI) **436 585-2OH** Mozart—Sacred Choral Works
(MOSC) **070978** Maurice Greene—Songs and
Keyboard Works
(MOSC) **070979** Sound the Trumpets from Shore to
Shore
(SONY) **SK66243** Music for Queen Mary
(VIRG) **VC7 59321-2** Shakespeare's Lutenist
(VIRG) **VC7 59521-2** The English Orpheus - Works by
John Dowland
(VIRG) **VC7 59606-2** Monteverdi—Madrigals, Book 8

KIRKBY-LUNN, Louise (mez)
   see CONCERT INDEX under:
(PEAR) **GEMMCDS9924(1)** Covent Garden on
Record, Vol.2 (pt 1)
(PEAR) **GEMMCDS9924(2)** Covent Garden on
Record, Vol.2 (pt 2)
(SUPR) **11 2136-2(4)** Emmy Destinn—Complete
Edition, Discs 9 & 10

KIRKESKOV, Dorte (pf)
   see CONCERT INDEX under:
(ROND) **RCD8319** Nielsen—Songs, Vol.1
(ROND) **RCD8323** Nielsen—Songs, Vol.2
(ROND) **RCD8327** Nielsen—Songs, Vol.4

KIRKLAND, Glenda (mez)
R. Strauss: Aegyptische Helena (Cpte)

KIRKWOOD, Gordon (pf)
   see CONCERT INDEX under:
(SYMP) **SYMCD1064** Schubert & Wolf—Lieder

KIRKWOOD, James (cond)
   see Sheaf Concert Orch

KIRKWOOD, William (bass)
Schoenberg: Moses and Aron (Cpte)

KIROV THEATRE CHORUS
   cond V. GERGIEV
Borodin: Prince Igor (Cpte)
Prokofiev: War and Peace (Cpte)
Rimsky-Korsakov: Sadko (Cpte)
Tchaikovsky: Queen of Spades (Cpte)
   see CONCERT INDEX under:
(PHIL) **442 011-2PH** Russian Orchestral Works .
(PHIL) **442 775-2PH** Russian Spectacular

KIROV THEATRE ORCHESTRA
   cond V. GERGIEV
Borodin: Prince Igor (Cpte)
Prokofiev: Romeo and Juliet (Cpte), War and Peace
(Cpte)
Rachmaninov: Symphony 2
Rimsky-Korsakov: Sadko (Cpte)
Shostakovich: Symphony 8
Tchaikovsky: Queen of Spades (Cpte), Sleeping
Beauty (Cpte)
   see CONCERT INDEX under:
(PHIL) **438 872-2PH** Songs and Dances of Death
(PHIL) **442 011-2PH** Russian Orchestral Works
(PHIL) **442 775-2PH** Russian Spectacular

KIRSCHBICHLER, Theodore (bass)
R. Strauss: Salome (Cpte)

KIRSCHSTEIN, Leonore (sop)
Hindemith: Cardillac (Cpte)
Mozart: Zauberflöte (Cpte)
   see CONCERT INDEX under:
(TEST) **SBT1036** Lisa Della Casa sings Richard
Strauss

KIRSHBAUM, Ralph (vc)
Bach: Solo Cello Suites
   see CONCERT INDEX under:
(CHAN) **CHAN6547** Walton—Choral and Orchestral
Works
(EMI) **CMS7 64790-2** Saint-Saëns—Complete Works
for Violin and Orchestra
(VIRG) **VC7 59565-2** Barber—Orchestral & Chamber
Works

KIRSTEN, Dorothy (sop)
   see CONCERT INDEX under:

(EMI) **CHS7 69741-2(1)** Record of Singing,
Vol.4—Anglo-American School (pt 1)
(RCA) **09026 61580-2(6)** RCA/Met 100 Singers, 100
Years (pt 6)

KISS, András (vn)
Bartók: Duos, Sz98
Stemdale Bennett: Piano Sextet, Op. 8
see CONCERT INDEX under:
(MARC) **8 223170** Berwald—Piano Trios, Vol.1
(MARC) **8 223404** Atterberg—Chamber Music, Vol.1
(MARC) **8 223405** Atterberg—Chamber Works

KISS, József (ob)
see CONCERT INDEX under:
(NAXO) **8 550511** Mozart/Beethoven—Quintets for
Piano and Wind etc
(NAXO) **8 550556** C.P.E.Bach/Marcello—Oboe
Works

KISS, Rózsa (sop)
Bach: St Matthew Passion, BWV244 (Cpte)

KISSIN, Evgeni (pf)
Chopin: Mazurkas (exc), Piano Sonata 3
Prokofiev: Piano Concerto 1, Piano Concerto 3
see CONCERT INDEX under:
(DG) **427 485-2GH** Kissin plays Tchaikovsky &
Scriabin
(DG) **435 617-2GH** Beethoven in Berlin—New Year's
Eve Concert
(MELO) **74321 25172-2(2)** Russian Piano School (pt 2
- Vols.9 & 10)
(MELO) **74321 25182-2** Russian Piano School, Vol. 10
(RCA) **RD60443** Evgeny Kissin—Carnegie Hall Debut
(RCA) **RD87947** Shostakovich: Orchestral Works
(RCA) **RD87948** Haydn: Concertos
(RCA) **09026 60400-2** Mozart—Piano Concertos
(RCA) **09026 60445-2** Chopin—Piano Works, Vol.1
(RCA) **09026 61548-2** Rachmaninov—Piano Concerto
No 3, etc
(SONY) **SK45931** Evgeni Kissin in Tokyo
(SONY) **SK52567** Schumann—Piano Works
(SONY) **SK64538** Haydn/Schubert—Piano Sonatas

KIT, Mikhail (bar)
Borodin: Prince Igor (Cpte)
Prokofiev: War and Peace (Cpte)

KITAIENKO, Dmitri (cond)
see Bergen PO

KITAZATO, Taka (ob)
Telemann: Musique de Table (exc)

KITCHEN, Linda (sop)
Meyerbeer: Crociato in Egitto (Cpte)
see CONCERT INDEX under:
(HYPE) **CDA66420** Vaughan Williams: Vocal Works
(HYPE) **CDA66569** Vaughan Williams—Choral Works
(MERI) **DUOCD89003** Haydn & Schubert: Masses, etc
(OPRA) **ORCH104** A Hundred Years of Italian Opera:
1820-1830

KITCHINER, John (bar)
Herrmann: Wuthering Heights (Cpte)
Sondheim: Pacific Overtures (exc)

KITE, Celia (sop)
Offenbach: Christopher Columbus (Cpte)

KITE, Christopher (fp)
see CONCERT INDEX under:
(MERI) **CDE84113** Mozart—Fortepiano Sonatas
(MERI) **CDE84145** Beethoven: Chamber Music on
Period Instruments

KITE, Christopher (pf)
see CONCERT INDEX under:
(NIMB) **NI5158** Mendelssohn: Orchestral Works

KITHARA
see CONCERT INDEX under:
(CHAN) **CHAN0562** Musica Mediterranea

KITSCHIN, Alexander (cond)
see orch

KITSCHIN, Alexander (pf)
see CONCERT INDEX under:
(MMOI) **CDMOIR422** Great Voices in Tchaikovsky

KITZINGER, Fritz (pf)
see CONCERT INDEX under:
(PEAR) **GEMMCD9119** Schumann—Legendary Song
Cycles
(PEAR) **GEMMCD9453** William Primrose—Viola
Recital
(RCA) **09026 61245-2** Ezio Pinza - Recital

KJELLGREN, Ingeborg (mez)
Verdi: Rigoletto (Cpte)

KLAAS, Rainer M. (pf)
see CONCERT INDEX under:
(MARC) **8 223383** Alkan—Chamber Works

KLÁN, Josef (bass)
Fibich: Šárka (Cpte)

KLÁNSKÝ, Ivan (pf)
see CONCERT INDEX under:
(SUPR) **11 1533-2** Suk—Chamber Works, Volume 3

KLARE, Susanne (mez)
Albinoni: Nascimento dell'Aurora (Cpte)
Gluck: Iphigénie en Tauride (Cpte)
Suder: Kleider machen Leute (Cpte)

KLARWEIN, Franz (ten)
Wagner: Meistersinger (Cpte)

KLAS, Eri (cond)
see Estonia Op Orch

KLEBER, Manfred (ten)
Hindemith: Nusch-Nuschi (Cpte)

KLECHEVSKY, Alexander (bn)
see CONCERT INDEX under:
(ETCE) **KTC1179** Denisov—Music for Cello

KLEE, Bernhard (cond)
see Berlin RSO

KLEIBER, Carlos (cond)
see Bavarian St Orch

KLEIBER, Erich (cond)
see Berlin St Op Orch

KLEIN, Kenneth (cond)
see NY Virtuosi

KLEIN, Kerstin (sop)
Mendelssohn: Elias (Cpte)

KLEIN, Markus (treb)
see CONCERT INDEX under:
(TELD) **2292-42573-2** Bach—Cantatas, Volume 19
(TELD) **2292-42578-2** Bach—Cantatas, Volume 22
(TELD) **2292-42602-2** Bach—Cantatas, Volume 26
(TELD) **2292-42603-2** Bach—Cantatas, Volume 27
(TELD) **4509-91758-2** Bach—Cantatas, Vol.4
(TELD) **4509-91759-2** Bach—Cantatas, Vol.5
(TELD) **4509-91760-2** Bach—Cantatas, Vol.6

KLEIN, Peter (ten)
Beethoven: Fidelio (Cpte)
*J. Strauss II: Fledermaus (Cpte), Nacht in Venedig
(Cpte)*
Lehár: Lustige Witwe (exc)
Mozart: Zauberflöte (Cpte)
*R. Strauss: Ariadne auf Naxos (Cpte), Rosenkavalier
(Cpte)*
Wagner: Meistersinger (Cpte)
see CONCERT INDEX under:
(DECC) **443 530-2LF2** Mozart—Die Entführung aus
dem Serail

KLEINDIENST, Stella (sop)
Gubaidulina: Jetzt immer Schnee

(DAS) KLEINE KONZERT
cond H. MAX
*C. P. E. Bach: Auferstehung und Himmelfahrt Jesu
(Cpte)*
*Telemann: Donner-Ode, Herr ist König, Tag des
Gerichts (Cpte)*
*W. F. Bach: Es ist eine Stimme, F89, Lasset uns
ablegen, F80*
see CONCERT INDEX under:
(CAPR) **10 208** C.P.E. Bach: Sacred Choral Works
(CAPR) **10 303** J. C. F. Bach: Secular Cantatas
(CAPR) **10 310/1** J. E. Bach—Passion Oratorio, etc.
(CAPR) **10 315** Telemann—Choral Music
(CAPR) **10 426** W. F. Bach—Cantatas, Vol.2

KLEINHENZ, Regina Johanna (sngr)
Killmayer: Yolimba (Cpte)

KLEINSCHMIDT, Michael (organ)
see CONCERT INDEX under:
(KOCH) **37030-2** Britten—Choral & Organ Works

KLEMENS, Mario (cond)
see Prague FISYO

KLEMPERER, Otto (cond)
see Berlin St Op Orch

KLEMPERER, Werner (narr)
Schoenberg: Gurrelieder

KLEPPER, Regina (sop)
Kreutzer: Nachtlager in Granada (Cpte)
Pergolesi: Orfeo, Stabat Mater

KLERK, Albert de (organ)
see CONCERT INDEX under:
(EMI) **CDC5 55000-2** Bach—Cantata Arias

KLETZKI, Paul (cond)
see Czech PO

KLEVIT, Lisa (chalumeau)
see CONCERT INDEX under:
(ARCH) **419 633-2AH** Telemann: Wind Concertos

KLIBONOFF, Jon (pf)
see CONCERT INDEX under:
(CATA) **09026 61824-2** Frâtres
(CATA) **09026 62568-2** Maria Bachmann—Kiss On
Wood

KLIEGEL, Maria (vc)
Brahms: Double Concerto
Dvořák: Cello Concerto
Elgar: Cello Concerto
Schumann: Cello Concerto
see CONCERT INDEX under:
(MARC) **8 223334** Schnittke—Works for Cello
(MARC) **8 223403** Virtuoso Cello Encores
(NAXO) **8 550519** Bloch/Bruch/Tchaikovsky—Cello
Works
(NAXO) **8 550654** Schubert/Schumann—Chamber
Works
(NAXO) **8 550655** Mendelssohn—Cello Works
(NAXO) **8 550656** Brahms—Cello Sonatas
(NAXO) **8 550785** Le Grand Tango

KLIEN, Walter (pf)
see CONCERT INDEX under:
(PHIL) **422 515-2PME7** The Complete Mozart Edition
Vol 15

KLIER, Manfred (hn)
see CONCERT INDEX under:
(EMI) **CZS7 67521-2** Schumann—Concertos

KLIETMANN, Martin (ten)
Handel: St John Passion (Cpte)

KLIMOV, Valery (vn)
Khachaturian: Violin Concerto

KLINCKERFUSS, Leonore (hpd)
Bach: Violin Sonatas, BWV1014-19

KLINDA, Ferdinand (organ)
see CONCERT INDEX under:
(OPUS) **9351 2020** Messiaen: Organ Works

KLINE, Olive (sop)
(RCA) **09026 61879-2** Grieg—Historic Recordings
(SIMA) **PSC1810(2)** Grieg—Songs (historical
recordings, pt 2)

KLINKO, Markus (hp)
see CONCERT INDEX under:
(EMI) **CDC7 54467-2** French Harp Music
(EMI) **CDC7 54884-2** French Harp Chamber Music

KLINT, Jørgen (bass)
*Nielsen: Maskarade (Cpte), Saul and David (Cpte),
Springtime in Funen*
see CONCERT INDEX under:
(PAUL) **PACD56** Nielsen: Songs

KLÖCKER, Dieter (cl)
see CONCERT INDEX under:
(ORFE) **C153861A** Romantic Lieder
(SCHW) **311045** Romantic Clarinet Concertos

KLOOSE, Alexandra (sngr)
Killmayer: Yolimba (Cpte)

KLÖPPER, Robert (ten)
Delius: Village Romeo and Juliet (Cpte)

KLOS, Friedemann (treb)
Mozart: Zauberflöte (Cpte)

KLOSE, Margarete (mez)
Mozart: Zauberflöte (Cpte)
*Wagner: Lohengrin (Cpte), Tristan und Isolde (Cpte),
Walküre (Cpte)*
see CONCERT INDEX under:
(EMI) **CMS7 64008-2(1)** Wagner Singing on Record
(pt 1)
(EMI) **CZS7 67123-2** Wagner: Der Ring des
Nibelungen
(MYTO) **3MCD93381** Wagner—Die Walküre, etc
(PREI) **89082** Margarete Klose (1902-1968)
(SCHW) **314502** Vienna State Opera—Live
Recordings (sampler)
(SCHW) **314562** Vienna State Opera Live, Vol.6
(TELD) **9031-76442-2** Wagner—Excerpts from the
1936 Bayreuth Festival

KŁOSIŃSKA, Izabella (sop)
see CONCERT INDEX under:
(SCHW) **314001** Szymanowski: Lieder

KLOUBOVÁ, Zdena (sop)
Janáček: Moravian folk poetry in songs (exc)

KLUG, Howard (cl)
see CONCERT INDEX under:
(ARAB) **Z6569** Milhaud—Jazz Works

KLUG, Thomas (vn)
see CONCERT INDEX under:
(DG) **437 788-2GH** Lourié—Chamber and Vocal
Works

KLUMLIKBOLDT, Werner (bar)
Wagner: Meistersinger (Cpte)

KLUSOŇ, Josef (va)
see CONCERT INDEX under:
(SUPR) **11 1461-2** Dvořák—Chamber Works -
Volume 11

KLUST, Hertha (pf)
see CONCERT INDEX under:
(TEST) **SBT1057** Beethoven—Lieder

KMENTT, Waldemar (ten)
Beethoven: Missa Solemnis, Symphony 9
J. Strauss II: Fledermaus (Cpte)
*Lehár: Giuditta (exc), Graf von Luxemburg (exc),
Lustige Witwe (exc), Zarewitsch (exc)*
Mozart: Idomeneo (Cpte), Zauberflöte (Cpte)
Puccini: Turandot (Cpte)
R. Strauss: Arabella (Cpte), Salome (Cpte)
Wagner: Rheingold (Cpte)
Weill: Dreigroschenoper (Cpte)
see CONCERT INDEX under:
(DECC) **414 100-2DM15** Wagner: Der Ring des
Nibelungen
(DG) **429 036-2GX5** Beethoven: Complete
Symphonies
(PHIL) **432 598-2PB3** Mendelssohn—Complete
Symphonies
(VANG) **08.2028.71** Bach—Cantatas

KNAPNIK, Eugeniusz (pf)
see CONCERT INDEX under:
(POLS) **PNCD045** Lutosławski: Selected Works

KNAPP, David C (hn)
see CONCERT INDEX under:
(DELO) **DE3084** Schumann: Orchestral Works

KNAPP, Josef (bar)
Lehár: Lustige Witwe (Cpte)
R. Strauss: Schweigsame Frau (Cpte)

KNAPP, Peter (bass)
Verdi: Trovatore (Cpte)
see CONCERT INDEX under:
(DECC) 433 908-2DM2 Falla—Orchestral Music

KNAPPERTSBUSCH, Hans (cond)
see Bavarian St Orch

KNARDAHL, Eva (pf)
Kielland: Villarkorn, Op. 13
Sinding: Piano Concerto
see CONCERT INDEX under:
(BIS) BIS-CD104 Grieg: Complete Piano Music, Vol.1
(BIS) BIS-CD105 Grieg: Complete Piano Music, Vol.2
(BIS) BIS-CD106 Grieg: Complete Piano Music, Vol.3
(BIS) BIS-CD107 Grieg: Complete Piano Music, Vol.4
(BIS) BIS-CD108 Grieg: Complete Piano Music, Vol.5
(BIS) BIS-CD109 Grieg: Complete Piano Music, Vol.6
(BIS) BIS-CD110 Grieg: Complete Piano Music, Vol.7
(BIS) BIS-CD111 Grieg: Complete Piano Music, Vol.8
(BIS) BIS-CD112 Grieg: Complete Piano Music, Vol.9
(BIS) BIS-CD159 Hindemith—Chamber Works
(NKF) NKFCD50004-2 Grieg—Violin Sonatas
(SIMA) PSC1021 Brahms—Piano Works
(SIMA) PSC1059 Brahms—Piano Works, Vol. 2
(SIMA) PSC1809(2) Grieg—Historical Piano Recordings (pt 2)

KNIBBS, Jean (contr)
see CONCERT INDEX under:
(HARM) HMX290 1528/33(2) A Purcell Companion (pt 2)

KNIEJSKI, Turid (hp)
see CONCERT INDEX under:
(BIS) BIS-CD428 Nielsen—Wind Chamber Music
(SIMA) PSC3108 Geirr Tveitt—Works for harp and orchestra

KNIGHT, Andrew (bass)
Lampe: Pyramus and Thisbe (Cpte)
see CONCERT INDEX under:
(HYPE) CDA66668 Dibdin—Three Operas

KNIGHT, Gillian (mez)
Berlioz: Damnation de Faust (Cpte)
Janáček: Cunning Little Vixen (Cpte)
Puccini: Madama Butterfly (Cpte), Rondine (Cpte)
Schoenberg: Moses und Aron (Cpte)
Sullivan: Gondoliers (Cpte), HMS Pinafore (Cpte),
Iolanthe (Cpte), Patience (Cpte), Pirates of Penzance
(Cpte), Yeomen of the Guard (Cpte)
Verdi: Forza del destino (Cpte), Rigoletto (Cpte),
Traviata (Cpte)
Wagner: Götterdämmerung (Cpte), Parsifal (Cpte)
see CONCERT INDEX under:
(DECC) 430 095-2DWO The World of Gilbert &
Sullivan, Vol.1
(DECC) 433 868-2DWO The World of Gilbert &
Sullivan - Volume 2
(PHIL) 438 800-2PM2 Mozart—Choral Works
(SONY) M3K79312 Puccini: Il Trittico

KNIGHT, Janice (cor ang)
see CONCERT INDEX under:
(HYPE) CDA66496 Villa-Lobos: Chamber Works

KNIJFF, Jan Piet (hpd)
Schnittke: Concerto grosso 4

KNIPLOVÁ, Naděžda (sop)
Janáček: Jenufa (Cpte)
see CONCERT INDEX under:
(DECC) 421 852-2DH2 Janáček: Operatic & Chamber Works

KNOBLICH, Hans Georg (sngr)
Flotow: Martha (Cpte)

KNODT, Erich (bass)
Wagner: Fliegende Holländer (Cpte)

KNOLL, Rudolf (bar)
Mozart: Don Giovanni (exc)

KNÖPPEL, Michael (bass)
Weill: Jasager (Cpte)

KNOR, Stanislav (pf)
see CONCERT INDEX under:
(SUPR) 11 1105-2 Gershwin & Milhaud—orchestral works

KNÖRZER, Ulrich (va)
see CONCERT INDEX under:
(CAPR) 10 452 Boccherini Edition, Vol.7

KNOWLES, Gregory (perc)
see CONCERT INDEX under:
(VIRG) VC5 45003-2 Contemporary Trumpet Music

KNOX, Garth (va)
see CONCERT INDEX under:
(AUVI) MO782025 Schoenberg—Chamber Music, Vol. 3

KNUDSEN, Sato (vc)
see CONCERT INDEX under:
(NORT) NR248-CD Silenced Voices - Victims of the Holocaust

KNÜPFER, Paul (bass)
see CONCERT INDEX under:
(SUPR) 11 2136-2(3) Emmy Destinn—Complete Edition, Discs 5 to 8

KNUSSEN, Oliver (cond)
see BBC SO

KNUTSON, David (alto)
Hindemith: Nusch-Nuschi (Cpte)

KOBAYASHI, Marie (mez)
Berg: Lulu (Cpte)

KÖBERLE, Ulrich (ten)
Delius: Village Romeo and Juliet (Cpte)
Schillings: Mona Lisa (Cpte)

KOBLITZ, Ingo (ten)
R. Strauss: Rosenkavalier (Cpte)

KOBYHYANSKY, Arnold (vn)
Vainberg: String Quartet 12

KOCH, Egmont (bar)
Wagner: Götterdämmerung (Cpte)

KOCH, Ferdinand (ten)
see CONCERT INDEX under:
(VOX) CDX2 5504 Bruckner/Liszt/Wagner—Orchestral Works

KOCH, Lothar (ob)
see CONCERT INDEX under:
(DG) 423 888-2GGA R. Strauss—Orchestral & Vocal Works

KOCH, Martin (cond)
see London Cast

KOCH, Ulrich (va)
R. Strauss: Don Quixote
see CONCERT INDEX under:
(BAYE) BR100058 Serenada Hungaria

KOCHERGA, Anatoly (bass)
Mussorgsky: Boris Godunov (Cpte), Khovanshchina
(Cpte), Songs and Dances of Death
Shostakovich: Lady Macbeth of Mtsensk (Cpte)
Tchaikovsky: Mazeppa (Cpte)

KOČÍ, Přemysl (bass)
Hába: Mother (Cpte)
Janáček: Makropulos Affair (Cpte)

KOČÍ, Viktor (ten)
Janáček: From the House of the Dead (Cpte), Káťa
Kabanová (Cpte), Makropulos Affair (Cpte)

KOCIÁN, Vojtech (ten)
Martinů: Miracles of Mary (Cpte)

KOCIAN QUARTET
Brahms: Piano Quartet 3, Piano Quintet, String Sextet
1, String Sextet 2
Bruckner: String Quintet
Dvořák: String Quartet 10, String Quartet 14
see CONCERT INDEX under:
(SUPR) 11 2166-2 Schulhoff—Chamber Works, Volume 1

KOCSIS, Zoltán (cond)
see Budapest Wind Ens

KOCSIS, Zoltán (pf)
Bartók: For Children (1945)
see CONCERT INDEX under:
(HUNG) HCD12991 20th Century Percussion Works
(PHIL) 412 118-2PH Debussy: Piano works
(PHIL) 416 831-2PH3 Bartok: Works for Piano &
Orchestra
(PHIL) 422 404-2PH Debussy: Piano Works
(PHIL) 434 104-2PH Bartók—Piano Works, Vol.1
(PHIL) 438 380-2PM2 Best of Grieg
(PHIL) 442 016-2PH Bartók—Piano Works, Vol.2
(PHIL) 442 405-2PM Kocsis plays Beethoven
(PHIL) 442 466-2PH Bartók—Piano Concertos

KÓCZIÁN, Johanna von (voc)
Weill: Dreigroschenoper (Cpte)

KODADOVÁ, Renata (hp)
see CONCERT INDEX under:
(SUPR) 11 1533-2 Suk—Chamber Works, Volume 3

KODÁLY QUARTET
Beethoven: String Quartet 1, String Quartet 2
Brahms: Piano Quintet
Haydn: String Quartet, Op. 42, String Quartet, Op. 51,
String Quartet, Op. 103, String Quartets, Op. 2 (exc),
String Quartets, Op. 9 (exc), String Quartets, Op.20
(exc), String Quartets, Op. 33 (exc), String Quartets,
Op.64 (exc), String Quartets, Op. 71, String Quartets,
Op. 74, String Quartets, Op. 77 (exc)
Indy: String Quartet 1, String Quartet 2
Kodály: String Quartet 1, String Quartet 2
Schubert: Adagio and Rondo concertante, D487,
String Quartet, D87, String Quartet, D804, Trout
Quintet, D667
Schumann: Piano Quintet, Op. 44
see CONCERT INDEX under:
(NAXO) 8 550886 Bartók—Chamber Works

KODAMA, Mari (pf)
see CONCERT INDEX under:
(ASV) CDDCA786 Prokofiev—Piano Works

KOECKERT, Rudolf (vn)
R. Strauss: Don Quixote

KOECKERT QUARTET
Schumann: String Quartet 1, String Quartet 3

KOENEN, Rolf (hpd)
Bach: Flute Sonatas, BWV1030-5 (exc)
Marais: Variations on 'Les folies d'Espagne'

KOENIG, Gottfried Michael (tape op)
see CONCERT INDEX under:
(WERG) WER60161-50 Ligeti: Instrumental Works

KOENIG, Jan Latham (cond)
see LPO

KOEPPEL, Brent (computer/tape op)
see CONCERT INDEX under:
(BRID) BCD9031 J. Harvey—Miscellaneous Works

KOERMENDI, Klára (pf)
see CONCERT INDEX under:
(NAXO) 8 550696 Satie—Piano Works, Vol.1

KOFFMANE, Robert (bar)
Wagner: Meistersinger (Cpte)

KOGAN, Leonid (vn)
see CONCERT INDEX under:
(EMI) CZS7 67732-2 Leonid Kogan - A profile
(RCA) 09026 61893-2 Pierre Monteux Edition

KOGAN, Oleg (vc)
see CONCERT INDEX under:
(O111) OPS30-121 Haydn—English and Scottish Songs

KOGEL, Richard (bass)
Orff: Kluge (Cpte), Mond (Cpte)

KOGOSOWSKI, Alan (pf)
see CONCERT INDEX under:
(CHAN) CHAN9261 Rachmaninov—Orchestral transcriptions

KÖHLER, Annette (mez)
Telemann: Don Quichotte (Cpte)

KÖHLER, Axel (alto)
Almeida: Giuditta (Cpte)
Hasse: Conversione di Sant' Agostino (Cpte)
Monteverdi: Incoronazione di Poppea (Cpte)
Telemann: Donner-Ode
see CONCERT INDEX under:
(CAPR) 10 431 Musical Table Entertainment
(CAPR) 10 547 Handel—Arias

KÖHLER, Christopher (hn)
see CONCERT INDEX under:
(EMI) CZS7 67521-2 Schumann—Concertos

KÖHLER, Markus (bar)
Krenek: Reisebuch, Op. 62 (Cpte)
Schreker: Gezeichneten (Cpte)

KOHN, Eugene (cond)
see Munich RO

KOHN, Karl Christian (bass)
Berg: Wozzeck (Cpte)
Busoni: Doktor Faust (Cpte)
Egk: Verlobung in San Domingo (Cpte)
Handel: Giulio Cesare (Cpte)
Hindemith: Cardillac (Cpte)
Mozart: Don Giovanni (Cpte)
R. Strauss: Arabella (Cpte), Capriccio (Cpte)
Weber: Freischütz (Cpte)

KOHNEN, Robert (hpd)
Couperin: Nouveaux Concerts (exc), Pièces de violes
Devienne: Bassoon Sonatas, Op. 24
Handel: Flute Sonatas (exc)
Leclair: Violin Sonatas, Op.1 (exc), Violin Sonatas, Op.2 (exc)
Marais: Pièces de viole VII (exc)
Rameau: Pièces de clavecin en concerts
Telemann: Musique de Table (exc)
Zelenka: Trio Sonatas
see CONCERT INDEX under:
(ACCE) ACC8537D French Oboe Music
(ACCE) ACC5019D Italian Flute Sonatas
(ACCE) ACC48013D Telemann—Works for Oboe & continuo
(ACCE) ACC57804D Works for oboe
(ACCE) ACC58019D German Chamber Music
(ACCE) ACC58436D Leclair: Flute Sonatas, Vol.2
(ACCE) ACC68014D Music for two bass viols
(PIER) PV788012 French Viola da gamba and Harpsichord Works

KOHOUT, Antonín (vc)
Brahms: String Sextet 1, String Sextet 2

KOHOUT, Karel (tbn)
see CONCERT INDEX under:
(SUPR) 11 1878-2 The Unknown Janáček

KOHT, Maja (sop)
Delius: Village Romeo and Juliet (Cpte)

KOIZUMI, Kazuhiro (cond)
see RPO

KOJIAN, Varujan (cond)
see Hong Kong PO

KOL, Bracha (rec)
see CONCERT INDEX under:
(CARL) PWK1138 Baroque Favourites

KOLASSI, Irma (mez)
see CONCERT INDEX under:
(EMI) CHS7 69741-2(3) Record of Singing, Vol.4—French School

KOLBEN, Robert (pf)
see CONCERT INDEX under:

(KOCH) 37109-2 Ullmann—Chamber Works

KOLBINGER, Karl (bn)
Haydn: Sinfonia concertante

KOLCHINSKY, Camilla (cond)
see Polish Nat RSO

KOLDITZ, Martin (alto)
see CONCERT INDEX under:
(CAPR) 10 367 Mendelssohn—Motets

KOLISCH, Rudolf (vn/va)
Schoenberg: Pierrot Lunaire

KOLISCH QUARTET
Mozart: String Quartet, K465, String Quartet, K589
see CONCERT INDEX under:
(ARCI) ARC103/4 Schoenberg—String Quartets

KOLK, Stanley (ten)
Orff: Carmina Burana

KOLL, Heinrich (va)
R. Strauss: Don Quixote

KOLLO, Ants (ten)
Tubin: Barbara von Tisenhusen (Cpte)

KOLLO, René (ten)
Beethoven: Fidelio (Cpte)
Korngold: Tote Stadt (Cpte)
Lehár: Lustige Witwe (exc)
Mahler: Lied von der Erde, Symphony 8
R. Strauss: Ariadne auf Naxos (Cpte), Frau ohne Schatten (Cpte)
Wagner: Götterdämmerung (Cpte), Lohengrin (Cpte), Meistersinger (Cpte), Parsifal (Cpte), Rienzi (Cpte), Siegfried (Cpte), Tannhäuser (Cpte), Tristan und Isolde (Cpte)
Weber: Freischütz (Cpte)
Weill: Dreigroschenoper (Cpte)
see CONCERT INDEX under:
(ACAN) 43 266 Bernd Weikl—Operatic Recital
(DECC) 430 804-2DC10 Mahler—Complete Symphonies
(DG) 423 481-2GX6 Beethoven: Complete Symphonies
(DG) 435 712-2GX2 Lehár—The Merry Widow. Suppé—Overtures
(EMI) CDC7 54776-2 René Kollo sings Wagner and Strauss

KOLMAKOVA, Loudmila (mez)
Mussorgsky: Marriage (Cpte)

KOLMAN, Barry (cond)
see Slovak RSO

KOLNIAK, Angela (sop)
Mozart: Nozze di Figaro (Cpte)

KOLOWRATNIK, Karl (sngr)
see CONCERT INDEX under:
(SCHW) 314632 Vienna State Opera Live, Vol.13

KOMAN, Hollace C. (organ)
see CONCERT INDEX under:
(KOCH) 37215-2 Italian Orchestral Music

KOMANCOVÁ, Ludmila (contr)
Janáček: Káťa Kabanová (Cpte)

KOMAREK, Dora (sop)
see CONCERT INDEX under:
(SCHW) 314572 Vienna State Opera Live, Vol.7
(SCHW) 314602 Vienna State Opera Live, Vol.10
(SCHW) 314632 Vienna State Opera Live, Vol.13
(SCHW) 314652 Vienna State Opera Live, Vol.15

KOMARNICZKY, Zita (sop)
Respighi: Belfagor (Cpte)

KOMATSU, Hidenori (bar)
Puccini: Madama Butterfly (Cpte)
see CONCERT INDEX under:
(CPO) CPO999 262-2 Romantic Duets
(HARM) HMC90 1420 Weill—The Seven Deadly Sins; Songs
(HARM) HMC90 5210 Duos Romantiques

KOMEN, Paul (pf)
Brahms: Cello Sonata 1, Cello Sonata 2
see CONCERT INDEX under:
(ETCE) KTC1074 Works for Oboe & Piano

KOMLÓSI, Ildikó (mez)
Wagner: Rheingold (Cpte)

KOMLÓSSY, Erzsébet (contr)
see CONCERT INDEX under:
(DECC) 421 810-2DM2 Dvořák & Kodály: Vocal Works
(DECC) 443 488-2DF2 Kodály—Háry János; Psalmus Hungaricus etc

KOMST, Marinus (timp)
see CONCERT INDEX under:
(DECC) 444 455-2DH Martin—Ballades; Concerto for 7 Wind Instruments

KONDO, Fusako (mez)
see CONCERT INDEX under:
(TIMP) 1C1010 Honegger—Chamber Works, Vol.3
(TIMP) 1C1011 Honegger—Chamber Works, Vol.4
(TIMP) 4C1012 Honegger—Chamber Works

KONDRASHIN, Kyrill (cond)
see BRSO

KONETZNI, Anny (sop)
Wagner: Parsifal (exc), Tristan und Isolde (exc)
see CONCERT INDEX under:

(SCHW) 314502 Vienna State Opera—Live Recordings (sampler)
(SCHW) 314512 Vienna State Opera Live, Vol.1
(SCHW) 314532 Vienna State Opera Live, Vol.3
(SCHW) 314562 Vienna State Opera Live, Vol.6
(SCHW) 314592 Vienna State Opera Live, Vol.9
(SCHW) 314632 Vienna State Opera Live, Vol.13
(SCHW) 314652 Vienna State Opera Live, Vol.15
(SCHW) 314662 Vienna State Opera Live, Vol.16
(SCHW) 314672 Vienna State Opera Live, Vol.17

KONETZNI, Hilde (sop)
Beethoven: Fidelio (Cpte)
Verdi: Don Carlo (exc)
Weber: Oberon (exc)
see CONCERT INDEX under:
(EMI) CHS7 69741-2(4) Record of Singing, Vol.4—German School
(EMI) CZS7 57123-2 Wagner: Der Ring des Nibelungen
(LYRC) SRO830 Smetana—The Bartered Bride, etc
(PREI) 90078 Hilde Konetzni
(PREI) 93261 Richard Strauss accompanies
(SCHW) 314502 Vienna State Opera—Live Recordings (sampler)
(SCHW) 314582 Vienna State Opera Live, Vol.5
(SCHW) 314582 Vienna State Opera Live, Vol.8
(SCHW) 314592 Vienna State Opera Live, Vol.9
(SCHW) 314602 Vienna State Opera Live, Vol.10
(SCHW) 314602 Vienna State Opera Live, Vol.10
(SCHW) 314672 Vienna State Opera Live, Vol.17

KÖNIG, Klaus (ten)
Beethoven: Symphony 9
K. A. Hartmann: Simplicius Simplicissimus (Cpte)
Mahler: Lied von der Erde
Suder: Kleider machen Leute (Cpte)
Wagner: Tannhäuser (Cpte), Walküre (exc)

KÖNIG ENSEMBLE
cond J. LATHAM-KÖNIG
Weill: Happy End (Cpte), Mahagonny-Gesänge (Cpte)

KONING, Kees-Jan de (bass)
Biber: Requiem in A, Vesperae

KONRÁD, György (va)
see CONCERT INDEX under:
(NAXO) 8 550439 Mozart—Works for Clarinet
(NAXO) 8 550511 Mozart/Beethoven—Quintets for Piano and Wind etc

KONSTANTINIDI, Aristotel (pf)
see CONCERT INDEX under:
(CDM) LDC288 038/40 Rimsky-Korsakov—Complete Songs

KONSULOV, Ivan (bar)
Puccini: Bohème (Cpte)
Tchaikovsky: Queen of Spades (Cpte)
see CONCERT INDEX under:
(OPUS) 9156 1824 Dvorský sings Operatic Arias

KONTARSKY, Alfons (pf)
Boulez: Structures, Bk 1, Structures, Bk 2

KONTARSKY, Aloys (pf)
Boulez: Structures, Bk 1, Structures, Bk 2
Messiaen: Merle noir

KONTARSKY, Bernhard (cond)
see Stuttgart Op Orch

KONTRA, Anton (vn)
Gade: Violin Concerto, Op. 56
see CONCERT INDEX under:
(CHAN) CHAN9209 Lumbye—Waltzes, Galops & Polkas

KONTRA QUARTET
see CONCERT INDEX under:
(BIS) BIS-CD503/4 Nielsen—Chamber Works
(BIS) BIS-CD516 Gade—String Quartets
(BIS) BIS-CD543 Grieg—String Quartets
(BIS) BIS-CD564 Kodaly—String Qaurtets Nos 1 and 2; Gavotte
(MARC) DCCD9203 Holmboe—String Quartets - Volume 1

KONWITSCHNY, Franz (cond)
see Berlin Deutsche Op Orch

KÓNYA, Sándor (ten)
see CONCERT INDEX under:
(RCA) 09026 61580-2(7) RCA/Met 100 Singers, 100 Years (pt 7)

KOÓ, Tamás (vc)
see CONCERT INDEX under:
(NAXO) 8 550511 Mozart/Beethoven—Quintets for Piano and Wind etc

KOOIJMANS, Ad (bar)
R. Strauss: Rosenkavalier (Cpte)

KOOISTRA, Foskien (vn)
see CONCERT INDEX under:
(CHNN) CCS4792 Henry Purcell & His Time

KOON, Theresa (sop)
S. Wagner: Bärenhäuter (Cpte)

KOOPMAN, Ton (cond)
see Amsterdam Baroque Ch

KOOPMAN, Ton (organ)
D. Ortiz: Trattado de glosas
Soler: Organ Concertos
see CONCERT INDEX under:
(CAPR) 10 254 Early English Organ Music

(CAPR) 10 256 Stanley: Organ Voluntaries
(DG) 427 801-2GDC Bach—Organ Works
(NOVA) 150 005-2 Bach: Organ Works, Volume 1
(NOVA) 150 036-2 Bach—Organ Works, Vol.3
(NOVA) 150 048-2 Buxtehude—Organ Works
(TELD) 4509-94458-2 Bach—Organ Works, Volume 1

KOOPMAN, Ton (hpd)
Bach: Wohltemperierte Klavier (exc)
Fiocco: Pièces de clavecin, Op. 1
Forqueray: Pièces de viole (exc)
Marais: Pièces de viole, III/I (exc), Pièces de viole, III/II (exc), Pièces de viole IV/II (exc), Pièces de viole V/II (exc)
see CONCERT INDEX under:
(ASTR) E8503 Merula—Arie e Capricci
(CAPR) 10 210 Bach: Keyboard Works
(PHIL) 422 518-2PME5 The Complete Mozart Edition Vol 18

KOOPMAN, Ton (hpd/dir)
see CONCERT INDEX under:
(PHIL) 422 507-2PME12 The Complete Mozart Edition Vol 7

KOOY, Peter (bass)
Bach: Cantata 42, Cantata 66, Cantata 78, Cantata 80, Cantata 198, Cantata 206, Cantata 207a, Christmas Oratorio, BWV248 (Cpte), Easter Oratorio, BWV249, Magnificat, BWV243, Mass, BWV233, Mass, BWV236, Mass in B minor, BWV232 (Cpte), Motets (Cpte), St John Passion, BWV245 (Cpte), St Matthew Passion, BWV244 (Cpte)
Fauré: Requiem (Cpte)
Gilles: Requiem
Monteverdi: Vespers
Mozart: Mass, K427
see CONCERT INDEX under:
(ERAT) 2292-45822-2 M-A.Charpentier—Motets
(HARM) HMC90 1167 Lully—Grands Motets
(HARM) HMC90 1272 Mendelssohn—Psalms; Ave Maria
(HARM) HMC90 1365 Bach—Cantatas for Bass
(HARM) HMC90 1422 Weill—Orchestral and Choral Works
(HARM) HMC90 1462 Purcell—Funeral Music for Queen Mary; Te Deum; Anthems
(HARM) HMC90 1479 Bach—Cantatas
(HARM) HMX290 1528/33(1) A Purcell Companion (pt 1)
(SONY) SK53981 Purcell—Anthems and Hymns
(VIRG) VC7 59237-2 Bach—Cantatas
(VIRG) VC7 59587-2 Bach—Masses etc

KOPČÁK, Sergej (bass)
see CONCERT INDEX under:
(OPUS) 9156 1824 Dvorský sings Operatic Arias

KOPLEFF, Florence (contr)
Beethoven: Symphony 9
Berlioz: Enfance du Christ (Cpte)
Milhaud: Pacem in Terris

KOPP, Miroslav (ten)
Martinů: Ariane (Cpte)
Smetana: Bartered Bride (Cpte), Dalibor (Cpte)
see CONCERT INDEX under:
(SUPR) 11 0752-2 Martinů—Spaliček, etc
(SUPR) 11 1878-2 The Unknown Janáček

KOPPELSTETTER, Martina (contr)
Bach: Mass in B minor, BWV232 (Cpte)

KORCHINSKA, Maria (hp)
see CONCERT INDEX under:
(DUTT) CDAX8014 British Gramophone Premieres

KORD, Kazimierz (cond)
see SRO

KORÉH, Endre (bass)
see CONCERT INDEX under:
(DECC) 443 530-2LF2 Mozart—Die Entführung aus dem Serail
(EMI) CHS7 69741-2(6) Record of Singing, Vol.4—Russian & Slavonic Schools

KORF, Anthony (cond)
see Parnassus

KORHONEN, Timo (gtr)
see CONCERT INDEX under:
(ONDI) ODE730-2 Twentieth Century Guitar Works
(ONDI) ODE770-2 Ponce—Guitar Works

KORJUS, Miliza (sop)
see CONCERT INDEX under:
(PREI) 89054 Miliza Korjus (1912-1980)
(PREI) 89209 Helge Roswaenge (1897-1972) - II

KORMAN, John (vn)
see CONCERT INDEX under:
(TELA) CD80059 Popular Orchestral Works

KÖRMENDI, Klára (pf)
Mosonyi: Piano Concerto in E minor
see CONCERT INDEX under:
(MARC) 8 223473 Lajtha—Piano Works
(MARC) 8 223558 Mosonyi—Piano Music for Four Hands
(NAXO) 8 550697 Satie—Piano Works, Volume 2
(NAXO) 8 550699 Satie—Piano Works, Volume 4

KORN, Artur (bass)
Beethoven: Symphony 9
Mozart: Nozze di Figaro (Cpte)

KORNEIEV, Alexander (cond)
see USSR RSO Sols Ens

KÖRNER, Ewald (cond)
see Slovak PO

KORNGOLD, Erich (cond)
see Austrian St Rad Orch

KORNIEV, Nikolai (cond)
see St Petersburg Chbr Ch

KORNIEVA, Natalia (sop)
Rachmaninov: Liturgy, Op. 31

KORNILOV, D.G. (pf)
see CONCERT INDEX under:
(PEAR) GEMMCDS9997/9(2) Singers of Imperial
Russia, Vol.1 (pt 2)

KOROLEVA, Ludmila (sop)
see CONCERT INDEX under:
(CDM) LDC288 027/8 Prokofiev—Film and Stage
Music

KOROLEWICZ-WAYDA, Janina (sop)
see CONCERT INDEX under:
(PEAR) GEMMCDS9004/6(1) Singers of Imperial
Russia, Vol.3 (pt 1)

KOROVINA, Tatiana (sngr)
Myslivecek: Abraham and Isaac

KORPÁS, Ferenc (bass)
Bach: St Matthew Passion, BWV244 (Cpte)

KORSOFF, Lucette (sop)
see CONCERT INDEX under:
(IRCC) IRCC-CD802 Souvenirs of Rare French
Opera

KORTE, Hans (sngr)
Weill: Silbersee (Cpte)

KORZYŃSKI, Andrzej (cond)
see OST

KOSBAHN, Gerda (sop)
Schillings: Mona Lisa (Cpte)

KOSCHAK, Dora (mez)
E.T.A. Hoffmann: Undine (Cpte)

KOSHETZ, Nina (sop)
see CONCERT INDEX under:
(MMOI) CDMOIR422 Great Voices in Tchaikovsky
(NIMB) NI7802 Divas 1906-1935

KOŠICE TEACHERS CHOIR
cond J. WILDNER
see CONCERT INDEX under:
(NAXO) 8 550495 Mozart—Sacred Choral Works

KOSINA, Miroslav (vn)
Bach: 2-Violin Concerto (exc)
see CONCERT INDEX under:
(SUPR) 11 1533-2 Suk—Chamber Works, Volume 3

KOSKINEN, Eeva (vn)
see CONCERT INDEX under:
(BIS) BIS-CD560 Sallinen—Orchestral Works

KOŠLER, Zdeněk (cond)
see Czech PO

KOSLOWSKY, Johanna (sop)
Fux: Death of John the Baptist (Cpte)
Landi: Mort d'Orfeo (Cpte)
see CONCERT INDEX under:
(CAPR) 10 208 C.P.E. Bach: Sacred Choral Works
(CPO) CPO999 139-2 The Apocryphal Bach
Cantatas

KOSSOFF, David (ob)
see CONCERT INDEX under:
(SCHW) 310832 Frank Martin—Orchestral Works

KOSTELANETZ, André (cond)
see Columbia SO

KOSTER, Ab (hn)
Mozart: Horn Concerti, Rondo, K371

KÖSTERS, Johannes M. (bar)
see CONCERT INDEX under:
(SONY) SK53975 Composers Inspired by the Poet
Friedrich Hölderlin

KOSTIA, Raili (contr)
Mozart: Zauberflöte (Cpte)

KOSUGI, Takehisa (voc)
see CONCERT INDEX under:
(KOCH) 37238-2 A Chance Operation - John Cage
Tribute

KOSZUT, Ursula (sop)
B.A. Zimmermann: Soldaten (Cpte)
Hindemith: Mathis der Maler (Cpte)
Nono: Intolleranza 1960 (Cpte)

KÖTH, Erika (sop)
Benatzky: Im weissen Rössl (exc)
Fall: Rose von Stambul (exc)
J. Strauss II: Fledermaus (Cpte), Zigeunerbaron
(Cpte)
Millöcker: Dubarry (exc)
Mozart: Entführung (exc)
Wagner: Siegfried (Cpte), Walküre (Cpte)
Zeller: Vogelhändler (exc)
see CONCERT INDEX under:
(DG) 431 110-2GB Great Voices - Fritz Wunderlich
(EMI) CDH5 65201-2 Leonie Rysanek - Operatic
Recital
(EMI) CHS7 69741-2(4) Record of Singing,
Vol.4—German School
(PHIL) 446 057-2PB14 Wagner—The Ring Cycle -
Bayreuth Festival 1967

KOTIK, Petr (cond)
see S.E.M. Ens Orch

KOTILAINEN, Juha (bar)
Sallinen: Kullervo (Cpte)

KOTLIAROV, Mikhail (ten)
see CONCERT INDEX under:
(DECC) 436 762-2DH Shostakovich—Orchestral &
Vocal Works

KOTOSKI, Dawn (sop)
Handel: Giustino (Cpte)

KOTOWSKA, Adela (pf)
see CONCERT INDEX under:
(PEAR) GEMMCD9939 Josef Hassid & Ida Haendel -
1940-42 Recordings

KÖTTER, Paul (ten)
see CONCERT INDEX under:
(SCHW) 314672 Vienna State Opera Live, Vol.17

KOTZIA, Eleftheria (gtr)
see CONCERT INDEX under:
(PEAR) SHECD9609 The Blue Guitar

KOUSNIETZOFF, Marie (sop)
see CONCERT INDEX under:
(PEAR) GEMMCDS9924(2) Covent Garden on
Record, Vol.2 (pt 2)

KOUSSEVITZKY, Serge (cond)
see BBC SO

KOUSSEVITZKY, Serge (db)
see CONCERT INDEX under:
(BIDD) WHL019 Koussevitzky—Double-bass
Recordings & Early Boston SO

KOUTNIK, Tomas (cond)
see Slovak RSO

KOVA, Marija (sop)
R. Ward: Crucible (Cpte)

KOVACEVICH, Stephen (cond)
see Australian CO

KOVACEVICH, Stephen (pf)
Beethoven: Bagatelles (exc), Cello Sonata 3, Cello
Sonata 5, Diabelli Variations, Piano Concerto 3,
Piano Concerto 4, Piano Concerto 5, Piano Sonata
30
Brahms: Lieder, Op.91, Lieder, Op.105, Piano
Concerto 1, Piano Concerto 2
Mozart: Piano Concerto 21, Piano Concerto 25
see CONCERT INDEX under:
(EMI) CDC5 55226-2 Beethoven—Piano Sonatas
(EMI) CDC5 55359-2 Schubert—Piano Works, Vol.1
(EMI) CDC7 54599-2 Beethoven—Piano Sonatas
(EMI) CDC7 54896-2 Beethoven—Piano Sonatas
(EMI) CDM7 63165-2 Jacqueline Du Pré—Early BBC
Recordings, Vol.1
(EMI) CZS5 68132-2 Les introuvables de Jacqueline
du Pré
(PHIL) 420 750-2PH Brahms: Piano Works
(PHIL) 422 514-2PME5 The Complete Mozart Edition
Vol 14
(PHIL) 426 660-2PSL Bartók—Piano Concertos
(PHIL) 438 380-2PM2 Best of Grieg
(PHIL) 438 812-2PM2 Bartók—Orchestral Works
(PHIL) 442 577-2PM2 Beethoven—Concertos,
Volume 1
(PHIL) 442 580-2PM2 Beethoven—Concertos,
Volume 2
(PHIL) 446 154-2PM2 Mozart—The Complete Piano
Trios

KOVACEVICH, Stephen (pf/dir)
Beethoven: Piano Concerto 5

KOVACIC, Ernst (vn)
Stevens: Violin Concerto
see CONCERT INDEX under:
(HYPE) CDA66473 Violin Duets
(LARG) Largo 5124 HK Gruber—...aus schatten duft
gewebt
(ONDI) ODE826-2 Sibelius—Early Chamber Music,
Vol. 1

KOVÁCS, Attila (bass)
Delius: Village Romeo and Juliet (Cpte)

KOVÁCS, Béla (cl)
see CONCERT INDEX under:
(NAXO) 8 550390 Mozart—Chamber Works for
Clarinet
(NAXO) 8 550439 Mozart—Works for Clarinet
(NAXO) 8 550511 Mozart/Beethoven—Quintets for
Piano and Wind etc

KOVÁCS, Imre (fl)
see CONCERT INDEX under:
(MARC) 8 223727 Truscott—Chamber Music
(NAXO) 8 550511 Mozart/Beethoven—Quintets for
Piano and Wind etc

KOVÁCS, János (cond)
see Hungarian St Orch

KOVÁCS, László (cond)
see Budapest Camerata

KOVALENKO, I. (ten)
Tchaikovsky: Eugene Onegin (Cpte)

KOVALENKO, Maria (sop)
see CONCERT INDEX under:
(NIMB) NI7865 Great Singers at the Mariinsky
Theatre

KOVALEV, Alexander (vc)
see CONCERT INDEX under:
(OLYM) OCD542 Glazunov—Chamber Works

KOVALYOV, Alexander (vc)
see CONCERT INDEX under:
(OLYM) OCD523 Shostakovich Quartet - Volume 3

KOVÁTS, Kolos (bass)
Bartók: Duke Bluebeard's Castle (Cpte)
Rossini: Guillaume Tell (Cpte)
see CONCERT INDEX under:
(CAPR) 10 451/5 Beethoven—Symphonies 1-9

KÖVES, Péter (bass)
Bach: St Matthew Passion, BWV244 (Cpte)
Mozart: Zauberflöte (Cpte)

KOVES, Toni (cimbalom)
see CONCERT INDEX under:
(SONY) SM3K46291 Stravinsky—Ballets, Vol.1

KOWALSKI, Jochen (alto)
Gluck: Orfeo ed Euridice (Cpte)
Handel: Samson (Cpte), Theodora (Cpte)
Orff: Carmina Burana
see CONCERT INDEX under:
(CAPR) 10 113 Berlin Opera Composers
(CAPR) 10 213 Handel and Mozart Arias for
Countertenor
(CAPR) 10 359 Jochen Kowalski—Lieder Recital
(CAPR) 10 416 Jochen Kowalski sings Opera Arias
(CAPR) 10 523 Jochen Kowalski sings Bach Cantatas
(CAPR) 10 532 Kowalski sings Bach and Handel
Sacred Arias

KOWOLLIK, Maria (mez)
Spohr: Faust (Cpte)

KOZDERKA, Ladislav (tpt)
see CONCERT INDEX under:
(SUPR) 11 1878-2 The Unknown Janáček

KOZDERKA, Vladimir (tpt)
see CONCERT INDEX under:
(SUPR) 11 0751-2 Martinů—Choral Works

KOŽENÁ, Magdalena (contr)
Zelenka: Requiem, ZWV48

KOZLOVSKY, Ivan (ten)
(EMI) CHS7 69741-2(6) Record of Singing,
Vol.4—Russian & Slavonic Schools

KOZLOWSKA, Joanna (sop)
Górecki: Symphony 3
Mozart: Finta giardiniera (Cpte)

KOZMA, Lajos (ten)
Liszt: Faust Symphony
Monteverdi: Orfeo (Cpte)
Vivaldi: Orlando Furioso (Cpte)
see CONCERT INDEX under:
(DECC) 421 810-2DM2 Dvořák & Kodály: Vocal
Works
(DECC) 433 080-2DM Kodály—Choral Works
(DECC) 443 488-2DF2 Kodály—Háry János; Psalmus
Hungaricus etc
(RCA) GD60941 Rarities - Montserrat Caballé

KOZNOWSKI, Zenon (bass)
R. Strauss: Salome (Cpte)

KOŽUŠNÍK, Karel (ten)
see CONCERT INDEX under:
(KOCH) 37230-2 Terezín Music Anthology, Volume 2

KRAAK, Meinard (ten)
see CONCERT INDEX under:
(PHIL) 438 528-2PM4(1) Schubert—Lieder (pt 1)

KRAAMWINKEL, Nicoline (vn)
(MERI) CDE84286 Ethel Smyth—Impressions that
Remain

KRACHMALNICK, Samuel (cond)
see NYC Op Orch

KRAEMER, Nicholas (cond)
see Raglan Baroque Players

KRAEMER, Nicholas (hpd)
Avison: Concerti after D. Scarlatti
Bach: 4-Harpsichord Concerto

KRAFT, Jean (mez)
Giordano: Andrea Chénier (Cpte)
Verdi: Otello (Cpte)

KRAFT, Kathleen (fl)
see CONCERT INDEX under:
(KOCH) 37138-2 Bach—Solo Cantatas

KRAFT, Norbert (gtr)
Paganini: Centone di sonate (exc)
see CONCERT INDEX under:
(CHAN) CHAN8784 Modern Solo Guitar Works
(CHAN) CHAN8937 Arrangements for Guitar and
Harpsichord
(CHAN) CHAN9033 Romantic Works for Guitar
(NAXO) 8 550729 Guitar Concertos
(NAXO) 8 553007 19th Century Guitar Favourites

KRAHMER, Renate (sop)
Mendelssohn: Elias (Cpte)

KRAINEV, Vladimir (pf)
see CONCERT INDEX under:
(RCA) 09026 60466-2 Modern Portraits II - Spivakov
(RCA) 74321 20297-2 Scriabin—Symphonies, etc
(RCA) 74321 24894-2 Homage to Schnittke

(TELD) 9031-73257-2   Prokofiev—Piano Concertos

KRAJNÝ, Boris (pf)
Ravel: Left-Hand Concerto, Piano Concerto
  see CONCERT INDEX *under:*
(SUPR) 11 0684-2   Ravel/Poulenc—Works for Piano and Orchestra

KRÁMER, Elisabeth (pf)
Orff: Catulli Carmina
Stravinsky: Noces
  see CONCERT INDEX *under:*
(WERG) WER6275-2   Orff—Trionfi

KRÁMER, Manfred (vn)
  see CONCERT INDEX *under:*
(ARCH) 419 633-2AH   Telemann: Wind Concertos

KRÄMMER, Hans (bar)
J. Strauss II: Fledermaus (Cpte)

KRAPP, Edgar (organ)
Kodály: Laudes Organi, Missa Brevis
  see CONCERT INDEX *under:*
(RCA) 09026 61186-2   Works for Trumpet & Organ
(WERG) WER6199-2   Messiaen—Organ Works

KRASA, Rudolf (bar)
  see CONCERT INDEX *under:*
(SUPR) 11 2136-2(3)   Emmy Destinn—Complete Edition, Discs 5 to 8

KRASNER, Louis (vn)
Berg: Violin Concerto
Schoenberg: Violin Concerto

KRÁSOVÁ, Marta (mez)
Dvořák: Stabat mater

KRASOVSKY, Emanuel (pf)
  see CONCERT INDEX *under:*
(CARL) PWK1137   Romantic Strings

KRASTEVA, Svetla (sop)
Gluck: Iphigénie en Tauride (Cpte)

KRATĚNOVÁ, Jana (sop)
Krása: Brundibár (Cpte)

KRATOCHVÍLOVÁ, Anna (sop)
Martinů: Miracles of Mary (Cpte)
  see CONCERT INDEX *under:*
(SUPR) 11 0752-2   Martinů—Spaliček, etc

KRAUS, Adalbert (ten)
Bach: Cantata 6, Cantata 21, Cantata 28, Cantata 31, Cantata 63, Cantata 66, Cantata 93, Cantata 106, Cantata 134, Cantata 194, Easter Oratorio, BWV249 (Cpte)
Pfitzner: Palestrina (Cpte)
Wagner: Meistersinger (Cpte)
  see CONCERT INDEX *under:*
(HANS) 98 801   Bach—Cantatas, Vol.39
(HANS) 98 802   Bach—Cantatas, Vol.40
(HANS) 98 803   Bach—Cantatas, Vol.41
(HANS) 98 804   Bach—Cantatas, Vol.42
(HANS) 98 807   Bach—Cantatas, Vol.45
(HANS) 98 808   Bach—Cantatas, Vol.46
(HANS) 98 809   Bach—Cantatas, Vol.47
(HANS) 98 810   Bach—Cantatas, Vol.48
(HANS) 98 812   Bach—Cantatas, Vol.50
(HANS) 98 813   Bach—Cantatas, Vol.51
(HANS) 98 814   Bach—Cantatas, Vol.52
(HANS) 98 816   Bach—Cantatas, Vol.54
(HANS) 98 819   Bach—Cantatas, Vol.57
(HANS) 98 820   Bach—Cantatas, Vol.58
(HANS) 98 821   Bach—Cantatas, Vol.59
(HANS) 98 822   Bach—Cantatas, Vol.60
(HANS) 98 824   Bach—Cantatas, Vol.62
(HANS) 98 825   Bach—Cantatas, Vol.63
(HANS) 98 826   Bach—Cantatas, Vol.64
(HANS) 98 828   Bach—Cantatas, Vol.66
(HANS) 98 829   Bach—Cantatas, Vol.67
(HANS) 98 835   Bach—Cantatas, Vol.69
(HANS) 98 856   Bach—Cantatas, Vol.5
(HANS) 98 858   Bach—Cantatas, Vol.7
(HANS) 98 859   Bach—Cantatas, Vol.8
(HANS) 98 861   Bach—Cantatas, Vol.10
(HANS) 98 863   Bach—Cantatas, Vol.12
(HANS) 98 864   Bach—Cantatas, Vol.13
(HANS) 98 866   Bach—Cantatas, Vol.15
(HANS) 98 867   Bach—Cantatas, Vol.16
(HANS) 98 868   Bach—Cantatas, Vol.17
(HANS) 98 869   Bach—Cantatas, Vol.18
(HANS) 98 871   Bach—Cantatas, Vol.19
(HANS) 98 871   Bach—Cantatas, Vol.20
(HANS) 98 872   Bach—Cantatas, Vol.21
(HANS) 98 874   Bach—Cantatas, Vol.23
(HANS) 98 875   Bach—Cantatas, Vol.24
(HANS) 98 876   Bach—Cantatas, Vol.25
(HANS) 98 877   Bach—Cantatas, Vol.26
(HANS) 98 878   Bach—Cantatas, Vol.27
(HANS) 98 879   Bach—Cantatas, Vol.28
(HANS) 98 882   Bach—Cantatas, Vol.31
(HANS) 98 883   Bach—Cantatas, Vol.32
(HANS) 98 885   Bach—Cantatas, Volume 34
(HANS) 98 886   Bach—Cantatas, Vol.35
(HANS) 98 887   Bach—Cantatas, Vol.36
(HANS) 98 890   Bach—Cantatas, Vol.37
(HANS) 98 891   Bach—Cantatas, Vol.38
(NOVA) 150 028-2   Bach—Cantatas
(NOVA) 150 029-2   Bach—Cantatas
(TELD) 2292-42573-2   Bach—Cantatas, Volume 19
(TELD) 2292-42576-2   Bach—Cantatas, Volume 20
(TELD) 4509-91758-2   Bach—Cantatas, Vol.4

KRAUS, Alfredo (ten)
Bizet: Jolie fille de Perth (Cpte)

Donizetti: Lucia di Lammermoor (Cpte), Lucrezia Borgia (Cpte)
Gounod: Roméo et Juliette (Cpte)
Massenet: Manon (Cpte), Werther (Cpte)
Mozart: Così fan tutte (Cpte)
Sorozábal: Katiuska (Cpte)
Verdi: Falstaff (Cpte), Rigoletto (Cpte), Traviata (Cpte)
Vives: Doña Francisquita (Cpte)
  see CONCERT INDEX *under:*
(EMI) CDC7 49067-2   Opera Arias and Duets
(EMI) CDM7 63104-2   Alfredo Krauss - Opera Recital
(EMI) CMS7 63244-2   The Art of Maria Callas
(PHIL) 442 785-2PH   The Incomparable Alfredo Kraus
(RCA) 09026 61580-2(8)   RCA/Met 100 Singers, 100 Years (pt 8)

KRAUS, Ernst (ten)
  see CONCERT INDEX *under:*
(SUPR) 11 2136-2(1)   Emmy Destinn—Complete Edition, Discs 1 & 2

KRAUS, Herbert (cond)
  see Vienna Mozart Ens

KRAUS, Herold (ten)
Wagner: Meistersinger (Cpte)

KRAUS, Lili (pf)
  see CONCERT INDEX *under:*
(MUSI) MACD-665   The Goldberg/Kraus Duo plays Mozart and Beethoven

KRAUS, Michael (ten)
B. Goldschmidt: Gewaltige Hahnrei (Cpte)
Busoni: Turandot (Cpte)
Krenek: Jonny spielt auf (Cpte)
Mozart: Zauberflöte (Cpte)
R. Strauss: Rosenkavalier (Cpte)
  see CONCERT INDEX *under:*
(DECC) 440 854-2DH   Ullmann—Der Kaiser von Atlantis
(LARG) Largo5130   Testimonies of War

KRAUS, Otakar (bar)
Lehár: Land des Lächelns (Cpte), Lustige Witwe (Cpte)

KRAUS, Philip (bar)
Beethoven: Fidelio (Cpte)

KRAUS, Richard (cond)
  see Bamberg SO

KRAUSE, Carlos (bass)
Verdi: Simon Boccanegra (Cpte)

KRAUSE, Monika (sop)
Lortzing: Undine (Cpte)
Puccini: Bohème (Cpte)

KRAUSE, Richard (ten)
R. Ward: Crucible (Cpte)

KRAUSE, Tom (bar)
Bach: Mass in B minor, BWV232 (Cpte), St Matthew Passion, BWV244 (Cpte)
Beethoven: Fidelio (Cpte), Missa Solemnis
Berlioz: Roméo et Juliette (Cpte)
Bizet: Carmen (Cpte)
Donizetti: Don Pasquale (Cpte)
Giordano: Andrea Chénier (Cpte)
Gluck: Alceste (1776) (Cpte)
Haydn: Mass 11
J. Strauss II: Fledermaus (Cpte)
Mendelssohn: Erste Walpurgisnacht
Mozart: Nozze di Figaro (Cpte), Requiem
Puccini: Turandot (Cpte)
R. Strauss: Elektra (Cpte), Salome (Cpte)
Rachmaninov: Bells
Tchaikovsky: Iolanta (Cpte)
Verdi: Otello (Cpte)
Wagner: Lohengrin (Cpte)
  see CONCERT INDEX *under:*
(DECC) 421 810-2DM2   Dvořák & Kodály: Vocal Works
(DECC) 425 722-2DM   Mozart—Masonic Music
(DECC) 430 159-2DM   Haydn, M.Haydn & Mozart: Sacred Choral Works
(DECC) 430 498-2DWO   The World of Mozart
(DECC) 433 175-2DM   Bach—Sacred Choral Works

KRAUSS, Clemens (cond)
  see Bayreuth Fest Orch

KRAUSS, Fritz (ten)
Wagner: Walküre (exc)

KRÄUTLER, Walter (ten)
Verdi: Nabucco (Cpte)
  see CONCERT INDEX *under:*
(DECC) 436 464-2DM   Ten Top Baritones & Basses

KRČEK, Jaroslav (cond)
  see Musica Bohemica

KREBBERS, Herman (vn)
Brahms: Violin Concerto
  see CONCERT INDEX *under:*
(MUSI) MACD-780   The Mengelberg Legacy
(PHIL) 420 700-2PSL   Bach: Violin Concertos
(PHIL) 442 580-2PM2   Beethoven—Concertos, Volume 2

KREBILL, Dorothy (mez)
Verdi: Traviata (Cpte)

KREBS, Helmut (ten)
Henze: Junge Lord (Cpte)
J.Strauss II: Fledermaus (Cpte)

Mozart: Requiem
  see CONCERT INDEX *under:*
(DG) 445 400-2GDO10   Ferenc Fricsay - A Portrait
(DG) 445 402-2GDO   Bartók—Orchestral Works
(ERAT) 4509-97407-2   Bach—Cantatas
(ERAT) 4509-98525-2   Bach—Cantatas

KRECHEK, Jaroslav (cond)
  see Capella Istropolitana

KREČMER, Rudolf (cond)
  see Prague Virtuosi

KREDER, Jean-Paul (cond)
  see ORTF Lyric Orch

KREEN, Uno (bass)
Tubin: Barbara von Tisenhusen (Cpte)

KREGER, James (vc)
  see CONCERT INDEX *under:*
(MUSI) MACD-649   Salute To France

KREIDER, Paul (bass)
Puccini: Bohème (Cpte)

KREISLER, Alexander von (cond)
  see Cincinatti Cons

KREISLER, Fritz (pf)
  see CONCERT INDEX *under:*
(BIDD) LAB009/10   The Kreisler Collection

KREISLER, Fritz (vn)
Beethoven: Violin Sonata 8, Violin Sonata 9
Mendelssohn: Violin Concerto, Op.64
Mozart: Violin Concerto, K218
  see CONCERT INDEX *under:*
(BIDD) LAB009/10   The Kreisler Collection
(BIDD) LAB049/50   Kreisler - The Berlin HMV Recordings (1926-7)
(BIDD) LAB068/9   The Kreisler Collection—1921-25
(BIDD) LAB075   Kreisler—1926-1927 Victor Recordings
(BIDD) LAB080   Kreisler—1928 Victor Recordings
(EMI) CDH7 64701-2   Kreisler plays Kreisler
(MMOI) CDMOIR418   Great Voices of the Century—John McCormack
(PEAR) GEMMCDS9996   Kreisler - Violin Concertos
(PEAR) GEMMCD9315   Kreisler/McCormack Duets
(PEAR) GEMMCD9324   Fritz Kreisler plays Encores
(PEAR) GEMMCD9330   Beethoven: Violin Sonatas, Vol.1
(PEAR) GEMMCD9354   Beethoven: Violin Sonatas, Vol.2
(RCA) 09026 61265-2(1)   Rachmaninov—The Complete Recordings (pt 1)
(RCA) 09026 61879-2   Grieg—Historic Recordings
(SYMP) SYMCD1071   Great Violinists, Vol.1
(TEST) SBT1005   Ten Top Tenors

KREISLER, Hugo (vc)
  see CONCERT INDEX *under:*
(BIDD) LAB009/10   The Kreisler Collection
(BIDD) LAB049/50   Kreisler - The Berlin HMV Recordings (1926-7)
(PEAR) GEMMCD9324   Fritz Kreisler plays Encores

KREISLER QUARTET
  see CONCERT INDEX *under:*
(EMI) CDH7 64701-2   Kreisler plays Kreisler

KREJČÍ, Jiří (ob)
  see CONCERT INDEX *under:*
(SUPR) 11 0999-2   Mozart—Wind Quintets & Quartet

KREJČÍK, Vladimír (ten)
Janáček: Cunning Little Vixen (Cpte), Excursions of Mr Brouček (Cpte), Jenufa (Cpte), Makropulos Affair (Cpte)
  see CONCERT INDEX *under:*
(DECC) 421 852-2DH2   Janáček: Operatic & Chamber Works
(DECC) 430 375-2DH2   Janáček—Operatic and Orchestral Works

KREKOW, Ude (bass)
Ligeti: Grand Macabre (Cpte)
Schreker: Schatzgräber (Cpte)

KREMER, Gidon (vn)
Bartók: Violin Sonata 1, Violin Sonata 2
Beethoven: Romances, Violin Concerto, Violin Sonata 4, Violin Sonata 5
Brahms: Double Concerto, Violin Concerto
Glass: Violin Concerto
Gubaidulina: Hommage, Offertorium
Mendelssohn: Violin and Piano Concerto, Violin Concerto (1822)
Nono: Hay que caminar, Lontananza nostalgica
Schnittke: Concerto Grosso 1, Concerto Grosso 5
Schumann: Piano Concerto, Violin Concerto, Violin Concerto, Op.129, Violin Sonata 1, Violin Sonata 2
Shostakovich: Violin Concerto 1
Sibelius: Violin Concerto
Vivaldi: Concerti, Op.8 (exc)
  see CONCERT INDEX *under:*
(DG) 415 138-2GH   Beethoven: Violin Sonatas, Vol. 1
(DG) 427 351-2GH   20th-Century Violin and Piano Works
(DG) 429 231-2GH   Modern Orchestral Works
(DG) 431 168-2GGA   Beethoven & Schubert: Works for Violin & Orchestra
(DG) 431 654-2GH   Schubert—Works for Violin and Piano
(DG) 431 803-2GH   Prokofiev—Violin and Piano Works
(DG) 437 092-2GH   Schubert—Violin Sonatinas
(DG) 437 535-2GH   Schubert—Soirée

(SUPR) **11 0752-2** Martinů—Spaliček, etc
cond **P. KÜHN**
see CONCERT INDEX under:
(SUPR) **CO-72646** Dvořák: Moravian Duets
(SUPR) **11 0751-2** Martinů—Choral Works
(SUPR) **11 0767-2** Martinů—Cantatas
cond **I. PAŘIK**
Myslivecek: Abraham and Isaac
cond **J. PINKAS**
Dvořák: Jacobin (Cpte)

KÜHNE, Rolf (bass)
Beethoven: Symphony 9

KÜHR, Klaus (vc)
see CONCERT INDEX under:
(ETCE) **KTC1045** Menotti: Chamber and Vocal
Works

KUIJKEN, Barthold (cond)
see Octophoros

KUIJKEN, Barthold (fl)
Rameau: Pièces de clavecin en concerts

KUIJKEN, Barthold (fl)
Handel: Flute Sonatas (exc)
Haydn: Divertimentos, HobIV
Leclair: Violin Sonatas, Op.1 (exc), Violin Sonatas,
Op.2 (exc)
Telemann: Fantaisies, TWV40: 2-13 (exc)
see CONCERT INDEX under:
(ACCE) **ACC9177D** Italian Flute Sonatas
(ACCE) **ACC58019D** German Chamber Music
(ACCE) **ACC58436D** Leclair: Flute Sonatas, Vol.2
(ACCE) **ACC68641D** Haydn: Baryton Trios
(DHM) **RD77026** Bach: Flute Sonatas
(SONY) **SK48045** Flute Concertos
(SONY) **S2K53964** C. P. E. Bach—Flute Sonatas

KUIJKEN, Sigiswald (cond)
see OAE

KUIJKEN, Sigiswald (vn)
Bach: Violin Sonatas, BWV1014-19
Rameau: Pièces de clavecin en concerts
see CONCERT INDEX under:
(ACCE) **ACC9292D** Mozart—Sonatas for Keyboard
and Violin, Vol.2
(DHM) **RD77026** Bach: Flute Sonatas
(RCA) **GD71964** Bach: Flute Works

KUIJKEN, Sigiswald (vn/dir)
see CONCERT INDEX under:
(ACCE) **ACC9395D** Bach—Cantatas

KUIJKEN, Sigiswald (vn/va da gamba)
see CONCERT INDEX under:
(ACCE) **ACC58019D** German Chamber Music
(ACCE) **ACC68014D** Music for two bass viols

KUIJKEN, Wieland (va da gamba)
Bach: Violin Sonatas, BWV1030-5
Blavet: Flute Sonatas, Op.2 (exc), Flute Sonatas,
Op.3 (exc)
Couperin: Nouveaux Concerts (exc), Pièces de
violes
Handel: Flute Sonatas (exc)
Leclair: Violin Sonatas, Op.1 (exc), Violin Sonatas,
Op.2 (exc)
Marais: Pièces de viole V/II (exc)
Rameau: Pièces de clavecin en concerts
Sainte-Colombe: Concerts à deux violes esgales
(exc)
see CONCERT INDEX under:
(ACCE) **ACC8537D** French Oboe Music
(ACCE) **ACC57802D** Purcell: Songs and Elegies
(ACCE) **ACC58436D** Leclair: Flute Sonatas, Vol.2
(ACCE) **ACC68014D** Music for two bass viols
(ASTR) **E8757** Purcell—Songs from Orpheus
Britannicus
(DHM) **RD77026** Bach: Flute Sonatas
(HARM) **HMX290 1528/33(2)** A Purcell Companion (pt
2)
(RCA) **GD71964** Bach: Flute Works

KUIJKEN, Wieland (vc)
see CONCERT INDEX under:
(ACCE) **ACC9177D** Italian Flute Sonatas
(ACCE) **ACC57804D** Works for oboe

KUIJKEN, Wieland (vc/va da gamba)
see CONCERT INDEX under:
(ACCE) **ACC58019D** German Chamber Music

KUIJKEN CONSORT
see CONCERT INDEX under:
(ACCE) **ACC77912D** German Church Cantatas and
Arias

KUIJKEN QUARTET
see CONCERT INDEX under:
(DENO) **CO-75850/2** Mozart—'Haydn' Quartets

KUISMA, Rainer (perc)
Crumb: Madrigals, Music for a Summer Evening

KULENKAMPFF, Georg (vn)
Beethoven: Violin Concerto
Bruch: Violin Concerto 1
Mendelssohn: Violin Concerto, Op.64
Schumann: Violin Concerto
Sibelius: Violin Concerto

KULKA, Janos (cond)
see BPO

KULKA, Konstanty (Andrzej) (vn)
see CONCERT INDEX under:
(DECC) **433 816-2DH2** Hindemith—Kammermusik

(POLS) **PNCD045** Lutosławski: Selected Works
(POLS) **PNCD065** Szymanowski: Chamber Works

KULLENBO, Lars (ten)
Lidholm: Dream Play (Cpte)

KULLMAN, Charles (ten)
see CONCERT INDEX under:
(MUSI) **MACD-749** Bruno Walter conducts Mahler
(PREI) **89057** Charles Kullmann (1903-1982)
(SCHW) **314512** Vienna State Opera Live, Vol.1

KULOWITSCH, Jack (db)
see CONCERT INDEX under:
(RCA) **09026 68181-2** French Chamber Works

KULP, Nancy (sngr)
Kern: Show Boat (Cpte)

KUN, Hu (vn)
Barber: Violin Concerto
Bernstein: Serenade
see CONCERT INDEX under:
(NIMB) **NI5192** Prokofiev: Orchestral Works
(NIMB) **NI5357** Hoddinott—Orchestral Works

KUNC, František (bass)
Janáček: Šárka (Cpte)

KUNDE, Gregory (ten)
A. Thomas: Hamlet (Cpte)
Bellini: Bianca e Fernando (Cpte)
Rossini: Armida (Cpte)

KUNDER, Friedmann (bass)
Wagner: Meistersinger (Cpte)

KUNDLÁK, Jozef (ten)
Bellini: Sonnambula (Cpte)
Schumann: Paradies und die Peri (Cpte)
Suchoň: Whirlpool (Cpte)

KÜNNEKE, Eduard (cond)
see Berlin St Op Orch

KUNZ, Claudio (treb)
Puccini: Gianni Schicchi (Cpte)
see CONCERT INDEX under:
(EURO) **GD69043** Puccini: Il Trittico

KUNZ, Erich (bar)
J. Strauss II: Fledermaus (Cpte), Nacht in Venedig
(Cpte), Wiener Blut (exc), Zigeunerbaron (Cpte)
Lehár: Land des Lächelns (Cpte), Lustige Witwe
(Cpte)
Mozart: Così fan tutte (exc), Zauberflöte (Cpte)
R. Strauss: Ariadne auf Naxos (Cpte)
Wagner: Meistersinger (Cpte)
see CONCERT INDEX under:
(EMI) **CDH5 65072-2** Glyndebourne Recorded - 1934-
1994
(EMI) **CHS7 69741-2(4)** Record of Singing,
Vol.4—German School
(PREI) **90168** Wagner—Die Meistersinger, Act 2, etc
(SCHW) **314532** Vienna State Opera Live, Vol.3
(TEST) **SBT1059** Erich Kunz—Opera and Song
Recital

KUNZ, Hanns-Friedrich (bass)
Bach: Cantata 146
see CONCERT INDEX under:
(HANS) **98 808** Bach—Cantatas, Vol.46
(HANS) **98 825** Bach—Cantatas, Vol.63
(HANS) **98 835** Bach—Cantatas, Vol.69
(HANS) **98 873** Bach—Cantatas, Vol.22
(HANS) **98 891** Bach—Cantatas, Vol.38
(TELD) **2292-42559-2** Bach—Cantatas, Volume 12
(TELD) **4509-91757-2** Bach—Cantatas, Vol.3

KUNZ, Ursula (mez)
Wagner: Walküre (Cpte)

KUNZEL, Erich (cond)
see Cincinnati Jazz Orch

KÜPER, Klaus-Jürgen (bar)
R.Strauss: Arabella (Cpte)

KUPPER, Anneliese (sop)
Bruckner: Te Deum
Mozart: Requiem
R. Strauss: Elektra (Cpte)

KUPSA, Friedemann (vc)
see CONCERT INDEX under:
(TROU) **TRO-CD03** Ethel Smyth—Chamber Works,
Vols.1 & 2
(TROU) **TRO-CD1405** Ethel Smyth—Chamber
Works & Songs, Vol.3

KURCZEWSKI, Jerzy (cond)
see Poznan Boys' Ch

KURITSKAYA, Ludmila (pf)
(OLYM) **OCD292** Kabalevsky—Cello Concertos;
Violin and Piano Works

KURKOWSKI, Michal (vn)
see CONCERT INDEX under:
(SCHW) **311116** Dvořák—Bagatelles, Op. 47;
Serenade, Op. 44

KURT, Melanie (sop)
see CONCERT INDEX under:
(IRCC) **IRCC-CD800** Souvenirs from Meyerbeer
Operas
(PEAR) **GEMMCDS9924(2)** Covent Garden on
Record, Vol.2 (pt 2)
(PEAR) **GEMMCDS9925(1)** Covent Garden on
Record—Vol.3 (pt 1)

KURTZ, Efrem (cond)
see NYPO

KURZ, Selma (sop)
see CONCERT INDEX under:
(PEAR) **GEMMCDS9924(1)** Covent Garden on
Record, Vol.2 (pt 1)
(PREI) **89110** Heinrich Schlusnus (1888-1952) - II

KUSCHE, Benno (bar)
J. Strauss II: Wiener Blut (exc)
Orff: Kluge (Cpte), Mond (Cpte)
Wagner: Meistersinger (Cpte)
see CONCERT INDEX under:
(ACAN) **43 268** Peter Anders sings German Opera
Arias
(EMI) **CMS5 65212-2** Wagner—Les introuvables du
Ring
(EURO) **GD69022** Oscar Straus: Operetta excerpts

KUSMIAK, Eugene (pf)
see CONCERT INDEX under:
(APR) **APR7016** The Auer Legacy, Vol.2

KUSNJER, Iván (bar)
Dvořák: Dimitrij (Cpte), Spectre's Bride
Martinů: Czech Rhapsody, Gilgamesh, Miracles of
Mary (Cpte)
Myslivecek: Abraham and Isaac
Orff: Carmina burana
Smetana: Dalibor (Cpte)
Zemlinsky: Lyrische Symphonie
see CONCERT INDEX under:
(CHAN) **CHAN9138** Martinů—Orchestral and Choral
Works
(SUPR) **11 0767-2** Martinů—Cantatas
(SUPR) **11 2214-2** Janáček—Moravian, Hukvaldy &
Silesian Songs
(SUPR) **11 2225-2** Janáček—26 Folk Ballads

KUSSMAUL, Rainer (vn)
see CONCERT INDEX under:
(OLYM) **OCD428** Haydn—Violin Concertos

KUSTER, Paul-Otto (ten)
Weill: Dreigroschenoper (Cpte)

KÜTTENBAUM, Annette (mez)
Schoeck: Massimilla Doni (Cpte)
Wagner: Götterdämmerung (Cpte), Parsifal (Cpte),
Rheingold (Cpte)

KUTTNER, Max (ten)
see CONCERT INDEX under:
(PREI) **89209** Helge Roswaenge (1897-1972) - II

KUUSK, Ivo (ten)
Tubin: Barbara von Tisenhusen (Cpte)

KUZMIN, Leonid (pf)
see CONCERT INDEX under:
(RUSS) **RDCD10021** Liszt—Piano Works

KUZNETSOV, Leo (ten)
Tchaikovsky: Eugene Onegin (Cpte)

KUZNETSOVA, Ludmilla (mez)
see CONCERT INDEX under:
(CHAN) **CHAN9397** Grechaninov—Choral &
Orchestral Works

KUZNETSOVA, Maria (sop)
see CONCERT INDEX under:
(PEAR) **GEMMCDS9004/6(1)** Singers of Imperial
Russia, Vol.3 (pt 1)
(SYMP) **SYMCD1105** The Harold Wayne Collection,
Vol.10

KVALBEIN, Aage (vc)
Grieg: Cello Sonata
see CONCERT INDEX under:
(VICT) **VCD19071** Grieg—Chamber Works, Vol.1

KVAM, Terje (cond)
see Hanover Band

KVAPIL, Jan (vn)
see CONCERT INDEX under:
(SUPR) **11 0767-2** Martinů—Cantatas

KVAPIL, Radoslav (pf)
Dvořák: Poetic Tone Pictures, Theme with
Variations
Janáček: Moravian folk poetry in songs (exc)
Smetana: Bagatelles and Impromptus, B40, Czech
Dances, T112
see CONCERT INDEX under:
(BIS) **BIS-CD234** Martinů—Chamber Works
(CALL) **CAL9206** Czech Piano Music
(CALL) **CAL9690** Smetana—Chamber and
Instrumental Works
(CALL) **CAL9699** Janáček—Chamber and Piano
Works
(NIMB) **NI5103** Music for Brass, Piano and
Percussion
(UNIC) **DKPCD9140** Anthology of Czech Piano Music
- Volume 3
(UNIC) **DKPCD9145** Voříšek—Piano Music
(UNIC) **DKPCD9149** Fibich—Anthology of Czech
Piano Music, Volume 5
(UNIC) **DKPCD9152** Smetana—Anthology of Czech
Piano Music, Volume 6
(UNIC) **DKPCD9156** Anthology of Czech Piano Music,
Volume 7

KWEKSILBER, Marjanne (sop)
Campra: Europe galante
Gluck: Orfeo ed Euridice (Cpte)
Handel: Messiah (Cpte)
see CONCERT INDEX under:

LAIL, Lorri (contr)
see CONCERT INDEX under:
(CPRI) **CAP21510** Rosenberg plays Rosenberg
(EMI) **CHS7 69741-2(5)** Record of Singing,
Vol.4—Scandinavian School

LAINE, Cleo (sngr)
Bernstein: On the Town (Cpte)

LAINE, Esko (db)
Boccherini: Sextets, G461-6 (exc)

LAIRD, Michael (tpt)
see CONCERT INDEX under:
(ARGO) **417 818-2ZH** American Music
(L'OI) **410 553-2OH** 18th Century Orchestral Works
(L'OI) **411 949-2OH** Telemann: Double & Triple
Concertos
(PHIL) **412 892-2PH** Vivaldi: Double Concertos
(PHIL) **420 954-2PH** Telemann—Trumpet Concertos

(MICHAEL) LAIRD BRASS ENSEMBLE
see CONCERT INDEX under:
(ARGO) **433 451-2ZH** Trumpet Voluntary—Music for
Organ and Brass

LAITER, Alexandre (ten)
Chausson: Roi Arthus (Cpte)
Saint-Saëns: Henry VIII (Cpte)
see CONCERT INDEX under:
(HARM) **HMC90 1422** Weill—Orchestral and Choral
Works

LAJOVIC, Uros (cond)
see Berlin RSO

LAKATOS, Alexander (va)
Schmidt: Clarinet and Piano Quintet 2
see CONCERT INDEX under:
(MARC) **8 223415** Schmidt—Chamber Works

LAKES, Gary (ten)
Beethoven: Symphony 9
Berlioz: Troyens (Cpte)
R. Strauss: Ariadne auf Naxos (Cpte)
Wagner: Walküre (Cpte)
Weber: Oberon (Cpte)
see CONCERT INDEX under:
(DG) **445 354-2GX14** Wagner—Der Ring des
Nibelungen

LAKI, Krisztina (sop)
E.T.A. Hoffmann: Undine (Cpte)
Einem: Dantons Tod (Cpte)
Handel: Partenope (Cpte)
Haydn: Schöpfung (Cpte)
Mendelssohn: Symphony 2
Mozart: Schauspieldirektor (Cpte)
Myslivecek: Bellerofonte (Cpte)
see CONCERT INDEX under:
(HANS) **98 859** Bach—Cantatas, Vol.8

LAKTIB, Radouane (voc/oud)
see CONCERT INDEX under:
(NONE) **7559-79275-2** Pieces of Africa

LALÁK, Bohumír (bass)
Martinů: Julietta (Cpte)

LALEMAN, Johan (organ)
see CONCERT INDEX under:
(RICE) **RIC062026** Concerto in forma di una messa

LALLEMENT, Bernard (cond)
see J-F. Gonzales Orch

LALLOUETTE, Olivier (bass)
Bizet: Carmen (Cpte)
Handel: Giulio Cesare (Cpte), Scipione (Cpte)
Lully: Alceste (Cpte)
Monteverdi: Ritorno d'Ulisse in patria (Cpte)

LAM, Basil (hpd)
see CONCERT INDEX under:
(EMI) **CHS7 69741-2(2)** Record of Singing,
Vol.4—Anglo-American School (pt 2)

LAMANDIER, Esther (sop)
see CONCERT INDEX under:
(ALIE) **AL1012** Sephardic Romances and Armenian
Songs
(ALIE) **AL1019** Domna

LAMANDIER, Esther (sop/hp)
Anon: Psalms (exc)

LAMASSE, Aleth (vc)
Haydn: Cello Concerto in C, Cello Concerto in D

LAMB, Timothy (treb)
Britten: Noye's Fludde (Cpte)

LAMBERGER, Eric (cl)
see CONCERT INDEX under:
(AUVI) **V4644** Debussy/Ravel—Orchestral Songs

LAMBERT, Constant (cond)
see CBO

LAMBERT, Juliet (sngr)
Gershwin: Strike Up the Band I (Cpte), Strike Up the
Band II

LAMBERTI, Giorgio (ten)
Puccini: Tosca (Cpte)
Respighi: Belfagor (Cpte)
see CONCERT INDEX under:
(EURO) **GD69043** Puccini: Il Trittico

LAMBIASE, Valeria (elec org)
see CONCERT INDEX under:
(SCHW) **310632** Globokar—Chamber Works

LAMBOUR, Christian (pf)
see CONCERT INDEX under:
(ETCE) **KTC1083** Telemann: Sonatas

LAMBRIKS, Marjon (mez)
Verdi: Traviata (exc)
Wagner: Parsifal (Cpte)

LAMKE, Jürgen (pf)
see CONCERT INDEX under:
(SCHW) **311672** Schulhoff—Chamber Music for
Violin, Cello and Piano
(SCHW) **312322** Schulhoff—Chamber Music with
wind instruments

LAMMERS, Malte (ob)
see CONCERT INDEX under:
(SCHW) **312322** Schulhoff—Chamber Music with
wind instruments

LAMMINMÄKI, Juhani (cond)
see Espoo CO

LAMON, Jeanne (cond)
see Tafelmusik

LAMON, Jeanne (vn)
see CONCERT INDEX under:
(HYPE) **CDA66247** Vivaldi: Vocal and Orchestral
Works
(SONY) **SK48044** Vivaldi—Concertos for Strings

LAMON, Jeanne (vn/dir)
Bach: Brandenburg Concertos
Biber: Harmonia artificioso—ariosa
see CONCERT INDEX under:
(SONY) **SK53365** Music for Trumpet and Orchestra

LAMOND, Frederic (pf)
see CONCERT INDEX under:
(APR) **APR5504** Lamond—The Complete Liszt
Recordings 1919-36

LAMOREAUX, Rosa (sop)
Berlioz: Messe Solennelle (Cpte)

LAMORLETTE, Roger (ob)
see CONCERT INDEX under:
(EMI) **CDC5 55036-2** Honegger/Poulenc—Perform
their own works
(PEAR) **GEMMCD9311** Poulenc d'après Poulenc

LAMOUREUX CONCERTS ORCHESTRA
(ERAT) **4509-96952-2** Duruflé—Requiem; Organ
Works
cond A. DORATI
see CONCERT INDEX under:
(PHIL) **442 272-2PM2** The Best of Bizet
cond J. FOURNET
Bizet: Pêcheurs de Perles (Cpte)
see CONCERT INDEX under:
(PHIL) **442 272-2PM2** The Best of Bizet
cond I. MARKEVITCH
see CONCERT INDEX under:
(PHIL) **442 631-2PM4** Clara Haskil—The Legacy
Volume 2: Concertos
(PHIL) **442 685-2PM12** Clara Haskil - The Legacy

LAMOUREUX ORCHESTRA
cond E. BIGOT
Bartók: Piano Concerto 2
cond P. DERVAUX
see CONCERT INDEX under:
(PHIL) **438 953-2PM2** Alarie/Simoneau - Arias &
Duets
cond R. DESORMIÈRE
Bartók: Rhapsody 1, Sz87
cond J. FOURNET
see CONCERT INDEX under:
(DG) **437 677-2GDO2** Irmgard Seefried - Opera
Recital
(PHIL) **438 970-2PM2** Camille Maurane
cond J. GRESSIER
see CONCERT INDEX under:
(EMI) **CZS7 67515-2** Offenbach—Operetta highlights
cond J-P. JACQUILLAT
see CONCERT INDEX under:
(EMI) **CDM7 64365-2** Chausson—Chamber,
Orchestra & Vocal Works
(EMI) **CMS5 65061-2(1)** The Fabulous Victoria de los
Angeles (pt 1)
cond A. JOUVE
(PHIL) **438 953-2PM2** Alarie/Simoneau - Arias &
Duets
cond I. MARKEVITCH
Mozart: Mass, K317
see CONCERT INDEX under:
(DG) **447 406-2GOR** Berlioz—Symphonie fantastique
etc
(EMI) **CDM7 64281-2** Boulanger—Vocal & Chamber
Works
cond J. MARTINON
(DG) **429 155-2GR** Works for Cello & Orchestra
(DG) **437 371-2GX2** Bizet/Lalo—Orchestral Works
cond M. RAVEL
see CONCERT INDEX under:
(PEAR) **GEMMCD9927** Ravel, Fauré and Debussy
cond H. ROSBAUD
Gluck: Orphée (Cpte)
cond A. ROS-MARBÀ
see CONCERT INDEX under:
(EMI) **CMS5 65061-2(1)** The Fabulous Victoria de los
Angeles (pt 1)

cond P. SACHER
see CONCERT INDEX under:
(PHIL) **438 970-2PM2** Camille Maurane
cond G. TZIPINE
see CONCERT INDEX under:
(EMI) **CMS7 63386-2** Borodin—Prince Igor &
Complete Solo Songs

LAMPRECHT, Doris (mez)
Handel: Scipione (Cpte)

LAMSON, Carl (pf)
see CONCERT INDEX under:
(BIDD) **LAB068/9** The Kreisler Collection—1921-25
(BIDD) **LAB075** Kreisler—1926-1927 Victor
Recordings
(BIDD) **LAB080** Kreisler—1928 Victor Recordings
(PEAR) **GEMMCD9324** Fritz Kreisler plays Encores

LAMY, Hervé (ten)
Delalande: Dies irae, S31, Miserere mei Deus
secundum, S27
see CONCERT INDEX under:
(FNAC) **592096** Rameau—Grand Motets
(FNAC) **592308** Lully—Grand Motets, Volume 1
(HARM) **HMC90 1167** Lully—Grands Motets
(HARM) **HMC90 1272** Mendelssohn—Psalms; Ave
Maria

(R.) LAMY SINGERS
cond H. CARSTE
see CONCERT INDEX under:
(DG) **431 110-2GB** Great Voices - Fritz Wunderlich
cond A. ROTHER
see CONCERT INDEX under:
(PREI) **90222** Maria Cebotari sings Richard Strauss

LANCE, Albert (ten)
see CONCERT INDEX under:
(PHIL) **442 272-2PM2** The Best of Bizet

LANCELOT, Jacques (cl)
see CONCERT INDEX under:
(ERAT) **4509-95361-2** Mozart—Wind Concertos

LANCELOT, James (cond)
see Durham Cath Ch

LANCELOT, James (organ)
Britten: Rejoice in the Lamb
see CONCERT INDEX under:
(ERAT) **2292-45937-2** Mozart—Wind Concertos
(PRIO) **PRCD228** Great European Organs No. 5

LANCHBERY, John (cond)
see Philh

LANCIE, John de (ob)
see CONCERT INDEX under:
(RCA) **GD87989** Works for Oboe

LANDAU, Siegfried (cond)
see Westphalian SO

LANDAUER, Bernhard (alto)
Biber: Arminio (Cpte)

LANDAUER, Walter (pf)
see CONCERT INDEX under:
(DUTT) **CDSJB1002** Barbirolli conducts French
Music

LANDER, Thomas (bass)
Purcell: Fairy Queen, Z629 (Cpte)

LANDES, Garah (pf)
see CONCERT INDEX under:
(KOCH) **37045-2** American Romantic Piano Music

LANDESMAN, Fran (sngr)
Kern: Show Boat (Cpte)

LANDOLF, Beatrix (vn)
see CONCERT INDEX under:
(DHM) **RD77188** C.P.E. Bach—Vocal & Chamber
Works

LANDOUZY, Lise (sop)
see CONCERT INDEX under:
(IRCC) **IRCC-CD800** Souvenirs from Meyerbeer
Operas

LANDOWSKA, Wanda (hpd)
(DANA) **DACOCD303** Great Musicians in
Copenhagen
(EMI) **CDH7 61008-2** Landowska plays Bach
(EMI) **CDH7 64934-2** D. Scarlatti—Keyboard Sonatas
(MSCM) **MM30444** Wanda Landowska - Harpsichord
Recital
(MSCM) **MM30445** Wanda Landowska plays Handel
(RCA) **GD60919** Bach—Harpsichord Works

LANDOWSKA, Wanda (pf)
see CONCERT INDEX under:
(BIDD) **LHW013** Landowska plays Mozart

LANDRINE, Bryan (sngr)
Porter: Anything Goes (Cpte)

LANDWEHR-HERRMANN, Gertraud (sop)
Telemann: Tag des Gerichts (Cpte)

LANDY, Tonny (ten)
Haydn: Fedeltà Premiata (Cpte)
Nielsen: Maskarade (Cpte)

LANE, Betty (sop)
Gershwin: Porgy and Bess (Cpte)
R. Strauss: Aegyptische Helena (Cpte)

LANE, Burton (pf)
see CONCERT INDEX under:

(PHIL) **432 416-2PH3** Haydn—L'incontro
improvviso/Arias
(PHIL) **432 420-2PH3** Haydn—Il mondo della
luna/Arias
 cond M. EICHENHOLZ
 see CONCERT INDEX under:
(EMI) **CDC7 54007-2** Mozart—Lieder
 cond L. FOSTER
 see CONCERT INDEX under:
(CLAV) **CD50-8803** Enescu—Chamber & Orchestral
Works
(CLAV) **CD50-8806** Busoni & Raff—Works for Piano &
Orchestra
(VIRG) **VC7 59024-2** Works for Guitar and Orchestra
 cond P-L GRAF
Spohr: Violin and Harp Concerto 1
 cond A. JORDAN
Haydn: Schöpfung (Cpte)
 see CONCERT INDEX under:
(PHIL) **432 420-2PH3** Haydn—Il mondo della
luna/Arias
 cond J. LÓPEZ-COBOS
Falla: Amor Brujo (Cpte), Canciones populares
españolas
Respighi: Ancient Airs and Dances, Botticelli
Pictures
Rossini: Barbiere di Siviglia (Cpte)
 see CONCERT INDEX under:
(DENO) **CO-77612** Haydn—Early Symphonies
(TELD) **4509-90846-2** Trumpet Concertos
(TELD) **4509-96800-2** Jennifer Larmore—Where Shall
I Fly?
 cond F. MARTIN
 see CONCERT INDEX under:
(JECK) **JD529-2** Martin: Concertos
 cond Y. MENUHIN
 see CONCERT INDEX under:
(VIRG) **CUV5 61204-2** Mozart—Orchestral Works
 cond V. NEGRI
Cimarosa: Requiem in G minor
 cond U. SEGAL
 see CONCERT INDEX under:
(CLAV) **CD50-9328** Mozart/Beethoven—Piano
Works
 cond A. ZEDDA
 see CONCERT INDEX under:
(VIRG) **CUV5 61206-2**
Prokofiev/Debussy/Milhaud—Orchestral Works

LAUSANNE CHORAL UNION
 cond F. MARTIN
Martin: Requiem

LAUSANNE INSTRUMENTAL ENSEMBLE
 cond M. CORBOZ
 see CONCERT INDEX under:
(ERAT) **2292-45923-2** Bach/Vivaldi—Sacred Choral
Works

LAUSANNE OPERA CHORUS
 cond I. ANGUELOV
Henze: Boulevard Solitude (Cpte)

LAUSANNE PRO ARTE CHOIR
 cond E. ANSERMET
Martin: Pilate
 see CONCERT INDEX under:
(DECC) **433 175-2DM** Bach—Sacred Choral Works
 cond R. BONYNGE
 see CONCERT INDEX under:
(DECC) **436 463-2DM** Ten Top Tenors
 cond N. JÄRVI
Stravinsky: Oedipus Rex (Cpte)
 see CONCERT INDEX under:
(CHAN) **CHAN9239** Stravinsky—Orchestral Works
(CHAN) **CHAN9240** Stravinsky—Choral and
Orchestral Works
 cond A. JORDAN
Haydn: Schöpfung (Cpte)
 see CONCERT INDEX under:
(ERAT) **4509-95307-2** Schubert/Schumann—Sacred
Choral Works
 cond J.LÓPEZ-COBOS
Poulenc: Gloria
 see CONCERT INDEX under:
(DECC) **425 627-2DM** Poulenc: Choral and Orchestral
Works

LAUSANNE VOCAL ENSEMBLE
 cond M. CORBOZ
 see CONCERT INDEX under:
(ERAT) **2292-45923-2** Bach/Vivaldi—Sacred Choral
Works
(ERAT) **4509-96961-2** Schubert—Stabat Mater;
Offertorium; Magnificat

LAUSANNE YOUTH CHOIR
 cond E. ANSERMET
Falla: Atlántida

LAUSCH, Eleanor (sop)
Wagner: Walküre (exc)

LAUSNAY, Georges de (pf)
 see CONCERT INDEX under:
(APR) **APR7028** Jacques Thibaud—Complete Solo
Recordings 1929-36
(MSCM) **MM30321** Jacques Thibaud—Violin Recital

LAUTENBACHER, Susanne (vn)
Bach: Violin Sonatas, BWV1014-19
 see CONCERT INDEX under:
(BAYE) **BR100058** Serenada Hungaria

LAUTTEN COMPAGNEY
 see CONCERT INDEX under:

(CAPR) **10 431** Musical Table Entertainment

LAUWERS, Henk (bass)
Puccini: Manon Lescaut (Cpte)

LAVAL, Danielle (pf)
 see CONCERT INDEX under:
(AUVI) **V4698** Rota—Piano Works
(AUVI) **V4729** Mendelssohn—Piano Works
(EMI) **CDM5 65154-2** Roussel—Orchestral Works

LAVENDER, John (pf)
(PEAR) **SHECD9611** Grainger—Piano Music for Four
Hands, Vol. 1
(PEAR) **SHECD9623** Grainger—Piano Music for Four
Hands, Vol.2
(PEAR) **SHECD9631** Grainger—Piano Music for Four
Hands, Vol.3

LAVENDER, Justin (ten)
Bellini: Puritani (Cpte)
Smyth: Wreckers (Cpte)

LAVILLA, Felix (pf)
 see CONCERT INDEX under:
(DG) **435 848-2GX2** Spanish Songs - Berganza

LAVIRGEN, Pedro (ten)
Moreno Torroba: Luisa Fernanda (Cpte)
Vives: Bohemios (Cpte), Doña Francisquita (Cpte)

LAVOIX, Claude (pf)
 see CONCERT INDEX under:
(CLAV) **CD50-9506** Collet—Cantos de España

LAW, Norman (cond)
 see Sellers Engin Band

LAW, Norman (tbn)
 see CONCERT INDEX under:
(CHAN) **CHAN4523** Concerto

LAWFORD, Simon (organ)
(DECC) **430 359-2DM** Baroque Church Music
(NIMB) **NI5243** Mathias—Sacred & Secular Choral
Music

LAWLER, Emmanuel (ten)
 see CONCERT INDEX under:
(MARC) **8 223461** Sullivan—Incidental Music

LAWLESS, James (spkr)
Britten: Paul Bunyan (Cpte)

LAWLOR, Thomas (bar)
Sullivan: HMS Pinafore (Cpte), Yeomen of the Guard
(Cpte)
 see CONCERT INDEX under:
(DECC) **433 868-2DWO** The World of Gilbert &
Sullivan - Volume 2

LAWRENCE, Amy (sop)
Schillings: Mona Lisa (Cpte)

LAWRENCE, Helen (sop)
B. Goldschmidt: Gewaltige Hahnrei (Cpte)
Verdi: Macbeth (Cpte)

LAWRENCE, Marjorie (sop)
(EMI) **CMS7 64008-2(1)** Wagner Singing on Record
(pt 1)
(EMI) **CMS7 64008-2(2)** Wagner Singing on Record
(pt 2)
(PREI) **89011** Marjorie Lawrence (1909-1979)

LAWRENCE-KING, Andrew (dhp)
 see CONCERT INDEX under:
(COLL) **Coll7016-2** Handel—Alexander's Feast
(EMI) **CDM7 69853-2** Baroque Classics
(HYPE) **CDA66229** Harp Music of the Italian
Renaissance
(HYPE) **CDA66307** My Mind to me a kingdom is
(HYPE) **CDA66518** The Harp of Ludovico
(HYPE) **CDA66619** The Study of Love
(VIRG) **VC7 59071-2** O Lusitano—Portuguese
Renaissance Music c1500
(VIRG) **VC7 59231-2** Sigismondo d'India—Solo Vocal
Music

LAWRENCE-KING, Andrew (hp)
D. Ortiz: Trattado de glosas
 see CONCERT INDEX under:
(ASTR) **E8503** Merula—Arie e Capricci
(EMI) **CDC7 54659-2** Josquin Desprez—Vocal Works
(HYPE) **CDA66330** Masterpieces of Mexican
Polyphony
(HYPE) **CDA66335** A Musicall Dreame
(HYPE) **CDA66653** The Voice in the Garden
(TELD) **4509-90841-2** A Gift of Nature - 17th Century
English Chamber Music

LAWRENCE-KING, Andrew (medieval hp)
 see CONCERT INDEX under:
(ECM) **837 360-2** Proensa—Songs of the
Troubadours
(HYPE) **CDA66238** The Service of Venus and Mars
(HYPE) **CDA66286** A Song for Francesca

LAWRENSON, John (bar)
Elgar: King Arthur (exc), Starlight Express (exc)
Handel: Theodora (Cpte)

LAWS, Hubert (fl)
 see CONCERT INDEX under:
(DG) **429 790-2GH** Spirituals in Concert

LAWSON, Colin (chalumeau)
 see CONCERT INDEX under:

(HARM) **HMU90 7104** Vivaldi/Chedéville—Oboe
Sonatas

LAWSON, Colin (cl)
 see CONCERT INDEX under:
(MERI) **CDE84145** Beethoven: Chamber Music on
Period Instruments

LAWSON, Denis (sngr)
Rodgers: Pal Joey (Cpte)

LAWSON, Mhairi (sop)
 see CONCERT INDEX under:
(O111) **OPS30-121** Haydn—English and Scottish
Songs

LAWSON, Peter (pf)
 see CONCERT INDEX under:
(CFP) **CD-CFP4329** Satie: Piano Works
(VIRG) **VC7 59008-2** American Piano Sonatas
(VIRG) **VC7 59316-2** American Piano Sonatas,
Volume 2

LAWSON, Winifred (sop)
Sullivan: Patience (Cpte)

LAWTON, Jeffrey (ten)
Martinů: Greek Passion (Cpte)

LAYFIELD, Malcolm (cond)
 see Goldberg Ens

LAYFIELD, Malcolm (vn/dir)
 see CONCERT INDEX under:
(MERI) **CDE84177** Haydn: Concertos

LAYTON, Elizabeth (vn)
Pärt: Passio
 see CONCERT INDEX under:
(VIRG) **VC7 59609-2** Vivaldi—Concertos

LAYTON, Stephen (cond)
 see Holst Sngrs

LAYTON, Stephen (organ)
 see CONCERT INDEX under:
(ARGO) **417 468-2ZH** G. Gabrieli: Choral and
Instrumental Works
(PRIO) **PRCD435** Great Cathedral Anthems, Vol.3

LAZAR, Hans-Jürgen (ten)
J. Strauss II: Zigeunerbaron (Cpte)

LAZAREV, Alexander (cond)
 see BBC SO

LÁZARO, Hipolito (ten)
 see CONCERT INDEX under:
(EMI) **CHS7 64860-2(2)** La Scala Edition - Vol.1,
1878-1914 (pt 2)
(MEMO) **HR4408/9(2)** Singers in Genoa, Vol.1 (disc
2)

LAZKY-OTTO, Ib (hn)
 see CONCERT INDEX under:
(UNIC) **DKPCD9110** Kuhlau—Orchestral works

LAZZARETTI, Bruno (ten)
Donizetti: Lucia di Lammermoor (Cpte), Poliuto
(Cpte)
F. David: Désert
(CAPR) **10 380** Breezes from the Orient, Vol.2

LAZZARI, Agostino (ten)
Puccini: Gianni Schicchi (Cpte)
Rossini: Mosè (Cpte)
 see CONCERT INDEX under:
(DECC) **411 665-2DM3** Puccini: Il trittico

LAZZARINI, Adriana (mez)
Mascagni: Cavalleria Rusticana (Cpte)
Verdi: Rigoletto (Cpte)

LE BLANC, Suzie (sop)
Schütz: Symphoniae sacrae, Op. 10 (Cpte)
 see CONCERT INDEX under:
(TELD) **4509-90798-2** Monteverdi—Il Ballo delle
ingrate

LE BLANC, Suzie (sop)
 see CONCERT INDEX under:
(TELD) **4509-95068-2** Purcell—Songs of Welcome &
Farewell

LE BRETON, M. (sngr)
 see CONCERT INDEX under:
(MUSD) **20239-2** Delibes—Opéras-Comiques

LE BROCQ, Mark (alto)
Purcell: Fairy Queen, Z629 (Cpte)

LE CORRE, Pascal (pf)
 see CONCERT INDEX under:
(CYBE) **CY809** Schmitt—Piano Works

LE COZ, Claudine (sngr)
Gluck: Rencontre imprévue (Cpte)
Lully: Alceste (Cpte)

LE GAILLARD, Yannick (hpd)
Blavet: Flute Sonatas, Op. 2 (exc), Flute Sonatas, Op.
3 (exc)
Handel: Water Music
Haydn: Seven Last Words

LE GUIN, Elisabeth (vc)
 see CONCERT INDEX under:
(HARM) **HMU90 7084/5** Bach—Violin Sonatas

LE HÉMONET, Pierre (bass)
Debussy: Pelléas et Mélisande (Cpte)

LE MAIGAT, Pierre-Yves (bass-bar)
Berg: Lulu (Cpte)

Offenbach: Brigands (Cpte)
see CONCERT INDEX under:
(EMI) CDM7 64687-2   French Works inspired by Edgar Allan Poe

LE PALUDIER, Christophe (alto)
Purcell: Fairy Queen, Z629 (Cpte)

LE PINIEC, Elisabeth (sop)
see CONCERT INDEX under:
(ARIO) ARN68015   Charpentier—Sacred Choral works

LE ROI, Gaële (sop)
see CONCERT INDEX under:
(MARC) 8 223755   Prix de Rome Cantatas

LE ROUX, François (bar)
A. Thomas: Hamlet (Cpte)
Bizet: Carmen (exc)
Debussy: Pelléas et Mélisande (Cpte)
Fauré: Pénélope (Cpte)
Offenbach: Brigands (Cpte)
Poulenc: Dialogues des Carmélites (Cpte)
see CONCERT INDEX under:
(EMI) CDM7 64687-2   French Works inspired by Edgar Allan Poe
(REM) REM311049   Duparc: Mélodies
(REM) REM311069   Hahn—Mélodies
(REM) REM311086   French Duets
(REM) REM311175   Fauré—Mélodies, Vol.1

LE SAGE, Eric (pf)
see CONCERT INDEX under:
(DENO) CO-75960   Märchenbilder—Paul Meyer plays Schumann
(DENO) CO-79282   French Clarinet Art

LE SAGE, Sally (sop)
Monteverdi: Lamento d'Arianna a 1, L'Arianna (exc)
see CONCERT INDEX under:
(DECC) 433 080-2DM   Kodály—Choral Works

LEACH, Joanna (fp)
Field: Nocturnes (exc)

LEANDERSON, Rolf (bar)
Nørgård: Gilgamesh (Cpte)

LEAPER, Adrian (cond)
see Bratislava RSO

LEAR, Angela (pf)
see CONCERT INDEX under:
(APR) APR5551   Angela Lear—The Original Chopin
(KING) KCLCD2031   Chopin—Piano Works

LEAR, Evelyn (sop)
Berg: Lulu (Cpte), Wozzeck (Cpte)
Bernstein: On the Town (Cpte)
Egk: Verlobung in San Domingo (Cpte)
Janáček: Glagolitic Mass (Cpte)
Mozart: Zauberflöte (Cpte)
R. Strauss: Rosenkavalier (Cpte)

LEATHERMAN, Alan (sngr)
Gershwin: Porgy and Bess (Cpte)

LEBEDA, Andreas (bar)
Monteverdi: Incoronazione di Poppea (Cpte)

LEBEDEVA, Ludmila (sop)
Mussorgsky: Boris Godunov (Cpte)

LEBEDEVA, Neyla (sop)
Tchaikovsky: Queen of Spades (Cpte)

LEBHERZ, Louis (bass)
Verdi: Aroldo (Cpte)

LEBLANC, Claudette (sop)
see CONCERT INDEX under:
(UNIC) DKPCD133   Debussy—Songs

LEBLANC, Suzette (sop)
see CONCERT INDEX under:
(HYPE) CDA66247   Vivaldi: Vocal and Orchestral Works

LEBRUN, Eric (organ)
see CONCERT INDEX under:
(MARC) 8 223636   In Memoriam Lili Boulanger
(NAXO) 8 553176   Poulenc—Choral Works
(NAXO) 8 553196   Duruflé—Sacred Choral and Organ Works, Volume 1
(NAXO) 8 553197   Duruflé—Sacred Choral and Organ Works, Volume 2

LECAUDEY, Jean-Pierre (organ)
Franck: Chorales
see CONCERT INDEX under:
(SONY) SK57488   Duruflé—Organ Works

LECHEVALIER, Sylvie (pf)
see CONCERT INDEX under:
(LARG) Largo5130   Testimonies of War

LECOCQ, Michel (ten)
Hasse: Piramo e Tisbe (Cpte)
Tchaikovsky: Eugene Onegin (Cpte)

LECONTE, Jean Michel (cond)
see French Rad and TV Orch

LECONTE, Pierre-Michel (cond)
see French Rad Lyric Orch

LECOQ, Michel (ten)
Lully: Bourgeois Gentilhomme

LEDBETTER, Victor (bar)
Handel: Messiah (Cpte)
(TELA) CD80362   Poulenc/Szymanowski—Stabat Mater

LEDGER, Philip (cond)
see ASMF

LEDGER, Philip (organ)
see CONCERT INDEX under:
(ASV) CDDCA584   W.S. Lloyd Webber—Various Works
(EMI) CDM5 65101-2   A Warlock Centenary Album

LEDGER, Philip (hpd/dir)
see CONCERT INDEX under:
(EMI) CDM7 69835-2   Vivaldi—Cello Concertos

LEDGER, Philip (pf)
see CONCERT INDEX under:
(ASV) CDDCA584   W.S. Lloyd Webber—Various Works
(CFP) CD-CFP4570   Choral Favourites
(DECC) 430 093-2DWO   The World of Vaughan Williams
(MERI) CDE84119   Britten: Songs and Instrumental Works

LEDNÁROVÁ, Henrietta (sop)
Respighi: Primavera

LEDROIT, Henri (alto)
see CONCERT INDEX under:
(HARM) HMC90 1167   Lully—Grands Motets
(RICE) RIC037011   Charpentier—Cantatas and Airs
(RICE) RIC041016   German Baroque Cantatas, Vol.2 - Buxtehude

LEDROIT, Michèle (sop)
see CONCERT INDEX under:
(RICE) RIC037011   Charpentier—Cantatas and Airs

LEE, Christopher (narr)
see CONCERT INDEX under:
(NIMB) NI5192   Prokofiev: Orchestral Works

LEE, Dennis (pf)
see CONCERT INDEX under:
(HYPE) CDA66409   Szymanowski—Piano Works

LEE, Jack (cond)
see Orig Broadway Cast

LEE, Josephine (pf)
see CONCERT INDEX under:
(CLAR) CDGSE78-50-52   Three Tenors
(SYMP) SYMCD1067   Russian & Polish Songs

LEE, Mark (organ)
see CONCERT INDEX under:
(PRIO) PRCD494   Magnificat and Nunc Dimittis

LEE, Mi-Kiung (vn)
Boccherini: Sextets, G461-6 (exc)
see CONCERT INDEX under:
(CLAV) CD50-8507   Chamber recital

LEE, Nelli (sop)
see CONCERT INDEX under:
(SONY) SMK57660   Rachmaninov/Stravinsky—Orchestral Works

LEE, Noël (pf)
see CONCERT INDEX under:
(ARIO) ARN68009   Massenet—Melodies
(ARIO) ARN68228   Debussy/Pierné/Ravel—Sonatas for Violin and Piano
(ARIO) ARN68258   Poulenc—Mélodies
(AUVI) V4440   Debussy: Piano Works
(ETCE) KTC1048   Debussy: Mélodies, Vol.2
(ETCE) KTC1098   Copland—Orchestral Works
(PHIL) 438 721-2PM2   Debussy—Complete Piano Music, Vol.2

LEE, Sylvia Olden (pf)
see CONCERT INDEX under:
(DG) 429 790-2GH   Spirituals in Concert

LEECH, Richard (ten)
Gounod: Faust (Cpte)
J. Strauss II: Fledermaus (Cpte)
Puccini: Bohème (Cpte)
R. Strauss: Rosenkavalier (Cpte), Salome (Cpte)
Verdi: Rigoletto (Cpte)
see CONCERT INDEX under:
(SONY) SX14K48198   Mahler—Complete Symphonies, etc
(TELA) CD80164   Berlioz—Orchestral Works

LEEDS FESTIVAL CHORUS
cond T. BEECHAM
see CONCERT INDEX under:
(DUTT) CDLX7003   Vintage Beecham
(VAI) VAIA1045   Beecham conducts Handel
cond L. BERNSTEIN
Mahler: Symphony 8
cond D. LLOYD-JONES
see CONCERT INDEX under:
(HYPE) CDA66565   Constant Lambert—Vocal & Orchestral Works
cond C. MACKERRAS
Handel: Israel in Egypt (Cpte)
cond J. WALLACE
see CONCERT INDEX under:
(NIMB) NI5175   French Revolution- orchestral music

LEEMING, Peter (bass)
Britten: Burning Fiery Furnace (Cpte), Death in Venice (Cpte)

LEES, Ben (tpt)
see CONCERT INDEX under:
(CNTO) CRCD2368   Sullivan—That Glorious Song of Old

LEESON-WILLIAMS, Nigel (bass-bar)
Cresswell: Modern Ecstasy

LEEUW, Reinbert (pf)
see CONCERT INDEX under:
(SCHW) 311612   Bartók/Shostakovich/Stravinsky—Chamber Works

LEEUW, Reinbert de (cond)
see Amsterdam Nieuw Sinfonietta

LEFEBRE, Pierre (ten)
Rossini: Gazza ladra (Cpte)
Spontini: Vestale (Cpte)

LEFÉBVRE, Claude (fl)
see CONCERT INDEX under:
(AUVI) V4644   Debussy/Ravel—Orchestral Songs

LEFÉBVRE, Henri (cl)
see CONCERT INDEX under:
(CLRI) CC0005   The Clarinet - Historical Recordings, Vol.1

LEFEBVRE, Philippe (organ)
Dupré: Vêpres de la Vierge

LEFEBVRE, Pierre (ten)
Franchetti: Cristoforo Colombo (Cpte)
Puccini: Fanciulla del West (Cpte)

LEFKOWITZ, Ronan (vn)
see CONCERT INDEX under:
(SONY) SK53126   Made in America

LEFORT, Marie-Françoise (sop)
see CONCERT INDEX under:
(DECC) 440 333-2DH   Ravel—Vocal Works

LEGAY, Henri (ten)
Bizet: Ivan IV (exc), Pêcheurs de Perles (Cpte)

LEGE ARTIS CHAMBER CHOIR
cond B. ABALYAN
Rachmaninov: Liturgy, Op. 31, O Mother of God

LEGGATE, Robin (ten)
Boito: Mefistofele (Cpte)
Elgar: Light of Life (Cpte)
Haydn: Armida (Cpte)
Offenbach: Contes d'Hoffmann (Cpte)
Puccini: Fanciulla del West (Cpte)
Verdi: Ballo in maschera (Cpte), Traviata (Cpte), Trovatore (Cpte)
see CONCERT INDEX under:
(OPRA) ORCH103   Italian Opera—1810-20

LEGGE, Anthony (pf)
see CONCERT INDEX under:
(CHAN) CHAN8749   Songs of the British Isles
(CHAN) CHAN8786   Schumann and Brahms—Lieder

LEGINSKA, Ethel (pf)
(OPAL) OPAL CD9839   Pupils of Theodore Leschetizky

LEGOUHY, Marguérite (mez)
Poulenc: Mamelles de Tirésias (Cpte)
Ravel: Enfant et les sortilèges (Cpte)

LEGRAND, Christiane (sop)
Berio: Laborintus II

LEGRAND, Michel (pf)
see CONCERT INDEX under:
(ERAT) 4509-92857-2   Satie—Piano Works
(ERAT) 4509-96386-2   American Piano Music

LEGROS, Adrien (bass)
Boïeldieu: Dame blanche (Cpte)

LEGUÉRINGEL, Franck (bar)
Auber: Gustav III (Cpte)
Bizet: Carmen (Cpte)

LEHANE, Maureen (mez)
Handel: Theodora (Cpte)
Pergolesi: Stabat Mater
R. Strauss: Elektra (Cpte)

LEHÁR, Franz (cond)
see Berlin SO

LEHEL, György (cond)
see Budapest SO

LEHIGH VALLEY CHAMBER ORCHESTRA
Copland: Dance Panels
Lipkis: Scaramouche

LEHMAN, Jeanne (sop)
see CONCERT INDEX under:
(EMI) CDC7 54586-2   Broadway Showstoppers
(EMI) CDC7 54883-2   Jerome Kern Treasury

LEHMANN, Lilli (sop)
(NIMB) NI7840/1   The Era of Adelina Patti
(PEAR) GEMMCDS9923(2)   Covent Garden on Record, Vol.1 (pt 2)
(SIMA) PSC1810(1)   Grieg—Songs (historical recordings, pt 1)

LEHMANN, Lotte (sop)
Schumann: Dichterliebe, Op. 48 (Cpte), Frauenliebe und -leben, Op. 42 (Cpte)
Wagner: Walküre (exc)
see CONCERT INDEX under:
(CLAR) CDGSE78-50-57   Lotte Lehmann sings Lieder
(EMI) CDH7 64029-2   Richard Tauber - Opera Recital
(EMI) CDH7 69787-2   Richard Tauber sings Operetta Arias

(EMI) **CHS7 64487-2**   R. Strauss—Der Rosenkavalier & Lieder
(EMI) **CMS7 64008-2(1)**   Wagner Singing on Record (pt 1)
(MMOI) **CDMOIR408**   Great Sopranos
(MMOI) **CDMOIR422**   Great Voices in Tchaikovsky
(NIMB) **NI7802**   Divas 1906-1935
(NIMB) **NI7830**   Richard Tauber in Opera
(NIMB) **NI7851**   Legendary Voices
(PEAR) **GEMMCDS9365**   R. Strauss: Der Rosenkavalier (abridged), etc
(PEAR) **GEMMCDS9925(2)**   Covent Garden on Record—Vol.3 (pt 2)
(PEAR) **GEMMCDS9926(2)**   Covent Garden on Record—Vol.4 (pt 2)
(PEAR) **GEMMCD9119**   Schumann—Legendary Song Cycles
(PREI) **89302**   The Young Lotte Lehmann
(SCHW) **314622**   Vienna State Opera Live, Vol.12

LEHMANN, Wilfred (cond)
see Melbourne SO

LEHNERT, Christa (sop)
see CONCERT INDEX *under:*
(ROSE) **3221**   Schumann—Miscellaneous Works

LEHNING, Steven (va da gamba)
see CONCERT INDEX *under:*
(HARM) **HMU90 7084/5**   Bach—Violin Sonatas

LEHR, LeRoy (bass)
Copland: Tender Land (Cpte)

LEHRBERGER, Thomas (ten)
Weill: Mahagonny (Cpte), Zar lässt sich Photographieren (Cpte)

LEHRNDORFER, Franz (organ)
Biber: Mystery Sonatas

LEHTINEN, Matti (narr)
Aho: Pergamon

LEHWALDER, Heidi (hp)
see CONCERT INDEX *under:*
(RCA) **09026 62552-2**   Debussy/Ravel—Chamber Works

LEIB, Günther (bass)
Wagner: Rienzi (Cpte)

LEIBOWITZ, René (cond)
see RPO

LEIBUR, Arvo (vn)
see CONCERT INDEX *under:*
(BIS) **BIS-CD541/2**   Tubin—The Complete Music for Violin, Viola and Piano

LEICESTER HAYMARKET THEATRE CAST
cond P. KERRYSON
Sondheim: Merrily We Roll Along (Cpte)

LEICHNER, Emil (pf)
see CONCERT INDEX *under:*
(ROMA) **RR1941**   Terezín - The Music 1941-44

LEIDER, Frida (sop)
see CONCERT INDEX *under:*
(CLAR) **CDGSE78-50-26**   Wagner: Tristan und Isolde excerpts
(CLAR) **CDGSE78-50-35/6**   Wagner—Historical recordings
(DANA) **DACOCD313/4**   Lauritz Melchior Anthology - Vol. 2
(DANA) **DACOCD315/6**   Lauritz Melchior Anthology - Vol. 3
(EMI) **CMS7 64008-2(2)**   Wagner Singing on Record (pt 2)
(LYRC) **LCD146**   Frida Leider sings Wagner
(MMOI) **CDMOIR408**   Great Sopranos
(NIMB) **NI7848**   Great Singers at the Berlin State Opera
(PEAR) **GEMMCDS9137**   Wagner—Der Ring des Nibelungen
(PEAR) **GEMMCDS9925(2)**   Covent Garden on Record—Vol.3 (pt 2)
(PEAR) **GEMMCDS9926(1)**   Covent Garden on Record—Vol.4 (pt 1)
(PEAR) **GEMMCDS9331**   Frida Leider sings Wagner
(PREI) **89004**   Frida Leider (1888-1975) - I
(PREI) **89301**   The Art of Frida Leider

LEIDLAND, Hilde (sop)
Dusapin: Medeamaterial (Cpte)
Mozart: Nozze di Figaro (Cpte)
Wagner: Götterdämmerung (Cpte), Parsifal (Cpte), Rheingold (Cpte), Siegfried (Cpte)

LEIFERKUS, Sergei (bar)
Beethoven: Fidelio (Cpte)
Janáček: Glagolitic Mass (Cpte)
Mussorgsky: Boris Godunov (Cpte)
Prokofiev: Ivan the Terrible Suite
Shostakovich: Symphony 13, Symphony 14
Tchaikovsky: Mazeppa (Cpte), Queen of Spades (Cpte)
Verdi: Otello (Cpte)
Wagner: Lohengrin (Cpte)
see CONCERT INDEX *under:*
(CHAN) **CHAN9374**   Rachmaninov—Songs
(CONI) **CDCF229**   Mussorgsky—Songs, Vol.1
(CONI) **75605 51248-2**   Mussorgsky—Songs, Vol.2
(DECC) **440 355-2DH**   Rachmaninov—Choral Works
(DG) **439 860-2GH**   Shostakovich—Orchestral Songs, Vol.1
(RCA) **RD60195**   Mussorgsky—Orchestral & Vocal Works

LEIGH, Barbara (sngr)
see CONCERT INDEX *under:*
(EMI) **CDANGEL 5**   Norton—Chu Chin Chow

LEIGH-HUNT, Barbara (spkr)
Elgar/Binyon: Wood magic

LEIGHTON SMITH, Laurence (cond)
see Moscow PO

LEINSDORF, Erich (cond)
see Boston SO

LEIPNITZ, Harald (spkr)
Mozart: Entführung (Cpte)

LEIPZIG GEWANDHAUS CHILDRENS CHOIR
cond K. MASUR
Mendelssohn: Paulus (Cpte)

LEIPZIG GEWANDHAUS ORCHESTRA
cond H. ABENDROTH
see CONCERT INDEX *under:*
(TAHR) **TAH106/7**   Hermann Abendroth-Historic Recordings
cond K. ANČERL
Prokofiev: Romeo and Juliet Suites
cond K. MASUR
Beethoven: Choral Fantasia, Romances, Triple Concerto
Brahms: Piano Concerto 2
Bruch: Violin Concerto 1
Mendelssohn: Paulus (Cpte), Symphony 3, Symphony 4, Violin Concerto, Op.64
Prokofiev: Alexander Nevsky, Scythian Suite
R. Strauss: Ariadne auf Naxos (Cpte)
Tchaikovsky: Francesca da Rimini, Piano Concerto 2, Romeo and Juliet, Symphony 1, Symphony 2
see CONCERT INDEX *under:*
(DG) **413 851-2GW2**   Modern American Favourites
(DG) **427 203-2GR**   Gershwin: Orchestral Works
(EMI) **CDM7 64850-2**   Liszt—Symphonic Poems
(EMI) **CMS7 62542-2**   Prokofiev—Piano Concertos, etc
(PHIL) **411 052-2PH**   Richard Strauss: Lieder
(PHIL) **412 237-2PH**   Horn Concertos
(PHIL) **420 932-2PH2**   Bruch—Orchestral Works
(PHIL) **426 290-2PH5**   Beethoven—Complete Symphonies
(PHIL) **432 282-2PSL3**   Bruch—Works for Violin and Orchestra
(PHIL) **438 706-2PM2**   Beethoven—Overtures; Minuets; Dances
(RCA) **74321 20286-2**   Mendelssohn—Symphonies 1-5
(TELD) **4509-95981-2**   Tchaikovsky—Symphonies
(TELD) **9031-75860-2**   Mendelssohn—Piano Concertos
(TELD) **9031-76456-2**   Tchaikovsky—Orchestral Works
cond G. RAMIN
Bach: St Matthew Passion, BWV244 (exc)
cond W. SAWALLISCH
Mendelssohn: Elias (Cpte)
cond P. SCHREIER
see CONCERT INDEX *under:*
(DECC) **440 680-2DH**   Great Sacred Arias
B. Goldschmidt: Mediterranean Songs (Cpte)
Eisler: Deutsche Sinfonie
Krenek: Jonny spielt auf (Cpte)
see CONCERT INDEX *under:*
(DECC) **440 854-2DH**   Ullmann—Der Kaiser von Atlantis
(DECC) **444 182-2DH**   Tanz Grotesk

LEIPZIG NEW BACH COLLEGIUM MUSICUM
cond M. POMMER
see CONCERT INDEX *under:*
(CAPR) **10 051**   Classical Trumpet Concertos
(CAPR) **10 069**   C.P.E. Bach—Oboe Concertos
(CAPR) **10 157**   Bach: Cantatas
(CAPR) **10 230**   Vivaldi: Oboe Concertos

LEIPZIG OPERA CHORUS
cond L. ZAGROSEK
Krenek: Jonny spielt auf (Cpte)

LEIPZIG RADIO CHORUS
Bach: Christmas Oratorio, BWV248 (Cpte), Mass in B minor, BWV232 (Cpte), St. Matthew Passion, BWV244 (Cpte)
Beethoven: Choral Fantasia, Missa Solemnis
Brahms: Deutsches Requiem, Op. 45 (Cpte)
Haydn: Mass 7, Mass 10, Mass 13
Mendelssohn: Elias (Cpte), Paulus (Cpte)
Mozart: Clemenza di Tito (Cpte), Entführung (Cpte), Idomeneo (Cpte), Requiem, Zauberflöte (Cpte)
Tchaikovsky: Eugene Onegin (Cpte)
Wagner: Götterdämmerung (Cpte), Meistersinger (Cpte), Parsifal (Cpte), Rienzi (Cpte), Tristan und Isolde (Cpte)
Weber: Freischütz (Cpte), Kampf und Sieg, J190 (exc)
see CONCERT INDEX *under:*
(CAPR) **10 451/5**   Beethoven—Symphonies 1-9
(PHIL) **422 522-2PME5**   The Complete Mozart Edition Vol 22
(PHIL) **422 545-2PME3**   The Complete Mozart Edition Vol.45
(PHIL) **426 275-2PH**   Mozart—Sacred Choral Works
(PHIL) **426 290-2PH5**   Beethoven—Complete Symphonies
(RCA) **74321 20286-2**   Mendelssohn—Symphonies 1-5

(SONY) **SK53975**   Composers Inspired by the Poet Friedrich Hölderlin

LEIPZIG RADIO SYMPHONY ORCHESTRA
see CONCERT INDEX *under:*
(PHIL) **422 545-2PME3**   The Complete Mozart Edition Vol.45
cond H. ABENDROTH
see CONCERT INDEX *under:*
(TAHR) **TAH102**   Hermann Abendroth - 1927-1941 Recordings
cond H. KEGEL
Wagner: Parsifal (Cpte)
Weber: Kampf und Sieg, J190 (exc)
cond M. POMMER
see CONCERT INDEX *under:*
(ONDI) **ODE771-2**   Weill—Orchestral and Vocal Works

LEIPZIG ST THOMAS CHURCH CHOIR
cond H. KEGEL
Wagner: Parsifal (Cpte)
cond G. RAMIN
Bach: St Matthew Passion, BWV244 (exc)

LEIPZIG SYMPHONY ORCHESTRA
cond H. KEGEL
Brahms: Deutsches Requiem, Op. 45 (Cpte)
cond H. NEUMANN
Henze: Voices (Cpte)

LEIPZIG UNIVERSITY CHOIR
cond M. POMMER
see CONCERT INDEX *under:*
(CAPR) **10 151**   Bach: Cantatas

LEISENHEIMER, Reinhard (ten)
Schreker: Ferne Klang (Cpte)

LEISNER, Emmi (contr)
see CONCERT INDEX *under:*
(PEAR) **GEMMCDS9137**   Wagner—Der Ring des Nibelungen
(PREI) **89201**   Helge Roswaenge (1897-1972) - I

LEISTER, Karl (cl)
Crusell: Clarinet Quintet, Op. 4
Mozart: Clarinet Quintet, K581
Spohr: Clarinet Concerto 1, Clarinet Concerto 2, Clarinet Concerto 3, Clarinet Concerto 4
see CONCERT INDEX *under:*
(BIS) **BIS-CD345**   Crusell: Clarinet Concertos
(DG) **419 237-2GH**   Schubert: Lieder
(DG) **419 875-2GCM3**   Brahms. Quintets and Sextets.
(DG) **427 639-2GH**   Poulenc: Chamber Works
(DG) **431 782-2GH**   Mozart—Chamber Works
(DG) **437 131-2GX2**   Brahms—Chamber Works
(PHIL) **422 509-2PME5**   The Complete Mozart Edition Vol 9

LEITAO, Manuel (ten)
Verdi: Traviata (Cpte)

LEITNER, Ferdinand (cond)
see Bamberg SO

LEITNER, Ferdinand (pf)
see CONCERT INDEX *under:*
(PREI) **89088**   Walther Ludwig (1902-1981)

LEITNER, Konrad (cond)
see Vienna Mozart Orch

LEITNER, Lotte (sop)
Mozart: Zauberflöte (Cpte)

LEITNER, Markus (alto)
Mozart: Zauberflöte (Cpte)

LÉJEUNE, Jerome (cond)
see Capella Ricercar

LEJEUNE-GILIBERT, Gabrielle (mez)
see CONCERT INDEX *under:*
(RCA) **GD60495(3)**   The Complete Caruso Collection (pt 3)

LELIO, Loretta di (sop)
Verdi: Don Carlo (Cpte)

LELIWA, Tadeusz (ten)
see CONCERT INDEX *under:*
(CLUB) **CL99-089**   Adamo Didur (1874-1946)

LEMAN CHORUS
cond A. GUADAGNO
(DECC) **436 301-2DA**   Renata Tebaldi & Franco Corelli—Arias & Duets

LEMARIOVÁ, Marcela (mez)
Hába: Mother (Cpte)
Janáček: Káta Kabanová (Cpte)
Martinů: Julietta (Cpte)

LEMBERG, Arno (spkr)
R.Strauss: Arabella (Cpte)

LEMESHEV, Sergei (ten)
Tchaikovsky: Eugene Onegin (Cpte)

LEMKOV, Tutte (sop)
Grieg: Peer Gynt (exc)

LEMMONÉ, John (fl)
see CONCERT INDEX *under:*
(LARR) **CDLRH221**   Dame Nellie Melba - Opera and Song Recital
(ROMO) **81011-2(2)**   Dame Nellie Melba (pt 2)

LEMNITZ, Tiana (sop)
Bach: St Matthew Passion, BWV244 (exc)
Mozart: Zauberflöte (Cpte)
Schillings: Glockenlieder (exc)

LEONI, Henri (sngr)
see CONCERT INDEX under:
(PEAR) GEMMCDS9050/2(2) Music from the New
York Stage, Vol. 1 (part 2)

LEONSKAJA, Elisabeth (pf)
Brahms: Piano Concerto 2, Piano Quintet, Piano
Sonata 1, Piano Sonata 3, Romanzen, Op. 33
(Cpte)
Chopin: Nocturnes
Dvořák: Piano Quintet, Op.81 (exc)
Schubert: Piano Sonata, D664, Piano Sonata, D959,
Trout Quintet, D667
Tchaikovsky: Piano Concerto 2, Piano Sonata, Op.
37
see CONCERT INDEX under:
(TELD) 9031-73282-2 Shostakovich—Piano
Concertos, etc
(TELD) 9031-74872-2 Schumann/Brahms—Lieder

LEOZ, Alfonso (ten)
Rossini: Otello (Cpte)

LEPETIT, Albrecht (ten)
see CONCERT INDEX under:
(CAPR) 10 367 Mendelssohn—Motets

LEPKOFF, †Jesse (fl)
see CONCERT INDEX under:
(ERAT) 4509-94830-2 The Unicorn—Medieval French
Songs

LEPORE, Carlo (bass)
see CONCERT INDEX under:
(STUD) SM12 2389 Paisiello—Music for Napoleon
Bonaparte's Chapel

LEPPARD, Raymond (cond)
see BBC Northern SO

LEPPARD, Raymond (hpd)
see CONCERT INDEX under:
(ASV) CDDCA663 Handel/Telemann—Oboe
Sonatas

LEPPARD, Raymond (hpd/dir)
Bach: Triple Concerto, BWV1044
see CONCERT INDEX under:
(CFP) CD-CFP4557 Baroque Favourites

LEPPÉE, Gjurgja (sop)
see CONCERT INDEX under:
(EMI) CHS7 69741-2(5) Record of Singing,
Vol.4—Scandinavian School

LEPRIN, Frédéric (ten)
Bizet: Carmen (Cpte)
Poulenc: Mamelles de Tirésias (Cpte)

LEQUENNE, A. (sngr)
see CONCERT INDEX under:
(MUSD) 20239-2 Delibes—Opéras-Comiques

LEQUIEN, Colette (va)
see CONCERT INDEX under:
(ERAT) 4509-96953-2 Fauré—Chamber Works

LERER, Norma (mez)
Fauré: Pénélope (Cpte)
Haydn: Isola Disabitata (Cpte)
see CONCERT INDEX under:
(HANS) 98 873 Bach—Cantatas, Vol.22

LERNER, Bennett (pf)
see CONCERT INDEX under:
(ETCE) KTC1019 American Piano Music
(ETCE) KTC1036 American piano music
(ETCE) KTC1061 Exposition Paris, 1937

LERNER, Jeffrey C. (cl)
see CONCERT INDEX under:
(BAY) BCD-1014 Classical Hollywood

LERNER, Mimi (mez)
see CONCERT INDEX under:
(EMI) CDC7 54643-2 Rossini—Bicentenary Gala
Concert

LEROUX, Xavier (pf)
see CONCERT INDEX under:
(IRCC) IRCC-CD802 Souvenirs of Rare French
Opera

LESAGE, Eric (pf)
see CONCERT INDEX under:
(AUVI) V4693 Beethoven—Works for Flute

LESCHETIZKY, Theodore (pf)
see CONCERT INDEX under:
(OPAL) OPALCD9839 Pupils of Theodore
Leschetizky

LESKAYA, Anna (sop)
see CONCERT INDEX under:
(RCA) GD60522 Alexander Kipnis—Opera & Song
Recital

LESLEY-GREEN, Carol (sop)
Sullivan: Yeomen of the Guard (exc)

LESNE, Brigitte (cond)
see Discantus

LESNE, Brigitte (mez)
see CONCERT INDEX under:
(VIRG) VC7 59602-2 Monteverdi—Motets

LESNE, Brigitte (mez/dir)
Anon: Codex Las Huelgas (exc)

LESNE, Gérard (alto)
Bach: Cantata 21, Cantata 42, Cantata 80,
Magnificat, BWV243, Mass, BWV233, Mass,
BWV236
Couperin: Leçons de Ténèbres
Galuppi: Arripe alpestri ad vallem, Confitebor tibi,
Domini
Handel: Poro (Cpte)
Stradella: San Giovanni Battista (Cpte)
see CONCERT INDEX under:
(HARM) HMC90 1280 Montéclair—Cantatas
(HRMO) HCD8720 Vivaldi—Sacred Vocal Works
(VIRG) VC5 45000-2 Bononcini—Vocal & Chamber
Works
(VIRG) VC5 45075-2 Charpentier—Leçons de
ténèbres, Vol. 2
(VIRG) VC5 45103-2 Alessandro Scarlatti—Motets
(VIRG) VC5 45107-2 Charpentier—Leçons de
ténèbres, Vol. 3
(VIRG) VC7 59058-2 Caldara—Solo Cantatas
(VIRG) VC7 59059-2 Handel—Italian Cantatas
(VIRG) VC7 59071-2 O Lusitano—Portuguese
Renaissance Music c1500
(VIRG) VC7 59232-2 Vivaldi—Sacred Works for Alto &
Orchestra
(VIRG) VC7 59237-2 Bach—Cantatas
(VIRG) VC7 59295-2 M-A. Charpentier—Tenebrae
Lessons for Good Friday
(VIRG) VC7 59587-2 Bach—Masses etc
(VIRG) VC7 59602-2 Monteverdi—Motets

LESSER, Laurence (vc)
Tchaikovsky: Souvenir de Florence
see CONCERT INDEX under:
(RCA) 09026 61778-2(25) The Heifetz Collection, Vol.
25

LESSING, Kolja (pf)
see CONCERT INDEX under:
(LARG) Largo 5117 Goldschmidt—Chamber Works
(LARG) Largo 5127 Igor Markevitch—Chamber
Works
(LARG) Largo 5128 Goldschmidt—Retrospectrum
(MARC) 8 223383 Alkan—Chamber Works

LESSING, Kolja (vn)
see CONCERT INDEX under:
(LARG) Largo 5127 Igor Markevitch—Chamber
Works
(LARG) Largo 5128 Goldschmidt—Retrospectrum

LESTELLY (ten)
Terrasse: Travaux d'Hercule (Cpte)

LESTER, Gabrielle (vn)
see CONCERT INDEX under:
(DG) 437 535-2GH Schubert—Soirée

LESTER, Harold (hpd)
Purcell: Dido (Cpte)
Vivaldi: Concerti, Op. 8 (exc)

LESTER, Richard (vc)
Boccherini: String Sextets, G454-9 (exc)
Vivaldi: Concerti, Op. 8 (exc)
see CONCERT INDEX under:
(CAPR) 10 453 Boccherini Edition, Vol.8
(DG) 437 535-2GH Schubert—Soirée

LESTER, Todd (voc)
Bernstein: West Side Story (Cpte)

LESTRIGANT, Etienne (ten)
Purcell: Dido (Cpte)
see CONCERT INDEX under:
(ARIO) ARN68015 Charpentier—Sacred Choral works
(HARM) HMX290 1528/33(1) A Purcell Companion (pt
1)

LETTINGA, Bouke (alto)
Biber: Requiem in F minor
Valls: Missa Scala Aretina

LEUTGEB, Johann (bar)
Ligeti: Grand Macabre (Cpte)

LEUVERINK, Gerrit Jan (va)
Schnittke: Concerto grosso 4

LEVALLIER, Adam (spkr)
Offenbach: Belle Hélène (Cpte)

LEVASSEUR, Jeanette (sngr)
Ganne: Hans (Cpte)
Offenbach: Madame l'Archiduc (Cpte)

LEVEAUX, Ursula (bn)
see CONCERT INDEX under:
(COLL) Coll1396-2 Maxwell Davies—Strathclyde
Concertos 7 & 8 etc

LEVEILLE, Ryan (perc)
Rorem: Eleven Studies

LEVERTOV, Gad (va)
see CONCERT INDEX under:
(CARL) PWK1141 French Impressions

LEVEY, Ethel (sngr)
see CONCERT INDEX under:
(PEAR) GEMMCDS9050/2(2) Music from the New
York Stage, Vol. 1 (part 2)

LEVI, Yoel (cond)
see Atlanta SO

LEVIN, Michelle (pf)
see CONCERT INDEX under:
(KOCH) 37070-2 Barber/Foss/Ornstein—Cello
Works

LEVIN, Robert (fp)
Mozart: Piano Concerto 9, Piano Concerto 12
see CONCERT INDEX under:
(L'OI) 444 571-2OH Mozart—Piano Concertos Nos 11
and 13;Rondo, K386
(SONY) SK53120 Haydn—Piano Trios
(SONY) SK53366 Mozart—Chamber Music for
Clarinet

LEVIN, Robert (pf)
see CONCERT INDEX under:
(ECM) 827 744-2 Kashkashian/Levin—Elegies
(ECM) 833 309-2 Hindemith—Viola Sonatas
(NKF) NKFCD50017-2 Sinding—Piano Works
(PHIL) 432 152-2PH Brahms—Choral Works
(SONY) SK64302 Clarinet & Piano Sonatas

LEVIN, Sylvan (cond)
see RCA SO

LEVIN, Todd (voc)
T. Levin: De Luxe

LEVIN, Walter (vn)
Schoenberg: String Trio

LEVINE, David (pf)
Reimann: Variations

LEVINE, Gilbert (cond)
see Cracow PO

LEVINE, James (cond)
see Bayreuth Fest Orch

LEVINE, James (pf)
see CONCERT INDEX under:
(RCA) 09026 62547-2 Divas in Song—Marilyn Horne's
60th Birthday

LEVINE, James (pf)
Schubert: Appergione Sonata, D821, Schöne Müllerin
(Cpte), Trout Quintet, D667, Winterreise (Cpte)
Schumann: Piano Quintet, Op.44
see CONCERT INDEX under:
(DG) 419 237-2GH Schubert: Lieder
(DG) 427 639-2GH Poulenc: Chamber Works
(DG) 431 782-2GH Mozart—Chamber Works

LEVINE, James (pf/dir)
see CONCERT INDEX under:
(DG) 431 625-2GH Gershwin—Orchestral works

LEVINE, Julius (db)
Schubert: Trout Quintet, D667
see CONCERT INDEX under:
(SONY) SM3K46527 Mozart—Legendary
Interpretations, IV

LEVINE, Maurice (cond)
see Broadway Cast

LEVINSKY, Ilya (ten)
Shostakovich: Lady Macbeth of Mtsensk (Cpte)

LEVITZKI, Mischa (pf)
see CONCERT INDEX under:
(APR) APR7014 Romantic Piano Rarities, Vol.2
(APR) APR7020 Mischa Levitzki—The Complete
HMV Recordings, 1927-33

LEVKO, Valentina (mez)
Kabalevsky: Requiem
Tchaikovsky: Queen of Spades (Cpte)

LEVKO-ANTOSCH, Olga (sop)
see CONCERT INDEX under:
(SCHW) 314572 Vienna State Opera Live, Vol.7
(SCHW) 314602 Vienna State Opera Live, Vol.10
(SCHW) 314632 Vienna State Opera Live, Vol.13

LEVY, Daniel (pf)
see CONCERT INDEX under:
(EDEL) ED1012 Schumann: Chamber Music with
Piano
(EDEL) ED1034 Grieg—Piano Works

LEVY, Mark (va da gamba)
see CONCERT INDEX under:
(L'OI) 433 043-2OH Telemann—Concertos
(L'OI) 433 187-2OH Mad Songs

LEVY, T. (cond)
see orch

LEWINGTON, James (ten)
Anon: Missa Salisburgensis, Plaudite tympana
G. Charpentier: Louise (Cpte)
Shostakovich: Lady Macbeth of Mtsensk (Cpte)

LEWIS, Sir Anthony (cond)
see ECO

LEWIS, Bertha (contr)
Sullivan: Patience (Cpte)
see CONCERT INDEX under:
(VIRG) VC7 59604-2 Debussy—Chamber Works

LEWIS, Bryn (hp)
Britten: Folk Songs (exc)

LEWIS, Cary (pf)
see CONCERT INDEX under:
(VANG) **08.4051.71** Gottschalk—Piano Works, Vol.2

LEWIS, Henry (cond)
see orch

LEWIS, Henry (sngr)
see CONCERT INDEX under:
(PEAR) **GEMMCDS9056/8** Music from the New York
Stage, Vol. 3: 1913-17
(PEAR) **GEMMCDS9059/61** Music from the New York
Stage, Vol. 4: 1917-20

LEWIS, Idris (cond)
see orch

LEWIS, Keith (ten)
A. Thomas: Hamlet (Cpte)
Bach: Mass in B minor, BWV232 (Cpte)
Beethoven: Christus am Oelberge, Op. 85, Mass in C,
Symphony 9
Berlioz: Grande Messe des Morts (Cpte)
Bruckner: Mass in D minor, Te Deum
Franck: Béatitudes (Cpte)
Handel: Messiah (Cpte)
Haydn: Mass 10
Mahler: Symphony 8
Mendelssohn: Elias (Cpte)
Mozart: Don Giovanni (Cpte), Requiem
Rossini: Mosè in Egitto (Cpte), Otello (Cpte), Tancredi
(Cpte)
Schumann: Genoveva (Cpte), Paradies und die Peri
(Cpte)
see CONCERT INDEX under:
(CHAN) **CHAN8476** Works by Rachmaninov and
Tchaikovsky
(RCA) **74321 20277-2** Beethoven—Complete
Symphonies

LEWIS, Marianne (organ)
Pärt: Berliner Messe

LEWIS, Mary (sop)
see CONCERT INDEX under:
(BEUL) **1PD13** Sir Malcolm Sargent conducts British
Music

LEWIS, Michael (bass)
Massenet: Werther (Cpte)

LEWIS, Richard (ten)
Beethoven: Christus am Oelberge, Op. 85, Missa
Solemnis
Elgar: Dream of Gerontius (Cpte)
Handel: Messiah (exc), Messias, K572 (Cpte)
Mahler: Lied von der Erde
Mozart: Così fan tutte (exc)
R. Strauss: Salome (Cpte)
Walton: Troilus and Cressida (exc)
see CONCERT INDEX under:
(CFP) **CD-CFP4532** Sacred Arias
(EMI) **CDH5 65072-2** Glyndebourne Recorded - 1934-
1994
(SONY) **SM2K47522** Beethoven & Haydn—Choral
Works

LEWIS, Vicki (sngr)
Gershwin: Girl crazy (Cpte)

LEWIS, William (ten)
V. Thomson: Mother of us all (Cpte)
see CONCERT INDEX under:
(VANG) **08.4016.71** Music of Samuel Barber

LHÉVINNE, Josef (pf)
see CONCERT INDEX under:
(APR) **APR7013** Romantic Piano Rarities, Vol.1

LIANG, Ning (sop)
see CONCERT INDEX under:
(CPO) **CPO999 269-2** Meyerbeer—Mélodies

LICAD, Cécile (pf)
Chopin: Piano Concerto 2
see CONCERT INDEX under:
(MUSM) **67124-2** Chopin—Piano Works

LICATA, Andrea (cond)
see Bellini Th Orch

LICETTE, Miriam (sop)
Gounod: Faust (Cpte)
see CONCERT INDEX under:
(PEAR) **GEMMCDS9925(1)** Covent Garden on
Record—Vol.3 (pt 1)
(PEAR) **GEMMCD9175** Heddle Nash - Serenade
(PEAR) **GEMMCD9319** Heddle Nash sings Opera
Arias & Songs
(PEAR) **GEMMCD9473** Heddle Nash—Vol.2

LICHA, Robert (ten)
R. Strauss: Rosenkavalier (Cpte)
Wagner: Meistersinger (Cpte)

LICHFIELD CATHEDRAL CHOIR
see CONCERT INDEX under:
(ABBE) **CDCA903** Christmas Music From Lichfield
Cathedral
(PRIO) **PRCD383** Psalms of David, Vol.4
cond A. LUMSDEN
see CONCERT INDEX under:
(PRIO) **PRCD505** Magnificat and Nunc Dimittis,
Volume 3

LICHT, Daniel (cond)
see OST

LICHTENBERGER, Hannes (bass)
R. Strauss: Rosenkavalier (Cpte)
Verdi: Battaglia di Legnano (Cpte)

LIDDELL, Nona (vn)
Haydn: Quatuor, HobII/G4

LIDDELL, Alvar (spkr)
Tavener: Whale

LIEB, Günther (bar)
Weber: Freischütz (Cpte)

LIEBAN, Julius (ten)
see CONCERT INDEX under:
(SUPR) **11 2136-2(3)** Emmy Destinn—Complete
Edition, Discs 5 to 8

LIEBERFELD, Dan (pf)
see CONCERT INDEX under:
(ROMO) **81012-2** Elisabeth Rethberg— Brunswick
Recordings 1924-1929

LIEBERMAN, Viktor (vn)
Schnittke: Concerto grosso 3

LIEBERMANN, Melinda (sop)
Glass: Akhnaten (Cpte)

LIEBMANN, Heike (contr)
R. Strauss: Rosenkavalier (Cpte)

LIEBSCHER, Wolfgang (bn)
see CONCERT INDEX under:
(EMI) **CDM7 69661-2** R. Strauss—Wind Concertos
(EMI) **CMS7 64342-2** R. Strauss—Orchestral Works,
Vol.1

LIÈGE ORCHESTRA
cond P. STRAUSS
Franck: Psyché

LIÈGE PHILHARMONIC ORCHESTRA
cond P. BARTHOLOMÉE
Lekeu: Andromède, Burgraves
Mozart: Sinfonia Concertante, K364, Violin Concerto,
K219
see CONCERT INDEX under:
(RICE) **RIC014024** Boesmans—Concertos

LIER, Ellen van (sop)
see CONCERT INDEX under:
(EURO) **GD69043** Puccini: Il Trittico

LIER, Kjell Axel (hp)
see CONCERT INDEX under:
(BIS) **BIS-CD377** Schnittke: Concertos

LIEWEHR, Fred (narr)
J. Strauss II: Wiener Blut (exc)

LIFE ON THE WATER
cond T. RILEY
Riley: In C

LIFSCHEY, Samuel (va)
R. Strauss: Don Quixote

LIFSCHITZ, Konstantin (pf)
Bach: Goldberg Variations
see CONCERT INDEX under:
(DENO) **CO-78907** Konstantin Lifschitz—Debut
Recording
(DENO) **CO-78908** Konstantin Lifschitz—Live in
Milano

LIGABUE, Ilva (sop)
Verdi: Falstaff (Cpte)

LIGENDZA, Catarina (sop)
Wagner: Götterdämmerung (Cpte), Meistersinger
(Cpte)
see CONCERT INDEX under:
(BELA) **450 121-2** Plácido Domingo
(DG) **431 104-2GB** Great Voices - Plácido Domingo
(DG) **435 211-2GX15** Wagner—Der Ring des
Nibelungen

LIGETI, Andras (cond)
see Budapest SO

LIGETI, György (tape op)
see CONCERT INDEX under:
(WERG) **WER60161-50** Ligeti: Instrumental Works

LIGHT MUSIC SOCIETY ORCHESTRA
cond V. DUNN
see CONCERT INDEX under:
(EMI) **CDM7 64131-2** Orchestral Music for Christmas

LIGHT SYMPHONY ORCHESTRA
cond HAYDN WOOD
see CONCERT INDEX under:
(EMI) **CDS7 54568-2** The Elgar Edition, Vol.3

LIGHTBAND, Robert (org/dir)
see CONCERT INDEX under:
(ABBE) **CDCA926** Choral Music from Dundee

LIGHTFOOT, Peter (bass-bar)
Massenet: Cid (Cpte)

LIGUGÉ ABBEY CHOIR
see CONCERT INDEX under:
(STUD) **SM1220.02** Immortel Grégorien

LIKA, Peter (bass)
Bach: Cantata 21, Magnificat, BWV243, St John
Passion, BWV245 (Cpte), St Matthew Passion,
BWV244 (Cpte)
Busoni: Arlecchino (Cpte)
Egk: Peer Gynt (Cpte)
Eisler: Deutsche Sinfonie
Flotow: Martha (Cpte)
Gluck: Alceste (1776) (Cpte)

Handel: Acis und Galatea, K566 (Cpte), Ode for St.
Cecilia's Day (Cpte)
Mendelssohn: Paulus (Cpte)
Rossini: Petite messe solennelle (Cpte)
Schumann: Manfred (Cpte)
Stravinsky: Noces
see CONCERT INDEX under:
(EMI) **CMS7 64783-2** Schubert—Sacred Works,
Vol.2

LIKHOPOI, Natalia (vn)
see CONCERT INDEX under:
(OLYM) **OCD292** Kabalevsky—Cello Concertos;
Violin and Piano Works

LILEY, Stephen (ten)
see CONCERT INDEX under:
(KOCH) **37202-2** Essentially Christmas

LILJE, Peeter (cond)
see Estonia Op Orch

LILJEFORS, Mats (cond)
see Swedish CO

LILL, John (pf)
Rachmaninov: Etudes-tableaux, Op. 33, Etudes-
tableaux, Op. 39, Piano Concerto 3, Piano Sonata 2
Tchaikovsky: Piano Concerto 1
see CONCERT INDEX under:
(ASV) **CDDCA584** W.S. Lloyd Webber—Various
Works
(ASV) **CDDCA753** Prokofiev—Piano Sonatas, Vol. 1
(ASV) **CDDCA754** Prokofiev—Piano Sonatas, Vol. 2
(ASV) **CDDCA755** Prokofiev—Piano Sonatas, Vol. 3
(ASV) **CDQS5055** Beethoven—Piano Sonatas, Vol. 1
(ASV) **CDQS5057** Beethoven—Piano Sonatas, Vol. 3
(CHAN) **CHAN9084/6** Beethoven—Piano Works
(CONI) **CDCF224** Arnold—Orchestral Works

LILLE NATIONAL ORCHESTRA
cond J-C. CASADESUS
Beethoven: Romances, Violin Concerto
Honegger: Roi David (Cpte)
Milhaud: Boeuf sur le toit
Poulenc: Voix Humaine (Cpte)
Six: Mariés de la Tour Eiffel (Cpte)
see CONCERT INDEX under:
(HARM) **HMC90 1434** Ravel—Orchestral Works

LILLESØE, Susse (sop)
Mussorgsky: Boris Godunov (Cpte)
Zemlinsky: Es war einmal (Cpte)

LILO (sngr)
Porter: Can-Can (Cpte)

LILOWA, Margarita (mez)
Mussorgsky: Boris Godunov (Cpte)
Offenbach: Contes d'Hoffmann (Cpte)
R. Strauss: Elektra (Cpte), Rosenkavalier (Cpte)
Tchaikovsky: Eugene Onegin (Cpte)
Wagner: Parsifal (Cpte), Walküre (Cpte)

LIMA, Luis (ten)
Massenet: Roi de Lahore (Cpte)
Vives: Bohemios (Cpte)

LIMANSKY, Gale (sngr)
Forrest/Wright: Kismet (Cpte)

LIMBERG CATHEDRAL CHILDREN'S CHOIR
cond A. GUADAGNO
Puccini: Bohème (Cpte)
cond E. INBAL
Mahler: Symphony 3, Symphony 8

LIMBRICK, Simon (perc)
see CONCERT INDEX under:
(CNTI) **CCD1008** Anderson: Mask and other works
(ECM) **847 537-2** Gavin Bryars—After the Requiem

LIMBURG SYMPHONY ORCHESTRA
cond S. MAS CONDE
R. Strauss: Bourgeois gentilhomme suite
Stravinsky: Pulcinella Suite

LIMOGES BAROQUE ENSEMBLE
see CONCERT INDEX under:
(ASTR) **E8530** Bach—Cantatas
(ASTR) **E8544** Bach—Cantatas
cond C. COIN
see CONCERT INDEX under:
(ASTR) **E8517** Boccherini—Cello Concertos, etc

LIMONGE, Bras (db)
see CONCERT INDEX under:
(CHNT) **LDC278 835** Villa-Lobos—Chôros for
Chamber Ensembles

LIMPT, Adriaan van (pf)
R. Strauss: Rosenkavalier (Cpte)

LIN, Cho-Liang (vn)
Arensky: Piano Trio 1
Brahms: String Sextet 1, String Sextet 2
Bruch: Scottish Fantasy, Violin Concerto 1
Mozart: Concertone, K190, Sinfonia concertante,
K364
Nielsen: Violin Concerto
Sibelius: Violin Concerto
Tchaikovsky: Piano Trio, Op. 50
see CONCERT INDEX under:
(SONY) **MK39310** Haydn Concertos
(SONY) **SK53969** Prokofiev/Stravinsky—Violin
Concertos

LIN, Gillian (pf)
Britten: Piano Concerto
Copland: Piano Concerto

LIN, Lucia (vn)
see CONCERT INDEX under:
(NEW) 80407-2 Sheng—Miscellaneous Works

LINAY, Samuel (treb)
Delius: Village Romeo and Juliet (Cpte)
Janáček: Fate (Cpte)
see CONCERT INDEX under:
(ASV) CDDCA758 Falla, Milhaud & Stravinsky—Operas

LINBERG, Jakob (archlte/theorbo)
Corelli: Trio Sonatas, Op. 1, Trio Sonatas, Op. 2

LINCER, William (va)
see CONCERT INDEX under:
(SONY) SMK47625 R. Strauss—Orchestral Works

LINCOLN CATHEDRAL CHOIR
cond C. WALSH
see CONCERT INDEX under:
(PRIO) PRCD454 Great Cathedral Anthems, Vol.4

LINCOLN CENTER CHAMBER MUSIC SOCIETY
see CONCERT INDEX under:
(KOCH) 37272-2 Music of Charles Wuorinen
cond O. KNUSSEN
see CONCERT INDEX under:
(VIRG) VC7 59308-2 Knussen—Chamber Music
cond D. SHIFRIN
Dvořák: Serenade, Op. 44, String Quintet, Op. 77
cond C. WUORINEN
see CONCERT INDEX under:
(KOCH) 37272-2 Music of Charles Wuorinen

LIND, Eva (sop)
Humperdinck: Hänsel und Gretel (Cpte)
J. Strauss II: Fledermaus (Cpte)
Mozart: Finta semplice (Cpte), Zauberflöte (Cpte)
R. Strauss: Ariadne auf Naxos (Cpte), Frau ohne Schatten (Cpte)

LIND, Lane (narr)
see CONCERT INDEX under:
(KONT) 32188 Nielsen—Vocal Works

LIND, Michael (tuba)
see CONCERT INDEX under:
(BIS) BIS-CD159 Hindemith—Chamber Works

LINDBERG, Christian (tbn)
see CONCERT INDEX under:
(BIS) BIS-CD159 Hindemith—Chamber Works
(BIS) BIS-CD298 The Romantic Trombone
(BIS) BIS-CD348 The Winter Trombone
(BIS) BIS-CD388 Solitary Trombone
(BIS) BIS-CD628 American Trombone Concertos
(BIS) BIS-CD658 British Trombone Concertos
(DECC) 444 455-2DH Martin—Ballades; Concerto for 7 Wind Instruments
(DENO) CO-78944 Takemitsu—Orchestral Works
(LDR) LDRCD1012 British Masters (Volume 2)

LINDBERG, Jacob (gtr)
see CONCERT INDEX under:
(BIS) BIS-CD327 Baroque Music for Lute & Guitar
(PEAR) SHECD9608 Romantic Songs for Tenor & Guitar

LINDBERG, Jakob (lte)
Dowland: First Book of Songs (Cpte)
see CONCERT INDEX under:
(BIS) BIS-CD290 Vivaldi: works for lute
(BIS) BIS-CD327 Baroque Music for Lute & Guitar
(BIS) BIS-CD341 Music for lutes
(BIS) BIS-CD390 Music from the time of Christian IV, Vol. 2
(BIS) BIS-CD391 Music from the time of Christian IV, Vol. 3
(BIS) BIS-CD399 La Serenissima I
(BIS) BIS-CD469 Holborne—Pavans, Galliards, Almains and other short Airs
(BIS) BIS-CD599 La Serenissima II

LINDBERG, Jakob (lte/dir)
Dowland: Lachrimae (exc)
see CONCERT INDEX under:
(BIS) BIS-CD390 Music from the time of Christian IV, Vol. 2

LINDBERG, Jakob (lte/orpharion)
see CONCERT INDEX under:
(BIS) BIS-CD469 Holborne—Pavans, Galliards, Almains and other short Airs
(BIS) BIS-CD722/4 Dowland—Complete Solo Lute Music

LINDBERG, Jakob (theorbo)
Corelli: Trio Sonatas, Op.3 (exc)

LINDBERG-TORLIND, Kerstin (sop)
see CONCERT INDEX under:
(CPRI) CAP21510 Rosenberg plays Rosenberg

LINDE, Hans-Martin (fl)
see CONCERT INDEX under:
(DHM) RD77188 C.P.E. Bach—Vocal & Chamber Works

LINDE, Hans-Martin (rec)
see CONCERT INDEX under:
(DHM) 74321 26617-2(1) Elly Ameling - The Early Recorings, Vols. 1-3

LINDEN, Jaap ter (va da gamba)
Couperin: Concerts Royaux
see CONCERT INDEX under:
(HARM) HMA190 1150 Couperin—Motets

LINDEN, Jaap ter (vc)
Bach: Musikalisches Opfer, BWV1079
see CONCERT INDEX under:
(ERAT) 4509-91728-2 Haydn—Piano Trios

LINDEN, Sylvia (sop)
Diabelli: Pastoral Mass, op 147

LINDEN SINGERS
cond S. BEDFORD
see CONCERT INDEX under:
(LOND) 425 159-2LM Salute to Percy Grainger

LINDER, Albert (hn)
Atterberg: Horn Concerto, Op. 28

LINDGREN, Ingrid (pf)
Crumb: Madrigals, Music for a Summer Evening

LINDGREN, Stefan (pf)
(MSVE) MSCD521 Berwald—Chamber Works

LINDHOLM, Berit (sop)
Berlioz: Troyens (Cpte)
Wagner: Walküre (Cpte)
see CONCERT INDEX under:
(DECC) 414 100-2DM15 Wagner: Der Ring des Nibelungen

LINDHOLM, Lisbeth (sop)
Schnittke: Requiem

LINDNER, Brigitte (sop)
Humperdinck: Königskinder (Cpte)
Lehár: Giuditta (Cpte)
Mozart: Zauberflöte (Cpte)
Suder: Kleider machen Leute (Cpte)
see CONCERT INDEX under:
(EMI) CZS7 67819-2 Brahms/Schumann—Requiems

LINDROOS, Peter (ten)
Bergman: Singing Tree (Cpte)
Nielsen: Saul and David (Cpte)
see CONCERT INDEX under:
(FINL) 4509-95849-2 Sibelius: Choral Works

LINDROOS, Petri (bass)
Bergman: Singing Tree (Cpte)

LINDSAY, Gavin (cornet)
see CONCERT INDEX under:
(DOYE) DOYCD005 Flower of Scotland

LINDSAY QUARTET
Beethoven: String Quartet 7, String Quartet 8, String Quartet 9, String Quartet 14
Brahms: Piano Quintet
Britten: String Quartet 3
Dvořák: Piano Quintet, Op.81
Haydn: String Quartet, Op. 51, String Quartets, op.54, String Quartets, Op. 55
Martinů: Piano Quintet 1
Mozart: String Quartet, K387, String Quintet, K516
Schubert: String Quartet, D112, String Quartet, D703, String Quartet, D804, String Quartet, D810, String Quartet, D887, String Quintet
Schumann: Piano Quintet, Op.44
Tippett: String Quartet 4
see CONCERT INDEX under:
(ASV) CDDCA749 The Bohemians, Volume 1
(ASV) CDDCA806 The Bohemians, Volume 5
(ASV) CDDCA825 Lindsay Quartet - 25 Years
(ASV) CDDCA879 British String Quartets
(ASV) CDDCA930 Ravel/Debussy/Stravinsky—String Quartets
(ASV) CDDCS207 Beethoven—String Quartets
(ASV) CDDCS301 Bartók—String Quartets
(ASV) CDDCS403 Beethoven—Late String Quartets
(ASV) CDQS6144 Haydn Quartets - Volume 1
(ASV) CDQS6145 Haydn Quartets—Volume 2
(ASV) CDQS6146 Haydn—String Quartets, Vol. 3
(CHAN) CHAN8366 Weber—Chamber Music for Clarinet
(CHAN) CHAN8683 English Chamber Works

LINDSLEY, Celina (sop)
Busoni: Turandot (Cpte)
Gurlitt: Wozzeck (Cpte)
Henze: Bassariden (Cpte)
Hindemith: Nusch-Nuschi (Cpte)
Martinů: Ariane (Cpte)
Mysliveček: Bellerofonte (Cpte)
Schoeck: Massimilla Doni (Cpte)
Zemlinsky: Kreidekreis (Cpte)
see CONCERT INDEX under:
(CAPR) 10 169 Mozart: Choral Works
(CAPR) 10 244 Schubert: Choral Music

LING, Jahja (cond)
see Florida Orch

LINK, Kurt (bar)
Schoenberg: Moses und Aron (Cpte)

LINN, Ben (sngr)
see CONCERT INDEX under:
(PEAR) GEMMCDS9056/8 Music from the New York Stage, Vol. 3: 1913-17

LINOS ENSEMBLE
Brahms: Serenade 2
Mozart: Divertimento, K252, Serenade, K361
Wagner: Siegfried Idyll

LINS, Martina (sop)
A. Scarlatti: Lamentazioni (exc)
C. P. E. Bach: Gott hat den Herrn auferwecket, H803
Fux: Death of John the Baptist (Cpte)

Telemann: Getreue Music-Meister (Cpte)
see CONCERT INDEX under:
(CAPR) 10 310/1 J. E. Bach—Passion Oratorio, etc.
(CAPR) 10 315 Telemann—Choral Music

LINTON, Charles (pf)
see CONCERT INDEX under:
(RCA) 09026 61580-2(2) RCA/Met 100 Singers, 100 Years (pt 2)

LINVAL, Monique (sop)
Bizet: Carmen (Cpte)
Delibes: Lakmé (Cpte)

LIOT, Raymond (sngr)
Ganne: Hans (Cpte)

LIPATTI, Dinu (pf)
Mozart: Piano Concerto 21
Schumann: Piano Concerto
see CONCERT INDEX under:
(ARCI) ARC112/3 Dinu Lipatti—Les Inédits
(EMI) CDH5 65166-2 Dinu Pipatti—Last Recital, Besançon, 1950
(EMI) CDH7 63038-2 Dinu Lipatti - Piano Recital
(EMI) CDH7 69800-2 Dinu Lipatti - Piano Recital
(EMI) CDH7 69802-2 Dinu Lipatti plays Chopin
(JECK) JD541-2 Bach & Chopin: Piano Works

LIPATTI, Madeleine (pf)
see CONCERT INDEX under:
(ARCI) ARC112/3 Dinu Lipatti—Les Inédits
(EMI) CHS7 69741-2(3) Record of Singing, Vol.4—French School

LIPKIN, Seymour (pf)
see CONCERT INDEX under:
(BIDD) LAW008 Grieg—Violin Sonatas
(BIDD) LAW015 Dohnányi/Weiner—Violin Sonatas
(SONY) SMK47628 Stravinsky—Choral and Orchestral Works

LIPKOWSKA, Lydia (sop)
see CONCERT INDEX under:
(MMOI) CDMOIR422 Great Voices in Tchaikovsky
(NIMB) NI7865 Great Singers at the Mariinsky Theatre
(PEAR) GEMMCDS9004/6(1) Singers of Imperial Russia, Vol.3 (pt 1)
(PEAR) GEMMCDS9925(1) Covent Garden on Record—Vol.3 (pt 1)

LIPMAN, Samuel (pf)
see CONCERT INDEX under:
(RCA) 09026 68131-2 Classics for Children—Boston Pops

LIPOVŠEK, Marjana (mez)
Bach: Christmas Oratorio, BWV248 (Cpte), Mass in B minor, BWV232 (Cpte), St. Matthew Passion, BWV244 (Cpte)
Beethoven: Missa Solemnis, Symphony 9
Brahms: Alto Rhapsody, Op. 53
Einem: Dantons Tod (Cpte)
Gounod: Faust (Cpte)
Handel: Messiah (Cpte)
J. Strauss II: Fledermaus (exc)
Martin: Cornet
Mendelssohn: Midsummer Night's Dream (exc)
Mozart: Requiem, Zauberflöte (exc)
Mussorgsky: Boris Godunov (Cpte), Khovanshchina (Cpte)
Pergolesi: Stabat Mater
R. Strauss: Elektra (Cpte), Frau ohne Schatten (Cpte)
Schoeck: Penthesilea (Cpte)
Schoenberg: Gurrelieder
Schubert: Mass, D950
Stravinsky: Oedipus Rex (Cpte)
Verdi: Requiem (Cpte)
Vivaldi: Gloria, RV589
Wagner: Götterdämmerung (Cpte), Rheingold (Cpte), Tristan und Isolde (Cpte)
see CONCERT INDEX under:
(DG) 427 306-2GH6 Beethoven: Complete Symphonies
(EURO) GD69043 Puccini: Il Trittico
(ORFE) C159871A Schubert: Lieder Recital
(ORFE) C179891A Marjana Lipovšek sings Famous Opera Arias
(SONY) SK52490 Brahms—Lieder
(SONY) SK53360 Mahler/Nono—Vocal Works
(SONY) SK57972 Schumann—Lieder

LIPP, Wilma (sop)
J. Strauss II: Wiener Blut (exc)
Janáček: Excursions of Mr Brouček (Cpte)
R. Strauss: Rosenkavalier (Cpte)
see CONCERT INDEX under:
(DECC) 443 530-2LF2 Mozart—Die Entführung aus dem Serail
(EURO) GD69022 Oscar Straus: Operetta excerpts
(PHIL) 438 760-2PM2 Brahms—Choral Works and Overtures

LIPPERT, Herbert (ten)
Haydn: Schöpfung (Cpte), Stabat Mater
J. Strauss II: Zigeunerbaron (Cpte)
Mozart: Zauberflöte (Cpte)
Schreker: Gezeichneten (Cpte)
see CONCERT INDEX under:
(DECC) 440 854-2DH Ullmann—Der Kaiser von Atlantis

(EMI) **CHS7 69741-2(2)** Record of Singing,
Vol.4—Anglo-American School (pt 2)

LLOYD, Frank (hn)
Britten: Serenade
see CONCERT INDEX *under:*
(ASV) **CDDCA645** Vivaldi—Concertos
(COLL) **Coll7037-2** Britten—Orchestral Song Cycles
(DOYE) **DOYCD017** Gregson—Brass Music - Volume
1
(NOVA) **150 043-2** Mozart—Works for Oboe and
Orchestra
(SALA) **SCD8904/5** Scelsi—Chamber Works

LLOYD, George (cond)
see Albany SO

LLOYD, Peter (fl)
see CONCERT INDEX *under:*
(CARL) **PCD991** French Flute Music

LLOYD, Robert (bass)
Beethoven: Missa Solemnis, Symphony 9
Berlioz: Benvenuto Cellini (Cpte), Béatrice et
Bénédict (Cpte), Damnation de Faust (Cpte), Roméo
et Juliette (Cpte)
Bizet: Carmen (Cpte)
Britten: Little Sweep (Cpte)
Donizetti: Lucia di Lammermoor (Cpte)
Elgar: Apostles (Cpte)
Gay: Beggar's Opera (Cpte)
Handel: Messiah (Cpte), Semele (Cpte)
Massenet: Esclarmonde (Cpte), Werther (Cpte)
Mozart: Clemenza di Tito (Cpte), Don Giovanni
(Cpte), Entführung (Cpte), Finta semplice (Cpte),
Mass, K427, Nozze di Figaro (Cpte), Requiem,
Zauberflöte (Cpte)
Mussorgsky: Songs and Dances of Death
Puccini: Bohème (Cpte), Fanciulla del West (Cpte)
Rossini: Barbiere di Siviglia (Cpte), Siège de Corinthe
(Cpte)
Saint-Saëns: Samson et Dalila (Cpte)
Schumann: Szenen aus Goethes Faust (Cpte)
Sullivan: Yeomen of the Guard (Cpte)
Vaughan Williams: Hugh the Drover (Cpte)
Verdi: Ballo in maschera (Cpte), Giovanna d'Arco
(Cpte), Macbeth (Cpte), Rigoletto (Cpte), Trovatore
(Cpte)
Wagner: Parsifal (Cpte), Rheingold (Cpte)
Walton: Troilus and Cressida (Cpte)
see CONCERT INDEX *under:*
(DECC) **425 681-2DM2** Tutto Pavarotti
(EMI) **CDM5 65101-2** A Warlock Centenary Album
(EMI) **CDM7 64716-2** Ireland—Piano Concerto, etc

LLOYD WEBBER, Julian (vc)
A. Lloyd Webber: Variations
Elgar: Cello Concerto
see CONCERT INDEX *under:*
(ASV) **CDDCA584** W.S. Lloyd Webber—Various
Works
(ASV) **CDDCA592** British Cello Music
(ASV) **CDDCA807** British Cello Works, Vol.2
(EMI) **CDM7 64726-2** Sullivan—Orchestral Works
(PHIL) **412 231-2PH** Travels with my Cello
(PHIL) **416 698-2PH** Encore! Travels with my cello,
Vol. 2
(PHIL) **422 387-2PH** Dvořák—Orchestral Works
(PHIL) **432 084-2PH** French Cello Works
(PHIL) **434 106-2PH** Works for Cello and Orchestra
(PHIL) **434 917-2PH** Cello Song
(PHIL) **442 530-2PH** English Idylls
(RCA) **RD70800** British cello works
(UNIC) **UKCD2074** The Delius Collection, Volume 4

LLOYD-EVANS, Philip (bar)
Janáček: Fate (Cpte)
Sullivan: HMS Pinafore (Cpte)

LLOYD-JONES, Beti (mez)
Sullivan: Patience (Cpte)

LLOYD-JONES, David (cond)
see English Northern Philh

LLUNA, Joan-Enric (cl)
Falla: Harpsichord Concerto
see CONCERT INDEX *under:*
(NOVA) **150 043-2** Mozart—Works for Oboe and
Orchestra

LO GIUDICE, Franco (ten)
Verdi: Requiem (Cpte)

LOACHE, Benjamin de (narr)
see CONCERT INDEX *under:*
(STOK) **LSCD20** Stokowski conducts Philadelphia
Rarities

LOBANOV, Vassili (pf)
see CONCERT INDEX *under:*
(CHNT) **LDC278 1018/9** Shostakovich: Chamber
Works

LOCATELLI TRIO
Albinoni: Sonate, Op. 4, Trattenimenti, Op. 6
Corelli: Sonatas, Op. 5
Locatelli: Violin Sonatas, Op. 6 (exc)
Tartini: Devil's Trill Sonata, Violin Sonatas and
Pastorale (1734) (exc)
see CONCERT INDEX *under:*
(HYPE) **CDA66485** Tartini—Violin Sonatas, Vol.2
(HYPE) **CDA66583** English 18th Century Violin
Sonatas

LOCHER, Paul (vn)
Holliger: Alb-Chehr

LOCHMANN, Daniel (treb)
Purcell: Dido (Cpte)
see CONCERT INDEX *under:*
(HYPE) **CDA66623** Purcell—Complete Anthems &
Services, Vol.3

LOCK, Robert (sngr)
Romberg: Student Prince (Cpte)

LOCKE BRASS CONSORT
see CONCERT INDEX *under:*
(KOCH) **37202-2** Essentially Christmas
cond M. KIBBLEWHITE
see CONCERT INDEX *under:*
(KOCH) **37202-2** Essentially Christmas
cond J. STOBART
see CONCERT INDEX *under:*
(CHAN) **CHAN8419** R. Strauss—Music for Symphonic
Brass
(CRD) **CRD3402** Symphonic Marches for Concert
Brass

LOCKHART, James (cond)
see ECO

LOCKHART, James (pf)
see CONCERT INDEX *under:*
(CFP) **CD-CFP4669** Margaret Price sings Romantic
Songs
(ORFE) **C031821A** Schumann: Lieder
(ORFE) **C058831A** Brahms—Lieder
(RCA) **09026 61635-2** Margaret Price sings Mozart

LOCKWOOD, Arthur (tpt)
see CONCERT INDEX *under:*
(DUTT) **CDAX8010** Hallé Orchestra Wartime
Recordings

LODÉON, Frederic (vc)
Schubert: Piano Trio 2
Tchaikovsky: Piano Trio, Op. 50
see CONCERT INDEX *under:*
(EMI) **CDC7 49165-2** Schubert: Works for Piano Trio
(EMI) **CMS7 62548-2** Fauré—Chamber Works, Vol.2

LOESSER, Arthur (pf)
see CONCERT INDEX *under:*
(APR) **APR7015** The Auer Legacy, Vol.1
(BIDD) **LAB013** Toscha Seidel—Sonatas by Brahms
and Grieg

LOGAN, Peter (ten)
see CONCERT INDEX *under:*
(GLOR) **GDCD016** Leo Sowerby—American Master
of Sacred Song

LOGES, Karl-Heinz (cond)
see LSO

LOGIE, Nicholas (va)
see CONCERT INDEX *under:*
(EMI) **CMS5 65115-2** Britten—Chamber Works

LOGUIN, Anders (perc)
see CONCERT INDEX *under:*
(BIS) **BIS-CD507** Schnittke—Cello Works

LOHMANN, Norbert (ten)
Lully: Bourgeois Gentilhomme

LOHNER, Helmut (bass)
J. Strauss II: Fledermaus (Cpte)

LOIBNER, Wilfriede (sop)
R. Strauss: Rosenkavalier (Cpte)

LOIBNER, Wilhelm (cond)
see Austrian St Rad Orch

LOIRE PHILHARMONIC ORCHESTRA
cond P. DERVAUX
see CONCERT INDEX *under:*
(EMI) **CDM7 63950-2** Pierné—Orchestral Works
(EMI) **CDM7 63951-2** Rabaud—Orchestral Works
(EMI) **CDM7 63953-2** D'Indy—Orchestral Works Vol
II
cond M. SOUSTROT
see CONCERT INDEX *under:*
(FORL) **UCD16681** The Great Italian Arias
(PIER) **PV788011** Trumpet Concertos
(PIER) **PV792051** Chausson/Fauré—Orchestral
Works

LOIRI, Vesa-Matti (sngr)
Sallinen: Kullervo (Cpte)

LOISEL, Jean-Marc (bass)
Saint-Saëns: Henry VIII (Cpte)

**LOISELEUR DES LONGCHAMPS, Jacques-François
(ten)**
Rameau: Hippolyte et Aricie (Cpte)

LOKKA, Maija (sop)
Madetoja: Juha (Cpte)

LOMAN, Judy (hp)
see CONCERT INDEX *under:*
(CBC) **SMCD5119** Adeste Fideles

LOMBANA, Sergio (ten)
Delius: Village Romeo and Juliet (Cpte)

LOMBARD, Alain (cond)
see Bordeaux Aquitaine Orch

LOMBARDO, Bernard (ten)
Cherubini: Lodoïska (Cpte)
Donizetti: Lucia di Lammermoor (Cpte)

LONDON, George (bass-bar)
Brahms: Deutsches Requiem, Op. 45 (Cpte)
Mozart: Zauberflöte (Cpte)
Offenbach: Contes d'Hoffmann (Cpte)

Puccini: Tosca (Cpte)
R. Strauss: Arabella (Cpte)
Wagner: Parsifal (Cpte), Rheingold (Cpte), Walküre
(Cpte)
see CONCERT INDEX *under:*
(DECC) **414 100-2DM15** Wagner: Der Ring des
Nibelungen
(EMI) **CHS7 69741-2(2)** Record of Singing,
Vol.4—Anglo-American School (pt 2)
(SONY) **SMK47638** Vaughan Williams—Orchestral
Works

LONDON, Maurine (sop)
Wagner: Siegfried (Cpte)

LONDON BAROQUE
Bach: Trio Sonatas, BWV1036-9
Corelli: Trio Sonatas, Op. 1, Trio Sonatas, Op. 2, Trio
Sonatas, Op. 3, Trio Sonatas, Op. 4
Handel: Trio Sonatas, Op.2 (exc), Trio Sonatas,
Op.5
Mozart: Church Sonatas (exc)
Purcell: Sonatas, Z790-801, Sonatas, Z802-11
W. Lawes: Fantasia-Suites a 4
see CONCERT INDEX *under:*
(AMON) **CD-SAR14** English Music of the 18th
Century
(AMON) **CD-SAR34** Mozart—Chamber Works
(HARM) **HMC90 1327** Purcell—Chamber Music
(HARM) **HMC90 1395** L. & W. Mozart/J.C.
Bach—Concertos and Sonatas
(HARM) **HMC90 1410** CPE Bach—Sonatas
(HARM) **HMC90 1511** C. P. E. Bach—Trio Sonatas
(HARM) **HMX290 1528/33(1)** A Purcell Companion (pt
1)
cond E. HIGGINBOTTOM
see CONCERT INDEX *under:*
(HYPE) **CDA66269** Mondonville: Motets
cond C. MEDLAM
Blow: Venus and Adonis (Cpte)
Monteverdi: Orfeo (Cpte)
see CONCERT INDEX *under:*
(HARM) **HMA190 1220** Sonatas by Muffat and
Schmelzer

LONDON BRASS
see CONCERT INDEX *under:*
(ARGO) **440 282-2ZH** Nyman—Time Will Pronounce
(CARL) **PCD919** Great Music from Great Occasions
at Westminster Abbey
cond M. NEARY
see CONCERT INDEX *under:*
(CARL) **PCD919** Great Music from Great Occasions
at Westminster Abbey
(CNTO) **CSACD3050** Music from the Coronation of H.
M. Queen Elizabeth II

LONDON BRASS VIRTUOSI
cond D. HONEYBALL
see CONCERT INDEX *under:*
(HYPE) **CDA66189** Music for Brass and Percussion

LONDON CAST
Rodgers: Carousel (exc)
cond S. CALVERT
F. Loewe: Brigadoon (Cpte)
cond R. EDWARDS
Willy Russell: Blood Brothers (Cpte)
cond M. KOCH
Bart: Oliver! (Cpte)
cond N. RHODEN
Gay: Beggar's Opera (Cpte)
cond S. SCHWARTZ
S. Schwartz: Godspell (exc)
cond C. WALKER
Sandy Wilson: Boy Friend (Cpte)
cond T. YORK
Rodgers: Pal Joey (Cpte)

LONDON CHAMBER CHOIR
cond L. HELTAY
Haydn: Salve Regina, HobXXIIIb/1, Stabat Mater

LONDON CHAMBER ORCHESTRA
see CONCERT INDEX *under:*
(VIRG) **CUV5 61126-2** Elgar/Vaughan
Williams—String Music
(VIRG) **CUV5 61145-2** Vivaldi—Four Seasons
(VIRG) **VC7 59609-2** Vivaldi—Concertos
cond S. LAYTON
MacMillan: Seven Last Words
cond C. WARREN-GREEN
Dvořák: Serenade, Op. 22
Mozart: Sinfonia Concertante, K297b
Suk: Serenade, Op. 6

LONDON CHAMBER PLAYERS
Monteverdi: Ballo delle ingrate
cond A. DELLER
Monteverdi: Ballo delle ingrate

LONDON CLASSICAL PLAYERS
cond R. NORRINGTON
Beethoven: Choral Fantasia, Piano Concerto 5,
Prometheus (exc), Symphony 1, Symphony 2,
Symphony 3, Symphony 4, Symphony 5, Symphony
6, Symphony 8, Symphony 9
Berlioz: Symphonie fantastique
Brahms: Begräbnisgesang, Op.13, Deutsches
Requiem, Op.45 (Cpte), Haydn Variations, Symphony
1, Symphony 2, Tragic Overture
Haydn: Symphony 101, Symphony 102, Symphony
103, Symphony 104
Mendelssohn: Symphony 3, Symphony 4

*Mozart: Don Giovanni (Cpte), Symphony 38,
Symphony 39, Symphony 40, Symphony 41,
Zauberflöte (Cpte)
Purcell: Fairy Queen, Z629 (Cpte)
Schubert: Symphony 4, Symphony 5, Symphony 6,
Symphony 8, Symphony 9
Schumann: Symphony 3, Symphony 4*
  see CONCERT INDEX *under:*
(EMI) **CDC5 55192-2** Haydn—Symphonies
(EMI) **CDC5 55348-2** Weber—Orchestral Works
(EMI) **CDC5 55479-2** Wagner—Orchestral Works
(EMI) **CDC7 49816-2** Beethoven: Orchestral Works
(EMI) **CDC7 54091-2** Rossini—Overtures
(EMI) **CDC7 54525-2** Mozart—Sacred Works

LONDON COLLEGIATE BRASS
  cond J. STOBART
  see CONCERT INDEX *under:*
(CRD) **CRD3434** British Music for Brass
(CRD) **CRD3444** Brass Ensemble music by 20th
Century British composers

LONDON COLLEGIUM MUSICUM
Walton: Belshazzar's Feast

LONDON CONCERT CHOIR
  cond N. CLEOBURY
  see CONCERT INDEX *under:*
(CONI) **CDCF167** Dickinson—Vocal Works

LONDON CORNETT AND SACKBUTT ENSEMBLE
  cond T. CAUDLE
Monteverdi: Orfeo (Cpte)
  cond A. PARROTT
*G. Gabrieli: Canzoni et Sonate (1615) (exc), Sacrae
symphoniae (1597) (exc)*

LONDON EARLY MUSIC CONSORT
  cond D. MUNROW
  see CONCERT INDEX *under:*
(ARCH) **415 292-2AH** Music of the Gothic Era

LONDON FESTIVAL ORCHESTRA
  cond S. BLACK
  see CONCERT INDEX *under:*
(DECC) **433 616-2DSP**
Addinsell/Gershwin—Orchestral Works
  cond R. POPLE
*Mozart: Sinfonia concertante, K297b, Sinfonia
Concertante, K364
R. Strauss: Metamorphosen
Schoenberg: Verklärte Nacht*
  see CONCERT INDEX *under:*
(ASV) **CDDCA769** Franck—Miscellaneous Works
(ASV) **CDDCA779** Vaughan Williams—Orchestral
Works
(ASV) **CDDCA782** Holst—Orchestral Works
(ASV) **CDQS6140** Haydn/Stamitz—Sinfonie
Concertanti
(DG) **445 822-2GH** Une flûte à l'opéra
(HYPE) **CDA66332** Malcolm Arnold—Orchestral
Works
(HYPE) **CDA66561/3** Mendelssohn—Complete String
Symphonies

LONDON FESTIVAL RECORDING ENSEMBLE
  cond B. HERRMANN
  see CONCERT INDEX *under:*
(DECC) **433 616-2DSP**
Addinsell/Gershwin—Orchestral Works

LONDON FILMWORKS ORCHESTRA
  cond C. TOWNS
Towns: Buccaneers (exc)

LONDON FORTEPIANO TRIO
*Beethoven: Piano Trios (exc)
Mozart: Divertimento, K254, Piano Trio, K496, Piano
Trio, K502, Piano Trio, K542, Piano Trio, K548, Piano
Trio, K564*

LONDON GABRIELI BRASS ENSEMBLE
  cond C. LARKIN
  see CONCERT INDEX *under:*
(HYPE) **CDA66470** Original 19th Century Music for
Brass
(HYPE) **CDA66517** From the Steeples and the
Mountains

LONDON HAFFNER WIND ENSEMBLE
  see CONCERT INDEX *under:*
(CHAN) **CHAN9152** Alwyn—Chamber Works -
Volume 1
(COLL) **Coll1348-2** Français—Chamber Works

LONDON HANDEL CHOIR
  cond D. DARLOW
Handel: Triumph of Time and Truth (Cpte)

LONDON HANDEL ORCHESTRA
  cond D. DARLOW
*Handel: Aminta e Fillide, Triumph of Time and Truth
(Cpte)*
  see CONCERT INDEX *under:*
(HYPE) **CDA66227** Emma Kirkby Collection

LONDON HARPSICHORD ENSEMBLE
  see CONCERT INDEX *under:*
(UNIC) **DKPCD9071** Vivaldi—Chamber Concertos
(UNIC) **DKPCD9128** Telemann—Six Oboe Concertos
- Volume 1

LONDON KING'S COLLEGE SINGERS
  cond E.H. WARRELL
  see CONCERT INDEX *under:*
(REGE) **REGCD106** Carols in Advent

LONDON MOZART PLAYERS
*Mozart: Piano Concerto 12, Piano Concerto 14, Piano
Concerto 19, Piano Concerto 27*
  see CONCERT INDEX *under:*
(CHAN) **CHAN9215** Mendelssohn—Works for Piano
& Orchestra
(EMI) **CDM7 69835-2** Vivaldi—Cello Concertos
  cond M. BAMERT
*Clementi: Symphonies, Op. 18, Symphony 1
Field: Piano Concerto 1, Piano Concerto 2
Krommer: Symphony 2, Symphony 4*
  see CONCERT INDEX *under:*
(CHAN) **CHAN9358** Stamitz—Symphonies
  cond H. BLECH
  see CONCERT INDEX *under:*
(TEST) **SBT1026** Irmgard Seefried
  cond A. FRANCIS
Offenbach: Christopher Columbus (Cpte)
  cond J. GLOVER
*Mozart: Maurerische Trauermusik, K477, Requiem
Walton: Façade (Cpte)*
  see CONCERT INDEX *under:*
(ASV) **CDDCA615** Mozart—Symphonies
(ASV) **CDDCA647** Mozart—Symphonies
(ASV) **CDDCA682** Britten—Vocal & Orchestral
Works
(ASV) **CDDCA683** Mozart—Arias
(ASV) **CDDCA717** Mozart—Symphonies
(ASV) **CDDCA761** Mozart—Symphonies
(ASV) **CDDCA762** Mozart—Symphonies
(ASV) **CDDCA795** Mozart—Wind Concertos
(GALL) **CD-499** Bassoon Concertos
  cond A. LITTON
  see CONCERT INDEX *under:*
(DECC) **440 293-2DH** Works for Guitar and
Orchestra
  cond H. SHELLEY
  see CONCERT INDEX *under:*
(HYPE) **CDA66411** Mozart & Kramar—Oboe
Concertos

LONDON MOZART TRIO
*Dvořák: Piano Trio 4
Schubert: Piano Trio 1*

LONDON MUSICA ANTIQUA
  cond M. URIDGE
  see CONCERT INDEX *under:*
(SYMP) **SYMCD1157** Five Centuries of Festive Fayre

LONDON MUSICI
  cond R. MARLOW
  see CONCERT INDEX *under:*
(CONI) **CDCF176** French Sacred Choral Works
(CONI) **75605 51232-2** Stravinsky—Mass;
Gesualdo—Responsoria
  cond M. STEPHENSON
*Handel: Messiah (exc)
Rossini: Sonate a quattro (exc)*
  see CONCERT INDEX *under:*
(CONI) **CDCF172** Malcolm Arnold: Concertos
(CONI) **CDCF173** Prokofiev: Orchestral & Chamber
Works
(CONI) **CDCF182** Panufnik: Orchestral Works
(CONI) **CDCF203** Vivaldi—Concertos
(CONI) **CDCF217** Panufnik—Orchestral Works
(CONI) **CDCF228** Arnold—Concertos

LONDON MUSICI CHAMBER CHOIR
  cond M. STEPHENSON
Handel: Messiah (exc)

LONDON MUSICIANS ORCHESTRA
  cond I. FRASER
  see CONCERT INDEX *under:*
(PHIL) **442 603-2PH** Julie Andrews sings Richard
Rodgers

LONDON OBOE BAND
  cond P. GOODWIN
  see CONCERT INDEX *under:*
(HARM) **HMU90 7122** Lully/Philidor—Stage Works

LONDON OPERA CHORUS
*Bellini: Sonnambula (Cpte)
Donizetti: Lucrezia Borgia (Cpte)
J. Adams: Death of Klinghoffer (Cpte)
Mozart: Don Giovanni (Cpte), Nozze di Figaro
(Cpte)
Ponchielli: Gioconda (Cpte)
Puccini: Tosca (Cpte)
Verdi: Ballo in maschera (Cpte), Luisa Miller (Cpte),
Traviata (exc), Trovatore (Cpte)*
  see CONCERT INDEX *under:*
(DECC) **425 681-2DM2** Tutto Pavarotti
(DECC) **436 463-2DM** Ten Top Tenors

LONDON ORATORY CHOIR
  cond J. HOBAN
Valls: Missa Scala Aretina

LONDON ORATORY JUNIOR CHOIR
  cond M. BEST
  see CONCERT INDEX *under:*
(HYPE) **CDA66569** Vaughan Williams—Choral Works
  cond J.E. GARDINER
*Bach: St Matthew Passion, BWV244 (Cpte)
Monteverdi: Vespers*

LONDON ORCHESTRA NOVA
  cond M. DAVIES
  see CONCERT INDEX *under:*
(EMI) **CDM7 64730-2** Vaughan Williams—Riders to
the Sea; Epithalamion, etc

LONDON PHILHARMONIC CHOIR
  cond C. ABBADO
Berlioz: Te Deum
  cond M. BAMERT
*Parry: Invocation to Music, Lotos Eaters, Soul's
Ransom*
  cond P. BOULEZ
Schoenberg: Gurrelieder
  cond A. BOULT
*Elgar: Kingdom (Cpte)
Vaughan Williams: Symphony 1, Symphony 7*
  cond J. FERENCSIK
Kodály: Psalmus Hungaricus
  see CONCERT INDEX *under:*
(EMI) **CMS7 64218-2** Delius—Vocal Works
  cond B. HAITINK
*Beethoven: Choral Fantasia
Shostakovich: Symphony 2, Symphony 3
Vaughan Williams: Symphony 1, Symphony 7*
  cond C. KRAUSS
  see CONCERT INDEX *under:*
(DECC) **433 477-2DM** Ferrier Edition - Volume 10
  cond A. LITTON
Mendelssohn: Midsummer Night's Dream (exc)
  cond Z. MEHTA
Orff: Carmina Burana
  cond K. NAGANO
Stravinsky: Perséphone (Cpte)
  cond L. SLATKIN
  see CONCERT INDEX *under:*
(RCA) **RD60813** Walton—Belshazzar's Feast
  cond G. SOLTI
  see CONCERT INDEX *under:*
(DECC) **436 403-2DWO** The World of Royal Music
(DECC) **440 318-2DWO** World of British Classics,
Volume II
  cond K. TENNSTEDT
Mahler: Symphony 8
  see CONCERT INDEX *under:*
(EMI) **CMS7 64471-2** Mahler—Symphonies, Vol.1
(EMI) **CMS7 64476-2** Mahler—Symphonies, Vol.2
(EMI) **CZS7 67819-2** Brahms/Schumann—Requiems
  cond B. THOMSON
*Elgar: Music Makers
Vaughan Williams: Dona nobis pacem, Mystical
Songs*
  cond F. WELSER-MÖST
Stravinsky: Oedipus Rex (Cpte)
  see CONCERT INDEX *under:*
(EMI) **CDC7 54858-2** Bartók/Kodály—Orchestral
works

LONDON PHILHARMONIC CHORUS
  cond R. MUTI
Cherubini: Coronation Mass in G
  cond F. WELSER-MÖST
Orff: Carmina Burana

LONDON PHILHARMONIC ORCHESTRA CELLOS
  cond G. SIMON
  see CONCERT INDEX *under:*
(CALA) **CACD0104** The London Cello Sound

LONDON PHILHARMONIC ORCHESTRA
  see CONCERT INDEX *under:*
(LASE) **15 511** Mozart: Symphonies and Overtures
(LYRI) **SRCD209** Holst—Orchestral Works
  cond A. DE ALMEIDA
A. Thomas: Hamlet (Cpte)
  cond W. ALWYN
Alwyn: Symphony 1, Symphony 4
  see CONCERT INDEX *under:*
(LYRI) **SRCD228** Alwyn—Symphonies
(LYRI) **SRCD229** Alwyn—Orchestral Works
(LYRI) **SRCD230** Alwyn—Orchestral Works
  cond R. ARMSTRONG
  see CONCERT INDEX *under:*
(EMI) **CDC5 55540-2** Roberto Alagna sings Operatic
Arias
  cond M. ARNOLD
Arnold: Symphony 3, Symphony 4
  see CONCERT INDEX *under:*
(EVER) **EVC9006** Vaughan
Williams/Arnold—Orchestral Works
(LYRI) **SRCD201** Malcolm Arnold: Orchestral Dances
(REFE) **RRCD-48** Arnold—Overtures
  cond D. ATHERTON
  see CONCERT INDEX *under:*
(LYRI) **SRCD209** Holst—Orchestral Works
  cond G. AYKAL
*Elgar: In the South
Saygun: Viola Concerto*
  cond M. BAMERT
*Parry: Concertstück, Invocation to Music, Lotos
Eaters, Soul's Ransom, Symphonic Variations,
Symphony 1, Symphony 2, Symphony 3, Symphony
4*
  see CONCERT INDEX *under:*
(CHAN) **CHAN8955** Parry—Orchestral Works
(CHAN) **CHAN9125** Rawsthorne—Piano Concertos
(CHAN) **CHAN9283** Martin—Orchestral Works,
Volume 1
(CHAN) **CHAN9312** Martin—Orchestral Works
(CHAN) **CHAN9380** Martin—Ballades
  cond J. BARBIROLLI
  see CONCERT INDEX *under:*
(BIDD) **LAB025** Jascha Heifetz plays
(EMI) **CDH5 65191-2** Heifetz plays
Mozart/Mendelssohn/Vieuxtemps
(EMI) **CDH7 64030-2** Heifetz plays Violin Concertos
(EMI) **CDH7 64251-2** Jascha Heifetz - Violin Works

cond R. LEPPARD
Bax: Symphony 7
Cavalli: Ormindo (Cpte)
Gluck: Orfeo ed Euridice (Cpte)
see CONCERT INDEX under:
(BBCR) **DMCD98** BBC Proms - The Centenary: 1895-1995
cond A. LITTON
Mendelssohn: Midsummer Night's Dream (exc)
Ravel: Boléro
Rimsky-Korsakov: Scheherazade
Shostakovich: Festive Overture, Symphony 10
cond J. LOCKHART
see CONCERT INDEX under:
(RCA) **09026 61635-2** Margaret Price sings Mozart
cond J. LÓPEZ-COBOS
Mendelssohn: Violin Concerto, Op. 64
Vieuxtemps: Violin Concerto 5
cond L. MAAZEL
A. Lloyd Webber: Variations
W. Lloyd Webber: Aurora
see CONCERT INDEX under:
(DECC) **417 252-2DH** Scriabin: Orchestral Works
cond Z. MACAL
Dvořák: Symphonic Variations, Symphony 9
cond C. MACKERRAS
Dvořák: Symphonic Variations, Symphony 7, Symphony 8, Symphony 9
Mozart: Symphony 40, Symphony 41
Walton: Symphony 1
see CONCERT INDEX under:
(CFP) **CD-CFP9000** Orchestral Favourites
(RCA) **RD60757** Bloch/Bruch—Cello Works
(RCA) **RD60758** Tchaikovsky—Cello Works
cond J. MAKSYMIUK
Grieg: Piano Concerto
Schumann: Piano Concerto
cond N. DEL MAR
see CONCERT INDEX under:
(CFP) **CD-CFP9003** Elgar: Orchestral Works
cond K. MASUR
Schnittke: Cello Concerto 1
Schumann: Cello Concerto, Symphony 1, Symphony 4
see CONCERT INDEX under:
(TELD) **4509-95501-2** Schumann—Symphonies Nos 1-4
cond Z. MEHTA
Orff: Carmina Burana
Puccini: Turandot (Cpte)
see CONCERT INDEX under:
(DECC) **417 011-2DH2** Pavarotti's Greatest Hits
(DECC) **425 681-2DM2** Tutto Pavarotti
cond J. MESTER
see CONCERT INDEX under:
(KOCH) **37012-2** Twenty Fanfares for the Common Man
cond A. MITCHELL
McEwen: Border Ballads
see CONCERT INDEX under:
(CHAN) **CHAN9345** McEwen—Orchestral Works
cond W. MORRIS
Mahler: Knaben Wunderhorn (exc)
cond R. MUTI
Cherubini: Coronation Mass in G
cond K. NAGANO
Stravinsky: Perséphone (Cpte), Rite of Spring (Cpte)
cond S. OZAWA
see CONCERT INDEX under:
(EMI) **CMS7 64617-2** The art of Itzhak Perlman
(EMI) **CZS4 83177-2(1)** Itzhak Perlman Edition (pt 1)
cond M. PLASSON
see CONCERT INDEX under:
(EMI) **CMS7 63104-2** Alfredo Krauss - Opera Recital
cond A. PREVIN
Chopin: Piano Concerto 2
cond J. PRITCHARD
see CONCERT INDEX under:
(EMI) **CDH5 65072-2** Glyndebourne Recorded - 1934-1994
(SONY) **MK37298** Puccini and Verdi Arias
(SONY) **MK39097** Puccini Heroines
cond A. RAHBARI
Dvořák: Golden Spinning-Wheel, Wild Dove
cond K. RANKL
see CONCERT INDEX under:
(PREI) **90190** Paul Schoeffler—Recital
cond S. RATTLE
Gershwin: Porgy and Bess (Cpte)
see CONCERT INDEX under:
(EMI) **CDH5 65072-2** Glyndebourne Recorded - 1934-1994
cond F. REINER
Wagner: Tristan und Isolde (Cpte)
cond K. RICHTER
Handel: Messiah (Cpte)
cond K.A. RICKENBACHER
see CONCERT INDEX under:
(CFP) **CD-CFP9008** Wagner Orchestral Works
cond L. RONALD
Mendelssohn: Violin Concerto, Op.64
see CONCERT INDEX under:
(EMI) **CDS7 54568-2** The Elgar Edition, Vol.3
cond M. ROSTROPOVICH
Shostakovich: Lady Macbeth of Mtsensk (Cpte)
cond M. SARGENT
Mozart: Violin Concerto, K218
see CONCERT INDEX under:
(BEUL) **1PD13** Sir Malcolm Sargent conducts British Music
(TEST) **SBT1007** Kell plays Mozart Clarinet Works

cond W. SAWALLISCH
Brahms: Academic Festival Overture, Haydn Variations, Piano Concerto 1, Piano Concerto 2, Schicksalslied, Op. 54, Symphony 1, Symphony 2, Symphony 3, Symphony 4, Tragic Overture
cond N. SHERIFF
see CONCERT INDEX under:
(LARG) **Largo5130** Testimonies of War
cond C. SILVESTRI
see CONCERT INDEX under:
(EMI) **CZS5 68229-2** Constantin Silvestri—A profile
cond L. SLATKIN
Elgar: In the South, Serenade, Symphony 1, Symphony 2
Prokofiev: Symphony 1
Walton: Portsmouth Point, Symphony 1
see CONCERT INDEX under:
(RCA) **RD60813** Walton—Belshazzar's Feast
(RCA) **09026 60073-2** Elgar—Orchestral Works
(RCA) **09026 61226-2** Britten—Orchestral Works
cond G. SOLTI
Bartók: Duke Bluebeard's Castle (Cpte), Violin Concerto 2
Bizet: Carmen (Cpte)
Elgar: Pomp and Circumstance Marches (exc), Violin Concerto
Haydn: Symphony 93, Symphony 99
Holst: Planets
Mozart: Don Giovanni (Cpte), Nozze di Figaro (Cpte)
Puccini: Bohème (Cpte)
R. Strauss: Ariadne auf Naxos (Cpte)
see CONCERT INDEX under:
(DECC) **417 645-2DH** Kiri - Portrait
(DECC) **417 719-2DM** Elgar: Orchestral Works
(DECC) **421 899-2DA** Teresa Berganza - Mozart Arias
(DECC) **425 689-2DX** Jorge Bolet plays Liszt
(DECC) **430 498-2DWO** The World of Mozart
(DECC) **436 290-2DM6** Haydn—London Symphonies
(DECC) **436 403-2DWO** The World of Royal Music
(DECC) **436 461-2DM** Ten Top Sopranos
(DECC) **436 462-2DM** Ten Top Mezzos
(DECC) **436 463-2DM** Ten Top Tenors
(DECC) **436 464-2DM** Ten Top Baritones & Basses
(DECC) **440 317-2DWO** World of British Classics, Volume 1
(DECC) **440 318-2DWO** World of British Classics, Volume II
(DECC) **443 856-2DF2** Elgar—Symphonies, etc
(LOND) **421 388-2LM** Elgar: Violin Concerto, etc
(RCA) **09026 61580-2(8)** RCA/Met 100 Singers, 100 Years (pt 8)
cond W. SUSSKIND
see CONCERT INDEX under:
(CFP) **CD-CFP9000** Orchestral Favourites
cond G. SZELL
Brahms: Piano Concerto 1
see CONCERT INDEX under:
(KOCH) **37035-2** Benno Moiseiwitsch—A Centenary Celebration
cond K. TENNSTEDT
Beethoven: Symphony 3
Brahms: Violin Concerto
Bruch: Violin Concerto 1
Mahler: Lied von der Erde, Symphony 5, Symphony 6, Symphony 7, Symphony 8
Mussorgsky: Night on the Bare Mountain
see CONCERT INDEX under:
(EMI) **CDC7 49759-2** Wagner: Opera Scenes and Arias
(EMI) **CMS7 64471-2** Mahler—Symphonies, Vol.1
(EMI) **CMS7 64476-2** Mahler—Symphonies, Vol.2
(EMI) **CMS7 64481-2** Mahler—Symphonies, Vol.3
(EMI) **CZS7 62707-2** Mahler—Vocal Works
(EMI) **CZS7 67819-2** Brahms/Schumann—Requiems
cond B. THOMSON
Bax: Between Dusk and Dawn, Christmas Eve, Festival Overture, Morning Song, Nympholept, Russian Suite, Saga Fragment, Symphonic Variations, Symphony 1, Symphony 2, Symphony 5, Symphony 6, Truth about the Russian Dancers, Winter Legends
Elgar: Music Makers, Sea Pictures, Symphony 1, Symphony 2
Saint-Saëns: Piano Concerto 2
Schumann: Piano Concerto
Stravinsky: Violin Concerto
Tchaikovsky: Violin Concerto
Vaughan Williams: Dona nobis pacem, Mystical Songs
Walton: Quest (Cpte), Symphony 1, Symphony 2, Troilus and Cressida Suite, Varii capricci, Wise Virgins (exc)
see CONCERT INDEX under:
(CHAN) **CHAN6538** Seascapes
(CHAN) **CHAN8454** Bax—Orchestral Works
(CHAN) **CHAN8461** Ireland—Orchestral Works
(CHAN) **CHAN8494** Bax—Orchestral Works
(CHAN) **CHAN8502** Vaughan Williams—Orchestral Works
(CHAN) **CHAN8579** Russian Cello Concertos
(CHAN) **CHAN8610** Elgar—Orchestral Works
(CHAN) **CHAN8828** Bax—Symphony No 7; Songs
(CHAN) **CHAN8959** Walton—Orchestral and Instrumental Works
(CHAN) **CHAN8968** Walton—Orchestral Works
(CHAN) **CHAN9003** Walton—Orchestral Works
(CHAN) **CHAN9148** Walton—Orchestral Works
(CHAN) **CHAN9168** Bax—Orchestral Works

cond S. VARVISO
see CONCERT INDEX under:
(DECC) **436 464-2DM** Ten Top Baritones & Basses
cond W. WALTON
see CONCERT INDEX under:
(LYRI) **SRCD224** Walton—Orchestral Works
cond F. WEINGARTNER
Beethoven: Contredanses, WoO17
see CONCERT INDEX under:
(DUTT) **CDAX8005** 'Philharmonic'
cond W. WELLER
see CONCERT INDEX under:
(DECC) **433 612-2DSP** Prokofiev—Popular Orchestral Works
cond F. WELSER-MÖST
Beethoven: Symphony 5
Bruckner: Symphony 5, Symphony 7
Dvořák: Violin Concerto
Glazunov: Violin Concerto
Lehár: Lustige Witwe (Cpte)
Mendelssohn: Symphony 3, Symphony 4
Orff: Carmina Burana
Schumann: Symphony 2, Symphony 3
Stravinsky: Firebird (Cpte), Oedipus Rex (Cpte), Symphonies of Wind Instruments
see CONCERT INDEX under:
(EMI) **CDC5 55090-2** Amanda Roocroft—Recital
(EMI) **CDC7 54089-2** J. Strauss II—Waltzes & Overtures
(EMI) **CDC7 54858-2** Bartók/Kodály—Orchestral works
cond D. WILLCOCKS
see CONCERT INDEX under:
(EMI) **CDM7 64730-2** Vaughan Williams—Riders to the Sea; Epithalamion, etc
cond B. WORDSWORTH
see CONCERT INDEX under:
(LYRI) **SRCD212** Foulds—Orchestral Works
cond T. YUASA
Prokofiev: Lt. Kijé Suite
Rimsky-Korsakov: Scheherazade

LONDON POPS ORCHESTRA
cond F. FENNELL
see CONCERT INDEX under:
(MERC) **434 330-2MM** Coates & Grainger—Country Gardens

LONDON PRO MUSICA
see CONCERT INDEX under:
(CARL) **PCD825** A Florentine Carnival

LONDON PROMENADE ORCHESTRA
cond A. FARIS
see CONCERT INDEX under:
(PHIL) **400 011-2PH** Ketèlbey: Orchestral Works

LONDON QUARTET
Alwyn: String Quartet 1, String Quartet 2

LONDON SCHUBERT CHORALE
(HYPE) **CDJ33020** Schubert—Complete Lieder, Vol.20
(HYPE) **CDJ33023** Schubert—Complete Lieder, Vol.23

LONDON SCHÜTZ CHOIR
cond R. NORRINGTON
Beethoven: Choral Fantasia, Symphony 9
Brahms: Begräbnisgesang, Op.13, Deutsches Requiem, Op.45 (Cpte)
Mozart: Don Giovanni (Cpte), Zauberflöte (Cpte)
Purcell: Fairy Queen, Z629 (Cpte)
see CONCERT INDEX under:
(DECC) **443 868-2DF2** Italian Baroque Sacred Works
(EMI) **CDC7 54525-2** Mozart—Sacred Works

LONDON SELECT CHOIR
cond T. BEECHAM
see CONCERT INDEX under:
(BEEC) **BEECHAM3** Delius—Vocal & Orchestral Works
(DUTT) **CDLX7011** Beecham conducts Delius

LONDON SINFONIETTA
see CONCERT INDEX under:
(ARGO) **430 209-2ZH** Torke—Chamber Works
cond J. ADAMS
J. Adams: Chamber Symphony, Grand Pianola Music
cond D. ATHERTON
Birtwistle: Punch and Judy (Cpte)
Tavener: Whale
Tippett: Ice Break (Cpte)
(CATA) **09026 62672-2** Revueltas—Night of the Mayas
(DECC) **421 852-2DH2** Janáček: Operatic & Chamber Works
(DECC) **430 375-2DH2** Janáček—Operatic and Orchestral Works
cond G. BENJAMIN
(NIMB) **NI5167** Benjamin—Antara; J. Harvey—Song Offerings; Boulez—Orch music
cond L. BERIO
(RCA) **09026 62540-2** Cathy Berberian sings Berio & Weill
cond P. BOULEZ
(SONY) **SM2K44571** Schoenberg: Choral Works

cond R. CHAILLY
Stravinsky: Rake's Progress (Cpte)
see CONCERT INDEX under:
(DECC) **433 079-2DM** Stravinsky—Orchestral Works
cond C. DUTOIT
Saint-Saëns: Carnaval des animaux
see CONCERT INDEX under:
(DECC) **414 460-2DH** Saint-Saëns—Orchestral
works
cond T. EDWARDS
see CONCERT INDEX under:
(VIRG) **VC7 59051-2** Messiaen—Choral Works
cond H. K. GRUBER
see CONCERT INDEX under:
(LARG) **Largo 5124** HK Gruber—...aus schatten duft
gewebt
cond E. HOWARTH
see CONCERT INDEX under:
(ETCE) **KTC1052** Birtwistle: Orchestral Works
cond O. KNUSSEN
Britten: Prince of the Pagodas (Cpte)
Goehr: Piano Concerto
see CONCERT INDEX under:
(ARGO) **443 203-2ZH** Copland—Ballet Music
(DG) **447 068-2GH** Stravinsky—The Flood, etc
(NMC) **NMCD009** Birtwistle—Choral and Orchestral
Works
(UNIC) **DKPCD9102** Goehr—Orchestral and Vocal
Works
(UNIC) **UKCD2010** Knussen—Orchestral & Vocal
Works
(VIRG) **VC7 59020-2** Takemitsu—Miscellaneous
Works
cond D. MASSON
see CONCERT INDEX under:
(BRID) **BCD9045** Benedict Mason—Chamber and
Orchestral Works
cond J. MCGLINN
Berlin: Annie Get Your Gun (Cpte)
F. Loewe: Brigadoon (Cpte)
Kern: Show Boat (Cpte)
Porter: Kiss Me, Kate (Cpte)
see CONCERT INDEX under:
(EMI) **CDC5 55189-2** The Busby Berkeley Album
(EMI) **CDC7 54586-2** Broadway Showstoppers
(EMI) **CDC7 54802-2** The Lorelei
(EMI) **CDC7 54883-2** Jerome Kern Treasury
cond K. NAGANO
Stravinsky: Histoire du soldat (exc)
see CONCERT INDEX under:
(ARGO) **430 209-2ZH** Torke—Chamber Works
cond S. RATTLE
see CONCERT INDEX under:
(DECC) **433 908-2DM2** Falla—Orchestral Music
(EMI) **CDC7 47991-2** The Simon Rattle Jazz Album
cond E-P. SALONEN
see CONCERT INDEX under:
(SONY) **M2K44762** Messiaen—Orchestral Works
(SONY) **SK45797** Stravinsky: Works for Piano &
Orchestra
(SONY) **SK45965** Esa-Pekka Salonen conducts
Stravinsky
(SONY) **SK46667** Stravinsky—Miscellaneous Works
(SONY) **SK46720** John Williams plays music of
Takemitsu
cond M. STENZ
see CONCERT INDEX under:
(NONE) **7559-79362-2** Górecki—Orchestral and Vocal
Works
cond M. TILSON THOMAS
see CONCERT INDEX under:
(CNTI) **CCD1020** Simon Bainbridge—Orchestral
Works
cond J. TUNICK
see CONCERT INDEX under:
(EMI) **CDC7 54527-2** Kiri Te Kanawa sings Kern
cond L. ZAGROSEK
see CONCERT INDEX under:
(ARGO) **443 528-2ZH** Torke—Music on the Floor
cond D. ZINMAN
Górecki: Symphony 3
see CONCERT INDEX under:
(NONE) **7559-79362-2** Górecki—Orchestral and Vocal
Works

LONDON SINFONIETTA CHORUS
cond D. ATHERTON
Tavener: Whale
Tippett: Ice Break (Cpte)
see CONCERT INDEX under:
(DECC) **430 375-2DH2** Janáček—Operatic and
Orchestral Works
cond R. CHAILLY
Stravinsky: Rake's Progress (Cpte)
cond T. EDWARDS
see CONCERT INDEX under:
(VIRG) **VC7 59051-2** Messiaen—Choral Works
cond J. MCGLINN
see CONCERT INDEX under:
(EMI) **CDC5 55189-2** The Busby Berkeley Album
(EMI) **CDC7 54883-2** Jerome Kern Treasury
cond E-P. SALONEN
see CONCERT INDEX under:
(SONY) **SK46667** Stravinsky—Miscellaneous Works

LONDON SINFONIETTA OPERA ORCHESTRA
cond D. RENZETTI
Rossini: Bianca e Falliero (Cpte)

LONDON SINFONIETTA VOICES
cond T. EDWARDS
see CONCERT INDEX under:
(VIRG) **VC7 59051-2** Messiaen—Choral Works

cond O. KNUSSEN
see CONCERT INDEX under:
(NMC) **NMCD009** Birtwistle—Choral and Orchestral
Works

LONDON STUDIO SYMPHONY ORCHESTRA
cond L. JOHNSON
Herrmann: North by Northwest (exc)

LONDON SYMPHONIC WIND ORCHESTRA
cond N. HESS
see CONCERT INDEX under:
(FLY) **FLYCD105** East Coast Pictures—The Wind
Band Music of Nigel Hess

LONDON SYMPHONY CHORUS
cond L. BERNSTEIN
Mahler: Symphony 8
cond R. BONYNGE
see CONCERT INDEX under:
(DECC) **433 706-2DMO3** Bellini—Beatrice di Tenda;
Operatic Arias
cond B. BRITTEN
Britten: War Requiem
see CONCERT INDEX under:
(DECC) **436 403-2DWO** The World of Royal Music
(LOND) **425 100-2LM** Britten: Orchestral & Vocal
Works
cond COLIN DAVIS
Handel: Messiah (Cpte)
cond E. DOWNES
see CONCERT INDEX under:
(DECC) **436 439-2DWO** The World of Borodin
cond P. GAMBA
see CONCERT INDEX under:
(DECC) **440 839-2DF2** Beethoven—Piano Concertos,
etc
cond G. MALCOLM
see CONCERT INDEX under:
(LOND) **436 396-2LM** Britten—Spring Symphony,
etc
cond G. SOLTI
see CONCERT INDEX under:
(DECC) **444 389-2DWO** The World of Borodin

LONDON SYMPHONY CHORUS
cond C. ABBADO
Berlioz: Te Deum
Prokofiev: Alexander Nevsky
Ravel: Daphnis et Chloé (Cpte)
see CONCERT INDEX under:
(DG) **415 353-2GH4** Mendelssohn—Complete
Symphonies, etc
(DG) **423 103-2GH** Debussy: Vocal & Orchestral
Works
(DG) **445 519-2GMA** Ravel—Orchestral Works
(DG) **447 419-2GOR** Prokofiev—Alexander
Nevsky;Lieutenant Kijé etc
(RCA) **09026 61354-2** Mussorgsky—Orchestral &
Choral Works
cond L. BERNSTEIN
Bernstein: Candide (1988) (Cpte)
see CONCERT INDEX under:
(SONY) **SM2K47522** Beethoven & Haydn—Choral
Works
cond P. BOULEZ
see CONCERT INDEX under:
(SONY) **SM3K64103** Berlioz—Orchestral and Vocal
Works
cond B. BRITTEN
Elgar: Dream of Gerontius (Cpte)
see CONCERT INDEX under:
(DECC) **430 094-2DWO** The World of Elgar
(DECC) **436 990-2DWO** The World of Benjamin
Britten
cond COLIN DAVIS
Beethoven: Mass in C, Missa Solemnis
Berlioz: Damnation de Faust (Cpte), Grande messe
des morts (Cpte), Te Deum
Mozart: Vespers, K339 (exc)
see CONCERT INDEX under:
(PHIL) **412 873-2PH** Mozart—Sacred Music
(PHIL) **438 800-2PM2** Mozart—Choral Works
cond R. FRÜHBECK DE BURGOS
see CONCERT INDEX under:
(CARL) **PCD915** Debussy—Orchestral Works
cond R. HICKOX
Bernstein: Chichester Psalms
Brahms: Deutsches Requiem, Op. 45 (Cpte)
Elgar: Apostles (Cpte), Caractacus (Cpte), Light of
Life (Cpte)
Fauré: Requiem (Cpte)
Haydn: Mass 11
Holst: Cloud Messenger, Hymn of Jesus
Mendelssohn: Elijah (Cpte)
Orff: Carmina Burana
Rossini: Stabat Mater
Tippett: Child of Our Time
Vaughan Williams: Dona nobis pacem, Sancta
Civitas
see CONCERT INDEX under:
(CARL) **PCD908** Great Opera Choruses
(CHAN) **CHAN8641/2** Elgar—Dream of Gerontius
Parry—Choral Works
(CHAN) **CHAN8788/9** Elgar—The Kingdom;
Orchestral Works
(CHAN) **CHAN8855** Britten—Choral Works
(CHAN) **CHAN8983/4** Britten—Choral and Orchestral
Works
(CHAN) **CHAN9082** Ferguson—Choral and
Orchestral Works
(DECC) **440 323-2DWO** World of British Classics,
Volume V

cond C. HOGWOOD
Beethoven: Symphony 9
cond G. KAPLAN
Mahler: Symphony 2
cond I. KERTÉSZ
Rossini: Stabat Mater
see CONCERT INDEX under:
(DECC) **443 488-2DF2** Kodály—Háry János; Psalmus
Hungaricus etc
cond K. NAGANO
Ravel: Daphnis et Chloé (Cpte)
cond A. PREVIN
Britten: Spring Symphony
Orff: Carmina Burana
Prokofiev: Alexander Nevsky
Rachmaninov: Bells
Vaughan Williams: Symphony 1
see CONCERT INDEX under:
(EMI) **CDM7 64723-2** Walton—Choral & Orchestral
Works
cond M. ROSTROPOVICH
Prokofiev: Alexander Nevsky, Ivan the Terrible Suite
cond G. ROZHDESTVENSKY
Howells: Missa Sabrinensis (Cpte), Stabat mater
cond B. THOMSON
Vaughan Williams: Symphony 1, Symphony 7,
Toward the Unknown Region
see CONCERT INDEX under:
(CHAN) **CHAN9262/3** Vaughan Williams—Orchestral
Works
cond M. TILSON THOMAS
Debussy: Martyre de St Sébastien (Cpte)
Mahler: Symphony 3
see CONCERT INDEX under:
(SONY) **SK53275** Stravinsky—Symphonies

LONDON SYMPHONY ORCHESTRA
Beethoven: Symphony 9
Wagner: Götterdämmerung (exc)
see CONCERT INDEX under:
(BEUL) **1PD13** Sir Malcolm Sargent conducts British
Music
(CARL) **PCD902** An Evening in Vienna
(CLAR) **CDGSE78-50-26** Wagner: Tristan und Isolde
excerpts
(CLAR) **CDGSE78-50-35/6** Wagner—Historical
recordings
(CLAR) **CDGSE78-50-46** Walter Widdop (1892-1949)
(EMI) **CES5 68519-2** Beethoven—Symphonies
(LYRC) **LCD146** Frida Leider sings Wagner
cond C. ABBADO
Bizet: Arlésienne Suites, Carmen (Cpte), Carmen
Suites (exc)
Chopin: Piano Concerto 1
Liszt: Piano Concerto 1
Mendelssohn: Symphony 3, Symphony 4, Symphony
5
Mozart: Piano Concerto 21, Piano Concerto 27,
Symphony 40, Symphony 41
Mussorgsky: Pictures
Pergolesi: Stabat Mater
Prokofiev: Alexander Nevsky
Ravel: Daphnis et Chloé (Cpte), Valses nobles et
sentimentales
Rossini: Barbiere di Siviglia (Cpte)
Schumann: Piano Concerto
Stravinsky: Firebird Suite (1919), Jeu de Cartes,
Petrushka (Cpte), Pulcinella, Rite of Spring (Cpte)
Tchaikovsky: Piano Concerto 1
Vivaldi: Concerti, Op.8 (exc)
Weber: Konzertstück
see CONCERT INDEX under:
(BELA) **450 121-2** Plácido Domingo
(DECC) **425 027-2DM** Prokofiev—Ballet Suites
(DG) **433 081-2DM** Hindemith—Orchestral Works
(DG) **415 353-2GH4** Mendelssohn—Complete
Symphonies, etc
(DG) **415 972-2GH** Ravel orchestral works
(DG) **419 869-2GGA** Rossini: Overtures
(DG) **423 103-2GH** Debussy: Vocal & Orchestral
Works
(DG) **423 104-2GH** Mendelssohn: Overtures
(DG) **423 238-2GC** Berg: Vocal and Orchestral
Works
(DG) **423 665-2GH** Ravel: Orchestral Works
(DG) **427 314-2GH** Ravel: Orchestral & Vocal Works
(DG) **431 104-2GB** Great Voices - Plácido Domingo
(DG) **439 409-2GCL** Liszt—Piano Works
(DG) **439 414-2GCL** Ravel—Orchestral & Vocal
Works
(DG) **445 501-2GMA** Bartók/Janáček—Orchestral
Works
(DG) **445 519-2GMA** Ravel—Orchestral Works
(DG) **447 419-2GOR** Prokofiev—Alexander
Nevsky;Lieutenant Kijé etc
(RCA) **09026 61354-2** Mussorgsky—Orchestral &
Choral Works
cond H. ABENDROTH
see CONCERT INDEX under:
(TAHR) **TAH102** Hermann Abendroth - 1927-1941
Recordings
cond Y. AHRONOVITCH
Rachmaninov: Piano Concerto 2, Piano Concerto 4
see CONCERT INDEX under:
(DG) **413 850-2GW2** Rachmaninov/Liszt—Piano
Concertos
cond A. ARGENTA
see CONCERT INDEX under:
(BEUL) **3PD10** Bliss & Tchaikovsky—Violin
Concertos
(DECC) **433 911-2DM2** Spanish Orchestral Music, Vol
3

(DECC) **433 628-2DSP**
Franck/Grieg/Schumann—Piano & Orchestral Works
(LOND) **440 490-2LM5(1)** Kirsten Flagstad Edition (pt 1)
(LOND) **440 492-2LM** Kirsten Flagstad Edition, Vol. 2
  cond L. FOSTER
  see CONCERT INDEX *under:*
(DG) **431 815-2GH** Wieniawski/Sarasate—Works for Violin and Orchestra
  cond A. FRANCIS
Crusell: Clarinet Concerto 2
Donizetti: Maria Padilla (Cpte)
Weber: Clarinet Concerto 2
  see CONCERT INDEX *under:*
(HYPE) **CDA66022** The Clarinet in Concert
  cond R. FRÜHBECK DE BURGOS
Bizet: Arlésienne Suites, Carmen Suites (exc)
Kodály: Háry János Suite
Tchaikovsky: Symphony 5
  see CONCERT INDEX *under:*
(CARL) **PCD915** Debussy—Orchestral Works
(CARL) **PCD924** Spanish Spectacular
(CARL) **PCD930** Elgar/Vaughan Williams—Orchestral Works
(CHAN) **CHAN8773** Ravel & Fauré—Works for Piano and Orchestra
  cond A. GALLIERA
  see CONCERT INDEX *under:*
(EMI) **CDM7 69501-2** Elisabeth Schwarzkopf—Romantic Heroines
  cond P. GAMBA
  see CONCERT INDEX *under:*
(DECC) **433 220-2DWO** The World of the Violin
(DECC) **440 839-2DF2** Beethoven—Piano Concertos, etc
  cond G. GAVAZZENI
  see CONCERT INDEX *under:*
(SONY) **MK39097** Puccini Heroines
  cond P. GEMIGNANI
Forrest/Wright: Kismet (Cpte)
  cond J. GEORGIADIS
  see CONCERT INDEX *under:*
(CARL) **PCD856** Works by J. Strauss
(CHAN) **CHAN8739** Johann Strauss and Family in London
  cond A. GIBSON
  see CONCERT INDEX *under:*
(EMI) **CDM7 69544-2** Berlioz: Vocal Works
  cond M. GIBSON
  see CONCERT INDEX *under:*
(ASV) **CDDCA907** Bottesini—Volume 3 - Passioni Amorose
  cond C.M. GIULINI
  see CONCERT INDEX *under:*
(EMI) **CES5 68519-2** Beethoven—Symphonies
  cond W. GOEHR
  see CONCERT INDEX *under:*
(EMI) **CHS7 69741-2(7)** Record of Singing, Vol.4—Italian School
(PEAR) **GEMMCD9151** Alfredo Campoli
  cond E. GOOSSENS
Hindemith: Violin Concerto
Rachmaninov: Symphonic Dances
Stravinsky: Rite of Spring (Cpte)
  see CONCERT INDEX *under:*
(EVER) **EVC9007** Villa-Lobos/Antill/Ginastera—Orchestral Works
  cond C. GROVES
  see CONCERT INDEX *under:*
(LYRI) **SRCD323** Grace Williams—Orchestral Works
  cond V. HANDLEY
  see CONCERT INDEX *under:*
(LYRI) **SRCD234** Rubbra—Orchestral Works
  cond H. HARTY
  see CONCERT INDEX *under:*
(DUTT) **CDAX8003** Walton—Gramophone premières
  cond L. HAZA
  see CONCERT INDEX *under:*
(GRP) **GRK75002** Arturo Sandoval—The Classical Album
  cond R. HEGER
  see CONCERT INDEX *under:*
(DANA) **DACOCD315/6** Lauritz Melchior Anthology - Vol. 3
(EMI) **CDH7 69789-2** Melchior sings Wagner
(EMI) **CMS7 64008-2(2)** Wagner Singing on Record (pt 2)
(PEAR) **GEMMCDS9075** Hugo Wolf Society, Volume I
(PEAR) **GEMMCDS9137** Wagner—Der Ring des Nibelungen
(PEAR) **GEMMCD9398** Friedrich Schorr
(PREI) **89046** Rosette Anday (1903-1977)
  cond HENRY WOOD
  see CONCERT INDEX *under:*
(DUTT) **CDAX8008** Sir Henry Wood conducts Proms Favourites
(PEAR) **GEMMCD9978** Irene Scharrer
  cond H.W. HENZE
  see CONCERT INDEX *under:*
(DG) **429 854-2GC2** Henze—Symphonies
  cond L. HEWARD
  see CONCERT INDEX *under:*
(EMI) **CHS5 65198-2** Maggie Teyte sings French Songs
  cond R. HICKOX
Alwyn: Piano Concerto 1, Symphony 1, Symphony 3, Violin Concerto

Arnold: Symphony 1, Symphony 2, Symphony 3, Symphony 4, Symphony 5, Symphony 6
Bloch: Schelomo
Brahms: Deutsches Requiem, Op. 45 (Cpte)
Elgar: Apostles (Cpte), Caractacus (Cpte), Cello Concerto, Light of Life (Cpte), Severn Suite, Violin Concerto
Holst: Cloud Messenger, Hymn of Jesus, Planets
Mendelssohn: Elijah (Cpte)
Orff: Carmina Burana
Tippett: Child of Our Time
Vaughan Williams: Dona nobis pacem, Sancta Civitas
Walton: Violin Concerto
  see CONCERT INDEX *under:*
(CARL) **PCD908** Great Opera Choruses
(CHAN) **CHAN8641/2** Elgar—Dream of Gerontius.
Parry—Choral Works
(CHAN) **CHAN8788/9** Elgar—The Kingdom; Orchestral Works
(CHAN) **CHAN8855** Britten—Choral Works
(CHAN) **CHAN8902** Alwyn—Orchestral Works
(CHAN) **CHAN8983/4** Britten—Choral and Orchestral Works
(CHAN) **CHAN8994** Ireland—Orchestral Works
(CHAN) **CHAN9082** Ferguson—Choral and Orchestral Works
(CHAN) **CHAN9093** Alwyn—Orchestral Works
(CHAN) **CHAN9100** Arnold—Film Music
(CHAN) **CHAN9196** Alwyn—Orchestral Works
(CHAN) **CHAN9243** Alwyn—Film Music
  cond P. HINDEMITH
  see CONCERT INDEX *under:*
(DECC) **433 081-2DM** Hindemith—Orchestral Works
  cond L. HOLDRIDGE
Holdridge: Pueblo del Sol
  cond G. HOLST
Holst: Planets
  see CONCERT INDEX *under:*
(PEAR) **GEMMCD9417** Holst conducts Holst
  cond J. HORENSTEIN
Mahler: Symphony 1, Symphony 3
  see CONCERT INDEX *under:*
(UNIC) **UKCD2016** Panufnik—Orchestral Works
  cond J. HORNER
Homer: Willow (exc)
  cond JAMES LEVINE
Dvořák: Cello Concerto
Verdi: Forza del destino (Cpte), Giovanna d'Arco (Cpte)
  see CONCERT INDEX *under:*
(EMI) **CDM7 69549-2** Ruggero Raimondi: Italian Opera Arias
  cond N. JÄRVI
Brahms: Double Concerto, Handel Variations, Hungarian Dances, Piano Quartet 1, Symphony 1, Symphony 2, Symphony 3, Symphony 4
Bruch: Violin Concerto 1
Schumann: Genoveva (exc), Julius Cäsar, Manfred (exc), Overture, Scherzo and Finale
  see CONCERT INDEX *under:*
(CHAN) **CHAN8614** Rachmaninov & Kalinnikov: Orchestral Works
(CHAN) **CHAN8783** Russian Orchestral Works
  cond E. JOCHUM
Elgar: Enigma Variations
(DG) **413 424-2GW2** Brahms—Orchestral Works
  cond E. JORDA
Falla: Sombrero de tres picos (Cpte)
  cond J. JUDD
Tchaikovsky: Andante cantabile, Op.11, Piano Concerto 1
  see CONCERT INDEX *under:*
(CARL) **MCD59** Vaughan Williams/R. Strauss—Oboe Works
  cond R. KAJANUS
  see CONCERT INDEX *under:*
(KOCH) **37133-2** Kajanus conducts Sibelius, Vol.3
  cond G. KAPLAN
Mahler: Symphony 2
  cond I. KERTÉSZ
Bartók: Duke Bluebeard's castle (Cpte)
Rossini: Stabat Mater
  see CONCERT INDEX *under:*
(DECC) **421 810-2DM2** Dvořák & Kodály: Vocal Works
(DECC) **425 044-2DM** Mozart—Works for Piano and Orchestra
(DECC) **425 097-2DM** Mozart—Piano Concertos, Vol. 10
(DECC) **425 681-2DM2** Tutto Pavarotti
(DECC) **425 722-2DM** Mozart—Masonic Music
(DECC) **430 046-2DC6** Dvořák—Complete Symphonies, etc
(DECC) **430 498-2DWO** The World of Mozart
(DECC) **433 080-2DM** Kodály—Choral Works
(DECC) **433 910-2DM** O Holy Night
(DECC) **443 488-2DF2** Kodály—Háry János; Psalmus Hungaricus etc
(DECC) **443 576-2DCS** Mozart—Piano Concertos, etc
(LOND) **443 727-2LC10** Mozart—The Piano Concertos
  cond K. KONDRASHIN
(PHIL) **446 200-2PM** Liszt—Piano Concertos; Piano Sonata
  cond J. KRIPS
Beethoven: Violin Concerto
  see CONCERT INDEX *under:*

(DECC) **443 530-2LF2** Mozart—Die Entführung aus dem Serail
(EMI) **CHS7 69741-2(7)** Record of Singing, Vol.4—Italian School
  cond A. LA ROSA PARODI
  see CONCERT INDEX *under:*
(TEST) **SBT1019** Tito Gobbi - Opera Arias & Songs
  cond P. LEDGER
  see CONCERT INDEX *under:*
(LYRI) **SRCD225** Bliss—Orchestral Works
  cond E. LEINSDORF
R. Strauss: Salome (Cpte)
Verdi: Aida (Cpte)
Wagner: Walküre (Cpte)
  see CONCERT INDEX *under:*
(DECC) **436 463-2DM** Ten Top Tenors
(RCA) **09026 61580-2(7)** RCA/Met 100 Singers, 100 Years (pt 7)
  cond G. LLOYD
(ALBA) **AR004** Lloyd—Piano Concerto No 4; Piano works
  cond K-H. LOGES
(DG) **431 104-2GB** Great Voices - Plácido Domingo
  cond P. MAAG
(DECC) **430 498-2DWO** The World of Mozart
(DECC) **433 727-2DM** Clarinet Concertos
(DECC) **443 578-2DCS** Mendelssohn—Orchestral Works
  cond L. MAAZEL
Puccini: Rondine (Cpte)
Tchaikovsky: Piano Concerto 1
  see CONCERT INDEX *under:*
(EMI) **CMS7 64429-2** Sviatoslav Richter—Un Portrait
(SONY) **M3K79312** Puccini: Il Trittico
  cond C. MACKERRAS
Brahms: Violin Concerto
Bruch: Violin Concerto 1
Dohnányi: Konzertstück, Op.12
Dvořák: Cello Concerto
Rimsky-Korsakov: Capriccio espagnol, Scheherazade
Sibelius: Legends (exc), Symphony 2
Tchaikovsky: Nutcracker (exc)
Walton: Symphony 2
  see CONCERT INDEX *under:*
(CFP) **CD-CFPD4456** Music by Eric Coates
(EMI) **CDC7 47841-2** Puccini: Opera Recital
(EMI) **CDM7 64726-2** Sullivan—Orchestral Works
(MERC) **434 352-2MM** Kaleidoscope
  cond G. MALCOLM
  see CONCERT INDEX *under:*
(LOND) **436 396-2LM** Britten—Spring Symphony, etc
  cond I. MARIN
Donizetti: Lucia di Lammermoor (Cpte)
Rossini: Semiramide (Cpte)
(DG) **435 387-2GH** Cheryl Studer sings Sacred Arias
  cond I. MARKEVITCH
  see CONCERT INDEX *under:*
(PHIL) **426 848-2PB4** Tchaikovsky: Symphonies
(PHIL) **438 335-2PM2** Tchaikovsky—Symphonies
(PHIL) **438 350-2PM2** Stravinsky—Ballets
(PHIL) **438 973-2PM2** Igor Markevitch conducts Stravinsky
(PHIL) **442 643-2PM** Rimsky-Korsakov—Orchestral Works
  see CONCERT INDEX *under:*
(PHIL) **426 640-2PSL** Prokofiev—Orchestral Works
  cond J. MARTINON
  see CONCERT INDEX *under:*
(DECC) **444 389-2DWO** The World of Borodin
  cond G-F. MASINI
Rossini: Elisabetta (Cpte)
  cond M. MATHIESON
(EMI) **CDGO 2059** British Film Music from the 40s and 50s
  cond J. MAUCERI
Rimsky-Korsakov: Scheherazade
  cond J. MCCARTHY
(ARAB) **Z6582** The Rossini Tenor
  cond N. MCGEGAN
(ARAB) **Z6598** Rockwell Blake, the Mozart Tenor
  cond J. MCGLINN
Porter: Anything Goes (Cpte)
(EMI) **CDC7 54071-2** Frederica von Stade sings Rodgers & Hart
(EMI) **CDC7 54203-2** Porter—Night and Day
  cond H. MENGES
  see CONCERT INDEX *under:*
(MERC) **432 011-2MM** Works for Piano and Orchestra
  cond D.A. MILLER
T. Levin: De Luxe
  cond M. MILLER
Paganini: Violin Concerto 1
Wieniawski: Violin Concerto 2
  cond P. MONTEUX
  see CONCERT INDEX *under:*
(BELA) **450 132-2** Rimsky-Korsakov—Scheherazade
(DECC) **425 956-2DM** Ravel: Orchestral Works
(DECC) **430 094-2DWO** The World of Elgar
(DECC) **440 612-2DF2** Brahms—Piano Concertos, etc
(DECC) **443 479-2DF2** Beethoven—Symphonies

Schumann: Symphony 3
Verdi: Falstaff (Cpte)
see CONCERT INDEX under:
(DG) 415 366-2GH Placido Domingo Recital
(DG) 415 844-2GGA Ravel/Mussorgsky—Orchestral
Works
(DG) 427 213-2GR French Orchestral Works
cond E. LEINSDORF
see CONCERT INDEX under:
(SHEF) CD-7/8 Prokofiev & Wagner: Orchestral
Works
cond Z. MEHTA
Beethoven: Violin Concerto
Mahler: Symphony 3
Saint-Saëns: Symphony 3
Verdi: Pezzi sacri (Cpte)
see CONCERT INDEX under:
(TELD) 4509-96200-2 The Three Tenors 1994
cond A. PREVIN
Bartók: Concerto for orchestra
Dvořák: My Home, Symphony 7, Symphony
9
Janáček: Sinfonietta
Prokofiev: Alexander Nevsky, Lt. Kijé Suite,
Symphony 1, Symphony 5
see CONCERT INDEX under:
(TELA) CD80206 Dvořák: Orchestral Works
cond E-P. SALONEN
Mahler: Symphony 4
Sibelius: En Saga, Kullervo, Legends
see CONCERT INDEX under:
(ONDI) ODE804-2 Saariaho—Orchestral and
Chamber Works
(SONY) SK53969 Prokofiev/Stravinsky—Violin
Concertos
(SONY) SK58952 Debussy—Orchestral and Vocal
Works
(SONY) SK66280 Lutosławski—Orchestral Works
cond A. WALLENSTEIN
see CONCERT INDEX under:
(RCA) GD87872 Jascha Heifetz Collection
(RCA) GD87963 Heifetz plays Korngold, Rózsa &
Waxman
(RCA) 09026 61778-2(08) The Heifetz Collection, Vol.
8
(RCA) 09026 61778-2(09) The Heifetz Collection, Vol.
9
(RCA) 09026 61778-2(20) The Heifetz Collection, Vol.
20
(RCA) 09026 61778-2(21) The Heifetz Collection, Vol.
21
(RCA) 09026 61778-2(24) The Heifetz Collection, Vol.
24
(RCA) 09026 61778-2(31) The Heifetz Collection, Vol.
31
(RCA) 09026 61778-2(43) The Heifetz Collection, Vol.
43

LOS ANGELES PIANO QUARTET
Fauré: Piano Quartet 1, Piano Quartet 2

LOSA, Alfonso (ten)
Verdi: Traviata (Cpte)

LOSCH, Liselotte (sop)
Mozart: Zauberflöte (Cpte)

LOTHAR, Susanne (narr)
see CONCERT INDEX under:
(SONY) SK53360 Mahler/Nono—Vocal Works

LOTRIĆ (TEN), Janez (ten)
see CONCERT INDEX under:
(NAXO) 8 553030 Opera Duets

LOTT, Felicity (sop)
Bach: Mass in B minor, BWV232 (Cpte), St Matthew
Passion, BWV244 (Cpte)
Brahms: Deutsches Requiem, Op. 45 (Cpte)
Britten: Peter Grimes (Cpte), Turn of the Screw
(Cpte)
Elgar: Coronation Ode (Cpte)
Handel: Messiah (exc)
Haydn: Mass 11
Lehár: Lustige Witwe (Cpte)
M-A. Charpentier: Te Deum H146
Mahler: Symphony 8
Mathias: Lux aeterna
Mozart: Così fan tutte (Cpte), Nozze di Figaro (Cpte)
Purcell: Birthday Ode, Z323
R. Strauss: Vier letzte Lieder
Schubert: Hirt auf dem Felsen, D965
Vaughan Williams: Symphony 1
Wolf: Goethe Lieder (exc), Italienisches Liederbuch
(Cpte), Mörike Lieder (exc)
see CONCERT INDEX under:
(ASV) CDDCA683 Mozart—Arias
(CARL) MCD22 Schumann—Lieder
(CARL) PCD2016 Schubert—Lieder
(CFP) CD-CFP4570 Choral Favourites
(CHAN) CHAN8538 R. Strauss: Orchestral & Vocal
Works
(CHAN) CHAN8557 R. Strauss—Vocal and
Orchestral Works
(CHAN) CHAN8572 R. Strauss: Orchestral & Vocal
Works
(CHAN) CHAN8631 R. Strauss: Orchestral & Vocal
Works
(CHAN) CHAN8657 Britten—Vocal Works
(CHAN) CHAN8722 Felicity Lott sings English Songs
(CHAN) CHAN8734 R. Strauss—Orchestral Works
and Songs
(CHAN) CHAN8744 R. Strauss: Orchestral and
Vocal Works

(CHAN) CHAN8758 R. Strauss—Opera Excerpts
(CHAN) CHAN9054 R. Strauss—Orchestral Songs,
Vol.1
(COLL) Coll7037-2 Britten—Orchestral Song Cycles
(COLL) Coll7039-2 Britten—The Folk Songs
(EMI) CDC7 49930-2 Sweet Power of Song
(EMI) CDC7 54411-2 On Wings of Song
(EMI) CMS7 64476-2 Mahler—Symphonies, Vol.2
(ERAT) 4509-96371-2 Gardiner—The Purcell
Collection
(FORL) UCD16730 Poulenc—Mélodies
(HARM) HMA190 1138 Melodies of the poems of
Victor Hugo
(HYPE) CDA66112 Souvenirs de Venise
(HYPE) CDA66801/2 Gounod—Songs
(HYPE) CDA67061/2 Britten—Purcell Realizations
(HYPE) CDJ33019 Schubert—Complete Lieder,
Vol.19
(PHIL) 420 648-2PM Vivaldi: Sacred Choral Music,
Vol.1
(PHIL) 420 649-2PM Vivaldi: Sacred Choral Music,
Vol.2
(UNIC) UKCD2073 The Delius Collection, Volume 3

LOTZ, Siegfried (db)
see CONCERT INDEX under:
(CAPR) 10 180 Gisela May sings Weill

LOUGHRAN, James (cond)
see Hallé

LOUGHTON HIGH SCHOOL FOR GIRLS' CHOIR
cond H. VON KARAJAN
Humperdinck: Hänsel und Gretel (Cpte)
R. Strauss: Rosenkavalier (Cpte)

LOUISVILLE ORCHESTRA
cond A. ENDO
Gottschalk: Cakewalk (Cpte)
cond M. GOULD
see CONCERT INDEX under:
(ALBA) TROY013/4-2 Morton Gould—Orchestral
Works
cond J. MESTER
Piston: Incredible Flutist (Cpte)
see CONCERT INDEX under:
(ALBA) AR012 Roy Harris—Orchestral Works
(ALBA) TROY013/4-2 Morton Gould—Orchestral
Works
(ALBA) TROY021-2 American Choral & Orchestral
Works
(ALBA) TROY024-2 American Orchestral Works
cond L. SLATKIN
(ALBA) TROY024-2 American Orchestral Works
cond L.L. SMITH
(ALBA) AR012 Roy Harris—Orchestral Works
(ALBA) TROY013/4-2 Morton Gould—Orchestral
Works
cond R. WHITNEY
see CONCERT INDEX under:
(ALBA) AR012 Roy Harris—Orchestral Works
(ALBA) TROY021-2 American Choral & Orchestral
Works

LOUP, François (bass)
Chausson: Roi Arthus (Cpte)
Debussy: Pelléas et Mélisande (Cpte)
Honegger: Jeanne d'Arc (Cpte)
Lully: Alceste (Cpte)

LOUREIRO DE SÁ, Marcos (bar)
see CONCERT INDEX under:
(FNAC) 592096 Rameau—Grand Motets

LOUVAY, Françoise (sop)
Boïeldieu: Dame blanche (Cpte)

LÖVAAS, Kari (sop)
Egk: Peer Gynt (Cpte)
Haydn: Fedeltà Premiata (Cpte), Vera Costanza
(Cpte)
Puccini: Messa di Gloria
R. Strauss: Rosenkavalier (Cpte)
Schumann: Szenen aus Goethes Faust (Cpte)
see CONCERT INDEX under:
(DG) 437 719-2GC Berg—Vocal Works

LOVANO, Lucien (bass)
Messager: Basoche (Cpte), Monsieur Beaucaire
(Cpte)
Milhaud: Christophe Colomb (Cpte)
Offenbach: Chanson de Fortunio (Cpte)
Planquette: Rip van Winkle (Cpte)
Terrasse: Travaux d'Hercule (Cpte)
see CONCERT INDEX under:
(DECC) 433 400-2DM2 Ravel & Debussy—Stage
Works

LOVANO, Lucien (narr)
Milhaud: Christophe Colomb (Cpte)

LOVE, Shirley (mez)
Janáček: Diary of one who disappeared
Stravinsky: Rake's Progress (Cpte)

LOVEDAY, Alan (vn)
Vivaldi: Concerti, Op. 8 (exc)

LOVETT, Martin (vc)
Schubert: Trout Quintet, D667

LOWBURY, Pauline (vn)
Simpson: Horn Quartet, Horn Trio, Violin Sonata
(1984)

LOWBURY PIANO TRIO
Simpson: Piano Trio (1988-9)

LOWE, Robert (cond)
see Orig London Cast

LOWENDUSKY, Gary (db)
J. Adams: Shaker Loops

LOWENTHAL, Jerome (pf)
Tchaikovsky: Concert Fantasia, Piano Concerto 1,
Piano Concerto 2, Piano Concerto 3

LOWER RHINE CHORAL SOCIETY
cond H. SCHMITT
see CONCERT INDEX under:
(SCHW) 313001 Pater Noster

LOWER RHINE COMMUNITY CHOIR
see CONCERT INDEX under:
(SCHW) 314050 Weill—Vocal and Choral Works
cond M-A. SCHLINGENSIEPEN
see CONCERT INDEX under:
(SCHW) 314050 Weill—Vocal and Choral Works

LOWERY, Melvin (ten)
Stravinsky: Rake's Progress (Cpte)

LOZANO, Fernando (cond)
see Mexico City PO

LSO BRASS ENSEMBLE
cond E. CREES
see CONCERT INDEX under:
(COLL) Coll1288-2 American Music for Brass

LUBBOCK, John (cond)
see St John's Smith Square Orch

LUBIMOV, Alexei (pf)
see CONCERT INDEX under:
(ERAT) 2292-45510-2 Mozart—Piano Sonatas
(ERAT) 2292-45990-2 Chopin—Piano Works
(ERAT) 4509-98474-2 Brahms—Piano Works

LUBIN, Germaine (sop)
see CONCERT INDEX under:
(CLUB) CL99-022 Germaine Lubin (1891-1979)
(EMI) CMS7 64008-2(2) Wagner Singing on Record
(pt 2)
(EPM) 150 052 Germaine Lubin—Opera & Song
Recital

LUBIN, Robert (pf)
see CONCERT INDEX under:
(BRID) BCD9051 Stravinsky—Piano Works

LUBIN, Steven (fp)
Mozart: Piano Concerto 20
see CONCERT INDEX under:
(HARM) HMU90 7094 Schubert—Piano Trios
(L'OI) 425 835-2OH Mozart—Concert and Opera
Arias
(L'OI) 433 848-2OH Schubert—Chamber and Vocal
Works

LUBIN, Steven (fp/dir)
Mozart: Piano Concerto 12, Piano Concerto 15, Piano
Concerto 23

LUBIN, Steven (pf)
see CONCERT INDEX under:
(HARM) HMU90 7037
Beethoven/Brahms/Krufft—Works for Horn

LUBLIN, Eliane (sop)
G. Charpentier: Louise (Cpte)

LUBOSHUTZ, Pierre (pf)
(BIDD) WHL019 Koussevitzky—Double-bass
Recordings & Early Boston SO

LUBOTSKY, Mark (vn)
Britten: Violin Concerto
Schnittke: Violin Concerto 1, Violin Concerto 2
see CONCERT INDEX under:
(BIS) BIS-CD286 Tubin: Orchestral Works
(ONDI) ODE800-2 Schnittke—Works for Violin and
Piano
(SONY) SK53271 Schnittke—Orchestral and
Chamber Works

LUCA, Giuseppe De (bar)
see CONCERT INDEX under:
(CLAR) CDGSE78-50-52 Three Tenors
(CLUB) CL99-587/8 Eugenia Burzio (1872-1922)
(CONI) CDHD201 Galli-Curci in Opera and Song
(EMI) CDH7 61051-2 Beniamino Gigli - Operatic
Arias
(EMI) CHS7 64860-2(2) La Scala Edition - Vol.1,
1878-1914 (pt 2)
(IRCC) IRCC-CD808 Souvenirs of 19th Century Italian
Opera
(MEMO) HR4408/9(1) Singers in Genoa, Vol.1 (disc
1)
(MMOI) CDMOIR417 Great Voices of the
Century—Beniamino Gigli
(MSCM) MM30352 Caruso—Italian Opera Arias
(MSOU) DFCDI-111 The Art of the Coloratura
(NIMB) NI7804 Giovanni Martinelli—Opera Recital
(NIMB) NI7806 Galli-Curci—Opera & Song Recital
(NIMB) NI7851 Legendary Voices
(NIMB) NI7852 Galli-Curci, Vol.1
(NIMB) NI7853 Galli-Curci, Vol.2
(NIMB) NI7854 Luigi-Volpi sings Verdi
(NIMB) NI7867 Legendary Baritones
(PEAR) EVC4(1) The Caruso Edition, Vol.4 (pt 1)
(PEAR) EVC4(2) The Caruso Edition, Vol.4 (pt 2)
(PEAR) GEMMCDS9924(2) Covent Garden on
Record, Vol.2 (pt 2)
(PEAR) GEMMCDS9925(1) Covent Garden on
Record—Vol.3 (pt 1)
(PEAR) GEMMCD9316 Beniamino Gigli

LUNDKVIST, Erik (organ)
Olsson: Te Deum
see CONCERT INDEX under:
(EMI) CDC7 54098-2   Sacred Songs

LUNGO, Laura del (mez)
see CONCERT INDEX under:
(IRCC) IRCC-CD808   Souvenirs of 19th Century Italian
Opera

LUNOW, Horst (bass)
Wagner: Meistersinger (Cpte)

LUPERI, Mario (bass)
Cherubini: Lodoïska (Cpte)

LUPONE, Patti (sngr)
see CONCERT INDEX under:
(PHIL) 446 406-2PH   Berlin—Heat Wave

LUPOVICI, Marcel (spkr)
Tomasi: Triomphe de Jeanne

LUPPI, Oreste (bass)
see CONCERT INDEX under:
(EMI) CHS7 64860-2(2)   La Scala Edition - Vol.1,
1878-1914 (pt 2)
(MEMO) HR4408/9(1)   Singers in Genoa, Vol.1 (disc
1)
(PEAR) GEMMCDS9924(2)   Covent Garden on
Record, Vol.2 (pt 2)
(SYMP) SYMCD1113   The Harold Wayne Collection,
Vol.13
(SYMP) SYMCD1126   The Harold Wayne Collection,
Vol.14

LUPTÁČIK, Jozef (cl)
see CONCERT INDEX under:
(OPUS) 9351 1894   French Chamber Works

LUPU, Radu (pf)
Grieg: Piano Concerto
Mozart: 2-Piano Concerto, K365
Schubert: Impromptus (exc), Moments musicaux,
D780, Piano Sonata, D664, Piano Sonata, D845,
Piano Sonata, D894, Piano Sonata, D958, Piano
Sonata, D960
Schumann: Piano Concerto
see CONCERT INDEX under:
(DECC) 417 599-2DH   Brahms: Piano Works
(DECC) 421 154-2DM   French Chamber Works
(DECC) 425 033-2DM   Schubert—Piano Sonatas
(DECC) 440 496-2DH   Schumann—Piano Works
(EMI) CDC7 47549-2   Schubert—Lieder Recital
(EMI) CDC7 54239-2   Schubert—Lieder
(SONY) SK44915   Mozart—Works for 2 Pianos &
Piano Duet

LUPU, Sherban (vn)
see CONCERT INDEX under:
(ASV) CDDCA902   Ginastera—Piano Works, Volume
3
(CNTI) CCD1017   Violin Diabolique: Music by Ernst
and Wieniawski

LURIE, Mitchell (cl)
see CONCERT INDEX under:
(TEST) SBT1053   Chamber Works

LUSH, Ernest (pf)
see CONCERT INDEX under:
(DECC) 433 220-2DWO   The World of the Violin
(EMI) CDM5 65101-2   A Warlock Centenary Album
(EMI) CDM7 63165-2   Jacqueline Du Pré—Early BBC
Recordings, Vol.1
(EMI) CDM7 63166-2   Jacqueline Du Pré—Early BBC
Recordings, Vol.2
(EMI) CDS7 54607-2   Stravinsky plays and conducts
Stravinsky
(EMI) CZS5 68132-2   Les introuvables de Jacqueline
du Pré
(LOND) 430 061-2LM   Kathleen Ferrier—Song Recital
(PREI) 90190   Paul Schoeffler—Recital
(SYMP) SYMCD1067   Russian & Polish Songs
(TEST) SBT1016   Pierre Fournier - recital

LUSMANN, Stephen (bar)
R. Strauss: Friedenstag (Cpte)

LUSSAN, Zélie de (mez)
see CONCERT INDEX under:
(IRCC) IRCC-CD802   Souvenirs of Rare French
Opera

LUSTMAN, Julie (pf)
see CONCERT INDEX under:
(BRID) BCD9039   The Great Regondi, Vol. 1
(BRID) BCD9055   The Great Regondi, Vol. 2

LÜTKEN, Augusta (sop)
see CONCERT INDEX under:
(SIMA) PSC1810(1)   Grieg—Songs (historical
recordings, pt 1)

LUTOSŁAWSKI, Witold (cond)
see BBC SO

LUTZ, Alfred (vn)
see CONCERT INDEX under:
(ETCE) KTC1045   Menotti: Chamber and Vocal
Works

LUTZ, David (pf)
see CONCERT INDEX under:
(TELD) 9031-74002-2   Mahler (orch Berio)—Lieder

LUTZ, Thomas (castanets)
see CONCERT INDEX under:
(DG) 435 860-2GH2   Berlioz—Mélodies

LUTZ, Walter (vc)
see CONCERT INDEX under:
(PREI) 89208   Karl Erb Lieder Album

LUTZE, Walter (cond)
see Berlin Deutsche Op Orch

LUTZKE, Myron (vc)
Schubert: Octet, D803
see CONCERT INDEX under:
(HARM) HMU90 7094   Schubert—Piano Trios
(SONY) SK53106   Kathleen Battle & Jean-Pierre
Rampal in Concert

**LUXEMBOURG RADIO & TV SYMPHONY
ORCHESTRA**
cond P. CAO
see CONCERT INDEX under:
(FORL) FF007   Liszt—Piano Concertos Nos 1 and 2;
Hungarian Rhapsodies
cond J-C. CASADESUS
see CONCERT INDEX under:
(FORL) UCD16516   Liszt: Orchestral works
cond D. CHORAFAS
Bruch: Violin Concerto 1
Mendelssohn: Violin Concerto, Op. 64
cond L. DE FROMENT
see CONCERT INDEX under:
(FORL) FF009   Weber—Clarinet Concertos Nos 1 and
2; Oberon Overture
(FORL) FF045   Grieg/Lalo—Orchestral Works
cond L. HAGER
Brahms: Tragic Overture

LUXEMBOURG RADIO SYMPHONY ORCHESTRA
Goetz: Piano Concerto 2
see CONCERT INDEX under:
(VOX) 115708-2   Mosonyi/Raff/Stavenhaegn—Piano
Concertos
(VOX) 115709-2   D'Albert/Bronsart/Liszt—Piano
Concertos
(VOX) 115713-2
Mendelssohn/Reinecke/Rheinberger—Piano
Concertos
(VOX) 115714-2   Balakirev/Lyapunov/Medtner—Piano
Concertos
(VOX) 115717-2   Chopin/Henselt/Hiller—Piano
Concertos
cond P. CAO
see CONCERT INDEX under:
(VOX) CDX2 5506   György Sándor plays Bartók
cond L. DE FROMENT
(VOX) 115712-2   Hiller/Litolff/Moscheles—Piano
Concertos
cond F. MARTIN
Martin: Piano concerto 2, Violin Concerto

LUXON, Benjamin (bar)
Alwyn: Miss Julie (Cpte)
Berlioz: Enfance du Christ (Cpte)
Britten: Rape of Lucretia (Cpte), War Requiem
Elgar: Dream of Gerontius (Cpte)
Handel: Messiah (Cpte)
Haydn: Orlando Paladino (Cpte), Ritorno di Tobia
(Cpte), Schöpfung (Cpte)
Korngold: Tote Stadt (Cpte)
Schubert: Schöne Müllerin (Cpte), Schwanengesang,
D957 (Cpte), Winterreise (Cpte)
Walton: Belshazzar's Feast, Troilus and Cressida
(Cpte)
see CONCERT INDEX under:
(CHAN) CHAN8475   Vaughan Williams—Songs
(CHAN) CHAN8643   Warlock Songs
(CHAN) CHAN8782   Quilter: Songs
(CHAN) CHAN8830   Bush—A Little Love Music
(CHAN) CHAN8831   Butterworth & Gurney: Songs
(CHAN) CHAN9185/6   Howells—Songs
(DECC) 421 810-2DM2   Dvořák & Kodály: Vocal
Works
(DECC) 430 160-2DM   Haydn: Masses & Keyboard
Concerto
(DECC) 430 360-2DM   Faure/Poulenc—Sacred Choral
Works
(DECC) 436 486-2DF2
Duruflé/Fauré/Poulenc—Choral Works
(EMI) CDM7 64730-2   Vaughan Williams—Riders to
the Sea; Epithalamion, etc
(EMI) CMS7 64218-2   Delius—Vocal Works
(LOND) 433 200-2LHO2   Britten—Owen Wingrave,
etc.
(PHIL) 432 416-2PH3   Haydn—L'incontro
improvviso/Arias

LUY, André (organ)
Martin: Requiem

LYDIAN STRING QUARTET
see CONCERT INDEX under:
(HARM) HMU90 7114   Schuman—String Quartets

LYKSETH-SCHJERVEN, Magna (sop)
see CONCERT INDEX under:
(SIMA) PSC1810(1)   Grieg—Songs (historical
recordings, pt 1)

LYMPANY, Dame Moura (pf)
Prokofiev: Piano Concerto 3
Rachmaninov: Piano Concerto 3, Preludes
see CONCERT INDEX under:
(CFP) CD-CFP4653   Debussy—Piano Works
(EMIL) CDZ110   Best-Loved Piano Classics
(EMIL) CDZ111   Best Loved Piano Classics Volume
2
(OLYM) OCD190   The Lympany Legend, Vol. 1

LYNCH, Charles (pf)
see CONCERT INDEX under:
(SYMP) SYMCD1075   May Harrison—Violinist and
Composer

LYNDON-GEE, Christopher (pf)
see CONCERT INDEX under:
(LARG) Largo 5127   Igor Markevitch—Chamber
Works

LYON FRANCO-GERMAN CHOIR
cond W. BADUN
Suppé: Requiem

LYON NATIONAL CHOIR
cond S. BAUDO
Beethoven: Christus am Oelberge, Op. 85
see CONCERT INDEX under:
(HARM) HMC90 5149   Poulenc: Sacred choral works
cond P. FOURNILLIER
Massenet: Grisélidis (Cpte)

LYON NATIONAL ORCHESTRA
cond S. BAUDO
Beethoven: Christus am Oelberge, Op. 85
Dutilleux: Symphony 1, Timbres, espace,
mouvement
see CONCERT INDEX under:
(HARM) HMC90 5149   Poulenc: Sacred choral works
cond E. KRIVINE
Berlioz: Symphonie fantastique, Troyens (exc)
Bizet: Arlésienne Suites, Symphony
Franck: Psyché, Symphony

LYON NATIONAL ORCHESTRA CHORUS
cond P. FOURNILLIER
Massenet: Vierge (Cpte)
cond B. TETU
Caplet: Inscriptions champêtre, Miroir de Jésus

LYON OPÉRA CHORUS
cond G. FERRO
Donizetti: Don Pasquale (Cpte)
see CONCERT INDEX under:
(VIRG) CUV5 61139-2   Rossini—Arias
cond P. FOURNILLIER
Massenet: Grisélidis (Cpte)
cond J.E. GARDINER
Offenbach: Brigands (Cpte)
Rossini: Comte Ory (Cpte)
cond K. NAGANO
Berlioz: Damnation de Faust (Cpte)
Busoni: Arlecchino (Cpte), Turandot (Cpte)
Debussy: Rodrigue et Chimène (Cpte)
Floyd: Susannah (Cpte)
Poulenc: Dialogues des Carmélites (Cpte)
Prokofiev: Love for 3 Oranges (Cpte)
cond J. NELSON
Berlioz: Béatrice et Bénédict (Cpte)

LYON OPERA ORCHESTRA
cond G. FERRO
Donizetti: Don Pasquale (Cpte)
see CONCERT INDEX under:
(VIRG) CUV5 61139-2   Rossini—Arias
cond L. FOSTER
see CONCERT INDEX under:
(EMI) CDC5 55151-2   Operetta Duets
cond J.E. GARDINER
Berlioz: Damnation de Faust (Cpte), Enfance du
Christ (Cpte)
Gluck: Iphigénie en Aulide (Cpte), Iphigénie en
Tauride (Cpte), Orphée (Cpte), Rencontre imprévue
(Cpte)
Offenbach: Brigands (Cpte)
Rossini: Comte Ory (Cpte)
see CONCERT INDEX under:
(EMI) CDC7 49689-2   Duparc/Ravel—Vocal Works
(ERAT) 2292-45517-2   Berlioz—Songs
cond K. NAGANO
Berlioz: Damnation de Faust (Cpte)
Busoni: Arlecchino (Cpte), Turandot (Cpte)
Canteloube: Chants d'Auvergne (exc)
Debussy: Boîte à joujoux, Rodrigue et Chimène
(Cpte)
Delibes: Coppélia (Cpte)
Floyd: Susannah (Cpte)
J. Adams: Death of Klinghoffer (Cpte)
Poulenc: Dialogues des Carmélites (Cpte)
Prokofiev: Love for 3 Oranges (Cpte), Peter and the
Wolf
R. Strauss: Salomé (Cpte)
see CONCERT INDEX under:
(ERAT) 2292-45820-2   Milhaud—Orchestral Works
(VIRG) VC7 59236-2   French Songs
cond J. NELSON
Berlioz: Béatrice et Bénédict (Cpte)

LYONS, Darius (fl)
see CONCERT INDEX under:
(RCA) 09026 61580-2(1)   RCA/Met 110 Singers, 100
Years (pt 1)

LYONS, Jeff (sngr)
Gershwin: Strike Up the Band I (Cpte), Strike Up the
Band II

LYRA BOREALIS ENSEMBLE
cond P. JÄRVI
see CONCERT INDEX under:
(KOCH) 37165-2   Kasemets—Chamber Works

LYRIC ART QUARTET
see CONCERT INDEX under:
(BAY) BCD-1014   Classical Hollywood

LYRIC QUARTET
see CONCERT INDEX under:
(METI) **MSVCD92003** Howells—Chamber Works

LYSELL, Bernt (vn)
see CONCERT INDEX under:
(MSVE) **MSCD521** Berwald—Chamber Works

LYSY, Alberto (vn)
see CONCERT INDEX under:
(CLAV) **CD50-8507** Chamber recital

LYSY, Antonio (vc)
see CONCERT INDEX under:
(CLAV) **CD50-8507** Chamber recital

LYSY, Oskar (va)
R. Strauss: Don Quixote

LYTTING, Katia (mez)
Bellini: Puritani (Cpte)
Rossini: Signor Bruschino (Cpte)

MA, Yo-Yo (vc)
Bach: Viola da gamba Sonatas, BWV1027-9
Beethoven: Cello Sonata 1, Cello Sonata 2, Piano
Quartet, Op. 16, Triple Concerto
Brahms: String Sextet 1, String Sextet 2
Dvořák: Piano Trio 3, Piano Trio 4
Elgar: Cello Concerto
Fauré: Piano Quartet 1, Piano Quartet 2
Schoenberg: Verklärte Nacht
Schumann: Piano Quartet, Op. 47
Shostakovich: Cello Sonata, Op.40, Piano Trio 2
Walton: Cello Concerto
see CONCERT INDEX under:
(DG) **415 276-2GH** Beethoven—Orchestral Works
(SONY) **MK39310** Haydn Concertos
(SONY) **SK39964** J.C.Bach & Boccherini Orchestral
Works
(SONY) **SK42206** Dvořák—Works for cello and
orchestra
(SONY) **SK42663** Schumann: Cello Works
(SONY) **SK48191** Brahms—Cello Sonatas
(SONY) **SK48382** Prokofiev/Tchaikovsky—Cello
Works
(SONY) **SK53112** Chopin—Chamber Works
(SONY) **SK53126** Made in America
(SONY) **SK57961** The New York Album
(SONY) **S2K45846** Brahms—Piano Quartets

MAAG, Peter (cond)
see Berne SO

MAAZEL, Lorin (cond)
see Berlin Deutsche Op Orch

MABRY, James (sngr)
Weill: Down in the Valley (Cpte)

MAC LOW, Jackson (voc)
see CONCERT INDEX under:
(KOCH) **37238-2** A Chance Operation - John Cage
Tribute

MACAL, Zdenek (cond)
see BRSO

MACALESTER TRIO
see CONCERT INDEX under:
(VOX) **115845-2** Chamber Works by Women
Composers

MCARDLE, Andrea (sngr)
J. Herman: Jerry's Girls (Cpte)

MCARTHUR, David (pf)
see CONCERT INDEX under:
(HERA) **HAVPCD152** Music for Clarinet and Piano

MACARTHUR, Edwin (cond)
see RCA Victor SO

MCARTHUR, Edwin (cond)
see RCA SO

MCARTHUR, Edwin (pf)
see CONCERT INDEX under:
(LOND) **440 490-2LM5(1)** Kirsten Flagstad Edition (pt
1)
(LOND) **440 490-2LM5(2)** Kirsten Flagstad Edition (pt
2)
(LOND) **440 493-2LM** Kirsten Flagstad Edition, Vol.
3
(LOND) **440 494-2LM** Kirsten Flagstad Edition, Vol.
4
(NIMB) **NI7871** Kirsten Flagstad in Song
(PEAR) **GEMMCD9092** Kirsten Flagstad - Songs
(RCA) **09026 61879-2** Grieg—Historic Recordings
(SIMA) **PSC1821(2)** Kirsten Flagstad, Vol.1 (pt 2)

MCASLAN, Lorraine (vn)
Beethoven: Violin Sonata 5, Violin Sonata 9
Britten: Violin Concerto
Mozart: Sinfonia Concertante, K364
see CONCERT INDEX under:
(CNTI) **CCD1022** Bridge/Britten—Works for Violin and
Piano
(COLL) **Coll1123-2** Britten & L. Berkeley: Orchestral
Works
(LYRI) **SRCD209** Holst—Orchestral Works

MACAUX, Geneviève (sop)
Bizet: Carmen (Cpte)

MCBRIDE, Brendan (ten)
see CONCERT INDEX under:
(OPRA) **ORCH104** A Hundred Years of Italian Opera:
1820-1830

MCCABE, Dan (bar)
see CONCERT INDEX under:
(ERAT) **4509-98480-2** Lamentations - Holy Week in
Provence

MCCABE, John (pf)
Bax: Violin Sonata 1, Violin Sonata 2
Howells: Howells' Clavichord, Lambert's Clavichord
Walton: Piano Quartet
see CONCERT INDEX under:
(ASV) **CDDCA592** British Cello Music
(ASV) **CDDCA807** British Cello Music, Vol.2
(CHAN) **CHAN8391** Bax—Chamber Works
(CNTI) **CCD1027** Brahms/Gal—Clarinet Sonatas
(CNTI) **CCD1028/9** Transatlantic Piano
(CNTI) **CCD1045** Bax—Piano Works
(LOND) **443 785-2LC12(2)** Haydn—The Keyboard
Sonatas (pt 2)
(SAGA) **EC3393-2** Satie—Piano Works

MCCABE, Robin (pf)
see CONCERT INDEX under:
(BIS) **BIS-CD184** French Flute Music

MCCALDIN, Clare (sop)
see CONCERT INDEX under:
(MERI) **CDE84153** French Choral Music

MCCALDIN, Denis (cond)
see Haydn Soc Orch

MCCANN, Paul (ten)
M. Berkeley: Baa Baa Black Sheep (Cpte)

MCCANN, Phillip (cond)
see Sellers Engin Band

MCCANN, Phillip (cornet)
see CONCERT INDEX under:
(CHAN) **CHAN4501** The World's Most Beautiful
Melodies
(CHAN) **CHAN4505** Black Dyke plays Rossini
(CHAN) **CHAN4513** British Bandsman Centenary
Concert
(CHAN) **CHAN6539** Classic Brass

MCCARTHY, John (cond)
see LSO

MCCARTHY, Michael (bass)
see CONCERT INDEX under:
(NAXO) **8 553129** Purcell—Choral and Organ Music

MCCARTY, Brian (tv)
J. Adams: Light over Water

MCCARTY, Patricia (va)
see CONCERT INDEX under:
(ECM) **445 350-2** Jarrett—Bridge of Light

MACCHI, Maria de (sop)
see CONCERT INDEX under:
(MEMO) **HR4408/9(2)** Singers in Genoa, Vol.1 (disc
2)

MACCHÌ, Mario (bass)
Verdi: Otello (Cpte)

MCCHRYSTAL, Gerard (sax)
see CONCERT INDEX under:
(CHAN) **CHAN9129** Debussy/Ravel—Orchestral
Works

MCCOLLUM, John (ten)
Beethoven: Symphony 9

MCCORMACK, Elizabeth (mez)
see CONCERT INDEX under:
(HYPE) **CDA66638** Villa-Lobos—Sacred Choral Music

MCCORMACK, John (ten)
see CONCERT INDEX under:
(BIDD) **LAB068/9** The Kreisler Collection—1921-25
(MMOI) **CDMOIR411** Sacred Songs and Arias
(MMOI) **CDMOIR418** Great Voices of the
Century—John McCormack
(NIMB) **NI7801** Great Singers, Vol.1
(PEAR) **GEMMCDS9075** Hugo Wolf Society, Volume I
(PEAR) **GEMMCDS9924(2)** Covent Garden on
Record, Vol.2 (pt 2)
(PEAR) **GEMMCD9315** Kreisler/McCormack Duets
(RCA) **09026 61580-2(2)** RCA/Met 100 Singers, 100
Years (pt 2)
(SUPR) **11 2136-2(4)** Emmy Destinn—Complete
Edition, Discs 9 & 10
(TEST) **SBT1005** Ten Top Tenors
(TEST) **SBT1008** Viva Rossini

MCCORMICK, Mary Ann (mez)
see CONCERT INDEX under:
(DG) **445 828-2GH** Webern—String Quartets and
Trios

MCCOSHAN, Daniel (ten)
Mozart: Nozze di Figaro (Cpte)
Walton: Troilus and Cressida (Cpte)
(EMI) **CDH5 65072-2** Glyndebourne Recorded - 1934-
1994

MCCOY, Seth (ten)
Rachmaninov: Monna Vanna (exc)

MCCRACKEN, James (ten)
Bizet: Carmen (Cpte)
Meyerbeer: Prophète (Cpte)
Schoenberg: Gurrelieder

MCCRAW, Michael (bn)
see CONCERT INDEX under:
(BIS) **BIS-CD617** Telemann—Recorder Concertos

MCCREESH, Paul (cond)
see Gabrieli Consort

MCCUE, William (bass)
Mozart: Nozze di Figaro (Cpte)

MACCULI, Sabina (sop)
Mozart: Betulia Liberata (Cpte)
see CONCERT INDEX under:
(DECC) **436 261-2DHO3** Puccini—Il Trittico

MCCULLOCH, Susan (sop)
Mozart: Nozze di Figaro (Cpte)
see CONCERT INDEX under:
(OPRA) **ORCH104** A Hundred Years of Italian Opera:
1820-1830

MCDANIEL, Barry (bar)
Haydn: Mass 10
Henze: Junge Lord (Cpte)
Mozart: Finta Giardiniera (Cpte)
Puccini: Messa di Gloria
Purcell: Dido (Cpte)
R. Strauss: Ariadne auf Naxos (Cpte)
Weill: Zar lässt sich Photographieren (Cpte)
see CONCERT INDEX under:
(EMI) **CDM7 63948-2** 20th Century French Orchestral
Works
(SONY) **SM3K45845** Webern—Complete Works

MCDONALD, Christie (sngr)
see CONCERT INDEX under:
(PEAR) **GEMMCDS9053/5** Music from the New York
Stage, Vol. 2: 1908—1913
(PEAR) **GEMMCDS9056/8** Music from the New York
Stage, Vol. 3: 1913-17

MACDONALD, George (cl)
see CONCERT INDEX under:
(ASV) **CDDCA568** Works for clarinet and orchestra

MACDONALD, John (elec kybd)
see CONCERT INDEX under:
(BRID) **BCD9031** J. Harvey—Miscellaneous Works

MACDONALD, Kenneth (ten)
Britten: Midsummer Night's Dream (Cpte)
Donizetti: Lucia di Lammermoor (Cpte)

MCDONALD, Robert (pf)
see CONCERT INDEX under:
(SONY) **SK52568** Midori—Encore!

MCDONALD, Susann (hp)
see CONCERT INDEX under:
(DELO) **DE3005** World of the Harp

MACDONALD, W. H. (sngr)
see CONCERT INDEX under:
(PEAR) **GEMMCDS9050/2(1)** Music from the New
York Stage, Vol. 1 (part 1)

MCDONALL, Lois (sop)
Donizetti: Maria Padilla (Cpte)
Wagner: Rheingold (Cpte)

MCDONNELL, Tom (bar)
Puccini: Fanciulla del West (Cpte)
Rossini: Tancredi (Cpte)
(RCA) **GD60941** Rarities - Montserrat Caballé

MACDOUGALL, Jamie (ten)
Boughton: Bethlehem (Cpte)
Britten: Folk Songs (exc)
Handel: Judas Maccabaeus (Cpte)
Purcell: King Arthur, Z628 (Cpte)
see CONCERT INDEX under:
(ARCH) **445 353-2AH** Mozart—Sacred Choral Works
(HYPE) **CDJ33020** Schubert—Complete Lieder,
Vol.20
(HYPE) **CDJ33022** Schubert—Complete Lieder,
Vol.22

MCEACHERN, Malcolm (bass)
see CONCERT INDEX under:
(EMI) **CDANGEL 5** Norton—Chu Chin Chow

MCFADDEN, Claron (sop)
Gluck: Orfeo ed Euridice (Cpte), Paride ed Elena
(Cpte)
Handel: Acis and Galatea (Cpte), Ottone (Cpte)
Monteverdi: Ritorno d'Ulisse in patria (Cpte)
Purcell: King Arthur, Z628 (Cpte)
Rameau: Indes galantes (Cpte)
see CONCERT INDEX under:
(CHNN) **CCS7895** Buxtehude—Cantatas
(SONY) **SK47184** Glenn Gould—The Composer

MCFADZEAN, John (treb)
see CONCERT INDEX under:
(ARGO) **443 215-2ZH** Britten—Christmas Music

MCFARLAND, Robert (bar)
Glass: Satyagraha (Cpte)

MACFARLANE, Clare (va)
see CONCERT INDEX under:
(CHAN) **CHAN9197** Alwyn—Chamber Music, Volume
2

MACFARLANE, George (sngr)
see CONCERT INDEX under:
(PEAR) **GEMMCDS9056/8** Music from the New York
Stage, Vol. 3: 1913-17

MCGEE, Robin (db)
Cerha: Art Chansons (exc)

MCGEGAN, Nicholas (cond)
see Capella Savaria

MCGEGAN, Nicholas (hpd)
Bach: Anna Magdalena Notenbuch (1725) (exc)

MCGEGAN, Nicholas (hpd/dir)
Handel: Radamisto (Cpte)
see CONCERT INDEX under:
(HARM) **HMU90 7066** Uccellini—Chamber Works
(HARM) **HMU90 7067** Nicola Matteis—Ayres for the
Violin

MCGLAUGHLIN, William (cond)
see Kansas City SO

MCGLINN, John (cond)
see London Sinfonietta

MCGLINN, John (sngr)
Berlin: Annie Get Your Gun (Cpte)
see CONCERT INDEX under:
(EMI) **CDC5 55189-2** The Busby Berkeley Album

MCGRAW, Michael (bn)
see CONCERT INDEX under:
(BIS) **BIS-CD271** Recorder Concertos
(DHM) **RD77201** Telemann—Wind Concertos

MACGREGOR, Alison (sngr)
G. Charpentier: Louise (Cpte)

MACGREGOR, Joanna (pf)
Bach: French Suites, BWV812-17
Britten: Piano Concerto
D. Scarlatti: Keyboard Sonatas (exc)
Krauze: Quatuor pour la Naissance
Messiaen: Quatuor
see CONCERT INDEX under:
(COLL) **Coll1053-2** Satie—Piano Works
(COLL) **Coll1102-2** Britten & Saxton: Orchestral
Works
(COLL) **Coll1107-2** Ives/Barber—Piano Works
(COLL) **Coll1139-2** Gershwin—Orchestral Works
(COLL) **Coll1299-2** American Piano Classics
(COLL) **Coll1404-2** Bartók/Debussy/Ravel—Piano
Works
(COLL) **Coll1414-2** Birtwistle—Orchestral Works

MCGRUDER, Jasper (narr)
Glass: Einstein on the Beach (Cpte)

MCGUIRE, James Michael (bar)
Haydn: Creation (Cpte)

MACHADO, Maria cella (hp)
see CONCERT INDEX under:
(CHNT) **LDC278 869/70** Villa-Lobos—Guitar Works

MACHI, Mario (bar)
Donizetti: Messa di Gloria e Credo

MACHOTKOVÁ, Marcela (sop)
Dvořák: Jacobin (Cpte)
Smetana: Two Widows (Cpte)

MACHULA, Tibor de (vc)
Hindemith: Cello Concerto

MACIAS, Reinaldo (ten)
Beethoven: Fidelio (Cpte)
Honegger: Aventures du Roi Pausole (Cpte)

MACIEJEWSKI, Stephan (bass)
Lully: Atys (Cpte)
see CONCERT INDEX under:
(AUVI) **AV6108** Bouzignac—Sacred choral music

MCILWHAM, George (bagpipe)
see CONCERT INDEX under:
(UNIC) **DKPCD9070** A Celebration of Scotland

MCINNES, Donald (va)
Schoenberg: Verklärte Nacht

MCINTYRE, Sir Donald (bass-bar)
Berlioz: Damnation de Faust (Cpte)
Handel: Messiah (Cpte)
Mahler: Symphony 8
Wagner: Parsifal (Cpte), Rheingold (Cpte), Siegfried
(Cpte), Walküre (Cpte)
see CONCERT INDEX under:
(ODE) **CDMANU1317** Wagner—Opera Excerpts

MACIOCCHI, Françoise (pf)
Rossini: Petite Messe Solennelle

MACKAY, Ann (sop)
Rameau: Naïs (Cpte)
see CONCERT INDEX under:
(ASV) **CDDCA684** Schubert—Lieder & Chamber
Works
(ASV) **CDDCA766** Handel—Works for Soprano and
Orchestra
(MERI) **CDE84253** Beethoven—Chamber and Vocal
Works

MCKAY, James (bn)
see CONCERT INDEX under:
(RCA) **RD87774** Vivaldi: Cello Concertos

MACKAY, Penelope (sop)
Britten: Death in Venice (Cpte)

MACKAY, Rita (sop)
Sullivan: Patience (Cpte)

MCKEE, Joseph (bass)
Britten: Paul Bunyan (Cpte)
Puccini: Bohème (Cpte)
V. Thomson: Mother of us all (Cpte)

MCKELLAR, Kenneth (ten)
see CONCERT INDEX under:
(DECC) **430 500-2DWO** World of Handel

MCKELLAR-FERGUSON, Kathleen (mez)
Beethoven: Symphony 9

MCKELLEN, Ian (narr)
Stravinsky: Histoire du soldat (exc)

MCKENNA, Kennedy (ten)
see CONCERT INDEX under:
(CLAR) **CDGSE78-50-26** Wagner: Tristan und Isolde
excerpts
(CLAR) **CDGSE78-50-35/6** Wagner—Historical
recordings
(PEAR) **GEMMCDS9137** Wagner—Der Ring des
Nibelungen

MCKENZIE, Julia (sngr)
Sondheim: Into the Woods (Cpte)

MCKENZIE, Mark (cond)
see OST

MACKENZIE, Neil (ten)
see CONCERT INDEX under:
(HYPE) **CDA66311/2** Monteverdi: St Barbara
Vespers

MACKENZIE, Norman (pf)
see CONCERT INDEX under:
(TELA) **CD80326** Brahms—Vocal works
(TELA) **CD80340** Schubert—Songs for Male Chorus

MACKERRAS, Sir Charles (cond)
see Australian CO

MACKEY, Hugh (bass)
see CONCERT INDEX under:
(CHAN) **CHAN8808** Early 20th Century English
Music

MACKEY, Steve (gtr)
see CONCERT INDEX under:
(NONE) **7559-79310-2** Short Stories

MACKIE, Meibon (bn)
see CONCERT INDEX under:
(CONI) **CDCF173** Prokofiev: Orchestral & Chamber
Works

MACKIE, Neil (ten)
Handel: Saul (Cpte), Semele (Cpte)
Haydn: Schöpfung (Cpte)
Leighton: Symphony 3
Maxwell Davies: Into the Labyrinth, Lighthouse
(Cpte)
Mozart: Requiem
Sullivan: Yeomen of the Guard (Cpte)
see CONCERT INDEX under:
(CHAN) **CHAN8760** Walton—Choral Works
(HYPE) **CDA66489** Leighton—Cathedral Music
(MERI) **DUOCD89002** German Lieder sung in English
(UNIC) **UKCD2009** A-Courting we will go

MACKINTOSH, Catherine (vn)
Corelli: Trio Sonatas, Op. 3 (exc), Trio Sonatas, Op. 4
(exc)
Mozart: Flute Sonatas, Zauberflöte (exc)
Purcell: Sonatas, Z802-11
Rameau: Pièces de clavecin en concerts
Vivaldi: Concerti, Op. 8 (exc)
see CONCERT INDEX under:
(CHAN) **CHAN8763** Purcell—Chamber Works Vol 3
(HYPE) **CDA66380** Bach—Violin Concertos
(L'OI) **410 553-2OH** 18th Century Orchestral Works
(L'OI) **411 949-2OH** Telemann: Double & Triple
Concertos
(L'OI) **417 123-2OH** Purcell: Songs and Airs
(L'OI) **421 500-2OH** Bach: Double Concertos
(L'OI) **433 053-2OH** Bach/Vivaldi—Orchestral Works
(MERI) **CDE84145** Beethoven: Chamber Music on
Period Instruments

MCKNIGHT, Anne (sop)
Puccini: Bohème (Cpte)

MCLACHLAN, Murray (pf)
Shchedrin: Preludes and Fugues (1963-70), Preludes
and Fugues (1972)
see CONCERT INDEX under:
(OLYM) **OCD214** Miaskovsky—Piano Sonatas
(OLYM) **OCD217** Miaskovsky—Piano Works
(OLYM) **OCD255** Prokofiev: Piano Sonatas, Vol.1
(OLYM) **OCD256** Prokofiev: Piano Sonatas, Vol.2
(OLYM) **OCD257** Prokofiev—Piano Sonatas, Volume
3
(OLYM) **OCD266** Kabalevsky—Piano Works, Vol.1
(OLYM) **OCD267** Kabalevsky—Piano Works, Vol.2
(OLYM) **OCD439** Tcherepnin—Piano Concertos
(OLYM) **OCD440** Tcherepnin—Piano Concertos

MCLAUGHLIN, John (gtr)
see CONCERT INDEX under:
(SONY) **MK45578** McLaughlin: Guitar Works

MCLAUGHLIN, Marie (sop)
Bernstein: On the Town (Cpte)
Handel: Allegro, il penseroso ed il moderato (Cpte)
Mozart: Così fan tutte (Cpte), Don Giovanni (Cpte),
Nozze di Figaro (Cpte), Requiem, Zauberflöte (Cpte)
Purcell: Dido (Cpte)
Sullivan: Mikado (Cpte)
see CONCERT INDEX under:
(DECC) **430 370-2DH** R. Strauss—Works for Horn
(HYPE) **CDA66659** R. Strauss—Lieder
(HYPE) **CDJ33013** Schubert—Complete Lieder,
Vol.13
(HYPE) **CDJ33014** Schubert—Complete Lieder,
Vol.14

MCLEAN, Hugh (organ)
see CONCERT INDEX under:
(DECC) **433 677-2DM** Gibbons—Sacred Works

MACLEOD, Stephan (bass)
see CONCERT INDEX under:
(CHNN) **CCS7895** Buxtehude—Cantatas

MCLEOD, Suzanne (mez)
Corghi: Divara (Cpte)

MCLOUGHLIN, Eileen (sop)
Monteverdi: Ballo delle ingrate

MCMAHON, Alan (spkr)
Lampe: Pyramus and Thisbe (Cpte)

MCMAHON, Michael (pf)
see CONCERT INDEX under:
(CBC) **MVCD1052** Lieder on Poems of Heinrich Heine
(MARQ) **ERAD113** Catherine Robbin—Song Recital

MCMAHON, Richard (pf)
see CONCERT INDEX under:
(CHAN) **CHAN6535** Stravinsky—Symphonies of Wind
Instruments
(PP) **PP10792** Chabrier—Piano Works

MCMARTIN, John (sngr)
Sondheim: Follies (Cpte)

MACMILLAN, Sir Ernest (cond)
see Toronto SO

MACMILLAN, James (cond)
see Scottish CO

MCMILLAN, Kevin (bar)
Nielsen: Symphony 3
Orff: Carmina Burana
see CONCERT INDEX under:
(CBC) **MVCD1052** Lieder on Poems of Heinrich Heine

MACMILLEN, Francis (vn)
see CONCERT INDEX under:
(APR) **APR7016** The Auer Legacy, Vol.2

MCNAIR, Sylvia (sop)
Bach: Mass in B minor, BWV232 (Cpte)
Beethoven: Egmont (Cpte), Missa Solemnis
Berlioz: Béatrice et Bénédict (Cpte)
Debussy: Martyre de St Sébastien (Cpte)
Gluck: Orfeo ed Euridice (Cpte)
Grieg: Peer Gynt (exc)
Handel: Messiah (Cpte), Semele (Cpte)
Haydn: Mass 10
Mahler: Symphony 2, Symphony 4, Symphony 8
Mozart: Clemenza di Tito (Cpte), Idomeneo (Cpte),
Mass, K317, Mass, K427, Nozze di Figaro (Cpte),
Requiem, Re Pastore (Cpte)
Orff: Carmina Burana
Rachmaninov: Songs, Op.34 (exc)
Rossini: Viaggio a Reims (Cpte)
Sullivan: Yeomen of the Guard (Cpte)
Vivaldi: Gloria, RV589
see CONCERT INDEX under:
(DG) **447 023-2GX12** Mahler—The Symphonies
(PHIL) **426 290-2PH5** Beethoven—Complete
Symphonies
(PHIL) **434 920-2PH** Handel/Mozart—Solo Motets
(PHIL) **442 129-2PH** Sure Thing—The Jerome Kern
Songbook
(PHIL) **446 081-2PH** The Echoing Air—The Music of
Henry Purcell
(TELA) **CD80164** Berlioz—Orchestral Works
(TELA) **CD80250** Barber—Popular Orchestral Works

MACNAMARA, Hilary (pf)
H. Ferguson: Partita, Op. 5b
see CONCERT INDEX under:
(HYPE) **CDA66375** Rachmaninov—Works of Piano
Duet

MCNAUGHT, Graeme (pf)
see CONCERT INDEX under:
(CHAN) **CHAN8960** Copland—Vocal Works

MCNAUGHTON, Tom (sngr)
see CONCERT INDEX under:
(PEAR) **GEMMCDS9053/5** Music from the New York
Stage, Vol. 2: 1908–1913

MCNEELY, Joel (cond)
see OST

MACNEIL, Cornell (bar)
Verdi: Aida (Cpte), Luisa Miller (Cpte)

MACNEVIN, Greg (tuba)
see CONCERT INDEX under:
(CNTO) **CRCD2368** Sullivan—That Glorious Song of
Old

MACOMBER, Curtis (vn)
Beach: Violin Sonata, Op. 34
Corigliano: Violin Sonata

MCPHEE, Colin (pf)
see CONCERT INDEX under:
(PEAR) **GEMMCD9177** Britten—Vocal Works

MACPHERSON, George (bass)
Puccini: Manon Lescaut (Cpte)
Walton: Troilus and Cressida (Cpte)

MCQUEEN, Helen (cor ang)
see CONCERT INDEX under:
(VIRG) **VC7 59520-2** American Orchestral Works

MACRAE, Gordon (sngr)
Rodgers: Carousel (film) (Cpte), Oklahoma (film)
(Cpte)

MAIER, Franzjosef (vn)
Biber: Mystery Sonatas

MAIER, Franzjosef (vn/dir)
Pergolesi: Serva Padrona
see CONCERT INDEX under:
(DHM) 74321 26617-2(1) Elly Ameling - The Early
Recorings, Vols. 1-3

MAIER, Fritz (bass)
R. Strauss: Rosenkavalier (Cpte)

MAIEVSKI, Maurice (ten)
Bizet: Carmen (Cpte)

MAIKL, Georg (ten)
Beethoven: Symphony 9
Wagner: Meistersinger (Cpte)
see CONCERT INDEX under:
(SCHW) 314572 Vienna State Opera Live, Vol.7
(SCHW) 314602 Vienna State Opera Live, Vol.10
(SCHW) 314622 Vienna State Opera Live, Vol.12
(SCHW) 314642 Vienna State Opera Live, Vol.14
(SCHW) 314672 Vienna State Opera Live, Vol.17

MAIKL, Liselotte (sop)
R. Strauss: Ariadne auf Naxos (Cpte), Salome
(Cpte)

MAILE, Hans (vn)
Reger: Piano Trio, op 2
see CONCERT INDEX under:
(SCHW) 311122 Early Twentieth Century Music
(THOR) CTH2012 Copland—Chamber Works

MAILLET, Jean (vn/dir)
see CONCERT INDEX under:
(PIER) PV794114 Graupner—Overtures for
Chalumeaux and Orchestra

MAINKA, Stefan (treb)
see CONCERT INDEX under:
(CAPR) 10 367 Mendelssohn—Motets

MAINZ BACH CHOIR
cond D. HELLMANN
Saint-Saëns: Oratorio de Noël, Op. 12

MAINZ BACH ORCHESTRA
cond D. HELLMANN
Saint-Saëns: Oratorio de Noël, Op. 12

MAINZ WIND ENSEMBLE
(WERG) WER60143-50 Français: Music for Wind
Ensemble
cond K.R. SCHÖLL
see CONCERT INDEX under:
(WERG) WER6087-2 Français plays Français
(WERG) WER60179-50 Egk/Mozart—Wind Music

MAIONE, Orazio (pf)
see CONCERT INDEX under:
(CARL) PCD964 Piano Concertos

MAIONICA, Silvio (bass)
Cilea: Adriana Lecouvreur (Cpte)
Giordano: Fedora (Cpte)
Puccini: Tosca (Cpte)
Verdi: Ballo in maschera (Cpte), Forza del Destino
(Cpte), Traviata (Cpte)
see CONCERT INDEX under:
(DECC) 411 665-2DM3 Puccini: Il trittico

MAIRENA, Manuel (bar)
Falla: Vida breve (Cpte)

MAISENBERG, Oleg (pf)
see CONCERT INDEX under:
(DG) 437 092-2GH Schubert—Violin Sonatinas
(DG) 445 820-2GH Schubert/Liszt—Duos and
Transcriptions
(HARM) HMC90 1301/2 Rachmaninov—Works for 2
Pianos & Piano Duet
(ORFE) C043831A Schubert: Piano Works
(ORFE) C060831A Milhaud: Works for wind and piano
(PRAG) PR250 038 Bartók—Violin and Piano Works

MAISEY, Susan (sop)
Sullivan: Pirates of Penzance (Cpte)

MAISKY, Mischa (vc)
Bach: Goldberg Variations, Solo Cello Suites, Viola
da gamba Sonatas, BWV1027-9
Bloch: Schelomo
Brahms: Double Concerto
Dvořák: Cello Concerto
Elgar: Cello Concerto
Schumann: Cello Concerto
Shostakovich: Cello Concerto 1, Cello Concerto 2
Tchaikovsky: Rococo Variations
see CONCERT INDEX under:
(DG) 423 099-2GH3 Schumann: Symphonies &
Concertos
(DG) 431 544-2GH Meditation
(DG) 431 801-2GH Beethoven—Cello Sonatas, etc
(DG) 435 781-2GH Adagio - Mischa Maisky
(DG) 437 514-2GH Beethoven—Cello Sonatas, etc
(DG) 439 863-2GH Cellissimo
(DG) 439 934-2GH2 Beethoven—Cello Sonatas, etc
(DG) 445 611-2GMA Elgar—Orchestral Works
(EMI) CDM7 63577-2 Franck & Debussy: Cello
Sonatas, etc
(PHIL) 412 230-2PH Works for Cello and Piano

MAISON, René (ten)
Beethoven: Fidelio (Cpte)
see CONCERT INDEX under:
(SCHW) 314542 Vienna State Opera Live, Vol.4

MAÎTRISE DE LA RADIOFFUSION FRANÇAISE
cond J. BARBIROLLI
see CONCERT INDEX under:
(EMI) CZS7 62669-2 French Orchestral Music
cond T. BEECHAM
Bizet: Carmen (Cpte)
cond E. BOUR
Ravel: Enfant et les sortilèges (Cpte)
cond L. MAAZEL
Ravel: Enfant et les Sortilèges (Cpte)
cond S. OZAWA
Bizet: Carmen (Cpte)
cond G. PRÊTRE
Massenet: Werther (Cpte)
cond H. TOMASI
Tomasi: Triomphe de Jeanne

(LA) MAÎTRISE DE LA RÉSURRECTION
cond J. RUDEL
G. Charpentier: Louise (Cpte)

MAÎTRISE NATIONALE DE VERSAILLES CHOIR
cond J-C. MALGOIRE
see CONCERT INDEX under:
(K617) K617026 Les Chemins du Baroque, Vol.2

MAJESKE, Daniel (vn)
see CONCERT INDEX under:
(DECC) 443 175-2DH Mozart—Orchestral Works
(SONY) SM3K45845 Webern—Complete Works

MAJEWSKI, Virginia (va)
see CONCERT INDEX under:
(RCA) GD87965 Dvořák & Brahms: Chamber Works
(RCA) 09026 61778-2(26) The Heifetz Collection, Vol.
26
(RCA) 09026 61778-2(34) The Heifetz Collection, Vol.
34
(RCA) 09026 61778-2(35) The Heifetz Collection, Vol.
35
(RCA) 09026 61778-2(41) The Heifetz Collection, Vol.
41

MAJKUT, Erich (spkr)
see CONCERT INDEX under:
(SCHW) 314602 Vienna State Opera Live, Vol.10

MAJKUT, Erich (ten)
J.Strauss II: Fledermaus (Cpte)
Lehár: Giuditta (exc)
Mozart: Nozze di Figaro (Cpte), Zauberflöte (Cpte)
R. Strauss: Rosenkavalier (Cpte)
Wagner: Meistersinger (Cpte)

MAJOR, Malvina (sop)
Mascagni: Amico Fritz (Cpte)
Mozart: Finta giardiniera (Cpte)

MAKARSKI, Michelle (vn)
see CONCERT INDEX under:
(ECM) 445 350-2 Jarrett—Bridge of Light

MÄKELÄ, Pertti (ten)
Sallinen: Kullervo (Cpte)

MAKKAY, Klára (sop)
Kodály: Missa Brevis

MAKSAKOV, Max (bass-bar)
see CONCERT INDEX under:
(MMOI) CDMOIR422 Great Voices in Tchaikovsky

MAKSAKOVA, Maria (mez)
see CONCERT INDEX under:
(DANT) LYS013/5 Tchaikovsky—The Queen of
Spades

MAKSYMIUK, Jerzy (cond)
see BBC Scottish SO

MAKUSHINA, Tatiana (sop)
see CONCERT INDEX under:
(EMI) CDC7 54839-2 Medtner plays Medtner

MALACHOVSKÝ, Ondrej (bass)
Suchoň: Whirlpool (Cpte)

MALAFRONTE, Judith (mez)
see CONCERT INDEX under:
(KOCH) 37163-2 Bach—Cantatas
(RCA) 09026 60970-2 Motets

MALAGÙ, Stefania (mez)
Catalani: Wally (Cpte)
Giordano: Andrea Chénier (Cpte)
Rossini: Barbiere di Siviglia (Cpte)
Verdi: Macbeth (Cpte), Otello (Cpte), Traviata (Cpte)
see CONCERT INDEX under:
(SONY) M3K79312 Puccini: Il Trittico

MALAKATE, Tina (sop)
see CONCERT INDEX under:
(DHM) 05472 77190-2
Monteverdi—Combattimento/Lamento d'Arianna

MALAKOVA, Petra (mez)
Verdi: Otello (Cpte)

MALANIUK, Ira (contr)
Mozart: Nozze di Figaro (Cpte)
R. Strauss: Arabella (Cpte)
Wagner: Götterdämmerung (Cpte), Meistersinger
(Cpte), Rheingold (exc), Walküre (exc)
see CONCERT INDEX under:
(DECC) 414 100-2DM15 Wagner: Der Ring des
Nibelungen
(EMI) CZS7 67123-2 Wagner: Der Ring des
Nibelungen
(FOYE) 15-CF2011 Wagner—Der Ring de Nibelungen

MALANOTTE, Edmondo (vn)
Vivaldi: Concerti, Op.8 (exc)

MALAS, Spiro (bass)
Donizetti: Elisir d'amore (Cpte), Fille du régiment
(Cpte)
Puccini: Tosca (Cpte)
R. Ward: Crucible (Cpte)
Rossini: Semiramide (Cpte)

MALAS-GODLEWSKA, Ewa (sop)
Jommelli: Armida abbandonata (Cpte)

MALASPINA, Giampiero (bar)
see CONCERT INDEX under:
(EMI) CHS7 69741-2(7) Record of Singing,
Vol.4—Italian School

MALCOLM, George (cond)
see ECO

MALCOLM, George (organ)
Britten: Rejoice in the Lamb
Poulenc: Organ Concerto
see CONCERT INDEX under:
(DECC) 425 627-2DM Poulenc: Choral and Orchestral
Works
(DECC) 430 500-2DWO World of Handel

MALCOLM, George (fp)
see CONCERT INDEX under:
(DECC) 440 474-2DH Mozart—Piano Music for Four
Hands

MALCOLM, George (hpd)
Bach: Flute Sonatas, BWV1030-5
see CONCERT INDEX under:
(DECC) 425 627-2DM Poulenc: Choral and Orchestral
Works
(DECC) 440 033-2DM Harpsichord Concertos
(DECC) 444 390-2DWO The World of The
Harpsichord
(PHIL) 412 632-2PH Recorder Sonatas
(RCA) 09026 61583-2(2) Julian Bream Edition (pt 2)
(RCA) 09026 61583-2(4) Julian Bream Edition (pt 4)
(RCA) 09026 61583-2(5) Julian Bream Edition (pt 5)
(RCA) 09026 61588-2 J. Bream Edition, Vol.5:
Concertos & Sonatas for Lte
(RCA) 09026 61599-2 J. Bream Edition, Vol.16: Julian
Bream & His Friends
(RCA) 09026 61603-2 J. Bream Edition, Vol.20: Bach
(VANG) 08.2003.72 Purcell—Celebrated
Songs,Sacred Airs and Concert Pieces

MAŁCUŻYŃSKI, Witold (pf)
see CONCERT INDEX under:
(EMI) CZS5 68226-2 Witold Malcuzynski—A profile
(POLS) PNCD066 Szymanowski: Piano Works

MALE QUARTET
see CONCERT INDEX under:
(PEAR) GEMMCD9175 Heddle Nash - Serenade
cond W. BRÜCKNER-RÜGGEBERG
Weill: Sieben Todsünden (Cpte)
cond J. PASTERNACK
see CONCERT INDEX under:
(ROMO) 81006-2 Rosa Ponselle (1897-1981)

MALE TRIO
cond F. BLACK
see CONCERT INDEX under:
(ROMO) 81009-2 Edith Mason—Complete
Recordings 1924-1928

MALFITANO, Catherine (sop)
Gounod: Roméo et Juliette (Cpte)
R. Strauss: Salome (Cpte)
Rossini: Stabat Mater

MALGOIRE, Jean-Claude (cond)
see Compagnie Barocco

MALIPIERO, Giovanni (ten)
see CONCERT INDEX under:
(EMI) CHS7 64864-2(2) La Scala Edition - Vol.2,
1915-46 (pt 2)
(EMI) CHS7 69741-2(7) Record of Singing,
Vol.4—Italian School

MALIPONTE, Adriana (sop)
Bizet: Carmen (Cpte)

MALKO, Nicolai (cond)
see Danish RSO

MALLABRERA, André (ten)
Boïeldieu: Voitures Versées (Cpte)
Massenet: Werther (Cpte)
Offenbach: Orphée aux enfers (Cpte)

MALLIÉ, Loïc (organ)
Liszt: Via crucis, S53
Mallié: Improvisation

MALLING, Amalie (pf)
Schoenberg: Piano Concerto
Schumann: Piano Concerto

MALLOCH, William (cond)
see Boston Early Music Sols

MALLOY, Matt (fl)
see CONCERT INDEX under:
(MODE) Mode 28/9 Cage—Roaratorio. Laughtears
etc

MALMBERG, Urban (bar)
Grieg: Peer Gynt (Cpte)
Mendelssohn: Hochzeit des Camacho (Cpte)
Offenbach: Contes d'Hoffmann (Cpte)
R. Strauss: Ariadne auf Naxos (Cpte)

Rossini: Barbiere di Siviglia (Cpte)
Saint-Saëns: Samson et Dalila (Cpte)
Schreker: Schatzgräber (Cpte)

MALMÖ SYMPHONY CHORUS
see CONCERT INDEX under:
(BIS) **BIS-CD437** Schnittke: Orchestral & Vocal Works

MALMÖ SYMPHONY ORCHESTRA
cond M. ATZMON
Pettersson: Symphony 5
cond J. DEPREIST
Shostakovich: Cello Concerto 1, Cello Concerto 2
see CONCERT INDEX under:
(BIS) **BIS-CD437** Schnittke: Orchestral & Vocal Works
(BIS) **BIS-CD501** Martinů—Orchestral Works
(BIS) **BIS-CD570** Malmö Symphony Orchestra
(BIS) **BIS-CD607** Sallinen—Orchestral Works
(BIS) **BIS-CD628** American Trombone Concertos
cond V. HANDLEY
see CONCERT INDEX under:
(CPRI) **CAP21417** Nilsson—Works for Piano and
Orchestra
cond P. JÄRVI
Gade: Violin Concerto, Op. 56
see CONCERT INDEX under:
(BIS) **BIS-CD550** Stenhammar—Vocal and Orchestral
Works
(BIS) **BIS-CD660** Sumera—Symphonies
(BIS) **BIS-CD682** Nystroem—Orchestral Works
(BIS) **BIS-CD690** Sumera—Orchestral Works
cond E. KLAS
Schnittke: Violin Concerto 1, Violin Concerto 2
cond L. MARKIZ
Bloch: Schelomo, Symphony (1903)
Elgar: Cello Concerto
Pettersson: Viola Concerto
Schnittke: Cello Concerto 2, Concerto Grosso 2,
Gogol Suite, In Memoriam, Labyrinths, Viola
Concerto
Schumann: Cello Concerto
cond O. SCHMIDT
Schmidt/Jansson: Öresund Symphony
cond L. SEGERSTAM
see CONCERT INDEX under:
(BIS) **BIS-CD437** Schnittke: Orchestral & Vocal Works
cond O. VÄNSKÄ
see CONCERT INDEX under:
(BIS) **BIS-CD593** Poulenc—Music for Two Pianos

MALMSBURY, Angela (cl)
see CONCERT INDEX under:
(ASV) **CDDCA795** Mozart—Wind Concertos

MALONE, Carol (sop)
Rossini: Cenerentola (Cpte)

MALSBURY, Angela (cl)
see CONCERT INDEX under:
(HYPE) **CDA66573** Prokofiev—Chamber Works

MALSKY, Ken (computer/tape op)
see CONCERT INDEX under:
(BRID) **BCD9031** J. Harvey—Miscellaneous Works

MALTA, Alexander (bass)
Berg: Wozzeck (Cpte)
Bizet: Carmen (exc)
Hindemith: Mathis der Maler (Cpte)
Leoncavallo: Bohème (Cpte)
Mozart: Don Giovanni (Cpte)
Shostakovich: Lady Macbeth of Mtsensk (Cpte)
Verdi: Rigoletto (Cpte), Traviata (Cpte)

MALVISI, Desdemona (sop)
Verdi: Lombardi (Cpte)

MALY, Alexander (bass)
Mozart: Zauberflöte (Cpte)
R. Strauss: Rosenkavalier (Cpte)

MALÝ, Lubomír (va)
Bruckner: String Quintet

MALYON, Julia (sop)
Wagner: Walküre (Cpte)

MAMOU, R (pf)
Field: Nocturnes (exc)

MAN, Annelie de (hpd)
see CONCERT INDEX under:
(BIS) **BIS-CD518** Denisov—Orchestral & Chamber
Works

MANAHAN, George (cond)
see Pro Arte Chorale

MANASEVICH, M.T. (vn)
see CONCERT INDEX under:
(PEAR) **GEMMCDS9001/3(2)** Singers of Imperial
Russia, Vol.2 (pt 2)

MANCA DI NISSA, Bernadette (contr)
Pergolesi: Frate 'nnamorato (Cpte)
Rossini: Gazza ladra (Cpte), Tancredi (Cpte)
Verdi: Falstaff (Cpte)

MANCHAVIN, Yuri (bass)
Tchaikovsky: Eugene Onegin (Cpte)
see CONCERT INDEX under:
(DANT) **LYS013/5** Tchaikovsky—The Queen of
Spades

MANCHESTER CATHEDRAL CHOIR
cond P. MAXWELL DAVIES
see CONCERT INDEX under:
(COLL) **Coll1390-2** Maxwell Davies—Orchestral
Works

MANCHESTER GRAMMAR SCHOOL BOYS' CHOIR
cond M. HANDFORD
Orff: Carmina Burana

MANCHET, Éliane (sop)
Debussy: Pelléas et Mélisande (Cpte)
G. Charpentier: Louise (Cpte)

MANCINI, Caterina (sop)
Rossini: Mosè (Cpte)

MANCINI, Henry (cond)
see Mancini Pops Orch

MANCINI, Luigi (bass)
Verdi: Traviata (Cpte)

MANCINI POPS ORCHESTRA
cond H. MANCINI
see CONCERT INDEX under:
(RCA) **RD60471** Mancini in Surround
(RCA) **RD60706** Cinema Italiano

MANDAC, Evelyn (sop)
Orff: Carmina Burana

MANDARIN, Emmanuel (organ)
see CONCERT INDEX under:
(ERAT) **2292-45825-2** LeJeune—Sacred Works

MANDEAL, Cristian (cond)
see Moldova PO

MANDELLI, Luisa (sop)
Donizetti: Elisir d'amore (Cpte)
Verdi: Rigoletto (Cpte), Traviata (Cpte)

MANDELRING QUARTET
see CONCERT INDEX under:
(LARG) **Largo 5115** Goldschmidt—Letzte Kapitel
(LARG) **Largo 5117** Goldschmidt—Chamber Works
(LARG) **Largo 5128** Goldschmidt—Retrospectrum

MANDIKIAN, Arda (mez)
Britten: Turn of the Screw (Cpte)

MANDONICO, Claudio (cond)
see Brescia Mndl and Gtr Orch

MANDOZZI, Graziano (pf)
see CONCERT INDEX under:
(SCHW) **312622** Wagner—Piano Works, Vol.2

MANDRIN, Emmanuel (cond)
see Demoiselles de Saint-Cyr

MANÉ, Helen (sop)
Donizetti: Messa di Gloria e Credo

MANFRED QUARTET
Schoenberg: String Quartet 1
Smetana: String Quartet 1, String Quartet 2

MANFREDINI, Cécile (sngr)
Lecocq: Jour et la Nuit (Cpte)

MANFRIN, Alain (tbn)
see CONCERT INDEX under:
(ACCO) **20202-2** Poulenc—Chamber Works

MANFRINI, Luigi (bass)
Puccini: Bohème (Cpte)
see CONCERT INDEX under:
(NIMB) **NI7853** Lauri-Volpi sings Verdi

MANGA, Silvana (sngr)
Donizetti: Gianni di Parigi (Cpte)

MANGANOTTI, Gianfranco (ten)
Verdi: Ballo in Maschera (Cpte), Ernani (Cpte)

MANGELSDORFF, Simone (sop)
Wagner: Rheingold (Cpte)
see CONCERT INDEX under:
(DG) **435 211-2GX15** Wagner—Der Ring des
Nibelungen

MANGERSNES, Magnar (cond)
see Bergen Cath Ch

MANGIN, Noel (bass)
Puccini: Bohème (Cpte)

MANHART, Emily (mez)
Bellini: Bianca e Fernando (Cpte)

MANHATTAN CHAMBER ORCHESTRA
cond R. A. CLARK
see CONCERT INDEX under:
(KOCH) **37221-2** Hovhaness—Orchestral Works
(KOCH) **37282-2** Henry Cowell—Chamber Works

MANHATTAN OPERA CHORUS
cond L. BERNSTEIN
Bizet: Carmen (Cpte)

MANHATTAN QUARTET
Shostakovich: String Quartet 6, String Quartet 10
see CONCERT INDEX under:
(SCHW) **310165** Shostakovich—String Quartets

MANIA, Paul (organ)
see CONCERT INDEX under:
(CLAR) **CDGSE78-50-57** Lotte Lehmann sings
Lieder

MANLEY, Paul (cond)
see Primavera CO

MANLEY, Paul (vn)
see CONCERT INDEX under:
(CARL) **PCD809** Vivaldi: Violin Concertos

MANN, Elizabeth (fl)
see CONCERT INDEX under:
(RCA) **09026 68181-2** French Chamber Works

MANN, Paul (spkr)
Glass: Einstein on the Beach (Cpte)

MANN, Robert (vn)
Schoenberg: String Trio
Schumann: Piano Quartet, Op. 47
see CONCERT INDEX under:
(SONY) **S2K47229** Carter—Chamber Works

MANN, Zdeněk (vn)
see CONCERT INDEX under:
(SUPR) **11 1533-2** Suk—Chamber Works, Volume 3

MANNARINI, Ida (mez)
see CONCERT INDEX under:
(PREI) **89016** Gina Cigna (b. 1900)
(PREI) **89023** Conchita Supervia (1895-1936)
(PREI) **89042** Nazzareno de Angelis (1881-1962)
(PREI) **89048** Apollo Granforte (1886-1975) - I

MANNBERG, Karl-Ove (vn)
Pettersson: 2-Violin Sonatas

MANNE, Shelly (perc)
see CONCERT INDEX under:
(EMI) **CMS7 64617-2** The art of Itzhak Perlman
(EMI) **CZS4 83177-2(3)** Itzhak Perlman Edition (pt 3)

MANNES, Leopold (pf)
see CONCERT INDEX under:
(SONY) **SMK58993** Pablo Casals plays Schumann at
Prades, 1952 & 1953

MANNHEIM QUARTET
see CONCERT INDEX under:
(NOVA) **150 006-2** Mozart: Chamber Works

MANNHEIMER, Iréne (pf)
Stenhammar: Late Summer Nights, Piano Concerto
1

MANNING, Frances (sop)
Janáček: Fate (Cpte)

MANNING, Jane (sop)
Berg: Lulu (Cpte)
Lumsdaine: Aria
Schoenberg: Moses and Aron (Cpte), Pierrot
Lunaire
see CONCERT INDEX under:
(CHAN) **CHAN6535** Stravinsky—Symphonies of Wind
Instruments
(CNTI) **CCD1008** Anderson: Mask and other works
(NMC) **NMCD011** Lutyens—Vocal and Chamber
Works
(NMC) **NMCD025** Artists' Series - Jane Manning
(NOVE) **NVLCD109** Weir—Mini-Operas

MANNING, Peter (vn)
see CONCERT INDEX under:
(EMI) **CDC7 54787-2** Janáček—Chamber Works
(HYPE) **CDA66257** Villa-Lobos: Works for Voice and
Strings
(TELA) **CD80387** Pärt—Fratres

MANNING, Rita (vn)
see CONCERT INDEX under:
(SPRO) **SPCV1001** Capital Virtuosi

MANNION, Rosa (sop)
Beethoven: Missa solemnis
Mozart: Ascanio in Alba (Cpte), Così fan tutte (Cpte)

MANNO, Vincenzo (ten)
Verdi: Aroldo (Cpte)

MANNOV, Johannes (bass)
Gade: Comala

MANOWARDA, Josef von (bass)
Wagner: Meistersinger (exc), Tristan und Isolde (exc),
Walküre (exc)
see CONCERT INDEX under:
(SCHW) **314512** Vienna State Opera Live, Vol.1
(SCHW) **314532** Vienna State Opera Live, Vol.3
(SCHW) **314562** Vienna State Opera Live, Vol.6
(SCHW) **314582** Vienna State Opera Live, Vol.8
(SCHW) **314592** Vienna State Opera Live, Vol.9
(SCHW) **314622** Vienna State Opera Live, Vol.12
(SCHW) **314632** Vienna State Opera Live, Vol.13
(SCHW) **314642** Vienna State Opera Live, Vol.14
(SCHW) **314662** Vienna State Opera Live, Vol.16
(SCHW) **314672** Vienna State Opera Live, Vol.17
(TELD) **9031-76442-2** Wagner—Excerpts from the
1936 Bayreuth Festival

MANSINGER, Vera (sop)
see CONCERT INDEX under:
(SCHW) **314602** Vienna State Opera Live, Vol.10

MANSUETO, Gaudio (bass)
see CONCERT INDEX under:
(EMI) **CHS7 64860-2(2)** La Scala Edition - Vol.1,
1878-1914 (pt 2)

MANTOVANI, Alessandro (sngr)
Cavalli: Calisto (Cpte)

MANTOVANI, Dino (bar)
Giordano: Andrea Chénier (Cpte)
Puccini: Fanciulla del West (Cpte), Tosca (Cpte)
Rossini: Barbiere di Siviglia (Cpte)

MANUEL, Paul (sngr)
Bernstein: West Side Story (Cpte)

MANUGUERRA, Matteo (bar)
Mascagni: Cavalleria rusticana (Cpte)
Massenet: Werther (Cpte)
Verdi: Battaglia di Legnano (Cpte), Masnadieri (Cpte),
Stiffelio (Cpte), Traviata (exc)
see CONCERT INDEX under:

(EMI) **CDM7 69500-2** Montserrat Caballé sings Bellini & Verdi Arias

MANURITTA, Giovanni (ten)
see CONCERT INDEX *under:*
(NIMB) **NI7836/7** Conchita Supervia (1895-1936)
(PREI) **89023** Conchita Supervia (1895-1936)

MANZ, Wolfgang (pf)
Dohnányi: Piano Quintet 1
see CONCERT INDEX *under:*
(DINT) **DICD920150** Russian Music for Two Pianos

MANZE, Andrew (cond)
see Cologne Stravaganza

MANZE, Andrew (vn)
see CONCERT INDEX *under:*
(CHAN) **CHAN0519** Telemann—La Changeante
(CHNN) **CCS5894** Pandolfi—Violin Sonatas
(ERAT) **4509-91728-2** Haydn—Piano Trios
(HARM) **HMU90 7091** Three Parts upon a Ground
(HARM) **HMU90 7134/5** Biber—Sonatas and Passagalias

MANZE, Andrew (vn/dir)
Vivaldi: Concerti, Op. 4 (exc)
see CONCERT INDEX *under:*
(CHAN) **CHAN0550** Scheibe—Sinfonias

MANZONE, Jacques Francis (vn)
see CONCERT INDEX *under:*
(EMI) **CDM7 69835-2** Vivaldi—Cello Concertos

MAR, Norman del (cond)
see Aarhus SO

MARAIRE, Dumisani (ngoma/hosho)
see CONCERT INDEX *under:*
(NONE) **7559-79275-2** Pieces of Africa

MARAIRE, Dumisani (voc)
see CONCERT INDEX *under:*
(NONE) **7559-79275-2** Pieces of Africa

MAŘÁK, Otakar (ten)
see CONCERT INDEX *under:*
(SUPR) **11 2136-2(2)** Emmy Destinn—Complete Edition, Discs 3 & 4

MARANDON, Monique (sop)
Rameau: Dardanus (Cpte)

MARANI, Antonio (bass)
Rossini: Torvaldo e Dorliska (Cpte)

MARBÀ, Antoni Ros (cond)
see Madrid SO

MARC, Alessandra (sop)
Beethoven: Symphony 9
Honegger: Roi David (Cpte)
Krenek: Jonny spielt auf (Cpte)
R. Strauss: Friedenstag (Cpte)
Verdi: Requiem (Cpte)
Zemlinsky: Lyrische Symphonie
see CONCERT INDEX *under:*
(DELO) **DE3108** Alessandra Marc—Opera Recital
(DELO) **DE3120** Wagner—Orchestral and Vocal Works
(ODE) **CDMANU1317** Wagner—Opera Excerpts

MARCANGELI, Anna (sop)
see CONCERT INDEX *under:*
(EMI) **CMS7 64165-2** Puccini—Trittico

MARCELLUS, Robert (cl)
see CONCERT INDEX *under:*
(SONY) **SM3K45845** Webern—Complete Works

MARCENO, Antonio (ten)
Verdi: Aida (Cpte)

MARC'HADOUR, Yvon le (bar)
Ravel: Enfant et les sortilèges (Cpte)

MARCHAT, Jean (narr)
Milhaud: Christophe Colomb (Cpte)

MARCHBANK, Peter (cond)
see SABC SO

MARCHESE, Catherine (bn)

MARCHÈSE, Catherine (bn)
see CONCERT INDEX *under:*
(SONY) **SK47184** Glenn Gould—The Composer
(MARC) **8 223636** In Memoriam Lili Boulanger

MARCHI, Alessandro de (hpd/dir)
see CONCERT INDEX *under:*
(ADES) **20271-2** Handel—Roman Cantatas

MARCHIGIANO PHILHARMONIC ORCHESTRA cond G. KUHN
Mozart: Così fan tutte (Cpte), Don Giovanni (Cpte)

MARCHIGIANO VINCENZO BELLINI LYRIC CHORUS cond G. KUHN
Mozart: Così fan tutte (Cpte), Don Giovanni (Cpte)

MARCHWINSKI, Jerzy (pf)
see CONCERT INDEX *under:*
(POLS) **PNCD065** Szymanowski: Chamber Works
(POLS) **PNCD067** Szymanowski: Songs

MARCONI, Francesco (ten)
see CONCERT INDEX *under:*
(EMI) **CHS7 64860-2(1)** La Scala Edition - Vol.1, 1878-1914 (pt 1)
(NIMB) **NI7840/1** The Era of Adelina Patti
(PEAR) **GEMMCDS9923(1)** Covent Garden on Record, Vol.1 (pt 1)
(SYMP) **SYMCD1069** The Harold Wayne Collection, Vol.2

(SYMP) **SYMCD1073** The Harold Wayne Collection, Vol.3

MARCOVICI, Silvia (vn)
see CONCERT INDEX *under:*
(BIS) **BIS-CD372** Sibelius: Orchestral Works

MARCUS, Marshall (vn)
Rossini: Sonate a Quattro

MARDONES, José (bass)
see CONCERT INDEX *under:*
(PEAR) **GEMMCDS9074(1)** Giovanni Zenatello, Vol.2 (pt 1)
(TEST) **SBT1008** Viva Rossini

MARÉCHAL, Jaqueline (sngr)
Lecocq: Rose Mousse (Cpte)

MARÉCHAL, Maurice (vc)
see CONCERT INDEX *under:*
(EMI) **CDC5 55036-2** Honegger/Poulenc—Perform their own works
(PEAR) **GEMMCD9348** Debussy: Orchestral & Chamber Works

MAREŠ, Vlastimil (cl)
see CONCERT INDEX *under:*
(SUPR) **11 0767-2** Martinů—Cantatas

MARESTIN, Valérie (sop)
Auber: Gustav III (Cpte)

MARETTE, Fany (sngr)
Hahn: Mozart (Cpte)

MARGALIT, Israela (pf)
Brahms: Piano Concerto 1
Korngold: Piano Trio, Op.1, Violin Sonata, Op.6
Mendelssohn: Capriccio brillant, Op. 22
Prokofiev: Piano Concerto 3
Saint-Saëns: Piano Concerto 2
Schumann: Piano Concerto
see CONCERT INDEX *under:*
(CHAN) **CHAN8582** Beethoven: Piano Sonatas
(EMI) **CDC5 55399-2** Delius—Chamber Works
(EMI) **CDC5 55400-2** Barber—Chamber and Instrumental Works
(KOCH) **37143-2** Grieg—Lyric Pieces
(KOCH) **37143-2** Schnittke/Shostakovich—Piano Concertos

MARGIONO, Charlotte (sop)
Beethoven: Fidelio (Cpte), Missa Solemnis
Brahms: Deutsches Requiem, Op. 45 (Cpte)
Mozart: Così fan tutte (Cpte), Don Giovanni (Cpte), Finta Giardiniera (Cpte), Nozze di Figaro (Cpte)
see CONCERT INDEX *under:*
(TELD) **2292-46452-2** Beethoven—Complete Symphonies

MARGISON, Richard (ten)
Beethoven: Symphony 9
Tchaikovsky: Mazeppa (Cpte)

MARGITA, Štefan (ten)
Martinů: Gilgamesh
Myslivecek: Bellerofonte (Cpte)

MARGOT, François (organ)
Gounod: Mass 2, Requiem

MARHERR-WAGNER, Elfriede (mez)
Mozart: Zauberflöte (exc)
Wagner: Götterdämmerung (exc)
see CONCERT INDEX *under:*
(EMI) **CMS7 64008-2(2)** Wagner Singing on Record (pt 2)
(LYRC) **LCD146** Frida Leider sings Wagner
(NIMB) **NI7848** Great Singers at the Berlin State Opera
(PEAR) **GEMMCDS9137** Wagner—Der Ring des Nibelungen
(PEAR) **GEMMCD9331** Frida Leider sings Wagner

MARIATEGUI, Suso (ten)
Verdi: Traviata (Cpte)

MARIETTI, Ines (sop)
Verdi: Traviata (Cpte)

MARIMPIETRI, Lydia (sop)
Catalani: Wally (Cpte)
Cherubini: Medea (Cpte)
see CONCERT INDEX *under:*
(EMI) **CMS7 64165-2** Puccini—Trittico

MARIN, Ion (cond)
see ECO

MARIN, José (sop)
Sorozábal: Katiuska (Cpte)

MARIN, Susana (pf)
see CONCERT INDEX *under:*
(RNE) **M3/03** Piano Works by Spanish Women Composers

MARINCOLA, Federico (gtr)
see CONCERT INDEX *under:*
(PIER) **PV794052** G. Morlaye—Pieces for Lute & Guitar

MARINCOLA, Federico (lte)
see CONCERT INDEX *under:*
(PIER) **PV794052** G. Morlaye—Pieces for Lute & Guitar

MARIN-DEGOR, Sophie (sop)
Dauvergne: Troqueurs (Cpte)
Gluck: Rencontre imprévue (Cpte)
Lully: Alceste (Cpte)
Mouret: Amours de Ragonde (Cpte)

Purcell: Dido (Cpte)

MARINKOVIC, Mateja (vn)
Reger: Preludes and Fugues, Op. 117 (exc), Preludes and Fugues, Op. 131a
see CONCERT INDEX *under:*
(ASV) **CDDCA868** Schnittke—Chamber Music, Volume 1

MARINOV, Pali (bass)
Stravinsky: Noces

MARINS, Elsa (ob)
see CONCERT INDEX *under:*
(CHNT) **LDC278 869/70** Villa-Lobos—Guitar Works

MARINUZZI, Gino (cond)
see EIAR Orch

MARION, Alain (fl)
Vivaldi: Concerti, Op.10
see CONCERT INDEX *under:*
(TIMP) **1C1010** Honegger—Chamber Works, Vol.3
(TIMP) **4C1012** Honegger—Chamber Works

MARION, Gloria (sop)
see CONCERT INDEX *under:*
(CLUB) **CL99-025** Giovanni Zenatello (1876-1949)
(PEAR) **GEMMCDS9074(2)** Giovanni Zenatello, Vol.2 (pt 2)
(PREI) **89038** Giovanni Zenatello (1876-1949)

MARIOTTI, Alfredo (bass)
Catalani: Wally (Cpte)
Mozart: Don Giovanni (Cpte)
Puccini: Bohème (Cpte), Tosca (Cpte)
Verdi: Macbeth (Cpte)
see CONCERT INDEX *under:*
(DECC) **436 261-2DHO3** Puccini—Il Trittico
(DECC) **436 301-2DA** Renata Tebaldi & Franco Corelli—Arias & Duets
(SONY) **M3K79312** Puccini: Il Trittico

MARIOTTI, Deborah (gtr)
see CONCERT INDEX *under:*
(EMI) **CZS7 67435-2** Rodrigo—Orchestral Works

MARKELOV, Yury (ten)
Rimsky-Korsakov: Tsar's Bride (Cpte)

MARKERT, Annette (contr)
Eisler: Deutsche Sinfonie
Handel: Floridante (Cpte)
R. Strauss: Salome (Cpte)
Saint-Saëns: Oratorio de Noël, Op. 12
see CONCERT INDEX *under:*
(CHRI) **CHR77119** Telemann—Cantatas for Alto

MARKEVITCH, Igor (cond)
see Concertgebouw

MARKGRAF, Wolfgang (bass)
Wagner: Meistersinger (exc)

MARKHAM, Ralph (pf)
Vaughan Williams: 2-Piano Concerto

MARKHAM, Richard (pf)
Rossini: Petite Messe Solennelle
see CONCERT INDEX *under:*
(CONI) **CDCF228** Arnold—Concertos
(CONI) **CDCF240** Arnold—Orchestral Works

MARKHOFF, Franz (bass)
see CONCERT INDEX *under:*
(SCHW) **314622** Vienna State Opera Live, Vol.12
(SCHW) **314642** Vienna State Opera Live, Vol.14

MARKIZ, Lev (cond)
see Amsterdam Nieuw Sinfonietta

MÄRKL, Markus (hpd)
see CONCERT INDEX *under:*
(HARM) **HMC90 1505** German Baroque Songs

MARKOV, Alexander (vn)
Paganini: Violin Concerto 1, Violin Concerto 2

MARKOV, Sabin (bass)
Mussorgsky: Boris Godunov (Cpte)
Puccini: Turandot (Cpte)

MARKOVÁ, Jiřina (sop)
Janáček: Excursions of Mr Brouček (Cpte)
Martinů: Miracles of Mary (Cpte)
Smetana: Dalibor (Cpte)
see CONCERT INDEX *under:*
(SONY) **SK45633** Edita Gruberová—Opera Arias
(STUD) **SM1223.27** Rossini—Complete unpublished Sacred Works

MARKOVICH, Alexander (pf)
Beethoven: Violin Sonata 9
Brahms: Violin Sonata 2
see CONCERT INDEX *under:*
(DG) **445 657-2GH** Bach/Beethoven/Mozart—Works for Violin and Piano
(TELD) **4509-90846-2** Trumpet Concertos
(TELD) **4509-94554-2** Carmen Fantasy—Virtuoso Music for Trumpet
(TELD) **9031-76349-2** Classical Violin Sonatas
(TELD) **9031-77705-2** Works for Trumpet & Piano

MARKOW, Emil (bass)
see CONCERT INDEX *under:*
(RCA) **GD87799** The Pearl Fishers Duet plus Duets and Scenes

MARKOWSKI, Andrzej (cond)
see Warsaw Nat PO

MARKS, Alan (pf)
Schumann: Fantasie, Piano Sonata 3
see CONCERT INDEX *under:*

(LARG) **Largo 5115** Goldschmidt—Letzte Kapitel

MARKS, Alfred (bar)
Berlin: Annie Get Your Gun (Cpte)
Gay: Beggar's Opera (Cpte)

MARKSON, Gerhard (cond)
see Hagen PO

MARKSON, Virginia (fl)
see CONCERT INDEX under:
(CBC) **SMCD5119** Adeste Fideles

MARKUS, Karl (ten)
Marschner: Hans Heiling (Cpte)
Weill: Sieben Todsünden (Cpte)

MARKWORT, Peter (ten)
R. Strauss: Elektra (Cpte)
Weill: Mahagonny (Cpte)

MARLBOROUGH FESTIVAL ORCHESTRA
cond A. SCHNEIDER
Beethoven: Triple Concerto

MARLEYN, Paul (vc)
see CONCERT INDEX under:
(UNIT) **88006-2** Russian Cello Sonatas

MARLOW, Richard (cond)
see Fretwork

MARLOW, Richard (organ)
see CONCERT INDEX under:
(CONI) **CDCF501** Carols from Trinity

MARLOWE, Anthony (ten)
Wagner: Tristan und Isolde (Cpte)

MARLOWE, Sylvia (hpd)
see CONCERT INDEX under:
(SONY) **SM2K47533** Music inspired by the Jewish
Religion

MAROTO, Francisco (sngr)
Sorozábal: Katiuska (Cpte)

MÁROVÁ, Libuše (mez)
Fibich: Bride of Messina (Cpte)
Janáček: Cunning Little Vixen (Cpte), Excursions of
Mr Brouček (Cpte)
Smetana: Kiss (Cpte)
see CONCERT INDEX under:
(DECC) **421 852-2DH2** Janáček: Operatic & Chamber
Works

MARRINER, Andrew (cl)
Weber: Clarinet Concerto 1, Clarinet Concerto 2

MARRINER, Sir Neville (cond)
see ASMF

MARRINER, Sir Neville (vn)
see CONCERT INDEX under:
(VANG) **08.2003.72** Purcell—Celebrated
Songs,Sacred Airs and Concert Pieces

MARS, Jacques (bar)
Bizet: Carmen (Cpte), Pêcheurs de perles (Cpte)
Poulenc: Dialogues des Carmélites (Cpte)

MARSALIS, Wynton (cornet)
see CONCERT INDEX under:
(SONY) **MK42137** Carnaval—Wynton Marsalis

MARSALIS, Wynton (tpt)
see CONCERT INDEX under:
(SONY) **MK39061** Let the bright Seraphim
(SONY) **MK39310** Haydn Concertos
(SONY) **SK37846** Trumpet Concertos
(SONY) **SK42478** Baroque Music for Trumpets
(SONY) **SK46672** Baroque Duets
(SONY) **SK47193** 20th Century Music for Trumpet
(SONY) **SK48235** A Carnegie Hall Christmas Concert
(SONY) **SK57497** Wynton Marsalis—The London
Concert

MARSCHALL, Eberhard (bn)
Mozart: Bassoon Concerto, K191

MARSCHALL, Werner (ten)
Hindemith: Nusch-Nuschi (Cpte)

MARSCHNER, Wolfgang (vn)
see CONCERT INDEX under:
(ORFE) **C197891A** Hindemith & Berg: Orchestral
Works

MARSH, Calvin (bar)
Rossini: Barbiere di Siviglia (Cpte)

MARSH, Jane (sop)
Schoeck: Penthesilea (Cpte)

MARSH, Lucy Isabelle (sop)
see CONCERT INDEX under:
(RCA) **09026 61879-2** Grieg—Historic Recordings

MARSHALL, Frank (pf)
see CONCERT INDEX under:
(NIMB) **NI7836/7** Conchita Supervia (1895-1936)

MARSHALL, Ingram (elec)
I. Marshall: Alcatraz

MARSHALL, Ingram (synth)
I. Marshall: Alcatraz

MARSHALL, Jane (cor ang)
Buller: Theatre of Memory

MARSHALL, Kimberly (organ)
see CONCERT INDEX under:
(AUVI) **V4645** The Historical Spanish Organ, Vol.
1—A. de Cabézon

MARSHALL, Larry (ten)
Beethoven: Missa Solemnis
Gershwin: Porgy and Bess (exc)

MARSHALL, Lois (sop)
see CONCERT INDEX under:
(EMI) **CHS7 63715-2** Mozart: Die Entführung, etc

MARSHALL, Margaret (sop)
Bach: Mass in B minor, BWV232 (Cpte), St Matthew
Passion, BWV244 (Cpte)
Elgar: Light of Life (Cpte)
Gluck: Orfeo ed Euridice (Cpte)
Handel: Messiah (exc)
Haydn: Mass 10, Schöpfung (Cpte)
Mozart: Litanies, K243, Mass, K317, Vespers, K321
Pergolesi: Stabat Mater
see CONCERT INDEX under:
(CHAN) **CHAN8788/9** Elgar—The Kingdom;
Orchestral Works
(DG) **437 719-2GC** Berg—Vocal Works
(EMIL) **CDZ7 67015-2** Mozart—Opera Arias
(PHIL) **420 648-2PM** Vivaldi: Sacred Choral Music,
Vol.1
(PHIL) **420 649-2PM** Vivaldi: Sacred Choral Music,
Vol.2
(PHIL) **422 522-2PME6** The Complete Mozart Edition
Vol 22
(PHIL) **432 416-2PH3** Haydn—L'incontro
improvviso/Arias

MARSHALL, Melanie (mez)
Purcell: Dido (Cpte)

MARSHALL, Wayne (organ)
Saint-Saëns: Symphony 3
see CONCERT INDEX under:
(CLLE) **COLCD118** I Will lift up mine eyes
(EMI) **CDC5 55048-2** Pulling out the stops!

MARSHALL, Wayne (hpd)
see CONCERT INDEX under:
(CLLE) **COLCD117** Rutter—Fancies

MARSHALL, Wayne (pf)
Gershwin: Porgy and Bess (Cpte)
see CONCERT INDEX under:
(VIRG) **VC7 59520-2** American Orchestral Works

MARSHEV, Oleg (pf)
see CONCERT INDEX under:
(DANA) **DACOCD391** Prokofiev—Piano Music -
Volume 1
(DANA) **DACOCD392** Prokofiev—Piano Music -
Volume 2

MARŠÍK, Bohumil (bass)
Janáček: Excursions of Mr Brouček (Cpte)
Martinů: Miracles of Mary (Cpte)

MARŠÍK, Bohuslav (bass)
Smetana: Dalibor (Cpte)

MARSON, John (hp)
Buller: Theatre of Memory

MARTEAU, Henri (vn)
see CONCERT INDEX under:
(SYMP) **SYMCD1071** Great Violinists, Vol.1

MARTELLI, Dominic (treb)
see CONCERT INDEX under:
(HYPE) **CDA66219** American Choral Works

MARTI, Bernabé (ten)
Bellini: Pirata (Cpte)
see CONCERT INDEX under:
(CFP) **CD-CFP4569** Puccini: Arias
(EMI) **CDM7 69500-2** Montserrat Caballé sings Bellini
& Verdi Arias

MARTIKAINEN, Olli-Pekka (perc)
(ONDI) **ODE802-2** Ibert/Jolivet/Nielsen—Flute
Concertos

MARTIN, Andrea (bar)
J. Strauss II: Fledermaus (Cpte)
Mozart: Così fan tutte (Cpte)
Salieri: Axur (Cpte)
see CONCERT INDEX under:
(NAXO) **8 550435** Mozart—Arias and Duets
(NAXO) **8 550495** Mozart—Sacred Choral Works

MARTIN, Andrew (vn)
see CONCERT INDEX under:
(CHAN) **CHAN8319** Encore! An Hour with Cantilena

MARTIN, David (pf)
see CONCERT INDEX under:
(CAMP) **RR2CD1331/2** Havergal Brian—Orchestral
Works

MARTIN, Drew (ten)
see CONCERT INDEX under:
(MUSM) **67110-2** Stravinsky—The Composer,
Volume V

MARTIN, Frank (cond)
see BPO

MARTIN, Frank (pf)
Martin: Vin herbé
see CONCERT INDEX under:
(CLAV) **CD50-9327** Lieder Recital—Heinz Rehfuss
(JECK) **JD563-2** Frank Martin interprets Frank
Martin

MARTIN, Ion (cond)
see Venice La Fenice Orch

MARTIN, Jaime (fl)
Falla: Harpsichord Concerto
see CONCERT INDEX under:
(ASV) **CDDCA922** Arnold—Clarinet Concertos

MARTIN, Janis (mez)
Janáček: Glagolitic Mass (Cpte)

MARTIN, Janis (sop)
Hindemith: Gesänge, Op. 9
Wagner: Rienzi (Cpte)
Zemlinsky: Traumgörge (Cpte)
see CONCERT INDEX under:
(SONY) **SMK48466** Boulez conducts
Schoenberg—Volume 3

MARTIN, Jean (pf)
Fauré: Nocturnes (exc), Thème et Variations, Op. 73
see CONCERT INDEX under:
(ARIO) **ARN268240** Weber—Piano Works
(NAXO) **8 550795** Fauré—Nocturnes, Volume 2
(NAXO) **8 550932** Reger—Piano Works

MARTIN, Joan (contr)
Falla: Retablo de Maese Pedro (Cpte)

MARTIN, Laurent (pf)
Alkan: Esquisses, Op. 63, Préludes, Op.31
see CONCERT INDEX under:
(MARC) **8 223500** Alkan—Piano Works
(MARC) **8 223657** Alkan—Piano Works

MARTIN, Marvis (sop)
Canteloube: Chants d'Auvergne (exc)

MARTIN, Mary (sngr)
Berlin: Annie get your Gun (Cpte)

MARTIN, Marya (fl)
Rorem: Bright Music

MARTIN, Michel (alto)
Offenbach: Madame l'Archiduc (Cpte)

MARTIN, Milagros (sop)
Bretón: Verbena de La Paloma (Cpte)

MARTIN, Philip (pf)
see CONCERT INDEX under:
(ALTA) **AIR-CD-9011** Philip Martin—Chamber & Vocal
Works
(CNTI) **CCD1007** Reizenstein: Piano Works
(HYPE) **CDA66459** Gottschalk—Piano works
(HYPE) **CDA66697** Gottschalk—Piano Music, Volume
2
(MARC) **8 223732** Addinsell—British Light Music

MARTIN, Thomas (db)
see CONCERT INDEX under:
(ASV) **CDDCA563** Works by Bottesini
(ASV) **CDDCA907** Bottesini—Volume 3 - Passioni
Amorose

MARTIN, Wolfgang (cond)
see Berlin St Op Orch

MARTINEAU, Annette (sngr)
Bazin: Voyage en Chine (Cpte)
Messager: Basoche (Cpte)
see CONCERT INDEX under:
(MUSD) **20239-2** Delibes—Opéras-Comiques

MARTINEAU, Malcolm (fp)
see CONCERT INDEX under:
(CLRI) **CC0004** The Early Clarinet Family

MARTINEAU, Malcolm (pf)
Britten: Folk Songs (exc)
Schubert: Schwanengesang, D957 (Cpte)
see CONCERT INDEX under:
(ASV) **CDDCA787** Finzi/Stanford—Clarinet
Concertos, etc
(ASV) **CDDCA891** Pastoral - British Clarinet Music
(ASV) **CDDCA922** Arnold—Clarinet Concertos
(CHAN) **CHAN9147** French Songs
(CHAN) **CHAN9277** French Songs
(CRD) **CRD3476** Fauré—Chansons, Vol.1
(CRD) **CRD3477** Fauré—Chansons, Vol.2
(DG) **445 294-2GH** Schubert—Lieder
(DG) **445 946-2GH** Bryn Terfel—The Vagabond
(EMIN) **CD-EMX2224** Schubert—Recital
(UNIT) **88016-2** Dweller in my Deathless Dreams

MARTINELLI, Germaine (sop)
(EMI) **CMS7 64008-2(1)** Wagner Singing on Record
(pt 1)

MARTINELLI, Giovanni (ten)
Verdi: Otello (Cpte)
see CONCERT INDEX under:
(MEMO) **HR4408/9(2)** Singers in Genoa, Vol.1 (disc
2)
(MMOI) **CDMOIR428** Rosa Ponselle and Giovanni
Martinelli sing Verdi
(NIMB) **NI7804** Giovanni Martinelli—Opera Recital
(NIMB) **NI7805** Rosa Ponselle—Opera & Song
Recital
(NIMB) **NI7846** Rosa Ponselle, Vol.2
(NIMB) **NI7856** Legendary Tenors
(PEAR) **GEMMCDS9452** The Emperor Tibbett
(PEAR) **GEMMCDS9925(1)** Covent Garden on
Record—Vol.3 (pt 1)
(PEAR) **GEMMCDS9926(2)** Covent Garden on
Record—Vol.4 (pt 2)
(PEAR) **GEMMCD9306** Ezio Pinza—Opera Recital
(PREI) **89062** Giovanni Martinelli (1885-1969)
(RCA) **GD87810** Rosa Ponselle - Opera & Song
Recital

(RCA) 09026 61580-2(2) RCA/Met 100 Singers, 100
Years (pt 2)
(ROMO) 81002-2 Emmy Destinn (1878-1930)
(ROMO) 81006-2 Rosa Ponselle (1897-1981)
(ROMO) 81007-2 Rosa Ponselle—Victor Recordings
1926-1929
(SUPR) 11 2136-2(5) Emmy Destinn—Complete
Edition, Discs 11 & 12
(TEST) SBT1005 Ten Top Tenors
(TEST) SBT1008 Viva Rossini

MARTINEZ, Dominick (treb)
Puccini: Tosca (Cpte)

MARTINEZ, Ivo (treb)
Puccini: Tosca (Cpte)

MARTINEZ, Odaline de la (cond)
see BBC PO

MARTINEZ, Sébastien (sngr)
Gounod: Sapho (Cpte)

MARTINI, Juan E. (cond)
see orch

MARTINI, Luise (sop)
J.Strauss II: Fledermaus (Cpte)

MARTINO, Adriane (mez)
see CONCERT INDEX under:
(DG) 419 257-2GH3 'Cav' and 'Pag', etc

MARTINO, Vito (ten)
Rossini: Siège de Corinthe (Cpte)

MARTINON, Jean (cond)
see FRNO

MARTINOTTI, Bruno (cond)
see Verona Arena Orch

MARTINOVICH, Boris (bass-bar)
Borodin: Prince Igor (Cpte)
Glinka: Life for the Tsar (Cpte)
Mussorgsky: Boris Godunov (Cpte)
see CONCERT INDEX under:
(RCA) 09026 61236-2 Leontyne Price - Prima Donna
Collection

MARTINPELTO, Hillevi (sop)
C.P.E. Bach: Auferstehung und Himmelfahrt Jesu
(Cpte)
Haeffner: Electra (Cpte)
Handel: Dixit Dominus
Lidholm: Dream Play (Cpte)
Mozart: Idomeneo (Cpte), Nozze di Figaro (Cpte)
Roman: Swedish Mass
Spohr: Faust (Cpte)

MARTINS, João Carlos (pf)
Bach: Goldberg Variations

MARTINŮ STRING QUARTET
see CONCERT INDEX under:
(ROMA) RR1941 Terezín - The Music 1941-44

MARTINUCCI, Nicola (ten)
Donizetti: Poliuto (Cpte)
Leoncavallo: Pagliacci (Cpte)
Puccini: Tabarro (Cpte), Turandot (Cpte)
Verdi: Aida (Cpte)

MARTIS, Delia de (sop)
see CONCERT INDEX under:
(PREI) 89008 Irene Minghini-Cattaneo (1892-1944)

MARTON, Eva (sop)
Bartók: Duke Bluebeard's Castle (Cpte)
Boito: Mefistofele (Cpte)
Catalani: Wally (Cpte)
Giordano: Andrea Chénier (Cpte)
Korngold: Violanta (Cpte)
Puccini: Fanciulla del West (Cpte), Tosca (Cpte),
Turandot (Cpte)
R. Strauss: Elektra (Cpte)
Respighi: Semirama (Cpte)
Wagner: Götterdämmerung (Cpte), Lohengrin (Cpte),
Siegfried (Cpte), Walküre (Cpte)
see CONCERT INDEX under:
(ACAN) 43 266 Bernd Weikl—Operatic Recital
(SONY) MK39097 Puccini Heroines
(SONY) SX14K48198 Mahler—Complete
Symphonies, etc

MARTOS, Maria José (sop)
Vives: Bohemios (Cpte)

MARTVON, Juraj (bar)
Suchoň: Whirlpool (Cpte)

MARTVONOVA, Anna (sop)
Suchoň: Whirlpool (Cpte)

MARTYNOV, Alexei (ten)
Karetnikov: Till Eulenspiegel (Cpte)
see CONCERT INDEX under:
(CDM) LDC238 038/40 Rimsky-Korsakov—Complete
Songs

MARTZY, Johanna (vn)
Brahms: Violin Concerto
Mendelssohn: Violin Concerto, Op.64

MARUSIN, Yuri (ten)
Prokofiev: War and Peace (Cpte)

MARVIN, Frederick (pf)
see CONCERT INDEX under:
(DORI) DIS80110 Dussek—Piano Sonatas, Volume
1
(DORI) DIS80125 Dussek—Piano Works, Volume 2

MARVIN, Stephen (vn)
see CONCERT INDEX under:
(SONY) SK48044 Vivaldi—Concertos for Strings

MARWOOD, Anthony (va)
Fauré: Piano Quintet 1, Piano Quintet 2

MARWOOD, Catherine (va)
Maxwell Davies: Strathclyde Concerto 5

(THE) MARWOOD ENSEMBLE
see CONCERT INDEX under:
(COLL) Coll1438-2 Françaix—Chamber Works

**MARYLAND UNIVERSITY CHORUS
cond A. DORATI**
Beethoven: Missa Solemnis

MARZOLLO, Dick (cond)
see SO

MAS, Margaret (sop)
see CONCERT INDEX under:
(EMI) CMS7 64165-2 Puccini—Trittico

MAS CONDE, Salvador (cond)
see Limburg SO

MASARYK, Jan (pf)
see CONCERT INDEX under:
(SUPR) 11 1491-2 Jarmila Novotna sings Czech
Songs and Arias

MASCAGNI, Pietro (cond)
see Holland Italian Op Orch

MASCAGNI, Pietro (pf)
see CONCERT INDEX under:
(SYMP) SYMCD1073 The Harold Wayne Collection,
Vol.3

MASCHERINI, Enzo (bar)
Verdi: Macbeth (Cpte)
see CONCERT INDEX under:
(CENT) CRC2164 Ferruccio Tagliavini—Early
Operatic Recordings

MASCHERONI, Edoardo (pf)
see CONCERT INDEX under:
(SYMP) SYMCD1111 The Harold Wayne Collection,
Vol.11

MASE, Raymond (tpt)
see CONCERT INDEX under:
(DG) 427 335-2GH Copland—Orchestral Works
(KOCH) 37141-2 Wolpe—Chamber Works

MASETTI, Umberto (pf)
see CONCERT INDEX under:
(PEAR) GEMMCDS9007/9(1) Singers of Imperial
Russia, Vol.4 (pt 1)

MASIMENKO, Eugene (bass-bar)
Kabalevsky: Colas Breugnon (Cpte)

MASINI, Galliano (ten)
see CONCERT INDEX under:
(EMI) CHS7 64864-2(2) La Scala Edition - Vol.2,
1915-46 (pt 2)

MASINI, Gian-Franco (cond)
see Grudgionz Fest Orch

MASINI, Guglielmo (bass)
see CONCERT INDEX under:
(EMI) CHS7 64864-2(1) La Scala Edition - Vol.2,
1915-46 (pt 1)

MASINI, Mafalda (mez)
Rossini: Italiana in Algeri (Cpte)

MASINI, Paolo (ten)
see CONCERT INDEX under:
(CLUB) CL99-509/10 Hina Spani (1896-1969)

MASKELL, Robert (hn)
see CONCERT INDEX under:
(CALA) CACD1017 French Chamber Music for
Woodwinds, Volume 1

MASKOVÁ, Dagmar (sop)
Liszt: Dante Symphony

MASLENNIKOV, Alexei (ten)
Mussorgsky: Boris Godunov (Cpte)
Shostakovich: Gamblers (Cpte)

MASON, Anne (mez)
see CONCERT INDEX under:
(OPRA) ORCH104 A Hundred Years of Italian Opera:
1820-1830

MASON, Anne (sop)
Donizetti: Emilia di Liverpool (Cpte), Eremitaggio di
Liverpool (Cpte)
Mayr: Medea (Cpte)
Mozart: Nozze di Figaro (Cpte)
see CONCERT INDEX under:
(OPRA) ORCH103 Italian Opera—1810-20

MASON, Barry (gtr)
see CONCERT INDEX under:
(AMON) CD-SAR45 Masters of the Baroque Guitar

MASON, Berkeley (pf)
see CONCERT INDEX under:
(EMI) CDS7 54607-2 Stravinsky plays and conducts
Stravinsky

MASON, Colin Scott (bar)
see CONCERT INDEX under:
(CLLE) COLCD115 Three Musical Fables

MASON, David (cond)
see Combattimento

MASON, Edith (sop)
see CONCERT INDEX under:
(ROMO) 81009-2 Edith Mason—Complete
Recordings 1924-1928
(SYMP) SYMCD1136 Opera in Chicago, Vol.1

MASON, Frances (vn)
see CONCERT INDEX under:
(EMI) CDM5 65101-2 A Warlock Centenary Album

MASON, Captain John R. (cond)
see HM Royal Marines Band, Portsmouth

MASON, Patrick (bar)
see CONCERT INDEX under:
(BRID) BCD9014 Elliott Carter: Vocal Works

MASON, Ralph (ten)
Janáček: Fate (Cpte)

MASON, Timothy (rec)
Mozart: Piano Quartet, K478, Piano Quartet, K493
see CONCERT INDEX under:
(L'OI) 411 949-2OH Telemann: Double & Triple
Concertos

MASON, William (bass)
G. Charpentier: Louise (Cpte)
Puccini: Bohème (Cpte)
Tchaikovsky: Eugene Onegin (Cpte)

MASOTTI, Giovanni (bass)
see CONCERT INDEX under:
(SYMP) SYMCD1126 The Harold Wayne Collection,
Vol.14

MASSA, Fulvio (ten)
Rossini: Occasione fa il ladro (Cpte), Scala di Seta
(Cpte), Signor Bruschino (Cpte)

MASSARD, Robert (bar)
Audran: Poupée (exc)
Berlioz: Benvenuto Cellini (Cpte)
Bizet: Carmen (Cpte)
Ganne: Saltimbanques (exc)
Gounod: Faust (Cpte)
Milhaud: Christophe Colomb (Cpte)

**MASSED BRASS BANDS
cond J. H. ILES**
see CONCERT INDEX under:
(BEUL) 1PD2 Crystal Palace Champions

**MASSENET FESTIVAL CHORUS
cond P. FOURNILLIER**
Massenet: Cléopâtre (Cpte)

MASSET, Françoise (sop)
see CONCERT INDEX under:
(ERAT) 4509-91722-2
Charpentier/Grigny/Lully—Sacred Choral and Organ
works

MASSEURS, Peter (tpt)
see CONCERT INDEX under:
(DECC) 433 702-2DH Shostakovich—Orchestral
Works
(DECC) 444 455-2DH Martin—Ballades; Concerto for
7 Wind Instruments
(ETCE) KTC1051 Berg. Schoenberg. Webern. Songs

MASSEY, Roy (cond)
see Hereford Cath Ch

MASSEY, Roy (organ)
Saint-Saëns: Mass, Op. 4

MASSIS, Annick (sop)
Rameau: Hippolyte et Aricie (Cpte)

MASSIS, René (bass-bar)
Chausson: Roi Arthus (Cpte)
Gluck: Iphigénie en Tauride (Cpte)
Halévy: Juive (Cpte)

MASSON, Diego (cond)
see English Northern Philh

MASSON, Luis (bass)
Fénelon: Chevalier Imaginaire (Cpte)
Vivaldi: Montezuma (Cpte)

MASSOT, Michel (tuba)
Boesmans: Extase

MASSOZ, Claude (bass)
Massenet: Cléopâtre (Cpte)

MASSUE, Nicholas (ten)
Verdi: Otello (Cpte)
see CONCERT INDEX under:
(PEAR) GEMMCDS9926(2) Covent Garden on
Record—Vol.4 (pt 2)

MASTERS, Rachel (hp)
Mozart: Flute and Harp Concerto, K299
see CONCERT INDEX under:
(CHAN) CHAN8972 Debussy & Ravel—Orchestral
works
(CHAN) CHAN9065 Alwyn—Orchestral Works
(CHAN) CHAN9094 Glière/Ginastera—Concertos
(CHAN) CHAN9380 Martin—Ballades
(CONI) CDCF217 Panufnik—Orchestral Works
(HYPE) CDA66219 American Choral Works

MASTERS, Robert (vn)
Brahms: String Sextet 1, String Sextet 2
see CONCERT INDEX under:
(ARGO) 433 215-2ZH Britten—Christmas Music
(CFP) CD-CFP4557 Baroque Favourites

MASTERSON, Valerie (sop)
Coward: Bitter Sweet (Cpte)

Forrest/Wright: Kismet (Cpte), Song of Norway
(Cpte), Timbuktu (exc)
Handel: Giulio Cesare (Cpte)
Rossini: Elisabetta (Cpte)
Sullivan: Mikado (exc), Pirates of Penzance (Cpte)
Wagner: Götterdämmerung (Cpte), Rheingold
(Cpte)
see CONCERT INDEX under:
(CARL) MCD15 Opera Spectacular
(DECC) 430 095-2DWO The World of Gilbert &
Sullivan, Vol.1
(DECC) 433 868-2DWO The World of Gilbert &
Sullivan - Volume 2
(GAMU) GAMD506 An Anthology Of English Song
(TER) CDVIR8317 If I Loved You - Love Duets from
the Musicals

MASTERTON-SMITH, Simon (bass)
Sondheim: Pacific Overtures (exc)
Sullivan: Pirates of Penzance (Cpte)

MASTILOVIC, Daniza (sop)
Wagner: Walküre (Cpte)
see CONCERT INDEX under:
(DG) 435 211-2GX15 Wagner—Der Ring des
Nibelungen
(PHIL) 446 057-2PB14 Wagner—The Ring Cycle -
Bayreuth Festival 1967

MASTROMEI, Gian-Piero (bar)
Verdi: Corsaro (Cpte), Simon Boccanegra (Cpte)

MASUR, Kurt (cond)
see Czech PO

MATA, Eduardo (cond)
see Dallas SO

MATAČIĆ, Lovro von (cond)
see Berlin Deutsche Op Orch

MATEI, Florin (va)
Enescu: String Octet

MATER, Ad (ob)
see CONCERT INDEX under:
(PHIL) 426 086-2PBQ Vivaldi—Double Concertos

MATHÉ, Christiane (pf)
see CONCERT INDEX under:
(SCHW) 312212 Martin—Piano Works

MÁTHÉ, Győző (va)
see CONCERT INDEX under:
(NAXO) 8 553090 Beethoven—Chamber Works

MATHÉ, Ulrike-Anima (vn)
Reger: Solo Violin Sonatas, Op. 91 (exc)

MATHESON-BRUCE, Graeme (ten)
Boughton: Bethlehem (Cpte)

MATHEZ, Jean-Pierre (tpt)
see CONCERT INDEX under:
(PHIL) 426 086-2PBQ Vivaldi—Double Concertos

MATHIAS, William (cond)
see BBC Welsh SO

MATHIESON, Muir (cond)
see LSO

MATHIS, Edith (sop)
Berlioz: Damnation de Faust (Cpte)
Dvořák: Stabat Mater
Handel: Ariodante (Cpte), Messias, K572 (Cpte)
Haydn: Infedeltà Delusa (Cpte), Jahreszeiten (Cpte),
Schöpfung (Cpte)
Henze: Junge Lord (Cpte)
Lortzing: Wildschütz (Cpte)
Mahler: Symphony 4
Mendelssohn: Symphony 2
Mozart: Apollo et Hyacinthus (Cpte), Ascanio in Alba
(Cpte), Clemenza di Tito (Cpte), Idomeneo (Cpte),
Lucio Silla (Cpte), Nozze di Figaro (Cpte), Requiem,
Sogno di Scipione (Cpte), Zaide (Cpte), Zauberflöte
(Cpte)
Nicolai: Lustigen Weiber von Windsor (Cpte)
R. Strauss: Rosenkavalier (Cpte)
Schoeck: Massimilla Doni (Cpte)
Schubert: Lazarus, D689
Schumann: Szenen aus Goethes Faust (Cpte)
Weber: Freischütz (Cpte)
Zemlinsky: Kleider machen Leute (Cpte)
see CONCERT INDEX under:
(ARCH) 439 369-2AX4 Bach—Cantatas, Vol.1
(ARCH) 439 374-2AX5 Bach—Cantatas, Volume 2 -
Easter
(ARCH) 439 380-2AX6 Bach—Cantatas, Volume 3 -
Ascension Day; Whitsun; Trinity
(ARCH) 439 387-2AX6 Bach Cantatas, Volume 4
(ARCH) 439 394-2AX5 Bach—Cantatas, Volume 5
(CPO) CPO999 262-2 Romantic Duets
(DENO) CO-78947 Schumann/Brahms—Lieder
(DG) 423 127-2GX4 Bruckner: Sacred Works for
Chorus
(DG) 423 133-2GH Brahms: Vocal Works
(DG) 429 042-2GX10 Mahler: Complete Symphonies
(DG) 429 664-2GSE3 Mendelssohn—Complete
Symphonies
(DG) 447 409-2GOR2 Bruckner—The Masses
(EMI) CMS7 64471-2 Mahler—Symphonies, Vol.1
(HYPE) CDJ33021 Schubert—Complete Lieder,
Vol.21
(NOVA) 150 010-2 Mozart—Lieder
(NOVA) 150 026-2 Schubert—Lieder
(PHIL) 426 275-2PH Mozart—Sacred Choral Works
(PHIL) 432 420-2PH3 Haydn—Il mondo della
luna/Arias

(ROSE) 3221 Schumann—Miscellaneous Works

MATHIS, Joyce (sop)
Verdi: Aida (Cpte)

MATHOT, Tini (organ)
Soler: Organ Concertos
see CONCERT INDEX under:
(CAPR) 10 254 Early English Organ Music

MATHOT, Tini (hpd)
see CONCERT INDEX under:
(PHIL) 422 518-2PME5 The Complete Mozart Edition
Vol 18

MATHOT, Tini (pf)
see CONCERT INDEX under:
(ERAT) 4509-91728-2 Haydn—Piano Trios

MATIĆ, Peter (spkr)
Weber: Freischütz (Cpte)

MÁTL, Lubomír (cond)
see Czech Phil Chor

MATORIN, Vladimir (bass)
Rachmaninov: Aleko (Cpte)

MATOUŠEK, Bohuslav (vn)
see CONCERT INDEX under:
(SUPR) 11 1119-2 Haydn: Violin Concertos

MATRIX ENSEMBLE
cond R. ZIEGLER
see CONCERT INDEX under:
(ASV) CDDCA758 Falla, Milhaud &
Stravinsky—Operas

MATRONE, Daniel (organ)
see CONCERT INDEX under:
(REM) REM311068 Reger—Organ Works

MATSUMOTO, Miwako (sop)
Boccherini: Stabat mater (1781)

MATSUZAWA, Yuki (pf)
see CONCERT INDEX under:
(PP) PP10394 Scriabin—Piano Works

MATTEI, Peter (bar)
Haeffner: Electra (Cpte)
see CONCERT INDEX under:
(BIS) BIS-CD550 Stenhammer—Vocal and Orchestral
Works
(BIS) BIS-CD654 Stenhammar—Songs

MATTEINI, Giuliana (mez)
Verdi: Don Carlo (Cpte)

MATTEO, Vicenzo di (bar)
Rossini: Pietra del paragone (Cpte)

MATTERS, Arnold (bar)
see CONCERT INDEX under:
(LYRC) SRO830 Smetana—The Bartered Bride, etc

MATTES, Willy (cond)
see Graunke SO

MATTEUZZI, William (ten)
Bellini: Puritani (Cpte)
Donizetti: Fille du Régiment (Cpte)
Puccini: Manon Lescaut (Cpte)
Rossini: Armida (Cpte), Barbiere di Siviglia (Cpte),
Cenerentola (Cpte), Gazza ladra (Cpte), Viaggio a
Reims (Cpte), Zelmira (Cpte)
Verdi: Rigoletto (Cpte)
see CONCERT INDEX under:
(DECC) 436 463-2DM Ten Top Tenors

MATTHES, Michaël (organ)
Saint-Saëns: Symphony 3

MATTHES, Walter (bar)
R. Strauss: Arabella (Cpte)

MATTHEWS, Andrea (sop)
Handel: Siroe, Rè di Persia (Cpte)
Rorem: Three Sisters Who Are Not Sisters (Cpte)
(NEWP) NPD85540 Handel/Bononcini—Muzio
Scevola

MATTHEWS, Brian (bass)
R. Strauss: Elektra (Cpte)

MATTHEWS, Charles (organ)
see CONCERT INDEX under:
(CONI) CDCF152 Purcell—Anthems for the Chapel
Royal

MATTHEWS, Denis (pf)
(EMI) CDH7 64928-2 Bach—Keyboard Works
(TEST) SBT1022 Brain,Kell & Goossens play
Schumann & Beethoven

MATTILA, Karita (sop)
Mozart: Cosi fan tutte (Cpte), Don Giovanni (Cpte),
Nozze di Figaro (Cpte)
Schubert: Fierrabras (Cpte), Mass, D950
Schumann: Paradies und die Peri (Cpte), Szenen aus
Goethes Faust (Cpte)
Sibelius: Kullervo
see CONCERT INDEX under:
(DG) 415 353-2GH4 Mendelssohn—Complete
Symphonies, etc
(ONDI) ODE792-2 Vocal and Chamber Works
(SONY) SK48242 R. Strauss—Orchestral Lieder
(SONY) SK53975 Composers Inspired by the Poet
Friedrich Hölderlin

MATTIUCCI, Franca (mez)
Puccini: Rondine (Cpte)

MATTONI, André von (spkr)
Mozart: Zauberflöte (exc)

MATTSEY, Jeff (bar)
see CONCERT INDEX under:
(RCA) 09026 61509-2 A Salute to American Music

MATUZ, István (fl)
Piemé: Flute Sonata, Op. 36

MATZ, Peter (cond)
see New World Phil

MATZENAUER, Margarete (mez)
see CONCERT INDEX under:
(IRCC) IRCC-CD800 Souvenirs from Meyerbeer
Operas
(PEAR) GEMMCDS9074(2) Giovanni Zenatello, Vol.2
(pt 2)

MATZKE, Werner (vc)
see CONCERT INDEX under:
(CAPR) 10 378 Musica Napoletana

MAUCERI, John (cond)
see Berlin Rad Ens

MAULTSBY, Nancy (mez)
Mendelssohn: Elias (Cpte)
Mozart: Requiem

MAURANE, Camille (bar)
Messager: Basoche (Cpte), P'tites Michu (exc)
Offenbach: Contes d'Hoffmann (Cpte)
Ravel: Enfant et les Sortilèges (Cpte)
see CONCERT INDEX under:
(EMI) CDM7 63944-2 Honegger—Orchestral Works
(EMI) CHS7 69741-2(3) Record of Singing,
Vol.4—French School
(PHIL) 438 970-2PM2 Camille Maurane

MAUREL, Victor (bar)
see CONCERT INDEX under:
(EMI) CHS7 64860-2(1) La Scala Edition - Vol.1,
1878-1914 (pt 1)
(MEMO) HR4408/9(1) Singers in Genoa, Vol.1 (disc
1)
(NIMB) NI7840/1 The Era of Adelina Patti
(NIMB) NI7867 Legendary Baritones
(PEAR) GEMMCDS9923(1) Covent Garden on
Record, Vol.1 (pt 1)
(SYMP) SYMCD1089 Historic Baritones of the French
School
(SYMP) SYMCD1101 The Harold Wayne Collection,
Vol.9
(SYMP) SYMCD1128 The Harold Wayne Collection,
Vol.15

MAURER, Elsie (contr)
B.A. Zimmermann: Soldaten (Cpte)

MAURETTE, Ariane (va da gamba)
see CONCERT INDEX under:
(ASV) CDGAU112 Marais—Pièces de Violes

MAURETTE, Jean-Luc (ten)
Berlioz: Troyens (Cpte)
Massenet: Cléopâtre (Cpte)
Rossini: Péchés de vieillesse II (Cpte), Péchés de
vieillesse III (exc)

MAURI, Giulio (bar)
Puccini: Turandot (Cpte)
Verdi: Trovatore (Cpte)

MAURICE, Glenda (mez)
see CONCERT INDEX under:
(ETCE) KTC1099 Glenda Maurice at Wigmore Hall

MAURO, Anna di (mez)
Mascagni: Cavalleria Rusticana (Cpte)
see CONCERT INDEX under:
(NAXO) 8 550495 Mascagni—Sacred Choral Works
(NAXO) 8 550684 Duets and Arias from Italian
Operas

MAURO, E. (ten)
see CONCERT INDEX under:
(RCA) GD60941 Rarities - Montserrat Caballé

MAURY, Claude (hn)
Telemann: Musique de Table (exc)

MAUS, Peter (ten)
Donizetti: Messa di Gloria e Credo
Hindemith: Nusch-Nuschi (Cpte)
Wagner: Meistersinger (Cpte), Parsifal (Cpte), Tristan
und Isolde (Cpte)
Wolf: Corregidor (Cpte)
see CONCERT INDEX under:
(HANS) 98 835 Bach—Cantatas, Vol.69

MAUSER, Siegfried (pf)
Hindemith: Cello Pieces, op 8, Cello Sonata, op 11/3,
Four Temperaments, Piano Concerto
(CPO) CPO999 020-2 Wilhelm Killmayer: Chamber
Works
(VIRG) VC5 45125-2 Zemlinsky—Piano Works
(VIRG) VC7 59017-2 K.A.Hartmann—Piano Works
(WERG) WER60145-50 Hindemith: Cello & Piano
Works, Vol.2

MAX, Hermann (cond)
see Kleine Konzert

MAXIÁN, František (pf)
Dvořák: Piano Concerto

MAXIM, Nicolae (fl)
Enescu: Wind Decet, Op. 14

MAXWELL, Donald (bar)
Britten: Midsummer Night's Dream (Cpte), Noye's
Fludde (Cpte), Rape of Lucretia (Cpte)
Coward: Bitter Sweet (Cpte)
Forrest/Wright: Kismet (Cpte), Song of Norway
(Cpte)
Howells: Missa Sabrinensis (Cpte)
Menotti: Amahl and the Night Visitors (Cpte)
Mozart: Nozze di Figaro (Cpte)
Orff: Carmina Burana
Romberg: Student Prince (Cpte)
Sullivan: Yeomen of the Guard (Cpte)
Tippett: Ice Break (Cpte)

MAXWELL, Linn (mez)
Purcell: Dido (Cpte)
V. Thomson: Mother of us all (Cpte)

MAXWELL, Melinda (ob)
Pärt: Passio

MAXWELL DAVIES, Sir Peter (cond)
see BBC PO

MAXWELL DAVIES, Sir Peter (pf)
see CONCERT INDEX under:
(UNIC) DKPCD9070   A Celebration of Scotland

MAY, Angelica (vc)
see CONCERT INDEX under:
(DHM) 74321 26617-2(1)   Elly Ameling - The Early
Recorings, Vols. 1-3

MAY, Brian (cond)
see OST

MAY, Edna (sngr)
see CONCERT INDEX under:
(PEAR) GEMMCDS9050/2(1)   Music from the New
York Stage, Vol. 1 (part 1)

MAY, Gisela (mez)
Mysliveček: Bellerofonte (Cpte)
see CONCERT INDEX under:
(CAPR) 10 180   Gisela May sings Weill

MAY, Jack (narr)
see CONCERT INDEX under:
(NIMB) NI5166   Vaughan Williams: Choral Works

(MICHAEL) MAY FESTIVAL CHORUS
cond J. LÓPEZ-COBOS
see CONCERT INDEX under:
(TELA) CD80149   Falla—Theatre Music

MAY FESTIVAL CHORUS
cond E. KUNZEL
Rodgers: Sound of Music (Cpte)

MAYER, Frederic (ten)
Weill: Kuhhandel (exc), Mahagonny (Cpte), Silbersee
(Cpte)

MAYER, Steven (pf)
see CONCERT INDEX under:
(ASV) CDDCA778   Liszt—Works for Piano and
Orchestra
(ASV) CDDCA783   Liszt versus Thalberg

MAYES, Paul (tpt)
see CONCERT INDEX under:
(CNTO) CRCD2368   Sullivan—That Glorious Song of
Old

MAYEUR, Jacqueline (contr)
Collasse: Racine Canticles

MAYGER, Graham (fl)
see CONCERT INDEX under:
(UNIC) DKPCD9131   Telemann—Oboe Concertos -
Volume 2

MAYHEW, Stella (sngr)
see CONCERT INDEX under:
(PEAR) GEMMCDS9050/2(2)   Music from the New
York Stage, Vol. 1 (part 2)
(PEAR) GEMMCDS9053/5   Music from the New York
Stage, Vol. 2: 1908—1913

MAYNARD, Ted (spkr)
Gershwin: Porgy and Bess (Cpte)

MAYNOR, Dorothy (sop)
see CONCERT INDEX under:
(EMI) CHS7 69741-2(1)   Record of Singing,
Vol.4—Anglo-American School (pt 1)

MAYO, Lydia (sop)
Boieldieu: Calife de Bagdad (Cpte)

MAYOR, Andrew (bar)
see CONCERT INDEX under:
(HYPE) CDA66608   Dibdin—Three Operas

MAYOR, Simon (mndl)
see CONCERT INDEX under:
(ACOU) CDACS012   The Mandolin Album
(ACOU) CDACS014   The Second Mandolin Album

MAYR, Ingrid (mez)
Einem: Dantons Tod (Cpte)
Mozart: Zauberflöte (Cpte)
R. Strauss: Rosenkavalier (Cpte)

MAYR, Richard (bass)
Beethoven: Symphony 9
see CONCERT INDEX under:
(EMI) CHS7 64487-2   R. Strauss—Der Rosenkavalier
& Lieder
(PEAR) GEMMCDS9365   R. Strauss: Der
Rosenkavalier (abridged), etc
(PEAR) GEMMCDS9925(2)   Covent Garden on
Record—Vol.3 (pt 2)

(SCHW) 314512   Vienna State Opera Live, Vol.1
(SCHW) 314622   Vienna State Opera Live, Vol.12
(SCHW) 314642   Vienna State Opera Live, Vol.14
(SCHW) 314652   Vienna State Opera Live, Vol.15
(SCHW) 314662   Vienna State Opera Live, Vol.16

MAYS, Sally (pf)
see CONCERT INDEX under:
(CNTI) CCD1009   Music of Barry Anderson

MAZALOUBAUD, Jean-Pierre (bass)
Shostakovich: Lady Macbeth of Mtsensk (Cpte)

MAZAROFF, Todor (ten)
see CONCERT INDEX under:
(SCHW) 314502   Vienna State Opera—Live
Recordings (sampler)
(SCHW) 314542   Vienna State Opera Live, Vol.4
(SCHW) 314572   Vienna State Opera Live, Vol.7
(SCHW) 314632   Vienna State Opera Live, Vol.13

MAZO, Ekaterina (sop)
Karetnikov: Till Eulenspiegel (Cpte)

MAZURA, Franz (bar)
Berg: Lulu (Cpte)
Pfitzner: Palestrina (Cpte)
Schoenberg: Moses and Aron (Cpte)
Wagner: Götterdämmerung (Cpte), Parsifal (Cpte)
see CONCERT INDEX under:
(DECC) 440 854-2DH   Ullmann—Der Kaiser von
Atlantis

MAZUROK, Yuri (bar)
Tchaikovsky: Eugene Onegin (Cpte), Queen of
Spades (Cpte)
Verdi: Trovatore (Cpte)

MAZZARRI, Liliana (sop)
(HYPE) CDA66745   Vivaldi—Opera Arias and
Sinfonias

MAZZEI, Enrico di (ten)
Puccini: Tosca (exc)

MAZZETTI, Sofia (sop)
see CONCERT INDEX under:
(RCA) 09026 68014-2   Pavarotti - The Early Years,
Vol.2

MAZZIE, Marin (sngr)
Sondheim: Passion (Cpte)

MAZZIERI, Maurizio (bass)
Haydn: Fedeltà Premiata (Cpte), Orlando Paladino
(Cpte)
Verdi: Masnadieri (Cpte), Simon Boccanegra (Cpte)

MAZZINI, Guido (bass)
Donizetti: Poliuto (Cpte)
Puccini: Bohème (Cpte)

MAZZOLA, Rudolf (bass)
Debussy: Pelléas et Mélisande (Cpte)

MAZZOLENI, Ester (sop)
see CONCERT INDEX under:
(EMI) CHS7 64860-2(2)   La Scala Edition - Vol.1,
1878-1914 (pt 2)
(IRCC) IRCC-CD808   Souvenirs of 19th Century Italian
Opera
(PEAR) GEMMCDS9073(2)   Giovanni Zenatello, Vol.1
(pt 2)
(PEAR) GEMMCDS9074(1)   Giovanni Zenatello, Vol.2
(pt 1)
(SYMP) SYMCD1113   The Harold Wayne Collection,
Vol.13
(SYMP) SYMCD1138   The Harold Wayne Collection,
Vol.16
(SYMP) SYMCD1148   The Harold Wayne Collection,
Vol.17
(SYMP) SYMCD1158   The Harold Wayne Collection,
Vol.18
(SYMP) SYMCD1168   The Harold Wayne Collection,
Vol.19

MAZZOLI, Ferruccio (bass)
Donizetti: Lucrezia Borgia (Cpte)
Puccini: Bohème (Cpte), Gianni Schicchi (Cpte)
Rossini: Guillaume Tell (Cpte), Mosè (Cpte)
Verdi: Aida (Cpte), Ballo in maschera (Cpte), Otello
(Cpte)

MAZZONI, Silvia (mez)
Mayr: Rosa Bianca (Cpte)
Verdi: Traviata (Cpte)

MEAD, Andrew (treb)
Britten: Midsummer Night's Dream (Cpte)

MEAD, Philip (pf)
see CONCERT INDEX under:
(CNTI) CCD1061   Montague—Orchestral and
Chamber Music

MEALE, J. Arthur (organ)
see CONCERT INDEX under:
(BEUL) 1PD5   Historic Organs, Volume 1

MEALY, Robert (vielle)
see CONCERT INDEX under:
(NALB) NA068CD   Machaut—Remede de Fortune

MEASHAM, David (cond)
see Melbourne SO

MECHALY, Gaëlle (sop)
Purcell: Dido (Cpte)

MECHERA, Erika (sop)
R. Strauss: Daphne (Cpte)

MECHLER, Thierry (organ)
see CONCERT INDEX under:
(MOTE) CD10881   Liszt & Rheinberger—Organ music

MEDEA QUARTET
see CONCERT INDEX under:
(METI) MSVCD92005   Mathias—String Quartets

MEDGYASZAY, Vilma (sop)
see CONCERT INDEX under:
(EMI) CDC5 55031-2   Bartók/Dohnányi—Play their
own works

MEDICI QUARTET
Dvořák: String Quartet 12
Elgar: Piano Quintet, String Quartet, Violin Sonata
Elgar/Binyon: Wood magic
Haydn: String Quartets, Op.20
Mendelssohn: String Quartet 2
Mozart: Clarinet Quintet, K581, String Quartet, K499
Schubert: String Quartet, D112, String Quartet, D810,
String Quintet
Shostakovich: Piano Quintet, Op.57
Smetana: String Quartet 1, String Quartet 2
see CONCERT INDEX under:
(MEDI) MQCD6005   Mozart's Journey to Prague
(NIMB) NI5140   Mendelssohn and Shostakovich
Octets
(NIMB) NI5191   Vaughan Williams: Chamber works
cond S. DARLINGTON
(NIMB) NI5256   Tippett—Choral Works
cond P. LEDGER
Britten: Little Sweep (Cpte)
cond R. MUTI
Verdi: Ballo in maschera (Cpte)
cond G. VASS
(MEDI) MQCD4002   A Song before Sunrise

MEDIEVAL ENSEMBLE OF LONDON
see CONCERT INDEX under:
(L'OI) 436 194-2OH2   Ockeghem—Complete Secular
Music

MEDJIMOREC, Heinz (pf)
see CONCERT INDEX under:
(EMI) CDC7 54881-2   Viennese Dance Music

MEDLAM, Charles (cond)
see London Baroque

MEDLAM, Charles (va da gamba)
see CONCERT INDEX under:
(HYPE) CDA66070   Purcell: Songs

MEDNIKOFF, Nikolai (pf)
see CONCERT INDEX under:
(BIDD) LAB017   Casals—The Victor Recordings

MEDTNER, Nicolas (pf)
see CONCERT INDEX under:
(EMI) CDC7 54839-2   Medtner plays Medtner
(TEST) SBT1027   Medtner—Piano Concertos, etc

MEE, William (tbn)
see CONCERT INDEX under:
(CNTO) CRCD2368   Sullivan—That Glorious Song of
Old

MEECHAM, Nicola (pf)
see CONCERT INDEX under:
(LARG) Largo 5125   Kurt Schwertsik—Für Christa

MEEKS, Michael (tpt)
see CONCERT INDEX under:
(VIRG) VJ7 59651-2   Vivaldi—Concertos

MEENA, James (cond)
see Collaborative Arts CO

MEENS, Hein (ten)
Keiser: Masagniello furioso (Cpte)
Schreker: Gezeichneten (Cpte)
see CONCERT INDEX under:
(ARCH) 437 090-2AT   Collectio Argentea 20: Bach
Family before J.S.

MEER, Janneke van der (vn)
see CONCERT INDEX under:
(OLYM) OCD460   Roussel—Chamber Music, Vol. 3

MEER, Richte van der (vc)
Devienne: Bassoon Sonatas, Op. 24
see CONCERT INDEX under:
(EMI) CDC5 55000-2   Bach—Cantata Arias

MEER, Richte van der (viol)
see CONCERT INDEX under:
(ACCE) ACC8864D   Symphonia Angelica

MEER, Ruud van der (bass)
Zelenka: Trio Sonatas
(DENO) CO-72886   Berlioz: Choral Works
(TELD) 2292-42433-2   Bach—Cantatas, Volume 15
(TELD) 2292-42506-2   Bach—Cantatas, Volume 10
(TELD) 2292-42556-2   Bach—Cantatas, Volume 11
(TELD) 2292-42559-2   Bach—Cantatas, Volume 12
(TELD) 2292-42560-2   Bach—Cantatas, Volume 13
(TELD) 2292-42566-2   Bach—Cantatas, Volume 16
(TELD) 2292-42571-2   Bach—Cantatas, Volume 17
(TELD) 2292-42572-2   Bach—Cantatas, Volume 18
(TELD) 2292-42575-2   Bach—Cantatas, Volume 19
(TELD) 2292-42576-2   Bach—Cantatas, Volume 20
(TELD) 2292-42577-2   Bach—Cantatas, Volume 21
(TELD) 2292-42581-2   Bach—Cantatas, Volume 22
(TELD) 2292-42582-2   Bach—Cantatas, Volume 23
(TELD) 2292-42583-2   Bach—Cantatas, Volume 24
(TELD) 2292-42601-2   Bach—Cantatas, Volume 25
(TELD) 2292-42602-2   Bach—Cantatas, Volume 26
(TELD) 2292-42603-2   Bach—Cantatas, Volume 27

MEMEO, Francesco (ten)
Puccini: Fanciulla del West (Cpte)

MENDELSSOHN, Vladimir (va)
Bruckner: Intermezzo and Trio, String Quintet
see CONCERT INDEX *under:*
(DENO) **C37-7505** Mozart: The complete works for
violin and orchestra, Vol. 2
(ECM) **831 959-2** Pärt—Arbos

(FANNY) MENDELSSOHN QUARTET
see CONCERT INDEX *under:*
(TROU) **TRO-CD01409** Milhaud—Early Works, Vol. 1

MENDELSSOHN QUARTET
see CONCERT INDEX *under:*
(MUSM) **67094-2** Antheil—Ballet Mécanique

MENDOZE, Christian (cond)
see Toulon Musica Antiqua

MENDOZE, Christian (rec/dir)
see CONCERT INDEX *under:*
(PIER) **PV794033** Vivaldi—Vocal and Wind Music

MENESES, Antonio (vc)
R. Strauss: Don Quixote

MENGELBERG, Willem (cond)
see BBC SO

MENGES, Herbert (cond)
see LSO

MENGES, Isolde (vn)
see CONCERT INDEX *under:*
(APR) **APR7015** The Auer Legacy, Vol.1
(BIDD) **LAB076** Menges plays Beethoven and
Brahms

MENICUCCI, Delfo (sngr)
Donizetti: Ajo nell'imbarazzo (Cpte)

MENNI, Giuseppe (bass)
see CONCERT INDEX *under:*
(PREI) **89048** Apollo Granforte (1886-1975) - I

MENOTTI, Tatiana (sop)
Puccini: Bohème (Cpte)

MENSA SONORA ENSEMBLE
see CONCERT INDEX *under:*
(PIER) **PV794114** Graupner—Overtures for
Chalumeaux and Orchestra

MENTZER, Susanne (mez)
Busoni: Arlecchino (Cpte)
Gounod: Faust (Cpte)
Mascagni: Cavalleria rusticana (Cpte)
Mendelssohn: Midsummer Night's Dream (exc)
Mozart: Don Giovanni (Cpte), Idomeneo (Cpte),
Nozze di Figaro (Cpte)
Rossini: Barbiere di Siviglia (Cpte), Turco in Italia
(Cpte)
see CONCERT INDEX *under:*
(EMI) **CDC7 54004-2** Chabrier: Vocal & Orchestral
Works
(KOCH) **37240-2** Women at an Exposition - 1893
Chicago World Fair
(PHIL) **422 545-2PME3** The Complete Mozart Edition
Vol.45

MENUHIN, Hepzibah (pf)
see CONCERT INDEX *under:*
(BIDD) **LAB066** Enescu—Violinist & Composer
(EMI) **CDM7 63988-2** Schubert, Mendelssohn &
Brahms—Chamber Works

MENUHIN, Jeremy (pf)
see CONCERT INDEX *under:*
(CHAN) **CHAN9173** Dvořák—Chamber Works
(EMI) **CDM7 63986-2** French Chamber Works

MENUHIN, Sir Yehudi (cond)
see Arnhem PO

MENUHIN, Sir Yehudi (va)
Berlioz: Harold in Italy
see CONCERT INDEX *under:*
(EMI) **CDM7 63985-2** Bartók—Violin and Viola Works
(EMI) **CDM7 63986-2** French Chamber Works
(EMI) **CHS5 65003-2** Walton conducts Walton

MENUHIN, Sir Yehudi (vn)
Bach: Solo Violin Partitas and Sonatas
Bartók: Solo Violin Sonata, Violin Sonata 1
Beethoven: Violin Concerto, Violin Sonata 5, Violin
Sonata 9
Berg: Violin Concerto
Berlioz: Rêverie et Caprice
Bloch: Violin Concerto
Brahms: Violin Sextet 1, String Sextet 2
Bruch: Violin Concerto 1
Delius: Violin Concerto
Elgar: Violin Concerto
Mendelssohn: Violin Concerto, Op.64
Nielsen: Violin Concerto
Paganini: Violin Concerto 1, Violin Concerto 2
Schumann: Violin Concerto
Sibelius: Violin Concerto
Tchaikovsky: Violin Concerto
(ARAB) **Z6563** Elgar—Orchestral Works
(BIDD) **LAB004** Menuhin plays Mozart Concertos
(BIDD) **LAB031** The young Yehudi Menuhin, Vol.1
(BIDD) **LAB032** The young Yehudi Menuhin, Vol.2
(BIDD) **LAB046** The Young Yehudi Menuhin
(BIDD) **LAB066** Enescu—Violinist & Composer
(CASC) **VEL2003** Memories of the Suisse Romande -
Ansermet conducts Berg

(DG) **415 874-2GCM4** Beethoven—Violin Sonatas
(DG) **445 400-2GDO10** Ferenc Fricsay - A Portrait
(EMI) **CDH7 61018-2** Yehudi Menuhin plays Bach
Violin Works
(EMI) **CDM7 63718-2** Mozart: Violin Concertos
(EMI) **CDM7 63985-2** Bartók—Violin and Viola Works
(EMI) **CDM7 63986-2** French Chamber Works
(EMI) **CDM7 63988-2** Schubert, Mendelssohn &
Brahms—Chamber Works
(EMI) **CDM7 64281-2** Boulanger—Vocal & Chamber
Works
(EMI) **CDM7 69112-2** Best of Saint-Saëns
(EMI) **CDS7 54564-2** The Elgar Edition, Vol.2
(EMI) **CHS5 65003-2** Walton conducts Walton
(EMI) **CZS7 62736-2** Poulenc—Chamber Works
(EMI) **CZS7 67310-2** Menuhin plays Popular Violin
Concertos
(MSCM) **MM30322** Enescu - Columbia Recordings
1920s-30s
(NEW) **NW375-2** Lukas Foss: Orchestral Works
(SONY) **SMK52688** Gould meets Menuhin
(TEST) **SBT1003** The Young Menuhin—Encores,
Vol.1

MENUHIN, Sir Yehudi (vn/dir)
see CONCERT INDEX *under:*
(CFP) **CD-CFP4557** Baroque Favourites
(EMI) **CDC7 54205-2** Vivaldi—Double Concertos
(EMI) **CES5 68517-2** Bach—Orchestral Works
(EMI) **CZS7 67310-2** Menuhin plays Popular Violin
Concertos
(EMI1) **CDZ7 67004-2** Mozart—Violin Concertos
(EMI1) **CDZ7 67005-2** Mozart—Violin Concertos, etc
(EMI) **CDZ114** Best of Baroque

MENZEL, Peter (bass)
Schreker: Gezeichneten (Cpte)

MERCENIER, Marcelle (pf)
see CONCERT INDEX *under:*
(RICE) **RIC014024** Boesmans—Concertos

MERCER, Gregory (ten)
V. Thomson: Lord Byron (Cpte)

MERCIER, Hélène (pf)
see CONCERT INDEX *under:*
(CHAN) **CHAN8905** Ravel—Works for Piano Duet
(CHAN) **CHAN9162** Mozart/Schubert—Piano Works
for Four Hands

MERCIER, Jacques (cond)
see Ile de France Nat Orch

MERCIER, Mel (bodhran)
see CONCERT INDEX *under:*
(MODE) **Mode 28/9** Cage—Roaratorio. Laughtears
etc

MERCIER, Peadher (bodhran)
see CONCERT INDEX *under:*
(MODE) **Mode 28/9** Cage—Roaratorio. Laughtears
etc

MERCKER, Karl-Ernst (ten)
Berg: Lulu (Cpte)
Jessel: Schwarzwaldmädel (exc)
Künneke: Vetter aus Dingsda (exc)
Offenbach: Vie Parisienne (exc)
Raymond: Maske in Blau (exc)
Wagner: Meistersinger (Cpte)
Zeller: Vogelhändler (exc)

MERCURIALI, Angelo (ten)
Bellini: Puritani (Cpte)
Cilea: Adriana Lecouvreur (Cpte)
Donizetti: Don Pasquale (Cpte)
Puccini: Fanciulla del West (Cpte), Madama Butterfly
(Cpte), Manon Lescaut (Cpte), Tosca (Cpte)
Verdi: Otello (Cpte), Traviata (Cpte)
see CONCERT INDEX *under:*
(EMI) **CDM7 69543-2** Maria Callas and Giuseppe Di
Stefano - Duets

MERCZ, Nóra (hp)
see CONCERT INDEX *under:*
(NAXO) **8 550741** Romantic Music for Flute and Harp

MERKER, Rose (sop)
see CONCERT INDEX *under:*
(SCHW) **314592** Vienna State Opera Live, Vol.9

MERLAK, Jasna Corrado (hp)
see CONCERT INDEX *under:*
(HYPE) **CDH88015** The Concerto in Europe

MERLI, Francesco (ten)
see CONCERT INDEX *under:*
(EMI) **CHS7 64864-2(2)** La Scala Edition - Vol.2,
1915-46 (pt 2)
(LYRC) **SRO805** Gina Cigna—Opera Recital
(NIMB) **NI7814** Claudia Muzio—Opera Arias & Songs
(PREI) **89010** Tancredi Pasero (1893-1983) - I
(PREI) **89026** Francesco Merli (1887-1976) - I

MERNIER, Benoît (organ)
see CONCERT INDEX *under:*
(RICE) **RIC052034** Charpentier—Sacred Choral
Works

MERREM-NIKISCH, Greta (sop)
see CONCERT INDEX *under:*
(EMI) **CDH7 69787-2** Richard Tauber sings Operetta
Arias

MERRETT, James Edward (db)
see CONCERT INDEX *under:*
(DUTT) **CDAX8014** British Gramophone Premieres

MERRILL, Robert (bar)
Bizet: Carmen (Cpte)
Donizetti: Lucia di Lammermoor (Cpte)
Leoncavallo: Pagliacci (Cpte)
Mascagni: Cavalleria Rusticana (Cpte)
Puccini: Bohème (Cpte), Manon Lescaut (Cpte)
Rossini: Barbiere di Siviglia (Cpte)
Verdi: Aida (Cpte), Ballo in maschera (Cpte), Falstaff
(Cpte), Forza del destino (Cpte), Rigoletto (Cpte),
Traviata (Cpte)
see CONCERT INDEX *under:*
(DECC) **411 665-2DM3** Puccini: Il trittico
(EMI) **CHS7 69741-2(2)** Record of Singing,
Vol.4—Anglo-American School (pt 2)
(RCA) **GD87799** The Pearl Fishers Duet plus Duets
and Scenes
(RCA) **09026 61509-2** A Salute to American Music
(RCA) **09026 61580-2(6)** RCA/Met 100 Singers, 100
Years (pt 6)
(SONY) **SM2K47533** Music inspired by the Jewish
Religion

MERRILL, William (pf)
see CONCERT INDEX *under:*
(PEAR) **SHECD9636** Sullivan—Guinevere and other
Ballads

MERRIMAN, Nan (mez)
Beethoven: Missa Solemnis
Mozart: Così fan tutte (Cpte)
Verdi: Falstaff (Cpte), Otello (Cpte)
see CONCERT INDEX *under:*
(DG) **437 677-2GDO2** Irmgard Seefried - Opera
Recital
(RCA) **GD60276** Toscanini conducts Boito & Verdi
(RCA) **GD60324** Beethoven—Complete Symphonies
(RCA) **GD60326** Verdi—Operas & Choral Works
(RCA) **09026 61581-2** Bernstein—Orchestral & Vocal
Works

MERRITT, Chris (ten)
Donizetti: Emilia di Liverpool (Cpte), Eremitaggio di
Liverpool (Cpte)
Glinka: Life for the Tsar (Cpte)
Rossini: Armida (Cpte), Bianca e Falliero (Cpte),
Donna del lago (Cpte), Zelmira (Cpte)
Verdi: Vespri siciliani (Cpte)
see CONCERT INDEX *under:*
(EMI) **CDC7 54643-2** Rossini—Bicentenary Gala
Concert
(OPRA) **ORCH103** Italian Opera—1810-20
(PHIL) **434 102-2PH** The Heroic Bel Canto Tenor

MERSCHER, Kristin (pf)
see CONCERT INDEX *under:*
(NAXO) **8 550654** Schubert/Schumann—Chamber
Works
(NAXO) **8 550655** Mendelssohn—Cello Works
(NAXO) **8 550656** Brahms—Cello Sonatas

MERSIOVSKY, Gertrud (organ)
Correa de Arauxo: Libro de Tientos y Discursos
(exc)

MERTENS, Klaus (bass)
A.J. Romberg: Lied von der Glocke
Bach: Christmas Oratorio, BWV248 (Cpte), Mass in B
Minor, BWV232 (Cpte), St Matthew Passion,
BWV244 (Cpte)
Handel: Acis and Galatea, K566 (Cpte), Ode for St.
Cecilia's Day (Cpte), Resurrezione (Cpte)
Monteverdi: Vespers
Mozart: Mass, K427
see CONCERT INDEX *under:*
(ACCE) **ACC93395D** Bach—Cantatas
(EMI) **CDC7 54003-2** Mozart—Masses and Church
Sonatas
(ERAT) **2292-45822-2** M-A.Charpentier—Motets
(ERAT) **4509-98536-2** Bach—Complete Cantatas,
Volume 1

MESGUICH, Daniel (narr)
Honegger: Roi David (Cpte)
Six: Mariés de la Tour Eiffel (Cpte)

MESPLÉ, Mady (sop)
Adam: Toréador (Cpte)
Auber: Fra Diavolo (Cpte)
Delibes: Lakmé (Cpte)
Massenet: Werther (Cpte)
Offenbach: Orphée aux enfers (Cpte)
Rossini: Guillaume Tell (Cpte)
see CONCERT INDEX *under:*
(EMI) **CDS7 49361-2** Offenbach: Operettas
(EMI) **CMS7 64095-2** Debussy—Mélodies
(SONY) **SMK48462** Boulez conducts Schoenberg

MESSIAEN, Olivier (organ)
Messiaen: Apparition de l'église éternelle, Nativité du
Seigneur
see CONCERT INDEX *under:*
(EMI) **CDC5 55037-2** French Organists play their own
works
(EMI) **CZS7 67400-2** Messiaen plays Messiaen

MESSIAEN, Olivier (pf)
Messiaen: Visions de l'Amen

(OLIVIER) MESSIAEN QUARTET
Messiaen: Quatuor

MESSIER, Lise (sop)
see CONCERT INDEX *under:*
(NALB) **NA008CD** Somei Satoh: Various Works

MESSIEREUR, Petr (vn)
see CONCERT INDEX *under:*

(CALL) **CAL9628** Mozart—Chamber Works
(SUPR) **11 0752-2** Martinů—Spaliček, etc
(SUPR) **11 0767-2** Martinů—Cantatas

MESSITER, Christine (fl)
see CONCERT INDEX *under:*
(CRYS) **Crystal CD810** Music of Alan Hovhaness

MESSITER, Malcolm (ob)
see CONCERT INDEX *under:*
(HYPE) **CDA66332** Malcolm Arnold—Orchestral
Works
(RCA) **RD60224** Baroque Oboe Concerti

MESSLER, Guy (tpt)
see CONCERT INDEX *under:*
(RCA) **09026 61200-2** Molter—Trumpet Concertos

MESSNER, Joseph (cond)
see orch

MESSTHALER, Ulrich (bass)
Handel: Flavio (Cpte)
see CONCERT INDEX *under:*
(HARM) **HMC90 1310** Schütz—The Nativity

MESTER, Jorge (cond)
see Louisville Orch

MESTER, Markus (tpt)
see CONCERT INDEX *under:*
(CAPR) **10 439** Modern Trumpet

METH, Max (cond)
see Broadway Cast

METSOMÄKI, Maaria (sop)
Madetoja: Juha (Cpte)

METTERNICH, Anton (bass)
Wagner: Meistersinger (Cpte)

METTERNICH, Josef (bar)
Humperdinck: Hänsel und Gretel (Cpte)
Wagner: Lohengrin (Cpte), Meistersinger (Cpte)
see CONCERT INDEX *under:*
(EMI) **CDH7 61001-2** R. Strauss—Lieder & Arias
(EMI) **CMS5 65212-2** Wagner—Les introuvables du
Ring

METZ, Henrik (pf)
see CONCERT INDEX *under:*
(KONT) **32047** Nielsen—Songs

METZGER, Julian (sngr)
Schreker: Gezeichneten (Cpte)

METZGER, Ottilie (contr)
see CONCERT INDEX *under:*
(IRCC) **IRCC-CD800** Souvenirs from Meyerbeer
Operas
(SUPR) **11 2136-2(3)** Emmy Destinn—Complete
Edition, Discs 5 to 8

METZMACHER, Ingo (cond)
see Bamberg SO

MEUNIER, Alain (vc)
see CONCERT INDEX *under:*
(ERAT) **2292-45772-2** Saint-Saëns—Works for
Chamber Ensemble
(SONY) **SK47184** Glenn Gould—The Composer

MEUNIER, Claudine (contr)
Berio: Laborintus II

MEUNIER, Jean-Louis (ten)
Debussy: Rodrigue et Chimène (Cpte)
Rameau: Hippolyte et Aricie (Cpte)

MEUNIER, Robert (lte)
see CONCERT INDEX *under:*
(BIS) **BIS-CD341** Music for lutes

**MEUTLBERG CHAMBER CHOIR
cond ROBERT WAGNER**
see CONCERT INDEX *under:*
(ROSE) **3221** Schumann—Miscellaneous Works

MEVEN, Peter (bass)
Debussy: Pelléas et Mélisande (Cpte)
Hindemith: Mathis der Maler (Cpte)
Pfitzner: Palestrina (Cpte)
Wagner: Walküre (exc)
Weber: Freischütz (Cpte)

MEWTON-WOOD, Noel (pf)
see CONCERT INDEX *under:*
(PEAR) **GEMMCD9939** Josef Hassid & Ida Haendel –
1940-42 Recordings

**MEXICO CITY CHORUS
cond F. LOZANO**
Beethoven: Symphony 9

**MEXICO CITY PHILHARMONIC ORCHESTRA
cond E. BÁTIZ**
see CONCERT INDEX *under:*
(ASV) **CDDCA653** Mexican Orchestral Works
(ASV) **CDDCA654** Ginastera—Orchestral Works
(ASV) **CDDCA657** Liadov—Orchestral Works
(ASV) **CDDCA665** Saint-Saëns—Orchestral Works
(ASV) **CDDCA686** Fauré—Orchestral Works
(ASV) **CDDCA735** Music of Spain
(EMI) **CDS7 47901-8** Villa-Lobos: Orchestral and
Chamber Works
(IMG) **IMGCD1605** Rachmaninov—Orchestral Works
cond F. LOZANO
Beethoven: Symphony 9
Brahms: Symphony 2
see CONCERT INDEX *under:*
(FORL) **FF045** Grieg/Lalo—Orchestral Works

**MEXICO STATE SYMPHONY ORCHESTRA
cond E. BÁTIZ**
see CONCERT INDEX *under:*
(ASV) **CDDCA665** Saint-Saëns—Orchestral Works
(ASV) **CDDCA887** Rodrigo—Guitar Concertos
(EMI) **CZS7 67435-2** Rodrigo—Orchestral Works

MEY, Guy de (ten)
Bach: Mass in B Minor, BWV232 (Cpte), St Matthew
Passion, BWV244 (Cpte)
Gluck: Rencontre imprévue (Cpte)
Handel: Alessandro (Cpte), Judas Maccabaeus
(Cpte), Resurrezione (Cpte)
Lully: Atys (Cpte)
Monteverdi: Incoronazione di Poppea (Cpte), Ritorno
d'Ulisse in patria (Cpte), Vespers
Mozart: Zauberflöte (Cpte)
Rameau: Platée (Cpte)
see CONCERT INDEX *under:*
(ERAT) **4509-98536-2** Bach—Complete Cantatas,
Volume 1
(RICE) **RIC037011** Charpentier—Cantatas and Airs
(RICE) **RIC041016** German Baroque Cantatas, Vol.2 -
Buxtehude
(RICE) **RIC048035/7** German Baroque Cantatas,
Vol.4 - Bruhns
(RICE) **RIC060048** German Baroque Cantatas, Vol. 5
(RICE) **RIC079061** German Baroque Cantatas, Vol.6 -
Funeral Cantatas
(RICE) **RIC109097/8** German Baroque Cantatas,
Vol.9 - Weckmann

MEYER, Kerstin (mez)
R. Strauss: Rosenkavalier (Cpte)
Verdi: Rigoletto (Cpte)
see CONCERT INDEX *under:*
(BIS) **BIS-CD017** Söderström and Meyer sing Duets

MEYER, Marcelle (pf)
see CONCERT INDEX *under:*
(EMI) **CDC7 54604-2** Milhaud plays and conducts
Milhaud
(EMI) **CZS5 68092-2** Les Introuvables de Marcelle
Meyer, Volume 2
(EPM) **150 122** Milhaud—Historic Recordings 1928-
1948

MEYER, Paul (cl)
see CONCERT INDEX *under:*
(DENO) **CO-75289** Clarinet Concertos
(DENO) **CO-75960** Märchenbilder—Paul Meyer plays
Schumann
(DENO) **CO-78917** 20th Century Music for
Unaccompanied Clarinet
(DENO) **CO-79282** French Clarinet Art
(DENO) **CO-79551** Weber—Clarinet Concertos

MEYER, Sabine (cl)
Brahms: Clarinet Quintet
Mozart: Clarinet Concerto, K622, Clarinet Quintet,
K581, Sinfonia Concertante, K297b
Yun: Clarinet Quintet
see CONCERT INDEX *under:*
(EMI) **CDC7 47351-2** Weber: Works for clarinet and
orchestra
(EMI) **CDC7 49736-2** Clarinet Music by Bruch, Mozart
& Schumann
(EMI) **CDC7 54239-2** Schubert—Lieder
(EMI) **CDC7 54842-2** Stamitz—Clarinet Concertos
(RCA) **09026 61976-2** Danzi—Flute & Clarinet Works

MEYER, Wolfgang (cl)
Beethoven: Piano Trios (exc)
Messiaen: Quatuor
Mozart: Clarinet Quintet, K581, Piano Trio, K498
see CONCERT INDEX *under:*
(LARG) **Largo 5127** Igor Markevitch—Chamber
Works

MEYER, Wolfgang (harm)
see CONCERT INDEX *under:*
(DECC) **425 204-2DNL** Ute Lemper sings Kurt Weill

(SABINE) MEYER WIND ENSEMBLE
see CONCERT INDEX *under:*
(EMI) **CDC7 54383-2** Kramář—Wind Octets

MEYER-ESCHE, Corinna (sop)
Spohr: Jessonda (Cpte)

MEYER-MAHR, Moritz (pf)
see CONCERT INDEX *under:*
(SIMA) **PSC1809(2)** Grieg—Historical Piano
Recordings (pt 2)

MEYERS, Anne Akiko (vn)
Bruch: Scottish Fantasy
Lalo: Symphonie espagnole
see CONCERT INDEX *under:*
(RCA) **09026 61700-2** Works for Violin & Orchestra
(RCA) **09026 62546-2** Salut d'amour

MEYERSON, Mitzi (organ)
see CONCERT INDEX *under:*
(HARM) **HMU90 7035** Sweeter than Roses - Purcell
Songs

MEYERSON, Mitzi (hpd)
Bach: Flute Sonatas, BWV1030-5 (exc), Trio
Sonatas, BWV525-530 (exc)
Duphly: Pièces de clavecin (exc)
Forqueray: Pièces de viole (exc)
see CONCERT INDEX *under:*
(ASV) **CDGAU102** Buxtehude—Suites and Variations
(ASV) **CDGAU112** Marais—Pièces de Violes
(HARM) **HMU90 7035** Sweeter than Roses - Purcell
Songs

MEYER-TOPSØE, Elisabeth (sop)
see CONCERT INDEX *under:*
(KONT) **32156** R. Strauss/Wagner—Lieder

MEYER-WELFING, Hugo (ten)
Mozart: Nozze di Figaro (Cpte)
Wagner: Meistersinger (Cpte)
see CONCERT INDEX *under:*
(EMI) **CHS7 69741-2(4)** Record of Singing,
Vol.4—German School
(VANG) **08.2010.71** Bach—Choral Works

MEYROWITZ, Selmar (cond)
see Berlin St Op Orch

MEZAC, Rose-Marie (sop)
Fauré: Requiem (Cpte)

MEZZENA, Bruno (pf)
Rossini: Péchés de vieillesse XII

MHEADHRA, Dáirine Ní (cond)
see Nua Nós

MIATELLO, Cristina (sop)
A. Scarlatti: Lamentazioni (Cpte)

MICCO, Anna Maria di (sop)
Rossini: Tancredi (Cpte)

MICCONI, Roberto (organ)
see CONCERT INDEX *under:*
(MOTE) **CD10561** Venetian Organ Music

MICHAEL, Audrey (mez)
Verdi: Luisa Miller (Cpte), Rigoletto (Cpte)
Wagner: Parsifal (Cpte)
see CONCERT INDEX *under:*
(ERAT) **4509-95307-2** Schubert/Schumann—Sacred
Choral Works

MICHAELIAN, Patricia (pf)
Bloch: Concerto Grosso 1

MICHAELIS, Ruth (sop)
R. Strauss: Arabella (Cpte)

MICHAELS, Mark (sngr)
Bernstein: West Side Story (Cpte)

MICHAELS-MOORE, Anthony (bar)
Mendelssohn: Erste Walpurgisnacht
Mercadante: Orazi e Curiazi (Cpte)
Orff: Carmina burana
Sullivan: Yeomen of the Guard (Cpte)
see CONCERT INDEX *under:*
(CARL) **MCD15** Opera Spectacular

MICHAILOVA, Maria (sop)*
see CONCERT INDEX *under:*
(MMOI) **CDMOIR422** Great Voices in Tchaikovsky
(PEAR) **GEMMCDS9001/3(2)** Singers of Imperial
Russia, Vol.2 (pt 2)
(PEAR) **GEMMCDS9007/9(1)** Singers of Imperial
Russia, Vol.4 (pt 1)
(PEAR) **GEMMCDS9007/9(2)** Singers of Imperial
Russia, Vol.4 (pt 2)

MICHALKO, Ján Vladimír (organ)
see CONCERT INDEX *under:*
(OPUS) **9351 2130** Franck: Organ Works

MICHALKOVÁ, Alzbeta (mez)
Mascagni: Cavalleria Rusticana (Cpte)
Puccini: Madama Butterfly (Cpte)
Suchoň: Whirlpool (Cpte)
Verdi: Rigoletto (Cpte)

MICHALSKI, Carl (cond)
see Vienna Op Orch

MICHALSKY, Anne (sop)
see CONCERT INDEX *under:*
(EMI) **CHS7 64487-2** R. Strauss—Der Rosenkavalier
& Lieder
(PEAR) **GEMMCDS9365** R. Strauss: Der
Rosenkavalier (abridged), etc
(SCHW) **314542** Vienna State Opera Live, Vol.4
(SCHW) **314592** Vienna State Opera Live, Vol.9
(SCHW) **314622** Vienna State Opera Live, Vol.12
(SCHW) **314632** Vienna State Opera Live, Vol.13
(SCHW) **314672** Vienna State Opera Live, Vol.17

MICHEAU, Janine (sop)
Bizet: Carmen (Cpte), Ivan IV (exc), Pêcheurs de
perles (Cpte)
Ganne: Saltimbanques (exc)
Gounod: Roméo et Juliette (Cpte)
Milhaud: Christophe Colomb (Cpte)
see CONCERT INDEX *under:*
(MUSD) **20239-2** Delibes—Opéras-Comiques
(PHIL) **438 970-2PM2** Camille Maurane

MICHEL, Bradle (tpt)
see CONCERT INDEX *under:*
(CARL) **PCD1051** Rachmaninov—Piano
Transcriptions

MICHEL, Danielle (mez)
Haydn: Mass 11
Suppé: Requiem

MICHEL, Solange (mez)
Bizet: Carmen (Cpte)
Debussy: Pelléas et Mélisande (Cpte)
G. Charpentier: Louise (Cpte)
Gounod: Faust (Cpte)
Ravel: Enfant et les sortilèges (Cpte)
see CONCERT INDEX *under:*
(EMI) **CHS7 69741-2(3)** Record of Singing,
Vol.4—French School

(MONT) **TCE8790** Debussy: Orchestral and Dramatic Works

MICHELANGELI, Arturo Benedetti (pf)
Beethoven: Piano Concerto 1, Piano Concerto 3, Piano Concerto 5, Piano Sonata 4
Brahms: Ballades
Debussy: Children's Corner, Images, Préludes (exc)
Haydn: Keyboard Concerto HobXVIII/4, Keyboard Concerto HobXVIII/11
Mozart: Piano Concerto 13, Piano Concerto 15
Rachmaninov: Piano Concerto 4
Ravel: Piano Concerto
Schubert: Piano Sonata, D537
see CONCERT INDEX *under:*
(DG) **413 449-2GH** Chopin: Piano Works
(EMI) **CDH7 64490-2** A.B. Michelangeli—Early Recordings
(MEMR) **999001** The Authorised Vatican Recordings-Michelangeli
(SIMA) **PSC1809(2)** Grieg—Historical Piano Recordings (pt 2)

MICHEL-DANSAC, Donatienne (sop)
Rameau: Nélée et Myrthis (Cpte), Pygmalion (Cpte)

MICHELETTI, Gaston (ten)
see CONCERT INDEX *under:*
(MSCM) **MM30451** Mascagni—Cavalleria Rusticana, etc
(NIMB) **NI7836/7** Conchita Supervia (1895-1936)

MICHELINI, Joëlle (sop)
Boieldieu: Calife de Bagdad (Cpte)

MICHELL, Edna (vn)
see CONCERT INDEX *under:*
(NEW) **NW375-2** Lukas Foss: Orchestral Works

MICHELUCCI, Roberto (vn)
Vivaldi: Concerti Grossi, Op. 3
see Michelangeli
(PHIL) **426 075-2PCC** Bach: Concertos
(PHIL) **426 086-2PBQ** Vivaldi—Double Concertos
(PHIL) **426 925-2PM19** The Complete Vivaldi Edition

MICHIELI, Jolanda (sop)
Verdi: Ernani (Cpte)

MICHIGAN UNIVERSITY MUSICAL SOCIETY CHORAL UNION
cond N. JÄRVI
Tchaikovsky: Snow Maiden (Cpte)

MICHNIEWSKI, Wojciech (cond)
see Sinfonia Varsovia

MIDBOE, David (bar)
Corghi: Divara (Cpte)

MIDDLETON, Arthur (bass)
see CONCERT INDEX *under:*
(PEAR) **GEMMCDS9074(2)** Giovanni Zenatello, Vol.2 (pt 2)

MIDDLETON, Karen (sop)
Wagner: Walküre (Cpte)

MID-GERMAN RADIO CHORUS
cond K. MASUR
Beethoven: Choral Fantasia

MIDGLEY, Maryetta (sop)
G. Charpentier: Louise (Cpte)
Puccini: Rondine (Cpte)
see CONCERT INDEX *under:*
(UNIC) **UKCD2071** The Delius Collection, Volume 1

MIDGLEY, Vernon (ten)
G. Charpentier: Louise (Cpte)
Puccini: Rondine (Cpte)
Rossini: Zelmira (Cpte)
see CONCERT INDEX *under:*
(CFP) **CD-CFP4637** Ketèlbey/Luigini—Orchestral Music
(UNIC) **UKCD2071** The Delius Collection, Volume 1

MIDGLEY, Walter (ten)
see CONCERT INDEX *under:*
(EMI) **CHS7 69741-2(2)** Record of Singing, Vol.4—Anglo-American School (pt 2)

MIDHOE, David (bar)
Delius: Village Romeo and Juliet (Cpte)

MIDI-PYRENEES REGIONAL CHOIR
cond M. PLASSON
Gounod: Roméo et Juliette (Cpte)

MIDORI, Miss (vn)
Bartók: Violin Concerto 1, Violin Concerto 2
Bruch: Scottish Fantasy
Paganini: Caprices, Op. 1
Sibelius: Violin Concerto
see CONCERT INDEX *under:*
(SONY) **SK44923** Dvořák—Orchestral Works
(SONY) **SK52568** Midori—Encore!

MIESSEN, Marijke (rec)
Telemann: Solos (1734) (exc)

MIGDAL, Marian (pf)
see CONCERT INDEX *under:*
(EMI) **CDM5 65073-2** Berwald—Orchestral Works

MIGENES (JOHNSON), Julia (sop)
Bizet: Carmen (Cpte)
Forrest/Wright: Kismet (Cpte)
Weill: Sieben Todsünden (Cpte)
see CONCERT INDEX *under:*
(ERAT) **4509-92875-2** Vienna - Operetta Arias

MIGLIETTE, Adrienne (sop)
see CONCERT INDEX *under:*
(DECC) **433 400-2DM2** Ravel & Debussy—Stage Works

MIGUEL, Pablo (pf)
Offenbach: Madame l'Archiduc (Cpte)
see CONCERT INDEX *under:*
(EMI) **CHS7 69741-2(1)** Record of Singing, Vol.4—Anglo-American School (pt 1)

MIHAILOV, Luben (ten)
see CONCERT INDEX *under:*
(EMI) **CMS7 63386-2** Borodin—Prince Igor & Complete Solo Songs

MIHÁLY, András (cond)
see Budapest Chbr Ens

MIHULE, Jiří (ob)
see CONCERT INDEX *under:*
(SUPR) **11 1445-2** Reicha/Beethoven—Compositions for Wind

MIILBERG, Hans (bass)
Tubin: Barbara von Tisenhusen (Cpte)

MIKAELI CHAMBER CHOIR
cond F. HAIDER
Donizetti: Linda di Chamounix (Cpte)
cond L. SEGERSTAM
Schnittke: Symphony 2

MIKASHOFF, Yvar (pf)
Stockhausen: Mantra

MIKHAILOV, Igor (bass)
Tchaikovsky: Eugene Onegin (Cpte)

MIKHAILOV, Lev (sax)
see CONCERT INDEX *under:*
(OLYM) **OCD165** Glazunov: Concertos

MIKKELSEN, Nis Bank (narr)
see CONCERT INDEX *under:*
(KONT) **32188** Nielsen—Vocal Works

MIKKELSEN, Terje (cond)
see Lithuanian Nat SO

MIKOREY, Karl (ten)
Wagner: Meistersinger (exc)

MÍKOVÁ, Alena (mez)
Janáček: From the House of the Dead (Cpte)

MIKULÁŠ, Peter (bass)
Beethoven: Mass in C
Bellini: Sonnambula (Cpte)
Brian: Symphony 1
Dvořák: Dimitrij (Cpte), Stabat mater, Te Deum
Mozart: Cosi fan tutte (Cpte)
Shostakovich: Symphony 13, Symphony 14
Suchoň: Whirlpool (Cpte)
Verdi: Requiem (Cpte), Simon Boccanegra (Cpte)
see CONCERT INDEX *under:*
(SUPR) **11 0816-2** Zelenka—Choral Works

MIKUS, Winfried (ten)
Keiser: Masagniello furioso (Cpte)

MILÁ, Lydia (sngr)
see CONCERT INDEX *under:*
(EMI) **CDC7 54883-2** Jerome Kern Treasury

MILAN, Susan (fl)
Mozart: Flute Quartets
see CONCERT INDEX *under:*
(CHAN) **CHAN8609** Flute Fantasie—Virtuoso French Flute Repertoire
(CHAN) **CHAN8613** Mozart: Works for Flute and Orchestra
(CHAN) **CHAN8840** La flûte enchantée
(CHAN) **CHAN8981/2** Gaubert—Works for Flute and Piano
(CHAN) **CHAN9051** Mozart/Salieri—Concertos
(CHAN) **CHAN9108** Beethoven—Chamber Works

MILAN ACADEMIA CHORUS
cond T. BRICCETTI
Mayr: Rosa Bianca (Cpte)

MILAN CHAMBER ORCHESTRA
cond P. VAGLIERI
Paisiello: Serva Padrona (Cpte)

MILAN LA SCALA CHORUS
see CONCERT INDEX *under:*
(SYMP) **SYMCD1113** The Harold Wayne Collection, Vol.13
cond C. ABBADO
Verdi: Aida (Cpte), Ballo in Maschera (Cpte), Don Carlos (Cpte), Macbeth (Cpte), Requiem (Cpte), Simon Boccanegra (Cpte)
see CONCERT INDEX *under:*
(RCA) **09026 68014-2** Pavarotti - The Early Years, Vol.2
cond U. BERRETTONI
Puccini: Bohème (Cpte)
cond R. CHAILLY
Rossini: Barbiere di Siviglia (Cpte)
cond G. GAVAZZENI
Donizetti: Anna Bolena (Cpte)
Rossini: Turco in Italia (Cpte)
cond F. GHIONE
see CONCERT INDEX *under:*
(EMI) **CDH7 63200-2** Tito Schipa—Recital
(MSCM) **MM30231** Don Pasquale & Tito Schipa Recital
cond C.M. GIULINI
Rossini: Italiana in Algeri (Cpte)

Verdi: Traviata (Cpte)
cond H. VON KARAJAN
Donizetti: Lucia di Lammermoor (Cpte)
Puccini: Madama Butterfly (Cpte)
Verdi: Trovatore (Cpte)
see CONCERT INDEX *under:*
(DG) **419 257-2GH3** 'Cav' and 'Pag', etc
(EMI) **CDM7 69543-2** Maria Callas and Giuseppe Di Stefano - Duets
(EMI) **CMS7 63244-2** The Art of Maria Callas
cond R. KUBELÍK
Verdi: Rigoletto (Cpte)
cond L. MAAZEL
Puccini: Fanciulla del West (Cpte), Manon Lescaut (Cpte)
Verdi: Aida (Cpte), Otello (Cpte)
cond L. VON MATAČIČ
Leoncavallo: Pagliacci (Cpte)
Puccini: Fanciulla del West (Cpte)
cond L. MOLAJOLI
see CONCERT INDEX *under:*
(EMI) **CDH7 69791-2** Dame Eva Turner sings Opera Arias and Songs
cond R. MUTI
Cherubini: Lodoïska (Cpte)
Gluck: Iphigénie en Tauride (Cpte)
Rossini: Donna del lago (Cpte)
Spontini: Vestale (Cpte)
Verdi: Attila (Cpte), Don Carlo (Cpte), Ernani (Cpte), Falstaff (Cpte), Forza del destino (Cpte), Requiem (Cpte), Rigoletto (Cpte), Traviata (Cpte), Vespri siciliani (Cpte)
cond G. NASTRUCCI
see CONCERT INDEX *under:*
(PREI) **89001** Toti dal Monte (1898-1975)
cond E. PANIZZA
see CONCERT INDEX *under:*
(EMI) **CHS7 64864-2(1)** La Scala Edition - Vol.2, 1915-46 (pt 1)
cond G. PRÊTRE
Leoncavallo: Pagliacci (Cpte)
Mascagni: Cavalleria Rusticana (Cpte)
cond C. SABAJNO
Puccini: Bohème (Cpte), Tosca (Cpte)
Verdi: Requiem (Cpte)
see CONCERT INDEX *under:*
(EMI) **CHS7 64864-2(1)** La Scala Edition - Vol.2, 1915-46 (pt 1)
(EMI) **CHS7 64008-2(1)** Wagner Singing on Record (pt 1)
(MSCM) **MM30231** Don Pasquale & Tito Schipa Recital
(NIMB) **NI7831** Mattia Battistini (1856-1928)
(NIMB) **NI7853** Lauri-Volpi sings Verdi
(PEAR) **GEMMCDS9074(2)** Giovanni Zenatello, Vol.2 (pt 2)
(PEAR) **GEMMCDS9926(1)** Covent Garden on Record—Vol.4 (pt 1)
cond V. DE SABATA
Puccini: Tosca (Cpte)
Verdi: Macbeth (Cpte)
see CONCERT INDEX *under:*
(EMI) **CDM7 63657-2** Schwarzkopf sings Opera Arias
(EMI) **CDM7 69543-2** Maria Callas and Giuseppe Di Stefano - Duets
(EMI) **CHS5 65506-2** Victor de Sabata conducts
(EMI) **CMS7 63244-2** The Art of Maria Callas
cond G. SANTINI
Verdi: Don Carlo (Cpte)
see CONCERT INDEX *under:*
(PREI) **89001** Toti dal Monte (1898-1975)
cond N. SANZOGNO
see CONCERT INDEX *under:*
(RCA) **09026 62541-2** Pavarotti - The Early Years, Vol.1
cond T. SERAFIN
Bellini: Norma (Cpte), Puritani (Cpte)
Cherubini: Medea (Cpte)
Donizetti: Elisir d'amore (Cpte)
Leoncavallo: Pagliacci (Cpte)
Mascagni: Cavalleria Rusticana (Cpte)
Puccini: Manon Lescaut (Cpte), Turandot (Cpte)
Verdi: Aida (Cpte), Forza del destino (Cpte), Rigoletto (Cpte)
see CONCERT INDEX *under:*
(EMI) **CMS7 63244-2** The Art of Maria Callas
cond G. SOLTI
Verdi: Simon Boccanegra (Cpte)
cond V. VENEZIANI
see CONCERT INDEX *under:*
(EMI) **CHS7 64864-2(2)** La Scala Edition - Vol.2, 1915-46 (pt 2)
cond A. VOTTO
Bellini: Sonnambula (Cpte)
Ponchielli: Gioconda (Cpte)
Puccini: Bohème (Cpte)
Verdi: Ballo in maschera (Cpte)
see CONCERT INDEX *under:*
(EMI) **CMS7 63244-2** The Art of Maria Callas

MILAN LA SCALA ORCHESTRA
see CONCERT INDEX *under:*
(PREI) **89001** Toti dal Monte (1898-1975)
cond C. ABBADO
Verdi: Aida (Cpte), Ballo in Maschera (Cpte), Don Carlos (Cpte), Macbeth (Cpte), Requiem (Cpte), Simon Boccanegra (Cpte)
see CONCERT INDEX *under:*
(BELA) **450 121-2** Plácido Domingo
(DG) **415 366-2GH** Plácido Domingo Recital
(DG) **431 104-2GB** Great Voices - Plácido Domingo

(RCA) 09026 68014-2 Pavarotti - The Early Years, Vol.2
(SONY) MK37228 Pavarotti sings Verdi
  cond G. ANTONICELLI
  see CONCERT INDEX *under:*
(EMI) CDH7 63200-2 Tito Schipa—Recital
(EMI) CHS7 64864-2(2) La Scala Edition - Vol.2, 1915-46 (pt 2)
(NIMB) NI7801 Great Singers, Vol.1
  cond U. BERRETTONI
Puccini: Bohème (Cpte)
  see CONCERT INDEX *under:*
(EMI) CDH7 61052-2 Beniamino Gigli—Arias and Duets (1932-1949)
(EMI) CDM7 63109-2 Tito Gobbi - Opera Aria Recital
(EMI) CHS7 64864-2(2) La Scala Edition - Vol.2, 1915-46 (pt 2)
(NIMB) NI7851 Legendary Voices
(PEAR) GEMMCDS9926(2) Covent Garden on Record—Vol.4 (pt 2)
(PREI) 89009 Gino Bechi (b. 1913)
(PREI) 89015 Carlo Tagliabue (1898-1978)
(TEST) SBT1019 Tito Gobbi - Opera Arias & Songs
  cond R. CHAILLY
Rossini: Barbiere di Siviglia (Cpte)
  cond A. EREDE
  see CONCERT INDEX *under:*
(EMI) CHS7 64864-2(2) La Scala Edition - Vol.2, 1915-46 (pt 2)
(LYRC) SRO805 Gina Cigna—Opera Recital
  cond O. DE FABRITIIS
  see CONCERT INDEX *under:*
(EMI) CDH7 61051-2 Beniamino Gigli - Operatic Arias
(MMOI) CDMOIR425 Three Tenors, Volume 2
  cond W. FURTWÄNGLER
  see CONCERT INDEX *under:*
(ACAN) 43 121 Wagner: Orchestral Works
  cond G. GAVAZZENI
Donizetti: Anna Bolena (Cpte)
Rossini: Turco in Italia (Cpte)
  see CONCERT INDEX *under:*
(EMI) CMS7 63244-2 The Art of Maria Callas
  cond F. GHIONE
  see CONCERT INDEX *under:*
(EMI) CDH7 61051-2 Beniamino Gigli - Operatic Arias
(EMI) CDH7 61052-2 Beniamino Gigli—Arias and Duets (1932-1949)
(EMI) CDH7 63200-2 Tito Schipa—Recital
(EMI) CHS7 64864-2(2) La Scala Edition - Vol.2, 1915-46 (pt 2)
(MMOI) CDMOIR409 Three Tenors—Björling, Gigli & Tauber
(MMOI) CDMOIR417 Great Voices of the Century—Beniamino Gigli
(MMOI) CDMOIR425 Three Tenors, Volume 2
(MSCM) MM30231 Don Pasquale & Tito Schipa Recital
(NIMB) NI7845 Giacomo Lauri-Volpi (1892-1979)
(NIMB) NI7853 Lauri-Volpi sings Verdi
(PEAR) GEMMCDS9925(2) Covent Garden on Record—Vol.3 (pt 2)
(PREI) 89012 Giacomo Lauri-Volpi (1894-1979)
(TEST) SBT1005 Ten Top Tenors
  cond C.M. GIULINI
Mozart: Piano Concerto 23
Rossini: Italiana in Algeri (Cpte)
Verdi: Traviata (Cpte)
  cond T.A. GUARNIERI
  see CONCERT INDEX *under:*
(EMI) CHS7 64864-2(1) La Scala Edition - Vol.2, 1915-46 (pt 1)
  cond H. VON KARAJAN
Puccini: Madama Butterfly (Cpte)
Verdi: Trovatore (Cpte)
  see CONCERT INDEX *under:*
(DG) 419 257-2GH3 'Cav' and 'Pag', etc
(EMI) CDM7 69543-2 Maria Callas and Giuseppe Di Stefano - Duets
(EMI) CMS7 63244-2 The Art of Maria Callas
  cond R. KUBELIK
Verdi: Rigoletto (Cpte)
  cond P. MAAG
  see CONCERT INDEX *under:*
(RCA) 09026 62541-2 Pavarotti - The Early Years, Vol.1
  cond L. MAAZEL
Puccini: Fanciulla del West (Cpte), Manon Lescaut (Cpte)
Verdi: Aida (Cpte), Otello (Cpte)
  cond G. MARINUZZI
  see CONCERT INDEX *under:*
(EMI) CHS7 64864-2(2) La Scala Edition - Vol.2, 1915-46 (pt 2)
(NIMB) NI7853 Lauri-Volpi sings Verdi
  cond L. VON MATACIC
Leoncavallo: Pagliacci (Cpte)
Puccini: Fanciulla del West (Cpte)
  cond L. MOLAJOLI
  see CONCERT INDEX *under:*
(MEMO) HR4408/9(2) Singers in Genoa, Vol.1 (disc 2)
(PREI) 89007 Aureliano Pertile (1885-1952) - I
(PREI) 89013 Giannina Arangi-Lombardi (1890-1951)
(PREI) 89040 Carlo Galeffi (1884-1961)
  cond R. MUTI
Cherubini: Lodoïska (Cpte)
Gluck: Iphigénie en Tauride (Cpte)
Pergolesi: Frate 'nnamorato (Cpte)

Rossini: Donna del lago (Cpte)
Spontini: Vestale (Cpte)
Verdi: Attila (Cpte), Don Carlo (Cpte), Ernani (Cpte), Falstaff (Cpte), Forza del destino (Cpte), Requiem (Cpte), Rigoletto (Cpte), Traviata (Cpte), Vespri siciliani (Cpte)
  see CONCERT INDEX *under:*
(EMI) CDC5 55017-2 Domingo Opera Classics
  cond G. NASTRUCCI
  see CONCERT INDEX *under:*
(PREI) 89007 Aureliano Pertile (1885-1952) - I
(PREI) 89048 Apollo Granforte (1886-1975) - I
(PREI) 89072 Aureliano Pertile (1885-1952) - II
  cond D. OLIVIERI
  see CONCERT INDEX *under:*
(MMOI) CDMOIR409 Three Tenors—Björling, Gigli & Tauber
(MMOI) CDMOIR417 Great Voices of the Century—Beniamino Gigli
  cond E. PANIZZA
  see CONCERT INDEX *under:*
(EMI) CHS7 64864-2(1) La Scala Edition - Vol.2, 1915-46 (pt 1)
  cond G. PRÊTRE
Leoncavallo: Pagliacci (Cpte)
Mascagni: Cavalleria Rusticana (Cpte)
  cond C. SABAJNO
Puccini: Bohème (Cpte), Tosca (Cpte)
Verdi: Requiem (Cpte)
  see CONCERT INDEX *under:*
(CLUB) CL99-025 Giovanni Zenatello (1876-1949)
(CLUB) CL99-509/10 Hina Spani (1896-1969)
(EMI) CDH7 61051-2 Beniamino Gigli - Operatic Arias
(EMI) CDH7 61052-2 Beniamino Gigli—Arias and Duets (1932-1949)
(EMI) CDH7 63200-2 Tito Schipa—Recital
(EMI) CHS7 64860-2(2) La Scala Edition - Vol.1, 1878-1914 (pt 2)
(EMI) CHS7 64864-2(1) La Scala Edition - Vol.2, 1915-46 (pt 1)
(EMI) CHS7 64864-2(2) La Scala Edition - Vol.2, 1915-46 (pt 2)
(EMI) CMS7 64008-2(1) Wagner Singing on Record (pt 1)
(MMOI) CDMOIR408 Great Sopranos
(MMOI) CDMOIR415 Sacred Songs and Arias
(MMOI) CDMOIR417 Great Voices of the Century—Beniamino Gigli
(MSCM) MM30231 Don Pasquale & Tito Schipa Recital
(NIMB) NI7850 Antonio Cortis (1891-1952)
(NIMB) NI7853 Lauri-Volpi sings Verdi
(NIMB) NI7856 Legendary Tenors
(PEAR) GEMMCDS9074(2) Giovanni Zenatello, Vol.2 (pt 2)
(PEAR) GEMMCDS9925(2) Covent Garden on Record—Vol.3 (pt 2)
(PEAR) GEMMCDS9926(1) Covent Garden on Record—Vol.4 (pt 1)
(PEAR) GEMMCDS9926(2) Covent Garden on Record—Vol.4 (pt 2)
(PEAR) GEMMCD9322 Tito Schipa sings Opera Arias and Songs
(PREI) 89001 Toti dal Monte (1898-1975)
(PREI) 89007 Aureliano Pertile (1885-1952) - I
(PREI) 89008 Irene Minghini-Cattaneo (1892-1944)
(PREI) 89037 Hina Spani (1896-1969)
(PREI) 89038 Giovanni Zenatello (1876-1949)
(PREI) 89043 Antonio Cortis (1891-1952)
(PREI) 89044 Dusolina Giannini (1902-1986)
(PREI) 89048 Apollo Granforte (1886-1975) - I
(PREI) 89072 Aureliano Pertile (1885-1952) - II
  cond V. DE SABATA
Puccini: Tosca (Cpte)
Verdi: Macbeth (Cpte)
  see CONCERT INDEX *under:*
(EMI) CDM7 63657-2 Schwarzkopf sings Opera Arias
(EMI) CDM7 69543-2 Maria Callas and Giuseppe Di Stefano - Duets
(EMI) CHS5 55506-2 Victor de Sabata conducts
(EMI) CMS7 63244-2 The Art of Maria Callas
  cond A. SABINO
  see CONCERT INDEX *under:*
(PREI) 89074 Tancredi Pasero (1893-1983) - II
  cond G. SANTINI
Verdi: Don Carlo (Cpte)
  see CONCERT INDEX *under:*
(EMI) CHS7 64864-2(1) La Scala Edition - Vol.2, 1915-46 (pt 1)
  cond N. SANZOGNO
  see CONCERT INDEX *under:*
(RCA) 09026 62541-2 Pavarotti - The Early Years, Vol.1
  cond T. SERAFIN
Bellini: Norma (Cpte), Puritani (Cpte)
Cherubini: Medea (Cpte)
Donizetti: Elisir d'amore (Cpte)
Leoncavallo: Pagliacci (Cpte)
Mascagni: Cavalleria Rusticana (Cpte)
Puccini: Manon Lescaut (Cpte), Turandot (Cpte)
Verdi: Aida (Cpte), Forza del destino (Cpte), Rigoletto (Cpte)
  see CONCERT INDEX *under:*
(EMI) CDC7 47282-2 Maria Callas - Operatic Recital
(EMI) CDC7 47966-2 Puccini and Bellini Arias
(EMI) CDM7 63182-2 The Incomparable Callas
(EMI) CDM7 63657-2 Schwarzkopf sings Opera Arias
(EMI) CDM7 69543-2 Maria Callas and Giuseppe Di Stefano - Duets
(EMI) CMS7 63244-2 The Art of Maria Callas

  cond G. SOLTI
Verdi: Simon Boccanegra (Cpte)
  see CONCERT INDEX *under:*
(DECC) 436 463-2DM Ten Top Tenors
  cond E. TIERI
  see CONCERT INDEX *under:*
(EMI) CHS7 69741-2(7) Record of Singing, Vol.4—Italian School
  cond A. TOSCANINI
  see CONCERT INDEX *under:*
(EMI) CHS7 64860-2(1) La Scala Edition - Vol.1, 1878-1914 (pt 1)
(EMI) CHS7 64864-2(2) La Scala Edition - Vol.2, 1915-46 (pt 2)
(RCA) GD60315 Toscanini Collection, Vol.71
  cond V. VENEZIANI
  see CONCERT INDEX *under:*
(EMI) CHS7 64864-2(2) La Scala Edition - Vol.2, 1915-46 (pt 2)
  cond A. VOTTO
Bellini: Sonnambula (Cpte)
Ponchielli: Gioconda (Cpte)
Puccini: Bohème (Cpte)
Verdi: Ballo in maschera (Cpte)
  see CONCERT INDEX *under:*
(EMI) CDM7 63110-2 Mirella Freni: Opera Recital
(EMI) CDM7 63182-2 The Incomparable Callas
(EMI) CDM7 69543-2 Maria Callas and Giuseppe Di Stefano - Duets
(EMI) CMS7 63244-2 The Art of Maria Callas

MILAN LA SCALA PHILHARMONIC ORCHESTRA
  cond C.M. GIULINI
Beethoven: Romances, Symphony 1, Symphony 2, Symphony 3, Symphony 4, Symphony 5, Symphony 7, Symphony 8, Violin Concerto
  see CONCERT INDEX *under:*
(SONY) SK53974 Beethoven—Orchestral Works
  cond R. MUTI
Bartók: Pictures, Sz46
Brahms: Serenade 1
Elgar: In the South
Stravinsky: Baiser de la fée (Cpte)
  see CONCERT INDEX *under:*
(SONY) SK53280 Italian Orchestral Works
(SONY) SK66279 Nino Rota—Orchestral Works

MILAN PHILHARMONIA
  cond C. COPPOLA
  see CONCERT INDEX *under:*
(SILV) SILVAD3001 At the Movies 1: Heroes & Tough Guys

MILAN POLYPHONIC CHOIR
  cond L. MAGIERA
Rossini: Petite messe solennelle

MILAN RAI CHORUS
  cond C.F. CILLARIO
Donizetti: Gianni di Parigi (Cpte)

MILAN RAI SYMPHONY ORCHESTRA
  cond C.F. CILLARIO
Donizetti: Gianni di Parigi (Cpte)

MILAN SYMPHONY ORCHESTRA
  cond L. MOLAJOLI
  see CONCERT INDEX *under:*
(PREI) 89013 Giannina Arangi-Lombardi (1890-1951)
  cond A. QUADRI
  see CONCERT INDEX *under:*
(EMI) CHS7 69741-2(7) Record of Singing, Vol.4—Italian School
(PREI) 89009 Gino Bechi (b. 1913)

MILANOV, Zinka (sop)
Mascagni: Cavalleria Rusticana (Cpte)
Puccini: Tosca (Cpte)
Verdi: Aida (Cpte), Requiem (Cpte), Trovatore (Cpte)
  see CONCERT INDEX *under:*
(EMI) CHS7 69741-2(7) Record of Singing, Vol.4—Italian School
(MYTO) 2MCD90317 Verdi—Un Ballo in maschera
(RCA) GD60276 Toscanini conducts Boito & Verdi
(RCA) GD87799 The Pearl Fishers Duet plus Duets and Scenes
(RCA) 09026 61580-2(5) RCA/Met 100 Singers, 100 Years (pt 5)

MILASHKINA, Tamara (sop)
Tchaikovsky: Eugene Onegin (Cpte), Queen of Spades (Cpte)

MILCHEVA, Alexandrina (mez)
Borodin: Prince Igor (Cpte)
Gluck: Cinesi (Cpte)
Leoncavallo: Bohème (Cpte)
Mussorgsky: Khovanshchina (Cpte)

MILDMAY, Audrey (sop)
Mozart: Don Giovanni (Cpte)
  see CONCERT INDEX *under:*
(EMI) CDH5 65072-2 Glyndebourne Recorded - 1934-1994

MILES, Alastair (bass)
Beethoven: Missa Solemnis
Berlioz: Enfance du Christ (Cpte)
Britten: Rape of Lucretia (Cpte)
Bruckner: Mass in D minor, Te Deum
Donizetti: Lucia di Lammermoor (Cpte)
Elgar: Caractacus (Cpte)
Handel: Messiah (Cpte), Messias, K572 (Cpte), Samson (Cpte), Saul (Cpte)
Haydn: Stabat Mater

(APR) **APR7023** Egon Petri, Vol.1
(PEAR) **GEMMCD9347** Ferruccio Busoni & Egon Petri
cond S. SKROWACZEWSKI
Prokofiev: Romeo and Juliet Suites
Shostakovich: Symphony 5
see CONCERT INDEX under:
(MERC) **432 011-2MM** Works for Piano and Orchestra

MINNESOTA CHORALE
cond J. REVZEN
Haydn: Jahreszeiten (Cpte), Schöpfung (Cpte)

MINNESOTA ORCHESTRA
cond A. DORATI
Bartók: Suite 2, Violin Concerto 2
cond N. MARRINER
see CONCERT INDEX under:
(EMI) **CDM7 64300-2** Holst/Purcell/Britten—Orchestral Works
(SONY) **MK39310** Haydn Concertos
(TELA) **CD82005** Wagner—Orchestral Music from Operas
cond J. REVZEN
see CONCERT INDEX under:
(KOCH) **37248-2** The Art of Arleen Auger
cond L. SLATKIN
Tchaikovsky: Nutcracker Suite, Swan Lake (exc)
cond E. DE WAART
Glazunov: Scènes de Ballet, Seasons
R. Strauss: Sinfonia Domestica, Suite, Op. 4

MINSK PHILHARMONIC ORCHESTRA
cond S. FRONTALINI
see CONCERT INDEX under:
(BONG) **GB2115-2** Ponchielli—Orchestral Works

MINSKY, Meir (cond)
see Košice St PO

MINTER, Drew (alto)
Handel: Agrippina (Cpte), Clori, Tirsi e Fileno (Cpte), Esther (Cpte), Floridante (Cpte), Giustino (Cpte), Messiah (Cpte), Ottone (Cpte), Sosarme (Cpte), Susanna (Cpte), Theodora (Cpte)
see CONCERT INDEX under:
(HARM) **HMC90 5183** Handel: Arias for Senesino
(HARM) **HMU90 7023** T.Campion—Ayres
(HARM) **HMU90 7035** Sweeter than Roses - Purcell Songs
(HARM) **HMU90 7053** Humfrey—Verse Anthems
(KOCH) **37138-2** Bach—Solo Cantatas
(KOCH) **37164-2** Bach—Cantatas, Vol.3

MINTON, Yvonne (mez)
Bach: Mass in B minor, BWV232 (Cpte)
Beethoven: Symphony 9
Berg: Lulu (Cpte)
Bizet: Carmen (Cpte)
Bruckner: Te Deum
Elgar: Dream of Gerontius (Cpte), Kingdom (Cpte)
Mahler: Symphony 8
Mozart: Clemenza di Tito (Cpte), Così fan tutte (Cpte), Nozze di Figaro (Cpte), Requiem
R. Strauss: Elektra (Cpte), Rosenkavalier (Cpte)
Rossini: Stabat Mater
Schoenberg: Gurrelieder, Lieder, Op. 22
Tippett: Knot Garden (Cpte)
Verdi: Pezzi sacri (Cpte)
Wagner: Parsifal (Cpte), Rheingold (Cpte), Walküre (Cpte)
see CONCERT INDEX under:
(DECC) **430 094-2DWO** The World of Elgar
(DECC) **430 792-2DC6** Beethoven—Complete Symphonies, etc
(DECC) **430 804-2DC10** Mahler—Complete Symphonies
(DG) **429 025-2GX10** Bruckner—Complete Symphonies, etc
(DG) **437 244-2GGA2** Berlioz/Franck—Vocal & Orchestral Works
(PHIL) **438 800-2PM2** Mozart—Choral Works
(SONY) **SMK48466** Boulez conducts Schoenberg—Volume 3
(SONY) **SM3K64103** Berlioz—Orchestral and Vocal Works

MINTY, Shirley (mez)
G. Charpentier: Louise (Cpte)
Haydn: Mass 9
Vaughan Williams: Hugh the Drover (Cpte)
see CONCERT INDEX under:
(EMI) **CDC7 54626-2** Operetta Arias
(EMI) **CDM7 64022-2** Vaughan Williams—Orchestral Works
(HYPE) **CDA66175** Music by Bliss, Britten and Holst
(L'OI) **421 478-2OH** Haydn—Masses
(L'OI) **421 654-2OH** Handel & Haydn: Choral works
(SONY) **M3K79312** Puccini: Il Trittico

MINTZ, Shlomo (va)
Mozart: Sinfonia Concertante, K364

MINTZ, Shlomo (vn)
Bach: Solo Violin Partitas and Sonatas
Beethoven: Romances, Violin Concerto
Dvořák: Violin Concerto
Mendelssohn: Violin Sonata, Op. 4, Violin Sonata (1838)
Paganini: Caprices, Op. 1
Prokofiev: Violin Concerto 1, Violin Concerto 2
Sibelius: Violin Concerto
Vivaldi: Concerti, Op. 8 (exc)
see CONCERT INDEX under:
(DG) **419 629-2GH** Violin Works
(DG) **427 676-2GH** French Works for Violin and Orchestra

(DG) **439 413-2GCL** Prokofiev—Orchestral Works
(DG) **445 501-2GMA** Bartók/Janáček—Orchestral Works
(DG) **445 557-2GMA** Prokofiev/Ravel—Violin Works

MINTZ, Shlomo (vn/dir)
see CONCERT INDEX under:
(MUSM) **67120-2** Vivaldi—Violin Concertos, Volume VI

MINZHILKIEV, Bulat (bass)
Borodin: Prince Igor (Cpte)
Mussorgsky: Khovanshchina (Cpte)
Rimsky-Korsakov: Sadko (Cpte)

MIORI, Ilaria (vn)
see CONCERT INDEX under:
(ONDI) **ODE826-2** Sibelius—Early Chamber Music, Vol. 1

MIQUELLE, Georges (vc)
see CONCERT INDEX under:
(MERC) **432 718-2MM** Bloch—Orchestral works

MIRA, Brigitte (sop)
Künneke: Vetter aus Dingsda (exc)
Offenbach: Vie Parisienne (exc)

MIRABAL, Linda (mez)
Vives: Doña Francisquita (Cpte)

MIRANDA, Ana-Maria (sop)
Galuppi: Magnificat in G

MIRECOURT TRIO
Beethoven: Piano Trios (exc)
see CONCERT INDEX under:
(MUSI) **MACD-635** American Chamber Works

MIRICIOIU, Nelly (sop)
Mercadante: Orazi e Curiazi (Cpte)
Puccini: Tosca (Cpte)
see CONCERT INDEX under:
(ETCE) **KTC1041** Nelly Miricioiu—Recital

MIRRING, Peter (vn)
Mozart: Flute Quartets

MIRRING QUARTET
see CONCERT INDEX under:
(CAPR) **10 801** Mozart: Serenades & Divertimenti

MIRTSCH, Senta (mez)
R. Strauss: Elektra (Cpte)

MIRYŃSKI, Janusz (vn)
see CONCERT INDEX under:
(CONI) **CDCF147** Van de Vate: Orchestral Works
(CONI) **CDCF168** Penderecki & Van de Vate—Orchestral Works

MISCHAKOFF, Mischa (vn)
see CONCERT INDEX under:
(APR) **APR7016** The Auer Legacy, Vol.2
(RCA) **GD60282** Haydn—Orchestral Works
(RCA) **GD60325** Brahms: Symphonies & Other Works

MIŠEJKA, Peter (vc)
Domažlicky: Czech Songs

MISHCHEVSKI, Anatole (ten)
Kabalevsky: Colas Breugnon (Cpte)

MISHENKIN, Arkady (ten)
Rimsky-Korsakov: Tsar's Bride (Cpte)

MISHURA-LEKHTMAN, Irina (mez)
Tchaikovsky: Snow Maiden (Cpte)

MISSENHARDT, Günther (bar)
Mozart: Entführung (Cpte)

MISSIN, William (alto)
see CONCERT INDEX under:
(PROU) **PROUCD125** Rejoice in the Lamb

MISTRAL, Nati (sop)
see CONCERT INDEX under:
(DECC) **417 786-2DM** Spanish Orchestral Works

MISTRY STRING QUARTET
Bax: Piano Quintet, String Quartet 2
see CONCERT INDEX under:
(UNIC) **DKPCD9082** Maconchy—String Quartets Vol. III
cond S. MONTAGUE
see CONCERT INDEX under:
(CNTI) **CCD1009** Music of Barry Anderson

MIT SYMPHONY ORCHESTRA
cond D. EPSTEIN
Barber: Piano Concerto

MITCHELL, Alasdair (cond)
see LPO

MITCHELL, Alastair (bn)
see CONCERT INDEX under:
(CLRI) **CC0004** The Early Clarinet Family

MITCHELL, Billy J. (spkr)
Gershwin: Porgy and Bess (Cpte)

MITCHELL, Brenda (sop)
see CONCERT INDEX under:
(ETCE) **KTC1070** Ferneyhough: Various Works

MITCHELL, Ian (cl)
Lumsdaine: What shall I sing?
see CONCERT INDEX under:
(UNIC) **UKCD2010** Knussen—Orchestral & Vocal Works

MITCHELL, Leona (sop)
Gershwin: Porgy and Bess (Cpte)

MITCHELL, Madeleine (sop)
Sullivan: Iolanthe (Cpte)

MITCHELL, Madeline (vc)
Krauze: Quatuor pour la Naissance
Messiaen: Quatuor

MITCHELL, Red (db)
see CONCERT INDEX under:
(EMI) **CMS7 64617-2** The art of Itzhak Perlman
(EMI) **CZS4 83177-2(3)** Itzhak Perlman Edition (pt 3)

MITCHELL, Scott (pf)
see CONCERT INDEX under:
(COLL) **Coll1103-2** Sonatas for Flute

MITCHELL, Warren (spkr)
Gay: Beggar's Opera (Cpte)

(GEOFFREY) MITCHELL CHOIR
cond A. FRANCIS
Donizetti: Maria Padilla (Cpte), Ugo, Conte di Parigi (Cpte)
Offenbach: Christopher Columbus (Cpte), Robinson Crusoé (Cpte)
see CONCERT INDEX under:
(OPRA) **ORC003** Donizetti—Gabriella di Vergy
cond J. JUDD
Meyerbeer: Dinorah (Cpte)
see CONCERT INDEX under:
(OPRA) **ORC004** Donizetti—Ne m'oubliez pas; Arias
cond A. MELVILLE
Boughton: Immortal Hour (Cpte)
cond D. PARRY
Donizetti: Assedio di Calais (Cpte), Emilia di Liverpool (Cpte), Eremitaggio di Liverpool (Cpte)
Mayr: Medea (Cpte)
Mercadante: Orazi e Curiazi (Cpte)
Meyerbeer: Crociato in Egitto (Cpte)
see CONCERT INDEX under:
(OPRA) **ORCH103** Italian Opera—1810-20
(OPRA) **ORCH104** A Hundred Years of Italian Opera: 1820-1830

MITCHINSON, John (ten)
Alwyn: Miss Julie (Cpte)
Elgar: Dream of Gerontius (Cpte)
Janáček: Glagolitic Mass (Cpte)
Mahler: Lied von der Erde, Symphony 8
Martinů: Greek Passion (Cpte)
Purcell: Dido (Cpte)
Stravinsky: Noces
Wagner: Tristan und Isolde (Cpte)
see CONCERT INDEX under:
(DECC) **430 159-2DM** Haydn, M.Haydn & Mozart: Sacred Choral Works
(SONY) **SM3K64103** Berlioz—Orchestral and Vocal Works

MITROPOULOS, Dimitri (cond)
see BRSO

MITSUI, Tsuyako (mez)
see CONCERT INDEX under:
(HANS) **98 882** Bach—Cantatas, Vol.31

MITTERER, Anita (vn)
Mozart: Piano Trio, K498

MITTERHOFER, Alfred (harm)
see CONCERT INDEX under:
(EMI) **CDC7 54881-2** Viennese Dance Music

MITTMAN, Leopold (pf)
see CONCERT INDEX under:
(APR) **APR7016** The Auer Legacy, Vol.2
(BIDD) **LAB055** Nathan Milstein - Early Columbia Recordings
(BIDD) **LAB096** Nathan Milstein-Columbia Recordings 1936-1942
(RCA) **09026 61879-2** Grieg—Historic Recordings

MIXOVÁ, Ivana (mez)
Dvořák: Jacobin (Cpte)
Janáček: Cunning Little Vixen (Cpte), Jenufa (Cpte), Káťa Kabanová (Cpte), Makropulos Affair (Cpte)
Martinů: Julietta (Cpte)
Smetana: Devil's Wall (Cpte)

MIXYLODIAN
cond P. SCHMIDT
see CONCERT INDEX under:
(CARL) **PCD970** Victoria and the Music of Imperial Spain

MIYAMOTO, Fumiaki (ob)
see CONCERT INDEX under:
(NOVA) **150 006-2** Mozart: Chamber Works

MIZUNO, Keiko (vn)
see CONCERT INDEX under:
(DENO) **C37-7486** Satie: Piano works

MKRTCHIAN, Lina (contr)
Karetnikov: Till Eulenspiegel (Cpte)

MOBERG, Ruth (sop)
see CONCERT INDEX under:
(BLUE) **ABCD028** Jussi Björling live at the Stockholm Opera

MOCHALOV, Alexei (bass)
Karetnikov: Till Eulenspiegel (Cpte)

MOCHIKI, Fumiko (mez)
Verdi: Traviata (Cpte)

MOCHIKI, Hiroshi (ten)
Verdi: Traviata (Cpte)

MODENA TEATRO COMUNALE ORCHESTRA
cond L. MAGIERA
see CONCERT INDEX *under:*
(RCA) 09026 62541-2 Pavarotti - The Early Years, Vol.1
(RCA) 09026 68014-2 Pavarotti - The Early Years, Vol.2

MODENO TEATRO COMUNALE CHORUS
cond C. DESDERI
Rossini: Pietra del paragone (Cpte)

MODERN ENSEMBLE
see CONCERT INDEX *under:*
(SONY) SK53290 Kurtag—Song Cycles
cond P. EÖTVÖS
see CONCERT INDEX *under:*
(SONY) SK53290 Kurtag—Song Cycles
(SONY) SK58945 Ligeti—Concertos
cond H. HOLLIGER
see CONCERT INDEX *under:*
(ECM) 437 441-2 Holliger—Scardanelli-Zyklus
cond I. METZMACHER
Cage: Sixteen Dances
Henze: Requiem
Nono: Prometeo (Cpte)
see CONCERT INDEX *under:*
(BRID) BCD9045 Benedict Mason—Chamber and Orchestral Works
(EMI) CDC7 54552-2 A Portrait of Charles Ives
(RCA) 09026 61180-2 Nancarrow—Studies
cond H. ZENDER
Schubert: Winterreise (Cpte)

MODESTI, Guiseppe (bass)
Cherubini: Medea (Cpte)
Donizetti: Linda di Chamounix (Cpte)
Giordano: Andrea Chénier (Cpte)
Puccini: Bohème (Cpte), Gianni Schicchi (Cpte)
Verdi: Aida (Cpte)

MÖDL, Martha (sop/mez)
Beethoven: Fidelio (Cpte)
Wagner: Götterdämmerung (Cpte), Parsifal (Cpte), Tristan und Isolde (exc), Walküre (Cpte)
see CONCERT INDEX *under:*
(EMI) CZS7 67123-2 Wagner: Der Ring des Nibelungen
(PHIL) 446 057-2PB14 Wagner—The Ring Cycle - Bayreuth Festival 1967

MODOS, Laszlo (bar)
Ligeti: Grand Macabre (Cpte)

MODRIAN, Joszef (ten)
see CONCERT INDEX *under:*
(MARC) 8 223430 Berwald—Piano Trios, Vol.2

MODUS NOVUS CHOIR
cond J. VAN IMMERSEEL
Mendelssohn: Hochzeit des Camacho (Cpte)

MOE, Eric (pf/hpd/org)
see CONCERT INDEX *under:*
(KOCH) 37130-2 John Cage—Thirteen Harmonies

MOELLER, Jobst (bar)
Lehár: Land des Lächelns (Cpte)

MOERSCHEL, Joel (vc)
see CONCERT INDEX *under:*
(NORT) NR228-CD Youthful Rapture—Chamber Music of Percy Graigner

MOFFAT, Julie (sop)
Various: Requiem of Reconciliation (Cpte)

MOFFO, Anna (sop)
Donizetti: Lucia di Lammermoor (Cpte)
Gluck: Orfeo ed Euridice (Cpte)
Mozart: Nozze di Figaro (Cpte)
Puccini: Bohème (Cpte), Madama Butterfly (Cpte), Rondine (Cpte)
R. Strauss: Capriccio (Cpte)
Verdi: Falstaff (Cpte), Luisa Miller (Cpte), Rigoletto (Cpte)
see CONCERT INDEX *under:*
(EMIL) CDZ7 67015-2 Mozart—Opera Arias
(RCA) GD87831 Moffo & Stokowski
(RCA) 09026 61580-2(7) RCA/Met 100 Singers, 100 Years (pt 7)

MOGENSEN, Morten (pf)
see CONCERT INDEX *under:*
(KONT) 32197 Syberg—Chamber Music, Vol. 2
(KONT) 32200 Nielsen—Works for Violin

MOGLIA, Alain (vn)
see CONCERT INDEX *under:*
(AUVI) V4697 Bach—Violin Concertos

MOGRELIA, Andrew (cond)
see Košice St PO

MOHÁCSI, Eva (sop)
Kodály: Missa Brevis

MOHR, Thomas (ten)
Busoni: Arlecchino (Cpte)
Marschner: Hans Heiling (Cpte)
Weill: Mahagonny-Gesänge (Cpte), Sieben Todsünden (Cpte)
see CONCERT INDEX *under:*
(WERG) WER6275-2 Orff—Trionfi

MOISEIWITSCH, Benno (pf)
see CONCERT INDEX *under:*
(APR) APR5505 Moiseiwitsch - Rachmaninov recordings, 1937-43

(APR) APR7005 Benno Moiseiwitsch—Solo Piano Recordings, 1938-50
(EMI) CDC7 54839-2 Medtner plays Medtner
(KOCH) 37035-2 Benno Moiseiwitsch—A Centenary Celebration
(OPAL) OPALCD9839 Pupils of Theodore Leschetizky
(RCA) 09026 61778-2(07) The Heifetz Collection, Vol. 7
(TEST) SBT1014 Delius—Orchestral Works
(TEST) SBT1023 Moiseiwitsch plays Schumann and Brahms

MOIZAN, Geneviève (sop)
Ganne: Saltimbanques (exc)

MOK, Gwendolyn (pf)
see CONCERT INDEX *under:*
(CALA) CACD1005 Ravel—Orchestral Works, Vol.2

MOK, Warren (ten)
Mendelssohn: Hochzeit des Camacho (Cpte)

MOKRENKO, Anatoly (bar)
Prokofiev: Ivan the Terrible

MOKRZYCKA (MOSCISCA), Maria (sop)
see CONCERT INDEX *under:*
(NIMB) NI7831 Mattia Battistini (1856-1928)
(PEAR) GEMMCD9936 Mattia Battistini, Vol.1

MOLAJOLI, Lorenzo (cond)
see La Scala Orch

MOLDOVA PHILHARMONIC ORCHESTRA
cond C. MANDEAL
Bretan: Arald (Cpte), Golem (Cpte)

MOLDVAY, József (bass)
Giordano: Andrea Chénier (Cpte)
Handel: Floridante (Cpte), St John Passion (Cpte)

MOLEDA, Krzysztof (ten)
Rossini: Signor Bruschino (Cpte)

MOLINARI, Enrico (bar)
see CONCERT INDEX *under:*
(ECM) 839 617-2 Bach & Carter—Instrumental & Chamber Works
(PREI) 89013 Giannina Arangi-Lombardi (1890-1951)

MOLINARI-PRADELLI, Francesco (cond)
see MMF Orch

MOLINARI-PRADELLI, Francesco (pf)
Rossini: Album de Musique (Cpte)

MOLL, Kurt (bass)
Beethoven: Fidelio (Cpte), Mass in C, Missa Solemnis
Haydn: Schöpfung (Cpte)
M-A. Charpentier: Magnificat, H74, Te Deum, H146
Mozart: Don Giovanni (Cpte), Entführung (Cpte), Mass, K139, Mass, K427, Nozze di Figaro (Cpte), Schauspieldirektor (Cpte), Zauberflöte (Cpte)
Prokofiev: Fiery Angel (Cpte)
R. Strauss: Daphne (Cpte), Elektra (Cpte), Intermezzo (Cpte), Rosenkavalier (exc), Salome (Cpte)
Schmidt: Notre Dame (Cpte)
Schubert: Winterreise (Cpte)
Shostakovich: Lady Macbeth of Mtsensk (Cpte)
Spohr: Jessonda (Cpte)
Verdi: Forza del destino (Cpte), Otello (Cpte), Rigoletto (Cpte)
Wagner: Fliegende Holländer (Cpte), Lohengrin (Cpte), Meistersinger (Cpte), Parsifal (Cpte), Siegfried (Cpte), Tannhäuser (Cpte), Tristan und Isolde (Cpte), Walküre (Cpte)
Weber: Freischütz (Cpte)
Wolf: Corregidor (Cpte)
see CONCERT INDEX *under:*
(ACAN) 44 2093-2 Brahms—Lieder
(ARCH) 439 380-2AX6 Bach—Cantatas, Volume 3 - Ascension Day; Whitsun; Trinity
(DG) 423 481-2GX6 Beethoven: Complete Symphonies
(DG) 445 354-2GX14 Wagner—Der Ring des Nibelungen
(HARM) HMC90 5210 Duos Romantiques
(ORFE) C021821A Schubert: Lieder

MOLL, Philip (hpd)
Bach: Flute Sonatas, BWV1030-5 (exc), Violin Sonatas, BWV1020-25 (exc)

MOLL, Philip (pf)
see CONCERT INDEX *under:*
(CAPR) 10 332 Mahler—Lieder
(DECC) 417 289-2DH Con amore
(DECC) 430 094-2DWO The World of Elgar
(DECC) 433 220-2DWO The World of the Violin
(DG) 423 696-2GH Lutosławski/Stravinsky—Concerted Works
(DG) 445 487-2GX3 Mutter plays Modern Works
(LOND) 421 388-2LM Elgar: Violin Concerto, etc
(PHIL) 412 623-2PH Schubert: Lieder
(RCA) GD86517 Galway plays Bach
(RCA) RD87756 Beethoven: Chamber Works for Flute
(RCA) 09026 60704-2 Violin Recital - Kyoko Takezawa
(RCA) 09026 61789-2 Concerto! Galway & Robles play Mozart

MØLLER, Annemarie (mez)
Mussorgsky: Boris Godunov (Cpte)
Schumann: Rose Pilgerfahrt (Cpte)

MØLLER, Arne Balk (vn)
see CONCERT INDEX *under:*
(BIS) BIS-CD710 Gubaidulina—Chamber Works

MØLLER, Ebbe Monrad (ob)
see CONCERT INDEX *under:*
(KONT) 32197 Syberg—Chamber Music, Vol. 2

MØLLER, Niels (ten)
Nielsen: Symphony 3
Wagner: Parsifal (Cpte)

MÖLLER, Stephan (pf)
see CONCERT INDEX *under:*
(SCHW) 313612 Wagner—Piano Works, Vol.1
(SCHW) 313622 Wagner—Piano Works, Vol.2

MÖLLER, Wouter (vc)
Telemann: Solos (1734) (exc), Sonate Metodiche (exc)
see CONCERT INDEX *under:*
(TELD) 4509-97465-2 Franz Brüggen Edition Vol. 3—English Ensemble Music
(TELD) 4509-97466-2 Frans Brüggen Edition Vol. 4—Early Baroque Recorder Music
(TELD) 4509-97467-2 Frans Brüggen Edition Vol. 5—Late Baroque Chamber Music

MOLLET, Pierre (bar)
Gounod: Roméo et Juliette (Cpte)
Martin: Mystère de la Nativité
see CONCERT INDEX *under:*
(CASC) VEL2010 Memories of the Suisse Romande - Suzanne Danco
(DECC) 433 400-2DM2 Ravel & Debussy—Stage Works
(EMI) CDM7 64281-2 Boulanger—Vocal & Chamber Works

MOLLIEN, Jean (bass)
Ganne: Hans (Cpte)
see CONCERT INDEX *under:*
(MUSD) 20239-2 Delibes—Opéras-Comiques

MOLLIN, Fred (cond)
see OST

MOLNÁR, András (ten)
Liszt: Faust Symphony

MOLSBERGER, Friedrich (bass)
Busoni: Turandot (Cpte)
Mendelssohn: Hochzeit des Camacho (Cpte)
R. Strauss: Salome (Cpte)
Schreker: Gezeichneten (Cpte)

MOLTKAU, Hans (ten)
see Munich RO

MOMPOU, Federico (pf)
see CONCERT INDEX *under:*
(EMI) CDC7 54836-2 Granados/Falla/Mompou/Nin

MONACHESI, Walter (bar)
Verdi: Simon Boccanegra (Cpte)

MONACO, Daniela de (contr)
Traetta: Buovo d'Antona (Cpte)

MONACO, Jerome Io (ten)
Verdi: Lombardi (Cpte)

MONACO, Mario Del (ten)
Bizet: Carmen (exc)
Boito: Mefistofele (Cpte)
Catalani: Wally (Cpte)
Cilea: Adriana Lecouvreur (Cpte)
Giordano: Fedora (Cpte)
J. Strauss II: Fledermaus (Cpte)
Ponchielli: Gioconda (Cpte)
Puccini: Manon Lescaut (Cpte), Tosca (Cpte), Turandot (Cpte)
Verdi: Forza del Destino (Cpte), Otello (Cpte), Rigoletto (Cpte)
Zandonai: Francesca da Rimini (exc)
see CONCERT INDEX *under:*
(DECC) 411 665-2DM3 Puccini: Il trittico
(DECC) 436 463-2DM Ten Top Tenors
(EMI) CHS7 69741-2(7) Record of Singing, Vol.4—Italian School

MONADNICK FESTIVAL CHORUS
cond J. BOLLE
V. Thomson: Lord Byron (Cpte)

MONADNICK FESTIVAL ORCHESTRA
cond J. BOLLE
V. Thomson: Lord Byron (Cpte)
see CONCERT INDEX *under:*
(ALBA) TROY017-2 Virgil Thomson—Vocal and Orchestral Works

MONAR, Isabel (mez)
Vives: Bohemios (Cpte)

MONCAYO VON HASE, Susanna (contr)
Hasse: Miserere in E minor, Requiem in C

MÖNCH, Georg (vn)
see CONCERT INDEX *under:*
(ETCE) KTC1119 Bartók—Works for Violin and Piano

MONCK, Sam (treb)
Britten: Little Sweep (Cpte)

MONCLOA, Calatlina (sop)
see CONCERT INDEX *under:*
(MARC) 8 223753 Montsalvatge/Rodrigo—Works

MONDRIAAN QUARTET
see CONCERT INDEX *under:*
(ETCE) KTC1093 G.Antheil—The String Quartets
(ETCE) KTC1124 Schnittke—Chamber Works

(RCA) 09026 61583-2(5) Julian Bream Edition (pt 5)
(RCA) 09026 61588-2 J. Bream Edition, Vol.5:
Concertos & Sonatas for Lte
(RCA) 09026 61605-2 J. Bream Edition, Vol.22: Gtr
Concertos

MONTFORT, Jeanne (mez)
Gounod: Faust (Cpte)

MONTGOMERY, Brian (bar)
Puccini: Fanciulla del West (Cpte)

MONTGOMERY, Kenneth (cond)
see Bournemouth Sinfonietta

MONTGOMERY, Mary Binney (pf)
see CONCERT INDEX under:
(BIDD) WHL012 Stokowski conducts French Music,
Vol.2

MONTGOMERY, Roger (cond)
see Jane's Minstrels

MONTGOMERY & STONE (sngrs)
see CONCERT INDEX under:
(PEAR) GEMMCDS9053/5 Music from the New York
Stage, Vol. 2: 1908–1913

MONTHY, Georg (bass)
Wagner: Tristan und Isolde (exc)
see CONCERT INDEX under:
(PREI) 90237 R Strauss—Daphne
(SCHW) 314542 Vienna State Opera Live, Vol.4
(SCHW) 314552 Vienna State Opera Live, Vol.5
(SCHW) 314572 Vienna State Opera Live, Vol.7
(SCHW) 314602 Vienna State Opera Live, Vol.10
(SCHW) 314632 Vienna State Opera Live, Vol.13
(SCHW) 314652 Vienna State Opera Live, Vol.15

MONTI, Nicola (ten)
Bellini: Sonnambula (Cpte)
Leoncavallo: Pagliacci (Cpte)
see CONCERT INDEX under:
(DECC) 433 706-2DMO3 Bellini—Beatrice di Tenda;
Operatic Arias
(EMI) CDM7 63109-2 Tito Gobbi - Opera Aria Recital

MONTICELLO TRIO
Maw: Piano Trio

MONTMOLLIN, Marie-Luise de (mez)
Martin: Vin herbé
see CONCERT INDEX under:
(DECC) 433 400-2DM2 Ravel & Debussy—Stage
Works

MONTREAL I MUSICI
Shostakovich: Piano Concerto 2
cond M. SHOSTAKOVICH
Shostakovich: Piano Concerto 1, Symphony for
Strings
cond Y. TUROVSKY
Handel: Concerti grossi, Op. 6
Mozart: Church Sonatas, Piano Concerto 12, Piano
Concerto 14
Schubert: German Dances and Trios, D90, Minuets
and Trios, D89, String Quartet, D810
Shostakovich: Chamber Symphony, Op. 110a,
Symphony 14
Tchaikovsky: Souvenir de Florence
Wassenaer: Concerti Armonici
see CONCERT INDEX under:
(CHAN) CHAN8444 Vivaldi—Chamber Works
(CHAN) CHAN8515 Works for string orchestra
(CHAN) CHAN8632 Honegger: Orchestral Works
(CHAN) CHAN8651 Vivaldi: Concertos
(CHAN) CHAN8800 Music on Hebrew Themes
(CHAN) CHAN8817 Britten: Orchestral Works
(CHAN) CHAN9149 Rimsky-Korsakov/Glinka—Vocal
Works

MONTREAL QUARTET
Brahms: Piano Quintet

MONTREAL SINFONIETTA
cond C. DUTOIT
see CONCERT INDEX under:
(DECC) 436 209-2DH Pergolesi & A Scarlatti—Choral
Works
(DECC) 440 327-2DH Stravinsky—Orchestral Works

MONTREAL SYMPHONY ORCHESTRA
cond C. DUTOIT
Berlioz: Roméo et Juliette (Cpte), Symphonie funèbre
et triomphale, Troyens (Cpte)
Bizet: Arlésienne Suites, Carmen Suites
Debussy: Images, Nocturnes, Pelléas et Mélisande
(Cpte)
Falla: Amor brujo (Cpte), Sombrero de tres picos
(Cpte)
Franck: Symphony
Gounod: Faust (exc)
Holst: Planets
Indy: Symphonie, Op. 25
Janáček: Glagolitic Mass (Cpte), Sinfonietta
Mendelssohn: Violin Concerto, Op. 64
Offenbach: Gaîté Parisienne (Cpte)
Prokofiev: Romeo and Juliet (exc)
R. Strauss: Bourgeois Gentilhomme Suite, Dance
Suite
Ravel: Daphnis et Chloé (Cpte)
Saint-Saëns: Symphony 3
Shostakovich: Symphony 1, Symphony 5, Symphony
9, Symphony 15
Tchaikovsky: Nutcracker (Cpte), Sleeping Beauty
(exc), Swan Lake (Cpte), Violin Concerto
see CONCERT INDEX under:
(DECC) 410 010-2DH Ravel: Orchestral Works

(DECC) 410 230-2DH Ravel: Orchestral Works
(DECC) 410 254-2DH Ravel: Orchestral works
(DECC) 414 408-2DH Suppé Overtures
(DECC) 421 440-2DH Fauré: Choral & Orchestral
Works
(DECC) 421 527-2DH Fête à la française
(DECC) 430 703-2DM Spanish Orchestral Works
(DECC) 430 714-2DM Ravel—Orchestral Works
(DECC) 430 729-2DM Respighi—Orchestral Works
(DECC) 436 210-2DH Bartók—Orchestral Works
(DECC) 436 474-2DM Stravinsky—Symphonies
(DECC) 436 483-2DM French Orchestral Works
(DECC) 436 837-2DH
Stravinsky/Szymanowski—Violin Concertos
(DECC) 440 331-2DH Prokofiev—Orchestral Works
(DECC) 440 332-2DH Ibert—Orchestral Works
(DECC) 440 333-2DH Ravel—Vocal Works
(DECC) 444 386-2DH Debussy—Orchestral Works
cond M. SHOSTAKOVICH
Shostakovich: Piano Concerto 2

MONTREAL SYMPHONY ORCHESTRA CHORUS
Berlioz: Roméo et Juliette (exc), Symphonie funèbre
et triomphale, Troyens (Cpte)
Debussy: Nocturnes, Pelléas et Mélisande (Cpte)
Holst: Planets
Janáček: Glagolitic Mass (Cpte)
Ravel: Daphnis et Chloé (Cpte)
see CONCERT INDEX under:
(DECC) 421 440-2DH Fauré: Choral & Orchestral
Works
(DECC) 436 210-2DH Bartók—Orchestral Works

MONTREAL TUDOR VOCAL ENSEMBLE
cond C. DUTOIT
Berlioz: Roméo et Juliette (Cpte)

MONTREUX FESTIVAL CHORUS
cond V. NEGRI
Cimarosa: Requiem in G minor

MONTSERRAT ABBEY CHOIR
see CONCERT INDEX under:
(STUD) SM1220.02 Immortel Grégorien
cond O. CUNILL
(FORL) UCD13919 Sacred Choral Works
cond G. ESTRADA
Anon: Christmas (exc)

MONTSERRAT ESCOLANIA
cond I. SEGARRA
Anon: Missa Salisburgensis, Plaudite tympana
see CONCERT INDEX under:
(SCHW) 313062 Casals—Sacred Choral Music

MONTSERRAT ESCOLANIA SOLOISTS
cond I. SEGARRA
Anon: Missa Salisburgensis, Plaudite tympana

MOODY, Howard (organ)
(MERI) CDE84112 Purcell: Sacred Choral Works

MOOG, Rainer (va)
see CONCERT INDEX under:
(CAPR) 10 633 Brahms—Piano Trios

MOOR, Chris de (bass)
Mozart: Messias, K572 (Cpte)

MOOR, Frank de (ten)
Puccini: Bohème (Cpte)

MOORE, Anthony Michaels (ten)
Spontini: Vestale (Cpte)

MOORE, Dudley (pf)
see CONCERT INDEX under:
(RCA) 09026 61678-2 Concerto! Steven Isserlis plays
Saint-Saëns

MOORE, F. (pf)
see CONCERT INDEX under:
(APR) APR7016 The Auer Legacy, Vol.2

MOORE, Gerald (pf)
Brahms: Deutsche Volkslieder (exc)
Schubert: Schöne Müllerin (Cpte), Winterreise
(Cpte)
Schumann: Geliebte, Op. 35 (Cpte), Liederkreis, Op.
39 (Cpte)
Wolf: Italienisches Liederbuch (Cpte), Mörike Lieder
(exc), Spanisches Liederbuch (Cpte)
(APR) APR7016 The Auer Legacy, Vol.2
(BIDD) LAB011 Brahms—Historic Chamber Music
Recordings
(CLAR) CDGSE78-50-47 The Harrison Sisters—An
English Musical Heritage
(CLAV) CD50-9300/4 Hommage à Tibor Varga
(CLAV) CD50-9314 Hommage à Tibor Varga, Volume
4
(CLRI) CC0005 The Clarinet - Historical Recordings,
Vol.1
(DG) 415 188-2GH Schubert—Lieder
(DG) 431 085-2GH Schubert—Lieder
(DG) 435 596-2GGA2 Schubert—Duets, Trios &
Quartets
(DG) 437 215-2GX9(1) Schubert—Lieder, Vol.1 (pt 1)
(DG) 437 215-2GX9(2) Schubert—Lieder, Vol.1 (pt 2)
(DG) 437 215-2GX9(3) Schubert—Lieder, Vol.1 (pt 3)
(DG) 437 215-2GX9(4) Schubert—Lieder, Vol.1 (pt 4)
(DG) 437 215-2GX9(5) Schubert—Lieder, Vol.1 (pt 5)
(DG) 437 215-2GX9(6) Schubert—Lieder, Vol.1 (pt 6)
(DG) 437 225-2GX9(1) Schubert—Lieder, Vol.2 (pt 1)
(DG) 437 225-2GX9(2) Schubert—Lieder, Vol.2 (pt 2)
(DG) 437 225-2GX9(3) Schubert—Lieder, Vol.2 (pt 3)

(DG) 437 225-2GX9(4) Schubert—Lieder, Vol.2 (pt 4)
(DG) 437 235-2GX3 Schubert—Lieder, Vol.3
(DUTT) CDLX7004 Elgar—Chamber Works
(DUTT) CDLX7013 The Unforgettable Isobel Baillie
(EMI) CDC5 55529-2 Delius—Cello Concerto, etc
(EMI) CDH5 65196-2 Schubert—Lieder
(EMI) CDH5 65502-2 Paul Tortelier
(EMI) CDH7 61003-2 Kathleen Ferrier sings Opera
and Songs
(EMI) CDH7 63030-2 Kirsten Flagstad - Wagner
Opera Arias
(EMI) CDH7 63198-2 Hans Hotter sings Bach &
Brahms
(EMI) CDH7 64028-2 Victoria de los Angeles sings
Spanish Songs
(EMI) CDH7 64250-2 Emmanuel Feuermann -
Recital
(EMI) CDH7 64252-2 Christoff sings Russian Arias &
Songs
(EMI) CDH7 64905-2 Wolf—Lieder Recital
(EMI) CDH7 69793-2 Elisabeth Schwarzkopf &
Irmgard Seefried sing Duets
(EMI) CDM5 65009-2 Janet Baker - Song Recital
(EMI) CDM5 65101-2 A Warlock Centenary Album
(EMI) CDM7 63653-2 Wolf: Lieder
(EMI) CDM7 63654-2 Schwarzkopf Encores
(EMI) CDM7 63656-2
Schubert/Schumann/Strauss—Lieder
(EMI) CDM7 63988-2 Schubert, Mendelssohn &
Brahms—Chamber Works
(EMI) CDM7 64716-2 Ireland—Piano Concerto, etc
(EMI) CHS5 65198-2 Maggie Teyte sings French
Songs
(EMI) CHS7 63025-2 Mussorgsky—Songs
(EMI) CHS7 69741-2(1) Record of Singing,
Vol.4—Anglo-American School (pt 1)
(EMI) CHS7 69741-2(2) Record of Singing,
Vol.4—Anglo-American School (pt 2)
(EMI) CHS7 69741-2(3) Record of Singing,
Vol.4—French School
(EMI) CHS7 69741-2(4) Record of Singing,
Vol.4—German School
(EMI) CHS7 69741-2(6) Record of Singing,
Vol.4—Russian & Slavonic Schools
(EMI) CHS7 69741-2(7) Record of Singing,
Vol.4—Italian School
(EMI) CMS5 65061-2(2) The Fabulous Victoria de los
Angeles (pt 2)
(EMI) CMS7 63559-2 Schubert: Song-Cycles &
Lieder
(EMI) CMS7 63563-2 Wolf—Mörike & Michelangelo
Lieder
(EMI) CMS7 63566-2 Schubert—Lieder
(EMI) CMS7 64074-2(1) Christa Ludwig—Recital (pt 1)
(EMI) CMS7 64074-2(2) Christa Ludwig—Recital (pt 2)
(EMI) CZS5 68132-2 Les introuvables de Jacqueline
du Pré
(EMI) CZS5 68485-2 Les Introuvables de János
Starker
(MMOI) CDMOIR411 Sacred Songs and Arias
(MMOI) CDMOIR418 Great Voices of the
Century—John McCormack
(NIMB) NI7851 Legendary Voices
(ORFE) C140101A Schubert: Lieder - Live at
Salzburg, 1957
(ORFE) C140201A Brahms: Lieder - Live at Salzburg,
1958
(ORFE) C140501A Beethoven: Lieder - Live at
Salzburg, 1965
(PEAR) GEMMCDS9085 Hugo Wolf Society, Volume
II
(PEAR) GEMMCD9045 William Primrose and Albert
Spalding
(PEAR) GEMMCD9134 Maggie Teyte - Chansons
(PEAR) GEMMCD9175 Heddle Nash - Serenade
(PEAR) GEMMCD9443 Feuermann—The Columbia
Records, Vol.2
(PEAR) GEMMCD9446 Feuermann—The Columbia
Records, Vol.3
(PEAR) GEMMCD9465 Alexander Kipnis
(PEAR) GEMMCD9473 Heddle Nash—Vol.2
(PEAR) GEMMCD9939 Josef Hassid & Ida Haendel -
1940-42 Recordings
(PREI) 89017 Gerhard Hüsch (1901-1984) sings
Schubert
(SYMP) SYMCD1140 The Harrison Sisters
(TEST) SBT1010 Ginette Neveu & Josef Hassid
(TEST) SBT1014 Delius—Orchestral Works
(TEST) SBT1016 Pierre Fournier - recital
(TEST) SBT1022 Brain,Kell & Goossens play
Schumann & Beethoven
(TEST) SBT1026 Irmgard Seefried

MOORE, Grace (sop)
see CONCERT INDEX under:
(PEAR) GEMMCDS9926(2) Covent Garden on
Record—Vol.4 (pt 2)
(RCA) 09026 61580-2(4) RCA/Met 100 Singers, 100
Years (pt 4)

MOORE, Philip (cond)
see York Minster Ch

MOORE, Roger (sngr)
Rodgers: King and I (Cpte)

MOORE, Thomas (vn)
see CONCERT INDEX under:
(CENT) CRC2176 Works by Soulima Stravinsky

MOORE, Walter (pf)
see CONCERT INDEX under:
(LARG) Largo5130 Testimonies of War

MOORE BY FOUR VOCAL JAZZ ENSEMBLE
cond P. BRUNELLE
see CONCERT INDEX under:
(COLL) Coll1449-2 Witness—Spirituals and Gospels,
Volume 1

MOPIN, Anne (sop)
Campra: Idoménée (Cpte)

MOQUET, Sylvie (bass viol)
see CONCERT INDEX under:
(FNAC) 592316 Clérambault—Chants & Motets for
the Royal House of Saint-Louis

MORA, Barry (bar)
Delius: Village Romeo and Juliet (Cpte)
Janáček: Fate (Cpte)

MORA, Fernando de la (ten)
Donizetti: Lucia di Lammermoor (Cpte)

MORAGUÈS, Pascal (cl)
Brahms: Clarinet Quintet

MORAGUÈS QUINTET
Mendelssohn: String Quartet 1, String Quartet 2
see CONCERT INDEX under:
(AUVI) V4684 Mozart—Chamber Works for Wind
(PHIL) 438 624-2PH2 Richter—The Authorised
Recordings: Beethoven

MORALES, Leonel (pf)
(MARC) 8 223753 Montsalvatge/Rodrigo—Works

MORALÈS, Maria (sop)
see CONCERT INDEX under:
(PHIL) 438 953-2PM2 Alarie/Simoneau - Arias &
Duets

MORALT, Rudolf (cond)
see Vienna St Op Orch

MORAN, Robert (cond)
see Piano Circus Band

MORANDI, Pier Giorgio (cond)
see Rome Op Orch

MORATH, Hélène (contr)
Martin: Vin herbé

MORAVEC, Ivan (pf)
Chopin: Ballades, Mazurkas (exc)
Dvořák: Piano Concerto
see CONCERT INDEX under:
(SUPR) 2SUP0027 Mozart: Orchestral Works

MORAZ, Patrick (prepared pf)
see CONCERT INDEX under:
(KOCH) 37238-2 A Chance Operation - John Cage
Tribute

MORDKOVITCH, Elena (pf)
see CONCERT INDEX under:
(CHAN) CHAN9184 Grieg—Violin Sonatas

MORDKOVITCH, Lydia (vn)
Alwyn: Violin Concerto
Bach: Solo Violin Partitas and Sonatas
Brahms: Double Concerto
Bruch: Violin Concerto 1
Dyson: Violin Concerto
Fauré: Violin Sonata 1
Kabalevsky: Violin Concerto
Khachaturian: Violin Concerto
Medtner: Violin Sonata 1, Violin Sonata 2
Moeran: Violin Concerto
Nielsen: Violin Sonata, Op.9, Violin Sonata 2
Prokofiev: Sonata, Op. 56, Violin Concerto 1, Violin
Concerto 2
R. Strauss: Violin Sonata
Schubert: Fantasie, D934, Sonata, D574
Shostakovich: Violin Concerto 1, Violin Concerto 2
Stravinsky: Violin Concerto
Ysaÿe: Violin Sonatas, Op.27
see CONCERT INDEX under:
(CHAN) CHAN8500 Russian Music for Violin and
Piano
(CHAN) CHAN8747 Szymanowski—Violin & Piano
Works
(CHAN) CHAN8748 Poème—Works for Violin and
Piano
(CHAN) CHAN8884 Stanford—Orchestral Works
(CHAN) CHAN9003 Bax—Orchestral Works
(CHAN) CHAN9073 Walton—Works for Violin and
Orchestra
(CHAN) CHAN9109 Franck/Messiaen/Saint-
Saëns—Violin & Piano Works
(CHAN) CHAN9184 Grieg—Violin Sonatas
(CHAN) CHAN9232 Respighi—Orchestral Works
(CHAN) CHAN9240 Stravinsky—Choral and
Orchestral Works
(CHAN) CHAN9351 Ravel/Respighi—Sonatas for
Violin and Piano
(CHAN) CHAN9377/8 Ireland—Chamber Works
(COLL) Coll1448-2 Scharwenka—Chamber Works,
Volume 2

MOREAUX, Christian (ob)
see CONCERT INDEX under:
(TIMP) 1C1010 Honegger—Chamber Works, Vol.3
(TIMP) 4C1012 Honegger—Chamber Works

MOREHOUSE-SPELMAN CHORUS
cond ROBERT SHAW
see CONCERT INDEX under:
(TELA) CD80109 Berlioz: Requiem, etc

MOREIRA, M. (contr)
see CONCERT INDEX under:
(ROSE) 3221 Schumann—Miscellaneous Works

MOREL, Christine (cond)
see C. Goudimel Ens

MOREL, Jean-Paul (cond)
see RCA Orch

MORELAND, Johanne (sop)
Verdi: Traviata (Cpte)

MORELLI, Adriana (sop)
see CONCERT INDEX under:
(SONY) MK44942 Domingo at the Philharmonic

MORELLI, Frank (bn)
Rorem: Winter Pages
see CONCERT INDEX under:
(DG) 431 665-2GX3 Mozart—Wind Concertos

MORELLI, Giuseppe (cond)
see Rome Op Orch

MORENO, Alfonso (gtr)
see CONCERT INDEX under:
(ASV) CDDCA887 Rodrigo—Guitar Concertos
(EMI) CDS7 47901-8 Villa-Lobos: Orchestral and
Chamber Works
(EMI) CZS7 67435-2 Rodrigo—Orchestral Works

MORENO, Hector (pf)
see CONCERT INDEX under:
(MARC) 8 223462 Guastavino—Piano Works

MORENO, José Miguel (gtr)
see CONCERT INDEX under:
(GLOS) GCD920103 The Spanish Guitar (1536-
1836)

MORENO, José Miguel (vihuela)
see CONCERT INDEX under:
(GLOS) GCD920103 The Spanish Guitar (1536-
1836)

MORENO, Myrna (mez)
(OPRA) ORCH103 Italian Opera—1810-20

MORENO TORROBA, Federico (cond)
see Madrid Concerts Orch

MORENO-BUENDIA, Manuel (cond)
see Madrid SO

MORESE, Giovanni (bass)
Puccini: Tosca (Cpte)

MORETTI, Isabelle (hp)
Caplet: Miroir de Jésus

MOREY, Cynthia (sop)
Sullivan: Iolanthe (exc)

MORF, Antony (cl)
see CONCERT INDEX under:
(BIS) BIS-CD513/4 Mozart—Chamber Works
(EDEL) ED1012 Schumann: Chamber Music with
Piano

MORGAN, Arwel Huw (bass)
A. Thomas: Hamlet (Cpte)

MORGAN, Gaynor (sop)
see CONCERT INDEX under:
(ASV) CDDCA758 Falla, Milhaud &
Stravinsky—Operas

MORGAN, Geoffrey (organ)
see CONCERT INDEX under:
(PRIO) PRCD416 Psalms of David, Vol.6

MORGAN, Ghislaine (sop)
see CONCERT INDEX under:
(REGE) REGSB701CD I saw the Lord

MORGAN, James (organ)
see CONCERT INDEX under:
(CONI) CDCF178 Brahms: Complete Motets

MORGAN, Morris (bar)
Suder: Kleider machen Leute (Cpte)

MORGAN, Rachel Ann (hp)
see CONCERT INDEX under:
(ETCE) KTC1049 Sweet as Bardic Harp-Songs with
Harp

MORGAN, Rachel Ann (mez/hp)
see CONCERT INDEX under:
(ETCE) KTC1049 Sweet as Bardic Harp-Songs with
Harp

MORGAN, Richard Lloyd (bass)
Bach: Mass in B minor, BWV232 (Cpte)

MORGAN, Tim (bar)
Sullivan: Gondoliers (Cpte)

MORGUNOV, Boris (narr)
Prokofiev: Ivan the Terrible

MORI, Orazio (bass)
Puccini: Fanciulla del West (Cpte), Tosca (Cpte),
Turandot (Cpte)
Verdi: Traviata (Cpte)
see CONCERT INDEX under:
(DECC) 436 261-2DHO3 Puccini—Il Trittico

MÖRIKE, Eduard (cond)
see Berlin Staatskapelle

MORINI, Erica (vn)
Mozart: Violin Concerto, K219
see CONCERT INDEX under:
(EMI) ZDMF7 64830-2 The Art of Nathan Milstein

MORINI, Guido (org/hpd)
Kapsperger: Chitarrone Book I (exc), Chitarrone Book
IV

MORINO, Giuseppe (ten)
Bizet: Pêcheurs de Perles (Cpte)
Donizetti: Favorita (Cpte), Gianni di Parigi (Cpte),
Maria di Rohan (Cpte)
see CONCERT INDEX under:
(NUOV) 6851 Giuseppe Morino—King of Bel Canto

MORISON, Elsie (sop)
Handel: Messiah (exc), Messias, K572 (Cpte)
Purcell: King Arthur, Z628 (Cpte)
see CONCERT INDEX under:
(CFP) CD-CFP4532 Sacred Arias
(DECC) 443 461-2DF2 Berlioz—L'Enfance du Christ,
etc
(DG) 429 042-2GX10 Mahler: Complete Symphonies

MORISON, Patricia (sngr)
Porter: Kiss me Kate (Cpte)

MORISSET-BALIER, Marie-André (organ)
Vierne: Messe basse, Op. 30, Messe basse, Op. 62
Widor: Symphony 2, Symphony 9

MØRK, Truls (vc)
Dvořák: Cello Concerto
Haydn: Cello Concerto in C, Cello Concerto in D
Nordheim: Tenebrae
Tchaikovsky: Rococo Variations
see CONCERT INDEX under:
(BIS) BIS-CD420 Britten—Orchestral Works
(EMI) CDC7 54205-2 Vivaldi—Double Concertos
(SIMA) PSC1022 Chamber Works for Oboe
(SIMA) PSC1029 Brahms—Works for Cello & Piano
(SIMA) PSC1063 Chopin/Schumann—Cello and
Piano Works
(VIRG) VC5 45034-2 Grieg/Sibelius—Cello Works

MORLEY, Matthew (organ)
see CONCERT INDEX under:
(NAXO) 8 550956 Bruckner—Motets

MORLEY, Sarah (pf)
see CONCERT INDEX under:
(UNIT) 88006-2 Russian Cello Sonatas

MORLEY, Simon (organ)
see CONCERT INDEX under:
(PRIO) PRCD429 Great Cathedral Anthems, Vol.5

MORNA, Liviu (vn)
Enescu: String Octet

MOROIANU, Mioara (vn)
Enescu: String Octet

MORONEY, Davitt (organ)
Biber: Mystery Sonatas

MORONEY, Davitt (hpd)
Bach: Art of Fugue, Musikalisches Opfer, BWV1079
Couperin: Concerts Royaux, Livre de clavecin II, Livre
de clavecin III
see CONCERT INDEX under:
(HARM) HMA190 1124/7 L. Couperin—Complete
Harpsichord Works
(HARM) HMA190 1150 Couperin—Motets
(HARM) HMU90 7024/5 Bach—Complete Sonatas for
Flute and Harpsichord
(L'OI) 433 053-2OH Bach/Vivaldi—Orchestral Works
(VIRG) VCD7 59011-2 Bach—French Suites etc
(VIRG) VC5 45166-2 The Purcell Manuscript
(VIRG) VC7 59272-2 Bach—Harpsichord Works

MORONEY, Davitt (virg)
see CONCERT INDEX under:
(VIRG) VC5 45166-2 The Purcell Manuscript

MOROZOV, Alexandr (bass)
Prokofiev: War and Peace (Cpte)

MOROZOV, Igor (bass)
Bellini: Beatrice di Tenda (Cpte)
see CONCERT INDEX under:
(NAXO) 8 553030 Opera Duets

MORPHY, Derek (bar)
see CONCERT INDEX under:
(CBC) SMCD5139 A Gilbert & Sullivan Gala

MORPURGO, Nelly (sop)
R. Strauss: Rosenkavalier (Cpte)

MORRESI, Giuseppe (bass)
Bellini: Sonnambula (Cpte)
Giordano: Andrea Chénier (Cpte)
Puccini: Fanciulla del West (Cpte), Madama Butterfly
(Cpte), Manon Lescaut (Cpte)
Verdi: Rigoletto (Cpte)
see CONCERT INDEX under:
(RCA) 09026 62541-2 Pavarotti - The Early Years,
Vol.1
(SONY) MK37228 Pavarotti sings Verdi

MORRIS, Gareth (fl)
see CONCERT INDEX under:
(EMI) CDH7 63039-2 Edwin Fischer plays Bach
Concertos

MORRIS, James (bass)
A. Thomas: Hamlet (Cpte)
Donizetti: Maria Stuarda (Cpte)
Fauré: Requiem (Cpte)
Gay: Beggar's Opera (Cpte)
Haydn: Schöpfung (exc)
Massenet: Roi de Lahore (Cpte)
Mozart: Requiem
Offenbach: Contes d'Hoffmann (Cpte)

R. Strauss: Salome (Cpte)
Stravinsky: Oedipus Rex (Cpte)
Verdi: Aida (Cpte), Trovatore (Cpte), Vespri Siciliani
(Cpte)
Wagner: Parsifal (Cpte), Rheingold (Cpte), Siegfried
(Cpte), Walküre (Cpte)
see CONCERT INDEX under:
(DG) 445 354-2GX14   Wagner—Der Ring des
Nibelungen
(EMI) CDS7 49487-2   Beethoven: Complete
Symphonies

MORRIS, Joan (mez)
Bolcom: Symphony 4

MORRIS, Richard (bar)
Maxwell Davies: Martyrdom of St Magnus (Cpte)

MORRIS, Timothy (organ)
see CONCERT INDEX under:
(CRD) CRD3491   Croft—Select Anthems

MORRIS, Victor (pf)
see CONCERT INDEX under:
(MERI) CDE84173   Elgar: Songs & Part-songs

MORRIS, Wyn (cond)
see Huddersfield Choral Soc

MORRISON, Anita (sop)
see CONCERT INDEX under:
(NUOV) 7109   Dallapiccola—Orchestral Works

MORRISON, Ann (sngr)
Gershwin: Lady, be Good! (Cpte)
see CONCERT INDEX under:
(EMI) CDC5 55189-2   The Busby Berkeley Album

MORRISON, Lewis (cl)
Maxwell Davies: Sinfonia concertante, Strathclyde
Concerto 4

MORRISON, Peter (bar)
see CONCERT INDEX under:
(CHAN) CHAN8362   Treasures of Operetta
(CHAN) CHAN8561   Treasures of Operetta, Vol. 2
(CHAN) CHAN8759   Treasures of Operetta III

MORRISON, Richard (bass)
Mozart: Mass, K427

MORSKOI, Gavriil (ten)
see CONCERT INDEX under:
(PEAR) GEMMCDS9001/3(1)   Singers of Imperial
Russia, Vol.2 (pt 1)

MORTENSEN, Gert (perc)
Nørgård: For a Change, Siddhartha (Cpte)
see CONCERT INDEX under:
(BIS) BIS-CD256   Works for percussion

MORTENSEN, Lars Ulrik (hpd)
Bach: French Overture, BWV831, Goldberg
Variations, Italian Concerto, BWV971, 3-Harpsichord
Concerti (exc), 4-Harpsichord Concerto
see CONCERT INDEX under:
(BIS) BIS-CD391   Music from the time of Christian IV,
Vol. 3
(CHAN) CHAN0531   Baroque Violin & Harpsichord
Sonatas
(CHAN) CHAN0541   Music from the Court of Frederick
the Great
(KONT) 32003   Tallis—Choral & Instrumental Works
(KONT) 32012   Bach—Harpsichord Works
(KONT) 32014   Telemann—Recorder Sonatas
(MOSC) 070978   Maurice Greene—Songs and
Keyboard Works

MORTIMER, Fred (cond)
see Fodens Motor Works Band

MORTIMER, Harry (cond)
see Yorkshire Imperial Band

MORTON, Richard (ten)
Britten: Rejoice in the Lamb
Dvořák: Mass in D
Elgar: Coronation Ode (Cpte)
see CONCERT INDEX under:
(CFP) CD-CFP4570   Choral Favourites
(HYPE) CDA66237   Dr Arne at Vauxhall Gardens

MORTON GOULD ORCHESTRA
cond M. GOULD
see CONCERT INDEX under:
(RCA) 09026 61667-2   Copland/Grofé—Orchestral
Works

MORY, Anny (sop)
Stravinsky: Noces

MORYN, Gilbert (sngr)
Lecocq: Jour et la Nuit (Cpte)
Messager: Monsieur Beaucaire (Cpte)

MOSAÏQUES QUARTET
Beethoven: String Quartet 5, String Quartet 6
Boccherini: Piano Quintets, G407-12 (exc), Piano
Quintets, G413-8 (exc)
Haydn: String Quartet, Op.103, String Quartets,
Op.20, String Quartets, Op.77
Mozart: Clarinet Quintet, K581, String Quartet, K464,
String Quartet, K465

MOSCA, Vitalba (mez)
Verdi: Rigoletto (Cpte)

MOSCONA, Nicola (bass)
Beethoven: Fidelio (Cpte)
Puccini: Bohème (Cpte)

Verdi: Ballo in maschera (Cpte), Otello (Cpte),
Requiem (Cpte), Trovatore (Cpte)
see CONCERT INDEX under:
(MYTO) 2MCD90317   Verdi—Un Ballo in maschera
(RCA) GD60276   Toscanini conducts Boito & Verdi

MOSCOW ALL-UNION RADIO CHOIR
see CONCERT INDEX under:
(EMI) CHS7 69741-2(6)   Record of Singing,
Vol.4—Russian & Slavonic Schools

**MOSCOW ALL-UNION RADIO SYMPHONY
ORCHESTRA**
cond R. GLIÈRE
Glière: Sheep's Spring (exc)
cond N. GOLOVANOV
see CONCERT INDEX under:
(RUSS) RDCD15004   Neuhaus plays Scriabin
cond V. SMIRNOV
see CONCERT INDEX under:
(EMI) CHS7 69741-2(6)   Record of Singing,
Vol.4—Russian & Slavonic Schools

MOSCOW ANIMA CHAMBER CHOIR
cond V. DUDAROVA
Miaskovsky: Symphony 6

MOSCOW ARTISTIC EDUCATION INSTITUTE CHOIR
cond D. KABALEVSKY
Kabalevsky: Requiem

MOSCOW BOYS' CAPPELLA
cond E. SVETLANOV
Mahler: Symphony 3

MOSCOW CHAMBER ORCHESTRA
cond R. BARSHAI
Shostakovich: Symphony 14
Vainberg: Symphony 7
see CONCERT INDEX under:
(EMI) CMS7 63522-2   Tippett—Chamber & Orchestral
Works

**MOSCOW CONSERVATOIRE INSTRUMENTAL
ENSEMBLE**
cond Y. NIKOLAEVSKY
see CONCERT INDEX under:
(EMI) CMS7 64429-2   Sviatoslav Richter—Un Portrait

MOSCOW CONTEMPORARY MUSIC ENSEMBLE
see CONCERT INDEX under:
(OLYM) OCD296   Moscow Contemporary Music
Ensemble - Volume 5
cond A. VINOGRADOV
see CONCERT INDEX under:
(CDM) LDC288 059   Contemporary
Listening—Raskatov
(CDM) LDC288 060   Contemporary
Listening—Kasparov
(CDM) LDC288 062   Contemporary
Listening—Ekimovski

MOSCOW IMPERIAL OPERA CHORUS
see CONCERT INDEX under:
(PEAR) GEMMCDS9001/3(2)   Singers of Imperial
Russia, Vol.2 (pt 2)

MOSCOW LITURGIC CHOIR
cond FATHER AMVROSY
Various: Russian Easter Liturgy

MOSCOW 'MALY' SYMPHONY ORCHESTRA
cond V. PONKIN
see CONCERT INDEX under:
(CDM) LDC288 027/8   Prokofiev—Film and Stage
Music

MOSCOW NEW CHOIR
cond E. RASTVOROVA
see CONCERT INDEX under:
(OLYM) OCD541   Georgy Sviridov—Choral Music

MOSCOW NEW OPERA ORCHESTRA
cond Y. SAMOILOV
see CONCERT INDEX under:
(OLYM) OCD528   Miaskovsky—Orchestral Works
(OLYM) OCD530   Miaskovsky—Cello Works

MOSCOW NEW RUSSIAN ORCHESTRA
cond C. PAÏTA
see CONCERT INDEX under:
(LODI) LO-CD791   Tchaikovsky—Orchestral Works

MOSCOW PATRIARCHAL CHOIR
cond A. GRINDENKO
Anon: Early Russian Plain Chant
Bortnyansky: Te Deum

MOSCOW PHILHARMONIC ORCHESTRA
cond D. BARRA
see CONCERT INDEX under:
(KOCH) 37159-2   Schnittke/Shostakovich—Piano
Concertos
cond R. BARSHAI
Shostakovich: Symphony 7
cond D. KABALEVSKY
see CONCERT INDEX under:
(OLYM) OCD269   Kabalevsky—Volume 4
cond D. KITAIENKO
Shostakovich: Symphony 5
see CONCERT INDEX under:
(OLYM) OCD269   Kabalevsky—Volume 4
(SHEF) CD26   The Moscow Sessions - II
(SHEF) CD27   The Moscow Sessions - III
cond K. KONDRASHIN
Brahms: Piano Concerto 2
Rachmaninov: Paganini Rhapsody

Shostakovich: Overture on Russian and Kirghiz Folk
Themes, Symphony 1, Symphony 2, Symphony 3,
Symphony 4, Symphony 5, Symphony 6, Symphony
7, Symphony 8, Symphony 9, Symphony 10,
Symphony 11, Symphony 12, Symphony 13,
Symphony 14, Symphony 15
Vainberg: Symphony 5
see CONCERT INDEX under:
(CHNT) LDC278 1007/8   Shostakovich: Symphonies,
Vol.4
(MERC) 432 002-2MM   Byron Janis
cond L. LEIGHTON SMITH
see CONCERT INDEX under:
(SHEF) CD25   The Moscow Sessions - I
(SHEF) CD26   The Moscow Sessions - II
(SHEF) CD27   The Moscow Sessions - III
cond G. ROZHDESTVENSKY
Shostakovich: New Babylon Suite
see CONCERT INDEX under:
(RUSS) RDCD11104   Elgar/Milhaud/Respighi—Works
for Cello & Orchestra
cond S. SAMOSUD
(RUSS) RDCD15005   Shostakovich plays
Shostakovich
cond A. ZHURAITIS
Vainberg: Trumpet Concerto

**MOSCOW RADIO AND TELEVISION SYMPHONY
ORCHESTRA**
cond R. ABDULLAYEV
Karayev: In the Path of Thunder, Seven Beauties

MOSCOW RADIO SYMPHONY ORCHESTRA
cond R. BARSHAI
Mahler: Symphony 9
cond V. FEDOSEYEV
Prokofiev: Violin Concerto 1, Violin Concerto 2
Tchaikovsky: Violin Concerto
cond A. GAUK
see CONCERT INDEX under:
(RUSS) RDCD15005   Shostakovich plays
Shostakovich
cond G. ROZHDESTVENSKY
(MERC) 432 002-2MM   Byron Janis
cond J. SPIEGELMAN
see CONCERT INDEX under:
(DELO) DE3139   Irving Fine—Orchestral Works

MOSCOW SOLOISTS ENSEMBLE
see CONCERT INDEX under:
(RCA) RD60464   Yuri Bashmet—Recital
(RCA) 74321 24894-2   Homage to Schnittke
cond Y. BASHMET
Schnittke: Trio Sonata
see CONCERT INDEX under:
(RCA) RD60368   Tchaikovsky & Grieg: Orchestral
Works

MOSCOW STANISLAVSKY TH CHORUS
cond G. ZHEMCHUZHIN
Kabalevsky: Colas Breugnon (Cpte)

MOSCOW STANISLAVSKY TH ORCHESTRA
cond G. ZHEMCHUZHIN
Kabalevsky: Colas Breugnon (Cpte)

MOSCOW STATE SYMPHONY ORCHESTRA
cond F. GLUSHCHENKO
Lyapunov: Ballada, Symphony 1
cond I. GOLOVSHIN
Rubinstein: Feramors, Piano Concerto 2, Piano
Concerto 4, Symphony 2

MOSCOW SYMPHONY ORCHESTRA
cond A. DE ALMEIDA
Tournemire: Symphony 1, Symphony 2, Symphony 4,
Symphony 5
see CONCERT INDEX under:
(MARC) 8 223602   Malipiero—Symphonies
(MARC) 8 223603   Malipiero—Symphonies
(MARC) 8 223604   Malipiero—Symphonies
(MARC) 8 223696   Malipiero—Symphonies
(MARC) 8 223697   Malipiero—Symphonies
(MARC) 8 223710   Guatemala, Volume 1
cond F. GLUSHCHENKO
(OLYM) OCD424   Kancheli—Orchestral Works
cond D. KABALEVSKY
Kabalevsky: Requiem
cond D. KITAIENKO
Prokofiev: Symphony 3, Symphony 4
R.Strauss: Also Sprach Zarathustra
Rachmaninov: Symphony 3
cond H. SHEK
N. Tcherepnin: Pavillon d'Armide

MOSCOW VIRTUOSI
Mozart: Concertone, K190, Sinfonia Concertante,
K364
see CONCERT INDEX under:
(RCA) RD60240   Vivaldi—Orchestral and Choral
works
(RCA) RD60370   Modern Portraits
cond V. SPIVAKOV
Bach: Suites, BWV1066-9
see CONCERT INDEX under:
(RCA) RD60240   Vivaldi—Orchestral and Choral
works
(RCA) RD60452   Schubert—Orchestral works
(RCA) RD87947   Shostakovich: Orchestral Works
(RCA) RD87948   Haydn: Concertos
(RCA) 09026 60400-2   Mozart—Piano Concertos
(RCA) 09026 60466-2   Modern Portraits II - Spivakov

(RCA) 09026 61964-2 Tchaikovsky—The Children's
Album
(RCA) 09026 68061-2 Stalin Cocktail
(RCA) 74321 24894-2 Homage to Schnittke

MOSCOW VIRTUOSI CHAMBER ORCHESTRA
cond V. SPIVAKOV
Shchedrin: Carmen Ballet

MOSCUCCI, Orietta (sop)
Verdi: Don Carlo (Cpte)

MOSELEY-MORGAN, Rebecca (sop)
Janáček: Fate (Cpte)

MOSER, Edda (sop)
Lehár: Giuditta (Cpte)
Mozart: Don Giovanni (Cpte), Mass, K317, Vespers,
K339, Zauberflöte (Cpte)
Wagner: Götterdämmerung (Cpte), Rheingold
(Cpte)
see CONCERT INDEX under:
(DG) 429 168-2GR Wagner: Excerpts from Der Ring
(DG) 435 211-2GX15 Wagner—Der Ring des
Nibelungen

MOSER, Thomas (ten)
Berlioz: Damnation de Faust (Cpte)
Cherubini: Lodoïska (Cpte)
Gluck: Cinesi (Cpte)
Haydn: Schöpfung (Cpte)
Mozart: Finta Giardiniera (Cpte), Finta semplice
(Cpte), Sogno di Scipione (Cpte), Zaïde (Cpte),
Zauberflöte (Cpte)
Schmidt: Buch mit Sieben Siegeln
Schreker: Ferne Klang (Cpte)
Spohr: Jessonda (Cpte)
Verdi: Aida (Cpte), Stiffelio (Cpte)
Wagner: Fliegende Holländer (Cpte)

MOSES, Geoffrey (bass)
Martinů: Greek Passion (Cpte)
Verdi: Rigoletto (Cpte)
Wagner: Tristan und Isolde (Cpte)

MOSKO, Stephen (cond)
see Netherlands Wind Ens

MOSKVITINA, Emilia (hp)
see CONCERT INDEX under:
(OLYM) OCD522 Grechaninov/Tchaikovsky—String
Quartets

MOSLEY, George (bar)
M. Berkeley: Baa Baa Black Sheep (Cpte)

MOSLEY, George (bass)
Purcell: Dido (Cpte), St Cecilia's Day Ode, Z339

MOSS, Harold (cond)
see Wingates Temperance Band

MOSSOP, Sue (mndl)
see CONCERT INDEX under:
(AMON) CD-SAR53 Music for Mandolin
(CONI) CDCF203 Vivaldi—Concertos

MOST, Ingeborg (contr)
Lortzing: Undine (Cpte)
Pfitzner: Von deutscher Seele (Cpte)
Weill: Kuhhandel (exc)

MOSTLY MOZART ORCHESTRA
cond G. SCHWARZ
Mozart: Clarinet Concerto, K622
see CONCERT INDEX under:
(DELO) DE3026 A. Auger - Bach and Handel arias

MOSTOWOY, Vladimir (ten)
Rachmaninov: Vespers, Op. 37 (Cpte)

MOTLEY, Byron (sngr)
see CONCERT INDEX under:
(PHIL) 446 406-2PH Berlin—Heat Wave

MOTT, Charles (bar)
(PEAR) GEMMCDS9951/5 The Elgar
Edition—Acoustic Recordings 1914-25

MOTZING, William (cond)
see Prague City PO

MOULD, Clifford (ten)
see CONCERT INDEX under:
(EMI) CDM7 64131-2 Orchestral Music for Christmas

MOULE, Timothy (treb)
see CONCERT INDEX under:
(ARGO) 436 120-2ZH Vaughan
Williams/Walton—Choral & Orchestral Works

MOULL, Geoffrey (cond)
see Bielefeld PO

MOUNTFORD, Philip (pf)
see CONCERT INDEX under:
(TREM) TREM101-2 Walter Leigh—Piano Music and
Songs

MOURA, Paulo (sax)
see CONCERT INDEX under:
(CHNT) LDC278 835 Villa-Lobos—Chôros for
Chamber Ensembles

MOWAT, Christopher (tbn)
see CONCERT INDEX under:
(COLL) Coll1390-2 Maxwell Davies—Orchestral
Works

MOWREY, Gaylord (pf)
M. Feldman: Why Patterns

MOXON, Alice (sop)
Sullivan: Sorcerer (Cpte)

MOYER, Frederick (pf)
Brahms: Hungarian Dances
Schmidt: Phantasiestücke

MOYLE, Julian (bar)
Lehár: Lustige Witwe (exc)
Sullivan: Iolanthe (exc)

MOYSE, Marcel (fl)
see CONCERT INDEX under:
(EMI) CDS7 54607-2 Stravinsky plays and conducts
Stravinsky
(PEAR) GEMMCD9348 Debussy: Orchestral &
Chamber Works

MOYZES QUARTET
Dvořák: String Quartet 12, String Quartet 14
Grechaninov: String Quartet 2, String Quartet 4
Mozart: String Quartet, K458, String Quartet, K465

MOZ-ART QUARTET
see CONCERT INDEX under:
(ETCE) KTC1171 Rachmaninov—String Quartets and
Romances

MOZART TRIO
Beethoven: Serenade, Op.8, String Trio, Op.3, String
Trios, Op. 9
Mozart: Flute Quartets, Piano Quartet, K478, Piano
Quartet, K493

MOZARTEAN PLAYERS
cond R. WILSON
Mozart: Piano Concerto 20

MOZES, Robert (vn)
see CONCERT INDEX under:
(CARL) PWK1141 French Impressions

MOZZAFIATO
see CONCERT INDEX under:
(SONY) SK53367 Beethoven—Chamber Works
(SONY) SK53965 Harmoniemusik after Mozart and
Rossini
(SONY) SK64306 Mozart/Pleyel—Wind Music

MOZZATO, Guido (vn)
Vivaldi: Concerti, Op.8 (exc)

MRÁČEK, Jan (vn)
Domažlický: Czech Songs

MRAVINSKY, Evgeny (cond)
see Czech PO

MRÁZ, Ladislav (bar)
Martinů: Bouquet
Smetana: Bartered Bride (Cpte), Devil's Wall (Cpte)
Vycpálek: Last things of Man

MRÁZOVÁ, Marie (contr)
Janáček: Cunning Little Vixen (Cpte), Jenufa (Cpte)
Martinů: Miracles of Mary (Cpte)
Smetana: Bartered Bride (Cpte)
Vycpálek: Czech Requiem
see CONCERT INDEX under:
(SUPR) 11 0767-2 Martinů—Cantatas
(SUPR) 11 0816-2 Zelenka—Choral Works

MRONGOVIUS, Karl-Hermann (pf)
(WERG) WER60131-50 Ligeti: Piano Works

MRÓZ, Leonard Andrzej (bass)
Mussorgsky: Boris Godunov (Cpte)
Shostakovich: Lady Macbeth of Mtsensk (Cpte)

MUCHA, Stanislav (vn)
Schmidt: Clarinet and Piano Quintet 2

MUCK, Conrad (vn)
(CAPR) 10 539 Schulhoff—Chamber Works

MUCK, Karl (cond)
see Bayreuth Fest Orch

MUCKENHEIM, Christa (sop)
Bach: Christmas Oratorio, BWV248 (Cpte)

MUDIE, Michael (cond)
see orch

MUELLER, Hartje (bass)
Verdi: Ernani (Cpte)

MUELLER, Zizi (fl)
see CONCERT INDEX under:
(NEW) NW357-2 Crumb. Madrigals and Chamber
works

MUFF, Alfred (bass)
Dessau: Hagadah Shel Pessach
Einem: Dantons Tod (Cpte)
R.Strauss: Frau ohne Schatten (Cpte)
Schreker: Gezeichneten (Cpte)
Wagner: Fliegende Holländer (Cpte)

MUGNONE, Leopoldo (pf)
see CONCERT INDEX under:
(SYMP) SYMCD1170 The Harold Wayne Collection,
Vol.20

MÜHLBACH, Christine (hp)
see CONCERT INDEX under:
(DG) 435 860-2GH2 Berlioz—Mélodies

MÜHLBERGER, Erna (sop)
R. Strauss: Rosenkavalier (Cpte)

MÜHLE, Anne-Marie (sop)
Monteverdi: Madrigals, Bk 8 (exc)
Mozart: Thamos, K345 (Cpte)

MÜHLFELD ENSEMBLE
see CONCERT INDEX under:
(CLRI) CC0007 New English Clarinet Music

MUKK, József (ten)
Bach: Cantata 80, Cantata 147, Cantata 208, Cantata
211, Cantata 212, Christmas Oratorio, BWV248
(Cpte), St Matthew Passion, BWV244 (Cpte)
Mascagni: Lodoletta (Cpte)

MULA-TCHAKO, Inva (sop)
see CONCERT INDEX under:
(SONY) SK46691 The First Placido Domingo
International Voice Competition

MULDOWNEY, Dominic (cond)
see Composers Ens

MULHOLLAND, Declan (sngr)
Gay: Beggar's Opera (Cpte)

MÜLLER, Carl-Heinz (bar)
Schubert: Winterreise (Cpte)

MÜLLER, Charlotte (mez)
see CONCERT INDEX under:
(PREI) 89035 Erna Berger (1900-1990) - I

MÜLLER, Eduard (hpd)
see CONCERT INDEX under:
(TELD) 4509-97452-2 Bach—Harpsichord Concertos

MÜLLER, Hanns Udo (cond)
see Berlin City Op Orch

MÜLLER, Hanns Udo (pf)
(PEAR) GEMMCDS9085 Hugo Wolf Society, Volume
II
(PEAR) GEMMCD9119 Schumann—Legendary Song
Cycles
(PREI) 89017 Gerhard Hüsch (1901-1984) sings
Schubert
(PREI) 89202 Gerhard Hüsch Sings

MÜLLER, Hartmut (bass)
Diabelli: Pastoral Mass, op 147

MÜLLER, Johannes (cond)
see Berlin RO

MÜLLER, Maria (sop)
Wagner: Fliegende Holländer (exc), Lohengrin
(Cpte)
see CONCERT INDEX under:
(EMI) CMS7 64008-2(1) Wagner Singing on Record
(pt 1)
(MYTO) 3MCD93381 Wagner—Die Walküre, etc
(SCHW) 314502 Vienna State Opera—Live
Recordings (sampler)
(TELD) 9031-76442-2 Wagner—Excerpts from the
1936 Bayreuth Festival

MULLER, Marianne (va da gamba)
Blavet: Flute Sonatas, Op. 2 (exc), Flute Sonatas, Op.
3 (exc)
see CONCERT INDEX under:
(ADES) 20235-2 Marais—Pièces de violes
(ERAT) 2292-45012-2 Couperin—Sacred Choral
Works

MULLER, Philippe (vc)
(DENO) CO-72508 French Piano Trios

MÜLLER, Rufus (ten)
Bach: St John Passion, BWV245 (Cpte)
Dowland: First Book of Songs (Cpte)
Mozart: Zauberflöte (Cpte)
see CONCERT INDEX under:
(HYPE) CDA66412 Purcell—Complete Odes &
Welcome Songs, Vol.3
(HYPE) CDA66497 O Tuneful Voice
(HYPE) CDA66649 Bamde—Lieder & Fortepiano
Music
(MERI) CDE84112 Purcell: Sacred Choral Works

MÜLLER-BRUHL, Helmut (cond)
see Capella Clementina

MÜLLER-HEUSER, Franz (bar)
Lully: Bourgeois Gentilhomme

MÜLLER-KRAY, Hans (cond)
see Berne St Orch

MÜLLER-MOLINARI, Helga (sop)
Rossini: Pietra del paragone (Cpte)

MÜLLER-MOLINARI, Helga (mez)
Donizetti: Messa da Requiem
Handel: Partenope (Cpte)
R. Strauss: Ariadne auf Naxos (Cpte), Rosenkavalier
(Cpte)

MÜLLER-THIEMENS, Heile (pf)
Schubert: Winterreise (Cpte)

MULLOVA, Viktoria (vn)
Bach: Solo Violin Partitas and Sonatas (exc), Violin
Sonatas, BWV1014-19 (exc)
Beethoven: Piano Trios (exc)
Brahms: Piano Trios 1, Violin Concerto
C.P.E. Bach: Sonata, H514
Mendelssohn: Violin Concerto, Op. 64, Violin
Concerto (1822)
Paganini: Violin Concerto 1
Sibelius: Violin Concerto
Tchaikovsky: Violin Concerto
Vieuxtemps: Violin Concerto 5
Vivaldi: Concerti, Op. 8 (exc), Concerto, RV577

MURDOCH, Katherine (va)
see CONCERT INDEX *under:*
(NORT) **NR227-CD** American Chamber Music with Flute

MURGATROYD, Andrew (ten)
Beethoven: Missa Solemnis
Purcell: Dido (Cpte)
Tavener: We shall see Him as He is
see CONCERT INDEX *under:*
(ABBE) **CDCA954** Dvořák/Elgar—Sacred Choral Works
(HYPE) **CDA66311/2** Monteverdi: St Barbara Vespers
(NIMB) **NI5144/8** Beethoven: Symphonies Nos 1-9

MURGU, Corneliu (ten)
Puccini: Fanciulla del West (Cpte)
Verdi: Otello (Cpte)

MURO, Bernardo De (ten)
see CONCERT INDEX *under:*
(EMI) **CHS7 64860-2(2)** La Scala Edition - Vol.1, 1878-1914 (pt 2)

MURPHY, Anne (bar hn)
see CONCERT INDEX *under:*
(DOYE) **DOYCD005** Flower of Scotland

MURPHY, Donna (sngr)
Sondheim: Passion (Cpte)

MURPHY, Heidi Grant (mez)
Wagner: Parsifal (Cpte)

MURPHY, Heidi Grant (sop)
Schumann: Paradies und die Peri (Cpte)

MURPHY, Maurice (cornet)
see CONCERT INDEX *under:*
(CHAN) **CHAN4513** British Bandsman Centenary Concert

MURPHY, Maurice (tpt)
see CONCERT INDEX *under:*
(ARAB) **Z6610** Shostakovich: Orchestral Works
(KOCH) **37179-2** Pinkham—Orchestral Works

MURPHY, Suzanne (sop)
Mozart: Nozze di Figaro (Cpte)
see CONCERT INDEX *under:*
(CHAN) **CHAN8476** Works by Rachmaninov and Tchaikovsky

MURPHY, William (bar)
see CONCERT INDEX *under:*
(SONY) **SM3K46291** Stravinsky—Ballets, Vol.1

MURRAY, Ann (mez)
Bach: Cantata 93, Magnificat, BWV243, Mass in B minor, BWV232 (Cpte)
Bellini: Norma (Cpte)
Brahms: Lieder, Op.91, Lieder, Op.105
Cilea: Adriana Lecouvreur (Cpte)
Debussy: Martyre de St Sébastien (Cpte)
Duruflé: Requiem
Falla: Sombrero de tres picos (Cpte)
Gay: Beggar's Opera (Cpte)
Gounod: Roméo et Juliette (Cpte)
Haydn: Mass 13, Schöpfung (Cpte)
Humperdinck: Hänsel und Gretel (Cpte)
M.-A. Charpentier: Magnificat, H74, Te Deum, H146
Monteverdi: Madrigals, Bk 8 (exc)
Mozart: Clemenza di Tito (Cpte), Finta semplice (Cpte), Lucio Silla (Cpte), Mass, K317, Nozze di Figaro (Cpte), Requiem, Zauberflöte (Cpte)
Offenbach: Contes d'Hoffmann (Cpte)
Puccini: Madama Butterfly (Cpte), Tosca (Cpte)
Purcell: Fairy Queen, Z629 (Cpte)
Rossini: Messa di gloria
Stravinsky: Pulcinella
Verdi: Battaglia di Legnano (Cpte), Don Carlos (Cpte)
Vivaldi: Gloria, RV589
see CONCERT INDEX *under:*
(COLL) **Coll7037-2** Britten—Orchestral Song Cycles
(DG) **431 751-2GC** Stravinsky—Songs
(EMI) **CDC7 49930-2** Sweet Power of Song
(EMI) **CDC7 54411-2** On Wings of Song
(FORL) **UCD16738** Great Handel Arias
(HANS) **98 825** Bach—Cantatas, Vol.63
(HANS) **98 828** Bach—Cantatas,Vol.66
(HANS) **98 871** Bach—Cantatas, Vol.20
(HANS) **98 872** Bach—Cantatas, Vol.21
(HANS) **98 882** Bach—Cantatas, Vol.31
(HYPE) **CDA66112** Souvenirs de Venise
(HYPE) **CDA66627** The Last Rose of Summer
(HYPE) **CDA66801/2** Gounod—Songs
(HYPE) **CDJ33003** Schubert—Complete Lieder, Vol. 3
(PHIL) **420 648-2PM** Vivaldi: Sacred Choral Music, Vol.1
(PHIL) **420 649-2PM** Vivaldi: Sacred Choral Music, Vol.2
(PHIL) **422 522-2PME6** The Complete Mozart Edition Vol 22

MURRAY, Doreen (sop)
G. Charpentier: Louise (Cpte)

MURRAY, Gordon (hpd)
see CONCERT INDEX *under:*
(HARM) **HMA190 5137** Arias and Cantatas for Soprano and Trumpet

MURRAY, John Horton (bar)
Verdi: Don Carlo (Cpte)

MURRAY, Michael (organ)
Dupré: Organ Symphony, Op. 25
Rheinberger: Organ Concerto 1
Saint-Saëns: Symphony 3
Vierne: Symphony 1, Symphony 3
see CONCERT INDEX *under:*
(TELA) **CD80049** Bach: Organ Works
(TELA) **CD80088** Bach in Los Angeles
(TELA) **CD80096** French Organ Music
(TELA) **CD80169** Michael Murray—Organ Recital
(TELA) **CD80179** Bach: Organ Works
(TELA) **CD80234** Franck: Organ Works
(TELA) **CD80286** Bach at St Bavo's

MURRAY, William (bass)
Henze: Bassariden (Cpte)
Mendelssohn: Hochzeit des Camacho (Cpte)
R. Strauss: Salome (Cpte)

MUSA SUSO, Foday (kora)
see CONCERT INDEX *under:*
(NONE) **7559-79275-2** Pieces of Africa

MUSCH, Hans (organ)
see CONCERT INDEX *under:*
(CHRI) **CD74606** Franck & Widor: Organ Works

MUSIC GROUP OF LONDON
Schubert: Octet, D803
see CONCERT INDEX *under:*
(EMI) **CDM5 65100-2** Vaughan Williams—Chamber Works

MUSIC PROJECTS LONDON
cond R. BERNAS
see CONCERT INDEX *under:*
(NMC) **NMCD004** Dillon—East 11th Street etc

MUSICA AETERNA
cond F. WALDMAN
see CONCERT INDEX *under:*
(PEAR) **GEMMCDS9138** Mozart—Piano Concertos, Volume 1

MUSICA BOHEMICA
cond J. KRČEK
Pascha: Prosae Pastorales

MUSICA FIAMMANTE
see CONCERT INDEX *under:*
(UNIC) **DKPCD9124** D.Scarlatti—Cantatas, Vol.3

MUSICA FIATA
cond ROLAND WILSON
Monteverdi: Selva morale e spirituale (exc)
Picchi: Canzoni da sonar (exc)
cond R. WILSON
see CONCERT INDEX *under:*
(DHM) **05472 77183-2** Music for the Bourgesoisie

MUSICA POLYPHONICA
cond L. DEVOS
see CONCERT INDEX *under:*
(ERAT) **2292-45202-2** M-A. Charpentier: Sacred Works

MUSICA SACRA ORCHESTRA
cond R. WESTENBURG
see CONCERT INDEX *under:*
(CATA) **09026 61822-2** Of Eternal Light
(RCA) **09026 60970-2** Motets

MUSICA SACRA SINGERS
cond R. SACCANI
Verdi: Aida (Cpte)

MUSICA SECRETA
see CONCERT INDEX *under:*
(AMON) **CD-SAR61** Barbara Strozzi—La virtuosissima cantatrice

MUSICA VARIA
Crumb: Madrigals, Music for a Summer Evening

MUSICA VITAE CHAMBER ORCHESTRA
see CONCERT INDEX *under:*
(BIS) **BIS-CD460** Nordic Music Vol. 1
(BIS) **BIS-CD461** Nordic Music Vol. 2
cond W. RAJSKI
see CONCERT INDEX *under:*
(BIS) **BIS-CD460** Nordic Music Vol. 1
(BIS) **BIS-CD461** Nordic Music Vol. 2

MUSICAL ART QUARTET
see CONCERT INDEX *under:*
(RCA) **09026 61778-2(05)** The Heifetz Collection, Vol. 5

MUSICALISCHE COMPAGNEY
see CONCERT INDEX *under:*
(MDG) **L3229** Schütz: Sacred Choral Works
(MDG) **L3230** Schütz: sacred choral works

MUSICI DE PRAGA
cond L. HLAVÁČEK
Mozart: Horn Concerti, Piano Concerto 19, Piano Concerto 27

(THE) MUSICIANS OF SWANNE ALLEY
see CONCERT INDEX *under:*
(HARM) **HMC90 5192** As I went to Walsingham
(VIRG) **VC7 59534-2** In the Streets and Theatres of London

(LES) MUSICIENS
Chausson: Piano Quartet, Piano Trio

(LES) MUSICIENS DU LOUVRE
cond M. MINKOWSKI
Handel: Amadigi di Gaula (Cpte), Concerti Grossi, Op. 3, Teseo (Cpte)

Lully: Phaëton (Cpte)
Marais: Alcyone (Cpte)
Mondonville: Titon et l'Aurore (Cpte)
Mouret: Amours de Ragonde (Cpte)
Rameau: Hippolyte et Aricie (Cpte), Platée (Cpte)
Stradella: San Giovanni Battista (Cpte)
see CONCERT INDEX *under:*
(ERAT) **2292-45974-2** Rebel—Orchestral Works

MUSIC'S RECREATION
see CONCERT INDEX *under:*
(MERI) **CDE84114** Recréation de musique
(MERI) **CDE84159** Telemann: Cantatas
(MERI) **CDE84182** Clérambault: Dramatic Cantatas

MUSIKFABRIK NRW
cond J. KALITZKE
Henze: Voices (exc)

MUSILOVÁ, Milada (contr)
Janáček: Makropulos Affair (Cpte)

MUSINU, Francesco (bass)
Paisiello: Nina (Cpte)
Rossini: Gazza ladra (Cpte)
Verdi: Traviata (Cpte), Vespri siciliani (Cpte)

MUSINU, Giuseppe (bass)
Donizetti: Fille du Régiment (Cpte)

MUSIQUE OBLIQUE ENSEMBLE
see CONCERT INDEX *under:*
(HARM) **HMC90 1417** Caplet—Orchestral and Vocal Works
cond P. HERREWEGHE
Fauré: Messe des Pêcheurs de Villerville, Requiem (Cpte)
Mahler: Lied von der Erde
Schoenberg: Pierrot lunaire
see CONCERT INDEX *under:*
(HARM) **HMC90 1322** Bruckner—Choral Works
(HARM) **HMC90 1422** Weill—Orchestral and Choral Works

MUSIQUE VIVANTE ENSEMBLE
cond L. BERIO
Berio: Laborintus II
cond D. MASSON
Boulez: Domaines
Globokar: Émigrés
Stockhausen: Aus den sieben Tagen (exc)

MUSKER, Kate (va)
see CONCERT INDEX *under:*
(ECM) **847 537-2** Gavin Bryars—After the Requiem
(KING) **KCLCD2027** South American Flute Music

MUSKETT, Doreen (hurdy-gurdy)
see CONCERT INDEX *under:*
(HYPE) **CDA66039** A Feather on the Breath of God

MUSOLENO, Rosemary (sop)
Haydn: Applausus (Cpte)

MUSQUER, Colette (pf)
see CONCERT INDEX *under:*
(FORL) **UCD16681** The Great Italian Arias

MUSTONEN, Andres (vn/dir)
see CONCERT INDEX *under:*
(FINL) **4509-95578-2** Telemann—Quartets

MUSTONEN, Olli (pf)
Alkan: Préludes, Op. 31
Chopin: Piano Concerto 1
Grieg: Piano Concerto
Shostakovich: Preludes, Op. 34
see CONCERT INDEX *under:*
(DECC) **436 255-2DH** Russian Piano Works
(DECC) **440 229-2DH** Stravinsky—Works for Piano and Orchestra
(DECC) **440 926-2DH** Prokofiev—Works for Violin and Piano

MUSY, Louis (bar)
Gounod: Faust (Cpte)
Offenbach: Contes d'Hoffmann (Cpte)

MUSY, Louis (bass)
G. Charpentier: Louise (Cpte)

MUSZELY, Melitta (sop)
see CONCERT INDEX *under:*
(EMI) **CMS5 65212-2** Wagner—Les introuvables du Ring

MUTI, Riccardo (cond)
see BPO

MUTIS, Andre (sngr)
Romberg: Student Prince (Cpte)

MUTTER, Anne-Sophie (vn)
Bartók: Violin Concerto 2
Beethoven: Violin Concerto
Berg: Violin Concerto
Brahms: Violin Concerto
Bruch: Violin Concerto 1
Lalo: Symphonie espagnole
Mendelssohn: Violin Concerto, Op.64
Moret: En rêve
Mozart: Violin Concerto, K211, Violin Concerto, K216, Violin Concerto, K218, Violin Concerto, K219
Rihm: Gesungene Zeit
Sarasate: Zigeunerweisen
Tchaikovsky: Violin Concerto
Vivaldi: Concerti, Op. 8 (exc)
see CONCERT INDEX *under:*
(DG) **415 276-2GH** Beethoven—Orchestral Works
(DG) **415 565-2GX4** Great Violin Concertos

(DG) **423 696-2GH**
Lutosławski/Stravinsky—Concerted Works
(DG) **427 687-2GH2** Beethoven: String Trios
(DG) **437 544-2GH** Carmen-Fantasie
(DG) **445 487-2GX3** Mutter plays Modern Works
(EMI) **CDC7 47005-2** Bach—Violin Concertos
(EMI) **CDC7 54302-2** Mozart—Concertos

MUZIO, Claudia (sop)
see CONCERT INDEX under:
(BOGR) **BIM705-2** Muzio—The Published Edisons,
1920-25
(EMI) **CHS7 64864-2(1)** La Scala Edition - Vol.2,
1915-46 (pt 1)
(NIMB) **NI7801** Great Singers, Vol.1
(NIMB) **NI7802** Divas 1906-1935
(NIMB) **NI7814** Claudia Muzio—Opera Arias & Songs
(PEAR) **GEMMCDS9925(1)** Covent Garden on
Record—Vol.3 (pt 1)
(ROMO) **81005-2** Claudia Muzio (1889-1936)
(ROMO) **81010-2** Claudia Muzio—Complete Pathé
Recordings, 1917-8

MUZZARELLI, Alfred (bass)
Wagner: Meistersinger (Cpte)
see CONCERT INDEX under:
(SCHW) **314562** Vienna State Opera Live, Vol.6
(SCHW) **314602** Vienna State Opera Live, Vol.10
(SCHW) **314642** Vienna State Opera Live, Vol.14

MUZZARELLI, Alfred (spkr)
R. Strauss: Ariadne auf Naxos (Cpte)
see CONCERT INDEX under:
(SCHW) **314632** Vienna State Opera Live, Vol.13
(SCHW) **314652** Vienna State Opera Live, Vol.15

MYERS, Barbara (sngr)
Forrest/Wright: Kismet (Cpte)

MYERS, Michael (ten)
Berlioz: Damnation de Faust (Cpte)
Schubert: Mass, D950
see CONCERT INDEX under:
(EMI) **CDS7 54251-2** Scriabin—Symphonies and Tone
Poems
(TELA) **CD80248** Beethoven: Choral Works

MYERS, Philip (hn)
Crumb: Haunted Landscape
Schuman: Colloquies
see CONCERT INDEX under:
(EMI) **CDC5 55400-2** Barber—Chamber and
Instrumental Works

MYERS, Raymond (bar)
Gounod: Faust (Cpte)
Verdi: Macbeth (Cpte)

MYERS, Timothy (tbn)
Bolcom: Sessions I

MYHUS, M. (mez)
Mussorgsky: Boris Godunov (Cpte)

MYRAT, Alexandre (cond)
see Monte Carlo PO

MYRLAK, Kazimierz (ten)
Gluck: Danza (Cpte)
Rossini: Signor Bruschino (Cpte)

MYSZAK, Stephanie (sngr)
Weill: Dreigroschenoper (Cpte)

NABARRO, Malcolm (cond)
see East England Orch

NABORÉ, William (pf)
see CONCERT INDEX under:
(DORO) **DRC3001** American 18th Century Piano
Works

NACHBAUER, Bernd (bass)
Suder: Kleider machen Leute (Cpte)

NACHEZ, Tivadar (vn)
see CONCERT INDEX under:
(SYMP) **SYMCD1071** Great Violinists, Vol.1

NADDEO, Maurizio (vc)
Veracini: Capriccio, Violin Sonatas, Op. 2 (exc)
Vivaldi: Manchester Sonatas
see CONCERT INDEX under:
(O111) **OPS30-9004** Vivaldi—String Concertos

NADLER, Sheila (mez)
J. Adams: Death of Klinghoffer (Cpte)

NADOR, Magda (sop)
Mozart: Schauspieldirektor (Cpte)

NAEGELE, Philipp (va)
Schubert: Trout Quintet, D667
see CONCERT INDEX under:
(BIS) **BIS-CD503/4** Nielsen—Chamber Works

NAFÉ, Alicia (mez)
Bellini: Adelson e Salvini (Cpte)
Bizet: Carmen (Cpte)
Falla: Amor Brujo (Cpte), Canciones populares
españolas, Vida breve (Cpte)
Mozart: Nozze di Figaro (Cpte)

NAGAI, Kazuko (mez)
Mahler: Symphony 8

NAGAI, Yukie (pf)
Debussy: Images (exc), Préludes (exc)
Ravel: Miroirs, Tombeau de Couperin
see CONCERT INDEX under:
(BIS) **BIS-CD489** Ravel: Arrangements for two
Pianos

NAGANO, Kent (cond)
see Berkeley SO

NAGANUMA, Yuriko (vn)
see CONCERT INDEX under:
(ARIO) **ARN68026** Baroque Choral and String Works

NAGAOKA, Sumiko (pf)
see CONCERT INDEX under:
(CHNN) **CG9101** Schumann—Piano Works

NAGLIA, Sandro (ten)
Handel: Poro (Cpte)
Monteverdi: Vespers

NAGY, Béla (vn)
see CONCERT INDEX under:
(MARC) **8 223727** Truscott—Chamber Music

NAGY, István-Zsolt (fl)
see CONCERT INDEX under:
(NIMB) **NI5392** J & M Haydn—Orchestral Works

NAGY, Robert (ob)
Barber: Vanessa (Cpte)

NAHR, William (ten)
Puccini: Bohème (Cpte)

NAJNAR, Jiří (va)
Dvořák: String Sextet
Schoenberg: Verklärte Nacht

NAKAMURA, Hiroko (pf)
Chopin: Piano Concerto 1
Stockhausen: Michaels Reise

NAKAMURA, Isao (perc)
Stockhausen: Michaels Reise

NAKARJAKOV, Sergei (tpt)
see CONCERT INDEX under:
(TELD) **4509-90846-2** Trumpet Concertos
(TELD) **4509-94554-2** Carmen Fantasy—Virtuoso
Music for Trumpet
(TELD) **9031-77705-2** Works for Trumpet & Piano

NAMARA, Marguerite (sop)
see CONCERT INDEX under:
(IRCC) **IRCC-CD802** Souvenirs of Rare French
Opera

NAMUR CHAMBER CHOIR
cond J-C. MALGOIRE
Gluck: Orfeo ed Euridice (Cpte)
Handel: Messias, K572 (Cpte)

NAMUR SYMPHONIC CHORUS
cond P. BARTHOLOMÉE
Lekeu: Andromède

NANCARROW, Conlon (pf)
Nancarrow: Studies for Player Piano (exc)
see CONCERT INDEX under:
(WERG) **WER6168-2** Nancarrow—Studies for Player
Piano

NANCY SYMPHONY ORCHESTRA
cond J. KALTENBACH
see CONCERT INDEX under:
(ACCO) **20283-2** Duparc—Orchestral Songs

NANNI, Oscar (bass)
Puccini: Madama Butterfly (Cpte)

NANTES INSTRUMENTAL ENSEMBLE
cond P. COLLEAUX
see CONCERT INDEX under:
(ARIO) **ARN68015** Charpentier—Sacred Choral works

NANTES VOCAL ENSEMBLE
cond P. COLLEAUX
M-A. Charpentier: In honorem sancti Xaverii
canticum, H355, Judicium Salomonis, H422
see CONCERT INDEX under:
(ARIO) **ARN68015** Charpentier—Sacred Choral works

NANUT, Anton (cond)
see Slovak PO

NAOUMOFF, Emile (pf)
see CONCERT INDEX under:
(MARC) **8 223636** In Memoriam Lili Boulanger
(SONY) **SK47184** Glenn Gould—The Composer

NAOURI, Laurent (bar)
Lully: Phaëton (Cpte)
Rameau: Hippolyte et Aricie (Cpte)

NAPIER, Marita (sop)
R. Strauss: Elektra (Cpte)
Schoenberg: Gurrelieder
Wagner: Rheingold (Cpte), Walküre (Cpte)
Weill: Zar lässt sich Photographieren (Cpte)
see CONCERT INDEX under:
(DG) **445 354-2GX14** Wagner—Der Ring des
Nibelungen

NAPLES RAI ORCHESTRA
cond C. FRANCI
Rossini: Inganno felice (Cpte)

NAPLES ROSSINI ORCHESTRA
cond F. CARACCIOLO
Pergolesi: Stabat Mater

NAPLES SAN CARLO OPERA CHORUS
cond F. MOLINARI-PRADELLI
Donizetti: Don Pasquale (Cpte)
Puccini: Bohème (Cpte), Gianni Schicchi (Cpte)
cond S. SASSANO
Rossini: Barbiere di Siviglia (exc)
cond T. SERAFIN
Donizetti: Linda di Chamounix (Cpte)
Rossini: Mosè (Cpte)

NAPLES SAN CARLO OPERA ORCHESTRA
cond F. MOLINARI-PRADELLI
Donizetti: Don Pasquale (Cpte)
Puccini: Bohème (Cpte), Gianni Schicchi (Cpte)
cond S. SASSANO
Rossini: Barbiere di Siviglia (exc)
cond T. SERAFIN
Donizetti: Linda di Chamounix (Cpte)
Rossini: Mosè (Cpte)

NAPLES SCARLATTI CHORUS
cond S. VARVISO
Rossini: Barbiere di Siviglia (Cpte)

NAPLES SCARLATTI ORCHESTRA
cond S. VARVISO
Rossini: Barbiere di Siviglia (Cpte)

NAPOLI, Catherine (sop)
Handel: Teseo (Cpte)
Mondonville: Titon et l'Aurore (Cpte)

NARÇON, Armand (bass)
Massenet: Werther (Cpte)
see CONCERT INDEX under:
(EMI) **CHS7 61038-2** Debussy—Pelléas et Mélisande,
etc

NARDI, Gregorio (pf)
see CONCERT INDEX under:
(DYNA) **CDS58** Liszt—Piano Works

NASEBAND, Dennis (treb)
Mozart: Zauberflöte (Cpte)

NASH, Dorothy (sop)
Sullivan: Mikado (Cpte)

NASH, Elizabeth (sop)
see CONCERT INDEX under:
(TREM) **TREM101-2** Walter Leigh—Piano Music and
Songs

NASH, Heddle (ten)
Elgar: Dream of Gerontius (Cpte)
Gounod: Faust (Cpte)
Mozart: Così fan tutte (Cpte)
see CONCERT INDEX under:
(DUTT) **CDAX8004** Sir Henry Wood conducts
Vaughan Williams
(DUTT) **CDLX7012** The Incomparable Heddle Nash
(EMI) **CDH5 65072-2** Glyndebourne Recorded - 1934-
1994
(PEAR) **GEMMCDS9926(1)** Covent Garden on
Record—Vol.4 (pt 1)
(PEAR) **GEMMCDS9926(2)** Covent Garden on
Record—Vol.4 (pt 2)
(PEAR) **GEMMCD9175** Heddle Nash - Serenade
(PEAR) **GEMMCD9319** Heddle Nash sings Opera
Arias & Songs
(PEAR) **GEMMCD9342** Vaughan Williams: Vocal
Works
(PEAR) **GEMMCD9473** Heddle Nash—Vol.2

NASH, John Heddle (bar)
Sullivan: Mikado (Cpte)

NASH, Royston (cond)
see New SO

NASH ENSEMBLE
Arensky: Piano Trio 1
Beethoven: Piano and Wind Quintet, Op. 16, Piano
Trios (exc), Septet, Op.20
Brahms: Clarinet Quintet, Horn Trio, Piano Quintet
Dvořák: Piano Quintet, Op.81, Piano Trio 4
Elgar: Piano Quintet, Violin Sonata
F. Berwald: Septet
Fauré: Bonne chanson, Op. 61, Piano Quartet 1,
Piano Quartet 2
Hummel: Septet, Op.74
Mozart: Clarinet Quintet, K581, Piano and Wind
Quintet, K452
Rimsky-Korsakov: Piano and Wind Quintet
Schubert: Notturno, D897, Octet, D803, Trout Quintet,
D667
Spohr: Nonet, Op.31, Octet, Op.32, Quintet, Op.52,
Septet, Op.147
Weber: Clarinet Quintet, J182, Flute Trio, J259
see CONCERT INDEX under:
(CRD) **CRD3410** Czech Chamber Works
(CRD) **CRD3437** Poulenc: Chamber & Vocal Works
(CRD) **CRD3446** Ravel: Chamber works
(HYPE) **CDA66192** Ferguson & Finzi: Chamber
Works
(NMC) **NMCD008** Simon Holt—Chamber Works
(UNIC) **UKCD2010** Knussen—Orchestral & Vocal
Works
(VIRG) **VC5 45016-2** Ravel—Chamber & Vocal Works
(VIRG) **VC7 59057-2** Schoenberg—Miscellaneous
Works
(VIRG) **VC7 59560-2** Mozart—Chamber Works
cond L. FRIEND
(HYPE) **CDA66137** Bliss: Vocal and Chamber Works
(HYPE) **CDA66754** Constant Lambert—Mr Bear
Squash-you-all-flat
(VIRG) **VC5 45016-2** Ravel—Chamber & Vocal Works
cond O. KNUSSEN
see CONCERT INDEX under:
(NMC) **NMCD024M** Turnage—Vocal and Chamber
Works
cond S. RATTLE
Schoenberg: Pierrot Lunaire
Webern: Concerto, Op. 24
see CONCERT INDEX under:

(CHAN) **CHAN6535** Stravinsky—Symphonies of Wind Instruments

NÄSLUND, Anders (bar)
Verdi: Rigoletto (Cpte)

NASRAWI, Douglas (ten)
Lully: Alceste (Cpte)
see CONCERT INDEX *under:*
(TELD) **4509-90796-2** Monteverdi—Il Ballo delle ingrate
(TELD) **4509-95068-2** Purcell—Songs of Welcome & Farewell

NASSERI, Hamid (sngr)
Egk: Verlobung in San Domingo (Cpte)

NAST, Minnie (sop)
see CONCERT INDEX *under:*
(SUPR) **11 2136-2(3)** Emmy Destinn—Complete Edition, Discs 5 to 8

NASTRUCCI, Gino (cond)
see Inst Ens

NASYEDKIN, Alexei (pf)
see CONCERT INDEX *under:*
(OLYM) **OCD523** Shostakovich Quartet - Volume 3

NAT, Yves (pf)
see CONCERT INDEX *under:*
(EMI) **CDH7 61012-2** Beethoven: Piano Sonatas

NATALI, Valiano (ten)
Donizetti: Lucia di Lammermoor (Cpte)

NATH, Pandit Pran (voc)
see CONCERT INDEX *under:*
(NONE) **7559-79310-2** Short Stories

NATHAN, Regina (sop)
Britten: Folk Songs (exc)

NATIONAL PHILHARMONIC CHORUS
cond J. GOLDSMITH
Goldsmith: Supergirl (exc)

NATIONAL PHILHARMONIC ORCHESTRA
cond K.H. ADLER
see CONCERT INDEX *under:*
(DECC) **417 011-2DH2** Pavarotti's Greatest Hits
(DECC) **425 681-2DM2** Tutto Pavarotti
(DECC) **433 010-2DM** Christmas Stars
(DECC) **433 710-2DH** O Holy Night
cond B. BARTOLETTI
Ponchielli: Gioconda (Cpte)
see CONCERT INDEX *under:*
(DECC) **430 724-2DM** Great Operatic Duets
cond R. BONYNGE
Bellini: Sonnambula (Cpte)
Delibes: Coppélia (Cpte)
Donizetti: Lucrezia Borgia (Cpte)
Gay: Beggar's Opera (Cpte)
Lecocq: Mam'zelle Angot Ballet (Cpte)
Massenet: Carillon, Cid (exc), Cigale, Esclarmonde (Cpte), Roi de Lahore (Cpte), Scènes alsaciennes, Thaïs (exc)
Meyerbeer: Patineurs
Tchaikovsky: Sleeping Beauty (Cpte), Swan Lake (Cpte)
Verdi: Traviata (exc), Trovatore (Cpte)
see CONCERT INDEX *under:*
(DECC) **417 011-2DH2** Pavarotti's Greatest Hits
(DECC) **417 645-2DH** Kiri - Portrait
(DECC) **425 681-2DM2** Tutto Pavarotti
(DECC) **430 724-2DM** Great Operatic Duets
(DECC) **433 220-2DWO** The World of the Violin
(DECC) **433 439-2DA** Great Love Duets
(DECC) **436 463-2DM** Ten Top Tenors
(LOND) **425 659-2LM** Britten: Orchestral Works
cond R. CHAILLY
Giordano: Andrea Chénier (Cpte)
Rossini: Guillaume Tell (Cpte), Turco in Italia (Cpte)
see CONCERT INDEX *under:*
(DECC) **443 850-2DF2** Rossini—Overtures
cond G. CHIARAMELLO
see CONCERT INDEX *under:*
(DECC) **410 015-2DH** Italian and Neapolitan Songs
(DECC) **417 011-2DH2** Pavarotti's Greatest Hits
(DECC) **425 681-2DM2** Tutto Pavarotti
cond O. DE FABRITIIS
Boito: Mefistofele (Cpte)
see CONCERT INDEX *under:*
(DECC) **425 681-2DM2** Tutto Pavarotti
cond G. GAVAZZENI
Mascagni: Cavalleria Rusticana (Cpte)
see CONCERT INDEX *under:*
(DECC) **425 681-2DM2** Tutto Pavarotti
cond C. GERHARDT
Alf Newman: Selznick International Pictures Fanfare
Bartók: Violin Concerto 1, Violin Concerto 2
Steiner: Gone with the Wind
see CONCERT INDEX *under:*
(CHES) Chesky **CD93** Earl Wild plays Chopin, Fauré & Liszt
(RCA) **GD80136** Now Voyager—Classic Film Scores of Max Steiner
(RCA) **GD80183** Classic Film Scores for Bette Davis
(RCA) **GD80185** Classic Film Scores of Korngold
(RCA) **GD80422** Casablanca—Classic Film Scores for Humphrey Bogart
(RCA) **GD80707** Citizen Kane—Classic Film Scores of Bernard Herrmann
(RCA) **GD80708** Sunset Boulevard—Classic Film Scores of Franz Waxman
(RCA) **GD80911** Spellbound—Classic Film Scores of Miklos Rozsa

(RCA) **GD80912** Captain Blood—Classic Film Scores for Errol Flynn
(RCA) **GD82792** The Spectacular World of Classic Film Scores
(VARE) **VSD5207** The Prince and the Pauper and other film music
cond J. GOLDSMITH
A. North: 2001 (exc)
Goldsmith: Blue Max (exc), Legend (exc), Supergirl (exc)
cond B. HERRMANN
Herrmann: Fantasticks, Psycho, Symphony 1
see CONCERT INDEX *under:*
(UNIC) **UKCD2065** Herrmann—Film Music Suites
(UNIC) **UKCD2066** Russian Orchestral Music
cond JAMES LEVINE
Bellini: Norma (Cpte)
Giordano: Andrea Chénier (Cpte)
Verdi: Otello (Cpte)
see CONCERT INDEX *under:*
(CFP) **CD-CFP4569** Puccini: Arias
(EMI) **CDM7 63104-2** Alfredo Krauss - Opera Recital
(RCA) **09026 61580-2(8)** RCA/Met 100 Singers, 100 Years (pt 8)
cond E. KOHN
see CONCERT INDEX *under:*
(EMI) **CDC5 55017-2** Domingo Opera Classics
(EMI) **CDC7 54053-2** Roman Heroes
cond R. LEPPARD
see CONCERT INDEX *under:*
(SONY) **MK39310** Haydn Concertos
(SONY) **SK37846** Trumpet Concertos
cond P. MAAG
Verdi: Luisa Miller (Cpte)
cond L. MAAZEL
Puccini: Villi (Cpte)
see CONCERT INDEX *under:*
(RCA) **RD60060** Noël! Noël! Noël!
cond G. PATANÈ
Leoncavallo: Pagliacci (Cpte)
see CONCERT INDEX *under:*
(DECC) **417 011-2DH2** Pavarotti's Greatest Hits
cond N. RESCIGNO
Puccini: Tosca (Cpte)
see CONCERT INDEX *under:*
(DECC) **417 011-2DH2** Pavarotti's Greatest Hits
(DECC) **425 681-2DM2** Tutto Pavarotti
(DECC) **433 439-2DA** Great Love Duets
cond M. ROSENSTOCK
Gould: Fall River Legend
cond G. SOLTI
Puccini: Tosca (Cpte)
Verdi: Ballo in maschera (Cpte)
see CONCERT INDEX *under:*
(DECC) **417 645-2DH** Kiri - Portrait
(DECC) **425 681-2DM2** Tutto Pavarotti
(DECC) **430 724-2DM** Great Operatic Duets
(DECC) **436 461-2DM** Ten Top Sopranos
cond L. STOKOWSKI
see CONCERT INDEX *under:*
(EMI) **CDM7 64140-2** Stokowski Showcase

NATIONAL PHILHARMONIC ORCHESTRA
cond A. COATES
Tchaikovsky: Romeo and Juliet, Symphony 6
cond J.O. EDWARDS
Bernstein: West Side Story (Cpte)
Kern: Show Boat (Cpte)
see CONCERT INDEX *under:*
(TER) **CDVIR8314** Is it really me?
cond A. FISTOULARI
see CONCERT INDEX *under:*
(DUTT) **CDK1200** This is Full Frequency Range Recording
cond C. KRAUSS
see CONCERT INDEX *under:*
(PREI) **90190** Paul Schoeffler—Recital
cond M. MATHIESON
(DUTT) **CDLXT2501** Bliss conducts Bliss
cond B. NEEL
see CONCERT INDEX *under:*
(DUTT) **CDK1200** This is Full Frequency Range Recording
cond V. OLOF
see CONCERT INDEX *under:*
(DUTT) **CDK1200** This is Full Frequency Range Recording
cond K. RANKL
see CONCERT INDEX *under:*
(PREI) **90190** Paul Schoeffler—Recital
cond M. SARGENT
see CONCERT INDEX *under:*
(DECC) **430 096-2DWO** The World of Kathleen Ferrier
(DECC) **433 470-2DM** Ferrier Edition - Volume 3
cond SIDNEY BEER
Tchaikovsky: Symphony 5
see CONCERT INDEX *under:*
(DUTT) **CDK1200** This is Full Frequency Range Recording

NATIONAL YOUTH ORCHESTRA OF GREAT BRITAIN
cond S. RATTLE
Stravinsky: Rite of Spring (Cpte)
cond C. SEAMAN
Dukas: Apprenti sorcier
Elgar: Enigma Variations
R. Strauss: Sinfonia domestica
Stravinsky: Firebird (Cpte)

NATOLA-GINASTERA, Aurora (vc)
see CONCERT INDEX *under:*
(ASV) **CDDCA855** Ginastera—Piano Music, Vol.1

NATZKE, Oscar (bass)
see CONCERT INDEX *under:*
(EMI) **CHS7 69741-2(2)** Record of Singing, Vol.4—Anglo-American School (pt 2)
(ODE) **CDODE1365** Oscar Natzke - A Legend in His Time

NAUDAIN, May (sngr)
see CONCERT INDEX *under:*
(PEAR) **GEMMCDS9056/8** Music from the New York Stage, Vol. 3: 1913-17

NAUMENKO, Alexander (bass)
Shostakovich: Gamblers (Cpte)

NAVARINI, Francesco (bass)
see CONCERT INDEX *under:*
(EMI) **CHS7 64860-2(1)** La Scala Edition - Vol.1, 1878-1914 (pt 1)
(MEMO) **HR4408/9(1)** Singers in Genoa, Vol.1 (disc 1)
(PEAR) **GEMMCDS9923(1)** Covent Garden on Record, Vol.1 (pt 1)

NAVARRA, André (vc)
see CONCERT INDEX *under:*
(ERAT) **4509-96953-2** Fauré—Chamber Works

NAVARRO, Garcia (cond)
see ECO

NAYDENOV, Alipi (cond)
see Rousse PSO

NAZARETH, Daniel (cond)
see Slovak PO

NBC SYMPHONY ORCHESTRA
cond F. BLACK
see CONCERT INDEX *under:*
(SYMP) **SYMCD1109** Great Violinists, Vol.5 - Adolf Busch
cond G. CANTELLI
(EMI) **CZS5 68217-2** Guido Cantelli—A profile
cond L. STOKOWSKI
see CONCERT INDEX *under:*
(PEAR) **GEMMCDS9044** Stokowski conducts Shostakovich
cond A. TOSCANINI
Atterberg: Symphony 6
Beethoven: Fidelio (Cpte), Missa Solemnis, Piano Concerto 1, Piano Concerto 3, Piano Concerto 4, Symphony 3, Symphony 8, Violin Concerto
Berlioz: Harold in Italy, Roméo et Juliette (exc)
Brahms: Piano Concerto 2, Serenade 2, Symphony 1
Cherubini: Requiem 1
Elgar: Enigma Variations
Franck: Symphony
Mozart: Symphony 40
Mussorgsky: Pictures
Puccini: Bohème (Cpte)
R. Strauss: Don Quixote, Tod und Verklärung
Saint-Saëns: Symphony 3
Schubert: Symphony 5, Symphony 8, Symphony 9
Shostakovich: Symphony 7
Sibelius: Symphony 2
Tchaikovsky: Manfred Symphony, Piano Concerto 1, Romeo and Juliet
Verdi: Ballo in maschera (Cpte), Otello (Cpte), Pezzi Sacri (exc), Requiem (Cpte), Traviata (Cpte)
see CONCERT INDEX *under:*
(ATS) **ATCD100** Toscanini conducts Italian Music
(DELL) **CDDA9020** Toscanini conducts music by his contemporaries
(DELL) **CDDA9021** Toscanini conducts French Works
(DELL) **CDDA9022** Toscanini conducts Schubert, Schumann & Brahms
(DELL) **CDDA9024** Toscanini conducts Tone Poems
(PEAR) **GEMMCDS9157** Jascha Heifetz - Concerto Recordings, Volume 1
(RCA) **GD60262** Toscanini Collection, Vol.32
(RCA) **GD60264** Wagner—Opera excerpts
(RCA) **GD60265** Debussy—Orchestral Works
(RCA) **GD60267** Toscanini Collection, Vol.45
(RCA) **GD60270** Beethoven—Symphony No 5 etc
(RCA) **GD60276** Toscanini conducts Boito & Verdi
(RCA) **GD60279** Toscanini Collection, Vol.24
(RCA) **GD60282** Haydn—Orchestral Works
(RCA) **GD60285** Mendelssohn—Symphonies, etc
(RCA) **GD60287** Mozart—Symphonies
(RCA) **GD60289** Toscanini Collection - Rossini Overtures
(RCA) **GD60294** Toscanini Collection - Sibelius
(RCA) **GD60296** Toscanini Collection, Vol.31
(RCA) **GD60305** Toscanini Collection - Wagner
(RCA) **GD60307** Toscanini Collection, Vol.38
(RCA) **GD60308** Toscanini Collection, Vol.40
(RCA) **GD60322** Toscanini Collection, Vol.39
(RCA) **GD60323** Toscanini Collection, Vol.28
(RCA) **GD60324** Beethoven—Complete Symphonies
(RCA) **GD60325** Brahms: Symphonies & Other Works
(RCA) **GD60326** Verdi—Operas & Choral Works
(RCA) **GD60449** Vladimir Horowitz plays Russian Works
(RCA) **GD60523** Horowitz plays Brahms, Liszt & Schubert
(RCA) **09026 61778-2(05)** The Heifetz Collection, Vol. 5

cond B. WALTER
see CONCERT INDEX *under:*
(PEAR) **GEMMCD9131** Bruno Walter live

NEAL, Joe (sngr)
Forrest/Wright: Kismet (Cpte)

NEALLEY, Ralph (sngr)
Gershwin: Porgy and Bess (Cpte)

NEARY, Alice (vc)
see CONCERT INDEX *under:*
(SONY) **SK66613** Tavener—Innocence

NEARY, Martin (cond)
see BBC SO

NEARY, Martin (organ)
see CONCERT INDEX *under:*
(ASV) **CDQS6011** Carols from Winchester Cathedral
(CARL) **PCD919** Great Music from Great Occasions at Westminster Abbey

NEBLETT, Carol (sop)
Korngold: Tote Stadt (Cpte)
Puccini: Fanciulla del West (Cpte)
see CONCERT INDEX *under:*
(BELA) **450 121-2** Plácido Domingo

NEBOLSIN, Eldar (pf)
see CONCERT INDEX *under:*
(DECC) **440 935-2DH** Chopin/Liszt—Piano Works

NEBOLSIN, Vassily (cond)
see Bolshoi Th Orch

NECOLESCU, Antonio (ten)
Liszt: Faust Symphony

NEDZADEL, Maria (sop)
see CONCERT INDEX *under:*
(LYRC) **LCD146** Frida Leider sings Wagner

NEEL, Boyd (cond)
see Boyd Neel Orch

(BOYD) NEEL ORCHESTRA
cond B. BRITTEN
see CONCERT INDEX *under:*
(DECC) **425 996-2DM** Britten—Vocal Works
cond B. NEEL
see CONCERT INDEX *under:*
(DECC) **430 096-2DWO** The World of Kathleen Ferrier
(DECC) **433 470-2DM** Ferrier Edition - Volume 3
(DECC) **433 471-2DM** Ferrier Edition - Volume 4
(DUTT) **CDAX8007** Boyd Neel conducts Britten & Vaughan Williams
(PEAR) **GEMMCD9151** Alfredo Campoli
cond ROY HENDERSON
see CONCERT INDEX *under:*
(DECC) **433 470-2DM** Ferrier Edition - Volume 3

(BOYD) NEEL STRING ORCHESTRA
cond B. BRITTEN
see CONCERT INDEX *under:*
(PEAR) **GEMMCD9177** Britten—Vocal Works
cond B. NEEL
Handel: Concerti grossi, Op.6

NEGRI, Giovanni Battista de (ten)
see CONCERT INDEX *under:*
(EMI) **CHS7 64860-2(1)** La Scala Edition - Vol.1, 1878-1914 (pt 1)
(MEMO) **HR4408/9(1)** Singers in Genoa, Vol.1 (disc 1)
(SYMP) **SYMCD1065** The Harold Wayne Collection, Vol.1

NEGRI, Vittorio (cond)
see ECO

NEGRO, Lucia (pf)
Messiaen: Poèmes pour Mi (exc)
see CONCERT INDEX *under:*
(BIS) **BIS-CD026** Shostakovich—Chamber Works
(BIS) **BIS-CD554** Stenhammar—Piano Music, Vol 1
(MSVE) **MSCD415** Kraus—Chamber Music
(MSVE) **MSCD521** Berwald—Chamber Works

NEIDICH, Charles (basset cl)
Mozart: Clarinet Concerto, K622
see CONCERT INDEX *under:*
(DG) **431 665-2GX3** Mozart—Wind Concertos

NEIDICH, Charles (cl)
see CONCERT INDEX *under:*
(SONY) **SK53367** Beethoven—Chamber Works
(SONY) **SK57968** Weber/Hummel/Reicha—Works for Clarinet
(SONY) **SK64302** Clarinet & Piano Sonatas
(SONY) **S2K66285** Brahms—String Quartets; Clarinet Quintet

NEIDICH, Charles (cl/basset cl)
see CONCERT INDEX *under:*
(SONY) **SK53356** Mozart—Chamber Music for Clarinet

NEIDICH, Charles (cl/dir)
see CONCERT INDEX *under:*
(SONY) **SK64306** Mozart/Pleyel—Wind Music

NEIDLINGER, Gustav (bass-bar)
Orff: Kluge (Cpte)
R. Strauss: Elektra (Cpte)
Wagner: Götterdämmerung (Cpte), Meistersinger (Cpte), Parsifal (Cpte), Rheingold (Cpte), Siegfried (Cpte)
see CONCERT INDEX *under:*
(DECC) **414 100-2DM15** Wagner: Der Ring des Nibelungen

(EMI) **CZS7 67123-2** Wagner: Der Ring des Nibelungen
(FOYE) **15-CF2011** Wagner—Der Ring de Nibelungen
(PHIL) **446 057-2PB14** Wagner—The Ring Cycle - Bayreuth Festival 1967

NEIKRUG, Marc (pf)
Beethoven: Violin Sonata 5, Violin Sonata 9, Violin Sonata 10
see CONCERT INDEX *under:*
(RCA) **RD60740** Mozart—Violin Sonatas, Vol.2
(RCA) **RD60743** Mozart—Violin Sonatas, Vol.3
(RCA) **RD60991** Beethoven—Complete Violin Sonatas
(RCA) **09026 60742-2** Mozart—Violin Sonatas, Vol.4
(RCA) **09026 60744-2** Mozart—Sonatas for Violin and Piano, Volume 5
(RCA) **09026 61276-2** Brahms—Viola Sonatas; Songs
(RCA) **09026 62697-2** Franck/Debussy/Fauré—Violin Sonatas
(RCA) **09026 68052-2** Schumann—Violin and Piano Works

NEILZ, Jacques (vc)
Messiaen: Quatuor

NEISER, Holger (treb)
see CONCERT INDEX *under:*
(WERG) **WER6173-2** T.W.Adorno—Chamber & Choral Works

NEJTEK, Pavel (db)
see CONCERT INDEX *under:*
(SUPR) **11 1461-2** Dvořák—Chamber Works - Volume 11

NEL, Anton (pf)
see CONCERT INDEX *under:*
(BRID) **BCD9027** Rodrigo—Piano Works

NELEPP, Georgi (ten)
see CONCERT INDEX *under:*
(DANT) **LYS013/5** Tchaikovsky—The Queen of Spades
(EMI) **CHS7 69741-2(6)** Record of Singing, Vol.4—Russian & Slavonic Schools
(PREI) **89080** Mark Reizen (1895-1992) - II

NELLI, Herva (sop)
Verdi: Ballo in maschera (Cpte), Otello (Cpte)
see CONCERT INDEX *under:*
(RCA) **GD60326** Verdi—Operas & Choral Works

NELSON, Elisabeth Comeaux (sop)
Britten: Paul Bunyan (Cpte)

NELSON, Gene (sngr)
Sondheim: Follies (Cpte)

NELSON, John (cond)
see Chicago Lyric Op Chor

NELSON, Judith (sop)
Handel: Alceste (Cpte), Apollo e Dafne, Messiah (exc), Resurrezione (Cpte)
Haydn: Mass 3
Purcell: Dido (Cpte), Fairy Queen, Z629 (Cpte)
see CONCERT INDEX *under:*
(HARM) **HMA190 5137** Arias and Cantatas for Soprano and Trumpet
(KOCH) **37044-2** Haydn—English Love Songs
(KOCH) **37163-2** Bach—Cantatas
(L'OI) **421 478-2OH** Haydn—Masses
(L'OI) **421 480-2OH** Monteverdi: Madrigali Erotici
(L'OI) **421 654-2OH** Handel & Haydn: Choral Works
(L'OI) **425 893-2OM6(1)** Purcell—Theatre Music (Part 1)
(L'OI) **425 893-2OM6(2)** Purcell—Theatre Music (Part 2)

NELSON, Marty (voc)
Bernstein: West Side Story (Cpte)

NELSOVA, Zara (vc)
see CONCERT INDEX *under:*
(BBCR) **BBCRD9111** Elgar—Cello Concerto etc

NELSSON, Woldemar (cond)
see Bayreuth Fest Orch

NĚMEČKOVÁ, Květoslava (sop)
Janáček: Amarus

NÉMET, János (boy alto)
Puccini: Tosca (Cpte)

NÉMETH, Judit (contr)
Bach: St Matthew Passion, BWV244 (Cpte)

NÉMETH, Judit (mez)
Bach: Cantata 80, Cantata 147, Cantata 208, Christmas Oratorio, BWV248 (Cpte)
Handel: St John Passion (Cpte)

NÉMETH, Maria (sop)
see CONCERT INDEX *under:*
(CLUB) **CL99-007** Maria Nemeth/Tiana Lemnitz
(NIMB) **NI7802** Divas 1906-1935
(PEAR) **GEMMCDS9926(2)** Covent Garden on Record—Vol.4 (pt 2)
(SCHW) **314542** Vienna State Opera Live, Vol.4
(SCHW) **314572** Vienna State Opera Live, Vol.7
(SCHW) **314602** Vienna State Opera Live, Vol.10
(SCHW) **314632** Vienna State Opera Live, Vol.13

NÉMETH, Pál (cond)
see Capella Savaria

NÉMETH, Pál (fl/dir)
see CONCERT INDEX *under:*
(HARM) **HMA190 3010** Bach—Wedding Cantatas, BWV202, 209 and 210
(QUIN) **QUI90 3010** Bach—Wedding Cantatas

NENDICK, Josephine (sop)
see CONCERT INDEX *under:*
(EMI) **CDM7 63948-2** 20th Century French Orchestral Works

NENTWIG, Franz Ferdinand (bass-bar)
Schreker: Schatzgräber (Cpte)

NÉQUECAUR, Pierre (bar)
Gounod: Philémon et Baucis (Cpte)

NERALIČ, Tomislav (bar)
Beethoven: Fidelio (Cpte)
see CONCERT INDEX *under:*
(SCHW) **314552** Vienna State Opera Live, Vol.5

NERAT, Harald (cond)
see Capella Istropolitana

NERI, Giulio (bass)
Verdi: Don Carlo (Cpte)

NERIKI, Shigeo (pf)
see CONCERT INDEX *under:*
(RCA) **RD60598** Works for Cello and Piano

NEROZZI, Lidia (mez)
Puccini: Madama Butterfly (Cpte)

NES, Jard van (contr)
Bach: Cantata 35, Cantata 170, Mass in B minor, BWV232 (Cpte), St Matthew Passion, BWV244 (Cpte)
Beethoven: Symphony 9
Brahms: Alto Rhapsody, Op. 53
Handel: Theodora (Cpte)
Mahler: Knaben Wunderhorn (exc), Lied von der Erde, Symphony 2, Symphony 3
Martin: Cornet
Mendelssohn: Elias (Cpte)
Mozart: Requiem, Zauberflöte (Cpte)
Schoenberg: Gurrelieder
Wagner: Götterdämmerung (Cpte)
see CONCERT INDEX *under:*
(DECC) **425 832-2DH** Berio—Vocal & Orchestral Works
(ETCE) **KTC1097** Loevendie—Miscellaneous Works
(OTTA) **OTRC98402** Works by Brahms and Mahler
(PHIL) **426 290-2PH5** Beethoven—Complete Symphonies
(SCHW) **311009** Schoenberg: Chamber Orchestral Works
(SCHW) **312632** Mahler/Busoni—Vocal/Orchestral Works

NESHYBA, Ladislav (bass)
Marschner: Hans Heiling (Cpte)
Verdi: Rigoletto (Cpte)

NESHYBOVÁ, Ivica (mez)
Verdi: Rigoletto (Cpte)

NESSI, Giuseppe (ten)
Puccini: Bohème (Cpte), Turandot (Cpte)
see CONCERT INDEX *under:*
(EMI) **CHS7 64864-2(1)** La Scala Edition - Vol.2, 1915-46 (pt 1)
(EMI) **CHS7 64864-2(2)** La Scala Edition - Vol.2, 1915-46 (pt 1)
(PREI) **89007** Aureliano Pertile (1885-1952) - I
(PREI) **89023** Conchita Supervia (1895-1936)

NESSINGER, Mary (mez)
T. Levin: De Luxe

NESTERENKO, Evgeny (bass)
Gounod: Faust (Cpte)
Rimsky-Korsakov: Mozart and Salieri (Cpte)
Shostakovich: Symphony 14
Tchaikovsky: Eugene Onegin (Cpte)
Verdi: Nabucco (Cpte), Trovatore (Cpte)

NETHERLAND WIND ENSEMBLE
see CONCERT INDEX *under:*
(ETCE) **KTC1130** Birtwistle—Works for Wind and Percussion
cond J. WOOD
see CONCERT INDEX *under:*
(ETCE) **KTC1130** Birtwistle—Works for Wind and Percussion

NETHERLANDS BACH SOCIETY BAROQUE ORCHESTRA
cond G. LEONHARDT
Biber: Requiem in F minor
Valls: Missa Scala Aretina

NETHERLANDS BACH SOCIETY CHOIR
cond T. KOOPMAN
Bach: St Matthew Passion, BWV244 (Cpte)
Mozart: Requiem
cond G. LEONHARDT
Biber: Requiem in F minor
Valls: Missa Scala Aretina

NETHERLANDS BACH SOCIETY COLLEGIUM MUSICUM
Bach: Mass in B minor, BWV232 (Cpte)

NETHERLANDS CHAMBER CHOIR
Rossini: Petite messe solennelle

(HYPE) **CDA66315** Handel: Music for Royal Occasions
(HYPE) **CDA66598** Purcell—Complete Odes & Welcome Songs, Vol.8
(HYPE) **CDA66609** Purcell—Complete Anthems & Services, Vol.2
(HYPE) **CDA66644** Purcell—Complete Anthems & Services, Vol.4
(HYPE) **CDA66656** Purcell—Complete Anthems & Services, Vol.5
(HYPE) **CDA66663** Purcell—Complete Anthems & Services, Vol.6
(HYPE) **CDA66677** Purcell—Anthems & Services, Vol.7

NEW COMPANY
cond E. DOWNES
Prokofiev: Eugene Onegin (Cpte)

NEW ENGLAND CHILDREN'S CHORUS
cond S. OZAWA
Orff: Carmina Burana

NEW ENGLAND CONSERVATORY CHORUS
cond A. COPLAND
(SONY) **SM3K46559** Copland Collection—1936-1948
cond C. MUNCH
Berlioz: Enfance du Christ (Cpte), Grande messe des morts (Cpte)
Ravel: Daphnis et Chloé (Cpte)
cond S. OZAWA
Berlioz: Roméo et Juliette (exc)
Orff: Carmina Burana
cond W. STEINBERG
Holst: Planets

NEW ENGLAND ORCHESTRA
cond J. SINCLAIR
see CONCERT INDEX under:
(KOCH) **37025-2** Ives—Orchestral Works

NEW EUROPEAN STRINGS CHAMBER ORCHESTRA
Bach: Goldberg Variations

NEW FRIENDS OF MUSIC ORCHESTRA
cond F. STIEDRY
see CONCERT INDEX under:
(BIDD) **LAB064** Recital by Joseph Szigeti
(BIDD) **LAB088** Primrose plays Handel, Mozart and Beethoven
(PEAR) **GEMMCD9045** William Primrose and Albert Spalding

NEW LEIPZIG QUARTET
see CONCERT INDEX under:
(CPO) **CPO999 002-2** Dessau—Complete String Quartets

NEW LIGHT SYMPHONY ORCHESTRA
cond J. AINSLIE MURRAY
see CONCERT INDEX under:
(EMI) **CDS7 54568-2** The Elgar Edition, Vol.3

NEW LONDON CHAMBER CHOIR
cond O. KNUSSEN
see CONCERT INDEX under:
(DG) **447 068-2GH** Stravinsky—The Flood, etc
cond J. WOOD
see CONCERT INDEX under:
(HYPE) **CDA66798** Poulenc—Secular Choral Music

NEW LONDON CHAMBER CHOIR
see CONCERT INDEX under:
(HYPE) **CDA66410** Stravinsky—Choral Works
cond J. WOOD
see CONCERT INDEX under:
(AMON) **CD-SAR24** La Rue and Josquin: Choral Works
(AMON) **CD-SAR56** The Brightest Heaven of Invention
(CHAN) **CHAN8478** Erik Bergman—Choral Works
(HYPE) **CDA66410** Stravinsky—Choral Works

NEW LONDON CHILDREN'S CHOIR
cond M. BEST
Vaughan Williams: Hugh the Drover (Cpte)
cond M. JANSONS
Tchaikovsky: Nutcracker (Cpte)
cond A. MELVILLE
Boughton: Bethlehem (Cpte)
cond M. ROSTROPOVICH
Prokofiev: Ivan the Terrible Suite
cond VLADIMIR ASHKENAZY
see CONCERT INDEX under:
(DECC) **436 762-2DH** Shostakovich—Orchestral & Vocal Works

NEW LONDON CONSORT
cond M. NEARY
see CONCERT INDEX under:
(SONY) **SK66243** Music for Queen Mary
cond P. PICKETT
Anon: Carmina Burana (exc), Feast of Fools, Llibre Vermell
Bach: Brandenburg Concertos
Blow: Venus and Adonis (Cpte)
M. Praetorius: Terpsichore (exc)
Monteverdi: Orfeo (Cpte), Vespers
Susato: Danserye (exc)
see CONCERT INDEX under:
(LINN) **CKD007** Music from the time of Columbus
(LINN) **CKD011** Elizabethan & Jacobean Consort Music
(L'OI) **433 148-2OH2** The Pilgrimage to Santiago

(L'OI) **436 460-2OH** Biber—Requiem; Chamber Works
(L'OI) **440 637-2OH** Monteverdi—Ballets

NEW LONDON ORCHESTRA
cond R. CORP
see CONCERT INDEX under:
(HYPE) **CDA66347** Poulenc & Hahn—Balletic Works
(HYPE) **CDA66365** Satie—Orchestral Works
(HYPE) **CDA66499** Prokofiev—Music for Children
(HYPE) **CDA66576** Virgil Thomson—Film Music
(HYPE) **CDA66594** Milhaud—Orchestral Works

NEW MUSIC THEATRE
cond T. RILEY
Riley: In C

NEW PALAIS ROYALE ORCHESTRA
cond M. PERESS
see CONCERT INDEX under:
(MUSM) **67094-2** Antheil—Ballet Mécanique

NEW PALAIS ROYALE PERCUSSION ENSEMBLE
cond M. PERESS
see CONCERT INDEX under:
(MUSM) **67094-2** Antheil—Ballet Mécanique

NEW PERFORMANCE GROUP
see CONCERT INDEX under:
(MODE) **Mode 14** Gitek—Choral and Chamber Works

NEW PHILHARMONIA CHORUS
cond J. BARBIROLLI
Verdi: Requiem (Cpte)
see CONCERT INDEX under:
(CFP) **CD-CFP4532** Sacred Arias
cond D. BARENBOIM
see CONCERT INDEX under:
(EMI) **CDM7 64634-2** Fauré/Bach—Choral Works
cond R. FRÜHBECK DE BURGOS
Orff: Carmina Burana
cond O. KLEMPERER
Beethoven: Missa Solemnis
Mozart: Don Giovanni (Cpte)
cond W. SAWALLISCH
see CONCERT INDEX under:
(PHIL) **432 598-2PB3** Mendelssohn—Complete Symphonies

NEW PHILHARMONIA ORCHESTRA
see CONCERT INDEX under:
(CFP) **CD-CFP4570** Choral Favourites
cond C. ABBADO
Tchaikovsky: Symphony 2
cond P.H. ADLER
see CONCERT INDEX under:
(RCA) **09026 61357-2** Leontyne Price Sings Mozart
cond E. ANSERMET
Stravinsky: Firebird (Cpte)
cond D. ATHERTON
(LYRI) **SRCD324** Mathias—Choral Works
(LYRI) **SRCD325** Mathias—Concertos
cond J. BARBIROLLI
Brahms: Piano Concerto 1
Mahler: Symphony 6
R. Strauss: Metamorphosen
Schoenberg: Pelleas und Melisande
Verdi: Requiem (Cpte)
see CONCERT INDEX under:
(CFP) **CD-CFP4532** Sacred Arias
(EMI) **CDC7 47537-2** English String Music
(EMI) **CDC7 47793-2** Mahler—Song-cycles
(EMI) **CDM7 63537-2** Brahms: Orchestral Works
(EMI) **CDM7 64724-2** Elgar—Orchestral Works
(EMI) **CDM7 69544-2** Berlioz: Vocal Works
(EMI) **CDM7 69563-2** Elgar: Orchestral Works
(EMI) **CZS7 62707-2** Mahler—Vocal Works
cond D. BARENBOIM
see CONCERT INDEX under:
(EMI) **CDM7 64626-2** Schumann—Concertos, etc
(EMI) **CDM7 64634-2** Fauré/Bach—Choral Works
(EMI) **CZS5 68132-2** Les introuvables de Jacqueline du Pré
cond B. BARTOLETTI
see CONCERT INDEX under:
(EMI) **CDS5 55017-2** Domingo Opera Classics
cond R. BONYNGE
Delibes: Sylvia (Cpte)
see CONCERT INDEX under:
(DECC) **433 010-2DM** Christmas Stars
(DECC) **436 301-2DA** Renata Tebaldi & Franco Corelli—Arias & Duets
cond A. BOULT
Elgar: Violin Concerto
R. Strauss: Don Quixote
Vaughan Williams: Symphony 3, Symphony 4, Symphony 6
see CONCERT INDEX under:
(EMI) **CDM7 64022-2** Vaughan Williams—Orchestral Works
cond B. BRITTEN
(LOND) **425 100-2LM** Britten: Orchestral & Vocal Works
cond COLIN DAVIS
(PHIL) **442 287-2PM2** Favourite Violin Concertos
cond A. COPLAND
see CONCERT INDEX under:
(SONY) **SM3K46559** Copland Collection—1936-1948
cond A. DAVIS
see CONCERT INDEX under:

(SONY) **SBK53257** Grieg—Orchestral Works
Beethoven: Romances
cond P. DERVAUX
see CONCERT INDEX under:
(EMI) **CMS7 64790-2** Saint-Saëns—Complete Works for Violin and Orchestra
cond A. DORATI
see CONCERT INDEX under:
(EMI) **CDM7 63985-2** Bartók—Violin and Viola Works
cond O. DE FABRITIIS
see CONCERT INDEX under:
(DECC) **417 686-2DC** Puccini—Operatic Arias
(DECC) **430 481-2DX2** Renata Tebaldi sings Opera Arias
cond A. FRANCIS
Donizetti: Ugo, Conte di Parigi (Cpte)
cond R. FRÜHBECK DE BURGOS
Orff: Carmina Burana
Ravel: Boléro
see CONCERT INDEX under:
(CFP) **CD-CFP4532** Sacred Arias
(DECC) **417 786-2DM** Spanish Orchestral Works
(EMI) **ZDMF7 64830-2** The Art of Nathan Milstein
cond A. GALLIERA
Beethoven: Violin Concerto
cond L. GARDELLI
Verdi: Corsaro (Cpte), Masnadieri (Cpte)
cond A. GIBSON
see CONCERT INDEX under:
(PHIL) **422 508-2PME4** The Complete Mozart Edition Vol 8
cond R. GIOVANINETTI
see CONCERT INDEX under:
(DG) **431 103-2GB** Great Voices—Montserrat Caballé
cond A. GUADAGNO
see CONCERT INDEX under:
(DECC) **433 010-2DM** Christmas Stars
(RCA) **GD60818** Great Operatic Duets
(RCA) **09026 61580-2(8)** RCA/Met 100 Singers, 100 Years (pt 8)
cond V. HANDLEY
see CONCERT INDEX under:
(LYRI) **SRCD235** Rubbra—Symphonies
cond J. HORENSTEIN
Nielsen: Saga-Drøm, Symphony 5
Tchaikovsky: Symphony 5
cond E. INBAL
Beethoven: Triple Concerto
see CONCERT INDEX under:
(PHIL) **442 580-2PM2** Beethoven—Concertos, Volume 2
cond JAMES LEVINE
Verdi: Vespri Siciliani (Cpte)
cond O. KLEMPERER
Bach: Mass in B minor, BWV232 (Cpte)
Beethoven: Choral Fantasia, Missa Solemnis
Bruckner: Symphony 5, Symphony 6
Mahler: Lied von der Erde, Symphony 9
Mozart: Così fan tutte (Cpte), Don Giovanni (Cpte), Nozze di Figaro (Cpte)
see CONCERT INDEX under:
(EMI) **CDM7 63358-2** Beethoven—Orchestral Works
(EMI) **CMS5 65212-2** Wagner—Les introuvables du Ring
(EMI) **CMS7 63272-2** Mozart: Late Symphonies
(EMI) **CMS7 63360-2** Beethoven: Complete Piano Concertos
(EMI) **CMS7 63613-2** Schumann—Symphonies, etc
(EMI) **CMS7 63835-2** Bruckner, Wagner & Hindemith—Orchestral Works
(EMI) **CMS7 64150-2** Klemperer conducts Rameau/Bach
(EMIL) **CDZ7 67015-2** Mozart—Opera Arias
cond J. KRENZ
see CONCERT INDEX under:
(PHIL) **442 287-2PM2** Favourite Violin Concertos
cond P. LEDGER
Elgar: Coronation Ode (Cpte)
cond E. LEINSDORF
Mozart: Così fan tutte (Cpte)
see CONCERT INDEX under:
(RCA) **GD60398** Leontyne Price sings Strauss arias
(RCA) **GD86722** R.Strauss: Orchestral and Vocal Works
cond R. LEPPARD
Mozart: Mass, K427
see CONCERT INDEX under:
(CFP) **CD-CFP4532** Sacred Arias
(PHIL) **426 977-2PCC** Works for Violin and Orchestra
(PHIL) **438 323-2PM2** Mozart—Violin Concertos
cond L. MAAZEL
Mussorgsky: Pictures
Prokofiev: Piano Concerto 3
see CONCERT INDEX under:
(SONY) **MK39097** Puccini Heroines
(SONY) **M3K79312** Puccini: Il Trittico
cond C. MACKERRAS
Mussorgsky: Pictures
Stravinsky: Petrushka (Cpte)
(DG) **431 166-2GR** French Works for Cello & Orchestra
cond L. MAGIERA
see CONCERT INDEX under:
(DECC) **417 011-2DH2** Pavarotti's Greatest Hits
(DECC) **425 681-2DM2** Tutto Pavarotti
cond I. MARKEVITCH
see CONCERT INDEX under:

(PHIL) **442 586-2PM2** Tchaikovsky—Complete Tone Poems
 cond E. MATA
 see CONCERT INDEX *under:*
(CATA) **09026 62672-2** Revueltas—Night of the Mayas
 cond D. MEASHAM
 see CONCERT INDEX *under:*
(UNIC) **UKCD2066** Russian Orchestral Music
 cond Z. MEHTA
Puccini: Tosca (Cpte)
Verdi: Trovatore (Cpte)
 see CONCERT INDEX *under:*
(RCA) **09026 61580-2(8)** RCA/Met 100 Singers, 100 Years (pt 8)
 cond R. MUTI
Cherubini: Requiem 2
Verdi: Aida (Cpte), Ballo in maschera (Cpte), Macbeth (Cpte)
 see CONCERT INDEX *under:*
(EMI) **CDC5 55017-2** Domingo Opera Classics
(EMI) **CDM7 69500-2** Montserrat Caballé sings Bellini & Verdi Arias
(EMI) **CDM7 69549-2** Ruggero Raimondi: Italian Opera Arias
(EMI) **CZS7 67314-2** Tchaikovsky—Symphonies
 cond G. PRÊTRE
G. Charpentier: Louise (Cpte)
 cond J. PRITCHARD
Chopin: Piano Concerto 2
 see CONCERT INDEX *under:*
(SONY) **MK39097** Puccini Heroines
 cond N. SANTI
 see CONCERT INDEX *under:*
(RCA) **09026 61236-2** Leontyne Price - Prima Donna Collection
(RCA) **61357-2** Leontyne Price Sings Mozart
(RCA) **09026 61580-2(8)** RCA/Met 100 Singers, 100 Years (pt 8)
 cond W. SAWALLISCH
 see CONCERT INDEX *under:*
(PHIL) **432 598-2PB3** Mendelssohn—Complete Symphonies
(PHIL) **442 302-2PM2** The Best of Mendelssohn
 cond T. SCHIPPERS
 see CONCERT INDEX *under:*
(RCA) **09026 61580-2(7)** RCA/Met 100 Singers, 100 Years (pt 7)
(RCA) **09026 61983-2** Leontyne Price sings Barber
 cond L. STOKOWSKI
 see CONCERT INDEX *under:*
(BBCR) **BBCRD9107**
Brahms/Klemperer/Ravel/Vaughan Williams—Orchestral Works
(DECC) **433 625-2DSP** Stokowski conducts Famous Russian Works
 cond E. DE WAART
 see CONCERT INDEX *under:*
(PHIL) **420 700-2PSL** Bach: Violin Concertos
(PHIL) **438 733-2PM2** R. Strauss—Music for Wind
 cond W. WALTON
 see CONCERT INDEX *under:*
(EMI) **CHS5 65003-2** Walton conducts Walton
 cond D. WILLCOCKS
Fauré: Pavane, Requiem (Cpte)
 see CONCERT INDEX *under:*
(EMI) **CDM7 64722-2** Vaughan Williams—Choral & Orchestral Works
(LYRI) **SRCD324** Mathias—Choral Works

NEW PHILHARMONIA WIND ENSEMBLE
 cond O. KLEMPERER
Mozart: Serenade, K375

NEW PHILHARMONIC ORCHESTRA
 cond A. JORDAN
Dukas: Ariane et Barbe-Bleue (Cpte)

NEW PRINCESS THEATRE ORCHESTRA, NEW YORK
 cond J. MCGLINN
 see CONCERT INDEX *under:*
(EMI) **CDC7 47454-2** Kiri sings Gershwin

NEW QUEEN'S HALL ORCHESTRA
 cond B. WORDSWORTH
 see CONCERT INDEX *under:*
(ARGO) **440 116-2ZH** Vaughan Williams—Orchestral Works
(EYE) **EOS5001** Wagner—Overtures and Preludes

NEW SADLER'S WELLS OPERA CHORUS
Coward: Bitter Sweet (Cpte)
Lehár: Lustige Witwe (exc)
Sullivan: HMS Pinafore (Cpte)
 see CONCERT INDEX *under:*
(TER) **CDVIR8314** Is it really me?

NEW SADLER'S WELLS OPERA ORCHESTRA
 cond S. PHIPPS
Sullivan: HMS Pinafore (Cpte)
 see CONCERT INDEX *under:*
(TER) **CDVIR8316** Sullivan—Overtures
 cond M. REED
Coward: Bitter Sweet (Cpte)
 cond B. WORDSWORTH
Lehár: Lustige Witwe (exc)
 see CONCERT INDEX *under:*
(TER) **CDVIR8314** Is it really me?

NEW STOCKHOLM CHAMBER ORCHESTRA
 cond O. KAMU
 see CONCERT INDEX *under:*
(BIS) **BIS-CD348** The Winter Trombone

 cond L. MARKIZ
 see CONCERT INDEX *under:*
(BIS) **BIS-CD377** Schnittke: Concertos

NEW SWINGLE SINGERS
 cond P. BOULEZ
Berio: Sinfonia

NEW SYMPHONY ORCHESTRA
 cond J. BARBIROLLI
 see CONCERT INDEX *under:*
(DANA) **DACOCD315/6** Lauritz Melchior Anthology - Vol. 3
 cond A. BOULT
Tchaikovsky: Swan Lake Suite
 cond A. COATES
 see CONCERT INDEX *under:*
(CLAR) **CDGSE78-50-54** Coates conducts Wagner, Weber & Mendelssohn
(PEAR) **GEMMCD9398** Friedrich Schorr
 cond A. COLLINS
Rachmaninov: Piano Concerto 3
 cond E. ELGAR
Elgar: Cello Concerto
 see CONCERT INDEX *under:*
(EMI) **CDS7 54564-2** The Elgar Edition, Vol.2
(EMI) **CDS7 54568-2** The Elgar Edition, Vol.3
 cond A. EREDE
 see CONCERT INDEX *under:*
(DECC) **436 463-2DM** Ten Top Tenors
 cond I. GODFREY
Sullivan: Gondoliers (Cpte), HMS Pinafore (Cpte), Iolanthe (Cpte), Patience (Cpte)
 see CONCERT INDEX *under:*
(DECC) **430 095-2DWO** The World of Gilbert & Sullivan, Vol.1
(DECC) **433 868-2DWO** The World of Gilbert & Sullivan - Volume 2
 cond R. NASH
 see CONCERT INDEX *under:*
(DECC) **433 868-2DWO** The World of Gilbert & Sullivan - Volume 2
 cond M. SARGENT
 see CONCERT INDEX *under:*
(BEUL) **1PD13** Sir Malcolm Sargent conducts British Music
(RCA) **09026 61778-2(11-15)** The Heifetz Collection, Vols. 11-15
(RCA) **09026 61778-2(30)** The Heifetz Collection, Vol. 30
 cond S. SKROWACZEWSKI
Chopin: Piano Concerto 1
 cond G. TOYE
 see CONCERT INDEX *under:*
(DUTT) **CDAX8006** The Delius Collection

NEW WORLD BRASS
 see CONCERT INDEX *under:*
(ARGO) **444 459-2ZH** Defining Dahl

NEW WORLD CHAMBER ENSEMBLE
 see CONCERT INDEX *under:*
(NEW) **NW273-2** Griffes: Vocal & Instrumental Works

NEW WORLD PHILHARMONIC
 cond P. MATZ
 see CONCERT INDEX *under:*
(EMI) **CDC5 55050-2** Kiri sings Cole Porter

NEW WORLD QUARTET
Brahms: String Quartet 1, String Quartet 2
 see CONCERT INDEX *under:*
(CARL) **MCD17** French Music For String Quartet
(VOX) **115775-2** Unknown String Quartets, Vol.2

NEW WORLD SYMPHONY
 cond J. NELSON
 see CONCERT INDEX *under:*
(ARGO) **440 212-2ZH** Schoenfield—Orchestral Works
 cond M. TILSON THOMAS
 see CONCERT INDEX *under:*
(ARGO) **436 737-2ZH** Tangazo—Music of Latin America
(ARGO) **444 459-2ZH** Defining Dahl

NEW WORLD VOCAL ENSEMBLE
 see CONCERT INDEX *under:*
(CHNN) **CCS2991** Ev'ry Time I Feel the Spirit

NEW YORK CHAMBER ORCHESTRA
 cond G. SCHWARZ
S. Albert: TreeStone
 see CONCERT INDEX *under:*
(DELO) **DE3092** Hanson—Orchestral Works

NEW YORK CHAMBER SYMPHONY ORCHESTRA
 cond G. SCHWARZ
 see CONCERT INDEX *under:*
(NEW) **80407-2** Sheng—Miscellaneous Works

NEW YORK CHAMBER SYMPHONY ORCHESTRA
 cond A. PANUFNIK
Panufnik: Arbor cosmica, Sinfonia sacra
 cond G. SCHWARZ
Kernis: Symphony in Waves
 see CONCERT INDEX *under:*
(DELO) **DE3067** Schubert—Orchestral Works
(DELO) **DE3074** Piston: Orchestral Works
(DELO) **DE3093** Diamond—Orchestral Works
(DELO) **DE3103** David Diamond—Orchestral Works
(DELO) **DE3105** Hanson—Choral and Orchestral Works
(DELO) **DE3106** Piston—Orchestral Works
(DELO) **DE3127** Creston—Orchestral Works, Vol.2

NEW YORK CHORAL ART SOCIETY
 cond L. BERNSTEIN
Liszt: Faust Symphony

NEW YORK CHORAL ARTISTS
 cond L. BERNSTEIN
Mahler: Symphony 3
 see CONCERT INDEX *under:*
(DG) **435 162-2GX13** Mahler—Complete Symphonies
 cond J. MCGLINN
 see CONCERT INDEX *under:*
(EMI) **CDC7 47454-2** Kiri sings Gershwin

NEW YORK CHORAL SOCIETY
 cond J.D. GOODWIN
 see CONCERT INDEX *under:*
(KOCH) **37026-2** Morton Gould—Choral Music

NEW YORK CHORAL SOCIETY ORCHESTRA
 cond J.D. GOODWIN
 see CONCERT INDEX *under:*
(KOCH) **37026-2** Morton Gould—Choral Music

NEW YORK CITY BALLET ORCHESTRA
 cond L. BERNSTEIN
Bernstein: Dybbuk (Cpte)

NEW YORK CITY GAY MEN'S CHORUS
 cond R. BASS
R. Strauss: Friedenstag (Cpte)

NEW YORK CITY OPERA CHILDREN'S CHORUS
 cond E. QUELER
Puccini: Edgar (Cpte)

NEW YORK CITY OPERA CHORUS
 see CONCERT INDEX *under:*
(SONY) **SK64133** The Essential Philip Glass
 cond C. KEENE
Glass: Satyagraha (Cpte)
 cond S. KRACHMALNICK
D. Moore: Carry Nation (Cpte)
 cond J. MAUCERI
Bernstein: Candide (1982) (Cpte)

NEW YORK CITY OPERA ORCHESTRA
 see CONCERT INDEX *under:*
(SONY) **SK64133** The Essential Philip Glass
 cond R. BONYNGE
 see CONCERT INDEX *under:*
(DECC) **430 724-2DM** Great Operatic Duets
 cond E. BUCKLEY
R. Ward: Crucible (Cpte)
 cond C. KEENE
Glass: Satyagraha (Cpte)
 cond S. KRACHMALNICK
D. Moore: Carry Nation (Cpte)
 cond J. MAUCERI
Bernstein: Candide (1982) (Cpte)

NEW YORK CITY SYMPHONY ORCHESTRA
 cond L. BERNSTEIN
Blitzstein: Airborne Symphony

NEW YORK CLARION CONCERTS CHORUS
 cond N. JENKINS
Rossini: Pietra del Paragone (Cpte)

NEW YORK CLARION CONCERTS ORCHESTRA
 cond N. JENKINS
Rossini: Pietra del Paragone (Cpte)

NEW YORK CONCERT CHORALE
 cond P. GEMIGNANI
Forrest/Wright: Kismet (Cpte)
 cond R. NORRINGTON
 see CONCERT INDEX *under:*
(EMI) **CDC7 54643-2** Rossini—Bicentenary Gala Concert
 cond J. RUDEL
Weill: Lost in the Stars (Cpte)

NEW YORK CONCERT SINGERS
 see CONCERT INDEX *under:*
(DELO) **DE3170** Beach—Cabildo; Six Short Pieces

NEW YORK CORNET AND SACBUT ENSEMBLE
 see CONCERT INDEX *under:*
(NEWP) **NC60021** Praetorius—Chorale Settings

NEW YORK HARMONIE ENSEMBLE
 cond S. RICHMAN
 see CONCERT INDEX *under:*
(MUSI) **MACD-649** Salute To France
(MUSI) **MACD-691** Dvorak & Friends - Czech Wind Music

NEW YORK LYCÉE FRANÇAIS CHILDREN'S CHOIR
 cond F. REINER
Bizet: Carmen (Cpte)

NEW YORK MALE CHORAL ARTISTS
 cond K. MASUR
Shostakovich: Symphony 13

NEW YORK METROPOLITAN OPERA CHILDREN'S CHOIR
 cond L. BERNSTEIN
Bizet: Carmen (Cpte)
 cond G. SOLTI
Verdi: Otello (Cpte)

NEW YORK METROPOLITAN OPERA CHORUS
 see CONCERT INDEX *under:*
(MSCM) **MM30352** Caruso—Italian Opera Arias
(NIMB) **NI7803** Enrico Caruso—Opera Recital
(PEAR) **EVC2** The Caruso Edition, Vol.2—1908-12
(PEAR) **EVC3(1)** The Caruso Edition, Vol.3 (pt 1)

(RCA) **GD60495(4)** The Complete Caruso Collection (pt 4)
(RCA) **GD60495(5)** The Complete Caruso Collection (pt 5)
  cond A. BODANZKY
Beethoven: Fidelio (Cpte)
  cond F. CALUSIO
  see CONCERT INDEX *under:*
(MYTO) **2MCD90317** Verdi—Un Ballo in maschera
  cond E. COOPER
  see CONCERT INDEX *under:*
(SONY) **MPK45693** Portrait—Ezio Pinza
  cond JAMES LEVINE
Donizetti: Elisir d'amore (Cpte)
Mozart: Nozze di Figaro (Cpte)
Puccini: Manon Lescaut (Cpte)
Verdi: Aida (Cpte), Don Carlo (Cpte), Luisa Miller (Cpte), Traviata (Cpte), Trovatore (Cpte)
Wagner: Götterdämmerung (Cpte), Parsifal (Cpte)
  see CONCERT INDEX *under:*
(DG) **445 354-2GX14** Wagner—Der Ring des Nibelungen
  cond E. LEINSDORF
Rossini: Barbiere di Siviglia (Cpte)
Verdi: Macbeth (Cpte)
Wagner: Tristan und Isolde (Cpte)
  cond D. MITROPOULOS
Barber: Vanessa (Cpte)
  see CONCERT INDEX *under:*
(RCA) **GD87911** Marian Anderson - Opera, Oratorio & Song Recital
  cond E. PANIZZA
Verdi: Otello (Cpte), Traviata (Cpte)
  see CONCERT INDEX *under:*
(MMOI) **CDMOIR404** Ezio Pinza—Recital
(MYTO) **2MCD90317** Verdi—Un Ballo in maschera
(PEAR) **GEMMCDS9452** The Emperor Tibbett
  cond J. PASTERNACK
  see CONCERT INDEX *under:*
(PEAR) **EVC4(1)** The Caruso Edition, Vol.4 (pt 1)
(RCA) **GD60495(5)** The Complete Caruso Collection (pt 5)
  cond W.B. ROGERS
  see CONCERT INDEX *under:*
(RCA) **GD60495(3)** The Complete Caruso Collection (pt 3)
  cond G. SCOGNAMIGLIO
  see CONCERT INDEX *under:*
(PEAR) **EVC3(1)** The Caruso Edition, Vol.3 (pt 1)
(RCA) **GD60495(5)** The Complete Caruso Collection (pt 5)
  cond G. SETTI
Bellini: Norma (exc)
  see CONCERT INDEX *under:*
(MMOI) **CDMOIR404** Ezio Pinza—Recital
(MMOI) **CDMOIR428** Rosa Ponselle and Giovanni Martinelli sing Verdi
(NIMB) **NI7801** Great Singers, Vol.1
(NIMB) **NI7804** Giovanni Martinelli—Opera Recital
(NIMB) **NI7805** Rosa Ponselle—Opera & Song Recital
(NIMB) **NI7845** Giacomo Lauri-Volpi (1892-1979)
(NIMB) **NI7851** Legendary Voices
(PEAR) **GEMMCDS9452** The Emperor Tibbett
(PEAR) **GEMMCDS9924(1)** Covent Garden on Record, Vol.2 (pt 1)
(PEAR) **GEMMCDS9926(2)** Covent Garden on Record—Vol.4 (pt 2)
(PEAR) **GEMMCD9306** Ezio Pinza—Opera Recital
(PREI) **89012** Giacomo Lauri-Volpi (1894-1979)
(PREI) **89050** Ezio Pinza (1892-1957)
(PREI) **89062** Giovanni Martinelli (1885-1969)
(PREI) **89073** Giuseppe de Luca (1876-1950) - II
(RCA) **GD87808** Lawrence Tibbett sings Opera Arias
(RCA) **GD87810** Rosa Ponselle - Opera & Song Recital
(RCA) **GD87811** Beniamino Gigli—Operatic Arias
(RCA) **09026 61245-2** Ezio Pinza - Recital
(RCA) **09026 61580-2(3)** RCA/Met 100 Singers, 100 Years (pt 3)
(ROMO) **81007-2** Rosa Ponselle—Victor Recordings 1926-1929
  cond B. WALTER
  see CONCERT INDEX *under:*
(MMOI) **CDMOIR404** Ezio Pinza—Recital

NEW YORK METROPOLITAN OPERA ORCHESTRA
  see CONCERT INDEX *under:*
(RCA) **09026 61580-2(3)** RCA/Met 100 Singers, 100 Years (pt 3)
  cond L. BERNSTEIN
Bizet: Carmen (Cpte)
  cond A. BODANZKY
Beethoven: Fidelio (Cpte)
Wagner: Siegfried (Cpte)
  cond F. CALUSIO
  see CONCERT INDEX *under:*
(MYTO) **2MCD90317** Verdi—Un Ballo in maschera
  cond F. CLEVA
(SONY) **MPK45693** Portrait—Ezio Pinza
  cond J. CONLON
  see CONCERT INDEX *under:*
(RCA) **09026 61509-2** A Salute to American Music
  cond E. COOPER
  see CONCERT INDEX *under:*
(EMI) **CHS7 69741-2(2)** Record of Singing, Vol.4—Anglo-American School (pt 2)
(SONY) **MPK45693** Portrait—Ezio Pinza
  cond JAMES LEVINE
Beethoven: Symphony 3

Donizetti: Elisir d'amore (Cpte)
Mozart: Nozze di Figaro (Cpte)
Mussorgsky: Pictures
Puccini: Manon Lescaut (Cpte)
Schoenberg: Cabaret Songs, Erwartung (Cpte)
Schubert: Symphony 8
Stravinsky: Rite of Spring (Cpte)
Verdi: Aida (Cpte), Don Carlo (Cpte), Luisa Miller (Cpte), Traviata (Cpte), Trovatore (Cpte)
Wagner: Götterdämmerung (Cpte), Parsifal (Cpte), Siegfried (exc), Walküre (Cpte)
  see CONCERT INDEX *under:*
(DG) **431 103-2GB** Great Voices—Montserrat Caballé
(DG) **431 104-2GB** Great Voices - Plácido Domingo
(DG) **435 874-2GH** Wagner—Overtures and Preludes
(DG) **445 354-2GX14** Wagner—Der Ring des Nibelungen
(SONY) **SK52489** Verdi—Ballet Music from the Operas
Rossini: Barbiere di Siviglia (Cpte)
Verdi: Macbeth (Cpte)
Wagner: Tristan und Isolde (Cpte)
  see CONCERT INDEX *under:*
(PREI) **89084** Kerstin Thorborg (1896-1970)
(RCA) **09026 61580-2(6)** RCA/Met 100 Singers, 100 Years (pt 6)
(RCA) **09026 61580-2(7)** RCA/Met 100 Singers, 100 Years (pt 7)
  cond D. MITROPOULOS
Barber: Vanessa (Cpte)
  see CONCERT INDEX *under:*
(RCA) **GD87911** Marian Anderson - Opera, Oratorio & Song Recital
(RCA) **09026 61580-2(5)** RCA/Met 100 Singers, 100 Years (pt 5)
(RCA) **09026 61580-2(6)** RCA/Met 100 Singers, 100 Years (pt 6)
  cond E. PANIZZA
Verdi: Otello (Cpte), Traviata (Cpte)
  see CONCERT INDEX *under:*
(MMOI) **CDMOIR404** Ezio Pinza—Recital
(MYTO) **2MCD90317** Verdi—Un Ballo in maschera
(PEAR) **GEMMCDS9452** The Emperor Tibbett
  cond W. PELLETIER
  see CONCERT INDEX *under:*
(MMOI) **CDMOIR404** Ezio Pinza—Recital
(RCA) **GD87808** Lawrence Tibbett sings Opera Arias
  cond G. SETTI
Bellini: Norma (exc)
  see CONCERT INDEX *under:*
(CONI) **CDHD201** Galli-Curci in Opera and Song
(EMI) **CDH7 61051-2** Beniamino Gigli - Operatic Arias
(MMOI) **CDMOIR404** Ezio Pinza—Recital
(MMOI) **CDMOIR428** Rosa Ponselle and Giovanni Martinelli sing Verdi
(NIMB) **NI7801** Great Singers, Vol.1
(NIMB) **NI7804** Giovanni Martinelli—Opera Recital
(NIMB) **NI7805** Rosa Ponselle—Opera & Song Recital
(NIMB) **NI7845** Giacomo Lauri-Volpi (1892-1979)
(NIMB) **NI7851** Legendary Voices
(NIMB) **NI7852** Galli-Curci, Vol.2
(PEAR) **GEMMCDS9452** The Emperor Tibbett
(PEAR) **GEMMCDS9926(2)** Covent Garden on Record—Vol.4 (pt 2)
(PEAR) **GEMMCD9306** Ezio Pinza—Opera Recital
(PEAR) **GEMMCD9316** Beniamino Gigli
(PEAR) **GEMMCD9367** Beniamino Gigli
(PREI) **89012** Giacomo Lauri-Volpi (1894-1979)
(PREI) **89050** Ezio Pinza (1892-1957)
(PREI) **89062** Giovanni Martinelli (1885-1969)
(PREI) **89073** Giuseppe de Luca (1876-1950) - II
(RCA) **GD87808** Lawrence Tibbett sings Opera Arias
(RCA) **GD87810** Rosa Ponselle - Opera & Song Recital
(RCA) **GD87811** Beniamino Gigli—Operatic Arias
(RCA) **09026 61245-2** Ezio Pinza - Recital
(RCA) **09026 61580-2(2)** RCA/Met 100 Singers, 100 Years (pt 2)
  cond B. WALTER
  see CONCERT INDEX *under:*
(MMOI) **CDMOIR404** Ezio Pinza—Recital
(PEAR) **GEMMCDS9926(2)** Covent Garden on Record—Vol.4 (pt 2)
(SONY) **MPK45693** Portrait—Ezio Pinza

NEW YORK METROPOLITAN OPERA SYNAGOGUE CHOIR
  cond L. BERNSTEIN
  see CONCERT INDEX *under:*
(SONY) **SM2K47533** Music inspired by the Jewish Religion

NEW YORK OPERA ORCHESTRA
  cond E. QUELER
Massenet: Cid (Cpte)
Puccini: Edgar (Cpte)
Verdi: Aroldo (Cpte)
  see CONCERT INDEX *under:*
(SONY) **MK39097** Puccini Heroines

NEW YORK ORATORIO SOCIETY
  cond E. QUELER
Verdi: Aroldo (Cpte)

NEW YORK PHILHARMONIC ORCHESTRA
Beethoven: Symphony 9
Gershwin: Rhapsody in Blue

---

  cond J. BARBIROLLI
Schumann: Violin Concerto
  see CONCERT INDEX *under:*
(DUTT) **CDSJB1001** Barbirolli in New York - 1938 Wagner Concert
  cond T. BEECHAM
  see CONCERT INDEX *under:*
(BEEC) **BEECHAM6** Sibelius/Mendelssohn/ Tchaikovsky—Orchestral Works
(DUTT) **CDAX8013** Beecham conducts Sibelius
  cond L. BERNSTEIN
Bartók: Concerto for Orchestra, Music for Strings, Percussion and Celesta
Beethoven: Fidelio (exc), Piano Concerto 3, Piano Concerto 5, Symphony 1, Symphony 2, Symphony 3, Symphony 7, Symphony 9
Bizet: Arlésienne Suites, Carmen Suites (exc)
Brahms: Haydn Variations, Piano Concerto 2, Serenade 2, Symphony 1, Symphony 2, Symphony 3, Violin Concerto
Bruckner: Symphony 9
Copland: Quiet city, Symphony 3
Gershwin: American in Paris
Haydn: Creation (Cpte), Mass 14
Janáček: Glagolitic Mass (Cpte)
Liszt: Faust Symphony
Mahler: Symphony 1, Symphony 2, Symphony 3, Symphony 4, Symphony 5, Symphony 6, Symphony 7
Nielsen: Symphony 2, Symphony 4, Symphony 5
Poulenc: Gloria
Prokofiev: Symphony 1, Symphony 5
Ravel: Daphnis et Chloé (Cpte)
Schumann: Symphony 1, Symphony 2
Shostakovich: Symphony 1, Symphony 5, Symphony 6, Symphony 7, Symphony 9, Symphony 14
Sibelius: Violin Concerto
Tchaikovsky: Francesca da Rimini, Romeo and Juliet, Symphony 4, Symphony 5, Symphony 6
  see CONCERT INDEX *under:*
(DG) **429 220-2GH** Ives—Orchestral Works
(DG) **429 231-2GH** Modern Orchestral Works
(DG) **435 162-2GX13** Mahler—Complete Symphonies
(SONY) **MPK44850** Shostakovich: Concertos
(SONY) **SMK47516** Beethoven—Orchestral Works
(SONY) **SMK47517** Beethoven—Orchestral Works
(SONY) **SMK47521** Beethoven—Orchestral Works
(SONY) **SMK47525** Berlioz—Orchestral Works
(SONY) **SMK47529** Bernstein conducts Bernstein
(SONY) **SMK47530** Bernstein conducts Bernstein
(SONY) **SMK47532** Bizet/Offenbach/Suppé—Orchestral Works
(SONY) **SMK47538** Brahms—Orchestral Works
(SONY) **SMK47541** Britten—Orchestral Works
(SONY) **SMK47543** Copland—Orchestral Works
(SONY) **SMK47544** Latin-American Orchestral Works
(SONY) **SMK47545** Debussy/Ravel—Orchestral Works
(SONY) **SMK47546** Debussy—Orchestral Works
(SONY) **SMK47547** Dvořák/Smetana—Orchestral Works
(SONY) **SMK47548** French Orchestral Works
(SONY) **SMK47549** Grieg/Sibelius—Orchestral Works
(SONY) **SMK47566** Hindemith—Orchestral Works
(SONY) **SMK47567** Holst/Barber/Elgar—Orchestral Works
(SONY) **SMK47568** Ives—Orchestral Works
(SONY) **SMK47571** Liszt/Rachmaninov/Ravel—Piano Concertos
(SONY) **SMK47572** Slavonic Orchestral Works
(SONY) **SMK47592** Mendelssohn—Orchestral Works
(SONY) **SMK47599** Hindemith/Nielsen—Concertos
(SONY) **SMK47600** Ballet Music from Famous Operas
(SONY) **SMK47601** Opera Overtures
(SONY) **SMK47603** Ravel—Orchestral Works
(SONY) **SMK47609** Schubert/Schumann—Orchestral Works
(SONY) **SMK47612** Schumann—Orchestral Works
(SONY) **SMK47618** Poulenc/Shostakovich—Piano Concertos
(SONY) **SMK47625** R. Strauss—Orchestral Works
(SONY) **SMK47628** Stravinsky—Choral and Orchestral Works
(SONY) **SMK47638** Vaughan Williams—Orchestral Works
(SONY) **SM2K47511** Bartók—Concertos
(SONY) **SM2K47522** Beethoven & Haydn—Choral Works
(SONY) **SM2K47526** Berlioz—Vocal and Orchestral Works
(SONY) **SM2K47533** Music inspired by the Jewish Religion
(SONY) **SM2K47550** Haydn—'Paris' Symphonies
(SONY) **SM2K47557** Haydn—'London' Symphonies, Vol.2
(SONY) **SM2K47563** Haydn—Choral & Orchestral Works
(SONY) **SM3K47154** Bernstein—Theatre Works Volume 1
(SONY) **SM3K47162** Bernstein plays and conducts Bernstein Volume III
(SONY) **SM3K47555** Haydn—'London' Symphonies, Vol.1
(SONY) **SM3K47585** Mahler—Symphonies
(SONY) **SM3K52632** Beethoven—Piano Concertos

cond P. BOULEZ
Stravinsky: Petrushka (Cpte)
  see CONCERT INDEX *under:*
(SONY) **SMK45838** Berg: Vocal & Orchestral Works
(SONY) **SMK45844** Varèse: Orchestral, Chamber and
Vocal Works
(SONY) **SMK48464** Boulez conducts Schoenberg -
Volume 2
(SONY) **SMK64107** Ravel/Roussel—Vocal &
Orchestral Works
(SONY) **SMK64108** Wagner—Orchestral Music
(SONY) **SM2K64100** Bartók/Scriabin—Orchestral
Works
(SONY) **SM3K45842** Ravel—Orchestral Works
(SONY) **SM3K64103** Berlioz—Orchestral and Vocal
Works
  cond E. KURTZ
Shostakovich: Symphony 9
  cond L. MAGIERA
  see CONCERT INDEX *under:*
(DECC) **444 450-2DH** Pavarotti in Central Park
  cond K. MASUR
Beethoven: Egmont (Cpte), Symphony 5
Berg: Lulu—Symphonie
Brahms: Academic Festival Overture, Symphony 2
Bruckner: Symphony 4
Dvořák: Slavonic Dances (exc), Symphony 8,
Symphony 9
Franck: Eolides, Symphony
Janáček: Sinfonietta
Mahler: Lieder eines fahrenden gesellen, Symphony
1, Symphony 9
Shostakovich: Symphony 13
Weill: Sieben Todsünden (Cpte)
  see CONCERT INDEX *under:*
(TELD) **9031-74007-2**
Ives/Brahms/Reger—Variations
  cond Z. MEHTA
Barber: Essay for Orchestra 3
Corigliano: Clarinet Concerto
Druckman: Prism
Paine: Symphony 2
Rochberg: Oboe Concerto
Schuman: Colloquies
Tchaikovsky: Piano Concerto 1
  see CONCERT INDEX *under:*
(DG) **423 063-2GH** Virtuoso Works for Violin
(SONY) **MK44942** Domingo at the Philharmonic
(SONY) **SK44923** Dvořák—Orchestral Works
  cond W. MENGELBERG
  see CONCERT INDEX *under:*
(PEAR) **GEMMCDS9922** New York Philharmonic -
150th Anniversary
(SYMP) **SYMCD1078** Willem Mengelberg conducts
  cond D. MITROPOULOS
Prokofiev: Romeo and Juliet (exc)
Saint-Saëns: Violin Concerto 3
Shostakovich: Symphony 10
  cond E. ORMANDY
Rachmaninov: Piano Concerto 3
  cond T. SCHIPPERS
Prokofiev: Alexander Nevsky
Tchaikovsky: Violin Concerto
  see CONCERT INDEX *under:*
(SONY) **MPK46727** Barber—Vocal Works
  cond G. SINOPOLI
Paganini: Violin Concerto 1
Saint-Saëns: Violin Concerto 3
  see CONCERT INDEX *under:*
(DG) **419 169-2GH** Wagner—Orchestral Works
(DG) **429 785-2GA** Mussorgsky/Ravel—Orchestral
Works
(DG) **437 534-2GA** Respighi—Orchestral Works
  cond J. STRANSKY
  see CONCERT INDEX *under:*
(PEAR) **GEMMCDS9922** New York Philharmonic -
150th Anniversary
  cond Y. TEMIRKANOV
Rimsky-Korsakov: Russian Easter Festival Ov,
Scheherazade
  cond A. TOSCANINI
  see CONCERT INDEX *under:*
(RCA) **GD60316** Toscanini Collection, Vol.64
(RCA) **GD60317** Toscanini Collection, Vol.65
(RCA) **GD60318** Toscanini Collection, Vol.66
  cond B. WALTER
Brahms: Deutsches Requiem, Op. 45 (Cpte)
Mahler: Symphony 4
  see CONCERT INDEX *under:*
(SONY) **SMK64466** R.
Strauss/Barber/Dvořák—Orchestral Works
(SONY) **SMK64467** J. Strauss
II/Brahms/Smetana—Orchestral Works
  cond A. WEISBERG
Crumb: Haunted Landscape

**NEW YORK PHILHARMONIC SYMPHONY
ORCHESTRA**
  cond J. BARBIROLLI
  see CONCERT INDEX *under:*
(BIDD) **LAB096** Nathan Milstein-Columbia
Recordings 1936-1942
(PEAR) **GEMMCDS9922** New York Philharmonic -
150th Anniversary
  cond T. BEECHAM
  see CONCERT INDEX *under:*
(PEAR) **GEMMCDS9922** New York Philharmonic -
150th Anniversary
(RCA) **09026 60929-2** R.Strauss—Tone Poems
  cond G. CANTELLI
Liszt: Piano Concerto 2

cond W. MENGELBERG
Beethoven: Symphony 1, Symphony 3
  see CONCERT INDEX *under:*
(RCA) **09026 60929-2** R.Strauss—Tone Poems
(SYMP) **SYMCD1078** Willem Mengelberg conducts
  cond F. REINER
  see CONCERT INDEX *under:*
(PEAR) **GEMMCDS9922** New York Philharmonic -
150th Anniversary
  cond A. RODZINSKI
  see CONCERT INDEX *under:*
(EMI) **CHS7 69741-2(1)** Record of Singing,
Vol.4—Anglo-American School (pt 1)
  cond L. STOKOWSKI
Prokofiev: Piano Concerto 3
  cond A. TOSCANINI
  see CONCERT INDEX *under:*
(PEAR) **GEMMCDS9373** Toscanini & the
NYPSO—1926-36
(PEAR) **GEMMCDS9922** New York Philharmonic -
150th Anniversary
(RCA) **GD60316** Toscanini Collection, Vol.64
(RCA) **GD60317** Toscanini Collection, Vol.65
(RCA) **GD60318** Toscanini Collection, Vol.66

NEW YORK SCHOLA CANTORUM
  cond E. QUELER
Puccini: Edgar (Cpte)
  see CONCERT INDEX *under:*
(SONY) **MK39097** Puccini Heroines
  cond L. STOKOWSKI
  see CONCERT INDEX *under:*
(SONY) **MPK46726** Ives—Orchestral and Vocal
Works

NEW YORK STADIUM SYMPHONY ORCHESTRA
  cond L. STOKOWSKI
Tchaikovsky: Francesca da Rimini, Hamlet
  see CONCERT INDEX *under:*
(EVER) **EVC9004** R. Strauss/Canning—Orchestral
Works

NEW YORK STUDIO ORCHESTRA
  cond J. TUNICK
  see CONCERT INDEX *under:*
(EMI) **CDC7 54266-2** Domingo and
Perlman—Together
(EMI) **CZS4 83177-2(3)** Itzhak Perlman Edition (pt 3)

NEW YORK VIRTUOSI
  cond K. KLEIN
  see CONCERT INDEX *under:*
(COLL) **Coll1097-2** Copland: Orchestral Works

NEW YORK VOCAL ARTS ENSEMBLE
  cond R. BEEGLE
  see CONCERT INDEX *under:*
(ARAB) **Z6586** Johann Strauss: Waltzes arranged for
Voices

NEW YORK Y CHAMBER ORCHESTRA
  cond G. SCHWARZ
Beethoven: Symphony 6

NEW ZEALAND CHAMBER ORCHESTRA
  cond N. BRAITHWAITE
  see CONCERT INDEX *under:*
(KOCH) **37058-2** Holst—Works for Chamber
Orchestra
(KOCH) **37139-2** Bridge/Delius—Works for Chamber
Orchestra

NEW ZEALAND QUARTET
  see CONCERT INDEX *under:*
(KOCH) **37192-2** Still—Summerland

NEW ZEALAND SYMPHONY ORCHESTRA
  cond F-P. DECKER
Reger: Hiller Variations, Mozart Variations, Op. 132
  see CONCERT INDEX *under:*
(NAXO) **8 553078** Hindemith—Orchestral Works
  cond M. FREDMAN
  see CONCERT INDEX *under:*
(NAXO) **8 553001** Delius—Orchestral Works
(NAXO) **8 553107** Britten—Orchestral Works
  cond A. HEENAN
(KIWI) **CDSLD-90** Lilburn—Symphonies
  cond J. HOPKINS
  see CONCERT INDEX *under:*
(CNTI) **CCD1069** Lilburn—Symphonies
(KIWI) **CDSLD-90** Lilburn—Symphonies
  cond J-Y. OSSONCE
  see CONCERT INDEX *under:*
(NAXO) **8 553124** Massenet—Hérodiade Orchestral
Suites Nos 1-3
(NAXO) **8 553125** Massenet—Hérodiade Orchestral
Suites Nos 4-7
  cond A. SCHENCK
Thompson: Symphony 2, Symphony 3
  see CONCERT INDEX *under:*
(KOCH) **37005-2** Menotti/Barber—Orchestral Works
(KOCH) **37010-2** Barber—Orchestral Works
(STRA) **SCD8012** Barber—Orchestral Works
  cond J. SEDARES
Rózsa: Symphony, Op. 6a, Vintner's Daughter, Op.
23a
  see CONCERT INDEX *under:*
(KOCH) **37191-2** Rózsa—Orchestral Works
(KOCH) **37224-2** B.Herrmann—The Devil and Daniel
Webster
(KOCH) **37232-2** Bloch—Orchestral Works
(KOCH) **37243-2** Barber/Dello Joio—Orchestral
Works
  cond W. SOUTHGATE
  see CONCERT INDEX *under:*

(CNTI) **CCD1034** Lyell Cresswell—Orchestral Works,
Vol.2
  cond H. WALLBERG
(DELO) **DE3108** Alessandra Marc—Opera Recital
(ODE) **CDMANU1317** Wagner—Opera Excerpts

NEWAY, Patricia (sop)
  see CONCERT INDEX *under:*
(VANG) **08.4016.71** Music of Samuel Barber

(THE) NEWBERRY CONSORT
  cond M. SPRINGFELS
  see CONCERT INDEX *under:*
(HARM) **HMU90 7022** Spanish Songs & Theatre
Music
(HARM) **HMU90 7038** Il Solazzo—Music for a
Medieval Banquet

NEWBOLD, Günther (cond)
  see Royal Flanders PO

NEWLEY, Anthony (sngr)
Bricusse: Scrooge (Cpte)

NEWMAN, Alfred (cond)
  see orch

NEWMAN, Anthony (cond)
  see Orch

NEWMAN, Anthony (hpd)
  see CONCERT INDEX *under:*
(DELO) **DE3186** Heigh Ho! Mozart
(SCHW) **310832** Frank Martin—Orchestral Works
(SONY) **SK53106** Kathleen Battle & Jean-Pierre
Rampal in Concert

NEWMAN, Arthur (bar)
Verdi: Otello (Cpte), Traviata (Cpte)

NEWMAN, Gareth (bn)
Maxwell Davies: Sinfonia concertante

NEWMAN, Henry (bass)
M. Berkeley: Baa Baa Black Sheep (Cpte)
Vaughan Williams: Hugh the Drover (Cpte)
Verdi: Traviata (Cpte)

NEWMAN, Lionel (cond)
  see orch

NEWMAN, Maria (va)
  see CONCERT INDEX *under:*
(COLO) **CST34 8048** Symphonic Hollywood, Volume
1

NEWMAN, Yvonne (mez)
Sullivan: Iolanthe (Cpte), Patience (Cpte)

NEWMANN, Herman (cond)
  see WNYC Concert Orch

NEWMARK, John (pf)
  see CONCERT INDEX *under:*
(DECC) **433 471-2DM** Ferrier Edition - Volume 4
(DECC) **433 473-2DM** Ferrier Edition - Volume 6
(DECC) **433 475-2DM** Ferrier Edition - Volume 8

NEWSOME, Roy (cond)
  see Besses o' the Barn Band

NEWTON, Ivor (pf)
  see CONCERT INDEX *under:*
(CLUB) **CL99-014** Dino Borgioli (1891-1960)
(EMI) **CHS7 64487-2** R. Strauss—Der Rosenkavalier
& Lieder
(MUSI) **MACD-644** The Art of Gregor Piatigorsky
(PEAR) **GEMMCD9447** Gregor Piatigorsky plays
Schumann, Beethoven, Weber & Brahms
(PEAR) **GEMMCD9939** Josef Hassid & Ida Haendel -
1940-42 Recordings
(PREI) **89207** Feodor Chaliapin Song
Book—Electrical Recordings
(TEST) **SBT1010** Ginette Neveu & Josef Hassid

NEZHDANOVA, Antonina (sop)
  see CONCERT INDEX *under:*
(NIMB) **NI7865** Great Singers at the Mariinsky
Theatre
(PEAR) **GEMMCDS9007/9(1)** Singers of Imperial
Russia, Vol.4 (pt 1)
(PEAR) **GEMMCDS9007/9(2)** Singers of Imperial
Russia, Vol.4 (pt 2)

NGUYEN-HUU, Ingo (sngr)
Schreker: Gezeichneten (Cpte)

NHK (TOKYO) CHAMBER SOLOISTS
  cond R. PATERNOSTRO
  see CONCERT INDEX *under:*
(CAPR) **10 348** Mozart Gala—Suntory Hall, Tokyo

NIBLEY, Reid (pf)
  see CONCERT INDEX *under:*
(VANG) **08.4051.71** Gottschalk—Piano Works, Vol.2

NICASTRO, Michelle (sngr)
Gershwin: Lady, be Good! (Cpte), Pardon My English
(Cpte)

NICE BAROQUE ENSEMBLE
  cond G. BEZZINA
Vivaldi: Dorilla in Tempe (Cpte)
  cond G. SCHMIDT-GADEN
Mozart: Apollo et Hyacinthus (Cpte)

NICE OPERA CHORUS
  cond G. BEZZINA
Vivaldi: Dorilla in Tempe (Cpte)
  cond J. CAREWE
Debussy: Pelléas et Mélisande (Cpte)

NICE PHILHARMONIC ORCHESTRA
cond J. CAREWE
Debussy: Pelléas et Mélisande (Cpte)
cond K. WEISE
Mozart: Piano Concerto 21, Piano Concerto 22

NICHITEANU, Liliana (mez)
Mussorgsky: Boris Godunov (Cpte)

NICHOL, Harry (ten)
see CONCERT INDEX under:
(OPRA) **ORCH103**   Italian Opera—1810-20

NICHOLAS, Harold (sngr)
H. Arlen: St Louis Woman (Cpte)

NICHOLAS, Michael (cond)
see Norwich Cath Ch

NICHOLL, Harry (ten)
see CONCERT INDEX under:
(CHAN) **CHAN8865**   Rossini: Opera Arias

NICHOLLS, Agnes (sop)
see CONCERT INDEX under:
(PEAR) **GEMMCDS9951/5**   The Elgar
Edition—Acoustic Recordings 1914-25

NICHOLLS, Chris (vn)
see CONCERT INDEX under:
(BRIT) **BML001**   Bernard van Dieren Collection

NICHOLLS, Christopher (cond)
see orch

NICHOLS, Mary (mez)
Bach: Mass in B minor, BWV232 (Cpte)
Monteverdi: Madrigals, Bk 8 (exc), Orfeo (Cpte)
see CONCERT INDEX under:
(BIS) **BIS-CD341**   Music for lutes
(EMI) **CDS7 49749-2**   Handel—Music for the Carmelite
Vespers
(VIRG) **VC7 59606-2**   Monteverdi—Madrigals, Book 8

NICHOLS, Robert (sngr)
Kern: Show Boat (Cpte)
Porter: Kiss Me, Kate (Cpte)

NICHOLSON, David (fl)
Maxwell Davies: Sinfonia concertante, Strathclyde
Concerto 6

NICHOLSON, Pamela (pf)
see CONCERT INDEX under:
(ASV) **CDDCA698**   Violin Virtuoso

NICHOLSON, Paul (cond)
see Parley of Instr

NICHOLSON, Paul (organ)
Handel: Organ Concertos (exc)
see CONCERT INDEX under:
(COLL) **Coll7016-2**   Handel—Alexander's Feast
(EMI) **CDC7 49555-2**   Tallis: Sacred Choral Works
(HYPE) **CDA66311/2**   Monteverdi: St Barbara
Vespers
(HYPE) **CDA66319**   Mundy—Sacred Choral Works
(HYPE) **CDA66564**   Roseingrave—Keyboard Works
(VIRG) **VC5 45147-2**   Lawes—Concord is Conquer'd
(VIRG) **VC7 59021-2**   Lawes—For ye Violls

NICHOLSON, Paul (hpd)
see CONCERT INDEX under:
(AMON) **CD-SAR42**   Arne—Instrumental Works
(HYPE) **CDA66564**   Roseingrave—Keyboard Works
(HYPE) **CDA66931/2**   Handel—Harpsichord Suites

NICHOLSON, Paul (hpd/org)
see CONCERT INDEX under:
(VIRG) **VC7 59324-2**   Purcell—O Solitude - Songs and
Airs

NICHOLSON, Paul (kybds/dir)
Arne: Favourite concertos
see CONCERT INDEX under:
(HYPE) **CDA66700**   English 18th-Century Keyboard
Concertos

NICK, Edmund (cond)
see Berlin St Op Orch

NICKLESS, David (treb)
see CONCERT INDEX under:
(HYPE) **CDA66707**   Purcell—Complete Anthems &
Services, Vol. 10

NICKLIN, Celia (ob)
see CONCERT INDEX under:
(ARGO) **417 818-2ZH**   American Music
(ASV) **CDDCA795**   Mozart—Wind Concertos
(CHAN) **CHAN8892**   Walton—Film Music, Vol 3
(DECC) **440 320-2DWO**   World of British Classics,
Volume IV
(DECC) **443 476-2DF2**   Vivaldi—L'estro armonico, Op
3
(PHIL) **412 892-2PH**   Vivaldi: Double Concertos
(PHIL) **420 954-2PH**   Telemann—Trumpet Concertos

NICOLAI, Claudio (bar)
Künneke: Vetter aus Dingsda (exc)
Mozart: Zauberflöte (Cpte)
Orff: Kluge (Cpte)
Weber: Freischütz (Cpte)

NICOLAI, Elena (mez)
Verdi: Don Carlo (Cpte), Forza del destino (Cpte)

NICOLAI, Theodor (bass)
Humperdinck: Königskinder (Cpte)

NICOLAS, Jacqueline (sop)
see CONCERT INDEX under:
(PIER) **PV786101**   Campra—French Cantatas

(PIER) **PV790013**   A. Scarlatti—Cantatas

NICOLAS, Marie-Annick (vn)
Fauré: Violin Sonata 1
Franck: Violin Sonata
see CONCERT INDEX under:
(AUVI) **V4697**   Bach—Violin Concertos

NICOLESCO, Mariana (sop)
Donizetti: Maria di Rohan (Cpte)
Puccini: Rondine (Cpte)

NICOLET, Aurèle (fl)
Cimarosa: Flute and Oboe Concertante in G
Mozart: Flute Quartets
Weber: Flute Trio, J259, Violin Sonatas, J99-104
see CONCERT INDEX under:
(ARCH) **427 113-2AGA**   Bach: Flute Sonatas
(ECM) **437 441-2**   Holliger—Scardanelli-Zyklus
(NOVA) **150 047-2**   Haydn: Chamber Works for Flute
(ORFE) **C060831A**   Milhaud: Works for wind and piano
(PHIL) **422 509-2PME5**   The Complete Mozart Edition
Vol 9
(PHIL) **422 514-2PME5**   The Complete Mozart Edition
Vol 14
(PHIL) **434 105-2PH**
Martin/Honegger/Martinů—Concertos and Chamber
Music
(PHIL) **442 012-2PH**   20th Century Wind Music
(PHIL) **442 299-2PM2**   Mozart—Complete Flute Works
(PHIL) **442 592-2PM2**   C P E Bach—Concertos

NICOLET, Christiane (fl)
see CONCERT INDEX under:
(NOVA) **150 047-2**   Haydn: Chamber Works for Flute

NICOLL, Harry (ten)
Sondheim: Pacific Overtures (exc)
Vaughan Williams: Hugh the Drover (Cpte)

NICOLOSI, Francesco (pf)
see CONCERT INDEX under:
(MARC) **8 223365**   Thalberg—Fantasies on operas by
Donizetti
(NAXO) **8 550611**   Mozart—Piano Variations, Vol.1
(NAXO) **8 550612**   Mozart—Piano Variations, Vol.2
(NAXO) **8 550613**   Mozart—Piano Variations, Vol.3

(LES) NIECES DE RAMEAU
Leclair: Recréation de musique I, Recréation de
musique II

NIED, Johannes (db)
Holliger: Beiseit

NIEDERALTAICHER SCHOLAREN
cond K. RUHLAND
see CONCERT INDEX under:
(SONY) **SK53117**   Motets of the 17th Century

NIEL, H. (ten)
Massenet: Werther (Cpte)

NIELSEN, Alice (sngr)
see CONCERT INDEX under:
(PEAR) **GEMMCDS9050/2(1)**   Music from the New
York Stage, Vol. 1 (part 1)

NIELSEN, Alice (sop)
see CONCERT INDEX under:
(PEAR) **GEMMCDS9074(1)**   Giovanni Zenatello, Vol.2
(pt 1)
(SYMP) **SYMCD1168**   The Harold Wayne Collection,
Vol.19

NIELSEN, Björn Carl (ob)
R. Strauss: Oboe Concerto

NIELSEN, Elof (ob)
see CONCERT INDEX under:
(PEAR) **GEMMCDS9095(2)**   Povla Frijsh (pt 2)

NIELSEN, Flora (mez)
see CONCERT INDEX under:
(EMI) **CHS7 69741-2(1)**   Record of Singing,
Vol.4—Anglo-American School (pt 1)
(EMI) **CMS7 64727-2**   Britten—Opera excerpts and
Folksongs

NIELSEN, Inge (sop)
Bach: Cantata 112, St. John Passion, BWV245
(Cpte)
Haydn: Seven Last Words, HobXX/2
Heise: Drot og Marsk (Cpte)
Mahler: Symphony 8
Mozart: Oca del Cairo (Cpte)
Nielsen: Springtime in Funen (Cpte)
Schumann: Rose Pilgerfahrt (Cpte)
Wagner: Parsifal (Cpte)
Zemlinsky: Geburtstag der Infantin (Cpte)
see CONCERT INDEX under:
(CHAN) **CHAN8853**   Nielsen: Choral Works
(HANS) **98 801**   Bach—Cantatas, Vol.39
(HANS) **98 820**   Bach—Cantatas, Vol.58
(HANS) **98 820**   Bach—Cantatas, Vol.60
(HANS) **98 867**   Bach—Cantatas, Vol.16
(PHIL) **422 522-2PME6**   The Complete Mozart Edition
Vol 22

NIEMANN, Edmund (pf)
Messiaen: Visions de l'Amen

NIEMIROWICZ, Dariusz (bass)
Puccini: Bohème (Cpte)
Rossini: Signor Bruschino (Cpte)
Weill: Kuhhandel (exc)

NIENSTEDT, Gerd (bass)
Berg: Lulu (Cpte)
Mozart: Requiem
Pfitzner: Palestrina (Cpte)

R.Strauss: Salome (Cpte)
Wagner: Meistersinger (Cpte), Parsifal (Cpte),
Rheingold (Cpte), Tannhäuser (Cpte), Tristan und
Isolde (Cpte), Walküre (Cpte)
see CONCERT INDEX under:
(PHIL) **438 800-2PM2**   Mozart—Choral Works
(PHIL) **446 057-2PB14**   Wagner—The Ring Cycle -
Bayreuth Festival 1967

NIESEMANN, Michael (ob)
see CONCERT INDEX under:
(ARCH) **419 633-2AH**   Telemann: Wind Concertos

NIESSNER, Anton (bar)
Lehár: Lustige Witwe (Cpte)

NIEUW ENSEMBLE
cond E. SPANJAARD
see CONCERT INDEX under:
(ETCE) **KTC1053**   Donatoni: Chamber and Vocal
Works
(ETCE) **KTC1070**   Ferneyhough: Various Works
(ETCE) **KTC1097**   Loevendie—Miscellaneous Works

NIGL, Georg (treb)
see CONCERT INDEX under:
(PHIL) **422 527-2PME**   The Complete Mozart Edition
Vol 27

NIGOGHOSSIAN, Sonia (mez)
Bellini: Bianca e Fernando (Cpte)
Offenbach: Périchole (Cpte)

NIJENHUIS, Fred (db)
see CONCERT INDEX under:
(TELD) **4509-97465-2**   Franz Brüggen Edition Vol.
3—English Ensemble Music

NIKITINA, Galina (mez)
see CONCERT INDEX under:
(PEAR) **GEMMCDS9007/9(2)**   Singers of Imperial
Russia, Vol.4 (pt 2)

NIKKANEN, Kurt (vn)
see CONCERT INDEX under:
(COLL) **Coll1203-2**   Bartók—Violin Sonatas

NIKOLAEVSKY, Yuri (cond)
see Moscow Cons Instr Ens

NIKOLAIDI, Elena (mez)
see CONCERT INDEX under:
(SCHW) **314562**   Vienna State Opera Live, Vol.6
(SCHW) **314572**   Vienna State Opera Live, Vol.7
(SCHW) **314582**   Vienna State Opera Live, Vol.8
(SCHW) **314602**   Vienna State Opera Live, Vol.10
(SCHW) **314632**   Vienna State Opera Live, Vol.13
(SCHW) **314652**   Vienna State Opera Live, Vol.15

NIKOLAIEVA, Tatyana (pf)
Bach: Goldberg Variations, Wohltemperierte Klavier
(exc)
Beethoven: Diabelli Variations, Piano Sonata 28,
Piano Sonata 29, Variations, Op. 35
Shostakovich: Preludes and Fugues, Op.87
see CONCERT INDEX under:
(HYPE) **CDA66620**   Shostakovich—Piano Works
(HYPE) **CDA66631/2**   Bach—Keyboard Works
(MEZH) **MK418024**   Nikolayeva plays Bach
(OLYM) **OCD561**   Beethoven—Piano Sonatas, Vol.1
(OLYM) **OCD562**   Beethoven—Piano Sonatas, Vol.2
(OLYM) **OCD563**   Beethoven—Piano Sonatas, Vol.3
(OLYM) **OCD564**   Beethoven—Piano Sonatas, Vol.4
(OLYM) **OCD565**   Beethoven—Piano Sonatas Nos 15-
17
(OLYM) **OCD566**   Beethoven—Piano Sonatas Nos 18-
22
(OLYM) **OCD567**   Beethoven—Piano Sonatas,
Volume 7
(OLYM) **OCD569**   Beethoven—Piano Sonatas,
Volume 9

NIKOLIĆ, Miomir (bass)
Verdi: Macbeth (Cpte)
Wagner: Meistersinger (Cpte)

NIKOLSKY, Gleb (bass)
Mussorgsky: Boris Godunov (Cpte)

NILON, Paul (ten)
Mayr: Medea (Cpte)
Mercadante: Orazi e Curiazi (Cpte)
see CONCERT INDEX under:
(OPRA) **ORCH103**   Italian Opera—1810-20
(OPRA) **ORCH104**   A Hundred Years of Italian Opera:
1820-1830

NILSSON, Alf (ob)
R. Strauss: Oboe Concerto
see CONCERT INDEX under:
(BIS) **BIS-CD285**   A Swedish Serenade

NILSSON, Arne (bn)
see CONCERT INDEX under:
(BIS) **BIS-CD288**   Vaňhal: Orchestral works

NILSSON, Birgit (sop)
J. Strauss II: Fledermaus (Cpte)
Mozart: Don Giovanni (Cpte)
Puccini: Fanciulla del West (Cpte), Tosca (Cpte),
Turandot (Cpte)
R. Strauss: Elektra (Cpte), Frau ohne Schatten
(Cpte), Salome (Cpte)
Verdi: Aida (Cpte)
Wagner: Götterdämmerung (Cpte), Siegfried (Cpte),
Tristan und Isolde (Cpte), Walküre (Cpte)
Weber: Oberon (Cpte)
see CONCERT INDEX under:
(BLUE) **ABCD009**   Birgit Nilsson live in Stockholm

(DECC) **414 100-2DM15** Wagner: Der Ring des
Nibelungen
(DECC) **436 461-2DM** Ten Top Sopranos
(EMI) **CDM7 63358-2** Beethoven—Orchestral Works
(EMI) **CMS5 65212-2** Wagner—Les introuvables du
Ring
(EMI) **CMS7 64008-2(1)** Wagner Singing on Record
(pt 1)
(PHIL) **446 057-2PB14** Wagner—The Ring Cycle -
Bayreuth Festival 1967
(RCA) **09026 61580-2(7)** RCA/Met 100 Singers, 100
Years (pt 7)
(RCA) **09026 61879-2** Grieg—Historic Recordings

NILSSON, Christer (tpt)
see CONCERT INDEX under:
(CHAN) **CHAN9209** Lumbye—Waltzes, Galops &
Polkas

NILSSON, Gunvor (mez)
Henze: English Cat (Cpte)
see CONCERT INDEX under:
(BIS) **BIS-CD438** Stenhammar: Vocal and Orchestral
Works

NILSSON, Helena (vc)
see CONCERT INDEX under:
(BIS) **BIS-CD652** Penderecki—Chamber Works

NILSSON, Helge (bass)
see CONCERT INDEX under:
(CPRI) **CAP21510** Rosenberg plays Rosenberg

NILSSON, Pia-Maria (sop)
see CONCERT INDEX under:
(MSVE) **MSCD417** Roman—Drottningholm Music

NILSSON, Raymond (ten)
Britten: Peter Grimes (Cpte)
Kodály: Psalmus Hungaricus

NILSSON, Sven (bass)
Wagner: Tristan und Isolde (Cpte)

NIMSGERN, Siegmund (bass-bar)
Bach: Christmas Oratorio, BWV248 (Cpte)
Bartók: Duke Bluebeard's Castle (Cpte)
Braunfels: Verkündigung (Cpte)
Flotow: Martha (Cpte)
Gluck: Alceste (1776) (Cpte)
Haydn: Schöpfung (exc)
Hindemith: Cardillac (Cpte)
Humperdinck: Hänsel und Gretel (Cpte)
Lully: Bourgeois Gentilhomme
Mozart: Nozze di Figaro (Cpte)
Pergolesi: Serva Padrona
Puccini: Turandot (Cpte)
Rossini: Mosè in Egitto (Cpte)
Schoenberg: Gurrelieder
Schreker: Ferne Klang (Cpte)
Wagner: Götterdämmerung (Cpte), Lohengrin (Cpte),
Parsifal (Cpte), Rheingold (Cpte), Siegfried (Cpte)
see CONCERT INDEX under:
(DHM) **GD77151** Bach—Secular Cantatas
(EURO) **GD69043** Puccini: Il Trittico
(HANS) **98 807** Bach—Cantatas, Vol.45
(HANS) **98 814** Bach—Cantatas, Vol.52
(HANS) **98 821** Bach—Cantatas, Vol.59
(HANS) **98 824** Bach—Cantatas, Vol.62
(HANS) **98 866** Bach—Cantatas, Vol.15
(HANS) **98 869** Bach—Cantatas, Vol.18
(HANS) **98 870** Bach—Cantatas, Vol.19
(HANS) **98 876** Bach—Cantatas, Vol.25
(SCHW) **312952** Hartmann—Orchestral and Vocal
Works
(SONY) **SMK48462** Boulez conducts Schoenberg
(SONY) **SMK48464** Boulez conducts Schoenberg -
Volume 2
(SONY) **SX14K48198** Mahler—Complete
Symphonies, etc
(TELD) **2292-42503-2** Bach—Cantatas, Volume 7
(TELD) **2292-42504-2** Bach—Cantatas, Volume 8
(TELD) **2292-42505-2** Bach—Cantatas, Volume 9
(TELD) **4509-91756-2** Bach—Cantatas, Vol.2

NIN, Joaquin (pf)
see CONCERT INDEX under:
(EMI) **CDC7 54836-2** Granados/Falla/Mompou/Nin

NINIĆ, Tonko (cond)
see Zagreb Sols

NINNO, Antonio di (ten)
see CONCERT INDEX under:
(DECC) **411 665-2DM3** Puccini: Il trittico

NIQUET, Hervé (cond)
see Concert Spirituel Orch

NIROUËT, Jean (alto)
Gilles: Requiem
Handel: Alessandro (Cpte)
Vivaldi: Dorilla in Tempe (Cpte)
see CONCERT INDEX under:
(ERAT) **2292-45202-2** M-A. Charpentier: Sacred
Works

NISHIZAKI, Takako (vn)
Beethoven: Violin Sonata 5, Violin Sonata 9
Mozart: Sinfonia Concertante, K364, Violin Concerto,
K216, Violin Concerto, K218, Violin Concerto, K219
see CONCERT INDEX under:
(MARC) **8 220308** Cui: Orchestral Works
(NAXO) **8 550414** Mozart & Saint-Saëns: Violin
Works

NISHRI, Varda (pf)
see CONCERT INDEX under:
(ROMA) **RR1941** Terezín - The Music 1941-44

NISSEN, Hanns Heinz (bass)
see CONCERT INDEX under:
(PREI) **90168** Wagner—Die Meistersinger, Act 2, etc

NISSEN, Hans Hermann (bass)
see CONCERT INDEX under:
(EMI) **CMS7 64008-2(1)** Wagner Singing on Record
(pt 1)
(EMI) **CMS7 64008-2(2)** Wagner Singing on Record
(pt 2)
(PREI) **89090** Hans Hermann Nissen (1893-1980)

NISSMAN, Barbara (pf)
see CONCERT INDEX under:
(NEWP) **NCD60092** Prokofiev—Piano Sonatas,
Vol.1
(NEWP) **NCD60093** Prokofiev—Piano Sonatas,
Vol.2
(NEWP) **NCD60094** Prokofiev—Piano Sonatas,
Vol.3

NITRANOVÁ, Marta (mez)
see CONCERT INDEX under:
(OPUS) **9156 1824** Dvorský sings Operatic Arias

NITSCHE, Horst (bass)
Mozart: Zauberflöte (Cpte)
R. Strauss: Rosenkavalier (Cpte), Salome (Cpte)
Verdi: Don Carlo (Cpte), Trovatore (Cpte)

NIVETTE, Juste (bass)
see CONCERT INDEX under:
(PEAR) **GEMMCDS9924(2)** Covent Garden on
Record, Vol.2 (pt 2)

NIXON, Darryl (hpd)
Boismortier: Sonatas, Op.26 (exc), Sonatas, Op.50
(exc)

NIXON, John Leigh (ten)
see CONCERT INDEX under:
(BIS) **BIS-CD341** Music for lutes

NIXON, Leigh (ten)
see CONCERT INDEX under:
(ARCH) **423 594-2AH** Handel—Vocal Works
(HARM) **HMX290 1528/33(2)** A Purcell Companion (pt
2)
(SONY) **SK66613** Tavener—Innocence

NIXON, Marni (sop)
Milhaud: Homme et son désir
Rodgers: King and I (film) (Cpte)

NIXON, Marnie (sngr)
Bernstein: West Side Story (Cpte)
F. Loewe: My Fair Lady (film) (Cpte)

NIZINENKO, Nikolai (bass)
Rimsky-Korsakov: Tsar's Bride (Cpte)
Shostakovich: Gamblers (Cpte)

NOACK, Erwin (sngr)
Krenek: Jonny spielt auf (Cpte)

NOAKES, Anna (fl)
see CONCERT INDEX under:
(ASV) **CDDCA875** Reger—Chamber Music, Volume 1
(ASV) **CDDCA898** Damase—Music for Flute, Harp
and Strings
(KING) **KCLCD2027** South American Flute Music

NOBLE, Dennis (bar)
Elgar: Dream of Gerontius (Cpte)
see CONCERT INDEX under:
(DUTT) **CDLX7012** The Incomparable Heddle Nash
(PEAR) **GEMMCDS9925(1)** Covent Garden on
Record—Vol.3 (pt 1)
(PEAR) **GEMMCD9175** Heddle Nash - Serenade
(PEAR) **GEMMCD9319** Heddle Nash sings Opera
Arias & Songs

NOBLE, John (bar)
Britten: Albert Herring (Cpte)
G. Charpentier: Louise (Cpte)
Massenet: Cendrillon (Cpte)
Orff: Carmina Burana
Schoenberg: Moses und Aron (Cpte)
Schumann: Szenen aus Goethes Faust (Cpte)
Shostakovich: Lady Macbeth of Mtsensk (Cpte)
Verdi: Corsaro (Cpte), Don Carlo (Cpte), Macbeth
(Cpte)
see CONCERT INDEX under:
(EMI) **CDM7 64022-2** Vaughan Williams—Orchestral
Works

NOCENTINI, Maria Costanza (sop)
Rossini: Pietra del paragone (Cpte)

NÖCKER, Hans Günter (bass-bar)
Egk: Verlobung in San Domingo (Cpte)
Handel: Giulio Cesare (Cpte)
Wagner: Götterdämmerung (Cpte)
see CONCERT INDEX under:
(ACAN) **43 267** Fritz Wunderlich sings Opera Arias

NODA, Yumiko (va)
Reger: Piano Trio, op 2

NOE, Marcel (bar)
see CONCERT INDEX under:
(CLAR) **CDGSE78-50-26** Wagner: Tristan und Isolde
excerpts

NOEHREN, Robert (organ)
see CONCERT INDEX under:
(DELO) **DE1028** Robert Noehren Plays Marcel Dupré
(DELO) **DE3028** Bach: Organ Works
(DELO) **DE3045** Organ Recital
(FACE) **FE8001** Dupré: Organ Works

NOËL, Hervé (tpt)
see CONCERT INDEX under:
(SCHW) **310652** Fumet/d'Indy/Honegger—Chamber
Works

NOGUERA, Louis (bass)
Bizet: Ivan IV (exc), Pêcheurs de Perles (Cpte)
Messager: Basoche (Cpte)

NOHARET, Philippe (vc)
see CONCERT INDEX under:
(REM) **REM311175** Fauré—Mélodies, Vol.1

NOJIMA, Minoru (pf)
Ravel: Gaspard de la nuit, Miroirs

NÖKLEBERG, Einar Steen (pf)
see CONCERT INDEX under:
(VICT) **VCD19007** Anne Gjevang in Recital

NOLAN, David (vn)
see CONCERT INDEX under:
(EMIN) **CD-EMX9508** Vaughan Williams—Orchestral
Works

NOLAN, Rodney (ten)
see CONCERT INDEX under:
(CHAN) **CHAN8800** Music on Hebrew Themes

NOLI, Alberto (bass)
Puccini: Bohème (Cpte)

NOLL, William (cond)
see Atlanta Choral Guild

NOLTE, Raimund (bass)
Rossini: Péchés de vieillesse II (Cpte), Péchés de
vieillesse III (exc)
Telemann: Don Quichotte (Cpte)

NONI, Alda (sop)
Mozart: Cosi fan tutte (exc)
R. Strauss: Ariadne auf Naxos (Cpte)
Rossini: Cenerentola (Cpte)
see CONCERT INDEX under:
(EMI) **CHS7 69741-2(7)** Record of Singing,
Vol.4—Italian School
(SCHW) **314582** Vienna State Opera Live, Vol.8

NOORMAN, Jantina (mez)
Purcell: Dido (Cpte)

NOORT, Henk (ten)
see CONCERT INDEX under:
(PREI) **90168** Wagner—Die Meistersinger, Act 2, etc

NOPRE, Gilles (cond)
see Rhenish PO

NORAS, Arto (vc)
Dvořák: Cello Concerto
Elgar: Cello Concerto
Lalo: Cello Concerto
Schumann: Cello Concerto

NORBERG-SCHULZ, Elizabeth (sop)
Brahms: Deutsches Requiem, Op. 45 (Cpte)
Mozart: Mass, K427, Zauberflöte (Cpte)
Pergolesi: Frate 'nnamorato (Cpte), Stabat Mater

NORBERT, Karl (bass)
see CONCERT INDEX under:
(SCHW) **314542** Vienna State Opera Live, Vol.4

NORDBERG, Hermann von (pf)
see CONCERT INDEX under:
(EMI) **CHS7 69741-2(4)** Record of Singing,
Vol.4—German School
(EMI) **CHS7 69741-2(6)** Record of Singing,
Vol.4—Russian & Slavonic Schools
(TEST) **SBT1026** Irmgard Seefried

NORDICA, Lillian (sop)
see CONCERT INDEX under:
(NIMB) **NI7840/1** The Era of Adelina Patti

NORDICA, Lillian (sop)
see CONCERT INDEX under:
(NIMB) **NI7840/1** The Era of Adelina Patti

NORDIN, Birgit (sop)
Verdi: Rigoletto (Cpte)

NORDINE, Ken (synths)
see CONCERT INDEX under:
(KOCH) **37238-2** A Chance Operation - John Cage
Tribute

NORDMANN, Marielle (hp)
see CONCERT INDEX under:
(SONY) **SK48184** Rampal plays Great Flute
Concertos
(SONY) **SK58919** Romantic Harp Concertos

NORDMO-LØVBERG, Aase (sop)
Beethoven: Symphony 9
see CONCERT INDEX under:
(BLUE) **ABCD028** Jussi Björling live at the Stockholm
Opera

NORDSTROM, Lyle (lte)
(HARM) **HMC90 5192** As I went to Walsingham
(VIRG) **VC7 59534-2** In the Streets and Theatres of
London

NORDWALL, Eva (hpd)
see CONCERT INDEX under:
(BIS) **BIS-CD053** Ligeti—Various Works

NORENA, Eidé (sop)
see CONCERT INDEX under:
(IRCC) **IRCC-CD800** Souvenirs from Meyerbeer
Operas
(NIMB) **NI7802** Divas 1906-1935
(PREI) **89041** Eidé Norena (1884-1968)

NØRHOLM, lb (narr)
Nørholm: Symphony 4
NORMAN, Jessye (sop)
Beethoven: Fidelio (Cpte), Missa Solemnis,
Symphony 9
Berlioz: Nuits d'été
Bizet: Carmen (Cpte)
Bruckner: Te Deum
Fauré: Pénélope (Cpte)
Gluck: Alceste (1776) (Cpte)
Haydn: Armida (Cpte), Vera Costanza (Cpte)
Mahler: Lied von der Erde, Lieder eines Fahrenden
Gesellen, Symphony 3
Mascagni: Cavalleria Rusticana (Cpte)
Mozart: Finta Giardiniera (Cpte), Nozze di Figaro
(Cpte)
Offenbach: Belle Hélène (Cpte), Contes d'Hoffmann
(Cpte)
Purcell: Dido (Cpte)
R. Strauss: Ariadne auf Naxos (Cpte), Salome
(Cpte)
Ravel: Shéhérazade
Schoenberg: Cabaret Songs, Erwartung (Cpte),
Gurrelieder
Stravinsky: Oedipus Rex (Cpte)
Tippett: Child of Our Time
Verdi: Corsaro (Cpte), Giorno di Regno (Cpte)
Wagner: Lohengrin (Cpte), Parsifal (Cpte), Tristan
und Isolde (exc), Walküre (Cpte), Wesendonk Lieder
see CONCERT INDEX under:
(DECC) 436 461-2DM   Ten Top Sopranos
(DG) 413 311-2GH   Brahms: Lieder
(DG) 423 613-2GH   Wagner—Opera excerpts
(DG) 429 025-2GX10   Bruckner—Complete
Symphonies, etc
(DG) 429 790-2GH   Spirituals in Concert
(DG) 445 354-2GX14   Wagner—Der Ring des
Nibelungen
(DG) 447 023-2GX12   Mahler—The Symphonies
(EMI) CDC7 49759-2   Wagner: Opera Scenes and
Arias
(EMI) CZS7 67819-2   Brahms/Schumann—Requiems
(ERAT) 2292-45368-2   Chausson: Songs
(PHIL) 400 019-2PH   Popular Sacred Songs
(PHIL) 411 052-2PH   Richard Strauss: Lieder
(PHIL) 412 623-2PH   Schubert: Lieder
(PHIL) 416 299-2PH   Richard Strauss: Lieder
(PHIL) 416 445-2PH   French songs
(PHIL) 422 048-2PH   Jessye Norman—Song Recital
(PHIL) 422 401-2PH   Jessye Norman - Lucky To Be
Me
(SONY) SK66826   Berg—Lieder
(SONY) SMK45838   Berg: Vocal & Orchestral Works
(SONY) SMK48466   Boulez conducts
Schoenberg—Volume 3
(SONY) SMK64107   Ravel/Roussel—Vocal &
Orchestral Works
(SONY) SX14K48198   Mahler—Complete
Symphonies, etc

NORMAN, Luke (bar)
see CONCERT INDEX under:
(GLOR) GDCD016   Leo Sowerby—American Master
of Sacred Song

NORMAN, Paul (bass)
see CONCERT INDEX under:
(GLOR) GDCD016   Leo Sowerby—American Master
of Sacred Song

NORRINGTON, Roger (cond)
see H. Schütz Ch

NORRIS, David Owen (pf)
Bax: Piano Quintet
Somervell: Maud (Cpte), Shropshire Lad (Cpte)
see CONCERT INDEX under:
(COLL) Coll7039-2   Britten—The Folk Songs

NORRKÖPING SYMPHONY ORCHESTRA
cond J. HIROKAMI
see CONCERT INDEX under:
(BIS) BIS-CD553   Atterberg—Orchestral Works
(BIS) BIS-CD619   Grieg—Piano Concerto (original
vers), etc
cond L. SEGERSTAM
Pettersson: Symphony 7, Symphony 11
Rott: Symphony
see CONCERT INDEX under:
(BIS) BIS-CD601   Reger—Orchestral Works

NORTH, Alex (cond)
see OST

NORTH, Nigel (gtr)
see CONCERT INDEX under:
(AMON) CD-SAR18   Guitar Collection
(AMON) CD-SAR23   Bach: Lute Music
(ARCH) 419 615-2AH   Vivaldi: Concertos
(BIS) BIS-CD341   Music for lutes
(HARM) HMU90 7104   Vivaldi/Chedeville—Oboe
Sonatas

NORTH, Nigel (lte)
Bach: Solo Violin Partitas and Sonatas (exc)
see CONCERT INDEX under:
(ARCA) A02   Purcell—Ayres and Songs from Orpheus
Britannicus
(HARM) HMU90 7104   Vivaldi/Chedeville—Oboe
Sonatas
(HARM) HMU90 7134/5   Biber—Sonatas and
Passagalias
(HYPE) CDA66228   Ancient Airs and Dances
(LINN) CKD006   Nigel North Lute Recital

NORTH, Nigel (lte/gtr)
see CONCERT INDEX under:
(VIRG) VC7 59324-2   Purcell—O Solitude - Songs and
Airs
NORTH, Nigel (lte/theorbo)
Piccinini: Intavolatura di liuto libro primo (exc)
NORTH, Nigel (theorbo)
W. Lawes: Royall Consorts
see CONCERT INDEX under:
(HARM) HMU90 7091   Three Parts upon a Ground
NORTH CAROLINA SYMPHONY ORCHESTRA
cond G. ZIMMERMANN
see CONCERT INDEX under:
(ALBA) AR001   R. Ward—Orchestral Works
NORTH GERMAN PHILHARMONIC ORCHESTRA
cond H. MÜLLER-BRÜHL
Dvořák: Piano Concerto
NORTH GERMAN RADIO CHORUS
cond G. ALBRECHT
Dessau: Hagadah Shel Pessach
Hindemith: Mathis der Maler (Cpte)
cond F. FRICSAY
Stravinsky: Oedipus Rex (Cpte)
cond J. E. GARDINER
Britten: War Requiem
cond E. INBAL
Berlioz: Damnation de Faust (Cpte), Grande Messe
des Morts (Cpte)
Mahler: Symphony 2, Symphony 8
Schoenberg: Gurrelieder
cond R. KUBELÍK
(DG) 429 042-2GX10   Mahler: Complete Symphonies
cond K. PENDERECKI
Penderecki: Polish Requiem
cond H. SCHMIDT-ISSERSTEDT
Mozart: Finta Giardiniera (Cpte)
cond G. WAND
see CONCERT INDEX under:
(RCA) 74321 20277-2   Beethoven—Complete
Symphonies
**NORTH GERMAN RADIO PHILHARMONIC
ORCHESTRA**
cond B. KLEE
see CONCERT INDEX under:
(SONY) SK53960   Gubaidulina—Piano Works
cond T. UKIGAYA
Krenek: Potpourri, Op. 54, Symphony 3
NORTH GERMAN RADIO SYMPHONY ORCHESTRA
cond H. BLOMSTEDT
see CONCERT INDEX under:
(DG) 437 719-2GC   Berg—Vocal Works
cond W. FURTWÄNGLER
Brahms: Haydn Variations, Symphony 1
cond C. GARBEN
Mozart: Piano Concerto 13, Piano Concerto 15
cond J. E. GARDINER
Britten: War Requiem
see CONCERT INDEX under:
(DG) 437 506-2GH   Brahms/Dvořák—Orchestral
Works
(DG) 439 894-2GH   Speak Low - Songs by Kurt Weill
cond K. PENDERECKI
Penderecki: Polish Requiem
cond H. SCHMIDT-ISSERSTEDT
Mozart: Finta Giardiniera (Cpte)
Reger: Romantische Suite, Symphonic Poems,
Op.128
see CONCERT INDEX under:
(ACAN) 43 268   Peter Anders sings German Opera
Arias
cond K. TENNSTEDT
Beethoven: Violin Concerto
cond G. WAND
Beethoven: Leonore (exc), Symphony 2, Symphony
3, Symphony 4, Symphony 5, Symphony 6
Bruckner: Symphony 3, Symphony 4, Symphony 5,
Symphony 6, Symphony 7, Symphony 8, Symphony
9
Mozart: German Dances, K600, Piano Concerto 24,
Piano Concerto 27, Serenade, K250, Symphony 40
Schubert: Symphony 3, Symphony 8, Symphony 9
Schumann: Symphony 3, Symphony 4
Stravinsky: Pulcinella Suite
Tchaikovsky: Symphony 5, Symphony 6
see CONCERT INDEX under:
(RCA) RD60827   Modern Pictures - Günter Wand
(RCA) 74321 20277-2   Beethoven—Complete
Symphonies
(RCA) 74321 20283-2   Brahms—Complete
Symphonies
NORTH JERSEY WIND SYMPHONY ORCHESTRA
cond A. HOVHANESS
Hovhaness: Requiem and Resurrection, Op. 224
NORTHERN CHAMBER ORCHESTRA
cond N. WARD
see CONCERT INDEX under:
(NAXO) 8 550721   Haydn—Symphonies
(NAXO) 8 550722   Haydn—Symphonies
(NAXO) 8 550724   Haydn—Symphonies, Vol. 9
(NAXO) 8 550729   Guitar Concertos
(NAXO) 8 550757   Haydn—Symphonies, Volume 10
(NAXO) 8 550871   Mozart—Symphonies
(NAXO) 8 550872   Mozart—Symphonies
(NAXO) 8 550873   Mozart—Symphonies Nos 11-14
(NAXO) 8 550874   Mozart—Symphonies

(REDC) RR008   Music by Alan Bush
NORTHERN SINFONIA
Stanley: Organ Concertos, Op. 10 (exc)
see CONCERT INDEX under:
(VIRG) VJ7 59655-2   French Impressions
cond S. BEDFORD
see CONCERT INDEX under:
(ASV) CDDCA568   Works for clarinet and orchestra
(COLL) Coll7037-2   Britten—Orchestral Song Cycles
(COLL) Coll7039-2   Britten—The Folk Songs
cond J. CASKEN
see CONCERT INDEX under:
(COLL) Coll1424-2   Casken—Orchestral Works
cond S. EDWARDS
see CONCERT INDEX under:
(ASV) CDDCB1101   Michael Berkeley—Clarinet
Concerto, etc
cond R. HICKOX
Bliss: Music for Strings, Pastoral
Walton: Bear (Cpte)
see CONCERT INDEX under:
(ASV) CDDCA591   Britten—Orchestral Works
(CHAN) CHAN9392   Vaughan Williams—Riders to the
Sea etc
(EMI) CDC7 47672-2   Elgar—Miniatures
(EMI) CDM5 65067-2   Delius—Orchestral Miniatures
(EMI) CDM7 64721-2   Moeran/Finzi—Orchestral
Works
cond G. MALCOLM
Handel: Concerti grossi, Op. 3, Concerti grossi,
Op.6
cond N. MARRINER
see CONCERT INDEX under:
(EMI) CDM7 69522-2   Britten—Vocal Works
cond J-B. POMMIER
(VIRG) VJ7 59655-2   French Impressions
cond S. RATTLE
Stravinsky: Pulcinella
cond H. SCHIFF
see CONCERT INDEX under:
(CHAN) CHAN9136   Schubert—Orchestral Works
(VIRG) VC7 59065-2   Haydn—Violin Concertos
cond Y.P. TORTELIER
Tchaikovsky: Rococo Variations
cond R. ZOLLMAN
(BIDD) LAW013   Dodgson—Orchestral & Vocal
Works
NORTHERN SINFONIA CHORUS
cond R. HICKOX
see CONCERT INDEX under:
(CHAN) CHAN9392   Vaughan Williams—Riders to the
Sea etc
NORTHWEST BOYCHOIR
cond G. SCHWARZ
(DELO) DE3141   Diamond—Vocal and Orchestral
Works
**NORTH-WEST GERMAN PHILHARMONIC
ORCHESTRA**
cond W.A. ALBERT
see CONCERT INDEX under:
(CPO) CPO999 037-2   Korngold—Orchestral Works
Vol.1
(CPO) CPO999 046-2   Korngold—Orchestral Works
Vol.2
(CPO) CPO999 077-2   Korngold—Orchestral Works
Vol.3
(CPO) CPO999 146-2   Korngold—Orchestral Works
Vol.4
cond D. ROGGEN
Villa-Lobos: Cello Concerto 1, Cello Concerto 2
cond M. YUROVSKY
Shostakovich: Gamblers (Cpte)
NORTH-WEST GERMAN RADIO CHORUS
cond W. BRÜCKNER-RÜGGEBERG
Weill: Mahagonny (Cpte)
cond W. SCHÜCHTER
Wagner: Lohengrin (Cpte)
NORTH-WEST GERMAN RADIO ORCHESTRA
cond W. BRÜCKNER-RÜGGEBERG
Weill: Mahagonny (Cpte)
NORTON, Angela (sngr)
Schuman: Question of Taste (Cpte)
NORTSOV, Panteleimon (bar)
Tchaikovsky: Eugene Onegin (Cpte)
(DANT) LYS013/5   Tchaikovsky—The Queen of
Spades
NORUP, Bent (bar)
Heise: Drot og Marsk (Cpte)
NORWEGIAN BRASS QUINTET
see CONCERT INDEX under:
(AURO) ACD4971   Nystedt—Chamber and Vocal
Works
NORWEGIAN CHAMBER ORCHESTRA
see CONCERT INDEX under:
(VICT) VCD19014   Hallgrømsson &
Nordheim—Chamber Orchestral Works
cond I. BROWN
Haydn: Cello Concerto in C, Cello Concerto in D
see CONCERT INDEX under:
(SIMA) PSC1035   Works for String Orchestra
(VIRG) VC5 45121-2   Britten—Orchestral Works

cond T. TØNNESEN
see CONCERT INDEX under:
(BIS) **BIS-CD147** Grieg—Music for String Orchestra

NORWEGIAN NATIONAL OPERA CHORUS
cond P. Å. ANDERSSON
Braein: Anne Pedersdotter (Cpte)

NORWEGIAN NATIONAL OPERA ORCHESTRA
cond P. Å. ANDERSSON
Braein: Anne Pedersdotter (Cpte)

NORWEGIAN QUARTET
Grieg: String Quartet in F, String Quartet, Op. 27
Holter: String Quartet 1, String Quartet 2
see CONCERT INDEX under:
(VICT) **VCD19048** Grieg—Complete String Quartets

NORWEGIAN RADIO ORCHESTRA
cond Ø. FJELDSTAD
see CONCERT INDEX under:
(LOND) **440 495-2LM** Kirsten Flagstad Edition, Vol.
5

NORWEGIAN SOLOISTS CHOIR
cond K. NYSTEDT
see CONCERT INDEX under:
(AURO) **ACD4971** Nystedt—Chamber and Vocal
Works

NORWEGIAN WIND ENSEMBLE
see CONCERT INDEX under:
(SIMA) **PSC1037** Mozart/Kvandal—Music for Wind
Ensemble
cond G. OSKAMP
R. Strauss: Sonatina 1, Suite, Op.4
cond O.K. RUUD
Berg: Chamber Concerto
Weill: Violin Concerto

NORWICH CATHEDRAL CHOIR
cond M. NICHOLAS
see CONCERT INDEX under:
(PRIO) **PRCD351** Great Cathedral Anthems, Vol.2
(PRIO) **PRCD409** Psalms of David, Vol.7
(PRIO) **PRCD470** Te Deum and Jubilate, Volume 2

NORWORTH, Jack (sngr)
see CONCERT INDEX under:
(PEAR) **GEMMCDS9053/5** Music from the New York
Stage, Vol. 2: 1908—1913
(PEAR) **GEMMCDS9059/61** Music from the New York
Stage, Vol. 4: 1917-20

NOSOTTI, Angelo (bass)
Mozart: Nozze di Figaro (Cpte)

NOTARISTEFANI, Virginia de (sop)
Puccini: Rondine (Cpte)

NOTÉ, Jean (bar)
see CONCERT INDEX under:
(SYMP) **SYMCD1089** Historic Baritones of the French
School

NOTHAS, Walter (vc)
Haydn: Sinfonia concertante

NOTO, Giuseppe (bass)
see CONCERT INDEX under:
(PEAR) **GEMMCDS9074(2)** Giovanni Zenatello, Vol.2
(pt 2)

NOTTI, Raymonde (sop)
Bizet: Carmen (Cpte)

NOTTINGHAM ORIANA CHOIR
cond ROY HENDERSON
see CONCERT INDEX under:
(DECC) **433 470-2DM** Ferrier Edition - Volume 3

NOUVEAU QUARTET
see CONCERT INDEX under:
(AMON) **CD-SAR42** Arne—Instrumental Works

(LE) NOUVEAU QUATUOR
see CONCERT INDEX under:
(AMON) **CD-SAR44** C.P.E. Bach: Trio Sonatas

NOUVEL PHILHARMONIQUE
cond G. PRÊTRE
Gounod: St Cecilia Mass

NOUVION, Bruno (tpt)
see CONCERT INDEX under:
(ACCO) **20202-2** Poulenc—Chamber Works

NOVA, Ettore (bass)
Salieri: Axur (Cpte)

NOVA SCHOLA GREGORIANA
cond A. TURCO
see CONCERT INDEX under:
(BONG) **GB5544/5-2** Palestrina—Messe mantovane

NOVACEK, John (pf)
see CONCERT INDEX under:
(KOCH) **37256-2** Rózsa—The Complete Music for
Solo Violin

NOVÁK, Richard (bass)
Dvořák: Kate and the Devil (Cpte)
Janáček: Cunning Little Vixen (Cpte), Excursions of
Mr Brouček (Cpte), From the House of the Dead
(Cpte), Glagolitic Mass (Cpte)
Martinů: Ariane (Cpte)
Puccini: Bohème (Cpte)
Smetana: Bartered Bride (Cpte)
(DECC) **430 375-2DH2** Janáček—Operatic and
Orchestral Works
(SUPR) **11 0751-2** Martinů—Choral Works
(SUPR) **11 0752-2** Martinů—Spaliček, etc

NOVÁK QUARTET
see CONCERT INDEX under:
(PHIL) **442 284-2PM2** Bartók—String Quartets

NOVÁKOVÁ, Alena (sop)
Janáček: Šárka (Cpte)

NOVAKOVA, Clara (fl)
see CONCERT INDEX under:
(EMI) **CDC7 54913-2** Saint-Saëns—La muse et le
poète

NOVÁKOVÁ, Jitka (vn)
(SUPR) **11 1533-2** Suk—Chamber Works, Volume 3

NOVÁKOVÁ, Kristina (hp)
see CONCERT INDEX under:
(OPUS) **9351 1894** French Chamber Works

NOVELLI, Francesco (bar)
Rossini: Barbiere di Siviglia (exc)

NOVELLO, Marie (pf)
see CONCERT INDEX under:
(OPAL) **OPALCD9839** Pupils of Theodore
Leschetizky

NOVIKOV, Viatcheslav (pf)
see CONCERT INDEX under:
(ONDI) **ODE826-2** Sibelius—Early Chamber Music,
Vol. 1

NOVIKOVA, Claudia (mez)
see CONCERT INDEX under:
(EMI) **CHS7 69741-2(6)** Record of Singing,
Vol.4—Russian & Slavonic Schools

NOVIKOVA, Tatiana (sop)
Borodin: Prince Igor (Cpte)

NOVOSIBIRSK PHILHARMONIC ORCHESTRA
cond A. KAZ
see CONCERT INDEX under:
(SONY) **SMK57660**
Rachmaninov/Stravinsky—Orchestral Works

NOVOTNÁ, Jarmila (sop)
see CONCERT INDEX under:
(EMI) **CDC7 54838-2** Franz Lehár
(PEAR) **GEMMCD9310** Franz Lehár conducts Richard
Tauber
(PREI) **90150** Lehár conducts Lehár
(RCA) **09026 61580-2(5)** RCA/Met 100 Singers, 100
Years (pt 5)
(SCHW) **314512** Vienna State Opera Live, Vol.1
(SUPR) **11 1491-2** Jarmila Novotna sings Czech
Songs and Arias

NOVOTNÝ, Břetislav (cond)
see Prague CO

NOVOYENIN, M. (ten)
see CONCERT INDEX under:
(DANT) **LYS013/5** Tchaikovsky—The Queen of
Spades

NOVŠAK, Primož (vn)
Brahms: Double Concerto

NOWAKOWSKI, Anton (organ)
see CONCERT INDEX under:
(DG) **423 127-2GX4** Bruckner: Sacred Works for
Chorus

NOWICKA, Barbara (mez)
Gluck: Corona (Cpte)

NOWSKI, Angelika (mez)
Gluck: Iphigénie en Tauride (Cpte)

NUA NÓS
cond D. N. MHEADHRA
see CONCERT INDEX under:
(NMC) **NMCD022** Gerald Barry—Instrumental &
Chamber Works

NUCCI, Leo (bar)
Cilea: Adriana Lecouvreur (Cpte)
Donizetti: Don Pasquale (Cpte), Elisir d'amore
(Cpte)
Giordano: Andrea Chénier (Cpte)
Mozart: Idomeneo (Cpte)
Puccini: Rondine (Cpte), Tosca (Cpte), Villi (Cpte)
Rossini: Barbiere di Siviglia (Cpte), Turco in Italia
(Cpte), Viaggio a Reims (Cpte)
Verdi: Aida (exc), Ballo in maschera (Cpte), Don
Carlos (Cpte), Falstaff (Cpte), Otello (Cpte), Rigoletto
(Cpte), Simon Boccanegra (Cpte), Traviata (Cpte),
Trovatore (Cpte)
see CONCERT INDEX under:
(DECC) **436 261-2DHO3** Puccini—Il Trittico
(DECC) **436 464-2DM** Ten Top Baritones & Basses

NUÑEZ, Antonio (vn)
Villa-Lobos: Cello Sonata 2, Piano Trio 2

NUNN, Richard (harm)
Rossini: Petite messe solennelle

NUOVO QUARTETTO
see CONCERT INDEX under:
(DENO) **CO-1029** Boccherini & Verdi: String Quartets

NUREMBERG OPERA CHORUS
cond W. FURTWÄNGLER
Wagner: Meistersinger (exc)

NUREMBERG SYMPHONY ORCHESTRA
cond R. KAUFMAN
see CONCERT INDEX under:
(COLO) **CST34 8048** Symphonic Hollywood, Volume
1

cond M. RÓZSA
Rózsa: Thief of Bagdad (exc)
cond K. SEIBEL
Rózsa: Jungle Book (exc)
see CONCERT INDEX under:
(COLO) **COL34 9004** Manfred Schenk sings Wagner

NURMELA, Karl (bar)
Leoncavallo: Pagliacci (Cpte)

NUYTS, Frank (cond)
see Bruges Collegium Instr

NWANOKU, Chi-Chi (db)
Goehr: Sing, Ariel, Op. 51
Rossini: Sonate a Quattro
Schubert: Trout Quintet, D667

NYBORG, Anders (spkr)
Nørholm: Symphony 2

NYFFENEGGER, Esther (vc)
Bach: Solo Cello Suites

NYGÅRD, Roald (spkr)
Braein: Anne Pedersdotter (Cpte)

NYHUS, Minna (contr)
Nørgård: Siddhartha (Cpte)

NYIREGYHÁZI, Ervin (pf)
see CONCERT INDEX under:
(VAI) **VAIA1003** Nyiregyhazi at the Opera

NYIREGYHÁZI BOYS' CHOIR
cond G. PATANÈ
Boito: Mefistofele (Cpte)

NYKÄNEN, Laura (contr)
Melartin: Symphony 4

NYMAN, Michael (cond)
see Orch

NYMAN, Michael (hpd)
Nyman: Zed and two noughts

NYMAN, Michael (pf/dir)
Nyman: Man Who Mistook His Wife for a Hat (Cpte),
Piano (exc), Prospero's Books

NYMAN, Tom (narr)
Aho: Pergamon

NYMAN, Tom (ten)
Bergman: Singing Tree (Cpte)
Rautavaara: Myth of Sampo

(MICHAEL) NYMAN BAND
Nyman: MGV, Prospero's Books

NYSTEDT, Knut (cond)
see Brass Ens

NYSTROM, Bradley (bar)
Schoenberg: Moses und Aron (Cpte)

NYZANKOWSKYI, Oleg de (ten)
Martin: Vin herbé

OAKLAND, Will (sngr)
see CONCERT INDEX under:
(PEAR) **GEMMCDS9053/5** Music from the New York
Stage, Vol. 2: 1908—1913

OBATA, Machiko (sop)
Weber: Oberon (Cpte)

OBER, Margarete (contr)
see CONCERT INDEX under:
(DANA) **DACOCD313/4** Lauritz Melchior Anthology -
Vol. 2
(RCA) **09026 61580-2(2)** RCA/Met 100 Singers, 100
Years (pt 2)

OBERFRANK, Géza (cond)
see Failoni CO

OBERST, Simon (sngr)
Handel: Saul (Cpte)

OBORIN, Lev (pf)
Khachaturian: Piano Concerto
see CONCERT INDEX under:
(PHIL) **412 570-2PH4** Beethoven Violin Sonatas

OBRAZTSOV, Anatoli (bass)
Grechaninov: Liturgy, Op. 79 (Cpte)

OBRAZTSOVA, Elena (mez)
Cilea: Adriana Lecouvreur (Cpte)
Mascagni: Cavalleria Rusticana (Cpte)
Prokofiev: Alexander Nevsky
Saint-Saëns: Samson et Dalila (Cpte)
Verdi: Aida (exc), Ballo in Maschera (Cpte), Luisa
Miller (Cpte), Rigoletto (Cpte), Trovatore (Cpte)
see CONCERT INDEX under:
(DG) **429 419-2GOR** Prokofiev—Alexander
Nevsky;Lieutenant Kijé etc

O'BRIEN, Vincent (pf)
see CONCERT INDEX under:
(PEAR) **GEMMCD9315** Kreisler/McCormack Duets

OBST, Michael (synth)
Stockhausen: Michaels Reise

OBUKHOVA, Nadezhda (mez)
see CONCERT INDEX under:
(DANT) **LYS013/5** Tchaikovsky—The Queen of
Spades
(EMI) **CHS7 69741-2(6)** Record of Singing,
Vol.4—Russian & Slavonic Schools

O'BYRNE, Gerard (ten)
Monteverdi: Vespers

ØIEN, Per (fl)
see CONCERT INDEX under:
(ASV) CDDCA741   Menotti/Luening—Orchestral
Works

OISTRAKH, David (cond)
see USSR SO

OISTRAKH, David (va/dir)
Mozart: Sinfonia Concertante, K364

OISTRAKH, David (vn)
Beethoven: Romances, Triple Concerto, Violin
Concerto
Brahms: Double Concerto, Violin Concerto
Khachaturian: Violin Concerto
Sibelius: Violin Concerto
Tchaikovsky: Violin Concerto
see CONCERT INDEX under:
(CHNT) LDC278 1018/9   Shostakovich: Chamber
Works
(DECC) 433 081-2DM   Hindemith—Orchestral Works
(DG) 413 844-2GW2   19th Century Violin Works
(DG) 447 427-2GOR2   D. Oistrakh plays Concertos
(EMI) CDC5 55035-2   Khachaturian conducts
Khachaturian
(PHIL) 412 570-2PH4   Beethoven Violin Sonatas
(PRAG) PR250 038   Bartók—Violin and Piano Works
(SUPR) 11 0582-2   David Oistrakh plays Beethoven &
Mozart

OISTRAKH, David (vn/dir)
see CONCERT INDEX under:
(DG) 447 427-2GOR2   D. Oistrakh plays Concertos
(EMI) CDM7 64868-2   Mozart—Works for Violin &
Orchestra

OISTRAKH, Igor (vn)
Mozart: Sinfonia Concertante, K364
Tchaikovsky: Piano Trio, Op. 50
see CONCERT INDEX under:
(DG) 447 427-2GOR2   D. Oistrakh plays Concertos
(RCA) 09026 61578-2   Vivaldi—Cello Concertos,
Vol.3

OKADA, Kiyoko (sop)
Rameau: Hippolyte et Aricie (Cpte)

OKAYAMA, Hiroyuki (bass)
Verdi: Traviata (Cpte)

OKAZAKI, Koji (bn)
see CONCERT INDEX under:
(DENO) C37-7487   Satie: Piano music for four hands

OKE, Alan (bar)
Lehár: Lustige Witwe (exc)
MacMillan: Visitatio Sepulchri (Cpte)
Sullivan: Gondoliers (Cpte)

OKENKO, Vladimir (ten)
see CONCERT INDEX under:
(STUD) SM1223.27   Rossini—Complete unpublished
Sacred Works

OKHOTNIKOV, Nikolai (bass)
Mussorgsky: Khovanshchina (Cpte)
Prokofiev: War and Peace (Cpte)

OKOLYCHEVA, Elena (contr)
Rimsky-Korsakov: Tsar's Bride (Cpte)

OKUMURA, Kazuo (vn)
Haydn: Sonatas, HobVI:1-6

ØLAFIMIHAN, Tinuke (sop)
Bernstein: West Side Story (Cpte)

OLCOTT, Chauncey (sngr)
see CONCERT INDEX under:
(PEAR) GEMMCDS9050/2(1)   Music from the New
York Stage, Vol. 1 (part 1)
(PEAR) GEMMCDS9053/5   Music from the New York
Stage, Vol. 2: 1908—1913
(PEAR) GEMMCDS9056/8   Music from the New York
Stage, Vol. 3: 1913-17

OLCZEWSKA, Maria (mez)
see CONCERT INDEX under:
(EMI) CHS7 64487-2   R. Strauss—Der Rosenkavalier
& Lieder
(EMI) CMS7 64008-2(2)   Wagner Singing on Record
(pt 2)
(PEAR) GEMMCDS9137   Wagner—Der Ring des
Nibelungen
(PEAR) GEMMCDS9365   R. Strauss: Der
Rosenkavalier (abridged), etc

OLD HOMESTEAD DOUBLE QUARTET
see CONCERT INDEX under:
(PEAR) GEMMCDS9050/2(1)   Music from the New
York Stage, Vol. 1 (part 1)

OLDENBURG, Fred (pf)
see CONCERT INDEX under:
(ETCE) KTC1124   Schnittke—Chamber Works
(ETCE) KTC1169   Ives—Music for String Quartet

OLDFATHER, Christopher (pf)
see CONCERT INDEX under:
(KOCH) 37258-2   Gubaidulina/Ustvolskaya—Works
for Cello
(SONY) S2K47229   Carter—Chamber Works

OLDHAM, Denver (pf)
see CONCERT INDEX under:
(NEW) NW328/9-2   Carpenter. Collected Piano
Works
(NEW) NW367-2   Nathaniel Dett: Piano Works

OLDHAM, Derek (ten)
Sullivan: Gondoliers (Cpte), Patience (Cpte), Pirates
of Penzance (Cpte), Sorcerer (Cpte)

OLEG, Raphaël (va)
see CONCERT INDEX under:
(DENO) CO-75636   Schubert—Violin and Viola Works

OLEG, Raphael (vn)
Beethoven: Piano Quartet, Op. 16, Piano Quartets,
WoO36
see CONCERT INDEX under:
(DENO) CO-75027   Schubert—Violin Sonatas
(DENO) CO-75636   Schubert—Violin and Viola Works

OLEJNÍČEK, Jiří (ten)
Janáček: Excursions of Mr Brouček (Cpte)

OLEXA, Vladimír (spkr)
Martinů: Echec au Roi

OLITZKA, Rosa (contr)
see CONCERT INDEX under:
(SIMA) PSC1810(2)   Grieg—Songs (historical
recordings, pt 2)

OLIVEIRA, Elmar (vn)
see CONCERT INDEX under:
(CARL) MCD27   Joachim—Orchestral Works

OLIVER, Aidan (treb)
Handel: Joshua (Cpte)
Vaughan Williams: Bunyan Sequence
see CONCERT INDEX under:
(CARL) PCD896   Fauré: Sacred Choral Works

OLIVER, Alexander (ten)
Handel: Ariodante (Cpte)
Meyerbeer: Dinorah (Cpte)
Mozart: Nozze di Figaro (Cpte)
Offenbach: Contes d'Hoffmann (Cpte), Robinson
Crusoé (Cpte)
Verdi: Ballo in maschera (Cpte), Corsaro (Cpte),
Traviata (exc)
see CONCERT INDEX under:
(DECC) 433 908-2DM2   Falla—Orchestral Music
(OPRA) ORC004   Donizetti—Ne m'oubliez pas; Arias

OLIVER, John (cond)
see J. Oliver Chorale

OLIVER, Robert (bass)
see CONCERT INDEX under:
(SONY) SM3K46291   Stravinsky—Ballets, Vol.1

(JOHN) OLIVER CHORALE
cond J. OLIVER
see CONCERT INDEX under:
(KOCH) 37178-2   Emblems

OLIVERI, Liliana (sop)
Maderna: Satyricon (Cpte)

OLIVERO, Magda (sop)
Alfano: Risurrezione (Cpte)
Giordano: Fedora (Cpte)
Zandonai: Francesca da Rimini (exc)
see CONCERT INDEX under:
(CENT) CRC2164   Ferruccio Tagliavini—Early
Operatic Recordings

OLIVIER, Sir Laurence (spkr)
see CONCERT INDEX under:
(EMI) CHS5 65003-2   Walton conducts Walton

OLIVIERI, Dino (cond)
see La Scala Orch

OLIVIERO, Lodovico (ten)
see CONCERT INDEX under:
(MYTO) 2MCD90317   Verdi—Un Ballo in maschera

OLLENDORFF, Fritz (bass)
Jessel: Schwarzwaldmädel (exc)
Rossini: Barbiere di Siviglia (Cpte)
Weber: Freischütz (Cpte)

OLLI, Kalevi (bass)
Madetoja: Juha (Cpte)

OLLMANN, Kurt (bar)
Bernstein: Candide (1988) (Cpte), On the Town
(Cpte), West Side Story (Cpte)
Gershwin: Oh, Kay! (Cpte)
Gounod: Roméo et Juliette (Cpte)
Haydn: Schöpfung (Cpte)

OLMEDA, Martine (mez)
Bizet: Carmen (Cpte)
Massenet: Cléopâtre (Cpte), Vierge (Cpte)

OLMI, Paolo (cond)
see Catania Teatro Massimo Bellini Orch

OLOF, Victor (cond)
see National SO

OLOFSSON, Åke (vc)
see CONCERT INDEX under:
(BIS) BIS-CD026   Shostakovich—Chamber Works

OLSEN, Derrik (bass)
Martin: Mystère de la Nativité, Pilate, Vin herbé

OLSEN, Frode (bass)
R. Strauss: Salome (Cpte)

OLSEN, Stanford (ten)
Mozart: Entführung (Cpte)
Rossini: Tancredi (Cpte)

OLSEN, Stein-Erik (gtr)
see CONCERT INDEX under:
(SIMA) PSC1031   Guitar Recital

OLSEN, Vidar (hn)
see CONCERT INDEX under:
(BIS) BIS-CD428   Nielsen—Wind Chamber Music

OLSSON, Tale (vn)
see CONCERT INDEX under:
(BIS) BIS-CD537   Schnittke Edition, Volume 12
(BIS) BIS-CD652   Penderecki—Chamber Works

OLTRABELLA, Augusta (sop)
see CONCERT INDEX under:
(EMI) CHS7 64864-2(2)   La Scala Edition - Vol.2,
1915-46 (pt 2)

OLVIS, William (ten)
Verdi: Macbeth (Cpte)

O'MARA, Joseph (sngr)
see CONCERT INDEX under:
(PEAR) GEMMCDS9050/2(1)   Music from the New
York Stage, Vol. 1 (part 1)

O'MARA, Joseph (ten)
see CONCERT INDEX under:
(SYMP) SYMCD1093   The Harold Wayne Collection,
Vol.7

OMBUENA, Vicente (ten)
Franchetti: Cristoforo Colombo (Cpte)
Puccini: Fanciulla del West (Cpte)
Verdi: Requiem (Cpte)

OMMERLÉ, Jeanne (sop)
V. Thomson: Lord Byron (Cpte)

ONCINA, Juan (ten)
Donizetti: Don Pasquale (Cpte)
Rossini: Cenerentola (Cpte), Comte Ory (Cpte)
see CONCERT INDEX under:
(EMI) CDH5 65072-2   Glyndebourne Recorded - 1934-
1994

ONCZAY, Csaba (vc)
Brahms: Clarinet Trio
see CONCERT INDEX under:
(MARC) 8 223170   Berwald—Piano Trios, Vol.1

ONDRAČKA, Vít (treb)
Krása: Brundibár (Cpte)

O'NEAL, Christopher (ob)
see CONCERT INDEX under:
(CARL) PCD939   Mozart: Orchestral Works

O'NEAL, James (ten)
Schoeck: Venus (Cpte)

ONEGIN, Sigrid (contr)
see CONCERT INDEX under:
(PREI) 89027   Sigrid Onegin (1889-1943)

O'NEILL, Dennis (ten)
Puccini: Fanciulla del West (Cpte)
Verdi: Requiem (Cpte)

O'NEILL, Nicholas (organ)
see CONCERT INDEX under:
(CNTO) CRCD2366   Music for a May Morning

O'NEILL, Robin (bn)
see CONCERT INDEX under:
(ASV) CDCOE814   Mozart—Wind Concertos
(ASV) CDDCA645   Vivaldi—Concertos
(HYPE) CDA66295   Villa-Lobos: Chamber Works
(NOVA) 150 043-2   Mozart—Works for Oboe and
Orchestra
(PHIL) 422 545-2PME3   The Complete Mozart Edition
Vol.45

ONESTI, Giorgio (bass)
Puccini: Bohème (Cpte), Gianni Schicchi (Cpte)

ONO, Yoko (tape op)
see CONCERT INDEX under:
(KOCH) 37238-2   A Chance Operation - John Cage
Tribute

ONOFRI, Enrico (vn)
Frescobaldi: Fiori musicali (Cpte)
Vivaldi: Concerti, Op. 8 (exc)

OORTMERSSEN, Jacques van (organ)
see CONCERT INDEX under:
(BIS) BIS-CD316   J. van Oortmerssen - Organ
Recital
(BIS) BIS-CD569   C.P.E.Bach—Organ Works

OOSTEN, Ben van (organ)
see CONCERT INDEX under:
(MDG) L3211/2   Vierne: Symphonies Nos. 1-3

OOSTERKAMP, Wout (bass)
Schreker: Gezeichneten (Cpte)

OPALACH, Jan (bass)
Handel: Imeneo (Cpte)
Stravinsky: Pulcinella
see CONCERT INDEX under:
(ARGO) 440 337-2ZH   Beaser—Orchestral and Vocal
Works
(BRID) BCD9014   Elliott Carter: Vocal Works
(EMI) CDC7 54643-2   Rossini—Bicentenary Gala
Concert

OPERA FESTIVAL CHORUS
cond O. KAMU
Sallinen: Iron Age Suite, Songs of Life and Death

OPERA NORTH CHORUS
cond P. DANIEL
M. Berkeley: Baa Baa Black Sheep (Cpte)
cond R. HICKOX
Walton: Troilus and Cressida (Cpte)

cond D. LLOYD-JONES
see CONCERT INDEX under:
(HYPE) CDA66565   Constant Lambert—Vocal &
Orchestral Works
cond M. TIPPETT
see CONCERT INDEX under:
(NIMB) NI5217   Tippett conducts Tippett

OPERA RESTOR'D
cond P. HOLMAN
Lampe: Cuckoo Concerto, Pyramus and Thisbe
(Cpte)
see CONCERT INDEX under:
(HYPE) CDA66608   Dibdin—Three Operas

OPERA STAGE CHORUS
cond R. HICKOX
Handel: Alcina (Cpte)

OPHÈLE, Emmanuelle (fl)
see CONCERT INDEX under:
(DG) 445 833-2GH   Boulez conducts Boulez

OPIE, Alan (bar)
Boughton: Bethlehem (Cpte)
Britten: Gloriana (Cpte), Rape of Lucretia (Cpte)
Offenbach: Christopher Columbus (Cpte), Robinson
Crusoé (Cpte)
Rossini: Barbiere di Siviglia (Cpte)
Vaughan Williams: Hugh the Drover (Cpte)
Verdi: Otello (Cpte)
Victory: Ultima Rerum (Cpte)
Walton: Bear (Cpte), Troilus and Cressida (Cpte)
Weill: Sieben Todsünden (Cpte)
see CONCERT INDEX under:
(HYPE) CDA66420   Vaughan Williams: Vocal Works
(HYPE) CDA66498   Britten—Canticles
(HYPE) CDA66569   Vaughan Williams—Choral Works

OPPENHEIM, David (cl)
Brahms: Clarinet Quintet
see CONCERT INDEX under:
(SONY) SM3K46527   Mozart—Legendary
Interpretations, IV

OPPENHEIM, Hans (cond)
see Inst Ens

OPPENHEIMER, Graham (va)
see CONCERT INDEX under:
(RCA) RD87173   Debussy: Orchestral works

OPPENS, Ursula (pf)
Carter: Piano Concerto
M. Feldman: Spring of Chosroes
Schnabel: Violin Sonata (1935)
see CONCERT INDEX under:
(MUSI) MACD-604   Contemporary American Piano
Works
(MUSI) MACD-650   Schoenberg—Song Cycles

OPPITZ, Gerhard (pf)
Beethoven: Choral Fantasia, Piano Trios (exc)
Brahms: Piano Pieces, Op.119, Piano Sonata 3
Fauré: Violin Sonata 1
R. Strauss: Violin Sonata
Schubert: Fantasie, D934, Notturno, D897, Piano Trio
1, Piano Trio 2, Sonata, D574
see CONCERT INDEX under:
(DG) 415 655-2GH   Bach: Harpsichord Concertos
(EURO) RD69245   Brahms: Complete Piano Works
(RCA) RD60856   Schumann—Piano Works
(RCA) RD60953   Liszt—Works for Piano and
Orchestra
(RCA) RD60954   Liszt—Piano Works
(RCA) 09026 60977-2   Schumann—Piano Works
(RCA) 09026 61568-2   Grieg—Complete Works for
Piano Solo, Vol.1
(RCA) 09026 61569-2   Grieg—Complete Works for
Piano Solo, Vol.2
(RCA) 09026 61620-2   Brahms—Piano Concertos, etc
(RCA) 09026 61811-2   Brahms—Piano Works
(RCA) 09026 61843-2   Concert in Villa Wahnfried
(RCA) 09026 61969-2   Beethoven—Piano Sonatas
(RCA) 74321 20297-2   Scriabin—Symphonies, etc

OPREAN, Adelina (vn)
Magnard: Piano Trio
see CONCERT INDEX under:
(HYPE) CDA66484   Enescu—Violin Sonatas

OPREAN, Justin (pf)
see CONCERT INDEX under:
(HYPE) CDA66484   Enescu—Violin Sonatas

OPRŠAL, Martin (glock)
see CONCERT INDEX under:
(SUPR) 11 1878-2   The Unknown Janáček

OPTHOF, Cornelius (bar)
(DECC) 433 706-2DMO3   Bellini—Beatrice di Tenda;
Operatic choral

ORADEA PHILHARMONIC ORCHESTRA
cond E. ACÉL
see CONCERT INDEX under:
(OLYM) OCD404   M. Haydn: Orchestral Works
(OLYM) OCD406   M. Haydn: Concertos
(OLYM) OCD407   M. Haydn: Symphonies
cond M. RAŢIU
see CONCERT INDEX under:
(OLYM) OCD407   M. Haydn: Symphonies
cond R. RÎMBU
see CONCERT INDEX under:
(OLYM) OCD434   Pichl—Symphonies
(OLYM) OCD435   M. Haydn—Symphonies, Vol.3

ORAISON, Jorge (gtr)
see CONCERT INDEX under:
(ETCE) KTC1023   Piazzolla—Tangos and Milongas

ORAMA, Heikki (bar)
E.T.A. Hoffmann: Undine (Cpte)

ORAMO, Sakari (cond)
see Finnish RSO

ORAN, Maria (sop)
Vives: Bohemios (Cpte)

ORAVECZ, György (pf)
Bretón: Piano Trio in E

ORAZI, Attilio d' (bar)
Puccini: Bohème (Cpte)

ØRBAEK, Hanne Mari (sop)
Monteverdi: Incoronazione di Poppea (Cpte)

ORBAN, Gödri (bn)
Enescu: Wind Decet, Op. 14

ORBELIAN, Constantine (pf)
Tchaikovsky: Piano Concerto 1
see CONCERT INDEX under:
(CHAN) CHAN8542   Khachaturian—Orchestral Works

(ANONYMOUS) ORCHESTRA
see CONCERT INDEX under:
(CFP) CD-CFP4569   Puccini: Arias
(DANA) DACOCD315/6   Lauritz Melchior Anthology -
Vol. 3
(NIMB) NI7802   Divas 1906-1935
(PREI) 89034   Giuseppe Lugo (1900-1980)
(RCA) 09026 61580-2(1)   RCA/Met 110 Singers, 100
Years (pt 1)
(RCA) 09026 61580-2(3)   RCA/Met 100 Singers, 100
Years (pt 3)
(RCA) 09026 61580-2(4)   RCA/Met 100 Singers, 100
Years (pt 4)
cond M. ABRAVANEL
see CONCERT INDEX under:
(SONY) MPK45694   Lily Pons—Opera & Song
Recital
cond A. ALBERGONI
see CONCERT INDEX under:
(CLUB) CL99-074   Conchita Supervia (1895-1936)
(EMI) CHS7 64864-2(1)   La Scala Edition - Vol.2,
1915-46 (pt 1)
(NIMB) NI7836/7   Conchita Supervia (1895-1936)
(PEAR) GEMMCDS9926(2)   Covent Garden on
Record—Vol.4 (pt 2)
(PREI) 89023   Conchita Supervia (1895-1936)
(PREI) 89063   Rosetta Pampanini (1896-1973)
(TEST) SBT1008   Viva Rossini
cond ALFRED NEWMAN
see CONCERT INDEX under:
(FOX) 07822 11006-2   Raksin/Herrmann—Laura/Jane
Eyre Original Soundtracks
cond K. ALWIN
see CONCERT INDEX under:
(PEAR) GEMMCDS9926(2)   Covent Garden on
Record—Vol.4 (pt 2)
(PREI) 89031   Elisabeth Schumann (1885-1952)
cond ANTHONY BERNARD
see CONCERT INDEX under:
(MMOI) CDMOIR411   Sacred Songs and Arias
cond ANTHONY NEWMAN
Alf Newman: Captain from Castile (exc)
cond G. ANTONICELLI
see CONCERT INDEX under:
(EMI) CHS7 64864-2(2)   La Scala Edition - Vol.2,
1915-46 (pt 2)
cond O.I. ARKADIEV
see CONCERT INDEX under:
(PEAR) GEMMCDS9004/6(1)   Singers of Imperial
Russia, Vol.3 (pt 1)
cond J. BARBIROLLI
see CONCERT INDEX under:
(CLAR) CDGSE78-50-49   Walter Widdop (1892-1949)
(CLAR) CDGSE78-50-50   Richard Crooks sings
Ballads & Sacred Songs
(EMI) CDH7 61051-2   Beniamino Gigli - Operatic
Arias
(EMI) CZS7 67359-2   Cortot plays Chopin
(MMOI) CDMOIR411   Sacred Songs and Arias
(MMOI) CDMOIR417   Great Voices of the
Century—Beniamino Gigli
(MMOI) CDMOIR425   Three Tenors, Volume 2
(MSOU) DFCDI-111   The Art of the Coloratura
(PEAR) GEMMCDS9926(1)   Covent Garden on
Record—Vol.4 (pt 1)
(PEAR) GEMMCD9314   Feodor Chaliapin - Aria and
Song Recital
(PEAR) GEMMCD9956   Joseph Hislop (1884-1977)
(PREI) 89004   Frida Leider (1888-1975) - I
(PREI) 89008   Irene Minghini-Cattaneo (1892-1944)
(PREI) 89044   Dusolina Giannini (1902-1986)
(TEST) SBT1008   Viva Rossini
cond H. BARLOW
see CONCERT INDEX under:
(MMOI) CDMOIR404   Ezio Pinza—Recital
(VAI) VAIA1072   Eleanor Steber Collection, Volume 1
cond J. BATTEN
see CONCERT INDEX under:
(EMI) CDH7 69791-2   Dame Eva Turner sings Opera
Arias and Songs
(PEAR) GEMMCD9175   Heddle Nash - Serenade
cond T. BEECHAM
see CONCERT INDEX under:
(EMI) CDH7 69791-2   Dame Eva Turner sings Opera
Arias and Songs

(NIMB) NI7802   Divas 1906-1935
(NIMB) NI7851   Legendary Voices
(PEAR) GEMMCDS9925(1)   Covent Garden on
Record—Vol.3 (pt 1)
(PEAR) GEMMCDS9926(2)   Covent Garden on
Record—Vol.4 (pt 2)
cond D. BELA
see CONCERT INDEX under:
(PEAR) GEMMCD9310   Franz Lehár conducts Richard
Tauber
cond V. BELLEZZA
see CONCERT INDEX under:
(PEAR) GEMMCDS9074(2)   Giovanni Zenatello, Vol.2
(pt 2)
(PEAR) GEMMCDS9925(2)   Covent Garden on
Record—Vol.3 (pt 2)
(PEAR) GEMMCDS9926(1)   Covent Garden on
Record—Vol.4 (pt 1)
cond H. VON BENDA
see CONCERT INDEX under:
(PREI) 89088   Walther Ludwig (1902-1981)
cond L. BERNSTEIN
Bernstein: Mass (Cpte)
see CONCERT INDEX under:
(SONY) SM2K47563   Haydn—Choral & Orchestral
Works
(SONY) SM3K47154   Bernstein—Theatre Works
Volume 1
cond U. BERRETTONI
see CONCERT INDEX under:
(EMI) CDH7 61051-2   Beniamino Gigli - Operatic
Arias
(EMI) CDH7 61052-2   Beniamino Gigli—Arias and
Duets (1932-1949)
(EMI) CHS7 69741-2(7)   Record of Singing,
Vol.4—Italian School
(PREI) 89009   Gino Bechi (b. 1913)
(PREI) 89015   Carlo Tagliabue (1898-1978)
cond K. BESL
see CONCERT INDEX under:
(EMI) CDH7 64029-2   Richard Tauber - Opera Recital
(NIMB) NI7830   Richard Tauber in Opera
cond E. BIGOT
see CONCERT INDEX under:
(EMI) CDM7 69548-2   Georges Thill sings French
Opera Arias
(EMI) CMS7 64008-2(1)   Wagner Singing on Record
(pt 1)
(FORL) UCD16727   L'Incomparable Georges Thill
(MSCM) MM30445   Wanda Landowska plays Handel
(NIMB) NI7856   Legendary Tenors
cond F. BLACK
see CONCERT INDEX under:
(ROMO) 81009-2   Edith Mason—Complete
Recordings 1924-1928
cond L. BLECH
see CONCERT INDEX under:
(EMI) CHS7 69741-2(5)   Record of Singing,
Vol.4—Scandinavian School
cond R. BLUM
see CONCERT INDEX under:
(SUPR) 11 1491-2   Jarmila Novotna sings Czech
Songs and Arias
cond N. BOULANGER
see CONCERT INDEX under:
(EMI) CDH7 61025-2   Fauré & Monteverdi Vocal
Works
cond R. BOURDON
see CONCERT INDEX under:
(CLAR) CDGSE78-50-52   Three Tenors
(CLUB) CL99-025   Giovanni Zenatello (1876-1949)
(CONI) CDHD201   Galli-Curci in Opera and Song
(EMI) CMS7 64008-2(1)   Wagner Singing on Record
(pt 1)
(MMOI) CDMOIR404   Ezio Pinza—Recital
(MMOI) CDMOIR408   Great Sopranos
(MMOI) CDMOIR411   Sacred Songs and Arias
(MMOI) CDMOIR417   Great Voices of the
Century—Beniamino Gigli
(MMOI) CDMOIR425   Three Tenors, Volume 2
(MMOI) CDMOIR428   Rosa Ponselle and Giovanni
Martinelli sing Verdi
(MSCM) MM30231   Don Pasquale & Tito Schipa
Recital
(MSOU) DFCDI-111   The Art of the Coloratura
(NIMB) NI7801   Great Singers, Vol.1
(NIMB) NI7804   Giovanni Martinelli—Opera Recital
(NIMB) NI7805   Rosa Ponselle—Opera & Song
Recital
(NIMB) NI7806   Galli-Curci—Opera & Song Recital
(NIMB) NI7807   Beniamino Gigli—Vol. 1: 1918-24
(NIMB) NI7810   Titta Ruffo—Opera Recital
(NIMB) NI7811   Ernestine Schumann-Heink—Opera &
Song Recital
(NIMB) NI7845   Giacomo Lauri-Volpi (1892-1979)
(NIMB) NI7846   Rosa Ponselle, Vol.2
(NIMB) NI7851   Legendary Voices
(NIMB) NI7853   Lauri-Volpi sings Verdi
(PEAR) GEMMCDS9074(2)   Giovanni Zenatello, Vol.2
(pt 2)
(PEAR) GEMMCDS9452   The Emperor Tibbett
(PEAR) GEMMCDS9925(2)   Covent Garden on
Record—Vol.3 (pt 2)
(PEAR) GEMMCDS9926(2)   Covent Garden on
Record—Vol.4 (pt 2)
(PEAR) GEMMCD9161   Edmond Clément (1867-
1928)
(PEAR) GEMMCD9306   Ezio Pinza—Opera Recital
(PEAR) GEMMCD9314   Feodor Chaliapin - Aria and
Song Recital
(PEAR) GEMMCD9316   Beniamino Gigli

(ROMO) 81002-2 Emmy Destinn (1878-1930)
(ROMO) 81011-2(1) Dame Nellie Melba (pt 1)
(ROMO) 81011-2(2) Dame Nellie Melba (pt 2)
(SUPR) 11 1337-2 Emmy Destinn (1878-1930)
(SUPR) 11 2136-2(5) Emmy Destinn—Complete
Edition, Discs 11 & 12
(TEST) SBT1005 Ten Top Tenors
  cond R. ROMANI
  see CONCERT INDEX under:
(MMOI) CDMOIR428 Rosa Ponselle and Giovanni
Martinelli sing Verdi
(NIMB) NI7851 Legendary Voices
  cond M. ROMERO
  see CONCERT INDEX under:
(NIMB) NI7836/7 Conchita Supervia (1895-1936)
  cond L. RONALD
  see CONCERT INDEX under:
(BIDD) LAB009/10 The Kreisler Collection
(LARR) CDLRH221 Dame Nellie Melba - Opera and
Song Recital
(PEAR) GEMMCDS9923(1) Covent Garden on
Record, Vol.1 (pt 1)
  cond A. ROUSSEL
  see CONCERT INDEX under:
(EMI) CDC7 54840-2 Composers in Person—Roussel
& Schmitt
  cond F. RUHLMANN
  see CONCERT INDEX under:
(MMOI) CDMOIR408 Great Sopranos
(MSCM) MM30451 Mascagni—Cavalleria Rusticana,
etc
(PREI) 89041 Eidé Norena (1884-1968)
  cond C. SABAJNO
  see CONCERT INDEX under:
(CLUB) CL99-509/10 Hina Spani (1896-1969)
(EMI) CDH7 63200-2 Tito Schipa—Recital
(EMI) CHS7 64860-2(1) La Scala Edition - Vol.1,
1878-1914 (pt 1)
(EMI) CHS7 64860-2(2) La Scala Edition - Vol.1,
1878-1914 (pt 2)
(EMI) CHS7 64864-2(1) La Scala Edition - Vol.2,
1915-46 (pt 1)
(MSCM) MM30231 Don Pasquale & Tito Schipa
Recital
(NIMB) NI7807 Beniamino Gigli—Vol. 1: 1918-24
(NIMB) NI7810 Titta Ruffo—Opera Recital
(NIMB) NI7831 Mattia Battistini (1856-1928)
(PEAR) GEMMCDS9923(1) Covent Garden on
Record, Vol.1 (pt 1)
(PEAR) GEMMCDS9924(1) Covent Garden on
Record, Vol.2 (pt 1)
(PEAR) GEMMCDS9925(1) Covent Garden on
Record—Vol.3 (pt 1)
(PEAR) GEMMCD9306 Ezio Pinza—Opera Recital
(PEAR) GEMMCD9322 Tito Schipa sings Opera Arias
and Songs
(PEAR) GEMMCD9936 Mattia Battistini, Vol.1
  cond A. SABINO
  see CONCERT INDEX under:
(PREI) 89074 Tancredi Pasero (1893-1983) - II
  cond M. SARGENT
Mozart: Violin Concerto, K268
  see CONCERT INDEX under:
(BEUL) 1PD13 Sir Malcolm Sargent conducts British
Music
(CLAR) CDGSE78-50-52 Three Tenors
(MUSI) MACD-749 Bruno Walter conducts Mahler
  cond F. SCHÖNBAUMSFELD
  see CONCERT INDEX under:
(EMI) CDH7 69787-2 Richard Tauber sings Operetta
Arias
  cond G. SCOGNAMIGLIO
  see CONCERT INDEX under:
(PEAR) EVC3(1) The Caruso Edition, Vol.3 (pt 1)
(RCA) GD60495(5) The Complete Caruso Collection
(pt 5)
  cond B. SEIDLER-WINKLER
  see CONCERT INDEX under:
(PEAR) GEMMCDS9001/3(1) Singers of Imperial
Russia, Vol.2 (pt 1)
(PEAR) GEMMCDS9924(1) Covent Garden on
Record, Vol.2 (pt 1)
(PEAR) GEMMCDS9924(2) Covent Garden on
Record, Vol.2 (pt 2)
(PREI) 89208 Karl Erb Lieder Album
(SUPR) 11 1337-2 Emmy Destinn (1878-1930)
(SUPR) 11 2136-2(1) Emmy Destinn—Complete
Edition, Discs 1 & 2
(SUPR) 11 2136-2(2) Emmy Destinn—Complete
Edition, Discs 3 & 4
(SUPR) 11 2136-2(3) Emmy Destinn—Complete
Edition, Discs 5 to 8
  cond G. SETTI
  see CONCERT INDEX under:
(NIMB) NI7804 Giovanni Martinelli—Opera Recital
(PEAR) GEMMCDS9924(1) Covent Garden on
Record, Vol.2 (pt 1)
(ROMO) 81007-2 Rosa Ponselle—Victor Recordings
1926-1929
  cond N. SHILKRET
  see CONCERT INDEX under:
(CLAR) CDGSE78-50-52 Three Tenors
(MMOI) CDMOIR422 Great Voices in Tchaikovsky
(MMOI) CDMOIR425 Three Tenors, Volume 2
(NIMB) NI7804 Giovanni Martinelli—Opera Recital
(PEAR) GEMMCDS9452 The Emperor Tibbett
(PEAR) GEMMCD9316 Beniamino Gigli
(PEAR) GEMMCD9367 Gigli—Arias and Duets
(RCA) GD87808 Lawrence Tibbett sings Opera
Arias

(ROMO) 81008-2 Mary Garden (1874-1967)
  cond E. SIVIERI
  see CONCERT INDEX under:
(RCA) GD87811 Beniamino Gigli—Operatic Arias
  cond A. SMALLENS
  see CONCERT INDEX under:
(PEAR) GEMMCDS9452 The Emperor Tibbett
(RCA) GD87808 Lawrence Tibbett sings Opera
Arias
  cond E. STERN
*Gershwin: Lady, be Good! (Cpte), Pardon My English
(Cpte)*
  see CONCERT INDEX under:
(NONE) 7559-79330-2 Patinkin—Experiment
(NONE) 7559-79345-2 I Wish It So - Dawn Upshaw
  cond I. STRAVINSKY
  see CONCERT INDEX under:
(ARHI) ADCD110 Mengelberg Edition - Volume 4
(SONY) SM2K46294 Stravinsky—Symphonies
  cond G. SZELL
  see CONCERT INDEX under:
(EMI) CDH7 64029-2 Richard Tauber - Opera Recital
(NIMB) NI7830 Richard Tauber in Opera
(TEST) SBT1005 Ten Top Tenors
  cond J. SZYFER
  see CONCERT INDEX under:
(EMI) CDM7 69548-2 Georges Thill sings French
Opera Arias
  cond F. TOURS
  see CONCERT INDEX under:
(NIMB) NI7867 Legendary Baritones
  cond N. TREEP
  see CONCERT INDEX under:
(LYRC) SRO830 Smetana—The Bartered Bride, etc
  cond E. VITALE
  see CONCERT INDEX under:
(EMI) CHS7 64860-2(2) La Scala Edition - Vol.1,
1878-1914 (pt 2)
  cond D. VOORHEES
  see CONCERT INDEX under:
(MMOI) CDMOIR404 Ezio Pinza—Recital
  cond S. WALDIMIR
  see CONCERT INDEX under:
(BLUE) ABCD016 Jussi Björling—Rare Records &
Alternative Takes
  cond A. WALLENSTEIN
  see CONCERT INDEX under:
(SUPR) 11 1491-2 Jarmila Novotna sings Czech
Songs and Arias
  cond B. WALTER
  see CONCERT INDEX under:
(PEAR) GEMMCDS9925(2) Covent Garden on
Record—Vol.3 (pt 2)
  cond H. WEIGERT
  see CONCERT INDEX under:
(NIMB) NI7830 Richard Tauber in Opera
  cond F. WEISSMANN
  see CONCERT INDEX under:
(DANA) DACOCD313/4 Lauritz Melchior Anthology -
Vol. 2
(EMI) CDH7 69787-2 Richard Tauber sings Operetta
Arias
(EMI) CDM7 69476-2 Richard Tauber - A Portrait
(EMI) CHS7 69741-2(7) Record of Singing,
Vol.4—Italian School
(EMI) CMS7 64008-2(1) Wagner Singing on Record
(pt 1)
(MMOI) CDMOIR425 Three Tenors, Volume 2
(PEAR) GEMMCDS9926(2) Covent Garden on
Record—Vol.4 (pt 2)
(PEAR) GEMMCD9339 Moriz Rosenthal—Piano
Recital
(PEAR) GEMMCD9381 Richard Tauber sings Lieder
(PEAR) GEMMCD9419 Herbert Ernst Groh—Opera
Recital
  cond P. WHITEMAN
  see CONCERT INDEX under:
(HALC) DHDL101 Two Sides of George Gershwin
  cond A. WILSON
  see CONCERT INDEX under:
(KOCH) 38703-2 Full Circle—Original Soundtrack,
etc
  cond A. WOLFF
  see CONCERT INDEX under:
(PREI) 89034 Giuseppe Lugo (1900-1980)
  cond V. YOUNG
V. Young: Quiet Man Suite (exc)
  see CONCERT INDEX under:
(RCA) 09026 61778-2(19) The Heifetz Collection, Vol.
19
  cond R. ZAMBONI
  see CONCERT INDEX under:
(EMI) CDH7 61052-2 Beniamino Gigli—Arias and
Duets (1932-1949)
  cond A. VON ZEMLINSKY
  see CONCERT INDEX under:
(SUPR) 11 1491-2 Jarmila Novotna sings Czech
Songs and Arias
  cond F. ZWEIG
  see CONCERT INDEX under:
(PEAR) GEMMCDS9926(2) Covent Garden on
Record—Vol.4 (pt 2)

ORCHESTRA OF THE AGE OF ENLIGHTENMENT
Rameau: Paladins (exc)
  see CONCERT INDEX under:
(VIRG) VC7 59266-2 Haydn—Orchestral Works
  cond A. HALSTEAD
  see CONCERT INDEX under:
(MSVE) MSCD419 Kraus—Symphonies

  cond P. HERREWEGHE
*C.P.E. Bach: Auferstehung und Himmelfahrt Jesu
(Cpte)*
  cond M. HUGGETT
  see CONCERT INDEX under:
(HARM) HMU90 7093 Telemann—Concertos and
Suites
  cond S. KUIJKEN
*C. P. E. Bach: Sinfonias, H657-62 (exc), Sinfonias,
H663-6*
  see CONCERT INDEX under:
(VIRG) VC7 59537-2 Haydn—Symphonies
(VIRG) VC7 59557-2 Haydn—Symphonies
(VIRG) VC7 59558-2 Mozart—Works for Horn &
Orchestra
  cond G. LEONHARDT
*Bach: Cantata 11, Cantata 211, Cantata 213, Easter
Oratorio, BWV249 (Cpte)*
  see CONCERT INDEX under:
(VIRG) VC7 59243-2 Purcell—Odes for Queen Mary
(VIRG) VC7 59541-2 C.P.E. Bach—Cello Concertos
  cond C. MACKERRAS
Beethoven: Violin Concerto
Mendelssohn: Violin Concerto, Op.64
  see CONCERT INDEX under:
(FORL) UCD16738 Great Handel Arias
  cond B. WEIL
*Schubert: Deutsche messe, Mass, D678, Mass, D950
(Cpte)*

ORCHESTRA OF THE EIGHTEENTH CENTURY
  cond F. BRÜGGEN
*Bach: Mass in B minor, BWV232 (Cpte), St. John
Passion, BWV245 (Cpte)*
Haydn: Symphony 97, Symphony 98
*Rameau: Abaris (exc), Dardanus (exc), Indes
Galantes (exc)*
Schubert: Symphony 6, Symphony 8, Symphony 9
  see CONCERT INDEX under:
(PHIL) 426 714-2PH Rameau & Purcell: Orchestral
Works
(PHIL) 434 799-2PH Mozart—Choral Works

ORCHESTRE DE LA BASTILLE (PARIS)
  cond MYUNG-WHUN CHUNG
Messiaen: Turangalîla Symphony
  see CONCERT INDEX under:
(DG) 431 778-2GH Bizet—Orchestral Works

ORCHESTRE DE LA CITÉ
  cond M. PIQUEMAL
  see CONCERT INDEX under:
(NAXO) 8 553176 Poulenc—Choral Works
(NAXO) 8 553196 Duruflé—Sacred Choral and Organ
Works, Volume 1
(NAXO) 8 553197 Duruflé—Sacred Choral and Organ
Works, Volume 2

**ORCHESTRE DE L'ASSOCIATION DES CONCERTS
PASDELOUP**
  cond P. COPPOLA
  see CONCERT INDEX under:
(DANT) LYS003/4 Charles Panzéra - Song Recital
(EMI) CMS7 64008-2(2) Wagner Singing on Record
(pt 2)
(PREI) 89011 Marjorie Lawrence (1909-1979)
  cond RHENÉ-BATON
  see CONCERT INDEX under:
(MUSI) MACD-767 Honegger conducts Honegger

ORCHESTRE DE PARIS
Beethoven: Symphony 9
  cond J. BARBIROLLI
  see CONCERT INDEX under:
(EMI) CZS7 62669-2 French Orchestral Music
  cond D. BARENBOIM
Brahms: Violin Concerto
Denisov: Symphony
Mozart: Requiem
*Saint-Saëns: Samson et Dalila (Cpte), Violin
Concerto 3*
Wieniawski: Violin Concerto 2
  see CONCERT INDEX under:
(BELA) 450 121-2 Plácido Domingo
(DG) 415 847-2GGA Saint-Saëns—Orchestral
Works
(DG) 435 069-2GGA Debussy—Orchestral Works
(DG) 437 244-2GGA2 Berlioz/Franck—Vocal &
Orchestral Works
(DG) 437 638-2GGA2 Berlioz—Vocal & Orchestral
Works
(DG) 439 407-2GCL Debussy—Orchestral Works
(DG) 445 536-2GMA Lalo/Saint-Saëns—Orchestral
Works
(EMI) CDM7 64634-2 Fauré/Bach—Choral Works
(EMI) CZS4 83177-2(1) Itzhak Perlman Edition (pt 1)
(EMI) CZS7 67306-2 Mozart—Works featuring Wind
Instruments
(ERAT) 2292-45417-2 Lieder with Orchestra
(ERAT) 2292-45493-2 Boulez: Orchestral Works
(SONY) SBK53255 Berlioz—Orchestral Works
  cond S. BAUDO
Dutilleux: Cello Concerto
Indy: Symphonie, Op. 25
  see CONCERT INDEX under:
(EMI) CDM7 63948-2 20th Century French Orchestral
Works
(EMI) CMS7 62643-2 Saint-Saëns—Complete Piano
Concertos
(EMI) CZS7 62669-2 French Orchestral Music
  cond S. BYCHKOV
Berlioz: Carnaval romain, Symphonie fantastique
Bizet: Arlésienne Suites, Carmen Suites
Mascagni: Cavalleria Rusticana (Cpte)

L. Johnson: First Men in the Moon (exc)
cond A. JONES
Towns: Wolves of Willoughby Chase (exc)
cond W. KILAR
see CONCERT INDEX under:
(OLYM) **OCD602** Wojciech Kilar—Film Music
cond A. KORZYNSKI
see CONCERT INDEX under:
(OLYM) **OCD601** Andrzej Korzyński—Music to the
films of Andrzej Wajda
cond D. LICHT
see CONCERT INDEX under:
(SILV) **FILMCD127** Vampire Circus—The Essential
Vampire Theme Collection
cond B. MAY
see CONCERT INDEX under:
(SILV) **FILMCD127** Vampire Circus—The Essential
Vampire Theme Collection
cond M. MCKENZIE
see CONCERT INDEX under:
(SILV) **FILMCD127** Vampire Circus—The Essential
Vampire Theme Collection
cond J. MCNEELY
McNeely: Iron Will (exc)
cond A. MEDVECZKY
Shore: M. Butterfly (exc)
cond W. MICHNIEWSKI
Preisner: Secret Garden (exc)
cond F. MOLLIN
see CONCERT INDEX under:
(SILV) **FILMCD127** Vampire Circus—The Essential
Vampire Theme Collection
cond A. NORTH
A. North: Agony and the Ecstasy (exc)
cond H. RABINOWITZ
Robbins: Remains of the Day (exc)
cond S. RATTLE
Doyle: Henry V (exc)
cond L. ROSENMAN
Rosenman: Lord of the Rings (exc)
cond N. ROTA
Rota: Romeo and Juliet (exc)
cond M. RÓZSA
see CONCERT INDEX under:
(CLOU) **CNS5006** Great Epic Film Scores
cond G. SCHURMANN
see CONCERT INDEX under:
(CLOU) **CNS5005** Schurmann—Horrors of the Black
Museum
cond J. SHEFFER
Goldenthal: Demolition Man (exc), Golden Gate
(exc)
cond V. SHOEN
S. Fine: Court Jester (exc)
cond D. SNELL
Doyle: Needful Things (exc)
cond R. STONE
see CONCERT INDEX under:
(SILV) **FILMCD127** Vampire Circus—The Essential
Vampire Theme Collection
cond D. TIOMKIN
Tiomkin: Fall of the Roman Empire (exc)
see CONCERT INDEX under:
(CLOU) **CNS5006** Great Epic Film Scores
cond C. TOWNS
Towns: Buccaneers (exc)
cond F. WAXMAN
Waxman: Nun's Story (exc), Spirit of St Louis (exc)
cond J.T. WILLIAMS
J.T. Williams: Home Alone (exc), Reivers (exc),
Schindler's List (exc)
see CONCERT INDEX under:
(FOX) **07822 11012-2** Star Wars Trilogy—Original
Soundtrack Anthology
cond D. WISEMAN
Wiseman: Tom and Viv (exc)
cond H. ZIMMER
Zimmer: Pacific Heights

O'RILEY, Christopher (pf)
see CONCERT INDEX under:
(CENT) **CRC2036** Busoni—Piano Works &
Transcriptions
(DELO) **DE3170** Beach—Cabildo; Six Short Pieces
(NONE) **7559-79343-2** Stravinsky—Piano Works

ORINCHUK, Leonid (pf)
see CONCERT INDEX under:
(OLYM) **OCD529** Glinka—Chamber Works

ORKIS, Lambert (fp)
Schubert: Impromptus (exc)
see CONCERT INDEX under:
(VIRG) **VC7 59630-2** Schubert—Lieder

ORKIS, Lambert (pf)
Crumb: Little Suite for Christmas, AD1979
Wernick: Piano Sonata (1982)
see CONCERT INDEX under:
(SONY) **SK53980** Franchomme/Chopin—Grand Duo
Concertante

ORLANDI, Ugo (mndl)
see CONCERT INDEX under:
(ERAT) **4509-92132-2** The Magic of the Mandolin

ORLANDO CONSORT
Anon: Worcester Fragments
see CONCERT INDEX under:
(METR) **METCD1002** Compère—Choral Works
(METR) **METCD1008** Popes and Antipopes

ORLANDO QUARTET
Brahms: String Quartet 2, String Quartet 3
Dvořák: String Quartet 12

Grieg: String Quartet, Op. 27
Mozart: String Quintet, K174, String Quintet, K406,
String Quintet, K515, String Quintet, K516, String
Quintet, K593, String Quintet, K614
Schumann: String Quartet 1
Smetana: String Quartet 1

ORLIAC, Jean-Claude (ten)
Gounod: Philémon et Baucis (Cpte)

ORLOV, Alexander (cond)
see Bolshoi Th Orch

ORLOV, Polikarp (bar)
see CONCERT INDEX under:
(PEAR) **GEMMCDS9001/3(1)** Singers of Imperial
Russia, Vol.2 (pt 1)

ORLOVSKY, Harold (vn)
Reger: Konzert im alten Stil

ORMANDY, Eugene (cond)
see BRSO

ORMISTON, Linda (mez)
Britten: Noye's Fludde (Cpte)
Saxton: Caritas (Cpte)
Sullivan: HMS Pinafore (Cpte)

O'ROURKE, Mícheál (pf)
Field: Nocturnes, Piano Concerto 1, Piano Concerto
2, Piano Sonata, H17, Sonatas, H8
see CONCERT INDEX under:
(CHAN) **CHAN9315** John Field—Piano Works
(CHAN) **CHAN9353** Chopin—Piano Works

OROZCO, Rafael (pf)
Albéniz: Cantos de España, Iberia
Schubert: Fantasy, D760, Piano Sonata, D960
see CONCERT INDEX under:
(AUVI) **V4724** Falla—Orchestral and Instrumental
Works

ORPHEI DRÄNGAR
cond E. ERICSON
see CONCERT INDEX under:
(EMI) **CDC7 54098-2** Sacred Songs
cond E-P. SALONEN
Stravinsky: Oedipus Rex (Cpte)

ORPHEI DRÄNGAR CHOIR
cond E. ERICSON
see CONCERT INDEX under:
(BIS) **BIS-CD383** Works for Male Chorus

ORPHEUS BOYS' CHOIR
cond P. BOULEZ
Schoenberg: Moses und Aron (Cpte)

ORPHEUS CHAMBER ENSEMBLE
see CONCERT INDEX under:
(BIS) **BIS-CD284** Roman: violin concertos and
sinfonias
cond K. EK
Langlais: Messe solennelle
Olsson: Te Deum

ORPHEUS STRING QUARTET
Beethoven: String Quartet 3, String Quartet 7
Schubert: String Quintet
see CONCERT INDEX under:
(ASV) **CDDCD457** Malipiero—Chamber Works

ORPINGTON JUNIOR SINGERS
cond L. BERNSTEIN
Mahler: Symphony 8

ORREGO, Rodrigo (ten)
Spohr: Faust (Cpte)

ORSANIC, Viatka (sop)
B. A. Zimmermann: Requiem (Cpte)

ØRSTED, Ole (elec)
Stockhausen: Mantra

ORTEGA, Ginesa (sngr)
Falla: Amor Brujo (Cpte)
Lorca: Canciones españolas antiguas

ORTF CHORUS
cond D-E. INGHELBRECHT
see CONCERT INDEX under:
(MONT) **TCE8790** Debussy: Orchestral and Dramatic
Works
cond J. MARTINON
see CONCERT INDEX under:
(EMI) **CDM7 63944-2** Honegger—Orchestral Works
(EMI) **CDM7 69587-2** Debussy: Orchestral Works,
Vol.1

ORTF LYRIC CHORALE
cond M. CARIVEN
Audran: Miss Helyett (Cpte)
Messager: Coups de Roulis (Cpte)
cond J-C. HARTEMANN
Offenbach: Madame l'Archiduc (Cpte)

ORTF LYRIC ORCHESTRA
cond E. BIGOT
Adam: Toréador (Cpte)
cond J. BREBION
see CONCERT INDEX under:
(MUSD) **20239-2** Delibes—Opéras-Comiques
cond M. CARIVEN
Audran: Miss Helyett (Cpte)
Messager: Coups de Roulis (Cpte)
cond J. DOUSSARD
Terrasse: Fiancée du Scaphandrier (Cpte)
cond J-C. HARTEMANN
Lecocq: Rose Mousse (Cpte)

Offenbach: Chanson de Fortunio (Cpte), Madame
l'Archiduc (Cpte)
cond J-P. KREDER
Messager: Passionêment (Cpte)

ORTF NATIONAL ORCHESTRA
cond M. DURUFLÉ
see CONCERT INDEX under:
(ERAT) **4509-98526-2** Duruflé—Vocal & Organ Works
cond J. MARTINON
see CONCERT INDEX under:
(EMI) **CDM7 63944-2** Honegger—Orchestral Works

ORTF PHILHARMONIC ORCHESTRA
cond C. BRUCK
Brahms: Violin Concerto

ORTH, Norbert (ten)
Leoncavallo: Bohème (Cpte)
Mozart: Entführung (Cpte)
Wagner: Meistersinger (Cpte)

ORTHMANN, Erich (cond)
see Berlin St Op Orch

ORTIZ, Cristina (pf)
Beethoven: Piano Concerto 1, Piano Concerto 2,
Piano Concerto 3, Piano Concerto 4, Piano Concerto
5, Piano Sonata 21
Saint-Saëns: Carnaval des animaux
Shostakovich: Piano Concerto 2
Stenhammar: Piano Concerto 2
see CONCERT INDEX under:
(CARL) **PCD846** French Impressionist Piano Music
(CARL) **PCD872** Chopin: Piano Works
(DECC) **414 348-2DH** Popular Works for Piano &
Orchestra
(DECC) **414 460-2DH** Saint-Saëns—Orchestral
works
(DECC) **430 628-2DH2** Villa-Lobos—Piano Concertos
(DECC) **430 726-2DM** Popular Works for Piano and
Orchestra
(DECC) **433 616-2DSP**
Addinsell/Gershwin—Orchestral Works
(EMI) **CDM7 69644-2** Poulenc—Choral, Piano and
Orchestral Works
(TRIN) **TRP027** Beethoven—Piano Sonatas

ORTON, Stephen (vc)
Walton: Piano Quartet
see CONCERT INDEX under:
(CONI) **CDCF218** Panufnik—String Quartets
(PHIL) **422 508-2PME4** The Complete Mozart Edition
Vol 8
(PHIL) **422 510-2PME3** The Complete Mozart Edition
Vol 10

ORVAL, Francis (hn)
see CONCERT INDEX under:
(PHIL) **438 365-2PM2** Brahms—Complete Trios

ORVAL ABBEY CHOIR
see CONCERT INDEX under:
(STUD) **SM1220.02** Immortel Grégorien

OSBORNE, Robert (bass-bar)
M. Monk: Atlas (Cpte)

OSINSKA, Eva (pf)
see CONCERT INDEX under:
(SONY) **SK53112** Chopin—Chamber Works

OSKAMP, Gérard (cond)
see Gothenburg SO

OSKARSSON, Guðjon (bass)
Braein: Anne Pedersdotter (Cpte)

OSLO CATHEDRAL CHOIR
cond R. GOODMAN
see CONCERT INDEX under:
(NIMB) **NI5144/8** Beethoven: Symphonies Nos 1-9
cond T. KVAM
Beethoven: Missa Solemnis
Grieg: Psalms, Op.74
Mendelssohn: Psalms, Op. 78 (Cpte)

OSLO PHILHARMONIC CHORUS
cond P. DREIER
Grieg: Peer Gynt (Cpte)
see CONCERT INDEX under:
(UNIC) **UKCD2019** Grieg—Orchestral & Vocal
Works
cond E-P. SALONEN
Grieg: Peer Gynt (exc)

OSLO PHILHARMONIC ORCHESTRA
see CONCERT INDEX under:
(LOND) **440 495-2LM** Kirsten Flagstad Edition, Vol.
5
cond A. BOULT
see CONCERT INDEX under:
(LOND) **440 490-2LM5(1)** Kirsten Flagstad Edition (pt
1)
cond M. CARIDIS
see CONCERT INDEX under:
(SIMA) **PSC3115** Valen—Symphonic Poems and
Orchestral Songs
cond Ø. FJELDSTAD
Sinding: Piano Concerto, Symphony 1
see CONCERT INDEX under:
(NKF) **NKFCD50011-2** Svendsen—Orchestral Works
(SIMA) **PSC3118** Jensen—Choral and Orchestral
Works
cond O. GRÜNER-HEGGE
see CONCERT INDEX under:
(SIMA) **PSC3118** Jensen—Choral and Orchestral
Works

PALIATSARAS, Konstantinos (ten)
see CONCERT INDEX under:
(DHM) **05472 77190-2**
Monteverdi—Combattimento/Lamento d'Arianna

PALING, Edwin (vn)
see CONCERT INDEX under:
(CHAN) **CHAN8834** R. Strauss: Orchestral and Vocal
Works

PALIVCOVÁ, Jarmila (sop)
Smetana: Bartered Bride (Cpte)

PALLADIAN ENSEMBLE
see CONCERT INDEX under:
(LINN) **CKD010** An Excess of Pleasure
(LINN) **CKD015** The Winged Lion
(LINN) **CKD036** Bach—Trio Sonatas

PÄLLI, Ilkka (vc)
see CONCERT INDEX under:
(BIS) **BIS-CD636** Gubaidulina—Bassoon and Cello
Works

PALLISER, Esther (sop)
see CONCERT INDEX under:
(SYMP) **SYMCD1093** The Harold Wayne Collection,
Vol.7

PALM, Mati (bass)
Tubin: Barbara von Tisenhusen (Cpte)

PALM, Thomas (pf)
Wolf: Goethe Lieder (exc)

PALM THEATRE ORCHESTRA
cond D. WISEMAN
Wiseman: Tom and Viv (exc)

PALMA, David (cond)
see Speculum Musicae

PALMA, Piero De (ten)
Bellini: Norma (Cpte), Sonnambula (Cpte)
Boito: Mefistofele (Cpte)
Donizetti: Favorita (Cpte), Linda di Chamounix (Cpte),
Lucrezia Borgia (Cpte)
Giordano: Andrea Chénier (Cpte), Fedora (Cpte)
Puccini: Bohème (Cpte), Gianni Schicchi (Cpte),
Madama Butterfly (Cpte), Manon Lescaut (Cpte),
Rondine (Cpte), Tosca (Cpte), Turandot (Cpte)
Rossini: Guillaume Tell (Cpte), Mosè (Cpte), Turco in
Italia (Cpte)
Verdi: Aida (Cpte), Ballo in maschera (Cpte), Don
Carlo (Cpte), Falstaff (Cpte), Forza del destino (Cpte),
Luisa Miller (Cpte), Otello (Cpte), Rigoletto (Cpte),
Simon Boccanegra (Cpte), Traviata (Cpte), Trovatore
(Cpte)
see CONCERT INDEX under:
(DECC) **436 261-2DHO3** Puccini—Il Trittico
(EMI) **CMS7 63244-2** The Art of Maria Callas
(EMI) **CMS7 64165-2** Puccini—Trittico
(RCA) **GD87799** The Pearl Fishers Duet plus Duets
and Scenes
(RCA) **09026 61236-2** Leontyne Price - Prima Donna
Collection
(RCA) **09026 61357-2** Leontyne Price Sings Mozart

PALMA, Susan (fl/alto fl)
see CONCERT INDEX under:
(DG) **427 677-2GH** Mozart—Concertos
(DG) **431 665-2GX3** Mozart—Wind Concertos

PALMER, Caroline (pf)
see CONCERT INDEX under:
(BIDD) **LAW005** Fuchs—Works for Cello and Piano
(ETCE) **KTC1111** Saint-Saëns—Works for Cello and
Piano
(ETCE) **KTC1153** Fauré—Works for Cello & Piano

PALMER, Christene (contr)
Sullivan: Pirates of Penzance (Cpte)
see CONCERT INDEX under:
(DECC) **433 868-2DWO** The World of Gilbert &
Sullivan - Volume 2

PALMER, David (ten)
Sullivan: Yeomen of the Guard (Cpte)

PALMER, Felicity (sop/mez)
Holst: Sávitri (Cpte)
Janáček: Glagolitic Mass (Cpte)
Monteverdi: Madrigals, Bk 8 (exc)
Mozart: Idomeneo (Cpte), Mass, K258, Nozze di
Figaro (Cpte), Sposo deluso (Cpte), Vespers, K339
Purcell: Dido (Cpte)
Rossini: Cenerentola (Cpte)
Schoenberg: Moses and Aron (Cpte)
Schumann: Szenen aus Goethes Faust (Cpte)
Stravinsky: Nightingale (Cpte)
Sullivan: HMS Pinafore (Cpte), Mikado (Cpte)
see CONCERT INDEX under:
(CHAN) **CHAN8641/2** Elgar—Dream of Gerontius.
Parry—Choral Works
(CHAN) **CHAN8788/9** Elgar—The Kingdom;
Orchestral Works
(DECC) **436 402-2DWO** The World of Wedding
Music
(DECC) **443 868-2DF2** Italian Baroque Sacred
Works
(EMI) **CDM5 65114-2** Britten—Vocal Works

PALMER, Gladys (contr)
Wagner: Götterdämmerung (exc)
see CONCERT INDEX under:
(PEAR) **GEMMCDS9137** Wagner—Der Ring des
Nibelungen

PALMER, Rudolph (cond)
see Brewer CO

PALMER, Todd (cl)
Rorem: Winter Pages

PALMER SINGERS
cond R. PALMER
Handel: Joshua (Cpte)

PALMIERI, Giovanni Battista (ten)
Bellini: Zaira (Cpte)
Salieri: Axur (Cpte)

PALNÉS, Alain (pf)
see CONCERT INDEX under:
(DENO) **C37-7487** Satie: Piano music for four hands

PALÓCZ, László (bass-bar)
see CONCERT INDEX under:
(DECC) **443 488-2DF2** Kodály—Háry János; Psalmus
Hungaricus etc

PALOMBINI, Vittoria (mez)
Puccini: Gianni Schicchi (Cpte)

PÅLSSON, Hans (pf)
see CONCERT INDEX under:
(BIS) **BIS-CD026** Shostakovich—Chamber Works
(CPRI) **CAP21417** Nilsson—Works for Piano and
Orchestra

PALUMBO, Massimo (pf)
see CONCERT INDEX under:
(NUOV) **7156** Respighi—Unpublished Piano Works

PAMEIJER, Eleonore (fl)
see CONCERT INDEX under:
(PHIL) **442 534-2PH** Janáček—Choral Works

PAMPANINI, Rosetta (sop)
see CONCERT INDEX under:
(CLUB) **CL99-014** Dino Borgioli (1891-1960)
(EMI) **CHS7 64864-2(1)** La Scala Edition - Vol.2,
1915-46 (pt 1)
(PEAR) **GEMMCDS9926(1)** Covent Garden on
Record—Vol.4 (pt 1)
(PREI) **89063** Rosetta Pampanini (1896-1973)

PAMPUCH, Helmut (ten)
Berg: Lulu (Cpte)
Wagner: Parsifal (Cpte), Rheingold (Cpte)

PANARIELLO, Ernesto (bass)
Cherubini: Lodoïska (Cpte)
Puccini: Fanciulla del West (Cpte), Manon Lescaut
(Cpte)
Verdi: Rigoletto (Cpte), Traviata (Cpte)

PANARO, Hugh (sngr)
see CONCERT INDEX under:
(EMI) **CDC7 54883-2** Jerome Kern Treasury

PANCELLA, Phyllis (mez)
Mozart: Nozze di Figaro (Cpte)
see CONCERT INDEX under:
(RCA) **09026 61509-2** A Salute to American Music

PANCIK, Josef (cond)
see Prague Chbr Ch

PANDANO, Vittorio (ten)
Donizetti: Lucia di Lammermoor (Cpte)
Puccini: Bohème (Cpte)

PANDOLFINI, Angelica (sop)
see CONCERT INDEX under:
(MEMO) **HR4408/9(1)** Singers in Genoa, Vol.1 (disc
1)
(SYMP) **SYMCD1073** The Harold Wayne Collection,
Vol.3

PANDOLFO, Paolo (va da gamba)
D. Ortiz: Trattado de glosas
Telemann: Essercizii musici (exc)
Vivaldi: Manchester Sonatas

PANE, Tullio (ten)
Giordano: Andrea Chénier (Cpte)
Puccini: Gianni Schicchi (Cpte), Turandot (Cpte)
see CONCERT INDEX under:
(EURO) **GD69043** Puccini: Il Trittico

PANENKA, Jan (pf)
Beethoven: Violin Sonata 5, Violin Sonata 9
Brahms: Piano Quartet 3, Piano Quintet
Martinů: Divertimento (1926), Sinfonietta giocosa
Schumann: Piano Quartet, Op. 47, Piano Quintet, Op.
44
see CONCERT INDEX under:
(SUPR) **11 0705-2** Slavonic Works for Violin & Piano
(SUPR) **11 0710-2** Violin Sonatas
(SUPR) **11 1532-2** Suk—Chamber Works, Volume 2
(SUPR) **11 1533-2** Suk—Chamber Works, Volume 3

PANERAI, Rolando (bar)
Bellini: Puritani (Cpte)
Donizetti: Elisir d'amore (Cpte), Lucia di Lammermoor
(Cpte)
Leoncavallo: Pagliacci (Cpte)
Mascagni: Cavalleria Rusticana (Cpte)
Mozart: Così fan tutte (Cpte)
Puccini: Bohème (Cpte), Gianni Schicchi (Cpte),
Madama Butterfly (Cpte)
Rossini: Italiana in Algeri (Cpte)
Verdi: Falstaff (Cpte), Oberto (Cpte), Trovatore
(Cpte)
see CONCERT INDEX under:
(DECC) **433 439-2DA** Great Love Duets
(DG) **419 257-2GH3** 'Cav' and 'Pag', etc

PALMER, Rudolph (cond)
(EMI) **CDM7 69543-2** Maria Callas and Giuseppe Di
Stefano - Duets
(EMI) **CMS7 63244-2** The Art of Maria Callas
(EURO) **GD69043** Puccini: Il Trittico

PANINA, Antonina (mez)
see CONCERT INDEX under:
(PEAR) **GEMMCDS9001/3(2)** Singers of Imperial
Russia, Vol.2 (pt 2)

PANIZZA, Ettore (cond)
see La Scala Orch

PANK, Siegfried (va da gamba)
see CONCERT INDEX under:
(CAPR) **10 101** C.P.E. Bach: Flute Works
(CAPR) **10 102** C.P.E. Bach: Viola da gamba Works
(CAPR) **10 234** Italian Recorder Works

PANKOV, Georgi (bass)
Tchaikovsky: Eugene Onegin (Cpte)

PANNONIC WIND ORCHESTRA
cond W. VAN ZUTPHEN
Cage: Fifty-eight

PANOCHA QUARTET
Schumann: Piano Quartet, Op. 47
see CONCERT INDEX under:
(SUPR) **11 0994-2** Martinů—String Quartets
(SUPR) **11 0999-2** Mozart—Wind Quintets & Quartet
(SUPR) **11 1461-2** Dvořák—Chamber Works -
Volume 11

PANTALEON ENSEMBLE
see CONCERT INDEX under:
(TUDO) **Tudor 767** Christmas Music

PANTSCHEFF, Ljubomir (bass)
Beethoven: Fidelio (Cpte)
Lehár: Lustige Witwe (exc)
Mozart: Zauberflöte (Cpte)
R. Strauss: Ariadne auf Naxos (Cpte), Rosenkavalier
(Cpte)
Wagner: Meistersinger (Cpte)

PANUFNIK, Andrzej (cond)
see BBC SO

PANULA, Jorma (cond)
see Danish Nat RSO

PANZARELLA, Anna Maria (sop)
Mozart: Requiem

PANZENBÖCK, Gerhard (bass)
R. Strauss: Rosenkavalier (Cpte)

PANZÉRA, Charles (bar)
see CONCERT INDEX under:
(BIDD) **LHW005** Alfred Cortot plays Schumann, Vol.
3
(DANT) **HPC004/5** Alfred Cortot plays Schumann
(DANT) **LYS003/4** Charles Panzéra - Song Recital
(EMI) **CDH7 64254-2** Charles Panzéra sings French
Songs
(PEAR) **GEMMCD9919** Panzéra sings Fauré,Duparc
& Schumann

PANZÉRA-BAILLOT, Madeleine (pf)
see CONCERT INDEX under:
(DANT) **LYS003/4** Charles Panzéra - Song Recital
(EMI) **CDH7 64254-2** Charles Panzéra sings French
Songs
(PEAR) **GEMMCD9919** Panzéra sings Fauré,Duparc
& Schumann

PAOLI, Antonio (ten)
see CONCERT INDEX under:
(EMI) **CHS7 64860-2(2)** La Scala Edition - Vol.1,
1878-1914 (pt 2)
(MEMO) **HR4408/9(2)** Singers in Genoa, Vol.1 (disc
2)

PAOLIS, Alessio de (ten)
Bizet: Carmen (Cpte)
Puccini: Turandot (Cpte)
see CONCERT INDEX under:
(PEAR) **GEMMCDS9452** The Emperor Tibbett

PAP, Robert (treb)
Mozart: Zauberflöte (Cpte)

PAPADAKOS, Dorothy (organ)
see CONCERT INDEX under:
(KOCH) **37258-2** Gubaidulina/Ustvolskaya—Works
for Cello

PAPADJIAKOU, Alexandra (contr)
Bellini: Zaira (Cpte)

PAPADOPOULOS, Kostas (bouzouki)
see CONCERT INDEX under:
(DG) **419 236-2GH** Songs my country taught me

PAPADOPOULOS, Marios (pf)
Shostakovich: Preludes and Fugues, Op. 87 (exc)
see CONCERT INDEX under:
(CARL) **PCD1009** Beethoven—Piano Sonatas
(HLCN) **CD-HLR143-2** Mussorgsky—Piano Works
(HYPE) **CDA66167** Janáček & Stravinsky: Piano
Works

PAPADOPOULOS, Marios (pf/dir)
see CONCERT INDEX under:
(HYPE) **CDA66167** Janáček & Stravinsky: Piano
Works

PAPAVRAMI, Tedi (vn)
see CONCERT INDEX under:
(HARM) **HMC90 5207** Virtuoso Works for Violin

PAPE, René (bass)
Beethoven: Missa solemnis (Cpte)

Puccini: Tosca (Cpte)
cond J. RUDEL
G. Charpentier: Louise (Cpte)
cond N. SANTI
see CONCERT INDEX under:
(DECC) 436 461-2DM   Ten Top Sopranos

PARIS OPERA ORCHESTRA
cond S. BAUDO
Honegger: Roi David (Cpte)
cond R. BENZI
see CONCERT INDEX under:
(PHIL) 442 272-2PM2   The Best of Bizet
cond P. BOULEZ
Berg: Lulu (Cpte)
cond H. BÜSSER
see CONCERT INDEX under:
(PEAR) GEMMCD9314   Feodor Chaliapin - Aria and
Song Recital
cond B. CAMPANELLA
see CONCERT INDEX under:
(EMI) CDM7 63104-2   Alfredo Krauss - Opera Recital
cond A. CLUYTENS
Gounod: Faust (Cpte)
cond P. DERVAUX
Poulenc: Dialogues des Carmélites (Cpte)
see CONCERT INDEX under:
(EMI) CDM7 63160-2   Dukas: Orchestral works
cond A. EREDE
Gounod: Roméo et Juliette (Cpte)
cond L. FOURESTIER
Saint-Saëns: Samson et Dalila (Cpte)
see CONCERT INDEX under:
(EMI) CHS7 69741-2(3)   Record of Singing,
Vol.4—French School
cond P. FOURNILLIER
Massenet: Amadis (Cpte)
cond R. LEPPARD
Rameau: Dardanus (Cpte)
cond L. MAAZEL
Mozart: Don Giovanni (Cpte)
cond S. OZAWA
Messiaen: Saint François d'Assise (Cpte)
cond G. PRÊTRE
Bizet: Carmen (Cpte), Pêcheurs de Perles (Cpte)
Gounod: Faust (Cpte)
Saint-Saëns: Samson et Dalila (Cpte)
see CONCERT INDEX under:
(EMI) CDC5 55017-2   Domingo Opera Classics
(EMI) CDC7 54437-2   Callas Rarities
(EMI) CDM7 63182-2   The Incomparable Callas
(EMI) CDM7 69112-2   Best of Saint-Saëns
(EMIN) CD-EMX2123   Maria Callas sings Operatic
Arias
cond N. RESCIGNO
see CONCERT INDEX under:
(EMI) CDC7 47943-2   Maria Callas sings Verdi Arias,
Vol.2
cond J. RUDEL
G. Charpentier: Louise (Cpte)
cond M. VELTRI
see CONCERT INDEX under:
(EMI) CDC7 49067-2   Opera Arias and Duets

PARIS OPÉRA-BASTILLE CHORUS
cond MYUNG-WHUN CHUNG
Saint-Saëns: Samson et Dalila (Cpte)
Shostakovich: Lady Macbeth of Mtsensk (Cpte)
Verdi: Otello (Cpte)

PARIS OPÉRA-BASTILLE ORCHESTRA
cond E. KOHN
see CONCERT INDEX under:
(SONY) SK46691   The First Placido Domingo
International Voice Competition
cond MYUNG-WHUN CHUNG
Messiaen: Ascension, Éclairs sur l'Au-Delà
Saint-Saëns: Samson et Dalila (Cpte), Symphony 3
Shostakovich: Lady Macbeth of Mtsensk (Cpte)
Verdi: Otello (Cpte)
see CONCERT INDEX under:
(DG) 445 947-2GH   Messiaen—Orchestral Works

PARIS OPÉRA-COMIQUE CHORUS
cond G. BRAIN
Rossini: Petite Messe Solennelle
cond G. CLOËZ
Puccini: Tosca (exc)
cond A. CLUYTENS
Bizet: Carmen (Cpte), Pêcheurs de Perles (Cpte)
Offenbach: Contes d'Hoffmann (Cpte)
Poulenc: Mamelles de Tirésias (Cpte)
cond E. COHEN
Massenet: Manon (Cpte), Werther (Cpte)
cond P. DERVAUX
Bizet: Pêcheurs de perles (Cpte)
cond A. LOMBARD
Delibes: Lakmé (Cpte)

PARIS OPÉRA-COMIQUE ORCHESTRA
cond G. CLOËZ
Puccini: Tosca (exc)
cond A. CLUYTENS
Bizet: Carmen (Cpte), Pêcheurs de perles (Cpte)
Offenbach: Contes d'Hoffmann (Cpte)
Poulenc: Mamelles de Tirésias (Cpte)
Ravel: Heure espagnole (Cpte)
see CONCERT INDEX under:
(EMI) CHS7 69741-2(3)   Record of Singing,
Vol.4—French School
cond E. COHEN
Massenet: Manon (Cpte), Werther (Cpte)
cond P. DERVAUX
Bizet: Pêcheurs de perles (Cpte)

cond L. FOURESTIER
see CONCERT INDEX under:
(EMI) CHS7 69741-2(3)   Record of Singing,
Vol.4—French School
cond A. LOMBARD
Delibes: Lakmé (Cpte)
cond G. PRÊTRE
Poulenc: Voix Humaine (Cpte)

PARIS ORCHESTRA CHORUS
cond D. BARENBOIM
Saint-Saëns: Samson et Dalila (Cpte)
see CONCERT INDEX under:
(DG) 435 069-2GGA   Debussy—Orchestral Works
(DG) 437 244-2GGA2   Berlioz/Franck—Vocal &
Orchestral Works
(DG) 437 638-2GGA2   Berlioz—Vocal & Orchestral
Works
(DG) 439 407-2GCL   Debussy—Orchestral Works
cond S. BYCHKOV
Mascagni: Cavalleria Rusticana (Cpte)
see CONCERT INDEX under:
(PHIL) 432 993-2PH   Paris 1920

PARIS ORCHESTRAL ENSEMBLE
cond P. HERREWEGHE
see CONCERT INDEX under:
(HARM) HMC90 1272   Mendelssohn—Psalms; Ave
Maria
cond A. JORDAN
see CONCERT INDEX under:
(ERAT) 4509-97239-2   Virtuoso Arias
cond J-J. KANTOROW
see CONCERT INDEX under:
(EMI) CDC7 54913-2   Saint-Saëns—La muse et le
poète
cond J-P. WALLEZ
Bach: 3-Harpsichord Concerti (exc), 4-Harpsichord
Concerto
see CONCERT INDEX under:
(NOVA) 150 014-2   Mozart—Gala Concert

**PARIS ORCHESTRE D'HARMONIE DES GARDIENS
DE LA PAIX**
cond D. DONDEYNE
see CONCERT INDEX under:
(CALL) CAL9859   French Orchestral Works

PARIS PHILHARMONIC ORCHESTRA
cond D. MILHAUD
see CONCERT INDEX under:
(CHNT) LDC278 1069   Milhaud—Orchestral and
Choral Works

PARIS RUSSIAN METROPOLITAN CHURCH CHOIR
cond N. AFONSKY
see CONCERT INDEX under:
(MMOI) CDMOIR411   Sacred Songs and Arias
(PREI) 89207   Feodor Chaliapin Song
Book—Electrical Recordings

PARIS RUSSIAN OPERA CHORUS
cond M. STEINMANN
(EMI) CDH7 61009-2   Chaliapin sings Russian Opera
Arias
cond O. TCHERNOYAROV
see CONCERT INDEX under:
(PEAR) GEMMCD9314   Feodor Chaliapin - Aria and
Song Recital

PARIS RUSSIAN OPERA ORCHESTRA
(EMI) CDH7 61009-2   Chaliapin sings Russian Opera
Arias

PARIS RUSSIAN ORTHODOX CATHEDRAL CHOIR
cond E. EVETZ
see CONCERT INDEX under:
(PHIL) 434 174-2PM   Russian Liturgical Chant

PARIS SACRE COEUR CHOIR
cond P. MAZE
see CONCERT INDEX under:
(MOTE) CD40081   French Choral and Organ Works

PARIS SORBONNE CHORUS
cond J. GRIMBERT
see CONCERT INDEX under:
(MARC) 8 223755   Prix de Rome Cantatas

PARIS SORBONNE ORCHESTRA
cond J. GRIMBERT
see CONCERT INDEX under:
(MARC) 8 223755   Prix de Rome Cantatas

PARIS SORBONNE UNIVERSITY CHOIR
cond J. GRIMBERT
Mozart: Ascanio in Alba (Cpte)

PARIS ST MAUR CNR BRASS ENSEMBLE
see CONCERT INDEX under:
(BNL) BNL112768   Litaize: Organ Works

PARIS ST MICHAEL ANGLICAN CHURCH CHOIR
cond P. MAZE
see CONCERT INDEX under:
(MOTE) CD40081   French Choral and Organ Works

PARIS STRING TRIO
see CONCERT INDEX under:
(CHNT) LDC278 821   Boëly—Works for Strings

PARIS SYMPHONY CHORUS
cond P. STOLL
Boïeldieu: Dame blanche (Cpte)

PARIS SYMPHONY ORCHESTRA
cond G. ENESCU
see CONCERT INDEX under:

(BIDD) LAB004   Menuhin plays Mozart Concertos
(BIDD) LAB046   The Young Yehudi Menuhin
(EMI) CDH7 61018-2   Yehudi Menuhin plays Bach
Violin Works
(EMI) CDH7 63718-2   Mozart: Violin Concertos
cond D. MILHAUD
see CONCERT INDEX under:
(EPM) 150 122   Milhaud—Historic Recordings 1928-
1948
cond P. MONTEUX
Stravinsky: Rite of Spring (Cpte)
see CONCERT INDEX under:
(BIDD) LAB004   Menuhin plays Mozart Concertos
(EMI) CDH7 61018-2   Yehudi Menuhin plays Bach
Violin Works
(EMI) CDH7 63718-2   Mozart: Violin Concertos
(MSCM) MM30322   Enescu - Columbia Recordings
1920s-30s
cond P. STOLL
Boïeldieu: Dame blanche (Cpte)
cond H. TOMASI
Gluck: Orphée (exc)

PARIS WIND QUINTET
see CONCERT INDEX under:
(EMI) CZS7 62736-2   Poulenc—Chamber Works

PARISII QUARTET
Boccherini: Oboe Quintets, G431-36
see CONCERT INDEX under:
(AUVI) V4730   Ravel/Debussy/Menu—String
Quartets

PÁRKÁNYI, Tibor (vc)
F. David: Piano Trios (exc)

PARKENING, Christopher (gtr)
see CONCERT INDEX under:
(EMI) CDC5 55052-2
Praetorius/Vivaldi/Warlock—Works arr guitar
(EMI) CDC7 54665-2   Rodrigo/Walton—Guitar Works

PARKER, Christine (sngr)
G. Charpentier: Louise (Cpte)

PARKER, Evan (sax)
see CONCERT INDEX under:
(ECM) 847 537-2   Gavin Bryars—After the Requiem

PARKER, John Kimura (pf)
Prokofiev: Piano Concerto 3
Tchaikovsky: Piano Concerto 1

PARKER, Patricia (mez)
Stravinsky: Noces

PARKER, William (bar)
Handel: Messiah (Cpte), Susanna (Cpte)

PARKER-SMITH, Jane (organ)
Janáček: Glagolitic Mass (Cpte)
see CONCERT INDEX under:
(ASV) CDDCA539   Popular French Romantics Vol. 1
(ASV) CDDCA610   Popular French Romantics Vol. 2
(ASV) CDDCA702   Jane Parker-Smith at the Grand
Organ of Armagh Cathedral

PARKES, Allan (bass)
Monteverdi: Madrigals, Bk 8 (exc)

PARKES, Peter (cond)
see Black Dyke Mills Band

PARKHOUSE, David (pf)
Elgar: Violin Sonata
see CONCERT INDEX under:
(DECC) 433 616-2DSP
Addinsell/Gershwin—Orchestral Works
(EMI) CDM5 65100-2   Vaughan Williams—Chamber
Works

PARKIN, Eric (pf)
Bax: Oliver Twist (exc)
Mayerl: Piano Transcriptions (exc), Piano
Transcriptions III (exc)
see CONCERT INDEX under:
(CHAN) CHAN8461   Ireland—Orchestral Works
(CHAN) CHAN8496   Bax: The Piano Music, Vol.1
(CHAN) CHAN8497   Bax: Piano Works, Volume 2
(CHAN) CHAN8560   Billy Mayerl: Piano Works
(CHAN) CHAN8637   Poulenc—Piano Works, Vol.1
(CHAN) CHAN8732   Bax: Piano Works
(CHAN) CHAN8837   Poulenc: Piano Works
(CHAN) CHAN8848   Mayerl—Piano Works
(CHAN) CHAN8864   G. Bush: Vocal & Choral Works
(CHAN) CHAN8887   Roussel—Piano Works
(CHAN) CHAN8888   Chaminade—Piano Works
(CHAN) CHAN9056   Ireland—Piano Works, Vol.1
(CHAN) CHAN9076   Dyson—Orchestral Works
(CHAN) CHAN9140   Ireland—Piano Works, Vol.2
(CHAN) CHAN9148   Mayerl—Piano Music, Vol.3
(CHAN) CHAN9148   Walton—Orchestral Works
(CHAN) CHAN9177   Barber—Piano Works
(CHAN) CHAN9250   Ireland—Piano Works, Vol.3
(CLOU) ACN6002   Gershwin: Piano Works
(PREA) PRCD1776   American Piano Music
(PRIO) PRCD468   Billy Mayerl—Piano Transcriptions,
Vol. 3
(SILV) SILVAD3006   The Jerome Kern Collection
(SILV) SONGCD906   Copland—Music for Piano
(UNIC) UKCD2071   The Delius Collection, Volume 1

PARKINS, Robert (organ)
see CONCERT INDEX under:
(NAXO) 8 550824   Brahms—Complete Organ Works

PARKMAN, Stefan (cond)
see Copenhagen Boys' Ch

PARKMAN, Stefan (ten)
Schnittke: Symphony 4

PARKS, Andrew (sngr)
Schuman: Mighty Casey (Cpte)

PARKS, Karen (sop)
Hammerstein: Carmen Jones (Cpte)

PARLE, Nicholas (hpd)
Telemann: Sonates Corellisantes

(LE) PARLEMENT DE MUSIQUE
see CONCERT INDEX *under:*
(0111) **OPS30-100** Hasse—Motets
(0111) **OPS55-9119** M-A. Charpentier—Office de
Ténèbres
   cond M. GESTER
A. Scarlatti: Lamentazioni (exc)
Brossard: Dialogus, Elévations (1698)
see CONCERT INDEX *under:*
(0111) **OPS30-9005** M.A.Charpentier—Vocal Works

(THE) PARLEY OF INSTRUMENTS
C. Bond: Concertos in Seven Parts
see CONCERT INDEX *under:*
(HYPE) **CDA66021** Monteverdi: Sacred vocal works
(HYPE) **CDA66237** Dr Arne at Vauxhall Gardens
(HYPE) **CDA66240** Philips—Consort Music
(HYPE) **CDA66255** Italian Baroque Trumpet Music
(HYPE) **CDA66658** Blow—Awake my lyre
(HYPE) **CDA67001/3** Purcell—Complete Ayres for the
Theatre
   cond R. GOODMAN
Bach: Cantata 208
Boyce: Solomon (Cpte)
Stanley: Concertos, Op. 2
see CONCERT INDEX *under:*
(HYPE) **CDA66074** German Consort Music, 1660-
1710
(HYPE) **CDA66108** Purcell's London: English Consort
Music
(HYPE) **CDA66160** Vivaldi: Music for lute and
mandoline
(HYPE) **CDA66227** Emma Kirkby Collection
(HYPE) **CDA66413** Telemann—Recorder Works
(HYPE) **CDA66578** Odes on the Death of Henry
Purcell
   cond E. HIGGINBOTTOM
see CONCERT INDEX *under:*
(HYPE) **CDA66373** M.Locke—Anthems,Motets and
the Oxford Ode
   cond D. HILL
see CONCERT INDEX *under:*
(HYPE) **CDA66200** M. Praetorius: Christmas music
(HYPE) **CDA66643** Philips—Motets
   cond P. HOLMAN
Arne: Favourite concertos
see CONCERT INDEX *under:*
(HYPE) **CDA66212** Purcell—Ayres for the Theatre
(HYPE) **CDA66328** Vivaldi—Recorder Concertos
(HYPE) **CDA66395** Music for Prince Charles
(HYPE) **CDA66413** Telemann—Recorder Works
(HYPE) **CDA66475** Monteverdi—Balli and Dramatic
Madrigals
(HYPE) **CDA66578** Odes on the Death of Henry
Purcell
(HYPE) **CDA66604** John Jenkins—Late Consort
Music
(HYPE) **CDA66637** Dowland—Lachrimae
(HYPE) **CDA66667** Four and Twenty Fiddlers
(HYPE) **CDA66700** English 18th-Century Keyboard
Concertos
(HYPE) **CDA66750** Purcell—The Symphony Songs
(HYPE) **CDA66768** John Amner—Cathedral Music
   cond JOHN SCOTT
Croft: Morning Service in D, Musica sacra (exc)
   cond P. NICHOLSON
T. Linley II: Shakespeare Ode

**(THE) PARLEY OF INSTRUMENTS BAROQUE
ORCHESTRA**
see CONCERT INDEX *under:*
(HYPE) **CDA67001/3** Purcell—Complete Ayres for the
Theatre

(THE) PARLEY OF INSTRUMENTS CHOIR
   cond R. GOODMAN
Boyce: Solomon (Cpte)
see CONCERT INDEX *under:*
(HYPE) **CDA66578** Odes on the Death of Henry
Purcell
   cond P. NICHOLSON
T. Linley II: Shakespeare Ode

PARLOW, Kathleen (vn)
see CONCERT INDEX *under:*
(APR) **APR7015** The Auer Legacy, Vol.1

PARMA TEATRO REGIO ORCHESTRA
   cond G. PATANÈ
see CONCERT INDEX *under:*
(DECC) **443 018-2DF2**
Pavarotti/Freni/Ricciarelli—Live

PARNAS, Leslie (vc)
Beethoven: Triple Concerto
Mozart: Clarinet Quintet, K581
Schubert: Trout Quintet, D667

(IL) PARNASO MUSICALE
see CONCERT INDEX *under:*
(CHRI) **CHR77119** Telemann—Cantatas for Alto

PARNASSUS
   cond A. KORF
Babbitt: Head of the Bed
see CONCERT INDEX *under:*
(KOCH) **37141-2** Wolpe—Chamber Works

PARNASSUS ENSEMBLE
see CONCERT INDEX *under:*
(ACCE) **ACC77912D** German Church Cantatas and
Arias

PARNASSUS ORCHESTRA
   cond M. STENZ
Henze: English Cat (Cpte)

PARNASSUS TRIO
Debussy: Piano Trio
Ravel: Piano Trio
see CONCERT INDEX *under:*
(MDG) **L3307/8** Hummel—Piano Trios
(MDG) **L3482** Lalo—Complete Piano Trios

PARNELL, Andrew (organ)
see CONCERT INDEX *under:*
(LAMM) **LAMM081D** Christmas at St Albans

PARNIS, William (ten)
see CONCERT INDEX *under:*
(PEAR) **GEMMCD9956** Joseph Hislop (1884-1977)

PARR, Gladys (contr)
see CONCERT INDEX *under:*
(DANA) **DACOCD315/6** Lauritz Melchior Anthology -
Vol. 3
(EMI) **CMS7 64008-2(1)** Wagner Singing on Record
(pt 1)

PARRAMON, Virginia (sop)
see CONCERT INDEX *under:*
(HARM) **HMC90 1482** Mompou—Vocal and
Orchestral Works

PARRENIN QUARTET
see CONCERT INDEX *under:*
(EMI) **CMS7 64365-2** Chausson—Chamber,
Orchestra & Vocal Works
(EMI) **CMS7 62542-2** Prokofiev—Piano Concertos,
etc
(EMI) **CMS7 62548-2** Fauré—Chamber Works, Vol.2

PARROTT, Andrew (cond)
see Boston Early Music Fest Orch

PARRY, David (cond)
see G. Mitchell Ch

PARRY, Marjorie (sop)
see CONCERT INDEX *under:*
(PEAR) **GEMMCD9175** Heddle Nash - Serenade

PARSI-PETTINELLA, Armida (mez)
see CONCERT INDEX *under:*
(EMI) **CHS7 64860-2(1)** La Scala Edition - Vol.1,
1878-1914 (pt 1)
(IRCC) **IRCC-CD800** Souvenirs from Meyerbeer
Operas
(PEAR) **GEMMCDS9073(1)** Giovanni Zenatello, Vol.1
(pt 1)
(SYMP) **SYMCD1113** The Harold Wayne Collection,
Vol.13
(SYMP) **SYMCD1138** The Harold Wayne Collection,
Vol.16

PARSONS, Brian (ten)
Rameau: Castor et Pollux (Cpte), Naïs (Cpte)

PARSONS, Geoffrey (pf)
Loewe: Gregor auf dem Stein, Op.38, Kaiser Karl V,
Op.99
Mahler: Knaben Wunderhorn
Schubert: Schöne Müllerin (Cpte), Winterreise
(Cpte)
Schumann: Dichterliebe, Op. 48 (Cpte), Gedichte,
Op. 35 (Cpte), Liederkreis, Op. 24 (Cpte), Liederkreis,
Op. 39 (Cpte)
Wolf: Goethe Lieder (exc), Italienisches Liederbuch
(Cpte), Mörike Lieder (exc), Spanisches Liederbuch
(Cpte)
see CONCERT INDEX *under:*
(BLUE) **ABCD009** Birgit Nilsson live in Stockholm
(COLL) **Coll1247-2** An Evening with Victoria De Los
Angeles
(DECC) **421 899-2DA** Teresa Berganza - Mozart
Arias
(DG) **437 719-2GC** Berg—Vocal Works
(EMI) **CDC5 55047-2** Liszt/Wagner/Berlioz—Romantic
Songs
(EMI) **CDC5 55147-2** Thomas Hampson Lieder Recital
(EMI) **CDC5 55345-2** Liebeslieder
(EMI) **CDC7 49997-2** Schubert—Lieder
(EMI) **CDC7 54436-2** Meyerbeer/Rossini—Songs
(EMI) **CDC7 54879-2** Beethoven—Lieder
(EMI) **CDM7 63553-2** Wolf: Lieder
(EMI) **CDM7 63554-2** Schwarzkopf Encores
(EMI) **CDM7 63656-2**
Schubert/Schumann/Strauss—Lieder
(EMI) **CMS7 64074-2(1)** Christa Ludwig—Recital (pt 1)
(EMI) **CMS7 64074-2(2)** Christa Ludwig—Recital (pt 2)
(HYPE) **CDA66100** Mahler: Songs
(HYPE) **CDA66320** Fauré—Songs
(ORFE) **C159871A** Dietrich Fischer-Dieskau
(ORFE) **C363941B** Lucia Popp - Lieder Recital
(PHIL) **416 298-2PH** Richard Strauss: Lieder
(PHIL) **422 048-2PH** Jessye Norman—Song Recital
(TELD) **2292-44923-2** Lieder aus Des Knaben
Wunderhorn
(TELD) **2292-44935-2** Schumann—Lieder
(TELD) **2292-44946-2** Mendelssohn—Lieder

(TELD) **2292-46334-2** Mozart—Lieder
(TELD) **4509-90873-2** Schubert—Lieder

PARSONS, Meredith (contr)
Wagner: Götterdämmerung (Cpte), Walküre (Cpte)
see CONCERT INDEX *under:*
(DG) **445 354-2GX14** Wagner—Der Ring des
Nibelungen

PARSONS, William (bass)
Bach: St Matthew Passion, BWV244 (exc)

PARTINGTON, Adrian (organ)
see CONCERT INDEX *under:*
(CARL) **PCD937** Tapestry of English Cathedral Music
(HYPE) **CDA66078** Cathedral & Organ Music
(HYPE) **CDA66313** Elgar—Cathedral Music
(HYPE) **CDA66446** S.S.Wesley—Cathedral Anthems,
Vol.1
(HYPE) **CDA66469** S.S.Wesley—Cathedral Anthems,
Vol.2
(PRIO) **PRCD384** Great European Organs, Vol.31

PARTRIDGE, Ian (ten)
Berlioz: Troyens (Cpte)
Handel: Chandos Anthem 10, Chandos Anthem 11,
Esther (Cpte), Triumph of Time and Truth (Cpte)
Haydn: Mass 9
M-A. Charpentier: Messe de minuit, H9, Te Deum
H146
Purcell: Fairy Queen, Z629 (Cpte), Indian Queen,
Z630 (exc)
Schubert: Schöne Müllerin, Winterreise (Cpte)
Schumann: Dichterliebe, Op.48 (Cpte), Liederkreis,
Op.39 (Cpte)
see CONCERT INDEX *under:*
(ARCH) **437 075-2AT** Collectio Argentea 5: Canti
Amorosi
(CHAN) **CHAN0504** Handel—Chandos Anthems Vol.
2
(CHAN) **CHAN0505** Handel—Chandos Anthems Vol.
3
(CHAN) **CHAN0517** Handel—Sacred Choral works
(CHAN) **CHAN8830** Bush—A Little Love Music
(CHAN) **CHAN9307** Schumann—Lieder
(COLL) **Coll1286-2** Britten—Choral Works
(COLL) **Coll1320-2** Baroque Choral Works
(COLL) **Coll7016-2** Handel—Alexander's Feast
(DECC) **430 263-2DM** Purcell—Sacred choral works
(DECC) **436 259-2DM** Handel/Blow—Choral Works
(DECC) **436 403-2DWO** The World of Royal Music
(DECC) **443 455-2DF2** Vivaldi—Sacred Choral Works
(DECC) **443 868-2DF2** Italian Baroque Sacred
Works
(EMI) **CDM5 65101-2** A Warlock Centenary Album
(EMI) **CDM7 64022-2** Vaughan Williams—Orchestral
Works
(ETCE) **KTC1063** Delius & Gurney: Songs
(ETCE) **KTC1078** English Songs—Peter Warlock and
Ralph Vaughan Williams
(HYPE) **CDA66015** Songs by Finzi and His Friends
(HYPE) **CDA66021** Monteverdi: Sacred vocal works
(ONDI) **ODE779-2** Britten/Berkeley—Works for Tenor
and Guitar
(PEAR) **SHECD9608** Romantic Songs for Tenor &
Guitar
(SONY) **SMK48462** Boulez conducts Schoenberg

PARTRIDGE, Jennifer (pf)
Schubert: Schöne Müllerin
Schumann: Dichterliebe, Op.48 (Cpte), Liederkreis,
Op.39 (Cpte)
see CONCERT INDEX *under:*
(DECC) **433 220-2DWO** The World of the Violin
(EMI) **CDM5 65101-2** A Warlock Centenary Album
(ETCE) **KTC1063** Delius & Gurney: Songs
(ETCE) **KTC1078** English Songs—Peter Warloch and
Ralph Vaughan Williams

PARVIS, Taurino (bar)
see CONCERT INDEX *under:*
(BONG) **GB1043-2** Italian Baritones of the Acoustic
Era
(MEMO) **HR4408/9(2)** Singers in Genoa, Vol.1 (disc
2)

PASCALIN, Olivier (spkr)
F. David: Désert

PASCO, Richard (spkr)
Britten: Noye's Fludde (Cpte)
Elgar/Binyon: Wood magic
Vaughan Williams: Bunyan Sequence
see CONCERT INDEX *under:*
(PEAR) **SHECD9602** Elgar: War Music

PASELLA, Guido (ten)
Donizetti: Don Pasquale (Cpte)

PASERO, Tancredi (bass)
Verdi: Aida (Cpte)
see CONCERT INDEX *under:*
(EMI) **CHS7 64864-2(1)** La Scala Edition - Vol.2,
1915-46 (pt 1)
(EMI) **CHS7 69741-2(7)** Record of Singing,
Vol.4—Italian School
(PREI) **89009** Gino Bechi (b. 1913)
(PREI) **89016** Tancredi Pasero (1893-1983) - I
(PREI) **89016** Gina Cigna (b. 1900)
(PREI) **89074** Tancredi Pasero (1893-1983) - II

PASHINSKY, Vladislav (bass)
Rimsky-Korsakov: Tsar's Bride (Cpte)

PASHLEY, Anne (sop)
Britten: Albert Herring (Cpte), Peter Grimes (Cpte)
see CONCERT INDEX *under:*

(DECC) **443 461-2DF2** Berlioz—L'Enfance du Christ, etc
(EMI) **CDM7 64634-2** Fauré/Bach—Choral Works

PASINI-VITALE, Lina (sop)
see CONCERT INDEX under:
(PEAR) **GEMMCDS9073(2)** Giovanni Zenatello, Vol.1 (pt 2)
(SYMP) **SYMCD1113** The Harold Wayne Collection, Vol.13
(SYMP) **SYMCD1148** The Harold Wayne Collection, Vol.17

PASINO, Gisella (mez)
Franchetti: Cristoforo Colombo (Cpte)
Puccini: Fanciulla del West (Cpte)
Ravel: Shéhérazade
Spontini: Vestale (Cpte)
Verdi: Otello (Cpte)

PASKUDA, Georg (ten)
R. Strauss: Arabella (Cpte)
Wagner: Fliegende Holländer (Cpte), Parsifal (Cpte), Tannhäuser (Cpte)

PASQUALE, Joseph de (va)
R. Strauss: Don Quixote
see CONCERT INDEX under:
(RCA) **GD87872** Jascha Heifetz Collection
(RCA) **GD87965** Dvořák & Brahms: Chamber Works
(RCA) **09026 61778-2(41)** The Heifetz Collection, Vol. 41
(RCA) **09026 61778-2(43)** The Heifetz Collection, Vol. 43
(SONY) **SBK53255** Berlioz—Orchestral Works

PASQUET, Nicolás (cond)
see Pécs SO

PASQUIER, Bruno (va)
Liszt: Harold in Italy (Berlioz)
Mozart: Sinfonia Concertante, K364
Schumann: Märchenbilder
see CONCERT INDEX under:
(AUVI) **V4679** Schmitt—Chamber Works
(EMI) **CMS7 62548-2** Fauré—Chamber Works, Vol.2
(SONY) **SK47230** Mozart—Chamber Works

PASQUIER, Régis (vn)
Berio: Sinfonia
Mozart: Sinfonia Concertante, K364, Violin Concerto, K219
see CONCERT INDEX under:
(AUVI) **V4679** Schmitt—Chamber Works
(HARM) **HMC90 1364** Ravel—Works for Violin and Piano
(SONY) **SK47230** Mozart—Chamber Works

PASSAGGIO, Stefano (va)
see CONCERT INDEX under:
(SCHW) **311122** Early Twentieth Century Music

PASSERINI, Cristiana (hp)
see CONCERT INDEX under:
(AKAD) **CDAK125** Tosti—Romanze

PASSIKIVI, Lilli (narr)
Aho: Pergamon

PASTERNACK, Josef (cond)
see orch

PASTERNAK, Wassili (ten)
Mussorgsky: Boris Godunov (Cpte)

PASTINE, Gianfranco (ten)
Rossini: Otello (Cpte)

PASVEER, Kathinka (alto fl)
Stockhausen: Michaels Reise

PÁSZTHY, Júlia (sop)
Bach: Cantata 208

PATAKI, Antál (ten)
Boito: Mefistofele (Cpte)

PATAKY, Koloman von (ten)
Mozart: Don Giovanni (Cpte)
see CONCERT INDEX under:
(EMI) **CDH5 65072-2** Glyndebourne Recorded - 1934-1994
(SCHW) **314512** Vienna State Opera Live, Vol.1
(SCHW) **314542** Vienna State Opera Live, Vol.4

PATANÈ, Franco (cond)
see MMF Orch

PATANÈ, Giuseppe (cond)
see Bologna Teatro Comunale Orch

PATERNOSTRO, Robert (cond)
see Berlin RSO

PATINKIN, Mandy (ten)
Forrest/Wright: Kismet (Cpte)
see CONCERT INDEX under:
(NONE) **7559-79330-2** Patinkin—Experiment

PATON, Iain (ten)
Purcell: King Arthur, Z628 (Cpte)

PATON, Julie (sngr)
Bernstein: West Side Story (Cpte)

PATRIASZ, Catherine (contr)
Bach: Mass in B minor, BWV232 (Cpte), St John Passion, BWV245 (Cpte)
Mozart: Requiem
Rossini: Petite messe solennelle
see CONCERT INDEX under:
(HARM) **HMC90 1479** Bach—Cantatas
(PHIL) **434 799-2PH** Mozart—Choral Works

PATRICK, David M. (organ)
see CONCERT INDEX under:
(PRIO) **PRCD371** Great European Organs No 28

PATRICK, Julian (bar)
D. Moore: Carry Nation (Cpte)

PATRICK, Julian (bass-bar)
see CONCERT INDEX under:
(SONY) **SM3K47154** Bernstein—Theatre Works Volume 1

PATRICK, Paul (vib)
see CONCERT INDEX under:
(PHIL) **432 075-2PH** Contemporary English Trumpet Concertos

PATRICK, Yvonne (sngr)
Sullivan: Gondoliers (Cpte), Iolanthe (Cpte), Mikado (Cpte)

PATTERSON, Elizabeth C. (cond)
see Gloriae Dei Cantores

PATTERSON, Ronald (vn)
see CONCERT INDEX under:
(ERAT) **2292-45368-2** Chausson: Songs

PATTI, Adelina (sop)
see CONCERT INDEX under:
(EMI) **CHS7 64860-2(1)** La Scala Edition - Vol.1, 1878-1914 (pt 1)
(NIMB) **NI7802** Divas 1906-1935
(NIMB) **NI7840/1** The Era of Adelina Patti
(PEAR) **GEMMCDS9923(1)** Covent Garden on Record, Vol.1 (pt 1)
(PEAR) **GEMMCD9312** Adelina Patti

PATTI, Adelina (spkr)
see CONCERT INDEX under:
(PEAR) **GEMMCD9312** Adelina Patti

PATTI, Gino Martinez (ten)
see CONCERT INDEX under:
(BONG) **GB1043-2** Italian Baritones of the Acoustic Era

PATTIERA, Tino (ten)
see CONCERT INDEX under:
(PREI) **89029** Meta Seinemeyer (1895-1929)

PATZAK, Julius (ten)
Beethoven: Fidelio (Cpte), Symphony 9
Haydn: Jahreszeiten (Cpte)
Mahler: Lied von der Erde
R. Strauss: Arabella (Cpte)
Schubert: Schöne Müllerin (Cpte)
see CONCERT INDEX under:
(ACAN) **44 2114-2** Schubert—Song Cycles
(DECC) **425 995-2DM** Brahms/Mahler—Lieder
(DG) **435 321-2GWP12** 150 Years - Vienna Philharmonic
(EMI) **CHS7 69741-2(4)** Record of Singing, Vol.4—German School
(EMI) **CZS7 67123-2** Wagner: Der Ring des Nibelungen
(MMOI) **CDMOIR422** Great Voices in Tchaikovsky
(NIMB) **NI7856** Legendary Tenors
(PEAR) **GEMMCD9383** Julius Patzak—Opera & Operetta Recital

PAUCKER, Georg (bass)
R. Strauss: Salome (Cpte)

PAUK, György (vn)
see CONCERT INDEX under:
(NAXO) **8 550749** Bartók—Violin Sonatas; Contrasts
(NAXO) **8 550886** Bartók—Chamber Works

PAUL, Charles (bar)
Poulenc: Dialogues des Carmélites (Cpte)

PAUL, Gerhard (narr)
Weber: Freischütz (Cpte)

PAUL, Jennifer S. (hpd)
A-L. Couperin: Pièces de Clavecin (exc)

PAUL, Konrad (bass)
Honegger: Jeanne d'Arc (Cpte)

PAUL, Pamela Mia (pf)
see CONCERT INDEX under:
(ARGO) **440 337-2ZH** Beaser—Orchestral and Vocal Works

PAUL, Reginald (pf)
see CONCERT INDEX under:
(CLAR) **CDGSE78-50-47** The Harrison Sisters—An English Musical Heritage
(SYMP) **SYMCD1140** The Harrison Sisters

PAUL, Thomas (bass)
Bach: Mass in B minor, BWV232 (Cpte)
Berlioz: Damnation de Faust (Cpte)
see CONCERT INDEX under:
(DELO) **DE3170** Beach—Cabildo; Six Short Pieces

PAULEY, Scott (theorbo)
see CONCERT INDEX under:
(CHNN) **CCS7595** Music for the King's Pleasure

PAULEY, Wilbur (bass)
M. Monk: Atlas (Cpte)
see CONCERT INDEX under:
(MUSM) **67110-2** Stravinsky—The Composer, Volume V
(NEWP) **NC60021** Praetorius—Chorale Settings
(RCA) **09026 60970-2** Motets

PAULI, Dan (hosho)
see CONCERT INDEX under:
(NONE) **7559-79275-2** Pieces of Africa

PAULI, Dietrich (ten)
Suder: Kleider machen Leute (Cpte)

PAULI, Piero (ten)
Puccini: Tosca (Cpte)

PAULIK, Anton (cond)
see Orch

PAULIK, Erich (bass)
J.Strauss II: Zigeunerbaron (Cpte)

PAULSEN, Melinda (mez)
Keiser: St. Mark Passion
see CONCERT INDEX under:
(TROU) **TRO-CD01405** Ethel Smyth—Chamber Works & Songs, Vol.3

PAULSEN, Thomas (treb)
Mozart: Zauberflöte (Cpte)

PAULY, Ernst (ten)
Zeller: Vogelhändler (exc)

PAULY, Rose (sop)
see CONCERT INDEX under:
(PEAR) **GEMMCDS9365** R. Strauss: Der Rosenkavalier (abridged), etc
(SCHW) **314512** Vienna State Opera Live, Vol.1
(SCHW) **314672** Vienna State Opera Live, Vol.17

PAUMGARTNER, Bernhard (cond)
see Vienna SO

PAUNOV, Milen (ten)
Mussorgsky: Boris Godunov (Cpte)

PAUNOVA, Mariana (contr)
Dukas: Ariane et Barbe-Bleue (Cpte)
Prokofiev: War and Peace (Cpte)

PAUSTIAN, Inger (sop)
Wagner: Parsifal (Cpte)

PAVAROTTI, Fernando (ten)
Verdi: Luisa Miller (Cpte)

PAVAROTTI, Luciano (ten)
Bellini: Norma (Cpte), Puritani (Cpte), Sonnambula (Cpte)
Boito: Mefistofele (Cpte)
Donizetti: Elisir d'amore (Cpte), Favorita (Cpte), Fille du régiment (Cpte), Lucia di Lammermoor (Cpte), Maria Stuarda (Cpte)
Giordano: Andrea Chénier (Cpte)
Leoncavallo: Pagliacci (Cpte)
Mascagni: Amico Fritz (Cpte), Cavalleria Rusticana (Cpte)
Mozart: Idomeneo (Cpte)
Ponchielli: Gioconda (Cpte)
Puccini: Bohème (Cpte), Madama Butterfly (Cpte), Manon Lescaut (Cpte), Tosca (Cpte), Turandot (Cpte)
R. Strauss: Rosenkavalier (Cpte)
Rossini: Guillaume Tell (Cpte), Petite messe solennelle, Stabat Mater
Verdi: Aida (Cpte), Ballo in maschera (Cpte), Don Carlo (Cpte), Luisa Miller (Cpte), Macbeth (Cpte), Otello (Cpte), Requiem (Cpte), Rigoletto (Cpte), Traviata (exc), Trovatore (Cpte)
see CONCERT INDEX under:
(DECC) **410 015-2DH** Italian and Neapolitan Songs
(DECC) **417 011-2DH2** Pavarotti's Greatest Hits
(DECC) **425 681-2DM2** Tutto Pavarotti
(DECC) **430 433-2DH** Carreras, Domingo and Pavarotti in Concert
(DECC) **430 716-2DM** Pavarotti—Gala Concert at the Albert Hall
(DECC) **430 724-2DM** Great Operatic Duets
(DECC) **433 010-2DM** Christmas Stars
(DECC) **433 437-2DA** Pavarotti—King of the High Cs
(DECC) **433 439-2DA** Great Love Duets
(DECC) **433 706-2DMO3** Bellini—Beatrice di Tenda; Operatic Arias
(DECC) **433 710-2DH** O Holy Night
(DECC) **436 461-2DM** Ten Top Sopranos
(DECC) **436 463-2DM** Ten Top Tenors
(DECC) **443 018-2DF2** Pavarotti/Freni/Ricciarelli—Live
(DECC) **444 450-2DH** Pavarotti in Central Park
(DG) **429 724-2GH2** Berlioz—Requiem, etc
(RCA) **09026 62541-2** Pavarotti - The Early Years, Vol.1
(RCA) **09026 68014-2** Pavarotti - The Early Years, Vol.2
(SONY) **MK37228** Pavarotti sings Verdi
(TELD) **4509-96200-2** The Three Tenors 1994

PAVLÍK, Ceněk (vn)
see CONCERT INDEX under:
(SUPR) **11 0111-2** Ceněk Pavlík—Violin Recital

PAVLOVÁ, Jitka (sop)
Fibich: Šárka (Cpte)
see CONCERT INDEX under:
(DECC) **421 852-2DH2** Janáček: Operatic & Chamber Works
(SUPR) **11 1878-2** The Unknown Janáček

PAVLOVSKI, Nina (sop)
Nørholm: Symphony 4

PAWELS, Jürgen von (narr)
Lehár: Friederike (Cpte), Giuditta (Cpte)

PAY, Antony (cond)
see ECO

PAY, Antony (cl)
 Mozart: Clarinet Concerto, K622
 see CONCERT INDEX under:
 (CRD) CRD3411 Mozart & Schumann: Chamber
 Works
 (L'OI) 433 674-2OH Vivaldi—Oboe Concertos
 (NMC) NMCD009 Birtwistle—Choral and Orchestral
 Works
 (PHIL) 422 833-2PC Mozart—Chamber Works
 (SONY) SMK48466 Boulez conducts
 Schoenberg—Volume 3

PAY, Antony (cl/dir)
 see CONCERT INDEX under:
 (CLAV) CD50-8602 Kramár—Clarinet Concertos
 (VIRG) VC7 59002-2 Weber—Works for Clarinet &
 Orchestra
 (VIRG) VC7 59287-2 Crusell—Clarinet Concertos

PAY, Sam (treb)
 Britten: Turn of the Screw (Cpte)

PAYEN, Paul (bar)
 Massenet: Manon (Cpte)

PAYNE, Joseph (organ)
 see CONCERT INDEX under:
 (NAXO) 8 553214 Early French Organ Music, Volume
 1
 (NAXO) 8 553215 Early French Organ Music, Volume
 2

PAYNE, Joseph (hpd)
 Albero: Keyboard Sonatas (Venice MS) (exc),
 Scarlatti Sonatas
 Roman: Harpsichord Suites

PAYNE, Patricia (mez)
 Beethoven: Mass in C, Missa Solemnis
 Britten: Peter Grimes (Cpte)
 Verdi: Ballo in maschera (Cpte)
 see CONCERT INDEX under:
 (SONY) M3K79312 Puccini: Il Trittico

PAYSEN, Stephen (perc)
 see CONCERT INDEX under:
 (NEW) NW357-2 Crumb. Madrigals and Chamber
 works

PEACOCK, Adrian (bass)
 Boughton: Bethlehem (Cpte)

PEACOCK, Lucy (sop)
 Hindemith: Mörder, Hoffnung der Frauen (Cpte)
 Weill: Kuhhandel (exc)

PEARCE, Alison (sop)
 see CONCERT INDEX under:
 (HYPE) CDA66104 Haydn: Welsh Folksong
 Arrangements

PEARCE, Colman (cond)
 see Ireland National SO

PEARCE, John (ten)
 Vaughan Williams: Hugh the Drover (Cpte)

PEARCE, Judith (fl)
 Maw: Flute Quartet
 see CONCERT INDEX under:
 (HYPE) CDA66172 Malcolm Arnold: Chamber Works,
 Vol. 2
 (HYPE) CDA66173 Malcolm Arnold: Chamber Works,
 Vol. 3
 (HYPE) CDA66175 Music by Bliss, Britten and Holst

PEARCE, Michael (bass)
 Handel: Dettingen Te Deum, King shall rejoice
 (Dettingen)

PEARCE, Michael (treb)
 see CONCERT INDEX under:
 (ARGO) 433 215-2ZH Britten—Christmas Music

PEARCE, Richard (organ)
 see CONCERT INDEX under:
 (CONI) CDCF176 French Sacred Choral Works
 (CONI) CDCF178 Brahms: Complete Motets

PEARL, David (treb)
 Puccini: Tosca (Cpte)

PEARLMAN, Martin (cond)
 see Boston Baroque

PEARLMAN, Martin (hpd)
 Haydn: Mass 11

PEARN, Michael (sngr)
 Bernstein: West Side Story (Cpte)

PEARS, Sir Peter (ten)
 Bach: St John Passion, BWV245 (Cpte)
 Britten: Albert Herring (Cpte), Burning Fiery Furnace
 (Cpte), Curlew River (Cpte), Death in Venice (Cpte),
 Midsummer Night's Dream (Cpte), Peter Grimes
 (Cpte), Prodigal Son (Cpte), Rape of Lucretia (Cpte),
 St Nicolas, Turn of the Screw (Cpte), War Requiem
 Elgar: Dream of Gerontius (Cpte)
 Puccini: Turandot (Cpte)
 Purcell: Fairy Queen, Z629 (Cpte)
 Schubert: Winterreise (Cpte)
 Schumann: Szenen aus Goethes Faust (Cpte)
 Walton: Troilus and Cressida (exc)
 see CONCERT INDEX under:
 (DECC) 425 996-2DM Britten—Vocal Works
 (DECC) 430 094-2DWO The World of Elgar
 (DECC) 436 201-2DM Schubert—Lieder
 (DECC) 436 990-2DWO The World of Benjamin
 Britten
 (DECC) 440 063-2DM Britten—Spring Symphony etc

(DECC) 443 461-2DF2 Berlioz—L'Enfance du Christ,
 etc
(DECC) 443 933-2DM Peter Pears sings Schubert
 and Schumann
(EMI) CDC7 54605-2 Poulenc and Britten play
 Poulenc and Britten
(EMI) CHS7 69741-2(2) Record of Singing,
 Vol.4—Anglo-American School (pt 2)
(EMI) CMS7 64727-2 Britten—Opera excerpts and
 Folksongs
(LOND) 425 100-2LM Britten: Orchestral & Vocal
 Works
(LOND) 425 159-2LM Salute to Percy Grainger
(LOND) 425 661-2LM Walton & Arnold: Orchestral &
 Vocal Works
(LOND) 425 716-2LM Britten: Canticles
(LOND) 433 200-2LHO2 Britten—Owen Wingrave,
 etc.
(LOND) 436 393-2LM Britten—The Little Sweep, etc
(LOND) 436 395-2LM Britten—Vocal Works
(LOND) 436 396-2LM Britten—Spring Symphony,
 etc
(PEAR) GEMMCD9177 Britten—Vocal Works
(RCA) 09026 61583-2(5) Julian Bream Edition (pt 5)
(RCA) 09026 61601-2 J. Bream Edition, Vol.18: Music
 for Voice & Gtr
(RCA) 09026 61602-2 J. Bream Edition, Vol.19:
 Elizabethan Lte Songs
(TELD) 9031-77614-2 Bach—Cantatas

PEARSON, Barbara (sop)
 Schoenberg: Moses and Aron (Cpte)

PEARSON, Donald (cond)
 see St John's Episcopal Cath Ch

PEARSON, Justin (vc)
 see CONCERT INDEX under:
 (HYPE) CDA66112 Souvenirs de Venise
 (KING) KCLCD2027 South American Flute Music

PEARSON, Leslie (organ)
 see CONCERT INDEX under:
 (CALA) CACD1007 Respighi—Orchestral Works
 (EMI) CDM7 69546-2 Lucia Popp

PEARSON, Leslie (hpd)
 see CONCERT INDEX under:
 (EMI) CDC7 47122-2 Mozart: Concert and Operatic
 Arias

PEARSON, Leslie (pf)
 see CONCERT INDEX under:
 (CFP) CD-CFP4637 Ketèlbey/Luigini—Orchestral
 Music

PEASE, James (bar)
 Britten: Peter Grimes (Cpte)

PEASGOOD, Siu (fl)
 see CONCERT INDEX under:
 (CHAN) CHAN0512 Telemann, Vol.2—Ouverture
 burlesque

PECHNER, Gerhard (bar)
 Verdi: Macbeth (Cpte)
 see CONCERT INDEX under:
 (RCA) 09026 61580-2(7) RCA/Met 100 Singers, 100
 Years (pt 7)

PECHOVÁ, Jarmila (sop)
 Smetana: Bartered Bride (Cpte)

PECHURIA, Tatiana (mez)
 Rimsky-Korsakov: Tsar's Bride (Cpte)

PECK, David (cl)
 see CONCERT INDEX under:
 (CARL) TCD77 Mozart—Wind Concertos

PECK, Richard (ten sax)
 Glass: Hydrogen Jukebox (Cpte)

PECKOVÁ, Dagmar (mez)
 Brian: Symphony 1
 see CONCERT INDEX under:
 (SUPR) 11 2214-2 Janáček—Moravian, Hukvaldy &
 Silesian Songs
 (SUPR) 11 2225-2 Janáček—26 Folk Ballads

PÉCS CHAMBER CHOIR
 cond M. ATZMON
 Haydn: Schöpfung (Cpte)

PÉCS SYMPHONY ORCHESTRA
 cond N. PASQUET
 see CONCERT INDEX under:
 (MARC) 8 223667 Lajtha—Orchestral Works, Volume
 1

PEDACI, Francesca (sngr)
 Cherubini: Lodoïska (Cpte)
 Mozart: Don Giovanni (Cpte)

PEDANI, Paolo (bar)
 Giordano: Andrea Chénier (Cpte)
 Verdi: Traviata (Cpte)

PEDERSON, Monte (bar)
 Schreker: Gezeichneten (Cpte), Irrelohe (Cpte)
 Tchaikovsky: Mazeppa (Cpte)

PEDICONI, Fiorella (sop)
 Paisiello: Nina (Cpte)
 Rossini: Torvaldo e Dorliska (Cpte)

PEDZIALEK, Mariusz (ob)
 see CONCERT INDEX under:
 (WERG) WER60172-50 Penderecki: Orchestral and
 Vocal Works

PEEBLES, Anthony (pf)
 see CONCERT INDEX under:
 (UNIC) UKCD2016 Panufnik—Orchestral Works

PEELERIN, Louise (ob)
 see CONCERT INDEX under:
 (NOVA) 150 016-2 Vivaldi—Concertos

PEERCE, Jan (ten)
 Beethoven: Fidelio (Cpte)
 Bizet: Carmen (Cpte)
 Puccini: Bohème (Cpte)
 R. Strauss: Ariadne auf Naxos (Cpte)
 Verdi: Ballo in maschera (Cpte), Traviata (Cpte)
 see CONCERT INDEX under:
 (ATS) ATCD100 Toscanini conducts Italian Music
 (EMI) CHS7 69741-2(2) Record of Singing,
 Vol.4—Anglo-American School (pt 2)
 (RCA) GD60276 Toscanini conducts Boito & Verdi
 (RCA) GD60324 Beethoven—Complete Symphonies
 (RCA) GD60326 Verdi—Operas & Choral Works
 (RCA) 09026 61580-2(5) RCA/Met 100 Singers, 100
 Years (pt 5)

PEETERS, Harry (bass)
 Donizetti: Poliuto (Cpte)
 Monteverdi: Orfeo (Cpte)
 Mozart: Idomeneo (Cpte), Zauberflöte (Cpte)
 R. Strauss: Salome (Cpte)
 Schumann: Szenen aus Goethes Faust (Cpte)
 Stravinsky: Oedipus Rex (Cpte)

PEETERS, Marcel (cond)
 see LSO

PEGIS, Christopher (vc)
 see CONCERT INDEX under:
 (CENT) CRC2176 Works by Soulima Stravinsky

PEGIS, Jonathan (vc)
 Schoenberg: Verklärte Nacht

PEHRSSON, Claas (rec)
 see CONCERT INDEX under:
 (BIS) BIS-CD159 Hindemith—Chamber Works
 (BIS) BIS-CD249 Works for Baroque Flute and
 Recorders
 (BIS) BIS-CD271 Recorder Concertos
 (BIS) BIS-CD617 Telemann—Recorder Concertos

PEIGNOT, Suzanne (sop)
 see CONCERT INDEX under:
 (PEAR) GEMMCD9311 Poulenc d'après Poulenc

PEILZ CHORAL UNION
 cond E. ANSERMET
 see CONCERT INDEX under:
 (BELA) 450 131-2 Fauré—Requiem
 (DECC) 433 400-2DM2 Ravel & Debussy—Stage
 Works

PEINEMANN, Edith (vn)
 see CONCERT INDEX under:
 (DG) 413 844-2GW2 19th Century Violin Works
 (ORFE) C254921A Kraus—Orchestral Works

PELIZZONI, Rinaldo (ten)
 Donizetti: Lucia di Lammermoor (Cpte)

PELKER, Gudrun (mez)
 Henze: Voices (exc)

PELL, Susanna (va da gamba)
 see CONCERT INDEX under:
 (HYPE) CDA66730 Purcell—Secular Solo Songs, Vol.
 3

PELL, William (ten)
 Wagner: Tannhäuser (Cpte)

PELLAROVÁ, Helena (sop)
 Zelenka: Requiem, ZWV48

PELLE, Nadia (sop)
 see CONCERT INDEX under:
 (CHAN) CHAN8800 Music on Hebrew Themes
 (CHAN) CHAN8924 Russian Vocal and Chamber
 works

PELLEGRINI QUARTET
 K. A. Hartmann: String Quartet 1, String Quartet 2

PELLERIN, Ray (organ)
 see CONCERT INDEX under:
 (NEWP) NCD60098 Weill—Vocal & Instrumental
 Works

PELLERIN, Raymond (alto)
 Handel: Sosarme (Cpte)

PELLETIER, Wilfrid (cond)
 see NY Met Op Orch

PELLICCIA, Arrigo (va)
 see CONCERT INDEX under:
 (PHIL) 438 323-2PM2 Mozart—Violin Concertos

PELLIÉ, Françoise (ondes martenot)
 Koechlin: Seven Stars Symphony

PELON, Caroline (sop)
 Rameau: Nélée et Myrthis (Cpte)
 see CONCERT INDEX under:
 (VIRG) VC5 45107-2 Charpentier—Leçons de
 ténèbres, Vol. 3

PÉNA, Michèle (sop)
 Offenbach: Orphée aux enfers (Cpte)

PEÑA, Paco (gtr)
 see CONCERT INDEX under:
 (NIMB) NI5093 Flamenco Guitar Music

PENDACHANSKA, Alexandrina (sop)
Glinka: Life for the Tsar (Cpte)
see CONCERT INDEX under:
(CAPR) 10 706 Young Voices of the Opera-
Alexandrina Pendachanska
(DECC) 440 355-2DH Rachmaninov—Choral Works

PENDARVIS, Janice (voc)
see CONCERT INDEX under:
(SONY) SK64133 The Essential Philip Glass

PENDERECKI, Krzysztof (cond)
see Italian Youth Orch

PENDLEBURY, Alan (bn)
see CONCERT INDEX under:
(VIRG) VC7 59285-2 Favourite Czech Orchestral
Works

PENDLEBURY, Sally Jane (vc)
see CONCERT INDEX under:
(CONI) CDCF905 Karen Jones—The Flute Album

PENDOWSKI, Michael (cond)
see Chicago SO

PENKOVA, Reni (mez)
see CONCERT INDEX under:
(EMI) CMS7 63386-2 Borodin—Prince Igor &
Complete Solo Songs

PENNARIO, Leonard (pf)
Brahms: Piano Trio 2
Dvořák: Piano Trio 3
Rachmaninov: Paganini Rhapsody
see CONCERT INDEX under:
(RCA) 09026 61778-2(27) The Heifetz Collection, Vol.
27
(RCA) 09026 61778-2(28) The Heifetz Collection, Vol.
28
(RCA) 09026 61778-2(33) The Heifetz Collection, Vol.
33
(RCA) 09026 61778-2(34) The Heifetz Collection, Vol.
34

PENNICCHI, Marinella (sop)
Monteverdi: Vespers
see CONCERT INDEX under:
(PHIL) 434 799-2PH Mozart—Choral Works

PENNO, Gino (ten)
Verdi: Macbeth (Cpte)

PENNSYLVANIA UNIVERSITY CHAMBER PLAYERS
cond R. WERNICK
see CONCERT INDEX under:
(NEW) NW357-2 Crumb. Madrigals and Chamber
works

PENNSYLVANIA UNIVERSITY GLEE CLUB
cond A. TOSCANINI
see CONCERT INDEX under:
(RCA) GD60328 Toscanini conducts the Philadelphia
Orch

PENNY, Andrew (cond)
see Ireland National SO

PENNY, Howard (vc)
Boccherini: String Sextets, G454-9 (exc)
see CONCERT INDEX under:
(CAPR) 10 453 Boccherini Edition, Vol.8

PENROSE, Timothy (alto)
Handel: Semele (Cpte)
Purcell: Fairy Queen, Z629 (Cpte)

PENSHURST CHORAL SOCIETY
cond M. BEST
Britten: St Nicolas

PENSON, Guy (clav)
see CONCERT INDEX under:
(RICE) RIC105081 Mozart—Keyboard Works

PENSON, Guy (hpd)
see CONCERT INDEX under:
(HYPE) CDA66391 Mozart: Sonatas for Keyboard and
Flute
(RICE) RIC069049 W.F. Bach—Keyboard Concertos
(RICE) RIC105081 Mozart—Keyboard Works

PENSON, Guy (pf)
see CONCERT INDEX under:
(HYPE) CDA66391 Mozart: Sonatas for Keyboard and
Flute

PENSON, Guy (tangent pf)
see CONCERT INDEX under:
(RICE) RIC105081 Mozart—Keyboard Works

PENTCHEVA, Mariana (contr)
Verdi: Rigoletto (Cpte)

PEPER, Uwe (ten)
Lehár: Lustige Witwe (Cpte)
Mozart: Entführung (Cpte)

PÉPIN, André (fl)
see CONCERT INDEX under:
(CASC) VEL2001 Martin—Orchestral Works

PERAHIA, Murray (pf)
Beethoven: Piano and Wind Quintet, Op. 16, Piano
Concerto 1, Piano Concerto 2, Piano Concerto 5
Brahms: Piano Quartet 1
Chopin: Piano Concerto 1, Piano Concerto 2, Piano
Sonata 2, Piano Sonata 3
Grieg: Piano Concerto
Mozart: Piano and Wind Quintet, K452
Schubert: Fantasy, D760, Piano Sonata, D959,
Winterreise (Cpte)

Schumann: Fantasie, Piano Concerto, Piano Sonata
2
see CONCERT INDEX under:
(SONY) MK42319 Beethoven—Piano Sonatas
(SONY) MK42401 Mendelssohn—Piano Works
(SONY) SK44915 Mozart—Works for 2 Pianos &
Piano Duet
(SONY) SK46437 Murray Perahia—The Aldeburgh
Recital
(SONY) SK47180 Murray Perahia plays Franck and
Liszt
(SONY) SK47181 Murray Perahia plays Brahms
(SONY) SK48233 Mozart—Piano Sonatas
(SONY) SK64397 Beethoven—Piano Sonatas
(SONY) SK64399 Chopin—Piano Works

PERAHIA, Murray (pf/dir)
Mozart: Piano Concerto 6, Piano Concerto 9, Piano
Concerto 13, Piano Concerto 17, Piano Concerto 18,
Piano Concerto 19, Piano Concerto 20, Piano
Concerto 21, Piano Concerto 22, Piano Concerto 23,
Piano Concerto 24, Piano Concerto 27, Piano
Concertos, K107
Schröter: Piano Concerto, Op. 3/3
see CONCERT INDEX under:
(SONY) SK39224 Mozart: Works for piano and
orchestra
(SONY) SK39225 Mozart: Piano Concertos Nos. 1-4
(SONY) SK42243 Mozart—Piano Concertos

PERCUSSION ENSEMBLE
see CONCERT INDEX under:
(NALB) NA055CD Harrison—The Perilous Chapel
cond W. SCHÄFER
Stravinsky: Noces
cond I. STRAVINSKY
see CONCERT INDEX under:
(EMI) CDS7 54607-2 Stravinsky plays and conducts
Stravinsky

PEREA, Emilio (ten)
see CONCERT INDEX under:
(MEMO) HR4408/9(2) Singers in Genoa, Vol.1 (disc
2)

PEREIRA, David (vc)
Schubert: String Quintet

PEREIRA, Malvina (sop)
see CONCERT INDEX under:
(PEAR) GEMMCDS9074(1) Giovanni Zenatello, Vol.2
(pt 1)

PERELSTEIN, Mabel (contr)
Penella: Gato Montés (Cpte)
Puccini: Gianni Schicchi (Cpte)
Vives: Doña Francisquita (Cpte)

PERÉNYI, Eszter (vn)
F. David: Piano Trios (exc)

PÉRÉNYI, Eszter (vn)
see CONCERT INDEX under:
(MARC) 8 223404 Atterberg—Chamber Music, Vol.1

PERÉNYI, Miklós (vc)
Mozart: Piano Quartet, K478, Piano Quartet, K493
Schubert: String Quintet
Tchaikovsky: Souvenir de Florence
see CONCERT INDEX under:
(HARM) HMA190 3026 C. P. E. Bach—Cello
Concertos
(SONY) SK58945 Ligeti—Concertos

PÉRÈS, Marcel (cond)
see Organum Ens

PERESS, Maurice (cond)
see New Palais Royale Orch

PEREZ, Dolores (sngr)
Barbieri: Barberillo de Lavapiès (Cpte)

PÉREZ, Victor Pablo (cond)
see Tenerife SO

PEREZ INIGO, Paloma (sop)
see CONCERT INDEX under:
(CARL) MCD45 Spanish Royal Gala

PERGAMENSCHIKOV, Boris (vc)
see CONCERT INDEX under:
(EMI) CDC7 54466-2 Brahms—Chamber Works

PERGOLA, Luciano della (ten)
Verdi: Macbeth (Cpte)

PERICK, Christof (cond)
see Berlin RSO

PÉRIER, Auguste (cl)
see CONCERT INDEX under:
(CLRI) CC0005 The Clarinet - Historical Recordings,
Vol.1

PÉRIER, Jean (bar)
see CONCERT INDEX under:
(SYMP) SYMCD1089 Historic Baritones of the French
School

PERILLO, Linda (sop)
Delalande: Dies irae, S31, Miserere mei Deus
secundum, S27
Purcell: King Arthur, Z628 (Cpte)

PERINI, Flora (mez)
see CONCERT INDEX under:
(CLAR) CDGSE78-50-52 Three Tenors
(MSCM) MM30352 Caruso—Italian Opera Arias
(PEAR) EVC4(1) The Caruso Edition, Vol.4 (pt 1)
(RCA) GD60495(6) The Complete Caruso Collection
(pt 6)

(ROMO) 81003-2 Galli-Curci—Acoustic Recordings,
Vol.1

PERKINS, Simon (bar)
see CONCERT INDEX under:
(MERI) CDE84153 French Choral Music

PERLASOVA, Evgenia (mez)
Borodin: Prince Igor (Cpte)

PERLEA, Jonel (cond)
see Bamberg SO

PERLEMUTER, Vlado (pf)
Beethoven: Piano and Wind Quintet, Op.16
Chopin: Ballades, Polonaises (exc)
Mozart: Piano and Wind Quintet, K452
see CONCERT INDEX under:
(EMI) CHS7 69741-2(3) Record of Singing,
Vol.4—French School
(NIMB) NI5005 Ravel—Piano Works, Vol 1
(NIMB) NI5165 Fauré: Piano Works

PERLMAN, Itzhak (bass)
Puccini: Tosca (Cpte)

PERLMAN, Itzhak (vn)
Bach: Solo Violin Partitas and Sonatas (exc)
Beethoven: Allegretto, Hess48, Piano Trios,
Romances, Violin Concerto, Violin Concerto, Violin
Sonata 5, Violin Sonata 9
Ben Haim: Violin Concerto
Berg: Violin Concerto
Brahms: Double Concerto, Violin Concerto
Bruch: Scottish Fantasy, Violin Concerto 1, Violin
Concerto 2
Castelnuovo-Tedesco: Violin Concerto 2
Dvořák: Romance, Op. 11, Violin Concerto
Glazunov: Violin Concerto
Goldmark: Violin Concerto
J. T. Williams: Schindler's List (exc)
Khachaturian: Violin Concerto
Korngold: Violin Concerto
Mendelssohn: Violin Concerto, Op.64
Mozart: Concertone, K190, Sinfonia Concertante,
K364, Violin Concerto, K211, Violin Concerto, K218,
Violin Sonata, K526, Violin Sonata, K547
Paganini: Caprices, Op. 1, Violin Concerto 1
Prokofiev: Violin Concerto 1, Violin Concerto 2
Saint-Saëns: Violin Concerto 3
Sarasate: Carmen Fantasy
Shostakovich: Violin Concerto 1
Sibelius: Violin Concerto
Sinding: Suite, Op. 10
Stravinsky: Violin Concerto
Tchaikovsky: Piano Trio, Op. 50, Sérénade
mélancolique, Souvenir d'un lieu cher, Op. 42 (exc),
Violin Concerto
Vivaldi: Concerti, Op. 8 (exc)
Wieniawski: Violin Concerto 2
see CONCERT INDEX under:
(DECC) 421 453-2DM4 Beethoven: Complete Violin
Sonatas
(DECC) 433 695-2DM Chamber Works
(DECC) 444 318-2DH Ravel/Debussy—Chamber
Music
(DG) 423 063-2GH Virtuoso Works for Violin
(DG) 427 813-2GDC Mozart: Violin Works & Wind &
Orchestra
(DG) 429 737-2GH Bach—Favourite Arias
(DG) 431 784-2GX4 Mozart—Violin Sonatas
(DG) 445 535-2GMA2 Mozart—Violin Concertos, etc
(DG) 445 549-2GMA Lalo/Saint-Saëns—Orchestral
Works
(EMI) CDC5 55360-2 The American Album
(EMI) CDC7 47170-2 Joplin: Rags
(EMI) CDC7 47399-2 Dvořák/Smetana—Works for
Violin & Piano
(EMI) CDC7 47403-2 Brahms—Violin Sonatas
(EMI) CDC7 47725-2 Virtuoso Works for Violin
(EMI) CDC7 47856-2 Bach: Violin Concertos
(EMI) CDC7 49604-2 Violin Arrangements by Jascha
Heifetz
(EMI) CDC7 54108-2 Tchaikovsky—Violin Works
(EMI) CDC7 54266-2 Domingo and
Perlman—Together
(EMI) CDM7 63533-2 Spanish Violin Works
(EMI) CDS7 54198-2 Beethoven—String Trios
(EMI) CDS7 54725-2 Brahms—Piano Trios
(EMI) CMS7 64617-2 The art of Itzhak Perlman
(EMI) CMS7 64922-2 Perlman plays Romantic Violin
Concertos
(EMI) CZS4 83177-2(1) Itzhak Perlman Edition (pt 1)
(EMI) CZS4 83177-2(2) Itzhak Perlman Edition (pt 2)
(EMI) CZS4 83177-2(3) Itzhak Perlman Edition (pt 3)
(RCA) RD60735 Mozart & Leclair—Chamber Works
(RCA) 07863 56520-2 Works for Violin and
Orchestra
(RCA) 09026 61454-2 Perlman plays Prokofiev
(SONY) MK34508 Duos by Paganini and Giuliani
(SONY) SK45819 Brahms: Violin Sonatas

PERLMAN, Itzhak (vn/dir)
Vivaldi: Concerti, Op. 8 (exc)
see CONCERT INDEX under:
(EMI) CDC7 47073-2 Bach: Concerto Transcriptions
(EMI) CDM7 64333-2 Vivaldi—Concertos
(EMI) CMS7 64617-2 The art of Itzhak Perlman
(EMI) CZS4 83177-2(1) Itzhak Perlman Edition (pt 1)

PERNERSTORFER, Alois (bass-bar)
R. Strauss: Schweigsame Frau (Cpte)
Verdi: Don Carlo (exc)
see CONCERT INDEX under:

(EMI) **CZS7 67123-2** Wagner: Der Ring des Nibelungen
(SCHW) **314572** Vienna State Opera Live, Vol.7

PERNET, André (bass)
Offenbach: Contes d'Hoffmann (Cpte)

PERNOT, Louis (lte)
D. Gaultier: Rhétorique des Dieux

PEROTIN, Gerard (perc)
Bartók: Sonata for 2 pianos and percussion

PERPIGNAN FESTIVAL ORCHESTRA
cond P. CASALS
Mozart: Sinfonia concertante, K364, Violin Concerto, K219
see CONCERT INDEX under:
(SONY) **SMK58984** Pablo Casals conducts Mozart at Perpignan, 1951

PERRAGUIN, Hélène (mez)
Berlioz: Troyens (Cpte)
Massenet: Amadis (Cpte)
Prokofiev: Love for 3 Oranges (Cpte)
R. Strauss: Salomé (Cpte)

PERRAS, John (cond)
see Centre d'Action Musicale de l'Ouest Orch

PERRAS, Margherita (sop)
see CONCERT INDEX under:
(NIMB) **NI7848** Great Singers at the Berlin State Opera
(PEAR) **GEMMCD9394** Helge Roswaenge—Operatic Recital
(PREI) **89082** Margarete Klose (1902-1968)
(PREI) **89088** Walther Ludwig (1902-1981)
(PREI) **89209** Helge Roswaenge (1897-1972) - II
(SCHW) **314632** Vienna State Opera Live, Vol.13

PERRIN, Cécile (sop)
Jommelli: Armida abbandonata (Cpte)

PERRY, Douglas (ten)
Glass: Satyagraha (Cpte)
V. Thomson: Mother of us all (Cpte)
see CONCERT INDEX under:
(SONY) **SK64133** The Essential Philip Glass

PERRY, Elisabeth (vn)
Nyman: Zed and two noughts

PERRY, Eugene (bar)
A. Davis: X (Cpte)
J. Adams: Death of Klinghoffer (Cpte)
see CONCERT INDEX under:
(DELO) **DE3170** Beach—Cabildo; Six Short Pieces

PERRY, Herbert (bass)
A. Davis: X (Cpte)

PERRY, Janet (sop)
Egk: Peer Gynt (Cpte)
Monteverdi: Madrigals, Bk 8 (exc)
Mozart: Thamos, K345 (Cpte), Zauberflöte (Cpte)
R. Strauss: Rosenkavalier (exc)
Wagner: Parsifal (Cpte)

PERRY, John (pf)
see CONCERT INDEX under:
(PHIL) **432 152-2PH** Brahms—Choral Works

PERRY, Nicholas (cornet)
Schütz: Symphoniae sacrae, Op. 10 (Cpte)

PERSINGER, Louis (pf)
see CONCERT INDEX under:
(BIDD) **LAB031** The young Yehudi Menuhin, Vol.1
(BIDD) **LAB044** Ruggiero Ricci—1938 Electrola Recordings
(TEST) **SBT1003** The Young Menuhin—Encores, Vol.1

PERSSON, Frederic (pf)
see CONCERT INDEX under:
(ROMO) **81012-2** Elisabeth Rethberg—Brunswick Recordings 1924-1929

PERSSON, Mats (bar)
Mahler: Symphony 8

PERSSON, Mats (pf)
Cage: Winter Music
see CONCERT INDEX under:
(HATH) **ARTCD6143** Morton Feldman—Works for Piano 2

PERT, Jill (contr)
Sullivan: Gondoliers (Cpte), Iolanthe (Cpte), Yeomen of the Guard (exc)

PERTILE, Aureliano (ten)
see CONCERT INDEX under:
(EMI) **CHS7 64864-2(1)** La Scala Edition - Vol.2, 1915-46 (pt 1)
(EMI) **CMS7 64008-2(1)** Wagner Singing on Record (pt 1)
(LYRC) **SRO805** Gina Cigna—Opera Recital
(NIMB) **NI7856** Legendary Tenors
(PEAR) **GEMMCDS9925(2)** Covent Garden on Record—Vol.3 (pt 2)
(PEAR) **GEMMCDS9926(1)** Covent Garden on Record—Vol.4 (pt 1)
(PREI) **89008** Aureliano Pertile (1885-1952) - I
(PREI) **89008** Irene Minghini-Cattaneo (1892-1944) - I
(PREI) **89072** Aureliano Pertile (1885-1952) - II

PERTUSI, Michele (bass)
Catalani: Wally (Cpte)
Mozart: Don Giovanni (Cpte), Nozze di Figaro (Cpte)

Puccini: Fanciulla del West (Cpte)
Rossini: Barbiere di Siviglia (Cpte), Cenerentola (Cpte), Petite messe solennelle (Cpte), Signor Bruschino (Cpte)
Verdi: Otello (Cpte), Rigoletto (Cpte)

PERTWEE, Jon (bar)
Bricusse: Scrooge (Cpte)

PĚRUŠKA, Jan (vn)
see CONCERT INDEX under:
(SUPR) **11 0751-2** Martinů—Choral Works

PESCHKO, Sebastian (pf)
see CONCERT INDEX under:
(TEST) **SBT1036** Lisa Della Casa sings Richard Strauss

PEŠEK, Libor (cond)
see Czech PO

PESKANOV, Mark (vn)
see CONCERT INDEX under:
(DELO) **DE3170** Beach—Cabildo; Six Short Pieces

PESKÓ, Zoltan (cond)
see Prague CO

(JEAN) PESNEAUD CHILDREN'S CHOIR
cond G. PRÊTRE
Bizet: Carmen (Cpte)

PESTALOZZI GYMNASIUM CHILDREN'S CHOIR
cond F. LUISI
see CONCERT INDEX under:
(EMI) **CDC5 55233-2** German Opera Arias

PETCHERSKY, Alma (pf)
(ASV) **CDDCA607** Villa-Lobos—Piano Works
(ASV) **CDQS6079** Spanish Piano Works

PETER, Albrecht (bar)
Orff: Mond (Cpte)
R. Strauss: Salome (Cpte)
Wagner: Tristan und Isolde (Cpte)
Weber: Freischütz (Cpte)

PETER, Oskar (tr)
Telemann: Essercizii musici (exc)

PETER, Renée (pf)
see CONCERT INDEX under:
(DECC) **443 467-2DF2** Stravinsky—Ballet Music

PETER, Uwe (ten)
Zemlinsky: Kleider machen Leute (Cpte), Kreidekreis (Cpte)

PETERBOROUGH STRING ORCHESTRA
see CONCERT INDEX under:
(HYPE) **CDH88014** Italian Oboe Concertos

PETERS, Brock (sngr)
Hammerstein: Carmen Jones (Cpte)

PETERS, Brock (spkr)
Gould: Fall River Legend

PETERS, Johanna (mez)
Britten: Albert Herring (Cpte)
Offenbach: Christopher Columbus (Cpte)

PETERS, Maria Angeles (sop)
Martín y Soler: Cosa Rara (Cpte)
Paisiello: Don Chisciotte (Cpte)

PETERS, Reinhard (cond)
see Collegium Aureum

PETERS, Roberta (sop)
Mozart: Zauberflöte (Cpte)
R. Strauss: Ariadne auf Naxos (Cpte)
Rossini: Barbiere di Siviglia (Cpte)
see CONCERT INDEX under:
(RCA) **09026 61580-2(6)** RCA/Met 100 Singers, 100 Years (pt 6)

PETERSEN, Dennis (ten)
Tchaikovsky: Queen of Spades (Cpte)

PETERSEN QUARTET
Beethoven: String Quartet 1, String Quartet 14
see CONCERT INDEX under:
(CAPR) **10 451** Boccherini Edition, Vol.5
(CAPR) **10 452** Boccherini Edition, Vol.7
(CAPR) **10 463** Schulhoff—String Quartets
(CAPR) **10 476** Grieg/Schumann—String Quartets
(CAPR) **10 511** Berg/Janáček/Dutilleux—String Quartets
(CAPR) **10 539** Schulhoff—Chamber Works
(CAPR) **10 605** Mozart—'Haydn' Quartets

PETERSON, Bernice (sngr)
Hammerstein: Carmen Jones (Cpte)

PETERSON, Glade (ten)
Bellini: Pirata (Cpte)

PETIBON, Patricia (sop)
Jommelli: Armida abbandonata (Cpte)

PETIT, Corinne (sngr)
Boïeldieu: Voitures Versées (Cpte)

PETIT, Georges (bar)
see CONCERT INDEX under:
(EPM) **150 122** Milhaud—Historic Recordings 1928-1948

PETIT, Marie-Ange (perc)
see CONCERT INDEX under:
(HARM) **HMC90 1298** M-A. Charpentier—Sacred Works
(HARM) **HMU90 7122** Lully/Philidor—Stage Works

PETIT, Marie-Madeleine (pf)
Messiaen: Quatuor

(LA) PETITE BANDE
see CONCERT INDEX under:
(ACCE) **ACC9395D** Bach—Cantatas
cond S. KUIJKEN
Bach: Brandenburg Concertos, Cantata 21, Magnificat, BWV243, Motets (Cpte), St John Passion, BWV245 (Cpte)
Corelli: Concerti grossi, op 6
Gluck: Orfeo ed Euridice (Cpte)
Handel: Alessandro (Cpte), Partenope (Cpte)
Haydn: Schöpfung (Cpte), Symphony 90, Symphony 91
Mozart: Così fan tutte (Cpte)
Rameau: Hippolyte et Aricie (exc), Zoroastre (Cpte)
see CONCERT INDEX under:
(DHM) **GD77010** Geminiani—Six Concerti Grossi
(DHM) **05472 77275-2** Haydn—Symphonies
(DHM) **05472 77294-2** Haydn—Symphonies
cond G. LEONHARDT
Bach: Mass in B minor, BWV232 (Cpte), St Matthew Passion, BWV244 (Cpte)
Campra: Europe galante
Lully: Bourgeois Gentilhomme
Rameau: Pygmalion (Cpte)

(LA) PETITE BANDE CHORUS
cond S. KUIJKEN
Bach: Motets (Cpte), St John Passion, BWV245 (Cpte)
Mozart: Così fan tutte (Cpte)
cond G. LEONHARDT
Bach: St Matthew Passion, BWV244 (Cpte)

PETITOT, Guillaume (bass)
Shostakovich: Lady Macbeth of Mtsensk (Cpte)

PETITS CHANTEURS À LA CROIX POTENCÉE
cond M. PLASSON
Offenbach: Orphée aux enfers (Cpte)

PETITS CHANTEURS DE PARIS
Fauré: Requiem (Cpte)

(LES) PETITS CHANTEURS DE SAINT-LOUIS
cond P. HERREWEGHE
Fauré: Messe des Pêcheurs de Villerville, Requiem (Cpte)

(LES) PETITS CHANTEURS DE VERSAILLES
cond T. BEECHAM
Bizet: Carmen (Cpte)

PETKOV, Angel (ten)
Mussorgsky: Boris Godunov (Cpte), Khovanshchina (Cpte)
Tchaikovsky: Queen of Spades (Cpte)

PETKOV, Anton (ten)
Borodin: Prince Igor (Cpte)

PETKOV, Dimiter (bass)
Mussorgsky: Boris Godunov (Cpte)
Prokofiev: War and Peace (Cpte)
Shostakovich: Lady Macbeth of Mtsensk (Cpte)
Tchaikovsky: Iolanta (Cpte)

PETR, Miloš (hn)
Mozart: Horn Concerti

PETRACCHI, Francesco (db)
Dvořák: String Quintet, Op.77
see CONCERT INDEX under:
(ASV) **CDDCA907** Bottesini—Volume 3 - Passioni Amorose

PETRACCHI, Franco (cond)
see LSO

PETRESCU, Adrian (ob)
Enescu: Wind Decet, Op. 14

PETRI, David (vc)
see CONCERT INDEX under:
(RCA) **RD87749** The Virtuoso Recorder

PETRI, Egon (pf)
see CONCERT INDEX under:
(APR) **APR7023** Egon Petri, Vol.1
(APR) **APR7024** Egon Petri, Vol.2
(APR) **APR7027** Egon Petri, Vol.3
(BIDD) **LAB007/8** The Art of Joseph Szigeti, Vol.2
(MUSI) **MACD-772** The Art of Egon Petri
(PEAR) **GEMMCD9347** Ferruccio Busoni & Egon Petri
(SYMP) **SYMCD1145** Busoni, Grainger & Petri

PETRI, Elisa (mez)
see CONCERT INDEX under:
(EMI) **CHS7 64860-2(2)** La Scala Edition - Vol.1, 1878-1914 (pt 2)
(PEAR) **GEMMCDS9073(1)** Giovanni Zenatello, Vol.1 (pt 1)

PETRI, Elisa (sop)
see CONCERT INDEX under:
(IRCC) **IRCC-CD808** Souvenirs of 19th Century Italian Opera
(NIMB) **NI7867** Legendary Baritones

PETRI, Hanne (hpd)
see CONCERT INDEX under:
(RCA) **RD87749** The Virtuoso Recorder

PETRI, Michala (rec)
Albinoni: Concerti, Op.7 (exc), Concerti, Op.9 (exc)
Bach: Flute Sonatas, BWV1030-5
Handel: Recorder Sonatas
Rossini: Italiana in Algeri (Cpte)
Telemann: Sonates sans basse, TWV40: 101-106

Vivaldi: Concerti, Op. 8 (exc), Concerto, RV443
see CONCERT INDEX under:
(PHIL) **400 075-2PH** Recorder Concertos
(PHIL) **410 041-2PH** Telemann: Recorder works
(PHIL) **412 632-2PH** Recorder Sonatas
(RCA) **RD60060** Noël! Noël! Noël!
(RCA) **RD87749** The Virtuoso Recorder
(RCA) **RD87885** Vivaldi: Concertos for Recorder

PETRICOLA, Emma (sop)
see CONCERT INDEX under:
(STU) **SM12 2389** Paisiello—Music for Napoleon
Bonaparte's Chapel

PETRIG, Caroline Maria (sop)
R. Strauss: Elektra (Cpte)

PETROSCHOFF, Vladimir (cond)
see Berlin Fest Orch

PETROV, Boris (pf)
Fauré: Violin Sonata 1
Franck: Violin Sonata

PETROV, Evgeny (cl)
see CONCERT INDEX under:
(ETCE) **KTC1177** Brahms—Music for Clarinet

PETROV, Ivan (bass)
Tchaikovsky: Eugene Onegin (Cpte)

PETROV, Nikolai (pf)
see CONCERT INDEX under:
(OLYM) **OCD198** Nikolai Petrov plays Fantasies
(OLYM) **OCD269** Kabalevsky—Volume 4

PETROV, Peter (bass)
Tchaikovsky: Queen of Spades (Cpte)

PETROVA, Fayina (contr)
see CONCERT INDEX under:
(DANT) **LYS013/5** Tchaikovsky—The Queen of
Spades

PETROVA, Valentina (sop)
Tchaikovsky: Eugene Onegin (Cpte)

PETRUSANEC, Franjo (bass)
Dvořák: Stabat mater

PETTINGER, Peter (pf)
see CONCERT INDEX under:
(CHAN) **CHAN8380** Elgar—Music for Violin and
Piano
(CHAN) **CHAN8438** Elgar—Piano Works
(CHAN) **CHAN8555** Russian Duos
(CNTI) **CCD1017** Violin Diabolique: Music by Ernst
and Wieniawski
(CNTI) **CCD1038** Works for Clarinet and Piano

PETTIT, David (pf)
see CONCERT INDEX under:
(HYPE) **CDA66573** Prokofiev—Chamber Works

PETZOLD, Martin (ten)
B. Goldschmidt: Gewaltige Hahnrei (Cpte)
Korngold: Wunder der Heliane (Cpte)
Krenek: Jonny spielt auf (Cpte)
Mozart: Zauberflöte (Cpte)
Schreker: Gezeichneten (Cpte)
see CONCERT INDEX under:
(DECC) **440 854-2DH** Ullmann—Der Kaiser von
Atlantis

PEYER, Gervase de (cl)
Brahms: Clarinet Quintet, Clarinet Sonata 1, Clarinet
Sonata 2
Messiaen: Quatuor
Mozart: Clarinet Quintet, K581
see CONCERT INDEX under:
(CHAN) **CHAN8506** Gervase de Peyer Recital
(CHAN) **CHAN8549** English Music for Clarinet and
Piano
(CHAN) **CHAN9377/8** Ireland—Chamber Works
(COLL) **Coll1097-2** Copland: Orchestral Works
(DECC) **430 498-2DWO** The World of Mozart
(DECC) **433 727-2DM** Clarinet Concertos
(EMI) **CMS7 64074-2(1)** Christa Ludwig—Recital (pt 1)
(LYRI) **SRCD325** Mathias—Concertos

PEYRON, Gisèle (sop)
see CONCERT INDEX under:
(EMI) **CDH7 61025-2** Fauré & Monteverdi Vocal
Works

PEYRON, Joseph (ten)
Audran: Poupée (exc)
Bazin: Maître Pathelin (Cpte)
Boïeldieu: Voitures Versées (Cpte)
Delibes: Lakmé (Cpte)
Ganne: Hans (Cpte)
Hahn: O mon bel inconnu (Cpte)
Lecocq: Rose Mousse (Cpte)
Milhaud: Christophe Colomb (Cpte)
Planquette: Rip van Winkle (Cpte)
Ravel: Enfant et les sortilèges (Cpte)
Tomasi: Don Juan de Mañara (Cpte)
see CONCERT INDEX under:
(MUSD) **20239-2** Delibes—Opéras-Comiques

PEZZETTI, Sergio (bass)
Rossini: Inganno felice (Cpte)

PEZZINO, Léonardo (ten)
Ravel: Enfant et les sortilèges (Cpte)
see CONCERT INDEX under:
(EMI) **CDS7 49361-2** Offenbach: Operettas

PFAFF, Oly (ten)
see CONCERT INDEX under:

(EMI) **CDC7 54037-2** Mozart—Masses and Church
Sonatas
(HANS) **98 859** Bach—Cantatas, Vol.8

PFEFFER, Anneli (sop)
Weber: Peter Schmoll (Cpte)

PFEIFFER, Ansgar (treb)
see CONCERT INDEX under:
(TELD) **2292-42631-2** Bach—Cantatas, Volume 36
(TELD) **4509-91762-2** Bach—Cantatas, Vol.8

PFEIFFER, Walter (vn)
see CONCERT INDEX under:
(TELD) **4509-95518-2** Bach—Violin Concertos

PFEIFLE, Alfred (ten)
R. Strauss: Rosenkavalier (Cpte)

PFEILER, Christa (mez)
see CONCERT INDEX under:
(VICT) **VCD19041** Grieg—Songs, Vol.4

PFISTER, Stephanie (vn)
see CONCERT INDEX under:
(HARM) **HMC90 1505** German Baroque Songs

PFITZNER, Hans (cond)
see Berlin St Op Orch

PFITZNER, Hans (pf)
see CONCERT INDEX under:
(EMI) **CDC5 55225-2** Pfitzner plays and conducts
Pfitzner
(PREI) **90029** Hans Pfitzner Accompanies &
Conducts

PFLANZL, Heinrich (bass)
Wagner: Meistersinger (Cpte)

**PFORZHEIM CHAMBER ORCHESTRA
cond F. WERNER**
see CONCERT INDEX under:
(ERAT) **4509-97407-2** Bach—Cantatas
(ERAT) **4509-98525-2** Bach—Cantatas

**PFORZHEIM SOUTH-WEST GERMAN CHAMBER
ORCHESTRA
cond V. CZARNECKI**
Boccherini: Stabat mater (1781)

PFÜLB, Tobias (treb)
Mozart: Zauberflöte (Cpte)

PHELPS, Cynthia (va)
Mozart: String Quintet, K174, String Quintet, K406,
String Quintet, K515, String Quintet, K516, String
Quintet, K593, String Quintet, K614
see CONCERT INDEX under:
(NUOV) **6802** Mozart—Chamber Works

PHELPS, Melissa (vc)
Schubert: String Quintet

**PHILADELPHIA BOYS' CHOIR
cond R. MUTI**
Leoncavallo: Pagliacci (Cpte)
Puccini: Tosca (Cpte)

**PHILADELPHIA CHORAL ARTS SOCIETY
cond C. DUTOIT**
see CONCERT INDEX under:
(DECC) **440 355-2DH** Rachmaninov—Choral Works
cond R. MUTI
see CONCERT INDEX under:
(EMI) **CDS7 54251-2** Scriabin—Symphonies and Tone
Poems

**PHILADELPHIA ORCHESTRA
cond D. BARENBOIM**
Elgar: Cello Concerto
cond T. BEECHAM
see CONCERT INDEX under:
(SONY) **SMK46683** Arnell/Berners/Delius—Orchestral
Works
cond C. DUTOIT
Persichetti: Piano Concerto
Rachmaninov: Rock, Op. 7, Symphony 2
see CONCERT INDEX under:
(DECC) **440 355-2DH** Rachmaninov—Choral Works
cond JAMES LEVINE
see CONCERT INDEX under:
(RCA) **74321 20294-2** Schumann—Symphonies 1-4
cond M. JANSONS
Mussorgsky: Songs and Dances of Death
Shostakovich: Symphony 10
cond C. MUNCH
see CONCERT INDEX under:
(SONY) **SBK53255** Berlioz—Orchestral Works
cond R. MUTI
Dvořák: Romance, Op.11, Violin Concerto
Leoncavallo: Pagliacci (Cpte)
Liszt: Faust Symphony
Mussorgsky: Pictures
Persichetti: Symphony 5
Prokofiev: Romeo and Juliet Suites (exc)
Puccini: Tosca (Cpte)
Rachmaninov: Paganini Rhapsody, Piano Concerto 2,
Piano Concerto 3
Rimsky-Korsakov: Scheherazade
Scriabin: Poème de l'extase
Shostakovich: Festive Overture, Symphony 5
Stravinsky: Rite of Spring (Cpte)
Tchaikovsky: Francesca da Rimini, Sleeping Beauty
(exc), Swan Lake Suite, Symphony 6
see CONCERT INDEX under:
(EMI) **CDC5 55120-2**
Debussy/Chausson/Ravel—Orchestral & Vocal
Works
(EMI) **CDC7 47022-2** Popular Orchestral Works

(EMI) **CDC7 47316-2** Respighi—Symphonic Poems
(EMI) **CDM7 64747-2** Franck—Orchestral Works
(EMI) **CDS7 49487-2** Beethoven: Complete
Symphonies
(EMI) **CDS7 54251-2** Scriabin—Symphonies and Tone
Poems
cond E. ORMANDY
Beethoven: Christus am Oelberge, Op. 85, Missa
Solemnis, Triple Concerto
Brahms: Double Concerto, Violin Concerto
Chopin: Piano Concerto 1, Piano Concerto 2
Dvořák: Cello Concerto, Violin Concerto
Mahler: Symphony 10
Paganini: Violin Concerto 1
Prokofiev: Piano Concerto 4
R. Strauss: Burleske, Don Quixote
Rachmaninov: Piano Concerto 3
Reger: Piano Concerto
Rossini: Boutique fantasque
Saint-Saëns: Symphony 3
Sibelius: Symphony 2, Symphony 7, Violin Concerto
Tchaikovsky: Sérénade mélancolique, Sleeping
Beauty (exc), Symphony 5, Symphony 6, Violin
Concerto
see CONCERT INDEX under:
(BIDD) **LAB054** Albert Spalding—Archive
Performances
(EMI) **CDM5 65175-2** Bartók/Hindemith—Orchestral
Works
(EMI) **CMS7 64922-2** Perlman plays Romantic Violin
Concertos
(EMI) **CZS4 83177-2(1)** Itzhak Perlman Edition (pt 1)
(EMI) **CZS4 83177-2(2)** Itzhak Perlman Edition (pt 2)
(MMOI) **CDMOIR408** Great Sopranos
(NIMB) **NI7847** Kirsten Flagstad (1895-1962)
(RCA) **GD87834** Romantic Piano Concertos
(RCA) **GD87911** Marian Anderson - Opera, Oratorio &
Song Recital
(RCA) **GD87915** Wagner: Arias and Duets
(RCA) **RD85666** Works for Piano and Orchestra
(RCA) **VD60486** Respighi: Orchestral Works
(RCA) **VD60489** Sibelius: Orchestral Works
(RCA) **09026 61265-2(1)** Rachmaninov—The
Complete Recordings (pt 1)
(RCA) **09026 61778-2(05)** The Heifetz Collection, Vol.
5
(RCA) **09026 61863-2** Saint-
Saëns/Falla/Franck—Piano Works
(RCA) **09026 61879-2** Grieg—Historic Recordings
(SIMA) **PSC1821(2)** Kirsten Flagstad, Vol.1 (pt 2)
(SONY) **MPK44850** Shostakovich: Concertos
(SONY) **SBK46329** Popular Orchestral works
(SONY) **SBK48263** Bartok—Orchestral Works
(SONY) **SBK48272** R. Strauss—Orchestral Works
(SONY) **SBK48278** Works for Cello and Orchestra
(SONY) **SBK48279**
Offenbach/Rachmaninov/Smetana—Orchestral
Works
(SONY) **SBK53255** Berlioz—Orchestral Works
(SONY) **SBK53256** Debussy—Orchestral Works
(SONY) **SBK53257** Grieg—Orchestral Works
(SONY) **SBK53258** Hindemith/Walton—Orchestral
Works
(SONY) **SBK53261**
Prokofiev/Shostakovich—Orchestral Works
(SONY) **SM3K46519** Mozart—Legendary
Interpretations
(TEST) **SBT1005** Ten Top Tenors
cond S. RACHMANINOV
see CONCERT INDEX under:
(CARL) **GLRS104** Rachmaninov plays Rachmaninov
(RCA) **09026 61265-2(1)** Rachmaninov—The
Complete Recordings (pt 1)
cond W. SAWALLISCH
Bruckner: Symphony 4
Dvořák: Cello Concerto, Scherzo Capriccioso,
Symphonic Variations, Symphony 7, Symphony 8,
Symphony 9
Tchaikovsky: Swan Lake (Cpte)
see CONCERT INDEX under:
(EMI) **CDC5 55026-2** Paganini/Saint-Saëns—Violin
Works
(EMI) **CDC5 55230-2** Hindemith—Orchestral Works
(EMI) **CMS7 64812-2** Dvořák—Orchestral Works
cond L. STOKOWSKI
Bloch: Schelomo
Rachmaninov: Piano Concerto 2
Stravinsky: Petrushka (Cpte), Rite of Spring (Cpte)
see CONCERT INDEX under:
(BIDD) **WHL005** Stokowski conducts Russian Music,
Vol.1
(BIDD) **WHL010** Stokowski conducts Russian Music,
Vol.1
(BIDD) **WHL011** Stokowski conducts French Music,
Vol.1
(BIDD) **WHL012** Stokowski conducts French Music,
Vol.2
(BIDD) **WHL013** Stokowski conducts French Music,
Vol.3
(BIDD) **WHL015** Stokowski conducts Tchaikovsky
(BIDD) **WHL017/8** Stokowski conducts Brahms
Symphonies
(BIDD) **WHL027** Stokowski conducts Dvořák, Liszt,
Chopin & Borodin
(BIDD) **WHL033** Stokowski conducts Beethoven and
Schubert
(CARL) **GLRS104** Rachmaninov plays Rachmaninov
(DELL) **CDDA9023** Stokowski conducts Sibelius and
Shostakovich
(DUTT) **CDAX8002** Stravinsky—Orchestral Works

(DUTT) **CDAX8009**   Stokowski conducts a Russian
Spectacular
(PEAR) **GEMMCDS9044**   Stokowski conducts
Shostakovich
(PEAR) **GEMMCD9448**   Stokowski conducts Wagner
(PEAR) **GEMMCD9488**   A Stokowski Fantasia
(RCA) **GD87808**   Lawrence Tibbett sings Opera
Arias
(RCA) **09026 60929-2**   R.Strauss—Tone Poems
(RCA) **09026 61265-2(1)**   Rachmaninov—The
Complete Recordings (pt 1)
(RCA) **09026 61265-2(2)**   Rachmaninov—The
Complete Recordings (pt 2)
(STOK) **LSCD20**   Stokowski conducts Philadelphia
Rarities
   cond A. TOSCANINI
   see CONCERT INDEX under:
(RCA) **GD60328**   Toscanini conducts the Philadelphia
Orch

PHILADELPHIA ROBIN HOOD DELL ORCHESTRA
   cond F. REINER
Brahms: Double Concerto

PHILHARMONIA BAROQUE ORCHESTRA
   cond N. McGEGAN
Corelli: Concerti grossi, Op.6 (exc)
Handel: Clori, Tirsi e Fileno (Cpte), Judas
Maccabaeus (Cpte), Messiah (Cpte), Resurrezione
(Cpte), Susanna (Cpte), Theodora (Cpte), Water
Music
Rameau: Naïs (exc), Temple de la Gloire (exc)
   see CONCERT INDEX under:
(HARM) **HMC90 5183**   Handel: Arias for Senesino
(HARM) **HMC90 5193**   Vivaldi: Flute Concertos
(HARM) **HMU90 7012**   Mozart—Horn Concertos, etc
(HARM) **HMU90 7016**   Handel: Arias for Montagnana
(HARM) **HMU90 7036**   Handel—Arias for Cuzzoni
(HARM) **HMU90 7056**   Handel—Arias for Durastanti

PHILHARMONIA CHOIR
   cond O. KLEMPERER
Bach: St Matthew Passion, BWV244 (exc)

PHILHARMONIA CHORUS
Beethoven: Symphony 9
Brahms: Alto Rhapsody, Op. 53, Deutsches Requiem,
Op. 45 (Cpte)
Cherubini: Coronation Mass in A
Donizetti: Lucia di Lammermoor (Cpte)
Fauré: Requiem (Cpte)
Hadley: Trees so high
Handel: Messiah (Cpte)
Lehár: Lustige Witwe (Cpte)
Mahler: Symphony 2, Symphony 8
Mendelssohn: Erste Walpurgisnacht, Symphony 2
Mozart: Così fan tutte (Cpte), Don Giovanni (Cpte),
Nozze di Figaro (Cpte), Requiem
Orff: Carmina Burana
Prokofiev: Cantata, Op. 74, Ivan the Terrible Suite
R. Strauss: Rosenkavalier (Cpte)
Rossini: Stabat Mater
Vaughan Williams: Symphony 1
Verdi: Pezzi sacri (Cpte), Requiem (Cpte)
Vivaldi: Gloria, RV589, Magnificat, RV611
   see CONCERT INDEX under:
(CALA) **CACD1002**   Debussy—Orchestral Works,
Vol.2
(CHAN) **CHAN9134**   Pärt—Collage
(EMI) **CDC7 47283-2**   Maria Callas - Mad Scenes &
Bel Canto Arias
(EMI) **CDM7 64144-2**   Klemperer conducts
Mendelssohn/Liszt/J.Strauss II
(EMI) **CHS5 65003-2**   Walton conducts Walton
   cond D. HILL
Rachmaninov: Vespers, Op.37 (Cpte)

PHILHARMONIA HUNGARICA
   cond G. A. ALBRECHT
   see CONCERT INDEX under:
(CPO) **CPO999 251-2**   Schulhoff—Symphonies
   cond W. BOSKOVSKY
   see CONCERT INDEX under:
(EMI) **CDM7 64627-2**   Liszt—Orchestral Works
   cond A. DORATI
Tchaikovsky: Serenade, Op.48
   see CONCERT INDEX under:
(DECC) **417 718-2DM**   Haydn: Symphonies
(DECC) **425 920-2DM4**   Haydn—Symphonies, Vol.5
(DECC) **425 930-2DM4**   Haydn—Symphonies, Vol.7
(DECC) **425 935-2DM4**   Haydn—Symphonies, Vol.8
(DECC) **430 100-2DM32(1)**   Haydn—Complete
Symphonies (Volumes 1-4)
(MERC) **432 017-2MM**   Bartók—Orchestral Works
   cond G. MAGA
Rubinstein: Piano Concerto 4
   see CONCERT INDEX under:
(VOX) **115712-2**   Hiller/Litolff/Moscheles—Piano
Concertos
(VOX) **115717-2**   Chopin/Henselt/Hiller—Piano
Concertos
Moszkowski: Piano Concerto
   cond G. VARGA
Rubinstein: Symphony 6

PHILHARMONIA ORCHESTRA
Mahler: Lied von der Erde
   see CONCERT INDEX under:
(ASV) **CDDCA713**   Tchaikovsky—Works for Violin and
Orchestra
(EMI) **CDC7 54626-2**   Operetta Arias
(EMI) **CDM7 69501-2**   Elisabeth
Schwarzkopf—Romantic Heroines

(EMI) **CDM7 69563-2**   Elgar: Orchestral Works
(NIMB) **NI5330**   Oboe Concertos
   cond O. ACKERMANN
J. Strauss II: Nacht in Venedig (Cpte), Zigeunerbaron
(Cpte)
Lehár: Land des Lächelns (Cpte), Lustige Witwe
(Cpte)
   see CONCERT INDEX under:
(EMI) **CDC7 47284-2**   Elisabeth Schwarzkopf sings
Operetta
(EMI) **CDH7 61001-2**   R. Strauss—Lieder & Arias
(EMI) **CDM7 63657-2**   Schwarzkopf sings Opera Arias
(TEST) **SBT1059**   Erich Kunz—Opera and Song
Recital
   cond A. DE ALMEIDA
Halévy: Juive (Cpte)
   cond K. ALWYN
   see CONCERT INDEX under:
(SILV) **FILMCD713**   Classic British Film Music
(SILV) **SILVAD3002**   At the Movies 2: Classic
Symphonic Film Music
   cond D. AMOS
   see CONCERT INDEX under:
(CRYS) **Crystal CD810**   Music of Alan Hovhaness
   cond ANTHONY BERNARD
   see CONCERT INDEX under:
(EMI) **CDH7 63198-2**   Hans Hotter sings Bach &
Brahms
   cond M. ARNOLD
   see CONCERT INDEX under:
(EMI) **CDC7 47284-2**   Arnold—Orchestral Works
   cond F. D'AVALOS
Brahms: Serenade 1, Symphony 1, Symphony 3,
Tragic Overture
Chausson: Symphony, Op. 20
Franck: Symphony
Martucci: Canzone dei ricordi, Piano Concerto 1
Mendelssohn: Erste Walpurgisnacht, Fair Melusina,
Midsummer Night's Dream (exc), Symphony 5
Schubert: Symphony 9
Wagner: Götterdämmerung (exc), Tannhäuser (exc)
   see CONCERT INDEX under:
(ASV) **CDDCA666**   D'Avalos conducts Wagner, Vol 3
(ASV) **CDDCA675**   Martucci—Complete Orchestral
Music, Vol. 1
(ASV) **CDDCA689**   Martucci—Complete Orchestral
Music, Vol. 2
(ASV) **CDDCA691**   Martucci—Complete Orchestral
Music, Vol. 4
(ASV) **CDDCA704**   Wagner—Overtures & Preludes
(ASV) **CDDCA744**   Brahms—Symphony No.2
(ASV) **CDDCA746**   Brahms—Symphony No 4.
Serenade No 2
(ASV) **CDDCA793**   Raff—Orchestral Works
(ASV) **CDDCA802**   Clementi—Orchestral Works,
Volume 1
(ASV) **CDDCA803**   Clementi—Orchestral Works,
Volume 2
(ASV) **CDDCA804**   Clementi—Orchestral Works,
Volume 3
(ASV) **CDDCS322**   Clementi—Complete Orchestral
Works
   cond K. BAKELS
Bruch: Violin Concerto 1
Saint-Saëns: Violin Concerto 3
   cond M. BAMERT
Hadley: Trees so high
Respighi: Concerto all'antica, Gregorian Concerto
Sainton: Island
   cond J. BARBIROLLI
Elgar: Cockaigne, Enigma Variations, Symphony 1
Vaughan Williams: Symphony 5
   see CONCERT INDEX under:
(EMI) **CDM7 69563-2**   Elgar: Orchestral Works
   cond E. BÁTIZ
Rimsky-Korsakov: Scheherazade, Tale of Tsar Saltan
(exc)
   see CONCERT INDEX under:
(IMG) **IMGCD1606**   Berlioz—Orchestral Works
   cond S. BEDFORD
Barber: Violin Concerto
Khachaturian: Violin Concerto
   cond R. BEHR
   see CONCERT INDEX under:
(EMI) **CDC5 55018-2**   Domingo sings and conducts
Tchaikovsky
   cond T. BENINTENDE-NEGLIA
   see CONCERT INDEX under:
(EMI) **CHS7 69741-2(7)**   Record of Singing,
Vol.4—Italian School
   cond L. BERIO
   see CONCERT INDEX under:
(TELD) **9031-74002-2**   Mahler (orch Berio)—Lieder
   cond H. BLECH
Goldmark: Violin Concerto 1
   cond A. BOULT
   see CONCERT INDEX under:
(EMI) **CDM7 69499-2**   Christa Ludwig sings Mahler
   cond K. BÖHM
Mozart: Così fan tutte (Cpte)
   see CONCERT INDEX under:
(EMI) **CDM7 63104-2**   Alfredo Krauss—Opera Recital
(EMI) **CMS5 65212-2**   Wagner—Les introuvables du
Ring
(EMI) **CDZ7 67015-2**   Mozart—Opera Arias
(TEST) **SBT1018**   Kirsten Flagstad
   cond M. BRABBINS
   see CONCERT INDEX under:
(ASV) **CDDCA931**   Hindemith—Works for
Viola,Volume 1

---

   cond N. BRAITHWAITE
   see CONCERT INDEX under:
(LYRI) **SRCD205**   Sterndale Bennett: Piano
Concertos, etc
   cond W. BRAITHWAITE
   see CONCERT INDEX under:
(EMI) **CDH7 63199-2**   Sena Jurinac—Opera and Song
Recital
(EMI) **CHS7 69741-2(5)**   Record of Singing,
Vol.4—Scandinavian School
(TEST) **SBT1018**   Kirsten Flagstad
   cond T. BREMNER
Jarre: Lawrence of Arabia (exc)
   see CONCERT INDEX under:
(SILV) **SILVAD3002**   At the Movies 2: Classic
Symphonic Film Music
   cond G. BURGON
   see CONCERT INDEX under:
(SILV) **FILMCD117**   The Television Scores of Geoffrey
Burgon
   cond Y. BUTT
   see CONCERT INDEX under:
(ASV) **CDDCA924**   Kodály—Orchestral Works
(ASV) **CDDCA934**   Goldmark—Orchestral Works
   cond S. BYCHKOV
Bruch: 2-Piano Concerto
Mendelssohn: 2-Piano Concerto in E
   cond G. CANTELLI
   see CONCERT INDEX under:
(EMI) **CZS5 68217-2**   Guido Cantelli—A profile
(TEST) **SBT1011**   Debussy—Orchestral Works
(TEST) **SBT1012**   Cantelli conducts Wagner & Brahms
(TEST) **SBT1017**   Orchestral Works - Cantelli
(TEST) **SBT1034**   Guido Cantelli conducts Rossini,
Mendelssohn & Beethoven
   cond CARL DAVIS
(DECC) **433 010-2DM**   Christmas Stars
   cond A. CLUYTENS
   see CONCERT INDEX under:
(EMI) **CHS5 65503-2**   Beethoven—Piano Concertos,
etc
   cond COLIN DAVIS
Berlioz: Harold in Italy
   see CONCERT INDEX under:
(EMI) **CMS7 63522-2**   Tippett—Chamber & Orchestral
Works
   cond L. COLLINGWOOD
   see CONCERT INDEX under:
(EMI) **CDH7 63199-2**   Sena Jurinac—Opera and Song
Recital
(EMI) **CHS7 69741-2(1)**   Record of Singing,
Vol.4—Anglo-American School (pt 1)
(EMI) **CHS7 69741-2(3)**   Record of Singing,
Vol.4—French School
(EMI) **CHS7 69741-2(4)**   Record of Singing,
Vol.4—German School
(TEST) **SBT1013**   Dame Joan Hammond—A
Celebration
   cond G. CURIEL
   see CONCERT INDEX under:
(TEST) **SBT1013**   Dame Joan Hammond—A
Celebration
   cond T. DART
   see CONCERT INDEX under:
(EMI) **CDM7 63655-2**   Schwarzkopf—The previously
unpublished recordings
   cond A. DAVIS
Beethoven: Romances (exc), Violin Concerto
Elgar: Enigma Variations, Pomp and Circumstance
Marches
   cond I. DOBROVEN
Beethoven: Piano Concerto 2, Piano Concerto 3,
Piano Concerto 4
Brahms: Violin Concerto
   see CONCERT INDEX under:
(EMI) **CDH7 63030-2**   Kirsten Flagstad - Wagner
Opera Arias
(EMI) **CDH7 63493-2**   Ginette Neveu—Recital
(EMI) **CDH7 64252-2**   Christoff sings Russian Arias &
Songs
(EMI) **CHS7 69741-2(4)**   Record of Singing,
Vol.4—German School
(EMI) **CMS7 64008-2(1)**   Wagner Singing on Record
(pt 1)
(TEST) **SBT1027**   Medtner—Piano Concertos, etc
(TEST) **SBT1042**   Brahms—Piano Concerto No.2, etc
   cond P. DOMINGO
   see CONCERT INDEX under:
(EMI) **CDC5 55018-2**   Domingo sings and conducts
Tchaikovsky
   cond C. DUTOIT
   see CONCERT INDEX under:
(DECC) **414 460-2DH**   Saint-Saëns—Orchestral
works
(DECC) **436 546-2DH**   Poulenc—Concertos
(DECC) **443 865-2DF2**   Saint-Saëns—Piano
Concertos
(ERAT) **2292-45971-2**   Tchaikovsky—Orchestral
Works
   cond J.O. EDWARDS
Forrest/Wright: Kismet (Cpte), Song of Norway
(Cpte), Timbuktu (exc)
Romberg: Student Prince (Cpte)
   see CONCERT INDEX under:
(TER) **CDVIR8314**   Is it really me?
(TER) **CDVIR8317**   If I Loved You - Love Duets from
the Musicals
   cond EDWIN FISCHER
   see CONCERT INDEX under:
(EMI) **CDH7 64928-2**   Bach—Keyboard Works

cond L. VON MATAČIĆ
Bruckner: Overture in G minor, Symphony 4
Lehár: Lustige Witwe (Cpte)
see CONCERT INDEX under:
(EMI) CDH7 61001-2   R. Strauss—Lieder & Arias
  cond M. MATHIESON
see CONCERT INDEX under:
(EMI) CDGO 2059   British Film Music from the 40s and
50s
  cond P. MAXWELL DAVIES
see CONCERT INDEX under:
(COLL) Coll1460-2   Maxwell Davies—Symphony No 5
etc
  cond H. MENGES
see CONCERT INDEX under:
(EMI) CHS5 65503-2   Beethoven—Piano Concertos,
etc
(EMI) CZS7 67735-2   Solomon—A Profile
  cond Y. MENUHIN
Mozart: Flute and Harp Concerto, K299
  cond M. MUDIE
(TEST) SBT1058   James Johnston - Opera Arias and
Songs
  cond R. MUTI
Cherubini: Coronation Mass in A, Marche religieuse
Donizetti: Don Pasquale (Cpte)
Gluck: Orfeo ed Euridice (Cpte)
Leoncavallo: Pagliacci (Cpte)
Mascagni: Cavalleria rusticana (Cpte)
Mozart: Violin Concerto, K211, Violin Concerto,
K218
Orff: Carmina Burana
Prokofiev: Ivan the Terrible
Tchaikovsky: Manfred Symphony
Verdi: Traviata (Cpte)
Vivaldi: Gloria, RV589, Magnificat, RV611
see CONCERT INDEX under:
(EMI) CDC7 47311-2   Maurice André plays Trumpet
Concertos
(EMI) CDM7 63104-2   Alfredo Krauss - Opera Recital
(EMI) CDM7 64329-2   Russian Piano Works
(EMI) CDM7 69500-2   Montserrat Caballé sings Bellini
& Verdi Arias
(EMI) CZS7 67314-2   Tchaikovsky—Symphonies
(EMI) CZS7 67521-2   Schumann—Concertos
  cond K. NAGANO
see CONCERT INDEX under:
(ASV) CDDCA786   Prokofiev—Piano Works
  cond G. NAVARRO
Rodrigo: Concierto de Aranjuez
  cond D. PARRY
Donizetti: Assedio di Calais (Cpte), Emilia di Liverpool
(Cpte), Eremitaggio di Liverpool (Cpte)
Mayr: Medea (Cpte)
Mercadante: Orazi e Curiazi (Cpte)
see CONCERT INDEX under:
(OPRA) ORCH103   Italian Opera—1810-20
(OPRA) ORCH104   A Hundred Years of Italian Opera:
1820-1830
  cond L. PEŠEK
Rachmaninov: Paganini Rhapsody, Piano Concerto
1
see CONCERT INDEX under:
(VIRG) VC7 59076-2   Janáček—Orchestral Music
  cond PETER THOMAS
Mozart: Flute Concerto, K313, Flute Concerto, K314
  cond J-B. POMMIER
see CONCERT INDEX under:
(DENO) CO-75258   Grieg/Franck/R.Strauss—Piano
Works
  cond G. PRÊTRE
see CONCERT INDEX under:
(EMI) CZS7 62690-2   Poulenc—Orchestral and Ballet
Works
  cond J. PRITCHARD
Berlioz: Rêverie et Caprice
Canteloube: Chants d'Auvergne (exc)
  cond S. RATTLE
Holst: Planets
Janáček: Sinfonietta, Taras Bulba
Shostakovich: Symphony 10
see CONCERT INDEX under:
(EMI) CDM7 64122-2   Sibelius—Orchestral Works
(EMI) CDM7 64737-2   Nielsen/Sibelius—Symphonies
(EMI) CMS7 64118-2   Sibelius—Complete
Symphonies, etc
  cond N. RESCIGNO
see CONCERT INDEX under:
(EMI) CDC7 47283-2   Maria Callas - Mad Scenes &
Bel Canto Arias
(EMI) CDC7 47730-2   Maria Callas sings Verdi Arias,
Vol.1
(EMI) CDM7 63182-2   The Incomparable Callas
(EMI) CMS7 63244-2   The Art of Maria Callas
(EMIN) CD-EMX2123   Maria Callas sings Operatic
Arias
  cond N. RICHARDSON
see CONCERT INDEX under:
(SILV) FILMCD127   Vampire Circus—The Essential
Vampire Theme Collection
(SILV) SILVAD3003   At the Movies 3: Horror &
Fantasy
  cond J. ROBERTSON
see CONCERT INDEX under:
(EMI) CDM7 63109-2   Tito Gobbi - Opera Aria Recital
(EMI) CHS7 69741-2(2)   Record of Singing,
Vol.4—Anglo-American School (pt 2)
(EMI) CHS7 69741-2(4)   Record of Singing,
Vol.4—German School
(TEST) SBT1019   Tito Gobbi - Opera Arias & Songs

(TEST) SBT1058   James Johnston - Opera Arias and
Songs
  cond S. ROBINSON
see CONCERT INDEX under:
(EMI) CDH7 61052-2   Beniamino Gigli—Arias and
Duets (1932-1949)
(EMI) CDH7 64028-2   Victoria de los Angeles sings
Spanish Songs
(TEST) SBT1013   Dame Joan Hammond—A
Celebration
  cond J-P. ROUCHON
see CONCERT INDEX under:
(ASV) CDDCA895   Berlioz—Vocal & Orchestral
Works
  cond J. RUDEL
Massenet: Cendrillon (Cpte)
see CONCERT INDEX under:
(EMI) CDM7 63104-2   Alfredo Krauss - Opera Recital
  cond P. SACHER
(DG) 423 696-2GH
Lutosławski/Stravinsky—Concerted Works
(DG) 445 487-2GXA   Mutter plays Modern Works
  cond E-P. SALONEN
Rachmaninov: Piano Concerto 2, Piano Concerto 3
Sibelius: Violin Concerto
Stravinsky: Firebird (Cpte), Jeu de cartes, Orpheus,
Petrushka
see CONCERT INDEX under:
(SONY) SK53289   Schoenberg/Liszt—Piano
Concertos
  cond K. SANDERLING
Mahler: Symphony 9
  cond W. SAWALLISCH
Brahms: Violin Concerto
Mozart: Piano Concerto 21, Piano Concerto 22
Orff: Kluge (Cpte), Mond (Cpte)
R. Strauss: Capriccio (Cpte)
see CONCERT INDEX under:
(EMI) CDC7 47834-2   R. Strauss/Hindemith—Horn
Concertos
(EMI) CDM7 63657-2   Schwarzkopf sings Opera Arias
(EMI) CDM7 69572-2   Weber: Overtures
(EMI) CMS5 65212-2   Wagner—Les introuvables du
Ring
  cond H. SCHIFF
Chopin: Piano Concerto 1, Piano Concerto 2
Lutosławski: Chain 2
Schnittke: Viola Concerto
  cond W. SCHÜCHTER
see CONCERT INDEX under:
(EMI) CDH5 65201-2   Leonie Rysanek - Operatic
Recital
(EMI) CDH7 64252-2   Christoff sings Russian Arias &
Songs
(EMI) CHS7 69741-2(4)   Record of Singing,
Vol.4—German School
  cond C. SCIMONE
Rossini: Maometto II (Cpte), Mosè in Egitto (Cpte)
  cond T. SERAFIN
Donizetti: Lucia di Lammermoor (Cpte)
see CONCERT INDEX under:
(EMI) CDC7 47282-2   Maria Callas - Operatic Recital
(EMI) CDC7 47966-2   Puccini and Bellini Arias
(EMI) CDM7 63182-2   The Incomparable Callas
(EMI) CMS7 63244-2   The Art of Maria Callas
  cond G. SÉBASTIAN
see CONCERT INDEX under:
(EMI) CDH7 63030-2   Kirsten Flagstad - Wagner
Opera Arias
(EMI) CHS5 69741-2(1)   Record of Singing,
Vol.4—Anglo-American School (pt 1)
(EMI) CMS5 65212-2   Wagner—Les introuvables du
Ring
  cond C. SILVESTRI
see CONCERT INDEX under:
(EMI) CZS5 68229-2   Constantin Silvestri—A profile
  cond G. SIMON
Respighi: Belkis, Queen of Sheba (exc), Brazilian
Impressions, Church Windows, Metamorphosen modi
XII
Six: Mariés de la Tour Eiffel (Cpte)
Various: Eventail de Jeanne
see CONCERT INDEX under:
(CALA) CACD0101   Orchestral works
(CALA) CACD1001   Debussy—Orchestral Works,
Vol.1
(CALA) CACD1002   Debussy—Orchestral Works,
Vol.2
(CALA) CACD1004   Ravel—Orchestral Works, Vol.1
(CALA) CACD1005   Ravel—Orchestral Works, Vol.2
(CALA) CACD1007   Respighi—Orchestral Works
(CALA) CACD1011   Borodin—Orchestral Works
(CALA) CACD1012   Mussorgsky—Orchestral Works
  cond Y. SIMONOV
see CONCERT INDEX under:
(COLL) Coll1207-2   Wagner—Orchestral Works
  cond G. SINOPOLI
Beethoven: Piano Concerto 1, Piano Concerto 2,
Romances, Violin Concerto
Bruch: Violin Concerto 1
Elgar: Cello Concerto, Pomp and Circumstance
Marches (exc), Symphony 1
Mahler: Kindertotenlieder, Klagende Lied, Symphony
1, Symphony 4, Symphony 5, Symphony 7,
Symphony 8, Symphony 9
Mascagni: Cavalleria rusticana (Cpte)
Mendelssohn: Symphony 4, Violin Concerto, op 64
Puccini: Madama Butterfly (Cpte), Manon Lescaut
(Cpte), Tosca (Cpte)
Rimsky-Korsakov: Russian Easter Festival Ov

Schoenberg: Pelleas und Melisande, Verklärte
Nacht
Schubert: Symphony 8
Sibelius: Violin Concerto
Tchaikovsky: Rococo Variations, Symphony 5, Violin
Concerto
Verdi: Forza del destino (Cpte)
Wagner: Tannhäuser (Cpte)
see CONCERT INDEX under:
(DG) 427 644-2GH   Debussy/Ravel—Orchestral
Works
(DG) 445 511-2GMA   Elgar—Orchestral Works
  cond L. SLATKIN
Vaughan Williams: Symphony 1, Symphony 5,
Symphony 6
see CONCERT INDEX under:
(RCA) RD60431   Dvořák—Works for Violin
(RCA) 09026 61193-2   Vaughan Williams—Orchestral
Works
(RCA) 09026 61194-2   Vaughan Williams—Orchestral
Works
(RCA) 09026 61196-2   Vaughan Williams—Orchestral
Works
(RCA) 09026 61631-2   Tchaikovsky—Works for Piano
& Orchestra
(RCA) 09026 62549-2   Haydn—London Symphonies,
Volume 1
  cond W. SUSSKIND
Bruch: Violin Concerto 1
Mozart: Cosi fan tutte (exc)
Prokofiev: Piano Concerto 3
Sibelius: Violin Concerto
see CONCERT INDEX under:
(EMI) CDH7 63201-2   Elisabeth Schwarzkopf—Early
Recordings
(EMI) CDH7 63495-2   Victoria de los Angeles—Early
Recordings
(EMI) CDH7 64028-2   Victoria de los Angeles sings
Spanish Songs
(EMI) CDM7 69501-2   Elisabeth
Schwarzkopf—Romantic Heroines
(EMI) CHS5 63703-2   Mozart: Piano Concertos, etc
(EMI) CHS7 69741-2(1)   Record of Singing,
Vol.4—Anglo-American School (pt 1)
(EMI) CZS5 68485-2   Les Introuvables de János
Starker
(EMI) CZS7 67310-2   Menuhin plays Popular Violin
Concertos
(OLYM) OCD190   The Lympany Legend, Vol. 1
(RCA) 09026 61778-2(07)   The Heifetz Collection, Vol.
7
(TEST) SBT1013   Dame Joan Hammond—A
Celebration
(TEST) SBT1016   Pierre Fournier - recital
(TEST) SBT1018   Kirsten Flagstad
(TEST) SBT1019   Tito Gobbi - Opera Arias & Songs
(TEST) SBT1028   Mozart—Violin Concertos
  cond E. SVETLANOV
Balakirev: Russian Ov. II, Symphony 1
Holst: Planets
Rimsky-Korsakov: Mlada (exc), Russian Easter
Festival Ov, Symphony 2
see CONCERT INDEX under:
(HYPE) CDA66586   Balakirev—Orchestral Works
  cond V. TAUSKY
Alwyn: Miss Julie (Cpte)
see CONCERT INDEX under:
(TEST) SBT1013   Dame Joan Hammond—A
Celebration
  cond B. THOMSON
see CONCERT INDEX under:
(CHAN) CHAN8867   Arnold: Dances
  cond M. TILSON THOMAS
(UNIC) UKCD2010   Knussen—Orchestral & Vocal
Works
  cond A. TONINI
see CONCERT INDEX under:
(EMI) CDC7 47283-2   Maria Callas - Mad Scenes &
Bel Canto Arias
(EMI) CDC7 54437-2   Callas Rarities
  cond Y.P. TORTELIER
Albéniz: Iberia
Falla: Sombrero de tres picos (Cpte)
see CONCERT INDEX under:
(CHAN) CHAN8989   Respighi—Orchestral Works
(CHAN) CHAN9092   Gershwin—Piano & Orchestral
Works
  cond A. VANDERNOOT
(EMI) CMS5 65252-2   Cziffra Edition, Volume 3
(EMI) CDM7 69499-2   Christa Ludwig sings Mahler
(EMI) CZS7 67474-2   Viva España!
  cond VLADIMIR ASHKENAZY
Beethoven: Symphony 5, Symphony 7
Dvořák: Cello Concerto
Mussorgsky: Pictures
Sibelius: Symphony 1, Symphony 3, Symphony 6,
Symphony 7
see CONCERT INDEX under:
(DECC) 417 762-2DM   Sibelius: Orchestral Works
(DECC) 421 069-2DM4   Sibelius: Complete
Symphonies
(DECC) 430 721-2DM   Beethoven—Orchestral Works
(DECC) 430 737-2DM   Sibelius—Orchestral Works
(DECC) 430 757-2DM   Sibelius—Orchestral Works
  cond H. WALLBERG
see CONCERT INDEX under:
(EMI) CDM7 69501-2   Elisabeth
Schwarzkopf—Romantic Heroines

cond W. WALTON
Walton: Troilus and Cressida (exc), Violin Concerto
see CONCERT INDEX under:
(EMI) **CHS5 65003-2** Walton conducts Walton
cond C. WARREN-GREEN
see CONCERT INDEX under:
(NIMB) **NI7016** Classical Trumpet Concertos
cond H. WEIGERT
see CONCERT INDEX under:
(EMI) **CMS5 65212-2** Wagner—Les introuvables du Ring
cond G. WELDON
Tchaikovsky: Sleeping Beauty (Cpte)
see CONCERT INDEX under:
(EMI) **CHS7 69741-2(1)** Record of Singing, Vol.4—Anglo-American School (pt 1)
(EMIN) **CD-EMX2198** A Delius Festival
cond W. WELLER
Mendelssohn: Symphony 2, Symphony 3, Symphony 4
see CONCERT INDEX under:
(CHAN) **CHAN9099** Mendelssohn—Orchestral Works
cond D. WILLCOCKS
see CONCERT INDEX under:
(CHAN) **CHAN8760** Walton—Choral Works
cond H. WOLFF
see CONCERT INDEX under:
(TELD) **9031-76350-2** Bartók—Orchestral Works
cond M. WOODS
see CONCERT INDEX under:
(CARL) **DPCD1048** Schumann—Symphonies
cond S. WRIGHT
see CONCERT INDEX under:
(NIMB) **NI5121** Virtuoso Trumpet Concertos
(NIMB) **NI7016** Classical Trumpet Concertos
cond D.V. YU
Tchaikovsky: Serenade, Op. 48, Souvenir de Florence
see CONCERT INDEX under:
(CARL) **MCD82** Russian Masterpieces

PHILHARMONIA ORCHESTRA CELLOS
cond G. SIMON
see CONCERT INDEX under:
(CALA) **CACD0104** The London Cello Sound

PHILHARMONIA QUARTET
see CONCERT INDEX under:
(TEST) **SBT1007** Kell plays Mozart Clarinet Works

PHILHARMONIA VIRTUOSI
cond R. KAPP
V. Thomson: Plow that broke the Plains, River
see CONCERT INDEX under:
(SCHW) **310832** Frank Martin—Orchestral Works

PHILHARMONIC CHAMBER CHOIR (LONDON)
cond D. TEMPLE
see CONCERT INDEX under:
(MERI) **CDE84173** Elgar: Songs & Part-songs

PHILHARMONIC QUARTET
see CONCERT INDEX under:
(OPUS) **9351 1894** French Chamber Works
(SYMP) **SYMCD1130** Joseph Holbrooke—Historic Recordings

PHILIPPE, André (bass)
Gounod: Roméo et Juliette (Cpte)
Offenbach: Contes d'Hoffmann (Cpte)

PHILIPPE, Michel (bass)
Berlioz: Troyens (Cpte)

PHILIPPE, Michel (ten)
Messiaen: Saint François d'Assise (Cpte)

PHILLIPS, Daniel (cond)
see Jesus College Ch

PHILLIPS, Edna (hp)
see CONCERT INDEX under:
(BIDD) **WHL013** Stokowski conducts French Music, Vol.3

PHILLIPS, Margaret (organ)
see CONCERT INDEX under:
(COLL) **Coll1270-2** 20th Century Christmas Music
(COLL) **Coll1343-2** Britten—Choral Works, Vol. II
(COLL) **Coll1370-2** Britten—Choral Works, Vol.3
(GAMU) **GAMCD514** 18th Century English Organ Music
(GAMU) **GAMCD522** 19th Century English Organ Music
(REGE) **REGCD105** From Chamber to Chantry
(YORK) **CD110** Saint-Saëns—Music for organ

PHILLIPS, Michael (organ)
see CONCERT INDEX under:
(ASV) **CDDCA881** English Church Music, Vol.3

PHILLIPS, Norman (bar)
Martinů: Ariane (Cpte)

PHILLIPS, Peter (cond)
see Chilingirian Qt

PHILLIPS, Sian (sngr)
Rodgers: Pal Joey (Cpte)

PHILLIPS, Todd (vn)
Mozart: Sinfonia Concertante, K364

PHILOMUSICA OF LONDON
cond G. GUEST
see CONCERT INDEX under:
(DECC) **443 868-2DF2** Italian Baroque Sacred Works

cond A. LEWIS
Purcell: King Arthur, Z628 (Cpte)

PHIPPS, Simon (cond)
see New Sadler's Wells Op Orch

PHOENIX SINGERS
cond R. SACCANI
Verdi: Aida (Cpte)

PHOENIX SYMPHONY ORCHESTRA
cond J. SEDARES
E. Bernstein: Hallelujah Trail Overture, Magnificent Seven (exc)
Herrmann: Symphony 1
Schuman: New England Triptych
see CONCERT INDEX under:
(KOCH) **37092-2** Copland—Orchestral Works

PIAF, Edith (spkr)
Cocteau: Bel indifférent

PIANO CIRCUS
Reich: Pianos
Riley: In C
see CONCERT INDEX under:
(ARGO) **433 522-2ZH** 20th Century Piano Works
(ARGO) **436 100-2ZH** Graham Fitkin—Works for Pianos
(ARGO) **440 294-2ZH** Music for Multiple Pianos
(ARGO) **443 527-2ZH** Loopholes

PIANO CIRCUS BAND
cond R. MORAN
see CONCERT INDEX under:
(ARGO) **436 128-2ZH** Moran—Vocal and Chamber Works
cond C. SMITH
see CONCERT INDEX under:
(ARGO) **436 128-2ZH** Moran—Vocal and Chamber Works

PIANODUO
see CONCERT INDEX under:
(CHNN) **CCS4592** Messiaen/Ives—Works for two pianos

PIANTINI, Carlos (cond)
see Italian International Orch

PIANTONI CERCLE CHORAL
cond E. ANSERMET
see CONCERT INDEX under:
(CASC) **VEL2010** Memories of the Suisse Romande - Suzanne Danco

PIARD, Marius (bn)
see CONCERT INDEX under:
(EMI) **CDS7 54607-2** Stravinsky plays and conducts Stravinsky

PIATIGORSKY, Gregor (vc)
Brahms: Double Concerto, Piano Trio 2
Dvořák: Cello Concerto, Piano Trio 3
Mendelssohn: Piano Trio 1
R. Strauss: Don Quixote
Schubert: Piano Trio 2
Tchaikovsky: Piano Trio, Op. 50, Souvenir de Florence
Walton: Cello Concerto
see CONCERT INDEX under:
(DANA) **DACOCD303** Great Musicians in Copenhagen
(MUSI) **MACD-644** The Art of Gregor Piatigorsky
(MUSI) **MACD-674** Piatigorsky—Recordings from the Pre-war era
(PEAR) **GEMMCD9447** Gregor Piatigorsky plays Schumann, Beethoven, Weber & Brahms
(RCA) **GD87871** Jascha Heifetz Collection
(RCA) **GD87872** Jascha Heifetz Collection
(RCA) **GD87873** Beethoven, Brahms & Schubert: Chamber Works
(RCA) **GD87963** Heifetz plays Korngold, Rózsa & Waxman
(RCA) **GD87965** Dvořák & Brahms: Chamber Works
(RCA) **09026 61778-2(10)** The Heifetz Collection, Vol. 10
(RCA) **09026 61778-2(11-15)** The Heifetz Collection, Vols. 11-15
(RCA) **09026 61778-2(21)** The Heifetz Collection, Vol. 21
(RCA) **09026 61778-2(25)** The Heifetz Collection, Vol. 25
(RCA) **09026 61778-2(26)** The Heifetz Collection, Vol. 26
(RCA) **09026 61778-2(27)** The Heifetz Collection, Vol. 27
(RCA) **09026 61778-2(28)** The Heifetz Collection, Vol. 28
(RCA) **09026 61778-2(30)** The Heifetz Collection, Vol. 30
(RCA) **09026 61778-2(31)** The Heifetz Collection, Vol. 31
(RCA) **09026 61778-2(33)** The Heifetz Collection, Vol. 33
(RCA) **09026 61778-2(34)** The Heifetz Collection, Vol. 34
(RCA) **09026 61778-2(35)** The Heifetz Collection, Vol. 35
(RCA) **09026 61778-2(37)** The Heifetz Collection, Vol. 37
(RCA) **09026 61778-2(41)** The Heifetz Collection, Vol. 41
(RCA) **09026 61778-2(42)** The Heifetz Collection, Vol. 42
(RCA) **09026 61778-2(43)** The Heifetz Collection, Vol. 43

(RCA) **09026 61778-2(44)** The Heifetz Collection, Vol. 44
(SONY) **SM3K45845** Webern—Complete Works

PIAU, Sandrine (sop)
Biber: Requiem in F minor
Campra: Idoménée (Cpte)
Collase: Racine Canticles
Handel: Messiah (Cpte), Scipione (Cpte)
Mendelssohn: Midsummer Night's Dream (Cpte)
Purcell: Fairy Queen, Z629 (Cpte), King Arthur, Z628 (Cpte)
Rameau: Castor et Pollux (Cpte), Indes galantes (Cpte), Pygmalion (Cpte)
Valls: Missa Scala Aretina
see CONCERT INDEX under:
(HARM) **HMC90 1351** Delalande—Sacred Choral Works
(HARM) **HMC90 1416** Delalande—Petits Motets
(HARM) **HMC90 1417** Caplet—Orchestral and Vocal Works
(VIRG) **VC5 45075-2** Charpentier—Leçons de ténèbres, Vol. 2

PICARDY REGIONAL ORCHESTRA (LE SINFONIETTA)
cond P. FOURNILLIER
Haydn: Applausus (Cpte)

PICCAVER, Alfred (ten)
see CONCERT INDEX under:
(NIMB) **NI7851** Legendary Voices
(PEAR) **GEMMCDS9925(2)** Covent Garden on Record—Vol.3 (pt 2)
(PREI) **89060** Alfred Piccaver (1884-1958)
(SCHW) **314632** Vienna State Opera Live, Vol.13

PICCHI, Mirto (ten)
Cherubini: Medea (Cpte)

PICCINNI, Andrea (bass)
Puccini: Bohème (Cpte), Tosca (Cpte)

PICCO, Millo (bass)
Verdi: Traviata (Cpte)

PICCOLI, Francesco (ten)
Donizetti: Lucia di Lammermoor (Cpte)

PICCOLLO, Silvia (sop)
A. Scarlatti: Maddalena (Cpte)

PICHARD, Anne (sop)
Campra: Idoménée (Cpte)
Montéclair: Jephté (Cpte)

PICHLER, Alexander (ten)
see CONCERT INDEX under:
(SCHW) **314652** Vienna State Opera Live, Vol.15

PICK, Hanns (bass)
Wagner: Meistersinger (Cpte)

PICKENS, James Vincent (ten)
Gershwin: Porgy and Bess (Cpte)

PICKERING, Martin (treb)
see CONCERT INDEX under:
(ABBS) **CDMVP827** 20 Christmas Carols from St George's Chapel, Windsor Castle

PICKERSGILL, William (bass-bar)
Schreker: Ferne Klang (Cpte)

PICKETT, Philip (cond)
see New London Consort

PICKETT, Philip (rec/dir)
see CONCERT INDEX under:
(L'OI) **433 043-2OH** Telemann—Concertos

PICK-HIERONIMI, Monica (sop)
Beethoven: Christus am Oelberge, Op. 85

PICKLER, Charles (va)
R. Strauss: Don Juan, Don Quixote

PICKLER, Robert (cond)
see Sydney SO

PICOTTI, Livio (alto)
Monteverdi: Vespers

PIDOUX, Roland (vc)
see CONCERT INDEX under:
(AUVI) **V4679** Schmitt—Chamber Works
(MARC) **8 223636** In Memoriam Lili Boulanger
(SONY) **SK47230** Mozart—Chamber Works

PIECK, Marijke (sop)
Verdi: Simon Boccanegra (Cpte)

PIECZONKA, Adrianne (sop)
Mozart: Zauberflöte (Cpte)

PIERARD, Catherine (mez)
Britten: Rape of Lucretia (Cpte)
Mozart: Zauberflöte (Cpte)

PIERARD, Catherine (sop)
Purcell: Dioclesian, Z627 (Cpte), Fairy Queen, Z629 (Cpte)
see CONCERT INDEX under:
(CHAN) **CHAN9185/6** Howells—Songs

PIERCE, Eluned (hp)
see CONCERT INDEX under:
(CHAN) **CHAN8525** Music from Estonia, Vol 1

PIERCE, Jacqueline (sop)
see CONCERT INDEX under:
(NEW) **80220-2** Angels' Visits

PIERCE, Joshua (pf)
see CONCERT INDEX under:

(KOCH) 37002-2 American Works for 2 Pianos & Orchestra

PIERCE, Judith (sop)
Wagner: Walküre (Cpte)

PIERI, M. (sngr)
see CONCERT INDEX under:
(MUSD) 20239-2 Delibes—Opéras-Comiques

PIERLOT, Philippe (fl)
see CONCERT INDEX under:
(ERAT) 2292-45772-2 Saint-Saëns—Works for Chamber Ensemble

PIERLOT, Philippe (va da gamba)

PIERLOT, Philippe (va da gamba/dir)
see CONCERT INDEX under:
(RICE) RIC118100 Le Tombeau de M. de Sainte-Colombe
(RICE) RIC098112 German Baroque Chamber Music, Vol.5

PIERLOT, Pierre (ob)
Albinoni: Concerti, Op. 9 (exc)
see CONCERT INDEX under:
(ERAT) 2292-45937-2 Mozart—Wind Concertos
(ERAT) 4509-95361-2 Mozart—Wind Concertos
(SONY) SK47230 Mozart—Chamber Works

PIEROTIC, Piero (bar)
see CONCERT INDEX under:
(SCHW) 314502 Vienna State Opera—Live Recordings (sampler)
(SCHW) 314542 Vienna State Opera Live, Vol.4
(SCHW) 314572 Vienna State Opera Live, Vol.7

PIEROTTI, Raquel (mez)
Bretón: Verbena de La Paloma (Cpte)
Rossini: Barbiere di Siviglia (Cpte), Comte Ory (Cpte)
Vives: Doña Francisquita (Cpte)

PIERRE, Francis (hp)
see CONCERT INDEX under:
(MARC) 8 223636 In Memoriam Lili Boulanger

PIERRE, Gregory (treb)
Britten: Midsummer Night's Dream (Cpte)

PIERRE, Joelle (sngr)
Planquette: Rip van Winkle (Cpte)

PIERSON, Edward (bar)
D. Moore: Carry Nation (Cpte)

PIERSON, Edward (voc)
Joplin: Treemonisha (Cpte)

PIETA, Richard (vn)
see CONCERT INDEX under:
(RICE) RIC014024 Boesmans—Concertos

PIETERSON, George (cl)
Hindemith: Clarinet Concerto
see CONCERT INDEX under:
(DECC) 444 455-2DH Martin—Ballades; Concerto for 7 Wind Instruments
(OTTA) OTRC29134 Brahms—Piano Trios
(PHIL) 438 365-2PM2 Brahms—Complete Trios
(PHIL) 438 742-2PM2 Debussy—Orchestral Music

PIETILÄINEN, Pauli (organ)
Aho: Pergamon

PIETSCH, Gernot (ten)
Puccini: Bohème (Cpte)

PIGERRE, Jean-Pierre (va)
see CONCERT INDEX under:
(ERAT) 2292-45368-2 Chausson: Songs

PIGLIUCCI, Giannicola (bar)
Verdi: Otello (Cpte)

PIGNEGUY, John (hn)
see CONCERT INDEX under:
(HYPE) CDA66172 Malcolm Arnold: Chamber Works, Vol. 2
(HYPE) CDA66173 Malcolm Arnold: Chamber Works, Vol. 3

PIGUET, Michel (ob)
Mozart: Oboe Concerto, K314
Telemann: Essercizii musici (exc)

PIGULLA, Franziska (spkr)
Mendelssohn: Oedipus (Cpte)

PIKAL, Guido (ten)
see CONCERT INDEX under:
(MARC) 8 223546 Furtwängler—Lieder and Choral Works

PIKE, Julian (ten)
Henze: English Cat (Cpte)

PIKULSKI, Maciej (pf)
see CONCERT INDEX under:
(FORL) UCD16692 Duparc—Mélodies

PILAR ALONSO, Maria del (sngr)
Bretón: Verbena de la Paloma (Cpte)

PILARCZYK, Helga (sop)
Berg: Wozzeck (exc)
Janáček: Glagolitic Mass (Cpte)
see CONCERT INDEX under:
(MERC) 432 006-2MM Orchestral Works

PILARL, Erica (sngr)
Schreker: Ferne Klang (Cpte)

PILAT, Richard (prepared pf)
see CONCERT INDEX under:

(BIS) BIS-CD272 Contemporary Music for Flute and Percussion

(TAMARA) PILIPCHUK VOCAL ENSEMBLE
see CONCERT INDEX under:
(OLYM) OCD296 Moscow Contemporary Music Ensemble - Volume 5

PILLER, Verena (contr)
Haydn: Mass 11

PILLINGER, Edward (cl)
Lumsdaine: What shall I sing?
see CONCERT INDEX under:
(UNIC) UKCD2010 Knussen—Orchestral & Vocal Works

PILOT, Ann Hobson (hp)
Ginastera: Harp Concerto
Mathias: Harp Concerto, Op. 50

PILTTI, Lea (sop)
see CONCERT INDEX under:
(ACAN) 43 128 Elisabeth Schwarzkopf—Vol. 2
(PREI) 93262 R.Strauss accompanies Reining,Dermota and Piltti

PILZ, August (cond)
see Odeon Orch

PINA, Erich (bass)
Wagner: Meistersinger (Cpte)

PINDELL, Reginald (bar)
Weill: Lost in the Stars (Cpte)

PINEAU, Jacques (spkr)
Bizet: Djamileh (Cpte)

PINEL, Anthony (organ)
see CONCERT INDEX under:
(MERI) CDE84168 Elgar: Choral Music
(MERI) CDE84188 Dvořák, Bruckner and Brahms: Choral Works

PINI, Anthony (vc)
Beethoven: Piano Trios (exc)
see CONCERT INDEX under:
(APR) APR5503 Solomon—The First HMV Recordings 1942-3
(DUTT) CDAX8014 British Gramophone Premieres
(TEST) SBT1002 Reginald Kell—Clarinet Works
(TEST) SBT1022 Brain,Kell & Goossens play Schubert & Beethoven

PINI, Carl (vn)
Rubbra: Violin Concerto

PINI-CORSI, Antonio (bar)
see CONCERT INDEX under:
(EMI) CHS7 64860-2(2) La Scala Edition - Vol.1, 1878-1914 (pt 2)
(MEMO) HR4408/9(1) Singers in Genoa, Vol.1 (disc 1)
(NIMB) NI7840/1 The Era of Adelina Patti
(PEAR) GEMMCDS9923(1) Covent Garden on Record, Vol.1 (pt 1)
(SYMP) SYMCD1149 Fernando De Lucia
(TEST) SBT1008 Viva Rossini

PINKAS, Jiří (cond)
see Brno Janáček Op Orch

PINKAS, Sally (pf)
see CONCERT INDEX under:
(NORT) NR248-CD Silenced Voices - Victims of the Holocaust

PINKERT, Regina (sop)
see CONCERT INDEX under:
(MEMO) HR4408/9(1) Singers in Genoa, Vol.1 (disc 1)
(PEAR) GEMMCDS9923(1) Covent Garden on Record, Vol.1 (pt 1)
(SYMP) SYMCD1113 The Harold Wayne Collection, Vol.13

PINNOCK, Trevor (cond)
see English Concert

PINNOCK, Trevor (hpd)
Bach: Flute Sonatas, BWV1030-5, Goldberg Variations
D. Scarlatti: Keyboard Sonatas (exc)
Handel: Belshazzar (Cpte)
Haydn: Stabat Mater
Rameau: Pièces de clavecin (exc), Pièces de clavecin en concerts (exc)
see CONCERT INDEX under:
(ARCH) 413 591-2AH The Harmonious Blacksmith
(CRD) CRD3307 Recital at the Victoria & Albert Museum
(CRD) CRD3347 A Choice Collection of Lessons and Ayres

PINNOCK, Trevor (hpd/dir)
Bach: Brandenburg Concertos, Suites, BWV1066-9, Triple Concerto, BWV1044, 3-Harpsichord Concerti (exc), 4-Harpsichord Concerto
Mozart: Symphony 40, Symphony 41
see CONCERT INDEX under:
(ARCH) 413 731-2AH Bach: Concerti
(ARCH) 415 518-2AH Baroque Orchestral Works
(ARCH) 415 991-2AH Bach harpsichord concertos
(ARCH) 415 992-2AH Bach—Concertos
(ARCH) 429 756-2AH Haydn: Sturm und Drang Symphonies, Vol.5
(ARCH) 431 678-2AH Haydn—Concertos
(ARCH) 435 262-2AH Christmas Concertos
(ARCH) 437 088-2AT Collectio Argentea 18: English Baroque Concertos

(ARCH) 439 893-2AH Telemann—Suites; Concerto in D
(ARCH) 447 043-2AH4 Mozart—The Late Symphonies
(CRD) CRD3311 Mozart & C.P.E.Bach: Keyboard Concertos
(CRD) CRD3348/9 Vivaldi—Concertos

PINNOCK, Trevor (virg)
see CONCERT INDEX under:
(CRD) CRD3307 Recital at the Victoria & Albert Museum

PINTO, Amelia (sop)
see CONCERT INDEX under:
(EMI) CHS7 64860-2(2) La Scala Edition - Vol.1, 1878-1914 (pt 2)
(IRCC) IRCC-CD808 Souvenirs of 19th Century Italian Opera
(MEMO) HR4408/9(2) Singers in Genoa, Vol.1 (disc 2)
(SYMP) SYMCD1111 The Harold Wayne Collection, Vol.11

PINTO, David (treb)
Britten: Noye's Fludde (Cpte)
see CONCERT INDEX under:
(DECC) 436 990-2DWO The World of Benjamin Britten

PINTO, Marie-Thérèse (sop)
Britten: Noye's Fludde (Cpte)
see CONCERT INDEX under:
(DECC) 436 990-2DWO The World of Benjamin Britten

PINZA, Ezio (bass)
Verdi: Requiem (Cpte)
see CONCERT INDEX under:
(EMI) CDH7 61051-2 Beniamino Gigli - Operatic Arias
(EMI) CHS7 64864-2(1) La Scala Edition - Vol.2, 1915-46 (pt 1)
(MMOI) CDMOIR404 Ezio Pinza—Recital
(MMOI) CDMOIR411 Sacred Songs and Arias
(MMOI) CDMOIR428 Rosa Ponselle and Giovanni Martinelli sing Verdi
(NIMB) NI7804 Giovanni Martinelli—Opera Recital
(NIMB) NI7805 Rosa Ponselle—Opera & Song Recital
(NIMB) NI7851 Legendary Voices
(NIMB) NI7852 Galli-Curci, Vol.2
(PEAR) GEMMCDS9452 The Emperor Tibbett
(PEAR) GEMMCDS9926(2) Covent Garden on Record—Vol.4 (pt 2)
(PEAR) GEMMCDS9306 Ezio Pinza—Opera Recital
(PEAR) GEMMCDS9367 Gigli—Arias and Duets
(PREI) 89050 Ezio Pinza (1892-1957)
(PREI) 89062 Giovanni Martinelli (1885-1969)
(RCA) GD87810 Rosa Ponselle - Opera & Song Recital
(RCA) GD87811 Beniamino Gigli—Operatic Arias
(RCA) 09026 61245-2 Ezio Pinza - Recital
(RCA) 09026 61580-2(3) RCA/Met 100 Singers, 100 Years (pt 3)
(ROMO) 81007-2 Rosa Ponselle—Victor Recordings 1926-1929
(ROMO) 81014-2 Elisabeth Rethberg (1894-1976)
(SCHW) 314512 Vienna State Opera Live, Vol.1
(SONY) MPK45693 Portrait—Ezio Pinza
(TEST) SBT1008 Viva Rossini

PIOLINO, François (ten)
Purcell: Fairy Queen, Z629 (Cpte)
see CONCERT INDEX under:
(HARM) HMC90 1351 Delalande—Sacred Choral Works

PIONTEK, Klaus (spkr)
Mendelssohn: Antigone (Cpte), Oedipus (Cpte)

PIPAL, Hans (sngr)
R. Strauss: Rosenkavalier (Cpte)

PIPPIN, Donald (cond)
see Orig Broadway Cast

PIQUEMAL, Michel (cond)
see M. Piquemal Voc Ens

PIQUEMAL, Michel (bar)
Fauré: Requiem (Cpte)
see CONCERT INDEX under:
(ARIO) ARN68071 Sauget—Vocal and orchestral works

(MICHEL) PIQUEMAL VOCAL ENSEMBLE
see CONCERT INDEX under:
(NAXO) 8 553196 Duruflé—Sacred Choral and Organ Works, Volume 1
cond M. PIQUEMAL
Fauré: Messe basse
see CONCERT INDEX under:
(NAXO) 8 553196 Duruflé—Sacred Choral and Organ Works, Volume 1
(NAXO) 8 553197 Duruflé—Sacred Choral and Organ Works, Volume 2

PIRADOV, Vladimir (cond)
see Bolshoi Th Orch

PIRASTI TRIO
see CONCERT INDEX under:
(ASV) CDDCA925 Holst/Stanford/Bax—Piano Trios

PIRAZZINI, Miriam (mez)
Cherubini: Medea (Cpte)
Puccini: Madama Butterfly (Cpte)

R. Strauss: Schweigsame Frau (Cpte)
*Wagner: Götterdämmerung (Cpte), Rheingold
(Cpte)*
see CONCERT INDEX under:
(DECC) **414 100-2DM15** Wagner: Der Ring des Nibelungen
(FOYE) **15-CF2011** Wagner—Der Ring de Nibelungen

PLUMMER, Christopher (narr)
Prokofiev: Ivan the Terrible Suite

PLUSHWIK, Gerhard (vc)
Mozart: Flute Quartets

PLUZHNIKOV, Konstantin (ten)
Borodin: Prince Igor (Cpte)
Mussorgsky: Khovanshchina (Cpte)
Scriabin: Symphony 1

**PLYMOUTH MUSIC SERIES CHORUS
cond P. BRUNELLE**
Britten: Paul Bunyan (Cpte)
Copland: Tender Land (Cpte)
see CONCERT INDEX under:
(COLL) **Coll1449-2** Witness—Spirituals and Gospels, Volume 1
(VIRG) **VC7 59022-2** Smyth—Vocal and Orchestral Works

**PLYMOUTH MUSIC SERIES ENSEMBLE SINGERS
cond P. BRUNELLE**
see CONCERT INDEX under:
(COLL) **Coll1449-2** Witness—Spirituals and Gospels, Volume 1

**PLYMOUTH MUSIC SERIES ORCHESTRA
cond P. BRUNELLE**
Britten: Paul Bunyan (Cpte)
Copland: Tender Land (Cpte)
see CONCERT INDEX under:
(VIRG) **VC7 59022-2** Smyth—Vocal and Orchestral Works

POBŁOCKA, Ewa (pf)
Panufnik: Piano Concerto
see CONCERT INDEX under:
(CONI) **75605 51750-2** Grieg—Piano and Orchestral Works

POCHAPSKY, Viacheslav (bass-bar)
Rachmaninov: Aleko (Cpte)

POCHON, Virginie (sngr)
Lully: Phaëton (Cpte)

PODAŘILOVÁ, Eva (celesta)
see CONCERT INDEX under:
(SUPR) **11 1878-2** The Unknown Janáček

PODBOLOTOV, Alexandre (ten)
Mussorgsky: Marriage (Cpte)

PODGER, Julian (ten)
see CONCERT INDEX under:
(ARGO) **436 833-2ZH** Purcell— Music for the Funeral of Queen Mary

PODGER, Rachel (vn)
see CONCERT INDEX under:
(O111) **OPS30-121** Haydn—English and Scottish Songs

PODLES, Ewa (contr)
Rossini: Tancredi (Cpte)
see CONCERT INDEX under:
(DECC) **436 261-2DHO3** Puccini—Il Trittico
(FORL) **UCD16683** Russian Songs

PODSKALSKÝ, Miroslav (bass)
see CONCERT INDEX under:
(STUD) **SM1223.27** Rossini—Complete unpublished Sacred Works

POELL, Alfred (bar)
Beethoven: Fidelio (Cpte)
Mozart: Nozze di Figaro (Cpte)
R. Strauss: Arabella (Cpte), Ariadne auf Naxos (Cpte), Rosenkavalier (Cpte)
Wagner: Meistersinger (Cpte)
see CONCERT INDEX under:
(CAMB) **CD-1032** From the Operas of Erich Wolfgang Korngold
(DECC) **425 959-2DM** Lisa della Casa sings R. Strauss
(EMI) **CZS7 67123-2** Wagner: Der Ring des Nibelungen
(PREI) **93261** Richard Strauss accompanies
(SCHW) **314551** Vienna State Opera Live, Vol.5
(SCHW) **314652** Vienna State Opera Live, Vol.15

POGGI, Ferrero (ten)
Rossini: Donna del lago (Cpte)
Verdi: Vespri siciliani (Cpte)

POGGI, Gianni (ten)
Puccini: Bohème (Cpte)
Verdi: Traviata (Cpte)

POGNARI, Hélène (pf)
see CONCERT INDEX under:
(MUSI) **MACD-620** 20th Century French Violin Works

POGORELICH, Ivo (pf)
Bach: English Suites, BWV806-811 (exc)
Chopin: Piano Concerto 2, Polonaises (exc), Preludes (exc)
D. Scarlatti: Keyboard Sonatas (exc)
Haydn: Keyboard Sonata 30, Keyboard Sonata 31
Liszt: Piano Sonata, S178
Prokofiev: Piano Sonata 6

Ravel: Gaspard de la nuit
Scriabin: Piano Sonata 2
Tchaikovsky: Piano Concerto 1
see CONCERT INDEX under:
(DG) **410 520-2GH** Beethoven & Schumann: Piano Works
(DG) **415 123-2GH** Chopin: Piano works
(DG) **437 460-2GH** Brahms—Piano Works
(DG) **437 763-2GH** Mozart—Piano Works

POGSON, Geoffrey (ten)
Bizet: Carmen (Cpte)
G. Lloyd: Iernin

POHJOLA, Liisa (pf)
see CONCERT INDEX under:
(BIS) **BIS-CD053** Ligeti—Various Works

POHL, Carla (sop)
Weill: Zar lässt sich Photographieren (Cpte)

POHL, Gisela (contr)
Hindemith: Nusch-Nuschi (Cpte)
Wagner: Parsifal (Cpte)

POHL, Hans-Dietrich (bar)
Puccini: Bohème (Cpte)

POHL, Rudolf (cond)
see Collegium Aureum

PÓKA, Balázs (bar)
Puccini: Bohème (Cpte)

POKORNÁ, Jindra (mez)
Janáček: Jenufa (Cpte)

POKORNÝ, Jiří (pf)
see CONCERT INDEX under:
(ROMA) **RR1941** Terezin - The Music 1941-44

POKROVSKY ENSEMBLE
Stravinsky: Noces (Cpte)
Traditional: Russian Village Wedding Songs (exc)

POLA, Bruno (bar)
Verdi: Traviata (Cpte)

POLACCO, Giorgio (cond)
see orch

POLÁŠEK, Oldřich (ten)
Dvořák: Kate and the Devil (Cpte)

POLDI, Piero (ten)
Verdi: Rigoletto (Cpte)

POLEZHAEV, Alexander (pf)
see CONCERT INDEX under:
(OLYM) **OCD530** Miaskovsky—Cello Works

POLGÁR, László (bass)
Beethoven: Fidelio (Cpte)
Donizetti: Poliuto (Cpte)
Liszt: Hungarian Coronation Mass, S11
Mascagni: Lodoletta (Cpte)
Mozart: Clemenza di Tito (Cpte), Don Giovanni (Cpte)
Respighi: Belfagor (Cpte), Semirama (Cpte)
Schreker: Gezeichneten (Cpte)
Schubert: Fierrabras (Cpte)
see CONCERT INDEX under:
(SONY) **SK45855** Mozart: Bastien und Bastienne

POLI, Afro (bar)
Mascagni: Cavalleria rusticana (Cpte)
Puccini: Bohème (Cpte)
see CONCERT INDEX under:
(EMI) **CHS7 64864-2(2)** La Scala Edition - Vol.2, 1915-46 (pt 2)
(MSCM) **MM30231** Don Pasquale & Tito Schipa Recital

POLI, Piero Francesco (ten)
Donizetti: Lucia di Lammermoor (Cpte)
Puccini: Turandot (Cpte)
Verdi: Ballo in maschera (Cpte), Traviata (Cpte)

POLIDORI, Graziano (bar)
Donizetti: Pazzi per progetto (Cpte)

POLI-RANDACCIO, Tina (sop)
see CONCERT INDEX under:
(EMI) **CHS7 64860-2(2)** La Scala Edition - Vol.1, 1878-1914 (pt 2)

POLISH CHAMBER ORCHESTRA
Haydn: Keyboard Concerto, HobXVIII/11
see CONCERT INDEX under:
(LINN) **CKD001** Polish Chamber Orchestra live in Glasgow
cond W. LUTOSŁAWSKI
see CONCERT INDEX under:
(POLS) **PNCD043** Lutosławski: Orchestral Works
cond J. MAKSYMIUK
Bartók: Divertimento
Britten: Frank Bridge Variations
Vivaldi: Concerti, Op. 8 (exc)
see CONCERT INDEX under:
(OLYM) **OCD392** Bacewicz—Orchestral and Chamber Works

**POLISH CHAMBER PHILHARMONIC ORCHESTRA
cond W. RAJSKI**
see CONCERT INDEX under:
(CHNT) **LDC278 962** Polish Works for Piano & Orchestra
(CLAV) **CD50-9018** Concertos for Oboe and Orchestra

**POLISH NATIONAL OPERA CHORUS
cond R. SATANOWSKI**
Szymanowski: Harnasie, Mandragora

**POLISH NATIONAL OPERA ORCHESTRA
cond R. SATANOWSKI**
Szymanowski: Harnasie, Mandragora
see CONCERT INDEX under:
(SCHW) **314001** Szymanowski: Lieder

**POLISH NATIONAL RADIO ORCHESTRA
cond A. WIT**
see CONCERT INDEX under:
(POLS) **PNCD020** Penderecki: Orchestral Works

**POLISH NATIONAL RADIO SYMPHONY ORCHESTRA
cond S. GUNZENHAUSER**
Paganini: Violin Concerto 1, Violin Concerto 2
see CONCERT INDEX under:
(NAXO) **8 550598** Dvořák—Symphonic Poems
cond M. HALÁSZ
Mahler: Blumine, Symphony 1, Symphony 7, Symphony 9
cond J. KASPSZYK
see CONCERT INDEX under:
(EMI) **CDM5 65082-2** Szymanowski—Orchestral Works
cond J. KATLEWICZ
(OLYM) **OCD313** Gorecki—Orchestral and Vocal Works
cond C. KOLCHINSKY
see CONCERT INDEX under:
(NAXO) **8 550758** Glazunov/Dvořák—Violin Concertos
cond A. LEAPER
Elgar: Cockaigne, Violin Concerto
Tchaikovsky: Symphony 2, Symphony 4
cond W. LUTOSŁAWSKI
see CONCERT INDEX under:
(EMI) **CDM5 65076-2** Lutosławski—Orchestral Works
(EMI) **CDM5 65305-2** Lutosławski—Orchestral Works
cond K. PENDERECKI
(EMI) **CDM5 65077-2** Penderecki—Orchestral and Vocal Works
cond J. SEMKOW
see CONCERT INDEX under:
(EMI) **CDM5 65082-2** Szymanowski—Orchestral Works
(EMI) **CDM5 65307-2** Szymanowski—Orchestral and Piano Works
cond T. STRUGAŁA
Paderewski: Piano Concerto
cond J. WILDNER
(NAXO) **8 550494** Works for Violin and Orchestra
cond A. WIT
Dvořák: Piano Concerto, Water Goblin
Mahler: Symphony 2, Symphony 5, Symphony 6
Prokofiev: Piano Concerto 2, Piano Concerto 5
Schumann: Symphony 2, Symphony 4
Smetana: Má vlast
Tchaikovsky: Francesca da Rimini, Storm, Symphony 3, Symphony 5, Symphony 6, Tempest
see CONCERT INDEX under:
(EBS) **EBS6063** Franz & Richard Strauss—Horn Concertos
(EURM) **350238** Weber—Works for Piano & Orchestra
(NAXO) **8 550566** Prokofiev—Piano Concertos
(NAXO) **8 550753** Ravel/Falla—Piano Concertos
(NAXO) **8 553005** Dvořák—Orchestral Works
(POLS) **PNCD050** R. Strauss: Orchestral Works

**POLISH RADIO & TV SYMPHONY ORCHESTRA
cond S. KAWALLA**
see CONCERT INDEX under:
(CONI) **CDCF147** Van de Vate: Orchestral Works
(CONI) **CDCF168** Penderecki & Van de Vate—Orchestral Works
cond T. STRUGAŁA
see CONCERT INDEX under:
(KOCH) **312652** Szymanowski—Orchestral and Choral Works

**POLISH RADIO AND TELEVISION CHOIR
cond T. STRUGAŁA**
see CONCERT INDEX under:
(KOCH) **312652** Szymanowski—Orchestral and Choral Works
cond S. WISLOCKI
see CONCERT INDEX under:
(KOCH) **312652** Szymanowski—Orchestral and Choral Works

**POLISH RADIO CHAMBER ORCHESTRA
cond A. DUCZMAL**
see CONCERT INDEX under:
(ASV) **CDQS6094** Grieg/Suk/Tchaikovsky—String Music

**POLISH RADIO SYMPHONY ORCHESTRA
cond T. WOJCIECHOWSKI**
see CONCERT INDEX under:
(CONI) **75605 51750-2** Grieg—Piano and Orchestral Works

**POLISH STATE PHILHARMONIC CHORUS
(KATOWICE)
cond J. KRENZ**
see CONCERT INDEX under:
(OLYM) **OCD385** Górecki—Choral & Orchestral Works

POLISH STATE PHILHARMONIC ORCHESTRA (KATOWICE)
cond O. DOHNÁNYI
see CONCERT INDEX *under:*
(MARC) 8 223207 Johann Strauss II Edition, Vol.7
(MARC) 8 223208 Johann Strauss II Edition, Vol.8
cond K. JEAN
see CONCERT INDEX *under:*
(NAXO) 8 550231 Berlioz: Orchestral Works
cond J. KRENZ
see CONCERT INDEX *under:*
(OLYM) OCD385 Górecki—Choral & Orchestral Works
cond J. WILDNER
see CONCERT INDEX *under:*
(MARC) 8 223209 Johann Strauss II Edition, Vol.9
(MARC) 8 223210 Johann Strauss II Edition, Vol.10

POLISH SYMPHONY ORCHESTRA
cond W. KILAR
see CONCERT INDEX *under:*
(OLYM) OCD602 Wojciech Kilar—Film Music

POLITKOVSKY, Vladimir (bar)
(DANT) LYS013/5 Tchaikovsky—The Queen of Spades

POLÍVKOVÁ, Jana (sop)
Hába: Mother (Cpte)

POLIVNICK, Paul (cond)
see Alabama SO

POLLACK, Christian (cond)
see Košice St PO

POLLAIN, René (va)
see CONCERT INDEX *under:*
(PEAR) GEMMCDS9922 New York Philharmonic - 150th Anniversary
(RCA) 09026 60929-2 R.Strauss—Tone Poems

POLLARD, Brian (bn)
see CONCERT INDEX *under:*
(TELD) 4509-97467-2 Frans Brüggen Edition Vol. 5—Late Baroque Chamber Music

POLLET, Françoise (sop)
Berlioz: Troyens (Cpte)
Honegger: Jeanne d'Arc (Cpte)
Poulenc: Voix Humaine (Cpte)
see CONCERT INDEX *under:*
(ACCO) 20283-2 Duparc—Orchestral Songs
(ACCO) 20441-2 Brahms—Lieder
(DG) 435 860-2GH2 Berlioz—Mélodies
(DG) 437 786-2GH Webern—Orchestral, Vocal & Chamber Works

POLLINI, Maurizio (cond)
see COE

POLLINI, Maurizio (pf)
Bartók: Piano Concerto 1, Piano Concerto 2
Beethoven: Piano Concerto 2, Piano Concerto 4, Piano Concerto 5, Piano Sonata 28, Piano Sonata 29
Berg: Piano Sonata
Brahms: Piano Concerto 1, Piano Quintet
Chopin: Etudes (exc), Piano Sonata 2, Piano Sonata 3, Polonaises (exc), Preludes (exc)
Debussy: Etudes
Mozart: Piano Concerto 19, Piano Concerto 23
Schoenberg: Piano Concerto
Schubert: Fantasy, D760, Piano Sonata, D845, Piano Sonata, D958, Piano Sonata, D959
Schumann: Fantasie, Piano Concerto, Piano Sonata 1
see CONCERT INDEX *under:*
(DG) 419 199-2GH2 Beethoven: Late Piano Sonatas
(DG) 419 229-2GH2 Schubert—Piano Works
(DG) 419 779-2GH Beethoven: Orchestral & Choral Works
(DG) 419 793-2GH3 Beethoven: Piano Concertos
(DG) 423 249-2GC Schoenberg: Piano Music
(DG) 427 322-2GH Liszt: Piano Works
(DG) 427 326-2GH Schubert: Piano Works
(DG) 427 642-2GH Beethoven: Piano Sonatas
(DG) 427 770-2GH Beethoven—Piano Sonatas
(DG) 429 570-2GH Beethoven: Late Piano Sonatas
(DG) 431 623-2GH Chopin—Piano Works
(DG) 439 770-2GH3 Beethoven—Piano Concertos
(DG) 445 522-2GMA Schumann—Piano Works
(DG) 447 431-2GOR 20th Century Piano Works
(EMI) CDM7 64354-2 Chopin—Piano Works

POLLOCK, Frank (sngr)
see CONCERT INDEX *under:*
(PEAR) GEMMCDS9056/8 Music from the New York Stage, Vol. 3: 1913-17

POLMEAR, Jeremy (cor ang)
see CONCERT INDEX *under:*
(UNIC) DKPCD9121 Sweet Melancholy

POLMEAR, Jeremy (ob)
see CONCERT INDEX *under:*
(UNIC) DKPCD9121 Sweet Melancholy

POLOZOV, Vyacheslav (ten)
Mussorgsky: Boris Godunov (Cpte)

POLS, Anneke (viol)
see CONCERT INDEX *under:*
(ACCE) ACC8864D Symphonia Angelica

POLSTER, Hermann Christian (bass)
Bach: St. Matthew Passion, BWV244 (Cpte)
Mendelssohn: Elias (Cpte), Paulus (Cpte)

Wagner: Meistersinger (Cpte), Parsifal (Cpte)

POLVERELLI, Laura (mez)
Jommelli: Armida abbandonata (Cpte)
Rossini: Cenerentola (Cpte)

POLVTSOVA, Jeanne (mez)
Rachmaninov: Vespers, Op. 37 (Cpte)

POLYANSKY, Valéry (cond)
see Russian St Polyphonic Cappella

POLYPHONY
cond S. LAYTON
MacMillan: Cantos Sagrados, Seven Last Words

PÖLZER, Julius (ten)
see CONCERT INDEX *under:*
(SCHW) 314512 Vienna State Opera Live, Vol.1
(SCHW) 314632 Vienna State Opera Live, Vol.13
(SCHW) 314662 Vienna State Opera Live, Vol.16

POMERANIAN PHILHARMONIC ORCHESTRA
cond T. UKIGAYA
Yun: Symphony 5
see CONCERT INDEX *under:*
(THOR) CTH2013 Martinů—Orchestral Works
(THOR) CTH2041 Lutosławski—Orchestral Works

POMERIUM MUSICES
cond A. BLACHLY
see CONCERT INDEX *under:*
(DORI) DOR90184 Busnois—In Hydraulis and other works

POMMER, Max (cond)
see Berlin CO

POMMERS, Leon (pf)
see CONCERT INDEX *under:*
(EMI) ZDMF7 64830-2 The Art of Nathan Milstein

POMMIER, Jean-Bernard (cond)
see Northern Sinfonia

POMMIER, Jean-Bernard (pf)
Chopin: Waltzes
see CONCERT INDEX *under:*
(ERAT) 2292-45598-2 Beethoven—Piano Sonatas, Vol.1
(ERAT) 2292-45812-2 Beethoven—Piano Sonatas, Vol.2
(VIRG) VJ7 59642-2 Brahms—Violin Sonatas

POMMIER, Jean-Bernard (pf/dir)
see CONCERT INDEX *under:*
(VIRG) VJ7 59655-2 French Impressions

POMPONI, Franco (sngr)
Schuman: Mighty Casey (Cpte)

PONDEPEYRE, Angeline (pf)
see CONCERT INDEX *under:*
(REM) REM311105 Poulenc—Melodies

PONGRACZ, Istvan (pf)
see CONCERT INDEX *under:*
(CLAV) CD50-9300/4 Hommage à Tibor Varga
(CLAV) CD50-9314 Hommage à Tibor Varga, Volume 4

PONKIN, Vladimir (cond)
see Leningrad PO

PONOMAREV, Viocheslav (vc)
see CONCERT INDEX *under:*
(ASV) CDDCA686 Fauré—Orchestral Works

PONS, Ismael (sngr)
Vives: Doña Francisquita (Cpte)

PONS, Josep (cond)
see Teatre Lliure CO

PONS, Juan (bar)
Donizetti: Lucia di Lammermoor (Cpte), Poliuto (Cpte)
Falla: Vida breve (Cpte)
Leoncavallo: Pagliacci (Cpte)
Mascagni: Cavalleria rusticana (Cpte), Iris (Cpte)
Penella: Gato Montés (Cpte)
Puccini: Fanciulla del West (Cpte), Madama Butterfly (Cpte), Tosca (Cpte)
Verdi: Aroldo (Cpte), Falstaff (Cpte), Forza del destino (Cpte), Traviata (Cpte)
see CONCERT INDEX *under:*
(DECC) 436 261-2DHO3 Puccini—Il Trittico

PONS, Lily (sop)
(MSOU) DFCDI-111 The Art of the Coloratura
(RCA) 09026 61580-2(4) RCA/Met 100 Singers, 100 Years (pt 4)
(SONY) MPK45694 Lily Pons—Opera & Song Recital

PONSEELE, Marcel (ob)
Telemann: Musique de Table (exc)
Zelenka: Trio Sonatas

PONSELLE, Carmela (mez)
see CONCERT INDEX *under:*
(ROMO) 81007-2 Rosa Ponselle—Victor Recordings 1926-1929

PONSELLE, Rosa (pf)
(RCA) GD87810 Rosa Ponselle - Opera & Song Recital

PONSELLE, Rosa (sop)
Bellini: Norma (exc)
Verdi: Traviata (exc)
see CONCERT INDEX *under:*

(MMOI) CDMOIR408 Great Sopranos
(MMOI) CDMOIR428 Rosa Ponselle and Giovanni Martinelli sing Verdi
(NIMB) NI7801 Great Singers, Vol.1
(NIMB) NI7802 Divas 1906-1935
(NIMB) NI7804 Giovanni Martinelli—Opera Recital
(NIMB) NI7805 Rosa Ponselle—Opera & Song Recital
(NIMB) NI7846 Rosa Ponselle, Vol.2
(NIMB) NI7851 Legendary Voices
(PEAR) GEMMCDS9926(1) Covent Garden on Record—Vol.4 (pt 1)
(PEAR) GEMMCDS9926(2) Covent Garden on Record—Vol.4 (pt 2)
(RCA) GD87810 Rosa Ponselle - Opera & Song Recital
(RCA) 09026 61580-2(3) RCA/Met 100 Singers, 100 Years (pt 3)
(ROMO) 81006-2 Rosa Ponselle (1897-1981)
(ROMO) 81007-2 Rosa Ponselle—Victor Recordings 1926-1929

PONTI, Michael (pf)
Brahms: Paganini Variations
F. X. Scharwenka: Piano Concerto, Op.56
Goetz: Piano Concerto 2
Liszt: Paganini Studies, S140
Melcer-Szczawinski: Piano Concerto 1
Moszkowski: Piano Concerto
Rubinstein: Piano Concerto 4
Thalberg: Piano Concerto
see CONCERT INDEX *under:*
(UNIC) DKPCD9110 Kuhlau—Orchestral works
(VOX) 115708-2 Mosonyi/Raff/Stavenhaegn—Piano Concertos
(VOX) 115709-2 D'Albert/Bronsart/Liszt—Piano Concertos
(VOX) 115712-2 Hiller/Litolff/Moscheles—Piano Concertos
(VOX) 115713-2 Mendelssohn/Reinecke/Rheinberger—Piano Concertos
(VOX) 115714-2 Balakirev/Lyapunov/Medtner—Piano Concertos
(VOX) 115717-2 Chopin/Henselt/Hiller—Piano Concertos

PONTI, Raffaele Delle (pf)
see CONCERT INDEX *under:*
(EMI) CHS7 64860-2(2) La Scala Edition - Vol.1, 1878-1914 (pt 2)
(PEAR) GEMMCDS9073(1) Giovanni Zenatello, Vol.1 (pt 1)

PONTIGGIA, Luigi (ten)
Mascagni: Amico Fritz (Cpte)

PÖNTINEN, Roland (pf)
Gade: Symphony 5
Scriabin: Piano Concerto
see CONCERT INDEX *under:*
(BIS) BIS-CD159 Hindemith—Chamber Works
(BIS) BIS-CD188 Stravinsky. Piano Works
(BIS) BIS-CD276 Roland Pöntinen plays Russian piano music
(BIS) BIS-CD287 Trumpet Works
(BIS) BIS-CD298 The Romantic Trombone
(BIS) BIS-CD300 Music for a Rainy Day
(BIS) BIS-CD317 Satie: Piano Works
(BIS) BIS-CD353 Beethoven: Piano Works.
(BIS) BIS-CD358 The Russian Viola
(BIS) BIS-CD364 The Russian Violin
(BIS) BIS-CD377 Schnittke: Concertos
(BIS) BIS-CD401 Tubin: Orchestral Works
(BIS) BIS-CD419 The Russian Flute
(BIS) BIS-CD547 Schnittke—Chamber Works
(BIS) BIS-CD593 Poulenc—Music for Two Pianos
(BIS) BIS-CD647 Grieg—Violin Sonatas
(BIS) BIS-CD651 Hindemith—Sonatas for Viola and Piano
(BIS) BIS-CD663/4 Janáček—Chamber and Instrumental Works

POOLE, John (cond)
see BBC Sngrs

POPA, Aurelian Octav (cl)
see CONCERT INDEX *under:*
(OLYM) OCD418 Aurelian Octav Popa plays Clarinet Concertos

POPA, Aurelian Octav (cl/dir)
see CONCERT INDEX *under:*
(OLYM) OCD406 M. Haydn: Concertos

POPA, Edouard (vn)
see CONCERT INDEX *under:*
(CHNT) LDC278 821 Boëly—Works for Strings

POPA, Péter (vn)
see CONCERT INDEX *under:*
(NAXO) 8 553090 Beethoven—Chamber Works

POPANGELOVA, Stefka (mez)
Mussorgsky: Boris Godunov (Cpte)
Tchaikovsky: Eugene Onegin (Cpte)

POPE, Cathryn (sop)
Mozart: Nozze di Figaro (Cpte)
Stravinsky: Rake's Progress (Cpte)

POPELLO-DAVIDOVA, Evgenia (mez)
see CONCERT INDEX *under:*
(NIMB) NI7865 Great Singers at the Mariinsky Theatre

POPESCU, Paul (cond)
see Iaşi Moldova PO

POPESCU, René Cristian (vn)
Enescu: String Octet

POPKEN, Ralf (alto)
Bach: Cantata 11, Cantata 211, Cantata 213, Easter
Oratorio, BWV249 (Cpte)
Handel: Agrippina (Cpte), Ottone (Cpte), Radamisto
(Cpte)
Hasse: Conversione di Sant' Agostino (Cpte)

POPLE, Peter (vn)
see CONCERT INDEX under:
(CRD) **CRD3457** Dvořák—Hausmusik

POPLE, Ross (cond)
see London Fest Orch

POPLE, Ross (vc)
Buller: Theatre of Memory
see CONCERT INDEX under:
(ASV) **CDDCA769** Franck—Miscellaneous Works

POPOV, Mincho (ten)
Borodin: Prince Igor (Cpte)
Glinka: Life for the Tsar (Cpte)
Mussorgsky: Boris Godunov (Cpte)
Tchaikovsky: Queen of Spades (Cpte)

POPOV, Stoyan (bass)
Mussorgsky: Khovanshchina (Cpte)

POPOV, Vladimir (ten)
Mussorgsky: Khovanshchina (Cpte)

POPOV, Yuri (pf)
see CONCERT INDEX under:
(OLYM) **OCD269** Kabalevsky—Volume 4

POPOVA, Maria Petrova (sop)
Mussorgsky: Khovanshchina (Cpte)

POPP, Lucia (sop)
Bach: St. Matthew Passion, BWV244 (Cpte)
Beethoven: Fidelio (Cpte)
Bizet: Djamileh (Cpte)
Brahms: Deutsches Requiem, Op. 45 (Cpte)
Flotow: Martha (Cpte)
Grieg: Peer Gynt (exc)
Handel: Giulio Cesare (Cpte), Messiah (Cpte)
Haydn: Schöpfung (Cpte)
J. Strauss II: Fledermaus (Cpte)
Janáček: Cunning Little Vixen (Cpte), Jenufa (Cpte)
Leoncavallo: Bohème (Cpte)
Mahler: Knaben Wunderhorn (exc), Symphony 8
Mendelssohn: Midsummer Night's Dream (exc),
Symphony 2
Mozart: Clemenza di Tito (Cpte), Così fan tutte
(Cpte), Don Giovanni (Cpte), Entführung (Cpte),
Idomeneo (Cpte), Nozze di Figaro (Cpte), Sogno di
Scipione (Cpte), Zauberflöte (exc)
Orff: Carmina Burana, Kluge (Cpte)
R. Strauss: Daphne (Cpte), Intermezzo (Cpte),
Rosenkavalier (Cpte)
Schoeck: Venus (Cpte)
Verdi: Nabucco (Cpte), Rigoletto (Cpte)
Wagner: Götterdämmerung (Cpte), Parsifal (Cpte),
Rheingold (Cpte), Tannhäuser (Cpte)
see CONCERT INDEX under:
(CFP) **CD-CFP4532** Sacred Arias
(DECC) **414 100-2DM15** Wagner: Der Ring des
Nibelungen
(DECC) **430 498-2DWO** The World of Mozart
(DECC) **430 804-2DC10** Mahler—Complete
Symphonies
(EMI) **CDC7 47019-2** Mozart—Opera Arias
(EMI) **CDC7 47407-2** Schubert: Sacred Choral works
(EMI) **CDC7 49318-2** R. Strauss—Lieder
(EMI) **CDC7 49319-2** Lucia Popp sings Slavonic
Opera Arias
(EMI) **CDC7 49700-2** Lucia Popp sings Viennese
Operetta
(EMI) **CDM7 64634-2** Fauré/Bach—Choral Works
(EMI) **CDM7 69223-2** Schubert—Choral Works
(EMI) **CDM7 69546-2** Lucia Popp
(EMI) **CMS7 64471-2** Mahler—Symphonies, Vol.1
(EMI) **CMS7 64778-2** Schubert—Sacred Works,
Vol.1
(EMI) **CMS7 64783-2** Schubert—Sacred Works,
Vol.2
(EMI) **CZS7 62707-2** Mahler—Vocal Works
(EMIL) **CDZ7 67015-2** Mozart—Opera Arias
(EURO) **GD69043** Puccini: Il Trittico
(HYPE) **CDJ33017** Schubert—Complete Lieder,
Vol.17
(ORFE) **C363941B** Lucia Popp - Lieder Recital
(PHIL) **442 073-2PB5** Beethoven—Complete
Symphonies, etc
(RCA) **RD60950** Lucia Popp - Jugendstil-Lieder
(SONY) **SK48242** R. Strauss—Orchestral Lieder
(SONY) **SM2K47522** Beethoven & Haydn—Choral
Works

POPP, Michael (cond)
see Estampie

POPPEN, Christoph (vn)
Messiaen: Quatuor, Thème et variations

POPPEN, Diemut (va)
Boccherini: Sextets, G461-6 (exc), String Sextets,
G454-9 (exc)
see CONCERT INDEX under:
(CAPR) **10 453** Boccherini Edition, Vol.8
(DG) **437 535-2GH** Schubert—Soirée

POPPERWELL, Stephen (ob)
see CONCERT INDEX under:

(KOCH) **37058-2** Holst—Works for Chamber
Orchestra

POPSAVOV, Miroslav (cond)
see Sofia Orthodox Ch

PORCELLI, Mario (bar)
Salieri: Axur (Cpte)

PORCHER, Hans Joachim (bass)
Killmayer: Yolimba (Cpte)
Mozart: Zauberflöte (Cpte)
Weber: Peter Schmoll (Cpte)

PORTAL, Enrique R. del (ten)
Vives: Doña Francisquita (Cpte)

PORTAL, Michel (cl)
Boulez: Domaines
Brahms: Clarinet Quintet, String Quintet 2
see CONCERT INDEX under:
(DECC) **421 581-2DH** Poulenc—Chamber Works
(EMI) **CDC7 54466-2** Brahms—Chamber Works
(EMI) **CMS7 62542-2** Prokofiev—Piano Concertos,
etc
(EMI) **CZS7 62736-2** Poulenc—Chamber Works

PORTAL, Sylvie (sop)
Fauré: Messe basse

PORTER, John (organ)
see CONCERT INDEX under:
(ABBS) **CDMVP827** 20 Christmas Carols from St
George's Chapel, Windsor Castle

PORTILLO, Joaquin (sngr)
Bretón: Verbena de la Paloma (Cpte)

PORTLAND QUARTET
Chadwick: String Quartet 1, String Quartet 2
Kreisler: String Quartet
R.Strauss: String Quartet, Op. 2
see CONCERT INDEX under:
(NORT) **NR232-CD** Piston—Piano and Chamber
Works
(NORT) **NR9001-CD** Piston—Sting Quartets Nos. 1-
3

PORTUGHEIS, Alberto (pf)
see CONCERT INDEX under:
(ASV) **CDDCA589** Khachaturian—Piano Works
(ASV) **CDDCA865** Ginastera—Piano Music, Vol.1
(ASV) **CDDCA880** Ginastera—Piano Music, Vol.2
(ASV) **CDDCA901** Rossini—Piano Pieces from Sins
of Old Age
(ASV) **CDDCA902** Ginastera—Piano Works, Volume
3

POSCH, Alois (db)
Gubaidulina: Hommage
Mozart: Serenade, K525
Schubert: Trout Quintet, D667
see CONCERT INDEX under:
(EMI) **CDC5 55108-2** R. Strauss/Mozart—Chamber
Works
(EMI) **CDC7 54881-2** Viennese Dance Music

POSCHNER-KLEBEL, Brigitte (sop)
Beethoven: Symphony 9
Mussorgsky: Khovanshchina (Cpte)
R. Strauss: Rosenkavalier (Cpte)
Schumann: Szenen aus Goethes Faust (Cpte)
see CONCERT INDEX under:
(DG) **435 486-2GH** Schubert/Schumann—Sacred
Choral Works

POSELLA, Leonard (fl/picc)
Schoenberg: Pierrot Lunaire

POSKIN, Francis (fl/picc)
see CONCERT INDEX under:
(DINT) **DICD920125** Walton—Façade

POSPÍŠIL, Michal (bass)
Zelenka: Requiem, ZWV48

POSSELT, Marita (sop)
B. Goldschmidt: Gewaltige Hahnrei (Cpte)
Krenek: Jonny spielt auf (Cpte)
Schreker: Gezeichneten (Cpte)

POST, Martin (ten)
Telemann: Getreue Music-Meister (Cpte)

POSTNIKOVA, Victoria (pf)
Busoni: Fantasia contrappuntistica, Piano Concerto,
Op. 39
Schnittke: Concerto Grosso 6
Tchaikovsky: Piano Concerto 1, Piano Concerto 2,
Piano Concerto 3, Piano Sonata, Op. 80, Seasons
see CONCERT INDEX under:
(ERAT) **2292-45772-2** Saint-Saëns—Works for
Chamber Ensemble
(ERAT) **2292-45969-2** Tchaikovsky—Complete Piano
Works

POTIER, Jacques (ten)
Honegger: Roi David (Cpte)
Saint-Saëns: Samson et Dalila (Cpte)

POTT, Charles (bass)
see CONCERT INDEX under:
(HYPE) **CDA66314** Purcell—Complete Odes &
Welcome Songs, Vol.1
(HYPE) **CDA66412** Purcell—Complete Odes &
Welcome Songs, Vol.3
(HYPE) **CDA66456** Purcell—Complete Odes &
Welcome Songs, Vol.4
(HYPE) **CDA66476** Purcell—Complete Odes &
Welcome Songs, Vol.5

POTTER, John (ten)
Monteverdi: Orfeo (Cpte)
Pärt: Passio
see CONCERT INDEX under:
(CHAN) **CHAN8478** Erik Bergman—Choral Works
(HARM) **HMU90 7053** Humfrey—Verse Anthems
(SAYD) **CD-SDL400** English National Songs
(TELD) **4509-90798-2** Monteverdi—Il Ballo delle
ingrate

POTTER, Philip (ten)
Sullivan: Patience (Cpte), Pirates of Penzance (Cpte),
Yeomen of the Guard (Cpte)
see CONCERT INDEX under:
(DECC) **433 868-2DWO** The World of Gilbert &
Sullivan - Volume 2

POTTS, Nigel (organ)
see CONCERT INDEX under:
(PRIO) **PRCD505** Magnificat and Nunc Dimittis,
Volume 3

POUGNET, Jean (vn)
see CONCERT INDEX under:
(DUTT) **CDAX8014** British Gramophone Premieres

POULENARD, Isabelle (sop)
Bach: Mass in B minor, BWV232 (Cpte)
Collasse: Racine Canticles
Handel: Alessandro (Cpte)
Pergolesi: Pro Jesu dum vivo, Stabat Mater
Rameau: Indes galantes (Cpte)
Vivaldi: Montezuma (Cpte)
see CONCERT INDEX under:
(HARM) **HMA190 1150** Couperin—Motets
(HYPE) **CDA66292** Fauré: Sacred Choral Works
(O111) **OPS39-9103** Clérambault—Secular Cantatas
(RICE) **RIC052034** Charpentier—Sacred Choral
Works

POULENC, Francis (pf)
see CONCERT INDEX under:
(ADES) **14114-2** Poulenc: Mélodies
(ADES) **14115-2** Poulenc: Mélodies
(EMI) **CDC5 55036-2** Honegger/Poulenc—Perform
their own works
(EMI) **CDC7 54605-2** Poulenc and Britten play
Poulenc and Britten
(EMI) **CHS7 69741-2(3)** Record of Singing,
Vol.4—French School
(EMI) **CZS7 62690-2** Poulenc—Orchestral and Ballet
Works
(PEAR) **GEMMCD9311** Poulenc d'après Poulenc

POULET, Gérard (vn)
see CONCERT INDEX under:
(ARIO) **ARN68228** Debussy/Pierné/Ravel—Sonatas
for Violin and Piano
(PHIL) **422 508-2PME4** The Complete Mozart Edition
Vol 8
(PHIL) **438 803-2PM2** Mozart—Violin Sonatas

POULSON, Lani (mez)
Mozart: Finta giardiniera (Cpte)

POULTER, Eileen (sop)
Purcell: Dido (Cpte)

POULTON, Robert (bar)
Berlioz: Enfance du Christ (Cpte)
Lehár: Lustige Witwe (Cpte)
Vaughan Williams: Hugh the Drover (Cpte)

POUNDS, Courtice (sngr)
see CONCERT INDEX under:
(EMI) **CDANGEL 5** Norton—Chu Chin Chow

POURADIER-DUTEIL, Monique (sop)
see CONCERT INDEX under:
(EMI) **CDS7 49361-2** Offenbach: Operettas

POWELL, Claire (mez)
Falla: Amor brujo (Cpte), Corregidor y la Molinera
(Cpte)
G. Lloyd: Iernin
R. Strauss: Rosenkavalier (Cpte)
see CONCERT INDEX under:
(CARL) **MCD15** Opera Spectacular

POWELL, Claude (cond)
see SO

POWELL, Josef (sngr)
see CONCERT INDEX under:
(PHIL) **446 406-2PH** Berlin—Heat Wave

POWELL, Roy (keyboards)
see CONCERT INDEX under:
(ARGO) **443 903-2ZH** First & Foremost

POWELL, Shezwae (mez)
Kern: Show Boat (Cpte)

POWELL, Thomas (bar)
Puccini: Bohème (Cpte)

POWER, Patrick (ten)
Balfe: Bohemian Girl (Cpte)
Beethoven: Symphony 9
Purcell: Dido (Cpte)

POWER BIGGS, Edward (George) (organ)
see CONCERT INDEX under:
(SONY) **SMK47625** R. Strauss—Orchestral Works

POWERS, James T. (sngr)
see CONCERT INDEX under:
(PEAR) **GEMMCDS9050/2(1)** Music from the New
York Stage, Vol. 1 (part 1)

POWERS, Tom (sngr)
see CONCERT INDEX under:
(PEAR) GEMMCDS9059/61   Music from the New York
Stage, Vol. 4: 1917-20

POZAS, Jorge (vc)
Falla: Harpsichord Concerto

POZEMKOVSKY, Georgi (ten)
see CONCERT INDEX under:
(EMI) CDH7 61009-2   Chaliapin sings Russian Opera
Arias

POZNAN AMADEUS CHAMBER ORCHESTRA
cond A. DUCZMAL
see CONCERT INDEX under:
(WERG) WER60172-50   Penderecki: Orchestral and
Vocal Works

POZNAN BOYS' CHOIR
cond J. KURCZEWSKI
see CONCERT INDEX under:
(OLYM) OCD313   Gorecki—Orchestral and Vocal
Works

POZNAN OPERA CHORUS
cond A. BOREJKO
see CONCERT INDEX under:
(LARG) Largo5130   Testimonies of War

POZNAN PHILHARMONIC ORCHESTRA
cond A. BOREJKO
see CONCERT INDEX under:
(LARG) Largo5130   Testimonies of War

PRADES FESTIVAL ORCHESTRA
cond P. CASALS
Schubert: Symphony 5
(SONY) SMK58982   Pablo Casals conducts Bach at
Prades, June 1950
cond E. ORMANDY
see CONCERT INDEX under:
(SONY) SMK58993   Pablo Casals plays Schumann at
Prades, 1952 & 1953

PRAGUE ACADEMIA WIND QUINTET
Reicha: Wind Quintets, Op.88 (exc), Wind Quintets,
Op.91 (exc)

PRAGUE CHAMBER CHOIR
cond J. PANCIK
see CONCERT INDEX under:
(CHAN) CHAN9257   Czech Choral Music

PRAGUE CHAMBER ORCHESTRA
cond B. GREGOR
Martinů: Divertimento (1926), Sinfonietta giocosa
cond L. HLAVÁČEK
Mozart: Serenade, K250
Vivaldi: Concerti, Op. 8 (exc)
see CONCERT INDEX under:
(RCA) 74321 21277-2   Mozart—Violin Concertos, etc
(RCA) 74321 21278-2   Mozart—Violin Concertos, etc
(SUPR) 11 1119-2   Haydn: Violin Concertos
cond C. MACKERRAS
Mozart: Serenade, K239, Serenade, K320, Serenade,
K525, Symphony 36, Symphony 38, Symphony 40,
Symphony 41
see CONCERT INDEX under:
(TELA) CD80165   Mozart—Early Symphonies
(TELA) CD80186   Mozart—Middle-period Symphonies
(TELA) CD80190   Mozart—Symphonies
(TELA) CD80203   Mozart: Symphonies
(TELA) CD80217   Mozart: Early Symphonies
(TELA) CD80242   Mozart: Early Symphonies
(TELA) CD80256   Mozart: Early Symphonies
(TELA) CD80272   Mozart: Early Symphonies
(TELA) CD80273   Mozart—Early Symphonies
cond B. NOVOTNÝ
see CONCERT INDEX under:
(DENO) CO-78919   Dvořák—Serenade for Strings
cond Z. PESKÓ
Myslíveček: Bellerofonte (Cpte)
cond F. VAJNAR
Brixi: Organ Concertos (exc)

PRAGUE CHILDREN'S CHOIR
cond J. BĚLOHLÁVEK
Dvořák: Stabat Mater
Martinů: Miracles of Mary (Cpte)
cond V. SMETÁČEK
Dvořák: St Ludmilla (Cpte)

PRAGUE CITY PHILHARMONIC ORCHESTRA
cond P. BATEMAN
see CONCERT INDEX under:
(SILV) FILMCD137   Dial M for Murder—A History of
Hitchcock
(SILV) FILMCD151   The Longest Day—Music from the
Classic War Films
(SILV) FILMCD153   True Grit—Music from the Classic
Films of John Wayne
(SILV) FILMCD159   To Catch A Thief—A History of
Hitchcock II
(SILV) FILMCD160   Schindler's List—Classic Film
Music of John Williams
cond W. MOTZING
see CONCERT INDEX under:
(SILV) FILMCD146   Fantastic Voyage—A Journey
Through Classic Fantasy Film Music
cond N. RAINE
see CONCERT INDEX under:
(SILV) FILMCD141   The Classic John Barry

PRAGUE FESTIVAL ORCHESTRA
cond P. URBANEK
Mahler: Symphony 1
see CONCERT INDEX under:
(LASE) 15 517   Dvořák: Orchestral Works

PRAGUE FILM SYMPHONY ORCHESTRA
cond M. KLEMENS
see CONCERT INDEX under:
(ROMA) RR1941   Terezín - The Music 1941-44

PRAGUE GIOIA DELLA MUSICA
cond M. BROWN
Handel: Messiah (Cpte)

PRAGUE MADRIGAL SINGERS
cond M. VENHODA
Pascha: Christmas Mass

PRAGUE NATIONAL THEATRE CHORUS
cond Z. CHALABALA
Smetana: Devil's Wall (Cpte)
cond B. GREGOR
Janáček: Jenufa (Cpte), Makropulos Affair (Cpte)
cond J. JIROUŠ
Hába: Mother (Cpte)
cond F. JÍLEK
Fibich: Bride of Messina (Cpte)
Smetana: Two Widows (Cpte)
cond Z. KOŠLER
Smetana: Dalibor (Cpte), Libuše (Cpte)
cond J. KROMBHOLC
Janáček: Káta Kabanová (Cpte)
Martinů: Julietta (Cpte)
cond J.H. TICHÝ
Smetana: Brandenburgers in Bohemia (Cpte)

PRAGUE NATIONAL THEATRE ORCHESTRA
cond K. BÖHM
Mozart: Don Giovanni (Cpte)
cond Z. CHALABALA
Smetana: Devil's Wall (Cpte)
cond B. GREGOR
Janáček: Jenufa (Cpte), Makropulos Affair (Cpte)
cond J. JIROUŠ
Hába: Mother (Cpte)
cond F. JÍLEK
Fibich: Bride of Messina (Cpte)
Smetana: Two Widows (Cpte)
cond Z. KOŠLER
Smetana: Dalibor (Cpte), Libuše (Cpte)
cond J. KROMBHOLC
Janáček: Káta Kabanová (Cpte)
Martinů: Julietta (Cpte)
cond J.H. TICHÝ
Smetana: Brandenburgers in Bohemia (Cpte)

PRAGUE OPERA ORCHESTRA
see CONCERT INDEX under:
(EMI) CHS7 69741-2(6)   Record of Singing,
Vol.4—Russian & Slavonic Schools

PRAGUE PHILHARMONIC CHOIR
(ARGO) 436 835-2ZH   Gorecki—Choral and
Orchestral Works
cond P. KÜHN
see CONCERT INDEX under:
(KOCH) 37230-2   Terezín Music Anthology, Volume 2
cond Z. MEHTA
Mahler: Symphony 2
cond J. NELSON
see CONCERT INDEX under:
(ARGO) 436 835-2ZH   Gorecki—Choral and
Orchestral Works
cond M. POLLINI
Rossini: Donna del Lago (Cpte)

PRAGUE PHILHARMONIC CHORUS
Various: Messa per Rossini (Cpte)
(SUPR) 11 1878-2   The Unknown Janáček
cond C. ABBADO
Mahler: Symphony 8
Rossini: Viaggio a Reims (Cpte)
see CONCERT INDEX under:
(DG) 445 238-2GH   Mussorgsky—Orchestral and
Choral Works
(DG) 447 023-2GX12   Mahler—The Symphonies
cond G. ALBRECHT
Dvořák: Spectre's Bride
Liszt: Dante Symphony
cond J. BĚLOHLÁVEK
Dvořák: Psalm 149, Stabat Mater
cond E. BRIZIO
see CONCERT INDEX under:
(STUD) SM1223.27   Rossini—Complete unpublished
Sacred Works
cond G. GELMETTI
Rossini: Gazza ladra (Cpte)
cond A. JORDAN
Wagner: Parsifal (Cpte)
cond V. NEUMANN
see CONCERT INDEX under:
(SUPR) C37-7230   Dvořák: Choral works
cond P. OLMI
Rossini: Siège de Corinthe (Cpte)
cond S. RATTLE
Liszt: Faust Symphony
cond D. RENZETTI
Rossini: Bianca e Falliero (Cpte)
cond C. SCIMONE
Rossini: Italiana in Algeri (Cpte)

PRAGUE RADIO CHORUS
cond G. ALBRECHT
Dvořák: Dimitrij (Cpte)
cond K. ANCERL
Smetana: Bartered Bride (Cpte)
cond J. BĚLOHLÁVEK
Martinů: Miracles of Mary (Cpte)
cond F. JÍLEK
Fibich: Bride of Messina (Cpte)
cond J. KROMBHOLC
Smetana: Two Widows (Cpte)
cond P. KÜHN
see CONCERT INDEX under:
(SUPR) 11 0751-2   Martinů—Choral Works
cond V. SMETÁČEK
Dvořák: St Ludmilla (Cpte)

PRAGUE RADIO SYMPHONY ORCHESTRA
cond K. ANCERL
Smetana: Bartered Bride (Cpte)
cond J. KROMBHOLC
Smetana: Má Vlast, Two Widows (Cpte)
cond R. KUBELÍK
Khachaturian: Violin Concerto
cond V. SMETÁČEK
Dvořák: St Ludmilla (Cpte)
cond V. VÁLEK
Saint-Saëns: Suite algérienne, Symphony 3
Schulhoff: Piano Concerto 1, Piano Concerto 2

PRAGUE SINFONIETTA
cond I. PAŘÍK
Myslíveček: Abraham and Isaac

PRAGUE SYMPHONY ORCHESTRA
see CONCERT INDEX under:
(SUPR) 11 0751-2   Martinů—Choral Works
cond P. ALTRICHTER
Brahms: Piano Concerto 1, Violin Concerto
cond S. BAUDO
Honegger: Cantate de Noël
cond J. BĚLOHLÁVEK
Martinů: Butterfly that stamped, Czech Rhapsody,
Echec au Roi, Miracles of Mary (Cpte), Revolt
Ravel: Left-Hand Concerto, Piano Concerto
Tchaikovsky: Capriccio Italien
see CONCERT INDEX under:
(SUPR) 11 0684-2   Ravel/Poulenc—Works for Piano
and Orchestra
cond E. BRIZIO
see CONCERT INDEX under:
(STUD) SM12 2389   Paisiello—Music for Napoleon
Bonaparte's Chapel
cond P. FOURNILLIER
Massenet: Scènes (Cpte)
cond L. HLAVÁČEK
see CONCERT INDEX under:
(SUPR) 11 1114-2   Schubert & Schumann: Works for
Violin & Orchestra
cond J. HRNČÍŘ
see CONCERT INDEX under:
(SUPR) 11 1114-2   Schubert & Schumann: Works for
Violin & Orchestra
cond V. NEUMANN
see CONCERT INDEX under:
(SUPR) 11 1105-2   Gershwin & Milhaud—orchestral
works
cond V. SMETÁČEK
Beethoven: Piano Concerto 5
Berlioz: King Lear, Rêverie et caprice
Foerster: From Shakespeare
see CONCERT INDEX under:
(SUPR) 11 0681-2   Roussel—Orchestral Works

PRAGUE VIRTUOSI
cond R. KREČMER
see CONCERT INDEX under:
(DINT) DICD920274
Stamitz/Dittersdorf/Haydn—Sinfonia Concertantes
cond O. VLČEK
see CONCERT INDEX under:
(DINT) DICD920234   Suk/Janáček—String Works

PRANDELLI, Giacinto (ten)
see CONCERT INDEX under:
(EMI) CHS7 69741-2(7)   Record of Singing,
Vol.4—Italian School
(EMI) CMS7 64165-2   Puccini—Trittico

PRAT, Jacques (vn)
see CONCERT INDEX under:
(ACCO) 20202-2   Poulenc—Chamber Works

PRATICÒ, Bruno (bar)
Bizet: Pêcheurs de Perles (Cpte)
Donizetti: Elisir d'amore (Cpte)
Paisiello: Don Chisciotte (Cpte)
Rossini: Barbiere di Siviglia (Cpte), Cambiale di
Matrimonio (Cpte), Signor Bruschino (Cpte)

PRATO VOCI BIANCHE GUIDO MONACO CHOR
cond B. BARTOLETTI
see CONCERT INDEX under:
(DECC) **436 261-2DHO3** Puccini—Il Trittico

PRATS, Jorge Luis (pf)
see CONCERT INDEX under:
(IMG) **IMGCD1605** Rachmaninov—Orchestral Works

PRATSCHKE, Sébastien (treb)
Mozart: Apollo et Hyacinthus (Cpte)

PRAŽÁK QUARTET
Beethoven: Grosse Fuge, String Quartet 13, String
Quartet 15
Crusell: Clarinet Quintet, Op. 4
Mozart: Clarinet Quintet, K581
see CONCERT INDEX under:
(NUOV) **6829/31** Mozart—The Six Haydn Quartets

PRECHT, Ulrika (sop)
Donizetti: Linda di Chamounix (Cpte)

PREDA, Maurizio (gtr)
Paganini: Lucca Sonatas

PREDIT, Mascia (sop)
see CONCERT INDEX under:
(EMI) **CHS7 69741-2(6)** Record of Singing,
Vol.4—Russian & Slavonic Schools

PRÉGARDIEN, Christoph (ten)
Bach: Cantata 11, Cantata 21, Cantata 206, Cantata
207a, Cantata 211, Cantata 213, Christmas Oratorio,
BWV248 (Cpte), Easter Oratorio, BWV249 (Cpte),
Magnificat, BWV243, Mass, BWV235, Mass,
BWV236, St John Passion, BWV245 (Cpte), St
Matthew Passion, BWV244 (Cpte)
C. P. E. Bach: Auferstehung und Himmelfahrt Jesu
(Cpte)
Handel: Acis and Galatea, K566 (Cpte), Ode for St.
Cecilia's Day (Cpte), Rodelinda (Cpte), Samson
(Cpte)
Haydn: Mass 10, Schöpfung (Cpte)
Killmayer: Yolimba (Cpte)
Monteverdi: Ritorno d'Ulisse in patria (Cpte),
Vespers
Mozart: Don Giovanni (Cpte), Mass, K427, Requiem
Schubert: Schöne Müllerin (Cpte)
Stradella: San Giovanni Battista (Cpte)
Telemann: Cantata, TWV1: 771, Schwanengesang,
TWV4: 6
Zelenka: Litanie lauretanae, ZWV152, Missa dei fili,
ZWV20
see CONCERT INDEX under:
(ASTR) **E8530** Bach—Cantatas
(ASTR) **E8544** Bach—Cantatas
(BIS) **BIS-CD540** Britten—Works for Tenor and
Orchestra
(CAPR) **10 310/1** J. E. Bach—Passion Oratorio, etc.
(CAPR) **10 315** Telemann—Choral Music
(DHM) **05472 77296-2** Schubert—Schiller Lieder
(DHM) **05472 77319-2** Heine Lieder
(ERAT) **2292-45822-2** M-A.Charpentier—Motets
(HARM) **HMC90 1479** Bach—Cantatas
(HYPE) **CDJ33023** Schubert—Complete Lieder,
Vol.23
(NOVA) **150 081-2** Mozart—The Freemason Music
(VIRG) **VC7 59587-2** Bach—Masses etc

PREGER, Kurt (spkr)
R. Strauss: Ariadne auf Naxos (Cpte)

PREIN, Johann Werner (bass)
Busoni: Turandot (Cpte)
Schreker: Ferne Klang (Cpte)

PREIS, Manfred (bass cl)
see CONCERT INDEX under:
(SONY) **SK53978** Prometheus

PREIS, Manfred (sax)
see CONCERT INDEX under:
(BIS) **BIS-CD536** French Works for Wind Quintet

PREMIERE ENSEMBLE
cond M. WIGGLESWORTH
Mahler: Lied von der Erde

PRENTICE, Charles (cond)
see orch

PRESCOTT, Jonathan (bass)
see CONCERT INDEX under:
(PHIL) **432 416-2PH3** Haydn—L'incontro
improvviso/Arias

PRESNELL, Harve (bar)
M. Willson: Unsinkable Molly Brown (Cpte)

PRESS, Roger (pf)
see CONCERT INDEX under:
(MERI) **CDE84160** Piano 'War Horses'

PRESSLER, Menahem (pf)
Beethoven: Choral Fantasia
Dvořák: Piano Quartet 2, Piano Quintet, Op.81

PRESTEL, Kurt (cond)
see Salzburg Mozarteum Orch

PRESTIA, Giacomo (bass)
Verdi: Otello (Cpte)

PRESTON, Robert (sngr)
M. Willson: Music Man (Cpte)

PRESTON, Simon (cond)
see AAM

PRESTON, Simon (organ)
Bach: Concertos, BWV592-7 (exc), Orgel-Büchlein,
BWV599-644 (exc), Trio Sonatas, BWV525-530
Britten: War Requiem
Handel: Organ Concertos (exc)
Poulenc: Organ Concerto
Purcell: Organ Voluntaries, Z717-20 (exc)
Saint-Saëns: Symphony 3
Vierne: Suite 3 (exc)
Widor: Symphony 5
see CONCERT INDEX under:
(BELA) **450 112-2** Carols for Advent—A Procession
With Carols on Advent Sunday
(DECC) **425 499-2DM** On Christmas night
(DECC) **430 091-2DWO** The World of the Organ
(DECC) **430 160-2DM** Haydn: Masses & Keyboard
Concerto
(DECC) **433 677-2DM** Gibbons—Sacred Works
(DECC) **436 402-2DWO** The World of Wedding
Music
(DECC) **436 403-2DWO** The World of Royal Music
(DG) **427 668-2GH** Bach: Organ Works
(DG) **435 381-2GH** Bach—Organ Works
(PHIL) **434 074-2PH** Trumpet and Organ Spectacular

PRESTON, Simon (hpd)
see CONCERT INDEX under:
(PHIL) **434 918-2PH2** Bach—Concertos

PRESTON, Simon (hpd/dir)
see CONCERT INDEX under:
(DG) **431 817-2GH** Baroque Trumpet Concertos

PRESTON, Stephen (fl)
Bach: Flute Sonatas, BWV1030-5, Partita, BWV1013,
Suites, BWV1066-9 (exc)
Vivaldi: Concerti, Op. 10
see CONCERT INDEX under:
(AMON) **CD-SAR19** Flute Recital
(CRD) **CRD3348/9** Vivaldi—Concertos
(L'OI) **410 553-2OH** 18th Century Orchestral Works

PRESTON-ROBERTS, Michael (bar)
Janáček: Fate (Cpte)

PRÊTRE, Georges (cond)
see FNO

PREVEDI, Bruno (ten)
Verdi: Nabucco (Cpte)
see CONCERT INDEX under:
(DECC) **417 686-2DC** Puccini—Operatic Arias

PREVES, Milton (va)
R. Strauss: Don Quixote

PREVIATI, Fabio (bar)
Bellini: Adelson e Salvini (Cpte)
Franchetti: Cristoforo Colombo (Cpte)
Puccini: Bohème (Cpte)
Rossini: Inganno felice (Cpte), Occasione fa il ladro
(Cpte)

PREVIN, André (cond)
see Chor

PREVIN, André (pf)
Beethoven: Piano and Wind Quintet, Op. 16, Piano
Trios (exc)
Brahms: Piano Trio 1
Debussy: Piano Trio
Mozart: Piano and Wind Quintet, K452, Piano Sonata,
K448
Ravel: Piano Trio
Schumann: Piano Quartet, Op.47, Piano Quartet
(1829)
see CONCERT INDEX under:
(DG) **439 886-2GH** Barber/Korngold—Violin
Concertos
(EMI) **CMS7 64617-2** The art of Itzhak Perlman
(EMI) **CZS4 83177-2(3)** Itzhak Perlman Edition (pt 3)
(PHIL) **434 914-2PH** Dvořák—Cello works
(PHIL) **442 129-2PH** Sure Thing—The Jerome Kern
Songbook
(RCA) **09026 68181-2** French Chamber Works
(SONY) **MPK44850** Shostakovich: Concertos
(SONY) **SMK47618** Poulenc/Shostakovich—Piano
Concertos

PREVIN, André (pf/dir)
Mozart: Piano Concerto 20, 2-Piano Concerto, K365
see CONCERT INDEX under:
(EMI) **CDC7 47161-2** André Previn plays Gershwin
(PHIL) **412 611-2PH** Gershwin—Orchestral Works

PREVITALI, Fernando (cond)
see Rome Op Orch

PRÉVOST, Christian (vn)
see CONCERT INDEX under:
(CHAN) **CHAN8651** Vivaldi: Concertos
(CHAN) **CHAN8817** Britten: Orchestral Works

PRÉVOST, Thomas (fl)
see CONCERT INDEX under:
(ACCO) **20202-2** Poulenc—Chamber Works
(ERAT) **2292-45772-2** Saint-Saëns—Works for
Chamber Ensemble

PRÉVOST, Thomas (picc)
see CONCERT INDEX under:
(ACCO) **20202-2** Poulenc—Chamber Works

PREY, Hermann (bar)
Bach: Mass in B minor, BWV232 (Cpte), St Matthew
Passion, BWV244 (Cpte)
Beethoven: Symphony 9
Brahms: Deutsches Requiem, Op. 45 (Cpte)
Flotow: Martha (Cpte)

Humperdinck: Königskinder (Cpte)
J.Strauss II: Zigeunerbaron (Cpte)
Korngold: Tote Stadt (Cpte)
Kreutzer: Nachtlager in Granada (Cpte)
Mahler: Symphony 8
Millöcker: Bettelstudent (Cpte), Gasparone (Cpte)
Mozart: Così fan tutte (Cpte), Finta Giardiniera (Cpte),
Nozze di Figaro (Cpte)
Orff: Kluge (Cpte)
Pfitzner: Palestrina (Cpte)
R. Strauss: Ariadne auf Naxos (Cpte), Capriccio
(Cpte), Schweigsame Frau (Cpte)
Rossini: Barbiere di Siviglia (Cpte)
Schubert: Lazarus, D689, Winterreise (Cpte)
Wagner: Meistersinger (Cpte)
Weber: Freischütz (Cpte), Oberon (Cpte)
see CONCERT INDEX under:
(DECC) **436 407-2DWO** The World of Schubert
(DENO) **CO-1254** Lieder recital
(DENO) **CO-1741** Mozart: Operatic Arias
(DENO) **C37-7720** Schumann: Lieder
(DG) **427 306-2GH6** Beethoven: Complete
Symphonies
(DG) **431 110-2GB** Great Voices - Fritz Wunderlich
(DG) **435 162-2GX13** Mahler—Complete
Symphonies
(PHIL) **442 050-2PB10** Mahler—Complete
Symphonies

PREYER, Stefan (treb)
Schubert: Mass, D678

PREZIOSA, Vincenzo (bass)
Puccini: Tosca (Cpte)

PŘIBILOVÁ, Gabriela (sop)
Krása: Brundibár (Cpte)

PŘIBYL, Vilém (ten)
Dvořák: Jacobin (Cpte)
Fibich: Šárka (Cpte)
Janáček: Excursions of Mr Brouček (Cpte), From the
House of the Dead (Cpte), Glagolitic Mass (Cpte),
Jenufa (Cpte)

PRICE, David (organ)
see CONCERT INDEX under:
(CNTO) **CRCD2368** Sullivan—That Glorious Song of
Old
(HYPE) **CDA66768** John Amner—Cathedral Music
(PRIO) **PRCD460** Psalms of David, Vol.8

PRICE, Janet (sop)
Donizetti: Ugo, Conte di Parigi (Cpte)
see CONCERT INDEX under:
(LYRI) **SRCD324** Mathias—Choral Works

PRICE, John (bn)
Danzi: Sextet

PRICE, Leontyne (sop)
Berlioz: Nuits d'été
Bizet: Carmen (Cpte)
Gershwin: Porgy and Bess (Cpte)
J. Strauss II: Fledermaus (Cpte)
Mozart: Così fan tutte (Cpte)
Puccini: Madama Butterfly (Cpte), Tosca (Cpte)
R. Strauss: Ariadne auf Naxos (Cpte)
Verdi: Aida (Cpte), Ballo in maschera (Cpte), Ernani
(Cpte), Forza del destino (Cpte), Requiem (Cpte),
Trovatore (Cpte)
see CONCERT INDEX under:
(DECC) **433 010-2DM** Christmas Stars
(DECC) **436 402-2DWO** The World of Wedding
Music
(DECC) **436 407-2DWO** The World of Schubert
(DECC) **436 461-2DM** Ten Top Sopranos
(RCA) **GD60398** Leontyne Price sings Strauss arias
(RCA) **GD86722** R.Strauss: Orchestral and Vocal
Works
(RCA) **09026 61236-2** Leontyne Price - Prima Donna
Collection
(RCA) **09026 61357-2** Leontyne Price Sings Mozart
(RCA) **09026 61499-2** Leontyne Price Recital
(RCA) **09026 61509-2** A Salute to American Music
(RCA) **09026 61580-2(7)** RCA/Met 100 Singers, 100
Years (pt 7)
(RCA) **09026 61983-2** Leontyne Price sings Barber
(SONY) **MPK46727** Barber—Vocal Works

PRICE, Dame Margaret (sop)
Beethoven: Symphony 9
Brahms: Deutsches Requiem, Op. 45 (Cpte)
Elgar: Kingdom (Cpte)
Mahler: Symphony 8
Mozart: Così fan tutte (Cpte), Don Giovanni (Cpte),
Nozze di Figaro (Cpte), Requiem, Zauberflöte (Cpte)
Puccini: Turandot (Cpte)
Schumann: Gedichte, Op.35 (Cpte), Liederkreis,
Op.39 (Cpte)
Vaughan Williams: Symphony 3
Verdi: Ballo in maschera (Cpte), Otello (Cpte)
Wagner: Tristan und Isolde (Cpte)
see CONCERT INDEX under:
(CFP) **CD-CFP4669** Margaret Price sings Romantic
Songs
(DECC) **430 724-2DM** Great Operatic Duets
(DECC) **433 439-2DA** Great Love Duets
(DG) **419 994-2GCM4** Berg, Schoenberg & Webern:
Chamber Works
(DG) **423 238-2GC** Berg: Vocal and Orchestral
Works
(DG) **427 314-2GH** Ravel: Orchestral & Vocal Works
(DG) **435 162-2GX13** Mahler—Complete
Symphonies

(DG) **439 414-2GCL** Ravel—Vocal and Orchestral Works
(EMI) **CDH5 65072-2** Glyndebourne Recorded - 1934-1994
(EMI) **CDM7 64730-2** Vaughan Williams—Riders to the Sea; Epithalamion, etc
(EMIL) **CDZ7 67015-2** Mozart—Opera Arias
(FORL) **UCD16698** Schubert—Lieder
(FORL) **UCD16711** Schumann—Lieder
(FORL) **UCD16728** The Romantic Lied
(HYPE) **CDA66666** Mendelssohn—Lieder
(HYPE) **CDJ33015** Schubert—Complete Lieder, Vol.15
(ORFE) **C031821A** Schumann: Lieder
(ORFE) **C058831A** Brahms—Lieder
(RCA) **09026 60901-2** Brahms—Lieder
(RCA) **09026 61635-2** Margaret Price sings Mozart

PRICE, Mr (cond)
see orch

PRICE, Olwen (mez)
see CONCERT INDEX *under:*
(TEST) **SBT1058** James Johnston - Opera Arias and Songs

PRICE, Patricia (mez)
Rossini: Tancredi (Cpte)

PRICE, Paul (chalumeau)
see CONCERT INDEX *under:*
(CLRI) **CC0004** The Early Clarinet Family

PRICE, Simon (perc)
see CONCERT INDEX *under:*
(ACOU) **CDACS014** The Second Mandolin Album

PRICE, Timothy Deryl (ten)
A. Davis: X (Cpte)

PRICE JONES, Penelope (sop)
see CONCERT INDEX *under:*
(ALTA) **AIR-CD-9011** Philip Martin—Chamber & Vocal Works

PRIDAY, Elizabeth (sop)
Handel: Israel in Egypt (Cpte), Semele (Cpte)
Purcell: Dido (Cpte), King Arthur, Z628 (Cpte)
see CONCERT INDEX *under:*
(ERAT) **4509-96371-2** Gardiner—The Purcell Collection

PRIDE, Timothy (alto)
see CONCERT INDEX *under:*
(ARGO) **436 833-2ZH** Purcell— Music for the Funeral of Queen Mary

PRIEM-BERGRATH, Han (cond)
see Berlin Phil Wind Qnt

PRIEST, Anita (organ)
Saint-Saëns: Symphony 3

PRIESTMAN, Brian (cond)
see French Rad & TV SO

PRIEW, Uta (contr)
Wagner: Götterdämmerung (Cpte), Rheingold (Cpte), Walküre (Cpte)

PRIGENT, Maurice (ten)
Ravel: Enfant et les sortilèges (Cpte)

PRIKOPA, Herbert (bar)
Ligeti: Grand Macabre (Cpte)
R. Strauss: Rosenkavalier (Cpte)

PRIMAVERA CHAMBER ORCHESTRA
cond P. MANLEY
see CONCERT INDEX *under:*
(UNIC) **DKPCD9134** Echoes from Russia

PRIMROSE, William (va)
Berlioz: Harold in Italy
Mozart: Sinfonia concertante, K364
see CONCERT INDEX *under:*
(BIDD) **LAB011** Brahms—Historic Chamber Music Recordings
(BIDD) **LAB088** Primrose plays Handel, Mozart and Beethoven
(BIDD) **WHL028** Koussevitzky conducts Berlioz
(PEAR) **GEMMCD9045** William Primrose and Albert Spalding
(PEAR) **GEMMCD9453** William Primrose—Viola Recital
(RCA) **GD87873** Beethoven, Brahms & Schubert: Chamber Works
(RCA) **GD87911** Marian Anderson - Opera, Oratorio & Song Recital
(RCA) **GD87965** Dvořák & Brahms: Chamber Works
(RCA) **09026 61778-2(09)** The Heifetz Collection, Vol. 9
(RCA) **09026 61778-2(10)** The Heifetz Collection, Vol. 10
(RCA) **09026 61778-2(11-15)** The Heifetz Collection, Vols. 11-15
(RCA) **09026 61778-2(25)** The Heifetz Collection, Vol. 25
(RCA) **09026 61778-2(26)** The Heifetz Collection, Vol. 26
(RCA) **09026 61778-2(31)** The Heifetz Collection, Vol. 31
(RCA) **09026 61778-2(32)** The Heifetz Collection, Vol. 32
(RCA) **09026 61778-2(33)** The Heifetz Collection, Vol. 33
(RCA) **09026 61778-2(34)** The Heifetz Collection, Vol. 34
(RCA) **09026 61778-2(35)** The Heifetz Collection, Vol. 35

(RCA) **09026 61778-2(37)** The Heifetz Collection, Vol. 37
(RCA) **09026 61778-2(41)** The Heifetz Collection, Vol. 41
(RCA) **09026 61778-2(42)** The Heifetz Collection, Vol. 42

PRINCE, Faith (sngr)
F. Loesser: Guys and Dolls (Cpte)

PRINCE OF WALES BRASS
see CONCERT INDEX *under:*
(ASV) **CDWHL2083** Christmas Fanfare

PRING, Katherine (mez)
Wagner: Götterdämmerung (Cpte), Rheingold (Cpte)

PRINZ, Alfred (cl)
Mozart: Clarinet Concerto, K622

PRIOR, John (treb)
Britten: Midsummer Night's Dream (Cpte)

PRITCHARD, Sir John (cond)
see BBC SO

PRO ARTE CHOIR
cond A. JORDAN
Fauré: Requiem (Cpte)

PRO ARTE CHORALE
cond G. MANAHAN
S. Satoh: Stabat Mater (1987)

PRO ARTE GUITAR TRIO
see CONCERT INDEX *under:*
(ASV) **CDWHL2079** Brazileira

PRO ARTE ORCHESTRA
cond J. ADDISON
see CONCERT INDEX *under:*
(EMI) **CDM7 64718-2** The Composer Conducts
cond R. ARNELL
see CONCERT INDEX *under:*
(EMI) **CDM7 64718-2** The Composer Conducts
cond BARRY ROSE
(EMI) **CDM7 64131-2** Orchestral Music for Christmas
cond B. HERRMANN
Herrmann: Wuthering Heights (Cpte)
cond A. RAWSTHORNE
see CONCERT INDEX *under:*
(EMI) **CDM7 64718-2** The Composer Conducts
cond J. SHEFFER
Goldenthal: Golden Gate (exc)

PRO ARTE QUARTET
Brahms: Piano Quartet 1
see CONCERT INDEX *under:*
(TEST) **SBT3055** Haydn—String Quartets, Volume 1
(TEST) **SBT4056** Haydn—String Quartets, Volume 2

PRO ARTE TRIO
see CONCERT INDEX *under:*
(MERI) **CDE84245** D. Stoll—Reflections on Vedic Scriptures

PRO ARTE WIND QUINTET
see CONCERT INDEX *under:*
(NIMB) **NI5327** French Wind Music

PRO CANTIONE ANTIQUA
see CONCERT INDEX *under:*
(DHM) **GD77228** Christmas Carols & Hymns of the 15th Century
cond M. BROWN
Palestrina: Missa Papae Marcelli, Stabat mater a 8
see CONCERT INDEX *under:*
(CARL) **PCD806** Renaissance Masterpieces
(CONI) **CDCF145** Sweet and Low - Glees and Partsongs
(HYPE) **CDA66715** Melgaz/Morago—Motets
cond B. TURNER
Byrd: Mass for three voices
Josquin Desprez: Missa 'L'homme armé' super voces musicales
Ockeghem: Missa Pro Defunctis
Peñalosa: Motets (exc)
Tallis: Lamentations of Jeremiah
see CONCERT INDEX *under:*
(ARCH) **437 072-2AT** Collectio Argentea 2: Palestrina, Lassus
(ASV) **CDQS6086** Palestrina—Sacred Works

PRO MUSICA CHAMBER CHOIR
cond N. JÄRVI
Grieg: Peer Gynt (exc), Sigurd Jorsalfar (Cpte)

PRO MUSICA CHOIR
cond S. EHRLING
Rosenberg: Symphony 4

PRO MUSICA ENSEMBLE
cond D. MILHAUD
see CONCERT INDEX *under:*
(EPM) **150 122** Milhaud—Historic Recordings 1928-1948

PROBST, Wolfgang (bar)
Nono: Intolleranza 1960 (Cpte)
Suder: Kleider machen Leute (Cpte)

PROCHÁZKOVÁ, Jaroslava (mez)
Janáček: Jenufa (Cpte), Makropulos Affair (Cpte)
Martinů: Julietta (Cpte)

PROCTER, Norma (contr)
Mahler: Symphony 3, Symphony 8
see CONCERT INDEX *under:*

(DECC) **436 990-2DWO** The World of Benjamin Britten
(DG) **429 042-2GX10** Mahler: Complete Symphonies
(LOND) **436 396-2LM** Britten—Spring Symphony, etc

PROEBSTL, Max (bass)
Handel: Giulio Cesare (Cpte)
R. Strauss: Salome (Cpte)
Wagner: Meistersinger (Cpte)

PROENZA, Pedro di (ten)
Honegger: Jeanne d'Arc (Cpte)

PRÖGLHÖF, Harald (bass)
Lehár: Giuditta (exc)
Mozart: Nozze di Figaro (Cpte), Zauberflöte (Cpte)
R. Strauss: Arabella (Cpte), Ariadne auf Naxos (Cpte), Daphne (Cpte), Rosenkavalier (Cpte)
Wagner: Meistersinger (Cpte)

PROHASKA, Felix (cond)
see Bamberg SO

PROHASKA, Jaro (bar)
Wagner: Fliegende Holländer (exc), Lohengrin (Cpte), Tristan und Isolde (Cpte)
see CONCERT INDEX *under:*
(SCHW) **314532** Vienna State Opera Live, Vol.3
(SCHW) **314592** Vienna State Opera Live, Vol.9
(TELD) **9031-76442-2** Wagner—Excerpts from the 1936 Bayreuth Festival

PROJECT ARS NOVA ENSEMBLE
see CONCERT INDEX *under:*
(NALB) **NA038CD** Music of Cyprus 1413-1422
(NALB) **NA048CD** Homage to Johannes Ciconia
(NALB) **NA068CD** Machaut—Remede de Fortune

PROKINA, Jelena (sop)
Mussorgsky: Khovanshchina (Cpte)

PROKINA, Yelena (sop)
Prokofiev: War and Peace (Cpte)

PROKOFIEV, Gabriel (narr)
see CONCERT INDEX *under:*
(HYPE) **CDA66499** Prokofiev—Music for Children

PROKOFIEV, Lina (narr)
see CONCERT INDEX *under:*
(CHAN) **CHAN8511** Prokofiev—Peter and the Wolf; Cinderella

PROKOFIEV, Oleg (narr)
see CONCERT INDEX *under:*
(HYPE) **CDA66499** Prokofiev—Music for Children

PROKOFIEV, Sergey (pf)
see CONCERT INDEX *under:*
(COND) **690.07.009** Horowitz—Piano Roll Recordings
(EMI) **CDCS 55223-2** Prokofiev & Glazunov - Composers in Person
(PEAR) **GEMMCD9470** Prokofiev plays Prokofiev

PROMETHEUS ENSEMBLE
see CONCERT INDEX *under:*
(ASV) **CDDCA664** French Chamber Works
(ASV) **CDDCA684** Schubert—Lieder & Chamber Works

PROTHEROE, Guy (cond)
see Spectrum

PROTSCHKA, Josef (ten)
Beethoven: Fidelio (Cpte)
Busoni: Turandot (Cpte)
Dvořák: Spectre's Bride
Hindemith: Cardillac (Cpte), Mathis der Maler (Cpte)
J. Strauss II: Fledermaus (exc)
Lortzing: Undine (Cpte)
Mendelssohn: Symphony 2
Pfitzner: Von deutscher Seele (Cpte)
R. Strauss: Ariadne auf Naxos (Cpte)
Schoeck: Massimilla Doni (Cpte)
Schreker: Schatzgräber (Cpte)
Schubert: Fierrabras (Cpte), Schöne Müllerin (Cpte)
Schumann: Dichterliebe, Op. 48 (Cpte), Liederkreis, Op.39 (Cpte)
Wagner: Fliegende Holländer (Cpte)
Wolf: Manuel Venegas, Spanisches Liederbuch (exc)
Zemlinsky: Traumgörge (Cpte)
see CONCERT INDEX *under:*
(CAPR) **10 129** Josef Protschka sings Mozart arias
(CAPR) **10 363** Mendelssohn—Lieder, Vol.2
(CAPR) **10 366** Mendelssohn—Lieder, Vol.1
(CAPR) **10 446/7** Mozart—Lieder
(EMI) **CMS7 64778-2** Schubert—Sacred Works, Vol.1
(EMI) **CMS7 64783-2** Schubert—Sacred Works, Vol.2
(SONY) **SK64301** Beethoven—Songs from the British Isles

PROTTI, Aldo (bar)
Verdi: Otello (Cpte), Rigoletto (Cpte), Traviata (Cpte)

PROUD, Malcolm (hpd)
see CONCERT INDEX *under:*
(CRD) **CRD3488** Hasse—Cantatas, Ballads and Sonatas
(MERI) **CDE84189** Handel—Italian Solo Cantatas and Instrumental Works

PROULX, Jean-Guy (organ)
see CONCERT INDEX *under:*

(REM) **REM311078** Musiques Symphoniques pour Grand Orgue

PROVENCE VOCAL ENSEMBLE
cond H. GUY
see CONCERT INDEX under:
(PIER) **PV788111** Poulenc—Choral Works

PROVINS, Jacques (sngr)
Hahn: O mon bel inconnu (Cpte)

PROVVISIONATO, Francesca (mez)
Donizetti: Elisir d'amore (Cpte)
Rossini: Occasione fa il ladro (Cpte), Scala di Seta (Cpte), Siège de Corinthe (Cpte)

PRUDENT, Jean (ten)
Bizet: Carmen (exc)

PRUDON, Huguette (sngr)
(EMI) **CZS7 67515-2** Offenbach—Operetta highlights

PRUETT, Jérôme (ten)
Henze: Boulevard Solitude (Cpte)

PRUNYI, Ilona (pf)
Boëllmann: Piano Quartet, Op. 10, Piano Trio, Op. 19
F. David: Piano Trios (exc)
Sterndale Bennett: Piano Sextet, Op. 8, Piano Sonata, Op. 13, Suite de pièces, Op. 24
Widor: Piano Quintet 1, Piano Trio
see CONCERT INDEX under:
(HUNG) **HCD31535** Bartók—Songs
(MARC) **8 223170** Berwald—Piano Trios, Vol.1
(MARC) **8 223404** Atterberg—Chamber Music, Vol.1
(MARC) **8 223405** Atterberg—Chamber Works
(MARC) **8 223578** Sterndale Bennett—Piano Works - Volume 3
(NAXO) **8 550555** Schubert—Piano Works for Four Hands

PRŮŠA, Karel (bass)
Dvořák: Jacobin (Cpte)
Janáček: Cunning Little Vixen (Cpte), From the House of the Dead (Cpte)
Martinů: Miracles of Mary (Cpte)
Smetana: Libuše (Cpte)
see CONCERT INDEX under:
(ROMA) **RR1941** Terezín - The Music 1941-44

PRUSSIAN STATE ORCHESTRA
cond H. VON KARAJAN
Bruckner: Symphony 8 (exc)
cond H.U. MÜLLER
see CONCERT INDEX under:
(PREI) **89065** Maria Reining (1903-1991)

PRUVOST, Jacques (bar)
Audran: Poupée (exc)
Bizet: Carmen (Cpte)
Hahn: Mozart (Cpte)
Messager: Coups de Roulis (Cpte), Monsieur Beaucaire (Cpte)
Offenbach: Chanson de Fortunio (Cpte), Madame l'Archiduc (Cpte)
Planquette: Rip van Winkle (Cpte)

PRÜWER, Julius (cond)
see Berlin St Op Orch

PRUZHANSKY, Arkady (ten)
Karetnikov: Till Eulenspiegel (Cpte)

PRYCE, Jonathan (sngr)
Bart: Oliver! (Cpte)

PRYCE-JONES, John (cond)
see D'Oyly Carte Op Orch

PRYLOVÁ, Libuše (sop)
Janáček: Makropulos Affair (Cpte)

PRYOR, Gwenneth (pf)
Brahms: Clarinet Sonata 1, Clarinet Sonata 2
see CONCERT INDEX under:
(CHAN) **CHAN8506** Gervase de Peyer Recital
(CHAN) **CHAN8549** English Music for Clarinet and Piano
(CHAN) **CHAN9377/8** Ireland—Chamber Works

(LA) PSALLETTE DE LORRAINE
cond B. FABRE-GARRUS
see CONCERT INDEX under:
(ASTR) **E8521** Helfer—Requiem for the Dukes of Lorraine

PSCHENITSCHNIKOVA, Natalia (fl)
Kancheli: Exil
see CONCERT INDEX under:
(ECM) **445 941-2** Kancheli—Abii ne Viderem

PUCHELT, Gerhard (pf)
Busoni: Violin Sonata 1, Violin Sonata 2

PUDDY, Keith (basset-hn)
see CONCERT INDEX under:
(CLRI) **CC0004** The Early Clarinet Family

PUDDY, Keith (chalumeau)
see CONCERT INDEX under:
(CLRI) **CC0004** The Early Clarinet Family

PUDDY, Keith (cl)
Brahms: Clarinet Quintet
Mozart: Clarinet Quintet, K581
see CONCERT INDEX under:
(CARL) **MCD38** 20th Century Music for Wind Trio
(CARL) **PCD939** Mozart: Orchestral Works
(CLRI) **CC0004** The Early Clarinet Family

PUERTO DE LA CRUZ 'REYES BARTLET' CHOIR
cond A. R. MARBÀ
Vives: Bohemios (Cpte)

PUGH, Katharina (contr)
see CONCERT INDEX under:
(HANS) **98 803** Bach—Cantatas, Vol.41

PUGH, William (ten)
Spohr: Faust (Cpte)

PUGLIESE, James (perc)
Glass: Hydrogen Jukebox (Cpte)

PUGLIESE, James (xylophone)
see CONCERT INDEX under:
(ARGO) **430 209-2ZH** Torke—Chamber Works

PUGLIESE, Michael (perc)
(NALB) **NA008CD** Somei Satoh: Various Works

PUGSLEY, Richard K. (bass)
see CONCERT INDEX under:
(GLOR) **GDCD016** Leo Sowerby—American Master of Sacred Song

PUHLMANN-RICHTER, Christa (mez)
Ligeti: Grand Macabre (Cpte)

PUJOL, Roger (bass)
Auber: Gustav III (Cpte)

PUMIR, Arnaud (organ)
Colin: Missa pro defunctis
Helfer: Missa pro defunctis

PURCELL, Pat (sop)
Janáček: Cunning Little Vixen (Cpte)

PURCELL BAND
see CONCERT INDEX under:
(HYPE) **CDA66264** Geminiani: Concertos & Sonatas

PURCELL QUARTET
Biber: Harmonia artificioso-ariosa
Corelli: Trio Sonatas, Op. 1, Trio Sonatas, Op. 2, Trio Sonatas, Op.3 (exc), Trio Sonatas, Op.4 (exc)
Leclair: Ouvertures et Sonates, Op. 13, Trio Sonatas, Op.4
Schütz: Symphoniae sacrae, Op. 10 (Cpte)
W. Lawes: Fantasia-Suites a 4, Royall Consorts
see CONCERT INDEX under:
(CHAN) **CHAN0502** Vivaldi—Trio Sonatas
(CHAN) **CHAN0511** Vivaldi—String Sonatas, Vol.2
(CHAN) **CHAN8591** Purcell—Chamber Works
(CHAN) **CHAN8663** Purcell: Chamber Works
(CHAN) **CHAN8763** Purcell—Chamber Works Vol 3
(HYPE) **CDA66193** Vivaldi—La Follia
(HYPE) **CDA66226** Corelli: La Folia and other Sonatas
(HYPE) **CDA66239** C.P.E. Bach: Chamber Works
(HYPE) **CDA66254** A. Scarlatti: Cantatas & La Folia
(HYPE) **CDA66264** Geminiani: Concertos & Sonatas
(HYPE) **CDA66310** Marais: Pièces de viole

(THE) PURCELL SIMFONY
Purcell: Indian Queen, Z630 (Cpte)
cond A. ROOLEY
Purcell: Don Quixote: The Musical (Cpte)

(THE) PURCELL SIMFONY VOICES
Purcell: Indian Queen, Z630 (Cpte)

PURCELL SINGERS
cond B. BRITTEN
Britten: Rejoice in the Lamb
see CONCERT INDEX under:
(LOND) **436 394-2LM** Britten—Vocal & Choral Works

PURNHAGEN, Gregory (bar)
Glass: Hydrogen Jukebox (Cpte)

PURSER, David (tbn)
see CONCERT INDEX under:
(BRID) **BCD9045** Benedict Mason—Chamber and Orchestral Works

PURSIO, Tuomas (bass)
Schumann: Manfred (Cpte)

PURVES, Christopher (bass)
Handel: Israel in Egypt (Cpte)
see CONCERT INDEX under:
(VIRG) **VC5 45107-2** Charpentier—Leçons de ténèbres, Vol. 3

PURVIS, Jennifer (pf)
(CLRI) **CC0006** Clarinet Virtuosi of the Past—Hermstedt

PURVIS, William (cond)
see Speculum Musicae

PURVIS, William (hn)
Mozart: Sinfonia Concertante, K297b
(DG) **431 665-2GX3** Mozart—Wind Concertos

PUSHEE, Graham (alto)
Cavalli: Calisto (Cpte)
Handel: Queen Caroline Te Deum, Ways of Zion do mourn
Telemann: Jauchze, jubilier und singe, TWV15: 5, Magnificat, TWV9: 17

PUSTELAK, Kazimierz (ten)
Mussorgsky: Boris Godunov (Cpte)

PUTELLI, Carlo (ten)
see CONCERT INDEX under:

(STUD) **SM12 2389** Paisiello—Music for Napoleon Bonaparte's Chapel

PUTILIN, Nikolai (bar)
Rimsky-Korsakov: Sadko (Cpte)
Tchaikovsky: Queen of Spades (Cpte)

PUTKONEN, Matti (bass)
Sallinen: Kullervo (Cpte)

PUTNAM, Ashley (sop)
Puccini: Bohème (Cpte)
V. Thomson: Mother of us all (Cpte)

PUTTAR, Nada (mez)
see CONCERT INDEX under:
(TEST) **SBT1036** Lisa Della Casa sings Richard Strauss

PUTTEN, Thea van der (contr)
R. Strauss: Rosenkavalier (Cpte)

PÜTZ, Ruth-Margret (sop)
Nicolai: Lustigen Weiber von Windsor (Cpte)

PUURA, Väino (bar)
Tubin: Barbara von Tisenhusen (Cpte)

PUYANA, Rafael (hpd)
Bach: Flute Sonatas, BWV1030-5, Viola da Gamba Sonatas, BWV1027-9

PYASETSKY, Valery (pf)
see CONCERT INDEX under:
(ETCE) **KTC1177** Brahms—Music for Clarinet

PYATT, David (hn)
see CONCERT INDEX under:
(EMIN) **CD-EMX2238** R. Strauss—Orchestral Works

QUADFLIEG, Will (narr)
Beethoven: Egmont (Cpte)
Mozart: Entführung (Cpte)

QUADRI, Argeo (cond)
see Catania Teatro Massimo Bellini Orch

QUADRO HOTTETERRE
Marais: Pièces en trio

QUAN, Linda (vn)
Schubert: Octet, D803

QUANDT, Kerstin (contr)
Pfitzner: Herz (Cpte)
S. Wagner: Bärenhäuter (Cpte),
Schwarzschwanenreich (Cpte)

QUANDT, Ludwig (vc)
Boccherini: Sextets, G461-6 (exc)

QUARANTA, Romolo (cl)
(CLRI) **CC0005** The Clarinet - Historical Recordings, Vol.1

QUARTA, Massimo (vn)
Vivaldi: Concerti, Op. 8 (exc)
see CONCERT INDEX under:
(ONDI) **ODE826-2** Sibelius—Early Chamber Music, Vol. 1

QUARTARARO, Florence (sop)
see CONCERT INDEX under:
(EMI) **CHS7 69741-2(1)** Record of Singing, Vol.4—Anglo-American School (pt 1)

QUARTET OF LONDON
see CONCERT INDEX under:
(CHAN) **CHAN8440** Alwyn—Chamber Works

QUARTETTO FAURÉ DI ROMA
Fauré: Piano Quartet 1, Piano Quartet 2

QUARTETTO ITALIANO
Beethoven: String Quartet 12, String Quartet 16
Brahms: Piano Quintet
Debussy: String Quartet
Ravel: String Quartet
see CONCERT INDEX under:
(PHIL) **420 797-2PM3** Beethoven: Middle Period String Quartets
(PHIL) **420 876-2PSL** Schubert, Dvořák & Borodin—String Quartets
(PHIL) **422 512-2PME8** The Complete Mozart Edition Vol 12
(PHIL) **426 046-2PM3** Beethoven: Early String Quartets
(PHIL) **426 050-2PM4** Beethoven: Late String Quartets
(PHIL) **426 097-2PC** Haydn: String Quartets
(PHIL) **446 163-2PM2** Schubert—Last Four Quartets

QUASTHOFF, Thomas (bar)
Bach: Mass, BWV235, St. John Passion, BWV245 (Cpte), St Matthew Passion, BWV244
Haydn: Anima del filosofo (Cpte)
see CONCERT INDEX under:
(PHIL) **426 275-2PH** Mozart—Sacred Choral Works
(RCA) **09026 61225-2** Schumann—Lieder
(RCA) **09026 61864-2** Schubert—Goethe Lieder

(I) QUATTRO TEMPERAMENTI
see CONCERT INDEX under:
(BIS) **BIS-CD403** Handel: Vocal and Chamber Works

QUATUOR NATIONAL D'AQUITAINE
see CONCERT INDEX under:
(CYBE) **CY805** Milhaud—String Quartets Vol. 2

QUEEN'S HALL LIGHT ORCHESTRA
cond C. WILLIAMS
see CONCERT INDEX under:
(EMI) **CDGO 2059** British Film Music from the 40s and 50s

QUEEN'S HALL ORCHESTRA
cond HENRY WOOD
see CONCERT INDEX under:
(BEUL) **1PD3** Sir Henry's Themes and Variations
(DUTT) **CDAX8004** Sir Henry Wood conducts Vaughan Williams
(DUTT) **CDAX8008** Sir Henry Wood conducts Proms Favourites
(DUTT) **2CDAX2002** The Best of Sir Henry J.Wood

QUEENSLAND PHILHARMONIC ORCHESTRA
cond J. GEORGIADIS
see CONCERT INDEX under:
(NAXO) **8 550928** Weber—Orchestral Works

QUEENSLAND SYMPHONY ORCHESTRA (BRISBANE)
cond W. A. ALBERT
Frankel: Symphony 2, Symphony 3
see CONCERT INDEX under:
(CPO) **CPO999 004-2** Hindemith—Orchestral Works Vol 1
(CPO) **CPO999 005-2** Hindemith—Orchestral Works Vol 2
(CPO) **CPO999 240-2** Frankel—Symphonies, etc
cond R. MILLS
see CONCERT INDEX under:
(VARE) **VSD5242** Waxman—The Legends of Hollywood, Vol.1
(VARE) **VSD5480** Waxman—Legends of Hollywood, Vol. 3

QUEFFÉLEC, Anne (pf)
D. Scarlatti: Keyboard Sonatas (exc)
see CONCERT INDEX under:
(CHAN) **CHAN8972** Debussy & Ravel—Orchestral works
(VIRG) **VC7 59233-2** Ravel—Piano Works, Vol.1
(VIRG) **VC7 59296-2** Satie—Piano Works, Vol.3
(VIRG) **VC7 59322-2** Ravel—Piano Works, Vol.2
(VIRG) **VC7 59515-2** Satie—Piano Works

QUELER, Eve (cond)
see NY Op Orch

QUERCIA, Mireille (sop)
Ohana: Cantigas
Stravinsky: Noces

QUEYRAS, Jean-Guihen (vc)
see CONCERT INDEX under:
(DG) **439 808-2GH** Boulez conducts Ligeti

QUILICO, Gino (bar)
Berlioz: Troyens (Cpte)
Bizet: Carmen (exc), Jolie fille de Perth (Cpte), Pêcheurs de Perles (Cpte)
Chausson: Roi Arthus (Cpte)
Donizetti: Don Pasquale (Cpte)
Gounod: Roméo et Juliette (Cpte)
Massenet: Manon (Cpte)
Puccini: Bohème (Cpte), Manon Lescaut (Cpte)
Rossini: Cenerentola (Cpte), Comte Ory (Cpte)
see CONCERT INDEX under:
(CBC) **SMCD5119** Adeste Fideles
(EMI) **CDC5 55151-2** Operetta Duets

QUILICO, Louis (bar)
Massenet: Esclarmonde (Cpte)
Milhaud: Pacem in Terris
see CONCERT INDEX under:
(CBC) **SMCD5119** Adeste Fideles

QUILLEVÉRÉ, Marcel (ten)
see CONCERT INDEX under:
(EMI) **CDS7 49361-2** Offenbach: Operettas

QUILLMAN, Gail (pf)
see CONCERT INDEX under:
(NEW) **NW376-2** Sowerby: Piano Works

QUINK
see CONCERT INDEX under:
(ETCE) **KTC1031** Byrd: Sacred Choral Works
(TELA) **CD80202** Carols around the world

QUINN, Gerard (bar)
Verdi: Trovatore (Cpte)

QUINTANA, Juan Manuel (va da gamba)
see CONCERT INDEX under:
(HARM) **HMC90 1505** German Baroque Songs

QUIRKE, Saul (treb)
Handel: Messiah (Cpte)
see CONCERT INDEX under:
(ARGO) **410 005-2ZH** Sacred Choral Works

QUITTMEYER, Susan (mez)
Verdi: Falstaff (Cpte)
Wagner: Rheingold (Cpte)

QUIVAR, Florence (contr)
Beethoven: Missa solemnis, Symphony 9
Berlioz: Roméo et Juliette (Cpte)
Gershwin: Porgy and Bess (Cpte)
Mahler: Symphony 2
Schumann: Paradies und die Peri (Cpte)
Sessions: When Lilacs last Bloom'd
Stravinsky: Oedipus Rex (Cpte)
Various: Messa per Rossini (Cpte)
Verdi: Ballo in maschera (Cpte), Luisa Miller (Cpte), Requiem (Cpte)
see CONCERT INDEX under:
(EMI) **CDS5 55121-2** Szymanowski—Choral Works
(SONY) **SX14K48198** Mahler—Complete Symphonies, etc
(TELA) **CD80149** Falla—Theatre Music

QUODLIBET
see CONCERT INDEX under:
(CRD) **CRD3450** Escobar: Sacred Choral Works

RAAMAT, Helvi (sop)
Tubin: Barbara von Tisenhusen (Cpte)

RAANOJA, Pia (sop)
see CONCERT INDEX under:
(BIS) **BIS-CD321** Nielsen—Orchestral Works
(BIS) **BIS-CD614/6** Nielsen—Symphonies and Concertos

RABEN, Larry (sngr)
see CONCERT INDEX under:
(EMI) **CDC5 55189-2** The Busby Berkeley Album

RABIN, Michael (vn)
Paganini: Caprices, Op.1

RABINER, Ellen (mez)
Purcell: Dido (Cpte)

RABINOF, Benno (vn)
see CONCERT INDEX under:
(APR) **APR7016** The Auer Legacy, Vol.2

RABINOVITCH, Alexandre (pf)
Messiaen: Visions de l'Amen
see CONCERT INDEX under:
(TELD) **4509-91378-2** Mozart—Sonatas for 2 pianos & for piano 4 hands
(TELD) **4509-92257-2** Brahms—Piano Works
(TELD) **9031-74717-2** Rachmaninov—Works for Two Pianos

RABINOVITCH, Max (pf)
see CONCERT INDEX under:
(APR) **APR7016** The Auer Legacy, Vol.2

RABINOWITZ, Harry (cond)
see OST

RABOL, Georges (pf)
see CONCERT INDEX under:
(NAXO) **8 553009** Chabrier—Piano Works, Volume 1
(NAXO) **8 553010** Chabrier—Piano Works, Volume 2
(NAXO) **8 553080** Chabrier—Piano Works, Volume 3
(O111) **OPS50-9114** Classics of the Americas, Vol. 4

RACHLEVSKY, Misha (cond)
see Kremlin CO

RACHLIN, Julian (vn)
Prokofiev: Violin Concerto 1
Saint-Saëns: Violin Concerto 3
Tchaikovsky: Violin Concerto 1
Wieniawski: Violin Concerto 2
see CONCERT INDEX under:
(SONY) **SK53272** Sibelius—Orchestral Works

RACHMANINOV, Natalie (pf)
see CONCERT INDEX under:
(RCA) **09026 61265-2(2)** Rachmaninov—The Complete Recordings (pt 2)

RACHMANINOV, Sergei (cond)
see Philadelphia

RACHMANINOV, Sergei (pf)
Rachmaninov: Piano Concerto 2, Piano Concerto 3
see CONCERT INDEX under:
(APR) **APR7013** Romantic Piano Rarities, Vol.1
(CARL) **GLRS104** Rachmaninov plays Rachmaninov
(DECC) **425 964-2DM** Rachmaninov from Ampico Piano Rolls
(MSCM) **MM30271** Rachmaninov plays the Romantics
(RCA) **GD87766** Rachmaninov plays Rachmaninov
(RCA) **09026 61265-2(1)** Rachmaninov—The Complete Recordings (pt 1)
(RCA) **09026 61265-2(2)** Rachmaninov—The Complete Recordings (pt 2)
(RCA) **09026 61265-2(3)** Rachmaninov—The Complete Recordings (pt 3)
(RCA) **09026 61879-2** Grieg—Historic Recordings
(SIMA) **PSC1809(2)** Grieg—Historical Piano Recordings (pt 2)

RACHMILOVICH, Jacques (cond)
see Santa Monica Orch

RACINE, Philippe (fl)
see CONCERT INDEX under:
(ACCO) **20123-2** Koechlin—Vocal and Chamber Works
(CLAV) **CD50-9003** Jolivet & Koechlin—Chamber Works
(ECM) **839 617-2** Bach & Carter—Instrumental & Chamber Works

RACKHAM SYMPHONY CHOIR
cond P. PARAY
P. Paray: Joan of Arc Mass

RACLOT, Daniel (vc)
see CONCERT INDEX under:
(ACCO) **20202-2** Poulenc—Chamber Works

RÁCZ, Ottó (ob)
see CONCERT INDEX under:
(NAXO) **8 553090** Beethoven—Chamber Works

RÁCZ, Zoltán (perc)
see CONCERT INDEX under:
(DECC) **443 894-2DH** Bartók—Chamber Works

RÁCZ, Zoltán (vc)
see CONCERT INDEX under:

(DECC) **425 935-2DM4** Haydn—Symphonies, Vol.8
(DECC) **430 100-2DM32(2)** Haydn—Complete Symphonies (Volumes 5-8)

RADCLIFFE CHORAL SOCIETY
cond C. MUNCH
Berlioz: Roméo et Juliette (Cpte)

RADEN, Gregory (cl)
Rorem: Eleven Studies

RADEV, Marianna (contr)
Rossini: Stabat Mater

RADIO FREE BERLIN DANCE ORCHESTRA
cond W. BRÜCKNER-RÜGGEBERG
Weill: Dreigroschenoper (Cpte)

RADIO LILLE ORCHESTRA
cond M. SUZAN
Bartók: Violin Concerto 2

RADIOTJÄNST ENTERTAINMENT ORCHESTRA
see CONCERT INDEX under:
(CPRI) **CAP21510** Rosenberg plays Rosenberg

RADIOTJÄNST SYMPHONY ORCHESTRA
cond H. ROSENBERG
see CONCERT INDEX under:
(CPRI) **CAP21510** Rosenberg plays Rosenberg

RADKEVICH, Victor (ten)
Grechaninov: Liturgy, Op. 79 (Cpte)

RADOUKANOV, Entcho (db)
see CONCERT INDEX under:
(BIS) **BIS-CD507** Schnittke—Cello Works

RADULESCU, Michael (organ)
(DHM) **05472 77276-2** Bach—Organ Works, Vol.2

RAEKALLIO, Matti (pf)
Moszkowski: Piano Concerto
Rubinstein: Piano Concerto 4
see CONCERT INDEX under:
(ONDI) **ODE729-2** Prokofiev: Piano Works
(ONDI) **ODE761-2** Prokofiev—Piano Sonatas
(ONDI) **ODE777-2** Paganini Studies

RAEL, Anthya (pf)
see CONCERT INDEX under:
(CRD) **CRD3391** Works for Cello
(MERI) **DUOCD89019/21** Beethoven—Sonatas for Violin and Piano

RAFFALLI, Tibère (ten)
Honegger: Roi David (Cpte)
Offenbach: Brigands (Cpte)
Verdi: Don Carlos (Cpte)

RAFFANELLI, Flora (sop)
Bellini: Pirata (Cpte)
see CONCERT INDEX under:
(EMI) **CDM7 69500-2** Montserrat Caballé sings Bellini & Verdi Arias

RAFFANTI, Dano (ten)
Bellini: Capuleti (Cpte)
Rossini: Donna del Lago (Cpte), Siège de Corinthe (Cpte)

RAFFEINER, Walter (ten)
Berg: Wozzeck (Cpte)
R. Strauss: Salome (Cpte)
S. Wagner: Schwarzschwanenreich (Cpte)
Weill: Happy End (Cpte), Kuhhandel (exc), Mahagonny-Gesänge (Cpte)

RAFFELL, Anthony (bass)
Berlioz: Troyens (Cpte)
Sullivan: Trial by Jury (Cpte), Yeomen of the Guard (Cpte)
see CONCERT INDEX under:
(DECC) **433 868-2DWO** The World of Gilbert & Sullivan - Volume 2

RAFFERTY, Michael (cond)
see Scottish Chbr Op Ens

RAFN, Eyrind (fl)
Kuhlau: Flute Quintets, Op. 51

RAFTERY, J. Patrick (ten)
Spontini: Vestale (Cpte)

RAGATZU, Rosella (sop)
Franchetti: Cristoforo Colombo (Cpte)

RAGAZ, Christine (vn)
Reger: Piano Trio, Op. 102

RAGGETT, Keith (ten)
Britten: Midsummer Night's Dream (Cpte)

RAGIN, Derek Lee (alto)
A. Scarlatti: Giardino d'amore
Gluck: Orfeo ed Euridice (Cpte)
Handel: Flavio (Cpte), Giulio Cesare (Cpte), Saul (Cpte), Scipione (Cpte), Teseo (Cpte)
Hasse: Cleofide (Cpte)
Purcell: Dido (Cpte)
see CONCERT INDEX under:
(CHNN) **CCS0890** Handel—Cantatas & Sonatas
(CHNN) **CCS2991** Ev'ry Time I Feel the Spirit
(ETCE) **KTC1069** Vivaldi: Cantatas
(TELA) **CD80181** Walton & Bernstein: Choral Works

RAGLAN BAROQUE PLAYERS
cond N. KRAEMER
Locatelli: Concertos, Op. 3

RAGON, Gilles (ten)
Cavalli: Calisto (Cpte)
Debussy: Rodrigue et Chimène (Cpte)

Jommelli: Armida abbandonata (Cpte)
Lully: Alceste (Cpte), Armide, Atys (Cpte)
M-A. Charpentier: In honorem sancti Xaverii
canticum, H355, Judicium Salomonis, H422, Médée
(Cpte)
Marais: Alcyone (Cpte)
Mouret: Amours de Ragonde (Cpte)
Rameau: Platée (Cpte)
　　see CONCERT INDEX *under:*
(ARIO) **ARN68015**　Charpentier—Sacred Choral works
(O111) **OPS39-9103**　Clérambault—Secular Cantatas

RAGOSSNIG, Konrad (gtr)
　　see CONCERT INDEX *under:*
(NOVA) **150 039-2**　Lieder with Guitar
Accompaniment

RAGOSSNIG, Konrad (lte)
　　see CONCERT INDEX *under:*
(ARCH) **415 294-2AH**　Terpsichore - Renaissance &
Early Baroque Dance Music

RAHBARI, Alexander (cond)
　　see Belgian Rad & TV Orch

RAHKONEN, Margit (pf)
　　see CONCERT INDEX *under:*
(NIMB) **NI5358**　The Virtuoso Violin

RAHMAN, Sophia (pf)
　　see CONCERT INDEX *under:*
(GAMU) **GAMCD537**　Works for Viola and Piano
(REDC) **RR008**　Music by Alan Bush

RAHME, Edmondo (ten)
Verdi: Trovatore (Cpte)

RAIMONDI, Gianni (ten)
Donizetti: Anna Bolena (Cpte)

RAIMONDI, Ruggero (bass)
Bellini: Norma (Cpte), Pirata (Cpte)
Bizet: Carmen (exc)
Debussy: Pelléas et Mélisande (Cpte)
Mozart: Don Giovanni (Cpte), Nozze di Figaro
(Cpte)
Mussorgsky: Boris Godunov (Cpte)
Puccini: Bohème (Cpte), Tosca (Cpte), Turandot
(Cpte)
Rossini: Barbiere di Siviglia (Cpte), Cenerentola
(Cpte), Italiana in Algeri (Cpte), Mosè in Egitto (Cpte),
Petite messe solennelle, Stabat Mater, Viaggio a
Reims (Cpte)
Verdi: Aida (Cpte), Attila (Cpte), Ballo in Maschera
(Cpte), Don Carlo (Cpte), Don Carlos (Cpte), Forza
del destino (Cpte), Lombardi (Cpte), Macbeth (Cpte),
Masnadieri (Cpte), Rigoletto (Cpte), Simon
Boccanegra (Cpte), Trovatore (Cpte), Vespri Siciliani
(Cpte)
　　see CONCERT INDEX *under:*
(EMI) **CDM7 69549-2**　Ruggero Raimondi: Italian
Opera Arias

RAINBIRD, James (treb)
Menotti: Amahl and the Night Visitors (Cpte)

RAINE, Nic (cond)
　　see Prague City PO

RAINER, Ingomar (hpd)
　　see CONCERT INDEX *under:*
(NOVA) **150 025-2**　C.P.E.Bach—Keyboard Works

RAINERO, Ruth (sop)
Purcell: Dido (Cpte)

RAINS, Claude (narr)
　　see CONCERT INDEX *under:*
(SONY) **SM2K52657**　Strauss—Lieder and Piano
Works

RAISA, Rosa (sop)
　　see CONCERT INDEX *under:*
(CLUB) **CL99-052**　Rosa Raisa (1893-1963)

RAISKY, Boris (cond)
　　see Belorussian St Rad & TV Orch

RAITT, John (sngr)
Berlin: Annie get your Gun (Cpte)

RAITZIN, Misha (ten)
Mussorgsky: Boris Godunov (Cpte)

RAJNA, Thomas (pf)
Granados: Danzas españolas, Goyescas
Rajna: Piano Concerto 2
Schumann: Piano Quartet, Op. 47, Piano Quintet, Op.
44
　　see CONCERT INDEX *under:*
(CRD) **CRD3322**　Granados—Piano Works, Vol.3
(CRD) **CRD3323**　Granados—Piano Works, Vol.4
(SAGA) **EC3391-2**　Stravinsky—Piano Works

RAJSKI, Wojciech (cond)
　　see Baltic Phil SO

RAJTER, L'udovít (cond)
　　see Bratislava RSO

RAK, Štěpán (gtr)
　　see CONCERT INDEX *under:*
(CHAN) **CHAN8622**　Remembering Prague

RAKOWSKI, Maciej (vn)
　　see CONCERT INDEX *under:*
(ASV) **CDDCA645**　Vivaldi—Concertos

RALF, Torsten (ten)
Beethoven: Fidelio (Cpte)
　　see CONCERT INDEX *under:*
(DUTT) **CDLX7007**　Beecham conducts Wagner

(EMI) **CMS7 64008-2(1)**　Wagner Singing on Record
(pt 1)
(PEAR) **GEMMCDS9926(2)**　Covent Garden on
Record—Vol.4 (pt 2)
(PREI) **89077**　Torsten Ralf (1901-1954)
(PREI) **90237**　R Strauss—Daphne
(SCHW) **314512**　Vienna State Opera Live, Vol.1
(SCHW) **314552**　Vienna State Opera Live, Vol.5

RALLIER, Serge (ten)
Poulenc: Mamelles de Tirésias (Cpte)

RAMAT GAN CHAMBER CHOIR
cond J.T. WILLIAMS
J. T. Williams: Schindler's List (exc)

RAMBERT, Mlle (sop)
Massenet: Manon (Cpte)

RAMEY, Samuel (bass)
A. Thomas: Hamlet (Cpte)
Bach: Mass in B minor, BWV232 (Cpte)
Bartók: Duke Bluebeard's Castle (Cpte)
Bellini: Norma (Cpte)
Bernstein: On the Town (Cpte)
Boito: Mefistofele (Cpte)
Bruckner: Te Deum
Donizetti: Lucia di Lammermoor (Cpte)
Floyd: Susannah (Cpte)
Forrest/Wright: Kismet (Cpte)
Gounod: Faust (Cpte)
Handel: Ariodante (Cpte), Semele (Cpte)
Haydn: Armida (Cpte)
Massenet: Chérubin (Cpte)
Mozart: Don Giovanni (Cpte), Nozze di Figaro (Cpte),
Zauberflöte (Cpte)
Mussorgsky: Boris Godunov (Cpte)
Puccini: Tosca (Cpte)
Rossini: Barbiere di Siviglia (Cpte), Donna del Lago
(Cpte), Gazza ladra (Cpte), Italiana in Algeri (Cpte),
Maometto II (Cpte), Messa di gloria, Otello (Cpte),
Petite messe solennelle, Semiramide (Cpte), Signor
Bruschino (Cpte), Turco in Italia (Cpte), Viaggio a
Reims (Cpte)
Saint-Saëns: Samson et Dalila (Cpte)
Stravinsky: Rake's Progress (Cpte)
Verdi: Aida (Cpte), Attila (Cpte), Don Carlo (Cpte),
Due Foscari (Cpte), Masnadieri (Cpte), Requiem
(Cpte), Rigoletto (Cpte)
　　see CONCERT INDEX *under:*
(DECC) **436 464-2DM**　Ten Top Baritones & Basses
(DG) **429 025-2GX10**　Bruckner—Complete
Symphonies, etc
(EMI) **CDC7 54643-2**　Rossini—Bicentenary Gala
Concert
(RCA) **09026 61509-2**　A Salute to American Music
(RCA) **09026 62547-2**　Divas in Song—Marilyn Horne's
60th Birthday

RAMIN, Günther (cond)
　　see Leipzig Gewandhaus

RAMIN, Philippe (hpd)
　　see CONCERT INDEX *under:*
(PIER) **PV790013**　A. Scarlatti—Cantatas

RAMIREZ, Alejandro (ten)
Hindemith: Nusch-Nuschi (Cpte)
　　see CONCERT INDEX *under:*
(ERAT) **2292-45926-2**　Charpentier—Sacred Choral
Works
(ERAT) **4509-96961-2**　Schubert—Stabat Mater;
Offertorium; Magnificat

RAMÍREZ, Alexander-Sergei (gtr)
　　see CONCERT INDEX *under:*
(DENO) **CO-75357**　Guitar Works
(DENO) **CO-78931**　Villa-Lobos/Ginastera—Guitar
Works

RAMIREZ, Ariel (kybds)
　　see CONCERT INDEX *under:*
(PHIL) **420 955-2PH**　Ramirez: Choral Works

RAMIREZ, Mari Carmen (sngr)
Barbieri: Barberillo de Lavapiès (Cpte)

RAMIRO, Yordi (ten)
Puccini: Gianni Schicchi (Cpte), Madama Butterfly
(Cpte)
Verdi: Rigoletto (Cpte)

RAMM, Gabriele (sop)
Weill: Happy End (Cpte), Mahagonny-Gesänge
(Cpte)

RAMPAL, Jean-Pierre (cond)
　　see ECO

RAMPAL, Jean-Pierre (fl)
Bach: Musikalisches Opfer, BWV1079, Suites,
BWV1066-9 (exc)
　　see CONCERT INDEX *under:*
(ERAT) **4509-95361-2**　Mozart—Wind Concertos
(SONY) **SK47230**　Mozart—Chamber Works
(SONY) **SK48184**　Rampal plays Great Flute
Concertos
(SONY) **SK53106**　Kathleen Battle & Jean-Pierre
Rampal in Concert

RAMPAL, Jean-Pierre (fl/dir)
　　see CONCERT INDEX *under:*
(SONY) **SK45930**　Concertos for Two Flutes
(SONY) **SK48184**　Rampal plays Great Flute
Concertos

RAMPF, Stefan (alto)
　　see CONCERT INDEX *under:*
(TELD) **2292-42609-2**　Bach—Cantatas, Volume 30

(TELD) **2292-42615-2**　Bach—Cantatas, Volume 31
(TELD) **2292-42617-2**　Bach—Cantatas, Volume 32
(TELD) **2292-42631-2**　Bach—Cantatas, Volume 36
(TELD) **2292-42632-2**　Bach—Cantatas, Volume 37
(TELD) **4509-91761-2**　Bach—Cantatas, Vol.7
(TELD) **4509-91762-2**　Bach—Cantatas, Vol.8

RAMPY, David (ten)
Nono: Intolleranza 1960 (Cpte)

RAMUZ, Charles-Ferdinand (narr)
　　see CONCERT INDEX *under:*
(CLAV) **CD50-8918**　Ansermet conducts Stravinsky

RANDALL, Tony (sngr)
　　see CONCERT INDEX *under:*
(RCA) **09026 62681-2**　Mr Jerry Hadley—Golden Days

RANDALU, Kalle (pf)
　　see CONCERT INDEX *under:*
(BIS) **BIS-CD690**　Sumera—Orchestral Works

RANDLE, Thomas (ten)
Purcell: Fairy Queen, Z629 (Cpte)
Tippett: Ice Break (Cpte)
Various: Requiem of Reconciliation (Cpte)

RANDON, Alain (bn)
　　see CONCERT INDEX *under:*
(ACCO) **20202-2**　Poulenc—Chamber Works

RANDOVÁ, Eva (mez)
Fibich: Šárka (Cpte)
Janáček: Cunning Little Vixen (Cpte), Glagolitic Mass
(Cpte), Jenůfa (Cpte)
Schreker: Irrelohe (Cpte)
Wagner: Lohengrin (Cpte)
　　see CONCERT INDEX *under:*
(EMI) **CDC7 49811-2**　Covent Garden Gala Concert
(HANS) **98 809**　Bach—Cantatas, Vol.47

RANDS, Leslie (bar)
Sullivan: Gondoliers (Cpte), Patience (Cpte), Sorcerer
(Cpte)

RANGARAJAN, Gautam (ten)
Goehr: Death of Moses

RÁNKI, Dezsö (pf)
　　see CONCERT INDEX *under:*
(TELD) **9031-76139-2**　Bartók—Piano Works

RANKIN, Bruce (sngr)
Romberg: Student Prince (Cpte)

RANKIN, Nell (mez)
Beethoven: Symphony 9

RANKL, Karl (cond)
　　see LPO

RANNE, Alexander (ten)
Rachmaninov: Liturgy, Op. 31

RANNOU, Blandine (hpd)
Couperin: Concerts Royaux, Livre de clavecin III

RANSOM, Dwight (voc)
Joplin: Treemonisha (Cpte)

RANSOME, Antony (bar)
Rameau: Naïs (Cpte)

RANTA, Ilmo (pf)
　　see CONCERT INDEX *under:*
(CPO) **CPO999 269-2**　Meyerbeer—Mélodies

RAPATTONI, Marco (pf)
　　see CONCERT INDEX *under:*
(AKAD) **CDAK125**　Tosti—Romanze

RAPF, Kurt (cond)
　　see Vienna Sinfonietta

RAPHAEL ENSEMBLE
Arensky: String Quartet 2
Brahms: String Sextet 1, String Sextet 2
Dvořák: String Quintet, Op. 97, String Sextet
Korngold: String Sextet, Op. 10
Schoenberg: Verklärte Nacht
Schubert: String Quintet, String Trio, D471
Tchaikovsky: Souvenir de Florence
　　see CONCERT INDEX *under:*
(HYPE) **CDA66516**　Martinu/Schulhoff—Sextets
(HYPE) **CDA66704**　Bruckner/R. Strauss—Chamber
Works

RAPHAEL QUARTET
　　see CONCERT INDEX *under:*
(ETCE) **KTC1050**　Puccini: Songs and Rare Pieces

RAPHAEL TRIO
Beethoven: Piano Trios (exc), Trio, Op. 38
Wolf-Ferrari: Piano Trio, Op. 5, Piano Trio, Op. 7

RAPHAELE CONCERT ORCHESTRA
cond E. RONDELL
(MOZA) **MECD1002**　Operetta Melodies
cond P. WALDEN
　　see CONCERT INDEX *under:*
(MOZA) **MECD1002**　Operetta Melodies

RAPHANEL, Ghyslaine (sop)
Bizet: Carmen (Cpte)
Massenet: Manon (Cpte)
Offenbach: Brigands (Cpte)

RAPPÉ, Jadwiga (contr)
Beethoven: Missa solemnis
Mahler: Symphony 2
Wagner: Rheingold (Cpte), Siegfried (Cpte)
　　see CONCERT INDEX *under:*
(PHIL) **426 275-2PH**　Mozart—Sacred Choral Works

REHER, Kurt (vc)
Schoenberg: Verklärte Nacht
Schubert: String Quintet

REHFUSS, Heinz (bar)
Falla: Atlántida
Gounod: Roméo et Juliette (Cpte)
Martin: Vin herbé
Ravel: Enfant et les Sortilèges (Cpte)
see CONCERT INDEX under:
(CLAV) **CD50-9327** Lieder Recital—Heinz Rehfuss
(DECC) **433 400-2DM2** Ravel & Debussy—Stage
Works
(DECC) **443 467-2DF2** Stravinsky—Ballet Music
(JECK) **JD563-2** Frank Martin interprets Frank
Martin

REHLING, Elisabeth (sop)
see CONCERT INDEX under:
(ROND) **RCD8323** Nielsen—Songs, Vol.2
(ROND) **RCD8327** Nielsen: Songs, Vol.4

REIBEL, Guy (cond)
see France Groupe Vocal

REIBOLD, Bruno (cond)
see orch

REIBOLD, Hugo (cond)
see orch

REICH, Cäcilie (sop)
R. Strauss: Arabella (Cpte)
(SCHW) **314532** Vienna State Opera Live, Vol.3

REICH, Günter (narr)
Schoenberg: Gurrelieder, Moses und Aron (Cpte)
see CONCERT INDEX under:
(SONY) **SM2K44571** Schoenberg: Choral Works
(WERG) **WER60185-50** Schoenberg: Choral &
Orchestral Works

REICH, Hermann (bass)
see CONCERT INDEX under:
(SCHW) **314562** Vienna State Opera Live, Vol.6
(SCHW) **314602** Vienna State Opera Live, Vol.10
(SCHW) **314642** Vienna State Opera Live, Vol.14

(STEVE) REICH AND MUSICIANS
*Reich: Music for Mallet Instruments, Voices and
Organ*
see CONCERT INDEX under:
(DG) **427 428-2GC2** Reich: Various Works

REICHELT, Ingeborg (sop)
see CONCERT INDEX under:
(ERAT) **4509-97407-2** Bach—Cantatas
(ERAT) **4509-98525-2** Bach—Cantatas
(HANS) **98 804** Bach—Cantatas, Vol.42
(HANS) **98 871** Bach—Cantatas, Vol.20
(HANS) **98 873** Bach—Cantatas, Vol.22
(HANS) **98 891** Bach—Cantatas, Vol.38

REICHENBERG, David (ob)
see CONCERT INDEX under:
(ARCH) **413 731-2AH** Bach: Concerti
(ARCH) **415 518-2AH** Baroque Orchestral Works
(ARCH) **415 674-2AH** Vivaldi: Concertos
(ARCH) **419 615-2AH** Vivaldi: Concertos
(HYPE) **CDA66227** Emma Kirkby Collection

REICHENBERG, David (ob d'amore)
see CONCERT INDEX under:
(ARCH) **413 731-2AH** Bach: Concerti

REICHENBERGER, Hugo (cond)
see Vienna St Op Orch

REICHERT, Willy (sngr)
Jessel: Schwarzwaldmädel (exc)

REICHMANN, Wolfgang (narr)
Mozart: Entführung (Cpte)
Weill: Dreigroschenoper (Cpte)

REICHWEIN, Leopold (cond)
see Vienna St Op Orch

REID, Jane (vn)
see CONCERT INDEX under:
(CHAN) **CHAN8319** Encore! An Hour with Cantilena

REID, Lesley (sop)
G. Charpentier: Louise (Cpte)

(DER) REIHE ENSEMBLE, VIENNA
cond F. CERHA
see CONCERT INDEX under:
(WERG) **WER60162-50** Ligeti: Choral and Orchestral
Works

REILLY, Tommy (harmonica)
see CONCERT INDEX under:
(CHAN) **CHAN6486** Serenade - Tommy Reilly
(CHAN) **CHAN8617** Works for Harmonica and
Orchestra
(CHAN) **CHAN8802** Works for Harmonica
(CHAN) **CHAN9248** Harmonica Concertos
(DECC) **440 320-2DWO** World of British Classics,
Volume IV

REILLY LEWIS, J (cond)
see Washington Nat Cath Ch Society

REIMANN, Arlbert (fp)
see CONCERT INDEX under:
(ORFE) **C097841A** Zelter: Lieder

REIMANN, Arlbert (pf)
Reimann: Michelangelo Lieder, Shine and Dark
*Schubert: Schöne Müllerin (Cpte), Winterreise
(Cpte)*

Shostakovich: Michelangelo Suite, Op. 145
see CONCERT INDEX under:
(DG) **429 766-2GH** Schubert—Lieder
(EMI) **CDM7 63569-2** Pfitzner: Lieder
(EMI) **CDM7 63570-2** Berg & Schoenberg: Lieder
(ORFE) **C053851A** Tchaikovsky: Songs
(ORFE) **C156861A** Hindemith Lieder
(TELD) **4509-97459-2** Eisler—Hollywood Songbook
(WERG) **WER60183-50** Reimann—Vocal Works

REIMER, Eva-Christine (sop)
Schillings: Mona Lisa (Cpte)

REIMER, Eva-Christine (sop)
Delius: Village Romeo and Juliet (Cpte)

REINECKE, Frank (vn)
see CONCERT INDEX under:
(EDA) **EDA008-2** Works by Ullmann and Schoenberg

REINECKE, Renate (sop)
R. Strauss: Elektra (Cpte)

REINER, Charles (pf)
see CONCERT INDEX under:
(MERC) **434 351-2MM** Szeryng plays Kreisler

REINER, Fritz (cond)
see Chicago SO

REINHARDT, Doris (mez)
see CONCERT INDEX under:
(MARC) **8 223636** In Memoriam Lili Boulanger

REINHARDT, Rolf (cond)
see South-West German RSO

REINHARDT, Rolf (pf)
see CONCERT INDEX under:
(VOX) **CDX2 5506** György Sándor plays Bartók

REINHART, Gregory (bass)
Beethoven: Symphony 9
Handel: Messiah (Cpte)
Lully: Alceste (Cpte)
*M-A. Charpentier: Arts Florissants (Cpte), Judicium
Salomonis, H422*
Prokofiev: Love for 3 Oranges (Cpte)
Rameau: Zoroastre (Cpte)
see CONCERT INDEX under:
(HARM) **HMA190 1150** Couperin—Motets

REINHOLD, Annette (contr)
see CONCERT INDEX under:
(CAPR) **10 367** Mendelssohn—Motets

REINING, Maria (sop)
*R. Strauss: Arabella (Cpte), Ariadne auf Naxos
(Cpte), Rosenkavalier (Cpte)*
Wagner: Walküre (exc)
see CONCERT INDEX under:
(EMI) **CDC7 54838-2** Franz Lehár
(EMI) **CHS7 69741-2(4)** Record of Singing,
Vol.4—German School
(EMI) **CMS7 64008-2(1)** Wagner Singing on Record
(pt 1)
(PREI) **89065** Maria Reining (1903-1991)
(PREI) **89083** Maria Reining
(PREI) **90150** Lehár conducts Lehár
(PREI) **90190** Paul Schoeffler—Recital
(PREI) **90237** R Strauss—Daphne
(PREI) **93262** R.Strauss accompanies
Reining,Dermota and Piltti
(SCHW) **314502** Vienna State Opera—Live
Recordings (sampler)
(SCHW) **314542** Vienna State Opera Live, Vol.4
(SCHW) **314552** Vienna State Opera Live, Vol.5
(SCHW) **314602** Vienna State Opera Live, Vol.10
(SCHW) **314632** Vienna State Opera Live, Vol.13
(SCHW) **314672** Vienna State Opera Live, Vol.17

REINMAR, Hans (bar)
see CONCERT INDEX under:
(PREI) **89209** Helge Roswaenge (1897-1972) - II

REINPRECHT, Johann (ten)
R. Strauss: Rosenkavalier (Cpte)

REISER, Tobi (cond)
see Salzburg Shepherd Boys

REISS, Albert (ten)
see CONCERT INDEX under:
(CLAR) **CDGSE78-50-33** Lauritz Melchior & Albert
Coates
(EMI) **CDH7 69789-2** Melchior sings Wagner
(PEAR) **GEMMCDS9137** Wagner—Der Ring des
Nibelungen

REISS, Janine (pf)
see CONCERT INDEX under:
(EMI) **CMS7 63386-2** Borodin—Prince Igor &
Complete Solo Songs

REITER, Alfred (bass)
Spohr: Faust (Cpte)

REITER, Walter (vn)
see CONCERT INDEX under:
(ARCH) **445 839-2AH** Vivaldi—Woodwind Concertos

REITH, Maria (sop)
Mozart: Zauberflöte (Cpte)

REIZEN, Mark (bass)
see CONCERT INDEX under:
(EMI) **CHS7 69741-2(5)** Record of Singing,
Vol.4—Russian & Slavonic Schools
(PREI) **89059** Mark Reizen (1895-1992) - I
(PREI) **89080** Mark Reizen (1895-1992) - II

REIZENSTEIN, Franz (pf)
see CONCERT INDEX under:
(BIDD) **LAB059/60** Henri Temianka—Recital

REJA, Jurij (ten)
Dvořák: Stabat mater

REMEDIOS, Alberto (ten)
*Wagner: Götterdämmerung (Cpte), Siegfried (Cpte),
Walküre (Cpte)*

REMIGIO, Carmela (sngr)
Bellini: Norma (Cpte)

RÉMILLARD, Chantal (vn)
see CONCERT INDEX under:
(SONY) **SK48044** Vivaldi—Concertos for Strings

REMMERT, Birgit (contr)
Beethoven: Missa solemnis
Honegger: Jeanne d'Arc (Cpte)
Mahler: Lied von der Erde
Mendelssohn: Erste Walpurgisnacht
see CONCERT INDEX under:
(PHIL) **438 873-2PH2** Bach—Magnificat and Masses
(TELD) **2292-46452-2** Beethoven—Complete
Symphonies

REMOR, Michela (mez)
Gluck: Iphigénie en Tauride (Cpte)

RENAISSANCE SINGERS
cond V. HANDLEY
see CONCERT INDEX under:
(CHAN) **CHAN8808** Early 20th Century English
Music
cond Y. P. TORTELIER
Ravel: Daphnis et Chloé (Cpte)
see CONCERT INDEX under:
(CHAN) **CHAN8914** Debussy and Ravel—Vocal and
Orchestral Works
(CHAN) **CHAN8952** Chausson & Fauré—Vocal and
Orchestral Works

RENARD, Guy (ten)
B.A. Zimmermann: Soldaten (Cpte)

RENARD, Paul (spkr)
Bizet: Carmen (Cpte)

RENARD CLARINET QUARTET
cond C. RAYBOULD
see CONCERT INDEX under:
(CLRI) **CC0005** The Clarinet - Historical Recordings,
Vol.1

RENARDY, Ossy (vn)
see CONCERT INDEX under:
(BIDD) **LAB061/2** Ossy Renardy - The Victor
Recordings (1940-1)

RENAUD, Maurice (bar)
see CONCERT INDEX under:
(IRCC) **IRCC-CD802** Souvenirs of Rare French
Opera
(NIMB) **NI7840/1** The Era of Adelina Patti
(NIMB) **NI7867** Legendary Baritones
(PEAR) **GEMMCDS9923(2)** Covent Garden on
Record, Vol.1 (pt 2)
(SYMP) **SYMCD1089** Historic Baritones of the French
School
(SYMP) **SYMCD1100** Harold Wayne Collection,
Vol.8

RENAUX, Nadine (sop)
see CONCERT INDEX under:
(EMI) **CZS7 67515-2** Offenbach—Operetta highlights

RENCONTRES MUSICALES ORCHESTRA
cond I. ANGUELOV
Henze: Boulevard Solitude (Cpte)

RENDALL, David (ten)
Bruckner: Te Deum
Elgar: Apostles (Cpte)
*Forrest/Wright: Kismet (Cpte), Song of Norway
(Cpte)*
Handel: Ariodante (Cpte)
Mozart: Requiem
Puccini: Rondine (Cpte)
Romberg: Student Prince (Cpte)
see CONCERT INDEX under:
(CHAN) **CHAN8712/7** Beethoven: Complete
Symphonies
(DG) **429 025-2GX10** Bruckner—Complete
Symphonies, etc

RENÉE, Madelyn (sop)
Verdi: Aida (Cpte)

RENN, Rosalinde (spkr)
Schumann: Manfred (Cpte)

RENNERT, Jonathan (organ)
see CONCERT INDEX under:
(PRIO) **PRCD374** Darke—Organ Works

RENNES CATHEDRAL MASTERSHIP CHOIR
see CONCERT INDEX under:
(STUD) **SM1220.02** Immortel Grégorien

RENTON, Frank (cond)
see Kneller Hall Band

RENZETTI, Donato (cond)
see London Sinf Op Orch

RENZI, Frances (pf)
see CONCERT INDEX under:
(KOCH) **37186-2** French Clarinet Music

RENZI, Paolo (ob)
see CONCERT INDEX under:

RHODES, Samuel (va)
Mozart: Clarinet Quintet, K581
Schoenberg: String Trio
Schumann: Piano Quartet, Op. 47, Piano Quintet, Op. 44

RHYS-DAVIES, Gareth (bar)
Janáček: Fate (Cpte)

RHYS-DAVIES, Jennifer (sop)
Mercadante: Orazi e Curiazi (Cpte)
Rossini: Barbiere di Siviglia (Cpte)
see CONCERT INDEX under:
(OPRA) ORCH104 A Hundred Years of Italian Opera: 1820-1830

RHYS-EVANS, Huw (ten)
Boïeldieu: Calife de Bagdad (Cpte)
Mendelssohn: Hochzeit des Camacho (Cpte)

RIALLAND, Louis (ten)
G. Charpentier: Louise (Cpte)
Gounod: Roméo et Juliette (Cpte)
Poulenc: Dialogues des Carmélites (Cpte)

RIBACCHI, Luisa (mez)
Puccini: Manon Lescaut (Cpte)
Verdi: Otello (Cpte), Rigoletto (Cpte)

RIBASENKO, Vladimir (bass)
Mussorgsky: Marriage (Cpte)

RIBBE, Hans-Joachim (bass)
Bach: St. Matthew Passion, BWV244 (Cpte)

RICCI, Enrique (cond)
see ECO

RICCI, George (vc)
see CONCERT INDEX under:
(BIDD) LAB044 Ruggiero Ricci—1938 Electrola Recordings

RICCI, Gian Luca (bar)
Paisiello: Serva Padrona (Cpte)

RICCI, Luigi (cond)
see Rome Op Orch

RICCI, Ruggiero (vn)
Brahms: Violin Concerto
see CONCERT INDEX under:
(BIDD) LAB044 Ruggiero Ricci—1938 Electrola Recordings
(DECC) 433 220-2DWO The World of the Violin
(DECC) 433 911-2DM2 Spanish Orchestral Music, Vol 3
(ETCE) KTC1038 Violin and piano recital
(UNIC) UKCD2048 Wieniawski—Virtuoso Showpieces

RICCI, Ruggiero (vn/dir)
see CONCERT INDEX under:
(UNIC) UKCD2067 Bach—Violin Concertos

RICCIARDI, Franco (ten)
Bellini: Sonnambula (Cpte)
Cilea: Adriana Lecouvreur (Cpte)
Donizetti: Lucrezia Borgia (Cpte)
Puccini: Bohème (Cpte), Manon Lescaut (Cpte)
Verdi: Aida (Cpte), Traviata (Cpte)

RICCIARELLI, Katia (sop)
Bellini: Capuleti (Cpte), Zaira (Cpte)
Bizet: Carmen (Cpte)
Donizetti: Elisir d'amore (Cpte), Poliuto (Cpte)
Puccini: Bohème (Cpte), Tosca (Cpte), Turandot (Cpte)
Rossini: Bianca e Falliero (Cpte), Donna del Lago (Cpte), Gazza ladra (Cpte), Petite messe solennelle, Stabat Mater, Viaggio a Reims (Cpte)
Verdi: Aida (exc), Ballo in Maschera (Cpte), Battaglia di Legnano (Cpte), Don Carlos (Cpte), Due Foscari (Cpte), Falstaff (Cpte), Luisa Miller (Cpte), Otello (Cpte), Requiem (Cpte), Simon Boccanegra (Cpte), Trovatore (Cpte)
see CONCERT INDEX under:
(BELA) 450 121-2 Plácido Domingo
(DECC) 443 018-2DF2 Pavarotti/Freni/Ricciarelli—Live
(RCA) GD86534 Verdi Arias and Duets
(RCA) 09026 61580-2(8) RCA/Met 100 Singers, 100 Years (pt 8)
(SONY) MK39097 Puccini Heroines
(VIRG) CUV5 61139-2 Rossini—Arias

RICE, Tristan (treb)
see CONCERT INDEX under:
(ABBS) CDMVP827 20 Christmas Carols from St George's Chapel, Windsor Castle

RICERCAR CONSORT
Haydn: Divertimenti, HobX (exc)
see CONCERT INDEX under:
(RICE) RIC037011 Charpentier—Cantatas and Airs
(RICE) RIC041016 German Baroque Cantatas, Vol.2 - Buxtehude
(RICE) RIC046023 German Baroque Cantatas, Vol.3
(RICE) RIC048035/7 German Baroque Cantatas, Vol.4 - Bruhns
(RICE) RIC054032 Italian Motets and Arias
(RICE) RIC060048 German Baroque Cantatas, Vol. 5
(RICE) RIC061041 Bach—Cantatas
(RICE) RIC079061 German Baroque Cantatas, Vol.6 - Funeral Cantatas
(RICE) RIC098112 German Baroque Chamber Music, Vol.5
(RICE) RIC109097/8 German Baroque Cantatas, Vol.9 - Weckmann

---

cond A. CHAMORRO
see CONCERT INDEX under:
(RICE) RIC069049 W.F. Bach—Keyboard Concertos

RICERCAR QUARTET
Telemann: Paris Quartets (Quadri) (exc)

RICHARD, Lawrence (bass)
Sullivan: Iolanthe (Cpte)

RICHARDS, Angela (sngr)
Gay: Beggar's Opera (Cpte)

RICHARDSON, Diane (pf)
see CONCERT INDEX under:
(NEW) NW273-2 Griffes: Vocal & Instrumental Works

RICHARDSON, Linda (mez)
G. Charpentier: Louise (Cpte)
Massenet: Werther (Cpte)
Ravel: Enfant et les sortilèges (Cpte)
Shostakovich: Lady Macbeth of Mtsensk (Cpte)
Vaughan Williams: Hugh the Drover (Cpte)
see CONCERT INDEX under:
(EMI) CDC7 54071-2 Frederica von Stade sings Rodgers & Hart
(EMI) CDC7 54586-2 Broadway Showstoppers
(EMI) CDC7 54626-2 Operetta Arias

RICHARDSON, Marilyn (sop)
Mozart: Zauberflöte (exc)

RICHARDSON, Mark (bar)
Sullivan: Mikado (Cpte)

RICHARDSON, Neil (cond)
see Philh

RICHARDSON, Sir Ralph (spkr)
Vaughan Williams: Symphony 7
see CONCERT INDEX under:
(DECC) 433 612-2DSP Prokofiev—Popular Orchestral Works

RICHARDSON, Stephen (bar)
Goehr: Death of Moses
MacMillan: Visitatio Sepulchri (Cpte)
Mozart: Kleine Freimaurer-Kantate, K623, Requiem
see CONCERT INDEX under:
(SONY) SK66243 Music for Queen Mary

RICHARDSON, Stephen (bass)
see CONCERT INDEX under:
(DG) 447 068-2GH Stravinsky—The Flood, etc

RICHARTZ, Paul (vn)
see CONCERT INDEX under:
(ACAN) 43 801 Elisabeth Schwarzkopf—Wartime Recordings

RICHERT, François (bass)
Donizetti: Roberto Devereux (Cpte)

RICHMAN, Steven (cond)
see NY Harmonie Ens

RICHTER, Carl (bar)
Puccini: Bohème (exc)

RICHTER, Ernst Theo (bar)
Busoni: Arlecchino (Cpte)

RICHTER, Karl (cond)
see Ansbach Bach Week Sols Ens

RICHTER, Karl (hpd)
see CONCERT INDEX under:
(ARCH) 427 113-2AGA Bach: Flute Sonatas

RICHTER, Konrad (pf)
Schubert: Winterreise (Cpte)
see CONCERT INDEX under:
(BAYE) BR100228 Ullmann—Orchestral Works
(PREI) 93331 Pfitzner: Lieder

RICHTER, Ladislav (ten)
Zelenka: Requiem, ZWV48

RICHTER, Maximilian (treb)
Mozart: Zauberflöte (Cpte)

RICHTER, Sviatoslav (pf)
Beethoven: Piano Concerto 1, Triple Concerto
Brahms: Piano Concerto 2, Piano Sonata 1, Piano Sonata 2
Britten: Piano Concerto
Chopin: Etudes (exc), Scherzos
Dvořák: Piano Concerto
Grieg: Piano Concerto
Hindemith: Ludus tonalis, Piano Sonata 2
Prokofiev: Piano Concerto 5
Rachmaninov: Piano Concerto 2, Preludes (exc)
Schubert: Fantasy, D760, Piano Sonata, D958, Piano Sonata, D960, Winterreise (Cpte)
Schumann: Bunte Blätter, Piano Concerto
Tchaikovsky: Piano Concerto 1
see CONCERT INDEX under:
(CHNT) LDC278 1018/9 Shostakovich: Chamber Works
(DECC) 436 454-2DH Haydn—Keyboard Sonatas
(DECC) 436 455-2DH Haydn—Piano Sonatas
(DECC) 436 456-2DH Schumann—Piano Works
(DG) 413 850-2GW2 Rachmaninov/Liszt—Piano Concertos
(DG) 423 573-2GDO Sviatoslav Richter—Piano Recital
(DG) 435 751-2GDO Richter plays Schumann
(DG) 447 355-2GDB2 Recital - Sviatoslav Richter
(EMI) CDC7 47507-2 Shostakovich—Chamber Works
(EMI) CDM7 64625-2 Schumann—Piano Works
(EMI) CMS7 64429-2 Sviatoslav Richter—Un Portrait

(MELO) 74321 25172-2(1) Russian Piano School (pt 1 - Vols.1 - 8)
(MELO) 74321 25178-2 Russian Piano School, Vol. 6
(OLYM) OCD286 Sviatoslav Richter, Vol.1 - Schubert
(OLYM) OCD287 Sviatoslav Richter - Vol.2
(OLYM) OCD288 Schubert—Piano Works
(OLYM) OCD334 Richter, Vol.4—Tchaikovsky Piano Works
(OLYM) OCD336 Richter, Vol.6—Beethoven Piano Sonatas
(OLYM) OCD337 Richter, Vol.7—Rachmaninov Piano Works
(OLYM) OCD339 Sviatoslav Richter - Volume 9
(ORFE) C334931A Schubert—Lieder
(PHIL) 438 477-2PH3 Richter—The Authorised Recordings: Brahms/Schumann
(PHIL) 438 480-2PH2 Richter—The Authorised Recordings: Mozart
(PHIL) 438 483-2PH2 Richter—The Authorised Recordings: Schubert
(PHIL) 438 486-2PH2 Richter—The Authorised Recordings: Beethoven
(PHIL) 438 613-2PH3 Richter—The Authorised Recordings: Bach
(PHIL) 438 617-2PH2 Richter—The Authorised Recordings: Haydn/Weber/B'hoven
(PHIL) 438 620-2PH3 Richter—The Authorised Recordings: Chopin/Liszt
(PHIL) 438 624-2PH2 Richter—The Authorised Recordings: Beethoven
(PHIL) 438 627-2PH2 Richter—The Authorised Recordings: Russian Piano Works
(PHIL) 446 200-2PM Liszt—Piano Concertos; Piano Sonata
(PYRA) PYR13500/1 Sviatoslav Richter at Pleyel
(PYRA) PYR13503 Sviatoslav Richter - Piano Recital
(RCA) RD60859 Sviatoslav Richter - Piano Recital

RICKARD, Paul (treb)
see CONCERT INDEX under:
(ABBS) CDMVP827 20 Christmas Carols from St George's Chapel, Windsor Castle

RICKARDS, Steven (alto)
Handel: Siroe, Rè di Persia (Cpte)
see CONCERT INDEX under:
(KOCH) 37163-2 Bach—Cantatas

RICKENBACHER, Karl Anton (cond)
see Bamberg SO

RICQUIER, Odette (sop)
Gounod: Roméo et Juliette (Cpte)
see CONCERT INDEX under:
(CLUB) CL99-101 Vanni Marcoux (1877-1962)

RIDDER, Anton de (ten)
Busoni: Doktor Faust (Cpte)
Korngold: Tote Stadt (Cpte)
R. Strauss: Capriccio (Cpte), Rosenkavalier (Cpte)

RIDDERBUSCH, Karl (bass)
Bach: Mass in B minor, BWV232 (Cpte), St Matthew Passion, BWV244 (Cpte)
Beethoven: Fidelio (Cpte)
E.T.A. Hoffmann: Undine (Cpte)
Flotow: Martha (Cpte)
Humperdinck: Königskinder (Cpte)
Mozart: Requiem
Pfitzner: Palestrina (Cpte)
R. Strauss: Capriccio (Cpte)
Wagner: Fliegende Holländer (Cpte), Götterdämmerung (Cpte), Lohengrin (Cpte), Meistersinger (Cpte), Parsifal (Cpte), Rheingold (Cpte), Siegfried (Cpte), Tristan und Isolde (Cpte)
see CONCERT INDEX under:
(DG) 423 127-2GX4 Bruckner: Sacred Works for Chorus
(DG) 435 211-2GX15 Wagner—Der Ring des Nibelungen
(DG) 437 368-2GX2 Beethoven—Orchestral Works
(DG) 439 423-2GCL Wagner—Der Ring des Nibelungen (highlights)
(DG) 447 409-2GOR2 Bruckner—The Masses

RIDDLE, Frederick (va)
see CONCERT INDEX under:
(CHAN) CHAN6545 Vaughan Williams—Orchestral Works
(DUTT) CDAX8003 Walton—Gramophone premières
(DUTT) CDAX8014 British Gramophone Premieres
(MUSI) MACD-665 The Goldberg/Kraus Duo plays Mozart and Beethoven
(TEST) SBT1007 Kell plays Mozart Clarinet Works

RIDEOUT, Patricia (spkr)
see CONCERT INDEX under:
(SONY) SM2K52664 Schoenberg—Piano Works

RIDGE QUARTET
Dvořák: Piano Quintet, Op.5, Piano Quintet, Op.81
J. Adams: Shaker Loops

RIDGLEY-WHITEHOUSE, Stephen (organ)
see CONCERT INDEX under:
(HERI) HRCD901 By Royal Command

RIDGLEY-WHITEHOUSE, Stephen (org/dir)
see CONCERT INDEX under:
(HERI) HRCD901 By Royal Command

RIDGLEY-WHITEHOUSE, Stephen (pf)
see CONCERT INDEX under:
(HERI) HRCD901 By Royal Command

RIDGWAY, Judith (pf)
see CONCERT INDEX under:
(CARL) **MCD57** Britten—Songs

RIDINGS, Lt-Col Richard A. (cond)
see Coldstream Guards Band

RIEBL, Thomas (va)
see CONCERT INDEX under:
(ACAN) **43 507** Brahms—Lieder

RIEDEL, Bernd (bar)
Lortzing: Wildschütz (Cpte)

RIEDEL, Karl (cond)
see RCA SO

RIEDELBAUCH, Wolfgang (ten)
Mozart: Zauberflöte (Cpte)

RIEDIKER, Hans (bass)
Holliger: Magische Tänzer (Cpte)

RIEDL, Franz (bass)
R. Strauss: Rosenkavalier (Cpte)

RIEFLING, Robert (pf)
see CONCERT INDEX under:
(NKF) **NKFCD50029-2** Grieg—Piano Works
(SIMA) **PSC1809(2)** Grieg—Historical Piano
Recordings (pt 2)

RIEGEL, Kenneth (ten)
Berg: Lulu (Cpte)
Berlioz: Damnation de Faust (Cpte)
Haydn: Mass 14
Henze: Bassariden (Cpte)
Liszt: Faust Symphony
Mahler: Symphony 8
Messiaen: Saint François d'Assise (Cpte)
Mozart: Don Giovanni (Cpte)
Mussorgsky: Boris Godunov (Cpte)
R. Strauss: Salome (Cpte)
Zemlinsky: Florentinische Tragödie, Geburtstag der
Infantin (Cpte)
see CONCERT INDEX under:
(DG) **435 162-2GX13** Mahler—Complete
Symphonies
(DG) **437 788-2GH** Lourié—Chamber and Vocal
Works
(SONY) **SM2K47563** Haydn—Choral & Orchestral
Works

RIEGER, Fritz (cond)
see BRSO

RIEGER, Wolfram (pf)
see CONCERT INDEX under:
(JECK) **JD677-2** Schoeck—Complete Lieder, Vol.7

RIEGLER, Friedl (sop)
Mozart: Zauberflöte (Cpte)

RIENER, Robert (bar)
Puccini: Gianni Schicchi (Cpte)
Verdi: Rigoletto (Cpte)
see CONCERT INDEX under:
(EURO) **GD69043** Puccini: Il Trittico

RIESMAN, Michael (cond)
see Orch

RIESMAN, Michael (kybds)
see CONCERT INDEX under:
(PNT) **434 873-2PTH** Jon Gibson—In Good
Company

RIESMAN, Michael (pf)
see CONCERT INDEX under:
(SONY) **SK64133** The Essential Philip Glass

RIESSLER, Michael (bass cl)
see CONCERT INDEX under:
(SCHW) **310632** Globokar—Chamber Works

RIEU, André (cond)
see Amsterdam CO

RIGA PHILHARMONIC ORCHESTRA
cond K. RUSMANIS
see CONCERT INDEX under:
(CONI) **CDCF236** Vasks—Message

RIGACCI, Bruno (cond)
see Livorno Cel-Teatro Orch

RIGACCI, Susanna (sop)
Donizetti: Elisir d'amore (Cpte), Pazzi per progetto
(Cpte)
Sacchini: Contadina in Corte (Cpte)

RIGBY, Jean (mez)
Bach: Magnificat, BWV243
Berlioz: Enfance du Christ (Cpte)
Bizet: Carmen (Cpte)
Britten: Rape of Lucretia (Cpte)
Bruckner: Mass in F minor, Psalm 150
Mahler: Lied von der Erde
Mendelssohn: Elijah (Cpte), Erste Walpurgisnacht,
Midsummer Night's Dream (exc)
Sullivan: Mikado (exc), Yeomen of the Guard (Cpte)
Verdi: Forza del destino (Cpte), Rigoletto (Cpte)
see CONCERT INDEX under:
(HYPE) **CDA66420** Vaughan Williams: Vocal Works
(TELD) **4509-92374-2** Elgar—The Music Makers;
String Pieces

RIGHETTI, Cesare (bar)
see CONCERT INDEX under:
(TELD) **4509-90798-2** Monteverdi—Il Ballo delle
ingrate

RIGNOLD, Hugo (cond)
see ROHO

RIGUTTO, Bruno (pf)
Bach: 3-Harpsichord Concerti (exc), 4-Harpsichord
Concerto
Chopin: Piano Concerto 1, Piano Concerto 2
Koechlin: Ballade
see CONCERT INDEX under:
(DENO) **CO-78927** Chopin—Piano Works, Volume 3
(EMI) **CZS7 62687-2** Fauré—Piano Works

RIHA, Vladimir (cl)
Beethoven: Piano Trios (exc)

RILEY, Stanley (bass)
Verdi: Trovatore (Cpte)

RILEY, Terry (cond)
see Life on the Water

RILEY, Terry (tambura)
see CONCERT INDEX under:
(NONE) **7559-79310-2** Short Stories

RILKE ENSEMBLE
cond S. EHRLING
Rosenberg: Symphony 4

RILLING, Helmuth (cond)
see Inst Ens

RILLING, Helmuth (organ)
Beethoven: Missa solemnis
Brahms: Deutsches Requiem, Op. 45 (Cpte)
Franck: Béatitudes (Cpte)
Handel: Messias, K572 (Cpte)
J.C. Bach: Amadis de Gaule (Cpte)
Various: Messa per Rossini (Cpte)
see CONCERT INDEX under:
(HANS) **98 965** Bach—Motets

RÎMBU, Romeo (cond)
see Oradea PO

RIME, Noémi (sop)
A. Scarlatti: Lamentazioni (exc)
Brossard: Dialogus, Elévations (1698)
Lully: Armide, Atys (Cpte)
M.-A. Charpentier: Malade Imaginaire, Médée (Cpte)
Mouret: Amours de Ragonde (Cpte)
Purcell: Fairy Queen, Z629 (Cpte)
Rameau: Indes galantes (Cpte)
see CONCERT INDEX under:
(ERAT) **4509-96967-2** Rameau—Les Grands Motets
(HARM) **HMC90 1416** Delalande—Petits Motets

RIMINI, Giacomo (bar)
see CONCERT INDEX under:
(CLUB) **CL99-052** Rosa Raisa (1893-1963)

RIMON, Meir (hn/dir)
see CONCERT INDEX under:
(CARL) **MCD31** Horn Concertos

RINALDI, Alberto (bar)
Cimarosa: Matrimonio segreto (Cpte)
Leoncavallo: Pagliacci (Cpte)

RINALDI-MILIANI, Stefano (bar)
Mozart: Don Giovanni (Cpte)

RINAUDO, Mario (bass)
Puccini: Bohème (Cpte), Madama Butterfly (Cpte)
Verdi: Forza del destino (Cpte), Rigoletto (Cpte)

RING, Blanche (sngr)
see CONCERT INDEX under:
(PEAR) **GEMMCDS9053/5** Music from the New York
Stage, Vol. 2: 1908–1913

RINGART, Anna (mez)
Berg: Lulu (Cpte)

RINGEISSEN, Bernard (pf)
Alkan: Études, Op.35, Études, Op.39 (exc)
see CONCERT INDEX under:
(EMI) **CDM7 64714-2** Poulenc—Piano Concertos
(HARM) **HMA190 927** Alkan—Piano Works

RINGHOLZ, Teresa (sop)
Rossini: Scala di Seta (Cpte)

RINTZLER, Marius (bass)
Busoni: Doktor Faust (Cpte)
Puccini: Madama Butterfly (Cpte)
Shostakovich: Symphony 13

RIO DE JANEIRO ASSOCIATION FOR CHORAL SONG
(MALE MEMBERS)
see CONCERT INDEX under:
(CHNT) **LDC278 835** Villa-Lobos—Chôros for
Chamber Ensembles

RIORDAN, Joseph (ten)
Sullivan: Gondoliers (Cpte)

RIPLEY, Gladys (contr)
Elgar: Dream of Gerontius (Cpte)
see CONCERT INDEX under:
(EMI) **CHS7 69741-2(1)** Record of Singing,
Vol.4—Anglo-American School (pt 1)

RIPOLLES, Dolores (sngr)
Bretón: Verbena de la Paloma (Cpte)

RIPPON, Michael (bass)
Handel: Israel in Egypt (Cpte)
Herrmann: Fantasticks, Wuthering Heights (Cpte)
Puccini: Tosca (Cpte)
Purcell: St Cecilia's Day Ode, Z328
R. Strauss: Salome (Cpte)
Schoenberg: Moses and Aron (Cpte)
Vaughan Williams: Hugh the Drover (Cpte)

Weill: Sieben Todsünden
see CONCERT INDEX under:
(DECC) **433 080-2DM** Kodály—Choral Works
(LYRI) **SRCD324** Mathias—Choral Works

RISCHE, Michael (pf)
see CONCERT INDEX under:
(SCHW) **312322** Schulhoff—Chamber Music with
wind instruments

RISCHNER, Alfons (cond)
see Stuttgart RSO

RISTORI, Gabrielle (mez)
Audran: Miss Helyett (Cpte), Poupée (exc)

RITCHIE, Elizabeth (sop)
Sullivan: HMS Pinafore (Cpte)
see CONCERT INDEX under:
(CLRI) **CC0006** Clarinet Virtuosi of the
Past—Hermstedt

RITCHIE, Margaret (sop)
Delius: Village Romeo and Juliet (Cpte)
see CONCERT INDEX under:
(EMI) **CHS7 69741-2(1)** Record of Singing,
Vol.4—Anglo-American School (pt 1)
(EMI) **CMS7 64727-2** Britten—Opera excerpts and
Folksongs

RITCHIE, Neil (treb)
Dvořák: Mass in D

RITCHIE, Stanley (vn)
Vivaldi: Concerti, Op. 11
see CONCERT INDEX under:
(HARM) **HMU90 7091** Three Parts upon a Ground
(HARM) **HMU90 7094** Schubert—Piano Trios

RITTER, John Steele (pf)
see CONCERT INDEX under:
(SONY) **SK47230** Mozart—Chamber Works
(SONY) **SK53106** Kathleen Battle & Jean-Pierre
Rampal in Concert

RITTERBUSCH, Sabine (sop)
Dessau: Hagadah Shel Pessach

RITZEN, Peter (pf)
see CONCERT INDEX under:
(MARC) **8 223525** Leschetizky—Piano Works

RITZMANN, Martin (ten)
Beethoven: Symphony 9

RIVA, Ambrogio (bass)
Rossini: Bianca e Falliero (Cpte)

RIVAS, Isabel (sngr)
Usandizaga: Golondrinas (Cpte)

RIVAZ, Anthony de (alto)
Saint-Saëns: Mass, Op. 4

RIVENQ, Nicolas (bar)
Bizet: Carmen (Cpte)
Dauvergne: Troqueurs (Cpte)
Massenet: Don Quichotte (Cpte)
Monteverdi: Orfeo (Cpte)
Montéclair: Jephté (Cpte)
Rameau: Indes galantes (Cpte)
Rossini: Comte Ory (Cpte)
Vivaldi: Montezuma (Cpte)
see CONCERT INDEX under:
(ERAT) **4509-96967-2** Rameau—Les Grands Motets

RIVERS, Earl (cond)
see Cincinnati Uni Th Orch

RIVERS, Malcolm (bass-bar)
G. Lloyd: Iernin, John Socman (exc)
Puccini: Fanciulla del West (Cpte)
Sondheim: Pacific Overtures (Cpte)
Sullivan: Mikado (Cpte), Pirates of Penzance (Cpte)
Walton: Troilus and Cressida (Cpte)

RIVERS, Sandra (pf)
see CONCERT INDEX under:
(EMI) **CDC7 54352-2** Sarah Chang - Debut
(RCA) **09026 62546-2** Salut d'amour

RIZZA, Gilda dalla (sop)
see CONCERT INDEX under:
(EMI) **CHS7 64864-2(1)** La Scala Edition - Vol.2,
1915-46 (pt 1)
(PEAR) **GEMMCDS9925(1)** Covent Garden on
Record—Vol.3 (pt 1)

RIZZI, Carlo (cond)
see LSO

RIZZI, Lucia (contr)
Bellini: Adelson e Salvini (Cpte)
Rossini: Italiana in Algeri (Cpte)

RIZZI, Marco (vn)
see CONCERT INDEX under:
(NUOV) **7109** Dallapiccola—Orchestral Works

RIZZOLI, Bruna (sop)
Donizetti: Don Pasquale (Cpte)
Puccini: Bohème (Cpte), Gianni Schicchi (Cpte)
Rossini: Mosè (Cpte)
Verdi: Aida (Cpte)

ROA, Miguel (cond)
see Madrid SO

ROACH, David (sax)
see CONCERT INDEX under:
(MILA) **74321 14081-2** Bernard Herrmann—Film
Scores

ROACH, Jeanette (contr)
Sullivan: Gondoliers (Cpte)

ROB, Irit (pf)
see CONCERT INDEX *under:*
(CHAN) **CHAN8593** Works for String Orchestra

ROBARTS, Jonathon (bass)
G. Lloyd: Iernin

ROBBIN, Catherine (mez)
Beethoven: Missa Solemnis, Symphony 9
Berlioz: Béatrice et Bénédict (Cpte)
Handel: Belshazzar (Cpte), Floridante (exc), Messiah
(exc), Orlando (Cpte)
Haydn: Stabat Mater
Mozart: Clemenza di Tito (Cpte)
see CONCERT INDEX *under:*
(CBC) **SMCD5098** Mahler—Lieder
(EMI) **CDC7 54525-2** Mozart—Sacred Works
(ERAT) **2292-45517-2** Berlioz—Songs
(L'OI) **436 585-2OH** Mozart—Sacred Choral Works
(MARQ) **ERAD113** Catherine Robbin—Song Recital

ROBBINS, John Franklyn (spkr)
see CONCERT INDEX *under:*
(CNTI) **CCD1009** Music of Barry Anderson

ROBBINS, Julien (bass)
Verdi: Traviata (Cpte)
Wagner: Parsifal (Cpte)

ROBBINS, Mark (hn)
see CONCERT INDEX *under:*
(DELO) **DE3084** Schumann: Orchestral Works

ROBERT, Sylvie (sop)
see CONCERT INDEX *under:*
(MARC) **8 223636** In Memoriam Lili Boulanger

ROBERT, Walter (pf)
see CONCERT INDEX *under:*
(BIDD) **LAB061/2** Ossy Renardy - The Victor
Recordings (1940-1)

ROBERTS, Bernard (pf)
Beethoven: Diabelli Variations
Elgar: Piano Quintet
see CONCERT INDEX *under:*
(NIMB) **NI7709** Beethoven—Piano Sonatas

ROBERTS, Cynthia (vn)
see CONCERT INDEX *under:*
(SONY) **SK48044** Vivaldi—Concertos for Strings

ROBERTS, Eric (bar)
Sondheim: Pacific Overtures (exc)
Sullivan: Mikado (Cpte), Pirates of Penzance (Cpte)

ROBERTS, Gareth (ten)
Vaughan Williams: Sancta civitas

ROBERTS, Joy (sop)
Offenbach: Christopher Columbus (Cpte)
see CONCERT INDEX *under:*
(L'OI) **425 893-2OM6(1)** Purcell—Theatre Music (Part
1)

ROBERTS, Rebecca (sop)
Offenbach: Périchole (Cpte)

ROBERTS, Stephen (bar)
Bach: St Matthew Passion, BWV244 (Cpte)
Birtwistle: Punch and Judy (Cpte)
Elgar: Apostles (Cpte), Caractacus (Cpte), Coronation
Ode (Cpte)
Fauré: Requiem (Cpte)
Haydn: Mass 11
M-A. Charpentier: Te Deum H146
Mozart: Litanies, K243, Mass, K258, Requiem,
Vespers, K321, Vespers, K339
Nielsen: Symphony 3
Orff: Carmina Burana
Telemann: Deus judicium tuum, Donner-Ode
see CONCERT INDEX *under:*
(ARGO) **436 833-2ZH** Purcell— Music for the Funeral
of Queen Mary
(CFP) **CD-CFP4570** Choral Favourites
(CHAN) **CHAN8760** Walton—Choral Works
(CHAN) **CHAN8972** Debussy & Ravel—Orchestral
works
(EMI) **CDM7 64730-2** Vaughan Williams—Riders to
the Sea; Epithalamion, etc
(HYPE) **CDA66015** Songs by Finzi and His Friends
(HYPE) **CDA66437** Stravinsky—Sacred Choral
Works

ROBERTS, Susan (sop)
Wagner: Parsifal (Cpte)
see CONCERT INDEX *under:*
(WERG) **WER6275-2** Orff—Trionfi

ROBERTS, Timothy (organ)
see CONCERT INDEX *under:*
(ARCH) **437 552-2AH2** Venetian Vespers
(ARCH) **437 833-2AH** Christmas Mass in Rome
(ARCH) **445 829-2AH** Purcell—Harmonia Sacra
(HYPE) **CDA66646** Blow—Fairest work of happy
Nature
(HYPE) **CDA66688** Festal Sacred Music of Bavaria
(VIRG) **VC7 59006-2** Gabrieli—A Venetian
Coronation,1595

ROBERTS, Timothy (fp)
(HYPE) **CDA66497** O Tuneful Voice
(HYPE) **CDA66649** Benda—Lieder & Fortepiano
Music
(HYPE) **CDA66740** The Romantic Muse—English
Music in the Time of Beethoven

ROBERTS, Timothy (hpd)
see CONCERT INDEX *under:*

(ARCH) **445 829-2AH** Purcell—Harmonia Sacra
(HYPE) **CDA66497** O Tuneful Voice
(HYPE) **CDA66646** Blow—Fairest work of happy
Nature
(NAXO) **8 550603** Gibbons—Consort and Keyboard
Music, Songs and Anthems
(NAXO) **8 550604** Byrd—Music for Viols, Voices and
Keyboard

ROBERTS, Timothy (spinet)
see CONCERT INDEX *under:*
(HYPE) **CDA66646** Blow—Fairest work of happy
Nature

ROBERTS WESLEYAN BRASS ENSEMBLE
cond R. SHEWAN
see CONCERT INDEX *under:*
(BAY) **BCD-1011** American Choral Music

ROBERTS WESLEYAN COLLEGE CHORALE
cond R. SHEWAN
see CONCERT INDEX *under:*
(BAY) **BCD-1011** American Choral Music

ROBERTSON, Christopher (bar)
Bellini: Puritani (Cpte)

ROBERTSON, David (cond)
see FNO

ROBERTSON, Duncan (ten)
Lalo: Namouna (Cpte)
Rossini: Barbiere di Siviglia (Cpte)
see CONCERT INDEX *under:*
(EMI) **CDC7 47283-2** Maria Callas - Mad Scenes &
Bel Canto Arias
(EMI) **CMS7 63244-2** The Art of Maria Callas

ROBERTSON, George (va)
see CONCERT INDEX *under:*
(ASV) **CDDCA875** Reger—Chamber Music, Volume 1

ROBERTSON, Iain (organ)
see CONCERT INDEX *under:*
(CHAN) **CHAN4501** The World's Most Beautiful
Melodies

ROBERTSON, James (cond)
see Philh

ROBERTSON, John (ten)
Mozart: Nozze di Figaro (Cpte)

ROBERTSON, Liz (sngr)
Strouse: Dance a Little Closer (Cpte)

ROBERTSON, Martin (sax)
see CONCERT INDEX *under:*
(CHAN) **CHAN9380** Martin—Ballades
(NMC) **NMCD024M** Turnage—Vocal and Chamber
Works

ROBERTSON, Nicholas (ten)
Bach: Cantata 211
Handel: Belshazzar (Cpte), Israel in Egypt (Cpte)
Monteverdi: Orfeo (Cpte)

ROBERTSON, Stuart (bar)
Sullivan: Gondoliers (Cpte), Pirates of Penzance
(Cpte), Sorcerer (Cpte)

ROBESON, Paul (bass-bar)
see CONCERT INDEX *under:*
(MMOI) **CDMOIR411** Sacred Songs and Arias

ROBIN, Donna (sop)
see CONCERT INDEX *under:*
(NAXO) **8 550435** Mozart—Arias and Duets

ROBIN, Mado (sop)
see CONCERT INDEX *under:*
(EMI) **CHS7 69741-2(3)** Record of Singing,
Vol.4—French School

ROBINŠAK, Branko (ten)
Bellini: Beatrice di Tenda (Cpte)

ROBINSON, C. (organ)
see CONCERT INDEX *under:*
(EMI) **CES5 68525-2** Berlioz/Saint-Saëns—Orchestral
Works

ROBINSON, Christopher (cond)
see St George's Chapel Ch

ROBINSON, Douglas (ten)
Bach: Cantata 21

ROBINSON, Eric (cond)
see orch

ROBINSON, Ethna (mez)
M-A. Charpentier: Te Deum, H146

ROBINSON, Faye (sop)
Haydn: Mass 13
Mahler: Symphony 8
Tippett: Byzantium, Child of our Time, Mask of Time,
Symphony 3
see CONCERT INDEX *under:*
(DECC) **430 263-2DM** Purcell—Sacred choral works

ROBINSON, Forbes (bass)
Britten: Peter Grimes (Cpte)

ROBINSON, Joseph (ob)
Rochberg: Oboe Concerto
see CONCERT INDEX *under:*
(EMI) **CDC5 55400-2** Barber—Chamber and
Instrumental Works

ROBINSON, Paul (cond)
see Košice St PO

ROBINSON, Paul (cond)
see Toronto CO

ROBINSON, Paul (bar)
Vaughan Williams: Hugh the Drover (Cpte)

ROBINSON, Paul (bass)
Goehr: Death of Moses

ROBINSON, Peter (cond)
see ENO Orch

ROBINSON, Sharon (vc)
Brahms: String Sextet 1, String Sextet 2

ROBINSON, Stacey (sngr)
Schuman: Mighty Casey (Cpte)

ROBINSON, Stanford (cond)
see LSO

ROBINSON CLEAVER, H (organ)
see CONCERT INDEX *under:*
(EMI) **CHS7 69741-2(2)** Record of Singing,
Vol.4—Anglo-American School (pt 2)

ROBISON, Paula (fl)
see CONCERT INDEX *under:*
(MMAS) **MMD 60195A** American Flute Music

ROBLES, Marisa (hp)
see CONCERT INDEX *under:*
(DECC) **425 723-2DM** Harp Concertos
(DECC) **433 869-2DWO** The World of the Harp
(DECC) **436 990-2DWO** The World of Benjamin
Britten
(RCA) **RD87173** Debussy: Orchestral works
(RCA) **RD87861** Mozart—Works for Flute &
Orchestra
(RCA) **09026 61677-2** Concerto! with Dudley Moore
(RCA) **09026 61789-2** Concerto! Galway & Robles
play Mozart
(VIRG) **VC7 59604-2** Debussy—Chamber Works

ROBLOU, David (hpd)
see CONCERT INDEX *under:*
(L'OI) **433 187-2OH** Mad Songs

ROBSON, Anthony (ob)
Albinoni: Concerti, Op. 7 (exc), Concerti, Op. 9 (exc)
see CONCERT INDEX *under:*
(VIRG) **VC5 45095-2** Bach—Concertos
(VIRG) **VC7 59266-2** Haydn—Orchestral Works

ROBSON, Anthony (ob/dir)
see CONCERT INDEX *under:*
(VIRG) **VC5 45095-2** Bach—Concertos

ROBSON, Christopher (alto)
Blow: Venus and Adonis (Cpte)
Handel: Messiah (Cpte)
Maxwell Davies: Resurrection (Cpte)
Monteverdi: Orfeo (Cpte), Vespers
Tippett: Ice Break (Cpte)
Vivaldi: Nisi Dominus
see CONCERT INDEX *under:*
(ARGO) **436 833-2ZH** Purcell— Music for the Funeral
of Queen Mary
(L'OI) **436 460-2OH** Biber—Requiem; Chamber
Works
(VIRG) **VC7 59243-2** Purcell—Odes for Queen Mary

ROBSON, Elizabeth (sop)
Sullivan: Iolanthe (exc)

ROBSON, Nigel (ten)
Britten: Rape of Lucretia (Cpte)
Handel: Alexander's Feast (Cpte), Jephtha (Cpte)
Monteverdi: Orfeo (Cpte), Vespers
Mozart: Idomeneo (Cpte)
Walton: Troilus and Cressida (Cpte)
see CONCERT INDEX *under:*
(ERAT) **2292-45466-2** Carissimi—Jonas
(SONY) **SK45965** Esa-Pekka Salonen conducts
Stravinsky

ROCCO, James (sngr)
Gershwin: Strike Up the Band I (Cpte), Strike Up the
Band II

ROCHE, Joseph (vn)
see CONCERT INDEX *under:*
(VOX) **115845-2** Chamber Works by Women
Composers

ROCHE, Pierre De La (cond)
see orch

ROCHESTER CATHEDRAL CHOIR
cond B. FERGUSON
see CONCERT INDEX *under:*
(PRIO) **PRCD461** Psalms of David, Vol.9

ROCHESTER POPS ORCHESTRA
cond L. SCHIFRIN
see CONCERT INDEX *under:*
(SILV) **SILVAD3001** At the Movies 1: Heroes & Tough
Guys
(SILV) **SILVAD3002** At the Movies 2: Classic
Symphonic Film Music

RODDE, Anne-Marie (sop)
Busoni: Turandot (Cpte)
Gilles: Requiem
Gluck: Rencontre imprévue (Cpte)
Gounod: Philémon et Baucis (Cpte)
Honegger: Jeanne d'Arc (Cpte)
see CONCERT INDEX *under:*
(ETCE) **KTC1048** Debussy: Mélodies, Vol.2

RODE, Wilhelm (bass-bar)
see CONCERT INDEX *under:*
(SCHW) **314632** Vienna State Opera Live, Vol.13

(OLYM) **OCD444** Enescu—Complete Orchestral Works, Volume 4
(OLYM) **OCD495** Enescu—Orchestral Works, Volume 5

ROMANIAN RADIO CHORUS
 cond H. ANDREESCU
 Enescu: Poème roumain, Op. 1

ROMANKO, Olga (sop)
 Verdi: Requiem (Cpte)
 see CONCERT INDEX under:
 (DECC) **436 261-2DHO3** Puccini—Il Trittico

ROMANO, Franco (bass)
 Donizetti: Lucrezia Borgia (Cpte)

ROMANOVA, Lydia (mez)
 Mussorgsky: Boris Godunov (Cpte)

ROMANOVÁ, Natalia (sop)
 Dvořák: Kate and the Devil (Cpte)
 see CONCERT INDEX under:
 (SUPR) **11 0751-2** Martinů—Choral Works

ROMANOVA, Nina (mez)
 Shostakovich: King Lear, Op.58a

ROMBOUT, Ernest (ob)
 see CONCERT INDEX under:
 (DECC) **440 605-2DH** Mozart/Haydn/Hummel—Works for Oboe

ROME ACADEMY ORCHESTRA
 cond V. BELLEZZA
 see CONCERT INDEX under:
 (EMI) **CHS7 69741-2(7)** Record of Singing, Vol.4—Italian School

ROME FAURÉ QUINTET
 Brahms: Piano Quintet
 Fauré: Piano Quintet 1, Piano Quintet 2

ROME OPERA CHORUS
 cond J. BARBIROLLI
 Puccini: Madama Butterfly (Cpte)
 cond V. BELLEZZA
 see CONCERT INDEX under:
 (EMI) **CMS7 64165-2** Puccini—Trittico
 cond J. LATHAM-KÖNIG
 Donizetti: Poliuto (Cpte)
 cond E. LEINSDORF
 Puccini: Madama Butterfly (Cpte), Tosca (Cpte), Turandot (Cpte)
 see CONCERT INDEX under:
 (RCA) **GD87799** The Pearl Fishers Duet plus Duets and Scenes
 cond Z. MEHTA
 Verdi: Aida (Cpte)
 cond D. OREN
 Puccini: Tosca (Cpte)
 cond J. PERLEA
 Puccini: Manon Lescaut (Cpte)
 Verdi: Aida (Cpte)
 see CONCERT INDEX under:
 (RCA) **09026 61580-2(5)** RCA/Met 100 Singers, 100 Years (pt 5)
 cond G. SANTINI
 Giordano: Andrea Chénier (Cpte)
 Mascagni: Cavalleria Rusticana (Cpte)
 Puccini: Madama Butterfly (Cpte)
 Verdi: Don Carlo (Cpte), Simon Boccanegra (Cpte)
 cond T. SCHIPPERS
 Puccini: Bohème (Cpte)
 cond T. SERAFIN
 Verdi: Aida (Cpte), Otello (Cpte), Requiem (Cpte)
 see CONCERT INDEX under:
 (EMI) **CMS7 64165-2** Puccini—Trittico
 cond G. SOLTI
 Verdi: Aida (Cpte)

ROME OPERA ORCHESTRA
 see CONCERT INDEX under:
 (RCA) **GD87799** The Pearl Fishers Duet plus Duets and Scenes
 (RCA) **09026 61580-2(5)** RCA/Met 100 Singers, 100 Years (pt 5)
 cond R. ARDUINI
 see CONCERT INDEX under:
 (NIMB) **NI7853** Lauri-Volpi sings Verdi
 (PREI) **89009** Gino Bechi (b. 1913)
 cond J. BARBIROLLI
 Puccini: Madama Butterfly (Cpte)
 cond V. BELLEZZA
 see CONCERT INDEX under:
 (EMI) **CMS7 64165-2** Puccini—Trittico
 cond R. CHAILLY
 see CONCERT INDEX under:
 (DECC) **436 463-2DM** Ten Top Tenors
 cond O. DE FABRITIIS
 see CONCERT INDEX under:
 (EMI) **CDH7 61052-2** Beniamino Gigli—Arias and Duets (1932-1949)
 (EMI) **CDM7 63109-2** Tito Gobbi - Opera Aria Recital
 (EMI) **CHS7 69741-2(7)** Record of Singing, Vol.4—Italian School
 cond F. FERRARIS
 see CONCERT INDEX under:
 (CFP) **CD-CFP4569** Puccini: Arias
 (EMI) **CDH7 63110-2** Mirella Freni: Opera Recital
 cond G. GAVAZZENI
 see CONCERT INDEX under:
 (RCA) **09026 68014-2** Pavarotti - The Early Years, Vol.2
 cond V. GUI
 see CONCERT INDEX under:

(EMI) **CHS7 69741-2(6)** Record of Singing, Vol.4—Russian & Slavonic Schools
 cond E. LEINSDORF
 Puccini: Madama Butterfly (Cpte), Tosca (Cpte), Turandot (Cpte)
 see CONCERT INDEX under:
 (RCA) **GD87799** The Pearl Fishers Duet plus Duets and Scenes
 (RCA) **09026 61580-2(5)** RCA/Met 100 Singers, 100 Years (pt 5)
 (RCA) **09026 61580-2(7)** RCA/Met 100 Singers, 100 Years (pt 7)
 cond Z. MEHTA
 Verdi: Aida (Cpte)
 see CONCERT INDEX under:
 (DECC) **430 433-2DH** Carreras, Domingo and Pavarotti in Concert
 cond P.G. MORANDI
 Paisiello: Don Chisciotte (Cpte)
 cond G. MORELLI
 see CONCERT INDEX under:
 (EMI) **CDH7 63495-2** Victoria de los Angeles—Early Recordings
 cond D. OLIVIERI
 see CONCERT INDEX under:
 (EMI) **CHS7 64864-2(2)** La Scala Edition - Vol.2, 1915-46 (pt 2)
 cond D. OREN
 Puccini: Tosca (Cpte)
 cond J. PERLEA
 Puccini: Manon Lescaut (Cpte)
 Verdi: Aida (Cpte)
 see CONCERT INDEX under:
 (RCA) **GD87799** The Pearl Fishers Duet plus Duets and Scenes
 cond F. PREVITALI
 see CONCERT INDEX under:
 (RCA) **09026 61580-2(7)** RCA/Met 100 Singers, 100 Years (pt 7)
 cond L. RICCI
 see CONCERT INDEX under:
 (EMI) **CHS7 64864-2(2)** La Scala Edition - Vol.2, 1915-46 (pt 2)
 (PREI) **89009** Gino Bechi (b. 1913)
 cond G. SANTINI
 Giordano: Andrea Chénier (Cpte)
 Mascagni: Cavalleria Rusticana (Cpte)
 Puccini: Madama Butterfly (Cpte)
 Verdi: Don Carlo (Cpte), Simon Boccanegra (Cpte)
 see CONCERT INDEX under:
 (CFP) **CD-CFP4569** Puccini: Arias
 (EMI) **CDM7 63109-2** Tito Gobbi - Opera Aria Recital
 (EMI) **CMS7 64165-2** Puccini—Trittico
 cond T. SCHIPPERS
 Puccini: Bohème (Cpte)
 cond T. SERAFIN
 Verdi: Aida (Cpte), Otello (Cpte), Requiem (Cpte)
 see CONCERT INDEX under:
 (EMI) **CHS7 64864-2(2)** La Scala Edition - Vol.2, 1915-46 (pt 2)
 (EMI) **CMS7 64165-2** Puccini—Trittico
 (RCA) **09026 61580-2(6)** RCA/Met 100 Singers, 100 Years (pt 6)
 (RCA) **09026 61580-2(7)** RCA/Met 100 Singers, 100 Years (pt 7)
 cond G. SOLTI
 Verdi: Aida (Cpte)

ROME PHILHARMONIC ORCHESTRA
 cond G. GAVAZZENI
 see CONCERT INDEX under:
 (RCA) **GD86534** Verdi Arias and Duets
 (RCA) **09026 61580-2(8)** RCA/Met 100 Singers, 100 Years (pt 8)

ROME POLYPHONIC CHORUS
 cond R. FASANO
 Gluck: Orfeo ed Euridice (Cpte)
 cond G. GAVAZZENI
 see CONCERT INDEX under:
 (RCA) **GD86534** Verdi Arias and Duets

ROME RAI CHORUS
 cond O. DE FABRITIIS
 Verdi: Forza del destino (exc)
 cond W. FURTWÄNGLER
 see CONCERT INDEX under:
 (EMI) **CZS7 67123-2** Wagner: Der Ring des Nibelungen
 cond G. GAVAZZENI
 Bellini: Pirata (Cpte)
 see CONCERT INDEX under:
 (EMI) **CDM7 69500-2** Montserrat Caballé sings Bellini & Verdi Arias

ROME RAI ORCHESTRA
 cond O. DE FABRITIIS
 Verdi: Forza del destino (exc)
 cond M. FRECCIA
 see CONCERT INDEX under:
 (MEMR) **999001** The Authorised Vatican Recordings-Michelangeli
 cond W. FURTWÄNGLER
 see CONCERT INDEX under:
 (ACAN) **43 121** Wagner: Orchestral Works
 (EMI) **CZS7 67123-2** Wagner: Der Ring des Nibelungen
 cond G. GAVAZZENI
 Bellini: Pirata (Cpte)
 see CONCERT INDEX under:
 (EMI) **CDM7 69500-2** Montserrat Caballé sings Bellini & Verdi Arias

(MEMR) **999001** The Authorised Vatican Recordings-Michelangeli
 cond J. SEREBRIER
 see CONCERT INDEX under:
 (ASV) **CDDCA706** Borodin—Symphonies
 cond A. SIMONETTO
 see CONCERT INDEX under:
 (EMI) **CDC7 54437-2** Callas Rarities
 (EMI) **CHS7 69741-2(7)** Record of Singing, Vol.4—Italian School

ROME SYMPHONY ORCHESTRA
 cond N. BONAVOLONTÀ
 see CONCERT INDEX under:
 (RCA) **09026 62541-2** Pavarotti - The Early Years, Vol.1
 (RCA) **09026 68014-2** Pavarotti - The Early Years, Vol.2
 cond R. MUTI
 see CONCERT INDEX under:
 (RCA) **09026 68014-2** Pavarotti - The Early Years, Vol.2

ROME TEATRO REALE OPERA ORCHESTRA
 cond L. RICCI
 see CONCERT INDEX under:
 (PREI) **89074** Tancredi Pasero (1893-1983) - II

ROMERO, Angel (gtr)
 Granados: Danzas españolas
 see CONCERT INDEX under:
 (PHIL) **412 624-2PH** Vivaldi: Guitar Concertos
 (PHIL) **426 076-2PCC** Vivaldi: Concertos
 (TELA) **CD80213** Angel Romero Guitar Recital

ROMERO, Angelo (bar)
 Donizetti: Campanello di notte (Cpte), Gianni di Parigi (Cpte)
 Rossini: Barbiere di Siviglia (Cpte)

ROMERO, Celedonio (gtr)
 Granados: Danzas españolas
 see CONCERT INDEX under:
 (DELO) **DE1005** Bach/Sanz—Transcriptions & Works for Guitar
 (PHIL) **412 624-2PH** Vivaldi: Guitar Concertos
 (PHIL) **426 076-2PCC** Vivaldi: Concertos

ROMERO, Celín (gtr)
 see CONCERT INDEX under:
 (PHIL) **412 624-2PH** Vivaldi: Guitar Concertos
 (PHIL) **426 076-2PCC** Vivaldi: Concertos

ROMERO, Modesto (cond)
 see orch

ROMERO, Pepe (gtr)
 Boccherini: Guitar Quintets, G445-453
 see CONCERT INDEX under:
 (PHIL) **412 624-2PH** Vivaldi: Guitar Concertos
 (PHIL) **426 076-2PCC** Vivaldi: Concertos
 (PHIL) **432 828-2PM** Splendour of Spain, Vol.8 - Rodrigo
 (PHIL) **438 016-2PH** Rodrigo—Guitar Works
 (PHIL) **442 150-2PH** Noches de España

RONALD, Sir Landon (cond)
 see LPO

RONALD, Sir Landon (pf)
 see CONCERT INDEX under:
 (NIMB) **NI7840/1** The Era of Adelina Patti
 (PEAR) **GEMMCD9312** Adelina Patti
 (SIMA) **PSC1809(1)** Grieg—Historical Piano Recordings (pt 1)

RONDELL, Erwin (cond)
 see Raphaele Concert Orch

RONDELLI, Barbara (sop)
 see CONCERT INDEX under:
 (HANS) **98 869** Bach—Cantatas, Vol.18

RONDIN, Mats (vc)
 see CONCERT INDEX under:
 (BIS) **BIS-CD663/4** Janáček—Chamber and Instrumental Works

RONGE, Gabriele Maria (sop)
 Zemlinsky: Traumgörge (Cpte)

RONI, Luigi (bass)
 Bellini: Zaira (Cpte)
 Mozart: Don Giovanni (Cpte)
 Puccini: Fanciulla del West (Cpte), Manon Lescaut (Cpte)
 Verdi: Aida (Cpte), Falstaff (Cpte)

ROOCROFT, Amanda (sop)
 Mozart: Così fan tutte (Cpte)
 Schoenberg: String Quartet 2
 Vaughan Williams: Symphony 1
 see CONCERT INDEX under:
 (EMI) **CDC5 55090-2** Amanda Roocroft—Recital
 (EMI) **CDC5 55396-2** Mozart & his Contemporaries
 (HYPE) **CDA66420** Vaughan Williams: Vocal Works

ROOLEY, Anthony (cond)
 see Consort of Musicke

ROOLEY, Anthony (chitarrone)
 see CONCERT INDEX under:
 (HYPE) **CDA66106** Olympia's Lament
 (HYPE) **CDA66227** Emma Kirkby Collection

ROOLEY, Anthony (lte)
 Dowland: Third and Last Booke of Songs (exc)
 see CONCERT INDEX under:
 (HYPE) **CDA66056** Purcell: Songs and Dialogues
 (HYPE) **CDA66227** Emma Kirkby Collection
 (L'OI) **417 123-2OH** Purcell: Songs and Airs

(MOSC) **070979** Sound the Trumpets from Shore to Shore
(VIRG) **VC7 59321-2** Shakespeare's Lutenist
(VIRG) **VC7 59521-2** The English Orpheus - Works by John Dowland

ROOLEY, Anthony (lte/dir)
Monteverdi: Madrigals, Bk 2 (Cpte), Madrigals, Bk.3 (Cpte)
see CONCERT INDEX *under:*
(BIS) **BIS-CD392** Music from the time of Christian IV, Vol. 4
(MOSC) **070986** The Mistress—Settings of Abraham Cowley's Poems
(MOSC) **070995** Monteverdi—Erotic Madrigals & their Sacred Contrafacta
(VIRG) **VC7 59035-2** T. Ravenscroft—Songs, Rounds & Catches

ROOLEY, Anthony (orpharion)
see CONCERT INDEX *under:*
(VIRG) **VC7 59521-2** The English Orpheus - Works by John Dowland

ROOTERING, Jan-Hendrik (bass)
Beethoven: Missa solemnis, Symphony 9
Donizetti: Messa da Requiem
Gluck: Rencontre imprévue (Cpte)
Mahler: Symphony 8
Mozart: Don Giovanni (Cpte), Requiem
Puccini: Fanciulla del West (Cpte), Turandot (Cpte)
R.Strauss: Frau ohne Schatten (Cpte)
Rossini: Semiramide (Cpte)
Schumann: Szenen aus Goethes Faust (Cpte)
Stravinsky: Oedipus Rex (Cpte)
Suder: Kleider machen Leute (Cpte)
Verdi: Luisa Miller (Cpte), Rigoletto (Cpte)
Wagner: Lohengrin (Cpte), Parsifal (Cpte), Rheingold (Cpte)
see CONCERT INDEX *under:*
(DG) **445 354-2GX14** Wagner—Der Ring des Nibelungen
(DG) **447 023-2GX12** Mahler—The Symphonies

ROQUE, Marcel (bar)
Massenet: Werther (Cpte)

ROQUETTY, Camille (bar)
Gounod: Roméo et Juliette (Cpte)

RORBACH, Krystyna (sop)
see CONCERT INDEX *under:*
(SCHW) **314001** Szymanowski: Lieder

RORHOLM, Marianne (contr)
Handel: Giulio Cesare (Cpte)
Puccini: Madama Butterfly (Cpte)
R. Strauss: Ariadne auf Naxos (Cpte), Salome (Cpte)
Sibelius: Kullervo
Wagner: Parsifal (Cpte)

ROS, Pere (va da gamba)
see CONCERT INDEX *under:*
(ARCH) **437 075-2AT** Collectio Argentea 5: Canti Amorosi

ROSAND, Aaron (vn)
Brahms: Hungarian Dances
Handel: Flute Sonatas (exc), Violin Sonatas (exc)
Joachim: Romance in B flat
see CONCERT INDEX *under:*
(HARM) **HMU90 7070** Walton—Orchestral Works

ROSARIO, Patricia (sop)
see CONCERT INDEX *under:*
(COLL) **Coll1349-2** Respighi—Vocal and Orchestral Works

ROSAT, Karine (sop)
Haydn: Mass 11

ROSBAUD, Hans (cond)
see Berlin St Op Orch

ROSCA, Marcel (bass)
Puccini: Bohème (Cpte), Gianni Schicchi (Cpte), Manon Lescaut (Cpte), Tabarro (Cpte)

ROSCHER, Matthias (bn)
see CONCERT INDEX *under:*
(SCHW) **311071** Trumpet Concertos

RÖSCHMANN, Dorothea (sop)
Bach: Cantata 204, Cantata 210
Handel: Giustino (Cpte)
Keiser: Masaniello furioso (Cpte)

ROSCOE, Martin (pf)
Dohnányi: Piano Concerto 1, Piano Concerto 2
G. Lloyd: Lament, Air and Dance, Violin Sonata
see CONCERT INDEX *under:*
(ALBA) **AR003** George Lloyd—Piano Works
(ASV) **CDDCA863** Dohnányi—Piano Works
(ASV) **CDDCA915** Dohnányi—Piano Quintets
(ASV) **CDDCA932** Beach/R. Clarke—Chamber Works
(EMIN) **CD-EMX2221** Pärt—Chamber Works
(HYPE) **CDA66911/4** Fauré—Complete Piano Works
(MARC) **8 223480** Bernard Stevens—Orchestral Works
(NAXO) **8 553016** Szymanowski—Piano Works, Vol. 1

ROSÉ, Alma (vn)
see CONCERT INDEX *under:*
(BIDD) **LAB056/7** Arnold Rosé & the Rosé String Quartet

ROSÉ, Arnold (vn)
see CONCERT INDEX *under:*

(BIDD) **LAB056/7** Arnold Rosé & the Rosé String Quartet

ROSE, Barry (cond)
see ECO

ROSE, Bernard (cond)
see Wren Orch

ROSE, George (sngr)
Strouse: Dance a Little Closer (Cpte)

ROSE, Gregory (cond)
see Singcircle

ROSE, Jerome (pf)
see CONCERT INDEX *under:*
(VOX) **115708-2** Mosonyi/Raff/Stavenhaegn—Piano Concertos
(VOX) **115717-2** Chopin/Henselt/Hiller—Piano Concertos

ROSE, Leonard (vc)
Beethoven: Triple Concerto
Brahms: Double Concerto
Dvořák: Cello Concerto
see CONCERT INDEX *under:*
(SONY) **SBK48278** Works for Cello and Orchestra
(SONY) **SMK47609** Schubert/Schumann—Orchestral Works

ROSE, Peter (bass)
Mozart: Nozze di Figaro (Cpte)
R. Strauss: Salome (Cpte)
Rossini: Barbiere di Siviglia (Cpte)
see CONCERT INDEX *under:*
(SONY) **S2K46836** Goldschmidt—Beatrice Cenci, etc

ROSE, Stuart (spkr)
Grieg: Peer Gynt (exc)

ROSE, Timothy (treb)
see CONCERT INDEX *under:*
(ARGO) **433 215-2ZH** Britten—Christmas Music

ROSE CONSORT OF VIOLS
see CONCERT INDEX *under:*
(AMON) **CD-SAR46** Elizabethan Christmas Anthems
(AMON) **CD-SAR55** Dowland—Lachrimae
(NAXO) **8 550603** Gibbons—Consort and Keyboard Music, Songs and Anthems
(NAXO) **8 550604** Byrd—Music for Viols, Voices and Keyboard
(NAXO) **8 550687** Jenkins—All in a Garden Green
(WOOD) **WOODM001-2** Born is the Babe—Renaissance Music
(WOOD) **WOODM002-2** Ah, Dear Heart

ROSÉ QUARTET
see CONCERT INDEX *under:*
(BIDD) **LAB056/7** Arnold Rosé & the Rosé String Quartet

ROSEKRANS, Charles (cond)
see Hungarian St Orch

RÖSEL, Peter (pf)
Beethoven: Choral Fantasia, Triple Concerto
see CONCERT INDEX *under:*
(EMI) **CMS7 64342-2** R. Strauss—Orchestral Works, Vol.1

ROSEN, Charles (pf)
Chopin: Piano Concerto 2
see CONCERT INDEX *under:*
(MUSI) **MACD-609** Chopin: Piano Works
(SONY) **SB2K53531** Beethoven—Late Piano Sonatas
(SONY) **SM3K45845** Webern—Complete Works

ROSEN, Marvin (pf)
see CONCERT INDEX *under:*
(KOCH) **37195-2** Fred the Cat - Half a Century of Piano Music

ROSEN, Max (vn)
see CONCERT INDEX *under:*
(ROMO) **81012-2** Elisabeth Rethberg — Brunswick Recordings 1924-1929

ROSEN, Nathaniel (vc)
Bach: Solo Cello Suites
see CONCERT INDEX *under:*
(JMR) **JMR5** Brahms/Mendelssohn/Schumann—Chamber Works

ROSENAK, Karen (celesta)
M. Feldman: Rothko Chapel

ROSENBAUM, Poul (pf)
Ruders: Dramaphonia
see CONCERT INDEX *under:*
(CHAN) **CHAN9336/8** Mussorgsky—Songs

ROSENBAUM, Susan (sngr)
Schuman: Mighty Casey (Cpte)

ROSENBERG, Hilding (cond)
see Radiotjänst SO

ROSENBERG, Hilding (narr)
see CONCERT INDEX *under:*
(CPRI) **CAP21510** Rosenberg plays Rosenberg

ROSENBERG, Hilding (pf)
see CONCERT INDEX *under:*
(CPRI) **CAP21510** Rosenberg plays Rosenberg

ROSENBERG, Peter (vn)
Reger: Konzert im alten Stil, Sinfonietta, Op. 90

ROSENBERGER, Carol (pf)
Beethoven: Piano and wind quintet, op 16, Piano Concerto 4, Piano Sonata 23, Piano Sonata 32

Hindemith: Four Temperaments
Mozart: Piano and wind quintet, K452
Schubert: Impromptus (exc), Piano Sonata, D960
see CONCERT INDEX *under:*
(DELO) **DE1002** Szymanowski—Piano Works
(DELO) **DE3006** Water Music of the Impressionists
(DELO) **DE3021** 20th-century Russian music
(DELO) **DE3061** Haydn: Orchestral Works
(DELO) **DE3064** Haydn: Orchestral Works
(DELO) **DE3092** Hanson—Orchestral Works
(DELO) **DE3109** R.Strauss—Orchestral Works
(DELO) **DE3130** Hanson—Orchestral Works
(DELO) **DE3186** Heigh Ho! Mozart

ROSENBUSCH, Thorsten (vn)
see CONCERT INDEX *under:*
(PHIL) **434 918-2PH2** Bach—Concertos

ROSENEK, Leo (pf)
see CONCERT INDEX *under:*
(EMI) **CHS7 64487-2** R. Strauss—Der Rosenkavalier & Lieder
(PREI) **89084** Kerstin Thorborg (1896-1970)

ROSENFELD, Julie (vn)
Debussy: Piano Trio
Ravel: Piano Trio
see CONCERT INDEX *under:*
(RCA) **09026 68181-2** French Chamber Works

ROSENGREN, Håkan (cl)
see CONCERT INDEX *under:*
(SONY) **SK53276** Nielsen—Orchestral Works

ROSENMAN, Leonard (cond)
see OST

ROSENSHEIN, Neil (ten)
Bernstein: Songfest
Haydn: Schöpfung (Cpte)
Loeffler: Irish Fantasies
Tchaikovsky: Eugene Onegin (Cpte)

ROSENSTOCK, Milton (cond)
see National PO

ROSENTHAL, Manuel (cond)
see French Rad Lyric Orch

ROSENTHAL, Moriz (pf)
see CONCERT INDEX *under:*
(APR) **APR7002** Moriz Rosenthal—The Complete HMV Recordings 1934-37
(APR) **APR7013** Romantic Piano Rarities, Vol.1
(EMI) **CDS7 49361-2** Offenbach: Operettas
(PEAR) **GEMMCD9339** Moriz Rosenthal—Piano Recital
(PEAR) **GEMMCD9963** Moriz Rosenthal—Vol.2

ROSENTHAL, Paul (va)
Tchaikovsky: Souvenir de Florence
see CONCERT INDEX *under:*
(RCA) **09026 61778-2(28)** The Heifetz Collection, Vol. 28

ROSENTHAL, Paul (vn)
see CONCERT INDEX *under:*
(RCA) **09026 61778-2(25)** The Heifetz Collection, Vol. 25

ROSETTA, Vittoria (harm)
Rossini: Petite messe solennelle

ROSIN, Armin (tbn)
see CONCERT INDEX *under:*
(JECK) **JD529-2** Martin: Concertos

ROSKILDE CATHEDRAL BOYS' CHOIR & CONGREGATION
cond P. MCCREESH
M. Praetorius: Lutheran Christmas Mass

ROS-MARBÀ, Antonio (cond)
see Barcelona Patronato Orch

ROSNER, Anton (ten)
Gazzaniga: Don Giovanni (Cpte)

ROSS, Alastair (organ)
see CONCERT INDEX *under:*
(MERI) **CDE84096** Seventeenth-Century German Works

ROSS, Christopher (bass)
Rossini: Barbiere di Siviglia (Cpte)

ROSS, Dave (perc)
see CONCERT INDEX *under:*
(ETCE) **KTC1071** L.Harrison—Music For Guitar And Percussion

ROSS, Diana (sngr)
see CONCERT INDEX *under:*
(SONY) **SK53358** Christmas in Vienna

ROSS, Elise (sop)
Boesmans: Attitudes
Weill: Sieben Todsünden

ROSS, Gill (sop)
Purcell: King Arthur, Z628 (Cpte)
see CONCERT INDEX *under:*
(ERAT) **4509-96371-2** Gardiner—The Purcell Collection

ROSS, Lesley Echo (sop)
Sullivan: Gondoliers (Cpte), Yeomen of the Guard (exc)

ROSS, Pamela (pf)
Schumann: Faschingsschwank aus Wien, Kreisleriana

ROSS, Scott (hpd)
Bach: Goldberg Variations
D. Scarlatti: Keyboard Sonatas
Handel: Keyboard Suites Set I

ROSSI, Alessandra (sop)
Rossini: Cambiale di Matrimonio (Cpte)

ROSSI, Annabella (sop)
Paisiello: Don Chisciotte (Cpte)

ROSSI, Arcangelo (bass)
see CONCERT INDEX under:
(TEST) SBT1008   Viva Rossini

ROSSI, Giulio (bass)
see CONCERT INDEX under:
(SYMP) SYMCD1077   The Harold Wayne Collection,
Vol.4

ROSSI, Jean (db)
see CONCERT INDEX under:
(TIMP) 1C1009   Honegger—Chamber Works, Vol.2
(TIMP) 4C1012   Honegger—Chamber Works

ROSSI, John Carmen (ten)
Verdi: Ballo in maschera (Cpte)
see CONCERT INDEX under:
(RCA) GD60326   Verdi—Operas & Choral Works

ROSSI, Lina (mez)
Verdi: Rigoletto (Cpte)

ROSSI, Mario (cond)
see Turin SO

ROSSIAUD, Doris (pf)
see CONCERT INDEX under:
(DECC) 443 467-2DF2   Stravinsky—Ballet Music

ROSSIER, Nicole (contr)
see CONCERT INDEX under:
(ERAT) 2292-45923-2   Bach/Vivaldi—Sacred Choral
Works

ROSSIGNOL, Martial (sngr)
Ganne: Hans (Cpte)

ROSSI-LEMENI, Nicola (bass)
Bellini: Norma (Cpte), Puritani (Cpte)
Donizetti: Anna Bolena (Cpte)
Rossini: Mosè (Cpte), Turco in Italia (Cpte)
Verdi: Forza del destino (Cpte)
see CONCERT INDEX under:
(EMI) CHS7 69741-2(7)   Record of Singing,
Vol.4—Italian School
(EMI) CMS7 63244-2   The Art of Maria Callas

RÖSSLER, Almut (organ)
Messiaen: Corps glorieux, Messe de la Pentecôte
see CONCERT INDEX under:
(SCHW) 315024   Messiaen—Organ Works

RÖSSL-MAJDAN, Hilde (mez)
Beethoven: Symphony 9
Janáček: Glagolitic Mass (Cpte)
Mahler: Symphony 2, Symphony 3
Mozart: Nozze di Figaro (Cpte)
R. Strauss: Ariadne auf Naxos (Cpte), Rosenkavalier
(Cpte)
see CONCERT INDEX under:
(DG) 429 036-2GX5   Beethoven: Complete
Symphonies
(EMI) CZS7 67123-2   Wagner: Der Ring des
Nibelungen
(VANG) 08.2010.71   Bach—Choral Works
(VANG) 08.2028.71   Bach—Cantatas

ROSSMANITH, Gabriele (sop)
Hindemith: Mathis der Maler (Cpte)

ROST, Andrea (sop)
Mahler: Symphony 8
Mozart: Nozze di Figaro (Cpte)
Verdi: Rigoletto (Cpte)
see CONCERT INDEX under:
(DG) 447 023-2GX12   Mahler—The Symphonies

ROSTAL, Max (va)
see CONCERT INDEX under:
(EMI) CMS7 64350-2   R. Strauss—Orchestral Works,
Vol.3

ROSTAL, Max (vn)
see CONCERT INDEX under:
(SYMP) SYMCD1068   Schubert: Works for Violin and
Piano
(SYMP) SYMCD1076   Violin & Piano Works

ROSTROPOVICH, Mstislav (cond)
see BPO

ROSTROPOVICH, Mstislav (pf)
see CONCERT INDEX under:
(LOND) 433 200-2LHO2   Britten—Owen Wingrave,
etc.

ROSTROPOVICH, Mstislav (vc)
Bach: Solo Cello Suites
Beethoven: Triple Concerto
Brahms: Cello Sonata 1, Cello Sonata 2, Double
Concerto
Bridge: Cello Sonata
Dutilleux: Cello Concerto
Dvořák: Cello Concerto
Lutosławski: Cello Concerto
R. Strauss: Don Quixote
Saint-Saëns: Cello Concerto 1
Schnittke: Cello Concerto 2
Schubert: Arpeggione Sonata, D821, String Quintet
Shostakovich: Cello Concerto 2

Tchaikovsky: Rococo Variations
see CONCERT INDEX under:
(DECC) 417 833-2DH   Rostropovich/Britten Recital
(DECC) 430 633-2DM   Haydn—Concertos
(DG) 427 687-2GH2   Beethoven: String Trios
(DG) 431 475-2GGA   Russian Orchestral Works
(DG) 437 952-2GX2   Great Cello Works
(DG) 445 947-2GX   Messiaen—Orchestral Works
(LOND) 421 859-2LM   Britten: Cello Works
(LOND) 425 100-2LM   Britten: Orchestral & Vocal
Works
(MELO) 74321 18290-2   Tchaikovsky—Chamber
Works
(RUSS) RDCD11104   Elgar/Milhaud/Respighi—Works
for Cello & Orchestra
(RUSS) RDCD15005   Shostakovich plays
Shostakovich
(SONY) MPK44850   Shostakovich: Concertos
(SONY) SK53271   Schnittke—Orchestral and
Chamber Works
(TELD) 9031-77311-2   CPE Bach/Vivaldi/Tartini—Cello
Concertos

ROSTROPOVICH, Mstislav (vc/dir)
Haydn: Cello Concerto in C, Cello Concerto in D
see CONCERT INDEX under:
(DG) 431 475-2GGA   Russian Orchestral Works
(DG) 437 952-2GX2   Great Cello Works

ROSWAENGE, Helge (ten)
Mozart: Zauberflöte (Cpte)
see CONCERT INDEX under:
(EMI) CMS7 64008-2(1)   Wagner Singing on Record
(pt 1)
(NIMB) NI7848   Great Singers at the Berlin State
Opera
(NIMB) NI7856   Legendary Tenors
(PEAR) GEMMCDS9085   Hugo Wolf Society, Volume
II
(PEAR) GEMMCDS9926(2)   Covent Garden on
Record—Vol.4 (pt 2)
(PEAR) GEMMCD9394   Helge Roswaenge—Operatic
Recital
(PREI) 89018   Helge Rosvaenge (1897-1972)
(PREI) 89201   Helge Rosvaenge (1897-1972) - I
(PREI) 89209   Helge Rosvaenge (1897-1972) - II
(SCHW) 314502   Vienna State Opera—Live
Recordings (sampler)
(SCHW) 314552   Vienna State Opera Live, Vol.5
(SCHW) 314622   Vienna State Opera Live, Vol.12
(TEST) SBT1005   Ten Top Tenors

ROSWAENGE, Ilonka (sop)
see CONCERT INDEX under:
(PREI) 89209   Helge Rosvaenge (1897-1972) - II

ROTA, Anna Maria (contr)
Puccini: Manon Lescaut (Cpte)

ROTA, Marcello (cond)
see Svizzera Italiana Orch

ROTA, Marcello (hn)
see CONCERT INDEX under:
(EDEL) ED1012   Schumann: Chamber Music with
Piano

ROTH, Daniel (organ)
see CONCERT INDEX under:
(MOTE) CD10491   Vierne: Organ Works
(MOTE) CD10981   Dupré: Organ Works

ROTH, Sigmund (bass)
Weill: Mahagonny (Cpte)
see CONCERT INDEX under:
(SCHW) 314562   Vienna State Opera Live, Vol.6
(SCHW) 314582   Vienna State Opera Live, Vol.8

ROTH QUARTET
Mendelssohn: String Quartet 3, String Quartet 5

ROTHENBERGER, Anneliese (sop)
Flotow: Martha (Cpte)
J.Strauss II: Fledermaus (Cpte)
Lehár: Land des Lächelns (Cpte)
Millöcker: Gasparone (Cpte)
Mozart: Entführung (Cpte), Zauberflöte (Cpte)
R. Strauss: Arabella (Cpte)
Verdi: Don Carlo (Cpte)
Zeller: Vogelhändler (Cpte)
see CONCERT INDEX under:
(EMIL) CDZ7 67015-2   Mozart—Opera Arias

ROTHIER, Léon (bass)
see CONCERT INDEX under:
(PEAR) EVC3(1)   The Caruso Edition, Vol.3 (pt 1)
(RCA) GD60495(5)   The Complete Caruso Collection
(pt 5)

ROTHMÜLLER, Marko (bar)
see CONCERT INDEX under:
(EMI) CHS7 69741-2(4)   Record of Singing,
Vol.4—German School
(LYRC) SRO830   Smetana—The Bartered Bride, etc
(SYMP) SYMCD1098/9   Marko Rothmüller—Lieder
Recital

ROTHSTEIN, Jack (cond)
see LJSO

ROTSCHOPF, Michael (spkr)
B. A. Zimmermann: Requiem (Cpte)

**ROTTERDAM PHILHARMONIC CHORUS (WOMEN'S
VOICES)**
cond J. TATE
Mendelssohn: Midsummer Night's Dream (exc)

ROTTERDAM PHILHARMONIC ORCHESTRA
cond J. CONLON
Mussorgsky: Khovanshchina (exc), Pictures
cond V. GERGIEV
see CONCERT INDEX under:
(PHIL) 426 740-2PH   Dmitri Hvorostovsky sings
Tchaikovsky & Verdi Arias
cond J. TATE
Mendelssohn: Midsummer Night's Dream (exc)
(EMI) CDC7 54581-2   R.Strauss—Orchestral Music
from Operas
cond E. DE WAART
R. Strauss: Rosenkavalier (Cpte)

RÖTTGER, Renate (sop)
Weill: Kuhhandel (exc)

ROTZSCH, Hans Joachim (ten)
Mendelssohn: Elias (Cpte)
R. Strauss: Ariadne auf Naxos (Cpte)
Wagner: Meistersinger (Cpte)

ROUCHON, Jean-Philippe (cond)
see Philh

ROUEN THÉÂTRE DES ARTS CHORUS
cond A. GUINGAL
Saint-Saëns: Henry VIII (Cpte)

ROUILLON, Philippe (bar)
Saint-Saëns: Henry VIII (Cpte)

ROULEAU, Joseph (bass)
A. Thomas: Hamlet (Cpte)
Berlioz: Enfance du Christ (Cpte)
Haydn: Mass 14
Rossini: Semiramide (Cpte)
see CONCERT INDEX under:
(DECC) 443 461-2DF2   Berlioz—L'Enfance du Christ,
etc
(EMI) CDC7 47283-2   Maria Callas - Mad Scenes &
Bel Canto Arias
(EMI) CMS7 63244-2   The Art of Maria Callas

ROUND, Thomas (ten)
Sullivan: Gondoliers (Cpte), HMS Pinafore (Cpte),
Iolanthe (Cpte), Trial by Jury (Cpte)
see CONCERT INDEX under:
(DECC) 430 095-2DWO   The World of Gilbert &
Sullivan, Vol.1
(DECC) 433 868-2DWO   The World of Gilbert &
Sullivan - Volume 2

ROUQUETTY, Camille (ten)
see CONCERT INDEX under:
(EPM) 150 122   Milhaud—Historic Recordings 1928-
1948

ROUSI, Martti (vc)
see CONCERT INDEX under:
(ONDI) ODE826-2   Sibelius—Early Chamber Music,
Vol. 1

ROUSKOVÁ, Anna (contr)
Janáček: Jenůfa (Cpte)

ROUSSE PHILHARMONIC SYMPHONY ORCHESTRA
cond A. NAYDENOV
Prokofiev: Ivan the Terrible

ROUSSEAU, Emile (bar)
Poulenc: Mamelles de Tirésias (Cpte)
see CONCERT INDEX under:
(EMI) CHS7 61038-2   Debussy—Pelléas et Mélisande,
etc

ROUSSEL, Albert (cond)
see orch

ROUSSEL, Albert (pf)
see CONCERT INDEX under:
(EMI) CDC7 54840-2   Composers in Person—Roussel
& Schmitt

ROUSSELIÈRE, Charles (ten)
see CONCERT INDEX under:
(IRCC) IRCC-CD802   Souvenirs of Rare French
Opera

ROUSSET, Christophe (cond)
see Talens Lyriques

ROUSSET, Christophe (organ)
see CONCERT INDEX under:
(FNAC) 592098   Du Mont—Motets en dialogue

ROUSSET, Christophe (hpd)
Bach: Goldberg Variations, Partitas, BWV825-30
Boccherini: Duets, G76, String Quintets, G340-5
(exc)
Couperin: Art de toucher le clavecin, Concerts
Royaux, Livre de clavecin I, Livre de clavecin II, Livre
de clavecin III, Livre de clavecin IV
Le Roux: Pièces de clavecin
Leclair: Violin Sonatas, Op. 5 (exc)
Rameau: Pièces de clavecin (exc), Pièces de
clavecin en concerts
Royer: Chasse de Zaïde (D14218), Pièces de
clavecin
see CONCERT INDEX under:
(ASTR) E8757   Purcell—Songs from Orpheus
Britannicus

cond J. PRITCHARD
Donizetti: Elisir d'amore (Cpte)
  cond S. RATTLE
Janáček: Cunning Little Vixen (Cpte)
  cond F. REINER
Wagner: Tristan und Isolde (Cpte)
  cond C. RIZZI
Rossini: Cenerentola (Cpte)
  cond W. SCHÜCHTER
  see CONCERT INDEX under:
(EMI) CDH5 65201-2   Leonie Rysanek - Operatic
Recital
  cond G. SINOPOLI
Mascagni: Cavalleria rusticana (Cpte)
Puccini: Manon Lescaut (Cpte), Tosca (Cpte)
Wagner: Tannhäuser (Cpte)
  cond G. SOLTI
Gluck: Orfeo ed Euridice (Cpte)
Verdi: Traviata (Cpte)
  cond R. STAPLETON
  see CONCERT INDEX under:
(CARL) MCD15   Opera Spectacular
  cond J. TATE
R.Strauss: Arabella (Cpte)

**ROYAL OPERA HOUSE, COVENT GARDEN
CHILDREN'S CHORUS**
  cond G. SOLTI
Puccini: Tosca (Cpte)

**ROYAL OPERA HOUSE ORCHESTRA, COVENT
GARDEN**
Menotti: Amahl and the Night Visitors (Cpte)
  cond J. BARKER
  see CONCERT INDEX under:
(EMI) CDC5 55017-2   Domingo Opera Classics
(EMI) CDC7 49811-2   Covent Garden Gala Concert
  cond T. BEECHAM
  see CONCERT INDEX under:
(ACAN) 43 268   Peter Anders sings German Opera
Arias
  cond V. BELLEZZA
  see CONCERT INDEX under:
(EMI) CDH7 61009-2   Chaliapin sings Russian Opera
Arias
  cond R. BONYNGE
Adam: Giselle (Cpte)
Donizetti: Fille du régiment (Cpte), Lucia di
Lammermoor (Cpte)
  see CONCERT INDEX under:
(DECC) 417 011-2DH2   Pavarotti's Greatest Hits
(DECC) 433 437-2DA   Pavarotti—King of the High Cs
  cond A. BOULT
  see CONCERT INDEX under:
(DECC) 430 500-2DWO   World of Handel
  cond B. BRITTEN
Britten: Peter Grimes (Cpte)
  see CONCERT INDEX under:
(DECC) 436 990-2DWO   The World of Benjamin
Britten
(LOND) 425 659-2LM   Britten: Orchestral Works
(LOND) 436 396-2LM   Britten—Spring Symphony,
etc
  cond COLIN DAVIS
Berlioz: Troyens (Cpte)
Britten: Peter Grimes (Cpte)
Massenet: Werther (Cpte)
Mozart: Clemenza di Tito (Cpte), Così fan tutte
(Cpte), Don Giovanni (Cpte)
Puccini: Bohème (Cpte), Tosca (Cpte)
Tippett: Knot Garden (Cpte)
Verdi: Ballo in maschera (Cpte), Trovatore (Cpte)
  cond L. COLLINGWOOD
  see CONCERT INDEX under:
(TEST) SBT1058   James Johnston - Opera Arias and
Songs
  cond E. DOWNES
  see CONCERT INDEX under:
(CFP) CD-CFP4569   Puccini: Arias
(DECC) 417 686-2DC   Puccini—Operatic Arias
(DECC) 436 461-2DM   Ten Top Sopranos
(DECC) 436 462-2DM   Ten Top Mezzos
  cond M. ERMLER
Adam: Giselle (Cpte)
Arensky: Tchaikovsky Variations
Delibes: Coppélia (exc)
Prokofiev: Romeo and Juliet (Cpte)
Tchaikovsky: Nutcracker (exc), Sleeping Beauty
(Cpte), Swan Lake (exc)
  cond L. FOSTER
Walton: Troilus and Cressida (Cpte)
  cond W. FURTWÄNGLER
  see CONCERT INDEX under:
(PEAR) GEMMCD9331   Frida Leider sings Wagner
  cond L. GARDELLI
  see CONCERT INDEX under:
(CFP) CD-CFP4569   Puccini: Arias
  cond G. GAVAZZENI
Mascagni: Amico Fritz (Cpte)
  cond A. GIBSON
  see CONCERT INDEX under:
(DECC) 436 462-2DM   Ten Top Mezzos
  cond C.M. GIULINI
Verdi: Don Carlo (Cpte)
  see CONCERT INDEX under:
(EMI) CDC5 55017-2   Domingo Opera Classics
(EMi) CDM7 69500-2   Montserrat Caballé sings Bellini
& Verdi Arias
(EMI) CDM7 69549-2   Ruggero Raimondi: Italian
Opera Arias

cond I. GODFREY
Sullivan: Trial by Jury (Cpte)
  see CONCERT INDEX under:
(DECC) 433 868-2DWO   The World of Gilbert &
Sullivan - Volume 2
  cond R. GOODALL
  see CONCERT INDEX under:
(EMI) CHS7 69741-2(2)   Record of Singing,
Vol.4—Anglo-American School (pt 2)
(EMI) CMS7 64727-2   Britten—Opera excerpts and
Folksongs
  cond B. HAITINK
Britten: Peter Grimes (Cpte)
  see CONCERT INDEX under:
(EMI) CDC7 49849-2   Famous Opera Choruses
  cond J. LANCHBERY
Hérold: Fille mal gardée (exc)
Lanchbery: Tales of Beatrix Potter
  cond H. LEWIS
  see CONCERT INDEX under:
(DECC) 436 462-2DM   Ten Top Mezzos
  cond L. MAAZEL
Verdi: Luisa Miller (Cpte)
  see CONCERT INDEX under:
(BELA) 450 121-2   Plácido Domingo
(DG) 415 366-2GH   Plácido Domingo Recital
  cond Z. MEHTA
Puccini: Fanciulla del West (Cpte)
  see CONCERT INDEX under:
(BELA) 450 121-2   Plácido Domingo
(DG) 431 104-2GB   Great Voices - Plácido Domingo
  cond F. MOLINARI-PRADELLI
  see CONCERT INDEX under:
(DECC) 425 493-2DM2   Joan Sutherland: The Art of
the Prima Donna
(DECC) 430 500-2DWO   World of Handel
(DECC) 436 402-2DWO   The World of Wedding
Music
  cond M. MUDIE
  see CONCERT INDEX under:
(EMI) CHS7 69741-2(7)   Record of Singing,
Vol.4—Italian School
(TEST) SBT1058   James Johnston - Opera Arias and
Songs
  cond R. MUTI
Bellini: Capuleti (Cpte)
  cond G. PATANÈ
  see CONCERT INDEX under:
(CFP) CD-CFP4569   Puccini: Arias
  cond J. PRITCHARD
Donizetti: Elisir d'amore (Cpte)
  cond A. QUADRI
Cimarosa: Maestro di cappella (Cpte)
  cond S. RATTLE
Janáček: Cunning Little Vixen (Cpte)
  cond H. RIGNOLD
  see CONCERT INDEX under:
(EMI) CHS5 65198-2   Maggie Teyte sings French
Songs
  cond C. RIZZI
Rossini: Cenerentola (Cpte)
  cond G. SOLTI
Gluck: Orfeo ed Euridice (Cpte)
Tchaikovsky: Eugene Onegin (Cpte)
Verdi: Traviata (Cpte)
  see CONCERT INDEX under:
(DECC) 436 461-2DM   Ten Top Sopranos
(DECC) 436 462-2DM   Ten Top Mezzos
  cond J. TATE
R.Strauss: Arabella (Cpte)
  see CONCERT INDEX under:
(EMI) CDC7 49863-2   French Opera Arias
  cond W. WALTON
Walton: Troilus and Cressida (exc)
  cond R. ZAMBONI
  see CONCERT INDEX under:
(EMI) CDH7 61052-2   Beniamino Gigli—Arias and
Duets (1932-1949)

ROYAL PHILHARMONIC CHOIR
  cond L. STOKOWSKI
  see CONCERT INDEX under:
(DECC) 433 625-2DSP   Stokowski conducts Famous
Russian Works
  cond B. WORDSWORTH
Bernstein: West Side Story (Cpte)

**ROYAL PHILHARMONIC ORCHESTRA (CELLO
ENSEMBLE)**
  see CONCERT INDEX under:
(EMI) CDC7 47433-2   Villa-Lobos: Bachianas
Brasileiras
(EMI) CDS7 47901-8   Villa-Lobos: Orchestral and
Chamber Works

ROYAL PHILHARMONIC ORCHESTRA
Holst: Choral Fantasia
Saint-Saëns: Symphony 3
  see CONCERT INDEX under:
(DECC) 433 625-2DSP   Stokowski conducts Famous
Russian Works
(RPO) CDRPO7014   Ashkenazy Live in Moscow
(TELA) CD80126   Works by Britten and Prokofiev
  cond K.H. ADLER
  see CONCERT INDEX under:
(DECC) 430 716-2DM   Pavarotti—Gala Concert at the
Albert Hall
  cond A. DE ALMEIDA
Canteloube: Chants d'Auvergne (exc)
  cond K. ALWYN
  see CONCERT INDEX under:
Bax: Malta GC (exc), Oliver Twist (exc)
  see CONCERT INDEX under:

(SILV) SILVAD3002   At the Movies 2: Classic
Symphonic Film Music
  cond D. AMOS
  see CONCERT INDEX under:
(KOCH) 37002-2   American Works for 2 Pianos &
Orchestra
  cond M. ARNOLD
  see CONCERT INDEX under:
(EMI) CDGO 2059   British Film Music from the 40s and
50s
(EMI) CDM7 64718-2   The Composer Conducts
  cond D. ATLAS
Stravinsky: Firebird Suite (1919), Symphony in E flat
  cond M. ATZMON
  see CONCERT INDEX under:
(DECC) 414 348-2DH   Popular Works for Piano &
Orchestra
(DECC) 430 726-2DM   Popular Works for Piano and
Orchestra
(DECC) 433 616-2DSP
Addinsell/Gershwin—Orchestral Works
  cond R.C. BACHMANN
Bachmann: Rotation 90 degrees north
  cond C. BADEA
Saint-Saëns: Phaéton
  cond J. BARBIROLLI
Sibelius: Symphony 2
  cond E. BATIZ
  see CONCERT INDEX under:
(ASV) CDDCA653   Mexican Orchestral Works
(ASV) CDDCA665   Saint-Saëns—Orchestral Works
(ASV) CDQS6033   Mozart—Orchestral Works
(EMI) CDC7 47433-2   Villa-Lobos: Bachianas
Brasileiras
(EMI) CDS7 47901-8   Villa-Lobos: Orchestral and
Chamber Works
(EMI) CZS7 67435-2   Rodrigo—Orchestral Works
(IMG) IMGCD1606   Berlioz—Orchestral Works
(IMG) IMGCD1609   Shostakovich—Orchestral Works
(NAXO) 8 550539   Respighi—Orchestral Works
  cond T. BEECHAM
Balakirev: Symphony 1, Tamara
Bizet: Arlésienne Suites
Borodin: Prince Igor (exc)
Delius: Sea Drift, Village Romeo and Juliet (Cpte)
Mozart: Clarinet Concerto, K622
Rimsky-Korsakov: Scheherazade
Schumann: Manfred (exc)
Tchaikovsky: Romeo and Juliet, Symphony 3
  see CONCERT INDEX under:
(BBCR) DMCD98   BBC Proms - The Centenary: 1895-
1995
(EMI) CDH5 65191-2   Heifetz plays
Mozart/Mendelssohn/Vieuxtemps
(EMI) CDH5 65502-2   Paul Tortelier
(EMI) CDM7 63379-2   Beecham conducts French
Orchestral Works
(EMI) CDM7 63397-2   Sibelius: Orchestral Works
(EMI) CDM7 63401-2   French Favourites
(EMI) CDM7 63405-2   British Orchestral Works
(EMI) CDM7 64027-2   Sibelius—Orchestral Works
(EMI) CDM7 69750-2   Schubert—Symphonies
(EMI) CDS7 47509-8   Beecham conducts Delius
(EMI) CHS7 63715-2   Mozart: Die Entführung, etc
(EMI) CMS7 64066-2   Haydn—London Symphonies
(EMI) CMS7 64389-2   Haydn—Symphonies
(EMIL) CDZ7 67015-2   Mozart—Opera Arias
(RCA) 09026 61778-2(18)   The Heifetz Collection, Vol.
18
(SONY) SMK46683   Arnell/Berners/Delius—Orchestral
Works
(SONY) SMK58934   Delius—Orchestral Works
  cond E. BERNSTEIN
  see CONCERT INDEX under:
(MILA) 74321 14081-2   Bernard Herrmann—Film
Scores
  cond U. BJÖRLIN
  see CONCERT INDEX under:
(EMI) CDM5 65073-2   Berwald—Orchestral Works
  cond Y. BUTT
Goldmark: Rustic wedding, Sakuntala
  see CONCERT INDEX under:
(ASV) CDDCA619   Elgar—Orchestral Works
(ASV) CDDCA665   Sibelius—Orchestral Works
(ASV) CDDCA709   Lalo—Orchestral Works
(ASV) CDDCA722   Grieg—Orchestral Works
(ASV) CDDCA878   Lalo/Gounod—Orchestral Works
(ASV) CDDCA903   Glazunov—Orchestral Works
  cond B. CAMERON
(EMI) CDM7 64716-2   Ireland—Piano Concerto, etc
  cond J-C. CASADESUS
  see CONCERT INDEX under:
(RPO) CDRPO7023   French Orchestral Works
  cond N. CLEOBURY
  see CONCERT INDEX under:
(PHIL) 416 698-2PH   Encore! Travels with my cello,
Vol. 2
  cond M. DAVIES
Delius: Violin Concerto
  see CONCERT INDEX under:
(EMIN) CD-EMX2196   A Delius Festival
  cond J. DEPREIST
Hindemith: Four Temperaments, Nobilissima visione
  cond A. DORATI
Dvořák: American Suite, Slavonic Dances
Haydn: Ritorno di Tobia (Cpte), Schöpfung (Cpte)
Orff: Carmina Burana
Stravinsky: Firebird (Cpte)
  cond P. DREIER
  see CONCERT INDEX under:

(AURO) **NCD4913** Works by Harold Saeverud
(SIMA) **PSC3108** Geirr Tveitt—Works for harp and orchestra
  cond C. DUTOIT
Tchaikovsky: Piano Concerto 1
  see CONCERT INDEX *under:*
(DECC) **433 220-2DWO** The World of the Violin
(DECC) **443 865-2DF2** Saint-Saëns—Piano Concertos
  cond P. ELLIS
  see CONCERT INDEX *under:*
(TRIN) **TRP040** Copland—Orchestral Works
  cond A. EREDE
Paganini: Violin Concerto 1, Violin Concerto 2
  see CONCERT INDEX *under:*
(EMI) **CDM7 63109-2** Tito Gobbi - Opera Aria Recital
(EMI) **CHS7 69741-2(7)** Record of Singing, Vol.4—Italian School
(TEST) **SBT1019** Tito Gobbi - Opera Arias & Songs
  cond M. ERMLER
Beethoven: Egmont (exc), Symphony 6
Bizet: Carmen Suites
Grieg: Peer Gynt Suites
  cond H. FARBERMAN
Glière: Symphony 3
Rachmaninov: Symphony 2
  cond C. FARNCOMBE
  see CONCERT INDEX *under:*
(DECC) **430 500-2DWO** World of Handel
  cond R. FARNON
  see CONCERT INDEX *under:*
(REFE) **RRCD-47** Robert Farnon—Concert Works
  cond J. FARRER
Dvořák: Slavonic Dances
  see CONCERT INDEX *under:*
(ASV) **CDDCA794** Dvořák—Symphonic Poems
  cond E. FENBY
  see CONCERT INDEX *under:*
(UNIC) **DKPCD9063** Delius—Choral & Orchestral Works
(UNIC) **UKCD2071** The Delius Collection, Volume 1
(UNIC) **UKCD2072** The Delius Collection, Volume 2
(UNIC) **UKCD2073** The Delius Collection, Volume 3
  cond A. FISTOULARI
  see CONCERT INDEX *under:*
(CFP) **CD-CFP4569** Puccini: Arias
(CFP) **CD-CFP4637** Ketélbey/Luigini—Orchestral Music
  cond C.P. FLOR
Dvořák: Serenade, Op.22, Symphony 8
Franck: Symphonic Variations, Symphony
  cond L. FOSTER
Paganini: Violin Concerto 1
Sarasate: Carmen Fantasy
  see CONCERT INDEX *under:*
(EMI) **CDM7 63533-2** Spanish Violin Works
(EMI) **CMS7 64617-2** The art of Itzhak Perlman
(EMI) **CMS7 64922-2** Perlman plays Romantic Violin Concertos
  cond A. FRANCIS
Offenbach: Robinson Crusoé (Cpte)
  see CONCERT INDEX *under:*
(OPRA) **ORC003** Donizetti—Gabriela di Vergy
  cond D. GAMLEY
  see CONCERT INDEX *under:*
(REFE) **RRCD-47** Robert Farnon—Concert Works
  cond L. GARDELLI
Rossini: Guillaume Tell (Cpte)
Verdi: Attila (Cpte), Forza del destino (Cpte), Giorno di Regno (Cpte), Lombardi (Cpte)
  see CONCERT INDEX *under:*
(EMI) **CDM7 69549-2** Ruggero Raimondi: Italian Opera Arias
  cond C. GIBAULT
Beethoven: Symphony 5
Schubert: Symphony 8
  cond A. GIBSON
  see CONCERT INDEX *under:*
(PHIL) **400 019-2PH** Popular Sacred Songs
  cond I. GODFREY
Sullivan: Pirates of Penzance (Cpte)
  see CONCERT INDEX *under:*
(DECC) **430 095-2DWO** The World of Gilbert & Sullivan, Vol.1
(DECC) **433 868-2DWO** The World of Gilbert & Sullivan - Volume 2
  cond E. GOOSSENS
Beethoven: Romances
Tchaikovsky: Violin Concerto
  see CONCERT INDEX *under:*
(DG) **413 844-2GW2** 19th Century Violin Works
(DG) **447 427-2GOR2** D. Oistrakh plays Concertos
  cond M.A. GÓMEZ-MARTÍNEZ
  see CONCERT INDEX *under:*
(DECC) **430 628-2DH2** Villa-Lobos—Piano Concertos
  cond C. GROVES
Vaughan Williams: Hugh the Drover (Cpte)
  see CONCERT INDEX *under:*
(ASV) **CDDCA787** Finzi/Stanford—Clarinet Concertos, etc
(CARL) **CDRPO5005** An English Celebration
(LYRI) **SRCD323** Grace Williams—Orchestral Works
  cond A. GUADAGNO
  see CONCERT INDEX *under:*
(EMI) **CDM7 69500-2** Montserrat Caballé sings Bellini & Verdi Arias
  cond V. GUI
Rossini: Barbiere di Siviglia (Cpte)
  see CONCERT INDEX *under:*
(EMI) **CDH5 65072-2** Glyndebourne Recorded - 1934-1994

  cond M. HALÁSZ
Dvořák: Cello Concerto
Elgar: Cello Concerto
  cond V. HANDLEY
Arnold: Symphony 7, Symphony 8
Boughton: Oboe Concerto 1, Symphony 3
Foulds: Dynamic Triptych
Holst: Planets, St Paul's Suite
Rubbra: Viola Concerto, Violin Concerto
Simpson: Symphony 3, Symphony 5
Vaughan Williams: Piano Concerto
  see CONCERT INDEX *under:*
(CHAN) **CHAN8464** Bax—Orchestral Works
(CHAN) **CHAN8625** Bax: Choral Works
(CONI) **CDCF171** Elgar/Bax—Works for Viola & Orchestra
(CONI) **CDCF175** 20th Century British Music for Piano and Orchestra
(CONI) **CDCF224** Arnold—Orchestral Works
(CONI) **CDCF240** Arnold—Orchestral Works
(HYPE) **CDA66450** Bantock—Orchestral Works
(HYPE) **CDA66630** Bantock—Orchestral Works
(UNIC) **DKPCD9040** Delius—Works for Violin & Orchestra
(UNIC) **UKCD2072** The Delius Collection, Volume 2
  cond G. HERBIG
Beethoven: Fidelio (exc), Symphony 3
  see CONCERT INDEX *under:*
(ASV) **CDDCA763** Emma Johnson plays Clarinet Concertos
(DENO) **CO-79551** Weber—Clarinet Concertos
  cond R. HICKOX
Bernstein: Chichester Psalms
Fauré: Requiem (Cpte)
  see CONCERT INDEX *under:*
(DECC) **440 323-2DWO** World of British Classics, Volume V
  cond J. HIROKAMI
Bruch: Violin Concerto 1
Sibelius: Violin Concerto
  cond J. HORENSTEIN
Rachmaninov: Piano Concerto 2, Piano Concerto 3
  see CONCERT INDEX *under:*
(CHAN) **CHAN8521/2** Rachmaninov—Works for Piano & Orchestra
  cond E. HOWARTH
(ASV) **CDACA1003** The Classical Oboe
  cond O.A. HUGHES
Verdi: Requiem (Cpte)
  cond P. JÄRVI
  see CONCERT INDEX *under:*
(TRIN) **TRP010** Dvořák—Orchestral Works
  cond J. JUDD
Holst: Planets
Tchaikovsky: Piano Concerto 1
  see CONCERT INDEX *under:*
(TRIN) **TRP024** Grieg—Piano Concerto, Op 16; Lyric Pieces
  cond O. KIELLAND
Kielland: Symphony 1
  cond P. KLETZKI
  see CONCERT INDEX *under:*
(EMI) **CZS7 67726-2** Paul Kletzki—A Profile
  cond K. KOIZUMI
Tchaikovsky: Marche slave, Romeo and Juliet, Symphony 5, Symphony 6
  cond R. KUBELÍK
  see CONCERT INDEX *under:*
(EMI) **CZS5 68223-2** Rafael Kubelík—A profile
  cond E. KURTZ
  see CONCERT INDEX *under:*
(EMI) **CZS7 67729-2** Efrem Kurtz - A profile
  cond R. LEIBOWITZ
(CHES) **Chesky CD50** Works for Piano & Orchestra
  cond H. LEWIS
Meyerbeer: Prophète (Cpte)
  cond A. LICATA
  see CONCERT INDEX *under:*
(TRIN) **TRP046** Prokofiev—Peter and the Wolf etc
  cond J. LING
Dupré: Organ Symphony, Op. 25
Rheinberger: Organ Concerto 1
  cond A. LITTON
Brahms: Academic Festival Overture, Symphony 1
Elgar: Enigma Variations
Rachmaninov: Isle of the Dead, Symphonic Dances, Symphony 1, Symphony 2, Symphony 3, Vocalise
  see CONCERT INDEX *under:*
(DECC) **433 519-2DH** Works for Violin and Orchestra
(EMI) **CDC7 54665-2** Rodrigo/Walton—Guitar Works
(VIRG) **VMT7 59279-2** Rachmaninov—Orchestral Works
  cond J. LOCKHART
Beethoven: Symphony 7, Symphony 8
  cond J. LÓPEZ-COBOS
Bruch: Scottish Fantasy
Lalo: Symphonie espagnole
Rachmaninov: Piano Concerto 2
Ravel: Piano Concerto
  cond Z. MACAL
Rachmaninov: Piano Concerto 3
  cond C. MACKERRAS
Elgar: Sea Pictures, Symphony 2
Shostakovich: Festive Overture, Symphony 5
Tchaikovsky: Sleeping Beauty (exc), Swan Lake Suite
  see CONCERT INDEX *under:*
(ARGO) **436 545-2ZH** Elgar—Orchestral Works

  cond N. DEL MAR
Elgar: Enigma Variations, Pomp and Circumstance Marches
  see CONCERT INDEX *under:*
(EMI) **CDH5 65502-2** Paul Tortelier
(UNIC) **DKPCD9108** Delius—Orchestral Works
(UNIC) **UKCD2071** The Delius Collection, Volume 1
(UNIC) **UKCD2072** The Delius Collection, Volume 2
(UNIC) **UKCD2073** The Delius Collection, Volume 3
  cond P. MAXWELL DAVIES
  see CONCERT INDEX *under:*
(COLL) **Coll1390-2** Maxwell Davies—Orchestral Works
  cond Y. MENUHIN
Beethoven: Symphony 9
Elgar: Cello Concerto, Enigma Variations
Nielsen: Symphony 4, Violin Concerto
Vaughan Williams: Symphony 5, 2-Piano Concerto
  cond R. NASH
Sullivan: Mikado (exc)
  see CONCERT INDEX *under:*
(DECC) **430 095-2DWO** The World of Gilbert & Sullivan, Vol.1
  cond D. PARRY
Meyerbeer: Crociato in Egitto (Cpte)
  cond A. PREVIN
Beethoven: Piano Concerto 4, Piano Concerto 5, Symphony 9
Berlioz: Corsaire, Symphonie fantastique
Brahms: Academic Festival Overture, Haydn Variations, Piano Concerto 1, Piano Concerto 2, Symphony 4, Tragic Overture
Chopin: Piano Concerto 2
Elgar: Enigma Variations, Pomp and Circumstance Marches
Holst: Planets
Prokofiev: Piano Concerto 3
Rachmaninov: Symphony 2
Rimsky-Korsakov: Tale of Tsar Saltan (exc)
Saint-Saëns: Piano Concerto 2, Piano Concerto 3, Piano Concerto 4, Piano Concerto 5
Tchaikovsky: Piano Concerto 1, Symphony 5
Vaughan Williams: Lark Ascending, Symphony 2, Symphony 5, Tallis Fantasia
Walton: Belshazzar's Feast, Henry V Suite, Viola Concerto, Violin Concerto
  see CONCERT INDEX *under:*
(EMI) **CDC7 47355-2** Mozart—Concert Arias
(TELA) **CD80125** Walton—Orchestral Works
(TELA) **CD80126** Works by Britten and Prokofiev
  cond J. PRITCHARD
(EMI) **CDH5 65072-2** Glyndebourne Recorded - 1934-1994
  cond N. RESCIGNO
Donizetti: Lucia di Lammermoor (Cpte)
(EMI) **CDM7 63512-2** Alfredo Krauss - Opera Recital
  cond P. ROBINSON
  see CONCERT INDEX *under:*
(SILV) **SILKD6004** Simple Gifts—Lesley Garrett
  cond W. ROWICKI
Liszt: Piano Concerto 2
Prokofiev: Piano Concerto 3
  cond M. RÓZSA
(SILV) **SILVAD3002** At the Movies 2: Classic Symphonic Film Music
  cond M. SARGENT
Sullivan: Yeomen of the Guard (Cpte)
(CHES) **Chesky CD93** Earl Wild plays Chopin, Fauré & Liszt
(DECC) **430 095-2DWO** The World of Gilbert & Sullivan, Vol.1
(EMI) **CDC5 55529-2** Delius—Cello Concerto, etc
(EMI) **CZS5 68132-2** Les introuvables de Jacqueline du Pré
(EMIN) **CD-EMX2198** A Delius Festival
  cond C. SEAMAN
Rachmaninov: Piano Concerto 2, Piano Concerto 4
  see CONCERT INDEX *under:*
(TRIN) **TRP036** Delius—Orchestral Works
  cond J. SEREBRIER
  see CONCERT INDEX *under:*
(ASV) **CDDCA785** Bloch/Serebrier—Works for Violin and Orchestra
(ASV) **CDDCA855** Four Seasons
(ASV) **CDDCA861** Wolf-Ferrari—Overtures & Intermezzos
(CARL) **MCD71** French Orchestral Works
  cond R. STANGER
(CHES) **Chesky CD50** Works for Piano & Orchestra
  cond R. STAPLETON
  see CONCERT INDEX *under:*
(CARL) **MCD15** Opera Spectacular
  cond L. STOKOWSKI
  see CONCERT INDEX *under:*
(DECC) **433 625-2DSP** Stokowski conducts Famous Russian Works
  cond E. STRATTA
  see CONCERT INDEX *under:*
(TELD) **9031-76997-2** Symphonic Tango
  cond Y. TEMIRKANOV
Grieg: Piano Concerto
Prokofiev: Violin Concerto 1
Rachmaninov: Paganini Rhapsody, Piano Concerto 2
Schumann: Piano Concerto
Shostakovich: Cello Concerto 1, Cello Concerto 2

Stravinsky: Petrushka (Cpte), Rite of Spring (Cpte)
Tchaikovsky: Violin Concerto
see CONCERT INDEX *under:*
(EMI) **CDC7 47348-2**   Khachaturian—Ballet Music
(RCA) **RD60195**   Mussorgsky—Orchestral & Vocal
Works
(RCA) **09026 61203-2**   Berlioz—Symphonie
fantastique
(RCA) **09026 61821-2**   Tchaikovsky—Complete
Symphonies, etc
   cond Y.P. TORTELIER
see CONCERT INDEX *under:*
(EMI) **CZS7 67521-2**   Schumann—Concertos
   cond VLADIMIR ASHKENAZY
Glazunov: Seasons (Cpte)
Prokofiev: Cello Concertino, Symphony-Concerto
Shostakovich: Fragments, Op.42, Piano Concerto 2,
Symphony 3, Symphony 5, Symphony 12, Violin
Concerto 1
Tchaikovsky: Nutcracker (Cpte)
see CONCERT INDEX *under:*
(DECC) **430 370-2DH**   R. Strauss—Works for Horn
(DECC) **430 542-2DH**   20th Century American Works
(DECC) **436 239-2DH**   Works for piano and orchestra
(DECC) **436 651-2DH**   Borodin—Orchestral Works
(DECC) **436 762-2DH**   Shostakovich—Orchestral &
Vocal Works
(DECC) **436 763-2DH**   Shostakovich—Orchestral
Works
(RPO) **CDRPO7014**   Ashkenazy Live in Moscow
(RPO) **CDRPO7015**   Ashkenazy in Moscow and
London
   cond G. WELDON
see CONCERT INDEX *under:*
(EMIL) **CDZ114**   Best of Baroque
   cond W. WELLER
see CONCERT INDEX *under:*
(DECC) **440 621-2DF2**   Mozart—Violin Concertos,
etc
   cond H.D. WETTON
Holst: Choral Symphony
   cond D. WILLCOCKS
H. Blake: Benedictus
see CONCERT INDEX *under:*
(UNIC) **DKPCD9046**   Holst—Choral Works
(UNIC) **DKPCD9057**   A Christmas Garland
   cond B. WORDSWORTH
Beethoven: Symphony 1, Symphony 7
Bernstein: West Side Story (Cpte)
see CONCERT INDEX *under:*
(ARGO) **443 170-2ZH**   Bliss—Orchestral Works
   cond P. ZUKOFSKY
Schnabel: Symphony 2

ROYAL PHILHARMONIC ORCHESTRA CELLOS
   cond G. SIMON
see CONCERT INDEX *under:*
(CALA) **CACD0104**   The London Cello Sound

ROYAL PHILHARMONIC SOCIETY ORCHESTRA
   cond E. ANSERMET
see CONCERT INDEX *under:*
(PEAR) **GEMMCD9291**   Fanny Davies plays
Schumann
   cond T. BEECHAM
see CONCERT INDEX *under:*
(BEEC) **BEECHAM3**   Delius—Vocal & Orchestral
Works
(DUTT) **CDLX7011**   Beecham conducts Delius

ROYAL SCOTTISH ORCHESTRA
   cond M. BAMERT
Schoenberg: Pelleas und Melisande
Webern: Passacaglia
see CONCERT INDEX *under:*
(CHAN) **CHAN8618**   Works for Clarinet and
Orchestra
   cond J. BROWN
Bernstein: Candide (1988) (exc)
   cond A. GIBSON
Elgar: Cockaigne, Coronation Ode (Cpte), Dream of
Gerontius (Cpte), Enigma Variations, Falstaff, Pomp
and Circumstance Marches, Spirit of England
Holst: Planets
Rachmaninov: Symphony 2
Sibelius: Symphony 1, Symphony 2, Symphony 4,
Symphony 5
Stravinsky: Symphony in C, Symphony in 3
movements
Walton: Symphony 1
see CONCERT INDEX *under:*
(CHAN) **CHAN6503**   Orchestral works
(CHAN) **CHAN6508**   Sibelius: Orchestral Works
(CHAN) **CHAN6533**   Nielsen/Sibelius—Orchestral
Works
(CHAN) **CHAN6538**   Seascapes
(CHAN) **CHAN6547**   Walton—Choral and Orchestral
Works
(CHAN) **CHAN6557**   Sibelius—Symphonies
(CHAN) **CHAN6586**   Sibelius—Orchestral & Vocal
Works
(CHAN) **CHAN6591**   Sibelius—Orchestral Works
(CHAN) **CHAN8301**   The Special Sound of Chandos
(CHAN) **CHAN8309**   Elgar—Overtures
(CHAN) **CHAN8316**   Berlioz: Overtures
(CHAN) **CHAN8345/6**   Stravinsky—Three Symphonies
and Ode
(CHAN) **CHAN8379**   Scottish Overtures
(CHAN) **CHAN8395/6**   Sibelius: Tone Poems
(CHAN) **CHAN8405**   Elgar—Orchestral Works
   cond N. JÄRVI
Bartók: Concerto for orchestra

Dvořák: Biblical Songs (Cpte), Golden Spinning-
Wheel, Heroic Song, My Home, Noon Witch, Slavonic
Dances, Slavonic Rhapsodies (exc), Symphony 1,
Symphony 2, Symphony 4, Symphony 5, Symphony
6, Symphony 7, Symphony 8, Symphony 9, Water
Goblin, Wild Dove
Enescu: Romanian Rhapsodies, Op. 11
Glazunov: Raymonda (exc), Seasons, Stenka Razin,
Violin Concerto
Kabalevsky: Violin Concerto
Khachaturian: Gayaneh (exc), Symphony 2, Violin
Concerto
Mahler: Blumine, Kindertotenlieder, Lieder eines
fahrenden Gesellen, Symphonisches Praeludium,
Symphony 1, Symphony 3, Symphony 4, Symphony
5, Symphony 6
Prokofiev: Alexander Nevsky, Cinderella Suite 2,
Cinderella Suite 3, Gambler Portraits, op 49, Romeo
and Juliet Suites, Scythian Suite, Semyon Kotko, op
81 bis, Sinfonietta, Symphony 1, Symphony 2,
Symphony 3, Symphony 4, Symphony 5, Symphony
6, Symphony 7, Symphony-Concerto, Violin Concerto
1, Violin Concerto 2, Waltz Suite (exc)
R. Strauss: Heldenleben, Lieder, Op. 68, Symphony
in F minor, Vier letzte Lieder
Rimsky-Korsakov: Scheherazade
Scriabin: Rêverie, Op. 24, Symphony 2
Shostakovich: Ballet Suite 4, Ballet Suite 5,
Symphony 1, Symphony 4, Symphony 5, Symphony
6, Symphony 7, Symphony 8, Symphony 10, Violin
Concerto 1, Violin Concerto 2
Stravinsky: Baiser de la fée
Tchaikovsky: Nutcracker (exc), Sleeping Beauty
(exc), Symphony 2
see CONCERT INDEX *under:*
(CHAN) **CHAN7000/1**   Shostakovich—Orchestral
Works
(CHAN) **CHAN8472**   Prokofiev—Orchestral Works
(CHAN) **CHAN8476**   Works by Rachmaninov and
Tchaikovsky
(CHAN) **CHAN8511**   Prokofiev—Peter and the Wolf;
Cinderella
(CHAN) **CHAN8525**   Music from Estonia, Vol 1
(CHAN) **CHAN8538**   R. Strauss: Orchestral & Vocal
Works
(CHAN) **CHAN8542**   Khachaturian—Orchestral Works
(CHAN) **CHAN8557**   R. Strauss—Vocal and
Orchestral Works
(CHAN) **CHAN8572**   R. Strauss: Orchestral & Vocal
Works
(CHAN) **CHAN8575**   Dvořák—Orchestral Works
(CHAN) **CHAN8587**   Shostakovich: Orchestral Works
(CHAN) **CHAN8611**   Russian Orchestral Works
(CHAN) **CHAN8631**   R. Strauss: Orchestral & Vocal
Works
(CHAN) **CHAN8656**   Music from Estonia, Volume 2
(CHAN) **CHAN8728**   Prokofiev—Orchestral Works
(CHAN) **CHAN8729**   Prokofiev—Ballet & Opera Suites
(CHAN) **CHAN8730**   Shostakovich—Ballet Suites
(CHAN) **CHAN8734**   R. Strauss—Orchestral and
Songs
(CHAN) **CHAN8744**   R. Strauss—Orchestral and
Vocal Works
(CHAN) **CHAN8758**   R. Strauss—Opera Excerpts
(CHAN) **CHAN8798/9**   Dvořák: Symphonic Poems
(CHAN) **CHAN8804**   Glazunov and Lyadov: Orchestral
Works
(CHAN) **CHAN8805**   Kalinnikov: Orchestral Works
(CHAN) **CHAN8806**   Prokofiev—Orchestral Works
(CHAN) **CHAN8834**   R. Strauss: Orchestral and Vocal
Works
(CHAN) **CHAN8927**   Khachaturian—Spartacus Ballet
Suites 1-3
(CHAN) **CHAN9054**   R. Strauss—Orchestral Songs,
Vol.1
   cond P. MAXWELL DAVIES
Maxwell Davies: Trumpet Concerto
   cond B. THOMSON
Leighton: Cello Concerto, Op. 31, Symphony 3
Martinů: Symphony 1, Symphony 2, Symphony 3,
Symphony 4, Symphony 5, Symphony 6
Nielsen: Symphony 1, Symphony 2, Symphony 3,
Symphony 4, Symphony 5, Symphony 6
T. Wilson: Introit, Piano Concerto
see CONCERT INDEX *under:*
(CHAN) **CHAN8858**   Britten—Vocal Works
(CHAN) **CHAN8882/3**   Rachmaninov: Works for Piano
& Orchestra

ROYAL SCOTTISH ORCHESTRA CHORUS
   cond A. GIBSON
Elgar: Coronation Ode (Cpte), Dream of Gerontius
(Cpte), Spirit of England
see CONCERT INDEX *under:*
(CHAN) **CHAN6547**   Walton—Choral and Orchestral
Works
   cond N. JÄRVI
Mahler: Symphony 3
Prokofiev: Alexander Nevsky
see CONCERT INDEX *under:*
(CHAN) **CHAN8476**   Works by Rachmaninov and
Tchaikovsky

ROYAL SCOTTISH ORCHESTRA JUNIOR CHORUS
   cond N. JÄRVI
Mahler: Symphony 3

ROYAL SHAKESPEARE COMPANY CHORUS
   cond J. O. EDWARDS
H. Arlen: Wizard of Oz (stage) (exc)

ROYAL SHAKESPEARE COMPANY ORCHESTRA
   cond J. O. EDWARDS
H. Arlen: Wizard of Oz (stage) (exc)

(LE) ROYAL TRIO
see CONCERT INDEX *under:*
(DHM) **05472 77176-2**   Music at the Court of Louis XIV

ROYALL, Christopher (alto)
Liszt: Missa choralis, S10
see CONCERT INDEX *under:*
(HYPE) **CDA66311/2**   Monteverdi: St Barbara
Vespers
(HYPE) **CDA66319**   Mundy—Sacred Choral Works

ROZARIO, Patricia (sop)
Britten: Rape of Lucretia (Cpte)
Canteloube: Chants d'Auvergne (exc)
Haydn: Stabat Mater
Tavener: Mary of Egypt (Cpte), We shall see Him as
He is
Vaughan Williams: Symphony 3
see CONCERT INDEX *under:*
(COLL) **Coll1428-2**   Tavener—To a Child dancing in
the Wind
(COLL) **Coll3052-2**   Patricia Rozario - Spanish
Recital
(HYPE) **CDJ33020**   Schubert—Complete Lieder,
Vol.20
(HYPE) **CDJ33022**   Schubert—Complete Lieder,
Vol.22
(SONY) **SK66613**   Tavener—Innocence

ROZHDESTVENSKY, Gennadi (cond)
see BBC SO

ROZHDESTVENSKY, Gennadi (narr)
Prokofiev: Cantata, Op. 74

ROZHDESTVENSKY, Gennadi (pf)
see CONCERT INDEX *under:*
(ERAT) **2292-45969-2**   Tchaikovsky—Complete Piano
Works

ROZHDESTVENSKY, Sasha (vn)
Schnittke: Concerto Grosso 6
see CONCERT INDEX *under:*
(RCA) **74321 24894-2**   Homage to Schnittke

ROZSA, Anna (sop)
see CONCERT INDEX *under:*
(PREI) **89007**   Aureliano Pertile (1885-1952) - I
(PREI) **89043**   Antonio Cortis (1891-1952)
(PREI) **89048**   Apollo Granforte (1886-1975) - I

ROZSA, Ernö (vn)
see CONCERT INDEX *under:*
(MARC) **8 223324**   Von Schillings—Orchestral Works

RÓZSA, Miklos (cond)
see Frankenland State SO

ROZSNYAI, Zoltán (cond)
see Hungarian St Orch

ROZSOS, István (ten)
Giordano: Andrea Chénier (Cpte)

RSFSR ACADEMIC RUSSIAN CHOIR
   cond K. KONDRASHIN
see CONCERT INDEX *under:*
(CHNT) **LDC278 1007/8**   Shostakovich: Symphonies,
Vol.4

RTBF NEW SYMPHONY ORCHESTRA
   cond E. DONEUX
Franck: Auber Variations, Piano Concerto
   cond J. SEREBRIER
see CONCERT INDEX *under:*
(CHAN) **CHAN8369**   Chausson—Orchestral Works

RTBF SYMPHONY ORCHESTRA
   cond B. PRIESTMAN
Franck: Ce qu'on entend sur la montagne
   cond J. SEREBRIER
(RCA) **RD87763**   Shostakovich: Film Music
   cond A. WALTER
Franck: Organiste I (exc)
Furtwängler: Symphony 3

RTE CHAMBER CHOIR
   cond R. SACCANI
Verdi: Aida (Cpte)

RTE CONCERT ORCHESTRA
   cond A. PENNY
H. Salter: Ghost of Frankenstein (exc), House of
Frankenstein (exc)
Sullivan: Ile enchantée (Cpte), Thespis (exc)
see CONCERT INDEX *under:*
(MARC) **8 223461**   Sullivan—Incidental Music
(MARC) **8 223665**   Vaughan Williams—Film Music
(MARC) **8 223695**   German—Orchestral Works,
Volume 1
   cond E. TOMLINSON
see CONCERT INDEX *under:*
(MARC) **8 223522**   British Light Music—Miniatures

RTE PHILHARMONIC CHOIR
   cond R. BONYNGE
Balfe: Bohemian Girl (Cpte)
   cond C. PEARCE
Victory: Ultima Rerum (Cpte)
   cond R. SACCANI
Verdi: Aida (Cpte)

RTE SYMPHONY ORCHESTRA
   cond C. PEARCE
see CONCERT INDEX *under:*

RUSO, Daniela (pf)

RUSÓ, Daniela (pf)
see CONCERT INDEX under:
(MARC) **8 223644** Bella—Piano Works
Grechaninov: Piano Trio 1, Piano Trio 2
Schmidt: Clarinet and Piano Quintet 2
(MARC) **8 223415** Schmidt—Chamber Works

RUSS, Giannina (sop)
see CONCERT INDEX under:
(EMI) **CHS7 64860-2(2)** La Scala Edition - Vol.1, 1878-1914 (pt 2)
(MEMO) **HR4408/9(2)** Singers in Genoa, Vol.1 (disc 2)
(PEAR) **GEMMCDS9923(2)** Covent Garden on Record, Vol.1 (pt 2)
(PEAR) **GEMMCDS9924(2)** Covent Garden on Record, Vol.2 (pt 2)
(SYMP) **SYMCD1113** The Harold Wayne Collection, Vol.13

RUSS, Karsten (ten)
Delius: Village Romeo and Juliet (Cpte)
Schillings: Mona Lisa (Cpte)

RUSSELL, Alexander (organ)
see CONCERT INDEX under:
(ROMO) **81008-2** Mary Garden (1874-1967)

RUSSELL, James (sngr)
Schuman: Mighty Casey (Cpte)

RUSSELL, Lillian (sngr)
see CONCERT INDEX under:
(PEAR) **GEMMCDS9050/2(1)** Music from the New York Stage, Vol. 1 (part 1)

RUSSELL, Linda (sop)
Rameau: Naïs (Cpte)

RUSSELL, Lynda (sop)
Bach: Christmas Oratorio, BWV248 (Cpte)
Haydn: Mass 7, Mass 14
Mozart: Betulia Liberata (Cpte)
see CONCERT INDEX under:
(ARGO) **436 120-2ZH** Vaughan Williams/Walton—Choral & Orchestral Works
(CHAN) **CHAN0517** Handel—Sacred Choral works
(COLL) **Coll1320-2** Baroque Choral Works
(DECC) **443 455-2DF2** Vivaldi—Sacred Choral Works

RUSSELL, Rogene (cor ang)
Benson: End of the World

RUSSIA SYMPHONY ORCHESTRA
Miaskovsky: Symphony 6
cond V. DUDAROVA
Kalinnikov: Symphony 1, Symphony 2
see CONCERT INDEX under:
(OLYM) **OCD292** Kabalevsky—Cello Concertos; Violin and Piano Works
(OLYM) **OCD513** Liadov—Orchestral Works

RUSSIAN FEDERATION STATE SYMPHONY ORCHESTRA
cond E. SVETLANOV
Shostakovich: Symphony 5
see CONCERT INDEX under:
(CANY) **EC3630-2** Tchaikovsky—The Complete Symphonies

RUSSIAN METROPOLITAN CHURCH CHOIR (PARIS)
cond N. AFONSKY
see CONCERT INDEX under:
(PEAR) **GEMMCD9314** Feodor Chaliapin - Aria and Song Recital

RUSSIAN NATIONAL ORCHESTRA
cond M. PLETNEV
Dvořák: Slavonic Dances
Prokofiev: Cinderella (Cpte), Summer Night, Op.123
Rachmaninov: Rock, Op.7, Symphony 2
Tchaikovsky: Manfred Symphony, Marche slave, Symphony 6, Tempest
see CONCERT INDEX under:
(DG) **439 892-2GH** Russian Overtures

RUSSIAN NATIONAL ORCHESTRA SOLOISTS ENSEMBLE
see CONCERT INDEX under:
(OLYM) **OCD529** Glinka—Chamber Works

RUSSIAN PHILHARMONIC ORCHESTRA
Salieri: Axur (Cpte)

RUSSIAN REPUBLIC CHOIRS
cond K. KONDRASHIN
Shostakovich: Symphony 2, Symphony 3, Symphony 13

RUSSIAN STATE ACADEMIC CHOIR
cond I. MARKEVITCH
see CONCERT INDEX under:
(PHIL) **438 973-2PM2** Igor Markevitch conducts Stravinsky

RUSSIAN STATE ACADEMIC ORCHESTRA
cond I. MARKEVITCH
see CONCERT INDEX under:
(PHIL) **438 973-2PM2** Igor Markevitch conducts Stravinsky

RUSSIAN STATE BRASS ORCHESTRA
cond N. SERGEYEV
Miaskovsky: Symphony 19

RUSSIAN STATE CHOIR
cond A. CHISTIAKOV
Rachmaninov: Aleko (Cpte)
Tchaikovsky: Snow Maiden (Cpte)

RUSSIAN STATE POLYPHONIC CAPPELLA
cond V. POLYANSKY
Schnittke: Concerto

RUSSIAN STATE SYMPHONY CAPPELLA
cond V. POLYANSKY
Grechaninov: Liturgy, Op. 79 (Cpte), Seven Days of the Passion (Cpte)
see CONCERT INDEX under:
(CHAN) **CHAN9397** Grechaninov—Choral & Orchestral Works
(CLAV) **CD50-9304/5** Rachmaninov—Works for Chorus

RUSSIAN STATE SYMPHONY ORCHESTRA
cond I. GOLOVSHIN
Balakirev: Russian Ov II, Symphony 2
Rubinstein: Don Quixote, Ivan the Terrible, Symphony 4
see CONCERT INDEX under:
(NAXO) **8 550792** Balakirev—Orchestral Works
cond V. POLYANSKY
Grechaninov: Liturgy, Op. 79 (Cpte)
Tchaikovsky: Marche slave, Symphony 6
see CONCERT INDEX under:
(CHAN) **CHAN9397** Grechaninov—Choral & Orchestral Works
cond E. SVETLANOV
Borodin: Petite Suite, Symphony 2
Mahler: Symphony 3
Rimsky-Korsakov: Symphony 1, Symphony 2
Suk: Asrael
see CONCERT INDEX under:
(RCA) **09026 61674-2** Borodin—Orchestral Works
(RCA) **09026 62684-2** Rimsky-Korsakov—Symphony No 3, etc

RUSSIUS, Klaus Henner (spkr)
Schumann: Manfred (Cpte)

RUST, Rebecca (vc)
see CONCERT INDEX under:
(MARC) **8 223298** Enescu & Villa-Lobos: Cello Works

RUTA, Franco (bass)
Donizetti: Lucrezia Borgia (Cpte)
Verdi: Traviata (Cpte)

RUTA, Tommaso (mndl)
see CONCERT INDEX under:
(PHIL) **426 086-2PBQ** Vivaldi—Double Concertos

RUTGERS, Elisabeth (sop)
R. Strauss: Ariadne auf Naxos (Cpte)
see CONCERT INDEX under:
(SCHW) **314632** Vienna State Opera Live, Vol.13
(SCHW) **314652** Vienna State Opera Live, Vol.15
(SCHW) **314672** Vienna State Opera Live, Vol.17

RUTHERFORD, Christian (hn)
see CONCERT INDEX under:
(CHAN) **CHAN0547** Telemann—Orchestral Works
(CONI) **CDCF220** Michael Haydn—Masses and Vespers
(PHIL) **432 152-2PH** Brahms—Choral Works

RUTLAND SINFONIA
cond B. COLLETT
see CONCERT INDEX under:
(PEAR) **SHECD9602** Elgar: War Music

RUTTER, John (cond)
see Cambridge Clare College Orch

RUUD, Ole Kristian (cond)
see Norwegian Wind Ens

RUUS, Arno (organ)
see CONCERT INDEX under:
(SCHW) **314050** Weill—Vocal and Choral Works

RUUTTUNEN, Esa (bar)
Sallinen: Kullervo (Cpte)
see CONCERT INDEX under:
(BIS) **BIS-CD656** Klami—Whirls-Ballet Suites etc

RUYLE, Bill (perc)
see CONCERT INDEX under:
(PNT) **434 873-2PTH** Jon Gibson—In Good Company

RUZDJAK, Vladimir (bar)
Mahler: Symphony 8

RUZICKA, Peter (cond)
see Berlin RSO

RŮŽIČKOVÁ, Zuzana (hpd)
Bach: Flute Sonatas, BWV1030-5, Violin Sonatas, BWV1014-19
see CONCERT INDEX under:
(CAMP) **RRCD1321** Martinů—Keyboard Concertos, etc
(ORFE) **C139861A** Music of the English Virginalists

RUZICZKA, Else (mez)
see CONCERT INDEX under:
(NIMB) **NI7848** Great Singers at the Berlin State Opera
(PEAR) **GEMMCD9451** Alexander Kipnis
(PREI) **89019** Alexander Kipnis (1891-1978)

RYAN, Jane (viol)
see CONCERT INDEX under:
(DECC) **430 263-2DM** Purcell—Sacred choral works

RYDELL, Roland (bar)
Tubin: Requiem for Fallen Soldiers

RYDÉN, Susanne (sop)
see CONCERT INDEX under:

(HARM) **HMC90 1310** Schütz—The Nativity

RYDL, Kurt (bass)
Beethoven: Fidelio (Cpte)
Einem: Dantons Tod (Cpte)
Gluck: Alceste (1776) (Cpte)
Haydn: Schöpfung (Cpte)
J. Strauss II: Fledermaus (Cpte)
Mozart: Zauberflöte (Cpte)
Offenbach: Contes d'Hoffmann (Cpte)
Puccini: Madama Butterfly (Cpte), Manon Lescaut (Cpte), Turandot (Cpte)
R.Strauss: Arabella (Cpte), Ariadne auf Naxos (Cpte), Frau ohne Schatten (Cpte), Rosenkavalier (Cpte), Salome (Cpte)
Schmidt: Buch mit Sieben Siegeln
Verdi: Ballo in maschera (Cpte), Nabucco (Cpte), Rigoletto (Cpte)
Wagner: Fliegende Holländer (Cpte), Meistersinger (Cpte), Parsifal (Cpte), Rheingold (Cpte), Siegfried (Cpte), Tannhäuser (Cpte)
Weber: Freischütz (Cpte)

RYE, John (narr)
Lumsdaine: Aria

RYPDAL, Terje (gtr)
Rypdal: Largo, Op.55, Q.E.D.

RYSANEK, Leonie (sop)
Beethoven: Fidelio (Cpte)
R. Strauss: Ariadne auf Naxos (Cpte), Frau ohne Schatten (Cpte), Salome (Cpte)
Verdi: Macbeth (Cpte), Otello (Cpte)
Wagner: Walküre (Cpte)
see CONCERT INDEX under:
(EMI) **CDH5 65201-2** Leonie Rysanek - Operatic Recital
(EMI) **CHS7 69741-2(4)** Record of Singing, Vol.4—German School
(PHIL) **446 057-2PB14** Wagner—The Ring Cycle - Bayreuth Festival 1967
(RCA) **09026 61580-2(7)** RCA/Met 100 Singers, 100 Years (pt 7)

RYSANEK, Lotte (sop)
R. Strauss: Frau ohne Schatten (Cpte)

S. E. M. ENSEMBLE ORCHESTRA
cond P. KOTIK
Cage: Atlas Eclipticalis, Concert for Piano

SAARBRÜCKEN RADIO CHAMBER ORCHESTRA
cond A. JANIGRO
see CONCERT INDEX under:
(WERG) **WER60162-50** Ligeti: Choral and Orchestral Works

SAARBRÜCKEN RADIO SYMPHONY ORCHESTRA
cond D.R. DAVIES
Schnittke: Viola Concerto
cond A. FRANCIS
Pettersson: Symphony 3, Symphony 4
cond G. MARKSON
see CONCERT INDEX under:
(MARC) **8 223334** Schnittke—Works for Cello
cond MYUNG-WHUN CHUNG
Rimsky-Korsakov: Invisible City of Kitezh (exc)
Shostakovich: Symphony 6
cond M. VIOTTI
Paganini: Violin Concerto 1, Violin Concerto 2

SAARINEN, Eeva-Liisa (mez)
Sallinen: Kullervo (Cpte)
Sibelius: Kullervo

SAARINEN, Eeva-Liisa (narr)
Aho: Pergamon

SABA, Geoffrey (pf)
see CONCERT INDEX under:
(CARL) **PCD858** Piano Transcriptions
(CARL) **PCD950** Schubert—Piano works

SABAJNO, Carlo (cond)
see La Scala Orch

SABAJNO, Carlo (pf)
see CONCERT INDEX under:
(NIMB) **NI7831** Mattia Battistini (1856-1928)
(PEAR) **GEMMCDS9923(1)** Covent Garden on Record, Vol.1 (pt 1)
(PEAR) **GEMMCD9936** Mattia Battistini, Vol.1
(SYMP) **SYMCD1069** The Harold Wayne Collection, Vol.2
(SYMP) **SYMCD1073** The Harold Wayne Collection, Vol.3

SABATA, Victor de (cond)
see BPO

SABATANO, Nina (sop)
Rossini: Barbiere di Siviglia (exc)

SABATINI, Daniele (perc)
see CONCERT INDEX under:
(SCHW) **310632** Globokar—Chamber Works

SABBATINI, Giuseppe (ten)
Mozart: Don Giovanni (Cpte)
Rossini: Petite messe solennelle (Cpte)
see CONCERT INDEX under:
(CAPR) **10 247** The Art of Bel Canto
(CAPR) **10 348** Mozart Gala—Suntory Hall, Tokyo

SABEL, Jakob (ten)
see CONCERT INDEX under:
(SCHW) **314532** Vienna State Opera Live, Vol.3

SABINO, Antonio (cond)
see La Scala Orch

SABO, Katja (mez)
R. Strauss: Salome (Cpte)

SABRIÉ, Isabelle (sop)
see CONCERT INDEX under:
(MARC) 8 223636   In Memoriam Lili Boulanger

SABROWSKI, Jörg (bar)
Delius: Village Romeo and Juliet (Cpte)

SABROWSKI, Jörg (sngr)
Schillings: Mona Lisa (Cpte)

SACCÀ, Roberto (ten)
Handel: Messias, K572 (Cpte)

SACCANI, Rico (cond)
see Ireland National SO

SACCHETTI, Antonio (bass)
Puccini: Madama Butterfly (Cpte), Manon Lescaut
(Cpte)
Verdi: Traviata (Cpte)

SACCHETTI, Arturo (organ)
see CONCERT INDEX under:
(EURM) 350224   Franck—Complete Harmonium
Music

SACCHI, Franca (contr)
Ponchielli: Gioconda (Cpte)

SACCOMANI, Lorenzo (bar)
Leoncavallo: Pagliacci (Cpte)

SACHER, Paul (cond)
see Collegium Musicum

(LES) SACQUEBOUTIERS DE TOULOUSE
cond B. FABRE-GARRUS
see CONCERT INDEX under:
(ASTR) E8521   Helfer—Requiem for the Dukes of
Lorraine

SADÉ, Gabriel (ten)
Dessau: Hagadah Shel Pessach

SADLER, Michael (sngr)
Sondheim: Pacific Overtures (exc)

SADLER'S WELLS OPERA CHORUS
cond A. FARIS
Sullivan: Iolanthe (exc), Mikado (Cpte)
cond R. GOODALL
Wagner: Götterdämmerung (exc)

SADLER'S WELLS OPERA ORCHESTRA
cond W. BRAITHWAITE
see CONCERT INDEX under:
(PEAR) GEMMCDS9925(1)   Covent Garden on
Record—Vol.3 (pt 1)
cond A. FARIS
Sullivan: Iolanthe (exc), Mikado (Cpte)
cond R. GOODALL
Wagner: Götterdämmerung (exc), Siegfried (exc)

SADLERS WELLS ORCHESTRA
cond W. WALTON
see CONCERT INDEX under:
(EMI) CHSS 65003-2   Walton conducts Walton

SÁDLO, Miloš (vc)
Shostakovich: Cello Concerto 1

SADLO, Peter (perc)
see CONCERT INDEX under:
(DG) 439 867-2GH   Bartók/Ravel—Works for 2 Pianos

SADOC, Jesse (tbn)
see CONCERT INDEX under:
(CHNT) LDC278 835   Villa-Lobos—Chôros for
Chamber Ensembles

SAEDÉN, Erik (bar)
see CONCERT INDEX under:
(CPRI) CAP21510   Rosenberg plays Rosenberg

SAEVERUD, Trond (vn)
Hvoslef: Violin Concerto

SAFFER, Lisa (sop)
Handel: Agrippina (Cpte), Judas Maccabaeus (Cpte),
Ottone (Cpte), Radamisto (Cpte), Resurrezione
(Cpte)
Purcell: Dido (Cpte)
see CONCERT INDEX under:
(HARM) HMU90 7036   Handel—Arias for Cuzzoni
(NEW) 80407-2   Sheng—Miscellaneous Works
(VIRG) VC7 59308-2   Knussen—Chamber Music

SAFIULIN, Anatoly (bass)
Shostakovich: Symphony 13, Symphony 14

SAFRI DUO
Bach: English Suites, BWV806-811 (exc), French
Suites, BWV812-17 (exc)
see CONCERT INDEX under:
(CHAN) CHAN9330   Fireplay—Percussion Works

SAGEMÜLLER, Dirk (bar)
Verdi: Rigoletto (Cpte)

SAGITTARIUS VOCAL ENSEMBLE
see CONCERT INDEX under:
(ERAT) 2292-45825-2   LeJeune—Sacred Works
(ERAT) 4509-91722-2
Charpentier/Grigny/Lully—Sacred Choral and Organ
works
cond M. LAPLÉNIE
Colin: Missa pro defunctis
Helfer: Missa pro defunctis
cond J-C. MALGOIRE
Lully: Alceste (Cpte)

cond M. MINKOWSKI
Lully: Phaëton (Cpte)
Rameau: Hippolyte et Aricie (Cpte)

SAGI-VELA, Luis (sngr)
Barbieri: Barberillo de Lavapiès (Cpte)

SAIDULA, Hermine (mez)
R. Strauss: Rosenkavalier (Cpte)

SAILER, Frederike (sop)
see CONCERT INDEX under:
(ERAT) 4509-97407-2   Bach—Cantatas

SAINT NICHOLAS SINGERS
cond G. HEALD-SMITH
see CONCERT INDEX under:
(CAMP) RR2CD1331/2   Havergal Brian—Orchestral
Works

SAINT PAUL CHAMBER ORCHESTRA
see CONCERT INDEX under:
(KOCH) 37248-2   The Art of Arleen Auger
(PHIL) 420 168-2PH   Violin Works
cond C. HOGWOOD
(DECC) 433 660-2DH   Martinů—Orchestral Works
cond J. REVZEN
Haydn: Jahreszeiten (Cpte), Schöpfung (Cpte)
cond A. WOLFF
Haydn: Symphony 85, Symphony 86
cond H. WOLFF
Haydn: Symphony 82, Symphony 83, Symphony 84,
Symphony 87
see CONCERT INDEX under:
(TELD) 9031-77192-2   Respighi—Orchestral Works
(TELD) 9031-73134-2   Bartók/Kodály—Hungarian
dances
(TELD) 9031-73135-2   Christmas with Thomas
Hampson
(TELD) 9031-73282-2   Shostakovich—Piano
Concertos, etc
(TELD) 9031-74006-2   Ravel/Debussy—Orchestral
Works
(TELD) 9031-77309-2
Bizet/Prokofiev/Haydn—Symphonies
(TELD) 9031-77311-2   CPE Bach/Vivaldi/Tartini—Cello
Concertos
cond P. ZUKERMAN
(SONY) SK39964   J.C.Bach & Boccherini Orchestral
Works

SAINT-CYR, Dom André (cond)
see St John the Baptist Ch Schola

SAINT-DENIS FESTIVAL CHORUS
cond J-C. CASADESUS
Honegger: Roi David (Cpte)

SAINT-ETIENNE LYRIC CHORUS
cond P. FOURNILLIER
Gounod: Sapho (Cpte)

SAINT-ETIENNE NOUVEL ORCHESTRA
cond P. FOURNILLIER
Gounod: Sapho (Cpte)
Massenet: Cléopâtre (Cpte)

SAINT-PALAIS, Mary (sop)
Campra: Idoménée (Cpte)
Dauvergne: Troqueurs (Cpte)
Montéclair: Jephté (Cpte)

SAITO KINEN ORCHESTRA
cond S. OZAWA
Beethoven: Symphony 7
Schubert: Symphony 8
Stravinsky: Oedipus Rex (Cpte)
see CONCERT INDEX under:
(PHIL) 432 176-2PH   Takemitsu—Orchestral Works
(PHIL) 438 137-2PH   Mozart/Tchaikovsky—Music for
Strings

SAKAMOTO, Ryuichi (synths)
see CONCERT INDEX under:
(KOCH) 37238-2   A Chance Operation - John Cage
Tribute

SAKARI, Petri (cond)
see Iceland SO

SAKHAROV, M. (pf)
see CONCERT INDEX under:
(EMI) CHS7 69741-2(6)   Record of Singing,
Vol.4—Russian & Slavonic Schools

SAKKAS, Spiros (sngr)
Xenakis: Oresteia (Cpte)

SAKS, Gidon (bass)
Schreker: Ferne Klang (Cpte)
Zemlinsky: Kreidekreis (Cpte)

SALA, Antonio (vc)
see CONCERT INDEX under:
(BIDD) LAB059/60   Henri Temianka—Recital

SALA, Giuseppe (ten)
see CONCERT INDEX under:
(SYMP) SYMCD1126   The Harold Wayne Collection,
Vol.14

SALE, Frank (ten)
Wagner: Tristan und Isolde (Cpte)

SALEVIC, Mischa (vn)
see CONCERT INDEX under:
(ETCE) KTC1045   Menotti: Chamber and Vocal
Works

SALISBURY CATHEDRAL BOYS' CHOIR
cond J. E. GARDINER
see CONCERT INDEX under:
(PHIL) 438 149-2PH   French Choral Works

SALISBURY CATHEDRAL CHOIR
see CONCERT INDEX under:
(MERI) CDE84068   Carols from Salisbury
cond R. KING
Handel: Deborah (Cpte)
cond R. SEAL
see CONCERT INDEX under:
(MERI) CDE84025   Anthems from Salisbury
(MERI) CDE84180   Anthems for America
cond G. SOLTI
(DECC) 436 403-2DWO   The World of Royal Music

SALLABA, Richard (ten)
R. Strauss: Ariadne auf Naxos (Cpte)
see CONCERT INDEX under:
(PREI) 90237   R Strauss—Daphne
(SCHW) 314602   Vienna State Opera Live, Vol.10
(SCHW) 314652   Vienna State Opera Live, Vol.15

SALMINEN, Matti (bass)
Mozart: Don Giovanni (Cpte), Entführung (Cpte),
Requiem, Zauberflöte (Cpte)
Sallinen: Kullervo (Cpte)
Wagner: Fliegende Holländer (Cpte),
Götterdämmerung (Cpte), Parsifal (Cpte), Rheingold
(Cpte), Siegfried (Cpte), Tannhäuser (Cpte), Tristan
und Isolde (Cpte), Walküre (Cpte)
see CONCERT INDEX under:
(BIS) BIS-CD520   Matti Salminen - Opera Recital
(DG) 445 354-2GX14   Wagner—Der Ring des
Nibelungen

SALMINEN, Sarianna (sngr)
Zemlinsky: Kleider machen Leute (Cpte)

SALMON, Philip (ten)
Handel: Israel in Egypt (Cpte), Saul (Cpte)
Lehár: Lustige Witwe (Cpte)
Massenet: Vierge (Cpte)
see CONCERT INDEX under:
(HYPE) CDA66062   Bruckner—Motets
(HYPE) CDA66076   British Choral Works
(HYPE) CDA66126   Britten: Choral Works
(PHIL) 432 152-2PH   Brahms—Choral Works

SALMOND, Felix (vc)
see CONCERT INDEX under:
(APR) APR7012   Myra Hess—A vignette

SALO, Per (organ)
Janáček: Glagolitic Mass (Cpte)

SALO, Per (pf)
Ives: Concord Sonata
see CONCERT INDEX under:
(KONT) 32101/2   Britten—Works for Cello
(KONT) 32147   Nørgård—Piano Works

SALOMAA, Petteri (bass)
Beethoven: Symphony 9
Bergman: Singing Tree (Cpte)
Grieg: Peer Gynt (exc)
Mendelssohn: Elias (Cpte)
Mozart: Betulia Liberata (Cpte), Nozze di Figaro
(Cpte), Zauberflöte (Cpte)
Prokofiev: Fiery Angel (Cpte)
Puccini: Madama Butterfly (Cpte)
Purcell: King Arthur, Z628 (Cpte)
Schreker: Gezeichneten (Cpte)
Verdi: Forza del destino (Cpte), Macbeth (Cpte)

SALOMON QUARTET
Haydn: String Quartet, Op. 42, String Quartet,
Op.103, String Quartets, Op.20 (exc), String Quartets,
Op. 33 (exc), String Quartets, Op. 50 (exc), String
Quartets, Op. 54, String Quartets, Op. 71 (exc), String
Quartets, Op. 74 (exc), String Quartets, Op.77
Mozart: Piano Quartet, K478, Piano Quartet, K493,
String Quartet, K387, String Quartet, K421, String
Quartet, K428, String Quartet, K458, String Quartet,
K464, String Quartet, K465, String Quartet, K575,
String Quartet, K590, String Quintet, K515, String
Quintet, K516, String Quintet, K593, String Quintet,
K614

SALOMONSSON, Kristina Hjärtsjö (sop)
Schnittke: Requiem

SALONEN, Esa-Pekka (cond)
see BPO

SALONGA, Lea (sngr)
Rodgers: King and I (Cpte)

SALTARELLI, Domenik (va)
see CONCERT INDEX under:
(PHIL) 426 076-2PCC   Vivaldi: Concertos

SALTARIN, Maurizio (ten)
Verdi: Otello (Cpte)

SALTER, Richard (bar)
Reimann: Unrevealed
Yun: Symphony 5
see CONCERT INDEX under:
(SONY) SK64301   Beethoven—Songs from the British
Isles

SALTER, Robert (vn)
see CONCERT INDEX under:
(RCA) 09026 62524-2   It's Peaceful Here

SALTER, Robert (vn/dir)
see CONCERT INDEX under:

(RCA) **RD60224** Baroque Oboe Concerti
(RCA) **09026 61275-2** Strings! The Definitive Collection

SALTIRE SINGERS
cond H. OPPENHEIM
see CONCERT INDEX *under:*
(ARCH) **447 156-2AP** Purcell—Fantasias and Vocal Works

SALTZMANN-STEVENS, Minnie (sop)
see CONCERT INDEX *under:*
(PEAR) **GEMMCDS9924(2)** Covent Garden on Record, Vol.2 (pt 2)

SALVADOR I, Guillermo (pf)
see CONCERT INDEX *under:*
(ASV) **CDDCA665** Saint-Saëns—Orchestral Works

SALVADOR II, Guillermo (pf)
see CONCERT INDEX *under:*
(ASV) **CDDCA665** Saint-Saëns—Orchestral Works

SALVADORI, Antonio (bar)
Bellini: Capuleti (Cpte)
Puccini: Fanciulla del West (Cpte)

SALVATI, Stella (contr)
see CONCERT INDEX *under:*
(STUD) **SM12 2389** Paisiello—Music for Napoleon Bonaparte's Chapel

SALVI, Bruno (vn)
Vivaldi: Concerti, Op. 8 (exc)

SALWAROWSKI, Jerzy (cond)
see Silesian PSO

SALWEN, Barry David (pf)
see CONCERT INDEX *under:*
(KOCH) **37106-2** Sessions—Complete Works for Solo Piano

SALYNIKOV, Andrei (ten)
Scriabin: Symphony 1

SALZBURG CAMERATA
cond S. VÉGH
see CONCERT INDEX *under:*
(CAPR) **10 192** Mozart—Chamber Orchestral Works

SALZBURG CAMERATA ACADEMICA
cond S. VÉGH
Haydn: String Quartet, Op.51
see CONCERT INDEX *under:*
(CAPR) **10 801** Mozart: Serenades & Divertimenti

SALZBURG CHAMBER CHOIR
cond L. HAGER
Mozart: Apollo et Hyacinthus (Cpte), Ascanio in Alba (Cpte), Sogno di Scipione (Cpte)
see CONCERT INDEX *under:*
(PHIL) **422 522-2PME6** The Complete Mozart Edition Vol 22

SALZBURG CHAMBER ORCHESTRA
cond H. NERAT
see CONCERT INDEX *under:*
(NAXO) **8 550609** Mozart—Cassations

SALZBURG CHAMBER SOLOISTS
see CONCERT INDEX *under:*
(DENO) **CO-78918** Mozart—Orchestral Works

SALZBURG FESTIVAL CHAMBER CHOIR
cond H. VON KARAJAN
Verdi: Trovatore (Cpte)

SALZBURG HOFMUSIK
cond W. BRUNNER
Biber: Arminio (Cpte)

SALZBURG MOZARTEUM CAMERATA ACADEMICA
cond S. VÉGH
Brahms: String Quintet 2
Mozart: Divertimenti, K136-8 (exc), Divertimento, K205, Divertimento, K247, Divertimento, K251, Divertimento, K287, Divertimento, K334, Piano Concerto 9, Piano Concerto 12, Piano Concerto 13, Piano Concerto 14, Piano Concerto 15, Piano Concerto 16, Piano Concerto 17, Piano Concerto 18, Piano Concerto 19, Piano Concerto 20, Piano Concerto 21, Piano Concerto 22, Piano Concerto 23, Piano Concerto 24, Piano Concerto 25, Piano Concerto 26, Piano Concerto 27
Schoenberg: Verklärte Nacht
see CONCERT INDEX *under:*
(CAPR) **10 185** Mozart—Serenades & Divertimenti
(CAPR) **10 302** Mozart—Serenades, Vol.6
(CAPR) **10 801** Mozart: Serenades & Divertimenti
(DECC) **433 042-2DH** Mozart—Piano Works

SALZBURG MOZARTEUM CHORUS
cond L. HAGER
Mozart: Lucio Silla (Cpte)
cond K. PRESTEL
Mozart: Don Giovanni (exc)

SALZBURG MOZARTEUM ORCHESTRA
cond H. GRAF
see CONCERT INDEX *under:*
(CAPR) **10 253** Mozart: Marches
(CAPR) **10 269** Mozart—Symphonies, Vol 2
(CAPR) **10 313** Mozart: Symphonies, Vol.3
(CAPR) **10 313** Mozart: Symphonies, Vol.4
(CAPR) **10 809** Mozart—Overtures, Dances & Marches

cond L. HAGER
Mozart: Apollo et Hyacinthus (Cpte), Ascanio in Alba (Cpte), Finta Giardiniera (Cpte), Finta semplice (Cpte), Lucio Silla (Cpte), Mitridate (Cpte), Sogno di Scipione (Cpte), Zaïde (Cpte)
see CONCERT INDEX *under:*
(PHIL) **422 522-2PME6** The Complete Mozart Edition Vol 22
cond K. PRESTEL
Mozart: Don Giovanni (exc)
cond B. WEIL
see CONCERT INDEX *under:*
(DENO) **CO-1741** Mozart: Operatic Arias

SALZBURG RADIO CHORUS
cond L. HAGER
Mozart: Lucio Silla (Cpte)

SALZBURG SHEPHERD BOYS
cond T. REISER
Keetman: Weihnachtslieder (exc)
Orff: Weihnachtsgeschichte

SALZEDO, Carlos (hp)
see CONCERT INDEX *under:*
(CLAR) **CDGSE78-50-47** The Harrison Sisters—An English Musical Heritage

SALZER, Ernst (bar)
Ligeti: Grand Macabre (Cpte)

SALZMANN, Jean-Marc (bar)
Dauverné: Troqueurs (Cpte)
Henze: Boulevard Solitude (Cpte)
M-A. Charpentier: Médée (Cpte)

SAMAROFF, Olga (pf)
see CONCERT INDEX *under:*
(SIMA) **PSC1809(2)** Grieg—Historical Piano Recordings (pt 2)

SAMKO, Milan (harm)
see CONCERT INDEX *under:*
(CAPR) **10 180** Gisela May sings Weill

SAMMARCO, Mario (bar)
see CONCERT INDEX *under:*
(EMI) **CHS7 64360-2(1)** La Scala Edition - Vol.1, 1878-1914 (pt 1)
(EMI) **CHS7 64360-2(2)** La Scala Edition - Vol.1, 1878-1914 (pt 2)
(PEAR) **GEMMCDS9073(2)** Giovanni Zenatello, Vol.1 (pt 2)
(PEAR) **GEMMCDS9924(1)** Covent Garden on Record, Vol.2 (pt 1)
(PEAR) **GEMMCDS9924(2)** Covent Garden on Record, Vol.2 (pt 2)
(SYMP) **SYMCD1111** The Harold Wayne Collection, Vol.11
(SYMP) **SYMCD1113** The Harold Wayne Collection, Vol.13
(SYMP) **SYMCD1158** The Harold Wayne Collection, Vol.18
(TEST) **SBT1008** Viva Rossini

SAMMARITANO, Silvestro (bass)
Puccini: Manon Lescaut (Cpte)
Spontini: Vestale (Cpte)
Verdi: Forza del destino (Cpte), Rigoletto (Cpte), Traviata (Cpte)

SAMMONS, Albert (vn)
see CONCERT INDEX *under:*
(DUTT) **CDAX8014** British Gramophone Premieres
(TEST) **SBT1014** Delius—Orchestral Works

SAMOILOV, Yevgeny (cond)
see Moscow New Op Orch

SAMOSUD, Samuel (cond)
see Bolshoi Th Orch

SAMPIERI, Michele (bar)
see CONCERT INDEX *under:*
(PEAR) **GEMMCDS9074(2)** Giovanni Zenatello, Vol.2 (pt 2)
(PEAR) **GEMMCDS9926(1)** Covent Garden on Record—Vol.4 (pt 1)

SAMUEL, Gerhard (cond)
see Cincinnati Philh

SAMUEL, Harold (pf)
see CONCERT INDEX *under:*
(BIDD) **LAB076** Menges plays Beethoven and Brahms

SAMUELS, Homer (pf)
see CONCERT INDEX *under:*
(CONI) **CDHD201** Galli-Curci in Opera and Song

SAMUELS, Ron (cl)
see CONCERT INDEX *under:*
(KOCH) **37186-2** French Clarinet Music

SAMUELSON, Mikael (bar)
Haeffner: Electra (Cpte)
Roman: Swedish Mass
Segerstam: Symphony 14

SAN ANTONIO SYMPHONY ORCHESTRA
cond V. ALESSANDRO
see CONCERT INDEX *under:*
(PHIL) **426 076-2PCC** Vivaldi: Concertos

SAN DIEGO CHAMBER ORCHESTRA
cond D. BARRA
see CONCERT INDEX *under:*
(KOCH) **37094-2** Ibert/Poulenc—Orchestral Works
(KOCH) **37134-2** Arnold—Orchestral Works
(KOCH) **37196-2** Bloch/Q.Porter—Orchestral Works

(KOCH) **37215-2** Italian Orchestral Music

SAN DIEGO MASTER CHORALE
cond Y. TALMI
Berlioz: Roméo et Juliette (exc), Troyens (exc)

SAN DIEGO SYMPHONY ORCHESTRA
cond L. SCHIFRIN
see CONCERT INDEX *under:*
(PRO) **CDS524** Hitchcock—Master of Mayhem
(SILV) **SILVAD3001** At the Movies 1: Heroes & Tough Guys
(SILV) **SILVAD3002** At the Movies 2: Classic Symphonic Film Music
(SILV) **SILVAD3003** At the Movies 3: Horror & Fantasy
cond Y. TALMI
Berlioz: Roméo et Juliette (exc), Troyens (exc)
Glière: Symphony 3

SAN FRANCISCO BOYS' CHORUS
cond H. BLOMSTEDT
Orff: Carmina Burana

SAN FRANCISCO CONTEMPORARY MUSIC PLAYERS
cond S. MOSKO
see CONCERT INDEX *under:*
(NALB) **NA055CD** Harrison—The Perilous Chapel

SAN FRANCISCO GIRL'S CHORUS
cond H. BLOMSTEDT
Orff: Carmina Burana

SAN FRANCISCO MUNICIPAL CHORUS
cond P. MONTEUX
see CONCERT INDEX *under:*
(RCA) **GD87911** Marian Anderson - Opera, Oratorio & Song Recital

SAN FRANCISCO OPERA ORCHESTRA
cond E. MACARTHUR
see CONCERT INDEX *under:*
(RCA) **GD87911** Wagner: Arias and Duets
cond E. MCARTHUR
see CONCERT INDEX *under:*
(NIMB) **NI7847** Kirsten Flagstad (1895-1962)

SAN FRANCISCO PHILHARMONIA BAROQUE ORCHESTRA
cond N. MCGEGAN
Handel: Apollo e Dafne, Oboe Concertos (exc)

SAN FRANCISCO SYMPHONY CHORUS
Brahms: Deutsches Requiem, Op. 45 (Cpte)
Grieg: Peer Gynt (exc)
Mahler: Symphony 2
Orff: Carmina Burana

SAN FRANCISCO SYMPHONY ORCHESTRA
Grieg: Peer Gynt (exc)
cond H. BLOMSTEDT
Bartók: Concerto for Orchestra, Kossuth
Brahms: Deutsches Requiem, Op. 45 (Cpte)
Bruckner: Symphony 6
Chopin: Piano Concerto 1
F. Berwald: Symphony 1, Symphony 4
Grieg: Piano Concerto
Mahler: Symphony 2
Mendelssohn: Symphony 3, Symphony 4
Nielsen: Symphony 1, Symphony 2, Symphony 3, Symphony 4, Symphony 5, Symphony 6
Orff: Carmina Burana
R. Strauss: Alpensinfonie, Don Juan, Heldenleben, Metamorphosen
Schubert: Overture, D591, Symphony 9
Sibelius: Symphony 4, Symphony 5
Wagner: Siegfried Idyll
Wuorinen: Golden Dance, Piano Concerto 3
see CONCERT INDEX *under:*
(DECC) **421 523-2DH** Hindemith: Orchestral Works
(DECC) **433 809-2DH** Hindemith—Orchestral Works
(DECC) **443 376-2DH** Harbison/Sessions—Orchestral Works
cond H. BLOMSTEDT
Bruckner: Symphony 4
cond E. MCARTHUR
see CONCERT INDEX *under:*
(SIMA) **PSC1821(2)** Kirsten Flagstad, Vol.1 (pt 2)
cond P. MONTEUX
Gruenberg: Violin Concerto
see CONCERT INDEX *under:*
(RCA) **GD87911** Marian Anderson - Opera, Oratorio & Song Recital
(RCA) **09026 61893-2** Pierre Monteux Edition
cond S. OZAWA
see CONCERT INDEX *under:*
(DG) **413 851-2GW2** Modern American Favourites
(DG) **427 203-2GR** Gershwin: Orchestral Works
cond E. DE WAART
J. Adams: Shaker Loops
Reich: Variations (1980)
see CONCERT INDEX *under:*
(TELA) **CD80096** French Organ Music

SAN PETRONIO CAPPELLA MUSICALE SOLOISTS
cond S. VARTOLO
see CONCERT INDEX *under:*
(BONG) **GB5523/5-2** Torelli—Complete Works for 1, 2, 4 Trumpets & Orchestra
(BONG) **GB5544/5-2** Palestrina—Messe mantovane

SANCHEZ, Angelica Uribe (sop)
C.H. Graun: Montezuma (Cpte)

SANCHEZ, Damián (cond)
see Inst Ens

SÁNCHEZ, Emilio (sngr)
Vives: Bohemios (Cpte)

SANCHEZ, Guadalupe (sop)
see CONCERT INDEX under:
(CARL) **MCD45** Spanish Royal Gala

SANCHIONI, Nunu (sop)
see CONCERT INDEX under:
(PREI) **89048** Apollo Granforte (1886-1975) - I

SAND, Annemarie (mez)
Smyth: Wreckers (Cpte)

SAND, Bo (cl)
see CONCERT INDEX under:
(KONT) **32032** Wind Chamber Music

SANDER, Martin (organ)
Reubke: Organ Sonata

SANDER, Otto (spkr)
Mendelssohn: Oedipus (Cpte)

SANDERLING, Kurt (cond)
see Czech PO

SANDERLING, Michael (vc)
see CONCERT INDEX under:
(CAPR) **10 539** Schulhoff—Chamber Works
(EDA) **EDA008-2** Works by Ullmann and Schoenberg

SANDERLING, Stefan (cond)
see Ireland National SO

SANDERLING, Thomas (cond)
see Berlin RSO

SANDERS, John (cond)
see Gloucester Cath Ch

SANDERS, Samuel (pf)
see CONCERT INDEX under:
(EMI) **CDC7 47399-2** Dvořák/Smetana—Works for Violin & Piano
(EMI) **CDC7 49604-2** Violin Arrangements by Jascha Heifetz
(EMI) **CDM7 63533-2** Spanish Violin Works
(EMI) **CMS7 64617-2** The art of Itzhak Perlman
(EMI) **CZS4 83177-2(1)** Itzhak Perlman Edition (pt 1)
(EMI) **CZS4 83177-2(2)** Itzhak Perlman Edition (pt 2)
(EMI) **CZS4 83177-2(3)** Itzhak Perlman Edition (pt 3)

SANDERSON, Michael (ten)
Lampe: Pyramus and Thisbe (Cpte)

SANDFORD, Kenneth (bar)
Sullivan: Gondoliers (Cpte), Iolanthe (Cpte), Mikado (Cpte), Patience (Cpte), Trial by Jury (Cpte), Yeomen of the Guard (Cpte)
see CONCERT INDEX under:
(DECC) **433 868-2DWO** The World of Gilbert & Sullivan - Volume 2

SANDGREN, Carolina (sop)
Mahler: Symphony 8

SANDISH, Dale (sngr)
Gershwin: Strike Up the Band I (Cpte), Strike Up the Band II

SANDISON, Gordon (bar)
Bizet: Carmen (Cpte)
Sullivan: HMS Pinafore (Cpte)

SANDKLEF, Per (vn)
see CONCERT INDEX under:
(MSVE) **MSCD415** Kraus—Chamber Music

SANDLUND, Staffan (bass)
Lidholm: Dream Play (Cpte)

SÁNDOR, Arpad (pf)
see CONCERT INDEX under:
(BIDD) **LAB049/50** Kreisler - The Berlin HMV Recordings (1926-7)
(EMI) **CDH7 64494-2** Heifetz plays Bach
(PEAR) **GEMMCDS9157** Jascha Heifetz - Concerto Recordings, Volume 1
(PEAR) **GEMMCD9324** Fritz Kreisler plays Encores
(RCA) **09026 61778-2(02)** The Heifetz Collection, Vol.2 - 1925-34
(RCA) **09026 61778-2(03)** The Heifetz Collection, Vol. 3
(SUPR) **11 1491-2** Jarmila Novotna sings Czech Songs and Arias

SÁNDOR, György (pf)
see CONCERT INDEX under:
(SONY) **SX4K68275** Bartók—Piano Works
(VOX) **CDX2 5506** György Sándor plays Bartók

SÁNDOR, János (cond)
see Budapest PO

SANDOR, John (ten)
Verdi: Masnadieri (Cpte)
see CONCERT INDEX under:
(LASE) **15 611** Suppé—Overtures
(LASE) **15 617** Grieg: Orchestral Works

SÁNDOR, Judit (mez)
Bruch: Violin Concerto 1
see CONCERT INDEX under:
(LASE) **15 511** Mozart: Symphonies and Overtures
(LASE) **15 606** Gershwin: Orchestral Works
(LASE) **15 616** French Ballet Music

SANDOVAL, Arturo (tpt)
see CONCERT INDEX under:
(GRP) **GRK75002** Arturo Sandoval—The Classical Album

ŞANDRU, Sanda (sop)
Bretan: Arald (Cpte), Golem (Cpte)

SANDSTRÖM, Mikael (perc)
see CONCERT INDEX under:
(ONDI) **ODE802-2** Ibert/Jolivet/Nielsen—Flute Concertos

SANDTNEROVÁ, Marta (mez)
Hába: Mother (Cpte)

SANDVE, Kjell Magnus (ten)
Braein: Anne Pedersdotter (Cpte)
Grieg: Sigurd Jorsalfar (Cpte)
see CONCERT INDEX under:
(SONY) **SK53276** Nielsen—Orchestral Works
(VICT) **VCD19041** Grieg—Songs, Vol.4

SANDVIK, Gro (fl)
see CONCERT INDEX under:
(BIS) **BIS-CD428** Nielsen—Wind Chamber Music

SANDVIK, Gro (rec)
see CONCERT INDEX under:
(BIS) **BIS-CD428** Nielsen—Wind Chamber Music

SANFORD, Sally (sop)
(ALBA) **TROY127-2** Purcell—From Rosy Bow'rs

SANGER, David (organ)
Vierne: Symphony 3, Symphony 4
see CONCERT INDEX under:
(BIS) **BIS-CD273** Organ Works
(MERI) **CDE84068** Carols from Salisbury
(MERI) **ECD84081** Bach—Organ Works

SANGIORGIO, Victor (pf)
see CONCERT INDEX under:
(COLL) **Coll1374-2** Stravinsky—Piano Works

SANGUINETI, Edoardo (narr)
Berio: Laborintus II

SANROMÁ, Jesús-María (pf)
see CONCERT INDEX under:
(BIDD) **LAB087** Hindemith plays Hindemith
(PEAR) **GEMMCD9020** Koussevitzky conducts Stravinsky and Mussorgsky
(RCA) **09026 61778-2(05)** The Heifetz Collection, Vol. 5

SANSALONE, Salvatore (vn)
see CONCERT INDEX under:
(ERAT) **2292-45368-2** Chausson: Songs

SANSOM, Mary (sop)
Sullivan: Gondoliers (Cpte), Iolanthe (Cpte), Patience (Cpte)
see CONCERT INDEX under:
(DECC) **433 868-2DWO** The World of Gilbert & Sullivan - Volume 2

SANSONNETTI, Marcelle (sngr)
Ganne: Hans (Cpte)

SÁNTA, Jolán (mez)
Mascagni: Lodoletta (Cpte)

SANTA CECILIA ACADEMY CHORUS, ROME
cond B. BARTOLETTI
Verdi: Ballo in maschera (Cpte)
cond L. BERNSTEIN
Puccini: Bohème (Cpte)
cond F. CAPUANA
Cilea: Adriana Lecouvreur (Cpte)
cond A. EREDE
Puccini: Turandot (Cpte)
Verdi: Otello (Cpte), Rigoletto (Cpte)
cond C.M. GIULINI
Verdi: Trovatore (Cpte)
cond L. MAAZEL
Puccini: Tosca (Cpte)
cond F. MOLINARI-PRADELLI
Puccini: Manon Lescaut (Cpte), Tosca (Cpte)
Verdi: Forza del Destino (Cpte), Traviata (Cpte)
cond J. PRITCHARD
Donizetti: Lucia di Lammermoor (Cpte)
cond T. SERAFIN
Boito: Mefistofele (Cpte)
Puccini: Bohème (Cpte), Madama Butterfly (Cpte)
cond G. SINOPOLI
Verdi: Rigoletto (Cpte)

SANTA CECILIA ACADEMY ORCHESTRA, ROME
cond B. BARTOLETTI
Verdi: Ballo in maschera (Cpte)
cond V. BELLEZZA
see CONCERT INDEX under:
(PREI) **89009** Gino Bechi (b. 1913)
cond L. BERNSTEIN
Puccini: Bohème (Cpte)
see CONCERT INDEX under:
(DG) **429 728-2GH** Debussy: Orchestral Works
cond R. BONYNGE
see CONCERT INDEX under:
(DECC) **436 301-2DA** Renata Tebaldi & Franco Corelli—Arias & Duets
cond G. CANTELLI
see CONCERT INDEX under:
(TEST) **SBT1017** Orchestral Works - Cantelli
cond F. CAPUANA
Cilea: Adriana Lecouvreur (Cpte)
cond A. EREDE
Puccini: Turandot (Cpte)
Verdi: Otello (Cpte), Rigoletto (Cpte)
see CONCERT INDEX under:
(DECC) **430 481-2DX2** Renata Tebaldi sings Opera Arias

cond G. GAVAZZENI
see CONCERT INDEX under:
(DECC) **417 686-2DC** Puccini—Operatic Arias
(DECC) **430 481-2DX2** Renata Tebaldi sings Opera Arias
(DECC) **436 463-2DM** Ten Top Tenors
(RCA) **GD86534** Verdi Arias and Duets
cond C.M. GIULINI
Verdi: Trovatore (Cpte)
see CONCERT INDEX under:
(RCA) **09026 62541-2** Pavarotti - The Early Years, Vol.1
cond L. MAAZEL
Puccini: Tosca (Cpte)
see CONCERT INDEX under:
(DECC) **436 463-2DM** Ten Top Tenors
cond F. MOLINARI-PRADELLI
Puccini: Manon Lescaut (Cpte), Tosca (Cpte)
Verdi: Forza del Destino (Cpte), Traviata (Cpte)
see CONCERT INDEX under:
(DECC) **430 481-2DX2** Renata Tebaldi sings Opera Arias
(DECC) **436 463-2DM** Ten Top Tenors
(DECC) **436 464-2DM** Ten Top Baritones & Basses
cond F. PATANÈ
(DECC) **417 686-2DC** Puccini—Operatic Arias
cond J. PRITCHARD
Donizetti: Lucia di Lammermoor (Cpte)
cond V. DE SABATA
see CONCERT INDEX under:
(EMI) **CHS5 65506-2** Victor de Sabata conducts
cond T. SERAFIN
Boito: Mefistofele (Cpte)
Puccini: Bohème (Cpte), Madama Butterfly (Cpte)
see CONCERT INDEX under:
(DECC) **417 686-2DC** Puccini—Operatic Arias
(DECC) **430 481-2DX2** Renata Tebaldi sings Opera Arias
cond G. SINOPOLI
Verdi: Rigoletto (Cpte)
cond A. VOTTO
see CONCERT INDEX under:
(PREI) **89009** Gino Bechi (b. 1913)

SANTA FÉ OPERA CHORUS
cond R. LEPPARD
V. Thomson: Mother of us all (Cpte)

SANTA FÉ OPERA ORCHESTRA
cond R. LEPPARD
V. Thomson: Mother of us all (Cpte)

SANTA MONICA ORCHESTRA
cond J. RACHMILOVICH
see CONCERT INDEX under:
(CAMB) **CD-1063** Louis Kaufman - Violin Works

SANT'AMBROGIO, John (vc)
Bolcom: Sessions I
see CONCERT INDEX under:
(TELA) **CD80059** Popular Orchestral Works

SANT'AMBROGIO, Sara (pf)
see CONCERT INDEX under:
(KOCH) **37000-2** Bernstein—Songs & Duets

SANTE, Sophia van (mez)
R. Strauss: Rosenkavalier (Cpte)

SANTI, Nello (cond)
see New Philh

SANTINI, Angelo (ten)
see CONCERT INDEX under:
(IRCC) **IRCC-CD808** Souvenirs of 19th Century Italian Opera

SANTINI, Gabriele (cond)
see La Scala Chor

SANTLEY, Sir Charles (bar)
see CONCERT INDEX under:
(NIMB) **NI7840/1** The Era of Adelina Patti
(SYMP) **SYMCD1093** The Harold Wayne Collection, Vol.7

SANTOS, Betina Maag (vn)
Telemann: Fantaisies, TWV40: 14-25

SANTOS, Murillo (pf)
(CHNT) **LDC278 835** Villa-Lobos—Chôros for Chamber Ensembles

SANTOS, Turibio (gtr)
(CHNT) **LDC278 835** Villa-Lobos—Chôros for Chamber Ensembles
(CHNT) **LDC278 869/70** Villa-Lobos—Guitar Works

SANZOGNO, Nino (cond)
see La Scala Orch

SAORGIN, René (organ)
Couperin: Messe à l'usage ordinaire des paroisses, Messe pour les couvents
Grigny: Premier livre d'orgue (exc)
see CONCERT INDEX under:
(HARM) **HMA190 942** Buxtehude—Organ Works

SAPAROVÁ, Jikta (mez)
Bellini: Sonnambula (Cpte)
Verdi: Rigoletto (Cpte)

SAPELL, Hermann (bar)
Wagner: Meistersinger (Cpte)
Weber: Freischütz (Cpte)

SAPORITO, James (perc)
see CONCERT INDEX under:
(CATA) **09026 62668-2** Maria Bachmann—Kiss On Wood

SAQUE, Elsa (sop)
see CONCERT INDEX under:
(ERAT) **2292-45926-2** Charpentier—Sacred Choral Works

(LES) SAQUEBOUTIERS DE TOULOUSE
see CONCERT INDEX under:
(HARM) **HMC90 1255** Schütz—Sacred Choral Works

SARABIA, Guillermo (bar)
Bizet: Pêcheurs de Perles (Cpte)
Zemlinsky: Florentinische Tragödie

SARACENI, Adelaide (sop)
see CONCERT INDEX under:
(MSCM) **MM30231** Don Pasquale & Tito Schipa Recital
(PREI) **89048** Apollo Granforte (1886-1975) - I

SARAGOSSE, Jean-Claude (bass)
Montéclair: Jephté (Cpte)

SARAM, Rohan de (vc)
see CONCERT INDEX under:
(AUVI) **MO782025** Schoenberg—Chamber Music, Vol. 3
(LYRI) **SRCD234** Rubbra—Orchestral Works
(PHIL) **426 925-2PM19** The Complete Vivaldi Edition

SARASATE, Pablo de (vn)
see CONCERT INDEX under:
(SYMP) **SYMCD1071** Great Violinists, Vol.1

SARASTE, Jukka-Pekka (cond)
see Avanti CO

SARBU, Mihail (pf)
see CONCERT INDEX under:
(DYNA) **CDS21/2** Franck—Chamber works

SARDI, Ivan (bass)
Henze: Junge Lord (Cpte)
Mozart: Don Giovanni (Cpte), Nozze di Figaro (Cpte)
Stravinsky: Oedipus Rex (Cpte)
Verdi: Requiem (Cpte), Traviata (Cpte)
Wagner: Meistersinger (Cpte)
see CONCERT INDEX under:
(DG) **437 677-2GDO2** Irmgard Seefried - Opera Recital

SARDINERO, Vicente (bar)
Mascagni: Amico Fritz (Cpte)
Puccini: Bohème (Cpte), Edgar (Cpte), Manon Lescaut (Cpte), Turandot (Cpte)
Usandizaga: Golondrinas (Cpte)
Verdi: Giorno di Regno (Cpte), Simon Boccanegra (Cpte)
see CONCERT INDEX under:
(SONY) **MK39097** Puccini Heroines

SARFATY, Regina (contr)
Beethoven: Fidelio (exc), Symphony 9
Bellini: Pirata (Cpte)
see CONCERT INDEX under:
(SONY) **SM3K46291** Stravinsky—Ballets, Vol.1

SARGENT, Sir Malcolm (cond)
see BBC SO

SARGENT, Sir Malcolm (narr/cond)
see CONCERT INDEX under:
(BEUL) **1PD13** Sir Malcolm Sargent conducts British Music

SÁRKÁNY, Kázmér (bass)
Giordano: Andrea Chénier (Cpte)
Rossini: Barbiere di Siviglia (Cpte)

SARPLE, Adrian (sngr)
Bernstein: West Side Story (Cpte)

SARRAGOSSE, Jean-Claude (bass)
Campra: Idoménée (Cpte)
Rameau: Castor et Pollux (Cpte)

SARRAZIN, Lionel (bass)
Bizet: Carmen (Cpte)
Gounod: Sapho (Cpte)
see CONCERT INDEX under:
(DECC) **440 333-2DH** Ravel—Vocal Works

SARRI, Gino (ten)
Donizetti: Lucia di Lammermoor (Cpte)
see CONCERT INDEX under:
(EMI) **CMS7 63244-2** The Art of Maria Callas

SARTI, Gastone (bar)
Donizetti: Pazzi per progetto (Cpte)

SARTI, Laura (mez)
Rossini: Barbiere di Siviglia (Cpte)

SASS, Sylvia (sop)
Bartók: Duke Bluebeard's Castle (Cpte)
Mozart: Don Giovanni (Cpte)
Respighi: Belfagor (Cpte)
Verdi: Stiffelio (Cpte)

SASSANO, Salvatore (cond)
see Naples San Carlo Op Orch

SASSARI SYMPHONY ORCHESTRA
cond G. CATALUCCI
Sacchini: Contadina in Corte (Cpte)

SASSOLI, Ada (hp)
see CONCERT INDEX under:

(RCA) **09026 61412-2** Nellie Melba - Recital
(ROMO) **81011-2(1)** Dame Nellie Melba (pt 1)

SASSON, Deborah (sop)
Wagner: Parsifal (Cpte)

SATANOWSKI, Robert (cond)
see Bydgoszcz PSO

SATO, Astuko (bn)
see CONCERT INDEX under:
(SCHW) **310832** Frank Martin—Orchestral Works

SATOH, Somei (voc/elec)
S. Satoh: Mantra (1986)

SATRE, Ana Raquel (mez)
Donizetti: Lucia di Lammermoor (Cpte)
Verdi: Otello (Cpte)
see CONCERT INDEX under:
(DECC) **430 481-2DX2** Renata Tebaldi sings Opera Arias

SATTLER, Joachim (ten)
Wagner: Tristan und Isolde (exc)
see CONCERT INDEX under:
(SCHW) **314532** Vienna State Opera Live, Vol.3

SATU MARE PHILHARMONIC ORCHESTRA
cond C. DUMBRĂVEANU
see CONCERT INDEX under:
(OLYM) **OCD418** Aurelian Octav Popa plays Clarinet Concertos

SAUER, Emil von (pf)
see CONCERT INDEX under:
(PEAR) **GEMMCD9403** Emil von Sauer plays Liszt
(PEAR) **GEMMCD9993** Arthur Friedheim—complete recordings, etc

SAUER, Franz (bass)
Wagner: Meistersinger (Cpte)

SAUER, Martin (pf)
see CONCERT INDEX under:
(NAXO) **8 550367** Chopin—Rondos & Variations

SAUERBAUM, Heinz (ten)
Weill: Mahagonny (Cpte)

SAUERBECK, Agnes (organ)
see CONCERT INDEX under:
(NALB) **NA015CD** Lou Harrison: Various Works

SAUGEY, Pierre (bar)
Messager: Basoche (Cpte), Coups de Roulis (Cpte)
Offenbach: Chanson de Fortunio (Cpte)
see CONCERT INDEX under:
(MUSD) **20239-2** Delibes—Opéras-Comiques

SAULESCO QUARTET
see CONCERT INDEX under:
(CPRI) **CAP21326** Wirén—Orchestral and Chamber works

SAUNDERS, Iris (sop)
Britten: Death in Venice (Cpte)

SAUNDERS, Jenny (sop)
Vaughan Williams: Hugh the Drover (Cpte)

SAUNDERS, Stephen (tbn)
see CONCERT INDEX under:
(DECC) **430 359-2DM** Baroque Church Music

SAURA, Francisco (sngr)
Barbieri: Barberillo de Lavapiès (Cpte)

SAUROLA, Pertti (bar)
see CONCERT INDEX under:
(FINL) **4509-95849-2** Sibelius: Choral Works

SAUROVA, Eva (sop)
Offenbach: Périchole (Cpte)
Wagner: Parsifal (Cpte)

SAUTEREAU, Nadine (sop)
Bizet: Carmen (Cpte)
Messager: Basoche (Cpte)
Ravel: Enfant et les sortilèges (Cpte)
see CONCERT INDEX under:
(EMI) **CDM7 63182-2** The Incomparable Callas

SAVAGE, Richard (bar)
Handel: Saul (Cpte)
Lehár: Lustige Witwe (Cpte)

SAVALL, Jordi (cond)
see Capella Reial Instr Ens

SAVALL, Jordi (va da gamba)
Bach: Flute Sonatas, BWV1030-5
D. Ortiz: Trattado de glosas
Forqueray: Pièces de viole (exc)
Gibbons: Fantasias Royals a 3 (exc), In Nomine (exc)
Machy: Pièces de viole (exc)
Marais: Pièces de viole, III/I (exc), Pièces de viole, III/II (exc) Pièces de viole IV/II (exc), Pièces de viole V/II (exc)
Sainte-Colombe: Concerts a deux violes esgales (exc)
see CONCERT INDEX under:
(ARCH) **437 075-2AT** Collectio Argentea 5: Canti Amorosi
(ASTR) **E8503** Merula—Arie e Capricci

SAVARESE, Ugo (bar)
Verdi: Traviata (Cpte)

SAVASTANO, Antonio (ten)
Verdi: Ballo in Maschera (Cpte), Don Carlos (Cpte), Macbeth (Cpte), Simon Boccanegra (Cpte)
see CONCERT INDEX under:
(SONY) **MK37228** Pavarotti sings Verdi

SAVIDGE, Peter (bar)
Handel: Hercules (Cpte)

SAVIGNOL, Jean (ten)
Shostakovich: Lady Macbeth of Mtsensk (Cpte)

SAVIGNOL, Pierre (bass)
Bizet: Ivan IV (exc)

SAVIJOKI, Jukka (gtr)
see CONCERT INDEX under:
(BIS) **BIS-CD411** Giuliani: Works for Flute and Guitar, Vol. 1
(BIS) **BIS-CD412** Giuliani: Works for Flute and Guitar, Vol. 2
(BIS) **BIS-CD413** Giuliani: Works for Flute and Guitar, Vol. 3
(ONDI) **ODE779-2** Britten/Berkeley—Works for Tenor and Guitar
(ONDI) **ODE781-2** Piazzolla—Works for Flute and Guitar

SAVIJOKI, Pekka (sax)
see CONCERT INDEX under:
(BIS) **BIS-CD159** Hindemith—Chamber Works

SAVILLE, Frances (sop)
see CONCERT INDEX under:
(SYMP) **SYMCD1093** The Harold Wayne Collection, Vol.7

SAVINO, Richard (gtr)
Boccherini: Guitar Quintets, G445-453 (exc)
Giuliani: Gran Quintetto, Op. 65
Mertz: Bardenklänge (exc)
see CONCERT INDEX under:
(HARM) **HMU90 7116** Giuliani/Paganini—Violin and Guitar Works

SAVOIARDO, Giovanni (bar)
Puccini: Fanciulla del West (Cpte)

SAVONLINNA OPERA FESTIVAL CHORUS
cond U. SÖDERBLOM
see CONCERT INDEX under:
(BIS) **BIS-CD508** Kokkonen—Complete Orchestral Music, Vol.4

SAVORY, Catherine (mez)
Martinů: Greek Passion (Cpte)

SAWA, Shigeru (mez)
Verdi: Traviata (Cpte)

SAWALLISCH, Wolfgang (cond)
see Bavarian Rad Chor

SAWALLISCH, Wolfgang (pf)
see CONCERT INDEX under:
(DG) **423 133-2GH** Brahms: Vocal Works
(EMI) **CDC7 47407-2** Schubert: Sacred Choral works
(EMI) **CDC7 49318-2** R. Strauss—Lieder
(EMI) **CMS7 64783-2** Schubert—Sacred Works, Vol.2
(EMI) **CMS7 64827-2** Mendelssohn—Lieder
(ORFE) **C185891A** Eichendorff Lieder - Live at Salzburg, 1975
(ORFE) **C333931B** Mahler—Des Knaben Wunderhorn Lieder

SAWKA, Johann (sngr)
see CONCERT INDEX under:
(SCHW) **314632** Vienna State Opera Live, Vol.13

SAWSTON VILLAGE COLLEGE CHAMBER CHOIR
cond S. CLEOBURY
Goehr: Death of Moses

SAXON STATE ORCHESTRA
cond K. BÖHM
see CONCERT INDEX under:
(BIDD) **LHW018** Backhaus plays Brahms, Volume 2
(PREI) **89049** Margarete Teschemacher (1903-1959)
(PREI) **89077** Torsten Ralf (1901-1954)
cond K. ELMENDORFF
Wagner: Walküre (exc)

SAYÃO, Bidú (sop)
see CONCERT INDEX under:
(IRCC) **IRCC-CD808** Souvenirs of 19th Century Italian Opera
(RCA) **09026 61580-2(4)** RCA/Met 100 Singers, 100 Years (pt 4)

SAYCE, Lynda (lte)
see CONCERT INDEX under:
(DERV) **DRVCD101** The Golden Age Restor'd

SAYER, Roger (organ)
see CONCERT INDEX under:
(PRIO) **PRCD461** Psalms of David, Vol.9

SCABBIA, Gaia (fl)
see CONCERT INDEX under:
(AKAD) **CDAK125** Tosti—Romanze

SCACCIATI, Bianca (sop)
see CONCERT INDEX under:
(PREI) **89010** Tancredi Pasero (1893-1983) - I

SCALAVINO, Umberto (sngr)
Puccini: Fanciulla del West (Cpte)

SCALCHI, Gloria (mez)
Rossini: Petite messe solennelle (Cpte)
see CONCERT INDEX under:
(DECC) **436 261-2DHO3** Puccini—Il Trittico

SCALES, Prunella (narr)
Sitwell: Poems
Walton: Façade (Cpte)

SCALTRITI, Roberto (bar)
Rossini: Pietra del paragone (Cpte)
Verdi: Rigoletto (Cpte), Traviata (Cpte), Trovatore
(Cpte)

SCAMPINI, Augusto (ten)
see CONCERT INDEX under:
(IRCC) **IRCC-CD808** Souvenirs of 19th Century Italian
Opera

SCANDIUZZI, Roberto (bass)
Franchetti: Cristoforo Colombo (Cpte)
Puccini: Bohème (Cpte), Turandot (Cpte)

SCANO, Gaetano (ten)
Rossini: Siège de Corinthe (Cpte)

SCARABELLI, Adelina (sop)
Rossini: Cenerentola (Cpte)

SCARAMBERG, Emile (ten)
see CONCERT INDEX under:
(PEAR) **GEMMCDS9923(2)** Covent Garden on
Record, Vol.1 (pt 2)
(SYMP) **SYMCD1113** The Harold Wayne Collection,
Vol.13

SCARAMOUCHE
see CONCERT INDEX under:
(CHNN) **CCS4792** Henry Purcell & His Time

SCARDONI, Mario (bass)
Gazzaniga: Gloria, Stabat Mater

SCARPINATI, Nicolas (bass)
see CONCERT INDEX under:
(PHIL) **432 416-2PH3** Haydn—L'incontro
improvviso/Arias

SCATTOLA, Carlo (bass)
Puccini: Bohème (Cpte)
see CONCERT INDEX under:
(NIMB) **NI7836/7** Conchita Supervia (1895-1936)

SCELLIER, Jacques (bass)
Messager: Basoche (Cpte)
see CONCERT INDEX under:
(MUSD) **20239-2** Delibes—Opéras-Comiques

SCHAAF, Jerrold van der (ten)
B.A. Zimmermann: Soldaten (Cpte)
Nono: Intolleranza 1960 (Cpte)

SCHAAF, Peter (pf)
Schubert: Winterreise (Cpte)

SCHAB, Jacques (pf)
see CONCERT INDEX under:
(CHNT) **LDC278 951** Denisov: Songs

SCHÄBLEN, Charlotte (mez)
see CONCERT INDEX under:
(MYTO) **3MCD93381** Wagner—Die Walküre, etc

SCHAD, Otto (perc)
see CONCERT INDEX under:
(VOX) **CDX2 5506** György Sándor plays Bartók

SCHADE, Michael (ten)
Bach: St Matthew Passion, BWV244
Haydn: Schöpfung (Cpte)
Mendelssohn: Elias (Cpte)
Sullivan: HMS Pinafore (Cpte)
Verdi: Otello (Cpte)
Wagner: Meistersinger (Cpte)

SCHADEBERG, Christine (sop)
see CONCERT INDEX under:
(BRID) **BCD9014** Elliott Carter: Vocal Works

SCHÄDLE, Lotte (sop)
Jessel: Schwarzwaldmädel (exc)
Mozart: Entführung (Cpte)
Weber: Freischütz (Cpte)
see CONCERT INDEX under:
(ARCH) **439 369-2AX4** Bach—Cantatas, Vol.1

SCHADOCK, Mathias (spkr)
see CONCERT INDEX under:
(SONY) **SK53978** Prometheus

SCHAECHTER, Dalia (mez)
Mendelssohn: Midsummer Night's Dream (exc)
see CONCERT INDEX under:
(DG) **435 486-2GH** Schubert/Schumann—Sacred
Choral Works

SCHAEFTLEIN, Jürg (ob)
(TELD) **4509-95518-2** Bach—Violin Concertos

SCHAER, Hanna (mez)
Caplet: Miroir de Jésus
Dukas: Ariane et Barbe-Bleue (Cpte)
Wagner: Parsifal (Cpte)
see CONCERT INDEX under:
(ERAT) **2292-45923-2** Bach/Vivaldi—Sacred Choral
Works
(ERAT) **4509-96961-2** Schubert—Stabat Mater;
Offertorium; Magnificat

SCHÄFER, Christine (sop)
Haydn: Schöpfung (Cpte)
Humperdinck: Hänsel und Gretel (Cpte)
Mendelssohn: Elias (Cpte), Midsummer Night's
Dream (exc)
see CONCERT INDEX under:
(WERG) **WER60183-50** Reimann—Vocal Works

SCHÄFER, Markus (ten)
Bach: Mass in B minor, BWV232 (Cpte), St Matthew
Passion, BWV244 (Cpte)
Beethoven: Joseph II Cantata, Leopold II Cantata

SCHÄFER, Wolfgang (cond)
see Frankfurt Kantorei

SCHÄFER-SUBRATA, Faridah (sop)
Bach: Mass in B minor, BWV232 (Cpte)

SCHALK, Franz (cond)
see VPO

SCHALL, Gary (marimba)
see CONCERT INDEX under:
(ARGO) **430 209-2ZH** Torke—Chamber Works

SCHARINGER, Anton (bass)
Bach: Mass in B minor, BWV232 (Cpte), St John
Passion, BWV245 (Cpte), St Matthew Passion,
BWV244 (Cpte)
Gazzaniga: Don Giovanni (Cpte)
Gurlitt: Wozzeck (Cpte)
Handel: Samson (Cpte), Theodora (Cpte)
Haydn: Schöpfung (Cpte)
J. Strauss II: Fledermaus (exc)
Mozart: Don Giovanni (Cpte), Finta Giardiniera
(Cpte), Nozze di Figaro (Cpte), Oca del Cairo (Cpte),
Zauberflöte (Cpte)
Telemann: St Matthew Passion (1746)
Weber: Freischütz (Cpte)

SCHARLEY, Denise (mez)
Honegger: Roi David (Cpte)
Poulenc: Dialogues des Carmélites (Cpte)
Ravel: Enfant et les sortilèges (Cpte)

SCHARRER, Irene (pf)
see CONCERT INDEX under:
(DUTT) **2CDAX2002** The Best of Sir Henry J.Wood
(PEAR) **GEMMCD9978** Irene Scharrer

SCHÄRTEL, Elisabeth (mez)
Wagner: Walküre (Cpte)
see CONCERT INDEX under:
(DG) **429 169-2GR** Wagner—Choruses
(PHIL) **446 057-2PB14** Wagner—The Ring Cycle -
Bayreuth Festival 1967

SCHARY, Elke (mez)
Puccini: Madama Butterfly (Cpte)

SCHASCHING, Rudolf (ten)
J. Strauss II: Zigeunerbaron (Cpte)
Lehár: Lustige Witwe (Cpte)
see CONCERT INDEX under:
(TELD) **2292-46452-2** Beethoven—Complete
Symphonies

SCHATZBERGER, Lesley (basset-hn)
see CONCERT INDEX under:
(AMON) **CD-SAR38** Mendelssohn—Chamber Works

SCHATZBERGER, Lesley (cl/basset-hn)
Stockhausen: Michaels Reise

SCHAUWECKER, Frederic (pf)
(CLAR) **CDGSE78-50-50** Richard Crooks sings
Ballads & Sacred Songs
(RCA) **09026 61879-2** Grieg—Historic Recordings

SCHECH, Marianne (sop)
Mozart: Zauberflöte (Cpte)
R. Strauss: Elektra (Cpte)
Wagner: Fliegende Holländer (Cpte), Tannhäuser
(Cpte)
see CONCERT INDEX under:
(DG) **437 677-2GDO2** Irmgard Seefried - Opera
Recital

SCHECK, Gustav (fl)
see CONCERT INDEX under:
(ACAN) **43 801** Elisabeth Schwarzkopf—Wartime
Recordings

SCHEELE-MÜLLER, Ida von (contr)
see CONCERT INDEX under:
(SUPR) **11 2136-2(3)** Emmy Destinn—Complete
Edition, Discs 5 to 8

SCHEFF, Walter (bar)
Blitzstein: Airborne Symphony, Native Land (exc)

SCHEIBNER, Andreas (bar)
Bach: St. Matthew Passion, BWV244 (Cpte)

SCHEIDEMANTEL, Karl (bar)
see CONCERT INDEX under:
(SIMA) **PSC1810(1)** Grieg—Songs (historical
recordings, pt 1)

SCHEIDER, Wolfgang (bar)
R. Strauss: Rosenkavalier (Cpte)

SCHEIDL, Theodor (bar)
see CONCERT INDEX under:
(PREI) **89201** Helge Roswaenge (1897-1972) - I

SCHEIN, Ann (pf)
Rorem: Night Music
see CONCERT INDEX under:
(SONY) **SK66826** Berg—Lieder

SCHELLENBERG, Arno (bar)
see CONCERT INDEX under:
(SCHW) **314672** Vienna State Opera Live, Vol.17

SCHELLENBERG, Henriette (sop)
see CONCERT INDEX under:
(TELA) **CD80248** Beethoven: Choral Works

SCHELLENBERGER, Dagmar (sop)
Gluck: Orfeo ed Euridice (Cpte)

SCHELLENBERGER, Hansjörg (cor ang)
see CONCERT INDEX under:
(DENO) **CO-76611** Oboe/Cor anglais and Harp
Recital
(DENO) **C37-7034** Mozart Music for oboe and cor
anglais

SCHELLENBERGER, Hansjörg (ob)
Bach: Flute Sonatas, BWV1030-5 (exc)
Beethoven: Piano and Wind Quintet, Op. 16
Marais: Variations on 'Les folies d'Espagne'
Mozart: Piano and Wind Quintet, K452
see CONCERT INDEX under:
(DENO) **CO-2301** Baroque Oboe Concertos
(DENO) **CO-76611** Oboe/Cor anglais and Harp
Recital
(DENO) **C37-7034** Mozart Music for oboe and cor
anglais
(DG) **427 639-2GH** Poulenc: Chamber Works
(DG) **429 750-2GH** Oboe Concertos

SCHELLOW, Erich (narr)
Weill: Dreigroschenoper (Cpte)
see CONCERT INDEX under:
(DG) **419 624-2GH** Beethoven: Vocal, Orchestral &
Wind Music

SCHEMTCHUK, Ludmila (mez)
Prokofiev: Alexander Nevsky

SCHENCK, Andrew (cond)
see Atlantic Sinfonietta

SCHENK, Bernd (hn)
see CONCERT INDEX under:
(DG) **435 860-2GH2** Berlioz—Mélodies

SCHENK, Manfred (bass)
Wagner: Lohengrin (Cpte)
see CONCERT INDEX under:
(COLO) **COL34 9004** Manfred Schenk sings Wagner

SCHENK, Otto (narr)
J. Strauss II: Fledermaus (Cpte)
R. Strauss: Ariadne auf Naxos (Cpte)

SCHENNEBERG, Eliette (mez)
see CONCERT INDEX under:
(EPM) **150 122** Milhaud—Historic Recordings 1928-
1948

SCHEPPAN, Hilde (sop)
Mozart: Zauberflöte (Cpte)
Wagner: Götterdämmerung (Cpte), Meistersinger
(Cpte)

SCHEPS, Ilya (pf)
see CONCERT INDEX under:
(CDM) **LDC288 038/40** Rimsky-Korsakov—Complete
Songs

SCHERBAKOV, Konstantin (pf)
Lyapunov: Studies, Op. 11
see CONCERT INDEX under:
(NAXO) **8 553207** Respighi—Orchestral Works

SCHERCHEN, Herman (cond)
see Czech PO

SCHERGAUT, Susanne (vn)
see CONCERT INDEX under:
(PHIL) **434 918-2PH2** Bach—Concertos

SCHERLER, Barbara (mez)
Berg: Lulu (Cpte)
Schreker: Ferne Klang (Cpte)

SCHERMAN, Thomas (cond)
see Little Orch Soc

SCHERMERHORN, Kenneth (cond)
see Hong Kong PO

SCHEY, Herman (bass)
see CONCERT INDEX under:
(ARCI) **ARC109** Klemperer conducts the
Concertgebouw, Vol.2

SCHEYRER, Gerda (sop)
see CONCERT INDEX under:
(EMI) **CZS7 67123-2** Wagner: Der Ring des
Nibelungen

SCHIAVAZZI, Piero (ten)
(MEMO) **HR4408/9(2)** Singers in Genoa, Vol.1 (disc
2)

SCHICKHAUS, Karl-Heinz (dulcimer/dir)
(TUDO) **Tudor 767** Christmas Music

SCHIDLOF, Peter (va)
Mozart: Concertone, K190, Sinfonia Concertante,
K364
Schubert: Trout Quintet, D667

SCHIEBLER, Beverly (vn)
see CONCERT INDEX under:
(TELA) **CD80059** Popular Orchestral Works

SCHIEFEN, Guido (vc)
see CONCERT INDEX under:

(CAPR) **10 452** Boccherini Edition, Vol.7

SCHIERI, Fritz (cond)
see Munich Chmbr Chor

SCHIFF, András (fp)
Mozart: Piano Quartet, K478, Piano Quartet, K493
see CONCERT INDEX *under:*
(DECC) **440 474-2DH** Mozart—Piano Music for Four Hands
(L'OI) **433 328-2OH** Mozart—Keyboard Works

SCHIFF, András (pf)
Bach: English Suites, BWV806-811, Goldberg Variations, Partitas, BWV825/30, Wohltemperierte Klavier (exc), 2-Part Inventions, BWV772/86, 3-Part Inventions, BWV787/801
Brahms: Piano Quintet
D. Scarlatti: Keyboard Sonatas (exc)
Mendelssohn: Piano Concerto 1, Piano Concerto 2, Songs without Words (exc)
Mozart: Piano and Wind Quintet, K452, Piano Concerto 9, Piano Concerto 12, Piano Concerto 13, Piano Concerto 14, Piano Concerto 15, Piano Concerto 16, Piano Concerto 17, Piano Concerto 18, Piano Concerto 19, Piano Concerto 20, Piano Concerto 21, Piano Concerto 22, Piano Concerto 23, Piano Concerto 24, Piano Concerto 25, Piano Concerto 26, Piano Concerto 27
Schubert: Piano Sonata, D537, Piano Sonata, D568, Piano Sonata, D958, Piano Sonata, D959, Schöne Müllerin (Cpte), Trout Quintet, D667, Winterreise (Cpte)
see CONCERT INDEX *under:*
(DECC) **425 612-2DH** Schubert—Lieder
(DECC) **430 232-2DH** Mozart: Piano Concertos
(DECC) **430 425-2DH** Schubert—Piano Works
(DECC) **430 498-2DWO** The World of Mozart
(DECC) **430 513-2DH** Mozart—Arias
(DECC) **433 042-2DH** Mozart—Piano Works
(DECC) **433 313-2DH2** Bach—Keyboard Works
(DECC) **436 123-2DH** Schumann—Lieder
(DECC) **440 297-2DH** Italian Songs
(DECC) **440 305-2DH** Schubert—Piano Sonatas
(DECC) **440 306-2DH** Schubert—Piano Sonatas
(DECC) **440 307-2DH** Schubert—Piano Sonatas
(DECC) **440 310-2DH** Schubert—Piano Sonatas
(DECC) **440 311-2DH** Schubert—Piano Sonatas, Vol. 7
(DECC) **443 893-2DH** Bartók—Violin Works
(DECC) **443 894-2DH** Bartók—Chamber Works
(DENO) **C37-7092** Andras Schiff plays Bartók
(DENO) **C37-7236** Bach: Keyboard Concertos
(DENO) **C37-7573** Schiff plays Schumann
(HUNG) **HCD11690** Bach—Keyboard Works
(HUNG) **HCD11885** Beethoven—Piano Works
(PHIL) **434 076-2PH** Heinz Holliger and Friends
(TELD) **4509-99051-2** Handel/Brahms/Reger—Piano Works
(TELD) **4509-99176-2** Schumann—Piano Works

SCHIFF, Heinrich (cond)
see COE

SCHIFF, Heinrich (vc)
Beethoven: Piano Trios (exc), Triple Concerto
Brahms: Piano Trio 1
Haydn: Cello Concerto in C, Cello Concerto in D
Schubert: String Quintet
Shostakovich: Cello Concerto 1, Cello Concerto 2
Vieuxtemps: Cello Concerto 1, Cello Concerto 2
see CONCERT INDEX *under:*
(DG) **431 166-2GR** French Works for Cello & Orchestra
(PHIL) **434 914-2PH** Dvořák—Cello works
(WERG) **WER60185-50** Schoenberg: Choral & Orchestral Works

SCHIFF, Zina (vn)
see CONCERT INDEX *under:*
(STRA) **SCD8011** Vaughan Williams: Orchestral Works

SCHIFRIN, Lalo (cond)
see Rochester Pops

SCHIKOVA, Peter (va)
Mozart: Flute Quartets

SCHILL, Olle (cl)
see CONCERT INDEX *under:*
(BIS) **BIS-CD321** Nielsen—Orchestral Works
(BIS) **BIS-CD614/6** Nielsen—Symphonies and Concertos
(BIS) **BIS-CD616** Nielsen—Concertos

SCHILLER, Adelheid (sop/contr)
see CONCERT INDEX *under:*
(EURO) **GD69043** Puccini: Il Trittico

SCHILLER, Allan (pf)
Chopin: Polonaises (exc), Waltzes (exc)

SCHILLER, Christoph (va)
see CONCERT INDEX *under:*
(ACCO) **20062-2** Scelsi—Chamber Works

SCHILLER, Frank (ten)
R. Strauss: Salome (Cpte)

SCHILLING, Thomas (alto)
see CONCERT INDEX *under:*
(TELD) **2292-42609-2** Bach—Cantatas, Volume 30
(TELD) **4509-91761-2** Bach—Cantatas, Vol.7

SCHILP, Marie-Luise (mez)
see CONCERT INDEX *under:*
(PREI) **90078** Hilde Konetzni
(PREI) **90168** Wagner—Die Meistersinger, Act 2, etc

SCHIML, Marga (mez)
Dvořák: Stabat Mater
Gluck: Cinesi (Cpte)
Mozart: Clemenza di Tito (Cpte)
Schumann: Paradies und die Peri (Cpte)
Wagner: Fliegende Holländer (Cpte), Götterdämmerung (Cpte), Parsifal (Cpte), Rheingold (Cpte), Walküre (Cpte)
Weber: Oberon (Cpte)
see CONCERT INDEX *under:*
(DG) **423 127-2GX4** Bruckner: Sacred Works for Chorus
(DG) **447 409-2GOR2** Bruckner—The Masses
(EURO) **GD69043** Puccini: Il Trittico

SCHINDLER, Xenia (hp)
see CONCERT INDEX *under:*
(CLAV) **CD50-9003** Jolivet & Koechlin—Chamber Works

SCHIØTZ, Aksel (ten)
see CONCERT INDEX *under:*
(EMI) **CHS7 69741-2(5)** Record of Singing, Vol.4—Scandinavian School

SCHIPA, Tito (ten)
see CONCERT INDEX *under:*
(CONI) **CDHD201** Galli-Curci in Opera and Song
(EMI) **CDH7 63200-2** Tito Schipa—Recital
(EMI) **CHS7 64864-2(1)** La Scala Edition - Vol.2, 1915-46 (pt 1)
(EMI) **CHS7 64864-2(2)** La Scala Edition - Vol.2, 1915-46 (pt 2)
(MMOI) **CDMOIR411** Sacred Songs and Arias
(MSCM) **MM30231** Don Pasquale & Tito Schipa Recital
(NIMB) **NI7801** Great Singers, Vol.1
(NIMB) **NI7806** Galli-Curci—Opera & Song Recital
(NIMB) **NI7851** Legendary Voices
(NIMB) **NI7852** Galli-Curci, Vol.2
(NIMB) **NI7856** Legendary Tenors
(PEAR) **GEMMCD9322** Tito Schipa sings Opera Arias and Songs
(RCA) **GD87969** Tito Schipa - Opera & Song Recital
(RCA) **09026 61580-2(4)** RCA/Met 100 Singers, 100 Years (pt 4)
(ROMO) **81004-2** Galli-Curci—Acoustic Recordings, Vol.2
(TEST) **SBT1005** Ten Top Tenors

SCHIPPER, Emil (bar)
see CONCERT INDEX *under:*
(EMI) **CMS7 64008-2(2)** Wagner Singing on Record (pt 2)
(PEAR) **GEMMCDS9137** Wagner—Der Ring des Nibelungen
(SCHW) **314512** Vienna State Opera Live, Vol.1
(SCHW) **314532** Vienna State Opera Live, Vol.3
(SCHW) **314592** Vienna State Opera Live, Vol.9
(SCHW) **314622** Vienna State Opera Live, Vol.12
(SCHW) **314632** Vienna State Opera Live, Vol.13
(SCHW) **314642** Vienna State Opera Live, Vol.14
(SCHW) **314662** Vienna State Opera Live, Vol.16
(SCHW) **314672** Vienna State Opera Live, Vol.17

SCHIPPERS, Thomas (cond)
see LSO

SCHIR, Bernhard (spkr)
B. A. Zimmermann: Requiem (Cpte)

SCHIRP, Wilhelm (bass)
see CONCERT INDEX *under:*
(PEAR) **GEMMCD9331** Frida Leider sings Wagner
(PREI) **90168** Wagner—Die Meistersinger, Act 2, etc
(SCHW) **314632** Vienna State Opera Live, Vol.13

SCHIRRER, René (bar)
Berlioz: Damnation de Faust (Cpte), Enfance du Christ (Cpte), Troyens (Cpte)
Chausson: Roi Arthus (Cpte)
Donizetti: Don Pasquale (Cpte)
Gluck: Iphigénie en Aulide (Cpte)
Halévy: Juive (Cpte)
Offenbach: Brigands (Cpte)
Rameau: Anacréon (Cpte), Castor et Pollux (Cpte)

SCHIRRMACHER, Ursula (sop)
see CONCERT INDEX *under:*
Jessel: Schwarzwaldmädel (Cpte)
Künneke: Vetter aus Dingsda (exc)
Offenbach: Vie Parisienne (exc)

SCHLACHTER, Wolfgang (ob)
see CONCERT INDEX *under:*
(SONY) **SK45930** Concertos for Two Flutes

SCHLAPP, Jan (va)
Mozart: Flute Quartets, Piano Quartet, K478, Piano Quartet, K493, Zauberflöte (exc)

SCHLEIERMACHER, Steffen (pf)
Cage: Winter Music
see CONCERT INDEX *under:*
(HATH) **ARTCD6143** Morton Feldman—Works for Piano 2

SCHLEMM, Anny (mez)
Wagner: Fliegende Holländer (Cpte)
Weill: Mahagonny (Cpte)

SCHLESWIG-HOLSTEIN MUSIC FESTIVAL ORCHESTRA
cond C. ESCHENBACH
Beethoven: Piano Concerto 1

SCHLICK, Barbara (sop)
A.J. Romberg: Lied von der Glocke

Bach: Cantata 21, Cantata 42, Cantata 66, Cantata 80, Christmas Oratorio, BWV248 (Cpte), Easter Oratorio, BWV249, Magnificat, BWV243, Mass in B minor, BWV232 (Cpte), St John Passion, BWV245 (Cpte), St Matthew Passion, BWV244 (Cpte)
Biber: Arminio (Cpte)
C. P. E. Bach: Auferstehung und Himmelfahrt Jesu (Cpte)
Handel: Acis und Galatea, K566 (Cpte), Giulio Cesare (Cpte), Messiah (Cpte), Ode for St. Cecilia's Day (Cpte), Resurrezione (Cpte), Rodelinda (Cpte)
Hasse: Piramo e Tisbe (Cpte)
Keiser: Masagniello furioso (Cpte)
Mozart: Mass, K427, Requiem
Telemann: Cantata, TWV1: 771, Donner-Ode, Getreue Music-Meister (Cpte), Schwanengesang, TWV4: 6, St Matthew Passion (1746) (Cpte)
W. F. Bach: Es ist eine Stimme, F89, Lasset uns ablegen, F80
see CONCERT INDEX *under:*
(ASTR) **E8530** Bach—Cantatas
(ASTR) **E8544** Bach—Cantatas
(CAPR) **10 208** C.P.E. Bach: Sacred Choral Works
(CAPR) **10 303** J. C. F. Bach: Secular Cantatas
(CAPR) **10 310/1** J. E. Bach—Passion Oratorio, etc
(CAPR) **10 315** Telemann—Choral Music
(CAPR) **10 426** W. F. Bach—Cantatas, Vol.2
(EMI) **CDC7 54037-2** Mozart—Masses and Church Sonatas
(ERAT) **2292-45822-2** M-A.Charpentier—Motets
(ERAT) **4509-98536-2** Bach—Complete Cantatas, Volume 1
(HARM) **HMC90 1479** Bach—Cantatas
(O111) **OPS30-88** Leo/Pergolesi—Salve Reginas
(VIRG) **VC7 59237-2** Bach—Cantatas

SCHLIEPHAKE, Ingrid (vn)
see CONCERT INDEX *under:*
(SCHW) **311122** Early Twentieth Century Music

SCHLINGENSIEPEN, Marc-Andreas (cond)
see R. Schumann CO

SCHLOSSER, Vera (sop)
Wagner: Walküre (Cpte)
see CONCERT INDEX *under:*
(DECC) **414 100-2DM15** Wagner: Der Ring des Nibelungen

SCHLOTER, Elmar (organ)
see CONCERT INDEX *under:*
(EMI) **CMS7 64778-2** Schubert—Sacred Works, Vol.1

SCHLUSNUS, Heinrich (bar)
see CONCERT INDEX *under:*
(MMOI) **CDMOIR422** Great Voices in Tchaikovsky
(NIMB) **NI7848** Great Singers at the Berlin State Opera
(NIMB) **NI7867** Legendary Baritones
(PREI) **89006** Heinrich Schlusnus (1888-1952) - I
(PREI) **89035** Erna Berger (1900-1990) - I
(PREI) **89110** Heinrich Schlusnus (1888-1952) - II
(PREI) **89205** Heinrich Schlusnus Lieder Album, Vol.1
(PREI) **89229** Helge Roswaenge (1897-1972) - II
(PREI) **89301** The Art of Frida Leider
(PREI) **89302** The Young Lotte Lehmann

SCHLÜSSEL, Sanford (pf)
see CONCERT INDEX *under:*
(BIDD) **LAB066** Enescu—Violinist & Composer
(MSCM) **MM30322** Enescu - Columbia Recordings 1920s-30s

SCHLÜTER, Erna (sop)
R. Strauss: Elektra (Cpte)

SCHMALFUSS, Gernot (ob)
see CONCERT INDEX *under:*
(CLAV) **CD50-9300/4** Hommage à Tibor Varga
(CLAV) **CD50-9311** Hommage à Tibor Varga, Volume 1

SCHMALFUSS, Peter (pf)
see CONCERT INDEX *under:*
(THOR) **CTH2005** Smetana—Piano Works

SCHMALSTICH, Clemens (cond)
see Berlin St Op Orch

SCHMALZ, Flora (mez)
see CONCERT INDEX *under:*
(MYTO) **3MCD93381** Wagner—Die Walküre, etc

SCHMECKENBECHER, Jochen (bar)
Dessau: Hagadah Shel Pessach

SCHMEDES, Dagmar (mez)
Wagner: Walküre (Cpte)
see CONCERT INDEX *under:*
(EMI) **CZS7 67123-2** Wagner: Der Ring des Nibelungen

SCHMEDES, Erik (ten)
see CONCERT INDEX *under:*
(SYMP) **SYMCD1081** The Harold Wayne Collection, Vol.5

SCHMEISSER, Tobias (treb)
Weill: Jasager (Cpte)

SCHMELZER, Peter (cond)
see European Master Orch

SCHMID, Edith (sop)
Mozart: Zauberflöte (Cpte)

SCHMID, Elmar (cl)
Gazzaniga: Don Giovanni (Cpte)

Holliger: Alb-Chehr, Beiseit
Magnard: Piano and Wind Quintet
Mozart: Piano and Wind Quintet, K452
see CONCERT INDEX *under:*
(DECC) **443 893-2DH** Bartók—Violin Works

SCHMID, Georg (va)
R. Strauss: Don Quixote

SCHMID, Kurt (cl)
Holliger: Alb-Chehr

SCHMID, Roman (ob)
Magnard: Piano and Wind Quintet

SCHMID, Ulrich (vc)
Villa-Lobos: Cello Concerto 1, Cello Concerto 2

SCHMIDINGER, Benjamin (treb)
Schubert: Mass, D950 (Cpte)

SCHMIDINGER, Josef (ten)
J.Strauss II: Zigeunerbaron (Cpte)
Lehár: Lustige Witwe (Cpte)

SCHMIDL, Peter (cl)
see CONCERT INDEX *under:*
(DG) **429 221-2GH** Mozart— Symphonies Nos 25 &
29; Clarinet Concerto

SCHMIDT, Andreas (bar)
Bach: St Matthew Passion, BWV244 (Cpte)
Beethoven: Fidelio (Cpte), Missa solemnis
Brahms: Deutsches Requiem, Op.45 (Cpte)
Fauré: Requiem (Cpte)
Gounod: Faust (Cpte)
Haydn: Jahreszeiten (Cpte), Mass 10, Schöpfung
(Cpte)
Henze: Bassariden (Cpte)
Hindemith: Cardillac (Cpte)
Humperdinck: Hänsel und Gretel (Cpte)
Lortzing: Undine (Cpte)
Mahler: Klagende Lied, Knaben Wunderhorn (exc)
Mozart: Don Giovanni (Cpte), Finta semplice (Cpte),
Mass, K317, Nozze di Figaro (Cpte), Zauberflöte
(Cpte)
Offenbach: Contes d'Hoffmann (Cpte)
Prokofiev: Lt. Kijé suite
R.Strauss: Frau ohne Schatten (Cpte)
Schubert: Schöne Müllerin (Cpte), Winterreise
(Cpte)
Various: Requiem of Reconciliation (Cpte)
Verdi: Macbeth (Cpte)
Wagner: Lohengrin (Cpte), Rheingold (Cpte),
Tannhäuser (Cpte)
Weber: Freischütz (Cpte)
Wolf: Italienisches Liederbuch (Cpte)
see CONCERT INDEX *under:*
(DG) **427 348-2GH2** Zemlinsky: Lieder
(DG) **435 486-2GH** Schubert/Schumann—Sacred
Choral Works
(DG) **437 536-2GH** Schubert—Lieder
(DG) **439 943-2GH** Schumann—Lieder
(HANS) **98 856** Bach—Cantatas, Vol.5
(HANS) **98 858** Bach—Cantatas, Vol.7
(HANS) **98 859** Bach—Cantatas, Vol.8
(HANS) **98 979** Mozart—Sacred Choral Works
(NOVA) **150 028-2** Bach—Cantatas
(NOVA) **150 029-2** Bach—Cantatas
(PHIL) **422 522-2PME6** The Complete Mozart Edition
Vol 22
(RCA) **09026 61184-2** Mahler (orch Berio)/R.
Strauss—Lieder
(SONY) **SK52555** New Year's Eve Concert 1992
(SONY) **SK57960** Zemlinsky—Posthumous Songs
(TELA) **CD80269** Mahler—Lieder

SCHMIDT, Carlo (ten)
Verdi: Don Carlo (Cpte)

SCHMIDT, Diane (accordion)
see CONCERT INDEX *under:*
(DELO) **DE3168** Hovhaness—The Rubaiyat

SCHMIDT, Eric (organ)
(BELA) **450 131-2** Fauré—Requiem

SCHMIDT, Felix (vc)
Boccherini: Cello Concerto, G480
see CONCERT INDEX *under:*
(CARL) **PCD930** Elgar/Vaughan Williams—Orchestral
Works

SCHMIDT, Franz Alfred (cond)
see Berlin St Op Orch

SCHMIDT, Georg (va)
see CONCERT INDEX *under:*
(SCHW) **310045** Hindemith: Works for Viola and
Orchestra

SCHMIDT, Helga (contr)
R.Strauss: Arabella (Cpte)

SCHMIDT, Helmut (pf)
see CONCERT INDEX *under:*
(EMI) **CDM7 69501-2** Elisabeth
Schwarzkopf—Romantic Heroines
(SCHW) **314050** Weill—Vocal and Choral Works

SCHMIDT, Jeff von der (hn)
see CONCERT INDEX *under:*
(HARM) **HMU90 7106** Kraft—Orchestral Works

SCHMIDT, Johannes (bass)
Weber: Peter Schmoll (Cpte)

SCHMIDT, Joseph (ten)
see CONCERT INDEX *under:*
(EMI) **CDM7 69478-2** A Portrait of Joseph Schmidt

SCHMIDT, Jytte Gorki (gtr)
see CONCERT INDEX *under:*
(EMI) **CHS7 69741-2(5)** Record of Singing,
Vol.4—Scandinavian School

SCHMIDT, Karl (cond)
see Berlin Staatskapelle

SCHMIDT, Kimberly (pf)
see CONCERT INDEX *under:*
(KOCH) **37240-2** Women at an Exposition - 1893
Chicago World Fair

SCHMIDT, Liselotte (sop)
Lehár: Land des Lächelns (exc)
see CONCERT INDEX *under:*
(EURO) **GD69022** Oscar Straus: Operetta excerpts

SCHMIDT, Manfred (ten)
Busoni: Doktor Faust (Cpte)
Hindemith: Mathis der Maler (Cpte)
Korngold: Violanta (Cpte)
Orff: Kluge (Cpte)
Wagner: Meistersinger (Cpte)

SCHMIDT, Marianna (hp)
see CONCERT INDEX *under:*
(SCHW) **311122** Early Twentieth Century Music

SCHMIDT, Ole (cond)
see Aarhus RAM Orch

SCHMIDT, Paul (bass)
R. Strauss: Friedenstag (Cpte)

SCHMIDT, Piers (cond)
see Mixolydian

SCHMIDT, Trudeliese (mez)
Hindemith: Mathis der Maler (Cpte)
Mahler: Symphony 8
Monteverdi: Combattimento di Tancredi e Clorinda
Mozart: Idomeneo (Cpte), Requiem, Zauberflöte
(Cpte)
Weill: Mahagonny-Gesänge (Cpte)
see CONCERT INDEX *under:*
(ARCH) **439 394-2AX5** Bach—Cantatas, Volume 5
(DG) **435 162-2GX13** Mahler—Complete
Symphonies
(EMI) **CMS7 64476-2** Mahler—Symphonies, Vol.2

SCHMIDT, Wilhelm (pf)
see CONCERT INDEX *under:*
(TEST) **SBT1026** Irmgard Seefried

SCHMIDT, Wolfgang (ten)
Mozart: Zauberflöte (Cpte)
Telemann: St Matthew Passion (1746)
Weill: Silbersee (Cpte)

SCHMIDT JOHANSEN, Mogens (bar)
Nielsen: Maskarade (Cpte)

SCHMIDT-BOELCKE, Werner (cond)
see Berlin SO

SCHMIDT-GADEN, Gerhard (cond)
see Collegium Aureum

SCHMIDT-GERTENBACH, Volker (cond)
see Berlin SO

SCHMIDT-ISSERSTEDT, Hans (cond)
see Berlin Deutsche Op Orch

SCHMID-WYSS, Hanni (pf)
see CONCERT INDEX *under:*
(JECK) **JD646-2** Frank Martin—Chamber Works

SCHMIEDEL, Reinhard (cond)
Krenek: Reisebuch, Op. 62 (Cpte)

SCHMIEDER, Manfred (bass)
(CAPR) **10 180** Gisela May sings Weill

SCHMIEGE, Marilyn (mez)
Hindemith: Mathis der Maler (Cpte)
Mozart: Nozze di Figaro (Cpte)
Rossini: Cenerentola (Cpte)
Schreker: Gezeichneten (Cpte)
Schumann: Paradies und die Peri (Cpte)

SCHMITHÜSEN, Ingrid (sop)
Bach: Cantata 78, Cantata 198
Mozart: Requiem

SCHMITT, Edith (sop)
Rossini: Petite Messe Solennelle

SCHMITT, Florent (cond)
see Walther Straram Orch

SCHMITT, Florent (cond)
see CONCERT INDEX *under:*
(EMI) **CDC7 54840-2** Composers in Person—Roussel
& Schmitt

SCHMITT, Hartmut (cond)
see Lower Rhine Choral Soc

SCHMITT, Helmut (cond)
(DG) **415 655-2GH** Bach: Harpsichord Concertos

SCHMITT, Minika (sop)
Wagner: Parsifal (Cpte)
see CONCERT INDEX *under:*
(EURO) **GD69043** Puccini: Il Trittico

SCHMITT-WALTER, Karl (bar)
Orff: Mond (Cpte)
R. Strauss: Capriccio (Cpte)
see CONCERT INDEX *under:*
(EMI) **CDM7 63657-2** Schwarzkopf sings Opera Arias

(EMI) **CHS7 69741-2(4)** Record of Singing,
Vol.4—German School
(PREI) **90222** Maria Cebotari sings Richard Strauss

SCHMITZ, Jutta Maria (sngr)
S. Wagner: Schwarzschwanenreich (Cpte)

SCHMITZ, Martin (ten)
see CONCERT INDEX *under:*
(CAPR) **10 310/1** J. E. Bach—Passion Oratorio, etc.

SCHMITZ, Peter (ten)
Monteverdi: Vespers

SCHMÖHE, Georg (cond)
see Berlin RSO

SCHNABEL, Artur (pf)
Bach: Toccatas, BWV910-16 (exc), 2-Harpsichord
Concerti (exc)
Beethoven: Piano Concerto 2, Piano Concerto 3,
Piano Concerto 4, Piano Concerto 5
Brahms: Piano Concerto 1, Piano Concerto 2
Schubert: Allegretto, D915, Impromptus (exc)
see CONCERT INDEX *under:*
(EMI) **CHS7 63703-2** Mozart: Piano Concertos, etc
(EMI) **CHS7 63765-2** Beethoven—Complete Piano
Sonatas
(EMI) **CHS7 64259-2** Schnabel plays Schubert
(MUSI) **MACD-674** Piatigorsky—Recordings from the
Pre-war era
(PEAR) **GEMMCDS9123** Beethoven—Piano Sonatas,
Vol.3
(PEAR) **GEMMCD9447** Gregor Piatigorsky plays
Schumann, Beethoven, Weber & Brahms

SCHNABEL, Karl Ulrich (pf)
Bach: 2-Harpsichord Concerti (exc)
see CONCERT INDEX *under:*
(EMI) **CHS7 63703-2** Mozart: Piano Concertos, etc

SCHNAUT, Gabriele (mez)
Beethoven: Fidelio (Cpte)
Hindemith: Cardillac (Cpte), Junge Magd, Mörder,
Hoffnung der Frauen (Cpte), Sancta Susanna (Cpte)
Schreker: Ferne Klang (Cpte), Schatzgräber (Cpte)
Stravinsky: Oedipus Rex (Cpte)
Wagner: Götterdämmerung (Cpte), Lohengrin (Cpte),
Walküre (Cpte)
see CONCERT INDEX *under:*
(CHAN) **CHAN9240** Stravinsky—Choral and
Orchestral Works
(HANS) **98 814** Bach—Cantatas, Vol.52
(HANS) **98 868** Bach—Cantatas, Vol.17
(HANS) **98 877** Bach—Cantatas, Vol.26
(HANS) **98 878** Bach—Cantatas, Vol.27
(HANS) **98 890** Bach—Cantatas, Vol.37

SCHNEE, Normunds (cor ang)
see CONCERT INDEX *under:*
(CONI) **CDCF236** Vasks—Message

SCHNEEBELI, Olivier (cond)
see Brussels Ludi Musici Ens

SCHNEEBERGER, Hansheinz (vn)
Reger: Violin Sonata 6, Violin Sonata 7
Spohr: Violin and Harp Concerto 1
see CONCERT INDEX *under:*
(DECC) **443 893-2DH** Bartók—Violin Works
(DECC) **443 894-2DH** Bartók—Chamber Works
(ECM) **437 440-2** Bach/Veress—Chamber Works
(ECM) **839 617-2** Bach & Carter—Instrumental &
Chamber Works
(LARG) **Largo 5128** Goldschmidt—Retrospectrum

SCHNEIDER, Alexander (cond)
see COE

SCHNEIDER, Alexander (vn)
Beethoven: Piano Trios (exc)
Brahms: String Sextet 1
Mozart: Clarinet Quintet, K581
Schubert: Piano Trio 1, Piano Trio 2, String Quintet
(SONY) **SMK58991** Pablo Casals plays Beethoven at
Prades and Perpignan, 1951 & 1953
(SONY) **SMK58993** Pablo Casals plays Schumann at
Prades, 1952 & 1953

SCHNEIDER, Beat (vc)
Mozart: Sinfonia Concertante, K297b
(NOVA) **150 016-2** Vivaldi—Concertos

SCHNEIDER, Bruno (hn)
Mozart: Horn Quintet, K407
see CONCERT INDEX *under:*
(CLAV) **CD50-9010** R. Strauss—Wind Concertos
(EMI) **CDC7 54239-2** Schubert—Lieder

SCHNEIDER, Edwin (pf)
see CONCERT INDEX *under:*
(BIDD) **LAB068/9** The Kreisler Collection—1921-25
(MMOI) **CDMOIR418** Great Voices of the
Century—John McCormack
(PEAR) **GEMMCDS9075** Hugo Wolf Society, Volume I
(PEAR) **GEMMCD9315** Kreisler/McCormack Duets
(TEST) **SBT1005** Ten Top Tenors

SCHNEIDER, Erich (ten)
see CONCERT INDEX *under:*
(PREI) **90168** Wagner—Die Meistersinger, Act 2, etc

SCHNEIDER, Gottfried (vn)
Godowsky: Impressions

SCHNEIDER, John (gtr)
see CONCERT INDEX *under:*

(ETCE) **KTC1071**   L.Harrison—Music For Guitar And Percussion

SCHNEIDER, Josef (vc)
see CONCERT INDEX *under:*
(SONY) **SK45930**   Concertos for Two Flutes

SCHNEIDER, Michael (cond)
see Cologne Camerata

SCHNEIDER, Michael (rec/fl)
Stradella: San Giovanni Battista (Cpte)
see CONCERT INDEX *under:*
* (ARCH) **419 633-2AH**   Telemann: Wind Concertos
(DHM) **RD77156**   Vivaldi: Concertos
(DHM) **RD77201**   Telemann—Wind Concertos

SCHNEIDER, Peter (cond)
see Bayreuth Fest Orch

SCHNEIDER, Urs (cond)
see Košice St PO

SCHNEIDERHAN, Wolfgang (vn)
Beethoven: Triple Concerto, Violin Concerto
Brahms: Double Concerto
Martin: Violin Concerto
see CONCERT INDEX *under:*
(DG) **413 145-2GW2**   Beethoven—Orchestral Works
(JECK) **JD645-2**   Frank Martin conducts Frank Martin

SCHNEIDERHAN, Wolfgang (vn/dir)
Mozart: Violin Concerto, K219
see CONCERT INDEX *under:*
(DG) **429 159-2GR**   Mozart: Violin Concertos

SCHNEIDERHEINZE, Johanna (contr)
Bach: St. Matthew Passion, BWV244 (Cpte)

SCHNEIDT, Hans Martin (cond)
see Berlin RSO

SCHNEYDER, Peter (bass)
see CONCERT INDEX *under:*
(NOVA) **150 081-2**   Mozart—The Freemason Music

SCHNITTKE, Irina (pf)
see CONCERT INDEX *under:*
(SONY) **SK53271**   Schnittke—Orchestral and Chamber Works

SCHNITZER, Petra Maria (sop)
Mozart: Zauberflöte (Cpte)

SCHNITZLER, Michael (va)
Mozart: String Quintet, K515, String Quintet, K516

SCHNORR, Simon (treb)
Mozart: Zauberflöte (Cpte)

SCHOBER, Maria (sop)
see CONCERT INDEX *under:*
(PREI) **90237**   R Strauss—Daphne
(SCHW) **314602**   Vienna State Opera Live, Vol.10

SCHOCK, Rudolf (ten)
Abraham: Blume von Hawaii (exc), Viktoria und ihr Husar (exc)
Beethoven: Fidelio (Cpte)
Benatzky: Im weissen Rössl (exc)
Fall: Rose von Stambul (exc)
J. Strauss II: Wiener Blut (exc)
Jessel: Schwarzwaldmädel (exc)
Künneke: Vetter aus Dingsda (exc)
Lehár: Friederike (exc), Land des Lächelns (exc), Schön ist die Welt (exc)
Offenbach: Vie Parisienne (exc)
R. Strauss: Ariadne auf Naxos (Cpte)
Raymond: Maske in Blau (exc)
Wagner: Fliegende Holländer (Cpte), Lohengrin (Cpte), Meistersinger (Cpte), Tristan und Isolde (Cpte)
Weber: Freischütz (exc)
Zeller: Vogelhändler (exc)
see CONCERT INDEX *under:*
(EMI) **CDH5 65201-2**   Leonie Rysanek - Operatic Recital
(EMI) **CHS7 69741-2(4)**   Record of Singing, Vol.4—German School
(EMI) **CMS5 65212-2**   Wagner—Les introuvables du Ring
(EURO) **GD69022**   Oscar Straus: Operetta excerpts
(TEST) **SBT1036**   Lisa Della Casa sings Richard Strauss

SCHOEFFLER, Paul (bass-bar)
Beethoven: Fidelio (Cpte), Symphony 9
Mozart: Cosi fan tutte (Cpte), Nozze di Figaro (Cpte)
R. Strauss: Ariadne auf Naxos (Cpte), Daphne (Cpte)
Wagner: Meistersinger (Cpte), Tristan und Isolde (Cpte)
see CONCERT INDEX *under:*
(DECC) **425 959-2DM**   Lisa della Casa sings R. Strauss
(DG) **435 321-2GWP12**   150 Years - Vienna Philharmonic
(EMI) **CHS7 69741-2(4)**   Record of Singing, Vol.4—German School
(PREI) **90083**   Maria Reining
(PREI) **90190**   Paul Schoeffler—Recital
(RCA) **GD60874**   R. Strauss—Scenes from Elektra & Salome
(SCHW) **314502**   Vienna State Opera—Live Recordings (sampler)
(SCHW) **314352**   Vienna State Opera Live, Vol.3
(SCHW) **314562**   Vienna State Opera Live, Vol.6
(SCHW) **314632**   Vienna State Opera Live, Vol.13

(ARNOLD) SCHOENBERG CHOIR
cond C. ABBADO
Mahler: Symphony 2
Schoenberg: Gurrelieder
Schubert: Fierrabras (Cpte)
see CONCERT INDEX *under:*
(DG) **447 023-2GX12**   Mahler—The Symphonies
cond N. HARNONCOURT
Beethoven: Fidelio (Cpte), Missa Solemnis
Handel: Samson (Cpte), Theodora (Cpte)
Haydn: Seven Last Words, HobXX/2, Stabat Mater
J. Strauss II: Zigeunerbaron (Cpte)
Mendelssohn: Erste Walpurgisnacht
Mozart: Litanies, K243, Lucio Silla (Cpte), Mass, K257
Vivaldi: Gloria, RV589
see CONCERT INDEX *under:*
(TELD) **2292-46452-2**   Beethoven—Complete Symphonies
(TELD) **4509-90494-2**   Mozart—Sacred Choral Works
cond E. HOWARTH
Ligeti: Grand Macabre (Cpte)
cond JAMES LEVINE
see CONCERT INDEX *under:*
(DG) **439 887-2GH**   Brahms—Orchestral & Vocal Works
cond L. MAAZEL
see CONCERT INDEX *under:*
(SONY) **SX14K48198**   Mahler—Complete Symphonies, etc
cond C. MACKERRAS
Delius: Village Romeo and Juliet (Cpte)
cond G. PATANÈ
see CONCERT INDEX *under:*
(DECC) **425 430-2DH**   Cecilia Bartoli sings Rossini Arias
cond A. PREVIN
Orff: Carmina burana

SCHOENBERG ENSEMBLE
cond R. DE LEEUW
see CONCERT INDEX *under:*
(SCHW) **312632**   Mahler/Busoni—Vocal/Orchestral Works
cond R. DE LEEUW
Gubaidulina: Jetzt immer Schnee, Perception
L. Andriessen: De Stijl, De Tijd
Messiaen: Canyons aux étoiles
see CONCERT INDEX *under:*
(PHIL) **442 532-2PH**   Ustvolskaya—Compositions, I, II, III
(PHIL) **442 534-2PH**   Janáček—Choral Works
(SCHW) **311009**   Schoenberg: Chamber Orchestral Works
(SCHW) **314005**   Webern—Complete Vocal Chamber Works

SCHOENBERG QUARTET
Berg: Lyric Suite, String Quartet
Schoenberg: String Quartet 1
Zemlinsky: String Quartet 2, String Quartet 3
see CONCERT INDEX *under:*
(OLYM) **OCD457**   Pijper—String Quartets
(OLYM) **OCD459**   Roussel—Chamber Music, Vol. 2
(OLYM) **OCD460**   Roussel—Chamber Music, Vol. 3

SCHOENFIELD, Paul (pf)
see CONCERT INDEX *under:*
(ALBA) **TROY036-2**   S.Paulus—Songs
(NEW) **NW334-2**   American Violin and Piano Works

SCHOLA CANTORUM
cond L. BERNSTEIN
Ravel: Daphnis et Chloé (Cpte)
see CONCERT INDEX *under:*
(SONY) **SMK47603**   Ravel—Orchestral Works

SCHOLA CANTORUM BASILIENSIS
see CONCERT INDEX *under:*
(ARCH) **447 156-2AP**   Purcell—Fantasias and Vocal Works
cond A. WENZINGER
(VANG) **08.5068.71**   William Byrd and his Age

SCHOLA GREGORIANA
cond M. BERRY
Anon: Divine Office: Vespers
see CONCERT INDEX *under:*
(HERA) **HAVPCD148**   13th Century Chants
(HERA) **HAVPCD151**   Anglo-Saxon Christmas
(HERA) **HAVPCD161**   Pentecost at Pontigny
(HERA) **HAVPCD168**   Abelard—12th-Century Chant

SCHOLA HUNGARICA
cond L. DOBSZAY
Anon: Christmas (exc), Saints' Days (exc)

SCHOLARS
see CONCERT INDEX *under:*
(NAXO) **8 550880**   French Chansons

(THE) SCHOLARS BAROQUE ENSEMBLE
Bach: St John Passion, BWV245 (Cpte)
Handel: Messiah (Cpte)
Purcell: Fairy Queen, Z629 (Cpte)

SCHOLES, Kim (vc)
Blackwood: Cello Sonata
Bridge: Cello Sonata

SCHOLL, Andreas (alto)
Handel: Messiah (Cpte)
Monteverdi: Orfeo (Cpte)
see CONCERT INDEX *under:*
(ASTR) **E8530**   Bach—Cantatas

(ASTR) **E8544**   Bach—Cantatas
(HARM) **HMC90 1505**   German Baroque Songs
(HARM) **HMC90 1552**   The Three Countertenors

SCHÖLL, Klaus Rainer (cond)
see Mainz Wind Ens

SCHÖLLHORN, Iris (organ)
see CONCERT INDEX *under:*
(HYPE) **CDA66688**   Festal Sacred Music of Bavaria

SCHOLZ, Dieter (bass)
Krenek: Jonny spielt auf (Cpte)

SCHOLZ, Kristine (pf)
Cage: Winter Music
see CONCERT INDEX *under:*
(HATH) **ARTCD6143**   Morton Feldman—Works for Piano 2

SCHOLZE, Rainer (bass)
K. A. Hartmann: Simplicius Simplicissimus (Cpte)
Massenet: Chérubin (Cpte)
Puccini: Fanciulla del West (exc)
Wagner: Tannhäuser (Cpte)
Zemlinsky: Kleider machen Leute (Cpte)

SCHOMBERG, Martin (ten)
Wagner: Meistersinger (Cpte)

SCHONBACH, Sanford (va)
(RCA) **GD87873**   Beethoven, Brahms & Schubert: Chamber Works
(RCA) **09026 61778-2(42)**   The Heifetz Collection, Vol. 42

SCHÖNBAUMSFELD, Franz (cond)
see Berlin St Op Orch

SCHÖNE, Lotte (sop)
see CONCERT INDEX *under:*
(CLUB) **CL99-020**   Maria Ivogün & Lotte Schöne—Opera Recital
(MMOI) **CDMOIR408**   Great Sopranos
(NIMB) **NI7833**   Schöne & Tauber in Operetta
(NIMB) **NI7848**   Great Singers at the Berlin State Opera
(PEAR) **GEMMCDS9926(1)**   Covent Garden on Record—Vol.4 (pt 1)
(PEAR) **GEMMCD9956**   Joseph Hislop (1884-1977)

SCHÖNE, Wolfgang (bass)
Bach: Cantata 31, Cantata 31, Cantata 63, Cantata 106, Christmas Oratorio, BWV248 (Cpte)
Berg: Lulu (Cpte)
Haydn: Jahreszeiten (Cpte)
J.C. Bach: Amadis de Gaule (Cpte)
Mendelssohn: Elias (Cpte)
Mozart: Zaide (Cpte)
Wagner: Parsifal (Cpte)
see CONCERT INDEX *under:*
(HANS) **98 801**   Bach—Cantatas, Vol.39
(HANS) **98 802**   Bach—Cantatas, Vol.40
(HANS) **98 803**   Bach—Cantatas, Vol.41
(HANS) **98 804**   Bach—Cantatas, Vol.42
(HANS) **98 806**   Bach—Cantatas, Vol.44
(HANS) **98 808**   Bach—Cantatas, Vol.46
(HANS) **98 809**   Bach—Cantatas, Vol.47
(HANS) **98 814**   Bach—Cantatas, Vol.52
(HANS) **98 816**   Bach—Cantatas, Vol.54
(HANS) **98 819**   Bach—Cantatas, Vol.57
(HANS) **98 822**   Bach—Cantatas, Vol.60
(HANS) **98 824**   Bach—Cantatas, Vol.62
(HANS) **98 826**   Bach—Cantatas, Vol.64
(HANS) **98 828**   Bach—Cantatas, Vol.66
(HANS) **98 829**   Bach—Cantatas, Vol.67
(HANS) **98 856**   Bach—Cantatas, Vol.5
(HANS) **98 859**   Bach—Cantatas, Vol.8
(HANS) **98 861**   Bach—Cantatas, Vol.10
(HANS) **98 863**   Bach—Cantatas, Vol.12
(HANS) **98 864**   Bach—Cantatas, Vol.13
(HANS) **98 866**   Bach—Cantatas, Vol.15
(HANS) **98 867**   Bach—Cantatas, Vol.16
(HANS) **98 868**   Bach—Cantatas, Vol.17
(HANS) **98 869**   Bach—Cantatas, Vol.18
(HANS) **98 870**   Bach—Cantatas, Vol.19
(HANS) **98 871**   Bach—Cantatas, Vol.20
(HANS) **98 872**   Bach—Cantatas, Vol.21
(HANS) **98 874**   Bach—Cantatas, Vol.23
(HANS) **98 875**   Bach—Cantatas, Vol.24
(HANS) **98 876**   Bach—Cantatas, Vol.25
(HANS) **98 877**   Bach—Cantatas, Vol.26
(HANS) **98 878**   Bach—Cantatas, Vol.27
(HANS) **98 879**   Bach—Cantatas, Vol.28
(HANS) **98 883**   Bach—Cantatas, Vol.32
(HANS) **98 886**   Bach—Cantatas, Vol.35
(HANS) **98 887**   Bach—Cantatas, Vol.36
(HANS) **98 891**   Bach—Cantatas, Vol.38

SCHÖNEBERG BOYS' CHOIR
cond C. VON DOHNÁNYI
Henze: Jungo Lord (Cpte)
cond E. JOCHUM
Orff: Carmina Burana
cond H. VON KARAJAN
Bizet: Carmen (Cpte)
Puccini: Bohème (Cpte)

SCHÖNEBERGER, Hans (cl)
see CONCERT INDEX *under:*
(ORFE) **C103841A**   Spohr: Lieder

SCHÖNHERR, Max (cond)
see Austrian RSO

SCHÖNING, Klaus (spkr)
see CONCERT INDEX *under:*

(MODE) **Mode 28/9** Cage—Roaratorio. Laughtears etc

SCHØNWANDT, Michael (cond)
see Berlin SO

SCHÖNZELER, Hans-Hubert (cond)
see Bournemouth Sinfonietta

SCHOOTEN, Frank (bass)
Bizet: Carmen (Cpte)

SCHÖPFLIN, Hans-Jürgen (ten)
Weber: Peter Schmoll (Cpte)

SCHOPPER, Michael (bass)
Bach: St Matthew Passion, BWV244 (Cpte)
Keiser: Masagniello furioso (Cpte)
Monteverdi: Incoronazione di Poppea (Cpte), Ritorno d'Ulisse in patria (Cpte)
Purcell: Fairy Queen, Z629
Schubert: Winterreise (Cpte)
Schumann: Paradies und die Peri (Cpte)
Stradella: San Giovanni Battista (Cpte)
Telemann: Don Quichotte (Cpte), Pimpinone (Cpte)
see CONCERT INDEX *under:*
(ARCH) **437 079-2AT** Collectio Argentea 9: De Profundis
(ARCH) **437 090-2AT** Collectio Argentea 20: Bach Family before J.S.
(TELD) **2292-42422-2** Bach—Cantatas, Volume 14
(TELD) **4509-91757-2** Bach—Cantatas, Vol.3

SCHORNSHEIM, Christine (fp)
see CONCERT INDEX *under:*
(CAPR) **10 424** Christine Schornsheim plays Harpsichord works

SCHORNSHEIM, Christine (hpd)
see CONCERT INDEX *under:*
(CAPR) **10 051** Classical Trumpet Concertos
(CAPR) **10 230** Vivaldi: Oboe Concertos
(CAPR) **10 234** Italian Recorder Works
(CAPR) **10 424** Christine Schornsheim plays Harpsichord works

SCHORR, Friedrich (bass-bar)
Beethoven: Fidelio (Cpte)
Wagner: Siegfried (Cpte)
see CONCERT INDEX *under:*
(CLAR) **CDGSE78-50-35/6** Wagner—Historical recordings
(CLAR) **CDGSE78-50-54** Coates conducts Wagner, Weber & Mendelssohn
(DANA) **DACOCD315/6** Lauritz Melchior Anthology - Vol. 3
(EMI) **CMS7 64008-2(1** Wagner Singing on Record (pt 1)
(EMI) **CMS7 64008-2(2)** Wagner Singing on Record (pt 2)
(MMOI) **CDMOIR411** Sacred Songs and Arias
(NIMB) **NI7848** Great Singers at the Berlin State Opera
(PEAR) **GEMMCDS9075** Hugo Wolf Society, Volume I
(PEAR) **GEMMCDS9137** Wagner—Der Ring des Nibelungen
(PEAR) **GEMMCDS9925(2)** Covent Garden on Record—Vol.3 (pt 2)
(PEAR) **GEMMCD9119** Schumann—Legendary Song Cycles
(PEAR) **GEMMCD9398** Friedrich Schorr
(RCA) **09026 61580-2(3)** RCA/Met 100 Singers, 100 Years (pt 3)
(ROMO) **81014-2** Elisabeth Rethberg (1894-1976)
(SCHW) **314622** Vienna State Opera Live, Vol.12
(SCHW) **314642** Vienna State Opera Live, Vol.14

SCHORTEMEIER, Dirk (sngr)
Lully: Bourgeois Gentilhomme

SCHORTEMEIER, Dirk (spkr)
Lortzing: Undine (Cpte)

SCHOSS, Gunther (spkr)
Mendelssohn: Antigone (Cpte), Oedipus (Cpte)

SCHOTENRÖHR, Christian (ten)
Weill: Kuhhandel (exc)

SCHOTT, Elemi (sngr)
Grieg: Peer Gynt (exc)

SCHOTTLER, Giorgio (bass)
Rossini: Barbiere di Siviglia (exc)

SCHOU, Jens (cl)
Holten: Clarinet Concerto

SCHOUTEN, Karl (va)
see CONCERT INDEX *under:*
(PHIL) **422 514-2PME5** The Complete Mozart Edition Vol 14

SCHRAMM, Ernst Gerold (bass)
Beethoven: Mass in C

SCHRAMM, Franz (bass)
see CONCERT INDEX *under:*
(SCHW) **314602** Vienna State Opera Live, Vol.10

SCHRAMM, Margit (sop)
Abraham: Blume von Hawaii (exc), Viktoria und ihr Husar (exc)
J. Strauss II: Wiener Blut (exc)
Jessel: Schwarzwaldmädel (exc)
Lehár: Friederike (exc), Land des Lächelns (exc)
Offenbach: Vie Parisienne (exc)
Raymond: Maske in Blau (exc)
see CONCERT INDEX *under:*
(EURO) **GD69022** Oscar Straus: Operetta excerpts

SCHRECKENBACH, Gabriele (mez)
Bach: Cantata 28, Cantata 36, Cantata 66, Cantata 112, Cantata 198
Busoni: Turandot (Cpte)
Gurlitt: Wozzeck (Cpte)
Hindemith: Mörder, Hoffnung der Frauen (Cpte), Nusch-Nuschi (Cpte), Sancta Susanna (Cpte), Todes Tod
Schumann: Paradies und die Peri (Cpte)
Wolf: Corregidor (Cpte)
Zemlinsky: Kreidekreis (Cpte)
see CONCERT INDEX *under:*
(CAPR) **10 169** Mozart: Choral Works
(CAPR) **10 244** Schubert: Choral Music
(CAPR) **10 332** Mahler—Lieder
(HANS) **98 802** Bach—Cantatas, Vol.40
(HANS) **98 806** Bach—Cantatas, Vol.44
(HANS) **98 810** Bach—Cantatas, Vol.48
(HANS) **98 813** Bach—Cantatas, Vol.51
(HANS) **98 818** Bach—Cantatas, Vol.56
(HANS) **98 819** Bach—Cantatas, Vol.57
(HANS) **98 859** Bach—Cantatas, Vol.8
(HANS) **98 861** Bach—Cantatas, Vol.10
(HANS) **98 863** Bach—Cantatas, Vol.12
(HANS) **98 864** Bach—Cantatas, Vol.13
(HANS) **98 868** Bach—Cantatas, Vol.17
(HANS) **98 871** Bach—Cantatas, Vol.20
(HANS) **98 873** Bach—Cantatas, Vol.22
(HANS) **98 878** Bach—Cantatas, Vol.27
(HANS) **98 886** Bach—Cantatas, Vol.35

SCHRECKENBERGER, Stephan (bass)
Mozart: Requiem
Telemann: Donner-Ode, Herr ist König, Tag des Gerichts (Cpte)
W. F. Bach: Es ist eine Stimme, F89, Lasset uns ablegen, F80
see CONCERT INDEX *under:*
(CAPR) **10 426** W. F. Bach—Cantatas, Vol.2

SCHRECKER, Bruno (vc)
see CONCERT INDEX *under:*
(CALA) **CACD1018** French Chamber Music for Woodwinds, Volume 2

SCHREIBER, Magdalene (sop)
see CONCERT INDEX *under:*
(HANS) **98 835** Bach—Cantatas, Vol.69
(HANS) **98 884** Bach—Cantatas, Vol.23

SCHREIBMAYER, Kurt (ten)
Wagner: Parsifal (Cpte), Rheingold (Cpte)

SCHREIER, Peter (cond)
see CPE Bach CO

SCHREIER, Peter (ten)
Bach: Cantata 36, Cantata 108, Christmas Oratorio, BWV248 (Cpte), Mass in B minor, BWV232 (Cpte), St Matthew Passion, BWV244 (Cpte)
Beethoven: Missa Solemnis, Symphony 9
Handel: Messias, K572 (Cpte)
Haydn: Jahreszeiten (Cpte)
Lortzing: Wildschütz (Cpte)
Mahler: Lied von der Erde
Mendelssohn: Elias (Cpte)
Mozart: Ascanio in Alba (Cpte), Clemenza di Tito (Cpte), Così fan tutte (Cpte), Don Giovanni (Cpte), Entführung (Cpte), Idomeneo (Cpte), Lucio Silla (Cpte), Oca del Cairo (Cpte), Requiem, Schauspieldirector (Cpte), Sogno di Scipione (Cpte), Zaïde (Cpte), Zauberflöte (Cpte)
R. Strauss: Ariadne auf Naxos (Cpte), Capriccio (Cpte), Daphne (Cpte)
Schmidt: Buch mit Sieben Siegeln
Schubert: Schöne Müllerin (Cpte), Winterreise (Cpte)
Stravinsky: Oedipus Rex (Cpte)
Wagner: Meistersinger (Cpte), Rheingold (Cpte), Rienzi (Cpte), Siegfried (Cpte), Tristan und Isolde (Cpte)
Weber: Freischütz (Cpte)
Wolf: Italienisches Liederbuch (Cpte)
see CONCERT INDEX *under:*
(ARCH) **439 369-2AX4** Bach—Cantatas, Vol.1
(ARCH) **439 374-2AX5** Bach—Cantatas, Volume 2 - Easter
(ARCH) **439 380-2AX6** Bach—Cantatas, Volume 3 - Ascension Day; Whitsun; Trinity
(ARCH) **439 387-2AX6** Bach Cantatas, Volume 4
(ARCH) **439 394-2AX5** Bach—Cantatas, Volume 5
(CAMP) **RRCD1313** Britten—Vocal and Orchestral Works
(CAPR) **10 151** Bach: Cantatas
(DECC) **425 612-2DH** Schubert—Lieder
(DG) **423 133-2GH** Brahms: Vocal Works
(DG) **435 596-2GGA2** Schubert—Duets, Trios & Quartets
(EMI) **CDM7 69223-2** Schubert—Choral Works
(EMI) **CMS7 64778-2** Schubert—Sacred Works, Vol.1
(HANS) **98 803** Bach—Cantatas, Vol.41
(HANS) **98 864** Bach—Cantatas, Vol.13
(HANS) **98 871** Bach—Cantatas, Vol.20
(HANS) **98 882** Bach—Cantatas, Vol.31
(HANS) **98 883** Bach—Cantatas, Vol.32
(HANS) **98 887** Bach—Cantatas, Vol.36
(HANS) **98 891** Bach—Cantatas, Vol.38
(HYPE) **CDJ33018** Schubert—Complete Lieder, Vol.18
(NOVA) **150 039-2** Lieder with Guitar Accompaniment
(PHIL) **422 522-2PME6** The Complete Mozart Edition Vol 22

(PHIL) **422 545-2PME3** The Complete Mozart Edition Vol.45
(PHIL) **442 073-2PB5** Beethoven—Complete Symphonies, etc
(RCA) **74321 20286-2** Mendelssohn—Symphonies 1-5
(TELD) **2292-46154-2** Schumann—Lieder

SCHREIER, Peter (ten/dir)
Bach: Christmas Oratorio, BWV248 (Cpte), St. Matthew Passion, BWV244 (Cpte)
see CONCERT INDEX *under:*
(PHIL) **422 522-2PME6** The Complete Mozart Edition· Vol 22

SCHREKER, Bruno (vc)
Schubert: String Quintet

SCHRENKEL, Vojtech (ten)
Bellini: Sonnambula (Cpte)
Puccini: Bohème (Cpte)

SCHREYER, Gerda (sop)
R. Strauss: Elektra (Cpte)
Wagner: Walküre (Cpte)

SCHRÖDER, Jaap (cond)
see Concerto Amsterdam

SCHRÖDER, Jaap (vn)
Handel: German Airs
see CONCERT INDEX *under:*
(DHM) **RD77188** C.P.E. Bach—Vocal & Chamber Works
(L'OI) **400 080-2OH** Bach—Violin Concertos
(L'OI) **421 500-2OH** Bach: Double Concertos
(L'OI) **443 196-2OM** Schubert/Mendelssohn—Violin Sonatas
(L'OI) **443 326-2OH** Bach—Harpsichord Concertos
(MSVE) **MSCD415** Kraus—Chamber Music
(TELD) **4509-92177-2** Telemann—Paris Quartets; Suites

SCHRÖDER, Jaap (vn/dir)
see CONCERT INDEX *under:*
(TELD) **4509-92180-2** Leclair/Naudot—Concertos

SCHRÖDER, Karl Ernst (lte)
see CONCERT INDEX *under:*
(HARM) **HMC90 1505** German Baroque Songs
(HARM) **HMC90 1552** The Three Countertenors

SCHRÖDER, Karl-Ernst (lte)
see CONCERT INDEX *under:*
(ARCA) **A21** Ars Subtilis Ytalica

SCHRÖDER, Olaf (spkr)
Honegger: Jeanne d'Arc (Cpte)

SCHROETER, Joachim (bass)
R. Strauss: Rosenkavalier (Cpte)

SCHRÖTER, Gisela (mez)
Mendelssohn: Elias (Cpte)
Wagner: Parsifal (Cpte)

SCHUB, André-Michel (pf)
Rorem: Bright Music

SCHUBACK, Thomas (cond)
see Drottningholm Baroque Ens

SCHUBACK, Thomas (pf)
see CONCERT INDEX *under:*
(BIS) **BIS-CD054** Lieder Recital
(MSVE) **MSCD623** Stenhammar: Songs

SCHUBERT, Claudia (contr)
Handel: Rodelinda (Cpte)
Mozart: Requiem
Telemann: St Matthew Passion (1746) (Cpte)
W. F. Bach: Es ist eine Stimme, F89, Lasset uns ablegen, F80
see CONCERT INDEX *under:*
(CAPR) **10 426** W. F. Bach—Cantatas, Vol.2

SCHUBERT, Erika (mez)
Wagner: Walküre (Cpte)
see CONCERT INDEX *under:*
(FOYE) **15-CF2011** Wagner—Der Ring de Nibelungen

SCHUBERT, Hedwig (sop)
J. Strauss II: Fledermaus (Cpte)

SCHUBERT, Richard (ten)
see CONCERT INDEX *under:*
(SCHW) **314592** Vienna State Opera Live, Vol.9

SCHUBERT ENSEMBLE OF LONDON
Hummel: Piano Quintet, op. 87
Schubert: Trout Quintet, D667
Schumann: Piano Quartet, Op. 47, Piano Quintet, Op. 44
see CONCERT INDEX *under:*
(COLL) **Coll1453-2** Distance &
Enchantment—Chamber Works by Judith Weir

(FRANZ) SCHUBERT QUARTET
Dittersdorf: String Quartets (exc), String Quintets (1789) (exc)
Haydn: String Quartet, Op.103, String Quartets, Op.77
Mozart: String Quartet, K465, String Quartet, K590
Tchaikovsky: String Quartet 1, String Quartet 3

SCHUCH, Clementine von (sop)
Offenbach: Vie Parisienne (exc)

SCHÜCHTER, Wilhelm (cond)
see Berlin Deutsche Op Orch

SCHUDEL, Regina (sop)
Gurlitt: Wozzeck (Cpte)
Mendelssohn: Hochzeit des Camacho (Cpte)

Schreker: Gezeichneten (Cpte)

SCHÜLER, Johannes (cond)
see Berlin St Op Orch

SCHULHOF, Otto (pf)
see CONCERT INDEX under:
(EMI) **CHS5 65185-2** Beethoven/Brahms—Cello
Sonatas

SCHULHOFF, Erwin (pf)
see CONCERT INDEX under:
(DECC) **444 819-2DH** Schulhoff—Concertos and
Piano Music

SCHULKOWSKY, Robyn (perc)
see CONCERT INDEX under:
(LAND) **CTLCD111** Cover him with grass

SCHULLER, Gunther (cond)
see Houston Grand Op Orch

SCHULMAN, Louise (va)
see CONCERT INDEX under:
(KOCH) **37110-2** Wuorinen—Orchestral & Chamber
Works

SCHULTE, Eike Wilm (bar)
Wagner: Lohengrin (Cpte), Rheingold (Cpte)

SCHULTE, Rolf (vn)
see CONCERT INDEX under:
(MUSM) **67152-2** Stravinsky—The Composer,
Volume VII

SCHULTZ, Carl (bar)
R. Strauss: Salome (Cpte)
Schreker: Schatzgräber (Cpte)
Schumann: Genoveva (Cpte)

SCHULTZ, Kirsten (sop)
see CONCERT INDEX under:
(EMI) **CDM5 65415-2** Nielsen—Symphonies, etc

SCHULTZ, Stephen (cond)
see American Baroque

SCHULTZ, Stephen (fl)
see CONCERT INDEX under:
(HARM) **HMC90 5193** Vivaldi: Flute Concertos
(KOCH) **37096-2** 18th Century French Cantatas

SCHULTZ, Tom (pf)
see CONCERT INDEX under:
(MUSM) **67110-2** Stravinsky—The Composer,
Volume V

SCHULTZE, Siegfried (pf)
see CONCERT INDEX under:
(BIDD) **LAB077/8** Huberman—Complete Brunwick
Recordings
(BIDD) **LAB081/2** Huberman—Columbia recordings
with piano
(EPM) **150 032** The Romantic Violin

SCHULZ, Christian (treb)
Mozart: Zauberflöte (Cpte)

SCHULZ, Else (sop)
see CONCERT INDEX under:
(SCHW) **314532** Vienna State Opera Live, Vol.3
(SCHW) **314552** Vienna State Opera Live, Vol.5
(SCHW) **314572** Vienna State Opera Live, Vol.7
(SCHW) **314652** Vienna State Opera Live, Vol.15

SCHULZ, Wolfgang (fl)
Mozart: Flute and Harp Concerto, K299
Schubert: Guitar Quartet, D96
see CONCERT INDEX under:
(DG) **427 639-2GH** Poulenc: Chamber Works
(DG) **429 738-2GH** Debussy & Ravel: Chamber
Works
(EMI) **CDC7 54881-2** Viennese Dance Music

SCHULZE, Siegfried (bass)
Bach: St Matthew Passion, BWV244 (exc)

SCHUMACHER, Marten (spkr)
Hindemith: Nusch-Nuschi (Cpte)

SCHUMAN, Patricia (sop)
Handel: Messiah (Cpte)
Rossini: Tancredi (Cpte)

SCHUMANN, Elisabeth (sop)
see CONCERT INDEX under:
(CLAR) **CDGSE78-50-46** Walter Widdop (1892-1949)
(DANA) **DACOCD315/6** Lauritz Melchior Anthology -
Vol. 3
(EMI) **CHS7 64487-2** R. Strauss—Der Rosenkavalier
& Lieder
(EMI) **CHS7 69741-2(4)** Record of Singing,
Vol.4—German School
(EMI) **CMS7 64008-2(1)** Wagner Singing on Record
(pt 1)
(MMOI) **CDMOIR408** Great Sopranos
(MMOI) **CDMOIR411** Sacred Songs and Arias
(PEAR) **GEMMCDS9365** R. Strauss: Der
Rosenkavalier (abridged), etc
(PEAR) **GEMMCDS9925(2)** Covent Garden on
Record—Vol.3 (pt 2)
(PEAR) **GEMMCDS9926(2)** Covent Garden on
Record—Vol.4 (pt 2)
(PREI) **89031** Elisabeth Schumann (1885-1952)
(SCHW) **314622** Vienna State Opera Live, Vol.12
(SCHW) **314632** Vienna State Opera Live, Vol.13
(SCHW) **314672** Vienna State Opera Live, Vol.17

(ROBERT) SCHUMANN CHAMBER ORCHESTRA
see CONCERT INDEX under:
(SCHW) **314050** Weill—Vocal and Choral Works

cond M-A. **SCHLINGENSIEPEN**
see CONCERT INDEX under:
(SCHW) **314050** Weill—Vocal and Choral Works

SCHUMANN-HEINK, Ernestine (contr)
see CONCERT INDEX under:
(NIMB) **NI7801** Great Singers, Vol.1
(NIMB) **NI7811** Ernestine Schumann-Heink—Opera &
Song Recital
(PEAR) **EVC3(1)** The Caruso Edition, Vol.3 (pt 1)
(PEAR) **GEMMCDS9923(1)** Covent Garden on
Record, Vol.1 (pt 1)
(PEAR) **GEMMCD9309** Enrico Caruso - Opera and
Song Recital
(RCA) **GD60495(4)** The Complete Caruso Collection
(pt 4)
(RCA) **09026 61580-2(1)** RCA/Met 110 Singers, 100
Years (pt 1)
(RCA) **09026 61879-2** Grieg—Historic Recordings
(SIMA) **PSC1810(2)** Grieg—Songs (historical
recordings, pt 2)

SCHUMANN-HEINK, Ernestine (sngr)
see CONCERT INDEX under:
(PEAR) **GEMMCDS9050/2(2)** Music from the New
York Stage, Vol. 1 (part 2)

SCHÜNEMANN, Hildegard (sop)
Wagner: Parsifal (Cpte)

SCHUNK, Robert (ten)
Beethoven: Symphony 9
Hindemith: Cardillac (Cpte)
Wagner: Fliegende Holländer (Cpte)

SCHÜRHOFF, Else (mez)
Humperdinck: Hänsel und Gretel (Cpte)
Mozart: Zauberflöte (Cpte)
Wagner: Meistersinger (Cpte)
see CONCERT INDEX under:
(SCHW) **314532** Vienna State Opera Live, Vol.3
(SCHW) **314672** Vienna State Opera Live, Vol.17

SCHURICHT, Carl (cond)
see FNO

SCHURMANN, Gerrard (cond)
see BBC SO

SCHUSTER, Walther R (organ)
see CONCERT INDEX under:
(MOTE) **CD10601** Organ recital

SCHÜTTE, Ulrich (bar)
Weill: Jasager (Cpte)

SCHÜTZ ACADEMY
cond H. ARMAN
see CONCERT INDEX under:
(CAPR) **10 409** Schütz and Venice

(HEINRICH) SCHÜTZ CHOIR
cond R. NORRINGTON
see CONCERT INDEX under:
(DECC) **433 174-2DM** Monteverdi—Choral Works

SCHÜTZ CONSORT
cond R. NORRINGTON
see CONCERT INDEX under:
(DECC) **433 174-2DM** Monteverdi—Choral Works
(EMI) **CDC7 54525-2** Mozart—Sacred Works

SCHÜTZE, Walter (cond)
see Berlin St Op Orch

SCHWAB, Ludwig (pf)
see CONCERT INDEX under:
(PEAR) **GEMMCD9315** Kreisler/McCormack Duets

SCHWAIGER, Rosi (sop)
Mozart: Nozze di Figaro (Cpte), Zauberflöte (Cpte)
R. Strauss: Rosenkavalier (Cpte)
see CONCERT INDEX under:
(CAMB) **CD-1032** From the Operas of Erich Wolfgang
Korngold

SCHWALB, Miklos (pf)
see CONCERT INDEX under:
(CLAV) **CD50-9300/4** Hommage à Tibor Varga
(CLAV) **CD50-9314** Hommage à Tibor Varga, Volume
4

SCHWALBÉ, Michel (vn)
see CONCERT INDEX under:
(DG) **415 301-2GH** Italian Baroque Concertos
(DG) **415 853-2GGA** R. Strauss: Orchestral Works
(DG) **439 422-2GCL** Vivaldi—Concertos

SCHWANBECK, Bodo (bass)
Berg: Lulu (Cpte)
R. Strauss: Rosenkavalier (Cpte)

SCHWARTS, Robert (ten)
Corghi: Divara (Cpte)

SCHWARTZ, Stephen (cond)
see London Cast

SCHWARZ, Bernhard (vc)
see CONCERT INDEX under:
(MARC) **8 223383** Alkan—Chamber Works

SCHWARZ, Gerard (cond)
see ECO

SCHWARZ, Gerard (tpt/dir)
Haydn: Trumpet Concerto
Hummel: Trumpet Concerto
(DELO) **DE3002** The Sound of Trumpets

SCHWARZ, Gotthold (bass)
Biber: Arminio (Cpte)
Busoni: Turandot (Cpte)

Fux: Death of John the Baptist (Cpte)
Handel: Rodelinda (Cpte)
Hasse: Conversione di Sant' Agostino (Cpte)
Schreker: Gezeichneten (Cpte)
Telemann: Cantata, TWV1: 771, Schwanengesang,
TWV4: 6
see CONCERT INDEX under:
(ASTR) **E8530** Bach—Cantatas
(ASTR) **E8544** Bach—Cantatas
(CAPR) **10 208** C.P.E. Bach: Sacred Choral Works
(CAPR) **10 367** Mendelssohn—Motets

SCHWARZ, Hanna (mez)
Bach: Cantata 106
Berg: Lulu (Cpte)
Humperdinck: Hänsel und Gretel (Cpte), Königskinder
(Cpte)
Mahler: Rückert Lieder
Mozart: Apollo et Hyacinthus (Cpte), Zauberflöte
(Cpte)
R.Strauss: Frau ohne Schatten (Cpte), Salome
(Cpte)
Schubert: Lazarus, D689
Schumann: Szenen aus Goethes Faust (Cpte)
Verdi: Rigoletto (Cpte)
Wagner: Götterdämmerung (Cpte), Parsifal (Cpte),
Rheingold (Cpte), Walküre (Cpte)
see CONCERT INDEX under:
(DG) **423 481-2GX6** Beethoven: Complete
Symphonies
(DG) **445 354-2GX14** Wagner—Der Ring des
Nibelungen
(HANS) **98 863** Bach—Cantatas, Vol.12
(PHIL) **422 522-2PME6** The Complete Mozart Edition
Vol 22

SCHWARZ, Irmgard (mez)
Delius: Village Romeo and Juliet (Cpte)

SCHWARZ, Joseph (bar)
see CONCERT INDEX under:
(NIMB) **NI7867** Legendary Baritones
(SIMA) **PSC1810(2)** Grieg—Songs (historical
recordings, pt 2)

SCHWARZ, Peter (cond)
see Berlin Ars-Nova Ens

SCHWARZ, Vera (sop)
see CONCERT INDEX under:
(EMI) **CDC7 54838-2** Franz Lehár
(EMI) **CDH7 69787-2** Richard Tauber sings Operetta
Arias
(EMI) **CDM7 69476-2** Richard Tauber - A Portrait
(PEAR) **GEMMCD9310** Franz Lehár conducts Richard
Tauber
(PEAR) **GEMMCD9327** The Vocal Prime of Richard
Tauber

SCHWARZ, Volker (spkr)
Eisler: Deutsche Sinfonie

SCHWARZENBERG, Elisabeth (sop)
Wagner: Parsifal (Cpte)

SCHWARZER, Regina (mez)
Biber: Arminio (Cpte)

SCHWARZKOPF, Dame Elisabeth (sop)
Bach: St Matthew Passion, BWV244 (exc)
Beethoven: Fidelio (Cpte), Symphony 9
Brahms: Deutsche Volkslieder (exc), Deutsches
Requiem, Op. 45 (Cpte)
Handel: Messiah (Cpte)
Humperdinck: Hänsel und Gretel (Cpte)
J.Strauss II: Fledermaus (Cpte), Nacht in Venedig
(Cpte), Zigeunerbaron (Cpte)
Lehár: Land des Lächelns (Cpte), Lustige Witwe
(Cpte)
Mahler: Knaben Wunderhorn (exc), Symphony 2,
Symphony 4
Mozart: Cosi fan tutte (Cpte), Don Giovanni (Cpte),
Nozze di Figaro (Cpte)
Offenbach: Contes d'Hoffmann (Cpte)
Orff: Kluge (Cpte)
Puccini: Turandot (Cpte)
R. Strauss: Capriccio (Cpte), Rosenkavalier (Cpte)
Verdi: Falstaff (Cpte), Requiem (Cpte)
Wagner: Meistersinger (Cpte)
Walton: Troilus and Cressida (exc)
Weber: Abu Hassan (Cpte)
Wolf: Italienisches Liederbuch (Cpte), Spanisches
Liederbuch (Cpte)
see CONCERT INDEX under:
(ACAN) **43 128** Elisabeth Schwarzkopf—Vol. 2
(ACAN) **43 801** Elisabeth Schwarzkopf—Wartime
Recordings
(EMI) **CDC7 47276-2** R. Strauss: Lieder with
Orchestra
(EMI) **CDC7 47284-2** Elisabeth Schwarzkopf sings
Operetta
(EMI) **CDC7 54839-2** Medtner plays Medtner
(EMI) **CDH7 61001-2** R. Strauss—Lieder & Arias
(EMI) **CDH7 63201-2** Elisabeth Schwarzkopf—Early
Recordings
(EMI) **CDH7 63702-2** Mozart: Lieder & Concert Arias
(EMI) **CDH7 64026-2** Schubert—Lieder
(EMI) **CDH7 64905-2** Wolf—Lieder Recital
(EMI) **CDH7 69793-2** Elisabeth Schwarzkopf &
Irmgard Seefried sing Duets
(EMI) **CDM7 63574-2** Elisabeth Schwarzkopf
Christmas Album
(EMI) **CDM7 63653-2** Wolf: Lieder
(EMI) **CDM7 63655-2** Schwarzkopf Encores
(EMI) **CDM7 63655-2** Schwarzkopf—The previously
unpublished recordings

(EMI) **CDM7 63656-2**
Schubert/Schumann/Strauss—Lieder
(EMI) **CDM7 63657-2** Schwarzkopf sings Opera Arias
(EMI) **CDM7 69501-2** Elisabeth
Schwarzkopf—Romantic Heroines
(EMI) **CHS5 65506-2** Victor de Sabata conducts
(EMI) **CHS7 69741-2(4)** Record of Singing,
Vol.4—German School
(EMI) **CMS5 65061-2(2)** The Fabulous Victoria de los
Angeles (pt 2)
(EMI) **CMS7 63310-2** Beethoven: Complete
Symphonies
(SONY) **S2K52657** Strauss—Lieder and Piano
Works

SCHWEIGER, Hans (bar)
Beethoven: Fidelio (Cpte)
R. Strauss: Ariadne auf Naxos (Cpte)
see CONCERT INDEX under:
(PREI) **90237** R Strauss—Daphne
(SCHW) **314532** Vienna State Opera Live, Vol.3

SCHWEIGER, Peter (spkr)
Schumann: Manfred (Cpte)

SCHWEIKERT, Sally (sop)
Schoenberg: Moses und Aron (Cpte)

SCHWEITZER, Albert (organ)
see CONCERT INDEX under:
(BEUL) **1PD5** Historic Organs, Volume 1

(ALBERT) SCHWEITZER WIND QUINTET
Reicha: Wind Quintets, Op.88 (exc), Wind Quintets,
Op.91 (exc), Wind Quintets, Op.99 (exc)
see CONCERT INDEX under:
(CPO) **CPO999 024-2** Reicha—Complete Wind
Quintets, Vol.3
(CPO) **CPO999 026-2** Reicha—Complete Wind
Quintets, Vol.5
(CPO) **CPO999 027-2** Reicha—Complete Wind
Quintets, Vol.6
(CPO) **CPO999 029-2** Reicha—Complete Wind
Quintets, Vol.8

SCHWEIZER, Verena (sop)
Hindemith: Cardillac (Cpte), Nusch-Nuschi (Cpte)
Saint-Saëns: Oratorio de Noël, Op. 12

SCHWERING, Elizabeth (sop)
R. Ward: Crucible (Cpte)

SCHWERTSIK, Christa (sngr)
see CONCERT INDEX under:
(LARG) **Largo 5125** Kurt Schwertsik—Für Christa

SCHWERTSIK, Kurt (pf)
see CONCERT INDEX under:
(LARG) **Largo 5125** Kurt Schwertsik—Für Christa

SCHWIER, Elisabeth (sop)
R. Strauss: Elektra (Cpte)

SCHYMBERG, Hjördis (sop)
Beethoven: Symphony 9
Gounod: Roméo et Juliette (exc)
Puccini: Bohème (exc)
see CONCERT INDEX under:
(BLUE) **ABCD016** Jussi Björling—Rare Records &
Alternative Takes
(BLUE) **ABCD028** Jussi Björling live at the Stockholm
Opera
(CARL) **GLRS103** The Magnificent Björling
(CONI) **CDHD214** Jussi Björling - Arias, Lieder and
Songs
(EMI) **CDH7 64707-2** Jussi Björling, Vol.2
(NIMB) **NI7842** Jussi Björling, Vol.2

SCIFFER, Jan (vc)
see CONCERT INDEX under:
(HYPE) **CDA66391** Mozart: Sonatas for Keyboard and
Flute

SCIMONE, Carolyn (sngr)
Schuman: Question of Taste (Cpte)

SCIMONE, Carolyn (sop)
see CONCERT INDEX under:
(ETCE) **KTC1139** Villa-Lobos—Songs, Vol.1

SCIMONE, Claudio (cond)
see Monte Carlo Op Orch

SCIUTTI, Graziella (sop)
Donizetti: Don Pasquale (Cpte)
Gluck: Orfeo ed Euridice (Cpte)
Mozart: Don Giovanni (Cpte), Nozze di Figaro
(Cpte)
Puccini: Rondine (Cpte)
Rossini: Italiana in Algeri (Cpte)
see CONCERT INDEX under:
(EMI) **CDH5 65072-2** Glyndebourne Recorded - 1934-
1994

SCOFIELD, Paul (spkr)
Purcell: Don Quixote: The Musical (Cpte)

SCOGNAMIGLIO, Gaetano (cond)
see orch

SCOGNAMIGLIO, Gaetano (pf)
see CONCERT INDEX under:
(BIDD) **LAB039** Elman—Victor Records with Caruso,
Alda & Str Quartet
(CLUB) **CL99-060** Enrico Caruso—Opera & Song
Recital
(MMOI) **CDMOIR422** Great Voices in Tchaikovsky
(PEAR) **EVC3(1)** The Caruso Edition, Vol.3 (pt 1)
(PEAR) **EVC3(2)** The Caruso Edition, Vol.3 (pt 2)
(RCA) **GD60495(4)** The Complete Caruso Collection
(pt 4)

(RCA) **GD60495(5)** The Complete Caruso Collection
(pt 5)

SCOTT, Christopher (pf)
see CONCERT INDEX under:
(HYPE) **CDA66244** Debussy: Works for Two Pianos

SCOTT, Cyril (pf)
see CONCERT INDEX under:
(GAMU) **GAMCD517** Ravel: Music for Two Pianos

SCOTT, Graham (pf)
see CONCERT INDEX under:
(GAMU) **GAMCD520** Scriabin—Piano Music

SCOTT, Henri (sngr)
see CONCERT INDEX under:
(PEAR) **GEMMCDS9059/61** Music from the New York
Stage, Vol. 4: 1917-20

SCOTT, James (cond)
see Yorkshire Imperial Band

SCOTT, John (cond)
see Berlin RSO

SCOTT, John (organ)
Britten: St Nicolas
see CONCERT INDEX under:
(CIRR) **CICD1007** Favourite Organ Works.
(CLLE) **COLCD109** Fauré: Sacred Choral Works
(CLLE) **COLCD114** Rutter—Sacred Choral Works
(DECC) **430 263-2DM** Purcell—Sacred choral works
(DECC) **436 403-2DWO** The World of Royal Music
(GUIL) **GRCD7022** John Scott—Organ Recital
(HYPE) **CDA66292** Fauré: Sacred Choral Works
(HYPE) **CDA66359** Mendelssohn—Choral Works
(HYPE) **CDA66368** Duruflé—Organ Works
(HYPE) **CDA66491/2** Mendelssohn—Organ Works
(HYPE) **CDA66569** Vaughan Williams—Choral Works
(HYPE) **CDH88036** Praise to the Lord
(NIMB) **NI5367** Mathias—Organ Works
(PRIO) **PRCD401** Great European Organs, Vol.34
(REGE) **REGCD103** Kodály: Choral Music
(REGE) **REGCD105** From Chamber to Chantry

SCOTT, Norman (bass)
Beethoven: Fidelio (exc), Symphony 9
Verdi: Ballo in maschera (Cpte)
see CONCERT INDEX under:
(RCA) **GD60324** Beethoven—Complete Symphonies
(RCA) **GD60326** Verdi—Operas & Choral Works

SCOTTI, Antonio (bar)
see CONCERT INDEX under:
(IRCC) **IRCC-CD802** Souvenirs of Rare French
Opera
(NIMB) **NI7857** Farrar in Italian Opera
(NIMB) **NI7859** Caruso, Farrar & Journet in French
Opera
(PEAR) **EVC1(2)** The Caruso Edition, Vol.1 (pt 2)
(PEAR) **EVC2** The Caruso Edition, Vol.2—1908-12
(PEAR) **EVC3(1)** The Caruso Edition, Vol.3 (pt 1)
(PEAR) **GEMMCDS9923(2)** Covent Garden on
Record, Vol.1 (pt 2)
(PEAR) **GEMMCDS9924(2)** Covent Garden on
Record, Vol.2 (pt 2)
(PEAR) **GEMMCDS9925(1)** Covent Garden on
Record—Vol.3 (pt 1)
(PEAR) **GEMMCD9309** Enrico Caruso - Opera and
Song Recital
(RCA) **GD60495(2)** The Complete Caruso Collection
(pt 2)
(RCA) **GD60495(3)** The Complete Caruso Collection
(pt 3)
(RCA) **GD60495(4)** The Complete Caruso Collection
(pt 4)
(RCA) **09026 61580-2(1)** RCA/Met 110 Singers, 100
Years (pt 1)
(SYMP) **SYMCD1100** Harold Wayne Collection,
Vol.8

SCOTTISH BAROQUE ENSEMBLE
cond LIONEL FRIEDMAN
see CONCERT INDEX under:
(CRD) **CRD3342** Scandinavian Serenade

SCOTTISH CHAMBER CHORUS
cond C. MACKERRAS
Mozart: Nozze di Figaro (Cpte), Zauberflöte (Cpte)

SCOTTISH CHAMBER OPERA ENSEMBLE
cond M. RAFFERTY
Maxwell Davies: Martyrdom of St Magnus (Cpte)

SCOTTISH CHAMBER ORCHESTRA
Beethoven: Romances, Violin Concerto
cond S. BEDFORD
see CONCERT INDEX under:
(COLL) **Coll1210-2** Twentieth-Century Flute
Concertos
cond J. BLAIR
see CONCERT INDEX under:
(DYNA) **DC-U25** Haydn: Violin Concertos
cond I. BOLTON
MacMillan: Visitatio Sepulchri (Cpte)
cond P. DANIEL
see CONCERT INDEX under:
(RCA) **09026 61277-2** Rebounds - Evelyn Glennie
cond A. GIBSON
Handel: Water Music
cond J. LAREDO
see CONCERT INDEX under:
(NIMB) **NI5112** Mendelssohn: Orchestral Works
cond C. MACKERRAS
Beethoven: Prometheus (Cpte)
Field: Piano Concerto 2, Piano Concerto 3

Mozart: Così fan tutte (Cpte), Nozze di Figaro (Cpte),
Piano Concerto 17, Piano Concerto 20, Piano
Concerto 21, Piano Concerto 22, Piano Concerto 24,
Piano Concerto 27, Zauberflöte (Cpte)
see CONCERT INDEX under:
(HYPE) **CDA66729** Weber—Piano Concertos
(HYPE) **CDA66800** Arriaga/Voříšek—Symphonies
(TELA) **CD80287** Mozart—Piano Concertos, etc
(TELA) **CD80367** Mozart—Horn Concerti
cond J. MACMILLAN
MacMillan: Búsqueda (Cpte)
see CONCERT INDEX under:
(CATA) **09026 61916-2** MacMillan—Veni, Veni
Emmanuel & Other Percussion Works
cond G. MALCOLM
Handel: Messiah (exc)
cond P. MAXWELL DAVIES
Maxwell Davies: Into the Labyrinth, Sinfonia, Sinfonia
concertante, Sinfonietta Accademica, Strathclyde
Concerto 1, Strathclyde Concerto 2, Strathclyde
Concerto 3, Strathclyde Concerto 4, Strathclyde
Concerto 5, Strathclyde Concerto 6, Symphony 4
see CONCERT INDEX under:
(COLL) **Coll1396-2** Maxwell Davies—Strathclyde
Concertos 7 & 8 etc
(UNIC) **DKPCD9070** A Celebration of Scotland
cond K. MONTGOMERY
see CONCERT INDEX under:
(EMIL) **CDZ114** Best of Baroque
cond J-P. SARASTE
Beethoven: Symphony 3
Mozart: Symphony 39, Symphony 41
see CONCERT INDEX under:
(CATA) **09026 61916-2** MacMillan—Veni, Veni
Emmanuel & Other Percussion Works
(VIRG) **VC7 59565-2** Barber—Orchestral & Chamber
Works
(VIRG) **VJ7 59657-2** Mother Goose
cond P. SCHREIER
see CONCERT INDEX under:
(EMI) **CDC7 54453-2** Bach—Cantatas
cond G. SCHWARZ
see CONCERT INDEX under:
(DELO) **DE3061** Haydn: Orchestral Works
(DELO) **DE3062** Haydn: Orchestral Works
(DELO) **DE3063** Haydn—Orchestral Works
(DELO) **DE3064** Haydn: Orchestral Works
cond J. SEREBRIER
(ASV) **CDDCA700** Mendelssohn—Orchestral Works
(ASV) **CDDCA719** Tchaikovsky—Orchestral Works
(ASV) **CDDCA760** Prokofiev—Vocal and Orchestral
Works
cond Y.P. TORTELIER
Mozart: Violin Concerto, K218, Violin Concerto,
K219
cond M. VELTRI
see CONCERT INDEX under:
(NIMB) **NI5106** Rossini—Opera Arias
(NIMB) **NI5224** Bellini & Donizetti: Arias

SCOTTISH EARLY MUSIC CONSORT
see CONCERT INDEX under:
(CHAN) **CHAN0581** Auld Scottish Sangs

SCOTTISH ENSEMBLE
see CONCERT INDEX under:
(VIRG) **VJ7 59641-2** J.S. & C.P.E. Bach—Violin &
Cello Concertos
(VIRG) **VJ7 59652-2** Popular Baroque Works
cond J. REES
Bach: Brandenburg Concertos
see CONCERT INDEX under:
(VIRG) **VJ5 61103-2** Vivaldi—Concertos
(VIRG) **VJ7 59652-2** Popular Baroque Works

**SCOTTISH NATIONAL ORCHESTRA WIND
ENSEMBLE**
cond P. JÄRVI
Mozart: Divertimento, K213, Serenade, K361

SCOTTISH OPERA CHORUS
cond J. BROWN
Bernstein: Candide (1988) (exc)
cond J. Y. OSSONCE
Chabrier: Briséis (Cpte)

SCOTTISH OPERA ORCHESTRA
cond J. BROWN
see CONCERT INDEX under:
(TER) **CDVIR8314** Is it really me?

SCOTTISH PHILHARMONIC SINGERS
cond G. MALCOLM
Handel: Messiah (exc)
cond M. VELTRI
see CONCERT INDEX under:
(NIMB) **NI5106** Rossini—Opera Arias
(NIMB) **NI5224** Bellini & Donizetti: Arias

SCOTTO, Renata (sop)
Bellini: Norma (Cpte)
Cherubini: Medea (Cpte)
Cilea: Adriana Lecouvreur (Cpte)
Giordano: Andrea Chénier (Cpte)
Leoncavallo: Pagliacci (Cpte)
Meyerbeer: Prophète (Cpte)
Puccini: Edgar (Cpte), Madama Butterfly (Cpte),
Tosca (Cpte), Villi (Cpte)
Verdi: Otello (Cpte), Rigoletto (Cpte), Traviata
(Cpte)
see CONCERT INDEX under:
(CFP) **CD-CFP4569** Puccini: Arias
(ETCE) **KTC2002** Renata Scotto: Aria and song
recital

SEJNA, Karel (cond)
see Brno St PO

SEKIYA, Shin (cond)
see Shin-Yu Kai Ch

SELANDIA ENSEMBLE
see CONCERT INDEX under:
(KONT) **32032** Wind Chamber Music

SELBIG, Ute (sop)
Mendelssohn: Vom Himmel hoch
Saint-Saëns: Oratorio de Noël, Op. 12
see CONCERT INDEX under:
(CAPR) **10 367** Mendelssohn—Motets

SELEZNIEV, Georgy (bass)
Borodin: Prince Igor (Cpte)

SELIG, Franz-Josef (bass)
Bach: St Matthew Passion, BWV244 (Cpte)
Busoni: Turandot (Cpte)
Mozart: Requiem
see CONCERT INDEX under:
(EMI) **CDC7 54037-2** Mozart—Masses and Church
Sonatas

SELIMSKI, Assen (bar)
Mussorgsky: Khovanshchina (Cpte)

SELIN, Elisabeth (rec)
Telemann: Sonates sans basse, TWV40: 101-106

SELIVANOV, Piotr (bar)
see CONCERT INDEX under:
(DANT) **LYS013/5** Tchaikovsky—The Queen of
Spades

SELLAR, David (treb)
Puccini: Tosca (Cpte)

SELLERS, Bruce (ten)
see CONCERT INDEX under:
(PHIL) **442 534-2PH** Janáček—Choral Works

SELLERS ENGINEERING BAND
cond N. LAW
see CONCERT INDEX under:
(CHAN) **CHAN4531** Legend in Brass
cond P. MCCANN
see CONCERT INDEX under:
(CHAN) **CHAN4531** Legend in Brass

SELLHEIM, Eckart (pf)
see CONCERT INDEX under:
(SONY) **SBK48171** Works for Cello and Piano

SELLHEIM, Friedrich-Jürgen (vc)
see CONCERT INDEX under:
(SONY) **SBK48171** Works for Cello and Piano

SELLICK, Phyllis (pf)
see CONCERT INDEX under:
(EMI) **CDM7 64044-2** Arnold—Orchestral Works
(NIMB) **NI5178** Piano Works for Three Hands

SELLS, Michael (ten)
Verdi: Falstaff (Cpte)

SELTZER, Dov (cond)
see Israel PO

SEMBRICH, Marcella (sop)
see CONCERT INDEX under:
(NIMB) **NI7840/1** The Era of Adelina Patti
(NIMB) **NI7860** Emma Eames & Pol Plançon
(PEAR) **EVC1(2)** The Caruso Edition, Vol.1 (pt 2)
(PEAR) **GEMMCDS9923(1)** Covent Garden on
Record, Vol.1 (pt 1)
(RCA) **GD60495(2)** The Complete Caruso Collection
(pt 2)
(RCA) **09026 61580-2(1)** RCA/Met 110 Singers, 100
Years (pt 1)
(ROMO) **81001-2** Emma Eames (1865-1952)

SEMELLAZ, François (sop)
Lully: Atys (Cpte)
Rameau: Nélée et Myrthis (Cpte)

SEMEZIS, Raphëelle (vc)
see CONCERT INDEX under:
(MARC) **8 223636** In Memoriam Lili Boulanger

(IL) SEMINARIO MUSICALE
see CONCERT INDEX under:
(VIRG) **VC7 59602-2** Monteverdi—Motets

(IL) SEMINARIO MUSICALE ENSEMBLE
Couperin: Leçons de Ténèbres
see CONCERT INDEX under:
(HRMO) **H/CD8720** Vivaldi—Sacred Vocal Works

SEMKOW, Jerzy (cond)
see BPO

SEMPÉ, Skip (hpd)
Anglebert: Harpsichord Works (exc)
Chambonnières: Harpsichord Suites
Forqueray: Pièces de viole (exc)
see CONCERT INDEX under:
(ARIO) **ARN68046** Italian Airs & Cantatas
(DHM) **RD77219** F. Couperin—Harpsichord Works
(DHM) **RD77252** Purcell—Airs and Instrumental
Music
(DHM) **05472 77222-2** Bach—Harpsichord Works

SEMPÉ, Skip (hpd/dir)
see CONCERT INDEX under:
(DHM) **RD77218** Lully—Divertissements
(DHM) **RD77220** Monteverdi e il suo Tempo
(DHM) **RD77252** Purcell—Airs and Instrumental
Music

(DHM) **05472 77190-2**
Monteverdi—Combattimento/Lamento d'Arianna
(DHM) **05472-77300-2** Buxtehude—Abendmusik

SENATOR, Boaz (bass)
Puccini: Bohème (Cpte)
Rossini: Zelmira (Cpte)

SENDREZ, Michel (pf)
Berlioz: Lélio (Cpte)

SENDROWITZ, Mitchell (bar)
Verdi: Traviata (Cpte)

SÉNÉCHAL, Michel (ten)
Bazin: Voyage en Chine (Cpte)
Bizet: Carmen (Cpte), Ivan IV (exc)
Boïeldieu: Dame blanche (Cpte)
Cilea: Adriana Lecouvreur (Cpte)
G. Charpentier: Louise (Cpte)
Giordano: Andrea Chénier (Cpte)
Honegger: Aventures du Roi Pausole (Cpte)
Massenet: Chérubin (Cpte)
Messiaen: Saint François d'Assise (Cpte)
Offenbach: Contes d'Hoffmann (Cpte), Orphée aux
enfers (Cpte), Périchole (Cpte)
Poulenc: Dialogues des Carmélites (Cpte)
Puccini: Bohème (Cpte), Madama Butterfly (Cpte),
Tosca (Cpte), Turandot (Cpte)
Ravel: Enfant et les Sortilèges (Cpte), Heure
espagnole (Cpte)
Tchaikovsky: Eugene Onegin (Cpte)
Verdi: Forza del destino (Cpte), Otello (Cpte)
Wagner: Meistersinger (Cpte)
see CONCERT INDEX under:
(EMI) **CDM7 64281-2** Boulanger—Vocal & Chamber
Works
(ERAT) **4509-95362-2** Mozart—Sacred Choral
Works
(MUSD) **20239-2** Delibes—Opéras-Comiques
(SONY) **M3K79312** Puccini: Il Trittico

SENGER, Alexander (ten)
R. Strauss: Daphne (Cpte)
see CONCERT INDEX under:
(HANS) **98 863** Bach—Cantatas, Vol.12

SENIGLOVÁ, Eva (sop)
Marschner: Hans Heiling (Cpte)

SENN, Martha (mez)
Honegger: Roi David (Cpte)
Mascagni: Cavalleria Rusticana (Cpte)
Mozart: Clemenza di Tito (Cpte)
Verdi: Rigoletto (Cpte)
see CONCERT INDEX under:
(DORI) **DOR90210** Falla—Vocal Works
(NUOV) **6809** Falla: Vocal & Instrumental Works

SENN, Martin-Ulrich (fl)
see CONCERT INDEX under:
(THOR) **CTH2012** Copland—Chamber Works

SEOW, Yitkin (pf)
Forrest/Wright: Song of Norway (Cpte)
see CONCERT INDEX under:
(ASV) **CDDCA684** Schubert—Lieder & Chamber
Works
(HYPE) **CDA66344** Satie—Piano Works

SEQUENTIA
Anon: Bordesholm Lament (Cpte), Codex Calixtinus
(exc), Codex Las Huelgas (exc)
(DHM) **RD77095** Vitry—Chansons and Motets
(DHM) **05472 77320-2** Hildegard von
Bingen—Canticles of Ecstasy

SEQUOIA QUARTET
Bartók: String Quartet 3
Ravel: String Quartet

SERAFIM, Fernando (ten)
see CONCERT INDEX under:
(ERAT) **2292-45926-2** Charpentier—Sacred Choral
Works

SERAFIN, Tullio (cond)
see La Scala Orch

SERAPHIM TRIO
Varkonyi: Piano Trio, Op.17

SERBESCU, Liana (pf)
Mendelssohn-Hensel: Jahr, Nachspiel
see CONCERT INDEX under:
(CPO) **CPO999 015-2** Mendelssohn-Hensel—Piano
Works Vol 2

SEREBRIER, José (cond)
see LSO

SERENATA OF LONDON
cond B. WILDE
see CONCERT INDEX under:
(CARL) **PCD1108** Chamber Orchestral Works

SERENI, Mario (bar)
Donizetti: Lucia di Lammermoor (Cpte)
Giordano: Andrea Chénier (Cpte)
Mascagni: Cavalleria Rusticana (Cpte)
Puccini: Bohème (Cpte), Madama Butterfly (Cpte),
Rondine (Cpte), Turandot (Cpte)
Verdi: Aida (Cpte), Ernani (Cpte), Traviata (Cpte)
see CONCERT INDEX under:
(RCA) **GD87799** The Pearl Fishers Duet plus Duets
and Scenes

SERGE, John (ten)
Rossini: Semiramide (Cpte)

SERGEYEV, Nikolai (cond)
see Russian St Brass Orch

SERIESE, Astrid (sop)
L. Andriessen: M is for Man

SERKIN, Peter (pf)
Goehr: Piano Concerto
Lieberson: Piano Concerto
see CONCERT INDEX under:
(NEW) **NW344-2** Modern Piano Works
(NEW) **80407-2** Sheng—Miscellaneous Works
(VIRG) **VC7 59308-2** Knussen—Chamber Music

SERKIN, Rudolf (pf)
Beethoven: Choral Fantasia, Piano Concerto 3, Piano
Concerto 4, Piano Concerto 5, Piano Trios (exc),
Triple Concerto
Brahms: Cello Sonata 1, Cello Sonata 2, Horn Trio,
Piano Concerto 2, Piano Quartet 1, Piano Quartet 2,
Piano Trio 2
Mozart: Piano Concerto 21, Piano Concerto 27
Prokofiev: Piano Concerto 4
R. Strauss: Burleske
Reger: Piano Concerto
Schubert: Fantasie, D934, Impromptus (exc), Piano
Trio 2, Trout Quintet, D667
see CONCERT INDEX under:
(ARCI) **ARC105** Serkin— Welte-Mignon Piano Rolls
(c.1928)
(DANA) **DACOCD303** Great Musicians in
Copenhagen
(EMI) **CDH7 63494-2** Beethoven & Bach: Chamber
Works
(EMI) **CHS5 65308-2**
Beethoven/Schubert/Mendelssohn—Chamber
Works
(PEAR) **GEMMCDS9141** The Busch Quartet -
Complete Schubert Recordings
(PEAR) **GEMMCD9942** Adolf Busch and Rudolf
Serkin
(SONY) **SMK58991** Pablo Casals plays Beethoven at
Prades and Perpignan, 1951 & 1953
(SONY) **S2K47522** Beethoven & Haydn—Choral
Works
(SONY) **SM2K58985** Pablo Casals at Perpignan and
Prades, 1951 & 1953
(SYMP) **SYMCD1109** Great Violinists, Vol.5 - Adolf
Busch
(TELA) **CD80061** Beethoven: Piano Concertos

SERKOYAN, Gérard (bass)
Saint-Saëns: Henry VIII (Cpte)

SERMET, Huseyin (pf)
see CONCERT INDEX under:
(AUVI) **V4679** Schmitt—Chamber Works
(AUVI) **V4687** Schmitt—Piano and Orchestral Works

SEROV, Eduard (cond)
see Leningrad CO

SERRA, Luciana (sop)
Donizetti: Ajo nell'imbarazzo (Cpte), Don Pasquale
(Cpte), Fille du Régiment (Cpte), Gianni di Parigi
(Cpte)
Gazzaniga: Don Giovanni (Cpte)
Mozart: Zauberflöte (Cpte)
Offenbach: Contes d'Hoffmann (Cpte)
Rossini: Siège de Corinthe (Cpte), Viaggio a Reims
(Cpte)

SERRAIOCCO, Danilo (bass-bar)
Cherubini: Lodoïska (Cpte)
Mayr: Rosa Bianca (Cpte)
Puccini: Fanciulla del West (Cpte), Tosca (Cpte)
Rossini: Inganno felice (Cpte)
see CONCERT INDEX under:
(DECC) **436 261-2DHO3** Puccini—Il Trittico

SERRANO, Enriqueta (sngr)
Sorozábal: Katiuska (Cpte)

SERRE, Jean-Louis (bar)
Mouret: Amours de Ragonde (Cpte)

SERVADEI, Annette (pf)
see CONCERT INDEX under:
(CARL) **PCD949** Annette Servadei—Piano Recital
(CNTI) **CCD1058** Sibelius—Piano Works, Vol.1
(CNTI) **CCD1059** Sibelius—Piano Works, Vol.2
(CNTI) **CCD1064** Dohnányi—Complete Piano Music,
Volume 1
(CNTI) **CCD1070** Sibelius—Piano Works, Vol 4
(CNTI) **CCD1071** Sibelius—Piano Works, Vol 5

SERVILE, Roberto (bar)
Rossini: Barbiere di Siviglia (Cpte)
see CONCERT INDEX under:
(CAPR) **10 380** Breezes from the Orient, Vol.2

SESSIONS, Roger (cond)
see CONCERT INDEX under:
(SONY) **SM3K46291** Stravinsky—Ballets, Vol.1

SETRAK, M. (pf)
Chopin: Piano Concerto 1
J. Wieniawski: Piano Concerto, Op. 20
see CONCERT INDEX under:
(CHNT) **LDC278 962** Polish Works for Piano &
Orchestra

SETTI, Giulio (cond)
see NY Met Op Chor

SETTMACHER, Ferdinand (bass)
R. Strauss: Rosenkavalier (Cpte)

SETZER, Franz (ten)
R. Strauss: Rosenkavalier (Cpte)

SETZER, Philip (vn)
Bartók: Duos, Sz98
Fuchs: Duos, Op. 55
see CONCERT INDEX under:
(DG) **431 772-2GH** Prokofiev—Chamber Works

SEVAN PHILHARMONIC ORCHESTRA
cond A. HOVHANESS
Hovhaness: Symphony 19

SEVENICH, Stefan (sngr)
Braunfels: Verkündigung (Cpte)

SEVENOAKS SCHOOL CHOIR
cond M. BEST
Britten: St Nicolas

SEVERIN, Peder (ten)
see CONCERT INDEX under:
(ROND) **RCD8319** Nielsen—Songs, Vol.1
(ROND) **RCD8323** Nielsen—Songs, Vol.2
(ROND) **RCD8327** Nielsen: Songs, Vol.4

SEVERINA, Gina (mez)
see CONCERT INDEX under:
(PEAR) **EVC1(2)** The Caruso Edition, Vol.1 (pt 2)
(RCA) **GD60495(2)** The Complete Caruso Collection (pt 2)

SEVILLE SYMPHONY ORCHESTRA
cond M. ROA
Vives: Doña Francisquita (Cpte)

SEWELL, Brian (bn)
see CONCERT INDEX under:
(CARL) **PCD939** Mozart: Orchestral Works

SEWEN, Marek (cond)
see Warsaw CO

SEYMOUR, Linda (contr)
see CONCERT INDEX under:
(EMI) **CDS7 54607-2** Stravinsky plays and conducts Stravinsky

SEYMOUR, Valerie (sop)
Sullivan: HMS Pinafore (Cpte)

SEYRIG, Delphine (narr)
see CONCERT INDEX under:
(VIRG) **VC7 59604-2** Debussy—Chamber Works

SFORZA, Camillo (ten)
Donizetti: Lucrezia Borgia (Cpte)
Verdi: Traviata (Cpte)

SGOUROS, Dimitris (pf)
Brahms: Piano Concerto 1, Piano Concerto 2

SHACHNAZARIYA, Edward (cond)
see USSR Academy SO

SHACKLOCK, Constance (mez)
see CONCERT INDEX under:
(TEST) **SBT1018** Kirsten Flagstad

SHADE, Nancy (sop)
B.A. Zimmermann: Soldaten (Cpte)

SHAFFER, Elaine (fl)
Mozart: Flute and Harp Concerto, K299

SHAFFER, Thomas (bar)
Britten: Paul Bunyan (Cpte)

SHAGIDULLIN, Albert (bass)
Mussorgsky: Boris Godunov (Cpte)

SHAHAM, Gil (vn)
Bruch: Violin Concerto 1
Kreisler: Violin Concerto in C
Mendelssohn: Violin Concerto, op 64
Paganini: Violin Concerto 1
Saint-Saëns: Violin Concerto 3
Sibelius: Violin Concerto
Tchaikovsky: Violin Concerto
Vivaldi: Concerti, Op.8 (exc)
see CONCERT INDEX under:
(DG) **431 815-2GH** Wieniawski/Sarasate—Works for Violin and Orchestra
(DG) **437 837-2GH** Paganini—Violin & Guitar Works
(DG) **439 886-2GH** Barber/Korngold—Violin Concertos

SHAHAM, Hagai (vn)
see CONCERT INDEX under:
(ARGO) **440 116-2ZH** Vaughan Williams—Orchestral Works

SHAKESNIDER, Wilma (sop)
Gershwin: Porgy and Bess (exc)

SHALEV, Adel (hpd)
see CONCERT INDEX under:
(KOCH) **37021-2** Mira Zakai—Song Recital

SHALLON, David (cond)
see Berlin RSO

SHANGHAI QUARTET
Grieg: String Quartet, Op. 27
Mendelssohn: String Quartet 2
see CONCERT INDEX under:
(DELO) **DE3162** Hovhaness—Quartets; Bagatelles
(DELO) **DE3186** Heigh Ho! Mozart

SHAPIRO, Harvey (vc)
see CONCERT INDEX under:
(EMI) **ZDMF7 64830-2** The Art of Nathan Milstein

SHAPIRO, Lois (fp)
see CONCERT INDEX under:

(CHNN) **CCS6494** Beethoven—Cello Variations

SHAPIRO, Marc (pf)
see CONCERT INDEX under:
(RCA) **09026 61893-2** Pierre Monteux Edition

SHAPIRO GRAVITTE, Debbie (sngr)
see CONCERT INDEX under:
(EMI) **CDC5 55189-2** The Busby Berkeley Album

SHARON, Boaz (pf)
see CONCERT INDEX under:
(UNIC) **DKPCD9155** Milhaud—Piano Works

SHARON QUARTET
see CONCERT INDEX under:
(DINT) **DICD920171** Mozart/Beethoven/Ravel—String Quartets

SHARONOV, Vasili (bar)
see CONCERT INDEX under:
(PEAR) **GEMMCDS9001/3(1)** Singers of Imperial Russia, Vol.2 (pt 1)
(PEAR) **GEMMCDS9997/9(1)** Singers of Imperial Russia, Vol.1 (pt 1)
(SYMP) **SYMCD1105** The Harold Wayne Collection, Vol.10

SHARP, Frederick (bar)
Delius: Village Romeo and Juliet (Cpte)
see CONCERT INDEX under:
(EMI) **CMS7 64727-2** Britten—Opera excerpts and Folksongs

SHARP, John (vc)
R. Strauss: Don Quixote

SHARP, Norma (sop)
Egk: Peer Gynt (Cpte)
Schumann: Szenen aus Goethes Faust (Cpte)
Wagner: Götterdämmerung (Cpte), Rheingold (Cpte), Siegfried (Cpte)

SHARP, William (bar)
Mozart: Kleine Freimaurer-Kantate, K623, Requiem
see CONCERT INDEX under:
(EMI) **CDC7 54851-2** Gershwin—Blue Monday, etc
(KOCH) **37000-2** Bernstein—Songs & Duets
(KOCH) **37028-2** Gershwin—Songs & Duets
(KOCH) **37050-2** Blitzstein—Songs
(KOCH) **37086-2** Unquiet Peace—The Lied Between the Wars
(KOCH) **37138-2** Bach—Solo Cantatas
(KOCH) **37163-2** Bach—Cantatas
(KOCH) **37164-2** Bach—Cantatas, Vol.3

SHARPE, Cedric (vc)
see CONCERT INDEX under:
(PREI) **89207** Feodor Chaliapin Song Book—Electrical Recordings

SHARPE, Ivan (ten)
see CONCERT INDEX under:
(OPRA) **ORCH104** A Hundred Years of Italian Opera: 1820-1830

SHARPE, Terence (bar)
Giordano: Andrea Chénier (Cpte)
Sullivan: Yeomen of the Guard (Cpte)
Vaughan Williams: Hugh the Drover (Cpte)
Verdi: Vespri Siciliani (Cpte)

SHARROW, Leonard (bn)
see CONCERT INDEX under:
(RCA) **GD60282** Haydn—Orchestral Works

SHASBY, Anne (pf)
see CONCERT INDEX under:
(CHAN) **CHAN6535** Stravinsky—Symphonies of Wind Instruments

SHATTUCK, Truly (sngr)
see CONCERT INDEX under:
(PEAR) **GEMMCDS9053/5** Music from the New York Stage, Vol. 2: 1908–1913

SHAW, Briony (vn)
see CONCERT INDEX under:
(SPRO) **SPCV1001** Capital Virtuosi

SHAW, Geoffrey (bass)
Monteverdi: Orfeo (Cpte)

SHAW, Ian (organ)
see CONCERT INDEX under:
(ASV) **CDGAU114** Tallis/Sheppard—Masses
(PRIO) **PRCD296** Evensong For St Cuthbert's Day
(PRIO) **PRCD343** Psalms of David, Vol.3

SHAW, Penny (sngr)
Verdi: Trovatore (Cpte)

SHAW, Philip (cornet)
see CONCERT INDEX under:
(CHAN) **CHAN4523** Concerto

SHAW, Robert (cond)
see Atlanta SO

SHAW, Robert (narr)
Blitzstein: Airborne Symphony

SHAW, Roderick (fp)
Devienne: Oboe Sonatas, Op. 71, Sonatas, Op. 23 (exc)

SHAW, Teresa (mez)
Purcell: Dido (Cpte)
see CONCERT INDEX under:
(PHIL) **432 152-2PH** Brahms—Choral Works

(ROBERT) SHAW CHAMBER SINGERS
cond ROBERT SHAW
see CONCERT INDEX under:

(TELA) **CD80340** Schubert—Songs for Male Chorus
(TELA) **CD80377** Songs of Angels-Christmas Hymns and Carols

(ROBERT) SHAW CHORALE
cond R. CELLINI
Leoncavallo: Pagliacci (Cpte)
Mascagni: Cavalleria Rusticana (Cpte)
Verdi: Trovatore (Cpte)
cond E. LEINSDORF
see CONCERT INDEX under:
(RCA) **09026 61245-2** Ezio Pinza - Recital
cond F. REINER
Bizet: Carmen (Cpte)
cond A. TOSCANINI
Beethoven: Missa Solemnis
Cherubini: Requiem 1
Verdi: Ballo in maschera (Cpte)
see CONCERT INDEX under:
(RCA) **GD60276** Toscanini conducts Boito & Verdi
(RCA) **GD60324** Beethoven—Complete Symphonies
(RCA) **GD60325** Brahms: Symphonies & Other Works
(RCA) **GD60326** Verdi—Operas & Choral Works

(ROBERT) SHAW FESTIVAL SINGERS
cond ROBERT SHAW
Rachmaninov: Vespers, Op. 37 (Cpte)
see CONCERT INDEX under:
(TELA) **CD80236** Poulenc: Choral Works
(TELA) **CD80326** Brahms—Vocal works

SHEA, Jere (sngr)
Sondheim: Passion (Cpte)

SHEAF CONCERT ORCHESTRA
cond J. KIRKWOOD
see CONCERT INDEX under:
(CHOR) **EECD109** Celebration of Christmas

SHEEN, Colin (tbn)
see CONCERT INDEX under:
(HYPE) **CDA66177** Bruckner—Sacred Choral Works
(HYPE) **CDA66245** Bruckner—Choral Works

SHEEN, Graham (bn)
Beethoven: Piano and Wind Quintet, Op. 16
Mozart: Piano and Wind Quintet, K452
see CONCERT INDEX under:
(PHIL) **412 892-2PH** Vivaldi: Double Concertos

SHEEN, Martin (sngr)
Rodgers: King and I (Cpte)

SHEFFER, Jonathan (cond)
see OST

SHEFFIELD, Leo (bar)
Sullivan: Pirates of Penzance (Cpte)

SHEFFIELD, Philip (ten)
G. Lloyd: John Socman (exc)
M. Berkeley: Baa Baa Black Sheep (Cpte)
see CONCERT INDEX under:
(CLLE) **COLCD104** English Partsongs

SHEFFIELD CHORALE
cond J. KIRKWOOD
see CONCERT INDEX under:
(CHOR) **EECD109** Celebration of Christmas

SHEFFIELD PHILHARMONIC CHORUS
cond J. BARBIROLLI
Elgar: Dream of Gerontius (Cpte)

SHEK, Henry (cond)
see Moscow SO

SHELBY, Karen (mez)
Janáček: Cunning Little Vixen (Cpte)

SHELLEY, Howard (cond)
see LMP

SHELLEY, Howard (pf)
Alwyn: Piano Concerto 1
Chopin: Piano Sonata 2, Preludes (exc)
Foulds: Dynamic Triptych
H. Ferguson: Partita, Op. 5b, Piano Sonata, Op. 8
Hindemith: Four Temperaments
Rachmaninov: Etudes-tableaux, Op. 33, Etudes-tableaux, Op. 39, Moments musicaux, Op.16, Morceaux de fantaisie, Op.3, Morceaux de salon, Op.10, Piano Sonata 1, Piano Sonata 2, Preludes (exc)
Tippett: Piano Concerto
Vaughan Williams: Piano Concerto
see CONCERT INDEX under:
(CHAN) **CHAN8814** Schumann—Piano Works
(CHAN) **CHAN8882/3** Rachmaninov: Works for Piano & Orchestra
(CHAN) **CHAN9018** Chopin—Piano Works
(CHAN) **CHAN9092** Gershwin—Piano & Orchestral Works
(CHAN) **CHAN9175** Chopin—Piano Works
(CHAN) **CHAN9196** Alwyn—Orchestral Works
(CHAN) **CHAN9233** Tippett—Orchestral Works
(CHAN) **CHAN9262/3** Vaughan Williams—Orchestral Works
(CHAN) **CHAN9325** Gershwin—Orchestral Works
(CHAN) **CHAN9374** Rachmaninov—Songs
(EMI) **CDC7 54346-2** Vaughan Williams/Ravel—Chamber Works
(EMI) **CDM7 64730-2** Vaughan Williams—Riders to the Sea; Epithalamion, etc
(HYPE) **CDA66009** Rachmaninov—Piano Works
(HYPE) **CDA66082** Rachmaninov—Piano Works
(HYPE) **CDA66198** Rachmaninov—Early Piano Works

(HYPE) **CDA66375** Rachmaninov—Works of Piano Duet
(HYPE) **CDA66486** Rachmaninov—Piano Transcriptions
(HYPE) **CDS44041/8** Rachmaninov—Complete Piano Music
(PHIL) **422 508-2PME4** The Complete Mozart Edition Vol 8

SHELLEY, Howard (pf/dir)
Mozart: Piano Concerto 9, Piano Concerto 12, Piano Concerto 13, Piano Concerto 14, Piano Concerto 17, Piano Concerto 19, Piano Concerto 20, Piano Concerto 21, Piano Concerto 23, Piano Concerto 24, Piano Concerto 27
see CONCERT INDEX *under:*
(CHAN) **CHAN9215** Mendelssohn—Works for Piano & Orchestra

SHELTON, Lucy (sop)
Goehr: Mouse Metamorphosed, Op. 54, Sing, Ariel, Op. 51
S. Albert: TreeStone
see CONCERT INDEX *under:*
(VIRG) **VC7 59308-2** Knussen—Chamber Music

SHELTON, Lucy (spkr)
see CONCERT INDEX *under:*
(DG) **447 068-2GH** Stravinsky—The Flood, etc

SHEMER, David (hpd)
see CONCERT INDEX *under:*
(CARL) **PWK1138** Baroque Favourites

SHENG, Bright (pf)
see CONCERT INDEX *under:*
(NEW) **80407-2** Sheng—Miscellaneous Works

SHEPHERD, Adrian (cond)
see Cantilena

SHEPHERD, James (cornet)
see CONCERT INDEX *under:*
(CHAN) **CHAN4513** British Bandsman Centenary Concert

SHEPHERD, Mark (organ)
see CONCERT INDEX *under:*
(PRIO) **PRCD505** Magnificat and Nunc Dimittis, Volume 3

SHEPHERD, Muriel (cond)
see Birmingham Bach Ch

SHEPPARD, Craig (pf)
Rossini: Petite messe solennelle
see CONCERT INDEX *under:*
(ASV) **CDDCA667** Prokofiev—Works for Violin & Piano
(CIRR) **CICD1010** Chopin: Piano Works

SHEPPARD, Honor (sop)
Monteverdi: L'Arianna (exc)
Purcell: Dido (Cpte), Indian Queen, Z630 (Cpte)
see CONCERT INDEX *under:*
(HARM) **HMX290 1528/33(2)** A Purcell Companion (pt 2)

SHEPPARD, Peter (vn)
Cui: Kaleidoscope, Violin Sonata in D
Telemann: Fantaisies, TWV40: 14-25

SHEPPARD, Susan (vc)
see CONCERT INDEX *under:*
(HARM) **HMU90 7104** Vivaldi/Chedéville—Oboe Sonatas

SHERIDAN, Margaret (sop)
see CONCERT INDEX *under:*
(PEAR) **GEMMCDS9925(2)** Covent Garden on Record—Vol.3 (pt 2)
(PREI) **89072** Aureliano Pertile (1885-1952) - II

SHERIFF, Noam (cond)
see Berlin RSO

SHERMAN, Russell (pf)
Liszt: Études d'exécution, S139

SHERRY, Fred (vc)
Rorem: Bright Music, Winter Pages
see CONCERT INDEX *under:*
(KOCH) **37110-2** Wuorinen—Orchestral & Chamber Works
(KOCH) **37112-2** Wolpe—Chamber Works
(KOCH) **37242-2** Wuorinen—Chamber Works
(NEW) **NW357-2** Crumb. Madrigals and Chamber works

SHETLER, Norman (pf)
Schubert: Schöne Müllerin (Cpte), Schwanengesang, D957 (Cpte)

SHEVELEV, Nikolai (bar)
see CONCERT INDEX *under:*
(PEAR) **GEMMCDS9007/9(2)** Singers of Imperial Russia, Vol.4 (pt 2)

SHEWAN, Robert (cond)
see Roberts Wesleyan Brass Ens

SHEYNKMAN, Emanuil (balalaika)
see CONCERT INDEX *under:*
(BIS) **BIS-CD351** Tubin: Orchestral Works

SHICOFF, Neil (ten)
Bizet: Carmen (Cpte)
Donizetti: Lucia di Lammermoor (Cpte)
Offenbach: Contes d'Hoffmann (Cpte)
Tchaikovsky: Eugene Onegin (Cpte)
Verdi: Attila (Cpte), Macbeth (Cpte), Rigoletto (Cpte), Traviata (Cpte)

SHIFRIN, David (cond)
see Lincoln Center Chbr Music Soc

SHIFRIN, David (basset cl)
Mozart: Clarinet Concerto, K622, Clarinet Quintet, K581

SHIFRIN, David (cl)
Beethoven: Piano and wind quintet, op 16
Mozart: Piano and wind quintet, K452
see CONCERT INDEX *under:*
(ARAB) **Z6608** Brahms—Trios, Vol.2
(RCA) **09026 68181-2** French Chamber Works

SHIKANO, Akihito (bass)
Verdi: Traviata (Cpte)

SHILKRET, Nathaniel (cond)
see orch

SHILLING, Eric (bar)
Sullivan: Iolanthe (exc)

SHILLING, Eric (narr)
see CONCERT INDEX *under:*
(SUPR) **11 1945-2** Orchestral Works

SHIMELL, William (bar)
Bach: Mass in B minor, BWV232 (Cpte)
Berlioz: Enfance du Christ (Cpte)
Cherubini: Lodoïska (Cpte)
Mozart: Don Giovanni (Cpte)
Stravinsky: Pulcinella (Cpte)
Vaughan Williams: Symphony 1
see CONCERT INDEX *under:*
(EMIN) **CDBOX-VW1** Vaughan Williams—Symphonies Nos 1-9, etc
(HYPE) **CDA66565** Constant Lambert—Vocal & Orchestral Works

SHIMON, Itamar (va)
see CONCERT INDEX *under:*
(CHNN) **CG9107** Music for Clarinet, Piano & Viola

SHIN, Young Ok (sop)
Bellini: Bianca e Fernando (Cpte)

SHINGLES, Stephen (va)
see CONCERT INDEX *under:*
(ASV) **CDDCA518** The English Connection
(DECC) **430 265-2DM** Telemann—Orchestral works

SHIN-YU KAI CHOIR
cond M. ATZMON
Haydn: Schöpfung (Cpte)
cond S. OZAWA
Orff: Carmina burana
Stravinsky: Oedipus Rex (Cpte)
cond S. SEKIYA
see CONCERT INDEX *under:*
(PHIL) **438 135-2PH** Takemitsu—A Song of Circles and Triangles

SHIN-YU KAI CHORUS
cond G. SINOPOLI
Mahler: Klagende Lied

SHIOKAWA, Yuuko (vn)
Mozart: Piano Quartet, K478, Piano Quartet, K493
see CONCERT INDEX *under:*
(DECC) **443 894-2DH** Bartók—Chamber Works

SHIPOVALNIKOV, Aleksei (cond)
see Slavyanka

SHIRAI, Mitsuko (mez)
Mahler: Symphony 4
Mendelssohn: Symphony 2
Schubert: Winterreise (Cpte)
Wolf: Manuel Venegas, Spanisches Liederbuch (exc)
see CONCERT INDEX *under:*
(BAYE) **BR100041** Choral and Vocal Works
(CAPR) **10 098** Mozart: Lieder recital
(CAPR) **10 099** Schumann—Lieder Recital
(CAPR) **10 171** Schubert: Lieder
(CAPR) **10 204** Brahms: Lieder
(CAPR) **10 335** Wolf—Lieder with Orchestra
(CAPR) **10 421** Berg—Lieder
(CAPR) **10 445** Schumann—Lieder
(CAPR) **10 446/7** Mozart—Lieder
(CAPR) **10 462** Songs with Viola
(CAPR) **10 497** R. Strauss—Lieder
(CAPR) **10 514** Schoenberg—Songs
(CAPR) **10 534** Hölderlin Songs

SHIRASAKA-TERATANI, Chieko (sngr)
Braunfels: Verkündigung (Cpte)

SHIRINKSY, Alexander (vn)
see CONCERT INDEX *under:*
(MEZH) **MK417109** Medtner—Works for Violin and Piano

SHIRLEY, Bill (ten)
F. Loewe: My Fair Lady (film) (Cpte)

SHIRLEY, George (ten)
Haydn: Orlando Paladino (Cpte)
Mozart: Cosi fan tutte (Cpte)
R. Strauss: Friedenstag (Cpte)
see CONCERT INDEX *under:*
(SONY) **SM3K46291** Stravinsky—Ballets, Vol.1
(SONY) **SM3K46292** Stravinsky—Ballets, Vol.2

SHIRLEY-QUIRK, John (bar)
Bach: St John Passion, BWV245 (Cpte), St Matthew Passion, BWV244 (Cpte)
Berlioz: Roméo et Juliette (Cpte)

Britten: Burning Fiery Furnace (Cpte), Curlew River (Cpte), Death in Venice (Cpte), Gloriana (Cpte), Midsummer Night's Dream (Cpte), Prodigal Son (Cpte), Rape of Lucretia (Cpte)
Dvořák: Stabat Mater
Elgar: Dream of Gerontius (Cpte), Kingdom (Cpte), Light of Life (Cpte)
Handel: Judas Maccabaeus (Cpte), Messiah (Cpte)
Mahler: Symphony 8
Orff: Carmina Burana
Purcell: Fairy Queen, Z629 (Cpte), St Cecilia's Day Ode, Z328
Rachmaninov: Bells
Schumann: Szenen aus Goethes Faust (Cpte)
Shostakovich: Symphony 13
Stravinsky: Pulcinella
Tippett: Child of Our Time
Vaughan Williams: Symphony 1
Walton: Bear (Cpte)
see CONCERT INDEX *under:*
(CFP) **CD-CFP4532** Sacred Arias
(CHAN) **CHAN8983/4** Britten—Choral and Orchestral Works
(DECC) **430 260-2DM** Bach—Cantatas
(DECC) **430 804-2DC10** Mahler—Complete Symphonies
(DECC) **436 920-2DM** Rachmaninov—Complete Songs
(DECC) **440 323-2DWO** World of British Classics, Volume V
(DECC) **443 009-2DF2** Mozart—Choral Works
(DECC) **443 455-2DF2** Vivaldi—Sacred Choral Works
(DG) **431 751-2GC** Stravinsky—Songs
(EMI) **CDM7 64723-2** Walton—Choral & Orchestral Works
(EMI) **CES5 68519-2** Beethoven—Symphonies
(EMI) **CMS7 64218-2** Delius—Vocal Works
(EMIN) **CD-EMX2198** A Delius Festival
(LOND) **425 159-2LM** Salute to Percy Grainger
(LOND) **425 716-2LM** Britten: Canticles
(LOND) **433 200-2LHO2** Britten—Owen Wingrave, etc.
(LYRI) **SRCD225** Bliss—Orchestral Works
(MERI) **CDE84119** Britten: Songs and Instrumental Works
(SONY) **SK66280** Lutosławski—Orchestral Works
(SONY) **SMK48462** Boulez conducts Schoenberg
(SONY) **SMK48463** Boulez conducts Schoenberg - Volume 1
(SONY) **SM3K64103** Berlioz—Orchestral and Vocal Works

SHIRLEY-QUIRK, John (narr)
see CONCERT INDEX *under:*
(SONY) **SM2K44571** Schoenberg: Choral Works

SHITKOVA, Albina (sop)
Kabalevsky: Colas Breugnon (Cpte)

SHKOLNIKOVA, Nelli (vn)
see CONCERT INDEX *under:*
(CALA) **CACD0101** Orchestral works

SHMITOV, Alexei (pf)
see CONCERT INDEX *under:*
(ETCE) **KTC1179** Denisov—Music for Cello

SHOEN, Vic (cond)
see OST

SHORE, Andrew (bass-bar)
Rossini: Barbiere di Siviglia (Cpte)

SHORR, Aaron (pf)
Cui: Kaleidoscope, Violin Sonata in D

SHORT, Nigel (alto)
Handel: Belshazzar (Cpte)
see CONCERT INDEX *under:*
(HYPE) **CDA66476** Purcell—Complete Odes & Welcome Songs, Vol.5
(HYPE) **CDA66494** Purcell—Complete Odes & Welcome Songs, Vol.6
(HYPE) **CDA66587** Purcell—Complete Odes & Welcome Songs, Vol.7
(HYPE) **CDA66677** Purcell—Anthems & Services, Vol.7

SHOSTAKOVICH, Dmitri (pf)
see CONCERT INDEX *under:*
(EMI) **CDC7 54606-2** Shostakovich plays Shostakovich
(RUSS) **RDCD15005** Shostakovich plays Shostakovich

SHOSTAKOVICH, Maxim (cond)
see BRSO

SHOSTAKOVICH JNR, Dmitri (pf)
Shostakovich: Piano Concerto 1, Piano Concerto 2

SHOSTAKOVICH QUARTET
Glazunov: String Quartet 6, String Quartet 7
see CONCERT INDEX *under:*
(OLYM) **OCD522** Grechaninov/Tchaikovsky—String Quartets
(OLYM) **OCD523** Shostakovich Quartet - Volume 3
(OLYM) **OCD531** Shostakovich—String Quartets, Vol.1
(OLYM) **OCD532** Shostakovich—String Quartets, Vol.2
(OLYM) **OCD533** Shostakovich—String Quartets, Vol.3
(OLYM) **OCD534** Shostakovich—String Quartets, Volume 4
(OLYM) **OCD535** Shostakovich—String Quartets, Volume 5

(OLYM) **OCD542** Glazunov—Chamber Works

SHOUMANOVA, Anelia (sngr)
Weill: Dreigroschenoper (Cpte)

SHUARD, Amy (sop)
see CONCERT INDEX under:
(CFP) **CD-CFP4569** Puccini: Arias
(TEST) **SBT1058** James Johnston - Opera Arias and
Songs

SHULMAN, Andrew (vc)
see CONCERT INDEX under:
(EMI) **CDC5 55085-2** Flute Recital
(EMI) **CDC7 54787-2** Janáček—Chamber Works

SHULMAN, Andrew (vn)
see CONCERT INDEX under:
(VIRG) **VC7 59609-2** Vivaldi—Concertos

SHULMAN, Nora (fl)
see CONCERT INDEX under:
(CBC) **SMCD5119** Adeste Fideles

SHUMAN, Mark (vc)
see CONCERT INDEX under:
(ASV) **CDDCA663** Handel/Telemann—Oboe
Sonatas

SHUMSKAYA, Elizaveta (sop)
see CONCERT INDEX under:
(PREI) **89061** Pavel Lisitian (born 1911)

SHUMSKY, Oscar (vn)
Bach: Solo Violin Partitas and Sonatas
Beethoven: Romances (exc), Violin Concerto
Glazunov: Violin Concerto
Mozart: Violin Concerto, K218, Violin Concerto,
K219
Rode: Violin Caprices
see CONCERT INDEX under:
(BIDD) **LAW008** Grieg—Violin Sonatas
(BIDD) **LAW015** Dohnányi/Weiner—Violin Sonatas

SHUMSKY, Oscar (vn/dir)
see CONCERT INDEX under:
(NIMB) **NI5325** Bach—Violin Concertos

SHUMSKY/REISMAN DUO
Varkonyi: Leda—Fantasy

SHUTOVA, Marina (mez)
see CONCERT INDEX under:
(CDM) **LDC288 038/40** Rimsky-Korsakov—Complete
Songs

SIBELIUS ACADEMY QUARTET
see CONCERT INDEX under:
(BIS) **BIS-CD458** Kokkonen—Chamber Works
(FINL) **4509-95851-2** Sibelius—Complete String
Quartets

(JEAN) SIBELIUS QUARTET
Sibelius: String Quartet, Op.56, String Quartet
(1889)
see CONCERT INDEX under:
(ONDI) **ODE831-2** Sallinen—String Quartets

SIBIRIAKOV, Lev (bass)
see CONCERT INDEX under:
(NIMB) **NI7865** Great Singers at the Mariinsky
Theatre
(PEAR) **GEMMCDS9001/3(2)** Singers of Imperial
Russia, Vol.2 (pt 2)
(PEAR) **GEMMCDS9007/9(2)** Singers of Imperial
Russia, Vol.4 (pt 2)
(PEAR) **GEMMCDS9925(1)** Covent Garden on
Record—Vol.3 (pt 1)

SICA, Gennaro (ten)
Mozart: Nozze di Figaro (Cpte)

SICE, Robert van (marimba/vib)
see CONCERT INDEX under:
(ETCE) **KTC1085** Marimba Concertos

SIDERER, Mathilde (sngr)
Lecocq: Jour et la Nuit (Cpte)
Terrasse: Travaux d'Hercule (Cpte)

SIDHOM, Peter (bar)
Smyth: Wreckers (Cpte)
Verdi: Rigoletto (Cpte), Traviata (Cpte)
see CONCERT INDEX under:
(CALA) **CACD1018** French Chamber Music for
Woodwinds, Volume 2

SIEBER, Gudrun (sop)
Hindemith: Nusch-Nuschi (Cpte)

SIEBERT, Dorothea (sop)
Wagner: Götterdämmerung (Cpte), Parsifal (Cpte),
Rheingold (Cpte)
see CONCERT INDEX under:
(PHIL) **446 057-2PB14** Wagner—The Ring Cycle -
Bayreuth Festival 1967

SIEBERT, Glenn (ten)
Schubert: Mass, D950

SIEBLER, Ulrike (fl)
see CONCERT INDEX under:
(TROU) **TRO-CD01405** Ethel Smyth—Chamber
Works & Songs, Vol.3

SIEDEN, Cyndia (sop)
Gluck: Orfeo ed Euridice (Cpte)
Mozart: Entführung (Cpte)
R.Strauss: Frau ohne Schatten (Cpte)
see CONCERT INDEX under:
(KOCH) **37086-2** Unquiet Peace—The Lied Between
the Wars

SIEGEL, Hermann (bass)
R. Strauss: Elektra (Cpte)

SIEGELE, Dankwart (bass)
Bellini: Puritani (Cpte)

SIEGEL-SCHWALL BAND
cond S. OZAWA
see CONCERT INDEX under:
(DG) **413 851-2GW2** Modern American Favourites

SIEGEN BACH CHORUS COLLEGIUM VOCALE
cond U. STÖTZEL
Telemann: St Matthew Passion (1746) (Cpte)

SIEGHART, Martin (cond)
see Stuttgart CO

SIEMS, Margarete (sop)
see CONCERT INDEX under:
(PEAR) **GEMMCDS9925(1)** Covent Garden on
Record—Vol.3 (pt 1)

SIEPI, Cesare (bass)
Beethoven: Missa Solemnis
Boito: Mefistofele (Cpte)
Donizetti: Lucia di Lammermoor (Cpte)
Mozart: Don Giovanni (Cpte), Nozze di Figaro
(Cpte)
Ponchielli: Gioconda (Cpte)
Puccini: Bohème (Cpte)
Verdi: Don Carlo (Cpte), Forza del Destino (Cpte),
Rigoletto (Cpte)
see CONCERT INDEX under:
(EMI) **CHS5 65506-2** Victor de Sabata conducts
(RCA) **GD60326** Verdi—Operas & Choral Works

SIEWART, Charlotte (sop)
Wagner: Götterdämmerung (Cpte)

SIEWERT, Ruth (contr)
Bruckner: Te Deum
Wagner: Parsifal (Cpte), Walküre (exc)
see CONCERT INDEX under:
(EMI) **CMS5 65212-2** Wagner—Les introuvables du
Ring
(EMI) **CZS7 67123-2** Wagner: Der Ring des
Nibelungen

SIEYES, Maurice (bar)
Massenet: Grisélidis (Cpte)

SIGHELE, Mietta (sop)
Verdi: Aida (Cpte)

SIGMUNDSSON, Kristin (bass)
Bach: St. John Passion, BWV245 (Cpte)
Mozart: Don Giovanni (Cpte), Zauberflöte (Cpte)
Schreker: Gezeichneten (Cpte)

SIGNOR, Franco (bass)
Donizetti: Martyrs (Cpte)

SIGNORE, Gino del (ten)
Verdi: Forza del destino (Cpte)

SIGNORETTI, Leopoldo (ten)
see CONCERT INDEX under:
(SYMP) **SYMCD1065** The Harold Wayne Collection,
Vol.1

SIGNORINI, Francesco (ten)
see CONCERT INDEX under:
(MEMO) **HR4408/9(1)** Singers in Genoa, Vol.1 (disc
1)

SIIRALA, Jussi (pf)
see CONCERT INDEX under:
(BIS) **BIS-CD159** Hindemith—Chamber Works

SIKI, Béla (pf)
see CONCERT INDEX under:
(ARCI) **ARC112/3** Dinu Lipatti—Les Inédits

SIKIRA, Alisa (sop)
Delius: Village Romeo and Juliet (Cpte)

SIKORA, Jozef (vc)
see CONCERT INDEX under:
(MARC) **8 223234** Johann Strauss II Edition, Vol.34

SILBANO, Silvana (mez)
Bellini: Zaira (Cpte)

SILD, Tarmo (bar)
Tubin: Barbara von Tisenhusen (Cpte)

SILESIAN PHILHARMONIC CHOIR
cond W. LUTOSŁAWSKI
see CONCERT INDEX under:
(POLS) **PNCD040** Lutosławski: Vocal and Orchestral
Works

**SILESIAN PHILHARMONIC SYMPHONY
ORCHESTRA**
cond J. SALWAROWSKI
see CONCERT INDEX under:
(CHNT) **LDC278 1092** Lessel—Works for Piano

SILESIAN QUARTET
see CONCERT INDEX under:
(ETCE) **KTC2017** Tansman—String Quartets, etc

SILJA, Anja (sop)
Berg: Wozzeck (Cpte)
Schoenberg: Erwartung (Cpte)
Wagner: Fliegende Holländer (Cpte),
Götterdämmerung (Cpte), Lohengrin (Cpte), Parsifal
(Cpte), Rheingold (Cpte), Tannhäuser (Cpte)
Weill: Mahagonny (Cpte)
see CONCERT INDEX under:
(PHIL) **446 057-2PB14** Wagner—The Ring Cycle -
Bayreuth Festival 1967

SILLICH, Aristodemo (bass)
see CONCERT INDEX under:
(NIMB) **NI7831** Mattia Battistini (1856-1928)
(PREI) **89045** Mattia Battistini (1856-1928)

SILLITO, Kenneth (cond)
see ASMF

SILLITO, Kenneth (vn)
Vaughan Williams: Concerto Accademico
Vivaldi: Concerti, Op. 8 (exc)
Walton: Piano Quartet, Violin Sonata
see CONCERT INDEX under:
(ASV) **CDDCA518** The English Connection
(CHAN) **CHAN8578** Hommages à Haydn, Roussel et
Fauré
(CHAN) **CHAN8621** French Chamber Music
(CHAN) **CHAN8771** Czech Chamber Works
(CHAN) **CHAN9258** Nielsen/Svendsen—Chamber
Works
(CHAN) **CHAN9262/3** Vaughan Williams—Orchestral
Works
(CHAN) **CHAN9292** Walton—Chamber Music
(COLL) **Coll1234-2** English Music for Strings
(CONI) **CDCF172** Malcolm Arnold: Concertos
(LYRI) **SRCD223** Holst—Orchestral Works
(PHIL) **422 503-2PME7** The Complete Mozart Edition
Vol 3
(PHIL) **422 545-2PME3** The Complete Mozart Edition
Vol.45
(PHIL) **426 082-2PBQ** Handel—Orchestral Works

SILLS, Barrett (vc)
Benson: End of the World

SILLS, Beverly (sop)
G. Charpentier: Louise (Cpte)
Rossini: Siège de Corinthe (Cpte)

SILOTI, Alexander (pf)
(PEAR) **GEMMCD9993** Arthur Friedheim—complete
recordings, etc

SILVA, Joana (sop)
see CONCERT INDEX under:
(ERAT) **2292-45926-2** Charpentier—Sacred Choral
Works

SILVA, Miguel da (va)
Beethoven: Piano Quartet, Op. 16, Piano Quartets,
WoO36

SILVA, Rohan de (pf)
see CONCERT INDEX under:
(COLL) **Coll1203-2** Bartók—Violin Sonatas
(RCA) **09026 61386-2** French Violin Sonatas

SILVASTI, Jorma (ten)
Mahler: Lied von der Erde
Sallinen: Kullervo (Cpte)

SILVEIRA, Elisabeth (contr)
see CONCERT INDEX under:
(ERAT) **4509-95307-2** Schubert/Schumann—Sacred
Choral Works

SILVER, Bonnie (hpd)
see CONCERT INDEX under:
(CHAN) **CHAN8937** Arrangements for Guitar and
Harpsichord

SILVERI, Paolo (bar)
see CONCERT INDEX under:
(EMI) **CHS7 69741-2(7)** Record of Singing,
Vol.4—Italian School

SILVERMAN, Robert (pf)
see CONCERT INDEX under:
(CBC) **MVCD1061** Franck—Piano Works

SILVERSTEIN, Joseph (cond)
see Utah SO

SILVERSTEIN, Joseph (vn)
see CONCERT INDEX under:
(NORT) **NR206-CD** Arthur Foote—Chamber Works
(NORT) **NR9004-CD** Dark Garden

SILVERTHORNE, Paul (va)
Haydn: Quatuor, HobII/G4
Schubert: Trio, D96
see CONCERT INDEX under:
(ASV) **CDDCA868** Schnittke—Chamber Music,
Volume 1
(EMI) **CDC5 55398-2** Britten—Chamber Works
(MERI) **CDE84232** Brahms/Dvořák—Gypsy Songs

SILVESTRELLI, Andrea (bass)
Mozart: Don Giovanni (Cpte)
Verdi: Don Carlo (Cpte)

SILVESTRI, Constantin (cond)
see Bournemouth SO

SIMA, Gabriele (sop)
Busoni: Turandot (Cpte)
Einem: Dantons Tod (Cpte)
Mozart: Zauberflöte (Cpte)
R. Strauss: Rosenkavalier (Cpte)
Rossini: Barbiere di Siviglia (Cpte)
Schoeck: Penthesilea (Cpte)
Wagner: Tannhäuser (Cpte)

SIMÁNDY, József (ten)
Kodály: Psalmus Hungaricus

SIMČISKO, Viktor (vn)
see CONCERT INDEX under:
(MARC) **8 223240** Johann Strauss II Edition, Vol.40

ŠIMČISKO, Viktor (vn)
Gluck: Trio Sonatas (1746)
Grechaninov: Piano Trio 1, Piano Trio 2
see CONCERT INDEX under:
(CAMP) **RRCD1317** Martinů/Kobayashi—Orchestral
Works
(MARC) **8 223629** Ippolitov-Ivanov—Orchestral Works

SIMCOCK, Iain (organ)
Pott: Christus
see CONCERT INDEX under:
(CARL) **PCD919** Great Music from Great Occasions
at Westminster Abbey
(HYPE) **CDA66330** Masterpieces of Mexican
Polyphony
(HYPE) **CDA66664** Poulenc—Choral Works
(HYPE) **CDA66668** Adeste Fideles
(HYPE) **CDA66669** Panis angelicus
(HYPE) **CDA66688** Festal Sacred Music of Bavaria
(HYPE) **CDA66757** Duruflé—Requiem
(PROU) **PROUCD135** Music for Trumpet and Organ

SIMCOCK, Iain (handbells)
see CONCERT INDEX under:
(COLL) **Coll1428-2** Tavener—To a Child dancing in
the Wind
(VIRG) **VC5 45035-2** Tavener—Thunder entered Her

SIMIC, Goran (bass)
Schreker: Irrelohe (Cpte)
Verdi: Ballo in maschera (Cpte)

SIMIONATO, Giulietta (mez)
Cilea: Adriana Lecouvreur (Cpte)
Donizetti: Anna Bolena (Cpte)
Gluck: Orfeo ed Euridice (Cpte)
J. Strauss II: Fledermaus (Cpte)
Ponchielli: Gioconda (Cpte)
Rossini: Italiana in Algeri (Cpte)
Verdi: Aida (Cpte), Don Carlo (Cpte), Falstaff (Cpte),
Forza del Destino (Cpte), Rigoletto (Cpte), Trovatore
(Cpte)
see CONCERT INDEX under:
(DECC) **411 665-2DM3** Puccini: Il trittico
(EMI) **CHS7 69741-2(7)** Record of Singing,
Vol.4—Italian School

SIMKOWSKY, Nikolaus (ten)
Monteverdi: Orfeo (Cpte)
R. Strauss: Rosenkavalier (Cpte)

SIMMONS, Raymond (tpt)
see CONCERT INDEX under:
(DECC) **436 239-2DH** Works for piano and orchestra

SIMON, Emil (cond)
see Cluj-Napoca PO

SIMON, Enid (hp)
see CONCERT INDEX under:
(LOND) **436 394-2LM** Britten—Vocal & Choral
Works

SIMON, François (narr)
see CONCERT INDEX under:
(CLAV) **CD50-8918** Ansermet conducts Stravinsky

SIMON, Geoffrey (cond)
see ECO

SIMON, Jan (pf)
Schulhoff: Piano Concerto 1, Piano Concerto 2

SIMON, Monique (sop)
Rameau: Hippolyte et Aricie (Cpte)

SIMONE, Bruno de (bar)
Pergolesi: Frate 'nnamorato (Cpte)
Puccini: Turandot (Cpte)
Rossini: Cambiale di Matrimonio (Cpte)

SIMONEAU, Léopold (ten)
Berlioz: Grande messe des morts (Cpte)
Bizet: Pêcheurs de Perles (Cpte)
Gluck: Orphée (Cpte)
Mozart: Così fan tutte (Cpte), Don Giovanni (Cpte)
see CONCERT INDEX under:
(EMI) **CDH5 65072-2** Glyndebourne Recorded - 1934-
1994
(EMI) **CHS7 63715-2** Mozart: Die Entführung, etc
(PHIL) **438 953-2PM2** Alarie/Simoneau - Arias &
Duets
(PHIL) **442 272-2PM2** The Best of Bizet

SIMONETTO, Alfredo (cond)
see Rome RAI Orch

SIMONIN, Christine (ondes martenot)
see CONCERT INDEX under:
(ACCO) **20123-2** Koechlin—Vocal and Chamber
Works

SIMONOV, Yuri (cond)
see Philh

(LA) SIMPHONIE DU MARAIS
cond H. REYNE
Delalande: Sinfonies pour les soupers du Roi

SIMPSON, David (vc)
Brahms: String Sextet 1, String Sextet 2

SIMPSON, Derek (vc)
see CONCERT INDEX under:
(CFP) **CD-CFP4557** Baroque Favourites

SIMPSON, Marietta (mez)
Bach: Magnificat, BWV243, Mass in B minor,
BWV232 (Cpte)
Gershwin: Porgy and Bess (Cpte)
Janáček: Glagolitic Mass (Cpte)

Mahler: Symphony 8
Schubert: Mass, D950
Vivaldi: Gloria, RV589
see CONCERT INDEX under:
(TELA) **CD80248** Beethoven: Choral Works
(TELA) **CD80362** Poulenc/Szymanowski—Stabat
Mater

SIMPSON, Olive (sop)
Towns: Buccaneers (exc)

SINAISKY, Vasili (cond)
see Leningrad PO

SINCLAIR, James (cond)
see New England Orch

SINCLAIR, Jeannette (sop)
Mozart: Nozze di Figaro (Cpte)
Rossini: Comte Ory (Cpte)

SINCLAIR, Monica (contr)
Delibes: Lakmé (exc)
Donizetti: Fille du régiment (Cpte)
Gounod: Faust (Cpte)
J.Strauss II: Zigeunerbaron (Cpte)
Mozart: Nozze di Figaro (Cpte)
Purcell: Dido (Cpte)
Rossini: Comte Ory (Cpte)
Walton: Troilus and Cressida (exc)
see CONCERT INDEX under:
(EMI) **CDC7 47283-2** Maria Callas - Mad Scenes &
Bel Canto Arias
(EMI) **CDH5 65072-2** Glyndebourne Recorded - 1934-
1994
(EMI) **CMS7 63244-2** The Art of Maria Callas

SINE NOMINE QUARTET
see CONCERT INDEX under:
(CLAV) **CD50-9404/5** Brahms—String Quartets
(CLAV) **CD50-9501** Arriaga—String Quartets
(ERAT) **4509-91721-2** Dutilleux—Piano Works and
Chamber Music
cond A. CHARLET
Gounod: Requiem

SINFONIA CHORUS
cond B. BROUGHTON
Rózsa: Julius Caesar (exc)
cond R. HICKOX
Bliss: Pastoral

SINFONIA DA CAMERA
see CONCERT INDEX under:
(ARAB) **Z6570** Saint-Saëns—Chamber Orchestral
Works
cond I. HOBSON
see CONCERT INDEX under:
(ARAB) **Z6569** Milhaud—Jazz Works

SINFONIA OF LONDON
cond J. BARBIROLLI
see CONCERT INDEX under:
(EMI) **CDC7 47537-2** English String Music
cond A. BLISS
see CONCERT INDEX under:
(EMI) **CDM7 64718-2** The Composer Conducts
cond B. BROUGHTON
Rózsa: Ivanhoe (exc), Julius Caesar (exc)
cond R. FRÜHBECK DE BURGOS
see CONCERT INDEX under:
(EMI) **CDM7 69502-2** On Wings of Song
cond J. HOLLINGSWORTH
see CONCERT INDEX under:
(EMI) **CDANGEL 5** Norton—Chu Chin Chow
cond N. DEL MAR
Brahms: Violin Concerto

SINFONIA VARSOVIA
Mozart: Piano Concerto 21, Piano Concerto 22, Piano
Concerto 24, Piano Concerto 27
cond E. KRIVINE
see CONCERT INDEX under:
(DENO) **CO-75597** Mozart—Chamber Works
(DENO) **CO-79442** Beyond Wagner
cond Y. MENUHIN
Mozart: Symphony 40, Symphony 41
see CONCERT INDEX under:
(VIRG) **CUV5 61204-2** Mozart—Orchestral Works
cond W. MICHNIEWSKI
Preisner: Secret Garden (exc)
cond J. SWOBODA
Beethoven: Piano Concerto 4

SINFONIA 21
cond E. DOWNES
Prokofiev: Eugene Onegin (Cpte)

SINFONYE
cond S. WISHART
see CONCERT INDEX under:
(HYPE) **CDA66283** Bella Domna
(HYPE) **CDA66625** The Sweet Look & the Loving
Manner
(HYPE) **CDA66685** Gabriel's Greeting

SINGAPORE SYMPHONY ORCHESTRA
cond C. HUEY
Lachner: Symphony 1
Spohr: Symphony 2

SINGCIRCLE
cond G. ROSE
see CONCERT INDEX under:
(CNTI) **CCD1061** Montague—Orchestral and
Chamber Music

SINGER, David (cl)
Mozart: Sinfonia Concertante, K297b
see CONCERT INDEX under:
(DG) **431 665-2GX3** Mozart—Wind Concertos

SINGER, Kurt (cond)
see Berlin St Op Orch

SINGER, Mark (sngr)
Rorem: Three Sisters Who Are Not Sisters (Cpte)

SINGEROVÁ, Marta (pf)
Martinů: La Jolla

SINGHER, Martial (bar)
see CONCERT INDEX under:
(EMI) **CMS7 64008-2(1)** Wagner Singing on Record
(pt 1)
(EPM) **150 122** Milhaud—Historic Recordings 1928-
1948
(PREI) **89011** Marjorie Lawrence (1909-1979)

SINGING CITY CHOIRS
cond E. ORMANDY
Beethoven: Missa Solemnis

SINIAWSKAIA, Tamara (sop)
see CONCERT INDEX under:
(RCA) **74321 32042-2** Scriabin—Symphonies, etc

SINIMBERGHI, Gino (ten)
see CONCERT INDEX under:
(NIMB) **NI7848** Great Singers at the Berlin State
Opera

SINNONE, Aldo (ten)
see CONCERT INDEX under:
(SCHW) **314512** Vienna State Opera Live, Vol.1

SINOPOLI, Giuseppe (cond)
see Berlin Deutsche Op Orch

SINYAVSKAYA, Tamara (mez)
Prokofiev: Ivan the Terrible Suite
Tchaikovsky: Eugene Onegin (Cpte)

SIPES, Theodore (bar)
see CONCERT INDEX under:
(BAY) **BCD-1011** American Choral Music

SIPKAY, Deborah (hp)
see CONCERT INDEX under:
(MARC) **8 223404** Atterberg—Chamber Music, Vol.1

SIPPOLA, Ulla (sop)
Rossini: Petite messe solennelle (Cpte)

SIRACUSA, Maria (fl)
see CONCERT INDEX under:
(SCHW) **310632** Globokar—Chamber Works

SIRBU, Mariana (vn)
see CONCERT INDEX under:
(DYNA) **CDS21/2** Franck—Chamber works
(PHIL) **442 145-2PH** Vivaldi—Violin Concertos

SIRKIÄ, Raimo (ten)
Mahler: Symphony 8

SIROKAY, Zsuzsanna (pf)
see CONCERT INDEX under:
(JECK) **JD536-2** The Romantic Clarinet

SITAR, Helmut (perc)
Tubin: Requiem for Fallen Soldiers

SÍTEK, Václav (bar)
Martinů: Field Mass

SITKOVETSKY, Dimitri (vn/dir)
Mozart: Violin Concerto, K218, Violin Concerto,
K219
see CONCERT INDEX under:
(NOVA) **150 012-2** Mozart—Violin Concertos
(NOVA) **150 017-2** Bach—Violin Concertos

SITKOVETSKY, Dmitry (vn)
Bach: Goldberg Variations, Solo Violin Partitas and
Sonatas
Beethoven: Piano Trios (exc), Romances, Serenade,
Op. 8, Violin Concerto
Schubert: Notturno, D897, Piano Trio 1, Piano Trio 2
Shostakovich: Violin Concerto 1, Violin Concerto 2
see CONCERT INDEX under:
(ORFE) **C047831A** Grieg—Violin Sonatas
(ORFE) **C103841A** Spohr: Lieder
(VIRG) **VCS 45002-2** 20th Century Violin Sonatas
(VIRG) **VCS 45074-2** Prokofiev—Violin Works

SITWELL, Dame Edith (narr)
see CONCERT INDEX under:
(LOND) **425 661-2LM** Walton & Arnold: Orchestral &
Vocal Works

SIVALL, Olle (ten)
Verdi: Rigoletto (Cpte)

SIVIERI, Enrico (cond)
see orch

SIVONEN, Ilkka (pf)
see CONCERT INDEX under:
(BIS) **BIS-CD508** Kokkonen—Complete Orchestral
Music, Vol.4

SIX BROWN BROTHERS (SAXOPHONE SEXTET)
see CONCERT INDEX under:
(PEAR) **GEMMCDS9056/8** Music from the New York
Stage, Vol. 3: 1913-17

(THE) SIXTEEN
cond H. CHRISTOPHERS
Bach: Christmas Oratorio, BWV248 (Cpte), Mass in B
minor, BWV232 (Cpte), Motets (Cpte)
Fayrfax: Aeternae laudis lilium, Missa Albanus

Handel: Chandos Anthem 10, Chandos Anthem 11,
Israel in Egypt (Cpte), Messiah (Cpte)
Purcell: Fairy Queen, Z629 (Cpte)
Teixeira: Te Deum
　see CONCERT INDEX *under:*
(CHAN) **CHAN0504**　Handel—Chandos Anthems Vol.
2
(CHAN) **CHAN0505**　Handel—Chandos Anthems Vol.
3
(CHAN) **CHAN0513**　Tallis: Sacred Choral Works
(CHAN) **CHAN0517**　Handel—Sacred Choral Works
(COLL) **Coll1270-2**　20th Century Christmas Music
(COLL) **Coll1286-2**　Britten—Choral Works
(COLL) **Coll1287-2**　American Collection
(COLL) **Coll1300-2**　Traditional Christmas Collection
(COLL) **Coll1314-2**　The Rose and the Ostrich
Feather
(COLL) **Coll1316-2**　Crown of Thorns - Eton
Choirbook, Vol.2
(COLL) **Coll1320-2**　Baroque Choral Works
(COLL) **Coll1342-2**　The Pillars of Eternity - Eton Choir
Book Vol III
(COLL) **Coll1343-2**　Britten—Choral Works, Vol. II
(COLL) **Coll1360-2**　Sacred Music from Venice and
Rome
(COLL) **Coll1370-2**　Britten—Choral Works, Vol.3
(COLL) **Coll1395-2**　The Flower of all Virginity
(COLL) **Coll1405-2**　Tavener—Choral Works
(COLL) **Coll1407-2**　Cardoso/Lôbo—Choral Works
(COLL) **Coll1425-2**　Purcell—Funeral Music for Queen
Mary
(COLL) **Coll5009-2**　Allegri & Lotti &
Palestrina—Sacred choral works
(COLL) **Coll7016-2**　Handel—Alexander's Feast
(HYPE) **CDA66259**　Sheppard—Sacred Choral
Works
(HYPE) **CDA66263**　Christmas Music from Medieval
and Renaissance Europe
(HYPE) **CDA66311/2**　Monteverdi: St Barbara
Vespers
(HYPE) **CDA66319**　Mundy—Sacred Choral Works
(HYPE) **CDA66325**　Taverner—Sacred Choral Works
(HYPE) **CDA66360**　Taverner—Missa Corona Spinea
(HYPE) **CDA66418**　John Sheppard—Church Music,
Vol.2
(HYPE) **CDA66427**　Taverner—Sacred Choral Works
(HYPE) **CDA66507**　Tavener—Choral Works
(HYPE) **CDA66570**　Sheppard—Church Music Volume
3
(HYPE) **CDA66603**　Sheppard—Cathedral Music,
Vol.2
(HYPE) **CDA66639**　Taverner—Choral Works
(MERI) **CDE84175**　Music from the Eton Choirbook
(VIRG) **VC7 59192-2**　Poulenc—Choral Works
(VIRG) **VC7 59311-2**　Poulenc—Choral Music, Vol 2
　cond T. KOOPMAN
Handel: Messiah (Cpte)
　cond E. SVETLANOV
Holst: Planets

(THE) SIXTEEN ORCHESTRA
　cond H. CHRISTOPHERS
Bach: Christmas Oratorio, BWV248 (Cpte), Mass in B
minor, BWV232 (Cpte)
Handel: Chandos Anthem 10, Chandos Anthem 11,
Israel in Egypt (Cpte), Messiah (Cpte), Organ
Concertos (exc)
Purcell: Fairy Queen, Z629 (Cpte)
Teixeira: Te Deum
　see CONCERT INDEX *under:*
(CHAN) **CHAN0504**　Handel—Chandos Anthems Vol.
2
(CHAN) **CHAN0505**　Handel—Chandos Anthems Vol.
3
(CHAN) **CHAN0517**　Handel—Sacred Choral works
(COLL) **Coll1270-2**　20th Century Christmas Music
(COLL) **Coll1320-2**　Baroque Choral Works
(COLL) **Coll1425-2**　Purcell—Funeral Music for Queen
Mary
(COLL) **Coll7016-2**　Handel—Alexander's Feast
(HYPE) **CDA66311/2**　Monteverdi: St Barbara
Vespers

SJÖBERG, Ingela Högerås (sop)
Schnittke: Requiem

SJÖGREN, Björn (va)
　see CONCERT INDEX *under:*
(MSVE) **MSCD415**　Kraus—Chamber Music

SJÖGREN, Kim (vn)
Kuhlau: Flute Quintets, Op. 51
Mozart: Violin Concerto, K216, Violin Concerto,
K219
　see CONCERT INDEX *under:*
(CHAN) **CHAN8894**　Nielsen—Concertos
(CHAN) **CHAN9209**　Lumbye—Waltzes, Galops &
Polkas

SJÖSTEDT, Margareta (mez)
R. Strauss: Elektra (Cpte)
　see CONCERT INDEX *under:*
(VANG) **08.2010.71**　Bach—Choral Works

SJÖSTRÖM, Gabriella (organ)
　see CONCERT INDEX *under:*
(BIS) **BIS-CD510**　Organ Music from the USA

SKAMPA, Milan (va)
Brahms: String Sextet 1, String Sextet 2

SKANAVI, Vladimir (pf)
　see CONCERT INDEX *under:*
(CDM) **LDC288 038/40**　Rimsky-Korsakov—Complete
Songs

SKAUG, Erna (sop)
　see CONCERT INDEX *under:*
(AURO) **ACD4971**　Nystedt—Chamber and Vocal
Works

SKEAPING, Lucie (mez)
　see CONCERT INDEX *under:*
(SAYD) **CD-SDL400**　English National Songs

SKEAPING, Roderick (vn)
　see CONCERT INDEX *under:*
(HARM) **HMX290 1528/33(2)**　A Purcell Companion (pt
2)

SKERJANC, Edvard (vc)
(CHAN) **CHAN8651**　Vivaldi: Concertos

SKIDMORE, Jeffrey (cond)
　see Ex Cathedra Baroque Orch

SKIGIN, Semion (pf)
　see CONCERT INDEX *under:*
(CONI) **CDCF229**　Mussorgsky—Songs, Vol.1
(CONI) **75605 51248-2**　Mussorgsky—Songs, Vol.2

SKINNER, John York (alto)
Handel: Partenope (Cpte)

SKINNER, Noel (pf)
　see CONCERT INDEX *under:*
(MERI) **CDE84245**　D. Stoll—Reflections on Vedic
Scriptures

SKITCH, Jeffrey (bar)
Sullivan: Gondoliers (Cpte), HMS Pinafore (Cpte)
　see CONCERT INDEX *under:*
(DECC) **430 095-2DWO**　The World of Gilbert &
Sullivan, Vol.1
(DECC) **433 868-2DWO**　The World of Gilbert &
Sullivan - Volume 2

SKOKAN, Franz (bass)
　see CONCERT INDEX *under:*
(SCHW) **314602**　Vienna State Opera Live, Vol.10

SKORODIN, Elaine (vn)
　see CONCERT INDEX *under:*
(KOCH) **37240-2**　Women at an Exposition - 1893
Chicago World Fair

SKOVAJSKA, Jiří (pf)
Martinů: Double Concerto
　see CONCERT INDEX *under:*
(CONI) **CDCF210**　Martinu—Orchestral Works

SKOVHUS, Boje (bar)
Beethoven: Fidelio (Cpte)
Britten: War Requiem
Lehár: Lustige Witwe (Cpte)
Leoncavallo: Pagliacci (Cpte)
Mozart: Nozze di Figaro (Cpte)
Orff: Carmina Burana
Schoeck: Venus (Cpte)
Spohr: Faust (Cpte)
　see CONCERT INDEX *under:*
(SONY) **SK57969**　Wolf/Korngold—Eichendorff
Lieder
(SONY) **SK66835**　Schubert—Schwanengesang and
Lieder

SKRAM, Knut (bar)
　see CONCERT INDEX *under:*
(BIS) **BIS-CD321**　Nielsen—Orchestral Works
(BIS) **BIS-CD614/6**　Nielsen—Symphonies and
Concertos
(VICT) **VCD19039**　Grieg—Songs, Vol.2
(VICT) **VCD19040**　Grieg—Complete Songs - Volume
III
(VICT) **VCD19041**　Grieg—Songs, Vol.4

SKROBACS, Lawrence (pf)
　see CONCERT INDEX *under:*
(ETCE) **KTC1029**　Yvonne Kenny at the Wigmore
Hall
(NEW) **80220-2**　Angels' Visits

SKROWACZEWSKI, Stanislaw (cond)
　see Hallé

ŠKVÁROVÁ, Yvona (contr)
　see CONCERT INDEX *under:*
(STUD) **SM1223.27**　Rossini—Complete unpublished
Sacred Works

SKVOR, Petr (vn)
Suk: Fairy Tale

SLABBERT, Wicus (sngr)
Zemlinsky: Kleider machen Leute (Cpte)

SLADDEN, Daniel (bass)
　see CONCERT INDEX *under:*
(ARGO) **433 215-2ZH**　Britten—Christmas Music

SLAGTER, Jacob (hn)
　see CONCERT INDEX *under:*
(DECC) **444 455-2DH**　Martin—Ballades; Concerto for
7 Wind Instruments
(OTTA) **OTRC29134**　Brahms—Piano Trios

SLANE, Philip (ten)
Handel: Saul (Cpte)

SLATER, Joseph (fl)
　see CONCERT INDEX *under:*
(DUTT) **CDAX8014**　British Gramophone Premieres

SLATINARU, Maria (sop)
Puccini: Tabarro (Cpte)

SLATKIN, Felix (cond)
　see Concert Arts Stgs

SLATKIN, Leonard (cond)
　see BRSO

SLATKIN, Leonard (pf)
　see CONCERT INDEX *under:*
(RCA) **RD60431**　Dvořák—Works for Violin
(RCA) **09026 61581-2**　Bernstein—Orchestral & Vocal
Works

SLÁVIK, Ján (vc)
Schmidt: Clarinet and Piano Quintet 2
　see CONCERT INDEX *under:*
(MARC) **8 223415**　Schmidt—Chamber Works

SLAVYANKA
　cond A. SHIPOVALNIKOV
Shvedov: Liturgy of St John Chrysostom (Cpte)

SLEMBECK, Dieter (ten)
Wagner: Parsifal (Cpte)

ŠLEPKOVSKÁ (MEZ), Denisa (mez)
Respighi: Primavera

SLEZAK, Leo (ten)
　see CONCERT INDEX *under:*
(NIMB) **NI7856**　Legendary Tenors
(PEAR) **GEMMCDS9924(2)**　Covent Garden on
Record, Vol.2 (pt 2)
(PREI) **89020**　Leo Slezak (1873-1946)
(SIMA) **PSC1810(1)**　Grieg—Songs (historical
recordings, pt 1)
(SYMP) **SYMCD1081**　The Harold Wayne Collection,
Vol.5

SLOBODSKAYA, Oda (sop)
　see CONCERT INDEX *under:*
(EMI) **CDC7 54839-2**　Medtner plays Medtner

SLOVÁK, Ladislav (cond)
　see Bratislava RSO

SLOVAK CHAMBER ORCHESTRA
　cond B. WARCHAL
Corelli: Concerti grossi, Op. 6
Dvořák: Serenade, Op.22
Suk: Serenade, Op.6
　see CONCERT INDEX *under:*
(CAMP) **RRCD1313**　Britten—Vocal and Orchestral
Works
(CPO) **CPO999 101-2**　M. Haydn—Symphonies
(CPO) **CPO999 152-2**　M. Haydn—Symphonies
(CPO) **CPO999 153-2**　M. Haydn—Symphonies
(OPUS) **9150 1473**　L.Mozart & Telemann: Orchestral
Works
(OPUS) **9350 1710**　Concertos For Trumpet and
Orchestra
(OPUS) **9350 1773**　20th Century Works for String
Orchestra
(OPUS) **9350 1812**　Mannheim Symphonies

SLOVAK FOLK ENSEMBLE CHORUS
　cond O. LENÁRD
Brian: Symphony 1

SLOVAK OPERA CHORUS
　cond A. LEAPER
Brian: Symphony 4
　cond O. LENÁRD
Brian: Symphony 1

SLOVAK PHILHARMONIC CHORUS
　cond C. ABBADO
Mussorgsky: Boris Godunov (Cpte), Khovanshchina
(Cpte)
Schoenberg: Gurrelieder
　cond ADRIANO
Respighi: Liriche (1921)
　see CONCERT INDEX *under:*
(MARC) **8 223315**　Bliss—Film Music
　cond M. DE BERNART
Donizetti: Maria di Rohan (Cpte)
　cond C. BREMBECK
Bach: Mass in B minor, BWV232 (Cpte)
　cond O. DOHNÁNYI
　see CONCERT INDEX *under:*
(NAXO) **8 550241**　Verdi—Opera Choruses
　cond R. DUARTE
Villa-Lobos: Discovery of Brazil Suites
　cond S. GUNZENHAUSER
Orff: Carmina burana
　cond W. HUMBURG
Puccini: Bohème (Cpte)
　cond Z. KOŠLER
Martinů: Gilgamesh
　cond E. KÖRNER
Marschner: Hans Heiling (Cpte)
　cond A. LEAPER
Brian: Symphony 4
　see CONCERT INDEX *under:*
(MARC) **8 223446**　Holbrooke—Orchestral Works
　cond O. LENÁRD
Bellini: Sonnambula (Cpte)
Brian: Symphony 1
Suchoň: Whirlpool (Cpte)
　cond F. LUISI
Donizetti: Favorita (Cpte)
　cond A. NANUT
Beethoven: Mass in C
　cond C. PIANTINI
Bizet: Pêcheurs de Perles (Cpte)
　cond A. RAHBARI
Brahms: Deutsches Requiem, Op.45 (Cpte)
Dvořák: Stabat mater, Te Deum
Leoncavallo: Pagliacci (Cpte)
Mascagni: Cavalleria Rusticana (Cpte)
Puccini: Madama Butterfly (Cpte), Tosca (Cpte)

SMIT, Henk (bass)
R. Strauss: Rosenkavalier (Cpte)

SMIT, Leo (pf)
see CONCERT INDEX under:
(SONY) SM2K66345 Copland—Complete Music for
Solo Piano

SMITH, Alan (organ)
see CONCERT INDEX under:
(CAMP) RR2CD1331/2 Havergal Brian—Orchestral
Works

SMITH, Alexis (sngr)
Sondheim: Follies (Cpte)

SMITH, Alma Jean (sop)
Gluck: Iphigénie en Tauride (Cpte)

SMITH, Andrew (bar)
Gershwin: Porgy and Bess (Cpte)

SMITH, Angus (ten)
see CONCERT INDEX under:
(ASV) CDGAU114 Tallis/Sheppard—Masses
(ASV) CDGAU122 Venice Preserved

SMITH, Brooks (pf)
see CONCERT INDEX under:
(RCA) GD87706 Beethoven: Violin Sonatas, Vol.3
(RCA) GD87873 Beethoven, Brahms & Schubert:
Chamber Works
(RCA) GD87965 Dvořák & Brahms: Chamber Works
(RCA) 09026 61778-2(08) The Heifetz Collection, Vol.
8
(RCA) 09026 61778-2(09) The Heifetz Collection, Vol.
9
(RCA) 09026 61778-2(16) The Heifetz Collection, Vol.
16
(RCA) 09026 61778-2(24) The Heifetz Collection, Vol.
24
(RCA) 09026 61778-2(26) The Heifetz Collection, Vol.
26
(RCA) 09026 61778-2(28) The Heifetz Collection, Vol.
28
(RCA) 09026 61778-2(31) The Heifetz Collection, Vol.
31
(RCA) 09026 61778-2(32) The Heifetz Collection, Vol.
32
(RCA) 09026 61778-2(33) The Heifetz Collection, Vol.
33
(RCA) 09026 61778-2(35) The Heifetz Collection, Vol.
35
(RCA) 09026 61778-2(40) The Heifetz Collection, Vol.
40
(RCA) 09026 61778-2(41) The Heifetz Collection, Vol.
41
(RCA) 09026 61778-2(42) The Heifetz Collection, Vol.
42
(RCA) 09026 61778-2(45) The Heifetz Collection, Vol.
45
(RCA) 09026 61778-2(46) The Heifetz Collection,
Vol.46 - The final recital

SMITH, Carol (mez)
Mascagni: Cavalleria Rusticana (Cpte)
see CONCERT INDEX under:
(CHAN) CHAN8865 Rossini: Opera Arias
(SONY) SM2K47522 Beethoven & Haydn—Choral
Works

SMITH, Craig (cond)
see Emmanuel Music Chor

SMITH, Cyril (pf)
see CONCERT INDEX under:
(EMI) CDM7 64044-2 Arnold—Orchestral Works
(NIMB) NI5178 Piano Works for Three Hands

SMITH, Daniel (bar)
see CONCERT INDEX under:
(RCA) 09026 61509-2 A Salute to American Music

SMITH, Daniel (bn)
see CONCERT INDEX under:
(ASV) CDDCA535 English Music for Bassoon and
Piano
(ASV) CDDCA565 Vivaldi—Bassoon Concertos, Vol
1
(ASV) CDDCA571 Vivaldi—Bassoon Concertos, Vol.
2
(ASV) CDDCA613 Chamber Works for Bassoon
(ASV) CDDCA662 Vivaldi—Bassoon Concertos, Vol.
3
(ASV) CDDCA751 Vivaldi—Bassoon Concerti, Vol.5
(ASV) CDDCA752 Vivaldi—Bassoon Concerti, Vol.6

SMITH, Dave (pf)
see CONCERT INDEX under:
(ECM) 847 537-2 Gavin Bryars—After the Requiem

SMITH, Dave (ten hn)
see CONCERT INDEX under:
(ECM) 847 537-2 Gavin Bryars—After the Requiem

SMITH, David (vc)
see CONCERT INDEX under:
(CRD) CRD3457 Dvořák—Hausmusik

SMITH, Donald George (ten)
Saint-Saëns: Samson et Dalila (Cpte)

SMITH, Erik (hpd)
see CONCERT INDEX under:
(PHIL) 422 545-2PME3 The Complete Mozart Edition
Vol.45

SMITH, Fenwick (fl)
see CONCERT INDEX under:
(HYPE) CDA66414 Koechlin—Flute Works

(NORT) NR227-CD American Chamber Music with
Flute
(NORT) NR248-CD Silenced Voices - Victims of the
Holocaust

SMITH, Geoff (kybds)
see CONCERT INDEX under:
(SONY) SK66605 Geoff Smith—Fifteen Wild
Decembers

SMITH, Gregg (cond)
see G. Smith Sngrs

SMITH, Henry Charles (tbn)
see CONCERT INDEX under:
(SONY) SM2K52671 Hindemith—Chamber Works

SMITH, Hopkinson (lte)
Bach: Solo Cello Suites (exc)
see CONCERT INDEX under:
(ASTR) E8528 Gallot—Works for Lute

SMITH, Hopkinson (theorbo)
Marais: Pièces de viole, III/I (exc), Pièces de viole,
III/II (exc), Pièces de viole IV/II (exc), Pièces de viole
V/II (exc)

SMITH, Hopkinson (vihuela)
Mudarra: Tres libros (Vocal works) (Cpte), Tres libros
(1546) (Cpte)
Narváez: Seys libros del delphin (exc)
see CONCERT INDEX under:
(ASTR) E7748 Milán—Libro de musica, Vol.1
(AUVI) E7777 Luys Milan—El Maestro

SMITH, Jeffrey (treb)
Puccini: Tosca (Cpte)

SMITH, Jennifer (sop)
Bach: Cantata 208, Mass in B minor, BWV232
(Cpte)
Handel: Allegro, il penseroso ed il moderato (Cpte),
Amadigi di Gaula (Cpte), Hercules (Cpte), Ottone
(Cpte)
Lully: Phaëton (Cpte)
Marais: Alcyone (Cpte)
Mondonville: Titon et l'Aurore (Cpte)
Monteverdi: Orfeo (Cpte)
Purcell: Fairy Queen, Z629 (Cpte), Indian Queen,
Z630 (Cpte), King Arthur, Z628 (Cpte), St Cecilia's
Day Ode, Z328, Tempest, Z631 (Cpte)
Rameau: Castor et Pollux (Cpte), Indes Galantes
(Cpte), Naïs (Cpte), Platée (Cpte)
Stravinsky: Pulcinella
see CONCERT INDEX under:
(ARCH) 437 834-2AH Christmas in Rome - Gloria
(DECC) 430 160-2DM Haydn: Masses & Keyboard
Concerto
(DECC) 433 908-2DM2 Falla—Orchestral Music
(DECC) 443 455-2DF2 Vivaldi—Sacred Choral Works
(ERAT) 2292-45923-2 Bach/Vivaldi—Sacred Choral
Works
(ERAT) 4509-96371-2 Gardiner—The Purcell
Collection

SMITH, Joshua (fl)
see CONCERT INDEX under:
(DECC) 443 175-2DH Mozart—Orchestral Works

SMITH, Kenneth (fl)
see CONCERT INDEX under:
(ASV) CDDCA739 Summer Works
(CONI) CDCF203 Vivaldi—Concertos

SMITH, Kevin (alto)
Ligeti: Grand Macabre (Cpte)

SMITH, Lawrance Leighton (cond)
see Louisville Orch

SMITH, Leonore (fl)
see CONCERT INDEX under:
(PHIL) 412 892-2PH Vivaldi: Double Concertos
(VIRG) VC7 59604-2 Debussy—Chamber Works

SMITH, Malcolm (bass)
Penderecki: Polish Requiem
Prokofiev: War and Peace (Cpte)
Weill: Sieben Todsünden (Cpte)

SMITH, Marla (vn)
see CONCERT INDEX under:
(DELO) DE3045 Organ Recital

SMITH, Martin (sngr)
Coward: Bitter Sweet (Cpte)

SMITH, Michael (cond)
see Llandaff Cath Ch

SMITH, Norman (tpt)
see CONCERT INDEX under:
(DELO) DE3002 The Sound of Trumpets

SMITH, Philip (pf)
see CONCERT INDEX under:
(RCA) RD60557 Evelyn Glennie - Light in Darkness

SMITH, Philip (tpt)
Copland: Quiet city

SMITH, Robert (treb)
see CONCERT INDEX under:
(DECC) 430 263-2DM Purcell—Sacred choral works

SMITH, Ronald (pf)
Bach: Solo Violin Partitas and Sonatas (exc)
Chopin: Etudes (exc)
Liszt: Beethoven Symphonies, S464 (exc)
see CONCERT INDEX under:
(EMI) CDH7 64928-2 Bach—Keyboard Works

(NIMB) NI5187 Balakirev, Mussorgsky, Scriabin:
Piano works

SMITH, Sandy (ten hn)
see CONCERT INDEX under:
(CHAN) CHAN4523 Concerto

SMITH, Steven (prod)
see CONCERT INDEX under:
(KOCH) 37238-2 A Chance Operation - John Cage
Tribute

SMITH, Steven (vn)
see CONCERT INDEX under:
(ASV) CDDCA769 Franck—Miscellaneous Works
(ASV) CDQS6140 Haydn/Stamitz—Sinfonie
Concertanti

SMITH QUARTET
see CONCERT INDEX under:
(CNTI) CCD1061 Montague—Orchestral and
Chamber Music
(LAND) CTLCD111 Cover him with grass

(GREGG) SMITH SINGERS
cond G. SMITH
see CONCERT INDEX under:
(KOCH) 37026-2 Morton Gould—Choral Music
cond L. STOKOWSKI
see CONCERT INDEX under:
(SONY) MPK46726 Ives—Orchestral and Vocal
Works

SMITHSONIAN CHAMBER PLAYERS
cond K. SLOWIK
see CONCERT INDEX under:
(DHM) 05472 77327-2 Couperin—Concerts Royaux
(DHM) 05472 77343-2 Metamorphosis

SMITS, Raphaëlla (gtr)
see CONCERT INDEX under:
(ACCE) ACC29182D Sor/Coste—Guitar Works

SMOLA, Emmerich (cond)
see Cologne RSO

SMOLA, Oldřich (va)
Domažlický: Czech Songs

SMUDA, Agnes (sngr)
Copland: Tender Land (Cpte)

SMYTHE, Russell (bar)
Donizetti: Assedio di Calais (Cpte)
Mozart: Finta giardiniera (Cpte)
Rameau: Hippolyte et Aricie (Cpte)
see CONCERT INDEX under:
(OPRA) ORCH103 Italian Opera—1810-20
(OPRA) ORCH104 A Hundred Years of Italian Opera:
1820-1830

SNASHALL, Mark (treb)
Herrmann: Wuthering Heights (Cpte)

SNEDDON, Thomas (treb)
see CONCERT INDEX under:
(CNTO) CSACD3050 Music from the Coronation of H.
M. Queen Elizabeth II

SNELL, David (cond)
see OST

SNELL, Howard (cond)
see Britannia Building Soc Band

SNELL, Howard (tpt)
see CONCERT INDEX under:
(LYRI) SRCD323 Grace Williams—Orchestral Works

(HOWARD) SNELL BRASS
cond H. SNELL
see CONCERT INDEX under:
(POLY) QPRL007D Howard Snell Brass - The Four
Seasons etc.
(POLY) QPRZ005D Premiere

SNELLINGS, Dirk (bass)
Hasse: Miserere in E minor, Requiem in C

SNIJDERS, John (pf)
see CONCERT INDEX under:
(ETCE) KTC1097 Loevendie—Miscellaneous Works

SNIPP, Peter (bar)
Rossini: Barbiere di Siviglia (Cpte)

SNÍTIL, Václav (vn)
see CONCERT INDEX under:
(SUPR) 11 1114-2 Schubert & Schumann: Works for
Violin & Orchestra

SNOOK, Gareth (sngr)
Kern: Show Boat (Cpte)

SNOOK, Robert (sngr)
Gershwin: Porgy and Bess (Cpte)

SNOWDEN, Jonathan (fl)
see CONCERT INDEX under:
(CONI) CDCF173 Prokofiev: Orchestral & Chamber
Works
(EMI) CDM7 64730-2 Vaughan Williams—Riders to
the Sea; Epithalamion, etc
(EMIN) CD-EMX2227 Holst—Orchestral Works

SNYDER, Barry (pf)
see CONCERT INDEX under:
(KOCH) 37281-2 Amy Beach/Rebecca Clarke—Cello
Works

SNYDER, John (perc)
see CONCERT INDEX under:
(PNT) 434 873-2PTH Jon Gibson—In Good
Company

SONNERIE ENSEMBLE
cond **M. HUGGETT**
see CONCERT INDEX *under:*
(VIRG) **VC5 45038-2** Bach—Cantatas
(VIRG) **VC5 45059-2** Bach—Cantatas

SONNERIE TRIO
Couperin: Concerts Royaux
Leclair: Violin Sonatas, Op. 5 (exc), Violin Sonatas, Op. 9 (exc)
Rameau: Pièces de clavecin en concerts
Telemann: Paris Quartets (Nouveaux quatuors) (exc), Paris Quartets (Quadri) (exc)
see CONCERT INDEX *under:*
(ASV) **CDGAU113** The Art of the Recorder
(TELD) **4509-90841-2** A Gift of Nature - 17th Century English Chamber Music

SÖNNERSTEDT, Bernhard (bar)
see CONCERT INDEX *under:*
(EMI) **CHS7 69741-2(5)** Record of Singing, Vol.4—Scandinavian School

SONNLEITNER, Johann (hpd)
Gibbons: Fantasias Royals a 3 (exc), In Nomine (exc)
Handel: German Airs
see CONCERT INDEX *under:*
(HYPE) **CDA66070** Purcell: Songs

SONNTAG, Ulrike (sop)
J.C. Bach: Amadis de Gaule (Cpte)
Stravinsky: Noces
see CONCERT INDEX *under:*
(HANS) **98 857** Bach—Cantatas, Vol.6
(HANS) **98 859** Bach—Cantatas, Vol.8
(TROU) **TRO-CD01409** Milhaud—Early Works, Vol. 1

SONSALLA, Gundula (gtr)
(CAPR) **10 180** Gisela May sings Weill

SØNSTEVOLD, Knut (bn)
see CONCERT INDEX *under:*
(BIS) **BIS-CD159** Hindemith—Chamber Works

SOÓS, Emese (sop)
Górecki: Symphony 2

SOOT, Fritz (ten)
see CONCERT INDEX *under:*
(LYRC) **LCD146** Frida Leider sings Wagner
(PREI) **89301** The Art of Frida Leider

SOPHISTICATED LADIES
Sibelius: String Quartet, Op.56, String Quartet (1889)

SORDELLO, Enzo (bar)
Puccini: Fanciulla del West (Cpte), Madama Butterfly (Cpte)

SØRENSEN, Christian (ten)
Nielsen: Maskarade (Cpte)

SØRENSEN, Hans (hn)
see CONCERT INDEX *under:*
(CLRI) **CC0002** Nielsen—Orchestral and Chamber Works

SORIANO, Gonzalo (pf)
see CONCERT INDEX *under:*
(EMI) **CDM7 64470-2** Mompou—Piano Works
(EMI) **CMS5 65061-2(1)** The Fabulous Victoria de los Angeles (pt 1)
(EMI) **CMS5 65061-2(2)** The Fabulous Victoria de los Angeles (pt 2)
(EMI) **CZS7 67474-2** Viva España!

ŠORMOVÁ, Naďa (sop)
Fibich: Bride of Messina (Cpte)
Smetana: Two Widows (Cpte)

SOROZÁBAL, Pablo (cond)
see Madrid Concerts Orch

SORRELL, Lise (mez)
Wagner: Walküre (Cpte)
see CONCERT INDEX *under:*
(FOYE) **15-CF2011** Wagner—Der Ring de Nibelungen

SOSKIN, Gabrielle (sop)
see CONCERT INDEX *under:*
(LOND) **436 393-2LM** Britten—The Little Sweep, etc

SOSNOWSKI, Tomasz (bn)
see CONCERT INDEX *under:*
(NOVA) **150 016-2** Vivaldi—Concertos

SOTIN, Hans (bass)
Beethoven: Fidelio (Cpte), Symphony 9
Busoni: Doktor Faust (Cpte)
Lortzing: Wildschütz (Cpte)
Mahler: Symphony 8
Mozart: Così fan tutte (Cpte), Mass, K427
R. Strauss: Salome (Cpte)
Rossini: Stabat Mater
Stravinsky: Oedipus Rex (Cpte)
Verdi: Aida (Cpte)
Wagner: Lohengrin (Cpte), Meistersinger (Cpte), Parsifal (Cpte), Tannhäuser (Cpte)
see CONCERT INDEX *under:*
(EMI) **CMS5 65212-2** Wagner—Les introuvables du Ring
(EMI) **CMS7 64476-2** Mahler—Symphonies, Vol.2
(PHIL) **442 050-2PB10** Mahler—Complete Symphonies

SOUČEK, Jaroslav (bar)
Janáček: Cunning Little Vixen (Cpte), Excursions of Mr Brouček (Cpte), From the House of the Dead (Cpte)
see CONCERT INDEX *under:*
(DECC) **421 852-2DH2** Janáček: Operatic & Chamber Works
(DECC) **430 375-2DH2** Janáček—Operatic and Orchestral Works
(SUPR) **C37-7230** Dvořák: Choral works

SOUEZ, Ina (sop)
Mozart: Così fan tutte (Cpte), Don Giovanni (Cpte)
see CONCERT INDEX *under:*
(DUTT) **CDLX7012** The Incomparable Heddle Nash
(EMI) **CDH5 65072-2** Glyndebourne Recorded - 1934-1994

SOUKUPOVÁ, Věra (mez)
Dvořák: Stabat Mater
Janáček: Glagolitic Mass (Cpte), Jenufa (Cpte)
Martinů: Julietta (Cpte)
Smetana: Brandenburgers in Bohemia (Cpte), Libuše (Cpte)
Stravinsky: Oedipus Rex (Cpte)
Wagner: Rheingold (Cpte), Siegfried (Cpte)
see CONCERT INDEX *under:*
(PHIL) **446 057-2PB14** Wagner—The Ring Cycle - Bayreuth Festival 1967
(SUPR) **11 1930-2** Janáček/Kabeláč—Choral and Orchestral Works

SOULACROIX, Gabriel (bar)
see CONCERT INDEX *under:*
(SYMP) **SYMCD1089** Historic Baritones of the French School

SOUMAR, Jan (bass)
Smetana: Bartered Bride (Cpte)

ŠOUNOVÁ-BROUKOVÁ, Daniela (sop)
Dvořák: Jacobin (Cpte), St Ludmilla (Cpte)
Smetana: Two Widows (Cpte)

SOUŠEK, Zdeněk (ten)
see CONCERT INDEX *under:*
(DECC) **430 375-2DH2** Janáček—Operatic and Orchestral Works

SOUSTROT, Bernard (tpt)
see CONCERT INDEX *under:*
(PIER) **PV788011** Trumpet Concertos

SOUSTROT, Marc (cond)
see Loire PO

SOUTER, Martin (organ)
Bach: Chorales, BWV651-668 (exc)
see CONCERT INDEX *under:*
(ISIS) **ISISCD002** Bach—Organ Works
(ISIS) **ISISCD008** Bach—Chorale Preludes, Volume 2

SOUTER, Martin (hpd)
D. Scarlatti: Keyboard Sonatas (exc)
Handel: Keyboard Suites, Set I (exc)
see CONCERT INDEX *under:*
(ISIS) **ISISCD010** The Royal Harpsichord of George III

SOUTER, Matthew (va)
see CONCERT INDEX *under:*
(CLRI) **CC0006** Clarinet Virtuosi of the Past—Hermstedt

SOUTH AFRICAN BROADCASTING CORPORATION SYMPHONY ORCHESTRA
cond **P. MARCHBANK**
see CONCERT INDEX *under:*
(MARC) **8 223485** Cyril Scott—Orchestral Works

SOUTH AFRICAN NATIONAL SYMPHONY ORCHESTRA
cond **A. STEPHENSON**
Rajna: Harp Concerto, Piano Concerto 2

SOUTH FLORIDA UNIVERSITY CHORUS
cond **ROBERT SHAW**
Mahler: Symphony 8

SOUTH GERMAN MADRIGAL CHOIR
cond **W. GÖNNENWEIN**
Mozart: Requiem

SOUTH GERMAN RADIO CHORUS
cond **G. ALBRECHT**
Henze: Bassariden (Cpte)
cond **E. INBAL**
Mahler: Symphony 8
cond **N. MARRINER**
Handel: Messiah (Cpte)
see CONCERT INDEX *under:*
(PHIL) **422 522-2PME6** The Complete Mozart Edition Vol 22

SOUTH WEST GERMAN RADIO ORCHESTRA
cond **M. GIELEN**
Mahler: Symphony 7
cond **P. SACHER**
see CONCERT INDEX *under:*
(ARCI) **ARC112/3** Dinu Lipatti—Les Inédits
cond **E. SMOLA**
see CONCERT INDEX *under:*
(CHAN) **CHAN9248** Harmonica Concertos

SOUTHEND BOYS' CHOIR
cond **C. ABBADO**
Berlioz: Te Deum
cond **A. DORATI**
Orff: Carmina Burana

cond **R. HICKOX**
see CONCERT INDEX *under:*
(CARL) **PCD908** Great Opera Choruses
(CHAN) **CHAN8855** Britten—Choral Works
cond **Z. MEHTA**
Orff: Carmina Burana
cond **R. MUTI**
Mascagni: Cavalleria rusticana (Cpte)
cond **G. SINOPOLI**
Mahler: Symphony 8
cond **K. TENNSTEDT**
see CONCERT INDEX *under:*
(EMI) **CMS7 64471-2** Mahler—Symphonies, Vol.1
cond **M. TILSON THOMAS**
Mahler: Symphony 3

SOUTHERN BAPTIST THEOLOGICAL SEMINARY CHORUS
cond **J. MESTER**
see CONCERT INDEX *under:*
(ALBA) **TROY021-2** American Choral & Orchestral Works

SOUTHERN FESTIVAL ORCHESTRA
cond **R. WHITE**
see CONCERT INDEX *under:*
(CHAN) **CHAN9110** Edwardian Echoes

SOUTHERN PHILHARMONIC ORCHESTRA
cond **F. STIEDRY**
Gluck: Orfeo ed Euridice (exc)

SOUTHERN VOICES
cond **R. HICKOX**
see CONCERT INDEX *under:*
(CHAN) **CHAN9214** Delius—Choral Works

SOUTHGATE, William (cond)
see NZ SO

SOUTHGATE CHRIST CHURCH CHOIR
cond **M. BEST**
Britten: St Nicolas

SOUTH-GERMAN GERMAN RADIO WIND QUINTET
see CONCERT INDEX *under:*
(WERG) **WER60161-50** Ligeti: Instrumental Works

SOUTHWARK CATHEDRAL CHOIR
cond **P. WRIGHT**
see CONCERT INDEX *under:*
(PRIO) **PRCD435** Great Cathedral Anthems, Vol.3

SOUTH-WEST GERMAN CHAMBER ORCHESTRA
cond **P. ANGERER**
see CONCERT INDEX *under:*
(CLAV) **CD50-0813** Clarinet Concertos
(VOX) **115709-2** D'Albert/Bronsart/Liszt—Piano Concertos
cond **V. CZARNECKI**
(EBS) **EBS6058** Boccherini—Cello Concerti
cond **J.E. DÄHLER**
Galuppi: Magnificat in G
Vivaldi: Gloria, RV589
cond **F. TILEGANT**
see CONCERT INDEX *under:*
(TELD) **9031-77620-2** Telemann—Orchestral Works
cond **F. WERNER**
see CONCERT INDEX *under:*
(ERAT) **4509-97407-2** Bach—Cantatas

SOUTH-WEST GERMAN RADIO CHORUS
cond **J. HORENSTEIN**
see CONCERT INDEX *under:*
(VOX) **CDX2 5504**
Bruckner/Liszt/Wagner—Orchestral Works

SOUTH-WEST GERMAN RADIO SYMPHONY ORCHESTRA
cond **O. ACKERMANN**
see CONCERT INDEX *under:*
(ACAN) **43 268** Peter Anders sings German Opera Arias
cond **J. BERGER**
(EBS) **EBS6065** Brixi—Organ Concertos
cond **E. BOUR**
Mozart: Piano Concerto 9, Piano Concerto 16, Piano Concerto 18, Piano Concerto 20, Piano Concerto 24, Piano Concerto 25
see CONCERT INDEX *under:*
(WERG) **WER60162-50** Ligeti: Choral and Orchestral Works
cond **M. GIELEN**
B. A. Zimmermann: Requiem (Cpte)
Bruckner: Symphony 7
Busoni: Piano Concerto, Op. 39
Mahler: Symphony 9
see CONCERT INDEX *under:*
(WERG) **WER60185-50** Schoenberg: Choral & Orchestral Works
cond **L. HAGER**
see CONCERT INDEX *under:*
(AMAT) **SRR8904/1** German Romantic Music
cond **J. HORENSTEIN**
see CONCERT INDEX *under:*
(VOX) **CDX2 5504**
Bruckner/Liszt/Wagner—Orchestral Works
cond **R. REINHARDT**
see CONCERT INDEX *under:*
(VOX) **CDX2 5506** György Sándor plays Bartók
cond **E. SMOLA**
(DG) **431 110-2GB** Great Voices - Fritz Wunderlich
cond **L. STOKOWSKI**
see CONCERT INDEX *under:*

(MUSI) **MACD-778**   Stokowski conducts French Music
cond P. STOLL
see CONCERT INDEX *under:*
(WERG) **WER6087-2**   Françaix plays Françaix
cond M. VIOTTI
see CONCERT INDEX *under:*
(CLAV) **CD50-9111**   Poulenc—Orchestral Works

SOUZAY, Gérard (bar)
Berlioz: Enfance du Christ (Cpte)
Debussy: Pelléas et Mélisande (Cpte)
see CONCERT INDEX *under:*
(BELA) **450 131-2**   Fauré—Requiem
(DECC) **425 975-2DM**   Gerard Souzay—Song Recital
(DECC) **440 065-2DM**   Schubert/Schumann—Lieder
(EMI) **CDM5 65161-2**   Duparc/Chausson—Mélodies
(EMI) **CHS7 69741-2(3)**   Record of Singing,
Vol.4—French School
(EMI) **CMS7 64079-2(1)**   Fauré—Complete Songs (pt
1)
(EMI) **CMS7 64079-2(2)**   Fauré—Complete Songs (pt
2)
(EMI) **CMS7 64095-2**   Debussy—Mélodies
(PHIL) **438 511-2PM4**   Schubert—Lieder
(PHIL) **438 964-2PM4(1)**   Souzay sings French Songs
(pt 1)
(PHIL) **438 964-2PM4(2)**   Souzay sings French Songs
(pt 2)
(PHIL) **442 272-2PM2**   The Best of Bizet
(PHIL) **442 744-2PM2**   Wolf/R.Strauss—Lieder

SOVIET CINEMA ORCHESTRA
cond E. KHACHATURIAN
Karetnikov: Till Eulenspiegel (Cpte)

SOVIET EMIGRÉ ORCHESTRA
cond L. GOZMAN
see CONCERT INDEX *under:*
(OLYM) **OCD196**   Tchaikovsky & Shostakovich
Orchestral Works

SOYER, Roger (bass)
Berlioz: Benvenuto Cellini (Cpte), Troyens (Cpte)
Bizet: Pêcheurs de Perles (Cpte)
Delibes: Lakmé (Cpte)
Donizetti: Maria Stuarda (Cpte)
Massenet: Werther (Cpte)
Rameau: Dardanus (Cpte)
see CONCERT INDEX *under:*
(EMIL) **CDZ7 67015-2**   Mozart—Opera Arias
(ERAT) **4509-95362-2**   Mozart—Sacred Choral
Works
(ERAT) **4509-98526-2**   Duruflé—Vocal & Organ Works

SPACAGNA, Maria (sop)
Mascagni: Lodoletta (Cpte)

ŠPAČEK, Jozef (bass)
Puccini: Madama Butterfly (Cpte), Tosca (Cpte)
Verdi: Rigoletto (Cpte)
see CONCERT INDEX *under:*
(ASV) **CDDCA802**   Clementi—Orchestral Works,
Volume 1
(ASV) **CDDCS322**   Clementi—Complete Orchestral
Works
(EURM) **350225**   Cherubini—Complete Keyboard
Music

SPAETER, Matthias (lte)
Dowland: First Book of Songs (Cpte)

SPAGNOLI, Pietro (bar)
Donizetti: Elisir d'amore (Cpte)
Monteverdi: Vespers
Puccini: Fanciulla del West (Cpte)
Rossini: Signor Bruschino (Cpte), Tancredi (Cpte)

SPALDING, Albert (vn)
see CONCERT INDEX *under:*
(BIDD) **LAB054**   Albert Spalding—Archive
Performances
(BIDD) **LAB088**   Primrose plays Handel, Mozart and
Beethoven
(BOGR) **BIM705-2**   Muzio—The Published Edisons,
1920-25
(PEAR) **GEMMCD9045**   William Primrose and Albert
Spalding
(ROMO) **81005-2**   Claudia Muzio (1889-1936)
(ROMO) **81010-2**   Claudia Muzio—Complete Pathé
Recordings, 1917-8

SPANELLYS, Georgette (sop)
Bizet: Carmen (Cpte)

SPANG-HANSSEN, Ulrik (organ)
see CONCERT INDEX *under:*
(PAUL) **PACD55**   Nielsen: Organ Works

SPANI, Hina (sop)
see CONCERT INDEX *under:*
(CLUB) **CL99-509/10**   Hina Spani (1896-1969)
(EMI) **CHS7 64864-2(2)**   La Scala Edition - Vol.2,
1915-46 (pt 2)
(EMI) **CMS7 64008-2(1)**   Wagner Singing on Record
(pt 1)
(MMOI) **CDMOIR408**   Great Sopranos
(PEAR) **GEMMCDS9074(2)**   Giovanni Zenatello, Vol.2
(pt 2)
(PREI) **89037**   Hina Spani (1896-1969)
(PREI) **89038**   Giovanni Zenatello (1876-1949)

SPANISH LYRIC ORCHESTRA
cond F. MORENO TORROBA
Barbieri: Barberillo de Lavapiès (Cpte)
Usandizaga: Golondrinas (Cpte)

SPANISH NATIONAL ORCHESTRA
cond R. FRÜHBECK DE BURGOS
see CONCERT INDEX *under:*
(EMI) **CZS7 67474-2**   Viva España!

SPANISH NATIONAL YOUTH ORCHESTRA
cond E. COLOMER
Falla: Atlántida (Cpte), Sombrero de tres picos
(Cpte)
see CONCERT INDEX *under:*
(AUVI) **V4724**   Falla—Orchestral and Instrumental
Works

SPANJAARD, Ed (cond)
see Nieuw Ens

SPANOGHE, Viviane (vc)
see CONCERT INDEX *under:*
(MARC) **8 223680**   Devreese—Orchestral Works

SPARF, Nils-Erik (va)
see CONCERT INDEX *under:*
(BIS) **BIS-CD435**   Britten—Orchestral & Vocal Works
(DG) **429 727-2GH**   Brahms—Lieder

SPARF, Nils-Erik (vn)
Vivaldi: Concerti, Op. 8 (exc)
see CONCERT INDEX *under:*
(BIS) **BIS-CD212**   Brahms: Complete Violin Sonatas
(BIS) **BIS-CD284**   Roman: violin concertos and
sinfonias
(BIS) **BIS-CD290**   Vivaldi: works for lute
(BIS) **BIS-CD525**   Sibelius—Complete Music for Violin
and Piano, Vol.1
(BIS) **BIS-CD625**   Sibelius—Music for Violin and
Piano, Volume 2
(CPRI) **CAP21326**   Wirén—Orchestral and Chamber
works
(MSVE) **MSCD415**   Kraus—Chamber Music

SPARNAAY, Harry (bass cl)
see CONCERT INDEX *under:*
(CNTI) **CCD1009**   Music of Barry Anderson

SPASSOV, Boris (cond)
see Sofia National Op Orch

SPATAFORA, Manuel (bar)
Puccini: Bohème (Cpte)
see CONCERT INDEX *under:*
(EMI) **CDM7 69543-2**   Maria Callas and Giuseppe Di
Stefano - Duets

SPATARO, Tomaso (ten)
Verdi: Falstaff (Cpte)

SPÄTH, Christoph (ten)
Mozart: Nozze di Figaro (Cpte)
Spohr: Faust (Cpte)
Wolf: Manuel Venegas

SPECTRE DE LA ROSE
see CONCERT INDEX *under:*
(NAXO) **8 550750**   Marais/Sainte-Colombe—Greatest
Masterworks

SPECTRUM
cond G. PROTHEROE
J. Harvey: Bhakti

SPECULUM MUSICAE
cond R. BLACK
see CONCERT INDEX *under:*
(BRID) **BCD9014**   Elliott Carter: Vocal Works
cond D. PALMA
see CONCERT INDEX *under:*
(BRID) **BCD9014**   Elliott Carter: Vocal Works
(BRID) **BCD9037**   Ruders—Chamber Works
cond W. PURVIS
see CONCERT INDEX *under:*
(BRID) **BCD9014**   Elliott Carter: Vocal Works
cond D. STAROBIN
see CONCERT INDEX *under:*
(BRID) **BCD9014**   Elliott Carter: Vocal Works

SPEISER, Elisabeth (sop)
Gluck: Orfeo ed Euridice (Cpte)
Handel: German Airs
Martin: Requiem
see CONCERT INDEX *under:*
(JECK) **JD561-2**   Early Songs by Berg, Schönberg
and Schreker
(JECK) **JD630-2**   Schubert: Lieder
(JECK) **JD5004-2**   Carissimi: Cantatas

SPELLMAN, Zacharia (tuba)
J. Adams: Light over Water

SPENCE, Patricia (mez)
Handel: Judas Maccabaeus (Cpte), Messiah (Cpte),
Ottone (Cpte), Resurrezione (Cpte)
Verdi: Traviata (Cpte)
see CONCERT INDEX *under:*
(OPRA) **ORCH104**   A Hundred Years of Italian Opera:
1820-1830
(RCA) **09026 61581-2**   Bernstein—Orchestral & Vocal
Works

SPENCER, Charles (pf)
see CONCERT INDEX *under:*
(DECC) **430 518-2DH**   Cecilia Bartoli—Rossini Recital
(RCA) **09026 61547-2**   Farewell to Salzburg
(RCA) **09026 61864-2**   Schubert—Goethe Lieder
(RCA) **09026 62652-2**   Christa Ludwig—Tribute to
Vienna
(SONY) **SK52490**   Brahms—Lieder

SPENCER, Robert (lte)
see CONCERT INDEX *under:*
(EMI) **CDM7 64130-2**   Christmas Music from King's

SPENCER, Robert (theorbo)
see CONCERT INDEX *under:*
(DECC) **440 079-2DM**   The Amorous Flute

SPERING, Christoph (cond)
see Cologne Chorus Musicus

SPERING, Christoph (org/dir)
Rossini: Péchés de vieillesse II (Cpte), Péchés de
vieillesse III (exc)

SPERRY, Paul (ten)
Maderna: Satyricon (Cpte)
see CONCERT INDEX *under:*
(ALBA) **TROY036-2**   S.Paulus—Songs

SPICER, Paul (cond)
see Birmingham Bach Ch

SPIEGELEIR, Olivier De (pf)
see CONCERT INDEX *under:*
(PAVA) **ADW7332**   Liszt/Debussy—Piano Works

SPIEGELMAN, Joel (cond)
see Moscow RSO

SPIERER, Leon (vn/dir)
Vivaldi: Concerti Grossi, Op.3

SPIESS, Ludovic (ten)
Mussorgsky: Boris Godunov (Cpte)

SPILLER, Anton (vn)
Villa-Lobos: Piano Trio 1, Piano Trio 3

SPINA, Mario (ten)
Leoncavallo: Pagliacci (Cpte)

SPINA, Pietro (sngr)
Cherubini: Lodoïska (Cpte)

SPINGLER, Renate (sop)
Dessau: Hagadah Shel Pessach

SPINK, Charlotte (sop)
MacMillan: Búsqueda (Cpte)

SPISAR, Oldřich (ten)
Hába: Mother (Cpte)

SPIVAKOV, Vladimir (cond)
see Armenian St Perc Ens

SPIVAKOV, Vladimir (vn)
Prokofiev: Violin Concerto 1
Tchaikovsky: Violin Concerto
see CONCERT INDEX *under:*
(RCA) **09026 62524-2**   It's Peaceful Here
(RCA) **74321 24884-2**   Homage to Schnittke

SPIVAKOV, Vladimir (vn/dir)
Mozart: Concertone, K190, Sinfonia Concertante,
K364
see CONCERT INDEX *under:*
(CIRR) **CICD1004**   Bach: Violin Concertos
(RCA) **RD60240**   Vivaldi—Orchestral and Choral
works
(RCA) **RD60369**   Vivaldi: Concertos
(RCA) **RD60370**   Modern Portraits
(RCA) **RD87948**   Haydn: Concertos
(RCA) **RD87991**   Bach: Concerti

SPLETTER, Carla (sop)
Mozart: Zauberflöte (Cpte)

SPOHR, Dietburg (cond)
see Bel Canto Ens

SPOLIANSKY, Mischa (pf)
see CONCERT INDEX *under:*
(EMI) **CDM7 69476-2**   Richard Tauber - A Portrait
(MMOI) **CDMOIR409**   Three Tenors—Björling, Gigli &
Tauber
(PEAR) **GEMMCD9370**   Richard Tauber sings Lieder

SPONG, Jon (pf)
see CONCERT INDEX *under:*
(NEW) **NW273-2**   Griffes: Vocal & Instrumental Works

SPOORENBERG, Erna (sop)
Haydn: Mass 14
Mahler: Symphony 8
see CONCERT INDEX *under:*
(DECC) **430 159-2DM**   Haydn, M.Haydn & Mozart:
Sacred Choral Works
(DECC) **443 009-2DF2**   Mozart—Choral Works
(DG) **429 042-2GX10**   Mahler: Complete Symphonies

SPORSÉN, Torgny (bass)
see CONCERT INDEX *under:*
(DG) **429 984-2GH**   Russian Orchestral Works

SPRANGER, Irene (fl)
see CONCERT INDEX *under:*
(CHAN) **CHAN0535**   Baroque Flute Concertos

SPRENKELS, Charlotte (hp)
see CONCERT INDEX *under:*
(ASV) **CDCOE813**   Mozart—Wind Concertos

SPRINGER, Ingeborg (mez)
Wagner: Parsifal (Cpte), Rienzi (Cpte)

SPRINGFELS, Mary (cond)
see Newberry Consort

SPRINGFELS, Mary (va da gamba)
see CONCERT INDEX *under:*
(HARM) **HMU90 7024/5**   Bach—Complete Sonatas for
Flute and Harpsichord
(HARM) **HMU90 7035**   Sweeter than Roses - Purcell
Songs
(HARM) **HMU90 7091**   Three Parts upon a Ground

SPRINGUEL, France (vc)
see CONCERT INDEX *under:*

(TELA) **CD80387** Pärt—Fratres

SPRINZENA, Nathaniel (ten)
Verdi: Trovatore (Cpte)

SPRONK, Jan (ob)
Schnittke: Concerto grosso 4
see CONCERT INDEX *under:*
(DECC) **444 455-2DH** Martin—Ballades; Concerto for
7 Wind Instruments

SPURR, Phyllis (pf)
see CONCERT INDEX *under:*
(DECC) **430 096-2DWO** The World of Kathleen Ferrier
(DECC) **433 471-2DM** Ferrier Edition - Volume 4
(DECC) **433 473-2DM** Ferrier Edition - Volume 6
(DECC) **433 475-2DM** Ferrier Edition - Volume 8
(DECC) **433 477-2DM** Ferrier Edition - Volume 10

SQUIRE, Haddon (pf)
see CONCERT INDEX *under:*
(BIDD) **LAB009/10** The Kreisler Collection
(PEAR) **GEMMCD9324** Fritz Kreisler plays Encores

SQUIRES, Shelagh (mez)
Wagner: Götterdämmerung (Cpte), Rheingold (Cpte),
Walküre (Cpte)

SRAMEK, Alfred (bar)
Beethoven: Fidelio (Cpte)
Mozart: Don Giovanni (Cpte)
R. Strauss: Ariadne auf Naxos (Cpte), Rosenkavalier
(Cpte)

ŠRUBAŘ, Theodor (bar)
Vycpálek: Czech Requiem
see CONCERT INDEX *under:*
(SUPR) **2SUP0025** Orff: Choral Works

ST ALBANS ABBEY CHOIR
cond BARRY ROSE
see CONCERT INDEX *under:*
(LAMM) **LAMM081D** Christmas at St Albans
cond F. WELSER-MÖST
Orff: Carmina Burana

ST ALBAN'S BACH CHOIR
cond BARRY ROSE
see CONCERT INDEX *under:*
(LAMM) **LAMM081D** Christmas at St Albans

ST. ALBAN'S SCHOOL CHOIR
cond C. ABBADO
Berlioz: Te Deum

**ST AMBROSE RC JUNIOR SCHOOL CHOIR,
SPEAKE**
cond E. WALTERS
see CONCERT INDEX *under:*
(CHAN) **CHAN8436** A Festival of Christmas

ST ANNE'S GYMNASIUM CHILDREN'S CHORUS
cond L. SEGERSTAM
see CONCERT INDEX *under:*
(CHAN) **CHAN8853** Nielsen: Choral Works

ST ANTHONY SINGERS
see CONCERT INDEX *under:*
(DECC) **430 260-2DM** Bach—Cantatas
cond COLIN DAVIS
see CONCERT INDEX *under:*
(DECC) **443 461-2DF2** Berlioz—L'Enfance du Christ,
etc
cond A. LEWIS
Purcell: Dido (Cpte), King Arthur, Z628 (Cpte)
(DECC) **436 462-2DM** Ten Top Mezzos
cond C. MACKERRAS
Purcell: Indian Queen, Z630 (exc)

**ST BAVO'S CATHEDRAL, HAARLEM (BOYS'
CHOIR)**
cond F. BRÜGGEN
Bach: Cantata 56

ST BRIDE'S CHURCH CHOIR, FLEET STREET
cond R. JONES
see CONCERT INDEX *under:*
(NAXO) **8 550956** Bruckner—Motets
(REGE) **REGSB701CD** I saw the Lord
cond A. WATTS
see CONCERT INDEX *under:*
(REGE) **REGSB701CD** I saw the Lord

ST CECILIA'S ABBEY, RYDE, NUNS' CHOIR
see CONCERT INDEX *under:*
(HERA) **HAVPCD157** Gregorian Chant Gaudete

ST CLEMENT DANES SCHOOL CHOIR
cond JAMES LEVINE
Puccini: Tosca (Cpte)
cond K. NAGANO
Puccini: Bohème (Cpte)
cond A. PREVIN
Britten: Spring Symphony
Orff: Carmina Burana

**ST DAVID'S EPISCOPAL CHURCH CHOIR,
BALTIMORE**
cond D. ZINMAN
see CONCERT INDEX *under:*
(TELA) **CD80164** Berlioz—Orchestral Works

ST ETIENNE MAÎTRISE SCHOLACHOEUR
cond P. FOURNILLIER
Massenet: Vierge (Cpte)

ST GEORGE'S CHAPEL CHOIR, WINDSOR CASTLE
cond M. BEST
Britten: St Nicolas

cond C. ROBINSON
see CONCERT INDEX *under:*
(ABBS) **CDMVP827** 20 Christmas Carols from St
George's Chapel, Windsor Castle
(HYPE) **CDA66273** Parry—Cathedral Music
(HYPE) **CDA66345** Tomkins—Cathedral Music
cond D. WILLCOCKS
Mathias: Lux aeterna
see CONCERT INDEX *under:*
(LYRI) **SRCD324** Mathias—Choral Works

ST GERVAIS CHORUS
cond P. COPPOLA
see CONCERT INDEX *under:*
(DANT) **LYS003/4** Charles Panzéra - Song Recital

ST GRÉGOIRE INSTITUTE CHOIR
(STUD) **SM1220.02** Immortel Grégorien

ST HEDWIG'S CATHEDRAL CHOIR, BERLIN
(CAPR) **10 380** Breezes from the Orient, Vol.2
cond R. BADER
Donizetti: Messa di Gloria e Credo
E.T.A. Hoffmann: Undine (Cpte)
cond R. CHAILLY
Schoenberg: Gurrelieder
cond K. FORSTER
Bruckner: Te Deum
cond F. FRICSAY
Beethoven: Symphony 9
Mozart: Requiem
Rossini: Stabat Mater
Verdi: Pezzi sacri (Cpte), Requiem (Cpte)
see CONCERT INDEX *under:*
(DG) **445 400-2GDO10** Ferenc Fricsay - A Portrait
(DG) **445 402-2GDO** Bartók—Orchestral Works
(DG) **445 410-2GDO** Kodály—Orchestral Works
(DG) **447 343-2GDB2** Stravinsky—Orchestral &
Choral Works
cond G.M. GUIDA
F. David: Désert
cond R. KEMPE
Brahms: Deutsches Requiem, Op.45 (Cpte)
Mozart: Requiem
Wagner: Meistersinger (Cpte)
cond C. PERICK
Schmidt: Notre Dame (Cpte)

ST HILL, Krister (ten)
Krenek: Jonny spielt auf (Cpte)

ST JAMES'S BAROQUE PLAYERS
cond I. BOLTON
Purcell: Dido (Cpte)
see CONCERT INDEX *under:*
(TELD) **4509-91192-2** Baroque Music of Bologna

ST JAMES'S SINGERS
cond I. BOLTON
Purcell: Dido (Cpte)
see CONCERT INDEX *under:*
(CONI) **CDCF167** Dickinson—Vocal Works

ST. JOHN, Scott (vn)
see CONCERT INDEX *under:*
(NAXO) **8 550690** Paganini—Music for Violin and
Guitar I
(NAXO) **8 550759** Paganini—Music for Violin &
Guitar, Vol.2

**ST JOHN THE BAPTIST CHURCH SCHOLA,
MONTREAL**
cond A. SAINT-CYR
Tournemire: Orgue mystique, Op. 57 (exc)

ST JOHN'S COLLEGE CHOIR, CAMBRIDGE
cond G. GUEST
Haydn: Mass 9, Mass 10, Mass 13, Mass 14
Liszt: Missa choralis, S10
Massenzio: Office of Compline (exc)
Mozart: Litanies, K243, Mass, K258, Requiem,
Vespers, K321, Vespers, K339
see CONCERT INDEX *under:*
(ASV) **CDGAU114** Tallis/Sheppard—Masses
(BELA) **450 111-2** Carols for Christmas
(CHAN) **CHAN8658** Poulenc & Charpentier: Sacred
Choral Works
(DECC) **430 159-2DM** Haydn, M.Haydn & Mozart:
Sacred Choral Works
(DECC) **430 160-2DM** Haydn: Masses & Keyboard
Concerto
(DECC) **430 263-2DM** Purcell—Sacred choral works
(DECC) **430 360-2DM** Faure/Poulenc—Sacred Choral
Works
(DECC) **430 498-2DWO** The World of Mozart
(DECC) **430 499-2DWO** World of Bach
(DECC) **433 678-2DH** Palestrina—Masses
(DECC) **436 402-2DWO** The World of Wedding
Music
(DECC) **436 403-2DWO** The World of Royal Music
(DECC) **436 407-2DWO** The World of Schubert
(DECC) **436 486-2DF2**
Duruflé/Fauré/Poulenc—Choral Works
(DECC) **436 990-2DWO** The World of Benjamin
Britten
(DECC) **443 455-2DF2** Vivaldi—Sacred Choral Works
(DECC) **443 868-2DF2** Italian Baroque Sacred
Works
cond C. ROBINSON
see CONCERT INDEX *under:*
(CHAN) **CHAN0559** Gibbons—Organ and Choral
Works

ST JOHN'S EPISCOPAL CATHEDRAL CHOIR
cond D. PEARSON
see CONCERT INDEX *under:*
(DELO) **DE3125** Sing we Merrily - Choral Music

ST JOHN'S SMITH SQUARE ORCHESTRA
cond J. LUBBOCK
Arnold: Guitar Concerto, Op.67
Haydn: Symphony 44, Symphony 49
Mendelssohn: Symphony 3, Symphony 4
Mozart: Symphony 40
Rodrigo: Concierto de Aranjuez
Schubert: Symphony 5
Stravinsky: Apollon musagète, Orpheus (Cpte)
Vivaldi: Concerti, Op. 10, Concerto, RV441
see CONCERT INDEX *under:*
(COLL) **Coll1373-2** C.P.E.Bach—Flute Concertos

ST JULIEN-LE-PAUVRE CHURCH CHOIR, PARIS
Anon: Byzantine Holy Week Chants

ST KLEMENS SCHOOL CHILDREN'S CHOIR
cond T. VETÖ
Nielsen: Springtime in Funen

ST LEGER, Frank (pf)
see CONCERT INDEX *under:*
(RCA) **09026 61412-2** Nellie Melba - Recital
(ROMO) **81011-2(2)** Dame Nellie Melba (pt 2)

ST LOUIS SYMPHONY CHORUS
cond L. SLATKIN
Bartók: Miraculous Mandarin (Cpte)
Mahler: Symphony 2
Orff: Carmina Burana
Tchaikovsky: Nutcracker (Cpte)

ST LOUIS SYMPHONY ORCHESTRA
cond L. BERNSTEIN
see CONCERT INDEX *under:*
(RCA) **09026 61581-2** Bernstein—Orchestral & Vocal
Works
cond V. GOLSCHMANN
Lalo: Symphonie espagnole
see CONCERT INDEX *under:*
(RCA) **09026 61261-2** Artur Rubinstein plays Spanish
Works
cond L. SLATKIN
Bartók: Concerto for Orchestra, Miraculous Mandarin
(Cpte)
Bizet: Carmen Suites (exc)
Bolcom: Symphony 4
Copland: Music for a Great City, Symphony 3
Elgar: Salut d'amour, Violin Concerto
Grieg: Peer Gynt (exc)
Mahler: Symphony 2
Orff: Carmina Burana
Prokofiev: Symphony 5
Schubert: Symphony 9
Shostakovich: Symphony 4
Tchaikovsky: Nutcracker (Cpte)
see CONCERT INDEX *under:*
(EMI) **CDC7 49463-2** Barber—Orchestral Works
(RCA) **RD60432** Tchaikovsky—Orchestral Works
(RCA) **RD60732** Barber—Orchestral Works
(RCA) **RD60798** Music of Walter Piston
(RCA) **RD77716** Classic Marches
(RCA) **09026 60985-2** Ravel—Piano Concertos, etc
(RCA) **09026 60993-2**
Haydn/Ginastera/Stravinsky—Orchestral Works
(RCA) **09026 61222-2** Ives—Orchestral Works
(RCA) **09026 61282-2** Schuman/Ives—American
Orchestral Works
(RCA) **09026 61699-2** Copland—Music for Films
(RCA) **09026 68045-2** Tchaikovsky—Orchestral
Works
(TELA) **CD80059** Popular Orchestral Works
(TELA) **CD80071** Debussy: Orchestral works
(TELA) **CD80072** Russian Orchestral Works
(TELA) **CD80080** Music for Strings

ST LUKE'S BAROQUE ORCHESTRA
cond R. PALMER
Telemann: Pimpinone (Cpte)

ST LUKE'S CHAMBER ENSEMBLE
cond C. WUORINEN
see CONCERT INDEX *under:*
(KOCH) **37110-2** Wuorinen—Orchestral & Chamber
Works

ST LUKE'S ORCHESTRA
Weill: Violin Concerto
cond J. ADAMS
see CONCERT INDEX *under:*
(NONE) **7559-79249-2** American Elegies
cond R. CRAFT
Stravinsky: Rake's Progress (Cpte)
see CONCERT INDEX *under:*
(MUSM) **67110-2** Stravinsky—The Composer,
Volume V
(MUSM) **67113-2** Stravinsky—The Composer -
Volume IV
(MUSM) **67152-2** Stravinsky—The Composer,
Volume VII
cond W.H. CURRY
A. Davis: X (Cpte)
cond C. MACKERRAS
Handel: Water Music
Haydn: Symphony 31, Symphony 45, Symphony 101,
Symphony 104
Mozart: Serenade, K361

Mozart: Don Giovanni (Cpte), Entführung (Cpte),
Exsultate, jubilate, K165, Mass, K317, Nozze di
Figaro (Cpte), Zauberflöte (Cpte)
Rossini: Stabat Mater
Verdi: Requiem (Cpte)
see CONCERT INDEX under:
(ARCH) **439 387-2AX6** Bach Cantatas, Volume 4
(DG) **423 127-2GX4** Bruckner: Sacred Works for
Chorus
(DG) **447 409-2GOR2** Bruckner—The Masses
(EMI) **CHS7 69741-2(4)** Record of Singing,
Vol.4—German School

STADLER, Maria (narr)
Lehár: Friederike (Cpte)

STADLER, Sergei (vn)
Tishchenko: Violin Concerto 2
see CONCERT INDEX under:
(OLYM) **OCD165** Glazunov: Concertos

STADLMAIR, Hans (cond)
see Munich CO

STAEGEMANN, Waldemar (ten)
see CONCERT INDEX under:
(EMI) **CDH7 69787-2** Richard Tauber sings Operetta
Arias

STAEMPFLI, Wally (sop)
see CONCERT INDEX under:
(ERAT) **2292-45923-2** Bach/Vivaldi—Sacred Choral
Works

STAFFORD, Ashley (alto)
A. Scarlatti: Dixit Dominus II
Handel: Alexander's Feast (Cpte), Israel in Egypt
(Cpte)
Purcell: Fairy Queen, Z629 (Cpte), Indian Queen,
Z630 (Cpte), King Arthur, Z628 (Cpte), St Cecilia's
Day Ode, Z328
see CONCERT INDEX under:
(ARCH) **423 405-2AH** Schütz—Sacred Choral Works
(ERAT) **4509-96371-2** Gardiner—The Purcell
Collection

(LA) STAGIONE
Stradella: San Giovanni Battista (Cpte)
cond M. SCHNEIDER
Abel: Symphonies, Op. 10
Gluck: Paride ed Elena (Cpte)
Handel: Rodelinda (Cpte)
Telemann: Cantata, TWV1: 771, Don Quichotte
(Cpte), Pimpinone (Cpte), Schwanengesang, TWV4:
6

(LA) STAGIONE VOCAL ENSEMBLE
cond M. SCHNEIDER
Gluck: Paride ed Elena (Cpte)

STAHLMAN, Sylvia (sop)
Haydn: Mass 11

STAIER, Andreas (fp)
Dussek: Piano Sonata, C133, Piano Sonatas, C149-
151
Schubert: Schöne Müllerin (Cpte), Winterreise
(Cpte)
see CONCERT INDEX under:
(CAPR) **10 444** Dussek—Piano Concertos
(DHM) **RD77160** Haydn—Keyboard Works
(DHM) **05472 77285-2** Haydn—Fortepiano Sonatas,
Vol.3
(DHM) **05472 77296-2** Schubert—Schiller Lieder
(DHM) **05472 77319-2** Heine Lieder
(TELD) **4509-94569-2** Salieri/Steffan—Concertos for
Fortepiano

STAIER, Andreas (hpd)
Bach: Triple Concerto, BWV1044
D. Scarlatti: Keyboard Sonatas (exc)
Telemann: Essercizii musici (exc)
see CONCERT INDEX under:
(DHM) **RD77025** C.P.E. Bach: Keyboard Works
(DHM) **RD77039** Bach—Keyboard Fantasies
(DHM) **RD77187** C.P.E. Bach: Sinfonias &
Concertos
(DHM) **05472 77306-2** Bach—Clavier-Übung I and II

STALDER, Hans-Rudolf (cl)
see CONCERT INDEX under:
(JECK) **JD536-2** The Romantic Clarinet

STALDER QUINTET
Onslow: Septet, Wind Quintet, Op.81/3

STALLMAN, Robert (fl)
Handel: Flute Sonatas (exc), Recorder Sonatas
(exc)
see CONCERT INDEX under:
(BIDD) **LAW013** Dodgson—Orchestral & Vocal
Works

STALLMAN, Robert (ob)
Vivaldi: Concerti, Op. 10, Concerto, RV441

(CARL) STAMITZ ORCHESTRA
Schubert: Octet, D803
see CONCERT INDEX under:
(REM) **REM311105** Poulenc—Melodies

STAMM, Harald (bass)
Haydn: Schöpfung (Cpte)
Hindemith: Cardillac (Cpte), Mathis der Maler (Cpte),
Nusch-Nuschi (Cpte)
Mahler: Symphony 8
Offenbach: Contes d'Hoffmann (Cpte)
Schoeck: Massimilla Doni (Cpte)
Schreker: Schatzgräber (Cpte)

Schumann: Genoveva (Cpte), Szenen aus Goethes
Faust (Cpte)

STAMP, Alison (sop)
see CONCERT INDEX under:
(GIME) **CDGIM339** Renaissance Sacred Choral
Works

STAMP, Richard (cond)
see London Academy

STAMPER, Richard (cond)
Arensky: Piano Trio 1
Tchaikovsky: Piano Trio, Op. 50

STÄMPFLI, Jakob (bass)
Haydn: Mass 11
see CONCERT INDEX under:
(ERAT) **4509-97407-2** Bach—Cantatas

STANCHEV, Dimiter (bass)
Mussorgsky: Khovanshchina (Cpte)
Prokofiev: Ivan the Terrible
Tchaikovsky: Eugene Onegin (Cpte)

STANDAGE, Silas (organ)
see CONCERT INDEX under:
(CONI) **CDCF214** Great is the Lord
(CONI) **CDCF220** Michael Haydn—Masses and
Vespers
(CONI) **CDCF517** A Child is Born

STANDAGE, Simon (cond)
see Collegium Musicum 90

STANDAGE, Simon (vn)
Bach: Triple Concerto, BWV1044
Telemann: Canons mélodieux, TWV40: 118-123,
Sonates Corellisantes
Vivaldi: Concerti, Op.4, Concerti, Op. 8 (exc),
Concerti, Op.9
see CONCERT INDEX under:
(ARCH) **410 646-2AH** Bach—Violin concertos
(ARCH) **413 731-2AH** Bach: Concerti
(ARCH) **415 674-2AH** Vivaldi: Concertos
(ARCH) **419 615-2AH** Vivaldi: Concertos
(ARCH) **427 316-2AH** Haydn: Violin Concertos
(CHAN) **CHAN0519** Telemann—La Changeante
(CHAN) **CHAN0528** Vivaldi—Double Concertos
(CHAN) **CHAN0531** Baroque Violin & Harpsichord
Sonatas
(CONI) **CDCF220** Michael Haydn—Masses and
Vespers
(CRD) **CRD3348/9** Vivaldi—Concertos
(L'OI) **433 045-2OH2** Mozart—Works for Violin and
Orchestra
(PHIL) **446 081-2PH** The Echoing Air—The Music of
Henry Purcell

STANDAGE, Simon (vn/dir)
A. Marcello: Concerto in B flat, Oboe Concerti, 'La
Cetra'
Albinoni: Concerti, Op. 7 (exc), Concerti, Op. 9 (exc)
Leclair: Concerti, Op. 7 (exc), Concertos, Op. 10
(exc)
see CONCERT INDEX under:
(CHAN) **CHAN0512** Telemann, Vol.2—Ouverture
burlesque
(CHAN) **CHAN0519** Telemann—La Changeante
(CHAN) **CHAN0525** Telemann—Domestic Music,
Vol.3
(CHAN) **CHAN0530** Baroque Violin Concertos
(CHAN) **CHAN0540** J.C.Bach—Orchestral Works
(CHAN) **CHAN0541** Music from the Court of Frederick
the Great
(CHAN) **CHAN0547** Telemann—Orchestral Works
(CHAN) **CHAN0564** Leclair—Violin Concertos,
Volume 2

STANĚK, Tomás (treb)
Krása: Brundibár (Cpte)

STANFORD UNIVERSITY CHORUS
cond P. MONTEUX
see CONCERT INDEX under:
(RCA) **09026 61893-2** Pierre Monteux Edition

STÅNGBERG, Anna (hp)
Olsson: Te Deum

STANGER, Peter (cond)
see Orig London Cast

STANGER, Russell (cond)
see RPO

STANIENDA, Jan (vn/dir)
see CONCERT INDEX under:
(LINN) **CKD001** Polish Chamber Orchestra live in
Glasgow

STANKOVSKY, Robert (cond)
see Bratislava RSO

STANZELEIT, Susanne (vn)
see CONCERT INDEX under:
(ASV) **CDDCA852** Bartók—Violin Works, Vol.1
(ASV) **CDDCA883** Bartók—Music for Violin and
Piano, Volume 2

STAPF, Silke (sop)
Telemann: Don Quichotte (Cpte)

STAPLETON, Jean (sngr)
Styne: Funny Girl (Cpte)

STAPLETON, Robin (cond)
see RPO

STAPP, Olivia (mez)
see CONCERT INDEX under:
(NEW) **NW273-2** Griffes: Vocal & Instrumental Works

STARCK, Claude (vc)
Brahms: Cello Sonata 1, Cello Sonata 2
Chopin: Cello Sonata
Grieg: Cello Sonata

STARKER, János (vc)
Beethoven: Triple Concerto
Brahms: Cello Sonata 1, Cello Sonata 2, Double
Concerto, Piano Trio 1, Piano Trio 2
Hindemith: Cello Concerto
R. Strauss: Don Quixote
Schumann: Cello Concerto
see CONCERT INDEX under:
(DELO) **DE1015** Janos Starker plays Kodály
(DELO) **DE3062** Haydn: Orchestral Works
(DELO) **DE3063** Haydn—Orchestral Works
(DELO) **DE3103** David Diamond—Orchestral Works
(EMI) **CZS5 68485-2** Les Introuvables de János
Starker
(MERC) **432 001-2MM** Works for Cello and Orchestra
(MERC) **432 010-2MM** Cello Concertos
(PHIL) **442 580-2PM2** Beethoven—Concertos,
Volume 2
(RCA) **RD60598** Works for Cello and Piano
(RCA) **09026 61562-2** Brahms/Schumann—Cello
Works

STAROBIN, David (cond)
see Speculum Musicae

STAROBIN, David (gtr)
see CONCERT INDEX under:
(BRID) **BCD9029** Giuliani—Solo Guitar Music
(BRID) **BCD9037** Ruders—Chamber Works
(BRID) **BCD9039** The Great Regondi, Vol. 1
(BRID) **BCD9055** The Great Regondi, Vol. 2

STARREVELD, Harrie (fl)
see CONCERT INDEX under:
(ETCE) **KTC1070** Ferneyhough: Various Works

STARREVELD, Harrie (fl/picc)
see CONCERT INDEX under:
(BRID) **BCD9031** J. Harvey—Miscellaneous Works

STARREVELD, Harrie (picc)
see CONCERT INDEX under:
(ETCE) **KTC1070** Ferneyhough: Various Works

STASIO, Anna di (mez)
Alfano: Risurrezione (Cpte)
Giordano: Andrea Chénier (Cpte)
Puccini: Madama Butterfly (Cpte)
Verdi: Rigoletto (Cpte), Trovatore (exc)
see CONCERT INDEX under:
(DECC) **411 665-2DM3** Puccini: Il trittico
(SONY) **M3K79312** Puccini: Il Trittico

STASOV, Leonid (spkr)
Gubaidulina: Perception

STATKIEWICZ, Edward (vn)
see CONCERT INDEX under:
(OLYM) **OCD392** Bacewicz—Orchestral and
Chamber Works

STAUCH, Adolf (pf)
see CONCERT INDEX under:
(EMI) **CHS7 69741-2(4)** Record of Singing,
Vol.4—German School

STAUDE, Hans-Jörg (bass)
R. Strauss: Rosenkavalier (Cpte)

STAUNTON, Imelda (sngr)
Sondheim: Into the Woods (Cpte)

STÁVA, Aleš (bass)
Dvořák: Kate and the Devil (Cpte)

STAVANGER SYMPHONY ORCHESTRA
cond G. LLEWELLYN
see CONCERT INDEX under:
(CHAT) **FCM1002** Svendsen—Orchestral Works

STAVROVSKAYA, Ludmila (mez)
(DANT) **LYS013/5** Tchaikovsky—The Queen of
Spades

STEBER, Eleanor (sop)
Barber: Vanessa (Cpte)
Beethoven: Fidelio (Cpte)
Wagner: Lohengrin (Cpte)
see CONCERT INDEX under:
(EMI) **CHS7 69741-2(1)** Record of Singing,
Vol.4—Anglo-American School (pt 5)
(RCA) **09026 61580-2(5)** RCA/Met 100 Singers, 100
Years (pt 5)
(SONY) **MPK46727** Barber—Vocal Works
(VAI) **VAIA1017** Leonard Warren—Early Recordings
(VAI) **VAIA1072** Eleanor Steber Collection, Volume 1

STEBLIANKO, Alexei (ten)
Mussorgsky: Khovanshchina (Cpte)

STEEGER, Gerhard (cond)
see Berlin Deutsche Op Orch

STEEL, John (sngr)
see CONCERT INDEX under:
(PEAR) **GEMMCDS9059/61** Music from the New York
Stage, Vol. 4: 1917-20

STEELE, Jonathan (alto)
Britten: Rejoice in the Lamb

STEELE-PERKINS, Crispian (tpt)
Bach: Cantata 51
Telemann: Musique de Table (exc)
see CONCERT INDEX under:

(CARL) **PCD821** Trumpet Concertos
(HYPE) **CDA66255** Italian Baroque Trumpet Music
(PHIL) **446 081-2PH** The Echoing Air—The Music of Henry Purcell
(SONY) **SK53365** Music for Trumpet and Orchestra
(VIRG) **VC7 59520-2** American Orchestral Works
(VIRG) **VJ7 59651-2** Vivaldi—Concertos

STEER, Michael (db)
see CONCERT INDEX *under:*
(KOCH) **37192-2** Still—Summerland

STEFANO, Donato Di (bar)
Verdi: Traviata (Cpte)

STEFANO, Giuseppe di (ten)
Bellini: Puritani (Cpte)
Donizetti: Elisir d'amore (Cpte), Lucia di Lammermoor (Cpte)
Leoncavallo: Pagliacci (Cpte)
Mascagni: Cavalleria Rusticana (Cpte)
Puccini: Bohème (Cpte), Manon Lescaut (Cpte), Tosca (Cpte)
Verdi: Ballo in maschera (Cpte), Rigoletto (Cpte), Traviata (Cpte), Trovatore (Cpte)
see CONCERT INDEX *under:*
(DECC) **417 686-2DC** Puccini—Operatic Arias
(DECC) **436 463-2DM** Ten Top Tenors
(EMI) **CDM7 69543-2** Maria Callas and Giuseppe Di Stefano - Duets
(EMI) **CHS5 65506-2** Victor de Sabata conducts
(EMI) **CHS7 69741-2(7)** Record of Singing, Vol.4—Italian School
(EMI) **CMS7 63244-2** The Art of Maria Callas
(RCA) **GD60326** Verdi—Operas & Choral Works
(RCA) **09026 61580-2(6)** RCA/Met 100 Singers, 100 Years (pt 6)

STEFANONI, Marco (bass)
Alfano: Risurrezione (Cpte)
Verdi: Don Carlo (Cpte)

STEFANSKI, Andrzej (pf)
see CONCERT INDEX *under:*
(POLS) **PNCD066** Szymanowski: Piano Works

STEFFAN, Katherine (mez)
see CONCERT INDEX *under:*
(CHAN) **CHAN8865** Rossini: Opera Arias

STEFFEK, Hanny (sop)
Gluck: Orfeo ed Euridice (Cpte)
Lehár: Lustige Witwe (Cpte)
Mozart: Così fan tutte (Cpte)

STEFFEK, Ronald (bass)
R. Strauss: Rosenkavalier (Cpte)

STEGENGA, Herre-Jan (vc)
see CONCERT INDEX *under:*
(OLYM) **OCD460** Roussel—Chamber Music, Vol. 3

STEGER, Ingrid (mez)
Wagner: Walküre (Cpte)
(DG) **435 211-2GX15** Wagner—Der Ring des Nibelungen

STEHLE, Adelina (sop)
see CONCERT INDEX *under:*
(MEMO) **HR4408/9(1)** Singers in Genoa, Vol.1 (disc 1)
(SYMP) **SYMCD1113** The Harold Wayne Collection, Vol.13

STEIGER, Anna (sop)
Mozart: Così fan tutte (Cpte)
see CONCERT INDEX *under:*
(ASV) **CDDCA758** Falla, Milhaud & Stravinsky—Operas

STEIN, Andreas (alto)
Mozart: Zauberflöte (Cpte)

STEIN, Cléna (db)
Boismortier: Sonatas, Op.26 (exc), Sonatas, Op.50 (exc)
see CONCERT INDEX *under:*
(HARM) **HMA190 5137** Arias and Cantatas for Soprano and Trumpet

STEIN, Horst (cond)
see Bamberg SO

STEIN, Leonard (pf)
see CONCERT INDEX *under:*
(NALB) **NA035CD** Singing Through

STEINBACH, Heribert (ten)
Pfitzner: Palestrina (Cpte)
Wagner: Meistersinger (Cpte)

STEINBERG, Julie (pf)
see CONCERT INDEX *under:*
(NALB) **NA015CD** Lou Harrison: Various Works
(NALB) **NA055CD** Harrison—The Perilous Chapel

STEINBERG, Pinchas (cond)
see Austrian RSO

STEINBERG, William (cond)
see Berlin St Op Orch

STEINER, Adolf (vc)
(ACAN) **43 801** Elisabeth Schwarzkopf—Wartime Recordings

STEINER-KRAUS, Edith (pf)
see CONCERT INDEX *under:*
(KOCH) **37109-2** Ullmann—Chamber Works

STEINGRUBER, Ilona (sop)
R. Strauss: Elektra (Cpte)
see CONCERT INDEX *under:*
(CAMB) **CD-1032** From the Operas of Erich Wolfgang Korngold
(DG) **437 677-2GDO2** Irmgard Seefried - Opera Recital

STEINHARDT, Arnold (va)
see CONCERT INDEX *under:*
(BIDD) **LAW012** Fuchs—Works for Violin and Piano

STEINHARDT, Arnold (vn)
see CONCERT INDEX *under:*
(BIDD) **LAW012** Fuchs—Works for Violin and Piano

STEINHARDT, Victor (pf)
see CONCERT INDEX *under:*
(BIDD) **LAW012** Fuchs—Works for Violin and Piano

STEINKOPF, Hanns (cond)
see Berlin Deutsche Op Orch

STEINMANN, Conrad (rec)
Telemann: Essercizii musici (exc)
see CONCERT INDEX *under:*
(HARM) **HMA190 1245** G.B. & G. Sammartini—Concerti & Sinfonie

STEINMANN, Max (cond)
see LSO

STEINMASSL, Hermine (sop)
Mozart: Zauberflöte (Cpte)

STEINSKY, Eva (sop)
Gazzaniga: Don Giovanni (Cpte)

STEINSKY, Ulrike (sop)
J. Strauss II: Fledermaus (Cpte)
Mozart: Zauberflöte (Cpte)

STELIBSKÝ, Josef (pf)
see CONCERT INDEX *under:*
(SUPR) **11 1491-2** Jarmila Novotna sings Czech Songs and Arias

STELLA, Antonietta (sop)
Donizetti: Linda di Chamounix (Cpte)
Giordano: Andrea Chénier (Cpte)
Puccini: Bohème (Cpte)
Verdi: Don Carlo (Cpte)
see CONCERT INDEX *under:*
(CFP) **CD-CFP4569** Puccini: Arias

STELLMAN, Maxine (mez)
Verdi: Traviata (Cpte)

STEMME, Nina (sop)
Lidholm: Dream Play (Cpte)
see CONCERT INDEX *under:*
(SONY) **SK46691** The First Placido Domingo International Voice Competition

STEMPNIK, Gerhard (cor ang)
see CONCERT INDEX *under:*
(BIS) **BIS-CD536** French Works for Wind Quintet

STENDORO, Giorgio (bar)
Puccini: Madama Butterfly (Cpte)

STENE, Randi (contr)
Janáček: Glagolitic Mass (Cpte)
R. Strauss: Salome (Cpte)
(CHAN) **CHAN9223** R. Strauss—A cappella choral works
(DG) **435 866-2GH** Kathleen Battle sings Italian Opera Arias
(DG) **437 519-2GH** Grieg—Orchestral Songs
(DG) **437 523-2GH** Grieg—Dramatic Works with Orchestra
(EMI) **CDC7 54117-2** Venetian Church Music
(VIRG) **VC5 45051-2** Grieg—Choral Works

STENGAARD, Frode (organ)
see CONCERT INDEX *under:*
(ROND) **RCD8329** Nielsen: Songs, Vol.5

STENHOUSE, Murray (tbn)
see CONCERT INDEX *under:*
(DOYE) **DOYCD005** Flower of Scotland

STENSVOLD, Terje (bass)
Braein: Anne Pedersdotter (Cpte)

STENZ, Markus (cond)
see London Sinfonietta

ŠTĔPÁN, Pavel (pf)
Mozart: Piano Concerto 19, Piano Concerto 27
see CONCERT INDEX *under:*
(SUPR) **11 1532-2** Suk—Chamber Works, Volume 2

STEPANSKY, Alan (vc)
Korngold: Piano Trio, Op.1
see CONCERT INDEX *under:*
(EMI) **CDC5 55400-2** Barber—Chamber and Instrumental Works

STEPANSKY, Joseph (vn)
see CONCERT INDEX *under:*
(RCA) **09026 61778-2(35)** The Heifetz Collection, Vol. 35

STÉPHANE CAILLAT CHORALE
cond M. DURUFLÉ
see CONCERT INDEX *under:*
(ERAT) **4509-98526-2** Duruflé—Vocal & Organ Works

STEPHEN, Pamela Helen (mez)
Mozart: Nozze di Figaro (Cpte)
see CONCERT INDEX *under:*

(CHAN) **CHAN9392** Vaughan Williams—Riders to the Sea etc.

STEPHENS, Alison (mndl)
see CONCERT INDEX *under:*
(AMON) **CD-SAR53** Music for Mandolin

STEPHENS, Suzanne (basset-hn)
Stockhausen: Michaels Reise

STEPHENSON, Allan (cond)
see SA Nat SO

STEPHENSON, Donald (ten)
Berlioz: Enfance du Christ (Cpte)

STEPHENSON, Elinor (sngr)
Bernstein: West Side Story (Cpte)

STEPHENSON, Mark (cond)
see London Musici

STEPHENSON, William (pf)
Liszt: Années de pèlerinage 2, Études d'exécution, S139 (exc)
see CONCERT INDEX *under:*
(OLYM) **OCD461** Busoni—Piano Music - Volume 1

STĘPIEŃ, Jozef (ten)
Szymanowski: Harnasie

STEPNER, Daniel (vn)
Bach: Triple Concerto, BWV1044
Schubert: Octet, D803
see CONCERT INDEX *under:*
(HARM) **HMU90 7059** Mozart—Quintets

STEPP, Christoph (cond)
see Bamberg SO

STERCZYNSKI, Jerzy (pf)
see CONCERT INDEX *under:*
(CHNT) **LDC278 1092** Lessel—Works for Piano

STERMAN, Andrew (sop sax/bass cl)
Glass: Hydrogen Jukebox (Cpte)

STERN, Eric (cond)
see LSO

STERN, Eric (pf)
see CONCERT INDEX *under:*
(NONE) **7559-79345-2** I Wish It So - Dawn Upshaw

STERN, Gershon (cond)
see Israel SO

STERN, Isaac (vn)
Beethoven: Piano Quartet, Op. 16, Triple Concerto
Brahms: Double Concerto, Piano Trio 1, String Sextet 1, String Sextet 2, Violin Concerto
Dvořák: Violin Concerto
Fauré: Piano Quartet 1, Piano Quartet 2
Mozart: Sinfonia concertante, K364
Schubert: String Quintet
Schumann: Piano Quartet, Op. 47
Shostakovich: Piano Trio 2
Vivaldi: Concerti, Op. 8 (exc)
see CONCERT INDEX *under:*
(SONY) **SK45816** Humoresque—Favourite Violin Encores
(SONY) **SK53107** Brahms—Violin Sonatas
(SONY) **SK53972** Mozart—Keyboard and Violin Sonatas
(SONY) **SK64309** Mozart—Violin Sonatas
(SONY) **SMK47521** Beethoven—Orchestral Works
(SONY) **SMK47599** Hindemith/Nielsen—Concertos
(SONY) **SMK58982** Pablo Casals conducts Bach at Prades, June 1950
(SONY) **SM2K47511** Bartók—Concertos
(SONY) **SM3K45845** Webern—Complete Works
(SONY) **S2K45846** Brahms—Piano Quartets

STERN, Maurice (ten)
R. Ward: Crucible (Cpte)

STERN, Michael (cond)
see Zurich Tonhalle Orch

STERNBERG, Harold (bass)
Verdi: Macbeth (Cpte)

STERNECK, Berthold (bass)
see CONCERT INDEX *under:*
(SCHW) **314622** Vienna State Opera Live, Vol.12
(SCHW) **314672** Vienna State Opera Live, Vol.17

STERNFIELD, Allan (pf)
see CONCERT INDEX *under:*
(KOCH) **37230-2** Terezín Music Anthology, Volume 2

STETSENKO, Boris (bar)
see CONCERT INDEX *under:*
(CDM) **LDC288 027/8** Prokofiev—Film and Stage Music

STEUBER, Lilian (pf)
see CONCERT INDEX *under:*
(RCA) **GD87872** Jascha Heifetz Collection
(RCA) **09026 61778-2(43)** The Heifetz Collection, Vol. 43

STEUERMANN, Eduard (pf)
Schoenberg: Pierrot Lunaire

STEUR, René (bass)
Biber: Requiem in A, Vesperae

STEVENS, Dora (sop)
see CONCERT INDEX *under:*
(DUTT) **CDAX8003** Walton—Gramophone premières

STEVENS, Garry (sngr)
Bernstein: West Side Story (Cpte)

(DG) **435 860-2GH2** Berlioz—Mélodies
cond K. BENDIX
see CONCERT INDEX under:
(BLUE) **ABCD028** Jussi Björling live at the Stockholm Opera
cond S. EHRLING
Verdi: Rigoletto (Cpte)
cond N. GREVILLIUS
see CONCERT INDEX under:
(BLUE) **ABCD028** Jussi Björling live at the Stockholm Opera
cond N. JÄRVI
Tchaikovsky: Mazeppa (Cpte)

STOCKHOLM ROYAL OPERA ORCHESTRA
cond K. BENDIX
see CONCERT INDEX under:
(BLUE) **ABCD028** Jussi Björling live at the Stockholm Opera
cond S. EHRLING
Verdi: Rigoletto (Cpte)
cond L. GARDELLI
see CONCERT INDEX under:
(BLUE) **ABCD028** Jussi Björling live at the Stockholm Opera
cond N. GREVILLIUS
Gounod: Roméo et Juliette (exc)
Puccini: Bohème (exc)
see CONCERT INDEX under:
(BLUE) **ABCD016** Jussi Björling—Rare Records & Alternative Takes
(BLUE) **ABCD028** Jussi Björling live at the Stockholm Opera
(EMI) **CDH7 61053-2** Jussi Björling sings Operatic Arias
(EMI) **CDH7 647472** Jussi Björling, Vol.2
(EMI) **CHS7 69741-2(5)** Record of Singing, Vol.4—Scandinavian School
(MMOI) **CDMOIR409** Three Tenors—Björling, Gigli & Tauber
(MMOI) **CDMOIR425** Three Tenors, Volume 2
cond E. KLAS
Schnittke: Peer Gynt (Cpte)

STOCKHOLM ROYAL ORCHESTRA
cond K. INGEBRETSEN
Lidholm: Dream Play (Cpte)

STOCKHOLM SINFONIETTA
cond N. JÄRVI
Gade: Symphony 1, Symphony 2, Symphony 3, Symphony 4, Symphony 5, Symphony 6, Symphony 7, Symphony 8
R. Strauss: Bourgeois gentilhomme Suite, Oboe Concerto
see CONCERT INDEX under:
(BIS) **BIS-CD387** Schubert: Orchestral Works
(BIS) **BIS-CD453** Schubert: Orchestral Works
cond O. KAMU
Schnittke: Symphony 4
cond S. PARKMAN
Schnittke: Requiem
cond E-P. SALONEN
see CONCERT INDEX under:
(BIS) **BIS-CD285** A Swedish Serenade
cond J-O. WEDIN
see CONCERT INDEX under:
(CPRI) **CAP21326** Wirén—Orchestral and Chamber works

STOCKHOLM SYMPHONIC WIND ORCHESTRA
cond B. PRIESTMAN
see CONCERT INDEX under:
(CPRI) **CAP21415** Works for Wind Orchestra
cond O. VÄNSKÄ
see CONCERT INDEX under:
(CPRI) **CAP21415** Works for Wind Orchestra

STOCKHOLM WIND QUINTET
see CONCERT INDEX under:
(CPRI) **CAP21326** Wirén—Orchestral and Chamber works

STÖCKIGT, Siegfried (pf)
see CONCERT INDEX under:
(DG) **413 851-2GW2** Modern American Favourites
(DG) **427 203-2GR** Gershwin: Orchestral Works

STOCKMARR, Johanna (pf)
see CONCERT INDEX under:
(PEAR) **GEMMCD9933** Grieg and his Circle play Grieg
(SIMA) **PSC1809(1)** Grieg—Historical Piano Recordings (pt 1)

STOCKMEIER, Wolfgang (organ)
see CONCERT INDEX under:
(CPO) **CPO999 039-2** Pepping—Organ Works

STOCKTON, Ann Mason (hp)
see CONCERT INDEX under:
(TEST) **SBT1053** Chamber Works

STOKES, Elisabeth (sop)
Rossini: Tancredi (Cpte)

STOKES, Nancy (sop)
Verdi: Traviata (Cpte)

STOKES, William (tpt)
see CONCERT INDEX under:
(NIMB) **NI5189** Telemann: Trumpet Concertos

STOKLASSA, Gertraut (sop)
Korngold: Violanta (Cpte)

STOKOWSKI, Leopold (cond)
see American SO

STOLL, Pierre (cond)
see Paris SO

STOLL, Stefan (sngr)
see CONCERT INDEX under:
(SONY) **S2K66836** Goldschmidt—Beatrice Cenci, etc

STOLL, Walter (bass)
Wagner: Meistersinger (Cpte)

STOLTE, Adele (sop)
R. Strauss: Ariadne auf Naxos (Cpte)
see CONCERT INDEX under:
(RCA) **74321 20286-2** Mendelssohn—Symphonies 1-5

STOLTZMAN, Lucy Chapman (vn)
see CONCERT INDEX under:
(BRID) **BCD9031** J. Harvey—Miscellaneous Works
(RCA) **RD60170** Twentieth Century Chamber Works

STOLTZMAN, Richard (cl)
Brahms: Clarinet Quintet, Clarinet Sonata 1, Clarinet Sonata 2
Weber: Clarinet Quintet, J182
see CONCERT INDEX under:
(RCA) **RD60170** Twentieth Century Chamber Works
(RCA) **RD60437** Guildhall Ensemble plays Finzi and Ashmore
(RCA) **09026 61677-2** Concerto! with Dudley Moore
(RCA) **09026 61790-2** Concerto! Stoltzman plays Copland etc.
(RCA) **09026 62537-2** Takemitsu—Cantos
(RCA) **09026 62552-2** Debussy/Ravel—Chamber Works

STOLZ, Robert (cond)
see Berlin SO

STOLZE, Gerhard (ten)
Berg: Wozzeck (Cpte)
Gounod: St Cecilia Mass
Orff: Antigonae (Cpte), Carmina Burana
R. Strauss: Elektra (Cpte), Salome (Cpte)
Wagner: Meistersinger (Cpte), Parsifal (Cpte), Rheingold (Cpte), Siegfried (Cpte), Tannhäuser (Cpte)
see CONCERT INDEX under:
(DECC) **414 100-2DM15** Wagner: Der Ring des Nibelungen
(DG) **429 168-2GR** Wagner: Excerpts from Der Ring
(DG) **435 211-2GX15** Wagner—Der Ring des Nibelungen
(DG) **439 423-2GCL** Wagner—Der Ring des Nibelungen (highlights)
(FOYE) **15-CF2011** Wagner—Der Ring de Nibelungen

STONE, Dorothy (fl)
M. Feldman: Why Patterns

STONE, Frederick (pf)
see CONCERT INDEX under:
(DECC) **430 096-2DWO** The World of Kathleen Ferrier
(DECC) **433 473-2DM** Ferrier Edition - Volume 6
(LOND) **430 061-2LM** Kathleen Ferrier—Song Recital

STONE, Norman (ten)
see CONCERT INDEX under:
(DUTT) **CDAX8006** The Delius Collection

STONE, Richard (cond)
see OST

STONE, William (bar)
Bach: Magnificat, BWV243, Mass in B minor, BWV232 (Cpte)
Hindemith: Requiem
Mahler: Symphony 8
Mozart: Mass, K427
Schubert: Mass, D167
Verdi: Simon Boccanegra (Cpte)
see CONCERT INDEX under:
(TELA) **CD80181** Walton & Bernstein: Choral Works

STOOP, Ernestine (hp)
see CONCERT INDEX under:
(PHIL) **442 534-2PH** Janáček—Choral Works

STORCHIO, Rosina (sop)
see CONCERT INDEX under:
(EMI) **CHS7 64860-2(2)** La Scala Edition - Vol.1, 1878-1914 (pt 2)
(MEMO) **HR4408/9(1)** Singers in Genoa, Vol.1 (disc 1)
(PEAR) **GEMMCDS9073(1)** Giovanni Zenatello, Vol.1 (pt 1)

STORCK, Helga (hp)
see CONCERT INDEX under:
(ETCE) **KTC1045** Menotti: Chamber and Vocal Works

STOROZHEV, Nikita (bass)
Mozart: Idomeneo (Cpte)
Mussorgsky: Boris Godunov (Cpte)
Prokofiev: Ivan the Terrible Suite
Shostakovich: Symphony 13, Symphony 14
Verdi: Don Carlos (Cpte)
see CONCERT INDEX under:
(ARGO) **436 835-2ZH** Gorecki—Choral and Orchestral Works
(CHAN) **CHAN9149** Rimsky-Korsakov/Glinka—Vocal Works
(DECC) **436 762-2DH** Shostakovich—Orchestral & Vocal Works

STOTT, Kathryn (pf)
G. Lloyd: Piano Concerto 3

Nyman: Piano Concerto
see CONCERT INDEX under:
(ALBA) **AR004** Lloyd—Piano Concerto No 4; Piano works
(CONI) **CDCF148** Debussy—Piano Works
(CONI) **CDCF159** Rachmaninov—Piano Works
(CONI) **CDCF169** Chopin—Piano Works
(CONI) **CDCF175** 20th Century British Music for Piano and Orchestra
(CONI) **CDCF180** Liszt—Piano Works
(CONI) **CDCF186** Bridge—Piano Works
(CONI) **CDCF191** Ravel—Piano Works
(CONI) **75605 51751-2** Fauré—Piano Works
(EMI) **CDC7 54419-2** Clarinet Recital
(HYPE) **CDA66610** Howells—Orchestral Works
(HYPE) **CDA66911/4** Fauré—Complete Piano Works
(UNIC) **DKPCD9147/8** Chopin—Piano Works
(UNIC) **DKPCD9158** Chabrier—Piano Works

STÖTZEL, Ulrich (cond)
see Cologne Stravaganza

STOUR MUSIC FESTIVAL CHAMBER ORCHESTRA
see CONCERT INDEX under:
(HARM) **HMA190 201** Blow—Vocal Works

STOUTZ, Edmond de (cond)
see Zurich CO

STOW, Penelope (sop)
see CONCERT INDEX under:
(MERI) **CDE84153** French Choral Music

STOWE, Sara (sop)
Purcell: Dido (Cpte)

STOYANOVA, Elena (sop)
Tchaikovsky: Queen of Spades (Cpte)

STRACCIARI, Riccardo (bar)
see CONCERT INDEX under:
(EMI) **CHS7 64860-2(2)** La Scala Edition - Vol.1, 1878-1914 (pt 2)
(EMI) **CHS7 64864-2(1)** La Scala Edition - Vol.2, 1915-46 (pt 1)
(MEMO) **HR4408/9(2)** Singers in Genoa, Vol.1 (disc 2)
(MMOI) **CDMOIR428** Rosa Ponselle and Giovanni Martinelli sing Verdi
(NIMB) **NI7801** Great Singers, Vol.1
(NIMB) **NI7867** Legendary Baritones
(PEAR) **GEMMCDS9924(1)** Covent Garden on Record, Vol.2 (pt 1)
(PREI) **89003** Riccardo Stracciari (1875-1955)
(SYMP) **SYMCD1113** The Harold Wayne Collection, Vol.13
(TEST) **SBT1008** Viva Rossini

STRACENSKÁ, Viktória (contr)
Janáček: Glagolitic Mass (Cpte)

STRACHWITZ, Ernst Leopold (narr)
Ligeti: Grand Macabre (Cpte)

STRACK, Friedrich (sngr)
R. Strauss: Rosenkavalier (Cpte)

STRACKE, Hans Richard (cond)
see Philh Hungarica

STRÁDALOVÁ, Cecílie (sop)
Janáček: Jenufa (Cpte)

STRADIVARIA ENSEMBLE
cond P. COLLEAUX
M-A. Charpentier: In honorem sancti Xaverii canticum, H355, Judicium Salomonis, H422

STRAGAPEDE, Antonio (bar)
Puccini: Fanciulla del West (Cpte)

STRAKA, Peter (ten)
Berg: Lulu (Cpte)
Mendelssohn: Symphony 2

STRANO, Francesco (vc)
see CONCERT INDEX under:
(PHIL) **426 086-2PBQ** Vivaldi—Double Concertos

STRANSKY, Josef (cond)
see NYPO

STRARAM, Walther (cond)
see Walther Straram Orch

STRASBOURG CATHÉDRALE MAÎTRISE
cond A. LOMBARD
Puccini: Turandot (Cpte)

STRASBOURG PERCUSSIONS
Xenakis: Pleiades
cond R. HAYRABEDIAN
Ohana: Cantigas
Stravinsky: Noces

STRASBOURG PHILHARMONIC ORCHESTRA
cond T. GUSCHLBAUER
Grieg: Piano Concerto
Rachmaninov: Piano Concerto 2
see CONCERT INDEX under:
(AUVI) **V4686** Indy—Orchestral Music
cond F. HAIDER
Donizetti: Roberto Devereux (Cpte)
cond A. LOMBARD
Gounod: Faust (Cpte)
Offenbach: Périchole (Cpte)
Puccini: Turandot (Cpte)
see CONCERT INDEX under:
(ERAT) **2292-45925-2** Berlioz—Orchestral Works
(ERAT) **4509-92867-2** Debussy—Orchestral Works
(RCA) **09026 61580-2(8)** RCA/Met 100 Singers, 100 Years (pt 8)

STRASBOURG UNIVERSITY GREGORIAN SCHOLA
see CONCERT INDEX under:
(STUD) SM1220.02   Immortel Grégorien

STRASBOURG UNIVERSITY MUSIC DEPARTMENT CHORUS
cond D. DEBART
Xenakis: Orestia (Cpte)

STRASFOGEL, Ignace (pf)
see CONCERT INDEX under:
(BIDD) LAB045   Hubay & Flesch —HMV Recordings
(RCA) 09026 61879-2   Grieg—Historic Recordings

STRASSER, Tamas (va)
see CONCERT INDEX under:
(VOX) 115845-2   Chamber Works by Women Composers

STRATAS, Teresa (sop)
Berg: Lulu (Cpte)
Kern: Show Boat (Cpte)
Lehár: Lustige Witwe (exc)
Leoncavallo: Pagliacci (Cpte)
see CONCERT INDEX under:
(DG) 435 712-2GX2   Lehár—The Merry Widow.
Suppé—Overtures

STRATHEARN, Paul (sngr)
Sondheim: Pacific Overtures (exc)

STRATTA, Ettore (cond)
see RPO

STRATTON QUARTET
see CONCERT INDEX under:
(DUTT) CDLX7004   Elgar—Chamber Works

STRAUCH, Pierre (vc)
see CONCERT INDEX under:
(ERAT) 2292-45770-2   Xenakis—Miscellaneous Works

STRAUSS, Edward (cond)
see Orch

STRAUSS, Paul (cond)
see Liège Orch

STRAUSS, Richard (cond)
see Bavarian St Orch

STRAUSS, Richard (pf)
see CONCERT INDEX under:
(PEAR) GEMMCDS9365   R. Strauss: Der Rosenkavalier (abridged), etc
(PREI) 90078   Hilde Konetzni
(PREI) 90083   Maria Reining
(PREI) 93261   Richard Strauss accompanies
(PREI) 93262   R.Strauss accompanies Reining,Dermota and Piltti

STRAUSS-SMITH, Lloyd (ten)
Delius: Village Romeo and Juliet (Cpte)

(LA) STRAVAGANZA, COLOGNE
cond A. MANZE
see CONCERT INDEX under:
(DENO) CO-78933   Telemann—Concertos
cond U. STÖTZEL
Telemann: St Matthew Passion (1746) (Cpte)

STRAVINSKY, Igor (cond)
see Boston SO

STRAVINSKY, Igor (pf)
see CONCERT INDEX under:
(EMI) CDS7 54607-2   Stravinsky plays and conducts Stravinsky

STRAVINSKY, Igor (spkr)
see CONCERT INDEX under:
(SONY) SM2K46294   Stravinsky—Symphonies

STRAVINSKY, Soulima (pf)
see CONCERT INDEX under:
(EMI) CDS7 54607-2   Stravinsky plays and conducts Stravinsky

STREETON, Jane (sop)
see CONCERT INDEX under:
(HYPE) CDA66608   Dibdin—Three Operas

STREHLE, Wilfried (va)
see CONCERT INDEX under:
(SCHW) 311088   Spohr—Instrumental Works

STREICH, Rita (sop)
Gluck: Orfeo ed Euridice (Cpte)
J.Strauss II: Fledermaus (Cpte)
Millöcker: Bettelstudent (Cpte)
Mozart: Don Giovanni (Cpte), Entführung (Cpte),
Nozze di Figaro (Cpte), Zauberflöte (Cpte)
R. Strauss: Ariadne auf Naxos (Cpte), Daphne (Cpte)
Wagner: Siegfried (Cpte)
Weber: Freischütz (Cpte)
see CONCERT INDEX under:
(DG) 437 677-2GDO2   Irmgard Seefried - Opera Recital
(DG) 437 680-2GDO2   Rita Streich - Lieder Recital
(EMI) CZS7 67123-2   Wagner: Der Ring des Nibelungen
(FOYE) 15-CF2011   Wagner—Der Ring de Nibelungen

STREIFF, Danièle (sop)
Massenet: Amadis (Cpte), Cléopâtre (Cpte)

STREISAND, Barbra (voc)
Styne: Funny Girl (Cpte)

STREIT, Kurt (ten)
Mozart: Così fan tutte (Cpte), Entführung (Cpte),
Zauberflöte (Cpte)

Sullivan: Yeomen of the Guard (Cpte)
see CONCERT INDEX under:
(EMI) CDC5 55430-2   Brahms/Schumann—Lieder

STRIBONEEN, Randel (sngr)
see CONCERT INDEX under:
(SONY) SM3K47154   Bernstein—Theatre Works Volume 1

STRICH, Elaine (sngr)
Coward: Sail Away (Cpte)

STRICKER, Frieder (ten)
Wagner: Meistersinger (Cpte)

STRICKER, Hans (treb)
see CONCERT INDEX under:
(TELD) 2292-44193-2   Bach—Cantatas, Volume 44
(TELD) 4509-91764-2   Bach—Cantatas, Vol.10

STRICKLAND, William (cond)
see Dumbarton Oaks CO

STRIENZ, Wilhelm (bass)
Mozart: Zauberflöte (Cpte)
see CONCERT INDEX under:
(PREI) 89071   Gerhard Hüsch (1901-1984) - II

STRIMLING, Gene (perc)
see CONCERT INDEX under:
(ETCE) KTC1071   L.Harrison—Music For Guitar And Percussion

STRING ORCHESTRA
see CONCERT INDEX under:
(DECC) 430 263-2DM   Purcell—Sacred choral works
cond BARRY ROSE
see CONCERT INDEX under:
(EMI) CDM7 64131-2   Orchestral Music for Christmas
cond B. REIBOLD
see CONCERT INDEX under:
(BIDD) LAB087   Hindemith plays Hindemith

STRING QUARTET
see CONCERT INDEX under:
(BIDD) LAB029   French Chamber works
(PEAR) GEMMCDS9996   Kreisler - Violin Concertos
(ROMO) 81012-2   Elisabeth Rethberg— Brunswick Recordings 1924-1929

STRINGER, Alan (tpt)
see CONCERT INDEX under:
(CRD) CRD3308   Trumpet & Organ at Liverpool Cathedral
(DECC) 430 633-2DM   Haydn—Concertos

STŘÍŠKA, Jaroslav (ten)
Janáček: From the House of the Dead (Cpte)
Martinů: Julietta (Cpte)

STROBL, Joseph (cond)
see Austrian St Rad Orch

STROHBAUER, Hans (ten)
Lehár: Lustige Witwe (Cpte)

STROINIGG, Frieda (mez)
see CONCERT INDEX under:
(SCHW) 314592   Vienna State Opera Live, Vol.9

STROMAN, Guy (sngr)
see CONCERT INDEX under:
(EMI) CDC5 55189-2   The Busby Berkeley Album

STRUB, Max (vn)
see CONCERT INDEX under:
(EMI) CDC5 55225-2   Pfitzner plays and conducts Pfitzner
(PREI) 90029   Hans Pfitzner Accompanies & Conducts

STRUB, Patrick (cond)
see Stuttgart Arcata Ens

STRUCKMANN, Falk (bar)
Bartók: Duke Bluebeard's castle (Cpte)
Beethoven: Fidelio (Cpte), Symphony 9
Busoni: Turandot (Cpte)
Wagner: Tristan und Isolde (Cpte)

STRUGAŁA, Tadeusz (cond)
see Polish Nat RSO

STRYCZEK, Karl-Heinz (bar)
Wagner: Rheingold (Cpte)

STUART, Ian (cl)
Stockhausen: Michaels Reise

STUART-ROBERTS, Deborah (mez)
Cilea: Adriana Lecouvreur (Cpte)

STUBBS, Stephen (cond)
see Tragicomedia

STUBBS, Stephen (gtr)
see CONCERT INDEX under:
(TELD) 4509-90841-2   A Gift of Nature - 17th Century English Chamber Music

STUBBS, Stephen (lte)
Kellner: Auserlesene Lauten-Stücke
Landi: Mort d'Orfeo (Cpte)
see CONCERT INDEX under:
(ECM) 837 360-2   Proensa—Songs of the Troubadours
(EMI) CDC7 54519-2   Bach & Weiss—Lute Suites
(HYPE) CDA66307   My Mind to me a kingdom is
(HYPE) CDA66335   A Musicall Dreame
(PIER) PV787092   Airs and Dances of Shakespeare's Time
(TELD) 4509-90798-2   Monteverdi—Il Ballo delle ingrate

STUBBS, Stephen (theorbo)
see CONCERT INDEX under:
(TELD) 4509-90841-2   A Gift of Nature - 17th Century English Chamber Music

STÜCKGOLD, Grete (sop)
see CONCERT INDEX under:
(SIMA) PSC1810(2)   Grieg—Songs (historical recordings, pt 2)

STUCKI, Marianne (fl)
see CONCERT INDEX under:
(ETCE) KTC1083   Telemann: Sonatas

STÜCKL, Annelies (contr)
Mozart: Zauberflöte (Cpte)

STUDER, Cheryl (sop)
Beethoven: Missa Solemnis
Brahms: Deutsches Requiem, Op.45 (Cpte)
Donizetti: Lucia di Lammermoor (Cpte), Messa da Requiem
Floyd: Susannah (Cpte)
Gounod: Faust (Cpte)
Lehár: Lustige Witwe (Cpte)
Mahler: Klagende Lied, Symphony 2, Symphony 8
Mozart: Don Giovanni (Cpte), Entführung (Cpte),
Nozze di Figaro (Cpte), Zauberflöte (Cpte)
R. Strauss: Elektra (Cpte), Frau ohne Schatten (Cpte), Salome (Cpte)
Rossini: Semiramide (Cpte), Viaggio a Reims (Cpte)
Schubert: Fierrabras (Cpte)
Verdi: Attila (Cpte), Otello (Cpte), Pezzi sacri (Cpte),
Requiem (Cpte), Traviata (Cpte), Vespri siciliani (Cpte)
Wagner: Götterdämmerung (Cpte), Lohengrin (Cpte),
Meistersinger (Cpte), Tannhäuser (Cpte), Walküre (Cpte)
Zemlinsky: Geburtstag der Infantin (Cpte)
see CONCERT INDEX under:
(DG) 435 387-2GH   Cheryl Studer sings Sacred Arias
(DG) 435 617-2GH   Beethoven in Berlin—New Year's Eve Concert
(DG) 435 867-2GH2   Barber—The Songs
(DG) 437 784-2GH   Cheryl Studer—Salzburg Recital
(DG) 439 768-2GH   Wagner—Gala - New Year's Eve Concert 1993
(DG) 439 865-2GH   Cheryl Studer sings Strauss and Wagner
(DG) 445 354-2GX14   Wagner—Der Ring des Nibelungen
(DG) 447 023-2GX12   Mahler—The Symphonies
(EMI) CDC7 49811-2   Covent Garden Gala Concert
(EMI) CDS7 49487-2   Beethoven: Complete Symphonies
(PHIL) 442 410-2PM   Queen of the Night—Cheryl Studer sings Mozart

STUDER, Ulrich (bar)
Gilles: Requiem
see CONCERT INDEX under:
(HARM) HMC90 1167   Lully—Grands Motets

STUDHOLME, Marion (sop)
Britten: Peter Grimes (Cpte)
Sullivan: Mikado (Cpte)

STUDIO ORCHESTRA
cond H. KRTSCHIL
see CONCERT INDEX under:
(CAPR) 10 180   Gisela May sings Weill

STUDT, Richard (vn)
see CONCERT INDEX under:
(DECC) 440 037-2DM   Bach—Concertos

STUDT, Richard (vn/dir)
see CONCERT INDEX under:
(EMIN) CD-EMX2221   Pärt—Chamber Works
(NAXO) 8 550823   English String Music
(NAXO) 8 550979   20th Century String Music
(UNIC) DKPCD9050   Vivaldi—Concertos

STULEN, Jan (cond)
see Hilversum Radio Chbr Orch

STUMPER, Rudolf (bass)
R. Strauss: Rosenkavalier (Cpte)

STUMPHIUS, Annegeer (sop)
Bach: St. John Passion, BWV245 (Cpte)
Gluck: Rencontre imprévue (Cpte)
Haydn: Jahreszeiten (Cpte)

STUPEL, Ilya (cond)
see Rubinstein PO

STURROCK, Kathron (pf)
see CONCERT INDEX under:
(CARL) PCD1050   Brahms—Violin Sonatas
(CHAN) CHAN8770   Bliss—Chamber Works
(GAMU) GAMCD534   R. Clarke—Songs with Piano and Violin

STUTTGART ARCATA ENSEMBLE
cond P. STRUB
Gluck: Don Juan (Cpte)

STUTTGART BACH COLLEGIUM
Beethoven: Missa Solemnis
Brahms: Deutsches Requiem, Op. 45 (Cpte)
Handel: Messias, K572 (Cpte)
J.C. Bach: Amadis de Gaule (Cpte)
see CONCERT INDEX under:
(HANS) 98 822   Bach—Cantatas, Vol.60
(HANS) 98 965   Bach—Motets
(NOVA) 150 028-2   Bach—Cantatas
(NOVA) 150 029-2   Bach—Cantatas

cond H. RILLING
Bach: Cantata 6, Cantata 21, Cantata 28, Cantata 31, Cantata 36, Cantata 63, Cantata 66, Cantata 93, Cantata 108, Cantata 112, Cantata 134, Cantata 146, Cantata 182, Cantata 194, Christmas Oratorio, BWV248 (Cpte), Easter Oratorio, BWV249 (Cpte), Mass, BWV235, St Matthew Passion, BWV244
Beethoven: Christus am Oelberge, Op. 85, Mass in C
Cherubini: Mass in D minor
Haydn: Jahreszeiten (Cpte), Schöpfung (Cpte)
Mendelssohn: Elias (Cpte)
see CONCERT INDEX under:
(HANS) 98 801 Bach—Cantatas, Vol.39
(HANS) 98 802 Bach—Cantatas, Vol.40
(HANS) 98 803 Bach—Cantatas, Vol.41
(HANS) 98 804 Bach—Cantatas, Vol.42
(HANS) 98 805 Bach—Cantatas, Vol.43
(HANS) 98 806 Bach—Cantatas, Vol.44
(HANS) 98 807 Bach—Cantatas, Vol.45
(HANS) 98 808 Bach—Cantatas, Vol.46
(HANS) 98 809 Bach—Cantatas, Vol.47
(HANS) 98 810 Bach—Cantatas, Vol.48
(HANS) 98 811 Bach—Cantatas, Vol.49
(HANS) 98 812 Bach—Cantatas, Vol.50
(HANS) 98 813 Bach—Cantatas, Vol.51
(HANS) 98 814 Bach—Cantatas, Vol.52
(HANS) 98 815 Bach—Cantatas, Vol.53
(HANS) 98 816 Bach—Cantatas, Vol.54
(HANS) 98 817 Bach—Cantatas, Vol.55
(HANS) 98 818 Bach—Cantatas, Vol.56
(HANS) 98 819 Bach—Cantatas, Vol.57
(HANS) 98 820 Bach—Cantatas, Vol.58
(HANS) 98 821 Bach—Cantatas, Vol.59
(HANS) 98 822 Bach—Cantatas, Vol.60
(HANS) 98 824 Bach—Cantatas, Vol.62
(HANS) 98 825 Bach—Cantatas, Vol.63
(HANS) 98 826 Bach—Cantatas, Vol.64
(HANS) 98 828 Bach—Cantatas, Vol.66
(HANS) 98 829 Bach—Cantatas, Vol.67
(HANS) 98 835 Bach—Cantatas, Vol.69
(HANS) 98 855 Bach—Cantatas, Vol.4
(HANS) 98 861 Bach—Cantatas, Vol.10
(HANS) 98 863 Bach—Cantatas, Vol.12
(HANS) 98 864 Bach—Cantatas, Vol.13
(HANS) 98 866 Bach—Cantatas, Vol.15
(HANS) 98 867 Bach—Cantatas, Vol.16
(HANS) 98 868 Bach—Cantatas, Vol.17
(HANS) 98 869 Bach—Cantatas, Vol.18
(HANS) 98 870 Bach—Cantatas, Vol.19
(HANS) 98 871 Bach—Cantatas, Vol.20
(HANS) 98 872 Bach—Cantatas, Vol.21
(HANS) 98 873 Bach—Cantatas, Vol.22
(HANS) 98 874 Bach—Cantatas, Vol.23
(HANS) 98 875 Bach—Cantatas, Vol.24
(HANS) 98 876 Bach—Cantatas, Vol.25
(HANS) 98 877 Bach—Cantatas, Vol.26
(HANS) 98 878 Bach—Cantatas, Vol.27
(HANS) 98 879 Bach—Cantatas, Vol.28
(HANS) 98 882 Bach—Cantatas, Vol.31
(HANS) 98 883 Bach—Cantatas, Vol.32
(HANS) 98 885 Bach—Cantatas, Vol.34
(HANS) 98 886 Bach—Cantatas, Vol.35
(HANS) 98 887 Bach—Cantatas, Vol.36
(HANS) 98 890 Bach—Cantatas, Vol.37
(HANS) 98 891 Bach—Cantatas, Vol.38
(HANS) 98 979 Mozart—Sacred Choral Works

STUTTGART BAROQUE ORCHESTRA
cond F. BERNIUS
Bach: Motets (Cpte)

STUTTGART CHAMBER CHOIR
cond F. BERNIUS
Bach: Cantata 206, Cantata 207a, Motets (Cpte)
Gluck: Orfeo ed Euridice (Cpte)
Monteverdi: Vespers
Zelenka: Litanie lauretanae, ZWV152, Missa dei fili, ZWV20
see CONCERT INDEX under:
(SONY) SK48037 Bruckner—Choral Works
cond B. WEIL
Gazzaniga: Don Giovanni (Cpte)

STUTTGART CHAMBER ORCHESTRA
cond D.R. DAVIES
see CONCERT INDEX under:
(ECM) 439 611-2 Works for Viola & Orchestra
(ECM) 445 941-2 Kancheli—Abii ne Viderem
cond K. MÜNCHINGER
Bach: Mass in B minor, BWV232 (Cpte), Musikalisches Opfer, BWV1079, Suites, BWV1066-9 (exc)
see CONCERT INDEX under:
(DECC) 430 499-2DWO World of Bach
(DECC) 430 706-2DM Popular Baroque Works
(DECC) 433 175-2DM Bach—Sacred Choral Works
cond H. RILLING
Bach: Mass, BWV236
Haydn: Mass 10
cond M. SIEGHART
see CONCERT INDEX under:
(ORFE) C254921A Kraus—Orchestral Works

STUTTGART GÄCHINGER KANTOREI
Beethoven: Missa solemnis
Brahms: Deutsches Requiem, Op. 45 (Cpte)
Franck: Béatitudes (Cpte)
Handel: Messias, K572 (Cpte)
J.C. Bach: Amadis de Gaule (Cpte)
Various: Messa per Rossini (Cpte)
see CONCERT INDEX under:
(HANS) 98 965 Bach—Motets

cond H. RILLING
Bach: Cantata 6, Cantata 28, Cantata 30, Cantata 36, Cantata 63, Cantata 66, Cantata 93, Cantata 106, Cantata 108, Cantata 112, Cantata 134, Cantata 146, Cantata 182, Cantata 194, Cantata 198, Christmas Oratorio, BWV248 (Cpte), Easter Oratorio, BWV249 (Cpte), Mass, BWV235, Mass, BWV236, St Matthew Passion, BWV244
Beethoven: Christus am Oelberge, Op. 85, Mass in C
Cherubini: Mass in D minor
Haydn: Jahreszeiten (Cpte), Mass 10, Schöpfung (Cpte)
Mendelssohn: Elias (Cpte)
Various: Requiem of Reconciliation (Cpte)
see CONCERT INDEX under:
(HANS) 98 801 Bach—Cantatas, Vol.39
(HANS) 98 802 Bach—Cantatas, Vol.40
(HANS) 98 803 Bach—Cantatas, Vol.41
(HANS) 98 805 Bach—Cantatas, Vol.43
(HANS) 98 806 Bach—Cantatas, Vol.44
(HANS) 98 807 Bach—Cantatas, Vol.45
(HANS) 98 808 Bach—Cantatas, Vol.46
(HANS) 98 809 Bach—Cantatas, Vol.47
(HANS) 98 810 Bach—Cantatas, Vol.48
(HANS) 98 811 Bach—Cantatas, Vol.49
(HANS) 98 812 Bach—Cantatas, Vol.50
(HANS) 98 813 Bach—Cantatas, Vol.51
(HANS) 98 814 Bach—Cantatas, Vol.52
(HANS) 98 815 Bach—Cantatas, Vol.53
(HANS) 98 816 Bach—Cantatas, Vol.54
(HANS) 98 817 Bach—Cantatas, Vol.55
(HANS) 98 818 Bach—Cantatas, Vol.56
(HANS) 98 819 Bach—Cantatas, Vol.57
(HANS) 98 820 Bach—Cantatas, Vol.58
(HANS) 98 821 Bach—Cantatas, Vol.59
(HANS) 98 822 Bach—Cantatas, Vol.60
(HANS) 98 824 Bach—Cantatas, Vol.62
(HANS) 98 825 Bach—Cantatas, Vol.63
(HANS) 98 826 Bach—Cantatas, Vol.64
(HANS) 98 828 Bach—Cantatas, Vol.66
(HANS) 98 829 Bach—Cantatas, Vol.67
(HANS) 98 835 Bach—Cantatas, Vol.69
(HANS) 98 855 Bach—Cantatas, Vol.4
(HANS) 98 856 Bach—Cantatas, Vol.5
(HANS) 98 857 Bach—Cantatas, Vol.6
(HANS) 98 858 Bach—Cantatas, Vol.7
(HANS) 98 859 Bach—Cantatas, Vol.8
(HANS) 98 861 Bach—Cantatas, Vol.10
(HANS) 98 863 Bach—Cantatas, Vol.12
(HANS) 98 864 Bach—Cantatas, Vol.13
(HANS) 98 866 Bach—Cantatas, Vol.15
(HANS) 98 867 Bach—Cantatas, Vol.16
(HANS) 98 868 Bach—Cantatas, Vol.17
(HANS) 98 869 Bach—Cantatas, Vol.18
(HANS) 98 870 Bach—Cantatas, Vol.19
(HANS) 98 871 Bach—Cantatas, Vol.20
(HANS) 98 872 Bach—Cantatas, Vol.21
(HANS) 98 873 Bach—Cantatas, Vol.22
(HANS) 98 874 Bach—Cantatas, Vol.23
(HANS) 98 875 Bach—Cantatas, Vol.24
(HANS) 98 876 Bach—Cantatas, Vol.25
(HANS) 98 877 Bach—Cantatas, Vol.26
(HANS) 98 878 Bach—Cantatas, Vol.27
(HANS) 98 879 Bach—Cantatas, Vol.28
(HANS) 98 882 Bach—Cantatas, Vol.31
(HANS) 98 883 Bach—Cantatas, Vol.32
(HANS) 98 885 Bach—Cantatas, Vol.34
(HANS) 98 886 Bach—Cantatas, Vol.35
(HANS) 98 887 Bach—Cantatas, Vol.36
(HANS) 98 890 Bach—Cantatas, Vol.37
(HANS) 98 891 Bach—Cantatas, Vol.38
(HANS) 98 979 Mozart—Sacred Choral Works
(NOVA) 150 028-2 Bach—Cantatas
(NOVA) 150 029-2 Bach—Cantatas

STUTTGART GEDÄCHTNISKIRCHE CHOIR
cond H. RILLING
see CONCERT INDEX under:
(HANS) 98 803 Bach—Cantatas, Vol.41
(HANS) 98 804 Bach—Cantatas, Vol.42
(HANS) 98 824 Bach—Cantatas, Vol.62
(HANS) 98 868 Bach—Cantatas, Vol.17
(HANS) 98 874 Bach—Cantatas, Vol.23
(HANS) 98 875 Bach—Cantatas, Vol.24
(HANS) 98 876 Bach—Cantatas, Vol.25

STUTTGART HYMNUS CHOIR (BOYS' VOICES)
cond K. MÜNCHINGER
see CONCERT INDEX under:
(DECC) 430 499-2DWO World of Bach

STUTTGART OPERA CHORUS
cond D.R. DAVIES
Glass: Akhnaten (Cpte)
cond B. KONTARSKY
B.A. Zimmermann: Soldaten (Cpte)
Nono: Intolleranza 1960 (Cpte)

STUTTGART OPERA ORCHESTRA
cond D.R. DAVIES
Glass: Akhnaten (Cpte)
cond G. GÖRLICH
see CONCERT INDEX under:
(MMOI) CDMOIR408 Great Sopranos
cond B. KONTARSKY
Nono: Intolleranza 1960 (Cpte)

STUTTGART PIANO TRIO
Beethoven: Piano Trios (exc)

STUTTGART RADIO CHORUS
cond K. ARP
Spohr: Faust (Cpte)

cond G. BERTINI
see CONCERT INDEX under:
(ORFE) C015821A Stravinsky: Choral and Vocal Works
cond K. BÖHM
Mozart: Nozze di Figaro (Cpte)
cond G. CHMURA
Schubert: Lazarus, D689
cond M. GIELEN
B. A. Zimmermann: Requiem (Cpte)
cond E. INBAL
Berlioz: Damnation de Faust (Cpte), Roméo et Juliette (Cpte)
cond F. LEITNER
Handel: Giulio Cesare (Cpte)
cond H. MÜLLER-KRAY
see CONCERT INDEX under:
(ACAN) 43 267 Fritz Wunderlich sings Opera Arias
cond A. RISCHNER
see CONCERT INDEX under:
(ACAN) 43 267 Fritz Wunderlich sings Opera Arias

STUTTGART RADIO ORCHESTRA
cond K. BÖHM
Mozart: Nozze di Figaro (Cpte)

STUTTGART RADIO SYMPHONY ORCHESTRA
Franck: Béatitudes (Cpte)
Various: Messa per Rossini (Cpte)
cond G. BERTINI
Ravel: Left-Hand Concerto, Piano Concerto
see CONCERT INDEX under:
(ORFE) C015821A Stravinsky: Choral and Vocal Works
cond G. CHMURA
Schubert: Lazarus, D689
cond R. FRÜHBECK DE BURGOS
Spohr: Clarinet Concerto 1, Clarinet Concerto 2, Clarinet Concerto 3, Clarinet Concerto 4
cond G. GELMETTI
Mozart: Sinfonia Concertante, K364, Symphony 40
see CONCERT INDEX under:
(EMI) CDC7 54248-2 Berg/Stravinsky—Violin Concertos, etc
cond H. GRAF
see CONCERT INDEX under:
(ORFE) C096841A Famous Opera Arias
cond C. LEONHARDT
Wagner: Walküre (exc)
cond N. MARRINER
Handel: Messiah (Cpte)
Mahler: Symphony 4
Mozart: Piano Concerto 16, Piano Concerto 19
R. Strauss: Metamorphosen, Oboe Concerto
Rachmaninov: Symphony 2, Vocalise
Schumann: Symphony in G minor, Symphony 2, Symphony 3, Symphony 4
Tchaikovsky: Suite 3, Suite 4
Vieuxtemps: Cello Concerto 1, Cello Concerto 2
see CONCERT INDEX under:
(CAPR) 10 063 Schumann: Orchestral Works
(CAPR) 10 308 Oboe Concertos
(CAPR) 10 309 Haydn: Concertos
(CAPR) 10 369 R. Strauss—Orchestral Works
(CAPR) 10 428 Britten/Honegger—Orchestral Works
(CAPR) 10 997 Schumann: Symphonies & Orchestral Works
(PHIL) 422 522-2PME6 The Complete Mozart Edition Vol 22
cond H. MÜLLER-KRAY
(ACAN) 43 267 Fritz Wunderlich sings Opera Arias
cond A. RISCHNER
see CONCERT INDEX under:
(ACAN) 43 267 Fritz Wunderlich sings Opera Arias
cond C. SCHURICHT
Brahms: Deutsches Requiem, Op. 45 (Cpte)
see CONCERT INDEX under:
(ACAN) 43 267 Fritz Wunderlich sings Opera Arias
cond S. SOLTESZ
(ORFE) C081841A Grace Bumbry: Famous Opera Arias

STUTTGART SCHOLA CANTORUM
cond C. GOTTWALD
see CONCERT INDEX under:
(WERG) WER6074-2 Cage—Miscellaneous Works
(WERG) WER60162-50 Ligeti: Choral and Orchestral Works
cond F. TRAVIS
Holliger: Siebengesang
cond H. ZENDER
Holliger: Magische Tänzer (Cpte)

STUTTGART STATE CHORUS
see CONCERT INDEX under:
(SONY) SK64133 The Essential Philip Glass

STUTTGART STATE ORCHESTRA
see CONCERT INDEX under:
(SONY) SK64133 The Essential Philip Glass
B.A. Zimmermann: Soldaten (Cpte)

STUTTGART STATE ORCHESTRA BRASS ENSEMBLE
cond D.R. DAVIES
see CONCERT INDEX under:
(ECM) 831 959-2 Pärt—Arbos

STUTTGART STRING SEXTET
Brahms: String Sextet 1, String Sextet 2

SULIKOWSKI, Jerzy (pf)
see CONCERT INDEX under:
(POLS) **PNCD067** Szymanowski: Songs

SULIOTIS, Elena (sop)
Verdi: Macbeth (Cpte), Nabucco (Cpte)
see CONCERT INDEX under:
(DECC) **436 261-2DHO3** Puccini—Il Trittico

SULLÉ, Sylvie (mez)
Honegger: Roi David (Cpte)

SULLIVAN, Gwynne (ten)
Walton: Troilus and Cressida (Cpte)

SULTAN, Grete (pf)
Cage: Etudes australes Bks I-IV

SULTANOV, Aleksei (pf)
see CONCERT INDEX under:
(TELD) **2292-46011-2** Russian Piano Sonatas

SULZENKO, Jirí (bass)
Puccini: Bohème (Cpte)

SULZMANN, Stan (sax)
see CONCERT INDEX under:
(ECM) **847 537-2** Gavin Bryars—After the Requiem

SUMAC, Yma (sngr)
Fain: Flahooley (Cpte)

SUMEGI, Daniel (bass)
Bellini: Beatrice di Tenda (Cpte)

SUMMEREDER, Roman (organ)
Schütz: Kleiner geistlichen Concerten, SWV282-305
(exc), Kleiner geistlichen Concerten, SWV306-37
(exc)

SUMMERLY, Jeremy (cond)
see Oxford Camerata

SUMMERS, Hilary (contr)
Handel: Messiah (Cpte)
Nyman: Noises, Sounds and Sweet Airs (Cpte)

SUMMERS, Jonathan (bar)
Balfe: Bohemian Girl (Cpte)
Britten: Gloriana (Cpte), Peter Grimes (Cpte)
Orff: Carmina Burana
Puccini: Fanciulla del West (Cpte), Madama Butterfly
(Cpte)
Saint-Saëns: Samson et Dalila (Cpte)
Vaughan Williams: Symphony 1
Verdi: Ballo in maschera (Cpte), Battaglia di Legnano
(Cpte), Traviata (exc)

SUMMERS, Lydia (mez)
see CONCERT INDEX under:
(VAI) **VAIA1017** Leonard Warren—Early Recordings

ŠUMPÍK, Pavel (tamb)
see CONCERT INDEX under:
(SUPR) **11 1878-2** The Unknown Janáček

SUNARA, Maja (mez)
see CONCERT INDEX under:
(RCA) **GD60941** Rarities - Montserrat Caballé

SUNG, Hugh (pf)
Brahms: Hungarian Dances
Handel: Flute Sonatas (exc), Violin Sonatas (exc)
Joachim: Romance in B flat

SUNNEGÅRDH, Thomas (ten)
Wagner: Rheingold (Cpte)

SUPERVIA, Conchita (mez)
see CONCERT INDEX under:
(CLUB) **CL99-074** Conchita Supervia (1895-1936)
(EMI) **CHS7 64864-2(1)** La Scala Edition - Vol.2,
1915-46 (pt 1)
(NIMB) **NI7801** Great Singers, Vol.1
(NIMB) **NI7836/7** Conchita Supervia (1895-1936)
(PEAR) **GEMMCDS9926(2)** Covent Garden on
Record—Vol.4 (pt 2)
(PREI) **89023** Conchita Supervia (1895-1936)
(TEST) **SBT1008** Viva Rossini

SUPOVÉ, Kathleen (elec kybd)
see CONCERT INDEX under:
(BRID) **BCD9031** J. Harvey—Miscellaneous Works

SURIAN, Giorgio (bar)
Gluck: Iphigénie en Tauride (Cpte)
Paisiello: Nina (Cpte)
Rossini: Bianca e Falliero (Cpte), Donna del lago
(Cpte), Viaggio a Reims (Cpte)
Verdi: Attila (Cpte), Forza del destino (Cpte),
Rigoletto (Cpte)

SURINACH, E. (sop)
see CONCERT INDEX under:
(CLUB) **CL99-014** Dino Borgioli (1891-1960)

SURYOVÁ, Daniela (contr)
Dvořák: Kate and the Devil (Cpte)
Fibich: Šárka (Cpte)
Janáček: Jenůfa (Cpte)

SUSCA, Vito (bass)
Verdi: Traviata (Cpte)

SUSLAK, Isolda (pf)
see CONCERT INDEX under:
(BIS) **BIS-CD501** Martinů—Orchestral Works

SÜSS, Margit-Anna (hp)
see CONCERT INDEX under:
(DENO) **CO-76611** Oboe/Cor anglais and Harp
Recital
(DG) **429 738-2GH** Debussy & Ravel: Chamber
Works

SÜSS, Reiner (bar)
Lortzing: Wildschütz (Cpte)
Mozart: Zaïde (Cpte)
Wagner: Tannhäuser (Cpte)

SUSSKIND, Walter (cond)
see Concert Arts Orch

SUSSMAN, Estel (sop)
see CONCERT INDEX under:
(MONT) **TCE8790** Debussy: Orchestral and Dramatic
Works

SUSSMUTH, Gernot (vn)
see CONCERT INDEX under:
(CAPR) **10 539** Schulhoff—Chamber Works

SUTCLIFFE, Tom (alto)
Bach: St Matthew Passion, BWV244 (Cpte)

SUTEJ, Vjeksolav (cond)
see ECO

SUTER, Jeremy (organ)
see CONCERT INDEX under:
(PRIO) **PRCD312** Stanford: Choral Works

SUTHAUS, Ludwig (ten)
Wagner: Meistersinger (Cpte), Tristan und Isolde
(Cpte), Walküre (Cpte)
see CONCERT INDEX under:
(EMI) **CZS7 67123-2** Wagner: Der Ring des
Nibelungen
(MYTO) **3MCD93381** Wagner—Die Walküre, etc

SUTHERLAND, Dame Joan (sop)
A. Thomas: Hamlet (Cpte)
Beethoven: Symphony 9
Bellini: Norma (Cpte), Puritani (Cpte), Sonnambula
(Cpte)
Bizet: Carmen (Cpte)
Cilea: Adriana Lecouvreur (Cpte)
Delibes: Lakmé (Cpte)
Donizetti: Elisir d'amore (Cpte), Fille du régiment
(Cpte), Lucia di Lammermoor (Cpte), Lucrezia Borgia
(Cpte), Maria Stuarda (Cpte)
Gay: Beggar's Opera (Cpte)
Gounod: Faust (Cpte)
Handel: Athalia (Cpte)
J. Strauss II: Fledermaus (Cpte)
Massenet: Esclarmonde (Cpte), Roi de Lahore
(Cpte)
Mozart: Don Giovanni (Cpte)
Offenbach: Contes d'Hoffmann (Cpte)
Puccini: Turandot (Cpte)
Rossini: Semiramide (Cpte)
Verdi: Masnadieri (Cpte), Requiem (Cpte), Rigoletto
(Cpte), Traviata (Cpte), Trovatore (Cpte)
Wagner: Siegfried (Cpte)
see CONCERT INDEX under:
(CFP) **CD-CFP4532** Sacred Arias
(DECC) **414 100-2DM15** Wagner: Der Ring des
Nibelungen
(DECC) **417 011-2DH2** Pavarotti's Greatest Hits
(DECC) **425 493-2DM2** Joan Sutherland: The Art of
the Prima Donna
(DECC) **430 500-2DWO** World of Handel
(DECC) **430 724-2DM** Great Operatic Duets
(DECC) **433 010-2DM** Christmas Stars
(DECC) **433 439-2DA** Great Love Duets
(DECC) **433 706-2DMO3** Bellini—Beatrice di Tenda;
Operatic Arias
(DECC) **436 402-2DWO** The World of Wedding
Music
(DECC) **436 461-2DM** Ten Top Sopranos

SUTTE, Jack (tpt)
Rorem: Eleven Studies

SUTTER, Christian (db)
Kancheli: Exil

SUTTON, Andrew (hn)
see CONCERT INDEX under:
(CNTO) **CRCD2368** Sullivan—That Glorious Song of
Old

SUTTON, Sheryl (narr)
Glass: Einstein on the Beach (Cpte)

SUTTON, Vern (ten)
Britten: Paul Bunyan (Cpte)
Copland: Tender Land (Cpte)

SUVINI, Luigi (cond)
see Dallapiccola Ens

SUZAN, Maurice (cond)
see Radio Lille Orch

SUZUKI, Azuko (sop)
Haydn: Anima del filosofo (Cpte)

SUZUKI, Hidemi (baroque vc)
see CONCERT INDEX under:
(DENO) **CO-73868/9** Bach: Flute Works
(DHM) **RD77909** Vivaldi: Cello Sonatas

SUZUKI, Hidemi (vc)
Handel: Violin Sonatas (exc)
Leclair: Violin Sonatas, Op. 5 (exc)

SUZUKI, Kai (treb)
Mozart: Zauberflöte (Cpte)

SUZUMI, Kishiko (vn)
Nørholm: Violin Concerto

SVAB, Alessandro (bar)
Rossini: Pietra del paragone (Cpte)

SVAB, Sdenek (hn)
see CONCERT INDEX under:
(CHNT) **LDC278 835** Villa-Lobos—Chôros for
Chamber Ensembles

SVANHOLM, Set (ten)
Wagner: Götterdämmerung (Cpte), Rheingold
(Cpte)
see CONCERT INDEX under:
(DECC) **414 100-2DM15** Wagner: Der Ring des
Nibelungen
(EMI) **CDH7 63030-2** Kirsten Flagstad - Wagner
Opera Arias
(EMI) **CMS5 65212-2** Wagner—Les introuvables du
Ring
(LOND) **440 490-2LM5(1)** Kirsten Flagstad Edition (pt
1)
(RCA) **09026 61580-2(6)** RCA/Met 100 Singers, 100
Years (pt 6)
(SCHW) **314502** Vienna State Opera—Live
Recordings (sampler)
(SCHW) **314582** Vienna State Opera Live, Vol.8
(SCHW) **314652** Vienna State Opera Live, Vol.15
(SCHW) **314663** Vienna State Opera Live, Vol.17
(TEST) **SBT1018** Kirsten Flagstad

SVÁROVSKÝ, Leoš (cond)
see Brno St PO

SVED, Alexander (bar)
see CONCERT INDEX under:
(EMI) **CHS7 64864-2(2)** La Scala Edition - Vol.2,
1915-46 (pt 2)
(MYTO) **2MCD90317** Verdi—Un Ballo in maschera
(SCHW) **314542** Vienna State Opera Live, Vol.4
(SCHW) **314572** Vienna State Opera Live, Vol.7
(SCHW) **314622** Vienna State Opera Live, Vol.12
(SCHW) **314632** Vienna State Opera Live, Vol.13
(TEST) **SBT1008** Viva Rossini

SVEDENBRANT, Georg (bass)
Verdi: Rigoletto (Cpte)
see CONCERT INDEX under:
(BLUE) **ABCD028** Jussi Björling live at the Stockholm
Opera

ŠVEHLA, Zdeněk (ten)
Janáček: Makropulos Affair (Cpte)
Martinů: Julietta (Cpte)
Smetana: Two Widows (Cpte)
see CONCERT INDEX under:
(DECC) **421 852-2DH2** Janáček: Operatic & Chamber
Works
(DECC) **430 375-2DH2** Janáček—Operatic and
Orchestral Works

ŠVEJDA, Miroslav (ten)
Fibich: Bride of Messina (Cpte)
Janáček: Excursions of Mr Brouček (Cpte), From the
House of the Dead (Cpte)
Smetana: Two Widows (Cpte)

SVENDÉN, Brigitta (mez)
Wagner: Götterdämmerung (Cpte), Rheingold (Cpte),
Siegfried (Cpte), Walküre (Cpte)
see CONCERT INDEX under:
(DG) **445 354-2GX14** Wagner—Der Ring des
Nibelungen

SVENSSON, Peter (ten)
Janáček: Glagolitic Mass (Cpte)
Kodály: Psalmus Hungaricus
Mozart: Zauberflöte (Cpte)
Stravinsky: Oedipus Rex (Cpte)
see CONCERT INDEX under:
(CHAN) **CHAN9240** Stravinsky—Choral and
Orchestral Works

SVERNER, Clara (pf)
see CONCERT INDEX under:
(MARC) **8 223556** Velasquez—Piano Works

**SVESHNIKOV RUSSIAN ACADEMY CHOIR
cond A. CHISTIAKOV**
Rimsky-Korsakov: Tsar's Bride (Cpte)

SVETLANOV, Evgeni (cond)
see Bolshoi Th Brass Ens

SVETLEV, Mikhail (ten)
Mussorgsky: Boris Godunov (Cpte)

**SVETOSLAV OBRETENOV NATIONAL CHORUS
cond E. TCHAKAROV**
Tchaikovsky: Queen of Spades (Cpte)

**SVIZZERA ITALIANA ORCHESTRA
cond M. ROTA**
(BONG) **GB2513-2** Mariella Devia—Opera Arias

SVOBODA, Michael (tbn/bar hn)
Stockhausen: Michaels Reise

ŠVORC, Antonín (bass)
Dvořák: St Ludmilla (Cpte)
Smetana: Libuše (Cpte)
see CONCERT INDEX under:
(DECC) **430 375-2DH2** Janáček—Operatic and
Orchestral Works

SWALLOW, Keith (pf)
see CONCERT INDEX under:
(CHAN) **CHAN8356** Weber—Chamber Music for
Clarinet
(CHAN) **CHAN8683** English Chamber Works
(HYPE) **CDA66271/2** Elgar:The Complete Choral
Songs

TAGLIAVINI, Franco (ten)
Berlioz: Te Deum

TAGNIN, Hugo (tam-tam)
see CONCERT INDEX under:
(CHNT) **LDC278 835** Villa-Lobos—Chôros for Chamber Ensembles

TAHA, Claudia (sop)
Spohr: Faust (Cpte)

TAILLON, Jocelyne (mez)
Debussy: Pelléas et Mélisande (Cpte)
Fauré: Pénélope (Cpte)
Gounod: Faust (Cpte), Roméo et Juliette (Cpte)
Monteverdi: Ritorno d'Ulisse in patria (Cpte)
Offenbach: Contes d'Hoffmann (Cpte)
Ravel: Enfant et les sortilèges (Cpte)
Rossini: Guillaume Tell (Cpte)

TAINTON, Carol (pf)
see CONCERT INDEX under:
(SCHW) **311122** Early Twentieth Century Music

TAIT, Catherine (vn)
see CONCERT INDEX under:
(ARAB) **Z6569** Milhaud—Jazz Works

TAJO, Italo (bass)
Puccini: Manon Lescaut (Cpte), Tosca (Cpte)
Verdi: Aida (Cpte), Macbeth (Cpte)

TAKÁCS, Klára (contr)
Giordano: Andrea Chénier (Cpte)
Liszt: Hungarian Coronation Mass, S11
Respighi: Belfagor (Cpte)
Verdi: Rigoletto (Cpte)

TAKÁCS, Tamara (mez)
Boito: Mefistofele (Cpte)
Giordano: Andrea Chénier (Cpte)
see CONCERT INDEX under:
(NAXO) **8 550476** Schubert—Lieder Recital

TAKÁCS QUARTET
Brahms: Piano Quintet, String Quartet 3
Schubert: String Quartet, D703, String Quartet, D804, String Quartet, D810, String Quintet
see CONCERT INDEX under:
(HUNG) **HCD12502/4** Bartók—Complete String Quartets

TAKAHASHI, Aki (pf)
M. Feldman: Piano Quintet

TAKAHASHI, Yuji (pf)
see CONCERT INDEX under:
(DENO) **CO-1052** Messiaen & Xenakis: Piano Works
(DENO) **C37-7486** Satie: Piano works
(DENO) **C37-7487** Satie: Piano music for four hands

TAKALO, Arttu (perc)
see CONCERT INDEX under:
(ONDI) **ODE802-2** Ibert/Jolivet/Nielsen—Flute Concertos

TAKAMI, Nagasama (va)
see CONCERT INDEX under:
(REM) **REM311175** Fauré—Mélodies, Vol.1

TAKASHIMA, Tomoko (cl)
see CONCERT INDEX under:
(NAXO) **8 553178** Krommer—Clarinet Concertos

TAKEZAWA, Kyoko (vn)
Elgar: Violin Concerto
Mendelssohn: Violin Concerto, Op. 64, Violin Concerto (1822)
Prokofiev: Violin Concerto 2
Tchaikovsky: Violin Concerto
see CONCERT INDEX under:
(RCA) **09026 60704-2** Violin Recital - Kyoko Takezawa
(RCA) **09026 61386-2** French Violin Sonatas
(RCA) **09026 61675-2** Bartók—Works for Violin & Orchestra
(RCA) **09026 61677-2** Concerto! with Dudley Moore

TAL, Yaara (pf)
Brahms: Hungarian Dances, Waltzes, Op. 39
see CONCERT INDEX under:
(SONY) **SK47199** Piano Music for four hands
(SONY) **SK48494** Mendelssohn—Piano music for four hands
(SONY) **SK53110** Gouvy—Piano Music for Four Hands
(SONY) **S2K58955** Schubert—Piano Music for Four Hands, Volume 1

TALALYAN, Genrikh (va)
see CONCERT INDEX under:
(MELO) **74321 18290-2** Tchaikovsky—Chamber Works

TALAN QUARTET
see CONCERT INDEX under:
(OLYM) **OCD543** Taneyev—String Quartets

TALBOT, John (pf)
Moeran: Violin Sonata in E minor

TALE QUARTET
see CONCERT INDEX under:
(BIS) **BIS-CD467** Schnittke: String Quartets
(BIS) **BIS-CD547** Schnittke—Chamber Works
(BIS) **BIS-CD652** Penderecki—Chamber Works

(LES) TALENS LYRIQUES
Collasse: Racine Canticles
Leclair: Ouvertures et Sonates, Op.13

cond C. ROUSSET
Handel: Scipione (Cpte)
Jommelli: Armida abbandonata (Cpte)

TALEXIS, Amelia (sop)
see CONCERT INDEX under:
(IRCC) **IRCC-CD802** Souvenirs of Rare French Opera
(PEAR) **GEMMCDS9924(2)** Covent Garden on Record, Vol.2 (pt 2)
(SYMP) **SYMCD1126** The Harold Wayne Collection, Vol.14

TALICH, Jan (va)
see CONCERT INDEX under:
(SUPR) **11 0767-2** Martinů—Cantatas
(SUPR) **11 1532-2** Suk—Chamber Works, Volume 2

TALICH, Vaclav (cond)
see Czech PO

TALICH QUARTET
Beethoven: String Quartet 7 (exc), String Quartet 8 (exc), String Quartet 9 (exc), String Quartet 10, String Quartet 13, String Quartet 14, String Quartet 15, String Quartet 16
Borodin: String Quartet 2
Brahms: Clarinet Quintet, String Quartet 3
Debussy: String Quartet
Dvořák: String Quartet 11, String Quartet 12, String Sextet
Ravel: String Quartet
Schoenberg: Verklärte Nacht
Tchaikovsky: String Quartet 1
see CONCERT INDEX under:
(CALL) **CAL6698** Haydn/Boccherini/Mendelssohn/Miča—Quartets
(CALL) **CAL9245** Mozart—Complete String Quartets, Vol.5
(CALL) **CAL9628** Mozart—Chamber Works
(CALL) **CAL9633/9** Beethoven: Complete String Quartets
(CALL) **CAL9635** Beethoven—String Quartets
(CALL) **CAL9690** Smetana—Chamber and Instrumental Works
(CALL) **CAL9699** Janáček—Chamber and Piano Works
(CALL) **CAL9893** Debussy & Ravel: String Quartets

TALLET, Marc (bass cittern)
Blavet: Flute Sonatas, Op. 2 (exc), Flute Sonatas, Op. 3 (exc)

TALLEY, Marian (sop)
see CONCERT INDEX under:
(PEAR) **GEMMCD9367** Gigli—Arias and Duets

TALLINN CAMERATA
see CONCERT INDEX under:
(FINL) **4509-95705-2** Estonian Chamber Music

TALLINN CHAMBER ORCHESTRA
cond T. KALJUSTE
see CONCERT INDEX under:
(ECM) **439 162-2** Pärt—Choral Works

TALLINN QUARTET
see CONCERT INDEX under:
(BIS) **BIS-CD574** Chamber Music from Estonia

TALLIS CHAMBER CHOIR
cond D. HINNELLS
Verdi: Trovatore (Cpte)
cond J. TATE
Beethoven: Missa Solemnis
cond M. VIOTTI
Donizetti: Elisir d'amore (Cpte)

TALLIS SCHOLARS
cond P. PHILLIPS
D. Lôbo: Missa Vox clamantis, Requiem (6vv)
Gesualdo: Responsoria (exc), Sacrarum cantionum (5vv) (exc)
Josquin Desprez: Missa La sol fa re mi, Missa Pange lingua
Lobo: Versa est in luctum
Victoria: Officium defunctorum (1605), Tenebrae Responsories
see CONCERT INDEX under:
(GIME) **CDGIMB400** The Palestrina Collection
(GIME) **CDGIM001** Palestrina—Missa Benedicta es
(GIME) **CDGIM002** Russian Orthodox Music
(GIME) **CDGIM003** Missa Nigra sum: Mass and motets
(GIME) **CDGIM004** Taverner: Choral works
(GIME) **CDGIM005** Tavener: Choral Works
(GIME) **CDGIM006** Tallis: Motets
(GIME) **CDGIM007** Tallis: English Anthems
(GIME) **CDGIM008** Palestrina & Primavera—Choral Works
(GIME) **CDGIM010** Christmas carols and motets
(GIME) **CDGIM011** Byrd: Sacred Choral Works
(GIME) **CDGIM013** Clemens Non Papa: Sacred Choral Works
(GIME) **CDGIM014** Cornysh—Choral Works
(GIME) **CDGIM016** Sheppard: Sacred Choral Works
(GIME) **CDGIM017** Sarum Chant
(GIME) **CDGIM018** Lassus: Sacred Choral Works
(GIME) **CDGIM019** Josquin Desprez—Masses
(GIME) **CDGIM020** Palestrina—Masses and Motets
(GIME) **CDGIM021** Cardoso: Sacred Choral Works
(GIME) **CDGIM023** Isaac—Missa de Apostolis
(GIME) **CDGIM024** Tomkins—The Great Service
(GIME) **CDGIM025** Tallis—Lamentations of Jeremiah
(GIME) **CDGIM026** Brumel—Sacred Choral Works
(GIME) **CDGIM027** Western Wind Masses

(GIME) **CDGIM029** Rore—Missa Praeter rerum seriem; Motets
(GIME) **CDGIM030** R White—Tudor Church Music
(GIME) **CDGIM339** Renaissance Sacred Choral Works
(GIME) **CDGIM343/4** Byrd—Sacred Choral Music
(GIME) **CDGIM345** Byrd—Masses and Motets
(GIME) **CDGIM994** The Tallis Scholars Live In Rome
(GIME) **CDGIM995** Taverner—Anniversary Album
(GIME) **CDGIM999** Tallis Scholars—South Bank Show
cond J. TAVENER
see CONCERT INDEX under:
(GIME) **CDGIM005** Tavener: Choral Works

TALLY, Harry (sngr)
see CONCERT INDEX under:
(PEAR) **GEMMCDS9050/2(2)** Music from the New York Stage, Vol. 1 (part 2)

TALMI, Er'ella (fl)
see CONCERT INDEX under:
(CARL) **PWK1133** Flute Album
(CARL) **PWK1141** French Impressions

TALMI, Yoav (cond)
see Golders Orkest

TALMI, Yoav (pf)
see CONCERT INDEX under:
(CARL) **PWK1133** Flute Album

TALVELA, Martti (bass)
Beethoven: Missa Solemnis, Symphony 9
Haydn: Jahreszeiten (Cpte)
Mahler: Symphony 8
Mozart: Don Giovanni (Cpte), Entführung (Cpte), Zauberflöte (Cpte)
Mussorgsky: Boris Godunov (Cpte)
Verdi: Requiem (Cpte), Rigoletto (Cpte)
Wagner: Parsifal (Cpte), Rheingold (Cpte), Tristan und Isolde (Cpte), Walküre (Cpte)
see CONCERT INDEX under:
(BIS) **BIS-CD325** Mussorgsky: Orchestral & Vocal Works
(DECC) **430 792-2DC6** Beethoven—Complete Symphonies, etc
(DECC) **430 804-2DC10** Mahler—Complete Symphonies
(DECC) **436 464-2DM** Ten Top Baritones & Basses
(DG) **435 211-2GX15** Wagner—Der Ring des Nibelungen
(PHIL) **446 057-2PB14** Wagner—The Ring Cycle - Bayreuth Festival 1967
(RCA) **09026 61580-2(8)** RCA/Met 100 Singers, 100 Years (pt 8)

TALVI, Ilkka (vn)
S. Albert: In Concordium
see CONCERT INDEX under:
(DELO) **DE3114** Creston—Orchestral Works
(DELO) **DE3119** Diamond—Orchestral Works

TAMADEUC ABBEY CHOIR
see CONCERT INDEX under:
(STUD) **SM1220.02** Immortel Grégorien

TAMAGNO, Francesco (ten)
(EMI) **CHS7 64860-2(1)** La Scala Edition - Vol.1, 1878-1914 (pt 1)
(EMI) **CHS7 64860-2(2)** La Scala Edition - Vol.1, 1878-1914 (pt 2)
(MEMO) **HR4408/9(1)** Singers in Genoa, Vol.1 (disc 1)
(NIMB) **NI7840/1** The Era of Adelina Patti
(NIMB) **NI7856** Legendary Tenors
(OPAL) **OPALCD9846** Francesco Tamagno—Complete Recordings
(PEAR) **GEMMCDS9923(2)** Covent Garden on Record, Vol.1 (pt 2)
(TEST) **SBT1008** Viva Rossini

TAMARIN, Ilya (ten)
see CONCERT INDEX under:
(RCA) **GD60522** Alexander Kipnis—Opera & Song Recital

TAMASSY, Eva (mez)
Weill: Silbersee (Cpte)

TAMAYO, Arturo (cond)
see BBC SO

TAMAYO, Pablo (sngr)
Moreno Torroba: Luisa Fernanda (Cpte)

TAMBLYN, Russ (sngr)
Bernstein: West Side Story (Cpte)

TAMBUCO PERCUSSION ENSEMBLE
cond E. MATA
see CONCERT INDEX under:
(DORI) **DOR90215** Chavez—Chamber Works

TAMEZ, Maria Luisa (sop)
C.H. Graun: Montezuma (Cpte)

TAMIR, Alexander (pf)
Brahms: Symphony 3, Variations, Op.23
Schubert: Divertissement à la Hongroise, D818, Divertissement, D823
see CONCERT INDEX under:
(CARL) **PWK1134** Dances Round the World
(CRD) **CRD3413** Brahms—Works for two pianos & one piano, four hands
(CRD) **CRD3424** Ravel—Works for Piano Duet

TAMPA BAY MASTER CHORALE
cond ROBERT SHAW
Mahler: Symphony 8

TAMPERE PHILHARMONIC ORCHESTRA
cond L. GRIN
Melartin: Symphony 2, Symphony 4, Symphony 5,
Symphony 6
Moszkowski: Piano Concerto
Rubinstein: Piano Concerto 4
cond L. SEGERSTAM
Segerstam: Symphony 15

TAN, Melvyn (fp)
Beethoven: Choral Fantasia, Piano Concerto 5
see CONCERT INDEX under:
(EMI) CDC5 55348-2   Weber—Orchestral Works
(EMI) CDC7 54526-2   Beethoven—Piano Works
(HYPE) CDA66281   Beethoven—Cello & Piano Works,
Vol.1
(HYPE) CDA66282   Beethoven—Cello & Piano Works,
Vol.2
(MERI) CDE84183   Donizetti: Songs
(MERI) ECD84080   Haydn: Vocal works
(RCA) 09026 62553-2   Mendelssohn—Works for Cello
& Piano
(VIRG) VER5 61160-2   Beethoven—Piano Sonatas

TAN, Melvyn (hpd)
see CONCERT INDEX under:
(AMON) CD-SAR22   Oboe Collection

TANDLER, Heinz (bass)
Wagner: Meistersinger (Cpte)

TANDURA, Elisabetta (sop)
Rossini: Adelaide di Borgogna (Cpte)

TANENBAUM, David (gtr)
see CONCERT INDEX under:
(NALB) NA055CD   Harrison—The Perilous Chapel

TANFIELD, Peter (vn)
see CONCERT INDEX under:
(MERI) CDE84227/8   Brahms—Chamber Works

TANG, Mu Hai (cond)
see BRSO

TANG, Muhai (cond)
see Royal Flanders PO

TANGERINE DREAM
see CONCERT INDEX under:
(SILV) SILVAD3003   At the Movies 3: Horror &
Fantasy

TANGLEWOOD FESTIVAL CHORUS
cond L. BERNSTEIN
Liszt: Faust Symphony
cond B. HAITINK
Brahms: Alto Rhapsody, Op. 53
cond S. OZAWA
Bartók: Miraculous Mandarin (Cpte)
Beethoven: Choral Fantasia
Berlioz: Damnation de Faust (Cpte), Grande messe
des morts (Cpte)
Mahler: Symphony 3
Mendelssohn: Midsummer Night's Dream (exc)
Poulenc: Gloria (Cpte), Stabat mater
R. Strauss: Elektra (Cpte)
Ravel: Daphnis et Chloé (Cpte)
Schoenberg: Gurrelieder
Sessions: When Lilacs last Bloom'd
Tchaikovsky: Queen of Spades (Cpte)
see CONCERT INDEX under:
(DG) 423 089-2GH   Fauré: Orchestral Works
(DG) 423 243-2GC   Ives: Orchestral Works

TANGUAY, Eva (sngr)
see CONCERT INDEX under:
(PEAR) GEMMCDS9053/5   Music from the New York
Stage, Vol. 2: 1908—1913

TANNENBERGEROVA, Yvette (sop)
see CONCERT INDEX under:
(SUPR) 11 1878-2   The Unknown Janáček

TANSINI, Ugo (cond)
see EIAR Orch

TANSKI, Claudius (pf)
Reubke: Piano Sonata

TANYEL, Seta (pf)
F. X. Scharwenka: Piano Quartet, Op. 37, Piano Trio,
Op. 45
Schubert: Trout Quintet, D667
see CONCERT INDEX under:
(CHAN) CHAN8519   Poulenc: Piano Duo Works
(CHAN) CHAN8603   Bax: Works for Piano Duet
(COLL) Coll1219-2   Seta Tanyel plays Chopin
(COLL) Coll1325-2   Scharwenka—Piano Works
(COLL) Coll1330-2   Chopin—Piano Works
(COLL) Coll1352-2   Scharwenka—Piano Works, Vol.2
(COLL) Coll1365-2   Scharwenka—Piano Works, Vol.3
(COLL) Coll1412-2   Moszkowski—Piano Works
(COLL) Coll1446-2   Scharwenka—Chamber Works,
Volume 2

TAPESTRY
see CONCERT INDEX under:
(BRIT) BML012   Songs from the Exotic

TAPIOLA CHAMBER CHOIR
cond U. SÖDERBLOM
Bergman: Singing Tree (Cpte)

TAPIOLA SINFONIETTA
cond P. JÄRVI
see CONCERT INDEX under:
(BIS) BIS-CD630   French Orchestral Music
cond J-J. KANTOROW
see CONCERT INDEX under:
(BIS) BIS-CD703   Schoenberg—Music for Strings
cond O. VÄNSKÄ
see CONCERT INDEX under:
(BIS) BIS-CD540   Britten—Works for Tenor and
Orchestra
(BIS) BIS-CD560   Sallinen—Orchestral Works

TAPPING, Roger (va)
see CONCERT INDEX under:
(CALA) CACD1017   French Chamber Music for
Woodwinds, Volume 1
(CALA) CACD1018   French Chamber Music for
Woodwinds, Volume 2

TAPPY, Eric (ten)
Berlioz: Enfance du Christ (Cpte)
Debussy: Pelléas et Mélisande (Cpte)
Haydn: Schöpfung (Cpte)
Martin: Mystère de la Nativité, Pilate, Requiem, Vin
herbé
Mozart: Zauberflöte (Cpte)

TARALLO, Nino (bar)
Puccini: Gianni Schicchi (Cpte)

TARASCHENKO, Vitaly (ten)
Rachmaninov: Aleko (Cpte)

TARASOVA, Marina (vc)
see CONCERT INDEX under:
(OLYM) OCD292   Kabalevsky—Cello Concertos;
Violin and Piano Works
(OLYM) OCD530   Miaskovsky—Cello Works

TARASSOVA, Marianna (mez)
Rimsky-Korsakov: Sadko (Cpte)

TARDOS, Anne (voc)
see CONCERT INDEX under:
(KOCH) 37238-2   A Chance Operation - John Cage
Tribute

TARLTON, Philip (bn)
Danzi: Sextet

TARR, Edward (tpt)
see CONCERT INDEX under:
(BIS) BIS-CD078   Holmboe—Miscellaneous Works
(BIS) BIS-CD159   Hindemith—Chamber Works

TARRAGO, Oscar (pf)
see CONCERT INDEX under:
(ASV) CDDCA654   Ginastera—Orchestral Works

TARTAKOV, Ioakim (bar)
see CONCERT INDEX under:
(PEAR) GEMMCDS9997/9(1)   Singers of Imperial
Russia, Vol.1 (pt 1)

TARUSKIN, Richard (cond)
see Cappella Nova

TASHI
see CONCERT INDEX under:
(RCA) 09026 62537-2   Takemitsu—Cantos

TASIN, Flavio (bar)
Verdi: Traviata (Cpte)

TASMANIAN SYMPHONY ORCHESTRA
cond D. FRANKS
see CONCERT INDEX under:
(ABCC) 8 7000 10   Rita Hunter—Opera Arias

TASSEL, Charles van (bar)
Schreker: Gezeichneten (Cpte)

TASSINARI, Pia (sop)
see CONCERT INDEX under:
(CENT) CRC2164   Ferruccio Tagliavini—Early
Operatic Recordings
(EMI) CHS7 64864-2(2)   La Scala Edition - Vol.2,
1915-46 (pt 2)

TAST, Werner (fl)
see CONCERT INDEX under:
(CAPR) 10 805   Mozart: Wind Concertos

TATARA, Michio (bar)
Stravinsky: Oedipus Rex (Cpte)

TATE, Jeffrey (cond)
see BPO

TATE MUSIC GROUP
see CONCERT INDEX under:
(UNIC) DKPCD9050   Vivaldi—Concertos

TATNELL, Roland (alto)
Purcell: St Cecilia's Day Ode, Z328

TATONE, Vito (ten)
Puccini: Manon Lescaut (Cpte)

TATOZZI, Vittorio (bar)
Verdi: Rigoletto (Cpte)

TÁTRAI, Vilmos (cond)
see Hungarian CO

TÁTRAI QUARTET
Haydn: String Quartet, Op. 51

TATTERMUSCHOVÁ, Helena (sop)
Janáček: Makropulos Affair (Cpte)

TAUB, Robert (pf)
Persichetti: Piano Concerto

TAUBE, Michael (pf)
see CONCERT INDEX under:
(PEAR) GEMMCD9443   Feuermann—The Columbia
Records, Vol.2
(PEAR) GEMMCD9446   Feuermann—The Columbia
Records, Vol.3

TAUBE, Sven-Bertil (gtr)
see CONCERT INDEX under:
(PHIL) 416 698-2PH   Encore! Travels with my cello,
Vol. 2

TAUBER, Richard (ten)
see CONCERT INDEX under:
(EMI) CDC7 54838-2   Franz Lehár
(EMI) CDH7 64029-2   Richard Tauber - Opera Recital
(EMI) CDH7 69787-2   Richard Tauber sings Operetta
Arias
(EMI) CDM7 69476-2   Richard Tauber - A Portrait
(LYRC) SRO830   Smetana—The Bartered Bride, etc
(MMOI) CDMOIR409   Three Tenors—Björling, Gigli &
Tauber
(MMOI) CDMOIR425   Three Tenors, Volume 2
(NIMB) NI7801   Great Singers, Vol.1
(NIMB) NI7830   Richard Tauber in Opera
(NIMB) NI7833   Schöne & Tauber in Operetta
(NIMB) NI7856   Legendary Tenors
(PEAR) GEMMCDS9926(2)   Covent Garden on
Record—Vol.4 (pt 2)
(PEAR) GEMMCD9327   Franz Lehár conducts Richard
Tauber
(PEAR) GEMMCD9327   The Vocal Prime of Richard
Tauber
(PEAR) GEMMCD9370   Richard Tauber sings Lieder
(PEAR) GEMMCD9381   Richard Tauber sings Lieder
(PREI) 89051   Elisabeth Rethberg (1894-1976)
(PREI) 90150   Lehár conducts Lehár
(SCHW) 314512   Vienna State Opera Live, Vol.1
(SIMA) PSC1810(2)   Grieg—Songs (historical
recordings, pt 2)
(TEST) SBT1005   Ten Top Tenors

TAUBEROVÁ, Maria (sop)
Martinů: Julietta (Cpte)

TAUBMAN, Leon (pf)
see CONCERT INDEX under:
(RCA) 09026 61879-2   Grieg—Historic Recordings

TAUBMANN, Horst (ten)
R. Strauss: Arabella (Cpte)

TAUSKY, Vilem (cond)
see Philh

TAVENER, Alan (cond)
see Cappella Nova

TAVENER, John (cond)
see Tallis Scholars

TAVENER, John (organ)
Tavener: Whale

TAVENER, John (pf)
see CONCERT INDEX under:
(COLL) Coll1428-2   Tavener—To a Child dancing in
the Wind

TAVERNER CHOIR
cond C. HOGWOOD
see CONCERT INDEX under:
(L'OI) 425 893-2OM6(1)   Purcell—Theatre Music (Part
1)
cond A. PARROTT
Anon: Festival of the Virgin Mary (exc)
Handel: Israel in Egypt (Cpte), Messiah (Cpte)
Monteverdi: Vespers
Purcell: Dido (Cpte), St Cecilia's Day Ode, Z328
(Cpte)
see CONCERT INDEX under:
(EMI) CDC7 47633-2   Praetorius & Schütz: Sacred
Choral Works
(EMI) CDC7 47998-2   Una Stravanganza dei Medici -
Florentine Intermedi (ed. Keyte)
(EMI) CDC7 49555-2   Tallis: Sacred Choral Works
(EMI) CDC7 49809-2   The Carol Album
(EMI) CDC7 54117-2   Venetian Church Music
(EMI) CDC7 54265-2   Gabrieli—Canzonas, Sonatas &
Motets
(EMI) CDC7 54659-2   Josquin Desprez—Vocal Works
(EMI) CDS7 49749-2   Handel—Music for the Carmelite
Vespers
(VIRG) VC5 45159-2   Purcell—Come ye sons of art
(VIRG) VC7 59326-2   Vivaldi—Sacred Choral Works
cond O. REES
see CONCERT INDEX under:
(HERA) HAVPCD155   Music from Renaissance
Portugal

TAVERNER CONSORT
cond A. PARROTT
Bach: Cantata 4, Easter Oratorio, BWV249, Mass in
B minor, BWV232 (Cpte)
Machaut: Messe de Nostre Dame
Monteverdi: Madrigals, Bk 8 (exc), Selva morale e
spirituale (exc), Vespers, Volgendo il ciel
Purcell: St Cecilia's Day Ode, Z328 (Cpte)
see CONCERT INDEX under:
(EMI) CDC7 47633-2   Praetorius & Schütz: Sacred
Choral Works
(EMI) CDC7 47699-2   Music for the Sistine Chapel
(EMI) CDC7 47998-2   Una Stravanganza dei Medici -
Florentine Intermedi (ed. Keyte)
(EMI) CDC7 49555-2   Tallis: Sacred Choral Works
(EMI) CDC7 49809-2   The Carol Album
(EMI) CDC7 54117-2   Venetian Church Music

TEDESCO, Sergio (ten)
Boito: Mefistofele (Cpte)
Mascagni: Iris (Cpte)

TEES, Stephen (va)
see CONCERT INDEX under:
(CHAN) **CHAN9065** Alwyn—Orchestral Works
(CHAN) **CHAN9270** Holst—Orchestral Works
(COLL) **Coll1428-2** Tavener—To a Child dancing in the Wind

TEETER, Lara (sngr)
Gershwin: Lady, be Good! (Cpte)

TEETERS, Donald (cond)
see Boston Cecilia

TEISEIRA, Susanna (contr)
see CONCERT INDEX under:
(ERAT) **4509-95307-2** Schubert/Schumann—Sacred Choral Works

TEL AVIV PHILHARMONIC CHOIR
cond Z. MEHTA
Mahler: Symphony 2

TELECKÝ, Milan (va)
Hummel: Viola Sonata, Op.5/3
see CONCERT INDEX under:
(CAMP) **RRCD1317** Martinů/Kobayashi—Orchestral Works
(OPUS) **9351 1894** French Chamber Works

TELLEFSEN, Arve (vn)
Nielsen: Violin Concerto
see CONCERT INDEX under:
(BIS) **BIS-CD026** Shostakovich—Chamber Works
(EMI) **CDM5 65073-2** Berwald—Orchestral Works
(NKF) **NKFCD50004-2** Grieg—Violin Sonatas

TELLEFSEN, Rut (narr)
(DG) **437 519-2GH** Grieg—Orchestral Songs

TELLINI, Ines Alfani (sop)
see CONCERT INDEX under:
(PREI) **89072** Aureliano Pertile (1885-1952) - II

TELVA, Marion (mez)
Bellini: Norma (exc)
see CONCERT INDEX under:
(NIMB) **NI7805** Rosa Ponselle—Opera & Song Recital
(ROMO) **81007-2** Rosa Ponselle—Victor Recordings 1926-1929

TEMIANKA, Henri (vn)
see CONCERT INDEX under:
(BIDD) **LAB059/60** Henri Temianka—Recital

TEMIANKA, Henri (vn/dir)
see CONCERT INDEX under:
(BIDD) **LAB059/60** Henri Temianka—Recital

TEMIRKANOV, Yuri (cond)
see Berlin RSO

TEMPERLEY, Jean (mez)
see CONCERT INDEX under:
(CFP) **CD-CFP4637** Ketèlbey/Luigini—Orchestral Music

TEMPLE, David (cond)
see Philharmonic Chbr Ch

TEMPLE UNIVERSITY CHORUS
cond E. ORMANDY
Beethoven: Christus am Oelberge, Op. 85

TEMPLE UNIVERSITY WOMEN'S CHOIR
cond E. ORMANDY
see CONCERT INDEX under:
(SONY) **SBK53256** Debussy—Orchestral Works

TENERIFE SYMPHONY ORCHESTRA
cond A. R. MARBÀ
Vives: Bohemios (Cpte), Doña Francisquita (Cpte)
cond V. P. PÉREZ
Gerhard: Symphony 1, Symphony 3
see CONCERT INDEX under:
(AUVI) **V4660** Gerhard—Orchestral Works
(ETCE) **KTC1095** Spanish Orchestral works

TENISCH, Markus (accordion)
Holliger: Alb-Chehr

TENNANT, Raymond (cond)
see Glasgow CWS Band

TENNEY, James (synths)
see CONCERT INDEX under:
(KOCH) **37238-2** A Chance Operation - John Cage Tribute

TENNSTEDT, Klaus (cond)
see BPO

TENSTAM, Ulrika (mez)
Mahler: Symphony 8

TEODORINI, Elena (sop)
see CONCERT INDEX under:
(EMI) **CHS7 64860-2(1)** La Scala Edition - Vol.1, 1878-1914 (pt 1)
(SYMP) **SYMCD1077** The Harold Wayne Collection, Vol.4

TERAKADO, Ryo (vn)
Handel: Violin Sonatas (exc)
Leclair: Violin Sonatas, Op. 5 (exc)
Rameau: Pièces de clavecin en concerts

TEREKIN, Konstantin (bass)
see CONCERT INDEX under:

(DANT) **LYS013/5** Tchaikovsky—The Queen of Spades

TERENTIEVA, Nina (mez)
Rimsky-Korsakov: Tsar's Bride (Cpte)

TERFEL, Bryn (bass-bar)
Beethoven: Symphony 9
Brahms: Deutsches Requiem, Op.45 (Cpte)
Britten: Gloriana (Cpte)
Cilea: Adriana Lecouvreur (Cpte)
Elgar: Apostles (Cpte)
Handel: Messiah (exc)
Lehár: Lustige Witwe (Cpte)
Mahler: Kindertotenlieder, Symphony 8
Monteverdi: Vespers
Mozart: Don Giovanni (Cpte), Nozze di Figaro (Cpte)
Prokofiev: Fiery Angel (Cpte)
Puccini: Tosca (Cpte)
R. Strauss: Salome (Cpte)
Schubert: Schwanengesang, D957 (Cpte)
Schumann: Szenen aus Goethes Faust (Cpte)
Stravinsky: Oedipus Rex (Cpte)
Sullivan: Yeomen of the Guard (Cpte)
Vaughan Williams: Dona nobis pacem, Sancta Civitas
Wagner: Lohengrin (Cpte)
see CONCERT INDEX under:
(ARGO) **433 214-2ZH** Elgar—Music inspired by children
(CHAN) **CHAN9214** Delius—Choral Works
(DG) **439 768-2GH** Wagner—Gala - New Year's Eve Concert 1993
(DG) **445 294-2GH** Schubert—Lieder
(DG) **445 946-2GH** Bryn Terfel: The Vagabond
(DG) **447 023-2GX12** Mahler—The Symphonies
(HYPE) **CDA66569** Vaughan Williams—Choral Works
(LOND) **448 134-2LH** Walton—Belshazzar's Feast, etc
(SAIN) **SCDC2013** Meirion Williams—Songs
(TELD) **4509-97868-2** The Last Night of the Proms 1994

TERKAL, Karl (ten)
Beethoven: Fidelio (Cpte)
Einem: Dantons Tod (Cpte)
Mozart: Zauberflöte (Cpte)
R. Strauss: Rosenkavalier (Cpte)

TERNER, Helga (sop)
Bach: St. Matthew Passion, BWV244 (Cpte)
Wagner: Parsifal (Cpte)

TERRANI, Lucia Valentini (mez)
Handel: Messiah (Cpte)
Haydn: Fedeltà Premiata (Cpte)
Pergolesi: Stabat Mater
Rossini: Cenerentola (Cpte), Donna del Lago (Cpte), Italiana in Algeri (Cpte), Petite messe solennelle, Stabat Mater, Viaggio a Reims (Cpte)
Verdi: Aida (Cpte), Don Carlos (Cpte), Falstaff (Cpte), Nabucco (Cpte)
Vivaldi: Gloria, RV589, Magnificat, RV611, Orlando Furioso (Cpte)
see CONCERT INDEX under:
(PHIL) **432 420-2PH3** Haydn—Il mondo della luna/Arias

TERRONI, Raphael (pf)
see CONCERT INDEX under:
(BMS) **BMS416CD** Berkeley—Music for Solo Piano and Piano Duets

TERROSI, Aldo (bar)
Puccini: Bohème (Cpte)

TERRY, Stephen (spkr)
Britten: Midsummer Night's Dream (Cpte)

TERRY, Stephen (treb)
Britten: Albert Herring (Cpte)

TERWEY, Joep (bn)
see CONCERT INDEX under:
(DECC) **444 455-2DH** Martin—Ballades; Concerto for 7 Wind Instruments

TERZAKIS, Zahos (ten)
Penderecki: Polish Requiem

TERZIAN, Anita (mez)
Gounod: Faust (Cpte)

TESAŘ, Zdeněk (cl)
see CONCERT INDEX under:
(SUPR) **11 1445-2** Reicha/Beethoven—Compositions for Wind

TESAROWICZ, Romuald (bass)
Mussorgsky: Boris Godunov (Cpte)
Rossini: Semiramide (Cpte)
Shostakovich: Lady Macbeth of Mtsensk (Cpte)

TESCHEMACHER, Margarete (sop)
Mozart: Nozze di Figaro (Cpte)
Wagner: Walküre (exc)
see CONCERT INDEX under:
(MMOI) **CDMOIR408** Great Sopranos
(PREI) **89049** Margarete Teschemacher (1903-1959)
(PREI) **90237** R Strauss—Daphne
(SCHW) **314672** Vienna State Opera Live, Vol.17

TESCHLER, Fred (bass)
R. Strauss: Elektra (Cpte)
Wagner: Parsifal (Cpte)

TESSMER, Heinrich (ten)
Mozart: Zauberflöte (Cpte)
see CONCERT INDEX under:
(LYRC) **SRO830** Smetana—The Bartered Bride, etc
(PEAR) **GEMMCDS9137** Wagner—Der Ring des Nibelungen

TESTI, Lorenzo (bar)
Verdi: Rigoletto (Cpte)

TÉTARD, Albert (vc)
Messiaen: Quatuor
see CONCERT INDEX under:
(EMI) **CDM5 65154-2** Roussel—Orchestral Works

TETRA
see CONCERT INDEX under:
(CONI) **CDCF903** By Arrangement—Tetra Guitar Quartet

TETRAZZINI, Luisa (sop)
see CONCERT INDEX under:
(CLUB) **CL99-060** Enrico Caruso—Opera & Song Recital
(EMI) **CHS7 63802-2(1)** Tetrazzini—The London Records (pt 1)
(EMI) **CHS7 63802-2(2)** Tetrazzini—The London Records (pt 2)
(NIMB) **NI7801** Great Singers, Vol.1
(NIMB) **NI7802** Divas 1906-1935
(NIMB) **NI7808** Luisa Tetrazzini—Opera & Song Recital
(NIMB) **NI7851** Legendary Voices
(PEAR) **EVC3(1)** The Caruso Edition, Vol.3 (pt 1)
(PEAR) **GEMMCDS9924(2)** Covent Garden on Record, Vol.2 (pt 2)
(PEAR) **GEMMCD9221** Luisa Tetrazzini—Vol.1
(PEAR) **GEMMCD9222** Luisa Tetrazzini—Vol.2
(PEAR) **GEMMCD9223** Luisa Tetrazzini—Vol.3
(PEAR) **GEMMCD9224** Luisa Tetrazzini—Vol.4
(PEAR) **GEMMCD9225** Luisa Tetrazzini—Vol.5
(RCA) **GD60495(4)** The Complete Caruso Collection (pt 4)
(RCA) **09026 61580-2(2)** RCA/Met 100 Singers, 100 Years (pt 2)
(SIMA) **PSC1810(2)** Grieg—Songs (historical recordings, pt 2)
(TEST) **SBT1008** Viva Rossini

TETSU, Yves (chalumeau)
see CONCERT INDEX under:
(PIER) **PV794114** Graupner—Overtures for Chalumeaux and Orchestra

TETU, Bernard (cond)
see Lyon Nat Orch Chor

TETZLAFF, Chris (vn)
Dvořák: Violin Concerto
Lalo: Symphonie Espagnole
(VIRG) **VC5 45056-2** Weill/Hindemith/Toch—Chamber Works
(VIRG) **VC5 45122-2** 20th Century Violin Sonatas
(VIRG) **VC7 59065-2** Haydn—Violin Concertos
(VIRG) **VC7 59076-2** Janáček—Orchestral Music

TEUFEL FAMILY
cond U.C. HARRER
see CONCERT INDEX under:
(PHIL) **426 860-2PH** Christmas in Vienna

TEUTSCH, Götz (vc)
Boccherini: Sextets, G461-6 (exc)

TEUTSCH, Karol (cond)
see Warsaw CO

TEVDORASHVII, Vasiko (voc)
see CONCERT INDEX under:
(ECM) **445 941-2** Kancheli—Abii ne Viderem

TEXIER, Vincent le (bass-bar)
Berlioz: Béatrice et Bénédict (Cpte)
Bizet: Carmen (Cpte)
Debussy: Pelléas et Mélisande (Cpte), Rodrigue et Chimène (Cpte)
Marais: Alcyone (Cpte)
Prokofiev: Love for 3 Oranges (Cpte)
R. Strauss: Salomé (Cpte)
Rameau: Platée (Cpte)
Ravel: Enfant et les sortilèges (Cpte)

TEYTE, Dame Maggie (sop)
see CONCERT INDEX under:
(EMI) **CHS5 65198-2** Maggie Teyte sings French Songs
(EMI) **CHS7 61038-2** Debussy—Pelléas et Mélisande, etc
(EMI) **CHS7 69741-2(1)** Record of Singing, Vol.4—Anglo-American School (pt 1)
(MMOI) **CDMOIR408** Great Sopranos
(PEAR) **GEMMCD9134** Maggie Teyte - Chansons

THALBEN-BALL, Sir George (organ)
see CONCERT INDEX under:
(BEUL) **1PD5** Historic Organs, Volume 1

THALHEIM, Armin (clav)
C. P. E. Bach: Keyboard Sonatas, H70-75

THALHEIM, Armin (hpd)
see CONCERT INDEX under:
(CAPR) **10 101** C.P.E. Bach: Flute Works

THAMES, Jeanine (sop)
see CONCERT INDEX under:
(UNIC) **DKPCD9102** Goehr—Orchestral and Vocal Works

THAMES CHAMBER CHOIR
cond B. HERRMANN
Hermann: Fantasticks

THAMES CHAMBER ORCHESTRA
cond M. DOBSON
see CONCERT INDEX under:
(CRD) **CRD3331** Baroque Concerto in England
cond J. HOBAN
Valls: Missa Scala Aretina
cond D. WILLCOCKS
Bach: St Matthew Passion, BWV244 (Cpte)

THARANDE, Jacques (sngr)
Terrasse: Fiancée du Scaphandrier (Cpte)

THÄRICHEN, Werner (timp)
see CONCERT INDEX under:
(SCHW) **311052** Virtuoso Kettledrum Concertos

THAU, Pierre (bass)
Berlioz: Troyens (Cpte)
Bizet: Carmen (Cpte)
Debussy: Pelléas et Mélisande (Cpte)
Saint-Saëns: Samson et Dalila (Cpte)

THAW, David (ten)
R. Strauss: Capriccio (Cpte)
Wagner: Meistersinger (Cpte)

THAYSEN, Eva Hess (sop)
see CONCERT INDEX under:
(KONT) **32203** Nielsen—Orchestral Works
(ROND) **RCD8329** Nielsen: Songs, Vol.5

THEATRE OF VOICES
cond P. HILLIER
see CONCERT INDEX under:
(ECM) **439 172-2** Byrd—Motets and Mass for Four
Voices
(HARM) **HMU90 7076** Lassus—St Matthew Passion
(HARM) **HMU90 7136** Josquin
Despres/Mouton—Vocal Works

THEBOM, Blanche (mez)
Mozart: Cosi fan tutte (exc)
Wagner: Tristan and Isolde (Cpte)
see CONCERT INDEX under:
(EMI) **CDH5 65072-2** Glyndebourne Recorded - 1934-
1994
(EMI) **CDH7 63199-2** Sena Jurinac—Opera and Song
Recital
(EMI) **CHS7 69741-2(1)** Record of Singing,
Vol.4—Anglo-American School (pt 1)

THEDÉEN, Torleif (vc)
Bloch: Schelomo
Elgar: Cello Concerto
Gubaidulina: Rejoice!
Schnittke: Cello Concerto 2, Concerto Grosso 2
Schumann: Cello Concerto
Shostakovich: Cello Concerto 1, Cello Concerto 2
see CONCERT INDEX under:
(BIS) **BIS-CD446** Britten—Cello Suites
(BIS) **BIS-CD468** Kokkonen: Orchestral Works
(BIS) **BIS-CD507** Schnittke—Cello Works
(BIS) **BIS-CD560** Sallinen—Orchestral Works
(BIS) **BIS-CD582** Wirén—Chamber Works
(BIS) **BIS-CD697** Schnittke—Chamber Works
(DG) **435 860-2GH2** Berlioz—Mélodies

THEIMER, Uwe (cond)
see Vienna Op Ball Orch

THEOBOLD, Simon (bar)
see CONCERT INDEX under:
(PEAR) **SHECD9602** Elgar: War Music

THEODORE, David (ob)
Vaughan Williams: Oboe Concerto
see CONCERT INDEX under:
(CHAN) **CHAN9051** Mozart/Salieri—Concertos
(CHAN) **CHAN9262/3** Vaughan Williams—Orchestral
Works
(EMIN) **CD-EMX2227** Holst—Orchestral Works
(HYPE) **CDA66705** Holst—Partsongs

THEODORIDOU, Sonia (sop)
Cavalli: Calisto (Cpte)

THERVEL, Gérard (bar)
Lully: Phaéton (Cpte)

THEUNS, Frank (rec)
Telemann: Musique de Table (exc)

THEURING, Günther (ten)
Monteverdi: Orfeo (Cpte)

THEYARD, Harry (ten)
Rossini: Siège de Corinthe (Cpte)

THIBAUD, Jacques (vn)
Beethoven: Piano Trios (exc)
Mozart: Violin Concerto, K268
Schubert: Piano Trio 1
see CONCERT INDEX under:
(APR) **APR7028** Jacques Thibaud—Complete Solo
Recordings 1929-36
(BIDD) **LAB028** Jacques Thibaud & Alfred Cortot
(BIDD) **LAB029** French Chamber works
(BIDD) **LHW002** Alfred Cortot plays Weber and
Mendelssohn
(BIDD) **LHW004** Alfred Cortot plays Schumann, Vol.
2
(BIDD) **LHW006** Alfred Cortot plays Debussy & Ravel
(EMI) **CDH7 63032-2** French Violin Sonatas
(EMI) **CHS7 64057-2** Cortot-Thibaud-Casals
Trio—Historic Recordings
(KOCH) **37705-2** Alfred Cortot as Conductor

(MSCM) **MM30321** Jacques Thibaud—Violin Recital
(PEAR) **GEMMCD9348** Debussy: Orchestral &
Chamber Works

THIBAUDET, Jean-Yves (pf)
Indy: Symphonie, Op. 25
Messiaen: Turangalîla Symphony
Rachmaninov: Paganini Rhapsody, Piano Concerto 1,
Piano Concerto 2, Piano Concerto 3
Wolf: Mörike Lieder (exc)
see CONCERT INDEX under:
(DECC) **430 512-2DH** Liszt—Lieder - Fassbaender
(DECC) **433 515-2DH2** Ravel—Solo Piano Works
(DECC) **436 736-2DH** Liszt—Piano Transcriptions
(DECC) **444 338-2DH** Brahms/Schumann—Piano
Works
(VIRG) **VC5 45034-2** Grieg/Sibelius—Cello Works

THIELEMANN, Christian (cond)
see Berlin Deutsche Op Orch

THIELMANN, Christel (va da gamba)
see CONCERT INDEX under:
(HARM) **HMC90 5192** As I went to Walsingham
(HYPE) **CDA66228** Ancient Airs and Dances
(VIRG) **VC7 59534-2** In the Streets and Theatres of
London

THIESSEN, John (tpt)
see CONCERT INDEX under:
(SONY) **SK53365** Music for Trumpet and Orchestra

THILL, Georges (ten)
Massenet: Werther (Cpte)
see CONCERT INDEX under:
(EMI) **CDM7 69548-2** Georges Thill sings French
Opera Arias
(EMI) **CMS7 64008-2(1)** Wagner Singing on Record
(pt 1)
(FORL) **UCD16727** L'Incomparable Georges Thill
(MMOI) **CDMOIR411** Sacred Songs and Arias
(NIMB) **NI7856** Legendary Tenors
(PEAR) **GEMMCDS9926(1)** Covent Garden on
Record—Vol.4 (pt 1)
(TEST) **SBT1005** Ten Top Tenors

THINAT, Françoise (pf)
Debussy: Images, La Mer

THINGBOE, Eva Lillian (mez)
Corghi: Divara (Cpte)

THIOLLIER, François-Joël (pf)
see CONCERT INDEX under:
(NAXO) **8 550683** Ravel—Piano Works, Volume 1
(NAXO) **8 550753** Ravel/Falla—Piano Concertos
(NAXO) **8 550754** French Music for Piano and
Orchestra
(NAXO) **8 553008** Ravel—Piano Works, Volume 2

THIRACHE, Julien (bar)
Bizet: Carmen (Cpte)
Poulenc: Mamelles de Tirésias (Cpte)

THIRION-VALLET, Pierre (bass)
see CONCERT INDEX under:
(ARCO) **AAOC93232** Mélodies Françaises

THIRY, Louis (organ)
see CONCERT INDEX under:
(CALL) **CAL9928** Messaien: Organ Works

THIVEL, Benoît (alto)
Collasse: Racine Canticles

THOM, Peter (voc)
Bernstein: West Side Story (Cpte)

THOMA, Gertrude (sop)
L. Andriessen: De Stijl

THOMAMÜLLER, Lieselotte (sop)
Wagner: Walküre (Cpte)
see CONCERT INDEX under:
(FOYE) **15-CF2011** Wagner—Der Ring de Nibelungen

THOMAS, Anne Marsden (organ)
see CONCERT INDEX under:
(PRIO) **PRCD368** Henry Smart—Organ Works

THOMAS, Bernard (cond)
see B. Thomas CO

THOMAS, Brian (vn)
Fauré: Requiem (Cpte)
see CONCERT INDEX under:
(CARL) **PCD809** Vivaldi: Violin Concertos
(CARL) **PCD825** A Florentine Carnival

THOMAS, David (bass)
Anon: Missa Salisburgensis, Plaudite tympana
Bach: Cantata 4, Cantata 82, Cantata 211, Cantata
212, Magnificat, BWV243, Mass in B minor, BWV232
(Cpte)
Berlioz: Enfance du Christ (Cpte)
Handel: Alceste (Cpte), Apollo e Dafne, Athalia
(Cpte), Comus, Esther (Cpte), Israel in Egypt (Cpte),
Judas Maccabaeus (Cpte), Messiah (exc), Orlando
(Cpte), Semele (Cpte), Susanna (Cpte), Theodora
(Cpte)
Haydn: Creation (Cpte), Mass 3
Monteverdi: Orfeo (Cpte), Ritorno d'Ulisse in patria
(Cpte), Selva morale e spirituale (exc), Vespers
Mozart: Mass, K427, Requiem
Purcell: Dido (Cpte), Don Quixote: The Musical
(Cpte), Fairy Queen, Z629 (Cpte), Indian Queen,
Z630 (Cpte), St Cecilia's Day Ode, Z328, Tempest,
Z631 (Cpte)
see CONCERT INDEX under:
(ARCH) **447 150-2AP2** Purcell—Choral Works

(EMI) **CDC7 47633-2** Praetorius & Schütz: Sacred
Choral Works
(EMI) **CDS7 49749-2** Handel—Music for the Carmelite
Vespers
(ERAT) **4509-96371-2** Gardiner—The Purcell
Collection
(HARM) **HMU90 7016** Handel: Arias for Montagnana
(HARM) **HMU90 7053** Humfrey—Verse Anthems
(HYPE) **CDA66021** Monteverdi: Sacred vocal works
(HYPE) **CDA66056** Purcell: Songs and Dialogues
(L'OI) **421 478-2OH** Haydn—Masses
(L'OI) **421 480-2OH** Monteverdi: Madrigali Erotici
(L'OI) **421 654-2OH** Handel & Haydn: Choral works
(L'OI) **425 893-2OM6(1)** Purcell—Theatre Music (Part
1)
(L'OI) **425 893-2OM6(2)** Purcell—Theatre Music (Part
2)
(VIRG) **VC5 45159-2** Purcell—Come ye sons of art
(VIRG) **VC7 59321-2** Shakespeare's Lutenist

THOMAS, Handel (bass)
Puccini: Manon Lescaut (Cpte)
Walton: Troilus and Cressida (Cpte)

THOMAS, James (organ)
see CONCERT INDEX under:
(PRIO) **PRCD511** Magnificat and Nunc Dimittis,
Volume 2

THOMAS, Jeffrey (cond)
see American Bach Sols

THOMAS, Jeffrey (ten)
Handel: Messiah (Cpte), Resurrezione (Cpte),
Susanna (Cpte), Theodora (Cpte)
Haydn: Mass 11
Mozart: Mass, K427
Purcell: Fairy Queen, Z629
see CONCERT INDEX under:
(EMI) **CDC7 54117-2** Venetian Church Music
(KOCH) **37164-2** Bach—Cantatas, Vol.3

THOMAS, Jeffrey (ten/dir)
see CONCERT INDEX under:
(KOCH) **37138-2** Bach—Solo Cantatas
(KOCH) **37163-2** Bach—Cantatas

THOMAS, Jess (ten)
Schoenberg: Gurrelieder
Wagner: Lohengrin (Cpte), Meistersinger (Cpte),
Parsifal (Cpte), Siegfried (Cpte)
see CONCERT INDEX under:
(DG) **429 168-2GR** Wagner: Excerpts from Der Ring
(DG) **435 211-2GX15** Wagner—Der Ring des
Nibelungen
(DG) **437 368-2GX2** Beethoven—Orchestral Works
(DG) **439 423-2GCL** Wagner—Der Ring des
Nibelungen (highlights)

THOMAS, John Charles (bar)
see CONCERT INDEX under:
(NIMB) **NI7867** Legendary Baritones

THOMAS, John Charles (sngr)
see CONCERT INDEX under:
(PEAR) **GEMMCDS9056/8** Music from the New York
Stage, Vol. 3: 1913-17
(PEAR) **GEMMCDS9059/61** Music from the New York
Stage, Vol. 4: 1917-20

THOMAS, Kelvin (bass)
Maxwell Davies: Martyrdom of St Magnus (Cpte)

THOMAS, Lewis (ten)
Walton: Troilus and Cressida (exc)

THOMAS, Marjorie (contr)
Handel: Messiah (exc), Messias, K572 (Cpte)
see CONCERT INDEX under:
(DG) **429 042-2GX10** Mahler: Complete Symphonies

THOMAS, Mary (sop)
Maxwell Davies: Miss Donnithorne's Maggot
Puccini: Rondine (Cpte)
Purcell: Dido (Cpte), King Arthur, Z628 (Cpte)

THOMAS, Milton (va)
Brahms: String Sextet 1
Tchaikovsky: Souvenir de Florence
see CONCERT INDEX under:
(RCA) **09026 61778-2(25)** The Heifetz Collection, Vol.
25
(RCA) **09026 61778-2(28)** The Heifetz Collection, Vol.
28

THOMAS, Nova (sop)
Balfe: Bohemian Girl (Cpte)

THOMAS, Pascal (bass)
Debussy: Pelléas et Mélisande (Cpte)

THOMAS, Peter (cond)
see Philh

THOMAS, Peter (vn)
see CONCERT INDEX under:
(NIMB) **NI5121** Virtuoso Trumpet Concertos
(NIMB) **NI7016** Classical Trumpet Concertos

THOMAS, Philip (pf)
see CONCERT INDEX under:
(BRIT) **BML001** Bernard van Dieren Collection

THOMAS, Ronald (cond)
see Bournemouth Sinfonietta

THOMAS, Ronald (vc)
see CONCERT INDEX under:
(NORT) **NR227-CD** American Chamber Music with
Flute

TILEGANT, Friedrich (cond)
see South-West German CO

TILLES, Nurit (pf)
Messiaen: Visions de l'Amen

TILLI, Johann (bass)
Dessau: Hagadah Shel Pessach
Gazzaniga: Don Giovanni (Cpte)
Mahler: Symphony 8
Schumann: Genoveva (Cpte)
Shostakovich: Lady Macbeth of Mtsensk (Cpte)

TILNEY, Colin (clav)
Bach: Wohltemperierte Klavier (exc)
Purcell: Choice Collection of Lessons

TILNEY, Colin (hpd)
Bach: English Suites, BWV806-811, Wohltemperierte
Klavier (exc)
D. Scarlatti: Keyboard Sonatas (exc)
see CONCERT INDEX under:
(ARCH) **437 075-2AT** Collectio Argentea 5: Canti
Amorosi
(L'OI) **433 053-2OH** Bach/Vivaldi—Orchestral Works

TILNEY, Colin (pf)
see CONCERT INDEX under:
(PREI) **89996** Kyra Vayne (b.1916)

TILSON THOMAS, Michael (cond)
see Boston SO

TILSON THOMAS, Michael (pf)
see CONCERT INDEX under:
(SONY) **MK39699** Gershwin: Piano and Orchestral
works

TILSON THOMAS, Michael (pf/dir)
see CONCERT INDEX under:
(SONY) **MK39699** Gershwin: Piano and Orchestral
works

TILVERN, Alan (spkr)
Gershwin: Porgy and Bess (Cpte)

TIMIȘOARA BANATUL PHILHARMONIC CHORUS
cond J-F. ANTONIOLI
J. Perrin: De Profundis, Op. 26

**TIMIȘOARA BANATUL PHILHARMONIC
ORCHESTRA**
cond J-F. ANTONIOLI
J. Perrin: Cello Concerto, De Profundis, Op. 26

TIMM, Jürnjacob (vc)
Beethoven: Triple Concerto

TINDALL, Paul (ten)
Handel: Israel in Egypt (Cpte)
Purcell: Dido (Cpte), St Cecilia's Day Ode, Z339

TINDEMANS, Margriet (va da gamba)
see CONCERT INDEX under:
(LAND) **CTLCD111** Cover him with grass

TINGAY, Gillian (hp)
see CONCERT INDEX under:
(ASV) **CDDCA898** Damase—Music for Flute, Harp
and Strings

TINKLER, Mark (treb)
Bernstein: Candide (1988) (exc)
Liszt: Missa choralis, S10

TINNEY, Hugh (pf)
Liszt: Harmonies poétiques, S173

TINSLEY, James (tpt)
see CONCERT INDEX under:
(NORT) **NR211-CD** Krebs: Chorale Preludes and
Fantasias

TINSLEY, Pauline (sop)
R. Strauss: Elektra (Cpte)

TIOMKIN, Dimitri (cond)
see OST

TIPO, Maria (pf)
Bach: Partitas, BWV825-30 (exc)
Chopin: Nocturnes
see CONCERT INDEX under:
(EMI) **CDC7 54147-2** Bach—Italian Concerto
(EMI) **CDC7 54766-2** Clementi—Piano Sonatas

TIPPETT, Sir Michael (cond)
see Bath Fest Orch

TIPPING, Christopher (alto)
Handel: Dettingen Te Deum, King shall rejoice
(Dettingen)

TIPTON, Janice (ocarina)
see CONCERT INDEX under:
(ETCE) **KTC1071** L.Harrison—Music For Guitar And
Percussion

TIRIMO, Martin (pf)
Chopin: Piano Concerto 1, Piano Concerto 2
Debussy: Préludes
Rachmaninov: Paganini Rhapsody, Piano Concerto
2
see CONCERT INDEX under:
(KING) **KCLCD2003** Masterpieces in Miniature

TIRINO, Thomas (pf)
MacDowell: Piano Concerto 1, Piano Concerto 2

TIRMONT, Dominique (bar)
Audran: Miss Helyett (Cpte)
Hahn: O mon bel inconnu (Cpte)
Messager: Coups de Roulis (Cpte), Passionément
(Cpte)
Offenbach: Madame l'Archiduc (Cpte)

Terrasse: Travaux d'Hercule (Cpte)

TITTA, Enzo (bass)
Verdi: Rigoletto (Cpte)

TITTERTON, Frank (ten)
see CONCERT INDEX under:
(DUTT) **CDAX8004** Sir Henry Wood conducts
Vaughan Williams
(PEAR) **GEMMCD9342** Vaughan Williams: Vocal
Works

TITUS, Alan (bar)
Bernstein: Mass (Cpte)
Catalani: Wally (Cpte)
Haydn: Fedeltà Premiata (Cpte)
Killmayer: Yolimba (Cpte)
Leoncavallo: Bohème (Cpte)
Mozart: Nozze di Figaro (Cpte)
Puccini: Bohème (Cpte)
Schumann: Genoveva (Cpte), Paradies und die Peri
(Cpte)
Verdi: Falstaff (Cpte)
see CONCERT INDEX under:
(SONY) **SM2K47563** Haydn—Choral & Orchestral
Works

TITUS, Graham (bass)
see CONCERT INDEX under:
(SONY) **SK66613** Tavener—Innocence

TITZE, Robert (bass)
see CONCERT INDEX under:
(ROSE) **3221** Schumann—Miscellaneous Works

TIVOLI AUGMENTED ORCHESTRA
cond R. STRAUSS
R. Strauss: Rosenkavalier film

TIVOLI CONCERT ORCHESTRA
cond S. FELUMB
see CONCERT INDEX under:
(EMI) **CHS7 69741-2(5)** Record of Singing,
Vol.4—Scandinavian School

TJEKNAVORIAN, Loris (cond)
see Armenian PO

TOBIASSON, Ingrid (contr)
Lidholm: Dream Play (Cpte)

TOBIN, John (ten)
Bach: St John Passion, BWV245 (Cpte)

TOCCO, James (pf)
see CONCERT INDEX under:
(CALA) **CACD0101** Orchestral works
(KING) **KCLCD2009** MacDowell—Piano Sonatas
(KING) **KCLCD2011** Griffes: Selected piano solos

TOCHA, Ulla (mez)
Weill: Zar lässt sich Photographieren (Cpte)

TOCZYSKA, Stefania (mez)
Glinka: Life for the Tsar (Cpte)
Mussorgsky: Boris Godunov (Cpte)
Prokofiev: War and Peace (Cpte)
Spontini: Olimpie (Cpte)
Tchaikovsky: Queen of Spades (Cpte)
Verdi: Requiem (Cpte), Trovatore (Cpte)
see CONCERT INDEX under:
(EMI) **CDS7 54251-2** Scriabin—Symphonies and Tone
Poems

TODD, Phil (sax)
see CONCERT INDEX under:
(KOCH) **38703-2** Full Circle—Original Soundtrack,
etc

TODD, Philip (ten)
Britten: Rejoice in the Lamb
Monteverdi: L'Arianna (exc)
see CONCERT INDEX under:
(HARM) **HMA190 201** Blow—Vocal Works

TODD, Richard (hn)
see CONCERT INDEX under:
(RCA) **09026 68181-2** French Chamber Works

TODOROV, Todor (ten)
see CONCERT INDEX under:
(EMI) **CMS7 63386-2** Borodin—Prince Igor &
Complete Solo Songs

TODOROVITCH, Marie-Ange (sop)
Massenet: Don Quichotte (Cpte)

TOKATYAN, Armand (ten)
see CONCERT INDEX under:
(CLUB) **CL99-052** Rosa Raisa (1893-1963)
(VAI) **VAIA1017** Leonard Warren—Early Recordings
(VAI) **VAIA1072** Eleanor Steber Collection, Volume 1

TOKODY, Ilona (sop)
Mascagni: Iris (Cpte)
see CONCERT INDEX under:
(EURO) **GD69043** Puccini: Il Trittico

TOKOS, Zoltan (gtr)
Boccherini: Guitar Quintets, G445-453 (exc)

TOKYO BAROQUE TRIO
Telemann: Paris Quartets (Nouveaux quatuors)

TOKYO LITTLE SINGERS
cond G KUHN
Verdi: Otello (Cpte)

**TOKYO METROPOLITAN SYMPHONY ORCHESTRA
CHORUS**
cond P. MAAG
Mendelssohn: Midsummer Night's Dream (exc)

TOKYO METROPOLITAN SYMPHONY ORCHESTRA
cond P. MAAG
Mendelssohn: Midsummer Night's Dream (exc)
cond H. WAKASUGI
R. Strauss: Dance Suite, Divertimento, Op.86,
Josephslegende (Cpte), Schlagobers
Wagner: Symphony in C, Symphony in E
see CONCERT INDEX under:
(DENO) **CO-78944** Takemitsu—Orchestral Works

TOKYO PHILHARMONIC ORCHESTRA
cond G KUHN
Verdi: Otello (Cpte)
cond R. PATERNOSTRO
Verdi: Traviata (Cpte)

TOKYO QUARTET
Brahms: Clarinet Quintet
Mozart: Flute Quartets, Oboe Quartet, K370, String
Quintet, K515, String Quintet, K516
Schubert: String Quartet, D46, String Quartet, D173,
String Quartet, D804, String Quartet, D810, String
Quartet, D887
Schumann: Piano Quintet, Op.44
Weber: Clarinet Quintet, J182
see CONCERT INDEX under:
(DG) **445 241-2GC3** Bartók—String Quartets
(RCA) **RD60462** Beethoven—Middle Period
Quartets
(RCA) **RD86673** Brahms: Piano and Chamber Works
(RCA) **09026 61284-2** Beethoven—Early String
Quartets
(RCA) **09026 61387-2** A Way A Lone
(RCA) **09026 62552-2** Debussy/Ravel—Chamber
Works

TOKYO SYMPHONY ORCHESTRA
cond R. PATERNOSTRO
see CONCERT INDEX under:
(SCHW) **314061** R. Strauss—Lieder
cond H. WAKASUGI
R. Strauss: Romanze, AV75, Symphony in F minor

TOLL, John (organ)
see CONCERT INDEX under:
(HARM) **HMU90 7104** Vivaldi/Chedéville—Oboe
Sonatas

TOLL, John (hpd)
see CONCERT INDEX under:
(HARM) **HMU90 7046** Vivaldi—Chamber Concertos
(HARM) **HMU90 7091** Three Parts upon a Ground
(HARM) **HMU90 7104** Vivaldi/Chedéville—Oboe
Sonatas

TOLZ BOYS' CHOIR
see CONCERT INDEX under:
(SONY) **SK53981** Purcell—Anthems and Hymns
cond C. ABBADO
Mahler: Symphony 8
Mussorgsky: Boris Godunov (Cpte)
Schumann: Szenen aus Goethes Faust (Cpte)
see CONCERT INDEX under:
(DG) **447 023-2GX12** Mahler—The Symphonies
cond J. E. GARDINER
Britten: War Requiem
cond E. ZU GUTTENBERG
Bach: St Matthew Passion, BWV244 (Cpte)
cond B. HAITINK
Mozart: Zauberflöte (Cpte)
cond N. HARNONCOURT
see CONCERT INDEX under:
cond B. KLEE
Schumann: Szenen aus Goethes Faust (Cpte)
cond R. KUBELIK
Pfitzner: Palestrina (Cpte)
see CONCERT INDEX under:
(DG) **429 042-2GX10** Mahler: Complete Symphonies

cond E. LEINSDORF
Korngold: Tote Stadt (Cpte)
cond G. LEONHARDT
Bach: St Matthew Passion, BWV244 (Cpte)
Lully: Bourgeois Gentilhomme
see CONCERT INDEX under:
(TELD) 2292-42500-2   Bach—Cantatas, Volume 4
(TELD) 2292-42502-2   Bach—Cantatas, Volume 6
(TELD) 2292-42633-2   Bach—Cantatas, Volume 38
(TELD) 2292-42634-2   Bach—Cantatas, Volume 39
(TELD) 4509-91755-2   Bach—Cantatas, Vol.1
(TELD) 4509-91756-2   Bach—Cantatas, Vol.2
(TELD) 4509-91762-2   Bach—Cantatas, Vol.8
(TELD) 4509-91763-2   Bach—Cantatas, Vol.9
cond D. RUNNICLES
Humperdinck: Hänsel und Gretel (Cpte)
cond W. SAWALLISCH
R.Strauss: Frau ohne Schatten (Cpte)
cond G. SCHMIDT-GADEN
Keetman: Weihnachtslieder (exc)
Orff: Orff-Schulwerk (Cpte), Weihnachtsgeschichte
Schütz: Kleiner geistlichen Concerten, SWV282-305
(exc), Kleiner geistlichen Concerten, SWV306-37
(exc)
cond I. SEGARRA
Anon: Missa Salisburgensis, Plaudite tympana
cond J. TATE
Humperdinck: Hänsel und Gretel (Cpte)
cond H. WALLBERG
Humperdinck: Königskinder (Cpte)
cond B. WEIL
Haydn: Schöpfung (Cpte)
see CONCERT INDEX under:
(SONY) SK53368   Haydn—Sacred Music

TOLZ BOYS' CHOIR SOLOISTS
cond I. SEGARRA
Anon: Missa Salisburgensis, Plaudite tympana

TOMÁNEK, Jaroslav (ten)
see CONCERT INDEX under:
(SUPR) 2SUP0025   Orff: Choral Works

TOMASCHEK, Adolf (ten)
R. Strauss: Rosenkavalier (Cpte)
Verdi: Ballo in maschera (Cpte)

TOMASI, Henri (cond)
see FNO

TOMASZEWSKI, Rolf (bar)
R. Strauss: Salome (Cpte)

.**TOMCKOWIACK, Gonzalo (ten)**
Verdi: Simon Boccanegra (Cpte)

TOMEI, Giulio (bass)
see CONCERT INDEX under:
(EMI) CDH7 61052-2   Beniamino Gigli—Arias and
Duets (1932-1949)

TOMEK, Richard (ten)
see CONCERT INDEX under:
(SCHW) 314602   Vienna State Opera Live, Vol.10
(SCHW) 314622   Vienna State Opera Live, Vol.12
(SCHW) 314632   Vienna State Opera Live, Vol.13
(SCHW) 314642   Vienna State Opera Live, Vol.14

TOMES, Susan (pf)
Fauré: Violin Sonata 1, Violin Sonata 2
see CONCERT INDEX under:
(COLL) Coll1453-2   Distance &
Enchantment—Chamber Works by Judith Weir
(HYPE) CDA66415   Bartók—Chamber Works
(HYPE) CDA66465   Brahms—Violin Sonatas
(HYPE) CDA66473   Violin Duets

TOMICICH, Aurio (bass)
Bellini: Adelson e Salvini (Cpte), Bianca e Fernando
(Cpte)
Fénelon: Chevalier Imaginaire (Cpte)
Maderna: Satyricon (Cpte)

TOMLINSON, Ernest (cond)
see Bratislava RSO

TOMLINSON, John (bass)
A. Thomas: Hamlet (Cpte)
Bartók: Cantata profana
Bellini: Capuleti (Cpte), Sonnambula (Cpte)
Birtwistle: Punch and Judy (Cpte)
Handel: Alcina (Cpte), Giulio Cesare (Cpte), Hercules
(Cpte), Messiah (Cpte)
Martinů: Greek Passion (Cpte)
Monteverdi: Orfeo (Cpte)
Mozart: Così fan tutte (Cpte), Don Giovanni (Cpte),
Nozze di Figaro (Cpte)
Puccini: Manon Lescaut (Cpte), Tosca (Cpte)
Rameau: Naïs (Cpte)
Rossini: Guillaume Tell (Cpte), Petite Messe
Solennelle
Stravinsky: Nightingale (Cpte), Oedipus Rex (Cpte)
Verdi: Forza del destino (Cpte), Requiem (Cpte),
Traviata (exc)
Wagner: Götterdämmerung (Cpte), Parsifal (Cpte),
Rheingold (Cpte), Siegfried (Cpte), Walküre (Cpte)
Weill: Sieben Todsünden
see CONCERT INDEX under:
(ASV) CDDCA666   D'Avalos conducts Wagner, Vol 3
(CHAN) CHAN8712/7   Beethoven: Complete
Symphonies
(OPRA) ORC003   Donizetti—Gabriella di Vergy
(SONY) SK45965   Esa-Pekka Salonen conducts
Stravinsky

TOMMASINI, Giuseppe (ten)
see CONCERT INDEX under:
(ROMO) 81005-2   Claudia Muzio (1889-1936)

TOMMASINI, Mario (bass)
Verdi: Macbeth (Cpte)

TOMMASO, Angelo (bass)
Rossini: Barbiere di Siviglia (exc)

TOMOWA-SINTOW, Anna (sop)
Beethoven: Missa Solemnis, Symphony 9
Brahms: Deutsches Requiem, Op. 45 (Cpte)
Korngold: Wunder der Heliane (Cpte)
Mozart: Don Giovanni (Cpte), Mass, K317, Nozze di
Figaro (Cpte), Requiem, Zauberflöte (exc)
R. Strauss: Ariadne auf Naxos (Cpte), Rosenkavalier
(Cpte)
Tchaikovsky: Eugene Onegin (Cpte)
Verdi: Requiem (Cpte)
Wagner: Lohengrin (Cpte)
see CONCERT INDEX under:
(ORFE) C106841A   Famous Opera Arias

TOMŠIČ, Dubravka (pf)
D. Scarlatti: Keyboard Sonatas (exc)

TOMTER, Lars Anders (va)
see CONCERT INDEX under:
(BIS) BIS-CD428   Nielsen—Wind Chamber Music
(SIMA) PSC1022   Chamber Works for Oboe
(VICT) VCD19006   Norwegian Chamber Works
(VIRG) VC5 45121-2   Britten—Orchestral Works
(VIRG) VC7 59309-2   Brahms/Schumann—Viola
Sonatas

TONBRIDGE SCHOOL CHOIR
cond M. BEST
Britten: St Nicolas

TONIETTI, Anne (narr)
see CONCERT INDEX under:
(PHIL) 438 973-2PM2   Igor Markevitch conducts
Stravinsky

TONINI, Antonio (cond)
see Philh

TØNNESEN, Terje (cond)
see Norwegian CO

TØNNESEN, Terje (vn)
see CONCERT INDEX under:
(SIMA) PSC1022   Chamber Works for Oboe
(VICT) VCD19006   Norwegian Chamber Works
(VICT) VCD19014   HallgrØmsson &
Nordheim—Chamber Orchestral Works
(VICT) VCD19070   Grieg—Complete Violin Sonatas

TØNNESEN, Terje (vn/dir)
see CONCERT INDEX under:
(VICT) VCD19014   HallgrØmsson &
Nordheim—Chamber Orchestral Works

TOOTEN, Luc (vc)
see CONCERT INDEX under:
(DINT) DICD920125   Walton—Façade

TOPART, Jean (narr)
Berlioz: Lélio (Cpte)

TOPAS, Liselotte (sop)
see CONCERT INDEX under:
(DANA) DACOCD315/6   Lauritz Melchior Anthology -
Vol. 3

TOPILIN, Vsevold (pf)
see CONCERT INDEX under:
(BIDD) LAB059/60   Henri Temianka—Recital

TÖPPER, Hertha (mez)
Bartók: Duke Bluebeard's Castle (Cpte)
Mozart: Nozze di Figaro (Cpte)
Stravinsky: Oedipus Rex (Cpte)
Wagner: Walküre (exc)
see CONCERT INDEX under:
(ARCH) 439 369-2AX4   Bach—Cantatas, Vol.1
(ARCH) 439 374-2AX5   Bach—Cantatas, Volume 2 -
Easter
(ARCH) 439 380-2AX6   Bach—Cantatas, Volume 3 -
Ascension Day; Whitsun; Trinity
(ARCH) 439 387-2AX6   Bach Cantatas, Volume 4
(ARCH) 439 394-2AX5   Bach—Cantatas, Volume 5
(ERAT) 4509-97407-2   Bach—Cantatas
(ERAT) 4509-98525-2   Bach—Cantatas

TORCHINSKY, Abe (tuba)
see CONCERT INDEX under:
(SONY) SM2K52671   Hindemith—Chamber Works

TORESELLA, Fanny (sop)
see CONCERT INDEX under:
(SYMP) SYMCD1065   The Harold Wayne Collection,
Vol.1

TORGOMIAN, Gérard (vn)
see CONCERT INDEX under:
(EMI) CDC7 54884-2   French Harp Chamber Music

TORJESEN, Sirl (sop)
see CONCERT INDEX under:
(AURO) ACD4973   Borealis

TORKE, Michael (cond)
see Argo Band

TORKE, Michael (pf)
see CONCERT INDEX under:
(ARGO) 430 209-2ZH   Torke—Chamber Works

TÖRÖK, František (vn)
see CONCERT INDEX under:
(MARC) 8 223415   Schmidt—Chamber Works

TORONTO CHAMBER ORCHESTRA
cond PAUL ROBINSON
see CONCERT INDEX under:

(RCA) RD60155   Vivaldi: Cello Concertos, Vol.2
(RCA) RD87774   Vivaldi: Cello Concertos
(RCA) 09026 61578-2   Vivaldi—Cello Concertos,
Vol.3

TORONTO CHILDREN'S CHORUS
cond J.A. BARTLE
see CONCERT INDEX under:
(CBC) SMCD5119   Adeste Fideles

TORONTO FESTIVAL SINGERS
cond I. STRAVINSKY
see CONCERT INDEX under:
(SONY) SM2K46294   Stravinsky—Symphonies

TORONTO SYMPHONY ORCHESTRA
cond J.A. BARTLE
see CONCERT INDEX under:
(CBC) SMCD5119   Adeste Fideles
cond A. DAVIS
see CONCERT INDEX under:
(CBC) SMCD5142   Ben Heppner sings Richard
Strauss
cond E. MACMILLAN
see CONCERT INDEX under:
(CBC) PSCD2005   Glenn Gould broadcast
performances

TORRE, Nestore della (bar)
see CONCERT INDEX under:
(SYMP) SYMCD1069   The Harold Wayne Collection,
Vol.2

TORRE, Raf de la (spkr)
Schumann: Manfred (Cpte)

TORRI, Rosina (sop)
Puccini: Bohème (Cpte)

TORTELIER, Maud (vc)
see CONCERT INDEX under:
(EMI) CDM7 69835-2   Vivaldi—Cello Concertos
(EMI) CMS7 63386-2   Borodin—Prince Igor &
Complete Solo Songs
(VIRG) VC7 59668-2   French Impressions

TORTELIER, Paul (cond)
see ECO

TORTELIER, Paul (vc)
Chopin: Cello Sonata
Elgar: Cello Concerto
R. Strauss: Don Quixote
Rachmaninov: Cello Sonata
Schubert: String Quintet
Tchaikovsky: Rococo Variations
see CONCERT INDEX under:
(EMI) CDC7 47939-2   Fauré—Orchestral Works
(EMI) CDH5 65502-2   Paul Tortelier
(EMI) CDM7 69835-2   Vivaldi—Cello Concertos
(EMI) CMS7 64350-2   R. Strauss—Orchestral Works,
Vol.3
(EMI) CZS7 67521-2   Schumann—Concertos
(ERAT) 4509-95359-2   Bach/Vivaldi—Cello Sonatas

TORTELIER, Paul (vc/dir)
see CONCERT INDEX under:
(VIRG) VC7 59668-2   French Impressions

TORTELIER, Yan Pascal (cond)
see BBC PO

TORTELIER, Yan Pascal (vn)
see CONCERT INDEX under:
(EMI) CDC7 47939-2   Fauré—Orchestral Works

TORTELIER, Yan Pascal (vn/dir)
see CONCERT INDEX under:
(CHAN) CHAN8952   Chausson & Fauré—Vocal and
Orchestral Works
(CHAN) CHAN8972   Debussy & Ravel—Orchestral
works

TORZEWSKI, Marek (ten)
Mozart: Finta giardiniera (Cpte)
see CONCERT INDEX under:
(SONY) SK53360   Mahler/Nono—Vocal Works

TOSCANI, Rina Gallo (sop)
Mascagni: Cavalleria rusticana (Cpte)

TOSCANINI, Arturo (cond)
see BBC SO

TOSCANO, Tina (sop)
Verdi: Rigoletto (Cpte)

TOSETTA, C. (sop)
Handel: Rinaldo (Cpte)

TOSI, Giancarlo (bass)
Bellini: Adelson e Salvini (Cpte)
Donizetti: Fille du Régiment (Cpte)

TOSO, Maria Teresa (mez)
Gazzaniga: Stabat Mater

TOSO, Piero (vn)
Albinoni: Concerti, Op. 9 (exc)
Vivaldi: Concerti, Op. 8

TOTENBERG, Roman (vn)
see CONCERT INDEX under:
(APR) APR7016   The Auer Legacy, Vol.2

TÓTH, István (db)
Schubert: Trout Quintet, D667
see CONCERT INDEX under:
(NAXO) 8 553090   Beethoven—Chamber Works

TÓTH, János (bass)
Bach: Christmas Oratorio, BWV248 (Cpte)
Giordano: Andrea Chénier (Cpte)
Respighi: Belfagor (Cpte)

TOULON MUSICA ANTIQUA
see CONCERT INDEX *under:*
(PIER) **PV794033** Vivaldi—Vocal and Wind Music
cond C. MENDOZE
see CONCERT INDEX *under:*
(PIER) **PV787092** Airs and Dances of Shakespeare's Time

TOULOUSE CAPITOLE CHORUS
cond M. PLASSON
Bizet: Pêcheurs de Perles (Cpte)
Gounod: Faust (Cpte), Roméo et Juliette (Cpte)
Massenet: Don Quichotte (Cpte), Manon (Cpte)
Offenbach: Belle Hélène (Cpte), Orphée aux enfers (Cpte), Périchole (Cpte)
see CONCERT INDEX *under:*
(EMI) **CDC7 49219-2** Operas Arias for Trumpet

TOULOUSE CAPITOLE ORCHESTRA
cond M. PLASSON
Bizet: Arlésienne (Cpte), Pêcheurs de Perles (Cpte)
Fauré: Cantique de Jean Racine, Requiem (Cpte)
Franck: Rédemption
Gounod: Faust (Cpte), Mors et Vita (Cpte), Roméo et Juliette (Cpte), Symphony 1, Symphony 2
Indy: Symphony 2
Lalo: Symphonie espagnole, Violin Concerto
Massenet: Don Quichotte (Cpte), Manon (Cpte)
Offenbach: Belle Hélène (Cpte), Orphée aux enfers (Cpte), Périchole (Cpte)
Roussel: Padmâvatî (Cpte)
see CONCERT INDEX *under:*
(DG) **435 437-2GH** Milhaud—Orchestral Works
(DG) **435 438-2GH** Honegger—Orchestral Works
(DG) **439 939-2GH** Milhaud—Orchestral Works
(EMI) **CDC5 55057-2** Bizet—Orchestral Works
(EMI) **CDC7 47648-2** Ravel: Orchestral Works
(EMI) **CDC7 47939-2** Fauré—Orchestral Works
(EMI) **CDC7 49219-2** Operas Arias for Trumpet
(EMI) **CDC7 49471-2** Satie: Orchestral Works
(EMI) **CDC7 49472-2** Debussy—Orchestral Works
(EMI) **CDC7 49652-2** Chabrier—Orchestral Works
(EMI) **CDC7 54004-2** Chabrier: Vocal & Orchestral Works
(EMI) **CDC7 54010-2** Berlioz—Orchestral Works
(EMI) **CDC7 54237-2** Berlioz—Orchestral Works
(EMI) **CDM7 63104-2** Alfredo Krauss - Opera Recital
(EMI) **CZS7 62745-2** Rachmaninov—Piano Works

TOULOUSE MID-PYRÉNÉES CHORUS
cond M. PLASSON
see CONCERT INDEX *under:*
(EMI) **CDC7 49472-2** Debussy—Orchestral Works
(EMI) **CDC7 54004-2** Chabrier: Vocal & Orchestral Works

TOULOUSE NATIONAL CHAMBER ORCHESTRA
cond B. BRATOEV
see CONCERT INDEX *under:*
(AUVI) **A6124** Britten: Orchestral works
cond J-C. MALGOIRE
see CONCERT INDEX *under:*
(AUVI) **V4697** Bach—Violin Concertos

TOULOUSE SAQUEBOUTIERS
cond P. HERREWEGHE
Monteverdi: Vespers

TOURAINE, Geneviève (sop)
see CONCERT INDEX *under:*
(DECC) **433 400-2DM2** Ravel & Debussy—Stage Works

TOURANGEAU, Huguette (mez)
Donizetti: Lucia di Lammermoor (Cpte), Maria Stuarda (Cpte)
Falla: Amor brujo (Cpte)
Massenet: Esclarmonde (Cpte), Roi de Lahore (Cpte)
Offenbach: Contes d'Hoffmann (Cpte)
Verdi: Rigoletto (Cpte)

TOUREL, Jennie (mez)
see CONCERT INDEX *under:*
(EMI) **CHS7 69741-2(1)** Record of Singing, Vol.4—Anglo-American School (pt 1)
(SONY) **SMK47638** Vaughan Williams—Orchestral Works
(SONY) **SMK58984** Pablo Casals conducts Mozart at Perpignan, 1951
(SONY) **SM2K47526** Berlioz—Vocal and Orchestral Works
(SONY) **SM2K47533** Music inspired by the Jewish Religion
(SONY) **SM3K47162** Bernstein plays and conducts Bernstein Volume III

TOURNÉ, Teresa (sop)
Bretón: Verbena de la Paloma (Cpte)
Chapí: Revoltosa (Cpte)
Moreno Torroba: Luisa Fernanda (Cpte)
Vives: Doña Francisquita (Cpte)

TOURS, Frank (cond)
see orch

TOUVRON, Guy (tpt)
Shostakovich: Piano Concerto 1
see CONCERT INDEX *under:*
(DECC) **436 798-2DH** Loussier—Concertos
(OPUS) **9350 1710** Concertos For Trumpet and Orchestra
(RCA) **09026 61186-2** Works for Trumpet & Organ
(RCA) **09026 61200-2** Molter—Trumpet Concertos
(SCHW) **311052** Virtuoso Kettledrum Concertos

TOVEY, Bramwell (cond)
see Hallé

TOWB, Suki (vc)
see CONCERT INDEX *under:*
(ASV) **CDGAD201** Vivaldi—Cello Sonatas

TOWNS, Colin (cond)
see London Filmworks Orch

TOWNS, Colin (synths)
see CONCERT INDEX *under:*
(KOCH) **38703-2** Full Circle—Original Soundtrack, etc

TOYE, Geoffrey (cond)
see LSO

TOYE, Jennifer (sop)
Sullivan: Gondoliers (Cpte), Iolanthe (Cpte), Patience (Cpte)
see CONCERT INDEX *under:*
(DECC) **430 095-2DWO** The World of Gilbert & Sullivan, Vol.1
(DECC) **433 868-2DWO** The World of Gilbert & Sullivan - Volume 2

TOYODA, Kiyomi (sop)
Mendelssohn: Midsummer Night's Dream (exc)

TOZER, Geoffrey (pf)
Ireland: Piano Concerto
Medtner: Piano Concerto 1, Piano Concerto 2, Piano Concerto 3, Sonata-Ballada, Op. 27, Violin Sonata 1, Violin Sonata 2
Respighi: Concerto in modo misolidio, Piano Concerto in A minor
Tchaikovsky: Piano Concerto 3
see CONCERT INDEX *under:*
(CHAN) **CHAN9040** Medtner—Piano Concertos, etc
(CHAN) **CHAN9050** Medtner—Piano Works, Vol.1
(CHAN) **CHAN9125** Rawsthorne—Piano Concertos
(CHAN) **CHAN9229** Rimsky-Korsakov—Orchestral Works
(CHAN) **CHAN9238** Stravinsky—Orchestral Works
(CHAN) **CHAN9240** Stravinsky—Choral and Orchestral Works
(CHAN) **CHAN9311** Respighi—Orchestral Works
(CHAN) **CHAN9327** Medtner—Songs
(CHAN) **CHAN9360** Liszt—Orchestral Works
(TALL) **TP001** Piano Works for Children

TOZZI, Giorgio (bass)
Barber: Vanessa (Cpte)
Berlioz: Enfance du Christ (Cpte)
Puccini: Bohème (Cpte), Turandot (Cpte)
Rossini: Barbiere di Siviglia (Cpte)
Verdi: Aida (Cpte), Forza del destino (Cpte), Luisa Miller (Cpte), Requiem (Cpte)
see CONCERT INDEX *under:*
(RCA) **GD87799** The Pearl Fishers Duet plus Duets and Scenes
(RCA) **09026 61580-2(5)** RCA/Met 100 Singers, 100 Years (pt 5)

TRACEY, Ian (organ)
see CONCERT INDEX *under:*
(CFP) **CD-CFP4558** Organ Recital
(CHAN) **CHAN9271** Poulenc/Guilmant/Widor—Organ Works
(MIRA) **MRCD901** Liverpool Encores

TRACK, Gerhard (cond)
see Bratislava RSO

TRAFICANTE, Valerie (pf)
see CONCERT INDEX *under:*
(CARL) **MCD71** French Orchestral Works

TRAGICOMEDIA
Landi: Mort d'Orfeo (Cpte)
see CONCERT INDEX *under:*
(TELD) **4509-90798-2** Monteverdi—Il Ballo delle ingrate
cond S. STUBBS
Bach: Anna magdalena Notenbuch (1725) (exc), Cantata 140 (exc)
see CONCERT INDEX *under:*
(HYPE) **CDA66307** My Mind to me a kingdom is
(HYPE) **CDA66335** A Musicall Dreame
(TELD) **4509-91971-2** Monteverdi—Madrigali concertati

TRAKAS, Christopher (bar)
see CONCERT INDEX *under:*
(KOCH) **37215-2** Italian Orchestral Music

TRAMA, Ugo (bass)
Puccini: Tosca (Cpte)

TRAMIER, Brigitte (hpd)
Anglebert: Harpsichord Works (exc)

TRAMPLER, Walter (va)
Schoenberg: Verklärte Nacht
see CONCERT INDEX *under:*
(CNTI) **CCD1020** Simon Bainbridge—Orchestral Works

TRAUBEL, Helen (sop)
see CONCERT INDEX *under:*
(EMI) **CHS7 69741-2(1)** Record of Singing, Vol.4—Anglo-American School (pt 1)
(RCA) **GD60264** Wagner—Opera excerpts
(RCA) **09026 61580-2(4)** RCA/Met 100 Singers, 100 Years (pt 4)
(RCA) **09026 61879-2** Grieg—Historic Recordings

TRAUBOTH, Andrea (sop)
Braunfels: Verkündigung (Cpte)

TRAVIS, Francis (cond)
see Basle SO

TRAVIS, Ron (spkr)
Gershwin: Porgy and Bess (Cpte)

TRAVNÍČEK QUARTET
Dvořák: String Quartet 12, String Quartet 13

TRAXEL, Josef (ten)
Bruckner: Te Deum

TREE, Michael (va)
Brahms: String Sextet 1, String Sextet 2

TREEP, Nico (cond)
see orch

TRÉGAN, Thierry (ten)
Bizet: Carmen (Cpte)

TREGUIER, Christian (bar)
Auber: Gustav III (Cpte)
Massenet: Grisélidis (Cpte)

TRÉHARD, Jean-Marie (gtr)
see CONCERT INDEX *under:*
(CALL) **CAL9204** Granados: Transcriptions for Guitar Duo

TREHARNE, Arwel (ten)
Lampe: Pyramus and Thisbe (Cpte)

TREKEL, Roman (bar)
Wagner: Tristan and Isolde (Cpte)
Weber: Freischütz (Cpte)

TRELEAVEN, John (ten)
Bernstein: Candide (1988) (Cpte)
Donizetti: Assedio di Calais (Cpte)
Verdi: Trovatore (Cpte)

TREML, Alois (bass)
B.A. Zimmermann: Soldaten (Cpte)

TREMPER, Susanne (sngr)
Weill: Dreigroschenoper (Cpte), Mahagonny-Gesänge (Cpte)

TREMPONT, Michel (ten)
A. Thomas: Hamlet (Cpte)
Auber: Fra Diavolo (Cpte)
Massenet: Chérubin (Cpte)
Offenbach: Brigands (Cpte), Orphée aux enfers (Cpte), Périchole (Cpte)
see CONCERT INDEX *under:*
(EMI) **CDS7 49361-2** Offenbach: Operettas

TRENK-TREBITSCH, Willy (voc)
Weill: Dreigroschenoper (Cpte)

TRENTIN, Roger (ten)
Offenbach: Belle Hélène (Cpte), Orphée aux enfers (Cpte)

TRENTON, Louise (sop)
see CONCERT INDEX *under:*
(CLAR) **CDGSE78-50-35/6** Wagner—Historical recordings
(PEAR) **GEMMCDS9137** Wagner—Der Ring des Nibelungen

TREPTE, Paul (cond)
see Ely Cath Ch

TREPTE, Paul (organ)
Saint-Saëns: Mass, Op. 4

TREPTOW, Günther (ten)
Henze: Junge Lord (Cpte)
Wagner: Meistersinger (Cpte), Tristan und Isolde (Cpte)

TREVISAN, Antonella (mez)
Verdi: Rigoletto (Cpte), Traviata (Cpte)

TREVOR, Caroline (mez)
Bach: Cantata 4, Easter Oratorio, BWV249
Mozart: Zauberflöte (Cpte)
see CONCERT INDEX *under:*
(AMON) **CD-SAR55** Dowland—Lachrimae
(COLL) **Coll1320-2** Baroque Choral Works

TREW, Graham (bar)
see CONCERT INDEX *under:*
(MERI) **CDE84185** Settings from A. E. Housman's 'A Shropshire Lad'

TREXLER, Roswitha (sngr)
Henze: Voices (Cpte)

TRHLIK, Otakar (cond)
see Slovak RSO

TRIANTI, Alexandra (sop)
see CONCERT INDEX *under:*
(PEAR) **GEMMCDS9075** Hugo Wolf Society, Volume I

TRIBUKAIT, Bengt (organ)
see CONCERT INDEX *under:*
(BIS) **BIS-CD510** Organ Music from the USA

(JOSEF) TRIEBENSEE ENSEMBLE
cond J. WEIERINK
Krommer: Partitas, Op. 45

TRIESTE TRIO
see CONCERT INDEX *under:*
(DG) **437 131-2GX2** Brahms—Chamber Works
(NUOV) **6857/8** Schubert—Piano Trios

TRIGEAU, Jacques (bar)
Offenbach: Périchole (Cpte)

TRIMARCHI, Domenico (bar)
Donizetti: Elisir d'amore (Cpte)

Haydn: Orlando Paladino (Cpte), Vera Costanza (Cpte)
Puccini: Tosca (Cpte)
Rossini: Barbiere di Siviglia (Cpte), Cenerentola (Cpte), Italiana in Algeri (Cpte)
see CONCERT INDEX *under:*
(PHIL) **432 416-2PH3** Haydn—L'incontro improvviso/Arias
(PHIL) **432 420-2PH3** Haydn—Il mondo della luna/Arias

TRINI, Monica (sop)
Verdi: Aida (Cpte)

TRINITY BOYS' CHOIR
cond L. BERNSTEIN
Stravinsky: Mass
cond O. DE FABRITIIS
Boito: Mefistofele (Cpte)
cond R. HICKOX
Britten: Midsummer Night's Dream (Cpte)
cond G. LLOYD
G. Lloyd: John Socman (exc)

TRINITY COLLEGE CHOIR, CAMBRIDGE
cond R. MARLOW
Bach: Motets (Cpte)
Schütz: Psalmen Davids, SWV22-47 (exc)
Sweelinck: Pseaumes des David III (exc)
Victoria: Lamentations of Jeremiah (exc), Tenebrae Responsories (exc)
see CONCERT INDEX *under:*
(CONI) **CDCF151** Poulenc—Sacred Choral Works
(CONI) **CDCF152** Purcell—Anthems for the Chapel Royal
(CONI) **CDCF155** Parry/Stanford—Choral Works
(CONI) **CDCF164** Walton: Sacred Choral Music
(CONI) **CDCF176** French Sacred Choral Works
(CONI) **CDCF178** Brahms: Complete Motets
(CONI) **CDCF212** Monteverdi—Motets
(CONI) **CDCF214** Great is the Lord
(CONI) **CDCF216** When David Heard
(CONI) **CDCF219** Miserere and Other Popular Choral Works
(CONI) **CDCF220** Michael Haydn—Masses and Vespers
(CONI) **CDCF230** Lassus—Regina coeli and Seasonal Motets
(CONI) **CDCF501** Carols from Trinity
(CONI) **CDCF517** A Child is Born
(CONI) **75605 51231-2** O.Gibbons—Hosanna to the Son of David
(CONI) **75605 51232-2** Stravinsky—Mass; Gesualdo—Responsoria

TRIO DI MILANO
see CONCERT INDEX *under:*
(DYNA) **CDS49** French Piano Trios

TRIO 1790
J. C. Bach: Sonatas, T313/1, Sonatas, T323/5 (exc)

TRIPP, Werner (fl)
Mozart: Flute and Harp Concerto, K299

TRITLE, Thomas (hn)
see CONCERT INDEX *under:*
(CHNT) **LDC278 835** Villa-Lobos—Chôros for Chamber Ensembles

TRITT, William (pf)
see CONCERT INDEX *under:*
(TELA) **CD80166** Gershwin: Orchestral Works

TRO, Silvia (sop)
Bretón: Verbena de La Paloma (Cpte)

TROEVA-MIRCHEVA, Rossitza (contr)
Mussorgsky: Boris Godunov (Cpte)
Tchaikovsky: Eugene Onegin (Cpte)

TROGU-RÖHRICH, Caterina (sop)
Traetta: Buovo d'Antona (Cpte)

TROITSKAYA, Natalia (sop)
Janáček: Glagolitic Mass (Cpte)
Rachmaninov: Bells

TROMP, Joost (fl)
see CONCERT INDEX *under:*
(TELD) **4509-97467-2** Frans Brüggen Edition Vol. 5—Late Baroque Chamber Music

TRONDHEIM SOLOISTS
cond B. FISKUM
see CONCERT INDEX *under:*
(VICT) **VCD19066** Grieg—Music for Strings
(VICT) **VCD19071** Grieg—Chamber Works, Vol.1

TRONDHEIM SYMPHONY CHORUS
cond O.K. RUUD
see CONCERT INDEX *under:*
(VIRG) **VC5 45051-2** Grieg—Choral Works

TRONDHEIM SYMPHONY ORCHESTRA
cond O. K. RUUD
Groven: Piano Concerto, Symphony 2
see CONCERT INDEX *under:*
(VICT) **VCD19018** Grieg—Songs with Orchestra
(VIRG) **VC5 45051-2** Grieg—Choral Works

TROOP, Mark (pf)
see CONCERT INDEX *under:*
(COLL) **Coll3052-2** Patricia Rozario - Spanish Recital

TROPIN, Robert (sngr)
Gounod: Mireille (Cpte)

TROST, Rainer (ten)
Lehár: Lustige Witwe (Cpte)

Mendelssohn: Paulus (Cpte)
Mozart: Così fan tutte (Cpte)
see CONCERT INDEX *under:*
(PHIL) **438 873-2PH2** Bach—Magnificat and Masses

TROTTER, Thomas (organ)
Janáček: Glagolitic Mass (Cpte)
see CONCERT INDEX *under:*
(ARGO) **433 152-2ZH** Thomas Trotter plays Widor
(DECC) **436 400-2DH** Messiaen—Organ Works
(DECC) **436 656-2DH** Organ Transcriptions - Thomas Trotter
(DECC) **440 283-2DH** Liszt—Organ Works
(HYPE) **CDA66062** Bruckner—Motets
(HYPE) **CDA66216** The Grand Organ
(HYPE) **CDA66219** American Choral Works
(HYPE) **CDA66245** Bruckner—Choral Works
(LOND) **443 451-2LH** Mozart—Organ Works

TROTTMANN, Barbara (sngr)
Corghi: Divara (Cpte)

TROUP, Malcolm (pf)
Messiaen: Vingt regards

TROUPOVA, Irena (sop)
Biber: Arminio (Cpte)

TROVARELLI, Antonella (mez)
Rossini: Pietra del paragone (Cpte)

TROY, Dermot (ten)
R. Strauss: Capriccio (Cpte)
Rossini: Comte Ory (Cpte)

TROYANOS, Tatiana (mez)
Bartók: Duke Bluebeard's Castle (Cpte)
Bellini: Norma (Cpte)
Bernstein: West Side Story (Cpte)
Bizet: Carmen (Cpte)
Massenet: Werther (Cpte)
Mozart: Così fan tutte (Cpte), Finta Giardiniera (Cpte), Nozze di Figaro (Cpte)
Purcell: Dido (Cpte)
R. Strauss: Ariadne auf Naxos (Cpte), Capriccio (Cpte), Rosenkavalier (Cpte)
Schoenberg: Gurrelieder
Wagner: Götterdämmerung (Cpte)
see CONCERT INDEX *under:*
(DG) **437 368-2GX2** Beethoven—Orchestral Works
(DG) **445 354-2GX14** Wagner—Der Ring des Nibelungen
(RCA) **09026 61509-2** A Salute to American Music

TRUC, Georges (cond)
see SO

TRUCCO, Victor (cond)
see RCA SO

TRUFFELLI, Romano (ten)
see CONCERT INDEX *under:*
(RCA) **GD86534** Verdi Arias and Duets

TRUMAN, Robert (vc)
see CONCERT INDEX *under:*
(HYPE) **CDA66705** Holst—Partsongs

TRUNDT, Henny (sop)
see CONCERT INDEX *under:*
(SCHW) **314532** Vienna State Opera Live, Vol.3
(SCHW) **314642** Vienna State Opera Live, Vol.14

TRUPP, Maria (contr)
R. Strauss: Rosenkavalier (Cpte)

TRURO CATHEDRAL CHOIR
cond D. BRIGGS
see CONCERT INDEX *under:*
(PRIO) **PRCD322** Choral Evensong From Truro Cathedral
(PRIO) **PRCD429** Great Cathedral Anthems, Vol.5

TRUSHIN, Vyatcheslav (va)
Vainberg: String Quartet 12

TRYON, Valerie (pf)
see CONCERT INDEX *under:*
(UNIC) **DKPCD9133** Debussy—Songs

TSCHAMMER, Hans (bass-bar)
Beethoven: Missa Solemnis
Wagner: Parsifal (Cpte), Rheingold (Cpte)

TSCHUPP, Räto (cond)
see Zurich Camerata

TSELOVALNIK, Evgenia (sop)
Mussorgsky: Khovanshchina (Cpte)
Shostakovich: Symphony 14

TSIDIPOVA, Valentina (sop)
Rimsky-Korsakov: Sadko (Cpte)

TSINGOPOULOS, Madeline (sngr)
Rorem: Childhood Miracle (Cpte), Three Sisters Who Are Not Sisters (Cpte)

TSIPCALO, Sergey (bar)
Rachmaninov: Liturgy, Op. 31

TS'ONG, Fou (pf)
Beethoven: Piano Concerto 4
Chopin: Mazurkas (exc), Nocturnes
see CONCERT INDEX *under:*
(COLL) **Coll1052-2** Debussy—Piano Works
(DECC) **425 044-2DM** Mozart—Works for Piano and Orchestra
(DECC) **425 088-2DM** Mozart—Piano Concertos, Vol. 1
(LOND) **443 727-2LC10** Mozart—The Piano Concertos
(SONY) **SBK53515** Chopin—Piano Works

TS'ONG, Fou (pf/dir)
Haydn: Keyboard Concerto, HobXVIII/11
Mozart: Piano Concerto 9, Piano Concerto 12, Piano Concerto 21, Piano Concerto 22, Piano Concerto 24, Piano Concerto 27

TSURUTA, Kinshi (biwa)
see CONCERT INDEX *under:*
(PHIL) **432 176-2PH** Takemitsu—Orchestral Works

TSUTSUI, Kaori (cl)
see CONCERT INDEX *under:*
(NAXO) **8 553178** Krommer—Clarinet Concertos

TUAND, Carlo (ten)
Bellini: Puritani (Cpte)

TUBB, Evelyn (sop)
Monteverdi: Madrigals, Bk 8 (exc)
Mozart: Zauberflöte (Cpte)
Purcell: Don Quixote: The Musical (Cpte)
see CONCERT INDEX *under:*
(CARL) **PCD881** Monteverdi—Solos and Duets
(HYPE) **CDA66476** Purcell—Complete Odes & Welcome Songs, Vol.5
(MOSC) **070979** Sound the Trumpets from Shore to Shore
(MOSC) **070987** The Mad Lover
(SONY) **SK66243** Music for Queen Mary
(VIRG) **VC7 59606-2** Monteverdi—Madrigals, Book 8

TÜBINGER, Hans (spkr)
B.A. Zimmermann: Soldaten (Cpte)

TUČEK, René (bar)
Dvořák: Jacobin (Cpte)
Janáček: Excursions of Mr Brouček (Cpte)
Smetana: Libuše (Cpte)

TUCKER, Gene (ten)
Berlioz: Messe Solennelle (Cpte)
Rachmaninov: Vespers, Op. 37 (Cpte)

TUCKER, Mark (ten)
Bach: Mass in B minor, BWV232 (Cpte)
Monteverdi: Orfeo (Cpte), Ritorno d'Ulisse in patria (Cpte), Vespers
Purcell: King Arthur, Z628 (Cpte)
Telemann: Deus judicium tuum, Donner-Ode
see CONCERT INDEX *under:*
(ERAT) **2292-45466-2** Carissimi—Jonas

TUCKER, Richard (ten)
Puccini: Madama Butterfly (Cpte)
Verdi: Aida (Cpte), Forza del destino (Cpte)
see CONCERT INDEX *under:*
(EMI) **CHS7 69741-2(2)** Record of Singing, Vol.4—Anglo-American School (pt 2)
(RCA) **GD60326** Verdi—Operas & Choral Works
(RCA) **09026 61580-2(6)** RCA/Met 100 Singers, 100 Years (pt 6)
(SONY) **SMK47638** Vaughan Williams—Orchestral Works

TUCKWELL, Barry (hn)
Czerny: Andante and Polacca, Schubert Fantasies, Op. 339
Herzogenberg: Piano Trio in D, Op. 61
Reinecke: Piano Trio, Op. 188
see CONCERT INDEX *under:*
(ASV) **CDDCA716** Koechlin—Works for Horn & Piano
(DECC) **430 370-2DH** R. Strauss—Works for Horn
(DECC) **430 633-2DM** Haydn—Concertos
(DECC) **433 695-2DM** Chamber Works
(DECC) **436 990-2DWO** The World of Benjamin Britten
(DECC) **443 838-2DF2** Italian Orchestral Works
(EMI) **CDM7 69569-2** Mozart—Horn Concertos, etc
(ETCE) **KTC1135** French Music for Horn
(LOND) **425 716-2LM** Britten: Canticles
(LOND) **436 395-2LM** Britten—Vocal Works

TUCKWELL, Barry (hn/dir)
Mozart: Horn Concerti

TUDOR, David (synths)
see CONCERT INDEX *under:*
(KOCH) **37238-2** A Chance Operation - John Cage Tribute

TUGARINOVA, Klavdila (contr)
see CONCERT INDEX *under:*
(MMOI) **CDMOIR422** Great Voices in Tchaikovsky

TUGARINOVA, Tatiana (mez)
Tchaikovsky: Eugene Onegin (Cpte)

TÜLLER, Niklaus (bass)
Zelenka: Requiem in C
see CONCERT INDEX *under:*
(HANS) **98 803** Bach—Cantatas, Vol.41
(HANS) **98 806** Bach—Cantatas, Vol.44
(HANS) **98 810** Bach—Cantatas, Vol.48
(HANS) **98 820** Bach—Cantatas, Vol.58
(HANS) **98 826** Bach—Cantatas, Vol.64
(HANS) **98 828** Bach—Cantatas, Vol.66
(HANS) **98 863** Bach—Cantatas, Vol.12
(HANS) **98 870** Bach—Cantatas, Vol.19
(HANS) **98 878** Bach—Cantatas, Vol.27
(HANS) **98 879** Bach—Cantatas, Vol.28
(HANS) **98 886** Bach—Cantatas, Vol.35
(HANS) **98 890** Bach—Cantatas, Vol.37
(JECK) **JD673-2** Schoeck—Complete Lieder, Vol.3

TULVE, Jaan-Eik (ten)
see Paris Gregorian Ch

TUMAGIAN, Eduard (bar)
Brahms: Deutsches Requiem, Op.45 (Cpte)

Leoncavallo: Pagliacci (Cpte)
Mascagni: Cavalleria Rusticana (Cpte)
Prokofiev: War and Peace (Cpte)
Puccini: Gianni Schicchi (Cpte), Tabarro (Cpte),
Turandot (Cpte)
Verdi: Rigoletto (Cpte), Simon Boccanegra (Cpte)
see CONCERT INDEX under:
(NAXO) **8 550684**   Duets and Arias from Italian
Operas

TUMAGIAN, Edward (bass)
Verdi: Otello (Cpte)

TUNELL, Lisa (contr)
Beethoven: Symphony 9

TUNICK, Jonathan (cond)
see London Sinfonietta

TUNNARD, Viola (cond)
see Elizabethan Sngrs

TUNNARD, Viola (pf)
see CONCERT INDEX under:
(LOND) **425 159-2LM**   Salute to Percy Grainger
(LOND) **436 394-2LM**   Britten—Vocal & Choral
Works

TUNNELL, Charles (vc)
Schubert: Trio, D96
see CONCERT INDEX under:
(ASV) **CDDCA645**   Vivaldi—Concertos
(HYPE) **CDA66295**   Villa-Lobos: Chamber Works
(SONY) **MK39061**   Let the bright Seraphim

TUNNELL, John (vn)
see CONCERT INDEX under:
(CARL) **PCD808**   Bach: Violin Concertos
(CARL) **PCD809**   Vivaldi: Violin Concertos
(NIMB) **NI5325**   Bach—Violin Concertos

TUNNICLIFF, Theresa (cl)
see CONCERT INDEX under:
(NUOV) **6802**   Mozart—Chamber Works

TUNNICLIFFE, Richard (vc)
Rossini: Sonate a Quattro

TUNSTALL, Helen (hp)
see CONCERT INDEX under:
(COLL) **Coll1286-2**   Britten—Choral Works
(COLL) **Coll1428-2**   Tavener—To a Child dancing in
the Wind
(NMC) **NMCD009**   Birtwistle—Choral and Orchestral
Works

TUOMELA, Tuula-Marja (sop)
Bergman: Singing Tree (Cpte)

TURA, Gennaro De (ten)
see CONCERT INDEX under:
(EMI) **CHS7 64860-2(2)**   La Scala Edition - Vol.1,
1878-1914 (pt 2)

TURBAN, Ingolf (vn)
see CONCERT INDEX under:
(CLAV) **CD50-8808**   Grieg—Violin Sonatas
(CLAV) **CD50-9017**   Respighi—Works for Violin and
Orchestra

TURBA-RABIER, Odette (sop)
Ravel: Enfant et les sortilèges (Cpte)

TURCHETTA, Sonia (contr)
Salieri: Axur (Cpte)

TURCHETTI, Anna Maria (sop)
see CONCERT INDEX under:
(TEST) **SBT1008**   Viva Rossini

TURCO, Alberto (cond)
see Nova Schola Gregoriana

TURCO, Enrico (bass)
Franchetti: Cristoforo Colombo (Cpte)
Gluck: Iphigénie en Tauride (Cpte)
Mozart: Don Giovanni (Cpte)
Puccini: Fanciulla del West (Cpte)

TURECK, Rosalyn (pf)
see CONCERT INDEX under:
(VAI) **VAIA1024**   Rosalyn Tureck recital, Teatro Colón,
BA

TURIN EIAR ORCHESTRA
   cond F. GHIONE
see CONCERT INDEX under:
(LYRC) **SRO805**   Gina Cigna—Opera Recital
   cond G. MARINUZZI
see CONCERT INDEX under:
(PREI) **89015**   Carlo Tagliabue (1898-1978)
   cond A. LA ROSA PARODI
see CONCERT INDEX under:
(PREI) **89015**   Carlo Tagliabue (1898-1978)
   cond U. TANSINI
see CONCERT INDEX under:
(LYRC) **SRO805**   Gina Cigna—Opera Recital
(PREI) **89015**   Carlo Tagliabue (1898-1978)

TURIN LYRIC CHORUS
   cond F. CLEVA
Catalani: Wally (Cpte)

TURIN PHILHARMONIC ORCHESTRA
   cond M. VIOTTI
Rossini: Signor Bruschino (Cpte)
see CONCERT INDEX under:
(CLAV) **CD50-8509**   Frank Martin—Piano Concertos

TURIN RADIO SYMPHONY ORCHESTRA
   cond G. GELMETTI
Rossini: Gazza ladra (Cpte)

TURIN RAI CHORUS
   cond E. BONCOMPAGNI
Alfano: Risurrezione (Cpte)
   cond C. SCIMONE
Donizetti: Elisir d'amore (Cpte)

TURIN RAI ORCHESTRA
   cond E. BONCOMPAGNI
Alfano: Risurrezione (Cpte)
   cond G. SANTINI
Verdi: Traviata (Cpte)
   cond C. SCIMONE
Donizetti: Elisir d'amore (Cpte)

TURIN SYMPHONY ORCHESTRA
   cond F. MOLINARI-PRADELLI
see CONCERT INDEX under:
(RCA) **09026 68014-2**   Pavarotti - The Early Years,
Vol.2
   cond M. ROSSI
see CONCERT INDEX under:
(RCA) **09026 68014-2**   Pavarotti - The Early Years,
Vol.2

TURIN TEATRO REGIO CHORUS
   cond B. CAMPANELLA
Donizetti: Don Pasquale (Cpte)

TURIN TEATRO REGIO ORCHESTRA
   cond B. CAMPANELLA
Donizetti: Ajo nell'imbarazzo (Cpte), Don Pasquale
(Cpte)

TÜRK, Gerd (ten)
Biber: Arminio (Cpte)
Mangold: Abraham
Monteverdi: Incoronazione di Poppea (Cpte),
Vespers
Mozart: Requiem

TÜRKE, Marina (sop)
Henze: Junge Lord (Cpte)

TURKOVIC, Milan (bn)
see CONCERT INDEX under:
(ARCH) **419 615-2AH**   Vivaldi: Concertos
(DG) **427 639-2GH**   Poulenc: Chamber Works
(DG) **431 782-2GH**   Mozart—Chamber Works
(SCHW) **311065**   Double Concertos
(TELD) **9031-77603-2**   Works by Leopold and
Wolfgang Amadeus Mozart

TURNBULL, James (alto)
see CONCERT INDEX under:
(CHAN) **CHAN8658**   Poulenc & Charpentier: Sacred
Choral Works

TURNBULL, Dr Walter J. (cond)
see Harlem Boys Ch

TURNER, Bruno (cond)
see Hamburg Early Music Wind Ens

TURNER, Charles (prepared pf)
see CONCERT INDEX under:
(KOCH) **37238-2**   A Chance Operation - John Cage
Tribute

TURNER, Claramae (mez)
Verdi: Ballo in maschera (Cpte)

TURNER, Dame Eva (narr)
see CONCERT INDEX under:
(EMI) **CDH7 69791-2**   Dame Eva Turner sings Opera
Arias and Songs

TURNER, Dame Eva (sop)
see CONCERT INDEX under:
(DUTT) **CDAX8004**   Sir Henry Wood conducts
Vaughan Williams
(EMI) **CDH7 69791-2**   Dame Eva Turner sings Opera
Arias and Songs
(NIMB) **NI7801**   Great Singers, Vol.1
(NIMB) **NI7802**   Divas 1906-1935
(NIMB) **NI7851**   Legendary Voices
(PEAR) **GEMMCDS9925(1)**   Covent Garden on
Record—Vol.3 (pt 1)
(PEAR) **GEMMCD9342**   Vaughan Williams: Vocal
Works

TURNER, Gavin (cond)
see William Byrd Ch

TURNER, Jane (mez)
Wagner: Götterdämmerung (Cpte), Rheingold
(Cpte)

TURNER, John (fl)
see CONCERT INDEX under:
(L'OI) **411 949-2OH**   Telemann: Double & Triple
Concertos

TUROVSKY, Eleonora (vn)
Kodály: Duo, Op. 7
see CONCERT INDEX under:
(CHAN) **CHAN8358**   Music for Violin and Cello
(CHAN) **CHAN8470**   J.C. Bach & Boccherini—Cello
Works
(CHAN) **CHAN8555**   Russian Duos
(CHAN) **CHAN8651**   Vivaldi: Concertos
(CHAN) **CHAN8652**   Russian Music for String Duo
(CHAN) **CHAN8817**   Britten: Orchestral Works
(CHAN) **CHAN8924**   Russian Vocal and Chamber
works

TUROVSKY, Yuli (cond)
see Montreal I Musici

TUROVSKY, Yuli (vc)
Brahms: Clarinet Trio
Dvořák: Piano Trio 4

Kodály: Cello Sonata, Op. 8, Duo, Op. 7
Miaskovsky: Cello Sonata 2
Prokofiev: Cello Sonata, Op. 119
Rachmaninov: Cello Sonata
Shostakovich: Cello Sonata, Op. 40
Smetana: Piano Trio in G minor
Tchaikovsky: Album for the Young
see CONCERT INDEX under:
(CHAN) **CHAN8358**   Music for Violin and Cello
(CHAN) **CHAN8458**   Debussy & Ravel: Chamber
Works
(CHAN) **CHAN8555**   Russian Duos
(CHAN) **CHAN8652**   Russian Music for String Duo
(CHAN) **CHAN8800**   Music on Hebrew Themes

TUROVSKY, Yuli (vc/dir)
see CONCERT INDEX under:
(CHAN) **CHAN8470**   J.C. Bach & Boccherini—Cello
Concertos

TURPIE, Karen (vn)
see CONCERT INDEX under:
(DG) **415 487-2GH**   Vivaldi: Guitar Concertos
(NOVA) **150 016-2**   Vivaldi—Concertos

TUSA, Andrew (ten)
Handel: Israel in Egypt (Cpte)
see CONCERT INDEX under:
(HYPE) **CDA66494**   Purcell—Complete Odes &
Welcome Songs, Vol.6

TUSCAN ORCHESTRA
   cond G. GELMETTI
Rossini: Barbiere di Siviglia (Cpte)

TUSCHER, Nata (sop)
Martin: Vin herbé

TUTSEK, Piroska (mez)
see CONCERT INDEX under:
(SCHW) **314542**   Vienna State Opera Live, Vol.4
(SCHW) **314672**   Vienna State Opera Live, Vol.17

TUXEN, Erik (cond)
see Danish RSO

TVERSKAYA, Olga (fp)
see CONCERT INDEX under:
(O111) **OPS30-121**   Haydn—English and Scottish
Songs
(O111) **OPS30-126**   Schubert—Violin Sonatas

TVRZSKÝ, Jaroslav (organ)
Honegger: Cantate de Noël

TWENTIETH CENTURY CLASSICS ENSEMBLE
   cond R. CRAFT
see CONCERT INDEX under:
(KOCH) **37263-2**   Schoenberg—A Survivor from
Warsaw, etc

TWENTIETH CENTURY FOX CHORUS
   cond ALFRED NEWMAN
see CONCERT INDEX under:
(RCA) **09026 61245-2**   Ezio Pinza - Recital

**TWENTIETH CENTURY FOX SYMPHONY
ORCHESTRA**
   cond ALFRED NEWMAN
see CONCERT INDEX under:
(RCA) **09026 61245-2**   Ezio Pinza - Recital

(TOBY) TWINING MUSIC
see CONCERT INDEX under:
(CATA) **09026 61981-2**   Toby Twining—Shaman

TWO CITIES SYMPHONY ORCHESTRA
   cond C. WILLIAMS
see CONCERT INDEX under:
(EMI) **CDGO 2059**   British Film Music from the 40s and
50s

TYLER, Marilyn (sop)
Wagner: Walküre (Cpte)
see CONCERT INDEX under:
(DECC) **414 100-2DM15**   Wagner: Der Ring des
Nibelungen

TYLŠAR, Bedřich (hn)
see CONCERT INDEX under:
(NAXO) **8 550459**   Czech Horn Concertos
(OPUS) **9150 1473**   L.Mozart & Telemann: Orchestral
Works
(SUPR) **11 1445-2**   Reicha/Beethoven—Compositions
for Wind

TYLŠAR, Zdeněk (hn)
Mozart: Horn Concerti, Rondo, K371, Serenade,
K320
see CONCERT INDEX under:
(NAXO) **8 550459**   Czech Horn Concertos
(OPUS) **9150 1473**   L.Mozart & Telemann: Orchestral
Works
(SUPR) **11 1445-2**   Reicha/Beethoven—Compositions
for Wind

TYRÉN, Arne (bass)
Verdi: Rigoletto (Cpte)

TYSALL, Annabella (sop)
see CONCERT INDEX under:
(WOOD) **WOODM001-2**   Born is the
Babe—Renaissance Music
(WOOD) **WOODM002-2**   Ah, Dear Heart

TYSKLIND, Stig (bass)
Haeffner: Electra (Cpte)

TZIPINE, Georges (cond)
see FNO

UCHIDA, Mitsuko (pf)
Chopin: Piano Sonata 2, Piano Sonata 3
Debussy: Etudes
Mozart: Piano Concerto 8, Piano Concerto 9, Piano
  Concerto 18, Piano Concerto 19, Piano Concerto 20,
  Piano Concerto 21, Piano Concerto 22, Piano
  Concerto 23, Piano Concerto 24, Piano Concerto 25,
  Piano Concerto 26, Piano Concerto 27
Schumann: Carnaval, Kreisleriana
  see CONCERT INDEX under:
(PHIL) 412 122-2PH   Mozart—Piano Works
(PHIL) 412 123-2PH   Mozart Piano Works
(PHIL) 412 616-2PH   Mozart—Piano Sonatas, Vol.1
(PHIL) 412 617-2PH   Mozart: Piano Sonatas, Vol.2
(PHIL) 412 741-2PH   Mozart: Piano Sonatas, Vol.3
(PHIL) 420 185-2PH   Mozart: Piano Sonatas, Vol.4
(PHIL) 420 186-2PH   Mozart: Piano Sonatas, Vol.5
(PHIL) 420 950-2PH   Kiri te Kanawa sings Mozart arias
(PHIL) 422 115-2PH6   Mozart—Complete Piano
  Sonatas
(PHIL) 422 517-2PME5 The Complete Mozart Edition
  Vol 17
(PHIL) 422 518-2PME5 The Complete Mozart Edition
  Vol 18
(PHIL) 422 545-2PME3 The Complete Mozart Edition
  Vol.45
(PHIL) 432 989-2PH2   Mitsuko Uchida live in Concert

UCHIDA, Reiko (pf)
Rorem: Eleven Studies

UDAETA, Juan (cond)
see Granada City Orch

UDAGAWA, Hideko (vn)
Brahms: Violin Concerto
Bruch: Violin Concerto 1

UDALOVA, Irina (sop)
Rimsky-Korsakov: Tsar's Bride (Cpte)

UDE, Armin (ten)
Mozart: Zaïde (Cpte), Zauberflöte (Cpte)
R. Strauss: Rosenkavalier (Cpte)
Saint-Saëns: Oratorio de Noël, Op. 12

UECKER, Korliss (sop)
Wagner: Parsifal (Cpte)

UEMURA, Kaori (va da gamba)
Couperin: Nouveaux Concerts (exc), Pièces de
  violes
Handel: Violin Sonatas (exc)
Leclair: Violin Sonatas, Op. 5 (exc)
Marais: Pièces de viole V/II (exc)
Rameau: Pièces de clavecin en concerts

UGGAMS, Leslie (sngr)
J. Herman: Jerry's Girls (Cpte)

UGHI, Uto (vn)
Brahms: Violin Concerto
Bruch: Violin Concerto 1
  see CONCERT INDEX under:
(RCA) RD60431   Dvořák—Works for Violin

UGORSKI, Anatol (pf)
Beethoven: Diabelli Variations
Messiaen: Catalogue d'oiseaux, Fauvette des
  Jardins
Mussorgsky: Pictures
Schubert: Fantasy, D760
Schumann: Davidsbündlertänze
Stravinsky: Petrushka
  see CONCERT INDEX under:
(DG) 435 881-2DH   Beethoven—Piano Works

UHDE, Hermann (bar)
Gounod: St Cecilia Mass
Wagner: Götterdämmerung (Cpte), Lohengrin (Cpte),
  Parsifal (Cpte), Rheingold (Cpte)
  see CONCERT INDEX under:
(FOYE) 15-CF2011   Wagner—Der Ring de Nibelungen

UHL, Fritz (ten)
Orff: Antigonae (Cpte)
R. Strauss: Arabella (Cpte), Elektra (Cpte)
Wagner: Fliegende Holländer (Cpte)

UHL, Oswald (vc)
  see CONCERT INDEX under:
(PREI) 90205   Strauss conducts Strauss, Vol.1

UHLEMANN, Irina (mez)
Delius: Village Romeo and Juliet (Cpte)

UITTENBOSCH, Anneke (hpd)
  see CONCERT INDEX under:
(TELD) 4509-97452-2   Bach—Harpsichord Concertos

UITTI, Frances-Marie (vc)
Scelsi: Ko-Tha, Trilogia
  see CONCERT INDEX under:
(ETCE) KTC1148   Jonathan Harvey—Works for Cello
(ETCE) KTC2016   John Cage—Works for Cello

UKENA, Paul (ten)
R. Ward: Crucible (Cpte)

UKIGAYA, Takao (cond)
see N German Rad PO

UKRAINE NATIONAL SYMPHONY ORCHESTRA
  cond T. KUCHAR
Prokofiev: Symphony 3

UKRAINE NATIONAL SYMPHONY ORCHESTRA
  cond T. KUCHAR
Prokofiev: Symphony 7
  cond A. PENNY
  see CONCERT INDEX under:

(MARC) 8 223721   Holbrooke—Orchestral Works

**UKRAINIAN RADIO AND TV SYMPHONY
ORCHESTRA**
  cond V. GNEDASH
Lyatoshynsky: Romeo and Juliet Suite

UKRAINIAN STATE SYMPHONY ORCHESTRA
  cond V. GNEDASH
Lyatoshynsky: Symphony 3
  cond T. KUCHAR
Lyatoshynsky: Grazhyna, Symphony 1, Symphony 2,
  Symphony 3, Symphony 4, Symphony 5
  see CONCERT INDEX under:
(NAXO) 8 550968/9   Prokofiev—Suites

ULANOWSKY, Paul (pf)
  see CONCERT INDEX under:
(CAMB) CD-1063   Louis Kaufman - Violin Works
(CLAR) CDGSE78-50-57   Lotte Lehmann sings
  Lieder

ULBRICH, Andrea (contr)
Franchetti: Cristoforo Colombo (Cpte)
Mascagni: Lodoletta (Cpte)

ULBRICH, Andrea (mez)
Mendelssohn: Hochzeit des Camacho (Cpte)

ULBRICH, Claudia (sngr)
Killmayer: Yolimba (Cpte)

ULBRICHT, Wilhelm (ten)
  see CONCERT INDEX under:
(PREI) 90168   Wagner—Die Meistersinger, Act 2, etc

ULFUNG, Ragnar (ten)
R. Strauss: Elektra (Cpte)

ULLNER, Niels (vc)
  see CONCERT INDEX under:
(BIS) BIS-CD682   Nystroem—Orchestral Works

ULSAMER, Josef (va da gamba)
  see CONCERT INDEX under:
(ARCH) 415 294-2AH   Terpsichore - Renaissance &
  Early Baroque Dance Music

ULSAMER COLLEGIUM
  see CONCERT INDEX under:
(ARCH) 415 294-2AH   Terpsichore - Renaissance &
  Early Baroque Dance Music
  cond H.M. SCHNEIDT
Schütz: Psalmen Davids, SWV22-47 (exc)

ULSTER ORCHESTRA
  cond V. HANDLEY
Bliss: Checkmate (exc), Colour Symphony
Brahms: Haydn Variations, Serenade 1
Delius: Florida Suite, North Country Sketches
Moeran: Masque Ov, Pieces for small orchestra,
  Symphony, Violin Concerto
Stanford: Clarinet Concerto, Irish Rhapsody 1, Irish
  Rhapsody 2, Irish Rhapsody 4, Irish Rhapsody 5,
  Piano Concerto 2, Symphony 1, Symphony 2,
  Symphony 3, Symphony 5, Symphony 6, Variations,
  Op.71
  see CONCERT INDEX under:
(CHAN) CHAN6538   Seascapes
(CHAN) CHAN6583   Dvořák—Orchestral Works
(CHAN) CHAN8473   Works by Bax, Bridge and
  Britten
(CHAN) CHAN8524   Grieg—Orchestral Works
(CHAN) CHAN8639   Moeran: Orchestral Works
(CHAN) CHAN8723   Grieg: Orchestral Works
(CHAN) CHAN8808   Early 20th Century English
  Music
(CHAN) CHAN8818   Bliss—Vocal and Orchestral
  works
(CHAN) CHAN8861   Stanford: Orchestral Works
(CHAN) CHAN8884   Stanford—Orchestral Works
  cond B. THOMSON
Bax: Symphony 4, Tintagel
Harty: Children of Lir, Comedy overture, Irish
  Symphony, Ode to a Nightingale, Variations on a
  Dublin Air, Violin Concerto
  see CONCERT INDEX under:
(CHAN) CHAN6538   Seascapes
(CHAN) CHAN6583   Harty—Orchestral Works
(CHAN) CHAN8301   The Special Sound of Chandos
(CHAN) CHAN8307   Bax—Tone Poems
(CHAN) CHAN8318   Elgar—Music inspired by
  children
(CHAN) CHAN8321   Harty—Orchestral Works
(CHAN) CHAN8367   Bax—Tone Poems Vol 2
(CHAN) CHAN9168   Bax—Orchestral Works
  cond Y. P. TORTELIER
Debussy: Après-midi, Boîte à joujoux
Ravel: Daphnis et Chloé (Cpte), Ma mère l'oye
  (Cpte)
Saint-Saëns: Symphony 2, Symphony 3
  see CONCERT INDEX under:
(CHAN) CHAN8735   Berlioz & Duparc: Songs
(CHAN) CHAN8850   Debussy & Ravel: Orchestral
  Works
(CHAN) CHAN8852   French Orchestral Works
(CHAN) CHAN8903   Debussy & Ravel—Orchestral
  Works
(CHAN) CHAN8914   Debussy and Ravel—Vocal and
  Orchestral Works
(CHAN) CHAN8952   Chausson & Fauré—Vocal and
  Orchestral Works
(CHAN) CHAN8972   Debussy & Ravel—Orchestral
  works
(CHAN) CHAN9023   20th Century French Orchestral
  Works

(CHAN) CHAN9114   Debussy/Ravel—Orchestral
  Works
(CHAN) CHAN9129   Debussy/Ravel—Orchestral
  Works

UMBACH, Adolf (cl)
  see CONCERT INDEX under:
(CLRI) CC0005   The Clarinet - Historical Recordings,
  Vol.1

UMEÅ SINFONIETTA
  cond J.-P. SARASTE
  see CONCERT INDEX under:
(BIS) BIS-CD288   Vañhal: Orchestral works

UNANDER-SCHARIN, Carl (ten)
Lidholm: Dream Play (Cpte)

UNGÁR, Tamás (pf)
Conyngham: Southern Cross
  see CONCERT INDEX under:
(CALA) CACD1012   Mussorgsky—Orchestral Works

UNGER, Gerhard (ten)
Humperdinck: Königskinder (Cpte)
Millöcker: Bettelstudent (Cpte)
Mozart: Entführung (Cpte), Finta Giardiniera (Cpte)
Offenbach: Vie Parisienne (exc)
Orff: Carmina Burana
R. Strauss: Ariadne auf Naxos (Cpte), Elektra (Cpte),
  Rosenkavalier (Cpte)
Wagner: Meistersinger (Cpte), Tannhäuser (Cpte)
Zeller: Vogelhändler (Cpte)
  see CONCERT INDEX under:
(EMI) CHS7 63715-2   Mozart: Die Entführung, etc

UNGER, Heinz (cond)
see CBC SO

UNGROVÁ, Markéta (sop)
  see CONCERT INDEX under:
(SUPR) 11 1878-2   The Unknown Janáček

UNICORN ENSEMBLE
  see CONCERT INDEX under:
(NAXO) 8 553131   Chominciamento di gioia

UNTERZAUCHER, Wolfgang (spkr)
Mendelssohn: Antigone (Cpte), Oedipus (Cpte)

UNWIN, Roderick (treb)
  see CONCERT INDEX under:
(HYPE) CDA66126   Britten: Choral Works

UPPSALA ACADEMIC CHAMBER CHOIR
  cond O. KAMU
Schnittke: Symphony 4
  cond S. PARKMAN
Schnittke: Requiem

UPSHAW, Dawn (sop)
Bach: Magnificat, BWV243
Canteloube: Chants d'Auvergne (exc)
Donizetti: Elisir d'amore (Cpte)
Gershwin: Oh, Kay! (Cpte)
Górecki: Symphony 3
Haydn: Creation (Cpte)
M-A. Charpentier: Magnificat, H74, Te Deum, H146
Massenet: Chérubin (Cpte)
Mozart: Finta Giardiniera (Cpte), Lucio Silla (Cpte),
  Nozze di Figaro (Cpte), Zauberflöte (Cpte)
R. Strauss: Ariadne auf Naxos (Cpte)
Schubert: Mass, D167
Vivaldi: Gloria, RV589
  see CONCERT INDEX under:
(AUVI) MO782024   Schoenberg—String Quartets
(NONE) 7559-79249-2   American Elegies
(NONE) 7559-79262-2   Dawn Upshaw-The girl with
  orange lips
(NONE) 7559-79317-2   Goethe Lieder
(NONE) 7559-79345-2   I Wish It So - Dawn Upshaw
(NONE) 7559-79362-2   Górecki—Orchestral and Vocal
  Works
(SONY) SK58952   Debussy—Orchestral and Vocal
  Works

URAY, Malthias (treb)
Mozart: Zauberflöte (Cpte)

URBAN, Johannes (bass)
R. Strauss: Rosenkavalier (Cpte)

URBANEK, Pavel (cond)
see Prague Fest Orch

URBANOVÁ, Eva (sop)
Smetana: Dalibor (Cpte)

URBANOVÁ, Vlasta (sop)
Hába: Mother (Cpte)

URBAS, Ivan (bass)
Puccini: Bohème (Cpte)
  see CONCERT INDEX under:
(HARM) HMC980 1420   Weill—The Seven Deadly Sins;
  Songs

URIA-MONZON, Béatrice (mez)
Bizet: Carmen (Cpte)
Franck: Rédemption
Prokofiev: Love for 3 Oranges (Cpte)
  see CONCERT INDEX under:
(NAXO) 8 553196   Duruflé—Sacred Choral and Organ
  Works, Volume 1

URIARTE, Begoña (pf)
  see CONCERT INDEX under:
(WERG) WER60131-50   Ligeti: Piano Works

URIBE, Maria Teresa (mez)
Shore: M. Butterfly (exc)

URIDGE, Michael (cond)
see London Musica Antiqua

URITSKY, Vyacheslav (vn)
see CONCERT INDEX under:
(NORT) **NR227-CD** American Chamber Music with Flute

URLUS, Jacques (ten)
see CONCERT INDEX under:
(PEAR) **GEMMCDS9925(1)** Covent Garden on Record—Vol.3 (pt 1)

UROBOROS ENSEMBLE
cond M. FINNISSY
see CONCERT INDEX under:
(ETCE) **KTC1096** Finnissy—Chamber Works

URQUHART, Peter (cond)
see Capella Alamire

URREY, Frederick (ten)
Handel: Siroe, Rè di Persia (Cpte)
Rorem: Three Sisters Who Are Not Sisters (Cpte)
see CONCERT INDEX under:
(NEWP) **NPD85540** Handel/Bononcini—Muzio Scevola
(RCA) **09026 60970-2** Motets

URSULEAC, Viorica (sop)
see CONCERT INDEX under:
(PREI) **89035** Erna Berger (1900-1990) - I
(SCHW) **314502** Vienna State Opera—Live Recordings (sampler)
(SCHW) **314512** Vienna State Opera Live, Vol.1
(SCHW) **314552** Vienna State Opera Live, Vol.5
(SCHW) **314562** Vienna State Opera Live, Vol.6
(SCHW) **314602** Vienna State Opera Live, Vol.10
(SCHW) **314642** Vienna State Opera Live, Vol.14
(SCHW) **314652** Vienna State Opera Live, Vol.15
(SCHW) **314662** Vienna State Opera Live, Vol.16

US TV CAST
Berlin: Annie get your Gun (Cpte)

USBECK, Mathias (treb)
Fauré: Requiem (Cpte)

USSR ACADEMY SYMPHONY ORCHESTRA
cond A. LAZAREV
Schoenberg: Violin Concerto
cond E. SHACHNAZARIYA
see CONCERT INDEX under:
(OLYM) **OCD5001** Glazunov—Orchestral Works
cond E. SVETLANOV
Khachaturian: Violin Concerto
see CONCERT INDEX under:
(OLYM) **OCD129** Lyapunov: Orchestral Works

USSR ACADEMY SYMPHONY ORCHESTRA SOLOISTS ENSEMBLE
cond G. ROZHDESTVENSKY
see CONCERT INDEX under:
(OLYM) **OCD194** Shostakovich: Vocal & Orchestral Works

USSR CINEMA SYMPHONY ORCHESTRA
cond E. KHACHATURIAN
Shostakovich: Gadfly Suite
see CONCERT INDEX under:
(OLYM) **OCD296** Moscow Contemporary Music Ensemble - Volume 5
cond V. PONKIN
see CONCERT INDEX under:
(OLYM) **OCD296** Moscow Contemporary Music Ensemble - Volume 5
cond S. REDWINE
see CONCERT INDEX under:
(STAN) **STZ112** Victor Young—For Whom the Bell Tolls

USSR MINISTRY OF CULTURE CHAMBER CHOIR
cond G. ROZHDESTVENSKY
see CONCERT INDEX under:
(OLYM) **OCD212** Honegger: Orchestral Works

USSR MINISTRY OF CULTURE CHORUS
cond G. ROZHDESTVENSKY
see CONCERT INDEX under:
(OLYM) **OCD194** Shostakovich: Vocal & Orchestral Works

USSR MINISTRY OF CULTURE STATE SYMPHONY ORCHESTRA
cond G. ROZHDESTVENSKY
Glazunov: Symphony 1, Symphony 7

USSR MINISTRY OF CULTURE SYMPHONY ORCHESTRA
cond G. ROZHDESTVENSKY
Miaskovsky: Symphony 1
Mussorgsky: Marriage (Cpte)
Shostakovich: Golden Hills Suite, Symphony 1, Symphony 3, Symphony 6, Symphony 10, Symphony 12, Symphony 13, Symphony 14
Tchaikovsky: Romeo and Juliet, Symphony 4
Tishchenko: Symphony 5
see CONCERT INDEX under:
(OLYM) **OCD130** Glazunov: Orchestral Works
(OLYM) **OCD194** Shostakovich: Vocal & Orchestral Works
(OLYM) **OCD212** Honegger: Orchestral Works
(OLYM) **OCD5001** Glazunov—Orchestral Works

USSR RADIO CHORUS
cond E. SVETLANOV
Scriabin: Symphony 1

USSR RADIO SYMPHONY ORCHESTRA SOLOISTS ENSEMBLE
cond A. KORNEIEV
see CONCERT INDEX under:
(OLYM) **OCD165** Glazunov: Concertos

USSR RADIO SYMPHONY ORCHESTRA
cond O. DIMITRIEDI
see CONCERT INDEX under:
(OLYM) **OCD130** Glazunov: Orchestral Works
(OLYM) **OCD5001** Glazunov—Orchestral Works
cond V. FEDOSEYEV
Scriabin: Symphony 1
Tchaikovsky: Swan Lake (Cpte)
cond Y. NIKOLAEVSKY
see CONCERT INDEX under:
(OLYM) **OCD165** Glazunov: Concertos
cond G. ROZHDESTVENSKY
see CONCERT INDEX under:
(OLYM) **OCD5001** Glazunov—Orchestral Works

USSR STATE ACADEMIC CHOIR
cond K. KONDRASHIN
Shostakovich: Symphony 13

USSR SYMPHONY ORCHESTRA
cond K. KONDRASHIN
Miaskovsky: Symphony 6
Mozart: Piano Concerto 21
Tchaikovsky: Piano Concerto 2
cond D. OISTRAKH
Shostakovich: Symphony 9
cond E. SVETLANOV
Scriabin: Poème de l'extase, Symphony 1
Shostakovich: Symphony 1
Tchaikovsky: Festival Overture, Francesca da Rimini, Manfred Symphony, Piano Concerto 2, Romeo and Juliet, Serenade, Op.48, Symphony 1, Symphony 2, Symphony 3, Symphony 5, Tempest
see CONCERT INDEX under:
(MELO) **74321 17095-2** Tchaikovsky—Orchestral Works
(MELO) **74321 17097-2** Tchaikovsky—Orchestral Works
(MELO) **74321 17101-2** Tchaikovsky—Symphonies, etc

USSR TV AND RADIO LARGE ORCHESTRA
cond A. DMITRIEV
see CONCERT INDEX under:
(MEZH) **MK417087** Russian Piano Concertos
cond V. FEDOSEYEV
see CONCERT INDEX under:
(CDM) **LDC288 004** Ciurlionis—Orchestral & Chamber Works
cond D. KABALEVSKY
see CONCERT INDEX under:
(OLYM) **OCD269** Kabalevsky—Volume 4
cond G. ROZHDESTVENSKY
see CONCERT INDEX under:
(MEZH) **MK417087** Russian Piano Concertos
(RUSS) **RDCD11104** Elgar/Milhaud/Respighi—Works for Cello & Orchestra

USSR TV AND RADIO SYMPHONY ORCHESTRA
cond M. SHOSTAKOVICH
Vainberg: Symphony 12

USTINOV, Sir Peter (narr)
see CONCERT INDEX under:
(DECC) **443 488-2DF2** Kodály—Háry János; Psalmus Hungaricus etc
(PHIL) **438 973-2PM2** Igor Markevitch conducts Stravinsky

USTINOVA, Elena (sop)
Rachmaninov: Bells

UTAH SYMPHONY ORCHESTRA
cond M. ABRAVANEL
Goldmark: Rustic Wedding
Milhaud: Homme et son désir, Pacem in Terris
see CONCERT INDEX under:
(VANG) **08.4030.71** Satie—Ballet and Orchestral Music
(VANG) **08.4051.71** Gottschalk—Piano Works, Vol.2
cond E. BERNSTEIN
E. Bernstein: Comancheros (exc), True Grit (exc)
cond V. KOJIAN
Korngold: Adventures of Robin Hood (exc)
cond J. RUDEL
see CONCERT INDEX under:
(DECC) **436 402-2DWO** The World of Wedding Music
cond J. SILVERSTEIN
see CONCERT INDEX under:
(HARM) **HMU90 7124** Perle/Danielpour—Piano Works

UTAH UNIVERSITY CHORUS
cond M. ABRAVANEL
Milhaud: Pacem in Terris

UTIGER, Mary (vn)
see CONCERT INDEX under:
(DHM) **RD77201** Telemann—Wind Concertos

UTKIN, Alexei (ob)
see CONCERT INDEX under:
(RCA) **RD60240** Vivaldi—Orchestral and Choral works
(RCA) **RD60370** Modern Portraits
(RCA) **RD87948** Haydn: Concertos
(RCA) **RD87991** Bach: Concerti

UTRECHT, Aleksandra (pf)
see CONCERT INDEX under:

(OLYM) **OCD392** Bacewicz—Orchestral and Chamber Works

UVA, Antonio d' (ten)
Rossini: Donna del Lago (Cpte)

UYS, Johanna (sop)
see CONCERT INDEX under:
(CLAR) **CDGSE78-50-54** Coates conducts Wagner, Weber & Mendelssohn

VACCHIANO, William (tpt)
see CONCERT INDEX under:
(SONY) **MPK44850** Shostakovich: Concertos
(SONY) **SMK47618** Poulenc/Shostakovich—Piano Concertos

VACELLIER, André (cl)
see CONCERT INDEX under:
(EMI) **CDS7 54607-2** Stravinsky plays and conducts Stravinsky

VACIK, Jan (ten)
Puccini: Fanciulla del West (Cpte)

VÁCZI, Zoltan (perc)
see CONCERT INDEX under:
(DECC) **443 894-2DH** Bartók—Chamber Works

VADUVA, Leontina (sop)
Bizet: Carmen (Cpte)
Verdi: Rigoletto (Cpte)

VÁGHELYI, Gábor (bar)
Giordano: Andrea Chénier (Cpte)

VAGHI, Giacomo (bass)
Verdi: Forza del destino (exc)

VAGLIERI, Paolo (cond)
see Milan CO

VAHLE, Petra (va)
see CONCERT INDEX under:
(BIS) **BIS-CD518** Denisov—Orchestral & Chamber Works
(BIS) **BIS-CD541/2** Tubin—The Complete Music for Violin, Viola and Piano

VAIDMAN, Vera (vn)
see CONCERT INDEX under:
(CARL) **PWK1137** Romantic Strings

VAILLANT, Ludovic (tpt)
see CONCERT INDEX under:
(EMI) **CDC7 54606-2** Shostakovich plays Shostakovich

VAINBERG, Moishei (pf)
Vainberg: Piano Quintet, Op. 18

VÄINMAA, Lauri (pf)
see CONCERT INDEX under:
(FINL) **4509-95704-2** Estonian Piano Music

VAJDA, József (bn)
see CONCERT INDEX under:
(NAXO) **8 550511** Mozart/Beethoven—Quintets for Piano and Wind etc
(NAXO) **8 553090** Beethoven—Chamber Works

VAJDA, Otto (bass)
R. Strauss: Rosenkavalier (Cpte)

VAJNAR, František (cond)
see Brno Janáček Op Orch

VAKARELIS, Janis (pf)
Liszt: Piano Concerto 2
Prokofiev: Piano Concerto 3

VALADE, Pierre-André (fl)
see CONCERT INDEX under:
(DG) **445 833-2GH** Boulez conducts Boulez

VALAITIS, Vladimir (bar)
Kabalevsky: Requiem
Tchaikovsky: Queen of Spades (Cpte)

VALÁSKOVÁ, Jana (sop)
Bellini: Sonnambula (Cpte)
Brian: Symphony 4
Respighi: Primavera
Suchoň: Whirlpool (Cpte)

VALDENASSI, Cecilia (sop)
Rossini: Donna del Lago (Cpte)

VALDENGO, Giuseppe (bar)
Donizetti: Don Pasquale (Cpte)
Verdi: Otello (Cpte)
see CONCERT INDEX under:
(EMI) **CHS7 69741-2(7)** Record of Singing, Vol.4—Italian School
(RCA) **GD60326** Verdi—Operas & Choral Works
(RCA) **09026 61580-2(6)** RCA/Met 100 Singers, 100 Years (pt 6)

VALDEPEÑAS, Joaquin (cl)
see CONCERT INDEX under:
(CBC) **MVCD1053** Schubert—Lieder

VALDES, Maximiano (cond)
see LSO

VÁLEK, Jiří (fl)
see CONCERT INDEX under:
(SUPR) **11 1533-2** Suk—Chamber Works, Volume 3

VÁLEK, Roman (cond)
see Baroque 1994 Ens

VÁLEK, Vladimír (cond)
see Dvořák CO

VALENCIA CHOIR
cond J. PONS
see CONCERT INDEX *under:*
(HARM) **HMC90 1482** Mompou—Vocal and
Orchestral Works

VALENCIA ORCHESTRA
cond M. GALDUF
Albéniz: Concierto fantástico, op.78, Iberia

VALENCIA PEQUEÑOS CANTORES
cond E. COLOMER
Falla: Atlántida (Cpte)

VALENCIA VOCAL ENSEMBLE
cond J-F. PAILLARD
Rameau: Indes Galantes (Cpte)

VALENCIN, Anne (sop)
see CONCERT INDEX *under:*
(EPM) **150 122** Milhaud—Historic Recordings 1928-
1948

VALENTA, Leopold (bass)
Mozart: Zauberflöte (Cpte)

VALENTA, Mira (contr)
see CONCERT INDEX *under:*
(ACCE) **ACC8864D** Symphonia Angelica

VALENTE, Benita (sop)
Gerhard: Cancionero de Pedrell, Shahrazada
Mahler: Symphony 2
Schubert: Mass, D950
Vaughan Williams: Symphony 1

VALENTE, Valentina (sop)
Mussorgsky: Boris Godunov (Cpte)

VALENTIK, Jan (spkr)
Suchoň: Whirlpool (Cpte)

VALENTINE, Timothy (cor ang)
see CONCERT INDEX *under:*
(NORT) **NR211-CD** Krebs: Chorale Preludes and
Fantasias

VALENTINE, Timothy (ob)
see CONCERT INDEX *under:*
(NORT) **NR211-CD** Krebs: Chorale Preludes and
Fantasias

VALENTINI, Fernando (bar)
see CONCERT INDEX *under:*
(EMI) **CMS7 64165-2** Puccini—Trittico

VALENTINI, Massimo (bass)
Salieri: Axur (Cpte)

VALENTINI, Romano (pf)
see CONCERT INDEX *under:*
(DENO) **CO-75448** Berio—Duets for Two Violins,
Volume 1

VALENTINO, Frank (bar)
Puccini: Bohème (exc)

VALENTINO, Stefano (bass)
Rossini: Barbiere di Siviglia (exc)

VALERO, Fernando (ten)
see CONCERT INDEX *under:*
(EMI) **CHS7 64860-2(1)** La Scala Edition - Vol.1,
1878-1914 (pt 1)
(MEMO) **HR4408/9(1)** Singers in Genoa, Vol.1 (disc
1)
(PEAR) **GEMMCDS9923(2)** Covent Garden on
Record, Vol.1 (pt 2)
(SYMP) **SYMCD1073** The Harold Wayne Collection,
Vol.3

VALETTI, Pablo (vn)
see CONCERT INDEX *under:*
(HARM) **HMC90 1505** German Baroque Songs

VALJAKKA, Taru (sop)
Shostakovich: Lady Macbeth of Mtsensk (Cpte)

VÁLKA, Josef (ten)
Janáček: Šárka (Cpte)

VÄLKKI, Anita (sop)
Madetoja: Juha (Cpte)
Wagner: Götterdämmerung (Cpte)
see CONCERT INDEX *under:*
(DECC) **414 100-2DM15** Wagner: Der Ring des
Nibelungen

VALLECILLO, Irma (pf)
see CONCERT INDEX *under:*
(ALBA) **TROY036-2** S.Paulus—Songs

VALLETTI, Cesare (ten)
Berlioz: Enfance du Christ (Cpte)
Donizetti: Linda di Chamounix (Cpte)
Puccini: Madama Butterfly (Cpte)
Rossini: Barbiere di Siviglia (Cpte), Italiana in Algeri
(Cpte)
(RCA) **09026 61580-2(6)** RCA/Met 100 Singers, 100
Years (pt 6)

VALLIER, Régine (mez)
Lecocq: Rose Mousse (Cpte)

VALLIN, Marie-Claude (sop)
see CONCERT INDEX *under:*
(ARIO) **ARN68015** Charpentier—Sacred Choral works
(SONY) **SK53368** Haydn—Sacred Music

VALLIN, Ninon (sop)
Massenet: Werther (exc)
Puccini: Tosca (exc)
see CONCERT INDEX *under:*

(EMI) **CDC7 54836-2** Granados/Falla/Mompou/Nin
(MMOI) **CDMOIR408** Great Sopranos

VALSTA, Tapani (pf)
see CONCERT INDEX *under:*
(BIS) **BIS-CD458** Kokkonen—Chamber Works

VALTA, Jan (cond)
see Žilina St CO

VALTASAARI, Tapani (bass)
Madetoja: Juha (Cpte)

VALTRIANI, Jeda (sop)
see CONCERT INDEX *under:*
(DECC) **411 665-2DM3** Puccini: Il trittico

VAN, Billy B. (sngr)
see CONCERT INDEX *under:*
(PEAR) **GEMMCDS9056/8** Music from the New York
Stage, Vol. 3: 1913-17

VAN & SCHENCK (sngrs)
see CONCERT INDEX *under:*
(PEAR) **GEMMCDS9056/8** Music from the New York
Stage, Vol. 3: 1913-17
(PEAR) **GEMMCDS9059/61** Music from the New York
Stage, Vol. 4: 1917-20

VAN ALLAN, Richard (bass)
Berlioz: Damnation de Faust (Cpte), Enfance du
Christ (Cpte)
Boughton: Bethlehem (Cpte)
Britten: Gloriana (Cpte), Peter Grimes (Cpte)
Cavalli: Ormindo (Cpte)
Donizetti: Lucrezia Borgia (Cpte)
Forrest/Wright: Kismet (Cpte), Song of Norway
(Cpte)
Mendelssohn: Erste Walpurgisnacht
Mozart: Così fan tutte (Cpte), Don Giovanni (Cpte)
Offenbach: Contes d'Hoffmann (Cpte)
Puccini: Tosca (Cpte)
Rossini: Guillaume Tell (Cpte)
Sullivan: HMS Pinafore (Cpte), Mikado (Cpte), Pirates
of Penzance (Cpte)
Tchaikovsky: Eugene Onegin (Cpte)
Vaughan Williams: Hugh the Drover (Cpte)
Verdi: Ballo in maschera (Cpte), Forza del destino
(Cpte), Luisa Miller (Cpte), Traviata (Cpte), Vespri
Siciliani (Cpte)
Walton: Troilus and Cressida (Cpte)
see CONCERT INDEX *under:*
(DECC) **433 439-2DA** Great Love Duets

VAN ALLAN, Richard (narr)
Berlioz: Béatrice et Bénédict (Cpte)

VAN BAASBANK, Adrian (bar)
Mozart: Lucio Silla (Cpte)

VAN BLERK, Gérard (pf)
see CONCERT INDEX *under:*
(BAYE) **BR100009** Ravel—Vocal & Chamber Works

VAN BOS, Coenraad (pf)
see CONCERT INDEX *under:*
(PEAR) **GEMMCDS9075** Hugo Wolf Society, Volume I
(PEAR) **GEMMCDS9085** Hugo Wolf Society, Volume
II
(RCA) **09026 61879-2** Grieg—Historic Recordings
(ROMO) **81014-2** Elisabeth Rethberg (1894-1976)

VAN BUREN, Gene (sngr)
see CONCERT INDEX *under:*
(PHIL) **446 406-2PH** Berlin—Heat Wave

VAN DAM, José (bass-bar)
Beethoven: Fidelio (Cpte), Missa Solemnis,
Symphony 9
Berlioz: Damnation de Faust (Cpte), Enfance du
Christ (Cpte)
Bizet: Carmen (exc), Jolie fille de Perth (Cpte)
Brahms: Deutsches Requiem, Op. 45 (Cpte)
Debussy: Pelléas et Mélisande (Cpte), Rodrigue et
Chimène (Cpte)
Duruflé: Requiem
Fauré: Pénélope (Cpte), Requiem (Cpte)
G. Charpentier: Louise (Cpte)
Gluck: Iphigénie en Aulide (Cpte)
Gounod: Faust (Cpte), Mors et Vita (Cpte), Roméo et
Juliette (Cpte)
Haydn: Schöpfung (Cpte)
Mahler: Symphony 8
Massenet: Don Quichotte (Cpte), Manon (Cpte)
Mendelssohn: Elias (Cpte)
Messiaen: Saint François d'Assise (Cpte)
Mozart: Così fan tutte (Cpte), Don Giovanni (Cpte),
Mass, K317, Nozze di Figaro (Cpte), Requiem,
Zauberflöte (Cpte)
Offenbach: Contes d'Hoffmann (Cpte)
Poulenc: Dialogues des Carmélites (Cpte)
R. Strauss: Frau ohne Schatten (Cpte), Salome
(Cpte), Salomé (Cpte)
Rameau: Dardanus (Cpte)
Ravel: Heure espagnole (Cpte)
Roussel: Padmâvatî (Cpte)
Schubert: Schwanengesang, D957 (Cpte)
Verdi: Aida (Cpte), Ballo in maschera (Cpte), Don
Carlo (Cpte), Otello (Cpte), Requiem (Cpte), Simon
Boccanegra (Cpte)
Wagner: Fliegende Holländer (Cpte), Parsifal (Cpte)
see CONCERT INDEX *under:*
(DG) **435 162-2GX13** Mahler—Complete
Symphonies
(EMI) **CDC7 49288-2** José van Dam sings French
Songs
(EMI) **CDC7 54818-2** Mélodies, Volume 2
(EMIL) **CDZ7 67015-2** Mozart—Opera Arias

(ERAT) **2292-45923-2** Bach/Vivaldi—Sacred Choral
Works
(FORL) **UCD16681** The Great Italian Arias
(FORL) **UCD16692** Duparc—Mélodies
(NOVA) **150 014-2** Mozart—Gala Concert
(SONY) **SMK64107** Ravel/Roussel—Vocal &
Orchestral Works
(VIRG) **VC7 59236-2** French Songs

VAN DE VOORDE, Oliver (treb)
Puccini: Gianni Schicchi (Cpte)

VAN DER GUCHT, Jan (ten)
see CONCERT INDEX *under:*
(DUTT) **CDLX7011** Beecham conducts Delius

VAN DER MEEL, Nico (ten)
Bach: Mass in B minor, BWV232 (Cpte), St. John
Passion, BWV245 (Cpte)
Landi: Mort d'Orfeo (Cpte)
Mendelssohn: Hochzeit des Camacho (Cpte)
Monteverdi: Vespers
Mozart: Don Giovanni (Cpte)

VAN DER PAS, Theo (pf)
see CONCERT INDEX *under:*
(BIDD) **LAB011** Brahms—Historic Chamber Music
Recordings
(EMI) **CDH7 64250-2** Emmanuel Feuermann -
Recital
(PEAR) **GEMMCD9443** Feuermann—The Columbia
Records, Vol.2

VAN DEYCK, Lucienne (contr)
Puccini: Manon Lescaut (Cpte), Suor Angelica
(Cpte)

VAN DOESELAAR, Leo (organ)
Bach: Cantata 35, Cantata 170
Fauré: Messe des Pêcheurs de Villerville, Requiem
(Cpte)
Rossini: Petite messe solennelle
see CONCERT INDEX *under:*
(DECC) **433 816-2DH2** Hindemith—Kammermusik
(ETCE) **KTC1054** Ravel. Music for Piano, Four
Hands
(ETCE) **KTC2003-1** W.F. Bach: Organ Works Vol. 1
(ETCE) **KTC2003-2** W.F. Bach: Complete Organ
Music Vol. II

VAN DOESELAAR, Leo (pf)
Dvořák: Legends, Op. 59

VAN DYCK, Ernest (ten)
see CONCERT INDEX *under:*
(SYMP) **SYMCD1172** The Harold Wayne Collection,
Vol.21

VAN DYCK, Stephan (ten)
Rameau: Hippolyte et Aricie (Cpte)

VAN EETVELDT, Frans (bass)
Puccini: Gianni Schicchi (Cpte)

VAN EVERA, Emily (sop)
Bach: Cantata 4, Easter Oratorio, BWV249, Mass in
B minor, BWV232 (Cpte)
Blow: Venus and Adonis (Cpte)
Handel: Israel in Egypt (Cpte), Messiah (Cpte)
Purcell: Dido (Cpte)
see CONCERT INDEX *under:*
(ASV) **CDGAU122** Venice Preserved
(BIS) **BIS-CD341** Music for Lute
(EMI) **CDC7 47998-2** Una Stravanganza dei Medici -
Florentine Intermedi (ed. Keyte)
(EMI) **CDC7 54117-2** Venetian Church Music
(EMI) **CDC7 49749-2** Handel—Music for the Carmelite
Vespers
(HARM) **HMC90 5192** As I went to Walsingham
(UNIC) **DKPCD9124** D.Scarlatti—Cantatas, Vol.3
(VIRG) **VC5 45159-2** Purcell—Come ye sons of art
(VIRG) **VC7 59326-2** Vivaldi—Sacred Choral Works
(VIRG) **VC7 59534-2** In the Streets and Theatres of
London

VAN GIJSEGEM, Ludwig (ten)
Puccini: Manon Lescaut (Cpte)
see CONCERT INDEX *under:*
(RICE) **RIC052034** Charpentier—Sacred Choral
Works

VAN GORP, Jean (bar)
Berlioz: Lélio (Cpte)

VAN KAMPEN, Christopher (vc)
Fauré: Piano Trio
Górecki: Lerchenmusik
Krause: Quatuor pour la Naissance
Messiaen: Quatuor
see CONCERT INDEX *under:*
(COLL) **Coll7039-2** Britten—The Folk Songs
(CRD) **CRD3446** Ravel: Chamber works
(DECC) **440 032-2DM** Monteverdi/Gesualdo—Motets
and Madrigals
(EMI) **CDM7 64130-2** Christmas Music from King's
(HYPE) **CDA66171** Malcolm Arnold: Chamber Works,
Vol. 1
(HYPE) **CDA66173** Malcolm Arnold: Chamber Works,
Vol. 3
(LARG) **Largo 5125** Kurt Schwertsik—Für Christa
(NMC) **NMCD009** Birtwistle—Choral and Orchestral
Works
(NMC) **NMCD024M** Turnage—Vocal and Chamber
Works
(VIRG) **VC5 45016-2** Ravel—Chamber & Vocal Works
(VIRG) **VC7 59604-2** Debussy—Chamber Works

VAN KEMPEN, Paul (cond)
see BPO

VAN MILL, Arnold (bass)
Verdi: Aida (Cpte)
Wagner: Meistersinger (Cpte), Parsifal (Cpte)

VAN ROOY, Anton (bass-bar)
see CONCERT INDEX under:
(PEAR) **GEMMCDS9923(2)** Covent Garden on
Record, Vol.1 (pt 2)
(SYMP) **SYMCD1100** Harold Wayne Collection,
Vol.8

VAN TULDER, Louis (ten)
Beethoven: Symphony 9

VAN WERING, Janny (hpd)
see CONCERT INDEX under:
(TELD) **4509-97452-2** Bach—Harpsichord Concertos

VAN ZWEDEN, Jaap (vn)
Schnittke: Concerto grosso 3, Concerto grosso 4
see CONCERT INDEX under:
(SONY) **SK53265** Vivaldi—Violin Concertos

VANBRUGH QUARTET
see CONCERT INDEX under:
(ASV) **CDDCA915** Dohnányi—Piano Quintets
(CHAN) **CHAN9295** Contemporary Irish String
Quartets
(COLL) **Coll1381-2** Dvořák/Janáček—String
Quartets
(HYPE) **CDA66626** Simpson—Chamber Works

VANCONTI, Carlotta (sop)
see CONCERT INDEX under:
(PEAR) **GEMMCD9310** Franz Lehár conducts Richard
Tauber

VANCOUVER SYMPHONY ORCHESTRA
cond R. BARSHAI
Mussorgsky: Night on the bare mountain
Tchaikovsky: Symphony 6

VANDEN EYNDEN, Jean-Claude (pf)
Franck: Auber Variations, Piano Concerto

VANDENBURG, Howard (ten)
Mozart: Zauberflöte (Cpte)

VANDERLINDE, Debra (sop)
V. Thomson: Lord Byron (Cpte)

VANDERNOOT, André (cond)
see Philh

VANDERSTEENE, Zeger (ten)
Lekeu: Andromède
see CONCERT INDEX under:
(PHIL) **434 799-2PH** Mozart—Choral Works

VANDERWAL, David (ten)
Pärt: Berliner Messe

VANDEVILLE, Jacques (ob)
see CONCERT INDEX under:
(ACCO) **20202-2** Poulenc—Chamber Works
(ARIO) **ARN68071** Sauget—Vocal and orchestral
works
(ERAT) **2292-45772-2** Saint-Saëns—Works for
Chamber Ensemble

VANE, Doris (sop)
Gounod: Faust (Cpte)
see CONCERT INDEX under:
(SYMP) **SYMCD1130** Joseph Holbrooke—Historic
Recordings

VANELLI, Gino (bar)
(CLUB) **CL99-014** Dino Borgioli (1891-1960)
(PREI) **89026** Francesco Merli (1887-1976) - I

VANESS, Carol (sop)
Beethoven: Missa Solemnis, Symphony 9
Gluck: Iphigénie en Tauride (Cpte)
Mozart: Clemenza di Tito (Cpte), Così fan tutte
(Cpte), Don Giovanni (Cpte), Nozze di Figaro (Cpte)
Puccini: Tosca (Cpte)
Verdi: Requiem (Cpte)
see CONCERT INDEX under:
(EMI) **CDC7 54329-2** Domingo sings Mozart Arias
(EMI) **CDH5 65072-2** Glyndebourne Recorded - 1934-
1994
(EMIL) **CDZ7 67015-2** Mozart—Opera Arias
(RCA) **09026 61509-2** A Salute to American Music

VANESSA-MAE (vn)
Beethoven: Violin Concerto
Tchaikovsky: Violin Concerto

VANGELIS, Odyssey Papathanassiou (kybds)
see CONCERT INDEX under:
(PHIL) **416 698-2PH** Encore! Travels with my cello,
Vol. 2

VANHECKE, François (sop)
Rameau: Pygmalion (Cpte)

VANHOVE, Frank (fl)
see CONCERT INDEX under:
(MARC) **8 223741** Maes—Orchestral Works

VANNI, Helen (mez)
V. Thomson: Mother of us all (Cpte)

VANNI-MARCOUX (bass)
see CONCERT INDEX under:
(CLUB) **CL99-101** Vanni Marcoux (1877-1962)
(PEAR) **GEMMCDS9924(2)** Covent Garden on
Record, Vol.2 (pt 2)

VANNUCCINI, Enrico (bass)
see CONCERT INDEX under:

(IRCC) **IRCC-CD808** Souvenirs of 19th Century Italian
Opera

VÄNSKÄ, Osmo (cond)
see Lahti Chbr Ens

VANTIN, Martin (ten)
Mozart: Entführung (Cpte), Nozze di Figaro (Cpte),
Zauberflöte (Cpte)
Wagner: Meistersinger (Cpte), Tristan und Isolde
(Cpte)

VANTONI, Carlotta (sop)
see CONCERT INDEX under:
(EMI) **CDH7 69787-2** Richard Tauber sings Operetta
Arias

VANZO, Alain (ten)
Bizet: Pêcheurs de Perles (Cpte)
Delibes: Lakmé (Cpte)
Fauré: Pénélope (Cpte)
Offenbach: Périchole (Cpte)

VARADY, Julia (sop)
Bartók: Duke Bluebeard's Castle (Cpte)
Beethoven: Missa solemnis (Cpte), Symphony 9
Cimarosa: Matrimonio segreto (Cpte)
Halévy: Juive (Cpte)
Mascagni: Cavalleria Rusticana (Cpte)
Meyerbeer: Amori di Teolinda
Mozart: Clemenza di Tito (Cpte), Idomeneo (Cpte),
Lucio Silla (Cpte), Nozze di Figaro (Cpte)
R.Strauss: Arabella (Cpte), Ariadne auf Naxos (Cpte),
Frau ohne Schatten (Cpte)
Shostakovich: Symphony 14
Spohr: Jessonda (Cpte)
Spontini: Olimpie (Cpte)
see CONCERT INDEX under:
(ACAN) **43 266** Bernd Weikl—Operatic Recital
(DECC) **425 681-2DM2** Tutto Pavarotti
(ORFE) **C053851A** Tchaikovsky: Songs
(ORFE) **C103841A** Spohr: Lieder
(ORFE) **C248921A** Mozart/Strauss—Lieder
(ORFE) **C323941A** Puccini—Famous Opera Arias

VARCOE, Stephen (bar)
A. Scarlatti: Dixit Dominus II
Bach: Cantata 140, Cantata 147, Mass in B minor,
BWV232 (Cpte), St John Passion, BWV245 (Cpte)
Blow: Venus and Adonis (Cpte)
C. P. E. Bach: Auferstehung und Himmelfahrt Jesu
(Cpte)
Campra: Messe de Requiem
Handel: Alessandro (Cpte), Alexander's Feast (Cpte),
Allegro, il penseroso ed il moderato (Cpte), Dettingen
Te Deum, Jephtha (Cpte), Messias, K572 (Cpte),
Partenope (Cpte), Solomon (Cpte), Triumph of Time
and Truth (Cpte), Ways of Zion do mourn
Holst: Sávitri (Cpte)
Monteverdi: Orfeo (Cpte)
Ponchielli: Gioconda (Cpte)
Purcell: Dioclesian, Z627 (exc), Fairy Queen, Z629
(Cpte), Indian Queen, Z630 (Cpte), King Arthur, Z628
(Cpte), St Cecilia's Day Ode, Z328, Tempest, Z631
(Cpte), Timon of Athens, Z632 (Cpte)
Schütz: Symphoniae sacrae, Op. 10 (Cpte)
Tavener: Mary of Egypt (Cpte)
see CONCERT INDEX under:
(ARCH) **429 782-2AH** Bach—Cantatas Nos 106, 118b
& 198
(ARCH) **437 090-2AT** Collectio Argentea 20: Bach
Family before J.S.
(CAPR) **10 310/1** J. E. Bach—Passion Oratorio, etc.
(CAPR) **10 315** Telemann—Choral Music
(CHAN) **CHAN0518** Vivaldi & Bach—Choral Works
(CHAN) **CHAN8478** Erik Bergman—Choral Works
(CHAN) **CHAN8743** English Orchestral Songs
(CHAN) **CHAN8864** G. Bush: Vocal & Choral Works
(CLLE) **COLCD109** Fauré: Sacred Choral Works
(CLLE) **COLCD121** Christmas Day in the Morning
(ERAT) **2292-45466-2** Carissimi—Jonas
(ERAT) **4509-96371-2** Gardiner—The Purcell
Collection
(HYPE) **CDA66161/2** Finzi Song Cycles to words by
Thomas Hardy
(HYPE) **CDA66248** La Procession - Eighty Years of
French Song
(HYPE) **CDA66261/2** War's Embers
(HYPE) **CDA66269** Mondonville: Motets
(HYPE) **CDA66385** Settings of A. E. Housman
(HYPE) **CDA66644** Purcell—Complete Anthems &
Services, Vol.4
(HYPE) **CDJ33002** Schubert—Complete Lieder, Vol.
2
(KOCH) **37263-2** Schoenberg—A Survivor from
Warsaw, etc
(PHIL) **422 522-2PME6** The Complete Mozart Edition
Vol 22

VARCOL, Liviu (ob)
see CONCERT INDEX under:
(CPO) **CPO999 142-2** Hindemith—Complete Wind
Concertos

VARDI, Arie (pf)
see CONCERT INDEX under:
(CARL) **PWK1132** Children's Corner

VARDI, Emanuel (va)
see CONCERT INDEX under:
(CHAN) **CHAN8770** Bliss—Chamber Works

VARGA, Gilbert (cond)
see BBC PO

VARGA, Gilbert (vn)
see CONCERT INDEX under:

(CLAV) **CD50-9300/4** Hommage à Tibor Varga
(CLAV) **CD50-9311** Hommage à Tibor Varga, Volume
1

VARGA, István (cl)
see CONCERT INDEX under:
(MARC) **8 223727** Truscott—Chamber Music

VARGA, Tibor (cond)
see Varga Fest Orch

VARGA, Tibor (vn)
Bruch: Violin Concerto 1
Tchaikovsky: Violin Concerto
see CONCERT INDEX under:
(CLAV) **CD50-9300/4** Hommage à Tibor Varga
(CLAV) **CD50-9314** Hommage à Tibor Varga, Volume
4
(DG) **445 400-2GDO10** Ferenc Fricsay - A Portrait
(DG) **445 402-2GDO** Bartók—Orchestral Works

VARGA, Tibor (vn/dir)
Mozart: Violin Concerto, K219
see CONCERT INDEX under:
(CLAV) **CD50-9300/4** Hommage à Tibor Varga
(CLAV) **CD50-9311** Hommage à Tibor Varga, Volume
1

(TIBOR) VARGA CHAMBER ORCHESTRA
see CONCERT INDEX under:
(CLAV) **CD50-9300/4** Hommage à Tibor Varga

(TIBOR) VARGA FESTIVAL ORCHESTRA
see CONCERT INDEX under:
(CLAV) **CD50-9300/4** Hommage à Tibor Varga
cond T. VARGA
Mozart: Symphony 36
see CONCERT INDEX under:
(CLAV) **CD50-9300/4** Hommage à Tibor Varga

VARGAS, Milagr (contr)
B.A. Zimmermann: Soldaten (Cpte)
Glass: Akhnaten (Cpte)
Maderna: Satyricon (Cpte)

VARGAS, Ramon (ten)
Bellini: Zaira (Cpte)
Puccini: Manon Lescaut (Cpte)
Rossini: Barbiere di Siviglia (Cpte), Scala di Seta
(Cpte)
Verdi: Falstaff (Cpte), Otello (Cpte)
see CONCERT INDEX under:
(CLAV) **CD50-9202** Donizetti/Rossini—Tenor Arias

VÁRJON, Dénes (pf)
see CONCERT INDEX under:
(NAXO) **8 550849** Schumann—Piano Works

VARNA PHILHARMONIC CHORUS
Shostakovich: Execution of Stepan Razin
Sviridov: Oratorio Pathétique

VARNAY, Astrid (sop/mez)
Giordano: Andrea Chénier (Cpte)
Mascagni: Cavalleria rusticana (Cpte)
Stravinsky: Rake's Progress (Cpte)
Wagner: Götterdämmerung (Cpte), Lohengrin (Cpte),
Siegfried (Cpte), Walküre (Cpte)
see CONCERT INDEX under:
(EMI) **CHS7 69741-2(1)** Record of Singing,
Vol.4—Anglo-American School (pt 1)
(FOYE) **15-CF2011** Wagner—Der Ring de Nibelungen

VARNER, Johanna (vc)
see CONCERT INDEX under:
(TROU) **TRO-CD03** Ethel Smyth—Chamber Works,
Vols.1 & 2

VARNIER, Jérome (bar)
Rameau: Hippolyte et Aricie (Cpte)

VARNIER, Jérôme (sngr)
Lully: Phaëton (Cpte)

VARSOVIA QUARTET
see CONCERT INDEX under:
(OLYM) **OCD328** Polish String Quartets

VARTOLO, Sergio (cond)
see San Petronio Cappella Musicale Orch

VARVISO, Silvio (cond)
see Bayreuth Fest Orch

VASARI
cond J. BACKHOUSE
see CONCERT INDEX under:
(UNIT) **88033-2** Howells/F. Martin—Choral Works

VÁSÁRY, Tamás (cond)
see Bournemouth Sinfonietta

VÁSÁRY, Tamás (pf)
Chopin: Nocturnes (exc), Piano Concerto 1, Piano
Concerto 2
Rachmaninov: Piano Concerto 2, Piano Concerto 4
see CONCERT INDEX under:
(ASV) **CDDCA792** Mozart—Piano Duets, Vol.1
(ASV) **CDDCA799** Mozart—Piano Duets, Vol.2
(CHAN) **CHAN8859** Martinů—Orchestral Works
(DG) **413 850-2GW2** Rachmaninov/Liszt—Piano
Concertos

VÁSÁRY, Tamás (pf/dir)
see CONCERT INDEX under:
(CHAN) **CHAN8993** Honegger—Orchestral Works

VASILIEVA, Alla (vc)
Vainberg: String Quartet 12

VASLE, Juan (bass)
Franck: Béatitudes (Cpte)

VIENNA PHILHARMONIC ORCHESTRA

Wagner: Walküre (exc)
see CONCERT INDEX under:
(DG) 435 321-2GWP12　150 Years - Vienna Philharmonic
(LOND) 440 490-2LM5(1)　Kirsten Flagstad Edition (pt 1)
　cond C. ABBADO
Beethoven: Coriolan, Symphony 1, Symphony 2, Symphony 3, Symphony 4, Symphony 5, Symphony 7, Symphony 8, Symphony 9
Berg: Wozzeck (Cpte)
Brahms: Hungarian Dances
Bruckner: Symphony 4, Symphony 7
Debussy: Pelléas et Mélisande (Cpte)
Mahler: Symphony 2, Symphony 3, Symphony 4, Symphony 9, Symphony 10 (exc)
Mendelssohn: Violin Concerto, Op. 64
Mozart: Mass, K139, Nozze di Figaro (Cpte), Piano Concerto 14, Piano Concerto 20, Piano Concerto 21, Piano Concerto 26
Rossini: Italiana in Algeri (Cpte)
Schoenberg: Gurrelieder
Schubert: Mass, D950
Tchaikovsky: Symphony 4, Violin Concerto
Verdi: Pezzi sacri (Cpte), Requiem (Cpte)
Wagner: Lohengrin (Cpte)
see CONCERT INDEX under:
(DG) 419 779-2GH　Beethoven: Orchestral & Choral Works
(DG) 419 793-2GH3　Beethoven: Piano Concertos
(DG) 423 662-2GH　New Year's Day Concert, Vienna, 1988
(DG) 427 306-2GH6　Beethoven: Complete Symphonies
(DG) 429 260-2GH　Contemporary Works
(DG) 431 628-2GH　Vienna New Year's Concert, 1991
(DG) 431 774-2GH　Schoenberg/Webern—Orchestral Works
(DG) 435 335-2GWP2　VPO plays Johann & Josef Strauss
(DG) 447 023-2GX12　Mahler—The Symphonies
　cond O. ACKERMANN
see CONCERT INDEX under:
(EMI) CHS7 69741-2(4)　Record of Singing, Vol.4—German School
(TEST) SBT1059　Erich Kunz—Opera and Song Recital
　cond V. ANDREAE
see CONCERT INDEX under:
(DECC) 433 628-2DSP　Franck/Grieg/Schumann—Piano & Orchestral Works
　cond J. BARBIROLLI
Brahms: Haydn Variations
see CONCERT INDEX under:
(EMI) CDM7 63537-2　Brahms: Orchestral Works
　cond L. BERNSTEIN
Beethoven: Fidelio (Cpte), String Quartet 14, String Quartet 16
Brahms: Academic Festival Overture, Double Concerto, Haydn Variations, Piano Concerto 1, Piano Concerto 2, Symphony 2, Symphony 3, Symphony 4, Tragic Overture, Violin Concerto
Bruckner: Symphony 9
Mahler: Kindertotenlieder, Symphony 5, Symphony 6, Symphony 8, Symphony 10 (exc)
R. Strauss: Rosenkavalier (Cpte)
Schumann: Cello Concerto, Symphony 2
Shostakovich: Symphony 6, Symphony 9
Sibelius: Symphony 1, Symphony 2, Symphony 5, Symphony 7
see CONCERT INDEX under:
(DG) 415 570-2GX4　Brahms: Symphonies & Overtures
(DG) 423 099-2GH3　Schumann: Symphonies & Concertos
(DG) 423 481-2GX6　Beethoven: Complete Symphonies
(DG) 429 221-2GH　Mozart— Symphonies Nos 25 & 29; Clarinet Concerto
(DG) 431 682-2GH　Mahler—Lieder
(DG) 435 162-2GX13　Mahler—Complete Symphonies
(DG) 435 321-2GWP12　150 Years - Vienna Philharmonic
(DG) 435 467-2GH3　Beethoven—Piano Concertos
(DG) 445 505-2GMA　Brahms/Beethoven—Orchestral Works
(DG) 445 554-2GMA　Haydn—Symphonies
　cond W. BOSKOVSKY
see CONCERT INDEX under:
(DECC) 425 425-2DA　Strauss Gala, Vol.1 - The Blue Danube
(DECC) 425 426-2DA　Strauss Gala, Vol.2 - Tales from the Vienna Woods
(DECC) 425 427-2DA　Strauss Gala, Vol.3 - Wine, Women and Song
(DECC) 425 428-2DA　Strauss Gala, Vol.4 - Vienna Blood
(DECC) 425 429-2DA　Strauss Gala, Vol.5 - Roses from the South
(DECC) 430 501-2DWO　World of Johann Strauss
(DG) 435 335-2GWP2　VPO plays Johann & Josef Strauss
　cond P. BOULEZ
Mahler: Symphony 6
　cond A. BOULT
see CONCERT INDEX under:
(LOND) 440 490-2LM5(1)　Kirsten Flagstad Edition (pt 1)

　cond K. BÖHM
Beethoven: Piano Concerto 4, Piano Concerto 5, Symphony 9
Brahms: Piano Concerto 1
Bruckner: Symphony 3, Symphony 4, Symphony 7
Mozart: Clarinet Concerto, K622, Così fan tutte (Cpte), Flute and Harp Concerto, K299, Piano Concerto 19, Piano Concerto 23, Requiem, Serenade, K525
R. Strauss: Arabella (Cpte), Ariadne auf Naxos (Cpte), Rosenkavalier (Cpte), Schweigsame Frau (Cpte)
Wagner: Meistersinger (Cpte)
see CONCERT INDEX under:
(DECC) 425 959-2DM　Lisa della Casa sings R. Strauss
(DG) 413 424-2GW2　Brahms—Orchestral Works
(DG) 413 432-2GW2　J. Strauss II—Overtures, Polkas & Waltzes
(DG) 419 793-2GH3　Beethoven: Piano Concertos
(DG) 429 509-2GR　Beethoven: Orchestral Works
(DG) 435 321-2GWP12　150 Years - Vienna Philharmonic
(DG) 435 335-2GWP2　VPO plays Johann & Josef Strauss
(DG) 437 368-2GX2　Beethoven—Orchestral Works
(DG) 437 928-2GX2　Beethoven—Symphonies & Overtures
(EMI) CHS7 69741-2(4)　Record of Singing, Vol.4—German School
(PREI) 90237　R Strauss—Daphne
　cond COLIN DAVIS
Berlioz: Symphonie fantastique
see CONCERT INDEX under:
(PHIL) 438 868-2PH　Mozart/Weber/Spohr—Clarinet Concertos
　cond I. DOBROVEN
see CONCERT INDEX under:
(PEAR) GEMMCD9341　Bach & Mozart: Violin Concertos
　cond C. VON DOHNÁNYI
Beethoven: Fidelio (Cpte)
Berg: Wozzeck (Cpte)
Glass: Violin Concerto
R. Strauss: Salome (Cpte)
Schnittke: Concerto Grosso 5
Schoenberg: Erwartung (Cpte)
Wagner: Fliegende Holländer (Cpte)
　cond F. FRICSAY
Mozart: Idomeneo (Cpte)
see CONCERT INDEX under:
(DG) 445 400-2GDO10　Ferenc Fricsay - A Portrait
(DG) 445 407-2GDO　Brahms—Orchestral Works
　cond W. FURTWÄNGLER
Bach: St Matthew Passion, BWV244 (exc)
Beethoven: Fidelio (Cpte), Symphony 6, Symphony 9
Brahms: Haydn Variations
Furtwängler: Symphony 2
Mozart: Don Giovanni (Cpte)
Wagner: Walküre (Cpte)
see CONCERT INDEX under:
(ACAN) 43 121　Wagner: Orchestral Works
(DG) 435 321-2GWP12　150 Years - Vienna Philharmonic
(DG) 435 324-2GWP　VPO under Wilhelm Furtwängler
(DG) 435 335-2GWP2　VPO plays Johann & Josef Strauss
(EMI) CDH5 65197-2　Furtwängler conducts Richard Strauss and Smetana
(EMI) CDM7 63657-2　Schwarzkopf sings Opera Arias
(EMI) CHS5 65353-2　Hindemith/Schubert/R. Strauss—Orchestral Works
(EMI) CHS7 64935-2　Wagner—Opera Excerpts
　cond J. E. GARDINER
Lehár: Lustige Witwe (Cpte)
　cond C.M. GIULINI
Brahms: Haydn Variations, Symphony 1, Symphony 2, Symphony 3, Symphony 4, Tragic Overture
Bruckner: Symphony 7, Symphony 8, Symphony 9
Franck: Symphonic Variations, Symphony
Verdi: Rigoletto (Cpte)
see CONCERT INDEX under:
(BELA) 450 121-2　Plácido Domingo
(DG) 415 366-2GH　Plácido Domingo Recital
(SONY) SK52567　Schumann—Piano Works
　cond B. HAITINK
Berlioz: Symphonie fantastique
Brahms: Piano Concerto 2
Bruckner: Symphony 3
　cond R. HEGER
(EMI) CHS7 64487-2　R. Strauss—Der Rosenkavalier & Lieder
(PEAR) GEMMCDS9365　R. Strauss: Der Rosenkavalier (abridged), etc
　cond H. HOLLREISER
see CONCERT INDEX under:
(DECC) 425 959-2DM　Lisa della Casa sings R. Strauss
　cond JAMES LEVINE
Beethoven: Missa Solemnis
Mozart: Mass, K427, Symphony 40, Symphony 41, Violin Concerto, K211, Violin Concerto, K218, Zauberflöte (Cpte)
R. Strauss: Ariadne auf Naxos (Cpte)
Smetana: Bartered Bride (exc), Má Vlast (exc)
see CONCERT INDEX under:
(DG) 427 813-2GDC　Mozart: Vorks for Violin & Orchestra
(DG) 437 544-2GH　Carmen-Fantasie

(DG) 437 806-2GH　Tchaikovsky—Ballet Music
(DG) 439 887-2GH　Brahms—Orchestral & Vocal Works
(DG) 445 535-2GMA2　Mozart—Violin Concertos, etc
(RCA) 09026 61580-2(8)　RCA/Met 100 Singers, 100 Years (pt 8)
　cond E. JOCHUM
Beethoven: Piano Concerto 2
Bruckner: Symphony 7
see CONCERT INDEX under:
(DG) 419 793-2GH3　Beethoven: Piano Concertos
　cond H. VON KARAJAN
Beethoven: Symphony 9
Bizet: Carmen (Cpte)
Brahms: Deutsches Requiem, Op. 45 (Cpte)
Bruckner: Symphony 7, Symphony 8, Symphony 9
Dvořák: Symphony 8
Gluck: Orfeo ed Euridice (Cpte)
Haydn: Schöpfung (Cpte)
J. Strauss II: Fledermaus (Cpte)
Mozart: Nozze di Figaro (Cpte), Zauberflöte (Cpte)
Mussorgsky: Boris Godunov (Cpte)
Puccini: Madama Butterfly (Cpte), Tosca (Cpte), Turandot (Cpte)
R. Strauss: Rosenkavalier (exc), Salome (Cpte)
Schumann: Symphony 4
Tchaikovsky: Violin Concerto
Verdi: Aida (Cpte), Ballo in maschera (Cpte), Don Carlo (Cpte), Otello (Cpte), Requiem (Cpte), Trovatore (Cpte)
Vivaldi: Concerti, Op. 8 (exc)
see CONCERT INDEX under:
(DECC) 430 481-2DX2　Renata Tebaldi sings Opera Arias
(DECC) 433 010-2DM　Christmas Stars
(DECC) 433 439-2DA　Great Love Duets
(DECC) 436 402-2DWO　The World of Wedding Music
(DECC) 436 407-2DWO　The World of Schubert
(DECC) 436 464-2DM　Ten Top Baritones & Basses
(DG) 415 366-2GH　Plácido Domingo Recital
(DG) 419 616-2GH　New Year's Concert in Vienna, 1987
(DG) 423 613-2GH　Wagner—Opera excerpts
(DG) 435 321-2GWP12　150 Years - Vienna Philharmonic
(DG) 435 335-2GWP2　VPO plays Johann & Josef Strauss
(EMI) CDH7 69793-2　Elisabeth Schwarzkopf & Irmgard Seefried sing Duets
(EMI) CDM7 63657-2　Schwarzkopf sings Opera Arias
(EMI) CDM7 69549-2　Ruggero Raimondi: Italian Opera Arias
(PREI) 90034　Maria Cebotari (1910-49)
(PREI) 90078　Hilde Konetzni
(RCA) 09026 61580-2(7)　RCA/Met 100 Singers, 100 Years (pt 7)
(RCA) 09026 61580-2(8)　RCA/Met 100 Singers, 100 Years (pt 8)
(TEST) SBT1059　Erich Kunz—Opera and Song Recital
　cond R. KEMPE
Wagner: Lohengrin (Cpte)
see CONCERT INDEX under:
(EMI) CES5 68525-2　Berlioz/Saint-Saëns—Orchestral Works
　cond I. KERTÉSZ
see CONCERT INDEX under:
(DECC) 430 773-2DC4　Schubert—Complete Symphonies, etc
　cond C. KLEIBER
Beethoven: Symphony 5, Symphony 7
Brahms: Symphony 4
see CONCERT INDEX under:
(SONY) SK45938　Carlos Kleiber conducts Johann Strauss
(SONY) SK48376　New Year's Concert - 1992
　cond E. KLEIBER
Mozart: Nozze di Figaro (Cpte)
R. Strauss: Rosenkavalier (Cpte)
see CONCERT INDEX under:
(ARCI) ARC102　Kleiber conducts Waltzes and Overtures
(DG) 435 335-2GWP2　VPO plays Johann & Josef Strauss
　cond O. KLEMPERER
Beethoven: Symphony 5
Schubert: Symphony 8
see CONCERT INDEX under:
(DG) 435 321-2GWP12　150 Years - Vienna Philharmonic
　cond H. KNAPPERTSBUSCH
Bruckner: Symphony 7
Schmidt: Husarenlied Variations
Schubert: Symphony 8
Wagner: Meistersinger (Cpte)
see CONCERT INDEX under:
(DECC) 436 407-2DWO　The World of Schubert
(DG) 435 321-2GWP12　150 Years - Vienna Philharmonic
(DG) 435 335-2GWP2　VPO plays Johann & Josef Strauss
(LOND) 440 490-2LM5(1)　Kirsten Flagstad Edition (pt 1)
(LOND) 440 495-2LM　Kirsten Flagstad Edition, Vol. 5
(PREI) 90951　Mozart—Symphonies
　cond K. KONDRASHIN
Beethoven: Violin Concerto
Dvořák: Symphony 9

cond C. KRAUSS
Haydn: Jahreszeiten (Cpte)
see CONCERT INDEX under:
(DG) 435 321-2GWP12   150 Years - Vienna
Philharmonic
(DG) 435 335-2GWP2   VPO plays Johann & Josef
Strauss
(KOCH) 37011-2   Legendary Conductors
(KOCH) 37129-2   Clemens Kraus Conducts
(PREI) 90112   Clemens Krauss conducts the VPO
cond J. KRIPS
Mozart: Don Giovanni (Cpte), Entführung (Cpte)
see CONCERT INDEX under:
(DECC) 443 530-2LF2   Mozart—Die Entführung aus
dem Serail
(DG) 435 335-2GWP2   VPO plays Johann & Josef
Strauss
(EMI) CDH7 63201-2   Elisabeth Schwarzkopf—Early
Recordings
(EMI) CDM7 63654-2   Schwarzkopf Encores
(EMIL) CDZ7 67015-2   Mozart—Opera Arias
(PREI) 90083   Maria Reining
cond R. KUBELÍK
see CONCERT INDEX under:
(EMI) CZS5 68223-2   Rafael Kubelík—A profile
cond F. LEHÁR
see CONCERT INDEX under:
(EMI) CDC7 54838-2   Franz Lehár
(EMI) CDM7 69476-2   Richard Tauber - A Portrait
(EMI) CHS7 69741-2(4)   Record of Singing,
Vol.4—German School
(PEAR) GEMMCD9310   Franz Lehár conducts Richard
Tauber
(PREI) 89065   Maria Reining (1903-1991)
(PREI) 90150   Lehár conducts Lehár
cond E. LEINSDORF
R. Strauss: Ariadne auf Naxos (Cpte)
cond L. MAAZEL
Dvořák: Symphony 7, Symphony 8, Symphony 9
Tchaikovsky: Hamlet, Manfred Symphony
see CONCERT INDEX under:
(DECC) 430 778-2DC3   Sibelius—Symphonies
(DECC) 430 787-2DC4   Tchaikovsky—Symphonies
(DG) 427 820-2GDC   J. Strauss: Waltzes
(DG) 435 335-2GWP2   VPO plays Johann & Josef
Strauss
(SONY) SK46694   New Year's Day Concert 1994
(SONY) SX14K48198   Mahler—Complete
Symphonies, etc
cond C. MACKERRAS
Janáček: Cunning Little Vixen, Cunning Little
Vixen Suite, Jenůfa (Cpte), Makropulos Affair (Cpte)
see CONCERT INDEX under:
(DECC) 421 852-2DH2   Janáček: Operatic & Chamber
Works
(DECC) 430 375-2DH2   Janáček—Operatic and
Orchestral Works
(DECC) 430 727-2DM
Janáček/Shostakovich—Orchestral Works
cond Z. MEHTA
Beethoven: Piano Concerto 4, Piano Concerto 5
Mahler: Symphony 2
Schmidt: Symphony 4
see CONCERT INDEX under:
(DECC) 436 471-2DM   Beethoven—Piano Works
(DG) 435 335-2GWP2   VPO plays Johann & Josef
Strauss
(SONY) SK45808   New Year's Day Concert 1990
cond P. MONTEUX
Mozart: Don Giovanni (Cpte)
see CONCERT INDEX under:
(DECC) 440 627-2DF2   Beethoven—Symphonies
cond R. MORALT
see CONCERT INDEX under:
(DECC) 425 959-2DM   Lisa della Casa sings R.
Strauss
(EMI) CHS7 69741-2(4)   Record of Singing,
Vol.4—German School
(EMI) CMS7 64008-2(1)   Wagner Singing on Record
(pt 1)
(PREI) 89018   Helge Rosvaenge (1897-1972)
(PREI) 89065   Maria Reining (1903-1991)
(TEST) SBT1059   Erich Kunz—Opera and Song
Recital
cond R. MUTI
Mozart: Clemenza di Tito (Cpte), Don Giovanni
(Cpte), Symphony 31, Symphony 41
Schubert: Rosamunde (exc), Symphony 1, Symphony
2, Symphony 8, Symphony 9
Schumann: Symphony 1, Symphony 4
see CONCERT INDEX under:
(EMI) CMS7 64873-2   Schubert—The Symphonies
(EMIL) CDZ7 67015-2   Mozart—Opera Arias
(PHIL) 438 493-2PH   New Year's Concert 1993
cond K. MÜNCHINGER
Mozart: Clarinet Concerto, K622, Flute and Harp
Concerto, K299
see CONCERT INDEX under:
(DECC) 436 407-2DWO   The World of Schubert
cond D. OISTRAKH
Mozart: Serenade, K525
Tchaikovsky: Symphony 5
cond A. PREVIN
Dvořák: Slavonic Dances
Haydn: Symphony 102, Symphony 104
J. Strauss II: Fledermaus (Cpte), Unter Donner und
Blitz
Orff: Carmina burana

cond C. KRAUSS
R. Strauss: Alpensinfonie, Also sprach Zarathustra,
Don Juan, Don Quixote, Heldenleben, Tod und
Verklärung, Vier letzte Lieder
see CONCERT INDEX under:
(DG) 437 790-2GH   R. Strauss—Orchestral Works
(PHIL) 434 914-2PH   Dvořák—Cello works
cond J. PRITCHARD
Mozart: Idomeneo (Cpte)
see CONCERT INDEX under:
(DECC) 436 462-2DM   Ten Top Mezzos
cond F. PROHASKA
see CONCERT INDEX under:
(PREI) 90034   Maria Cebotari (1910-49)
cond F. REINER
Verdi: Requiem (Cpte)
see CONCERT INDEX under:
(DECC) 443 930-2DM   Jussi Björling sings Opera
Arias
cond F. SCHALK
Beethoven: Symphony 6, Symphony 8
cond H. SCHMIDT-ISSERSTEDT
Beethoven: Symphony 1, Symphony 2, Symphony 3,
Symphony 7, Symphony 9
cond C. SCHURICHT
Bruckner: Symphony 5
see CONCERT INDEX under:
(DG) 435 321-2GWP12   150 Years - Vienna
Philharmonic
cond C. SILVESTRI
see CONCERT INDEX under:
(EMI) CMS5 68229-2   Constantin Silvestri—A profile
(EMI) CZS7 67310-2   Menuhin plays Popular Violin
Concertos
cond G. SOLTI
Mendelssohn: Symphony 4
Mozart: Entführung (Cpte), Mass, K427, Requiem,
Zauberflöte (Cpte)
R. Strauss: Arabella (Cpte), Elektra (Cpte), Frau ohne
Schatten (Cpte), Rosenkavalier (Cpte), Salome
(Cpte)
Schubert: Symphony 5, Symphony 8
Shostakovich: Symphony 5
Verdi: Otello (Cpte), Requiem (Cpte)
Wagner: Götterdämmerung (Cpte), Lohengrin (Cpte),
Meistersinger (Cpte), Parsifal (Cpte), Rheingold
(Cpte), Ring des Nibelungen Introduction, Siegfried
(Cpte), Tannhäuser (Cpte), Walküre (Cpte)
see CONCERT INDEX under:
(DECC) 410 137-2DH   Wagner: Excerpts from The
Ring
(DECC) 414 100-2DM15   Wagner: Der Ring des
Nibelungen
(DECC) 417 011-2DH2   Pavarotti's Greatest Hits
(DECC) 430 511-2DH   R. Strauss—Lieder
(DECC) 433 437-2DA   Pavarotti—King of the High Cs
(DECC) 433 439-2DA   Great Love Duets
(DECC) 433 710-2DH   O Holy Night
(DECC) 436 461-2DM   Ten Top Sopranos
(DECC) 436 462-2DM   Ten Top Mezzos
(DECC) 436 464-2DM   Ten Top Baritones & Basses
(DECC) 440 618-2DF2   R. Strauss—Tone Poems
(LOND) 440 490-2LM5(1)   Kirsten Flagstad Edition (pt
1)
(LOND) 440 495-2LM   Kirsten Flagstad Edition, Vol.
5
cond R. STRAUSS
see CONCERT INDEX under:
(DG) 435 321-2GWP12   150 Years - Vienna
Philharmonic
(DG) 435 333-2GWP   VPO under Richard Strauss
(PREI) 90216   Strauss conducts Strauss, Vol.2
cond G. SZELL
Bruckner: Symphony 7
see CONCERT INDEX under:
(DG) 435 335-2GWP2   VPO plays Johann & Josef
Strauss
(EPM) 150 032   The Romantic Violin
cond B. WALTER
Brahms: Symphony 3
Mahler: Lied von der Erde, Symphony 4, Symphony
9
Mozart: Symphony 38
Wagner: Walküre (exc)
see CONCERT INDEX under:
(DECC) 430 096-2DWO   The World of Kathleen Ferrier
(DECC) 433 477-2DM   Ferrier Edition - Volume 10
(DG) 435 321-2GWP12   150 Years - Vienna
Philharmonic
(DG) 435 335-2GWP2   VPO plays Johann & Josef
Strauss
(EMI) CDH7 61003-2   Kathleen Ferrier sings Opera
and Songs
(KOCH) 37011-2   Legendary Conductors
(MUSI) MACD-749   Bruno Walter conducts Mahler
(NIMB) NI7851   Legendary Voices
(PEAR) GEMMCD9940   Bruno Walter conducts &
plays Mozart
(PREI) 90114   Bruno Walter conducts the Vienna
Philharmonic
(PREI) 90141   Walter directs the VPO
(PREI) 90157   Beethoven/Wagner—Orchestral Works
cond F. WEINGARTNER
Beethoven: Symphony 3, Symphony 8, Symphony 9
see CONCERT INDEX under:
(MSCM) MM30269   Weingartner conducts Beethoven

VIENNA PHILHARMONIC QUARTET
Schubert: String Quartet, D810

VIENNA PIANO TRIO
Brahms: Piano Trio, Op. posth, Piano Trio 1, Piano
Trio 2, Piano Trio 3

VIENNA PRO MUSICA ORCHESTRA
cond M. GIELEN
see CONCERT INDEX under:
(VOX) CDX2 5506   György Sándor plays Bartók
cond J. HORENSTEIN
see CONCERT INDEX under:
(VOX) CDX2 5504
Bruckner/Liszt/Wagner—Orchestral Works
(VOX) CDX2 5306   The Art of Ivry Gitlis
cond J. PERLEA
see CONCERT INDEX under:
(VOX) CDX2 5502   Cassado performs Cello
Masterpieces
cond H. SWAROWSKY
see CONCERT INDEX under:
(VOX) CDX2 5505   The Art of Ivry Gitlis

VIENNA RADIO SYMPHONY ORCHESTRA
cond M. CARIDIS
Kalomiris: Symphony 1
cond B. PRIESTMAN
see CONCERT INDEX under:
(CBC) PSCD2002   Maureen Forrester sings Handel
Arias

VIENNA SCHRAMMEL QUARTET
see CONCERT INDEX under:
(PEAR) GEMMCD9383   Julius Patzak—Opera &
Operetta Recital

VIENNA SINFONIETTA
cond K. RAPF
Dittersdorf: Symphonies after Ovid

VIENNA SINGAKADEMIE CHORUS
cond O. CAETANI
Donizetti: Poliuto (Cpte)
cond W. FURTWÄNGLER
Bach: St Matthew Passion, BWV244 (exc)
Beethoven: Symphony 9
see CONCERT INDEX under:
(DG) 435 321-2GWP12   150 Years - Vienna
Philharmonic
cond E. INBAL
Beethoven: Symphony 9
cond K. MÜNCHINGER
Bach: Mass in B minor, BWV232 (Cpte)

VIENNA SINGVEREIN
cond L. BERNSTEIN
Mahler: Symphony 8
see CONCERT INDEX under:
(DG) 435 162-2GX13   Mahler—Complete
Symphonies
cond K. BÖHM
Haydn: Jahreszeiten (Cpte)
cond M. CARIDIS
Kalomiris: Symphony 1
cond P. GÜLKE
Schreker: Irrelohe (Cpte)
cond N. HARNONCOURT
Mozart: Zauberflöte (Cpte)
cond E. INBAL
Shostakovich: Symphony 2
cond H. VON KARAJAN
Bach: Mass in B minor, BWV232 (Cpte), St Matthew
Passion, BWV244 (Cpte)
Beethoven: Missa Solemnis, Symphony 9
Brahms: Deutsches Requiem, Op. 45 (Cpte)
Haydn: Schöpfung (Cpte)
Mozart: Mass, K317, Requiem, Zauberflöte (Cpte)
Verdi: Aida (Cpte), Requiem (Cpte)
see CONCERT INDEX under:
(DG) 429 036-2GX5   Beethoven: Complete
Symphonies
(EMI) CMS7 63310-2   Beethoven: Complete
Symphonies
cond F. REINER
Verdi: Requiem (Cpte)
cond W. SAWALLISCH
see CONCERT INDEX under:
(PHIL) 438 760-2PM2   Brahms—Choral Works and
Overtures
cond G. SOLTI
Mahler: Symphony 8
see CONCERT INDEX under:
(DECC) 430 804-2DC10   Mahler—Complete
Symphonies

VIENNA STATE OPERA CHORUS
cond C. ABBADO
Berg: Wozzeck (Cpte)
Debussy: Pelléas et Mélisande (Cpte)
Mozart: Mass, K139, Nozze di Figaro (Cpte)
Mussorgsky: Khovanshchina (Cpte)
Rossini: Italiana in Algeri (Cpte)
Schoenberg: Gurrelieder
see CONCERT INDEX under:
(DG) 431 774-2GH   Schoenberg/Webern—Orchestral
Works
(DG) 435 486-2GH   Schubert/Schumann—Sacred
Choral Works
(DG) 447 023-2GX12   Mahler—The Symphonies
cond C. ADLER
Mahler: Symphony 3
cond K. ALWIN
see CONCERT INDEX under:
(SCHW) 314512   Vienna State Opera Live, Vol.1
(SCHW) 314542   Vienna State Opera Live, Vol.4
(SCHW) 314632   Vienna State Opera Live, Vol.13
(SCHW) 314662   Vienna State Opera Live, Vol.16
cond L. BERNSTEIN
Beethoven: Fidelio (Cpte)
Mahler: Symphony 8

VLASOV, Vitali (ten)
Tchaikovsky: Queen of Spades (Cpte)

(ALEXIS) VLASSOF CHORUS
cond I. STRAVINSKY
see CONCERT INDEX under:
(EMI) CDS7 54607-2   Stravinsky plays and conducts
Stravinsky
cond H. TOMASI
Gluck: Orphée (Cpte)

(ALEXIS) VLASSOF ORCHESTRA
cond H. TOMASI
Gluck: Orphée (Cpte)

VLATKOVIČ, Radovan (hn)
Gubaidulina: Hommage
Mozart: Piano and Wind Quintet, K452
see CONCERT INDEX under:
(EMI) CDM7 64851-2   Mozart/R. Strauss—Horn
Concertos

VLČEK, Oldřich (cond)
see Prague Virtuosi

VLIEGEN, Marianne (mez)
Puccini: Suor Angelica (Cpte)

VOCAL ENSEMBLE
cond J-C. MALGOIRE
Vivaldi: Montezuma (Cpte)

VOCAL SOLOISTS (sngrs)
Wagner: Ring des Nibelungen Introduction

VOCES INTIMAE QUARTET
see CONCERT INDEX under:
(BIS) BIS-CD026   Shostakovich—Chamber Works
(BIS) BIS-CD053   Ligeti—Various Works

VOCES QUARTET
Enescu: String Quartet 1, String Quartet 2
see CONCERT INDEX under:
(MDG) L3236   Arriaga: String Quartets

VOCHT, Louis de (cond)
see Antwerp Concerts Orch

VODENICHAROV, Boyan (pf)
see CONCERT INDEX under:
(ETCE) KTC1122   Prokofiev—Early Piano Works

VODIČKA, Leo Marian (ten)
Dvořák: Dimitrij (Cpte), St Ludmilla (Cpte)
Janáček: Amarus, Moravian folk poetry in songs
(exc)
Smetana: Dalibor (Cpte), Kiss (Cpte), Libuše (Cpte)
see CONCERT INDEX under:
(SONY) SK45633   Edita Gruberová—Opera Arias

VODRÁŽKA, Jaroslav (organ)
see CONCERT INDEX under:
(SUPR) 11 1930-2   Janáček/Kabeláč—Choral and
Orchestral Works

VOGEL, Adolf (bass)
see CONCERT INDEX under:
(SCHW) 314562   Vienna State Opera Live, Vol.6

VOGEL, Alfred (bass)
see CONCERT INDEX under:
(SCHW) 314652   Vienna State Opera Live, Vol.15

VOGEL, Allan (cor ang)
Beethoven: Piano and wind quintet, op 16
Mozart: Piano and wind quintet, K452

VOGEL, Barbara (sop)
Mozart: Nozze di Figaro (Cpte)

VOGEL, Christian (bass)
Wagner: Rheingold (Cpte)

VOGEL, Harald (organ)
see CONCERT INDEX under:
(DHM) RD77202   Bach—Complete Organ Works,
Vol.1

VOGEL, Siegfried (bass)
Mozart: Idomeneo (Cpte)
R. Strauss: Ariadne auf Naxos (Cpte), Elektra (Cpte)
Wagner: Meistersinger (Cpte), Rienzi (Cpte)
Weber: Freischütz (Cpte)

VOGEL, Volker (ten)
Schoenberg: Gurrelieder
Zemlinsky: Kleider machen Leute (Cpte)

VOGLER, Tim (vn)
see CONCERT INDEX under:
(EDA) EDA008-2   Works by Ullmann and Schoenberg

VOGLER QUARTET
Bartók: String Quartet 2
Beethoven: String Quartet 9
Berg: Lyric Suite
Brahms: String Quartet 2, String Quartet 3
Schumann: String Quartet 1, String Quartet 3
Verdi: String Quartet
see CONCERT INDEX under:
(RCA) 09026 61816-2
Debussy/Janáček/Shostakovich—String Quartets

VOGT, Annette (mez)
Delius: Village Romeo and Juliet (Cpte)

VOGT, Joachim (ten)
Henze: Voices (Cpte)

VOGT, Lars (pf)
Grieg: Piano Concerto
Schumann: Piano Concerto
see CONCERT INDEX under:
(EMI) CDC7 54446-2   Lars Vogt—Piano Recital

(EMI) CDC7 54548-2
Komarova/Mussorgsky/Tchaikovsky—Piano Works

VOGT, Richard (spkr)
Weill: Lost in the Stars (Cpte)

VOICES OF ASCENSION
cond D. KEENE
see CONCERT INDEX under:
(DELO) DE3186   Heigh Ho! Mozart

VOIGT, Deborah (sop)
Berlioz: Troyens (Cpte)
Mahler: Symphony 8
Weber: Oberon (Cpte)
see CONCERT INDEX under:
(EMI) CDC7 54643-2   Rossini—Bicentenary Gala
Concert

VOINEAG, Ionel (ten)
Bretan: Arald (Cpte)

VOISE, Olivier (cl)
see CONCERT INDEX under:
(AUVI) V4644   Debussy/Ravel—Orchestral Songs

VOKETAITIS, Arnold (bar)
Massenet: Cid (Cpte)

VOKETAITIS, Arnold (bass-bar)
D. Moore: Carry Nation (Cpte)

VOLANS, Kevin (hpd)
see CONCERT INDEX under:
(LAND) CTLCD111   Cover him with grass

VOLHARDING ORCHESTRA
cond J. HEMPEL
L. Andriessen: M is for Man

VOLKEN, Edmund (dulcimer)
Holliger: Alb-Chehr

VOLKEN, Marcel (accordion)
Holliger: Alb-Chehr

VÖLKER, Franz (ten)
Wagner: Lohengrin (Cpte)
see CONCERT INDEX under:
(NIMB) NI7848   Great Singers at the Berlin State
Opera
(PEAR) GEMMCD9383   Julius Patzak—Opera &
Operetta Recital
(PREI) 89005   Franz Völker (1899-1965) - I
(PREI) 89070   Franz Völker (1899-1965) - II
(SCHW) 314502   Vienna State Opera—Live
Recordings (sampler)
(SCHW) 314532   Vienna State Opera Live, Vol.3
(SCHW) 314552   Vienna State Opera Live, Vol.5
(SCHW) 314592   Vienna State Opera Live, Vol.9
(SCHW) 314602   Vienna State Opera Live, Vol.10
(SCHW) 314622   Vienna State Opera Live, Vol.12
(SCHW) 314642   Vienna State Opera Live, Vol.14
(SCHW) 314662   Vienna State Opera Live, Vol.16
(SCHW) 314672   Vienna State Opera Live, Vol.17
(TELD) 9031-76442-2   Wagner—Excerpts from the
1936 Bayreuth Festival

VOLKOV, Alexander (pf)
Beethoven: Piano Trios (exc)
Brahms: Clarinet Trio

VOLKOVA, Svetlana (mez)
Prokofiev: War and Peace (Cpte)

VOLLESTAD, Per (bar)
Mozart: Così fan tutte (Cpte)
see CONCERT INDEX under:
(SIMA) PSC1051   Schumann & Wolf—Lieder Recital
(SIMA) PSC1071   Schubert—Lieder
(VIRG) VC5 45051-2   Grieg—Choral Works

VOLZ, Manfred (bass)
Berlioz: Damnation de Faust (Cpte)

(ALEXANDER) VON SCHLIPPENBACH JAZZ BAND
cond M. GIELEN
B. A. Zimmermann: Requiem (Cpte)

VONÁSEK, Rudolf (ten)
Janáček: Makropulos Affair (Cpte)
Smetana: Bartered Bride (Cpte)

VONK, Hans (cond)
see Hague PO

VOORHEES, Donald (cond)
see orch

VORONEZH CHAMBER CHOIR
see CONCERT INDEX under:
(HYPE) CDA66410   Stravinsky—Choral Works
cond J. WOOD
see CONCERT INDEX under:
(HYPE) CDA66410   Stravinsky—Choral Works

VOS, Wim (perc)
Messiaen: Canyons aux étoiles

VOSS, Ralf Friedrich (spkr)
Honegger: Jeanne d'Arc (Cpte)

VOTAPEK, Ralph (pf)
see CONCERT INDEX under:
(MUSI) MACD-649   Salute to France

VOTAVA, Antonín (ten)
Smetana: Brandenburgers in Bohemia (Cpte), Devil's
Wall (Cpte)

VOTIPKA, Thelma (mez)
Verdi: Otello (Cpte)

VOTTO, Antonino (cond)
see La Scala Orch

VOZZA, Corinna (mez)
Donizetti: Lucia di Lammermoor (Cpte)
Mascagni: Cavalleria Rusticana (Cpte)
Verdi: Forza del destino (Cpte), Rigoletto (Cpte)
see CONCERT INDEX under:
(EMI) CMS7 64165-2   Puccini—Trittico
(RCA) GD60941   Rarities - Montserrat Caballé
(RCA) 09026 61236-2   Leontyne Price - Prima Donna
Collection

VRASPIR, Lubomir (ten)
Dvořák: St Ludmilla (Cpte)

VRIEND, Jan Willem de (cond)
see Amsterdam Bach Sols

VRIES, Han de (ob)
Telemann: Sonate Metodiche (exc)
see CONCERT INDEX under:
(CALA) CACD1005   Ravel—Orchestral Works, Vol.2
(EMI) CDC5 55000-2   Bach—Cantata Arias

VRONSKÝ, Petr (cond)
see Brno St PO

VROOMAN, Richard van (ten)
Cimarosa: Requiem in G minor

VYBÍRALOVÁ, Ludmila (vn)
see CONCERT INDEX under:
(SUPR) 11 1533-2   Suk—Chamber Works, Volume 3

VYVYAN, Jennifer (sop)
Britten: Turn of the Screw (Cpte)
Purcell: Fairy Queen, Z629 (Cpte)
Schumann: Szenen aus Goethes Faust (Cpte)
see CONCERT INDEX under:
(DECC) 436 990-2DWO   The World of Benjamin
Britten
(LOND) 433 200-2LHO2   Britten—Owen Wingrave,
etc
(LOND) 436 393-2LM   Britten—The Little Sweep, etc
(LOND) 436 396-2LM   Britten—Spring Symphony,
etc

WAAL, Rian de (pf)
Brahms: Piano Quintet
see CONCERT INDEX under:
(CHNN) CG9106   Mendelssohn—Piano Works
(HYPE) CDA66496   Leopold Godowsky—Piano
Transcriptions

WAARDENBURG, Erika (hp)
see CONCERT INDEX under:
(OLYM) OCD459   Roussel—Chamber Music, Vol. 2

WAART, Edo de (cond)
see Dutch Rad PO

WACHSMUTH, Hans-Jürgen (ten)
Wagner: Parsifal (Cpte)

WÄCHTER, Waltraut (vn)
(ONDI) ODE771-2   Weill—Orchestral and Vocal
Works

WADSWORTH, Charles (pf)
Rorem: Winter Pages

WADSWORTH, Derek (cond)
see Czech SO

WAECHTER, Eberhard (bar)
Berg: Wozzeck (Cpte)
J. Strauss II: Fledermaus (Cpte)
Lehár: Lustige Witwe (Cpte)
Mozart: Don Giovanni (Cpte), Idomeneo (Cpte),
Nozze di Figaro (Cpte)
Offenbach: Vie Parisienne (exc)
R. Strauss: Arabella (Cpte), Capriccio (Cpte),
Rosenkavalier (Cpte), Salome (Cpte)
Wagner: Rheingold (Cpte), Tannhäuser (Cpte),
Tristan und Isolde (Cpte)
Weber: Freischütz (Cpte)
see CONCERT INDEX under:
(DECC) 414 100-2DM15   Wagner: Der Ring des
Nibelungen

WAGEMAN, Rose (mez)
Korngold: Tote Stadt (Cpte)

WAGENFÜHRER, Roland (ten)
Wagner: Meistersinger (Cpte)

WAGLER, Dietrich (organ)
see CONCERT INDEX under:
(PRIO) PRCD332   Great European Organs No 24

WAGMANN, Rose (mez)
Hindemith: Mathis der Maler (Cpte)

WAGNER, Axel (bass)
see CONCERT INDEX under:
(PREI) 93368   Mendelssohn—Lieder

WAGNER, Friederike (sop)
Bach: Mass in B minor, BWV232 (Cpte)
(NAXO) 8 550431   Bach—Soprano Cantatas

WAGNER, James (ten)
J.C. Bach: Amadis de Gaule (Cpte)
Various: Messa per Rossini (Cpte)
(SCHW) 314050   Weill—Vocal and Choral Works

WAGNER, José (sngr)
Weill: Kuhhandel (exc)

WAGNER, Pop (bar)
Britten: Paul Bunyan (Cpte)

WAGNER, Reinhardt (cond)
see Camargue PO

WAGNER, Robert (cond)
see Innsbruck Cons Ch

WAGNER, Siegfried (cond)
see Bayreuth Fest Orch

WAGNER, Sieglinde (mez)
Dvořák: Requiem
Mozart: Zauberflöte (Cpte)
R. Strauss: Elektra (Cpte)
Wagner: Fliegende Holländer (Cpte),
Götterdämmerung (Cpte), Parsifal (Cpte), Walküre
(Cpte)
see CONCERT INDEX *under:*
(DG) 423 127-2GX4   Bruckner: Sacred Works for
Chorus
(EMI) CDH5 65201-2   Leonie Rysanek - Operatic
Recital
(EMI) CMS5 65212-2   Wagner—Les introuvables du
Ring
(PHIL) 446 057-2PB14   Wagner—The Ring Cycle -
Bayreuth Festival 1967

WAGNER, Stefan (vn)
see CONCERT INDEX *under:*
(SCHW) 311672   Schulhoff—Chamber Music for
Violin, Cello and Piano

WAGNER, Wolfgang (db)
Mendelssohn: Sextet, Op.110

WAGSTAFF, Lindsay (sop)
see CONCERT INDEX *under:*
(CHAN) CHAN9363   Adams/Lang—Wind Music

WAHL, Anders de (narr)
see CONCERT INDEX *under:*
(CPRI) CAP21510   Rosenberg plays Rosenberg

WAHLGREN, Per-Arne (bar)
Zemlinsky: Es war einmal (Cpte)

WAHLUND, Sten (bar)
Lidholm: Dream Play (Cpte)

WAILING, Michael B. (sngr)
Porter: Anything Goes (Cpte)

WAIT, Mark (pf)
Bryars: Jesus' Blood

WAKABAYASHI, Nobu (vn)
see CONCERT INDEX *under:*
(CARL) PCD1050   Brahms—Violin Sonatas

WAKAMATSU, Natsumi (vn)
Rameau: Pièces de clavecin en concerts

WAKASUGI, Hiroshi (cond)
see Cologne RSO

WAKEFIELD, Henrietta (sop)
Verdi: Traviata (Cpte)

WAKEFIELD, John (ten)
Cavalli: Ormindo (Cpte)
Handel: Messiah (Cpte)
Sullivan: Mikado (Cpte)

WAKEHAM, Michael (bar)
Sullivan: Gondoliers (Cpte)

WALCH, Silvia (vn)
Boccherini: Sextets, G461-6 (exc)
see CONCERT INDEX *under:*
(CAPR) 10 453   Boccherini Edition, Vol.8

WALCHA, Helmut (organ)
see CONCERT INDEX *under:*
(ARCH) 419 904-2AX12(1)   Bach: Organ Works
(ARCH) 427 133-2AGA   Buxtehude: Organ Works

WALDEN, Peter (cond)
see Raphaele Concert Orch

WALDEN, Timothy (vc)
see CONCERT INDEX *under:*
(VIRG) VC7 59285-2   Favourite Czech Orchestral
Works

WALDENAU, Elisabeth (mez)
Mozart: Nozze di Figaro (Cpte)

WALDHANS, Jiří (cond)
see Brno St PO

WALDIMIR, Sune (cond)
see orch

WALDMAN, Frederick (cond)
see Musica aeterna

WALES, Pauline (mez)
Sullivan: Iolanthe (Cpte), Mikado (exc), Pirates of
Penzance (Cpte)
see CONCERT INDEX *under:*
(DECC) 430 095-2DWO   The World of Gilbert &
Sullivan, Vol.1
(DECC) 433 868-2DWO   The World of Gilbert &
Sullivan - Volume 2

WALEVSKA, Christine (vc)
see CONCERT INDEX *under:*
(PHIL) 438 797-2PM2   Haydn—Concertos

WALKER, Alan (treb)
see CONCERT INDEX *under:*
(CHAN) CHAN8658   Poulenc & Charpentier: Sacred
Choral Works

WALKER, Arnetia (sngr)
Gershwin: Pardon My English (Cpte)

WALKER, Blythe (sop)
Rachmaninov: Monna Vanna (exc)

WALKER, Chris (cond)
see London Cast

WALKER, Drummond (ten)
Spohr: Faust (Cpte)

WALKER, Esther (sngr)
see CONCERT INDEX *under:*
(PEAR) GEMMCDS9059/61   Music from the New York
Stage, Vol. 4: 1917-20

WALKER, Helen (sop)
Purcell: Dido (Cpte)

WALKER, James (fl)
see CONCERT INDEX *under:*
(DECC) 433 220-2DWO   The World of the Violin

WALKER, Kim (bn)
Boismortier: Sonatas, Op.26 (exc), Sonatas, Op.50
(exc)
see CONCERT INDEX *under:*
(DECC) 436 415-2DH   R. Strauss—Orchestral Works
(GALL) CD-499   Bassoon Concertos
(REGE) REGCD104   The Bel Canto Bassoon

WALKER, Malcolm (narr)
Debussy: Pelléas et Mélisande (Cpte)
Gluck: Rencontre imprévue (Cpte)
see CONCERT INDEX *under:*
(ASV) CDDCA758   Falla, Milhaud &
Stravinsky—Operas

WALKER, Nellie (contr)
Handel: Messiah (Cpte)
Sullivan: Pirates of Penzance (Cpte)
see CONCERT INDEX *under:*
(CLAR) CDGSE78-50-35/6   Wagner—Historical
recordings
(PEAR) GEMMCDS9137   Wagner—Der Ring des
Nibelungen

WALKER, Nina (pf)
Rossini: Soirées musicales
see CONCERT INDEX *under:*
(EMI) CDM5 65101-2   A Warlock Centenary Album
(EMI) CDM7 64716-2   Ireland—Piano Concerto, etc
(SONY) SM3K47154   Bernstein—Theatre Works
Volume 1

WALKER, Norman (bass)
Elgar: Dream of Gerontius (Cpte)
see CONCERT INDEX *under:*
(EMI) CHS7 69741-2(2)   Record of Singing,
Vol.4—Anglo-American School (pt 2)
(SYMP) SYMCD1130   Joseph Holbrooke—Historic
Recordings

WALKER, Penelope (mez)
Britten: Midsummer Night's Dream (Cpte)
Mathias: Lux aeterna
see CONCERT INDEX *under:*
(OPRA) ORCH103   Italian Opera—1810-20
(OPRA) ORCH104   A Hundred Years of Italian Opera:
1820-1830

WALKER, Sarah (mez)
Beethoven: Symphony 9
Britten: Peter Grimes (Cpte)
Buller: Proença
Fauré: Bonne chanson, Op. 61
Gay: Beggar's Opera (Cpte)
Handel: Giulio Cesare (Cpte), Hercules (Cpte)
Mendelssohn: Midsummer Night's Dream (exc)
Mozart: Requiem
Stravinsky: Rake's Progress (Cpte)
Tchaikovsky: Eugene Onegin (Cpte)
Tippett: Child of our Time, Ice Break (Cpte), Mask of
Time
Vaughan Williams: Hugh the Drover (Cpte)
Verdi: Traviata (Cpte)
Wagner: Walküre (Cpte)
see CONCERT INDEX *under:*
(CHAN) CHAN8457   Falla—El amor brujo; Nights in
the gardens of Spain
(CRD) CRD3401   Schumann: Lieder
(CRD) CRD3464   Schubert: Lieder
(CRD) CRD3473   Dreams and Fancies
(CRD) CRD3476   Fauré—Chansons, Vol.1
(CRD) CRD3477   Fauré—Chansons, Vol.2
(GAMU) GAMD506   An Anthology Of English Song
(HYPE) CDA66165   The Sea
(HYPE) CDA66323   Duparc: Mélodies
(HYPE) CDA66420   Vaughan Williams: Vocal Works
(HYPE) CDA67061/2   Britten—Purcell Realizations
(HYPE) CDJ33006   Schubert—Complete Lieder, Vol 8
(MERI) CDE84167   Cabaret Songs
(MERI) CDE84232   Brahms/Dvořák—Gypsy Songs
(UNIC) DKPCD9063   Delius—Choral & Orchestral
Works
(UNIC) UKCD2073   The Delius Collection, Volume 3
(VIRG) VC5 45016-2   Ravel—Chamber & Vocal Works

WALKER, Timothy (gtr)
Buller: Proença
see CONCERT INDEX *under:*
(CARL) MCD57   Britten—Songs

WALKER SMITH, Nicola (sngr)
see CONCERT INDEX *under:*
(SONY) SK66605   Geoff Smith—Fifteen Wild
Decembers

WALL, Roberta (sngr)
Gershwin: Pardon My English (Cpte)

WALLACE, Ian (bass)
Mozart: Nozze di Figaro (Cpte)
Rossini: Barbiere di Siviglia (Cpte), Cenerentola
(Cpte), Comte Ory (Cpte)
see CONCERT INDEX *under:*
(BBCR) BBCRD9106   The Music of Eric Coates
(EMI) CDH5 65072-2   Glyndebourne Recorded - 1934-
1994

WALLACE, John (cond)
see Wallace Collection

WALLACE, John (cornet)
see CONCERT INDEX *under:*
(EMI) CDC5 55086-2   Trumpet Recital

WALLACE, John (tpt)
Goehr: Sing, Ariel, Op. 51
Maxwell Davies: Trumpet Concerto
see CONCERT INDEX *under:*
(EMI) CDC5 55086-2   Trumpet Recital
(NIMB) NI5103   Music for Brass, Piano and
Percussion
(NIMB) NI5121   Virtuoso Trumpet Concertos
(NIMB) NI5189   Telemann: Trumpet Concertos
(NIMB) NI7016   Classical Trumpet Concertos

WALLACE, Mervyn (ten)
Gershwin: Porgy and Bess (Cpte)

WALLACE COLLECTION
   cond J. WALLACE
see CONCERT INDEX *under:*
(COLL) Coll1229-2   The Wallace Collection
(NIMB) NI5103   Music for Brass, Piano and
Percussion
(NIMB) NI5129   Sousa: Marches
(NIMB) NI5175   French Revolution- orchestral music
   cond S. WRIGHT
see CONCERT INDEX *under:*
(NIMB) NI5103   Music for Brass, Piano and
Percussion
(TELA) CD80204   Gabrieli and St Mark's—Venetian
Brass Music

WALLBERG, Heinz (cond)
see Bamberg SO

WALLÉN, Martti (bass)
Bergman: Singing Tree (Cpte)

WALLENDORF, Klaus (hn)
see CONCERT INDEX *under:*
(ORFE) C153861A   Romantic Lieder

WALLENSTEIN, Alfred (cond)
see BPO

WALLENSTEIN, Alfred (vc)
see CONCERT INDEX *under:*
(PEAR) GEMMCDS9922   New York Philharmonic -
150th Anniversary
(RCA) 09026 60929-2   R.Strauss—Tone Poems

WALLER, Adalbert (bass)
S. Wagner: Bärenhäuter (Cpte)

WALLEZ, Amaury (bn)
see CONCERT INDEX *under:*
(DECC) 421 581-2DH   Poulenc—Chamber Works
(EMI) CZS7 62736-2   Poulenc—Chamber Works

WALLEZ, Jean-Pierre (cond)
see Instr Ens of France

WALLEZ, Jean-Pierre (vn)
Beethoven: Romances, Violin Concerto
Bruch: Violin Concerto
Mendelssohn: Violin Concerto, Op. 64
see CONCERT INDEX *under:*
(DECC) 436 798-2DH   Loussier—Concertos

WALLFISCH, Elizabeth (vn)
Brahms: String Sextet 1, String Sextet 2
Corelli: Trio Sonatas, Op. 3 (exc)
Locatelli: Concertos, Op. 3
Rossini: Sonate a Quattro
see CONCERT INDEX *under:*
(HYPE) CDA66380   Bach—Violin Concertos
(MERI) CDE84195   Vivaldi: Orchestral and Vocal
Works

WALLFISCH, Elizabeth (vn/dir)
Biber: Harmonia artificioso–ariosa
see CONCERT INDEX *under:*
(VIRG) VC5 45095-2   Bach—Concertos
(VIRG) VC7 59266-2   Haydn—Orchestral Works

WALLFISCH, Peter (pf)
Brahms: Cello Sonata 1, Cello Sonata 2
see CONCERT INDEX *under:*
(CHAN) CHAN8499   English Music for Cello and Piano
(CHAN) CHAN9132   Leighton—Chamber Works

WALLFISCH, Raphael (vc)
Barber: Cello Concerto
Brahms: Cello Sonata 1, Cello Sonata 2, Double
Concerto
Britten: Cello Symphony
Dohnányi: Konzertstück, Op.12
Dvořák: Cello Concerto
Finzi: Cello Concerto
Hindemith: Cello Concerto

R. Strauss: Elektra (Cpte)
Schoenberg: Moses und Aron (Cpte)
Tippett: Child of Our Time (Cpte)
Vaughan Williams: Hugh the Drover (Cpte)
Wagner: Götterdämmerung (Cpte), Walküre (Cpte)
see CONCERT INDEX under:
(DECC) 414 100-2DM15   Wagner: Der Ring des Nibelungen
(DECC) 430 160-2DM   Haydn: Masses & Keyboard Concerto
(DECC) 430 804-2DC10   Mahler—Complete Symphonies
(DECC) 433 175-2DM   Bach—Sacred Choral Works
(DECC) 436 407-2DWO   The World of Schubert
(DECC) 443 009-2DF2   Mozart—Choral Works
(DECC) 443 455-2DF2   Vivaldi—Sacred Choral Works
(EMI) CDM7 64218-2   Vaughan Williams—Riders to the Sea; Epithalamion, etc
(EMI) CMS7 64218-2   Delius—Vocal Works
(HANS) 98 801   Bach—Cantatas, Vol.39
(HANS) 98 802   Bach—Cantatas, Vol.40
(HANS) 98 803   Bach—Cantatas, Vol.41
(HANS) 98 805   Bach—Cantatas, Vol.43
(HANS) 98 806   Bach—Cantatas, Vol.44
(HANS) 98 807   Bach—Cantatas, Vol.45
(HANS) 98 808   Bach—Cantatas, Vol.46
(HANS) 98 809   Bach—Cantatas, Vol.47
(HANS) 98 811   Bach—Cantatas, Vol.49
(HANS) 98 813   Bach—Cantatas, Vol.51
(HANS) 98 814   Bach—Cantatas, Vol.52
(HANS) 98 818   Bach—Cantatas, Vol.56
(HANS) 98 819   Bach—Cantatas, Vol.57
(HANS) 98 820   Bach—Cantatas, Vol.58
(HANS) 98 821   Bach—Cantatas, Vol.59
(HANS) 98 822   Bach—Cantatas, Vol.60
(HANS) 98 826   Bach—Cantatas, Vol.64
(HANS) 98 863   Bach—Cantatas, Vol.12
(HANS) 98 869   Bach—Cantatas, Vol.18
(HANS) 98 870   Bach—Cantatas, Vol.19
(HANS) 98 872   Bach—Cantatas, Vol.21
(HANS) 98 874   Bach—Cantatas, Vol.23
(HANS) 98 875   Bach—Cantatas, Vol.24
(HANS) 98 876   Bach—Cantatas, Vol.25
(HANS) 98 877   Bach—Cantatas, Vol.26
(HANS) 98 878   Bach—Cantatas, Vol.27
(HANS) 98 879   Bach—Cantatas, Vol.28
(HANS) 98 883   Bach—Cantatas, Vol.32
(HANS) 98 885   Bach—Cantatas, Vol.34
(HANS) 98 886   Bach—Cantatas, Vol.35
(HANS) 98 887   Bach—Cantatas, Vol.36
(HANS) 98 890   Bach—Cantatas, Vol.37
(LOND) 436 396-2LM   Britten—Spring Symphony, etc
(TELD) 4509-93687-2   Bach—Cantatas

WATTS, Jane (organ)
see CONCERT INDEX under:
(PRIO) PRCD237   Great European Organs No. 7
(PRIO) PRCD286   Great European Organs, No. 18
(PRIO) PRCD294   Great European Organs No.19
(PRIO) PRCD377   Great European Organs, Vol.29
(PRIO) PRCD414   Great European Organs, Vol.32
(PRIO) PRCD491   Great European Organs, Vol 37
(UNIC) DKPCD9057   A Christmas Garland

WATTS, Nathan (treb)
Mozart: Zauberflöte (Cpte)

WATZKE, Rudolf (bass)
Beethoven: Symphony 9
see CONCERT INDEX under:
(DANA) DACOCD315/6   Lauritz Melchior Anthology - Vol. 3
(PREI) 89201   Helge Roswaenge (1897-1972) - I
(TAHR) FURT1004/7   Furtwängler conducts the Berlin Philharmonic

WAUGH, Nancy (contr)
see CONCERT INDEX under:
(DECC) 433 400-2DM2   Ravel & Debussy—Stage Works

WAXMAN, Franz (cond)
see OST

WAYENBERG, Daniel (pf)
see CONCERT INDEX under:
(CHNN) CG9107   Music for Clarinet, Piano & Viola

WAYNFLETE SINGERS
cond R. HICKOX
Mahler: Klagende Lied (Cpte)
see CONCERT INDEX under:
(CHAN) CHAN9214   Delius—Choral Works
cond D. HILL
see CONCERT INDEX under:
(ARGO) 430 836-2ZH   English Sacred Choral Music
(ARGO) 436 120-2ZH   Vaughan Williams/Walton—Choral & Orchestral Works
cond A. LITTON
see CONCERT INDEX under:
(LOND) 448 134-2LH   Walton—Belshazzar's Feast, etc

WEARING, Catherine (sop)
Britten: Little Sweep (Cpte)

WEATHERS, Felicia (sop)
R. Strauss: Elektra (Cpte)
see CONCERT INDEX under:
(DECC) 417 686-2DC   Puccini—Operatic Arias

WEAVER, James (bass)
see CONCERT INDEX under:
(KOCH) 37163-2   Bach—Cantatas

WEBB, Barbara (sop)
Britten: Curlew River (Cpte)
Gershwin: Porgy and Bess (exc)

WEBBER, Aaron (treb)
see CONCERT INDEX under:
(HYPE) CDA66693   Purcell—Complete Anthems and Services, Volume 9
(HYPE) CDA66707   Purcell—Complete Anthems & Services, Vol. 10
(HYPE) CDA66716   Purcell—Complete Anthems and Services, Volume 11
(HYPE) CDA66757   Duruflé—Requiem

WEBBER, Geoffrey (cond)
see Gonville & Caius College Ch

WEBBER, Geoffrey (organ)
see CONCERT INDEX under:
(ABBE) CDCA914   The English Anthem, Vol.4

WEBER, Heinrich (ten)
Anon: Missa Salisburgensis, Plaudite tympana
Egk: Peer Gynt (Cpte)
Killmayer: Yolimba (Cpte)
Korngold: Violanta (Cpte)
Mascagni: Iris (Cpte)
Puccini: Fanciulla del West (Cpte)

WEBER, Janice (pf)
Liszt: Études d'exécution, S139
see CONCERT INDEX under:
(CARL) PCD1051   Rachmaninov—Piano Transcriptions

WEBER, Joe (sngr)
see CONCERT INDEX under:
(PEAR) GEMMCDS9050/2(1)   Music from the New York Stage, Vol. 1 (part 1)

WEBER, Kurt (cl)
see CONCERT INDEX under:
(NOVA) 150 026-2   Schubert—Lieder

WEBER, Ludwig (bass)
Mozart: Zauberflöte (Cpte)
R. Strauss: Rosenkavalier (Cpte)
Wagner: Parsifal (Cpte), Rheingold (Cpte)
see CONCERT INDEX under:
(DUTT) CDLX7007   Beecham conducts Wagner
(EMI) CHS7 69741-2(4)   Record of Singing, Vol.4—German School
(EMI) CMS7 64008-2(2)   Wagner Singing on Record (pt 2)
(FOYE) 15-CF2011   Wagner—Der Ring de Nibelungen
(LYRC) LCD146   Frida Leider sings Wagner

WEBER, Margrit (pf)
see CONCERT INDEX under:
(DG) 445 400-2GDO10   Ferenc Fricsay - A Portrait
(DG) 445 403-2GDO   R. Strauss—Orchestral Works
(DG) 445 405-2GDO   Stravinsky—Orchestral Works
(DG) 447 343-2GDB2   Stravinsky—Orchestral & Choral Works

WEBER, Peter (bass)
Schoeck: Penthesilea (Cpte)

WEBER, Peter (ten)
Mozart: Zauberflöte (Cpte)
R. Strauss: Ariadne auf Naxos (Cpte)
Verdi: Ballo in maschera (Cpte)

(CARL MARIA VON) WEBER MEN'S CHOIR
cond G. ALBRECHT
Dessau: Hagadah Shel Pessach
cond S. SOLTESZ
Mendelssohn: Antigone (Cpte), Oedipus (Cpte)

WEBERN, Anton (cond)
see BBC SO

WEBSTER, Ferguson (pf)
see CONCERT INDEX under:
(TEST) SBT1003   The Young Menuhin—Encores, Vol.1

WEBSTER, Gillian (sop)
Britten: Peter Grimes (Cpte)

WEBSTER, Roger (cornet)
see CONCERT INDEX under:
(CHAN) CHAN4523   Concerto
(POLY) QPRL049D   Boosey & Hawkes National Brass Band Gala Concert 1991

WEDIN, Jan-Olav (cond)
see Stockholm Sinfonietta

WEDIN, Lage (bass)
Haeffner: Electra (Cpte)

WEEMS, Nancy (pf)
see CONCERT INDEX under:
(BAY) BCD-1014   Classical Hollywood

WEGMANN, Christoph (treb)
see CONCERT INDEX under:
(TELD) 2292-42632-2   Bach—Cantatas, Volume 37
(TELD) 2292-42633-2   Bach—Cantatas, Volume 38
(TELD) 2292-42634-2   Bach—Cantatas, Volume 39
(TELD) 4509-91762-2   Bach—Cantatas, Vol.8
(TELD) 4509-91763-2   Bach—Cantatas, Vol.9
(TELD) 9031-74798-2   Bach—Arias and Duets

WEGNER, Ekkehard (ten)
Bach: St. Matthew Passion, BWV244 (Cpte)

WEGNER, Walburga (sop)
see CONCERT INDEX under:
(ACAN) 43 268   Peter Anders sings German Opera Arias

WEHLE, Reiner (cl)
see CONCERT INDEX under:
(NOVA) 150 006-2   Mozart: Chamber Works

WEI, Xue (vn)
Brahms: Violin Concerto
Bruch: Violin Concerto 1
Headington: Violin Concerto
Mendelssohn: Violin Concerto, Op. 64
R. Strauss: Violin Concerto
Saint-Saëns: Violin Concerto 3
see CONCERT INDEX under:
(ASV) CDDCA698   Violin Virtuoso
(ASV) CDDCA713   Tchaikovsky—Works for Violin and Orchestra
(ASV) CDDCA892   Saint-Saëns—Violin Works

WEICHERT, Caroline (pf)
see CONCERT INDEX under:
(ACCO) 20025-2   Shostakovich: Piano Works

WEICHERT, Elsa (contr)
see CONCERT INDEX under:
(SCHW) 314592   Vienna State Opera Live, Vol.9

WEICHERT, Matthias (bass)
Krenek: Jonny spielt auf (Cpte)

WEICHHOLD, Monika (mez)
see CONCERT INDEX under:
(EMI) CZS7 67819-2   Brahms/Schumann—Requiems

WEIDINGER, Christine (sop)
Handel: Rinaldo (Cpte)
Mozart: Mitridate (Cpte)

WEIERINK, Jeroen (cond)
see J. Triebensee Ens

WEIGEL, Wolfgang (gtr)
see CONCERT INDEX under:
(SCHW) 312362   Spanish Guitar Concertos

WEIGERT, Hermann (cond)
see Berlin St Op Orch

WEIGLE, Jörg-Peter (cond)
see Dresden PO

WEIGLE, Sebastian (hn)
see CONCERT INDEX under:
(CAPR) 10 805   Mozart: Wind Concertos

WEIKERT, Ralf (cond)
see Munich RSO

WEIKL, Bernd (bar)
Dessau: Hagadah Shel Pessach
Gluck: Alceste (1776) (Cpte)
Haydn: Schöpfung (Cpte)
Humperdinck: Hänsel und Gretel (Cpte)
Leoncavallo: Bohème (Cpte)
Mozart: Don Giovanni (Cpte)
Orff: Carmina burana
Pfitzner: Palestrina (Cpte)
R. Strauss: Elektra (Cpte)
Schubert: Winterreise (Cpte)
Tchaikovsky: Eugene Onegin (Cpte)
Verdi: Rigoletto (Cpte)
Wagner: Götterdämmerung (Cpte), Meistersinger (Cpte), Tannhäuser (Cpte), Tristan und Isolde (Cpte)
Weber: Freischütz (Cpte)
see CONCERT INDEX under:
(ACAN) 43 266   Bernd Weikl—Operatic Recital
(DG) 445 354-2GX14   Wagner—Der Ring des Nibelungen
(EMI) CZS7 62707-2   Mahler—Vocal Works
(PHIL) 426 290-2PH5   Beethoven—Complete Symphonies

WEIL, Bruno (cond)
see Archibudelli

WEIL, Terence (vc)
see CONCERT INDEX under:
(EMI) CHS7 69741-2(2)   Record of Singing, Vol.4—Anglo-American School (pt 2)

WEINER, Stanley (va)
S. Weiner: Viola Concerto

WEINER, Stanley (vn)
S. Weiner: Violin Concerto 4

WEINGARTNER, Felix (cond)
see LPO

WEINHAPPEL, Thomas (alto)
Schubert: Mass, D678

WEINMEISTER, Gabriele (vn)
see CONCERT INDEX under:
(CPO) CPO999 020-2   Wilhelm Killmayer: Chamber Works

WEIR, Gillian (organ)
Saint-Saëns: Symphony 3
see CONCERT INDEX under:
(CHAN) CHAN8861   Stanford: Orchestral Works
(COLL) Coll7031-2   Messiaen—Organ Works
(DECC) 433 080-2DM   Kodály—Choral Works
(KOSS) KC1013   Organ Works

WEIR, Scot (ten)
Franck: Béatitudes (Cpte)
Mendelssohn: Hochzeit des Camacho (Cpte)
Mozart: Mass, K427
see CONCERT INDEX under:
(HANS) 98 979   Mozart—Sacred Choral Works

WEIRICH, Robert (pf)
see CONCERT INDEX under:

(KOCH) **37281-2** Amy Beach/Rebecca Clarke—Cello Works

WEISBACH, Hans (cond)
see Vienna SO

WEISBERG, Arthur (cond)
see NYPO

WEISE, Klaus (cond)
see Nice PO

WEISE, Manfred (cl)
see CONCERT INDEX under:
(EMI) **CDM7 69661-2**   R. Strauss—Wind Concertos
(EMI) **CMS7 64342-2**   R. Strauss—Orchestral Works, Vol.1

WEISHEIT, Silke (contr)
see CONCERT INDEX under:
(CAPR) **10 310/1**   J. E. Bach—Passion Oratorio, etc.
(CAPR) **10 315**   Telemann—Choral Music

WEISS, Catherine (vn)
Corelli: Trio Sonatas, Op. 4 (exc)

WEISS, Franz (narr)
see CONCERT INDEX under:
(PREI) **89034**   Giuseppe Lugo (1900-1980)

WEISS, Herbert (treb)
Puccini: Tosca (Cpte)

WEISS, Ursula (vn)
see CONCERT INDEX under:
(MOSC) **070978**   Maurice Greene—Songs and Keyboard Works

WEISSENBERG, Alexis (pf)
Mussorgsky: Pictures
Tchaikovsky: Piano Concerto 1
see CONCERT INDEX under:
(EMI) **CDM7 64747-2**   Franck—Orchestral Works
(EMI) **CDM7 69112-2**   Best of Saint-Saëns

WEISSENBORN, Günther (pf)
(DG) **437 680-2GDO2**   Rita Streich - Lieder Recital

WEISSMANN, Frieder (cond)
see Berlin SO

WEISSMANN, Frieder (pf)
see CONCERT INDEX under:
(CLAR) **CDGSE78-50-57**   Lotte Lehmann sings Lieder

WELBECK LIGHT QUARTET
see CONCERT INDEX under:
(PEAR) **PASTCD9744**   Campoli's Choice

WELCH, Jonathan (ten)
Puccini: Bohème (Cpte)

WELDON, George (cond)
see Philh

WELIN, Karl-Erik (organ)
see CONCERT INDEX under:
(WERG) **WER60161-50**   Ligeti: Instrumental Works

WELITSCH, Alexander (bass)
Verdi: Don Carlo (exc)

WELITSCH, Ljuba (sop)
J. Strauss II: Fledermaus (Cpte)
R. Strauss: Rosenkavalier (Cpte)
see CONCERT INDEX under:
(EMI) **CHS7 69741-2(4)**   Record of Singing, Vol.4—German School

WELKER, Hartmut (bar)
Beethoven: Fidelio (Cpte)
Korngold: Wunder der Heliane (Cpte)
Schmidt: Notre Dame (Cpte)
Schoenberg: Gurrelieder
Schubert: Fierrabras (Cpte)
Wagner: Lohengrin (Cpte)
Zemlinsky: Traumgörge (Cpte)

WELLBAUM, Lisa (hp)
see CONCERT INDEX under:
(DECC) **443 175-2DH**   Mozart—Orchestral Works

WELLER, Dieter (bass)
Flotow: Martha (Cpte)
Ligeti: Grand Macabre (Cpte)
Schreker: Schatzgräber (Cpte)
Zemlinsky: Geburtstag der Infantin (Cpte)

WELLER, Lawrence (bar)
Britten: Paul Bunyan (Cpte)

WELLER, Walter (cond)
see CBSO

WELLER QUARTET
Haydn: String Quartet, Op. 103, String Quartets, Op. 1 (exc), String Quartets, Op. 33 (exc)

WELLINGTON, Christopher (va)
see CONCERT INDEX under:
(ASV) **CDDCA769**   Franck—Miscellaneous Works
(EMI) **CDM5 65101-2**   A Warlock Centenary Album

WELLINGTON COLLEGE CHOIRS (BERKSHIRE)
cond S. ANDERSON
see CONCERT INDEX under:
(HERA) **HAVPCD153**   Give us the Wings of Faith

WELLS, Jeffrey (bass-bar)
Verdi: Traviata (Cpte)

WELLS, Mary (sop)
Britten: Little Sweep (Cpte)
Purcell: Fairy Queen, Z629 (Cpte)

WELLS, Patricia (sop)
see CONCERT INDEX under:
(SONY) **SM2K47563**   Haydn—Choral & Orchestral Works

WELLS, Robin (organ)
see CONCERT INDEX under:
(HERA) **HAVPCD142**   Christmas at Charterhouse

WELLS CATHEDRAL CHOIR
cond A. CROSSLAND
see CONCERT INDEX under:
(PRIO) **PRCD337**   Psalms of David, Volume 2

WELLS CATHEDRAL VICARS CHORAL
cond A. NETHSINGHA
see CONCERT INDEX under:
(ABBE) **CDCA924**   The Vicars Choral of Wells Cathedral

WELSBY, Norman (bar)
Wagner: Götterdämmerung (Cpte), Rheingold (Cpte)

WELSER-MÖST, Franz (cond)
see LPO

WELSH, Moray (vc)
Brahms: String Sextet 1, String Sextet 2
Goehr: Romanza, Op.24
see CONCERT INDEX under:
(ASV) **CDDCA907**   Bottesini—Volume 3 - Passioni Amorose
(CHAN) **CHAN6542**   Grainger—Famous Folk-settings
(CHAN) **CHAN9345**   McEwen—Orchestral Works
(EMI) **CDC5 55398-2**   Britten—Chamber Works
(EMI) **CDC5 55399-2**   Delius—Chamber Works
(HYPE) **CDA66171**   Malcolm Arnold: Chamber Works, Vol. 1
(RCA) **GD86517**   Galway plays Bach

WELSH, Scott (sngr)
see CONCERT INDEX under:
(PEAR) **GEMMCDS9059/61**   Music from the New York Stage, Vol. 4: 1917-20

WELSH NATIONAL OPERA CHORUS
cond D. ATHERTON
see CONCERT INDEX under:
(LYRI) **SRCD324**   Mathias—Choral Works
cond R. BONYNGE
A. Thomas: Hamlet (Cpte)
Bellini: Norma (Cpte)
Cilea: Adriana Lecouvreur (Cpte)
Verdi: Masnadieri (Cpte)
cond R. CHAILLY
Giordano: Andrea Chénier (Cpte)
cond R. GOODALL
Wagner: Tristan und Isolde (Cpte)
cond C. MACKERRAS
Britten: Gloriana (Cpte)
Janáček: Fate (Cpte)
Sullivan: HMS Pinafore (Cpte), Mikado (Cpte), Pirates of Penzance (Cpte)
Tchaikovsky: Eugene Onegin (Cpte)
cond C. RIZZI
Gounod: Faust (Cpte)
Verdi: Rigoletto (Cpte)
see CONCERT INDEX under:
(PHIL) **442 785-2PH**   The Incomparable Alfredo Kraus
cond G. SOLTI
Puccini: Tosca (Cpte)
cond L. STOKOWSKI
see CONCERT INDEX under:
(DECC) **433 625-2DSP**   Stokowski conducts Famous Russian Works

WELSH NATIONAL OPERA ORCHESTRA
cond R. ARMSTRONG
see CONCERT INDEX under:
(EMI) **CDM7 69522-2**   Britten—Vocal Works
cond R. BONYNGE
A. Thomas: Hamlet (Cpte)
Bellini: Norma (Cpte)
Cilea: Adriana Lecouvreur (Cpte)
Messager: Deux Pigeons (Cpte)
Verdi: Masnadieri (Cpte)
cond R. GOODALL
Wagner: Tristan und Isolde (Cpte)
cond C. MACKERRAS
Britten: Gloriana (Cpte)
Janáček: Fate (Cpte)
Sullivan: HMS Pinafore (Cpte), Mikado (Cpte), Pirates of Penzance (Cpte)
Tchaikovsky: Eugene Onegin (Cpte)
see CONCERT INDEX under:
(ARGO) **433 214-2ZH**   Elgar—Music inspired by children
(ARGO) **433 704-2ZH**   Delius—Orchestral Works
cond C. RIZZI
Gounod: Faust (Cpte)
Verdi: Rigoletto (Cpte)
see CONCERT INDEX under:
(PHIL) **442 785-2PH**   The Incomparable Alfredo Kraus
(TELD) **9031-73283-2**   Hampson and Hadley

WELTING, Ruth (sop)
Humperdinck: Hänsel und Gretel (Cpte)
Massenet: Cendrillon (Cpte)
Mozart: Schauspieldirektor (Cpte)
R. Strauss: Rosenkavalier (Cpte)
see CONCERT INDEX under:
(DG) **429 025-2GX10**   Bruckner—Complete Symphonies, etc

(DG) **437 250-2GGA**   Bruckner—Orchestral & Vocal Works

WEMAN, Lena (fl)
see CONCERT INDEX under:
(MSVE) **MSCD415**   Kraus—Chamber Music

WEND, Flore (sop)
see CONCERT INDEX under:
(DECC) **433 400-2DM2**   Ravel & Debussy—Stage Works

WENDLER, Anton (ten)
J. Strauss II: Fledermaus (Cpte)

WENGLOR, Ingeborg (sop)
Beethoven: Symphony 9

WENGRAF, Senta (narr)
J.Strauss II: Fledermaus (Cpte)

WENHASTON BOYS' CHOIR
cond C. BARNETT
see CONCERT INDEX under:
(COLL) **Coll7039-2**   Britten—The Folk Songs

WENHOLD, André (bar)
Pfitzner: Herz (Cpte)
S. Wagner: Bärenhäuter (Cpte), Schwarzschwanenreich (Cpte)

WENK, Erik (bass)
see CONCERT INDEX under:
(ERAT) **4509-97407-2**   Bach—Cantatas

WENKEL, Ortrun (contr)
Henze: Bassariden (Cpte)
Humperdinck: Königskinder (Cpte)
Mozart: Requiem, Zauberflöte (exc)
R. Strauss: Daphne (Cpte)
Shostakovich: Jewish Folk Poetry, Op 79, Marina Tsvetaeva Poems
Wagner: Götterdämmerung (Cpte), Rheingold (Cpte), Siegfried (Cpte), Walküre (Cpte)
see CONCERT INDEX under:
(EMI) **CMS7 64471-2**   Mahler—Symphonies, Vol.1
(SONY) **SMK48462**   Boulez conducts Schoenberg

WENKOFF, Wenko (ten)
see CONCERT INDEX under:
(SCHW) **314552**   Vienna State Opera Live, Vol.5

WENNBERG, Siv (sop)
Wagner: Rienzi (Cpte)

WENNING, Hermann (spkr)
Nono: Intolleranza 1960 (Cpte)

WENT, David (organ)
see CONCERT INDEX under:
(ASV) **CDDCA851**   English Church Music, Vol.1

WENZINGER, August (cond)
see SCB

WERBA, Erik (pf)
Wolf: Italienisches Liederbuch (Cpte)
see CONCERT INDEX under:
(DG) **437 348-2GDO2**   Irmgard Seefried - Lieder Recital
(DG) **437 680-2GDO2**   Rita Streich - Lieder Recital
(FINL) **4509-95606-2**   Kim Borg - Songs and Arias
(ORFE) **C297921B**   Irmgard Seefried—Salzburg Recital, 1957
(ORFE) **C331931A**   Christa Ludwig - Lieder Recital

WERFF, Ivo-Jan van der (va)
F. X. Scharwenka: Piano Quartet, Op. 37, Piano Trio, Op. 45

WERKE, Freydis Ree (hn)
see CONCERT INDEX under:
(UNIC) **DKPCD9110**   Kuhlau—Orchestral works

WERNER, Alfred (bar)
J. Strauss II: Fledermaus (Cpte)

WERNER, Fritz (cond)
see Pforzheim CO

WERNER, Joseph (cond)
see CONCERT INDEX under:
(VANG) **08.4051.71**   Gottschalk—Piano Works, Vol.2

WERNER, Regina (sop)
Wagner: Parsifal (Cpte)

WERNICK, Richard (cond)
see Pennsylvania Univ Chbr Players

WERNIGK, William (ten)
Wagner: Meistersinger (Cpte)
see CONCERT INDEX under:
(EMI) **CHS7 64487-2**   R. Strauss—Der Rosenkavalier & Excerpts
(SCHW) **314532**   Vienna State Opera Live, Vol.3
(SCHW) **314552**   Vienna State Opera Live, Vol.5
(SCHW) **314562**   Vienna State Opera Live, Vol.6
(SCHW) **314572**   Vienna State Opera Live, Vol.7
(SCHW) **314582**   Vienna State Opera Live, Vol.8
(SCHW) **314592**   Vienna State Opera Live, Vol.9
(SCHW) **314602**   Vienna State Opera Live, Vol.10
(SCHW) **314622**   Vienna State Opera Live, Vol.12
(SCHW) **314632**   Vienna State Opera Live, Vol.13
(SCHW) **314652**   Vienna State Opera Live, Vol.15

WESSEL, Kai (alto)
Bach: Cantata 66, Easter Oratorio, BWV249, Mass in B Minor, BWV232 (Cpte), St Matthew Passion, BWV244 (Cpte)
Biber: Requiem in A, Vesperae
Handel: Rodelinda (Cpte)
Telemann: Getreue Music-Meister (Cpte)
see CONCERT INDEX under:

WHEELER, Victoria (sop)
R. Strauss: Elektra (Cpte)

WHELAN, David (bar)
Puccini: Bohème (Cpte)

WHETTON, Alan (sax)
see CONCERT INDEX under:
(ACOU) CDACS014 The Second Mandolin Album

WHISTLER, Simon (va)
Mozart: String Quintet, K515, String Quintet, K516, String Quintet, K593, String Quintet, K614

WHITCOMBE, Michael (sax)
see CONCERT INDEX under:
(KOCH) 37094-2 Ibert/Poulenc—Orchestral Works

WHITE, David (bass cl/sax)
Goehr: Sing, Ariel, Op. 51

WHITE, Frances (sngr)
see CONCERT INDEX under:
(PEAR) GEMMCDS9059/61 Music from the New York Stage, Vol. 4: 1917-20

WHITE, Jeremy (bass)
G. Lloyd: Iernin
Handel: Israel in Egypt (Cpte)
see CONCERT INDEX under:
(HYPE) CDA66311/2 Monteverdi: St Barbara Vespers

WHITE, Nicholas (organ)
see CONCERT INDEX under:
(MERI) CDE84153 French Choral Music

WHITE, Peter (organ)
see CONCERT INDEX under:
(DECC) 430 159-2DM Haydn, M.Haydn & Mozart: Sacred Choral Works
(DECC) 430 498-2DWO The World of Mozart
(DECC) 430 499-2DWO World of Bach
(DECC) 436 402-2DWO The World of Wedding Music

WHITE, Robert (bagpipe)
see CONCERT INDEX under:
(HYPE) CDA66039 A Feather on the Breath of God

WHITE, Robert (ten)
see CONCERT INDEX under:
(VIRG) VJ7 59644-2 Handel—Favourite Arias

WHITE, Robin (cond)
see Southern Fest Orch

WHITE, Wendy (mez)
Stravinsky: Rake's Progress (Cpte)
Verdi: Luisa Miller (Cpte), Traviata (Cpte)
Wagner: Parsifal (Cpte)
see CONCERT INDEX under:
(RCA) 09026 61581-2 Bernstein—Orchestral & Vocal Works

WHITE, Willard (bass)
Britten: Gloriana (Cpte)
Gershwin: Porgy and Bess (Cpte)
Handel: Acis and Galatea (Cpte)
Joplin: Treemonisha (Cpte)
Kern: Show Boat (Cpte)
Mendelssohn: Elijah (Cpte)
Monteverdi: Orfeo (Cpte)
Mozart: Requiem
R. Strauss: Aegyptische Helena (Cpte)
Tippett: Child of Our Time
Zemlinsky: Symphonische Gesänge, Op. 20
see CONCERT INDEX under:
(CHAN) CHAN8960 Copland—Vocal Works
(EMI) CDH5 65072-2 Glyndebourne Recorded - 1934-1994
(EMI) CDS7 54270-2 Rattle Conducts Britten

WHITEHEAD, James (vc)
see CONCERT INDEX under:
(EMI) CHS5 65198-2 Maggie Teyte sings French Songs

WHITEHILL, Clarence (bass-bar)
see CONCERT INDEX under:
(PEAR) GEMMCDS9924(1) Covent Garden on Record, Vol.2 (pt 1)
(RCA) 09026 61580-2(2) RCA/Met 100 Singers, 100 Years (pt 2)
(SYMP) SYMCD1081 The Harold Wayne Collection, Vol.5

WHITELEY, Franklyn (bass)
Puccini: Bohème (Cpte)

WHITELEY, John Scott (organ)
see CONCERT INDEX under:
(PRIO) PRCD324 Jongen—Organ Works, Vol.1
(PRIO) PRCD365 Edward Bairstow—Choral Works
(PRIO) PRCD486 The Psalms of David, Volume 10
(YORK) CD101 Great Romantic Organ Music
(YORK) CD846 Christmas at York Minster

WHITEMAN, Paul (cond)
see Orch

WHITFIELD, John (cond)
see Endymion Ens

WHITNEY, Robert (cond)
see Louisville Orch

WHITTAKER, David (fl)
see CONCERT INDEX under:
(EMI) CDM7 64130-2 Christmas Music from King's
(EMI) CMS7 64074-2(2) Christa Ludwig—Recital (pt 2)

WHITTLESEY, Christine (sop)
Gubaidulina: Hommage
see CONCERT INDEX under:
(BRID) BCD9045 Benedict Mason—Chamber and Orchestral Works
(DG) 439 910-2GH Birtwistle—Secret Theatre;Tragoedia etc
(SONY) SK53290 Kurtag—Song Cycles

WHITWORTH, John (alto)
Purcell: King Arthur, Z628 (Cpte)

WIBAUT, Frank (pf)
see CONCERT INDEX under:
(CHAN) CHAN6601 Elgar—Choral Works

WICK, Denis (cond)
see London Wind Orch

WICKENS, Derek (ob)
see CONCERT INDEX under:
(ASV) CDACA1003 The Classical Oboe
(UNIC) UKCD2060 Britten—Early Chamber Music

WICKHAM, Edward (cond)
see Clerks' Group

WICKHAM, Henry (bass)
Duruflé: Requiem

WICKS, Dennis (bass)
Berlioz: Troyens (Cpte)
R. Strauss: Salome (Cpte)
Schoenberg: Moses und Aron (Cpte)
see CONCERT INDEX under:
(SONY) M3K79312 Puccini: Il Trittico

WIDDOP, Walter (ten)
Wagner: Götterdämmerung (exc)
see CONCERT INDEX under:
(CLAR) CDGSE78-50-26 Wagner: Tristan und Isolde excerpts
(CLAR) CDGSE78-50-35/6 Wagner—Historical recordings
(CLAR) CDGSE78-50-46 Walter Widdop (1892-1949)
(CLAR) CDGSE78-50-52 Three Tenors
(CLAR) CDGSE78-50-54 Coates conducts Wagner, Weber & Mendelssohn
(DUTT) CDAX8004 Sir Henry Wood conducts Vaughan Williams
(EMI) CMS7 64008-2(2) Wagner Singing on Record (pt 2)
(PEAR) GEMMCDS9137 Wagner—Der Ring des Nibelungen
(PEAR) GEMMCDS9925(1) Covent Garden on Record—Vol.3 (pt 1)
(PEAR) GEMMCDS9926(1) Covent Garden on Record—Vol.4 (pt 1)
(PEAR) GEMMCD9342 Vaughan Williams: Vocal Works

WIDGREN, Olof (narr)
see CONCERT INDEX under:
(CPRI) CAP21510 Rosenberg plays Rosenberg

WIDLUND, Mats (pf)
Stenhammar: Piano Concerto 1

WIDMER, Kurt (bass)
Cimarosa: Requiem in G minor
Saint-Saëns: Oratorio de Noël, Op. 12
see CONCERT INDEX under:
(ERAT) 2292-45202-2 M-A. Charpentier: Sacred Works

WIDMER, Oliver (bar)
Mozart: Zauberflöte (Cpte)
Schreker: Gezeichneten (Cpte)
Wolf: Manuel Venegas
see CONCERT INDEX under:
(HANS) 98 979 Mozart—Sacred Choral Works

WIDOR, Charles-Marie (organ)
see CONCERT INDEX under:
(EMI) CDC5 55037-2 French Organists play their own works

WIEDEMANN, Hermann (bass)
Wagner: Parsifal (exc)
see CONCERT INDEX under:
(SCHW) 314532 Vienna State Opera Live, Vol.3
(SCHW) 314562 Vienna State Opera Live, Vol.6
(SCHW) 314602 Vienna State Opera Live, Vol.10
(SCHW) 314622 Vienna State Opera Live, Vol.12
(SCHW) 314642 Vienna State Opera Live, Vol.14
(SCHW) 314652 Vienna State Opera Live, Vol.15

WIEDENHOFER, Thomas (narr)
Lehár: Giuditta (Cpte)

WIEDER-ATHERTON, Sonia (vc)
see CONCERT INDEX under:
(AUVI) V4644 Debussy/Ravel—Orchestral Songs
(AUVI) V4666 Prokofiev/Shostakovich—Sonatas for Cello and Piano

WIEDERHUT, Eberhard (bass)
Anon: Missa Salisburgensis, Plaudite tympana

WIEDERKER, Jean-Jacques (vc)
see CONCERT INDEX under:
(SCHW) 310652 Fumet/d'Indy/Honegger—Chamber Works

(JEAN-JACQUES) WIEDERKER CHAMBER ORCHESTRA
cond F. BOUANICHE
see CONCERT INDEX under:
(SCHW) 310652 Fumet/d'Indy/Honegger—Chamber Works

WIEDL, Wilhelm (treb)
see CONCERT INDEX under:
(TELD) 2292-42572-2 Bach—Cantatas, Volume 18
(TELD) 2292-42576-2 Bach—Cantatas, Volume 20
(TELD) 2292-42577-2 Bach—Cantatas, Volume 21
(TELD) 2292-42578-2 Bach—Cantatas, Volume 22
(TELD) 2292-42582-2 Bach—Cantatas, Volume 23
(TELD) 2292-42583-2 Bach—Cantatas, Volume 24
(TELD) 2292-42584-2 Bach—Cantatas, Volume 25
(TELD) 2292-42602-2 Bach—Cantatas, Volume 26
(TELD) 2292-42603-2 Bach—Cantatas, Volume 27
(TELD) 4509-91758-2 Bach—Cantatas, Vol.4
(TELD) 4509-91759-2 Bach—Cantatas, Vol.5
(TELD) 4509-91760-2 Bach—Cantatas, Vol.6

WIEDNER-ZAJAC, Elzbieta (pf)
see CONCERT INDEX under:
(DORI) DIS80121 Masques—Polish Piano Works

WIEDSTRUCK, Yvonne (sop)
see CONCERT INDEX under:
(CPO) CPO999 158-2 Pfitzner—Das dunkle Reich

WIEGOLD, Mary (sop)
Lumsdaine: What shall I sing?
see CONCERT INDEX under:
(NMC) NMCD003 Mary Wiegold's Songbook

WIELE, Aimée van de (hpd)
see CONCERT INDEX under:
(EMI) CZS7 62690-2 Poulenc—Orchestral and Ballet Works

WIEMANN, Ernst (bass)
Weber: Freischütz (Cpte)

WIEN, Erika (mez)
see CONCERT INDEX under:
(VANG) 08.2010.71 Bach—Choral Works

WIENER, Jean (pf)
see CONCERT INDEX under:
(EPM) 150 122 Milhaud—Historic Recordings 1928-1948

WIENER, Julia (sop)
see CONCERT INDEX under:
(EMI) CMS7 63386-2 Borodin—Prince Igor & Complete Solo Songs

WIENER, Otto (bass)
R. Strauss: Rosenkavalier (Cpte)
Wagner: Lohengrin (Cpte), Meistersinger (Cpte)

WIENER TSCHUSCHENKAPELLE
cond J. E. GARDINER
Lehár: Lustige Witwe (Cpte)

WIENS, Edith (sop)
Bach: Cantata 6
Mahler: Symphony 4, Symphony 8
Mendelssohn: Midsummer Night's Dream (exc)
Mozart: Mass, K427, Oca del Cairo (Cpte)
Saint-Saëns: Oratorio de Noël, Op. 12
Vaughan Williams: Dona nobis pacem
Wagner: Parsifal (Cpte)
see CONCERT INDEX under:
(CBC) MVCD1053 Schubert—Lieder
(EMI) CMS7 64476-2 Mahler—Symphonies, Vol.2
(HANS) 98 811 Bach—Cantatas, Vol.49
(HANS) 98 813 Bach—Cantatas, Vol.51
(HANS) 98 864 Bach—Cantatas, Vol.13
(RCA) 74321 20277-2 Beethoven—Complete Symphonies

WIESLANDER, Maria (hpd)
see CONCERT INDEX under:
(MSVE) MSCD415 Kraus—Chamber Music

WIESLER, Manuela (fl)
see CONCERT INDEX under:
(BIS) BIS-CD272 Contemporary Music for Flute and Percussion
(BIS) BIS-CD419 The Russian Flute
(BIS) BIS-CD630 French Orchestral Music

WIETER, Georg (bass)
Mozart: Nozze di Figaro (Cpte)
Orff: Kluge (Cpte)
Wagner: Meistersinger (Cpte)

WIGET, Ueli (pf)
Henze: Requiem

WIGGLESWORTH, Mark (cond)
see Premiere Ens

WIGHTMAN, Brian (bn)
see CONCERT INDEX under:
(HYPE) CDA66172 Malcolm Arnold: Chamber Works, Vol. 2
(HYPE) CDA66173 Malcolm Arnold: Chamber Works, Vol. 3

WIJNKOOP, Alexander van (cond)
see Berne Camerata

WILANÓW QUARTET
see CONCERT INDEX under:
(ACCO) 201142 Lutosławski—Chamber Works
(OLYM) OCD387 Bacewicz—Chamber Works
(POLS) PNCD065 Szymanowski: Chamber Works

WILBRAHAM, John (tpt)
see CONCERT INDEX under:
(EMI) CZS7 62736-2 Poulenc—Chamber Works

WILBRINK, Hans (bar)
Wagner: Meistersinger (Cpte)

WILLSON, Tim (ten)
Verdi: Trovatore (Cpte)

WILSING, Jörn W (bar)
Leoncavallo: Bohème (Cpte)
R. Strauss: Intermezzo (Cpte)

WILSON, Al H. (sngr)
see CONCERT INDEX under:
(PEAR) GEMMCDS9050/2(1) Music from the New
York Stage, Vol. 1 (part 1)
(PEAR) GEMMCDS9050/2(2) Music from the New
York Stage, Vol. 1 (part 2)

WILSON, Alan (organ)
see CONCERT INDEX under:
(EMI) CDC7 49555-2 Tallis: Sacred Choral Works

WILSON, Allan (cond)
see Orch

WILSON, Catherine (mez)
Britten: Albert Herring (Cpte)
Purcell: Dido (Cpte)

WILSON, Christopher (lte)
Dowland: First Book of Songs (Cpte), Lachrimae
see CONCERT INDEX under:
(AMON) CD-SAR29 In Nomine: English Consort
Works
(CHAN) CHAN0538 Elizabethan Lute Songs
(VIRG) VC7 59034-2 Elizabethan Lute Music
(VIRG) VC7 59539-2 Nights' Black Bird
(VIRG) VC7 59586-2 Goe Nightly Cares

WILSON, Christopher (vihuela)
see CONCERT INDEX under:
(HYPE) CDA66653 The Voice in the Garden

WILSON, Elizabeth (vc)
Pärt: Passio

WILSON, Georges (spkr)
Honegger: Jeanne d'Arc (Cpte)
Stravinsky: Oedipus Rex (Cpte)

WILSON, Glen (fp)
see CONCERT INDEX under:
(DENO) C37-7505 Mozart: The complete works for
violin and orchestra, Vol. 2
(ETCE) KTC1035 Mozart: Lieder

WILSON, Glen (hpd)
D. Scarlatti: Keyboard Sonatas (exc)
Telemann: Solos (1734) (exc)

WILSON, Gordon (cond)
Verdi: Trovatore (Cpte)

WILSON, Gran (ten)
Stravinsky: Pulcinella

WILSON, Ian (tpt)
see CONCERT INDEX under:
(L'OI) 410 553-2OH 18th Century Orchestral Works
(L'OI) 411 949-2OH Telemann: Double & Triple
Concertos

WILSON, Lambert (narr)
Franck: Rédemption
Stravinsky: Oedipus Rex (Cpte)

WILSON, Mescal (pf)
Szymanowski: Symphony 4

WILSON, Paul (ten)
Saxton: Caritas (Cpte)

WILSON, Ransom (cond)
see Cologne Musica Fiata

WILSON, Roland (cond)
see Musica Fiata

WILSON, Scott (hn)
see CONCERT INDEX under:
(DELO) DE3084 Schumann: Orchestral Works

WILSON, Steuart (ten)
see CONCERT INDEX under:
(EMI) CDS7 54560-2 The Elgar Edition, Vol.1

WILSON, Tim (tpt)
J. Adams: Light over Water

WILSON, Timothy (alto)
Handel: Israel in Egypt (Cpte)
Tavener: Akathist of Thanksgiving
see CONCERT INDEX under:
(VIRG) VC5 45159-2 Purcell—Come ye sons of art

WILSON HYDE, Eric (bar)
Sullivan: HMS Pinafore (Cpte)

WILSON-JOHNSON, David (bar)
Bach: Cantata 11, Cantata 211, Cantata 213, Easter
Oratorio, BWV249 (Cpte), Mass in B minor, BWV232
(Cpte)
Birtwistle: Punch and Judy (Cpte)
Boughton: Immortal Hour (Cpte)
Brahms: Deutsches Requiem, Op. 45 (Cpte)
Britten: Peter Grimes (Cpte)
Donizetti: Lucrezia Borgia (Cpte)
Elgar: Caractacus (Cpte)
G. Lloyd: John Socman (exc)
Hadley: Trees so high
Handel: Belshazzar (Cpte)
Haydn: Mass 11
Maxwell Davies: Black Pentecost
Mozart: Mass, K317, Requiem
Parry: Soul's Ransom
Purcell: Fairy Queen, Z629 (Cpte)
Smyth: Wreckers (Cpte)
Somervell: Maud (Cpte), Shropshire Lad (Cpte)

Stainer: Crucifixion
Tippett: Ice Break (Cpte)
see CONCERT INDEX under:
(CARL) PCD896 Fauré: Sacred Choral Works
(CHAN) CHAN8476 Works by Rachmaninov and
Tchaikovsky
(CHAN) CHAN8788/9 Elgar—The Kingdom;
Orchestral Works
(DG) 447 068-2GH Stravinsky—The Flood, etc
(HYPE) CDA66769 Vivaldi—Sacred Music, Volume
1
(SONY) SK45965 Esa-Pekka Salonen conducts
Stravinsky
(SONY) SMK48463 Boulez conducts Schoenberg -
Volume 1
(VIRG) VC7 59243-2 Purcell—Odes for Queen Mary

**WIMBELDON KING'S COLLEGE SCHOOL BOYS'
CHOIR**
cond J. HORNER
Horner: Willow (exc)

WIMBERGER, Peter (bass-bar)
R. Strauss: Frau ohne Schatten (Cpte)

WIMMER, Hans-Georg (bass)
Telemann: Donner-Ode, Getreue Music-Meister
(Cpte), St Matthew Passion (1746) (Cpte)
see CONCERT INDEX under:
(CAPR) 10 310/1 J. E. Bach—Passion Oratorio, etc.
(CAPR) 10 315 Telemann—Choral Music

WINANT, William (perc)
M. Feldman: Rothko Chapel
see CONCERT INDEX under:
(NALB) NA015CD Lou Harrison: Various Works
(NALB) NA035CD Singing Through
(NALB) NA055CD Harrison—The Perilous Chapel

WINBERGH, Gösta (ten)
A. Thomas: Hamlet (Cpte)
Beethoven: Symphony 9
Chausson: Roi Arthus (Cpte)
Donizetti: Don Pasquale (Cpte)
Gluck: Iphigénie en Tauride (Cpte)
Haydn: Schöpfung (Cpte)
Liszt: Faust Symphony
Mozart: Clemenza di Tito (Cpte), Don Giovanni
(Cpte), Entführung (Cpte)
see CONCERT INDEX under:
(DG) 427 306-2GH6 Beethoven: Complete
Symphonies

WINCENC, Carol (fl)
see CONCERT INDEX under:
(ARGO) 440 212-2ZH Schoenfield—Orchestral
Works

WINCENE, Carol (fl)
Glass: Hydrogen Jukebox (Cpte)
Mozart: Flute Quartets, Piano Sonata, K533 (exc)
see CONCERT INDEX under:
(NEW) NW375-2 Lukas Foss: Orchestral Works

WINCHESTER CATHEDRAL CHOIR
cond D. HILL
Handel: Blessed are they that considereth the poor,
Coronation Anthems
Haydn: Mass 7, Mass 14
see CONCERT INDEX under:
(ARGO) 430 836-2ZH English Sacred Choral Music
(ARGO) 436 120-2ZH Vaughan
Williams/Walton—Choral & Orchestral Works
(ARGO) 436 833-2ZH Purcell— Music for the Funeral
of Queen Mary
(HYPE) CDA66400 Tallis: Sacred Choral Works
(HYPE) CDA66424 Tye—Sacred Choral Works
(HYPE) CDA66477 Weelkes—Cathedral Music
(HYPE) CDA66643 Philips—Motets
(VIRG) VC5 45035-2 Tavener—Thunder entered Her
cond C. HOGWOOD
Mozart: Mass, K427
see CONCERT INDEX under:
(L'OI) 436 585-2OH Mozart—Sacred Choral Works
cond M. NEARY
see CONCERT INDEX under:
(ASV) CDQS6011 Carols from Winchester Cathedral
cond G. SOLTI
see CONCERT INDEX under:
(DECC) 436 403-2DWO The World of Royal Music

WINCHESTER CATHEDRAL CHORISTERS
cond M. BERRY
see CONCERT INDEX under:
(HERA) HAVPCD168 Abelard—12th-Century Chant

WINCHESTER QUIRISTERS
cond D. HILL
see CONCERT INDEX under:
(HYPE) CDA66400 Tallis: Sacred Choral Works
cond C. HOGWOOD
Mozart: Mass, K427
see CONCERT INDEX under:
(L'OI) 436 585-2OH Mozart—Sacred Choral Works
cond R. KING
see CONCERT INDEX under:
(UNIT) 88002-2 My Beloved Spake

WINCHESTER VOCAL ARTS
cond D. HILL
see CONCERT INDEX under:
(HYPE) CDA66400 Tallis: Sacred Choral Works

WIND BAND
see CONCERT INDEX under:
(CLRI) CC0005 The Clarinet - Historical Recordings,
Vol.1

cond C. RAYBOULD
see CONCERT INDEX under:
(CLRI) CC0005 The Clarinet - Historical Recordings,
Vol.1

WINDGASSEN, Wolfgang (ten)
Beethoven: Fidelio (Cpte)
Wagner: Götterdämmerung (Cpte), Lohengrin (Cpte),
Parsifal (Cpte), Rheingold (Cpte), Siegfried (Cpte),
Tannhäuser (Cpte), Tristan und Isolde (Cpte)
see CONCERT INDEX under:
(DECC) 414 100-2DM15 Wagner: Der Ring des
Nibelungen
(EMI) CZS7 67123-2 Wagner: Der Ring des
Nibelungen
(FOYE) 15-CF2011 Wagner—Der Ring de Nibelungen
(PHIL) 446 057-2PB14 Wagner—The Ring Cycle -
Bayreuth Festival 1967

WINDISCH, Ludwig (bass)
see CONCERT INDEX under:
(PREI) 90168 Wagner—Die Meistersinger, Act 2, etc

WINDMÜLLER, Yaron (bar)
see CONCERT INDEX under:
(CPO) CPO999 158-2 Pfitzner—Das dunkle Reich

WINDS, Erich-Alexander (spkr)
R. Strauss: Ariadne auf Naxos (Cpte)

WINDSOR, Lorna (sop)
Mozart: Ascanio in Alba (Cpte)

WINFIELD, John (ten)
G. Lloyd: John Socman (exc)
Schoenberg: Moses und Aron (Cpte)
see CONCERT INDEX under:
(OPRA) ORC003 Donizetti—Gabriella di Vergy

WINFIELD, Roger (ob)
see CONCERT INDEX under:
(LYRI) SRCD226 L. Berkeley—Orchestral Works

WINGATES TEMPERANCE BAND
cond H. MOSS
see CONCERT INDEX under:
(BEUL) 1PD2 Crystal Palace Champions

WINGERDEN, Jeanette van (rec)
see CONCERT INDEX under:
(TELD) 4509-97467-2 Frans Brüggen Edition Vol.
5—Late Baroque Chamber Music

WINKELMANN, Hermann (ten)
see CONCERT INDEX under:
(SYMP) SYMCD1081 The Harold Wayne Collection,
Vol.5

WINKLER, Adriana (vn)
Enescu: String Octet

WINKLER, Hermann (ten)
Berg: Wozzeck (Cpte)
Hindemith: Mathis der Maler (Cpte)
Mozart: Idomeneo (Cpte)
R.Strauss: Arabella (Cpte), Elektra (Cpte)
Schoeck: Massimilla Doni (Cpte)
Zemlinsky: Kleider machen Leute (Cpte)

WINKLER, Michael-Christfried (organ)
Saint-Saëns: Oratorio de Noël, Op. 12
see CONCERT INDEX under:
(CAPR) 10 367 Mendelssohn—Motets

WINN, James (pf)
see CONCERT INDEX under:
(KOCH) 37272-2 Music of Charles Wuorinen

WINN, Peter (treb)
see CONCERT INDEX under:
(ARGO) 433 215-2ZH Britten—Christmas Music

WINNIPEG GILBERT & SULLIVAN SOCIETY
cond B. TOVEY
see CONCERT INDEX under:
(CBC) SMCD5139 A Gilbert & Sullivan Gala

(THE) WINNIPEG SINGERS
cond B. TOVEY
see CONCERT INDEX under:
(CBC) SMCD5139 A Gilbert & Sullivan Gala

WINNIPEG SYMPHONY ORCHESTRA
cond B. TOVEY
see CONCERT INDEX under:
(CBC) SMCD5139 A Gilbert & Sullivan Gala

WINOGRODSKA, Grazyna (mez)
Penderecki: Polish Requiem

WINSAUER, Waltraud (mez)
Mozart: Zauberflöte (Cpte)
R. Strauss: Rosenkavalier (Cpte)

WINSCHERMANN, Helmut (cond)
see German Bach Sols

WINSLADE, Glenn (ten)
Handel: Messiah (exc)
Lehár: Lustige Witwe (exc)
Mozart: Idomeneo (Cpte)

WINTER, Kate (sop)
see CONCERT INDEX under:
(EMI) CDS7 54607-2 Stravinsky plays and conducts
Stravinsky

WINTER, Louise (mez)
see CONCERT INDEX under:
(COLL) Coll1349-2 Respighi—Vocal and Orchestral
Works

WINTER, Paul (bar)
Verdi: Traviata (Cpte)

WINTERTHUR STATE ORCHESTRA
cond V. DESARZENS
Martin: Vin herbé

WINTERTHUR SYMPHONY ORCHESTRA
cond C. DAHINDEN
see CONCERT INDEX *under:*
(MUSI) **MACD-667** Louis Kaufman plays 20th Century
Concertos

WION, G. (sngr)
see CONCERT INDEX *under:*
(MUSD) **20239-2** Delibes—Opéras-Comiques

WIPFLER, Wolfgang (hn)
see CONCERT INDEX *under:*
(CAPR) **10 482** Nobody knows de trouble I see

WIRKKALA, Merja (sop)
Madetoja: Juha (Cpte)

WIRTZ, Dorothea (sop)
C.H. Graun: Montezuma (Cpte)
R. Strauss: Daphne (Cpte)

WIRZ, Clara (mez)
Janáček: Diary of one who disappeared

WISE, David (vn)
see CONCERT INDEX *under:*
(DUTT) **CDAX8012** Malcolm Sargent conducts
English Music

WISE, Patricia (sop)
Berg: Lulu (Cpte)
see CONCERT INDEX *under:*
(ERAT) **4509-95362-2** Mozart—Sacred Choral
Works

WISEMAN, Debbie (cond)
see Palm Court Th Orch

WISEMAN, Debbie (pf)
Wiseman: Tom and Viv (exc)

WISHART, Stevie (cond)
see Sinfonye

WISLOCKI, Stanislaw (cond)
see Katowice Polish Rad & TV Great SO

WISPELWEY, Pieter (vc)
Bach: Solo Cello Suites
Brahms: Cello Sonata 1, Cello Sonata 2
Schubert: String Quintet
see CONCERT INDEX *under:*
(CHNN) **CCS6294** Vivaldi—Cello Sonatas
(CHNN) **CCS6494** Beethoven—Cello Variations
(CHNN) **CCS7395** Haydn—Works for Cello and
Orchestra
(CHNN) **CCS7495** 20th Century Solo Cello Works
(GLOB) **GLO5074** Britten—Cello Suites
(GLOB) **GLO5089** Crumb/Escher/Kodály—Cello Solo
Sonatas

WISSICK, Brent (baroque vc)
see CONCERT INDEX *under:*
(ALBA) **TROY127-2** Purcell—From Rosy Bow'rs

WISSICK, Brent (va da gamba)
see CONCERT INDEX *under:*
(ALBA) **TROY127-2** Purcell—From Rosy Bow'rs

WISSKIRCHEN, Paul (organ)
see CONCERT INDEX *under:*
(MOTE) **CD40101** Guilmant: Organ Works, Vol.1

WISTREICH, Richard (bass)
Handel: Belshazzar (Cpte)
Mozart: Zauberflöte (Cpte)
Purcell: Fairy Queen, Z629 (Cpte)
Schütz: Symphoniae sacrae, Op. 10 (Cpte)
T. Linley II: Shakespeare Ode
see CONCERT INDEX *under:*
(BIS) **BIS-CD341** Music for lutes
(L'OI) **421 480-2OH** Monteverdi: Madrigali Erotici
(MERI) **CDE84096** Seventeenth-Century German
Works

WIT, Antoni (cond)
see Cracow RSO

WITCOMB, Nicholas (treb)
see CONCERT INDEX *under:*
(HYPE) **CDA66585** Purcell—Complete Anthems &
Services, Vol.1
(HYPE) **CDA66623** Purcell—Complete Anthems &
Services, Vol.3
(HYPE) **CDA66644** Purcell—Complete Anthems &
Services, Vol.4
(HYPE) **CDA66656** Purcell—Complete Anthems &
Services, Vol.5
(HYPE) **CDA66663** Purcell—Complete Anthems &
Services, Vol.6

WITH, Dora (mez)
see CONCERT INDEX *under:*
(SCHW) **314532** Vienna State Opera Live, Vol.3
(SCHW) **314592** Vienna State Opera Live, Vol.9
(SCHW) **314602** Vienna State Opera Live, Vol.10
(SCHW) **314622** Vienna State Opera Live, Vol.12
(SCHW) **314632** Vienna State Opera Live, Vol.13
(SCHW) **314642** Vienna State Opera Live, Vol.14

WITT, Josef (ten)
R. Strauss: Arabella (Cpte), Ariadne auf Naxos
(Cpte)
Verdi: Macbeth (Cpte)
Wagner: Meistersinger (Cpte)
see CONCERT INDEX *under:*
(SCHW) **314532** Vienna State Opera Live, Vol.3
(SCHW) **314572** Vienna State Opera Live, Vol.7
(SCHW) **314582** Vienna State Opera Live, Vol.8
(SCHW) **314652** Vienna State Opera Live, Vol.15

WITT, Kerstin (mez)
R. Strauss: Salome (Cpte)

WITT SMITH, Susan de (pf)
see CONCERT INDEX *under:*
(KOCH) **37144-2** American Music for Flute and
Piano
(KOCH) **37154-2** Still—Miscellaneous Works
(KOCH) **37192-2** Still—Summerland

WITTE, Erich (ten)
Wagner: Meistersinger (Cpte), Rheingold (Cpte)
Weber: Abu Hassan (Cpte)
see CONCERT INDEX *under:*
(FOYE) **15-CF2011** Wagner—Der Ring de Nibelungen

WITTE, Wolfgang (ten)
Verdi: Ballo in maschera (Cpte)

WITTEK, Helmut (treb)
Mahler: Symphony 4
see CONCERT INDEX *under:*
(DG) **435 162-2GX13** Mahler—Complete
Symphonies
(TELD) **2292-42428-2** Bach—Cantatas, Volume 41
(TELD) **2292-42634-2** Bach—Cantatas, Volume 39
(TELD) **2292-42635-2** Bach—Cantatas, Volume 40
(TELD) **2292-42738-2** Bach—Cantatas, Volume 42
(TELD) **2292-44179-2** Bach—Cantatas, Volume 43
(TELD) **2292-44193-2** Bach—Cantatas, Volume 44
(TELD) **2292-44194-2** Bach—Cantatas, Volume 45
(TELD) **4509-91763-2** Bach—Cantatas, Vol.9
(TELD) **4509-91764-2** Bach—Cantatas, Vol.10
(TELD) **9031-74798-2** Bach—Arias and Duets

WITTE-WALDBAUER, Margarete (contr)
see CONCERT INDEX *under:*
(ROSE) **3221** Schumann—Miscellaneous Works

WITTGES, Herbert (bar)
Schoenberg: Moses und Aron (Cpte)

WITTGES, Max (bass-bar)
R. Strauss: Friedenstag (Cpte)

WITTING, Eugene (ten)
(PEAR) **GEMMCDS9004/6(2)** Singers of Imperial
Russia, Vol.3 (pt 2)
(PEAR) **GEMMCDS9007/9(2)** Singers of Imperial
Russia, Vol.4 (pt 2)

WITTING, Gerhard (ten)
Wagner: Meistersinger (Cpte)

WITTRISCH, Marcel (ten)
see CONCERT INDEX *under:*
(EMI) **CMS7 64008-2(1)** Wagner Singing on Record
(pt 1)
(NIMB) **NI7848** Great Singers at the Berlin State
Opera
(PREI) **89049** Margarete Teschemacher (1903-
1959)
(PREI) **89082** Margarete Klose (1902-1968)
(PREI) **90034** Maria Cebotari (1910-49)

WIXELL, Ingvar (bar)
Donizetti: Elisir d'amore (Cpte), Lucrezia Borgia
(Cpte)
Leoncavallo: Pagliacci (Cpte)
Mozart: Don Giovanni (Cpte), Nozze di Figaro (Cpte),
Zaide (Cpte)
Puccini: Bohème (Cpte), Madama Butterfly (Cpte),
Tosca (Cpte)
Verdi: Ballo in maschera (Cpte), Giorno di Regno
(Cpte), Rigoletto (Cpte), Trovatore (Cpte)
see CONCERT INDEX *under:*
(EMI) **CDM5 65081-2** Stenhammar—Orchestral &
Vocal Works
(SONY) **M3K79312** Puccini: Il Trittico

WLASCHIHA, Ekkehard (bass)
Bach: St. Matthew Passion, BWV244 (Cpte)
Beethoven: Fidelio (Cpte)
Wagner: Götterdämmerung (Cpte), Lohengrin (Cpte),
Parsifal (Cpte), Siegfried (Cpte)
see CONCERT INDEX *under:*
(DG) **445 354-2GX14** Wagner—Der Ring des
Nibelungen

WNYC CONCERT ORCHESTRA
cond H. NEWMANN
see CONCERT INDEX *under:*
(PEAR) **GEMMCDS9095(2)** Povla Frijsh (pt 2)

WODEHOUSE, Ian (treb)
Britten: Midsummer Night's Dream (Cpte)

WOESTER, Heinz (spkr)
see CONCERT INDEX *under:*
(DECC) **443 530-2LF2** Mozart—Die Entführung aus
dem Serail

WOHLERS, Rüdiger (ten)
Haydn: Schöpfung (exc)

WOHLERT, Peter (cond)
see Berlin CO

WOHLFAHRT, Erwin (ten)
Mozart: Nozze di Figaro (Cpte)
Wagner: Rheingold (Cpte), Siegfried (Cpte), Tristan
und Isolde (Cpte)
see CONCERT INDEX *under:*
(DG) **435 211-2GX15** Wagner—Der Ring des
Nibelungen
(PHIL) **446 057-2PB14** Wagner—The Ring Cycle -
Bayreuth Festival 1967

WOHLFARTH, Brigitte (sop)
Spohr: Faust (Cpte)

WOJCIECHOWSKI, Tadeusz (cond)
see Polish RSO

WOLANSKI, Jan (bass)
Rossini: Signor Bruschino (Cpte)

WOLANSKY, Raymond (bar)
B.A. Zimmermann: Soldaten (Cpte)
Orff: Carmina Burana

WÖLDIKE, Mogens (cond)
see Danish St RSO

WOLF, Gerd (bass)
R. Strauss: Ariadne auf Naxos (Cpte)

WOLF, Ilse (sop)
see CONCERT INDEX *under:*
(DECC) **430 359-2DM** Baroque Church Music

WOLF, Markus (va)
Mozart: String Quintet, K515, String Quintet, K516

WOLFF, Albert (cond)
see orch

WOLFF, Beverly (mez)
D. Moore: Carry Nation (Cpte)
Rossini: Pietra del Paragone (Cpte)

WOLFF, Christian (narr)
Lehár: Friederike (Cpte)

WOLFF, Ernst Victor (pf)
(PEAR) **GEMMCDS9085** Hugo Wolf Society, Volume
II

WOLFF, Fritz (ten)
see CONCERT INDEX *under:*
(EMI) **CMS7 64008-2(2)** Wagner Singing on Record
(pt 2)

WOLFF, Hugh (cond)
see Philh

WOLFFBERG, Inge (voc)
Weill: Dreigroschenoper (Cpte)

WOLFRUM, Paul (bar)
Weill: Mahagonny (Cpte)

WOLKEN (ten)
see CONCERT INDEX *under:*
(SCHW) **314562** Vienna State Opera Live, Vol.6
(SCHW) **314622** Vienna State Opera Live, Vol.12
(SCHW) **314642** Vienna State Opera Live, Vol.14

WOLOSOFF, Bruce (pf)
Busoni: Elegien, Piano Sonata, Op.20a

WOLPE, Katharina (pf)
see CONCERT INDEX *under:*
(SYMP) **SYMCD1107** Schoenberg—Piano Works

WOLTERS, Rainer (vn)
see CONCERT INDEX *under:*
(RCA) **09026 60900-2** Galway plays Bach

WOMEN'S PHILHARMONIC ORCHESTRA
cond J. FALLETTA
see CONCERT INDEX *under:*
(KOCH) **37169-2** The Women's Philharmonic -
Orchestral Works

WONG, Randall (sop)
Hasse: Cleofide (Cpte)
M. Monk: Atlas (Cpte)

WOOBURN SINGERS
cond C. ABBADO
Berlioz: Te Deum

WOOD, Haydn (cond)
see Light SO

WOOD, Sir Henry (cond)
see BBC SO

WOOD, Sir Henry (pf)
see CONCERT INDEX *under:*
(SYMP) **SYMCD1093** The Harold Wayne Collection,
Vol.7

WOOD, James (cond)
see Ens

WOOD, James (bass)
R. Strauss: Friedenstag (Cpte)

WOOD, James (perc)
see CONCERT INDEX *under:*
(AMON) **CD-SAR22** Oboe Collection

WOOD, Lorraine (ob)
see CONCERT INDEX *under:*
(ARCH) **439 893-2AH** Telemann—Suites; Concerto in
D
(ARCH) **445 839-2AH** Vivaldi—Woodwind Concertos

WOOD, Mark (perc)
see CONCERT INDEX *under:*
(KOCH) **37187-2** 20th-Century American Oboe
Works

WOODHOUSE, Nigel (mndl)
see CONCERT INDEX under:
(CONI) **CDCF203**   Vivaldi—Concertos

WOODLAND, Rae (sop)
see CONCERT INDEX under:
(LYRI) **SRCD225**   Bliss—Orchestral Works

WOODLEY, Arthur (bass-bar)
Stravinsky: Rake's Progress (Cpte)
Weill: Lost in the Stars (Cpte)
see CONCERT INDEX under:
(EMI) **CDC7 54851-2**   Gershwin—Blue Monday, etc

WOODMAN, Thomas (bar)
V. Thomson: Lord Byron (Cpte)
see CONCERT INDEX under:
(KOCH) **37168-2**   Silent Noon—Songs of Vaughan
Williams

WOODROW, Alan (ten)
Shostakovich: Lady Macbeth of Mtsensk (Cpte)
Sondheim: Pacific Overtures (exc)
see CONCERT INDEX under:
(RCA) **GD71964**   Bach: Flute Works

WOODROW, James (gtr)
see CONCERT INDEX under:
(KING) **KCLCD2027**   South American Flute Music

WOODS, Carol (sngr)
Weill: Lost in the Stars (Cpte)

WOODS, Denise (sop)
see CONCERT INDEX under:
(RCA) **09026 61509-2**   A Salute to American Music

WOODS, Elaine (sop)
see CONCERT INDEX under:
(SONY) **SK64301**   Beethoven—Songs from the British
Isles

WOODS, Michael (cond)
see Philh

WOODS, Pamela (ob)
see CONCERT INDEX under:
(TELA) **CD80205**   Oboe Music by English Composers

WOODS, Philip (hn)
see CONCERT INDEX under:
(CNTO) **CRCD2368**   Sullivan—That Glorious Song of
Old

WOODS, Sheryl (sop)
Glass: Satyagraha (Cpte)

WOODWARD, Roger (pf)
see CONCERT INDEX under:
(ETCE) **KTC1103**   Takemitsu—Complete Piano
Works
(ETCE) **KTC1126**   Scriabin—Piano Works

WOOLF, Gabriel (narr)
see CONCERT INDEX under:
(CHAN) **CHAN8748**   Poème—Works for Violin and
Piano

WOOLF, Simon (treb)
Purcell: St Cecilia's Day Ode, Z328

WOOLLAM, Kenneth (ten)
Tippett: Child of Our Time (Cpte)

WOOLLETT, Elizabeth (sop)
Sullivan: Gondoliers (Cpte), Iolanthe (Cpte)

WOOLLEY, Robert (organ)
Corelli: Trio Sonatas, Op. 3 (exc)
see CONCERT INDEX under:
(CHAN) **CHAN0553**   Post-Restoration English Organ
Works
(CHAN) **CHAN0559**   Gibbons—Organ and Choral
Works
(CHAN) **CHAN8763**   Purcell—Chamber Works Vol 3

WOOLLEY, Robert (fp)
J. C. Bach: Keyboard Sonatas, Op. 17

WOOLLEY, Robert (hpd)
Corelli: Trio Sonatas, Op. 4 (exc)
Seixas: Keyboard Sonatas I (exc), Keyboard Sonatas
II (exc)
see CONCERT INDEX under:
(ASV) **CDGAD201**   Vivaldi—Cello Sonatas
(HYPE) **CDA66239**   C.P.E. Bach: Chamber Works
(HYPE) **CDA66254**   A. Scarlatti: Cantatas & La Folia

WOOLLEY, Scot (pf)
Korngold: Polykrates Potpourri, Schneemann

WORCESTER CATHEDRAL CHOIR
see CONCERT INDEX under:
(CARL) **PCD937**   Tapestry of English Cathedral Music
(HYPE) **CDA66078**   Cathedral & Organ Music
(HYPE) **CDA66271/2**   Elgar:The Complete Choral
Songs
cond DAVID HUNT
see CONCERT INDEX under:
(HYPE) **CDA66313**   Elgar—Cathedral Music
cond DON HUNT
Saint-Saëns: Mass, Op. 4
see CONCERT INDEX under:
(ABBE) **CDCA943**   Tudor Church Music, Vol.1
(ABBE) **CDCA957**   Tudor Church Music, Volume 2
(HYPE) **CDA66446**   S.S.Wesley—Cathedral Anthems,
Vol.1
(HYPE) **CDA66469**   S.S.Wesley—Cathedral Anthems,
Vol.2
cond C. ROBINSON
see CONCERT INDEX under:
(CHAN) **CHAN6601**   Elgar—Choral Works

WORDSWORTH, Barry (cond)
see BBC Concert Orch

WORFF, Franz (bass)
see CONCERT INDEX under:
(SCHW) **314582**   Vienna State Opera Live, Vol.8
(SCHW) **314602**   Vienna State Opera Live, Vol.10

WORKMAN, Charles Herbert (bar)
Rossini: Armida (Cpte)

WORLD PHILHARMONIC ORCHESTRA
cond L. MAAZEL
see CONCERT INDEX under:
(AUVI) **AV6113**   Live Recording - Rio de Janeiro

WORLD SYMPHONY ORCHESTRA
cond M. ATZMON
Haydn: Schöpfung (Cpte)

WÖRLE, Robert (ten)
B.A. Zimmermann: Soldaten (Cpte)
B. Goldschmidt: Gewaltige Hahnrei (Cpte)
Busoni: Arlecchino (Cpte), Turandot (Cpte)
Gurlitt: Wozzeck (Cpte)
Hasse: Conversione di Sant' Agostino (Cpte)
Mozart: Zauberflöte (Cpte)
Schreker: Ferne Klang (Cpte), Gezeichneten (Cpte)

WORTHLEY, Max (ten)
Monteverdi: Lamento d'Arianna a 1, L'Arianna (exc)

WORTHY, Johnny (ten)
Gershwin: Porgy and Bess (Cpte)

WOSKA, Elisabeth (spkr)
R. Strauss: Intermezzo (Cpte)

WOTTRICH, Erich (ten)
B. Goldschmidt: Gewaltige Hahnrei (Cpte)
Gurlitt: Wozzeck (Cpte)
Schreker: Gezeichneten (Cpte)
Schumann: Szenen aus Goethes Faust (Cpte)
see CONCERT INDEX under:
(LARG) **Largo5130**   Testimonies of War
(SONY) **S2K66836**   Goldschmidt—Beatrice Cenci, etc

WOYTOWICZ, Stefania (sop)
Dvořák: Stabat Mater
Górecki: Symphony 3
see CONCERT INDEX under:
(KOCH) **312652**   Szymanowski—Orchestral and
Choral Works
(OLYM) **OCD313**   Gorecki—Orchestral and Vocal
Works
(POLS) **PNCD040**   Lutosławski: Vocal and Orchestral
Works

WRAY, Margaret Jane (sop)
Mahler: Symphony 8
Shostakovich: Lady Macbeth of Mtsensk (Cpte)

WREN BAROQUE SOLOISTS
cond M. ELLIOTT
see CONCERT INDEX under:
(UNIC) **DKPCD9130**   Caldara—Madrigals and
Cantatas

WREN ORCHESTRA
see CONCERT INDEX under:
(DECC) **430 359-2DM**   Baroque Church Music
cond BERNARD ROSE
see CONCERT INDEX under:
(DECC) **430 359-2DM**   Baroque Church Music
cond S. CLEOBURY
see CONCERT INDEX under:
(DECC) **436 402-2DWO**   The World of Wedding
Music
cond G. GUEST
Mozart: Litanies, K243, Mass, K258, Vespers, K321,
Vespers, K339
see CONCERT INDEX under:
(DECC) **436 402-2DWO**   The World of Wedding
Music
(DECC) **443 455-2DF2**   Vivaldi—Sacred Choral Works

WRIGHT, Andrew (organ)
see CONCERT INDEX under:
(ARGO) **410 005-2ZH**   Sacred Choral Works

WRIGHT, Colin (ten)
Sullivan: Mikado (exc)
see CONCERT INDEX under:
(DECC) **430 095-2DWO**   The World of Gilbert &
Sullivan, Vol.1
(DECC) **433 868-2DWO**   The World of Gilbert &
Sullivan - Volume 2

WRIGHT, Harold (cl)
Brahms: Clarinet Quintet
Mozart: Clarinet Quintet, K581

WRIGHT, Joyce (sop)
Sullivan: Gondoliers (Cpte), HMS Pinafore (Cpte)
see CONCERT INDEX under:
(DECC) **430 095-2DWO**   The World of Gilbert &
Sullivan, Vol.1
(DECC) **433 868-2DWO**   The World of Gilbert &
Sullivan - Volume 2

WRIGHT, Keith (organ)
Stanford: Services, Op. 12, Services, Op. 81
see CONCERT INDEX under:
(PRIO) **PRCD437**   Stanford—Complete Morning &
Evening Services, Vol.1

WRIGHT, Moya (hp)
Rajna: Harp Concerto

WRIGHT, Patricia (sop)
see CONCERT INDEX under:

(CNTI) **CCD1046**   Bax—Songs
(GAMU) **GAMCD534**   R. Clarke—Songs with Piano
and Violin

WRIGHT, Peter (cond)
see Southwark Cath Ch

WRIGHT, Peter (organ)
see CONCERT INDEX under:
(PRIO) **PRCD257**   Great Cathedral Anthems
(PRIO) **PRCD406**   Great European Organs No 35

WRIGHT, Simon (cond)
see Philh

WRIGHT, Simon (organ)
see CONCERT INDEX under:
(EMI) **CDC5 55086-2**   Trumpet Recital
(NIMB) **NI5330**   Oboe Concertos

WRIGHT, Simon (hpd)
see CONCERT INDEX under:
(EMI) **CDC5 55086-2**   Trumpet Recital

WRIGHT, Simon (pf)
see CONCERT INDEX under:
(EMI) **CDC5 55086-2**   Trumpet Recital

WRIGLEY, Yolande (pf)
see CONCERT INDEX under:
(ASV) **CDDCA796**   Cello Sonatas
(ASV) **CDDCA896**   Bax—Complete works for Cello
and Piano

WÜHRER, Friedrich (pf)
see CONCERT INDEX under:
(EMI) **CHS7 69741-2(4)**   Record of Singing,
Vol.4—German School

WULF, Martina (sop)
R. Strauss: Elektra (Cpte)

WULKOPF, Cornelia (mez)
Egk: Peer Gynt (Cpte)
Mozart: Apollo et Hyacinthus (Cpte)
Puccini: Fanciulla del West (Cpte)
Schubert: Lazarus, D689

WULSTAN, David (cond)
see Clerkes of Oxenford

WUNDERER, Gabriele (sop)
Corghi: Divara (Cpte)

WUNDERLICH, Fritz (ten)
Bach: Christmas Oratorio, BWV248 (Cpte)
Beethoven: Missa Solemnis
Berg: Wozzeck (Cpte)
Egk: Verlobung in San Domingo (Cpte)
Handel: Giulio Cesare (Cpte)
Haydn: Schöpfung (Cpte)
Janáček: Excursions of Mr Brouček (Cpte)
Mahler: Lied von der Erde
Mozart: Entführung (Cpte), Zauberflöte (Cpte)
Nicolai: Lustigen Weiber von Windsor (Cpte)
R. Strauss: Daphne (Cpte), Schweigsame Frau
(Cpte)
Wagner: Fliegende Holländer (Cpte), Tannhäuser
(Cpte)
see CONCERT INDEX under:
(ACAN) **43 267**   Fritz Wunderlich sings Opera Arias
(DG) **423 956-2GDO**   Schubert: Lieder
(DG) **429 933-2GDO**   Fritz Wunderlich—Lieder Recital
(DG) **431 110-2GB**   Great Voices - Fritz Wunderlich
(NIMB) **NI7851**   Legendary Voices

WUNROW, Theresa Elder (hp)
see CONCERT INDEX under:
(DELO) **DE3106**   Piston—Orchestral Works
(DELO) **DE3126**   The Incredible Walter Piston

WUORINEN, Charles (cond)
see American Cpsrs Orch

WUORINEN, Charles (pf)
see CONCERT INDEX under:
(KOCH) **37112-2**   Wolpe—Chamber Works

WÜRDINGER, Walter (mndl)
see CONCERT INDEX under:
(PHIL) **422 527-2PME**   The Complete Mozart Edition
Vol 27

WÜRTTEMBERG CHAMBER CHOIR
Wolf: Manuel Venegas

WÜRTTEMBERG CHAMBER ORCHESTRA
cond J. FAERBER
Haydn: Keyboard Concerto, HobXVIII:11
Neuner: Oboe Concerto
Shostakovich: Piano Concerto 1
Winter: Oboe Concerto
see CONCERT INDEX under:
(RCA) **RD60244**   C.P.E. Bach: Flute Concertos
(RCA) **RD60247**   Quantz—Flute Concertos
(RCA) **09026 60900-2**   Galway plays Bach
(RCA) **09026 61200-2**   Molter—Trumpet Concertos
(RCA) **09026 61976-2**   Danzi—Flute & Clarinet Works
cond H. RILLING
Bach: Cantata 30, Cantata 198
see CONCERT INDEX under:
(HANS) **98 815**   Bach—Cantatas, Vol.53
(HANS) **98 817**   Bach—Cantatas, Vol.55
(HANS) **98 819**   Bach—Cantatas, Vol.57
(HANS) **98 822**   Bach—Cantatas, Vol.60
(HANS) **98 828**   Bach—Cantatas, Vol.66
(HANS) **98 855**   Bach—Cantatas, Vol.4
(HANS) **98 856**   Bach—Cantatas, Vol.5
(HANS) **98 857**   Bach—Cantatas, Vol.6
(HANS) **98 858**   Bach—Cantatas, Vol.7
(HANS) **98 859**   Bach—Cantatas, Vol.8

(HANS) 98 871　Bach—Cantatas, Vol.20
(HANS) 98 877　Bach—Cantatas, Vol.26
(NOVA) 150 028-2　Bach—Cantatas
(NOVA) 150 029-2　Bach—Cantatas

WÜRTTEMBERG PHILHARMONIC ORCHESTRA
　cond J.-M. BURFIN
　see CONCERT INDEX under:
　(MARC) 8 223659　d'Indy—Orchestral Works
　cond G. NOPRE
　see CONCERT INDEX under:
　(MARC) 8 223654　Indy—Orchestral Works
　(MARC) 8 223659　d'Indy—Orchestral Works

WUSTMAN, John (pf)
　see CONCERT INDEX under:
　(ACAN) 43 579　Songs by Berg, Mahler & Ogermann
　(DECC) 417 813-2DH　Regine Crespin sings French Vocal Works
　(TELA) CD80326　Brahms—Vocal works

WÜSTMANN, Erika (sop)
　R. Strauss: Ariadne auf Naxos (Cpte)

WYATT, Walker (bass)
　see CONCERT INDEX under:
　(TELD) 2292-42502-2　Bach—Cantatas, Volume 6
　(TELD) 4509-91756-2　Bach—Cantatas, Vol.2

WYNBERG, Simon (gtr)
　F. Fossa: Guitar Trios, Op. 18 (exc)
　see CONCERT INDEX under:
　(ASV) CDDCA645　Vivaldi—Concertos
　(CHAN) CHAN8512　Guitar Music of Ferranti and Ferrer
　(HYPE) CDA66295　Villa-Lobos: Chamber Works
　(NAXO) 8 550690　Paganini—Music for Violin and Guitar I
　(NAXO) 8 550759　Paganini—Music for Violin & Guitar, Vol.2

WYNDER, Gloria (contr)
　R. Ward: Crucible (Cpte)

WYNER, Susan Davenny (mez)
　Ravel: Enfant et les sortilèges (Cpte)

WYNNE, Delyth (hp)
　see CONCERT INDEX under:
　(PHIL) 432 152-2PH　Brahms—Choral Works

WYN-ROGERS, Catherine (contr)
　Bach: Christmas Oratorio, BWV248 (Cpte)
　Bruckner: Mass in D minor, Te Deum
　Elgar: Dream of Gerontius (Cpte)
　Gay: Beggar's Opera (Cpte)
　Haydn: Mass 7, Mass 14
　see CONCERT INDEX under:
　(ARCH) 437 834-2AH　Christmas in Rome - Gloria
　(ARCH) 445 353-2AH　Mozart—Sacred Choral Works
　(HYPE) CDA66420　Vaughan Williams: Vocal Works
　(HYPE) CDA66569　Vaughan Williams—Choral Works
　(HYPE) CDJ33022　Schubert—Complete Lieder, Vol.22

WYSS, Gerard (pf)
　(DENO) CO-75636　Schubert—Violin and Viola Works
　(DENO) CO-78947　Schumann/Brahms—Lieder

WYSS, Sophie (sop)
　see CONCERT INDEX under:
　(EMI) CMS7 64727-2　Britten—Opera excerpts and Folksongs

WYTTENBACH, Jürg (cond)
　see Cello Ens

WYTTENBACH, Jürg (pf)
　see CONCERT INDEX under:
　(ACCO) 20061-2　Scelsi: Choral & Orchestral Works
　(ECM) 839 617-2　Bach & Carter—Instrumental & Chamber Works

WYZNER, Franz (bass)
　Einem: Dantons Tod (Cpte)

XALAPA SYMPHONY ORCHESTRA
　cond H. DE LA FUENTE
　see CONCERT INDEX under:
　(CARL) MCD63　Mexican Orchestral Works
　(CATA) 09026 62672-2　Revueltas—Night of the Mayas

XARHAKOS, Stavros (cond)
　see Athens Exp Orch

XENAKIS ENSEMBLE
　cond H. KERSTENS
　see CONCERT INDEX under:
　(ERAT) 2292-45030-2　Xenakis: Miscellaneous Works

XUEREB, Pierre-Henri (va)
　see CONCERT INDEX under:
　(TIMP) 1C1009　Honegger—Chamber Works, Vol.2
　(TIMP) 1C1010　Honegger—Chamber Works, Vol.3
　(TIMP) 4C1012　Honegger—Chamber Works

YABLONSKAYA, Oxana (pf)
　Brahms: Cello Sonata 1, Cello Sonata 2
　Tchaikovsky: Morceaux, Op. 51, Piano Sonata, Op. 37
　see CONCERT INDEX under:
　(CONN) CD4194　Rachmaninov—Piano Works

YABLONSKI, Dmitry (vc)
　Brahms: Cello Sonata 1, Cello Sonata 2

YACHMI-CAUCIG, Rohangiz (contr)
　J. Strauss II: Fledermaus (Cpte)
　Mozart: Così fan tutte (Cpte)

R. Strauss: Rosenkavalier (Cpte)
Wagner: Parsifal (Cpte)

YAHIA, Mino (bass)
　Egk: Verlobung in San Domingo (Cpte)

YAHR, Carol (mez)
　Debussy: Pelléas et Mélisande (Cpte)

YAKAR, Rachel (sop)
　Campra: Europe galante
　Debussy: Pelléas et Mélisande (Cpte)
　Honegger: Aventures du Roi Pausole (Cpte)
　Lully: Bourgeois Gentilhomme, Phaëton (Cpte)
　Martucci: Canzone dei ricordi
　Mozart: Idomeneo (Cpte), Requiem, Zauberflöte (Cpte)
　Poulenc: Dialogues des Carmélites (Cpte)
　Rameau: Pygmalion (Cpte)
　see CONCERT INDEX under:
　(CLAV) CD50-9506　Collet—Cantos de España
　(ERAT) 2292-45923-2　Bach/Vivaldi—Sacred Choral Works
　(HARM) HMC90 1455　Lekeu—Vocal and Chamber Works
　(SONY) SMK45844　Varèse: Orchestral, Chamber and Vocal Works

YAKHONTOV, A. (bass)
　Tchaikovsky: Eugene Onegin (Cpte)

YAMAJ, Yoshihisa (ten)
　Albinoni: Nascimento dell'Aurora (Cpte)

YAMASHITA, Kazuhito (gtr)
　see CONCERT INDEX under:
　(RCA) 09026 60237-2　Giuliani—Chamber Works with guitar

YAMPOLSKY, Vladimir (pf)
　see CONCERT INDEX under:
　(SUPR) 11 0582-2　David Oistrakh plays Beethoven & Mozart

YANG, Win-Sin (vc)
　Schubert: String Quintet

YANIGISAWA, Yasuo (bass)
　Verdi: Traviata (Cpte)

YAPRIDZE, Anton (bass)
　Tchaikovsky: Eugene Onegin (Cpte)

YAROSLAVTSEV, Valeri (bass)
　Tchaikovsky: Eugene Onegin (Cpte), Queen of Spades (Cpte)

YASSA, Ramzi (pf)
　Chopin: Andante Spianato and Grande Polonaise, Ballades

YATES, Sophie (hpd)
　see CONCERT INDEX under:
　(CHAN) CHAN0545　French Baroque Harpsichord Works
　(CHAN) CHAN0560　Spanish and Portuguese Hapsichord Music

YATES, Sophie (virg)
　see CONCERT INDEX under:
　(CHAN) CHAN0574　English Virginals Music
　(CHAN) CHAN0578　The Early Byrd

YEADON, Daniel (vc)
　see CONCERT INDEX under:
　(CONI) CDCF220　Michael Haydn—Masses and Vespers

YEATS, Caitriona (hp)
　see CONCERT INDEX under:
　(NORT) NR227-CD　American Chamber Music with Flute

YEEND, Frances (sop)
　P. Paray: Joan of Arc Mass
　(RCA) GD60874　R. Strauss—Scenes from Elektra & Salome

YEH, John Bruce (cl)
　Messiaen: Quatuor

YELISEEV, Leo (ten)
　Kabalevsky: Colas Breugnon (Cpte)

YENDOLL, Vyvyan (va)
　see CONCERT INDEX under:
　(KOCH) 37058-2　Holst—Works for Chamber Orchestra

YEPES, Narciso (gtr)
　Boccherini: Guitar Quintets, G445-453 (exc)
　Rodrigo: Concierto de Aranjuez, Fantasía
　see CONCERT INDEX under:
　(DG) 435 848-2GX2　Spanish Songs - Berganza

YGGDRASIL QUARTET
　see CONCERT INDEX under:
　(BIS) BIS-CD691　Jón Leifs—String Quartets

YI-KWEI-SZE (bass)
　Berlioz: Roméo et Juliette (Cpte)
　P. Paray: Joan of Arc Mass

YINON, Israel (cond)
　see Brno St PO

YIP, Wing-Sie (cond)
　see Košice St PO

YLÖNEN, Marko (vc)
　Rautavaara: Cello Concerto

YODER, Paul (bar)
　Henze: Cimarron

YODER, Pearl (sop)
　see CONCERT INDEX under:
　(PREI) 89209　Helge Roswaenge (1897-1972) - II

YOKOYAMA, Katsuya (shakuhachi)
　see CONCERT INDEX under:
　(PHIL) 432 176-2PH　Takemitsu—Orchestral Works

YORDANOFF, Luben (vn)
　Messiaen: Quatuor
　see CONCERT INDEX under:
　(EMI) CDM7 69112-2　Best of Saint-Saëns

YORK, John (pf)
　see CONCERT INDEX under:
　(CALA) CACD1017　French Chamber Music for Woodwinds, Volume 1
　(CALA) CACD1018　French Chamber Music for Woodwinds, Volume 2
　(MARC) 8 223718　English Cello Sonatas

YORK, Michael (narr)
　see CONCERT INDEX under:
　(DELO) DE3168　Hovhaness—The Rubaiyat

YORK, Trevor (cond)
　see London Cast

YORK MINSTER CHOIR
　see CONCERT INDEX under:
　(YORK) CD846　Christmas at York Minster
　cond F. JACKSON
　see CONCERT INDEX under:
　(CHAN) CHAN6520　On Christmas Night
　cond P. MOORE
　see CONCERT INDEX under:
　(PRIO) PRCD805　Edward Bairstow—Choral Works
　(PRIO) PRCD486　The Psalms of David, Volume 10

YORK PIANO TRIO
　Dvořák: Piano Trio 3, Piano Trio 4
　see CONCERT INDEX under:
　(MERI) CDE84200　Mendelssohn/Schumann—Piano Trios

YORKSHIRE IMPERIAL BAND
　cond JAMES SCOTT
　see CONCERT INDEX under:
　(CHAN) CHAN4513　British Bandsman Centenary Concert
　cond H. MORTIMER
　see CONCERT INDEX under:
　(CHAN) CHAN4513　British Bandsman Centenary Concert

YOSHIDA, Hiroyuki (ten)
　Verdi: Otello (Cpte)

YOSHINO, Naoko (hp)
　see CONCERT INDEX under:
　(PHIL) 442 012-2PH　20th Century Wind Music
　(VIRG) VJ5 61108-2　Mozart—Concertos

YOUDE, Jenny (contr)
　see CONCERT INDEX under:
　(HYPE) CDA66292　Fauré: Sacred Choral Works

YOUN, Kwanghchul (bass)
　see CONCERT INDEX under:
　(SONY) SK46691　The First Placido Domingo International Voice Competition

YOUNG, Alexander (ten)
　Elgar: Kingdom (Cpte)
　Handel: Israel in Egypt (Cpte), Judas Maccabaeus (Cpte), Theodora (Cpte)
　Haydn: Creation (Cpte), Mass 14
　Purcell: St Cecilia's Day Ode, Z328
　see CONCERT INDEX under:
　(EMI) CDC7 47283-2　Maria Callas - Mad Scenes & Bel Canto Arias

YOUNG, Charles (sngr)
　(EMI) CDANGEL 5　Norton—Chu Chin Chow

YOUNG, Emma (vn)
　Prokofiev: Sonata, Op. 56

YOUNG, John Bell (pf)
　see CONCERT INDEX under:
　(NEWP) NPD85513　Friedrich Nietzsche—Piano Works

YOUNG, La Monte (pf)
　see CONCERT INDEX under:
　(PNT) 434 873-2PTH　Jon Gibson—In Good Company

YOUNG, Thomas J. (ten)
　A. Davis: X (Cpte)
　J. Adams: Death of Klinghoffer (Cpte)

YOUNG, Victor (cond)
　see Orch

YOUNG RUSSIA STATE SYMPHONY ORCHESTRA, MOSCOW
　cond V. BALEY
　see CONCERT INDEX under:
　(CDM) RUS288 085　Lyatoshynsky—Orchestral Works

YOUTH ECHO CHOIR
　cond A. LEAPER
　Brian: Symphony 4
　cond O. NAXOS
　Brian: Symphony 1

YSAS, Rosa Maria (contr)
　Vives: Bohemios (Cpte), Doña Francisquita (Cpte)

YSAŸE, Eugène (vn)
　see CONCERT INDEX under:

(SYMP) **SYMCD1071** Great Violinists, Vol.1

YSAŸE QUARTET
Mozart: String Quartet, K387, String Quartet, K421, String Quartet, K428, String Quartet, K458, String Quartet, K464, String Quartet, K465

YU, Djong Victorin (cond)
see Philh

YUASA, Takuo (cond)
see LPO

YUDINA, Maria (pf)
see CONCERT INDEX under:
(MELO) **74321 25172-2(1)** Russian Piano School (pt 1 - Vols.1 - 8)
(MELO) **74321 25176-2** Russian Piano School, Vol. 4

YUKOV, Igor (pf)
see CONCERT INDEX under:
(CHNT) **LDC278 1018/9** Shostakovich: Chamber Works

YURISICH, Gregory (bar)
Mozart: Don Giovanni (Cpte)

YURLOV RUSSIAN CHOIR
cond K. KONDRASHIN
Miaskovsky: Symphony 6
Shostakovich: Symphony 13
cond G. ROZHDESTVENSKY
Shostakovich: Symphony 3, Symphony 13

YUROV, Yuri (va)
see CONCERT INDEX under:
(TELD) **4509-90422-2** Tchaikovsky—Chamber Works

YUROVSKY, Mikhail (cond)
see Berlin RSO

YUZHIN, David (ten)
see CONCERT INDEX under:
(NIMB) **NI7865** Great Singers at the Mariinsky Theatre
(PEAR) **GEMMCDS9001/3(1)** Singers of Imperial Russia, Vol.2 (pt 1)
(PEAR) **GEMMCDS9001/3(2)** Singers of Imperial Russia, Vol.2 (pt 2)

YVONNE GOUVERNÉ CHOIR
cond R. DESORMIÈRE
see CONCERT INDEX under:
(EMI) **CHS7 61038-2** Debussy—Pelléas et Mélisande, etc

ZABALETA, Nicanor (hp)
Mozart: Flute and Harp Concerto, K299

ZABELA-VRUBEL, Nadezhda (sop)
see CONCERT INDEX under:
(PEAR) **GEMMCDS9004/6(1)** Singers of Imperial Russia, Vol.3 (pt 1)

ZABORONOK, Andrey (cond)
see Bolshoi Children's Ch

ZACCARIA, Nicola (bass)
Bellini: Norma (Cpte), Sonnambula (Cpte)
Donizetti: Lucia di Lammermoor (Cpte), Lucrezia Borgia (Cpte)
Puccini: Bohème (Cpte), Fanciulla del West (Cpte), Turandot (Cpte)
Rossini: Barbiere di Siviglia (Cpte), Italiana in Algeri (Cpte), Tancredi (Cpte)
Verdi: Aida (Cpte), Ballo in maschera (Cpte), Don Carlo (Cpte), Falstaff (Cpte), Rigoletto (Cpte), Trovatore (Cpte)
Vivaldi: Orlando Furioso (Cpte)
see CONCERT INDEX under:
(EMI) **CDM7 69543-2** Maria Callas and Giuseppe Di Stefano - Duets

ZACCARINI, Franco (bass)
see CONCERT INDEX under:
(PREI) **89048** Apollo Granforte (1886-1975) - I

ZACHARIAS, Christian (pf)
Beethoven: Triple Concerto
Mozart: Piano Concerto 16, Piano Concerto 19, Piano Concerto 22, Piano Concerto 23, Piano Concerto 24, Piano Concerto 27

ZACHRISSON, Gösta (ten)
Prokofiev: Fiery Angel (Cpte)

ZACKRISSON, Gösta (ten)
see CONCERT INDEX under:
(BIS) **BIS-CD438** Stenhammar: Vocal and Orchestral Works

ZÁDOR, Dezsö (bar)
Wagner: Götterdämmerung (exc)
see CONCERT INDEX under:
(PEAR) **GEMMCDS9137** Wagner—Der Ring des Nibelungen
(SUPR) **11 2136-2(3)** Emmy Destinn—Complete Edition, Discs 5 to 8

ZÁDORI, Mária (sop)
Handel: Floridante (Cpte), St John Passion (Cpte)
see CONCERT INDEX under:
(HARM) **HMA190 3010** Bach—Wedding Cantatas, BWV202, 209 and 210
(QUIN) **QUI90 3010** Bach—Wedding Cantatas

ZADVORNY, Sergei (bass)
Rossini: Armida (Cpte)
Tchaikovsky: Eugene Onegin (Cpte)

ZAEPFFEL, Alain (alto)
M-A. Charpentier: Judicium Salomonis, H422
see CONCERT INDEX under:
(ADES) **20217-2** A. Scarlatti—Duo Cantatas, Vol.1
(ERAT) **2292-45926-2** Charpentier—Sacred Choral Works

ZAGONARA, Adelio (ten)
Puccini: Manon Lescaut (Cpte), Turandot (Cpte)
Verdi: Aida (Cpte)
see CONCERT INDEX under:
(EMI) **CMS7 64165-2** Puccini—Trittico

ZAGORINSKY, Alexander (vc)
see CONCERT INDEX under:
(ETCE) **KTC1177** Brahms—Music for Clarinet
(ETCE) **KTC1179** Denisov—Music for Cello

ZAGÓRZANKA, Barbara (sop)
see CONCERT INDEX under:
(SCHW) **314001** Szymanowski: Lieder

ZAGREB SOLOISTS
see CONCERT INDEX under:
(RCA) **GD86517** Galway plays Bach
cond A. JANIGRO
(CBC) **PSCD2002** Maureen Forrester sings Handel Arias
(VANG) **08.4016.71** Music of Samuel Barber
cond T. NINIĆ
see CONCERT INDEX under:
(ASV) **CDDCA751** Vivaldi—Bassoon Concerti, Vol.5
(ASV) **CDDCA752** Vivaldi—Bassoon Concerti, Vol.6
(CARL) **PCD1000** Bartók/Shostakovich—Orchestral Works

ZAGROSEK, Lothar (cond)
see Austrian RSO

ZAHAB, Roger (vn)
see CONCERT INDEX under:
(KOCH) **37130-2** John Cage—Thirteen Harmonies
(KOCH) **37238-2** A Chance Operation - John Cage Tribute

ZAHARIA, Constantin (ten)
Saint-Saëns: Samson et Dalila (Cpte)
Verdi: Otello (Cpte)

ZAHRADNÍČEK, Jiří (ten)
Smetana: Two Widows (Cpte)
see CONCERT INDEX under:
(DECC) **430 375-2DH2** Janáček—Operatic and Orchestral Works

ZAHRADNÍK, Bohuslav (cl)
see CONCERT INDEX under:
(CALL) **CAL9628** Mozart—Chamber Works
(SUPR) **11 0999-2** Mozart—Wind Quintets & Quartet

ZAJAC, Karen (contr)
Schoenberg: Moses und Aron (Cpte)

ZAJICK, Dolora (mez)
Prokofiev: Alexander Nevsky
Verdi: Aida (Cpte), Don Carlo (Cpte), Forza del destino (Cpte), Requiem (Cpte), Trovatore (Cpte)

ZAK, Yonathan (pf)
see CONCERT INDEX under:
(KOCH) **37021-2** Mira Zakai—Song Recital

ZAKAI, Mira (contr)
Mussorgsky: Boris Godunov (Cpte)
Schoenberg: Moses und Aron (Cpte)
see CONCERT INDEX under:
(DECC) **430 804-2DC10** Mahler—Complete Symphonies
(KOCH) **37021-2** Mira Zakai—Song Recital

ZAKHAROFF, Boris (pf)
see CONCERT INDEX under:
(APR) **APR7015** The Auer Legacy, Vol.1

ZAKOWSKY, Rainer (ten)
R. Strauss: Rosenkavalier (Cpte)

ZALEWSKI, Włodzimierz (bar)
Mussorgsky: Boris Godunov (Cpte)

ZALLINGER, Meinhard von (cond)
see Bavarian St Orch

ZAMBALIS, Stella (mez)
Bernstein: West Side Story (Cpte)

ZAMBELLI, Corrado (bass)
Verdi: Trovatore (Cpte)

ZAMBERG, Viktor (bass)
Kabalevsky: Colas Breugnon (Cpte)

ZAMBON, Giuseppe (alto)
see CONCERT INDEX under:
(DENO) **CO-78904** Pergolesi/Feo—Sacred Vocal Works

ZAMBON, Giuseppe (ten)
Traetta: Buovo d'Antona (Cpte)

ZAMBONI, Maria (sop)
see CONCERT INDEX under:
(EMI) **CHS7 64864-2(1)** La Scala Edition - Vol.2, 1915-46 (pt 1)

ZAMBONI, Rinaldo (cond)
see orch

ZAMKOCHIAN, Berj (organ)
see CONCERT INDEX under:
(RCA) **09026 61500-2** Munch conducts French Orchestral Works

ZAMMIT, Giuseppe (ten)
Verdi: Trovatore (Cpte)

ZAMPIERI, Giuseppe (ten)
Donizetti: Lucia di Lammermoor (Cpte)
J. Strauss II: Fledermaus (Cpte)
Verdi: Traviata (Cpte)

ZAMPIERI, Mara (sop)
Puccini: Fanciulla del West (Cpte)
Verdi: Macbeth (Cpte)

ZANASI, Furio (bass)
Handel: Giulio Cesare (Cpte)

ZANASI, Mario (bar)
Leoncavallo: Pagliacci (Cpte)

ZANCANARO, Giorgio (bar)
Giordano: Andrea Chénier (Cpte)
Puccini: Tosca (Cpte)
Verdi: Attila (Cpte), Forza del destino (Cpte), Rigoletto (Cpte), Traviata (Cpte), Trovatore (exc), Vespri siciliani (Cpte)

ZANCU, Dan (bass)
Bretan: Arald (Cpte), Golem (Cpte)

ZANDER, Benjamin (cond)
see Boston PO

ZANELLI, Renato (bar/ten)
see CONCERT INDEX under:
(NIMB) **NI7856** Legendary Tenors
(NIMB) **NI7867** Legendary Baritones
(PEAR) **GEMMCDS9926(1)** Covent Garden on Record—Vol.4 (pt 1)

ZANETTI, Monique (sop)
Campra: Idoménée (Cpte), Messe de Requiem
Lully: Atys (Cpte)
M-A. Charpentier: Malade Imaginaire, Médée (Cpte)
Monteverdi: Vespers
see CONCERT INDEX under:
(HARM) **HMC90 1280** Montéclair—Cantatas
(O111) **OPS30-100** Hasse—Motets

ZANETTI, Orfeo (ten)
Verdi: Don Carlo (Cpte)

ZANIBONI, A. (vn)
see CONCERT INDEX under:
(PEAR) **GEMMCDS9001/3(1)** Singers of Imperial Russia, Vol.2 (pt 1)

ZANINI, Nicoletta (mez)
Verdi: Rigoletto (Cpte)

ZANLONGHI, Pascale (hp)
see CONCERT INDEX under:
(TIMP) **1C1010** Honegger—Chamber Works, Vol.3
(TIMP) **4C1012** Honegger—Chamber Works

ZANNINI, Laura (mez)
Berg: Lulu (Cpte)
Verdi: Traviata (Cpte)

ZANOLLI, Silvana (sop)
Verdi: Traviata (Cpte)

ZAPPA, Frank (pf)
see CONCERT INDEX under:
(KOCH) **37238-2** A Chance Operation - John Cage Tribute

ZARDO, Carlo (bass)
Verdi: Macbeth (Cpte)

ZAREMBA, Eléna (mez)
Mussorgsky: Boris Godunov (Cpte)
Shostakovich: King Lear, Op. 58a, Lady Macbeth of Mtsensk (Cpte)
Wagner: Rheingold (Cpte)
see CONCERT INDEX under:
(DG) **445 238-2GH** Mussorgsky—Orchestral and Choral Works

ZARESKA, Eugenia (mez)
Martin: Pilate
Mussorgsky: Boris Godunov (Cpte)

ZAUN, Fritz (cond)
see Berlin St Op Orch

ZAVADILÍK, Leoš (vn)
see CONCERT INDEX under:
(SUPR) **11 1878-2** The Unknown Janáček

ZAYDE, Jascha (pf)
see CONCERT INDEX under:
(APR) **APR7016** The Auer Legacy, Vol.2

ZBRUEVA, Evgenia (contr)
see CONCERT INDEX under:
(NIMB) **NI7865** Great Singers at the Mariinsky Theatre
(PEAR) **GEMMCDS9004/6(2)** Singers of Imperial Russia, Vol.3 (pt 2)
(PEAR) **GEMMCDS9007/9(1)** Singers of Imperial Russia, Vol.4 (pt 1)

ZEANI, Virginia (sop)
see CONCERT INDEX under:
(DECC) **417 686-2DC** Puccini—Operatic Arias

ZEAVIN, Carol (vn)
see CONCERT INDEX under:
(KOCH) **37110-2** Wuorinen—Orchestral & Chamber Works

ZEC, Nikolaus (bass)
see CONCERT INDEX under:
(SCHW) **314542** Vienna State Opera Live, Vol.4
(SCHW) **314562** Vienna State Opera Live, Vol.6

(SCHW) **314592** Vienna State Opera Live, Vol.9
(SCHW) **314602** Vienna State Opera Live, Vol.10
(SCHW) **314632** Vienna State Opera Live, Vol.13
(SCHW) **314642** Vienna State Opera Live, Vol.14
(SCHW) **314652** Vienna State Opera Live, Vol.15

ZECCHI, Carlo (cond)
see Czech PO

ZECCHILLO, Giuseppe (bass)
Puccini: Tosca (Cpte)

ZEDDA, Alberto (cond)
see Collegium Instr Brugense

ZEDELIUS, Maria (sop)
Telemann: St Matthew Passion (1746)
see CONCERT INDEX under:
(ARCH) **437 079-2AT** Collectio Argentea 9: De
Profundis
(ARCH) **437 090-2AT** Collectio Argentea 20: Bach
Family before J.S.

ZEDNIK, Heinz (ten)
Berg: Wozzeck (Cpte)
Bizet: Carmen (Cpte)
J. Strauss II: Fledermaus (Cpte)
Lehár: Lustige Witwe (Cpte)
Mozart: Entführung (Cpte), Nozze di Figaro (Cpte),
Zauberflöte (Cpte)
Mussorgsky: Boris Godunov (Cpte), Khovanshchina
(Cpte)
Prokofiev: Fiery Angel (Cpte)
Puccini: Tosca (Cpte), Turandot (Cpte)
R. Strauss: Ariadne auf Naxos (Cpte), Rosenkavalier
(Cpte)
Schreker: Irrelohe (Cpte)
Shostakovich: Lady Macbeth of Mtsensk (Cpte)
Tchaikovsky: Mazeppa (Cpte)
Wagner: Parsifal (Cpte), Rheingold (Cpte), Siegfried
(Cpte)
see CONCERT INDEX under:
(DG) **445 354-2GX14** Wagner—Der Ring des
Nibelungen

ZEEUW, Chantal de (organ)
see CONCERT INDEX under:
(PIER) **PV783041** Liszt—Organ Works

ZEEUW, Ger de (perc)
Messiaen: Canyons aux étoiles

ZEFIRO ENSEMBLE
Zelenka: Trio Sonatas (exc)

ZEH, Walter (bar)
R. Strauss: Rosenkavalier (Cpte), Salome (Cpte)

ZEHETMAIR, Thomas (vn)
Beethoven: Violin Sonata 5, Violin Sonata 9
Brahms: Violin Concerto
Devienne: Bassoon Quartets, Op.73
Paganini: Caprices, Op. 1
Schumann: Fantasie, Op. 131
see CONCERT INDEX under:
(PHIL) **434 076-2PH** Heinz Holliger and Friends
(TELD) **4509-91444-2** Dvořák/Schumann—Violin
Concertos, etc
(TELD) **4509-97449-2**
Berg/Hartmann/Janáček—Violin Concertos

ZEHETMAIR, Thomas (vn/dir)
see CONCERT INDEX under:
(TELD) **2292-46340-2** Mozart—Violin Concertos Nos
2 3 and 5
(TELD) **4509-97449-2**
Berg/Hartmann/Janáček—Violin Concertos

ZEJST, Martin van der (alto)
Bach: Motets (Cpte)

ZELAZNY, Piotr (va)
see CONCERT INDEX under:
(KONT) **32197** Syberg—Chamber Music, Vol. 2

ZELLER, Richard (bar)
V. Thomson: Lord Byron (Cpte)

ZELLER, Robert (cond)
see Vienna St Op Orch

ZELNICK, Robert (vn)
see CONCERT INDEX under:
(VOX) **115845-2** Chamber Works by Women
Composers

ZELTSER, Mark (pf)
see CONCERT INDEX under:
(DG) **415 276-2GH** Beethoven—Orchestral Works

ZEMEL CHOIR
cond G. SIMON
Bloch: Sacred Service

ZEMLINSKY, Alexander von (cond)
see Berlin City Op Orch

ZEMPLÉNI, Mária (sop)
Respighi: Belfagor (Cpte)

ZENATELLO, Giovanni (ten)
see CONCERT INDEX under:
(CLUB) **CL99-025** Giovanni Zenatello (1876-1949)
(CLUB) **CL99-509/10** Hina Spani (1896-1929)
(EMI) **CHS7 64860-2(2)** La Scala Edition - Vol.1,
1878-1914 (pt 2)
(IRCC) **IRCC-CD808** Souvenirs of 19th Century Italian
Opera
(PEAR) **GEMMCDS9073(1)** Giovanni Zenatello, Vol.1
(pt 1)
(PEAR) **GEMMCDS9073(2)** Giovanni Zenatello, Vol.1
(pt 2)

(PEAR) **GEMMCDS9074(1)** Giovanni Zenatello, Vol.2
(pt 1)
(PEAR) **GEMMCDS9074(2)** Giovanni Zenatello, Vol.2
(pt 2)
(PEAR) **GEMMCDS9924(1)** Covent Garden on
Record, Vol.2 (pt 1)
(PEAR) **GEMMCDS9924(2)** Covent Garden on
Record, Vol.2 (pt 2)
(PEAR) **GEMMCDS9925(2)** Covent Garden on
Record—Vol.3 (pt 2)
(PEAR) **GEMMCDS9926(1)** Covent Garden on
Record—Vol.4 (pt 1)
(PREI) **89038** Giovanni Zenatello (1876-1949)
(SUPR) **11 2136-2(5)** Emmy Destinn—Complete
Edition, Discs 11 & 12
(SYMP) **SYMCD1073** The Harold Wayne Collection,
Vol.3
(SYMP) **SYMCD1138** The Harold Wayne Collection,
Vol.16
(SYMP) **SYMCD1148** The Harold Wayne Collection,
Vol.17
(SYMP) **SYMCD1158** The Harold Wayne Collection,
Vol.18
(SYMP) **SYMCD1168** The Harold Wayne Collection,
Vol.19

ŽENATÝ, Ivan (vn)
see CONCERT INDEX under:
(SUPR) **11 1522-2** Janáček—Orchestral Works, Vol.
3

ZENDER, Hans (cond)
see Basle SO

ZENNARO, Iorio (ten)
Rossini: Armida (Cpte), Inganno felice (Cpte),
Occasione fa il ladro (Cpte)

ZEPPERITZ, Rainer (db)
Schubert: Trout Quintet, D667

ZERBINI, Antonio (bass)
Verdi: Forza del destino (Cpte), Traviata (Cpte)

ZERHAUOVÁ, Jitka (contr)
Beethoven: Mass in C

ZEROLA, Nicola (ten)
(MEMO) **HR408/9(2)** Singers in Genoa, Vol.1 (disc
2)

ZERTSALOVA, Natalia (pf)
Tchaikovsky: Piano Trio, Op. 50

ZEUMER, Gerti (sop)
Mahler: Symphony 8
see CONCERT INDEX under:
(DG) **435 162-2GX13** Mahler—Complete
Symphonies

ZEUTHEN, Morten (vc)
Holten: Sinfonia concertante
Nørgård: Between
see CONCERT INDEX under:
(UNIC) **DKPCD9114** Ruders—Orchestral Works

ZEYST, Martin van der (alto)
Bach: Motets (Cpte)

ZHADAN, Ivan (ten)
see CONCERT INDEX under:
(EMI) **CHS7 69741-2(6)** Record of Singing,
Vol.4—Russian & Slavonic Schools

ZHANG, Jianyi (ten)
Liszt: Faust Symphony

ZHEMCHUZHIN, Georgy (cond)
see Moscow Stanislavsky Th Orch

ZHISLIN, Grigori (va)
see CONCERT INDEX under:
(CONI) **CDCF168** Penderecki & Van de
Vate—Orchestral Works

ZHUKOV, Igor (pf)
see CONCERT INDEX under:
(MEZH) **MK417087** Russian Piano Concertos

ZHUKOVSKAYA, Glafira (sop)
Tchaikovsky: Eugene Onegin (Cpte)

ZHURAITIS, Algis (cond)
see Moscow PO

ZICHNER, Frank-Immo (pf)
see CONCERT INDEX under:
(EDA) **EDA008-2** Works by Ullmann and Schoenberg

ŽÍDEK, Ivo (ten)
Dvořák: Stabat Mater
Fibich: Bride of Messina (Cpte)
Janáček: From the House of the Dead (Cpte), Jenůfa
(Cpte), Makropulos Affair (Cpte)
Martinů: Julietta (Cpte)
Smetana: Brandenburgers in Bohemia (Cpte), Devil's
Wall (Cpte)
Stravinsky: Oedipus Rex (Cpte)
see CONCERT INDEX under:
(DECC) **430 375-2DH2** Janáček—Operatic and
Orchestral Works

ZIEGLER, Benno (bar)
(PEAR) **GEMMCD9327** The Vocal Prime of Richard
Tauber

ZIEGLER, Delores (mez)
Bach: Mass in B minor, BWV232 (Cpte)
Donizetti: Roberto Devereux (Cpte)
Haydn: Mass 10

Mahler: Symphony 8
Mozart: Clemenza di Tito (Cpte), Così fan tutte
(Cpte), Mass, K317, Mass, K427, Requiem,
Zauberflöte (Cpte)
Verdi: Falstaff (Cpte)
Weber: Oberon (Cpte)
see CONCERT INDEX under:
(EMI) **CDH5 65072-2** Glyndebourne Recorded - 1934-
1994
(EMI) **CDS7 49487-2** Beethoven: Complete
Symphonies

ZIEGLER, Robert (cond)
see Matrix Ens

ZIESAK, Ruth (sop)
Bach: Cantata 206, Cantata 207a, Christmas
Oratorio, BWV248 (Cpte), Mass, BWV236, Mass in B
minor, BWV232 (Cpte)
Beethoven: Fidelio (Cpte)
Haydn: Jahreszeiten (Cpte), Mass 10, Schöpfung
(Cpte)
Humperdinck: Hänsel und Gretel (Cpte)
Mahler: Symphony 2
Mozart: Clemenza di Tito (Cpte), Requiem,
Zauberflöte (Cpte)
Orff: Catulli Carmina
Weber: Freischütz (Cpte)
Wolf: Goethe Lieder (exc), Italienisches Liederbuch
(Cpte), Mörike Lieder (exc)
see CONCERT INDEX under:
(SONY) **SK57960** Zemlinsky—Posthumous Songs

ZIGHERA, Bernard (pf)
Stravinsky: Petrushka (Cpte)
see CONCERT INDEX under:
(BIDD) **WHL019** Koussevitzky—Double-bass
Recordings & Early Boston SO

ZIJLSTRA, Nancy (sop)
see CONCERT INDEX under:
(ERAT) **2292-45822-2** M-A.Charpentier—Motets

ZIKA, Zdenka (sop)
(SCHW) **314662** Vienna State Opera Live, Vol.16

ZIKMUNDOVÁ, Eva (sop)
Hába: Mother (Cpte)
Janáček: Cunning Little Vixen (Cpte)
see CONCERT INDEX under:
(DECC) **430 375-2DH2** Janáček—Operatic and
Orchestral Works

ZILBERSTEIN, Lilya (pf)
Rachmaninov: Piano Concerto 2, Piano Concerto 3,
Preludes (exc)
Shostakovich: Piano Sonata 1
see CONCERT INDEX under:
(DG) **431 123-2GH** Brahms: Piano Works
(DG) **435 385-2GH** Schubert/Liszt—Piano Works
(DG) **437 524-2GH** Grieg—Orchestral Works
(DG) **437 805-2GH**
Medtner/Mussorgsky/Taneyev—Piano Works
(DG) **439 927-2GH** Debussy/Ravel—Piano Works

ZILIANI, Alessandro (ten)
see CONCERT INDEX under:
(EMI) **CHS7 64864-2(2)** La Scala Edition - Vol.2,
1915-46 (pt 2)

ŽILINA STATE CHAMBER ORCHESTRA
cond J. VALTA
Martinů: La Jolla
Respighi: Botticelli Pictures

ZILIO, Elena (mez)
Donizetti: Gianni di Parigi (Cpte)
Paisiello: Don Chisciotte (Cpte)

ZIMANOWSKI, Robert (vn)
Szymanowski: Violin Concerto 1
see CONCERT INDEX under:
(ACCO) **20062-2** Scelsi—Chamber Works
(ACCO) **20093-2** Janáček—Chamber Works
(ACCO) **22053-2** Schumann: Violin Sonatas
(CLAV) **CD50-9003** Jolivet & Koechlin—Chamber
Works

ZIMBALIST, Efrem (vn)
see CONCERT INDEX under:
(APR) **APR7016** The Auer Legacy, Vol.2
(PEAR) **GEMMCDS9996** Kreisler - Violin Concertos

ZIMERMAN, Krystian (pf)
Brahms: Piano Concerto 1, Piano Concerto 2
Chopin: Piano Concerto 1, Piano Concerto 2
Debussy: Préludes
R. Strauss: Violin Sonata
Respighi: Violin Sonata
Schubert: Impromptus (exc)
Stravinsky: Noces
see CONCERT INDEX under:
(DG) **423 090-2GH** Chopin—Piano Works
(DG) **423 571-2GH** Liszt: Works for Piano and
Orchestra
(DG) **431 469-2GGA** Works for Violin and Piano
(DG) **431 664-2GH** Lutosławski—Orchestral Works
(DG) **431 780-2GH** Liszt—Piano Works
(DG) **435 467-2GH3** Beethoven—Piano Concertos
(OLYM) **OCD392** Bacewicz—Orchestral and
Chamber Works

ZIMERMAN, Krystian (pf/dir)
Beethoven: Piano Concerto 1, Piano Concerto 2
see CONCERT INDEX under:
(DG) **435 467-2GH3** Beethoven—Piano Concertos

ZIMMER, Hans (cond)
see OST

ZIMMER, Rudolf (bar)
Verdi: Trovatore (Cpte)

ZIMMERMANN, Erich (ten)
Wagner: Meistersinger (exc), Tristan und Isolde (Cpte)
see CONCERT INDEX under:
(SCHW) 314562   Vienna State Opera Live, Vol.6
(SCHW) 314592   Vienna State Opera Live, Vol.9
(SCHW) 314602   Vienna State Opera Live, Vol.10
(SCHW) 314642   Vienna State Opera Live, Vol.14
(TELD) 9031-76442-2   Wagner—Excerpts from the 1936 Bayreuth Festival

ZIMMERMANN, Erika (sop)
Wagner: Götterdämmerung (Cpte), Parsifal (Cpte), Rheingold (Cpte)
see CONCERT INDEX under:
(FOYE) 15-CF2011   Wagner—Der Ring de Nibelungen

ZIMMERMANN, Frank Peter (vn)
Beethoven: Romances, Violin Concerto
Dvořák: Violin Concerto
Glazunov: Violin Concerto
Mozart: Sinfonia Concertante, K364
Prokofiev: Violin Concerto 1, Violin Concerto 2
Saint-Saëns: Violin Concerto 3
Sibelius: Violin Concerto
Tchaikovsky: Violin Concerto
see CONCERT INDEX under:
(EMI) CDC7 49862-2   Bach: Concertos
(EMI) CDC7 54248-2   Berg/Stravinsky—Violin Concertos, etc
(EMI) CDC7 54305-2   Violin Sonatas
(EMI) CDC7 54541-2   French Violin and Piano Works

ZIMMERMANN, Gerhardt (cond)
see North Carolina SO

ZIMMERMANN, Margarita (mez)
Albinoni: Nascimento dell'Aurora (Cpte)
Rossini: Petite messe solennelle
see CONCERT INDEX under:
(PHIL) 422 522-2PME6   The Complete Mozart Edition Vol 22

ZIMMERMANN, Mark (sngr)
Bizet: Jolie fille de Perth (Cpte)
Puccini: Manon Lescaut (Cpte)
Rossini: Maometto II (Cpte)

ZIMMERMANN, Renate (mez)
Weill: Kuhhandel (exc)

ZIMMERMANN, Tabea (va)
Bartók: Viola Concerto
Devienne: Bassoon Quartets, Op.73
Gubaidulina: Hommage
Hindemith: Schwanendreher
Mozart: Sinfonia Concertante, K364
Schubert: Winterreise (Cpte)
see CONCERT INDEX under:
(CAPR) 10 462   Songs with Viola
(ECM) 437 440-2   Bach/Veress—Chamber Works
(EMI) CDC5 55107-2   Schnittke/Kopytman—Viola Concertos
(EMI) CDC7 49736-2   Clarinet Music by Bruch, Mozart & Schumann
(EMI) CDC7 54394-2   Modern Viola Works
(HYPE) CDH88015   The Concerto in Europe
(PHIL) 434 076-2PH   Heinz Holliger and Friends
(SCHW) 311065   Double Concertos
(WERG) WER60172-50   Penderecki: Orchestral and Vocal Works

ZIMMERMANN, Udo (cond)
see Inst. Ens

ZIMOSKI, Mark (synths)
C. Young: Haunted Summer (exc)

ZINETTI, Giuseppina (sop)
see CONCERT INDEX under:
(PREI) 89010   Tancredi Pasero (1893-1983) - I
(PREI) 89013   Giannina Arangi-Lombardi (1890-1951)

ZINGARA TRIO
cond E. HEATH
Beethoven: Triple Concerto

ZINGER, Pablo (pf)
see CONCERT INDEX under:
(NALB) NA058CD   Guastavino—Canciones Argentinas

ZINMAN, David (cond)
see Baltimore SO

ZINTL, Barbara (sop)
Honegger: Jeanne d'Arc (Cpte)

ZIPPER, Hans (pf)
see CONCERT INDEX under:
(EMI) CHS7 69741-2(4)   Record of Singing, Vol.4—German School

ZIPPERLING, Rainer (va da gamba)
see CONCERT INDEX under:
(CPO) CPO999 209-2   Abel—Chamber Works
(DHM) RD77201   Telemann—Wind Concertos
(RICE) RIC118100   Le Tombeau de M. de Sainte-Colombe

ZIRKELBACH, Corinna (hp)
see CONCERT INDEX under:

(TROU) TRO-CD01405   Ethel Smyth—Chamber Works & Songs, Vol.3

ZÍTEK, Václav (bar)
Dvořák: Jacobin (Cpte)
Fibich: Bride of Messina (Cpte), Šárka (Cpte)
Janáček: Cunning Little Vixen (Cpte), Jenufa (Cpte), Makropulos Affair (Cpte)
Martinů: Miracles of Mary (Cpte)
Smetana: Kiss (Cpte), Libuše (Cpte)
see CONCERT INDEX under:
(DECC) 430 375-2DH2   Janáček—Operatic and Orchestral Works

ZIURAITIS, Algis (cond)
see Bolshoi Th Orch

ZIVONI, Yossi (vn)
see CONCERT INDEX under:
(MERI) CDE84229   Mendelssohn—Violin Sonatas

ZLATOGOROVA, Bronislava (mez)
Tchaikovsky: Eugene Onegin (Cpte)
see CONCERT INDEX under:
(DANT) LYS013/5   Tchaikovsky—The Queen of Spades
(PREI) 89080   Mark Reizen (1895-1992) - II

ZLESÁK, Antonin (ten)
Martinů: Julietta (Cpte)
Stravinsky: Oedipus Rex (Cpte)

ZOBEL, Philibert (cond)
see Bec-Hellouin Abbey Ch

ZOFF, Jutta (hp)
Saint-Saëns: Oratorio de Noël, Op. 12

ZOGHBY, Linda (sop)
Haydn: Isola Disabitata (Cpte), Ritorno di Tobia (Cpte)
see CONCERT INDEX under:
(PHIL) 432 416-2PH3   Haydn—L'incontro improvviso/Arias

ZOHAR, Israel (cl)
see CONCERT INDEX under:
(EMI) CMS7 64617-2   The art of Itzhak Perlman

ZÖLLER, Karlheinz (fl)
Messiaen: Merle noir

ZOLLMAN, Ronald (cond)
see Northern Sinfonia

ZOON, Jacques (fl)
Maderna: Hyperion (Cpte)
see CONCERT INDEX under:
(DECC) 444 455-2DH   Martin—Ballades; Concerto for 7 Wind Instruments

ZORGNIOTTI, Mario (bass)
Verdi: Traviata (Cpte)

ZORINA, Verina (narr)
see CONCERT INDEX under:
(ARHI) ADCD110   Mengelberg Edition - Volume 4

ZOROBERTO, Anna (sop)
Gluck: Iphigénie en Tauride (Cpte)
Verdi: Simon Boccanegra (Cpte)

ZOROVA, Vessela (mez)
Prokofiev: Ivan the Terrible

ZSOLT, Mr (cond)
see Budapest Cons Orch

ZUBICKY, Gregor (ob)
see CONCERT INDEX under:
(SIMA) PSC1022   Chamber Works for Oboe

ZUCCA, Donald (sngr)
Gershwin: Porgy and Bess (Cpte)

ZUCCHI, Reiko Noda (sop)
see CONCERT INDEX under:
(STUD) SM12 2389   Paisiello—Music for Napoleon Bonaparte's Chapel

ZUKERMAN, Eugenia (fl)
see CONCERT INDEX under:
(DELO) DE3186   Heigh Ho! Mozart

ZUKERMAN, Pinchas (cond)
see ECO

ZUKERMAN, Pinchas (va)
Mozart: Sinfonia Concertante, K364, String Quintet, K515, String Quintet, K516
Nørgård: Remembering Child
see CONCERT INDEX under:
(DG) 437 248-2GGA   Brahms—Viola Sonatas
(EMI) CDS7 54198-2   Beethoven—String Trios
(EMI) CMS7 64617-2   The art of Itzhak Perlman
(EMI) CZS4 83177-2(1)   Itzhak Perlman Edition (pt 1)
(RCA) RD60735   Mozart & Leclair—Chamber Works
(RCA) 09026 61276-2   Brahms—Viola Sonatas; Songs
(RCA) 09026 61284-2   Beethoven—Early String Quartets
(RCA) 09026 68052-2   Schumann—Violin and Piano Works

ZUKERMAN, Pinchas (vn)
Beethoven: Allegretto, Hess48, Piano Trios (exc), Romances, Violin Concerto, Violin Sonata 5, Violin Sonata 9, Violin Sonata 10
Brahms: Violin Concerto, Violin Sonata 1
Elgar: Salut d'amour, Violin Concerto
Mozart: Concertone, K190
Vivaldi: Concerti, Op. 8 (exc)
see CONCERT INDEX under:
(DG) 437 248-2GGA   Brahms—Viola Sonatas

(DG) 439 529-2GGA   Delius/Vaughan Williams/Walton—Orchestral Works
(DG) 447 405-2GOR   Berg/Stravinsky—Chamber Works
(EMI) CDC7 47856-2   Bach: Violin Concertos
(EMI) CDM7 64631-2   Beethoven—Violin Sonatas
(EMI) CMS7 69707-2   Impressions of Jacqueline du Pré
(EMI) CZS4 83177-2(1)   Itzhak Perlman Edition (pt 1)
(RCA) RD60718   Bach—Violin Concertos
(RCA) RD60735   Mozart & Leclair—Chamber Works
(RCA) RD60740   Mozart—Violin Sonatas, Vol.2
(RCA) RD60743   Mozart—Violin Sonatas, Vol.3
(RCA) RD60991   Beethoven—Complete Violin Sonatas
(RCA) 09026 60742-2   Mozart—Violin Sonatas, Vol.4
(RCA) 09026 60744-2   Mozart—Sonatas for Violin and Piano, Volume 5
(RCA) 09026 62697-2   Franck/Debussy/Fauré—Violin Sonatas
(RCA) 09026 68052-2   Schumann—Violin and Piano Works
(SONY) SMK47592   Mendelssohn—Orchestral Works
(SONY) SMK48466   Boulez conducts Schoenberg—Volume 3

ZUKERMAN, Pinchas (vn/dir)
see CONCERT INDEX under:
(PHIL) 420 168-2PH   Violin Works
(SONY) SK39964   J.C.Bach & Boccherini Orchestral Works

ZUKOFSKY, Paul (cond)
see RPO

ZUKOFSKY, Paul (vn)
Glass: Einstein on the Beach (Cpte)
M. Feldman: Spring of Chosroes
Schnabel: Violin Sonata (1935)
see CONCERT INDEX under:
(MOBS) CP2103   Cage—Violin Music
(NEW) 80396-2   Babbitt/Diamond/Persichetti—Orchestral Works

ZUPNIK, Marilyn (ob)
see CONCERT INDEX under:
(ASV) CDDCA663   Handel/Telemann—Oboe Sonatas

ZURICH CAMERATA
cond R. TSCHUPP
see CONCERT INDEX under:
(JECK) JD506-2   Flute Concertos

ZURICH CHAMBER ENSEMBLE
cond C. KELLER
see CONCERT INDEX under:
(ACCO) 149158   Eisler: Chamber Works

ZURICH CHAMBER MUSIC
see CONCERT INDEX under:
(JECK) JD506-2   The Romantic Clarinet

ZURICH CHAMBER ORCHESTRA
cond E. DE STOUTZ
Haydn: Keyboard Concerto HobXVIII/4, Keyboard Concerto HobXVIII/11
Mozart: Bassoon Concerto, K191, Clarinet Concerto, K622
see CONCERT INDEX under:
(EMI) CDC7 54086-2   Classical Trumpet Concertos

ZURICH COLLEGIUM MUSICUM
cond P. SACHER
see CONCERT INDEX under:
(DG) 437 952-2GX2   Great Cello Works

ZURICH OPERA HOUSE CHORUS
cond N. HARNONCOURT
Mozart: Clemenza di Tito (Cpte), Entführung (Cpte), Idomeneo (Cpte), Zauberflöte (Cpte)
cond R. WEIKERT
Zemlinsky: Kleider machen Leute (Cpte)

ZURICH OPERA HOUSE MOZART ORCHESTRA
cond N. HARNONCOURT
Mozart: Entführung (Cpte), Idomeneo (Cpte)

ZURICH OPERA ORCHESTRA
cond N. HARNONCOURT
Mozart: Clemenza di Tito (Cpte), Zauberflöte (Cpte)
cond R. WEIKERT
Zemlinsky: Kleider machen Leute (Cpte)

ZURICH STRING SEXTET
Brahms: String Sextet 2

ZURICH TONHALLE ORCHESTRA
cond O. ACKERMANN
see CONCERT INDEX under:
(JECK) JD541-2   Bach & Chopin: Piano Works
cond H. KNAPPERTSBUSCH
see CONCERT INDEX under:
(PREI) 90083   Maria Reining
(PREI) 90190   Paul Schoeffler—Recital
cond F. PATANÈ
see CONCERT INDEX under:
(DECC) 436 463-2DM   Ten Top Tenors
cond M. STERN
Prokofiev: Violin Concerto 1, Violin Concerto 2

ZUTPHEN, Wim van (cond)
see Pannonic Wind Orch

ZWART, Titia de (viol)
see CONCERT INDEX under:
(ACCE) ACC8864D   Symphonia Angelica

ZWEIG, Fritz (cond)
see Berlin City Op Orch

ZWEIG, Mimi (vn)
Shostakovich: Piano Quintet, Op. 57
Tchaikovsky: Album for the Young

ZYLIS-GARA, Teresa (sop)
Chausson: Roi Arthus (Cpte)
Mozart: Requiem
R. Strauss: Ariadne auf Naxos (Cpte)
see CONCERT INDEX *under:*
(POLS) **PNCD067**   Szymanowski: Songs

Concert index

① **20123-2** (5/92)
Koechlin—Vocal and Chamber Works
Koechlin: Lilian I; Lilian II; Vers le soleil; Stéle funéraire. (K. Graf, P. Racine, C. Simonin, D. Cholette, D. Cholette)

① **20202-2** (9/93)
Poulenc—Chamber Works
Poulenc: Violin Sonata; Oboe Sonata; Elégie (1957); 2-Clarinet Sonata; Cello Sonata; Sextet; Flute Sonata; Piano, oboe and bassoon trio; Clarinet Sonata; Villanelle; Clarinet and Bassoon Sonata; Horn, Trumpet and Trombone Sonata. (G. Amar, T. Prévost, T. Prévost, J-L. Capezzali, J. Vandeville, R. Fontaine, F. Gauthier, H. Joulain, A. Randon, J-J. Justafré, C. Carry-Colas, P. Mink, B. Nouvion, A. Manfrin, J. Prat, D. Raclot, J-P. Armengaud)

① **20283-2** (4/95)
Duparc—Orchestral Songs
Duparc: Manoir de Rosemonde; Chanson triste; Invitation au voyage; Vie antérieure; Phidylé; Au pays où se fait la guerre; Testament; Vague et la cloche; Lénore; Danse lente; Aux étoiles. (F. Pollet, Nancy SO/J. Kaltenbach)

① **20441-2** (12/95)
Brahms—Lieder
Brahms: Lieder, Op. 3 (exc); Lieder, Op. 6 (exc); Lieder, Op. 7 (exc); Lieder, Op. 32 (exc); Lieder, Op. 43 (exc); Lieder, Op. 49 (exc); Lieder, Op. 63 (exc); Lieder, Op. 71 (exc); Lieder, Op. 85 (exc); Lieder, Op. 86 (exc); Lieder, Op. 91 (exc); Lieder, Op. 94 (exc); Lieder, Op. 95 (exc); Lieder, Op. 96 (exc); Lieder, Op. 105 (exc); Lieder, Op. 106 (exc); Lieder, Op. 107 (exc); Lieder, Op. 59 (exc). (F. Pollet, R. Vignoles, L. Verney)

① **22053-2** (6/90)
Schumann—Violin Sonatas
Schumann: Violin Sonata 1; Violin Sonata 2; Violin Sonata 3. (R. Zimansky, C. Keller)

Acoustics

① **CDACS012** (3/92)
The Mandolin Album
Mayor: Jump the Gun; Two Seagulls; Maple Flames; *Handel:* Solomon (exc); *Mayor:* Exchange; When Summer Comes Again; *Vivaldi:* Concerto, RV425; *Berlioz:* Nuits d'été (exc); *Mayor:* Tune for a Mop Fair; Jericho Waltz; Wheelin' and Dealin'; *Bach:* Solo Violin Partitas and Sonatas (exc); *Mayor:* Mosstrooper Medley. (S. Mayor, H. James, H. James)

① **CDACS014** (3/92)
The Second Mandolin Album
Brahms: Hungarian Dances (exc); *Mayor:* Buttermere Waltz; Hoppings; *Haydn:* Symphony 104 (exc); *Bach:* 3-Part Inventions, BWV787-801 (exc); *Mayor:* Pipped at the Post; Two Days in Tuscany; Great Bear; *Vivaldi:* Concerto, RV532; *Mayor:* Old Man of the Mountains; *D. Scarlatti:* Keyboard Sonatas (exc); *Handel:* Water Music (exc); *Mayor:* Dead Sea Dances. (S. Mayor, H. James, S. Price, A. Whetton)

Adès

① **14114-2** (8/90)
Poulenc: Mélodies
Poulenc: Poèmes Apollinaire (1938); Bestiaire; Poèmes Apollinaire (1946) (exc); Montparnasse; Grenouillère; Banalités; Epitaphe; Chansons gaillardes; Priez pour paix; Calligrammes. (P. Bernac, F. Poulenc)

① **14115-2** (8/90)
Poulenc: Mélodies
Poulenc: Poèmes de Paul Éluard; Fraîcheur et le feu; Miroirs brûlants (exc); Tel jour, telle nuit; Poèmes de Louis Aragon (exc); Disparu; Paul et Virginie; Parisiana; Métamorphoses; Travail du peintre. (P. Bernac, F. Poulenc)

① **14161-2** (10/90)
Shostakovich: String Quartets
Shostakovich: String Quartet 3; String Quartet 7; String Quartet 11. (Fine Arts Qt)

① **20217-2** (9/90)
A. Scarlatti—Duo Cantatas, Vol.1
A. Scarlatti: Sonno; Clori e Mirtillo; Marc'Antonio e Cleopatra; Doralbo e Niso. (V. Dietschy, A. Zaepffel, Gradiva Ens)

① **20235-2** (2/94)
Marais—Pièces de violes
Marais: Pièces de viole I/I (exc); Pièces de viole II/II (exc); Pièces de viole III/II (exc); Pièces de viole IV/II (exc); Pièces de viole V/II (exc). (M. Muller, S. Abramowicz, E. Ferré, P. Monteilhet)

① **20271-2** (9/94)
Handel—Roman Cantatas
Handel: Tu fedel?; No se emenderà jamàs; Nel dolce dell'oblio; Mentre il tutto; Armida abbandonata. (M. C. Kiehr, Teatro Armonico, A. de Marchi (hpd/dir))

Akademia

① **CDAK103** (7/91)
Rossini—Potpourri from Péchés de vieillesse
Rossini: Péchés de vieillesse V (exc); Péchés de vieillesse VI (exc); Péchés de vieillesse VII (exc); Péchés de vieillesse IV (exc); Péchés de vieillesse IX (exc). (J. Swann)

① **CDAK125** (1/95)
Tosti—Romanze
Tosti: Serenata; Sogno; 'A Vucchella; Segreto; Ideale; Mattinata (1903); Anima mia; Donna, vorrei morir; Pensol; Vorrei morire; Aprile; Ancora!; Mattinata; Ultima canzone; Malià; Non t'amo più; Pescatore canta; Tristezza; O falce di luna calante; Alba separa; Mi guitarra dice; Ricordati di me; Vuoi note. (E. Palacio, G. Scabbia, H. Liviabella, B. Giuffredi, C. Passerini, M. Decimo, M. Rapattoni)

Albany

① **AR001** (9/89)
R. Ward—Orchestral Works
R. Ward: Jubilation; Symphony 4; Saxophone Concerto; Sonic Structure. (J. Houlik, North Carolina SO/G. Zimmermann)

① **AR003** (5/89)
George Lloyd—Piano Works
G. Lloyd: Road through Samarkand; St. Antony and the Bogside Beggar; Aggressive Fishes; Intercom Baby; African Shrine. (M. Roscoe)

① **AR004** (8/89)
Lloyd—Piano Concerto No 4; Piano works
G. Lloyd: Piano Concerto 4; Lily-leaf and the Grasshopper; Transformation of the Naked Ape. (K. Stott, LSO/G. Lloyd)

① **AR012** (6/89)
Roy Harris—Orchestral Works
R. Harris: Symphony 1933; Symphony 5; Violin Concerto. (G. Fulkerson, Louisville Orch/L.L. Smith/J. Mester/R. Whitney)

① **TROY013/4-2** (10/89)
Morton Gould—Orchestral Works
Gould: Housewarming; American Symphonette 2; Symphony of Spirituals; Flourishes; Viola Concerto; Columbia; Soundings. (Louisville Orch/L.L. Smith/J. Mester/M. Gould, R. Glazer)

① **TROY015-2** (8/89)
G. Lloyd—Orchestral Works
G. Lloyd: Symphony 6; Symphony 10; John Socman (exc). (BBC PO, BBC Phil Brass/G. Lloyd)

① **TROY017-2** (4/90)
Virgil Thomson—Vocal and Orchestral Works
V. Thomson: Symphony on a Hymn Tune; Symphony 2; Lord Byron (exc); Shipwreck and Love Scene; Solemn Music; Joyful Fugue. (M. Hill, Monadnock Fest Orch, Budapest SO/J. Bolle)

① **TROY021-2** (6/90)
American Choral & Orchestral Works
Toch: Jephta, op 89; *Barber:* Die natali, op 37; *Prayers of Kierkegaard; Creston:* Corinthians: XIII. (G. Capone, S. Bap Theo Sem Chor, Louisville Orch/J. Mester/R. Whitney)

① **TROY024-2** (6/90)
American Orchestral Works
Dello Joio: Haydn Homage; *Persichetti:* Symphony 8; *Schickele:* Pentangle. (K. Albrecht, Louisville Orch/L. Slatkin/J. Mester)

① S. **TROY036-2** (5/92)
S.Paulus—Songs
Paulus: Bittersuite; All my pretty ones; Artsongs. (R. Jacobson, P. Sperry, H. Hagegård, W. Jones, P. Schoenfield, I. Vallecillo)

① **TROY127-2** (10/95)
Purcell—From Rosy Bow'rs
Purcell: St Cecilia's Day Ode, Z328 (exc); Birthday Ode, Z323 (exc); Fairy Queen, Z629 (exc); Don Quixote, Z578 (exc); Dioclesian, Z627 (exc); Tyrannic Love, Z613 (exc); Tempest, Z631 (exc); Oedipus, Z583 (exc); Indian Queen, Z630 (exc); If music be the food of love, Z379/3; Blessed Virgin's Expostulation, Z196; Evening Hymn, Z193; Hornpipes (exc); Choice Collection of Lessons (exc);

Musick's hand-maid, Part 2 (exc). (S. Sanford, B. Wissick, B. Wissick, R. Erickson, R. Erickson)

① **TROY146-2** (11/95)
Antheil—Piano Works
Antheil: Airplane Sonata; Sonata sauvage; Femme 100 Têtes (exc); Little Shimmy; Transatlantic (exc); Piano Sonata 4; Valentine Waltzes. (M. Verbit)

Alienor

① **AL1012** (11/86)
Sephardic Romances and Armenian Songs
Anon: Rosa enflorece; Yo m'enamori; Madre de la novia; Hija mia; Carza chica; *Traditional:* Puncha Puncha; *Anon:* Y una madre; David y Absalon; Morenica sos; Durme mi angelico; Noches buenas; El Conde niño; El villano vil; Sirena; Gerineldo; Ilono; Ak Egartho. (E. Lamandier)

① **AL1019** (2/88)
Domna
Machaut: Dame, vostre doulz viaire; Dou mal qui m'a longuement; Foy porter; J'aim la flour de valour; *Peter von Aberg:* O starker Got; *Monk of Salzburg:* Kum senfter Trost; *Peter von Sachsen:* Maria gnuchtig; *Vidal:* Pos tomatz; *Bernart de Ventadorn:* Quan l'erba fresc; *Folquet de Marseille:* En chantan; *Riquier:* Jhesu Cristz; *Anon:* Per tropo fede; *Gherardello da Firenze:* I' vo' bene; *Lorenzo da Firenze:* Non vedi tu, Amor; *Anon:* Lucente stella. (E. Lamandier)

Altarus

① **AIR-CD-9011** (12/95)
Philip Martin—Chamber & Vocal Works
Philip Martin: Piano Trio 1; Elegies; Night Songs; Light Music; Rainbow comes and goes. (P. Price Jones, R. Colan, P. Martin, Crawford Trio)

① **AIR-CD-9020** (10/92)
Scriabin—Piano Works
Scriabin: Piano Sonata 8; Preludes, Op. 67; Piano Sonata 9; Poèmes, Op.69; Piano Sonata 10; Poèmes, Op.71; Vers la flamme; Danses, Op.73; Preludes, Op.74. (D. Amato)

① **AIR-CD-9025** (4/95)
Sorabji—Piano Works
Sorabji: Quaere reliqua; St Bertrand de Comminges; Toccatinetta; Sutras; Passeggiata arlecchinesca. (D. Amato)

① **AIR-CD-9040** (9/95)
Grainger—Salute to Scotland
Grainger: Hill-Song 1; Songs of the North; Scotch Folksongs; Scotch Strathspey and Reel. (R. Stevenson)

① **AIR-CD-9052** (5/92)
Eckhardt-Gramatté—Piano Sonatas
Eckhardt-Gramatté: Piano Sonata 1; Piano Sonata 2; Piano Sonata 3; Piano Sonata 4; Piano Sonata 5; Piano Sonata 6. (M-A. Hamelin)

① **AIR-CD-9091** (9/90)
Ronald Stevenson: Piano Works
Stevenson: Passacaglia on DSCH; Busoni Prelude, Fugue and Fantasy; Recitative and Air. (R. Stevenson)

Amati

① **SRR8904/1** (10/91)
German Romantic Music
Bruckner: Overture in G minor; *Schumann:* Violin Concerto, Op. 129; *Spohr:* Symphony 3. (S. Gawriloff, South-West German RSO/L. Hager)

Amon Ra

① **CD-SAR12** (7/87)
Hummel—Works for Violin & Piano
Hummel: Violin Sonata, Op. 50; Viola Sonata, Op. 5/3; Nocturne, Op. 99. (R. Holmes, R. Burnett)

① **CD-SAR14** (4/87)
English Music of the 18th Century
Avison: Sonatas, Op. 5 (exc); *Arne:* Keyboard Sonatas (exc); Trio Sonatas (1757) (exc); *Handel:* Dresden Trio Sonatas (exc); *Abel:* Sonatas, Op. 9 (exc); *Stanley:* Organ Concertos, Op. 10 (exc). (London Baroque)

① **CD-SAR18** (6/87)
Guitar Collection
Mudarra: Tres libros (1546) (exc); *Le Roy/Ballard:* Branle de Poictou; Pimontoyse; *Milán:* El Maestro: Fantasias (exc); *Narváez:* Seys libros del delphin (exc); *Corbetta:* Sinfonia a 2; *Sanz:* Spanish Guitar Instruction II (exc); Spanish Guitar Instruction I (exc); *Visée:* Suite in D minor; *Giuliani:* Grande Ouverture, Op. 61; *Sor:* Mozart Variations, Op. 9; *Carulli:* Beethoven Variations, Op. 169; *Mertz:* Lied ohne Worte. (N. North, M. Cole)

Arabesque

C. Reoira, N. North, J. Lindberg, A. Pleeth, English
Concert/T. Pinnock)

① **415 991-2AH** (9/87)
Bach harpsichord concertos
Bach: Harpsichord Concerto, BWV1052; Harpsichord
Concerto, BWV1053; Harpsichord Concerto, BWV1054.
(English Concert, T. Pinnock (hpd/dir))

① **415 992-2AH** (2/87)
Bach—Concertos
Bach: Harpsichord Concerto, BWV1055; Harpsichord
Concerto, BWV1056; Harpsichord Concerto, BWV1057;
Harpsichord Concerto, BWV1058. (English Concert, T.
Pinnock (hpd/dir))

① **419 615-2AH** (6/87)
Vivaldi: Concertos
Vivaldi: Concerto, RV159; Concerto, RV271; Concerto,
RV484; Concerto, RV436; Concerto, RV540; Concerto,
RV545. (S. Standage, M. Turkovic, L. Beznosiuk, R.
Goodman, N. North, D. Reichenberg, English Concert/T.
Pinnock)

① **419 633-2AH** (8/87)
Telemann: Wind Concertos
Telemann: Flute Concerto 4; 3-Oboe & 3-Violin Concerto;
2-Chalumeaus Concerto 1; Trumpet Concerto; Recorder
and Flute Concerto; Violin, Cello & Trumpet Concerto. (M.
Schneider, W. Hazelzet, P. Westermann, M. Niesemann,
P. Dhont, E. Hoeprich, L. Klevit, F. Immer, R. Goebel
(vn/dir), M. Krämer, W. Erhard, P. Carrai, Cologne Musica
Antiqua/R. Goebel)

① **419 904-2AX12(1)** (10/89)
Bach: Organ Works
Bach: Toccata and Fugue, BWV565; Toccata and Fugue,
BWV540; Toccata and Fugue, BWV538; Toccata, Adagio
and Fugue, BWV564; Fantasia and Fugue, BWV542;
Fantasia, BWV562; Passacaglia and Fugue, BWV582;
Fantasia, BWV572; Fantasia and Fugue, BWV537;
Prelude and Fugue, BWV548; Prelude and Fugue,
BWV547; Prelude and Fugue, BWV541; Prelude and
Fugue, BWV544; Prelude and Fugue, BWV534; Prelude
and Fugue,BWV546; Prelude and Fugue, BWV543; Trio
Sonatas, BWV525-530; Prelude and Fugue, BWV545;
Prelude and Fugue, BWV536; Prelude and Fugue,
BWV531; Prelude and Fugue, BWV533; Prelude and
Fugue, BWV532; Prelude and Fugue, BWV550; Prelude
and Fugue, BWV539; Prelude and Fugue, BWV551;
Fugue, BWV574; Fugue, BWV579; Prelude and Fugue,
BWV535; Fugue, BWV578; Pastorale, BWV590; Canzona,
BWV588; Allabreve, BWV589; Duets, BWV802-805; Art of
Fugue (exc); Orgel-Büchlein, BWV599-644. (H. Walcha)

① **419 904-2AX12(2)** (10/89)
Bach: Organ Works
Bach: Clavier-Übung III, BWV669-689; Meine Seele erhebt
den Herren, BWV733; Nun freut euch, BWV734; Vom
Himmel hoch, BWV700; Vom Himmel hoch Variations,
BWV769; Chorales, BWV651-668; Valet will ich dir geben,
BWV736; Schübler Chorales, BWV645-650; Sei gegrüsset,
BWV768; Art of Fugue. (H. Walcha)

① **423 098-2AH** (1/88)
Haydn—Symphonies
Haydn: Symphony 6; Symphony 7; Symphony 8. (English
Concert/T. Pinnock)

① **423 149-2AX6** (3/88)
Handel: Orchestral Works
Handel: Water Music; Fireworks Music; Concerti a due cori
(exc); Concerti grossi, Op. 3; Concerti grossi, Op. 6;
Concerto grosso: Alexander's Feast. (English Concert/T.
Pinnock)

① **423 405-2AH** (11/88)
Schütz—Sacred Choral Works
Schütz: Freue dich des Weibes deiner Jugend, SWV453;
Psalmen Davids, SWV22-47 (exc); Symphoniarum
sacrarum, SWV398-418 (exc); Geistliche Chormusik,
SWV369-97 (exc); Musicalische Exequien. (A. Stafford, M.
Chance, F. Lang, Monteverdi Ch, EBS, His Majesties
Sagbutts and Cornetts/J.E. Gardiner)

① **423 594-2AH** (2/89)
Handel—Vocal Works
Handel: Dixit Dominus; Nisi Dominus; Salve Regina. (A.
Auger, L. Dawson, D. Montague, L. Nixon, J.M. Ainsley, S.
Birchall, Westminster Abbey Ch, Westminster Abbey
Orch/S. Preston)

① **423 703-2AX3** (1/89)
Zelenka: Orchestral Works
Zelenka: Capriccio I; Capriccio II; Capriccio III; Capriccio
IV; Capriccio V; Concerto a 8 in G; Sinfonia, ZWV189;
Hipocondrie, ZWV187; Overture, ZWV188. (Berne
Camerata/A. van Wijnkoop)

① **427 113-2AGA** (9/89)
Bach: Flute Sonatas
Bach: Flute Sonatas, BWV1030-5 (exc); Violin Sonatas,
BWV1020-25 (exc); Partita, BWV1013. (A. Nicolet, K.
Richter)

① **427 118-2AGA** (6/89)
Buxtehude & Pachelbel: Chamber Works
Buxtehude: Trio Sonata, BuxWV271; Trio Sonata,
BuxWV273; Trio Sonata, BuxWV266; *Pachelbel:* Partie in
G; Musicalische Ergötzung (exc); Canon and Gigue; Aria
con variazioni in A. (Cologne Musica Antiqua/R. Goebel)

① **427 124-2AGA** (5/89)
Purcell—Sacred Choral Works
Purcell: Te Deum and Jubilate, Z232; My heart is inditing,
Z30; O sing unto the Lord, Z44; They that go down to the
sea in ships, Z57; Praise the Lord, O Jerusalem, Z46.
(Oxford Christ Church Cath Ch, English Concert/S.
Preston)

① **427 133-2AGA** (3/90)
Buxtehude: Organ Works
Buxtehude: Prelude, Fugue and Chaconne, BuxWV137;
Prelude and Fugue, BuxWV139; Prelude and Fugue,
BuxWV140; Prelude and Fugue, BuxWV141; Prelude and
Fugue, BuxWV145; Prelude and Fugue, BuxWV146;
Prelude and Fugue, BuxWV149; Ciacona, BuxWV159;
Ciacona, BuxWV160; Passacaglia, BuxWV161; Prelude
and Fugue, BuxWV142. (H. Walcha)

① **427 316-2AH** (5/89)
Haydn: Violin Concertos
Haydn: Violin Concerto, HobVIIa/1; Violin Concerto,
HobVIIa/3; Violin Concerto, HobVIIa/4; *Salomon:*
Romance. (S. Standage, English Concert/T. Pinnock)

① **429 400-2AH** (7/90)
Haydn: Sturm und Drang Symphonies, Vol.4
Haydn: Symphony 43; Symphony 51; Symphony 52.
(English Concert/T. Pinnock)

① **429 756-2AH** (9/90)
Haydn: Sturm und Drang Symphonies, Vol.5
Haydn: Symphony 42; Symphony 44; Symphony 46.
(English Concert, T. Pinnock (hpd/dir))

① **429 782-2AH** (5/91)
Bach—Cantatas Nos 106, 118b & 198
Bach: Cantata 106; Cantata 118; Cantata 198. (N.
Argenta, M. Chance, A. Rolfe Johnson, S. Varcoe,
Monteverdi Ch, EBS/J.E. Gardiner)

① **431 678-2AH** (9/92)
Haydn—Concertos
Haydn: Oboe Concerto; Trumpet Concerto; Keyboard
Concerto, HobXVIII/11. (P. Goodwin, M. Bennett, T.
Pinnock (hpd/dir), English Concert/T. Pinnock)

① **435 262-2AH** (12/91)
Christmas Concertos
M-A. Charpentier: Noëls, H531 (exc); Noëls sur les
instruments, H534 (exc); *Molter:* Concerto Pastorale in G;
Vivaldi: Concerto, RV537; *Sammartini:* Concerti grossi
(exc); *Telemann:* Concerto polonois; *Handel:* Concerti a
due cori (exc); *Corelli:* Concerti Grossi, Op.6 (exc).
(English Concert, T. Pinnock (hpd/dir))

① **435 393-2AH** (9/92)
Italian 4-Violin Concertos
Torelli: 4-Violin Concerto; *Mossi:* Concerti, Op.4 (exc);
Giuseppe Valentini: Concerti grossi, Op. 7 (exc); *Locatelli:*
Concerti, Op.4 (exc); *Leo:* 4-Violin Concerto. (Cologne
Musica Antiqua/R. Goebel)

① **437 072-2AT** (1/93)
Collectio Argentea 2: Palestrina, Lassus
Palestrina: Missa Aeterna Christi munera; Motets, Bk 2
(1581) (exc); Motets, Bk 3 (1575) (exc); *Lassus:* Ave
regina caelorum II a 6; Salve regina mater a 8; O mors;
Psalmi Davidis poenitentiales (exc). (PCA, Hamburg Early
Music Wind Ens/B. Turner)

① **437 075-2AT** (1/93)
Collectio Argentea 5: Canti Amorosi
Monteverdi: Madrigals, Bk 7 (exc); Madrigals, Bk 9 (exc);
Madrigals, Bk 8 (exc); Scherzi musicali (1632) (exc);
Caccini: Nuove musiche (1602) (exc); *India:* Le musiche I
(1609); *Saracini:* Musiche (1614) (exc); Seconde musiche
(1620) (exc); *Peri:* Varie musiche (exc); *Gagliano:* Valli
profonde; *Del Turco:* Occhi belli; *Calestani:* Damigella tutta
bella. (N. Rogers, I. Partridge, C. Keyte, Inst Ens/J.
Jürgens, C. Tilney, A. Bailes, J. Savall, P. Ros)

① **437 079-2AT** (1/93)
Collectio Argentea 9: De Profundis
Schütz: Erbarm dich mein, O Herre Gott; *Tunder:* An
Wasserflüssen Babylon; Ach Herr, lass deine liebe
Engelein; *Bruhns:* De profundis clamavi; *Weckmann:* Wie
liegt die Stadt so wuste; *Strungk:* Ich ruf zu dir, Herr Jesu

Christ. (M. Zedelius, M. Schopper, Cologne Musica
Antiqua/R. Goebel)

① **437 081-2AT** (1/93)
Collectio Argentea 11: Muffat & Biber
Biber: Pauern Kirchfahrt Sonata; 2-violin and trombone
Sonata; Sonatas (1683) (exc); Battalia a 10; *Georg Muffat:*
Indissolubilis Amicitia Suite; COncerto grosso in A minor.
(VCM/N. Harnoncourt)

① **437 082-2AT** (1/93)
Collectio Argentea 12: Vivaldi/Bononcini—Cantatas
Bononcini: Cantate e duetti (exc); *Vivaldi:* Cessate, omai
cessate, RV684; O mie porpore più belle, RV685; Amor hai
vinto, RV683. (R. Jacobs/S. Kuijken, L. van Dael, W.
Kuijken, R. Kohnen, Complesso Barocco, A. Curtis
(hpd/dir))

① **437 086-2AT** (1/93)
Collectio Argentea 16: Le Parnasse Francais
Marais: La gamme (exc); *Rebel:* Tombeau de M. de Lully;
Couperin: La Sultane Sonata; *Leclair:* Ouvertures et
Sonates, Op.13 (exc); Trio, Op.14 (exc). (Cologne Musica
Antiqua/R. Goebel)

① **437 088-2AT** (1/93)
Collectio Argentea 18: English Baroque Concertos
Stanley: Concertos, Op.2 (exc); *Arne:* Favourite Concertos
(exc); *Boyce:* Symphonies (exc); *Geminiani:* Concerti
Grossi (Corelli, Op.5) (exc); *Hellendaal:* Concertos, Op.3
(exc); *Avison:* Concerti after D. Scarlatti (exc). (English
Concert, T. Pinnock (hpd/dir))

① **437 089-2AT** (1/93)
Collectio Argentea 19: German Chamber Music before
Bach
Reincken: Hortus musicus (exc); *Buxtehude:* Trio Sonata,
BuxWV273; *Rosenmüller:* Sonate (exc); *Westhoff:* La
guerra Sonata; *Pachelbel:* Partie in G; Canon and Gigue.
(Cologne Musica Antiqua/R. Goebel)

① **437 090-2AT** (1/93)
Collectio Argentea 20: Bach Family before J.S.
J. M. Bach I: Ach bleib bei uns, Herr Jesu Christ; Liebster
Jesu, hör mein Flehen; Ach, wie sehnlich; *G.C. Bach:*
Siehe, wie fein und lieblich ist; *J. Christoph Bach:* Herr,
wende dich; Meine Freundin, du bist schön. (M. Zedelius,
D. Cordier, P. Elliott, H. Meens, M. Schopper, S. Varcoe,
Rheinische Kantorei, Cologne Musica Antiqua/R. Goebel)

① **437 327-2AH** (2/93)
Bach—Cantatas
Bach: Cantata 36; Cantata 61; Cantata 62. (N. Argenta, P.
Lang, A. Rolfe Johnson, O. Bär, Monteverdi Ch, EBS/J.E.
Gardiner)

① **437 549-2AH2** (5/93)
Heinichen—Dresden Concertos
Heinichen: Concerto, S211; Concerto, S213; Darmstadt
Concerto, S214; Venezia Concerto, S214; Concerto, S215;
Concerto, S217; Concerto, S226; Concerto, S231;
Concerto, S232; Concerto, S233; Concerto, S234;
Concerto, S235; Serenata, S204; Sonata, S208; Concerto
Movement, S240. (Cologne Musica Antiqua/R. Goebel)

① **437 552-2AH2** (4/93)
Venetian Vespers
Anon: Festival of the Virgin Mary (exc); Praeambulum;
Banchieri: Organ Suonarino (exc); *Cavalli:* Lauda
Jerusalem; *Faccio:* Intonazione; *Finetti:* O Maria; G.
Gabrieli: Intonationi d'organo (exc); *Grandi:* Motets (1621)
(exc); O quam tu pulchra es a 1; *Marini:* Eco a tre violini;
Monteverdi: Selva morale e spirituale (exc); Messa et salmi
(exc); *Rigatti:* Messa e salmi (1640) (exc); Messa e salmi
ariosi (exc). (Gabrieli Consort, Gabrieli Players/P.
McCreesh, T. Roberts)

① **437 555-2AH** (6/93)
Bach—Harpsichord Works
Bach: Prelude and Fugue, BWV894; Toccatas, BWV910-
16 (exc); Aria, BWV989; Capriccio, BWV992. (K. Gilbert)

① **437 558-2AH** (6/93)
Telemann—Orchestral Suites
Telemann: Overture-Suite, TWV55: C 6; Overture-Suite,
TWV55: D 19; Overture-Suite, TWV55: B 10. (English
Concert/T. Pinnock)

① **437 792-2AH4** (11/93)
Mozart—Early Symphonies
Mozart: Symphony 1; Symphony, K19a; Symphony 4;
Symphony 5; Symphony, K45a; Symphony 6; Symphony
7; Symphony 8; Symphony 9; Symphony, K76; Symphony,
K45b; Symphony, K81; Symphony, K97; Symphony, K95;
Symphony 11; Symphony, K74g; Symphony, K75;
Symphony, K96; Symphony 10; Symphony 12; Symphony
13; Symphony 14; Symphony 15. (English Concert/T.
Pinnock)

① **437 833-2AH** (1/94)
Christmas Mass in Rome
Palestrina: Missa Hodie Christus natus est; Motets, Bk 3
(1575) (exc); *Josquin Desprez:* Praeter rerum seriem;
Victoria: Quem vidistis pastores?; O magnum mysterium;
Frescobaldi: O Iesu mi dulcissime; Canzoni with Titles
(exc); Fiori musicali (exc); *Pasquini:* Toccata I; *G.F. Anerio:*
Dialogo pastorale (exc); *Mazzocchi:* Nasceris, alme puer;
Carissimi: Exulta gaude; Desiderata nobis. (Gabrieli
Consort, Gabrieli Players/P. McCreesh, T. Roberts)

① **437 834-2AH** (3/94)
Christmas in Rome - Gloria
Vivaldi: Gloria, RV589; *A. Scarlatti:* O di Betlemme altera;
Corelli: Concerti Grossi, Op. 6 (exc). (N. Argenta, J. Smith,
C. Wyn-Rogers, English Concert Ch, English Concert/T.
Pinnock)

① **439 369-2AX4** (3/94)
Bach—Cantatas, Vol.1
Bach: Cantata 13; Cantata 28; Cantata 58; Cantata 61;
Cantata 63; Cantata 64; Cantata 65; Cantata 131; Cantata
82; Cantata 111; Cantata 121; Cantata 124; Cantata 132;
Cantata 171. (E. Mathis, S. Armstrong, L. Schädle, A.
Reynolds, H. Töpper, P. Schreier, E. Haefliger, D. Fischer-
Dieskau, T. Adam, Munich Bach Ch, Munich Bach Orch/K.
Richter)

① **439 374-2AX5** (5/94)
Bach—Cantatas, Volume 2 - Easter
Bach: Cantata 92; Cantata 126; Cantata 23; Cantata 1;
Cantata 182; Cantata 4; Cantata 6; Cantata 158; Cantata
67; Cantata 104; Cantata 12; Cantata 108; Cantata 87. (E.
Mathis, A. Reynolds, H. Töpper, P. Schreier, E. Haefliger,
D. Fischer-Dieskau, T. Adam, Munich Bach Ch, Munich
Bach Orch/K. Richter)

① **439 380-2AX6** (7/94)
Bach—Cantatas, Volume 3 - Ascension Day; Whitsun;
Trinity
Bach: Cantata 11; Cantata 44; Cantata 34; Cantata 68;
Cantata 175; Cantata 129; Cantata 39; Cantata 76;
Cantata 135; Cantata 21; Cantata 24; Cantata 30; Cantata
93; Cantata 147; Cantata 10. (E. Mathis, U. Buckel, A.
Reynolds, H. Töpper, P. Schreier, E. Haefliger, J. van
Kesteren, D. Fischer-Dieskau. K. Moll, K. Engen, Munich
Bach Ch, Munich Bach Orch/K. Richter, Ansbach Bach
Week Sols Ens)

① **439 387-2AX6** (1/95)
Bach Cantatas, Volume 4
Bach: Cantata 9; Cantata 187; Cantata 178; Cantata 45;
Cantata 105; Cantata 102; Cantata 199; Cantata 179;
Cantata 137; Cantata 33; Cantata 78; Cantata 17; Cantata
51; Cantata 100; Cantata 27; Cantata 8; Cantata 148. (E.
Mathis, M. Stader, U. Buckel, J. Hamari, H. Töpper, P.
Schreier, E. Haefliger, J. van Kesteren, D. Fischer-
Dieskau, K. Engen, Munich Bach Ch, Munich Bach Orch,
Ansbach Bach Week Sols Ens/K. Richter)

① **439 394-2AX5** (1/95)
Bach—Cantatas, Volume 5
Bach: Cantata 96; Cantata 5; Cantata 56; Cantata 180;
Cantata 38; Cantata 55; Cantata 115; Cantata 139;
Cantata 60; Cantata 26; Cantata 116; Cantata 70; Cantata
140; Cantata 130; Cantata 32; Cantata 106. (E. Mathis, U.
Buckel, T. Schmidt, H. Töpper, P. Schreier, E. Haefliger, D.
Fischer-Dieskau, T. Adam, K. Engen, Munich Bach Ch,
Munich Bach Orch/K. Richter)

① **439 780-2AH2** (12/95)
Bach—Orchestral Suites etc
Bach: Suites, BWV1066-9 (exc); Cantata 110 (exc); Cantata 174
(exc); Easter Oratorio, BWV249 (exc); Cantata 42 (exc);
Cantata 52 (exc). (English Concert Ch, English Concert/T.
Pinnock)

① **439 866-2AH** (7/94)
Handel—Marian Cantatas and Arias
Handel: Haec est regina virginum; Ah, che troppo
ineguali; Donna che in ciel; Giunta l'ora fatal. (A.S. von
Otter, chor, Cologne Musica Antiqua/R. Goebel)

① **439 893-2AH** (8/94)
Telemann—Suites; Concerto in D
Telemann: 3-Trumpet and Oboe Concerto; Overture-Suite,
TWV55: g min 4; Musique de Table (exc). (M. Bennett, M.
Harrison, N. Thompson, P. Goodwin, L. Wood, English
Concert, T. Pinnock (hpd/dir))

① **439 900-2AH5** (11/94)
Beethoven—Symphonies
Beethoven: Symphony 1; Symphony 2; Symphony 3;
Symphony 4; Symphony 5; Symphony 6; Symphony 7;
Symphony 8; Symphony 9. (L. Orgonášová, A.S. von
Otter, A. Rolfe Johnson, G. Cachemaille, Monteverdi Ch,
ORR/J.E. Gardiner)

① **439 915-2AH4** (1/95)
Mozart—Salzburg Symphonies
Mozart: Symphony 16; Symphony 17; Symphony 18;
Symphony 19; Symphony 20; Symphony 21; Symphony
22; Symphony 23; Symphony 24; Symphony 25;
Symphony 26; Symphony 27; Symphony 28; Symphony
29; Symphony 30. (English Concert/T. Pinnock)

① **445 353-2AH** (10/94)
Mozart—Sacred Choral Works
Mozart: Mass, K317; Exsultate, jubilate, K165; Vespers,
K339. (B. Bonney, C. Wyn-Rogers, J. MacDougall, S.
Gadd, English Concert Ch, English Concert/T. Pinnock)

① **445 824-2AH** (12/95)
Gluck/Rebel/Telemann—Orchestral Works
Rebel: Elémens; *Telemann:* Sonata in E minor; *Gluck:*
Alessandro. (Cologne Musica Antiqua/R. Goebel)

① **445 829-2AH** (7/95)
Purcell—Harmonia Sacra
Purcell: Lord, what is man, Z192; O solitude, Z406; In the
black, dismal dungeon of despair, Z190; Lord, I can suffer
thy rebukes, Z136; Organ Voluntaries, Z717-20 (exc); In
guilty night, Z134; Plung'd in the confines of despair, Z142;
Awake, ye dead, Z182; Earth trembled, Z197; With sick
and famish'd eyes, Z200; O, I'm sick of life, Z140; Close
thine eyes, Z184; Funeral Sentences (exc); Grounds (exc);
My op'ning eyes are purg'd, Z D72. (Gabrieli Consort,
Gabrieli Players/P. McCreesh, T. Roberts, T. Roberts)

① **445 839-2AH** (10/95)
Vivaldi—Woodwind Concertos
Vivaldi: Concerto, RV156; Concerti, Op.8 (exc); Concerto,
RV485; Concerto, RV166; Concerto, RV577; Concerto,
RV444; Concerto, RV575. (P. Holtslag, C. Latham, P.
Goodwin, L. Wood, A. Grazzi, P. Hanson, W. Reiter, J.
Coe, D. Watkin, English Concert/T. Pinnock)

① **445 882-2AH** (10/95)
Purcell—Ode on St Cecilia's Day; Anthems
Purcell: St Cecilia's Day Ode, Z328; My beloved spake,
Z28; O sing unto the Lord, Z44. (Gabrieli Consort, Gabrieli
Players/P. McCreesh)

① **447 043-2AH4** (12/95)
Mozart—The Late Symphonies
Mozart: Symphony 31; Symphony 32; Symphony 33;
Symphony 34; Symphony 35; Symphony 36; Symphony
38; Symphony 39; Symphony 40; Symphony 41. (English
Concert, T. Pinnock (hpd/dir))

① **447 150-2AP2** (7/95)
Purcell—Choral Works
Purcell: Morning and Evening Service, Z230 (exc); Te
Deum and Jubilate, Z232; Evening Service, Z231; O God,
thou hast cast us out, Z36; O Lord God of hosts, Z37;
Remember not, Lord, our offences, Z50; Lord, how long
wilt thou be angry?, Z25; O God, thou art my God, Z35;
Funeral Sentences (exc); Jehova, quam multi sunt, Z135;
My heart is inditing, Z30; O sing unto the Lord, Z44; My
beloved spake, Z28; They that go down to the sea in ships,
Z57; Praise the Lord, O Jerusalem, Z46. (D. Thomas,
Oxford Christ Church Cath Ch, English Concert/S.
Preston)

① **447 153-2AP** (7/95)
Purcell—Fantasias
Purcell: Viola da gamba fantasias, Z732-4; Viola da gamba
fantasies, Z735-43; Viola da gamba fantasia, Z745; In
Nomine, Z746; In Nomine, Z747; Chaconne, Z730. (VCM,
English Concert/T. Pinnock)

① **447 155-2AP** (7/95)
Coronation Music for King James II
Blow: God spake sometime in visions; Let Thy hand be
strengthened; Behold, O God, our defender; *H. Lawes:*
Zadok the priest; *Purcell:* My heart is inditing, Z30; I was
glad; *Child:* O Lord, grant the King a long life; *Turner:* King
shall rejoice. (Westminster Abbey Ch, orch/S. Preston)

① **447 156-2AP** (7/95)
Purcell—Fantasias and Vocal Works
Purcell: Viola da gamba fantasias, Z732-4; Viola da gamba
fantasies, Z735-43; Viola da gamba fantasia, Z745; In
Nomine, Z746; In Nomine, Z747; 'Tis wine was made to
rule the day, Z546; Oh! what a scene of mirth; When the
cock begins to crow, ZD172; How pleasant is this flowery
plain, Z543; In thee, O Lord, Z16. (SCB, Saltire Sngrs, Inst
Ens/H. Oppenheim)

① **447 281-2AMA** (7/95)
Haydn—Symphonies
Haydn: Symphony 42; Symphony 45; Symphony 46.
(English Concert/T. Pinnock)

① **447 291-2AMA** (12/95)
Mozart—Works for Piano and Orchestra
Mozart: Piano Concerto 9; Piano Concerto 17; Rondo,
K382. (M. Bilson, EBS/J. E. Gardiner)

| **Arcobaleno** |

① **AAOC93232** (6/95)
Mélodies Françaises
Duparc: Lamento; Manoir de Rosemonde; Extase; Élégie;
Soupir; *Saint-Saëns:* Pas d'armes; Chanson à boire;
Danse macabre; *Ropartz:* Heine Poèmes; *Ravel:* Don
Quichotte à Dulcinée; *Poulenc:* Priez pour paix; Hymne;
Dernier poème; Disparu. (P. Thirion-Vallet, D. Baldwin)

| **Archive Documents** |

① **ADCD107** (12/91)
Mengelberg Edition—Volume 1
Brahms: Symphony 3; *Debussy:* Après-midi; *Franck:*
Psyché (exc); *Liszt:* Préludes. (Concertgebouw/W.
Mengelberg)

① **ADCD108** (6/93)
Mengelberg Edition, Vol.2
Tchaikovsky: Symphony 6; *Borodin:* In the Steppes of
Central Asia; *Grieg:* Peer Gynt Suites (exc).
(Concertgebouw/W. Mengelberg)

① **ADCD110** (12/93)
Mengelberg Edition - Volume 4
Stravinsky: Baiser de la Fée (exc); Choral Variations;
Perséphone (exc); *Hindemith:* Violin Concerto. (Boston
SO, Westminster Ch, V. Zorina, orch/I. Stravinsky, P.
Helmann, Concertgebouw/W. Mengelberg)

① **ADCD111** (12/93)
Mengelberg Edition - Volume 5
Beethoven: Symphony 7; *Cherubini:* Anacréon (exc);
Mendelssohn: Midsummer Night's Dream (exc). (BBC SO,
Berlin RO, Concertgebouw/W. Mengelberg)

① **ADCD112** (5/95)
The Mengelberg Edition, Volume 6
Bach: Suites, BWV1066-9 (exc); Harpsichord Concerto,
BWV1056; *Vivaldi:* Concerti, Op.8 (exc); *J.C. Bach:*
Keyboard Concerto, T295/1 (exc); *Mozart:* Serenade,
K525. (A. Jambor, M. Flipse, Concertgebouw/W.
Mengelberg)

| **Argo** |

① **410 005-2ZH** (7/83)
Sacred Choral Works
Palestrina: Exsultate Deo; Peccantem me quotidie; Tu es
Petrus a 6; *Lotti:* Crucifixus a 8; *Victoria:* Lauda Sion;
Allegri: Miserere mei; *Monteverdi:* Adoramus te, Christe;
Cantate Domino I; *Cavalli:* Salve Regina; *G. Gabrieli:*
Jubilate Deo. (S. Quirke, A. Wright, Westminster Cath
Ch/S. Cleobury)

① **410 552-2ZH** (11/83)
Fauré: Orchestral Works
Fauré: Pelléas et Mélisande Suite (exc); Pavane;
Fantaisie; Masques et Bergamasques. (Chor, W. Bennett,
ASMF/N. Marriner)

① **414 042-2ZH** (12/84)
Christmas Carols at King's College, Cambridge
Traditional: O little town of Bethlehem; Stille Nacht; In the
bleak mid-winter; Hark! the herald angels sing; Away in a
manger; Once in Royal David's city; Up! Good Christen
folk; Sussex Carol; Ding dong! merrily on high; First
Nowell; First good joy that Mary had; Sing lullaby; God rest
you merry, gentlemen; Holly and the Ivy; I saw three ships;
O come, all ye faithful. (King's College Ch, D. Briggs/S.
Cleobury)

① **414 595-2ZH** (9/86)
Vaughan Williams—Orchestral Works
Vaughan Williams: Tallis Fantasia; Greensleeves Fantasia;
Dives and Lazarus Variants; Lark ascending. (I. Brown,
ASMF/N. Marriner)

① **417 468-2ZH** (2/88)
G. Gabrieli: Choral and Instrumental Works
G. Gabrieli: Symphoniae sacrae II (exc); Canzoni et
Sonate (1615) (exc); Symphoniae sacrae (1597) (exc);
Canzoni (1608) (exc); Jubilate Deo; Timor et tremor; O
magnum mysterium. (C. Brett, W. Kendall, P. Hall, I.
Caddy, R. Farnes, S. Layton, King's College Ch, PJBE/S.
Cleobury)

① **417 818-2ZH** (11/87)
American Music
Barber: Adagio for Strings; *Ives:* Symphony 3; *Copland:*
Quiet city; *Cowell:* Hymn and Fuguing tune No.10;
Creston: Rumor. (C. Nicklin, M. Laird, ASMF/N. Marriner)

① **430 200-2ZH** (2/91)
The Emperor's Fanfare
Soler: Emperor's Fanfare; *Wagner:* Tristan und Isolde
(exc); *Jongen:* Pièces, Op. 37 (exc); *Bach:* Toccata and
Fugue, BWV565; *Albinoni:* Adagio; *Alain:* Litanies;

Arion

instruments, H534 (exc); Noëls, H531 (exc); Canticum in nativitatem Domini, H314; Lebègue: Troisième livre d'orgue (exc); Raison: Second livre d'orgue (exc). (M-C. Vallin, E. Le Piniec, G. Ragon, E. Lestrigant, J-L. Bindi, D. Ferran, Nantes Voc Ens, Nantes Instr Ens/P. Colleaux)

ⓘ **ARN68026** (12/89)
Baroque Choral and String Works
Vivaldi: Salve Regina, RV616; Pergolesi: Concertino No. 2; Salve Regina in F minor; Violin Concerto in B flat. (J. Bowman, Y. Naganuma, J-W. Audoli Inst Ens/J-W. Audoli)

ⓘ **ARN68035** (6/89)
Britten—Vocal and String works
Britten: Illuminations; Phaedra; Simple Symphony. (C. Eda-Pierre, J-W. Audoli Inst Ens/J-W. Audoli)

ⓘ **ARN68046** (9/89)
Italian Airs & Cantatas
Caccini: Bella ragion; Nuove musiche (1602) (exc); Monteverdi: Salve Regina a 1; Si dolce è'l tormento; Ego flos campi; Frescobaldi: Arie musicali Bk 1 (exc); Arie musicali Bk 2 (exc); India: Le musiche V (1623) (exc); Le musiche IV (1621) (exc); Vivaldi: Piango, gemo, sospiro, RV675; Grandi: O quam tu pulchra es a 1; Handel: Vedendo amor. (J. Bowman, S. Sempé, J. Bernfeld)

ⓘ **ARN68047** (10/89)
The organs of Malaga Cathedral
Soler: Organ Concertos (exc); Keyboard Sonatas II (exc); Anon: Ligaduras; Tiento Lleno; Cabanilles: Tientos (exc); Barrera: Organ Sonata (1782); Organ Sonata (1784). (M.G. Filippi, M. Henking)

ⓘ **ARN68071** (8/90)
Sauget—Vocal and orchestral works
Sauget: Sonate d'église; Garden Concerto; Oiseau a vut. (M. Piquemal, J. Vandeville, J-P. Brosse, J-W. Audoli Inst Ens/J-W. Audoli)

ⓘ **ARN68084** (10/90)
Messiaen & Xenakis—Choral works
Messiaen: Rechants; O sacrum convivium!; Xenakis: Nuits. (France Groupe Vocal)

ⓘ **ARN68228** (9/94)
Debussy/Pierné/Ravel—Sonatas for Violin and Piano
Debussy: Violin Sonata; Pierné: Violin Sonata; Ravel: Violin Sonata (1897); Violin Sonata (1923-27). (G. Poulet, N. Lee)

ⓘ **ARN68258** (3/94)
Poulenc—Mélodies
Poulenc: Travail du peintre; Chansons gaillardes; Tel jour, telle nuit; Poèmes de Paul Éluard. (B. Kruysen, N. Lee)

Astrée

ⓘ **E7703/4** (3/86)
Mozart—The Last Piano Sonatas
Mozart: Piano Sonata, K533; Piano Sonata, K533; Fantasia, K475; Piano Sonata, K545; Piano Sonata, K570; Piano Sonata, K576. (P. Badura-Skoda)

ⓘ **E7715** (11/88)
Dowland: Lute Works
Dowland: Pavans (exc); Galliards (exc); Jigs, Corantos, Toys, etc (exc); Ballad Settings (exc); Fantasies (exc); Almains (exc). (P. O'Dette)

ⓘ **E7716** (8/88)
Pierre Boulez: Piano Sonatas
Boulez: Piano Sonata 1; Piano Sonata 2; Piano Sonata 3. (C. Helffer)

ⓘ **E7748** (5/91)
Milán—Libro de musica, Vol.1
Milán: El Maestro: Fantasias (exc); El Maestro: Pavanas (exc); El Maestro: Tentos (exc). (H. Smith)

ⓘ **E7780** (12/93)
Lassus—5 Part Motets
Lassus: Angelus Domini locutus est; Emendemus in melius; Multarum hic resonat; Pater Abraham miserere; Quid prodest homini; Si bona suscepimus; Stabunt justi; Verba mea auribus percipe; Veni dilecte mi; Pater noster a 6 (1585). (Hanover Childrens' Ch, Collegium Vocale/P. Herreweghe)

ⓘ **E8503** (1/94)
Merula—Arie e Capricci
Merula: Curtio precipitato, Op.13 (exc); Madrigals, Bk.2 (exc); Capriccio cromatico; Toccata del secondo tono. (M. Figueras, J-P. Canihac, A. Lawrence-King, R. Lislevand, L. Duftschmid, J. Savall, T. Koopman)

ⓘ **E8507** (2/94)
Josquin Desprez—Missa Ave maris stella; Motets
Josquin Desprez: Missa Ave Maris Stella; Monstra te esse matrem; Salve regina a 4; Gaude Virgo, Mater Christi;

Alma redemptoris mater/Ave regina celorum; Vultum tuum. (A Sei Voci)

ⓘ **E8508** (1/94)
Strele do dia - Cantigas de Santa María
Alfonso el Sabio: Por nos de dutta tirar; Mira gres fremosos faz por; Santa María, strella do dia; Santa Maria Sinal; De tod a chaga; En a gran coita; Pode por Santa Maria; Soltar pode muit; Pero que seja a gente; Pero cantigas de loor. (Catalan Capella Reial, Hespèrion XX/J. Savall)

ⓘ **E8517** (4/94)
Boccherini—Cello Concertos, etc
Boccherini: Cello Concerto, G476; Cello Concerto, G480; Cello Concerto, G482; Concert Arias, G544-558 (exc). (M. Almajano, C. Coin (vc/dir), Limoges Baroque Ens/C. Coin)

ⓘ **E8521** (3/95)
Helfer—Requiem for the Dukes of Lorraine
Helfer: Missa pro defunctis; Anon: Funeral Chants (exc); L'Estocart: Du fond de ma pensée; Sweelinck: De profundis; Du Caurroy: Dixiesme fantasie; M. Lasson: In manibus tuis; Anon: Funeral Orations for Charles III (exc). (E. Green, A Sei Voci, Lorraine Psallette, Toulouse Sacqueboutiers, J. Chamboux, J. Bernfeld/B. Fabre-Garrus)

ⓘ **E8523** (1/95)
Bach—Harpsichord Concertos
Bach: Harpsichord Concerto, BWV1054; Harpsichord Concerto, BWV1052; Triple Concerto, BWV1044; Wohltemperierte Klavier (exc). (P. Hantaï, Concert Français, P. Hantaï (hpd/dir))

ⓘ **E8524** (9/95)
Allegri—Miserere, Mass & Motets
Allegri: Miserere mei; Missa Vidi turbam magnam; De ore prudentis; Repleti sunt omnes; Cantate domino. (A Sei Voci/B. Fabre-Garrus, D. Ferran)

ⓘ **E8528** (8/95)
Gallot—Works for Lute
Gallot: Pieces in F sharp minor (exc); Pieces in A minor (exc); Pieces in F (exc); Pieces in D minor (exc); Pieces in C (exc). (H. Smith)

ⓘ **E8530** (2/95)
Bach—Cantatas
Bach: Cantata 49; Cantata 115; Cantata 180. (B. Schlick, A. Scholl, C. Prégardien, G. Schwarz, Concerto Vocale, Limoges Baroque Ens, C. Coin (vc/dir))

ⓘ **E8531** (10/94)
Debussy—Piano Works, Vol.3
Debussy: Pour le piano; Plus que lente; Valse romantique; Children's Corner; Tarantelle styrienne. (P. Cassard)

ⓘ **E8532** (10/95)
Arriaga—Orchestral Works
Arriaga: Symphony in D; Esclavos felices (exc); Overture, Op. 1. (Concert des Nations, Capella Reial Instr Ens/J. Savall)

ⓘ **E8543** (9/95)
Bull—Doctor Bull's Good Night
J. Bull: In Nomines (exc); Pavans (exc); Galliards (exc); King's Hunt; Almans (exc); Toys (exc); Why ask you; Fantasias (exc); Dutch Dance; Pavans and Galliards (exc); Bull's Goodnight; Salvator Mundi Deus. (P. Hantaï)

ⓘ **E8544** (12/95)
Bach—Cantatas
Bach: Cantata 85; Cantata 183; Cantata 199; Cantata 175. (B. Schlick, A. Scholl, C. Prégardien, G. Schwarz, Concerto Vocale, Limoges Baroque Ens, C. Coin (vc/dir))

ⓘ **E8707** (2/92)
Encina—Romances and Villancicos
Encina: Sañosa porfia; Levanta Pascual, levanta; Qu'es de ti, desconsolado?; Mortal tristura me dieron; Amor con fortuna; Fata la parte; Ay triste, que vengo; Cucú, cucú; Despierta, despierta; Triste España sin ventura!; A tal perdida tan triste; Quedate, carillo, adios; Si abrá en este baldres!; El que rige y el regido; Mas vale trocar; Oy comamos y bebamos. (Hespèrion XX/J. Savall)

ⓘ **E8708** (11/89)
Tye: Consort Music
Tye: O Lux; Rubum quem; Christus resurgens; Amavit; Lawdes Deo; Sit fast; Dum transsissets a 5; In Nomine a 4; In Nomine a 6; In Nomines a 5. (Hespèrion XX/J. Savall)

ⓘ **E8713** (2/90)
Charpentier—Vocal Works
M-A. Charpentier: Canticum in honorem BVM, H400; Prelude a 3, H509; Pour la conception de la vierge, H313; Nativité de la vierge, H309; Salve regina, H23; Pour la fête de l'Epiphanie, H395; Prelude pour le 2de Magnificat,

---

H533; Magnificat, H80; Stabat Mater, H15; Litanies, H83. (Concert des Nations/J. Savall)

ⓘ **E8724** (2/92)
Jenkins—Consort Music for Viols
Jenkins: Fantasias in 6 parts (exc); Pavans in 6 parts; In Nomines in 6 parts. (Hespèrion XX, M. Behringer)

ⓘ **E8729** (2/92)
Intermedios del Barroco Hispanico
M. Romero: Caiase de un espino; Aguilera de Heredia: Tiento de Batalla; Lope de Vega: De pechos sobre una torre; Cabanilles: Passacalles (exc); Machado: Afuera, afuera que sale; Aguilera de Heredia: Ensalada; Lope de Vega: Como retumban los remos; Correa de Arauxo: Batalla des Morales; F. Guerrero: Si tus penas no pruevo; Cabanilles: Tientos (exc); Castro: Desde las torres del alma; Cabanilles: Corrente italiana; Castro: Entre dos Alamos verdes; Kerll: Batalla Imperial; Marín: Ojos, que me desdenais; Anon: No hay que decirle el primor. (M. Figueras, Hespèrion XX/J. Savall)

ⓘ **E8731** (7/91)
L. Couperin—Harpsichord Works, Vol 1
L. Couperin: Harpsichord Works I (exc); Harpsichord Works III (exc); Harpsichord Works IV (exc); Harpsichord Works V (exc). (B. Verlet)

ⓘ **E8732** (7/91)
L. Couperin—Harpsichord Works, Vol.2
L. Couperin: Harpsichord Works III (exc); Harpsichord Works IV (exc); Harpsichord Works V (exc); Harpsichord Works II (exc). (B. Verlet)

ⓘ **E8733** (4/93)
L. Couperin—Harpsichord Works, Vol 3
L. Couperin: Harpsichord Works I (exc); Harpsichord Works II (exc); Harpsichord Works IV (exc); Harpsichord Works V (exc). (B. Verlet)

ⓘ **E8734** (4/93)
L. Couperin—Harpsichord Works, Vol.4
L. Couperin: Harpsichord Works I (exc); Harpsichord Works II (exc); Harpsichord Works III (exc); Harpsichord Works IV (exc). (B. Verlet)

ⓘ **E8735** (4/93)
L. Couperin—Harpsichord Works, Vol.5
L. Couperin: Harpsichord Works I (exc); Harpsichord works II (exc); Harpsichord Works III (exc); Harpsichord Works V (exc). (B. Verlet)

ⓘ **E8752** (7/94)
Brahms—Piano Works
Brahms: Piano Sonata 3; Schumann Variations; Variations, Op 21/2. (A. Bonatta)

ⓘ **E8757** (9/93)
Purcell—Songs from Orpheus Britannicus
Purcell: Rival Sisters, Z609 (exc); Fly swift, ye hours, Z369; Gentle Shepherds, Z464; Aureng-Zebe, Z573 (exc); Pausanias, Z585 (exc); I came, I saw, Z375; If music be the food of love, Z379/3; Bess of Bedlam, Z370; Timon of Athens, Z632 (exc); Don Quixote, Z578 (exc); King Arthur, Z628 (exc); Tyrannic Love, Z613 (exc); Fatal hour comes on apace, Z421; O Solitude, Z406; Dioclesian, Z627 (exc); Bonduca, Z574 (exc); Fairy Queen, Z629 (exc); Musick's Hand-maid Part 2 (exc); Grounds (exc); Hornpipes (exc); Choice Collection of Lessons (exc). (A. Mellon, W. Kuijken, C. Rousset)

ⓘ **E8762** (7/92)
El Cancionero Palacio
Francisco de la Torre: Danza Alta; Mena: Aquella mora garrida; A sonbra de mis cabellos; Bella malmaridada; Peñalosa: Por las sierras de Madrid; Román: O voy; J. Ponce: Torre de la niña; Ave color vini clari; Milán: Mios fueron, mi coraçon; Garçimuñoz: Pues bien, para ésta; Badajóz el músico: O desdichado de mi; Anchieta: Dos ánades; Alonso: Tricotea; Encina: Pues que jamas olvidaros; Anon: Rodrigo Martínez; Al alva venid; Tres morillas; Qué me queréis, cavallero?; A los baños de amor; Harto de tanta porfía; Pase el agoa, ma Julieta; El cervel mi fa; Si d'amor pena sentis; Ay, que non ay!. (Hespèrion XX/J. Savall)

ⓘ **E8763** (7/92)
El Cancionero de la Colombina
Francisco de la Torre: Dime, triste coraçon; Enrique: Pues con sobra de tristura; Mi querer tanto vos quiere; Triana: Querer vieja yo?; Quién vos dió tal señorio?; Pinguele, rrespinguete; Dinos, madre del donsel; Urreda: Donde estás que non te veo; Muy triste sera mi vida; Nunca fué pena major; Hurtado de Xeres: No tenga madie sperança; Comago: Que's mi vida preguntáys; Señora, qual soy venido; Belmonte: Nunca fue pena mayor; Anon: Propiñan de Melyor; Cómo no le andaré yo?; Lealtat, o lealtat; Muy crueles bozes dan; O en te Israel; Buenas nuevas de alegria; Quien tiene vida en esperança; Niña y viña. (Hespèrion XX/J. Savall)

① **E8764** (6/93)
El Cancionero de Medinaceli
P. Guerrero: Di, perra mora; *F. Guerrero*: Prado verde y florido; Dexó la venda; Ojos claros; *Cebrián*: Lágrimas di mi consuelo; *Morata*: Pués que me tienes; Pues que no puedo olvidarte; *Cabezón*: Susanne un jour Fantasia; *Mudarra*: Tres Libros (vocal works) (exc); *Anon*: A biente y siete de Março; Puse mis amores; Buelve tus claros ojos; Corten espadas afiladas; Ay Jesus; Aquella voz de Christo; Guárdame las vacas. (Hespérion XX/J. Savall)

① **E8766** (10/93)
Guerrero—Sacrae Cantiones
F. Guerrero: Ave Maria a 4; Alma Redemptoris mater a 4; Beata Dei genitrix a 6; Pater Noster a 8; O Domine Jesu a 4; O sacrum convivium a 5; Laudate Dominum a 8; Gabriel archangelus a 4; Ave virgo sanctissima a 5; Salve Regina a 4; Regina coeli a 8; O altitudo a 8; Trahe me post te a 5; Duo Seraphim a 12; Ave Maria a 8. (Capella Reial Voc Ens, Hespérion XX/J. Savall)

① **E8768** (7/92)
Soler—Harpsichord Works, Vol.1
Soler: Keyboard Sonatas I (exc); Keyboard Sonatas II (exc); Preludes (exc). (B. van Asperen)

① **E8769** (7/92)
Soler—Harpsichord Works, Vol. 2
Soler: Preludes (exc); Keyboard Sonatas I (exc); Keyboard Sonatas II (exc). (B. van Asperen)

① **E8770** (7/92)
Soler—Harpsichord Works, Vol.3
Soler: Keyboard Sonatas I (exc); Keyboard Sonatas II (exc); Preludes (exc). (B. van Asperen)

① **E8771** (7/92)
Soler—Harpsichord Works, Vol.4
Soler: Keyboard Sonatas I (exc); Keyboard Sonatas II (exc); Fandango; Preludes (exc). (B. van Asperen)

ASV

① **CDACA1003** (9/86)
The Classical Oboe
Vivaldi: Concerto, RV461; *A. Marcello*: Oboe Concerto in D minor; *Haydn*: Oboe Concerto. (D. Wickens, RPO/A. Howarth)

① **CDCOE803** (3/87)
Chamber Concertos
Bach: Violin and Oboe Concerto, BWV1060; *Mozart*: Sinfonia Concertante, K297b; *Vivaldi*: Concerto, RV556. (M. Blankestijn, D. Boyd, COE/A. Schneider)

① **CDCOE807** (9/88)
Beethoven—Music for Wind Instruments
Beethoven: Sextet, Op. 71; Quintet, Hess19; Rondino, WoO25; Octet, Op. 103. (COE Wind Sols)

① **CDCOE810** (4/89)
Orchestral Works
A. Marcello: Oboe Concerto in D minor; *Vivaldi*: Concerto, RV487; *Mozart*: Symphony 25; Rondo, K371; *Wolf*: Italian Serenade; *J. Strauss II*: Blauen Donau, Op. 314; Kaiser, Op. 437. (D. Boyd, M. Wilkie, J. Williams, COE/A. Schneider)

① **CDCOE811** (10/89)
Works for Clarinet and Orchestra
Mozart: Clarinet Concerto, K622; *Copland*: Clarinet Concerto; *R. Strauss*: Duet Concertino. (R. Hosford, R. Hosford, M. Wilkie, COE/A. Schneider/T. Fischer)

① **CDCOE812** (4/90)
Music for Wind Instruments
Krommer: Octet-Partita, Op. 57; *Janáček*: Mládí; *Seiber*: Serenade (1925); *Hummel*: Octet-Partita in E flat; *Dvořák*: Slavonic Dances (exc). (COE Wind Sols)

① **CDCOE813** (9/91)
Mozart—Wind Concertos
Mozart: Flute Concerto, K313; Bassoon Concerto, K191; Flute and Harp Concerto, K299. (T. Fischer (fl/dir), M. Wilkie/S. Végh, C. Sprenkels, COE)

① **CDCOE814** (9/91)
Mozart—Wind Concertos
Mozart: Oboe Concerto, K314; Sinfonia Concertante, K297b; Clarinet Concerto, K622. (D. Boyd, R. Hosford, R. O'Neill, J. Williams, R. Hosford, COE/P. Berglund/A. Schneider)

① **CDDCA517** (2/85)
The French Connection
Ravel: Tombeau; *Debussy*: Danse sacrée et danse profane; *Fauré*: Dolly; *Ibert*: Divertissement. (O. Ellis, ASMF/N. Marriner)

① **CDDCA518** (2/85)
The English Connection
Vaughan Williams: Lark ascending; Tallis Fantasia; *Elgar*: Serenade; *Tippett*: Corelli Fantasia. (I. Brown, M. Latchem, K. Sillito, S. Shingles, D. Vigay, ASMF/N. Marriner)

① **CDDCA534** (6/86)
Barber—Orchestral Works
Barber: Piano Concerto; Medea's Meditation, Op. 23a; Adagio for Strings. (T. Joselson, LSO/A. Schenck)

① **CDDCA535** (9/89)
English Music for Bassoon and Piano
Hurlstone: Bassoon Sonata; *Elgar*: Romance, Op. 62; *Jacob*: Sketches; *Arne*: Keyboard Sonatas (exc); *Dunhill*: Lyric Suite; *Vaughan Williams*: Studies in English folk song; *Avison*: Violin Sonata in F. (Daniel Smith, R. Vignoles)

① **CDDCA539** (4/86)
Popular French Romantics Vol. 1
Widor: Symphony 1 (exc); Symphony 9 (exc); *Guilmant*: Scherzo, Op. 80; Gigout: Ten Organ Pieces (exc); *Bonnet*: Pièces nouvelles, Op.7 (exc); *Lefébure-Wély*: Sortie in B flat; *Vierne*: Suite 3 (exc); Suite 2 (exc). (J. Parker-Smith)

① **CDDCA559** (11/86)
Works for clarinet and orchestra
Crusell: Clarinet Concerto 2; *Weber*: Clarinet Concertino; *H. J. Baërmann*: Clarinet Quintet, Op.23 (exc); *Rossini*: Introduction, theme and variations in B flat. (E. Johnson, ECO/C. Groves)

① **CDDCA563** (6/87)
Works by Bottesini
Bottesini: Gran duo concertante; Andante sostenuto; Clarinet and Double Bass Duetto; Gran Concerto in F. (E. Johnson, J-L. Garcia, T. Martin, ECO/A. Litton)

① **CDDCA565** (1/88)
Vivaldi—Bassoon Concertos, Vol 1
Vivaldi: Concerto, RV467; Concerto, RV491; Concerto, RV500; Concerto, RV499; Concerto, RV466; Concerto, RV486. (Daniel Smith, ECO/P. Ledger)

① **CDDCA568** (2/88)
Works for clarinet and orchestra
Copland: Clarinet Concerto; *Finzi*: Clarinet Concerto; *Mourant*: Pied Piper. (G. Macdonald, Northern Sinfonia/S. Bedford)

① **CDDCA571** (1/88)
Vivaldi—Bassoon Concertos, Vol. 2
Vivaldi: Concerto, RV474; Concerto, RV487; Concerto, RV476; Concerto, RV469; Concerto, RV494; Concerto, RV470. (Daniel Smith, ECO/P. Ledger)

① **CDDCA584** (11/87)
W.S. Lloyd Webber—Various Works
W. Lloyd Webber: Missa Sanctae Mariae Magdalenae; Saviour (exc); Divine Compassion (exc); In the half-light; Air varié; Badinage de Noël; Song without words; Scherzo in G minor; Arabesque; Presto for Perseus; Romantic Evening; Rent for love; Utopia; Over the bridge; Pretty washer-maiden; So lovely the rose. (J. Graham-Hall, Richard Hickox Sngrs/R. Hickox, J. Lloyd Webber, J. Lill, P. Ledger, P. Ledger, I. Watson)

① **CDDCA585** (9/87)
Works for Clarinet and Orchestra
Weber: Clarinet Concerto 1; *Crusell*: Introduction, Theme and Variations on a Swedish Air; *Tartini*: Concertino for Clarinet and Strings; *Debussy*: Première rapsodie. (E. Johnson, ECO/Y.P. Tortelier)

① **CDDCA589** (11/87)
Khachaturian—Piano Works
Khachaturian: Piano Concerto; Sonatina; Toccata. (A. Portugheis, LSO/L. Tjeknavorian)

① **CDDCA591** (3/88)
Britten—Orchestral Works
Britten: Frank Bridge Variations; Simple Symphony; Prelude and Fugue, Op.29. (Northern Sinfonia/R. Hickox)

① **CDDCA592** (9/88)
British Cello Music
Britten: Tema-Sacher; *Rawsthorne*: Cello Sonata; *Ireland*: Holy Boy; *Arnold*: Cello Fantasy; *Walton*: Passacaglia. (J. Lloyd Webber, J. McCabe)

① **CDDCA599** (5/88)
Saint-Saëns—Orchestral Works
Saint-Saëns: Symphony 2; Suite algérienne; Phaéton. (LSO/Y. Butt)

① **CDDCA607** (9/88)
Villa-Lobos—Piano Works
Villa-Lobos: Valsa da dor; Bachianas Brasileiras 4; Ciclo brasileiro; Chôros 5. (A. Petchersky)

① **CDDCA610** (3/89)
Popular French Romantics Vol. 2
Saint-Saëns: Préludes et fugues, Op. 109 (exc); *Widor*: Symphony 4 (exc); *Vierne*: Symphony 1 (exc); Triptyque, Op. 58 (exc); *Guilmant*: Grand Choeur in D; *Franck*: Prélude, Fugue et Variation; *Renaud*: Toccata in D minor; *Mulet*: Carillon-sortie. (J. Parker-Smith)

① **CDDCA613** (10/88)
Chamber Works for Bassoon
Danzi: Bassoon Quartet, Op.40/3; *Jacob*: Bassoon Suite; *Reicha*: Bassoon Quintet. (Daniel Smith, Coull Qt)

① **CDDCA615** (7/88)
Mozart—Symphonies
Mozart: Symphony 34; Symphony 35; Symphony 39. (LMP/J. Glover)

① **CDDCA619** (11/88)
Elgar—Orchestral Works
Elgar: In the South; Coronation March; Light of Life (exc); Froissart. (RPO/Y. Butt)

① **CDDCA621** (10/88)
La Clarinette Française
Saint-Saëns: Clarinet Sonata; *Debussy*: Préludes (exc); *Milhaud*: Duo concertante; *Poulenc*: Clarinet Sonata; *Ravel*: Pièce en forme de habanera; Pavane pour une infante défunte; *Pierné*: Canzonetta; *Milhaud*: Scaramouche (exc). (E. Johnson, G. Back)

① **CDDCA627** (12/88)
Delius—A Song of Summer
Delius: Song of Summer; Brigg Fair; In a Summer Garden; Song before Sunrise; Summer Night on the River; Village Romeo and Juliet (exc). (Philh/O.A. Hughes)

① **CDDCA631** (4/89)
Shostakovich—String Quartets
Shostakovich: String Quartet 4; String Quartet 8; String Quartet 11. (Coull Qt)

① **CDDCA645** (9/89)
Vivaldi—Concertos
Vivaldi: Concerto, RV531; Concerto, RV547; Concerto, RV539; Concerto, RV441; Concerto, RV104; Concerto, RV93; Concerto, RV570. (O. Hegedus, D. Begde, M. Rakowski, C. Tunnell, F. Lloyd, T. Chidell, W. Bennett, N. Black, R. O'Neill, S. Wynberg, ECO/G. Malcolm)

① **CDDCA647** (8/89)
Mozart—Symphonies
Mozart: Symphony 31; Symphony 36; Symphony 38. (LMP/J. Glover)

① **CDDCA649** (7/89)
Sibelius—Orchestral Works
Sibelius: Pelleas and Melisande; Valse romantique; Spring Song; Swanwhite. (RPO/Y. Butt)

① **CDDCA652** (10/89)
Celebration for Flute & Orchestra
Saint-Saëns: Odelette; Romance, Op. 37; Ascanio (exc); *Hüe*: Flute Fantasia; *Gaubert*: Nocturne; *Doppler*: Fantaisie, Op. 26; *Fauré*: Fantaisie; *Godard*: Suite, Op. 116. (W. Bennett, ECO/S. Bedford)

① **CDDCA653** (8/89)
Mexican Orchestral Works
Revueltas: Ventanas; Musica para Charlar; Caminos; *Chávez*: Symphony 4; Sinfonia de Antigona. (RPO, Mexico City PO/E. Bátiz)

① **CDDCA654** (8/89)
Ginastera—Orchestral Works
Ginastera: Harp Concerto; Estancia Suite; Piano Concerto 1. (N. Allen, O. Tarrago, Mexico City PO/E. Bátiz)

① **CDDCA657** (9/89)
Liadov—Orchestral Works
Liadov: Fanfares; Polonaise, Op.49; Enchanted Lake, Op.62; Baba-Yaga, Op.56; Kikimora, Op.63; About olden times, Op. 21b; Musical Snuffbox, Op.32; Russian Folksongs, Op.58; Polonaise, Op.55. (Mexico City PO/E. Bátiz)

① **CDDCA659** (11/89)
The Romantic Clarinet
Weber: Clarinet Concerto 2; *Spohr*: Clarinet Concerto 1; *Crusell*: Clarinet Concerto 3. (E. Johnson, ECO/G. Schwarz)

① **CDDCA662** (11/89)
Vivaldi—Bassoon Concertos, Vol. 3
Vivaldi: Concerto, RV488; Concerto, RV472; Concerto, RV481; Concerto, RV479; Concerto, RV501; Concerto, RV477. (Daniel Smith, ECO/P. Ledger)

① **CDDCA663** (9/89)
Handel/Telemann—Oboe Sonatas
Handel: Oboe Sonatas; *Telemann*: Essercizii musici (exc);

Musique de Table (exc); Getreue Music-Meister (exc);
Sonate Metodiche (exc). (M. Zupnik, M. Shuman, R.
Leppard)

① **CDDCA664** (11/89)
French Chamber Works
Debussy: Danse sacrée et danse profane; Sonata for
Flute, Viola and Harp; *Ravel*: Introduction and Allegro;
Roussel: Sérénade. (Prometheus Ens)

① **CDDCA665** (1/90)
Saint-Saëns—Orchestral Works
Saint-Saëns: Symphony 3; Danse Macabre; Wedding
Cake; Carnaval des Animaux. (N. Rawsthorne, J.F. Osorio,
G. Salvador I, G. Salvador II, LPO, Mexico St SO, RPO,
Mexico City PO/E. Bátiz)

① **CDDCA666** (3/90)
D'Avalos conducts Wagner, Vol 3
Wagner: Siegfried Idyll; Lohengrin (exc); Meistersinger
(exc); Walküre (exc). (J. Tomlinson, Philh/F. d'Avalos)

① **CDDCA667** (11/89)
Prokofiev—Works for Violin & Piano
Prokofiev: Violin Sonata 1; Violin Sonata 2; Melodies,
Op.35b. (M. Fujikawa, C. Sheppard)

① **CDDCA669** (11/89)
Prokofiev—Songs
Prokofiev: Ugly Duckling; Children's Songs, Op.68 (Cpte);
Russian Folksongs, Op. 104 (exc); Poems, Op.23 (Cpte);
Songs without Words, Op.35 (Cpte). (C. Farley, R.
Vignoles)

① **CDDCA675** (12/89)
Martucci—Complete Orchestral Music, Vol. 1
Martucci: Symphony 1; Novelletta; Nocturne, Op.70/1;
Tarantella. (Philh/F. d'Avalos)

① **CDDCA682** (5/90)
Britten—Vocal & Orchestral Works
Britten: Illuminations; Nocturne; Sinfonietta, Op. 1. (A.
Rolfe Johnson, Northern Sinfonia/J. Glover)

① **CDDCA683** (2/90)
Mozart—Arias
Mozart: Exsultate, jubilate, K165; Voi avete un cor fedele,
K217; Vado, ma dove?, K583; Chi sà, K582; Nehmt
meinen Dank, K383; Bella mia fiamma, K528; Zaïde (exc);
Mitridate (exc). (F. Lott, LMP/J. Glover)

① **CDDCA684** (6/90)
Schubert—Lieder & Chamber Works
Schubert: Trout Quintet, D667; Forelle, D550; Hirt auf dem
Felsen, D965. (A. Mackay, Y. Seow, C. Craker,
Prometheus Ens)

① **CDDCA686** (3/90)
Fauré—Orchestral Works
Fauré: Violin Concerto; Berceuse, op 16; Elégie; Masques
et bergamasques (exc); Shylock Suite (exc); Pelléas et
Mélisande Suite (exc). (R. Bonucci, V. Ponomarev, Mexico
City PO/E. Bátiz)

① **CDDCA687** (6/90)
Bartók—Piano Works
Bartók: Hungarian Peasant Songs, Sz71; Suite, Sz62;
Allegro barbaro, Sz49; Rondos on Folktunes, Sz284; Easy
Pieces; Burlesques, Sz247; Romanian folkdances, Sz56;
Romanian Dances, Sz243. (P. Frankl)

① **CDDCA689** (5/90)
Martucci—Complete Orchestral Music, Vol. 2
Martucci: Symphony 2; Colore orientale, Op. 44/3;
Andante, op. 69/2. (G. Ives, Philh/F. d'Avalos)

① **CDDCA691** (7/90)
Martucci—Complete Orchestral Music, Vol. 4
Martucci: Piano Concerto 2; Canzonetta, Op.55/1;
Gavotta, Op.55/2; Giga, Op.61/3; Serenata, Op.57/1;
Minuetto, Op.57/2; Momento musicale, Op.57/3. (F.
Caramiello, Philh/F. d'Avalos)

① **CDDCA695** (5/90)
Debussy—Piano Works, Vol. 1
Debussy: Images; Children's Corner; Estampes. (G.
Fergus-Thompson)

① **CDDCA698** (9/90)
Violin Virtuoso
Brahms: Hungarian Dances (exc); *Sarasate*: Danzas
españolas (exc); *Elgar*: Capricieuse; *Mendelssohn*: Songs
without words (exc); *Wieniawski*: Capriccio-valse, op 7;
Traditional: Deep River; *Paradies*: Siciliene; *Dinicu*: Hora
Staccato; *Rachmaninov*: Songs, Op. 38 (exc); Songs, Op.
21 (exc); *Heuberger*: Opernball (exc); *Gluck*: Orfeo ed
Euridice (exc); *Prokofiev*: Love for 3 Oranges Suite (exc);
Tchaikovsky: Souvenir d'un lieu cher, op 42 (exc);
Gershwin: Porgy and Bess (exc); *Castelnuovo-Tedesco*:
Etudes d'ondes. (X. Wei, Pam Nicholson)

① **CDDCA700** (7/90)
Mendelssohn—Orchestral Works
Mendelssohn: Symphony 3; Symphony 4; Octet, Op. 20
(exc). (Scottish CO/J. Serebrier)

① **CDDCA701** (6/90)
The Virtuoso Clarinettist
Weber: Variations, J128; *Spohr*: Fantasy and Variations,
op 81; *Donizetti*: Studio 1; *Kalliwoda*: Morceau de salon;
Lovreglio: Fantasia, op 45; *Waterson*: Morceau de
Concert; *Ponchielli*: Convegno; *Rossini*: Stabat Mater
(exc); *Panizza*: Ballabile con Variazioni; *Messager*: Solo de
concours. (C. Bradbury, O. Davies, D. Watson)

① **CDDCA702** (9/90)
Jane Parker-Smith at the Grand Organ of Armagh
Cathedral
Guilmant: Organ Sonata 5; *Jongen*: Pièces, Op. 37 (exc);
Brewer: Marche héroïque; *Wood*: Nunc dimittis; *Fleury*:
Prelude, Andante and Toccata; *Karg-Elert*: Pieces, Op.
142 (exc); *Saint-Martin*: Toccata de la Libération. (J.
Parker-Smith)

① **CDDCA704** (10/90)
Wagner—Overtures & Preludes
Wagner: Faust Overture; Feen (exc); Liebesverbot (exc);
Rienzi (exc); Fliegende Holländer (exc). (Philh/F.
d'Avalos)

① **CDDCA705** (7/90)
Fauré—Works for Violin
Fauré: Violin Sonata 1; Violin Sonata 2; Andante, op 75;
Berceuse, op 16. (M. Fujikawa, J.F. Osorio)

① **CDDCA706** (6/90)
Borodin—Symphonies
Borodin: Symphony 1; Symphony 2; Symphony 3. (Rome
RAI Orch/J. Serebrier)

① **CDDCA709** (10/90)
Lalo—Orchestral Works
Lalo: Roi d'Ys (exc); Scherzo; Symphony in G minor;
Rapsodie norvégienne. (RPO/Y. Butt)

① **CDDCA711** (9/90)
Debussy—Piano Works, Vol. 3
Debussy: Isle Joyeuse; D'un cahier d'esquisses; Rêverie;
Mazurka; Page d'Album; Plus que Lente; Valse
Romantique; Danse; Tarantelle styrienne; Hommage à
Haydn; Masques; Ballade; Petit Nègre; Morceau de
Concours; Elégie; Berceuse héroïque; Nocturne. (G.
Fergus-Thompson)

① **CDDCA713** (9/90)
Tchaikovsky—Works for Violin and Orchestra
Tchaikovsky: Violin Concerto; Sérénade mélancolique;
Valse-scherzo, op 34; Souvenir d'un lieu cher, op 42 (exc).
(X. Wei, Philh, S. Accardo)

① **CDDCA714** (8/90)
Bloch—Works for Violin & Piano
Bloch: Baal Shem; Violin Sonata 1; Violin Sonata 2.
(/Lionel Friedman, A. Schiller)

① **CDDCA716** (9/90)
Koechlin—Works for Horn & Piano
Koechlin: Horn Sonata, op 70; Pieces, op 180; Morceau de
lecture; Sonneries, Op. 123 (exc); Sonneries, Op 142
(exc); Sonneries, op 153 (exc). (B. Tuckwell, D.
Blumenthal)

① **CDDCA717** (4/91)
Mozart—Symphonies
Mozart: Symphony 29; Symphony 25; Symphony 33.
(LMP/J. Glover)

① **CDDCA719** (3/91)
Tchaikovsky—Orchestral Works
Tchaikovsky: Serenade, Op. 48; Elegy; Suite 4; Andante
cantabile, Op.11; Sleeping Beauty (exc). (Scottish CO/J.
Serebrier)

① **CDDCA720** (10/90)
Debussy—Piano Works, Vol. 4
Debussy: Préludes (exc); Images oubliées; Arabesques.
(G. Fergus-Thompson)

① **CDDCA722** (1/91)
Grieg—Orchestral Works
Grieg: Symphonic Dances; Sigurd Jorsalfar, Op. 56; Lyric
Suite, Op. 54 (exc). (RPO/Y. Butt)

① **CDDCA732** (5/91)
Clarinet Celebration
Weber: Duo concertant, J204; Variations, J128;
Schumann: Fantasiestücke, Op. 73; *Lovreglio*: Fantasia,
Op. 45; *Burgmüller*: Duo, Op. 15; *Giampieri*: Carnevale di
Venezia. (E. Johnson, G. Back)

① **CDDCA735** (9/91)
Music of Spain
Turina: Procesión del Rocío; Oración del torero; *Granados*:
Danzas españolas (exc); Goyescas (exc); *Albéniz*:
Catalonia; *Falla*: Amor Brujo (exc); Vida breve (exc).
(Mexico City PO/E. Bátiz)

① **CDDCA739** (1/91)
Summer Works
Delius: Koanga (exc); *Ranish*: Flute sonata; *R. R. Bennett*:
Summer Music; *P. Lamb*: Flute sonata; *Elgar*: Nursery
Suite (exc); *Dunhill*: Flute suite; *C. Scott*: Extatic Shepherd;
Arnold: Flute sonata, Op. 121. (K. Smith, P. Rhodes)

① **CDDCA741** (5/91)
Menotti/Luening—Orchestral Works
Luening: Legend (1951); Lyric Scene (1958); *Menotti*:
Sebastian (Cpte). (E. Larsen, P. Oien, Oslo PO, LSO/J.
Serebrier)

① **CDDCA744** (9/91)
Brahms—Symphony No.2
Brahms: Symphony 2; Haydn Variations; Academic
Festival Overture. (Philh/F. d'Avalos)

① **CDDCA746** (9/91)
Brahms—Symphony No 4. Serenade No 2
Brahms: Symphony 4; Serenade 2; Hungarian Dances
(exc). (Philh/F. d'Avalos)

① **CDDCA747** (7/91)
Emma Johnson plays Weber
Weber: Clarinet Concerto 1; Clarinet Concerto 2; Clarinet
Concertino; Duo concertant, J204. (E. Johnson, ECO/Y.P.
Tortelier/G. Schwarz/C. Groves, G. Back)

① **CDDCA749** (11/91)
The Bohemians, Volume 1
Janáček: String Quartet 1; String Quartet 2; *Dvořák*:
Cypresses. (Lindsay Qt)

① **CDDCA751** (4/92)
Vivaldi—Bassoon Concerti, Vol.5
Vivaldi: Concerto, RV489; Concerto, RV493; Concerto,
RV484; Concerto, RV504; Concerto, RV480; Concerto,
RV503. (Daniel Smith, Zagreb Sols/T. Ninić)

① **CDDCA752** (4/92)
Vivaldi—Bassoon Concerti, Vol.6
Vivaldi: Concerto, RV497; Concerto, RV485; Concerto,
RV483; Concerto, RV478; Concerto, RV498; Concerto,
RV473; Concerto, RV502. (Daniel Smith, Zagreb Sols/T.
Ninić)

① **CDDCA753** (9/91)
Prokofiev—Piano Sonatas, Vol. 1
Prokofiev: Piano Sonata 1; Piano Sonata 2; Piano Sonata
3; Visions fugitives; Piano Sonatinas, Op. 54. (J. Lill)

① **CDDCA754** (6/91)
Prokofiev—Piano Sonatas, Vol. 2
Prokofiev: Piano Sonata 4; Piano Sonata 5; Piano Sonata
6; Pieces, Op. 59 (exc). (J. Lill)

① **CDDCA755** (4/91)
Prokofiev—Piano Sonatas, Vol. 3
Prokofiev: Piano Sonata 7; Piano Sonata 8; Piano Sonata
9. (J. Lill)

① **CDDCA758** (7/91)
Falla, Milhaud & Stravinsky—Operas
Falla: Retablo de maese Pedro (Cpte); *Milhaud*: Malheurs
d'Orphée (Cpte); *Stravinsky*: Renard. (S. Linay, Adrian
Thompson, M. Best, M. Walker, A. Steiger, P. Harrhy, P.
Donnelly, M. Best, Gaynor Morgan, P. Bardon, S. Bickley,
H. Hetherington, P. Harrhy, P. Donnelly, N. Cavallier,
Matrix Ens/R. Ziegler)

① **CDDCA759** (10/91)
Transcriptions of Bach's Chaconne
Bach: Solo Violin Partitas and Sonatas (exc); Schübler
Chorales, BWV645-650 (exc); Chorales, BWV651-668
(exc); Nun freut euch, BWV734; Orgel-Büchlein, BWV599-
644 (exc); Prelude and Fugue, BWV543; In dulci jubilo,
BWV729; Cantata 147 (exc); Flute Sonatas, BWV1030-5
(exc); Cantata 208 (exc); Solo Violin Partitas and Sonatas
(exc); Toccata and Fugue, BWV565. (G. Fergus-
Thompson)

① **CDDCA760** (7/91)
Prokofiev—Vocal and Orchestral Works
Prokofiev: Ugly Duckling; Summer day; Autumnal sketch,
Op. 8; Winter bonfire; Symphony 1. (C. Farley, Paisley
Abbey Ch, Scottish CO/J. Serebrier)

① **CDDCA761** (4/91)
Mozart—Symphonies
Mozart: Symphony 37; Symphony 40; Symphony 41.
(LMP/J. Glover)

sacrae (1597) (exc); Canzon IX (1597); O magnum mysterium; Sacrae symphoniae (1597) (exc); *G. Bassano:* Canite Tuba; Frais et gaillard; Deus qui Beatum Marcum; *J. Bassano:* Fantasias a 5 (exc); *Monteverdi:* Selva morale e spirituale (exc). (E. van Evera, S. Hemington-Jones, S. Berridge, Angus Smith, Gentlemen of the Chappell, His Majesties Sagbutts and Cornetts/P. Bassano)

ⓘ **CDGAU124** (10/91)
Carver—Scottish Renaissance Polyphony Vol 1
Carver: O bone Jesu; Missa Dum sacrum mysterium; Gaude flore virginali. (Cappella Nova/A. Tavener)

ⓘ **CDGAU125** (10/91)
Krebs—Organ works in the style of Bach
Krebs: Prelude and Fugue in D; Herzlich lieb hab ich dich; Zeuch ein zu deinen Toren; Trio in D minor; BACH Fugue; Trio in E flat; Herr Gott dich loben alle wir; Fantasia sopra Wer nun den lieben Gott; Wir glauben all an einen Gott; Prelude and Fugue in C; Fantasia a giusto Italiano. (G. Barber)

ⓘ **CDGAU133** (7/94)
Nicholas Ludford, Volume 3
Ludford: Missa Christi Virgo; Domine Jesu Christe; *Anon:* Festival of the Virgin Mary (exc). (Cardinall's Musick/A. Carwood)

ⓘ **CDGAU137** (12/92)
Vivaldi—Choral Works
Vivaldi: Domine ad adiuvandum, RV593; Beatus vir, RV597; Stabat Mater; Magnificat, RV610. (Ex Cathedra Chbr Ch, Ex Cathedra Baroque Orch/J. Skidmore)

ⓘ **CDGAU138** (7/95)
Ramsey—Choral Music
R. Ramsey: How are the mighty fallen; Almighty and everlasting God I; When David heard; O come, let us sing; Service (exc); In guilty night; Sleep, fleshy birth; Thou maist be proud; Go perjured man; What hears, dear Prince; Inclina, Domine; O Sapientia; In Monte Oliveti; O vos omnes; Te Deum and Jubilate a 5. (Magnificat Ch, Magnificat Players/P. Cave)

ⓘ **CDGAU139** (3/95)
Ockeghem—Missa Mi-Mi, etc
Ockeghem: Salve Regina I; Missa Mi-Mi; *Busnois:* Victimae Paschali Laudes; *Ockeghem:* Alma Redemptoris Mater; *Obrecht:* Quod Chorus Vatum; *Isaac:* Angeli, Archangeli. (Clerk's Group/E. Wickham)

ⓘ **CDGAU140** (1/95)
The Music of Nicholas Ludford, Volume 4
Ludford: Missa Lapidaverunt Stephanum; Ave Maria ancilla trinitatis; *Anon:* Sarum Chant (exc). (Cardinall's Musick/A. Carwood)

ⓘ **CDGAU141** (7/95)
Delalande—Choral Works
Delalande: Cantate Domino, S72; De Profundis, S23; Regina Coeli, S53. (Ex Cathedra Chbr Ch, Ex Cathedra Baroque Orch/J. Skidmore)

ⓘ **CDGAU142** (6/95)
Fayrfax—Complete Works, Vol. 1
Fayrfax: Missa O Quam Glorifica; Ave Dei patris filia; Somewhat musing; *Anon:* That was my joy; *Fayrfax:* To complayne me; *Anon:* Sarum Chant (exc). (Cardinall's Musick/A. Carwood)

ⓘ **CDQS6011** (12/88)
Carols from Winchester Cathedral
Traditional: I saw three ships; Holly and the Ivy; First Nowell; God rest you merry, gentlemen; In dulci jubilo; O come, all ye faithful; Spotless Rose; Jesus Christ the apple tree; *Daquin:* Nouveau livre de noëls (exc); *Traditional:* Once in royal David's city; Könige; Il est né; Zither carol; O little town of Bethlehem; *Dandrieu:* Noëls (exc). (Winchester Cath Ch/M. Neary, M. Neary)

ⓘ **CDQS6021** (7/88)
Holst/Vaughan Williams—Wind Music
Holst: Suite 1; *Vaughan Williams:* English Folk Song Suite; Toccata Marziale; *Holst:* Suite 2; Hammersmith. (London Wind Orch/D. Wick)

ⓘ **CDQS6033** (11/89)
Mozart—Orchestral Works
Mozart: Symphony 31; Symphony 36; Nozze di Figaro (exc). (LPO, RPO/E. Bátiz)

ⓘ **CDQS6055** (12/92)
Beethoven—Piano Sonatas, Vol.1
Beethoven: Piano Sonata 1; Piano Sonata 2; Piano Sonata 19; Piano Sonata 20. (J. Lill)

ⓘ **CDQS6057** (3/93)
Beethoven—Piano Sonatas, Vol. 3
Beethoven: Piano Sonata 5; Piano Sonata 6; Piano Sonata 7. (J. Lill)

ⓘ **CDQS6079** (12/92)
Spanish Piano Works
Albéniz: Suite española 1; *Granados:* Allegro de concierto; *Falla:* Fantasia bética. (A. Petchersky)

ⓘ **CDQS6086** (12/92)
Palestrina—Sacred Works
Palestrina: Missa Papae Marcelli; Domine Jesus in qua nocte; Motets, Bk 2 (1581) (exc); Stabat mater a 8; Peccantem me quotidie. (PCA/B. Turner)

ⓘ **CDQS6094** (3/94)
Grieg/Suk/Tchaikovsky—String Music
Grieg: Holberg Suite; Elegiac Melodies; *Tchaikovsky:* Serenade, Op. 48; *Suk:* Serenade, Op. 6. (Swiss CO, Polish Radio CO/A. Duczmal)

ⓘ **CDQS6127** (7/94)
Liszt/Schumann—Organ Works
Liszt: Fantasia and Fugue, S259; Prelude and Fugue, S260; Variations, S673; *Schumann:* Sketches, Op. 58. (J. Bate)

ⓘ **CDQS6140** (7/95)
Haydn/Stamitz—Sinfonie Concertanti
Haydn: Sinfonia concertante; *C. Stamitz:* Sinfonia concertante in C, K9; Sinfonia concertante in D, K19. (R. Friedman, S. Smith, R. Best, London Fest Orch/R. Pople)

ⓘ **CDQS6144** (5/95)
Haydn Quartets - Volume 1
Haydn: String Quartets, Op. 76 (exc); String Quartets, Op. 50 (exc); String Quartets, Op. 20 (exc). (Lindsay Qt)

ⓘ **CDQS6145** (5/95)
Haydn Quartets—Volume 2
Haydn: String Quartets, Op. 64 (exc); String Quartet, Op. 42; String Quartets, Op. 76 (exc). (Lindsay Qt)

ⓘ **CDQS6146** (7/95)
Haydn—String Quartets, Vol. 3
Haydn: String Quartets, Op. 20 (exc); String Quartets, Op. 33 (exc); String Quartets, Op. 71 (exc). (Lindsay Qt)

ⓘ **CDWHL2053** (9/92)
Eric Coates—Orchestral Works
Coates: Three Elizabeths Suite; Ballad; By the Sleepy Lagoon; Three Bears Suite; London Suite. (East England Orch/M. Nabarro)

ⓘ **CDWHL2066** (10/92)
Rêverie
Debussy: Arabesques (exc); Rêverie; Suite bergamasque (exc); *Scriabin:* Etudes, Op. 42 (exc); *Bach:* Cantata 147 (exc); Cantata 140 (exc); *Glinka:* Farewell to St Petersburg (exc); *Godowsky:* Triakontameron (exc); *Saint-Saëns:* Carnaval des animaux (exc); *Schumann:* Arabeske; Kinderszenen (exc); *Brahms:* Piano Pieces, Op. 118 (exc); *Grieg:* Lyric Pieces, Op. 43 (exc); Lyric Pieces, Op 54 (exc); *Ravel:* Tombeau de Couperin (exc); Pavane pour une infante défunte. (G. Fergus-Thompson)

ⓘ **CDWHL2067** (11/92)
Shepherd's Hey - Wind Music
Grainger: Molly on the shore, BFMS23; Irish tune from County Derry; Shepherd's Hey, BFMS31; Lincolnshire Posy; *Milhaud:* Suite française; *Poulenc:* Suite française. (London Wind Orch/D. Wick)

ⓘ **CDWHL2074** (8/93)
The Authentic George Gershwin, Vol. 1
Gershwin: Capitol Revue (exc); I was so young; La La Lucille (exc); Limehouse nights; Scandals 1921 (exc); Rhapsody in Blue; Lady, Be Good! (exc); Tell me more (exc); Piano Concerto (exc). (J. Gibbons)

ⓘ **CDWHL2075** (8/93)
The Music of Eric Coates - Volume 2
Coates: Suite in three parts (Cpte); Jester at the Wedding Suite; Four Centuries. (East England Orch/M. Nabarro)

ⓘ **CDWHL2076** (10/93)
Clarinet Masquerade
Farkas: Old Hungarian Dances (exc); *Mozart:* Divertimenti, K439b; *Tomasi:* Divertissements; *Garner:* Misty; *Jobim:* Garota de Ipanema; *Y. Desportes:* Suite française; *Stark:* Serenade, Op. 55; *Gershwin:* Porgy and Bess (exc); *Sid Phillips:* Cadenza; *C. Fernandez:* Muskrat Sousa; *Albinoni:* Sinfonie, Op. 2 (exc). (Thurston Cl Qt)

ⓘ **CDWHL2077** (8/93)
The Authentic Gershwin, Vol.2
Gershwin: Tip-Toes (exc); Three-quarter blues (exc); Oh, Kay! (exc); Preludes; Strike Up The Band I (exc); Strike Up The Band II (exc); Funny Face (exc); American in Paris; Show Girl (exc); Girl Crazy (exc). (J. Gibbons)

ⓘ **CDWHL2079** (1/94)
Brazileira
Wüsthoff: Concerto de Samba (exc); *L. Almeida:* Brazilliance; *Villa-Lobos:* Cirandas (exc); A Lenda do Caboclo; O Trenzinho do Caipira; Bachianas Brasileiras 4; *Piazzolla:* Grand Tango; *York:* Rosetta; *Milhaud:* Scaramouche. (Pro Arte Gtr Trio)

ⓘ **CDWHL2082** (3/95)
The Authentic Gershwin, Volume 3
Gershwin: Of Thee I Sing (exc); Second Rhapsody; Shocking Miss Pilgrim (exc); Cuban Overture; Pardon My English (exc); I Got Rhythm Variations; Catfish Row; Shall We Dance? (exc); Goldwyn Follies (exc); Porgy and Bess (exc). (J. Gibbons)

ⓘ **CDWHL2083** (12/93)
Christmas Fanfare
Traditional: Christmas Fanfare (Green); O come, all ye faithful; Joy to the world; Stille Nacht; Hark! the herald angels sing; In the bleak midwinter; Away in a manger; God rest you merry, gentlemen; O little one sweet; Patapan; Past three a clock; Sussex carol; Good King Wenceslas; Coventry Carol; Walking in the air; Ding dong! merrily on high; O little town of Bethlehem; Deck the hall; Santa Claus is coming to town; Once in Royal David's City; We wish you a merry Christmas; *Prokofiev:* Lt Kijé Suite (exc); *Bach:* Cantata 140 (exc); Cantata 147 (exc); *Corelli:* Concerti grossi, Op. 6 (exc); *Berlioz:* Enfance du Christ (exc). (Prince of Wales Brass)

Athene

ⓘ **ATHCD4** (12/93)
Clementi—Keyboard Sonatas
Clementi: Keyboard Sonatas, Op.7 (exc); Keyboard Sonatas, Op.13 (exc); Keyboard Sonatas, Op.24 (exc); Keyboard Sonatas, Op.25 (exc). (P. Katin)

Arturo Toscanini Society

ⓘ **ATCD100** (5/94)
Toscanini conducts Italian Music
Tommasini: Good-Humoured Ladies (exc); *Boccherini:* String Quintets, G271-6 (exc); *Cherubini:* String Quartet 1 (exc); *Bazzini:* Saul Overture; *Verdi:* String Quartet (exc); *Martucci:* Novelletta; *Bolzoni:* Minuetto; Al castello medioevale I; *Busoni:* Berceuse élégiaque; Rondo Arlecchinesco, Op.46; *Mancinelli:* Scene veneziane (exc); *Bossi:* Intermezzi goldoniani (exc); *Sinigaglia:* Baruffe chiozzotte; Piemonte (exc); *Wolf-Ferrari:* Segreto di Susanna (exc); *Tommasini:* Carnevale a Venezia; *Rieti:* Symphony 4; *Olivieri:* Inno di Garibaldi. (J. Peerce, NBC SO/A. Toscanini)

Audiofon

ⓘ **72040** (8/92)
Pavel and Lazar Berman live in recital
Beethoven: Violin Sonata 8; *Bloch:* Baal Shem (exc); *Brahms:* Violin Sonata 3; *Mozart:* Violin Sonata, K304; *Prokofiev:* Violin Sonata 2. (P. Berman, L. Berman)

ⓘ **72041** (6/92)
Lazar Berman - Piano Recital
Liszt: Winterreise, S561 (exc); Lieder, S558 (exc); Tristan und Isolde—paraphrase, S447; Années de pèlerinage 2 (exc); Harmonies poétiques, S173 (exc); Mephisto Waltz 1, S514; *Rachmaninov:* Moments Musicaux, Op.16 (exc). (L. Berman)

Aurora

ⓘ **ACD4971** (5/93)
Nystedt—Chamber and Vocal Works
Nystedt: Lucis creator optime; Pia memoria; Rhapsody in Green; Motets. (E. Skaug, O. Eriksen, Norwegian Brass Quintet, Bergen Cath Ch/M. Magnersnes, Brass Ens, Norwegian Sols Ch, Oslo PO/K. Nystedt)

ⓘ **ACD4973** (9/93)
Borealis
Janson: Tarantella; *Nordensten:* Ricochet, Op.75; *Söderlind:* Kjaerleiksleng i svarmerus; *Bibalo:* Savage. (S. Torjesen, Borealis Ens/C. Eggen)

ⓘ **ARCD1910** (3/88)
Halvor Haug—Orchestral Works
Haug: Symphony 1; Silence for Strings; Sinfonietta. (LSO/P. Dreier)

ⓘ **NCD4913** (8/87)
Works by Harold Saeverud
Saeverud: Symphony 9; Rondo amoroso; Galdreslåtten; Kjempevisleslåtten. (L. Ward, RPO/P. Dreier)

Auvidis

ⓘ **AV6108** (1/89)
Bouzignac—Sacred choral music
Bouzignac: Te Deum; Ego gaudebo in Domino; Alleluya; Deus dixit; Noë, noë; Hodie cum gaudio; O mors; Salve

Prélude, Fugue et Variation; Pastorale; Prière; Final, Op. 21; Fantaisie in A; Pièces (1878) (exc); Chorales. (W. Rübsam)

ⓘ BR100095 (2/91)
Chaconne
Bach: Solo Violin Partitas and Sonatas (exc); Dowland: First Book of Songs (exc); Britten: Nocturnal. (M. Seiffge, C. Hampe)

ⓘ BR100228 (10/94)
Ullmann—Orchestral Works
Ullmann: Piano Concerto, Op.25; Variations and Double Fugue, Op.5; Symphony 2. (Konrad Richter, Brno St PO/I. Yinon)

BBC Radio Classics

ⓘ BBCRD9106 (3/95)
The Music of Eric Coates
Coates: Merrymakers; London Suite; Three Elizabeths Suite; Calling All Workers; Jester at the Wedding Suite; Dam Busters; Green Hills o' Somerset; Stonecracker John. (I. Wallace, BBC Concert Orch/A. Boult)

ⓘ BBCRD9107 (3/95)
Brahms/Klemperer/Ravel/Vaughan Williams—Orchestral Works
Klemperer: Ziel (exc); Vaughan Williams: Tallis Fantasia; Ravel: Rapsodie espagnole; Brahms: Symphony 4. (New Philh/L. Stokowski)

ⓘ BBCRD9111 (5/95)
Elgar—Cello Concerto etc
Britten: Young Person's Guide; Elgar: Cello Concerto; Purcell: Abdelazer, Z570 (exc); Vaughan Williams: In the Fen Country. (Z. Nelsova, BBC SO, RLPO/C. Groves/M. Arnold)

ⓘ BBCRD9114 (3/95)
Beethoven—Orchestral Works
Beethoven: Symphony 6; Romances (exc); Egmont (exc); Prometheus (exc). (H. Bean, BBC SO/A. Boult)

ⓘ BBCRD9124 (12/95)
Szymanowski/Panufnik—Symphonies
Panufnik: Sinfonia Votiva; Szymanowski: Symphony 3; Symphony 4. (P. Langridge, P. Paleczny, BBC Sngrs, BBC Sym Chor, BBC SO/M. Elder/N. Del Mar/A. Panufnik)

ⓘ BBCRD9129 (10/95)
Bridge/Britten/Pärt—Orchestral Works
Bridge: Poems (1916); Britten: Gloriana Suite; Sinfonia da Requiem; Passacaglia, Op. 33b; Pärt: Cantus in memory of Benjamin Britten. (BBC Northern SO/N. Del Mar, BBC SO/G. Rozhdestvensky)

ⓘ DMCD98 (10/95)
BBC Proms - The Centenary: 1895-1995
Berlioz: Symphonie funèbre et triomphale (exc); Tchaikovsky: Nutcracker Suite; Elgar: Symphony 1; Gluck: Orfeo ed Euridice (exc); Wagner: Tannhäuser (exc); R. Strauss: Rosenkavalier (exc); Janáček: Sinfonietta; Shostakovich: Taiti trot. (J. Baker, BBC Chor, BBC SO, LPO, RPO, Hallé/J. Pritchard/M. Sargent/A. Boult/R. Leppard/T. Beecham/J. Barbirolli/R. Kempe/G. Rozhdestvensky)

Belart

ⓘ 450 111-2 (12/94)
Carols for Christmas
Traditional: Ding dong! merrily on high; O little town of Bethlehem; Il est né; Twelve days of Christmas; Up! good Christen folk; Stille Nacht; Good King Wenceslas; While shepherds watched; God rest you merry, Gentlemen; Holly and the Ivy; Away in a manger; Rutter: Shepherd's pipe carol; Traditional: First Nowell; I saw three ships; Suo Gan; Hark! the herald angels sing. (St John's College Ch/G. Guest, S. Cleobury)

ⓘ 450 112-2 (12/94)
Carols for Advent—A Procession With Carols on Advent Sunday
Traditional: Veni, Redemptor gentium; 'Twas in the year that King Uzziah died; Vox clara ecce intonat; Spotless Rose; I sing of a maiden; Remember, O thou man; Jordanis oras praebia; Gabriel's message; King Jesus hath a garden; Blessed Son of God; O come, o come Emmanuel. (King's College Ch/D. Willcocks, S. Preston)

ⓘ 450 121-2 (6/94)
Plácido Domingo
Wagner: Meistersinger (exc); Massenet: Werther (exc); Bizet: Carmen (exc); Verdi: Luisa Miller (exc); Rigoletto (exc); Weber: Oberon (exc); Verdi: Ballo in maschera (exc); Puccini: Fanciulla del West (exc); Berlioz: Damnation de Faust (exc); Verdi: Macbeth (exc). (P. Domingo, D. Fischer-Dieskau, P. Lagger, C. Ligendza, K. Ricciarelli, C. Neblett, A. Wilkens, I. Cotrubas, Berlin

Deutsche Op Chor, Berlin Deutsche Op Orch, Cologne RSO, LSO, ROHO, VPO, BRSO, La Scala Orch, Paris Orch/E. Jochum/R. Chailly/C. Abbado/L. Maazel/C.M. Giulini/R. Kubelik/Z. Mehta/D. Barenboim)

ⓘ 450 129-2 (5/94)
Images of Spain
Chabrier: España; Falla: Amor brujo (exc); Ravel: Boléro; Alborada del gracioso; Pavane; Rimsky-Korsakov: Capriccio espagnol. (Boston Pops/A. Fiedler, Warsaw Nat PO/J. Semkow, BPO/L. Maazel, Boston SO/S. Ozawa)

ⓘ 450 131-2 (5/94)
Fauré—Requiem
Fauré: Requiem (Cpte); Pelléas et Mélisande Suite; Masques et Bergamasques. (S. Danco, G. Souzay, E. Schmidt, Peilz Chor Union, SRO/E. Ansermet)

ⓘ 450 132-2 (6/94)
Rimsky-Korsakov—Scheherazade
Rimsky-Korsakov: Scheherazade; May Night (exc); Sadko. (LSO/P. Monteux, SRO/E. Ansermet)

ⓘ 450 143-2 (5/94)
Best of British
Bliss: Things to Come (exc); Welcome the Queen; Elgar: Pomp and Circumstance Marches. (LSO/A. Bliss)

ⓘ 450 145-2 (5/94)
Debussy—Orchestral Works
Debussy: La Mer; Nocturnes; Après-midi. (Concertgebouw, Netherlands Rad Women's Ch/E. Inbal/J. Fournet)

Beulah

ⓘ 1PD12 (2/95)
Boult's BBC Years
Beethoven: Symphony 8; Humperdinck: Hänsel und Gretel (exc); Tchaikovsky: Capriccio italien; Serenade, Op. 48. (BBC SO/A. Boult)

ⓘ 1PD13 (7/95)
Sir Malcolm Sargent conducts British Music
Holst: Perfect Fool (exc); Britten: Instruments of the Orchestra; Vaughan Williams: Hugh the Drover (exc); Elgar: I sing the birth; Pomp and Circumstance Marches (exc); Coleridge Taylor: Othello (exc); Bax: Coronation March. (Mary Lewis, T. Davies, RCS, LPO, LSO, New SO, orch/M. Sargent, M. Sargent)

ⓘ 1PD2 (11/93)
Crystal Palace Champions
Ireland: Downland Suite; Elgar: Severn Suite (exc); Bliss: Kenilworth; Meyerbeer: Prophète (exc); Holst: Moorside Suite; Bath: Honour and Glory; Iles: Sing a song; Championship Medley 3; Handel: Messiah (exc); Iles: Homeland Melodies. (Fodens Motor Works Band, Massed Brass Bands, Black Dyke Mills Band, Wingates Temperance Band/F. Mortimer/J. H. Iles/W. Halliwell/H. Moss)

ⓘ 1PD3 (1/94)
Sir Henry's Themes and Variations
Delius: Dance Rhapsody 1; Holbrooke: Blind Mice Variations; Rameau: Fêtes d'Hébé (exc); Handel: Rodrigo (exc); Almira (exc); Dvořák: Symphonic Variations; Glinka: Ruslan and Lyudmila (exc); Bruckner: Overture in G minor; Dohnányi: Symphonic Minuets, Op. 34; Handel: Samson (exc). (Queen's Hall Orch/Henry Wood)

ⓘ 1PD5 (9/94)
Historic Organs, Volume 1
Saint-Saëns: Carnaval des animaux (exc); Wagner: Lohengrin (exc); S.S. Wesley: Holsworthy Church Bells; Sibelius: Finlandia; Widor: Symphony 8 (exc); Elgar: Organ Sonata 1 (exc); MacDowell: Woodland Sketches (exc); Watling: Cantilène in B minor; Batiste: Pilgrim's Song of Hope; Bach: Prelude and Fugue, BWV533; Clérambault: Premier livre d'Orgue (exc); Daquin: Nouveau livre de noëls (exc); Franck: Prélude, fugue et variation; Saint-Saëns: Préludes et fugues, Op.99 (exc); Carnaval des animaux (exc). (R. Goss-Custard, G. Thalben-Ball, G.D. Cunningham, J.A. Meale, A. Schweitzer, M. Dupré)

ⓘ 1PD8 (6/94)
Sibelius—Orchestral Works
Sibelius: Symphony 1; Symphony 7; Karelia Ov. (LSO/A. Collins)

ⓘ 3PD10 (9/95)
Bliss & Tchaikovsky—Violin Concertos
Bliss: Violin Concerto; Theme and Cadenza; Tchaikovsky: Violin Concerto. (A. Campoli, LPO/A. Bliss, LSO/A. Argenta)

ⓘ 3PD8 (6/94)
Sibelius—Orchestral Works
Sibelius: Symphony 3; Pohjola's Daughter; Pelleas and Melisande (exc); Nightride and Sunrise. (LSO/A. Collins)

Biddulph

ⓘ LAB004 (1/90)
Menuhin plays Mozart Concertos
Mozart: Violin Concerto, K216; Violin Concerto, K271a; Violin Concerto, KAnh294a. (Y. Menuhin, Paris SO/G. Enescu/P. Monteux)

ⓘ LAB005/6 (1/90)
The Art of Joseph Szigeti, Vol.1
Bach: Solo Violin Partitas and Sonatas (exc); Solo Violin Partitas and Sonatas (exc); Solo Violin Partitas and Sonatas (exc); Solo Violin Partitas and Sonatas (exc); Paganini: Caprices, Op. 1 (exc); Caprices, Op. 1 (exc); Caprices, Op. 1 (exc); Caprices, Op. 1 (exc); Veracini: Violin Sonatas, Op.2 (exc); Tartini: Violin Sonatas (1745) (exc); Exaudet: Minuet; Beethoven: Menuet, WoO10/2; Violin Sonata 8 (exc); Brahms: Violin Sonata 3 (exc); Dvořák: Slavonic Dances (exc); Slavonic Dances (exc); Hubay: Blumenleben, Op.30 (exc); Bloch: Baal Shem (exc); Debussy: Petite Suite (exc); Milhaud: Printemps; Saudades do Brasil (exc); Kreisler: Francoeur Siciliano and Rigaudon; Liebesleid; Tambourin chinois. (J. Szigeti, K. Ruhrseitz)

ⓘ LAB007/8 (1/90)
The Art of Joseph Szigeti, Vol.2
Tartini: Violin Concerto, D96 (exc); Handel: Violin Sonatas, J99-104 (exc); Mozart: Violin Sonata, K304; Weber: Violin Sonatas, J99-104 (exc); Schubert: Piano Sonata, D850 (exc); Brahms: Violin Sonata 3; Elgar: Serenade; Adieu; Warlock: Capriol Suite (exc); Lie: Snow; Chabrier: Pièces pittoresques (exc); Ravel: Pièce en forme de habanera; Falla: Vida Breve (exc); Rimsky-Korsakov: Tale of Tsar Saltan (exc); Scriabin: Etudes, Op.8 (exc); Prokofiev: Symphony 1 (exc); Stravinsky: Pastorale; Petrushka (exc); Szymanowski: Myths, Op.30 (exc); Hubay: Scènes de la Csárda (exc); Bartók: Romanian Folkdances, S256; For Children (1908/09) (exc). (J. Szigeti, N. Magaloff, E. Petri, B. Bartók)

ⓘ LAB009/10 (7/90)
The Kreisler Collection
Bach: Solo Violin Partitas and Sonatas (exc); Suites, BWV1066-9 (exc); Sulzer: Sarabande, Op.8; F. Schubert II: Bagatelles, Op.13 (exc); Tchaikovsky: Souvenirs de Hapsal, Op.2 (exc); Kreisler: Couperin Aubade provençal; Chanson Louis XIII; Couperin précieuse; Dittersdorf Scherzo; Boccherini Allegretto; Cartier Chasse; Liebesfreud; Liebesleid; Tambourin chinois; Caprice viennois; Bach: Solo Violin Partitas and Sonatas (exc); Brahms: Hungarian Dances (exc); Tchaikovsky: Souvenirs de Hapsal, Op.2 (exc); Cottenet: Chanson méditation; Marie: Cinquantaine; Rubinstein: Melodies, Op.3 (exc); Drigo: Arlekinda (exc); Chaminade: Sérénade espagnole; Kreisler: Apple Blossoms (exc); Liebesleid; H. Kreisler: Viennese Folksong Fantasy; Pergolesi: Tre giorni son che Nina; Beethoven: Menuet, WoO10/2; Andante favori, WoO57; Schumann: Klavierstücke, Op.85 (exc); Wagner: Meistersinger (exc); Jeral: Sérénade viennois; Kreisler: Marche miniature viennoise; Syncopation; Traditional: Londonderry Air; Mozart: Violin Concerto, K218; Bruch: Violin Concerto 1. (F. Kreisler, anon, H. Squire, F. Kreisler, H. Kreisler, C. Keith, orch/L. Ronald, RAHO/E. Goossens)

ⓘ LAB011 (6/90)
Brahms—Historic Chamber Music Recordings
Brahms: Violin Sonata 2; Viola Sonata 2; Cello Sonata 1. (J. Heifetz, E. Bay, W. Primrose, G. Moore, E. Feuermann, T. Van der Pas)

ⓘ LAB013 (6/90)
Toscha Seidel—Sonatas by Brahms and Grieg
Brahms: Violin Sonata 1; Violin Sonata 2; Grieg: Violin Sonata 3. (T. Seidel, A. Loesser)

ⓘ LAB015 (1/91)
Heifetz—Early Victor Recordings, 1917-18
Wieniawski: Scherzo-tarantelle, Op. 16; Violin Concerto 2 (exc); Schubert: Ave Maria, D839; Elgar: Capricieuse; Drigo: Airs de ballet (exc); Beethoven: Ruinen von Athen (exc); Glazunov: Méditation, Op. 32; Bazzini: Ronde des lutins; Sarasate: Danzas españolas (exc); Danzas españolas (exc); Introduction and Tarantella, Op.43; Paganini: Moto perpetuo, Op.11; Caprices, Op.1 (exc); Moszkowski: Pieces, Op.45 (exc); Kreisler: Francoeur Siciliano and Rigaudon; Porpora Menuet; Mendelssohn: Lieder, Op. 34 (exc); Chopin: Nocturnes (exc); Achron: Hebrew Melody. (J. Heifetz, A. Benoist, Victor Orch/J. Pasternack)

ⓘ LAB017 (10/91)
Casals—The Victor Recordings
Bach: Toccata, Adagio and Fugue, BWV564 (exc); English Suites, BWV806-811 (exc); Schubert: Moments musicaux, D780 (exc); Chopin: Preludes (exc); Nocturnes (exc); Schumann: Klavierstücke, Op.85 (exc); Wagner:

Meistersinger (exc); Tannhäuser (exc); *Bruch:* Kol Nidrei; *Rubinstein:* Melodies, Op.3 (exc); *Popper:* Stücke, Op. 11 (exc); Vito, Op.54/5; *Hillemacher:* Gavotte tendre; *Sgambati:* Serenata napoletana, Op.24/2; *Godard:* Jocelyn (exc); *Saint-Saëns:* Carnaval des Animaux (exc); *Fauré:* Songs, Op.7 (exc); *Debussy:* Petite Suite (exc); *Granados:* Danzas españolas (exc); Goyescas (exc). (P. Casals, N. Mednikoff)

Ⓘ **LAB025** (1/91)
Jascha Heifetz plays
Franck: Violin Sonata; *Saint-Saëns:* Introduction and Rondo capriccioso; Havanaise; *Vieuxtemps:* Violin Concerto 4. (J. Heifetz, A. Rubinstein, LPO, LSO/J. Barbirolli)

Ⓘ **LAB028** (9/91)
Jacques Thibaud & Alfred Cortot
Bach: Brandenburg Concertos (exc); *Haydn:* Keyboard Trio 25; *Beethoven:* Violin Sonata 9. (J. Thibaud, P. Casals, A. Cortot, R. Cortet, Paris Cons CO)

Ⓘ **LAB029** (11/91)
French Chamber works
Franck: Piano Quintet; *Chausson:* Concert, Op. 21; *Fauré:* Berceuse, Op.16. (J. Thibaud, A. Cortot, International Qt, Stg Qt)

Ⓘ **LAB031** (4/91)
The young Yehudi Menuhin, Vol.1
Fiocco: Pièces de clavecin, Op.1 (exc); *Anon:* Romanesca; *Monasterio:* Sierra Morena; *F. Ries:* Capricciosa; *Saenger:* Concert Miniatures, Op.130 (exc); *Handel:* Dettingen Te Deum (exc); *Mozart:* Violin Concerto, K216 (exc); *Leclair:* Violin Sonatas, Op.9 (exc); *Spohr:* Duets, Op.39 (exc); *Serrano:* Canción del olvidó (exc); *Samazeuilh:* Chant d'Espagne; *Bloch:* Baal Shem (exc); *Bruch:* Violin Concerto 1. (Y. Menuhin, L. Persinger, LSO/L. Ronald)

Ⓘ **LAB032** (4/91)
The young Yehudi Menuhin, Vol.2
Bach: Solo Violin Partitas and Sonatas (exc); *Beethoven:* Violin Sonata 1; *Mozart:* Violin Sonata, K296 (exc); *Corelli:* Sonatas, Op.5 (exc); *Monsigny:* Aline, reine de Golconde (exc); *Nováček:* Concert caprices, Op. 5 (exc); *Rimsky-Korsakov:* Tsar's Bride (exc); *Paganini:* Violin Concerto 2 (exc). (Y. Menuhin, H. Giesen)

Ⓘ **LAB033/4** (6/91)
Jan Kubelík—The Acoustic Recordings (1902-13)
Ambrosio: Romance, Op.9; *Drdla:* Serenade 1; *Saint-Lubin:* Lucia Sextet; *Wieniawski:* Faust Fantaisie (exc); *Sarasate:* Carmen Fantasy (exc); *Paganini:* Paisiello's Introduction and Variations; *Bazzini:* Ronde des lutins; *Ambrosio:* Serenade, Op.4; *Nachéz:* Hungarian Dance 1; *Wieniawski:* Faust Fantaisie (exc); *Paganini:* God save the King variations; Moto Perpetuo, Op.11; *Saint-Lubin:* Lucia Sextet; *Drdla:* Serenade 1; *Schumann:* Kinderszenen (exc); *Bazzini:* Ronde des lutins; *Hubay:* Blumenleben, Op.30 (exc); *Wieniawski:* Scherzo-tarantelle, Op.16; *Raff:* Pieces, Op.85 (exc); *Drdla:* Visione; Souvenir; *Sarasate:* Zigeunerweisen; Danzas españolas (exc); *Fibich:* Moods, Op. 41, Part 2 (exc); *Sgambati:* Serenata napoletana, Op.24/2; *Drdla:* Berceuse, Op.56; *Saint-Saëns:* Carnaval des Animaux (exc); *Paganini:* Violin Concerto 1 (exc); Caprices, Op.1 (exc); *Randegger:* Pierrot sérénade; Pierrot sérénade; *Wieniawski:* Mazurkas, Op.19 (exc); *Sarasate:* Danzas españolas (exc); *F. Ries:* Suite, Op. 34 (exc); *Mozart:* Romanze, KAnh205; *Gluck:* Orfeo ed Euridice (exc); *Tchaikovsky:* Violin Concerto (exc); *Drdla:* Souvenir; *Dvořák:* Humoresques, Op.101 (exc); *Sarasate:* Zigeunerweisen; *Wieniawski:* Violin Concerto 2 (exc); *Sarasate:* Danzas españolas (exc); *Fiorillo:* Etude-caprices, Op. 3 (exc); *Rubinstein:* Soirées, Op. 44. (J. Kubelík, anon, G. Lapierre)

Ⓘ **LAB039** (10/91)
Elman—Victor Records with Caruso, Alda & Str Quartet
Kahn: Ave Maria; *Massenet:* Élégie; *Denza:* Si vous l'aviez compris; *Leoncavallo:* Sérénade française; *Hollman:* Chanson d'amour; *Rabey:* Dans tes yeux en pleurs; *Gounod:* Ave Maria; *G. Braga:* Melodies (exc); *Dittersdorf:* String Quartets (exc); *Haydn:* String Quartets, Op.76 (exc); *Mozart:* String Quartet, K421 (exc); *Schubert:* String Quartet, D804 (exc); *Tchaikovsky:* String Quartet 1 (exc); *Mozart:* String Quartet, K428 (exc). (M. Elman, E. Caruso, P. Kahn, G. Scognamiglio, F. Alda, F. La Forge, Elman Qt)

Ⓘ **LAB044** (12/91)
Ruggiero Ricci—1938 Electrola Recordings
Paganini: Violin Concerto 2 (exc); Moses in Egypt Variations; *Ysaÿe:* Rêve d'enfant, Op. 14; *Rachmaninov:* Songs, Op. 34 (exc); *Sarasate:* Danzas españolas (exc); Introduction and Tarantella, Op. 43; Zigeunerweisen (exc); *Bach:* Solo Violin Partitas and Sonatas (exc); *Mattheson:* Suites (1714) (exc); *Suk:* Pieces, Op. 17 (exc); *Beethoven:* String Trios, Op. 9 (exc). (R. Ricci, C. Fürstner, L. Persinger, J. DePasquale, G. Ricci)

Ⓘ **LAB045** (12/91)
Hubay & Flesch —HMV Recordings
Hubay: Cremona lutenist (exc); Berceuse, Op.79/7; Scènes de la Csárda (exc); Scènes de la Csárda (exc); *Bach:* Suites, BWV1066-9 (exc); *Handel:* Flute Sonatas (exc); *Hubay:* Ugy-e jani?; *Handel:* Dettingen Te Deum (exc); *Paganini:* Caprices, Op.1 (exc); *Handel:* Choice of Hercules (exc); *Fauré:* Berceuse, Op.16; *Falla:* Canciones populares españolas (exc); *Dobroven:* Melody hebraïque. (J. Hubay, O. Herz, Budapest Cons Orch/Mr Zsolt, M. Basilides, C. Flesch, I. Strasfogel)

Ⓘ **LAB046** (12/91)
The Young Yehudi Menuhin
Tartini: Devil's Trill Sonata; *Schubert:* Ave Maria, D839; *Wieniawski:* Scherzo-tarantelle, Op.16; *Moszkowski:* Pieces, Op.45 (exc); *Rimsky-Korsakov:* Tale of Tsar Saltan (exc); *Kreisler:* Francoeur Siciliano and Rigaudon; *Falla:* Vida Breve (exc); *Debussy:* Préludes (exc); *Ravel:* Tzigane; *Lalo:* Symphonie espagnole. (Y. Menuhin, A. Balsam, Paris SO/G. Enescu)

Ⓘ **LAB049/50** (9/92)
Kreisler - The Berlin HMV Recordings (1926-7)
Bach: Solo Violin Partitas and Sonatas (exc); *Beethoven:* Violin Concerto; *Mendelssohn:* Violin Concerto, Op.64; *Brahms:* Violin Concerto; *Mendelssohn:* Songs without words (exc); *Schumann:* Romanzen, Op.94 (exc); *Brahms:* Hungarian Dances (exc); *Debussy:* Préludes (exc); Petite Suite (exc); *Falla:* Vida breve (exc); Vida breve (exc); *C. Scott:* Pieces, Op. 47 (exc); *Corelli:* Trio Sonatas, Op.2 (exc); *Bizet:* Arlésienne Suites (exc); *Kreisler:* Marche miniature viennoise; Syncopation. (F. Kreisler, H. Kreisler, M. Raucheisen, A. Sándor, Berlin St Op Orch/L. Blech)

Ⓘ **LAB054** (10/92)
Albert Spalding—Archive Performances
Spohr: Violin Concerto 8; *Mendelssohn:* Violin Concerto, Op.64; *Spalding:* Etchings; Wind in the Pines; Dragonfly; *Schubert:* Ständchen, D889. (A. Spalding, Philadelphia/E. Ormandy, A. Benoist)

Ⓘ **LAB055** (10/92)
Nathan Milstein - Early Columbia Recordings
Bach: Solo Violin Partitas and Sonatas (exc); Solo Violin Partitas and Sonatas (exc); *Vitali:* Ciacona; *Vivaldi:* Sonatas, Op.2 (exc); Violin Sonata, RV10; *Tartini:* Devil's Trill Sonata; *Gallo:* Trio Sonatas (exc); *Nardini:* Violin Sonatas (exc). (N. Milstein, L. Mittman)

Ⓘ **LAB056/7** (12/92)
Arnold Rosé & the Rosé String Quartet
Bach: Solo Violin Partitas and Sonatas (exc); 2-Violin Concerto; Suites, BWV1066-9 (exc); *Beethoven:* String Quartet 4; String Quartet 10; String Quartet 14. (Arnold Rosé, Alma Rosé, CO, Rosé Qt)

Ⓘ **LAB059/60** (2/93)
Henri Temianka—Recital
Pugnani: Violin Sonatas, Op.7 (exc); *Bach:* Violin Sonatas, BWV1014-19 (exc); *Handel:* Flute Sonatas (exc); *Schumann:* Romanzen, Op.94 (exc); *Wieniawski:* Polonaise, Op.21; Scherzo-Tarantelle, Op.16; *Sarasate:* Danzas españolas (exc); *Saint-Saëns:* Introduction and Rondo Capriccioso; *Szymanowski:* Romance; King Roger (exc); *Bridge:* Cradle Song, H96; Moto perpetuo, H4c; *Arensky:* Piano Trio 1; *Schubert:* Rondo, D438; *Sibelius:* Humoresques, Opp.87/89 (exc); *Wieniawski:* Polonaise, Op.21. (H. Temianka, J. Graudan, F. Reizenstein, A. Sala, E. Joyce, Temianka CO, H. Temianka (vn/dir), V. Topilin)

Ⓘ **LAB061/2** (12/92)
Ossy Renardy - The Victor Recordings (1940-1)
Paganini: Caprices, Op.1; Grand Sonata in A; *Ernst:* Hungarian Airs; *Mozart:* Adagio, K261; *Brahms:* FAE Sonata; *Dvořák:* Ballad, B139; *Zarzycki:* Mazurka, Op.26; *Saint-Saëns:* Violin Concerto 1. (O. Renardy, W. Robert)

Ⓘ **LAB063** (3/93)
Nathan Milstein - American Columbia Recordings
Tchaikovsky: Violin Concerto; *C. Stamitz:* Violin Concerto in B flat (exc); *Mozart:* Violin Sonata, K296; *Beethoven:* Violin Sonata 8; *Suk:* Pieces, Op.17 (exc). (N. Milstein, A. Balsam, Chicago SO/F. Stock)

Ⓘ **LAB064** (11/92)
Recital by Joseph Szigeti
Bach: Violin Concerto, BWV1052; Cantata 156 (exc); *Tartini:* Violin Concerto, D45; *Mozart:* Divertimento, K287. (J. Szigeti, New Friends of Music Orch/F. Stiedry, Orch/W. Goehr/M. Goberman)

Ⓘ **LAB066** (6/93)
Enescu—Violinist & Composer
Corelli: Sonatas, Op.5 (exc); *Handel:* Violin Sonatas (exc); *Pugnani:* Sonatas, Op.8 (exc); *Beethoven:* Ruinen von Athen (exc); *Wagner:* Albumblatt; *Ambrosio:* Serenade, Op.4; *Kreisler:* Couperin Aubade provençal; Pugnani Tempo di menuetto; *Chausson:* Poème; *Enescu:* Violin Sonata 3. (G. Enescu, Y. Menuhin, S. Schlüssel, E.C. Harris, H. Menuhin)

Ⓘ **LAB068/9** (9/93)
The Kreisler Collection—1921-25
Brahms: Waltzes, Op.39 (exc); *Grieg:* Lyric Pieces, Op.43 (exc); *Dawes:* Melody in A; *Drdla:* Souvenir; *Kreisler:* Aucassin and Nicolette; Toy Soldier; *Rimsky-Korsakov:* Golden Cockerel (exc); Scheherazade (exc); *F. Logan:* Pale Moon; *C. Scott:* Pieces, Op.47 (exc); Cherry Ripe; *Chopin:* Mazurkas (exc); *Paderewski:* Miscellanea, Op.16 (exc); *Heuberger:* Opernball (exc); *Kramer:* Entr'acte, Op.46/2; *Openshaw:* Love sends a little gift; *Seitz:* World is waiting; *Haydn:* Symphony 96 (exc); *Tchaikovsky:* Violin Concerto (exc); *Friedberg:* Old French Gavotte; *Schütt:* Morceaux, Op.53 (exc); *Poldini:* Marionnettes (exc); *Grainger:* Molly on the Shore; *Balogh:* Dirge of the North; *Korngold:* Tote Stadt (exc); *Handel:* Serse (exc); *Tchaikovsky:* Souvenirs de Hapsal, Op.2 (exc); *Bass:* Chansonette; *Brandl:* Liebe Augustin (exc); *Dawes:* Melody in A; *Herbert:* Orange Blossoms (exc); *Kreisler:* Caprice viennois; *Balogh:* Caprice antique; *Cadman:* Legend of the Canyon; *Lalo:* Symphonie espagnole (exc); *Bach:* Menuet, BWV Anh114; *L. Koželuch:* Ritrovata figlia (exc); *Kreisler:* Russian Folksong paraphrase; *Liliuokalani:* Aloha Oe; *Dvořák:* Symphony 9 (exc); *Cadman:* American Indian Songs, Op.45 (exc); *Traditional:* I saw from the beach; *Rachmaninov:* Songs, Op.26 (exc); *R. Strauss:* Lieder, Op.27 (exc); *Larchet:* Padriac the fiddler. (F. Kreisler, C. Lamson, J. McCormack, E. Schneider)

Ⓘ **LAB070/1** (7/94)
Szigeti recordings with Bartók and Foldes
Bach: Solo Violin Partitas and Sonatas (exc); *Corelli:* Sonatas, Op.5 (exc); *Schubert:* Violin Sonata, D384; Piano Sonata, D850 (exc); *Brahms:* Hungarian Dances (exc); *Dvořák:* Slavonic Dances (exc); *Hubay:* Scènes de la Csárda (exc); *Kodály:* Háry János Suite (exc); *Mussorgsky:* Fair at Sorochintsï (exc); *Lalo:* Roi d'Ys (exc); *Debussy:* Suite bergamasque (exc); Violin Sonata; *Falla:* Sombrero de tres picos Suites (exc); *Milhaud:* Saudades do Brasil (exc); *Bloch:* Baal Shem; *Ives:* Violin Sonata 4; *Bartók:* Rhapsody 1; Contrasts. (J. Szigeti, A. Foldes, B. Bartók, B. Goodman)

Ⓘ **LAB075** (12/93)
Kreisler—1926-1927 Victor Recordings
Romberg: Student Prince (exc); *Friml:* Rose Marie (exc); *Lemare:* Andantino; *Cadman:* At dawning; *Lehár:* Giuditta (exc); *E. Owen:* Invocation; *Rimsky-Korsakov:* Songs, Op.2 (exc); *Tchaikovsky:* Morceaux, Op.10 (exc); *Rachmaninov:* Songs, Op.38 (exc); *Lehár:* Frasquita (exc); *Kreisler:* Caprice viennois; Liebesfreud; Liebesleid; *Berlin:* Blue skies; *Friml:* Dance of the Maidens; *Kreisler:* Shepherd's Madrigal; Gypsy Caprice; Schön Rosmarin; *Falla:* Canciones populares españolas (exc); *Albéniz:* España, Op.165 (exc); *Dvořák:* Humoresques, Op.101 (exc). (F. Kreisler, C. Lamson)

Ⓘ **LAB076** (11/93)
Menges plays Beethoven and Brahms
Beethoven: Violin Sonata 9; *Brahms:* Violin Sonata 2; Violin Sonata 3. (I. Menges, A. de Greef, H. Samuel)

Ⓘ **LAB077/8** (3/94)
Huberman—Complete Brunwick Recordings
Bach: Suites, BWV1066-9 (exc); *Gluck:* Orfeo ed Euridice (exc); *Beethoven:* Violin Sonata 9; *Mendelssohn:* Violin Concerto, Op.64 (exc); *Lalo:* Symphonie espagnole (exc); *Chopin:* Nocturnes (exc); *Tchaikovsky:* Souvenir d'un lieu cher, Op.42 (exc); Violin Concerto (exc); *Brahms:* Hungarian Dances (exc); Hungarian Dances (exc); *Bruch:* Kol Nidrei; *Elgar:* Capricieuse; *Paganini:* Violin Concerto 2 (exc); *Bazzini:* Ronde des lutins; *Vieuxtemps:* Ballade and Polonaise, Op.38; *Wieniawski:* Capriccio-Valse, Op.7; Violin Concerto 2 (exc); Mazurkas, Op.19 (exc); *Zarzycki:* Mazurka, Op.26; *Sarasate:* Danzas españolas (exc); Carmen Fantasy. (B. Huberman, P. Frenkel, S. Schultze)

Ⓘ **LAB080** (12/93)
Kreisler—1928 Victor Recordings
Dohnányi: Ruralia Hungarica; *Debussy:* Petite Suite (exc); Préludes (exc); *Drdla:* Souvenir; *Massenet:* Thaïs (exc); *E. Nevin:* Mighty lak' a rose; Rosary; *Foster:* Old Folks at Home; *Falla:* Vida breve (exc); *Albéniz:* España, Op.165 (exc); *Kreisler:* Tambourin chinois; *Winternitz:* Dance of the Marionettes; *Kreisler:* Beethoven Rondino; *Dvořák:* Slavonic Dances (exc); Violin Sonatina (exc); Gipsy Melodies (exc). (F. Kreisler, C. Lamson)

Ⓘ **LAB081/2** (9/94)
Huberman—Columbia recordings with piano
Bach: Orgel-Büchlein, BWV599-644 (exc); Suites, BWV1066-9 (exc); *Schubert:* Moments Musicaux, D780 (exc); Ave Maria, D839; *Chopin:* Nocturnes (exc); Waltzes (exc); Waltzes (exc); Waltzes (exc); *Brahms:* Hungarian Dances (exc); Waltzes, Op.39 (exc); *Tchaikovsky:* Souvenir d'un lieu cher, Op.42 (exc); *Bruch:* Kol Nidrei; *Elgar:* Capricieuse; *Sarasate:* Danzas españolas (exc);

Frühlingsstimmen, Op. 410; *H. Eccles:* Violin Sonata (exc); Violin Sonata (exc); *Laska:* Wiegenlied; *Beethoven:* Menuet, WoO10/2; *Koussevitzky:* Chanson triste, Op.2; Double Bass Concerto (exc); Valse Miniature, Op.1/2. (S. Koussevitzky, P. Luboshutz, B. Zighera, Boston SO/S. Koussevitzky)

① **WHL021/2** (2/95)
Frederick Stock and the Chicago Symphony Orchestra
Wagner: Meistersinger (exc); *Brahms:* Hungarian Dances (exc); *Goldmark:* Im Frühling; *Suk:* Fairy Tale (exc); *Glazunov:* Ruses d'amour (exc); *Tchaikovsky:* Symphony 5; *Paganini:* Moto perpetuo, Op.11; *Walton:* Scapino; *Dohnányi:* Suite, Op. 19; *R. Strauss:* Also sprach Zarathustra; *Stock:* Waltz, Op.8. (Chicago SO/F. Stock)

① **WHL027** (11/95)
Stokowski conducts Dvořák, Liszt, Chopin & Borodin
Dvořák: Symphony 9; *Liszt:* Hungarian Rhapsodies, S359 (exc); *Chopin:* Mazurkas (exc); Preludes (exc); *Borodin:* Prince Igor (exc). (Philadelphia/L. Stokowski)

① **WHL028** (7/95)
Koussevitzky conducts Berlioz
Berlioz: Carnaval Romain; Damnation de Faust (exc); Harold in Italy. (W. Primrose, Boston SO/S. Koussevitzky)

① **WHL033** (11/95)
Stokowski conducts Beethoven and Schubert
Beethoven: Symphony 7; *Schubert:* Symphony 8; Rosamunde (exc); Moments musicaux, D780 (exc). (Philadelphia/L. Stokowski)

Biographies in Music

① **BIM705-2** (5/90)
Muzio—The Published Edisons, 1920-25
Bachelet: Chère nuit; *Bellini:* Bianca e Fernando (exc); *Bizet:* Carmen (exc); *Boito:* Mefistofele (exc); *Buzzi-Peccia:* Mal d'amore; *Catalani:* Wally (exc); Loreley (exc); *Cilea:* Adriana Lecouvreur (exc); *Giordano:* Andrea Chénier (exc); Madame Sans-Gêne (exc); *Chopin:* Aspiration; *Gluck:* Paride ed Elena (exc); *Gomes:* Salvator Rosa (exc); Guagni-Benvenuti: Guardamil; *Handel:* Rinaldo (exc); *Herbert:* Orange Blossoms (exc); *Leoncavallo:* Pagliacci (exc); Zazà (exc); *Mascagni:* Amico Fritz (exc); A. Mascheroni: Eternamente; *Massenet:* Hérodiade (exc); *Monahan:* Shepherd's love; *Meyerbeer:* Africaine (exc); *Offenbach:* Contes d'Hoffmann (exc); *Parisotti:* Se tu m'ami; *Puccini:* Bohème (exc); *Rossini:* Separazione; *Sodero:* Crisantemi; *Tchaikovsky:* Eugene Onegin (exc); *Verdi:* Trovatore (exc); Forza del Destino (exc); Lombardi (exc); Vespri Siciliani (exc). (C. Muzio, orch, Anon, M. Laurenti, A. Spalding, R. Gaylor)

Birmingham Bach Choir

① **BBCCD2** (12/93)
There shall a star
Traditional: Torches; As with gladness; There shall a star; *Humperdinck:* Hänsel und Gretel (exc); *Prokofiev:* Lt Kijé Suite (exc); *Traditional:* Tomorrow shall be my dancing day; Away in a manger; Shepherds had an Angel; *M. Praetorius:* Es ist ein Ros'; *Traditional:* Benedicamus Domino; Bethlehem Down; What Cheer?; In dulci jubilo; Little child on the earth; In the bleak midwinter; Stille Nacht; Noël Nouvelet; Sing lullaby; Sussex carol; Nowell: Dieu vous garde. (Birmingham Bach Ch, Fine Arts Brass Ens/M. Shepherd, R. Dacey/P. Spicer)

BIS

① **BIS-CD017** (9/93)
Söderström and Meyer sing Duets
Kodály: Bicinia hungarica (exc); *Tchaikovsky:* Duets, Op. 46 (exc); *Dvořák:* Moravian Duets, B62 (exc); Moravian Duets, B60 (exc); *Purcell:* Welcome Song, Z335; King Arthur, Z628 (exc); Indian Queen, Z630 (exc); *Wennerberg:* Sutlers; Girls; *Geijer:* Dance; *Rossini:* Soirées musicales (exc); Duetto buffo di due gatti. (E. Söderström, K. Meyer, J. Eyron)

BIS-CD026 (9/92)

① **BIS-CD026** (9/92)
Shostakovich—Chamber Works
Shostakovich: Piano Trio 2; String Quartet 8; Blok Poems, Op. 127. (H. Pålsson, A. Tellefsen, F. Helmerson, Voces Intimae Qt, J. Delman, E. Dekov, Å. Olofsson, L. Negro)

① **BIS-CD053** (6/88)
Ligeti—Various Works
Ligeti: Double Concerto; San Francisco Polyphony; String Quartet 1; Continuum; Musica ricercata. (G. von Bahr, T. Lännerholm, L. Pohjola, E. Nordwall, Voces Intimae Qt, Swedish RSO/E. Howarth)

① **BIS-CD054** (5/94)
Lieder Recital
R. Strauss: Lieder, Op.10 (exc); *Schubert:* An Mignon, D161, An den Tod, D518; An den Mond, D193; An die

Leier, D737; An die Musik, D547; An mein Herz, D860; *Gounod:* A toi mon coeur; *Foerster:* An die Laute; *Brahms:* Lieder, Op. 46 (exc); Lieder, Op. 49 (exc); Lieder, Op. 71 (exc); *Hahn:* À Chloris; *Mozart:* An Chloe, K524; Ich würd' auf meinem Pfad, K390; *Wolf:* Mörike Lieder (exc). (H. Hagegård, T. Schuback)

① **BIS-CD078** (7/93)
Holmboe—Miscellaneous Works
Holmboe: Cello Concerto, Op. 120; Benedic Domino, Op. 59; Triade, Op. 123; Brass Quintet, Op. 79. (E.B. Bengtsson, Danish Nat RSO/J. Ferencsik, Camerata Chbr Ch/P. Enevold, E. Tarr, E. Westenholz, Swedish Brass Qnt)

① **BIS-CD104** (11/87)
Grieg: Complete Piano Music, Vol.1
Grieg: Lyric Pieces, Op.12; Lyric Pieces, Op.38; Lyric Pieces, Op.43; Lyric Pieces, Op.47. (E. Knardahl)

① **BIS-CD105** (11/87)
Grieg: Complete Piano Music, Vol.2
Grieg: Lyric Pieces, Op.54; Lyric Pieces, Op.57; Lyric Pieces, Op.62. (E. Knardahl)

① **BIS-CD106** (11/87)
Grieg: Complete Piano Music, Vol.3
Grieg: Lyric Pieces, Op.65; Lyric Pieces, Op.68; Lyric Pieces, Op.71. (E. Knardahl)

① **BIS-CD107** (8/88)
Grieg: Complete Piano Music, Vol.4
Grieg: Piano Pieces, Op.1; Tone-pictures, Op.3; Humoresques, Op.6; Funeral March; Piano Sonata, Op. 7. (E. Knardahl)

① **BIS-CD108** (8/88)
Grieg: Complete Piano Music, Vol.5
Grieg: Folksongs and Dances, Op.17; Improvisations, Op.29; Pictures, Op.19; Album Leaves, Op.28. (E. Knardahl)

① **BIS-CD109** (8/88)
Grieg: Complete Piano Music, Vol.6
Grieg: Ballade, Op.24; Peer Gynt Suite 1; Peer Gynt Suite 2; Sigurd Jorsalfar. (E. Knardahl)

① **BIS-CD110** (8/88)
Grieg: Complete Piano Music, Vol.7
Grieg: Holberg Suite; Elegiac Melodies, Op. 34; Waltz caprices, Op. 37; Prayer and Temple Dance; Nordic Melodies, Op.63. (E. Knardahl)

① **BIS-CD111** (8/88)
Grieg: Complete Piano Music, Vol.8
Grieg: Folksongs, Op.66; Song transcriptions, Op.41; Song transcriptions, Op.52. (E. Knardahl)

① **BIS-CD112** (8/88)
Grieg: Complete Piano Music, Vol.9
Grieg: Peasant Dances, Op.72; Stimmungen, Op.73; Piano Pieces (1908). (E. Knardahl)

① **BIS-CD131** (9/90)
Nielsen: Organ Works & Motets
Nielsen: Commotio; Little Preludes; Preludes; Motets. (E. Westenholz, Camerata Chbr Ch/P. Enevold)

① **BIS-CD147** (1/87)
Grieg—Music for String Orchestra
Grieg: Holberg Suite; Melodies, Op. 53; Nordic Melodies, Op. 63; Lyric Pieces (exc); Elegiac Melodies. (Norwegian CO/T. Tønnesen)

① **BIS-CD159** (3/94)
Hindemith—Chamber Works
Hindemith: Plöner Musiktag (exc); Trumpet Sonata; Trombone Sonata; Bass Tuba Sonata; Horn Sonata; Bassoon Sonata. (C. Pehrsson/A-P. Jonsson, A. Mjönes, P. Savijoki, K. Sønstevold, E. Tarr, C. Lindberg, M. Lind, E. Westenholz, R. Pöntinen, S. Harlos, J. Siirala, E. Knardahl, Malmö Brass Ens)

① **BIS-CD167/8** (5/90)
Nielsen: Complete Piano Music
Nielsen: Suite; Piano Music for Young and Old; Pieces, Op.59; Piano Piece; Dream of 'Silent Night'; Pieces, Op.3; Symphonic Suite; Humoresque; Festival Prelude; Chaconne; Theme with Variations. (E. Westenholz)

① **BIS-CD184** (9/89)
French Flute Music
Taffanel: Andante Pastorale et Scherzettino; *Widor:* Suite, Op.34; *Bozza:* Impressions; *Caplet:* Rêverie et Petite Valse; *Jolivet:* Chant de Linos; Incantations; *Debussy:* Syrinx; *Ferroud:* Pièces. (R. Aitken, R. McCabe)

① **BIS-CD188** (6/88)
Stravinsky. Piano Works
Stravinsky: Rite of Spring (Cpte); Firebird Suite (1919) (exc); Petrushka. (D. Achatz, R. Pöntinen)

① **BIS-CD212** (12/88)
Brahms: Complete Violin Sonatas
Brahms: Violin Sonata 1; Violin Sonata 2; Violin Sonata 3. (N-E. Sparf, E. Westenholz)

① **BIS-CD222** (10/84)
Sibelius: Orchestral Works
Sibelius: Symphony 5; Andante festivo; Karelia Ov. (Gothenburg SO/N. Järvi)

① **BIS-CD227** (10/86)
Tubin: Orchestral Works
Tubin: Symphony 4; Symphony 9; Toccata. (Bergen SO, Gothenburg SO/N. Järvi)

① **BIS-CD232** (1/84)
Contemporary Percussion Works
Cage: Second Construction; *Cowell:* Pulse; *Lundquist:* Sisu; *Taïra:* Hiéroptonie V. (Kroumata Perc Ens)

① **BIS-CD234** (2/93)
Martinu—Chamber Works
Martinů: Etudes and Polkas; Flute Sonata; Piano Sonata. (G. von Bahr, K. Hindart, R. Kvapil)

① **BIS-CD249** (10/88)
Works for Baroque Flute and Recorders
Babell: Sixth Flute Concerto; *Bach:* Suites, BWV1066-9 (exc); *Telemann:* Recorder and Flute Concerto. (P. Evison, C. Pehrsson, Drottningholm Baroque Ens)

① **BIS-CD256** (4/89)
Works for percussion
Nørgård: I Ching; *Xenakis:* Psappha; *Gudmundsen-Holmgreen:* Triptykon. (G. Mortensen, Danish RSO/J. Panula)

① **BIS-CD263** (11/85)
Sibelius: Orchestral Works
Sibelius: Symphony 4; Canzonetta; Oceanides. (Gothenburg SO/N. Järvi)

① **BIS-CD270** (2/86)
Sibelius: Songs with orchestra
Sibelius: King Christian II (exc); Songs, Op.38 (exc); Twelfth Night, Op. 60 (exc); Songs, Op.36 (exc); Rapids-Shooter's Brides; Songs, Op.38 (exc); Songs, Op.37 (exc); Songs, Op.17 (exc); Arioso, Op. 3; Songs, Op.13 (exc); Luonnotar; Serenade (1895). (M.A. Häggander, J. Hynninen, Gothenburg SO/J. Panula)

① **BIS-CD271** (2/86)
Recorder Concertos
Vivaldi: Concerto, RV485; Concerto, RV104; *Telemann:* Recorder & Bassoon Concerto; Recorder Concerto 1. (C. Pehrsson, M. McGraw, Drottningholm Baroque Ens)

① **BIS-CD272** (2/86)
Contemporary Music for Flute and Percussion
Jolivet: Suite en concert; *L. Andriesson:* Flute Concerto 1; *Cage:* Amores; *Sandström:* Drums (1980). (M. Wiesler, R. Pilat, Kroumata Perc Ens)

① **BIS-CD273** (10/85)
Organ Works
S. Wesley: Duet for organ; *Hesse:* Fantasia in C minor; *J. C. Bach:* Duets, Op. 18 (exc); *Merkel:* Organ Sonata, Op. 30; *J.C. Kellner:* Quartetto in E flat. (H. Fagius, D. Sanger)

① **BIS-CD276** (9/85)
Roland Pöntinen plays Russian piano music
Stravinsky: Petrushka; *Rachmaninov:* Etudes-tableaux, Op. 33 (exc); Etudes-tableaux, Op. 39 (exc); *Scriabin:* Piano Sonata 7; *Khachaturian:* Toccata; *Shostakovich:* Fantastic Dances; *Prokofiev:* Toccata, Op. 11. (R. Pöntinen)

① **BIS-CD284** (5/85)
Roman: violin concertos and sinfonias
Roman: Violin Concerto, BeRI/50; Violin Concerto, BeRI/43; Violin Concerto, BeRI/52; Sinfonia, BeRI/14; Sinfonia, BeRI/17; Sinfonia, BeRI/26. (Orpheus Chbr Ens, N-E. Sparf)

① **BIS-CD285** (4/85)
A Swedish Serenade
Wirén: Serenade, Op. 11; *Larsson:* Little Serenade, Op. 12; *Söderlund:* Oboe Concertino; *Lidholm:* Music for strings. (A. Nilsson, Stockholm Sinfonietta/E-P. Salonen)

① **BIS-CD286** (2/86)
Tubin: Orchestral Works
Tubin: Prélude solennel; Suite on Estonian Dances; Violin Concerto 1. (M. Lubotsky, Gothenburg SO/N. Järvi)

① **BIS-CD287** (11/85)
Trumpet Works
Arban: Norma Variations; *Françaix:* Trumpet Sonatine; *Tisné:* Héraldiques; *Honegger:* Intrada; *Maxwell Davies:* Trumpet Sonata; *Rabe:* Shazam!; *J. Hartmann:* Fantasia

brilliante on the air 'Rule Britannia'. (H. Hardenberger, R. Pöntinen)

ⓘ **BIS-CD288** (5/86)
Vañhal: Orchestral works
Vañhal: 2-Bassoon Concerto; Symphony in F; Symphony in A minor. (A. Wallin, A. Nilsson, Umeå Sinfonietta/J-P. Saraste)

ⓘ **BIS-CD290** (4/86)
Vivaldi: works for lute
Vivaldi: Trio, RV82; Trio, RV85; Concerto, RV93; Concerto, RV540. (J. Lindberg, N-E. Sparf, M. Huggett, M. Huggett, Drottningholm Baroque Ens)

ⓘ **BIS-CD291** (9/86)
20th-Century Music for Wind Quintet
Barber: Summer Music, Op. 31; Saeverud: Slåtter, Op. 21a; Jolivet: Sérénade (1945); Hindemith: Kleine Kammermusik, Op. 24/2. (Bergen Wind Qnt)

ⓘ **BIS-CD298** (9/85)
The Romantic Trombone
Ropartz: Pièce in E flat minor; Mercadante: Salve Maria (exc); Saint-Saëns: Cavatine, Op. 144; Gaubert: Morceau symphonique; Jongen: Aria et Polonaise, Op. 128; Stojowski: Fantaisie (1905); Alfvén: Herdsmaiden's Dance; Weber: Romance. (C. Lindberg, R. Pöntinen)

ⓘ **BIS-CD300** (11/85)
Music for a Rainy Day
Satie: Gnossiennes; Debussy: Suite bergamasque (exc); Seymer: Sológa; Prokofiev: Love for 3 Oranges Suite (exc); Grieg: Lyric Pieces, Op. 65 (exc); Schumann: Kinderszenen (exc); Stenhammar: Fantasies, Op. 11 (exc); Beethoven: Bagatelles (exc); Scriabin: Poèmes, Op. 32 (exc); Falla: Amor Brujo (exc); Chopin: Nocturnes (exc); Preludes (exc). (R. Pöntinen)

ⓘ **BIS-CD311** (4/87)
Sibelius: Orchestral Works
Sibelius: Symphony 7; Valse triste; Nightride and Sunrise; Scenes with cranes; Canzonetta; Valse romantique. (Gothenburg SO/N. Järvi)

ⓘ **BIS-CD312** (6/87)
Sibelius: Orchestral Works
Sibelius: Pohjola's Daughter; Rakastava; Tapiola; Andante lirico. (Gothenburg SO/N. Järvi)

ⓘ **BIS-CD314** (4/87)
Sibelius: Choral Works
Sibelius: Origin of Fire; Finnish Jaeger Battalion March; Have you courage?; Song of the Athenians; Academic March; Finlandia. (S. Tiilikainen, Laulun Ystävät Male Ch, Gothenburg SO/N. Järvi)

ⓘ **BIS-CD316** (11/87)
J. van Oortmerssen - Organ Recital
Du Caurroy: Dixiesme Fantasie; Guilain: Pièces d'orgue (exc); Balbastre: Noëls en variations (exc); Noëls en variations (exc); Boëly: Offertoire; Anon: Batalha de 6. Tom; Cancion; Mestres: Toccata sexto tono; Cantabile Amoroso; Toccata pastoril; Carrera y Lanchares: Versos. (J. van Oortmerssen)

ⓘ **BIS-CD317** (4/87)
Satie: Piano Works
Satie: Gnossiennes; Embryons desséchés; Avant-dernières pensées; Pièces froides; Sonatine bureaucratique; Gymnopédies; Véritables préludes flasques; Valses du précieux dégoûté; Sarabandes (exc). (R. Pöntinen)

ⓘ **BIS-CD321** (8/86)
Nielsen—Orchestral Works
Nielsen: Symphony 3; Clarinet Concerto; Maskarade (exc). (P. Raanoja, K. Skram, O. Schill, Gothenburg SO/Myung-Whun Chung)

ⓘ **BIS-CD325** (6/87)
Mussorgsky: Orchestral & Vocal Works
Mussorgsky: Pictures; Night on the Bare Mountain; Songs and Dances of Death. (M. Talvela, Finnish RSO/L. Segerstam/N. Järvi)

ⓘ **BIS-CD327** (11/87)
Baroque Music for Lute & Guitar
Kellner: Auserlesene Lauten-Stücke (exc); Visée: Suite in D minor; Bach: Prelude, BWV999; Fugue, BWV1000; Anon: Balcarres Lute Book (exc); Roncalli: Sonata 8; Weiss: Suite II in F; Tombeau sur la mort de M. Comte de Logy. (J. Lindberg, J. Lindberg)

ⓘ **BIS-CD337** (11/88)
Tubin: Orchestral Works
Tubin: Double Bass Concerto; Valse triste; Ballade; Violin Concerto 2; Estonian Dance Suite. (G. Garcia, H. Ehrén, Gothenburg SO/N. Järvi)

ⓘ **BIS-CD341** (12/86)
Music for lutes
Terzi: Canzone a otto voci; Pacolini: Passemezzo di zorzi; Passemezzo milanese; Passemezzo della battaglia; Anon: Temprar potess'io; Piccinini: Canzone a tre liutti; Lassus: Madonna mia pietà; Rore: Amor, se cosi dolce; R. Johnson II: Masque Dances; Parsons: Songe called Trumpetts; Vallet: Suite; Waelrant: Als ich u vinde; O villanella. (J. Lindberg, R. Meunier, N. North, P. O'Dette, E. Van Evera, P. Elliott, A. King, R. Wistreich, D. Miller, M. Nichols, R. Covey-Crump, P. Long, J.L. Nixon, Ens/R. Goodman)

ⓘ **BIS-CD343/4** (10/91)
Bach: Organ Works, Vol.4
Bach: Prelude and Fugue, BWV539; Wo soll ich fliehen hin, BWV694; Christ lag in Todesbanden, BWV695; Durch Adam's Fall, BWV705; Fantasia con imitacione, BWV563; Concertos, BWV592-7 (exc); Aria, BWV587; Prelude and Fugue, BWV536; Christum wir sollen loben schon, BWV696; Gelobet seist du, BWV697; Herr Christ, der einig Gottes SOhn, BWV698; Nun komm, der Heiden Heiland, BWV699; Vom Himmel hoch, BWV701; Gottes Sohn, BWV703; Lob sei dem allmächtigen Gott, BWV704; Fugue, BWV576; Pastorale, BWV590; O Gott, du frommer Gott, BWV767; Liebster Jesu, BWV706; Ich hab' mein' Sach' Gott, BWV707; Herr Jesu Christ, BWV709; Trio Sonatas, BWV525-530 (exc); Prelude and Fugue, BWV541; Trio, BWV586; Vom Himmel hoch, BWV700; Das Jesulein soll doch mein Trost, BWV702; Wir Christenleut, BWV710; Toccata, Adagio and Fugue, BWV564. (H. Fagius)

ⓘ **BIS-CD345** (9/87)
Crusell: Clarinet Concertos
Crusell: Clarinet Concerto 1; Clarinet Concerto 2; Clarinet Concerto 3. (K. Leister, Lahti SO/O. Vänskä)

ⓘ **BIS-CD347** (11/87)
Svendsen—Orchestral Works
Svendsen: Symphony 1; Symphony 2; Swedish Folk Tunes. (Gothenburg SO/N. Järvi)

ⓘ **BIS-CD348** (8/88)
The Winter Trombone
Vivaldi: Concerti, Op. 8 (exc); Milhaud: Concertino d'hiver; Larsson: Trombone Concertino, Op. 45/7; Telemann: Oboe Concerto 2; Pöntinen: Blå Vinter. (C. Lindberg, New Stockholm CO/O. Kamu)

ⓘ **BIS-CD351** (8/88)
Tubin: Orchestral Works
Tubin: Symphony 1; Balalaika Concerto; Music for Strings. (E. Sheynkman, Swedish RSO/N. Järvi)

ⓘ **BIS-CD352** (9/87)
Bernstein: Piano Arrangements
Bernstein: West Side Story Symphonic Dances; Fancy Free; Touches. (D. Achatz)

ⓘ **BIS-CD353** (8/88)
Beethoven: Piano Works.
Beethoven: Variations, Op. 35; Bagatelles (exc); Piano Sonata 12. (R. Pöntinen)

ⓘ **BIS-CD358** (2/88)
The Russian Viola
Rubinstein: Pieces, Op. 11/2 (exc); Glinka: Viola Sonata; Glazunov: Elégie, Op. 44; Stravinsky: Elegy; Shostakovich: Viola Sonata. (N. Imai, R. Pöntinen)

ⓘ **BIS-CD359** (10/87)
Sibelius—Orchestral Works
Sibelius: Swanwhite (exc); Belshazzar's Feast (exc); Dryad; Dance intermezzo; Pan and Echo. (Gothenburg SO/N. Järvi)

ⓘ **BIS-CD364** (4/88)
The Russian Viola
Shostakovich: Violin Sonata, Op. 134; Stravinsky: Duo concertant (exc); Schnittke: Violin Sonata 1. (C. Bergqvist, R. Pöntinen)

ⓘ **BIS-CD366** (4/88)
Sibelius: Piano Transcriptions, Vol.1
Sibelius: Karelia Suite; Wood Nymph; Finlandia; King Christian II (exc); Have you courage?; Song of the Athenians; Valse triste; Dryad; Dance intermezzo; Pelleas and Melisande. (E.T. Tawaststjerna)

ⓘ **BIS-CD367** (4/88)
Sibelius—Piano Transcriptions, Vol. 2
Sibelius: Belshazzar's Feast (Cpte); Bell Melody; Scaramouche; Finnish Jaeger Battalion March; Scout March; Valse lyrique; Autrefois; Valse chevaleresque; Suite mignonne; Suite champêtre; Suite caractéristique; Tempest Suites. (E.T. Tawaststjerna)

ⓘ **BIS-CD368** (4/88)
Mozart: Works for Flute and Orchestra
Mozart: Flute Concerto, K313; Flute Concerto, K314;

Andante, K315; Rondo, KAnh184. (M. Helasvuo, Ostrobothnian CO/J. Kangas)

ⓘ **BIS-CD372** (1/89)
Sibelius: Orchestral Works
Sibelius: Violin Concerto; Overture in A minor; Menuetto; In memoriam. (S. Marcovici, Gothenburg SO/N. Järvi)

ⓘ **BIS-CD377** (4/88)
Schnittke: Concertos
Schnittke: Concerto Grosso 1; Oboe and Harp Concerto; Piano Concerto. (C. Bergqvist, P. Swedrup, R. Pöntinen, H. Jahren, K.A. Lier, New Stockholm CO/L. Markiz)

ⓘ **BIS-CD383** (7/88)
Works for Male Chorus
Traditional: Hey, let's carouse; In our meadow; Peterson-Berger: On the fell in sunshine; Söderman: Peasant wedding (exc); Wikander: King Lily of the Valley; Bartók: Old Hungarian Folksongs, Sz50; Tormis: Songs of Hamlet; Suchoň: Slovakian Folksongs, J; N. David: Wir zogen in das Feld; R. Strauss: Männerchöre (1935) (exc); Reger: An das Meer; Barber: Stopwatch; Bossi: Brivido; Milhaud: Psaumes de David (exc); Saint-Saëns: Saltarelle; Verdi: Trovatore (exc); Gounod: Faust (exc). (Orphei Drängar Ch, Swedish RSO/E. Ericson/L. Segerstam)

ⓘ **BIS-CD384** (1/89)
Sibelius: Orchestral Works
Sibelius: Spring Song; Bard; Valse lyrique; Autrefois; Valse chevaleresque; Suite mignonne; Suite champêtre; Suite caractéristique; Presto. (M. Einarson, C. Forsberg, Gothenburg SO/N. Järvi)

ⓘ **BIS-CD387** (9/88)
Schubert: Orchestral Works
Schubert: Symphony 5; Symphony 6; Overture, D591. (Stockholm Sinfonietta/N. Järvi)

ⓘ **BIS-CD388** (10/89)
Solitary Trombone
Berio: Sequenza V; Xenakis: Keren; Kagel: Atem; Eliasson: Disegno; Cage: Sliding Trombone; Stockhausen: In Freundschaft. (C. Lindberg)

ⓘ **BIS-CD389** (2/89)
Music from the time of Christian IV, Vol. 1
Anon: Danish Mass; Bertolusi: Ego fios campi; Mancinus: Cantio Nova; Pedersen: Mass; Schattenberg: Amor Jesu dulcissimus; Jesu decus Angelicum; Jesu tua dilectio; O Jesu mi dulcissime. (Hilliard Ens/P. Hillier)

ⓘ **BIS-CD390** (2/89)
Music from the time of Christian IV, Vol. 2
Orologio: Intrada XXI; Intrada V; Intrada I; Intrada XIX; Borchgrevinck: Paduana and Galliard; Gistou: Paduana and Galliard; Greebe: Paduana and Galliard; Ørm: Pavana; Huet: Fantasia Graegorii; Anon: Petrus Fabricus Lutebook (exc); Dowland: Prelude, P102; Fantasies (exc); Jigs, Corantos, Toys, etc (exc); Brade: Paduana and Galliard; T. Simpson: Opus newer Paduanen (exc); Foucart: Courentes. (J. Lindberg, Royal Danish Brass, Dowland Consort, J. Lindberg (lte/dir))

ⓘ **BIS-CD391** (2/89)
Music from the time of Christian IV, Vol. 3
Dowland: Second Booke of Songs (exc); Scheidemann: Englische Mascarada; Schildt: Gleich wie das Feuer; Paduana Lacrymae; Terkelsen: Hylas does not want to get married; Daphnis' worried thoughts; Coridon's Lament; Myrtillo's Lament; Daphnis begs his Galathee; To know a faithful heart; Very sorrowful Daphnis; Drinking Song; Voigtländer: Als er guten Bescheid; Sommerliedlein. (R. Covey-Crump, U. Cold, J. Lindberg, L.U. Mortensen)

ⓘ **BIS-CD392** (2/89)
Music from the time of Christian IV, Vol. 4
Pedersen: Madrigals, Book 2 (exc); G. Gabrieli: Amor s'e in lei con honestate; A. Gabrieli: In nobil sangue; Luzzaschi: T'amo mia vita; H. Nielsen: T'amo mia vita; Pedersen: T'amo mia vita; Dering: T'amo mia vita; Borchgrevinck: Baci amorosi e cari; Aagesen: Crudel, lascia sto core; Gistou: Quel Augellin che canta; Brachrogge: Io ardo in vivo foco; Vecchi: Tindola, non dormire. (Consort of Musicke, A. Rooley (lte/dir))

ⓘ **BIS-CD395** (11/89)
Alfvén: Orchestral Works
Alfvén: Symphony 1; Drapa; Upsala-rapsodi; Revelation Cantata (exc). (Stockholm PO/N. Järvi)

ⓘ **BIS-CD399** (10/89)
La Serenissima I
Dalza: Alla venetiana; Spinacino: Adieu mes amours; Recercare; Crema: Recercar sexto; Recercar quinto; Saltarello ditto la bertoncina; Saltarello ditto el giorgio; Capirola: Capirola Lutebook (exc); Milano: Fantasias (exc); Ricercars (exc); Crema: Recercar decimoquinto; Mon amy; Entre mes bras; Spinacino: Bassadans; Dalza: Alla ferrarese. (J. Lindberg)

① **BIS-CD697** (11/95)
Schnittke—Chamber Works
Schnittke: Piano trio (1992); Praeludium; Stille Musik; A Paganini; Madrigal (exc); Moz-Art. (O. Krysa, A. Fischer, T. Thedéen, T. Tchekina)

① **BIS-CD703** (10/95)
Schoenberg—Music for Strings
Schoenberg: Verklärte Nacht; String Quartet 2; Chamber Symphony 1. (C. Högman, Tapiola Sinfonietta/J-J. Kantorow)

① **BIS-CD710** (11/95)
Gubaidulina—Chamber Works
Gubaidulina: Silenzio; In Erwartung; De profundis; Et expecto. (G. Draugsvoll, A. B. Møller, H. Brendstrup, Raschèr Sax Qt, Kroumata Perc Ens)

① **BIS-CD722/4** (11/95)
Dowland—Complete Solo Lute Music
Dowland: Almains (exc); Ballad Settings (exc); Fantasies (exc); Galliards (exc); Jigs, Corantos, Toys, etc. (exc); Pavans (exc); Sir Henry Guilforde's Almaine; Preludium; Come away, P60; Mounsier's Almain; Pavans (Mylius 1622). (J. Lindberg)

Bluebell

① **ABCD006** (8/88)
Jussi Björling Live - Holland 1939, Norway 1954
Verdi: Requiem (exc); *Meyerbeer:* Africaine (exc); *Bizet:* Carmen (exc); *Massenet:* Manon (exc); *Gounod:* Faust (exc); *Puccini:* Bohème (exc); *Handel:* Serse (exc); *Niedermeyer:* Pietà, Signore; *Verdi:* Requiem (exc); *Alfvén:* Songs, Op. 28 (exc); *Sibelius:* Songs, Op.36 (exc); *Grieg:* Melodies of the Heart, Op. 5 (exc); Songs, Op.25 (exc). (J. Björling, Hilversum RO/F. Weissmann, Bergen SO/C. Garaguly)

① **ABCD009** (6/92)
Birgit Nilsson live in Stockholm
R. Strauss: Vier letzte Lieder; *Sibelius:* Songs, Op.17 (exc); Songs, Op.37 (exc); Songs, Op.13 (exc); *R. Strauss:* Lieder, Op. 27 (exc); Lieder, Op. 10 (exc); Lieder, Op. 41 (exc); *Frumerie:* Songs of the Heart, Op.27 (exc); *Rangström:* Girl under the New Moon; Amazon; *Grieg:* Songs, Op.60 (exc); Songs, Op.25 (exc); Songs, Op.48 (exc); *Melartin:* Twenty years; *Sieczyriski:* Wien, du Stadt meiner Träume. (B. Nilsson, Swedish RSO/L. Segerstam, G. Parsons)

① **ABCD016** (8/92)
Jussi Björling—Rare Records & Alternative Takes
Borodin: Prince Igor (exc); *Dahl:* Bacchanal; *Nyblom:* Flaming Golden Stream; *O. Thiel:* Was it a dream?; *Enders:* Little Princess; *J. Strauss II:* Zigeunerbaron (exc); *Millöcker:* Bettelstudent (exc); *Offenbach:* Belle Hélène (exc); *Rossini:* Stabat mater (exc); *Verdi:* Trovatore (exc); Rigoletto (exc); *Mascagni:* Cavalleria rusticana (exc); *Gounod:* Roméo et Juliette (exc); *Foster:* Jeanie with the light brown hair; *Hardelot:* Because; *Puccini:* Manon Lescaut (exc); *Mascagni:* Cavalleria rusticana (exc); *Gounod:* Roméo et Juliette (exc); *Traditional:* In Heaven; God's innocent Lamb; *Beneken:* Oh, how peacefully; *Wennerberg:* Psalm 4. (J. Björling, H. Schymberg, A-L. Björling, orch/N. Grevillius/S. Waldimir, Stockholm Royal Orch, Stockholm Concert Soc Orch, Inst Ens)

① **ABCD028** (3/92)
Jussi Björling live at the Stockholm Opera
Puccini: Manon Lescaut (exc); *Mascagni:* Cavalleria Rusticana (exc); *Leoncavallo:* Pagliacci (exc). (H. Schymberg, J. Björling, H. Hasslo, B. Lundborg, A. Nordmo-Løvberg, B. Björling, M. Sehlmark, G. Svedenbrant, R. Moberg, Stockholm Royal Op Chor, Stockholm Royal Op Orch/N. Grevillius/K. Bendix/L. Gardelli)

BNL

① **BNL112742** (8/90)
Vierne: 24 Pièces de fantaisie
Vierne: Suite 1; Suite 2; Suite 3; Suite 4. (O. Latry)

① **BNL112753** (10/89)
Lübeck: Organ Works
Lübeck: Prelude and Fugue in D minor; Prelude and Fugue in C minor; Prelude and Fugue in G minor; Ich ruf zu dir; Prelude and Fugue in E; Prelude and Fugue in G minor; Nun lasst uns Gott; Prelude and Fugue in F; Prelude and Fugue in G. (B. Coudurier)

① **BNL112754** (10/89)
Bruhns & Hanff: Organ Works
Bruhns: Prelude in G; Prelude and Fugue in E minor I; Nun komm der Heiden Heiland; Prelude and Fugue in G minor; Prelude and Fugue in E minor II; *Hanff:*

Ach Gott, von Himmel sieh darein; Auf meinen lieben Gott; Ein feste Burg; Erbarm dich mein, o Herre Gott I; Erbarm dich mein, o Herre Gott II; Helft mir Gott's Güte preisen; Wär Gott nicht mit uns diese Zeit. (B. Coudurier)

① **BNL112768** (10/90)
Litaize: Organ Works
Litaize: Cortège (1951); Lied; Scherzo; Epiphanie; Jeux de rhythmes; Prélude et Danse Fuguée; Prélude liturgique; Pentecôte. (O. Latry, D. Comtet, Paris St Maur CNR Brass Ens)

Bongiovanni

① **GB1043-2** (12/94)
Italian Baritones of the Acoustic Era
Verdi: Rigoletto (exc); *Leoncavallo:* Roland von Berlin (exc); *Verdi:* Forza del destino (exc); *Petrella:* Jone (exc); *Donizetti:* Elisir d'amore (exc); *Robaudi:* Alla stella confidente; *Tirindelli:* Mistica; *Marchetti:* Ruy Blas (exc); *Gastaldon:* Musica proibita; Ti vorrei rapire; *Donizetti:* Favorita (exc); *Massenet:* Hérodiade (exc); *Tirindelli:* Myosotis; *Verdi:* Aida (exc); Forza del destino (exc); Forza del destino (exc); *Bizet:* Carmen (exc); *A. Thomas:* Hamlet (exc); *Gounod:* Faust (exc). (F.M. Bonini, F. Corradetti, T. Parvis, G. Bellantoni, G. Campanari, L. Montesanto, G. Viviani, E. Badini, G.M. Patti, N. Fusati, A. de Revers, L. Mellerio, anon, orch, anon)

① **GB2115-2** (1/94)
Ponchielli—Orchestral Works
Ponchielli: Garibaldi Elegia; Sinfonia; Sinfonia; Scena campestre; Lituani (exc); Promessi sposi (exc); Gavotte poudrée. (Minsk PO/S. Frontalini)

① **GB2513-2** (10/94)
Mariella Devia—Opera Arias
Bellini: Capuleti (exc); Sonnambula (exc); Puritani (exc); *Donizetti:* Lucia di Lammermoor (exc); *Gounod:* Roméo et Juliette (exc); *G. Charpentier:* Louise (exc); *Delibes:* Lakmé (exc). (M. Devia, Svizzera Italiana Orch/M. Rota)

① **GB5523/5-2** (5/95)
Torelli—Complete Works for 1, 2, 4 Trumpets & Orchestra
Torelli: Suonata, G1; Sinfonia, G2; Sonata, G3; Sinfonia, G4; Sonata, G5; Sonata, G6; Sonata, G7; Sinfonia, G8; Sinfonia, G9; Sinfonia, G10; Sinfonia, G11; Sonata, G13; Sinfonia, G15; Sinfonia, G16; Sinfonia, G17; Concerto con trombe, G18; Sinfonia, G19; Sinfonia, G20; Sinfonia, G21; Sinfonia, G22; Sinfonia, G23; Concerto con due trombe, G24; Sonata, G25; Sinfonia, G26; Concerto con trombe, G27; Sinfonia, G29; Sinfonia, G30; Sinfonia, G31; Concerto con trombe, G32; Sinfonia, G33. (San Petronio Cappella Musicale Orch/S. Vartolo)

① **GB5544/5-2** (5/95)
Palestrina—Messe mantovane
Palestrina: Missa in festis Apostolorum I; Missa in festis Apostolorum II; Missa Sine Nomine a 5; Missa in Semiduplicibus Maioribus I; Missa in Semiduplicibus Maioribus II. (San Petronio Cappella Musicale Sols/S. Vartolo, Nova Schola Gregoriana/A. Turco)

Bridge

① **BCD9001** (1/87)
Aleck Karis piano recital
Carter: Night Fantasies; *Chopin:* Fantasie, Op. 49; *Schumann:* Carnaval. (A. Karis)

① **BCD9014** (2/90)
Elliott Carter: Vocal Works
Carter: Frost Poems; Mirror on which to dwell; Syringa; In sleep, in thunder. (P. Mason, Speculum Musicae, C. Schadeberg/D. Starobin/D. Palma, Katherine Ciesinski, J. Opalach/W. Purvis, J. Garrison/R. Black)

① **BCD9027** (7/92)
Rodrigo—Piano Works
Rodrigo: Piano Suite; Preludio al gallo mañanero; Zarabanda lejana; Pastorale (1926); Bagatela; Serenata española; Sonada de adiós; Danzas de España; Danza de la Amapola; Evocaciones; Preludio de Añoranza; Sonatas of Castille; Berceuse de primavera; Berceuse de Otoño; Air de Ballet; Album de Cecilia; A l'ombre de Torre Bermeja; Piezas (1938); Estampas andaluzas; Piezas Infantiles; Sonatina para dos Muñecas; Gran Marcha de los Subsecretarios; Atardecer. (G. Allen, A. Nel)

① **BCD9029** (3/92)
Giuliani—Solo Guitar Music
Giuliani: Grande Ouverture, Op. 61; Leçons Progressives, Op. 51 (exc); Variations, Op. 20; Préludes, Op. 83 (exc); Rondeaux Progressives, Op. 14 (exc); Choix de mes Fleurs, Op. 46 (exc); Bagatelles, Op. 73 (exc); Etude, Op. 100/13; Variations, Op. 101. (D. Starobin)

① **BCD9031** (11/92)
J. Harvey—Miscellaneous Works
J. Harvey: From Silence; Natajara; Ritual Melodies. (K. Bennett, H. Starreveld, L.C. Stoltzman, M. Thompson, D. Anderson, R. Eckhardt, K. Supové, J. MacDonald, D. Dabby, D. Atherton, B. Koeppel, K. Malsky, P. Sohn/B. Vercoe)

① **BCD9037** (5/93)
Ruders—Chamber Works
Ruders: Psalmodies; Vox in Rama; Nightshade. (D. Starobin, Speculum Musicae/D. Palma, Capricorn/O. Knussen)

① **BCD9039** (12/95)
The Great Regondi, Vol. 1
Regondi: Morceau de Concert, Op. 12; Serenade in A; Etudes. (D. Starobin, D. Rogers, J. Lustman)

① **BCD9044** (12/94)
Elliott Carter—Eight Compositions (1948-1993)
Carter: Gra; Enchanted Preludes; Duo; Scrivo in Vento; Changes; Con Leggerezza Pensosa; Riconoscenza; Cello Sonata. (Group for Contemporary Music)

① **BCD9045** (10/94)
Benedict Mason—Chamber and Orchestral Works
B. Mason: String Quartet 1; Double Concerto; Self-Referential Songs. (C. Whittlesey, M. Thompson, D. Purser, Arditti Qt, London Sinfonietta/D. Masson, Modern Ens/I. Metzmacher)

① **BCD9051** (3/95)
Stravinsky—Piano Works
Stravinsky: Petrushka; Valse; Ragtime; Piano-Rag Music; Cinq doigts; Piano Sonata (1924); Serenade in A; Tango; Circus Polka; Three Easy Pieces. (A. Karis, R. Lubin)

① **BCD9055** (12/95)
The Great Regondi, Vol. 2
Regondi: As slow upon the shades of night; Avviso; Absence; Tell me heart!; Leisure moments (exc); Introduction and Caprice, Op. 23; Remembrance; Rêverie nocturne, Op. 19. (D'A. Fortunato, D. Rogers, D. Starobin, J. Lustman)

British Music Label

① **BML001** (2/94)
Bernard van Dieren Collection
Van Dieren: Songs (1917); Wer zum erstenmale liebt; Wenn ich auf dem Lager liege; Und wüssten's die Blumen; Mädchenlied; Asra; Ich wandelte unter den Bäumen; Mit deinen blauen Augen; Mir träumte von einem Königskind; Roses étaient toutes rouges; Spring Song; Harp Estemporales; Violin Sonata; Piccolo Pralinudettino Fridato; Sonata tyroica. (L. Andrew, C. Nicholls, S. Goossens, Philip Thomas, E. Davies, J. Ayerst, Emperor Qt)

① **BML012** (12/95)
Songs from the Exotic
N. Hayes: Basket; *Hallgrimsson:* Syrpa; *Weir:* Exotic songs (on the rocks); *Finnissy:* Beuk o' Newcassel Sangs; *G. Jackson:* French Song; *S. Harrison:* Nara ki itou; *Crane:* Balanescu; *A. Fisher:* Leviathan; *Skempton:* Colomen. (Tapestry)

British Music Society

① **BMS416CD** (3/94)
Berkeley—Music for Solo Piano and Piano Duets
L. Berkeley: Piano Sonata, Op. 20; Preludes, Op. 23; Short Pieces, Op. 4; Palm Court Waltz; Sonatina, Op. 39; Variations, Op. 73. (R. Terroni, N. Beedie)

Cala

① **CACD0101** (3/87)
Orchestral works
Wagner: Lohengrin (exc); *Tchaikovsky:* Violin Concerto; *Beethoven:* Symphony 5; *Rossini:* Guillaume Tell (exc); *Debussy:* Après-midi; *Paganini:* Moses in Egypt Variations; *Gershwin:* Rhapsody in Blue; *Vaughan Williams:* Greensleeves Fantasia; *Rimsky-Korsakov:* Capriccio espagnol. (N. Shkolnikova, G. Karr, J. Tocco, Philh, LSO/G. Simon)

① **CACD0104** (9/95)
The London Cello Sound
Balcombe: Greensleeves Suite; *Bernstein:* West Side Story (exc); *Casals:* Sardana; *Rachmaninov:* Songs, Op. 34 (exc); *Saint-Saëns:* Carnaval des animaux (exc). (LPO Vcs, RPO Vcs, BBC SO Vcs, Philh Vcs/G. Simon)

① **CACD1001** (5/91)
Debussy—Orchestral Works, Vol.1
Debussy: La Mer; Première rapsodie; Petite Suite; Suite

bergamasque (exc); Arabesques; Préludes (exc); Estampes (exc). (J. Campbell, Philh/G. Simon)

ⓘ **CACD1002** (5/91)
Debussy—Orchestral Works, Vol.2
Debussy: Nocturnes; Isle joyeuse; Estampes (exc); Tarantelle styrienne; Préludes (exc); Préludes (exc); Children's Corner. (Philh Chor, Philh/G. Simon)

ⓘ **CACD1004** (11/91)
Ravel—Orchestral Works, Vol.1
Ravel: La Valse; Miroirs (exc); Tzigane; Ma Mère l'oye (exc); Jeux d'eau; Mélodies populaires grecques; Boléro. (S. Chase, S. Burgess, Philh/G. Simon)

ⓘ **CACD1005** (11/91)
Ravel—Orchestral Works, Vol.2
Ravel: Rapsodie espagnole; Gaspard de la nuit (exc); Enfant et les sortilèges (exc); Piano Concerto; Pavane; Pièce en forme de habanera; Daphnis et Chloé Suites (exc). (H. de Vries, G. Mok, Philh/G. Simon)

ⓘ **CACD1007** (3/93)
Respighi—Orchestral Works
Respighi: Ballad of the Gnomes; Adagio con variazioni; Botticelli Pictures; Organ Suite. (A. Baillie, L. Pearson, Philh/G. Simon)

ⓘ **CACD1010** (2/93)
Bliss—Choral and Orchestral Works
Bliss: Morning Heroes; Investiture Antiphonal Fanfare (1969); Prayer of St. Francis of Assisi. (B. Blessed, East London Chor, Harlow Chor, E. Herts Chor, LPO/M. Kibblewhite)

ⓘ **CACD1011** (3/94)
Borodin—Orchestral Works
Borodin: Prince Igor (exc); String Quartet 2 (exc); In the Steppes of Central Asia; Petite Suite; Requiem. (M. Field, I. Boughton, BBC Sym Chor, S. Chase, Philh/G. Simon)

ⓘ **CACD1012** (11/93)
Mussorgsky—Orchestral Works
Mussorgsky: Night on the Bare Mountain; Fair at Sorochintsí (exc); Pictures; On the southern shore of the Crimea; Khovanshchina (exc); From my tears; Scherzo in B flat. (T. Ungár, Philh/G. Simon)

ⓘ **CACD1014** (12/93)
Mozart—Orchestral Works
Mozart: Violin Concerto, K216; Violin Concerto, K219; Sinfonia Concertante, K364. (S. Chase, R. Chase, Hanover Band/R. Goodman)

ⓘ **CACD1017** (2/95)
French Chamber Music for Woodwinds, Volume 1
Debussy: Saxophone rapsodie; Syrinx; Première rapsodie; Sonata for Flute, Viola and Harp; Petit nègre; Petite pièce; Saxophone rapsodie; *Saint-Saëns:* Odelette; Clarinet Sonata; Feuillet d'album, Op.81; Bassoon Sonata; Caprice, Op.79; Oboe Sonata; Romance, Op.37; Tarantelle, Op.6. (W. Bennett, N. Daniel, J. Campbell, D. Campbell, R. Gough, R. Kennard, R. Maskell, R. Watkins, S. Haram, R. Tapping, C. Benson, J. Drake, J. York, I. Jones, N. Daniel)

ⓘ **CACD1018** (2/95)
French Chamber Music for Woodwinds, Volume 2
Ravel: Introduction and Allegro; Pièce en forme de habanera; *Poulenc:* Oboe Sonata; Invitation au château; Villanelle; 2-Clarinet Sonata; Piano, Oboe and Bassoon Trio; Sextet; Clarinet and Bassoon Sonata; Rapsodie nègre; Clarinet Sonata; Mouvements perpétuels; Flute Sonata. (P. Sidhom, W. Bennett, N. Daniel, J. Campbell, D. Campbell, R. Gough, R. Watkins, I. Jones, P. Carter, C. West, C. Benson, J. Drake, J. York, Allegri Qt, J. Elias, J. Guter, R. Tapping, B. Schrecker)

ⓘ **CACD1019** (5/95)
Sirmen—String Quartets
Sirmen: String Quartet 1; String Quartet 2; String Quartet 3; String Quartet 4; String Quartet 5; String Quartet 6. (Allegri Qt)

ⓘ **CACD77001** (12/95)
Black Angels
Crumb: Black Angels; *Webern:* String Quartet, Op. 28; *Lutosławski:* String Quartet (1964). (Cikada Qt)

Calig

ⓘ **CAL50940** (11/95)
Glazunov—Works for String Orchestra
Glazunov: Suite, Op. 35; Elegy, Op. 105; Prelude and Fugue (Fridays); Vendredis; Various: Variations on a Russian Folk Song. (Amati Ens/A. Balogh)

Calliope

ⓘ **CAL6623** (11/95)
Tallis/Whyte—Sacred Choral Music
Tallis: Mass a 7; Suscipe quaeso Dominus; Salvator mundi Domine; *Whyte:* Regina coeli; Portio mea Domine; Domine quis habitavit; Christe qui lux es et dies III. (Clerkes of Oxenford/D. Wulstan)

ⓘ **CAL6648** (11/95)
Beethoven—Piano Sonatas
Beethoven: Piano Sonata 30; Piano Sonata 31; Piano Sonata 32. (I. Södergren)

ⓘ **CAL6698** (11/95)
Haydn/Boccherini/ Mendelssohn/Mica—Quartets
Haydn: String Quartets, Op.74 (exc); *Mendelssohn:* String Quartet 2; *F.A. Mica II:* String Quartet 6; *Boccherini:* String Quartets, G242-7 (exc). (Talich Qt)

ⓘ **CAL9204** (9/88)
Granados: Transcriptions for Guitar Duo
Granados: Danzas españolas (exc); Moresque; Capricho español; Goyescas (exc); Valses poéticos; Danzas caracteristica; Rapsodia aragonesa; Tonadillas (exc). (J. Horreaux, J-M. Tréhard)

ⓘ **CAL9206** (8/88)
Czech Piano Music
Janáček: Along an Overgrown Path (exc); *Smetana:* Polkas, B94; Polkas, B95; Souvenirs de Bohème. (R. Kvapil)

ⓘ **CAL9211** (9/88)
Clara Schumann: Piano Works
C. Schumann: Preludes and fugues, Op.16; Romances, Op.21; *R.Schumann* Variations; Pièces, Op. 15 (exc); Romance in B minor; Romances, Op.11; Romances, Op.22. (H. Boschi, A. Jodry)

ⓘ **CAL9245** (11/93)
Mozart—Complete String Quartets, Vol.5
Mozart: String Quartet, K589; String Quartet, K590; Adagio and Fugue, K546. (Talich Qt)

ⓘ **CAL9611** (12/89)
Gibbons: Sacred Choral Works
Gibbons: Praise the Lord, O my soul; Lord, we beseech thee; O clap your hands; Now shall the praises of the Lord; Lord, I will sing to Thee; Lord, thy answer I did hear; Thy beauty, Israel, is gone; O Lord of Hosts; O Lord in thy wrath; I am the resurrection; Come, kiss me with those lips of thine; O my love, how comely now; When one among the Twelve there was; Song of joy unto the Lord we sing; Who's this, that leaning on her friend; How sad and solitary now; Sing praises Is'rel to the Lord; Now in the Lord my heart doth pleasure take; See, see, the word is incarnate; Hosanna to the son of David; Sing unto the Lord; Blessed are all they; O Lord, how do my woes increase; Preces and Psalm 145; O Lord, I lift my heart to thee. (Clerkes of Oxenford/D. Wulstan)

ⓘ **CAL9628** (7/87)
Mozart—Chamber Works
Mozart: Clarinet Quintet, K581; Violin Sonata, K481; Violin Sonata, K376. (B. Zahradník, Talich Qt, P. Messiereur, S. Bogunia)

ⓘ **CAL9633/9** (1/89)
Beethoven: Complete String Quartets
Beethoven: String Quartet 1; String Quartet 2; String Quartet 3; String Quartet 4; String Quartet 5; String Quartet 6; String Quartet 7; String Quartet 8; String Quartet 9; String Quartet 10; String Quartet 11; String Quartet 12; String Quartet 13; String Quartet 14; String Quartet 15; String Quartet 16; Grosse Fuge. (Talich Qt)

ⓘ **CAL9635** (3/87)
Beethoven—String Quartets
Beethoven: String Quartet 11; String Quartet 12; Grosse Fuge. (Talich Qt)

ⓘ **CAL9650** (1/91)
Schumann: Piano Works
Schumann: Kinderszenen; Carnaval; Symphonic Studies II. (I. Södergren)

ⓘ **CAL9685** (5/90)
Liszt: Piano Works
Liszt: Piano Sonata, S178; Lugubre gondola, S200; Bagatelle sans tonalité, S216a; Nuages gris, S199; Am Grabe Richard Wagners, S202; En rêve, S207; Lieder, S558 (exc); Csárdás, S225 (exc). (M. Rudy)

ⓘ **CAL9690** (10/88)
Smetana—Chamber and Instrumental Works
Smetana: String Quartet 1; String Quartet 2; Polkas, B94; Polkas, B95; Souvenirs de Bohème (exc). (Talich Qt, R. Kvapil)

ⓘ **CAL9692** (2/89)
Scriabin: Piano Works
Scriabin: Piano Sonata 8; Piano Sonata 9; Piano Sonata 10; Etudes, Op.65; Preludes, Op.67; Poèmes, Op.69; Poèmes, Op.71; Vers la flamme; Danses, Op.73; Preludes, Op.74. (M. Rudy)

ⓘ **CAL9699** (4/89)
Janáček—Chamber and Piano Works
Janáček: String Quartet 1; String Quartet 2; Along an Overgrown Path (exc). (R. Kvapil, Talich Qt)

ⓘ **CAL9703/17(1)** (2/93)
Bach—Complete Organ Works (pt 1)
Bach: Prelude and Fugue, BWV531; Ach Herr, mich armen Sünder, BWV742; Allein Gott, BWV715; Neumeister Chorales, BWV1090-1120 (exc); Lobt Gott, BWV732; Fantasia and Fugue, BWV561; Vater unser im Himmelreich, BWV737; Vater unser im Himmelreich, BWV762; Herr Jesu Christ, BWV726; Christ lag in Todesbanden, BWV718; Gelobet seist du, BWV722; Auf meinen lieben Gott, BWV744; Prelude, BWV568; Fugue, BWV576; Wie schön leucht' der Morgenstern, BWV739; Pedal-Exercitium, BWV598; Prelude, BWV569; Gottes Sohn, BWV724; Fugue, BWV577; Erbarm' dich, BWV721; In dulci jubilo, BWV729; Fugue, BWV575; Auf meinen lieben Gott, BWV744; Allein Gott, BWV717; Allein Gott, BWV711; Prelude and Fugue, BWV549; Vom Himmel hoch, BWV738; Fugue, BWV131a; In dulci jubilo, BWV751; Ach Gott, vom Himmel, BWV741; Prelude and Fugue, BWV551; Partita, BWV766; Toccata, BWV566; Fantasia and Fugue, BWV904; Pastorale, BWV590; O Gott, du frommer Gott, BWV767; O Lamm Gottes; Nun freut euch, BWV734; Partita, SWV770; Valet will ich dir geben, BWV735; Prelude and Fugue, BWV550; Fugue, BWVAnh90. (A. Isoir)

ⓘ **CAL9703/17(2)** (2/93)
Bach—Complete Organ Works (pt 2)
Bach: Prelude and Fugue, BWV543; Allein Gott, BWV716; Das Jesulein soll doch mein Trost, BWV702; Fantasia, BWV572; Ich hab mein Sach Gott, BWV708; Ich hab' mein' Sach' Gott, BWV707; Ein Feste Burg, BWV720; Fugue, BWV579; Liebster Jesu, BWV731; Liebster Jesu, BWV730; Fugue, BWV574; Christus, der uns selig macht, BWV747; Allabreve, BWV589; Prelude and Fugue, BWV533; Meine Seele erhebt den Herren, BWV733; Prelude and Fugue, BWV532; Liebster jesu, BWV706; Christum wir sollen loben schon, BWV696; Prelude and Fugue, BWV534; Gottes Sohn, BWV703; Wo soll ich fliehen hin, BWV694; Wir glauben all an einen Gott, BWV765; Prelude and fugue, BWV535; Herr Christ, der einig Gottes Sohn, BWV698; Fantasia, BWV562; Nun komm, der Heiden Heiland, BWV699; Gelobet seist du, BWV697; Ach Gott und Herr, BWV714; Jesu, meine Freude, BWV713; Fantasia and Fugue, BWV537; Toccata and Fugue, BWV565; Toccata, adagio and Fugue, BWV564; Toccata and Fugue, BWV538; Toccata and Fugue, BWV540; Fantasia and fugue, BWV542; Concertos, BWV592-7 (exc); Liebster Jesu, BWV754; Fugue, BWV578; Fantasia con imitazione, BWV563; Canzona, BWV588; Passacaglia and Fugue, BWV582; Herr Jesu Christ, BWV709; Lob sei dem allmächtigen Gott, BWV704; Wer nur den lieben, BWV690; Wer nur den lieben, BWV691; Durch Adam's Fall, BWV705; Sei gegrüsset, BWV768; Vom Himmel hoch, BWV701; Trio, BWV584; Schübler Chorales, BWV645-650; Herr Christ, der einig' Gottes Sohn, BWVAnh55; Christ lag in Todesbanden, BWV695. (A. Isoir)

ⓘ **CAL9703/17(4)** (2/93)
Bach—Complete Organ Works (pt 4)
Bach: Prelude and Fugue, BWV548; Prelude and Fugue, BWV541; Prelude and Fugue, BWV544; Prelude and Fugue, BWV545; Trio, BWV583; Prelude and Fugue, BWV536; Trio Sonatas, BWV525-530; Prelude and Fugue, BWV536; Valet will ich dir geben, BWV736; Herzlich tut mich verlangen, BWV727; Chorales, BWV651-668 (exc); Preludes, BWV939-43 (exc); Jesus, meine Zuversicht, BWV728; Prelude and Fugue, BWV546; Trio, BWV1027a; Prelude and Fugue, BWV536; Prelude and Fugue, BWV552; Clavier-Übung III, BWV669-689 (exc). (A. Isoir)

ⓘ **CAL9703/17(5)** (2/93)
Bach—Complete Organ Works (pt 5)
Bach: Duets, BWV802-805; Vom Himmel Hoch Variations, BWV769; Prelude and Fugue, BWV543; Chorales, BWV651-668 (exc); Ricercar, BWV1079:5a. (A. Isoir)

ⓘ **CAL9710** (8/89)
Bach—Complete Works for Organ Vol 8
Bach: Passacaglia and Fugue, BWV582; Herr Jesu Christ, BWV709; Lob sei dem allmächtigen Gott, BWV704; Wer nur den lieben, BWV690; Wer nur den lieben, BWV691; Durch Adam's Fall, BWV705; Sei gegrüsset, BWV768; Vom Himmel hoch, BWV701; Trio, BWV584; Schübler Chorales, BWV645-650. (A. Isoir)

① CAL9828 (9/88)
Chabrier: Piano Works
Chabrier: Pièces pittoresques; Bourrée fantasque;
Impromptu; Marche des Cipayes; Air de Ballet; Pièces
posthumes (exc). (A. D'Arco)

① CAL9831/4 (8/88)
Debussy: Piano works
Debussy: Préludes; Images; Children's Corner; Berceuse
héroïque; Etudes; Nocturne; Pour le piano; Estampes;
Suite bergamasque; Epigraphes antiques; Petit nègre;
Arabesques; Plus que lente; Isle joyeuse; Ravel: Ma mère
l'oye; Sites auriculaires (exc). (T. Paraskivesco, J.
Rouvier)

① CAL9841 (11/89)
Fauré: Mélodies
Fauré: Songs, Op.5 (exc); Songs, Op.6 (exc); Songs, Op.7
(exc); Songs, Op.8 (exc); Songs, op.18 (exc); Songs,
Op.23 (exc); Songs, Op.27 (exc); Songs, Op.39 (exc);
Songs, Op.43 (exc); Songs, Op.46 (exc); Songs, Op.51
(exc); Bonne chanson, Op.61; Horizon chimérique. (J.
Herbillon, T. Paraskivesco)

① CAL9859 (8/88)
French Orchestral Works
Berlioz: Symphonie funèbre et triomphale; Schmitt:
Dionysiaques; Koechlin: Quelques chorals; Fauré: Chant
funéraire. (Gardiens de la Paix Orch/J. Dondeyne)

① CAL9893 (11/89)
Debussy & Ravel: String Quartets
Debussy: String Quartet; Ravel: String Quartet; Chansons
madécasses. (J. Herbillon, C. Lardé, P. Degenne, T.
Paraskivesco, Talich Qt)

① CAL9907 (6/90)
Organ Works
Couperin: Messe à l'usage ordinaire des paroisses; Jullien:
Premier livre d'orgue; Anglebert: Quatuor; L.
Couperin: Harpsichord Works II (exc); Harpsichord Works
III (exc); Harpsichord Works IV (exc); Fantaisies (exc). (A.
Isoir)

① CAL9916 (6/90)
17th Century French Noëls and Suites
Dandrieu: Noëls (exc); Guilain: Pièces d'orgue (exc);
Nivers: Livre d'orgue III (exc); Boyvin: Livre d'orgue II
(exc); Raison: Premier livre d'orgue (exc). (A. Isoir)

① CAL9928 (9/87)
Messaien: Organ Works
Messiaen: Nativité du seigneur; Banquet céleste;
Apparition de l'église éternelle. (L. Thiry)

Cambria

① CD-1032 (5/92)
From the Operas of Erich Wolfgang Korngold
Korngold: Ring des Polykrates (exc); Violanta (exc); Tote
Stadt (exc); Tote Stadt (exc); Wunder der Heliane (exc);
Kathrin (exc); Kathrin (exc); Kathrin (exc); Kathrin (exc);
Kathrin (exc); Kathrin (exc). (G. Janowitz, H. Hoppe, H.
Hillebrecht, I. Steingruber, A. Dermota, A. Poell, R.
Schwaiger, R. Christ, Austrian St Rad Orch/W. Loibner/J.
Strobl/E. Korngold/G. Kassowitz)

① CD-1063 (8/92)
Louis Kaufman - Violin Works
Martinů: Violin Concerto 2; Khachaturian: Violin Concerto;
Achron: Stimmungen, Op.32; Rimsky-Korsakov: Golden
Cockerel (exc); Traditional: Londonderry Air; Tchaikovsky:
String Quartet 1 (exc). (L. Kaufman, P. Ulanowsky, French
Rad and TV Orch/J.M. Leconte, Santa Monica Orch/J.
Rachmilovich, Columbia SO/B. Herrmann)

① CD-1066 (3/93)
Korngold in Vienna
Korngold: Much Ado About Nothing Suite; Tomorrow;
Schneemann (exc); Violanta (exc); Theme and Variations,
Op. 42. (Austrian RSO/M. Schönherr)

Campion

① RRCD1313 (3/92)
Britten—Vocal and Orchestral Works
Britten: Simple Symphony; Frank Bridge Variations;
Serenade. (P. Schreier, P. Damm, Slovak CO/B.
Warchal)

① RRCD1317 (9/92)
Martinů/Kobayashi—Orchestral Works
Kobayashi: Violin Concerto 1; Martinů: Serenade 4; Viola
Rhapsody. (V. Šimčisko, M. Telecký, Bratislava Chbr Ens,
Slovak RSO/V. Horák/O. Lenárd/O. Trhlik)

① RRCD1321 (7/94)
Martinů—Harpsichord Concertos, etc
Martinů: Harpsichord Concerto; Piano Concerto 4; Piano

Concerto 5. (Z. Růžičková, K. Havlikova, Slovak Radio
CO/Z. Košler, Slovak RSO/O. Lenárd/T. Koutnik)

① RRCD1334 (10/95)
J.C. Bach—Orchestral Works
J. C. Bach: Grand Overtures, Op. 18 (exc); Keyboard
Concertos, T295/1 (exc); Symphonies, Op. 6 (exc);
Sinfonia concertante, T284/6; Symphonies, Op. 9 (exc).
(Lukas Consort, V. Lukas (fp/dir)/V. Lukas)

① RRCD1335 (11/95)
Inese Galante - Début Recital
Bellini: Norma (exc); Gounod: Roméo et Juliette (exc);
Puccini: Rondine (exc); Bizet: Carmen (exc); Leoncavallo:
Pagliacci (exc); Puccini: Bohème (exc); Verdi: Traviata
(exc); Caccini: Ave Maria; Gounod: Ave Maria; Franck:
Panis angelicus; Mozart: Zauberflöte (exc); Verdi: Vespri
Siciliani (exc); Boito: Mefistofele (exc); Puccini: Gianni
Schicchi (exc); Villa-Lobos: Bachianas Brasileiras 5. (I.
Galante, Latvian Nat SO/A. Vilumanis)

① RR2CD1331/2 (5/95)
Havergal Brian—Orchestral Works
Brian: Fantastic Variations; Festal dance; In Memoriam;
Herrick songs; Doctor Merryheart; English Suite 1;
Burlesque Variations; For valour. (D. Martin, A. Smith, St
Nicholas Sngrs, Hull Youth SO/G. Heald-Smith)

Cantoris

① CRCD2366 (11/92)
Music for a May Morning
Anon: Sumer is icumen in; O lusty May; Dindirin, dindirin;
Amo amas; Watkin's Ale; Welsh Allemaine; Traditional:
Bobby Shaftoe; H. Hughes: She moved through the fair; B.
Rogers: Hymnus Eucharisticus; Morley: Balletts (1595)
(exc); Banchieri: Contrappunto bestiale alla mente;
Cornysh: Ah, Robin; Hassler: Tanzen und Springen;
Janequin: Au joly jeu; Pearsall: Who shall have my lady
fair?; Hatton: When ev'ning's twilight; Bishop: Forester
sound the cheerful horn; Vaughan Williams: Shakespeare
Songs (exc); Elizabethan Partsongs (exc); Britten: Friday
Afternoons, Op.7 (exc); R.R. Bennett: Aviary (exc); Seiber:
Hungarian Folksongs (exc); Ford: Musicke of Sundrie
Kindes I (exc); A. Holborne: Coranto 'The Fairie Round';
Various Consort Pieces (exc); J. Bull: Gigge; King's Hunt;
Byrd: Sellinger's Round, Bk84; Sweelinck: Pavana
Lachrimae. (Magdalen/G. Ives, L. Kenny, N. O'Neill)

① CRCD2367 (7/93)
For All the Saints
Attwood: Blessed is the man; Victoria: O quam gloriosum;
Bainton: And I saw a new heaven; Byrd: Gradualia 1/I:
Feast of All Saints (exc); Bairstow: Blessed city, heavenly
Salem; Leighton: Give me wings of faith; Britten: Hymn to
St Peter; Hymn to the Virgin; Dering: Cantica sacra (1618)
(exc); W.H. Harris: Strengthen ye; Whitlock: Glorious in
heaven; Stanford: For all the Saints; Vaughan Williams:
Organ Preludes on Welsh Hymn-Tunes (exc); Langlais:
Incantation. (Jesus College Ch/D. Phillips, T. Horton)

① CRCD2368 (7/93)
Sullivan—That Glorious Song of Old
Traditional: It came upon the midnight clear; Sullivan: Te
Deum (1872) (exc); Lead Kindly Light; Golden Legend
(exc); On Shore and Sea (exc); Light of the World (exc); O
Israel; Te Deum (1900); Strain upraise; Prodigal Son (exc).
(K. Flowers, B. Lees, P. Mayes, P. Woods, A. Sutton, M.
Kennedy, S. Dunn, W. Mee, G. Macnevin, W. Ruby,
Britten-Pears Chbr Ch, Ely Cath Ch, D. Price/P. Trepte)

① CSACD3050 (9/94)
Music from the Coronation of H. M. Queen Elizabeth II
Anon: Rejoice in the Lord alway; Dyson: Be strong and of
good courage; Handel: Coronation Anthems (exc); W. H.
Harris: Let my prayer come up; Howells: Behold, O God
our defender; Parry: I was glad; Purcell: Choice Collection
of Lessons (exc); Stanford: Communion Service, Op. 128
(exc); Various: National Anthems (exc); Vaughan Williams:
Mass in G minor; O taste and see; Old Hundredth;
Walton: Coronation Te Deum; Orb and sceptre; Crown
Imperial; S. S. Wesley: Thou wilt keep him. (T. Sneddon,
A. Crowley, M. Bennett, M. Baker, Westminster Abbey Ch,
ECO, London Brass/M. Neary)

Canyon Classics

① EC3630-2 (12/94)
Tchaikovsky—The Complete Symphonies
Tchaikovsky: Symphony 1; Symphony 2; Symphony 3;
Symphony 4; Symphony 5; Symphony 6; Manfred
Symphony. (Russian Federation St SO/E. Svetlanov)

① EC3698-2 (5/94)
Bartók—String Quartets
Bartók: String Quartet 1; String Quartet 2; String Quartet 3;
String Quartet 4; String Quartet 5; String Quartet 6. (Bartók
Qt)

Capriccio

① 10 051 (8/89)
Classical Trumpet Concertos
Otto: Trumpet Concerto in E flat; Molter: Trumpet Concerto
3; Richter: Trumpet Concerto in D; Sperger: Trumpet
Concerto in D. (L. Güttler, C. Schornsheim, F. Kircheis,
Leipzig New Bach Collegium Musicum/M. Pommer)

① 10 063 (6/86)
Schumann: Orchestral Works
Schumann: Symphony 1; Manfred (exc); Overture,
Scherzo and Finale. (Stuttgart RSO/N. Marriner)

① 10 069 (10/88)
C.P.E. Bach—Oboe Concertos
C. P. E. Bach: Oboe Concerto, H466; Oboe Concerto,
H468; J. C. Bach: Oboe Concerto, T290/7. (B. Glaetzner,
Leipzig New Bach Collegium Musicum, Berlin CO/M.
Pommer)

① 10 098 (7/87)
Mozart: Lieder recital
Mozart: Ridente la calma, K152; Dans un bois solitaire,
K308; Oiseaux, si tous les ans, K307; Traumbild, K530;
Verschweigung, K518; An Chloe, K524; Als Luise die
Briefe, K520; Lied der Trennung, K519; Sei du mein Trost,
K391; Komm, liebe Zither, K351; Zauberer, K472; Kleine
Spinnerin, K531; Sehnsucht nach dem Frühling, K596;
Veilchen, K476; Im Frühlingsanfang, K597; Zufriedenheit,
K473; Abendempfindung, K523; Ich würd' auf meinem
Pfad, K390; Lied zur Gesellenreise, K468; Zufriedenheit,
K349; Einsam bin ich, K475a. (M. Shirai, H. Höll)

① 10 099 (6/87)
Schumann—Lieder Recital
Schumann: Liederkreis, Op. 39 (Cpte); Maria Stuart Lieder,
Op. 135 (Cpte); Lieder und Gesänge, Op. 98a (exc);
Gedichte, Op. 35 (exc). (M. Shirai, H. Höll)

① 10 101 (10/88)
C.P.E. Bach: Flute Works
C. P. E. Bach: Flute Sonata, H548; Flute Sonata, H551;
Flute Sonata, H554; Flute Sonata, H556; Flute Sonata,
H555; Flute Sonata, H564. (E. Haupt, S. Pank, A.
Thalheim)

① 10 102 (10/88)
C.P.E. Bach: Viola da gamba Works
C. P. E. Bach: Viola da gamba Sonata, H558; Viola da
gamba Sonata, H559; Sonata, H510; Fantasia, H284. (S.
Pank, C. Jaccottet, C. Jaccottet)

① 10 103 (9/87)
C.P.E. Bach: Sinfonias
C. P. E. Bach: Sinfonia, H654; Sinfonia, H656; Sinfonia,
H649; Sinfonia, H650; Sinfonia, H653. (CPE Bach
Orch/Hans Haenchen)

① 10 104 (10/88)
C.P.E. Bach: Flute Concertos
C. P. E. Bach: Flute Concerto, H431; Flute Concerto,
H438; Keyboard Concerto, H425. (E. Haupt, CPE Bach
Orch/Hans Haenchen)

① 10 109 (3/89)
Josef Protschka sings Mozart arias
Mozart: Zauberflöte (exc); Entführung (exc); Finta
giardiniera (exc); Clemenza di Tito (exc); Così fan tutte
(exc); Don Giovanni (exc); Mitridate (exc); Idomeneo (exc).
(J. Protschka, Munich RO/K. Eichhorn)

① 10 113 (9/88)
Berlin Opera Composers
C.H. Graun: Rodelinda (exc); Artaserse (exc); Cleopatra e
Cesare (exc); Telemann: Flavius Bertaridus (exc);
Bononcini: Polifemo (exc); Griselda (exc); Hasse: Lucio
Papirio (exc); Clemenza di Tito (exc); Frederick the Great:
Ré pastore (exc); J.F. Agricola: Achille in Sciro (exc). (J.
Kowalski, Berlin CO/M. Pommer)

① 10 134 (7/87)
Flute and Recorder Concertos
Blavet: Flute Concerto in A minor; Geminiani: Concerti
Grossi, Op. 3 (exc); Telemann: Don Quichotte Overture-
Suite; Recorder and Flute Concerto. (E. Hering, E-B. Hilse,
Berlin Ancient Music Academy)

① 10 135 (10/88)
C.P.E. Bach: Organ Works
C. P. E. Bach: Keyboard Concerto, H444; Keyboard
Concerto, H446; Prelude, H107; Fantasia and Fugue,
H75.5. (R. Münch, CPE Bach Orch/Hans Haenchen)

① 10 151 (9/89)
Bach: Cantatas
Bach: Cantata 55; Cantata 84; Cantata 199. (V. Hruba-
Freiberger, P. Schreier, Leipzig Univ Ch, Leipzig New
Bach Collegium Musicum/M. Pommer)

① **10 409** (5/93)
Schütz and Venice
Schütz: Psalmen Davids, SWV22-47 (exc); Symphoniarum sacrarum, SWV398-418 (exc); Stehe auf, SWV499; Magnificat, SWV468; *G. Gabrieli*: Symphoniae sacrae II (exc); Lieto godea; *M. Praetorius*: Puericinium II (exc); *Monteverdi*: Selva morale e spirituale (exc). (Schütz Academy/H. Arman)

① **10 416** (10/92)
Jochen Kowalski sings Opera Arias
Hasse: Artaserse (exc); *Gluck*: Orphée (exc); *Handel*: Rinaldo (exc); *Mozart*: Ascanio in Alba (exc); *Gluck*: Telemaco (exc); *Donizetti*: Linda di Chamounix (exc); *Rossini*: Tancredi (exc). (J. Kowalski, Berlin RSO/H. Fricke)

① **10 419** (11/92)
Berg—Lieder
Berg: Early Songs; Songs, Op.2; Ferne Lieder; Mignon; Erster Verlust; Über den Bergen; Im Morgengrauen; Grabschrift; Am Abend; Fraue, du Süsse; Ich will die Fluren meiden; Schliesse mir die Augen beide; An Leukon; Näherin; Regen; Er klagt; Sternenfall; Herbstgefühl; Sehnsucht I; Spaziergang. (M. Shirai, H. Höll)

① **10 420** (8/94)
Handel—Overtures
Handel: Alcina (exc); Ariodante (exc); Berenice (exc); Solomon (exc); Agrippina (exc); Rodrigo (exc). (ASMF/K. Sillito)

① **10 424** (4/95)
Christine Schornsheim plays Harpsichord works
Hasse: Keyboard Sonata in E flat; *C. H. Graun*: Keyboard Sonata in D minor; *Benda*: Piano Sonatinas (exc); *C. F. C. Fasch*: Andantino con VII Variazioni; *Schulz*: Diverses pièces, Op. 1 (exc); *C. P. E. Bach*: Borchward, H79; Pott, H80; Gleim, H89; Bergius, H90; Stahl, H94; Boehmer, H81; Louise, H114. (C. Schornsheim, C. Schornsheim)

① **10 426** (11/94)
W. F. Bach—Cantatas, Vol.2
W. F. Bach: Sinfonia, F64; Dies ist der Tag, F85; Erzittert und fallet, F83. (B. Schlick, C. Schubert, W. Jochens, S. Schreckenberger, Rheinische Kantorei, Kleine Konzert/H. Max)

① **10 428** (1/94)
Britten/Honegger—Orchestral Works
Britten: Sinfonietta, Op. 1; Sinfonia da Requiem; *Honegger*: Symphony 3. (Stuttgart RSO/N. Marriner)

① **10 430** (9/93)
Krauss—Symphonies, Vol.2
Kraus: Sinfonia per la chiesa; Symphony in C II; Symphonie funèbre; Symphony in C sharp minor. (Concerto Cologne)

① **10 431** (6/93)
Musical Table Entertainment
Reusner: Neue Lauten-Früchte (exc); *Brade*: Newe ausserlesene Paduanen (1609) (exc); *B. Praetorius*: Paduanen und Galliarden (1616) (exc); *Zangius*: Zu Dienst will ich ihr singen; Jungfrau ich sag es; Ade meins Herzens Krönlein; Fahr hin all Freud; *Eccard*: Fröhlich will ich singen; Unser lieben Hühnerchen. (A. Köhler, Lautten Compagney)

① **10 436** (6/93)
Classical Trumpet Concertos
Hummel: Trumpet Concerto; *M. Haydn*: Trumpet Concerto, MH60; Trumpet Concerto, MH104; *Haydn*: Trumpet Concerto; *L. Mozart*: Trumpet Concerto. (R. Friedrich, ASMF/N. Marriner)

① **10 439** (6/93)
Modern Trumpet
Stravinsky: Fanfare (1964); *Honegger*: Intrada; *Henze*: Trumpet Sonatina; *Hindemith*: Trumpet Sonata; *Wolpe*: Trumpet Piece; *Skalkottas*: Trumpet Concertino; *Apostel*: Sonatina, Op. 42a; *Killmayer*: Trumpet Pieces; *Gubaidulina*: Ballads; Song without words; Trio; *Carter*: Canon for 3. (R. Friedrich, W. Bauer, M. Mester, T. Duis)

① **10 444** (10/95)
Dussek—Piano Concertos
Dussek: Keyboard Concerto, C97; Keyboard Concerto, C187; Sufferings of the Queen of France, C98. (A. Staier, Cologne Concerto)

① **10 445** (11/93)
Schumann—Lieder
Schumann: Myrthen, Op. 25 (exc); Gedichte, Op. 90 (Cpte); Gedichte, Op. 36 (exc); Gedichte, Op. 37 (exc); Lieder, Op. 40 (exc); Romanzen und Balladen, Op. 64 (exc); Spanisches Liederspiel, Op. 74 (exc); Lieder und Gesänge, Op. 77 (exc); Gesänge, Op. 83 (exc). (M. Shirai, H. Höll)

① **10 446/7** (10/94)
Mozart—Lieder
Mozart: Veilchen, K476; Oiseaux, si tous les ans, K307; Dans un bois solitaire, K308; Zufriedenheit, K349; Komm, liebe Zither, K351; Verdankt sei es dem Glanz der Grossen, K392; Ich würd' auf meinem Pfad, K390; Sei du mein Trost, K391; Betrogene Welt, K474; Zufriedenheit, K473; Zauberer, K472; Alte, K517; Verschwiegung, K518; Traumbild, K530; Abendempfindung, K523; Sehnsucht nach dem Frühling, K596; Im Frühlingsanfang, K597; Kinderspiel, K598; Kleiner Friedrichs Geburtstag, K529; Lied der Freiheit, K506; Kleine Spinnerin, K531; An Chloe, K524; Lied der Trennung, K519; Beim Auszug in das Feld, K552; An die Freude, K53; Wie unglücklich bin ich nit, K147; O heiliges Band, K148; Als Luise die Briefe, K520; German Church Songs, K343; Lied zur Gesellenreise, K468; Kleine deutsche Kantate, K619. (J. Protschka, H. Deutsch, M. Shirai, H. Höll)

① **10 448** (3/94)
Zemlinsky—Orchestral Works and Songs
Zemlinsky: Symphonische Gesänge, Op.20; König Kandaules (exc); Ballettstücke. (F. Grundheber, Hamburg PO/G. Albrecht)

① **10 449** (8/94)
Felix/Fanny Mendelssohn—Orchestral/Vocal Works
Mendelssohn: Symphony 4; Infelice, Op.94; *Mendelssohn-Hensel*: Io d'amor. (H. Kwon, Hamburg PO/G. Albrecht)

① **10 451** (5/93)
Boccherini Edition, Vol.5
Boccherini: String Quartets, G248-9 (exc); String Quartets, G177-82 (exc); String Quartets, G189-94 (exc); String Quartet, G213. (Petersen Qt)

① **10 451/5** (12/87)
Beethoven—Symphonies 1-9
Beethoven: Symphony 1; Symphony 2; Symphony 3; Symphony 4; Symphony 5; Symphony 6; Symphony 7; Symphony 8; Symphony 9. (A. Hargan, U. Walther, E. Büchner, K. Kováts, Berlin Rad Chor, Leipzig Rad Chor, Dresden PO/H. Kegel)

① **10 452** (4/94)
Boccherini Edition, Vol.7
Boccherini: String Quintets, G277-82 (exc); String Quintets, G325-30 (exc); String Quintets, G391-6 (exc); String Quintets, G397-402 (exc). (Petersen Qt, U. Knörzer, G. Schiefen)

① **10 453** (4/94)
Boccherini Edition, Vol.8
Boccherini: String Quintets, G319-24 (exc); String Quintets, G331-6 (exc); String Quartets, G220-5 (exc); Duet, G62. (M. Seiler, S. Walch, D. Poppen, R. Lester, H. Penny)

① **10 458** (5/93)
Boccherini Edition, Vol.4
Boccherini: Symphony, G519; Symphony, G520; Symphony, G521; Symphony, G522. (New Berlin CO, M. Erdleben (vn/dir))

① **10 459** (10/95)
Music from Charlottenburg Castle
Corelli: String Sonatas (exc); Trio Sonatas, Op. 2 (exc); *Ariosti*: Cantatas (exc); *Torelli*: Trio Sonatas, Op. 1 (exc); Concerti musicali, Op. 6 (exc); *Bononcini*: Polifemo (exc); *Cefalo* (exc); *Steffani*: Scherzo Guardati. (A. Monoyios, Berlin Barock Compagney)

① **10 462** (9/95)
Songs with Viola
R. Strauss: Lieder, Op. 31 (exc); *Brahms*: Lieder, Op. 91; *A. Busch*: Nun die Schatten dunkeln; Wonne der Wehmut; Aus den Himmelsaugen; Lieder: Poèms, Op. 5; *Dargomïzhsky*: Elegy; *Marx*: Durch Einsamkeiten; *Reutter*: Antike Oden, Op. 57; *Gounod*: Evening Song. (M. Shirai, T. Zimmermann, H. Höll)

① **10 463** (9/95)
Schulhoff—String Quartets
Schulhoff: String Quartet 1; String Quartet 2; Pieces for String Quartet. (Petersen Qt)

① **10 464** (8/94)
Visée—Pieces for Theorbo
Visée: Theorbo Suite in G; Theorbo Suite in C minor; Theorbo Suite in A; Theorbo Suite in E minor; Ouverture de la Grotte de Versailles; Logistille de Roland; Baricades Mistérieuses; Ménetou. (Y. Imamura)

① **10 476** (1/94)
Grieg/Schumann—String Quartets
Grieg: String Quartet, Op. 27; String Quartet in F; *Schumann*: String Quartet 1. (Petersen Qt)

① **10 479** (6/94)
Busoni—Orchestral Works
Busoni: Turandot Suite; Nocturne Symphonique, Op.43; Rondo arlecchinesco, Op.46; Divertimento, Op.52; Doktor Faust Studies; Clarinet Concertino, Op.48; Tanzwalzer, Op.53. (J-C. Gérard, U. Rodenhäuser, Berlin RSO/G. Albrecht)

① **10 482** (6/93)
Nobody knows of trouble I see
B. A. Zimmermann: Trumpet Concerto; *Berio*: Sequenza X; *Rihm*: Sine nomine; *Scelsi*: Pezzi; *Killmayer*: Broken Farewell. (R. Friedrich, W. Bauer, W. Wipfler, O. Seifert, U. Füssel, T. Duis, Frankfurt RSO/D. Kitaienko)

① **10 489** (7/95)
Brunetti—Symphonies
Brunetti: Symphony 26; Symphony 22; Symphony 36. (Cologne Concerto)

① **10 495** (12/94)
Flute Concertos - Michael Faust
Martin: Flute Ballade; *Nielsen*: Flute Concerto; *Bernstein*: Halil; *Ibert*: Flute Concerto. (M. Faust, Cologne RSO/A. Francis/S. Baudo)

① **10 497** (2/95)
R. Strauss—Lieder
R. Strauss: Lieder, Op. 10 (exc); Lieder, Op. 15 (exc); Lieder, Op. 21 (exc); Lieder, Op. 22; Lieder, Op. 26 (exc); Lieder, Op. 27 (exc); Lieder, Op. 29 (exc); Lieder, Op. 32 (exc); Lieder, Op. 39 (exc); Lieder, Op. 56 (exc); Krämerspiegel (exc); Lieder, Op. 67 (exc). (M. Shirai, H. Höll)

① **10 501** (2/95)
Elgar—Orchestral Works
Elgar: Enigma Variations; Wand of Youth Suite 1; Wand of Youth Suite 2. (ASMF/N. Marriner)

① **10 511** (2/95)
Berg/Janáček/Dutilleux—String Quartets
Berg: String Quartet; *Janáček*: String Quartet 2; *Dutilleux*: Ainsi la Nuit. (Petersen Qt)

① **10 514** (5/95)
Schoenberg—Songs
Schoenberg: Cabaret Songs (exc); Drüben geht die Sonne scheiden; Lieder, Op.2; Lieder, Op.3 (exc); Lieder, Op.6 (exc); Gedenken; Lieder, Op.12 (exc); Lieder, Op.14; Folksong Arrangements. (M. Shirai, H. Höll)

① **10 523** (6/95)
Jochen Kowalski sings Bach Cantatas
Bach: Anna Magdalena Notenbuch (1725) (exc); Cantata 170; Cantata 53; Cantata 200. (J. Kowalski, ASMF/K. Sillito)

① **10 532** (8/94)
Kowalski sings Bach and Handel Sacred Arias
Bach: Mass in B minor, BWV232 (exc); St Matthew Passion, BWV244 (exc); *Handel*: Messiah (exc); Israel in Egypt (exc); Belshazzar (exc); Allegro, il penseroso, ed il moderato (exc). (J. Kowalski, ASMF/N. Marriner)

① **10 534** (12/94)
Hölderlin Songs
Ullmann: Abendphantasie; Frühling; *Eisler*: Hölderlin-Fragmente; *Komma*: Hölderlin Fragments; *Reutter*: Hölderlin Lieder, Op.67; *Fröhlich*: Rückkehr in die Heimat; *Cornelius*: Sonnenuntergang; *Jarnach*: Lieder, Op.7 (exc); *Hauer*: Hölderlin-Lieder, Op.12 (exc); *Pfitzner*: Lieder, Op.29 (exc); *Fortner*: Geh unter, schöne Sonne; *Britten*: Hölderlin Fragments (exc). (M. Shirai, H. Höll)

① **10 539** (11/95)
Schulhoff—Chamber Works
Schulhoff: Sextet; String Quartet, Op. 25; Violin and Cello Duo; Violin Sonata. (C. Muck, G. Sussmuth, R. J. Kimstedt, M. Sanderling, H-J. Eschenburg, Petersen Qt)

① **10 547** (6/95)
Handel—Arias
Handel: Admeto (exc); Orlando (exc); Rodelinda (exc); Alcina (exc); Rinaldo (exc); Giulio Cesare (exc); Radamisto (exc); Flavio (exc). (A. Köhler, Halle Op House Handel Fest Orch/H. Arman)

① **10 553** (9/95)
Schubert—Piano Sonatas
Schubert: Piano Sonata, D557; Piano Sonata, D566; Piano Sonata, D575; Piano Sonata, D664. (M. Endres)

① **10 605** (11/92)
Mozart—'Haydn' Quartets
Mozart: String Quartet, K387; String Quartet, K421; String Quartet, K428; String Quartet, K458; String Quartet, K464; String Quartet, K465. (Petersen Qt)

Caprice

Carlton Classics

midnight clear; I can tell the world; God rest you merry, gentlemen; Stille Nacht; First Nowell. (RCS, J. Birch/L. Heltay)

⊕ **PCD1050** (10/93)
Brahms—Violin Sonatas
Brahms: Violin Sonata 1; Violin Sonata 2; Violin Sonata 3. (N. Wakabayashi, K. Sturrock)

⊕ **PCD1051** (12/93)
Rachmaninov—Piano Transcriptions
Rachmaninov: Preludes (exc); Daisies; Lilacs; Romance; Polka de W. R.; Aleko Dances; Songs, Op.34 (exc); Polka Italienne; *Rimsky-Korsakov:* Tale of Tsar Saltan (exc); *Bach:* Solo Violin Partitas and Sonatas (exc); *Kreisler:* Liebesleid; Liebesfreud; *Liszt:* Hungarian Rhapsodies, S244 (exc); *Tchaikovsky:* Songs, Op.16 (exc); *Mendelssohn:* Midsummer Night's Dream (exc). (J. Weber, B. Michel)

⊕ **PCD1054** (12/93)
Mozart—Wind Concertos
Mozart: Bassoon Concerto, K191; Clarinet Concerto, K622; Oboe Concerto, K314. (A. Baccini, M. Carulli, S. Azzolini, ECCO/E. Aadland)

⊕ **PCD1108** (2/95)
Chamber Orchestral Works
Sibelius: Suite champêtre; Canzonetta; *Tchaikovsky:* Elegy; *Dvořák:* Waltzes; Nocturne; Humoresques, Op. 101 (exc); *Elgar:* Salut d'amour; Sospiri; *Grieg:* Melodies, Op. 53; Nordic Melodies, Op. 63; Elegiac Melodies. (Serenata of London/B. Wilde)

⊕ **PCD2016** (10/95)
Schubert—Lieder
Schubert: Forelle, D550; An Silvia, D891; Heidenröslein, D257; Du bist die Ruh, D776; Musensohn, D764; An die Musik, D547; Auf dem Wasser zu singen, D774; Sei mir gegrüsst, D741; Litanei, D343; Junge Nonne, D828; Ave Maria, D839; Im Frühling, D882; Gretchen am spinnrade, D118; Nacht und Träume, D827; Ganymed, D544; Nur wer die Sehnsucht kennt, D877/4; Seligkeit, D433. (F. Lott, G. Johnson)

⊕ **PCD2017** (10/95)
Elgar/Fauré/Ravel—Orchestral Works
Fauré: Masques et bergamasques; *Elgar:* Chanson de Nuit; Chanson de Matin; *Fauré:* Pavane; *Delius:* First Cuckoo; *Ravel:* Pavane; *Warlock:* Capriol Suite; *Butterworth:* Banks of green willow; *Satie:* Gymnopédies (exc). (English Sinfonia/C. Groves)

⊕ **PCD805** (8/85)
Music of the Masters
Beethoven: Prometheus (exc); *Mozart:* Divertimenti, K136-8 (exc); *Rossini:* Barbiere di Siviglia (exc); *Fauré:* Pavane; *Wagner:* Siegfried Idyll. (COE/J. Judd)

⊕ **PCD806** (7/86)
Renaissance Masterpieces
Tallis: Spem in alium; Lamentations of Jeremiah; *Allegri:* Miserere mei. (PCA/M. Brown)

⊕ **PCD808** (5/86)
Bach: Violin Concertos
Bach: 2-Violin Concerto; Violin Concerto, BWV1041; Violin Concerto, BWV1042. (J. Laredo (vn/dir), J. Tunnell, Scottish CO)

⊕ **PCD809** (5/86)
Vivaldi: Violin Concertos
Vivaldi: Concerti Grossi, Op. 3 (exc); Concerti Grossi, Op. 3 (exc); Concerti Grossi, Op. 3 (exc); Concerto RV551. (J. Laredo (vn/dir), J. Tunnell, P. Manley, B. Thomas, H. Hallgrimsson, Scottish CO)

⊕ **PCD811** (7/86)
Vivaldi—Violin Concertos
Vivaldi: Concerto, RV533; Concerto, RV535; Concerto, RV539; Concerto, RV563; Concerto, RV560. (J. Laredo (vn/dir), Scottish CO)

⊕ **PCD817** (6/86)
Bach: Keyboard Works
Bach: Chromatic Fantasia and Fugue, BWV903; French Suites, BWV812-17 (exc); Italian Concerto, BWV971; Capriccio, BWV992. (R. Aldwinckle)

⊕ **PCD821** (6/86)
Trumpet Concertos
Haydn: Trumpet Concerto; *Torelli:* Concerto con tromba, G18; *M. Haydn:* Trumpet Concerto, MH60; *Telemann:* 2-Oboe & Trumpet Concerto 1; *Neruda:* Trumpet Concerto in E flat; *Humphries:* Trumpet Concerto, Op. 2/12. (C. Steele-Perkins, N. Black, Jeremy Brown, ECO/A. Halstead)

⊕ **PCD822** (6/86)
Italian Madrigals
Lassus: Matona mia cara; S'io esca vivo; *Negri:* Torneo amoroso; Leggiadra Marina; Alte mendozza; *Marenzio:*

Cruda Amarilli; *Arcadelt:* Bianco e dolce cigno; *Monte:* Leggiadre ninfe; *Caimo:* Piangete valli; *Gastoldi:* Viver lieto voglio; *A. Gabrieli:* Duo rose fresche; *Gesualdo:* Moro, lasso; Luci serene e chiare; *Mainerio:* Ballo furlano; *Wert:* Vezzosi augelli; *Monteverdi:* Madrigals, Bk.6 (exc); Madrigals, Bk.4 (exc); Scherzi musicali (1632) (exc); *Vecchi:* So ben, mi, c'ha bon tempo. (Amaryllis Consort)

⊕ **PCD823** (9/86)
Organ Spectacular
Bach: Toccata and Fugue, BWV565; *Franck:* Chorales (exc); *Meyerbeer:* Prophète (exc); *Guilmant:* March, Op. 15; *Saint-Saëns:* Fantaisie in E flat; *Brahms:* Chorale Preludes, Op. 122 (exc); *Liszt:* Prelude and Fugue, S260; *Vierne:* Suite 3 (exc). (D. Hill)

⊕ **PCD824** (6/86)
Mendelssohn—Orchestral Works
Mendelssohn: Symphony 4; Hebrides; Fair Melusina; Heimkehr aus der Fremde (exc). (Berne SO/P. Maag)

⊕ **PCD825** (2/87)
A Florentine Carnival
Isaac: A la battaglia; A la battaglia; Palle, palle; Ne più bella di queste; La morra; Donna di dentro dalla tua casa; Quis dabit capiti meo aquam; *Coppini:* Lanzi maine; *Anon:* Saltarello Fiorentina; Ben venga maggio; Canto de profumieri; Canto di capi tondi; Liffe, liffe; Questro mostrasi adirata; Trionfo della mea Minerva; Canto di lanzi suonatori di rubechine; Carro della morte. (London Pro Musica, B. Thomas)

⊕ **PCD827** (11/86)
The Art of the Coloratura
Handel: Allegro, il penseroso ed il moderato (exc); *Mozart:* Zauberflöte (exc); Vorrei spiegarvi, K418; *Arne:* Artaxerxes (exc); *Benedict:* Wren; *Proch:* Air and Variations; *Milhaud:* Chansons de Ronsard; *Alabiev:* Nightingale; *Glière:* Soprano Concerto. (B. Hoch, Hong Kong PO/K. Schermerhorn)

⊕ **PCD828** (11/86)
Beethoven—Piano Sonatas
Beethoven: Piano Sonata 14; Piano Sonata 23; Piano Sonata 8. (J. Ogdon)

⊕ **PCD834** (3/87)
Chopin—Piano Works
Chopin: Fantasie, Op. 49; Berceuse; Barcarolle; Polonaises (exc); Nocturnes (exc); Piano Sonata 3. (J. Ogdon)

⊕ **PCD835** (3/87)
The Romance of the Flute and Harp
Hasselmans: Source, Op. 44; Feuilles d'automne; *Godard:* Suite, Op. 116 (exc); *Godefroid:* Etude de concert, Op. 193; *Fauré:* Berceuse, Op. 16; Impromptu, Op. 86; *Doppler:* Mazurka; *Mendelssohn:* Songs without words (exc); *J. Thomas:* Watching the wheat; *Saint-Saëns:* Carnaval des animaux (exc); *Bizet:* Jolie fille de Perth Suite (exc); *Parish Alvars:* Serenade; *Debussy:* Syrinx; Suite bergamasque (exc). (Philippa Davies, T. Owen)

⊕ **PCD846** (6/87)
French Impressionist Piano Music
Debussy: Arabesques; Préludes (exc); Images (exc); Children's Corner (exc); Suite bergamasque (exc); Isle joyeuse; *Chabrier:* Pièces pittoresques (exc); *Satie:* Gymnopédies (exc); *Fauré:* Impromptus (exc); *Ibert:* Histoires (exc); *Poulenc:* Mélancolie; *Milhaud:* Saudades do Brasil (exc); *Ravel:* Jeux d'eau; Miroirs (exc). (C. Ortiz)

⊕ **PCD850** (7/87)
Harpsichord recital
Rameau: Pièces de clavecin (exc); *Daquin:* Premier livre de pièces de clavecin (exc); *Gibbons:* Preludes (exc); *Byrd:* Bells, BN98; *A. Holborne:* Noels' Galliard; *L. Couperin:* Harpsichord Works V (exc); Harpsichord Works II (exc); *Couperin:* Livre de clavecin II (exc); *D. Scarlatti:* Keyboard Sonatas (exc); *Mozart:* Piano Sonata, K331 (exc); Fantasia, K397. (R. Aldwinckle)

⊕ **PCD853** (9/87)
Guitar Works
Ponce: Valse; *Piazzolla:* Muerte del Angel; *Barrios:* Waltzes, Op. 8 (exc); Choro da saudade; Julia florida; *Lauro:* Valses venezolanos (1963) (exc); Valses venezolanos (1968) (exc); *Brouwer:* Canción de cuna; Ojos brujos; *Pernambuco:* Sons de carrilhões (exc); Interrogando; Sonho de magia; *Reis:* Si ela perguntar; *Villa-Lobos:* Preludes. (M. Kayath)

⊕ **PCD856** (9/87)
Works by J. Strauss
J. Strauss II: Champagner, Op. 211; Blauen Donau, Op. 314; Unter Donner und Blitz; Kaiser, Op. 437; Tritsch-Tratsch; Wiener Blut; Pizzicato Polka; Wo die Zitronen

blüh'n; Perpetuum mobile; Radetzky March. (LSO/J. Georgiadis)

⊕ **PCD858** (10/87)
Piano Transcriptions
Liszt: Faust—paraphrase, S407; *Grainger:* Rosenkavalier ramble; *R.Strauss:* Lieder, Op. 17 (exc); *Wagner:* Tristan und Isolde (exc); *Ravel:* La Valse; *Offenbach:* Contes d'Hoffmann (exc); *Grainger:* Waltz of the Flowers—paraphrase; *Gershwin:* Strike Up The Band I (exc); Goldwyn Follies (exc). (G. Saba)

⊕ **PCD861** (11/87)
Serenade
Elgar: Serenade; *Grieg:* Holberg Suite; *Mozart:* Serenade, K525; Serenade, K239. (Serenata of London)

⊕ **PCD864** (11/87)
Bach: Harpsichord Concertos
Bach: Harpsichord Concerto, BWV1052; Harpsichord Concerto, BWV1055; Harpsichord Concerto, BWV1056; Harpsichord Concerto, BWV1057. (St James's Baroque Plyrs, I. Bolton (hpd/dir))

⊕ **PCD872** (12/87)
Chopin: Piano Works
Chopin: Etudes (exc); Nocturnes (exc); Andante Spianato and Grande Polonaise; Mazurkas (exc); Impromptus (exc); Fantaisie-impromptu; Scherzos (exc); Ballades (exc); Waltzes (exc). (C. Ortiz)

⊕ **PCD873** (3/88)
English Madrigals
Morley: Balletts (1595) (exc); *Anon:* King's Morisco; *R.Ramsey:* Sleep, fleshy birth; *East:* Poor is the life; *Gibbons:* Silver swan; Ground, MBXX/26; What is our life?; *Bennet:* All creatures now; *Weelkes:* Balletts and Madrigals (exc); *Peerson:* Primrose; *Ford:* Musicke of Sundrie Kindes I (exc); *Ward:* Come, sable night; Retire, my troubled soul; *Farmer:* Fair Phyllis I saw sitting all alone; *Tomkins:* Oyez! has any found a lad?; *Byrd:* Though Amaryllis dance in green; Pavan and 2 Galliards, BK15 (exc); *Greaves:* Come away, sweet love; *Wilbye:* Madrigals, Second Set (exc); Madrigals, First Set (exc); *Famaby:* Fain would I wed. (Amaryllis Consort/C. Brett, R. Aldwinckle)

⊕ **PCD876** (5/88)
Guitar Classics from Spain
Tárrega: Preludios (exc); Capricho árabe; Recuerdos de la Alhambra; *Granados:* Tonadillas (exc); *Albéniz:* Suite española 1 (exc); Piezás características (exc); Mallorca; *Moreno Torroba:* Prelude in E; Sonatina in A; Nocturno; *Rodrigo:* Piezas españolas (exc); *Traditional:* Noi de la mare. (M. Kayath)

⊕ **PCD881** (4/88)
Monteverdi—Solos and Duets
Monteverdi: Madrigals, Bk.7 (exc); Ritorno d'Ulisse in Patria (exc); Cantate Domino II; Sancta Maria; Exulta, filia Sion; O bone Jesu, o piissime Jesu; Selva morale e spirituale (exc). (E. Kirkby, E. Tubb, Consort of Musicke/A. Rooley)

⊕ **PCD894** (8/88)
Great Baroque Arias, Part I
Handel: Ode for St Cecilia's Day (exc); Serse (exc); Semele (exc); Acis and Galatea (exc); Joshua (exc); Jephtha (exc); Alexander's Feast (exc); Samson (exc); *Bach:* Cantata 208 (exc); *Weldon:* Tempest (exc); *Purcell:* Dido (exc); *Vivaldi:* Orlando Furioso (exc). (G. Fisher, J. Bowman, J.M. Ainsley, M. George, King's Consort/R. King)

⊕ **PCD896** (10/88)
Fauré: Sacred Choral Works
Fauré: Requiem (Cpte); Messe basse; Maria, Mater gratiae; Tantum ergo, Op. 65/2. (A. Oliver, H. Escott, D. Wilson-Johnson, Westminster Cath Ch, CLS/D. Hill)

⊕ **PCD902** (4/89)
An Evening in Vienna
J. Strauss II: Fledermaus (exc); Frühlingsstimmen, Op. 410; Annen-Polka, Op. 117; Rosen aus dem Süden; Wein, Weib und Gesang; Auf der Jagd, Op. 373; Explosionen, Op. 43; Windsor-Klänge; *Jos Strauss:* Feuerfest!; *Ziehrer:* Busserl, Op. 389. (LSO, J. Georgiadis)

⊕ **PCD908** (4/89)
Great Opera Choruses
Bizet: Carmen (exc); *Verdi:* Trovatore (exc); Nabucco (exc); Macbeth (exc); *Gounod:* Faust (exc); *Verdi:* Aida (exc); *Borodin:* Prince Igor (exc). (Southend Boys' Ch, LSC, LSO/R. Hickox)

⊕ **PCD915** (6/89)
Debussy—Orchestral Works
Debussy: La Mer; Nocturnes; Après-midi. (LSC, LSO/R. Frühbeck de Burgos)

① **PCD919** (10/89)
Great Music from Great Occasions at Westminster Abbey
Bliss: Royal Fanfares (1960) (exc); *Parry:* I was glad; *Walton:* Set me as a seal; *S.S. Wesley:* Wash me throughly; Thou wilt keep him; *Stanford:* Services, Op. 10 (exc); *Anon:* Rejoice in the Lord alway; *D. Grant:* Psalm 23; *Vaughan Williams:* O clap your hands; Old Hundredth; *McKie:* Psalm 121; *Anon:* Lord, for thy tender mercy's sake; *Alcock:* Psalm 90; *Widor:* Symphony 5 (exc). (Westminster Abbey Ch, London Brass, I. Simcock, M. Neary/M. Neary)

① **PCD924** (11/89)
Spanish Spectacular
Rimsky-Korsakov: Capriccio espagnol; *Albéniz:* Suite española 1 (exc); *Falla:* Amor brujo (exc); *Ravel:* Alborada del gracioso; *Granados:* Goyescas (exc); *Falla:* Sombrero de tres picos Suites (exc). (LSO/R. Frühbeck de Burgos)

① **PCD930** (1/90)
Elgar/Vaughan Williams—Orchestral Works
Elgar: Cello Concerto; *Vaughan Williams:* Tallis Fantasia; Greensleeves Fantasia. (F. Schmidt, LSO/R. Frühbeck de Burgos)

① **PCD937** (9/90)
Tapestry of English Cathedral Music
P.G. Aston: Alleluya Psallat II; *Byrd:* Short Service (exc); *Britten:* Te Deum in C; Jubilate Deo in C; *Andrews:* Ah see the fair; *Gibbons:* O clap your hands; *W. Mundy:* O Lord, the maker of all things; *W.H. Harris:* Bring us, O Lord; *Tomkins:* O sing unto the Lord; *Gray:* What are these that glow from afar?; *Howells:* Rhapsodies, op 17 (exc); *Worcester Service* (exc). (Worcester Cath Ch, Don Hunt, A. Partington)

① **PCD939** (11/90)
Mozart: Orchestral Works
Mozart: Sinfonia concertante, K297b; Symphony 25; Nozze di Figaro (exc); Finta Giardiniera (exc). (C. O'Neal, K. Puddy, B. Sewell, M. Baines, English Sinfonia/C. Groves)

① **PCD949** (7/91)
Annette Servadei—Piano Recital
Mendelssohn: Andante and Rondo capriccioso, Op.14; Kinderstücke (exc); Fantaisies, Op.16 (exc); Songs without words (exc); Preludes and Fugues, Op.35 (exc); *Schumann:* Arabeske; Waldszenen (exc); Fantasiestücke, Op.12 (exc); Albumblätter, Op.124 (exc); Romanzen, Op.28 (exc); Faschingsschwank aus Wien (exc); Thema (1854); *Brahms:* Piano Pieces, Op.117 (exc); Waltzes, Op.39 (exc); Piano Pieces, Op.118 (exc); Piano Pieces, Op.119 (exc); Rhapsodies, Op.79 (exc). (A. Servadei)

① **PCD950** (9/91)
Schubert—Piano works
Schubert: Impromptus (exc); Piano Sonata, D625; Piano Sonata, D959. (G. Saba)

① **PCD953** (12/91)
Mendelssohn—Works for Piano & Orchestra
Mendelssohn: Piano Concerto 1; Piano Concerto 2; Capriccio brillant, Op.22. (A. Kuerti, LPO/P. Freeman)

① **PCD964** (3/92)
Piano Concertos
Bach: Harpsichord Concerto, BWV1052; *Haydn:* Keyboard Concerto, HobXVIII/11; *Mozart:* Piano Concerto 8. (O. Maione, G. d'Atri, P. Bruni, ECCO/E. Aadland)

① **PCD967** (5/92)
Schubert—Orchestral Works
Schubert: Symphony 3; Symphony 4; Overture, D591; Overture, D4; Verschworenen (exc). (English Sinfonia/C. Groves)

① **PCD968** (3/93)
Schubert—Orchestral Works
Schubert: Symphony 2; Symphony 6; Zwillingsbrüder (exc). (English Sinfonia/C. Groves)

① **PCD970** (5/92)
Victoria and the Music of Imperial Spain
Victoria: Missa surge propera; *Padilla:* Missa Ego flos campi; Stabat mater; *Victoria:* Alma Redemptoris Mater. (Mixyolodian/P. Schmidt)

① **PCD978** (9/92)
Haydn—Symphonies
Haydn: Symphony 43; Symphony 28; Symphony 34. (ECCO/E. Aadland)

① **PCD979** (3/92)
Vivaldi—Concertos
Vivaldi: Concerto, RV443; Concerto, RV535; Concerti, Op. 10 (exc); Concerto, RV93; Concerto, RV413; Concerto, RV498. (G.G. Viscardi, D.D. Ciacci, G. Falco, G.G. Viscardi, E. Segre, G. Sollima, C. Gonella, ECCO/E. Aadland)

① **PCD991** (9/92)
French Flute Music
Gaubert: Flute Sonata 1; *Caplet:* Rêverie et Petite Valse; *Fauré:* Fantaisie; *Saint-Saëns:* Romance, Op.37; *Büsser:* Prélude; *Poulenc:* Flute Sonata; *Roussel:* Andante and Scherzo, Op.51; *Ferroud:* Pièces. (P. Lloyd, R. Holt)

① **PWK1132** (6/90)
Children's Corner
Beethoven: Bagatelles (exc); Sonatinas (exc); *Bach:* Anna Magdalena Notenbuch (1725) (exc); *Mozart:* Fantasia, K397; *Schumann:* Album für die Jugend (exc); Kinderszenen (exc); *Grieg:* Lyric Pieces, Op.12 (exc); *Bartók:* For Children (1945) (exc); *A. Hajdu:* Milky Way (exc); *Debussy:* Children's Corner. (A. Vardi)

① **PWK1133** (6/90)
Flute Album
Schumann: Romanzen, op 94; *Donizetti:* Flute and Harp Sonata; *Kuhlau:* Flute Sonata, op 85 (exc); *Chopin:* Rossini Variations; *Mozart:* Violin Sonata, K15; *Bach:* Flute Sonatas, BWV1030-5 (exc); *Handel:* Flute Sonatas (exc); *Telemann:* Getreue Music-Meister (exc). (E. Talmi, Y. Talmi)

① **PWK1134** (6/90)
Dances Round the World
Dvořák: Slavonic Dances (exc); *Barber:* Souvenirs, op 28 (exc); *Debussy:* Petite Suite (exc); *Brahms:* Hungarian Dances (exc); Waltzes, op 39 (exc); *Grieg:* Norwegian Dances, op 35 (exc); *Schubert:* Waltzes, D779 (exc); *Moszkowski:* Danzas españolas (exc); *Rossini:* Soirées musicales (exc). (B. Eden, A. Tamir)

① **PWK1137** (6/90)
Romantic Strings
Dvořák: Violin Sonatina; *Schubert:* Violin Sonata, D385; *Kreisler:* Schön Rosmarin; Liebesleid; Liebesfreud; *Tchaikovsky:* Valse-scherzo, op 34; Souvenir d'un lieu cher, op 42 (exc). (V. Vaidman, E. Krasovsky)

① **PWK1138** (6/90)
Baroque Favourites
Telemann: Kleine Cammer-Music (exc); Essercizii musici (exc); *Vivaldi:* Sonatas, op 13 (exc); *Eyck:* Fluyten Lust-hof (exc); *Handel:* Recorder Sonatas (exc); *Corelli:* Sonatas, op 5 (exc); *Fontana:* Sonate a 1,2,3 (exc); *Frescobaldi:* Canzona in A minor; *Cima:* Sonata in D minor. (B. Kol, A. Brodo, D. Shemer)

① **PWK1139** (6/90)
Flute Serenade
Mozart: Flute Quartets (exc); *Beethoven:* Serenade, Op. 25; *Schubert:* String Trio, D471 (exc); *Hoffmeister:* Flute Quartet in A. (Israel Fl Ens)

① **PWK1141** (6/90)
French Impressions
Ravel: Introduction and Allegro; *Debussy:* Sonata for Flute, Viola and Harp; *Caplet:* Conte Fantastique; *Roussel:* Trio, Op. 58. (A. Giles, E. Talmi, A. Arnheim, R. Kaminkovsky, R. Mozes, Y. Kaminkovsky, Y. Alperin, G. Levertov, Jerusalem Stg Trio)

① **TCD77** (4/94)
Mozart—Wind Concertos
Mozart: Clarinet Concerto, K622; Bassoon Concerto, K191; Flute Concerto, K313; Oboe Concerto, K314; Horn Concerti. (A. Dorough, R. Atherholt, D. Peck, B. Kamins, W. Ver Meulen, Houston SO/C. Eschenbach)

Cascavelle

① **VEL2001** (11/92)
Martin—Orchestral Works
Martin: Petite Symphonie Concertante; Sturm (exc); Cello Concerto; Flute Ballade. (D. Fischer-Dieskau, P. Fournier, A. Pépin, SRO/E. Ansermet/F. Martin)

① **VEL2002** (11/92)
Memories of the Suisse Romande - Beecham conducts Mozart
Mozart: Symphony 31; Symphony 35; Symphony 39. (SRO/T. Beecham)

① **VEL2003** (11/92)
Memories of the Suisse Romande - Ansermet conducts Berg
Berg: Violin Concerto; Orchestral Pieces, Op. 6; Wozzeck Songs. (S. Danco, Y. Menuhin, SRO/E. Ansermet)

① **VEL2007** (11/92)
Martinů—Orchestral Works
Martinů: Fresques de Piero della Francesca; Symphony 4; Parables. (SRO/E. Ansermet)

① **VEL2008** (11/92)
Casadesus plays Piano Concertos
Mozart: Piano Concerto 26; *Liszt:* Piano Concerto 2; *Falla:*

Nights in the Gardens of Spain. (R. Casadesus, SRO/E. Ansermet)

① **VEL2009** (11/92)
Cello Concertos
Martinů: Cello Concerto 1; *Schumann:* Cello Concerto; *Shostakovich:* Cello Concerto 1. (P. Fournier, SRO/W. Sawallisch/F. Fricsay/J. Horenstein)

① **VEL2010** (1/93)
Memories of the Suisse Romande - Suzanne Danco
Britten: Illuminations; *Falla:* Canciones populares españolas; *Smetana:* Bartered Bride (exc); *Chabrier:* Sulamite; *Debussy:* Pelléas et Mélisande (exc); Enfant prodigue (exc). (S. Danco, SRO/E. Ansermet/I. Karr, Piantoni Cercle Choral, A. Vessières, P. Mollet)

Castle

① **CJCD10002** (6/86)
Sibelius—Orchestral Works
Sibelius: Finlandia; Valse triste; Karelia Suite; Legends (exc); Pohjola's Daughter. (LSO/G. Rozhdestvensky)

Catalyst

① **09026 61822-2** (12/93)
Of Eternal Light
M. Monk: Return to Earth; *Messiaen:* O sacrum convivium!; *R.I. Gordon:* Water Music; *Ligeti:* Lux aeterna; *Sherman:* Graveside; *Moran:* Seven Sounds Unseen. (Musica Sacra/R. Westenburg)

① **09026 61824-2** (12/93)
Frâtres
Corigliano: Violin Sonata; *Pärt:* Fratres; *Moravec:* Violin Sonata; *Glinsky:* Toccata-Scherzo; *Messiaen:* Quatuor (exc). (M. Bachmann, J. Klibonoff)

① **09026 61825-2** (1/94)
Glass—Organ Works
Glass: Dance II; Dance IV; Mad Rush; Contrary Motion; Satyagraha (exc). (D. Joyce)

① **09026 61916-2** (9/93)
MacMillan—Veni, Veni Emmanuel & Other Percussion Works
MacMillan: Veni, veni, Emmanuel; After the tryst; ...as others see us...; Dawn Rituals; Untold. (E. Glennie, R. Crouch, P. Evans, Scottish CO/J-P. Saraste/J. MacMillan)

① **09026 61979-2** (7/94)
Memento Bittersweet
Hersch: Tango Bittersweet; *K. Oldham:* Piano Concerto, Op. 14; *DeBlasio:* God is our righteousness; *Gannon:* Triad-O-Rama; *Hampton:* Variations on 'Amazing Grace'. (R. Dalessio, T. Stacy, D. Gilbert, D. Grabois, S. Dibner, E. Friedlander, N. Goluses, F. Hersch, I. Hobson, H. Huff, Aspen wind Qnt, Kansas City SO/W. McGlaughlin)

① **09026 61980-2** (7/95)
John Cage—In a Landscape
Cage: Dream (1948); Bacchanale (1940); Souvenir; In a Landscape; Suite (1948); Valentine Out of Season (1944); Prelude for Meditation (1944); Music for Marcel Duchamp (1947). (S. Drury)

① **09026 61981-2** (2/95)
Toby Twining—Shaman
Twining: Hymn; Richi Richi Rubel; Munu Munu; Shaman; Sanctus; Between Stars; Hee-oo-oom-ha; Hotel Destiné; Hell's Kitchen Hootenanny; Numa Exotic; Agnus Dei; Himalaya. (T. Twining Music, P. Stewart)

① **09026 62668-2** (5/95)
Maria Bachmann—Kiss On Wood
MacMillan: Kiss on Wood; *Bolcom:* Violin Sonata 2; *Copland:* Nocturne; *Schnittke:* Violin Sonata 1; *Dresher:* Double Ikat (exc). (M. Bachmann, J. Klibonoff, J. Saporito)

① **09026 62672-2** (2/95)
Revueltas—Night of the Mayas
Revueltas: Homenaje a Garcia Lorca; Sensemayá; Ocho x Radio; Toccata; Alcancías; Danzo; Noche de los Mayas Suite. (New Philh/E. Mata, London Sinfonietta/D. Atherton, Xalapa SO/H. de la Fuente)

CBC Records

① **MVCD1052** (6/93)
Lieder on Poems of Heinrich Heine
Schumann: Dichterliebe, Op. 48 (Cpte); *Brahms:* Lieder, Op. 96 (exc); *Liszt:* Vergiftet sind meine Lieder, S289; Du bist wie eine blume, S287; Fichtenbaum steht einsam, S309; Am Rhein, S272; *Mendelssohn:* Lieder, Op. 34 (exc); Lieder, Op. 19a (exc); Lieder, Op. 86 (exc); *Schubert:* Schwanengesang, D957 (exc). (K. McMillan, M. McMahon)

① **MVCD1053** (5/93)
Schubert—Lieder
Schubert: Seligkeit, D433; Frühlingsglaube, D686; Lied im Grünen, D917; Lachen und Weinen, D777; Jüngling an der Quelle, D300; Auf dem Wasser zu singen, D774; Junge Nonne, D828; Verschworenen (exc); Claudine von Villa Bella (exc); Einsame, D800; Nacht und Träume, D827; Mutter Erde, D788; Hirt auf dem Felsen, D965; Fischerweise, D881; Heidenröslein, D257; An Silvia, D891; Liebhaber in allen Gestalten, D558; An die Musik, D547. (E. Wiens, J. Valdepeñas, R. Jansen)

① **MVCD1061** (6/94)
Franck—Piano Works
Franck: Danse lente; Plaintes d'une poupée; Organiste I (exc); Prélude, aria et final; Prélude, Choral et Fugue; Prélude, Fugue et Variation. (R. Silverman)

① **PSCD2002** (12/92)
Maureen Forrester sings Handel Arias
Handel: Serse (exc); Rodelinda (exc); Ottone (exc); Giulio Cesare (exc); Jephtha (exc); Jephtha (exc); Theodora (exc); Samson (exc); Hercules (exc). (M. Forrester, Vienna RSO/B. Priestman, Vienna St Op Orch/R. Zeller, ECO/J. Somary, Zagreb Sols/A. Janigro)

① **PSCD2004** (7/94)
Glenn Gould broadcast performances
Beethoven: Piano Concerto 3; Variations, Op. 34; Variations, Op. 35. (G. Gould, CBC SO/H. Unger)

① **PSCD2005** (7/94)
Glenn Gould broadcast performances
Bach: Harpsichord Concerto, BWV1052; Partitas, BWV825-30 (exc); 3-Part Inventions, BWV787-801; Italian Concerto, BWV971. (G. Gould, Toronto SO/E. MacMillan)

① **SMCD5096** (9/92)
Mozart/Copland/Weber—Clarinet Concertos
Mozart: Clarinet Concerto, K622; *Weber:* Clarinet Concertino; *Copland:* Clarinet Concerto. (J. Campbell, Canadian Nat Arts Centre Orch/F-P. Decker)

① **SMCD5098** (5/92)
Mahler—Lieder
Mahler: Lieder eines fahrenden Gesellen; Rückert Lieder; Kindertotenlieder. (C. Robbin/R. Armenian, Kitchener-Waterloo SO)

① **SMCD5119** (12/93)
Adeste Fideles
Traditional: Cloche de Noël; Flambeau, Jeanette, Isabelle; *Adam:* Minuit, Chrétiens (exc); *Berlioz:* Enfance du Christ (exc); *Traditional:* Patapan; Fum, fum, fum; *Gounod:* Ave Maria; *Franck:* Panis angelicus; *Traditional:* O come, all ye faithful; Gesù bambino; Ninna Nanna; *Bach:* Cantata 208 (exc); *Traditional:* Es ist ein Ros' entsprungen; Maria Wiegenlied; *Schubert:* Ave Maria, D839; *Traditional:* Stille Nacht; O Tannenbaum; Carol of the bells; Sleigh; Coventry Carol; Huron Carol; I wonder as I wander; Christmas Song; White Christmas; Have Yourself a Merry Little Christmas. (L. Quilico, G. Quilico, N. Shulman, V. Markson, J. Loman, Toronto Children's Chor, Toronto SO/J.A. Bartle)

① **SMCD5125** (12/94)
Glitter and Be Gay—Coloratura Soprano Arias
Bernstein: Candide (1988) (exc); *Delibes:* Lakmé (exc); *J. Strauss II:* Fledermaus (exc); *Offenbach:* Contes d'Hoffmann (exc); *R. Strauss:* Ariadne auf Naxos (exc); *Gluck:* Orfeo ed Euridice (exc); *Mozart:* Zaïde (exc); Entführung (exc); Vorrei spiegarvi, K418. (T. Dahl, Calgary PO/M. Bernardi)

① **SMCD5139** (6/95)
A Gilbert & Sullivan Gala
Sullivan: Gondoliers (exc); HMS Pinafore (exc); Iolanthe (exc); Mikado (exc); Pirates of Penzance (exc); Trial by Jury (exc); Yeomen of the Guard (exc). (T. Dahl, M. Forrester, T. Chiles, R. Suart, D. Grant, D. Morphy, Winnipeg Sngrs, Winnipeg G & S Soc, Winnipeg SO/B. Tovey)

① **SMCD5142** (11/95)
Ben Heppner sings Richard Strauss
R. Strauss: Guntram (exc); Feuersnot (exc); Frau ohne Schatten (exc); Intermezzo Interludes (exc); Liebe der Danae (exc); Daphne (exc); Schweigsame Frau (exc); Rosenkavalier (exc). (B. Heppner, Toronto SO/A. Davis)

CdM Russian Season

① **LDC288 004** (6/91)
Ciurlionis—Orchestral & Chamber Works
Čiurlionis: Sea; In the Forest; String Quartet. (Vilnius Qt, USSR TV & Rad Orch/V. Fedoseyev)

① **LDC288 027/8** (9/92)
Prokofiev—Film and Stage Music
Prokofiev: Lt. Kijé Suite; Hamlet; Eugene Onegin (Cpte).

(L. Koroleva, B. Stetsenko, Blagovest Ch, Moscow Maly SO/V. Ponkin)

① **LDC288 038/40** (7/93)
Rimsky-Korsakov—Complete Songs
Rimsky-Korsakov: Songs, Op.2 (exc); Songs, Op.2 (exc); Songs, Op.2 (exc); Songs, Op.3 (exc); Songs, Op.3 (exc); Songs, Op.3 (exc); Songs, Op.4 (exc); Songs, Op.4 (exc); Songs, Op.4 (exc); Songs, Op.7 (exc); Songs, Op.7 (exc); Songs, Op.7 (exc); Songs, Op.8 (exc); Songs, Op.8 (exc); Songs, Op.8 (exc); Songs, Op.8 (exc); Songs, Op.25 (exc); Songs, Op.25 (exc); Songs, Op.26 (exc); Songs, Op.26 (exc); Songs, Op.26 (exc); Songs, Op.27 (exc); Songs, Op.27 (exc); Songs, Op.27 (exc); Songs, Op.27 (exc); Songs, Op.39 (exc); Songs, Op.39 (exc); Songs, Op.39 (exc); Songs, Op.40 (exc); Songs, Op.40 (exc); Songs, Op.40 (exc); Songs, Op.41 (exc); Songs, Op.41 (exc); Songs, Op.42 (exc); Songs, Op.42 (exc); In spring, Op.43 (exc); In spring, Op.43 (exc); To the poet, Op.45 (exc); To the poet, Op.45 (exc); By the sea, Op.46 (exc); By the sea, Op.46 (exc); By the sea, Op.46 (exc); Songs, Op.50 (exc); Songs, Op.50 (exc); Songs, Op.51 (exc); Songs, Op.51 (exc); Songs, Op.51 (exc); Songs, Op.55 (Cpte); Songs, Op.56 (Cpte). (N. Gerassimova, M. Shutova, A. Martynov, M. Lanskoy, S. Baikov, V. Skanavi, E. Cheglakova, A. Konstantinidi, I. Scheps)

① **LDC288 059** (9/93)
Contemporary Listening—Raskatov
Raskatov: Song Circle I; Sentimental Sequences; Misteria Brevis; Let there be night; Dolce Farniente; txetrU. (Moscow Contemp Music Ens/A. Vinogradov)

① **LDC288 060** (9/93)
Contemporary Listening—Kasparov
Kasparov: Landscape; Nevermore (exc); Credo; Cantus firmus; Postlude; Variations (1990); Silencium. (Moscow Contemp Music Ens/A. Vinogradov)

① **LDC288 062** (9/93)
Contemporary Listening—Ekimovski
Ekimovski: Chamber Variations; Double Chamber Variations; Cantabile Quartet; Mandala; Prelude and Fugue; Up in the hunting dogs. (Moscow Contemp Music Ens/A. Vinogradov, L. Golub)

① **RUS088 085** (1/95)
Lyatoshynsky—Orchestral Works
Lyatoshynsky: Polish Suite, Op. 60; Overture, Op. 20; Intermezzo; Lyric Poem, Op. 66; Fantastic March, Op. 3. (Young Russia State SO/V. Baley)

Centaur

① **CRC2025** (9/89)
Dohnányi: Piano Works
Dohnányi: Pieces, Op.2 (exc); Rhapsodies (exc); Winterreigen, Op.13 (exc); Pieces, Op.17 (exc); Pieces, Op.23 (exc); Concert Etudes, Op.28 (exc); Coppélia Waltz; Pieces, Op.41 (exc); Ruralia Hungarica (exc). (M. Hallman)

① **CRC2036** (10/89)
Busoni—Piano Works & Transcriptions
Bach: Solo Violin Partitas and Sonatas (exc); *Busoni:* Fantasia contrappuntistica (exc); *Liszt:* Mephisto Waltz 1, S514. (C. O'Riley)

① **CRC2050** (4/91)
Crumb: Piano Works
Crumb: Gnomic Variations; Makrokosmos I; Piano Pieces (1962). (J. Jacob)

① **CRC2101** (12/91)
Christmas on Guitar
Traditional: Angels we have heard on high; O come all ye faithful; First Nowell; Joy to the world; *Adam:* Minuit, Chrétiens (exc); *Bach:* Cantata 147; *Schubert:* Ave Maria, D839; *Traditional:* Greensleeves (What Child is this?); It came upon the midnight clear; I wonder as I wander; *Bach:* Cantata 140; Yon: Gesù Bambino; *Traditional:* Stille Nacht; Deck the hall. (G. de Chiaro)

① **CRC2164** (3/94)
Ferruccio Tagliavini—Early Operatic Recordings
Donizetti: Elisir d'amore (exc); *Verdi:* Rigoletto (exc); *Puccini:* Bohème (exc); *Mascagni:* Amico Fritz (exc); *Cilea:* Arlesiana (exc); *Verdi:* Falstaff (exc); *Wolf-Ferrari:* Quattro rusteghi (exc); *Bellini:* Sonnambula (exc); *Lombardi* (exc); *Puccini:* Tosca (exc); *Rossini:* Barbiere di Siviglia (exc); *Puccini:* Tosca (exc); *Massenet:* Manon (exc); A. Thomas: Mignon (exc); *Puccini:* Bohème (exc). (Ferruccio Tagliavini, M. Olivero, P. Tassinari, M. Huder, E. Mascherini, EIAR Orch/U. Tansini)

① **CRC2176** (2/95)
Works by Soulima Stravinsky
S. Stravinsky: Piano Trio; Encounters; Violin and Piano Pieces; Violin and Piano Etudes. (T. Moore, C. Pegis, E. Gilgore)

① **CRC2205** (5/95)
Ives—Orchestral Works
Ives: Universe Symphony; Orchestral Set II; Unanswered Question. (Cincinnati Philh/G. Samuel, CCM Perc Ens, CCM Chbr Ch)

Classic FM

① **CFMCD1783** (9/95)
Vision of Peace
Anon: Lent (exc); Pentecost (exc); Holy Week (exc); Holy Week (exc); Festival of the Virgin Mary (exc); Requiem (exc); Processions and Dedications (exc); Feast Days (exc); Saints' Days (exc); Funeral Chants (exc); Gregorian Chants for the Church's year (exc); Scriptural meditation; *Bévenot:* Compline (exc). (Ampleforth Abbey Monastic Ch)

Chandos

① **CHAN0501** (8/89)
Bach & Buxtehude: Organ Works
Bach: Prelude and Fugue, BWV533; Prelude and Fugue, BWV546; Orgel-Büchlein, BWV599-644 (exc); Liebster Jesu, BWV731; *Buxtehude:* Prelude and Fugue, BuxWV153; Herr Christ, der einig Gottes Sohn, BuxWV192; Wie schön leuchtet der Morgenstern, BuxWV223; Passacaglia, BuxWV161. (P. Kee)

① **CHAN0502** (9/90)
Vivaldi—Trio Sonatas
Vivaldi: Trio Sonata, RV76; Trio Sonata, RV72; Sonatas, Op. 1 (exc); Trio Sonata, RV70; Trio Sonata, RV71; Violin Sonata, RV29. (Purcell Qt)

① **CHAN0504** (8/89)
Handel—Chandos Anthems Vol. 2
Handel: Chandos Anthem 4a; Chandos Anthem 5b; Chandos Anthem 6. (L. Dawson, I. Partridge, The Sixteen, The Sixteen Orch/H. Christophers)

① **CHAN0505** (2/90)
Handel—Chandos Anthems Vol. 3
Handel: Chandos Anthem 7; Chandos Anthem 8; Chandos Anthem 9. (P. Kwella, J. Bowman, I. Partridge, M. George, The Sixteen, The Sixteen Orch/H. Christophers)

① **CHAN0506** (10/89)
Bach—Organ Works
Bach: Fantasia and Fugue, BWV542; Orgel-Büchlein, BWV599-644 (exc); Prelude and Fugue, BWV531; Chorales, BWV651-668 (exc); Erbarm' dich, BWV721; Prelude and Fugue, BWV544. (P. Kee)

① **CHAN0511** (6/91)
Vivaldi—String Sonatas, Vol.2
Vivaldi: Sonatas, Op. 1 (exc); Violin Sonata, RV2; Manchester Sonatas (exc); Trio Sonata, RV68; Trio Sonata, RV77. (Purcell Qt)

① **CHAN0512** (4/92)
Telemann, Vol.2—Ouverture burlesque
Telemann: Violin Concerto 9; Violin Concerto in F sharp minor; Ouverture burlesque; 2-Flute, Violin and Cello Concerto; 2-Violin Concerto in G. (R. Brown, S. Peasgood, M. Comberti, J. Coe, Collegium Musicum 90, S. Standage (vn/dir))

① **CHAN0513** (2/91)
Tallis: Sacred Choral Works
Tallis: Spem in alium; Te lucis ante terminum I; O nata lux; Lamentations of Jeremiah; O sacrum convivium; Jesu salvator saeculi; Salvator mundi I; Loquebantur variis linguis; Gaude gloriosa Dei mater. (The Sixteen/H. Christophers)

① **CHAN0517** (3/92)
Handel—Sacred Choral works
Handel: Nisi Dominus; Silete Venti; Dixit Dominus. (L. Dawson, Lynda Russell, C. Brett, I. Partridge, M. George, The Sixteen, The Sixteen Orch/H. Christophers)

① **CHAN0518** (7/91)
Vivaldi & Bach—Choral Works
Vivaldi: Introduzione in Gloria, RV642; Gloria, RV589; *Bach:* Magnificat, BWV243. (E. Kirkby, T. Bonner, M. Chance, J.M. Ainsley, S. Varcoe, Collegium Musicum 90 Chor, Collegium Musicum 90/R. Hickox)

① **CHAN0519** (4/92)
Telemann—La Changeante
Telemann: Violin Concerto in A minor; Flute and Violin Concerto in E minor; 4-Violin Concerto in A; Violin Concerto 3; La Changeante Suite; Concerto, TWV40: 202. (R. Brown, M. Comberti, M. Golding, A. Manze, Collegium Musicum 90, S. Standage (vn/dir), S. Standage)

ⓘ **CHAN0525** (4/93)
Telemann—Domestic Music, Vol.3
Telemann: Musique de Table (exc); Singe-, Spiel- und Generalbass-Übungen (exc); Concerts et six Suites (exc); Moralische Cantaten II (exc); 2-Violin Sonata; Serious and lighthearted odes (exc); Quartet, TWV43: G 12. (Collegium Musicum 90, S. Standage (vn/dir))

ⓘ **CHAN0527** (12/92)
Bach—Organ Works, Vol.3
Bach: Toccata and Fugue, BWV565; Chorales, BWV651-668 (exc); Prelude and Fugue, BWV553; Prelude and Fugue, BWV554; Prelude and Fugue, BWV555; Prelude and Fugue, BWV556; Prelude and Fugue, BWV557; Prelude and Fugue, BWV558; Prelude and Fugue, BWV559; Prelude and Fugue, BWV560; Prelude and Fugue, BWV549; Allein Gott, BWV711; Neumeister Chorales, BWV1090-1120 (exc); Ach Gott und Herr, BWV714. (P. Kee)

ⓘ **CHAN0528** (3/93)
Vivaldi—Double Concertos
Vivaldi: Concerto, RV505; Concerto, RV535; Concerto, RV511; Concerto, RV531; Concerto, RV523; Concerto, RV554. (Collegium Musicum 90, S. Standage)

ⓘ **CHAN0530** (5/93)
Baroque Violin Concertos
Bach: Violin Concerto, BWV1052; Violin Concerto, BWV1056; *Bonporti:* Concerti a quattro, Op.11 (exc); *Vivaldi:* Concerto, RV208. (S. Standage (vn/dir), Collegium Musicum 90)

ⓘ **CHAN0531** (6/93)
Baroque Violin & Harpsichord Sonatas
Leclair: Violin Sonatas, Op. 5 (exc); Violin Sonatas, Op. 9 (exc); *Mondonville:* Sonatas, Op. 3 (exc); *Guillemain:* Violin Sonatas, Op. 1 (exc); *Duphly:* Pièces de clavecin (exc); *Forqueray:* Pièces de viole (exc). (S. Standage, L.U. Mortensen)

ⓘ **CHAN0535** (6/93)
Baroque Flute Concertos
Agrell: Flute Concerto in D; *Scheibe:* Flute Concerto in A; Flute Concerto in D; *Hasse:* Flute Concerto in G. (M. Bania, I. Spranger, Concerto Copenhagen/A. Manze)

ⓘ **CHAN0538** (10/94)
Elizabethan Lute Songs
Campion: Ayres, Bk.1 (exc); Ayres (1601) (exc); *Ford:* Musicke of Sundrie Kindes I (exc); *Danyel:* Songs for the Lute (exc); *Rosseter:* What then is love but mourning; No grave for woe; Shall I come if I swim?; *Dowland:* First Book of Songs (exc); Second Booke of Songs (exc); *Anon:* Miserere my Maker; *A. Holborne:* Heres paternus; Night Watch; Muy linda; Fantasia 3. (M. Chance, C. Wilson)

ⓘ **CHAN0539** (10/93)
Buxtehude/Bruhns—Organ Works
Buxtehude: Auf meinen lieben Gott, BuxWV179; Gott der Vater wohn uns bei, BuxWV190; Nun komm, der Heiden Heiland, BuxWV211; Nimm von uns, BuxWV207; Puer natus, BuxWV217; Von Gott will ich, BuxWV221; *Bruhns:* Prelude and Fugue in E minor I; Prelude and Fugue in E minor II; Prelude and Fugue in G; Prelude and Fugue in G minor; Nun komm der Heiden Heiland. (P. Kee)

ⓘ **CHAN0540** (12/93)
J.C.Bach—Orchestral Works
J. C. Bach: Grand Overtures, Op. 18 (exc); Adriano in Siria (exc); Symphonies, Op. 6 (exc); Sinfonia concertante, T289/4. (AAM, S. Standage)

ⓘ **CHAN0541** (5/94)
Music from the Court of Frederick the Great
C.P.E. Bach: Trio Sonata, H578; *Benda:* Sonata in A minor; *Frederick the Great:* Flute Sonata in C; *C.P.E. Bach:* Kenner I (exc); *Graun:* Trio in G minor; *Quantz:* Flute Concerto in A. (R. Brown, M. Comberti, J. Coe, L.U. Mortensen, S. Standage (vn/dir))

ⓘ **CHAN0544** (2/94)
French Baroque Flute Music
Leclair: Violin Sonatas, Op. 2 (exc); *Blavet:* Flute Sonatas, Op. 2 (exc); *Rameau:* Pièces de clavecin en concerts (exc); *M. La Barre:* Flûte transversière II (exc); *Hotteterre:* Airs et Brunettes (exc); *Leclair:* Violin Sonatas, Op. 9 (exc). (R. Brown, M Caudle, J. Johnstone)

ⓘ **CHAN0545** (11/93)
French Baroque Harpsichord Works
Anglebert: Harpsichord Works (exc); *Couperin:* Art de toucher le clavecin (exc); Livre de clavecin I (exc); *Forqueray:* Pièces de viole (exc); *Rameau:* Pièces de clavecin (exc). (S. Yates)

ⓘ **CHAN0547** (7/94)
Telemann—Orchestral Works
Telemann: 3-Horn & Violin Concerto; Overture-Suite, TWV55: C 5; Overture-Suite in F, TWV55: F 11; Concerto

in G. (A. Halstead, C. Rutherford, R. Diaz, Collegium Musicum 90, S. Standage (vn/dir))

ⓘ **CHAN0550** (7/94)
Scheibe—Sinfonias
Scheibe: Sörge- og Klagesange over Dronning Lovise (exc); Sinfonia a 16 in D; Sinfonia a 4 in B flat I; Sinfonia a 4 in B flat II; Sörgesange over Kong Frederik V (exc); Sinfonia a 4 in A; Tempel des Ruhmes (exc). (Concerto Copenhagen, A. Manze (vn/dir))

ⓘ **CHAN0553** (9/94)
Post-Restoration English Organ Works
C. Gibbons: Verse in D minor; Verse in A minor; *Locke:* Voluntaries (exc); *Anon:* Voluntary for double organ; *Blow:* Verse in G; Verse in A minor; Verse in C; Verse for the Double Organ in G; Verse in G minor; Voluntary for the Cornet and Echo; *Purcell:* Organ Voluntaries, Z717-20 (exc); Verse, Z716; *Clarke:* Suite in D (exc); Trumpet Tune and Air; *Croft:* Voluntary in G; Voluntary in A minor; Voluntary in D; *Anon:* Voluntary for the Trumpet Stop. (R. Woolley)

ⓘ **CHAN0559** (11/94)
Gibbons—Organ and Choral Works
Gibbons: If ye be risen again with Christ; O Lord, in Thy wrath; Almighty God, who by Thy Son; O clap your hands; We praise Thee, O Father; So God loved the world; O God the king of glory; Fantasias; Preludes. (St John's College Ch/C. Robinson, R. Woolley)

ⓘ **CHAN0560** (11/94)
Spanish and Portuguese Haprsichord Music
Cabezón: Diferencias sobre La dama de demanda; Diferencias sobre el canto llano del Caballero; Diferencias sobre la Gallarda Milanesa; Pavana con su glosa; *Tientos III;* Farbordones; Cantus firmus; *Ximénez:* Obra del Primer Tono de lleno; *Coelho:* Flores de Música (exc); *Anon:* Españoleta; *Carreira:* Canção a Quatro glosada; *H. Cabezón:* Dulce memoria; *Cabanilles:* Passacalles (exc); Tientos (exc). (S. Yates)

ⓘ **CHAN0562** (3/95)
Musica Mediterranea
Willaert: A quand'haveva; O bene mio; *Nola:* Cingari simo venit'a giocare; *D. Ortiz:* Trattado de glosas (exc); *Mudarra:* Tres Libros (vocal works) (exc); *Barberiis:* Madonna qual certezza; *Valderrábano:* Discantar sobre un punto; *A. Valente:* Tenore del passo e mezzo; *Molinaro:* Lute Bk I (exc); *Picchi:* Intavolatura di Balli (exc); *Piccinini:* Chiaccone; *Bottegari:* Non si vedde giamai; *G. Bassano:* Vestiva i colli; *Rossi:* Arie di passacaglia; *Arañés:* Sarao de la Chacona; *Anon:* Riu, riu, chiu; Recercar; Donna vagh'e leggiadra; Folias. (Kithara)

ⓘ **CHAN0564** (2/95)
Leclair—Violin Concertos, Volume 2
Leclair: Concertos, Op. 7 (exc); Concertos, Op. 7 (exc); Concertos, Op. 10 (exc). (R. Brown, Collegium Musicum 90, S. Standage (vn/dir)/S. Standage)

ⓘ **CHAN0574** (12/95)
English Virginals Music
Byrd: Prelude, BK12; Fantasia, BK13; Pavan, BK54; Galliard, BK55; Barley Break, BK92; Pavan and Galliard, BK3; Woods so wild, BK85; Hugh Ashton's Ground, BK20; Bells, BK98; *Gibbons:* Fantasias (exc); *Anon:* My Lady Carey's Dompe; *Tomkins:* Barafostus' Dream; *Aston:* Homepype; *J. Bull:* In Nomine. (S. Yates)

ⓘ **CHAN0578** (8/95)
The Early Byrd
Byrd: All in a garden green, BK56; Lavolta, BK90; O mistress mine, BK83; Wilson's Wild, BK37; Farewell, false love; O Lord, how vain; Psalmes, Sonets and Songs (1588) (exc); Triumph with pleasant melody; Truth at the First; Ad Dominum cum tribularer; Cantiones Sacrae (1575) (exc). (S. Yates, I Fagiolini, Fretwork)

ⓘ **CHAN0581** (10/95)
Auld Scottish Sangs
Traditional: Scots Musical Museum (exc); *Oswald:* Collection of Scot's Tunes (exc); *Niël Gow:* Collection of Strathspey Reels (exc); Second Collection of Strathspey Reels (exc); *Traditional:* McIntosh's Lament; *Haydn:* What can a young lassie do; Auld Rob Morris; Robert Bruce's March to Bannockburn; *Beethoven:* Songs, WoO158c (exc); Scottish Songs, WoO156 (exc); Scottish Songs, Op. 108 (exc); National Airs with Variations, Op. 107 (exc); *Weber:* Scottish National Songs (exc); *Hummel:* Scottish Airs (exc); *J. Koželuch:* Scottish Airs (exc). (Scottish Early Music Consort)

ⓘ **CHAN4501** (11/92)
The World's Most Beautiful Melodies
Dvořák: Gipsy Melodies (exc); *Gounod:* Ave Maria; *Brahms:* Volks-Kinderlieder (exc); *Purcell-Cockram:* Passing by; *Puccini:* Madama Butterfly (exc); *Tchaikovsky:* Songs, Op. 6 (exc); *Dvořák:* Rusalka (exc); *Puccini:* Turandot (exc); *Delibes:* Filles de Cadiz (exc); *Traditional:* My

love is like a red, red rose; *Schubert:* Du bist die Ruh', D776; *Debussy:* Préludes (exc); *Puccini:* Gianni Schicchi (exc); *Mozart:* Nozze di Figaro (exc); *Sullivan:* Lost chord. (P. McCann, I. Robertson, Black Dyke Mills Band/P. Parkes)

ⓘ **CHAN4505** (7/93)
Black Dyke plays Rossini
Rossini: Scala di seta (exc); Barbiere di Siviglia (exc); Barbiere di Siviglia (exc); Cenerentola (exc); Tancredi (exc); Guillaume Tell (exc); Boutique Fantasque (exc). (P. McCann, J. Clough, Black Dyke Mills Band/P. Parkes/T. Walmsley)

ⓘ **CHAN4506** (9/93)
Life Divine—4 Famous Test-Pieces
Fletcher: Labour and Love; *Bliss:* Kenilworth; *C. Jenkins:* Life Divine; *Hespe:* Three Musketeers. (Black Dyke Mills Band/P. Parkes/D. Broadbent)

ⓘ **CHAN4507** (9/93)
A Tribute to Elgar, Delius and Vaughan Williams
Handel: Overture in D minor; *Elgar:* Wand of Youth Suite 1 (exc); Wand of Youth Suite 2 (exc); Bavarian Dances; *Delius:* Marche-caprice; *Holst:* Perfect Fool (exc). (Black Dyke Mills Band/P. Parkes)

ⓘ **CHAN4508** (7/93)
Epic Brass—British Music for Brass Band
Vinter: James Cook; *Fletcher:* Epic Symphony; *Elgar:* Severn Suite; *Ireland:* Comedy Overture; *Ball:* Wayfarer Sinfonietta. (Black Dyke Mills Band/R. Newsome)

ⓘ **CHAN4513** (11/93)
British Bandsman Centenary Concert
Steadman-Allen: Centenary Fanfare (1987); Beacons; *J. Ord Hume:* BB & CF; *Sullivan:* Yeomen of the Guard (exc); *P. Graham:* Brilliante; *Paganini:* Moto perpetuo, Op. 11; *Grieg:* Elegiac melodies (exc); *Ball:* Journey into Freedom; *Broadbent:* British Bandsman; *Howarth:* Legends; *Rimsky-Korsakov:* Tale of Tsar Saltan (exc); *Sullivan:* Pineapple Poll (exc); *Elgar:* Pomp and Circumstance Marches (exc); *Sullivan:* Lost chord. (W. Lang, M. Murphy, J. Shepherd, P. McCann, R. Childs, N. Childs, Besses o' the Barn Band, Black Dyke Mills Band, Yorkshire Imperial Band/H. Mortimer/R. Newsome/P. Parkes/James Scott)

ⓘ **CHAN4514** (9/93)
Black Dyke Mills Band play Overtures
Verdi: Forza del destino (exc); *Suppè:* Schöne Galathee (exc); Leichte Kavallerie (exc); *Nicolai:* Lustigen Weiber von Windsor (exc); *Rossini:* Italiana in Algeri (exc); *Donizetti:* Fille du régiment (exc); *Weber:* Oberon (exc); *Auber:* Domino noir (exc). (Black Dyke Mills Band/P. Parkes/D. Hurst)

ⓘ **CHAN4522** (3/94)
'Volcano'—live at the Royal Albert Hall, London
Simpson: Volcano; *P. Huber:* Symphonic Music; *Vinter:* John O'Gaunt; *Calvert:* Introduction, Elegy and Caprice; *Gregson:* Connotations. (Black Dyke Mills Band/P. Parkes)

ⓘ **CHAN4523** (10/94)
Concerto
Horovitz: Euphonium Concerto; *Sparke:* Concerto Grosso; *Rimsky-Korsakov:* Trombone Concerto; *D. Wright:* Trio Concerto; *G. Wood:* Scherzino. (R. Childs, R. Webster, P. Shaw, S. Smith, N. Law, Black Dyke Mills Band/P. Parkes)

ⓘ **CHAN4528** (1/94)
The Lion and the Eagle
Sullivan: Yeomen of the Guard (exc); *French:* Phil the Fluter's Ball (exc); *Various:* National Anthems (exc); *Holst:* Suite 2 (exc); *G. Langford:* Scottish Lament; *Stephen Foster Fantasy;* *Elgar:* Pomp and Circumstance Marches (exc); *Sousa:* Stars and Stripes Forever; *Ball:* Rhapsody on Negro Spirituals I; *Sharpe:* Music of George Gershwin. (Black Dyke Mills Band/R. Newsome)

ⓘ **CHAN4531** (11/95)
Legend in Brass
Ball: Kingdom Triumphant; *Curnow:* Legend in Brass; *C. Jenkins:* Coriolanus; *Leidzen:* Sinfonietta; *R. Newton:* Percussion Variations; *R. Redhead:* Pastoral Symphony. (Sellers Engin Band/P. McCann/N. Law)

ⓘ **CHAN6502** (1/91)
Delius—Orchestral Works
Delius: First cuckoo; Summer night on the river; Song before sunrise; Aquarelles; Hassan (exc); Fennimore and Gerda Intermezzo; Sonata for strings; Irmelin Prelude. (Bournemouth Sinfonietta/N. del Mar)

ⓘ **CHAN6503** (3/91)
Orchestral works
Rossini: Boutique fantasque (exc); *Dukas:* Apprenti sorcier; *Saint-Saëns:* Danse macabre. (SNO/A. Gibson)

Embarquement pour Cythère; 2-piano Sonata. (S. Tanyel, Jeremy Brown)

① **CHAN8521/2** (9/87)
Rachmaninov—Works for Piano & Orchestra
Rachmaninov: Piano Concerto 1; Piano Concerto 2; Piano Concerto 3; Piano Concerto 4; Paganini Rhapsody. (E. Wild, RPO/J. Horenstein)

① **CHAN8524** (8/87)
Grieg—Orchestral Works
Grieg: Peer Gynt Suites (exc); Elegiac Melodies; Sigurd Jorsalfar, Op. 56; Symphonic Dances. (Ulster Orch/V. Handley)

① **CHAN8525** (11/89)
Music from Estonia, Vol 1
Eller: Elegia; Five Pieces; Dawn; Raid: Symphony 1. (E. Pierce, SNO/N. Järvi)

① **CHAN8536/7** (2/88)
Mozart—Piano Trios
Mozart: Divertimento, K254; Piano Trio, K496; Piano Trio, K502; Piano Trio, K542; Piano Trio, K548; Piano Trio, K564. (Borodin Trio)

① **CHAN8538** (3/88)
R. Strauss: Orchestral & Vocal Works
R. Strauss: Also sprach Zarathustra; Don Juan; Lieder, Op. 43 (exc); Lieder, Op. 27 (exc). (F. Lott, SNO/N. Järvi)

① **CHAN8542** (11/87)
Khachaturian—Orchestral Works
Khachaturian: Piano Concerto; Gayaneh (exc); Masquerade (exc). (C. Orbelian, SNO/N. Järvi)

① **CHAN8549** (11/87)
English Music for Clarinet and Piano
Finzi: Bagatelles; Horovitz: Sonatina; Richardson: Roundelay; Ireland: Fantasy-sonata; Arnold: Clarinet Sonatina, Op.29; P.Harvey: Gershwin Suite. (G. de Peyer, G. Pryor)

① **CHAN8550** (10/87)
Brahms & Schumann: Viola & Piano Works
Brahms: Viola Sonata 1; Viola Sonata 2; Schumann: Märchenbilder. (N. Imai, R. Vignoles)

① **CHAN8555** (4/88)
Russian Duos
Shostakovich: Preludes, Op.34 (exc); Glazunov: Elegy, Op.17; Spanish Serenade, Op.20/2; Minstrel's Song, Op.71; Prokofiev: Stone Flower (exc); Cinderella (exc); Romeo and Juliet (exc); Tale of the Buffoon (exc). (E. Turovsky, Y. Turovsky, P. Pettinger)

① **CHAN8557** (12/87)
R. Strauss—Vocal and Orchestral Works
R. Strauss: Alpensinfonie; Lieder, Op. 48 (exc); Lieder, Op. 37 (exc); Lieder, Op. 88 (exc); Lieder, Op. 27 (exc). (F. Lott, E. Paling, SNO/N. Järvi)

① **CHAN8560** (6/88)
Billy Mayerl: Piano Works
Mayerl: Legends of King Arthur (exc); Japanese Pictures (exc); April's Fool; Harp of the Winds; Marigold; Railroad Rhythm; Shallow Waters; From a Spanish Lattice; Song of the Fir-Tree; Nimble-Fingered Gentleman; Evening Primrose; Four Aces (exc); Joker. (E. Parkin)

① **CHAN8561** (7/88)
Treasures of Operetta, Vol. 2
Jacobi: Sybil (exc); Posford: Balalaika (exc); Monckton: Quaker Girl (exc); Millöcker: Arme Jonathan (exc); Ziehrer: Schätzmeister (exc); German: Merrie England (exc); Ziehrer: Fremdenführer (exc); Lehár: Lustige Witwe (exc); Benatzky: Im weissen Rössl (exc); Lehár: Paganini (exc); Messager: Monsieur Beaucaire (exc); J. Strauss II: Casanova (exc). (M. Hill Smith, P. Morrison, Ambrosian Sngrs, Chandos Concert Orch/S. Barry)

① **CHAN8572** (3/88)
R. Strauss: Orchestral & Vocal Works
R.Strauss: Sinfonia domestica; Till Eulenspiegel; Lieder, Op. 10 (exc); Lieder, Op. 56 (exc). (F. Lott, SNO/N. Järvi)

① **CHAN8575** (5/88)
Dvořák—Orchestral Works
Dvořák: Symphony 3; Carnival; Symphonic Variations. (SNO/N. Järvi)

① **CHAN8578** (9/88)
Hommages à Haydn, Roussel et Fauré
Debussy: Hommage à Haydn; Dukas: Hommage élégiaque; Hahn: Thème varié; Indy: Menuet, Op.65; Ravel: Menuet sur le nom de Haydn; Widor: Fugue; Delage: À Roussel; Honegger: Hommage à Albert Roussel; Poulenc: Pièce brève; Tansman: Suite variée (exc); Ibert: Toccata; Beck: Fox-trot; Hoérée: Fanfare; Milhaud: Quatrain à Albert Roussel; Ravel: Berceuse; Schmitt: In memoriam Gabriel Fauré; Koechlin: Hommage à Gabriel Fauré; Ladmirault: Hommage à Gabriel Fauré; Roger-Ducasse: Hommage à Gabriel Fauré. (M. Fingerhut, M. Cable, W. Bennett, K. Sillito, C. Benson)

① **CHAN8579** (6/88)
Russian Cello Concertos
Glazunov: Chant du ménéstrel; Kabalevsky: Cello Concerto 2; Khachaturian: Cello Concerto. (R. Wallfisch, LPO/B. Thomson)

① **CHAN8582** (3/88)
Beethoven: Piano Sonatas
Beethoven: Piano Sonata 1; Piano Sonata 14; Piano Sonata 23. (I. Margalit)

① **CHAN8587** (7/88)
Shostakovich: Orchestral Works
Shostakovich: Symphony 9; Festive Overture; Katerina Izmaylova (exc); Taiti trot. (SNO/N. Järvi)

① **CHAN8591** (1/89)
Purcell—Chamber Works
Purcell: Sonatas, Z790-801 (exc); Pavan, Z752; Pavans, Z748-51 (exc). (R. Browder, Purcell Qt)

① **CHAN8593** (8/88)
Works for String Orchestra
Bloch: Concerto grosso 1; Barber: Adagio for Strings; Grieg: Holberg Suite; Puccini: Crisantemi. (Israel CO/Y. Talmi, I. Rob)

① **CHAN8603** (7/89)
Bax: Works for Piano Duet
Bax: 2-Piano Sonata; Red Autumn; Hardanger; Poisoned fountain; Devil that tempted St Anthony; Moy Mell. (Jeremy Brown, S. Tanyel)

① **CHAN8609** (11/88)
Flute Fantasie—Virtuoso French Flute Repertoire
Groviez: Romance et Scherzo; Gaubert: Fantaisie; Enescu: Cantabile e presto; Sancan: Sonatine; Taffanel: Andante pastorale et Scherzettino; Gaubert: Nocturne; Fauré: Morceau de lecture; Büsser: Prélude; Fauré: Fantaisie; Ganne: Andante et Scherzo. (S. Milan, I. Brown)

① **CHAN8610** (5/89)
Elgar—Orchestral Works
Elgar: Enigma Variations; Sanguine Fan (Cpte); Grania and Diarmid (exc). (J. Miller, LPO/B. Thomson)

① **CHAN8611** (10/88)
Russian Orchestral Works
Kalinnikov: Symphony 1; Glazunov: Sea; Spring. (SNO/N. Järvi)

① **CHAN8613** (4/89)
Mozart: Works for Flute and Orchestra
Mozart: Flute Concerto, K313; Flute Concerto, K314; Andante, K315; Rondo, KAnh184. (S. Milan, ECO/R. Leppard)

① **CHAN8614** (5/90)
Rachmaninov & Kalinnikov: Orchestral Works
Rachmaninov: Symphony 3; Kalinnikov: Intermezzo 1; Intermezzo 2. (LSO/N. Järvi)

① **CHAN8616** (10/90)
Beethoven: Piano Works
Beethoven: Variations, Op. 35; Variations, Op. 34; Rondos, Op. 51; Bagatelles (exc). (L. Lortie)

① **CHAN8617** (10/88)
Works for Harmonica and Orchestra
Vaughan Williams: Romance; Tausky: Concertino; Moody: Little Suite; Jacob: Pieces. (T. Reilly, ASMF/N. Marriner)

① **CHAN8618** (10/88)
Works for Clarinet and Orchestra
Copland: Clarinet Concerto; Lutoslawski: Dance Preludes; Nielsen: Clarinet Concerto. (J. Hilton, SNO/M. Bamert)

① **CHAN8620** (5/89)
Ravel: Piano Music, Vol.1
Ravel: Pavane pour une infante défunte; Tombeau de Couperin; Sérénade grotesque; Jeux d'eau; Valses nobles et sentimentales; La Valse. (L. Lortie)

① **CHAN8621** (12/88)
French Chamber Music
Ravel: Introduction and Allegro; Debussy: Danse sacrée et danse profane; Sonata for flute, viola and harp; Saint-Saëns: Fantaisie, Op.124; Roussel: Sérénade. (S. Kanga, ASMF Chbr Ens, K. Sillito)

① **CHAN8622** (9/88)
Remembering Prague
Rak: First Love; Hiroshima; Danza Mauretana; Cry of the Guitar; Hora; Remembering Prague; Czech Chorale; Pavanne. (S. Rak)

① **CHAN8625** (10/89)
Bax: Choral Works
Bax: Enchanted Summer; Walsinghame; Fatherland. (A. Williams-King, L. McWhirter, M. Hill, Brighton Fest Chor, RPO/V. Handley)

① **CHAN8628** (12/88)
Bax—Symphony No 7; Songs
Bax: Symphony 7; Glamour; Slumber Song; Eternity; Lyke-wake. (M. Hill, LPO/B. Thomson)

① **CHAN8631** (1/89)
R. Strauss: Orchestral & Vocal Works
R. Strauss: Don Quixote; Romanze, Av75; Lieder, Op. 27 (exc); Lieder, Op. 33 (exc). (R. Wallfisch, F. Lott, SNO/N. Järvi, J. Harrington)

① **CHAN8632** (12/88)
Honegger: Orchestral Works
Honegger: Concerto da Camera; Prélude, arioso et fugue; Symphony 2. (T. Hutchins, P-V. Plante, Montreal i Musici/Y. Turovsky)

① **CHAN8634** (6/89)
Bartók: String Quartets
Bartók: String Quartet 3; String Quartet 4; String Quartet 5. (Chilingirian Qt)

① **CHAN8637** (10/88)
Poulenc—Piano Works, Vol.1
Poulenc: Suite in C; Biches (exc); Mouvements perpétuels; Soirées de Nazelles; Intermezzi (exc); Valse-improvisation; Pièces (1928); Badinage; Napoli. (E. Parkin)

① **CHAN8639** (9/89)
Moeran: Orchestral Works
Moeran: Rhapsody 1; Rhapsody 2; Rhapsody 3; In the mountain country. (M. Fingerhut, Ulster Orch/V. Handley)

① **CHAN8641/2** (2/89)
Elgar—Dream of Gerontius. Parry—Choral Works
Elgar: Dream of Gerontius (Cpte); Parry: Blest Pair of Sirens; I was glad. (F. Palmer, A. Davies, G. Howell, LSC, LSO/R. Hickox)

① **CHAN8643** (2/89)
Warlock Songs
Warlock: Wind from the West; Whenas the rye; My ghostly Fader; Lullaby; As ever I saw; Take, o take those lips away; Bayly berith the bell away; Sweet content; Mourn no moe; There is a lady sweet and kind; Play Acting; Captain Stratton's Fancy; Mr Belloc's Fancy; Late Summer; Hey troly loly lo; Bachelor; Reset sweet nymphs; Piggesnie; Sleep; Autumn Twilight; Milkmaids; I held love's head; Thou gav'st me leave to kiss; Yarmouth Fair; Ha'nacker Mill; Night; My Own Country; Walking the Woods; Traditional: First Mercy; Warlock: Jolly Shepherd; Passing by; Fox. (B. Luxon, D. Willison)

① **CHAN8647** (10/89)
Ravel: Piano Music, Vol.2
Ravel: Gaspard de la nuit; Menuet antique; Menuet sur le nom de Haydn; A la manière de Borodine; A la manière de Chabrier; Prélude; Miroirs; Sonatine. (L. Lortie)

① **CHAN8651** (4/89)
Vivaldi: Concertos
Vivaldi: Concerto, RV542; Concerto, RV548; Concerto, RV537; Concerto, RV575; Concerto, RV447; Concerti Grossi, Op. 3 (exc). (E. Turovsky, G. Soly, T. Baskin, J. Thompson, R. Early, C. Prévost, L. Hall, A. Aubut, B. Hurtubise, E. Skerjanc, Montreal I Musici/Y. Turovsky)

① **CHAN8652** (7/89)
Russian Music for String Duo
Stravinsky: Suite italienne (violin); Glière: Pieces, Op.39; A. Tcherepnin: String Duo, Op.49; Prokofiev: Sonata, Op.56. (E. Turovsky, Y. Turovsky)

① **CHAN8655** (6/89)
Haydn, Mozart & Beethoven: Chamber Works
Haydn: Keyboard Trio 27; Mozart: Piano Trio, K498; Beethoven: Piano Trios (exc). (Borodin Trio, J. Campbell)

① **CHAN8656** (11/89)
Music from Estonia, Volume 2
Lemba: Symphony in C sharp minor; Tobias: Julius Caesar Ov; Eller: Twilight; Tormis: Overture 2; Pärt: Cantus in memory of Benjamin Britten. (SNO/N. Järvi)

① **CHAN8657** (6/89)
Britten—Vocal Works
Britten: Illuminations; Chansons françaises; Serenade. (F. Lott, A. Rolfe Johnson, M. Thompson, SNO/B. Thomson)

① **CHAN8658** (3/89)
Poulenc & Charpentier: Sacred Choral Works
M-A. Charpentier: Messe de minuit, H9; Poulenc: Motets pour le temps de Noël; Salve regina; Motets pour un temps de pénitence. (A. Walker, A. Flutter, J. Turnbull, B. Cooper, A. Rupp, St John's College Ch, CLS/G. Guest)

Ⓒ **CHAN8818** (7/91)
Bliss—Vocal and Orchestral works
Bliss: Cello Concerto; Hymn to Apollo; Enchantress. (R. Wallfisch, L. Finnie, Ulster Orch/V. Handley)

Ⓒ **CHAN8821** (8/90)
Diepenbrock: Orchestral Works
Diepenbrock: Birds Overture; Marsyas; Elektra Suite; Hymne. (E. Verhey, Hague PO/H. Vonk)

Ⓒ **CHAN8824** (12/90)
Walton: Vocal Works
Walton: Christopher Columbus; Daphne; Through gilded trellises; Long steel grass; Old Sir Faulk; Anon in love; Song for the Lord Mayor's Table; Twelve. (J. Gomez, P. Forbes, L. Finnie, R. Gleave, M. Hill, A. Davies, J. Oxley, P. Harvey, S. Gay, Westminster Sngrs, CLS/R. Hickox)

Ⓒ **CHAN8828** (8/90)
Vaughan Williams: Orchestral Works
Vaughan Williams: Symphony 8; Hymn-tune preludes; Greensleeves fantasia; Partita. (LSO/B. Thomson)

Ⓒ **CHAN8830** (9/92)
Bush—A Little Love Music
G. Bush: Greek Love Songs; End of Love; Songs of Wonder; Little love-music; Jonson Songs. (T. Cahill, I. Partridge, B. Luxon, G. Bush)

Ⓒ **CHAN8831** (11/90)
Butterworth & Gurney: Songs
Butterworth: Shropshire Lad (Cpte); Bredon Hill; *Gurney:* Apple Orchard; Fields are full; Twa corbies; Severn meadows; Desire in Spring; Ha'nacker Mill; Down by the Salley Gardens; Hawk and Buckle; By a bierside; Sleep; Black Stitchel; Folly of being comforted; In Flanders; Epitaph; Fiddler of Dooney; Carol of the Skiddaw Yowes; Scribe; On the Downs; I praise the tender flower; Cranham Woods. (B. Luxon, D. Willison)

Ⓒ **CHAN8832/3** (11/90)
Schumann: Chamber Works
Schumann: Piano Trio 1; Piano Trio 2; Piano Trio 3; Fantasiestücke, Op. 88. (Borodin Trio)

Ⓒ **CHAN8834** (12/90)
R. Strauss: Orchestral and Vocal Works
R. Strauss: Macbeth; Rosenkavalier (exc); Lieder, Op. 44 (exc). (L. Finnie, E. Paling, SNO/N. Järvi)

Ⓒ **CHAN8840** (10/90)
La flûte enchantée
Jolivet: Flute Concerto; *Chaminade:* Flute Concertino, Op.107; *Martin:* Flute Ballade; *Godard:* Suite, Op. 116; *Saint-Saëns:* Ascanio (exc); *Ibert:* Flute Concerto. (S. Milan, M. Dussek, CLS/R. Hickox)

Ⓒ **CHAN8841** (5/91)
Walton—Film Music, Vol 4
Walton: Richard III (exc); Macbeth (exc); Major Barbara (exc). (I. Watson, ASMF/N. Marriner, J. Gielgud)

Ⓒ **CHAN8847** (12/90)
Poulenc: Piano Works
Poulenc: Humoresque; Villageoises; Improvisations; Intermezzi; Suite française; Novelettes; Novelette sur un thème de Falla; Presto; Thème varié. (E. Parkin)

Ⓒ **CHAN8848** (11/90)
Mayerl—Piano Works
Mayerl: Four Aces (exc); Mistletoe; Autumn crocus; Hollyhock; White heather; Dances in syncopation, Op. 73; Sweet William; Parade of the Sandwich-Board Men; Hop-'O-My-Thumb; Jill all alone; Aquarium Suite; Bats in the belfry; Green Tulips. (E. Parkin)

Ⓒ **CHAN8850** (10/90)
Debussy & Ravel: Orchestral Works
Debussy: Images; *Ravel:* Rapsodie espagnole; Alborada del gracioso. (Ulster Orch/Y.P. Tortelier)

Ⓒ **CHAN8851** (2/91)
Prokofiev—Piano Works, Vol.1
Prokofiev: Piano Sonata 5; Romeo and Juliet Pieces; Pieces, Op. 32; March and Scherzo. (Boris Berman)

Ⓒ **CHAN8852** (2/91)
French Orchestral Works
Dukas: Apprenti sorcier; Péri (Cpte); *Chabrier:* España; Suite pastorale. (Ulster Orch/Y.P. Tortelier)

Ⓒ **CHAN8853** (4/91)
Nielsen—Choral Works
Nielsen: Hymnus Amoris; Sleep; Springtime in Funen; Motets. (I. Nielsen, P. Elming, A. Elkrog, P. Høyer, J. Ditlevsen, Copenhagen Boys' Ch, P. Grønlund, S. Byriel, St Anne's Gymnasium Children's Chor, Danish Nat Rad Ch, Danish Nat RSO/L. Segerstam/S. Parkman)

Ⓒ **CHAN8855** (4/91)
Britten—Choral Works
Britten: Spring Symphony; Welcome Ode; Psalm 150. (E. Gale, A. Hodgson, M. Hill, Southend Boys' Ch, City of London Girls, City of London Boys, K-H. Goedicke, LSC, LSO/R. Hickox)

Ⓒ **CHAN8859** (5/91)
Martinů—Orchestral Works
Martinů: Sinfonietta giocosa; La Jolla; Toccata e due canzoni. (J. Jacobson, Bournemouth Sinfonietta, T. Vásáry)

Ⓒ **CHAN8861** (11/90)
Stanford: Orchestral Works
Stanford: Concert Piece, Op. 181; Irish Rhapsody 3; Symphony 7. (R. Wallfisch, G. Weir, Ulster Orch/V. Handley)

Ⓒ **CHAN8864** (1/91)
G. Bush: Vocal & Choral Works
G. Bush: Summer Serenade; Hesperides Songs; Menagerie; Farewell, Earth's Bliss. (Adrian Thompson, E. Parkin, S. Varcoe, Westminster Sngrs, CLS/R. Hickox)

Ⓒ **CHAN8865** (2/91)
Rossini: Opera Arias
Rossini: Italiana in Algeri (exc); Donna del Lago (exc); Signor Bruschino (exc); Adelaide di Borgogna (exc); Otello (exc); Barbiere di Siviglia (exc); Bianca e Falliero (exc); Cenerentola (exc). (D. Jones, C. Smith, K. Steffan, H. Nicholl, G. Finley, S. Birchall, Richard Hickox Sngrs, CLS/R. Hickox)

Ⓒ **CHAN8866** (9/92)
Alwyn—Concertos
Alwyn: Oboe Concerto; Concerto grosso 1; Concerto grosso 2; Concerto grosso 3. (N. Daniel, CLS/R. Hickox)

Ⓒ **CHAN8867** (10/90)
Arnold: Dances
Arnold: Cornish Dances, Op. 91; Scottish Dances, Op. 59; English Dances, Op. 27; English Dances, Op. 33; Irish Dances, Op. 126; Solitaire (exc). (Philh/B. Thomson)

Ⓒ **CHAN8870** (12/90)
Sir William Walton's Film Music Vol. 2
Walton: Battle of Britain (exc); Spitfire Prelude and Fugue; Escape me never (exc); Three sisters; Wartime Sketchbook. (ASMF/N. Marriner)

Ⓒ **CHAN8873** (9/92)
Franck/Vieuxtemps—Works for Viola
Franck: Violin Sonata; *Vieuxtemps:* Viola Sonata, Op. 36; Morceaux, Op.61 (exc); Elégie, Op. 30. (N. Imai, R. Vignoles)

Ⓒ **CHAN8874** (4/92)
Dvořák—Chamber Works
Dvořák: String Quartet 13; String Quartet, B120; Waltzes, Op. 54. (Chilingirian Qt, D. McTier)

Ⓒ **CHAN8878** (4/91)
Diepenbrock: Symphonic Songs
Diepenbrock: Hymne an die Nacht (exc); Nacht; Wenige wissen das Geheimnis; Im grossen Schweigen. (L. Finnie, C. Homberger, R. Holl, Hague PO/H. Vonk)

Ⓒ **CHAN8881** (2/91)
Prokofiev—Piano Works, Vol 2
Prokofiev: Visions fugitives; Sarcasms, Op. 17; Tales of an old grandmother; Piano Sonata 7. (Boris Berman)

Ⓒ **CHAN8882/3** (4/91)
Rachmaninov: Works for Piano & Orchestra
Rachmaninov: Piano Concerto 1; Piano Concerto 2; Piano Concerto 3; Piano Concerto 4; Paganini Rhapsody. (H. Shelley, SNO/B. Thomson)

Ⓒ **CHAN8884** (3/91)
Stanford—Orchestral Works
Stanford: Symphony 4; Irish Rhapsody 6; Oedipus (exc). (L. Mordkovitch, Ulster Orch/V. Handley)

Ⓒ **CHAN8887** (10/91)
Roussel—Piano Works
Roussel: Rustiques; Ségovia; Doute; Sonatine; Prelude and Fugue; Pieces, Op.49; Suite. (E. Parkin)

Ⓒ **CHAN8888** (8/91)
Chaminade—Piano Works
Chaminade: Pierrette, Op. 41; Contes bleus 2; Minuetto, Op. 23; Danse créole, Op. 94; Sérénade, Op. 29; Air de Ballet, Op. 30; Romances sans paroles, Op. 76 (exc); Pièces humoristiques, Op. 87 (exc); Guitare, Op. 32; Sous le masque, Op. 116; Pas des sylphes; Etudes de concert, Op. 35 (exc); Lisonjera, Op. 50; Air à danser, Op. 164; Callirhoé (exc); Toccata, Op. 39; Feuillets d'Album, Op. 98 (exc); Lolita, Op. 54. (E. Parkin)

Ⓒ **CHAN8891** (9/91)
Franck—Organ Works
Franck: Chorales (exc); Pièces (1878) (exc); Prélude, fugue et variation; Petit Offertoire. (P. Kee)

Ⓒ **CHAN8892** (4/91)
Walton—Film Music, Vol 3
Walton: Henry V (Cpte); *Farnaby:* Rosa Solis; *Anon:* Watkin's Ale; *Canteloube:* Chants d'Auvergne (exc). (I. Watson, C. Nicklin, Westminster Cath Ch, ASMF Chor, ASMF/N. Marriner, C. Plummer)

Ⓒ **CHAN8894** (4/91)
Nielsen—Concertos
Nielsen: Violin Concerto; Clarinet Concerto; Flute Concerto. (K. Sjøgren, N. Thomsen, T. Lund Christiansen, Danish Nat RSO/M. Schønwandt)

Ⓒ **CHAN8897** (1/91)
Czech Orchestral Works
Martinů: Symphony 6; *Janáček:* Sinfonietta; *Suk:* Fantastické scherzo, Op. 25. (Czech PO/J. Bělohlávek)

Ⓒ **CHAN8902** (7/92)
Alwyn—Orchestral Works
Alwyn: Symphony 4; Elizabethan Dances; Festival March. (LSO/R. Hickox)

Ⓒ **CHAN8903** (10/91)
Debussy & Ravel—Orchestral Works
Ravel: Boléro; La Valse; *Debussy:* Khamma; Jeux (Cpte). (Ulster Orch/Y. P. Tortelier)

Ⓒ **CHAN8905** (3/91)
Ravel—Works for Piano Duet
Ravel: Rapsodie espagnole; Boléro; Ma mère l'oye; Introduction and Allegro; La Valse. (L. Lortie, H. Mercier)

Ⓒ **CHAN8913** (3/92)
Respighi—Vocal and Orchestral Works
Respighi: Birds; Botticelli Pictures; Tramonto; Adagio con variazioni. (L. Finnie, R. Wallfisch, Bournemouth Sinfonietta/T. Vásáry)

Ⓒ **CHAN8914** (10/91)
Debussy and Ravel—Vocal and Orchestral Works
Debussy: Nocturnes; *Ravel:* Shéhérazade; Shéhérazade; Shéhérazade. (L. Finnie, Renaissance Sngrs, Grosvenor High Sch Ch, Ulster Orch/Y.P. Tortelier)

Ⓒ **CHAN8924** (10/91)
Russian Vocal and Chamber works
Arensky: Piano Trio 2; *Shostakovich:* Blok Poems, Op. 127; *Prokofiev:* Overture, Op. 34. (Borodin Trio, N. Pelle, E. Turovsky, R. Golani, J. Campbell)

Ⓒ **CHAN8926** (6/91)
Prokofiev—Piano Works, Vol.3
Prokofiev: Piano Sonata 4; Music for Children; Pieces, Op. 52. (Boris Berman)

Ⓒ **CHAN8927** (5/91)
Khachaturian—Spartacus Ballet Suites 1-3
Khachaturian: Spartacus Suite 1; Spartacus Suite 2; Spartacus Suite 3. (SNO/N. Järvi)

Ⓒ **CHAN8930** (2/92)
Wagner—Arias
Wagner: Tannhäuser (exc); Lohengrin (exc); Götterdämmerung (exc); Tristan und Isolde (exc). (G. Jones, Cologne RSO/R. Paternostro)

Ⓒ **CHAN8936** (9/91)
Finzi—Choral works
Finzi: God is gone up; Welcome sweet and sacred feast; Short Elegies, Op. 5; Thou didst delight my eyes; My lovely one; Partsongs, Op. 17; Magnificat; White-flowering days; All this night; Lo, the full, final sacrifice. (Finzi Sngrs, H. Bicket/P. Spicer)

Ⓒ **CHAN8937** (11/91)
Arrangements for Guitar and Harpsichord
Vivaldi: Concerto, RV93; *Haydn:* String Quartets, Op. 2 (exc); *Boccherini:* Guitar Quintets, G445-453 (exc); *Rodrigo:* Fantasía. (N. Kraft, B. Silver)

Ⓒ **CHAN8952** (12/91)
Chausson & Fauré—Vocal and Orchestral Works
Chausson: Poème de l'amour et de la mer; Poème; *Fauré:* Pelléas et Mélisande Suite; Pavane. (L. Finnie, Renaissance Sngrs, Ulster Orch, Y. P. Tortelier (vn/dir)/Y. P. Tortelier)

Ⓒ **CHAN8955** (9/91)
Parry—Orchestral Works
Parry: Symphony 5; Elegy for Brahms; From Death to Life. (LPO/M. Bamert)

① **CHAN9075** (11/92)
Gade—Choral and Orchestral Works
Gade: Elf-king's daughter, Op. 30; Echoes from Ossian; Songs, Op. 13. (E. Johansson, A. Gjevang, P. Elming, Danish Nat Rad Ch, Danish Nat Rad Chbr Ch, Danish Nat RSO/D. Kitaienko/S. Parkman)

① **CHAN9076** (8/93)
Dyson—Orchestral Works
Dyson: Concerto da Chiesa; Concerto da Camera; Concerto leggiero. (E. Parkin, CLS/R. Hickox)

① **CHAN9077** (10/92)
Holst & Jacob—Chamber Works
Holst: Quintet, H11; Wind Quintet, H67; *Jacob:* Sextet, Op. 3. (A. Goldstone, Elysian Wind Qnt)

① **CHAN9079** (1/93)
British Music for Clarinet and Piano
Arnold: Clarinet Sonatina, Op. 29; *Bliss:* Pastoral; *H. Ferguson:* Short Pieces, Op. 6; *Dunhill:* Phantasy Suite, Op. 91; *Hurlstone:* Characteristic Pieces; *Stanford:* Clarinet Sonata; *Stoker:* Sonatina. (E. Jóhannesson, P. Jenkins)

① **CHAN9080** (11/92)
Janáček—Orchestral Works
Janáček: Taras Bulba; Cunning Little Vixen (exc); Jealousy; Fiddler's Child. (Czech PO/J. Bělohlávek)

① **CHAN9082** (4/93)
Ferguson—Choral and Orchestral Works
H. Ferguson: Partita, Op. 5a; Overture, Op. 16; Ballads, Op. 1; Dream of the Rood. (Anne Dawson, B. Rayner Cook, LSC, LSO/R. Hickox)

① **CHAN9084/6** (1/93)
Beethoven—Piano Works
Beethoven: Piano Concerto 1; Piano Concerto 2; Piano Concerto 3; Piano Concerto 4; Piano Concerto 5; Bagatelles (exc); Presto, WoO52; Allegretto, WoO56. (J. Lill, CBSO/W. Weller)

① **CHAN9092** (3/93)
Gershwin—Piano & Orchestral Works
Gershwin: Piano Concerto; Rhapsody in Blue; Second Rhapsody. (H. Shelley, Philh/Y. P. Tortelier)

① **CHAN9093** (2/93)
Alwyn—Orchestral Works
Alwyn: Symphony 2; Overture to a Masque; Magic Island; Derby Day; Fanfare for a Joyful Occasion. (LSO/R. Hickox)

① **CHAN9094** (2/93)
Glière/Ginastera—Concertos
Ginastera: Harp Concerto; *Glière:* Harp Concerto, Op. 74; Soprano Concerto. (E. Hulse, R. Masters, CLS/R. Hickox)

① **CHAN9096** (2/93)
Prokofiev—Orchestral Works
Prokofiev: War and Peace Suite; Summer Night, Op. 123; Russian Overture. (Philh/N. Järvi)

① **CHAN9097** (12/92)
Hindemith/Reger—Organ Works
Hindemith: Organ Sonatas; *Reger:* Pieces, Op. 65 (exc); Chorale Preludes, Op. 67 (exc); Pieces, Op. 129 (exc); Introduction and Passacaglia. (P. Kee)

① **CHAN9099** (1/93)
Mendelssohn—Orchestral Works
Mendelssohn: Symphony 1; Symphony 5; Hebrides. (Philh/W. Weller)

① **CHAN9100** (2/93)
Arnold—Film Music
Arnold: Bridge on the River Kwai (exc); Inn of the Sixth Happiness (exc); Hobson's Choice (exc); Whistle down the wind (exc); Sound Barrier; *Alford:* Colonel Bogey. (LSO/R. Hickox)

① **CHAN9101** (3/93)
Beethoven—Piano Sonatas
Beethoven: Piano Sonata 5; Piano Sonata 6; Piano Sonata 7. (L. Lortie)

① **CHAN9106** (4/93)
Walton—Orchestral Works
Walton: Viola Concerto; Hindemith Variations; Sonata for Strings. (N. Imai, LPO/J.L. Koenig)

① **CHAN9108** (4/93)
Beethoven—Chamber Works
Beethoven: Duets, WoO27 (exc); Trio, WoO37; Serenade, Op. 25. (S. Milan, L. Chilingirian, L. Williams, S. Azzolini, I. Brown)

① **CHAN9109** (4/93)
Franck/Messiaen/Saint-Saëns—Violin & Piano Works
Franck: Violin Sonata; *Messiaen:* Thème et Variations;

Saint-Saëns: Violin Sonata 1. (L. Mordkovitch, M. Gusak-Grin)

① **CHAN9110** (5/93)
Edwardian Echoes
Anchiffe: Nights of Gladness; *Baynes:* Destiny; *Bucalossi:* Grasshopper's Dance; *Caryll:* Pink Lady (exc); *Herman Finck:* In the Shadows; *Fletcher:* Parisian Sketches; *German:* Merrie England (exc); Nell Gwyn; Haydn Wood: Paris Suite (exc); *M. Phillips:* Rebel Maid (exc); *Monckton:* Arcadians (exc); Our Miss Gibbs (exc); Runaway Girl (exc). (M. Hill Smith, Southern Fest Orch/R. White)

① **CHAN9113** (3/93)
Grieg—Orchestral Works
Grieg: Sigurd Jorsalfar, Op. 56; Symphonic Dances; Peer Gynt (exc); Songs, Op. 39 (exc); Songs, Op. 25 (exc); Songs, Op. 33 (exc); Norway, Op. 58 (exc). (S. Kringelborn, Stockholm PO/G. Rozhdestvensky)

① **CHAN9114** (3/93)
Debussy/Ravel—Orchestral Works
Debussy: La Mer; Printemps; *Ravel:* Piano Trio. (Ulster Orch/Y. P. Tortelier)

① **CHAN9119** (4/93)
Prokofiev—Piano Works, Vol.7
Prokofiev: Piano Sonata 2; Dumka; Pieces, Op. 59; Cinderella Pieces, Op. 102; Schubert Waltzes. (Boris Berman)

① **CHAN9125** (4/93)
Rawsthorne—Piano Concertos
Rawsthorne: Concerto 1; Piano Concerto 2; 2-Piano Concerto. (G. Tozer, T-A. Cislowski, LPO/M. Bamert)

① **CHAN9127** (5/93)
Vienna Premiere - Volume III
E. Strauss: Blauäuglein; Österreichs Völker-Treue; Schleier und Krone; *Fahrbach II:* Storchschnäbel; *J. Strauss I:* Carneval in Paris; Freiheits; *J. Strauss II:* Nur nicht mucken!; *J. Strauss III:* Unter den Linden; *Jos Strauss:* Pauline II; Wallonen; Zeit-Bilder; Millöcker: Klopf an!; *Ziehrer:* Casimir, Op. 511; Lustigmacherin. (London Viennese Orch/J. Rothstein)

① **CHAN9129** (5/93)
Debussy/Ravel—Orchestral Works
Debussy: Rapsodie; Pour le piano (exc); Isle joyeuse; Marche écossaise; Plus que lente; Suite bergamasque (exc); Tarantelle styrienne; *Ravel:* Barque sur l'océan; Menuet antique; Fanfare; Pavane. (G. McChrystal, Ulster Orch/Y.P. Tortelier)

① **CHAN9131** (5/93)
Enescu/Shostakovich/Strauss—Chamber Works
Enescu: String Octet; *R. Strauss:* Capriccio (exc); *Shostakovich:* Pieces, Op.11. (ASMF Chbr Ens)

① **CHAN9132** (5/93)
Leighton—Chamber Works
Leighton: American Hymn Tune Fantasy; Alleluia Pascha Nostrum; Variations, Op.30; Piano Sonata, Op.64. (J. Hilton, R. Wallfisch, P. Wallfisch)

① **CHAN9134** (6/93)
Pärt—Collage
Pärt: Collage; Summa; If Bach had been a Beekeeper; Fratres; Symphony 2; Festina Lente; Credo. (Boris Berman, Philh Chor, Philh/N. Järvi)

① **CHAN9136** (6/93)
Schubert—Orchestral Works
Schubert: Symphony 3; Symphony 5; Overture, D591. (Northern Sinfonia/H. Schiff)

① **CHAN9138** (5/93)
Martinů—Orchestral and Choral Works
Martinů: Lidice; Field Mass; Symphony 4. (I. Kusnjer, Czech Phil Chor, Czech PO/J. Bělohlávek)

① **CHAN9139** (6/93)
Bax/Howells—Choral Works
Bax: This Worldes Joie; Mater Ora Filium; Greek Folk Songs; I sing of a maiden; *Howells:* Madrigals; Long, long ago; Summer is coming; Take him, earth. (Finzi Sngrs/P. Spicer)

① **CHAN9140** (6/93)
Ireland—Piano Works, Vol.2
Ireland: In Those Days; London Pieces; Leaves from a Child's Sketchbook; Darkened Valley; Pieces (1921); Equinox; Sonatina; Prelude in E flat; Ballade; Greenways. (E. Parkin)

① **CHAN9141** (9/93)
Mayerl—Piano Music, Vol.3
Mayerl: Filigree; Miniatures, Op.76; Siberian lament; In My Garden—Summertime; Japanese Pictures (exc); Beguine Impromptu; Big Top; Legends of King Arthur (exc); Honky-

tonk; In My Garden—Autumntime; Romanesque; Insect Oddities; Leprechaun's Leap. (E. Parkin)

① **CHAN9142** (8/93)
Marilyn Hill Smith sings Ivor Novello
Novello: King's Rhapsody (exc); Dancing Years (exc); Perchance to Dream (exc); Arc de triomphe (exc); Glamorous Night (exc); Gay's the Word (exc); Careless Rapture (exc); Valley of Song (exc); Little Damozel; Keep the home fires burning; Fairy laughter; Spring of the Year. (M. Hill Smith, G. Langford, Chandos Concert Orch/S. Barry)

① **CHAN9147** (6/93)
French Songs
Debussy: Proses lyriques; *Duparc:* Invitation au voyage; Extase; Vie antérieure; *Poulenc:* Bestiaire; Banalités; Chemins de l'amour; Souris; *Satie:* Ludions; Diva de l'Empire; Mélodies (1916). (D. Jones, M. Martineau)

① **CHAN9148** (1/94)
Walton—Orchestral Works
Walton: Façade Suites (exc); Siesta; Sinfonia concertante; Portsmouth Point; *Arnold:* Popular Birthday. (E. Parkin, LPO/J. Latham-König/B. Thomson)

① **CHAN9149** (9/93)
Rimsky-Korsakov/Glinka—Vocal Works
Rimsky-Korsakov: Sadko (Cpte); Songs, Op.42 (exc); Songs, Op.3 (exc); *Glinka:* I recall a wonderful moment; Farewell to St Petersburg (exc); Wedding Song; I am here; How sweet it is to be with you; Fire of longing; Say not that it grieves the heart; Farewell to St Petersburg (exc); Declaration; Doubt. (V. Bogachev, N. Storozhev, Montreal I Musici/Y. Turovsky, V. Bogachev, N. Storozhev)

① **CHAN9152** (10/93)
Alwyn—Chamber Works - Volume 1
Alwyn: Flute Concerto; Oboe and Harp Suite; Naiades; Music for 3 Players; Flute Trio. (K. Hill, N. Daniel, J. Farrall, L. Chen, C. Dearnley, J. Jones, J. Drake, London Haffner Wnd Ens, N. Daniel (ob/dir))

① **CHAN9158** (7/93)
Sibelius—Orchestral Works
Sibelius: Pelleas and Melisande; Swanwhite (exc); King Christian II (exc). (S. Tiilikainen, Iceland SO/P. Sakari)

① **CHAN9161** (7/93)
Howells—Music for Strings
Howells: Suite for Strings; Concerto for strings; Elegy; Serenade. (CLS/R. Hickox)

① **CHAN9162** (7/93)
Mozart/Schubert—Piano Works for Four Hands
Mozart: Piano Sonata, K448; Andante and Variations, K501; *Schubert:* Fantasie, D940. (L. Lortie, H. Mercier)

① **CHAN9168** (2/94)
Bax—Orchestral Works
Bax: Festival Overture; Christmas Eve; Orchestral Sketches (exc); Paean; Nympholept; Tintagel. (LPO, Ulster Orch/B. Thomson)

① **CHAN9169** (10/93)
Barber/Bristow—Orchestral Works
Barber: Symphony 2; Adagio for Strings; *Bristow:* Symphony 2. (Detroit SO/N. Järvi)

① **CHAN9173** (10/93)
Dvořák—Chamber Works
Dvořák: Piano Quintet, Op.81; Terzetto, Op.74; Drobnosti, B149; Gavotte, B164. (J. Menuhin, Chilingirian Qt)

① **CHAN9174** (11/93)
20th Century American Works for Winds
Barber: Summer Music, Op. 31; *Beach:* Pastorale (1942); *Fine:* Partita; *Harbison:* Wind Quintet (1978); *Villa-Lobos:* Quinteto em forma de chôros; *Schuller:* Suite (1945). (Reykjavik Wind Qnt)

① **CHAN9175** (11/93)
Chopin—Piano Works
Chopin: Piano Sonata 3; Impromptus; Fantaisie-impromptu; Barcarolle. (H. Shelley)

① **CHAN9176** (10/93)
Honegger—Orchestral Works
Honegger: Symphony 3; Symphony 5; Symphonic Movements (exc). (Danish Nat RSO/N. Järvi)

① **CHAN9177** (10/93)
Barber—Piano Works
Barber: Ballade; Excursions; Nocturne; Piano Sonata, Op. 26; Souvenirs, Op. 28. (E. Parkin)

① **CHAN9178** (11/93)
Rimsky-Korsakov—Orchestral Works
Rimsky-Korsakov: Symphony 1; Symphony 2; Capriccio espagnol. (Bergen PO/D. Kitaienko)

ⓘ **CHAN9271** (11/94)
Poulenc/Guilmant/Widor—Organ Works
Poulenc: Organ Concerto; *Guilmant:* Symphony 1; *Widor:* Symphony 5. (I. Tracey, BBC PO/Y. P. Tortelier)

ⓘ **CHAN9273** (9/94)
Howells—Piano Music
Howells: Gadabout; Sarum sketches; Pieces, Op. 14; Slow Dance; Cobler's Hornpipe; Snapshots, Op. 30; Chosen Tune; Lambert's Clavichord (exc); Musica sine Nomine; Sonatina (exc). (M. Fingerhut)

ⓘ **CHAN9277** (9/94)
Spanish Songs
Falla: Canciones populares españolas; *Granados:* Tonadillas (exc); *Guridi:* Canciones castellanas; *Montsalvatge:* Canciones negras; *Obradors:* Canciones clásicas españolas (exc); *Vito; Turina:* Poema in forma de canciones. (D. Jones, M. Martineau)

ⓘ **CHAN9278** (10/94)
The Edge of Space
Downey: Edge of Space; *Jacob:* Bassoon Concerto; *J. Andriessen:* Concertino. (R. Thompson, LSO, ECO Wind Ens, ECO/G. Simon)

ⓘ **CHAN9283** (7/94)
Martin—Orchestral Works, Volume 1
Martin: Wind Concerto; Erasmi Monumentum; Etudes. (LPO/M. Bamert)

ⓘ **CHAN9284** (5/95)
Mozart—Wind Music
Mozart: Serenade, K375; Serenade, K388; Adagio, K411; Adagio, K580a. (Netherlands Wind Ens)

ⓘ **CHAN9287** (9/94)
Nielsen—Orchestral Works
Nielsen: Helios; Symphonic Rhapsody; Saga-Drøm; Evening at Giske Suite; Paraphrase; Bøhmisk-Dansk folketone; Rhapsody Overture; Pan and Syrinx. (Danish Nat RSO/G. Rozhdestvensky)

ⓘ **CHAN9289** (8/94)
Brahms/Schumann—Piano Works
Brahms: Schumann Variations; *Schumann:* Blumenstück; Bunte Blätter. (L. Lortie)

ⓘ **CHAN9292** (10/94)
Walton—Chamber Music
Walton: Toccata; Duets for children; Façade (exc); Violin Pieces; Bagatelles; Anon in love; Winds; Tritons. (J. M. Ainsley, K. Sillito, C. Bonell, H. Milne, G. Dowdeswell)

ⓘ **CHAN9295** (10/94)
Contemporary Irish String Quartets
Kinsella: String Quartet 3; *I. Wilson:* Winter's Edge; *Beckett:* String Quartet 1; *Boydell:* String Quartet 2. (Vanbrugh Qt)

ⓘ **CHAN9301/2** (1/95)
Messiaen—Orchestral Works
Messiaen: Oiseaux exotiques; Haïkaï; Couleurs; Ville d'en haut; Vitrail et des oiseaux; Et exspecto resurrectionem. (P. Donohoe, Netherlands Wind Ens/R. de Leeuw)

ⓘ **CHAN9307** (12/94)
Schumann—Lieder
Schumann: Myrthen, Op. 25 (Cpte); Lieder und Gesa-a4nge, Op. 27 (Cpte); Gesänge, Op. 31 (exc). (L. Dawson, I. Partridge, J. Drake)

ⓘ **CHAN9311** (1/95)
Respighi—Orchestral Works
Respighi: Belfagor Overture; Toccata; *Bach:* Nun komm, der Heiden Heiland, BWV699; Meine Seele, erhebt den Herren, BWV733; Schübler Chorales, BWV645-650 (exc); *Respighi:* Fantasia slava. (G. Tozer, BBC PO/E. Downes)

ⓘ **CHAN9312** (1/95)
Martin—Orchestral Works
Martin: Symphonie concertante; Symphonie; Passacaglia (1944). (LPO/M. Bamert)

ⓘ **CHAN9313** (3/95)
Alfvén—Orchestral Works
Alfvén: Midsummer Vigil, Op. 19; Upsala-rapsodi; Dalarapsodi; Legend of the Skerries, Op. 20; Gustav Adolf II Suite (exc). (Iceland SO/P. Sakari)

ⓘ **CHAN9315** (3/95)
John Field—Piano Works
Field: Air du bon roi Henri IV, H20; Irish Dance, H3; Sehnsuchtswalzer, H15; Nocturne sur l'air de Martini, H15; Rondeau écossais, H23; Andante inédit, H64; Russian Song Variations, H41; Kamarinskaya Variations, H22; Marche triomphale, H16; Nouvelle fantaisie, H35; Nocturne, H16; Polonaise en rondeau, H21; Fantaisie sur un air russe (c1823); Album Leaves in C minor; Rondo, H18. (M. O'Rourke)

ⓘ **CHAN9321** (5/95)
Khachaturian/Ippolitov-Ivanov—Orchestral Works
Ippolitov-Ivanov: Caucasian sketches; *Khachaturian:* Symphony 3; Triumph Poem. (BBC PO/F. Glushchenko)

ⓘ **CHAN9325** (4/95)
Gershwin—Orchestral Works
Gershwin: Strike up the Band II (exc); Girl Crazy (exc); I Got Rhythm Variations; American in Paris; Catfish Row. (H. Shelley, BBC PO/Y. P. Tortelier)

ⓘ **CHAN9327** (12/95)
Medtner—Songs
Medtner: Angel, Op. 1a; Songs, Op. 13 (exc); Songs, Op. 28 (exc); Songs, Op. 29 (exc); Songs, Op. 32 (exc); Songs, Op. 36 (exc); Songs, Op. 37 (exc); Songs, Op. 52 (exc); Noon, Op. 59/1; Songs, Op. 24. (L. Andrew, G. Tozer)

ⓘ **CHAN9330** (4/95)
Fireplay—Percussion Works
A. Koppel: Toccata; Fuzzy; Fireplay; *Pape:* CaDance 4 2; *Miki:* Marimba Spiritual II; *Nørgård:* Echo Zone I-III. (Safri Duo)

ⓘ **CHAN9336/8** (4/95)
Mussorgsky—Songs
Mussorgsky: Where art thou, little star?; Hour of Jollity; Sadly rustled the leaves; Prayer; Tell me why; Old man's song; King Saul; Lullaby; Dear one, why are thine eyes?; Feast; What are words of love to you?; Ragamuffin; Pride; He-Goat; Song of the flea; Darling Savishna; Classicist; Eremushka's lullaby; From my tears; Hebrew song; Garden by the Don; Orphan; Gathering mushrooms; Evening song; Sunless; Nursery; Songs and Dances of Death; Child's song; Sphinx; Softly the spirit flew; It scatters and breaks; Seminarist; Wanderer; Is spinning man's work?; Vision; From my tears; Not like thunder; I have many palaces and gardens; But if I could meet thee again; Wild wind blows; Night; Kalistratushka; Outcast; Salammbô (exc); Meines Herzen Sehnsucht; Gopak; You drunken sot; Magpie; Forgotten; On the Dnieper. (A. Haugland, P. Rosenbaum)

ⓘ **CHAN9345** (6/95)
McEwen—Orchestral Works
McEwen: Solway Symphony; Hills O' Heather; Where the Wild Thyme blows. (M. Welsh, LPO/A. Mitchell)

ⓘ **CHAN9349** (6/95)
Stokowski Encores
Handel: Chandos Anthem 2 (exc); *G. Gabrieli:* Sacrae symphoniae (1597) (exc); *Handel:* Suite in D; *Mattheson:* Suites (1714) (exc); *Mozart:* Piano Sonata, K331 (exc); *Beethoven:* Piano Sonata 14 (exc); *Schubert:* Schwanengesang, D957 (exc); *Franck:* Panis angelicus; *Chopin:* Piano Sonata 2 (exc); *Debussy:* Préludes (exc); *Ippolitov-Ivanov:* In the Manger; *Shostakovich:* Counterplan Suite (exc); *Tchaikovsky:* Andante Cantabile, Op.11; *Albéniz:* Iberia (exc); *Sousa:* Stars and Stripes Forever. (BBC PO/M. Bamert)

ⓘ **CHAN9351** (6/95)
Ravel/Respighi—Sonatas for Violin and Piano
Ravel: Violin Sonata (1897); Violin Sonata (1923-27); *Respighi:* Violin Sonata. (L. Mordkovitch, C. Benson)

ⓘ **CHAN9353** (6/95)
Chopin—Piano Works
Chopin: Andante spianato and Grande Polonaise; Ballades; Polonaises (exc). (M. O'Rourke)

ⓘ **CHAN9355** (9/95)
Delius—Orchestral Works
Delius: Dance Rhapsody 1; Dance Rhapsody 2; North Country Sketches; In a Summer Garden; Village Romeo and Juliet (exc). (Bournemouth SO/R. Hickox)

ⓘ **CHAN9358** (5/95)
Stamitz—Symphonies
C. Stamitz: Symphonies, Op. 24 (exc); Symphonies, Op. 13 (exc); Symphony in D. (LMP/M. Bamert)

ⓘ **CHAN9360** (9/95)
Liszt—Orchestral Works
Liszt: Piano Concerto 1; Piano Concerto 2; Mazeppa; Préludes. (G. Tozer, SRO/N. Järvi)

ⓘ **CHAN9362** (10/95)
French Wind Music
Ibert: Pièces brèves; *Françaix:* Quintette (1948); *Milhaud:* Cheminée du roi René; *Damase:* Variations, Op. 22; *Pierné:* Pastorale (exc); *Poulenc:* Novelettes (exc); *Fauré:* Dolly (exc); *Debussy:* Petit nègre. (Reykjavik Wind Qnt)

ⓘ **CHAN9363** (10/95)
Adams/Lang—Wind Music
J. Adams: Short ride; Grand Pianola Music; *D. Lang:* Are you experienced?; Under Orpheus. (L. Wagstaff, K. Amps, R. Holton, D. Lang, E. Cover, S. Grotenhuis, Netherlands Wind Ens/S. Mosko)

ⓘ **CHAN9374** (10/95)
Rachmaninov—Songs
Rachmaninov: At the gate of the holy abode; Do you remember the evening; From the Gospel of St John; I shall tell you nothing; Letter to Stanislavsky; Song of the disillusioned; Songs, Op. 4 (exc); Songs, Op. 8 (exc); Songs, Op. 14 (exc); Songs, Op. 21 (exc); Songs, Op. 26 (exc); Songs, Op. 34 (exc); Were you hiccoughing. (S. Leiferkus, H. Shelley)

ⓘ **CHAN9376** (11/95)
Ireland—Orchestral Works
Ireland: Downland Suite; Orchestral Poem; Concertino pastorale; Symphonic Studies. (CLS/R. Hickox)

ⓘ **CHAN9377/8** (12/95)
Ireland—Chamber Works
Ireland: Violin Sonata 1; Violin Sonata 2; Fantasy-Sonata; Cello Sonata; Holy Boy; Phantasie Trio; Piano Trio 2; Piano Trio 3. (L. Mordkovitch, K. Georgian, I. Brown, G. de Peyer, G. Pryor)

ⓘ **CHAN9380** (10/95)
Martin—Ballades
Martin: Piano Ballade; Trombone Ballade; Ballade (1949); Saxophone Ballade; Ballade (1972); Flute Ballade. (R. Elms, I. Bousfield, P. Dixon, M. Robertson, P. Dukes, R. Masters, R. Elms, C. Chambers, LPO/M. Bamert)

ⓘ **CHAN9382** (10/95)
Holst/Lambert—Piano Works
Holst: Toccata; Chrissemas Day, Op. 46/1; Folk Song Arrangements, Op. 46/2; Nocturne; Jig; Arpeggio Study; Pièces; Piece for Yvonne; Dances; *C. Lambert:* Piano Sonata; Elegiac Blues; Elegy. (A. Goldstone, C. Clemmow)

ⓘ **CHAN9392** (11/95)
Vaughan Williams—Riders to the Sea etc.
Vaughan Williams: Riders to the Sea (Cpte); Household Music; Flos campi. (I. Attrot, L. Dawson, L. Finnie, K. M. Daymond, P. H. Stephen, P. Dukes, Northern Sinfonia Chor, Northern Sinfonia/R. Hickox)

ⓘ **CHAN9397** (12/95)
Grechaninov—Choral & Orchestral Works
Grechaninov: Symphony 1; Snowflakes, Op. 47 (Cpte); Missa Sancti Spiritus, Op. 169 (Cpte). (L. Kuznetsova, T. Jeranje, Russian St Sym Cappella, Russian St SO/V. Polyansky)

Channel Classics

ⓘ **CCSBOX10** (10/92)
Mozart—Piano Concertos
Mozart: Piano Concerto 5; Piano Concerto 9; Piano Concerto 8; Piano Concerto 12; Rondo, K382; Piano Concerto 13; Piano Concerto 14; Piano Concerto 11; Piano Concerto 15; Piano Concerto 16; Piano Concerto 6; Piano Concerto 17; Piano Concerto 18; Piano Concerto 19; Piano Concerto 20; Piano Concerto 21; Piano Concerto 22; Piano Concerto 23; Piano Concerto 24; Piano Concerto 25; Piano Concerto 26; Piano Concerto 27. (J. Van Immerseel (fp/dir), Anima Eterna)

ⓘ **CCS0690** (10/92)
Mozart—Keyboard Concertos Vol 2
Mozart: Piano Concerto 8; Rondo, K382; Piano Concerto 12. (Anima Eterna, J. Van Immerseel (fp/dir))

ⓘ **CCS0890** (2/92)
Handel—Cantatas & Sonatas
Handel: Lungi da me pensier tiranno; Siete rose rugiadose; Udite il mio consiglio; Cara sempre di Gloria; Oboe Sonatas (exc). (D.L. Ragin, Cologne Divitia Ens)

ⓘ **CCS0990** (10/92)
Mozart—Keyboard Concertos Vol 3
Mozart: Piano Concerto 11; Piano Concerto 13; Piano Concerto 14. (Anima Eterna, J. Van Immerseel (fp/dir))

ⓘ **CCS1491** (12/91)
Beethoven—Songs
Beethoven: Scottish Songs, Op. 108 (exc); Irish Songs, WoO152 (exc); Variations, WoO79; Piano Trios (exc); Ländler, WoO15. (M. Kweksilber, V. Beths, G. Beths, A. Bylsma, S. Hoogland)

ⓘ **CCS1691** (12/91)
Chamber music from Theresienstadt 1941-45
G. Klein: Piano Sonata; Trio; String Quartet, Op. 2; Fantasie a Fuga; *Ullmann:* String Quartet 3. (V. Eskin, Hawthorne Qt)

ⓘ **CCS2991** (8/92)
Ev'ry Time I Feel the Spirit
Traditional: Ole time religion; Witness; Steal away to Jesus; Little David; Deep river; Motherless child; Were you there; There's a man going round; I don't feel no ways

tired; Heaven; Oh, what a beautiful city; This little light of mine; Ev'ry time I feel de spirit; Give me Jesus. (D.L. Ragin, New World Voc Ens, M. Hogan)

ⓘ **CCS4592** (5/93)
Messiaen/Ives—Works for two pianos
Messiaen: Visions de l'Amen; *Ives:* Quarter-tone pieces; *Van Zeeland:* Initials. (Pianoduo)

ⓘ **CCS4792** (5/94)
Henry Purcell & His Time
Locke: Broken Consort I (exc); *W. Lawes:* Fantasia-Suites a 4 (exc); *Jenkins:* Fantasias in 3 parts (2 vns, b viol) (exc); *C. Simpson:* Prelude; Divisions on a Ground; *Baltzar:* John Come Kiss Me Now Divisions; *Purcell:* Pavans, Z748-51 (exc); Pavan, Z752; Fantasia, Z731. (Scaramouche, K. Junghänel, F. Kooistra)

ⓘ **CCS5093** (10/93)
Telemann—Chamber Music
Telemann: Sonates Corellisantes (exc); Paris Quartets (Nouveaux quatuors) (exc); Essercizii Musici (exc); Quartet, TWV43: a 3; Quartet, TWV43: g 4. (Florilegium Ens)

ⓘ **CCS5894** (7/94)
Pandolfi—Violin Sonatas
Pandolfi: Violin Sonatas, op. 3 (exc); Violin Sonatas, Op. 4 (exc); *Anon:* Harpsichord Suites (Flor) (exc). (A. Manze, R. Egarr, F. Jacobs)

ⓘ **CCS6294** (11/94)
Vivaldi—Cello Sonatas
Vivaldi: Cello Sonata, Rv44; Cello Sonata, RV45; Cello Sonata, RV46; Cello Sonata, RV39; Cello Sonata, RV40; Cello Sonata, RV42. (P. Wispelwey, Florilegium Ens)

ⓘ **CCS6494** (4/95)
Beethoven—Cello Variations
Beethoven: Handel Variations, WoO45; Mozart Variations, Op. 66; Mozart Variations, WoO46; Horn Sonata. (P. Wispelwey, L. Shapiro)

ⓘ **CCS7195** (6/95)
Beethoven—Sonatas & Bagatelles
Beethoven: Piano Sonata 16; Piano Sonata 32; Bagatelles (exc). (M. Chung)

ⓘ **CCS7395** (7/95)
Haydn—Works for Cello and Orchestra
Haydn: Cello Concerto in C; Cello Concerto in D; Symphony 104. (P. Wispelwey, Florilegium Ens)

ⓘ **CCS7495** (7/95)
20th Century Solo Cello Works
Ligeti: Cello Sonata (1948-53); *Sculthorpe:* Requiem; *Hindemith:* Solo Cello Sonata, Op. 25/3; *Sessions:* Cello Pieces (1966); *Meijering:* Belle Dame Sans Merci. (P. Wispelwey)

ⓘ **CCS7595** (12/95)
Music for the King's Pleasure
Leclair: Ouvertures et Sonates, Op. 13 (exc); Récréation de musique II; *Boismortier:* Sonatas, Op. 34 (exc); *Corrette:* Concerto comique 25. (Florilegium Ens, J. Rogers, S. Pauley)

ⓘ **CCS7895** (7/95)
Buxtehude—Cantatas
Buxtehude: Nimm von uns, Herr, BuxWV78; Jesu, meines Lebens Leben, BuxWV62; Fried- und Freudenreiche, BuxWV76 (exc); Führwahr, er trug unsere Krankheit, BuxWV31; Herzlich lieb, BuxWV41; Herr ist mit mir, BuxWV15. (C. McFadden, F. Dukel, J. Kenny, M. van Altena, S. MacLeod, Collegium Vocale, Royal Consort, Anima Eterna/J. van Immerseel)

ⓘ **CG9101** (11/92)
Schumann—Piano Works
Schumann: Fantasiestücke, Op.111; Waldszenen; Piano Sonata 3. (S. Nagaoka)

ⓘ **CG9103** (7/93)
Guitar Duets
Dowland: Ballad settings (exc); *Sor:* Divertissement, Op.34; *Granados:* Goyescas (exc); *Kleynjans:* Climats; *Bach:* Trio Sonatas, BWV525-530 (exc); Wohltemperierte Klavier (exc); *Albéniz:* España, Op.165 (exc); Cantos de España (exc); Mallorca; *Falla:* Vida breve (exc); Sombrero de tres picos Suites (exc). (T. Kropat, T. Krumeich)

ⓘ **CG9106** (6/93)
Mendelssohn—Piano Works
Mendelssohn: Andante and rondo capriccioso, Op.14; Preludes and Fugues, Op.35 (exc); Fantasy, Op.28; Variations sérieuses, Op.54; Scherzo a capriccio. (R. de Waal)

ⓘ **CG9107** (4/93)
Music for Clarinet, Piano & Viola
Bruch: Pieces, Op.83; *Mozart:* Piano Trio, K498;

Schumann: Märchenerzählungen. (H. de Graaf, I. Shimon, D. Wayenberg)

ⓘ **CG9110** (10/92)
Szymanowski—Piano Works
Szymanowski: Etudes, Op.4; Etudes, Op.33; Mazurkas, Op.62; Masques, Op.34 (exc); Variations, Op.10. (A. Vernède)

Le Chant du Monde

ⓘ **LDC278 1007/8** (5/89)
Shostakovich: Symphonies, Vol.4
Shostakovich: Symphony 11; Symphony 12; Symphony 13. (A. Eisen, RSFSR Academic Russian Ch, Moscow PO/K. Kondrashin)

ⓘ **LDC278 1018/9** (6/90)
Shostakovich: Chamber Works
Shostakovich: Cello sonata, op 40; Violin sonata, op 134; Viola sonata; Piano Trio 2. (D. Oistrakh, S. Richter, I. Monighetti, V. Lobanov, F. Druynin, M. Muntyan, G. Feighin, V. Feighin, I. Yukov)

ⓘ **LDC278 1064/5** (5/92)
Brahms—Complete Piano Variations
Brahms: Handel Variations; Schumann Variations; Variations, Op.23; String Sextet 1 (exc); Haydn Variations; Variations, Op.21/1; Variations, Op.21/2; Paganini Variations. (J. Colom, C. Deleito)

ⓘ **LDC278 1068** (8/92)
Chabrier—Une Education Manquée/Mélodies
Chabrier: Éducation manquée (Cpte); Roi malgré lui (exc); Chanson pour Jeanne; Île heureuse; Gwendoline (exc); Ballade des gros dindons; Pastorale des cochons roses. (C. Castelli, C. Collart, X. Depraz, Orch/C. Bruck, C. Castelli, H. Boschi)

ⓘ **LDC278 1069** (9/92)
Milhaud—Orchestral and Choral Works
Milhaud: Château de feu; Mort du tyran; Introduction et marche funèbre; Suite provençale; Catalogue de fleurs, Op.60. (Paris PO/D. Milhaud, Paris Cons/S. Baudo)

ⓘ **LDC278 1092** (10/93)
Lessel—Works for Piano
Lessel: Piano Concerto, Op.14; Adagio et rondeau, Op.9; Variations, Op.15/1; Variations, Op.15/2. (J. Sterczynski, Silesian PSO/J. Salwarowski)

ⓘ **LDC278 821** (8/87)
Boëly—Works for Strings
Boëly: String Quartet 1; String Quartet 3; String Trio, Op. 5/1. (E. Popa, Paris String Trio)

ⓘ **LDC278 835** (6/87)
Villa-Lobos—Chôros for Chamber Ensembles
Villa-Lobos: Chôros 1; Chôros 2; Chôros 2; Chôros 3; Chôros 4; Chôros 5; Chôros 7; Chôros bis; Wind Quintet. (Rio de Janeiro Assoc for Choral Song, C. Rato, B. Limonge, J. Botelho, G. Carneiro, P. Moura, N. Devos, A. Barbosa, S. Svab, T. Tritle, C. Gomes de Oliveira, J. Sadoc, M. Santos, T. Santos, G. Pareschi, W. Clis, H. Tagnin)

ⓘ **LDC278 869/70** (11/87)
Villa-Lobos—Guitar Works
Villa-Lobos: Etudes; Preludes; Bachianas Brasileiras 5 (exc); Suite populaire brésilienne; Distribuição de flores; Chôros 1; Guitar Concerto; Sexteto mistico. (T. Santos, L. Guimaraes, M. Bomfim, C. Rato, E. Marins, A. Bruno, S. Vieira, M. cella Machado, N. Devos, Brazilian CO/B. Bessler)

ⓘ **LDC278 901** (9/88)
Villa-Lobos—String Quartets
Villa-Lobos: String Quartet 4; String Quartet 5; String Quartet 6. (Bessler-Reis Qt)

ⓘ **LDC278 951** (4/90)
Denisov—Songs
Denisov: Bonfire of Snow; Bunin Poems; To Flora. (E. Vassilieva, J. Schab)

ⓘ **LDC278 962** (11/90)
Polish Works for Piano & Orchestra
Chopin: Piano Concerto 2; Allegro de Concert; *Tausig:* Hungarian Gypsy Airs. (M. Setrak, Polish Chmbr PO/W. Rajski)

ⓘ **LDC278 970/1** (5/91)
Schubert: Piano Trios
Schubert: Piano Trio 1; Piano Trio 2; Piano Trio, D28; Notturno, D897. (Rubinstein Trio)

Chanticleer Records

ⓘ **CR-8803** (12/94)
Our Heart's Joy—A Chanticleer Christmas
Mouton: Ave Maria gratia plena; *A. Gabrieli:* Quem vidistis

pastores; *M. Praetorius:* In dulci jubilo; *F. Guerrero:* Virgen Sancta; *Traditional:* E la don don; Riu, riu, chiu; *Biebl:* Ave Maria; *Traditional:* There is no rose; *Britten:* Hymn to the Virgin; *Traditional:* Tomorrow shall be my dancing day; Il est né; O come, o come Emmanuel; I wonder as I wander; Christmas Spirituals; Stille Nacht. (Chanticleer)

ⓘ **CR-8805** (7/94)
Brumel/Josquin Desprez—Choral Works
Brumel: Missa Berzerette savoyenne; Laudate Dominum; Sicut lilium; Lamentation; Lauda Sion Salvatorem; *Josquin Desprez:* Bergerette savoyenne. (Chanticleer)

ⓘ **CR-8808** (7/94)
Josquin Desprez/Agricola—Masses and Motets
Brumel: Mater Patris et filia; *Josquin Desprez:* Missa Mater Patris; Domine, non secundum; *A. Agricola:* Nobis Sancte Spiritus; Regina coeli; O crux ave; Magnificat. (Chanticleer)

Chatsworth

ⓘ **FCM1002** (9/94)
Svendsen—Orchestral Works
Svendsen: Symphony 2; Romance, Op. 26; Carnival in Paris; Norwegian Artist's Carnival; Norwegian Rhapsody 2. (M. Thorsen, Stavanger SO/G. Llewellyn)

Chesky

ⓘ **Chesky AD1** (9/91)
Medtner—Piano works
Medtner: Improvisation, Op. 47; Sonate-Idylle, Op. 56; Forgotten melodies, Op. 39. (E. Wild)

ⓘ **Chesky CD32** (10/90)
Earl Wild plays his transcriptions of Gershwin
Gershwin: Porgy and Bess (exc); *Wild:* Gershwin Variations; Virtuoso Etudes. (E. Wild)

ⓘ **Chesky CD50** (11/92)
Works for Piano & Orchestra
Grieg: Piano Concerto; *Liszt:* Hungarian Fantasia, S123; *Saint-Saëns:* Piano Concerto 2. (E. Wild, RPO/R. Leibowitz/R. Stanger, RCA Victor SO/M. Freccia)

ⓘ **Chesky CD58** (9/92)
Rachmaninov—Piano Works
Rachmaninov: Chopin Variations, Op. 22; Corelli Variations; Songs, Op. 34 (exc); Songs, Op. 4 (exc); Songs, Op. 14 (exc). (E. Wild)

ⓘ **Chesky CD93** (2/94)
Earl Wild plays Chopin, Fauré & Liszt
Chopin: Piano Concerto 1; *Liszt:* Piano Concerto 1; *Fauré:* Ballade, Op. 19. (E. Wild, RPO/M. Sargent, National PO/C. Gerhardt)

Chorale Classics

ⓘ **EECD109** (12/89)
Celebration of Christmas
Rutter: Star Carol; *Traditional:* Maiden Most Gentle; Ding dong! merrily on high; Quem pastores laudavere; *Mathias:* Babe is born; *Traditional:* Könige; Sussex Carol; *Berlioz:* Enfance du Christ (exc); *Traditional:* Away in a manger; *Rutter:* Jesus Child; *Traditional:* In dulci jubilo; *Rutter:* Mary's Lullaby; *Traditional:* Carol of the bells; Still, still, still; *Rutter:* Shepherd's pipe carol; Nativity carol. (Sheffield Chorale, Sheaf Concert Orch/J. Kirkwood)

Christophorus

ⓘ **CD74606** (7/91)
Franck & Widor: Organ Works
Widor: Symphony 5; *Franck:* Chorales (exc); Pièces (1878) (exc). (H. Musch)

ⓘ **CHR74584** (3/93)
Sacred Music of the 12th Century
Hildegard of Bingen: O magne Pater; O aeterne Deus; Ave generosa; O frondens virga; O felix anima; Ave Maria, o auctrix vitae; O quam mirabilis; O virtus sapientae; O vis aeternitatis; *Abelard:* Planctus David; O quanta qualia; *Anon:* Promat chorus hodie; Annus novus in gaudio; Fulget dies celebris. (Augsburg Early Music Ens)

ⓘ **CHR77119** (12/92)
Telemann—Cantatas for Alto
Telemann: Tirsis am Scheidewege; Seufzen; Ach Herr, strafe mich nicht. (A. Markert, Parnaso Musicale)

Cirrus

ⓘ **CICD1004** (12/87)
Bach: Violin Concertos
Bach: Violin Concerto, BWV1041; Violin Concerto, BWV1042; 2-Violin Concerto. (A. Futer, Moscow Virtuosi, V. Spivakov (vn/dir))

Ⓓ **CICD1005** (12/87)
Wagner: Orchestral Works
Wagner: Meistersinger (exc); Tannhäuser (exc); Götterdämmerung (exc); Tristan und Isolde (exc). (LSO/W. Morris)

Ⓓ **CICD1007** (12/87)
Favourite Organ Works.
Bach: Toccata and Fugue, BWV565; *Mozart:* Fantasia, K608; *S.S.Wesley:* Air and Gavotte; *Mendelssohn:* Organ Sonatas (exc); *Schumann:* Pedal Studies, Op. 56 (exc); *Franck:* Chorales (exc); *Saint-Saëns:* Fantaisie in E flat; *Gigout:* Ten Organ Pieces (exc); *Boëllmann:* Suite Gothique (exc). (John Scott)

Ⓓ **CICD1010** (12/87)
Chopin: Piano Works
Chopin: Fantasie, Op.49; Ballades (exc); Impromptus (exc); Barcarolle; Nocturnes (exc); Waltzes (exc); Polonaises (exc). (C. Sheppard)

Claremont

Ⓓ **CDGSE78-50-26** (7/89)
Wagner: Tristan und Isolde excerpts
Wagner: Tristan und Isolde (exc); Tristan und Isolde (exc); Tristan und Isolde (exc). (L. Melchior, W. Widdop, F. Leider, G. Ljungberg, G. Guszalewicz, I. Andrésen, H. Fry, C. Victor, E. Habich, M. Noe, K. McKenna, SO, LSO/A. Coates/L. Blech/L. Collingwood, Berlin St Op Orch)

Ⓓ **CDGSE78-50-33** (7/90)
Lauritz Melchior & Albert Coates
Wagner: Tannhäuser (exc); Siegfried (exc); Siegfried (exc); Siegfried (exc); Siegfried (exc); Siegfried (exc); Götterdämmerung (exc). (L. Melchior, A. Reiss, N. Gruhn, R. Bockelmann, LSO, orch/A. Coates)

Ⓓ **CDGSE78-50-35/6** (11/91)
Wagner—Historical recordings
Wagner: Walküre (exc); Rheingold (exc); Rheingold (exc). (W. Widdop, H. Fry, F. Schorr, G. Ljungberg, L. Trenton, F. Austral, F. Leider, E. Suddaby, N. Walker, A. Fear, K. McKenna, LSO/A. Coates, SO/L. Collingwood, Berlin St Op Orch/L. Blech)

Ⓓ **CDGSE78-50-46** (11/92)
Walter Widdop (1892-1949)
Wagner: Lohengrin (exc); Tristan und Isolde (exc); Walküre (exc); Götterdämmerung (exc); *Bach:* Mass in B minor, BWV232 (exc); *Handel:* Jephtha (exc); *Gounod:* Faust (exc); *Manson:* Songs of Love and Youth (exc); *Wallace:* Maritana (exc); *Handel:* Judas Maccabaeus (exc). (W. Widdop, G. Ljungberg, C. Victor, F. Austral, E. Schumann, LSO/L. Collingwood/A. Coates, Orch/J. Harrison, anon/J. Barbirolli)

Ⓓ **CDGSE78-50-47** (3/93)
The Harrison Sisters—An English Musical Heritage
Dvořák: Gipsy Melodies (exc); *Elgar:* Salut d'amour; *Delius:* Violin Sonata 1; Cello Sonata; *Smetana:* From the homeland (exc); *Brahms:* Cello Sonata 1; *Wagner:* Meistersinger (exc); *Elgar:* Cello Concerto (exc); *van Biene:* Broken melody; *Popper:* Characterstücke, Op. 3 (exc). (May Harrison, Margaret Harrison, B. Harrison, Princess Victoria, A. Bax, R. Paul, Margaret Harrison, G. Moore, H. Craxton, C. Salzedo, orch)

Ⓓ **CDGSE78-50-50** (9/93)
Richard Crooks sings Ballads & Sacred Songs
O. Straus: Walzertraum (exc); *Lincke:* Frau Luna (exc); *Foster:* Ah! may the red rose; Come, where my love lies dreaming; *Traditional:* All through the night; *Coates:* Birdsongs at Eventide; *M. Phillips:* Open your window to the morn; *S. Adams:* Nirvana; *Liddle:* How lovely are Thy dwellings; *S. Adams:* Star of Bethlehem; Holy City; *Stainer:* Crucifixion (exc); *Hardelot:* Because; *Geehl:* For you alone; *Landenburg:* Too late tomorrow; *Macmurrough:* Macushla; *Herbert:* Naughty Marietta (exc); *Sanderson:* Until; *Silésu:* Little love, a little kiss. (R. Crooks, orch/J. Barbirolli, F. la Forge, M. Andrews, J. Crawford, H. Dawson, F. Schauwecker)

Ⓓ **CDGSE78-50-52** (5/94)
Three Tenors
Puccini: Bohème (exc); *Mascagni:* Cavalleria rusticana (exc); *Massenet:* Élégie; *Verdi:* Rigoletto (exc); *Leoncavallo:* Pagliacci (exc); *Flotow:* Martha (exc); *Donizetti:* Elisir d'amore (exc); *Mozart:* Don Giovanni (exc); *Massenet:* Manon (exc); *Wagner:* Meistersinger (exc); *Puccini:* Tosca (exc); *Wagner:* Lohengrin (exc); *Borodin:* Prince Igor (exc); *Gounod:* Reine de Saba (exc); *Woodforde-Finden:* Request; *Clutsam:* I know of two bright eyes; *R. Strauss:* Lieder, Op.29 (exc). (E. Caruso, R. Crooks, W. Widdop, orch/C. Nicholls/W. Pelletier/N. Shilkret/R. Bourdon, Berlin St Op Orch/C. Schmalstich/L. Collingwood/M. Sargent, P. Kahn, J. Lee, BNOC Orch/A. Buesst, A. Galli-Curci, F. Perini, G. De Luca, M. Elman/W.B. Rogers)

Ⓓ **CDGSE78-50-54** (2/95)
Coates conducts Wagner, Weber & Mendelssohn
Wagner: Tannhäuser (exc); Tannhäuser (exc); Tannhäuser (exc); Tannhäuser (exc); Tannhäuser (exc); Tannhäuser (exc); *Weber:* Freischütz (exc); *Mendelssohn:* Elijah (exc). (B. Jones, W. Widdop, L. Melchior, F. Schorr, E. Halland, J. Uys, Cape Town Melodic Ch, chor, New SO, LSO, SO, Cape Town SO/A. Coates)

Ⓓ **CDGSE78-50-57** (11/95)
Lotte Lehmann sings Lieder
Schumann: Myrthen, Op.25 (exc); Lieder und Gesänge, Op.77 (exc); Myrthen, Op.25 (exc); *Bach:* Anna Magdalena Notenbuch (1725) (exc); *Schubert:* Erlkönig, D328; *Wolf:* Goethe Lieder (exc); Mörike Lieder (exc); Italienisches Liederbuch (exc); *R. Strauss:* Lieder, Op.10 (exc); Lieder, Op.17 (exc); Lieder, Op.27 (exc); *Brahms:* Lieder, Op.32 (exc); Lieder, Op.96 (exc); Lieder, Op.46 (exc); Deutsche Volkslieder (exc); Lieder, Op.43 (exc); Lieder, Op.47 (exc); Lieder, Op.105 (exc). (Lotte Lehmann, anon, Berlin St Op Orch/F. Weissmann, P. Mania, F. Weissmann, P. Ulanowsky)

Clarinet Classics

Ⓓ **CC0001** (9/92)
Copland/'Les Six'—Clarinet Works
Copland: Clarinet Sonata; *Tailleferre:* Arabesque; Solo Clarinet Sonata; *Honegger:* Clarinet Sonatina; *Poulenc:* Clarinet Sonata; *Milhaud:* Duo concertante; Clarinet Sonatina, Op. 100. (V. Soames, J. Drake)

Ⓓ **CC0002** (3/93)
Nielsen—Orchestral and Chamber Works
Nielsen: Clarinet Concerto; Serenata in vano; Wind Quintet. (H.G. Jespersen, S.C. Felumb, L. Cahuzac, A. Oxenvad, H. Sørensen, K. Larsson, L. Jensen, L. Hegner, Copenhagen Op Orch/J. Frandsen)

Ⓓ **CC0003** (8/93)
Clarinet Virtuosi of the Past: Heinrich Baermann
H. J. Baërmann: Air varié; Clarinet Quintet, Op.23 (exc); *Mendelssohn:* Concert Piece, Op.113; Concert Piece, Op.114; *Weber:* Clarinet Quintet, J182; Melody, J119; Variations, J128. (V. Soames, R. Heaton, J. Drake, Duke Qt)

Ⓓ **CC0004** (10/93)
The Early Clarinet Family
Anon: Chalumeaux Airs; *Handel:* 2-Clarinets and Horn Ov, HWV424; *Graupner:* 3-Chalumeaux Suite; *Beethoven:* Duets, WoO27 (exc); *Danzi:* Basset-horn Sonata, Op.62. (K. Puddy, K. Puddy, K. Puddy, G. Brodie, G. Brodie, P. Price, S. Dent, A. Mitchell, M. Martineau)

Ⓓ **CC0005** (2/94)
The Clarinet - Historical Recordings, Vol.1
Bassi: Rigoletto fantasia; *Boisdeffre:* Chanson Neapolitan (exc); *J. Mohr:* Air varié; *Weber:* Clarinet Concertino (exc); *Mozart:* Clarinet Concerto, K622 (exc); *Renard:* Marche grotesque (exc); *Schumann:* Fantasiestücke, Op. 73; *A. Frank:* Suite for 2 clarinets; *Bliss:* Clarinet Quintet (exc); *Bassi:* Mélodie d'I Puritani (exc); *Weber:* Clarinet Concerto 1 (exc); *Benedict:* Carnevale di Venezia; *C. Baermann:* Duo concertant, Op. 33; *Mozart:* Clarinet Quintet, K581 (exc); *Debussy:* Première rapsodie; *Marty:* Première fantaisie; *Meister:* Erwin Fantaisie. (M. Gomez, C. Draper, H.P. Draper, Renard Cl Qt, R. Kell, F. Thurston, R. Clarke, Griller Qt, A. Umbach, C. Esberger, R. Quaranta, A. Giammatteo, F.J. Brissett, B. Goodman, G. Hamelin, A. Périer, H. Lefèbvre, anon, wind band, SO/C. Raybould, G. Moore, Budapest Qt, orch/P. Coppola, Garde Republicaine Band)

Ⓓ **CC0006** (3/94)
Clarinet Virtuosi of the Past—Hermstedt
Mozart: Clemenza di Tito (exc); *Müller:* Clarinet Quartet 2; *Paer:* Sargino (exc); *Spohr:* Lieder, Op. 103 (Cpte); Faust (exc); Alruna Variations. (E. Ritchie, V. Soames, A. Colman, M. Souter, A. Blayden, J. Purvis)

Ⓓ **CC0007** (10/94)
New English Clarinet Music
Powers: Trio; *Lutyens:* Trio, Op. 135; *LeFanu:* Lullaby; Nocturne; *Graham Williams:* Song within; *R. Marsh:* Ferry Music. (Mühlfeld Ens)

Classics for Pleasure

Ⓓ **CD-CFPD4456** (9/89)
Music by Eric Coates
Coates: London Suite; Saxo-Rhapsody; Calling all workers; Merrymakers; Wood Nymphs; Summer Days Suite (exc); Three Elizabeths Suite; By the Sleepy Lagoon; Music Everywhere; From Meadow to Mayfair Suite; Cinderella; Dam Busters; Three Men (exc); Three Bears Suite; London Again. (RLPO/C. Groves, J. Brymer, CBSO/R. Kilbey, LSO/C. Mackerras)

Ⓓ **CD-CFP4304** (2/89)
Delius: Orchestral Works
Delius: Fennimore and Gerda Intermezzo; First cuckoo; Summer Night on the River; Song before Sunrise; Sleigh Ride; Irmelin Prelude; Village Romeo and Juliet (exc); Koanga (exc). (LPO/V. Handley)

Ⓓ **CD-CFP4329** (12/89)
Satie: Piano Works
Satie: Gymnopédies; Croquis et agaceries; Sonatine bureaucratique; Préludes du fils des étoiles (exc); Chapitres tournés en tous sens; Gnossiennes (exc); Passacaille; Heures séculaires et instantanées; Nouvelles pièces froides; Piège de Méduse; Nocturnes (exc). (P. Lawson)

Ⓓ **CD-CFP4479** (6/92)
Bach—Organ Works
Bach: Toccata and Fugue, BWV565; Liebster Jesu, BWV731; Orgel-Büchlein, BWV599-644 (exc); Fantasia, BWV572; Prelude and Fugue, BWV545; Schübler Chorales, BWV645-650 (exc); Prelude and Fugue, BWV552. (N. Rawsthorne)

Ⓓ **CD-CFP4532** (8/89)
Sacred Arias
Mozart: Mass, K427 (exc); *Handel:* Messiah (exc); *Bach:* Cantata 147 (exc); *Handel:* Messiah (exc); *Haydn:* Creation (exc); *Mendelssohn:* Elijah (exc); *Handel:* Judas Maccabaeus (exc); *Mozart:* Exsultate jubilate, K165 (exc); *Mendelssohn:* Elijah (exc); *Verdi:* Requiem (exc); Requiem (exc); *Fauré:* Requiem (exc); *Rossini:* Stabat Mater (exc). (K. Te Kanawa, New Philh/R. Leppard, Richard Lewis, RLPO/M. Sargent, J. Sutherland, G. Jones Orch/Geraint Jones, E. Morison, J. Shirley-Quirk, ASMF/D. Willcocks, J. Baker/R. Frühbeck de Burgos, LSO, D. Fischer-Dieskau, M. Caballé, F. Cossotto, New Philh Chor/J. Barbirolli, N. Gedda/C.M. Giulini, V. de los Angeles, Paris Cons/A. Cluytens, R. Gambill, MMF Orch/R. Muti, Philh, L. Popp, ECO/G. Fischer)

Ⓓ **CD-CFP4547** (1/89)
Shostakovich: Piano Concertos
Shostakovich: Piano Concerto 1; Piano Concerto 2; Unforgettable Year 1919 (exc). (D. Alexeev, P. Jones, ECO/J. Maksymiuk)

Ⓓ **CD-CFP4557** (11/89)
Baroque Favourites
Pachelbel: Canon and Gigue (exc); *Purcell:* Chaconne, Z730; *Vivaldi:* Concerti grossi, op 3 (exc); *Corelli:* Concerti grossi, op 6 (exc); *Gluck:* Orfeo ed Euridice (exc); *Monteverdi:* Madrigals, Bk 8 (exc); *Handel:* Concerti grossi, op 6 (exc). (ASMF/N. Marriner, Y. Menuhin (vn/dir), R. Masters, E. Goren, S. Humphreys, Bath Fest CO, Derek Simpson, Bath Fest Orch, G. English, H. Cuénod, Bath Fest Ens, R. Leppard (hpd/dir)/Y. Menuhin)

Ⓓ **CD-CFP4558** (1/90)
Organ Recital
Handel: Water Music (exc); *Fiocco:* Pièces de clavecin, Op.1 (exc); *Bach:* Toccata and Fugue, BWV565; Suites, BWV1066-9 (exc); *Purcell:* 2 Trumpet Tunes and Air; *Bossi:* Scherzo, Op. 49/2; *Walton:* Crown Imperial; *Cocker:* Tuba Tune; *Thalben-Ball:* Elegy; *Reger:* Introduction and Passacaglia; *Mulet:* Esquisses byzantines (exc); *Yon:* Humoresque; *Widor:* Symphony 5 (exc). (I. Tracey)

Ⓓ **CD-CFP4568** (8/90)
Delius: Orchestral Works
Delius: Brigg Fair; In a Summer Garden; Eventyr; Song of Summer. (Hallé/V. Handley)

Ⓓ **CD-CFP4569** (8/90)
Puccini: Arias
Puccini: Bohème (exc); Bohème (exc); Manon Lescaut (exc); Manon Lescaut (exc); Manon Lescaut (exc); Tosca (exc); Tosca (exc); Tosca (exc); Madama Butterfly (exc); Madama Butterfly (exc); Fanciulla del West (exc); Turandot (exc); Turandot (exc); Turandot (exc); Suor Angelica (exc); Gianni Schicchi (exc). (N. Gedda, ROHO/G. Patanè, R. Scotto, National PO/James Levine, C. Craig, Orch, M. Collins, M. Caballé, B. Marti, LSO/C. Mackerras, A. Stella/A. Erede, F. Corelli/F. Ferraris, M. Freni/L. Magiera, ROH Chor/L. Gardelli, G. Campora, Rome Op Orch/G. Santini, A. Shuard/E. Downes, F. Cavalli, RPO/A. Fistoulari)

Ⓓ **CD-CFP4570** (1/91)
Choral Favourites
Handel: Messiah (exc); *Bach:* Cantata 147 (exc); *Haydn:* Creation (exc); *Purcell:* Bell Anthem, Z49; *Schubert:* Psalm 23, D706; *Fauré:* Requiem (exc); *Elgar:* Coronation Ode (exc); *Delius:* To be sung of a summer night; *Britten:* St Nicolas; Ceremony of Carols (exc); *W.H. Harris:* Faire is the heaven; *Wood:* Hail, gladdening light; *Dykes:* Holy! Holy! Holy!. (King's College Ch, ASMF/D. Willcocks/P.

Ledger, F. Grier, P. Ledger, New Philh, F. Lott, A. Hodgson, R. Morton, S. Roberts, CUMS, Kneller Hall Band, R. Tear, O. Ellis, I. Hare, PJBE)

① **CD-CFP4577** (2/91)
A Viennese Evening
J. Strauss II: Zigeunerbaron (exc); Rosen aus den Süden; *E. Strauss*: Alpenrose; *J. Strauss II*: Champagner, Op. 211; Pesther Csárdás; Perpetuum Mobile; Fledermaus (exc); Morgenblätter, Op. 279; *E. Strauss*: Unter der Enns; *J. Strauss II*: Explosionen, Op. 43; Im Krapfenwald'l, Op. 336; *J. strauss I*: Radetzky March. (Hallé/B. Tovey)

① **CD-CFP4586** (12/91)
Carols from King's
Traditional: Sussex Carol; And all in the morning; Tomorrow shall be my dancing day; Könige; Cherry Tree Carol; All my heart this night rejoices; Stille Nacht; Hail blessed Virgin Mary; It came upon the midnight clear; Ding dong merrily on high; I saw a maiden; In the bleak midwinter; Maria durch ein' Dornwald ging; Lord at first did Adam make; Child is born in Bethlehem; Babe is born I wys; *M. Praetorius*: Psallite unigenito; *Traditional*: While shepherds watched. (S. Varcoe, Kings College Ch, J. Wells/D. Willcocks)

① **CD-CFP4598** (12/92)
Britten—Orchestral Works
Britten: Frank Bridge Variations; Matinées Musicales; Soirées Musicales. (ECO/A. Gibson)

① **CD-CFP4617** (6/93)
Elgar—Orchestral Works
Elgar: Falstaff; Cockaigne; Introduction and Allegro. (LPO/V. Handley)

① **CD-CFP4637** (3/94)
Ketèlbey/Luigini—Orchestral Music
Ketèlbey: In a Persian Market; In a Monastery Garden; Chal Romano; In the Mystic Land of Egypt; Clock and the Dresden Figures; Bells across the Meadows; In a Chinese Temple Garden; In the Moonlight; Sanctuary of the Heart; *Luigini*: Ballet égyptien (exc). (J. Temperley, V. Midgley, L. Pearson, Ambrosian Sngrs, Philh/J. Lanchbery, RPO/A. Fistoulari)

① **CD-CFP4638** (3/94)
Sheppard/Tallis—Motets
Sheppard: Gaude gaude gaude Maria virgo; Laudem dicite Deo; In pace in idipsum; In manus tuas I a 4; Verbum caro factum est; *Tallis*: Spem in alium; O nata lux; Ecce tempus idoneum; Loquebantur variis linguis; Gaude gloriosa Dei mater. (Clerkes of Oxenford/D. Wulstan)

① **CD-CFP4653** (10/94)
Debussy—Piano Works
Debussy: Suite bergamasque (exc); Petit nègre; Arabesques; Images (exc); Children's Corner; Plus que lente; Préludes (exc); Etudes (exc); Isle joyeuse. (M. Lympany)

① **CD-CFP4667** (7/95)
Ravel—Orchestral Works
Ravel: Piano Concerto; Left-hand Concerto; La Valse; Valses nobles et sentimentales. (P. Fowke, LPO/S. Baudo)

① **CD-CFP4669** (11/95)
Margaret Price sings Romantic Songs
Schumann: Frauenliebe und -leben, Op.42 (Cpte); *Schubert*: Auf der Riesenkoppe, D611; Hirt auf dem Felsen, D965; *Tchaikovsky*: Songs, Op.6 (exc); *Liszt*: O lieb, so lang du lieben kannst!, S298; Loreley, S273; Stille Wasserrose, S321; Wie sollen wir Wunderbares sein, S314; Kling leise, mein Lied, S301. (M. Price, J. Brymer, J. Lockhart)

① **CD-CFP9000** (11/87)
Orchestral Favourites
Tchaikovsky: 1812; *Borodin*: Prince Igor (exc); *Glinka*: Ruslan and Lyudmila (exc); *Tchaikovsky*: Marche slave; *Wagner*: Lohengrin (exc); *Mussorgsky*: Night on the Bare Mountain. (LPO/C. Mackerras/W. Susskind/A. Davison)

① **CD-CFP9003** (11/87)
Elgar—Orchestral Works
Elgar: Cello Concerto; In the South; Elegy. (R. Cohen, LPO/N. del Mar)

① **CD-CFP9008** (11/87)
Wagner Orchestral Works
Wagner: Walküre (exc); Götterdämmerung (exc); Lohengrin (exc); Meistersinger (exc). (LPO/K.A. Rickenbacher)

① **CD-CFP9011** (3/88)
Popular Orchestral Works
Dukas: Apprenti sorcier; *Chabrier*: Joyeuse marche; España; *Berlioz*: Damnation de Faust (exc); *Ravel*: Boléro. (Hallé/J. Loughran)

① **CD-CFP9012** (3/88)
Gershwin. Works for Piano and Orchestra
Gershwin: Rhapsody in Blue; Piano Concerto; American in Paris. (D. Blumenthal, ECO/S. Bedford)

① **CD-CFP9015** (12/87)
Waltzes by Johann Strauss II
J. Strauss II: Blauen Donau, Op. 314; Künstlerleben, Op. 316; Wein, Weib und Gesang; Accelerationen, Op. 234; Wiener Blut; Frühlingsstimmen, Op. 410; G'schichten aus dem Wienerwald, Op. 325; Kaiser, Op. 437. (Hallé/B. Thomson)

Claves

① **CD50-0813** (9/86)
Clarinet Concertos
Pleyel: Clarinet Concerto, Ben106; *Molter*: Clarinet Concerto 6; *Mercadante*: Clarinet Concerto, Op. 101. (T. Friedli, South-West German CO/P. Angerer)

① **CD50-8003/4** (6/88)
Albéniz—Piano Works
Albéniz: Iberia; Suite española 1; Cantos de España. (R. Requejo)

① **CD50-8203** (12/85)
Krommer—Flute & Oboe Concertos
Krommer: Flute Concerto, Op. 30; Flute and Oboe Concertino, Op. 65; Oboe Concerto, Op. 52. (P-L. Graf, H. Holliger, ECO/H. Holliger/P-L. Graf)

① **CD50-8206** (3/84)
Venetian Music for Voice and Instruments
Strozzi: Ariette, Op. 2 (exc); Ariette, Op. 6 (exc); *Molinaro*: Lute Bk I (exc); *Sances*: Misera, hor si ch'il pianto; O perduti diletti; *Monteverdi*: Messa et salmi (exc); *Milanuzzi*: Ut re mi; *Fontei*: Auree stelle; *Miniscalchi*: Fuggir pur mi convien; Fuggir voglio; In me vivete; *Palestrina*: Vestiva i colli; *Rore*: Anchor che col partire; *Lamoretti*: Bell' il vana tua beltade. (T. Berganza, Ens, J.E. Dähler (hpd/dir), Y. Imamura)

① **CD50-8406** (9/85)
Mozart—Chamber Works
Mozart: Oboe Quintet, K406; Oboe Quartet, K370; Adagio, K580a. (I. Goritzki, I. Goritzki, Berne Qt)

① **CD50-8505** (9/86)
Mozart—Works for Flute and Orchestra
Mozart: Flute Concerto, K313; Flute Concerto, K314; Andante, K315; *MOzart*: Rondo, K373. (P-L. Graf, ECO/R. Leppard)

① **CD50-8507** (3/87)
Chamber recital
Tchaikovsky: Souvenir de Florence; *Bloch*: From Jewish Life (exc); *Atterberg*: Suite 3; *Puccini*: Crisantemi; *Wagner*: Wesendonk Lieder (exc). (A. Lysy, M-K. Lee, P. Coletti, N. Chastain, A. Lysy, E. Vassallo, Camerata Lysy)

① **CD50-8508** (8/86)
Debussy—Piano Duet Works
Debussy: La mer; Marche écossaise; Petite Suite; Epigraphes antiques. (Crommelynck Duo)

① **CD50-8509** (3/87)
Frank Martin—Piano Concertos
Martin: Piano Concerto 1; Piano Concerto 2; Piano Ballade. (J-F. Antonioli, Turin PO/M. Viotti)

① **CD50-8602** (2/87)
Kramár—Clarinet Concertos
Krommer: Clarinet Concerto, Op. 36; Clarinet Concerto, Op. 86; 2-Clarinet Concerto, Op. 35. (T. Friedli, ECO/A. Pay, A. Pay (cl/dir))

① **CD50-8611** (2/88)
Schubert—Lieder
Schubert: Götter Griechenlands, D677; Dass sie hier gewesen, D775; Adelaide, D95; Stimme der Liebe, D412; An die Leier, D737; Geheimnis, D491; Atys, D585; Nachtstück, D672; Heidenröslein, D257; Auflösung, D807; Einsame, D800; Heidenröslein, D257; Fischerweise, D881; Jüngling an der Quelle, D300; Liebhaber in allen Gestalten, D558; Rosenband, D280; Sommernacht, D289; Herbst, D945; Winterabend, D938; Im Abendrot, D799; Nacht und Träume, D827; Sterne, D684; Wandrers Nachtlied II, D768. (E. Haefliger, J. E. Dähler)

① **CD50-8802** (9/91)
Schubert—Works for Piano Duet, Vol 1
Schubert: Polonaises, D599; Divertissement à la Hongroise, D818; Marches héroïques, D602; German Dance, D618. (Crommelynck Duo)

① **CD50-8803** (10/88)
Enescu—Chamber & Orchestral Works
Enescu: Chamber Symphony, Op.33; Wind Decet, Op.14; Intermezzi, Op.12. (Lausanne CO/L. Foster)

① **CD50-8806** (8/89)
Busoni & Raff—Works for Piano & Orchestra
Busoni: Konzertstück; *Raff*: Ode au printemps; Piano Concerto. (J-F. Antonioli, Lausanne CO/L. Foster)

① **CD50-8808** (2/91)
Grieg—Violin Sonatas
Grieg: Violin Sonata 1; Violin Sonata 2; Violin Sonata 3. (I. Turban, J-J. Dünki)

① **CD50-8814/6** (7/89)
Boccherini—Cello Concertos
Boccherini: Cello Concerto, G474; Cello Concerto, G475; Cello Concerto, G476; Cello Concerto, G477; Cello Concerto, G478; Cello Concerto, G479; Cello Concerto, G480; Cello Concerto, G481; Cello Concerto, G482; Cello Concerto, G483; Cello Concerto, G573; Cello Concerto in E flat. (D. Geringas, Padua CO/B. Giuranna)

① **CD50-8901** (10/91)
Schubert—Works for Piano Duet, Vol 2
Schubert: Sonata, D812; Rondo, D608; Variations, D813. (Crommelynck Duo)

① **CD50-8913/4** (3/91)
Mozart—Violin Concertos, etc
Mozart: Violin Concerto, K207; Violin Concerto, K211; Violin Concerto, K216; Violin Concerto, K218; Violin Concerto, K219; Adagio, K261; Rondo, K269; Rondo, K373. (F. Gulli, Venice and Padua CO/B. Giuranna)

① **CD50-8915** (7/90)
J. Strauss II—Waltzes (orig pf vers)
J. Strauss II: Frühlingsstimmen, Op. 410; G'schichten aus dem Wienerwald, Op. 325; Morgenblätter, Op. 279; Wo die Zitronen blühn; Wiener Blut; Wein Weib und Gesang; Blauen Donau, Op. 314. (Crommelynck Duo)

① **CD50-8918** (1/91)
Ansermet conducts Stravinsky
Stravinsky: Histoire du soldat (exc); Histoire du soldat (exc); Japanese Lyrics; *Traditional*: Song of the Volga Boatmen. (J.V. Gilles, F. Simon, W. Jacques, C-F. Ramuz, Y. Furusawa, SRO/E. Ansermet)

① **CD50-9001** (10/90)
Byrd—Keyboard Works
Byrd: Fantasia, BK25; Fantasia, BK62; Carman's WHistle, BK36; Pavan and Galliard, BK60; Pavan and Galliard, BK71; Pavan and Galliard, BK4; Woods so wild, BK85; Queen's Alman, BK10; Bells, BK98; Walsingham, BK8; All in a garden green, BK56; Volte, BK91; Ut re mi fa sol la, BK64. (U. Duetschler)

① **CD50-9003** (10/90)
Jolivet & Koechlin—Chamber Works
Koechlin: Flute Sonata, Op. 52; Primavera Quintet, op 156; *Jolivet*: Chant de Linos; Flute Sonata. (P. Racine, R. Zimansky, M. Clemann, C. Coray, X. Schindler, D. Cholette)

① **CD50-9010** (2/91)
R. Strauss—Wind Concertos
R. Strauss: Duet Concertino; Oboe Concerto; Horn Concerto 2. (I. Goritzki, T. Friedli, K. Thunemann, B. Schneider, Lausanne CO/M. Aeschbacher)

① **CD50-9016** (2/91)
Teresa Berganza—Recital
Monteverdi: Lamento d'Arianna a 1; *Vivaldi*: Piango, gemo, sospiro, RV675; *Haydn*: Arianna a Naxos; *Rossini*: Giovanna d'Arco. (T. Berganza, ECO/M. Viotti)

① **CD50-9017** (10/91)
Respighi—Works for Violin and Orchestra
Respighi: Chaconne; Concerto all'antica; Pastorale; Concerto a cinque. (I. Turban, N. Black, G. Ashton, S. Williams, I. Watson, ECO/M. Viotti)

① **CD50-9018** (9/91)
Concertos for Oboe and Orchestra
Fiala: Oboe Concerto in B flat; *Krommer*: Oboe Concerto, Op. 37; *Kalliwoda*: Concertino, Op. 110; *Martinů*: Oboe Concerto. (I. Goritzki, Polish Chmbr PO/W. Rajski)

① **CD50-9111** (5/92)
Poulenc—Orchestral Works
Poulenc: Animaux modèles; Biches (exc); Mariés de la tour Eiffel; Marches et Intermède. (South-West German RSO/M. Viotti)

① **CD50-9115** (3/93)
Shostakovich—Works for Strings
Shostakovich: Chamber Symphony, Op.110a; Symphony for Strings; String Quartet 15. (Kremlin COM. Rachlevsky)

① **CD50-9116** (6/93)
Tchaikovsky—Music for Strings
Tchaikovsky: Serenade, Op.48; String Quartet 1; Elegy;

Souvenir d'un lieu cher, Op.42 (exc). (Kremlin CO/M. Rachlevsky)

Ⓛ **CD50-9118** (11/93)
Weber—Lieder
Weber: Meine Lieder, meine Sänge, J73; Klage, J63; Kleine Fritz, J74; Was zieht zu deinen Zauberkreise, J68; Ich sah ein Röschen am Wege stehn, J67; Er an Sie, J57; Meine Farben, J62; Liebe-Glühen, J140; Über die Berge mit Ungestüm; Es stürmt auf der Flur, J161; Minnelied; Reigen; Sind es Schmerzen; Mein Verlangen; Wenn ich ein Vöglein wär', J233; Mein Schatzerl is hübsch, J234; Liebesgruss aus der Ferne; Herzchen, mein Schätzchen; Veilchen im Thale; Ich denke dein, J48; Horch'!, Leise horch', Geliebte!; Elle était simple et gentilette. (D. Fischer-Dieskau, H. Höll)

Ⓛ **CD50-9202** (11/92)
Donizetti/Rossini—Tenor Arias
Donizetti: Linda di Chamounix (exc); Duca d'Alba (exc); Elisir d'Amore (exc); Anna Bolena (exc); Don Pasquale (exc); Lucia di Lammermoor (exc); Rossini: Barbiere di Siviglia (exc); Italiana in Algeri (exc); Occasione fa il ladro (exc); Donna del lago (exc). (R. Vargas, ECO/M. Viotti)

Ⓛ **CD50-9205** (6/93)
Canciones Españolas
Falla: Tus ojillos negros; Granados: Canciones amatorias (Cpte); Leoz: Tríptico de canciones; Nin: Cantos de España (exc); Amor es como un niña; Tirana; Confiado jilguerillo; Majas de Paris; Obradors: Canciones clásicas españolas (exc); Rodrigo: Madrigales amatorios (Cpte); Turina: Poema en forma de canciones. (M. Bayo, J.A. Alvarez-Parejo)

Ⓛ **CD50-9215** (12/92)
Turina—Orchestral Works
Turina: Danzas Gitanas, Op.55; Rapsodia sinfónica; Tema y variaciones, Op.100; Serenata, Op.87; Oración del torero. (Granada City Orch/J. de Udaeta)

Ⓛ **CD50-9300/4** (11/93)
Hommage à Tibor Varga
Bach: Violin and Oboe Concerto, BWV1060; Violin Concerto, BWV1042; 2-Violin Concerto; Mozart: Violin Concerto, K219; Symphony 36; Tchaikovsky: Violin Concerto; Bruch: Violin Concerto 1; Hubay: Blumenleben, Op. 30 (exc); Chopin: Nocturnes (exc); Ferrara: Burleska; Kreisler: Francoeur Siciliano and Rigaudon; Stravinsky: Berceuse; Dohnányi: Ruralia hungarica (exc); Principe: Campielo; Geszler: Humming Top; Sarasate: Introduction and Tarantella, Op. 43; Szymanowski: Myths, Op. 30 (exc); Falla: Vida Breve (exc); Paganini: Moses in Egypt Variations (exc). (T. Varga, G. Schmalfuss, G. Varga, G. Moore, I. Pongracz, M. Schwalb, H. Greenslade, Varga CO, Varga Fest Orch, T. Varga (vn/dir)/T. Varga, Vienna Fest Orch/J-M. Auberson)

Ⓛ **CD50-9304/5** (6/95)
Rachmaninov—Works for Chorus
Rachmaninov: Liturgy, Op. 31; O mother of God; Chorus of Spirits; Panteley the healer. (Russian St Sym Cappella/V. Polyansky)

Ⓛ **CD50-9311** (11/93)
Hommage à Tibor Varga, Volume 1
Bach: Violin and Oboe Concerto, BWV1060; Violin Concerto, BWV1042; 2-Violin Concerto. (G. Varga, G. Schmalfuss, Varga CO, Varga Fest Orch, T Varga (vn/dir))

Ⓛ **CD50-9314** (11/93)
Hommage à Tibor Varga, Volume 4
Hubay: Blumenleben, Op. 30 (exc); Chopin: Nocturnes (exc); Ferrara: Burleska; Kreisler: Francoeur Siciliano and Rigaudon; Stravinsky: Berceuse; Dohnányi: Ruralia hungarica (exc); Principe: Campielo; Geszler: Humming Top; Sarasate: Introduction and Tarantella, Op.43; Szymanowski: Myths, Op.30 (exc); Falla: Vida Breve (exc); Paganini: Moses in Egypt Variations. (T. Varga, G. Moore, I. Pongracz, M. Schwalb, H. Greenslade)

Ⓛ **CD50-9317** (7/94)
Tchaikovsky—Chamber Orchestral Works
Tchaikovsky: Souvenir de Florence; String Quartet 3; Snow Maiden (exc). (Kremlin CO/M. Rachlevsky)

Ⓛ **CD50-9327** (5/94)
Lieder Recital—Heinz Rehfuss
Schubert: Frühlingsglaube, D686; Winterreise (exc); Wanderer, D489; Wanderer an den Mond, D870; An die Laute, D905; Schwanengesang, D957 (exc); Schumann: Myrthen, Op.25 (exc); Romanzen und Balladen, Op.49 (exc); Liebesfrühling, Op.37 (exc); Dichterliebe, Op.48 (exc); Wolf: Mörike Lieder (exc); Goethe Lieder (exc). (H. Rehfuss, F. Martin)

Ⓛ **CD50-9328** (9/94)
Mozart/Beethoven—Piano Works
Mozart: Piano Concerto 22; Rondo, K511; Beethoven: Piano Sonata 5. (T. Fellner, Lausanne CO/U. Segal)

Ⓛ **CD50-9404/5** (10/94)
Brahms—String Quartets
Brahms: String Quartet 1; String Quartet 2; String Quartet 3. (Sine Nomine Qt)

Ⓛ **CD50-9413** (1/95)
Schubert—Works for Piano Four Hands, Vol III
Schubert: Rondo, D951; Allegro, D947; Fantasie, D940; Grande marche funèbre, D859; Variations, D624. (Crommelynck Duo)

Ⓛ **CD50-9415** (2/95)
Miaskovsky—Orchestral Works
Miaskovsky: Sinfonietta, Op. 32/2; Pieces, Op. 46/1; Sinfonietta, Op. 58. (Kremlin CO/M. Rachlevsky)

Ⓛ **CD50-9501** (9/95)
Arriaga—String Quartets
Arriaga: String Quartet 1; String Quartet 2; String Quartet 3. (Sine Nomine Qt)

Ⓛ **CD50-9502** (11/95)
Baroque Viola Sonatas
C. Stamitz: Viola Sonata in B flat; Hummel: Viola Sonata, Op. 5/3; Dittersdorf: Viola Sonata in E flat; Vaňhal: Viola Sonata. (A. B. Duetschler, U. Duetschler)

Ⓛ **CD50-9506** (10/95)
Collet—Cantos de España
Collet: Canciones, Op. 69; Canciones, Op. 80; Poema, Op. 48; Amantes de Galicia; Cantos, Op. 42; Pena. (R. Yakar, C. Lavoix)

Cloud Nine Records

Ⓓ **ACN6002** (10/89)
Gershwin: Piano Works
Gershwin: Shall we dance? (exc); Lady, Be Good! (exc); Strike up the Band I (exc); Oh, Kay! (exc); Rosalie (exc); Funny Face (exc); Treasure Girl (exc); Girl Crazy (exc); Pardon My English (exc); Show Girl (exc); Damsel in distress (exc); Porgy and Bess (exc); Shocking Miss Pilgrim (exc); Goldwyn Follies (exc); Tra-la-la; By Strauss. (E. Parkin)

Ⓓ **ACN7014** (11/88)
Herrmann—Classic Fantasy Film Scores
Herrmann: Seventh Voyage of Sinbad (exc); Three Worlds of Gulliver (exc); Mysterious Island (exc); Jason and the Argonauts (exc). (OST/B. Herrmann)

Ⓓ **CNS5005** (10/93)
Schumann—Horrors of the Black Museum
Schumann: Horrors of the Black Museum (exc); Cone of Silence (exc); Attack on the Iron Coast (exc); Claretta (exc); Lost Continent (exc); Konga (exc); Bedford Incident (exc); Long Arm (exc); Ceremony (exc); Smugglers' Rhapsody. (OST/G. Schumann)

Ⓓ **CNS5006** (10/93)
Great Epic Film Scores
Rózsa: El Cid (exc); Tiomkin: Fall of the Roman Empire (exc); Magnificent Showman (exc); 55 Days At Peking (exc). (OST/M. Rózsa/D. Tiomkin)

Club 99

Ⓛ **CL99-007** (1/94)
Maria Nemeth/Tiana Lemnitz
Korngold: Tote Stadt (exc); Verdi: Trovatore (exc); Aida (exc); Puccini: Tosca (exc); Verdi: Ballo in maschera (exc); Mozart: Entführung (exc); Wagner: Fliegende Holländer (exc); Weber: Oberon (exc); Wagner: Wesendonk Lieder (exc); Schubert: Am Grabe Anselmos, D504. (M. Németh, T. Lemnitz, M. Raucheisen, orch)

Ⓛ **CL99-014** (12/90)
Dino Borgioli (1891-1960)
Bellini: Puritani (exc); Bellini: Sonnambula (exc); Giordano: Fedora (exc); Boito: Mefistofele (exc); A. Thomas: Mignon (exc); Bizet: Pêcheurs de Perles (exc); Bellini: Puritani (exc); Donizetti: Don Pasquale (exc); Bizet: Pêcheurs de Perles (exc); Puccini: Favorita (exc); Elisir d'amore (exc); Mascagni: Amico Fritz (exc); Rossini: Barbiere di Siviglia (exc); Puccini: Bohème (exc); Donizetti: Don Pasquale (exc); R. Strauss: Lieder, Op. 27 (exc); Donaudy: O del mio amato ben; Hageman: Do not go, my love. (D. Borgioli, E. Surinach, B. Franci, R. Pampanini, G. Vanelli, A. Brosa, orch, I. Newton)

Ⓛ **CL99-020** (1/94)
Maria Ivogün & Lotte Schöne—Opera Recital
Puccini: Turandot (exc); Mozart: Zauberflöte (exc); Cosi fan tutte (exc); Nicolai: Lustigen Weiber von Windsor (exc);

Massenet: Manon (exc); Cornelius: Barbier von Bagdad (exc); Bellini: Sonnambula (exc); J. Strauss II: Blauen Donau, Op. 314; Handel: Allegro, il penseroso ed il moderato (exc); J. Strauss II: Fledermaus (exc); Verdi: Traviata (exc); Mozart: Rè pastore (exc); Entführung (exc); Zauberflöte (exc); Verdi: Rigoletto (exc); Rossini: Barbiere di Siviglia (exc). (M. Ivogün, L. Schöne, Berlin St Op Orch/F. Zweig/L. Blech/E. Orthmann, K. Erb, orch)

Ⓛ **CL99-022** (5/91)
Germaine Lubin (1891-1979)
Wagner: Tannhäuser (exc); Lohengrin (exc); Siegfried (exc); Walküre (exc); Schubert: Erlkönig, D328; Schumann: Lieder und Gesänge, Op. 51 (exc); Myrthen, Op. 25 (exc); Reyer: Sigurd (exc); Chopin: Etudes (exc); Bach: Cantata 68 (exc); Puccini: Tosca (exc); Wagner: Tristan und Isolde (exc). (G. Lubin, orch/H. Defosse, E.I. Kahn, J. Krieger)

Ⓛ **CL99-025** (11/91)
Giovanni Zenatello (1876-1949)
Giordano: Andrea Chénier (exc); Bizet: Carmen (exc); Leoncavallo: Pagliacci (exc); Puccini: Tosca (exc); Verdi: Ballo in maschera (exc); Bizet: Carmen (exc); Puccini: Manon Lescaut (exc); Verdi: Otello (exc); Otello (exc); Giordano: Andrea Chénier (exc); Leoncavallo: Pagliacci (exc); Verdi: Aida (exc). (G. Zenatello, M. Gay, A. Granforte, Apollo Chor, M. Rappold, orch, La Scala Orch/R. Bourdon/C. Sabajno, G. Marion, A. Boemi)

Ⓛ **CL99-031** (7/90)
Dmitri Smirnov—Opera & Song Recital
Puccini: Tosca (exc); Manon Lescaut (exc); Tabarro (exc); Bohème (exc); Rossini: Barbiere di Siviglia (exc); Boito: Mefistofele (exc); Bizet: Pêcheurs de perles (exc); Massenet: Manon (exc); Manon (exc); Manon (exc); Donizetti: Elisir d'amore (exc); Verdi: Rigoletto (exc); Traviata (exc); Mascagni: Cavalleria Rusticana (exc); Leoncavallo: Mattinata. (D. Smirnov, orch)

Ⓛ **CL99-034** (1/94)
Marcel Journet (1867-1933)
Massenet: Thaïs (exc); A. Thomas: Hamlet (exc); Luce: Vos yeux / Du rêve; Wagner: Walküre (exc); G. Charpentier: Louise (exc); Bizet: Jolie fille de Perth (exc); Gounod: Faust (exc); M. Journet, M. Cozette, F. Heldy, M. Berthon, C. Vezzani, SO/H. Busser, anon/R. Bourdon/P. Coppola)

Ⓛ **CL99-042** (12/91)
Frieda Hempel (1885-1955) & Hermann Jadlowker (1877-1953)
Puccini: Bohème (exc); Gounod: Roméo et Juliette (exc); Meyerbeer: Huguenots (exc); Donizetti: Fille du Régiment (exc); Bizet: Carmen (exc); Donizetti: Lucia di Lammermoor (exc); T. Giordani: Caro mio ben; Carissimi: Vittoria! vittoria!; Schubert: Schwanengesang, D957 (exc); Winterreise (exc); Caccini: Nuove musiche (1602) (exc); Lotti: Arminio (exc). (F. Hempel, H. Jadlowker, orch, anon)

Ⓛ **CL99-052** (1/94)
Rosa Raisa (1893-1963)
Bellini: Norma (exc); Verdi: Trovatore (exc); Meyerbeer: Africaine (exc); Ponchielli: Gioconda (exc); Boito: Mefistofele (exc); Verdi: Trovatore (exc); Giordano: Andrea Chénier (exc); Puccini: Tosca (exc); Mascagni: Cavalleria rusticana (exc); Ponchielli: Gioconda (exc); Mascagni: Cavalleria rusticana (exc); Verdi: Trovatore (exc); Aida (exc); Aida (exc); Ernani (exc); Vespri siciliani (exc); Anon: Eili, eili. (R. Raisa, A. Tokatyan, G. Rimini, G. Crimi, orch)

Ⓛ **CL99-060** (7/90)
Enrico Caruso—Opera & Song Recital
Verdi: Aida (exc); Trovatore (exc); Puccini: Bohème (exc); Bohème (exc); P. M. Costa: Sei morta nella vita mia; Donizetti: Dom Sébastien (exc); Verdi: Rigoletto (exc); Bizet: Carmen (exc); Flotow: Martha (exc); Verdi: Trovatore (exc); Aida (exc); Boito: Mefistofele (exc); Alvarez: Partida; Donizetti: Elisir d'amore (exc); De Curtis: Canta pe'me. (E. Caruso, F. Alda, G. Farrar, L. Tetrazzini, J. Jacoby, P. Amato, L. Homer, orch/W.B. Rogers, G. Scognamiglio, anon, V. Bellezza, S. Cottone)

Ⓛ **CL99-074** (9/90)
Conchita Supervia (1895-1936)
Bizet: Carmen (exc); Saint-Saëns: Samson et Dalila (exc); Grieg: Peer Gynt (exc); A. Thomas: Mignon (exc); Puccini: Bohème (exc); Gounod: Faust (exc); R. Strauss: Rosenkavalier (exc); Humperdinck: Hänsel und Gretel (exc); Mozart: Nozze di Figaro (exc). (C. Supervia, V. Bettoni, I.M. Ferraris, orch/A. Albergoni/G. Cloëz/A. Capdevila)

Ⓛ **CL99-089** (1/94)
Adamo Didur (1874-1946)
Tchaikovsky: Queen of Spades (exc); Meyerbeer: Huguenots (exc); Boito: Mefistofele (exc); Mefistofele (exc); Meyerbeer: Robert le Diable (exc); Mugnone: Vita

brettone (exc); *Donizetti:* Elisir d'amore (exc); *Verdi:* Aida (exc); *Halévy:* Juive (exc); *Flotow:* Martha (exc); *Leoni:* Oracolo (exc); *Offenbach:* Contes d'Hoffmann (exc); *Gomes:* Salvator Rosa (exc); *A. Thomas:* Mignon (exc); *Gounod:* Faust (exc); *Traditional:* Folksongs of Little Russia; *Tosti:* Si tu le voulais; *Moniuszko:* O mother; *Noskowski:* Our mountaineers. (A. Didur, T. Leliwa, anon, orch)

Ⓓ **CL99-101** (1/94)
Vanni Marcoux (1877-1962)
Février: Monna Vanna (exc); *Massenet:* Don Quichotte (exc); Don Quichotte (exc); Cléopâtre (exc); Panurge (exc); *Berlioz:* Damnation de Faust (exc); *A. Thomas:* Hamlet (exc); *G. Charpentier:* Louise (exc); *Laparra:* Habanera (exc); *Mozart:* Don Giovanni (exc); *Mussorgsky:* Boris Godunov (exc); Boris Godunov (exc); *Schubert:* Forelle, D550; Winterreise (exc); *Hahn:* Je me metz; Offrande. (Vanni-Marcoux, O. Ricquier, M. Cozette, orch, anon, anon)

Ⓓ **CL99-109** (7/91)
Johanna Gadski (1871-1932)
Mascagni: Cavalleria rusticana (exc); *Mozart:* Zauberflöte (exc); Nozze di Figaro (exc); *Verdi:* Ballo in maschera (exc); Trovatore (exc); Aida (exc); Aida (exc); *R. Strauss:* Salome (exc); *Thuille:* Lobetanz (exc); *Wagner:* Lohengrin (exc); Tannhäuser (exc); Tristan und Isolde (exc); Fliegende Holländer (exc); Walküre (exc); Walküre (exc); Siegfried (exc); Götterdämmerung (exc); *Schubert:* Du bist die Ruh', D776; Erlkönig, D328; Gretchen am Spinnrade, D118. (J. Gadski, orch, anon)

Ⓓ **CL99-509/10** (9/90)
Hina Spani (1896-1969)
Granados: Tonadillas (exc); *Nin:* Cantos de España (exc); *Obradors:* Coplas de curro dulce; *López Buchardo:* Canción del carretero; *Ugarte:* Dia del fiesta; *Brahms:* Volkskinderlieder (exc); Lieder, Op. 72 (exc); *Parisotti:* Se tu m'ami; *Paradis:* Quel ruscelletto; *Tirindelli:* O primavera; *Verdi:* Trovatore (exc); *Wagner:* Lohengrin (exc); *Catalani:* Wally (exc); *Gounod:* Faust (exc); *Caccini:* Nuove musiche (1602) (exc); *Ciampi:* Tre cicisbei ridicoli (exc); *A. Scarlatti:* Donna ancora è fedele (exc); *Puccini:* Madama Butterfly (exc); *Massenet:* Manon (exc); *Puccini:* Tosca (exc); *Dvořák:* Gipsy melodies (exc); *Wagner:* Lohengrin (exc); *Verdi:* Ballo in maschera (exc); *Leoncavallo:* Pagliacci (exc); *Puccini:* Bohème (exc); *Verdi:* Trovatore (exc); *Puccini:* Manon Lescaut (exc); *Verdi:* Otello (exc); *Puccini:* Manon Lescaut (exc); Madama Butterfly (exc); *Mascagni:* Cavalleria rusticana (exc); *Puccini:* Tosca (exc). (H. Spani, P. Masini, A. Granforte, G. Zenatello, La Scala Orch, orch/C. Sabajno/G. Nastrucci)

Ⓓ **CL99-587/8** (1/91)
Eugenia Burzio (1872-1922)
Cilea: Adriana Lecouvreur (exc); *Mascagni:* Cavalleria rusticana (exc); *Verdi:* Forza del destino (exc); *Ponchielli:* Gioconda (exc); *Verdi:* Aida (exc); Trovatore (exc); *Boito:* Mefistofele (exc); *Verdi:* Forza del destino (exc); *Puccini:* Fanciulla del West (exc); *E. Romano:* Zulma (exc); *Bellini:* Norma (exc); *Meyerbeer:* Africaine (exc); *Gounod:* Ave Maria; *Boito:* Mefistofele (exc); *Verdi:* Forza del destino (exc); Otello (exc); Otello (exc); *Cilea:* Adriana Lecouvreur (exc); *Pacini:* Saffo (exc); *Verdi:* Ballo in maschera (exc); *Donizetti:* Favorita (exc); *Ponchielli:* Gioconda (exc); *Mascagni:* Cavalleria rusticana (exc). (E. Burzio, G. Acerbi, A. Magini-Coletti, G. De Luca, orch)

Collegium

Ⓓ **COLCD100** (6/87)
Rutter: Sacred Music
Rutter: Gloria; O clap your hands; All things bright and beautiful; Lord is my shepherd; Gaelic Blessing; For the beauty of the earth; Praise ye the Lord; God be in my head; Open thou mine eyes; Prayer of St Patrick; Lord bless you and keep you. (Cambridge Sngrs, CLS, PJBE/J. Rutter)

Ⓓ **COLCD104** (4/87)
English Partsongs
Stanford: Partsongs, Op. 119 (exc); *Delius:* To be sung of a Summer Night; *Elgar:* Choral Songs, Op. 53 (exc); My love dwelt in a northern land; *Vaughan Williams:* Shakespeare Songs (Cpte); *Britten:* Flower Songs (Cpte); *Moeran:* Sailor and Young Nancy; *Grainger:* Brigg Fair; Londonderry Air; *Chapman:* Three Ravens; *Holst:* Welsh Folk Songs, H183 (exc); *Bairstow:* Oak and the ash; *Stanford:* Quick! we have but a second. (M. Padmore, Cambridge Sngrs/J. Rutter, P. Sheffield, N. Sears)

Ⓓ **COLCD105** (11/87)
Flora Gave Me Fairest Flowers - English Madrigals
Morley: Balletts (1595) (exc); *East:* Quicke, quicke, away; *Gibbons:* Dainty fine bird; Silver Swan; *Byrd:* Though Amaryllis dance in green; This sweet and merry month of May; Lullaby my sweet little baby; *Weelkes:* Balletts and Madrigals (exc); Ayres (1608) (exc); Ayres (1608) (exc); *Wilbye:* Madrigals, Second Set (exc); Madrigals, First Set (exc); *Tomkins:* Too much I once lamented; Adieu, ye city-prisoning towers; *Farmer:* Little pretty bonny lass; *Bennet:* Round about in a fair ring; *R. Ramsey:* Sleep, fleshy birth. (Cambridge Sngrs/J. Rutter)

Ⓓ **COLCD106** (12/87)
Christmas Night
Traditional: In dulci jubilo; Adam lay ybounden; Christmas Night; Once, as I remember; Spotless rose; In the bleak mid-winter; *Rutter:* There is a flower; *Traditional:* Cherry Tree Carol; I wonder as I wander; *Rutter:* Candlelight Carol; *Traditional:* O Tannenbaum; Tomorrow shall be my dancing day; Virgin most pure; I sing of a maiden; *Ballet:* Lute-book lullaby; *Traditional:* Könige; Myn lyking; O little one sweet; *Ebeling:* All my heart this night rejoices; *Traditional:* I saw a maiden; Away in a manger; *Rutter:* Nativity carol. (Cambridge Sngrs, CLS/J. Rutter, G. Finley, N. Sears)

Ⓓ **COLCD107** (6/88)
Faire is the Heaven
Parsons: Ave Maria; *Tallis:* Loquebantur variis linguis; *Byrd:* Miserere mei; Haec dies a 6; Ave verum corpus; *Tallis:* If ye love me; *Farrant:* Hide not thou thy face; *Anon:* Lord, for thy tender mercy's sake; *Gibbons:* O clap your hands; *Byrd:* Bow thine ear; *Gibbons:* Hosanna to the Son of David; *Purcell:* Lord, how long wilt thou be angry?, Z25; Funeral Sentences (exc); Hear my prayer, O Lord, Z15; *Stanford:* Motets, Op.38 (exc); *Wood:* This joyful Eastertide; *Traditional:* Sing lullaby; Spotless rose; *Walton:* What cheer?; *Vaughan Williams:* O taste and see; *Britten:* Hymn to the Virgin; *Traditional:* Jesus Christ the apple tree; *W. H. Harris:* Faire is the heaven. (Cambridge Sngrs/J. Rutter)

Ⓓ **COLCD108** (10/88)
Poulenc: Sacred Choral Works
Poulenc: Gloria (Cpte); Salve regina; Ave verum corpus; Exultate Deo; Litanies à la Vierge noire; Motets pour un temps de pénitence; Motets pour le temps de Noël. (D. Deam, M. Seers, Cambridge Sngrs, CLS/J. Rutter)

Ⓓ **COLCD109** (1/89)
Fauré: Sacred Choral Works
Fauré: Requiem (Cpte); Ave verum; Tantum ergo, Op. 65/2; Ave Maria, Op. 93; Maria, Mater gratiae; Cantique de Jean Racine; Messe basse. (C. Ashton, S. Varcoe, John Scott, Cambridge Sngrs, CLS/J. Rutter)

Ⓓ **COLCD110** (4/90)
Byrd: Sacred Choral Works
Byrd: Sing joyfully unto God our strength; Turn our captivity; Praise our Lord all ye Gentiles; Emendemus in melius; Siderum rector; Plorans plorabit; Gradualia 1/ii: Miscellaneous (exc); Attolite portas; Laudibus in sanctis; Gradualia 1/i: Feast of All Saints (exc); Ave verum corpus; Gradualia 2: Pentecost (exc); Gradualia 2: Feast of Peter and Paul (exc); Gradualia 2: Nativity (exc); Gradualia 2: Votive Mass (exc). (Cambridge Sngrs/J. Rutter)

Ⓓ **COLCD111** (12/89)
Christmas with the Cambridge Singers
Traditional: Joy to the world; *Sweelinck:* Hodie Christus natus est; *Rutter:* Angels' Carol; *Traditional:* Ding dong! merrily on high; Twas in the moon of winter time; Personent hodie; Sussex Carol; In dulci jubilo; Gloucestershire Wassail; *Handel:* Messiah (exc); *Adam:* Minuit, Chrétiens (exc); *Rutter:* What sweeter music; *Victoria:* O magnum mysterium; *Traditional:* Still, still, still; Coventry Carol; Greensleeves (What Child is this?); *Berlioz:* Enfance du Christ (exc); *Traditional:* Sing lullaby; Quem pastores laudavere; *Britten:* New Year Carol; *Traditional:* Stille nacht. (Cambridge Sngrs, CLS/J. Rutter)

Ⓓ **COLCD113** (4/92)
Hail, gladdening Light
Anon: Rejoice in the Lord alway; *Purcell:* Remember not, Lord, our offences, Z50; *Amner:* Come, let's rejoice; *Tomkins:* When David heard; *Bairstow:* I sat down under his shadow; *Goss:* These are they which follow the Lamb; *Taverner:* Christe Jesu, pastor bone; *Philips:* O beatum et sacrosanctum diem; *Howells:* Nunc dimittis; *Vaughan Williams:* O vos omnes; *Dering:* Cantica sacra (1618) (exc); *Stanford:* Motets, Op. 38 (exc); *Wood:* Hail, gladdening Light; *Tavener:* Hymn to the Mother of God; Dormition Hymn; *Elgar:* They are at rest; *Walton:* Litany; *Morley:* Nolo mortem peccatoris; *Tallis:* O nata lux; *Rutter:* Loving Shepherd of thy sheep; *Stone:* Lord's Prayer; *Sheppard:* In manus tuas I a 4; *W.H. Harris:* Bring us, O Lord. (Cambridge Sngrs/J. Rutter)

Ⓓ **COLCD114** (4/92)
Rutter—Sacred Choral Works
Rutter: Magnificat; Falcon; O praise the Lord of heaven; Behold, the tabernacle of God. (P. Forbes, Cambridge Sngrs, CLS/J. Rutter, St Paul's Cath Ch, Andrew Lucas, John Scott)

Ⓓ **COLCD115** (12/91)
Three Musical Fables
Rutter: Reluctant Dragon; Brother Heinrich's Christmas; Wind in the Willows. (R. Baker, B. Kay, J. Jackman, G. Ives, A. Holt, S. Carrington, A. Hume, C.S. Mason, King's Sngrs, Cambridge Sngrs, CLS/R. Hickox/J. Rutter)

Ⓓ **COLCD116** (4/92)
Ave Gracia Plena
Anon: Festival of the Virgin Mary (exc); *F. Guerrero:* Ave virgo sanctissima a 5; *Traditional:* There is no rose; *Victoria:* Vidi speciosam; Ave Maria, gratia plena a 4; Ave Maria, gratia plena a 8; *Palestrina:* Stabat mater a 8; *Bruckner:* Ave maria (1861); *Verdi:* Pezzi sacri (exc); *Stravinsky:* Ave Maria; *Tchaikovsky:* Sacred pieces (exc); *Villette:* Hymne à la Vierge; *Dering:* Ave virgo gratiosa; *Howells:* Regina caeli; *Traditional:* Hail! blessed Virgin Mary; *Swayne:* Magnificat; *Holst:* Ave Maria; *Byrd:* Gradualia 1/i: Annunciation of the BVM (exc). (Cambridge Sngrs/J. Rutter)

Ⓓ **COLCD117** (3/93)
Rutter—Fancies
Rutter: Fancies; Suite antique; Childhood Lyrics; When Icicles hang. (D. Dobing, W. Marshall, Cambridge Sngrs, CLS/J. Rutter)

Ⓓ **COLCD118** (12/92)
I Will lift up mine eyes
Howells: Gloucester Service (exc); Like as the hart; Fear of the Lord; Requiem; Long, long ago; All my hope; *Stanford:* Services, Op. 81 (exc); Services, Op. 10 (exc); Anthems, Op.113 (exc); I heard a voice from heaven; When mary thro' the garden went; Services, Op. 115 (exc). (Cambridge Sngrs/J. Rutter, W. Marshall)

Ⓓ **COLCD119** (11/93)
A Cappella
Britten: Hymn to St Cecilia; *Brahms:* Lieder und Romanzen, Op. 44 (exc); *Schumann:* Doppelchörige Gesänge, Op. 141; *Pearsall:* Lay a garland; *Delius:* Splendour falls; *Ravel:* Chansons; *Debussy:* Chansons de Charles d'Orléans; *Poulenc:* Chansons françaises. (Cambridge Sngrs/J. Rutter)

Ⓓ **COLCD120** (11/93)
The Lark in the Clear Air
Rutter: Traditional Songs (Cpte); *Vaughan Williams:* English Folksongs (Cpte); *Traditional:* I know where I'm going; *H. Hughes:* She moved through the fair; *Traditional:* Lark in the clear air; *H. Hughes:* Down by the Salley Gardens; *Traditional:* Sprig of thyme; Bold grenadier; Keel Row; Cuckoo (England); She's like the Swallow; Willow song; Willow tree; Miller of the Dee; O can ye sew cushions?; Afton Water. (Cambridge Sngrs, CLS/J. Rutter)

Ⓓ **COLCD121** (12/93)
Christmas Day in the Morning
Traditional: I saw three ships; Riu, riu, chiu; *Rutter:* Mary's lullaby; *Traditional:* Sans Day Carol; Flambeau, Jeanette, Isabelle; *Rutter:* Star Carol; *Traditional:* Quelle est cette odeur agréable; Wexford Carol; Balulalow; *Warlock:* I saw a fair maiden; *Rutter:* Jesus Child; *Traditional:* Quittez, pasteurs; *Tavener:* Lamb; *Vaughan Williams:* Fantasia on Christmas Carols; *Traditional:* Blessed be that maid Mary; *Rutter:* Donkey Carol; Wild wood carol; *Traditional:* Go, tell it on the mountain; *Rutter:* Very best time of year; *Traditional:* Deck the hall; *Rutter:* Shepherd's pipe carol; Christmas lullaby; *Traditional:* We wish you a merry Christmas. (S. Varcoe, Cambridge Sngrs, CLS/J. Rutter)

Collins Classics

Ⓓ **Coll1019-2** (2/90)
Britten—Orchestral Works
Britten: Gloriana Suite; Sea Interludes, Op. 33a; Passacaglia, Op. 33b; Sinfonia da Requiem. (LSO/S. Bedford)

Ⓓ **Coll1052-2** (6/91)
Debussy—Piano Works
Debussy: Images oubliées; Estampes; Images. (F. Ts'ong)

Ⓓ **Coll1053-2** (5/91)
Satie—Piano Works
Satie: Sports et divertissements; Pièces froides (exc); Embryons desséchés; Véritables préludes flasques; Valses du précieux dégoûté; Gymnopédies; Avant-dernières pensées; Vieux séquins et vieilles cuirasses; Prélude de la Porte héroïque du ciel; Heures séculaires et instantanées; Gnossiennes (exc); Je te veux; Parade (exc). (J. MacGregor)

Ⓓ **Coll1097-2** (3/91)
Copland: Orchestral Works
Copland: Appalachian Spring Suite; Clarinet Concerto;

Colosseum

Condon Collection

Conifer

(exc); *Guridi*: Canciones castellanas (exc); *Obradors*: Vito. (J. Gomez, J. Constable)

○ **CDCF501** (12/90)
Carols from Trinity
P. Nicolai: Wachet auf, ruft uns die Stimme; *Traditional*: Advent Responsory; *Bach*: Schübler Chorales, BWV645-650 (exc); *Traditional*: Of the Father's heart begotten; Angelus ad virginem; Holly and the Ivy; I sing of a Maiden; Ding dong! Merrily on high; O come all ye faithful; There is no rose; *Brahms*: Chorale Preludes, Op.122 (exc); *Traditional*: Stille Nacht; O little town of Bethlehem; I saw three ships; Sweet was the song; *Holst*: Carols, H133 (exc); *Traditional*: Away in a manger; *Handl*: Resonet in laudibus; *Traditional*: Up! good Christen folk; First Nowell; *Berlioz*: Enfance du Christ (exc); *Traditional*: Könige; Unto us is born a son; Coventry carol; *Walton*: What cheer?; *Traditional*: Hark! the herald angels sing; *Bach*: In dulci jubilo, BWV729. (Trinity Coll Ch, Cambridge, R. Marlow/R. Marlow, G. Jackson)

○ **CDCF509** (7/92)
Fandango - Spanish Dances for Guitar
Rodrigo: Piezas españolas; *Aguado*: Fandango Variations; *Murcia*: Baroque Dances; *Sanz*: Spanish Guitar Instruction I (exc); Spanish Guitar Instruction II (exc); *Pavanas*; *Llobet*: Catalan Folksongs; *Pujol Vilarrubí*: Spanish Pieces. (T. Kerstens)

○ **CDCF512** (5/93)
The Erik Satie Show
Satie: Gymnopédies; Piège de Méduse; Croquis et agaceries; Poudre d'or; Chapitres tournés en tous sens; Piccadilly; Prélude en tapisserie; Véritables préludes flasques; Je te veux; Sonatine bureaucratique; Pièces froides; Sports et divertissements; Vexations; Préludes du fils des étoiles. (P. Dickinson)

○ **CDCF517** (12/93)
A Child is Born
Traditional: Wake, o wake!; Gabriel fram heven-king; Edi beo lhu; *Britten*: Hymn to the Virgin; *Gibbons*: This is the record of John; *Traditional*: Child is born in Bethlehem; Once in Royal David's City; Rejoice with heart and voice; Hodie Christus natus est; Great and Mighty Wonder; O little one sweet; In dulci jubilo; *Vaughan Williams*: Hodie (exc); *Amner*: Little flock; *Traditional*: While shepherds watched; Shepherd's Cradle Song; *Tavener*: Lamb; *Traditional*: As with gladness; Here is the little door; In the bleak midwinter; Tomorrow shall be my dancing day; Illuminare Jerusalem; Coventry carol; Benedicamus Domino; *Dandrieu*: Noëls (exc); *Gigout*: Rapsodie sur des Noëls; *Mulet*: Esquisses byzantines (exc). (Trinity Coll Ch, Cambridge, P. Rushforth, S. Standage/R. Marlow)

• ○ **CDCF518** (9/94)
Serenade
Mertz: Schubertian Songs; *Paganini*: Grand Sonata in A (exc); *Ghiribizzi*, MS43 (exc); Guitar Sonatinas, MS85 (exc); *Regondi*: Introduction and Caprice, Op.23; *Schubert*: Piano Sonata, D894 (exc); Moments musicaux, D780 (exc); *Chopin*: Preludes (exc); *Tárrega*: Preludios (exc); Capricho árabe; Mazurkas (exc); *Pavana*; Alborada. (T. Kerstens)

○ **CDCF903** (11/93)
By Arrangement—Tetra Guitar Quartet
Bernstein: West Side Story (exc); *Weill*: Dreigroschenoper (exc); *Prokofiev*: Lt Kijé Suite (exc); *Bock*: Fiddler on the Roof (exc); *Walton*: Façade Suites (exc). (Tetra)

○ **CDCF905** (10/94)
Karen Jones—The Flute Album
Fauré: Songs, Op. 7 (exc); *Morceau de concours*; *Dutilleux*: Sonatine; *Villa-Lobos*: Assobio a jato; *Godard*: Suite, Op. 116; *Fürstenau*: Adagio and Variations, Op. 133; *Debussy*: Prélude à l'après-midi d'un faune; *Saint-Saëns*: Romance, Op. 36; *Ascanio* (exc); *Doppler*: Casilda fantaisie; *Borne*: Carmen Fantasy. (K. Jones, A. Brewer, S. J. Pendlebury, C. Edwards)

○ **CDHD201** (3/94)
Galli-Curci in Opera and Song
Rossini: Semiramide (exc); *Bellini*: Sonnambula (exc); Sonnambula (exc); Sonnambula (exc); *Donizetti*: Lucia di Lammermoor (exc); Lucia di Lammermoor (exc); Lucia di Lammermoor (exc); *Verdi*: Trovatore (exc); Traviata (exc); *Rimsky-Korsakov*: Golden Cockerel (exc); *A. Scarlatti*: Solitudini amene (exc); *Donizetti*: Don Pasquale (exc); *Verdi*: Rigoletto (exc); Rigoletto (exc); *Bishop*: Lo, here the gentle lark; Echo Song; *Yradier*: Paloma. (A. Galli-Curci, T. Schipa, G. De Luca, orch/R. Bourdon, NY Met Op Orch/G. Setti, H. Samuels)

○ **CDHD214** (9/94)
Jussi Björling - Arias, Lieder and Songs
Flotow: Martha (exc); *Verdi*: Rigoletto (exc); Rigoletto (exc); Trovatore (exc); *Gounod*: Faust (exc); *Meyerbeer*: Africaine (exc); *Verdi*: Aida (exc); *Bizet*: Carmen (exc);

Ponchielli: Gioconda (exc); *Massenet*: Manon (exc); *Puccini*: Tosca (exc); Tosca (exc); Fanciulla del West (exc); *Rossini*: Stabat mater (exc); *Verdi*: Requiem (exc); *R. Strauss*: Lieder, Op.27 (exc); *Beethoven*: Adelaide, Op.46; *Schrader*: Summer night; *Traditional*: Ack Värmerland, du skóma; *Millöcker*: Bettelstudent (exc). (J. Björling, H. Schymberg, H. Ebert, orch/N. Grevillius)

○ **75605 51231-2** (8/95)
O.Gibbons—Hosanna to the Son of David
Gibbons: Almighty and everlasting God; Behold, thou hast made my days; Blessed are all they; Deliver us, O Lord; Glorious and powerful God; Hosanna to the Son of David; I am the resurrection; Lift up your heads; O all true faithful hearts; O Clap your hands; O Lord, how do my woes increase; O Lord, I lift my heart to thee; O Lord, in thee is all my trust; O Lord, in thy wrath; Out of the deep; Praise the Lord, O my soul; See, see, the word is incarnate; This is the record of John. (Trinity Coll Ch, Cambridge, Fretwork/R. Marlow)

○ **75605 51232-2** (6/95)
Stravinsky—Mass; Gesualdo—Responsoria
Stravinsky: Mass; Pater noster; Ave Maria; Dove descending; *Gesualdo*: Da pacem; Assumpta est Maria; Illumina nos; Responsoria (exc). (Trinity Coll Ch, Cambridge, London Musici/R. Marlow)

○ **75605 51239-2** (6/95)
Hugh Wood—String Quartets Nos 1-4
Hugh Wood: String Quartet 1; String Quartet 2; String Quartet 3; String Quartet 4. (Chilingirian Qt)

○ **75605 51248-2** (10/95)
Mussorgsky—Songs, Vol.2
Mussorgsky: Epitaph; Sphinx; Not like thunder; Softly the spirit flew; Pride; Is spinning man's work; Vision; It scatters and breaks; On the Dnieper; Eremushka's lullaby; Feast; Classicist; From my tears; Sunless. (S. Leiferkus, S. Skigin)

○ **75605 51750-2** (8/95)
Grieg—Piano and Orchestral Works
Grieg: Piano Concerto; Symphonic Dances; Elegiac Melodies; Lyric Pieces; Peer Gynt Suites; Holberg Suite; Lyric Suite, Op. 54; Lyric Pieces, Op. 43 (exc). (E. Poblocka, Polish RSO/T. Wojciechowski)

○ **75605 51751-2** (5/95)
Fauré—Piano Works
Fauré: Impromptus (exc); Nocturnes (exc); Romances sans paroles, Op. 17; Barcarolles (exc); Barcarolles (exc); Nocturnes (exc); Impromptu, Op. 86; Mazurka, Op. 32; Valses-caprices (exc). (K. Stott)

Connoisseur Society

○ **CD4186** (10/94)
Turina—Piano Works
Turina: Mujeres de Sevilla, Op.89; Mujeres Españolas, Op.17; Mujeres Españolas, Op.73; Danzas Andaluzas; Bailete, Op.79. (D. Buechner)

○ **CD4194** (6/94)
Rachmaninov—Piano Works
Rachmaninov: Corelli Variations; Etudes-tableaux, Op.33 (exc); Moments musicaux, Op.16 (exc); Preludes (exc); Morceaux de salon, Op.10 (exc); Lilacs; Daisies; *Mendelssohn*: Midsummer Night's Dream (exc). (O. Yablonskaya)

Continuum

○ **CCD1006** (7/89)
Busoni: Fantasias and Toccata
Busoni: Fantasia contrappuntistica; Bach Fantasia; Toccata. (J. Ogdon)

○ **CCD1007** (2/90)
Reizenstein: Piano Works
Reizenstein: Legend; Scherzo; Suite; Piano Sonata 2; Lambeth Walk Variations. (P. Martin)

○ **CCD1008** (7/90)
Anderson: Mask and other works
B. Anderson: Mask; Songs Penyeach; Sound the Tucket; Colla voce. (K. Lukas, S. Limbrick, M. Allen, I. Dearden, J. Alvarez, P. Harlowe/S. Montague, J. Manning, G. Grey, M. Khouri, I. Dearden, B. Slushin, S. Montague)

○ **CCD1009** (11/91)
Music of Barry Anderson
B. Anderson: Electroacoustic Fanfare; Arc; Piano Pieces (exc); Domingus. (H. Sparnaay, Mistry Qt, I. Dearden, J. Alvarez/S. Montague, S. Mays/S. Montague, S. Montague, J.F. Robbins)

○ **CCD1016** (9/90)
Bridge—Piano Works, Vol 1
Bridge: Gargoyle; Dedication; Improvisations; Winter

Pastoral; Hidden Fires; Miniature Pastorals 2; Miniature Pastorals 1; In Autumn; Fairy Tale Suite; Arabesque; Sea Idyll; Capriccio 2; Capriccio 1. (Peter Jacobs)

○ **CCD1017** (7/90)
Violin Diabolique: Music by Ernst and Wieniawski
Ernst: Hungarian Airs; Polonaise; Adagio sentimentale; Rondo Papageno; *Wieniawski*: Adagio élégiaque; Grand caprice, op 1; Fantasie orientale; Russian Carnival. (S. Lupu, P. Pettinger)

○ **CCD1018** (6/91)
Frank Bridge—Piano Works Vol.2
Bridge: Etude rhapsodique; Berceuse; Dramatic Fantasia; Poems; Pieces (1912); Characteristic Pieces; Lament; Canzonetta; Pensées fugitives 1; Scherzettino; Moderato; Vignettes de Marseille. (Peter Jacobs)

○ **CCD1019** (6/91)
Frank Bridge—Piano Works Vol.3
Bridge: Sketches; Hour Glass; Graziella; Miniature Pastorals 3; Miniature Suite; Lyrics; Come Sweet Death; Piano Sonata. (Peter Jacobs)

○ **CCD1020** (5/91)
Simon Bainbridge—Orchestral Works
Bainbridge: Fantasia for Double Orchestra; Viola Concerto; Concertante in moto perpetuo. (W. Trampler, N. Daniel, London Sinfonietta/M. Tilson Thomas, BBC SO, Composers Ens/S. Bainbridge)

○ **CCD1022** (4/92)
Bridge/Britten—Works for Violin and Piano
Britten: Suite, Op. 6; Reveille; *Bridge*: Violin Sonata; Romanze; Cradle Song, H96; Norse Legend; Serenade; Heart's ease. (L. McAslan, J.J. Blakely)

○ **CCD1024** (11/91)
Reizenstein—Chamber works
Reizenstein: Piano Quintet, Op. 23; Violin Sonata, Op. 20; Oboe Sonatina, Op. 11. (Melos Ens, E. Gruenberg, D. Wilde, J. Craxton, L. Crowson)

○ **CCD1027** (8/93)
Brahms/Gal—Clarinet Sonatas
Brahms: Clarinet Sonata 1; Clarinet Sonata 2; *Gál*: Clarinet Sonata, Op. 84. (M. Khouri, J. McCabe)

○ **CCD1028/9** (6/91)
Transatlantic Piano
J. Adams: Phrygian Gates; *Previn*: Invisible Drummer; *Copland*: Piano Sonata; *Carter*: Piano Sonata; *Rochberg*: Carnival Music; *R.R. Bennett*: Noctuary. (J. McCabe)

○ **CCD1034** (12/92)
Lyell Cresswell—Orchestral Works, Vol.2
Cresswell: O!; Salm; Speak for us, great sea. (NZ SO/W. Southgate)

○ **CCD1038** (6/92)
Works for Clarinet and Piano
Ireland: Fantasy-Sonata; *Bax*: Clarinet Sonata; *Finzi*: Bagatelles; *Horovitz*: Sonatina; *Arnold*: Clarinet Sonatina, Op. 29. (M. Khouri, P. Pettinger)

○ **CCD1042** (10/92)
Medieval Dance Music
Anon: Danses royales (exc); Estampie (13th cent); Ductia; Estampies royals (exc); Estampie (14th cent); Istanpitta Gaetta; Danca Amorosa; Troto; Saltarello; Lamento di Tristano; Rotta; Manfredina; Rotta della manfredina. (Dufay Collective)

○ **CCD1043** (12/91)
Music for Christmas
Britten: Ceremony of Carols; *Maxwell Davies*: Ave Rex Angelorum; *Traditional*: Child of Light; *Weir*: Illuminare, Jerusalem; *Tavener*: Nativity; *Walton*: All this time; *Traditional*: All and Some; *Leighton*: O a Rose; L. Berkeley: In Wintertime; *Poulenc*: Motets pour le temps de Noël. (Elysian Sngrs/M. Greenall)

○ **CCD1044** (5/93)
Dale—Piano Works
Dale: Piano Sonata; Night Fancies; Prunella. (Peter Jacobs)

○ **CCD1045** (11/92)
Bax—Piano Works
Bax: Piano Sonata in E flat; Legend; Piano Sonata 2. (J. McCabe)

○ **CCD1046** (5/93)
Bax—Songs
Bax: Eternity; Far in a Western Brookland; Market Girl; Traditional Songs of France (exc); White peace; Song in the Twilight; Out and Away; Irish Songs (1921) (exc); Shieling Song; To Eire; Irish Songs (1922) (exc); Milking Sian; Flute; Magnificat; I have house and land in Kent; O dear! what can the matter be?; *Campion*: Ayres, Bk 1

(exc); *Traditional:* There is no rose. (P. Wright, R. Greager, C. Keyte, R. Barnes)

① **CCD1047** (11/92)
Fauré—The Middle Years
Fauré: Nocturnes (exc); Barcarolles (exc); Préludes; Valses-caprices (exc). (Peter Jacobs)

① **CCD1049** (10/92)
Balfour Gardiner—Piano Music
Gardiner: Pieces; Humoresque; Salamanca; Joyful Homecoming; Michaelchurch; Noël; Prelude 2; Shenadoah; Mere. (Peter Jacobs)

① **CCD1058** (3/94)
Sibelius—Piano Works, Vol.1
Sibelius: Pieces, Op. 24; Impromptus, Op. 5; Pieces, Op. 34. (A. Servadei)

① **CCD1059** (3/94)
Sibelius—Piano Works, Vol.2
Sibelius: Valse triste; Spagnuolo; Mandolinato; Morceau romantique; Cavalier; Pensées lyriques, Op. 40; Finnish Folksongs; Pieces, Op. 58; Longing. (A. Servadei)

① **CCD1061** (4/95)
Montague—Orchestral and Chamber Music
Montague: From the White Edge of Phrygia; String Quartet 1; Haiku; Tigida Pipa. (S. Montague, P. Mead, Smith Qt, Singcircle/G. Rose, Florida Orch/J. Lang)

① **CCD1064** (5/95)
Dohnányi—Complete Piano Music, Volume 1
Dohnányi: Pieces, Op. 2; Passacaglia, Op. 6; Variations, Op. 4. (A. Servadei)

① **CCD1066** (10/93)
Trevor Hold—Piano works
Hold: Kemp's Nine Daies Wonder; Lilford Owl; Kaleidoscopes. (Peter Jacobs)

① **CCD1069** (8/94)
Lilburn—Symphonies
Lilburn: Symphony 1; Symphony 2; Symphony 3. (NZ SO/J. Hopkins)

① **CCD1070** (12/95)
Sibelius—Piano Works, Vol 4
Sibelius: Melody for the Bells, Op. 65; Pieces, Op. 75; Pieces, Op. 76; Pieces, Op. 85; Pieces, Op. 94; Bagatelles, Op. 97. (A. Servadei)

① **CCD1071** (12/95)
Sibelius—Piano Works, Vol 5
Sibelius: Valse lyrique, Op. 96a; Autrefois, Op. 96b; Valse chevaleresque, Op. 96c; Pieces, Op. 99; Pieces, Op. 101; Pieces, Op. 103; Esquisses, Op. 114; Finlandia. (A. Servadei)

CPO

① **CPO999 002-2** (5/95)
Dessau—Complete String Quartets
Dessau: String Quartet 1; String Quartet 2; String Quartet 3; String Quartet 4; String Quartet 5; String Quartet 6; String Quartet 7. (New Leipzig Qt)

① **CPO999 004-2** (12/91)
Hindemith—Orchestral Works Vol 1
Hindemith: Cupid and Psyche; Nobilissima Visione; Philharmonisches Konzert; Symphonic Metamorphosis. (Queensland SO/W.A. Albert)

① **CPO999 005-2** (12/91)
Hindemith—Orchestral Works Vol 2
Hindemith: Lustige Sinfonietta; Rag Time; Symphonische Tänze. (Queensland SO/W.A. Albert)

① **CPO999 006-2** (12/91)
Hindemith—Orchestral Works Vol 3
Hindemith: Nusch-Nuschi; Concert Music, Op. 50; Harmonie der Welt. (Melbourne SO/W.A. Albert)

① **CPO999 008-2** (11/94)
Hindemith—Orchestral Works - Volume 5
Hindemith: Mathis der Maler; Symphonia serena; Requiem (exc). (Sydney SO/W.A. Albert)

① **CPO999 015-2** (7/89)
Mendelssohn-Hensel—Piano Works Vol 2
Mendelssohn-Hensel: Piano Sonata in C minor; Piano Sonata in G minor; Piano Sonata Movement; Lieder, Op. 6 (exc). (L. Serbescu)

① **CPO999 018-2** (3/89)
A. Mahler—Complete Songs
A. Mahler: Lieder (1910); Lieder (1915); Lieder (1924). (I. Lippitz, B. Heller-Reichenbach)

① **CPO999 020-2** (10/89)
Wilhelm Killmayer: Chamber Works
Killmayer: String Quartet 1; String Trio; Piano Quartet;

Brahms-Bildnis; Vanitas Vanitatum. (S. Mauser, C. Altenburger, G. Weinmeister, B. Westphal, J. Berger)

① **CPO999 024-2** (3/89)
Reicha—Complete Wind Quintets, Vol.3
Reicha: Wind Quintets, Op.91 (exc); Wind Quintets, Op.100 (exc); Andantes and adagio (exc). (A. Schweitzer Qnt)

① **CPO999 026-2** (3/91)
Reicha—Complete Wind Quintets, Vol.5
Reicha: Wind Quintets, Op. 88 (exc); Wind Quintets, Op. 91 (exc); Wind Quintets, Op. 100 (exc). (A. Schweitzer Qnt)

① **CPO999 027-2** (3/91)
Reicha—Complete Wind Quintets, Vol.6
Reicha: Wind Quintets, Op. 91 (exc); Wind Quintets, Op. 100 (exc); Wind Quintets, Op. 99 (exc). (A. Schweitzer Qnt)

① **CPO999 029-2** (3/91)
Reicha—Complete Wind Quintets, Vol.8
Reicha: Wind Quintets, Op. 91 (exc); Wind Quintets, Op. 100 (exc); Andantes and adagio (exc). (A. Schweitzer Qnt)

① **CPO999 037-2** (10/91)
Korngold—Orchestral Works Vol.1
Korngold: Schneemann (exc); Schauspiel; Sinfonietta. (NW German PO/W.A. Albert, L. Farkas)

① **CPO999 039-2** (7/91)
Pepping—Organ Works
Pepping: Organ Concerto 2; Wie schön leuchtet der Morgenstern; Fugues (1942); Organ Partita 1. (W. Stockmeier)

① **CPO999 044-2** (12/90)
Viardot-Garcia—Songs
Viardot-Garcia: Madrid; Sérénade; Havanaise; Bonjour mon coeur; Grands oiseaux blancs; Petite chevière; Chêne et le roseau; Chanson de la pluie; Enfant et la mère; Désespoir; Adieu les beaux jours; Scène d'Hermione; Seize ans; Danse; Oiselet; Aime-moi; *Jommelli:* Calandrina; *Gluck:* Orphée (exc). (K. Ott/C. Keller)

① **CPO999 046-2** (10/91)
Korngold—Orchestral Works Vol.2
Korngold: Much Ado About Nothing Suite; Sursum corda, Op. 13; Piano Concerto. (NW German PO/W.A. Albert, S. de Groote)

① **CPO999 051-2** (7/91)
Karg-Elert—Works for Harmonium
Karg-Elert: Partita, Op. 37; Sonata, Op. 36; Passacaglia, Op. 25. (H.C. Jacobs)

① **CPO999 055-2** (3/90)
Wolpe—Piano Works
Wolpe: Adagios (1920) (exc); Stehende Musik; Tango; Rag-Caprice; Displaced Spaces; Form IV: Broken Sequences; Characteristic Marches (exc); Studies on Basic Rows (exc); Dance in the form of a Chaconne; Toccata (1941); Encouragements (exc). (G.D. Madge)

① **CPO999 077-2** (10/91)
Korngold—Orchestral Works Vol.3
Korngold: Baby Serenade, Op. 24; Cello Concerto, Op. 37; Symphonic Serenade, Op. 39. (NW German PO/W.A. Albert, J. Berger)

① **CPO999 079-2** (5/91)
Pfitzner—Violin Concerto, etc
Pfitzner: Violin Concerto, Op. 34; Duo, Op. 43; Scherzo. (S. Gawriloff, J. Berger, Bamberg SO/W.A. Albert)

① **CPO999 080-2** (5/91)
Pfitzner—Symphonies, etc
Pfitzner: Kleine Sinfonie, Op. 44; Symphony, Op. 46; Fest auf Solhaug. (Bamberg SO/W.A. Albert)

① **CPO999 084-2** (12/94)
Boccherini—Complete Symphonies, Volume 1
Boccherini: Concerto, G491; Symphony, G523; Symphony, G490. (Neuss German Chbr Acad/J. Goritzki)

① **CPO999 099-2** (4/93)
Krenek—Piano Pieces
Krenek: Toccata and Chaconne, Op. 13; Little Suite, Op. 13a; Variations, Op. 79; Washington Variations, Op. 120; Echoes from Austria, Op. 166. (G.D. Madge)

① **CPO999 100-2** (7/93)
C.P.E. Bach—Sonatas for Connoisseurs & Amateurs
C.P.E. Bach: Kenner I; Kenner II; Kenner III; Kenner IV; Kenner V; Kenner VI. (G. Antalffy, G. Antalffy)

① **CPO999 101-2** (8/93)
M. Haydn—Symphonies
M. Haydn: Symphony, MH23; Symphony, MH37; Symphony, MH26. (Slovak CO/B. Warchal)

---

① **CPO999 113-2** (8/93)
Moniuszko—Overtures
Moniuszko: Halka (exc); Countess (exc); Verbum Nobile (exc); Fairy Tale; Jawnuta (exc); Raftsman (exc); Paria (exc). (Bydgoszcz PSO/R. Satanowski)

① **CPO999 129-2** (11/95)
J. C. Bach—Opera Overtures, Vol. 1
J. C. Bach: Favourite Overtures (exc); Catone in Utica (exc); Birthday Cantata (exc); Overture, T277/4; Giulia Overture. (Hanover Band/A. Halstead)

① **CPO999 135-2** (4/94)
Pfitzner—Cello Concertos
Pfitzner: Cello Concerto, Op. 42; Cello Concerto, Op.52; Cello Concerto, Op. posth. (D. Geringas, Bamberg SO/W.A. Albert)

① **CPO999 136-2** (7/93)
Pfitzner—Orchestral Works
Pfitzner: Symphony, Op.36a; Elegie und Reigen; Fantasie. (Bamberg SO/W.A. Albert)

① **CPO999 139-2** (9/92)
The Apocryphal Bach Cantatas
Bach: Cantata 217; Cantata 218; Cantata 219; Cantata 220; Cantata 221; Cantata 222. (J. Koslowsky, K. Wessel, H. Geraerts, P. Langshaw, Alsfeld Voc Ens, Steintor Barock/W. Helbich)

① **CPO999 142-2** (11/95)
Hindemith—Complete Wind Concertos
Hindemith: Clarinet Concerto; Horn Concerto; Trumpet and Bassoon Concerto; Wind and Harp Concerto. (U. Mehlhart, M. L. Neunecker, R. Friedrich, C. Wilkening, W. Büchsel, L. Varcol, C. Cassedanne, Frankfurt RSO/W. A. Albert)

① **CPO999 146-2** (10/91)
Korngold—Orchestral Works Vol.4
Korngold: Symphony, Op. 40; Theme and Variations, Op. 42; Straussiana. (NW German PO/W.A. Albert)

① **CPO999 152-2** (8/93)
M. Haydn—Symphonies
M. Haydn: Symphony, MH62; Symphony, MH63; Symphony, MH64. (Slovak CO/B. Warchal)

① **CPO999 153-2** (8/93)
M. Haydn—Symphonies
M. Haydn: Symphony, MH65; Symphony, MH69; Symphony, MH50; Symphony, MH51. (Slovak CO/B. Warchal)

① **CPO999 158-2** (4/95)
Pfitzner—Das dunkle Reich
Pfitzner: Dunkle Reich; Blumen Rache; Fons salutifer, Op. 48. (Y. Wiedstruck, Y. Jänicke, Y. Windmüller, S. Bruns, Berlin Rad Chor, Berlin RSO/R. Reuter)

① **CPO999 166-2** (6/95)
Milhaud—Symphonies
Milhaud: Symphony 7; Symphony 8; Symphony 9. (Basle RSO/A. Francis)

① **CPO999 170-2** (10/95)
Donizetti—String Quartets
Donizetti: String Quartet 7; String Quartet 8; String Quartet 9. (Revolutionary Drawing Room)

① **CPO999 171-2** (4/95)
Sullivan—Orchestral Works
Sullivan: Irish Symphony; Imperial March; Victoria and Merrie England Suite 1; In Memoriam. (BBC Concert Orch/O. A. Hughes)

① **CPO999 178-2** (1/95)
Boccherini—Symphonies, Volume 8
Boccherini: Symphony, G520; Symphony, G522; Symphony, G500. (Neuss German Chbr Acad/J. Goritzki)

① **CPO999 198-2** (8/94)
B.A.Zimmermann—Music for Cello and Piano
B.A. Zimmermann: Enchiridion; Solo Cello Sonata; Solo Cello Studies; Intercomunicazione. (M. Bach, B. Wambach)

① **CPO999 209-2** (7/95)
Abel—Chamber Works
Abel: Sonatas, Op. 6 (exc); Viola da Gamba Pieces, WKO186-212 (exc); 2-Flute Trio in F; 3-Flute Trio in G; Sonata, WKO148. (Stagione, R. Zipperling)

① **CPO999 221-2** (2/95)
Frankel—Music for Strings
Frankel: Aftermath, Op. 17; Solemn Speech and Discussion; Sketches, Op. 2; Concertante Lirico, Op. 27; Youth Music, Op. 12. (R. Dan, Seattle NW CO/A. Francis)

① **CPO999 223-2** (2/95)
The Apocryphal Bach Motets
Bach: Jauchzet dem Herrn, BWV Anh160; Unser Wandel

ist im Himmel, BWV ANh165; Nun danket alle Gott, BWV Anh164; Ich lasse dich nicht, BWV Anh159; Merk auf, BWV Anh163; Lob und Ehre, BWV Anh162. (Alsfeld Voc Ens/W. Helbich)

ⓘ **CPO999 240-2 (7/94)**
Frankel—Symphonies, etc
Frankel: Symphony 1; Symphony 5; May Day. (Queensland SO/W. A. Albert)

ⓘ **CPO999 251-2 (1/95)**
Schulhoff—Symphonies
Schulhoff: Symphony 1; Symphony 2; Symphony 3. (Philh Hungarica/G. A. Albrecht)

ⓘ **CPO999 262-2 (11/95)**
Romantic Duets
Reinecke: Duets, Op. 12; Duets, Op. 109; *Schumann:* Gedichte, Op. 37 (exc); Lieder, Op. 43; Spanisches Liederspiel, Op. 74 (exc); Duette, Op. 78; Jugend Lieder, Op. 79 (exc); Sommerruh; *Cornelius:* Zweistimmige Lieder, Op. 6; Duets, Op. 16; Ich und Du; Am Meer; Zu den Bergen. (E. Mathis, H. Komatsu, C. Garben)

ⓘ **CPO999 269-2 (7/95)**
Meyerbeer—Mélodies
Meyerbeer: Ricordanza; Chant de Mai; Folle de St Joséph; Marguerite du poète; Jeune mère; Canzonette italiane; Scirocco; Sie und ich; Meeresstille; Fantaisie; Lavandière; Revenant du vieux Château; Fille de l'air. (N. Liang, I. Ranta)

ⓘ **CPO999 277-2 (7/95)**
Berthold Goldschmidt—Orchestral Works
B. Goldschmidt: Cello Concerto; Ciaconna sinfonica; Chronica Suite. (D. Geringas, Magdeburg PO/M. Husmann)

CRD

ⓘ **CRD3307 (11/90)**
Recital at the Victoria & Albert Museum
Anon: My Lady Wynktylds Rownde; *Byrd:* Queen's Alman, BK10; Bells, BK98; *Handel:* Keyboard Suites Set I (exc); *Croft:* Suite 3 (exc); *Arne:* Keyboard Sonatas (exc); *J. C. Bach:* Keyboard Sonatas, Op. 5 (exc). (T. Pinnock, T. Pinnock)

ⓘ **CRD3308 (11/87)**
Trumpet & Organ at Liverpool Cathedral
M-A. Charpentier: Te deum, H146 (exc); *Stanley:* Organ Voluntaries, Book 1 (exc); *Purcell:* Trumpet Sonata 1; *Boyce:* Voluntaries (exc); *Clarke:* Suite in D (exc); *Baldassare:* Sonata in F; *Roman:* Harpsichord Suites (exc); *Fiocco:* Pièces de clavecin, Op.1 (exc); *Purcell:* Choice Collection of Lessons (exc); *Bach:* Cantata 147 (exc); *Stubley:* Voluntary in C; *Viviani:* Capricci, Op.4 (exc). (A. Stringer, N. Rawsthorne)

ⓘ **CRD3311 (5/89)**
Mozart & C.P.E.Bach: Keyboard Concertos
C. P. E. Bach: Keyboard Concerto, H417; Keyboard Concertos, H471-6 (exc); *Mozart:* Piano Concertos, K107 (exc). (T. Pinnock (hpd/dir), English Concert)

ⓘ **CRD3312/3 (8/89)**
Arriaga & Wikmanson: String Quartets
Arriaga: String Quartet 1; String Quartet 2; String Quartet 3; *Wikmanson:* String Quartet 2. (Chilingirian Qt)

ⓘ **CRD3316 (9/87)**
Fauré—Works for Cello and Piano
Fauré: Cello Sonata 1; Cello Sonata 2; Sicilienne; Elégie. (T. Igloi, C. Benson)

ⓘ **CRD3322 (5/88)**
Granados—Piano Works, Vol.3
Granados: Escenas románticas; Piezas sobre Cantos Populares Españoles; Danza lenta. (T. Rajna)

ⓘ **CRD3323 (11/88)**
Granados—Piano Works, Vol.4
Granados: Valse de concierto; Valses poéticos; Capricho español; Rapsodia aragonesa; Carezza; Oriental; Impromptus. (T. Rajna)

ⓘ **CRD3331 (6/87)**
Baroque Concerto in England
Anon: Concerto grosso in F; *Boyce:* Concerto grosso in E minor; Concerto grosso in B minor; *Woodcock:* Oboe Concerto in E flat; Flute Concerto in D. (W. Bennett, N. Black, Thames CO/M. Dobson)

ⓘ **CRD3342 (10/87)**
Scandinavian Serenade
Grieg: Holberg Suite; *Nielsen:* Little Suite; *Sibelius:* Canzonetta; *Wirén:* Serenade, Op. 11. (Scottish Baroque Ens/Lionel Friedman)

ⓘ **CRD3347 (4/89)**
A Choice Collection of Lessons and Ayres
Playford: Musick's Hande-Maide (exc); *Locke:* Melothesia (exc); *Purcell:* Musick's Hand-maid, Part 2 (exc); Choice Collection of Lessons (exc); *Draghi:* Ground; *Blow:* Mortlack's Ground; *Greene:* Overtures (exc); *Arne:* Keyboard Sonatas (exc); *Nares:* Setts of Lessons (exc); *Paradis:* Keyboard Sonatas (exc). (T. Pinnock)

ⓘ **CRD3348/9 (8/88)**
Vivaldi—Concertos
Vivaldi: Concerti, Op.8; Concerto, RV429; Concerto, RV424. (S. Preston, S. Standage, A. Pleeth, English Concert, T. Pinnock (hpd/dir))

ⓘ **CRD3366 (5/89)**
Italian String Quartets
Verdi: String Quartet; *Puccini:* Crisantemi; *Donizetti:* String Quartet 13. (Alberni Qt)

ⓘ **CRD3372 (4/89)**
Tallis & Taverner: Sacred Choral Works
Tallis: Sancte Deus, sancte fortis; Audivi vocem; Honor virtus et potestas; O sacrum convivium; Salvator mundi I; *Taverner:* Western Wynde Mass; Mater Christi. (New College Ch/E. Higginbottom)

ⓘ **CRD3374 (10/92)**
Handel—The Chamber Music Vol. 2
Handel: Oboe Sonatas (exc); Violin Movement, HWV408 (exc); Violin Movement, HWV412 (exc); Violin Sonatas (exc). (Ecole d'Orphée)

ⓘ **CRD3377 (10/92)**
Handel—The Chamber Music Vol. 5
Handel: Sinfonia in B flat, HWV338; Trio Sonatas, Op. 2 (exc); Dresden Trio Sonatas; Trio Sonata, HWV403. (Ecole d'Orphée)

ⓘ **CRD3378 (10/92)**
Handel—The Chamber Music Vol. 6
Handel: Recorder Sonatas; Trio Sonata, HWV405; Violin Sonatas (exc). (Ecole d'Orphée)

ⓘ **CRD3383 (7/88)**
Ravel—Piano Works, Vol.1
Ravel: Miroirs; Sonatine; Menuet antique; Valses nobles et sentimentales; Pavane pour une infante défunte. (P. Crossley)

ⓘ **CRD3384 (7/88)**
Ravel—Piano Works, Vol.2
Ravel: Gaspard de la nuit; Tombeau de Couperin; Jeux d'eau; Sérénade grotesque; Menuet sur le nom de Haydn; Prélude; A la manière de Borodine; A la manière de Chabrier. (P. Crossley)

ⓘ **CRD3391 (1/92)**
Works for Cello
Grieg: Cello sonata; *Franck:* Violin Sonata; *Dvořák:* Rondo, B171. (R. Cohen, R. Vignoles, A. Rael)

ⓘ **CRD3396 (8/89)**
Virtuoso Transcriptions for Piano
Bach: Solo Violin Partitas and Sonatas (exc); *Schubert:* Schöne Müllerin (exc); *Kreisler:* Liebesleid; Liebesfreud; *Busoni:* Sonatina 6; *Glinka:* Farewell to St Petersburg (exc); Violin Movement, K547 (exc); *Schulz-Evler:* Blauen Donau Concert Arabesques; *Weber:* Invitation to the Dance, J260. (P. Fowke)

ⓘ **CRD3401 (6/90)**
Schumann: Lieder
Schumann: Myrthen, Op. 25 (exc); Jugend Lieder, Op. 79 (exc); Maria Stuart Lieder, Op. 135 (Cpte); Gedichte, Op. 36 (exc); Lieder, Op. 40 (exc); Gedichte, Op. 35 (exc); Romanzen und Balladen, Op. 45 (exc); Gesänge, Op. 31 (exc). (Sarah Walker, R. Vignoles)

ⓘ **CRD3402 (10/92)**
Symphonic Marches for Concert Brass
Verdi: Aida (exc); *Mozart:* Zauberflöte (exc); *Tchaikovsky:* Symphony 6 (exc); *Puccini:* Turandot (exc); *Grieg:* Sigurd Jorsalfar, Op. 56 (exc); *J. Strauss I:* Radetzky March; *Berlioz:* Symphonie fantastique (exc); *Mussorgsky:* Capture of Kars. (Locke Brass Consort/J. Stobart)

ⓘ **CRD3404 (6/92)**
Brahms—Organ Works
Brahms: Prelude and Fugue in A minor; O Traurigkeit, O Herzeleid; Prelude and Fugue in A minor; Fugue in A flat minor; Chorale Preludes, Op. 122. (N. Danby)

ⓘ **CRD3410 (7/89)**
Czech Chamber Works
Dvořák: Serenade, Op.44; *Krommer:* Octet-Partita, Op.79; Octet-Partita, Op.67. (Nash Ens)

ⓘ **CRD3411 (6/89)**
Mozart & Schumann: Chamber Works
Mozart: Piano Trio, K498; *Schumann:*

Märchenerzählungen; Fantasiestücke, Op.73. (I. Brown, A. Pay, R. Chase)

ⓘ **CRD3413 (5/91)**
Brahms—Works for two pianos & one piano, four hands
Brahms: Haydn Variations; Waltzes, Op. 39; Neue Liebeslieder. (B. Eden, A. Tamir)

ⓘ **CRD3417 (12/93)**
Beethoven—Violin Sonatas, Vol.3
Beethoven: Violin Sonata 8; Violin Sonata 9; Violin Sonata 10. (E. Gruenberg, D. Wilde)

ⓘ **CRD3420 (12/91)**
Byrd: Cantiones Sacrae (1589)
Byrd: In resurrectione tua (exc); Aspice Domine de sede (exc); Vide Domine afflictionem (exc); Domine tu iurasti (exc); Vigilate (exc); Domine secundum multitudinem (exc); Tristitia et anxietas (exc); Ne irascaris Domine (exc); O quam gloriosum (exc). (New College Ch/E. Higginbottom)

ⓘ **CRD3423 (1/88)**
Fauré—Piano Works, Vol.4
Fauré: Préludes; Impromptus; Thème et Variations, Op.73. (P. Crossley)

ⓘ **CRD3424 (3/91)**
Ravel—Works for Piano Duet
Ravel: La Valse; Rapsodie espagnole; Ma mère l'oye. (B. Eden, A. Tamir)

ⓘ **CRD3426 (2/88)**
Fauré: Piano Works, Vol.5
Fauré: Valses-caprices; Romances sans paroles, Op. 17; Ballade, Op. 19; Mazurka, Op. 32. (P. Crossley)

ⓘ **CRD3429 (4/87)**
Tallis: Sacred Choral Works
Tallis: Gaude gloriosa Dei mater; Magnificat and Nunc Dimittis; Dum transisset Sabbatum; In jejunio et fletu; Derelinquat impius; Candidi facti sunt Nazarei; Salvator mundi II; Absterge Domine. (New College Ch/E. Higginbottom)

ⓘ **CRD3430/1 (6/92)**
Tippett—Piano Sonatas
Tippett: Piano Sonata 1; Piano Sonata 2; Piano Sonata 3; Piano Sonata 4. (P. Crossley)

ⓘ **CRD3434 (9/86)**
British Music for Brass
Elgar: Severn Suite; *Vaughan Williams:* Henry V; *Holst:* Moorside Suite; *Ireland:* Comedy Ov. (London Collegiate Brass/J. Stobart)

ⓘ **CRD3435 (10/91)**
Mozart—Violin Sonatas
Mozart: Violin Sonata, K377; Violin Sonata, K301; Violin Sonata, K305; Violin Sonata, K379. (H. Davis, V. Black)

ⓘ **CRD3437 (10/86)**
Poulenc: Chamber & Vocal Works
Poulenc: Bal masqué; Bestiaire; Piano, oboe and bassoon trio; Sextet. (T. Allen, Nash Ens)

ⓘ **CRD3439 (7/87)**
Byrd—Motets
Byrd: Laudibus in sanctis (exc); Domine salva nos (exc); Domine, non sum dignus (exc); Cunctis diebus (exc); Haec dicit Dominus (exc); Haec dies a 6 (exc); Miserere mei (exc); Tribulatio proxima est (exc); Circumdederunt me (exc); Fac cum servo tuo (exc); Exsurge Domine (exc). (New College Ch/E. Higginbottom)

ⓘ **CRD3440 (12/87)**
Vivaldi: Cello Sonatas
Vivaldi: Cello Sonata, RV47; Cello Sonata, RV41; Cello Sonata, RV43; Cello Sonata, RV45. (Ecole d'Orphée)

ⓘ **CRD3441 (12/87)**
Vivaldi: Cello Sonatas
Vivaldi: Cello Sonata, RV40; Cello Sonata, RV46; Cello Sonata, RV44; Cello Sonata, RV42; Cello Sonata, RV39. (Ecole d'Orphée)

ⓘ **CRD3444 (9/87)**
Brass Ensemble music by 20th Century British composers
Walton: First Shoot; *Tippett:* Festal Brass with Blues; *Britten:* Russian Funeral; *Ireland:* Downland Suite. (London Collegiate Brass/J. Stobart)

ⓘ **CRD3446 (6/88)**
Ravel: Chamber works
Ravel: Introduction and Allegro; Violin and Cello Sonata; Piano Trio. (Nash Ens, M. Crayford, C. van Kampen, I. Brown)

ⓘ **CRD3449 (10/89)**
Jonathan Haas - Virtuoso Timpanist
L. Fischer: Symphony for 8 Timpani; *Druschetzky:* Partita

in C; Oboe and Timpani Concerto. (J. Haas, G. Hunt, Bournemouth Sinfonietta/H. Farberman)

① **CRD3450** (4/90)
Escobar: Sacred Choral Works
Escobar: Missa Pro defunctis; Hostis Herodes; Asperges me; Stabat mater; Clamabat autem mulier; Deus tuorum militum; Beatus es; Salve regina; Ave maris stella. (Quodlibet)

① **CRD3451** (12/88)
Gibbons: Sacred Choral Works
Gibbons: Second Service (exc); O Lord, in thy wrath; O God, the king of glory; Sing unto the Lord; O clap your hands; See, see, the word is incarnate; Glorious and powerful God; Fantasias (exc). (New College Ch, D. Burchell/E. Higginbottom)

① **CRD3454** (3/90)
Howells—Choral & Organ Music, Vol 1
Howells: Sequence for St Michael; Lambert's Clavichord (exc); Hymn for St Cecilia; Howells' Clavichord (exc); House of the Mind; Flourish for a bidding (exc); New College Service; St Louis (exc); O pray for the peace; King of Glory. (New College Ch, D. Burchell, E. Higginbottom/E. Higginbottom)

① **CRD3455** (12/91)
Howells—Choral & Organ Music, Vol.2
Howells: Behold, O God our defender; Missa Aedis Christi; Psalm-Preludes, Op.32 (exc); Pieces (exc); Traditional: Sing Lullaby; Here is the little door; Spotless Rose; Howells: Pieces (exc); Where wast thou. (New College Ch/E. Higginbottom, E. Higginbottom)

① **CRD3457** (10/92)
Dvořák—Hausmusik
Dvořák: Terzetto, Op. 74; Waltzes, Op. 54; Drobnosti, B149; Gavotte, B164; Bagatelles, B79. (H. Davis, P. Pople, R. Best, R. Best, David Smith, V. Black, Alberni Qt)

① **CRD3458** (4/91)
Schumann: Chamber Works
Schumann: Piano Trio 2; Piano Trio 3; Fantasiestücke, Op. 88. (Israel Pf Trio)

① **CRD3460** (3/90)
Medtner: Piano Works, Vol.3
Medtner: Piano Sonata, Op.22; Romantic sketches, op 54 (exc); Fairy Tales, op 8; Novelles, op 17; Piano Sonata, op 30. (H. Milne)

① **CRD3463** (10/91)
S.S. Wesley—Anthems and Organ Works
S.S. Wesley: Ascribe unto the Lord; Blessed be the God and Father; Thou wilt keep him; Wash me throughly; Cast me not away; Wilderness; Andante in E minor; Pieces for Chamber Organ - Set 1 (exc); Larghetto. (New College Ch, E. Higginbottom (org/dir), E. Higginbottom)

① **CRD3464** (4/91)
Schubert: Lieder
Schubert: Musensohn, D764; Ganymed, D544; Schäfers Klagelied, D121; Rastlose Liebe, D138; Suleika I, D720; Suleika II, D717; An den Mond, D296; Fischer, D225; Erlkönig, D328; Wandrers Nachtlied II, D768; Sterne, D939; An den Mond, D193; Einsame, D800; Nachtstück, D672; Zwerg, D771; Im Abendrot, D799; Nachtviolen, D752; Junge Nonne, D828; Nacht und Träume, D827. (Sarah Walker, R. Vignoles)

① **CRD3467** (9/94)
Tomkins—The Third Service and Anthems
Tomkins: Third Service; O Lord, let me know mine end; O that the salvation were given; Know you not; In Nomine (1652); In Nomine (1648); Voluntary in G; Voluntary in C; Voluntary in A minor. (New College Ch/E. Higginbottom, D. Burchell)

① **CRD3471** (8/93)
Schumann—Piano Works, Vol.2
Schumann: Piano Sonata 2; Presto passionato; Symphonic Studies. (H. Milne)

① **CRD3472** (11/94)
Suk—Works for String Quartet
Suk: String Quartet 1; String Quartet 2; Meditation, Op.35a; Ballade, Op.3/1; String Quartet Balada. (Suk Qt)

① **CRD3473** (10/92)
Dreams and Fancies
Ireland: If there were dreams to sell; Delius: Norwegian Songs (1889-90) (exc); C. A. Gibbs: Songs, Op. 15 (exc); Songs, op. 30 (exc); Vaughan Williams: House of Life (exc); Shove Songs (exc); Warlock: Fox; Jillian of Berry; Traditional: First mercy; Weelkes: Night; Sullivan: Orpheus with his lute; Howells: King David; Gavotte; Come sing and Dance; Traditional: Little road to Bethlehem; Monkey's Carol; Bridge: Isobel; R. Clarke: Seal man; Aspidistra; H. Nelson: Dirty work; Hoiby: Jabberwocky; Quilter: Songs,

---

Op. 3 (exc); *Gurney: Sleep; Dunhill: Cloths of heaven.* (Sarah Walker, R. Vignoles)

① **CRD3476** (5/93)
Fauré—Chansons, Vol.1
Fauré: Songs, Op.5 (exc); Songs, Op.1 (exc); Songs, Op.7 (exc); Aurore (1871); Songs, Op.6 (exc); Songs, Op.23; Songs, Op.2 (exc); Songs, Op.46 (exc); Songs, Op.51 (exc); Songs, Op.83 (exc); Songs, Op.87 (exc); Jardin Clos; Songs, Op.18 (exc); Songs, Op.85 (exc); En prière; Songs, Op.43 (exc); Songs, Op.76 (exc). (Sarah Walker, M. Martineau)

① **CRD3477** (8/93)
Fauré—Chansons, Vol.2
Fauré: Songs, Op.1 (exc); Songs, op.3 (exc); Songs, Op.5 (exc); Songs, Op.8 (exc); Puisqu'ici-bas; Tarentelle, Op.10/2; Songs, Op.27 (exc); Songs, Op.39 (exc); Songs, Op.43 (exc); Songs, Op.46 (exc); Songs, Op.51 (exc); Songs, Op.76 (exc); Songs, Op.85 (exc); Songs, Op.87 (exc); Don silencieux; Chanson; C'est la paix!; Vocalise-étude; Pelléas et Mélisande Suite (exc). (Sarah Walker, M. Martineau)

① **CRD3483** (10/92)
Boyce—Select Anthems
Boyce: O where shall wisdom be found?; Wherewithal shall a young man; I have surely built thee an house; O praise the Lord; Turn thee unto me; O give thanks (1762); By the waters of Babylon; Lord is King be the people; Voluntaries (exc). (New College Ch/E. Higginbottom, G. Cooper)

① **CRD3484** (9/92)
Greene—Select Anthems
Greene: Lord let me know mine end; King shall rejoice (1743); How long wilt thou forget me; God is our hope and strength; Have mercy upon me, O God (1743); Let God arise; O clap your hands together; Thou, O God, art praised in Zion (exc); Voluntarys (exc). (New College Ch/E. Higginbottom, G. Cooper)

① **CRD3485** (9/92)
Weber—Piano Works
Weber: Piano Sonata 1; Piano Sonata 2; Rondo brillante, J252; Invitation to the Dance, J260. (H. Milne)

① **CRD3486** (11/92)
Weber/Liszt—Piano Works
Weber: Piano Sonata 3; Piano Sonata 4; Polacca brillante, J268; Liszt: Polacca brillante, S455 (exc). (H. Milne)

① **CRD3487** (8/93)
Cries and Ballads of London
T. Ravenscroft: New oysters; Three blinde mice; Round of three country dances in one; Well fare the nightingale; Come follow me; Browning madame; Dowland: Second Booke of Songs (exc); A. Holborne: Voyce of the ghost; Old almaine; C. Woodcock: Browning my dere; Tye: In Nomines a 5 (exc); Weelkes: Cries of London; Ford: Cate of Bardy; A. Ferrabosco II: 3-Viol Pavan; Coprario: 3-Viol Almaine; Eyck: Fluyten Lust-hof (exc); Cobbold: New fashions; Anon: Nutmigs and Ginger; Traditional: Grimstock; Anon: Greensleeves; Sellinger's round. (Red Byrd, Circa 1500/N. Hadden)

① **CRD3488** (11/94)
Hasse—Cantatas, Ballads and Sonatas
Hasse: Quel vago seno; Fille, dolce mio bene; Conversione di Sant' Agostino (exc); Venetian Ballads; Trio Sonatas, Op. 2 (exc); Keyboard Sonatas, Op. 7 (exc). (J. Baird, N. Hadden, E. Headley, M. Proud)

① **CRD3491** (8/95)
Croft—Select Anthems
Croft: God is gone up; Musica Sacra (exc); Voluntary in A minor; Voluntary in D. (New College Ch/E. Higginbottom, T. Morris)

① **CRD3493/4** (12/95)
Medtner—Complete Works for Violin and Piano
Medtner: Violin Sonata 1; Violin Sonata 2; Violin Sonata 3; Nocturnes, Op.16; Canzonas and Danzas, Op.43. (M. Parikian, H. Milne)

Crystal

① **Crystal CD733** (5/95)
Moonflowers, Baby!—Clarinet & Piano Works
Hindemith: Clarinet Sonata in B flat; Honegger: Clarinet Sonatina; Françaix: Tema con variazioni; Vaughan Williams: Studies in English Folk Song; Milhaud: Duo Concertante; Caprice, Op. 335a; Bozza: Pulcinella; Kupferman: Moonflower, Baby!. (J. Cohler, J. Gordon)

① **Crystal CD810** (4/95)
Music of Alan Hovhaness
Hovhaness: And God Created Great Whales, Op. 229/1; Concerto 8; Elibris, Op. 50; Alleluia and Fugue, Op. 40b; Anahid, Op. 57. (C. Messiter, Philh/D. Amos)

Cybelia

① **CY805** (4/87)
Milhaud—String Quartets Vol. 2
Milhaud: String Quartet 5; String Quartet 8; String Quartet 11; String Quartet 13. (Quatuor National d'Aquitaine)

① **CY809** (3/87)
Schmitt—Piano Works
Schmitt: Pièces romantiques, Op. 42; Valses nocturnes, Op. 31 (Cpte); Mirages, Op. 70. (P. Le Corre)

① **CY867** (4/87)
Langlais—Organ Works
Langlais: Symphony 1; Folkioric Suite; Triptyque. (P. Cogen)

Danacord

① **DACOCD303** (8/92)
Great Musicians in Copenhagen
Dvořák: Carnival; Cello Concerto (exc); Tchaikovsky: Piano Concerto 1 (exc); Debussy: Children's Corner (exc); Poulenc: Concert champêtre (exc); Beethoven: Piano Concerto 4 (exc); Chopin: Etudes (exc); Paganini: Caprices, Op.1 (exc). (N. Milstein, G. Piatigorsky, V. Horowitz, R. Serkin, W. Landowska, Danish RSO/F. Busch/N. Malko)

① **DACOCD311/2** (8/88)
Lauritz Melchior Anthology - Vol.1
Verdi: Traviata (exc); Trovatore (exc); Nessler: Trompeter von Säckingen (exc); L. Friedman: Meet me tonight in dreamland; Kjerulf: My heart and my lyre; Heise: Eagle ascends; Though the tide turns; Gade: Oft when I ride; Bechgaard: Sailor's Farewell; Sailor's Farewell; J. P. E. Hartmann: Little Christine (exc); Heise: My lord and king; Fair is the gentle spring; Eagle ascends; Hassler: Entrust all your doings; Berggreen: Welcome again; Weyse: Blessed Day; Anon: Praise the Lord; Berggreen: Just think one day; Anon: Praise to Thee; Weyse: Ever dauntless; Mortensen: Dimlit fogs of night; Wennerberg: Gluntarne (exc); Lange-Müller: Florence, city of flowers; Allen: Sun smiles so kind; Andersen: Now all chasms are bursting; So many birds are flying; Puccini: Tosca (exc); Wagner: Walküre (exc); Lohengrin (exc); J. P. E. Hartmann: Little Christine (exc); Kjellerup: Beloved mine; Heise: When that I was; Andersen: Waves of Kongea; Rygaard: Flag; Denmark; Bonnén: When peace came over the land; Hovalt: Christiansborg. (L. Melchior, H. Hansen, A. Neumann, Anon, Brass Ens, Anon, Orch, Anon)

① **DACOCD313/4** (8/88)
Lauritz Melchior Anthology - Vol. 2
Wagner: Rienzi (exc); Lohengrin (exc); Tannhäuser (exc); Tannhäuser (exc); Walküre (exc); Walküre (exc); Walküre (exc); Siegfried (exc); Siegfried (exc); Parsifal (exc); Parsifal (exc); Wesendonk Lieder (exc); Meistersinger (exc); Verdi: Aida (exc); Meyerbeer: Africaine (exc); Weingartner: Liebesfeier, Op. 16/2; Trunk: Mir träumte von einer Königskind; Als ob ein Toter im Grab; In meiner Heimat; Erster Strahl; R. Strauss: Lieder, Op. 27 (exc); Sjöberg: Tonerna; Klenau: To my bride; Hageman: Do not go, my love. (L. Melchior, E. Bettendorf, F. Leider, M. Ober, orch/F. Weissmann/P. Breisach)

① **DACOCD315/6** (8/88)
Lauritz Melchior Anthology - Vol. 3
Wagner: Walküre (exc); Meistersinger (exc); Rienzi (exc); Lohengrin (exc); Tannhäuser (exc); Tannhäuser (exc); Tristan und Isolde (exc); Tristan und Isolde (exc); Walküre (exc); Walküre (exc); Walküre (exc); Walküre (exc); Götterdämmerung (exc); Meistersinger (exc); Meistersinger (exc); Meistersinger (exc); Meyerbeer: Africaine (exc); Leoncavallo: Pagliacci (exc); Verdi: Otello (exc). (L. Melchior, F. Leider, G. Guszalewicz, F. Schorr, L. Topas, R. Watzke, O. Helgers, E. Schumann, G. Parr, B. Williams, Orch, LSO, Berlin St Op Orch, New SO/J. Barbirolli, L. Blech/A. Coates/R. Heger/L. Collingwood)

① **DACOCD336/7** (11/95)
Brailowsky—The Berlin Recordings, Vol. 1
Chopin: Piano Concerto 1; Piano Sonata 2; Barcarolle; Ballades (exc); Mazurkas (exc); Nocturnes (exc); Preludes (exc); Preludes (exc); Waltzes (exc); Waltzes (exc); Waltzes (exc); Impromptus (exc); Fantaisie-Impromptu; Etudes (exc); Etudes (exc); Etudes (exc); Etudes (exc); Etudes (exc); Polonaises (exc). (A. Brailowsky, BPO/J. Prüwer)

① **DACOCD338/9** (11/95)
Brailowsky—The Berlin Recordings, Vol. 2
Liszt: Piano Concerto 1; Hungarian Rhapsodies, S244 (exc); Hungarian Rhapsodies, S244 (exc); Hungarian Rhapsodies, S244 (exc); Valse impromptu, S213; Concert Studies, S145 (exc); Liebesträume, S541 (exc); Tannhäuser-paraphrase, S442; Fliegende

Schwanengesang, S560 (exc); Lob der Thränen, S557. (J. Bolet)

ⓓ **417 011-2DH2** (7/86)
Pavarotti's Greatest Hits
Verdi: Rigoletto (exc); Franck: Panis angelicus; Bellini: Vanne, o rosa fortunata; Gounod: Faust (exc); Verdi: Requiem (exc); Aida (exc); Schubert: Ave Maria, D839; Leoncavallo: Pagliacci (exc); Ponchielli: Gioconda (exc); Donizetti: Elisir d'amore (exc); Puccini: Tosca (exc); Denza: Funiculì-Funiculà; Puccini: Turandot (exc); Donizetti: Fille du régiment (exc); Puccini: Bohème (exc); R. Strauss: Rosenkavalier (exc); Leoncavallo: Mattinata; Rossini: Soirées musicales (exc); De Curtis: Torna a Surriento; Donizetti: Favorita (exc); Bizet: Carmen (exc); Bellini: Puritani (exc); Verdi: Trovatore (exc). (L. Pavarotti, LSO/R. Bonynge, National PO/K.H. Adler, Bologna Teatro Comunale Orch, Vienna Volksoper Orch/L. Magiera, VPO/G. Solti/G. Patanè, New Philh, ECO/N. Rescigno/A. Guadagno, LPO/Z. Mehta, E. Garrett, ROH Chor, ROHO, BPO/H. von Karajan, Philh/P. Gamba/G. Chiaramello, J. Sutherland, N. Ghiaurov, G. Luccardi)

ⓓ **417 252-2DH** (4/89)
Scriabin: Orchestral Works
Scriabin: Poème de l'extase; Piano Concerto; Prometheus. (Vladimir Ashkenazy, Ambrosian Sngrs, LPO, Cleveland Orch/L. Maazel)

ⓓ **417 289-2DH** (9/87)
Con amore
Kreisler: Gitana; Liebesleid; Pugnani Praeludium and Allegro; Liebesfreud; Poldini: Marionnettes (exc); Wieniawski: Scherzo-tarantelle, Op. 16; Etudes-Caprices, Op. 18 (exc); Elgar: Salut d'amour; Capricieuse; Tchaikovsky: Morceaux, Op. 51 (exc); Nováček: Concert caprices, Op. 5 (exc); Debussy: Beau soir; Chopin: Nocturnes (exc); Gossec: Rosine (exc); Chaminade: Sérénade espagnole; Saint-Saëns: Etudes, Op. 52 (exc); Brahms: Hungarian Dances (exc). (K-W. Chung, P. Moll)

ⓓ **417 438-2DH** (7/87)
Poulenc: Piano Works
Poulenc: Soirées de Nazelles; Novelettes; Novelette sur un thème de Falla; Pastourelle; Mouvements perpétuels; Valse; Improvisations (exc); Pièces (1928). (P. Rogé)

ⓓ **417 476-2DH** (9/87)
Chopin: Preludes & Impromptus
Chopin: Preludes; Impromptus; Fantaisie-impromptu. (Vladimir Ashkenazy)

ⓓ **417 523-2DH** (2/87)
Liszt: Piano Works, Vol.8
Liszt: Concert Studies, S144; Concert Studies, S145; Consolations, S172; Don Juan réminiscences, S418. (J. Bolet)

ⓓ **417 599-2DH** (8/87)
Brahms: Piano Works
Brahms: Rhapsodies, Op. 79; Piano Pieces, Op. 117; Piano Pieces, Op. 118; Piano Pieces, Op. 119. (R. Lupu)

ⓓ **417 643-2DM** (9/88)
Chamber Works for Clarinet & Strings
Mozart: Clarinet Quintet, K581; Brahms: Clarinet Quintet, H. J. Baërmann: Clarinet Quintet, Op. 23 (exc). (A. Boskovsky, Vienna Octet)

ⓓ **417 645-2DH** (11/87)
Kiri - Portrait
Canteloube: Chants d'Auvergne (exc); Gay: Beggar's Opera (exc); Handel: Messiah (exc); Brahms: Deutsches Requiem, Op. 45 (exc); Mozart: Vado ma dove?, K583; Nozze di Figaro (exc); Puccini: Tosca (exc); Bizet: Carmen (exc); Villa-Lobos: Bachianas Brasileiras 5. (K. Te Kanawa, ECO/J. Tate, National PO/R. Bonynge, Chicago SO/G. Solti, Vienna CO/G. Fischer, LPO, L. Harrell, Inst. Ens, Chicago Sym Chor)

ⓓ **417 686-2DC** (1/89)
Puccini—Operatic Arias
Puccini: Madama Butterfly (exc); Tosca (exc); Tosca (exc); Turandot (exc); Turandot (exc); Bohème (exc); Bohème (exc); Fanciulla del West (exc); Gianni Schicchi (exc); Manon Lescaut (exc). (F. Weathers, Vienna Op. Orch/A. Quadri, G. di Stefano, Santa Cecilia Academy Orch/F. Patanè, A. Cerquetti, MMF Orch/G. Gavazzeni, R. Tebaldi, New Philh/O. de Fabritiis, B. Prevedi, ROHO/E. Downes, C. Bergonzi/T. Serafin, M. Chiara, Vienna Volksoper Orch/N. Santi, V. Zeani, J. Björling/A. Erede)

ⓓ **417 715-2DM** (7/87)
Bach—Orchestral Works
Bach: Suites, BWV1066-9 (exc); Violin and Oboe Concerto, BWV1060; Flute Concerto, BWV1056. (ASMF/N. Marriner, C. Kaine, T. Miller, W. Bennett)

ⓓ **417 718-2DM** (7/87)
Haydn: Symphonies
Haydn: Symphony 94; Symphony 96; Symphony 100. (Philh Hungarica/A. Dorati)

ⓓ **417 719-2DM** (7/87)
Elgar: Orchestral Works
Elgar: Pomp and Circumstance Marches; Enigma Variations; Cockaigne. (LPO, Chicago SO/G. Solti)

ⓓ **417 732-2DM** (12/87)
Beethoven—Piano Sonatas
Beethoven: Piano Sonata 14; Piano Sonata 23; Piano Sonata 21. (Vladimir Ashkenazy)

ⓓ **417 762-2DM** (12/88)
Sibelius: Orchestral Works
Sibelius: Finlandia; Karelia Suite; Tapiola; En Saga. (Philh/Vladimir Ashkenazy)

ⓓ **417 771-2DM** (4/89)
de Falla: Orchestral & Stage Works
Falla: Nights in the Gardens of Spain; Sombrero de tres picos (Cpte); Vida breve (exc). (A. de Larrocha, T. Berganza, SRO/S. Comissiona/E. Ansermet)

ⓓ **417 778-2DM** (5/89)
English Orchestral Music
Vaughan Williams: Greensleeves Fantasia; English Folk Song Suite; Elgar: Serenade; Butterworth: Banks of Green Willow; Warlock: Capriol Suite; Delius: First cuckoo; Village Romeo and Juliet (exc). (ASMF/N. Marriner)

ⓓ **417 786-2DM** (10/89)
Spanish Orchestral Works
Falla: Amor brujo (Cpte); Granados: Goyescas (exc); Albéniz: Suite española 1. (N. Mistral, New Philh/R. Frühbeck de Burgos)

ⓓ **417 792-2DM** (2/90)
Debussy: Piano Works
Debussy: Suite bergamasque; Children's Corner; Images; Arabesques. (P. Rogé)

ⓓ **417 795-2DM** (7/90)
Spanish Fireworks
Albéniz: Navarra; Suite española 1 (exc); Iberia (exc); Falla: Amor brujo (exc); Sombrero de tres picos (exc); Granados: Allegro de concierto; Goyescas (exc); Piezas sobre cantos populares españoles (exc); M. Albéniz: Sonata in D; Mompou: Impressions intimes (exc); Turina: Danzas andaluzas (exc); Danzas gitanas I (exc). (A. de Larrocha)

ⓓ **417 798-2DM** (7/90)
Ashkenazy plays Chopin Favourites
Chopin: Nocturnes (exc); Waltzes (exc); Fantaisie-impromptu; Mazurkas (exc); Scherzos (exc); Waltzes (exc); Nocturnes (exc); Waltzes (exc); Nocturnes (exc); Mazurkas (exc); Polonaises (exc); Ballades (exc). (Vladimir Ashkenazy)

ⓓ **417 813-2DH** (11/88)
Regine Crespin sings French Vocal Works
Berlioz: Nuits d'été; Ravel: Shéhérazade; Debussy: Chansons de Bilitis; Poulenc: Banalités (exc); Courte paille (exc); Chansons villageoises (exc); Poèmes de Louis Aragon. (R. Crespin, SRO/E. Ansermet, J. Wustman)

ⓓ **417 833-2DH** (9/87)
Rostropovich/Britten Recital
Debussy: Cello Sonata; Schubert: Arpeggione Sonata, D821; Schumann: Stücke, Op. 102. (M. Rostropovich, B. Britten)

ⓓ **417 887-2DH2** (6/88)
Albéniz: Piano Works
Albéniz: Iberia; Navarra; Suite española 1. (A. de Larrocha)

ⓓ **421 010-2DH** (8/88)
Schumann—Piano Works, Vol.2
Schumann: Carnaval; Humoreske; Novelletten (exc). (Vladimir Ashkenazy)

ⓓ **421 069-2DM4** (12/87)
Sibelius: Complete Symphonies
Sibelius: Symphony 1; Symphony 2; Symphony 3; Symphony 4; Symphony 5; Symphony 6; Symphony 7. (Philh/Vladimir Ashkenazy)

ⓓ **421 092-2DM** (5/88)
Brahms: Violin Sonatas
Brahms: Violin Sonata 1; Violin Sonata 2; Violin Sonata 3. (J. Suk, J. Katchen)

ⓓ **421 147-2DM** (5/89)
Allegri & Palestrina: Sacred Choral Works
Allegri: Miserere mei; Palestrina: Stabat mater a 8; Hodie beata virgo; Senex puerum portabat; Magnificat a 8;

Litaniae de BVM I a 8. (R. Goodman, King's College Ch/D. Willcocks)

ⓓ **421 154-2DM** (1/89)
French Chamber Works
Franck: Violin Sonata; Debussy: Violin Sonata; Sonata for Flute, Viola and Harp; Ravel: Introduction and Allegro. (K-W. Chung, R. Lupu, O. Ellis, Melos Ens)

ⓓ **421 290-2DH** (2/89)
Schumann—Piano Works, Vol.3
Schumann: Waldszenen; Kinderszenen; Piano Sonata 1. (Vladimir Ashkenazy)

ⓓ **421 337-2DM3** (2/90)
Bach: Organ Works, Vol.1
Bach: Prelude and Fugue, BWV531; Prelude and Fugue, BWV532; Prelude and Fugue, BWV533; Prelude and Fugue, BWV535; Prelude and Fugue, BWV548; Prelude and Fugue, BWV549; Prelude and Fugue, BWV550; Prelude and Fugue, BWV551; Toccata and Fugue, BWV538; Toccata and Fugue, BWV540; Toccata and Fugue, BWV565; Fantasia and Fugue, BWV537; Fantasia, BWV542; Fantasia and Fugue, BWV561; Fantasia, BWV562; Fantasia, BWV570; Fantasia, BWV572; Fugue, BWV575; Fugue, BWV576; Fugue, BWV577; Fugue, BWV579; Fugue, BWV581; Fugue, BWV946; Trio, BWV583; Trio, BWV585; Passacaglia and Fugue, BWV582; Toccata, Adagio and Fugue, BWV564; Kleines harmonisches Labyrinth, BWV591; Pedal-Exercitium, BWV598. (P. Hurford)

ⓓ **421 440-2DH** (1/89)
Fauré: Choral & Orchestral Works
Fauré: Requiem (Cpte); Pelléas et Mélisande Suite (exc); Pavane. (K. Te Kanawa, S. Milnes, Montreal Sym Chor, Montreal SO/C. Dutoit)

ⓓ **421 453-2DM4** (1/89)
Beethoven: Complete Violin Sonatas
Beethoven: Violin Sonata 1; Violin Sonata 2; Violin Sonata 3; Violin Sonata 4; Violin Sonata 5; Violin Sonata 6; Violin Sonata 7; Violin Sonata 8; Violin Sonata 9; Violin Sonata 10. (I. Perlman, Vladimir Ashkenazy)

ⓓ **421 523-2DH** (10/88)
Hindemith: Orchestral Works
Hindemith: Mathis der Maler; Trauermusik; Symphonic Metamorphosis. (G. Walther, San Francisco SO/H. Blomstedt)

ⓓ **421 527-2DH** (6/89)
Fête à la française
Chabrier: Joyeuse marche; España; Dukas: Apprenti sorcier; Satie: Gymnopédies (exc); Saint-Saëns: Samson et Dalila (exc); Bizet: Jeux d'enfants; A. Thomas: Raymond (exc); Ibert: Divertissement. (Montreal SO/C. Dutoit)

ⓓ **421 581-2DH** (8/89)
Poulenc—Chamber Works
Poulenc: Sextet; Clarinet Sonata; Flute Sonata; Oboe Sonata; Piano, oboe and bassoon trio. (P. Gallois, M. Bourgue, M. Portal, A. Wallez, A. Cazalet, P. Rogé)

ⓓ **421 590-2DH2** (4/89)
Rachmaninov: Complete Piano Concertos
Rachmaninov: Piano Concerto 1; Piano Concerto 2; Piano Concerto 3; Piano Concerto 4. (Vladimir Ashkenazy, Concertgebouw/B. Haitink)

ⓓ **421 713-2DH** (5/89)
Satie: Piano Works
Satie: Poudre d'or; Avant-dernières pensées; Pièces froides; Chapitres tournés en tous sens; Nocturnes (exc); Véritables préludes flasques; Rêveries nocturnes; Prélude de la porte héroïque du ciel; Heures séculaires et instantanées; Descriptions automatiques; Croquis et agaceries; Nouvelles pièces froides; Valses du précieux dégoûté. (P. Rogé)

ⓓ **421 718-2DH3** (3/89)
Beethoven—Piano Concertos
Beethoven: Piano Concerto 1; Piano Concerto 2; Piano Concerto 3; Piano Concerto 4; Piano Concerto 5; Choral Fantasia. (Cleveland Orch, Cleveland Orch Chor, Vladimir Ashkenazy (pf/dir))

ⓓ **421 810-2DM2** (5/89)
Dvořák & Kodály: Choral Works
Dvořák: Requiem; Kodály: Psalmus Hungaricus; Hymn of Zrinyi. (P. Lorengar, E. Komlóssy, R. Ilosfalvy, T. Krause, Ambrosian Sngrs, LSO, L. Kozma, Brighton Fest Chor, Wandsworth Sch Boys' Ch, B. Luxon/I. Kertész/L. Heltay)

ⓓ **421 818-2DH2** (11/90)
Ballet Gala
Minkus: Grand pas; Pugni: Pas de quatre; Offenbach: Papillon (exc); Pugni: Esmeralda (exc); Drigo: Corsaire (exc); Auber: Grand Pas Classique; C. Lambert: Rendez-vous; Pugni: Esmeralda (exc); Tommasini: Good-

① **425 721-2DM** (12/90)
Vivaldi: Concertos
Vivaldi: Concerti grossi, Op. 3 (exc); Concerto, RV401;
Concerto, RV569; Concerto, RV539; Concerti, Op. 4 (exc);
Concerto, RV537. (ASMF/N. Marriner, K. Heath, T. Brown,
R. Davis, C. Kaine, J. Wilbraham, P. Jones)

① **425 722-2DM** (11/90)
Mozart—Masonic Music
Mozart: O heiliges Band, K148; Dir, Seele des Weltalls,
K429; Lied zur Gesellenreise, K468; Maurerfreude, K471;
Maurerische Trauermusik, K477; Zerfliesset heut', K483;
Ihr unsre neuen Leiter, K484; Kleine deutsche Kantate,
K619; Kleine Freimaurer-Kantate, K623; Lasst uns mit
geschlungen Händen, K623a. (W. Krenn, T. Krause,
Edinburgh Fest Chor, G. Fischer, G. Fischer, LSO/I.
Kertész)

① **425 723-2DM** (12/90)
Harp Concertos
Handel: Organ Concertos (exc); *Boïeldieu:* Harp Concerto;
Dittersdorf: Harp Concerto; *Anon:* Theme, Variations and
Rondo; *Handel:* Theme and Variations in G minor;
Beethoven: Variations, WoO64. (M. Robles, ASMF/I.
Brown)

① **425 790-2DH** (4/94)
Mahler—Lieder
Mahler: Kindertotenlieder; Lieder eines fahrenden
Gesellen; Rückert Lieder; Knaben Wunderhorn (exc). (B.
Fassbaender, Berlin Deutsches SO/R. Chailly)

① **425 832-2DH** (8/90)
Berio—Vocal & Orchestral Works
Berio: Formazioni; Folk Songs; Sinfonia. (J. van Nes,
Electric Phoenix, Concertgebouw/R. Chailly)

① **425 838-2DH** (4/91)
Beethoven: Piano Sonatas
Beethoven: Piano Sonata 14; Piano Sonata 23; Piano
Sonata 21. (Vladimir Ashkenazy)

① **425 862-2DH** (4/91)
Poulenc—Piano Works
Poulenc: Humoresque; Nocturnes; Suite in C; Thème
varié; Improvisations (exc); Intermezzi; Villageoises;
Presto. (P. Rogé)

① **425 920-2DM4** (6/91)
Haydn—Symphonies, Vol.5
Haydn: Symphony 60; Symphony 61; Symphony 62;
Symphony 63; Symphony 64; Symphony 65; Symphony
66; Symphony 67; Symphony 68; Symphony 69;
Symphony 70; Symphony 71. (Philh Hungarica/A. Dorati)

① **425 930-2DM4** (6/91)
Haydn—Symphonies, Vol.7
Haydn: Symphony 84; Symphony 85; Symphony 86;
Symphony 87; Symphony 88; Symphony 89; Symphony
90; Symphony 91; Symphony 92; Symphony 93;
Symphony 94; Symphony 95. (Philh Hungarica/A. Dorati)

① **425 935-2DM4** (6/91)
Haydn—Symphonies, Vol.8
Haydn: Symphony 96; Symphony 97; Symphony 98;
Symphony 99; Symphony 100; Symphony 101; Symphony
102; Symphony 103; Symphony 104; Sinfonia
Concertante; Symphony A; Symphony B. (Philh
Hungarica/A. Dorati, I. Engl, L. Baranyi, I. Ozim, Z. Rácz)

① **425 940-2DM4** (4/92)
Schumann—Piano Works, Vol.5
Schumann: Kreisleriana; Novelletten (exc); Piano Sonata
2. (Vladimir Ashkenazy)

① **425 956-2DM** (5/90)
Ravel: Orchestral Works
Ravel: Daphnis et Chloé (Cpte); Rapsodie espagnole;
Pavane. (ROH Chor, LSO/P. Monteux)

① **425 959-2DM** (4/90)
Lisa della Casa sings R. Strauss
R. Strauss: Vier letzte Lieder; Arabella (exc); Arabella
(exc); Ariadne auf Naxos (exc); Capriccio (exc). (L. della
Casa, H. Gueden, P. Schoeffler, A. Poell, F. Bierbach,
VPO/K. Böhm/H. Moralt/H. Hollreiser)

① **425 960-2DM** (4/90)
Mozart—Chamber Works
Mozart: Piano Quartet, K478; Piano Quartet, K493; Horn
Quintet, K407. (C. Curzon, Amadeus Qt, D. Brain, Griller
Qt, M. Gilbert)

① **425 964-2DM** (4/90)
Rachmaninov from Ampico Piano Rolls
Rachmaninov: Morceaux de fantaisie, Op.3; Morceaux de
salon, Op.10 (exc); Preludes (exc); Etudes-tableaux,
Op.39 (exc); Lilacs; Polka de W. R.; *Mussorgsky:* Gopak;
Schubert: Schöne Müllerin (exc); *Rimsky-Korsakov:* Tale of

Tsar Saltan (exc); *Various:* National Anthems (exc);
Kreisler: Liebesleid; Liebesfreud. (S. Rachmaninov)

① **425 975-2DM** (7/91)
Gerard Souzay—Song Recital
Fauré: Songs, Op. 6 (exc); Songs, Op. 8 (exc); Songs, Op.
7 (exc); Songs, Op. 46 (exc); Songs, Op. 76 (exc); Songs,
Op. 51 (exc); Songs, Op. 83 (exc); Songs, Op. 58 (exc);
Chausson: Mélodies, Op. 2 (exc); Mélodies, Op.36 (exc);
Poème de l'amour et de la mer (exc); *Boësset:* Me veux-tu
voir mourir; *Bataille:* Tambourin; Cachez, beaux yeux; Ma
bergère non légère; *Canteloube:* Chants d'Auvergne (exc);
Fauré: Horizon chimérique; Songs, Op. 58 (exc). (G.
Souzay, J. Bonneau)

① **425 995-2DM** (9/92)
Brahms/Mahler—Lieder
Brahms: Liebeslieder Walzer, Op. 52; Neue Liebeslieder
Walzer, Op. 65 (exc); *Mahler:* Kindertotenlieder. (I.
Seefried, K. Ferrier, J. Patzak, H. Günter, C. Curzon, H.
Gál, Concertgebouw/O. Klemperer)

① **425 996-2DM** (9/92)
Britten—Vocal Works
Britten: Serenade; Michelangelo Sonnets; Winter Words.
(P. Pears, D. Brain, Boyd Neel Orch/B. Britten, B. Britten)

① **430 046-2DC6** (4/92)
Dvořák—Complete Symphonies, etc
Dvořák: Symphony 1; Symphony 2; Symphony 3;
Symphony 4; Symphony 5; Symphony 6; Symphony 7;
Symphony 8; Symphony 9; Carnival; In nature's realm; My
home; Scherzo capriccioso. (LSO/I. Kertész)

① **430 053-2DM6** (2/91)
Brahms—Piano Works
Brahms: Ballades; Handel Variations; Paganini Variations;
Variations, Op. 21/1; Variations, Op. 21/2; Waltzes, Op.
39; Schumann Variations; Scherzo, Op. 4; Piano Sonata 1;
Piano Sonata 2; Rhapsodies, Op. 79; Piano Sonata 3;
Piano Pieces, Op. 117; Piano Pieces, Op. 76; Piano
Pieces, Op. 118; Piano Pieces, Op. 119; Hungarian
Dances; Piano Pieces, Op. 116. (J. Katchen/J-P. Marty)

① **430 089-2DWO** (12/90)
King's World of Christmas
Traditional: Hark! the herald angels sing; First nowell;
While shepherds watched; I saw three ships; Ding dong!
merrily on high; Away in a manger; In dulci jubilo;
Unto us is born a son; O come, all ye faithful; Away in a
manger; O little town of Bethlehem; Holly and the Ivy; God
rest you merry, gentlemen; Past three a clock; See amid
the winter's snow. (King's College Ch/D. Willcocks)

① **430 091-2DWO** (6/91)
The World of the Organ
Widor: Symphony 5 (exc); *Bach:* Schübler Chorales,
BWV645-650 (exc); *Mozart:* Fantasia, K608; *Walton:*
Crown Imperial; *Clarke:* Suite in D (exc); *Handel:* Saul
(exc); *Purcell:* Choice Collection of Lessons (exc); *Elgar:*
Imperial March; *Vierne:* Symphony 1 (exc); *Wagner:*
Tannhäuser (exc); *Guilmant:* March, Op. 15; *Schumann:*
Pedal Studies, Op. 56 (exc); *Karg-Elert:* Choral-
Improvisationen, Op. 65 (exc). (S. Preston)

① **430 093-2DWO** (6/91)
The World of Vaughan Williams
Vaughan Williams: Greensleeves Fantasia; Linden Lea;
House of Life (exc); Songs of Travel (exc); Lark ascending;
Shakespeare Songs; English Folk Song Suite; O clap your
hands; O taste and see; Fantasia on Christmas Carols. (I.
Brown, ASMF/N. Marriner, R. Tear, P. Ledger, L. Heather,
King's College Ch/D. Willcocks, Boston Pops/A. Fiedler,
Canterbury Cath Ch, PJBE/D. Flood/A. Wicks, H. Alan,
LSO)

① **430 094-2DWO** (6/91)
The World of Elgar
Elgar: Pomp and Circumstance Marches (exc); Serenade;
Partsongs, Op. 53 (exc); Salut d'amour; Introduction and
Allegro; Enigma Variations (exc); Give unto the Lord;
Dream of Gerontius (exc). (LSO/A. Bliss, ASMF/N.
Marriner, L. Halsey Sngrs/L. Halsey, K-W. Chung, P. Moll,
ECO/B. Britten/P. Monteux, Canterbury Cath Ch/D.
Flood/A. Wicks, P. Pears, Y. Minton, LSC, King's College
Ch)

① **430 095-2DWO** (6/91)
The World of Gilbert & Sullivan, Vol.1
Sullivan: HMS Pinafore (exc); Mikado (exc); Yeomen of the
Guard (exc); Pirates of Penzance (exc); Iolanthe (exc);
Gondoliers (exc). (J. Reed, J. Skitch, J. Wright, G. Knight,
J. Hindmarsh, D'Oyly Carte Op Chor, New SO/I. Godfrey,
C. Wright, V. Masterson, P.A. Jones, P. Wales, RPO/R.
Nash, E. Harwood/M. Sargent, O. Brannigan, J. Allister, D.
Adams, T. Round, A. Styler, J. Toye)

① **430 096-2DWO** (6/91)
The World of Kathleen Ferrier
Traditional: Blow the wind southerly; Keel row; *Anon:* My

bonny lad; *Bridge:* Go not happy day; *Britten:* Folk Songs
(exc); *Traditional:* Kitty my love; *Handel:* Rodelinda (exc);
Serse (exc); *Gluck:* Orfeo ed Euridice (exc); *Mendelssohn:*
Elijah (exc); *Bach:* St Matthew Passion, BWV244 (exc);
Schubert: Gretchen am Spinnrade, D118; Junge Nonne,
D828; An die Musik, D547; Musensohn, D764; *Brahms:*
Lieder, Op. 94 (exc); Lieder, Op. 47 (exc); *Mahler:* Rückert
Lieder (exc). (K. Ferrier, P. Spurr, F. Stone, LSO/M.
Sargent, Boyd Neel Orch/B. Neel, National SO, VPO/B.
Walter)

① **430 100-2DM32(1)** (6/91)
Haydn—Complete Symphonies (Volumes 1-4)
Haydn: Symphony 1; Symphony 2; Symphony 3;
Symphony 4; Symphony 5; Symphony 6; Symphony 7;
Symphony 8; Symphony 9; Symphony 10; Symphony 11;
Symphony 12; Symphony 13; Symphony 14; Symphony
15; Symphony 16; Symphony 17; Symphony 18;
Symphony 19; Symphony 20; Symphony 21; Symphony
22; Symphony 23; Symphony 24; Symphony 25;
Symphony 26; Symphony 27; Symphony 28; Symphony
29; Symphony 30; Symphony 31; Symphony 32;
Symphony 33; Symphony 34; Symphony 35; Symphony
36; Symphony 37; Symphony 38; Symphony 39;
Symphony 40; Symphony 41; Symphony 42; Symphony
43; Symphony 44; Symphony 45; Symphony 46;
Symphony 47; Symphony 48; Symphony 49; Symphony
50; Symphony 51; Symphony 52; Symphony 53;
Symphony 54; Symphony 55; Symphony 56; Symphony
57; Symphony 58; Symphony 59. (Philh Hungarica/A.
Dorati)

① **430 100-2DM32(2)** (6/91)
Haydn—Complete Symphonies (Volumes 5-8)
Haydn: Symphony 60; Symphony 61; Symphony 62;
Symphony 63; Symphony 64; Symphony 65; Symphony
66; Symphony 67; Symphony 68; Symphony 69;
Symphony 70; Symphony 71; Symphony 72; Symphony
73; Symphony 74; Symphony 75; Symphony 76;
Symphony 77; Symphony 78; Symphony 79; Symphony
80; Symphony 81; Symphony 82; Symphony 83;
Symphony 84; Symphony 85; Symphony 86; Symphony
87; Symphony 88; Symphony 89; Symphony 90;
Symphony 91; Symphony 92; Symphony 93; Symphony
94; Symphony 95; Symphony 96; Symphony 97;
Symphony 98; Symphony 99; Symphony 100; Symphony
101; Symphony 102; Symphony 103; Symphony 104;
Sinfonia Concertante; Symphony A; Symphony B. (Philh
Hungarica/A. Dorati, I. Engl, L. Baranyi, I. Ozim, Z. Rácz)

① **430 149-2DH** (10/93)
Brahms/Schumann—Works for Clarinet
Brahms: Clarinet Sonata 1; Clarinet Sonata 2; *Schumann:*
Fantasiestücke, Op. 73. (F. Cohen, Vladimir Ashkenazy)

① **430 159-2DM** (6/91)
Haydn, M.Haydn & Mozart: Sacred Choral Works
Haydn: Mass 12; *M. Haydn:* Ave Regina; *Mozart:* Ave
verum corpus, K618. (E. Spoorenberg, B. Greevy, J.
Mitchinson, T. Krause, P. White, St John's College Ch,
ASMF/G. Guest)

① **430 160-2DM** (6/91)
Haydn: Masses & Keyboard Concerto
Haydn: Mass 8; Mass 7; Keyboard Concerto, HobXVIII/1.
(J. Smith, H. Watts, R. Tear, B. Luxon, S. Preston, St
John's College Ch, ASMF/G. Guest/N. Marriner)

① **430 226-2DH** (4/91)
Verdi—Choruses
Verdi: Nabucco (exc); Lombardi (exc); Macbeth (exc);
Masnadieri (exc); Trovatore (exc); Traviata (exc); Ballo in
maschera (exc); Don Carlo (exc); Aida (exc); Otello (exc);
Requiem (exc). (Chicago Sym Chor, Chicago SO/G.
Solti)

① **430 232-2DH** (11/90)
Mozart: Piano Concertos
Mozart: 3-Piano Concerto, K242; 2-Piano Concerto, K365;
Piano Concerto 20. (A. Schiff, D. Barenboim, G. Solti
(pf/dir), ECO)

① **430 260-2DM** (7/91)
Bach—Cantatas
Bach: Cantata 170; Cantata 159; Cantata 82. (J. Baker, R.
Tear, J. Shirley-Quirk, St Anthony Sngrs, ASMF/N.
Marriner)

① **430 261-2DM** (2/92)
Handel—Orchestral Works
Handel: Concerti grossi, Op. 3; Alcina (exc); Ariodante
(exc). (ASMF/N. Marriner)

① **430 263-2DM** (7/91)
Purcell—Sacred choral works
Purcell: Te Deum and Jubilate, Z232; Funeral Sentences:
Remember not, Lord, our offences, Z50; March and
Canzona, Z860; Funeral Sentences (exc); I was glad; O
Lord God of Hosts, Z37; O give thanks unto the Lord, Z33.
(J. Bowman, C. Brett, P. Esswood, I. Partridge, A. Dawson,

F. Robinson, S. Dean, L. Atkinson, M. Creese, S.
Keenlyside, R. King, R. Smith, Paul Williams, ECO, S.
Cleobury, J. Ryan, Symphoniae Sacrae, Stg Orch, John
Scott, St John's College Ch/G. Guest)

ⓘ **430 265-2DM** (7/91)
Telemann—Orchestral works
Telemann: Overture-Suite in C; Viola da gamba Concerto
1; Don Quichotte Overture-Suite; Overture-Suite in D. (S.
Shingles, ASMF/N. Marriner)

ⓘ **430 268-2DM** (7/91)
Mozart—Symphonies
Mozart: Symphony 25; Symphony 26; Symphony 27;
Symphony 29; Symphony 32. (ASMF/N. Marriner)

ⓘ **430 295-2DM** (8/92)
Janáček/Smetana—String Quartets
Janáček: String Quartet 1; String Quartet 2; Smetana:
String Quartet 1. (Gabrieli Qt)

ⓘ **430 352-2DH** (5/91)
Bartók: Orchestral Works
Bartók: Music for Strings, Percussion and Celesta;
Divertimento; Miraculous Mandarin (exc). (Chicago SO/G.
Solti)

ⓘ **430 359-2DM** (7/91)
Baroque Church Music
G. Bassano: Ave Regina; G. Gabrieli: Hodie Christus natus
est; Symphoniae sacrae (1597) (exc); A. Gabrieli: Laudate
Dominum; Pergolesi: Miserere II in C minor. (I. Wolf, D.
James, R. Covey-Crump, R. Suart, Magdalen Oxford Coll
Ch, S. Lawford, Wren Orch/Bernard Rose, J. Iveson, S.
Saunders, D. Purser, R. Gowman)

ⓘ **430 360-2DM** (9/91)
Faure/Poulenc—Sacred Choral Works
Fauré: Requiem (Cpte); Cantique de Jean Racine; Messe
basse; Poulenc: Mass in G; Salve Regina. (J. Bond, B.
Luxon, S. Cleobury, A. Brunt, St John's College Ch,
ASMF/G. Guest)

ⓘ **430 370-2DH** (9/92)
R. Strauss—Works for Horn
R. Strauss: Horn Concerto 1; Horn Concerto 2; Andante,
Av86a; Capriccio (exc); Alphorn; Introduction, Theme and
Variations. (B. Tuckwell, M. McLaughlin, RPO/Vladimir
Ashkenazy, Vladimir Ashkenazy)

ⓘ **430 375-2DH2** (10/91)
Janáček—Operatic and Orchestral Works
Janáček: From the House of the Dead (Cpte); Mládí;
Nursery rhymes (Cpte). (D. Jedlička, J. Janská, J.
Zahradníček, V. Krejčík, R. Novák, A. Švorc, B. Blachut, I.
Žídek, J. Souček, E. Zikmundová, Z. Souček, V. Zítek, Z.
Švehla, Vienna St Op Chor, VPO/C. Mackerras, London
Sinfonietta Chor, London Sinfonietta/D. Atherton)

ⓘ **430 425-2DH** (11/92)
Schubert—Piano Works
Schubert: Impromptus; Moments musicaux, D780;
Ungarische Melodie, D817; Deutsche Tänze, D820; Grazer
Galopp, D925. (A. Schiff)

ⓘ **430 433-2DH** (10/90)
Carreras, Domingo and Pavarotti in Concert
Cilea: Arlesiana (exc); Cardillo: Core 'ngrato; Lara:
Granada; Giordano: Andrea Chénier (exc); Meyerbeer:
Africaine (exc); Lehár: Land des Lächelns (exc); Puccini:
Tosca (exc); Turandot (exc); Turandot (exc); Crescenzo:
Rondine al nido; De Curtis: Torna a Surriento; Sorozábal:
Tabernera del puerto (exc); Bernstein: West Side Story
(exc); Mendoza y Cortez: Cielito lindo; A. Lloyd Webber:
Cats (exc); Louiguy: Vie en rose; Leoncavallo: Mattinata;
Lacalle: Amapola; Di Capua: O sole mio; Puccini:
Caminito; Annibale: 'O paese d' 'o sole. (J. Carreras, P.
Domingo, L. Pavarotti, MMF Orch, Rome Op Orch/Z.
Mehta)

ⓘ **430 448-2DM** (5/91)
The Solti Collection—Wagner Overtures
Wagner: Fliegende Holländer (exc); Tannhäuser (exc);
Meistersinger (exc); Tristan und Isolde (exc). (Chicago
SO/G. Solti)

ⓘ **430 481-2DX2** (8/91)
Renata Tebaldi sings Opera Arias
Puccini: Madama Butterfly (exc); Bohème (exc); Tosca
(exc); Boito: Mefistofele (exc); Verdi: Aida (exc); Otello
(exc); Trovatore (exc); Forza del destino (exc); Rossini:
Guillaume Tell (exc); Cilea: Adriana Lecouvreur (exc);
Refice: Cecilia (exc); Puccini: Gianni Schicchi (exc); Suor
Angelica (exc); Giordano: Andrea Chénier (exc); Catalani:
Wally (exc); Verdi: Don Carlo (exc); Ballo in maschera
(exc); Giovanna d'Arco (exc); Puccini: Turandot (exc);
Ponchielli: Gioconda (exc); Puccini: Rondine (exc);
Mascagni: Cavalleria Rusticana (exc); Cilea: Arlesiana
(exc). (R. Tebaldi, Santa Cecilia Academy Orch/T. Serafin,
C. Bergonzi/F. Molinari-Pradelli, VPO/H. von Karajan, A.R.

Satre, A. Cesarini, Geneva Grand Th Orch/A. Erede, MMF
Orch/L. Gardelli/G. Gavazzeni, Monte Carlo Nat Op
Orch/F. Cleva, New Philh/O. de Fabritiis)

ⓘ **430 498-2DWO** (6/91)
The World of Mozart
Mozart: Serenade, K525 (exc); Piano Concerto 21 (exc);
Nozze di Figaro (exc); Symphony 40 (exc); Piano Sonata,
K331 (exc); Così fan tutte (exc); Clarinet Concerto, K622
(exc); Ave verum corpus, K618; Maurerische Trauermusik,
K477; Requiem (exc); Symphony 25 (exc); Musikalischer
Spass (exc). (ASMF/N. Marriner, Vladimir Ashkenazy
(pf/dir), Philh, K. Te Kanawa, LPO/G. Solti, COE, A. Schiff,
L. Popp, B. Fassbaender, T. Krause, Vienna Op Orch/I.
Kertész, G. de Peyer, LSO/P. Maag, St John's College Ch,
P. White/G. Guest, ASMF Chor, Vienna Mozart Ens/W.
Boskovsky)

ⓘ **430 499-2DWO** (10/91)
World of Bach
Bach: Suites, BWV1066-9 (exc); Cantata 147 (exc);
Toccata and Fugue, BWV565; Brandenburg Concertos
(exc); Christmas Oratorio, BWV248 (exc); Cantata 140
(exc); Cantata 12 (exc); Mass in B minor, BWV232 (exc);
St Matthew Passion, BWV244 (exc). (ASMF/N. Marriner,
St. John's College Ch, P. White/G. Guest, P. Hurford,
Lübecker Kantorei, Stuttgart CO/K. Münchinger, SRO/E.
Ansermet, K. Ferrier, LPO/A. Boult, Stuttgart Hymnus
Boys' Ch)

ⓘ **430 500-2DWO** (10/91)
World of Handel
Handel: Solomon (exc); Rodelinda (exc); Judas
Maccabaeus (exc); Water Music - Suite (exc); Semele
(exc); Berenice (exc); Samson (exc); Israel in Egypt (exc);
Organ Concertos (exc); Coronation Anthems (exc);
Messiah (exc). (ASMF/N. Marriner, Handel Op Chor,
RPO/C. Farncombe, LSO/G. Szell, K. McKellar, ROHO/A.
Boult, J. Sutherland/F. Molinari-Pradelli, G. Malcolm,
King's College Ch, ECO/D. Willcocks, A. Reynolds, M.
Horne, Vienna Cantata Orch/H. Lewis, ASMF Chor)

ⓘ **430 501-2DWO** (10/91)
World of Johann Strauss
J. Strauss II: Blauen Donau, Op. 314; Pizzicato Polka;
Rosen aus dem Süden; Auf der Jagd, Op. 373; Tausend
und eine Nacht; G'schichten aus dem Wienerwald, Op.
325; Perpetuum mobile; Wiener Blut; Egyptischer Marsch,
Op. 335; Frühlingsstimmen, Op. 410. (VPO/W.
Boskovsky)

ⓘ **430 511-2DH** (9/91)
R. Strauss—Lieder
R. Strauss: Vier letzte Lieder; Lieder, Op. 21 (exc); Lieder,
Op. 10 (exc); Lieder, Op. 27 (exc); Lieder, Op. 36 (exc);
Lieder, Op. 15 (exc); Malven; Lieder, Op. 43 (exc); Lieder,
Op. 69 (exc); Lieder, Op. 17 (exc). (K. Te Kanawa, VPO/G.
Solti, G. Solti)

ⓘ **430 512-2DH** (9/92)
Liszt—Lieder - Fassbaender
Liszt: O lieb so lang du lieben kannst, S298; Freudvoll und
Leidvoll, S280; Mignons Lied, S275; Es war ein König in
Thule, S278; Über allen Gipfeln ist Ruh, S306; Du von der
Himmel bist, S279/2; Ich möchte hingehn, S296; Und wir
dachten der Toten, S338; Lasst mich ruhen, S317; Blume
und Duft, S324; Du bist wie eine Blume, S287; Am Rhein,
S272; Was Liebe sei, S288; Hohe Liebe, S307; Einst,
S332; Wieder möcht' ich dir begegnen, S322; Ihr Auge,
S310; Drei Zigeuner, S320. (B. Fassbaender, J-Y.
Thibaudet)

ⓘ **430 513-2DH** (12/91)
Mozart—Arias
Mozart: Nozze di Figaro (exc); Chi sà, K582; Così fan tutte
(exc); Alma grande e nobil core, K578; Don Giovanni (exc);
Clemenza di Tito (exc); Ch'io mi scordi di te, K505. (C.
Bartoli, A. Schiff, Vienna CO/G. Fischer)

ⓘ **430 518-2DH** (4/91)
Cecilia Bartoli—Rossini Recital
Rossini: Pastorella; Beltà crudele; Trovatore; Péchés de
vieillesse II (exc); Péchés de vieillesse I (exc); Mi lagnerò
tacendo; Pompadour; Ariette à l'ancienne; Nizza; Âme
délaissée; Canzonetta spagnuola; Giovanna d'Arco; Anon:
Légende de Marguérite. (C. Bartoli, C. Spencer)

ⓘ **430 542-2DH** (7/91)
20th Century American Works
Gershwin: Piano Concerto; Preludes; Copland: Salón
México; Piano Blues (exc); Barber: Ballade. (P. Jablonski,
RPO/Vladimir Ashkenazy)

ⓘ **430 628-2DH2** (5/92)
Villa-Lobos—Piano Concertos
Villa-Lobos: Piano Concerto 1; Piano Concerto 2; Piano
Concerto 3; Piano Concerto 4; Piano Concerto 5. (C. Ortiz,
RPO/M.A. Gómez-Martínez)

ⓘ **430 633-2DM** (2/92)
Haydn—Concertos
Haydn: Cello Concerto in C; Horn Concerto 1; Horn
Concerto 2; Trumpet Concerto. (M. Rostropovich, B.
Tuckwell, A. Stringer, ECO/B. Britten, ASMF/N. Marriner)

ⓘ **430 703-2DM** (8/91)
Spanish Orchestral Works
Rodrigo: Concierto de Aranjuez; Falla: Amor Brujo (exc);
Nights in the Gardens of Spain. (C. Bonell, A. de Larrocha,
Montreal SO/C. Dutoit, LPO/R. Frühbeck de Burgos)

ⓘ **430 705-2DM** (8/91)
Copland—Orchestral Works
Copland: Salón México; Appalachian Spring Suite; Rodeo;
Dance Symphony; Fanfare for the Common Man. (Detroit
SO/A. Dorati)

ⓘ **430 706-2DM** (8/91)
Popular Baroque Works
Pachelbel: Canon and Gigue (exc); Albinoni: Adagio;
Bach: Suites, BWV1066-9 (exc); Handel: Organ Concertos
(exc). (Stuttgart CO/K. Münchinger)

ⓘ **430 707-2DM** (8/91)
Tchaikovsky—Ballet Music
Tchaikovsky: Swan Lake Suite; Nutcracker Suite; Romeo
and Juliet. (Chicago SO/G. Solti)

ⓘ **430 710-2DM** (8/91)
Organ Spectacular
Widor: Symphony 5 (exc); Karg-Elert: Choral-
Improvisationen, Op. 65 (exc); Franck: Chorales (exc);
Bach: Toccata and Fugue, BWV565; Mendelssohn:
Midsummer Night's Dream (exc); Widor: Symphony 6
(exc); Boëllmann: Suite gothique; Liszt: Fantasia and
Fugue, S529. (P. Hurford)

ⓘ **430 714-2DM** (8/91)
Ravel—Orchestral Works
Ravel: Boléro; La Valse; Daphnis et Chloé Suites (exc);
Pavane. (Montreal SO/C. Dutoit)

ⓘ **430 716-2DM** (8/91)
Pavarotti—Gala Concert at the Albert Hall
Puccini: Tosca (exc); Turandot (exc); De Curtis: Torna a
Surriento; Verdi: Macbeth (exc); Giorno di Regno (exc);
Lombardi (exc); Luisa Miller (exc); Donizetti: Lucia di
Lammermoor (exc); Cilea: Arlesiana (exc); Berlioz:
Troyens (exc). (L. Pavarotti, RPO/K.H. Adler)

ⓘ **430 721-2DM** (12/91)
Beethoven—Orchestral Works
Beethoven: Symphony 6; Egmont (exc); Leonore (exc).
(Philh/Vladimir Ashkenazy)

ⓘ **430 724-2DM** (12/91)
Great Operatic Duets
Verdi: Traviata (exc); Puccini: Tosca (exc); Ponchielli:
Gioconda (exc); Bellini: Norma (exc); Verdi: Ballo in
maschera (exc); Puccini: Manon Lescaut (exc); Verdi:
Otello (exc). (J. Sutherland, L. Pavarotti, K. Te Kanawa, G.
Aragall, M. Caballé, A. Baltsa, S. Milnes, M. Price, J.
Carreras, London Op Chor, National PO, Bologna Teatro
Comunale Orch, NYC Op Orch/R. Bonynge/G. Solti/B.
Bartoletti/R. Chailly)

ⓘ **430 726-2DM** (12/91)
Popular Works for Piano and Orchestra
Gershwin: Rhapsody in Blue; Addinsell: Warsaw Concerto;
Litolff: Concerto symphonique, Op. 102 (exc); Gottschalk:
Grande fantaisie triumphal; Liszt: Hungarian Fantasia,
S123. (K. Labèque, M. Labèque, Cleveland Orch/R.
Chailly, C. Ortiz, RPO/M. Atzmon, J. Bolet, LSO/I.
Fischer)

ⓘ **430 727-2DM** (12/91)
Janáček/Shostakovich—Orchestral Works
Janáček: Sinfonietta; Taras Bulba; Shostakovich: Age of
Gold Suite. (VPO/C. Mackerras, LPO/B. Haitink)

ⓘ **430 729-2DM** (8/94)
Respighi—Orchestral Works
Respighi: Pines of Rome; Fountains of Rome; Roman
Festivals. (Montreal SO/C. Dutoit)

ⓘ **430 732-2DM** (8/91)
Debussy—Orchestral Works
Debussy: La Mer; Nocturnes; Après-midi. (Cleveland
Orch/Vladimir Ashkenazy, Cleveland Orch Chor)

ⓘ **430 737-2DM** (8/92)
Sibelius—Orchestral Works
Sibelius: Symphony 2; Karelia Suite; Finlandia.
(Philh/Vladimir Ashkenazy)

ⓘ **430 757-2DM** (7/93)
Sibelius—Orchestral Works
Sibelius: Finlandia; Karelia Suite; Tapiola; En Saga;
Luonnotar. (E. Söderström, Philh/Vladimir Ashkenazy)

① **430 759-2DM** (7/93)
Piano Favourites
Beethoven: Bagatelles (exc); Piano Sonata 14; *Chopin:*
Mazurkas (exc); Nocturnes (exc); Polonaises (exc);
Waltzes (exc); *Mussorgsky:* Pictures (exc); *Ravel:* Pavane
pour une infante défunte; *Schumann:* Arabeske;
Kinderszenen (exc); *Liadov:* Musical snuffbox, Op. 32.
(Vladimir Ashkenazy)

① **430 773-2DC4** (4/92)
Schubert—Complete Symphonies, etc
Schubert: Symphony 1; Symphony 2; Symphony 3;
Symphony 4; Symphony 5; Symphony 6; Symphony 8;
Symphony 9; Overture, D591; Teufels Lustschloss (exc);
Fierrabras (exc). (VPO/I. Kertész)

① **430 778-2DC3** (2/92)
Sibelius—Symphonies
Sibelius: Symphony 1; Symphony 2; Symphony 3;
Symphony 4; Symphony 5; Symphony 6; Symphony 7.
(VPO/L. Maazel)

① **430 787-2DC4** (4/92)
Tchaikovsky—Symphonies
Tchaikovsky: Symphony 1; Symphony 2; Symphony 3;
Symphony 4; Symphony 5; Symphony 6; Romeo and
Juliet. (VPO/L. Maazel)

① **430 792-2DC6** (4/92)
Beethoven—Complete Symphonies, etc
Beethoven: Symphony 1; Symphony 2; Symphony 3;
Symphony 4; Symphony 5; Symphony 6; Symphony 7;
Symphony 8; Symphony 9; Egmont (exc); Coriolan;
Leonore (exc). (P. Lorengar, Y. Minton, S. Burrows, M.
Talvela, Chicago Sym Chor, Chicago SO/G. Solti)

① **430 799-2DC4** (4/92)
Brahms—Complete Symphonies, etc
Brahms: Symphony 1; Symphony 2; Symphony 3;
Symphony 4; Academic Festival Overture; Tragic Overture.
(Chicago SO/G. Solti)

① **430 804-2DC10** (4/92)
Mahler—Complete Symphonies
Mahler: Symphony 1; Symphony 2; Symphony 3;
Symphony 4; Symphony 5; Symphony 6; Symphony 7;
Symphony 8; Symphony 9. (K. Te Kanawa, H. Harper, A.
Auger, L. Popp, I. Buchanan, H. Dernesch, M. Zakai, Y.
Minton, H. Watts, R. Kollo, J. Shirley-Quirk, M. Talvela,
Vienna Boys' Ch, Vienna St Op Chor, Vienna Singverein,
Chicago Sym Chor, Glen Ellyn Children's Chor, Chicago
SO/G. Solti)

① **430 839-2DH** (5/92)
Virtuoso Guitar Transcriptions
Rachmaninov: Preludes (exc); *Falla:* Vida Breve (exc);
Albéniz: Suite española 1 (exc); *Sarasate:* Danzas
españolas (exc); *Paganini:* Caprices, Op. 1 (exc);
Paradies: Siciliene; *Bach:* Solo Violin Partitas and
Sonatas (exc). (N. Hall)

① **430 843-2DH** (11/91)
Scriabin—Orchestral Works
Scriabin: Symphony 3; Poème de l'extase; Rêverie, Op.
24. (Berlin RSO/Vladimir Ashkenazy)

① **433 010-2DM** (12/91)
Christmas Stars
Traditional: Joy to the World; Twelve Days of Christmas;
Greensleeves (What Child is this?); Good King Wenceslas;
O come, all ye faithful; *Schubert:* Ave Maria, D839;
Schubert/Melichar: Mille cherubini in coro; *Gounod:*
Repentir; *Adam:* Minuit, Chrétiens (exc); *Yon:* Gesù
Bambino; *Traditional:* Stille Nacht; Angels from the realms
of glory; Sweet little Jesus boy; *Gounod:* Ave Maria;
Traditional: Hark! the Herald Angels sing. (J. Sutherland,
Ambrosian Sngrs, New Philh/R. Bonynge, R. Tebaldi/A.
Guadagno, L. Pavarotti, National PO/K.H. Adler, K. Te
Kanawa, Philh/Carl Davis, L. Price, VPO/H. von Karajan,
P. Clark, London Voices)

① **433 042-2DH** (5/93)
Mozart—Piano Works
Mozart: Piano Concerto 8; Piano Concerto 11; Rondo,
K386. (A. Schiff, Salzburg Mozarteum Camerata
Academica/S. Végh)

① **433 070-2DWO** (10/91)
World of Chopin
Chopin: Waltzes (exc); Nocturnes (exc); Etudes (exc);
Waltzes (exc); Polonaises (exc); Etudes (exc); Berceuse;
Piano Sonata 2 (exc); Polonaises (exc); Preludes (exc);
Mazurkas (exc); Nocturnes (exc); Fantaisie-impromptu;
Etudes (exc). (J. Bolet, Vladimir Ashkenazy, W. Kempff, J.
Katchen, A. de Larrocha)

① **433 078-2DM6** (6/92)
Shostakovich—String Quartets
Shostakovich: String Quartet 1; String Quartet 2; String
Quartet 3; String Quartet 4; String Quartet 5; String
Quartet 6; String Quartet 7; String Quartet 8; String
Quartet 9; String Quartet 10; String Quartet 11; String
Quartet 12; String Quartet 13; String Quartet 14; String
Quartet 15. (Fitzwilliam Qt)

① **433 079-2DM** (5/92)
Stravinsky—Orchestral Works
Stravinsky: Fairy's Kiss Divertimento; Suites; Histoire du
soldat Suite; Octet. (London Sinfonietta/R. Chailly)

① **433 080-2DM** (8/92)
Kodály—Choral Works
Kodály: Psalmus Hungaricus; Missa brevis; Pange lingua;
Psalm 114. (E. Gale, S. le Sage, H. Francis, A. Hodgson,
L. Kozma, I. Caley, M. Rippon, G. Weir, C. Bowers-
Broadbent, Brighton Fest Chor, Wandsworth Sch Boys'
Ch, LSO/L. Heltay/I. Kertész)

① **433 081-2DM** (9/92)
Hindemith—Orchestral Works
Hindemith: Violin Concerto; Symphonic Metamorphosis;
Mathis der Maler. (D. Oistrakh, LSO/P. Hindemith/C.
Abbado, SRO/P. Kletzki)

① **433 174-2DM** (5/92)
Monteverdi—Choral Works
Monteverdi: Madrigals, Bk.6 (exc); Madrigals, Bk 8 (exc);
Ballo delle ingrate; Madrigals, Bk.5 (exc); Selva morale e
spirituale (exc). (Schütz Consort, H. Schütz Ch/R.
Norrington)

① **433 175-2DM** (5/92)
Bach—Sacred Choral Works
Bach: Cantata 67; Cantata 130; Magnificat, BWV243. (E.
Ameling, H. van Bork, H. Watts, W. Krenn, T. Krause,
Vienna Academy Ch, Stuttgart CO/K. Münchinger,
Lausanne Pro Arte Ch, SRO/E. Ansermet)

① **433 220-2DWO** (5/92)
The World of the Violin
Massenet: Thaïs (exc); *Elgar:* Salut d'amour; Capricieuse;
Saint-Saëns: Introduction and Rondo capriccioso; *Prince
Albert:* Melody for the Violin; *Wieniawski:* Scherzo-
tarantelle, Op. 16; *Sarasate:* Danzas españolas (exc);
Beethoven: Romances (exc); *Kreisler:* Liebesfreud;
Liebesleid; Schön Rosmarin; *Falla:* Vida breve (exc);
Paganini: Caprices, Op. 1 (exc); *Vecsey:* Vent; *Sarasate:*
Zigeunerweisen. (N. Kennedy, National PO/R. Bonynge, K-
W. Chung, P. Moll, RPO/C. Dutoit, I. Brown, J. Partridge,
A. Campoli, D. Ibbott, W. Boskovsky (vn/dir), Vienna
Mozart Ens, R. Holmes, J. Walker, R. Ricci, E. Lush,
LSO/P. Gamba)

① **433 313-2DH2** (10/93)
Bach—Keyboard Works
Bach: French Suites, BWV812-17; Italian Concerto,
BWV971; French Overture, BWV831. (A. Schiff)

① **433 316-2DH** (9/92)
Verismo Arias - Mirella Freni
Cilea: Arlesiana (exc); Adriana Lecouvreur (exc);
Giordano: Andrea Chénier (exc); *Catalani:* Wally (exc);
Loreley (exc); *Alfano:* Risurrezione (exc); *Zandonai:*
Francesca da Rimini (exc); *Puccini:* Gianni Schicchi (exc);
Mascagni: Cavalleria Rusticana (exc); Lodoletta (exc); Iris
(exc). (M. Freni, Venice La Fenice Orch/B. Abbado)

① **433 400-2DM2** (6/93)
Ravel & Debussy—Stage Works
Ravel: L'enfant et les Sortilèges (Cpte); *Debussy:* Martyre
de St Sébastien (Cpte); *Ravel:* Heure espagnole (Cpte).
(F. Wend, M-L. de Montmollin, G. Touraine, A. Migliette, S.
Danco, J. Bise, G. Bobillier, L. Lovano, P. Mollet, H.
Cuénod, Geneva Motet Ch, SRO/E. Ansermet, S. Danco,
N. Waugh, M-L. de Montmollin, Peilz Chor Union, S.
Danco, P. Derenne, M. Hamel, H. Rehfuss, A. Vessières)

① **433 437-2DA** (12/93)
Pavarotti—King of the High Cs
Bellini: Puritani (exc); *Donizetti:* Fille du Régiment (exc);
Favorita (exc); *Puccini:* Bohème (exc); *Rossini:* Guillaume
Tell (exc); *R. Strauss:* Rosenkavalier (exc); *Verdi:*
Trovatore (exc). (A. Auger, G. Flossmann, L. Pavarotti, P.
Baillie, R. Bunger, H. Lackner, E. Garrett, ROH Chor &
Orch, L. Pavarotti, M. de Montmollin, G. Touraine (exc); L.
Pavarotti, Vienna Op Chor, ROHO, Vienna Op Orch, BPO, VPO/R.
Bonynge/E. Downes/N. Rescigno/H. von Karajan/G. Solti)

① **433 439-2DM** (12/93)
Great Love Duets
Puccini: Bohème (exc); Madama Butterfly (exc); *Manon
Lescaut* (exc); Tosca (exc); *Verdi:* Otello (exc); Traviata
(exc). (J. Sutherland, R. Tebaldi, M. Freni, M. Price, C.
Ludwig, L. Pavarotti, F. Corelli, C. Cossutta, R. Panerai, G.
Maffeo, N. Ghiaurov, R. van Allan, National PO, VPO,
BPO, SRO/R. Bonynge/G. Solti/H. von Karajan/A.
Guadagno/N. Rescigno)

① **433 470-2DM** (6/92)
Ferrier Edition - Volume 3
Gluck: Orfeo ed Euridice (exc); *Handel:* Rodelinda (exc);

① **430 471-2DM** (6/92)
Ferrier Edition - Volume 4
Schumann: Frauenliebe und -leben, Op. 42 (Cpte); Lieder
und Gesänge, Op. 51 (exc); Myrthen, Op. 25 (exc);
Schubert: Gretchen am Spinnrade, D118; Junge Nonne,
D828; An die Musik, D547; Musensohn, D764; Ganymed,
D544; Du liebst mich nicht, D756; Lachen und Weinen,
D777; *Traditional:* Stille Nacht; O come all ye faithful. (K.
Ferrier, J. Newmark, P. Spurr, B. Britten, Boyd Neel
Orch/R. Neel)

① **433 473-2DM** (6/92)
Ferrier Edition - Volume 6
Stanford: Irish Idyll, Op. 77 (exc); Songs, Op. 140 (exc);
Parry: English Lyrics, Set 6 (exc); *Vaughan Williams:*
House of Life (exc); *Bridge:* Go not, happy day; *Warlock:*
Sleep; Pretty Ring Time; *Britten:* Folk Songs (exc);
Traditional: Kitty, my love; *Purcell:* Bess of Bedlam, Z370;
Fairy Queen, Z629 (exc); *Handel:* Atalanta (exc); Admeto
(exc); *Wolf:* Mörike Lieder (exc); *Jensen:* Altar; *Bach:*
Sacred Songs, BWV489-507 (exc); Sacred Songs,
BWV439-488 (exc); Anna Magdalena Notenbuch (1725)
(exc). (K. Ferrier, F. Stone, P. Spurr, M. Silver, J.
Newmark)

① **433 474-2DM** (6/92)
Ferrier Edition - Volume 7
Bach: Mass in B minor, BWV232 (exc); St Matthew
Passion, BWV244 (exc); St John Passion, BWV245 (exc);
Handel: Samson (exc); Messiah (exc); Judas Maccabaeus
(exc). (K. Ferrier, LPO/A. Boult)

① **433 475-2DM** (6/92)
Ferrier Edition - Volume 8
Anon: My bonny lad; *Traditional:* Keel row; Blow the wind
southerly; I have a bonnet trimmed with blue; My boy
Willie; I know where I'm going; Fidgety bairn; I will walk
with my love; *Britten:* Folk Songs (exc); *Traditional:* Willow,
willow; *Anon:* Stuttering lovers; *Quilter:* Songs, Op. 3 (exc);
Elizabethan Lyrics, Op. 12 (exc); To Julia (exc); *Arnold
Book of Old Songs* (exc); *Traditional:* Have you seen the
whyte lillie grow?; Ye banks and braes; Drink to me only; H.
Hughes: Down by the Salley Gardens; *Traditional:* Lover's
curse. (K. Ferrier, J. Newmark, P. Spurr)

① **433 476-2DM** (6/92)
Ferrier Edition - Volume 9
Schubert: Junge Nonne, D828; Rosamunde (exc); Du
liebst mich nicht, D756; Tod und das Mädchen, D531;
Suleika I, D720; Du bist die Ruh, D776; *Brahms:* Lieder,
Op.105 (exc); Lieder, Op.96 (exc); Lieder, Op.47 (exc);
Lieder, Op.43 (exc); *Schumann:* Frauenliebe und -Leben,
Op.42 (Cpte). (K. Ferrier, B. Walter)

① **433 477-2DM** (6/92)
Ferrier Edition - Volume 10
Brahms: Alto Rhapsody, Op. 53; Lieder, Op.91; *Mahler:*
Rückert Lieder (exc). (K. Ferrier, LP Ch, LPO/C. Krauss,
M. Gilbert, P. Spurr, VPO/B. Walter)

① **433 515-2DH2** (11/92)
Ravel—Solo Piano Works
Ravel: Sérénade grotesque; Menuet antique; Pavane pour
une infante défunte; Jeux d'eau; Sonatine; Miroirs;
Gaspard de la nuit; Menuet sur le nom de Haydn; Valses
nobles et sentimentales; Prélude; A la manière de
Borodine; A la manière de Chabrier; Tombeau de
Couperin. (J-Y. Thibaudet)

① **433 519-2DH** (1/92)
Works for Violin and Orchestra
Saint-Saëns: Introduction and Rondo capriccioso;
Massenet: Thaïs (exc); *Sarasate:* Zigeunerweisen;
Chausson: Poème; *Ravel:* Tzigane; *Ysaÿe:* Caprice
d'après l'Étude. (J. Bell, RPO/A. Litton)

① **433 612-2DSP** (1/92)
Prokofiev—Popular Orchestral Works
Prokofiev: Peter and the Wolf; Symphony 1; Lt. Kijé Suite;
Love for 3 Oranges Suite (exc). (R. Richardson, LSO/M.
Sargent, Paris Cons/A. Boult, LPO/W. Weller)

① **433 616-2DSP** (1/92)
Addinsell/Gershwin—Orchestral Works
Addinsell: Warsaw Concerto; *Gershwin:* Cuban Overture;
Rhapsody in Blue; I Got Rhythm Variations; American in
Paris. (C. Ortiz, RPO/M. Atzmon, Cleveland Orch/L.
Maazel, S. Black (pf/dir), London Fest Orch, D. Parkhouse,
London Fest Rec Ens/S. Black, Herrmann/S. Black)

① **433 625-2DSP** (1/92)
Stokowski conducts Famous Russian Works
Tchaikovsky: Marche Slave; *Borodin:* Prince Igor (exc);

Mussorgsky: Night on the bare mountain; *Rimsky-Korsakov:* Capriccio espagnol; *Tchaikovsky:* 1812. (LSO, Royal Phil Chor, WNO Chor, RPO, New Philh, Grenadier Guards Band/L. Stokowski)

Ⓒ **433 628-2DSP** (1/92)
Franck/Grieg/Schumann—Piano & Orchestral Works
Grieg: Piano Concerto; *Franck:* Symphonic Variations; *Schumann:* Piano Concerto. (C. Curzon, LSO/Ø. Fjeldstad, LPO/A. Boult, F. Gulda, VPO/V. Andreae)

Ⓒ **433 651-2DH** (6/93)
Shura Cherkassky Live, Vol.3
Paderewski: Humoresques de concert, Op.14 (exc); *Tchaikovsky:* Songs, Op.6 (exc); *Chopin:* Waltzes (exc); *Rachmaninov:* Polka de W.R.; Morceaux de fantaisie, Op.3 (exc); *Shostakovich:* Golden Age Polka; *Scriabin:* Pieces, Op.2 (exc); *Balakirev:* Islamey; *Cherkassky:* Prélude pathétique; *Sinding:* Rustle of Spring, Op.32/3; *Albéniz:* España, Op.165 (exc); *Mozart:* Piano Sonata, K331 (exc); *Debussy:* Arabesques (exc); *Rebikov:* Christmas Tree; *Moszkowski:* Liebeswalzer, Op.57/5; *Sibelius:* Pieces, Op.24 (exc). (S. Cherkassky)

Ⓒ **433 652-2DH** (1/95)
Shura Cherkassky Live, Volume 6
Schumann: Carnaval; Fantasiestücke, Op. 111; Symphonic Studies. (S. Cherkassky)

Ⓒ **433 653-2DH** (10/91)
Shura Cherkassky Live
Albéniz: España, Op.165 (exc); *Chopin:* Ballades (exc); Etudes (exc); Preludes (exc); Nocturnes (exc); *Rachmaninov:* Polka de W. R.; *Rubinstein:* Melodies, Op.3 (exc); *Schubert:* Piano Sonata, D664; Moments musicaux, D780 (exc); *Scriabin:* Preludes, Op.11 (exc). (S. Cherkassky)

Ⓒ **433 654-2DH** (1/93)
Cherkassky Live - 80th Birthday Recital
Bach: Solo Violin Partitas and Sonatas (exc); *Schumann:* Symphonic Studies; *Chopin:* Nocturnes (exc); Tarantelle; *Ives:* Three Page Sonata; *Hofmann:* Kaleidoskop, Op.40; *Pabst:* Eugene Onegin Paraphrase; *Gould:* Boogie Woogie Etude. (S. Cherkassky)

Ⓒ **433 656-2DH** (1/95)
Shura Cherkassky Live, Volume 5
Liszt: Fantasia and Fugue, S463; Piano Sonata, S178; Hungarian Rhapsodies, S244 (exc); Liebesträume, S541 (exc). (S. Cherkassky)

Ⓒ **433 660-2DH** (3/93)
Martinů—Orchestral Works
Martinů: La Jolla; Rêvue de Cuisine (1927); Toccata e due canzoni; Merry Christmas 1941; Ricercari. (St Paul CO/C. Hogwood)

Ⓒ **433 675-2DM** (10/92)
Byrd—Three Masses
Byrd: Mass for three voices; Mass for four voices; Mass for five voices. (King's College Ch/D. Willcocks)

Ⓒ **433 676-2DM** (10/92)
Tallis—Choral Works
Tallis: Spem in alium; In manus tuas; In jejunio et fletu; Te lucis ante terminum I; Te lucis ante terminum II; Ecce tempus idoneum; Veni Redemptor gentium; O nata lux; Salvator mundi I; Derelinquat impius; Videte miraculum; Organ Lesson; Sancte Deus, sancte fortis. (CUMS, King's College Ch, A. Davis/D. Willcocks)

Ⓒ **433 677-2DM** (10/92)
Gibbons—Sacred Works
Gibbons: Now shall the praises of the Lord; Preces and Psalm 145; Second Service (exc); This is the record of John; See, see, the word is incarnate; Glorious and powerful God; Short Service (exc); Almighty and everlasting God; O Lord in Thy wrath; Hosanna to the Son of David; Loosemore: O Lord, increase my faith; *Gibbons:* O clap your hands. (King's College Ch, Jacobean Consort of Viols, S. Preston, H. McLean/D. Willcocks/B. Ord)

Ⓒ **433 678-2DH** (10/92)
Palestrina—Masses
Palestrina: Assumpta est Maria a 6; Missa Assumpta est Maria; Antiphon—Veni sponsa Christi; Motet—Veni sponsa Christi; Missa Veni sponsa Christi; Magnificat VI toni. (St John's College Ch/G. Guest)

Ⓒ **433 695-2DM** (9/92)
Chamber Works
Franck: Violin Sonata; *Brahms:* Horn Trio; *Schumann:* Adagio and Allegro, Op. 70; *Saint-Saëns:* Romance, Op. 67. (I. Perlman, B. Tuckwell, Vladimir Ashkenazy)

Ⓒ **433 702-2DH** (3/93)
Shostakovich—Orchestral Works
Shostakovich: Piano Concerto 1; Jazz Suite 1; Jazz Suite 2; Taiti Trot. (P. Masseurs, R. Brautigam, Concertgebouw/R. Chailly)

Ⓒ **433 706-2DMO3** (2/93)
Bellini—Beatrice di Tenda; Operatic Arias
Bellini: Beatrice di Tenda (Cpte); Norma (exc); Puritani (exc); Sonnambula (exc). (J. Sutherland, L. Pavarotti, C. Opthof, J. Veasey, J. Ward, J. Sutherland, M. Elkins, P. Duval, N. Monti, R. Capecchi, R. Cross, E. Flagello, F. Corena, London Sym Chor, MMF Chor, Ambrosian Op Chor, LSO, MMF Orch/R. Bonynge)

Ⓒ **433 710-2DH** (12/91)
O Holy Night
Adam: Minuit, Chrétiens (exc); *Niedermeyer:* Pietà, Signore; *Franck:* Panis angelicus; *Mercadante:* Sette ultime parole (exc); *Schubert:* Ave Maria, D839; *Yon:* Gesù, bambino; *Gluck:* Orfeo ed Euridice (exc); *Rossini:* Stabat Mater (exc); *Verdi:* Requiem (exc); *Gounod:* Ave Maria; *Schubert/Melichar:* Mille cherubini in coro; *Bizet:* Agnus Dei; *Berlioz:* Grande messe des morts (exc); *Traditional:* O come, all ye faithful. (L. Pavarotti, National PO/K.H. Adler, Philh/P. Gamba, LSO/I. Kertész, VPO/G. Solti, Wandsworth Sch Boys' Ch, London Voices)

Ⓒ **433 727-2DM** (7/93)
Clarinet Concertos
Mozart: Clarinet Concerto, K622; *Weber:* Clarinet Concerto 2; *Spohr:* Clarinet Concerto 1. (G. de Peyer, LSO/P. Maag/Colin Davis)

Ⓒ **433 729-2DM** (5/93)
Mendelssohn—Orchestral Works
Mendelssohn: 2-Piano Concerto in E; Piano Concerto (1822); String Symphony 12. (J. Ogdon, B. Lucas, ASMF/N. Marriner)

Ⓒ **433 809-2DH** (4/93)
Hindemith—Orchestral Works
Hindemith: Nobilissima visione; Schwanendreher; Concert Music, Op. 50. (G. Walther, San Francisco SO/H. Blomstedt)

Ⓒ **433 816-2DH2** (11/92)
Hindemith—Kammermusik
Hindemith: Kammermusik, Op. 24/1; Kleine Kammermusik, Op. 24/2; Kammermusik, Op. 36/1; Kammermusik, Op. 36/2; Kammermusik, Op. 36/3; Kammermusik, Op. 36/4; Kammermusik, Op. 46/1; Kammermusik, Op. 46/2. (K. Kulka, K. Kashkashian, N. Blume, L. Harrell, R. Brautigam, L. Van Doeselaar, Concertgebouw/R. Chailly)

Ⓒ **433 829-2DH** (2/93)
Stravinsky—Works for Two Pianos
Stravinsky: 2-Piano Sonata; Concerto for two solo pianos; Rite of Spring; Scherzo. (Vladimir Ashkenazy, A. Gavrilov)

Ⓒ **433 868-2DWO** (2/93)
The World of Gilbert & Sullivan - Volume 2
Sullivan: HMS Pinafore (exc); Mikado (exc); Patience (exc); Iolanthe (exc); Gondoliers (exc); Ruddigore (exc); Sorcerer (exc); Yeomen of the Guard (exc); Princess Ida (exc); Pirates of Penzance (exc). (J. Hindmarsh, J. Wright, P.A. Jones, V. Masterson, P. Wales, J. Toye, M. Sansom, A. Hood, E. Harwood, G. Knight, L. Holland, C. Palmer, J. Allister, T. Round, C. Wright, P. Potter, J. Skitch, D. Adams, J. Reed, K. Sandford, M. Rayner, A. Styler, T. Lawlor, A. Raffell, G. Cook, D'Oyly Carte Op Chor, New SO, RPO, ROHO/I. Godfrey/R. Nash/M. Sargent)

Ⓒ **433 869-2DWO** (2/93)
The World of the Harp
Albéniz: Recuerdos de viaje (exc); Piezás caracteristicas (exc); *Bach:* Wohltemperierte Klavier (exc); *Beethoven:* Variations, WoO64; *Bidaola:* Viejo zortzico; *Brahms:* Lieder, Op. 49 (exc); *Britten:* Ceremony of Carols (exc); *Chopin:* Mazurkas (exc); Preludes (exc); *Eberl:* Theme, Variations and Rondo Pastorale; *Falla:* Sombrero de tres picos (exc); *Fauré:* Impromptu, Op. 86; *Hasselmans:* Source, Op. 44; *Pierné:* Impromptu-caprice, Op. 9; *Salzedo:* Chanson dans la nuit. (M. Robles)

Ⓒ **433 908-2DM2** (9/92)
Falla—Orchestral Music
Falla: Amor Brujo (Cpte); Vida breve (exc); Sombrero de tres picos (Cpte); Nights in the Gardens of Spain; Retablo de maese Pedro (Cpte); Psyché; Harpsichord Concerto. (P. Lorengar, J. Smith, J. Smith, K. Te Kanawa, T. Berganza, M. de Gabarain, M. Horne, N. Jenkins, A. Oliver, P. Knapp, A. de Larrocha, R. Vignoles, Martin Katz, F. Lavilla, J. Constable, Ambrosian Sngrs, LPO/R. Frühbeck de Burgos/J. López-Cobos, London Sinfonietta/S. Rattle, SRO/E. Ansermet)

Ⓒ **433 911-2DM2** (6/93)
Spanish Orchestral Music, Vol 3
Glinka: Jota aragonesa; *Rimsky-Korsakov:* Capriccio Espagnol; *Massenet:* Danzas españolas; *Lalo:* Symphonie Espagnole; *Chabrier:* España; *Debussy:* Images (exc); *Ravel:* Rapsodie espagnole; Alborada del gracioso; Boléro. (SRO/E. Ansermet, LSO/A. Argenta, R. Ricci)

Ⓒ **433 920-2DM2** (9/92)
Spanish Piano Works, Vol.1
Soler: Keyboard Sonatas I (exc); Keyboard Sonatas II (exc); *M. Albéniz:* Sonata in D; *Granados:* Goyescas; Piezas sobre cantos populares españoles; Escenas románticas. (A. de Larrocha)

Ⓒ **433 923-2DM2** (9/92)
Spanish Piano Works, Vol.2
Granados: Danzas españolas; Allegro de concierto; *Albéniz:* Suite española 1; Suite española 2; Cantos de España. (A. de Larrocha)

Ⓒ **433 926-2DM2** (9/92)
Spanish Piano Works, Vol.3
Albéniz: Iberia; Navarra; Recuerdos de viaje (exc); Pavana caprico; España, Op. 165 (exc); *Falla:* Pièces espagnoles; Fantasía bética. (A. de Larrocha)

Ⓒ **433 929-2DM2** (9/92)
Spanish Piano Works, Vol.4
Falla: Sombrero de tres picos; Amor brujo; *Turina:* Danzas Gitanas 1 (exc); Danzas Andaluzas (exc); *Halffter:* Danzas; *Montsalvatge:* Sonatina para Yvette; Divertimento 2; *Nin-Culmell:* Tonadas (exc); *Surinach:* Canciones y Danzas; *Mompou:* Impressions intimes; Larrocha prelude; Musica Callada (exc); Cançons i danses (exc). (A. de Larrocha)

Ⓒ **436 075-2DH** (2/92)
Rossini Heroines
Rossini: Zelmira (exc); Nozze di Teti e di Peleo (exc); Maometto II (exc); Donna del Lago (exc); Elisabetta (exc); Semiramide (exc). (C. Bartoli, Venice La Fenice Chor, Venice La Fenice Orch/I. Martin)

Ⓒ **436 076-2DH** (2/93)
Beethoven—Piano Sonatas
Beethoven: Piano Sonata 30; Piano Sonata 31; Piano Sonata 32. (Vladimir Ashkenazy)

Ⓒ **436 123-2DH** (7/94)
Schumann—Lieder
Schumann: Liederkreis, Op. 39 (Cpte); Gedichte, Op. 90 (Cpte); Lieder, Op. 40 (exc); Lieder und Gesänge, Op. 98a (exc); Lieder und Gesänge, Op. 96 (exc). (R. Holl, A. Schiff)

Ⓒ **436 201-2DM** (8/93)
Schubert—Lieder
Schubert: Schöne Müllerin (Cpte); Schwanengesang, D957 (exc); Einsame, D800; An die Laute, D905. (P. Pears, B. Britten)

Ⓒ **436 202-2DM** (9/94)
Italian Songs
A. Scarlatti: Pompeo (exc); *Bellini:* Malinconia, ninfa gentile; *Cimara:* Stornello; *Donizetti:* Soirées d'automne (exc); *Gluck:* Paride ed Elena (exc); *Mascagni:* Serenata; Tua stella; *Mercadante:* Sposa del marinaro; *Paradis:* M'ha presa alla sua ragna; *Parisotti:* Se tu m'ami; *Ponchielli:* Noi leggevamo insieme; *Puccini:* È l'uccellino; *Ricci:* Carrettiere del Vomero; *Rossini:* Soirées musicales (exc); *Tosti:* Sogno; *Zandonai:* Assiuolo. (R. Tebaldi, R. Bonynge)

Ⓒ **436 204-2DM** (5/94)
Tchaikovsky—Songs
Tchaikovsky: Songs, Op. 6 (exc); Songs, Op. 6 (exc); Songs, Op. 16 (exc); Songs, Op. 16 (exc); Songs, Op. 25 (exc); Songs, Op. 27 (exc); Songs, Op. 28 (exc); Songs, Op. 28 (exc); Songs, Op. 38 (exc); Songs, Op. 47 (exc); Songs, Op. 47 (exc); Songs, Op. 54 (exc); Songs, Op. 60 (exc); Songs, Op. 65 (exc); Songs, Op. 73 (exc); Mezza notte; My genius; Zemfira's song; To forget; Take my heart away. (E. Söderström, Vladimir Ashkenazy)

Ⓒ **436 209-2DH** (8/93)
Pergolesi & Scarlatti—Choral Works
A. Scarlatti: Salve Regina; *Pergolesi:* Stabat Mater; Salve Regina. (J. Anderson, C. Bartoli, Montreal Sinfonietta/C. Dutoit)

Ⓒ **436 210-2DH** (3/94)
Bartók—Orchestral Works
Bartók: Miraculous Mandarin (Cpte); Portraits, Sz37; Divertimento. (Montreal Sym Chor, Montreal SO/C. Dutoit)

Ⓒ **436 224-2DM** (9/93)
Italian Concertos
Albinoni: Concerti, Op. 5 (exc); *Corelli:* Concerti grossi, Op. 6 (exc); Concerti grossi, Op. 6 (exc); *G. Gabrieli:* Canzon IX (1597); *Geminiani:* Concerti grossi, Op. 3 (exc); *Manfredini:* Concerti grossi, Op. 3 (exc); *Torelli:* Concerti musicali, Op. 6 (exc); *Locatelli:* Concerti grossi, Op. 1 (exc). (ASMF/N. Marriner)

ⓘ **436 736-2DH** (2/94)
Liszt—Piano Transcriptions
Liszt: Rigoletto—paraphrase, S434; Valse à capriccio, S401; Faust—paraphrase, S407; Eugene Onegin polonaise, S429; Fliegende Holländer—paraphrase, S440; Tannhäuser—paraphrase, S444; Lohengrin—paraphrase, S446; Tristan und Isolde—paraphrase, S447; Figaro Fantasia, S697. (J.-Y. Thibaudet)

ⓘ **436 762-2DH** (8/94)
Shostakovich—Orchestral & Vocal Works
Shostakovich: Symphony 2; October, Op. 131; Festive Overture; Song of the Forests. (M. Kotliarov, N. Storozhev, Brighton Fest Chor, New London Children's Ch, RPO/Vladimir Ashkenazy)

ⓘ **436 763-2DH** (4/94)
Shostakovich—Orchestral Works
Shostakovich: Symphony 8; Funeral-Triumphal Prelude; Novorossiisk Chimes. (RPO/Vladimir Ashkenazy)

ⓘ **436 798-2DH** (8/94)
Loussier—Concertos
Loussier: Violin Concerto (1988); Trumpet Concerto; Tableaux vénetiens. (J-P. Wallez, G. Touvron, A. Arpino, Prague CO)

ⓘ **436 832-2DH** (8/94)
Rossini—String Sonatas, Volume 2
Rossini: Sonate a quattro (exc); Overture obbligata and contrabasso in D; Sinfonia di Bologna; Sinfonia al Conventello. (Bologna Teatro Comunale Orch/R. Chailly)

ⓘ **436 837-2DH** (10/93)
Stravinsky/Szymanowski—Violin Concertos
Stravinsky: Violin Concerto; *Szymanowski*: Violin Concerto 1; Violin Concerto 2. (C. Juillet, Montreal SO/C. Dutoit)

ⓘ **436 866-2DH** (2/95)
Fauré—Violin and Piano Works
Fauré: Violin Sonata 1; Violin Sonata 2; Morceau de concours; Andante, Op. 75; Romance, Op. 28; Berceuse, Op. 16. (P. Amoyal, P. Rogé)

ⓘ **436 920-2DM** (5/94)
Rachmaninov—Complete Songs
Rachmaninov: Songs, Op. 4 (Cpte); Songs, Op. 8 (Cpte); Songs, Op. 14 (Cpte); Songs, Op. 21 (Cpte); Songs, Op. 26 (Cpte); Songs, Op. 34 (Cpte); Songs, Op. 38 (Cpte); Daisies; Lilacs; At the gate of the Holy abode; Song of the disillusioned; Flower has faded; Do you remember the evening; Were you hiccoughing; I shall tell you nothing; Again you leapt, my heart; April; Twilight has fallen; Powdered Paint; Night; Letter to Stanislavsky; From the Gospel of St John. (E. Söderström, Vladimir Ashkenazy, J. Shirley-Quirk)

ⓘ **436 990-2DWO** (6/93)
The World of Benjamin Britten
Britten: Young Persons Guide; Spring Symphony (exc); Noyes Fludde (exc); Serenade (exc); Billy Budd (exc); Ceremony of Carols (exc); Hymn to the Virgin; War Requiem (exc); Peter Grimes (exc); Folk Songs (exc); Simple Symphony. (ISO/B. Britten, J. Vyvyan, N. Procter, P. Pears, ROH Chor, ROHO, T. Anthony, O. Brannigan, D. Pinto, D. Angadi, S. Alexander, C. Clack, M-T. Pinto, E. O'Donovan, E Suffolk Children's Orch, ECO/N. del Mar, B. Tuckwell, P. Glossop, D. Bowman, G. Dempsey, Ambrosian Op Chor, St John's College Ch/G. Guest, M. Robles, G. Vishnevskaya, Bath Ch, LSC, Highgate Sch Ch, B. Britten)

ⓘ **436 991-2DH** (11/94)
Poulenc—Mélodies
Poulenc: Banalités; Fiançailles pour rire; Bestiaire; Mélodies (1956) (exc); Poèmes de Louise de Vilmorin; Chansons gaillardes; Métamorphoses; Hyde Park; Poèmes Apollinaire (1938) (exc); Ce doux petit visage; Main dominée par le coeur; Miroirs brûlants; Chemins de l'amour; Colloque. (C. Dubosc, G. Cachemaille, P. Rogé)

ⓘ **440 032-2DM** (2/94)
Monteverdi/Gesualdo—Motets and Madrigals
Gesualdo: Sacrarum cantionum (5vv) (exc); O vos omnes; Ecco, morirò dunque; Dolcissima mia vita; Moro, lasso; *Monteverdi*: Cantate Domino II; Domine ne in furore; Adoramus te, Christe; Madrigals, Bk 6 (exc); Madrigals, Bk 5 (exc); Madrigals, Bk 4 (exc). (Monteverdi Ch, A. Davis, C. Van Kampen, S. Carrington/J. E. Gardiner)

ⓘ **440 033-2DM** (9/94)
Harpsichord Concertos
Arne: Favourite Concertos (exc); Overtures in 8 parts (exc); *C. P. E. Bach*: Keyboard Concerto, H441; *Haydn*: Keyboard Concerto, HobXVIII/2; Overture in D, HobIa/7bis; *J. C. Bach*: Keyboard Concerto, T300/1. (G. Malcolm, ASMF/N. Marriner)

ⓘ **440 037-2DM** (1/94)
Bach—Concertos
Bach: Oboe d'amore Concerto, BWV1055; Oboe Concerto, BWV1053; Triple Concerto, BWV1063; 3-Violin Concerto, BWV1064. (W. Bennett, N. Black, C. Kaine, R. Thomas, R. Studt, ASMF/N. Marriner)

ⓘ **440 063-2DM** (9/94)
Britten—Spring Symphony etc
Britten: Spring Symphony; Sea Interludes, Op.33a; Young Person's Guide. (J. Vincent, K. Ferrier, P. Pears, St Willibrord's Boys' Ch, Netherlands Rad Chor, Concertgebouw/E. van Beinum)

ⓘ **440 065-2DM** (1/95)
Schubert/Schumann—Lieder
Schubert: Jüngling und der Tod, D545; Wanderer an den Mond, D870; Schwanengesang, D957 (exc); Schiffer, D536; Ganymed, D544; Erster Verlust, D226; Forelle, D550; Nacht und Träume, D827; Seligkeit, D433; Wer sich der Einsamkeit ergibt, D478; Fischerweise, D881; Erlkönig, D328; *Schumann*: Dichterliebe, Op.48 (Cpte). (G. Souzay, J. Bonneau, D. Baldwin)

ⓘ **440 079-2DM** (10/95)
The Amorous Flute
Anon: Faronells Ground; Bird Fancyer's Delight; Select Preludes and Vollentarys; Recorder Sonata in G; *Dieupart*: Suittes divisées (exc); *D. Purcell*: Sonata in D minor; *N. Matteis I*: Ground after the Scotch Humour; *Parcham*: Solo in G; *Handel*: Recorder Sonatas (exc). (D. Munrow, D. Munrow, O. Brookes, O. Brookes, R. Spencer, R. Spencer, C. Hogwood)

ⓘ **440 229-2DH** (1/94)
Stravinsky—Works for Piano and Orchestra
Stravinsky: Piano and Wind Concerto; Ebony Concerto; Capriccio; Movements. (O. Mustonen, D. Ashkenazy, Berlin Deutsches SO/Vladimir Ashkenazy)

ⓘ **440 281-2DH** (2/94)
Rachmaninov/Scriabin/Prokofiev—Piano Sonatas
Rachmaninov: Piano Sonata 2; *Scriabin*: Piano Sonata 9; Piano Sonata 5; *Prokofiev*: Piano Sonata 7. (P. Jablonski)

ⓘ **440 283-2DH** (10/94)
Liszt—Organ Works
Liszt: Fantasia and Fugue, S259; Variations, S673; Evocation, S658; Prelude and Fugue, S260. (T. Trotter)

ⓘ **440 293-2DH** (3/94)
Works for Guitar and Orchestra
Paganini: Violin Concerto 2; *Castelnuovo-Tedesco*: Guitar Concerto 1; *Sarasate*: Zigeunerweisen. (N. Hall, LMP/A. Litton)

ⓘ **440 297-2DH** (11/93)
Italian Songs
Beethoven: Partenza, WoO124; Ariettas, Op. 82 (exc); In questa tomba oscura, WoO133; *Mozart*: Ridente la calma, K152; *Schubert*: Didone abbandonata, D510; Im Haine, D738; An die Leier, D737; Pastorella al prato, D528; Canzonen, D688; Pensa, che questo istante, D76; Willkommen und Abschied, D767; *Haydn*: Arianna a Naxos. (C. Bartoli, A. Schiff)

ⓘ **440 305-2DH** (12/93)
Schubert—Piano Sonatas
Schubert: Piano Sonata, D840; Piano Sonata, D845; Piano Sonata, D571. (A. Schiff)

ⓘ **440 306-2DH** (12/93)
Schubert—Piano Sonatas
Schubert: Piano Sonata, D566; Piano Sonata, D784; Piano Sonata, D850. (A. Schiff)

ⓘ **440 307-2DH** (6/94)
Schubert—Piano Sonatas
Schubert: Piano Sonata, D557; Piano Sonata, D575; Piano Sonata, D894. (A. Schiff)

ⓘ **440 310-2DH** (6/95)
Schubert—Piano Sonatas
Schubert: Piano Sonata, D960; Piano Sonata, D279; Piano Sonata, D625. (A. Schiff)

ⓘ **440 311-2DH** (11/95)
Schubert—Piano Sonatas, Vol. 7
Schubert: Piano Sonata, D157; Piano Sonata, D459; Piano Sonata, D664. (A. Schiff)

ⓘ **440 317-2DWO** (4/94)
World of British Classics, Volume I
Various: National Anthems (exc); *Elgar*: Pomp and Circumstance Marches; In the South; Cockaigne. (LPO/G. Solti, ASMF/N. Marriner)

ⓘ **440 318-2DWO** (4/94)
World of British Classics, Volume II
Holst: Planets; Perfect Fool (exc); Egdon Heath. (LP Ch, LPO/G. Solti/A. Boult)

ⓘ **440 320-2DWO** (4/94)
World of British Classics, Volume IV
Vaughan Williams: Greensleeves Fantasia; English Folk Song Suite; Tallis Fantasia; Oboe Concerto; Concerto grosso; Romance. (C. Nicklin, T. Reilly, ASMF/N. Marriner)

ⓘ **440 323-2DWO** (4/94)
World of British Classics, Volume V
Delius: First cuckoo; Summer Night on the River; Air and Dance; Koanga (exc); Village Romeo and Juliet (exc); Hassan (exc); Fennimore and Gerda Intermezzo; Song before Sunrise; Sea Drift. (ASMF/N. Marriner, J. Shirley-Quirk, LSC, RPO/R. Hickox)

ⓘ **440 327-2DH** (9/94)
Stravinsky—Orchestral Works
Stravinsky: Dumbarton Oaks; Concerto in D; Apollon musagète (Cpte); Danses concertantes. (Montreal Sinfonietta/C. Dutoit)

ⓘ **440 331-2DH** (1/94)
Prokofiev—Concertos
Prokofiev: Violin Concerto 1; Violin Concerto 2; Love for 3 Oranges Suite. (J. Bell, Montreal SO/C. Dutoit)

ⓘ **440 332-2DH** (6/94)
Ibert—Orchestral Works
Ibert: Bacchanale; Bostoniana; Escales; Flute Concerto; Louisville Concerto; Suite symphonique (1930); Hommage à Mozart. (T. Hutchins, Montreal SO/C. Dutoit)

ⓘ **440 333-2DH** (10/95)
Ravel—Vocal Works
Ravel: Enfant et les sortilèges (Cpte); Shéhérazade; Shéhérazade. (C. Alliot-Lugaz, C. Dubosc, M-F. Lefort, O. Beaupré, C. Carlson, G. Gautier, D. Henry, L. Sarrazin, Montreal SO/C. Dutoit)

ⓘ **440 355-2DH** (8/94)
Rachmaninov—Choral Works
Rachmaninov: Bells; Spring, Op. 20; Russian Songs, Op. 41. (A. Pendachanska, K. Kaludov, S. Leiferkus, Philadelphia Choral Arts Soc, Philadelphia/C. Dutoit)

ⓘ **440 474-2DH** (6/94)
Mozart—Piano Music for Four Hands
Mozart: Piano Duet Sonata, K521; Andante and Variations, K501; Piano Duet Sonata, K497; Adagio and Allegro, K594; Fantasia, K608. (A. Schiff, G. Malcolm)

ⓘ **440 496-2DH** (4/95)
Schumann—Piano Works
Schumann: Humoreske; Kinderszenen; Kreisleriana. (R. Lupu)

ⓘ **440 605-2DH** (12/94)
Mozart/Haydn/Hummel—Works for Oboe
Haydn: Oboe Concerto; *Mozart*: Oboe Concerto, K314; *Hummel*: Introduction, Theme and Variations in F. (E. Rombout, Concertgebouw CO)

ⓘ **440 612-2DF2** (10/95)
Brahms—Piano Concertos, etc
Brahms: Piano Concerto 1; Piano Concerto 2; Handel Variations; Paganini Variations. (J. Katchen, LSO/P. Monteux/J. Ferencsik)

ⓘ **440 618-2DF2** (5/94)
R. Strauss—Tone Poems
R. Strauss: Heldenleben; Also sprach Zarathustra; Don Juan; Till Eulenspiegel; Alpensinfonie. (VPO, Chicago SO, BRSO/G. Solti)

ⓘ **440 621-2DF2** (5/94)
Mozart—Violin Concertos, etc
Mozart: Violin Concerto, K207; Violin Concerto, K211; Violin Concerto, K216; Violin Concerto, K218; Violin Concerto, K219; Rondo, K269; Adagio, K261; Rondo, K373. (M. Fujikawa, RPO/W. Weller)

ⓘ **440 627-2DF2** (12/94)
Beethoven—Symphonies
Beethoven: Symphony 1; Symphony 3; Symphony 6; Symphony 8. (VPO/P. Monteux)

ⓘ **440 679-2DH** (9/94)
Carnaval!
Adam: Pantins de Violette (exc); Si j'étais roi (exc); *Balfe*: Puits d'amour (exc); *Boïeldieu*: Fête au village voisin (exc); *F. David*: Perle du Brésil (exc); *Delibes*: Roi l'a dit (exc); *Grétry*: Fausses apparences (exc); *Hérold*: Pré aux clercs (exc); *Massenet*: Don César de Bazan (exc); *Massé*: Reine Topaze (exc); *Messager*: Madame Chrysanthème (exc); *Offenbach*: Mari à la porte (exc); *A. Thomas*: Songe d'une nuit d'été (exc). (S. Jo, ECO/R. Bonynge)

ⓘ **440 680-2DH** (3/95)
Great Sacred Arias
Handel: Messias, K572 (exc); *Bach*: Christmas Oratorio, BWV248 (exc); St John Passion, BWV245 (exc); St

Matthew Passion, BWV244 (exc); *Mozart:* Litanies, K243 (exc); *Davidde penitente,* K469 (exc); *Haydn:* Schöpfung (exc); *Jahreszeiten* (exc); *Mendelssohn:* Elias (exc). (U. Heilmann, Leipzig Gewandhaus/P. Schreier)

① **440 836-2DF2** (10/94)
Ravel—Piano Works
Ravel: Gaspard de la nuit; Valses nobles et sentimentales; Jeux d'eau; Miroirs; Sonatine; Tombeau de Couperin; Prélude; Menuet sur le nom de Haydn; A la manière de Borodine; Menuet antique; Pavane pour une infante défunte; A la manière de Chabrier; Ma mère l'Oye. (P. Rogé, D-F. Rogé)

① **440 839-2DF2** (9/95)
Beethoven—Piano Concertos, etc
Beethoven: Piano Concerto 3; Piano Concerto 4; Piano Concerto 5; Choral Fantasia. (J. Katchen, London Sym Chor, LSO/P. Gamba)

① **440 853-2DH** (3/94)
Haas/Krása—String Quartets
P. Haas: String Quartet 2; String Quartet 3; *Krása:* String Quartet (1921). (Hawthorne Qt)

① **440 854-2DH** (12/94)
Ullmann—Der Kaiser von Atlantis
Ullmann: Kaiser von Atlantis (Cpte); Abendphantasie; Frühling; Wo bist du. (M. Kraus, F. Mazura, M. Petzold, C. Oelze, W. Berry, H. Lippert, I. Vermillion, Leipzig Gewandhaus/L. Zagrosek, J. Alder)

① **440 926-2DH** (5/95)
Prokofiev—Works for Violin and Piano
Prokofiev: Violin Sonata 1; Melodies, Op. 35b; Violin Sonata 2. (J. Bell, O. Mustonen)

① **440 935-2DH** (7/94)
Chopin/Liszt—Piano Works
Chopin: Allegro de concert; Piano Sonata 3; Waltzes (exc); *Liszt:* Années de pèlerinage 2 (exc); Hungarian Rhapsodies, S244 (exc). (E. Nebolsin)

① **443 003-2DF2** (5/94)
Tchaikovsky—Orchestral Works
Tchaikovsky: 1812; Marche slave; Capriccio italien; Hamlet; Voyevoda; Francesca da Rimini; Romeo and Juliet; Fate; Tempest. (Detroit SO, Washington NSO/A. Dorati)

① **443 009-2DF2** (5/94)
Mozart—Choral Works
Mozart: Requiem; Mass, K317; Litanies, K195; Exsultate, jubilate, K165. (E. Spoorenberg, I. Cotrubas, H. Watts, R. Tear, J. Shirley-Quirk, Oxford Schola Cantorum, ASMF Chor, ASMF/N. Marriner)

① **443 018-2DF2** (5/94)
Pavarotti/Freni/Ricciarelli—Live
Verdi: Traviata (exc); Aida (exc); Macbeth (exc); Forza del destino (exc); Lombardi (exc); Corsaro (exc); Falstaff (exc); Otello (exc); Ballo in maschera (exc); *Puccini:* Turandot (exc); Turandot (exc); *Verdi:* Traviata (exc); *Massenet:* Werther (exc); *Verdi:* Vespri Siciliani (exc); *Ponchielli:* Gioconda (exc); *Donizetti:* Elisir d'amore (exc); Fille du régiment (exc); *Meyerbeer:* Africaine (exc); *Boito:* Mefistofele (exc); *Mascagni:* Amico Fritz (exc); *Verdi:* Traviata (exc); *Puccini:* Tosca (exc); *Donizetti:* Elisir d'amore (exc); *Verdi:* Aida (exc). (M. Freni, K. Ricciarelli, L. Pavarotti, Verona Arena Orch, Ater Orch, Parma Teatro Regio Orch/A. Gatto/L. Magiera/B. Martinotti/G. Patanè)

① **443 021-2DF2** (12/94)
Debussy—Piano Works
Debussy: Suite bergamasque; Children's Corner; Images; Arabesques; Préludes (exc); Pour le piano; Estampes; Isle joyeuse; Rêverie. (P. Rogé)

① **443 172-2DH** (11/94)
Ives/Varèse—Orchestral Works
Ives: Symphony 4; Unanswered Question; *Varèse:* Amériques. (Cleveland Orch/C. von Dohnányi)

① **443 173-2DH** (4/95)
Bartók/Martinů/Janáček—Orchestral Works
Bartók: Dance Suite; *Martinů:* Quartet Concerto. (Cleveland Orch/C. von Dohnányi)

① **443 175-2DH** (2/95)
Mozart—Orchestral Works
Mozart: Serenade, K525; Flute and Harp Concerto, K299; Sinfonia Concertante, K364. (J. Smith, L. Wellbaum, D. Majeske, R. Vernon, Cleveland Orch/C. von Dohnányi)

① **443 322-2DH** (2/95)
Schumann—Piano Works, Vol.6
Schumann: Abegg Variations; Fantasie; Faschingsschwank aus Wien. (Vladimir Ashkenazy)

① **443 324-2DH** (7/95)
Respighi/Saint-Saëns—Violin Concertos
Saint-Saëns: Violin Concerto 3; *Respighi:* Gregorian Concerto; Autumn Poem. (P. Amoyal, FNO/C. Dutoit)

① **443 376-2DH** (7/94)
Harbison/Sessions—Orchestral Works
Harbison: Oboe Concerto; Symphony 2; *Sessions:* Symphony 2. (W. Bennett, San Francisco SO/H. Blomstedt)

① **443 444-2DH** (1/95)
Hungarian Connections
Bartók: Hungarian Sketches; Romanian folkdances, Sz68; *Kodály:* Háry János Suite; *Liszt:* Faust Episodes, S110 (exc); Hungarian Rhapsodies, S359 (exc); *Leó Weiner:* Prinz Csonger Suite (exc). (L. Kaptain, Chicago SO/G. Solti)

① **443 452-2DH** (11/94)
Mozart Portraits—Bartoli
Mozart: Così fan tutte (exc); Nozze di Figaro (exc); Don Giovanni (exc); Davidde penitente, K469 (exc); Exsultate, jubilate, K165. (C. Bartoli, Vienna CO/G. Fischer)

① **443 455-2DF2** (12/94)
Vivaldi—Sacred Choral Works
Vivaldi: Gloria, RV588; Gloria, RV589; Magnificat, RV610; Dixit Dominus, RV594; Beatus vir, RV597. (Lynda Russell, P. Kwella, J. Smith, I. Buchanan, P. Castle, A. Wilkens, H. Watts, M. Cockerham, K. Bowen, I. Partridge, A. King, J. Shirley-Quirk, St John's College Ch, King's College Ch, Wren Orch, ASMF, ECO/G. Guest/P. Ledger/S. Cleobury)

① **443 458-2DF2** (9/95)
Mozart—Serenades
Mozart: Serenade, K525; Serenade, K239; Serenade, K320; Symphony, K62a; Serenade, K250. (Vienna Mozart Ens/W. Boskovsky)

① **443 461-2DF2** (12/94)
Berlioz—L'Enfance du Christ, etc
Berlioz: Enfance du Christ (Cpte); Tristia (exc); Sara la baigneuse; Mort de Cléopâtre. (E. Morison, A. Pashley, P. Pears, E. Fleet, J. Cameron, J. Frost, J. Rouleau, St Anthony Sngrs, Goldsbrough Orch, ECO/Colin Davis)

① **443 464-2DF2** (9/95)
Rimsky-Korsakov—Scheherazade, etc
Rimsky-Korsakov: Scheherazade; May Night (exc); Tale of Tsar Saltan (exc); Tale of Tsar Saltan (exc); Russian Easter Festival Ov; Christmas Eve (exc); Sadko; Dubinushka; Snow Maiden (exc). (Geneva Motet Ch, SRO/E. Ansermet)

① **443 467-2DF2** (9/95)
Stravinsky—Ballet Music
Stravinsky: Petrushka (Cpte); Rite of Spring (Cpte); Noces (Cpte); Firebird (Cpte). (B. Retchitzka, L. Devallier, H. Cuénod, H. Rehfuss, J. Horneffer, R. Peter, D. Rossiaud, R. Aubert, Geneva Motet Ch, SRO/E. Ansermet)

① **443 476-2DF2** (12/94)
Vivaldi—L'estro armonico, Op 3
Vivaldi: Concerti Grossi, Op. 3; Concerto, RV456; Concerto, RV498; Concerto, RV441; Concerto, RV574. (W. Bennett, N. Black, C. Nicklin, M. Gatt, T. Brown, R. Davis, I. Brown, ASMF/N. Marriner)

① **443 479-2DF2** (12/94)
Beethoven—Symphonies
Beethoven: Symphony 3; Symphony 4; Symphony 5; Symphony 7; Egmont (exc); König Stefan (exc). (LSO/P. Monteux)

① **443 485-2DF2** (12/94)
Bach—Great Organ Works
Bach: Toccata and Fugue, BWV565; Herzlich tut mich verlangen, BWV727; Schübler Chorales, BWV645-650 (exc); Fantasia and Fugue, BWV542; Liebster Jesu, BWV730; Passacaglia and Fugue, BWV582; Prelude and Fugue, BWV552; Chorales, BWV651-668 (exc); Fantasia and Fugue, BWV537; Toccata, Adagio and Fugue, BWV564; In dulci jubilo, BWV729; Prelude and Fugue, BWV543; Fantasia and Fugue, BWV572; Prelude and Fugue, BWV532; Nun freut euch, BWV734; Wo soll ich fliehen hin, BWV694; Fantasia and Fugue, BWV562; Toccata and Fugue, BWV538. (P. Hurford)

① **443 488-2DF2** (10/95)
Kodály—Háry János; Psalmus Hungaricus
Kodály: Háry János (Cpte); Peacock Variations; Peacock; Psalmus Hungaricus. (E. Komlóssy, L. Palócz, G. Melis, Z. Bende, O. Szönyi, Margit László, P. Ustinov, L. Kozma, Edinburgh Fest Chor, Brighton Fest Chor, Wandsworth Sch Boys' Ch, LSC, LSO/I. Kertész)

① **443 530-2LF2** (7/95)
Mozart—Die Entführung aus dem Serail
Mozart: Entführung (Cpte); Zauberflöte (exc); Così fan tutte (exc); Nozze di Figaro (exc); Don Giovanni (exc); Schauspieldirektor (exc). (W. Lipp, E. Loose, W. Ludwig, P. Klein, E. Koréh, H. Woester, Vienna St Op Chor, VPO, LSO/J. Krips)

① **443 570-2DCS** (4/95)
Schubert—Piano Works
Schubert: Piano Sonata, D850; Impromptus (exc); Moments musicaux, D780. (C. Curzon)

① **443 576-2DCS** (5/95)
Mozart—Piano Concertos, etc
Mozart: Piano Concerto 8; Piano Concerto 9; Rondo, K386. (Vladimir Ashkenazy, LSO/I. Kertész)

① **443 577-2DCS** (4/95)
Stravinsky—Orchestral Works
Stravinsky: Pulcinella Suite; Apollon musagète (Cpte); Capriccio. (J. Ogdon, ASMF/N. Marriner)

① **443 578-2DCS** (7/95)
Mendelssohn—Orchestral Works
Mendelssohn: Symphony 3; Hebrides; Midsummer Night's Dream (exc). (LSO/P. Maag)

① **443 579-2DCS** (4/95)
Schubert—Piano Works
Schubert: Piano Sonata, D664; Piano Sonata, D784; Ungarische Melodie, D817; Waltzes, D145. (Vladimir Ashkenazy)

① **443 580-2DCS** (5/95)
España
Chabrier: España; *Rimsky-Korsakov:* Capriccio espagnol; *Granados:* Danzas españolas; *Moszkowski:* Danzas españolas; *Debussy:* Images. (LSO, SRO/A. Argenta)

① **443 772-2DH** (12/94)
Stravinsky—Ballet Music
Stravinsky: Agon (Cpte); Orpheus (Cpte); Jeu de cartes (Cpte). (Berlin Deutsches SO/Vladimir Ashkenazy)

① **443 776-2DH** (12/95)
Ives/Ruggles/Seeger—Orchestral Works
Ives: Orchestral Set I; Orchestral Set II; *Ruggles:* Suntreader; Men and Mountains; *R. C. Seeger:* Andante. (Cleveland Orch Chor, Cleveland Orch/C. von Dohnányi)

① **443 838-2DH** (7/95)
Italian Orchestral Works
Rossini: Sonate a quattro; *Donizetti:* String Quartet in D (1828); *Cherubini:* Horn Sonatas (exc); *Bellini:* Oboe Concerto. (R. Lord, B. Tuckwell, ASMF/N. Marriner)

① **443 847-2DF2** (7/95)
Bach—Concertos
Bach: Brandenburg Concertos; Violin and Oboe Concerto, BWV1060; Flute Concerto, BWV1056. (W. Bennett, T. Miller, C. Kaine, ECO, ASMF/B. Britten/N. Marriner)

① **443 850-2DF2** (9/95)
Rossini—Overtures
Rossini: Guillaume Tell (exc); Signor Bruschino (exc); Viaggio a Reims (exc); Scala di seta (exc); Gazza ladra (exc); Turco in Italia (exc); Italiana in ALgeri (exc); Barbiere di Siviglia (exc); Torvaldo e Dorliska (exc); Cambiale di matrimonio (exc); Otello (exc); Semiramide (exc); Siège de Corinthe (exc); Tancredi (exc). (National PO/R. Chailly)

① **443 856-2DF2** (7/95)
Elgar—Symphonies, etc
Elgar: Symphony 1; Symphony 2; Cockaigne; In the South. (LPO/G. Solti)

① **443 865-2DF2** (7/95)
Saint-Saëns—Piano Concertos
Saint-Saëns: Piano Concerto 1; Piano Concerto 2; Piano Concerto 3; Piano Concerto 4; Piano Concerto 5. (P. Rogé, Philh, RPO, LPO/C. Dutoit)

① **443 868-2DF2** (7/95)
Italian Baroque Sacred Works
Pergolesi: Stabat mater; *D. Scarlatti:* Stabat mater; *A. Scarlatti:* Domine refugium factus es nobis; O magnum mysterium; *Pergolesi:* Magnificat in C; *Lotti:* Crucifixus a 8; *A. Bononcini:* Stabat mater; *Caldara:* Crucifixus. (E. Harwood, F. Palmer, J. Baker, A. Hodgson, P. Esswood, P. Langridge, I. Partridge, C. Keyte, St John's College Ch, King's College Ch, London Schütz Ch, Argo CO, ASMF, Philomusica of London/G. Guest/R. Norrington/D. Willcocks)

① **443 893-2DH** (11/94)
Bartók—Violin Works
Bartók: Violin Sonata 2; Contrasts; Solo Violin Sonata. (L. Fenyves, A. Engegard, H. Schneeberger, E. Schmid, A. Schiff)

① **443 894-2DH** (11/94)
Bartók—Chamber Works
Bartók: Violin Sonata 1; Duos, Sz98 (exc); Sonata for 2 Pianos and Percussion. (Y. Shiokawa, L. Fenyves, H. Schneeberger, A. Schiff, B. Canino, Z. Rácz, Z. Váczi)

① **443 930-2DM** (10/95)
Jussi Björling sings Opera Arias
Ponchielli: Gioconda (exc); Puccini: Fanciulla del West (exc); Giordano: Fedora (exc); Cilea: Arlesiana (exc); Verdi: Ballo in maschera (exc); Puccini: Manon Lescaut (exc); Verdi: Requiem (exc); Mascagni: Cavalleria rusticana (exc); Lehár: Land des Lächelns (exc). (J. Björling, R. Tebaldi, L. Dani, R. Corsi, MMF Chor, MMF Orch/A. Erede, VPO/F. Reiner, Inst Ens)

① **443 933-2DM** (10/95)
Peter Pears sings Schubert and Schumann
Schumann: Dichterliebe, Op. 48 (Cpte); Schubert: Im Frühling, D882; Auf dem Wasser zu singen, D774; Nachtstück, D672; An die Entfernte, D765; Lachen und Weinen, D777; Abendstern, D806; Schwanengesang, D957 (exc); Sprache der Liebe, D410; Einsame, D800; Geistertanz, D116; Atys, D585; Auflösung, D807; Nacht und Träume, D827. (P. Pears, B. Britten)

① **443 968-2DH** (10/95)
Poulenc—Chamber Works
Poulenc: Capriccio; 2-Piano Sonata; Elégie (1959); Sonata for Four Hands; Embarquement pour Cythère; Violin Sonata; Elégie (1957). (C. Juillet, A. Cazalet, P. Rogé, J-P. Collard)

① **444 182-2DH** (5/95)
Tanz Grotesk
Hindemith: Dämon (Cpte); Schreker: Geburtstag der Infantin Suite; Schulhoff: Mondsüchtige (Cpte). (Leipzig Gewandhaus/L. Zagrosek)

① **444 318-2DH** (12/95)
Ravel/Debussy—Chamber Music
Debussy: Violin Sonata; Cello Sonata; Ravel: Piano Trio. (I. Perlman, L. Harrell, Vladimir Ashkenazy)

① **444 323-2DF2** (9/95)
Mozart—Symphonies Nos 25, 29, 38 & 40; Serenata notturna
Mozart: Symphony 25; Symphony 29; Symphony 38; Symphony 40; Serenade, K239. (ECO/B. Britten)

① **444 338-2DH** (10/95)
Brahms/Schumann—Piano Works
Brahms: Paganini Variations; Schumann: Arabeske; Symphonic Studies; Symphonic Studies II. (J-Y. Thibaudet)

① **444 386-2DH** (8/95)
Debussy—Orchestral Works
Debussy: Printemps; Boîte à joujoux; Children's Corner; Plus que lente. (Montreal SO/C. Dutoit)

① **444 389-2DWO** (9/95)
The World of Borodin
Borodin: Prince Igor (exc); String Quartet 2 (exc); Prince Igor (exc); Scherzo in A flat; In the Steppes of Central Asia; For the shores; Symphony 2. (N. Ghiaurov, Z. Ghiaurov, Vladimir Ashkenazy, Borodin Qt, London Sym Chor, LSO, SRO/G. Solti/E. Downes/E. Ansermet/J. Martinon)

① **444 390-2DWO** (11/95)
The World of The Harpsichord
Bach: Italian Concerto, BWV971; Chromatic Fantasia and Fugue, BWV903; Toccatas, BWV910-16 (exc); French Suites, BWV812-17 (exc); Paradis: Keyboard Sonatas (exc); Daquin: Premier livre de pièces de clavecin (exc); Rimsky-Korsakov: Tale of Tsar Saltan (exc); Rameau: Pièces de clavecin (exc); Couperin: Livre de clavecin III (exc); Templeton: Bach goes to town; Malcolm: Bach before the mast. (G. Malcolm)

① **444 408-2DH** (6/95)
Prokofiev—Piano Sonatas Nos 6-8
Prokofiev: Piano Sonata 6; Piano Sonata 7; Piano Sonata 8. (Vladimir Ashkenazy)

① **444 450-2DH** (2/95)
Pavarotti in Central Park
Verdi: Vespri siciliani (exc); Luisa Miller (exc); Donizetti: Lucia di Lammermoor (exc); Cilea: Arlesiana (exc); Leoncavallo: Mattinata; Mascagni: Serenata; Bixio: Mia canzone al vento; Ellington: I let a song go out of my heart; Traditional: I can go to God; Di Lazzaro: Chitarra romana; Sibella: Girometta; Denza: Occhi di fata; Borne: Carmen Fantasy; Crescenzo: Rondine al nido; De Curtis: Non ti scordar di me; Massenet: Werther (exc); Puccini: Tosca (exc); Di Capua: 'O sole mio; Puccini: Turandot (exc). (L. Pavarotti, A. Griminelli, Harlem Boys Ch, NYPO/W. J. Turnbull/L. Magiera)

① **444 455-2DH** (10/95)
Martin—Ballades; Concerto for 7 Wind Instruments
Martin: Flute Ballade; Saxophone Ballade; Piano Ballade; Trombone Ballade; Wind Concerto. (J. Zoon, J. Spronk, G. Pieterson, J. Terwey, J. Slagter, P. Masseurs, C. Lindberg, K. Blokker, J. Harle, M. Komst, R. Brautigam, Concertgebouw/R. Chailly)

① **444 458-2DH** (12/95)
Solti—Carnegie Hall Project
Wagner: Meistersinger (exc); Brahms: Haydn Variations; Shostakovich: Symphony 9; R. Strauss: Don Juan; Smetana: Bartered Bride (exc). (Solti Orchestral Project/G. Solti)

① **444 567-2DM** (10/95)
Organ Masterpieces I
Widor: Symphony 5 (exc); Vierne: Pièces en stile libre (exc); Karg-Elert: Choral-Improvisationen, Op. 65 (exc); Alain: Litanies; Liszt: Prelude and Fugue, S260; Reger: Pieces, Op. 59 (exc); Widor: Symphony 6 (exc); Langlais: Paraphrases grégoriennes (exc); Reger: Introduction and Passacaglia; Vierne: Symphony 1 (exc); Boëllmann: Suite gothique. (P. Hurford)

① **444 568-2DM** (10/95)
Organ Masterpieces II
Franck: Chorales; Pastorale; Prélude, Fugue et Variation; Pièces (1878) (exc). (P. Hurford)

① **444 569-2DM** (10/95)
Organ Masterpieces III
Bach: Toccata and Fugue, BWV565; Herzlich tut mich verlangen, BWV727; Schübler Chorales, BWV645-650 (exc); Fantasia and Fugue, BWV542; Liebster Jesu, BWV730; Passacaglia and Fugue, BWV582; Toccata, Adagio and Fugue, BWV564; In dulci jubilo, BWV729; Prelude and Fugue, BWV552. (P. Hurford)

① **444 570-2DM** (10/95)
Organ Masterpieces IV
Mendelssohn: Organ Sonatas (exc); Preludes and Fugues, Op. 37; Brahms: Chorale Preludes, Op. 122 (exc). (P. Hurford)

① **444 819-2DH** (12/95)
Schulhoff—Concertos and Piano Music
Schulhoff: Piano Concerto 2; Double Concerto; Concertino for String Quartet and Orchestra; Jazz Etudes (exc); Esquisses de Jazz (exc); Partita (exc). (B. Wild, A. Madžar, E. Schulhoff, Hawthorne Qt, Deutsche Kammerphilharmonie/A. Delfs)

Dell'Arte

① **CDDA9020** (1/90)
Toscanini conducts music by his contemporaries
Brahms: Handel Variations; Roger-Ducasse: Sarabande; Sibelius: Legends (exc); R. Harris: Symphony 3; Paganini: Moto perpetuo, Op.11; Kabalevsky: Colas Breugnon (exc). (Chor, NBC SO/A. Toscanini)

① **CDDA9021** (6/90)
Toscanini conducts French Works
Debussy: Marche écossaise; Meyerbeer: Dinorah (exc); Roussel: Festin de l'araignée ballet; Franck: Symphony. (NBC SO/A. Toscanini)

① **CDDA9022** (6/90)
Toscanini conducts Schubert, Schumann & Brahms
Brahms: Serenade 1 (exc); Schubert: Symphony 2; Schumann: Symphony 2. (NBC SO/A. Toscanini)

① **CDDA9023** (6/92)
Stokowski conducts Sibelius and Shostakovich
Sibelius: Symphony 4; Valse triste; Tempest Suites (exc); Shostakovich: Symphony 6. (Philadelphia/L. Stokowski)

① **CDDA9024** (10/95)
Toscanini conducts Tone Poems
Graener: Flöte von Sanssouci; Liszt: Orpheus; Sibelius: En Saga; Liszt: Von der Wiege bis zum Grabe; Hungarian Rhapsodies, S359 (exc); Sousa: Stars and Stripes Forever. (NBC SO/A. Toscanini)

① **CDDBS7001** (11/87)
Earl Wild plays Rachmaninov Song Transcriptions
Rachmaninov: Songs, Op. 14 (exc); Songs, Op. 21 (exc); Songs, Op. 4 (exc); Songs, Op. 34 (exc); Songs, Op. 26 (exc); Songs, Op. 38 (exc). (E. Wild)

① **CDDBS7005** (2/89)
Schumann—Piano Works
Schumann: Piano Sonata 1; Papillons; Fantasiestücke, Op. 12 (exc); Romanzen, Op. 28 (exc); Waldszenen (exc). (E. Wild)

Delos

① **DE1002** (9/87)
Szymanowski—Piano Works
Szymanowski: Masques, Op. 34; Etudes, Op. 4; Etudes, Op. 33; Mazurkas, Op. 62; Mazurkas, Op. 50 (exc). (C. Rosenberger)

① **DE1005** (2/87)
Bach/Sanz—Transcriptions & Works for Guitar
Bach: Solo Violin Partitas and Sonatas (exc); Solo Cello Suites (exc); Sanz: Spanish Guitar Instruction I (exc); Spanish Guitar Instruction II (exc). (Celedonio Romero)

① **DE1013** (11/90)
Copland: Piano Works
Copland: Variations; Piano Fantasy; Passacaglia; Night Thoughts. (C. Fierro)

① **DE1015** (1/89)
Janos Starker plays Kodály
Kodály: Cello Sonata, Op.8; Duo, Op.7; Bottermund: Paganini Variations. (J. Starker, J. Gingold)

① **DE1028** (7/91)
Robert Noehren Plays Marcel Dupré
Dupré: Pieces, Op. 27 (exc); Suite bretonne, Op. 21 (exc); Preludes and Fugues, Op. 7; Chorales, Op. 28 (exc); Cortège et Litanie. (R. Noehren)

① **DE3002** (10/84)
The Sound of Trumpets
Altenburg: Concerto for 7 Trumpets; Vivaldi: Concerto, RV537; Biber: Sonata 'Scti Polycarpi'; Torelli: Suonata, G1; Telemann: Trumpet Concerto. (G. Schwarz (tpt/dir), E. Carroll/M. Gould, R. Sirinek, N. Smith, John Miller, N. Balm, R. Mase, NY Y CO)

① **DE3005** (10/84)
World of the Harp
Salzedo: Chanson dans la nuit; M. Albéniz: Sonata in D; Traditional: Believe me, if all those endearing young charms; Greensleeves (Alas! my love); Debussy: Préludes (exc); Albéniz: Recuerdos de Viaje (exc); Watkins: Petite Suite (exc); A. Ortiz: Guabina; Llanos; Francisque: Treasure of Orpheus; Tournier: Jazz Band; Au matin; Zabel: Source, Op. 23; Parish Alvars: Mandoline; Grandjany: Siciliana. (S. McDonald)

① **DE3006** (6/86)
Water Music of the Impressionists
Liszt: Années de pèlerinage 3 (exc); Griffes: Fountain of Acqua Paolo; Ravel: Gaspard de la nuit (exc); Jeux d'eau; Debussy: Estampes (exc); Images (exc); Préludes (exc). (C. Rosenberger)

① **DE3013** (6/87)
Beethoven—Orchestral Works
Beethoven: Symphony 1; Symphony 8; Prometheus (exc). (Los Angeles CO, LSO/G. Schwarz)

① **DE3021** (10/84)
20th-century Russian music
Stravinsky: Histoire du Soldat Suite; Shostakovich: Piano Concerto 1; Prokofiev: Symphony 1. (C. Rosenberger, S. Burns, Los Angeles CO/G. Schwarz)

① **DE3026** (11/86)
A. Auger - Bach and Handel arias
Handel: Messiah (exc); Giulio Cesare (exc); Atalanta (exc); Alexander's Feast (exc); Rinaldo (exc); Samson (exc); Bach: Cantata 209 (exc); Anna Magdalena Notenbuch (1725) (exc); Cantata 202 (exc); St Matthew Passion, BWV244 (exc). (A. Auger, Mostly Mozart Orch/G. Schwarz)

① **DE3028** (3/87)
Bach: Organ Works
Bach: Toccata and Fugue, BWV565; Erbarm' dich, BWV721; Orgel-Büchlein, BWV599-644 (exc); O Gott, du frommer Gott, BWV767; Trio Sonatas, BWV525-530 (exc); Prelude and Fugue, BWV541; Fantasia and Fugue, BWV537. (R. Noehren)

① **DE3038** (9/95)
Beethoven—String Quartets, Vol.8
Beethoven: String Quartet 6; String Quartet 16; Grosse Fuge. (Orford Qt)

① **DE3039** (9/95)
Beethoven—String Quartets
Beethoven: String Quartet 1; String Quartet 2; String Quartet 3; String Quartet 4; String Quartet 5; String Quartet 6; String Quartet 7; String Quartet 8; String Quartet 9; String Quartet 10; String Quartet 11; String Quartet 12; String Quartet 13; String Quartet 14; String Quartet 15; String Quartet 16; Grosse Fuge. (Orford Qt)

ⓓ **DE3040** (3/87)
Wagner—Orchestral Excerpts from the Operas
Wagner: Tannhäuser (exc); Rheingold (exc);
Götterdämmerung (exc); Meistersinger (exc). (Seattle
SO/G. Schwarz)

ⓓ **DE3044** (6/87)
Rachmaninov—Piano Works
Rachmaninov: Piano Sonata 2; Preludes (exc); Etudes-
tableaux, Op. 33 (exc); Moments musicaux, Op. 16 (exc);
Daisies; Etudes-tableaux, Op.39 (exc). (J. Browning)

ⓓ **DE3045** (11/87)
Organ Recital
Widor: Symphony 6 (exc); *Brahms:* Chorale Preludes, Op.
122 (exc); *Bach:* Prelude and Fugue, BWV543; Chorales,
BWV651-668 (exc); *Alain:* Janequin Variations; *Hindemith:*
Organ Sonatas (exc); *Karg-Elert:* Sinfonische Kanzonen,
Op. 85 (exc); *Messiaen:* Nativité du Seigneur (exc). (R.
Noehren, Detroit Mariner's Church Ch, M. Smith)

ⓓ **DE3052** (9/90)
R. Strauss: Orchestral Works
R. Strauss: Also sprach Zarathustra; Salome (exc);
Intermezzo Interludes (exc). (Seattle SO/G. Schwarz)

ⓓ **DE3061** (9/88)
Haydn: Orchestral Works
Haydn: Symphony 22; Symphony 104; Keyboard
Concerto, HobXVIII/2. (C. Rosenberger, Scottish CO/G.
Schwarz)

ⓓ **DE3062** (9/88)
Haydn: Orchestral Works
Haydn: Symphony 21; Symphony 96; Cello Concerto in C.
(J. Starker, Scottish CO/G. Schwarz)

ⓓ **DE3063** (10/92)
Haydn—Orchestral Works
Haydn: Cello Concerto in D; Symphony 61; Symphony
103. (J. Starker, Scottish CO/G. Schwarz)

ⓓ **DE3064** (5/90)
Haydn: Orchestral Works
Haydn: Symphony 51; Symphony 100; Keyboard
Concerto, HobXVIII:4. (C. Rosenberger, Scottish CO/G.
Schwarz)

ⓓ **DE3067** (5/92)
Schubert—Orchestral Works
Schubert: Symphony 5; Symphony 8; Deutsche Tänze,
D820. (NY Chbr SO/G. Schwarz)

ⓓ **DE3073** (3/90)
Hanson: Orchestral Works
Hanson: Symphony 1; Symphony 2; Elegy in memory of
Serge Koussevitzky. (Seattle SO/G. Schwarz)

ⓓ **DE3074** (9/90)
Piston—Orchestral Works
Piston: Symphony 2; Symphony 6; Sinfonietta. (Seattle
SO, NY Chbr SO/G. Schwarz)

ⓓ **DE3075** (10/89)
Soweby: Organ Works
Sowerby: Fantasy for Flute Stops; Requiescat in pace;
Organ Symphony. (C. Crozier)

ⓓ **DE3078** (9/90)
Barber, Bernstein and Gershwin
Barber: School for Scandal Ov; *Gershwin:* American in
Paris; *Bernstein:* Arias and Barcarolles. (J. Bunnell, D.
Duesing, Seattle SO/G. Schwarz)

ⓓ **DE3081** (5/90)
Tchaikovsky: Orchestral Works
Tchaikovsky: 1812; Hamlet; Tempest. (Oregon SO/J.
DePreist)

ⓓ **DE3084** (5/90)
Schumann: Orchestral Works
Schumann: Overture, scherzo and finale; Konzertstück,
Op.86; Symphony 1. (R. Bonneve, M. Robbins, D. Knapp,
S. Wilson, Seattle SO/G. Schwarz)

ⓓ **DE3090** (7/91)
Organ Recital
Mendelssohn: Organ Sonatas (exc); *Schumann:* B-A-C-H
Fugues, Op. 60 (exc); *Liszt:* Prelude and Fugue, S260
(exc); *Reubke:* Organ Sonata (exc). (C. Crozier)

ⓓ **DE3092** (2/91)
Hanson—Orchestral Works
Hanson: Symphony 3; Symphony 6; Fantasy Variations.
(C. Rosenberger, NY CO, Seattle SO/G. Schwarz)

ⓓ **DE3093** (4/91)
Diamond—Orchestral Works
Diamond: Symphony 2; Symphony 4; Concerto (1940).
(Seattle SO, NY Chbr SO/G. Schwarz)

ⓓ **DE3094** (5/92)
R. Strauss—Orchestral Works
R. Strauss: Heldenleben; Macbeth; Serenade, Op.7.
(Seattle SO/G. Schwarz)

ⓓ **DE3103** (4/93)
David Diamond—Orchestral Works
Diamond: Romeo and Juliet; Psalm; Kaddish; Symphony
3. (J. Starker, NY Chbr SO, Seattle SO/G. Schwarz)

ⓓ **DE3105** (7/92)
Hanson—Choral and Orchestral Works
Hanson: Symphony 4; Serenade, Op. 35; Lament for
Beowulf; Pastorale, Op. 38; Merry Mount (exc). (Seattle
SO, Seattle Sym Chorale, NY Chbr SO/G. Schwarz)

ⓓ **DE3106** (7/92)
Piston—Orchestral Works
Piston: Symphony 4; Capriccio; Serenata; New England
Sketches. (T.E. Wunrow, Seattle SO, NY Chbr SO/G.
Schwarz)

ⓓ **DE3108** (6/92)
Alessandra Marc—Opera Recital
Verdi: Forza del destino (exc); Aida (exc); *Catalani:* Wally
(exc); *Cilea:* Adriana Lecouvreur (exc); *Puccini:* Tosca
(exc); Turandot (exc); *G. Charpentier:* Louise (exc);
Wagner: Tannhäuser (exc). (A. Marc, NZ SO/H.
Wallberg)

ⓓ **DE3109** (10/92)
R.Strauss—Orchestral Works
R. Strauss: Rosenkavalier (exc); Burleske; Frau ohne
Schatten Fantasy. (C. Rosenberger, Seattle SO/G.
Schwarz)

ⓓ **DE3114** (12/92)
Creston—Orchestral Works
Creston: Symphony 3; Partita, Op.12; Out of the Cradle;
Invocation and Dance, Op.58. (S. Goff, I. Talvi, Seattle
SO/G. Schwarz)

ⓓ **DE3115** (7/93)
A Tribute to William Schuman
Ives: America Variations; *Schuman:* New England Triptych;
Symphony 5; Judith. (Seattle SO/G. Schwarz)

ⓓ **DE3119** (1/94)
Diamond—Orchestral Works
Diamond: Symphony 1; Enormous Room; Violin Concerto
2. (I. Talvi, Seattle SO/G. Schwarz)

ⓓ **DE3120** (4/94)
Wagner—Orchestral and Vocal Works
Wagner: Siegfried (exc); Lohengrin (exc); Tristan und
Isolde (exc); Walküre (exc); Faust Overture. (A. Marc,
Seattle SO/G. Schwarz)

ⓓ **DE3121** (4/94)
Transformations for Strings
Webern: Slow Movement (1905); *R. Strauss:*
Metamorphosen; *Honegger:* Symphony 2. (Seattle Sym
Stgs/G. Schwarz, S. Gulkis, R. Davis, C. Butler)

ⓓ **DE3125** (10/92)
Sing we Merrily - Choral Music
S. Campbell: Sing we merrily; *Rutter:* For the beauty of the
earth; *Bairstow:* Let all mortal flesh keep silence;
Traditional: Tomorrow shall be my dancing day; *Sumsion:*
There is a green hill; *Piccolo:* O hear us, Lord; *Ireland:*
Greater love hath no man; *Vaughan Williams:* Loch
Lomond; *Britten:* Jubilate Deo in C; *Susa:* Song to the
lamb; *Hallock:* Lord is my light; *Bernstein:* Mass (exc); M.
Fink: What sweeter music; *Bairstow:* Let all... Op.11; D.
Pearson: Advent Procession; *P.E. Baker:* Easter Anthem;
Near: And all in the morning; *Weaver:* Epiphany alleluias.
(St John's Episcopal Cath Ch/D. Pearson)

ⓓ **DE3126** (2/94)
The Incredible Walter Piston
Piston: Incredible Flutist Suite; English Horn Fantasy;
Suite; Concerto for Quartet, Wind and Percussion; Psalm
and Prayer. (S. Goff, G. Danielson, T. E. Wunrow, Juilliard
Qt, Seattle Sym Chorale, Seattle SO/G. Schwarz)

ⓓ **DE3127** (10/94)
Creston—Orchestral Works, Vol.2
Creston: Symphony 5; Toccata, Op. 68; Choreografic
Suite, Op. 86a. (Seattle SO, NY Chbr SO/G. Schwarz)

ⓓ **DE3130** (3/93)
Hanson—Orchestral Works
Hanson: Piano Concerto; Symphony 7; Symphony 5;
Mosaics. (C. Rosenberger, Seattle Sym Chorale, Seattle
SO/G. Schwarz)

ⓓ **DE3136** (12/93)
Nielsen/Loeffler/Prokofiev—Chamber Works
Loeffler: Rhapsodies; *Nielsen:* Wind Quintet; *Prokofiev:*
Quintet, Op. 39. (Chbr Music NW)

ⓓ **DE3139** (7/94)
Irving Fine—Orchestral Works
Fine: Blue Towers; Diversions for Orchestra; Music for
Piano; Toccata concertante; Symphony. (Moscow RSO/J.
Spiegelman)

ⓓ **DE3140** (5/93)
Portraits of Freedom
Copland: Fanfare for the Common Man; Lincoln Portrait;
Canticle of Freedom; Outdoor Ov; *R. Harris:* American
Creed; When Johnny comes marching (1934). (J. E.
Jones, Seattle Sym Chorale, Seattle SO/G. Schwarz)

ⓓ **DE3141** (4/95)
Diamond—Vocal and Orchestral Works
Diamond: This Sacred Ground; Symphony 8.
(E. Parce, Seattle Girls' Ch, Northwest Boychoir, Seattle
Sym Chorale, Seattle SO/G. Schwarz)

ⓓ **DE3146** (7/95)
The Schumann Edition
Schumann: Symphony 1; Symphony 2; Symphony 3;
Symphony 4; Overture, Scherzo and Finale; Symphonic
Studies (exc); Konzertstück, Op. 86; Piano Concerto;
Manfred (exc). (B. Davidovich, Seattle SO/G. Schwarz)

ⓓ **DE3147** (2/95)
Things Visible and Invisible
Alain: Danses (1937/9); *Langlais:* Paraphrases
grégoriennes; *Messiaen:* Messe de la Pentecôte. (C.
Crozier)

ⓓ **DE3157** (7/94)
Hovhaness—Orchestral Works
Hovhaness: Symphony 2; Prayer of St Gregory, Op. 62b;
Prelude and Quadruple Fugue, Op. 128; And God Created
Great Whales, Op. 229/1; Alleluia and Fugue, Op. 40b;
Celestial Fantasy, Op. 44. (Seattle SO/G. Schwarz)

ⓓ **DE3160** (5/95)
Hanson—The Mystic Trumpeter
Hanson: Dies Natalis I; Mystic Trumpeter; Lumen in
Christo; Lux aeterna. (J. E. Jones, Seattle Sym Chorale,
Seattle SO/G. Schwarz)

ⓓ **DE3162** (3/95)
Hovhaness—Quartets; Bagatelles
Hovhaness: Bagatelles, Op. 30; String Quartet 1; String
Quartet 2 (exc); String Quartet 3; String Quartet 4; *Z. Long:*
Song of the Ch'in. (Shanghai Qt)

ⓓ **DE3168** (7/95)
Hovhaness—The Rubaiyat
Hovhaness: Rubaiyat of Omar Khayyam, Op. 282;
Symphony 1; Meditation on Orpheus; Fantasy on
Japanese Woodprints. (M. York, D. Schmidt, R. Johnson,
Seattle SO/G. Schwarz)

ⓓ **DE3170** (12/95)
Beach—Cabildo; Six Short Pieces
Beach: Cabildo (Cpte); Hermit Thrush at Eve, Op. 92/1;
Give me not love, Op. 61; In the Twilight, Op. 85;
Shakespeare Songs, Op. 37 (exc); Songs, Op. 11 (exc);
Songs, Op. 1 (exc). (S. M. Hanan, A. D. Griffey, C.
Hellekant, E. Perry, P. Groves, T. Paul, L. Flanigan, New
York Concert Sngrs, M. Peskanov, C. Brey, C. O'Riley)

ⓓ **DE3186** (12/95)
Heigh Ho! Mozart
Menken: Pocahontas (exc); *Churchill:* Snow White (exc);
Snow White (exc); *Menken:* Beauty and the Beast (exc);
Fain: Peter Pan (exc); *Menken:* Little Mermaid (exc);
Sherman & Sherman: Jungle Book (exc); *E. John:* Lion
King (exc); *Churchill:* Three Little Pigs (exc); *Al Hoffman:*
Cinderella (exc); *J-J. Perry:* Main Street Electrical Parade;
Sherman & Sherman: Mary Poppins (exc); *Churchill:*
Bambi (exc); *Sherman & Sherman:* Winnie the Pooh (exc);
Menken: Aladdin (exc); *Harline:* Pinocchio (exc). (E.
Zukerman, P. Barritt, C. Rosenberger, Anthony Newman,
Voices of Ascension/D. Keene, Shanghai Qt, LAQG, Millar
Brass Ens/M. Cichowicz, ECO/D. Fraser)

Denon

ⓓ **CO-1029** (11/86)
Boccherini & Verdi: String Quartets
Boccherini: String Quartets, G165-70 (exc); String
Quartets, G220-5 (exc); *Verdi:* String Quartet. (Nuovo
Quartetto)

ⓓ **CO-1052** (11/86)
Messiaen & Xenakis: Piano Works
Messiaen: Etudes de rythme; *Xenakis:* Evryali; Herma. (Y.
Takahashi)

ⓓ **CO-1054** (12/86)
Rachmaninov: Piano Works
Rachmaninov: Piano Sonata 2; Etudes-tableaux, Op. 33;
Etudes-tableaux, Op. 39 (exc); Preludes (exc). (H.
Grimaud)

① 429 193-2GCM9 (8/90)
Dvořák: String Quartets
Dvořák: String Quartet 1; String Quartet 2; String Quartet 3; String Quartet 4; String Quartet 5; String Quartet 6; String Quartet 7; String Quartet 8; String Quartet 9; String Quartet 10; String Quartet 11; String Quartet 12; String Quartet 13; String Quartet 14; Andante appassionato; String Quartet, B120; Waltzes, Op. 54; Cypresses. (Prague Qt)

① 429 219-2GH (4/90)
Cello Concertos
Haydn: Cello Concerto in C; *C.P.E. Bach:* Cello Concerto, H439; *Boccherini:* Cello Concerto, G482. (M. Haimovitz, ECO/A. Davis)

① 429 220-2GH (8/90)
Ives—Orchestral Works
Ives: Symphony 2; Central Park in the dark; Unanswered question; Set of three short pieces (exc); Gong on the Hook; Tone Roads (exc); Halloween. (NYPO/L. Bernstein)

① 429 221-2GH (8/90)
Mozart— Symphonies Nos 25 & 29; Clarinet Concerto
Mozart: Symphony 25; Symphony 29; Clarinet Concerto, K622. (P. Schmidl, VPO/L. Bernstein)

① 429 225-2GH (4/90)
Bach: Oboe Concertos
Bach: Oboe Concerto, BWV1053; Oboe Concerto, BWV1055; Oboe Concerto, BWV1059. (D. Boyd (ob/dir), COE)

① 429 231-2GH (1/92)
Modern Orchestral Works
Bernstein: Jubilee Games; *Del Tredici:* Tattoo; *Rorem:* Violin Concerto. (G. Kremer, NYPO, Israel PO/L. Bernstein)

① 429 232-2GH (6/90)
Guitar Concertos
Rodrigo: Concierto de Aranjuez; *Fantasía; Villa-Lobos:* Guitar Concerto. (G. Söllscher, Orpheus CO)

① 429 233-2GH (7/90)
Schoenberg: Works for String Orchestra
Schoenberg: Chamber Symphony 1; Chamber Symphony 2; Verklärte Nacht. (Orpheus CO)

① 429 260-2GH (4/90)
Contemporary Works
Boulez: Notations (exc); *Ligeti:* Atmosphères; Lontano; *Nono:* Liebeslied; *Rihm:* Départ. (Vienna Jeunesse Ch, VPO/C. Abbado)

① 429 306-2GX9 (3/91)
Beethoven—Complete Piano Sonatas
Beethoven: Piano Sonata 1; Piano Sonata 2; Piano Sonata 3; Piano Sonata 4; Piano Sonata 5; Piano Sonata 6; Piano Sonata 7; Piano Sonata 8; Piano Sonata 9; Piano Sonata 10; Piano Sonata 11; Piano Sonata 12; Piano Sonata 13; Piano Sonata 14; Piano Sonata 15; Piano Sonata 16; Piano Sonata 17; Piano Sonata 18; Piano Sonata 19; Piano Sonata 20; Piano Sonata 21; Piano Sonata 22; Piano Sonata 23; Piano Sonata 24; Piano Sonata 25; Piano Sonata 26; Piano Sonata 27; Piano Sonata 28; Piano Sonata 29; Piano Sonata 30; Piano Sonata 31; Piano Sonata 32. (W. Kempff)

① 429 396-2GH (4/91)
Prokofiev—Orchestral Works
Prokofiev: Peter and the Wolf; Symphony 1; Overture, Op.34b; March, Op.99. (Sting, COE/C. Abbado)

① 429 404-2GH (5/91)
Hindemith: Orchestral Works
Hindemith: Mathis der Maler; Concert Music, Op.50; Symphonic Metamorphosis. (Israel PO/L. Bernstein)

① 429 488-2GDC (5/90)
Serenades for String Orchestra
Dvořák: Serenade, op 22; *Elgar:* Serenade; *Tchaikovsky:* Serenade, op 48. (Orpheus CO)

① 429 494-2GDC (6/90)
Intermezzo
Mascagni: Cavalleria Rusticana (exc); *Cilea:* Adriana Lecouvreur (exc); *Puccini:* Manon Lescaut (exc); *Leoncavallo:* Pagliacci (exc); *Massenet:* Thaïs (exc); *Wolf-Ferrari:* Gioielli della Madonna (exc); *Verdi:* Traviata (exc); *Schmidt:* Notre Dame (exc); *Mussorgsky:* Khovanshchina (exc); *Puccini:* Suor Angelica (exc); *Giordano:* Fedora (exc); *Mascagni:* Amico Fritz (exc); *Offenbach:* Contes d'Hoffmann (exc); *Ponchielli:* Gioconda (exc). (Gothenburg SO/N. Järvi)

① 429 509-2GR (10/90)
Beethoven: Orchestral Works
Beethoven: Symphony 7; Egmont (exc); Coriolan; Prometheus (exc). (VPO/K. Böhm)

① 429 570-2GH (7/90)
Beethoven: Late Piano Sonatas
Beethoven: Piano Sonata 30; Piano Sonata 31; Piano Sonata 32. (M. Pollini)

① 429 644-2GSE3 (7/90)
Brahms: Symphonies
Brahms: Symphony 1; Symphony 2; Symphony 3; Symphony 4. (BPO/H. von Karajan)

① 429 648-2GSE9 (3/91)
Bruckner: Symphonies
Bruckner: Symphony 1; Symphony 2; Symphony 3; Symphony 4; Symphony 5; Symphony 6; Symphony 7; Symphony 8; Symphony 9. (BPO/H. von Karajan)

① 429 664-2GSE3 (8/91)
Mendelssohn—Complete Symphonies
Mendelssohn: Symphony 1; Symphony 2; Symphony 3; Symphony 4; Symphony 5. (E. Mathis, L. Rebmann, W. Hollweg, Berlin Deutsche Op Chor, BPO/H. von Karajan)

① 429 672-2GSE2 (7/90)
Schumann: Symphonies
Schumann: Symphony 1; Symphony 2; Symphony 3; Symphony 4. (BPO/H. von Karajan)

① 429 724-2GH2 (7/92)
Berlioz—Requiem, etc
Berlioz: Grande Messe des Morts (Cpte); Corsaire; Benvenuto Cellini (exc); Carnaval Romain. (L. Pavarotti, Ernst Senff Chor, BPO/James Levine)

① 429 727-2GH (4/91)
Brahms—Lieder
Brahms: Zigeunerlieder, Op. 103 (exc); Lieder, Op. 97 (exc); Lieder, Op. 84 (exc); Lieder, Op. 43 (exc); Lieder, Op. 57 (exc); Lieder, Op. 72 (exc); Lieder, Op. 63 (exc); Lieder, Op. 32 (exc); Lieder, Op. 107 (exc); Lieder, Op. 106 (exc); Lieder, Op. 47 (exc); Lieder, Op. 49 (exc); Lieder, Op. 91. (A.S. von Otter, N-E. Sparf, B. Forsberg)

① 429 728-2GH (1/91)
Debussy: Orchestral Works
Debussy: La Mer; Images; Après-midi. (Santa Cecilia Academy Orch/L. Bernstein)

① 429 737-2GH (3/92)
Bach—Favourite Arias
Bach: Cantata 197 (exc); Cantata 58 (exc); Cantata 204 (exc); Cantata 97 (exc); Cantata 115 (exc); Cantata 171 (exc); Mass in B minor, BWV232 (exc); Cantata 202 (exc); Cantata 36 (exc); Cantata 187 (exc); Cantata 84 (exc); Cantata 105 (exc). (K. Battle, I. Perlman, St Luke's Orch/J. Nelson)

① 429 738-2GH (4/91)
Debussy & Ravel: Chamber Works
Ravel: Introduction and Allegro; Pavane; Violin and Cello Sonata; *Debussy:* Syrinx; Sonata for Flute, Viola and Harp; Chansons de Bilitis narrations. (C. Deneuve, Vienna-Berlin Ens, W. Schulz, M-A. Süss, G. Hetzel, G. Faust, W. Christ)

① 429 739-2GH (12/90)
Mozart: Piano Works
Mozart: Fantasia, K475; Piano Sonata, K457; Fantasia, K397; Piano Sonata, K331. (M-J. Pires)

① 429 750-2GH (5/91)
Oboe Concertos
Mozart: Oboe Concerto, K314; *Bellini:* Oboe Concerto; *R. Strauss:* Oboe Concerto. (H. Schellenberger, BPO/James Levine)

① 429 765-2GH (1/91)
Brahms—Orchestral & Choral Works
Brahms: Tragic Overture; Symphony 3; Schicksalslied, Op. 54. (Ernst Senff Chor, BPO/C. Abbado)

① 429 766-2GH (6/92)
Schubert—Lieder
Schubert: Schwanengesang, D957 (Cpte); Sehnsucht, D879; Wanderer an den Mond, D870; Wiegenlied, D867; Am Fenster, D878; Herbst, D945. (B. Fassbaender, A. Reimann)

① 429 783-2GH (4/91)
Mozart—Orchestral Works
Mozart: Gallimathias musicum, K32; Musikalischer Spass; Marches, K335; German Dances, K567; German Dances, K602 (exc); German Dances, K605; Contredanse, K587; Contredanse, K607; Contredanse, K610. (Orpheus CO)

① 429 785-2GH (5/91)
Mussorgsky/Ravel—Orchestral Works
Mussorgsky: Pictures; Night on the Bare Mountain; *Ravel:* Valses Nobles et Sentimentales. (NYPO/G. Sinopoli)

① 429 790-2GH (5/91)
Spirituals in Concert
Traditional: In that great getting up morning; Sinner, please don't let this harvest pass; Over my head I hear music; Oh, what a beautiful city; Lord, how come me here; I believe/In this field; Ride on, King Jesus; Swing low, sweet chariot; You can tell the world; Scandalize my name; Great day; Oh, glory; Calvary; Talk about a child that do love Jesus; Gospel train; My God is so high; There is a balm in Gilead; He's got the whole world in His hands. (K. Battle, J. Norman, H. Laws, N. Allen, S.O. Lee, chor, orch/James Levine)

① 429 854-2GC2 (12/90)
Henze—Symphonies
Henze: Symphony 1; Symphony 2; Symphony 3; Symphony 4; Symphony 5; Symphony 6. (BPO, LSO/H.W. Henze)

① 429 857-2GC (3/91)
Janáček—Piano Works
Janáček: Along an Overgrown Path; In the mists; Piano Sonata (1905); Thema con variazione. (R. Firkušný)

① 429 933-2GDO (11/90)
Fritz Wunderlich—Lieder Recital
Schumann: Dichterliebe, Op. 48 (Cpte); *Beethoven:* Adelaide, Op.46; Zärtliche Liebe, WoO123; Kuss, Op.128; Resignation, WoO149; *Schubert:* Im Abendrot, D799; An die Laute, D905; Liebe eines Schiffers an die Dioskuren, D360; Musensohn, D764; An Silvia, D891; Einsame, D800; Schwanengesang, D957 (exc); An die Musik, D547. (F. Wunderlich, H. Giesen)

① 429 984-2GH (3/91)
Russian Orchestral Works
Tchaikovsky: 1812; Marche slave; *Borodin:* In the Steppes of Central Asia; Prince Igor (exc); *Rimsky-Korsakov:* Russian Easter Festival Ov; Capriccio Espagnol. (Gothenburg Sym Chor, Gothenburg Sym Brass, T. Sporsén, Gothenburg SO/N. Järvi)

① 431 085-2GH (2/91)
Schubert—Lieder
Schubert: Rastlose Liebe, D138; Wandrers Nachtlied I, D224; Heidenröslein, D257; Erlkönig, D328; König in Thule, D367; Jägers Abendlied, D368; An Schwager Kronos, D369; Seligkeit, D433; Wanderer, D489; Forelle, D550; Sei mir gegrüsst, D741; Musensohn, D764; Wandrers Nachtlied II, D768; Auf dem Wasser zu singen, D774; Du bist die Ruh', D776; Lachen und Weinen, D777; Im Abendrot, D799; Einsame, D800; Ständchen, D889; An Silvia, D891; Schwanengesang, D957 (exc); Winterreise (exc). (D. Fischer-Dieskau, G. Moore)

① 431 103-2GB (5/93)
Great Voices—Montserrat Caballé
Gounod: Faust (exc); *Meyerbeer:* Huguenots (exc); *A. Charpentier:* Louise (exc); *Bizet:* Carmen (exc); *Gounod:* Roméo et Juliette (exc); *R. Strauss:* Salome (exc); *Puccini:* Manon Lescaut (exc). (M. Caballé, P. Domingo, New Philh/R. Giovaninetti, FNO/L. Bernstein, NY Met Op Orch/James Levine)

① 431 104-2GB (5/93)
Great Voices - Plácido Domingo
Bizet: Carmen (exc); *Puccini:* Manon Lescaut (exc); Fanciulla del West (exc); *Verdi:* Traviata (exc); Macbeth (exc); *Wagner:* Meistersinger (exc); *Cardillo:* Core 'ngrato; *Lara:* Granada; *Leoncavallo:* Mattinata; *Frentre:* Ay, ay, ay; *De Curtis:* Non ti scordar di me. (P. Domingo, T. Berganza, M. Caballé, I. Cotrubas, D. Fischer-Dieskau, P. Lagger, C. Ligendza, Ambrosian Sngrs, Bavarian St Op Chor, Berlin Deutsche Op Chor, LSO, NY Met Op Orch, ROHO, Bavarian St Orch, La Scala Orch, Berlin Deutsche Op Orch/C. Abbado/James Levine/Z. Mehta/C. Kleiber/E. Jochum/K-H. Loges/M. Peeters)

① 431 110-2GB (5/93)
Great Voices - Fritz Wunderlich
Mozart: Zauberflöte (exc); Entführung (exc); *Verdi:* Traviata (exc); *Tchaikovsky:* Eugene Onegin (exc); *Lortzing:* Zar und Zimmermann (exc); Waffenschmied (exc); *Rossini:* Barbiere di Siviglia (exc); *Verdi:* Rigoletto (exc); Don Carlos (exc); *Puccini:* Bohème (exc); Tosca (exc); *Schubert:* Heidenröslein, D257; *Beethoven:* Zärtliche Liebe, WoO123; *Denza:* Funiculi-Funicula; *May:* Lied geht um die Welt (exc). (F. Wunderlich, BPO/R. Böhm, Bavarian St Orch/E. Jochum, H. Gueden, Bavarian Rad Chor, BRSO/B. Bartoletti, Bavarian St Op Orch/O. Gerdes, I. Hallstein, Bamberg SO/H. Gierster, H. Prey, E. Köth, Munich RO/H. Moltkau/K. Eichhorn/H. Stein, South-West German RSO/E. Smola, H. Giesen, R. Lamy Sngrs, Graunke SO/H. Carste)

① **435 069-2GGA** (11/91)
Debussy—Orchestral Works
Debussy: Nocturnes; Printemps; Martyre de St Sébastien (exc). (Paris Orch Chor, Paris Orch/D. Barenboim)

① **435 070-2GGA** (11/91)
Mozart—Symphonies
Mozart: Symphony 32; Symphony 33; Symphony 35; Symphony 36. (BPO/H. von Karajan)

① **435 072-2GGA** (11/91)
Schubert—Piano Works
Schubert: Moments Musicaux, D780; Allegretto, D915; Scherzi, D593; Waltzes, D969. (D. Barenboim)

① **435 074-2GGA2** (11/91)
Dvořák—Orchestral Works
Dvořák: My Home; Hussite; In Nature's Realm; Carnival; Othello; Water Goblin; Noon Witch; Golden Spinning-Wheel; Wild Dove; Symphonic Variations. (BRSO/R. Kubelik)

① **435 162-2GX13** (2/92)
Mahler—Complete Symphonies
Mahler: Symphony 1; Symphony 2; Symphony 3; Symphony 4; Symphony 5; Symphony 6; Symphony 7; Symphony 8; Symphony 9; Symphony 10 (exc). (B. Hendricks, C. Ludwig, H. Wittek, M. Price, J. Blegen, G. Zeumer, A. Baltsa, T. Schmidt, K. Riegel, H. Prey, J. Van Dam, Westminster Ch, NY Choral Artists, Brooklyn Boys' Chor, Vienna Boys' Ch, Vienna St Op Chor, Vienna Singverein, Concertgebouw, NYPO, VPO/L. Bernstein)

① **435 211-2GX15** (4/92)
Wagner—Der Ring des Nibelungen
Wagner: Rheingold (Cpte); Walküre (Cpte); Siegfried (Cpte); Götterdämmerung (Cpte). (D. Fischer-Dieskau, J. Veasey, G. Stolze, E. Wohlfahrt, Z. Kélémen, S. Mangelsdorff, D. Grobe, R. Kerns, O. Dominguez, M. Talvela, K. Ridderbusch, H. Donath, E. Moser, A. Reynolds, J. Vickers, G. Janowitz, R. Crespin, T. Stewart, M. Talvela, L. Rebmann, D. Mastilovic, C. Ordassy, I. Steger, H. Jenckel, B. Ericson, C. Ahlin, L. Brockhaus, Jess Thomas, T. Stewart, H. Dernesch, C. Gayer, H. Brilioth, K. Ridderbusch, T. Stewart, G. Janowitz, C. Ludwig, L. Rebmann, L. Chookasian, C. Ligendza, G. Stolze, Berlin Deutsche Op Chor, BPO/H. von Karajan)

① **435 321-2GWP12** (2/92)
150 Years - Vienna Philharmonic
Haydn: Symphony 102; Ravel: Piano Concerto; Schoenberg: Pelleas und Melisande; R. Strauss: Tod und Verklärung; Brahms: Symphony 2; Beethoven: Grosse Fuge; Leonore (exc); Symphony 9; Bruckner: Symphony 9; Schubert: Symphony 8; Beethoven: Symphony 5; Schubert: Symphony 9; Schmidt: Husarenlied Variations; Beethoven: Missa Solemnis; Stravinsky: Pulcinella Suite; Dukas: Apprenti sorcier; Bruckner: Symphony 5; R. Strauss: Sinfonia Domestica; Till Eulenspiegel; Wagner: Meistersinger (exc); Mozart: Symphony 38; Mahler: Symphony 4. (VPO, L. Bernstein (pf/dir)/L. Bernstein/K. Böhm/W. Furtwängler, I. Seefried, R. Anday, A. Dermota, P. Schoeffler, Vienna Singakademie Chor/H. von Karajan/O. Klemperer/H. Knappertsbusch, T. Eipperle, L. Willer, J. Patzak, G. Hann, Vienna St Op Chor/C. Krauss/C. Schuricht/R. Strauss/H. Gueden/B. Walter)

① **435 324-2GWP** (2/92)
VPO under Wilhelm Furtwängler
Brahms: Symphony 2; Beethoven: Grosse Fuge; Leonore (exc). (VPO/W. Furtwängler)

① **435 333-2GWP** (2/92)
VPO under Richard Strauss
R. Strauss: Sinfonia Domestica; Till Eulenspiegel; Wagner: Meistersinger (exc). (VPO/R. Strauss)

① **435 335-2GWP2** (2/92)
VPO plays Johann & Josef Strauss
J. Strauss II: Du und Du, Op. 367; Annen-Polka, Op. 117; Blauen Donau, Op. 314; Kaiser, Op. 437; Leichtes Blut, Op. 319; Perpetuum Mobile; Vergnügungszug; Jos Strauss: Sphärenklänge; J. Strauss II: Kaiser, Op. 437; Frühlingsstimmen, Op. 410; Pizzicato Polka; Jos Strauss: Dorfschwalben aus Österreich; J. Strauss I: Radetzky March; J. Strauss II: Waldmeister (exc); Accelerationen, Op. 234; G'schichten aus dem Wienerwald, Op. 325; Auf der Jagd, Op. 373; Rosen aus dem Süden; Wein, Weib und Gesang; Fledermaus (exc); Ballo in maschera Quadrille, Op. 272; Tritsch-Tratsch; Kaiser, Op. 437. (VPO/E. Kleiber/C. Krauss/G. Szell/B. Walter/H. Knappertsbusch/K. Böhm/H. von Karajan/W. Furtwängler/W. Boskovsky/J. Krips/L. Maazel/C. Abbado/Z. Mehta)

① **435 349-2GH** (4/92)
Brahms—Orchestral and Choral Works
Brahms: Nänie, Op. 82; Symphony 4; Haydn Variations. (Berlin Rad Chor, BPO/C. Abbado)

① **435 381-2GH** (6/92)
Bach—Organ Works
Bach: Toccata, Adagio and Fugue, BWV564; Fantasia and Fugue, BWV542; Schübler Chorales, BWV645-650; Toccata and Fugue, BWV540; Passacaglia and Fugue, BWV582. (S. Preston)

① **435 383-2GH** (6/92)
Martin—Chamber Orchestral Works
Martin: Wind Concerto; Polyptyque; Etudes. (M. Blankestijn, COE/T. Fischer)

① **435 385-2GH** (9/92)
Schubert/Liszt—Piano Works
Liszt: Lieder, S558 (exc); Années de pèlerinage 2 (exc); Schubert: Piano Sonata, D850. (L. Zilberstein)

① **435 387-2GH** (11/92)
Cheryl Studer sings Sacred Arias
Schubert: Ave Maria, D839; Mendelssohn: Hear my Prayer; Bach: Christmas Oratorio, BWV248 (exc); Handel: Messiah (exc); Mozart: Vespers, K339 (exc); Gounod: Repentir; Fauré: Requiem (exc); Gounod: Ave Maria; Poulenc: Gloria (exc); Bernstein: Mass (exc); Bruch: Jubilate, Op.3. (C. Studer, Ambrosian Sngrs, LSO/I. Marin)

① **435 389-2GH** (7/93)
Points of Departure
Lerdahl: Waves; Druckman: Nor Spell nor Charm; Bolcom: Orphée-Sérénade; Gandolfi: Points of Departure. (Orpheus CO)

① **435 437-2GH** (7/92)
Milhaud—Orchestral Works
Milhaud: Symphony 1; Symphony 2; Suite provençale. (Toulouse Capitole Orch/M. Plasson)

① **435 438-2GH** (9/93)
Honegger—Orchestral Works
Honegger: Tempête; Pastorale d'été; Horace victorieux; Symphonic Movements (exc); Traversée des Andes; Vol sur l'Atlantique. (Toulouse Capitole Orch/M. Plasson)

① **435 439-2GH** (6/92)
Prokofiev—Piano Sonatas
Prokofiev: Piano Sonata 3; Piano Sonata 7; Piano Sonata 8. (A. Gavrilov)

① **435 440-2GH** (7/92)
Kathleen Battle at Carnegie Hall
Handel: Serse (exc); Giulio Cesare (exc); Mozart: Als Luise die Briefe, K520; Ridente la calma, K152; Liszt: S'il est un charmant gazon, S284; Comment, disaient-ils, S276; Enfant, si j'étais roi, S283; Oh! quand je dors, S282; R. Strauss: Lieder, Op.68 (exc); Mädchenblumen: Songs, Op.34 (exc); Songs, Op.21 (exc); Songs, Op.4 (exc); Gershwin: Porgy and Bess (exc); Traditional: Good News; G. Charpentier: Louise (exc); J. Strauss II: Fledermaus (exc); Traditional: Over my Head I hear Music; He's got the whole world in His hands; Swing low, sweet chariot. (K. Battle, M. Garrett)

① **435 467-2GH3** (11/92)
Beethoven—Piano Concertos
Beethoven: Piano Concerto 1; Piano Concerto 2; Piano Concerto 3; Piano Concerto 4; Piano Concerto 5. (K. Zimerman, VPO/L. Bernstein, K. Zimerman (pf/dir))

① **435 486-2GH** (6/93)
Schubert/Schumann—Sacred Choral Works
Schubert: Mass, D167; Tantum ergo, D962; Psalm 23, D706; Schumann: Requiem für Mignon, Op.98b. (B. Bonney, B. Poschner-Klebel, D. Schaechter, M. Hintermeier, J. Pita, A. Schmidt, Vienna St Op Chor, COE/C. Abbado)

① **435 591-2GGA** (9/92)
Liszt—Piano Works
Liszt: Consolations, S172; Liebesträume, S541; Années de pèlerinage 2 (exc); Rigoletto—paraphrase, S434. (D. Barenboim)

① **435 594-2GGA** (9/92)
Rachmaninov—Orchestral Works
Rachmaninov: Symphony 1; Rock, Op.7; Aleko (exc); Vocalise. (BPO/L. Maazel)

① **435 596-2GGA2** (10/92)
Schubert—Duets, Trios & Quartets
Schubert: Hermann und Thusnelda, D322; Antigone und Oedip, D542; Cronnan, D282; Sing-Übungen, D619; Selma und Selmar, D286; Licht und Liebe, D352; Hektors Abschied, D312; Nur wer die Sehnsucht kennt, D877/1; Szene aus Faust, D126; Hochzeitsbraten, D930; Advokaten, D37; Punschlied, D277; Verschwunden sind die Schmerzen, D88; Trinklied, D148; Tanz, D826; Des Tages Weihe, D763; Hymne an den Unendlichen, D232; An die Sonne, D439; Nun lasst uns den Leib begraben,

D168; Gott im Ungewitter, D985; Gott der Weltschöpfer, D986; Geselligkeit, D609; Gebet, D815. (E. Ameling, J. Baker, P. Schreier, H. Laubenthal, D. Fischer-Dieskau, G. Moore, Berlin RIAS Chbr Ch)

① **435 617-2GH** (5/92)
Beethoven in Berlin—New Year's Eve Concert
Beethoven: Egmont (exc); Ah! perfido, Op. 65; Leonore (exc); Choral Fantasia. (C. Studer, B. Ganz, E. Kissin, Berlin RIAS Chbr Ch, BPO/C. Abbado)

① **435 712-2GX2** (8/92)
Lehár—The Merry Widow. Suppé—Overtures
Lehár: Lustige Witwe (Cpte); Suppé: Morgen, ein Mittag, ein Abend in Wien (exc); Leichte Kavallerie (exc); Pique Dame (exc); Schöne Galathee (exc); Banditenstreiche (exc); Dichter und Bauer (exc). (E. Harwood, R. Kollo, Z. Kélémen, W. Hollweg, T. Stratas, W. Krenn, D. Grobe, Berlin Deutsche Op Chor, BPO/H. von Karajan)

① **435 744-2GDO3** (4/93)
Beethoven—Piano Concertos, etc
Beethoven: Piano Concerto 1; Piano Concerto 2; Piano Concerto 3; Piano Concerto 4; Piano Concerto 5; Rondos, Op.51. (W. Kempff, BPO/P. Van Kempen)

① **435 751-2GDO** (11/92)
Richter plays Schumann
Schumann: Fantasiestücke, Op.12 (exc); Marches, Op.76 (exc); Waldszenen; Novelletten (exc); Toccata; Abegg Variations. (S. Richter)

① **435 757-2GH2** (9/92)
Borodin—Orchestral Works
Borodin: Symphony 1; Symphony 2; Symphony 3; Prince Igor (exc); String Quartet 2 (exc); In the Steppes of Central Asia; Petite Suite. (Gothenburg Sym Chor, Gothenburg SO/N. Järvi)

① **435 766-2GH** (9/92)
Debussy—Orchestral Works
Debussy: Après-midi; Images; Printemps. (Cleveland Orch/P. Boulez)

① **435 781-2GH** (10/92)
Adagio - Mischa Maisky
Saint-Saëns: Carnaval des Animaux (exc); Fauré: Elégie; Glazunov: Chant du ménéstrel; Tchaikovsky: Nocturne, Op.19/4; Bruch: Kol Nidrei; R. Strauss: Romanze, Av75; Haydn: Violin Concerto, HobVIIa:1 (exc). (M. Maisky, Paris Orch/S. Bychkov)

① **435 800-2GH** (3/93)
Brahms—Violin Sonatas
Brahms: Violin Sonata 1; Violin Sonata 2; Violin Sonata 3. (A. Dumay, M-J. Pires)

① **435 848-2GX2** (12/92)
Spanish Songs - Berganza
Alfonso el Sabio: Rosa de rosas; Fuenllana: Orphenica lyra (exc); Anon: Dindirin, dindirin; Mudarra: Tres Libros (vocal works) (exc); Anon: Nuevas te traygo; Hombres con gran plazer; Valderrábano: De donde venis, amore?; Milán: El Maestro: Sonetos (exc); Triana: Dinos, madre del donsel; Encina: Romerico; Vasquez: Vos me matastes; Milán: El Maestro: Villancicos (exc); Narváez: Con qué la lavaré?; Vasquez: En la fuente del rosel; Alfonso el Sabio: Santa María, strella do dia; Anchieta: Con amores, la mi madre; Francisco de la Torre: Pámpano verde; Esteve: Alma, sintamos; Granados: Tonadillas (exc); Durán: Canciones castellanas (exc); Turina: Saeta; Canto a Sevilla (exc); Poema en forma de canciones (exc); Montsalvatge: Canciones negras; Falla: Canciones populares españolas; García Lorca: Canciones españolas antiguas. (T. Berganza, N. Yepes, F. Lavilla)

① **435 856-2GH** (2/93)
Schumann—Orchestral Works
Schumann: Symphony 1; Symphony 4; Manfred (exc). (BPO/James Levine)

① **435 860-2GH2** (7/94)
Berlioz—Works
Berlioz: Nocturne; Maure jaloux; Amitié, reprends ton empire; Canon libre à la quinte; Pleure, pauvre Colette; Montagnard exilé; Scènes de Faust (exc); Scènes de Faust (exc); Mélodies, Op. 2 (exc); Mélodies, Op. 2 (exc); Mélodies, Op. 2 (exc); Mélodies, Op. 2 (exc); Elégie en prose; Captive; Sara la baigneuse; Je crois en vous; Chansonette; Matin; Trébuchet; Jeune Pâtre breton; Chant des Bretons; Tristia (exc); Zaïde; Champs; Prière du matin; Belle Isabeau; Chasseur danois. (F. Pollet, A.S. Von Otter, J. Aler, T. Allen, C. Garben, Stockholm Royal Op Chor, B. Schenk, C. Mühlbach, G. Söllscher, T. Thedéen, T. Lutz)

1353

① **435 864-2GH** (4/93)
Barber/Ives—String Quartets
Ives: String Quartet 1; String Quartet 2; Set of Three Short Pieces (exc); *Barber*: String Quartet, Op.11. (Emerson Qt)

① **435 866-2GH** (12/93)
Kathleen Battle sings Italian Opera Arias
Bellini: Capuleti (exc); *Rossini*: Tancredi (exc); *Donizetti*: Don Pasquale (exc); Linda di Chamounix (exc); *Bellini*: Sonnambula (exc); *Rossini*: Viaggio a Reims (exc). (K. Battle, R. Croft, R. Stene, M.S. Doss, Ambrosian Op Chor, LPO/B. Campanella)

① **435 867-2GH2** (5/94)
Barber—The Songs
Barber: Slumber song of the Madonna; There's Nae Lark; Love at the Door; Serenades; Love's Caution; Night Wanderers; Of that so sweet imprisonment; Strings in the Earth and Air; Beggar's song; In the dark pinewood; Songs, Op.2 (Cpte); Songs, Op.10 (Cpte); Songs, Op.13 (Cpte); Dover Beach, Op.3; Songs, Op.18 (Cpte); Nuvoletta, Op.25; Mélodies passagères, Op.27 (Cpte); Hermit Songs, Op.29 (Cpte); Despite and Still, Op.41 (Cpte); Songs, Op.45 (Cpte). (C. Studer, T. Hampson, J. Browning, Emerson Qt)

① **435 873-2GH** (5/93)
Vivaldi—Oboe Concertos
Vivaldi: Concerto, RV450; Concerto, RV463; Concerto, RV548; Concerto, RV453; Concerto, RV461; Concerto, RV447. (D. Boyd, M. Blankestijn, COE)

① **435 874-2GH** (10/93)
Wagner—Overtures and Preludes
Wagner: Rienzi (exc); Tannhäuser (exc); Meistersinger (exc); Lohengrin (exc); Fliegende Holländer (exc). (NY Met Op Orch/James Levine)

① **435 881-2DH** (2/93)
Beethoven—Piano Works
Beethoven: Piano Sonata 32; Bagatelles (exc); Rondo a capriccio, Op.129. (A. Ugorski)

① **435 882-2GH** (2/93)
Mozart—Piano Sonatas
Mozart: Piano Sonata, K279; Piano Sonata, K280; Piano Sonata, K311; Piano Sonata, K576. (M-J. Pires)

① **435 883-2GH** (8/93)
German Orchestral Works
Schoenberg: Verklärte Nacht; *R. Strauss*: Metamorphosen; *Wagner*: Siegfried Idyll. (BPO/James Levine)

① **437 092-2GH** (4/93)
Schubert—Violin Sonatinas
Schubert: Violin Sonata, D384; Violin Sonata, D385; Violin Sonata, D408. (G. Kremer, O. Maisenberg)

① **437 128-2GX2** (2/93)
Brahms/Wolf—String Quartets
Brahms: String Quartet 1; String Quartet 2; String Quartet 3; *Wolf*: String Quartet in D minor. (LaSalle Qt)

① **437 131-2GX2** (2/93)
Brahms—Chamber Works
Brahms: Piano Trio 1; Piano Trio 2; Piano Trio 3; Horn Trio; Clarinet Trio. (Trieste Trio, C. Eschenbach, E. Drolc, G. Seifert, K. Leister, G. Donderer)

① **437 206-2GX3** (11/93)
Liszt—Années de pèlerinage
Liszt: Années de pèlerinage 1; Années de pèlerinage 2; Venezia e Napoli, S162; Années de pèlerinage 3. (L. Berman)

① **437 215-2GX9(1)** (3/93)
Schubert—Lieder, Vol-1 (pt 1)
Schubert: Leichenphantasie, D7; Vatermörder, D10; Jüngling am Bache, D30; Totengräberlied, D44; Schatten, D50; Sehnsucht, D52; Verklärung, D59; Pensa, che questo istante, D76; Taucher, D77; Andenken, D99; Geisternähe, D100; Totenopfer, D101; Trost, D97; Betende, D102; Lied aus der Ferne, D107; Abend, D108; Lied der Liebe, D109; Erinnerungen, D98; Adelaide, D95; An Emma, D113; Romanze, D114; An Laura, D115; Geistertanz, D116; Mädchen aus der Fremde, D117; Nachtgesang, D119; Trost in Tränen, D120; Schäfers Klagelied, D121; Sehnsucht, D123; Am See, D124; Auf einen Kirchhof, D151; Als ich sie erröten sah, D153; Bild, D155; Mondabend, D141; Lodas Gespenst, D150; Sänger, D149; Erwartung, D159; Am Flusse, D160; An Mignon, D161; Nähe des Geliebten, D162. (D. Fischer-Dieskau, G. Moore)

① **437 215-2GX9(2)** (3/93)
Schubert—Lieder, Vol.1 (pt 2)
Schubert: Sängers Morgenlied, D165; Amphiaraos, D166; Das war ich, D174; Sterne, D176; Vergebliche Liebe, D177; Liebesrausch, D179; Sehnsucht der Liebe, D180;

Erste Liebe, D182; Trinklied, D183; Stimme der Liebe, D187; Naturgenuss, D188; An die Freude, D189; Jüngling am Bache, D192; An den Mond, D193; Mainacht, D194; An die Nachtigall, D196; An die Apfelbäume, D197; Seufzer, D198; Liebeständelei, D206; Liebende, D207; Traum, D213; Laube, D214; Meeres Stille, D216; Grablied, D218; Finden, D219; Wandrers Nachtlied I, D224; Fischer, D225; Erster Verlust, D226; Erinnerung, D229; Täuschung, D230; Abend, D221; Geist der Liebe, D233; Tischlied, D234; Liedler, D209; Ballade, D134; Abends unter der Linde, D235; Mondnacht, D238; Huldigung, D240; Alles um Liebe, D241. (D. Fischer-Dieskau, G. Moore)

① **437 215-2GX9(3)** (3/93)
Schubert—Lieder, Vol.1 (pt 3)
Schubert: Geheimnis, D250; An den Frühling, D587; Bürgschaft, D246; Rattenfänger, D255; Schatzgräber, D256; Heidenröslein, D257; Bundeslied, D258; An den Mond, D259; Wonne der Wehmut, D260; Wer kauft Liebesgötter?, D261; Goldschmiedsgesell, D560; Morgenkuss, D264; Abendständchen, D265; Morgenlied, D266; Weiberfreund, D271; An die Sonne, D272; Tischlerlied, D274; Totenkranz für ein Kind, D275; Abendlied, D276; Fröhlichkeit, D262; Lob des Tokayers, D248; Furcht der Geliebten, D285; Rosenband, D280; An sie, D288; Sommernacht, D289; Frühen Gräber, D290; Dem Unendlichen, D291; Ossians Lied, D278; Mädchen von Inistore, D281; Labetrank, der Liebe, D302; An die Geliebte, D303; Mein Gruss an den Mai, D305; Skolie, D306; Sternenwelten, D307; Macht der Liebe, D308; Gestörte Glück, D309; Sterne, D313; Nachtgesang, D314; An Rosa I, D315. (D. Fischer-Dieskau, G. Moore)

① **437 215-2GX9(4)** (3/93)
Schubert—Lieder, Vol.1 (pt 4)
Schubert: An Rosa II, D316; Schwanengesang, D318; Zufriedene, D320; Liane, D298; Augenlied, D297; Geistes-Gruss, D142; Hoffnung, D295; An den Mond, D296; Rastlose Liebe, D138; Erlkönig, D328; Schmetterling, D633; Berge, D634; Genügsamkeit, D143; An die Natur, D372; Klage, D371; Morgenlied, D381; Abendlied, D382; Flüchtling, D402; An den Klavier, D388; Entzückung an Laura, D390; Vier Weltalter, D391; Pflügerlied, D392; Einsiedelei, D393; An die Harmonie, D394; Herbstnacht, D404; Lied, D403; Herbstabend, D405; Entfernten, D350; Fischerlied, D351; Sprache der Liebe, D410; Abschied von der Harfe, D406; Stimme der Liebe, D412; Entzückung, D413; Geist der Liebe, D414; Klage, D415; Julius an Theone, D419; Klage an den Mond, D436; Frühlingslied, D398; Auf den Tod einer Nachtigall, D399. (D. Fischer-Dieskau, G. Moore)

① **437 215-2GX9(5)** (3/93)
Schubert—Lieder, Vol.1 (pt 5)
Schubert: Knabenzeit, D400; Winterlied, D401; Minnelied, D429; Frühe Liebe, D430; Blumenlied, D431; Leidende, D432; Seligkeit, D433; Erntelied, D434; Grosse Halleluja, D442; Gestirne, D444; Liebesgötter, D446; An den Schlaf, D447; Gott im Frühling, D448; Gute Hirt, D449; Nacht, D358; Fragment aus dem Aeschylus, D450; An die untergehende Sonne, D457; An mein Klavier, D342; Freude der Kinderjahre, D455; Heimweh, D456; An den Mond, D468; An Chloen, D462; Hochzeitlied, D463; In der Mitternacht, D464; Trauer der Liebe, D465; Perle, D466; Liedesend, D473; Lied des Orpheus, D474; Abschied, D475; Rückweg, D476; Alte Liebe rostet nie, D477; Wer sich der Einsamkeit ergibt, D478; Wer nie sein Brot mit Tränen ass, D480; An die Türen, D479; König in Thule, D367; Jägers Abendlied, D368; An Schwager Kronos, D369; Sänger am Felsen, D482; Lied, D483. (D. Fischer-Dieskau, G. Moore)

① **437 215-2GX9(6)** (3/93)
Schubert—Lieder, Vol.1 (pt 6)
Schubert: Wanderer, D489; Hirt, D490; Lied eines Schiffers an die Dioskuren, D360; Geheimnis, D491; Zum Punsche, D492; Am Bach im Frühling, D361; An eine Quelle, D530; Bei dem Grabe meines Vaters, D496; Am Grabe Anselmos, D504; Abendlied, D499; Zufriedenheit, D362; Herbstlied, D502; Skolie, D507; Lebenslied, D508; Leiden der Trennung, D509; Alinde, D904; An die Laute, D905; Frohsinn, D520; Lied, D522; Trost, D523; Schäfer und der Reiter, D517; Lob der Tränen, D711; Alpenjäger, D524; Wie Ulfru fischt, D525; Fahrt zum Hades, D526; Schlaflied, D527; Blumensprache, D519; Abendröte, D690; Flug der Zeit, D515; Tod und das Mädchen, D531; Lied vom Reifen, D532; Täglich zu singen, D533; Am Strome, D539; Philoktet, D540; Memnon, D541; Auf dem See, D543; Ganymed, D544; Jüngling und der Tod, D545; Trost im Liede, D546. (D. Fischer-Dieskau, G. Moore)

① **437 225-2GX9(1)** (3/93)
Schubert—Lieder, Vol.2 (pt 1)
Schubert: An die Musik, D547; Pax vobiscum, D551; Hänflings Liebeswerbung, D552; Auf der Donau, D553; Schiffer, D536; Nach einem Gewitter, D561; Fischerlied, D562; Grab, D569; Strom, D565; An den Tod, D518;

Abschied, D578; Forelle, D550; Gruppe aus dem Tartarus, D583; Elysium, D584; Atys, D585; Erlafsee, D586; Alpenjäger, D588; Kampf, D594; Knabe in der Wiege, D579; Auf der Riesenkoppe, D611; An den Mond in einer Herbstnacht, D614; Grablied für die Mutter, D616; Einsamkeit, D620; Blumenbrief, D622; Marienbild, D623; Litanei, D343; Blondel zu Marien, D626; Abendrot, D627; Sonett I, D628; Sonett II, D629; Sonett III, D630; Vom Mitleiden Mariä, D632; Gebüsche, D646; Wanderer, D649; Abendbilder, D650; Himmelsfunken, D651; An die Freunde, D654; Sehnsucht, D636; Hoffnung, D637; Jüngling am Bache, D638; Hymne I, D659; Hymne II, D660; Hymne III, D661. (D. Fischer-Dieskau, G. Moore)

① **437 225-2GX9(2)** (3/93)
Schubert—Lieder, Vol.2 (pt 2)
Schubert: Hymne IV, D662; Marie, D658; Beim Winde, D669; Sternennächte, D670; Trost, D671; Nachtstück, D672; Prometheus, D674; Götter Griechenlands, D677; Nachthymne, D687; Vögel, D691; Knabe, D692; Fluss, D693; Abendröte, D690; Schiffer, D694; Sterne, D684; Morgenlied, D685; Frühlingsglaube, D686; Liebeslauschen, D698; Orest auf Tauris, D548; Entsühnte Orest, D699; Freiwilliges Versinken, D700; Jüngling auf dem Hügel, D702; Sehnsucht, D516; Zürnenden Diana, D707; Im Walde, D708; Gefangenen Sänger, D712; Unglückliche, D713; Versunken, D715; Geheimes, D719; Grenzen der Menschheit, D716; Jüngling an der Quelle, D300; Blumen Schmerz, D731; Sei mir gegrüsst, D741; Epistel, D749; Wachtelschlag, D742; Ihr Grab, D736; Nachtviolen, D752; Aus Heliopolis I, D753; Aus Heliopolis II, D754; Selige Welt, D743; Schwanengesang, D744; Du liebst mich nicht, D756; Liebe hat gelogen, D751. (D. Fischer-Dieskau, G. Moore)

① **437 225-2GX9(3)** (3/93)
Schubert—Lieder, Vol.2 (pt 3)
Schubert: Todesmusik, D758; Schatzgräbers Begehr, D761; An die Leier, D737; Im Haine, D738; Musensohn, D764; An die Entfernte, D765; Am Flusse, D766; Willkommen und Abschied, D767; Wandrers Nachtlied II, D768; Zürnende Barde, D785; Am See, D746; Viola, D786; Drang in die Ferne, D770; Zwerg, D771; Wehmut, D772; Mutter Erde, D788; Auf dem Wasser zu singen, D774; Pilgerweise, D789; Geheimnis, D793; Pilgrim, D794; Dass sie hier gewesen, D775; Du bist die Ruh, D776; Lachen und Weinen, D777; Greisengesang, D778; Dithyrambe, D801; Sieg, D805; Abendstern, D806; Auflösung, D807; Gondelfahrer, D808; Glaube, Hoffnung und Liebe, D955; Im Abendrot, D799; Einsame, D800; Sängers Habe, D832; Totengräbers Heimweh, D842; Blinde Knabe, D833; Nacht und Träume, D827; Normans Gesang, D846; Lied des gefangenen Jägers, D843; Im Walde, D834; Auf der Bruck, D853; Heimweh, D851; Allmacht, D852; Fülle der Liebe, D854. (D. Fischer-Dieskau, G. Moore)

① **437 225-2GX9(4)** (3/93)
Schubert—Lieder, Vol.2 (pt 4)
Schubert: Wiedersehn, D855; Abendlied für die Entfernte, D856; Lied des Florio, D857/2; An mein Herz, D860; Liebliche Stern, D861; Tiefes Leid, D876; Am Fenster, D878; Sehnsucht, D879; Im Freien, D880; Fischerweise, D881; Totengräberweise, D869; Im Frühling, D882; Lebensmut, D883; Um Mitternacht, D862; Über Wildemann, D884; Romanze des Richard Löwenherz, D907; Trinklied, D888; Ständchen, D889; Hippolits Lied, D890; An Silvia, D891; Wanderer an den Mond, D870; Zügenglöcklein, D871; Bei dir allein, D866/2; Irdisches Glück, D866/4; Wiegenlied, D867; Vater mit dem Kind, D906; Jägers Liebeslied, D909; Schiffers Scheidelied, D910; Incanto degli occhi, D902/1; Traditor deluso, D902/2; Modo di prender moglie, D902/3; Lied im Grünen, D917; Weinen, D926; Vor meiner Wiege, D927; Wallensteiner Lanzknecht beim Trunk, D931; Kreuzzug, D932; Fischers Liebesglück, D933; Winterabend, D938; Sterne, D939; Herbst, D945; Widerschein, D949; Abschied von der Erde, D829. (D. Fischer-Dieskau, G. Moore)

① **437 235-2GX3** (3/93)
Schubert—Lieder, Vol.3
Schubert: Schöne Müllerin (Cpte); Winterreise (Cpte); Schwanengesang, D957 (Cpte). (D. Fischer-Dieskau, G. Moore)

① **437 244-2GGA2** (1/93)
Berlioz/Franck—Vocal & Orchestral Works
Berlioz: Roméo et Juliette (Cpte); *Franck*: Chasseur maudit; Nocturne; Rédemption (exc). (Y. Minton, F. Araiza, J. Bastin, C. Ludwig, Paris Orch Chor, Paris Orch/D. Barenboim)

① **437 248-2GGA** (1/93)
Brahms—Viola Sonatas
Brahms: Viola Sonata 1; Viola Sonata 2; FAE Sonata. (P. Zukerman, P. Zukerman, D. Barenboim)

① 437 249-2GGA (1/93)
Brahms—Piano Works
Brahms: Piano Pieces, Op.116; Piano Pieces, Op.117;
Piano Pieces, Op.118; Piano Pieces, Op.119. (W.
Kempff)

① 437 250-2GGA (1/93)
Bruckner—Orchestral & Vocal Works
Bruckner: Symphony 0; Helgoland; Psalm 150. (R.
Welting, Chicago Sym Chor, Chicago SO/D. Barenboim)

① 437 252-2GGA (2/93)
Liszt/Schumann/Brahms—Piano Works
Liszt: Piano Sonata, S178; Hungarian Rhapsodies, S244
(exc); *Schumann:* Piano Sonata 2; *Brahms:* Rhapsodies,
Op.79. (M. Argerich)

① 437 254-2GGA (1/93)
Smetana/Janáček—Orchestral Works
Janáček: Sinfonietta; *Smetana:* Richard III; Wallenstein's
Camp; Hakon Jarl; Prague Carnival. (BRSO/R. Kubelik)

① 437 255-2GGA (1/93)
Strauss family—Waltzes & Polkas
J. Strauss II: G'schichten aus dem Wienerwald, Op. 325;
Auf der Jagd, Op. 373; Pizzicato Polka; Unter Donner und
Blitz; Wiener Blut; Blauen Donau, Op. 314; Kaiser, Op.
437; Annen-Polka, Op. 117; Tritsch-Tratsch; *Jos Strauss:*
Delirien; *J. Strauss II:* Perpetuum mobile. (BPO/H. von
Karajan)

① 437 348-2GDO2 (7/93)
Irmgard Seefried - Lieder Recital
Mozart: Veilchen, K476; Verschweigung, K518; Lied der
Trennung, K519; Kinderspiel, K598; Kleine Spinnerin,
K531; An Chloe, K524; Als Luise die Briefe, K520;
Sehnsucht nach dem Frühling, K596; Dans un bois
solitaire, K308; Abendempfindung, K523; *Schubert:* Auf
dem Wasser zu singen, D774; Seligkeit, D433; Lachen und
Weinen, D777; Junge Nonne, D828; König in Thule, D367;
Forelle, D550; Lied im Grünen, D917; Fischerweise, D881;
An die Musik, D547; *Brahms:* Lieder, Op.59 (exc); Lieder,
Op.106 (exc); *Mussorgsky:* Nursery; *Bartók:* Village
Scenes; *Wolf:* Mörike Lieder (exc); *R. Strauss:* Lieder,
Op.17 (exc); Lieder, Op.29 (exc); Lieder, Op.37 (exc);
Lieder, Op.10 (exc); Lieder, Op.27 (exc); *Schumann:*
Myrthen, Op.25 (exc); Liederkreis, Op.24 (exc);
Frauenliebe und -Leben, Op.42 (Cpte). (I. Seefried, E.
Werba)

① 437 352-2GDO2 (6/93)
Beethoven—Cello Sonatas
Beethoven: Cello Sonata 1; Cello Sonata 2; Cello Sonata
3; Cello Sonata 4; Cello Sonata 5; Handel Variations,
WoO45; Mozart Variations, WoO46; Mozart Variations,
Op.66. (P. Fournier, F. Gulda)

① 437 368-2GX2 (4/95)
Beethoven—Orchestral Works
Beethoven: Symphony 3; Symphony 9; Egmont (exc);
Coriolan; Prometheus (exc). (G. Jones, T. Troyanos, Jess
Thomas, K. Ridderbusch, Vienna St Op Chor, VPO/K.
Böhm)

① 437 371-2GX2 (5/95)
Bizet/Lalo—Orchestral Works
Bizet: Symphony; Jolie fille de Perth Suite; Jeux d'enfants;
Lalo: Cello Concerto; Namouna Suites; Rapsodie
norvégienne. (P. Fournier, FRNO, Lamoureux Orch/J.
Martinon)

① 437 404-2GX2 (10/94)
Famous Ballet Works
Offenbach: Gaîté Parisienne (exc); *Gounod:* Faust (exc);
Tchaikovsky: Sleeping Beauty (exc); *Delibes:* Coppélia
(exc); *Chopin:* Sylphides (Cpte); *Ravel:* Boléro. (BPO/H.
von Karajan)

① 437 460-2GH (1/93)
Brahms—Piano Works
Brahms: Piano Pieces, Op.76 (exc); Rhapsodies, Op.79;
Piano Pieces, Op.117; Piano Pieces, Op.118 (exc). (I.
Pogorelich)

① 437 470-2GX2 (10/94)
Mendelssohn—Songs without words
Mendelssohn: Songs without Words; Kinderstücke;
Gondellied (Klavierstücke; Albumblatt, Op.117. (D.
Barenboim)

① 437 506-2GH (6/93)
Brahms/Dvořák—Orchestral Works
Brahms: Hungarian Dances (exc); *Dvořák:* Symphonic
Variations; Czech Suite, B93. (N German RSO/J.E.
Gardiner)

① 437 507-2GH3 (12/93)
Nielsen—Complete Symphonies
Nielsen: Symphony 1; Symphony 2; Symphony 3;

Symphony 4; Symphony 5; Symphony 6. (S. Isokoski, J.
Hynninen, Gothenburg SO/N. Järvi)

① 437 514-2GH (12/93)
Beethoven—Cello Sonatas, etc
Beethoven: Cello Sonata 3; Cello Sonata 4; Cello Sonata
5; Handel Variations, WoO45. (M. Maisky, M. Argerich)

① 437 515-2GH (6/94)
Berg/Korngold/R. Strauss—Lieder
R. Strauss: Lieder, Op.36 (exc); Lieder, Op.32 (exc);
Lieder, Op.37 (exc); Lieder, Op.46 (exc); Lieder, Op.39
(exc); Lieder, Op.19 (exc); *Berg:* Early Songs; *Korngold:*
Einfache Lieder, Op.9 (exc); Lieder, Op.18; Lieder, Op.38
(exc); Abschiedslieder, Op.14 (exc); Sonett.für Wien,
Op.41. (A.S. von Otter, B. Forsberg)

① 437 519-2GH (6/93)
Grieg—Orchestral Songs
Grieg: Songs, Op. 21 (exc); Peer Gynt (exc); Songs, Op.39
(exc); Songs, Op.25 (exc); Songs, Op.33 (exc); Norway,
Op.58 (exc); Mountain thrall, Op.32; Southern Convent,
Op. 20; Bergljot, Op. 42. (B. Bonney, R. Stene, H.
Hagegård, R. Tellefsen, Gothenburg Sym Chor,
Gothenburg SO/N. Järvi)

① 437 520-2GH (6/93)
Grieg—Works for String Orchestra
Grieg: Holberg Suite; Elegiac Melodies; Melodies, Op.53;
Nordic Melodies, Op. 63; Lyric Pieces. (Gothenburg SO/N.
Järvi)

① 437 521-2GH (6/93)
Grieg—Songs
Grieg: Haugtussa, Op.67 (Cpte); Melodies of the heart,
Op.5 (exc); Songs, Op.25 (exc); Songs, Op.26 (exc);
Songs, Op.33 (exc); Songs, Op.39 (exc); Songs, Op.48
(Cpte); Songs, Op.49 (exc); Songs, Op.60 (exc); Songs,
Op.61 (exc). (A.S. von Otter, B. Forsberg)

① 437 522-2GH (12/93)
Grieg—Lyric Pieces
Grieg: Lyric Pieces, Op.12 (exc); Lyric Pieces, Op.38 (exc);
Lyric Pieces, Op.43 (exc); Lyric Pieces, Op.47 (exc); Lyric
Pieces, Op.54 (exc); Lyric Pieces, Op.57 (exc); Lyric
Pieces, Op.62 (exc); Lyric Pieces, Op.65 (exc); Lyric
Pieces, Op.68 (exc); Lyric Pieces, Op.71 (exc). (A.
Gavrilov)

① 437 523-2GH (6/93)
Grieg—Dramatic Works with Orchestra
Grieg: Land Sighting, Op.31; Olav Trygvason; Peer Gynt
Suites. (R. Stene, A. Gjevang, H. Hagegård, Gothenburg
Sym Chor, Gothenburg SO/N. Järvi)

① 437 524-2GH (7/93)
Grieg—Orchestral Works
Grieg: Piano Concerto; Lyric Suite, Op.54 (exc); In
Autumn. (L. Zilberstein, Gothenburg SO/N. Järvi)

① 437 525-2GH (9/93)
Grieg—Violin Sonatas
Grieg: Violin Sonata 1; Violin Sonata 2; Violin Sonata 3. (A.
Dumay, M-J. Pires)

① 437 528-2GH (8/93)
Mendelssohn—Symphonies for Strings
Mendelssohn: String Symphony 8; String Symphony 9;
String Symphony 10. (Orpheus CO)

① 437 532-2GH (11/93)
Ravel/Prokofiev—Piano Works
Prokofiev: Romeo and Juliet Pieces; Pieces, Op.4 (exc);
Pieces, Op.12 (exc); *Ravel:* Gaspard de la Nuit; Pavane
pour une infante défunte. (A. Gavrilov)

① 437 533-2GH (7/93)
Respighi—Orchestral Works
Respighi: Birds; Ancient Airs and Dances (exc); Botticelli
Pictures. (Orpheus CO)

① 437 534-2GH (9/93)
Respighi—Orchestral Works
Respighi: Fountains of Rome; Pines of Rome; Roman
Festivals. (NYPO/G. Sinopoli)

① 437 535-2GH (4/93)
Schubert—Soirée
Schubert: Polonaise, D580; German Dances and Trios,
D90; Rondo, D438; Minuets and Trios, D89; Concertstück,
D345. (G. Kremer, G. Lester, D. Poppen, R. Lester, COE)

① 437 536-2GH (6/93)
Schubert—Lieder
Schubert: Schwanengesang, D957 (exc); Vor meiner
Wiege, D927; Kreuzzug, D932; Fischers Liebesglück,
D933; Winterabend, D938; Sterne, D939. (A. Schmidt, R.
Jansen)

① 437 537-2GH (11/93)
American Chamber Works
Harbison: String Quartet 2; *Schuller:* String Quartet 3;
Wernick: String Quartet 4. (Emerson Qt)

① 437 538-2GH (6/95)
Schumann—Piano Works
Schumann: Waldszenen; Arabeske; Romanzen, Op.28;
Faschingsschwank aus Wien. (M-J. Pires)

① 437 544-2GH (12/93)
Carmen-Fantasie
Sarasate: Zigeunerweisen; Wieniawski: Légende, Op.17;
Tartini: Devil's Trill Sonata; *Ravel:* Tzigane; *Massenet:*
Thaïs (exc); *Sarasate:* Carmen Fantasy; *Fauré:* Berceuse,
Op.16. (A-S. Mutter, VPO/James Levine)

① 437 546-2GH (7/93)
Mozart—Piano Sonatas
Mozart: Piano Sonata, K281; Piano Sonata, K282; Piano
Sonata, K533. (M-J. Pires)

① 437 638-2GGA2 (7/93)
Berlioz—Vocal & Orchestral Works
Berlioz: Grande Messe des Morts (Cpte); Carnaval romain;
Damnation de Faust (exc); *Various:* National Anthems
(exc). (P. Domingo, Paris Orch Chor, Paris Orch/D.
Barenboim)

① 437 641-2GGA2 (7/93)
Schumann—Symphonies, etc
Schumann: Symphony 1; Symphony 2; Symphony 3;
Symphony 4; Manfred (exc). (Chicago SO/D. Barenboim)

① 437 677-2GH (9/93)
Irmgard Seefried - Opera Recital
Mozart: Rè Pastore (exc); Idomeneo (exc); Così fan tutte
(exc); *Bizet:* Carmen (exc); *Handel:* Giulio Cesare (exc);
Mozart: Nozze di Figaro (exc); Don Giovanni (exc);
Beethoven: Fidelio (exc); *Respighi:* Tramonto; *Mozart:*
Così fan tutte (exc); *Weber:* Freischütz (exc); *A. Thomas:*
Mignon (exc); *Lortzing:* Wildschütz (exc); *R. Strauss:*
Rosenkavalier (exc). (I. Seefried, Vienna SO, Berlin RSO,
BPO, Bavarian St Orch, BRSO, Lucerne Fest Strings,
Lamoureux Orch, Bamberg SO, Staatskapelle Dresden/F.
Leitner/K. Böhm/F. Fricsay/E. Jochum/R. Baumgartner/J.
Fournet/C. Stepp, M. Schech, E. Haefliger, N. Merriman,
D. Fischer-Dieskau, I. Sardi, R. Streich, I. Steingruber, K.
Böhme, Dresden St Op Chor)

① 437 680-2GDO2 (10/93)
Rita Streich - Lieder Recital
Mozart: An Chloe, K524; Kleine Spinnerin, K531; Lied der
Trennung, K519; Veilchen, K476; Zauberer, K472;
Sehnsucht nach dem Frühling, K596; Moto di gioia, K579;
Oiseaux, si tous les ans, K307; Dans un bois solitaire,
K308; Kinderspiel, K598; Sei du mein Trost, K391;
Verschweigung, K418; Warnung, K433; *Schubert:* Forelle,
D550; Auf dem Wasser zu singen, D774; Seligkeit, D433;
Wolf: Wohin mit der Freud'? Wiegenlied (1878); Kleine;
Nachtgruss, UP92; *R. Strauss:* Lieder, Op.69 (exc);
Milhaud: Chansons de Ronsard; *Traditional:* 's Schätzli;
Canto delle risaiole; Au clair de la lune; Z' Lauterbach han;
Schubert: Heidenröslein, D257; Claudine von Villa Bella
(exc); So sasst mich scheinen, D877/3; Nähe des
Geliebten, D162; Liebhaber in allen Gestalten, D558; Hirt
auf dem Felsen, D965; An den Mond, D193; Vögel, D691;
Lied im Grünen, D917; *Schumann:* Myrthen, Op.25 (exc);
Liederkreis, Op.39 (exc); Jugend Lieder, Op.79 (exc);
Lieder und Gesänge, Op.77 (exc); *Brahms:* Lieder, Op.106
(exc); Lieder, Op. 107 (exc); Lieder, Op.84 (exc); Lieder,
Op.49 (exc); *Wolf:* Eichendorff Lieder (exc); Goethe Lieder
(exc); Mörike Lieder (exc). (R. Streich, E. Werba, G.
Weissenborn, H. Geusser)

① 437 719-2GC (8/93)
Berg—Vocal Works
Berg: Early Songs; Wein; Early Songs. (M. Marshall, S.
Hass, K. Lõvaas, G. Parsons, Vienna SO/G.
Rozhdestvensky, N German RSO/H. Blomstedt)

① 437 763-2GH (8/95)
Mozart—Piano Works
Mozart: Piano Sonata, K283; Piano Sonata, K331;
Fantasia, K397. (I. Pogorelich)

① 437 783-2GH (10/93)
Haydn—Orchestral Works
Haydn: Symphony 60; Symphony 91; Armida (exc).
(Orpheus CO)

① 437 784-2GH (10/93)
Cheryl Studer—Salzburg Recital
Schubert: Ganymed, D544; Im Frühling, D882; Nur wer die
Sehnsucht kennt, D877/4; Gretchen am Spinnrade, D118;
Rastlose Liebe, D138; *Debussy:* Ariettes oubliées; *R.
Strauss:* Lieder, Op.10 (exc); Lieder, Op.17 (exc); Lieder,
Op.27 (exc); Lieder, Op.29 (exc); Lieder, Op.41 (exc);

ⓘ **439 869-2GH** (10/94)
Ives—Orchestral Works
Ives: Orchestral Set I; Unanswered Question; Theatre Orchestra Set; Symphony 3; Set 1. (G. Kalish, Orpheus CO)

ⓘ **439 886-2GH** (9/94)
Barber/Korngold—Violin Concertos
Barber: Violin Concerto; *Korngold*: Violin Concerto; Much Ado About Nothing Suite (exc). (G. Shaham, LSO/A. Previn, A. Previn)

ⓘ **439 887-2GH** (6/95)
Brahms—Orchestral & Vocal Works
Brahms: Symphony 3; Tragic Overture; Alto Rhapsody, Op.53. (A.S. von Otter, A. Schoenberg Ch, VPO/James Levine)

ⓘ **439 889-2GH** (8/95)
Schumann—Music for Oboe and Piano
Schumann: Adagio and Allegro, Op. 70; Fantasiestücke, Op. 73; Romanzen, Op. 94; Stücke, Op. 102; Klavierstücke, Op. 85 (exc). (D. Boyd, M-J. Pires)

ⓘ **439 892-2GH** (12/94)
Russian Overtures
Glinka: Ruslan and Lyudmila (exc); *Borodin*: Prince Igor (exc); *Shostakovich*: Festive Overture; *Prokofiev*: Semyon Kotko (exc); *Kabalevsky*: Colas Breughnon (exc); *Rimsky-Korsakov*: Tsar's Bride (exc); *Mussorgsky*: Khovanshchina (exc); *Tchaikovsky*: Overture in F; *Glazunov*: Ouverture Solennelle. (Russian Nat Orch/M. Pletnev)

ⓘ **439 894-2GH** (12/94)
Speak Low - Songs by Kurt Weill
Weill: Sieben Todsünden (Cpte); Lady in the dark (exc); Propaganda Songs (exc); Nannas Lied; Happy End (exc); Je ne t'aime pas; Abschiedsbrief; One touch of Venus (exc). (A.S. von Otter, B. Forsberg, N German RSO/J.E. Gardiner)

ⓘ **439 895-2GH** (2/95)
Flute Concertos of the Sans-Souci
C.P.E. Bach: Flute Concerto, H445; *F. Benda*: Flute Concerto in E minor; *Frederick the Great*: Flute Concerti (exc); *Quantz*: Flute Concerto in G. (P. Gallois, CPE Bach CO/P. Schreier)

ⓘ **439 896-2GH** (3/95)
Debussy—Orchestral Works
Debussy: Nocturnes; Première Rapsodie; Jeux; La Mer. (F. Cohen, Cleveland Orch Chor, Cleveland Orch/P. Boulez)

ⓘ **439 910-2GH** (9/95)
Birtwistle—Secret Theatre;Tragoedia etc
Birtwistle: Tragoedia; Distances; Celan Settings; Secret Theatre. (C. Whittlesey, Paris InterContemporain Ens/P. Boulez)

ⓘ **439 914-2GH** (12/94)
Mozart—String Quartets
Mozart: String Quartet, K428; String Quartet, K464; String Quartet Rondo, KAnh72. (Emerson Qt)

ⓘ **439 923-2GH2** (9/95)
Schumann—Complete Symphonies
Schumann: Symphony 1; Symphony 2; Symphony 3; Symphony 4. (Staatskapelle Dresden/G. Sinopoli)

ⓘ **439 927-2GH** (2/95)
Debussy/Ravel—Piano Works
Debussy: Pour le piano; Estampes; *Ravel*: Miroirs; Sonatine; Jeux d'eau. (L. Zilberstein)

ⓘ **439 932-2GH** (10/94)
Haydn—Symphonies, etc
Haydn: Symphony 98; Symphony 100; Mondo della luna (exc). (COE/C. Abbado)

ⓘ **439 934-2GH2** (2/95)
Beethoven—Cello Sonatas, etc
Beethoven: Cello Sonata 1; Cello Sonata 2; Cello Sonata 3; Cello Sonata 4; Cello Sonata 5; Mozart Variations, Op.66; Mozart Variations, WoO46; Handel Variations, WoO45. (M. Maisky, M. Argerich)

ⓘ **439 939-2GH** (6/95)
Milhaud—Orchestral Works
Milhaud: Symphony 6; Symphony 7; Overture méditerranéenne. (Toulouse Capitole Orch/M. Plasson)

ⓘ **439 943-2GH** (3/95)
Schumann—Lieder
Schumann: Gedichte, Op.35 (Cpte); Liederkreis, Op.39 (Cpte); Lieder, Op.40 (exc). (A. Schmidt, R. Jansen)

ⓘ **439 972-2GGA2** (1/95)
Verdi—Overtures & Preludes
Verdi: Oberto (exc); Giorno di regno (exc); Nabucco (exc); Ernani (exc); Giovanna d'Arco (exc); Alzira (exc); Attila

(exc); Masnadieri (exc); Macbeth (exc); Corsaro (exc); Battaglia di Legnano (exc); Luisa Miller (exc); Rigoletto (exc); Traviata (exc); Vespri siciliani (exc); Aroldo (exc); Ballo in maschera (exc); Forza del destino (exc); Aida (exc). (BPO/H. von Karajan)

ⓘ **439 975-2GGA2** (4/95)
Wolf—Lieder
Wolf: Italienisches Liederbuch (Cpte); Eichendorff Lieder (exc); Nachruf; In der Fremde I; In der Fremde II; In der Fremde VI; Rückkehr; Michelangelo Gedichte (Cpte). (C. Ludwig, D. Fischer-Dieskau, D. Barenboim)

ⓘ **439 981-2GGA** (3/95)
Paganini—Violin Works
Paganini: Violin Concerto 1; Sonata Napoleone; Palpiti, Op. 13; Perpetuela. (S. Accardo, LPO/C. Dutoit)

ⓘ **439 982-2GGA** (1/95)
Sibelius—Orchestral Works
Sibelius: Symphony 5; Symphony 6; Legends (exc). (BPO/H. von Karajan)

ⓘ **445 238-2GH** (2/95)
Mussorgsky—Orchestral and Choral Works
Mussorgsky: St John's Night; Destruction of Sennacherib; Salammbô (exc); Oedipus in Athens (exc); Joshua; Pictures. (E. Zaremba, Prague Phil Chor, BPO/C. Abbado)

ⓘ **445 241-2GC3** (10/94)
Bartók—String Quartets
Bartók: String Quartet 1; String Quartet 2; String Quartet 3; String Quartet 4; String Quartet 5; String Quartet 6. (Tokyo Qt)

ⓘ **445 294-2GH** (10/94)
Schubert—Lieder
Schubert: Gruppe aus dem Tartarus, D583; Litanei, D343; Forelle, D550; An die Leier, D737; Lachen und Weinen, D777; Schwanengesang, D957 (exc); Meeres Stille, D216; Wanderer, D489; Erlkönig, D328; Tod und das Mädchen, D531; Heidenröslein, D257; Wandrers Nachtlied II, D768; An die Musik, D547; Auf der Bruck, D853; Schäfers Klagelied, D121; An Silvia, D891; Du bist die Ruh', D776; An die Laute, D905; Rastlose Liebe, D138; Ganymed, D544; Musensohn, D764. (B. Terfel, M. Martineau)

ⓘ **445 354-2GX14** (11/94)
Wagner—Der Ring des Nibelungen
Wagner: Rheingold (Cpte); Walküre (Cpte); Siegfried (Cpte); Götterdämmerung (Cpte). (J. Morris, C. Ludwig, S. Jerusalem, H. Zednik, E. Wlaschiha, M.A. Häggander, M. Baker, S. Lorenz, B. Svendén, K. Moll, J-H. Rootering, H-K. Hong, D. Kesling, M. Parsons, G. Lakes, J. Norman, H. Behrens, K. Moll, M. Napier, L. Kelm, M. Mims, R. Runkel, A. Wilkens, D. Kesling, M. Parsons, R. Engert-Ely, R. Goldberg, K. Moll, K. Battle, M. Salminen, B. Weikl, C. Studer, H. Schwarz, H. Dernesch, T. Troyanos, A. Gruber, NY Met Op Chor, NY Met Op Orch/James Levine)

ⓘ **445 400-2GDO10** (11/94)
Ferenc Fricsay - A Portrait
Beethoven: Symphony 9; *Bartók*: Violin Concerto 2; Dance Suite; Cantata profana; *R. Strauss*: Don Juan; Duet Concertino; Burleske; Till Eulenspiegel; *Liebermann*: Furioso; *Blacher*: Paganini Variations; *Egk*: French Suite; *Einem*: Piano Concerto; *Stravinsky*: Rite of Spring (Cpte); Petrushka (Cpte); Movements; *Rossini*: Barbiere di Siviglia (exc); Tancredi (exc); Signor Bruschino (exc); Gazza ladra (exc); Semiramide (exc); *Verdi*: Nabucco (exc); Traviata (exc); Forza del Destino (exc); Aida (exc); Vespri siciliani (exc); *Brahms*: Symphony 2; Haydn Variations; Alto Rhapsody, Op. 53; *Mozart*: Requiem; Adagio and Fugue, K546; *Tchaikovsky*: Symphony 6; Violin Concerto; *Kodály*: Marosszék Dances; Symphony in C; Psalmus Hungaricus; *Smetana*: Má Vlast (exc). (I. Seefried, M. Forrester, E. Haefliger, D. Fischer-Dieskau, Berlin St Hedwig's Cath Ch, BPO/F. Fricsay, H. Krebs, T. Varga, Berlin RIAS Chbr Ch, Berlin RIAS Orch, H. Geusser, W. Fugmann, M. Weber, D. Herzog, Berlin RSO, VPO, E. Grümmer, G. Pitzinger, H. Hotter, Y. Menuhin)

ⓘ **445 402-2GDO** (11/94)
Bartók—Orchestral Works
Bartók: Violin Concerto 2; Dance Suite; Cantata profana. (H. Krebs, D. Fischer-Dieskau, T. Varga, Berlin RIAS Chbr Ch, Berlin St Hedwig's Cath Ch, BPO, Berlin RIAS Orch/F. Fricsay)

ⓘ **445 403-2GDO** (11/94)
R. Strauss—Orchestral Works
R. Strauss: Don Juan; Duet Concertino; Burleske; Till Eulenspiegel. (H. Geusser, W. Fugmann, M. Weber, Berlin RIAS Orch, BPO/F. Fricsay)

ⓘ **445 404-2GDO** (11/94)
Liebermann/Blacher/Egk/Einem—Orchestral Works
Liebermann: Furioso; *Blacher*: Paganini Variations; *Egk*:

French Suite; *Einem*: Piano Concerto; Ballade, Op.23. (G. Herzog, Berlin RIAS Orch, Berlin RSO/F. Fricsay)

ⓘ **445 405-2GDO** (11/94)
Stravinsky—Orchestral Works
Stravinsky: Rite of Spring (Cpte); Petrushka (Cpte); Movements. (M. Weber, Berlin RIAS Orch, Berlin RSO/F. Fricsay)

ⓘ **445 406-2GDO** (11/94)
Rossini/Verdi—Overtures and Preludes
Rossini: Barbiere di Siviglia (exc); Tancredi (exc); Signor Bruschino (exc); Gazza ladra (exc); Semiramide (exc); *Verdi*: Nabucco (exc); Traviata (exc); Forza del destino (exc); Aida (exc); Vespri siciliani (exc). (Berlin RIAS Orch/F. Fricsay)

ⓘ **445 407-2GDO** (11/94)
Brahms—Orchestral Works
Brahms: Symphony 2; Haydn Variations; Alto Rhapsody, Op.53. (M. Forrester, Berlin RIAS Chbr Ch, VPO, Berlin RSO/F. Fricsay)

ⓘ **445 410-2GDO** (11/94)
Kodály—Orchestral Works
Kodály: Marosszék Dances; Symphony in C; Psalmus Hungaricus. (E. Haefliger, Berlin St Hedwig's Cath Ch, Berlin RIAS Orch, Berlin RSO/F. Fricsay)

ⓘ **445 487-2GX3** (12/94)
Mutter plays Modern Works
Stravinsky: Violin Concerto; *Lutosławski*: Partita; Chain 2; *Bartók*: Violin Concerto 2; *Moret*: En rêve; *Berg*: Violin Concerto; *Rihm*: Gesungene Zeit. (A-S. Mutter, P. Moll, Philh/P. Sacher, BBC SO/W. Lutosławski, Boston SO/S. Ozawa, Chicago SO/James Levine)

ⓘ **445 501-2GMA** (12/94)
Bartók/Janáček—Orchestral Works
Bartók: Miraculous Mandarin (Cpte); Portraits, Sz37; *Janáček*: Sinfonietta. (S. Mintz, Ambrosian Sngrs, LSO, BPO/C. Abbado)

ⓘ **445 505-2GMA** (12/94)
Brahms/Beethoven—Orchestral Works
Brahms: Symphony 1; *Beethoven*: Egmont (exc); Coriolan. (VPO/L. Bernstein)

ⓘ **445 511-2GMA** (12/94)
Elgar—Orchestral Works
Elgar: Cello Concerto; Enigma Variations; Serenade. (M. Maisky, Philh/G. Sinopoli)

ⓘ **445 517-2GMA** (1/95)
Mozart—Piano Works
Mozart: Piano Sonata, K281; Piano Sonata, K330; Piano Sonata, K333; Adagio, K540; Rondo, K485. (V. Horowitz)

ⓘ **445 519-2GMA** (12/94)
Ravel—Orchestral Works
Ravel: Daphnis et Chloé (Cpte); Alborada del gracioso; Boléro. (LSC, LSO/C. Abbado)

ⓘ **445 520-2GMA** (3/95)
Schnittke—Chamber Works
Schnittke: Concerto grosso 1; Quasi una sonata; Moz-Art; A Paganini. (G. Kremer, T. Grindenko, Y. Smirnov, G. Kremer (vn/dir), Y. Smirnov, Y. Smirnov, COE/H. Schiff)

ⓘ **445 522-2GMA** (3/95)
Schumann—Piano Works
Schumann: Piano Concerto; Symphonic Studies; Arabeske. (M. Pollini, BPO/C. Abbado)

ⓘ **445 532-2GMA2** (1/95)
Haydn—Paris Symphonies
Haydn: Symphony 82; Symphony 83; Symphony 84; Symphony 85; Symphony 86; Symphony 87. (BPO/H. von Karajan)

ⓘ **445 535-2GMA2** (1/95)
Mozart—Violin Concertos, etc
Mozart: Violin Concerto, K207; Violin Concerto, K211; Violin Concerto, K216; Violin Concerto, K218; Violin Concerto, K219; Adagio, K261; Rondo, K269; Rondo, K373. (I. Perlman, VPO/James Levine)

ⓘ **445 549-2GMA** (7/95)
Lalo/Saint-Saëns—Orchestral Works
Berlioz: Rêverie et caprice; *Lalo*: Symphonie espagnole; *Saint-Saëns*: Violin Concerto 3. (I. Perlman, Paris Orch/D. Barenboim)

ⓘ **445 554-2GMA** (12/95)
Haydn—Symphonies
Haydn: Symphony 88; Symphony 92; Symphony 94. (VPO/L. Bernstein)

ⓘ **445 557-2GMA** (11/95)
Prokofiev—Chamber Works
Prokofiev: Violin Sonata 1; Violin Sonata 2; *Ravel*: Violin Sonata (1923-27). (S. Mintz, Y. Bronfman)

① **445 561-2GMA** (12/95)
Greensleeves - English Music for Strings
Elgar: Introduction and Allegro; Serenade; Elegy; *Vaughan Williams:* Tallis Fantasia; Greensleeves Fantasia; *Britten:* Simple Symphony. (Orpheus CO)

① **445 652-2GH** (1/95)
Beethoven—Violin Sonatas
Beethoven: Violin Sonata 6; Violin Sonata 7; Violin Sonata 8. (G. Kremer, M. Argerich)

① **445 657-2GH** (4/95)
Bach/Beethoven/Mozart—Works for Violin and Piano
Beethoven: Violin Sonata 5; *Bach:* Solo Violin Partitas and Sonatas (exc); *Mozart:* Adagio, K261. (D. Garrett, A. Markovich)

① **445 820-2GH** (10/95)
Schubert/Liszt—Duos and Transcriptions
Ernst: Erlkönig, Op. 26; *Liszt:* Grand duo concertant, S128; Lugubre gondola, S134; Soirées de Vienne, S427 (exc); Lieder, S558 (exc); *Schubert:* Trock'ne Blumen Variations, D802. (G. Kremer, O. Maisenberg)

① **445 822-2GH** (5/95)
Une flûte à l'opéra
Verdi: Traviata (exc); *Godard:* Jocelyn (exc); *Rossini:* Guillaume Tell (exc); *Massenet:* Thaïs (exc); *Verdi:* Ballo in maschera (exc); *Massé:* Noces de Jeannette (exc); *Bizet:* Carmen (exc). (P. Gallois, London Fest Orch/R. Pople)

① **445 825-2GH** (9/95)
Bartók—Orchestral Works
Bartók: Dance Suite; Pictures, Sz46; Hungarian Sketches; Divertimento. (Chicago SO/P. Boulez)

① **445 827-2GH** (4/95)
Messiaen—Orchestral Works
Messiaen: Chronochromie; Ville d'en haut; Et expecto resurrectionem. (Cleveland Orch/P. Boulez)

① **445 828-2GH** (2/95)
Webern—String Quartets and Trios
Webern: Slow Movement (1905); Movements, Op.5; String Quartet; Bagatelles; Rondo; String Trio Movement; Pieces for String Quartet; String Trio, Op.20; String Quartet, Op.28. (M.A. McCormick, Emerson Qt)

① **445 833-2GH** (12/95)
Boulez conducts Boulez
Boulez: Notations; Structures Bk 2; explosante-fixe. (S. Cherrier, E. Ophèle, P-A. Valade, P-L. Aimard, F. Boffard, Paris InterContemporain Ens/P. Boulez)

① **445 834-2GH** (12/95)
The 20th-Century Cello
Kodály: Cello Sonata, Op. 8; *Britten:* Cello Suite 3; *Berio:* Mots sont allés; *Henze:* Capriccio. (M. Haimovitz)

① **445 857-2GH2** (8/95)
Stenhammar—Orchestral Works
Stenhammar: Symphony 1; Symphony 2; Excelsior!; Serenade, Op.31. (Gothenburg SO/N. Järvi)

① **445 864-2GH** (9/95)
Shostakovich—String Quartets
Shostakovich: String Quartet 4; String Quartet 11; String Quartet 14. (Hagen Qt)

① **445 880-2GH** (10/95)
Franck/Debussy/Ravel—Violin Works
Franck: Violin Sonata; *Debussy:* Violin Sonata; *Ravel:* Berceuse; Pièce en forme de Habanera; Tzigane. (A. Dumay, M-J. Pires)

① **445 881-2GH** (11/95)
Schumann—Lieder
Schumann: Frauenliebe und -leben, Op. 42 (Cpte); Gedichte, Op. 35 (exc); Lieder und Gesänge, Op. 127 (exc); Gesänge, Op. 31 (exc); Gesänge, Op. 107 (exc); Gesänge, Op. 125 (exc); Lieder, Op. 40; Jugend Lieder, Op. 79 (exc); Romanzen und Balladen, Op. 45 (exc); Romanzen und Balladen, Op. 64 (exc); Minnespiel, Op. 101 (exc); Lieder und Gesänge, Op. 51 (exc); Gedichte, Op. 37 (exc). (A. S. von Otter, B. Forsberg)

① **445 946-2GH** (8/95)
Bryn Terfel—The Vagabond
Vaughan Williams: Songs of Travel; *Finzi:* Let us garlands bring; *Butterworth:* Bredon Hill; *Ireland:* Sea Fever; *Vagabond;* Bells of San Marie; *Butterworth:* Shropshire Lad. (B. Terfel, M. Martineau)

① **445 947-2GH** (8/95)
Messiaen—Orchestral Works
Messiaen: Concert à quatre; Offrandes oubliées; Sourire; Tombeau resplendissant. (C. Cantin, H. Holliger, M. Rostropovich, Y. Loriod, Paris Opéra-Bastille Orch/Myung-Whun Chung)

① **447 023-2GX12** (12/95)
Mahler—The Symphonies
Mahler: Symphony 1; Symphony 2; Symphony 3; Symphony 4; Symphony 5; Symphony 6; Symphony 7; Symphony 8; Symphony 9; Symphony 10 (exc). (C. Studer, J. Norman, S. McNair, A. Rost, W. Meier, F. von Stade, A.S. von Otter, R. Lang, P. Seiffert, B. Terfel, J-H. Rootering, Vienna Boys' Ch, Tolz Boys' Ch, A. Schoenberg Ch, Vienna St Op Chor, Berlin Rad Chor, Prague Phil Chor, BPO, VPO, Chicago SO/C. Abbado)

① **447 068-2GH** (10/95)
Stravinsky—The Flood, etc
Stravinsky: Flood (Cpte); Abraham and Isaac; *Huxley Variations;* Requiem Canticles; *Wuorinen:* Reliquary for Igor Stravinsky. (S. Bickley, P. Hall, D. Wilson-Johnson, S. Richardson, M. Berkeley, B. Jacobson, L. Shelton, New London Chbr Ch, London Sinfonietta/O. Knussen)

① **447 069-2GH** (12/95)
Verdi/Puccini/Muzio—Works for String Quartet
Puccini: Crisantemi; *Verdi:* String Quartet; *Luisa Miller* (exc). (Hagen Qt)

① **447 343-2GDB2** (11/95)
Stravinsky—Orchestral & Choral Works
Stravinsky: Rite of Spring (Cpte); Petrushka (Cpte); Movements; Divertimento; Capriccio; Symphony of Psalms. (M. Weber, M. Haas, Berlin RIAS Chor, Berlin RIAS Children's Chor, Berlin St Hedwig's Cath Ch, Berlin RIAS Orch, Berlin RSO/F. Fricsay)

① **447 352-2GDB2** (12/95)
Gundula Janowitz - A Portrait
Mozart: Ah, lo previdi, K272; A questo seno, K374; Alma grande e nobil core, K578; Vado, ma dove?, K583; Bella mia fiamma, K528; Misera! dove son, K369; *Wagner:* Tannhäuser (exc); Lohengrin (exc); Rienzi (exc); *Weber:* Freischütz (exc); Oberon (exc); *Schubert:* Suleika I, D720; Suleika II, D717; Du bist die Ruh', D776; Schwestergruss, D762; Forelle, D550; Jäger, ruhe von der Jagd, D838; Raste Krieger!, D837; Ave Maria, D839. (G. Janowitz, I. Gage, Vienna SO/W. Boettcher, Berlin Deutsche Op Orch/F. Leitner)

① **447 355-2GDB2** (12/95)
Recital - Sviatoslav Richter
Bach: Wohltemperierte Klavier (exc); *Haydn:* Keyboard Sonata 32; *Schubert:* Allegretto, D915; Ländler, D145 (exc); *Chopin:* Polonaises (exc); Etudes (exc); *Schumann:* Abegg Variations; *Debussy:* Estampes; Préludes (exc); *Scriabin:* Piano Sonata 5; *Rachmaninov:* Preludes (exc); *Prokofiev:* Visions fugitives (exc); Piano Sonata 8. (S. Richter)

① **447 389-2GH** (9/95)
Hindemith—Orchestral Works
Hindemith: Mathis der Maler; Nobilissima Visione; Symphonic Metamorphosis. (BPO/C. Abbado)

① **447 399-2GOR** (5/95)
Bartók—Piano Concertos
Bartók: Piano Concerto 1; Piano Concerto 2; Piano Concerto 3. (G. Anda, Berlin RSO/F. Fricsay)

① **447 404-2GOR** (9/95)
Beethoven—Piano Sonatas
Beethoven: Piano Sonata 8; Piano Sonata 14; Piano Sonata 21; Piano Sonata 23. (W. Kempff)

① **447 405-2GOR** (7/95)
Berg/Stravinsky—Chamber Works
Berg: Chamber Concerto; *Stravinsky:* Dumbarton Oaks; Instrumental Miniatures; Ebony Concerto. (M. Arrignon, P. Zukerman, D. Barenboim, Paris InterContemporain Ens/P. Boulez)

① **447 406-2GOR** (7/95)
Berlioz—Symphonie fantastique etc
Berlioz: Symphonie fantastique; *Cherubini:* Anacréon (exc); *Auber:* Muette de Portici (exc). (Lamoureux Orch/I. Markevitch)

① **447 409-2GOR2** (5/95)
Bruckner—The Masses
Bruckner: Mass in D minor; Mass in E minor; Mass in F minor. (E. Mathis, M. Stader, M. Schiml, C. Hellmann, W. Ochman, E. Haefliger, K. Ridderbusch, K. Borg, Bavarian Rad Chor, BRSO/E. Jochum)

① **447 414-2GOR** (10/95)
Falla/Stravinsky—Ballet Music
Falla: Amor brujo; Sombrero de tres picos Suites (exc); *Stravinsky:* Firebird Suite (1919). (G. Bumbry, Berlin RSO/L. Maazel)

① **447 416-2GOR2** (11/95)
Mozart—Symphonies
Mozart: Symphony 35; Symphony 36; Symphony 38;

Symphony 39; Symphony 40; Symphony 41. (BPO/K. Böhm)

① **447 419-2GOR** (6/95)
Prokofiev—Alexander Nevsky;Lieutenant Kijé etc
Prokofiev: Alexander Nevsky; Lt. Kijé Suite; Scythian Suite. (E. Obraztsova, LSC, LSO, Chicago SO/C. Abbado)

① **447 423-2GOR2** (6/95)
Tchaikovsky—Symphonies
Tchaikovsky: Symphony 4; Symphony 5; Symphony 6. (Leningrad PO/K. Sanderling/E. Mravinsky)

① **447 426-2GOR** (12/95)
Debussy/Mussorgsky/Ravel—Orchestral Works
Debussy: La Mer; *Mussorgsky:* Pictures; *Ravel:* Boléro. (BPO/H. von Karajan)

① **447 427-2GOR2** (6/95)
D. Oistrakh plays Concertos
Bach: Violin Concerto, BWV1041; Violin Concerto, BWV1042; 2-Violin Concerto; *Beethoven:* Romances; *Brahms:* Violin Concerto; *Tchaikovsky:* Violin Concerto. (D. Oistrakh, D. Oistrakh (vn/dir), I. Oistrakh, RPO/E. Goossens, Staatskapelle Dresden/F. Konwitschny, Vienna SO)

① **447 430-2GOR** (6/95)
Martha Argerich—Début Recital
Chopin: Scherzos (exc); *Brahms:* Rhapsodies, Op.79; *Prokofiev:* Toccata, Op.11; *Ravel:* Jeux d'eau; *Chopin:* Barcarolle; *Liszt:* Hungarian Rhapsodies, S244 (exc); Piano Sonata, S178. (M. Argerich)

① **447 431-2GOR** (6/95)
20th Century Piano Works
Stravinsky: Petrushka; *Prokofiev:* Piano Sonata 7; *Webern:* Variations, Op.27; *Boulez:* Piano Sonata 2. (M. Pollini)

① **447 435-2GOR** (12/95)
Honegger—Symphonies; Stravinsky—Concerto
Honegger: Symphony 2; Symphony 3; *Stravinsky:* Concerto in D. (BPO/H. von Karajan)

① **447 438-2GOR** (12/95)
Prokofiev/Ravel—Piano Concertos
Prokofiev: Piano Concerto 3; *Ravel:* Piano Concerto; Gaspard de la nuit. (M. Argerich, BPO/C. Abbado)

Deutsche Harmonia Mundi

① **GD77010** (11/90)
Geminiani—Six Concerti Grossi
Geminiani: Concerti grossi, Op. 2 (exc); Concerti grossi, Op. 3 (exc); Concerti grossi, Op. 7 (exc); Concerti grossi (Corelli, Op. 5) (exc). (Petite Bande/S. Kuijken)

① **GD77013** (12/90)
Bach—Keyboard Works
Bach: Art of Fugue; French Overture, BWV831; Italian Concerto, BWV971; Prelude, Fugue and Allegro, BWV998. (G. Leonhardt, B. van Asperen)

① **GD77085** (5/90)
Schubert & Schumann—Lieder
Schubert: Hirt auf dem Felsen, D965; Seligkeit, D433; Gretchen am Spinnrade, D118; Du liebst mich nicht, D756; Heimliches Lieben, D922; Im Frühling, D882; Vögel, D691; Jüngling an der Quelle, D300; Musensohn, D764; *Schumann:* Myrthen, Op. 25 (exc); Lieder und Gesänge, Op. 77 (exc); Lieder und Gesänge, Op. 51 (exc); Gedichte, Op. 35 (exc); Minnespiel, Op. 101 (exc); Jugend Lieder, Op. 79 (exc); Gedichte, Op. 90 (exc); Lieder und Gesänge, Op. 27 (exc); Liederkreis, Op. 39 (exc); Romanzen und Balladen, Op. 53 (exc); Gesänge, Op. 125 (exc). (E. Ameling, J. Demus, H. Deinzer)

① **GD77151** (10/90)
Bach—Secular Cantatas
Bach: Cantata 202; Cantata 209; Cantata 211; Cantata 212. (E. Ameling, G. English, S. Nimsgern, Collegium Aureum)

① **GD77228** (12/91)
Christmas Carols & Hymns of the 15th Century
Anon: Christmas (exc); *Traditional:* Ecce quod natura; Hayl Mary Ful of Grace; Jhesu, fili virginis; Nova, nova; Coventry Carol; Nowell: Dieu vous garde; *Binchois:* A solis ortus cardine; *Traditional:* Nowel, Nowel, Owt of Your Slepe; There is no rose. (PCA)

① **RD77025** (9/89)
C.P.E. Bach: Keyboard Works
C. P. E. Bach: Württemberg Sonatas (exc); La Folia Variations, H263 (exc); Keyboard Sonatas, H46-49 (exc); Fantasia, H300 (exc); Kenner V (exc); Fantasia, H291 (exc). (A. Staier)

① **RD77026** (1/90)
Bach: Flute Sonatas
Bach: Flute Sonatas, BWV1030-5 (exc); Trio Sonatas,

BWV1036-9 (exc); Partita, BWV1013. (Barthold Kuijken, M. Hantai, S. Kuijken, G. Leonhardt, W. Kuijken)

ⓘ **RD77033** (2/90)
Vivaldi: Chamber Concertos
Vivaldi: Concerto, RV94; Concerto, RV107; Concerto, RV99; Concerto, RV88; Concerto, RV105; Concerto, RV95; Concerto, RV87. (Cologne Camerata)

ⓘ **RD77039** (10/89)
Bach—Keyboard Fantasies
Bach: Prelude, BWV922; Fantasia and Fugue, BWV904; Prelude, BWV921; Fantasia, BWV919; Prelude and Fugue, BWV894; Prelude and Fugue, BWV902:1; Prelude and Fugue, BWV901; Chromatic Fantasia and Fugue, BWV903; Fantasia, BWV917; Fantasia, BWV906. (A. Staier)

ⓘ **RD77088** (10/90)
Schein—Vocal Works
Schein: Ringstum mich schwebet Traurigkeit; Kickehihi; Heulen und schmerzlichs Weinen; O seidne Härelein; Ihr Brüder; Diletti pastorali (exc); Frischauf, ihr Klosterbrüder mein; O Scheiden, o bitter Scheiden. (Cantus Cölln, K. Junghänel lte/dir))

ⓘ **RD77095** (1/92)
Vitry—Chansons and Motets
Philippe de Vitry: O canenda; Je qui; Colla iugo; Firmissime; Cum statua; Firmissime; Impudenter circuivi; Ay, amours!; Garrit gallus; Providence la senée; Floret; Aman novi; Petre clemens; Talant j'ai que d'obeir; Tribum; Tuba sacrae fidei; Tribum; Se j'onques a mon vivant; Douce playsence; Vos quid admiramini. (Sequentia)

ⓘ **RD77154** (12/91)
Concerto Delle Donne
Marenzio: Cantate ninfe; Passando con pensier; Bianchi cigni; Luzzaschi: O dolcezze amarissime; Non sa che sia dolore; T'amo mia vita; Cor mio deh non languire; Occhi del pianto mio; Monteverdi: Madrigals, Bk.8 (exc); Strozzi: Bella madre d'amore; Che dolce udire; Il gran Giove; Carissimi: Poiché le sdegno intese; A. Scarlatti: Cor mio. (Consort of Musicke/A. Rooley)

ⓘ **RD77156** (2/91)
Vivaldi: Concertos
Vivaldi: Concerti, Op.10 (exc); Concerti, Op.10 (exc); Sonata, RV779. (M. Schneider, K. Kaiser, Cologne Camerata)

ⓘ **RD77160** (5/91)
Haydn—Keyboard Sonatas
Haydn: Keyboard Sonata 58; Keyboard Sonata 59; Keyboard Sonata 60; Keyboard Sonata 61; Keyboard Sonata 62. (A. Staier)

ⓘ **RD77182** (11/90)
Lechner: Sacred & Secular Songs
Lechner: Deutsche Sprüche; Come nave; Ach herzigs Herz; Wie war mir nur; Nackend bin ich; Erst und ander Kapitel; Gott bhüte dich; Freu dich heut; Zart edles Gmüt; Hört, was sich hat zugetragen; Musicus wollt fröhlich sein; Ach, wer wird mir; Aus tiefer Not; Nach meiner Lieb; Wohl dem; Ich ging einmal spazieren; Frau, ich bin euch von Herzen; O Tod; Ach Lieb; Ganz schön betrübt; Mai viel schöner. (Cantus Cölln, K. Junghänel lte/dir))

ⓘ **RD77187** (4/91)
C.P.E. Bach: Sinfonias & Concertos
C.P.E. Bach: Sinfonias, H657-62 (exc); Keyboard Concertos, H471-6 (exc); Oboe Concerto, H468. (H-P. Westermann, A. Staier, Freiburg Baroque Orch/T. Hengelbrock)

ⓘ **RD77188** (4/92)
C.P.E. Bach—Vocal & Chamber Works
C.P.E. Bach: Trio Sonata, H571; Phillis and Thirsis; Flute and Violin Duett, H598; Little Pieces, H600; Trio Sonata, H567. (R. Hofmann, N. Rogers, H-M. Linde, C. Huntgeburth, J. Schröder, B. Landolf, P. Carrai, R. Junghanns)

ⓘ **RD77201** (12/91)
Telemann—Wind Concertos
Telemann: Recorder Concerto 2; Oboe Concerto 6; Flute Concerto in D; Recorder & Viola da gamba Concerto 1; 2-Violin & Bassoon Concerto in D. (M. Schneider, K. Kaiser, H-P. Westermann, M. McGraw, M. Utiger, H. Bäss, R. Zipperling, Cologne Camerata)

ⓘ **RD77202** (8/92)
Bach—Complete Organ Works, Vol.1
Bach: Fantasia, BWV572; Pastorale, BWV590; Vom Himmel hoch, BWV700; Vom Himmel hoch, BWV701; Toccata, Adagio and Fugue, BWV564; Gelobet seist du, BWV722; Gelobet seist du, BWV723; Wir Christenleut', BWV710; In dulci jubilo, BWV729; Sarabande con partite, BWV990; Fantasia C minor; Prelude and Fugue, BWV535a; Prelude and Fugue, BWV535. (Harald Vogel)

ⓘ **RD77218** (1/91)
Lully—Divertissements
Lully: Divertissement I; Divertissement II; Divertissement III. (G. Laurens, Capriccio Stravagante, S. Sempé (hpd/dir))

ⓘ **RD77219** (1/91)
F. Couperin—Harpsichord Works
Couperin: Art de toucher le clavecin (exc); Livre de clavecin I (exc); Livre de clavecin II (exc); Livre de clavecin III (exc); Livre de clavecin IV (exc). (S. Sempé)

ⓘ **RD77220** (10/91)
Monteverdi e il suo Tempo
Monteverdi: Madrigals, Bk.7 (exc); Castello: Sonatas (exc); Monteverdi: Ohimè ch'io cado; Merula: Chiaccona a 2; Frescobaldi: Secondo libro di toccate (exc); Riccio: Canzon; Frescobaldi: Secondo libro di toccate (exc); Monteverdi: Scherzi musicali (1632) (exc); Marini: Passacaglia a 4; Malvezzi: Sinfonia; Monteverdi: Madrigals, Bk 8 (exc); Madrigals, Bk.6 (exc); Si dolce e'1 tormento. (G. Laurens, Capriccio Stravagante, S. Sempé (hpd/dir))

ⓘ **RD77231** (3/92)
Purcell—Instrumental Music
Purcell: Chaconne, Z730; Fairy Queen, Z629 (exc); Dido (exc); King Arthur, Z628 (exc); Abdelazer, Z570 (exc). (Freiburg Baroque Orch/T. Hengelbrock)

ⓘ **RD77250** (7/91)
Bach's Sons—Chamber Music
J. C. Bach: Quintets, Op. 11 (exc); J. C. F. Bach: Flute Quartets, HWVI (exc); C. P. E. Bach: Trio Sonata, H570; Sonata, H512; Sinfonia, H585. (Adieux)

ⓘ **RD77252** (9/92)
Purcell—Airs and Instrumental Music
Purcell: Choice Collection of Lessons (exc); If music be the food of love, Z379/1; Fantasia, Z731; Fairy Queen, Z629 (exc); St Cecilia's Day Ode, Z328 (exc); Hornpipes (exc); Overture, Z772; Lord, what is man?, Z192; Chaconne, Z730; Oedipus, Z583 (exc); Lovely Albina, Z394; Viola da gamba Fantasies, Z735-43; Grounds (exc); Pavans, Z748-51 (exc); Evening Hymn, Z193. (H. Crook, Capriccio Stravagante, S. Sempé (hpd/dir), S. Sempé)

ⓘ **RD77757** (9/91)
Haydn/Kraft—Cello Concertos
Haydn: Cello Concerto in C; Cello Concerto in D; A. Kraft: Cello Concerto, Op. 4. (A. Bylsma, Tafelmusik/J. Lamon)

ⓘ **RD77867** (2/90)
Boccherini: Cello Concertos & Symphonies
Boccherini: Cello Concerto, G480; Cello Concerto, G483; Symphonies, G493-8 (exc); Symphonies, G503-8 (exc). (A. Bylsma, Tafelmusik/J. Lamon)

ⓘ **RD77868** (12/90)
Bach: Organ Works
Bach: Toccatas, BWV910-16 (exc); Liebster Jesu, BWV731; Christ lag in Todesbanden, BWV718; Valet will ich dir geben, BWV736; Lobt Gott, BWV732; Clavier-Übung III, BWV669-689 (exc); Prelude and Fugue, BWV533. (G. Leonhardt)

ⓘ **RD77909** (6/90)
Vivaldi: Cello Sonatas
Vivaldi: Cello Sonata, RV39; Cello Sonata, RV40; Cello Sonata, RV41; Cello Sonata, RV42; Cello Sonata, RV43; Cello Sonata, RV44. (A. Bylsma, J. Ogg, H. Suzuki)

ⓘ **RD77924** (5/92)
French Harpsichord Music
Rameau: Pièces de clavecin (exc); Duphly: Pièces de clavecin (exc); Royer: Pièces de clavecin (exc); Le Roux: Pièces de clavessin (exc). (G. Leonhardt)

ⓘ **05472 77176-2** (8/93)
Music at the Court of Louis XIV
Marais: La gamme (exc); Pièces de viole II/I (exc); Pièces de viole II/2 (exc); Visée: Allemande (Tombeau de Vieux Gallot); Rondeau (Le Montsermeil); Silvains de M. Couperin; Jacques Morel: Pièces de viole I (exc); Hotteterre: Rochers, vous etes muets; Troisième suite, Op.8; Blavet: Flute Sonatas, Op.2 (exc). (Royal Trio, W. Hazelzet, K. Junghänel)

ⓘ **05472 77181-2** (6/93)
Rosenmüller—Italian Cantatas
Rosenmüller: Beatus vir (4vv, 5 stgs); Magnificat (5vv); Benedicam Dominum; De profundis; Confitebor (4vv, 5 stgs); Gloria (4vv). (Cantus Cölln, K. Junghänel lte/dir))

ⓘ **05472 77183-2** (8/93)
Music for the Bourgeoisie
G. Gabrieli: Sacrae symphoniae (1597) (exc); Scheidt: Canzon à 4 tromboni; Canzon à Cornet vel Viol; Vierdanck: Als ich einmahl; Capriccio; Moritz: Canzon à 8; Pohle: Sonata à 6; 2-Violin and 4-Trombone Sonata; Siefert:

Canzon à 8; Weckmann: Sonata II à 4; Sonata IX à 4; Diessener: Sonata à 6; Rosenmüller: Sonata à 3; Vierdanck: Sonata à 4; Förster: Sonata à 3; Sonata à 7. (Musica Fiata/R. Wilson)

ⓘ **05472 77190-2** (2/94)
Monteverdi—Combattimento/Lamento d'Arianna
Farina: Capriccio Stravagante; Il Verso: Lasciatemi morire; Zanetti: Intrada; Mussi: Canzon, Op.5 (exc); Monteverdi: Lamento d'Arianna a 1; Combattimento di Tancredi e Clorinda. (G. Laurens, T. Malakate, J. Aymonino, K. Paliatsaras, Capriccio Stravagante, S. Sempé (hpd/dir))

ⓘ **05472 77222-2** (1/94)
Bach—Harpsichord Works
Bach: Solo Violin Partitas and Sonatas (exc); Partitas, BWV825-30 (exc); Harpsichord Concerto, BWV1054; Harpsichord Concerto, BWV1055. (S. Sempé, Capriccio Stravagante)

ⓘ **05472 77275-2** (10/93)
Haydn—Symphonies
Haydn: Symphony 93; Symphony 94; Symphony 95. (Petite Bande/S. Kuijken)

ⓘ **05472 77276-2** (4/93)
Bach—Organ Works, Vol.2
Bach: Prelude and Fugue, BWV552; Clavier-Übung III, BWV669-689 (exc); Duets, BWV802-805. (M. Radulescu)

ⓘ **05472 77278-2** (7/93)
Bach—Organ Works, Vol.3
Bach: Toccata and Fugue, BWV565; Herr Jesu CHrist, BWV709; Herr Jesu Christ, BWV726; Herzlich tut mich verlangen, BWV727; Prelude and Fugue, BWV550; Prelude and Fugue, BWV533; Prelude and Fugue, BWV549; Prelude and Fugue, BWV541; Prelude and Fugue, BWV539; Wo soll ich fliehen hin, BWV694; Nun komm, der Heiden Heiland, BWV699; Gottes Sohn, BWV703; Herr Christ, der einig Gottes Sohn, BWV698; Lob sei dem allmächtigen Gott, BWV704; Gelobet seist du, BWV697; Vom Himmel hoch, BWV701; Christum wir sollen loben schon, BWV696; In dulci jubilo, BWV751. (L. Ghielmi)

ⓘ **05472 77282-2** (10/93)
Monteverdi—Madrigali Amorosi
Monteverdi: Madrigals, Bk. 6 (exc); Madrigals, Bk.7 (exc); Madrigals, Bk.8 (exc); Madrigals, Bk 8 (exc); Scherzi musicali (1632) (exc). (Cantus Cölln, K. Junghänel lte/dir))

ⓘ **05472 77283-2** (10/93)
G.B. & G. Sammartini—Sonatas
Sammartini: Flute Sonatas, Op.2 (exc); Solos, Op.13 (exc); Recorder Sonata, Sibley 15; Recorder Sonata, Sibley 24; G. Sammartini: Cello Sonatas, Op.4 (exc); Harpsichord Sonata in A; Organ Sonata 6. (Cologne Camerata, S. Bauer, S. Bauer)

ⓘ **05472 77285-2** (2/94)
Haydn—Fortepiano Sonatas, Vol.3
Haydn: Variations, HobXVII/3; Variations, HobXVII/6; Kaiser Variations; Keyboard Sonata 34; Keyboard Sonata 53. (A. Staier)

ⓘ **05472 77289-2** (4/94)
Bach/Vivaldi—Orchestral Works
Bach: Suites, BWV1066-9 (exc); Cantata 42 (exc); 3-Violin Concerto, BWV1064; Vivaldi: Concerto, RV158; Olimpiade (exc); Concerti Grossi, Op. 3 (exc). (Freiburg Baroque Orch/T. Hengelbrock)

ⓘ **05472 77294-2** (10/94)
Haydn—Symphonies
Haydn: Symphony 96; Symphony 97; Symphony 98. (Petite Bande/S. Kuijken)

ⓘ **05472 77295-2** (10/94)
Handel/Purcell—Works
Purcell: Dioclesian Suite (exc); Dioclesian, Z627 (exc); If music be the food of love, Z379/1; O! how happy's he, Z403; Lost is my quiet for ever, Z502; Handel: Concerti grossi, Op. 6 (exc); Amarilli vezzosa. (N. Argenta, M. Chance, Freiburg Baroque Orch/Ga. von der Goltz)

ⓘ **05472 77296-2** (1/94)
Schubert—Schiller Lieder
Schubert: Bürgschaft, D246; Hoffnung, D637; Hektors Abschied, D312; An Emma, D113; Mädchens Klage, D191; Gruppe aus dem Tartarus, D583; Pilgrim, D794; Alpenjäger, D588; Leichenphantasie, D7; Götter Griechenlands, D677; Sehnsucht, D636. (C. Prégardien, A. Staier)

ⓘ **05472 77298-2** (5/94)
Schelle—Baroque Christmas Music
Schelle: Actus musicus; Vom Himmel kam; Uns ist ein Kind geboren (5vv); Ach mein herzliebes Jesulein; Machet die Thore weit; Nun Komm der Heiden Heiland. (Capella Ducale, Cologne Musica Fiata/R. Wilson)

Discover International

Disques Montaigne

Dorian

rode out; Ach mein herzliebes Jesulein; Angeles del zielo; Verbum Patris hodie; Tau garço; O staris in presepio; Hodie christus natus est; Personent hodie; Nowell sing we. (Alberquerque Música Antigua)

ⓘ **DIS80110** (5/95)
Dussek—Piano Sonatas, Volume 1
Dussek: Piano Sonata, C80; Piano Sonata, C242; Piano Sonata, C259. (F. Marvin)

ⓘ **DIS80121** (9/95)
Masques—Polish Piano Works
Lutosławski: Bucolics; *Szymanowski:* Mazurkas, Op. 50 (exc); Preludes, Op. 1 (exc); Masques, Op. 34; *Zarębski:* Berceuse, Op. 22; Tarantelle, Op. 25; Grande polonaise, Op. 6. (E. Wiedner-Zając)

ⓘ **DIS80125** (7/95)
Dussek—Piano Works, Volume 2
Dussek: Piano Sonata, C39; Piano Sonata, C61; Piano Sonata, C151; Piano Sonata, C211. (F. Marvin)

ⓘ **DIS80131** (11/95)
The Early Josquin
Josquin Desprez: Missa L'ami Baudichon; Credo; Magnificat; Missa sine nomine (exc); *Ockeghem:* Credo. (Capella Alamire/P. Urquhart)

ⓘ **DOR90177** (4/95)
La Rocque 'n' Roll
Traditional: J'ai vû le loup; *Le Roy:* Has tu point veu; M'avoit promis; Mes pas semez; J'ay le rebours; M. Praetorius: Terpsichore (exc); *Chardavoine:* Mignonne; Jeune fillette; G. Bassano: Frais et gaillard; Ung gay bergère; *Phalèse:* Gaillarde d'escosse; Danserye (exc); Alemande de Liège; *Planson:* Ma bergère; Jeune fillette; *L. Bourgeois:* Psalm 137; *Anon:* Estans assis; *Champion:* Psalm 137; *Goudimel:* Psalm 137; *Attaingnant:* Prélude; *Sermisy:* Tant que vivray; *Certon:* O madame; *Ballard:* Branles de village; *Bachelar:* Jeune fillette variations; *Du Caurroy:* Jeune fillette; *Mangeant:* Jean de Nivelle. (Baltimore Consort)

ⓘ **DOR90184** (4/95)
Busnois—In Hydraulis and other works
Busnois: In hydraulis; Anthoni usque limina; Victimae paschali laudes; Regina coeli I; A que ville; Bel acueil; Je ne puis vivre ainsi; Missa O crux lignum; *Anon:* Easter Sunday; Divine Office: Compline (exc). (Pomerium Musices/A. Blachly)

ⓘ **DOR90202** (11/95)
Impressions—Camerata Bariloche
Guastavino: Cantilenas argentinas (exc); Presencias (exc); *Ginastera:* Impresiones de la Puna; *Gianneo:* Piezas criollas (exc); *Zorzi:* Adagio elegíaco. (C. Barile, P. Cohen, Camerata Bariloche)

ⓘ **DOR90203** (9/95)
Borodin/Stravinsky/Shostakovich—String Quartet Works
Borodin: String Quartet 2; *Stravinsky:* Pieces (1914); *Shostakovich:* String Quartet 3. (Lafayette Qt)

ⓘ **DOR90210** (11/95)
Falla—Vocal Works
Falla: Amor Brujo; Canciones populares españolas; Homenajes (exc); Sombrero de tres picos Suites (exc). (M. Senn, S. Bolivar SO/E. Mata)

ⓘ **DOR90211** (8/95)
Latin American Ballets
Villa-Lobos: Uirapuru; *Ginastera:* Estancia Suite; *Chávez:* Caballos de vapor Suite. (S. Bolívar SO/E. Mata)

ⓘ **DOR90215** (9/95)
Chavez—Chamber Works
Chávez: Xochipilli; Suite for Double Quartet; Tambuco; Energía; Toccata. (Camerata, Tambuco/E. Mata)

Doron Music

ⓘ **DRC3001** (8/94)
American 18th Century Piano Works
Reinagle: Philadelphia Sonatas (exc); *Moller:* Sonata VIII; J. Hewitt: Mark, My Alford; W. Brown: Rondos (exc); *Traditional:* Yankee Doodle. (W. Naboré)

Doyen

ⓘ **DOYCD002** (2/91)
Euphonium Music
B. Bowen: Euphonium Music; *Curnow:* Euphonium Rhapsody; J.W. Phillips: Romance; *Stephens:* Solo Rhapsody; Howarth: Cantabile for John Fletcher; *Golland:* Euphonium Concerto 1; *Sparke:* Euphonium Fantasy. (R. Childs, N. Childs, Britannia Building Soc Band/H. Snell)

ⓘ **DOYCD004** (8/92)
Rule Brittania
Fučik: Entry of the Gladiators; *Bizet:* Carmen (exc);

rode out; Ach mein herzliebes Jesulein; *Shostakovich:* Flea (exc); *Bach:* Harpsichord Concerto, BWV1056 (exc); *Goffin:* Rhapsody in Brass; *Rossini:* Boutique fantasque (exc); *Traditional:* Old Chalet; *Respighi:* Pines of Rome; *Kabalevsky:* Comedians (exc); *Puccini:* Turandot (exc); *Traditional:* Steal away to Jesus; L. Pearson: Fantasy Variations; *Botsford:* Black and White Rag; *Sparke:* Partita. (Britannia Building Soc Band/H. Snell)

ⓘ **DOYCD005** (9/92)
Flower of Scotland
W. Rimmer: Australasian; *Sparke:* Capriccio; *Ball:* Softly sounds the little bell; Star Lake; R. Williamson: Flower of Scotland; R. Heath: Frolic for Trombones; *Rodgers:* Carousel (exc); *Borodin:* Prince Igor (exc); *Crüger:* Nun danket alle Gott; *Gershwin:* Strike Up the Band I (exc); D. Rose: Holiday for Strings; *Foster:* Beautiful Dreamer; P. Graham: Prelude to a New Age; *Hazell:* Mr Jums; *Friedmann:* Slavonic Rhapsody 2. (G. Lindsay, A. Murphy, B. Deans, M. Stenhouse, D. Platt, Glasgow CWS Band/H. Snell/R. Tennant)

ⓘ **DOYCD011** (7/93)
Pictures at an Exhibition
Byrd: Earl of Oxford's March, BK93; *Howarth:* Bandsman's Tale; American Dream; In Memoriam R.K.; *Gershwin:* Girl Crazy (exc); *Mussorgsky:* Pictures. (Britannia Building Soc Band/H. Snell)

ⓘ **DOYCD013** (12/92)
A Night at the Opera
Wagner: Tannhäuser (exc); J. Strauss II: Fledermaus (exc); *Saint-Saëns:* Samson et Dalila (exc); *Verdi:* Traviata (exc); Forza del Destino (exc); *Wagner:* Walküre (exc). (Grimethorpe Colliery Band/E. Howarth)

ⓘ **DOYCD017** (9/93)
Gregson—Brass Music - Volume 1
Gregson: Horn Concerto (1971); Connotations; Dances and Arias; Of Men and Mountains. (F. Lloyd, Desford Colliery Caterpillar Band/E. Gregson)

Dutton Laboratories

ⓘ **CDAX8002** (5/93)
Stravinsky—Orchestral Works
Stravinsky: Petrushka (Cpte); Firebird Suite (1919); Pastorale; Fireworks; *Shostakovich:* Preludes, Op.34 (exc). (Philadelphia/L. Stokowski)

ⓘ **CDAX8003** (12/93)
Walton—Gramophone premieres
Walton: Symphony 1; Viola Concerto; Daphne; Through Gilded Trellises; Old Sir Faulk. (D. Stevens, F. Riddle, H. Foss, LSO/H. Harty/W. Walton)

ⓘ **CDAX8004** (10/93)
Sir Henry Wood conducts Vaughan Williams
Vaughan Williams: Wasps (exc); Serenade to Music; Symphony 2; Greensleeves Fantasia. (L. Stiles-Allen, I. Baillie, E. Suddaby, E. Turner, M. Balfour, M. Brunskill, A. Desmond, M. Jarred, Parry Jones, H. Nash, F. Titterton, W. Widdop, Roy Henderson, N. Allin, R. Easton, H. Williams, BBC SO, Queen's Hall Orch/Henry Wood)

ⓘ **CDAX8005** (11/93)
'Philharmonic'
Balakirev: Russian Ov II; *Bizet:* Jeux d'enfants; R. Strauss: Don Juan; *Beethoven:* Contredanses, WoO17; *Weinberger:* Chestnut Tree. (LPO/H. Harty/A. Dorati/F. Busch/F. Weingartner/C. Lambert)

ⓘ **CDAX8006** (3/94)
The Delius Collection
Delius: Brigg Fair; In a Summer Garden; First cuckoo; Summer Night on the River; Village Romeo and Juliet (exc); Dance; Preludes; Piano Pieces (exc); *Grainger:* Brigg Fair. (N. Stone, E. Howard Jones, Oriana Madrigal Soc/C. Kennedy Scott, LSO, New SO/G. Toye)

ⓘ **CDAX8007** (5/94)
Boyd Neel conducts Britten & Vaughan Williams
Britten: Simple Symphony; Frank Bridge Variations; *Vaughan Williams:* Concerto Accademico; Tallis Fantasia. (F. Grinke, Boyd Neel Orch/B. Neel)

ⓘ **CDAX8008** (9/94)
Sir Henry Wood conducts Proms Favourites
Coates: London Suite; London Bridge; *Grainger:* Molly on the Shore, BFMS1; Mock Morris; Handel in the Strand; *Wagner:* Meistersinger (exc); *Berlioz:* Carnaval Romain; *Gounod:* Marche funèbre d'une marionette; *Elgar:* Pomp and Circumstance Marches (exc); Henry Wood: Sea-Song Fantasia; *Järnefelt:* Praeludium. (Queen's Hall Orch, British SO, LPO, LSO, SO/Henry Wood)

ⓘ **CDAX8009** (11/94)
Stokowski conducts a Russian Spectacular
Mussorgsky: Night on the Bare Mountain; Boris Godunov

(exc); Pictures (exc); Khovanshchina (exc); *Borodin:* Prince Igor (exc). (Philadelphia/L. Stokowski)

ⓘ **CDAX8010** (2/95)
Hallé Orchestra Wartime Recordings
Borodin: Prince Igor (exc); Symphony 2; *Liadov:* Kikimora, Op. 63; *Shostakovich:* Piano Concerto 1; *Tchaikovsky:* Sleeping Beauty (exc). (E. Joyce, A. Lockwood, Hallé/C. Lambert/L. Heward/A. Boult/M. Sargent)

ⓘ **CDAX8012** (5/95)
Malcolm Sargent conducts English Music
Ireland: London Overture; *Harty:* John Field Suite; Coleridge Taylor: Song of Hiawatha, Op. 30 (exc); *Gardiner:* Shepherd Fennell's Dance; *Vaughan Williams:* Lark ascending; *Holst:* Hymn of Jesus. (Webster Booth, D. Wise, Huddersfield Choral Soc, Liverpool PO/M. Sargent)

ⓘ **CDAX8013** (7/95)
Beecham conducts Sibelius
Sibelius: Symphony 7; Pelleas and Melisande (exc); Pelleas and Melisande (exc); Tempest Suites (exc); Scènes historiques I (exc); In Memoriam; Legends (exc). (NYPO, LPO/T. Beecham)

ⓘ **CDAX8014** (12/95)
British Gramophone Premieres
Bax: Nonet; *Delius:* Violin Sonata 3; H. Ferguson: Octet, Op.4; *Moeran:* String Trio. (J. Slater, L. Goossens, F. Thurston, P. Juler, D. Brain, C. James, J.E. Merrett, V. Watson, M. Korchinska, A. Sammons, J. Pougnet, F. Riddle, A. Pini, K. Long, Griller Qt)

ⓘ **CDK1200** (5/95)
This is Full Frequency Range Recording
Bizet: Arlésienne Suites (exc); *Berlioz:* Damnation de Faust (exc); *Glière:* Red Poppy Suite (exc); *Tchaikovsky:* Marche slave; *Wagner:* Götterdämmerung (exc); *Saint-Saëns:* Danse macabre; *Tchaikovsky:* Oprichnik (exc); *Wolf-Ferrari:* Gioielli della Madonna (exc); *Delius:* Irmelin Prelude; *Chabrier:* España. (National SO/Sidney Beer/A. Fistoulari/B. Neel/V. Olof)

ⓘ **CDLXT2501** (8/95)
Bliss conducts Bliss
Bliss: Colour Symphony; Introduction and Allegro; Things to Come (exc); Things to Come (exc); Men of Two Worlds (exc). (E. Joyce, LSO/A. Bliss, National SO/M. Mathieson)

ⓘ **CDLXT2502** (7/95)
Thomas Jensen conducts Nielsen, Vol.1
Nielsen: Symphony 1; Symphony 5; Helios. (Danish St RSO/E. Tuxen/T. Jensen)

ⓘ **CDLXT2503** (8/95)
Anthony Collins conducts Delius
Delius: Paris; In a Summer Garden; Summer Night on the River; Brigg Fair; First Cuckoo; Song of Summer. (LSO/A. Collins)

ⓘ **CDLX7001** (7/93)
Beecham conducts Favourite Overtures, Volume 1
Rossini: Scala di seta (exc); Guillaume Tell (exc); Gazza ladra (exc); Semiramide (exc); *Mendelssohn:* Hebrides; Ruy Blas; *Suppé:* Morgen, ein Mittag, ein Abend in Wien (exc); *Nicolai:* Lustigen Weiber von Windsor (exc). (LPO/T. Beecham)

ⓘ **CDLX7002** (10/93)
The Beecham Touch
Dvořák: Slavonic Rhapsodies (exc); *Debussy:* Après-midi; *Respighi:* Rossiniana (exc); *Bizet:* Jolie Fille de Perth (exc); *Berlioz:* Damnation de Faust (exc). (LPO/T. Beecham)

ⓘ **CDLX7003** (6/94)
Vintage Beecham
Handel: Solomon (exc); *Dvořák:* Legends (exc); *Offenbach:* Contes d'Hoffmann (exc); *Bizet:* Carmen Suites (exc); *Delius:* Koanga (exc); *Mendelssohn:* Midsummer Night's Dream (exc); *Mendelssohn:* Midsummer Night's Dream (exc); J. Strauss II: Frühlingsstimmen, Op. 410; *Borodin:* Prince Igor (exc); Prince Igor (exc). (Leeds Fest Chor, LPO/T. Beecham)

ⓘ **CDLX7004** (1/94)
Elgar—Chamber Works
Elgar: Piano Quintet; String Quartet; Capricieuse; Serenade; Adieu. (J. Hassid, J. Szigeti, H. Cohen, G. Moore, N. Magaloff, Stratton Qt)

ⓘ **CDLX7005** (7/94)
Dame Myra Hess
Schumann: Piano Concerto; Carnaval; *Franck:* Symphonic Variations; *Bach:* Cantata 147 (exc). (M. Hess, SO/W. Goehr, CBO/B. Cameron)

① **CDLX7006** (1/94)
Tchaikovsky—Orchestral Works
Tchaikovsky: Symphony 4; Romeo and Juliet; Hamlet.
(Hallé, CBO/C. Lambert)

① **CDLX7007** (6/94)
Beecham conducts Wagner
Wagner: Meistersinger (exc); Meistersinger (exc);
Fliegende Holländer (exc); Tannhäuser (exc); Lohengrin
(exc); Götterdämmerung (exc). (T. Lemnitz, T. Ralf, H.
Janssen, L. Weber, ROH Chor, LPO/T. Beecham)

① **CDLX7008** (8/94)
Bruno Walter conducts the LSO
Beethoven: Coriolan; *Haydn:* Symphony 86; *Schumann:*
Symphony 4; *Smetana:* Bartered Bride (exc); *Corelli:*
Concerti Grossi, Op.6 (exc). (LSO/B. Walter)

① **CDLX7009** (10/94)
Beecham conducts Favourite Overtures, Volume 2
Mozart: Nozze di Figaro (exc); Don Giovanni (exc);
Zauberflöte (exc); *Weber:* Oberon (exc); Freischütz (exc);
Brahms: Tragic Overture; *Wagner:* Faust Overture; *Berlioz:*
Carnaval Romain; *Rossini:* Scala di seta (exc). (LPO,
BPO/T. Beecham)

① **CDLX7011** (10/94)
Beecham conducts Delius
Delius: Appalachia; Koanga (exc); Hassan (exc); Hassan
(exc); First Cuckoo; Summer Night on the River;
Norwegian Songs (1889-90) (exc); Norwegian Songs
(1888) (exc). (D. Labbette, J. van der Gucht, T. Beecham,
BBC Chor, London Select Ch, ROH Chor, LPO, RPS
Orch/T. Beecham)

① **CDLX7012** (2/95)
The Incomparable Heddle Nash
Puccini: Bohème (exc); *Mozart:* Così fan tutte (exc); Così
fan tutte (exc); Don Giovanni (exc); *Rossini:* Barbiere di
Siviglia (exc); *Verdi:* Rigoletto (exc); Rigoletto (exc); *Bizet:*
Jolie fille de Perth (exc); *J. Strauss II:* Fledermaus (exc). (I.
Souez, D. Labbette, S. Andreva, H. Nash, J. Brownlee, D.
Noble, R. Alva, R. Easton, LPO/T. Beecham,
Glyndebourne Fest Orch/F. Busch, orch/C. Raybould)

① **CDLX7013** (7/95)
The Unforgettable Isobel Baillie
Handel: Samson (exc); *Bach:* Cantata 68 (exc); Cantata
201 (exc); *Mozart:* Finta giardiniera (exc); *Handel:*
Rodelinda (exc); *Haydn:* Creation (exc); *Handel:* Messiah
(exc); Messiah (exc); *Mendelssohn:* Elijah (exc); *Handel:*
Theodora (exc); Joshua (exc); *Mozart:* Nozze di Figaro
(exc); *Offenbach:* Contes d'Hoffmann (exc); *Schubert:* Hirt
auf dem Felsen, D965; An die Musik, D547; *Arne:* Tempest
(exc). (I. Baillie, C. Draper, G. Ison, G. Moore, Hallé, CBO,
Liverpool PO, orch/W. Braithwaite/B. Cameron/L.
Heward/M. Sargent/C. Prentice/S. Robinson)

① **CDLX7014** (12/95)
Beecham conducts Schubert Symphonies
Schubert: Symphony 5; Symphony 6; Symphony 8.
(LPO/T. Beecham)

① **CDLX7016** (9/95)
The Art of Sir Hamilton Harty
Bax: Overture to a Picaresque Comedy; *Berlioz:* Roméo et
Juliette (exc); Tristia (exc); *Sibelius:* Valse triste; *Smetana:*
Bartered Bride (exc); *Schubert:* Marches militaires, D733
(exc); *Handel:* Fireworks Music Suite; Water Music Suite.
(LPO/H. Harty)

① **CDSJB1001** (3/95)
Barbirolli in New York - 1938 Wagner Concert
Wagner: Rienzi (exc); Tannhäuser (exc); Tristan und
Isolde (exc); Meistersinger (exc); Siegfried Idyll. (NYPO/J.
Barbirolli)

① **CDSJB1002** (7/95)
Barbirolli conducts French Music
Debussy: Après-midi; *Fauré:* Pelléas et Mélisande Suite
(exc); *Ibert:* Divertissement; *Saint-Saëns:* Carnaval des
animaux; *Bizet:* Arlésienne Suites (exc). (W. Landauer, M.
Rawicz, Hallé/J. Barbirolli)

① **2CDAX2002** (9/94)
The Best of Sir Henry J.Wood
Bach: Brandenburg Concertos (exc); *Haydn:* Symphony
45; *Schubert:* Symphony 8; *Litolff:* Concerto Symphonique,
Op.102 (exc); *Rachmaninov:* Preludes (exc); *Bruckner:*
Overture in G minor; *Beethoven:* Symphony 5; *Brahms:*
Haydn Variations; *Dvořák:* Symphonic Variations. (I.
Scharrer, LSO, British SO, Queen's Hall Orch, SO/Henry
Wood)

① **2CDAX2003** (3/95)
Beecham conducts Haydn/Brahms/Franck
Brahms: Symphony 2; *Franck:* Symphony; *Haydn:*
Symphony 93; Symphony 99; Symphony 104. (LPO/T.
Beecham)

Dynamic

① **CDS21/2** (9/92)
Franck—Chamber works
Franck: Trios, Op. 1; Violin Sonata; Duo, Op. 14;
Andantino quietoso; Trio, Op. 2. (M. Sarbu, M. Sirbu, R.
Colan, M. Dancila)

① **CDS49** (5/89)
French Piano Trios
Fauré: Piano Trio; *Ravel:* Piano Trio; *Debussy:* Piano Trio.
(Trio di Milano)

① **CDS55** (8/89)
Dino Ciani - Piano Recital
Beethoven: Variations, Op. 35; *Schumann:* Piano Sonata
1; *Balakirev:* Islamey; *Liszt:* Études d'exécution, S139
(exc); *Chopin:* Etudes (exc); Nocturnes (exc); *Scriabin:*
Etudes, Op.8 (exc). (D. Ciani)

① **CDS58** (4/90)
Liszt—Piano Works
Liszt: Fantasia and Fugue, S529; Variations, S180;
Berceuse, S174; Geistliche Lieder, S562 (exc); Puritani
réminiscences, S390. (G. Nardi)

① **DC-U25** (1/89)
Haydn: Violin Concertos
Haydn: Violin Concerto, HobVIIa/1; Violin Concerto,
HobVIIa/3; Violin Concerto, HobVIIa/4. (A. Cappelletti,
Scottish CO/J. Blair)

Earthsounds

① **CDEASM003** (5/93)
The Son of the Stars - Piano Music of Satie
Satie: Gnossiennes; Avant-dernières pensées; Première
pensée Rose & Croix; Préludes du fils des étoiles;
Chapitres tournés en tous sens; Gymnopédies; Piège de la
Méduse; Rêverie du pauvre; Je te veux; Prélude de la
porte héroïque du ciel. (J. Lenehan)

EBS

① **EBS6058** (9/92)
Boccherini—Cello Concerti
Boccherini: Cello Concerto in E flat; Cello Concerto, G480;
Cello Concerto, G475; Cello Concerto, G573; Cello
Concerto, G479; Cello Concerto, G482; Cello Concerto,
G476; Cello Concerto, G478; Cello Concerto, G474; Cello
Concerto, G483. (J. Berger, South-
West German CO/V. Czarnecki)

① **EBS6063** (3/92)
Franz & Richard Strauss—Horn Concerts
R. Strauss: Horn Concerto 1; Horn Concerto 2; *F. Strauss:*
Horn Concerto. (I. James, Polish Nat RSO/A. Wit)

① **EBS6065** (9/92)
Brixi—Organ Concertos
Brixi: Organ Concertos; Preludes; Fugues. (S-J. Bleicher,
South-West German RSO/J. Berger)

ECM New Series

① **434 275-2** (10/92)
Tormis—Forgotten Peoples
Tormis: Livonian Heritage (Cpte); Votic Wedding Songs
(Cpte); Izhorian Epic (Cpte); Ingrian Evenings (Cpte);
Vespian Paths (Cpte); Karelian Destiny (Cpte). (Estonian
Phil Chbr Ch/T. Kaljuste)

① **437 040-2** (9/93)
Bach/Veress—Chamber Works
Bach: Solo Cello Suites (exc); *Veress:* Violin Sonata; Cello
Sonata; String Trio. (H. Schneeberger, T. Zimmermann, T.
Demenga)

① **437 441-2** (7/93)
Holliger—Scardanelli-Zyklus
Holliger: Jahreszeiten; Übungen zu Scardanelli; air; Turm-
Musik (exc); Ostinato funebre. (A. Nicolet, London
Voices/T. Edwards, Modern Ens/H. Holliger)

① **437 684-2** (6/93)
Walter Frye—Vocal Works
Frye: Missa Flos Regalis; Trinitatis dies; Salve virgo; O
florens rosa; Ave regina celorum; Sospitati dedit; Tout a
par moy; So ys emprentid; Myn hertis lust; Alas, alas.
(Hilliard Ens)

① **437 956-2** (5/93)
20th Century works for Organ and Soprano
Bryars: Black River; *Górecki:* O Domina nostra, Op.55;
Milhaud: Organ Preludes (exc); *Satie:* Messe des Pauvres.
(S. Leonard, C. Bowers-Broadbent)

---

① **439 162-2** (11/93)
Pärt—Choral Works
Pärt: Te Deum; Silouans Song; Magnificat; Berliner Messe.
(Estonian Phil Chbr Ch, Tallinn CO/T. Kaljuste)

① **439 172-2** (9/94)
Byrd—Motets and Mass for Four Voices
Byrd: Gradualia 1/ii: Corpus Christi (exc); Mass for four
voices; Clarifica me, Pater, BK47; Clarifica me, Pater,
BK48; Clarifica me, Pater, BK49; Gloria tibi Trinitas, BK50;
Taverner: In Nomine; *Tallis:* O ye tender babes; *R.
Edwards:* In goinge to my naked bedde; *Sheppard:* Vaine,
vaine, vaine. (Theatre Of Voices/P. Hillier, C. Bowers-
Broadbent)

① **439 611-2** (11/93)
Works for Viola & Orchestra
Britten: Lachrymae; *Hindemith:* Trauermusik; *Penderecki:*
Viola Concerto. (K. Kashkashian, Stuttgart CO/D.R.
Davies)

① **445 234-2** (8/95)
12 Hommages à Paul Sacher
Ginastera: Puneña; *Fortner:* Zum Spielen; *Henze:*
Capriccio; *Beck:* Epigramme für Paul Sacher; *Dutilleux:*
Strophes; *Lutosławski:* Sacher Variation; *Berio:* Mots sont
allés; *C. Halffter:* eSACHERe Variations; *Britten:* Tema-
Sacher; *K. Huber:* Transpositio ad infinitum; *Holliger:*
Chaconne; *Boulez:* Messagesquisse. (P. Demenga, T.
Demenga, Cello Ens/J. Wyttenbach)

① **445 350-2** (9/94)
Jarrett—Bridge of Light
Jarrett: Elegy; Adagio; Violin Sonata; Bridge of Light. (M.
Butler, M. Makarski, P. McCarty, K. Jarrett, Fairfield
Orch/T. Crawford)

① **445 351-2** (5/94)
Gavin Bryars—Vita Nova
Bryars: Incipit Vita Nova; Glorious Hill; Elements; Sub
Rosa. (D. James, Hilliard Ens, A. Dreyer, U. Lachner, R.
Firth, Chbr Ens, G. Bryars Ens)

① **445 369-2** (10/94)
Officium
Morales: Parce mihi domine; *Anon:* Primo tempore;
Sanctus; Regnantem sempiterna; *La Rue:* O salutaris
hostia; *Anon:* Procedentem sponsum; Pulcherrima rosa;
Pérotin: Beata viscera; *Anon:* De spineto nata rosa; Credo;
Dufay: Ave maris stella; *Anon:* Virgo flagellatur; Oratio
Ieremiae. (J. Garbarek, Hilliard Ens)

① **445 941-2** (4/95)
Kancheli—Abii ne Viderem
Kancheli: Morning Prayers; Evening Prayers; Abii ne
viderem. (V. Tevdorashvii, N. Pschenitschnikova, K.
Kashkashian, Hilliard Ens, Stuttgart CO/D. R. Davies)

① **447 390-2** (9/95)
Sandor Veress
Veress: Passacaglia Concertante; Musica Concertante;
Song of the Seasons. (London Voices/T. Edwards, Berne
Camerata, H. Holliger (ob/dir)/H. Holliger)

① **827 744-2** (9/86)
Kashkashian/Levin—Elegies
Britten: Lachrymae; *Vaughan Williams:* Romance; *Carter:*
Elegy (1943); *Glazunov:* Elégie, Op. 44; *Liszt:* Romance
oubliée, S132; *Kodály:* Adagio (1905); *Vieuxtemps:* Elégie,
Op. 30. (K. Kashkashian, R. Levin)

① **831 959-2** (9/87)
Pärt—Arbos
Pärt: Arbos; An den Wassern zu Babel; Pari intervallo; De
profundis; Es sang vor langen Jahren; Summa; Stabat
mater. (Hilliard Ens, Stuttgart St Orch Brass Ens/D.R.
Davies, C. Bowers-Broadbent, S. Bickley, G. Kremer, V.
Mendelssohn, L. Dawson, D. James, R. Covey-Crump, T.
Demenga)

① **833 309-2** (10/88)
Hindemith—Viola Sonatas
Hindemith: Solo Viola Sonata, Op.31/4; Solo Viola Sonata,
Op.25/1; Solo Viola Sonata (1937); Solo Viola Sonata,
Op.11/5; Viola Sonata, Op.11/4; Viola Sonata, Op.25/4;
Viola Sonata (1939). (K. Kashkashian, R. Levin)

① **837 360-2** (7/89)
Proensa—Songs of the Troubadours
Guillaume IX: Farai un vers; *Giraut de Bornelh:* Reis
glorios; *Raimon de Miraval:* Aissi cum es genser pascors;
Marcabru: L'autrier jost' una sebissa; *Bernart de
Ventadorn:* Be m'au perdut lai enves Ventadorn; Quan vei
la lauzeta mover; *Vidal:* Pos tornatz; *Raquier:* Be.m degra
de chantar tener. (P. Hillier, S. Stubbs, A. Lawrence-King,
E. Headley)

① **837 751-2** (2/90)
Perotin—Sacred Choral Works
Pérotin: Viderunt omnes; Alleluia; Posui adiutorium; Dum

sigillum summi patris; Alleluia, Nativitas; Beata viscera; Sederunt principes; *Anon:* Veni creator spiritus; O Maria virginei; Isias cecinit. (Hilliard Ens/P. Hillier)

ⓘ **839 617-2** (12/90)
Bach & Carter—Instrumental & Chamber Works
Bach: Solo Cello Suites (exc); *Carter:* Esprit rude/Esprit doux; Riconoscenza; Triple duo; Enchanted preludes. (P. Racine, E. Molinari, T. Demenga, H. Schneeberger, P. Cleemann, G. Huber, J. Wyttenbach)

ⓘ **847 537-2** (9/91)
Gavin Bryars—After the Requiem
Bryars: After the Requiem; Alaric (1989); Old Tower of Löbenicht; Allegrasco. (R. Heaton, R. Heaton, E. Parker, S. Sulzmann, R. Warleigh, J. Argüelles, Dave Smith, Dave Smith, A. Balanescu, A. Balanescu, K. Musker, A. Hinnigan, G. Bryars, B. Frisell, M. Allen, S. Limbrick)

ⓘ **847 539-2** (1/92)
Pärt—Miserere; Festina lente; Sarah was ninety-years old
Pärt: Sarah was ninety-years old; Miserere; Festina lente. (Western Wind Chbr Ch, Hilliard Ens, Bonn Beethovenhalle Orch/P. Hillier/D. R. Davies)

Edition Abseits

ⓘ **EDA008-2** (11/95)
Works by Ullmann and Schoenberg
Ullmann: Weise von Liebe und Tod; *Schoenberg* Variations, Op. 3a; *Schoenberg:* Klavierstücke, Op. 19; Ode to Napoleon. (G. Westphal, R. Hermann, T. Vogler, F. Reinecke, S. Fehlandt, M. Sanderling, M. Allan, G. Herzfeld, F-I. Zichner)

Edelweiss

ⓘ **ED1012** (6/90)
Schumann—Chamber Music with Piano
Schumann: Märchenerzählungen; Romanzen, op 94; Adagio and Allegro, op 70; Fantasiestücke, op 73; Märchenbilder. (P. Borgonovo, A. Morf, M. Rota, N. Chumachenco, D. Levy)

ⓘ **ED1034** (3/93)
Grieg—Piano Works
Grieg: Piano Sonata, Op. 7; Lyric Pieces, Op. 12 (exc); Lyric Pieces, Op. 38 (exc); Lyric Pieces, Op. 43 (exc); Lyric Pieces, Op. 47 (exc); Lyric Pieces, Op. 54 (exc); Lyric Pieces, Op. 57 (exc); Lyric Pieces, Op. 62 (exc); Lyric Pieces, Op. 65 (exc); Lyric Pieces, Op. 68 (exc); Lyric Pieces, Op. 71 (exc). (D. Levy)

Nonesuch

ⓘ **7559-79212-2** (9/90)
Beethoven: Piano Sonatas, Op.31
Beethoven: Piano Sonata 16; Piano Sonata 17; Piano Sonata 18. (R. Goode)

ⓘ **7559-79213-2** (4/91)
Beethoven—Piano Sonatas
Beethoven: Piano Sonata 5; Piano Sonata 6; Piano Sonata 7. (R. Goode)

ⓘ **7559-79242-2** (4/91)
Kronos Quartet—Black Angels
Shostakovich: String Quartet 8; *Tallis:* Spem in alium; *Crumb:* Black Angels; *Marta:* Doom; Sigh; *Ives:* They are there!. (Kronos Qt)

ⓘ **7559-79249-2** (7/91)
American Elegies
Ives: Unanswered Question; Down East; At the river; Serenity; Thoreau; Cradle Song; *I. Marshall:* Fog Tropes; *M. Feldman:* Madame Press; *J. Adams:* Eros Piano; *Diamond:* Ravel Elegy. (D. Upshaw, P. Crossley, St Luke's Orch/J. Adams)

ⓘ **7559-79261-2** (12/93)
Horszowski—A Portrait
Mozart: Fantasia, K397; *Chopin:* Nocturnes (exc); Mazurkas (exc); *Debussy:* Children's Corner; *Beethoven:* Piano Sonata 2; Piano Sonata 6; *Mozart:* Piano Sonata, K332; Piano Sonata, K576; *Bach:* English Suites, BWV806-811 (exc); *Schumann:* Arabeske; Kinderszenen. (M. Horszowski)

ⓘ **7559-79262-2** (11/91)
Dawn Upshaw-The girl with orange lips
Falla: Psyché; *Ravel:* Mallarmé Poems; *Stravinsky:* Japanese Lyrics; Bal'mont Poems; *Delage:* Poèmes hindous; *Kim:* Where Grief Slumbers. (D. Upshaw, Inst Ens)

ⓘ **7559-79264-2** (12/93)
Mieczyslaw Horszowski 100th Birthday Recording
Bach: French Suites, BWV812-17 (exc); *Chopin:* Mazurkas

ⓘ **7559-79275-2** (11/92)
Pieces of Africa
Maraire: Mai Nozipo; Kutambarra; *H. Hakmoun:* Saade; *Suso:* Tilliboyo; *Tamusuza:* Ekitundu Ekisooka; *El Din:* Escalay; *Addy:* Wawshishijay; *Volans:* String Quartet 1. (Kronos Qt, D. Maraire, D. Maraire, H. Hakmoun, R. Laktib, S. Hakmoun, F. Musa Suso, H. El Din, O. Addy, D. Pauli, Oakland Interfaith Gospel Ch/T. Kelly)

ⓘ **7559-79285-2** (8/94)
The Burton Lane Songbook, Vol.2
B. Lane: Carmelina (exc); Hold on to Your Hats (exc); Love on Toast (exc); Dancing Lady (exc); Kid Millions (exc); Ship Ahoy (exc); Royal Wedding (exc); Dancing on a Dime (exc); Lady's In Love With You; Where have I seen your Face Before; Give a Girl a Break (exc); Look Who's Here; On a Clear Day (exc). (M. Feinstein, B. Lane)

ⓘ **7559-79287-2** (4/94)
Gershwin—Piano Rolls
Gershwin: Tip-Toes (exc); Novelette in Fourths; Lady, be good (exc); Rhapsody in Blue; Gershwin Songbook (exc); When you want'em; Tell me more (exc); Scandals 1920 (exc); American in Paris. (G. Gershwin, F. Milne)

ⓘ **7559-79292-2** (10/93)
Baroque Guitar Transcriptions
D. Scarlatti: Keyboard Sonatas (exc); *Rameau:* Pièces de clavecin (exc); *Couperin:* Livre de clavecin II (exc); Livre de clavecin III (exc); *Bach:* Wohltemperierte Klavier (exc). (S. Assad, O. Assad)

ⓘ **7559-79310-2** (8/93)
Short Stories
Cowell: Euphometric; *Mackey:* Physical Property; *Pärt:* Dixon: Spoonful; *S. Johnson:* How it happens (exc); *Gubaidulina:* String Quartet 2; *Nath:* It is my turn. (Kronos Qt, P.P. Nath, S. Mackey, K. Bhatt, T. Riley, J. Constant)

ⓘ **7559-79311-2** (4/94)
John Adams—Hoodoo Zephyr
J. Adams: Coast; Disappointment Lake; Tourist Song; Tundra; Bump; Cerulean; Hoodoo Zephyr. (J. Adams, J. Adams)

ⓘ **7559-79317-2** (8/94)
Goethe Lieder
Schumann: Lieder und Gesänge, Op. 51 (exc); Lieder und Gesänge, Op. 96 (exc); Lieder und Gesänge, Op. 98a (exc); *Schubert:* Rastlose Liebe, D138; Gretchen am Spinnrade, D118; Nur wer die Sehnsucht kennt, D877/4; Suleika I, D720; Versunken, D715; Wandrers Nachtlied II, D768; Ganymed, D544; An den Mond, D296; *Wolf:* Goethe Lieder (exc); *Mozart:* Veilchen, K476. (D. Upshaw, R. Goode)

ⓘ **7559-79328-2** (3/94)
Beethoven—Complete Piano Sonatas
Beethoven: Piano Sonata 1; Piano Sonata 2; Piano Sonata 3; Piano Sonata 4; Piano Sonata 5; Piano Sonata 6; Piano Sonata 7; Piano Sonata 8; Piano Sonata 9; Piano Sonata 10; Piano Sonata 11; Piano Sonata 12; Piano Sonata 13; Piano Sonata 14; Piano Sonata 15; Piano Sonata 16; Piano Sonata 17; Piano Sonata 18; Piano Sonata 19; Piano Sonata 20; Piano Sonata 21; Piano Sonata 22; Piano Sonata 23; Piano Sonata 24; Piano Sonata 25; Piano Sonata 26; Piano Sonata 27; Piano Sonata 28; Piano Sonata 29; Piano Sonata 30; Piano Sonata 31; Piano Sonata 32. (R. Goode)

ⓘ **7559-79330-2** (11/94)
Patinkin—Experiment
Hupfeld: As Time Goes By; *Kern:* You Were Never Lovelier (exc); *Menken:* Little Shop of Horrors (stage) (exc); *Sondheim:* Company (exc); Merrily We Roll Along (exc); Follies (exc); So Many People; *Bernstein:* West Side Story (exc); *Waller:* Ain't Misbehavin' (exc); *Chapin:* Taxi; *C-M. Schönberg:* Misérables (exc); *Warren:* Billy Rose's Diamond Horseshoe (exc); *Rodgers:* Babes in Arms (exc); *Berlin:* Always; *B. Lane:* Finian's Rainbow (exc); *Porter:* Nymph Errant (exc). (M. Patinkin, Orch/E. Stern)

ⓘ **7559-79343-2** (5/95)
Stravinsky—Piano Works
Stravinsky: Histoire du Soldat; Petrushka; Apollo. (C. O'Riley)

ⓘ **7559-79345-2** (12/94)
I Wish It So - Dawn Upshaw
Bernstein: Candide (1988) (exc); Madwoman of Central Park West (exc); West Side Story (exc); *Blitzstein:* Juno (exc); No for an Answer (exc); Reuben, Reuben (exc); *Sondheim:* Anyone can Whistle (exc); Saturday Night (exc); Girls of Summer (exc); Merrily We Roll Along (exc); Evening Primrose (exc); *Weill:* One Touch of Venus (exc);

*Preludes (exc); *Schumann:* Papillons. (M. Horszowski)

Lady in the Dark (exc); Lost in the Stars (exc). (D. Upshaw, orch/E. Stern, E. Stern, L. Stifelman)

ⓘ **7559-79348-2** (3/95)
Górecki—Choral Works
Górecki: Miserere; Amen; Euntes ibant, Op. 32; Wisło moja; Szeroka Woda. (Chicago Sym Chor, Chicago Lyric Op Chor/J. Nelson, Lira Chbr Chor/L. Ding)

ⓘ **7559-79362-2** (9/95)
Górecki—Orchestral and Vocal Works
Górecki: Kleines Requiem, Op. 66; Harpsichord Concerto, Op. 40; Good Night, Op. 63. (J. Constable, E. Chojnacka, D. Upshaw, S. Bell, D. Hockings, London Sinfonietta/D. Zinman/M. Stenz)

Emergo Classics

ⓘ **EC3992-2** (10/94)
The Unfinished Mozart
Mozart: Allegro, K312; Andantino, KAnh46; Sonata Movement, K372; Sonata Movement, KAnh42; Sonata Movement, KAnh43; Violin Sonata, K402; Violin Sonata, K403; Violin Sonata, K404; Sonata Movement, KAnh47; Sonata Movement, KAnh48; Sonata Movement, K357; Sonata Movement, K396; String Quartet Rondo, KAnh72; String Quartet Minuet, KAnh74; String Quartet Minuet, KAnh68; Piano Trio Movements, K442; String Quintet Movement, KAnh79; String Quintet Movement, KAnh80; String Quintet Movement, KAnh81; String Quintet Movement, KAnh82; Clarinet Quintet Movement, KAnh88; Clarinet Quintet Movement, KAnh90; Clarinet Quintet Movement, KAnh91; String Trio Movement, KAnh66; Allegro assai, KAnh95; Adagio, KAnh94; Piano and Wind Quintet, K452a; Allegro, K288. (Netherlands Sols Ens)

ⓘ **EC3993-2** (7/94)
Mussorgsky/Rachmaninov—Piano Works
Mussorgsky: Pictures; *Rachmaninov:* Morceaux de fantaisie, Op.3 (exc); *Preludes* (exc); Etudes-Tableaux, Op. 33 (exc); Etudes-Tableaux, Op.39 (exc). (N. Grubert)

EMI

ⓘ **CDANGEL 5** (11/94)
Norton—Chu Chin Chow
Norton: Chu Chin Chow (exc); Chu Chin Chow (exc); Chu Chin Chow (exc); Chu Chin Chow (exc). (J. Bryan, B. Leigh, I. te Wiata, C. Young, Orch/M. Collins, M. McEachern, Gaumont British Orch/Man. V. Essex, C. Pounds, F. Cochrane, Orig London Cast/Percy Fletcher, M. Grimaldi, E. Darling, U. Connors, I. Humphris, Chor, Sinfonia of London/J. Hollingsworth)

ⓘ **CDC5 55000-2** (7/94)
Bach—Cantata Arias
Bach: Cantata 93 (exc); Cantata 177 (exc); Cantata 94 (exc); Cantata 202 (exc); Cantata 144 (exc); Cantata 89 (exc); Cantata 21 (exc); Christmas Oratorio, BWV248 (exc); Cantata 187 (exc); Cantata 199 (exc); Cantata 98 (exc); Cantata 1 (exc); Cantata 75 (exc); Cantata 74 (exc); Mass, BWV233 (exc). (E. Ameling, H. de Vries, R. van der Meer, A. de Klerk)

ⓘ **CDC5 55001-2** (3/95)
Elgar—Orchestral Works
Elgar: Enigma Variations; Falstaff; Grania and Diarmid (exc). (CBSO/S. Rattle)

ⓘ **CDC5 55017-2** (6/94)
Domingo Opera Classics
Verdi: Aida (exc); *Mozart:* Cosi fan tutte (exc); *Verdi:* Ballo in maschera (exc); *Puccini:* Manon Lescaut (exc); *Verdi:* Don Carlo (exc); *Handel:* Giulio Cesare (exc); *Boito:* Mefistofele (exc); *Mozart:* Don Giovanni (exc); *Meyerbeer:* Africaine (exc); *Puccini:* Fanciulla del West (exc); *Verdi:* Forza del Destino (exc); *Puccini:* Tosca (exc); *Mascagni:* Nerone (exc); *Gounod:* Faust (exc); *Puccini:* Tosca (exc); *Verdi:* Otello (exc). (P. Domingo, R. Grist, M. Caballé, ROH Chor, Ambrosian Op Chor, New Philh, Munich RO, ROHO, National PO, LSO, La Scala Orch, Paris Op Orch, Philh/R. Muti/E. Stern, R. Bartoletti/C.M. Giulini/J. Rudel/J. Barker/G. Prêtre/James Levine)

ⓘ **CDC5 55018-2** (4/94)
Domingo sings and conducts Tchaikovsky
Tchaikovsky: Romeo and Juliet; Songs, Op. 6 (exc); Capriccio italien; Eugene Onegin (exc); 1812. (P. Domingo, O. Harnoy, Philh/P. Domingo/R. Behr)

ⓘ **CDC5 55026-2** (11/94)
Paganini/Saint-Saëns—Violin Works
Paganini: Violin Concerto 1; *Saint-Saëns:* Havanaise; Introduction and Rondo Capriccioso. (S. Chang, Philadelphia/W. Sawallisch)

ⓘ **CDC5 55031-2** (5/95)
Bartók/Dohnányi—Play their own works
Bartók: Bagatelles, Sz38 (exc); Easy Pieces (exc);

Romanian Dances, Sz43 (exc); Burlesques, Sz47 (exc); Allegro barbaro, Sz49; Suite, Sz62; Mikrokosmos, Bk 5 (exc); Mikrokosmos, Bk 6 (exc); Hungarian Folk Tunes; Hungarian Folksongs, Sz64 (exc); Hungarian Folksongs, Sz64 (exc); For Children (1908-09) (exc); Romanian Folkdances, Sz56; Dohnányi: Nursery Variations. (V. Medgyaszay, M. Basilides, F. Székelyhidy, J. Szigeti, B. Bartók, E. Dohnányi, LSO/L. Collingwood)

① CDC5 55035-2 (7/94)
Khachaturian conducts Khachaturian
Khachaturian: Masquerade (exc); Violin Concerto; Gayaneh (exc). (D. Oistrakh, Philh/A. Khachaturian)

① CDC5 55036-2 (6/94)
Honegger/Poulenc—Perform their own works
Honegger: Pastorale d'été; Cello Concerto; *Poulenc:* Mouvements perpétuels; Piano, oboe and bassoon trio; Novelettes; Nocturnes (exc); Improvisations (exc); Aubade. (R. Lamorlette, G. Dhérin, M. Maréchal, F. Poulenc, Paris Cons, SO/A. Honegger, Walther Straram Orch/W. Straram)

① CDC5 55037-2 (5/94)
French Organists play their own works
Widor: Symphony 5 (exc); Symphonie gothique (exc); Vierne: Improvisations (1928) (exc); Suite 1 (exc); *Dupré:* Suite bretonne, Op.21 (exc); Preludes and Fugues, Op.7 (exc); *Messiaen:* Banquet céleste; Ascension. (C-M. Widor, L. Vierne, M. Dupré, O. Messiaen)

① CDC5 55047-2 (5/94)
Liszt/Wagner/Berlioz—Romantic Songs
Berlioz: Mélodies, Op. 2 (exc); Origine de la harpe; Elégie en prose; *Liszt:* Vätergruft, S281; Go not, happy day, S335; Es rauschen die Winde, S294; Ihr Auge, S310; Über allen Gipfeln ist Ruh, S306; Am Rhein, S272; Es muss ein Wunderbares sein, S314; Vergiftet sind meine Lieder, S289; Tombe et la rose, S285; Comment, disaient-ils, S276; Oh, quand je dors, S282; *Wagner:* Mélodies (exc); Tout n'est qu'images fugitives; Deux Grenadiers; Faust Lieder, Op.5 (exc); Tannenbaum. (T. Hampson, G. Parsons)

① CDC5 55048-2 (10/94)
Pulling out the stops!
G. Martini: Toccata; *M-A. Charpentier:* Te Deum, H146 (exc); *Bach:* Cantata 147 (exc); Suites, BWV1066-9 (exc); Schübler Chorales, BWV645-650 (exc); *Telemann:* Marches, TWV50: 31-42; *Bach:* Chorales, BWV651-668 (exc); *Clarke:* Suite in D (exc); *Rachmaninov:* Songs, Op.34 (exc); *Grieg:* Elegiac Melodies (exc); Folksongs and Dances, Op.17 (exc); *Traditional:* Wedding March from Nordmøre; *Olsen:* Canto Amoroso, Op.36/1; *Lindberg:* Old tune from Dalecarlia. (O.E. Antonsen, W. Marshall)

① CDC5 55050-2 (7/94)
Kiri sings Cole Porter
Porter: Born to Dance (exc); Broadway Melody (exc); Can-Can (exc); Gay Divorce (exc); High Society (exc); Jubilee (exc); Kiss Me Kate (exc); Paris (exc); Red, Hot and Blue (exc); Rosalie (exc); Seven Lively Arts (exc); Something to shout about (exc). (K. Te Kanawa, New World Phil/P. Matz)

① CDC5 55051-2 (6/94)
John Adams—Orchestral Works
J. Adams: Harmonielehre; Chairman Dances; Tromba lontana; Short Ride. (CBSO/S. Rattle)

① CDC5 55052-2 (10/94)
Praetorius/Warlock—Works arr guitar
Vivaldi: Concerto, RV93; *Warlock:* Capriol Suite; *Vivaldi:* Concerto, RV425; Trio, RV82; *M. Praetorius:* Terpsichore (exc). (C. Parkening, I. Brown, L. Handy, J. Constable, ASMF/I. Brown)

① CDC5 55057-2 (5/95)
Bizet—Orchestral Works
Bizet: Symphony; Roma; Patrie. (Toulouse Capitole Orch/M. Plasson)

① CDC5 55085-2 (7/94)
Flute Recital
Fauré: Fantaisie; *Poulenc:* Flute Sonata; *Caplet:* Rêverie et Petite Valse; *Dutilleux:* Sonatine; *Bach:* Flute Sonatas, BWV1030-5 (exc); *Prokofiev:* Flute Sonata. (P. E. Davies, J. Alley, A. Shulman)

① CDC5 55086-2 (11/94)
Trumpet Recital
Fantini: Trumpet Sonatas (exc); *Tartini:* Trumpet Concerto; *Françaix:* Trumpet Sonatine; *Arban:* Actéon Variations; *Enescu:* Legend; *Höhne:* Slavonic Fantasy; *Goedicke:* Concert Etude, Op.49; *Eben:* Chagall Windows. (J. Wallace, J. Wallace, M. Alexander, S. Wright, S. Wright, S. Wright)

① CDC5 55090-2 (10/94)
Amanda Roocroft—Recital
Handel: Samson (exc); Giulio Cesare (exc); *Mozart:* Così fan tutte (exc); Idomeneo (exc); *Puccini:* Rondine (exc); Gianni Schicchi (exc); Manon Lescaut (exc); *Verdi:* Otello (exc); *Dvořák:* Rusalka (exc); *G. Charpentier:* Louise (exc); *Duparc:* Chanson triste; *R. Strauss:* Lieder, Op.27 (exc); Lieder, Op.39 (exc). (A. Roocroft, LPO/F. Welser-Möst)

① CDC5 55091-2 (9/94)
Turnage—Orchestral Works
Turnage: Drowned Out; Kai; Screaming Popes; Momentum. (U. Heinen, Birmingham Contemp Mus Group, CBSO/S. Rattle)

① CDC5 55096-2 (12/94)
Ikos
Anon: Festival of the Virgin Mary (exc); *Górecki:* Totus tuus, Op.60; *Amen;* *Pärt:* Magnificat; *Anon:* Saints' Days (exc); *Pärt:* Beatitudes; *Tavener:* Magnificat; Nunc Dimittis; *Anon:* Requiem (exc); *Tavener:* Funeral Ikos. (Kings College Ch/S. Cleobury, D. Goode)

① CDC5 55107-2 (8/94)
Schnittke/Kopytman—Viola Concertos
Schnittke: Viola Concerto; Monologue; *Kopytman:* Cantus V. (T. Zimmermann, Jerusalem SO/D. Shallon)

① CDC5 55108-2 (2/95)
R. Strauss/Mozart—Chamber Works
Mozart: String Quintet, K406; *R. Strauss:* Capriccio (exc); Metamorphosen. (A. Posch, Vienna Stg Sextet)

① CDC5 55120-2 (7/94)
Debussy/Chausson/Ravel—Orchestral & Vocal Works
Chausson: Poème de l'amour et de la mer; *Debussy:* La mer; *Ravel:* Barque sur l'océan. (W. Meier, Philadelphia/R. Muti)

① CDC5 55121-2 (8/94)
Szymanowski—Choral Works
Szymanowski: Stabat mater; Litany, Op.59; Symphony 3. (E. Szmytka, F. Quivar, J. Garrison, J. Connell, CBSO Chor, CBSO/S. Rattle)

① CDC5 55122-2 (7/94)
Honegger—Orchestral Works
Honegger: Symphony 2; Symphony 3; Symphonic Movements (exc). (Oslo PO/M. Jansons)

① CDC5 55123-2 (1/95)
Julian Bream plays Bach
Bach: Prelude, Fugue and Allegro, BWV998; Suite, BWV996; Solo Violin Partitas and Sonatas (exc). (J. Bream)

① CDC5 55140-2 (8/94)
Rachmaninov—Orchestral Works
Rachmaninov: Symphony 2; Scherzo; Vocalise. (St Petersburg PO/M. Jansons)

① CDC5 55147-2 (1/95)
Thomas Hampson Lieder Recital
Franz: Lieder, Op. 1 (exc); Lieder, Op. 4 (exc); *Loewe:* Findlay; *Schumann:* Myrthen, Op. 25 (exc); Lieder und Gesänge, Op. 27 (exc); *Grieg:* Songs, Op. 48; *Beethoven:* An die ferne Geliebte, Op. 98; *Schumann:* Dichterliebe, Op. 48 (Cpte). (T. Hampson, G. Parsons)

① CDC5 55152-2 (6/95)
Operetta Duets
Friml: Rose Marie (exc); *Romberg:* Desert Song (exc); New Moon (exc); Student Prince (exc); *Hahn:* Ciboulette (exc); *Messager:* Véronique (exc); Yvain: Ta bouche (exc); *Christiné:* Phi-Phi (exc); *Offenbach:* Barbe-bleue (exc); *Millöcker:* Gasparone (exc); *Heuberger:* Opernball (exc); *J. Strauss II:* Zigeunerbaron (exc); Wiener Blut (exc); *Lehár:* Land des Lächelns (exc); Lustige Witwe (exc). (B. Hendricks, G. Quilico, Lyon Op Orch/L. Foster)

① CDC5 55166-2 (7/95)
Schubert/Beethoven/Reinecke—Viola Works
Beethoven: Notturno, Op.42; *Reinecke:* Phantasiestücke, Op.43; *Schubert:* Arpeggione Sonata, D821. (G. Caussé, F-R. Duchâble)

① CDC5 55167-2 (7/95)
Brahms—Piano Variations
Brahms: Schumann Variations; Handel Variations; Variations, Op.21/2; Theme and Variations. (M. Rudy)

① CDC5 55189-2 (12/94)
The Busby Berkeley Album
Warren: Gold Diggers of 1933 (exc); Gold Diggers of 1935 (exc); 42nd Street (exc); Dames (exc). (J. Blazer, D. Shapiro Gravitte, A. Morrison, J. Sylvester, N. Long, B. Barrett, G. Stroman, S. Chandler, L. Raben, J. McGlinn, D. Engel, London Sinfonietta Chor, London Sinfonietta/J. McGlinn)

① CDC5 55192-2 (12/94)
Haydn—Symphonies
Haydn: Symphony 99; Symphony 100; Windsor Castle Overture. (LCP/R. Norrington)

① CDC5 55212-2 (4/95)
Schoenberg—Orchestral Works
Schoenberg: Chamber Symphony 1; Erwartung (Cpte); Variations, Op.31. (P. Bryn-Julson, Birmingham Contemp Mus Group, CBSO/S. Rattle)

① CDC5 55223-2 (5/95)
Prokofiev & Glazunov - Composers in Person
Prokofiev: Piano Concerto 3; Pieces, Op.4 (exc); Visions fugitives (exc); Symphony 1 (exc); Piano Sonata 4 (exc); Pieces, Op.32 (exc); *Glazunov:* Seasons. (S. Prokofiev, LSO/P. Coppola, orch/A. Glazunov)

① CDC5 55224-2 (6/95)
Villa-Lobos conducts Villa-Lobos
Villa-Lobos: Bachianas Brasileiras 2 (exc); Bachianas Brasileiras 5; Miniatures (exc); Modinhas e Canções I (exc); Momoprecoce; Bachianas Brasileiras 4; Chôros 10. (V. de los Angeles, F. Fuller, M. Tagliaferro, H. Villa-Lobos, Jeunesses Musicales Chor, FRNO/H. Villa-Lobos)

① CDC5 55225-2 (5/95)
Pfitzner plays and conducts Pfitzner
Pfitzner: Christ-Elflein (exc); Palestrina (exc); Duo, Op.43; Lieder, Op.7 (exc); Lieder, Op.9 (exc); Lieder, Op.10 (exc); Lieder, Op.19 (exc); Lieder, Op.22 (exc); Lieder, Op.26 (exc); Lieder, Op.29 (exc); Lieder, Op.32 (exc); Lieder, Op.40 (exc). (G. Hüsch, M. Strub, L. Hoelscher, H. Pfitzner, Berlin St Op Orch/H. Pfitzner)

① CDC5 55226-2 (11/95)
Beethoven—Piano Sonatas
Beethoven: Piano Sonata 16; Piano Sonata 17; Piano Sonata 18. (S. Kovacevich)

① CDC5 55230-2 (6/95)
Hindemith—Orchestral Works
Hindemith: Symphonic Metamorphosis; Mathis der Maler; Nobilissima Visione. (Philadelphia/W. Sawallisch)

① CDC5 55231-2 (7/95)
Trumpet Concertos
Haydn: Trumpet Concerto; *Hertel:* Trumpet Concerto in E flat; *A. Marcello:* Oboe Concerto in D minor; *Hummel:* Trumpet Concerto. (M. André, F. Liszt CO/J. Rolla)

① CDC5 55233-2 (9/95)
German Opera Arias
Korngold: Tote Stadt (exc); *Lortzing:* Zar und Zimmermann (exc); Wildschütz (exc); *Marschner:* Hans Heiling (exc); Vampyr (exc); *Weber:* Euryanthe (exc); *Spohr:* Faust (exc); *Kreutzer:* Nachtlager in Granada (exc); *Schreker:* Ferne Klang (exc); *Humperdinck:* Königskinder (exc); *Wagner:* Tannhäuser (exc); Walküre (exc). (T. Hampson, Pestalozzi Children's Ch, Munich RO/F. Luisi)

① CDC5 55345-2 (12/95)
Liebeslieder
Mozart: An Chloe, K524; Veilchen, K476; Abendempfindung, K523; *Weber:* Was zieht zu deinen Zauberkreise, J68; Er an Sie, J57; Ich sah ein Röschen am Wege stehn, J67; *Schubert:* Nähe des Geliebten, D162; Bei dir allein, D866/2; Du bist die Ruh', D776; *Mendelssohn:* Lieder, Op.86 (exc); Lieder, Op.19a (exc); Lieder, Op.34 (exc); *Schumann:* Myrthen, Op.25 (exc); *Brahms:* Lieder, Op.59 (exc); Lieder, Op.47 (exc); Lieder, Op.63 (exc); *Wolf:* Eichendorff Lieder (exc); *R. Strauss:* Lieder, Op.21 (exc); Lieder, Op.27 (exc); Lieder, Op.19 (exc); Lieder, Op.10 (exc). (O. Bär, G. Parsons)

① CDC5 55348-2 (9/95)
Weber—Orchestral Works
Weber: Symphony 1; Symphony 2; Konzertstück. (M. Tan, LCP/R. Norrington)

① CDC5 55358-2 (8/95)
Barbara Hendricks sings Barber & Copland
Copland: Quiet City; Dickinson Poems (exc); *Barber:* Adagio for Strings; Songs, Op.13 (exc); Knoxville. (B. Hendricks, LSO/M. Tilson Thomas)

① CDC5 55359-2 (7/95)
Schubert—Piano Works, Vol.1
Schubert: Piano Sonata, D960; Allegretto, D915; Ländler, D790. (S. Kovacevich)

① CDC5 55360-2 (6/95)
The American Album
Bernstein: Serenade; *Barber:* Violin Concerto; *Foss:* American Pieces. (I. Perlman, Boston SO/S. Ozawa)

① CDC5 55396-2 (12/95)
Mozart & his Contemporaries
Mozart: Così fan tutte (exc); Don Giovanni (exc); Idomeneo (exc); Alma grande e nobil core, K578; Basta vincesti,

(exc); Années de pèlerinage 2 (exc); Consolations, S172 (exc). (T. Barto)

Ⓓ **CDC7 49604-2** (12/89)
Violin Arrangements by Jascha Heifetz
Ponce: Estrellita; Moszkowski: Pieces, op 45 (exc); Drigo: Airs de Ballet (exc); Rachmaninov: Songs, Op. 21 (exc); Ravel: Valses nobles et sentimentales (exc); Chopin: Nocturnes (exc); Poulenc: Presto; Saint-Saëns: Carnaval des animaux (exc); Gershwin: Preludes; Albéniz: Suite española 1 (exc); Schumann: Waldszenen (exc); Rameau: Pièces de clavecin (exc); Achron: Hebrew Melody; Paradis: Keyboard Sonatas (exc); Elgar: Capricieuse; Debussy: Children's Corner (exc); Foster: Old folks at home. (I. Perlman, S. Sanders)

Ⓓ **CDC7 49652-2** (9/88)
Chabrier—Orchestral Works
Chabrier: Joyeuse marche; España; Suite pastorale; Roi malgré lui (exc); Prélude pastorale; Bourrée fantasque; Pièces pittoresques (exc). (Toulouse Capitole Orch/M. Plasson)

Ⓓ **CDC7 49663-2** (1/89)
Works for Violin & Orchestra
Bruch: Violin Concerto 1; Mendelssohn: Violin Concerto, Op. 64; Schubert: Rondo, D438. (N. Kennedy, ECO/J. Tate)

Ⓓ **CDC7 49672-2** (9/89)
Mozart: Sacred Choral Works
Mozart: Vespers, K321; Vespers, K339; Ave verum corpus, K618. (L. Dawson, D. James, R. Covey-Crump/P. Hillier, King's College Ch, Cambridge Classical Plyrs/S. Cleobury)

Ⓓ **CDC7 49689-2** (4/89)
Duparc/Ravel—Vocal Works
Ravel: Shéhérazade; Mélodies hébraïques; Mélodies populaires grecques; Vocalise; Duparc: Invitation au voyage; Au pays où se fait la guerre; Vie antérieure; Manoir de Rosemonde; Phidylé; Chanson triste. (B. Hendricks, Lyon Op Orch/J.E. Gardiner)

Ⓓ **CDC7 49700-2** (6/88)
Lucia Popp sings Viennese Operetta
Lehár: Lustige Witwe (exc); Giuditta (exc); Land des Lächelns (exc); Friederike (exc); Suppé: Boccaccio (exc); Millöcker: Dubarry (exc); Zeller: Obersteiger (exc); Lincke: Frau Luna (exc); J. Strauss II: Tänzerin Fanny Elssler (exc); Casanova (exc); Stolz: Favorit (exc); Frühjahrsparade (exc); Dostal: Ungarische Hochzeit (exc). (L. Popp, Ambrosian Op. Chor, ASMF/N. Marriner)

Ⓓ **CDC7 49702-2** (7/89)
Satie: Piano Works, Vol.1
Satie: Allegro; Valse-Ballet; Fantaisie-Valse; Sarabandes; Fête; Morceaux en forme de poire; Nocturnes; Petites pièces montées; Gymnopédies; Premier Minuet; Avant-dernières pensées. (A. Ciccolini, G. Tacchino)

Ⓓ **CDC7 49703-2** (7/89)
Satie: Piano Works, Vol.2
Satie: Ogives; Première pensée Rose & Croix; Sonneries de la Rose & Croix; Préludes du fils des étoiles; Préludes du Nazaréen; Prélude d'Eginhard; Danses gothiques; Prélude de la porte héroïque du ciel; Prière; Vexations; Rêverie du pauvre; Versets laïques et somptueux. (A. Ciccolini)

Ⓓ **CDC7 49713-2** (7/89)
Satie: Piano Works, Vol.3
Satie: Caresse; Danse de travers; Petite musique; Dreaming Fish; Carnet d'esquisses; Pieces (1906-13); Passacaille; Prélude en tapisserie; Musiques intimes; Petits Chorals; Rêveries nocturnes; Aperçus désagréables; En habit de cheval. (A. Ciccolini, G. Tacchino)

Ⓓ **CDC7 49714-2** (7/89)
Satie: Piano Works, Vol.4
Satie: Nouvelles pièces froides; Préludes flasques; Véritables préludes flasques; Descriptions automatiques; Embryons desséchés; Croquis et agaceries; Chapitres tournés en tous sens; Vieux séquins et vieilles cuirasses; Sonatine bureaucratique; Menus propos enfantins; Enfantillages pittoresques; Peccadilles importunes; Nouvelles enfantines; Sports et divertissements; Heures séculaires et instantanées; Valses du précieux dégoûté. (A. Ciccolini)

Ⓓ **CDC7 49736-2** (8/89)
Clarinet Music by Bruch, Mozart & Schumann
Bruch: Pieces, Op. 83 (exc); Mozart: Piano Trio, K498; Schumann: Märchenerzählungen. (S. Meyer, T. Zimmermann, H. Höll)

Ⓓ **CDC7 49759-2** (11/88)
Wagner: Opera Scenes and Arias
Wagner: Tristan und Isolde (exc); Tannhäuser (exc);

Fliegende Holländer (exc); Götterdämmerung (exc). (J. Norman, Ambrosian Op Chor, LPO/K. Tennstedt)

Ⓓ **CDC7 49760-2** (7/89)
Satie: Piano Works, Vol.5
Satie: Gnossiennes; Pièces froides; Jack-in-the-box; Petite ouverture; Je te veux; Poudre d'or; Piccadilly; Piège de Méduse; Pantins dansent; Belle excentrique. (A. Ciccolini, G. Tacchino)

Ⓓ **CDC7 49765-2** (6/88)
My Spirit Sang All Day
Finzi: Partsongs, Op. 17 (exc); S.Wilson: To a Lady Seen from the Train; Gibberish; Holst: Bring us in good ale; Choral Folk Songs, H136 (exc); Vaughan Williams: Seeds of Love; Rest; Rubbra: My tocher's the jewel; Beauty is but a painted hell; Lovatt: Little Green Lane; Morris: Blow away the morning dew; Elgar: Choral Songs, Op.53 (exc); Bridge: Bee; O weary hearts!; Hilli-ho; Bairstow: Music, when soft voices die; Parry: Partsongs (1909) (exc); Wood: There comes a new moon; When winds that move not; Moeran: Songs of Springtime (exc); Grainger: Brigg Fair; Stanford: Partsongs, Op. 106 (exc); Quick! we have but a second. (King's Sngrs)

Ⓓ **CDC7 49797-2** (1/90)
Mussorgsky—Orchestral Works
Mussorgsky: Pictures; Night on the Bare Mountain; Khovanshchina (exc). (Oslo PO/M. Jansons)

Ⓓ **CDC7 49809-2** (12/89)
The Carol Album
Traditional: O come, o come Emmanuel; Stille Nacht; Il est né; Nova! nova!; Marche des rois; Babe of Bethlehem; Y la Virgen; Glory to God on high; Thys endere nyghth; Bach: O Jesulein süss; Traditional: God rest you merry, gentlemen; Sweet was the song; Quem pastores laudavere; Quanno nascete ninno; Riu, riu, chiu; Gabriel fram heven-king; Christum wir sollen loben schon; Coventry Carol; Gaudete!; In hac anni circulo; Alleluya: A nywe werk is come on honde; Greensleeves (The Old Year); Ding dong merrily on high. (Taverner Ch, Taverner Consort, Taverner Plyrs/A. Parrott)

Ⓓ **CDC7 49811-2** (9/89)
Covent Garden Gala Concert
Meyerbeer: Africaine (exc); Puccini: Bohème (exc); Fanciulla del West (exc); Verdi: Macbeth (exc); Aida (exc); Otello (exc); Otello (exc); Traviata (exc); J. Strauss II: Fledermaus (exc); Moreno Torroba: Chulapona (exc); Soutullo: Ultimo Romantico (exc). (C. Studer, E. Randová, P. Domingo, T. Allen, ROHO/J. Barker)

Ⓓ **CDC7 49816-2** (11/89)
Beethoven: Orchestral Works
Beethoven: Symphony 7; Egmont (exc); Coriolan. (LCP/R. Norrington)

Ⓓ **CDC7 49841-2** (2/90)
Fauré—Mélodies
Fauré: Songs, Op.7 (exc); Songs, Op.46 (exc); Songs, Op. 58 (exc); Songs, Op.83 (exc); Songs, Op.27 (exc); Songs, Op.39 (exc); Songs, Op.43 (exc); Songs, Op.46 (exc); Poèmes d'un jour; Songs, Op.18 (exc); Songs, Op.8 (exc); Songs, Op.23 (exc); Bonne chanson; Op.61. (B. Hendricks, M. Dalberto)

Ⓓ **CDC7 49842-2** (5/90)
Liszt: Piano Works
Liszt: Années de pèlerinage 3 (exc); Valses oubliées, S215 (exc); Années de pèlerinage 1 (exc); Concert Studies, S145; Liebesträume, S541; Buch der Lieder, S531 (exc); Tristan und Isolde—paraphrase, S447. (M. Rudy)

Ⓓ **CDC7 49843-2** (7/90)
Bach—Cantatas
Bach: Cantata 51; Cantata 82; Cantata 202; Cantata 208 (exc). (B. Hendricks, CPE Bach Orch/P. Schreier)

Ⓓ **CDC7 49849-2** (12/89)
Famous Opera Choruses
Beethoven: Fidelio (exc); Berlioz: Troyens (exc); Bizet: Carmen (exc); Donizetti: Lucia di Lammermoor (exc); Giordano: Andrea Chénier (exc); Mascagni: Cavalleria Rusticana (exc); Verdi: Aida (exc); Nabucco (exc); Otello (exc); Trovatore (exc); Wagner: Lohengrin (exc); Weber: Freischütz (exc). (J.M. Ainsley, A. Miles, H. Field, Haberdashers' Aske's Sch Ch, ROH Chor, ROHO/B. Haitink)

Ⓓ **CDC7 49857-2** (11/89)
Second Viennese School
Schoenberg: Orchestral Pieces, Op.16; Webern: Pieces, Op.6; Berg: Lulu—Symphonie. (A. Auger, CBSO/S. Rattle)

Ⓓ **CDC7 49862-2** (3/90)
Bach: Concertos
Bach: Violin Concerto, BWV1041; Violin Concerto,

BWV1042; Violin and Oboe Concerto, BWV1060. (F.P. Zimmermann, N. Black, ECO/J. Tate)

Ⓓ **CDC7 49863-2** (2/90)
French Opera Arias
G. Charpentier: Louise (exc); Debussy: Enfant prodigue (exc); Berlioz: Damnation de Faust (exc); Offenbach: Contes d'Hoffmann (exc); Gluck: Iphigénie en Tauride (exc); Massenet: Manon (exc); Cid (exc); Hérodiade (exc); Bizet: Pêcheurs de perles (exc); Verdi: Don Carlos (exc). (K. Te Kanawa, ROHO/J. Tate)

Ⓓ **CDC7 49930-2** (11/90)
Sweet Power of Song
Beethoven: Irish Songs, WoO152 (exc); Irish Songs, WoO154 (exc); Schumann: Jugend Lieder, Op. 79 (exc); Brahms: Duets, Op. 61 (exc); Berlioz: Trébuchet; Pleure, pauvre Colette; Gounod: D'un coeur; Arithmétique; Saint-Saëns: Desdichado; Pastorale; Fauré: Pleurs d'or, Op. 72; Tarentelle, Op. 10/2; Chausson: Duos, Op.11. (F. Lott, A. Murray, G. Johnson, G. Solodchin, J. Williams)

Ⓓ **CDC7 49947-2** (3/90)
Debussy—Orchestral Works
Debussy: Jeux (Cpte); Images; Roi Lear. (CBSO/S. Rattle)

Ⓓ **CDC7 49964-2** (4/90)
Early Twentieth Century Orchestral Works
Respighi: Roman Festivals; Ravel: Daphnis et Chloé Suites (exc); Dukas: Apprenti sorcier. (Oslo PO/M. Jansons)

Ⓓ **CDC7 49980-2** (2/91)
Manuel Barrueco plays Bach and De Visée
Bach: Prelude, Fugue and Allegro, BWV998; Solo Violin Partitas and Sonatas (exc); Visée: Ouverture de la Grotte de Versailles; Suite in B minor (1686). (M. Barrueco)

Ⓓ **CDC7 49995-2** (7/90)
Dvořák: Orchestral Works
Dvořák: Symphony 5; Othello; Scherzo capriccioso. (Oslo PO/M. Jansons)

Ⓓ **CDC7 49997-2** (7/90)
Schubert—Lieder
Schubert: Schwanengesang, D957 (Cpte); Wanderer an den Mond, D870; Zügenglöcklein, D871; Im Freien, D880. (O. Bär, G. Parsons)

Ⓓ **CDC7 54004-2** (2/91)
Chabrier: Vocal & Orchestral Works
Chabrier: Gwendoline (exc); Gwendoline (exc); Ode à la musique; Habanera; Valses romantiques; Larghetto; Sulamite. (B. Hendricks, S. Mentzer, P. del Vescovo, Toulouse Mid-Pyrénées Chor, Toulouse Capitole Orch/M. Plasson)

Ⓓ **CDC7 54007-2** (7/91)
Mozart—Lieder
Mozart: Sehnsucht nach dem Frühling, K596; Ich würd' auf meinem Pfad, K390; Zauberer, K472; Kleine Spinnerin, K531; Verschweigung, K518; Lied der Trennung, K519; Zufriedenheit, K473; Als Luise die Briefe, K520; Sei du mein Trost, K391; Veilchen, K476; Abendempfindung, K523; An Chloe, K524; Kleine deutsche Kantate, K619; Ridente la calma, K152; Dans un bois solitaire, K308; Oiseaux si tous les ans, K307; Moto di gioia, K579; Komm, liebe Zither, K351; Ch'io mi scordi di te, K505. (B. Hendricks, M-J. Pires, G. Söllscher, Lausanne CO/M. Eichenholz)

Ⓓ **CDC7 54010-2** (9/90)
Berlioz: Orchestral Works
Berlioz: Symphonie fantastique; Carnaval romain; Corsaire. (Toulouse Capitole Orch/M. Plasson)

Ⓓ **CDC7 54037-2** (10/91)
Mozart—Masses and Church Sonatas
Mozart: Mass, K257; Mass, K258; Mass, K259; Church Sonatas (exc). (A. Monoyios, B. Schlick, E. Graf, U. Groenewold, O. Pfaff, M. Schäfer, F-J. Selig, K. Mertens, Cologne Chbr Ch, Collegium Cartusianum/P. Neumann)

Ⓓ **CDC7 54053-2** (11/90)
Roman Heroes
Mascagni: Nerone (exc); Handel: Giulio Cesare (exc); Bellini: Norma (exc); Berlioz: Benvenuto Cellini (exc); Verdi: Attila (exc); Handel: Ezio (exc); Spontini: Vestale (exc); Wagner: Rienzi (exc); Puccini: Tosca (exc). (P. Domingo, Ambrosian Op Chor, National PO/E. Kohn, P. Domingo jnr)

Ⓓ **CDC7 54056-2** (10/90)
Suppé—Overtures
Suppé: Leichte Kavallerie (exc); Tantalusqualen (exc); Morgen, ein Mittag, ein Abend in Wien (exc); Wiener Jubel (exc); Dichter und Bauer (exc); Irrfahrt um's Glück (exc); Frau Meisterin (exc); Pique Dame (exc). (ASMF/N. Marriner)

Ⓓ **CDC7 54062-2** (11/90)
Kiri Te Kanawa—Italian Opera Arias
Puccini: Turandot (exc); Suor Angelica (exc); *Cilea*:
Adriana Lecouvreur (exc); *Giordano*: Andrea Chénier
(exc); *Leoncavallo*: Pagliacci (exc); *Boito*: Mefistofele (exc);
Verdi: Trovatore (exc); Traviata (exc); Forza del destino
(exc). (K. Te Kanawa, LSO/Myung-Whun Chung)

Ⓓ **CDC7 54071-2** (2/91)
Frederica von Stade sings Rodgers & Hart
Rodgers: Babes in Arms (exc); Chee-Chee (exc); Too
Many Girls (exc); I'd Rather Be Right (exc); Heads Up
(exc); On Your Toes (exc); Connecticut Yankee (exc);
Betsy (exc); Pal Joey (exc); Two Weeks with Pay (exc);
Dearest Enemy (exc); Lido Lady (exc); Boys from
Syracuse (exc). (F. von Stade, R. Ashe, L. Richardson, P.
Bartlett, Ambrosian Chor, LSO/J. McGlinn)

Ⓓ **CDC7 54086-2** (9/91)
Classical Trumpet Concertos
Mozart: Oboe Concerto, K314; *Haydn*: Oboe Concerto;
Bellini: Oboe Concerto; *Hummel*: Introduction, Theme and
Variations in F. (M. André, Zurich CO/E. de Stoutz)

Ⓓ **CDC7 54089-2** (12/91)
J. Strauss II—Waltzes & Overtures
J. Strauss II: Künstlerleben, Op. 316; Rosen aus dem
Süden; Zigeunerbaron (exc); G'schichten aus dem
Wienerwald, Op. 325; Kaiser, Op. 437; Fledermaus (exc);
Blauen Donau, Op. 314. (LPO/F. Welser-Möst)

Ⓓ **CDC7 54091-2** (4/91)
Rossini—Overtures
Rossini: Scala di seta (exc); Signor Bruschino (exc);
Italiana in Algeri (exc); Barbiere di Siviglia (exc); Gazza
ladra (exc); Semiramide (exc); Guillaume Tell (exc).
(LCP/R. Norrington)

Ⓓ **CDC7 54094-2** (3/91)
Janáček—Piano Works
Janáček: Piano Sonata (1905); In the mists;
Reminiscence; Along an Overgrown Path; Moravian
Dances. (M. Rudy)

Ⓓ **CDC7 54096-2** (10/91)
Ligeti—Choral Works
Ligeti: Lux aeterna; Drei Phantasien; Loneliness; Pápainé;
Night and Morning; Hungarian Studies; Mátraszentimre
Songs. (France Groupe Vocal/G. Reibel)

Ⓓ **CDC7 54098-2** (4/91)
Sacred Songs
Gounod: Ave Maria; *Franck*: Panis Angelicus; *Schubert*:
Ave Maria, D839; *Niedermeyer*: Pietà Signore; *Mascagni*:
Salve o Maria; *Mendelssohn*: Hear my prayer; *Gounod*: St
Cecilia Mass (exc); *Rossini*: Stabat Mater (exc);
Penderecki: Polish Requiem (exc); *Bernstein*: Symphony 3
(exc); *A. Lloyd Webber*: Requiem (exc); *Traditional*:
Amazing Grace; *J. M. Black*: When the Saints; *Traditional*:
Sometimes I feel like a motherless child. (B. Hendricks, O.
Samnegård, E. Lundkvist, U. Johansson, Inst Ens, E.
Ericson Chbr Ch, Orphei Drängar, Stockholm CO, Swedish
RSO/E. Ericson)

Ⓓ **CDC7 54108-2** (2/91)
Tchaikovsky—Violin Works
Tchaikovsky: Violin Concerto; *Tartini*: Devil's Trill Sonata;
Kreisler: Liebesleid; *Prokofiev*: Love for 3 Oranges Suite
(exc); *Bloch*: Baal Shem (exc); *Wieniawski*: Etudes-
Caprices, Op.18 (exc); *Tchaikovsky*: String Quartet 1 (exc);
Bazzini: Ronde des lutins. (I. Perlman, Israel PO/Z. Mehta,
J.G. Guggenheim)

Ⓓ **CDC7 54117-2** (8/91)
Venetian Church Music
G. Gabrieli: Intonationi d'organo (exc); Symphoniae sacrae
II (exc); Canzoni et Sonate (1615) (exc); Fuga IX toni;
Monteverdi: Adoramus te, Christe; Exulta, filia Sion; Currite
populi; Christe, adoramus te; *Grandi*: Motets (1610) (exc);
Castello: Sonatas (exc); *Legrenzi*: Sonatas, Op.8 (exc);
Lotti: Crucifixus a 6; Crucifixus a 10; *Vivaldi*: Clarae stellae,
RV625. (E. Van Evera, Jeffrey Thomas, R. Stene,
Taverner Ch, Taverner Consort, Taverner Plyrs/A.
Parrott)

Ⓓ **CDC7 54147-2** (11/91)
Bach—Italian Concerto
Bach: Cantata 147 (exc); Chromatic Fantasia and Fugue,
BWV903; Preludes, BWV924-932 (exc); Preludes,
BWV933-38; Preludes, BWV939-43; Prelude, BWV999;
Fughetta, BWV961; Fugue, BWV952; Fugue, BWV953;
Prelude and Fugue, BWV902/1; Prelude and Fughetta,
BWV902; Prelude and Fughetta, BWV899; Prelude and
Fughetta, BWV900; Prelude and Fugue, BWV895; Italian
Concerto, BWV971. (M. Tipo)

Ⓓ **CDC7 54158-2** (7/91)
Ravel—Piano Concertos, etc
Ravel: Piano Concerto; Left-Hand Concerto; Tombeau de
Couperin. (C. Ousset, CBSO/S. Rattle)

Ⓓ **CDC7 54191-2** (9/92)
La Dolce Vita
Giramo: Festa, riso; *Willaert*: O dolce vita mia; *Nola*: Tri
ciechi siamo; *Anon*: Pavana d'España; *Nola*: Chi la
gagliarda; *Macque*: Gagliarda seconda; *Anon*: Amanza
mia; *Cornet*: Parmi di star; *Anon*: Corten espadas afiladas;
Willaert: Ave virgo sponsa Dei; *Piccinini*: Colascione;
Anon: Catalina, Catalina!; *D. Ortiz*: Ricercada IV; *Willaert*:
O dolce vita mia; *Lambardi*: Toccata e gagliarda; *Willaert*:
Qual dolcezza giamai; *Mudarra*: Tres libros (1546) (exc);
Agostini: Non t'aricordi; *Anon*: Chi passa per 'sta strada;
Willaert: Vecchie letrose. (King's Sngrs, Tragicomedia, S.
Carrington)

Ⓓ **CDC7 54203-2** (10/91)
Porter—Night and Day
Porter: Jubilee (exc); Rosalie (exc); Born to Dance (exc);
Greenwich Village Follies (exc); Hitchy-Koo (1919) (exc);
Who said Gay Paree?; Fool there was; Seven Lively Arts (exc);
Don't fence me in; Broadway Melody (exc); Du Barry was a
Lady (exc); Broadway Melody (exc); Bull Dog; Something
for the Boys (exc). (T. Hampson, LSO/J. McGlinn)

Ⓓ **CDC7 54204-2** (8/91)
Ravel—Orchestral Works
Ravel: Fanfare; Shéhérazade; Alborada del gracioso;
Miroirs (exc); Ma mère l'oye (Cpte); La Valse. (M. Ewing,
CBSO/S. Rattle)

Ⓓ **CDC7 54205-2** (10/91)
Vivaldi—Double Concertos
Vivaldi: Concerto, RV529; Concerti Grossi, Op.3 (exc);
Concerto, RV547; Concerto, RV546; Concerto, RV548;
Concerto, RV542; Concerto, RV541. (Y. Menuhin (vn/dir),
L. Chen, T. Mørk, N. Black, D. Bell, Polish CO)

Ⓓ **CDC7 54211-2** (6/94)
Bartók—Works for Violin & Orchestra
Bartók: Violin Concerto 2; Rhapsody 1, Sz87; Rhapsody 2,
Sz90. (K-W. Chung, CBSO/S. Rattle)

Ⓓ **CDC7 54233-2** (5/93)
Brahms—Piano Works
Brahms: Piano Pieces, Op.76; Rhapsodies, Op.79;
Waltzes, Op.39. (M. Rudy)

Ⓓ **CDC7 54237-2** (2/92)
Berlioz—Orchestral Works
Berlioz: Harold in Italy; Benvenuto Cellini (exc); Waverley.
(G. Caussé, Toulouse Capitole Orch/M. Plasson)

Ⓓ **CDC7 54239-2** (8/93)
Schubert—Lieder
Schubert: Schwanengesang, D957 (exc); Lachen und
Weinen, D777; Refrainlieder, D866 (exc); Auf dem Strom,
D943; Sehnsucht, D879; An den Mond, D193; Versunken,
D715; Hirt auf dem Felsen, D965; Du liebst mich nicht,
D756; Liebe hat gelogen, D751; Junge Nonne, D828;
Klaglied, D23; Ave Maria, D839; Lied der Delphine,
D857/1; Heidenröslein, D257. (B. Hendricks, B. Schneider,
S. Meyer, R. Lupu)

Ⓓ **CDC7 54248-2** (3/92)
Berg/Stravinsky—Violin Concertos, etc
Berg: Violin Concerto; *Stravinsky*: Violin Concerto; *Ravel*:
Tzigane. (F.P. Zimmermann, Stuttgart RSO/G. Gelmetti)

Ⓓ **CDC7 54265-2** (2/92)
Gabrieli—Canzonas, Sonatas & Motets
G. Gabrieli: Dulcis Jesu; Sacrae symphoniae (1597) (exc);
Canzoni et Sonate (1615) (exc); Jubilate II a 8; O Jesu mi
dulcissime II; Hic est filius Deus; Miserere mei II; Audite
principes. (Taverner Consort, Taverner Ch, Taverner
Plyrs/A. Parrott)

Ⓓ **CDC7 54266-2** (3/92)
Domingo and Perlman—Together
Toselli: Serenade; *Ponce*: Estrellita; *Massenet*: Élégie;
Kálmán: Csárdásfürstin (exc); *Kreisler*: Old Refrain;
Rachmaninov: Songs, Op. 4 (exc); *Offenbach*: Contes
d'Hoffmann (exc); *Tosti*: Ideale; *Traditional*: Danny Boy;
Handel: Serse (exc); *Romberg*: Student Prince (exc);
Godard: Jocelyn (exc); *Tchaikovsky*: Songs, Op. 6 (exc);
R. Strauss: Lieder, Op. 27 (exc). (P. Domingo, I. Perlman,
NY Studio Orch/J. Tunick)

Ⓓ **CDC7 54273-2** (1/92)
Sibelius—Orchestral Works
Sibelius: Symphony 1; Finlandia; Karelia Suite. (Oslo
PO/M. Jansons)

Ⓓ **CDC7 54281-2** (11/91)
Prokofiev—Piano Sonatas
Prokofiev: Piano Sonata 6; Piano Sonata 7; Piano Sonata
8. (P. Donohoe)

Ⓓ **CDC7 54297-2** (4/92)
Haydn—Symphonies
Haydn: Symphony 60; Symphony 70; Symphony 90.
(CBSO/S. Rattle)

Ⓓ **CDC7 54301-2** (1/92)
Saxophone Concertos
Debussy: Rapsodie; *Ibert*: Concertino da camera; *Villa-
Lobos*: Saxophone Fantasia; *Glazunov*: Saxophone
Concerto, Op.109; *R. R. Bennett*: Saxophone Concerto; *D.
Heath*: Out of the Cool. (J. Harle, ASMF/N. Marriner)

Ⓓ **CDC7 54302-2** (1/92)
Mozart—Concertos
Mozart: Violin Concerto, K207; Adagio, K261; Sinfonia
Concertante, K364. (A-S. Mutter, B. Giuranna, ASMF/N.
Marriner)

Ⓓ **CDC7 54305-2** (6/92)
Violin Sonatas
Debussy: Violin Sonata; *Ravel*: Violin Sonata (1923-27);
Violin Sonata (1897); *Janáček*: Violin Sonata. (F.P.
Zimmermann, A. Lonquich)

Ⓓ **CDC7 54329-2** (3/92)
Domingo sings Mozart Arias
Mozart: Finta Giardiniera (exc); Idomeneo (exc); Don
Giovanni (exc); Don Giovanni (exc); Entführung (exc);
Clemenza di Tito (exc); Davidde penitente, K469 (exc);
Zauberflöte (exc); Nozze di Figaro (exc); Così fan tutte
(exc); Così fan tutte (exc). (P. Domingo, C. Vaness,
Munich RO/E. Kohn)

Ⓓ **CDC7 54330-2** (1/93)
Arrangements for Trumpet and Organ
Bach: Cantata 75 (exc); *Purcell*: Fairy Queen, Z629 (exc);
Stanley: Sonata in D minor; *Handel*: Oboe Concertos
(exc); *Bach*: Cantata 22 (exc); *Corelli*: Oboe Concerto;
Loeillet de Gant: Recorder Sonatas, Op.3 (exc);
Boismortier: Sonatas, Op.91 (exc); *Bach*: Chorales,
BWV651-668 (exc). (M. André, H. Bilgram)

Ⓓ **CDC7 54346-2** (2/92)
Vaughan Williams/Ravel—Chamber Works
Vaughan Williams: String Quartet 1; On Wenlock Edge;
Ravel: String Quartet. (Britten Qt, P. Langridge, H.
Shelley)

Ⓓ **CDC7 54352-2** (1/93)
Sarah Chang - Debut
Sarasate: Carmen Fantasy; *Elgar*: Salut d'amour;
Khachaturian: Gayaneh (exc); *Elgar*: Capricieuse; *Kreisler*:
Pugnani Tempo di menuetto; *Paganini*: Caprices, Op. 1
(exc); *Chopin*: Nocturnes (exc); *Shostakovich*: Preludes,
Op. 34 (exc); *Gershwin*: Porgy and Bess (exc); *Liszt*:
Consolations, S172 (exc); *Tchaikovsky*: Souvenir d'un lieu
cher, Op. 42 (exc); *Prokofiev*: Love for 3 Oranges Suite
(exc). (S. Chang, S. Rivers)

Ⓓ **CDC7 54367-2** (5/92)
Chopin—Piano Works
Chopin: Preludes (exc); Cantabile; Nocturnes (exc);
Contredanse. (T. Barto)

Ⓓ **CDC7 54381-2** (12/91)
R. Strauss—Lieder
R. Strauss: Lieder, Op. 21 (exc); Lieder, Op. 10 (exc);
Lieder, Op. 39 (exc); Lieder, Op. 27 (exc); Lieder, Op. 69
(exc); Lieder, Op. 48 (exc); Lieder, Op. 67 (exc); Lieder,
Op. 68 (exc); Lieder, Op. 29 (exc); Lieder, Op. 17 (exc);
Lieder, Op. 19 (exc); Lieder, Op. 41 (exc). (B. Hendricks,
R. Gothóni)

Ⓓ **CDC7 54382-2** (3/93)
Albéniz/Turina—Works for Guitar
Albéniz: Suite española 1; *Turina*: Fandanguillo; Sevillana,
Op.29; Ráfaga; Hommage à Tárrega; Guitar Sonata,
Op.61. (M. Barrueco)

Ⓓ **CDC7 54383-2** (5/92)
Krommer—Wind Octets
Krommer: Octet-Partita, Op.76; Octet-Partita, Op.71;
Octet-Partita, Op.57; Octet-Partita, Op.78. (Meyer Wind
Ens)

Ⓓ **CDC7 54394-2** (3/92)
Modern Viola Works
Shostakovich: Viola Sonata; *Britten*: Lachrymae;
Stravinsky: Elegy. (T. Zimmermann, H. Höll)

Ⓓ **CDC7 54407-2** (12/93)
English String Music
Elgar: Introduction and Allegro; *Vaughan Williams*: Tallis
Fantasia; *Walton*: Sonata for Strings. (CLS/R. Hickox)

Ⓓ **CDC7 54411-2** (7/92)
On Wings of Song
Purcell: Birthday Ode, Z323 (exc); Indian Queen, Z630
(exc); Lost is my quiet for ever, Z502; King Arthur, Z628
(exc); What can we poor females do?, Z518; *Mendelssohn*:

Leoncavallo: Mattinata; Tosti: Ideale; Beethoven: Adelaide, Op.46; R. Strauss: Lieder, Op.27 (exc). (J. Björling, H. Schymberg, A-L. Björling, H. Ebert, orch, Stockholm Royal Op Orch, Stockholm Concert Soc Orch/N. Grevillius)

ⓒ **CDH7 64905-2** (10/93)
Wolf—Lieder Recital
Wolf: Mörike Lieder (exc); Goethe Lieder (exc); Spanisches Liederbuch (exc); Alte Weisen (Cpte); Italienisches Liederbuch (exc); Songs for a woman's voice (exc). (E. Schwarzkopf, G. Moore)

ⓒ **CDH7 64928-2** (6/94)
Bach—Keyboard Works
Bach: Brandenburg Concertos (exc); 3-Harpsichord Concerti (exc); Harpsichord Concerto, BWV1053; Fantasia, BWV906; Fantasia and Fugue, BWV904; Chromatic Fantasia and Fugue, BWV903. (Edwin Fischer, Edwin Fischer (pf/dir), R. Smith, D. Matthews, Philh/Edwin Fischer)

ⓒ **CDH7 64934-2** (8/94)
D. Scarlatti—Keyboard Sonatas
D. Scarlatti: Keyboard Sonatas (exc); Keyboard Sonatas (exc); Keyboard Sonatas (exc). (W. Landowska)

ⓒ **CDH7 69787-2** (12/89)
Richard Tauber sings Operetta Arias
J. Strauss II: Fledermaus (exc); Fledermaus (exc); Zigeunerbaron (exc); Zigeunerbaron (exc); Lehár: Lustige Witwe (exc); Lustige Witwe (exc); Zigeunerliebe (exc); Paganini (exc); Friederike (exc); Land des Lächelns (exc); Kálmán: Zirkusprinzessin (exc); Gräfin Mariza (exc); Heuberger: Opernball (exc); Sieczyński: Wien, du Stadt meiner Träume; O. Straus: Walzertraum (exc); Zeller: Vogelhändler (exc); Stolz: Lied ist aus (exc). (R. Tauber, V. Schwarz, Lotte Lehmann, K. Branzell, G. Merrem-Nikisch, W. Staegemann, C. Vantoni, Chor, Orch, Berlin Staatskapelle, Odeon Künstlerorchester, Berlin Kunstlertheater Orch/F. Weissmann/E. Hauke/E. Korngold/F. Lehár/F. Schönbaumsfeld)

ⓒ **CDH7 69789-2** (10/89)
Melchior sings Wagner
Wagner: Rienzi (exc); Tannhäuser (exc); Tannhäuser (exc); Lohengrin (exc); Walküre (exc); Walküre (exc); Siegfried (exc); Siegfried (exc); Siegfried (exc); Götterdämmerung (exc); Tristan und Isolde (exc); Meistersinger (exc); Meistersinger (exc). (L. Melchior, A. Reiss, N. Gruhn, LSO, Berlin St Op Orch/J. Barbirolli/A. Coates/R. Heger/L. Collingwood/L. Blech)

ⓒ **CDH7 69791-2** (9/89)
Dame Eva Turner sings Opera Arias and Songs
E. Turner: Introductory talk; Verdi: Trovatore (exc); Aida (exc); Aida (exc); Aida (exc); Ponchielli: Gioconda (exc); Gioconda (exc); Puccini: Tosca (exc); Madama Butterfly (exc); Turandot (exc); Mascagni: Cavalleria rusticana (exc); Wagner: Lohengrin (exc); Tannhäuser (exc); Grieg: Melodies of the Heart, Op. 5 (exc); Tosti: Addio; Ronald: Summertime (exc); Del Riego: Homing; Hardelot: Because; Sometimes in my dreams. (E. Turner, E. Turner, E. Rubadi, F. Ciniselli, L. Paci, B. Carmassi, orch, anon/T. Beecham/L. Molajoli/S. Robinson/J. Batten, La Scala Chor, La Scala Orch, anon)

ⓒ **CDH7 69793-2** (3/89)
Elisabeth Schwarzkopf & Irmgard Seefried sing Duets
Humperdinck: Hänsel und Gretel (exc); R.Strauss: Rosenkavalier (exc); Monteverdi: Madrigals, Bk.7 (exc); Madrigals, Bk 8 (exc); Madrigals, Bk.1 (exc); Madrigals, Bk.8 (exc); Carissimi: E pur vuole; Lungi omai deh spiega; Il mio core è un mar; A piè d'un verde alloro; Dvořák: Moravian Duets, B60 (Cpte); Moravian Duets, B62 (exc). (E. Schwarzkopf, I. Seefried, G. Moore, Philh/J. Krips, VPO/H. von Karajan)

ⓒ **CDH7 69800-2** (6/89)
Dinu Lipatti - Piano Recital
Bach: Partitas, BWV825-30 (exc); Orgel-Büchlein, BWV5-644 (exc); Cantata 147 (exc); Flute Sonatas, BWV1030-5 (exc). D. Scarlatti: Keyboard Sonatas (exc); Mozart: Piano Sonata, K310 (exc); Schubert: Impromptus (exc). (D. Lipatti)

ⓒ **CDH7 69802-2** (7/89)
Dinu Lipatti plays Chopin
Chopin: Waltzes (exc); Barcarolle; Nocturnes (exc); Mazurkas (exc). (D. Lipatti)

ⓒ **CDM5 65009-2** (11/94)
Janet Baker - Song Recital
Fauré: Songs, Op.18 (exc); Songs, Op.83; Songs, Op.39 (exc); Songs, Op.58 (exc); Songs, Op.23 (exc); Songs, Op.1 (exc); Songs, Op.4 (exc); Songs, Op.46 (exc); Schubert: Am Grabe Anselmos, D504; Abendstern, D806; Vögel, D691; Götter Griechenlands, D677; Gondelfahrer, D808; Auflösung, D807; R. Strauss: Lieder, Op.39 (exc); Stanford: Belle Dame sans merci; Parry: English Lyrics, Set 5 (exc); English Lyrics, Set 2

antérieure; Phidylé; Chanson triste; Manoir de Rosemonde; Lamento; Chausson: Serres chaudes, Op. 24 (exc); Mélodies, Op.2 (exc); Shakespeare Songs, Op.28 (exc); Mélodies, Op.8 (exc); Mélodies, Op.36 (exc). (G. Souzay, D. Baldwin)

ⓒ **CDM5 65175-2** (9/94)
Bartók/Hindemith—Orchestral Works
Bartók: Music for Strings, Percussion and Celesta; Miraculous Mandarin (exc); Hindemith: Symphonic Metamorphosis. (Philadelphia/E. Ormandy)

ⓒ **CDM5 65182-2** (10/94)
Nielsen/Sibelius—Orchestral Works
Nielsen: Symphony 5; Sibelius: Luonnotar; Nightride and Sunrise; Oceanides. (G. Jones, Danish RSO/R. Kubelík, LSO/A. Dorati)

ⓒ **CDM5 65250-2** (3/95)
Cziffra Edition, Volume 1
Liszt: Piano Sonata, S178; Harmonies poétiques, S173 (exc); Concert Studies, S145 (exc); Paganini Studies, S140 (exc); Paganini Studies, S140 (exc); Midsummer Night's Dream—paraphrase, S410. (G. Cziffra)

ⓒ **CDM5 65251-2** (3/95)
Cziffra Edition, Volume 2
Chopin: Piano Concerto 1; Ballades (exc); Polonaises (exc); Impromptus (exc); Etudes (exc); Etudes (exc); Etudes (exc); Waltzes (exc); Nocturnes (exc). (G. Cziffra, Paris Orch/G. Cziffra Jnr)

ⓒ **CDM5 65252-2** (3/95)
Cziffra Edition, Volume 3
Liszt: Piano Concerto 1; Piano Concerto 2; Tchaikovsky: Piano Concerto 1. (G. Cziffra, Philh/A. Vandernoot)

ⓒ **CDM5 65253-2** (3/95)
Cziffra Edition, Volume 4
Daquin: Premier livre de pièces de clavecin (exc); Lully: Gavotte en rondeau, Rameau: Pièces de clavecin (exc); Dardanus (exc); Couperin: Livre de clavecin I (exc); Livre de clavecin II (exc); Livre de clavecin III (exc); Livre de clavecin IV (exc); Ravel: Tombeau de Couperin (exc); Sonatine; Jeux d'eau. (G. Cziffra)

ⓒ **CDM5 65254-2** (3/95)
Cziffra Edition, Volume 5
Mozart: Piano Sonata, K310; Beethoven: Piano Sonata 22; Schumann: Symphonic Studies; Novelletten (exc). (G. Cziffra)

ⓒ **CDM5 65255-2** (3/95)
Cziffra Edition, Volume 6
Bach: Schübler Chorales, BWV645-650 (exc); Orgel-Büchlein, BWV599-644 (exc); D. Scarlatti: Keyboard Sonatas (exc); Couperin: Livre de clavecin II (exc); Lully: Gavotte; Rameau: Dardanus (exc); Mozart: Piano Sonata, K331 (exc); Mendelssohn: Midsummer Night's Dream (exc); Bizet: Arlésienne (exc); Franck: Prélude, Choral et Fugue; Debussy: Plus que lente; Dohnányi: Concert Etudes, Op. 28 (exc); Khachaturian: Gayaneh (exc). (G. Cziffra)

ⓒ **CDM5 65305-2** (7/95)
Lutosławski—Orchestral Works
Lutosławski: Concerto for Orchestra (1954); Venetian Games (1961); Livre pour orchestre; Mi-Parti. (Polish Nat RSO/W. Lutosławski)

ⓒ **CDM5 65307-2** (4/95)
Szymanowski—Orchestral and Piano Works
Szymanowski: Harnasie; Symphony 4; Mazurkas, Op.50 (exc); Variations, Op.3. (F. Blumental, Polish Rad Chor, Cracow RSO/A. Wit, Polish Nat RSO/J. Semkow)

ⓒ **CDM5 65415-2** (12/95)
Nielsen—Symphonies, etc
Nielsen: Symphony 3; Symphony 4; At the bier. (K. Schultz, P. Rasmussen, Danish RSO/H. Blomstedt)

ⓒ **CDM7 63104-2** (10/89)
Alfredo Krauss - Opera Recital
Mozart: Così fan tutte (exc); Bellini: Puritani (exc); Donizetti: Lucia di Lammermoor (exc); Fille du Régiment (exc); Verdi: Rigoletto (exc); Traviata (exc); Puccini: Bohème (exc); Gounod: Roméo et Juliette (exc); Bizet: Jolie fille de Perth (exc); Massenet: Werther (exc); Manon (exc). (Alfredo Kraus, M. Caballé, A. Ferrin, S. Elenkov, J-N. Béguelin, Philh/K. Böhm/J. Rudel/R. Muti, Ambrosian Op Chor, RPO/N. Rescigno, Paris Op Chor, Paris Op Orch/B. Campanella, National PO/James Levine, Toulouse Capitole Orch/M. Plasson, French Rad New PO/G. Prêtre, LPO)

ⓒ **CDM7 63109-2** (10/89)
Tito Gobbi - Opera Aria Recital
Cilea: Arlesiana (exc); Leoncavallo: Zazà (exc); Verdi: Don Carlo (exc); Otello (exc); Forza del destino (exc); Mozart: Nozze di Figaro (exc); Verdi: Ballo in maschera (exc); Donizetti: Elisir d'amore (exc); Verdi: Nabucco (exc);

ⓒ **CDM5 65067-2** (2/94)
Delius—Orchestral Miniatures
Delius: Summer Evening; Sleigh Ride; Fennimore and Gerda Intermezzo; First cuckoo; Summer night on the river; Song before sunrise; Koanga (exc); Irmelin Prelude; Hassan (exc); Air and Dance. (Northern Sinfonia/R. Hickox)

ⓒ **CDM5 65073-2** (6/94)
Berwald—Orchestral Works
F. Berwald: Queen of Golconda (exc); Piano Concerto; Bayadères; Violin Concerto, Op.2; Serious and joyful fancies. (A. Tellefsen, M. Migdal, RPO/U. Björlin)

ⓒ **CDM5 65076-2** (2/95)
Lutosławski—Orchestral Works
Lutosławski: Symphony 1; Symphony 2; Symphonic Variations; Funeral music (1958). (Polish Nat RSO/W. Lutosławski)

ⓒ **CDM5 65077-2** (10/94)
Penderecki—Orchestral and Vocal Works
Penderecki: Anaklasis; Hiroshima Threnody; Fonogrammi; De natura sonoris I; Capriccio (vn); Canticum Canticorum Salomonis; De natura sonoris II; Dream of Jacob. (M. Wilkomirska, Cracow Phil Choir, Polish Nat RSO, LSO/K. Penderecki)

ⓒ **CDM5 65079-2** (12/94)
Schoenberg/Bartók/Hindemith—Orchestral Works
Schoenberg: Verklärte Nacht; Bartók: Divertimento; Hindemith: Trauermusik. (C. Aronowitz, ECO/D. Barenboim)

ⓒ **CDM5 65081-2** (5/94)
Stenhammar—Orchestral & Vocal Works
Stenhammar: Piano Concerto 2; Serenade, Op.31; Florez and Blanzeflor. (I. Wixell, J. Sólyom, Munich PO, Swedish RSO/S. Westerberg)

ⓒ **CDM5 65082-2** (7/94)
Szymanowski—Orchestral Works
Szymanowski: Concert Overture, Op.12; Symphony 2; Symphony 3. (W. Ochman, Polish Rad Chor, Polish Nat RSO/J. Semkow/J. Kaspszyk)

ⓒ **CDM5 65098-2** (8/94)
Berners—Orchestral Works
Berners: Triumph of Neptune (exc); Fugue; Nicholas Nickleby; Morceaux; Fantaisie espagnole. (RLPO/B. Wordsworth)

ⓒ **CDM5 65100-2** (10/94)
Vaughan Williams—Chamber Works
Vaughan Williams: Phantasy Quintet; Violin Sonata; String Quartet 2; Studies in English Folk Song. (H. Bean, D. Parkhouse, Music Group of London, E. Croxford)

ⓒ **CDM5 65101-2** (9/94)
A Warlock Centenary Album
Warlock: Capriol Suite; Serenade for strings; Curlew; Traditional: Bethlehem down; Adam lay y-bounden; I saw a maiden; Balulalow; Warlock: Where riches is everlasting; Shrouding of the Duchess of Malfi; Lady's Birthday; Pretty ring time; Autumn twilight; Captain Stratton's fancy; Yarmouth Fair. (J. Baker, I. Partridge, R. Hammersley, F. Harvey, R. Lloyd, O. Brannigan, D. Butt, J. Craxton, H. Bean, F. Mason, C. Wellington, E. Croxford, J. Partridge, G. Moore, N. Walker, E. Lush, Gavin Williams, P. Ledger, Guildford Cath Ch, Westminster Abbey Ch, King's College Ch, Bacchdian Sngrs, English Sinfonia, Bournemouth Sinfonietta/N. Dilkes/N. Del Mar/Barry Rose/D. Willcocks)

ⓒ **CDM5 65114-2** (7/95)
Britten—Vocal Works
Britten: Phaedra; Folk Songs (exc); Illuminations. (J. Gomez, F. Palmer, Endymion Ens/J. Whitfield)

ⓒ **CDM5 65131-2** (4/95)
Vaughan Williams—Choral and Orchestral Works
Vaughan Williams: Toward the Unknown Region; Norfolk Rhapsody 1; Tallis Fantasia; Dives and Lazarus Variants, In Windsor Forest. (CBSO Chor, CBSO, CBSO, Bournemouth Sym Chor, Bournemouth Sinfonietta/N. del Mar)

ⓒ **CDM5 65154-2** (7/95)
Roussel—Orchestral Works
Roussel: Piano Concerto; Cello Concertino; Pour une fête de printemps; Suite, Op.33. (D. Laval, A. Tétard, Paris Orch/J-P. Jacquillat)

ⓒ **CDM5 65161-2** (9/94)
Duparc/Chausson—Mélodies
Duparc: Invitation au voyage; Extase; Vague et la cloche; Sérénade florentine; Élégie; Soupir; Testament; Vie

Macbeth (exc); *Giordano:* Andrea Chénier (exc); *Wolf-Ferrari:* Gioielli della madonna (exc); *Puccini:* Fanciulla del West (exc); *Rossini:* Guillaume Tell (exc); *Donizetti:* Elisir d'amore (exc); *Verdi:* Simon Boccanegra (exc); *Cilea:* Adriana Lecouvreur (exc); *Giordano:* Fedora (exc); *Verdi:* Falstaff (exc); Otello (exc). (T. Gobbi, La Scala Orch, RPO, Philh, LSO, Rome Op Orch/U. Berrettoni/A. Erede/J. Robertson/W. Braithwaite/G. Santini/O. de Fabritiis, N. Monti)

① **CDM7 63110-2** (10/89)
Mirella Freni: Opera Recital
Mozart: Nozze di Figaro (exc); *Bellini:* Puritani (exc); *Verdi:* Traviata (exc); *Bizet:* Carmen (exc); Pêcheurs de Perles (exc); *Massenet:* Manon (exc); *G. Charpentier:* Louise (exc); *Puccini:* Gianni Schicchi (exc); Rondine (exc); Tosca (exc); Manon Lescaut (exc); Turandot (exc); Madama Butterfly (exc); Suor Angelica (exc); *Cilea:* Adriana Lecouvreur (exc). (M. Freni, Rome Op Orch/F. Ferraris, La Scala Orch/A. Votto, Orch/L. Magiera)

① **CDM7 63113-2** (11/89)
Rossini—Overtures
Rossini: Barbiere di Siviglia (exc); Semiramide (exc); Scala di seta (exc); Gazza ladra (exc); Italiana in Algeri (exc); Guillaume Tell (exc). (Philh/H. von Karajan)

① **CDM7 63136-2** (12/89)
Offenbach & Waldteufel: Orchestral Works
Offenbach: Gaîté parisienne (Cpte); *Waldteufel:* España; Patineurs; Estudiantina; Acclamations. (Monte Carlo PO/M. Rosenthal/W. Boskovsky)

① **CDM7 63160-2** (1/90)
Dukas: Orchestral works
Dukas: Symphony; Ariane et Barbe-bleue (exc); Apprenti sorcier; Péri (Cpte). (FRNO, Paris Op Orch, Philh/J. Martinon/P. Dervaux/I. Markevitch)

① **CDM7 63165-2** (9/89)
Jacqueline Du Pré—Early BBC Recordings, Vol.1
Bach: Solo Cello Suites (exc); *Britten:* Cello Sonata (exc); *Falla:* Suite populaire espagnole. (J. Du Pré, S. Kovacevich, E. Lush)

① **CDM7 63166-2** (9/89)
Jacqueline Du Pré—Early BBC Recordings, Vol.2
Brahms: Cello Sonata 2; *Couperin:* Nouveaux Concerts (exc); *Handel:* Oboe Concertos (exc). (J. Du Pré, E. Lush, W. Pleeth)

① **CDM7 63182-2** (2/90)
The Incomparable Callas
Bellini: Norma (exc); *Donizetti:* Lucia di Lammermoor (exc); *Verdi:* Ernani (exc); Aida (exc); *Ponchielli:* Gioconda (exc); *Puccini:* Tosca (exc); *Bizet:* Carmen (exc); *Saint-Saëns:* Samson et Dalila (exc); *Gluck:* Orphée (exc); *Gounod:* Roméo et Juliette (exc); *Massenet:* Cid (exc); *A. Thomas:* Mignon (exc). (M. Callas, La Scala Orch/T. Serafin, M. Elkins, Philh/N. Rescigno, Paris Cons/A. Votto, N. Sautereau, J. Berbié, Paris Op Orch/G. Prêtre, FRNO)

① **CDM7 63350-2** (5/90)
R. Strauss—Orchestral Works
R. Strauss: Don Juan; Tod und verklärung; Salome (exc); Metamorphosen. (Philh/O. Klemperer)

① **CDM7 63358-2** (8/90)
Beethoven—Orchestral Works
Beethoven: Symphony 6; Egmont (exc); Prometheus (exc). (Philh, New Philh, B. Nilsson/O. Klemperer)

① **CDM7 63368-2** (6/90)
Malcolm Arnold—Orchestral Works
Arnold: Symphony 2; Symphony 5; Peterloo Overture. (Bournemouth SO/C. Groves, CBSO/M. Arnold)

① **CDM7 63369-2** (7/90)
Walton—Orchestral Works
Walton: Spitfire Prelude and Fugue; Scapino; Crown Imperial; Orb and Sceptre; Johannesburg Festival Overture; Capriccio burlesco; Hamlet (exc); Richard III (exc). (RLPO/C. Groves)

① **CDM7 63379-2** (7/90)
Beecham conducts French Orchestral Works
Bizet: Carmen Suites (exc); *Fauré:* Pavane; Dolly; *Debussy:* Après-midi; *Saint-Saëns:* Rouet d'Omphale; *Delibes:* Roi s'amuse (exc). (FRNO, RPO/T. Beecham)

① **CDM7 63397-2** (7/90)
Sibelius: Orchestral Works
Sibelius: Tempest Suites (exc); Scènes historiques I (exc); Scènes historiques II; Karelia Suite (exc); Finlandia. (RPO, BBC SO, LPO/T. Beecham)

① **CDM7 63401-2** (9/92)
French Favourites
Chabrier: Gwendoline (exc); *Gounod:* Faust (exc); *Massenet:* Cendrillon (exc); *Bizet:* Roma (exc); *Grétry:*

Zémire et Azor (exc); *Bizet:* Patrie; *Massenet:* Vierge (exc); *Chabrier:* España. (RPO, FRNO, LPO/T. Beecham)

① **CDM7 63405-2** (6/92)
British Orchestral Works
Bantock: Fifine at the Fair; *Bax:* Garden of Fand; *Berners:* Triumph of Neptune (exc). (R. Alva, LPO, RPO/T. Beecham)

① **CDM7 63528-2** (11/90)
Trumpet Concertos
Handel: Flute Sonatas (exc); *Albinoni:* Concerti, Op.7 (exc); *Telemann:* 2-Oboe & Trumpet Concerto 2; *Hertel:* Trumpet Concerto in E flat. (M. André, ECO/C. Mackerras)

① **CDM7 63533-2** (11/90)
Spanish Violin Works
Sarasate: Carmen Fantasy; Zigeunerweisen; *Falla:* Suite populaire espagnole; *Granados:* Danzas españolas (exc); *Halffter:* Danzas (exc); *Sarasate:* Danzas españolas (exc); Caprice basque; *Albéniz:* España, Op.165 (exc). (I. Perlman, RPO/L. Foster, S. Sanders, Pittsburgh SO/A. Previn)

① **CDM7 63537-2** (11/90)
Brahms—Orchestral Works
Brahms: Piano Concerto 2; Tragic Overture; Academic Festival Overture. (D. Barenboim, New Philh, VPO/J. Barbirolli)

① **CDM7 63569-2** (9/90)
Pfitzner: Lieder
Pfitzner: Lieder, Op.26 (exc); Lieder, Op.11 (exc); Lieder, Op.22 (exc); Lieder, Op.21 (exc); Lieder, Op.15 (exc); Lieder, Op.9; Lieder, Op.7 (exc); Lieder, Op.10 (exc); Sonnets, Op.41 (exc); An den Mond; Lieder, Op.26 (exc); Lieder, Op.32 (exc). (D. Fischer-Dieskau, K. Engel, A. Reimann, H. Reutter)

① **CDM7 63570-2** (9/90)
Berg & Schoenberg: Lieder
Schoenberg: Lieder, Op.2 (exc); Lieder, Op.3 (exc); Deinem Blick, Op.6 (exc); Balladen, Op.12 (exc); Lieder, Op.14 (exc); Am Strande; Lieder, Op.48 (exc); *Berg:* Vielgeliebte, schöne Frau; Geliebte Schöne; Schattenleben; Schlummerlose Nächte; Es wandelt, was wir schauen; Im Morgengrauen; Grabschrift; Erster Verlust; Er klagt; Über den Bergen; Am Strande; Sehnsucht II; Sehnsucht III; Ich liebe dich; Ferne Lieder; Regen; Winter; Traurigkeit; Spaziergang. (D. Fischer-Dieskau, A. Reimann)

① **CDM7 63574-2** (12/90)
Elisabeth Schwarzkopf Christmas Album
Traditional: Stille Nacht; O come, all ye faithful; O du fröhliche; *Brahms:* Volkskinderlieder (exc); *F. Gluck:* In einem kühlen Grunde; *Franck:* Panis angelicus; *Traditional:* First Nowell; In dulci jubilo; *Humperdinck:* Weihnachten; *Anon:* Von Himmel hoch; *Traditional:* I saw three ships; Maria auf dem Berge; *Anon:* All creatures of our God and King. (E. Schwarzkopf, Ambrosian Sngrs, D. Vaughan, Philh/C. Mackerras, J. Bream)

① **CDM7 63577-2** (2/91)
Franck & Debussy: Cello Sonatas, etc
Franck: Violin Sonata; *Debussy:* Cello Sonata; Plus que lente; Préludes (exc). (M. Maisky, M. Argerich)

① **CDM7 63617-2** (11/90)
Wagner—Orchestral Works, Vol. 1
Wagner: Rienzi (exc); Tannhäuser (exc); Lohengrin (exc); Tristan und Isolde (exc). (Philh/O. Klemperer)

① **CDM7 63618-2** (11/90)
Wagner—Orchestral Works, Vol.2
Wagner: Meistersinger (exc); Rheingold (exc); Walküre (exc); Siegfried (exc); Götterdämmerung (exc); Götterdämmerung (exc); Parsifal (exc). (Philh/O. Klemperer)

① **CDM7 63653-2** (12/90)
Wolf: Lieder
Wolf: Mörike Lieder (exc); Goethe Lieder (exc); Songs for a woman's voice (Cpte); Alte Weisen (exc); Spanisches Liederbuch (exc); Eichendorff Lieder (exc); Mörike Lieder (exc); Mörike Lieder (exc); Vier Gedichte (exc). (E. Schwarzkopf, G. Moore, G. Parsons)

① **CDM7 63654-2** (12/90)
Schwarzkopf Encores
Bach: Anna Magdalena Notenbuch (1725) (exc); *Gluck:* Rencontre imprévue (exc); *Beethoven:* Lieder, Op. 83 (exc); *Loewe:* Kleiner Haushalt, Op.71; *Wagner:* Wesendonk Lieder (exc); *Brahms:* Lieder, Op. 106 (exc); Deutsche Volkslieder (exc); Deutsche Volkslieder (exc); *Mahler:* Lieder und Gesänge (exc); Rückert Lieder (exc); Knaben Wunderhorn (exc); *Tchaikovsky:* Songs, Op. 38 (exc); *Wolf-Ferrari:* Canzoniere (exc); *J. Martini:* Plaisir d'amour; *Hahn:* Si mes vers; *Debussy:* Mandoline; *Quilter:*

Arnold Book of Old Songs (exc); *Arne:* Love's Labours Lost (exc); Tempest (exc); *Traditional:* 's Schätzli; O du liebs Ängeli; Maria auf dem Berge; Danny Boy; *J. Strauss II:* Frühlingsstimmen, Op. 410 (exc). (E. Schwarzkopf, G. Moore, G. Parsons, VPO/J. Krips)

① **CDM7 63655-2** (12/90)
Schwarzkopf—The previously unpublished recordings
Bach: Cantata 199; Mass in B minor, BWV232 (exc); *Mozart:* Nehmt meinen Dank, K383; *Gieseking:* Kinderlieder (Cpte); *R. Strauss:* Vier letzte Lieder. (E. Schwarzkopf, K. Ferrier, Philh, Vienna SO/H. von Karajan/T. Dart/A. Galliera, W. Gieseking)

① **CDM7 63656-2** (12/90)
Schubert/Schumann/Strauss—Lieder
Schubert: Vögel, D691; Liebhaber in allen Gestalten, D558; Heidenröslein, D257; Forelle, D550; Einsame, D800; Jüngling an der Quelle, D300; An mein Klavier, D342; Erlkönig, D328; Suleika I, D720; Suleika II, D717; Hänflings Liebeswerbung, D552; Meeres Stille, D216; Gretchen am Spinnrade, D118; *Schumann:* Myrthen, Op. 25 (exc); Lieder und Gesänge, Op. 77 (exc); Myrthen, Op. 25 (exc); Gesänge, Op. 31 (exc); *R. Strauss:* Lieder, Op. 36 (exc); Lieder, Op. 69 (exc); Lieder, Op. 49 (exc); Lieder, Op. 37 (exc); Lieder, Op. 41 (exc); Lieder, Op. 67 (exc); Lieder, Op. 10 (exc). (E. Schwarzkopf, G. Moore, G. Parsons)

① **CDM7 63657-2** (12/90)
Schwarzkopf sings Opera Arias
Mozart: Nozze di Figaro (exc); Così fan tutte (exc); Don Giovanni (exc); *Verdi:* Requiem (exc); *Humperdinck:* Hänsel und Gretel (exc); *Lehár:* Lustige Witwe (exc); *J. Strauss II:* Fledermaus (exc); *Puccini:* Turandot (exc); *R. Strauss:* Ariadne auf Naxos (exc); Rosenkavalier (exc); Capriccio (exc). (E. Schwarzkopf, VPO, Philh, La Scala Chor, La Scala Orch, E. Grümmer, K. Schmitt-Walter/H. von Karajan/W. Furtwängler/V. de Sabata/O. Ackermann/T. Serafin/W. Sawallisch)

① **CDM7 63944-2** (3/92)
Honegger—Orchestral Works
Honegger: Symphonic Movements (exc); Pastorale d'été; Cantate de Noël. (C. Maurane, ORTF Chor, ORTF Nat Orch/J. Martinon)

① **CDM7 63945-2** (3/92)
French Ballet Music
Poulenc: Biches (exc); *Milhaud:* Création du monde; *Dutilleux:* Loup (exc). (Paris Cons/G. Prêtre)

① **CDM7 63948-2** (3/92)
20th Century French Orchestral Works
Boulez: Soleil des eaux; *Koechlin:* Bandar-Log; *Messiaen:* Chronochromie; Et exspecto resurrectionem. (J. Nendick, L. Devos, B. McDaniel, BBC SO, BBC Chor/P. Boulez/A. Dorati, Paris Orch/S. Baudo)

① **CDM7 63950-2** (3/92)
Pierné—Orchestral Works
Pierné: Images; Viennoise; Paysages Franciscains; Cathédrales. (Loire PO/P. Dervaux)

① **CDM7 63951-2** (3/92)
Rabaud—Orchestral Works
Rabaud: Mârouf (exc); Églogue, Op.7; Divertissement, Op.2; Procession nocturne, Op.6. (Loire PO/P. Dervaux)

① **CDM7 63953-2** (3/92)
D'Indy—Orchestral Works Vol II
Indy: Istar, Op.42; Wallenstein, Op.12; Forêt enchantée. (Loire PO/P. Dervaux)

① **CDM7 63985-2** (4/91)
Bartók—Violin & Viola Concertos
Bartók: Violin Concerto 1; Viola Concerto; Rhapsody 1, Sz87; Rhapsody 2, Sz90. (Y. Menuhin, Y. Menuhin, New Philh/A. Dorati, BBC SO/P. Boulez)

① **CDM7 63986-2** (4/91)
French Chamber Works
Ravel: Piano Trio; *Debussy:* Violin Sonata; Sonata for Flute, Viola and Harp; *Fauré:* Andante, Op.75; Berceuse, Op.16. (Y. Menuhin, G. Cassadó, L. Kentner, J. Février, M. Debost, L. Laskine, J. Menuhin, Y. Menuhin)

① **CDM7 63988-2** (4/91)
Schubert, Mendelssohn & Brahms—Chamber Works
Schubert: Fantasie, D934; *Mendelssohn:* Violin Sonata (1838); *Brahms:* Horn Trio. (Y. Menuhin, L. Kentner, G. Moore, H. Menuhin, A. Civil)

① **CDM7 64022-2** (5/92)
Vaughan Williams—Orchestral Works
Vaughan Williams: Serenade to music; English Folk Song Suite; Norfolk Rhapsody 1; Greensleeves Fantasia; In the Fen Country; Lark Ascending. (N. Burrowes, S. Armstrong, S. Longfield, M. Hayward, A. Hodgson, G. Jennings, S. Minty, M. Dickinson, I. Partridge, B. Dickerson, W. Evans,

K. Bowen, R. Angas, J. Carol Case, J. Noble, C. Keyte, H. Bean, LPO, LSO, New Philh/A. Boult)

ⓘ **CDM7 64027-2** (3/92)
Sibelius—Orchestral Works
Sibelius: Symphony 4; Symphony 6; Tempest Suites (exc); Legends (exc); Bard. (LPO, RPO/T. Beecham)

ⓘ **CDM7 64044-2** (10/91)
Arnold—Orchestral Works
Arnold: 2-Piano Concerto; Symphony 1; Solitaire (exc); Tam O'Shanter; English Dances, Op.27 (exc); English Dances, Op.33 (exc). (C. Smith, P. Sellick, CBSO, Bournemouth SO, Philh/M. Arnold)

ⓘ **CDM7 64122-2** (2/92)
Sibelius—Orchestral Works
Sibelius: Symphony 5; Symphony 7; Scenes with Cranes; Nightride and Sunrise. (CBSO, Philh/S. Rattle)

ⓘ **CDM7 64130-2** (12/91)
Christmas Music from King's
Sweelinck: Hodie Christus natus est; *Palestrina:* Motets, Bk 3 (1575) (exc); *Victoria:* O magnum mysterium; Senex puerum portabat; *Byrd:* Gradualia 1/i: Purification of the BVM (exc); Hodie beata virgo; *Gibbons:* Hosanna to the Son of David; *Weelkes:* Hosanna to the Son of David; Gloria in excelsis Deo; *Eccard:* When to the temple Mary went; *Traditional:* Boar's Head Carol; Holly and the Ivy; Angelus ad virginem; Angelus ad virginem; I sing of a maiden; *Watt's* Cradle Song; Tomorrow shall be my dancing day; *Campion:* Ayres, Bk 1 (exc); *Traditional:* Jesus Christ the apple tree; Most glorious Lord of life; That Lord that lay in Assë stall; Where riches is everlasting. (Kings College Ch, A. Davis, D. Whittaker, C. van Kampen, R. Spencer/D. Willcocks)

ⓘ **CDM7 64131-2** (2/91)
Orchestral Music for Christmas
Holy-Hutchinson: Carol Symphony; *Vaughan Williams:* Fantasia on Christmas carols; And all in the morning; Wassail Song; *Traditional:* Bethlehem down; Adam lay y-bounden; *Quilter:* Children's Overture; *Tomlinson:* English folk-dances Suite 1. (PAO/Barry Rose, J. Barrow, Gavin Williams, Stg Orch, R. Hammersley, C. Mould, Guildford Cath Ch, Light Music Soc Orch/V. Dunn)

ⓘ **CDM7 64140-2** (4/92)
Stokowski Showcase
Beethoven: Leonore (exc); *Mozart:* Don Giovanni (exc); *Schubert:* Rosamunde (exc); *Tchaikovsky:* Songs, Op.73 (exc); *Sousa:* Stars and Stripes Forever; *Chabrier:* España, (exc); *Saint-Saëns:* Danse Macabre; *Berlioz:* Carnaval Romain; *Ippolitov-Ivanov:* Caucasian Sketches (exc); *Rossini:* Guillaume Tell (exc). (National PO/L. Stokowski)

ⓘ **CDM7 64143-2** (8/92)
Klemperer conducts Gluck/Beethoven/Berlioz
Gluck: Iphigénie en Aulide (exc); *Beethoven:* Leonore (exc); *Berlioz:* Symphonie fantastique. (Philh/O. Klemperer)

ⓘ **CDM7 64144-2** (9/92)
Klemperer conducts Mendelssohn/Liszt/J.Strauss II
J. Strauss II: Fledermaus (exc); *Liszt:* Piano Concerto 1; *Mendelssohn:* Midsummer Night's Dream (exc). (A. Fischer, H. Harper, J. Baker, Philh Chor, Philh/O. Klemperer)

ⓘ **CDM7 64193-2** (6/92)
Dvořák—Orchestral Works
Dvořák: Symphony 8; Scherzo capriccioso; Legends (exc). (Hallé/J. Barbirolli)

ⓘ **CDM7 64281-2** (8/92)
Boulanger—Vocal & Chamber Works
Boulanger: Du fond de l'abîme; Psalm 24; Psalm 129; Vieille prière bouddhique; Pie Jesu; Violin Pieces. (O. Dominguez, R. Amade, M. Sénéchal, P. Mollet, A. Fauqueur, J-J. Grunenwald, E. Brasseur Chorale, Lamoureux Orch/I. Markevitch, Y. Menuhin, C. Curzon)

ⓘ **CDM7 64300-2** (7/94)
Holst/Purcell/Britten—Orchestral Works
Holst: Planets; *Purcell:* Abdelazer, Z570 (exc); *Britten:* Young Person's Guide. (Toronto SO/A. Davis, Taverner Plyrs/A. Parrott, Minnesota Orch/N. Marriner, Toronto Children's Chor)

ⓘ **CDM7 64326-2** (11/92)
Haydn/Vivaldi—Cello Concertos
Haydn: Cello Concerto in C; Cello Concerto in D; *Vivaldi:* Concerto, RV413; Concerto, RV417. (L. Harrell, ASMF/N. Marriner, ECO/P. Zukerman)

ⓘ **CDM7 64329-2** (11/92)
Russian Piano Works
Tchaikovsky: Piano Concerto 1; Morceaux, Op.19 (exc); *Balakirev:* Islamey; *Prokofiev:* Pieces, Op.4 (exc); Piano Concerto 1. (A. Gavrilov, Philh/R. Muti, LSO/S. Rattle)

ⓘ **CDM7 64331-2** (11/92)
Sibelius—Orchestral Works
Sibelius: Finlandia; Legends (exc) En Saga; Tapiola; Karelia Suite. (BPO/H. von Karajan)

ⓘ **CDM7 64332-2** (11/92)
Tchaikovsky—Ballet highlights
Tchaikovsky: Swan Lake (exc); Sleeping Beauty (exc); Nutcracker (exc). (LSO/A. Previn)

ⓘ **CDM7 64333-2** (11/92)
Vivaldi—Concertos
Vivaldi: Concerti, Op.8 (exc); Concerto, RV199; Concerti grossi, Op.3 (exc); Concerti, Op.4 (exc). (I. Perlman (vn/dir), LPO, Israel PO)

ⓘ **CDM7 64354-2** (11/92)
Chopin—Piano Works
Chopin: Piano Concerto 1; Nocturnes (exc); Ballades (exc); Polonaises (exc). (M. Pollini, Philh/P. Kletzki)

ⓘ **CDM7 64357-2** (11/92)
Debussy/Ravel—Orchestral Works
Debussy: La Mer; *Ravel:* Boléro; *Debussy:* Après-midi; *Ravel:* Alborada del gracioso; La Valse. (BPO, Paris Orch/H. von Karajan)

ⓘ **CDM7 64365-2** (4/93)
Chausson—Chamber, Orchestra & Vocal Works
Chausson: Chanson perpétuelle, Op.37; Concert, Op. 21; Poème de l'amour et de la mer. (A. Esposito, P. Barbizet, C. Ferras, Parrenin Qt, V. de los Angeles, Lamoureux Orch/J-P. Jacquillat)

ⓘ **CDM7 64470-2** (12/92)
Mompou—Piano Works
Mompou: Cançons i danses; Suburbis; Scènes d'enfants; Fêtes lointaines; Pessebres; Paisajes. (G. Soriano, C. Bravo)

ⓘ **CDM7 64523-2** (12/92)
Albéniz—Piano Works
Albéniz: Cantos de España; Suite española 2 (exc); Recuerdos de Viaje (exc); Mallorca; Piezás características (exc); Vega; Azulejos. (A. de Larrocha)

ⓘ **CDM7 64527-2** (12/92)
Falla—Piano Works
Falla: Pièces espagnoles; Vida breve (exc); Sombrero de tres picos (exc); Amor brujo (exc); Fantasía bética. (A. de Larrocha)

ⓘ **CDM7 64625-2** (3/93)
Schumann—Piano Works
Schumann: Fantasie; Faschingsschwank aus Wien; Papillons. (S. Richter)

ⓘ **CDM7 64626-2** (3/93)
Schumann—Concertos, etc
Schumann: Cello Concerto; Piano Concerto; Introduction and Allegro, Op.92. (J. Du Pré, D. Barenboim, New Philh/D. Barenboim, LPO/D. Fischer-Dieskau)

ⓘ **CDM7 64627-2** (6/93)
Liszt—Orchestral Works
Liszt: Hungarian Rhapsodies, S359 (exc); Hungarian Rhapsodies, S359 (exc); Rákóczy March; Ungarischer Sturmmarsch. (Philh Hungarica, LPO/W. Boskovsky)

ⓘ **CDM7 64630-2** (3/93)
Berlioz—Orchestral Works
Berlioz: Symphonie fantastique; Corsaire; Béatrice et Bénédict (exc); Carnaval Romain. (FNO/L. Bernstein, LSO/A. Previn)

ⓘ **CDM7 64631-2** (3/93)
Beethoven—Violin Sonatas
Beethoven: Violin Sonata 5; Violin Sonata 8; Violin Sonata 9. (P. Zukerman, D. Barenboim)

ⓘ **CDM7 64634-2** (3/93)
Fauré/Bach—Choral Works
Fauré: Requiem (Cpte); Pavane; *Bach:* Magnificat, BWV243. (S. Armstrong, D. Fischer-Dieskau, Edinburgh Fest Chor, Paris Orch/D. Barenboim, L. Popp, A. Pashley, J. Baker, R. Tear, T. Hemsley, New Philh Chor, New Philh)

ⓘ **CDM7 64687-2** (9/93)
French Works inspired by Edgar Allan Poe
Caplet: Masque de la mort rouge; *Debussy:* Chûte de la maison Usher (Cpte); *Schmitt:* Palais Hanté. (C. Barbaux, F. Le Roux, P-Y. Le Maigat, J-P. Lafont, F. Cambreling, Monte Carlo PO/G. Prêtre)

ⓘ **CDM7 64714-2** (8/93)
Poulenc—Piano Concertos
Poulenc: Aubade; Piano Concerto; 2-Piano Concerto. (G. Tacchino, B. Ringeissen, Paris Cons, Monte Carlo PO/G. Prêtre)

ⓘ **CDM7 64716-2** (2/94)
Ireland—Piano Concerto, etc
Ireland: Piano Concerto; London Overture; Mai-Dun; Greater love hath no man; Sea Fever; Songs sacred and profane (exc); Comedy Ov. (J. Baker, R. Lloyd, G. Moore, C. Horsley, N. Walker, Chichester Cath Ch/J. Birch, RPO/B. Cameron, Hallé, LSO/J. Barbirolli, GUS Band/G. Brand)

ⓘ **CDM7 64717-2** (9/93)
Brian—Orchestral Works
Brian: Symphony 7; Symphony 31; Tinker's Wedding Ov. (RLPO/C. Mackerras)

ⓘ **CDM7 64718-2** (8/94)
The Composer Conducts
Rawsthorne: Street Corner; Madame Chrysanthéme (exc); *J. Addison II:* Carte Blanche (exc); *Arnell:* Great detective (exc); *Bliss:* Checkmate (exc); *Arnold:* Grand Grand Ov. (PAO/A. Rawsthorne/J. Addison/R. Arnell, Sinfonia of London/A. Bliss, RPO/M. Arnold)

ⓘ **CDM7 64721-2** (8/94)
Moeran/Finzi—Orchestral Works
Moeran: Serenade; Sinfonietta; *Finzi:* Fall of the Leaf; New Year Music. (Northern Sinfonia/R. Hickox)

ⓘ **CDM7 64722-2** (6/94)
Vaughan Williams—Choral & Orchestral Works
Vaughan Williams: Tudor Portraits; Benedicite; Dives and Lazarus Variants. (H. Harper, E. Bainbridge, J. Carol Case, Bach Ch, New Philh, LSO, Jacques Orch/D. Willcocks)

ⓘ **CDM7 64723-2** (10/93)
Walton—Choral & Orchestral Works
Walton: Belshazzar's Feast; Portsmouth Point; Scapino; Britten Improvisations. (J. Shirley-Quirk, LSC, LSO/A. Previn)

ⓘ **CDM7 64724-2** (2/94)
Elgar—Orchestral Works
Elgar: Symphony 2; Sospiri; Elegy. (Hallé, New Philh/J. Barbirolli)

ⓘ **CDM7 64726-2** (4/94)
Sullivan—Orchestral Works
Sullivan: Cello Concerto; *Elgar:* Romance, Op.62; *Sullivan:* Irish Symphony; Di Ballo. (J. Lloyd Webber, LSO/C. Mackerras, RLPO/C. Groves)

ⓘ **CDM7 64730-2** (4/94)
Vaughan Williams—Riders to the Sea; Epithalamion, etc
Vaughan Williams: Riders to the Sea (Cpte); Merciless Beauty; Epithalamion. (N. Burrowes, M. Price, H. Watts, B. Luxon, P. Stevens, Ambrosian Sngrs, London Orch Nova/M. Davies, P. Langridge, Endellion Qt, S. Roberts, J. Snowden, H. Shelley, Bach Ch, LPO/D. Willcocks)

ⓘ **CDM7 64731-2** (3/94)
Vaughan Williams/Elgar/Butterworth—Songs
Vaughan Williams: On Wenlock Edge; Songs of Travel; *Elgar:* Pleading; Was it some golden star?; Oh, soft was the song; Twilight; Torch; River; *Butterworth:* Love blows as the wind blows. (R. Tear, T. Allen, CBSO/S. Rattle/V. Handley)

ⓘ **CDM7 64737-2** (11/93)
Nielsen/Sibelius—Symphonies
Nielsen: Symphony 4; Pan and Syrinx; *Sibelius:* Symphony 5. (CBSO, Philh/S. Rattle)

ⓘ **CDM7 64747-2** (9/93)
Franck—Orchestral Works
Franck: Symphony; Symphonic Variations; Chasseur Maudit. (A. Weissenberg, Paris Orch, BPO/H. von Karajan, Philadelphia/R. Muti)

ⓘ **CDM7 64850-2** (10/94)
Liszt—Symphonic Poems
Liszt: Tasso; Préludes; Orpheus; Mazeppa; Mephisto Waltz 2, S111. (Leipzig Gewandhaus/K. Masur)

ⓘ **CDM7 64851-2** (10/94)
Mozart/R. Strauss—Horn Concertos
Mozart: Horn Concerti; Rondo, K371; *R. Strauss:* Horn Concerto 1. (R. Vlatković, ECO/J. Tate)

ⓘ **CDM7 64868-2** (3/94)
Mozart—Works for Violin & Orchestra
Mozart: Violin Concerto, K218; Violin Concerto, K219; Rondo, K269; Rondo, K373; Adagio, K261. (D. Oistrakh (vn/dir), BPO)

ⓘ **CDM7 69018-2** (12/87)
J. Strauss II—Waltzes
J.Strauss II: Fledermaus (exc); *J. Strauss II:* Annen-Polka, Op. 117; Blauen Donau, Op. 314; *J.Strauss II:* Zigeunerbaron (exc); Tritsch-Tratsch; *J. Strauss II:* Kaiser, Op. 437. (BPO/H. von Karajan)

J-M. Frémeau, L. Pezzino, M. Mesplé, J. Laforge Choral Ens, Monte Carlo PO, M. Rosenthal)

Ⓓ **CDS7 49487-2** (1/89)
Beethoven: Complete Symphonies
Beethoven: Symphony 1; Symphony 2; Symphony 3; Symphony 4; Symphony 5; Symphony 6; Symphony 7; Symphony 8; Symphony 9; Fidelio (exc); Leonore (exc); Consecration of the House Ov. (C. Studer, D. Ziegler, P. Seiffert, J. Morris, Westminster Ch, Philadelphia/R. Muti)

Ⓓ **CDS7 49749-2** (6/89)
Handel—Music for the Carmelite Vespers
Handel: Dixit Dominus; Laudate pueri; Te decus virgineum; Nisi Dominus; Haec est regina virginum; Saeviat tellus; Salve regina; *Anon:* Carmelite Vespers Plainchant. (J. Feldman, E. Kirkby, E. Van Evera, M. Cable, M. Nichols, J. Cornwell, D. Thomas, Taverner Ch, Taverner Plyrs/A. Parrott)

Ⓓ **CDS7 49775-2** (8/88)
Tchaikovsky—Chamber Works
Tchaikovsky: String Quartet 1; String Quartet 2; String Quartet 3; Souvenir de Florence. (Borodin Qt, Y. Bashmet, N. Gutman)

Ⓓ **CDS7 54198-2** (2/93)
Beethoven—String Trios
Beethoven: String Trio, Op.3; Serenade, Op.8; String Trios, Op.9. (I. Perlman, P. Zukerman, L. Harrell)

Ⓓ **CDS7 54251-2** (7/91)
Scriabin—Symphonies and Tone Poems
Scriabin: Symphony 1; Symphony 2; Poème de l'extase; Symphony 3; Prometheus. (S. Toczyska, M. Myers, Westminster Ch, Philadelphia/R. Muti, D. Alexeev, Philadelphia Choral Arts Soc)

Ⓓ **CDS7 54270-2** (11/91)
Rattle Conducts Britten
Britten: American Ov; Ballad of Heroes; Diversions; Building of the House; Praise we great men; Suite on English Folk Tunes; Canadian Carnival; Young Apollo; Chansons françaises; Scottish Ballad; Occasional Ov; Sinfonia da Requiem. (R. Tear, P. Donohoe, A. Hargan, M. King, W. White, J. Gomez, P. Fowke, CBSO Chor, CBSO/S. Rattle)

Ⓓ **CDS7 54362-2** (4/92)
Mozart—Complete Variations for Piano Solo
Mozart: Variations, K24; Variations, K25; Variations, K179; Variations, K180; Variations, K354; Variations, K265; Variations, K353; Variations, K264; Variations, K352; Variations, K398; Variations, K455; Variations, K500; Variations, K54; Variations, K573; Variations, K613. (D. Barenboim)

Ⓓ **CDS7 54514-2** (8/93)
Mendelssohn—String Quartets
Mendelssohn: String Quartet 1; String Quartet 2; String Quartet 3; String Quartet 4; String Quartet 5; String Quartet 6. (Cherubini Qt)

Ⓓ **CDS7 54560-2** (6/92)
The Elgar Edition, Vol.1
Elgar: Symphony 1; Falstaff; Symphony 2; Dream of Gerontius (exc); Civic Fanfare; *Various:* National Anthems (exc); *Elgar:* Dream of Gerontius (exc); Music Makers (exc). (M. Balfour, S. Wilson, T. Davies, H. Heyner, H. Stevens, Three Choirs Fest Chor, RCS, LSO, RAHO/E. Elgar)

Ⓓ **CDS7 54564-2** (2/93)
The Elgar Edition, Vol.2
Elgar: Enigma Variations; Violin Concerto; Wand of Youth Suite 1; Wand of Youth Suite 2; Nursery Suite; Severn Suite; Land of Hope and Glory; Banner of St George (exc); *Various:* National Anthems (exc); *Croft:* O God our help; *Elgar:* Light of Life (exc); Mazurka, Op.10/1; Serenade mauresque; Contrasts; Chanson de nuit; Chanson de matin; Bavarian Dances (exc); Bavarian Dances (exc); Crown of India (Cpte); *Bach:* Fantasia and Fugue, BWV537. (Y. Menuhin, Chor, LSO, RAHO, New SO, LPO/E. Elgar, M. Balfour)

Ⓓ **CDS7 54568-2** (8/93)
The Elgar Edition, Vol.3
Elgar: Froissart; Cockaigne; In the South; Falstaff (exc); Cello Concerto; Beau Brummel (exc); Rosemary; Salut d'amour; Minuet, Op.21; Sérénade lyrique; May Song; Carissima; Beau Brummel (exc); Improvisations; Pomp and Circumstance Marches (exc); Pomp and Circumstance Marches (exc); Pomp and Circumstance Marches (exc); Pomp and Circumstance Marches (exc); Kingdom (exc); Pomp and Circumstance Marches (exc); Cockaigne; Serenade; Elegy; Caractacus (exc); Mina; Mina; Coronation March. (B. Harrison, LPO, RAHO, LSO, New SO, BBC SO/E. Elgar, E. Elgar/L. Collingwood/L. Ronald, New Light SO/J. Ainslie Murray, Light SO/Haydn Wood)

Ⓓ **CDS7 54587-2** (10/93)
Beethoven—String Quartets, Vol.1
Beethoven: String Quartet 1; String Quartet 3; String Quartet 4; String Quartet 7; String Quartet 10; String Quartet 12; String Quartet 13; String Quartet 14. (Alban Berg Qt)

Ⓓ **CDS7 54592-2** (10/93)
Beethoven—String Quartets, Vol.2
Beethoven: String Quartet 2; String Quartet 5; String Quartet 6; String Quartet 8; String Quartet 9; String Quartet 11; String Quartet 15; String Quartet 16; Grosse Fuge; String Quartet 13 (exc). (Alban Berg Qt)

Ⓓ **CDS7 54607-2** (5/93)
Stravinsky plays and conducts Stravinsky
Stravinsky: Noces; Octet; Capriccio; Symphony of Psalms; Pastorale; Firebird (exc); Petrushka (Vn/Pf); Songs of the Nightingale; Rag-time; Piano-Rag Music; Suite italienne (violin) (exc); Serenade in A; Duo Concertant; Concerto for two solo pianos. (K. Winter, L. Seymour, Parry Jones, Roy Henderson, BBC Chor, B. Mason, L. Heward, E. Lush, E. Benbow, Perc Ens/I. Stravinsky, M. Moyse, E. Godeau, G. Dhérin, M. Piard, E. Foveau, P. Vignal, A. Lafosse, R. Delbos, I. Stravinsky, Walther Straram Orch/E. Ansermet, Vlassof Chor, S. Dushkin, L. Gromer, G. Durand, A. Vacellier, G. Grandmaison, Inst Ens, S. Stravinsky)

Ⓓ **CDS7 54725-2** (2/95)
Brahms—Piano Trios
Brahms: Piano Trio 1; Piano Trio 2; Piano Trio 3; Piano Trio, Op. posth.. (I. Perlman, L. Harrell, Vladimir Ashkenazy)

Ⓓ **CDS7 54829-2** (2/94)
Brahms—String Quartets
Brahms: String Quartet 1; String Quartet 2; String Quartet 3. (Alban Berg Qt)

Ⓓ **CES5 68517-2** (11/95)
Bach—Orchestral Works
Bach: Violin Concerto, BWV1041; 2-Violin Concerto; Violin Concerto, BWV1042; Violin and Oboe Concerto, BWV1060; Suites, BWV1066-9 (exc). (Y. Menuhin (vn/dir), C. Ferras, L. Goossens, Bath Fest Orch/Y. Menuhin)

Ⓓ **CES5 68518-2** (11/95)
Beethoven—Orchestral Works
Beethoven: Symphony 1; Symphony 3; Symphony 5; Fidelio (exc); Prometheus (exc); Egmont (exc). (Munich PO, BPO/R. Kempe)

Ⓓ **CES5 68519-2** (11/95)
Beethoven—Symphonies
Beethoven: Symphony 6; Symphony 8; Symphony 9. (S. Armstrong, A. Reynolds, R. Tear, J. Shirley-Quirk, LSO, LSO/C.M. Giulini, Munich PO/R. Kempe)

Ⓓ **CES5 68525-2** (11/95)
Berlioz/Saint-Saëns—Orchestral Works
Berlioz: Symphonie fantastique; Carnaval romain; *Saint-Saëns:* Symphony 3; Carnaval des Animaux. (J. Ogdon, B. Lucas, C. Robinson, BPO, VPO, CBSO/R. Kempe/L. Frémaux)

Ⓓ **CHS5 65003-2** (11/94)
Walton conducts Walton
Walton: Symphony 1; Belshazzar's Feast; Violin Concerto; Viola Concerto; Partita; Johannesburg Festival Overture; Façade Suites (exc); Portsmouth Point; Wise Virgins (exc); Crown Imperial; Orb and Sceptre; Wise Virgins (exc); Hamlet (exc); Richard III (exc); Henry V Suite; Spitfire Prelude and Fugue; Henry V (exc); Henry V Suite (exc). (Donald Bell, Y. Menuhin, Y. Menuhin, chor, Philh Chor, Philh, New Philh, LSO, Sadlers Wells Orch/W. Walton, L. Olivier/R. Douglas)

Ⓓ **CHS5 65185-2** (10/94)
Beethoven/Brahms—Cello Sonatas
Beethoven: Cello Sonata 1; Cello Sonata 2; Cello Sonata 3; Cello Sonata 4; Cello Sonata 5; *Brahms:* Cello Sonata 2; *Beethoven:* Menuet, WoO10/2. (P. Casals, M. Horszowski, O. Schulhof)

Ⓓ **CHS5 65198-2** (10/94)
Maggie Teyte sings French Songs
Berlioz: Nuits d'été (exc); *Chausson:* Mélodies, Op.2 (exc); Mélodies, Op.2 (exc); Poème de l'amour et de la mer (exc); Chanson perpétuelle, Op.37; *Duparc:* Invitation au voyage; Phidylé; Chanson triste; Extase; *Ravel:* Epigrammes; Histoires naturelles (exc); Shéhérazade; *Massenet:* Élégie; *Fauré:* Songs, Op.2 (exc); Songs, Op.4 (exc); Songs, Op.5 (exc); Songs, Op.7 (exc); Songs, Op.8 (exc); Songs, Op.18 (exc); Songs, Op.23 (exc); Songs, Op.39 (exc); Songs, Op.46 (exc); Bonne chanson, Op.61 (exc); Bonne chanson, Op.61 (exc); Songs, Op.83 (exc); *Debussy:* Ariettes oubliées (exc); Âme évaporée; Beau soir; Poèmes de Baudelaire (exc); Proses lyriques (exc); *Hahn:* Si mes vers; Heure exquise; Offrande; Sourdine; Études latines (exc). (M. Teyte, G. Moore, LSO/L. Heward, Blech Qt, ROHO/H. Rignold, orch/L. Lucas, J. Whitehead)

Ⓓ **CHS5 65308-2** (1/95)
Beethoven/Schubert/Mendelssohn—Chamber Works
Beethoven: String Quartet 1; String Quartet 9; String Quartet 11; String Quartet 12; String Quartet 14; String Quartet 15; String Quartet 16; Violin Sonata 3; *Schubert:* String Quartet, D112; *Mendelssohn:* String Quartet, Op.81 (exc). (A. Busch, R. Serkin, Busch Qt, Busch Qt)

Ⓓ **CHS5 65353-2** (10/95)
Hindemith/Schubert/R. Strauss—Orchestral Works
R. Strauss: Don Juan; *Hindemith:* Harmonie der Welt; *Schubert:* Symphony 9. (VPO/W. Furtwängler)

Ⓓ **CHS5 65503-2** (11/95)
Beethoven—Piano Concertos, etc
Beethoven: Piano Concerto 2; Piano Concerto 3; Piano Concerto 4; Piano Concerto 5; Piano Sonata 14. (Solomon, Philh/A. Cluytens/H. Menges, BBC SO/A. Boult)

Ⓓ **CHS5 65506-2** (9/95)
Victor de Sabata conducts
Verdi: Requiem (Cpte); Traviata (exc); Vespri siciliani (exc); *Wolf-Ferrari:* Quattro rusteghi (exc); Segreto di Susanna (exc); *Respighi:* Fountains of Rome; *Rossini:* Guillaume Tell (exc). (E. Schwarzkopf, O. Dominguez, G. di Stefano, C. Siepi, La Scala Chor, La Scala Orch, Santa Cecilia Academy Orch/V. de Sabata)

Ⓓ **CHS7 61038-2** (8/88)
Debussy—Pelléas et Mélisande, etc
Debussy: Pelléas et Mélisande (Cpte); Fêtes galantes I (Cpte); Fêtes galantes II (Cpte); Chansons de Bilitis (Cpte); Promenoir des deux amants (Cpte); Proses lyriques (exc); Ballades de François Villon (exc); Pelléas et Mélisande (exc); Ariettes oubliées (exc). (J. Jansen, I. Joachim, H. Etcheverry, P. Cabanel, G. Cernay, L.B. Sedira, A. Narçon, E. Rousseau, M. Teyte, M. Garden, A. Cortot, C. Debussy, Y. Gouverné Ch, SO/R. Desormière)

Ⓓ **CHS7 61047-2** (5/89)
The Art of Segovia—The HMV Recordings 1927-39
Bach: Solo Violin Partitas and Sonatas (exc); Solo Cello Suites (exc); Solo Cello Suites (exc); Prelude, BWV999; Suite, BWV996 (exc); Solo Violin Partitas and Sonatas (exc); *Ponce:* Suite in A minor; *Sor:* Mozart Variations, Op. 9; *Visée:* Pieces for guitar (exc); *Moreno Torroba:* Sonatina in A (exc); *Mendelssohn:* String Quartet 1 (exc); *Malats:* Serenata española; *Tárrega:* Recuerdos de la Alhambra; Estudios (exc); *Froberger:* Gigue; *Albéniz:* Suite española 1 (exc); *Moreno Torroba:* Suite castellana (exc); Prelude in E; Nocturno; *Turina:* Fandanguillo; *Granados:* Danzas españolas (exc); *Ponce:* Valse; *Castelnuovo-Tedesco:* Sonata, Op. 77 (exc); *Ponce:* Guitar Sonata 3 (exc); Postlude; Mazurka. (A. Segovia)

Ⓓ **CHS7 63025-2** (8/89)
Mussorgsky—Songs
Mussorgsky: Sadly rustled the leaves; Where art thou, little star; Hour of Jollity; Tell me why; I have many palaces and gardens; What are words of love to you?; King Saul; Old man's song; But if I could meet thee again; Wild wind blows; Night; Kalistratushka; Salammbô (exc); Prayer; Outcast; Lullaby; Dear one, why are thine eyes?; From my tears; Gopak; Darling Savishna; Seminarist; Hebrew song; Magpie; Gathering mushrooms; Feast; Ragamuffin; He-Goat; Garden by the Don; Classicist; Orphan; Child's song; Nursery; Eremushka's lullaby; Peepshow; Evening song; Forgotten; Sunless; Songs and Dances of Death; Epitaph; Sphinx; Not like thunder; Softly the spirit flew; Is spinning man's work; It scatters and breaks; Vision; Pride; Wanderer; On the Dnieper; Song of the flea. (B. Christoff, A. Labinsky, G. Moore, FRNO/G. Tzipine)

Ⓓ **CHS7 63538-2** (3/90)
Horowitz—The HMV Recordings, 1930-51
Bach: Nun freut euch, BWV734; *D. Scarlatti:* Keyboard Sonatas (exc); Keyboard Sonatas (exc); *Haydn:* Keyboard Sonata 62; *Chopin:* Etudes (exc); Etudes (exc); Etudes (exc); Impromptus (exc); Nocturnes (exc); Mazurkas (exc); Mazurkas (exc); Mazurkas (exc); Scherzos (exc); *Debussy:* Etudes (exc); *Poulenc:* Pastourelle (exc); Pièces (1928) (exc); *Beethoven:* Variations, WoO80; *Schumann:* Arabeske; Toccata; Fantasiestücke, Op. 12 (exc); Presto passionato; *Liszt:* Harmonies poétiques, S173 (exc); Piano Sonata, S178; *Rachmaninov:* Piano Concerto 3; Preludes (exc); *Rimsky-Korsakov:* Tale of Tsar Saltan (exc); *Stravinsky:* Petrushka (exc); *Prokofiev:* Toccata, Op. 11; *Stravinsky:* Petrushka (exc). (V. Horowitz, LSO/A. Coates)

Ⓓ **CHS7 63703-2** (6/91)
Mozart: Piano Concertos, etc
Mozart: 2-Piano Concerto, K365; Piano Concerto 19; Piano Concerto 20; Piano Concerto 21; Piano Concerto

24; Piano Concerto 27; Piano Sonata, K332; Piano Sonata, K570; Rondo, K511. (A. Schnabel, K.U. Schnabel, LSO, Philh/M. Sargent/A. Boult/J. Barbirolli/W. Susskind)

Ⓓ **CHS7 63715-2** (3/91)
Mozart: Die Entführung, etc
Mozart: Entführung (Cpte); Clemenza di Tito (exc); Zauberflöte (exc); Entführung (exc); Idomeneo (exc); Misero! o sogno, K431. (L. Marshall, I. Hollweg, L. Simoneau, G. Unger, G. Frick, H. Laubenthal, Beecham Choral Soc, RPO/T. Beecham, L. Simoneau, Paris Champs-Élysées Orch/A. Jouve)

Ⓓ **CHS7 63765-2** (7/91)
Beethoven—Complete Piano Sonatas
Beethoven: Piano Sonata 1; Piano Sonata 2; Piano Sonata 3; Piano Sonata 4; Piano Sonata 5; Piano Sonata 6; Piano Sonata 7; Piano Sonata 8; Piano Sonata 9; Piano Sonata 10; Piano Sonata 11; Piano Sonata 12; Piano Sonata 13; Piano Sonata 14; Piano Sonata 15; Piano Sonata 16; Piano Sonata 17; Piano Sonata 18; Piano Sonata 19; Piano Sonata 20; Piano Sonata 21; Piano Sonata 22; Piano Sonata 23; Piano Sonata 24; Piano Sonata 25; Piano Sonata 26; Piano Sonata 27; Piano Sonata 28; Piano Sonata 29; Piano Sonata 30; Piano Sonata 31; Piano Sonata 32. (A. Schnabel)

Ⓓ **CHS7 63802-2(1)** (9/92)
Tetrazzini—The London Records (pt 1)
Verdi: Rigoletto (exc); *A. Thomas:* Mignon (exc); *Delibes:* Lakmé (exc); *Meyerbeer:* Dinorah (exc); *Donizetti:* Lucia di Lammermoor (exc); *Mozart:* Nozze di Figaro (exc); *Rossini:* Barbiere di Siviglia (exc); *Verdi:* Traviata (exc); *Mozart:* Don Giovanni (exc); *Gounod:* Roméo et Juliette (exc); *J. Strauss II:* Frühlingsstimmen, Op. 410; *Verdi:* Ballo in maschera (exc); *Donizetti:* Lucia di Lammermoor (exc); *Benedict:* Carnival of Venice Variations; *Bellini:* Sonnambula (exc); *Bizet:* Pêcheurs de perles (exc); *Tosti:* Aprile; Serenata; *Gounod:* Mireille (exc); *Chapí:* Hijas del Zebedeo (exc); *Donizetti:* Linda di Chamounix (exc); *Verdi:* Vespri Siciliani (exc); *Rossini:* Semiramide (exc); *Grieg:* Peer Gynt (exc); *F. David:* Perle du Brésil (exc); *Bizet:* Carmen (exc); *Verdi:* Traviata (exc); *Delibes:* Lakmé (exc); *Mozart:* Don Giovanni (exc); *Verdi:* Aida (exc); *Donizetti:* Linda di Chamounix (exc); *A. Thomas:* Hamlet (exc); Mignon (exc); *Proch:* Air and Variations. (L. Tetrazzini, orch/P. Pitt, P. Pitt, chor)

Ⓓ **CHS7 63802-2(2)** (9/92)
Tetrazzini—The London Records (pt 2)
Bellini: Sonnambula (exc); *Verdi:* Traviata (exc); *Meyerbeer:* Huguenots (exc); *Bellini:* Puritani (exc); *Venzano:* O che assorta; *Bishop:* Home, sweet home; *Ricci:* Crispino e la comare (exc); *Meyerbeer:* Etoile du Nord (exc); *A. Thomas:* Mignon (exc); *Mozart:* Zauberflöte (exc); *Lotti:* Arminio (exc); *Verdi:* Forza del destino (exc); *A. Tate:* Somewhere a voice is calling; *Veracini:* Rosalinda (exc); *Gounod:* Faust (exc); *G. Braga:* Melodies (exc); *Pergolesi:* Tre giorni son che Nina; *Lemaire:* Vous dansez, Marquise; *Lama:* Piccolo amore; Cara piccina; *V. Valente:* Nuttata napulitana; *Hoschna:* Madame Sherry (exc); *De Curtis:* So 'nnammurato 'e te!; *Lama:* 'O mare canta!; *Drigo:* Arlekinda (exc); *Lama:* Come le rose. (L. Tetrazzini, A. Baggiore, T. Amici, inst ens, orch/P. Pitt, P. Pitt)

Ⓓ **CHS7 64057-2** (12/91)
Cortot-Thibaud-Casals Trio—Historic Recordings
Beethoven: Piano Trios (exc); Mozart Variations, WoO46; Piano Trios (exc); Violin Sonata 9; *Brahms:* Double Concerto; *Haydn:* Keyboard Trio 25; *Mendelssohn:* Piano Trio 1; *Schubert:* Piano Trio 1; *Schumann:* Piano Trio 1. (J. Thibaud, P. Casals, A. Cortot, Barcelona Casals Orch/A. Cortot)

Ⓓ **CHS7 64259-2** (5/92)
Schnabel plays Schubert
Schubert: Piano Sonata, D850; Moments musicaux, D780; March, D606; Piano Sonata, D959; Piano Sonata, D960. (A. Schnabel)

Ⓓ **CHS7 64487-2** (4/93)
R. Strauss—Der Rosenkavalier & Lieder
R. Strauss: Rosenkavalier (exc); Lieder, Op.27 (exc); Lieder, Op.17 (exc); Lieder, Op.41 (exc); Lieder, Op.48 (exc); Lieder, Op.21 (exc); Lieder, Op.36 (exc); Lieder, Op.69 (exc); Lieder, Op.17 (exc); Lieder, Op.29 (exc); Lieder, Op.48 (exc); Lieder, Op.15 (exc); Lieder, Op.43 (exc); Lieder, Op.56 (exc); Lieder, Op.56 (exc); Lieder, Op.27 (exc); Lieder, Op.29 (exc); Lieder, Op.17 (exc). (Lotte Lehmann, M. Olczewska, R. Mayr, E. Schumann, V. Madin, B. Paalen, H. Gallos, A. Michalsky, K. Ettl, W. Wernigk, Vienna St Op Chor, VPO/R. Heger, Vienna St Op Orch/K. Alwin, orch/L. Collingwood/F. Weissmann, I. Newton, K. Alwin, L. Rosenek, anon, anon, Berlin St Op Orch)

Ⓓ **CHS7 64491-2** (7/93)
Rubinstein plays Chopin, Vol.1
Chopin: Piano Concerto 1; Piano Concerto 2; Waltzes (exc); Nocturnes (exc). (A. Rubinstein, LSO/J. Barbirolli)

Ⓓ **CHS7 64697-2** (10/93)
Rubinstein plays Chopin, Vol.2
Chopin: Waltzes (exc); Mazurkas (exc); Scherzos; Barcarolle; Berceuse; Polonaises (exc); Andante spianato and grande polonaise. (A. Rubinstein)

Ⓓ **CHS7 64708-2** (7/93)
Solomon plays Beethoven
Beethoven: Piano Sonata 27; Piano Sonata 28; Piano Sonata 29; Piano Sonata 30; Piano Sonata 31; Piano Sonata 32. (Solomon)

Ⓓ **CHS7 64860-2(1)** (4/94)
La Scala Edition - Vol.1, 1878-1914 (pt 1)
Verdi: Vespri Siciliani (exc); *Bellini:* Sonnambula (exc); *Verdi:* Don Carlo (exc); *Ponchielli:* Gioconda (exc); *Verdi:* Traviata (exc); Otello (exc); Otello (exc); Otello (exc); *Halévy:* Juive (exc); Juive (exc); *Donizetti:* Favorita (exc); *Verdi:* Otello (exc); *Wagner:* Lohengrin (exc); *Verdi:* Ernani (exc); *Rossini:* Barbiere di Siviglia (exc); *Mascagni:* Cavalleria Rusticana (exc); *Bellini:* Norma (exc); *Verdi:* Otello (exc); Falstaff (exc); *Donizetti:* Lucrezia Borgia (exc); *Puccini:* Manon Lescaut (exc); *Leoncavallo:* Medici (exc); *Mascagni:* Guglielmo Ratcliff (exc); *Saint-Saëns:* Samson et Dalila (exc); *Giordano:* Andrea Chénier (exc); *Bellini:* Puritani (exc); *Mascagni:* Iris (exc); *Massenet:* Roi de Lahore (exc); *Wagner:* Lohengrin (exc); *Tchaikovsky:* Eugene Onegin (exc); *Puccini:* Bohème (exc); Bohème (exc). (La Scala Orch/A. Toscanini, A. Patti, A. Barili, G. Kaschmann, S. Cottone, F. Marconi, G. Bellincioni, F. Tamagno, anon, V. Maurel, L. Escalais, F. Navarini, M. Battistini, orch/C. Sabajno, G. Oxilia, F. Viñas, F. Valero, T. Arkel, G.B. De Negri, E. Teodorini, E. Garbin, G. Pacini, A. Parsi-Pettinella, M. Sammarco, A. Bonci, F. De Lucia, G. Borgatti, E. Giraldoni, E. Caruso, E. Carelli)

Ⓓ **CHS7 64860-2(2)** (4/94)
La Scala Edition - Vol.1, 1878-1914 (pt 2)
Puccini: Bohème (exc); *Boito:* Mefistofele (exc); *De Lara:* Méssaline (exc); *Boito:* Mefistofele (exc); *Donizetti:* Linda di Chamounix (exc); *Franchetti:* Germania (exc); Germania (exc); Germania (exc); *Berlioz:* Damnation de Faust (exc); *Giordano:* Siberia (exc); Siberia (exc); Siberia (exc); *Verdi:* Rigoletto (exc); Aida (exc); *Donizetti:* Don Pasquale (exc); Don Pasquale (exc); *Tchaikovsky:* Queen of Spades (exc); *Verdi:* Traviata (exc); *Franchetti:* Figlia di Iorio (exc); *Ponchielli:* Gioconda (exc); Gioconda (exc); Gioconda (exc); *Mascagni:* Cavalleria Rusticana (exc); *Spontini:* Vestale (exc); *Saint-Saëns:* Samson et Dalila (exc); *Mascagni:* Isabeau (exc); *Puccini:* Fanciulla del West (exc); *Bellini:* Norma (exc); *Verdi:* Nabucco (exc); *Wagner:* Tristan und Isolde (exc); *Verdi:* Rigoletto (exc); Rigoletto (exc); Rigoletto (exc). (O. Luppi, orch/E. Vitale, F. Chaliapin, La Scala Orch/C. Sabajno, F. Tamagno, anon, G. Mansueto, G. De Tura, chor, E. Bruno, E. Caruso, S. Cottone, A. Pinto, M. Sammarco, A. Magini-Coletti, G. Zenatello, R. Delle Ponti, R. Storchio, G. De Luca, T. Ruffo, G. Finzi-Magrini, C. Boninsegna, A. Pini-Corsi, E. Badini, L. Sobinov, A. Didur, R. Stracciari, E. Giraldoni, E. Petri, P. Amato, R. Grassi, E. Burzio, G. Anselmi, E. Mazzoleni, A. Paoli, B. De Muro, T. Poli-Randaccio, G. Russ, V. Guerrini, C. Galeffi, E. Ferrari-Fontana, H. Lázaro, G. Pareto)

Ⓓ **CHS7 64864-2(1)** (4/94)
La Scala Edition - Vol.2, 1915-46 (pt 1)
Rossini: Barbiere di Siviglia (exc); Barbiere di Siviglia (exc); Mosè in Egitto (exc); *Donizetti:* Don Pasquale (exc); *Boito:* Mefistofele (exc); *Donizetti:* Lucia di Lammermoor (exc); *Bellini:* Sonnambula (exc); *Verdi:* Rigoletto (exc); *Boito:* Nerone (exc); Nerone (exc); *Giordano:* Andrea Chénier (exc); *Humperdinck:* Hänsel und Gretel (exc); *Verdi:* Aida (exc); *Ponchielli:* Gioconda (exc); *Verdi:* Trovatore (exc); Trovatore (exc); *Puccini:* Madama Butterfly (exc); Turandot (exc); Turandot (exc); *Verdi:* Don Carlo (exc); *Donizetti:* Fille du Régiment (exc); *Verdi:* Trovatore (exc); Trovatore (exc); Traviata (exc); *Spontini:* Vestale (exc); *Donizetti:* Elisir d'amore (exc); Elisir d'amore (exc). (R. Stracciari, E. De Hidalgo, N. De Angelis, D. Borgioli, B. Gigli, E. Pinza, T. dal Monte, M. Fleta, M. Journet, A. Pertile, C. Supervia, I.M. Ferraris, G. Arangi-Lombardi, G. Cobelli, C. Muzio, B. Franci, G. Masini, R. Pampanini, M. Zamboni, A. Baracchi, E. Venturini, G. Nessi, T. Pasero, I. Minghini-Cattaneo, G. Dalla Rizza, S. Baccaloni, T. Schipa, La Scala Chor, La Scala Orch, chor, orch/G. Polacco/C. Sabajno/A. Albergoni/L. Molajoli/G. Santini/E. Panizza/A. Guarnieri)

Ⓓ **CHS7 64864-2(2)** (4/94)
La Scala Edition - Vol.2, 1915-46 (pt 2)
Rossini: Guillaume Tell (exc); *Verdi:* Rigoletto (exc); *Puccini:* Madama Butterfly (exc); *Giordano:* Andrea Chénier (exc); *Verdi:* Nabucco (exc); Trovatore (exc); *Ponchielli:* Gioconda (exc); *Massenet:* Werther (exc); *Puccini:* Manon Lescaut (exc); *Verdi:* Otello (exc); *Puccini:* Turandot (exc); Suor Angelica (exc); *Boito:* Mefistofele (exc); *Wolf-Ferrari:* Campiello (exc); *Mascagni:* Amico Fritz (exc); *Puccini:* Bohème (exc); *Verdi:* Macbeth (exc); *Puccini:* Bohème (exc); *Verdi:* Rigoletto (exc); Ballo in maschera (exc); *Giordano:* Fedora (exc); *Verdi:* Otello (exc); *Bellini:* Puritani (exc); *Verdi:* Falstaff (exc); Traviata (exc). (H. Spani, L. Pagliughi, G. Masini, B. Gigli, E. Stignani, G. Cigna, T. Schipa, A. Ziliani, F. Merli, G. Lauri-Volpi, A. Oltrabella, P. Tassinari, M. Favero, G. Lugo, A. Sved, L. Albanese, A. Poli, G. Malipiero, G. Bechi, T. Gobbi, M. Caniglia, M. Carosio, M. Stabile, G. Nessi, L. Donaggio, La Scala Chor, La Scala Orch, Rome Op Orch, orch, Philh/C. Sabajno/V. Veneziani/L. Ricci/L. Molajoli/F. Ghione/M. Cordone/G. Antonicelli/G. Marinuzzi/U. Berrettoni/T. Serafin/A. Erede/D. Olivieri/A. Toscanini)

Ⓓ **CHS7 64935-2** (4/94)
Wagner—Opera Excerpts
Wagner: Tannhäuser (exc); Lohengrin (exc); Walküre (exc); Götterdämmerung (exc); Götterdämmerung (exc); Fliegende Holländer (exc); Tristan und Isolde (exc); Meistersinger (exc); Parsifal (exc). (K. Flagstad, VPO, Philh, BPO/W. Furtwängler)

Ⓓ **CHS7 69741-2(1)** (4/92)
Record of Singing, Vol.4—Anglo-American School (pt 1)
Hook: Hours of Love; *Bizet:* Jolie fille de Perth (exc); *Puccini:* Rondine (exc); *Handel:* Atalanta (exc); *Villa-Lobos:* Serestas (exc); *G. Charpentier:* Louise (exc); *Hahn:* Études latines (exc); *Mozart:* Zauberflöte (exc); *Korngold:* Tote Stadt (exc); *Wagner:* Tannhäuser (exc); Lohengrin (exc); *Gluck:* Alceste (1776) (exc); *Saint-Saëns:* Samson et Dalila (exc); *Bizet:* Carmen (exc); *Wolf:* Mörike Lieder (exc); *Elgar:* Sea Pictures (exc); *Bach:* Mass in B minor, BWV232 (exc). (M. Ritchie, Philh/L. Collingwood, G. Catley, LSO/S. Robinson, D. Kirsten, RCA Victor Orch/J-P. Morel, F. Quartararo, E. Houston, P. Miguel, E. Steber/W. Susskind, M. Teyte, G. Moore, D. Maynor, Boston SO/S. Koussevitzky, J. Hammond, A. Varnay/G. Sébastian, H. Traubel, NYPSO/A. Rodzinski, R. Bampton, Victor SO/W. Pelletier, B. Thebom/W. Braithwaite, J. Tourel, F. Nielsen, G. Ripley/G. Weldon, K. Ferrier, Vienna SO/H. von Karajan)

Ⓓ **CHS7 69741-2(2)** (4/92)
Record of Singing, Vol.4—Anglo-American School (pt 2)
Monro: My lovely Celia; *Boughton:* Immortal Hour (exc); *Britten:* Folk Songs (exc); *Herbert:* Naughty Marietta (exc); *Mozart:* Don Giovanni (exc); *Vaughan Williams:* Hugh the Drover (exc); *Ponchielli:* Gioconda (exc); *Purcell:* King Richard II, Z581 (exc); *Peel:* In Summertime on Bredon; *Villa-Lobos:* Miniatures (exc); *Nin:* Villancicos (exc); *Wolf:* Goethe Lieder (exc); *Leoncavallo:* Pagliacci (exc); *Massenet:* Hérodiade (exc); *Handel:* Judas Maccabaeus (exc); *Mussorgsky:* Boris Godunov (exc); *Handel:* Scipione (exc). (D. Lloyd, Webster Booth, J. Cockerill, P. Pears, B. Britten, J. Peerce/A. Fistoulari, W. Midgley, ROHO/R. Goodall, J. Johnston/J. Robertson, R. Tucker, NY Met Op Orch/E. Cooper, A. Deller, B. Lam, T. Weil, R. Irwin, F. Fuller, H. Villa-Lobos, I. Gorin, A. Baller, M. Harrell, L. Warren, RCA Orch/R. Cellini, R. Merrill, N. Walker, orch, G. London, V. Pleasants, O. Natzke, H. Robinson Cleaver, Philh/L. Collingwood/J-P. Morel, G. Moore)

Ⓓ **CHS7 69741-2(3)** (4/92)
Record of Singing, Vol.4—French School
Dell' Acqua: Chanson Provençale; *Séverac:* Ma poupée chérie; *Mozart:* Dans un bois solitaire, K308; *Hahn:* Rossignol des lilas; *Fauré:* En prière; *Rimsky-Korsakov:* Songs, Op. 2 (exc); *Respighi:* Stornellatrice; *Anon:* Amor amaro; *Ravel:* Mélodies populaires grecques (exc); *Godard:* Vivandière (exc); *Saint-Saëns:* Samson et Dalila (exc); *Berlioz:* Troyens (exc); *Lipatti:* Sensation; Amoureuse; Pas; Capital de la douleur; *Massenet:* Werther (exc); *Duparc:* Invitation au voyage; *Gounod:* Mélodies (1855) (exc); *Bassani:* Posate, dormite; *Lalo:* Roi d'ys (exc). (M. Robin, orch/G. Briez, M. Angelici, M. Fauré, I. Joachim, L. Bergmann, G. Boué, A. Collard, G. Guillamat, V. Perlemuter, R. Doria, T. Janopoulo, V. de los Angeles, G. Moore, S. Danco, E. Bellinzona, I. Kolassi, S. Michel, Paris Opéra-Comique Orch/L. Fourestier, H. Bouvier, Paris Op Orch, R. Gorr, Philh/L. Collingwood, H. Cuénod, M. Lipatti, R. Jobin/A. Cluytens, P. Bernac, F. Poulenc, C. Maurane, L. Bienvenu, G. Souzay, J. Bonneau, S. Juyol)

Ⓓ **CHS7 69741-2(4)** (4/92)
Record of Singing, Vol.4—German School
Schubert: Schweizerlied, D559; Claudine von Villa Bella (exc); *Mozart:* Zauberflöte (exc); Nehmt meinen Dank, K383; *Beethoven:* Fidelio (exc); *Brahms:* Liebeslieder Walzer, Op. 52 (exc); *Wolf:* Mörike Lieder (exc); *Lehár:* Eva (exc); *Reger:* Schlichte Weisen, Op.76 (exc); *Tchaikovsky:* Queen of Spades (exc); *Verdi:* Aida (exc); *Puccini:* Tosca (exc); *R. Strauss:* Arabella (exc); *Menotti:* Consul (exc); *R. Strauss:* Lieder, Op. 27 (exc); *Wolf:* Goethe Lieder (exc); *Mozart:* Don Giovanni (exc); *R.*

Strauss: Capriccio (exc); *Mozart:* Zauberflöte (exc); *Schubert:* Schöne Müllerin (exc); *Weber:* Freischütz (exc); *Lortzing:* Undine (exc); *Schumann:* Liederkreis, Op.39 (exc); *Schubert:* Jüngling an der Quelle, D300; *Mozart:* Zauberflöte (exc); Così fan tutte (exc); *Beethoven:* Fidelio (exc); *Brahms:* Lieder, Op. 86 (exc); *Wagner:* Tannhäuser (exc); *Schubert:* Fahrt zum Hades, D526; *Mozart:* Zauberflöte (exc); *Pfitzner:* Lieder, Op.2 (exc); *Weber:* Freischütz (exc). (E. Schumann, G. Moore, E. Köth, Berlin St Op Orch/A. Rother, M. Stader, orch/H. Erisman, E. Schwarzkopf, Philh/A. Galliera, I. Seefried, H. von Nordberg, F. Wührer, M. Reining, VPO/F. Lehár, E. Grümmer, H. Diez, S. Jurinac/L. Collingwood, L. Welitsch/J. Krips, G. Brouwenstijn, Hilversum RO/P. Van Kempen, Leonie Rysanek/W. Schüchter, I. Borkh, H. Konetzni, E. Höngen, H. Zipper, H. Meyer-Welfing/R. Moralt, A. Dermota/K. Böhm, W. Ludwig/O. Ackermann, J. Patzak, M. Raucheisen, P. Anders, Berlin Deutsche Op Orch, R. Schock, D. Fischer-Dieskau, K. Schmitt-Walter, A. Stauch, E. Kunz, M. Rothmüller/J. Robertson, P. Schoeffler, Vienna St Op Chor, Vienna St Op Orch, H. Hotter, L. Weber/I. Dobroven, T. Herrmann, G. Frick, Berlin Deutsche Op Chor, Berlin SO, F. Beckmann, J. Herrmann, B. Seidler-Winkler/B. Seidler-Winkler)

Ⓓ **CHS7 69741-2(5)** (4/92)
Record of Singing, Vol.4—Scandinavian School
Purcell: Dido (exc); *Sibelius:* Songs, Op.37 (exc); *Dowland:* Second Booke of Songs (exc); *Cilea:* Adriana Lecouvreur (exc); *Bizet:* Pêcheurs de perles (exc); *Gounod:* Roméo et Juliette (exc); *Offenbach:* Contes d'Hoffmann (exc); *Wolf:* Goethe Lieder (exc); *Wagner:* Tannhäuser (exc); *Gounod:* Mors et vita (exc); *Debussy:* Chansons de Bilitis (exc). (K. Flagstad, Philh/W. Braithwaite, L. Lail, S-G. Andrén, A. Schiøtz, J.G. Schmidt, S. Islandi, Tivoli Concert Orch/S. Felumb, N. Gedda/A. Galliera, J. Björling, Stockholm Royal Op Orch/N. Grevillius, H. Hasslo, orch, B. Sönnerstedt, F. Jensen, J. Berglund/L. Blech, K. Borg, Exclusive Orch, G. Leppée, L. Demant)

Ⓓ **CHS7 69741-2(6)** (4/92)
Record of Singing, Vol.4—Russian & Slavonic Schools
Mussorgsky: Night; Khovanshchina (exc); *Offenbach:* Périchole (exc); *Tchaikovsky:* Songs, Op.6 (exc); *Mussorgsky:* Fair at Sorochintsï (exc); *Rimsky-Korsakov:* Snow Maiden (exc); *Verstovsky:* Askold's Grave (exc); *Nápravník:* Dubrovsky (exc); *Smetana:* Dalibor (exc); *Rimsky-Korsakov:* Sadko (exc); *Tchaikovsky:* Mazeppa (exc); *Verdi:* Nabucco (exc); *Borodin:* Sleeping Princess; *Tchaikovsky:* Songs, Op.47 (exc); *Rubinstein:* Persian Songs, Op.34 (exc); *Kodály:* Sadly rustle the leaves. (M. Predit, G. Moore, Z. Dolukhanova, orch, C. Novikova, N. Obukhova, M. Sakharov, G. Vinogradov, Bolshoi Th Orch/S. Samosud, I. Zhadan/A. Orlov, G. Nelepp, Moscow All-Union Rad Ch, Moscow All-Union RSO/V. Smirnov, I. Kozlovsky, B. Blachut, Prague Op Orch, J. Charvát, P. Lisitsian/N. Golovanov, A. Ivanov, B. Christoff, Rome Op Orch/V. Gui, M. Reizen, A. Coates, B. Gmyrya, L. Ostrin, E. Koréh, H. von Nordberg)

Ⓓ **CHS7 69741-2(7)** (4/92)
Record of Singing, Vol.4—Italian School
Donizetti: Elisir d'amore (exc); *Verdi:* Trovatore (exc); *A. Thomas:* Mignon (exc); *Falvo:* Dicitencello vuie; *Boito:* Mefistofele (exc); *Massenet:* Werther (exc); *Verdi:* Otello (exc); *Donizetti:* Favorita (exc); *Giordano:* Andrea Chénier (exc); *Tosti:* 'A Vucchella; *Puccini:* Tosca (exc); *Verdi:* Don Carlo (exc); *Bellini:* Sonnambula (exc); *Glinka:* Life for the Tsar (exc); *Mussorgsky:* Boris Godunov (exc); *Massenet:* Werther (exc); *Verdi:* Trovatore (exc); *Donizetti:* Favorita (exc); *Bizet:* Pêcheurs de perles (exc); *Puccini:* Turandot (exc); *Bellini:* Capuleti (exc); *A. Scarlatti:* Su venite e consiglio; *Respighi:* Nebbie; *Bellini:* Fervido desiderio; *Puccini:* Manon Lescaut (exc); *Verdi:* Don Carlo (exc); Trovatore (exc); *Rossini:* Armida (exc); *Puccini:* Bohème (exc). (Ferruccio Tagliavini, RCA Victor Orch/A. Dorati, B. Gigli, C. Elmo, orch/U. Berrettoni, G. di Stefano, La Scala Orch/E. Tieri, L. Infantino, RPO/A. Erede, G. Malipiero, G. Prandelli, Milan SO/A. Quadri, M. del Monaco, P. Silveri, LSO/W. Goehr, T. Gobbi, Rome Op Orch/O. de Fabritiis, G. Valdengo, Kingsway SO, G. Malaspina, ROH Chor, ROHO/M. Mudie, G. Bechi, R. Arié/J. Krips, N. Rossi-Lemeni, Philh/T. Benintende-Neglia, T. Pasero, G. Simionato, F. Barbieri, M. Caruso, E. Stignani, Rome Academy Orch/V. Bellezza, A. Noni, E. Arizmendi/J.E. Martini, M. Carosio/A. Fistoulari, M. László, L. Cortese, A. Anzellotti, G. Favaretto, G. Gatti, G. Moore, R. Tebaldi, SRO, M. Grandi, Z. Milanov/F. Weissmann, M. Callas, Rome RAI Orch/A. Simonetto, S. Scuderi)

Ⓓ **CMS5 65061-2(1)** (4/94)
The Fabulous Victoria de los Angeles (pt 1)
Ravel: Shéhérazade; Mélodies Populaires Grecques; Mélodies Hébraïques; *Duparc:* Invitation au voyage; Phidylé; *Debussy:* Enfant prodigue (exc); *Chausson:* Poème de l'amour et de la mer; *Montsalvatge:* Canciones Negras; *Granados:* Canciones Amatorias (exc); *Rodrigo:* Madrigales Amatorios (Cpte); *Esplá:* Canciones playeras; *Toldrá:* Cançons; *Traditional:* Dama d'Arago; Cant del ocells; Cançó de Sega; *Mompou:* Combat del Somni; *Rodrigo:* Tríptic de Mosén Cinto; *Debussy:* Chansons de Bilitis; Fêtes galantes I; Noël des enfants; *Ravel:* Chants populaires (exc); *Hahn:* Trois jours; Rossignol des Lilas; *Fauré:* Songs, Op.6 (exc); Songs, Op.8 (exc); Songs, Op.39 (exc); Poèmes d'un jour (exc); *Falla:* Canciones Populares Españolas. (V. de los Angeles, Paris Cons/G. Prêtre, Lamoureux Orch/J-P. Jacquillat/R. Frühbeck de Burgos/A. Ros-Marbà, Barcelona Patronato Orch, G. Soriano)

Ⓓ **CMS5 65061-2(2)** (4/94)
The Fabulous Victoria de los Angeles (pt 2)
Toldrá: Canciones Gallegas (exc); *Turina:* Tríptico, Op.45 (exc); *Rodrigo:* Villancicos (exc); *Falla:* Psyché; Soneto a Córdoba; *Sacrati:* Proserpina (exc); *A. Scarlatti:* Pirro e Demetrio (exc); *Handel:* Joshua (exc); *Schubert:* Tod und das Mädchen, D531; Schöne Müllerin (exc); An die Musik, D547; *Brahms:* Lieder, Op.59 (exc); Lieder, Op.84 (exc); *Fauré:* Songs, Op.27 (exc); Songs, Op.46 (exc); *Purcell:* Indian Queen, Z630 (exc); Lost is my quiet for ever, Z502; *Haydn:* Schlaf in deiner engen Kammer; *J.C. Bach:* Canzonette (exc); *Beethoven:* Irish Songs, WoO154 (exc); Irish Songs, WoO152 (exc); Welsh Songs, WoO155 (exc); *Schubert:* Nur wer die Sehnsucht kennt, D877/4; *Berlioz:* Trébuchet; *Dvořák:* Moravian Duets, B69 (exc); *Tchaikovsky:* Duets, Op.46 (exc); *Saint-Saëns:* Pastorale; *Fauré:* Pleurs d'or, Op.72; *Brahms:* Lieder, Op.94 (exc); *Mozart:* Partenza, K436. (V. de los Angeles, G. Soriano, A. Challan, French Stg Trio, J-C. Gérard, E. Schwarzkopf, D. Fischer-Dieskau, G. Moore)

Ⓓ **CMS5 65115-2** (7/95)
Britten—Chamber Works
Britten: String Quartet 1; String Quartet 2; String Quartet 3; String Quartet (1931); Rhapsody; Quartettino; Elegy; Phantasy in F minor; Oboe Phantasy; Divertimenti; Alla marcia. (Endellion Qt, G. Jackson, D. Boyd, N. Logie)

Ⓓ **CMS5 65119-2** (10/95)
Delius—Orchestral Works
Delius: Brigg Fair; Appalachia; In a Summer Garden; Hassan (exc); Song before Sunrise; Koanga (exc); First Cuckoo; Summer Night on the River; Late Swallows; Village Romeo and Juliet (exc); Irmelin Prelude; Song of Summer; Fennimore and Gerda Intermezzo. (R. Tear, A. Jenkins, Ambrosian Sngrs, Hallé, LSO/J. Barbirolli)

Ⓓ **CMS5 65212-2** (10/94)
Wagner—Les introuvables du Ring
Wagner: Rheingold (exc); Walküre (exc); Walküre (exc); Walküre (exc); Walküre (exc); Siegfried (exc); Götterdämmerung (exc); Götterdämmerung (exc); Götterdämmerung (exc); Götterdämmerung (exc); Götterdämmerung (exc). (L. Otto, M. Muszely, K. Flagstad, H. Dernesch, B. Nilsson, S. Wagner, J. Blatter, R. Siewert, H. Melchert, R. Schock, S. Svanholm, W. Cochran, B. Kusche, J. Metternich, D. Fischer-Dieskau, F. Frantz, H. Hotter, H. Sotin, G. Frick, Berlin Deutsche Op Chor, Berlin Deutsche Op Orch/F. Konwitschny, Berlin Staatskapelle/R. Kempe, Philh/K. Böhm/L. Ludwig/G. Sébastian/W. Sawallisch/W. Furtwängler/H. Weigert, New Philh/O. Klemperer, BRSO/R. Kubelík)

Ⓓ **CMS5 65459-2** (7/95)
Brahms—String Quartets
Brahms: String Quartet 1; String Quartet 2; String Quartet 3. (Britten Qt)

Ⓓ **CMS7 62542-2** (7/89)
Prokofiev—Piano Concertos, etc
Prokofiev: Piano Concerto 1; Piano Concerto 2; Piano Concerto 3; Piano Concerto 4; Piano Concerto 5; Overture, Op.34; Visions fugitives. (M. Béroff, Leipzig Gewandhaus/K. Masur, M. Portal, Parrenin Qt)

Ⓓ **CMS7 62548-2** (5/89)
Fauré—Chamber Works, Vol.2
Fauré: Piano Quartet 1; Piano Quartet 2; Piano Quintet 1; Piano Quintet 2; String Quartet. (J-P. Collard, A. Dumay, B. Pasquier, F. Lodéon, Parrenin Qt)

Ⓓ **CMS7 63015-2** (8/89)
Beethoven—Cello Sonatas, etc
Beethoven: Cello Sonata 1; Cello Sonata 2; Cello Sonata 3; Cello Sonata 4; Cello Sonata 5; Mozart Variations, Op.66; Mozart Variations, WoO46; Handel Variations, WoO45. (J. Du Pré, D. Barenboim)

Ⓓ **CMS7 63244-2** (2/90)
The Art of Maria Callas
Bellini: Norma (exc); Pirata (exc); Sonnambula (exc); Puritani (exc); *Cherubini:* Medea (exc); *Donizetti:* Anna Bolena (exc); Lucia di Lammermoor (exc); *Gluck:* Iphigénie en Tauride (exc); *Mascagni:* Cavalleria Rusticana (exc); *Ponchielli:* Gioconda (exc); *Puccini:* Madama Butterfly (exc); Tosca (exc); *Rossini:* Barbiere di Siviglia (exc); Turco in Italia (exc); *Spontini:* Vestale (exc); *Verdi:* Ballo in maschera (exc); Macbeth (exc); Traviata (exc); Trovatore (exc); Vespri Siciliani (exc). (M. Callas, M. Filippeschi, N. Rossi-Lemeni, La Scala Chor, La Scala Orch/T. Serafin, Philh/N. Rescigno/A. Votto, R. Panerai, M. Sinclair, J. Lanigan, D. Robertson, J. Rouleau, G. Sarri, R. Arié, MMF Chor, MMF Orch, Paris Cons/G. Prêtre, A.M. Canali, C. Forti, N. Gedda/H. von Karajan/V. de Sabata, E. Ticozzi, G. di Stefano, F. Calabrese/G. Gavazzeni, Alfredo Kraus, P. de Palma, Lisbon San Carlos Nat Th Chor, Lisbon San Carlos Nat Th Orch/F. Ghione)

Ⓓ **CMS7 63272-2** (4/90)
Mozart: Late Symphonies
Mozart: Symphony 25; Symphony 29; Symphony 31; Symphony 33; Symphony 34; Symphony 35; Symphony 36; Symphony 38; Symphony 39; Symphony 40; Symphony 41. (Philh, New Philh/O. Klemperer)

Ⓓ **CMS7 63310-2** (1/90)
Beethoven: Complete Symphonies
Beethoven: Symphony 1; Symphony 2; Symphony 3; Symphony 4; Symphony 5; Symphony 6; Symphony 7; Symphony 8; Symphony 9; Coriolan; Egmont (exc). (E. Schwarzkopf, E. Höngen, E. Haefliger, O. Edelmann, Vienna Singverein, Philh/H. von Karajan)

Ⓓ **CMS7 63360-2** (3/90)
Beethoven: Complete Piano Concertos
Beethoven: Piano Concerto 1; Piano Concerto 2; Piano Concerto 3; Piano Concerto 4; Piano Concerto 5; Choral Fantasia. (D. Barenboim, John Alldis Ch, New Philh/O. Klemperer)

Ⓓ **CMS7 63386-2** (6/90)
Borodin—Prince Igor & Complete Solo Songs
Borodin: Prince Igor (Cpte); Those folk; Song of the dark forest; From my tears; Sea princess; Pretty girl no longer loves me; Magic Garden; Arabian melody; Fishermaiden; Listen to my song; Sleeping princess; Pride; Sea; Why art thou so early, dawn?; My songs are poisoned; False note; For the shores. (C. Chekerliski, J. Wiener, T. Todorov, B. Christoff, R. Penkova, L. Mihailov, A. Milkovsky, K. Dulguerov, B. Christoff, M. Tortelier, A. Tcherepnin, J. Reiss, Lamoureux Orch/G. Tzipine, Sofia National Op Chor, Sofia National Op Orch/J. Semkow)

Ⓓ **CMS7 63522-2** (12/91)
Tippett—Chamber & Orchestral Works
Tippett: Concerto for Double String Orch; Piano Sonata 1; Piano Sonata 2; String Quartet 1; Piano Concerto; Corelli Fantasia. (J. Ogdon, Philh/Colin Davis, Edinburgh Qt, Moscow CO/R. Barshai, Bath Fest Orch/M. Tippett)

Ⓓ **CMS7 63559-2** (9/90)
Schubert: Song-Cycles & Lieder
Schubert: Schöne Müllerin (Cpte); Winterreise (Cpte); Schwanengesang, D957 (exc); Schwanengesang, D957 (exc); Schwanengesang, D957 (exc); Schwanengesang, D957 (exc); Erlkönig, D328; Nacht und Träume, D827; Du bist die Ruh', D776. (D. Fischer-Dieskau, G. Moore)

Ⓓ **CMS7 63563-2** (9/90)
Wolf—Mörike & Michelangelo Lieder
Wolf: Mörike Lieder (exc); Sechs Gedichte (exc); Michelangelo Gedichte (Cpte). (D. Fischer-Dieskau, G. Moore)

Ⓓ **CMS7 63566-2** (9/90)
Schubert—Lieder
Schubert: Lachen und Weinen, D777; Dass sie hier gewesen, D775; Sei mir gegrüsst, D741; Du bist die Ruh', D776; Im Walde, D708; Seligkeit, D433; Heidenröslein, D257; Ständchen, D889; Fischers Liebesglück, D933; Fischerweise, D881; Jüngling an der Quelle, D300; An die Laute, D905; Forelle, D550; Auf der Riesenkoppe, D611; An die Entfernte, D765; Auf dem Wasser zu singen, D774; Schiffer, D536; Wanderer, D649; Nachtgesang, D314; Zügenglöcklein, D871; Jüngling und der Tod, D545; Heimweh, D456; Lied im Grünen, D917; Tod und das Mädchen, D531; Winterabend, D938; Zürnende Barde, D785; Strom, D565; Litanei, D343; Alinde, D904; Nähe des Geliebten, D162; Normans Gesang, D846; Lied des gefangenen Jägers, D843; Greisengesang, D778; Nachtstück, D672; Götter Griechenlands, D677; Fischer, D225; Bürgschaft, D246. (D. Fischer-Dieskau, G. Moore, K. Engel)

Ⓓ **CMS7 63613-2** (12/90)
Schumann—Symphonies, etc
Schumann: Symphony 1; Symphony 2; Symphony 3; Symphony 4; Szenen aus Goethes Faust (exc). (Philh, New Philh/O. Klemperer)

Ⓓ **CMS7 63835-2** (10/91)
Bruckner, Wagner & Hindemith—Orchestral Works
Bruckner: Symphony 8; *Wagner:* Walküre (exc); *Hindemith:* Nobilissima Visione. (N. Bailey, New Philh, Philh/O. Klemperer)

Concerto 3; Piano Concerto 4; Piano Concerto 5; Piano Concerto 6; Piano Concerto 8; Piano Concerto 9; Piano Concerto 11; Piano Concerto 12; Piano Concerto 13; Piano Concerto 14; Piano Concerto 15; Piano Concerto 16; Piano Concerto 17; Piano Concerto 18; Piano Concerto 19; Piano Concerto 20; Piano Concerto 21; Piano Concerto 22; Piano Concerto 23; Piano Concerto 24; Piano Concerto 25; Piano Concerto 26; Piano Concerto 27; Rondo, K382. (D. Barenboim (pf/dir), ECO)

ⓘ **CZS7 62863-2** (10/90)
Beethoven—Piano Sonatas
Beethoven: Piano Sonata 1; Piano Sonata 2; Piano Sonata 3; Piano Sonata 4; Piano Sonata 5; Piano Sonata 6; Piano Sonata 7; Piano Sonata 8; Piano Sonata 9; Piano Sonata 10; Piano Sonata 11; Piano Sonata 12; Piano Sonata 13; Piano Sonata 14; Piano Sonata 15; Piano Sonata 16; Piano Sonata 17; Piano Sonata 18; Piano Sonata 19; Piano Sonata 20; Piano Sonata 21; Piano Sonata 22; Piano Sonata 23; Piano Sonata 24; Piano Sonata 25; Piano Sonata 26; Piano Sonata 27; Piano Sonata 28; Piano Sonata 29; Piano Sonata 30; Piano Sonata 31; Piano Sonata 32. (D. Barenboim)

ⓘ **CZS7 62935-2** (3/91)
Bruckner—Symphonies
Bruckner: Symphony 1; Symphony 2; Symphony 3; Symphony 4; Symphony 5; Symphony 6; Symphony 7; Symphony 8; Symphony 9. (Staatskapelle Dresden/E. Jochum)

ⓘ **CZS7 67123-2** (2/91)
Wagner: Der Ring des Nibelungen
Wagner: Rheingold (Cpte); Walküre (Cpte); Siegfried (Cpte); Götterdämmerung (Cpte). (F. Frantz, I. Malaniuk, W. Windgassen, G. Neidlinger, J. Patzak, J. Greindl, G. Frick, A. Poell, L. Fehenberger, E. Grümmer, R. Siewert, S. Jurinac, M. Gabory, H. Rössl-Majdan, W. Windgassen, H. Konetzni, M. Mödl, E. Cavelti, G. Frick, J. Hellwig, M. Gabory, G. Scheyrer, D. Schmedes, O. Bennings, I. Malaniuk, E. Cavelti, H. Rössl-Majdan, L. Suthaus, A. Pernerstorfer, F. Frantz, J. Greindl, R. Streich, M. Klose, J. Greindl, M. Klose, A. Poell, S. Jurinac, H. Rössl-Majdan, Rome RAI Chor, Rome RAI Orch/W. Furtwängler)

ⓘ **CZS7 67294-2** (4/92)
Mozart—Piano Sonatas
Mozart: Piano Sonata, K279; Piano Sonata, K280; Piano Sonata, K281; Piano Sonata, K282; Piano Sonata, K283; Piano Sonata, K284; Piano Sonata, K309; Piano Sonata, K310; Piano Sonata, K311; Piano Sonata, K330; Piano Sonata, K331; Piano Sonata, K332; Piano Sonata, K333; Fantasia, K475; Piano Sonata, K457; Piano Sonata, K533; Piano Sonata, K545; Piano Sonata, K570; Piano Sonata, K576. (D. Barenboim)

ⓘ **CZS7 67306-2** (10/91)
Mozart—Works featuring Wind Instruments
Mozart: Sinfonia Concertante, K297b; Flute Concerto, K313; Andante, K315; Oboe Concerto, K314; Serenade, K361. (P. Graeme, T. King, I. James, M. Gatt, M. Debost, M. Bourgue, ECO, Paris Orch/D. Barenboim)

ⓘ **CZS7 67310-2** (11/91)
Menuhin plays Popular Violin Concertos
Bach: Violin Concerto; Mozart: Violin Concerto, K216; Violin Concerto, K219; Beethoven: Violin Concerto; Mendelssohn: Violin Concerto, Op. 64; Brahms: Violin Concerto; Bruch: Violin Concerto 1. (Y. Menuhin (vn/dir), C. Ferras, Bath Fest Orch, Y. Menuhin, VPO/C. Silvestri, Philh/K. Kurtz, BPO/R. Kempe/W. Susskind)

ⓘ **CZS7 67314-2** (9/91)
Tchaikovsky—Symphonies
Tchaikovsky: Symphony 1; Symphony 2; Symphony 3; Symphony 4; Symphony 5; Symphony 6; Romeo and Juliet. (Philh, New Philh/R. Muti)

ⓘ **CZS7 67359-2** (6/92)
Cortot plays Chopin
Chopin: Berceuse; Polish Songs (exc); Etudes (exc); Impromptus (exc); Impromptus (exc); Etudes (exc); Waltzes (exc); Berceuse; Ballades (exc); Preludes (exc); Piano Sonata 3; Preludes (exc); Nocturnes (exc); Piano Sonata 2; Polonaises (exc); Ballades; Fantasie, Op.49; Tarantelle; Barcarolle; Etudes (exc); Etudes (exc); Waltzes (exc); Piano Concerto 2; Impromptus (exc); Waltzes (exc); Preludes; Etudes (exc); Liszt: Chants polonais, S480 (exc); Chopin: Nocturnes (exc); Nocturnes (exc); Nocturnes (exc); Etudes (exc); Preludes (exc). (A. Cortot, orch/J. Barbirolli)

ⓘ **CZS7 67379-2** (1/92)
Beethoven Edition - Arrau
Beethoven: Piano Concerto 1; Piano Concerto 2; Piano Concerto 3; Piano Concerto 4; Piano Concerto 5; Variations, WoO80; Piano Sonata 14; Piano Sonata 18; Piano Sonata 21; Piano Sonata 22; Piano Sonata 23;

Piano Sonata 26; Piano Sonata 28; Piano Sonata 31; Piano Sonata 32. (C. Arrau, Philh/A. Galliera)

ⓘ **CZS7 67400-2** (6/92)
Messiaen plays Messiaen
Messiaen: Banquet céleste; Diptyque; Apparition de l'église éternelle; Ascension; Nativité du Seigneur; Corps glorieux; Messe de la Pentecôte; Livre d'orgue. (O. Messiaen)

ⓘ **CZS7 67435-2** (9/92)
Rodrigo—Orchestral Works
Rodrigo: Concierto serenata; Concierto pastoral; Concierto heróico; Concierto madrigal; Concierto de estío; Concierto de Aranjuez; Fantasia; Concierto andaluz; Concierto en modo galante; Per la flor del lliri blau; Música para un jardín; A la busca del más allá; Zarabanda lejana y villancico; Piezas infantiles; Soleriana (exc). (L. Hansen, A.L. Ara, R. Cohen, A. Moreno, D. Mariotti, M. Garibay, C. López, J. Ruiz, N. Allen, J.F. Osorio, RPO, LSO, Mexico St SO/E. Bátiz)

ⓘ **CZS7 67474-2** (7/92)
Viva España!
Chabrier: España; Albéniz: Iberia (exc); Ravel: Rapsodie espagnole; Turina: Danzas fantásticas; Rodrigo: Concierto de Aranjuez; Falla: Vida breve (exc); Amor brujo (Cpte); Nights in the Gardens of Spain; Sombrero de tres picos (exc). (Paris Cons/P. Dervaux/R. Frühbeck de Burgos/A. Cluytens, Spanish Nat Orch, A. Diaz, G. Soriano, Philh/A. Vandemoot/C.M. Giulini, O. Dominguez)

ⓘ **CZS7 67515-2** (5/93)
Offenbach—Operetta highlights
Offenbach: Vie parisienne (exc); Belle Hélène (exc); Orphée aux enfers (exc). (M. Roux, M. Hamel, W. Clément, L. Dachary, N. Renaux, L. Berton, D. Dassy, C. Devos, Duvaleix, B. Demigny, G. Rey, A. Doniat, C. Collart, A. Grandjean, H. Prudon, F. Betti, Raymond St Paul Chor, Lamoureux Orch/J. Gressier)

ⓘ **CZS7 67521-2** (8/93)
Schumann—Concertos
Schumann: Piano Concerto; Introduction and Allegro, Op.92; Violin Concerto; Cello Concerto; Konzertstück, Op.86. (D. Barenboim, G. Kremer, P. Tortelier, G. Seifert, N. Hauptmann, K. Köhler, M. Klier, Philh, LPO, BPO, RPO/R. Muti/K. Tennstedt/D. Fischer-Dieskau/Y.P. Tortelier)

ⓘ **CZS7 67564-2** (6/93)
Mozart—Symphonies
Mozart: Symphony 28; Symphony 29; Symphony 30; Symphony 40; Symphony 41. (ASMF/N. Marriner)

ⓘ **CZS7 67723-2** (9/93)
Carlo Maria Giulini—A Profile
Ravel: Alborada del gracioso; Daphnis et Chloé Suites (exc); Britten: Sea interludes, Op. 33a; Young Person's Guide; Tchaikovsky: Symphony 2; Schumann: Manfred (exc); Franck: Psyché (exc); Symphony. (Philh/C.M. Giulini)

ⓘ **CZS7 67726-2** (9/93)
Paul Kletzki—A Profile
Glinka: Jota Aragonesa; Rimsky-Korsakov: Tale of Tsar Saltan (exc); Tchaikovsky: Andante cantabile, Op.11; Sibelius: Symphony 2; Schubert: Rosamunde (exc); Mahler: Symphony 4; Symphony 5 (exc). (E. Loose, Philh, RPO/P. Kletzki)

ⓘ **CZS7 67729-2** (9/93)
Efrem Kurtz - A profile
Rimsky-Korsakov: Snow Maiden (exc); Golden Cockerel Suite (exc); Liadov: Kikimora, Op.63; Shostakovich: Symphony 1; Khachaturian: Masquerade (exc); Glinka: Life for the Tsar (exc); Rimsky-Korsakov: Dubinushka; Liadov: Baba-Yaga, Op.56; Enchanted Lake, Op.62; Musical Snuff-box, Op.32; Kabalevsky: Comedians; Prokofiev: Symphony 1. (Philh, RPO/E. Kurtz)

ⓘ **CZS7 67732-2** (9/93)
Leonid Kogan - A profile
Brahms: Violin Concerto; Lalo: Symphonie espagnole; Tchaikovsky: Sérénade mélancolique; Beethoven: Violin Concerto; Tchaikovsky: Violin Concerto. (L. Kogan, Philh/K. Kondrashin, Paris Cons/C. Silvestri)

ⓘ **CZS7 67767-2** (9/93)
Solomon—A Profile
Beethoven: Piano Concerto 1; Piano Concerto 3; Grieg: Piano Concerto; Schumann: Piano Concerto; Beethoven: Piano Sonata 27. (Solomon, Philh/H. Menges)

ⓘ **CZS7 67819-2** (5/94)
Brahms/Schumann—Requiems
Brahms: Deutsches Requiem, Op.45 (Cpte); Schumann: Requiem, Op.148; Requiem für Mignon, Op.98b. (J. Norman, H. Donath, B. Lindner, A. Andonian, D. Soffel, M. Georg, M. Weichhold, N. Gedda, J. Hynninen, D. Fischer-

Dieskau, LP Ch, BBC Sym Chor, Düsseldorf Musikverein, LPO/K. Tennstedt, Düsseldorf SO/B. Klee)

ⓘ **ZDMF7 64830-2** (5/94)
The Art of Nathan Milstein
Glazunov: Violin Concerto; Prokofiev: Violin Concerto 2; Saint-Saëns: Violin Concerto 3; Tchaikovsky: Violin Concerto; Brahms: Violin Concerto; Beethoven: Violin Concerto; Dvořák: Violin Concerto; Vivaldi: Concerti Grossi, Op.3 (exc); Sonatas, Op.2 (exc); Handel: Violin Sonatas (exc); Flute Sonatas (exc); T.A. Vitali: Ciacona; Corelli: Sonatas, Op.5 (exc); Tartini: Devil's Trill Sonata; Bach: Suites, BWV1066-9 (exc); Mozart: Violin Sonata, K296; Violin Sonata, K304; Beethoven: Violin Sonata 5; Prokofiev: Violin Sonata 2; Rachmaninov: Vocalise; Mussorgsky: Fair at Sorochíntsí (exc); Glazunov: Meditation, Op.32; Tchaikovsky: Valse-Scherzo, Op.34; Souvenir d'un lieu cher, Op.42 (exc); Rimsky-Korsakov: Russian Fantasia; Tale of Tsar Saltan (exc); Brahms: Hungarian Dances (exc); Massenet: Thaïs (exc); Gluck: Orfeo ed Euridice (exc); Chopin: Nocturnes (exc); Falla: Canciones populares españolas (exc); Wieniawski: Scherzo-Tarantelle, Op.16; Debussy: Préludes (exc); Sarasate: Introduction and Tarantella, Op.43; Kreisler: Pugnani Praeludium and Allegro. (N. Milstein, Pittsburgh SO/W. Steinberg, New Philh/R. Frühbeck de Burgos, Philh/A. Fistoulari/E. Leinsdorf, E. Morini, H. Shapiro, CO, L. Pommers, A. Balsam, R. Firkušný, orch/R. Irving, N. Milstein (vn/dir))

EMI Eminence

ⓘ **CD-EMX2123** (2/90)
Maria Callas sings Operatic Arias
Rossini: Barbiere di Siviglia (exc); Verdi: Macbeth (exc); Don Carlo (exc); Puccini: Tosca (exc); Gluck: Alceste (1776) (exc); Bizet: Carmen (exc); Saint-Saëns: Samson et Dalila (exc); Massenet: Manon (exc); G. Charpentier: Louise (exc). (M. Callas, N. Gedda, R. Duclos Ch, Philh, Paris Cons, FRNO, Paris Op Orch/A. Galliera/N. Rescigno/G. Prêtre)

ⓘ **CD-EMX2152** (12/89)
Tchaikovsky: Orchestral Works
Tchaikovsky: 1812; Romeo and Juliet; Marche slave; Francesca da Rimini. (RLPO/S. Edwards)

ⓘ **CD-EMX2165** (2/91)
Orchestral Works for Young People
Britten: Young Person's Guide; Ravel: Ma Mère l'oye (exc); Prokofiev: Peter and the Wolf. (W. Rushton, LPO/S. Edwards)

ⓘ **CD-EMX2179** (12/91)
Vaughan Williams—Orchestral Works
Vaughan Williams: Oboe Concerto; Partita; Tallis Fantasia; Greensleeves Fantasia; English Folk Song Suite. (J. Small, RLPO/V. Handley)

ⓘ **CD-EMX2185** (3/92)
Delius—Orchestral Works
Delius: Paris; Double Concerto; Cello Concerto. (R. Wallfisch, T. Little, RLPO/C. Mackerras)

ⓘ **CD-EMX2198** (12/91)
A Delius Festival
Delius: Songs of Farewell; Late Swallows; Song before Sunrise; To be sung of a Summer Night; Village Romeo and Juliet (exc); Cynara; Margot la Rouge (exc); Wanderer's Song; Koanga (exc). (R. Tear, J. Shirley-Quirk, RCS, Baccholian Sngrs, King's College Ch, Hallé, RLPO, RPO, Philh M. Sargent/J. Barbirolli/P. Ledger/M. Davies/E. Groves/G. Weldon)

ⓘ **CD-EMX2210** (9/93)
Vivaldi—Concertos
Vivaldi: Concerto, RV463; Concerto, RV156; Concerto, RV537; Concerti, Op.11 (exc); Concerto, RV129; Concerti, Op.10 (exc); Concerti Grossi, Op.3 (exc). (Hanover Band/A. Halstead)

ⓘ **CD-EMX2218** (3/94)
Bach—Organ Works, Vol.1
Bach: Toccata and Fugue, BWV565; Herzlich tut mich verlangen, BWV727; Fugue, BWV577; Erbarm' dich, BWV721; Fugue, BWV579; Prelude and Fugue, BWV541; Pastorale, BWV590; Clavier-Übung III, BWV669-689 (exc); Orgel-Büchlein, BWV599-644 (exc); Passacaglia and Fugue, BWV582. (P. Hurford)

ⓘ **CD-EMX2221** (6/94)
Pärt—Chamber Works
Pärt: Fratres; Cantus in memory of Benjamin Britten; Summa; Spiegel im Spiegel; Festina lente; Tabula rasa. (T. Little, M. Roscoe, Bournemouth Sinfonietta, R. Studt (vn/dir))

ⓘ **CD-EMX2224** (8/94)
Schubert—Recital
Schubert: Einsame, D800; Ständchen, D889; An Silvia,

D891; Jüngling an der Quelle, D300; Lied eines Schiffers an die Dioskuren, D360; Gruppe aus dem Tartarus, D583; Götter Griechenlands, D677; Im Walde, D708; Wanderer an den Mond, D870; Freiwilliges Versinken, D700; Himmelsfunken, D651; Prometheus, D674; Gondelfahrer, D808; Sterne, D939; Auf der Bruck, D853; Heidenröslein, D257; Im Haine, D738; Nachtviolen, D752; Bei dir allein, D866/2; Du bist die Ruh', D776. (S. Keenlyside, M. Martineau)

℗ **CD-EMX2226** (12/94)
Bach—Organ Works, Vol 2
Bach: Concertos, BWV592-7 (exc); Vater unser im Himmelreich, BWV737; Aria, BWV587; Tag, der ist, BWV719; Trio Sonatas, BWV525-530 (exc); Chorales, BWV651-668 (exc); Liebster Jesu, BWV731; Valet will ich dir geben, BWV735; Nun freut euch, BWV734; Toccata, Adagio and Fugue, BWV564. (P. Hurford)

℗ **CD-EMX2227** (12/94)
Holst—Orchestral Works
Holst: St Paul's Suite; Fugal Concerto; Brook Green Suite; Somerset Rhapsody; Perfect Fool (exc). (J. Snowden, D. Theodore, ECO/Y. Menuhin)

℗ **CD-EMX2229** (3/95)
Elgar—Chamber Works
Elgar: String Quartet; Canto popolare; Piano Quintet. (P. Lane, Vellinger Qt, J. Boyd)

℗ **CD-EMX2231** (3/95)
Britten—Orchestral Works
Britten: Gloriana Suite; Sea Interludes, Op. 33a; Pas de Six Suite. (RLPO/T. Yuasa)

℗ **CD-EMX2232** (3/95)
Dvořák—Orchestral Works
Dvořák: Romance, Op.11; Legends; Nocturne. (S. Gonley, ECO/C. Mackerras)

℗ **CD-EMX2237** (12/95)
Rachmaninov/Scriabin—Piano Works
Rachmaninov: Preludes (exc); Etudes-tableaux, Op.39 (exc); Moments musicaux, Op.16 (exc); Morceaux de fantaisie, Op.3 (exc); *Scriabin:* Preludes, Op.11 (exc). (A. Gavrilov)

℗ **CD-EMX2238** (8/95)
R. Strauss—Orchestral Works
R. Strauss: Horn Concerto 1; Horn Concerto 2; Duet Concertino; Serenade, Op.7. (J. Farrall, J. Andrews, D. Pyatt, Britten Sinf/N. Cleobury)

℗ **CD-EMX2239** (11/95)
Vaughan Williams/Delius—Piano Concertos
Delius: Piano Concerto; *Finzi:* Eclogue; *Vaughan Williams:* Piano Concerto. (P. Lane, RLPO/V. Handley)

℗ **CD-EMX2244** (9/95)
French Violin Sonatas
Debussy: Violin Sonata; *Poulenc:* Violin Sonata; *Ravel:* Violin Sonata (1923-27); Tzigane. (T. Little, P. Lane)

℗ **CD-EMX9502** (10/87)
Debussy: Orchestral Works
Debussy: La mer; Après-midi; Jeux (Cpte). (LPO/S. Baudo)

℗ **CD-EMX9503** (10/87)
Elgar—Orchestral Works
Elgar: Enigma Variations; Introduction and Allegro; Serenade. (LPO/V. Handley)

℗ **CD-EMX9508** (10/87)
Vaughan Williams—Orchestral Works
Vaughan Williams: Lark ascending; Dives and Lazarus Variants; Wasps (Cpte). (D. Nolan, LPO/V. Handley)

℗ **CDBOX-VW1** (1/95)
Vaughan Williams—Symphonies Nos 1-9, etc
Vaughan Williams: Symphony 1; Symphony 2; Symphony 3; Symphony 4; Symphony 5; Symphony 6; Symphony 7; Symphony 8; Symphony 9; Flos campi; Serenade to Music. (A. Barlow, A. Hargan, J. Rodgers, W. Shimell, C. Balmer, Liverpool Phil Ch, RLPO/V. Handley)

EMI Laser

℗ **CDZ110** (1/89)
Best-Loved Piano Classics
Chopin: Fantaisie-impromptu; *Brahms:* Waltzes, Op.39 (exc); *Mozart:* Piano Sonata, K331 (exc); *Beethoven:* Menuet, WoO10/2; *Schumann:* Kinderszenen (exc); *Liszt:* Concert Studies, S144 (exc); *Chopin:* Etudes (exc); *Dvořák:* Humoresques, Op.101 (exc); *MacDowell:* Woodland Sketches (exc); *Chaminade:* Etudes de concert, Op. 35 (exc); *Beethoven:* Bagatelles (exc); *Debussy:* Suite bergamasque (exc); Children's Corner (exc); *Rachmaninov:* Preludes (exc); *Rubinstein:* Melodies, Op.3 (exc); *Granados:* Goyescas (exc); *Falla:* Amor brujo (exc); *Albéniz:* España, Op. 165 (exc). (M. Lympany)

℗ **CDZ111** (1/92)
Best Loved Piano Classics Volume 2
Bach: Cantata 147 (exc); *Daquin:* Premier livre de pièces de clavecin (exc); *Handel:* Keyboard Suites Set I (exc); *Beethoven:* Piano Sonata 14 (exc); Rondo a capriccio, Op. 129; *Debussy:* Images (exc); Préludes (exc); *Chopin:* Waltzes (exc); Mazurkas (exc); *Albéniz:* España, Op. 165 (exc); *Ravel:* Jeux d'eau; *Paderewski:* Humoresques de concert, Op. 14 (exc); *Schumann:* Waldszenen (exc); *Satie:* Gymnopédies (exc); *Scriabin:* Etudes, Op. 8 (exc). (M. Lympany)

℗ **CDZ114** (1/89)
Best of Baroque
Albinoni: Adagio; *Bach:* Suites, BWV1066-9 (exc); *Gluck:* Orfeo ed Euridice (exc); *Handel:* Messiah (exc); Berenice (exc); *Bach:* 2-Violin Concerto; *Handel:* Solomon (exc); *Pachelbel:* Canon and Gigue (exc); *Handel:* Serse (exc); Water Music Suite. (RLPO/C. Groves, Scottish CO/K. Montgomery, Y. Menuhin (vn/dir), C. Ferras, Y. Menuhin (vn/dir), C. Ferras, Festival CO, ASMF/N. Marriner, R. Kilbey Stgs/R. Kilbey, RPO/G. Weldon)

℗ **CDZ7 67004-2** (6/91)
Mozart—Violin Concertos
Mozart: Violin Concerto, K207; Violin Concerto, K216; Violin Concerto, K219. (Y. Menuhin (vn/dir), Bath Fest Orch)

℗ **CDZ7 67005-2** (6/91)
Mozart—Violin Concertos, etc
Mozart: Violin Concerto, K211; Violin Concerto, K218; Sinfonia Concertante, K364. (R. Barshai, Bath Fest orch, Y. Menuhin (vn/dir))

℗ **CDZ7 67011-2** (7/91)
Mozart: Symphonies
Mozart: Symphony 31; Symphony 39; Symphony 40. (ECO/D. Barenboim)

℗ **CDZ7 67015-2** (7/91)
Mozart—Opera Arias
Mozart: Nozze di Figaro (exc); Nozze di Figaro (exc); Nozze di Figaro (exc); Entführung (exc); Entführung (exc); Don Giovanni (exc); Don Giovanni (exc); Don Giovanni (exc); Così fan tutte (exc); Così fan tutte (exc); Così fan tutte (exc); Zauberflöte (exc); Zauberflöte (exc); Zauberflöte (exc). (C. Desderi, LPO/B. Haitink, M. Price, VPO/R. Muti, F. Cossotto, Philh/C.M. Giulini, A. Moffo, A. Rothenberger/J. Krips, I. Hollweg, RPO/T. Beecham, G. Frick, R. Soyer, H. Donath, G. Bumbry, T. Allen, N. Gedda, New Philh/O. Klemperer, M. Ewing, M. Marshall, A. Baltsa, J. Van Dam, C. Vaness, F. Araiza, G. Taddei/K. Böhm, W. Berry, Bavarian St Op Orch/W. Sawallisch, S. Jerusalem, BRSO, L. Popp)

L'Empreinte Digitale

℗ **ED13036** (12/95)
Fulbert de Chartres—Cantor of the Year 1000
Anon: Stirps Jesse a 1; Stirps Jesse - organum; Stirps Jesse a 3 - Flos filius; Stirps Jesse - double organum; Stirps Jesse a 4 - Eius; Stirps Jesse a 4 - Flos filius; Chorus nove; Benedicamus Domino a 1; Benedicamus Domino - Stirps Jesse; Antiphons and Responses; Deus, Pater piissime; Aurea personet lyra; Alleluia dies sanctificatus; Solem justitie a 1; Solem justitie - organum; Solem justitie a 3 - Solem; Solem justitie a 3 - Cernere; Ad nutum Domini. (Venance Fortunat Ens/A-M. Deschamps)

English Recording Company

℗ **ERC5001** (6/92)
English String Music
Holst: St Paul's Suite; *Elgar:* Serenade; Introduction and Allegro; *Warlock:* Capriol Suite; Serenade for strings. (Britannia CO/D. Falkowski)

EPM Classical Collector

℗ **150 032** (10/91)
The Romantic Violin
Lalo: Symphonie espagnole; *Tchaikovsky:* Violin Concerto; *Sarasate:* Carmen Fantasy; Danzas españolas (exc); *Bruch:* Kol Nidrei; *Chopin:* Waltzes (exc). (B. Huberman, VPO/G. Szell, Berlin St Op Orch/W. Steinberg, S. Schultze)

℗ **150 052** (5/91)
Germaine Lubin—Opera & Song Recital
Weber: Freischütz (exc); *Wagner:* Lohengrin (exc); Tannhäuser (exc); Tristan und Isolde (exc); Walküre (exc); Siegfried (exc); Götterdämmerung (exc); *Schubert:* Erlkönig, D328; *Schumann:* Myrthen, Op. 25 (exc); *Debussy:* Promenoir des deux amants (exc); *Wolf:* Spanisches Liederbuch (exc); Mörike Lieder (exc); *Schumann:* Lieder und Gesänge, Op. 51 (exc); *Chopin:*

Etudes (exc); *Durante:* Vergin, tutto amor. (G. Lubin, orch, anon/H. Defosse, J. Krieger, E.I. Kahn, R. Verdière)

℗ **150 122** (9/93)
Milhaud—Historic Recordings 1928-1948
Milhaud: Choéphores (exc); Printemps I; Poèmes juifs (exc); *Satie:* Mélodies (1916); *Milhaud:* Homme et son désir; Soirées de Pétrograd (exc); Boeuf sur le toit; Poèmes de Jean Cocteau; Saudades do Brasil (exc); Euménides (exc); Création du Monde; Salade (exc); Chants hébraïques; Enlèvement d'Europe; Abandon d'Ariane; Délivrance de Thésée; Songes; Piano Concerto 1; Saudades do Brasil (exc); Automne (exc); Amours de Ronsard (exc); Concertino de printemps; Suite provençale; Fête de la musique; Scaramouche. (D. Milhaud, J. Bathori, Desormière Ens/D. Milhaud, R. Bénédetti, J. Wiener, M. Singher, J. Planel, G. Petit, A. Valencin, M. Brega, J. Hazart, Pro Musica Ens, Paris SO, M. Long, FRNO, orch, R. Mahé, E. Schenneberg, C. Rouquetty, P. Froumenty, Y. Astruc/R. Desormière, E. Fels, R. Gourgues, J. Claverie, M. Meyer, E. Chastenet/L. de Vocht, Antwerp Caecilia Chorale, Antwerp Concerts Orch, C. Croiza)

Erato

℗ **2292-45012-2** (8/90)
Couperin—Sacred Choral Works
Couperin: Leçons de ténèbres; Magnificat anima mea; Victoria Christo resurgenti. (M. van der Sluis, G. Laurens, P. Monteilhet, M. Muller, L. Boulay)

℗ **2292-45030-2** (10/90)
Xenakis—Choral Works
Xenakis: Khoai; Naama; Komboï; Ile de Gorée. (E. Chojnacka, S. Gualda, Xenakis Ens/H. Kerstens)

℗ **2292-45202-2** (12/84)
M-A. Charpentier: Sacred Works
M-A. Charpentier: Te Deum, H146; Laudate Dominum, H223; Magnificat, H79. (B. Degelin, L. Jansen, J. Nirouët, J. Caals, K. Widmer, Ghent Madrigal Ch, Ghent Cantabile, Musica Polyphonica/L. Devos)

℗ **2292-45219-2** (7/85)
Sacred Choral Works
D. Scarlatti: Stabat mater; *Cavalli:* Salve Regina; *Gesualdo:* Sacrarum canticorum (5vv) (exc); *Clemens non Papa:* O Maria vernans rosa. (Monteverdi Ch, EBS/J.E. Gardiner)

℗ **2292-45242-2** (12/86)
Honegger—Orchestral Music
Honegger: Symphony 1; Symphonic Movements; Pastorale d'été. (BRSO/C. Dutoit)

℗ **2292-45368-2** (10/88)
Chausson: Songs
Chausson: Mélodies, Op. 2 (exc); Poème de l'amour et de la mer; Chanson perpétuelle, Op. 37. (J. Norman, M. Dalberto, L. Anderson, R. Patterson, S. Sansalone, J-P. Pigerre, Monte Carlo PO/A. Jordan)

℗ **2292-45417-2** (4/90)
Lieder with Orchestra
Mahler: Kindertotenlieder; *Wagner:* Wesendonk Lieder; *Wolf:* Mörike Lieder (exc). (W. Meier, Paris Orch/D. Barenboim)

℗ **2292-45431-2** (4/90)
Mozart—Symphonies
Mozart: Symphony 25; Symphony 29; Symphony 33. (Amsterdam Baroque Orch/T. Koopman)

℗ **2292-45466-2** (11/90)
Carissimi—Oratorios
Carissimi: Jonas; Jephte; Judicium Extremum. (S. Varcoe, His Majesties Sagbutts and Cornetts, Monteverdi Ch, EBS, M. Tucker, N. Robson, R. Holton/J.E. Gardiner, S.H. Jones)

℗ **2292-45481-2** (7/90)
Falla—Piano Works
Falla: Fantasía bética; Homenaje Debussy; Pièces espagnoles; Sombrero de tres picos; Amor brujo; Homenaje Dukas; Vals-capricho; Serenata andaluza; Nocturno. (J-F. Heisser)

℗ **2292-45493-2** (10/90)
Boulez: Orchestral Works
Boulez: Rituel in memoriam Maderna; Messagesquisse; Notations (exc). (Paris Orch/D. Barenboim)

℗ **2292-45494-2** (12/90)
Boulez—Cantatas and Orchestral Works
Boulez: Visage nuptial; Soleil des eaux; Figures, Doubles, Prismes. (P. Bryn-Julson, E. Laurence, BBC Sngrs, BBC SO/P. Boulez)

℗ **2292-45499-2** (9/92)
Martinů—Orchestral Works
Martinů: Double Concerto; Quartet Concerto; Ricercari. (J-

Pièces de clavecin (exc); *Pozzoli*: Etude; Deep River; *Ibert*: Pièces (exc); *Grandjany*: Automne; *Debussy*: Valse romantique; Préludes (exc); *Bochsa*: Etude; *Tansman*: Pour les enfants; *Saint-Saëns*: Fantaisie, Op. 95; *Matielli*: Adagio; *Fauré*: Impromptu, Op. 86. (L. Laskine)

ⓓ **4509-92132-2** (12/93)
The Magic of the Mandolin
Vivaldi: Concerto, RV532; Concerto, RV425; Concerto, RV93; *Paisiello*: Mandolin Concerto in E flat; Mandolin Concerto in C; *Caudioso*: Mandolin Concerto. (U. Orlandi, D. Frati, B. Bianchi, Solisti Veneti/C. Scimone)

ⓓ **4509-92135-2** (12/93)
The Magic of the Harpsichord
Galuppi: Andantino; *Couperin*: Livre de clavecin II (exc); Livre de clavecin III (exc); *Rameau*: Pièces de clavecin (exc); *D. Scarlatti*: Keyboard Sonatas (exc); *Bach*: French Suites, BWV812-17 (exc); *Cimarosa*: Keyboard Sonata in G minor; Keyboard Sonata in A minor; *Handel*: Keyboard Suites Set I (exc). (R. Veyron-Lacroix)

ⓓ **4509-92137-2** (8/93)
Varese—Orchestral Works, Vol. 1
Varèse: Amériques; Offrandes; Hyperprism; Octandre; Arcana. (P. Bryn-Julson, FNO/K. Nagano)

ⓓ **4509-92403-2** (10/94)
Chopin—Piano Works
Chopin: Preludes; Impromptus; Fantaisie-Impromptu; Polonaises (exc); Ballades; Piano Sonata 2; Piano Sonata 3. (F-R. Duchâble)

ⓓ **4509-92406-2** (1/92)
Liszt—Concertos
Liszt: Piano Concerto 1; Piano Concerto 2; Hungarian Fantasia, S123. (F-R. Duchâble, LPO/J. Conlon)

ⓓ **4509-92857-2** (12/93)
Satie—Piano Works
Satie: Avant-dernières pensées; Caresse; Chapitres Tournés en tous sens; Gymnopédies; Jack-in-the-box; Pieces (1906-13); Préludes Flasques; Rêveries nocturnes; Sonatine bureaucratique; Sports et divertissements. (M. Legrand)

ⓓ **4509-92864-2** (12/93)
Bach—Piano Concertos
Bach: Harpsichord Concerto, BWV1052; Harpsichord Concerto, BWV1055; Harpsichord Concerto, BWV1056. (M-J. Pires, Lisbon Gulbenkian Orch/M. Corboz)

ⓓ **4509-92867-2** (12/93)
Debussy—Orchestral Works
Debussy: Après-midi; La Mer; Nocturnes; Première rapsodie. (Rhine Op Chor, Strasbourg PO/A. Lombard, Monte Carlo Op Orch/A. Jordan)

ⓓ **4509-92871-2** (8/94)
Franck—Orchestral Works
Franck: Symphony; Symphonic Variations; Prélude, Choral et Fugue. (P. Devoyon, P. Entremont, FRNO/J. Martinon)

ⓓ **4509-92874-2** (12/93)
An American Christmas
Traditional: Zion rise; Rejoice, ye shining worlds on high; *Anon*: Who is this that comes from afar; In those days came John the Baptist; *Traditional*: Hark! hark! what news the angels bring; Virgin most pure; Virgin unspotted; Methinks I see an heav'nly host; *Anon*: Heavenly Courtier; *Traditional*: Pretty Home; *Anon*: Midnight Cry; *Traditional*: Wayfaring Stranger; Slow Traveller; I wonder as I wander; Coventry Carol; Lovely Vine; O come, all ye Faithful; Still Water; While Shepherds watched; Shepherds, rejoice; *Anon*: Fulfilment; *Traditional*: Hush! my dear; Jesus the Light of the World; Joy to the world. (Boston Camerata/J. Cohen)

ⓓ **4509-92875-2** (1/94)
Vienna - Operetta Arias
Heuberger: Opernball (exc); *Kálmán*: Gräfin Mariza (exc); *Lehár*: Frasquita (exc); Lustige Witwe (exc); Paganini (exc); Schön ist die Welt (exc); Zarewitsch (exc); *O. Straus*: Tapfere Soldat (exc); *J. Strauss II*: Fledermaus (exc); Wiener Blut (exc); *Stolz*: Favorit (exc); Venus im Seide (exc). (J. Migenes, Vienna Volksoper Orch/L. Schifrin)

ⓓ **4509-94808-2** (8/94)
Rimsky-Korsakov—Orchestral Works
Rimsky-Korsakov: Capriccio Espagnol; Russian Easter Festival Ov; Tsar's Bride (exc); May Night (exc); Golden Cockerel Suite (exc). (Bolshoi SO/A. Lazarev)

ⓓ **4509-94817-2** (11/94)
Brahms—Orchestral Works
Brahms: Symphony 1; Symphony 2; Symphony 3; Symphony 4; Academic Festival Overture; Haydn Variations; Tragic Overture. (Chicago SO/D. Barenboim)

ⓓ **4509-94825-2** (11/94)
Ventadorn—Le Fou sur le Pont (Troubadour Songs)
Bernart de Ventadorn: Can vei la lauzta mover; Non es meravilla s'eu chan; Pos me pregatz seignor; Tant ai mo cor ple de joya; Lanquan vei la foilla; Bel m'es can eu vei la brolha; En Cossirer en en esmai; Era.m cosselhatz, senhor; *Amics Bernart de Ventadorn*; Per melhs cobrir lo mal pes; Can l'erba fresch'el folha par; Lo gens temps de pascor; Cantarai d'aqueszt trobadors. (Camerata Mediterranea/J. Cohen)

ⓓ **4509-94830-2** (11/94)
The Unicorn—Medieval French Songs
P. de Thaon: Serena en mer hante; *Anon*: En mai au douz tens nouvel; *M. de France*: Issi avint qu'un cers; D'un gupil; Danse de gupil; *Anon*: Ensement com la panthere; *P. de Thaon*: Monosceros; *T. de Champagne*: Aussi come unicorne sui; *G. de Coincy*: Saint Leochade Cycle; *Anon*: Au renouvel; Belle Doette; *M. de Paris*: Je chevauchoie l'autrier. (A. Azéma, C. A. Fulton, S. Kammen, J. Lepkoff)

ⓓ **4509-95307-2** (8/94)
Schubert/Schumann—Sacred Choral Works
Schubert: Mass, D950; *Schumann*: Requiem für Mignon, Op. 98b; Mass, Op. 147. (A. Michael, B. Balleys, L. Bizimeche-Eisinger, E. Silveira, S. Teiseira, A. Baldin, C. Homberger, M. Schäfer, M. Brodard, Round Chbr Ch, Lausanne Pro Arte Ch, Lisbon Gulbenkian Chor, SRO, Lisbon Gulbenkian Orch/A. Jordan/M. Corboz)

ⓓ **4509-95359-2** (8/94)
Bach/Vivaldi—Cello Sonatas
Bach: Viola da gamba Sonatas, BWV1027-9; *Vivaldi*: Cello Sonata, RV40; Cello Sonata, RV41; Cello Sonata, RV43; Cello Sonata, RV45; Cello Sonata, RV46; Cello Sonata, RV47. (P. Tortelier, R. Veyron-Lacroix)

ⓓ **4509-95361-2** (8/94)
Mozart—Wind Concertos
Mozart: Flute and Harp Concerto, K299; Flute Concerto, K313; Andante, K315; Clarinet Concerto, K622; Oboe Concerto, K314; Bassoon Concerto, K191. (L. Laskine, J-P. Rampal, J. Lancelot, P. Pierlot, P. Hongne, J-F Paillard CO/J-F. Paillard, Vienna SO, Bamberg SO/T. Guschlbauer, ECO/J-P. Rampal)

ⓓ **4509-95362-2** (8/94)
Mozart—Sacred Choral Works
Mozart: Mass, K317; Vespers, K321; Exsultate jubilate, K165; Vespers, K339; Ave verum corpus, K618; Mass, K220; Misericordias Domini, K222. (P. Wise, R. Hansmann, M. Bürgener, A. Bartelloni, M. Cousins, M. Sénéchal, H.K. Ecker, R. Soyer, Lisbon Gulbenkian Chor, M-C. Alain, O. Alain, Lisbon Gulbenkian Orch, P. Caillard Chorale, Vienna Baroque Ens/T. Guschlbauer)

ⓓ **4509-95789-2** (2/95)
Zarzuelas-The Passion of Spain
Guerrero y Torres: Huésped del Sevillano (exc); *Soriano*: Guitarrico (exc); *Penella*: Gato Montés (exc); *Vives*: Bohemios (exc); *Barbieri*: Barberillo de Lavapiés (exc); *Giménez*: Barbero de Sevilla (exc); *Vert*: Leyenda del beso (exc); *Calleja*: Emigrantes (exc); *Sorozábal*: Tabernera del Puerto (exc); *Caballero*: Dúo de la Africana (exc); *Serrano*: Trust de los Tenorios (exc). (J. Carreras, I. Rey, ECO/E. Ricci)

ⓓ **4509-96222-2** (12/94)
Messiaen—Piano Works
Messiaen: Virgil regards; Petites esquisses d'oiseaux; Préludes; Etudes de rythme. (Y. Loriod)

ⓓ **4509-96371-2** (7/95)
Gardiner—The Purcell Collection
Purcell: King Arthur, Z628 (Cpte); Indian Queen, Z630 (Cpte); Birthday Ode, Z323; Funeral Sentences; St Cecilia's Day Ode, Z328; Tempest, Z631 (Cpte); Timon of Athens, Z632 (Cpte); Dioclesian, Z627 (exc). (J. Smith, G. Fisher, E. Priday, G. Ross, A. Stafford, P. Elliott, S. Varcoe, Monteverdi Ch, EBS/J.E.Gardiner, M. Hill, J. Elwes, R. Hardy, D. Thomas, D. Harris, F. Lott, C. Brett, J. Williams, T. Allen, Monteverdi Orch, Equale Brass, B. Gordon, C. Hall, R. Earle, L. Dawson, R. Covey-Crump, M. George)

ⓓ **4509-96382-2** (8/95)
Vivaldi—Sinfonias and Concertos for Strings
Vivaldi: Sinfonia, RV146; Concerto, RV134; Concerto, RV152; Sinfonia, RV140; Concerto, RV114; Concerto, RV120; Concerto, RV163; Concerto, RV157; Sinfonia, RV168; Concerto, RV151; Concerto, RV167; Concerto, RV133; Concerto, RV158; Concerto, RV128; Sinfonia, RV132; Sinfonia, RV116; Concerto, RV143; Concerto, RV118; Sinfonia, RV137. (Solisti Veneti/C. Scimone)

ⓓ **4509-96386-2** (7/95)
American Piano Music
Barber: Ballade; *Beach*: Improvisations, Op. 148;

Bernstein: Anniversaries (1949/51); *Cage*: Bacchanale (1940); *Copland*: Piano Blues; *Gershwin*: Preludes; *Gottschalk*: Manchega; Banjo; *Gould*: Boogie Woogie Etude; *Joplin*: Entertainer; Maple leaf Rag; *MacDowell*: New England Idyls; *Nancarrow*: Prelude. (M. Legrand)

ⓓ **4509-96952-2** (3/95)
Duruflé—Requiem; Organ Works
Duruflé: Requiem; Suite, Op 5 (exc); Prélude, Adagio et choral varié, Op. 4. (H, Bouvier, X. Depraz, P. Caillard Chorale, S. Caillat Chorale, M-M. Duruflé-Chevalier, Lamoureux Concerts Orch/M. Duruflé, M. Duruflé)

ⓓ **4509-96953-2** (3/95)
Fauré—Chamber Works
Fauré: Piano Quintet 1; Piano Quintet 2; String Quartet; Piano Quartet 1; Piano Quartet 2; Piano Trio. (J. Hubeau, Via Nova Qt, R. Gallois-Montbrun, C. Lequien, A. Navarra)

ⓓ **4509-96961-2** (3/95)
Schubert—Stabat Mater; Offertorium; Magnificat
Schubert: Stabat Mater, D383; Magnificat, D486; Offertorium, D963. (S. Armstrong, H. Schaer, A. Ramirez, P. Huttenlocher, Lausanne Voc Ens, Lausanne CO/M. Corboz)

ⓓ **4509-96967-2** (8/95)
Rameau—Les Grands Motets
Rameau: Deus noster refugium; In convertendo; Quam dilecta. (S. Daneman, N. Rime, P. Agnew, N. Rivenq, N. Cavallier, Arts Florissants Chor, Arts Florissants Orch/W. Christie)

ⓓ **4509-97239-2** (6/95)
Virtuoso Arias
Rossini: Barbiere di Siviglia (exc); *Bellini*: Sonnambula (exc); *Delibes*: Lakmé (exc); *Verdi*: Rigoletto (exc); *Meyerbeer*: Dinorah (exc); *Donizetti*: Lucia di Lammermoor (exc); *R. Strauss*: Ariadne auf Naxos (exc); *Bernstein*: Candide (1956) (exc); *Yoon*: Barley Field; *Mozart*: Zauberflöte (exc). (S. Jo, Monte Carlo PO/P. Olmi, Paris Orch Ens/A. Jordan)

ⓓ **4509-97407-2** (5/95)
Bach—Cantatas
Bach: Cantata 8; Cantata 26; Cantata 43; Cantata 61; Cantata 85; Cantata 130; Cantata 182. (F. Sailer, I. Reichelt, C. Hellmann, H. Töpper, H. Krebs, J. Stämpfli, E. Wenk, F. Kelch, Heilbronn Schütz Ch, Pforzheim CO, South-West German CO/F. Werner)

ⓓ **4509-98474-2** (5/95)
Brahms—Piano Works
Brahms: Handel Variations; Ballades; Rhapsodies, Op. 79. (A. Lubimov)

ⓓ **4509-98480-2** (11/95)
Lamentations - Holy Week in Provence
Bouzignac: Unus ex vobis; Ha, plange, filia Jerusalem; *Carpentras*: Vexilla regis; *Gilles*: Lamentations; *Anon*: Lent (exc); *Ceppede*: Mais qui vous meut; *Vitré*: Comme trois forgerons; *Godolin*: Sur l'arbre de la Crotz. (A. Azéma, A. Azéma, F. Jodry, W. Hite, C. Kale, D. McCabe, P. Guttry, Boston Schola Cantorum, Boston Camerata/J. Cohen)

ⓓ **4509-98492-2** (9/95)
Schumann—Lieder
Schumann: Gesänge, Op. 142 (exc); Lieder und Gesänge, Op. 127 (exc); Romanzen und Balladen, Op. 45 (exc); Liederkreis, Op. 24 (Cpte); Dichterliebe, Op. 48 (Cpte); Myrthen, Op. 25 (exc); Spanisches Liederspiel, Op. 74 (exc); Liederkreis, Op. 39 (exc); Liederkreis, Op. 39 (exc). (D. Fischer-Dieskau, H. Höll)

ⓓ **4509-98493-2** (9/95)
Schubert—Lieder Recital
Schubert: An Schwager Kronos, D369; Hoffnung, D295; Auf der Donau, D553; Strom, D565; Wanderer, D565; Götter Griechenlands, D677; Freiwilliges Versinken, D700; Zwerg, D771; Wehmut, D772; Totengräbers Heimweh, D842; Auf der Bruck, D853; Sängers Habe, D832; Am Fenster, D878; Fischerweise, D881; Zügenglöcklein, D871; Kreuzzug, D932; Fischers Liebesglück, D933; Sterne, D939; Einsame, D800; Im Abendrot, D799; Schwanengesang, D957 (exc). (D. Fischer-Dieskau, H. Höll)

ⓓ **4509-98525-2** (6/95)
Bach—Cantatas
Bach: Cantata 6; Cantata 31; Cantata 67; Cantata 76; Cantata 80; Cantata 87. (I. Reichelt, H. Töpper, H. Krebs, F. Kelch, Heilbronn H Schütz Chor, Pforzheim CO/F. Werner)

ⓓ **4509-98526-2** (8/95)
Duruflé—Vocal & Organ Works
Duruflé: Mass, Op. 11; Motets, Op. 10; Danses, Op. 6; Scherzo, Op. 2; Prélude et Fugue sur le nom d'Alain, Op.

7. (R. Soyer, M-M. Duruflé-Chevalier, Stéphane Caillat Chorale, ORTF Nat Orch/M. Duruflé)

① **4509-98536-2** (9/95)
Bach—Complete Cantatas, Volume 1
Bach: Cantata 21; Cantata 131; Cantata 106; Cantata 196; Cantata 71; Cantata 150; Cantata 31; Cantata 185; Cantata 4. (B. Schlick, K. Wessel, G. de Mey, K. Mertens, Amsterdam Baroque Ch, Amsterdam Baroque Orch/T. Koopman)

Etcetera

① **KTC1012** (11/89)
Bartók: Piano Works
Bartók: Hungarian Peasant Songs, Sz71; Dirges, Sz45; Allegro barbaro; Sz249; Bagatelles, Sz38. (R. Hagopian)

① **KTC1019** (12/88)
American Piano Music
Copland: Piano Pieces; *V. Thomson:* Sentimental Tangos; Portraits (1983) (exc); *Bowles:* Preludes; Latin-American Pieces; *Barber:* Ballade; *Bernstein:* Touches; *Ramey:* Piano Fantasy. (B. Lerner)

① **KTC1021** (5/89)
Music for a Summer's Day
Pierné: Variations, libres et finale, op. 51; *Debussy:* Sonata for flute, viola and harp; *Ravel:* Sonatine; *Roussel:* Sérénade. (Netherlands Harp Ens)

① **KTC1023** (10/92)
Piazzolla—Tangos and Milongas
Piazzolla: Muerte del Angel; Guitar Pieces; Contrabajeando; Jacinto Chiciana; Milonga del Angel; Retrato de Alfredo Gobbi; Milonga en ay Menor; Otoño Porteño. (J. Oraison)

① **KTC1025** (1/89)
Sor: Guitar Works
Sor: Variations, Op. 40; Airs, Op. 19; Calme, Op. 50; Guitar Sonata, Op. 25. (L. Eisenhardt)

① **KTC1028** (7/85)
R. Strauss: Lieder
R. Strauss: Lieder, Op.10; Lieder, Op.27; Lieder, Op.22; Lieder, Op.29. (R. Alexander, T. Crone)

① **KTC1029** (7/90)
Yvonne Kenny at the Wigmore Hall
Schubert: Frühlingsglaube, D686; Wehmut, D772; Ganymed, D544; *R. Strauss:* Lieder, Op.48 (exc); Lieder, Op.41 (exc); Lieder, Op.68 (exc); *Poulenc:* Fiançailles pour rire (Cpte); *Rodrigo:* Madrigales amatorios (Cpte); *Copland:* Old American Songs 1 (exc); Old American Songs 2 (exc); *Traditional:* I know where I'm going. (Y. Kenny, L. Skrobacs)

① **KTC1030** (7/89)
Dowland: Songs and Lute Works
Dowland: First Booke of Songs (exc); Second Booke of Songs (exc); Third and Last Booke of Songs (exc); Pilgrimes Solace (exc); In darknesse let mee dwell; Pavans (exc); Lachrimae (exc); Jigs, Corantos, Toys, etc (exc); Almains (exc). (A. Dalton, Y. Imamura)

① **KTC1031** (9/90)
Byrd: Sacred Choral Works
Byrd: Mass for four voices; Gradualia 1/ii: Corpus Christi (exc); Ave verum corpus; Gradualia 2: Pentecost (exc); Gradualia 1/i: Feast of All Saints (exc); Prevent us, O Lord; Come to me, grief for ever; Retire, my soul; Come help, o God. (Quink)

① **KTC1035** (3/87)
Mozart: Lieder
Mozart: An Chloe, K524; Lied der Trennung, K519; Dans un bois solitaire, K308; Oiseaux, si tous les ans, K307; Sei du mein Trost, K391; Alte, K517; Veilchen, K476; Abendempfindung, K523; Zauberer, K472; Als Luise die Briefe, K520; Traumbild, K530; Ah, spiegarti, o Dio, K178; Moto di gioia, K579; Ridente la calma, K152; Im Frühlingsanfang, K597; Zufriedenheit, K473; Verschweigung, K518. (R. Alexander, G. Wilson)

① **KTC1036** (12/89)
American piano music
R. Harris: American Ballads; *Bowles:* Dance; Cross-Country; Sonatina (1932/5); *Copland:* Moods; Sonnet II; Petit portrait; *Blitzstein:* Guests (exc); *Barber:* Love Song; *Ramey:* Canzona; *Schuman:* Voyage; *Copland:* Sentimental Melody. (B. Lerner)

① **KTC1037** (2/87)
Bernstein: Songs
Bernstein: I hate music; Bonne cuisine (exc); Two Love Songs; So pretty; Piccola Serenata; Silhouette; Mass (exc); Pennsylvania Avenue (exc); Candide (1982) (exc); Peter Pan (exc). (R. Alexander, T. Crone)

① **KTC1038** (9/86)
Violin and piano recital
Franck: Violin Sonata; *Prokofiev:* Violin Sonata 2; *Ysaÿe:* Violin Sonatas, Op.27 (exc); *Paganini:* God save the King Variations; *Bach:* Solo Violin Partitas and Sonatas (exc). (R. Ricci, M. Argerich)

① **KTC1040** (10/87)
Ravel orchestrations
Ravel: Ma mère l'oye (Cpte); *Debussy:* Pour le piano (exc); Tarantelle styrienne; *Schumann:* Carnaval (exc); *Chabrier:* Pièces pittoresques (exc). (European CO Per Musica/J. Reynolds)

① **KTC1041** (5/90)
Nelly Miricioiu—Recital
Duparc: Invitation au voyage; Soupir; Chanson triste; *Granados:* Tonadillas (exc); *Respighi:* Notturno; Pioggia; Ma come potrei; Ultima ebbrezza; Invito alla danza; *Proch:* Air and Variations; *Puccini:* Rondine (exc); Tosca (exc); *Catalani:* Wally (exc). (N. Miricioiu, D. Harper)

① **KTC1042** (7/87)
Korngold piano sonatas
Korngold: Piano Sonata 1; Piano Sonata 2; Piano Sonata 3. (M. Verschoor)

① **KTC1044** (8/89)
German Lieder Recital
Zemlinsky: Maeterlinck Songs; *Schreker:* Funf Gesänge; Lieder, Op. 4; *Marx:* Lieder und Gesänge (exc); Lieder und Gesänge (exc). (D. Dorow, M. Damerini)

① **KTC1045** (7/88)
Menotti: Chamber and Vocal Works
Menotti: Notturno; Canti della lontananza; English Songs; Cantilena e Scherzo. (K. Armstrong, H. Francesch, H. Storck, A. Lutz, M. Salevic, S. Blaumer, K. Kühr)

① **KTC1046** (6/87)
Songs by Britten
Britten: Birthday Hansel; Charm of Lullabies; Folk Songs (exc); Folk Songs (exc). (Y. Kenny, C. Watkinson, T. Crone)

① **KTC1048** (4/88)
Debussy: Mélodies, Vol.2
Debussy: Jane; Caprice; Rondeau; Aimons-nous et dormons; Fille aux cheveux de lin; En sourdine; Poèmes de Banville (Cpte); Proses lyriques (Cpte); Poèmes de Stéphane Mallarmé (Cpte). (A-M. Rodde, N. Lee)

① **KTC1049** (12/87)
Sweet as Bardic Harp-Songs with Harp
Anon: Sleeps the noon in the deep blue sky; *Traditional:* Rannoch Herding Song; Greensleeves (Oh who is fair); Brian Boru's March; *Anon:* Spinning Wheel; *Traditional:* All through the night; *Anon:* Love for Wales; Longing; Queen's Dream; Gentle dove; *Traditional:* David of the White Rock; Counting the goats; *Anon:* Kishmul cradle croon; *Ellis:* Sunset Song; *Gwynn Williams:* Morning Light; Flower maiden; *T. Moore:* Irish Melodies (exc). (R. A. Morgan, R. A. Morgan)

① **KTC1050** (5/88)
Puccini: Songs and Rare Pieces
Puccini: Terra e mare; Storiella d'amore; È l'uccellino; Morire?; Inno a Diana; Menti all'avviso; Salve Regina; Sole e amore; Avanti Urania!; Piccolo tango; Foglio d'album; String Quartet; Crisantemi; Minuets; Scherzo. (R. Alexander, T. Crone, Raphael Qt)

① **KTC1051** (12/88)
Berg. Schoenberg. Webern. Songs
Webern: Lieder (1901-04); *Berg:* Schliesse mir die Augen beide; Early songs; An Leukon; Songs, Op. 2; *Schoenberg:* Cabaret songs. (D. Dorow, R. Jansen, T. Crone, R. de Reede, P. Masseurs, W. Goudswaard)

① **KTC1052** (4/88)
Birtwistle: Orchestral Works
Birtwistle: Carmen Perpetuum; Silbery Air; Secret Theatre. (London Sinfonietta/E. Howarth)

① **KTC1053** (7/88)
Donatoni: Chamber and Vocal Works
Donatoni: Spiri; Fili; De Près; Etwas ruhiger im Ausdruck; Refrain. (D. Dorow, Nieuw Ens/E. Spanjaard)

① **KTC1054** (11/88)
Ravel. Music for Piano, Four Hands
Ravel: Ma mère l'oye; Rapsodie espagnole; Boléro; Fanfare. (W. Jordans, L. Van Doeselaar)

① **KTC1055** (9/88)
Barber. Works
Barber: Songs, Op. 2 (Cpte); Songs, Op. 10 (Cpte); Songs, Op. 13 (Cpte); Songs, Op. 18 (Cpte); Nuvoletta, Op. 25 (Cpte); Hermit Songs, Op. 29 (Cpte); Despite and Still, Op. 41 (Cpte). (R. Alexander, T. Crone)

① **KTC1056** (1/90)
Italian Airs and Harpsichord Works
Caccini: Nuove musiche (1602) (exc); Nuove musiche (1614) (exc); *Picchi:* Toccata; Intavolatura di Balli (exc); *Monteverdi:* Salve, o Regina; *Frescobaldi:* Arie musicali Bk 1 (exc); Arie musicali Bk 2 (exc); Secondo libro di Toccate (exc); *B. Storace:* Passamezzo (exc). (M. van Egmond, C. Farr)

① **KTC1058** (12/88)
Grieg: Piano Works
Grieg: Lyric Pieces, Op.12 (exc); Lyric Pieces, Op.43 (exc); Lyric Pieces, Op.54 (exc); Lyric Pieces, Op.65 (exc); Lyric Pieces, Op.71 (exc); Song Transcriptions, Op.52 (exc); Ballade, Op.24; Holberg Suite. (H. Antoni)

① **KTC1059** (10/88)
Prokofiev. Cello Music
Prokofiev: Cello Sonata, Op. 119; Adagio, Op. 97b; Ballade, Op. 15; Music for Children (exc); Stone Flower (exc); Tale of the Buffoon (exc). (D. Ferschtman, R. Brautigam)

① **KTC1061** (1/89)
Exposition Paris, 1937
Auric: Seine au Matin; *Delannoy:* Diner sur l'Eau; *Ibert:* Espiègle au village de Lilliput; *Milhaud:* Tour de l'Exposition; *Poulenc:* Bourrée au pavillon d'Auvergne; *Sauguet:* Nuit coloniale; *Schmitt:* Retardée; *Tailleferre:* Pavillon d'Alsace; *A. Tcherepnin:* Autour des montagnes russes; *Martinů:* Train hauté; *Mompou:* Souvenirs de l'exposition; *Rieti:* Danseuse aux lions; *Honegger:* Scenic Railway; *Halffter:* Espagnolade; *Tansman:* Géant; *Mihalovici:* Danseur roumain; *Harsányi:* Tourbillon mécanique. (B. Lerner)

① **KTC1063** (12/89)
Delius & Gurney: Songs
Delius: Norwegian Songs (1889-90) (exc); Norwegian Songs (1888) (exc); Norwegian Songs (1889-90) (exc); *Gurney:* Fields are full; Severn meadows; Desire in spring; Singer; Epitaph; Folly of being comforted; Bread and cherries; All night under the moon; Down by the Salley Gardens; Snow; Cloths of Heaven; Brown is my love. (I. Partridge, J. Partridge)

① **KTC1064** (3/89)
Baroque Opera Arias
Purcell: Dido (exc); *Handel:* Serse (exc); Rodelinda (exc); Ariodante (exc); Rinaldo (exc); Hercules (exc); *Gluck:* Orfeo ed Euridice (exc). (C. Watkinson, Amsterdam Bach Sols/J.W. de Vriend)

① **KTC1066** (5/89)
Carter—String Quartets
Carter: String Quartet 2; String Quartet 3; Elegy (1946). (Arditti Qt)

① **KTC1068** (8/89)
Charles Ives: Songs, Vol. 2
Ives: Circus Band; Night Song; Old Flame; Night of Frost in May; Ich Grolle Nicht; Feldeinsamkeit; Alte Mutter; Weil' auf mir; Ilmenau; Rosamunde II; Qu'il m'irait bien; Elégie; Chanson de Florian; Children's Hour; Harpalus; There is a lane; Mirage; Farewell to Land; Evidence; Camp Meeting; Watchman; His exaltation; At the River; from 'Paracelsus'; Remembrance; At Sea; Ann Street; They are There. (R. Alexander, T. Crone)

① **KTC1069** (8/89)
Vivaldi: Cantatas
Vivaldi: Alla caccia, RV670; Perfidissimo cor, RV674; Sorge vermiglia, RV667; Care selve, RV671; Pianti, sospiri, RV676; Qual per ignoto, RV677. (D.L. Ragin, V. de Hoog, C. Farr)

① **KTC1070** (5/90)
Ferneyhough: Various Works
Ferneyhough: Chûte d'Icare; Superscriptio; Intermedio alla ciaccona; Etudes transcendantales; Mnemosyne. (B. Mitchell, H. Starreveld, H. Starreveld, A. Angster, I. Arditti, Nieuw Ens/E. Spanjaard)

① **KTC1071** (9/91)
L.Harrison—Music For Guitar And Percussion
L. Harrison: Canticle 3; Suite 1; Plaint and Variations; Serenado; Serenade (1978); Waltz. (J. Schneider, J. Tipton, D. Ross, G. Strimling, Cal Arts Perc Ens/J. Bergamo)

① **KTC1074** (2/90)
Works for Oboe & Piano
Rubbra: Oboe Sonata, Op.100; Duo, Op.156; *Grabert:* Oboe Sonata, Op.52; *Britten:* Temporal Variations; *Röntgen:* Oboe Sonata 1. (P. Bree, P. Bree, P. Komen)

① **KTC1076** (5/90)
Tausig: Wagner Transcriptions and Paraphrases
Tausig: Tristan paraphrases; Walküre transcriptions; Kaisermarsch transcription. (D. Hennig)

Eurodisc

Walzer (exc). (R. Schock, W. Lipp, L. Schmidt, F. Gruber, M. Schramm, B. Kusche, Günther Arndt Ch, Berlin SO/R. Stolz)

① **GD69043** (4/90)
Puccini: Il Trittico
Puccini: Tabarro (Cpte); Suor Angelica (Cpte); Gianni Schicchi (Cpte). (S. Nimsgern, I. Tokody, G. Lamberti, T. Pane, G. Auer, W. Baniewicz, L. Popp, M. Lipovšek, M. Schiml, D. Jennings, B. Calm, M.G. Ferroni, M. Georg, V. Errante, E. van Lier, K. Hautermann, M. Schmitt, A. Schiller, R. Panerai, H. Donath, P. Seiffert, W. Baniewicz, T. Pane, V. Errante, C. Kunz, G. Auer, F. Federici, R. Riener, M. Georg, Bavarian Rad Chor, Munich RO/G. Patanè)

① **RD69245** (10/90)
Brahms: Complete Piano Works
Brahms: Piano Sonata 1; Piano Pieces, Op. 119; Handel Variations; Ballades; Variations, Op. 21/1; Variations, Op. 21/2; Piano Pieces, Op. 118; Piano Pieces, Op. 117; Piano Sonata 2; Piano Pieces, Op. 76; Rhapsodies, Op. 79; Scherzo, Op. 4; Piano Pieces, Op. 116; Paganini Variations; Schumann Variations; Waltzes, Op. 39; Piano Sonata 3. (G. Oppitz)

Europa Musica

① **350202** (5/91)
Corelli—Complete Works
Corelli: Trio Sonatas, Op. 1; Trio Sonatas, Op. 2; Trio Sonatas, Op. 3; Trio Sonatas, Op. 4; Sonatas, Op. 5; Violin Sonata in A; Violin Sonatas, (1697) (exc); Concerti grossi, Op. 6; Overture; Trumpet Sonata; Fuga; Trio Sonatas, Op.posth; String Sonatas (exc). (C. Chiarappa (vn/dir), Accademia Bizantina)

① **350204** (7/91)
Mendelssohn—String Symphonies
Mendelssohn: String Symphony 1; String Symphony 2; String Symphony 3; String Symphony 4; String Symphony 5; String Symphony 6; String Symphony 7; String Symphony 8; String Symphony 9; String Symphony 10; String Symphony 11; String Symphony 12. (Amadeus CO/A. Duczmal)

① **350224** (3/92)
Franck—Complete Harmonium Music
Franck: Cinq pièces; Organiste II; Organiste I; Quasi marcia, Op. 22; Offertoire sur un air bréton. (A. Sacchetti)

① **350225** (4/92)
Cherubini—Complete Keyboard Music
Cherubini: Capriccio; Fantasia; Harpsichord Sonatas. (P. Spada)

① **350238** (5/92)
Weber—Works for Piano & Orchestra
Weber: Piano Concerto 1; Piano Concerto 2; Konzertstück. (M. Drewnowski, Polish Nat RSO/A. Wit)

The Everest Collection

① **EVC9003** (4/95)
Copland/Gershwin/Gould—Orchestral Works
Copland: Appalachian Spring; *Gould:* Spirituals; *Gershwin:* American in Paris. (Pittsburgh SO/W. Steinberg, LSO/W. Susskind)

① **EVC9004** (4/95)
R. Strauss/Canning—Orchestral Works
R. Strauss: Don Juan; Till Eulenspiegel; Salome (exc); *Canning:* Hymn Tune Fantasy. (NY Stadium SO, Houston SO/L. Stokowski)

① **EVC9006** (5/95)
Vaughan Williams/Arnold—Orchestral Works
Vaughan Williams: Job (Cpte); Wasps (exc); *Arnold:* Scottish Dances, Op. 59. (LPO/A. Boult/M. Arnold)

① **EVC9007** (4/95)
Villa-Lobos/Antill/Ginastera—Orchestral Works
Villa-Lobos: Bachianas Brasileiras 2 (exc); *Antill:* Corroboree (exc); *Ginastera:* Panambi Suite; Estancia Suite. (LSO/E. Goossens)

Eye of the Storm

① **EOS5001** (6/95)
Wagner—Overtures and Preludes
Wagner: Rienzi (exc); Tannhäuser (exc); Lohengrin (exc); Tristan und Isolde (exc); Meistersinger (exc); Parsifal (exc). (NQHO/B. Wordsworth)

Facet

① **FE8001** (7/91)
Dupré: Organ Works
Dupré: Pieces, Op. 27 (exc); Suite bretonne, Op. 21 (exc);

Preludes and Fugues, Op. 7 (exc); Chorales, Op. 28 (exc); Cortège et Litanie (exc). (R. Noehren)

① **FE8101** (2/91)
Bronislaw Kaper plays his Famous Film Themes
Kaper: Mutiny on the Bounty (exc); Lili (exc); Glass Slipper (exc); Butterfield 8 (exc); Auntie Mame (exc); Chocolate Soldier (exc); Invitation (exc); Brothers Karamazov (exc); Green Dolphin Street (exc); Swan (exc); Lord Jim (exc); San Francisco (exc). (B. Kaper)

Fidelio Classics

① **9201** (9/93)
Wagner—The Ring - An orchestral adventure
Wagner: Götterdämmerung (exc); Rheingold (exc); Siegfried (exc); Walküre (exc). (Netherlands Rad PO/E. de Waart)

Finlandia

① **4509-95578-2** (9/95)
Telemann—Quartets
Telemann: Musique de Table (exc); Paris Quartets (Nouveaux quatuors) (exc); Concerts et six Suites (exc). (Hortus Musicus, A. Mustonen (vn/dir))

① **4509-95584-2** (11/95)
Beethoven—Cello Sonatas, Vol.1
Beethoven: Handel Variations, WoO45; Cello Sonata, Op. 64; Cello Sonata 1. (A. Karttunen, T. Hakkila)

① **4509-95606-2** (12/94)
Kim Borg - Songs and Arias
Mozart: Zauberflöte (exc); *Rossini:* Barbiere di Siviglia (exc); *Verdi:* Don Carlo (exc); *Borodin:* Prince Igor (exc); *Tchaikovsky:* Eugene Onegin (exc); *Mussorgsky:* Khovanshchina (exc); Boris Godunov (exc); *Sibelius:* Songs, Op. 13 (exc); Songs, Op. 17 (exc); Songs, Op. 36 (exc); Songs, Op. 18 (exc); Row, row, duck; Finlandia; *Kilpinen:* Reflections, Opp. 33-4 (exc); *Mussorgsky:* Songs and Dances of Death; Where art thou, little star; Garden by the Don; Song of the Flea; *Schubert:* König in Thule, D367; Prometheus, D674; Erlkönig, D328; Wer sich der Einsamkeit ergibt, D478; Wer nie sein Brot mit Tränen ass, D480; An die Türen, D479; *Schumann:* Romanzen und Balladen, Op. 49 (exc); *Brahms:* Ernste Gesänge, Op. 121; *Wolf:* Mörike Lieder (exc); Michelangelo Gedichte (Cpte); *Loewe:* Balladen, Op. 20 (exc); Kleiner Haushalt, Op. 71. (K. Borg, E. Werba, M. Raucheisen, Munich PO, Bamberg SO, Berlin RSO/A. Rother/H. Stein)

① **4509-95704-2** (7/95)
Estonian Piano Music
Mägi: Ancient Kannel; *Kangro:* Suite, Op. 1; *Rääts:* Toccata; *Sumera:* 1981 Piece; *Tüür:* Piano Sonata; *Vähi:* Fata Morgana; *Pärt:* Partita. (L. Väinmaa)

① **4509-95705-2** (5/95)
Estonian Chamber Music
Eespere: Trivium; *Põldmäa:* Sonatina; *Mägi:* Cantus and Processus; *Kangro:* Idioms, Op. 43a; *Sumera:* For BBB; *Vähi:* Salvador D. (Tallinn Camerata)

① **4509-95849-2** (10/88)
Sibelius: Choral Works
Sibelius: Finlandia; Lover, Op.14; In the moonlight; Partsongs, Op.18 (exc); Natus in curas, Op.21; Partsongs, Op.84 (Cpte); Resemblance; Jonah's voyage; Finnish Jaeger Battalion March; Partsongs, Op.108 (Cpte); Fridolin's folly; One hears the storm outside; Roaring of a wave. (P. Lindroos, P. Saurola, Helsinki Univ Male Ch, Helsinki Garrison Band/E. Juuri/M. Hyökki)

① **4509-95851-2** (8/92)
Sibelius—Complete String Quartets
Sibelius: String Quartet (1885); String Quartet (1889); String Quartet, op.4; String Quartet, Op.56. (Sibelius Academy Qt)

① **4509-95856-2** (10/88)
Sibelius: Orchestral Works
Sibelius: Violin Concerto; Karelia Suite; Finlandia. (M. Fried, Helsinki PO/O. Kamu)

① **4509-95859-2** (8/92)
Sibelius—Orchestral Works
Sibelius: Humoresques, Opp.87/89; Rakastava; Pelleas and Melisande. (L. Kavacos, Espoo CO/J. Lamminmäki)

① **4509-96867-2** (4/95)
Madetoja—Orchestral Works
Madetoja: Ostrobothnians Suite; Symphony 3; Okon Fuoko Suite 1. (Finnish RSO/J-P. Saraste)

① **4509-97892-2** (11/95)
Baltic Works for String Orchestra, Vol. 1
Balakauskas: Ostrobothnian Symphony; *Vasks:* Stimmen Symphony; *Narbutaite:* Opus Lugubre. (Ostrobothnian CO/J. Kangas)

① **4509-97893-2** (11/95)
Baltic Works for String Orchestra, Vol. 2
Kutavičius: Northern Gates; *Vasks:* Cantabile; *Juozapaitis:* Perpetuum mobile; *Urbaitis:* Lithuanian Folk Music; *Tüür:* Insular Deserta; *Rekašius:* Music for Strings. (Ostrobothnian CO/J. Kangas)

Fly Records

① **FLYCD105** (3/94)
East Coast Pictures—The Wind Band Music of Nigel Hess
N. Hess: Thames Journey; East Coast Pictures; Stephenson's Rocket; Global Variations. (London Symphonic Wind Orch/N. Hess)

FNAC Music

① **592096** (2/94)
Rameau—Grand Motets
Rameau: Deus noster refugium; Quam dilecta; In convertendo. (V. Gens, I. Desrochers, J-P. Fouchécourt, H. Lamy, P. Harvey, M. Loureiro de Sà, S. Imbodem, Concert Spirituel Orch/H. Niquet)

① **592098** (9/93)
Du Mont—Motets en dialogue
Du Mont: Litanies de la vierge à 5; Symphonia à 3 in G minor; Allemanda à 3 in G minor; Dialogus agréli; Allemande in A minor; Pavane à 3 in D minor; Sarabande à 3 in D minor; Echo in lectulo meo; Allemande sur les Anches; In Te Domine à 3; Dialogus de anima; Pavane. (Talens Lyriques, C. Rousset, C. Rousset)

① **592267** (3/94)
Dufaut—Lute Suites
Dufaut: Lute Suite in A minor; Lute Suite in C; Lute Suite in G minor; Pavane in E minor; Lute Suite in C minor; Lute Suite in D; Lute Suite in G minor; Lute Suite in G minor II. (P. Monteilhet)

① **592292** (12/94)
Satie—Orchestral & Vocal Works
Satie: Socrate; Musique d'ameublement; Piège de Méduse (Cpte); Relâche (Cpte). (J-P. Fouchécourt, Erwartung Ens/B. Desgraupes)

① **592308** (11/94)
Lully—Grand Motets, Volume 1
Lully: Te Deum; Miserere; Plaude laetare Gallia. (I. Desrochers, D. Favat, R. Duguay, H. Lamy, P. Harvey, Concert Spirituel Orch/H. Niquet)

① **592316** (2/95)
Clérambault—Chants & Motets for the Royal House of Saint-Louis
Clérambault: Premier livre d'orgue (exc); Justificeris Domine; Miserere mei Deus; Magnificat; Exultet in Domino; O salutaris hostia; O felix Maria; Cantate Vincentium; Domine salvum fac Regem; Hodie Christus natus est; Gloria in excelsis Deo; Domine ante te; Immolabit haedum; Factum est silentium; Exultate Deo; De profundis clamavi; Benedictus. (Demoiselles de Saint-Cyr/E. Mandrin, S. Moquet, J. Boyer)

Fonè

① **91F02** (12/93)
Calace—Works for Mandolins
Calace: Danza Spagnola, Op. 105; Mattino d'autunno, Op. 164; Concerto, Op. 155; Impressionismo, Op. 145; Intermezzo, Op. 146; Pavana, Op. 54; Bolero, Op. 26; Mazurka, Op. 141; Tarantella, Op. 18; Impressioni orientali, Op. 132. (Calace Qnt, Brescia Mndl and Gtr Orch/C. Mandonico)

Forlane

① **FF007** (11/94)
Liszt—Piano Concertos Nos 1 and 2; Hungarian Rhapsodies
Liszt: Piano Concerto 1; Piano Concerto 2; Hungarian Rhapsodies, S244 (exc). (F. Clidat, Luxembourg Rad & TV SO/P. Cao)

① **FF009** (11/94)
Weber—Clarinet Concertos Nos 1 and 2; Oberon Overture
Weber: Clarinet Concerto 1; Clarinet Concerto 2; Oberon (exc). (S. Dangain, Luxembourg Rad & TV SO/L. de Froment)

① **FF045** (11/94)
Grieg/Lalo—Orchestral Works
Grieg: Peer Gynt Suites; Lyric Suite, Op. 54 (exc); *Lalo:*

Roi d'Ys (exc). (Mexico City PO/F. Lozano, Luxembourg Rad & TV SO/L. de Froment)

① **UCD13919** (3/87)
Sacred Choral Works
Anon: Festival of the Virgin Mary; Advent (exc); Mass (exc). (Montserrat Abbey Ch/O. Cunill/I. Segarra)

① **UCD16516** (8/85)
Liszt: Orchestral works
Liszt: Préludes; Totentanz; Hungarian Fantasia, S123; Faust Episodes, S110 (exc). (F. Clidat, Luxembourg Rad & TV SO/J-C. Casadesus)

① **UCD16552** (8/86)
Josquin Desprez—Choral Works
Josquin Desprez: Missa de beata virgine; Memor esto verbi tui; Qui velatus facie fuisti (exc); Planxit autem David; Déploration de Johannes Ockeghem. (A Sei Voci)

① **UCD16567** (2/89)
Haydn: Orchestral Works
Haydn: Horn Concerto 1; Horn Concerto 2; Vera Costanza (exc); Fedeltà premiata (exc); Speziale (exc). (D. Bourgue, Versailles Camerata/A. du Closel)

① **UCD16645** (11/92)
Paul Plishka sings Ukranian Songs
Barvynsky: Oh fields!; *Fomenko:* Mighty Knieper; *Lepkyi:* Song of the Cranes; *Lysenko:* Days pass; Boundless field; Oh Hetmans; Oh, Dnieper!; *Traditional:* About a young maiden; Ballad of Dovbush; Cossack's longing; Song of Bayda; Ukrainian Drinking Song. (P. Plishka, T. Hrynkiv)

① **UCD16681** (8/93)
The Great Italian Arias
Leoncavallo: Pagliacci (exc); *Puccini:* Bohème (exc); *Rossini:* Guillaume Tell (exc); Barbiere di Siviglia (exc); *Donizetti:* Lucrezia Borgia (exc); *Boito:* Mefistofele (exc); *Verdi:* Nabucco (exc); Attila (exc); Don Carlo (exc); Rigoletto (exc); *Giordano:* Andrea Chénier (exc); *Puccini:* È l'uccellino. (J. Van Dam, C. Musquer, Loire PO/M. Soustrot)

① **UCD16683** (5/95)
Russian Songs
Rachmaninov: Songs, Op.4 (exc); Songs, Op.14 (exc); Songs, Op.26 (exc); *Mussorgsky:* Nursery; *Tchaikovsky:* Songs, Op.47 (exc); *Zemfira's* Song; *Mussorgsky:* Songs and Dances of Death. (E. Podles, G. Johnson)

① **UCD16692** (1/94)
Duparc—Mélodies
Duparc: Invitation au voyage; Sérénade florentine; Vague et la cloche; Extase; Phidylé; Manoir de Rosemonde; Lamento; Testament; Chanson triste; Élégie; Soupir; Vie antérieure; Galop; Sérénade; Au pays où se fait la guerre; Romance de Mignon; Fuite. (J. Van Dam, F. Bonnafous, M. Pikulski)

① **UCD16698** (3/94)
Schubert—Lieder
Schubert: An die Laute, D905; Im Frühling, D882; Lachen und Weinen, D777; Nacht und Träume, D827; Frühlingsglaube, D686; An die Musik, D547; Seligkeit, D433; Fischerweise, D881; An Silvia, D891; Tod und das Mädchen, D531; Litanei, D343; Allmacht, D852; Nur wer die Sehnsucht kennt, D877/4; Rastlose Liebe, D138; Meeres Stille, D216; Ganymed, D544; Wandrers Nachtlied II, D768; Musensohn, D764; Suleika I, D720; Suleika II, D717; Erlkönig, D328. (M. Price, G. Johnson)

① **UCD16711** (10/94)
Schumann—Lieder
Schumann: Myrthen, Op. 25 (exc); Lieder und Gesänge, Op. 51 (exc); Gedichte, Op. 37 (exc); Frauenliebe und - leben, Op. 42 (Cpte); Gedichte, Op. 36 (Cpte); Jugend Lieder, Op. 79 (exc). (M. Price, T. Dewey)

① **UCD16727** (8/95)
L'Incomparable Georges Thill
Massenet: Hérodiade (exc); *Verdi:* Aida (exc); *Halévy:* Juive (exc); *Gluck:* Alceste (1776) (exc); *Massenet:* Cid (exc); *Meyerbeer:* Huguenots (exc); *Leoncavallo:* Pagliacci (exc); *Wagner:* Lohengrin (exc); *Verdi:* Traviata (exc); *Rossini:* Guillaume Tell (exc); *Méhul:* Joseph (exc); *Massenet:* Sapho (exc); *Gounod:* Roméo et Juliette (exc); *Messager:* Fortunio (exc); *Bruneau:* Attaque du moulin (exc). (G. Thill, orch/F. Heurteur/E. Bigot/P. Gaubert/P. Chagnon/A. Bruneau)

① **UCD16728** (2/95)
The Romantic Lied
Wolf: Mörike Lieder (exc); *Cornelius:* Trauer und Trost, Op.3; *Liszt:* Freudvoll und leidvoll, S280; Über allen Gipfeln ist Ruh, S306; Mignons Lied, S275; Der du von dem Himmel bist, S279; *Wagner:* Wesendonk Lieder. (M. Price, G. Johnson)

① **UCD16730** (8/94)
Poulenc—Mélodies
Poulenc: Bestiaire; Cocardes; Poèmes de Louise Lalanne; À sa guitare; Tel jour, telle nuit; Miroirs brûlants (exc); Banalités; Métamorphoses; Souris; Dame de Monte Carlo. (F. Lott, G. Johnson)

① **UCD16738** (8/95)
Great Handel Arias
Handel: Alcina (exc); Ariodante (exc); Giulio Cesare (exc); Serse (exc). (A. Murray, OAE/C. Mackerras)

Four Hands Music

① **FHMD891** (10/89)
Schubert: Piano Duets, Vol.1
Schubert: Marches héroïques, D602; German Dance, D618; Fantasie, D9; Sonata, D617; Polonaises, D599. (I. Beyer, H. Dagul)

① **FHMD892** (7/93)
Schubert—Piano Duets, Vol.2
Schubert: Fantasie, D48; Rondo, D608; German Dance, D618; Variations, D624; Allegro moderato, D968; Overture, D675. (I. Beyer, H. Dagul)

① **FHMD893** (6/94)
Schubert—Piano Duets, Volume 3
Schubert: Sonata, D812; Variations, D813; Marches, D819 (exc). (I. Beyer, H. Dagul)

① **FHMD894** (4/95)
Schubert—Piano Duets, Volume 4
Schubert: Marches Militaires, D733; Divertissement à la Hongroise, D818; Marches, D819 (exc). (I. Beyer, H. Dagul)

① **FHMD9111** (5/92)
Mozart—Works for Piano Duet
Mozart: Piano Duet Sonata, K497; Andante and Variations, K501; Piano Duet Sonata, K521. (I. Beyer, H. Dagul)

① **FHMD9212** (10/92)
Piano Duets - Children's Games
Bizet: Jeux d'enfants; *Jongen:* Jeux d'enfants; *Ladmirault:* Dan Lullaby; *Schumann:* Klavierstücke, Op. 85. (I. Beyer, H. Dagul)

Twentieth Century-Fox

① **07822 11006-2** (11/94)
Raksin/Herrmann—Laura/Jane Eyre Original Soundtracks
Alf Newman: 20th Century Fox Fanfare; *Raksin:* Laura (exc); *Herrmann:* Jane Eyre (exc). (OST, orch/Alfred Newman/B. Herrmann)

① **07822 11012-2** (11/94)
Star Wars Trilogy—Original Soundtrack Anthology
Alf Newman: 20th Century Fox Fanfare; *J. T. Williams:* Star Wars (exc); Empire Strikes Back (exc); Return of the Jedi (exc). (OST, LSO/J. T. Williams)

Foyer

① **15-CF2011** (6/88)
Wagner—Der Ring de Nibelungen
Wagner: Rheingold (Cpte); Walküre (Cpte); Siegfried (Cpte); Götterdämmerung (Cpte). (H. Hotter, I. Malaniuk, E. Witte, P. Kuen, G. Neidlinger, B. Falcon, G. Stolze, H. Uhde, M. von Ilosvay, L. Weber, J. Greindl, E. Zimmermann, H. Plümacher, G. Litz, R. Vinay, R. Resnik, A. Varnay, J. Greindl, B. Friedland, L. Thomamüller, B. Falcon, L. Sorrell, E. Schubert, G. Litz, S. Plate, M. von Ilosvay, W. Windgassen, H. Hotter, R. Streich, J. Greindl, H. Uhde, N. Hinsch-Gröndahl, I. Malaniuk, M. von Ilosvay, R. Resnik, Bayreuth Fest Chor, Bayreuth Fest Orch/C. Krauss)

FSM

① **FCD91220** (12/91)
French Baroque Christmas Music
Delalande: Symphonies des Noëls (exc); *M-A. Charpentier:* Noëls, H531 (exc); Noëls sur les instruments, H534 (exc); *Lebègue:* Troisième livre d'orgue (exc); *Daquin:* Nouveau livre de noëls (exc); *Dandrieu:* Noëls (exc); *Corrette:* Organ Concertos, op.26 (exc). (German Baroque sols, R. Ewerhart (org/dir))

Future Classics

① **FCM1004** (5/95)
Music from the Eton Choirbook
Davy: Matthew Passion; *Lambe:* Nesciens mater; *Nesbet:* Magnificat. (Eton Coll Chapel Ch/R. Allwood)

Gallo

① **CD-499** (8/89)
Bassoon Concertos
Mozart: Bassoon Concerto, K191; *Wolf-Ferrari:* Suite-concertino, Op.16; *Hummel:* Bassoon Concerto in F. (K. Walker, LMP/J. Glover)

Gamut Classics

① **GAMCD514** (5/91)
18th Century English Organ Music
Stanley: Organ Voluntaries, Book 2 (exc); Organ Voluntaries, Book 1 (exc); *J. James:* Voluntary; *Boyce:* Voluntaries (exc); *Heron:* Organ Voluntaries (exc); *Roseingrave:* Voluntarys and Fugues (exc); *Walond:* Organ Voluntaries, Op. 2 (exc); Organ Voluntaries, Op. 1 (exc); *J. Bennett:* Voluntary; *Kirkman:* Voluntary; *Keeble:* Voluntary; *Nares:* Introduction and Fugue in A. (Margaret Phillips)

① **GAMCD516** (3/91)
The Piano Music of Ivor Gurney and Edward Elgar
Elgar: Concert Allegro; Skizze; In Smyrna; Adieu; *Gurney:* To E.M.H.; Picture; Revery; Nocturne in A flat; Nocturne in B; Prelude in F sharp; Prelude in C; Prelude in C minor; Prelude in D flat; Preludes (1919-20). (A. Gravill)

① **GAMCD517** (2/91)
Ravel: Music for Two Pianos
Ravel: Rapsodie espagnole; Introduction and Allegro; Sites auriculaires (exc); Shéhérazade (exc); La Valse; Frontispice. (S. Coombs, Cyril Scott)

① **GAMCD518** (9/91)
British Piano Trios
R. Clarke: Piano Trio; *Ireland:* Phantasie Trio; *Bridge:* Phantasy, H79. (Hartley Trio)

① **GAMCD520** (10/91)
Scriabin—Piano Music
Scriabin: Pieces, Op. 2 (exc); Pieces, Op. 9 (exc); Preludes, Op. 16; Preludes, Op. 22; Preludes, Op. 27; Preludes, Op. 31; Preludes, Op. 33; Preludes, Op. 74; Piano Sonata 9; Piano Sonata 3. (G. Scott)

① **GAMCD522** (7/91)
19th Century English Organ Music
S. Wesley: Voluntaries, Op. 6 (exc); *T. Adams:* Voluntaries (1824) (exc); *H.T. Smart:* Andante in A; Andante in F; Fantasia with Choral; *W. T. Best:* English Psalm Tune Preludes; Air with variations; *Chipp:* Sketches, Op. 11 (exc); *Ouseley:* Preludes and Fugues (exc); Andante 2 (exc); *Heap:* Study 3; *Hopkins:* Andante grazioso. (Margaret Phillips)

① **GAMCD526** (3/92)
The Britten Connection
Bridge: Dramatic Fantasia; Gargoyle; *Britten:* Walztes; Night Piece; *L. Berkeley:* Preludes, Op. 23; *Stevenson:* Sonatina Serenissima; *C. Matthews:* Studies; *Ireland:* Ballade of London Nights. (A. Goldstone)

① **GAMCD527** (2/92)
Canticles from Ely
Stanford: Services, Op. 115 (exc); Services, Op. 115 (exc); *T.T. Noble:* Evening Service, Op. 17 (exc); *Jackson:* Benedicite in G; *Stanford:* Services, Op. 10 (exc); *Bairstow:* Lamentation; *Stanford:* Services, Op. 12 (exc); Services, Op. 12 (exc). (Ely Cath Ch/P. Trepte)

① **GAMCD528** (3/92)
The Piano Music of John Ogdon
Ogdon: Five Preludes; Sonatina; Piano Sonata 4; Twenty-five Preludes. (B. Lucas)

① **GAMCD529** (4/92)
A Garland for the Queen
Bliss: Aubade, T76; *Bax:* What is it like; *Tippett:* Dance, Clarion Air; *Vaughan Williams:* Silence and Music; *L. Berkeley:* Spring at this hour; *Ireland:* Hills; *Howells:* Inheritance; *Finzi:* White-flowering days; *Rawsthorne:* Canzonet; *Rubbra:* Salutation; *Britten:* A.M.D.G.; Sacred and Profane. (Cambridge Univ Chbr Ch/T. Brown)

① **GAMCD530** (5/92)
Dupré—Organ Music
Dupré: Preludes and Fugues, Op. 36 (exc); Evocation, Op. 37; Antiennes pour le temps de Noël, Op. 48; Poème symphonique; Choral and Fugue, Op. 57. (J. Filsell)

① **GAMCD534** (5/93)
R. Clarke—Songs with Piano and Violin
R. Clarke: June Twilight; Dream; Cherry Blossom Wand; Cloths of Heaven; Shy One; Seal Man; Down by the Salley Gardens; Infant Joy; Tiger; Tiger; Tears; God made a tree; Come, oh come; Greeting; Donkey; Cradle Song; Eight o'clock; Psalm of David; Aspidistra; Old English

Songs; Irish Country Songs; Midsummer Moon; Chinese Puzzle; Lullaby. (P. Wright, J. Rees, K. Sturrock)

Ⓒ **GAMCD535** (11/93)
Barber—Choral Music
Barber: Reincarnation, Op. 16; Virgin Martyrs, Op. 8/1; Stopwatch; Agnus Dei, Op. 11; Antony and Cleopatra (exc); Twelfth Night; Hermit Songs, Op. 29 (exc); Songs, Op. 13 (exc); Let down the bars, O Death, Op. 8/2; To be sung on the water; Vanessa (exc). (Cambridge Univ Chbr Ch/T. Brown)

Ⓒ **GAMCD536** (6/94)
American Piano Trios
Beach: Piano Trio, Op.150; *Ives:* Piano Trio; *Bloch:* Nocturnes; *Copland:* Vitebsk; *Cowell:* Trio. (Hartley Trio)

Ⓒ **GAMCD537** (4/94)
Works for Viola and Piano
R. Clarke: Viola Sonata; *Maconchy:* Viola Sketches; *Shostakovich:* Viola Sonata. (P. Dukes, S. Rahman)

Ⓒ **GAMD506** (4/92)
An Anthology Of English Song
Purcell: Oedipus, Z583 (exc); *Elgar:* Is she not passing fair?; *Ireland:* Sea Fever; *Vaughan Williams:* Linden Lea; House of Life (exc); Songs of Travel (exc); *Hageman:* Do not go, my love; *Leslie:* Annabelle Lee; *Woodforde-Finden:* Indian Love Lyrics (exc); *Quilter:* Songs, Op. 3 (exc); *C. A. Gibbs:* Cherry Tree; *M.V. White:* To Mary; *Gwynn Williams:* My little Welsh home; *Bond:* Perfect Day; *Parry:* English Lyrics, Set 2 (exc); *Handel:* Tolomeo (exc); *Coates:* Birdsongs at Eventide; *Traditional:* Blow the wind southerly. (V. Masterson, Sarah Walker, S. Burrows, P. Jeffes, T. Allen, R. Herincx, J. Constable)

Ⓒ **GOUPCD153** (2/90)
Tudor Anthems
Byrd: Haec dies a 6; This day Christ was born; *Gibbons:* O Lord, in thy wrath; Hosanna to the Son of David; *Dering:* Cantica sacra (1618) (exc); *Weelkes:* Hosanna to the Son of David; When David heard; *Anon:* Lord, for thy tender mercy's sake; *Tomkins:* When David heard; *Philips:* Ascendit Deus a 5; *Parsons:* Ave Maria; *Tallis:* Salvator mundi I; *W. Mundy:* O Lord, the maker of all things. (Oxford Christ Church Cath Ch/S. Preston)

Gimell

Ⓒ **CDGIMB400** (1/94)
The Palestrina Collection
Palestrina: Missa Benedicta es; Missa Nigra sum; Missa Papae Marcelli; Missa brevis; Missa Nasce la gioia mia; Missa Assumpta est Maria; Assumpta est Maria a 6; Missa Sicut lilium inter spinas; Sicut lilium inter spinas I; *Anon:* Benedicta es; Nigra sum; Assumpta est Maria; *Josquin Desprez:* Benedicta es; *Lhéritier:* Nigra sum; *Primavera:* Nasce la gioia mia. (Tallis Scholars/P. Phillips)

Ⓒ **CDGIM001** (7/90)
Palestrina—Missa Benedicta es
Palestrina: Missa Benedicta es; *Anon:* Benedicta es; *Josquin Desprez:* Benedicta es. (Tallis Scholars/P. Phillips)

Ⓒ **CDGIM002** (6/91)
Russian Orthodox Music
Anon: Medieval Russian Motets; *Ivan the Terrible:* Kuimi pokhvalienui mi; *Stravinsky:* Ave Maria; Pater noster; *Rachmaninov:* Lord's Prayer; *Tavener:* Great Canon; *Bortnyansky:* Mnogaya lieta. (Tallis Scholars/P. Phillips)

Ⓒ **CDGIM003** (8/87)
Missa Nigra sum: Mass and motets
Palestrina: Missa Nigra sum; *Anon:* Nigra sum; *Lhéritier:* Nigra sum; *Victoria:* Nigra sum; *De Silva:* Nigra sum. (Tallis Scholars/P. Phillips)

Ⓒ **CDGIM004** (7/86)
Tavener: Choral works
Tavener: Missa Gloria tibi Trinitas; Kyrie a 4; Dum transisset Sabbatum I. (Tallis Scholars/P. Phillips)

Ⓒ **CDGIM005** (6/91)
Tavener: Choral Works
Tavener: Ikon of Light; Funeral Ikos; Lamb. (Tallis Scholars, Chilingirian Qt/P. Phillips/J. Tavener)

Ⓒ **CDGIM006** (3/86)
Tallis: Motets
Tallis: Spem in alium; Salvator mundi I; Salvator mundi II; Sancte Deus, sancte fortis; Gaude gloriosa dei mater; Miserere nostri; Loquebantur variis linguis. (Tallis Scholars/P. Phillips)

Ⓒ **CDGIM007** (12/86)
Tallis: English Anthems
Tallis: If ye love me; Hear the voice and prayer; New commandment; O Lord, give thy holy spirit; Purge me, O Lord; Verily, verily say I unto you; Remember not, O Lord

God; Out of the deep; O Lord, in thee is all my trust; Christ rising again; Blessed are those that be undefiled; Psalm Tunes. (Tallis Scholars/P. Phillips)

Ⓒ **CDGIM008** (1/87)
Palestrina & Primavera—Choral Works
Palestrina: Missa brevis; Missa Nasce la gioia mia; *Primavera:* Nasce la gioia mia. (Tallis Scholars/P. Phillips)

Ⓒ **CDGIM010** (12/86)
Christmas carols and motets
Traditional: Angelus ad virginem; There is no rose; Nowell: Dieu vous garde; Coventry Carol; Coventry Carol; *Byrd:* Lullaby my sweet little baby; *Josquin Desprez:* Ave Maria...virgo serena; *Verdelot:* Ave Maria; *Victoria:* Ave Maria, gratia plena a 4; Ave Maria, gratia plena a 8; *M. Praetorius:* Es ist ein Ros'; *H. Praetorius:* Joseph lieber, Joseph mein; In dulci jubilo; *M. Praetorius:* Wachet auf. (Tallis Scholars/P. Phillips)

Ⓒ **CDGIM011** (6/87)
Byrd: Sacred Choral Works
Byrd: Great Service (exc); O God, the proud are risen against me; O Lord make thy servant; Sing joyfully unto God our strength. (Tallis Scholars/P. Phillips)

Ⓒ **CDGIM013** (12/87)
Clemens Non Papa: Sacred Choral Works
Clemens Non Papa: Missa Pastores quidnam vidistis; Missa Pastores quidnam vidistis; Tribulationes civitatem; Pater peccavi a 8; Ego flos campi a 7. (Tallis Scholars/P. Phillips)

Ⓒ **CDGIM014** (4/89)
Cornysh—Choral Works
Cornysh: Salve regina; Ave Maria, mater Dei; Gaude virgo mater Christi; Magnificat; Ah, Robin; Adieu, adieu, my heartes lust; Adieu courage; Woefully arrayed; Stabat mater. (Tallis Scholars/P. Phillips)

Ⓒ **CDGIM016** (1/90)
Sheppard: Sacred Choral Works
Sheppard: Media vita; Christe redemptor omnium; Reges Tharsis; Sacris solemniis; In manus tuas a 3; In manus tuas I a 4; In manus tuas II a 4; Verbum caro factum est. (Tallis Scholars/P. Phillips)

Ⓒ **CDGIM017** (12/88)
Sarum Chant
Anon: Christmas (exc); Christmas (exc); Christmas (exc); Christmas (exc); Christmas (exc). (Tallis Scholars/P. Phillips)

Ⓒ **CDGIM018** (7/89)
Lassus: Sacred Choral Works
Lassus: Missa Osculetur me; Osculetur me; Hodie completi sunt; Timor et tremor; Alma redemptoris mater a 8; Salve regina mater a 8; Ave regina caelorum II a 6; Regina coeli a 7. (Tallis Scholars/P. Phillips)

Ⓒ **CDGIM019** (7/89)
Josquin Desprez—Masses
Anon: L'homme armé; *Josquin Desprez:* Missa 'L'homme armé' super voces musicales; Missa 'L'homme armé' sexti toni. (Tallis Scholars/P. Phillips)

Ⓒ **CDGIM020** (9/90)
Palestrina—Sacred Works and Motets
Anon: Assumpta est Maria; *Palestrina:* Missa Assumpta est Maria; Assumpta est Maria a 6; Missa Sicut lilium inter spinas; Sicut lilium inter spinas I. (Tallis Scholars/P. Phillips)

Ⓒ **CDGIM021** (10/90)
Cardoso: Sacred Choral Works
M. Cardoso: Missa Pro defunctis; Non mortui; Sitivit anima mea; Mulier quae erat; Nos autem gloriari; Magnificat Secundi Toni. (Tallis Scholars/P. Phillips)

Ⓒ **CDGIM023** (10/91)
Isaac—Missa de Apostolis
Isaac: Missa de apostolis a 6; Optime...pastor; Tota pulchra es; Regina caeli laetare; Resurrexi; Virgo prudentissima a 6. (Tallis Scholars/P. Phillips)

Ⓒ **CDGIM024** (3/92)
Tomkins—The Great Service
Tomkins: Third Service; When David heard; Then David mourned; Almighty God, the fountain of all wisdom; O sing unto the Lord; O God, the proud are risen against me; Be strong and of a good courage; Woe is me. (Tallis Scholars/P. Phillips)

Ⓒ **CDGIM025** (5/92)
Tallis—Lamentations of Jeremiah
Tallis: Lamentations of Jeremiah; Absterge Domine; Derelinquat impius; Mihi autem nimis; O sacrum convivium; In jejunio et fletu; O salutaris hostia; In manus tuas; O nata lux; Salve intemerata. (Tallis Scholars/P. Phillips)

Ⓒ **CDGIM026** (9/92)
Brumel—Sacred Choral Works
Brumel: Missa Et ecce terrae motus; Lamentation; Magnificat secundi toni. (Tallis Scholars/P. Phillips)

Ⓒ **CDGIM027** (9/92)
Western Wind Masses
Sheppard: Western Wynde Mass; *Taverner:* Western Wynde Mass; *Tye:* Western Wind Mass. (Tallis Scholars/P. Phillips)

Ⓒ **CDGIM029** (6/94)
Rore—Missa Praeter rerum seriem; Motets
Josquin Desprez: Praeter rerum seriem; *Rore:* Missa Praeter rerum seriem; Sacrae cantiones (exc); Ave regina; Descendi in ortum meum. (Tallis Scholars/P. Phillips)

Ⓒ **CDGIM030** (6/95)
R White—Tudor Church Music
Whyte: Christe, qui lux es et dies III; Christe, qui lux es et dies IV; Exaudiat te Dominus; Lamentations; Magnificat; Portio mea Domine; Regina coeli. (Tallis Scholars/P. Phillips)

Ⓒ **CDGIM339** (7/86)
Renaissance Sacred Choral Works
Allegri: Miserere mei; *W. Mundy:* Vox patris caelestis; *Palestrina:* Missa Papae Marcelli. (A. Stamp, Tallis Scholars/P. Phillips)

Ⓒ **CDGIM343/4** (7/93)
Byrd—Sacred Choral Music
Byrd: Great Service (exc); O God, the proud are risen against me; O Lord make thy servant; Sing joyfully unto God our strength; Mass for five voices; Mass for four voices; Mass for three voices; Ave verum corpus; Infelix ego. (Tallis Scholars/P. Phillips)

Ⓒ **CDGIM345** (3/86)
Byrd—Masses and Motets
Byrd: Mass for five voices; Mass for four voices; Mass for three voices; Ave verum corpus. (Tallis Scholars/P. Phillips)

Ⓒ **CDGIM994** (9/94)
The Tallis Scholars Live In Rome
Palestrina: Motets, Bk 3 (1575) (exc); Missa Papae Marcelli; Stabat mater a 8; Alma Redemptoris mater (8vv); Magnificat Primi Toni; Nunc dimittis (8vv); *Allegri:* Miserere mei. (Tallis Scholars/P. Phillips)

Ⓒ **CDGIM995** (12/95)
Tavener—Anniversary Album
Tavener: Missa Gloria tibi trinitas; Kyrie a 4; Dum transisset Sabbatum I; Western Wynde Mass. (Tallis Scholars/P. Phillips)

Ⓒ **CDGIM999** (1/91)
Tallis Scholars—South Bank Show
Allegri: Miserere mei; *Clemens non Papa:* Pater peccavi a 8; *Josquin Desprez:* Missa 'L'homme armé' sexti toni (exc); *Cornysh:* Salve regina; *Tavener:* Dum transisset Sabbatum I; *Tallis:* Gaude gloriosa Dei mater; Psalm Tunes; *Byrd:* O Lord, make thy servant; Mass for four voices (exc). (Tallis Scholars/P. Phillips)

Globe

Ⓒ **GLO5074** (8/92)
Britten—Cello Suites
Britten: Cello Suite 1; Cello Suite 2; Cello Suite 3. (P. Wispelwey)

Ⓒ **GLO5089** (12/94)
Crumb/Escher/Kodály—Cello Solo Sonatas
Crumb: Cello Sonata (1955); *Escher:* Cello Sonata (1945-48); *Kodály:* Cello Sonata, Op. 8. (P. Wispelwey)

Gloriae Dei Cantores

Ⓒ **GDCD016** (9/95)
Leo Sowerby—American Master of Sacred Song
Sowerby: Great is the Lord; Psalms (1928) (exc); Psalms (1928) (exc); Psalms (1928) (exc); Turn thou to Thy God; Whoso dwelleth; Carillon; Angel stood by the Altar of the Temple (exc); Arioso; Lovely Infant; Magnificat and Nunc dimittis in E minor; All they from Saba shall come; Jesu, bright and morning star; Canon, Chacony and Fugue; Of God of Light; Thou art my strength; Prelude on 'Were you there'; Christians, to the Paschal Victim; Festival Musick; Come, Holy Ghost; Bright, Blithe and Brisk; O God, the Protector of All. (C. Helfrich, K. M. Hamilton, P. Logan, L. Norman, R. K. Pugsley, P. Norman, F. Hempel, D. Chalmers, J. E. Jordan Jr, Gloriae Dei Cantores, Gloriae Dei Brass Ens/E. C. Patterson)

Glossa

ⓓ **GCD920103** (8/95)
The Spanish Guitar (1536-1836)
Narváez: Seys libros del delphin (exc); Paseávase el rey moro; *López:* Fantasia; *Milán:* El Maestro: Pavanas (exc); *Mudarra:* Tres libros (1546) (exc); *Murcia:* Baroque Dances (exc); *Giga; Guerau:* Poema harmónico (exc); *Sanz:* Spanish Guitar Instruction II (exc); *Sor:* Minuets, Op. 11 (exc); Mozart Variations, Op. 9. (J. M. Moreno, J. M. Moreno)

ⓓ **GCD920201** (11/94)
Music in the time of Velázquez
Sanz: Spanish Guitar Instruction II (exc); Spanish Guitar Instruction I (exc); *Martín y Coll:* Flores de música (exc); *Hidalgo:* Templo de Palas (exc); Los celos hacen estrellas (exc); Ay, que me río de Amor; Estatua de Prometeo (exc); Cuydado pastor; *Marín:* Ojos que me desdenais; Song Collection (1690) (exc); *Selma y Salaverde:* Primo libro de Canzoni (exc); *Susanna passeggiata; Ruiz de Ribayaz:* Luz y norte musical para caminar (exc); *Guerau:* Poema harmónico (exc); *Durón:* Salir (exc). (Romanesca)

Gothic

ⓓ **G49037** (7/91)
Music of Paris in the 1920s & 1930s
Dupré: Preludes and Fugues, Op. 7 (exc); *Guilmant:* Fughetta de concert, Op. 29b (exc); *Duruflé:* Prélude, Adagio et Choral varié, Op. 4 (exc); *Langlais:* Poèmes évangéliques (exc); *Messiaen:* Nativité du Seigneur (exc); Apparition de l'église éternelle (exc); *Vierne:* Suite 3 (exc). (M. Keiser)

Gramavision

ⓓ **GV79439-2** (7/91)
Modern String Quartets
Bartók: String Quartet 4; *Gubaidulina:* String Quartet 3; *Schnittke:* String Quartet 2. (Arditti Qt)

ⓓ **GV79440-2** (11/90)
Works for String Quartet
Beethoven: Grosse fuge; *Crawford-Seeger:* String Quartet; *Nancarrow:* String Quartet 3; *Reynolds:* Coconino; *Xenakis:* Tetras. (Arditti Qt)

GRP

ⓓ **GRK75002** (1/95)
Arturo Sandoval—The Classical Album
L. Mozart: Trumpet Concerto; *Hummel:* Trumpet Concerto; *Arutiunian:* Trumpet Concerto; *A. Sandoval:* Trumpet Concerto. (A. Sandoval, LSO/L. Haza)

Guild

ⓓ **GRCD7022** (4/89)
John Scott—Organ Recital
Gigout: Ten Organ Pieces (exc); *Guilmant:* March, Op. 15; *Langlais:* Méditations sur l'apocalypse (exc); *Mulet:* Esquisses byzantines (exc); *Liszt:* Fantasia and Fugue, S259. (John Scott)

ⓓ **GRCD7025** (4/91)
A Grand Chorus—Organ Recital
Guilmant: Grand Choeur in D; *Purcell:* Voluntary on the Old 100th, Z721; Choice Collection of Lessons (exc); *Bridge:* Organ Pieces, H63 (exc); *Parry:* Birds (exc); *Preston:* Alleluyas; *Howells:* Pieces (exc); *Elgar:* Imperial March; *Vierne:* Suite 2 (exc); Suite 3 (exc). (A. Lumsden)

Halcyon

ⓓ **DHDL101** (9/91)
Two Sides of George Gershwin
Gershwin: American in Paris; Rhapsody in Blue; Rhapsody in Blue (exc); Preludes; Tip-Toes (exc); Oh, Kay! (exc); Funny Face (exc). (G. Gershwin, Victor SO, Orch/N. Shilkret/P. Whiteman)

Hänssler

ⓓ **98 801** (2/95)
Bach—Cantatas, Vol.39
Bach: Cantata 176; Cantata 20; Cantata 2. (I. Nielsen, C. Watkinson, V. Gohl, H. Watts, M. Kessler, T. Altmeyer, Adalbert Kraus, A. Baldin, W. Heldwein, W. Schöne, Stuttgart Gächinger Kantorei, Frankfurt Kantorei, Stuttgart Bach Collegium/H. Rilling)

ⓓ **98 802** (2/95)
Bach—Cantatas, Vol.40
Bach: Cantata 39; Cantata 135; Cantata 7. (A. Auger, G. Schreckenbach, H. Watts, Adalbert Kraus, F. Gerihsen, P.

Huttenlocher, W. Schöne, Stuttgart Gächinger Kantorei, Stuttgart Bach Collegium/H. Rilling)

ⓓ **98 803** (2/95)
Bach—Cantatas, Vol.41
Bach: Cantata 167; Cantata 24; Cantata 177. (A. Auger, K. Graf, H. Gardow, J. Hamari, H. Watts, K. Pugh, Adalbert Kraus, P. Schreier, N. Tüller, W. Heldwein, W. Schöne, Stuttgart Gedächtniskirche Ch, Stuttgart Gächinger Kantorei, Stuttgart Bach Collegium/H. Rilling)

ⓓ **98 804** (2/95)
Bach—Cantatas, Vol.42
Bach: Cantata 185; Cantata 88; Cantata 170. (A. Auger, I. Reichelt, J. Hamari, H. Laurich, V. Gohl, A. Baldin, Adalbert Kraus, P. Huttenlocher, W. Schöne, Frankfurt Kantorei, Stuttgart Gedächtniskirche Ch, Stuttgart Bach Collegium/H. Rilling)

ⓓ **98 805** (2/95)
Bach—Cantatas, Vol.43
Bach: Cantata 54; Cantata 186; Cantata 107. (A. Auger, J. Hamari, H. Watts, K. Equiluz, A. Baldin, P. Huttenlocher, J. Bröcheler, Stuttgart Gächinger Kantorei, Stuttgart Bach Collegium/H. Rilling)

ⓓ **98 806** (2/95)
Bach—Cantatas, Vol.44
Bach: Cantata 187; Cantata 136; Cantata 178. (M. Friesenhausen, H. Laurich, H. Watts, G. Schreckenbach, K. Equiluz, A. Baldin, W. Schöne, N. Tüller, Stuttgart Gächinger Kantorei, Stuttgart Bach Collegium/H. Rilling)

ⓓ **98 807** (2/95)
Bach—Cantatas, Vol.45
Bach: Cantata 45; Cantata 105; Cantata 168. (A. Auger, N. Burns, J. Hamari, H. Watts, V. Gohl, A. Baldin, Adalbert Kraus, T. Altmeyer, P. Huttenlocher, W. Heldwein, S. Nimsgern, Stuttgart Gächinger Kantorei, Frankfurt Kantorei, Stuttgart Bach Collegium/H. Rilling)

ⓓ **98 808** (2/95)
Bach—Cantatas, Vol.46
Bach: Cantata 94; Cantata 46; Cantata 179. (A. Auger, H. Donath, E. Paaske, H. Watts, A. Baldin, Adalbert Kraus, K. Equiluz, H-F. Kunz, W. Schöne, Stuttgart Gächinger Kantorei, Stuttgart Bach Collegium/H. Rilling)

ⓓ **98 809** (2/95)
Bach—Cantatas, Vol.47
Bach: Cantata 101; Cantata 102; Cantata 77. (A. Auger, H. Donath, E. Randová, H. Watts, J. Hamari, A. Baldin, K. Equiluz, Adalbert Kraus, J. Bröcheler, W. Schöne, Stuttgart Gächinger Kantorei, Stuttgart Bach Collegium/H. Rilling)

ⓓ **98 810** (2/95)
Bach—Cantatas, Vol.48
Bach: Cantata 199; Cantata 113; Cantata 25. (A. Auger, G. Schreckenbach, Adalbert Kraus, P. Huttenlocher, N. Tüller, Frankfurt Kantorei, Stuttgart Gächinger Kantorei, Stuttgart Bach Collegium/H. Rilling)

ⓓ **98 811** (2/95)
Bach—Cantatas, Vol.49
Bach: Cantata 35; Cantata 33; Cantata 164. (E. Wiens, J. Hamari, H. Watts, F. Lang, L-M. Harder, P. Huttenlocher, W. Heldwein, Stuttgart Gächinger Kantorei, Stuttgart Bach Collegium/H. Rilling)

ⓓ **98 812** (2/95)
Bach—Cantatas, Vol.50
Bach: Cantata 138; Cantata 161; Cantata 95. (A. Auger, R. Bollen, H. Laurich, A. Baldin, Adalbert Kraus, P. Huttenlocher, W. Heldwein, Stuttgart Gächinger Kantorei, Frankfurt Kantorei, Stuttgart Bach Collegium/H. Rilling)

ⓓ **98 813** (2/95)
Bach—Cantatas, Vol.51
Bach: Cantata 99; Cantata 8; Cantata 27. (A. Auger, E. Wiens, H. Watts, G. Schreckenbach, L-M. Harder, Adalbert Kraus, J. Bröcheler, P. Huttenlocher, W. Heldwein, Stuttgart Gächinger Kantorei, Stuttgart Bach Collegium/H. Rilling)

ⓓ **98 814** (2/95)
Bach—Cantatas, Vol.52
Bach: Cantata 148; Cantata 114; Cantata 96. (H. Donath, G. Schnaut, H. Watts, J. Hamari, M. Höfgen, K. Equiluz, Adalbert Kraus, S. Nimsgern, W. Schöne, Stuttgart Gächinger Kantorei, Frankfurt Kantorei, Stuttgart Bach Collegium/H. Rilling)

ⓓ **98 815** (2/95)
Bach—Cantatas, Vol.53
Bach: Cantata 47; Cantata 149; Cantata 169. (A. Auger, M. Georg, C. Watkinson, A. Baldin, P. Huttenlocher, Stuttgart Gächinger Kantorei, Stuttgart Bach Collegium, Württemberg CO/H. Rilling)

ⓓ **98 816** (2/95)
Bach—Cantatas, Vol.54
Bach: Cantata 5; Cantata 162; Cantata 180. (A. Auger, A. Rogers, C. Watkinson, A. Baldin, K. Equiluz, Adalbert Kraus, W. Heldwein, W. Schöne, Stuttgart Gächinger Kantorei, Frankfurt Kantorei, Stuttgart Bach Collegium/H. Rilling)

ⓓ **98 817** (2/95)
Bach—Cantatas, Vol.55
Bach: Cantata 49; Cantata 98; Cantata 188. (A. Auger, J. Hamari, A. Baldin, L-M. Harder, W. Heldwein, P. Huttenlocher, Stuttgart Gächinger Kantorei, Stuttgart Bach Collegium, Württemberg CO/H. Rilling)

ⓓ **98 818** (2/95)
Bach—Cantatas, Vol.56
Bach: Cantata 109; Cantata 38; Cantata 89. (A. Auger, G. Schreckenbach, H. Watts, K. Equiluz, L-M. Harder, P. Huttenlocher, Stuttgart Gächinger Kantorei, Stuttgart Bach Collegium/H. Rilling)

ⓓ **98 819** (2/95)
Bach—Cantatas, Vol.57
Bach: Cantata 80; Cantata 115; Cantata 55. (A. Auger, G. Schreckenbach, H. Watts, L-M. Harder, Adalbert Kraus, P. Huttenlocher, W. Schöne, Stuttgart Gächinger Kantorei, Württemberg CO, Stuttgart Bach Collegium/H. Rilling)

ⓓ **98 820** (2/95)
Bach—Cantatas, Vol.58
Bach: Cantata 163; Cantata 139; Cantata 116. (A. Auger, I. Nielsen, H. Watts, L-M. Harder, Adalbert Kraus, P. Huttenlocher, N. Tüller, Stuttgart Gächinger Kantorei, Stuttgart Bach Collegium/H. Rilling)

ⓓ **98 821** (2/95)
Bach—Cantatas, Vol.59
Bach: Cantata 52; Cantata 60; Cantata 26; Cantata 90. (A. Auger, D. Soffel, H. Watts, Adalbert Kraus, P. Huttenlocher, S. Nimsgern, Stuttgart Gächinger Kantorei, Stuttgart Bach Collegium/H. Rilling)

ⓓ **98 822** (2/95)
Bach—Cantatas, Vol.60
Bach: Cantata 62; Cantata 132; Cantata 91. (A. Auger, H. Donath, I. Nielsen, H. Watts, A. Baldin, K. Equiluz, Adalbert Kraus, P. Huttenlocher, W. Schöne, Stuttgart Gächinger Kantorei, Frankfurt Kantorei, Stuttgart Bach Collegium, Württemberg CO/H. Rilling)

ⓓ **98 824** (2/95)
Bach—Cantatas, Vol.62
Bach: Cantata 110; Cantata 40; Cantata 121. (A. Auger, K. Graf, H. Gardow, V. Gohl, D. Soffel, A. Baldin, Adalbert Kraus, S. Nimsgern, W. Schöne, Stuttgart Gächinger Kantorei, Stuttgart Gedächtniskirche Ch, Stuttgart Bach Collegium/H. Rilling)

ⓓ **98 825** (2/95)
Bach—Cantatas, Vol.63
Bach: Cantata 57; Cantata 64; Cantata 151. (A. Auger, N. Gamo-Yamamoto, H. Laurich, A. Murray, Adalbert Kraus, W. Heldwein, P. Huttenlocher, H-F. Kunz, Stuttgart Gächinger Kantorei, Frankfurt Kantorei, Stuttgart Bach Collegium/H. Rilling)

ⓓ **98 826** (2/95)
Bach—Cantatas, Vol.64
Bach: Cantata 133; Cantata 152; Cantata 122. (A. Auger, H. Donath, D. Soffel, H. Watts, A. Baldin, Adalbert Kraus, P. Huttenlocher, W. Schöne, N. Tüller, Stuttgart Gächinger Kantorei, Frankfurt Kantorei, Stuttgart Bach Collegium, Inst Ens/N. Rilling)

ⓓ **98 828** (2/95)
Bach—Cantatas, Vol.66
Bach: Cantata 148; Cantata 114; Cantata 197. (A. Auger, C. Cuccaro, D. Soffel, M. Georg, A. Murray, A. Baldin, Adalbert Kraus, P. Huttenlocher, W. Schöne, N. Tüller, Stuttgart Gächinger Kantorei, Stuttgart Bach Collegium, Württemberg CO/H. Rilling)

ⓓ **98 829** (2/95)
Bach—Cantatas, Vol.67
Bach: Cantata 193; Cantata 120; Cantata 69. (A. Auger, H. Donath, J. Hamari, H. Laurich, Adalbert Kraus, W. Schöne, Stuttgart Gächinger Kantorei, Stuttgart Bach Collegium/H. Rilling)

ⓓ **98 835** (2/95)
Bach—Cantatas, Vol.69
Bach: Cantata 157; Cantata 150; Cantata 97. (H. Donath, M. Schreiber, H. Gardow, M. Jetter, Adalbert Kraus, P. Maus, P. Huttenlocher, H-F. Kunz, Stuttgart Gächinger Kantorei, Inst Ens, Stuttgart Bach Collegium/H. Rilling)

ⓓ **98 855** (2/95)
Bach—Cantatas, Vol.4
Bach: Cantata 51; Cantata 56; Cantata 82. (A. Auger, D.

Fischer-Dieskau, Stuttgart Gächinger Kantorei,
Württemberg CO, Stuttgart Bach Collegium/H. Rilling)

① **98 856** (2/95)
Bach—Cantatas, Vol.5
Bach: Cantata 117; Cantata 145; Cantata 174. (M. Georg,
Adalbert Kraus, A. Schmidt, C. Cuccaro, J. Hamari, A.
Baldin, W. Schöne, Stuttgart Gächinger Kantorei,
Württemberg CO/H. Rilling)

① **98 857** (2/95)
Bach—Cantatas, Vol.6
Bach: Cantata 50; Cantata 140; Cantata 29. (A. Auger, A.
Baldin, P. Huttenlocher, U. Sonntag, E. Graf, Stuttgart
Gächinger Kantorei, Württemberg CO/H. Rilling)

① **98 858** (2/95)
Bach—Cantatas, Vol.7
Bach: Cantata 11; Cantata 100; Cantata 200. (C. Cuccaro,
M. Georg, Adalbert Kraus, A. Schmidt, A. Auger, J.
Hamari, P. Huttenlocher, Stuttgart Gächinger Kantorei,
Württemberg CO/H. Rilling)

① **98 859** (2/95)
Bach—Cantatas, Vol.8
Bach: Cantata 14; Cantata 9; Cantata 195. (K. Laki, A.
Baldin, P. Huttenlocher, U. Sonntag, G. Schreckenbach,
Adalbert Kraus, W. Schöne, S. Inou-Heller, E. Graf, O.
Pfaff, A. Schmidt, Stuttgart Gächinger Kantorei,
Württemberg CO/H. Rilling)

① **98 861** (2/95)
Bach—Cantatas, Vol.10
Bach: Cantata 137; Cantata 129; Cantata 78. (A. Auger, G.
Schreckenbach, Adalbert Kraus, W. Heldwein, P.
Huttenlocher, C. Watkinson, A. Baldin, W. Schöne,
Stuttgart Gächinger Kantorei, Stuttgart Bach Collegium/H.
Rilling)

① **98 863** (2/95)
Bach—Cantatas, Vol.12
Bach: Cantata 147; Cantata 71; Cantata 192. (A. Auger, H.
Watts, K. Equiluz, W. Schöne, K. Graf, H. Gardow, H.
Schwarz, G. Schreckenbach, A. Senger, Adalbert Kraus,
L-M. Harder, N. Tüller, P. Huttenlocher, H. Donath,
Frankfurt Kantorei, Stuttgart Gächinger Kantorei, Stuttgart
Bach Collegium/H. Rilling)

① **98 864** (2/95)
Bach—Cantatas, Vol.13
Bach: Cantata 4; Cantata 172; Cantata 85. (E. Wiens, C.
Watkinson, P. Schreier, W. Schöne, E. Csapó, D. Soffel,
Adalbert Kraus, A. Auger, G. Schreckenbach, W.
Heldwein, Stuttgart Gächinger Kantorei, Frankfurt Kantorei,
Stuttgart Bach Collegium/H. Rilling)

① **98 866** (2/95)
Bach—Cantatas, Vol.15
Bach: Cantata 70; Cantata 131; Cantata 79. (A. Auger, V.
Gohl, L-M. Harder, S. Nimsgern, Adalbert Kraus, W.
Schöne, J. Hamari, P. Huttenlocher, Stuttgart Gächinger
Kantorei, Stuttgart Bach Collegium/H. Rilling)

① **98 867** (2/95)
Bach—Cantatas, Vol.16
Bach: Cantata 61; Cantata 191; Cantata 1. (H. Donath,
Adalbert Kraus, W. Schöne, N. Gamo-Yamamoto, I.
Nielsen, P. Huttenlocher, Stuttgart Gächinger Kantorei,
Stuttgart Bach Collegium/H. Rilling)

① **98 868** (2/95)
Bach—Cantatas, Vol.17
Bach: Cantata 10; Cantata 130; Cantata 17. (A. Auger, M.
Neubauer, A. Baldin, W. Schöne, K. Graf, G. Schnaut,
Adalbert Kraus, G. Schreckenbach, W. Heldwein, Stuttgart
Gächinger Kantorei, Stuttgart Gedächtniskirche Ch,
Stuttgart Bach Collegium/H. Rilling)

① **98 869** (2/95)
Bach—Cantatas, Vol.18
Bach: Cantata 19; Cantata 76; Cantata 104. (B. Rondelli,
Adalbert Kraus, S. Nimsgern, A. Auger, H. Watts, W.
Schöne, Stuttgart Gächinger Kantorei, Stuttgart Bach
Collegium/H. Rilling)

① **98 870** (2/95)
Bach—Cantatas, Vol.19
Bach: Cantata 143; Cantata 190; Cantata 41. (E. Csapó,
Adalbert Kraus, W. Schöne, H. Watts, K. Equiluz, N. Tüller,
H. Donath, M. Höffgen, S. Nimsgern, Frankfurt Kantorei,
Stuttgart Gächinger Kantorei, Stuttgart Bach Collegium/H.
Rilling)

① **98 871** (2/95)
Bach—Cantatas, Vol.20
Bach: Cantata 16; Cantata 171; Cantata 153; Cantata 58.
(G. Schreckenbach, P. Schreier, P. Huttenlocher, A.
Auger, J. Hamari, A. Baldin, W. Heldwein, A. Murray,
Adalbert Kraus, I. Reichelt, W. Schöne, Stuttgart
Gächinger Kantorei, Stuttgart Bach Collegium,
Württemberg CO/H. Rilling)

① **98 872** (2/95)
Bach—Cantatas, Vol.21
Bach: Cantata 65; Cantata 123; Cantata 154; Cantata 124.
(Adalbert Kraus, W. Schöne, H. Watts, P. Huttenlocher, A.
Murray, A. Baldin, W. Heldwein, A. Auger, Stuttgart
Gächinger Kantorei, Stuttgart Bach Collegium/H. Rilling)

① **98 873** (2/95)
Bach—Cantatas, Vol.22
Bach: Cantata 32; Cantata 155; Cantata 3. (A. Auger, W.
Heldwein, I. Reichelt, N. Lerer, F. Melzer, H-F. Kunz, G.
Schreckenbach, L-M. Harder, P. Huttenlocher, Stuttgart
Gächinger Kantorei, Stuttgart Bach Collegium/H. Rilling)

① **98 874** (2/95)
Bach—Cantatas, Vol.23
Bach: Cantata 13; Cantata 73; Cantata 111. (A. Auger, C.
Watkinson, Adalbert Kraus, W. Heldwein, M. Schreiber, W.
Schöne, H. Watts, L-M. Harder, P. Huttenlocher, Stuttgart
Gächinger Kantorei, Stuttgart Gedächtniskirche Ch,
Stuttgart Bach Collegium/H. Rilling)

① **98 875** (2/95)
Bach—Cantatas, Vol.24
Bach: Cantata 72; Cantata 156; Cantata 83. (A. Auger, H.
Laurich, H. Watts, K. Equiluz, Adalbert Kraus, W. Schöne,
W. Heldwein, Stuttgart Gedächtniskirche Ch, Stuttgart
Gächinger Kantorei, Stuttgart Bach Collegium/H. Rilling)

① **98 876** (2/95)
Bach—Cantatas, Vol.25
Bach: Cantata 125; Cantata 81; Cantata 144. (A. Auger, J.
Hamari, M. Höffgen, H. Watts, K. Equiluz, Adalbert Kraus,
W. Schöne, S. Nimsgern, Stuttgart Gedächtniskirche Ch,
Stuttgart Gächinger Kantorei, Stuttgart Bach Collegium/H.
Rilling)

① **98 877** (2/95)
Bach—Cantatas, Vol.26
Bach: Cantata 92; Cantata 84; Cantata 18. (A. Auger, E.
Csapó, H. Watts, G. Schnaut, Adalbert Kraus, W. Schöne,
Stuttgart Gächinger Kantorei, Stuttgart Bach Collegium,
Württemberg CO, Inst Ens/H. Rilling)

① **98 878** (2/95)
Bach—Cantatas, Vol.27
Bach: Cantata 181; Cantata 126; Cantata 127. (A. Auger,
G. Schnaut, G. Schreckenbach, H. Watts, K. Equiluz,
Adalbert Kraus, L-M. Harder, N. Tüller, W. Schöne,
Stuttgart Gächinger Kantorei, Stuttgart Bach Collegium/H.
Rilling)

① **98 879** (2/95)
Bach—Cantatas, Vol.28
Bach: Cantata 23; Cantata 22; Cantata 159. (A. Auger, J.
Hamari, H. Watts, A. Baldin, Adalbert Kraus, N. Tüller, W.
Schöne, P. Huttenlocher, Stuttgart Gächinger Kantorei,
Stuttgart Bach Collegium/H. Rilling)

① **98 882** (2/95)
Bach—Cantatas, Vol.31
Bach: Cantata 158; Cantata 67; Cantata 42. (A. Auger, J.
Hamari, T. Mitsui, A. Murray, Adalbert Kraus, P. Schreier,
W. Heldwein, P. Huttenlocher, Stuttgart Gächinger
Kantorei, Stuttgart Bach Collegium, Inst Ens/H. Rilling)

① **98 883** (2/95)
Bach—Cantatas, Vol.32
Bach: Cantata 12; Cantata 103; Cantata 166. (D. Soffel, H.
Watts, Adalbert Kraus, P. Schreier, A. Baldin, W. Schöne,
W. Heldwein, Stuttgart Gächinger Kantorei, Stuttgart Bach
Collegium/H. Rilling)

① **98 885** (2/95)
Bach—Cantatas, Vol.34
Bach: Cantata 86; Cantata 37; Cantata 43. (A. Auger, J.
Hamari, H. Watts, Adalbert Kraus, A. Baldin, L-M. Harder,
W. Heldwein, P. Huttenlocher, Stuttgart Gächinger
Kantorei, Stuttgart Bach Collegium/H. Rilling)

① **98 886** (2/95)
Bach—Cantatas, Vol.35
Bach: Cantata 128; Cantata 37; Cantata 44; Cantata 59.
(A. Auger, G. Schreckenbach, C. Watkinson, H. Watts, A.
Baldin, Adalbert Kraus, W. Schöne, P. Huttenlocher, N.
Tüller, Stuttgart Gächinger Kantorei, Stuttgart Bach
Collegium/H. Rilling)

① **98 887** (2/95)
Bach—Cantatas, Vol.36
Bach: Cantata 183; Cantata 74; Cantata 34. (A. Auger, H.
Donath, J. Hamari, H. Laurich, H. Watts, P. Schreier,
Adalbert Kraus, W. Heldwein, P. Huttenlocher, W. Schöne,
Stuttgart Gächinger Kantorei, Stuttgart Bach Collegium/H.
Rilling)

① **98 890** (2/95)
Bach—Cantatas, Vol.37
Bach: Cantata 173; Cantata 68; Cantata 184. (J.
Beckmann, A. Auger, G. Schnaut, H. Watts, Adalbert

Kraus, N. Tüller, P. Huttenlocher, Stuttgart Gächinger
Kantorei, Stuttgart Bach Collegium/H. Rilling)

① **98 891** (2/95)
Bach—Cantatas, Vol.38
Bach: Cantata 175; Cantata 165; Cantata 75. (A. Auger, I.
Reichelt, C. Watkinson, A. Rogers, J. Hamari, V. Gohl, P.
Schreier, K. Equiluz, Adalbert Kraus, A. Baldin, P.
Huttenlocher, W. Schöne, H-F. Kunz, Stuttgart Gächinger
Kantorei, Frankfurt Kantorei, Stuttgart Bach Collegium/H.
Rilling)

① **98 965** (10/91)
Bach—Motets
Bach: Motets (Cpte); O Jesu Christ, BWV118; Ich lasse
dich nicht, BWV Anh159; Jauchzet dem Herrn, BWV
Anh160; Gerecht kommt um. (Stuttgart Gächinger
Kantorei, Stuttgart Bach Collegium, H. Rilling)

① **98 979** (9/92)
Mozart—Sacred Choral Works
Mozart: Mass, K427; Requiem; Kyrie, K341. (C. Oelze, I.
Verebics, I. Danz, S. Weir, A. Schmidt, O. Widmer,
Stuttgart Gächinger Kantorei, Stuttgart Bach Collegium/H.
Rilling)

① **98 995** (1/95)
Grieg—Orchestral Works
Grieg: Holberg Suite; Elegiac Melodies; Peer Gynt Suites;
Lyric Pieces. (ASMF/N. Marriner)

Harmonia Mundi

① **HMA190 1068** (12/87)
Monteverdi—Monteverdi
Monteverdi: Madrigals, Bk.7 (exc); Tirsi e Clori; Madrigals,
Bk 8 (exc). (Arts Florissants Voc Ens, Arts Florissants Instr
Ens/W. Christie)

① **HMA190 1077** (3/91)
Du Mont—Sacred Choral Works
Du Mont: Memorare; Dialogus de anima; Magnificat; Super
flumina Babylonis. (Paris Chapelle Royale Chor/P.
Herreweghe)

① **HMA190 1084** (5/87)
Monteverdi—Madrigals
Monteverdi: Madrigals, Bk.5 (exc); Taci, Armelin, deh taci;
Madrigals, Bk.8 (exc); Madrigals, Bk 8 (exc); Madrigals,
Bk.4 (exc); Madrigals, Bk.7 (exc); Madrigals, Bk.6 (exc).
(Concerto Vocale)

① **HMA190 1088** (4/88)
Vivaldi—Violin Sonatas
Vivaldi: Violin Sonata, RV2; Manchester Sonatas (exc);
Violin Sonata, RV25; Violin Sonata, RV29. (Boston
Museum Trio)

① **HMA190 1106** (5/87)
Medieval English Music
Plummer: Anna Mater Matris Christi; *Anon*: Alleluia: Hic est
vere martir; Singularis laudis digna; Doleo super te;
Worcester Fragments (exc); Civitatis nusquam conditur; Tu
civium primas; Mater Christi nobilis; Mass (exc); Alleluja: A
newê wort; *Traditional*: There is no rose; *Anon*: Tota
pulcra es amica mea; *Traditional*: Marvel not, Joseph;
Anon: O potores exquisiti. (Hilliard Ens)

① **HMA190 1124/7** (4/90)
L. Couperin—Complete Harpsichord Works
L. Couperin: Harpsichord Works I (Cpte); Harpsichord
Works II (Cpte); Harpsichord Works III (Cpte); Harpsichord
Works IV (Cpte); Harpsichord Works V (Cpte). (D.
Moroney)

① **HMA190 1138** (5/87)
Melodies of the poems of Victor Hugo
Gounod: Sérénade; *Bizet*: Guitare; Adieux de l'hôtesse;
Lalo: Guitare; *Delibes*: Églogue; *Fauré*: Songs, Op.1 (exc);
Songs, Op.5 (exc); Puisqu'ici-bas; *Wagner*: Mélodies (exc);
Liszt: Oh! quand je dors, S282; Comment, disaient-ils,
S276; *Saint-Saëns*: Soirée en mer; Fiancée du Timbalier;
M.V.White: Chantez, chantez, jeune Inspirée; *Hahn*:
Rêverie; Si mes vers; *Franck*: S'il est un charmant gazon.
(F. Lott, G. Johnson)

① **HMA190 1150** (12/87)
Couperin—Motets
Couperin: Magnificat anima mea; O misterium ineffabile;
Laetentur coeli; Tantum ergo; Regina coeli; Victoria Christo
resurgenti; Domine salvum fac regem; Venite exultemus
Domino; Lauda Sion salvatorem; Jucunda vox Ecclesiae.
(J. Feldman, I. Poulenard, G. Reinhart, J. ter Linden, D.
Moroney)

① **HMA190 1183** (5/87)
Works for Lute and Voice
Caccini: Nuove musiche (1602) (exc); *Bottrigari*: So ben mi
c'ha bon tempo; Mi parto; *Ferrari*: M'amo tanto costei;
Averto ò cor; *Melli*: Capriccio chromatico; *Purcell*: Oedipus,

801 (exc); Overture, Z771; Welcome Song, Z336 (exc); Overture, Z772; Overture, Z770. (London Baroque)

ⓘ **HMC90 1351** (7/91)
Delalande—Sacred Choral Works
Delalande: Te Deum, S32; Confitebor tibi Domine, S56; Super flumina. (V. Gens, S. Piau, A. Steyer, J-P. Fouchécourt, F. Piolino, J. Corréas, Arts Florissants Chor, Arts Florissants Orch/W. Christie)

ⓘ **HMC90 1364** (8/92)
Ravel—Works for Violin and Piano
Ravel: Violin Sonata (1897); Violin Sonata (1923-27); Mélodies Hébraïques (exc); Tzigane; Berceuse; Pièce en forme de habanera. (R. Pasquier, B. Engerer)

ⓘ **HMC90 1365** (10/92)
Bach—Cantatas for Bass
Bach: Cantata 82; Cantata 56; Cantata 158. (P. Kooy, Chapelle Royale Ch, Chapelle Royale Orch/P. Herreweghe)

ⓘ **HMC90 1366** (4/92)
Vivaldi—Sonate a tre
Vivaldi: Sonatas, Op.1 (exc); Trio Sonata, RV68; Trio Sonata, RV70; Trio Sonata, RV71; Trio Sonata, RV77. (Ens 415)

ⓘ **HMC90 1372** (5/92)
Froberger—Harpsichord Works
Froberger: Keyboard Works, Bk. 2 (exc); Keyboard Works, Bk. 4 (exc); Keyboard Works, Various I (exc); Keyboard Works, Various II (exc). (C. Rousset)

ⓘ **HMC90 1391** (2/93)
Roland de Lassus—Chansons & Moreshe
Lassus: Libro de Villanelle (1581) (exc); Las me fault-il; Quand mon mary vient; Chansons françaises nouvelles (exc); Puce j'ay; Nuict froide et sombre; Vignon vignon vignette; Fuyons tous d'amour; Triste coeur rempli; O foible esprit; En un chasteau; Elle s'en va de moy; Lucescit jam o socii; Je l'ayme bien; Mais qui pourroit (6vv); O lucia miau; Temps peut bien; J'ay un mary; Quand mon mary vient. (C. Janequin Ens)

ⓘ **HMC90 1395** (4/93)
L. & W. Mozart/J.C. Bach—Concertos and Sonatas
J.C. Bach: Violin Sonatas, T329/1 (exc); Keyboard Concertos, T293/4 (exc); *L. Mozart:* Church and Chamber Sonatas (exc); *Mozart:* Piano Concertos, K107. (London Baroque)

ⓘ **HMC90 1400** (9/93)
Haydn—Piano Trios
Haydn: Keyboard Trio 21; Keyboard Trio 22; Keyboard Trio 23. (E. Höbarth, C. Coin, P. Cohen)

ⓘ **HMC90 1401** (10/93)
Hassler—Sacred Vocal Works
Hassler: Missa I super Dixit Maria; Ad Dominum; O admirabile; Usquequo; Domine Deus; Vater unser im Himmelreich; *Lechner:* Si bona suscepimus. (Paris Chapelle Royale European Ens/P. Herreweghe)

ⓘ **HMC90 1405** (11/93)
Schumann—Violin Sonatas
Schumann: Violin Sonata 1; Violin Sonata 2; Romanzen, Op.94. (O. Charlier, B. Engerer)

ⓘ **HMC90 1408/9** (12/92)
Schubert—The Last Quartets
Schubert: String Quartet, D810; String Quartet, D804; String Quartet, D887; String Quartet, D703. (Melos Qt)

ⓘ **HMC90 1410** (1/93)
CPE Bach—Sonatas
C.P.E. Bach: Sonata, H510; Viola da gamba Sonata, H558; Viola da gamba Sonata, H559; Keyboard Sonatas, H24-9 (exc); Württemberg Sonatas (exc). (London Baroque, R. Egarr)

ⓘ **HMC90 1416** (4/93)
Delalande—Petits Motets
Delalande: Miserere à voix seule; Vanum est vobis; Miserator et misericors; Cantique quatrième; *Lemaire:* Assumpta est Maria; *Morin:* Regina coeli. (V. Gens, S. Piau, N. Rime, A. Steyer, Arts Florissants Chor, Arts Florissants Orch/W. Christie)

ⓘ **HMC90 1417** (2/93)
Caplet—Orchestral and Vocal Works
Caplet: Conte fantastique; Divertissements; Prières; Sonnets; Septet. (S. Coste, S. Piau, S. Deguy, Musique Oblique Ens, L. Cabel)

ⓘ **HMC90 1419** (6/93)
Prokofiev/Khachaturian/Kókai
Prokofiev: Overture, Op.34; Quintet, Op.39; *Khachaturian:* Clarinet Trio; *Kókai:* Quartettino. (W. Boeykens Ens)

ⓘ **HMC90 1420** (12/93)
Weill—The Seven Deadly Sins; Songs
Weill: Sieben Todsünden (Cpte); Complainte de la Seine; Youkali; Nannas Lied; Wie lange noch; Es regnet; Berlin im Licht. (B. Fassbaender, K-H. Brandt, H. Sojer, H. Komatsu, I. Urbas, C. Garben, Hanover Rad PO/C. Garben)

ⓘ **HMC90 1422** (8/93)
Weill—Orchestral and Choral Works
Weill: Berliner Requiem; Vom Tod im Wald; Violin Concerto. (A. Laiter, P. Kooy, E. Glab, Paris Chapelle Royale Chor, Musique Oblique Ens/P. Herreweghe)

ⓘ **HMC90 1426** (10/93)
Monteverdi—Il combattimento di Tancredi e Clorinda
Monteverdi: Il combattimento di Tancredi e Clorinda; Madrigals, Bk 8 (exc); Madrigals, Bk.7 (exc); Scherzi musicali (1632) (exc); Madrigals, Bk.6 (exc). (Arts Florissants Chor, Arts Florissants Orch/W. Christie)

ⓘ **HMC90 1432** (5/93)
Falla—Vocal & Orchestral Works
Falla: Canciones populares españolas; Harpsichord Concerto; Gran teatro del mundo; Psyché. (V. de los Angeles, Cor Lieder Camera, Teatre lliure CO/J. Pons)

ⓘ **HMC90 1434** (8/93)
Ravel—Orchestral Works
Ravel: Left-Hand Concerto; Piano Concerto; La Valse; Boléro. (G. Pludermacher, Lille Nat Orch/J-C. Casadesus)

ⓘ **HMC90 1453** (5/95)
Une fête chez Rabelais
Certon: La, la, la, je ne l'ose dire; *Clemens non Papa:* Chansons (exc); *G. Coste:* Chansons (exc); *Compère:* Nous sommes de l'ordre; *De Bussy:* Las il n'a nul mal; *Fresneau:* Fricassée; Souspir d'amours; *Gombert:* Chansons (exc); *Guiard:* Or oiez les introites; *Hesdin:* Ramonez moy; *Josquin Desprez:* Scaramella va alla guerra; *La Rue:* Autant en Emporte le Vent; *Ninot le Petit:* N'as tu point; *Pipelare:* Fors seulement; *Sermisy:* Je ne menge point; Las, je m'y plains; Vien tost; *Vermont le jeune:* Ce n'est pas trop; *Willaert:* Dessus le marché d'Arras; *Anon:* Viol music. (C. Janequin Ens/D. Visse)

ⓘ **HMC90 1455** (4/95)
Lekeu—Vocal and Chamber Works
Lekeu: Molto adagio; Piano Quartet; Larghetto; Adagio; Poèmes. (R. Yakar, I. Veyrier, Musique Oblique Ens)

ⓘ **HMC90 1462** (5/94)
Purcell—Funeral Music for Queen Mary; Te Deum; Anthems
Purcell: Funeral Sentences (exc); March and Canzona, Z860; Te Deum and Jubilate, Z232 (exc); Bell Anthem, Z49; Remember not, Lord, our offences, Z50; Blow up the Trumpet in Sion, Z10; Hear my prayer, O Lord, Z15; My heart is inditing, Z30; O Lord God of hosts, Z37. (T. Bonner, P. Kwella, K. Wessel, P. Agnew, W. Kendall, P. Kooy, Collegium Vocale/P. Herreweghe)

ⓘ **HMC90 1465** (5/94)
Chabrier/Ravel—Piano Works
Chabrier: Pièces pittoresques; Bourrée fantasque; Impromptu; Habanera; Pièces posthumes (exc); Air de ballet; *Ravel:* A la manière de Chabrier. (A. Planès)

ⓘ **HMC90 1466/7** (5/94)
Mozart—Violin Sonatas, Vol.1: Palatine Sonatas
Mozart: Violin Sonata, K301; Violin Sonata, K302; Violin Sonata, K303; Violin Sonata, K304; Violin Sonata, K305; Violin Sonata, K306; Variations, K359; Variations, K360. (C. Banchini, T. Vesselinova)

ⓘ **HMC90 1468/9** (10/94)
Mozart—Violin Sonatas, Vol.2
Mozart: Violin Sonata, K376; Violin Sonata, K296; Violin Sonata, K377; Violin Sonata, K378; Violin Sonata, K379; Violin Sonata, K380; Violin Sonata, K481. (C. Banchini, T. Vesselinova)

ⓘ **HMC90 1470** (2/95)
Mozart—Violin Sonatas, Vol.3
Mozart: Violin Sonata, K454; Violin Sonata, K526; Violin Sonata, K547. (C. Banchini, T. Vesselinova)

ⓘ **HMC90 1471** (9/94)
Bouzignac—Te Deum; Motets
Bouzignac: Ecce festivitas amoris; Ecce homo; Unus ex vobis; In pace in idipsum; Ha magne, filia Jerusalem; Vulnerasti cor meum; Alleluya, venite amici; Flos in floris tempore; O mors; Clamant clavi; Ecce aurora; Dum silentium; Jubilate Deo; Salve Jesus piissime; Ave Maria; Tota pulchra es; Te Deum. (Pages de la Chapelle, Arts Florissants Chor, O. Gibbons Viol Ens, Arts Florissants Instr Ens/W. Christie)

ⓘ **HMC90 1472** (3/94)
Saint-Saëns—Orchestral and Chamber Music
Saint-Saëns: Piano Quintet; Carnaval des animaux; Assassinat, Op. 128. (Musique Oblique Ens)

ⓘ **HMC90 1476** (12/94)
Chants from the Benevento Cathedral
Anon: Holy Week (exc); Easter Sunday (exc); Easter Sunday (exc). (Organum Ens/M. Pérès)

ⓘ **HMC90 1479** (3/94)
Bach—Cantatas
Bach: Cantata 11; Cantata 43; Cantata 44. (B. Schlick, C. Patriasz, C. Prégardien, P. Kooy, Collegium Vocale/P. Herreweghe)

ⓘ **HMC90 1482** (4/94)
Mompou—Vocal and Orchestral Works
Mompou: Improperiae; Combat del somni; Suburbis; Scènes d'enfants. (V. Parramon, J. Artysz, Valencia Ch, Teatre Lliure CO/J. Pons)

ⓘ **HMC90 1489** (6/94)
Nielsen—Orchestral Works
Nielsen: Clarinet Concerto; Pan and Syrinx; Amor and the Poet (exc); Little Suite. (W. Boeykens, Beethoven Academy/J. Caeyers)

ⓘ **HMC90 1491** (2/95)
Songs on Poems by Pierre de Ronsard
Regnard: Ni nuit ne jour; Dedans ce bois; Contre mon gré; Mon triste coeur; Heureux ennui; Las, toi qui es de moi; Bois Janin à moi; *Boni:* Rossignol mon mignon; Las! sans espoir; Quand je dors; Ha, bel accueil; Comment au départir; *Le Jeune:* Je suis tellement langoureux; Quand tu tournes tes yeux; De peu de bien; *Monte:* Quand de la lèvre; Si trop souvent; Premier jour du mois de mai; *Rippe:* Fantasie II. (C. Janequin Ens/D. Visse, E. Bellocq)

ⓘ **HMC90 1492** (10/94)
Grieg—Violin Sonatas
Grieg: Violin Sonata 1; Violin Sonata 2; Violin Sonata 3. (O. Charlier, B. Engerer)

ⓘ **HMC90 1495** (1/95)
Corsican chant from Franciscan manuscripts
Anon: Corsican Cantilena (exc); Corsican Kyrial (17th Cent) (exc); Corsican Manuale (exc); Corsican Kyrial (18th Cent) (exc). (Organum Ens/M. Pérès)

ⓘ **HMC90 1496** (5/95)
Purcell—Harpsichord Suites
Purcell: Choice Collection of Lessons (exc); Grounds (exc); Hornpipes (exc); Musick's hand-maid, Part 2 (exc). (K. Gilbert)

ⓘ **HMC90 1500** (11/94)
Gerhard—Orchestral & Vocal Works
Gerhard: Alegrías; Cancionero de Pedrell (exc); Haiku (Cpte); Pandora Suite. (J. Benet, Teatre Lliure CO/J. Pons)

ⓘ **HMC90 1503** (3/95)
Debussy—Piano Works
Debussy: Images; Images oubliées; Estampes. (G. Pludermacher)

ⓘ **HMC90 1505** (5/95)
German Baroque Songs
Nauwach: Teutsche Villanellen (exc); *H. Albert:* Arien (exc); *A. Krieger:* Liebesgluth verkehrt den Muth; Ihr bleibet nicht Bestand verpflicht; Liebe Macht herrscht Tag und Nacht; Rheinsche Wein; *Krieger:* Schmilz, hartes Herz; Verliebtes Weinen und Lachen; Heissverliebte; An die Einsamkeit; Holde Nacht; *Hammerschmidt:* Kunst des Küssens; *Gömer:* Nacht; An den Schlaf; *Fischer:* Praeludium and Chaconne VIII; *Krieger:* Sonata, Op. 2; *Hagen:* Locatelli Menuetto. (A. Scholl, P. Valetti, S. Pfister, F. Heumann, J. M. Quintana, A. Verzier, K. E. Schröder, M. Märkl)

ⓘ **HMC90 1511** (9/95)
C. P. E. Bach—Trio Sonatas
C. P. E. Bach: Trio Sonata, H582; Trio Sonata, H576; Trio Sonata, H577; Trio Sonata, H584; Trio Sonata, H590. (London Baroque)

ⓘ **HMC90 1514** (9/95)
Haydn—Keyboard Trios, Volume 4
Haydn: Keyboard Trio 24; Keyboard Trio 25; Keyboard Trio 26. (E. Höbarth, C. Coin, P. Cohen)

ⓘ **HMC90 1552** (8/95)
The Three Countertenors
Di Capua: 'O sole mio; *Bizet:* Carmen (exc); *Massenet:* Cid (exc); *Bernstein:* West Side Story (exc); *Saint-Saëns:* Samson et Dalila (exc); *Scholl:* White as Lilies; *Offenbach:* Périchole (exc); *C. François:* My Way; *Donizetti:* Elisir d'Amore (exc). (P. Bertin, A. Scholl, D. Visse, F. Couturier, K.E. Schröder, Camargue PO/Reinhardt Wagner)

① **HMC90 242** (3/86)
Purcell: Songs
Purcell: Come, let us drink, Z245; Miller's Daughter, Z277; Sir Walter enjoying his damsel, Z273; Health to the nut brown lass, Z240; Prithee be n't so sad and serious, Z269; I gave her cakes and I gave her ale, Z256; Young John the Gard'ner, Z292; Once, twice, thrice I Julia tried, Z265; Of all the instruments, Z263; Under this stone, Z286; Since time so kind to us does prove, Z272; 'Tis woman makes us love, Z281; If ever I more riches did desire, Z544; Laudate Dominum, Z108. (Deller Consort/A. Deller)

① **HMC90 5149** (7/85)
Poulenc: Sacred choral works
Poulenc: Stabat Mater; Litanies à la Vierge noire; Salve Regina. (M. Lagrange, Lyon Nat Ch, Lyon Nat Orch/S. Baudo)

① **HMC90 5183** (4/88)
Handel: Arias for Senesino
Handel: Giulio Cesare (exc); Rodelinda (exc); Tolomeo (exc); Riccardo Primi (exc); Orlando (exc); Flavio (exc). (D. Minter, Philh Baroque Orch/N. McGegan)

① **HMC90 5192** (2/88)
As I went to Walsingham
Anon: Walsingham Galliard; My true love hath my heart; As I went to Walsingham; Squiers Galliard; Walsingham; Primiero; *J. Johnson:* Delight Pavan; Walsingham; Go merely wheele; *Alison:* Lady Frances Sidneys Almayne; Goe from my window; Mr Allisons Almayne; Lady Frances Sidneys Goodnight; *Byrd:* O dear life; O Lord how vain; Come to me grief for ever; *Collard:* Walsingham; *G. Tessier:* In a grove most rich of shade; *A. Holborne:* Walsingham. (E. Van Evera, P. O'Dette, L. Nordstrom, C. Thielmann, Musicians of Swanne Alley)

① **HMC90 5193** (8/88)
Vivaldi: Flute Concertos
Vivaldi: Concerto, RV427; Concerto, RV438; Concerto, RV440; Concerto, RV533; Concerti, Op. 10 (exc); Concerto, RV436; Concerto, RV429. (J. See, S. Schultz, Philh Baroque Orch/N. McGegan)

① **HMC90 5207** (3/91)
Virtuoso Works for Violin
Sarasate: Carmen Fantasy; Caprice basque; Danzas españolas (exc); Zigeunerweisen; *Paganini:* Caprices, Op. 1 (exc); Paisiello's Introduction and Variations; Moto perpetuo, Op. 11; *Peci:* Albanian dances. (T. Papavrami, C. Larrieu)

① **HMC90 5210** (9/91)
Duos Romantiques
Mendelssohn: Duets, Op. 63 (exc); Abendlied; Wie Kann ich froh; Wasserfahrt; *Rubinstein:* Engel, Op. 48/1; Wanderers Nachtlied; Lotosblume; Waldlied; *Liszt:* O Meer im Abendstrahl, S344; *Cornelius:* Zu den Bergen; Duets, Op. 16 (exc); Ich und Du; *Schumann:* Lieder, Op. 43 (exc); Spanisches Liederspiel, Op. 74 (exc); Gedichte, Op. 37 (exc); *Brahms:* Duets, Op. 28 (exc). (B. Fassbaender, H. Komatsu, K. Moll, C. Garben)

① **HMI98 7007** (12/94)
Albéniz—Piano Sonatas
Albéniz: Piano Sonata 3; Piano Sonata 4; Piano Sonata 5; Automne. (A. Guinovart)

① **HMU90 7012** (3/89)
Mozart—Horn Concertos, etc
Mozart: Horn Concerti; Rondo, K371; Rondo, K514. (L. Greer, Philh Baroque Orch/N. McGegan)

① **HMU90 7016** (8/90)
Handel: Arias for Montagnana
Handel: Ezio (exc); Sosarme (exc); Esther (exc); Acis and Galatea (exc); Tolomeo (exc); Orlando (exc); Athalia (exc); Deborah (exc). (D. Thomas, Philh Baroque Orch/N. McGegan)

① **HMU90 7020** (6/91)
Kapsperger—Lute Works
Kapsperger: Lute Book I (exc); Chitarrone Book IV (exc); Chitarrone Book I (exc). (P. O'Dette)

① **HMU90 7022** (7/92)
Spanish Songs & Theatre Music
Hidalgo: Celos aun del aire matan (exc); *Falconieri:* Primo libro di canzone (exc); *Hidalgo:* Crédito; Selma y Salaverde: Canzon prima a due; *Hidalgo:* En los floridos páramos; Ay amor; Templo de Palas (exc); *Selma y Salaverde:* Canzon terza; Canzon prima; *Hidalgo:* Los celos hacen estrellas (exc); *Selma y Salaverde:* Canzon ottavo. (Newberry Consort/M. Springfels)

① **HMU90 7023** (6/91)
T.Campion—Ayres
Campion: Ayres (1601) (exc); Ayres, Bk 1 (exc); Ayres Bk 2 (exc); Ayres, Bk 3 (exc); Ayres, Bk 4 (exc). (D. Minter, P. O'Dette)

① **HMU90 7024/5** (11/91)
Bach—Complete Sonatas for Flute and Harpsichord
Bach: Flute Sonatas, BWV1030-5; Partita, BWV1013; Violin Sonatas, BWV1020-25 (exc); Flute Sonatas, BWV1030-5 (exc). (J. See, M. Springfels, D. Moroney)

① **HMU90 7029** (5/91)
Pachelbel—Hexachordum Apollinis
Pachelbel: Ciaccona I in D; Hexachordum Apollinis; Ciaccona in F minor. (J. Butt)

① **HMU90 7033/4** (8/93)
Mozart—The Complete Piano Trios
Mozart: Divertimento, K254; Piano Trio, K496; Piano Trio, K502; Piano Trio, K542; Piano Trio, K548; Piano Trio, K564. (Mozartean Players)

① **HMU90 7035** (1/93)
Sweeter than Roses - Purcell Songs
Purcell: O Solitude, Z406; St Cecilia's Day Ode, Z328 (exc); Rival Sisters, Z609 (exc); Indian Queen, Z630 (exc); If music be the food of love, Z379/3; Not all my torments, Z400; Bess of Bedlam, Z370; Oedipus, Z583 (exc); Pausanias, Z585 (exc); Birthday Ode, Z321 (exc); Lord what is man?, Z192; Sleep, Adam, sleep, Z195; Evening Hymn, Z193; Fatal hour comes on apace, Z421; St Cecilia's Day Ode, Z339 (exc); Welcome Song, Z324 (exc); Fairy Queen, Z629 (exc). (D. Minter, P. O'Dette, M. Meyerson, M. Meyerson, M. Springfels)

① **HMU90 7036** (12/91)
Handel—Arias for Cuzzoni
Handel: Rodelinda (exc); Riccardo Primi (exc); Giulio Cesare (exc); Scipione (exc); Ottone (exc); Tamerlano (exc); Alessandro (exc); Flavio (exc). (L. Saffer, Philh Baroque Orch/N. McGegan)

① **HMU90 7037** (9/92)
Beethoven/Brahms/Krufft—Works for Horn
Beethoven: Horn Sonata; *Brahms:* Horn Trio; *Krufft:* Horn Sonata. (L. Greer, S. Lubin, S. Chase)

① **HMU90 7038** (7/93)
Il Solazzo—Music for a Medieval Banquet
Anon: Badessa; Bel fiore danza; Nova stella; Cominciamento di gioia; Troto; Principio di virtu; *Jacopo da Bologna:* Non al suo amante; *Landini:* Bionda treçça; Dolcie signiore; Donna, s'i t'ò fallito; Gran disio; *Ciconia:* O rosa bella; Ligiarda donna; *Zacharia de Terano:* Rosetta; Fior gentil; *Bartolino da Padova:* Alba columba. (Newberry Consort/M. Springfels)

① **HMU90 7043** (10/95)
Dolcissima ed amorosa
Milano: Fantasia (Castelfranco MS); Fantasia dolcissima et amorosa; Fantasias (exc); Ricercars (exc); Borrono da Milano: Pavana ditta la Desparata; Tocha tocha la Canella; Pavana la Gombertina; Saltarello chiamato el Mazolo; Saltarellos (exc); Fantasias (exc); *Ripa:* Fantasias (exc); *Eccho; Dall'Aquila:* Unidentified Ricercar; Il est bon; Ricercar 101; Nous bergiers; Traditora 2; Traditora 3; Ricercars (exc); Battaglia. (P. O'Dette)

① **HMU90 7046** (4/92)
Vivaldi—Chamber Concertos
Vivaldi: Concerto, RV95; Concerto, RV99; Concerto, RV105; Concerto, RV94; Concerto, RV103; Trio Sonata, RV86; Trio Sonata, RV84. (M. Verbruggen, P. Goodwin, J. Holloway, D. Godburn, J. Toll, S. Comberti)

① **HMU90 7047** (7/92)
Cabanilles—Organ Works
Cabanilles: Tientos (exc); Paseos; Passacalles (exc); Xácara. (J. Butt)

① **HMU90 7048** (10/92)
Billings—Anthems and Fuguing Tunes
Billings: New-England psalm-singer (exc); Singing Master's Assistant (exc); Psalm-Singer's Amusement (exc); Suffolk Harmony (exc); Continental Harmony (exc); Lord is ris'n indeed. (His Majestie's Clerkes/P. Hillier)

① **HMU90 7053** (3/93)
Humfrey—Verse Anthems
Humfrey: O give thanks unto the Lord; O Lord my God; Have mercy upon me (3vv); By the waters of Babylon; Lift up your heads; Hear, O heav'ns; Hear my prayer, O God; Hear my crying, O God; Like as the hart. (D. Dean, D. Minter, R. Covey-Crump, J. Potter, D. Thomas, Cambridge Clare College Ch, Romanesca/N. McGegan)

① **HMU90 7056** (3/93)
Handel—Arias for Durastanti
Handel: Agrippina (exc); Radamisto (exc); Muzio Scevola (exc); Ottone (exc); Giulio Cesare (exc); Arianna (exc). (L. Hunt, Philh Baroque Orch/N. McGegan)

① **HMU90 7059** (7/93)
Mozart—Quintets
Mozart: Clarinet Quintet, K581; Horn Quintet, K407; String Quintet, K516. (Aston Magna, D. Stepner)

① **HMU90 7066** (7/94)
Uccellini—Chamber Works
Uccellini: Sonatas, Op. 2 (exc); Sonatas, Op. 3 (exc); Sonatas, Op. 4 (exc); Sonatas, Op. 7 (exc). (Arcadian Academy, N. McGegan (hpd/dir))

① **HMU90 7067** (9/92)
Nicola Matteis—Ayres for the Violin
N. Matteis I: Ayres for the Violin, Bk.1; Ayres for the Violin, Bk.2; Ayres for the Violin, Bk.4. (Arcadian Academy, N. McGegan (hpd/dir))

① **HMU90 7068** (4/93)
Lord Herbert of Cherbury's Lute Book
Anon: Chacogne; En me revenant; *Gautier d'Angleterre:* Lord Herbert's Courantes; *Reys:* Lord Herbert's Sarabande; Perrichon Courante; Despond: Filou variations; *Bacheler:* Lord Herbert's Miscellany; Dowland Variations; Jeune fillette variations; *R. Johnson I:* Lord Herbert's Miscellany; *Lorenzini:* Lord Herbert's Fantasia; *Cato:* Janequin Fantasia; *Hely:* Lord Herbert's Fantasias; *Sarabrand; Herbert of Cherbury:* Pavan. (P. O'Dette)

① **HMU90 7070** (11/92)
Walton—Orchestral Works
Walton: Violin Concerto; Henry V Suite; Spitfire Prelude and Fugue; Capriccio Burlesco. (A. Rosand, Florida PO/J. Judd)

① **HMU90 7076** (9/94)
Lassus—St Matthew Passion
Lassus: St Matthew Passion (Cpte); *Anon:* Easter Sunday (exc); Easter Sunday (exc). (Theatre of Voices/P. Hillier)

① **HMU90 7084/5** (10/93)
Bach—Violin Sonatas
Bach: Violin Sonatas, BWV1014-19; Violin Sonata, BWV1019a; Violin Sonatas, BWV1020-25 (exc). (E. Blumenstock, E. Le Guin, S. Lehning, J. Butt)

① **HMU90 7086/B** (1/94)
Prokofiev—Piano Sonatas
Prokofiev: Piano Sonata 1; Piano Sonata 2; Piano Sonata 3; Piano Sonata 4; Piano Sonata 5; Piano Sonata 6; Piano Sonata 7; Piano Sonata 8; Piano Sonata 9; Lt Kijé Suite (exc). (F. Chiu)

① **HMU90 7091** (2/94)
Three Parts upon a Ground
Purcell: Fantasia, Z731; *Buonamente:* Sonata a tre violini; *G. Gabrieli:* Canzoni et Sonate (1615) (exc); *Marini:* Eco a tre violini; Sonata a tre; *Uccellini:* Sonata, Op. 9 (exc); *Fontana:* Sonate a 1,2,3 (exc); *Constantin:* 3-Violin Pavan; *Schmelzer:* Sonata a tre; *Hacquart:* Harmonia parnassia (exc); *Rosier:* 3-Violin Suite; *Pachelbel:* Canon and Gigue. (J. Holloway, S. Ritchie, A. Manze, N. North, M. Springfels, J. Toll)

① **HMU90 7092** (10/94)
Persichetti—Divertimenti for Winds
Persichetti: Divertimento, Op. 42; Psalm, Op. 53; Choral Prelude, op. 160; Pageant, Op. 59; Masquerade, Op. 102; O Cool is the Valley, Op. 118; Parable, Op. 121. (LSO Winds/D. Amos)

① **HMU90 7093** (1/94)
Telemann—Concertos and Suites
Telemann: Recorder & Viola da Gamba Concerto 1; Overture-Suite, TWV55: D 6; Overture-Suite, TWV55: a min 2; Sinfonia, TWV50: 3. (M. Verbruggen, S. Cunningham, OAE/M. Huggett)

① **HMU90 7094** (7/94)
Schubert—Piano Trios
Schubert: Piano Trio 1; Notturno, D897; Piano Trio, D28. (S. Ritchie, M. Lutzke, S. Lubin)

① **HMU90 7099** (12/93)
On Yoolis Night
Anon: Advent (exc); Christmas (exc); Christmas (exc); Christmas (exc); Christmas (exc); Christmas (exc); Christmas (exc); *Traditional:* Alleluya: a nywe werk is come on honde; Gabriel fram heven-king; Puellare gremium; Ecce quod natura; There is no rose; Nowel, Nowel, Owt of Your Slepe; Prolis nativitas; Balaam de quo vaticinans; Ave Maria; Lullay: I saw a swete semly syght; Prolis eterne genitor; De supernis sedibus; Lullay: Als I lay on Yoolis night; Orto sole serene; Perperit virgo. (Anon 4)

① **HMU90 7103** (6/94)
Blow/Locke/Purcell—Organ Works
Purcell: Organ Voluntaries, Z717-20; Verse, Z716; Choice Collection of Lessons (exc); Grounds (exc); Voluntary on the Old 100th, Z721; Trumpet Voluntary; *Blow:* Organ Voluntaries; *Locke:* Voluntaries. (J. Butt)

① **HMU90 7104** (11/93)
Vivaldi/Chedéville—Oboe Sonatas
Vivaldi: Sonata, RV53; Trio Sonata, RV81; Sonata, RV779; Sonatas, Op.13 (exc); Sonatas, Op.13 (exc). (P. Goodwin, G. Hennessey, C. Lawson, F. Eustace, J. Holloway, S. Sheppard, N. North, N. North, J. Toll, J. Toll)

① **HMU90 7106** (2/94)
Kraft—Orchestral Works
William Kraft: Timpani Concerto; Piano Concerto; Evening Voluntaries; Veils and Variations. (J. von der Schmidt, M. Golabek, T. Akins, Alabama SO/P. Polivnick, Berkeley SO/K. Nagano)

① **HMU90 7108** (3/95)
Matteis—Ayres for the Violin, Volume 2
N. Matteis I: Ayres for the Violin, Bk 2 (exc); Ayres for the Violin, Bk 3 (exc); Ayres for the Violin, Bk 4 (exc). (Arcadian Academy)

① **HMU90 7114** (8/94)
Schuman—String Quartets
Schuman: String Quartet 2; String Quartet 3; String Quartet 5. (Lydian Qt)

① **HMU90 7116** (5/95)
Giuliani/Paganini—Violin and Guitar Works
Paganini: Grand Sonata in A; Sonata concertata in A; *Giuliani:* Duo concertante, Op. 25. (M. Huggett, R. Savino)

① **HMU90 7117** (5/94)
Mendelssohn—Piano Sonatas
Mendelssohn: Piano Sonata, Op.6; Piano Sonata, Op.105; Piano Sonata, Op.106; Rondo capriccioso. (F. Chiu)

① **HMU90 7122** (4/95)
Lully/Philidor—Stage Works
A. Philidor: Mariage de la Grosse Cathos; *Lully:* Bourgeois gentilhomme; Cadmus; Nopces de Village. (London Ob Band, M-A. Petit/P. Goodwin)

① **HMU90 7124** (5/95)
Perle/Danielpour—Piano Works
Perle: Etudes; Piano Concerto 2; *Danielpour:* Metamorphosis. (M. Boriskin, Utah SO/J. Silverstein)

① **HMU90 7125** (9/95)
The Lily & the Lamb
Anon: O gloriosa domina; Pe milde lomb isprad o rode; Ave maria gracia plena; O Maria stella maris; Stabat iuxta Christi crucem; Stillat in stellam radium; Salve virgo singularis; Stond wel moder under roode; O Maria virgo pia; In te concipitur, Jesu Christes milde moder; Veni mater gracie/Dou way, Robin; O mors moreris/O vita vera/Mors; Salve virgo tonantis solium; Miserere miseris; Ave maria salus hominum; Memor esto tuorum; Ave regina celorum. (Anon 4)

① **HMU90 7134/5** (2/95)
Biber—Sonatas and Passagalias
Biber: Sonatae (1681); Sonata violino solo; Pastorella Sonata; Lute Passacaglia; Mystery Sonatas (exc). (Romanesca, N. North, A. Manze)

① **HMU90 7136** (11/95)
Josquin Despres/Mouton—Vocal Works
Josquin Desprez: Missa De beata virgine; *Mouton:* Nesciens Mater; Ave Maria virgo serena; Ave sanctissima Maria; O Maria piissima; Ave Maria gemma virginum. (Theatre of Voices/P. Hillier)

① **HMU90 7150** (8/95)
Prokofiev—Piano Works, Vol. 4
Prokofiev: Romeo and Juliet Pieces; Cinderella Pieces, Op. 95; Cinderella Pieces, Op. 97; Pieces, Op. 96. (F. Chiu)

① **HMU90 7160** (11/95)
Dowland—Complete Lute Works, Vol. 1
Dowland: Pavans (Mylius 1622); Almains (exc); Ballad Settings (exc); Fantasies (exc); Galliards (exc); Jigs, Corantos, Toys, etc (exc); Pavans (exc). (P. O'Dette)

① **HMX290 1528/33(1)** (7/95)
A Purcell Companion (pt 1)
Purcell: Dido (Cpte); Funeral Sentences (exc); March and Canzona, Z860; Te Deum and Jubilate, Z232 (exc); Bell Anthem, Z49; Remember not, Lord, our offences, Z50; Blow up the Trumpet in Sion, Z10; Hear my prayer, O Lord, Z15; My heart is inditing, Z30; O Lord God of hosts, Z37; Fantasia, Z731; Sonatas, Z802-11 (exc); Pavan, Z752; Chaconne, Z730; Pavans, Z748-51; Sonatas Z790-801 (exc); Overture, Z771; Welcome Song, Z336 (exc); Overture, Z772; Overture, Z770. (G. Laurens, P. Cantor, J. Feldman, D. Visse, A. Mellon, B. Borden, E. Lestrigant, M. Laplénie, Arts Florissants Voc Ens, Arts Florissants Instr Ens/W. Christie, T. Bonner, P. Kwella, K. Wessel, P. Agnew, W. Kendall, P. Kooy, Collegium Vocale/P. Herreweghe, London Baroque)

① **HMX290 1528/33(2)** (7/95)
A Purcell Companion (pt 2)
Purcell: King Arthur, Z628 (exc); Bonduca, Z574 (exc); Don Quixote, Z578 (exc); Fairy Queen, Z629 (exc); Indian Queen, Z630 (exc); King Arthur, Z628 (exc); King Richard II, Z581 (exc); Dioclesian, Z627 (exc); Pausanias, Z585 (exc); Oedipus, Z583 (exc); Not all my torments, Z400; Evening Hymn, Z193; Organ Voluntaries, Z717-20; Verse, Z716; Choice Collection of Lessons (exc); Grounds (exc); Voluntary on the Old 100th, Z721; Trumpet Voluntary; *Blow:* Organ Voluntaries; *Locke:* Voluntaries; *Purcell:* O Solitude, Z406; If music be the food of love, Z379/1. (H. Sheppard, J. Knibbs, R. Hardy, A. Deller, M. Deller, P. Elliott, L. Nixon, M. Bevan, N. Beavan, Deller Ch, King's Musick/A. Deller, A. Deller, W. Kuijken, W. Christie, R. Skeaping, J. Butt)

① **HMX290 772/83(1)** (2/93)
Bach—Complete Organ Works (pt 1)
Bach: Prelude and Fugue, BWV532; Prelude and Fugue, BWV550; Prelude and Fugue, BWV533; Prelude and Fugue, BWV531; Prelude and Fugue, BWV535; Prelude and Fugue, BWV549; Prelude and Fugue, BWV534; Prelude and Fugue, BWV539; Fugue, BWV577; Fugue, BWV575; Fugue, BWV578; Fugue, BWV579; Toccata and Fugue, BWV565; Toccata, Adagio and Fugue, BWV564; Toccata and Fugue, BWV540; Toccata and Fugue, BWV538; Toccata, BWV566; O Gott, du frommer Gott, BWV767; Partita, BWV766; Sei gegrüsset, BWV768; Pastorale, BWV590; Canzona, BWV588; Allabreve, BWV589; Orgel-Büchlein, BWV599-644 (exc). (L. Rogg)

① **HMX290 772/83(2)** (2/93)
Bach—Complete Organ Works (pt 2)
Bach: Ein feste Burg, BWV720; Nun freut euch, BWV734; Chorales, BWV651-668 (exc); Valet will ich dir geben, BWV736; Herzlich tut mich verlangen, BWV727; Passacaglia and Fugue, BWV582; Fantasia and Fugue, BWV542; Fantasia and Fugue, BWV537; Fantasia, BWV572; Fantasia, BWV562; Herr Christ, der einig Gottes Sohn, BWV698; Gelobet seist du, BWV697; Nun komm, der Heiden Heiland, BWV699; Lob sei dem allmächtigen Gott, BWV704; Vom Himmel hoch, BWV701; Christum wir sollen loben schon, BWV696; Gottes Sohn, BWV703; Meine Seele erhebt den Herren, BWV733; Herr Jesu Christ, BWV709; Liebster Jesu, BWV706; Wer nur den lieben, BWV690; Wer nur den lieben, BWV691; Liebster Jesu, BWV731; Vom Himmel hoch, BWV738; Ach Gott und Herr, BWV714; Allein Gott, BWV711. (L. Rogg)

① **HMX290 772/83(2)** (2/93)
Bach—Complete Organ Works (pt 3)
Bach: Wir Christenleut', BWV710; Christ lag in Todesbanden, BWV718; Christ lag in Todesbanden, BWV695; Allein Gott, BWV717; Jesu, meine Freude, BWV713; In dich hab ich gehoffet, BWV712; Wir glauben all' an einen Gott, BWV740; Trio Sonatas, BWV525-530; Trio, BWV583; Prelude and Fugue, BWV552; Clavier-Übung III, BWV669-689 (exc); Schübler Chorales, BWV645-650; Vom Himmel hoch Variations, BWV769; Prelude and Fugue, BWV543; Prelude and Fugue, BWV548; Prelude and Fugue, BWV547; Prelude and Fugue, BWV541; Prelude and Fugue, BWV546; Prelude and Fugue, BWV545; Prelude and Fugue, BWV544; Prelude and Fugue, BWV536. (L. Rogg)

Harmonic

① **H/CD8505** (4/91)
Debussy: Piano Works
Debussy: Préludes (exc); Estampes (exc); Isle joyeuse (exc); Suite bergamasque (exc). (P. Badura-Skoda)

① **H/CD8720** (3/91)
Vivaldi—Sacred Vocal Works
Vivaldi: Stabat Mater; Nisi Dominus; Filiae mestae, RV638; Vestro Principi divino, RV633. (G. Lesne, Seminario Musicale Ens)

Hat-Hut

① **ARTCD6143** (12/95)
Morton Feldman—Works for Piano 2
M. Feldman: Intermission 1; Intermission 2; Intermission 5; Intermission 6; Piano Piece (1952); Last Pieces; Five Pianos. (S. Schleiermacher, I. Mundry, M. Persson, K. Scholz, N. Vigeland)

Helicon

① **CD-HLR143-2** (1/89)
Mussorgsky—Piano Works
Mussorgsky: Pictures; Gopak; Souvenirs d'enfance (exc); Intermezzo in modo classico; Kinderscarn; Larme; Au village. (M. Papadopoulos)

Herald

① **HAVPCD115** (4/89)
Howells: Organ Works
Howells: Short Organ Pieces; St Louis; Flourish for a bidding; Intrata; Slow airs. (P. Kenyon)

① **HAVPCD125** (6/90)
Franck: Organ Works
Franck: Fantaisie in A; Fantaisie, Op. 16; Organiste II (exc); Pastorale; Chorales (exc). (M. Howard)

① **HAVPCD142** (12/91)
Christmas at Charterhouse
M. Praetorius: Come, thou redeemer of the earth; *Traditional:* This is the truth sent from above; Bethlehem Down; *Brahms:* Chorale Preludes, Op. 122 (exc); *Traditional:* Adam lay y-bounden; King Jesus hath a garden; Quelle est cette odeur agréable?; Once in Royal David's City; Ding dong! merrily on high; In dulci jubilo; *Bach:* In dulci jubilo, BWV729; *Traditional:* O come, all ye faithful; Hark! the herald angels sing; Huic Magi. (Charterhouse Special Ch/R. Burton, R. Wells)

① **HAVPCD145** (3/92)
French Organ Works
Vierne: Symphony 3; *Widor:* Symphony 9; *Tournemire:* Suite évocatrice, Op.74. (J. Filsell)

① **HAVPCD148** (12/92)
13th Century Chants
Anon: Advent (exc); Advent (exc); Christmas (exc); Christmas (exc); Holy Week (exc); Holy Week (exc); Easter Sunday (exc); Easter Sunday (exc); Pentecost (exc); Feast Days (exc); Festival of the Virgin Mary (exc); Saints' Days (exc). (Schola Gregoriana/M. Berry)

① **HAVPCD151** (4/93)
Anglo-Saxon Christmas
Anon: Christmas (exc); Christmas (exc); Christmas (exc); Christmas (exc). (Schola Gregoriana/M. Berry)

① **HAVPCD152** (10/92)
Music for Clarinet and Piano
Arnold: Clarinet Sonatina, Op. 29; *Dunhill:* Phantasy Suite, Op. 91; *Finzi:* Bagatelles; *M. Henry:* Jazz Song; *Ireland:* Fantasy-Sonata; *McCabe:* Clarinet Pieces (1964). (N. Carpenter, D. McArthur)

① **HAVPCD155** (10/92)
Give us the Wings of Faith
Anon: Requiem (exc); Feast Days (exc); *Dunstable:* Quam pulchra es; *Byrd:* Gradualia 1/ii: Corpus Christi (exc); *Gibbons:* This is the record of John; *Stainer:* How beautiful upon the mountains; *Elgar:* Ave verum corpus, Op. 2/1; Ave Maria, Op. 2/2; *Parry:* Crossing the Bar; *Harwood:* O how glorious; *Bullock:* Give us the wings of faith; *Vaughan Williams:* O how amiable; *L. J. White:* Prayer of St Richard; *Bainton:* And I saw a new heaven; *Dyson:* Evening Service in D (exc); Ye that do your Master's will; *Britten:* Hymn of St Columba; *Anon:* Ave Maris Stella; *S. Anderson:* Hymn to St Cecilia; *W. H. Harris:* O what their joy. (Wellington College Chs, T. Byram-Wigfield/A. Anderson)

① **HAVPCD155** (1/94)
Music from Renaissance Portugal
P. de Cristo: Magnificat a 8; Ave Maria a 8; Sanctissimi quinque martires; De profundis; Lachrimans sitivit anima mea; Ave regina caelorum; *D. Lôbo:* Missa pro defunctis; *Anon:* Si pie Domine; *A. Fernandez:* Libera me Domine; Alma redemptoris mater; *Carreira:* Stabat mater. (Tavener Ch/O. Rees)

① **HAVPCD157** (3/93)
Gregorian Chant Gaudete
Anon: Advent (exc); Advent (exc); Christmas (exc); Christmas (exc); Epiphany (exc); Epiphany (exc); Epiphany (exc); Lent (exc); Lent (exc); Lent (exc); Holy Week (exc); Holy Week (exc); Holy Week (exc); Easter Sunday (exc); Easter Sunday (exc); Ascension Day (exc); Pentecost (exc); Corpus Christi (exc); Corpus Christi (exc); Corpus Christi (exc); Divine Office: Lauds (exc); Funeral chants (exc); Funeral chants (exc); Funeral chants (exc); Te saeculorum principem. (St Cecilia's Abbey, Ryde, Nuns' Ch)

① **HAVPCD161** (11/93)
Pentecost at Pontigny
Anon: Pentecost (exc); Pentecost (exc); Pentecost (exc); Pentecost (exc); Pentecost (exc); *Dunstable:* Veni, Sancte Spiritus; *Nucius:* Dum congelerentur; *Anon:* Clangat tuba; Thomas gemma; Ave, mundi rosa. (Schola Gregoriana/M. Berry)

① **HAVPCD163** (12/93)
In the Bleak Midwinter
Traditional: Once in Royal David's City; In the bleak midwinter; Up! good Christen folk; Tomorrow shall be my dancing day; Of the Father's heart begotten; Spotless

Rose; Lord at first did Adam make; God rest you merry, gentlemen; Christmas Day; Noël Nouvelet; Ding dong! merrily on high; O little town of Bethlehem; Coventry Carol; Bethlehem Down; O come, all ye faithful; Away in a manger; Zither Carol; Hark! the herald angels sing. (Edinburgh Cath Ch/T. Byram-Wigfield)

ⓘ **HAVPCD168** (3/95)
Abelard—12th-Century Chant
Abelard: O quanta qualia; Planctus David; Mater salvatoris; Ne derelinquas me; Epithalamica; Magnum salutis gaudium; De profundis; *Anon:* Divine Office: Various (exc); Feast Days (exc); Feast Days (exc); Sponsus; Samson dux fortissime; *St Bernard:* Quam pium. (Schola Gregoriana, Winchester Cath Choristers/M. Berry)

ⓘ **HAVPCD176** (9/95)
Bax/Villette—Choral Music
Bax: Epithalamium; I sing of a maiden; Lord, thou hast told us; Magnificat; Mater ora filium; This worldes joie; *Villette:* Attende Domine; Hymne à la Vierge; O magnum mysterium; O sacrum convivium; Salve Regina. (Rodolfus Ch/R. Allwood, C. Hughes)

Heritage Recordings

ⓘ **HRCD901** (8/91)
By Royal Command
Mendelssohn: Duets, Op. 63 (exc); Lieder, Op. 47 (exc); Lieder, Op. 8 (exc); Lieder, Op. 34 (exc); Lieder, Op. 57 (exc); Waldschloss, Op. posth; Schlafloser Augen Leuchte, Op. posth; Lieder, Op. 9 (exc); Lieder, Op. 86 (exc); Songs without Words (exc); Songs without Words (exc); Organ Sonatas (exc); Four Little Organ Pieces (exc); Paulus (exc); Hear my prayer; *Prince Albert:* Grüss an der Bruder; Grüss aus dem Ferne; Schmerz der Liebe; Klage der Liebe; Ständchen. (S. Gritton, J. Bowen, C. Dowdle, Heritage Sngrs, S. Ridgley-Whitehouse, S. Ridgley-Whitehouse, S. Ridgley-Whitehouse (org/dir))

Hungaroton

ⓘ **HCD11385** (10/87)
20th Century Vocal Works
Boulez: Improvisation sur Mallarmé I; Improvisation sur Mallarmé II; *Schoenberg:* Pierrot lunaire; *Webern:* Lieder, Op. 8; Canons, Op. 16. (E. Sziklay, Budapest Chbr Ens/A. Mihály)

ⓘ **HCD21690** (12/87)
Bach—Keyboard Works
Bach: Chromatic Fantasia and Fugue, BWV903; Partitas, BWV825/30 (exc); Toccatas, BWV910-16 (exc); English Suites, BWV806-811 (exc). (A. Schiff)

ⓘ **HCD11885** (4/89)
Beethoven—Piano Works
Beethoven: Bagatelles (exc); Allegretto, WoO61; Waltz, WoO84; Ecossaise, WoO86; Waltz, WoO85; Allegretto, WoO61a; Polonaise, Op. 89. (A. Schiff)

ⓘ **HCD12502/4** (3/85)
Bartók—Complete String Quartets
Bartók: String Quartet 1; String Quartet 2; String Quartet 3; String Quartet 4; String Quartet 5; String Quartet 6. (Takács Qt)

ⓘ **HCD12631** (12/86)
Bernstein in Budapest
Bartók: Music for Strings, Percussion and Celesta; *Bernstein:* Divertimento; *Brahms:* Hungarian Dances (exc). (BRSO/L. Bernstein)

ⓘ **HCD12991** (11/90)
20th Century Percussion Works
Varèse: Ionisation; *Chávez:* Toccata; *Cage:* 4'33"; Double Music; Amores; Third Construction. (Z. Kocsis, Amadinda Perc Group)

ⓘ **HCD31358** (6/91)
Reich—Music for Mallet Instruments
Reich: Music for Mallet Instruments, Voices and Organ; Music for Pieces of Wood; Sextet. (Amadinda Perc Group)

ⓘ **HCD31535** (7/93)
Bartók—Songs
Bartók: Songs, Sz61; Songs, Sz63; Hungarian Folksongs, Sz64 (exc); Songs, Sz61; Hungarian Folksongs, Sz101. (J. Hamari, I. Prunyi, Hungarian St Orch/J. Kovács)

Hunters Moon

ⓘ **HMPCD0589** (7/93)
Enchanting Melodies
Lange: Spring's Message; *Czibulka:* Stephanie-Gavotte, Op. 312; *Heinrich:* In the Shadows; *G.D. Wilson:* Shepherd Boy; *Jaell:* Chant Romantique; *Durand:* Waltz in E flat; *Bądarzewska-Baranowska:* Maiden's Prayer;

Wyman: Silvery Waves; *Watson:* Fairies' Gathering; *Kinkel:* Angel's Serenade; *S. Smith:* Sleigh-Bells; *Galos:* Chant du Berger; *Sanderson:* Sincerité; *Thomé:* Simple Aveu; *Fibich:* Moods, Op. 41, Part 2 (exc); *Elgar:* Salut d'amour; *G. Moore:* Lullaby; *Ketterer:* Gaëtana; *Rubinstein:* Soirées, Op. 44 (exc); *Chopin:* Nocturnes (exc); *Balakirev:* Spanish Melody; *Raff:* Polka de la Reine. (A. Etherden)

Hyperion

ⓘ **CDA66009** (10/88)
Rachmaninov—Piano Works
Rachmaninov: Chopin Variations, Op.22; Corelli Variations; Morceaux de fantaisie, Op.3 (exc); *Mendelssohn:* Midsummer Night's Dream (exc). (H. Shelley)

ⓘ **CDA66014** (7/89)
Music for clarinet and piano, Vol. 1
Stanford: Clarinet Sonata; *H. Ferguson:* Short Pieces, Op. 6; *Finzi:* Bagatelles; *Hurlstone:* Characteristic pieces. (T. King, C. Benson)

ⓘ **CDA66015** (9/91)
Songs by Finzi and His Friends
Finzi: To a Poet; Oh fair to see; *Milford:* If it's ever spring again; Colour; So sweet love seemed; *Gurney:* Sleep; Down by the salley gardens; Hawk and Buckle; *Gill:* In Memoriam; *Farrar:* O mistress mine!. (I. Partridge, S. Roberts, C. Benson)

ⓘ **CDA66021** (11/87)
Monteverdi: Sacred vocal works
Monteverdi: Su le penne; Selva morale e spirituale (exc); Messa et salmi (exc). (E. Kirkby, I. Partridge, D. Thomas, Parley of Instr)

ⓘ **CDA66022** (1/88)
The Clarinet in Concert
Bruch: Clarinet and Viola Concerto; *Mendelssohn:* Concert Piece, Op. 113; Concert Piece, Op. 114; *Crusell:* Introduction, Theme and Variations on a Swedish Air. (T. King, N. Imai, G. Dobrée, LSO/A. Francis)

ⓘ **CDA66038** (9/86)
Echoes of a Waterfall
Hasselmans: Source, Op. 44; Prelude, Op. 52; Chanson de mai, Op. 40; *Parish Alvars:* Divertissement, Op. 38; *Godefroid:* Bois solitaire; Etude de concert, Op. 193; *Glinka:* Mozart Variations; *J. Thomas:* Echoes of a Waterfall; Watching the Wheat; Megan's Daughter; *Spohr:* Variations, Op. 36. (S. Drake)

ⓘ **CDA66039** (7/85)
A Feather on the Breath of God
Hildegard of Bingen: O Jerusalem; O presul vere civitatis; O ignis spiritus; Columba aspexit; Ave generosa; O viridissima virga; O Euchari, in leta vita; O ecclesia. (E. Kirkby, Gothic Voices, D. Muskett, R. White/C. Page)

ⓘ **CDA66044** (11/89)
English Music for Clarinet and Piano
Howells: Clarinet Sonata; *Bliss:* Pieces, T9 (exc); *Reizenstein:* Arabesques; *A. Cooke:* Clarinet Sonata. (T. King, C. Benson)

ⓘ **CDA66045** (8/88)
Hahn: Songs
Hahn: Fontaines; À Chloris; Tyndaris; Chère blessure; Air; Quand je fus pris; Étoiles; Automne; Infidélité; Si mes vers; Enamourée; Chansons grises; D'une prison; Offrande; Incrédule; Fêtes galantes. (M. Hill, G. Johnson)

ⓘ **CDA66056** (6/88)
Purcell: Songs and Dialogues
Purcell: In all our Cynthia's shining sphere, Z496; Dioclesian, Z627 (exc); Old Bachelor, Z607 (exc); Amphitryon, Z572 (exc); Go, tell Amynta, gentle swain, Z489; Why, my Daphne, why complaining, Z525; What can we poor females do, Z518; Fenice, fond deceiver, Z492; In some kind dream, Z497; What a sad fate is mine, Z428; Lost is my quiet for ever, Z502; Stript of their green our groves appear, Z444; King Arthur, Z628 (exc). (E. Kirkby, D. Thomas, A. Rooley)

ⓘ **CDA66062** (7/86)
Bruckner—Motets
Bruckner: Locus iste; Os justi; Afferentur regi; Ave Maria (1861); Vexilla regis; Ecce sacerdos magnus; Tota pulchra es; Virga Jesse; Pange lingua; Inveni David; Christus factus est. (Corydon Sngrs/M. Best, P. Salmon, T. Trotter)

ⓘ **CDA66070** (12/89)
Purcell: Songs
Purcell: If music be the food of love, Z379/2; If music be the food of love, Z379/3; O! fair Cederia, Z402; Aureng-Zebe, Z573 (exc); Wedding Ode, Z325 (exc); Fly swift, ye hours, Z369; Double Dealer, Z592 (exc); Not all my torments Z400; King Arthur, Z628 (exc); Love thou can'st

---

hear, Z396; Dioclesian, Z627 (exc); Pausanias, Z585 (exc); Sophonisba, Z590 (exc); Ah! cruel nymph, Z352; Oedipus, Z583 (exc). (P. Esswood, J. Sonnleitner, C. Medlam)

ⓘ **CDA66074** (9/91)
German Consort Music, 1660-1710
Rosenmüller: Sonate da Camera (exc); *Schmelzer:* Sacro-Profanus (exc); *G. Böhm:* Keyboard suites (exc); *Fischer:* Journal du Printems (exc); *Telemann:* Ouverture a 4 in C. (Parley of Instr/R. Goodman/P. Holman)

ⓘ **CDA66076** (10/87)
British Choral Works
Howells: Requiem; Take him, earth; *Vaughan Williams:* Mass in G minor; Te Deum in G. (J. Coxwell, M. Seers, M. Chance, P. Salmon, J. Best, Corydon Sngrs/M. Best)

ⓘ **CDA66077** (6/89)
Crusell: Clarinet Quartets Nos 1-3
Crusell: Clarinet Quartet 1; Clarinet Quartet 2; Clarinet Quartet 3. (T. King, Allegri Qt)

ⓘ **CDA66078** (3/90)
Cathedral & Organ Music
Sumsion: Te Deum; They that go down; In exile; Down Ampney; Introduction and Theme; *Howells:* Scribe; Inheritance; *Finzi:* Lo, the full, final sacrifice. (Worcester Cath Ch, A. Partington, D. Hunt Sngrs/Don Hunt, Don Hunt)

ⓘ **CDA66082** (10/88)
Rachmaninov—Piano Works
Rachmaninov: Preludes (exc); Prelude (1891); Prelude (1917). (H. Shelley)

ⓘ **CDA66090** (12/86)
Rare piano encores
Rossini: Péchés de vieillesse X (exc); *Mozart:* Don Giovanni (exc); *Gershwin:* Promenade; *Reger:* Schlichte Weisen, Op. 76 (exc); *Grainger:* Blithe bells; *Wagner:* Albumblatt; *Gaertner:* Viennese Dances (exc); *Rachmaninov:* Songs, Op. 8 (exc); *Bizet:* Carmen (exc); *Rubinstein:* Valse caprice; *Grieg:* Melodies of the Heart, Op. 5 (exc); *Bruckner:* Erinnerung; *Liszt:* Valses oubliées, S215 (exc); Soirées de Vienne, S427 (exc); Valse à capriccio, S401. (L. Howard)

ⓘ **CDA66100** (4/87)
Mahler: Songs
Mahler: Lieder und Gesänge; Lieder eines fahrenden Gesellen; Im Lenz; Winterlied. (J. Baker, G. Parsons)

ⓘ **CDA66104** (10/91)
Haydn: Welsh Folksong Arrangements
Haydn: Away, my herd; Break of Day; Rising Sun; David of the White Rock; Rising of the Lark; Crystal Ground; Jenny's Mantle; Dimpled Cheek; March of the Men of Harlech; Lambs' Fold Vale; Despairing Bard; Minstrels of Chirk Castle; All Through the Night; Ash Grove; Sleeping Beauty. (A. Pearce, S. Drake)

ⓘ **CDA66106** (2/87)
Olympia's Lament
India: Le musiche IV (1623) (exc); Le musiche IV (1621) (exc); Le musiche I (1609) (exc); Le musiche V (1623) (exc); *Monteverdi:* Scherzi musicali (1632) (exc); Ohimè ch'io cado; Lamento d'Olimpia; Voglio di vita uscir. (E. Kirkby, A. Rooley)

ⓘ **CDA66108** (11/88)
Purcell's London: English Consort Music
G. Keller: Trumpet Sonatas (exc); *N. Matteis I:* Divisions on a Ground in D minor (exc); *Baltzar:* Pavan and Galliard in C (exc); *Blow:* Chaconne in G (exc); *J. Eccles:* Judgment of Paris (exc); *Anon:* Sonata in D (exc); *Croft:* Twin Rivals Suite (exc); *Purcell:* Choice Collection of Lessons (exc). (Parley of Instr/R. Goodman/P. Holman)

ⓘ **CDA66112** (3/88)
Souvenirs de Venise
Rossini: Soirées musicales (exc); Soirées musicales (exc); *Beethoven:* Songs, WoO158a (exc); *Schubert:* Gondelfahrer, D808; *Mendelssohn:* Lieder, Op. 57 (exc); *Jensen:* Wenn durch die Piazzetta, Op.50/3; Leis' rudern hier, mein Gondolier, Op.50/4; *Glinka:* Venetian Night; *Taneyev:* Venice at Night; *Gounod:* Mélodies (1855) (exc); *Massenet:* Souvenir de Venise; *Fauré:* Songs, Op.7 (exc); *Hahn:* Venezia (exc). (F. Lott, A. Murray, A. Rolfe Johnson, R. Jackson, G. Johnson, B. Brooks, J. Pearson, H. d'Alton)

ⓘ **CDA66114** (6/86)
Victoria: Sacred Choral Works
Victoria: O quam gloriosum; Missa O quam gloriosum; Missa Ave maris stella. (Westminster Cath Ch/D. Hill)

ⓘ **CDA66121** (7/86)
Organ Fireworks Vol 1
Bonnet: Variations de concert, Op. 1; *Guilmant:* Grand choeur triomphale; March, Op. 15; *Whitlock:* Extemporizations (exc); *Brewer:* Marche héroïque;

Monnikendam: Toccata 2; *D. Johnson:* Trumpet tune in D; *Widor:* Symphony 7 (exc); *Preston:* Alleluyas; *Høvland:* Toccata (1973). (C. Herrick)

ⓒ **CDA66126** (5/86)
Britten: Choral Works
Britten: Rejoice in the Lamb; Wedding Anthem; Festival Te Deum; Boy was Born. (M. Seers, J. Coxwell, R. Unwin, M. Chance, P. Salmon, Q. Hayes, Westminster Cath Ch, Corydon Sngrs/M. Best)

ⓒ **CDA66129** (1/89)
Victoria: Sacred Choral Works
Victoria: Ave Maria, gratia plena a 4; Ave maris stella (1581); Ne timeas, Maria; Sancta Maria, succurre miseris; Vidi speciosam; Missa Vidi speciosam. (Westminster Cath Ch, J. O'Donnell/D. Hill)

ⓒ **CDA66133** (11/88)
Martinů: Chamber Works
Martinů: Madrigal stanzas; Madrigals (1937); Madrigals (1948); Madrigal Sonata. (Dartington Ens)

ⓒ **CDA66135** (12/89)
H. Lawes: Psalms, Ayres and Dialogues
H. Lawes: My soul the Great God's praises sing; Lark; Sweet, stay awhile; Amintor's welladay; This mossy bank; Man's life is but vain; Hark, shepherd swains; Thee and thy wondrous deeds; I laid me down; In quel gelato core; I prithee send me; Slide soft you silver floods; Sing fair Clorinda; Orpheus's Hymn; Come, sad turtle; Farewell, despairing hopes; Sitting by the streams. (Consort of Musicke/A. Rooley)

ⓒ **CDA66137** (9/88)
Bliss: Vocal and Chamber Works
Bliss: Rout; Rhapsody; Conversation; Women of Yueh; Madame Noy; Oboe Quintet. (E. Gale, A. Rolfe Johnson, Nash Ens/L. Friend)

ⓒ **CDA66144** (12/86)
The Garden of Zephirus
Dufay: J'atendray tant; Mon cuer me fait; Adieu ces bons vins; *Anon:* N'a pas long temps; Je la remire; *Anthonello de Caserta:* Amour m'a le ceur; *Briquet:* Ma seul amour; *Landini:* Nessun ponga speranca; Giunta vaga biltà; *Reynea:* Va t'en, mon cuer; *Matheus de Sancto Johanne:* Fortune, faulce; *Francus de Insula:* Amours nont cure; *Brollo:* Qui le sien. (Gothic Voices, I. Barford/C. Page)

ⓒ **CDA66156** (10/86)
The Symphony in Europe
Boccherini: Symphonies, G509-14 (exc); *Maldere:* Symphony, Op. 4/1; *Schwindl:* Symphony 'périodique' in F; *S. Wesley:* Symphony in A. (ECCO/J. Faerber)

ⓒ **CDA66157** (9/91)
Parry: Chamber Music
Parry: Violin Sonata; Short Pieces; Fantasie-Sonata. (E. Gruenberg, R. Vignoles)

ⓒ **CDA66160** (10/86)
Vivaldi: Music for lute and mandoline
Vivaldi: Concerto RV532; Concerto RV425; Concerto, RV93; Concerto RV540; Trio, RV85; Trio, RV82. (Parley of Instr/R. Goodman/P. Holman)

ⓒ **CDA66161/2** (3/90)
Finzi Song Cycles to words by Thomas Hardy
Finzi: Earth and Air and Rain; Till Earth Outwears; I said to Love; Young Man's Exhortation; Before and after Summer. (M. Hill, S. Varcoe, C. Benson)

ⓒ **CDA66165** (11/87)
The Sea
Ireland: Sea Fever; *Haydn:* Canzonetas I (exc); Canzonetas II (exc); *Dibdin:* Tom Bowling; *Walton:* Song for the Lord Mayor's Table (exc); *Wolf:* Eichendorff Lieder (exc); *Fauré:* Songs, Op.23 (exc); Songs, Op.51 (exc); Horizon chimérique; *Schubert:* Lied eines Schiffers an die Dioskuren, D360; *Borodin:* Sea; Sea Princess; *Debussy:* Proses lyriques (exc); *Ives:* Swimmers; *Schumann:* Gesänge, Op. 125 (exc); *Berlioz:* Nuits d'été (exc); *Mendelssohn:* Wasserfahrt; *Brahms:* Duets, Op. 20 (exc); *Traditional:* Mermaid; Sail on, sail on. (Sarah Walker, T. Allen, R. Vignoles)

ⓒ **CDA66167** (11/89)
Janáček & Stravinsky: Piano Works
Janáček: Piano Sonata (1905); Capriccio; *Stravinsky:* Piano and Wind Concerto. (M. Papadopoulos, M. Papadopoulos, RPO)

ⓒ **CDA66168** (3/87)
Treasures of the Spanish Renaissance
F. Guerrero: Surge propera; O altitudo a 8; O Domine Jesu a 4; O sacrum convivium a 5; Ave virgo sanctissima a 5; Regina coeli a 8; *Lobo:* Versa est in luctum; Ave Maria; O quam suavis est, Domine; *Vivanco:* Magnificat. (Westminster Cath Ch/D. Hill)

ⓒ **CDA66171** (1/89)
Malcolm Arnold: Chamber Works, Vol. 1
Arnold: Violin Sonata 1; Violin Sonata 2; Pieces, Op. 84; Viola Sonata, Op. 17; Cello Duo, Op. 85; Piano Trio, Op. 54. (M. Crayford, I. Brown, R. Chase, C. van Kampen, M. Welsh)

ⓒ **CDA66172** (1/89)
Malcolm Arnold: Chamber Works, Vol. 2
Arnold: Flute Sonatina, Op. 19; Oboe Sonatina, Op. 28; Clarinet Sonatina, Op. 29; Recorder Sonatina, Op. 41; Bassoon Fantasia, Op. 86; Clarinet Fantasia, Op. 87; Horn Fantasia, Op. 88; Flute Fantasia, Op. 89; Oboe Fantasia, Op. 90; Trio, Op.6. (J. Pearce, B. Wightman, G. Hulse, M. Collins, J. Pigneguy, R. Chase, I. Brown)

ⓒ **CDA66173** (1/89)
Malcolm Arnold: Chamber Works, Vol. 3
Arnold: Quintet, Op. 7; Oboe Quartet, Op. 61; Flute Sonata, Op. 121; Flute and Viola Duo, Op. 10; Divertimento, Op. 37; Shanties, Op.4. (M. Crayford, I. Brown, R. Chase, C. van Kampen, J. Pearce, G. Hulse, M. Collins, J. Pigneguy, B. Wightman)

ⓒ **CDA66175** (11/88)
Music by Bliss, Britten and Holst
Bliss: Pastoral; *Britten:* Gloriana Choral Dances; *Holst:* Rig Veda - Group 3. (S. Minty, M. Hill, J. Pearce, T. Owen, Holst Sngrs, Holst Orch/H.D. Wetton)

ⓒ **CDA66177** (9/86)
Bruckner—Sacred Choral Works
Bruckner: Mass in E minor; Libera me; Aequale. (Corydon Sngrs, ECO Wind Ens/M. Best, C. Sheen, R. Brenner, P. Brown)

ⓒ **CDA66181** (10/87)
Widor: Organ works
Widor: Symphony 5; Symphony 1 (exc); Nouvelles pièces (exc). (/D. Hill)

ⓒ **CDA66182** (12/89)
Works by D. Scarlatti
D. Scarlatti: Stabat mater; Salve Regina; Keyboard Sonatas (exc). (C. Harris, N. Clapton, Oxford Christ Church Cath Ch/F. Grier, F. Grier)

ⓒ **CDA66185** (7/87)
Livia Rév—Piano Recital
Bach: Preludes, BWV933-38 (exc); Preludes, BWV924-932 (exc); *Daquin:* Premier livre de pièces de clavecin (exc); *Mozart:* Variations, K265; *Beethoven:* Bagatelles (exc); *Schumann:* Album für die Jugend (exc); *Chopin:* Nocturnes (exc); *Liszt:* Études d'exécution, S139 (exc); *Bizet:* Jeux d'enfants (exc); *Fauré:* Dolly (exc); *Tchaikovsky:* Album for the young (exc); *Villa-Lobos:* Prole do bebê I (exc); *Jolivet:* Chansons naïves (exc); *Prokofiev:* Music for Children (exc); *Debussy:* Children's Corner (exc); *Petit nègre; *Bartók:* Easy Pieces (exc); For Children (1945) (exc); *Magin:* Three Pieces; *Matačić:* Miniature Variations. (L. Rév)

ⓒ **CDA66186** (6/87)
Time Stands Still
Dowland: First Book of Songs (exc); Third and Last Booke of Songs (exc); Farre from triumphing court; *Campion:* Ayres (1601); Ayres, Bk 1 (exc); *Ford:* Musicke of Sundrie Kindes I (exc); *Danyel:* Songs for the Lute (exc); *Ferrabosco I:* Pavan; *Handford:* Now each creature; *H. Lawes:* Gather ye rosebuds; *Rosseter:* What then is love but mourning; *Anon:* Lost is my liberty; Mignonne allons. (E. Kirkby/A. Rooley)

ⓒ **CDA66189** (7/87)
Music for Brass and Percussion
Copland: Fanfare for the Common Man; *Grieg:* Funeral March; *Janáček:* Sinfonietta (exc); *R. Strauss:* Festmusik der Stadt Wien; *Vaughan Williams:* Henry V; *Britten:* Russian Funeral; *Holst:* Moorside Suite. (London Brass Virtuosi/D. Honeyball)

ⓒ **CDA66190** (9/87)
Victoria: Choral Works
Victoria: O magnum mysterium; Missa O magnum mysterium; Ascendens Christus in altum; Missa Ascendens Christus in altum. (Westminster Cath Ch/D. Hill)

ⓒ **CDA66192** (7/91)
Ferguson & Finzi: Chamber Works
H. Ferguson: Octet, Op. 4; Bagatelles, Op. 9; Violin Sonata 2; *Finzi:* Elegy, Op. 22. (L. Chilingirian, C. Benson, Nash Ens)

ⓒ **CDA66193** (7/87)
Vivaldi—La Follia
Vivaldi: Trio Sonata, RV60; Sonatas, Op. 1 (exc); Trio Sonata, RV74; Manchester Sonatas (exc). (Purcell Qt)

ⓒ **CDA66195** (7/87)
Telemann—Chamber Works
Telemann: Sonata, TWV42: d 10; Essercizii Musici (exc); Essercizii Musici (exc); Quartet, TWV43: G 6; Quartet, TWV43: g 2; Quartet, TWV43: a 3. (Chandos Baroque Plyrs)

ⓒ **CDA66198** (9/87)
Rachmaninov—Early Piano Works
Rachmaninov: Piano Sonata 2; Morceau de fantaisie (1899); Song without words (?1887); Pièce (1917); Fughetta (1899); Fragments (1917); Oriental Sketch (1917); Nocturnes (1887/8); Pièces (?1887). (H. Shelley)

ⓒ **CDA66200** (6/87)
M. Praetorius: Christmas music
M. Praetorius: Polyhymnia caduceatrix et panegyrica (exc); Puericinium (exc); Musae Sioniae VI (exc); Terpsichore (exc). (Westminster Cath, Parley of Instr/D. Hill)

ⓒ **CDA66201** (11/87)
Liszt—Piano Works, Vol.1
Liszt: Valses oubliées, S215; Mephisto Waltz 2, S515; Mephisto Waltz 3, S216; Mephisto Waltz 4, S696; Bagatelle sans tonalité, S216a; Ländler, S211; Albumblatt, S166; Valse impromptu, S213; Caprices-valses, S214 (exc); Mephisto Waltz 1, S514. (L. Howard)

ⓒ **CDA66209** (5/90)
Britten: Songs
Britten: Michelangelo Sonnets; Canticle 1; Winter Words; Folk Songs (exc). (A. Rolfe Johnson, G. Johnson)

ⓒ **CDA66212** (9/87)
Purcell—Ayres for the Theatre
Purcell: Abdelazer, Z570 (exc); Timon of Athens, Z632 (exc); Gordian Knot Unty'd, Z597 (exc); Bonduca Z574 (exc); Virtuous Wife, Z611 (exc); Chaconne, Z730. (Parley of Instr/P. Holman)

ⓒ **CDA66215** (1/88)
Works for Clarinet and Orchestra
Lutosławski: Dance preludes; *Seiber:* Concertino; *H. Blake:* Clarinet Concerto. (T. King, ECO/A. Litton/H. Blake)

ⓒ **CDA66216** (11/87)
The Grand Organ
Wagner: Meistersinger (exc); *Liszt:* Consolations, S172 (exc); *Mendelssohn:* Midsummer Night's Dream (exc); Athalie (exc); *Weber:* Jubel-Ouverture; *Saint-Saëns:* Carnaval des animaux (exc); Danse Macabre; *Prokofiev:* Toccata, Op.11. (T. Trotter)

ⓒ **CDA66219** (9/87)
American Choral Works
Barber: Agnus Dei, Op. 11; *Bernstein:* Chichester Psalms; *Copland:* In the Beginning; Motets. (D. Martelli, C. Denley, R. Masters, G. Kettel, T. Trotter, Corydon Sngrs/M. Best)

ⓒ **CDA66220** (2/88)
Britten: Choral music
Britten: Ceremony of Carols; Missa brevis; Hymn to the Virgin; Hymn of St Columba; This way to the Tomb (exc); Jubilate Deo in E flat. (Westminster Cath Ch, S. Williams/D. Hill)

ⓒ **CDA66226** (9/87)
Corelli: La Follia and other Sonatas
Corelli: Trio Sonatas, Op. 1 (exc); Trio Sonatas, Op. 2 (exc); Trio Sonatas, Op. 3 (exc); Trio Sonatas, Op. 4 (exc); Sonatas, Op. 5 (exc); Sonatas, Op. 5 (exc). (Purcell Qt, L. Campbell)

ⓒ **CDA66227** (9/87)
Emma Kirkby Collection
Monteverdi: Selva morale e spirituale (exc); Voglio di vita uscir; Scherzi musicali (1632) (exc); *India:* Le Musiche V (1623) (exc); Le musiche I (1609) (exc); *Bach:* Cantata 208 (exc); Cantata 202 (exc); *Campion:* Now hath Flora; Move now with measured sound; *East:* You meaner beauties; *Purcell:* Stript of their green our groves appear, Z444; *Machaut:* Foy porter; *Dowland:* Third and Last Booke of Songs (exc); *Hildegard of Bingen:* Columba aspexit; *H. Lawes:* Lark; *Handel:* Triumph of Time and Truth (exc). (E. Kirkby, Parley of Instr/R. Goodman/P. Holman, A. Rooley, D. Reichenberg, Taverner Plyrs/A. Parrott, Consort of Musicke/A. Rooley, A. Rooley, Gothic Voices/C. Page, London Handel Orch/D. Darlow)

ⓒ **CDA66228** (4/88)
Ancient Airs and Dances
Molinaro: Lute Bk I (exc); *Galilei:* Polymnia; *Anon:* Ancient Airs and Dances; *Caroso:* Laura soave; *Boësset:* Divine Amaryllis; *Gianoncelli:* Tasteggiata; Bergamasca; Besard: Bransles de Village; Airs de cour; *Roncalli:* Passacaglia. (R. Covey-Crump, J. Holloway, N. North, P. O'Dette, C. Thielmann)

long, great God, Z189; Not all my torments, Z400; Oedipus, Z583 (exc); King Arthur, Z628 (exc); Knotting Song, Z371; Fairy Queen, Z629 (exc); Welcome Song, Z344 (exc); Tyrannic Love, Z613 (exc); Rival Sisters, Z609 (exc); Fatal hour comes on apace, Z421; If music be the food of love, Z379/1; St Cecilia's Day Ode, Z339 (exc); Evening hymn, Z193 (exc). (J. Bowman, King's Consort/R. King)

ⓒ **CDA66290** (7/88)
Italian Vocal Music
Martucci: Canzone dei Ricordi; Nocturne, Op. 70/1; *Respighi:* Tramonto. (C. Madalin, ECO/A. Bonavera)

ⓒ **CDA66292** (10/89)
Fauré: Sacred Choral Works
Fauré: Requiem (Cpte); Cantique de Jean Racine; Messe basse; Ave verum; Tantum ergo, Op. 65/2. (M. Seers, I. Poulenard, J. Coxwell, C. Jackson, J. Youde, M. George, John Scott, Corydon Sngrs, ECO/M. Best)

ⓒ **CDA66294** (11/88)
Pergolesi—Sacred Choral Works
Pergolesi: Stabat Mater; Salve Regina; In coelestibus regnis. (G. Fisher, M. Chance, King's Consort/R. King)

ⓒ **CDA66295** (9/89)
Villa-Lobos: Chamber Works
Villa-Lobos: Wind Quintet; Modinha; Bachianas Brasileiras 6; Distribuição de flores; Assobio a jato; Chôros 2; Canção do amor; Wind Trio. (W. Bennett, N. Black, J. Knight, T. King, R. O'Neill, C. Tunnell, S. Wynberg)

ⓒ **CDA66296** (7/89)
Martinů—Cello Sonatas
Martinů: Cello Sonata 1; Cello Sonata 2; Cello Sonata 3. (S. Isserlis, Peter Evans)

ⓒ **CDA66300** (4/90)
The Clarinet in Concert—Vol 2
Spohr: Alruna Variations; *Rietz:* Clarinet Concerto, Op. 29; *Solère:* Sinfonie concertante; *Heinze:* Konzertstück. (T. King, G. Dobrée, ECO/J. Judd/A. Litton)

ⓒ **CDA66301** (12/88)
Liszt—Piano Works, Vol.2
Liszt: Ballade 1; Ballade 2; Légendes, S175; Berceuse, S174; Impromptu, S191; Piano Piece, S189; Polonaises, S223. (L. Howard)

ⓒ **CDA66302** (10/89)
Liszt—Piano Works, Vol.3
Liszt: Fantasia and Fugue, S529; Weinen, Klagen, Sorgen, Zagen Prelude, S179; Variations, S180; Funeral Odes; Grosses Konzertsolo, S176. (L. Howard)

ⓒ **CDA66305** (1/89)
My Spirit Hath Rejoiced—Settings of Magnificat & Nunc Dimittis
T. T. Noble: Evening Service, Op. 6 (exc); *Howells:* Gloucester Service (exc); *Murrill:* Evening Service in E (exc); *Harwood:* Evening Service, Op. 6 (exc); *Darke:* Evening Service in F (exc); *Sumsion:* Evening Service in G (exc); *Dyson:* Evening Service in D. (St Paul's Cath Ch, C. Dearnley/John Scott)

ⓒ **CDA66307** (1/90)
My Mind to me a kingdom is
Anon: My mind to me a kingdom is; When Daphne from fair Phoebus; Leaves be green; *Traditional:* Daphne; *Anon:* Willow Song; *Traditional:* Greensleeves (Alas! my love); *Anon:* Fortune my foe; *Traditional:* Joy, no; *Anon:* Fortune my foe; O death, rock me asleep; Goe from my window; *R. Nicholson:* In a merry May morn; *Morley:* Joyne hands; Joyne hands; *Dowland:* Lachrimae (exc); *Byrd:* Lullaby, my sweet little baby (exc); *Hume:* Virgin's Muse (exc); *Bennet:* Venus' birds (exc). (D. Cordier, A. Lawrence-King, N. Hadden, S. Stubbs, Tragicomedia/S. Stubbs)

ⓒ **CDA66309** (4/90)
Vivaldi—La Pastourella
Vivaldi: Concerto, RV87; Concerto, RV94; Concerto, RV95; Concerto, RV105; Concerto, RV107; Trio Sonata, RV86. (Chandos Baroque Plyrs)

ⓒ **CDA66310** (4/90)
Marais: Pièces de viole
Marais: Pièces en trio (exc); Pièces de viole III/1 (exc); Pièces de viole II/1 (exc). (Purcell Qt)

ⓒ **CDA66311/2** (4/89)
Monteverdi: St Barbara Vespers
Monteverdi: Vespers; *Palestrina:* Gaude, Barbara a 5; *Amigione:* Sonatas. (N. Jenkin, M. Seers, C. Royall, A. Murgatroyd, N. MacKenzie, M. Padmore, S. Birchall, J. White, The Sixteen, J. West, P. Nicholson, The Sixteen Orch/H. Christophers)

ⓒ **CDA66313** (1/89)
Elgar—Cathedral Music
Elgar: Ave verum corpus, Op. 2/1; Ave Maria, Op. 2/2; Ave

maris, Op. 2/3; Angelus, Op. 56; I Sing the Birth; Lo! Christ the Lord is Born; Great is the Lord; Ecce sacerdos magnus; O salutaris hostia 1; O salutaris hostia 2; O salutaris hostia 3; Fear not, O Land; O Hearken Thou, Op. 64; Give unto the Lord. (Worcester Cath Ch, A. Partington/David Hunt)

ⓒ **CDA66314** (2/89)
Purcell—Complete Odes & Welcome Songs, Vol.1
Purcell: Birthday Ode, Z320; Birthday Ode, Z332; St Cecilia's Day Ode, Z339. (G. Fisher, T. Bonner, J. Bowman, M. Chance, C. Daniels, J.M. Ainsley, M. George, C. Pott, King's Consort/R. King)

ⓒ **CDA66315** (7/89)
Handel: Music for Royal Occasions
Handel: Birthday Ode for Queen Anne (Cpte); Queen Caroline Te Deum; Wedding anthem, HWV263. (G. Fisher, J. Bowman, J.M. Ainsley, M. George, New College Ch, King's Consort/R. King)

ⓒ **CDA66316** (1/90)
Palestrina—Sacred Choral Works
Palestrina: Missa O Rex gloriae; Viri Galilaei; O Rex gloriae. (Westminster Cath Ch/J. O'Donnell)

ⓒ **CDA66319** (1/90)
Mundy—Sacred Choral Works
W. Mundy: O Lord, the maker of all things; Videte miraculum; Sive vigilem; Ah, helpless wretch; Vox patris caelestis; Kyrie; O Lord, the world's saviour; Evening Service in medio chori; Secret sins; Beatus et sanctus; Adolescentulus sum ego. (C. Royall, The Sixteen, P. Nicholson/H. Christophers)

ⓒ **CDA66320** (1/90)
Fauré—Songs
Fauré: Songs, Op.1 (exc); Songs, Op.4 (exc); Songs, Op.5 (exc); Songs, Op.7 (exc); Songs, Op.6 (exc); Poèmes d'un jour (exc); Songs, Op.23 (exc); Songs, Op.39 (exc); En prière; Songs, Op.46 (exc); Chanson d'Eve, Op.95; Songs, Op.51 (exc); Songs, Op. 58 (exc). (J. Baker, G. Parsons)

ⓒ **CDA66323** (9/89)
Duparc: Mélodies
Duparc: Invitation au voyage; Sérénade florentine; Testament; Phidylé; Extase; Vague et la cloche; Chanson triste; Galop; Romance de Mignon; Sérénade; Fuite; Lamento; Élégie; Manoir de Rosemonde; Au pays où se fait la guerre; Soupir; Vie antérieure. (Sarah Walker, T. Allen, R. Vignoles)

ⓒ **CDA66324** (11/89)
Chopin: Piano Works
Chopin: Preludes; Berceuse; Fantasie, Op.49. (L. Rév)

ⓒ **CDA66325** (3/91)
Taverner—Sacred Choral Works
Anon: Archangeli Michaelis interventione; *Taverner:* Kyrie a 4; Missa O Michael; Dum transisset Sabbatum I. (The Sixteen/H. Christophers)

ⓒ **CDA66326** (1/90)
Bach—Solo Cantatas
Bach: Cantata 170; Cantata 54; Cantata 169. (J. Bowman, King's Consort/R. King)

ⓒ **CDA66327** (7/92)
Spanish Music of the Golden Age
Sanz: Spanish Guitar Instruction I (exc); Spanish Guitar Instruction II (exc); *Granduque:* Hidalgo: Pasacalle; *Guerau:* Poema harmónico (exc); *Ruiz de Ribayaz:* Luz y norte musical para caminar (exc); *Anon:* Spanish dances; *Marin:* Song Collection (1690). (M.D.M. Fernández Doval, Extempore Stg Ens)

ⓒ **CDA66328** (8/89)
Vivaldi—Recorder Concertos
Vivaldi: Concerto, RV441; Concerto, RV444; Concerti, Op. 8 (exc); Concerto, RV445; Concerto, RV442; Concerto, RV443. (P. Holtslag, Parley of Instr/P. Holman)

ⓒ **CDA66329** (1/90)
Holst—Choral Works
Holst: Psalms, H117; Male Choruses. H186: Evening watch; Partsongs, H162; Nunc dimittis. (Holst Sngrs, Holst Orch/H.D. Wetton)

ⓒ **CDA66330** (12/90)
Masterpieces of Mexican Polyphony
H. Franco: Salve regina a 5; *J. G. de Padilla:* Domine ad adjuvandum; Mirabilia testimonia; Lamentations of Jeremiah a 16; Salve regina; *López Capillas:* Alleluia; Dic nobis, Maria; Magnificat quarti voci; *A. de Salazar:* O sacrum convivium. (Westminster Cath Ch, A. Watts, A. Lawrence-King, I. Simcock/J. O'Donnell)

ⓒ **CDA66332** (3/90)
Malcolm Arnold—Orchestral Works
Arnold: Sinfonietta 1; Sinfonietta 2; Sinfonietta 3; Flute

Concerto 1; Oboe Concerto. (E. Beckett, M. Messiter, London Fest Orch/R. Pople)

ⓒ **CDA66335** (12/90)
A Musicall Dreame
R. Jones: Through your strangeness frets my heart; Sweet Kate; Once did I serve a cruel heart; Will said to his mammy; Hark! Wot ye what?; My complaining is but feigning; On a time in summer season; Farewell, fond youth; Grief of my best love's absenting; And is it night?; *Ite caldi sospiri; Hume:* Captaine Humes Poeticall Musicke (exc); Captaine Humes Poeticall Musicke (exc); *Dowland:* Pavans (exc); Second Booke of Songs (exc); *Farnaby:* Giles Farnaby - His Dreame; His rest; Farnaby's Conceit; His humour; *Notari:* Prime musiche nuove (exc); *Coprario:* In darkness let me dwell. (M. Chance, D. Cordier, Tragicomedia/S. Stubbs, E. Headley, A. Lawrence-King, S. Stubbs)

ⓒ **CDA66336** (10/89)
Music for The Lion-Hearted King
Anon: Mundus vergen; Novus miles sequitur; *Gace Brulé:* A la douçour de la bele seron; *Anon:* Sol sub nube latuit; Hac in anni ianua; Anglia, planctus itera; Etas auri reditur; Vetus abit littera; In occasu sideris; *Blondel de Nesle:* Amours dont sui espris; *Anon:* Pange melos lacrimosum; *Blondel de Nesle:* Ma joie me semont; *Anon:* Ver pacis apperit; Latex silice. (Gothic Voices/C. Page)

ⓒ **CDA66340** (2/90)
Romantic Harp Music of the 19th Century, Vol. 3
Pierné: Impromptu-Caprice, Op. 9; *J. Thomas:* David of the White Rock Fantasia; Harp Study; *Fauré:* Châtelaine, Op. 110; Impromptu, Op. 86; *Hasselmans:* Mazurka, Op. 31; Nocturne, Op. 43; *Parish Alvars:* Fantaisie et Variations; *Zabel:* Valse Caprice, Op. 37; *Glinka:* Nocturne in E flat; *Debussy:* Suite bergamasque (exc). (S. Drake)

ⓒ **CDA66344** (12/89)
Satie—Piano Works
Satie: Gymnopédies; Gnossiennes; Embryons desséchés; Croquis et Agaceries; Sports et Divertissements; Heures séculaires et instantanées; Valses du précieux dégoûté; Sonatine bureaucratique; Nocturnes. (Y. Seow)

ⓒ **CDA66345** (3/90)
Tomkins—Cathedral Music
Tomkins: O sing unto the Lord; Then David mourned; My beloved spake; Above the stars my saviour dwells; Third Service (exc); Glory be to God on high; Almighty God, the fountain of all wisdom; When David heard; My shepherd is the living Lord; Sing unto God; Behold, the hour cometh; O God, the proud are risen against me. (St George's Chapel Ch, R. Judd/C. Robinson)

ⓒ **CDA66346** (5/90)
Liszt—Piano Works, Vol.5
Liszt: Danse macabre, S555; Chants polonais, S480; Idée fixe, S395; Francs-juges, S471; Pilgrims' March, S473; Valse des Sylphes, S475; Roi Lear, S474. (L. Howard)

ⓒ **CDA66347** (10/89)
Poulenc & Hahn—Balletic Works
Poulenc: Sinfonietta; Aubade; *Hahn:* Bal de Béatrice d'Este Suite. (J. Evans, New London Orch/R. Corp)

ⓒ **CDA66357** (1/90)
Liszt—Piano Works, Vol.4
Liszt: Études d'exécution, S139; Mariotte; Adagio in C; Élégie, S168. (L. Howard)

ⓒ **CDA66358** (2/90)
Machaut—Choral Works
Machaut: Messe de Nostre Dame; Je ne cesse de prier; Ma fin est mon commencement. (Hilliard Ens/P. Hillier)

ⓒ **CDA66359** (4/90)
Mendelssohn—Choral Works
Mendelssohn: Verleih uns Frieden; Kyrie; Ehre sei Gott in der Höhe; Sacred Pieces, Op. 23 (exc); Heilig, heilig ist Gott; Anthems, op 79 (Cpte); Psalms, Op. 78 (Cpte); Hear my prayer. (Corydon Sngrs, Jeremy Dawson, R. Covey-Crump, John Scott, ECO/M. Best)

ⓒ **CDA66360** (1/90)
Taverner—Missa Corona Spinea
Taverner: Missa Corona spinea; Gaude plurimum; In pace. (The Sixteen/H. Christophers)

ⓒ **CDA66365** (1/90)
Satie—Orchestral Works
Satie: Parade (Cpte); Aventures de Mercure (Cpte); Relâche (Cpte); Gymnopédies (exc); Gnossiennes. (New London Orch/R. Corp)

ⓒ **CDA66368** (1/91)
Duruflé—Organ Works
Duruflé: Prélude sur l'Introit de l'Epiphanie; Prélude et Fugue sur le nom d'Alain, Op. 7; Suite, Op. 5; Scherzo, Op. 2; Prélude, Adagio et Choral varié, Op. 4; Fugue sur le

carillon de Soissons. (St Paul's Cath Men's Ch, John Scott)

ⓘ **CDA66370** (6/91)
Sacred and Secular Music from six centuries
Machaut: Quant je sui mis au retour; *Hermannus Contractus:* Salve regina; *Godefroy de St Victoire:* Planctus ante nescia; *Dufay:* Gloria ad modem tubae; Vergene bella; *Fayrfax:* Most clere of colour; *Tallis:* O nata lux; *Byrd:* Ne irascaris Domine; *Traditional:* Dezí, flor resplandeçiente; Nuevas, nuevas; *Peñalosa:* Motets (exc); *Flecha:* El Jubilate; *Isaac:* Tota pulchra es; *Janequin:* Chant des oiseaux; *Goudimel:* Bonjour mon coeur. (Hilliard Ens)

ⓘ **CDA66371/2** (12/90)
Liszt—Piano Works, Vol.6
Liszt: Freischütz overture, S575; Don Juan réminiscences, S418; Aida—paraphrase, S436; Eugene Onegin polonaise, S429; Ruslan and Ludmila march, S406; Almira sarabande and chaconne, S181; Benvenuto Cellini motifs, S396; Faust—paraphrase, S407; Tristan und Isolde—paraphrase, S447; Lucia di Lammermoor réminiscences, S397; Lucia di Lammermoor march, S398; Tony hunting chorus, S404; Africaine illustrations, S415; Auber pieces, S387; Norma réminiscences, S394. (L. Howard)

ⓘ **CDA66373** (9/91)
M.Locke—Anthems,Motets and the Oxford Ode
Locke: Oxford Act Song; How doth the city sit solitary; Super flumina Babylonis; O be joyful; Audi, Domine, Lord, let me know mine end; Jesu auctor clementie; Be thou exalted. (New College Ch, Parley of Instr/E. Higginbottom)

ⓘ **CDA66374** (9/90)
The English Anthem, Vol.1
Stainer: I saw the Lord; *Wood:* Hail, gladdening light; *Gardiner:* Evening hymn; *Naylor:* Vox dicentis clama; *S.S. Wesley:* Blessed be the God and Father; *Stanford:* Motets, op 38 (exc); *Bairstow:* Blessed city, heavenly Salem; Let all mortal flesh keep silence; *Ireland:* Greater love hath no man; *Hadley:* My beloved spake; *Finzi:* God is gone up. (St Paul's Cath Ch, Andrew Lucas/John Scott)

ⓘ **CDA66375** (2/91)
Rachmaninov—Works of Piano Duet
Rachmaninov: Suite 1; Suite 2; Symphonic Dances, Op. 45. (H. Shelley, H. Macnamara)

ⓘ **CDA66376** (7/90)
Simpson: Chamber Works
Simpson: String Quartet 3; String Quartet 6; String Trio. (Delmé Qt)

ⓘ **CDA66380** (4/90)
Bach—Violin Concertos
Bach: 2-Violin Concerto; Violin Concerto, BWV1042; Violin Concerto, BWV1041; Violin and Oboe Concerto, BWV1060. (C. Mackintosh, Elizabeth Wallfisch, P. Goodwin, King's Consort/R. King)

ⓘ **CDA66383** (6/91)
Albinoni & Vivaldi—Wind Concertos
Albinoni: Concerti, Op.9 (exc); *Vivaldi:* Concerto, RV560; Concerto, RV455; Concerto, RV559. (P. Goodwin, King's Consort/R. King)

ⓘ **CDA66385** (9/90)
Settings of A. E. Housman
Gurney: Western Playland; Ludlow and Teme; *Vaughan Williams:* On Wenlock Edge. (Adrian Thompson, S. Varcoe, Delmé Qt, I. Burnside)

ⓘ **CDA66387** (10/91)
LeJeune—Masses
Le Jeune: Magnificat; Benedicite Dominum; Missa ad Placitum. (New College Ch, E. Higginbottom (org/dir))

ⓘ **CDA66391** (5/90)
Mozart: Sonatas for Keyboard and Flute
Mozart: Violin Sonata, K10; Violin Sonata, K11; Violin Sonata, K12; Violin Sonata, K13; Violin Sonata, K15; Violin Sonata, K15. (M. Grauwels, G. Penson, G. Penson, J. Sciffer)

ⓘ **CDA66393** (3/90)
Mozart: Complete Original Music for Flute - 3
Mozart: Flute Concerto, K313; Andante, K315; Flute and Harp Concerto, K299. (M. Grauwels, G. Herbert, Québec Violons du Roy/B. Labadie)

ⓘ **CDA66394** (9/90)
Howells—Organ Works
Howells: Psalm-Preludes, Op. 32; Rhapsodies, Op. 17; Psalm-Preludes, Set 2. (C. Dearnley)

ⓘ **CDA66395** (9/91)
Music for Prince Charles
Gibbons: Double bass Fantasias a 4; Double bass

Fantasias a 3 (exc); Fantasias a 3 (exc); *Lupo:* Fantasy-airs a 3 (exc); Fantasy-airs a 4 (exc); Fantasies a 4 (exc). (Parley of Instr/P. Holman)

ⓘ **CDA66397** (1/92)
Mendelssohn—String Quartets
Mendelssohn: String Quartet 1; String Quartet 2; String Quartet, Op.81 (exc). (Coull Qt)

ⓘ **CDA66398** (1/92)
Schutz—Christmas Story; Gabrieli—Motets
Schütz: Christmas Story, SWV435; *G. Gabrieli:* Symphoniae sacrae II (exc); Audite principes; O magnum mysterium. (R. Holton, J.M. Ainsley, M. George, King's Consort Ch, King's Consort/R. King)

ⓘ **CDA66400** (5/90)
Tallis: Sacred Choral Works
Tallis: O salutaris hostia; In jejunio et fletu; Salvator mundi I; Salvator mundi II; In manus tuas; Lamentations of Jeremiah; O sacrum convivium; O nata lux; Te lucis ante terminum I; Spem in alium. (Winchester Cath Ch, Winchester Quiristers, Winchester Vocal Arts, T. Byram-Wigfield/D. Hill)

ⓘ **CDA66409** (7/91)
Szymanowski—Piano Works
Szymanowski: Masques, Op.34; Metopes; Etudes, Op.4; Fantasy. (D. Lee)

ⓘ **CDA66410** (2/92)
Stravinsky—Choral Works
Traditional: Voronezh Bridal folk songs; *Stravinsky:* Noces; Russian Peasant Songs; Russian Peasant Songs; Ave Maria; Pater Noster; Credo; *Gesualdo:* Da pacem; Assumpta est Maria; Illumina nos; *Stravinsky:* Dove descending; Introitus. (Voronezh Chbr Ch, New London Chmbr Ch, Ens/J. Wood)

ⓘ **CDA66411** (4/91)
Mozart & Kramar—Oboe Concertos
Mozart: Oboe Concerto, K314; *Krommer:* Oboe Concerto, Op.52; Oboe Concerto, Op.37. (S. Francis, LMP/H. Shelley)

ⓘ **CDA66412** (11/90)
Purcell—Complete Odes & Welcome Songs, Vol.3
Purcell: Welcome Song, Z324; Welcome Song, Z335; Birthday Ode, Z321. (G. Fisher, T. Bonner, J. Bowman, J. Kenny, R. Covey-Crump, R. Müller, M. George, C. Pott, King's Consort/R. King)

ⓘ **CDA66413** (10/91)
Telemann—Recorder Works
Telemann: Recorder Overture-Suite; Recorder Concerto 1; Recorder Concerto 2; Trumpet Sinfonia. (P. Holtslag, Parley of Instr/P. Holman/R. Goodman)

ⓘ **CDA66414** (10/90)
Koechlin—Flute Works
Koechlin: Morceau de lecture, op 218; Lilian II (exc); Lilian I; Flute Sonata, Op. 52; 2-Flute Sonata, Op. 75; Chants, op 157b. (F. Smith, M. Amlin, J. West, L. Buyse)

ⓘ **CDA66415** (4/91)
Bartók—Chamber Works
Bartók: Solo Violin Sonata; Rhapsody 1; Rhapsody 2; Contrasts. (K. Osostowicz, M. Collins, S. Tomes)

ⓘ **CDA66416** (1/91)
Debussy—Piano Works
Debussy: Images (exc); Isle joyeuse; Préludes (exc). (L. Rév)

ⓘ **CDA66418** (12/92)
John Sheppard—Church Music, Vol.2
Sheppard: Jesu salvator seculi II; Deus tuorum militum II; Ave maris stella; Jesu salvator seculi I; Missa Cantate; Salvator mundi Domine. (The Sixteen/H. Christophers)

ⓘ **CDA66420** (9/90)
Vaughan Williams: Vocal Works
Vaughan Williams: Serenade to Music; Flos Campi; Mystical Songs; Fantasia on Christmas Carols. (E. Connell, L. Kitchen, Anne Dawson, A. Roocroft, Sarah Walker, J. Rigby, D. Montague, C. Wyn-Rogers, J.M. Ainsley, M. Hill, A. Davies, M. Davies, T. Allen, A. Opie, G. Howell, J. Connell, N. Imai, Corydon Sngrs, ECO/M. Best)

ⓘ **CDA66421/2** (9/91)
Liszt—Piano Works, Vol.7
Liszt: Ave Maria, S182; Ave maris stella, S506; Invocation; Hymnes, S173a; Harmonies poétiques, S154; Harmonies poétiques, S173; Alleluja and Ave Maria, S183; Zum Haus des Herrn, S505; O Roma nobilis, S546a; Slavimo slavno slaveni! S503; Ave Maria II in D; Ave Maria II in D flat; In festo transfigurationis, S188; Hymne du Pape, S530; Sancta Dorothea, S187; Ave Maria IV, S545; Hungarian Coronation Mass, S501; Stabat Mater; Urbi et orbi, S184; Vexilla regis prodeunt, S185. (L. Howard)

ⓘ **CDA66423** (12/90)
The Marriage of Heaven and Hell
Anon: Je ne chant pas; Trois sereurs; Plus bele que flors; Par un martinet; De la virge Katerine; Ave parens; Super te Jerusalem; A vous douce debonnaire; Mout souvent; Quant voi l'aloete; En non Dieu; Je m'en vois; Festa januaria; *Blondel de Nesle:* En tous tans que vente bise; *Muset:* Trop volontiers chanteroie; *Bernart de Ventadorn:* Can vei la lauzta mover; *Gautier de Dargies:* Autre que je ne seuill fas. (Gothic Voices/C. Page)

ⓘ **CDA66424** (1/91)
Tye—Sacred Choral Works
Tye: Orbis factor Kyrie; Euge Bone Mass; Quaesumus omnipotens; Miserere mei, Deus; Omnes gentes plaudite; Peccavimus cum patribus. (Winchester Cath Ch/D. Hill)

ⓘ **CDA66427** (4/92)
Taverner—Sacred Choral Works
Taverner: O Wilhelme, pastor bone; Dum transisset Sabbatum I; Missa Sancti Wilhelmi; Ex eius tumba. (The Sixteen/H. Christophers)

ⓘ **CDA66434** (4/91)
Bach—Organ Works
Bach: Toccata and Fugue, BWV565; Toccata and Fugue, BWV540; Toccata and Fugue, BWV538; Toccata, Adagio and Fugue, BWV564; Passacaglia and Fugue, BWV582. (C. Herrick)

ⓘ **CDA66436** (3/91)
English Ballet Music
C. Lambert: Horoscope (exc); *Bliss:* Checkmate (exc); *Walton:* Façade Suites (exc). (English Northern Philh/D. Lloyd-Jones)

ⓘ **CDA66437** (9/91)
Stravinsky—Sacred Choral Works
Stravinsky: Symphony of Psalms; Pater noster; Ave Maria; Credo; Mass; Canticum sacrum. (J.M. Ainsley, S. Roberts, Westminster Cath Ch, CLS, J. O'Donnell)

ⓘ **CDA66438** (5/92)
Liszt—Piano Works, Vol.13
Liszt: À la Chappelle Sixtine, S461; Preludes and Fugue, S462; Fantasia and Fugue, S463. (L. Howard)

ⓘ **CDA66439** (10/91)
Hear my Prayer
Mendelssohn: Hear my Prayer; *B. Rose:* Feast Song for St. Cecilia; *Brahms:* Deutsches Requiem, Op. 45 (exc); *Allegri:* Miserere mei; *J. Harvey:* Come Holy Ghost; *Tavener:* I will lift up; *Wise:* Ways of Zion do mourn; *Stanford:* Services, Op. 81 (exc); *Britten:* Festival Te Deum. (J. Budd, St Paul's Cath Ch, Adrian Lucas/John Scott)

ⓘ **CDA66440** (4/91)
Handel—Italian Duets
Handel: Tanti strali al sen; A miravi io son intento; Troppo cruda; Conservate, raddioppiate; Langue, geme e sospira; No, di voi non vuo fidarmi; Sono liete, fortunate; Fronda leggiera e mobile; Se tu non lasci amore. (G. Fisher, J. Bowman, King's Consort, R. King (hpd/dir))

ⓘ **CDA66444** (9/91)
Brahms: Lieder
Brahms: Lieder, Op. 59 (exc); Lieder, Op. 46 (exc); Lieder, Op. 86 (exc); Lieder, Op. 84 (exc); Lieder, Op. 72 (exc); Lieder, Op. 71 (exc); Lieder, Op. 3 (exc); Lieder, Op. 95 (exc); Romanzen, Op. 33 (exc); Lieder, Op. 105 (exc); Lieder, Op. 47 (exc); Lieder, Op. 106 (exc); Lieder, Op. 63 (exc); Lieder, Op. 43 (exc); Lieder, Op. 96 (exc); Lieder, Op. 97 (exc). (E. Ameling, R. Jansen)

ⓘ **CDA66446** (10/91)
S.S.Wesley—Cathedral Anthems, Vol.1
S.S. Wesley: Blessed be the God and Father; Thou wilt keep him; Let us lift up our heart; Ascribe unto the Lord; Cast me not away; Wilderness. (Worcester Cath Ch, A. Partington/Don Hunt)

ⓘ **CDA66447** (10/91)
Awake, Sweet Love
Campion: Ayres, Bk 1 (exc); *Dowland:* Fantasies (exc); *Anon:* Come tread the paths; *Ford:* Musicke of Sundrie Kindes I (exc); *Dowland:* Galliards (exc); *E. Johnson:* Eliza is the fayrest quene; *Danyel:* Rosa (exc); *Dowland:* Pavan; *Hunnis:* In terror trapp'd; *Dowland:* Prelude, P102; *Danyel:* Songs for the Lute (exc); *Dowland:* First Book of Songs (exc); Second Booke of Songs (exc); Third and Last Booke of Songs (exc); Pilgrimes Solace (exc). (J. Bowman, D. Miller, King's Consort)

ⓘ **CDA66449** (9/91)
Simpson—Brass Band Music
Simpson: Energy; Four Temperaments; Introduction and Allegro; Volcano; Vortex. (Desford Colliery Caterpillar Band/J. Watson)

Tutte le vecchie; *Macque:* Prima stravaganza; Gagliarda prima; Toccata a modo di trombetta; *Michi:* Arie Spirituali (exc); *Frescobaldi:* Primo libro di Toccate (exc); Secondo libro di Toccate (exc); *Monteverdi:* Vespers (exc). (A. Lawrence-King)

ⓘ **CDA66519** (4/92)
The English Anthem, Vol.2
Battishill: O Lord, look down from heaven; *Stainer:* Awake, awake (exc); *Stanford:* Motets, Op.38 (exc); *Bainton:* And I saw a new heaven; *Joubert:* O Lorde, the maker of al thing; *Mathias:* As truly as God is our Father; *Bairstow:* Save us, O Lord; *Ouseley:* O Saviour of the world; *Gowers:* Viri Galilaei; *Holloway:* Lord, what is man?; *Finzi:* Lo, the full, final sacrifice. (St Paul's Cath Ch/John Scott)

ⓘ **CDA66520** (3/91)
Haydn—Symphonies, Vol.1
Haydn: Symphony 73; Symphony 74; Symphony 75. (Hanover Band/R. Goodman)

ⓘ **CDA66521** (6/91)
Haydn—Symphonies, Vol. 2
Haydn: Symphony 90; Symphony 91; Symphony 92. (Hanover Band/R. Goodman)

ⓘ **CDA66522** (10/91)
Haydn—Symphonies, Vol.3
Haydn: Symphony 45; Symphony 46; Symphony 47. (Hanover Band/R. Goodman)

ⓘ **CDA66523** (12/91)
Haydn—Symphonies, Vol.4
Haydn: Symphony 6; Symphony 7; Symphony 8. (Hanover Band/R. Goodman)

ⓘ **CDA66524** (3/92)
Haydn—Symphonies Vol.5
Haydn: Symphony 1; Symphony 2; Symphony 3; Symphony 4; Symphony 5. (Hanover Band, R. Goodman (hpd/dir))

ⓘ **CDA66525** (5/92)
Haydn—Symphonies, Vol.6
Haydn: Symphony 76; Symphony 77; Symphony 78. (Hanover Band/R. Goodman)

ⓘ **CDA66526** (9/92)
Haydn—Symphonies, Vol.7
Haydn: Symphony 70; Symphony 71; Symphony 72. (Hanover Band/R. Goodman)

ⓘ **CDA66527** (10/92)
Haydn—Symphonies, Vol.8
Haydn: Symphony 82; Symphony 83; Symphony 84. (Hanover Band, R. Goodman (hpd/dir))

ⓘ **CDA66528** (12/92)
Haydn—Symphonies, Vol.9
Haydn: Symphony 101; Symphony 102; Windsor Castle Overture. (Hanover Band/R. Goodman)

ⓘ **CDA66529** (12/92)
Haydn—Symphonies, Vol.10
Haydn: Symphony 9; Symphony 10; Symphony 11; Symphony 12. (Hanover Band, R. Goodman (hpd/dir))

ⓘ **CDA66530** (2/93)
Haydn—Symphonies, Vol.11
Haydn: Symphony 42; Symphony 43; Symphony 44. (Hanover Band/R. Goodman)

ⓘ **CDA66531** (7/93)
Haydn—Symphonies, Vol.12
Haydn: Symphony 48; Symphony 49; Symphony 50. (Hanover Band/R. Goodman)

ⓘ **CDA66532** (8/93)
Haydn—Symphonies, Vol.13
Haydn: Symphony 93; Symphony 94; Symphony 95. (Hanover Band/R. Goodman)

ⓘ **CDA66533** (12/93)
Haydn—Symphonies, Vol.14
Haydn: Symphony 17; Symphony 18; Symphony 19; Symphony 20; Symphony 21. (Hanover Band/R. Goodman)

ⓘ **CDA66534** (3/94)
Haydn—Symphonies, Vol.15
Haydn: Symphony 13; Symphony 14; Symphony 15; Symphony 16. (Hanover Band/R. Goodman)

ⓘ **CDA66535** (11/94)
Haydn—Symphonies, Vol.16
Haydn: Symphony 85; Symphony 86; Symphony 87. (Hanover Band/R. Goodman)

ⓘ **CDA66536** (6/95)
Haydn—Symphonies, Vol. 17
Haydn: Symphony 22; Symphony 23; Symphony 24; Symphony 25. (Hanover Band/R. Goodman)

ⓘ **CDA66561/3** (12/91)
Mendelssohn—Complete String Symphonies
Mendelssohn: String Symphony 1; String Symphony 2; String Symphony 3; String Symphony 4; String Symphony 5; String Symphony 6; String Symphony 7; String Symphony 8; String Symphony 9; String Symphony 10; String Symphony 11; String Symphony 12. (London Fest Orch/R. Pople)

ⓘ **CDA66564** (9/92)
Roseingrave—Keyboard Works
Roseingrave: Suits of Lessons (exc); Voluntarys and Fugues (exc); Double Fugues (exc); Harpsichord Concerto. (P. Nicholson, P. Nicholson)

ⓘ **CDA66565** (6/92)
Constant Lambert—Vocal & Orchestral Works
C. Lambert: Rio Grande; Aubade héroïque; Summer's Last Will and Testament. (S. Burgess, W. Shimell, J. Gibbons, Op North Chor, Leeds Fest Chor, English Northern Philh/D. Lloyd-Jones)

ⓘ **CDA66569** (8/92)
Vaughan Williams—Choral Works
Vaughan Williams: Song of Thanksgiving; Choral Hymns; Magnificat; Shepherds of the Delectable Mountains; Old Hundredth. (J. Gielgud, L. Dawson, L. Kitchen, C. Wyn-Rogers, J.M. Ainsley, J. Bowen, Adrian Thompson, A. Opie, B. Terfel, J. Best, John Scott, R. Judd, London Oratory Jnr Ch, Corydon Sngrs, CLS/M. Best)

ⓘ **CDA66570** (12/92)
Sheppard—Church Music Volume 3
Sheppard: Gaude gaude gaude Maria virgo; Deum transisset Sabbatum I; Spiritus Sanctus procedens II; In manus tuas II a 4; Audivi vocem de caelo; Libera nos, salva nos II; Beata nobis gaudia; Impetum fecerunt unanimes; Sancte Dei preciose; Sacris solemniis. (The Sixteen/H. Christophers)

ⓘ **CDA66573** (9/92)
Prokofiev—Chamber Works
Prokofiev: Overture, Op.34; String Quartet 1; String Quartet 2. (A. Malsbury, D. Pettit, Coull Qt)

ⓘ **CDA66575** (3/93)
Liszt—Piano Works, Vol.18
Liszt: Capriccio alla turca, S388; March, S388a; Fantasie, S389; Midsummer Night's Dream—paraphrase, S410; Einsam bin ich, S453; Nibelungen and Faust excerpts, S496; Symphonisches Zwischenspiel, S497; Pastorale, S508. (L. Howard)

ⓘ **CDA66576** (8/92)
Virgil Thomson—Film Music
V. Thomson: Fugues and Cantilenas; Louisiana Story Suite; Acadian Songs and Dances; Plow that Broke the Plains. (New London Orch/R. Corp)

ⓘ **CDA66578** (3/93)
Odes on the Death of Henry Purcell
Clarke: Come, come along; *Finger:* Farewell Suite; *H. Hall:* Yes, my Aminta; *T. Morgan:* Purcell's Farewell; *Blow:* Ode on the death of Mr Henry Purcell. (R. Holton, R. Covey-Crump, C. Daniels, S. Birchall, Parley of Instr Ch, Parley of Instr/R. Goodman/P. Holman)

ⓘ **CDA66579** (11/92)
Mendelssohn—String Quartets
Mendelssohn: String Quartet in E flat; String Quartet 4; String Quartet 6. (Coull Qt)

ⓘ **CDA66581/2** (12/93)
Bartók—String Quartets
Bartók: String Quartet 1; String Quartet 2; String Quartet 3; String Quartet 4; String Quartet 5; String Quartet 6. (New Budapest Qt)

ⓘ **CDA66583** (5/93)
English 18th Century Violin Sonatas
Geminiani: Violin Sonatas, Op.1 (exc); *R. Jones:* Chamber Air's (exc); *Arne:* Violin Solo in E; *J. Gibbs:* Solos, Op.1 (exc); *Giardini:* Violin Sonatas, Op.1 (exc); *Heilendaal:* Celebrated Rondo; *T. Linley II:* Violin Sonata in A. (Locatelli Trio)

ⓘ **CDA66584** (9/92)
Chaminade—Piano Works
Chaminade: Chaconne, Op.8; Pièces humoristiques, Op.87 (exc); Air de Ballet, Op.30; Poèmes Provençales, Op. 127 (exc); Romance, Op.137; Etudes, Op.101; Etudes de Concert, Op.35 (exc); Thème Varié, Op.89; Sérénade, Op.29; Romances sans paroles, Op.76 (exc); Etude mélodique, Op.118; Etude pathétique, Op.124; Lisonjera, Op.50; Valse romantique, Op.115; Deuxième Valse, Op.77; Etude scholastique, Op.139. (Peter Jacobs)

ⓘ **CDA66585** (7/92)
Purcell—Complete Anthems & Services, Vol.1
Purcell: O sing unto the Lord, Z44; O praise God in His

holiness, Z42; Praise the Lord, O Jerusalem, Z46; It is a good thing to give thanks, Z18; O give thanks unto the Lord, Z33; Let mine eyes, Z24; My beloved spake, Z28. (N. Witcomb, J. Finnis, P. Hallchurch, J. Bowman, C. Daniels, M. George, R. Evans, King's Consort/R. King)

ⓘ **CDA66586** (9/92)
Balakirev—Orchestral Works
Balakirev: Symphony 2; Tamara; Overture on Russian themes. (Philh/E. Svetlanov)

ⓘ **CDA66587** (3/93)
Purcell—Complete Odes & Welcome Songs, Vol.7
Purcell: Welcome Song, Z336; Welcome Song, Z341; Yorkshire Feast Song, Z333. (G. Fisher, S. Hamilton, J. Bowman, N. Short, R. Covey-Crump, C. Daniels, M. George, R. Evans, King's Consort/R. King)

ⓘ **CDA66588** (9/92)
Lancaster & Valois
Machaut: Donnez, signeurs; Quand je ne voy; Riches d'amour; Pas de tor; *SOlage:* Tres gentil cuer; *Pycard:* Credo; *Sturgeon:* Salve mater domini; *Fonteyns:* Regali ex progenie; *Cesaris:* Se vous scaviez; Mon seul vouloir; *Cordier:* Ce jour de l'an; *Anon:* Puis qu'autrement; Soit tart; Le ior; Avrai je ja; Sanctus (14th cent); Je vueil vivre. (Gothic Voices, C. Page (lte/dir))

ⓘ **CDA66594** (12/92)
Milhaud—Orchestral Works
Milhaud: Carnaval de Londres; Apothéose de Molière; Boeuf sur le toit; Carnaval d'Aix. (J. Gibbons, New London Orch/R. Corp)

ⓘ **CDA66597** (11/92)
Chopin—Piano Works
Chopin: Polonaises (exc); Bolero; Allegro de concert; Berceuse; Tarantelle. (N. Demidenko)

ⓘ **CDA66598** (3/93)
Purcell—Complete Odes & Welcome Songs, Vol.8
Purcell: Birthday Ode, Z323; Welcome Song, Z343; Welcome Song, Z340. (G. Fisher, T. Bonner, J. Bowman, M. Chance, M. Padmore, J.M. Ainsley, M. George, R. Evans, New College Ch, King's Consort/R. King)

ⓘ **CDA66603** (8/93)
Sheppard—Cathedral Music, Vol.2
Sheppard: Aeterne Rex altissime; Second service (exc); Dum transisset sabbatum II; Hostis Herodes impie; In manus tuas a 3; Te Deum; Western Wynde Mass. (The Sixteen/H. Christophers)

ⓘ **CDA66604** (12/92)
John Jenkins—Late Consort Music
Jenkins: Fantasia-suites in 4 parts (3 vns, b viol) (exc); Fantasia-suites in 4 parts (2 vns, 2 b viols) (exc); Airs for lyra consort (exc). (Parley of Instr/P. Holman)

ⓘ **CDA66605** (10/92)
Organ Fireworks, Vol.4
D. Johnson: Trumpet tune in A; *Lemare:* Toccata di Concerto, Op.59; *Buck:* Star-Spangled Banner Variations, Op.23; *Guilmant:* Judas Maccabaeus paraphrase; *Whitlock:* Pieces for organ (exc); *D. Bourgeois:* Howells Variations, Op. 87; *Vierne:* Pièces en stile libre (exc); *Batiste:* Grand offertoire in D; *Shostakovich:* Lady Macbeth of Mtsensk (exc); *Bonnet:* Pièces nouvelles, Op.7 (exc); *Widor:* Symphony 6 (exc); *Lefébure-Wély:* Sortie in E flat. (C. Herrick)

ⓘ **CDA66607** (12/92)
Scriabin—Complete Etudes
Scriabin: Pieces, Op.2 (exc); Etudes, Op.8; Etudes, Op.42; Pieces, Op.49 (exc); Pieces, Op.56 (exc); Etudes, Op.65. (P. Lane)

ⓘ **CDA66608** (5/93)
Dibdin—Three Operas
Dibdin: Ephesian Matron (Cpte); Brickdust Man (Cpte); Grenadier (Cpte). (B. Mills, J. Streeton, M. Padmore, A. Knight, Y. Barclay, K. West, S. Bisatt, K. West, A. Mayor, Opera Restor'd/P. Holman)

ⓘ **CDA66609** (11/92)
Purcell—Complete Anthems & Services, Vol.2
Purcell: Behold now, praise the Lord, Z3; Blessed are they that fear the Lord, Z5; I will give thanks, Z20; My song shall be alway, Z31; Te Deum and Jubilate, Z232. (J. Bowman, R. Covey-Crump, M. George, New College Ch, King's Consort/R. King)

ⓘ **CDA66610** (3/93)
Howells—Orchestral Works
Howells: Piano Concerto 2; Dances; Concerto for Strings. (K. Stott, M. Stewart, RLPO/V. Handley)

ⓘ **CDA66614** (4/93)
Josquin—Missa Pange Lingua
Josquin Desprez: Missa Pange Lingua; Vultum tuum; Planxit autem David. (Westminster Cath Ch/J. O'Donnell)

D141; Klage an den Mond, D436; Mainacht, D194; Unglückliche, D713; Morgenkuss, D264; Kolmas Klage, D217; Lied, D403; Winterabend, D938; Wanderer an den Mond, D870; Im Freien, D880; Am Fenster, D878; Blinde Knabe, D833; Junge Nonne, D828; Gondelfahrer, D808; An die Sonne, D270. (M. Price, G. Johnson)

① **CDJ33016** (3/93)
Schubert—Complete Lieder, Vol.16
Schubert: Leichenphantasie, D7; Laura am Klavier, D388; Entzückung an Laura, D390; Entzückung an Laura, D577; An die Freude, D189; An Emma, D113; Mädchen aus der Fremde, D117; Geheimnis, D793; Bürgschaft, D246; Jüngling am Bache, D638; Vier Weltalter, D391; Sehnsucht, D52; Pilgrim, D794. (T. Allen, G. Johnson)

① **CDJ33017** (6/93)
Schubert—Complete Lieder, Vol.17
Schubert: Lied, D373; Lodas Gespenst, D150; Klage, D371; Lorma, D376; Herbstabend, D405; Einsiedelei, D393; Herbstnacht, D404; Lied in der Abwesenheit, D416; Frühlingslied, D398; Winterlied, D401; Minnelied, D429; Aus Diego Manazares, D538; Pflicht und Liebe, D467; An den Mond, D468; Litanei, D343; Geheimnis, D491; Am Grabe Anselmos, D504; An die Nachtigall, D497; Klage um Ali Bey, D496a; Phidile, D500; herbstlied, D502; Lebenslied, D508; Leiden der Trennung, D509; An mein Klavier, D342. (L. Popp, G. Johnson)

① **CDJ33018** (7/93)
Schubert—Complete Lieder, Vol.18
Schubert: Finden, D219; Nacht, D358; An den Schlaf, D447; Blumenlied, D431; Auf den Tod einer Nachtigall, D399; Entelied, D434; An die Harmonie, D394; Heimweh, D456; Abendlied, D499; An die Entfernte, D765; Drang in die Ferne, D770; Heimweh, D851; Auf der Bruck, D853; Urn Mitternacht, D862; Blume und der Quell, D874; Liebliche Stern, D861; Tiefes Leid, D876; Im Walde, D834; Im Frühling, D882; Lebensmut, D883; Über Wildemann, D884; An mein Herz, D860. (P. Schreier, G. Johnson)

① **CDJ33019** (2/94)
Schubert—Complete Lieder, Vol.19
Schubert: Nachtviolen, D752; Gott im Frühling, D448; Im Haine, D738; Blumen Schmerz, D731; Blumensprache, D519; Rose, D745; Vergissmeinnicht, D792; Liebliche Stern, D861; Am See, D746; Sterne, D176; Sternennächte, D670; Nach einem Gewitter, D561; Beim Winde, D669; Auf dem Wasser zu singen, D774; Abendlied, D276; Auf dem See, D543; Suleika I, D720; Suleika II, D717. (F. Lott, G. Johnson)

① **CDJ33020** (6/94)
Schubert—Complete Lieder, Vol.20
Schubert: Winterlied, D242a; Ossians Lied, D278; Mädchen von Inistore, D281; Als ich sie erröten sah, D153; Schwanengesang, D318; Totenkranz für ein Kind, D275; Fröhlichkeit, D262; Zufriedene, D320; Alles um Liebe, D241; Geist der Liebe, D233; Erste Liebe, D182; Täuschung, D230; Liebesrausch, D164; Huldigung, D240; Heidenröslein, D257; Nachtgesang, D314; Morgenstern, D172; Bergknappenlied, D268; Trinklied, D169; Schwertlied, D170; Nun lasst uns den Leib begraben, D168; Grablied, D218; Jesus Christus unser Heiland, D168a; Hoffnung, D251; Punschlied, D253; Klage um Ali Bey, D140; Abendständchen, D265; Tischlerlied, D274; Wiegenlied, D304; Macht der Liebe, D308; Trinklied, D183; Trinklied, D267. (P. Rozario, C. Denley, J.M. Ainsley, I. Bostridge, J. MacDougall, S. Keenlyside, M. George, London Schubert Chorale, G. Johnson)

① **CDJ33021** (8/94)
Schubert—Complete Lieder, Vol.21
Schubert: Schlaflied, D527; Sehnsucht, D516; Liebe, D522; Forelle, D550; Nur wer die Liebe kennt, D513a; Flug der Zeit, D515; Trost, D523; Abgeblühte Linde, D514; Lied vom Reifen, D532; An eine Quelle, D530; An die Musik, D547; Schäfer und der Reiter, D517; Hänflings Liebeswerbung, D552; Schweizerlied, D559; Liebhaber in allen Gestalten, D558; Abschied, D578; Erlafsee, D586; Lied eines Kindes, D596; Evangelium Johannis, D607; Lob der Tränen, D711; Grablied für die Mutter, D616; Blumenbrief, D622; Blondel zu Marien, D626; Vom Mitleiden Mariä, D632. (E. Mathis, G. Johnson)

① **CDJ33022** (1/95)
Schubert—Complete Lieder, Vol.22
Schubert: Trinklied, D148; Morgenlied, D266; An Sie, D288; Mädchen aus der Fremde, D252; Abend, D221; Punschlied, D277; An die Sonne, D272; Leben ist ein Traum, D269; Drei Sänger, D329; Erinnerung, D229; Abendroth, D236; Genügsamkeit, D143; An Rosa I, D315; An Rosa II, D316; Bild, D155; Furcht der Geliebten, D285; Skolie, D306; Cora an die Sonne, D263; Sterne, D313; Lob des Tokayers, D248; Vaterlandslied, D287; Gebet, D171; Hermann und Thusnelda, D322; Selma und Selmar, D286; Lorma, D327; Cronnan, D282; Hymne an den Unendlichen, D232; Grab, D330. (L. Anderson, P. Rozario,

C. Denley, C. Wyn-Rogers, J. MacDougall, J. M. Ainsley, S. Keenlyside, M. George, G. Johnson)

① **CDJ33023** (7/95)
Schubert—Complete Lieder, Vol.23
Schubert: Tod Oscars, D375; Grab, D377; Entfernten, D350; Pflügerlied, D392; Abschied von der Harfe, D406; Jüngling an der Quelle, D300; Abendlied, D382; Stimme der Liebe, D412; Romanze, D144; Geist der Liebe, D414; Klage, D415; Julius an Theone, D419; Leidende, D432; Leidende, D432b; Frühe Liebe, D430; Knabenzeit, D400; Edone, D445; Liebesgötter, D446; An Chloen, D363; Freude der Kinderjahre, D455; Wer sich der Einsamkeit ergibt, D478; Wer nie sein Brot mit Tränen ass, D480; An die Türen, D479; Hirt, D490; Am ersten Maimorgen, D344; Bei dem Grabe meines Vaters, D496; Mailied, D503; Zufriedenheit, D362; Skolie, D507. (C. Prégardien, London Schubert Chorale, G. Johnson)

① **CDP11001** (6/94)
Psalms from St Paul's, Vol.1
Anon: Psalm 1; Psalm 2; Psalm 3; Psalm 4; Psalm 5; Psalm 6; Psalm 7; Psalm 8; Psalm 9; Psalm 10; Psalm 11; Psalm 12; Psalm 13; Psalm 14; Psalm 15; Psalm 16; Psalm 17. (St Paul's Cath Ch/John Scott, Andrew Lucas)

① **CDP11002** (2/95)
Psalms from St Paul's, Volume 2
Anon: Psalm 18; Psalm 19; Psalm 20; Psalm 21; Psalm 22; Psalm 23; Psalm 24; Psalm 25; Psalm 26; Psalm 27; Psalm 28; Psalm 29. (St Paul's Cath Ch/John Scott, Andrew Lucas)

① **CDP11003** (10/95)
Psalms from St Paul's, Volume 3
Anon: Psalm 30; Psalm 31; Psalm 32; Psalm 33; Psalm 34; Psalm 35; Psalm 36; Psalm 37; Psalm 38; Psalm 39; Psalm 40. (St Paul's Cath Ch/John Scott, Andrew Lucas)

① **CDS44041/8** (3/94)
Rachmaninov—Complete Piano Music
Rachmaninov: Morceaux de fantaisie, Op.3; Preludes (exc); Prelude (1891); Prelude (1917); Morceaux de salon, Op.10; Moments musicaux, Op.16; Piano Sonata 2; Morceau de fantaisie (1899); Song Without Words (?1887); Pièce (1917); Fughetta (1899); Fragments (1917); Oriental Sketch (1917); Nocturnes (1887/8); Pièces (?1887); Etudes-tableaux Op.33; Etudes-tableaux, Op.39; Piano Sonata 1; Piano Sonata 2; Chopin Variations, Op.22; Corelli Variations; Morceaux de fantaisie, Op.3 (exc); Mendelssohn: Midsummer Night's Dream (exc); Rimsky-Korsakov: Tale of Tsar Saltan (exc); Kreisler: Liebesleid; Liebesfreud; Bizet: Arlésienne Suites (exc); Schubert: Schöne Müllerin (exc); Mussorgsky: Fair at Sorochintsî (exc); Bach: Solo Violin Partitas and Sonatas (exc); Rachmaninov: Daisies; Lilacs; Polka de W.R.; Songs, Op.34 (exc); Mendelssohn: Midsummer Night's Dream (exc); Tchaikovsky: Songs, Op.16 (exc). (H. Shelley)

① **CDS44051/3** (6/94)
Mendelssohn—Complete String Quartets
Mendelssohn: String Quartet in E flat; String Quartet 1; String Quartet 2; String Quartet 3; String Quartet 4; String Quartet 5; String Quartet 6; String Quartet, Op. 81. (Coull Qt)

① **CDS44061/3** (6/95)
Debussy—Piano Music
Debussy: Suite bergamasque; Pour le Piano; Estampes; Children's Corner; Images; Isle joyeuse; Préludes; Masques. (L. Rév)

IMG Records

① **IMGCD1605** (2/95)
Rachmaninov—Orchestral Works
Rachmaninov: Piano Concerto 3; Vocalise; Prince Rostislav. (J. L. Prats, Mexico City PO/E. Bátiz)

① **IMGCD1606** (7/94)
Berlioz—Orchestral Works
Berlioz: Symphonie Fantastique; Corsaire; Carnaval romain. (Philh, RPO/E. Bátiz)

① **IMGCD1609** (2/95)
Shostakovich—Orchestral Works
Shostakovich: Symphony 9; Overture on Russian and Kirghiz Folk Themes; Novorossiisk Chimes; October, Op. 131. (RPO/E. Bátiz)

Imperial Sound

① **RAZCD901** (12/92)
Sunlight on the Garden
Hoffstetter: String Quartets, Op.3 (exc); *Haydn:* String Quartets, Op.33 (exc); *Vachon:* String Quartets, Op.7 (exc); *Bridge:* Cherry ripe; Idylls (exc); *Schubert:* String Quartet, D87 (exc); *Bloch:* Night; *Puccini:* Crisantemi; *Mendelssohn:* String Quartet, Op.81 (exc); *Gluck:*

Allegretto; Britten: Divertimenti (exc); *J.B. Jadin:* Quartets, Op.1 (exc); *Leighton:* Variations, Op.43 (exc). (Rasumovsky Qt)

International Record Collectors

① **IRCC-CD800** (9/92)
Souvenirs from Meyerbeer Operas
Meyerbeer: Huguenots (exc); Huguenots (exc); Huguenots (exc); Huguenots (exc); Huguenots (exc); Robert le Diable (exc); Robert le Diable (exc); Robert le Diable (exc); Robert le Diable (exc); Prophète (exc); Prophète (exc); Prophète (exc); Prophète (exc); Prophète (exc); Dinorah (exc); Dinorah (exc); Dinorah (exc); Dinorah (exc). (E. Norena, A. Parsi-Pettinella, L. Landouzy, A. Affre, M. Lafargue, A. Gresse, J-F. Delmas, chor, B.A. de Montalant, E. Clément, M. Journet, N. de Angelis, F. Viñas, S. Cahier, M. Kurt, M. Matzenauer, O. Metzger, L. Homer, G. Huguet, F. Hempel, M. Ancona, L. Fugère, orch, anon)

① **IRCC-CD802** (8/92)
Souvenirs of Rare French Opera
Donizetti: Lucia di Lammermoor (exc); *De Lara:* Méssaline (exc); Méssaline (exc); *Reyer:* Sigurd (exc); Sigurd (exc); Sigurd (exc); *Leroux:* Reine Fiammette (exc); V.A. Duvernoy: Hellé (exc); *Février:* Gismonda (exc); *Massenet:* Ariane (exc); *Saint-Saëns:* Barbares (exc); *Gounod:* Polyeucte (exc); Tribut de Zamora (exc); Reine de Saba (exc); *Février:* Monna Vanna (exc); *Bruneau:* Virginie (exc); *Nougués:* Aigle (exc); *T. Dubois:* Aben-Hamet (exc); *Massenet:* Roma (exc); Roma (exc); *Bourgault-Ducoudray:* Thamara (exc); *Bruneau:* Attaque du moulin (exc). (L. Korsoff, A. Scotti, A. Ghasne, M. Renaud, R. Caron, L. Escalais, M. Carré, M. Namara, L. Muratore, C. Rousselière, Z. de Lussan, M. Rappold, F. Ansseau, G. Féraldy, H. Albers, M. Imbert, L. Dupré, L. Beyle, A. Affre, A. Talexis, X. Leroux, anon, orch/P. Coppola)

① **IRCC-CD808** (6/94)
Souvenirs of 19th Century Italian Opera
Apolloni: Ebreo (exc); *Petrella:* Jone (exc); *Ruggi:* Due Ciabattini (exc); *Petrella:* Contessa d'Amalfi (exc); *Faccio:* Amleto (exc); *Usiglio:* Educande di Sorrento (exc); *Marchetti:* Ruy Blas (exc); Ruy Blas (exc); Ruy Blas (exc); *Campana:* Esmeralda (exc); *Gomes:* Guarany (exc); Guarany (exc); Guarany (exc); Guarany (exc); *Ponchielli:* Promessi Sposi (exc); Lina (exc); *Bottesini:* Ero e Leandro (exc). (A. DiGiorgio, A. Scampini, G. De Luca, F. Corradetti, A. Santini, C. Owen, E. Petri, E. Bucalo, T. Desana, C. Boninsegna, L. Colazza, L. del Lungo, E. Caronna, E. Foggi, B. Sayão, E. Mazzoleni, G. Zenatello, A. Amadi, P. Amato, E. Vannuccini, M. Carosio, A. Pinto, anon, orch)

Isis

① **ISISCD002** (10/94)
Bach—Organ Works
Bach: Toccata and Fugue, BWV565; Toccata, Adagio and Fugue, BWV564; Fantasia and Fugue, BWV542; Prelude and Fugue, BWV547; Prelude and Fugue, BWV536; Passacaglia and Fugue, BWV582. (M. Souter)

① **ISISCD008** (5/95)
Bach—Chorale Preludes, Volume 2
Bach: Chorales, BWV651-668 (exc); Schübler Chorales, BWV645-650; Liebster Jesu, BWV731; Prelude and Fugue, BWV541. (M. Souter)

① **ISISCD010** (12/95)
The Royal Harpsichord of George III
Handel: Keyboard Suites, Set II (exc); *Arne:* Keyboard Sonatas (exc); *J. C. Bach:* Keyboard Sonatas, Op. 5 (exc); *Chilcot:* Harpsichord Suites (exc); *Mozart:* Minuet, K2; Minuet, K4; Minuet, K5. (M. Souter)

Jade

① **JADC102** (10/94)
Lassus—Tenebrae Office & Lamentations of Jeremiah
Lassus: Lamentations of Jeremiah; Tenebrae Responsories; *Anon:* Holy Week (exc). (J-P. Gipon Voc Ens/J-P. Gipon)

① **JADC131** (9/95)
The Spirit of Gregorian Chant
Anon: Mass (exc); Mass (exc); Mass (exc); Mass (exc); Mass (exc). (Burgos Santo Domingo de Silos Monastery Ch)

Jecklin

① **JD5004-2** (3/89)
Carissimi: Cantatas
Carissimi: Lamento in morte di Maria Stuarda; In un mar di pensieri; Amor mio, che cosa è questa; Deh memoria e che più chiedi; Suonerà l'ultima tromba. (E. Speiser, H.L. Hirsch)

① **JD506-2** (11/87)
Flute Concertos
Cimarosa: 2-Flute Concerto; *Gluck:* Flute Concerto; *Orfeo ed Euridice* (exc); *Pokorny:* Flute Concerto. (P.-L. Graf, G. Guéneux, Zurich Camerata/R. Tschupp)

① **JD529-2** (9/89)
Martin: Concertos
Martin: Harpsichord Concerto; Trombone Ballade; Piano Ballade. (C. Jaccottet, A. Rosin, S. Benda, Lausanne CO/F. Martin)

① **JD536-2** (11/87)
The Romantic Clarinet
Spohr: Fantasy and Variations, Op. 81; *Alruna* Variations; *Weber:* Duo concertant, J204; Variations, J128; *Küffner:* Introduction, Theme and Variations. (H-R. Stalder, J. von Vintschger, Z. Sirokay, Zurich Chbr Music)

① **JD541-2** (4/90)
Bach & Chopin: Piano Works
Bach: Harpsichord Concerto, BWV1052; *Chopin:* Piano Concerto 1; Nocturnes (exc); Etudes (exc). (D. Lipatti, Concertgebouw/E. van Beinum, Zurich Tonhalle Orch/O. Ackermann)

① **JD561-2** (1/89)
Early Songs from Berg, Schönberg and Schreker
Berg: Early Songs; *Schreker:* Lieder, Op.4 (exc); Lieder, Op.7 (exc); *Berg:* Songs, Op.2; Schliesse mir die Augen beide; *Schoenberg:* Lieder, Op. 2. (E. Speiser, I. Gage)

① **JD563-2** (3/90)
Frank Martin interprets Frank Martin
Martin: Jedermann Monologe; Minnelieder; Chants de Noël; Preludes; Flute Ballade; Cello Ballade. (H. Rehfuss, F. Martin, E. Ameling, P. Odé, R. Willoughby, H. Honegger)

① **JD630-2** (2/91)
Schubert: Lieder
Schubert: Knabe, D692; Götter Griechenlands, D677; Sehnsucht, D879; Lachen und Weinen, D777; Heimliches Lieben, D922; Am Grabe Anselmos, D504; Rose, D745; Gretchen am Spinnrade, D118; An mein Herz, D860; Im Abendrot, D799; Winterabend, D938; Wanderer an den Mond, D870; Nachtstück, D672; Abschied, D475; Wandrers Nachtlied I, D224; Abendbilder, D650; Frühlingsglaube, D686; Ganymed, D544; Lied der Anne Lyle, D830; Beim Winde, D669; Schlaflied, D527. (E. Speiser, J. Buttrick)

① **JD645-2** (10/91)
Frank Martin conducts Frank Martin
Martin: Maria-Triptychon; Petite Symphonie Concertante; Passacaglia (1962). (I. Seefried, W. Schneiderhan, SRO/F. Martin, BPO)

① **JD646-2** (10/91)
Frank Martin—Chamber Works
Martin: String Trio; Pavane couleur; Trio populaires irlandaises; Piano Quintet. (H. Schmid-Wyss, Zurich Chmbr Ens)

① **JD673-2** (3/94)
Schoeck—Complete Lieder, Vol.3
Schoeck: Gott und die Bajadere, Op.34; Wanderung im Gebirge, Op.45; Hafis-Lieder, Op.33; Sommerabend; Entschwundene. (N. Tüller, C. Keller)

① **JD677-2** (3/94)
Schoeck—Complete Lieder, Vol.7
Schoeck: Wandsbecker Liederbuch, Op.52; Im Nebel; Wiegenlied; Lieder, Op.51; Lieder, Op.35. (J. Banse, D. Henschel, W. Rieger)

① **J4420/1-2** (11/91)
Schubert: Piano Sonatas, Vol.1
Schubert: Piano Sonata, D784; Piano Sonata, D845; Piano Sonata, D894; Piano Sonata, D959. (T. Leonhardt)

① **J4422/3-2** (11/91)
Schubert: Piano Sonatas, Vol.2
Schubert: Piano Sonata, D664; Piano Sonata, D850; Piano Sonata, D958; Piano Sonata, D960. (T. Leonhardt)

J.Martin Stafford

① **JMSCD1** (5/95)
Thurston Dart plays English Organ Music
Byrd: Fantasia, BK25; Fantasia, BK26; *J. Bull:* Untitled Fantasia; Salvator Mundi Deus; *Gibbons:* Fantasia; In Nomine; *Tomkins:* Fancy; *Blow:* Verset in D minor; *Locke:* Voluntaries (exc); *Purcell:* Verset; Voluntary on the old 100th, Z721; *Greene:* Voluntary; *Handel:* Fugue in F; Suite; *Purcell:* Organ Voluntaries, Z717-20 (exc); Verse, Z716; *Nares:* Introduction and Fugue; *Boyce:* Voluntaries (exc); *Stanley:* Organ Voluntaries, Book 3 (exc). (T. Dart)

John Marks Records

① **JMR5** (3/95)
Brahms/Mendelssohn/Schumann—Chamber Works
Brahms: Cello Sonata 1; Cello Sonata 2; *Schumann:* Fantasiestücke, Op. 73; *Mendelssohn:* Song without Words, Op. 109. (N. Rosen, D. Stevenson)

Kingdom

① **KCLCD2001** (6/88)
Gordon Fergus-Thompson plays Scriabin and Balakirev
Balakirev: Lark; Piano Sonata (1900-05); *Scriabin:* Poèmes, Op.32; Piano Sonata 3; Vers la flamme. (G. Fergus-Thompson)

① **KCLCD2003** (12/88)
Masterpieces in Miniature
Liszt: Concert Studies, S144 (exc); *Debussy:* Préludes (exc); *Albéniz:* Cantos de España (exc); *Schumann:* Fantasiestücke, Op. 12 (exc); *Bartók:* For Children (1945) (exc); *Chopin:* Fantaisie-impromptu; *Schubert:* Impromptus (exc); *Brahms:* Waltzes, Op.39 (exc); *Chopin:* Nocturnes (exc); Waltzes (exc); *Schubert:* Ländler, D145 (exc); Waltzes, D365 (exc); Waltzes, D779 (exc); *Rachmaninov:* Preludes (exc); *Beethoven:* Bagatelles (exc); *Liszt:* Rigoletto—paraphrase, S434. (M. Tirimo)

① **KCLCD2005** (3/89)
20th Century Harpsichord Music
Martinů: Harpsichord Pieces; Harpsichord Sonata; Harpsichord Impromptus; *V. Thomson:* Portraits (1940) (exc); Portrait (1956); *Persichetti:* Harpsichord Sonata 7; *Albright:* Harpsichord Fancies; *Adler:* Harpsichord Sonata; *Sowash:* Unicorn; Theme and Variations; *Templeton:* Topsy-Turvy Suite (exc). (B. Harbach)

① **KCLCD2009** (7/89)
MacDowell—Piano Sonatas
MacDowell: Piano Sonata 1; Piano Sonata 2; Piano Sonata 3. (J. Tocco)

① **KCLCD2011** (6/89)
Griffes: Selected piano solos
Griffes: Rhapsody; Fantasy Pieces, Op. 6; Piano Sonata; Pleasure-dome of Kubla Khan; Tone-Pictures, Op. 5; Legend (1915); Preludes. (J. Tocco)

① **KCLCD2012** (6/89)
Lennox Berkeley—Piano Music
L. Berkeley: Short pieces, Op. 4; Pieces, Op. 2; Polka, Op. 5a; Mazurkas, Op. 32/1; Paysage (1944); Improvisation, Op. 55/2; Mazurka, Op. 101/2; Preludes, Op. 23; Piano Sonata, Op. 20. (C. Headington)

① **KCLCD2013** (3/90)
Twentieth Century Flute Music
Vaughan Williams: Suite de ballet; *Martinů:* Flute Sonata; *Debussy:* Syrinx; *Copland:* Flute Duo; *Honegger:* Danse de la Chèvre; *Poulenc:* Flute Sonata. (M. Cox, N. Clayton)

① **KCLCD2016** (10/90)
Brahms: Piano Works
Brahms: Piano Sonata 3; Piano Pieces, op 76; Rhapsodies, op 79. (J. Plowright)

① **KCLCD2017** (11/90)
Twentieth century British Piano Music
Elgar: Adieu; In Smyrna; Serenade; *Delius:* Preludes; *Moeran:* Summer Valley; *Headington:* Ballade-image; *Cinquanta; Patterson:* Tunnel of Time; *Britten:* Holiday Diary; *Ireland:* Island Spell. (C. Headington)

① **KCLCD2019** (10/90)
Nielsen: Piano Works
Nielsen: Theme with Variations; Pieces, Op. 59; Chaconne; Humoresque; Pieces, Op. 3; Suite. (E. Katahn)

① **KCLCD2020** (2/91)
The Art of the Lute-Harpsichord
Bach: Suite, BWV996; *Dowland:* Galliards (exc); Pavans (exc); *D. Scarlatti:* Keyboard Sonatas (exc); *Duphly:* Pièces de clavecin (exc); *Weiss:* Suite I in D. (K. Heindel)

① **KCLCD2027** (12/92)
South American Flute Music
Ginastera: Impresiones de la Puna; Duo, Op.13; *Villa-Lobos:* Bachianas Brasileiras 6; Chôros 2; Assobio a jato; Distribuição de flores; *Piazzolla:* Histoire du Tango. (A. Noakes, M. Argiros, L. Craven, M. Denman, R. Friedman, K. Musker, S. New, J. Woodrow, J. Pearson)

① **KCLCD2031** (4/93)
Chopin—Piano Works
Chopin: Piano Sonata 2; Piano Sonata 3; Nocturnes (exc); Berceuse. (A. Lear)

Kiwi-Pacific Records

① **CDSLD-90** (3/94)
Lilburn—Symphonies
Lilburn: Symphony 1; Symphony 2; Symphony 3. (NZ SO/J. Hopkins/A. Heenan)

Koch International Classics

① **312652** (4/94)
Szymanowski—Orchestral and Choral Works
Szymanowski: Stabat Mater; Symphony 3; Kasprowicz Fragments, Op. 5. (S. Woytowicz, K. Szostek-Radkowa, A. Hiolski, Polish Rad & TV Ch, Polish Radio & TV SO, Katowice Polish Rad & TV Great SO/S. Wislocki/T. Strugała/J. Maksymiuk)

① **37000-2** (6/90)
Bernstein—Songs & Duets
Bernstein: On the Town (exc); Wonderful Town (exc); Peter Pan (exc); Songfest (exc); Arias and Barcarolles. (J. Kaye, W. Sharp, M. Barrett, S. Blier, S. Sant'Ambrogio)

① **37002-2** (10/90)
American Works for 2 Pianos & Orchestra
Gould: Dance variations; *Piston:* 2-Piano Concerto; *Copland:* Rodeo (exc); Danzón cubano; Salón México. (J. Pierce, D. Jonas, RPO/D. Amos)

① **37003-2** (11/90)
Grainger—Orchestral Works
Grainger: Warriors; Hill Song 1; Hill Song 2; Danish Folk-Music Suite; Irish Tune from County Derry; Beautiful fresh flower. (Melbourne SO/G. Simon)

① **37005-2** (4/91)
Menotti/Barber—Orchestral Works
Barber: Souvenirs Suite; *Menotti:* Amahl and the Night Visitors (exc); Sebastian Suite. (NZ SO/A. Schenck)

① **37008-2** (4/91)
Romantic French & German Organ Music
Jongen: Toccata; *Karg-Elert:* Impressions, Op. 72 (exc); *Vierne:* Suite 4 (exc); Triptyque, Op. 58 (exc); Suite 3 (exc); *Tournemire:* Méditation (exc); *Reger:* Pieces, Op. 59 (exc); *Dupré:* Symphonie-Passion (exc); Variations sur un vieux Noël. (M.H. Long)

① **37010-2** (1/91)
Barber—Orchestral Works
Barber: Essay for Orchestra 3; Medea Suite; Fadograph. (NZ SO/A. Schenck)

① **37011-2** (1/91)
Legendary Conductors
Haydn: Symphony 88; *Mozart:* Symphony 39; *Gluck:* Alceste (1776) (exc); *Beethoven:* Leonore (exc). (VPO/C. Krauss, Berlin St Op Orch/E. Kleiber, Concertgebouw/W. Mengelberg/B. Walter)

① **37012-2** (7/91)
Twenty Fanfares for the Common Man
Copland: Fanfare for the Common Man; Ceremonial Fanfare; Inaugural Fanfare; *Hanson:* Chorale and Fanfare; Fanfare for the Signal Corps; *R. Harris:* Fanfare for the Forces; *Cowell:* Fanfare to the Forces of the Latin American Allies; *Wagenaar:* Fanfare for Airmen; *Gould:* Fanfare for Freedom; Columbian Fanfares; *Bernstein:* Fanfare for JFK; Fanfare for the 25th Anniversary (1961); *Shivaree; D. Taylor:* Fanfare for Russia; *V. Thomson:* Fanfare for France; *Piston:* Ceremonial Fanfare; Fanfare for the Fighting French; *Creston:* Fanfare for Paratroopers. (LPO/J. Mester)

① **37021-2** (5/91)
Mira Zakai—Song Recital
Ravel: Chansons madécasses; *Mahler:* Lieder und gesänge (exc); *Berg:* Songs, Op. 2; *Webern:* Lieder, Op. 3; *Handel:* Mi, palpita il cor. (M. Zakai, Yonathan Zak, A. Biron, M. Haran, A. Shalev)

① **37025-2** (2/91)
Ives—Orchestral Works
Ives: Country Band March; Ragtime Dances; Postlude; Set 1 (exc); Yale-Princeton; Theatre Orchestra Set; Set of Three Short Pieces (exc); Orchestral Set I. (New England Orch/J. Sinclair)

① **37026-2** (1/91)
Morton Gould—Choral Music
Gould: Of Time and the River; A capella; Quotations. (NY Choral Soc, NY Choral Soc Orch/J.D. Goodwin, G. Smith Sngrs/G. Smith)

① **37027-2** (7/91)
American Chamber Works
Rochberg: Piano Quartet (1983); *Harbison:* Variations (1982); Twilight Music (1984). (American Chbr Players)

① 37028-2 (7/91)
Gershwin—Songs & Duets
Gershwin: Rosalie (exc); Damsel in distress (exc); Hi-Ho!; Treasure Girl (exc); Strike up the band I (exc); Funny Face (exc); Our Nell (exc); Strike up the band II (exc); Primrose (exc); Till Then; Pardon my English (exc); Show Girl (exc); Lady, be good! (exc); Porgy and Bess (exc); Of thee I sing (exc). (J. Kaye, W. Sharp, S. Blier)

① 37030-2 (5/91)
Britten—Choral & Organ Works
Britten: Te Deum in C; Hymn of St Columba; Jubilate Deo in C; Hymn to St Cecilia; Prelude and Fugue; Hymn to St Peter; Rejoice in the Lamb. (St Thomas Ch/G. Hancock, M. Kleinschmidt, P. Berry)

① 37035-2 (10/91)
Benno Moiseiwitsch—A Centenary Celebration
Beethoven: Piano Concerto 5; *Liszt:* Hungarian Fantasia, S123; *Medtner:* Fairy Tales, Op.34 (exc); *Prokofiev:* Pieces, Op.4 (exc); *Godowsky:* Fledermaus Potpourri. (B. Moiseiwitsch, LPO/G. Szell/C. Lambert)

① 37036-2 (4/92)
Creston—Orchestral Works
Creston: Corinthians: XIII; Walt Whitman; Symphony 2. (Cracow PO/D. Amos)

① 37043-2 (10/91)
Songs of Frederick Delius
Delius: Norwegian Songs (1889-90) (exc); Verlaine Songs (exc); Lune blanche; Chanson d'Automne; Danish Songs (exc); Norwegian Songs (1888) (exc); English Songs. (R. Golden, S. Sulich)

① 37044-2 (11/91)
Haydn—English Love Songs
Haydn: Canzonettas I (exc); O tuneful voice; Spirit's Song; Canzonettas II (exc); Arianna a Naxos. (J. Nelson, E. Thornburgh)

① 37045-2 (7/91)
American Romantic Piano Music
Griffes: Fantasy Pieces, Op. 6; Piano Sonata; Tone-Pictures, Op. 5; *MacDowell:* Piano Sonata 4. (G. Landes)

① 37050-2 (10/91)
Blitzstein—Songs
Blitzstein: Reuben, Reuben (exc); Cradle will Rock (exc); No for an Answer (exc); Airborne Symphony (exc); Regina (exc); This is the Garden (exc); Juno (exc); From Marion's Book (exc); Jimmie's Got a Goil; Stay in my Arms; Goloopchik (exc); Zipperfly; Magic Barrel (exc). (K. Holvik, W. Sharp, S. Blier)

① 37051-2 (4/92)
More Music for Martha Graham
Menotti: Errand into the Maze; *Hindemith:* Hérodiade; *Schuman:* Night Journey. (Atlantic Sinfonietta/A. Schenck)

① 37053-2 (11/91)
The Young Otto Klemperer
Weill: Kleine Dreigroschenmusik (exc); *R. Strauss:* Till Eulenspiegel; Salome (exc); *Brahms:* Symphony 1. (Berlin St Op Orch/O. Klemperer)

① 37056-2 (10/92)
Coleridge-Taylor—Chamber Works
Coleridge Taylor: Petite suite de concert; Ballade, Op. 4; Negro Melodies (exc); Clarinet Quintet. (M. Ludwig, M. Ludwig, Hawthorne Qt, V. Eskin)

① 37057-2 (4/92)
Byrd—Grounds and Variations
Byrd: My Lady Nevell's Ground, BK57; O mistress mine, BK83; John come kiss me now, BK81; Pavan and Galliard, BK2; Carman's Whistle, BK36; Walsingham, BK8; Hugh Ashton's Ground, BK20; Fortune, BK6; Sellinger's Round, BK84. (E. Thornburgh)

① 37058-2 (4/92)
Holst—Works for Chamber Orchestra
Holst: Brook Green Suite; Lyric Movement; Fugal Concerto; Morris Dance Tunes; St Paul's Suite. (V. Yendoll, A. Still, S. Popperwell, New Zealand CO/N. Braithwaite)

① 37059-2 (4/92)
Furtwängler—The Early Recordings
Bach: Brandenburg Concertos (exc); Suites, BWV1066-9 (exc); *Mozart:* Nozze di Figaro (exc); Entführung (exc); Serenade, K525; *Schubert:* Rosamunde (exc); *Beethoven:* Egmont (exc); Symphony 5; *Weber:* Freischütz (exc); *Rossini:* Gazza ladra (exc); Barbiere di Siviglia (exc). (BPO/W. Furtwängler)

① 37061-2 (3/92)
Beecham conducts Sibelius
Sibelius: En saga; Legends (exc); Bard; In memoriam; Valse triste; Symphony 4. (LPO/T. Beecham)

① 37069-2 (11/92)
American String Quartets
Q. Porter: String Quartet 3; *Barber:* String Quartet, Op. 11; *Piston:* String Quartet 1. (Chester Qt)

① 37070-2 (10/93)
Barber/Foss/Ornstein—Cello Works
Barber: Cello Sonata; *Foss:* Capriccio; *Ornstein:* Cello Sonata, Op. 52. (Y. Hanani, M. Levin)

① 37072-2 (2/93)
Leo Blech conducts
Berlioz: Carnaval Romain; *Smetana:* Má Vlast (exc); *Liszt:* Hungarian Rhapsodies, S359 (exc); *Schubert:* Symphony 9. (BPO, Berlin St Op Orch, LSO/L. Blech)

① 37073-2 (4/92)
Furtwängler—Early Recordings 1926-1937
Weber: Freischütz (exc); Invitation to the Dance; *Mendelssohn:* Midsummer Night's Dream (exc); Hebrides; *Berlioz:* Damnation de Faust (exc); *Wagner:* Lohengrin (exc); Tristan und Isolde (exc); Götterdämmerung (exc); *Brahms:* Hungarian Dances (exc); *J. Strauss II:* Fledermaus (exc); *R. Strauss:* Till Eulenspiegel. (BPO/W. Furtwängler)

① 37076-2 (3/92)
Richard Strauss conducts Mozart
Mozart: Symphony 39; Symphony 40; Symphony 41. (Berlin St Op Orch/R. Strauss)

① 37077-2 (3/92)
The Young John Barbirolli
Haydn: Symphony 104; *Mozart:* Serenade, K525; *Purcell:* Married Beau, Z603 (exc); *Tchaikovsky:* Swan Lake Suite; *Grieg:* Peer Gynt Suites (exc). (Barbirolli CO, LPO, Barbirolli SO/J. Barbirolli)

① 37085-2 (5/92)
Schütz—Motets
Schütz: Geistliche Chormusik, SWV369-97 (exc); Cantiones sacrae (exc); Das ist mir lieb, SWV51. (Emmanuel Music Choir/C. Smith)

① 37086-2 (7/93)
Unquiet Peace—The Lied Between the Wars
Weill: Berliner Requiem (exc); Silbersee (exc); Dreigroschenoper (exc); Love Life (exc); Berlin im Licht; Mahagonny (exc); Lady in the Dark (exc); Happy End (exc); Marie Galante (exc); Je ne t'aime pas; Street Scene (exc); One touch of Venus (exc); Firebrand of Florence (exc); Nannas Lied; Youkali; Knickerbocker Holiday (exc). (A. Réaux, R. Kapilow)

① 37087-2 (6/92)
Songs of Kurt Weill
Weill: Berliner Requiem (exc); Silbersee (exc); Dreigroschenoper (exc); Love Life (exc); Berlin im Licht; Mahagonny (exc); Lady in the Dark (exc); Happy End (exc); Marie Galante (exc); Je ne t'aime pas; Street Scene (exc); One touch of Venus (exc); Firebrand of Florence (exc); Nannas Lied; Youkali; Knickerbocker Holiday (exc). (A. Réaux, R. Kapilow)

① 37092-2 (4/92)
Copland—Orchestral Works
Copland: Tender Land Suite; Latin-American sketches; Red Pony Suite. (Phoenix SO/J. Sedares)

① 37094-2 (4/92)
Ibert/Poulenc—Orchestral Works
Ibert: Divertissement; Concertino da camera; *Poulenc:* Sinfonietta. (M. Whitcombe, San Diego CO/D. Barra)

① 37096-2 (9/92)
18th Century French Cantatas
Montéclair: Bergère; Mort de Didon; Pan et Syrinx; *Clérambault:* Médée. (J. Baird, American Baroque, S. Schultz)

① 37102-2 (7/93)
Aureole
Debussy: Sonata for Flute, Viola and Harp; *Devienne:* Duos, Op. 5 (exc); *Fauré:* Morceau de concours (1898); *Ibert:* Interludes; *Ravel:* Sonatine. (Aureole)

① 37106-2 (12/92)
Sessions—Complete Works for Solo Piano
Sessions: Piano Sonata 1; Piano Sonata 2; Piano Sonata 3; Pages from a Diary; Pieces; Waltz. (B.D. Salwen)

① 37109-2 (10/92)
Ullmann—Chamber Works
Ullmann: Piano Sonata 5; Piano Sonata 6; Piano Sonata 7;

String Quartet 3. (Group for New Music, R. Kolben, E. Steiner-Kraus)

① 37110-2 (7/93)
Wuorinen—Orchestral & Chamber Works
Wuorinen: Five; Archangel; Archaeopteryx; Hyperion. (D. Taylor, B. Hudson, C. Zeavin, L. Schulman, F. Sherry, St Luke's Chbr Ens, St Luke's Orch/C. Wuorinen)

① 37112-2 (2/94)
Wolpe—Chamber Works
Wolpe: Quartet (1955); Violin Sonata (1949); Trio (1963-64). (H. Solberger, S. Taylor, J. Fleezanis, F. Sherry, D. Kennedy, A. Karis, G. Ohlsson, C. Wuorinen)

① 37113-2 (2/95)
Sessions—Chamber Works
Sessions: Quintet (1958); Stravinsky Canons; String Quartet (1938); Cello Pieces (1966). (Group for Contemporary Music, J. Gordon)

① 37118-2 (10/92)
My Own Country - Songs of Peter Warlock
Warlock: Late summer; I have a garden; My own country; Lullaby; Sweet content; Ha'nacker Mill; Night; To the Memory of a Great Singer; Traditional: Birds; Frostbound Wood; First Mercy; *Warlock:* Pretty Ring Time; *Anon:* Have you seen but a white lily grow?; *Warlock:* Cradle Song; Cloths of Heaven; Sleep; Lillygay. (R. Golden, L. Rothfuss)

① 37121-2 (7/93)
The Group for Contemporary Music
J. Harvey: String Quartet 1; *Peterson:* String Quartet 1; *Wuorinen:* String Quartet 2. (Group for Contemporary Music)

① 37126-2 (11/92)
Victor de Sabata conducts the BPO
Verdi: Aida (exc); *Wagner:* Tristan und Isolde (exc); *Kodály:* Galánta Dances; *Respighi:* Roman Festivals. (BPO/V. de Sabata)

① 37129-2 (5/93)
Clemens Kraus Conducts
Brahms: Symphony 3; *R. Strauss:* Bourgeois Gentilhomme Suite; Salome (exc). (VPO/C. Krauss)

① 37130-2 (11/95)
John Cage—Thirteen Harmonies
Zahab: Vexing Lightfall; *Cage:* Harmonies; Harmonies. (R. Zahab, E. Moe)

① 37133-2 (2/94)
Kajanus conducts Sibelius, Vol.3
Sibelius: Symphony 3; Symphony 5; Finnish Jaeger Battalion March. (LSO, Helsinki PO/R. Kajanus)

① 37134-2 (6/92)
Arnold—Orchestral Works
Arnold: Serenade; Sinfonietta 1; Sinfonietta 2; 2-Violin Concerto. (I. Gruppman, V. Gruppman, San Diego CO/D. Barra)

① 37138-2 (12/92)
Bach—Cantatas
Bach: Cantata 51; Cantata 54; Cantata 55; Cantata 82. (J. Baird, D. Minter, W. Sharp, K. Kraft, J. Abberger, B. Baugess, American Bach Sols, Jeffrey Thomas (ten/dir)/J. Thomas)

① 37139-2 (11/92)
Bridge/Delius—Works for Chamber Orchestra
Bridge: Suite for strings; Cherry ripe; There is a willow; Sir Roger de Coverley; *Delius:* Sonata for Strings. (New Zealand CO/N. Braithwaite)

① 37141-2 (12/92)
Wolpe—Chamber Works
Wolpe: In 2 Parts; Brecht Lieder; Quartet (1950); Hamlet; Piece in 2 instrumental units; To the Dancemaster; Trumpet Piece; Trumpet and 7 instruments. (J. Castle, R. Mase, Parnassus/A. Korf)

① 37143-2 (3/93)
Grieg—Lyric Pieces
Grieg: Lyric Pieces, Op. 38 (exc); Lyric Pieces, Op. 47 (exc); Lyric Pieces, Op. 54 (exc); Lyric Pieces, Op. 57 (exc); Lyric Pieces, Op. 62 (exc); Lyric Pieces, Op. 68 (exc); Lyric Pieces, Op. 71 (exc). (I. Margalit)

① 37144-2 (4/94)
American Music for Flute and Piano
Barber: Canzone, Op. 38; *Bloch:* Last Poems; *E. Burton:* Flute Sonatina; *Copland:* Flute Duo; Flute Vocalise; *Muczynski:* Flute Sonata; *Q. Porter:* Blues lointaines; *Rochberg:* Between Two Worlds. (A. Still, S. De Witt Smith)

① **37700-2** (12/92)
Albert Coates Conducts, Vol.1 - Russian Favourites
Glinka: Ruslan and Lyudmila (exc); Kamarinskaya;
Borodin: In the Steppes of Central Asia; Prince Igor (exc);
Liadov: Russian Folksongs, Op.58; *Mussorgsky:* Fair at
Sorochintsï (exc); *Tchaikovsky:* Marche Slave; *Rimsky-
Korsakov:* May Night (exc); Dubinushka; Maid of Pskov
(exc); Mlada (exc); Snow Maiden (exc); *Stravinsky:*
Firebird (exc). (LSO/A. Coates)

① **37702-2** (9/93)
Piero Coppola conducts
Ravel: Valses nobles et sentimentales; Boléro; *Honegger:*
Symphonic Movements (exc); *Saint-Saëns:* Symphony 3.
(A. Cellier, Paris Cons, SO/P. Coppola)

① **37704-2** (4/93)
Albert Coates conducts the LSO, Vol.2
Liszt: Hungarian Rhapsodies, S359 (exc); *Weber:* Oberon
(exc); *Wagner:* Rheingold (exc); Walküre (exc);
Götterdämmerung (exc); *Humperdinck:* Hänsel and Gretel
(exc); *Dvořák:* Carnival; *R. Strauss:* Don Juan; *Bach:*
Fantasia and Fugue, BWV537; *R. Strauss:* Tod und
Verklärung; *Respighi:* Fountains of Rome; *Holst:* Planets
(exc); *Ravel:* La Valse. (LSO/A. Coates)

① **37705-2** (11/93)
Alfred Cortot as Conductor
Couperin: Nouveaux Concerts (exc); *Bach:* Brandenburg
Concertos; *Brahms:* Double Concerto. (Paris Ecole
Normale CO/A. Cortot, J. Thibaud, P. Casals, Barcelona
Casals Orch)

① **38703-2** (9/95)
Full Circle—Original Soundtrack, etc
Towns: Full Circle (exc); Trumpet Concerto; 1930
Cityscape. (G. Ashton, P. Todd, Orch/A. Wilson, OST, C.
Towns)

Koch Schwann

① **310002** (9/90)
Salzburg Serenades
Anon: Sextet; Sextet-Parthia; *Neukomm:* Serenade;
Assmayer: Octet; *Wölfl:* Sextet; *M. Haydn:* Divertimento,
MH418. (Consortium Classicum)

① **310011** (10/89)
Cambini; Danzi; Reicha—Wind Quintets
Danzi: Wind Quintets, Op.67 (exc); *Cambini:* Wind Quintet
3; *Reicha:* Wind Quintets, Op. 100 (exc). (Aulos Wind
Qnt)

① **310019** (4/90)
Brazilian Piano Music
Villa-Lobos: Prole do bebê II (exc); Cirandas (exc);
Guarnieri: Ponteios 24; Ponteios 42; Ponteios 44; Ponteios
45; Ponteios 49; Ponteios 50; *Nazareth:* Escorregando;
Duvidoso; Apanhei-te, Cavaquinho; Bambino; Garoto;
Faceira; Remando; Favorito. (M. Verzoni)

① **310022** (10/89)
Françaix—Chamber Works
Françaix: Wind Quintet 1; Wind Quintet 2; Wind Quartet
(1933); Divertissement (1947). (Aulos Wind Qnt)

① **310035** (8/90)
Gottschalk—Piano Works
Gottschalk: Banjo; Union; Ricordati; Pasquinade; Savane;
Scherzo-romantique; Souvenir de Porto Rico; Gallina; Ojos
Criollos; Last Hope; Bananier; Bamboula, RO20. (K.
Kaufmann)

① **310045** (6/88)
Hindemith: Works for Viola and Orchestra
Hindemith: Kammermusik, op 36/4; Schwanendreher;
Concert Music, Op. 48. (G. Schmidt, BRSO/R. Heger/R.
Kubelik)

① **310047** (6/92)
Krenek—Piano Sonatas, Vol.1
Krenek: Piano Sonata 1; Piano Sonata 3; Piano Sonata 5.
(G.D. Madge)

① **310048** (6/92)
Krenek—Piano Sonatas, Vol.2
Krenek: Piano Sonata 7; Piano Sonata 2; Piano Sonata 4;
Piano Sonata 6. (G.D. Madge)

① **310051** (6/93)
Works for Wind Instruments
Janáček: Mládí; *P. Haas:* Wind Quintet, Op. 10; *Foerster:*
Wind Quintet, Op. 95. (K. Berger, Aulos Wind Qnt)

① **310087** (10/91)
Music for Wind Ensemble
Briccialdi: Wind Quintet, Op. 124; *Rossini:* Sonate a
quattro (exc); *C. E. Lefebvre:* Suite, Op. 57; *Taffanel:* Wind
Quintet. (Aulos Wind Qnt)

① **310094** (9/92)
Haydn—Keyboard Sonatas
Haydn: Keyboard Sonata 8; Keyboard Sonata 9; Keyboard
Sonata 11; Keyboard Sonata 16; Keyboard Sonata 13. (C.
Faron)

① **310165** (6/93)
Shostakovich—String Quartets
Shostakovich: String Quartet 6; String Quartet 7; String
Quartet 8. (Manhattan Qt)

① **310412** (11/93)
Górecki—Orchestral Works
Górecki: Symphony 1; Chorus I; Olden Style Pieces.
(Cracow PO/R. Bader)

① **310632** (7/93)
Globokar—Chamber Works
Globokar: Discours III; Toucher; Discours VI; Voix
instrumentalisée; Accord. (M. Vilotijević, M. Siracusa, H.
Holliger, M. Riessler, S. Viola, M. Chiapperino, V.
Lambiase, D. Sabatini, J-P. Drouet, Domus)

① **310652** (6/95)
Fumet/d'Indy/Honegger—Chamber Works
Fumet: Nuit; *Indy:* Concerto, Op. 89; *Honegger:* Dit des
Jeux suite. (P. Dechorgnat, J. Ferrandis, H. Noël, J-J.
Wiederker, J-J. Wiederker CO/F. Bouaniche)

① **310832** (3/94)
Frank Martin—Orchestral Works
Martin: Wind Concerto; Petite symphonie concertante;
Flute Ballade. (E. Brown, D. Kossoff, Daniel Goldberg, A.
Sato, P. Gordon/M. Gould, K. Finn, V. Drake, Anthony
Newman, C. Hoca, R. Kohloff, M. Hinton, M. Gunji, Philh
Virtuosi/R. Kapp)

① **310942** (2/95)
Steven Kimbrough—Lieder Recital
Schoenberg: In hellen Träumen; Warum bist du
aufgewacht; Mannesbangen; Mailied; Gruss in die Ferne;
K. Weigl: Gesänge, Op. 1 (Cpte); Liebeslied; *Korngold:*
Entführung; Und wie mag die Liebe; Lieder, Op. 4 (exc);
Lieder, Op. 7 (exc); Rosenblatt; *Korngold:*
Unvergänglichkeit (Cpte); Lieder, Op. 38 (exc). (S.
Kimbrough, D. Baldwin)

① **311009** (8/89)
Schoenberg: Chamber Orchestral Works
Schoenberg: Chamber Symphony 1; Pieces for chamber
orchestra; Lied der Waldtaube; Orchestral Pieces, Op. 16.
(J. van Nes, Schoenberg Ens/R. de Leeuw)

① **311035** (12/89)
Orchestral Works
Sarrier: Symphony in D; *Soler:* Keyboard Sonatas I (exc);
Keyboard Sonatas I (exc); *Arriaga:* Symphony in D. (Berlin
RIAS Sinfonietta/J. Velazco)

① **311045** (11/88)
Romantic Clarinet Concertos
Danzi: Introduction, Op. 45; *Kalliwoda:* Introduction, Op.
128; *Lindpaintner:* Clarinet Concertino; *Reissiger:* Clarinet
Concertino. (D. Klöcker, Berlin RSO/J. López-Cobos)

① **311052** (10/88)
Virtuoso Kettledrum Concertos
Prin: Echo de Psyché; *Hertel:* Timpani Concerto;
Thärichen: Timpani Concerto; *Anon:* Adagio and Allegro
for timpani. (W. Thärichen, N. Bardach, G. Touvron, W.
Karius, Berlin RSO/V. Handley)

① **311065** (4/90)
Double Concertos
Bruch: Clarinet and Viola Concerto; *Lutosławski:* Double
Concerto; *R. Strauss:* Duet Concertino. (E. Brunner, T.
Zimmermann, M. Turkovic, M. Graf, Bamberg SO/L.
Zagrosek)

① **311071** (3/89)
Trumpet Concertos
Hertel: Concerto a cinque in D; Trumpet Concerto in D;
Hummel: Trumpet Concerto; *J.A. Gros:* Trumpet Concerto.
(W. Basch, K. Kärcher, G. Vetter, K. Ventulett, M. Roscher,
Orpheus CO)

① **311078** (11/88)
Schreker: Orchestral Works
Schreker: Chamber Symphony; Prelude to a Drama; Valse
lente; Nachtstücke. (Berlin RSO/M. Gielen/K.A.
Rickenbacher)

① **311088** (1/90)
Spohr—Instrumental Works
Spohr: Variations, Op.8; Concerto, Op.131; Variations,
Op.6. (E. Sebestyen, H. Ganz, H. Beyerle, W. Strehle, M.
Ostertag, Berlin RSO/G. Albrecht)

① **311116** (4/90)
Dvořák—Bagatelles, Op. 47; Serenade, Op. 44
Dvořák: Bagatelles, B79; Bagatelles, B79; Serenade, op

44. (L. Casleanu, M. Kurkowski, C. Brunnert, D.R. Davies,
Bonn Beethovenhalle Orch/D.R. Davies)

① **311122** (7/90)
Early Twentieth Century Music
Zemlinsky: Sinfonietta; *Stephan:* Music for 7 stringed
instruments; *Reger:* Suite, op 103a. (Berlin RSO/B. Klee,
B. Hartog, I. Schliephake, S. Passaggio, G. Donderer, A.
Akahoshi, C. Tainton, M. Schmidt, H. Maile/U. Lajovic)

① **311135** (9/90)
Schubertiana
Heuberger: Schubert Variations; *Schubert:* Waltzes, D969;
Galop and Ecossaises, D735 (exc); Marches Militaires,
D733 (exc); Divertissement à la Hongroise, D818 (exc);
Waltzes, D779 (exc); Deutsche Tänze, D820. (Berlin
RSO/M. Bamert)

① **311136** (1/92)
Dohnanyi plays and conducts
Mozart: Piano Concerto 17; *Dohnányi:* Ruralia Hungarica
(exc); Nursery Variations. (Budapest PO/E. Dohnányi,
LSO, E. Dohnányi/L. Collingwood, E. Dohnányi (pf/dir))

① **311164** (5/92)
Mozart—Violin Concertos
Mozart: Violin Concerto, K207; Violin Concerto, K211;
Violin Concerto, K216; Violin Concerto, K218; Violin
Concerto, K219. (A. Cappelletti, ECCO/E. Aadland)

① **311232** (12/94)
Messiaen—Works for Piano and Orchestra
Messiaen: Sourire; Et exspecto resurrectionem; Oiseaux
exotiques; Ville d'en Haut; Vitrail et des oiseaux. (Y.
Loriod, BRSO, Berlin RSO/K. A. Rickenbacher)

① **311342** (5/94)
Hindemith plays and conducts
Hindemith: Mathis der Maler; String Trio 2; String Quartet,
Op.22. (S. Goldberg, P. Hindemith, E. Feuermann, Amar
Qt, BPO/P. Hindemith)

① **311382** (12/92)
Milhaud—Orchestral Works
Milhaud: Saudades do Brasil; Carnaval de Londres; Rag
Caprices. (Capella Cracoviensis/K.A. Rickenbacher)

① **311392** (5/93)
Milhaud—Little Symphonies and Little Operas
Milhaud: Chamber Symphony 1; Chamber Symphony 2;
Chamber Symphony 3; Chamber Symphony 4; Chamber
Symphony 5; Chamber Symphony 6; Enlèvement
d'Europe; Abandon d'Ariane; Délivrance de Thésée.
(Capella Cracoviensis/K.A. Rickenbacher)

① **311612** (5/95)
Bartók/Shostakovich/Stravinsky—Chamber Works
Bartók: Solo Violin Sonata; *Stravinsky:* Elegy;
Shostakovich: Viola Sonata. (R. Hillyer, R. de Leeuw)

① **311672** (5/95)
Schulhoff—Chamber Music for Violin, Cello and Piano
Schulhoff: Violin and Cello Duo; Violin Sonata 2; Cello
Sonata. (S. Wagner, B. Gmelin, J. Lamke)

① **311972** (4/95)
Humperdinck—Orchestral Works
Humperdinck: Shakespeare Suite 1; Shakespeare Suite 2;
Overture 1; Humoresque. (Bamberg SO/K.A.
Rickenbacher)

① **312212** (5/94)
Martin—Piano Works
Martin: Preludes; Guitare; Clair de lune; Etude rhythmique;
Esquisse; Fantaisie. (C. Mathé)

① **312322** (9/95)
Schulhoff—Chamber Music with wind instruments
Schulhoff: Concertino; Divertissement; Flute Sonata; Hot-
Sonata. (T. Oepen, V. Donandt, H-U. Heinzmann, M.
Lammers, W. Hermann, B. Groth, J. Lamke, D. Bensmann,
M. Rische)

① **312362** (5/95)
Spanish Guitar Concertos
Marco: Concierto Guadiana; *Cruz de Castro:* Guitar
Concerto; *Benguerel:* Tempo. (W. Weigel, European
Master Orch/P. Schmelzer)

① **312592** (8/95)
Dvořák/Brahms/Reger—Duets
Brahms: Duets, Op. 20; Duets, Op. 66 (exc); Duets, Op.
61; Balladen and Romanzen, Op. 75 (exc); *Dvořák:*
Moravian Duets, B62; Moravian Duets, B60; *Reger:* Duets,
Op. 111a. (J. Banse, B. Fassbaender, C. Garben)

① **312632** (5/94)
Mahler/Busoni—Vocal/Orchestral Works
Mahler: Lieder eines fahrenden Gesellen; *Busoni:*
Berceuse élégiaque; *Mahler:* Kindertotenlieder. (J.
Bröcheler, J. van Nes, Schoenberg Ens/R. De Leeuw)

Ⓒ **312952** (5/94)
Hartmann—Orchestral and Vocal Works
K. A. Hartmann: Symphony 2; Gesangsszene zu Giraudoux' 'Sodom und Gomorrha'; Sinfonia Tragica. (S. Nimsgern, Bamberg SO/K. A. Rickenbacher)

Ⓒ **312982** (4/94)
Tan Dun—Orchestral Works
Tan Dun: On Taoism; Orchestral Theatre I; Death and Fire. (BBC Scottish SO/T. Dun)

Ⓒ **313001** (2/90)
Pater Noster
Anon: Pater noster—Plainchant; *Obrecht:* Pater noster; *Paminger:* Pater noster; *Schütz:* Symphoniarum Sacrarum, SWV398-418 (exc); *Homilius:* Pater noster; *Verdi:* Pater noster; *Reger:* Pater noster; *Stravinsky:* Pater noster; *Stockmeier:* Pater noster. (Lower Rhine Choral Soc/H. Schmitt)

Ⓒ **313062** (1/92)
Casals—Sacred Choral Music
Casals: Nigra sum; Tota pulchra es; Cançó a la verge; Rosarium; O vos omnes; Eucaristica; Recordare; Oracio a la Verge de Montserrat; Salve, Montserratina. (Montserrat Escolania/I. Segarra)

Ⓒ **313612** (6/93)
Wagner—Piano Works, Vol.1
Wagner: Piano Sonata, Op. 4; Piano Sonata, Op. 1; Album Sonata. (S. Möller)

Ⓒ **313622** (6/93)
Wagner—Piano Works, Vol.2
Wagner: Fantasia; Albumblatt; Metternich Albumblatt; Ankunft; Schott Albumblatt; Polka; Züricher Vielliebchen; Polonaise; Polonaise, Op. 2; Notenbrief; Elegie. (S. Möller, G. Mandozzi)

Ⓒ **314001** (12/89)
Szymanowski: Lieder
Szymanowski: Songs, Op. 31; Songs, Op. 26; Songs, Op. 42; Songs, Op. 5. (I. Kłosińska, K. Rorbach, B. Zagórzanka, K. Szostek-Radkowa, Polish Nat Op Orch/R. Satanowski)

Ⓒ **314005** (5/90)
Webern—Complete Vocal Chamber Works
Webern: Entflieht auf leichten Kähnen I; Entflieht auf leichten Kähnen II; Pieces for String Quartet; Lieder (1914); Lieder, Op. 8; Lieder, Op. 13; Lieder, Op. 14; Lieder, Op. 15; Canons, Op. 16; Rhymes, Op. 17; Lieder, Op. 18; Lieder, Op. 19. (D. Dorow, Netherlands Chbr Ch, Schoenberg Ens/R. de Leeuw)

Ⓒ **314050** (4/92)
Weill—Vocal and Choral Works
Weill: Recordare; Legende vom toten Soldaten; At Potsdam; Berliner Requiem; Walt Whitman Songs; Kiddush. (J. Wagner, W. Holzmair, Lower Rhine Community Ch, Düsseldorf Evangelist Church Students' Ch, Hanover Girls' Ch, R. Schumann CO, Düsseldorf SO Wind Ens, Helmut Schmidt/M-A. Schlingensiepen, A. Ruus)

Ⓒ **314063** (5/92)
Songs with Guitar
Giuliani: Ariette, Op. 95 (exc); *Spohr:* Lieder, Op. 72 (exc); *Beethoven:* Adelaide, Op. 46; *Schubert:* Gott im Frühling, D448; Nacht und Träume, D827; Wanderer, D489; Abschied von der Harfe, D406; *Brahms:* Deutsche Volkslieder (exc); Volks-Kinderlieder (exc). (E. Parcells, F. Justen)

Ⓒ **314081** (6/92)
R. Strauss—Lieder
R. Strauss: Vier letzte Lieder; Lieder, Op. 10 (exc); Lieder, Op. 27 (exc); Lieder, Op. 41 (exc); Lieder, Op. 48 (exc); Lieder, Op. 56 (exc). (G. Jones, Tokyo SO/R. Paternostro)

Ⓒ **314322** (3/95)
Ensemble Belcanto—Lieder Recital
Eisler: Woodburry songs; *Rühm:* Schöpfung; Foetus; Sprechquartette; *Schwehr:* Deutsche Tänze; *Van de Vate:* Cocaine Lil. (Bel Canto Ens/D. Spohr)

Ⓒ **314372** (8/95)
Schulhoff—Orchestral Works
Schulhoff: Plameny (exc); Symphony 1; Suite. (Brno St PO/I. Yinon)

Ⓒ **314502** (6/94)
Vienna State Opera—Live Recordings (sampler)
Bizet: Carmen (exc); *Wagner:* Walküre (exc); *R. Strauss:* Rosenkavalier (exc); *Verdi:* Don Carlo (exc); *Wagner:* Meistersinger (exc); *Mozart:* Nozze di Figaro (exc); *Wagner:* Lohengrin (exc); Fliegende Holländer (exc); *Borodin:* Prince Igor (exc); *Schmidt:* Notre Dame (exc); *Verdi:* Aida (exc); *Mozart:* Zauberflöte (exc); *Wagner:* Walküre (exc); *Verdi:* Ballo in maschera (exc); *Wagner:* Götterdämmerung (exc); *R. Strauss:* Frau ohne Schatten (exc); *Mascagni:* Cavalleria Rusticana (exc); *Wagner:* Rienzi (exc); *R. Strauss:* Rosenkavalier (exc). (S. Svanholm, V. Ursuleac, T. Mazaroff, P. Pierotic, P. Schoeffler, M. Klose, M. Müller, H. Hotter, H. Braun, A. Jerger, M. Lorenz, M. Reining, W. Grossmann, A. Konetzni, M. Ahlersmeyer, H. Konetzni, H. Roswaenge, M. Jeritza, F. Völker, E. Hadrabová, M. Gerhard, Vienna St Op Chor, Vienna St Op Orch/K. Böhm/W. Furtwängler/H. Knappertsbusch/C. Krauss/J. Krips/W. Loibner/L. Ludwig/R. Moralt/H. Reichenberger/H. Tietjen/B. Walter)

Ⓒ **314512** (7/94)
Vienna State Opera Live, Vol.1
R. Strauss: Rosenkavalier (exc); *Tchaikovsky:* Eugene Onegin (exc); *Verdi:* Otello (exc); *Rossini:* Barbiere di Siviglia (exc); *Benedict:* Carnival of Venice Variations; *Bellini:* Sonnambula (exc); *Verdi:* Aida (exc); *Wagner:* Tannhäuser (exc); Meistersinger (exc); Parsifal (exc); *Albert:* Tiefland (exc); *Gounod:* Faust (exc); *Wagner:* Götterdämmerung (exc); Götterdämmerung (exc); Meistersinger (exc); Lohengrin (exc); Lohengrin (exc); *Lehár:* Giuditta (exc); Giuditta (exc). (V. Ursuleac, R. Mayr, E. Hadrabová, M. Gerhart, H. Gallos, B. Paalen, K. von Pataky, C. Kullman, T. dal Monte, L. Montesanto, A. Sinnone, G. Lauri-Volpi, G. Rünger, J. Kalenberg, R. Bockelmann, K. Thorborg, J. Pölzer, R. Pauly, E. Pinza, L. Melchior, A. Konetzni, J. von Manowarda, K. Flagstad, T. Ralf, L. Helletsgruber, L. Hofmann, E. Schipper, M. Hussa, R. Tauber, J. Novotná, Vienna St Op Chor, Vienna St Op Orch/C. Krauss/H. Reichenberger/V. de Sabata/G. del Campo/R. Heger/F. Weingartner/K. Alwin/H. Knappertsbusch/J. Krips/F. Lehár)

Ⓒ **314532** (11/94)
Vienna State Opera Live, Vol.3
R. Strauss: Salome (exc); Salome (exc); *Mozart:* Idomeneo (exc); *Weber:* Freischütz (exc); *Wagner:* Meistersinger (exc); Siegfried (exc); Götterdämmerung (exc). (J. Witt, E. Schürhoff, E. Schulz, P. Schoeffler, A. Dermota, D. With, H. Alsen, H. Schweiger, C. Bissuti, K. Ettl, H. Hotter, J. Sattler, M. Bugarinovic, J. Sabel, E. Réthy, E. Böttcher, A. Konetzni, E. Kunz, M. Rus, F. Völker, E. Rethberg, J. von Manowarda, J. Prohaska, C. Reich, J. Kalenberg, H. Wiedemann, M. Lorenz, R. Anday, W. Wernigk, L. Helletsgruber, H. Trundt, E. Schipper, M. Angerer, Vienna St Op Chor, Vienna St Op Orch/R. Strauss/J. Krips)

Ⓒ **314542** (12/94)
Vienna State Opera Live, Vol.4
Verdi: Aida (exc); Don Carlo (exc); *Leoncavallo:* Pagliacci (exc); *Gounod:* Faust (exc); *Wagner:* Tannhäuser (exc); Fliegende Holländer (exc); *Puccini:* Tosca (exc); Turandot (exc); *Leoncavallo:* Pagliacci (exc); *Saint-Saëns:* Samson et Dalila (exc); *Verdi:* Aida (exc). (J. Björling, M. Németh, K. Thorborg, A. Sved, L. Hofmann, T. Mazaroff, P. Pierotic, M. Reining, P. Tutsek, C. Bissuti, H. Alsen, M. Bokor, F. Ginrod, A. Kipnis, E. Réthy, A. Jerger, K. Norbert, J. Kalenberg, B. Paalen, S. Björling, K. Ettl, G. Monthy, A. Michalsky, R. Anday, R. Maison, K. von Pataky, N. Zec, Vienna St Op Chor, Vienna St Op Orch/V. de Sabata/B. Walter/K. Alwin/J. Krips/W. Furtwängler/R. Heger/L. Reichwein/R. Moralt/W. Loibner/H. Reichenberger)

Ⓒ **314552** (11/94)
Vienna State Opera Live, Vol.5
R. Strauss: Aegyptische Helena (exc); Frau ohne Schatten (exc); Daphne (exc). (V. Ursuleac, F. Völker, M. Bokor, H. Roswaenge, A. Jerger, T. Ralf, H. Konetzni, E. Höngen, H. Alsen, E. Loose, W. Wenkoff, E. Boettcher, M. Frutschnigg, J. Herrmann, E. Schulz, G. Monthy, M. Rus, W. Wernigk, A. Poell, T. Neralič, R. Neumann, M. Reining, A. Dermota, A. Rauch, Vienna St Op Chor, Vienna St Op Orch/C. Krauss/K. Böhm/R. Moralt)

Ⓒ **314562** (1/95)
Vienna State Opera Live, Vol.6
Wagner: Tristan und Isolde (exc); Parsifal (exc); Parsifal (exc); Götterdämmerung (exc); *Verdi:* Aida (exc); *Wagner:* Walküre (exc); Siegfried (exc); Meistersinger (exc). (M. Lorenz, V. Ursuleac, A. Jerger, E. Zimmermann, B. Paalen, N. Zec, H. Gallos, H. Duhan, H. Wiedemann, V. Madin, A. Arnold, Wolken, W. Wernigk, A. Muzzarelli, H. Reich, K. Ettl, A. Konetzni, M. Klose, P. Schoeffler, S. Roth, H. Braun, Adolf Vogel, J. von Manowarda, D. Ilitsch, E. Nikolaidi, M. Ahlersmeyer, H. Alsen, L. Hofmann, J. Kalenberg, Vienna St Op Chor, Vienna St Op Orch/W. Furtwängler/L. Reichwein/H. Knappertsbusch/L. Ludwig/C. Krauss)

Ⓒ **314572** (2/95)
Vienna State Opera Live, Vol.7
Bizet: Carmen (exc); *Pfitzner:* Palestrina (exc); *Schmidt:* Notre Dame (exc); *Verdi:* Aida (exc); *Smetana:* Bartered Bride (exc). (T. Mazaroff, E. Réthy, E. Brems, A. Arnold, P. Pierotic, G. Monthy, D. Komarek, O. Levko-Antosch, M. Bokor, J. Witt, A. Jerger, E. Szánthó, H. Alsen, K. Ettl, F. Destal, G. Maikl, W. Wernigk, A. Gregorig, K. Friedrich, E. Schulz, M. Németh, K. Thorborg, A. Sved, A. Dermota, E. Kaufmann, E. Nikolaidi, A. Pernerstorfer, Vienna St Op Chor, Vienna St Op Orch/B. Walter/R. Moralt)

Ⓒ **314582** (4/95)
Vienna State Opera Live, Vol.8
Verdi: Ballo in maschera (exc); Aida (exc); Falstaff (exc). (M. Lorenz, M. Ahlersmeyer, H. Konetzni, E. Nikolaidi, A. Noni, S. Roth, M. Rus, F. Worff, S. Svanholm, D. Ilitsch, H. Hotter, J. von Manowarda, G. Hann, K. Kronenberg, E. Réthy, A. Kern, A. Dermota, J. Witt, M. Bugarinovic, W. Wernigk, Vienna St Op Chor, Vienna St Op Orch/K. Böhm/V. Gui/C. Krauss)

Ⓒ **314592** (8/95)
Vienna State Opera Live, Vol.9
Wagner: Rheingold (exc); Walküre (exc); Siegfried (exc); Götterdämmerung (exc). (J. Prohaska, N. Zec, H. Alsen, A. Konetzni, L. Hofmann, F. Völker, H. Konetzni, R. Merker, K. Thorborg, L. Helletsgruber, E. Flesch, M. Bokor, D. With, A. Michalsky, F. Stroinigg, B. Paalen, E. Weichert, R. Schubert, G. Kappel, E. Zimmermann, J. Kalenberg, E. Schipper, W. Achsel, R. Anday, J. von Manowarda, G. Rünger, E. Szánthó, Vienna St Op Orch/J. Krips/B. Walter/R. Heger)

Ⓒ **314602** (3/95)
Vienna State Opera Live, Vol.10
Mozart: Nozze di Figaro (exc); *Wagner:* Meistersinger (exc); *Bizet:* Carmen (exc); *Puccini:* Turandot (exc); *Verdi:* Don Carlo (exc); *Nicolai:* Lustigen Weiber von Windsor (exc); *Wagner:* Meistersinger (exc); Tannhäuser (exc); Siegfried (exc); Götterdämmerung (exc); *Verdi:* Falstaff (exc); *Puccini:* Gianni Schicchi (exc). (L. Hofmann, H. Alsen, G. Maikl, G. Monthy, H. Wiedemann, V. Madin, A. Arnold, E. Fritsch, R. Tomek, J. Kiepura, E. Réthy, M. Németh, A. Kipnis, N. Ardelli, H. Konetzni, E. Nikolaidi, L. Helletsgruber, M. Reining, M. Ahlersmeyer, K. Bollhammer, E. Majkut, M. Cebotari, M. Rohs, A. Jerger, V. Ursuleac, F. Völker, E. Zimmermann, E. Szánthó, A. Muzzarelli, H. Reich, K. Ettl, J. Kalenberg, R. Sallaba, V. Mansinger, K. Thorborg, M. Lorenz, W. Wernigk, M. Bugarinovic, D. With, D. Komarek, A. Dermota, O. Levko-Antosch, N. Zec, E. Godin, M. Schober, O. Drapal, F. Worff, W. Achsel, F. Skokan, F. Schramm, Vienna St Op Chor, Vienna St Op Orch/K. Böhm/C. Krauss/K. Alwin/H. Reichenberger/B. Walter/F. Weingartner/H. Knappertsbusch/W. Furtwängler/W. Loibner)

Ⓒ **314622** (11/95)
Vienna State Opera Live, Vol.12
R. Strauss: Rosenkavalier (exc); *Wagner:* Tannhäuser (exc); Meistersinger (exc); *Gounod:* Faust (exc); *R. Strauss:* Salome (exc); *Wagner:* Walküre (exc); *Giordano:* Andrea Chénier (exc); *Mascagni:* Cavalleria rusticana (exc); *Leoncavallo:* Pagliacci (exc). (Lotte Lehmann, E. Hadrabová, V. Madin, E. Schumann, A. Michalsky, R. Tomek, B. Sterneck, B. Paalen, W. Wernigk, J. Kalenberg, R. Mayr, F. Schorr, G. Maikl, F. Markhoff, K. Ettl, L. Hofmann, K. Thorborg, E. Laholm, H. Wiedemann, H. Roswaenge, J. Berglund, L. Helletsgruber, A. Sved, G. Graarud, M. Jeritza, E. Schipper, J. von Manowarda, Wolken, F. Völker, M. Bokor, R. Anday, D. With, E. Szánthó, Vienna St Op Chor, Vienna St Op Orch/H. Knappertsbusch/R. Heger/F. Weingartner/J. Krips/H. Reichenberger/C. Krauss)

Ⓒ **314632** (6/95)
Vienna State Opera Live, Vol.13
Mozart: Nozze di Figaro (exc); *Puccini:* Fanciulla del West (exc); *Leoncavallo:* Pagliacci (exc); *Mascagni:* Cavalleria Rusticana (exc); *Salmhofer:* Iwan Tarassenko (exc); *Schmidt:* Notre Dame (exc); *Wagner:* Parsifal (exc); *Weber:* Freischütz (exc); *Wagner:* Fliegende Holländer (exc); Tannhäuser (exc); *Verdi:* Aida (exc). (A. Jerger, M. Reining, P. Schoeffler, M. Perras, D. With, O. Levko-Antosch, K. Ettl, W. Wernigk, H. Gallos, V. Madin, D. Komarek, A. Piccaver, G. Monthy, E. Schumann, E. Schipper, A. Konetzni, T. Mazaroff, K. Kolowratnik, R. Tomek, F. Szkokan, J. Sawka, H. Alsen, N. Zec, F. Destal, E. Nikolaidi, E. Rutgers, J. Pölzer, A. Muzzarelli, W. Rode, J. von Manowarda, W. Schirp, B. Gigli, M. Németh, R. Anday, A. Sved, A. Kipnis, Vienna St Op Chor, Vienna St Op Orch/W. Loibner/H. Duhan/K. Alwin/H. Knappertsbusch/R. Moralt/L. Reichwein)

Ⓒ **314642** (8/95)
Vienna State Opera Live, Vol.14
Wagner: Rheingold (exc); Walküre (exc); Götterdämmerung (exc); Meistersinger (exc); Parsifal (exc). (J. von Manowarda, B. Paalen, V. Ursuleac, G. Graarud, V. Madin, J. Kalenberg, E. Zimmermann, H. Wiedemann, F. Markhoff, L. Helletsgruber, D. With, E. Szánthó, F. Schorr, M. Jeritza, F. Hüni-Mihacsek, F. Völker, R. Mayr, E. Hadrabová, M. Bokor, R. Anday, A. Michalsky, H. Trundt, E. Schipper, R. Bockelmann, N. Zec, G. Maikl, H. Duhan, A. Arnold, Wolken, R. Tomek, A.

Muzzarelli, H. Reich, K. Ettl, G. Rünger, Vienna St Op Chor, Vienna St Op Orch/C. Krauss)

① 314652 (10/95)
Vienna State Opera Live, Vol.15
R. Strauss: Arabella (exc); Friedenstag (Cpte); Ariadne auf Naxos (exc). (V. Ursuleac, M. Bokor, A. Jerger, A. Kern, G. Rünger, R. Mayr, H. Hotter, H. Alsen, J. Witt, H. Wiedemann, C. Bissuti, N. Zec, A. Dermota, H. Gallos, G. Monthy, K. Kamann, W. Franter, Y. Madin, M. Bugarinovic, A. Konetzni, S. Svanholm, E. Schulz, A. Pichler, A. Muzzarelli, F. Jelinek, H. Baier, D. Komarek, E. Nikolaidi, E. Rutgers, A. Poell, W. Wernigk, Alfred Vogel, R. Sallaba, Vienna St Op Chor, Vienna St Op Orch/C. Krauss/R. Moralt, V. Ursuleac)

① 314662 (9/95)
Vienna State Opera Live, Vol.16
Wagner: Rienzi (exc); Lohengrin (exc); Walküre (exc); Walküre (exc); Walküre (exc); Götterdämmerung (exc); Leoncavallo: Pagliacci (exc); R. Strauss: Frau ohne Schatten (exc); Wagner: Götterdämmerung (exc); Götterdämmerung (exc); Verdi: Don Carlo (exc); Otello (exc). (F. Völker, R. Anday, H. Gallos, K. Ettl, Z. Zika, J. von Manowarda, E. Schipper, G. Rünger, V. Ursuleac, R. Mayr, H. Konetzni, J. Pölzer, A. Konetzni, E. Szánthó, W. Achsel, K. Hammes, A. Jerger, Vienna St Op Chor, Vienna St Op Orch/J. Krips/F. Ruhlmann/C. Krauss/H. Knappertsbusch/K. Alwin)

① 314672 (1/95)
Vienna State Opera Live, Vol.17
Mozart: Zauberflöte (exc); Weber: Freischütz (exc); Wagner: Lohengrin (exc); R. Strauss: Elektra (exc); Wagner: Götterdämmerung (exc); Tannhäuser (exc); Wolf-Ferrari: Gioielli della Madonna (exc); R. Strauss: Rosenkavalier (exc); Rosenkavalier (exc). (E. Berger, M. Reining, J. von Manowarda, C. Bissuti, T. Lemnitz, E. Rutgers, M. Bohnen, F. Völker, V. Soetber, W. Franter, P. Kötter, M. Teschemacher, H. Alsen, A. Konetzni, R. Pauly, E. Schipper, S. Svanholm, D. Söderqvist, E. Schürhoff, P. Tutsek, H. Konetzni, M. Lorenz, A. Schellenberg, G. Maikl, V. Madin, H. Gallos, K. Ettl, N. Ardelli, M. Bokor, A. Jerger, B. Sterneck, E. Schumann, E. Flesch, B. Paalen, A. Michalsky, Vienna St Op Chor, Vienna St Op Orch/H. Knappertsbusch)

① 315012 (8/92)
Jongen—Orchestral Works
Jongen: Symphonie concertante; Suite; Allegro appassionato. (/H. Schoonbroodt, Liège SO/R. Defossez, T-M. Gilissen, French Rad & TV SO/B. Priestman)

① 315024 (3/92)
Messiaen—Organ Works
Messiaen: Livre d'Orgue; Ascension; Verset pour la fête de la Dédicace. (A. Rössler)

① 315272 (10/95)
Debussy/Fauré/Poulenc—Violin Sonatas
Debussy: Violin Sonata; Fauré: Violin Sonata 1; Poulenc: Violin Sonata. (I. van Keulen, R. Brautigam)

① 317003 (10/91)
Mozart—Organ Works
Mozart: Fantasia, K608; Adagio and Allegro, K594; Andante, K616; Adagio and Rondo, K617; Suite, K399; Fugue, K401; Gigue, K574; Adagio and Fugue, K546; Fugue, K154; Fugue, K153; Adagio, K356; Mass, K275 (exc); Liszt: Evocation, S658 (exc); Mozart: Fugue, K443. (M. Haselböck)

Kontrapunkt

① 32001 (11/87)
La Rue/Wert—Sacred Choral Works
La Rue: Missa pro defunctis; Wert: Ascendente Jesu in naviculam; Amen, amen dico vobis; Adesti dolori meo; Egressus Jesus; Vox in Rama audita est. (Ars Nova/B. Holten)

① 32003 (12/88)
Tallis—Choral & Instrumental Works
Tallis: Videte miraculum; Felix namque I; O nata lux; Salvator mundi I; Felix namque II; Lamentations of Jeremiah. (L.U. Mortensen, Ars Nova/B. Holten)

① 32008 (5/89)
Gombert/La Rue—Sacred Choral Works
Gombert: Musae Jovis; Lugebat David Absalon; La Rue: Missa L'homme armé. (Ars Nova/B. Holten)

① 32012 (1/89)
Bach—Harpsichord Works
Bach: Toccatas, BWV910-16 (exc); Aria, BWV989; Chromatic Fantasia and Fugue, BWV903. (L.U. Mortensen)

① 32014 (11/89)
Telemann—Recorder Sonatas
Telemann: Getreue Music-Meister (exc); Sonata, TWV41: f 2; Essercizii Musici (exc). (V. Boeckman, F. Hansen, L.U. Mortensen)

① 32028/30 (2/90)
Schoenberg—Lieder
Schoenberg: Waldesnacht; Mein Herz; Sang ein Bettlerpärlein; Mädchenfrühling; Nicht doch!; Mannesbangen; Deinem Blick; Lieder, Op.1; Lieder, Op. 2; Lieder, Op. 3; Gruss in die Ferne; Lieder, Op.6; Balladen, Op.12; Lieder, Op.14; Buch der hängenden Gärten; Gedenken; Am Strande; Folksong Arrangements; Lieder, Op.48. (S. Lange, L.T. Bertelsen, T. Lønskov)

① 32032 (6/90)
Wind Chamber Music
Debussy: Petite Suite; Syrinx; Pierné: Pastorale; Bozza: Pièces pour une musique de nuit; J. Bentzon: Racconto 3; Høffding: Dialogues; Riisager: Divertimento; Français: Wind Quartet (1933). (Selandia Ens, I. Holck, N. Eje, B. Sand)

① 32033/4 (9/90)
Brahms—Complete String Quartets
Brahms: String Quartet 1; String Quartet 2; String Quartet 3. (Danish Qt)

① 32038 (10/90)
Gombert—Sacred Choral Works
Gombert: Magnificat I; Credo; Ave Maria; Si ignoras te; Ave salus mundi; Magnificat VIII. (Ars Nova/B. Holten)

① 32047 (7/91)
Nielsen—Songs
Nielsen: Little Danish Songs, FS114 (exc); Danish Songs (exc); Strophic Songs, FS42 (exc); Mother (exc). (K. Westi, H. Metz)

① 32049 (12/94)
Nørholm—String Quartets
Nørholm: String Quartet 3; String Quartet 4; String Quartet 7; String Quartet 8. (Danish Qt)

① 32098 (3/93)
Gade—Violin Sonatas
Gade: Violin Sonata 1; Violin Sonata 2; Violin Sonata 3. (S. Elbaek, E. Westenholz)

① 32101/2 (2/93)
Britten—Works for Cello
Britten: Cello Suite 1; Cello Suite 2; Cello Suite 3; Cello Sonata; Tema-Sacher. (K.B. Dinitzen, P. Salo)

① 32124 (5/93)
Gade—Piano Works, Vol.2
Gade: Folkdances, Op. 31; Folkdance and Romance; Idylls, Op. 34; Fantasy Pieces, Op. 41; From the sketchbook; Arabeske, Op. 27. (E. Westenholz)

① 32147 (8/93)
Nørgård—Piano Works
Nørgård: Piano Sonata 2; Grooving; Turn; Achilles and the Tortoise. (P. Salo)

① 32150/1 (10/93)
Nielsen—Chamber Works
Nielsen: String Quartet, FS4; String Quartet, FS11; String Quartet, FS23; String Quartet, FS36; String Quartet Movements, FS3c. (Danish Qt)

① 32156 (1/94)
Strauss/Wagner—Lieder
R. Strauss: Vier letzte Lieder; Lieder, Op. 10 (exc); Lieder, Op. 27 (exc); Wagner: Wesendonk Lieder. (E. Meyer-Topsøe, Copenhagen PO/H.N. Bihlmaier)

① 32164 (12/94)
Gade—Works for Violin and Piano
Gade: Aquarelles, Op. 19 (exc); Idylls, Op. 34 (exc); Folkedanse, Op. 62; Violin Sonata in A (exc); Fantasiestücke, Op. 43; Capriccio. (S. Elbaek, E. Westenholz)

① 32171 (9/95)
Nielsen—Symphony No 5; Symphonic Rhapsody, etc
Nielsen: Symphony 5; Bøhmisk-dansk folketone; Symphonic Rhapsody. (Odense SO/E. Serov)

① 32178 (11/94)
Nielsen—Orchestral Works
Nielsen: Symphony 2; Snefrid; Amor and the Poet (exc). (Odense SO/E. Serov)

① 32185 (9/94)
Prokofiev—Violin Sonatas; Melodies
Prokofiev: Violin Sonata 1; Violin Sonata 2; Melodies, Op. 35b. (N. Madojan, E. Westenholz)

① 32188 (3/95)
Nielsen—Vocal Works
Nielsen: Hagbarth and Signe; Ebbe Skammelsen; St John's eve play. (H. Bonde-Hansen, L.T. Bertelsen, L. Lind, N.B. Mikkelsen, Funen Acad Children's Ch, Odense Phil Ch, Odense SO/T. Vetö)

① 32194 (7/95)
Danish Orchestral Works
Gade: Echoes from Ossian; Abrahamsen: Symphony; Horneman: Aladdin (exc); Nørgård: Twilight. (Aarhus RAM Orch/O. Schmidt/S.K. Hansen)

① 32195 (5/95)
Grieg—Violin Sonatas
Grieg: Violin Sonata 1; Violin Sonata 2; Violin Sonata 3. (N. Madojan, E. Westenholz)

① 32197 (6/95)
Syberg—Chamber Music, Vol. 2
Syberg: Allegro Sonatissimo; Scherzando; String Trio. (S. Elbaek, P. Zelazny, T. S. Hermansen, M. Mogensen, T. L. Christiansen, E. M. Meller)

① 32200 (7/95)
Nielsen—Works for Violin
Nielsen: Violin Sonata, Op. 9; Violin Sonata 2; Prelude, FS104; Prelude, FS128. (S. Elbaek, M. Mogensen)

① 32202 (12/95)
Ibert—Chamber Music with Flute
Ibert: Aria; Entr'acte (1937); Histoires; Interludes; Jeux; Mouvements; Pièces brèves; Pièce; Jardinier de Samos Suite. (T. L. Christiansen, Collegium Musicum Sols)

① 32203 (11/95)
Nielsen—Orchestral Works
Nielsen: Symphony 3; String Quartet Movements, FS3c (exc); Maskarade. (E.H. Thaysen, L.T. Bertelsen, Odense SO/E. Serov)

Koss Classics

① KC1013 (12/92)
Organ Works
Guilmant: Scherzo symphonique, Op. 55/2; Duruflé: Scherzo, Op. 2; Bossi: Scherzo, Op. 49/2; Giga, Op. 73; Vierne: Symphony 6 (exc); Pièces en style libre (exc); Langlais: Hommage à Frescobaldi; Widor: Symphony 6 (exc); Bach: Trio Sonatas, BWV525-530 (exc); H. Parker: Organ Sonata, Op. 65; Yon: Humoresque; Dandrieu: Noëls (exc); Reger: Pieces, Op. 65 (exc); Gigout: Ten Organ Pieces (exc); Bonnet: Pièces nouvelles, Op. 7 (exc); Jongen: Organ Pieces, Op. 53 (exc); Whitlock: Pieces for Organ (exc); Lefébure-Wély: Sortie in B flat. (G. Weir)

K617

① K617024 (9/93)
Les Chemins du Baroque, Vol.3
F. Guerrero: O celestial medicina; Trahe me post te; Pan divino, gracioso; Fernandes: Elegit eum Dominus; Lienas: Mass (5vv) (exc); Aguilera de Heredia: Salbe de 1 tono; Victoria: Ave maria gratia plena a 8; Anon: Festival of the Virgin Mary (exc). (Compaña musical, La Fenice/J. Cabré, Y. Repérant)

① K617025 (9/93)
Les Chemins du Baroque, Vol.1
Araujo: Hola, Hala; Silencio, Pasito; Dixit Dominus; Salve Regina; Zipoli: Missa San Ignacio; Torrejón y Velasco: Invitatorio de difuntos; Magnificat sexti toni; D. de Salazar: Salga el Torillo. (Cordoba Children's Ch, Elyma Ens/G. Garrido)

① K617026 (9/93)
Les Chemins du Baroque, Vol.2
Anon: Festival of the Virgin Mary (exc); Araujo: Dixit Dominus; M-A. Charpentier: Messe pour plusieurs instruments, H513 (exc); Nisi Dominus, H231; Ave maris stella, H67; Magnificat, H74; Anon: Domine ad adjuvandum; Zumaya: Lauda Jerusalem. (Compaña musical, Maîtrise Nationale Ch, Grande Ecurie/J-C. Malgoire)

Lammas

① LAMM081D (12/93)
Christmas at St Albans
Rutter: Shepherd's Pipe Carol; Traditional: Greensleeves (What Child is this?); I sing of a maiden; Before the Marvel of this Night; There is no rose; Zither Carol; Good King Wenceslas; Warlock: I saw a fair maiden; Traditional: Tomorrow shall be my dancing day; Buxtehude: In dulci jubilo, BuxWV197; Traditional: Small wonder the star; God rest you merry, gentlemen; Quittez pasteurs; Coventry Carol; Berlioz: Enfance du Christ (exc); Traditional: Away in a manger; De Virgin Mary had a baby-boy; Holy Son of

God; It came upon the midnight clear; Eia Susanni; Sussex Carol. (St Alban's Abbey Ch, St Alban's Bach Ch, A. Parnell/Barry Rose)

Landor

① **CTLCD111** (10/91)
Cover him with grass
Volans: String Quartet 1; Mbira; She who sleeps; White Man Sleeps (1982). (Smith Qt, K. Volans, D. James, R. Schulkowsky, R. Hill, M. Tindemans)

Largo

① **Largo 5115** (11/91)
Goldschmidt—Letzte Kapitel
B. Goldschmidt: Letzte Kapitel; String Quartet 2; Belsatzar; String Quartet 3. (Berlin Ars-Nova Ens, A. Marks, Mandelring Qt/P. Schwarz)

① **Largo 5117** (11/92)
Goldschmidt—Chamber Works
B. Goldschmidt: String Quartet 1; Piano Sonata, Op. 10; Clarinet Quartet. (I. Hausmann, K. Lessing, Mandelring Qt)

① **Largo 5124** (9/94)
HK Gruber—...aus schatten duft gewebt
H. K. Gruber: Rote Teppich; Violin Concerto 1; Episoden, Op. 20; Pieces, Op. 11; Bossa Nova, Op. 21e. (E. Kovacic, P. Crossley, London Sinfonietta/H. K. Gruber)

① **Largo 5125** (9/94)
Kurt Schwertsik—Für Christa
Schwertsik: da uhu schaud me so draurech au; Gedichte an Ljuba, Op. 53; ich sein blumenbein, Op. 38; Späte Liebeslieder; Nocturnes, Op. 10b. (C. Schwertsik, C. van Kampen, K. Schwertsik, N. Meecham)

① **Largo 5127** (10/95)
Igor Markevitch—Chamber Works
Markevitch: Galop; Noces; Serenade; Envol d'Icare. (Cologne Markevitch Ens, K. Lessing, K. Lessing, W. Meyer, D. Jensen, C. Lyndon-Gee, F. Lang, J. Gagelmann, R. Haeger)

① **Largo 5128** (3/95)
Goldschmidt—Retrospectrum
B. Goldschmidt: Retrospectrum; Variations, Op. 32; Violin Capriccio; Capriccio, Op. 11; Little Legend; Scherzo; From the Ballet; Encore; String Quartet 4. (K. Lessing, K. Lessing, H. Schneeberger, Gaede Trio, Mandelring Qt)

① **Largo5130** (7/95)
Testimonies of War
Blacher: Alla marcia; Dance Scenes; Chiarina; Partita, Op. 24; Sonatinas, Op. 14 (exc); Psalmen; Shortall: Fanfare; Weill: Workers' Choruses (exc); Divertimento, Op. 5 (exc); B. Goldschmidt: Psalmen; Milhaud: Chorale; Vaughan Williams: Valiant for truth. (E. Wottrich, M. Kraus, S. Lechevalier, W. Moore, Poznań Op Chor, BBC Sym Chor, Wallace Collection, Berlin RSO, LPO, Poznań PO/N. Sheriff/A. Borejko/S. Jackson/B. Goldschmidt)

Larrikin

① **CDLRH221** (3/89)
Dame Nellie Melba - Opera and Song Recital
Puccini: Bohème (exc); Verdi: Rigoletto (exc); Traviata (exc); Traviata (exc); Mozart: Nozze di Figaro (exc); Gounod: Faust (exc); Donizetti: Lucia di Lammermoor (exc); Traditional: Comin' thro' the rye; Claribel: Come back to Erin; Foster: Old folks at home; Bishop: Home, sweet home; Traditional: Believe me, if all those endearing young charms; Ye banks and braes; Bishop: Lo, here the gentle lark; Duparc: Chanson triste; M.V. White: John Anderson, my Jo; Traditional: Annie Laurie; Dvořák: Gipsy Melodies (exc); Traditional: Auld Lang Syne; Wetzger: By the Brook; Melba: Farewell Speech. (N. Melba, E. Caruso, J. Brownlee, orch/W.B. Rogers, H. Craxton/L. Ronald, G. Lapierre, N. Melba, Coldstream Guards Band/M. Rogan, N. Melba, J. Lemmoné, N. Melba)

LaserLight

① **15 506** (10/90)
Rossini: Overtures
Rossini: Barbiere di Siviglia (exc); Italiana in Algeri (exc); Scala di Seta (exc); Tancredi (exc); Semiramide (exc); Siège de Corinthe (exc); Gazza Ladra (exc). (Plovdiv PO/R. Raychev)

① **15 511** (5/90)
Mozart: Symphonies and Overtures
Mozart: Symphony 41; Symphony 40; Zauberflöte (exc). (LPO, J. Sándor, Hungarian CO/V. Tátrai)

① **15 515** (3/91)
Beethoven: Orchestral Works
Beethoven: Violin Concerto; Romances; Menuet, WoO10/2. (M. Szenthelyi, Hungarian St. Orch/G. Györiványi-Ráth)

① **15 517** (3/91)
Dvořák: Orchestral Works
Dvořák: Symphony 9; Romance, Op.11; Carnival. (Prague Fest Orch/P. Urbanek, M. Szenthelyi, Hungarian St. Orch/T. Pál)

① **15 520** (10/90)
Rossini: Overtures
Rossini: Cambiale di matrimonio (exc); Cenerentola (exc); Matilde di Shabran (exc); Viaggio a Reims (exc); Guillaume Tell (exc); Boutique fantasque (exc). (Plovdiv PO/R. Raychev)

① **15 522** (11/90)
Schubert: Chamber Works
Schubert: Trout Quintet, D667; Rondo, D438; Impromptus (exc). (D. Dechenne, E. Verhey, F. Erblich, J. Decroos, P. Jansen, Colorado Qt, J. Jandó)

① **15 523** (10/90)
Beethoven: Orchestral Works
Beethoven: Piano Concerto 5; Coriolan; Leonore (exc). (A. Dikov, Sofia PO/E. Tabakov, Dresden PO/H. Kegel)

① **15 525** (5/90)
Mozart—Violin Concertos
Mozart: Violin Concerto, K216; Violin Concerto, K218; Violin Concerto, K.219. (C. Altenburger, German Bach Sols/H. Winschermann)

① **15 606** (11/90)
Gershwin: Orchestral Works
Gershwin: American in Paris; Rhapsody in Blue; Porgy and Bess (exc). (J. Jandó, Budapest PO, J. Sándor, Budapest Stgs)

① **15 611** (11/90)
Suppé—Overtures
Suppé: Leichte Kavallerie (exc); O du mein Österreich; Fatinitza (exc); Pique Dame (exc); Dichter und Bauer (exc); Banditenstreiche (exc); Schöne Galathee (exc); Flotten Burschen (exc); Morgen, ein Mittag, ein Abend in Wien (exc). (Hungarian St Op Orch, J. Sandor)

① **15 616** (5/90)
French Ballet Music
Delibes: Sylvia (exc); Coppélia (exc); Gounod: Faust (exc). (Berlin RSO/H. Fricke, Budapest PO, J. Sándor)

① **15 617** (11/90)
Grieg: Orchestral Works
Grieg: Piano Concerto; Peer Gynt Suites (exc); Peer Gynt Suites (exc). (J. Jandó, Budapest PO, J. Sandor, Vienna SO/Y. Ahronovitch)

LDR

① **LDRCD1001** (7/89)
British Masters
Ireland: Maritime Overture; Jacob: Timpani Concerto; G. Lloyd: Forest of Arden; Cabezón: Tiento del Segundo Tono; D. Bourgeois: Serenade, Op. 22; Holst: Songs of the West. (T. Fry, City of London Wind Ens/G. Brand)

① **LDRCD1008** (4/90)
Beethoven & Schnittke: String Quartets
Beethoven: String Quartet 13; Grosse Fuge; Schnittke: String Quartet 3. (Britten Qt)

① **LDRCD1010** (5/90)
Haydn: Keyboard Works
Haydn: Keyboard Sonata 31; Keyboard Sonata 33; Keyboard Sonata 60; Variations, HobXVII/6. (Y.E. Mei)

① **LDRCD1012** (3/90)
British Masters (Volume 2)
Ireland: Comedy Ov; D. Bourgeois: Trombone Concerto; Bach: Orgel-Büchlein, BWV599-644 (exc); Horovitz: Paganini Variations; Holst: Moorside Suite. (City of London Wind Ens/G. Brand, C. Lindberg, City of London Brass Qt)

Léman Classics

① **LC42601** (7/92)
Guitar Works
Ponce: La Folia Variations; Villa-Lobos: Preludes; Ginastera: Guitar Sonata, Op. 47. (J. Freire)

① **LC44801** (10/93)
Works for Oboe and Piano
Finzi: Interlude; Howells: Oboe Sonata (1943); Patterson: Duologue (1984). (N. Daniel, J. Drake)

Libra

① **LRCD156** (5/90)
Georgian Harpsichord Music
Handel: Tolomeo (exc); Chilcot: Harpsichord Suites (exc); Pasquali: Lesson 4; Paradis: Keyboard Sonatas (exc); Arne: Keyboard sonatas (exc); J.C. Bach: Keyboard sonatas, op 5 (exc); Haydn: Keyboard Sonata in C; Earl of Kelly: Favourite Minuets. (G. Gifford)

Linn Records

① **CKD001** (12/91)
Polish Chamber Orchestra live in Glasgow
Mozart: Divertimenti, K136-8 (exc); Vivaldi: Concerti grossi, Op. 3 (exc); Bach: Violin Concerto, BWV1041; Bartók: Divertimento; Elgar: Introduction and Allegro. (Polish CO, J. Stanienda (vn/dir))

① **CKD002** (11/91)
French works for cello and piano
Debussy: Cello Sonata; Martin: Cello Ballade; Poulenc: Cello Sonata. (W. Conway, Peter Evans)

① **CKD006** (12/92)
Nigel North Lute Recital
Weiss: Infidele Sonata; Prelude, Fantasia and Fugue in C; Tombeau sur la mort de M. Comte de Logy; Vivaldi: Concerti grossi, Op.3 (exc); Bach: Solo violin Partitas and Sonatas (exc). (N. North)

① **CKD007** (7/92)
Music from the time of Columbus
Urreda: Muy triste sera mi vida; J. Ponce: Como está; Anchieta: Con amores, la mi madre; Encina: Triste España, sin ventural; Mas vale trocar; Ay triste, que vegno; Quedate, carillo, adios; Mortal tristura me dieron; Francisco de la Torre: Danza alta; Mondéjar: Solo fin de mis males; Anon: Viva el gran Rey; Cómo no le andaré yo; Niña y viña; Calabaça; Al alva venid; Dale, si le das; A las maytines erá; Propiñan de melyor; Perdi la mia rueca. (C. Bott, New London Consort/P. Pickett)

① **CKD009** (10/93)
Lutosławski/Rachmaninov/Webern—Cello Works
Lutosławski: Grave; Webern: Pieces, Op. 11; Rachmaninov: Cello Sonata. (W. Conway, Peter Evans)

① **CKD010** (7/93)
An Excess of Pleasure
Uccellini: Sonatas, Op. 2 (exc); N. Matteis I: Ayres for the Violin, Bk.1 (exc); Ayres for the Violin, Bk.4 (exc); Locke: Broken Consort in D; C. Simpson: John come kiss me now divisions; Blow: Sonata in A; Marini: Sonata; Anon: Ciaconna; Geminiani: Scots Airs (exc); Purcell: Two in one upon a ground. (Palladian Ens)

① **CKD011** (4/94)
Elizabethan & Jacobean Consort Music
Morley: Balletts (1595) (exc); Ayres (1600) (exc); Anon: Tarleton's Jig; This merry pleasant spring; Byrd: My Lord of Oxenford's Mask; Maynard: Wonders of the World (exc); Brade: Coral; Jenkins: Why sigh'st thou; Lauder: My Lord of Marche Paven; Anon: Galliard; Coleman: Did you not once, Lucinda; A. Holborne: Reade's Almain; Lupo: Masque Music; Campion: Ayres, Bk 4 (exc); Anon: Baratostus' Dreame; Watkin's Ale; Nutmigs and Ginger; Melvill: O lusty May. (C. Bott, M. George, New London Consort/P. Pickett)

① **CKD015** (1/95)
The Winged Lion
Castello: Sonatas (exc); Vitali: Ciacona; Uccellini: Sonatas, Op. 5 (exc); Sonatas, Op. 4 (exc); Vivaldi: Concerto, RV100; Trio Sonata, RV84; Buonamente: Suite (1626); Cavalli: Canzoni (exc); Murcia: Baroque Dances (exc); Amor; Turini: Sonata a tre (1624). (Palladian Ens, W. Carter)

① **CKD036** (8/95)
Bach—Trio Sonatas
Bach: Trio Sonatas, BWV525-530 (exc); Duets, BWV802-805; Canons, BWV1087. (Palladian Ens)

Lodia

① **LO-CD791** (12/95)
Tchaikovsky—Orchestral Works
Tchaikovsky: Romeo and Juliet; Symphony 4; Capriccio Italien. (Moscow New Russian Orch/C. Païta)

London

① **421 388-2LM** (8/89)
Elgar: Violin Concerto, etc
Elgar: Violin Concerto; Salut d'amour; Capricieuse. (K-W. Chung, LPO/G. Solti, P. Moll)

① **421 390-2LM** (8/89)
Delius: Orchestral Works
Delius: Song before sunrise; First cuckoo; Summer Night on the River; Air and Dance; Village Romeo and Juliet (exc); Hassan (exc); Fennimore and Gerda Intermezzo; Koanga (exc). (ASMF/N. Marriner)

① **421 391-2LM** (8/89)
British Music
Warlock: Capriol Suite; *Butterworth:* Shropshire Lad; English Idylls; Banks of Green Willow; *Britten:* Frank Bridge Variations. (ASMF/N. Marriner)

① **421 859-2LM** (10/89)
Britten: Cello Works
Britten: Cello Suite 1; Cello Suite 2; Cello Sonata. (M. Rostropovich, B. Britten)

① **425 100-2LM** (9/89)
Britten: Orchestral & Vocal Works
Britten: Cello Symphony; Sinfonia da Requiem; Cantata misericordium. (M. Rostropovich, P. Pears, D. Fischer-Dieskau, London Sym Chor, ECO, LSO, New Philh/B. Britten)

① **425 159-2LM** (1/90)
Salute to Percy Grainger
Grainger: Shepherd's Hey, BFMS16; Willow willow; I'm seventeen come Sunday; Bold William Taylor; There was a pig; My Robin is to the Greenwood gone; Lord Maxwell's Goodnight; Duke of Marlborough's Fanfare; Let's dance gay in green meadow; Scotch Strathspey and Reel; Pretty maid milking her cow; Sprig of Thyme; Lisbon; Shallow brown; Lost lady found; Molly on the shore, BFMS1; Shenandoah; Irish Tune from County Derry; Brigg Fair; Green Bushes. (P. Pears, J. Shirley-Quirk, Ambrosian Sngrs, Linden Sngrs, V. Tunnard, B. Britten, ECO/B. Britten/S. Bedford, Wandsworth Sch Boys' Ch)

① **425 646-2LM3** (7/90)
Tippett: Symphonies
Tippett: Symphony 1; Symphony 2; Symphony 3; Suite for Prince Charles; Symphony 4. (H. Harper, LSO/Colin Davis, Chicago SO/G. Solti)

① **425 659-2LM** (12/90)
Britten: Orchestral Works
Britten: Young Person's Guide; Peter Grimes (exc); Matinées musicales; Soirées musicales. (LSO, ROHO, National PO/B. Britten/R. Bonynge)

① **425 661-2LM** (9/90)
Walton & Arnold: Orchestral & Vocal Works
Walton: Façade (Cpte); Siesta; Scapino; Portsmouth Point; *Arnold:* English Dances, Op.33; English Dances, Op. 27. (E. Sitwell, P. Pears, EOG Ens/A. Collins, LPO/A. Boult)

① **425 715-2LM** (9/90)
Britten: Chamber Works
Britten: Sinfonietta, op 1; String Quartet 2; String Quartet 3. (Amadeus Qt, Vienna Octet)

① **425 716-2LM** (9/90)
Britten: Canticles
Britten: Canticle 1; Canticle 2; Canticle 3; Canticle 4; Canticle 5; Birthday Hansel; Sweeter than Roses. (P. Pears, B. Britten, J. Hahessy, B. Tuckwell, J. Shirley-Quirk, O. Ellis, J. Bowman)

① **430 061-2LM** (7/91)
Kathleen Ferrier—Song Recital
Stanford: Songs, Op. 140 (exc); Irish Idyll, Op. 77 (exc); *Parry:* English Lyrics, Set 6 (exc); *Vaughan Williams:* House of Life (exc); *Bridge:* Go not, happy day; *Warlock:* Sleep; Pretty Ring Time; *Britten:* Folk Songs (exc); *Traditional:* Kitty my love; *H. Ferguson:* Discovery; *Wordsworth:* Red skies; Wind; Clouds; *Rubbra:* Psalms, Op. 61. (K. Ferrier, F. Stone, E. Lush)

① **433 200-2LHO2** (11/93)
Britten—Owen Wingrave, etc.
Britten: Owen Wingrave (Cpte); Hölderlin Fragments; Poet's Echo. (B. Luxon, J. Shirley-Quirk, N. Douglas, S. Fisher, H. Harper, J. Vyvyan, J. Baker, P. Pears, Wandsworth Sch Boys' Ch, ECO/B. Britten, G. Vishnevskaya, M. Rostropovich, B. Britten, P. Pears)

① **436 393-2LM** (11/93)
Britten—The Little Sweep, etc
Britten: Little Sweep (Cpte); Gemini Variations; Children's Crusade. (D. Hemmings, J. Vyvyan, N. Evans, A. Cantelo, T. Anthony, P. Pears, M. Ingram, Marilyn Baker, R. Fairhurst, L. Vaughan, G. Soskin, Alleyn's Sch Ch, EOG Orch/B. Britten, G. Jeney, Z. Jeney, Wandsworth Sch Boys' Ch, chbr ens/R. Burgess)

① **436 394-2LM** (9/93)
Britten—Vocal & Choral Works
Britten: Ceremony of Carols; Boy was born; Friday Afternoons, Op. 7 (exc); Psalm 150. (M. Harnett, E. Simon,

Purcell Sngrs, All Saints Ch, Copenhagen Boys Ch, Downside School Boys Ch, V. Tunnard/B. Britten)

① **436 395-2LM** (9/93)
Britten—Vocal Works
Britten: Illuminations; Serenade; Nocturne. (P. Pears, B. Tuckwell, LSO, ECO/B. Britten)

① **436 396-2LM** (9/93)
Britten—Spring Symphony, etc
Britten: Spring Symphony; Cantata Academica; Hymn to St. Cecilia. (J. Vyvyan, N. Procter, H. Watts, P. Pears, O. Brannigan, ROH Chor, London Sym Chor, Emanuel School Boys' Ch, ROHO, LSO/B. Britten/G. Malcolm)

① **440 490-2LM5(1)** (12/95)
Kirsten Flagstad Edition (pt 1)
Wagner: Wesendonk Lieder; *Mahler:* Kindertotenlieder; Lieder eines fahrenden Gesellen; *Sibelius:* Songs, Op. 17 (exc); Songs, Op. 37 (exc); Songs, Op. 38 (exc); Songs, Op. 36 (exc); Arioso, Op. 3; Songs, Op. 13 (exc); Twelfth Night, Op. 60 (exc); *Grieg:* Songs, Op. 18 (exc); Songs, Op. 60 (exc); Songs, Op. 59 (exc); Songs, Op. 21 (exc); *Alnaes:* Hundred violins; Yearnings of Spring; About love; February morning; Lie: Key; Letter; *Grieg:* Garborg Songs (1895); Songs, Op. 70 (exc); Songs, Op. 39 (exc); Songs, Op. 69 (exc); Songs, Op. 18 (exc); Songs, Op. 21 (exc); Songs, Op. 26 (exc); Songs, Op. 25 (exc); Songs, Op. 48 (exc); Songs, Op. 60 (exc); Melodies of the Heart, Op. 5 (exc); *Wagner:* Walküre (exc); Walküre (exc); Lohengrin (exc); Parsifal (exc); Götterdämmerung (exc). (K. Flagstad, S. Svanholm, E. McArthur, VPO, Oslo PO, Norwegian St RO, LSO/A. Boult/H. Knappertsbusch/G. Solti/Ø. Fjeldstad)

① **440 490-2LM5(2)** (12/95)
Kirsten Flagstad Edition (pt 2)
Brahms: Ernste Gesänge, Op. 121; Lieder, Op. 7 (exc); Lieder, Op. 49 (exc); Lieder, Op. 105 (exc); Lieder, Op. 72 (exc); Lieder, Op. 95 (exc); Lieder, Op. 96 (exc); Lieder, Op. 59 (exc); *Schubert:* Dem Unendlichen, D291; Erlkönig, D328; Am Grabe Anselmos, D504; Mädchens Klage, D191; Ave Maria, D839. (K. Flagstad, E. McArthur)

① **440 491-2LM** (12/95)
Kirsten Flagstad Edition, Vol. 1
Wagner: Wesendonk Lieder; *Mahler:* Kindertotenlieder; Lieder eines fahrenden Gesellen. (K. Flagstad, Vienna SO/H. Knappertsbusch/A. Boult)

① **440 492-2LM** (12/95)
Kirsten Flagstad Edition, Vol. 2
Sibelius: Songs, Op. 17 (exc); Songs, Op. 37 (exc); Songs, Op. 38 (exc); Songs, Op. 36 (exc); Arioso, Op. 3; Songs, Op. 13 (exc); Twelfth Night, Op. 60 (exc); *Grieg:* Songs, Op. 18 (exc); Songs, Op. 60 (exc); Songs, Op. 59 (exc); Songs, Op. 21 (exc); *Alnaes:* Hundred violins; Yearnings of Spring; About love; February morning; Lie: Key; Letter. (K. Flagstad, E. McArthur/Ø. Fjeldstad)

① **440 493-2LM** (12/95)
Kirsten Flagstad Edition, Vol. 3
Grieg: Garborg Songs (1895); Melodies of the heart, Op. 5 (exc); Songs, Op. 70 (exc); Songs, Op. 39 (exc); Songs, Op. 69 (exc); Songs, Op. 18 (exc); Songs, Op. 21 (exc); Songs, Op. 26 (exc); Songs, Op. 25 (exc); Songs, Op. 48 (exc); Songs, Op. 60 (exc). (K. Flagstad, E. McArthur)

① **440 494-2LM** (12/95)
Kirsten Flagstad Edition, Vol. 4
Brahms: Ernste Gesänge, Op. 121; Lieder, Op. 7 (exc); Lieder, Op. 49 (exc); Lieder, Op. 105 (exc); Lieder, Op. 72 (exc); Lieder, Op. 95 (exc); Lieder, Op. 96 (exc); Lieder, Op. 59 (exc); *Schubert:* Dem Unendlichen, D291; Erlkönig, D328; Am Grabe Anselmos, D504; Mädchens Klage, D191; Ave Maria, D839. (K. Flagstad, E. McArthur)

① **440 495-2LM** (12/95)
Kirsten Flagstad Edition, Vol. 5
Wagner: Walküre (exc); Walküre (exc); Lohengrin (exc); Parsifal (exc); Götterdämmerung (exc). (K. Flagstad, VPO/H. Knappertsbusch/G. Solti, Oslo PO, Norwegian Rad Orch/Ø. Fjeldstad)

① **443 451-2LH** (10/95)
Mozart—Organ Works
Mozart: Suite, K399 (exc); Adagio and Allegro, K594; Londoner Notenskizzenbuch (exc); Andante, K15ii; Adagio, K540; Allegro, K72a; Fugue, K401; Gigue, K574; Prelude and Fugue, K394; Andantino, K236; Andante, K616; Adagio, K356; Fantasia, K608. (T. Trotter)

① **443 727-2LC10** (9/95)
Mozart—The Piano Concertos
Mozart: Piano Concerto 1; Piano Concerto 2; Piano Concerto 3; Piano Concerto 4; Piano Concerto 5; Piano Concerto 6; 3-Piano Concerto, K242; Piano Concerto 8; Piano Concerto 9; 2-Piano Concerto, K365; Piano Concerto 11; Piano Concerto 12; Piano Concerto 13; Piano Concerto 14; Piano Concerto 15; Piano Concerto

16; Piano Concerto 17; Piano Concerto 18; Piano Concerto 19; Piano Concerto 20; Piano Concerto 21; Piano Concerto 22; Piano Concerto 23; Piano Concerto 24; Piano Concerto 25; Piano Concerto 26; Piano Concerto 27; Rondo, K382; Rondo, K386. (Vladimir Ashkenazy (pf/dir), D. Barenboim (pf/dir), F. Ts'Ong, Philh, ECO, LSO/I. Kertész, Vladimir Ashkenazy)

① **443 785-2LC12(1)** (12/95)
Haydn—The Keyboard Sonatas (pt 1)
Haydn: Keyboard Sonata 1; Keyboard Sonata 2; Keyboard Sonata 3; Keyboard Sonata 4; Keyboard Sonata 5; Keyboard Sonata 6; Keyboard Sonata 7; Keyboard Sonata 8; Keyboard Sonata 9; Variations, HobXVII/7; Keyboard Sonata 10; Keyboard Sonata 11; Keyboard Sonata 12; Keyboard Sonata 13; Keyboard Sonata 14; Keyboard Sonata 15; Keyboard Sonata 16; Keyboard Sonata 17; Keyboard Sonata 18; Keyboard Sonata 19; Keyboard Sonata 20; Keyboard Sonata 28; Keyboard Sonata, HobXVI/16; Keyboard Sonata 29; Keyboard Sonata 30; Keyboard Sonata 31; Keyboard Sonata 32; Keyboard Sonata 33; Keyboard Sonata 34; Keyboard Sonata 35; Keyboard Sonata 36; Keyboard Sonata 37; Keyboard Sonata 38; Keyboard Sonata 39; Keyboard Sonata 40; Keyboard Sonata 41; Keyboard Sonata, HobXVI/17; Keyboard Sonata 42; Keyboard Sonata 43; Keyboard Sonata 44; Keyboard Sonata 45; Keyboard Sonata 46; Menuets, HobIX/8; Keyboard Sonata 47; Keyboard Sonata 48; Keyboard Sonata 49; Keyboard Sonata 50. (J. McCabe)

① **443 785-2LC12(2)** (12/95)
Haydn—The Keyboard Sonatas (pt 2)
Haydn: Keyboard Sonata 51; Keyboard Sonata 52; Keyboard Sonata 53; Keyboard Sonata 54; Keyboard Sonata 55; Keyboard Sonata 56; Keyboard Sonata 57; Keyboard Sonata 58; Keyboard Sonata 59; Keyboard Sonata 60; Keyboard Sonata 61; Keyboard Sonata 62; Variations, HobXVII/3; Fantasia, HobXVII/4; Variations, HobXVII/3; Adagio, HobXVII/9; Variations, HobXVII/5; Variations, HobXVII/2; Capriccio, HobXVII/1; Seven Last Words. (J. McCabe)

① **444 114-2LH** (10/95)
Walton—Orchestral Works
Walton: Scapino; Violin Concerto; Symphony 2. (T. Little, Bournemouth SO/A. Litton)

① **448 134-2LH** (10/95)
Walton—Belshazzar's Feast, etc
Walton: Belshazzar's Feast; Henry V Suite; Crown Imperial. (B. Terfel, Waynflete Sngrs, Inviti, Bournemouth Sym Chor, Bournemouth SO/A. Litton)

Lorelt

① **LNT101** (9/92)
British Women Composers - Volume 1
Wallen: It all depends on you; *L. Cooper:* Road is wider than long; *Maconchy:* My dark heart; *Lefanu:* Old woman of Beare. (Lontano/O. de la Martinez)

① **LNT104** (5/94)
Martin Butler—Tin-Pan Ballet
Butler: Tin-Pan Ballet; Bluegrass Variations; Jazz Machines; On the rocks; Going with the grain. (R. Crouch, M. Butler, Lontano/O. de la Martinez)

Lyric

① **LCD146** (6/90)
Frida Leider sings Wagner
Wagner: Tristan und Isolde (exc); Tristan und Isolde (exc); Tristan und Isolde (exc); Götterdämmerung (exc); Götterdämmerung (exc); Götterdämmerung (exc); Götterdämmerung (exc); Götterdämmerung (exc). (F. Leider, E. Marherr-Wagner, L. Melchior, F. Soot, K. Thorborg, L. Weber, H. Janssen, M. Nedzadel, orch, LPO, Berlin St Op Orch, LSO/L. Blech/A. Coates/J. Barbirolli/T. Beecham, ROH Chor)

① **SRO805** (11/90)
Gina Cigna—Opera Recital
Gounod: Faust (exc); *Verdi:* Forza del destino (exc); *Ponchielli:* Gioconda (exc); *Giordano:* Andrea Chénier (exc); *Cilea:* Adriana Lecouvreur (exc); *Bellini:* Norma (exc); *Verdi:* Ballo in maschera (exc); *Catalani:* Wally (exc); *Puccini:* Fanciulla del West (exc); Turandot (exc); *Verdi:* Aida (exc); Otello (exc). (G. Cigna, C. Elmo, A. Pertile, F. Merli, orch/L. Molajoli, Turin EIAR Orch/U. Tansini/F. Ghione, La Scala Orch/A. Erede)

① **SRO830** (2/92)
Smetana—The Bartered Bride, etc
Smetana: Bartered Bride (Cpte); *Weber:* Freischütz (exc); *Bizet:* Carmen (exc); *Wagner:* Lohengrin (exc); *J. Strauss II:* Rosen aus dem Süden; *O. Straus:* Land without Music (exc); *Tauber:* Tapfere Soldat (exc); *Tauber:* Old Chelsea (exc); *Romberg:* Desert Song (exc); *German:* Merrie England (exc); *Tosti:* Addio. (H. Konetzni, R. Tauber, H. Tessmer,

F. Krenn, M. Rothmüller, M. Jarred, A. Matters, S. Kalter,
S. Andreva, G. Hinze, G. Clifford, ROH Chor, LPO/T.
Beecham, R. Tauber, orch/N. Treep, P. Kahn)

Lyrinx

ⓒ **LYRCD066** (9/87)
Jacques Champion de Chambonnières—Harpsichord
works
Chambonnières: Pavanes (exc); Allemandes (exc);
Sarabandes (exc); Courantes (exc); Gigues (exc); Autre
brusque in F; Autre, BT65; Chaconne in F; Rondeau in F;
Drollerie; Printemps; Gaillarde and Double. (F. Lengellé)

ⓒ **LYRCD070** (4/92)
Horszowski at Prades
Mozart: Piano Sonata, K332; *Debussy:* Children's Corner;
Beethoven: Piano Sonata 15; *Chopin:* Ballades (exc). (M.
Horszowski)

Lyrita

ⓒ **SRCD201** (12/90)
Malcolm Arnold: Orchestral Dances
Arnold: Cornish Dances, Op. 91; English Dances, Op. 27;
English Dances, Op. 33; Scottish Dances, Op. 59; Irish
Dances, Op. 126; Solitaire (exc). (LPO/M. Arnold)

ⓒ **SRCD202** (11/90)
Rubbra—Orchestral Works
Rubbra: Symphony 3; Symphony 4; Tribute, Op. 56;
Resurgam, Op. 149. (Philh/N. del Mar)

ⓒ **SRCD204** (11/90)
Sterndale Bennett: Works for Piano and Orchestra
Sterndale Bennett: Piano Concerto 1; Piano Concerto 3;
Caprice, Op 22. (M. Binns, LPO/N. Braithwaite)

ⓒ **SRCD205** (11/90)
Sterndale Bennett: Piano Concertos, etc
Sterndale Bennett: Piano Concerto 2; Piano Concerto 5;
Adagio. (M. Binns, Philh/N. Braithwaite)

ⓒ **SRCD208** (4/93)
Hurlstone—Orchestral Works
Hurlstone: Variations (1896); Magic Mirror; Hungarian
Variations. (LPO/N. Braithwaite)

ⓒ **SRCD209** (6/93)
Holst—Orchestral Works
Holst: Winter Idyll; Cotswold Symphony (exc); Song of the
Night; Invocation; Sita (exc); Morning of the Year
(exc); Lure. (L. McAslan, A. Baillie, LPO, LSO/D.
Atherton)

ⓒ **SRCD212** (5/93)
Foulds—Orchestral Works
Foulds: Cabaret; Pasquinade Symphonique 2; April -
England; Hellas; Mantras. (LPO/B. Wordsworth)

ⓒ **SRCD222** (7/92)
Holst—Orchestral Works
Holst: Beni Mora; Fugal Overture; Hammersmith;
Japanese Suite; Scherzo; Somerset Rhapsody. (LPO,
LSO/A. Boult)

ⓒ **SRCD223** (4/93)
Holst—Orchestral Works
Holst: Songs without words (exc); 2-Violin Concerto;
Golden Goose (exc); Capriccio; Fugal Concerto; Moorside
Suite (exc); Lyric Movement; Brook Green Suite. (E.
Hurwitz, K. Sillito, C. Aronowitz, W. Bennett, P. Graeme,
ECO/I. Holst)

ⓒ **SRCD224** (7/92)
Walton—Orchestral Works
Walton: Capriccio burlesco; Music for Children; Portsmouth
Point; Quest (exc); Scapino; Siesta; Sinfonia Concertante.
(P. Katin, LSO, LPO/W. Walton)

ⓒ **SRCD225** (9/92)
Bliss—Orchestral Works
Bliss: Mêlée fantasque; Rout; Adam Zero (exc); Hymn to
Apollo; Serenade (1929); World is charged. (R. Woodland,
J. Shirley-Quirk, Ambrosian Sngrs, LSO/A. Bliss/P.
Ledger/B. Priestman)

ⓒ **SRCD226** (3/93)
L. Berkeley—Orchestral Works
Britten: Mont Juic; *L. Berkeley:* Serenade, Op. 12;
Divertimento, Op. 18; Partita, Op. 66; Sinfonia concertante,
Op. 84 (exc); Symphony 3. (R. Winfield, LPO/L. Berkeley)

ⓒ **SRCD228** (10/92)
Alwyn—Symphonies
Alwyn: Symphony 2; Symphony 3; Symphony 5. (LPO/W.
Alwyn)

ⓒ **SRCD229** (12/92)
Alwyn—Orchestral Works
Alwyn: Derby Day; Magic Island; Elizabethan Dances
(exc); Sinfonietta (1970); Festival March. (LPO/W. Alwyn)

ⓒ **SRCD230** (12/92)
Alwyn—Orchestral Works
Alwyn: Concerto Grosso 2; Autumn Legend; Lyra Angelica.
(O. Ellis, G. Browne, LPO/W. Alwyn)

ⓒ **SRCD231** (9/92)
Bax—Orchestral Works
Bax: Northern Ballad 1; Mediterranean; Garden of Fand;
Tintagel; November Woods. (LPO/A. Boult)

ⓒ **SRCD234** (10/92)
Rubbra—Orchestral Works
Rubbra: Symphony 6; Symphony 8; Soliloquy. (R. de
Saram, LSO/V. Handley, Philh/N. del Mar)

ⓒ **SRCD235** (12/92)
Rubbra—Symphonies
Rubbra: Symphony 2; Festival Ov; Symphony 7. (New
Philh, LSO/Handley/A. Boult)

ⓒ **SRCD323** (6/95)
Grace Williams—Orchestral Works
Grace Williams: Fantasia on Welsh Nursery Tunes;
Carillons; Penillion; Trumpet Concerto; Sea Sketches. (A.
Camden, H. Snell, R. Allan, LSO, RPO, ECO/C. Groves/D.
Atherton)

ⓒ **SRCD324** (2/95)
Mathias—Choral Works
Mathias: Ave Rex, Op.45; Elegy for a Prince, Op. 59; This
Worlde's Joie, Op. 67. (G. Evans, J. Price, K. Bowen, M.
Rippon, WNO Chor, Bach Ch, St George's Chapel Ch,
LSO, New Philh/D. Atherton/D. Willcocks)

ⓒ **SRCD325** (7/95)
Mathias—Concertos
Mathias: Clarinet Concerto; Harp Concerto; Piano
Concerto 3. (G. de Peyer, O. Ellis, P. Katin, LSO, New
Philh/D. Atherton)

Marco Polo

ⓒ **DCCD9003** (11/92)
Rasmussen/Sorensen—String Quartets
Rasmussen: Solos and Shadows; Surrounded by Scales;
Sørensen: Alman; Adieu; Angels' Music. (Arditti Qt)

ⓒ **DCCD9203** (6/94)
Holmboe—String Quartets - Volume 1
Holmboe: String Quartet 1; String Quartet 3; String Quartet
4. (Kontra Qt)

ⓘ **8 220114** (8/87)
Wagner: Overtures and Marches
Wagner: Polonia; Rule Britannia; Grosser Festmarsch;
Kaisermarsch. (Hong Kong PO/V. Kojian)

ⓘ **8 220308** (10/86)
Cui: Orchestral Works
Cui: Suite concertante; Suite miniature 1; Suite 3. (T.
Nishizaki, Hong Kong PO/K. Schermerhorn)

ⓘ **8 220309** (6/86)
Glazunov: Orchestral Works
Glazunov: Overture, Op. 3; Finnish Sketches; Cortège
solennel; Triumphal March; Spring; Poème épique. (Hong
Kong PO/K. Schermerhorn)

ⓘ **8 220345** (3/86)
Alfred Hill: Orchestral Works
Hill: Symphony 4; Symphony 6; Sacred Mountain.
(Melbourne SO/W. Lehmann)

ⓘ **8 223134** (4/89)
Honegger—Film Music
Honegger: Misérables (exc); Roue; Traversée des Andes;
Vol sur l'Atlantique; Napoléon. (Bratislava RSO/Adriano)

ⓘ **8 223151** (7/93)
Glazunov—Piano Music, Vol.1
Glazunov: Sacha Suite, Op. 2; Pieces, Op. 22; Sabela
Waltzes, Op. 23; Etudes, Op. 31; Petite valse, Op. 36;
Nocturne, Op. 37; Concert waltz, Op. 41; Miniatures, Op.
42; Prelude and Mazurkas, Op. 25. (T. Fránova)

ⓘ **8 223153** (7/93)
Glazunov—Piano Works, Vol.3
Glazunov: Piano Sonata 1; Piano Sonata 2; Prelude and
Fugue in E minor. (T. Fránova)

ⓘ **8 223156** (10/90)
Miaskovsky—Piano Sonatas, Vol.1
Miaskovsky: Piano Sonata 2; Piano Sonata 3; Piano
Sonata 5. (E. Hegedüs)

ⓘ **8 223162** (7/89)
Pfitzner: Orchestral Works
Pfitzner: Piano Concerto; Christ-Elflein (exc); Herz (exc).
(W. Harden, Bratislava RSO/H. Beissel)

ⓘ **8 223170** (10/93)
Berwald—Piano Trios, Vol.1
F. Berwald: Piano Trio 1; Piano Trio 2; Piano Trio 3. (A.
Kiss, C. Onczay, I. Prunyi)

ⓘ **8 223178** (10/90)
Miaskovsky: Piano Sonatas, Vol.2
Miaskovsky: Piano Sonata 6; Piano Sonata 7; Piano
Sonata 8; Piano Sonata 9. (E. Hegedüs)

ⓘ **8 223201** (1/90)
Johann Strauss II Edition, Vol.1
J. Strauss II: Gunstwerber, Op. 4; Herzenslust, Op. 3;
Phönix-Schwingen; Debut-Quadrille, Op. 2; Zehner-Polka;
Klangfiguren, Op. 251; Maskenzug, Op. 240; Nocturne-
Quadrille; Freut euch des Lebens, Op. 340; Fledermaus
Polka, Op. 362; Bei uns z'Haus, Op. 361; Veilchen.
(Košice St PO/A. Walter)

ⓘ **8 223202** (1/90)
Johann Strauss II Edition, Vol.2
J. Strauss II: Czech-Polka, Op. 13; Jungen Wiener, Op. 17;
Satanella-Polka; Cytheren-Quadrille, Op. 6; Solon-
Sprüche; Fantasieblümchen, Op. 241; Wo die Zitronen
blüh'n; Indra-Quadrille, Op. 122; Tik-Tak; Vermählungs-
Toaste; Neue Pizzicato-Polka, Op. 449; Jubel-Marsch, Op.
126. (Košice St PO/A. Walter)

ⓘ **8 223203** (1/90)
Johann Strauss II Edition, Vol.3
J. Strauss II: Berglieder, Op. 18; Jux-Polka, Op. 17; Wiener
Punch-Lieder; Dämonen-Quadrille, Op. 19; Freudengruss,
Op. 217; Liebeslieder, Op. 114; Vergnügungszug;
Satanella-Quadrille; Oesterreicher; Aesculap-Polka, Op.
130; Lind-Gesänge, Op. 21; Amazonen-Polka, Op. 9.
(Košice St PO/A. Walter)

ⓘ **8 223204** (4/90)
Johann Strauss II Edition, Vol.4
J. Strauss II: Hopser-Polka, Op. 28; Serail Tänze; Austria-
Marsch, Op. 20; Veilchen-Polka; Knall-Kügerln, Op. 140;
Motor-Quadrille, Op. 129; Bürger-Ball-Polka, Op. 145;
Dividenden, Op. 252; Verbrüderungs-Marsch; Im
Krapfenwald'l, Op. 336; O schöner Mai. (Košice St PO/R.
Edlinger)

ⓘ **8 223205** (4/90)
Johann Strauss II Edition, Vol.5
J. Strauss II: Heiligenstädter Rendezvous, Op. 78;
Nachfalter, Op. 157; Quadrille sur des airs françaises;
Musen-Polka, Op. 147; Wiener Chronik; Russische
Marsch-Fantasie; Elisen, Op. 151; Kennst du mich?, Op.
381; Hesperus, Op. 249; Italienischer Walzer, Op. 407;
Pariser Polka. (Košice St PO/O. Dohnányi)

ⓘ **8 223206** (4/90)
Johann Strauss II Edition, Vol.6
J. Strauss II: Warschauer; Wellen und Wogen; Caroussel,
Op. 133; Camelien, Op.248; Myrthen-Kränze, Op. 154;
Nordstern; Bluette, Op. 271; Konkurrenzen, Op. 267;
Chansonetten, Op. 259; Ballsträusschen, Op. 380; Kuss-
Walzer, Op. 400. (Košice St PO/O. Dohnányi)

ⓘ **8 223207** (7/90)
Johann Strauss II Edition, Vol.7
J. Strauss II: Zeitgeister; Nachklänge, Op. 38; Odeon;
Schneeglöckchen; Neuhauser, Op. 137; Kron, Op. 139;
Ballg'schichten, Op. 150; Furioso-Polka, Op. 260;
Deutscher Kreiger-Marsch, Op. 284; Colonnen, Op. 262;
Kreigers Liebchen, Op. 379; Nordseebilder. (Polish St
PO/O. Dohnányi)

ⓘ **8 223208** (7/90)
Johann Strauss II Edition, Vol.8
J. Strauss II: Sanguiniker; Pepita; Wilhelm Genesungs;
Schallwellen; Wiedersehen; Ballo in maschera Quadrille,
Op. 272; Carnevals-Botschafter, Op. 270; Leichtes Blut,
Op. 319; Saison; Cagliostro, Op. 370; Banditen-Galopp,
Op. 378; Lagunen-Walzer. (Polish St PO/O. Dohnányi)

ⓘ **8 223209** (7/90)
Johann Strauss II Edition, Vol.9
J. Strauss II: Carnevalsbilder, Op. 357; Annen-Polka, Op.
117; Indigo-Marsch, Op. 349; Albion-Polka, Op. 102;
Gedanken auf den Alpen, Op. 172; Festival, Op. 341;
Habsburg Hoch, Op. 408; Nachtveilchen, Op. 170; Luzifer,
Op. 266; Kaiser, Op. 437. (Polish St PO/J. Wildner)

ⓘ **8 223210** (9/90)
Johann Strauss II Edition, Vol.10
J. Strauss II: Morgenblätter, Op. 279; Bauern-Polka, Op.
276; Juristenball, Op. 280; Myrthenblüthen, Op. 395;
Blumenfest, Op. 111; Panacea-Klänge; Diabolin-Polka,
Op. 244; Lieder-Quadrille, Op. 275; Pesther Csárdás,
Feuilleton, Op. 193. (Polish St PO/J. Wildner)

32/2; Salut, Op. 45; Alleluia, Op. 25; Rondeau
chromatique, Op. 12; Variations, Op. 1; Super flumina
Babylonis, Op. 52. (L. Martin)

ⓘ **8 223659** (1/95)
d'Indy—Orchestral Works
Indy: Etranger (exc); Tableaux, Op. 36; Fantaisie, Op. 31;
Fervaal (exc); Saugefleurie, Op. 21. (P. Cousu,
Württemberg PO/G. Nopre/J-M. Burfin)

ⓘ **8 223660** (2/95)
S. Wagner/Schillings/C. Harris—Orchestral Works
Schillings: Kassandra; Eleusische Fest; S. Wagner:
Sehnsucht; C. Harris: Paradise Lost; Festival March. (M.
Neubauer, Thüringian SO/K. Bach)

ⓘ **8 223665** (10/95)
Vaughan Williams—Film Music
Vaughan Williams: 49th Parallel (exc); Story of a Flemish
Farm Suite; Coastal Command; England of Elizabeth
Suite. (RTE Concert Orch/A. Penny)

ⓘ **8 223667** (4/95)
Lajtha—Orchestral Works, Volume 1
Lajtha: Suite 3; Symphonic Pictures; Symphony 7. (Pécs
SO/N. Pasquet)

ⓘ **8 223674** (2/95)
Truscott—Orchestral Works
Truscott: Suite in G; Elegy; Symphony in E. (Ireland
National SO/G. Brain)

ⓘ **8 223680** (11/94)
Devreese—Orchestral Works
G. Devreese: Tombelène; Violin Concerto 1; Cello
Concertino. (G. de Neve, V. Spanoghe, Belgian Rad & TV
Orch/F. Devreese)

ⓘ **8 223681** (11/94)
Devreese—Film music
Devreese: Benvenuta Suite; Soir, un Train (exc); Oeuvre
au Noir Suite; Belle (exc). (Belgian Rad & TV Orch/F.
Devreese)

ⓘ **8 223683** (12/95)
Suppé—Overtures, Volume 3
Suppé: Leichte Kavallerie (exc); Tricoche und Cacolet
(exc); Boccaccio (exc); Afrikareise (exc); Fatinitza (exc);
Humorous Variations; Heimkehr von der Hochzeit (exc);
Herzenseintracht; Franz Schubert (exc); Triumph Overture.
(Košice St PO/A. Walter)

ⓘ **8 223689** (3/95)
Schmitt—Orchestral Works
Schmitt: Danse d'Abisag, Op. 75; Habeyssée, Op. 110;
Rêves, Op. 65; Symphony 2. (H. Segerstam, Rhineland-
Pfalz State PO/L. Segerstam)

ⓘ **8 223695** (11/95)
German—Orchestral Works, Volume 1
German: Richard III; Theme and Diversions; Seasons.
(RTE Concert Orch/A. Penny)

ⓘ **8 223696** (2/95)
Malipiero—Symphonies
Malipiero: Symphony 5; Symphony 6; Symphony 8;
Symphony 11. (Moscow SO/A. de Almeida)

ⓘ **8 223697** (2/95)
Malipiero—Symphonies
Malipiero: Sinfonia dello Zodiaco; Symphony 9; Symphony
10. (Moscow SO/A. de Almeida)

ⓘ **8 223701** (10/95)
Donizetti—Instrumental Concertos
Donizetti: Sinfonia in G minor; Flute Sonata; Oboe Sonata;
Double Concerto; Cor anglais Concertino; Clarinet
Concertino; Sinfonia in D minor. (Budapest Camerata/L.
Kovács)

ⓘ **8 223704** (8/95)
Koechlin—Orchestral Works
Koechlin: Symphonic pieces, Op. 20 (exc); Sur les flots
lointains, Op. 130; Buisson ardent; Sur les flots lointains
(stgs). (Rhineland-Pfalz State PO/L. Segerstam)

ⓘ **8 223710** (5/95)
Guatemala, Volume 1
Martínez-Sobral: Acuarelas Chapinas; Castillo: Sinfonieta;
Xibalbá; Guatemala I; Guatemala II. (Moscow SO/A. de
Almeida)

ⓘ **8 223718** (8/95)
English Cello Sonatas
Ireland: Cello Sonata; Moeran: Cello Sonata; Rubbra:
Cello Sonata, Op. 60. (R. Wallfisch, J. York)

ⓘ **8 223721** (12/95)
Holbrooke—Orchestral Works
Holbrooke: Children of Don (exc); Birds of Rhiannon; Dylan
(exc). (Ukraine National SO/A. Penny)

ⓘ **8 223727** (6/95)
Truscott—Chamber Music
Truscott: Flute Trio; Clarinet Sonata 1; Violin Sonata in C;
Meditation; Cello Sonata in A minor. (I. Kovács, I. Varga,
B. Nagy, V. Eckhardt, L. Barsóny, J. K. Domonkos, M.
Lugossy)

ⓘ **8 223732** (4/95)
Addinsell—British Light Music
Addinsell: Goodbye Mr Chips (exc); Ring around the Moon
(exc); Smokey Mountains Concerto; Isle of Apples; Prince
and the Showgirl (exc); Tune in G; Tom Brown's
Schooldays (exc); Festival; Journey to Romance; Fire over
England (exc); Tale of Two Cities (exc). (P. Martin, R.
Elms, BBC Concert Orch/K. Alwyn)

ⓘ **8 223741** (11/95)
Maes—Orchestral Works
Maes: Symphony 2; Viola Concerto; Concertante Overture;
Arabesque and Scherzo. (L. DeNeve, F. Vanhove, Royal
Flanders PO/G. Oskamp)

ⓘ **8 223751** (9/95)
Caplet/Debussy—Orchestral Works
Debussy: Children's Corner; Estampes (exc); Suite
bergamasque (exc); Caplet: Suite Persane (exc); Légende;
Marche triomphale. (Rhineland-Pfalz State PO/L.
Segerstam)

ⓘ **8 223753** (9/95)
Montsalvatge/Rodrigo—Works
Montsalvatge: Concierto breve; Sinfonía de réquiem;
Rodrigo: Zarabanda lejana y Villancico. (C. Moncloa, L.
Morales, Madrid SO/A. R. Marbà)

ⓘ **8 223755** (10/95)
Prix de Rome Cantatas
Caplet: Myrrha; Tout est lumière; Debussy: Printemps;
Ravel: Aurore; Matinée de Provence; Tout est lumière;
Bayadères; Nuit. (S. Coste, B. Desnoues, G. LeRoi, M.
Duguay, J-F. Lapointe, Paris Sorbonne Chor, Paris
Sorbonne Orch/J. Grimbert)

Marquis

ⓘ **ERAD113** (7/94)
Catherine Robbin—Song Recital
Purcell: If music be the food of love, Z379/3; Schubert:
Fischer, D225; König in Thule, D367; Suleika II, D717;
Brahms: Lieder, Op. 43 (exc); Lieder, Op.47 (exc); Lieder,
Op. 58 (exc); Honegger: Saluste du Bartas; Britten: Folk
Songs (exc); P. Tate: Lark in the clear air; Warlock: Birds;
Finzi: Let us garlands bring (exc); Bissell: Eastern Canada
Folk Songs (exc); Maritime Folk Songs (exc); G. Ridout:
Eastern Canada Folksongs (exc). (C. Robbin, M.
McMahon)

Mastersound

ⓘ **DFCDI-111** (4/92)
The Art of the Coloratura
J. Strauss II: Blauen Donau, Op. 314; Benedict: Wren;
Alabiev: Nightingale; Dell' Acqua: Villanelle; Delibes: Filles
de Cadiz; Proch: Air and Variations; Offenbach: Contes
d'Hoffmann (exc); Delibes: Lakmé (exc); Verdi: Rigoletto
(exc); Donizetti: Lucia di Lammermoor (exc); Rossini:
Barbiere di Siviglia (exc); Barbiere di Siviglia (exc);
Rimsky-Korsakov: Golden Cockerel (exc); Sadko (exc);
Kern: I dream too much (exc); Olivieri: J'attendrai; Various:
National Anthems (exc); (L. Pons, G. De Luca, orch/A.
Kostelanetz, F. La Forge/G. Cloëz/R. Bourdon/J.
Barbirolli/W. Pelletier)

Kevin Mayhew Ltd

ⓘ **KM93071405410** (12/93)
Christmas is Coming
Traditional: Christmas is coming; Here we come a-
wassailing; Deck the hall; Mummer's Song; How far is it to
Bethlehem?; Come all you worthy gentlemen; Sans Day
Carol; I saw three ships; Little Donkey; Infant Holy; Child in
a manger; Joseph lieber Joseph mein; Stille Nacht; Away
in a manger; Mary's Boy Child; Quelle est cette odeur
agréable; Echo carol; See amid the winter's snow; Unto us
is born a son; Coventry carol; Personent hodie; We three
Kings; Sussex Carol; Good King Wenceslas;
Gloucestershire Wassail; Twelve Days of Christmas; We
wish you a merry Christmas. (Jenkins Family Sngrs/N.
Jenkins)

Medici-Whitehall

ⓘ **MQCD4002** (9/94)
A Song before Sunrise
Delius: Fennimore and Gerda Intermezzo; Song before
Sunrise; Elgar: Serenade; Vaughan Williams:
Greensleeves Fantasia; Delius: Aquarelles; Warlock:

Serenade for Strings; Holst: Brook Green Suite; Delius:
First cuckoo; Summer Night on the River; Elgar:
Introduction and Allegro. (Medici Qt, Oxford Orch da
Camera/G. Vass)

ⓘ **MQCD6005** (11/92)
Mozart's Journey to Prague
Mozart: Serenade, K525 (exc); String Quartet, K464 (exc);
String Quartet, K465 (exc); String Quartet, K421 (exc).
(Medici Qt)

Melodiya

ⓘ **74321 17095-2** (12/94)
Tchaikovsky—Orchestral Works
Tchaikovsky: Symphony 4; Fate; Capriccio italien. (USSR
SO/E. Svetlanov)

ⓘ **74321 17097-2** (12/94)
Tchaikovsky—Orchestral Works
Tchaikovsky: Symphony 6; Voyevoda; Andante cantabile,
Op.11. (USSR SO/E. Svetlanov)

ⓘ **74321 17101-2** (12/94)
Tchaikovsky—Symphonies, etc
Tchaikovsky: Symphony 1; Symphony 2; Symphony 3;
Symphony 4; Symphony 5; Symphony 6; Francesca da
Rimini; Serenade, Op. 48; Romeo and Juliet; Fate;
Capriccio Italien; Tempest; Voyevoda; Andante cantabile,
Op. 11. (USSR SO/E. Svetlanov)

ⓘ **74321 18290-2** (10/94)
Tchaikovsky—Chamber Works
Tchaikovsky: String Quartet 1; String Quartet 2; String
Quartet 3; String Quartet (1865); Souvenir de Florence.
(Borodin Qt, G. Talalyan, M. Rostropovich)

ⓘ **74321 25172-2(1)** (8/95)
Russian Piano School (pt 1 - Vols.1 - 8)
Tchaikovsky: Morceaux, Op. 51 (exc); Morceaux, Op. 72
(exc); Morceaux, Op. 72 (exc); Arensky: Forgotten
Rhythms (exc); Borodin: Petite Suite (exc); Rachmaninov:
Morceaux de salon, Op. 10 (exc); Medtner: Novelles, Op.
17 (exc); Goldenweiser: Kabardino-Balkarsky Songs and
Dances; Rachmaninov: Suite 2; Mozart: Rondo, K511;
Piano Sonata, K448; Debussy: Préludes (exc); Préludes
(exc); Prokofiev: Visions fugitives (exc); Bach: Trio Sonatas,
BWV525-530 (exc); Allein Gott, BWV711; Chorales,
BWV651-668 (exc); Schübler Chorales, BWV645-650
(exc); Chorales, BWV651-668 (exc); Mozart: Piano
Sonata, K282; Piano Sonata, K576; Fantasia and Fugue,
K394; Variations, K500; Stravinsky: Serenade in A; Bartók:
Mikrokosmos, Bk 5 (exc); Mikrokosmos, Bk 6 (exc);
Hindemith: Piano Sonata 3; Berg: Piano Sonata; Krenek:
Piano Sonata 2; Mozart: Fantasia, K475; Schubert:
Impromptus; Schumann: Piano Sonata 1; Chopin:
Nocturnes (exc); Scherzos (exc); Rachmaninov: Moments
musicaux, Op. 16 (exc); Scriabin: Piano Sonata 4; Poème
tragique; Valse, Op. 38; Etudes, Op. 8 (exc); Prokofiev:
Tales of an old grandmother; Visions fugitives (exc);
Sarcasms, Op. 17 (exc); Pieces, Op. 12 (exc); Bach: Italian
Concerto, BWV971; Fugue, BWV944; Haydn: Keyboard
Sonata 60; Beethoven: Piano Sonata 12; Chopin: Ballades
(exc); Bach: Prelude and Fugue BWV532; Beethoven:
Variations, WoO80; Weber: Piano Sonata 2; Liszt:
Rhapsodie espagnole, S254; Prokofiev: Visions fugitives
(exc); Liszt: Études d'exécution, S139; Hungarian
Rhapsodies, S244 (exc). (A. Goldenweiser, G. Ginsburg,
H. Neuhaus, S. Neuhaus, S. Feinberg, M. Yudina, V.
Sofronitzky, S. Richter, Emil Gilels, L. Berman)

ⓘ **74321 25172-2(2)** (8/95)
Russian Piano School (pt 2 - Vols.9 & 10)
Tchaikovsky: Nutcracker Suite (exc); Shchedrin: Anna
Karenina (exc); Prokofiev: Piano Sonata 7; Mozart: Piano
Sonata, K570; Rachmaninov: Etudes-tableaux, Op. 39
(exc); Preludes (exc); Lilacs; Scriabin: Preludes, Op. 27;
Pieces, Op. 51; Preludes, Op. 37; Etudes, Op. 42 (exc);
Prokofiev: Visions fugitives (exc); Pieces, Op. 32 (exc);
Kissin: Inventions. (M. Pletnev, E. Kissin)

ⓘ **74321 25173-2** (8/95)
Russian Piano School, Vol. 1
Tchaikovsky: Morceaux, Op. 51 (exc); Morceaux, Op. 72
(exc); Morceaux, Op. 72 (exc); Arensky: Forgotten
Rhythms (exc); Borodin: Petite Suite (exc); Rachmaninov:
Morceaux de salon, Op. 10 (exc); Medtner: Novelles, Op.
17 (exc); Goldenweiser: Kabardino-Balkarsky Songs and
Dances; Rachmaninov: Suite 2. (A. Goldenweiser, G.
Ginsburg)

ⓘ **74321 25174-2** (8/95)
Russian Piano School, Vol. 2
Mozart: Rondo, K511; Piano Sonata, K448; Debussy:
Préludes (exc); Préludes (exc); Prokofiev: Visions fugitives.
(H. Neuhaus, S. Neuhaus)

Ⓓ **74321 25175-2** (8/95)
Russian Piano School, Vol. 3
Bach: Trio Sonatas, BWV525-530 (exc); Allein Gott, BWV711; Chorales, BWV651-668 (exc); Schübler Chorales, BWV645-650 (exc); Chorales, BWV651-668 (exc); *Mozart:* Piano Sonata, K282; Piano Sonata, K576; Fantasia and Fugue, K394; Variations, K500. (S. Feinberg)

Ⓓ **74321 25176-2** (8/95)
Russian Piano School, Vol. 4
Stravinsky: Serenade in A; *Bartók:* Mikrokosmos, Bk 5 (exc); Mikrokosmos, Bk 6 (exc); *Hindemith:* Piano Sonata 3; *Berg:* Piano Sonata; *Krenek:* Piano Sonata 2. (M. Yudina)

Ⓓ **74321 25177-2** (8/95)
Russian Piano School, Vol. 5
Mozart: Fantasia, K475; *Schubert:* Impromptus (exc); *Schumann:* Piano Sonata 1; *Chopin:* Nocturnes (exc); Scherzos (exc); *Rachmaninov:* Moments musicaux, Op. 16 (exc); *Scriabin:* Piano Sonata 4; Poème tragique; Valse, Op. 38; Etudes, Op. 8 (exc); *Prokofiev:* Tales of an old grandmother; Visions fugitives (exc); Sarcasms, Op. 17 (exc); Pieces, Op. 12 (exc). (V. Sofronitzky)

Ⓓ **74321 25178-2** (8/95)
Russian Piano School, Vol. 6
Bach: Italian Concerto, BWV971; Fugue, BWV944; *Haydn:* Keyboard Sonata 60; *Beethoven:* Piano Sonata 12; *Chopin:* Ballades (exc). (S. Richter)

Ⓓ **74321 25179-2** (8/95)
Russian Piano School, Vol. 7
bach: Prelude and Fugue BWV532; *Beethoven:* Variations, WoO80; *Weber:* Piano Sonata 2; *Liszt:* Rhapsodie espagnole, S254; *Prokofiev:* Visions fugitives (exc). (Emil Gilels)

Ⓓ **74321 25181-2** (8/95)
Russian Piano School, Vol. 9
Tchaikovsky: Nutcracker Suite; *Shchedrin:* Anna Karenina (exc); *Prokofiev:* Piano Sonata 7; *Mozart:* Piano Sonata, K570. (M. Pletnev)

Ⓓ **74321 25182-2** (8/95)
Russian Piano School, Vol. 10
Rachmaninov: Etudes-tableaux, Op. 39 (exc); Preludes (exc); Lilacs; *Scriabin:* Preludes, Op. 27; Pieces, Op. 51; Preludes, Op. 37; Etudes, Op. 42 (exc); *Prokofiev:* Visions fugitives (exc); Pieces, Op. 32 (exc); *Kissin:* Inventions. (E. Kissin)

Memoir Records

Ⓓ **CDMOIR404** (7/91)
Ezio Pinza—Recital
Verdi: Ernani (exc); *Mussorgsky:* Boris Godunov (exc); *Mozart:* Nozze di Figaro (exc); Don Giovanni (exc); Zauberflöte (exc); *Gounod:* Faust (exc); Faust (exc); *A. Thomas:* Caïd (exc); *Handel:* Serse (exc); *Puccini:* Bohème (exc); *Bellini:* Norma (exc); *Verdi:* Simon Boccanegra (exc); Vespri Siciliani (exc); Requiem (exc); Don Carlo (exc); *Tosti:* Chanson de l'adieu; *Paisiello:* Amor contrastato (exc); *Mussorgsky:* Song of the Flea. (E. Pinza, NY Met Op Chor, NY Met Op Orch, orch/R. Bourdon/E. Panizza/B. Reibold/B. Walter/H. Barlow/W. Pelletier/G. Setti/D. Voorhees)

Ⓓ **CDMOIR408** (2/92)
Great Sopranos
Wagner: Tannhäuser (exc); Parsifal (exc); *Weber:* Oberon (exc); *Beethoven:* Fidelio (exc); *Mozart:* Zauberflöte (exc); Nozze di Figaro (exc); *Offenbach:* Périchole (exc); *Massenet:* Manon (exc); *Donizetti:* Fille du Régiment (exc); *Spontini:* Vestale (exc); *Puccini:* Madama Butterfly (exc); Turandot (exc); *Catalani:* Wally (exc). (Lotte Lehmann, F. Leider, M. Teschemacher, K. Flagstad, T. Lemnitz, E. Schumann, M. Teyte, N. Vallin, T. dal Monte, R. Ponselle, M. Seinemeyer, L. Schöne, H. Spani, Berlin St Op Orch, LSO, Stuttgart Op Orch, Philadelphia, BPO, orch, La Scala Orch/F. Weissmann/J. Barbirolli/G. Görlich/E. Ormandy/T. Beecham/G.W. Byng/F. Ruhlmann/J. Pasternack/R. Bourdon/F. Zweig/C. Sabajno)

Ⓓ **CDMOIR409** (9/92)
Three Tenors—Björling, Gigli & Tauber
Meyerbeer: Africaine (exc); *Puccini:* Tosca (exc); Tosca (exc); *Millöcker:* Bettelstudent (exc); *Rossini:* Soirées musicales (exc); *Tosti:* Ideale; *Grieg:* Melodies of the Heart, Op. 5 (exc); *De Curtis:* Torna a Surriento; *Yradier:* Paloma; *Traditional:* Kommt a Vogerl geflogen; *Gounod:* Faust (exc); *Ponchielli:* Gioconda (exc); *Flotow:* Martha (exc); *Leoncavallo:* Mattinata; *Sieczyński:* Wien, du Stadt meiner Träume; *Traditional:* Ack Värmerland, du sköna; *Geehl:* For you alone; *De Curtis:* Senza nisciuno; *Di Capua:* O sole mio; *Puccini:* Turandot (exc). (J. Björling, R. Tauber, B. Gigli, orch/N. Grevillius, La Scala Orch/F. Ghione/W. Goehr, Stockholm Royal Op Orch/D. Olivieri, M. Spoliansky/I. Lewis, Dajos Bela Orch)

Ⓓ **CDMOIR411** (1/93)
Sacred Songs and Arias
Bizet: Agnus Dei; *Verdi:* Requiem (exc); Requiem (exc); *Rossini:* Stabat Mater (exc); Stabat Mater (exc); *Franck:* Panis angelicus; *Handel:* Serse (exc); *Faure:* Crucifix; *Gounod:* Ave Maria; *Bach:* Cantata 147 (exc); *Mendelssohn:* Elias (exc); *Mozart:* Exsultate, jubilate, K165 (exc); *Handel:* Messiah (exc); *Haydn:* Creation (exc); *Traditional:* Swing low, sweet chariot; *Grechaninov:* Liturgy, Op. 79 (exc). (G. Thill, J. Björling, E. Pinza, E. Caruso, F. Austral, B. Gigli, T. Schipa, M. Journet, J. McCormack, F. Schorr, E. Schumann, P. Dawson, I. Baillie, P. Robeson, F. Chaliapin, ROH Chor, Berlin St Op Chor, Paris Russian Met Church Ch, orch, La Scala Orch, ROHO, Berlin St Op Orch, G. Moore, LSO, Hallé, R. Clapham/Anthony Bernard/N. Grevillius/C. Sabajno/J. Barbirolli/B. Seidler-Winkler/R. Bourdon/W.B. Rogers/A. Melichar/L. Collingwood/L. Heward/N. Afonsky/G.W. Byng)

Ⓓ **CDMOIR417** (6/93)
Great Voices of the Century—Beniamino Gigli
Puccini: Bohème (exc); *Giordano:* Andrea Chénier (exc); *Mascagni:* Cavalleria Rusticana (exc); *Boito:* Mefistofele (exc); *Verdi:* Rigoletto (exc); Forza del destino (exc); *Donizetti:* Elisir d'amore (exc); *Bizet:* Pêcheurs de perles (exc); Pêcheurs de perles (exc); *Meyerbeer:* Africaine (exc); *Flotow:* Martha (exc); *Toselli:* Serenade; *Bixio:* Canzone dell'amore; *De Curtis:* Carmela; *Denza:* Occhi di fata; *Di Chiara:* Spagnola; *Cottrau:* Addio a Napoli. (B. Gigli, D. Giannini, G. De Luca, orch, La Scala Orch/E. Goossens/J. Pasternack/C. Sabajno/F. Ghione/R. Bourdon/J. Barbirolli/D. Olivieri/W. Goehr/L. Collingwood)

Ⓓ **CDMOIR418** (5/93)
Great Voices of the Century—John McCormack
Donizetti: Elisir d'amore (exc); *Handel:* Semele (exc); Atalanta (exc); *Mozart:* Don Giovanni (exc); Ridente la calma, K152; *Bizet:* Pêcheurs de perles (exc); *Verdi:* Traviata (exc); *Rachmaninov:* Songs, Op.26 (exc); *Wolf:* Goethe Lieder (exc); Spanisches Liederbuch (exc); *Foster:* Jeanie with the light brown hair; *J. Patterson:* Garden where the Praties Grow; *Macmurrough:* Macushla; *Traditional:* Foggy, foggy dew; Star of the County Down; *Crouch:* Kathleen Mavourneen; *A. Sanders:* Little Town; *E. Ball:* Barry of Ballymore (exc); *Dufferin:* Terence's farewell to Kathleen; *Haynes:* Off to Philadelphia; *C. Marshall:* I hear you calling me. (J. McCormack, L. Bori, E. Schneider, G. Moore, S. Clay, orch, F. Kreisler/J. Pasternack/W.B. Rogers)

Ⓓ **CDMOIR422** (6/94)
Great Voices in Tchaikovsky
Tchaikovsky: Queen of Spades (exc); Queen of Spades (exc); Queen of Spades (exc); Queen of Spades (exc); Queen of Spades (exc); Maid of Orleans (exc); Iolanta (exc); Iolanta (exc); Iolanta (exc); Eugene Onegin (exc); Eugene Onegin (exc); Eugene Onegin (exc); Eugene Onegin (exc); Eugene Onegin (exc); Songs, Op.6 (exc); Songs, Op.47 (exc); Songs, Op.38 (exc); Songs, Op.47 (exc); Songs, Op.60 (exc); Songs, Op.38 (exc). (J. Rogatchewsky, H. Schlusnus, M. Michailova, K. Tugarinova, X. Belmas, A. Didur, M. Jeritza, L. Lipkowska, V. Kastorsky, M. Maksakov, L. Sobinov, Lotte Lehmann, D. Smirnov, J. Patzak, G. Baklanoff, N. Koshetz, L. Tibbett, F. Chaliapin, E. Caruso, anon, A. Kitschin, G. Scognamiglio, orch, Berlin St Op Orch/A. Melichar/A. Kitschin/Wolfgang Martin, Inst Ens/N. Shilkret)

Ⓓ **CDMOIR425** (12/94)
Three Tenors, Volume 2
Verdi: Aida (exc); *Puccini:* Manon Lescaut (exc); *Wagner:* Meistersinger (exc); *Offenbach:* Belle Hélène (exc); *M. Sandoval:* Eres tú; *Moszkowski:* Serenata, Op.15/1; *Lehár:* Frasquita (exc); *Donaudy:* O bei nidi d'amore; *Friml:* Vagabond King (exc); *Puccini:* Bohème (exc); *Leoncavallo:* Pagliacci (exc); *Donizetti:* Elisir d'amore (exc); *Lortzing:* Undine (exc); *Bizet:* Carmen (exc); *Giordano:* Andrea Chénier (exc); *Offenbach:* Contes d'Hoffmann (exc); *Alfvén:* Songs, Op.28 (exc); *R. Strauss:* Lieder, Op.17 (exc); *Lehár:* Land des Lächelns (exc); Friederike (exc); *Di Capua:* Maria Mari; *Cottrau:* Santa Lucia. (J. Björling, B. Gigli, R. Tauber, orch, Stockholm Royal Op Orch, La Scala Orch, Berlin Staatskapelle, Berlin Künstlertheater Orch/N. Grevillius/J. Pasternack/E. Hauke/R. Bourdon/F. Ghione/O. de Fabritiis, H. Ebert/F. Weissmann/N. Shilkret/J. Barbirolli)

Ⓓ **CDMOIR428** (7/95)
Rosa Ponselle and Giovanni Martinelli sing Verdi
Verdi: Aida (exc); Aida (exc); Aida (exc); Aida (exc); Aida (exc); Trovatore (exc); Trovatore (exc); Trovatore (exc); Trovatore (exc); Ernani (exc); Ernani (exc); Forza del destino (exc); Forza del destino (exc); Forza del destino (exc). (R. Ponselle, E. Baker, G. Martinelli, R. Stracciari, E. Pinza, NY Met Op Chor, NY Met Op Orch, orch/R. Bourdon/G. Setti/J. Pasternack/W.B. Rogers/R. Romani)

Memoria

Ⓓ **991006** (3/94)
Brahms—Symphonies
Brahms: Symphony 1; Symphony 2; Symphony 3; Symphony 4. (Leningrad PO/E. Mravinsky)

Ⓓ **999001** (10/95)
The Authorised Vatican Recordings-Michelangeli
Debussy: Images; *Ravel:* Gaspard de la nuit; *Chopin:* Andante spianato and Grande Polonaise; *Debussy:* Préludes (exc); *Beethoven:* Piano Concerto 5; Piano Sonata 3; *Schumann:* Piano Concerto; *Liszt:* Totentanz. (A.B. Michelangeli, Rome RAI Orch/M. Freccia/G. Gavazzeni)

Memories

Ⓓ **HR4408/9(1)** (11/92)
Singers in Genoa, Vol.1 (disc 1)
Massenet: Roi de Lahore (exc); *Verdi:* Otello (exc); *Rossini:* Guillaume Tell (exc); *Verdi:* Otello (exc); Simon Boccanegra (exc); Otello (exc); *Brediceanu:* Vai, mindruto; *Mascagni:* Cavalleria Rusticana (exc); *A. Thomas:* Hamlet (exc); *Meyerbeer:* Africaine (exc); *Puccini:* Manon Lescaut (exc); *Gounod:* Roméo et Juliette (exc); *Verdi:* Ernani (exc); *Halévy:* Juive (exc); *Donizetti:* Don Pasquale (exc); *Cilea:* Adriana Lecouvreur (exc); *Verdi:* Falstaff (exc); *Donizetti:* Lucia di Lammermoor (exc); *Verdi:* Luisa Miller (exc); *Donizetti:* Lucrezia Borgia (exc); *Bellini:* Puritani (exc); *Donizetti:* Favorita (exc); *Berlioz:* Damnation de Faust (exc); *Bizet:* Pêcheurs de Perles (exc); *Leoncavallo:* Bohème (exc); *Cilea:* Adriana Lecouvreur (exc); *Verdi:* Traviata (exc); Rigoletto (exc); *Mascagni:* Iris (exc); *Boito:* Mefistofele (exc). (A. Cotogni, A. Aramburo, F. Signorini, G.B. de Negri, V. Arimondi, F. Tamagno, H. Darclée, F. Valero, R. Blanchart, F. Viñas, C. Ferrani, R. Pinkert, G. Kaschmann, F. Navarini, A. Pini-Corsi, E. Corsi, E. Garbin, A. Stehle, V. Maurel, N. Melba, F. Giraud, I. de Frate, A. Bonci, O. Luppi, G. De Luca, E. Caruso, R. Storchio, A. Pandolfini, E. Ventura, T. Ruffo, M. Farneti, T. Arkel, anon, orch)

Ⓓ **HR4408/9(2)** (11/92)
Singers in Genoa, Vol.1 (disc 2)
Mascagni: Cavalleria Rusticana (exc); *Rossini:* Barbiere di Siviglia (exc); Barbiere di Siviglia (exc); *Wagner:* Walküre (exc); *Puccini:* Manon Lescaut (exc); *Giordano:* Fedora (exc); *Rossini:* Barbiere di Siviglia (exc); *Bellini:* Norma (exc); *Donizetti:* Favorita (exc); Lucia di Lammermoor (exc); *Verdi:* Trovatore (exc); *Wagner:* Meistersinger (exc); *Bellini:* Norma (exc); *Giordano:* Andrea Chénier (exc); *Marchetti:* Ruy Blas (exc); *Puccini:* Manon Lescaut (exc); *Wagner:* Walküre (exc); *Puccini:* Fanciulla del West (exc); Tosca (exc); Fanciulla del West (exc); *Verdi:* Otello (exc); Otello (exc); Rigoletto (exc); Rigoletto (exc); *Giordano:* Marcella (exc); *Verdi:* Ballo in maschera (exc). (G. Bellincioni, R. Stracciari, V. Bettoni, G. Borgatti, L. Cavalieri, E. Carelli, M. Barrientos, M. de Macchi, G. Bellantoni, J. Palet, G. Pacini, A. Pinto, G. Russ, V. Guerrini, E. Giraldoni, T. Parvis, P. Schiavazzi, C. Formichi, I. Calleja, L. Montesanto, G. Martinelli, A. Paoli, N. Zerola, H. Lázaro, D. Viglione-Borghese, E. Perea, G. Danise, anon, orch, La Scala Orch/L. Molajoli, E. Ventura)

Mercury

Ⓓ **432 001-2MM** (3/91)
Works for Cello and Orchestra
Dvořák: Cello Concerto; *Bruch:* Kol Nidrei; *Tchaikovsky:* Rococo Variations. (J. Starker, LSO/A. Dorati)

Ⓓ **432 002-2MM** (9/91)
Byron Janis
Liszt: Piano Concerto 1; Piano Concerto 2; Hungarian Rhapsodies, S244 (exc); Valses oubliées, S215 (exc); Années de pèlerinage 1 (exc); *Schumann:* Romanzen, Op. 28 (exc); Novelletten (exc); *Falla:* Sombrero de tres picos Suites (exc); *Guion:* Harmonica Player. (B. Janis, Moscow PO/K. Kondrashin, Moscow RSO/G. Rozhdestvensky)

Ⓓ **432 003-2MM** (4/91)
Ravel & Ibert: Orchestral Works
Ravel: Rapsodie espagnole; Alborada del Gracioso; Pavane; La Valse; Tombeau; *Ibert:* Escales. (Detroit SO/P. Paray)

Ⓓ **432 006-2MM** (3/91)
Orchestral Works
Schoenberg: Orchestral Pieces, Op. 16; *Webern:* Pieces, Op. 10; *Berg:* Orchestral Pieces, Op. 6; Lulu—Symphonie. (H. Pilarczyk, LSO/A. Dorati)

Meridian

Howells: O my dear hert; Peacock Pie (exc); *Ridout*: Prism of Life; Epitaph for Amy; Lewis Sonnets; *Warlock*: Love for Love; Sleep; My own Country; *Steptoe*: Cock Robin. (J. Bowman, P. Goodwin, T. Grunberg, Downshire Players/P. Ash)

ⓘ **CDE84159** (1/90)
Telemann: Cantatas
Telemann: Ihr Völker, hört; Erguess dich zur Salbung; Erscheine Gott; Packe dich, gelähmter Drache; Essercizii Musici (exc). (J. Baird, J. Bowman, Music's Recreation)

ⓘ **CDE84160** (5/90)
Piano 'War Horses'
Prokofiev: Piano Sonata 7; *Debussy*: Pour le piano; *Rachmaninov*: Corelli Variations. (R. Press)

ⓘ **CDE84167** (3/89)
Cabaret Songs
Gershwin: By Strauss; Strike up the Band I (exc); Jolly Jack Tar; Goldwyn Follies (exc); *Coward*: World Weary; G. *Wright*: Diss; *Duke*: Paris in New York; *Britten*: Cabaret Songs; *Mallory*: Indian Summer; Unfortunate Coincidence; Words of Comfort; Résumé; *Ives*: Side Show; Circus Band; *Dankworth*: Lines to Ralph Hodgson, Esq; Bread and Butter; English Teeth; *Gershwin*: Oh, Kay! (exc); Pardon my English (exc); Lady, Be Good (exc); *Duke*: Ages Ago. (Sarah Walker, R. Vignoles)

ⓘ **CDE84168** (10/89)
Elgar: Choral Music
Elgar: Imperial March; Give unto the Lord; Ave verum corpus, Op. 2/1; Hear thy children; Te Deum and Benedictus; God be merciful unto us; Apostles (exc); Great is the Lord. (S. Foulkes, Bristol Cath Ch, Bristol Cath Special Ch, A. Pinel, M. Archer/M. Archer)

ⓘ **CDE84169** (6/90)
Mozart: Clarinet Works
Mozart: Clarinet Concerto, K622; Clarinet Quintet, K581; Piano Trio, K498. (J. Farrell, J. Farrell, Divertimenti/P. Daniel, P. Barritt, R. Isserlis, M. Gerrard, S. Comberti, G. Jackson, G. Johnson)

ⓘ **CDE84173** (12/89)
Elgar: Songs & Part-songs
Elgar: O happy eyes, Op.18/1; Love, Op.18/2; To her beneath; Is she not passing fair?; Shepherd's song; Weary wind of the west; Evening scene; Windlass song; Poet's life; Song of autumn; Death on the hills; Serenade, Op.73/2; Credo in E minor; Was it some golden star?; Speak, music, Op.41/2; Lo! Christ the Lord is born; O mightiest of the mighty; River; How calmly the evening; Goodmorrow. (J. Brecknock, V. Morris, Philharmonic Chbr Ch/D. Temple)

ⓘ **CDE84175** (11/89)
Music from the Eton Choirbook
Browne: Salve regina; Stabat mater dolorosa; *Anon*: Nesciens mater; *Lambe*: Nesciens mater; Stella caeli; *Cornysh*: Ave Maria, mater Dei; R. *Wilkinson*: Salve regina a 9; *Davy*: Stabat mater. (The Sixteen/H. Christophers)

ⓘ **CDE84177** (11/90)
Haydn: Concertos
Haydn: Violin Concerto, HobVIIa/1; Cello Concerto in C; Violin and Keyboard Concerto, HobXVIII/6. (M. Layfield (vn/dir), W. Conway, D. Francis, Goldberg Ens/M. Layfield)

ⓘ **CDE84180** (11/90)
Anthems for America
Weelkes: Hosanna to the Son of David; *Philips*: Ave Jesu Christe; Ecce vicit Leo; *Weelkes*: Alleluia, I heard a voice; W.H. *Harris*: Faire is the heaven; Bring us, O Lord; *Stanford*: Motets, Op. 38 (exc); *Traditional*: Spotless Rose; *Finzi*: God is gone up; *Byrd*: Vigilate; *Purcell*: Jehova, quam multi sunt, Z135; *Traditional*: Coventry Carol; *Leighton*: Mass, Op. 66 (exc); *Schütz*: Geistliche Chormusik, SWV369-97 (exc); Weib, was weinest du, SWV443; Es gingen zweene Menschen, SWV444. (Salisbury Cath Ch/R. Seal)

ⓘ **CDE84182** (1/91)
Clérambault: Dramatic Cantatas
Clérambault: Orphée; Zéphire et Flore; Léandre et Héro; Sonata Magnifique. (J. Baird, Music's Re-creation)

ⓘ **CDE84183** (4/90)
Donizetti: Songs
Donizetti: Canto d'Ugolino; Amor funesto; Trovatore in caricatura; Spirto di Dio; Viva il matrimonio; Renégat; Noé; Départ pour la chasse; Coeur pour abri; Hart. (I. Caddy, M. Tan, A. Halstead, S. Comberti)

ⓘ **CDE84185** (11/90)
Settings from A.E. Housman's 'A Shropshire Lad'
Somervell: Shropshire Lad (Cpte); *Butterworth*: Shropshire Lad (Cpte); *Gurney*: Western Playland (Cpte); *Peel*: When

the lad for longing sighs; Reveille; In Summertime on Bredon. (G. Trew, R. Vignoles, Coull Qt)

ⓘ **CDE84188** (4/90)
Dvořák, Bruckner and Brahms: Choral Works
Dvořák: Mass in D; *Bruckner*: Christus factus est; Tota pulchra es; Locus iste; Ave Maria (1861); *Brahms*: Motets, op 110 (exc); Geistliches Lied, op 30. (Bristol Cath Ch, A. Pinel/M. Archer)

ⓘ **CDE84189** (12/91)
Handel—Italian Solo Cantatas and Instrumental Works
Handel: Violin Sonatas (exc); Keyboard Suites, Set I (exc); Solitudini care; Occhi miei; Qual fior che all'alba ride; Udite il mio consiglio. (J. Baird, M. Proud, J. Dornenburg)

ⓘ **CDE84193** (3/92)
Mendelssohn—String Symphonies, etc
Mendelssohn: String Symphony 7; String Symphony 8; String Quartet, Op. 81. (Goldberg Ens/M. Layfield)

ⓘ **CDE84195** (10/90)
Vivaldi: Orchestral and Vocal Works
Vivaldi: Concerti, op 8 (exc); In furore giustissimae, RV626; Incoronazione di Dario (exc); Griselda (exc); Fida ninfa (exc). (Elizabeth Wallfisch, K. Eckersley, Fiori Musicali, P. Rapson)

ⓘ **CDE84200** (3/92)
Mendelssohn/Schumann—Piano Trios
Mendelssohn: Piano Trio 1; *Schumann*: Fantasiestücke, Op. 88; *Mendelssohn*: Piano Trio 2. (York Trio)

ⓘ **CDE84210** (3/93)
Haydn—Keyboard Sonatas
Haydn: Keyboard Sonata 39; Keyboard Sonata 41; Keyboard Sonata 44; Keyboard Sonata 48; Keyboard Sonata 49. (J. Cload)

ⓘ **CDE84213** (8/92)
Walther—Organ Works
Walther: Torelli Concertos (exc); Telemann Concertos (exc); Taglietti Concerto in B flat; Meck Concerto in B minor; Schmücke dich; Herr Gott; Hilf mir Gott; Es ist das Heil; Jesu meine Freude; Herr Jesu Christ. (S. Farr)

ⓘ **CDE84227/8** (11/92)
Brahms—Chamber Works
Brahms: Piano Trio 1; Piano Trio 2; Piano Trio 3; Horn Trio. (S. Stirling, Dussek Pf Trio, P. Tanfield, M. Dussek)

ⓘ **CDE84229** (9/93)
Mendelssohn—Violin Sonatas
Mendelssohn: Violin Sonata, Op. 4; Violin Sonata (1838); Violin Sonata (1820). (Y. Zivoni, A. Goldstone)

ⓘ **CDE84232** (4/94)
Brahms/Dvořák—Gypsy Songs
Brahms: Zigeunerlieder, Op. 103 (exc); Lieder, Op. 69 (exc); Lieder, Op. 85 (exc); Lieder, Op. 95 (exc); Lieder, Op. 107 (exc); Lieder, Op. 91; *Dvořák*: Gipsy Melodies; In Folk Tone, B146. (Sarah Walker, P. Silverthorne, J. Jacobson, R. Vignoles)

ⓘ **CDE84236** (6/93)
Hummel—Chamber Music - Volume 2
Hummel: Violin Sonata, Op. 50; Bella capricciosa, Op. 55; Viola Sonata, Op. 5/3; Rondo, Op. 19; Flute Sonata, Op. 64. (C. Conway, N. Blume, C. Croshaw)

ⓘ **CDE84237** (7/93)
Romantic Sonatas for Piano Duet
Moscheles: Piano Sonata, Op. 47; *Fibich*: Piano Sonata, Op. 28; *Goetz*: Sonata, Op. 17. (A. Goldstone, C. Clemmow)

ⓘ **CDE84245** (10/94)
D. Stoli—Reflections on Vedic Scriptures
D. Stoli: Piano Quartet; Piano Sonata; 2-Piano Sonata; String Trio. (Pro Arte Trio, D. Ward, N. Skinner)

ⓘ **CDE84253** (4/94)
Beethoven—Chamber and Vocal Works
Beethoven: Piano Trios (exc); Scottish Songs, Op. 108 (exc); Scottish Songs, WoO156 (exc). (English Piano Trio, A. Mackay)

ⓘ **CDE84259** (10/94)
Fauré—Works for Violin and Piano
Fauré: Violin Sonata 1; Violin Sonata 2; Sicilienne; Berceuse, Op. 16. (K. Smietana, J.J. Blakely)

ⓘ **CDE84268** (3/95)
Brahms—Chamber Works
Brahms: Hungarian Dances; Piano Studies; Rhapsodies, Op. 79. (L.D. Alvanis)

ⓘ **CDE84269** (1/95)
Suk Piano Works, Volume 1
Suk: Spring, Op. 22a; About Friendship, Op. 36; Things lived and dreamt, Op. 30; Piano Pieces, Op. 7 (exc). (N. Immelman)

ⓘ **CDE84286** (10/95)
Ethel Smyth—Impressions that Remain
Smyth: Violin Sonata, Op. 7; Cello Sonata, Op. 5; Trio in D Minor. (Chagall Trio, N. Kraamwinkel, T. Gill, J. Rolton)

ⓘ **CDE84298/9** (3/96)
Delius—The Complete Works for Violin and Piano
Delius: Violin Sonata 1; Violin Sonata 2; Violin Sonata 3; Violin Sonata in B; Légende; Romance (1892); Fennimore and Gerda Interludes; Hassan (exc); Lullaby. (L. Jones, Malcolm Miller)

ⓘ **DUOCD89002** (1/90)
German Lieder sung in English
Schubert: Heidenröslein, D257; Schöne Müllerin (exc); Jägers Abendlied, D368; Ständchen, D889; Licht und Liebe, D352; Wachtelschlag, D742; Herbst, D945; Einsame, D800; Rosenband, D280; *Mahler*: Rückert Lieder (exc); *Brahms*: Lieder, Op. 46 (exc); Lieder, Op. 107 (exc); Lieder, Op. 86 (exc); Lieder, Op. 32 (exc); Lieder, Op. 71 (exc); Deutsche Volkslieder (exc); *Schumann*: Gedichte, Op. 35 (exc); *Wolf*: Mörike Lieder (exc); Eichendorff Lieder (exc); *Loewe*: Wandrers Nachtlied; *Mendelssohn*: Lieder, Op. 57 (exc). (K. Livingstone, N. Mackie, J.J. Blakely)

ⓘ **DUOCD89003** (2/90)
Haydn & Schubert: Masses, etc
Haydn: Mass 7; Mass 7 (exc); *Schubert*: Salve Regina, D676; Mass, D167; *Haydn*: Flute-clock pieces, HobXIX (exc). (L. Kitchen, L. Atkinson, M. Glanville, I. Hare, Haydn Soc Chor, Haydn Soc Orch/D. McCaldin)

ⓘ **DUOCD89009** (12/91)
The Romantic Englishman
Spofforth: Hail! smiling morn; *Walmisley*: Music, all powerful; *Webbe I*: Discord, dire sister; *Horsley*: Come, gentle zephyr; *Goss*: List! for the breeze; *Beale*: Come, let us join the roundelay; *Battishill*: Sylvia blushes when I woo her; T. *Philips*: Crows in the cornfield; *Hatton*: When ev'ning's twilight; *Bishop*: By the simplicity of Venus' doves; *Parry*: Partsongs (1904-12); *Stainer*: Cupid look about thee; *Benedict*: Lily of Killarney (exc); *Pearsall*: There is a paradise on earth; *Sterndale Bennett*: Come live with us; *Molloy*: Tomorrow will be Friday; *Sullivan*: Long day closes. (Hilliard Ens, L-L. Kiesel)

ⓘ **DUOCD89019/21** (12/92)
Beethoven—Sonatas for Violin and Piano
Beethoven: Violin Sonata 1; Violin Sonata 2; Violin Sonata 3; Violin Sonata 4; Violin Sonata 5; Violin Sonata 6; Violin Sonata 7; Violin Sonata 8; Violin Sonata 9; Violin Sonata 10. (R. Cohen, A. Rael)

ⓘ **DUOCD89023** (2/94)
Beethoven—Piano Works
Beethoven: Variations, WoO80; Piano Sonata 13; Allegretto, WoO53; Allegretto, WoO56; Bagatelles (exc). (T. Leonhardt)

ⓘ **ECD84070** (3/85)
Chopin: Piano works
Chopin: Piano Sonata 2; Etudes (exc); Nocturnes (exc); Andante spianato and Grande Polonaise. (J. Bingham)

ⓘ **ECD84080** (1/86)
Haydn: Vocal works
Haydn: Ploughman; Logie of Buchan; Sleepy Bodie; O can ye sew cushions; White cockade; Canzonettas II (exc); Arianna a Naxos; Creation (exc); Canzonettas I (exc); Bonny Brucket Lassie; My Heart's in the Highlands. (J. Bott, M. Tan, A. Bury, L. Beznosiuk, A. Pleeth, F. Kelly)

ⓘ **ECD84081** (3/87)
Bach—Organ Works
Bach: Toccata and Fugue, BWV565; Prelude and Fugue, BWV553; Prelude and Fugue, BWV554; Prelude and Fugue, BWV555; Prelude and Fugue, BWV556; Prelude and Fugue, BWV557; Prelude and Fugue, BWV558; Prelude and Fugue, BWV560; Allabreve, BWV589; Ach Gott und Herr, BWV714; Prelude and Fugue, BWV532. (D. Sanger)

ⓘ **ECD84083** (9/86)
Haydn: Keyboard Works
Haydn: Adagio, HobXVII/9; Keyboard Sonata 50; Keyboard Sonata 54; Keyboard Sonata 55. (J. Cload)

ⓘ **ECD84093** (8/86)
Josquin Desprez: Motets
Josquin Desprez: Inviolata, integra et castra es, Maria; Stabat mater dolorosa; Virgo salutifer; Salve regina a 4; Praeter rerum seriem; Veni, Sancte Spiritus; Virgo prudentissima. (New College Ch/E. Higginbottom)

ⓘ **ECD84117** (3/87)
Haydn: String Quartets
Haydn: String Quartet, Op.1/0; String Quartet, Op.42; String Quartet, Op.103. (English Qt)

ⓘ **MACD-609** (4/91)
Chopin: Piano Works
Chopin: Polonaises (exc); Piano Sonata 2; Ballades (exc);
Barcarolle. (C. Rosen)

ⓘ **MACD-612** (11/90)
Walter Gieseking—Historical Broadcasts, 1944-50
Bach: Chromatic Fantasia and Fugue, BWV903; Mozart:
Piano Sonata, K331; Beethoven: Piano Sonata 31; D.
Scarlatti: Keyboard Sonatas (exc); Debussy: Images (exc);
Ravel: Gaspard de la Nuit (exc); Mozart: Piano Sonata,
K576. (W. Gieseking)

ⓘ **MACD-620** (12/90)
20th Century French Violin Works
Milhaud: Concertino de Printemps; Danses de
Jacaremirim; Violin Concerto 2; Poulenc: Violin Sonata;
Sauguet: Concerto d'Orphée. (L. Kaufman, FRNO/D.
Milhaud, A. Balsam, H. Pognari/J.M. Leconte)

ⓘ **MACD-621** (6/91)
Scriabin—Piano Sonatas, Vol.2
Scriabin: Piano Sonata 6; Piano Sonata 7; Piano Sonata 8;
Piano Sonata 9; Piano Sonata 10. (Boris Berman)

ⓘ **MACD-635** (11/91)
American Chamber Works
L. Harrison: Double Concerto; Cowell: Cleistogamy;
Combinations; Reale: Piano Trio (1980). (K. Goldsmith, T.
King, Mirecourt Trio, Mills College Gamelan Ens)

ⓘ **MACD-643** (11/91)
Mozart & Schumann—Chamber Works
Mozart: Piano Quartet, K478; Piano Quartet, K493;
Schumann: Piano Quintet, Op.44. (C. Arrau, C. Curzon,
Budapest Qt)

ⓘ **MACD-644** (10/91)
The Art of Gregor Piatigorsky
Brahms: Cello Sonata 1; Shostakovich: Cello Sonata,
Op.40; Weber: Violin Sonatas, J99-104 (exc); Francoeur:
Cello Sonata in E (exc); Scriabin: Romance in A minor;
Tchaikovsky: Morceaux, Op. 51 (exc); Chopin: Nocturnes
(exc); Weber: Violin Sonatas, J99-104 (exc). (G.
Piatigorsky, R. Stewart, I. Newton)

ⓘ **MACD-649** (7/92)
Salute To France
Hahn: Bal de Béatrice d'Este Suite; Milhaud: Chamber
Symphony 4; Ibert: Cello Concerto; Suite Symphonique
(1930); Poulenc: Aubade. (J. Kreger, R. Votapek, NY
Harmonie Ens/S. Richman)

ⓘ **MACD-650** (6/92)
Schoenberg—Song Cycles
Schoenberg: Cabaret Songs (exc); Lieder, Op.2; Buch der
hängenden Gärten. (P. Bryn-Julson, U. Oppens)

ⓘ **MACD-662** (6/92)
Cortot plays Weber and Liszt
Weber: Piano Sonata 2; Liszt: Piano Sonata, S178;
Concert Studies, S144 (exc); Concert Studies, S144 (exc);
Chants polonais, S480 (exc); Hungarian Rhapsodies, S244
(exc). (A. Cortot)

ⓘ **MACD-665** (4/92)
The Goldberg/Kraus Duo plays Mozart and Beethoven
Mozart: Violin Sonata, K296; Violin Sonata, K377; Violin
Sonata, K378; Violin Sonata, K379; Violin Sonata, K380;
Violin Sonata, K404; Violin Sonata, K481; Duo, K423; Duo,
K424; Beethoven: Violin Sonata 5; Violin Sonata 9; Violin
Sonata 10. (S. Goldberg, L. Kraus, F. Riddle, P.
Hindemith)

ⓘ **MACD-667** (1/92)
Louis Kaufman plays 20th Century Concertos
Larsson: Violin Concerto, Op.42; Barber: Violin Concerto;
Vaughan Williams: Concerto Accademico. (L. Kaufman,
Swedish RSO/S. Frykberg, Lucerne Fest Orch/W. Goehr,
Winterthur SO/C. Dahinden)

ⓘ **MACD-674** (3/92)
Piatigorsky—Recordings from the Pre-war era
Schumann: Cello Concerto; Beethoven: Cello Sonata 2;
Brahms: Cello Sonata 1; Mendelssohn: Songs without
words (exc); Moszkowski: Pieces, Op.45 (exc);
Tchaikovsky: Songs, Op.6 (exc). (G. Piatigorsky, A.
Schnabel, A. Rubinstein, K. Szreter, LPO/J. Barbirolli)

ⓘ **MACD-691** (8/92)
Dvorak & Friends - Czech Wind Music
Dvořák: Serenade, Op.44; Slavonic Dances (exc);
Krommer: Partitas, Op. 45; Mysliveček: Octet 2. (C.
Kavalovski, S. Brubaker, NY Harmonie Ens/S. Richman)

ⓘ **MACD-749** (12/93)
Bruno Walter conducts Mahler
Mahler: Lied von der Erde; Rückert Lieder (exc); Rückert
Lieder (exc); Symphony 5 (exc). (K. Thorborg, C. Kullman,
VPO/B. Walter, orch/M. Sargent)

ⓘ **MACD-767** (4/94)
Honegger conducts Honegger
Honegger: Tempête; Pastorale d'été; Symphonic
Movements (exc); Aventures du roi Pausole (exc); Chant
de Nigamon; Symphony 3. (SO, Odeon Grand Orch/A.
Honegger, Pasdeloup Orch/Rhené-Baton)

ⓘ **MACD-772** (3/94)
The Art of Egon Petri
Chopin: Preludes (exc); Busoni: Indianisches Tagebuch;
Elegien (exc); Perpetuum Mobile; Fantasia
Contrappuntistica (exc); Medtner: Fairy Tales, Op.20; Forgotten
Melodies, Op.38 (exc); Schumann: Fantasiestücke, Op.12;
Mozart: Piano Concerto 9 (exc); Bach: Prelude, Fugue and
Allegro, BWV998; Cantata 208 (exc); Chorales, BWV651-
668 (exc); Applicatio, BWV841-843; Liszt: Forelle, S564;
Chopin: Nocturnes (exc); Haydn: Variations, HobXVII:6;
Gluck: Orfeo ed Euridice (exc); Alceste (1776) (exc);
Beethoven: Piano Sonata 27; Schubert: Divertissement,
D823 (exc); Chopin: Nocturnes (exc); Piano Sonata 3;
Beethoven: Piano Sonata 30; Piano Sonata 31; Piano
Sonata 32; Liszt: Venezia e Napoli, S162; Chopin:
Polonaises (exc). (E. Petri, C. Bussotti)

ⓘ **MACD-778** (2/94)
Stokowski conducts French Music
Ibert: Escales; Ravel: Alborada del gracioso; Debussy:
Images (exc); Ravel: Alborada del gracioso; Debussy:
Op.109. (FRNO, Hessian RO, South-West German RSO/L.
Stokowski)

ⓘ **MACD-780** (7/94)
The Mengelberg Legacy
Tchaikovsky: Symphony 5; Dvořák: Violin Concerto;
Beethoven: Symphony 3; Debussy: Fantaisie; Brahms:
Symphony 3; Violin Concerto; Schubert: Arpeggione
Sonata, D821; Bruch: Violin Concerto 1; Wagner:
Tannhäuser (exc); Beethoven: Egmont (exc). (M. Neuss,
H. Krebbers, B. Gustabo, G. Cassadó, W. Gieseking,
Concertgebouw/W. Mengelberg)

ⓘ **MACD-809** (10/94)
Mengelberg conducts Tchaikovsky
Tchaikovsky: Symphony 4; Symphony 5; Symphony 6;
Romeo and Juliet; Serenade, Op.48 (exc).
(Concertgebouw/W. Mengelberg)

ⓘ **MACD-824** (3/95)
Beethoven—Symphonies
Beethoven: Symphony 4; Symphony 5; Symphony 6;
Symphony 7. (BPO/W. Furtwängler)

Music Masters (UK)

ⓘ **MMD 60195A** (11/90)
American Flute Works
Copland: Flute Duo; Barber: Mélodies passagères, op 27;
Canzone, op 38; Beaser: Flute Variations; R. Harris: Flute
Study. (P. Robison, T. Hester)

Music Masters (USA)

ⓘ **67094-2** (4/94)
Antheil—Ballet Mécanique
Antheil: Ballet Mécanique; Jazz Symphony; Violin, Piano
and Drum Sonata 2; String Quartet 1. (C. Castleman, R.
Hodgkinson, I. Davis, R. Lawson, Mendelssohn Qt, New
Palais Royale Perc Ens, New Palais Royale Orch/M.
Peress)

ⓘ **67098-2** (6/94)
Beethoven—Piano Sonatas
Beethoven: Piano Sonata 30; Piano Sonata 31; Piano
Sonata 32. (V. Feltsman)

ⓘ **67110-2** (9/94)
Stravinsky—The Composer, Volume V
Stravinsky: Suites; Études, Op. 7; Norwegian Moods;
Concerto for two solo pianos; Ode (1943); Rag-time;
Piano-Rag Music; Renard (Cpte). (T. Baker, D. Martin, D.
Evitts, W. Pauley, M. Wait, T. Schultz, St Luke's Orch/R.
Craft)

ⓘ **67113-2** (6/94)
Stravinsky—The Composer - Volume IV
Stravinsky: Greeting prelude; Various: National Anthems
(exc); Stravinsky: Dumbarton Oaks; Instrumental
Miniatures; Chorus; Falla; Scherzo à la Russe; Scènes de
Ballet; Agon; Choral Variations; Balanchine Chorale.
(Gregg Smith Sngrs, St. Luke's Orch/R. Craft)

ⓘ **67120-2** (10/94)
Vivaldi—Violin Concertos, Volume VI
Vivaldi: Concerto, RV223; Concerto, RV349; Concerto,
RV248; Concerto, RV229; Concerto, RV343; Concerto,
RV267. (S. Mintz (vn/dir), Israel CO)

ⓘ **67124-2** (10/95)
Chopin—Piano Works
Chopin: Ballades (exc); Etudes (exc); Nocturnes (exc);
Scherzos (exc). (C. Licad)

ⓘ **67152-2** (10/95)
Stravinsky—The Composer, Volume VII
Stravinsky: Histoire du Soldat Suite; Marseillaise; Valse;
Sketches for a sonata; Pribaoutki; Cats' Cradle Songs;
Monumentum pro Gesualdo; Mass; Dove descending;
Canticum sacrum. (St Luke's Orch/R. Craft, C. Ciesinski, J.
Humphries, D. Evitts, M. Wait, R. Schulte)

ⓘ **7021-2** (5/93)
Hovhaness/Harrison—Orchestral Works
Hovhaness: Symphony 2; Lousadzak; L. Harrison:
Symphony 2. (K. Jarrett, American Cpsrs Orch/D.R.
Davies)

Music Memoria

ⓘ **MM30231** (10/90)
Don Pasquale & Tito Schipa Recital
Donizetti: Don Pasquale (Cpte); Elisir d'amore (exc); Elisir
d'amore (exc); Lucia di Lammermoor (exc); Bellini:
Sonnambula (exc); Sonnambula (exc); Verdi: Rigoletto
(exc); Leoncavallo: Pagliacci (exc); Cilea: Arlesiana (exc);
Mascagni: Ave Maria; Rimsky-Korsakov: Songs, Op. 2
(exc). (E. Badini, A. Saraceni, T. Schipa, A. Poli, G.
Callegari, La Scala Chor, La Scala Orch/C. Sabajno, T.
Schipa, A. Galli-Curci, T. dal Monte, orch/R. Bourdon/F.
Ghione)

ⓘ **MM30269** (5/91)
Weingartner conducts Beethoven
Beethoven: Symphony 7; Symphony 8; Prometheus (exc).
(VPO/F. Weingartner)

ⓘ **MM30271** (11/91)
Rachmaninov plays the Romantics
Chopin: Piano Sonata 2; Nocturnes (exc); Waltzes (exc);
Waltzes (exc); Liszt: Müllerlieder, S565 (exc);
Mendelssohn: Songs without Words (exc); Schumann:
Carnaval; Liszt: Concert Studies, S145 (exc); Polonaises,
S223 (exc). (S. Rachmaninov)

ⓘ **MM30272** (10/91)
Joseph Szigeti
Beethoven: Violin Concerto; Mendelssohn: Violin
Concerto, Op.64; Paganini: Caprices, Op.1 (exc). (J.
Szigeti, British SO/B. Walter, LPO/T. Beecham)

ⓘ **MM30320** (10/91)
Joseph Szigeti
Handel: Violin Sonatas (exc); Bach: Solo Violin Partitas
and Sonatas (exc); Mozart: Violin Sonata, K304; Bach:
Solo Violin Partitas and Sonatas (exc). (J. Szigeti, N.
Magaloff)

ⓘ **MM30321** (10/91)
Jacques Thibaud—Violin Recital
Bach: Brandenburg Concertos (exc); Debussy: Violin
Sonata; Préludes (exc); Fauré: Berceuse, Op.16; Mozart:
Serenade, K250 (exc); Albéniz: España, Op.165 (exc);
Desplanes: Intrada; Saint-Saëns: Havanaise; Déluge (exc);
Granados: Danzas españolas (exc); Falla: Vida breve
(exc). (J. Thibaud, A. Cortot, T. Janopoulo, G. de Lausnay,
Paris Ecole Normale CO, A. Cortot (pf/dir))

ⓘ **MM30322** (12/91)
Enescu - Columbia Recordings 1920s-30s
Handel: Violin Sonatas (exc); Corelli: Sonatas, Op.5 (exc);
Pugnani: Sonatas, Op.8 (exc); Kreisler: Pugnani Tempo di
Menuetto; Chausson: Poème; Bach: 2-Violin Concerto. (G.
Enescu, S. Schlüssel, Y. Menuhin, Paris SO/P. Monteux)

ⓘ **MM30352** (7/91)
Caruso—Italian Opera Arias
Verdi: Rigoletto (exc); Rigoletto (exc); Rigoletto (exc);
Traviata (exc); Aida (exc); Aida (exc); Trovatore (exc);
Trovatore (exc); Ballo in maschera (exc); Macbeth (exc);
Forza del destino (exc); Donizetti: Favorita (exc); Lucia di
Lammermoor (exc); Puccini: Tosca (exc); Bohème (exc);
Gomes: Schiavo (exc); Mascagni: Cavalleria rusticana
(exc); Rossini: Petite messe solennelle (exc). (E. Caruso,
A. Gluck, J. Jacoba, A. Galli-Curci, F. Perini, G. De Luca,
L. Homer, M. Egener, A. Bada, M. Journet, orch, NY Met
Op Chor, NY Met Op Orch)

ⓘ **MM30373** (12/91)
Gounod—Mélodies
Gounod: Mélodies (1855) (exc); Au rossignol; Reine de
Saba (exc); Vierge d'Athènes; Cinq Mars (exc); Dites, la
jeune belle; Vallon; Soir; Viens! les gazons sont verts!; A la
brise; Quanti mai; Chanson de printemps; Mignon; Absent;
Sérénade; Philémon et Baucis (exc). (R. Doria, J.
Boguet)

Variations; Pomp and Circumstance Marches (exc); Salut d'amour. (Bratislava RSO/A. Leaper)

① **8 550231** (1/91)
Berlioz: Orchestral Works
Berlioz: Carnaval Romain; King Lear; Benvenuto Cellini (exc); Corsaire; Damnation de Faust (exc); Roméo et Juliette (exc). (Polish St PO/K. Jean)

① **8 550238** (8/91)
Borodin—Symphonies
Borodin: Symphony 1; Symphony 2; Symphony 3. (Bratislava RSO/S. Gunzenhauser)

① **8 550241** (4/91)
Verdi—Opera Choruses
Verdi: Nabucco (exc); Don Carlo (exc); Traviata (exc); Battaglia di Legnano (exc); Trovatore (exc); Ernani (exc); Otello (exc); Macbeth (exc); Forza del Destino (exc); Aida (exc). (Slovak Phil Chor, Bratislava RSO/O. Dohnányi)

① **8 550250** (3/91)
R. Strauss: Orchestral Works
R. Strauss: Don Juan; Till Eulenspiegel; Tod und Verklärung. (Slovak PO/Z. Košler)

① **8 550264** (4/91)
Mozart—Symphonies
Mozart: Symphony 27; Symphony 33; Symphony 36. (Capella Istropolitana/B. Wordsworth)

① **8 550276** (11/90)
French Violin Sonatas
Debussy: Violin Sonata; *Poulenc:* Violin Sonata; *Saint-Saëns:* Violin Sonata 1; *Ravel:* Violin Sonata (1897). (D-S. Kang, P. Devoyon)

① **8 550281** (10/90)
Brahms: Orchestral Works
Brahms: Symphony 4; Academic Festival Overture; Tragic Overture. (Belgian Rad & TV Orch/A. Rahbari)

① **8 550342** (2/91)
R. Strauss: Orchestral Works
R. Strauss: Aus Italien; Liebe der Danae (exc); Rosenkavalier (exc). (Slovak PO/Z. Košler)

① **8 550343** (5/92)
Italian and French Opera Arias
Verdi: Rigoletto (exc); Aida (exc); *Bizet:* Carmen (exc); *Gounod:* Faust (exc); *Massenet:* Werther (exc); *Puccini:* Villi (exc); Tosca (exc); Turandot (exc); Manon Lescaut (exc); Madama Butterfly (exc); *Lara:* Granada; *De Curtis:* Torna a Surriento; *Di Capua:* O sole mio. (P. Dvorský, Bratislava RSO/O. Lenárd)

① **8 550354** (5/92)
Brahms—Piano Works
Brahms: Piano Pieces, Op.117; Piano Pieces, Op.118; Piano Pieces, Op.119; Scherzo, Op.4. (I. Biret)

① **8 550367** (5/93)
Chopin—Rondos & Variations
Chopin: Rondo, Op. 1; Rondo, Op. 5; Introduction and Rondo, Op. 16; Rondo in C; Mazurkas (exc); Introduction and Variations (1826); Introduction and Variations, Op. 12; Souvenir de Paganini; Hexameron Variations; Introduction, Theme and Variations. (I. Biret, M. Sauer)

① **8 550368** (4/92)
Chopin—Works for Piano & Orchestra
Chopin: Piano Concerto 1; Fantasia on Polish Airs; Andante spianato and Grande polonaise. (I. Biret, Košice St PO/R. Stankovsky)

① **8 550369** (4/92)
Chopin—Works for Piano & Orchestra
Chopin: Piano Concerto 2; Krakowiak; Variations, Op. 2. (I. Biret, Košice St PO/R. Stankovsky)

① **8 550378** (7/91)
Weber—Works for Clarinet and Orchestra
Weber: Clarinet Concerto 1; Clarinet Concerto 2; Clarinet Concertino. (E. Ottersamer, Košice St PO/J. Wildner)

① **8 550381** (9/91)
Prokofiev—Orchestral Suites
Prokofiev: Lt. Kijé Suite; Love for 3 Oranges Suite (exc); Romeo and Juliet Suites (exc); Cinderella Suite 1. (Košice St PO/A. Mogrelia)

① **8 550382** (9/91)
Haydn—Symphonies Nos 45,48 and 102
Haydn: Symphony 45; Symphony 48; Symphony 102. (Capella Istropolitana/B. Wordsworth)

① **8 550383** (12/91)
Mozart—Tenor Arias
Mozart: Idomeneo (exc); Entführung (exc); Don Giovanni (exc); Cosi fan tutte (exc); Clemenza di Tito (exc). (J. Dickie, Capella Istropolitana/J. Wildner)

① **8 550390** (2/94)
Mozart—Chamber Works for Clarinet
Mozart: Clarinet Quintet, K581; Violin Sonata, K380; Clarinet Quintet Movement, KAnh90. (J. Balogh, B. Kovács, J. Balogh, Danubius Qt)

① **8 550401** (4/93)
Schumann—Piano Works
Schumann: Kreisleriana; Waldszenen; Blumenstück. (P. Gulda)

① **8 550411** (3/92)
Janacek—Orchestral works
Janáček: Taras Bulba; Sinfonietta; Lachian dances. (Bratislava RSO/O. Lenárd)

① **8 550414** (4/91)
Mozart & Saint-Saëns: Violin Works
Mozart: Violin Concerto, K207; Violin Concerto, K211; Rondo, K269; Piano Concerto 21 (exc). (T. Nishizaki, Capella Istropolitana/J. Wildner)

① **8 550416** (2/92)
Handel—Harpsichord Suites
Handel: Keyboard Suites, Set I (exc); Capriccio, HWV481; Keyboard Suites, Set II (exc); Sonatina in D minor; Sonata in G minor; Toccata in G minor. (A. Cuckston)

① **8 550431** (9/92)
Bach—Soprano Cantatas
Bach: Cantata 199; Cantata 202; Cantata 209. (F. Wagner, Capella Istropolitana/C. Brembeck)

① **8 550435** (12/91)
Mozart—Arias and Duets
Mozart: Entführung (exc); Nozze di Figaro (exc); Don Giovanni (exc); Zauberflöte (exc); Cosi fan tutte (exc). (A. Martin, D. Robin, Capella Istropolitana/J. Wildner, Vienna Mozart Orch/K. Leitner)

① **8 550439** (2/94)
Mozart—Works for Clarinet
Mozart: Piano Trio, K498; Violin Sonata, K378; Piano Trio, K496. (B. Kovács, J. Balogh, G. Konrád, J. Jandó, Danubius Qt)

① **8 550452** (9/95)
Clementi—Piano Music
Clementi: Keyboard Sonatas, Op.25 (exc); Keyboard Sonatas, Op. 37 (exc); Keyboard Sonatinas, Op. 36; Keyboard Sonatas, Op. 24 (exc). (B. Szokolay)

① **8 550459** (3/93)
Czech Horn Concertos
Fiala: 2-Horn Concerto in E flat; *Pokorný:* 2-Horn Concerto in F; *Rosetti:* 2-Horn Concerto in A flat; 2-Horn Concerto in E flat. (Z. Tylšár, B. Tylšár, Capella Istropolitana/F. Vajnar)

① **8 550466** (3/92)
Rachmaninov—Preludes, Vol.2
Rachmaninov: Preludes (exc); *Kreisler:* Liebesleid; Liebesfreud. (I. Biret)

① **8 550476** (3/93)
Schubert—Lieder Recital
Schubert: An die Musik, D547; Heidenröslein, D257; Forelle, D550; Auf dem Wasser zu singen, D774; Du bist die Ruh', D776; Im Frühling, D882; Wandrers Nachtlied II, D768; Nacht und Träume, D827; Zwerg, D771; Gretchen am Spinnrade, D118; Junge Nonne, D828; Heiss mich nicht reden, D877/2; So lasst mich scheinen, D877/3; Nur wer die Sehnsucht kennt, D877/4; Suleika I, D720; Suleika II, D717; Tod und das Mädchen, D531; Erlkönig, D328. (T. Takács, J. Jandó)

① **8 550486** (9/92)
Rimsky-Korsakov—Orchestral Works
Rimsky-Korsakov: Snow Maiden (exc); Golden Cockerel Suite (exc); Mlada (exc). (Bratislava RSO/D. Johanos)

① **8 550494** (12/93)
Works for Violin and Orchestra
Lalo: Symphonie espagnole; *Ravel:* Tzigane; *Saint-Saëns:* Havanaise; Sarasate: Zigeunerweisen. (M. Bisengaliev, Polish Nat RSO/J. Wildner)

① **8 550495** (3/93)
Mozart—Sacred Choral Works
Mozart: Mass, K317; Vespers, K339 (exc); Sub tuum praesidium, K198; Ave verum corpus, K618; Exsultate jubilate, K165. (P. Coles, A. di Mauro, J. Dickie, A. Martin, Košice Teachers Ch, Camerata Cassovia/J. Wildner)

① **8 550505** (11/93)
Debussy—Orchestral Works
Debussy: Images; Martyre de St Sébastien; Marche écossaise; Berceuse héroïque. (Belgian Rad & TV Orch/A. Rahbari)

① **8 550508** (5/93)
Chopin—Piano Works
Chopin: Ballades; Berceuse; Etudes (exc); Fantasie, Op. 49; Galop marquis; Largo; Funeral March, Op. 72/2; Cantabile. (I. Biret)

① **8 550509** (8/94)
Brahms—Piano Works
Brahms: Variations, Op. 21/1; Variations, Op. 21/2; Piano Studies. (I. Biret)

① **8 550511** (4/93)
Mozart/Beethoven—Quintets for Piano and Wind etc
Beethoven: Piano and Wind Quintet, Op.16; *Mozart:* Piano and Wind Quintet, K452; Adagio and Rondo, K617. (J. Jandó, J. Kiss, B. Kovács, J. Kevehází, J. Vajda, J. Jandó, I. Kovács, G. Konrád, T. Koó)

① **8 550519** (11/94)
Bloch/Bruch/Tchaikovsky—Cello Works
Bloch: Schelomo; *Bruch:* Kol Nidrei; *Tchaikovsky:* Rococo Variations; Nocturne, Op. 19/4; Pezzo capriccioso. (M. Kliegel, Ireland National SO/G. Markson)

① **8 550539** (8/92)
Respighi—Orchestral Works
Respighi: Pines of Rome; Fountains of Rome; Roman Festivals. (RPO/E. Bátiz)

① **8 550544** (4/93)
Mozart—String Quartets, Vol.5
Mozart: String Quartet, K589; String Quartet, K160; String Quartet, K169; String Quartet, K168. (Eder Qt)

① **8 550545** (2/95)
Mozart—String Quartets, Volume 6
Mozart: String Quartet, K172; String Quartet, K173; String Quartet, K575. (Eder Qt)

① **8 550546** (2/95)
Mozart—String Quartets, Volume 7
Mozart: String Quartet, K170; String Quartet, K171; String Quartet, K421. (Eder Qt)

① **8 550547** (4/95)
Mozart—String Quartets, Volume 8
Mozart: String Quartet, K499; String Quartet, K590; Adagio and Fugue, K546. (Eder Qt)

① **8 550555** (12/92)
Schubert—Piano Works for Four Hands
Schubert: Allegro, D947; Marches caractéristiques, D968b; Divertissement à la hongroise, D818. (J. Jandó, I. Prunyi)

① **8 550556** (6/93)
C.P.E.Bach/Marcello—Oboe Works
C.P.E. Bach: Oboe Concerto, H466; Oboe Concerto, H468; Solo Flute Sonata, H562; *A. Marcello:* Oboe Concerto in D minor. (J. Kiss, F. Erkel CO)

① **8 550566** (11/92)
Prokofiev—Piano Concertos
Prokofiev: Piano Concerto 3; Piano Concerto 4; Piano Concerto 1. (K.W Paik, Polish Nat RSO/A. Wit)

① **8 550572** (4/93)
Lamentations
Whyte: Lamentations; *Tallis:* Lamentations of Jeremiah; *Palestrina:* Lamentationum Hieremiae; *Lassus:* Lamentations of Jeremiah; *Brito:* Lamentations Jeremiae. (Oxford Camerata/J. Summerly)

① **8 550574** (7/93)
Byrd—Sacred Choral Works
Byrd: Mass for four voices; Mass for five voices; Infelix ego. (Oxford Camerata/J. Summerly)

① **8 550576** (11/94)
Tallis—Mass for four voices; Motets
Tallis: Mass a 4; Loquebantur variis linguis; Salvator mundi I; O sacrum convivium; Audivi vocem; Sancte Deus, sancte fortis; Virate miraculum; Te lucis ante terminum I; In manus tuas. (Oxford Camerata/J. Summerly)

① **8 550577** (6/93)
Grieg—Lyric Pieces Vol. 2
Grieg: Lyric Pieces, Op.12 (exc); Lyric Pieces, Op.38 (exc); Lyric Pieces, Op.43 (exc); Lyric Pieces, Op.47 (exc); Lyric Pieces, Op.54 (exc); Lyric Pieces, Op.57 (exc); Lyric Pieces, Op.62 (exc); Lyric Pieces, Op.65 (exc); Lyric Pieces, Op.71 (exc). (B. Szokolay)

① **8 550581** (3/93)
French Organ Music
Guilmant: Grand Choeur in D; Cantilène pastorale; *Vierne:* Pièces en stile libre (exc); Stèle pour un enfant défunt; *M-A. Charpentier:* Te Deum, H146 (exc); *Langlais:* Méditations (1962); *Bonnet:* Romance sans paroles; *Boëllmann:* Suite gothique; *Widor:* Symphony 5 (exc); *Malengreau:* Suite Mariale. (/S. Lindley)

① **8 550582** (3/93)
English Organ Music
C.S. Lang: Tuba Tune; *Howells:* Psalm-Preludes, Op. 32; *Elgar:* Organ Sonata 1; *Vaughan Williams:* Organ Preludes on Welsh Hymn-Tunes (exc); *Whitlock:* Hymn Preludes (exc); *Cocker:* Tuba Tune. (G. Green)

① **8 550598** (5/94)
Dvořák—Symphonic Poems
Dvořák: Noon Witch; Golden Spinning-Wheel; Wild Dove. (Polish Nat RSO/S. Gunzenhauser)

① **8 550600** (10/93)
Dvořák—Overtures
Dvořák: Vanda (exc); In Nature's Realm; Carnival; Othello; My Home. (BBC PO/S. Gunzenhauser)

① **8 550603** (2/95)
Gibbons—Consort and Keyboard Music, Songs and Anthems
Gibbons: Pavan and Galliard a 6; Fantasias a 2 (exc); Go from my window; Fantasia a 6 (exc); Double Bass Fantasias a 4 (exc); Galliard; In Nomine; Lord Salisbury Pavan and Galliard; Preludes (exc); Masks (exc); Almans (exc); Behold, thou hast made my days; Madrigals, First Set (exc); Glorious and powerful God. (T. Bonner, Red Byrd, T. Roberts, Rose Consort)

① **8 550604** (6/95)
Byrd—Music for Viols, Voices and Keyboard
Byrd: Pavan and Galliard a 6, BE17/15; Psalmes, Sonets and Songs (1588) (exc); Rejoice unto the Lord; John come kiss me now, BK81; Fantasia a 6, BE17/13; Have mercy upon me, O God; In Nomine a 4, BE17/17; In angel's weed; Fair Britain Isle; Fantasia a 4, BE17/4; Triumph with pleasant melody; Pavan and Galliard, BK14 (exc); Qui passe, BK19; Fantasia a 6 III; In Nomines a 5 (exc); Christ rising again. (Rose Consort, Red Byrd, T. Roberts, T. Bonner)

① **8 550605** (2/93)
Favourite Soprano Arias
Bellini: Puritani (exc); Capuleti (exc); Sonnambula (exc); *Donizetti:* Linda di Chamounix (exc); Lucia di Lammermoor (exc); *Puccini:* Turandot (exc); Gianni Schicchi (exc); Rondine (exc); *Verdi:* Rigoletto (exc). (L. Orgonášová, Bratislava RSO/W. Humburg)

① **8 550606** (11/92)
Soprano Arias from Italian Operas
Verdi: Don Carlo (exc); Otello (exc); Forza del destino (exc); *Catalani:* Wally (exc); *Puccini:* Manon Lescaut (exc); Tosca (exc); Suor Angelica (exc); Gianni Schicchi (exc); Turandot (exc); Villi (exc); Bohème (exc). (M. Gauci, Belgian Rad & TV Orch/A. Rahbari)

① **8 550609** (4/93)
Mozart—Cassations
Mozart: Cassation, K63; Cassation, K99; Cassation, K100. (Salzburg CO/H. Nerat)

① **8 550611** (9/94)
Mozart—Piano Variations, Vol.1
Mozart: Variations, K24; Variations, K25; Variations, K54; Variations, K179; Variations, K180; Variations, K354. (F. Nicolosi)

① **8 550612** (9/94)
Mozart—Piano Variations, Vol.2
Mozart: Variations, K264; Variations, K265; Variations, K352; Variations, K353; Variations, K398. (F. Nicolosi)

① **8 550613** (9/94)
Mozart—Piano Variations, Vol.3
Mozart: Variations, K455; Variations, K460; Variations, K500; Variations, K573; Variations, K613. (F. Nicolosi)

① **8 550654** (7/93)
Schubert/Schumann—Chamber Works
Schubert: Arpeggione Sonata, D821; *Schumann:* Fantasiestücke, Op. 73; Stücke, Op. 102; Adagio and Allegro, Op. 70. (M. Kliegel, K. Merscher)

① **8 550655** (7/94)
Mendelssohn—Cello Works
Mendelssohn: Cello Sonata 1; Variations concertantes, Op. 17; Cello Sonata 2; Song without words, Op. 109. (M. Kliegel, K. Merscher)

① **8 550656** (12/93)
Brahms—Cello Sonatas
Brahms: Cello Sonata in D; Cello Sonata 1; Cello Sonata 2. (M. Kliegel, K. Merscher)

① **8 550657** (6/94)
Haydn—Keyboard Sonatas, Vol.1
Haydn: Keyboard Sonata 59; Keyboard Sonata 60; Keyboard Sonata 61; Keyboard Sonata 62. (J. Jandó)

① **8 550676** (9/93)
Beethoven—Piano Variations
Beethoven: Variations, Op. 35; Variations, WoO80; Variations, Op. 34; Variations, WoO70. (J. Jandó)

① **8 550679** (6/94)
Bach—Keyboard Works
Bach: 2-Part Inventions, BWV772-86; 3-Part Inventions, BWV787-801; Anna Magdalena Notenbuch (1725) (exc). (J. Sebestyén)

① **8 550681** (4/94)
Mendelssohn—Works for Piano & Orchestra
Mendelssohn: Piano Concerto 1; Piano Concerto 2; Capriccio brillant, Op. 22; Rondo brillant, Op. 29. (B. Frith, Košice St PO/R. Stankovsky)

① **8 550683** (2/95)
Ravel—Piano Works, Volume 1
Ravel: Parade; Pavane pour une infante défunte; Sérénade grotesque; A la manière de Chabrier; A la manière de Borodine; Menuet antique; Jeux d'eau; Menuet sur le nom de Haydn; Prélude; Sonatine; Miroirs. (F-J. Thiollier)

① **8 550684** (12/94)
Duets and Arias from Italian Operas
Donizetti: Elisir d'amore (exc); *Leoncavallo:* Pagliacci (exc); *Mascagni:* Cavalleria Rusticana (exc); *Ponchielli:* Gioconda (exc); *Verdi:* Forza del destino (exc); Rigoletto (exc). (A. di Mauro, G. Aragall, Tumagian, Bratislava RSO/A. Rahbari)

① **8 550687** (8/94)
Jenkins—All in a Garden Green
Jenkins: Pavans in 6 parts (exc); Fantasias in 5 parts (exc); Divisions on a Ground (exc); Fantasias in 4 parts (exc); All in a Garden Green Fantasia; Newarke Seidge Pavan and Galliard; Airs in 4 parts (exc); Fantasia-Suites in 2 parts (fantasia-air-corant) (exc); Fantasias in 3 parts (viols) (exc); In Nomines in 6 parts (exc). (Rose Consort)

① **8 550688** (7/95)
Spohr—Clarinet Works
Spohr: Clarinet Concerto 1; Clarinet Concerto 3; Potpourri, Op. 60. (E. Ottensamer, Košice St PO, Bratislava RSO/J. Wildner)

① **8 550689** (7/95)
Spohr—Clarinet Works
Spohr: Clarinet Concerto 2; Clarinet Concerto 4; Fantasy and Variations, Op. 81. (E. Ottensamer, Slovak RSO/J. Wildner)

① **8 550690** (12/94)
Paganini—Music for Violin and Guitar I
Paganini: Sonatas, Op. 3; Sonata concertata in A; Variations, Op. 14; Cantabile, Op. 17. (S. St John, S. Wynberg)

① **8 550692** (8/94)
Bach—Keyboard Works
Bach: Partitas, BWV825-30 (exc); Prelude and Fughetta, BWV902; Capriccio, BWV992. (W. Rübsam)

① **8 550696** (11/93)
Satie—Piano Works, Vol.1
Satie: Nocturnes; Première pensée Rose & Croix; Sonneries de la Rose & Croix; Rêverie de l'enfance de Pantagruel; Rêverie du Pauvre; Rêveries nocturnes; Prélude de la porte héroïque du ciel; Ogives; Sarabandes. (K. Koermendi)

① **8 550697** (7/94)
Satie—Piano Works, Volume 2
Satie: Musiques intimes; Caresse; Petits chorals; Danse de travers; Pièces froides; Nouvelles pièces froides; Préludes flasques; Nouvelles enfantines; Petite Musique; Pages mystiques; Prélude en tapisserie; Pantins dansent; Danses gothiques. (K. Körmendi)

① **8 550699** (6/95)
Satie—Piano Works, Volume 4
Satie: Piccadilly; Dreaming Fish; Piège de Méduse; Diva de l'Empire; Jack-in-the-box; Heures séculaires et instantanées; Peccadilles importunes; Morceaux en forme de poire; En habit de cheval; Petites pièces montées; Aperçus désagréables; Belle excentrique. (K. Körmendi, G. Eckhardt)

① **8 550704** (5/94)
Bach—Art of Fugue, Vol.2
Bach: Art of Fugue (exc); Passacaglia and Fugue, BWV582; Sei gegrüsset, BWV768. (W. Rübsam)

① **8 550709** (10/94)
Bach—Keyboard Works
Bach: French Suites, BWV812-17 (exc); Italian Concerto, BWV971; Chromatic Fantasia and Fugue, BWV903. (W. Rübsam)

① **8 550715** (10/94)
Schumann—Piano Works
Schumann: Piano Sonata 2; Nachtstücke; Arabeske; Klavierstücke, Op. 32; Toccata; Presto passionato. (B. Glemser)

① **8 550721** (1/94)
Haydn—Symphonies
Haydn: Symphony 26; Symphony 35; Symphony 49. (Northern CO/N. Ward)

① **8 550722** (11/94)
Haydn—Symphonies
Haydn: Symphony 6; Symphony 7; Symphony 8. (Northern CO/N. Ward)

① **8 550724** (6/95)
Haydn—Symphonies, Vol. 9
Haydn: Symphony 22; Symphony 29; Symphony 60. (Northern CO/N. Ward)

① **8 550729** (4/94)
Guitar Concertos
Castelnuovo-Tedesco: Guitar Concerto 1; *Rodrigo:* Concierto de Aranjuez; *Villa-Lobos:* Guitar Concerto. (N. Kraft, Northern CO/N. Ward)

① **8 550741** (12/94)
Romantic Music for Flute and Harp
Bizet: Carmen (exc); *Massenet:* Thaïs (exc); *Durand:* Waltz in E flat; *Bizet:* Arlésienne Suites (exc); *Debussy:* Petite Suite (exc); *Ravel:* Rapsodie espagnole (exc); *Durand:* Chaconne, Op. 62; *Gluck:* Orfeo ed Euridice (exc); *Mozart:* Andante, K315; *Chopin:* Rossini Variations; *Schuécker:* Mazurka, Op. 12; *Rimsky-Korsakov:* Sadko (exc); *Tchaikovsky:* Morceaux, Op. 51 (exc); *J. Strauss II:* Tritsch-Tratsch. (J. Bálint, N. Mercz)

① **8 550744** (10/94)
Wieniawski—Violin Showpieces
Wieniawski: Souvenir de Moscou, Op. 6; Capriccio-Valse, Op. 7; Variations, Op. 15; Polonaise, Op. 4; Russian Carnival; Gigue, Op. 27; Saltarello; Mazurkas, Op. 12 (exc); Mazurkas, Op. 19; Kujawiak in A minor; Légende, Op. 17; Scherzo-tarantelle, Op. 16. (M. Bisengaliev, J. Lenehan)

① **8 550745** (12/95)
Goldmark—Orchestral Works
Goldmark: Im Frühling; Rustic Wedding; In Italien. (Ireland National SO/S. Gunzenhauser)

① **8 550749** (9/94)
Bartók—Violin Sonatas; Contrasts
Bartók: Violin Sonata 1; Violin Sonata 2; Contrasts. (G. Pauk, K. Berkes, J. Jandó)

① **8 550750** (2/94)
Marais/Sainte-Colombe—Greatest Masterworks
Marais: La gamme (exc); Pièces de viole, II/2 (exc); Pièces de viole, III/II (exc); Pièces de viole, IV/II (exc); *Sainte-Colombe:* Concerts à deux violes esgales (exc); *Marais:* Pièces de viole, I/I (exc). (Spectre de la Rose)

① **8 550752** (10/94)
Saint-Saëns—Orchestral Works
Saint-Saëns: Caprice andalous; Introduction and Rondo capriccioso; Morceau de concert, Op. 62; Romance, Op. 48; Violin Concerto 3. (D-S. Kang, Katowice RSO/A. Wit)

① **8 550753** (3/95)
Ravel/Falla—Piano Concertos
Ravel: Piano Concerto; Left-Hand Concerto; *Falla:* Nights in the Gardens of Spain. (F-J. Thiollier, Polish Nat RSO/A. Wit)

① **8 550754** (1/95)
French Music for Piano and Orchestra
Fauré: Ballade, Op. 19; *Franck:* Symphonic Variations; *Indy:* Symphonie, Op. 25. (F-J. Thiollier, Ireland National SO/A. de Almeida)

① **8 550757** (5/95)
Haydn—Symphonies, Volume 10
Haydn: Symphony 30; Symphony 55; Symphony 63. (Northern CO/N. Ward)

① **8 550758** (4/95)
Glazunov/Dvořák—Violin Concertos
Glazunov: Violin Concerto; *Dvořák:* Violin Concerto; Romance, Op. 11. (I. Kaler, Polish Nat RSO/C. Kolchinsky)

① **8 550759** (12/94)
Paganini—Music for Violin & Guitar, Vol.2
Paganini: Sonatas, Op. 2; Cantabile e Valtz; Variazioni di bravura; Duetto amoroso; Gran Viola Sonata. (S. St John, S. Wynberg)

① **8 550990** (2/95)
Weber—Piano Works, Vol.3
Weber: Piano Sonata 3; Momento capriccioso, J56; Castor et Pollux Variations, J40; Variations, J53; Variations, J55. (A. Paley)

① **8 550998** (9/95)
Hildegard of Bingen—Heavenly Revelations
Hildegard of Bingen: O Euchari, in leta vita; O virga mediatrix; Ave generosa; Laus Trinitati; Kyrie eleison; O presul vere civitatis; O ignis spiritus; Ordo Virtutum (exc); O pastor animarum; O viridissima virga; O virga ac diadema. (Oxford Camerata/J. Summerly)

① **8 553001** (10/95)
Delius—Orchestral Works
Delius: Paris; Brigg Fair; Eventyr; Irmelin Prelude; Koanga (exc). (NZ SO/M. Fredman)

① **8 553005** (8/95)
Dvořák—Orchestral Works
Dvořák: Czech Suite, B93; Festival March; Heroic Song; Hussite. (Polish Nat RSO/A. Wit)

① **8 553006** (2/95)
Weber—Piano Works, Vol.4
Weber: Piano Sonata 4; Rondo brillante, J252; Polacca brillante, J268; Adieux; Joseph Variations, J141. (A. Paley)

① **8 553007** (1/95)
19th Century Guitar Favourites
Aguado: Menuett; Andante; Lessons (exc); Studies (exc); *Sor:* Minuets, Op. 11 (exc); Studies, Op. 6 (exc); Studies, Op. 31 (exc); Studies, Op. 35 (exc); Minuetto, Op. 22; *Tárrega:* Rosita; Mazurkas; Estudios (exc); Gran vals; Preludios (exc); Alborada; Recuerdos de la Alhambra; Maria. (N. Kraft)

① **8 553008** (7/95)
Ravel—Piano Works, Volume 2
Ravel: Valses nobles et sentimentales; Gaspard de la nuit; Tombeau de Couperin; Valse. (F-J. Thiollier)

① **8 553009** (2/95)
Chabrier—Piano Works, Volume 1
Chabrier: Bourrée fantasque; Pièces posthumes (exc); Petite valse; Habanera; Pièces pittoresques. (G. Rabol)

① **8 553010** (2/95)
Chabrier—Piano Works, Volume 2
Chabrier: Marche des Cipayes; Julia; Impromptu; Pièces posthumes (exc); Capriccio; Souvenirs de Brunehaut. (G. Rabol)

① **8 553016** (9/95)
Szymanowski—Piano Works, Vol. 1
Szymanowski: Mazurkas, Op. 50 (exc); Metopes; Etudes, op. 4; Piano Sonata 2. (M. Roscoe)

① **8 553025** (6/95)
Psalms of the French Reformation
Goudimel: Psalms; Psalm 104; Cantique de Siméon; Par le désert; *L'Estocart:* Psalms; *Sweelinck:* Donnez au Seigneur gloire. (C. Goudimel Ens/C. Morel)

① **8 553030** (2/95)
Opera Duets
Rossini: Guillaume Tell (exc); *Bizet:* Pêcheurs de Perles (exc); *Donizetti:* Lucia di Lammermoor (exc); *Verdi:* Vespri Siciliani (exc); Forza del destino (exc); Otello (exc). (J. Lotrič, I. Morozov, Slovak RSO/J. Wildner, Slovak Op Chor)

① **8 553033** (10/95)
Bach—Organ Works
Bach: Prelude and Fugue, BWV535; O Gott, du frommer Gott, BWV767; Trio, BWV584; Valet will ich dir geben, BWV736; Prelude and Fugue, BWV550; Canzona, BWV588; Wir glauben all' an einen Gott, BWV740; Allabreve, BWV589. (W. Rübsam)

① **8 553050** (3/95)
Scandinavian Wind Quintets
Fernström: Wind Quintet, Op. 59; *Kvandal:* Wind Quintet, Op. 34; Sacred Folktunes, Op. 23b; *Nielsen:* Wind Quintet. (Oslo Wind Qnt)

① **8 553078** (6/95)
Hindemith—Orchestral Works
Hindemith: Mathis der Maler; Nobilissima Visione; Symphonic Metamorphosis. (NZ SO/F-P. Decker)

① **8 553080** (2/95)
Chabrier—Piano Works, Volume 3
Chabrier: España; Valses romantiques; Joyeuse marche; Prélude pastorale; Cortège burlesque; Souvenirs de Munich; Air de Ballet; Suite de valses. (G. Rabol, S. Dugas)

① **8 553085** (7/95)
J. C. Bach—Sinfonias, Vol. 3
J. C. Bach: Symphonies, Op. 9; Sinfonia Concertante in A; Sinfonia Concertante, T284/6. (Budapest Camerata/H. Gmür)

① **8 553087** (10/95)
Dufay—Missa L'homme armé
Dufay: Missa L'homme armé; Supremum est mortalibus; *Anon:* L'homme armé; Pentecost (exc); Gregorian Chants for the Church's Year (exc). (Oxford Camerata/J. Summerly)

① **8 553090** (11/95)
Beethoven—Chamber Works
Beethoven: Quintet, Hess19; Septet, Op. 20; Sextet, Op. 81b. (O. Rácz, J. Balogh, J. Vajda, J. Kevеházi, János Kevеházi, S. Berki, I. Hegyi, P. Popa, G. Máthé, Peter Szabó, I. Tóth)

① **8 553103** (4/95)
Mozart—String Quintets, Volume 1
Mozart: String Quintet, K174; String Quintet, K515; String Quintet, K174 (exc). (Eder Qt, J. Fehérvári)

① **8 553107** (10/95)
Britten—Orchestral Works
Britten: Sinfonia da Requiem; Sea Interludes, Op. 33a; Passacaglia, Op. 33b; American Ov. (NZ SO/M. Fredman)

① **8 553124** (9/95)
Massenet—Herôdiade Orchestral Suites Nos 1-3
Massenet: Hérodiade (exc); Suite 1; Scènes hongroises; Scènes dramatiques. (NZ SO/J-Y. Ossonce)

① **8 553125** (9/95)
Massenet—Herôdiade Orchestral Suites Nos 4-7
Massenet: Scènes pittoresques; Scènes napolitaines; Scènes de féerie; Scènes alsaciennes. (NZ SO/J-Y. Ossonce)

① **8 553127** (6/95)
Haydn—Keyboard Sonatas, Volume 4
Haydn: Keyboard Sonata 36; Keyboard Sonata 37; Keyboard Sonata 38; Keyboard Sonata 39; Keyboard Sonata 40; Keyboard Sonata 41. (J. Jandó)

① **8 553128** (7/95)
Haydn—Keyboard Sonatas, Volume 5
Haydn: Keyboard Sonata 48; Keyboard Sonata 49; Keyboard Sonata 50; Keyboard Sonata 51; Keyboard Sonata 52. (J. Jandó)

① **8 553129** (2/95)
Purcell—Choral and Organ Music
Purcell: Organ Voluntaries, Z717-20 (exc); Jehova, quam multi sunt, Z135; Remember not, Lord, our offences, Z50; I will sing unto the Lord, Z22; O God, the King of Glory, Z34; O God, thou art my God, Z35; O God, thou hast cast us out, Z36; Lord, how long wilt thou be angry?, Z25; Hear my prayer, O Lord, Z15; Blow up the trumpet in Sion, Z10; Funeral Sentences; Queen's Epicedium, Z383. (C-A. Lane, A. Carwood, M. McCarthy, L. Cummings, Oxford Camerata/J. Summerly)

① **8 553131** (6/95)
Chominciamento di gioia
Anon: Istanpittas (exc); Trotto; Saltarelli (exc). (Unicorn Ens)

① **8 553136** (6/95)
Prokofiev—Chamber Works
Prokofiev: String Quartet 1; String Quartet 2; Cello Sonata, Op. 119. (Aurora Qt, M. Grebanier, J. Guggenheim)

① **8 553173** (6/95)
Charpentier—Choral Works
M-A. Charpentier: Confitebor tibi, H220; Laudate pueri, H203; Litanies, H89; Nisi Dominus, H160; Transfige dulcissime Jesu, H251; Messe des morts, H7. (Concert Spirituel Voc Ens/H. Niquet)

① **8 553176** (10/95)
Poulenc—Choral Works
Poulenc: Stabat Mater; Gloria; Litanies à la Vierge noire. (D. Borst, E. Lebrun, Ile de France Regional Ch, Orch de la Cité/M. Piquemal)

① **8 553178** (6/95)
Krommer—Clarinet Concertos
Krommer: Clarinet Concerto, Op. 36; 2-Clarinet Concerto, Op. 35; 2-Clarinet Concerto, Op. 91. (K. Tsutsui, T. Takashima, N. Esterházy Sinfonia, M. Berkes (cl/dir))

① **8 553196** (11/95)
Duruflé—Sacred Choral and Organ Works, Volume 1
Duruflé: Requiem; Motets, Op. 10; Scherzo, Op. 2; Notre père, Op. 14; Prélude et Fugue sur le nom d'Alain, Op. 7. (B. Uria-Monzon, D. Henry, E. LeBrun, M. Piquemal Voc Ens, Orch de la Cité/M. Piquemal)

① **8 553197** (11/95)
Duruflé—Sacred Choral and Organ Works, Volume 2
Duruflé: Mass, Op. 11; Prélude, Adagio et Choral varié, Op. 4; Suite, Op. 5. (D. Henry, E. LeBrun, M. Piquemal Voc Ens, Orch de la Cité/M. Piquemal)

① **8 553207** (11/95)
Respighi—Orchestral Works
Respighi: Piano Concerto in A minor; Toccata; Fantasia slava. (K. Scherbakov, Slovak RSO/H. Griffiths)

① **8 553214** (10/95)
Early French Organ Music, Volume 1
Marchand: Deuxième livre d'orgue; *Compère:* Ave Maria gratia plena; Paranymphus salutat virginem; *Japart:* Fortuna d'un gran tempo; *G. Corrette:* Messe du huitième ton; *Grigny:* Premier livre d'orgue (exc); *Fugue.* (J. Payne)

① **8 553215** (10/95)
Early French Organ Music, Volume 2
Titelouze: Hymnes de l'Eglise (exc); Magnificat (exc); *Jullien:* Premier livre d'orgue (exc); *Lebègue:* Offertoire en C; Vierge pucelle; Trio; Dessus de Cromhorne; Tierce en taille; *Roberday:* Fugue and Caprice 3; *Du Mont:* Allemande; *L. Couperin:* Fantaisies (exc); *Anon:* Magnificat; Ave Maris Stella; *Attaingnant:* Parce Domine; Sanctus and Benedictus; Magnificat; *Raison:* Premier livre d'orgue; *Gigault:* Kyrie; Fugue grave; *Anglebert:* Organ works (exc). (J. Payne)

① **8 553353** (11/95)
Boulez—Piano Sonatas
Boulez: Piano Sonata 1; Piano Sonata 2; Piano Sonata 3. (I. Biret)

New Albion

① **NA008CD** (9/90)
Somei Satoh: Various Works
S. Satoh: Heavenly spheres (1979); Birds in warped time II (1980); Incarnation II (1977); Gate into the stars (1962); Litania (1973). (L. Messier, F. Almond, M. Pugliese, M. Leng Tan)

① **NA015CD** (11/90)
Lou Harrison: Various Works
L. Harrison: La Koro Sutro; Varied Trio; Suite for Violin and American Gamelan. (Berkeley Univ Chor, Berkeley Univ Chbr Chor, K. Gottlieb, A. Sauerbeck, American Gamelan/P. Brett, D. Abel, W. Winant, J. Steinberg/J. Bergamo)

① **NA035CD** (9/91)
Singing Through
Cage: Flower; Mirakus; Eight Whiskus; Wonderful Widow of eighteen springs; Nowth upon Nacht; Sonnekus; Forever and Sunsmell; Solo for Voice 49; Solo for Voice 52; Solo for Voice 67; Music for (exc). (J. La Barbara, W. Winant, L. Stein, S. Evans)

① **NA038CD** (4/93)
Music of Cyprus 1413-1422
Anon: Cyprus codex (exc); Bonne é belle; Danse d'Abroz. (PAN Ens)

① **NA048CD** (5/93)
Homage to Johannes Ciconia
Ciconia: Amor per ti sempre; Caçando un giorno; O Padua; Regina gloriosa; Aler m'en veus; Io crido amor; O rosa bella; Poy che morir mi convien; Ben che da vui donna; Ray au soleyl; Petrum Marcello venetum; Che nel servir anticho; Per quella strada; Una panthera; Gli atti col dançar frances; Sus un' fontayne; O Petre Christi discipule; Doctorum principem; O virum omnimoda. (PAN Ens)

① **NA055CD** (2/94)
Harrison—The Perilous Chapel
L. Harrison: Harp Suite; Serenade (1978); Perilous Chapel; Fugue (1941); Song of Quetzalcoatl; May Rain. (J. Duykers, D. Tanenbaum, J. Steinberg, W. Winant, San Francisco Contemp Music Plyrs/S. Mosko, Perc Ens)

① **NA058CD** (1/94)
Guastavino—Canciones Argentinas
Guastavino: Canciones argentinas; Canciones coloniales; Piececitos; Cita; Se equivicó la paloma; Canciones; Rosa y el sauce; Pueblito, mi pueblo. (U. Espaillat, P. Zinger)

① **NA062CD** (6/94)
Revueltas—The String Quartets
Revueltas: String Quartet 1; String Quartet 2; String Quartet 3; String Quartet 4. (Latin American Qt)

① **NA068CD** (10/94)
Machaut—Remede de Fortune
Machaut: Qui n'aroit autre deport; Tels rit au main; Joie, plaisence; En amer a douce vie; Dame, de qui toute; Dame, a vous sans retolir; Dame, mon cuer en vous remaint; Rose, liz; Trop plus est bele (exc); Liement me

① **NI5327** (1/93)
French Wind Music
Ibert: Pièces brèves; *Françaix:* Wind Quintet 1; *Auric:* Wind Trio; *Honegger:* Danse de la Chèvre; *Milhaud:* Cheminée du roi René. (Pro Arte Wind Quintet)

① **NI5328** (10/92)
Taverner to Tavener
Taverner: Kyrie a 4; *Henry VIII:* Pastyme with good companye; *Parsons:* Ave Maria; *Dering:* Cantica sacra (1618) (exc); *Gibbons:* Hosanna to the Son of David; *Blow:* Salvator mundi; *Purcell:* Jehova, quam multi sunt, Z135; *Greene:* Lord let me know mine end; *Crotch:* How dear are thy counsels; *Walton:* Litany; *Ley:* Prayer of King Henry VI; *W.H. Harris:* Love of love; *Harper:* Universe; *Tavener:* Hymn to the Holy Spirit. (Oxford Christ Church Cath Ch/S. Darlington)

① **NI5330** (12/92)
Oboe Concertos
Françaix: Horloge de Flore; *Martinů:* Oboe Concerto; *R. Strauss:* Oboe Concerto. (J. Anderson, Philh, S. Wright)

① **NI5331** (11/92)
Haydn—Symphonies Nos 14-17
Haydn: Symphony 14; Symphony 15; Symphony 16; Symphony 17. (Austro-Hungarian Haydn Orch/A. Fischer)

① **NI5341** (1/94)
Haydn—Orchestral Works
Haydn: Symphony 89; Symphony 91; Vera costanza (exc). (Austro-Hungarian Haydn Orch/A. Fischer)

① **NI5353** (9/94)
Beethoven—String Quartets, Op 18 Nos 4,5 and 6
Beethoven: String Quartet 4; String Quartet 5; String Quartet 6. (Brandis Qt)

① **NI5357** (7/93)
Hoddinott—Orchestral Works
Hoddinott: Passaggio, Op.94; Heaventree of Stars, Op.102; Doubles, Op.106; Star Children, Op.135. (H. Kun, D. Cowley, R. Armstrong, BBC Welsh SO/T. Otaka)

① **NI5358** (9/93)
The Virtuoso Violin
Vecsey: Vent; *Moszkowski:* Pieces, Op.45 (exc); *Sarasate:* Introduction and Tarantella, Op.43; *Chopin:* Nocturnes (exc); *Herbert:* A la valse; *Albéniz:* España, Op.165 (exc); *Elgar:* Capricieuse; *Dinicu:* Hora staccato; *Paganini:* Streghe; *Hubay:* Blumenleben, Op.30 (exc); *Brahms:* Hungarian Dances (exc); *Kroll:* Banjo and Fiddle; *Beethoven:* Ruinen von Athen (exc); *Bazzini:* Ronde des Lutins. (L. Daeshik Kang, M. Rahkonen)

① **NI5360** (10/93)
Taverner—Music for Our Lady and Divine Office
Taverner: Ex eius tumba; Audivi vocem; Kyrie a 4; Alleluia, veni electa mea; Magnificat a 5; Ave Dei; Dum transisset sabbatum I; Dum transisset sabbatum II. (Oxford Christ Church Cath Ch/S. Darlington)

① **NI5362/3** (7/93)
Bartók—Orchestral Works
Bartók: Wooden Prince Suite; Portraits, Sz37; Music for Strings, Percussion and Celesta; Divertimento. (G. Hetzel, Hungarian St SO/A. Fischer)

① **NI5364** (3/94)
Walton—Choral Works
Walton: Litany; Missa Brevis; Chichester Service; Set me as a seal; Antiphon; Jubilate; Make we joy; All this time; What cheer; Where does the uttered; Twelve; King Herod. (Oxford Christ Church Cath Ch/S. Darlington)

① **NI5366** (8/93)
20th Century British Orchestral Works
Finzi: Eclogue; *Bridge:* Cherry ripe; Entr'actes; Lament; Sally in our Alley; Sir Roger de Coverley; There is a willow; Irish melody; *Parry:* English Suite. (Martin Jones, English Stg Orch/W. Boughton)

① **NI5367** (6/93)
Mathias—Organ Works
Mathias: Fanfare; Processional; Invocations, Op. 35; Fantasy, Op. 78; Berceuse, Op. 95/3; Jubilate, Op. 67/2; Antiphonies, Op. 88/2; Fenestra; Recessional, Op. 96/4; Chorale. (John Scott)

① **NI5369** (12/93)
Hoddinott—Piano Sonatas
Hoddinott: Piano Sonata 1; Piano Sonata 2; Piano Sonata 3; Piano Sonata 4; Piano Sonata 5. (Martin Jones)

① **NI5370** (5/95)
Hoddinott—Piano Sonatas
Hoddinott: Piano Sonata 6; Piano Sonata 7; Piano Sonata 8; Piano Sonata 9; Piano Sonata 10. (Martin Jones)

① **NI5377** (2/94)
Bach—Organ Works, Vol.4
Bach: Toccatas BWV910-16 (exc); Fugue, BWV951; Fugue, BWV575; Prelude and Fugue, BWV553; Prelude and Fugue, BWV554; Prelude and Fugue, BWV555; Prelude and Fugue, BWV556; Prelude and Fugue, BWV557; Prelude and Fugue, BWV558; Prelude and Fugue, BWV559; Prelude and Fugue, BWV560; Fantasia con imitazione, BWV563; Fugue, BWV950; Toccatas BWV910-16 (exc). (K. Bowyer)

① **NI5390** (6/95)
Blue Guitar
Tippett: Blue guitar; *Britten:* Nocturnal; *R. R. Bennett:* Impromptus; *Walton:* Bagatelles; *L. Berkeley:* Sonatina, Op. 52/1. (C. Ogden)

① **NI5392** (8/93)
J & M Haydn—Orchestral Works
M. Haydn: Flute Concerto, MH81; Flute Concerto, MH105; Symphony in F (1770); *Haydn:* Symphony 22. (I-Z. Nagy, Austro-Hungarian Haydn Orch/A. Fischer)

① **NI5405/6** (9/94)
Szymanowski—Piano Music, Volume 1
Szymanowski: Preludes, Op. 1; Variations, Op. 3; Variations, Op. 10; Etudes, Op. 4; Piano Sonata 1; Piano Sonata 2; Fantasy; Prelude and Fugue in C sharp minor. (Martin Jones)

① **NI5408** (1/95)
Langlais—Works for Organ
Langlais: Symphony 1; Symphony 2; Suite française (exc); Suite brève; Poem of Happiness. (K. Bowyer)

① **NI5410** (3/95)
Hindemith/Schulhoff/Weill—String Quartets
Hindemith: String Quartet, Op. 22; *Schulhoff:* String Quartet 1; *Weill:* String Quartet. (Brandis Qt)

① **NI5411** (1/95)
Hindemith/Schoenberg/Pepping—Organ Works
Hindemith: Organ Sonatas; *Schoenberg:* Variations, Op. 40; Organ Fragments; *Pepping:* Fugues (1943). (K. Bowyer)

① **NI5419/20** (3/95)
Haydn—'Paris' Symphonies
Haydn: Symphony 82; Symphony 83; Symphony 84; Symphony 85; Symphony 86; Symphony 87. (Austro-Hungarian Haydn Orch/A. Fischer)

① **NI5422** (7/95)
Brahms/Liszt/Schumann—Piano Works
Brahms: Piano Sonata 3; *Liszt:* Années de pèlerinage 2 (exc); *Schumann:* Toccata. (M. Anderson)

① **NI5423** (7/95)
Bach—Organ Works, Volume 6
Bach: Toccata, Adagio and Fugue, BWV564; Trio Sonatas, BWV525-530 (exc); Valet will ich dir geben, BWV735; Valet will ich dir geben, BWV736; Prelude and Fugue, BWV533; Prelude and Fugue, BWV535; Trio, BWV584; Toccata and Fugue in E; Wenn wir in höchsten Nöten sein, BWV Anh78. (K. Bowyer)

① **NI7015** (7/94)
Orchestral Favourites, Volume IV - Elgar
Elgar: Pomp and Circumstance Marches (exc); Cockaigne; Elegy; Introduction and Allegro; Sospiri; Enigma Variations. (English SO/W. Boughton)

① **NI7016** (2/95)
Classical Trumpet Concertos
Haydn: Trumpet Concerto; *Neruda:* Trumpet Concerto; *Hummel:* Trumpet Concerto; *F. Weber:* Trumpet Variations in F; *C.F.C. Fasch:* Trumpet Concerto in E. (J. Wallace, J. Anderson, P. Thomas, Philh/C. Warren-Green/S. Wright)

① **NI7705** (10/89)
Schumann/Franck—Piano Works
Franck: Prélude, Choral et Fugue; *Schumann:* Symphonic Studies; Kreisleriana. (S. Cherkassky)

① **NI7709** (11/95)
Beethoven—Piano Sonatas
Beethoven: Piano Sonata 30; Piano Sonata 31; Piano Sonata 32. (B. Roberts)

① **NI7801** (10/89)
Great Singers, Vol.1
Bellini: Norma (exc); Puritani (exc); Puritani (exc); Sonnambula (exc); *Bizet:* Carmen (exc); *Donizetti:* Lucrezia Borgia (exc); *Leoncavallo:* Pagliacci (exc); *Mascagni:* Amico Fritz (exc); *Mozart:* Don Giovanni (exc); Zauberflöte (exc); *Puccini:* Bohème (exc); Turandot (exc); *Rossini:* Barbiere di Siviglia (exc); *Refice:* Ombra di Nube; *Saint-Saëns:* Samson et Dalila (exc); *Verdi:* Ballo in maschera (exc). (M. Favero, T. Schipa, La Scala Orch/L. Antonicelli, A. Galli-Curci, orch/G. Polacco, G. Muzio/L.

Refice, R. Ponselle, NY Met Op Chor, NY Met Op Orch/G. Setti, L. Tetrazzini, E. Turner/S. Robinson, E. Schumann-Heink, C. Supervia/G. Cloëz, M. Anderson/L. Collingwood, E. Caruso, B. Gigli/E. Goossens, G. Lauri-Volpi, J. McCormack/W.B. Rogers, R. Tauber, Vienna St Op Orch/K. Alwin, R. Stracciari, L. Tibbett/R. Bourdon)

① **NI7802** (10/89)
Divas 1906-1935
Beethoven: Fidelio (exc); *Boito:* Mefistofele (exc); *Borodin:* Prince Igor (exc); *Donaudy:* O del mio amato ben; *Gounod:* Roméo et Juliette (exc); *Massenet:* Don César de Bazan (exc); Manon (exc); *Mozart:* Zauberflöte (exc); *Puccini:* Bohème (exc); Madama Butterfly (exc); *Rimsky-Korsakov:* Sadko (exc); *A. Thomas:* Mignon (exc); *Verdi:* Aida (exc); Ballo in maschera (exc); Rigoletto (exc); Trovatore (exc); *Yradier:* Calasera. (L. Tetrazzini, N. Melba, A. Patti, F. Hempel, A. Galli-Curci, R. Ponselle, Lotte Lehmann, E. Turner, N. Koshetz, E. Norena, M. Németh, C. Muzio, orch, A. Barili, H. Romani/M. Gurlitt/T. Beecham/L. Molajoli/W.B. Rogers)

① **NI7803** (10/89)
Enrico Caruso—Opera Recital
Donizetti: Dom Sébastien (exc); Duca d'Alba (exc); Elisir d'amore (exc); *Goldmark:* Königin von Saba (exc); *Gomes:* Schiavo (exc); *Halévy:* Juive (exc); *Leoncavallo:* Pagliacci (exc); *Massenet:* Manon (exc); Manon (exc); *Meyerbeer:* Africaine (exc); *Puccini:* Manon Lescaut (exc); Tosca (exc); *Verdi:* Aida (exc); Ballo in maschera (exc); Ballo in maschera (exc); Forza del destino (exc); Rigoletto (exc); Rigoletto (exc); Trovatore (exc). (E. Caruso, orch, anon, NY Met Op Chor/J. Pasternack)

① **NI7804** (10/89)
Giovanni Martinelli—Opera Recital
Giordano: Andrea Chénier (exc); Andrea Chénier (exc); Fedora (exc); *Leoncavallo:* Pagliacci (exc); Pagliacci (exc); *Mascagni:* Cavalleria Rusticana (exc); Cavalleria Rusticana (exc); *Rossini:* Guillaume Tell (exc); *Tchaikovsky:* Eugene Onegin (exc); *Verdi:* Aida (exc); Ernani (exc); Forza del destino (exc); Forza del destino (exc); Traviata (exc); Trovatore (exc). (G. Martinelli, F. Lapitino, orch/W.B. Rogers/J. Pasternack/R. Bourdon, G. De Luca, R. Ponselle, E. Pinza, NY Met Op Chor, NY Met Op Orch/G. Setti/N. Shilkret, G. Anthony, chor)

① **NI7805** (10/89)
Rosa Ponselle—Opera & Song Recital
Arensky: On wings of dream; *Bellini:* Norma (exc); Norma (exc); *Di Capua:* Maria, mari; *De Curtis:* Carmela; *Bond:* Perfect day; *Ponchielli:* Gioconda (exc); *Rimsky-Korsakov:* Songs, Op. 2 (exc); *Spontini:* Vestale (exc); *Verdi:* Aida (exc); Aida (exc); Ernani (exc); Traviata (exc); Otello (exc). (R. Ponselle, orch/R. Bourdon, G. Martinelli, E. Pinza, NY Met Op Chor, NY Met Op Orch/G. Setti, M. Telva, M. Elman, R. Romani/J. Pasternack)

① **NI7806** (5/90)
Galli-Curci—Opera & Song Recital
Gounod: Roméo et Juliette (exc); *Auber:* Manon Lescaut (exc); *Rossini:* Barbiere di Siviglia (exc); *Meyerbeer:* Dinorah (exc); *Bellini:* Puritani (exc); *Verdi:* Traviata (exc); Traviata (exc); Traviata (exc); *A. Thomas:* Mignon (exc); *Donizetti:* Don Pasquale (exc); *Bellini:* Sonnambula (exc); Sonnambula (exc); dell' Acqua: Villanelle; *Donizetti:* Linda di Chamounix (exc); *Verdi:* Rigoletto (exc); *Donizetti:* Lucia di Lammermoor (exc); Lucia di Lammermoor (exc); *Bishop:* Pretty Mocking Bird. (A. Galli-Curci, orch/R. Bourdon/R. Bourdon, T. Schipa, G. De Luca)

① **NI7807** (5/90)
Beniamino Gigli—Vol. 1: 1918-24
Ponchielli: Gioconda (exc); *Boito:* Mefistofele (exc); *Puccini:* Tosca (exc); Tosca (exc); *Donizetti:* Favorita (exc); *Gounod:* Faust (exc); *Mascagni:* Iris (exc); *Lalo:* Roi d'Ys (exc); *Leoncavallo:* Pagliacci (exc); *Giordano:* Andrea Chénier (exc); *Meyerbeer:* Africaine (exc); *Catalani:* Loreley (exc); *Flotow:* Martha (exc); *Cannio:* O surdato 'nnammurato; *De Curtis:* Tu sola; *Saint-Saëns:* Carnaval des animaux (exc); *Drigo:* Arlekinda (exc); *Buzzi-Peccia:* Povero Pulcinella; *Denza:* Funiculì-Funiculà. (B. Gigli, orch/C. Sabajno/J. Pasternack/R. Bourdon)

① **NI7808** (10/90)
Luisa Tetrazzini—Opera & Song Recital
Donizetti: Lucia di Lammermoor (exc); *Rossini:* Barbiere di Siviglia (exc); *Bellini:* Sonnambula (exc); *Donizetti:* Lucia di Lammermoor (exc); *Eckert:* Eco; *A. Thomas:* Mignon (exc); *Verdi:* Rigoletto (exc); Ballo in maschera (exc); *Delibes:* Lakmé (exc); *Proch:* Air and Variations; *Verdi:* Trovatore (exc); *Brahms:* Lieder, Op. 84 (exc); Variazioni: O che assorta; *Verdi:* Traviata (exc); *Veracini:* Rosalinda (exc); *Pergolesi:* Tre giorni son che Nina; *Verdi:* Vespri siciliani (exc); Rigoletto (exc). (L. Tetrazzini, J. Jacoby, E. Caruso, P. Amato, orch)

Ⓓ **NI7809** (12/90)
Caruso in Song
Crescenzo: Tarantella sincera; *Geehl:* For you alone; *Hardelot:* Because; *Rossini:* Soirées musicales (exc); *Szulc:* Hantise d'amour; *Ciociano:* Cielo turchino; *Pennino:* Pecchè; *Cottrau:* Santa Lucia; *Di Capua:* O sole mio; *Alvarez:* Partida; *Niedermeyer:* Pietà, Signore; *Billi:* Campane a sera; *Alvarez:* A Granada; *Cohan:* Over there; *Fucito:* Sultano a Tte; *Califona:* Vieni sul mar; *Pergolesi:* Tre giorni son che Nina; *Handel:* Serse (exc); *Rossini:* Petite messe solennelle (exc). (E. Caruso, orch/W.B. Rogers/J. Pasternack)

Ⓓ **NI7810** (11/90)
Titta Ruffo—Opera Recital
A. Thomas: Hamlet (exc); *Verdi:* Traviata (exc); *Ponchielli:* Gioconda (exc); Gioconda (exc); *Leoncavallo:* Pagliacci (exc); Zazà (exc); *Ferradini:* Non penso a lei; *Donizetti:* Favorita (exc); *Massenet:* Thaïs (exc); *Verdi:* Otello (exc); Otello (exc); Otello (exc); Nabucco (exc); *Meyerbeer:* Africaine (exc); *Verdi:* Ballo in maschera (exc); *Puccini:* Tosca (exc); *Rossini:* Barbiere di Siviglia (exc); *Verdi:* Rigoletto (exc); Falstaff (exc); *Ponchielli:* Gioconda (exc). (T. Ruffo, orch/C. Sabajno/W.B. Rogers/J. Pasternack, E. Caruso, B. Gigli/R. Bourdon)

Ⓓ **NI7811** (2/91)
Ernestine Schumann-Heink—Opera & Song Recital
Donizetti: Lucrezia Borgia (exc); *Arditi:* Leggero invisibile; *Becker:* Frühlingszeit; *Meyerbeer:* Prophète (exc); Prophète (exc); *Wagner:* Rheingold (exc); *Millöcker:* I und mei Bua; *Wagner:* Rienzi (exc); *Handel:* Rinaldo (exc); *Schubert:* Erlkönig, D328; *Wagner:* Wesendonk Lieder (exc); *H. Reimann:* Spinnerliedchen; *Molloy:* Kerry Dance; *Brahms:* Lieder, Op. 49 (exc); *C. Böhm:* Lieder, Op. 326 (exc); *Traditional:* Du, du liegst mir im Herzen; *Lieurance:* By the Waters of Minnetonka; *Wagner:* Rheingold (exc); Götterdämmerung (exc). (E. Schumann-Heink, orch, H. Witherspoon, J. Hofmann/R. Bourdon)

Ⓓ **NI7814** (4/91)
Claudia Muzio—Opera Arias & Songs
Mascagni: Cavalleria rusticana (exc); *Puccini:* Bohème (exc); Bohème (exc); Tosca (exc); *Verdi:* Forza del destino (exc); Otello (exc); Trovatore (exc); Traviata (exc); *Giordano:* Andrea Chénier (exc); *Boito:* Mefistofele (exc); *Cilea:* Adriana Lecouvreur (exc); Arlesiana (exc); *Bellini:* Sonnambula (exc); *Buzzi-Peccia:* Colombetta; *Parisotti:* Se tu m'ami; *Delibes:* Filles de Cadiz; Bonjour, Suzon; *Refice:* Ombra di nube; *Reger:* Schlichte Weisen, Op.76 (exc). (C. Muzio, orch/L. Molajoli/L. Refice, F. Merli)

Ⓓ **NI7830** (12/92)
Richard Tauber in Opera
R. Strauss: Rosenkavalier (exc); *Wagner:* Walküre (exc); *Kienzl:* Evangelimann (exc); *Smetana:* Bartered Bride (exc); *Puccini:* Tosca (exc); Tosca (exc); *Verdi:* Trovatore (exc); *Mozart:* Don Giovanni (exc); Zauberflöte (exc); *Tchaikovsky:* Eugene Onegin (exc); *Bizet:* Carmen (exc); *Puccini:* Bohème (exc); *Korngold:* Tote Stadt (exc); *Puccini:* Madama Butterfly (exc); Turandot (exc); *Wagner:* Meistersinger (exc); *Lortzing:* Undine (exc); *Offenbach:* Contes d'Hoffmann (exc). (R. Tauber, E. Bettendorf, Lotte Lehmann, Berlin St Op Chor, Berlin Schauspielhaus Orch, Berlin Staatskapelle, Berlin St Op Orch, orch/K. Besl/G. Szell/H. Weigert/E. Hauke, chor)

Ⓓ **NI7831** (10/92)
Mattia Battistini (1856-1928)
Tchaikovsky: Eugene Onegin (exc); *Verdi:* Ballo in maschera (exc); Ernani (exc); *Flotow:* Martha (exc); *Donizetti:* Favorita (exc); Dom Sébastien (exc); *Hérold:* Zampa (exc); *Berlioz:* Damnation de Faust (exc); *Massenet:* Werther (exc); *A. Thomas:* Hamlet (exc); *Nouguès:* Quo vadis? (exc); *Verdi:* Traviata (exc); *Donizetti:* Linda di Chamounix (exc); *Verdi:* Macbeth (exc); *Donizetti:* Favorita (exc); *Verdi:* Don Carlo (exc). (M. Battistini, E. Corsi, L. Colazza, A. Sillich, M. Mokrzycka, La Scala Chor, anon, C. Sabajno, orch/C. Sabajno)

Ⓓ **NI7832** (8/92)
Maria Ivogün (1891-1987)
Bishop: Lo, here the gentle lark; *Handel:* Allegro, il penseroso ed il moderato (exc); *Donizetti:* Don Pasquale (exc); Lucia di Lammermoor (exc); *Rossini:* Barbiere di Siviglia (exc); *Verdi:* Traviata (exc); *Chopin:* Nocturnes (exc); *Meyerbeer:* Huguenots (exc); *Nicolai:* Lustigen Weiber von Windsor (exc); *Schubert:* Ständchen, D889; Winterreise (exc); *J. Strauss II:* Frühlingsstimmen, Op. 410; G'schichten aus dem Wienerwald, Op. 325; *Kreisler:* Liebesfreud; *Traditional:* O du liebs ängeli; Z' Lauterbach han; 's Schätzli; Maria auf dem Berge; *J. Strauss II:* Blauen Donau, Op. 314; Fledermaus (exc). (M. Ivogün, M. Raucheisen, orch, Berlin St Op Orch/L. Blech)

Ⓓ **NI7833** (12/92)
Schöne & Tauber in Operetta
Lehár: Paganini (exc); *Suppé:* Schöne Galathee (exc); *Berté:* Dreimäderlhaus (exc); *J. Strauss II:* Fledermaus (exc); Lustige Krieg (exc); Indigo und die Vierzig Räuber (exc); Cagliostro in Wien (exc); *Kálmán:* Gräfin Mariza (exc); *Millöcker:* Arme Jonathan (exc); *Zeller:* Vogelhändler (exc); Obersteiger (exc); *Nessler:* Trompeter von Säckingen (exc); *Lehár:* Zigeunerliebe (exc); Land des Lächelns (exc); Lustige Witwe (exc); *Kálmán:* Zirkusprinzessin (exc); *J. Strauss II:* G'schichten aus dem Wienerwald, Op. 325. (L. Schöne, R. Tauber, Berlin St Op Orch, Vienna Th an der Wien Orch, Berlin Schauspielhaus Orch, Berlin Künstlertheater Orch, Berlin Staatskapelle, Odeon Künstlerorchester, orch/H. Weigert/A. Paulik/E. Hauke/F. Lehár/E. Korngold)

Ⓓ **NI7836/7** (3/93)
Conchita Supervia (1895-1936)
Rossini: Italiana in Algeri (exc); Barbiere di Siviglia (exc); Barbiere di Siviglia (exc); Cenerentola (exc); *Gounod:* Faust (exc); *A. Thomas:* Mignon (exc); *Saint-Saëns:* Samson et Dalila (exc); *Delibes:* Bonjour, Suzon; Églogue; *Falla:* Canciones populares españolas; *Baldomir:* Meus Amores; *Serrano:* Alegría del Batallón (exc); Mal de Amores (exc); *Yradier:* Paloma; *Valverde:* Clavelitos; *Bizet:* Carmen (exc). (C. Supervia, A. Vavon, A. Bernadet, G. Micheletti, C. Scattola, G. Manuritta, CO, orch/A. Albergoni/G. Cloëz/A. Capdevila/M. Romero, F. Marshall/P. Godes)

Ⓓ **NI7840/1** (7/93)
The Era of Adelina Patti
Verdi: Falstaff (exc); Don Carlos (exc); *Tosti:* Dopo; *Rameau:* Pièces de clavecin (exc); *Gluck:* Rencontre imprévue (exc); *Yradier:* Calasera; *Meyerbeer:* Prophète (exc); *Bizet:* Carmen (exc); *Massenet:* Hérodiade (exc); Manon (exc); Hérodiade (exc); *A. Thomas:* Hamlet (exc); *Adam:* Chalet (exc); *Wagner:* Lohengrin (exc); Meistersinger (exc); *F. Erkel:* Hunyadi László (exc); *Donizetti:* Favorita (exc); *Mozart:* Don Giovanni (exc); Don Giovanni (exc); Nozze di Figaro (exc); *Flotow:* Martha (exc); *Bellini:* Puritani (exc); *Donizetti:* Lucrezia Borgia (exc); *Bellini:* Sonnambula (exc); *Rossini:* Barbiere di Siviglia (exc); *Mozart:* Don Giovanni (exc); *Verdi:* Ernani (exc); *Donizetti:* Lucia di Lammermoor (exc); *Verdi:* Otello (exc); *Mozart:* Nozze di Figaro (exc); *Gounod:* Soir; *R. Strauss:* Lieder, Op.17 (exc); *Gomes:* Guarany (exc); *Hatton:* Simon the cellarer; *Hook:* 'Twas within a mile; *Bishop:* Home, sweet home. (V. Maurel, P. Plançon, E. Eames, L. Fugère, A. Patti, F. Viñas, E. Calvé, M. Renaud, F. de Lucia, F. Tamagno, N. Melba, F. Litvinne, W. Hesch, L. Nordica, M. Ancona, E. de Reszke, M. Sembrich, F. Marconi, M. Battistini, Lilli Lehmann, C. Santley, anon, L. Ronald, J. Huguet, A. Pini-Corsi, orch, A. Barili)

Ⓓ **NI7842** (10/93)
Jussi Björling, Vol.2
Beethoven: Adelaide, Op.46; *Schubert:* An Silvia, D891; Schwanengesang, D957 (exc); An die Leier, D737; *R. Strauss:* Lieder, Op.27 (exc); *Sibelius:* Songs, Op.36 (exc); *Alfvén:* Songs, Op.28 (exc); *Eklöf:* Morning; *Sjöberg:* Tonerna; *Tosti:* Ideale; *Puccini:* Tosca (exc); Tosca (exc); Fanciulla del West (exc); Bohème (exc); *Verdi:* Rigoletto (exc); Rigoletto (exc); *Flotow:* Martha (exc); *Gounod:* Faust (exc); *Bizet:* Carmen (exc); *Offenbach:* Belle Hélène (exc); *J. Strauss II:* Zigeunerbaron (exc); *Millöcker:* Bettelstudent (exc). (J. Björling, H. Schymberg, H. Ebert, orch/N. Grevillius)

Ⓓ **NI7845** (7/93)
Giacomo Lauri-Volpi (1892-1979)
Bellini: Puritani (exc); *Boito:* Mefistofele (exc); *Massenet:* Werther (exc); *Puccini:* Tosca (exc); *Mascagni:* Cavalleria Rusticana (exc); *Leoncavallo:* Pagliacci (exc); *Puccini:* Bohème (exc); *Verdi:* Trovatore (exc); *Bellini:* Puritani (exc); Norma (exc); *Meyerbeer:* Huguenots (exc); *Gomes:* Schiavo (exc); *Offenbach:* Contes d'Hoffmann (exc); *Bizet:* Carmen (exc); *Gounod:* Faust (exc); *Meyerbeer:* Africaine (exc); *Giordano:* Andrea Chénier (exc); *Puccini:* Madama Butterfly (exc); Manon Lescaut (exc); Fanciulla del West (exc); Turandot (exc). (G. Lauri-Volpi, L. Borgonovo, NY Met Op Chor, NY Met Op Orch/G. Setti, La Scala Orch/F. Ghione, orch/R. Bourdon, SO/M. Cordone)

Ⓓ **NI7846** (10/93)
Rosa Ponselle, Vol.2
Puccini: Madama Butterfly (exc); Tosca (exc); *Verdi:* Forza del destino (exc); Trovatore (exc); *Mascagni:* Cavalleria Rusticana (exc); *Tosti:* Addio; *Herbert:* Mademoiselle Modiste (exc); *Rimsky-Korsakov:* Sadko (exc); *Puccini:* Manon Lescaut (exc); *Halévy:* Juive (exc); *Wagner:* Lohengrin (exc); *Verdi:* Aida (exc); Aida (exc); *Massenet:* Élégie; *Gounod:* Ave Maria; *Charles:* When I have sung my songs. (R. Ponselle, G. Martinelli, E. Baker, chor, orch, R. Romani/R. Romani/R. Bourdon)

Ⓓ **NI7847** (7/93)
Kirsten Flagstad (1895-1962)
Wagner: Walküre (exc); Walküre (exc); Tannhäuser (exc); Lohengrin (exc); Lohengrin (exc); *Weber:* Oberon (exc); *Beethoven:* Fidelio (exc); Ah! perfido, Op.65; *Wagner:* Tristan und Isolde (exc); Götterdämmerung (exc). (K. Flagstad, orch/H. Lange, Philadelphia/E. Ormandy, San Francisco Op Orch/E. McArthur)

Ⓓ **NI7848** (10/93)
Great Singers at the Berlin State Opera
Mozart: Entführung (exc); *Beethoven:* Fidelio (exc); *Donizetti:* Don Pasquale (exc); *Wagner:* Rienzi (exc); Fliegende Holländer (exc); Tannhäuser (exc); Tannhäuser (exc); Tristan und Isolde (exc); Meistersinger (exc); *Verdi:* Trovatore (exc); Traviata (exc); *Humperdinck:* Hänsel und Gretel (exc); *Puccini:* Bohème (exc); Turandot (exc); *R. Strauss:* Rosenkavalier (exc); Rosenkavalier (exc). (M. Perras, E. Berger, H. Gottlieb, M. Wittrisch, W. Domgraf-Fassbaender, G. Sinimberghi, F. Völker, F. Schorr, T. Lemnitz, L. Melchior, F. Leider, E. Marherr-Wagner, M. Lorenz, H. Schlusnus, H. Roswaenge, G. Hüsch, M. Cebotari, L. Schöne, E. Ruziczka, A. Kipnis, Berlin St Op Orch, Berlin Staatskapelle, orch, LSO/B. Seidler-Winkler/F. Zweig/A. Melichar/L. Blech/A. Coates/C. Schmalstich/J. Schüler/H.U. Müller/E. Orthmann/C. Krauss)

Ⓓ **NI7849** (3/94)
Frieda Hempel (1885-1955)
Verdi: Rigoletto (exc); *Donizetti:* Lucia di Lammermoor (exc); *Rossini:* Barbiere di Siviglia (exc); *Mozart:* Nozze di Figaro (exc); Zauberflöte (exc); Zauberflöte (exc); *Adam:* Toréador (exc); *Meyerbeer:* Huguenots (exc); *Gounod:* Mireille (exc); *Meyerbeer:* Robert le Diable (exc); *Offenbach:* Contes d'Hoffmann (exc); *Verdi:* Traviata (exc); Ernani (exc); Ballo in maschera (exc); Rigoletto (exc); *J. Strauss II:* Wein, Weib und Gesang; *Lortzing:* Wildschütz (exc); *Mangold:* Zweigesang. (F. Hempel, P. Amato, orch, B. Seidler-Winkler)

Ⓓ **NI7850** (3/94)
Antonio Cortis (1891-1952)
Verdi: Rigoletto (exc); Trovatore (exc); *Bizet:* Carmen (exc); *Gounod:* Faust (exc); *Massenet:* Manon (exc); Werther (exc); *Mascagni:* Cavalleria Rusticana (exc); Iris (exc); *Puccini:* Tosca (exc); Turandot (exc); Bohème (exc); Bohème (exc); *Donizetti:* Favorita (exc); *Giordano:* Cena delle Beffe (exc); *Vives:* Doña Francisquita (exc); *Gaztambide:* Vieja (exc); *Serrano:* Alegría del Batallón (exc); *Cortis:* Calabazas; Tropezón. (A. Cortis, La Scala Orch/C. Sabajno, orch)

Ⓓ **NI7851** (12/93)
Legendary Voices
Bellini: Sonnambula (exc); *Gomes:* Schiavo (exc); *Puccini:* Tosca (exc); *Herbert:* Mademoiselle Modiste (exc); *A. Thomas:* Mignon (exc); *Verdi:* Rigoletto (exc); Aida (exc); *Mascagni:* Cavalleria Rusticana (exc); *Verdi:* Ernani (exc); *Mozart:* Zauberflöte (exc); *Schubert:* Erlkönig, D328; *Schumann:* Myrthen, Op.25 (exc); *Wagner:* Walküre (exc); Tristan und Isolde (exc); *Ponchielli:* Gioconda (exc); *Millöcker:* Bettelstudent (exc); *Cilea:* Arlesiana (exc); *Tchaikovsky:* Eugene Onegin (exc). (L. Tetrazzini, E. Caruso, R. Ponselle, T. Schipa, G. De Luca, E. Turner, A. Piccaver, E. Pinza, A. Kipnis, Lotte Lehmann, K. Flagstad, J. Björling, T. Gobbi, F. Wunderlich, orch/R. Romani, NY Met Op Chor, NY Met Op Orch/G. Setti, G. Anthony/T. Beecham/M. Gurlitt/R. Bourdon, Berlin St Op Orch/E. Orthmann, G. Moore, Odeon CO, VPO/B. Walter/H. Lange/N. Grevillius, La Scala Orch/U. Berrettoni, Bavarian St Orch/M. von Zallinger)

Ⓓ **NI7852** (8/94)
Galli-Curci, Vol.2
Delibes: Lakmé (exc); *Donizetti:* Lucia di Lammermoor (exc); Lucia di Lammermoor (exc); *Verdi:* Rigoletto (exc); *F. David:* Perle du Brésil (exc); *Bizet:* Pêcheurs de Perles (exc); *Proch:* Air and Variations; *Verdi:* Trovatore (exc); Trovatore (exc); *Rimsky-Korsakov:* Golden Cockerel (exc); Sadko (exc); *A. Thomas:* Hamlet (exc); *Donizetti:* Lucia di Lammermoor (exc); *Verdi:* Rigoletto (exc); Traviata (exc); *Gounod:* Philémon et Baucis (exc). (A. Galli-Curci, B. Gigli, L. Homer, E. Pinza, A. Bada, G. De Luca, T. Schipa, orch, NY Met Op Orch/G. Setti)

Ⓓ **NI7853** (7/94)
Lauri-Volpi sings Verdi
Verdi: Luisa Miller (exc); Rigoletto (exc); Forza del destino (exc); Aida (exc); Aida (exc); Aida (exc); Aida (exc); Otello (exc). (G. Lauri-Volpi, L. Manfrini, I. Minghini-Cattaneo, E. Rethberg, G. De Luca, M. Caniglia, M. Basiola I, La Scala Chor, Rome Op Orch/R. Arduini, La Scala Orch/F. Ghione, G. Bechi/C. Sabajno, Berlin St Op Orch/F. Zweig, orch/R. Bourdon/G. Marinuzzi)

Ⓓ **NI7856** (9/94)
Legendary Tenors
Verdi: Otello (exc); *Tchaikovsky:* Eugene Onegin (exc); *Verdi:* Luisa Miller (exc); *Massenet:* Manon (exc); *Goldmark:* Königin von Saba (exc); *Verdi:* Otello (exc); *Rimsky-Korsakov:* May Night (exc); *Tosti:* Ideale; *Mascagni:* Cavalleria rusticana (exc); *Leoncavallo:* Zazà (exc); *A. Thomas:* Mignon (exc); *Flotow:* Martha (exc);

Wagner: Walküre (exc); Mozart: Don Giovanni (exc);
Boïeldieu: Dame blanche (exc); Massenet: Manon (exc);
Leoncavallo: Pagliacci (exc); Giordano: Andrea Chénier
(exc); Puccini: Turandot (exc); Massenet: Werther (exc).
(F. Tamagno, D. Smirnov, A. Bonci, E. Clément, L. Slezak,
E. Caruso, L. Sobinov, G. Lauri-Volpi, A. Pertile, G.
Martinelli, J. Patzak, H. Roswaenge, L. Melchior, R.
Tauber, D. Devriès, G. Thill, B. Gigli, R. Zanelli, J. Björling,
T. Schipa, anon, F. La Forge, orch, LSO, La Scala Orch/J.
Barbirolli/W. Goehr/G. Cloëz/E. Bigot/C. Sabajno/N.
Grevillius/M. Cordone)

① **NI7857** (10/94)
  Farrar in Italian Opera
  Mozart: Nozze di Figaro (exc); Don Giovanni (exc); Wolf-
  Ferrari: Donne curiose (exc); Segreto di Susanna (exc);
  Puccini: Bohème (exc); Bohème (exc); Bohème (exc);
  Bohème (exc); Tosca (exc); Tosca (exc); Madama Butterfly
  (exc); Madama Butterfly (exc); Madama Butterfly (exc);
  Madama Butterfly (exc); Madama Butterfly (exc). (G.
  Farrar, E. Caruso, A. Scotti, G. Ciaparelli-Viafora, J.
  Jacoby, orch)

① **NI7859** (10/94)
  Caruso, Farrar & Journet in French Opera
  Gounod: Philémon et Baucis (exc); Massenet: Manon
  (exc); A. Thomas: Mignon (exc); Massenet: Jongleur de
  Notre Dame (exc); Bizet: Pêcheurs de perles (exc);
  Pêcheurs de perles (exc); Gounod: Faust (exc); Faust
  (exc); Faust (exc); Faust (exc); Faust (exc); Faust (exc);
  Faust (exc); Faust (exc); Faust (exc); Faust (exc); Faust
  (exc). (G. Farrar, E. Caruso, M. Journet, orch/W.B. Rogers,
  M. Ancona, A. Scotti)

① **NI7860** (1/95)
  Emma Eames & Pol Plançon
  Meyerbeer: Robert le Diable (exc); Etoile du Nord (exc);
  Dinorah (exc); Bizet: Carmen (exc); Gounod: Faust (exc);
  Faust (exc); Roméo et Juliette (exc); Roméo et Juliette
  (exc); Berlioz: Damnation de Faust (exc); Damnation de
  Faust (exc); A. Thomas: Caïd (exc); Mozart: Nozze di
  Figaro (exc); Nozze di Figaro (exc); Don Giovanni (exc);
  Zauberflöte (exc); Zauberflöte (exc); Wagner: Lohengrin
  (exc); Schubert: Gretchen am Spinnrade, D118; Rossini:
  Stabat mater (exc); Bellini: Sonnambula (exc). (E. Eames,
  P. Plançon, E. de Gogorza, M. Sembrich, L. Homer, anon,
  orch)

① **NI7865** (3/95)
  Great Singers at the Mariinsky Theatre
  Moniuszko: Halka (exc); Ponchielli: Gioconda (exc); Verdi:
  Traviata (exc); Traviata (exc); Tchaikovsky: Eugene
  Onegin (exc); Queen of Spades (exc); Queen of Spades
  (exc); Queen of Spades (exc); Glinka: Life for the Tsar
  (exc); Rimsky-Korsakov: Snow Maiden (exc); Rubinstein:
  Demon (exc); Serov: Judith (exc); Mozart: Zauberflöte
  (exc); Auber: Fra Diavolo (exc); Meyerbeer: Huguenots
  (exc); Gounod: Mireille (exc); Massenet: Thaïs (exc); A.
  Thomas: Hamlet (exc); Delibes: Lakmé (exc); Lakmé (exc);
  Verdi: Requiem (exc); Boito: Mefistofele (exc). (A.
  Nezhdanova, M. Kovalenko, E. Bronskaya, L. Lipkowska,
  O. Boronat, E. Katulskaya, E. Popello-Davidova, E.
  Zbrueva, A. Labinsky, D. Yuzhin, D. Smirnov, E. Vitting, L.
  Sobinov, M. Karakash, V. Kastorsky, L. Sibiriakov, orch)

① **NI7866** (7/95)
  Caruso in Opera, Volume 2
  Flotow: Martha (exc); Verdi: Rigoletto (exc); Trovatore
  (exc); Trovatore (exc); Donizetti: Don Pasquale (exc);
  Favorita (exc); Mascagni: Cavalleria rusticana (exc);
  Puccini: Bohème (exc); Bohème (exc); Tosca (exc);
  Meyerbeer: Huguenots (exc); Bizet: Carmen (exc);
  Leoncavallo: Bohème (exc); Tchaikovsky: Eugene Onegin
  (exc); Giordano: Andrea Chénier (exc); Andrea Chénier
  (exc); Gounod: Reine de Saba (exc); Verdi: Macbeth (exc);
  Rubinstein: Nero (exc); Meyerbeer: Africaine (exc);
  Puccini: Bohème (exc). (E. Caruso, N. Melba, orch, anon)

① **NI7867** (10/95)
  Legendary Baritones
  Massenet: Jongleur de Notre Dame (exc); Tosti: Au temps
  du grand roi; Verdi: Falstaff (exc); Traviata (exc); Ballo in
  maschera (exc); Massenet: Roi de Lahore (exc); Verdi:
  Otello (exc); Puccini: Tosca (exc); Verdi: Ernani (exc);
  Falstaff (exc); Due Foscari (exc); Wagner: Tannhäuser
  (exc); Meyerbeer: Hans Heiling (exc); Leoncavallo: Zazà
  (exc); Verdi: Rigoletto (exc); Giordano: Andrea Chénier
  (exc); Rossini: Barbiere di Siviglia (exc); Lortzing:
  Wildschütz (exc); Verdi: Attila (exc). (L. Fugère, V. Maurel,
  A. Magini-Coletti, M. Battistini, M. Ancona, R. Renaud, E.
  Giraldoni, R. Stracciari, G. De Luca, T. Ruffo, P. Amato, J.
  Schwarz, H. Schlusnus, R. Zanelli, C. Galeffi, J.C.
  Thomas, L. Tibbett, G. Hüsch, I. Gorin, E. Petri, orch,
  Victor SO, Berlin St Op Orch/F. Tours/N. Shilkret/F.
  Weissmann/B. Reibold)

① **NI7871** (12/95)
  Kirsten Flagstad in Song
  Beethoven: Lieder, Op.48 (exc); Zärtliche Liebe, WoO123;

R. Strauss: Lieder, Op.17 (exc); Lieder, Op.10 (exc);
Lieder, Op.27 (exc); Alnaes: Happiness; Grieg: Songs,
Op.26 (exc); Songs, Op.60 (exc); Songs, Op.69 (exc);
Songs, Op.25 (exc); Songs, Op.70 (exc); Melodies of the
heart, Op.5 (exc); Songs, Op.48 (exc); Haugtussa, Op.67
(Cpte); Bridge: Love went a'riding; Dvořák: Gipsy Melodies
(exc); C. Scott: Lullaby; J.H. Rogers: At parting; Charles:
When I have sung my songs. (K. Flagstad, E. McArthur)

① **NI8803** (12/95)
  Chopin—Grand Piano Project
  Chopin: Piano Sonata 2; Nocturnes (excs); Polonaises
  (exc); Scherzos (exc); Waltzes (exc); Berceuse. (J.
  Hofmann)

NKF

① **NKFCD50002-2** (12/89)
  Grieg—Orchestral Works
  Grieg: Symphonic Dances; Holberg Suite; Old Norwegian
  Romance. (Oslo PO/M. Jansons)

① **NKFCD50004-2** (12/89)
  Grieg—Violin Sonatas
  Grieg: Violin Sonata 1; Violin Sonata 2; Violin Sonata 3. (A.
  Tellefsen, E. Knardahl)

① **NKFCD50009-2** (12/89)
  Svendsen—Orchestral Works
  Svendsen: Norwegian Rhapsody 1; Norwegian Rhapsody
  2; Norwegian Rhapsody 3; Norwegian Rhapsody 4;
  Zorahayda: Norwegian Artists' Carnival. (Bergen SO/K.
  Andersen)

① **NKFCD50011-2** (12/89)
  Svendsen—Orchestral Works
  Svendsen: Symphony 2; Festival Polonaise; Carnival in
  Paris; Romance, Op. 26. (O.B. Hansen, Oslo PO/Ø.
  Fjeldstad)

① **NKFCD50017-2** (12/89)
  Sinding—Piano Works
  Sinding: Marche grotesque, Op. 32/1; Rustle of Spring,
  Op. 32/3; Serenade, Op. 33/4; Scherzo, Op 33/6;
  Caprices, Op. 44 (exc); Prélude, Op. 34/1; Crépuscules,
  Op. 34/4; Chanson, Op. 34/5; Piano Sonata; Variations,
  Op. 2. (K. Baekkelund, R. Levin)

① **NKFCD50029-2** (10/94)
  Grieg—Piano Works
  Grieg: Ballade, Op. 24; Piano Sonata, Op. 7; Peasant
  Dances, Op. 72 (exc). (R. Riefling)

NMC

① **NMCD003** (4/92)
  Mary Wiegold's Songbook
  Dowland: Ballad Settings (exc); Galliards (exc); Pavans
  (exc); Weir: Romance of Count Arnaldos (exc); C. Matthews:
  Cantata; Strugnell's Haiku; Bainbridge: Michelangelo song;
  Skempton: How slow the wind; Birtwistle: White and Light;
  Wilby: Easter Wings; K. Tippett: Sun - The Living Son;
  Woolrich: Turkish Mouse; Muldowney: On Suicide;
  Beamish: Tuscan Lullaby; Northcott: Maidens came;
  Bedford: Even Now. (M. Wiegold, Composers Ens/D.
  Muldowney)

① **NMCD004** (9/92)
  Dillon—East 11th Street etc
  Dillon: East 11th St; Femme invisible; Windows and
  Canopies. (Music Projects London/R. Bernas)

① **NMCD006** (11/92)
  Cashian/Butler/Nicholls—Works for String Quartet
  Cashian: String Quartet 1; Butler: Songs and Dances; D.
  Nicholls: Winter Landscape. (Bingham Qt)

① **NMCD008** (5/93)
  Simon Holt—Chamber Works
  Holt: ... era madrugada; Canciones; Shadow realm;
  Sparrow Night. (F. Kimm, Nash Ens)

① **NMCD009** (8/93)
  Birtwistle—Choral and Orchestral Works
  Birtwistle: Melencolia I; Ritual Fragment; Meridian. (M.
  King, A. Pay, M. Thompson, C. van Kampen, H. Tunstall,
  London Sinfonietta Voices, London Sinfonietta/O.
  Knussen)

① **NMCD011** (10/93)
  Lutyens—Vocal and Chamber Works
  Lutyens: Chamber Concerto 1; Valley of Hatsu-se; Tempi,
  Op. 42; Isis and Osiris (exc); Triolet I; Triolet II;
  Requiescat. (J. Manning, Jane's Minstrels/R.
  Montgomery)

① **NMCD022** (4/95)
  Gerald Barry—Instrumental & Chamber Works
  G. Barry: Au Milieu; Sur les Pointes; Triorchic Blues;
  Swinging Tripes; Triorchic Blues; Piano Quartet; Bob;

Untitled; Sextet. (N. Kawai, M. d'Arcy, Nua Nós/D. N.
Mheadhra)

① **NMCD024M** (9/95)
  Turnage—Vocal and Chamber Works
  Turnage: On All Fours; Lament for a Hanging Man;
  Sarabande; Release. (F. Kimm, M. Robertson, C. Van
  Kampen, I. Brown, Nash Ens/O. Knussen)

① **NMCD025** (10/95)
  Artists' Series - Jane Manning
  Weir: Don't let that horse; P. P. Nash: In a walled garden;
  Connolly: Poems of Wallace Stevens II; Bauld: Farewell
  Already; Elias: Peroration; Payne: Adlestrop; A. Gilbert:
  Beastly Jingles. (J. Manning, Jane's Minstrels/R.
  Montgomery)

Northeastern

① **NR206-CD** (7/90)
  Arthur Foote—Chamber Works
  Foote: Piano Trio 2; Character Pieces, Op.9; Pieces, Op.1.
  (J. Silverstein, J. Eskin, V. Eskin)

① **NR211-CD** (12/89)
  Krebs: Chorale Preludes and Fantasias
  Krebs: Fantasia in G minor; Kommt her zu mir; Herr Jesu
  Christ; Es ist gewisslich; Herzlich lieb hab' ich dich;
  Liebster Jesu; Wachet auf prelude; Wachet auf fugue;
  Fantasia 4 in F; In allen meinen Taten; Jesu meine
  Freude; Was mein gott will; O Gott, du frommer Gott;
  Komme heiliger Geist; Gott der Vater wohn' uns bei. (E.
  Swanborn, T. Valentine, T. Valentine, J. Tinsley)

① **NR227-CD** (9/90)
  American Chamber Music with Flute
  Copland: Threnody I; Threnody II; Flute Vocalise; Flute
  Duo; Foote: Sarabande and Rigaudon; Pieces, Op.31; At
  dusk; Nocturne and Scherzo. (F. Smith, C. Yeats, S.
  Chase, L. Chang, V. Uritsky, M. Thompson, K. Murdoch,
  Ronald Thomas, B. Coppock, R. Hodgkinson)

① **NR228-CD** (3/90)
  Youthful Rapture—Chamber Music of Percy Grainger
  Grainger: Handel in the Strand; Harvest Hymn; Lord
  Peter's Stable-Boy; Scandinavian Suite; Mock Morris; My
  Robin is to the Greenwood gone; Maiden and the Frog;
  Sussex Mummer's Christmas Carol; Molly on the Shore;
  Youthful Rapture; Arrival Platform Humlet; Colonial Song.
  (J. Smirnoff, J. Smirnoff, J. Moerschel, S. Drury)

① **NR232-CD** (9/90)
  Piston—Piano and Chamber Works
  Piston: Piano Quintet; Piano Sonata; Passacaglia;
  Improvisation. (L. Hokanson, Portland Qt)

① **NR233-CD** (1/90)
  The Young Schubert
  Schubert: Piano Sonata, D157; Adagio, D178; Piano
  Sonata, D279; Fantasie, D2e; Andante, D29; Minuet,
  D600; Trio, D610; Variations, D156. (L. Hokanson)

① **NR238-CD** (9/91)
  Imaginées - Cello and piano works
  Debussy: Cello Sonata; N. Boulanger: Pièces; Auric:
  Imaginées II; Ravel: Don Quichotte à Dulcinée; Messiaen:
  Quatuor (exc); Poulenc: Cello Sonata. (N. Fischer, J.K.
  Fischer)

① **NR248-CD** (5/93)
  Silenced Voices - Victims of the Holocaust
  Kaprálová: Dubnova, Op. 13; G. Klein: Duo; Schulhoff:
  String Quartet 1; Concertino; Flute Sonata. (F. Smith, S-J.
  Huang, M. Ludwig, S. Knudsen, E. Barker, S. Pinkas, V.
  Eskin, Hawthorne Qt)

① **NR9001-CD** (9/90)
  Piston—Sting Quartets Nos. 1-3
  Piston: String Quartet 1; String Quartet 2; String Quartet 3.
  (Portland Qt)

① **NR9004-CD** (1/90)
  Dark Garden
  Beach: Songs, Op. 1 (exc); Browning Songs, Op. 44 (exc);
  By the still waters; Songs, Op. 26 (exc); Shakespeare
  Songs, Op. 37 (exc); Romance; Burns Songs, Op. 43
  (exc); Humming Bird; Songs, Op. 12 (exc); Hymn of Trust;
  Compositions (1898); Songs, Op. 21 (exc); Songs, Op. 51
  (exc); Dark Garden; Lento espressivo; Songs, Op. 19
  (exc); From Grandmother's Garden; Songs, Op. 11 (exc);
  Rendezvous, Op. 120. (D. Fortunato, J. Silverstein, V.
  Eskin)

Novalis

① **150 005-2** (4/88)
  Bach: Organ Works, Volume 1
  Bach: Prelude and Fugue, BWV552; O Gott, du frommer
  Gott, BWV767; Fantasia and Fugue, BWV542; Chorales
  BWV651-668 (exc); Schübler Chorales, BWV645-650

(exc); Orgel-Büchlein, BWV599-644 (exc); Toccata and Fugue, BWV565. (T. Koopman)

ⓘ **150 006-2** (11/88)
Mozart: Chamber Works
Mozart: Horn Quintet, K407; Oboe Quartet, K370; Clarinet Quintet, K581. (M-L. Neunecker, F. Miyamoto, R. Wehle, Mannheim Qt)

ⓘ **150 010-2** (9/87)
Mozart—Lieder
Mozart: An die Freude, K53; Wie unglücklich bin ich nit, K147; Oiseaux, si tous les ans, K307; Dans un bois solitaire, K308; Zufriedenheit, K349; Ich würd' auf meinem Pfad, K390; Sei du mein Trost, K391; Zauberer, K472; Zufriedenheit, K473; Veilchen, K476; Alte, K517; Verschweigung, K518; Als Luise die Briefe, K520; Abendempfindung, K523; An Chloe, K524; Kleine Spinnerin, K531; Sehnsucht nach dem Frühling, K596; Im Frühlingsanfang, K597; Kinderspiel, K598. (E. Mathis, K. Engel)

ⓘ **150 012-2** (11/87)
Mozart—Violin Concertos
Mozart: Violin Concerto, K207; Violin Concerto, K211; Violin Concerto, K216. (D. Sitkovetsky (vn/dir), ECO)

ⓘ **150 014-2** (5/88)
Mozart—Gala Concert
Mozart: Così fan tutte (exc); Mentre ti lascio, K513; Bacio di mano, K541; Zauberflöte (exc); Nozze di Figaro (exc); Don Giovanni (exc). (J. Van Dam, Paris Orch Ens/J-P. Wallez)

ⓘ **150 016-2** (2/88)
Vivaldi—Concertos
Vivaldi: Concerto, RV278; Concerto, RV498; Concerto, RV158; Concerto, RV401; Concerto, RV455; Concerto, RV575. (T. Füri (vn/dir), K. Turpie, B. Schneider, T. Demenga, L. Peelerin, T. Sosnowski, Berne Camerata/T. Füri)

ⓘ **150 017-2** (5/88)
Bach—Violin Concertos
Bach: Violin Concerto, BWV1041; Violin Concerto, BWV1042; 2-Violin Concerto; Violin and Oboe Concerto, BWV1060. (D. Sitkovetsky (vn/dir), J-L. Garcia, N. Black, ECO)

ⓘ **150 018-2** (6/88)
Harpsichord Recital
Frescobaldi: Secondo libro di Toccate (exc); Byrd: Pavan and Galliard, BK60; Froberger: Keyboard Works, Various I (exc); Purcell: Musick's Hand-maid, Part 2 (exc); Handel: Keyboard Suites Set I (exc); Rameau: Pygmalion (exc); Bach: Concertos, BWV972-987 (exc); Couperin: Livre de clavecin III (exc); D. Scarlatti: Keyboard Sonatas (exc). (K. Gilbert)

ⓘ **150 022-2** (1/89)
Romantic Serenades
Suk: Serenade, Op. 6; Elgar: Serenade; Fuchs: Serenade, Op. 21. (Berne Camerata)

ⓘ **150 025-2** (2/89)
C.P.E.Bach—Keyboard Works
C. P. E. Bach: Keyboard Concerto, H479; Keyboard Concerto, H444; Sonatina, H453. (R. Fuller, I. Rainer, Vienna Academy Orch, M. Haselböck (hpd/dir), M. Haselböck (org/dir))

ⓘ **150 026-2** (2/90)
Schubert—Lieder
Schubert: Frühlingsglaube, D686; An die untergehende Sonne, D457; Rose, D745; Suleika I, D720; Suleika II, D717; Wonne der Wehmut, D260; Gott im Frühling, D448; An die Nachtigall, D497; Lachen und Weinen, D777; Forelle, D550; Hirt auf dem Felsen, D965; Am Grabe Anselmos, D504; Nur wer die Sehnsucht kennt, D877/4; So lasst mich scheinen, D877/3; Erster Verlust, D226; Rastlose Liebe, D138; Gretchen am Spinnrade, D118; Mädchen, D652; Wiegenlied, D498. (E. Mathis, K. Weber, K. Engel)

ⓘ **150 028-2** (1/89)
Bach—Cantatas
Bach: Cantata 117; Cantata 11; Cantata 82. (C. Cuccaro, M. Georg, Adalbert Kraus, A. Schmidt, D. Fischer-Dieskau, Stuttgart Gächinger Kantorei, Stuttgart Bach Collegium, Württemberg CO/H. Rilling)

ⓘ **150 029-2** (1/89)
Bach—Cantatas
Bach: Cantata 145; Cantata 51; Cantata 140; Cantata 56. (C. Cuccaro, A. Auger, Adalbert Kraus, A. Baldin, A. Schmidt, P. Huttenlocher, D. Fischer-Dieskau, Stuttgart Gächinger Kantorei, Stuttgart Bach Collegium, Württemberg CO/H. Rilling)

ⓘ **150 031-2** (9/89)
Stalder & Reindl: Orchestral Works
Stalder: Symphony 5; Flute Concerto in B flat; Reindl: Sinfonia Concertante in D. (W. Bennett, J-L. Garcia, ECO/H. Griffiths)

ⓘ **150 036-2** (8/89)
Bach—Organ Works, Vol.3
Bach: Toccata and Fugue, BWV538; Sei gegrüsset, BWV768; Fantasia, BWV572; Trio Sonatas, BWV525-530 (exc); Clavier-Übung III, BWV669-689 (exc); Prelude and Fugue, BWV543. (T. Koopman)

ⓘ **150 039-2** (10/89)
Lieder with Guitar Accompaniment
Mozart: Veilchen, K476; Zufriedenheit, K349; Komm, liebe Zither, K351; Sehnsucht nach dem Frühling, K596; Haydn: An den Mond; Beethoven: Andenken, WoO136; Mendelssohn: Pagenlied, Op. posth; Weber: Canzonettas; König einst gefangen sass, J195; Zeit, J97; Wiegenlied, J96; Spohr: Lieder, Op. 72 (exc); Schubert: Schäfers Klagelied, D121; Nachtstück, D672; Wanderer, D489; Brahms: Deutsche Volkslieder (exc). (P. Schreier, K. Ragossnig)

ⓘ **150 043-2** (4/90)
Mozart—Works for Oboe and Orchestra
Mozart: Flute Concerto, K313; Oboe Concerto, K314; Sinfonia Concertante, K297b. (T. Indermühle, J-E. Lluna, F. Lloyd, R. O'Neill, ECO/L. Hager)

ⓘ **150 045-2** (4/90)
Haydn—Symphonies
Haydn: Symphony 94; Symphony 73; Symphony 30. (Vienna Academy Orch/M. Haselböck)

ⓘ **150 047-2** (12/90)
Haydn: Chamber Works for Flute
Haydn: Divertimentos, HobIV (exc); Keyboard Trio 15; Keyboard Trio 16. (A. Nicolet, C. Nicolet, R. Filippini, B. Canino)

ⓘ **150 048-2** (6/90)
Buxtehude—Organ Works
Buxtehude: Prelude, Fugue and Chaconne, BuxWV137; Ein feste Burg, BuxWV184; Passacaglia, BuxWV161; Nun komm, der Heiden Heiland, BuxWV211; In dulci jubilo, BuxWV197; Fugue, BuxWV174; Puer natus, BuxWV217; Prelude and Fugue, BuxWV139; Nun lob mein Seel', BuxWV212; Prelude and Fugue, BuxWV163; Wie schön leuchtet der Morgenstern, BuxWV223; Prelude and Fugue, BuxWV149. (T. Koopman)

ⓘ **150 049-2** (9/90)
Vivaldi—Violin Concertos
Vivaldi: Concerti, Op.8 (exc); Concerto, RV551; Concerti grossi, Op.3 (exc). (T. Füri (vn/dir), Berne Camerata)

ⓘ **150 052-2** (10/91)
Bach—Organ Works, Vol.4
Bach: Prelude and Fugue, BWV541; Liebster Jesu, BWV730; Liebster Jesu, BWV731; Fugue, BWV578; Wir glauben all' an einen Gott, BWV740; Chorales, BWV651-668 (exc); Fantasia in C minor; Passacaglia and Fugue, BWV582; Pastorale, BWV590. (/T. Koopman)

ⓘ **150 053-2** (4/91)
Mozart—Symphonies
Mozart: Symphony 41; Symphony 35; Symphony 17. (ECO/L. Hager)

ⓘ **150 054-2** (10/91)
Mozart—Organ Works
Mozart: Fantasia, K608; Adagio and Allegro, K594; Andante, K616; Adagio, K356; Fugue, K153; Fugue, K154; Fugue, K401; Gigue, K574; Suite, K399. (M. Haselböck)

ⓘ **150 057-2** (10/91)
Tchaikovsky—Chamber Orchestral Works
Tchaikovsky: Serenade, Op.48; Suite 4; Andante Cantabile, Op.11. (ECO/J. Judd)

ⓘ **150 069-2** (2/91)
Liszt—Organ Works
Liszt: Prelude and Fugue, S260; Evocation, S658; Variations, S673; Fantasia and Fugue, S259. (G. Kaunzinger)

ⓘ **150 070-2** (7/91)
Schoeck—Orchestral Works
Schoeck: Violin Concerto; Serenade, Op. 1; Suite, Op. 59. (U. Hoelscher, ECO/H. Griffiths)

ⓘ **150 081-2** (10/93)
Mozart—The Freemason Music
Mozart: Kleine Freimaurer-Kantate, K623; Zerfliesset heut', K483; Lobesgesang auf die feierliche Johannislöge, K148; Lied zur Gesellenreise, K468; Ihr unsre neuen Leiter, K484; Maurerfreude, K471; Maurerische Trauermusik, K477; Kleine deutsche Kantate, K619; Dir, Seele des

Weltalls, K429. (C. Prégardien, H. Wildhaber, G. Hornik, P. Schneyder, Chorus Viennensis, Vienna Academy Orch/M. Haselböck, M. Haselböck, M. Haselböck)

Novello

ⓘ **NVLCD109** (3/90)
Weir—Mini-Operas
Weir: Consolations of Scholarship; Missa del Cid; King Harald's Saga. (J. Manning, L. Hirst, N. Herrett, Lontano/O. de la Martinez, Combattimento/D. Mason)

Nuova Era

ⓘ **6742** (10/89)
Mozart—Violin Sonatas, Vol.3
Mozart: Violin Sonata, K481; Violin Sonata, K303; Variations, K359; Variations, K360. (S. Accardo, B. Canino)

ⓘ **6743** (10/89)
Mozart—Violin Sonatas, Vol.4
Mozart: Violin Sonata, K378; Violin Sonata, K302; Violin Sonata, K304; Violin Sonata, K403. (S. Accardo, B. Canino)

ⓘ **6797/8** (3/90)
Beethoven: Late Piano Sonatas
Beethoven: Piano Sonata 28; Piano Sonata 29; Piano Sonata 30; Piano Sonata 31; Piano Sonata 32. (A. Ciccolini)

ⓘ **6802** (6/91)
Mozart—Chamber Works
Mozart: Clarinet Quintet, K581; Horn Quintet, K407; Oboe Quartet, K370. (A. Loppi, T. Tunnicliff, R. Graham, S. Accardo, M. Batjer, T. Hoffman, C. Phelps, R. Filippini)

ⓘ **6809** (5/90)
Falla—Vocal & Instrumental Works
Falla: Amor brujo (Cpte); Canciones populares españolas; Serenata; Serenata andaluza. (M. Senn, M.R. Bodini, Carme/L. Izquierdo)

ⓘ **6826** (12/90)
Mussorgsky/Balakirev—Piano works
Balakirev: Islamey; Berceuse; Mussorgsky: Souvenirs d'enfance; Kinderscherz; Duma; Capricieuse; Seamstress. (M. Campanella)

ⓘ **6829/31** (11/91)
Mozart—The Six Haydn Quartets
Mozart: String Quartet, K387; String Quartet, K421; String Quartet, K428; String Quartet, K458; String Quartet, K464; String Quartet, K465. (Pražák Qt)

ⓘ **6851** (10/89)
Giuseppe Morino—King of Bel Canto
Mozart: Così fan tutte (exc); Meyerbeer: Huguenots (exc); Donizetti: Elisir d'amore (exc); Fille du régiment (exc); Duca d'Alba (exc); Bellini: Pirata (exc); Puritani (exc); Gounod: Faust (exc); Roméo et Juliette (exc); Lalo: Roi d'Ys (exc); Bizet: Pêcheurs de perles (exc); Massenet: Manon (exc). (G. Morino, Warmia Nat PO/B. Amaducci)

ⓘ **6857/8** (5/91)
Schubert—Piano Trios
Schubert: Piano Trio 1; Piano Trio 2; Piano Trio, D28; Notturno, D897. (Trieste Trio)

ⓘ **7109** (3/94)
Dallapiccola—Orchestral Works
Dallapiccola: Muriel Couvreux Concerto; Frammenti di Saffo; Liriche di Anacreonte; Carmina Alcaei; Tartiniana seconda. (A. Morrison, M. Rizzi, B. Canino, Dallapiccola Ens/L. Suvini)

ⓘ **7156** (10/93)
Respighi—Unpublished Piano Works
Respighi: Piano Sonata in A minor; Piano Sonata in F minor; Melodie; Allegro da Concerto; Piano Suite 1; Piano Suite 2 (exc); Prelude in B flat minor; Prelude in D minor. (M. Palumbo)

Ode

ⓘ **CDMANU1317** (11/92)
Wagner—Opera Excerpts
Wagner: Fliegende Holländer (exc); Parsifal (exc); Tannhäuser (exc); Meistersinger (exc). (A. Marc, C. Doig, D. McIntyre, NZ SO/H. Wallberg)

ⓘ **CDODE1365** (12/92)
Oscar Natzke - A Legend in His Time
Handel: Samson (exc); Mozart: Zauberflöte (exc); Zauberflöte (exc); Don Giovanni (exc); Rossini: Barbiere di Siviglia (exc); Mussorgsky: Song of the Flea; Ketèlbey: Sanctuary of the Heart; In a Monastery Garden; W.H. Weiss: Village Blacksmith; Beethoven: Lieder, Op.48 (exc); Zärtliche Liebe, WoO123; Schumann: Romanzen und

Balladen, Op.49 (exc); *Tchaikovsky*: Songs, Op.47 (exc); *Malashkin*: Oh could I but express in song; *Lehmann*: In a Persian Garden (exc); *Hewitt*: Out where the big ships go; *Traditional*: Shenandoah; Blow the man down; Hullaballo balay; Drunken Sailor; Rio Grande; Billy boy; *L. Fischer*: Kritikaster (exc); *M. Phillips*: Wimmen oh wimmen. (O. Natzke, H. Greenslade, chor, orch/H. Geehl/W. Braithwaite)

L'Oiseau-Lyre

Ⓛ **400 080-2OH** (3/83)
Bach—Violin Concertos
Bach: 2-Violin Concerto; Violin Concerto, BWV1041; Violin Concerto, BWV1042. (J. Schröder, C. Hirons, AAM/C. Hogwood)

Ⓛ **410 553-2OH** (12/83)
18th Century Orchestral Works
Pachelbel: Canon and Gigue; *Vivaldi*: Concerti Grossi, Op. 3 (exc); Concerto, RV537; *Gluck*: Orfeo ed Euridice (exc); *Handel*: Solomon (exc); Berenice (exc); Water Music (exc). (J. Holloway, M. Huggett, C. Mackintosh, E. Wilcock, S. Preston, M. Laird, I. Wilson, AAM/C. Hogwood)

Ⓛ **411 811-2OH2** (8/86)
Bach: Keyboard Suites
Bach: French Suites, BWV812-17; Suite, BWV819; Suite, BWV818a. (C. Hogwood)

Ⓛ **411 832-2OH** (2/85)
Mozart: Choral Works
Mozart: Exsultate, jubilate, K165; Ergo interest, K143; Regina coeli, K108; Regina coeli, K127. (E. Kirkby, Westminster Cath Boys' Ch, AAM/C. Hogwood)

Ⓛ **411 949-2OH** (8/84)
Telemann: Double & Triple Concertos
Telemann: 3-Trumpet Concerto 1; Quartet, TWV43: B 2; Recorder and Flute Concerto; Concerto polonois; Flute, Oboe d'amore & Viola d'amore Concerto. (F. Immer, M. Laird, I. Wilson, C. Mackintosh, C. Hirons, T. Jones, T. Mason, J. Turner/S. Preston, C. Shanks, M. Huggett, AAM, C. Hogwood (hpd/dir))

Ⓛ **414 329-2OH** (8/85)
Vivaldi—Vocal and Instrumental Works
Vivaldi: Stabat mater; Nisi Dominus; Concerto, RV153. (J. Bowman, AAM/C. Hogwood)

Ⓛ **414 473-2OH** (3/86)
Handel: Italian Cantatas
Handel: Tu fedel?; Mi, palpita il cor; Alpestre monte; Tra le fiamme. (E. Kirkby, AAM/C. Hogwood)

Ⓛ **417 123-2OH** (9/86)
Purcell: Songs and Airs
Purcell: Fairy Queen, Z629 (exc); Birthday Ode, Z321 (exc); If music be the food of love, Z379/3; Not all my torments, Z400; Olinda in the shades unseen, Z404; Urge me no more, Z426; Bess of Bedlam, Z370; Lovely Albina, Z394; Pausanias, Z585 (exc); Tempest, Z631 (exc); When first Amintas sued for a kiss, Z430; Timon of Athens, Z632 (exc); Evening Hymn, Z193. (E. Kirkby, C. Hogwood, A. Rooley, R. Campbell, C. Mackintosh)

Ⓛ **417 622-2OH** (5/88)
Mozart—Wind Concertos
Mozart: Flute and Harp Concerto, K299; Bassoon Concerto, K191; Flute Concerto, K313; Andante, K315. (L. Beznosiuk, D. Bond, F. Kelly, AAM/C. Hogwood)

Ⓛ **421 429-2OH** (12/88)
Mozart: Chamber Works
Mozart: Clarinet Quintet, K581; Oboe Quartet, K370; Horn Quintet, K407. (AAM Chbr Ens)

Ⓛ **421 478-2OH** (6/89)
Haydn—Masses
Haydn: Mass 5; Mass 6; Mass 1a. (J. Nelson, S. Minty, C. Watkinson, R. Covey-Crump, M. Hill, D. Thomas, Oxford Christ Church Cath Ch, AAM/S. Preston)

Ⓛ **421 480-2OH** (5/89)
Monteverdi: Madrigali Erotici
Monteverdi: Madrigals, Bk.7 (exc); Madrigals, Bk.8 (exc); Madrigals, Bk 8 (exc). (E. Kirkby, J. Nelson, P. Holden, P. Elliott, A. King, D. Thomas, R. Wistreich, Consort of Musicke/A. Rooley)

Ⓛ **421 500-2OH** (9/89)
Bach: Double Concertos
Bach: Violin and Oboe Concerto, BWV1060; 2-Harpsichord Concerti (exc); 2-Violin Concerto (exc). (S. Hammer, C. Mackintosh, J. Schröder, C. Hirons, C. Rousset, AAM, C. Hogwood (hpd/dir)/C. Hogwood)

Ⓛ **421 654-2OH** (8/89)
Handel & Haydn: Choral works
Handel: Birthday Ode for Queen Anne (Cpte); Blessed are they that considereth the poor; *Haydn*: Mass 2. (J. Nelson,

E. Kirkby, S. Minty, J. Bowman, M. Hill, D. Thomas, Oxford Christ Church Cath Ch, AAM/S. Preston)

Ⓛ **425 835-2OH** (4/91)
Mozart—Concert and Opera Arias
Mozart: Rè pastore (exc); Voi avete un cor fedele, K217; Ah, lo previdi, K272; Zaïde (exc); Nehmt meinen Dank, K383; Ch'io mi scordi di te, K505. (E. Kirkby, AAM/C. Hogwood, S. Lubin)

Ⓛ **425 892-2OH** (8/91)
Elizabethan Songs: The Lady Musick
R. Edwards: When grypinge griefes; *Campion*: Ayres (1601) (exc); *Dowland*: Second Booke of Songs (exc); Pilgrimes Solace (exc); *Danyel*: Songs for the Lute (exc); *Pilkington*: Rest sweet nymphs; Musick deare solace; Come all ye; *Morley*: Ayres (1600) (exc); *Robert Jones*: Musicall Dreame (exc); *Bartlet*: Sweete birdes. (E. Kirkby/A. Rooley)

Ⓛ **425 893-2OM6(1)** (4/91)
Purcell—Theatre Music (Part 1)
Purcell: Abdelazer, Z570 (exc); Distressed Innocence, Z577 (exc); Married Beau, Z603 (exc); Gordian Knot Unty'd, Z597 (exc); Sir Anthony Love, Z588 (exc); Bonduca, Z574 (exc); Circe, Z575 (exc); Virtuous Wife, Z611 (exc); Old Bachelor, Z607 (exc); Don Quixote, Z578 (exc); Amphitryon, Z572 (exc); Double Dealer, Z592 (exc); Richmond Heiress, Z608 (exc); Rival Sisters, Z609 (exc); Henry II, Z580 (exc); Tyrannic Love, Z613 (exc); Overture, Z772; Theodosius, Z606 (exc); Libertine, Z600 (exc); Massacre of Paris, Z604 (exc); Oedipus, Z583 (exc); Overture, Z771; King Richard II, Z581 (exc); Sir Barnaby Whigg, Z589 (exc); Sophonisba, Z590 (exc). (J. Roberts, J. Nelson, C. Keyte, E. Lane, J. Bowman, M. Hill, P. Elliott, A. Byers, P. Bamber, E. Kirkby, D. Thomas, R. Covey-Crump, Taverner Ch, AAM/C. Hogwood)

Ⓛ **425 893-2OM6(2)** (4/91)
Purcell—Theatre Music (Part 2)
Purcell: My wife has a tongue, Z594; Fool's Preferment, Z571; Indian Emperor, Z598 (exc); Why, my Daphne, why complaining, Z525; Wife's excuse, Z612 (exc); Cleomenes, Z576 (exc); Regulus, Z586 (exc); Marriage-Hater Match'd, Z602 (exc); Love Triumphant, Z582 (exc); Rule a Wife and Have a Wife, Z587 (exc); Female Vertuosos, Z596 (exc); Epsom Wells, Z579 (exc); Maid's Last Prayer, Z601 (exc); Aureng-Zebe, Z573 (exc); Canterbury Guests, Z591 (exc); Fatal Marriage, Z595 (exc); Spanish Friar, Z610 (exc); Pausanias, Z585 (exc); Mock Marriage, Z605 (exc); Oroonoko, Z584 (exc); Pavans, Z748-51; Pavan, Z752; Sonata, Z780; Chaconne, Z730. (J. Nelson, J. Bowman, M. Hill, P. Elliott, A. Byers, P. Bamber, E. Kirkby, D. Thomas, R. Covey-Crump, AAM/C. Hogwood)

Ⓛ **430 082-2OH3** (12/90)
Haydn: Symphonies
Haydn: Symphony 21; Symphony 22; Symphony 24; Symphony 28; Symphony 30; Symphony 31; Symphony 23; Symphony 32; Symphony 34. (AAM/C. Hogwood)

Ⓛ **433 012-2OH3** (4/92)
Haydn—Symphonies Volume 5
Haydn: Symphony 35; Symphony 38; Symphony 39; Symphony 41; Symphony 58; Symphony 59; Symphony 65. (AAM/C. Hogwood)

Ⓛ **433 043-2OH** (11/92)
Telemann—Concertos
Telemann: Recorder Overture-Suite; Recorder Concerto 1; Recorder & Viola da gamba Concerto 1. (P. Pickett (rec/dir), M. Levy, New London Consort)

Ⓛ **433 045-2OH2** (4/92)
Mozart—Works for Violin and Orchestra
Mozart: Violin Concerto, K207; Violin Concerto, K211; Violin Concerto, K216; Violin Concerto, K218; Violin Concerto, K219; Rondo, K269; Adagio, K261; Rondo, K373. (S. Standage, AAM/C. Hogwood)

Ⓛ **433 052-2OH** (1/92)
Vivaldi—Works for Cello
Vivaldi: Concerto, RV406; Concerto, RV402; Concerto, RV414; Cello Sonata, RV44; Cello Sonata, RV39; Cello Sonata, RV42. (C. Coin, E. Ferré, AAM, C. Hogwood)

Ⓛ **433 053-2OH** (3/92)
Bach/Vivaldi—Orchestral Works
Bach: 3-Harpsichord Concerti (exc); 3-Harpsichord Concerti (exc); 3-Harpsichord Concerti (exc); 4-Harpsichord Concerto; *Vivaldi*: Concerti Grossi, Op.3 (exc). (C. Hirons, J. Holloway, M. Huggett, C. Mackintosh, E. Wilcock, D. Moroney, C. Rousset, C. Tilney, C. Hogwood (hpd/dir), AAM/C. Hogwood)

Ⓛ **433 054-2OH** (5/92)
Bach—Keyboard Works
Bach: Italian Concerto, BWV971; French Overture, BWV831; Duets, BWV802-805; Chromatic Fantasia and Fugue, BWV903. (C. Rousset)

Ⓛ **433 148-2OH2** (7/92)
The Pilgrimage to Santiago
Anon: Codex Las Huelgas (exc); Codex Calixtinus (exc); *Alfonso el Sabio*: A Madre de Deus; De grad'a Santa Maria; Ben com'aos; Non e gran causa; Non sofre Santa María; Por dereito ten a Virgen; Quen a Virgen bervira; *Codax*: Aj deus se sab'ora meu amigo (exc); Aj ondas que eu vin veer (exc); Atlas undas que venez sur la mar (exc); Eno sagrado en vigo (exc); Esperanza de totz ferms esperans (exc); Mia jrmana fremosa (exc); Mundad' ei comigo (exc); Ondas do mar de vigo (exc); Quantas sabedes amar amigo (exc). (New London Consort/P. Pickett)

Ⓛ **433 187-2OH** (2/93)
Mad Songs
Purcell: Bess of Bedlam. Z370; Don Quixote, Z578 (exc); Fool's Preferment, Z571 (exc); Not all my torments, Z400; *J. Eccles*: Mad Lover (exc); She Ventures, and He Wins (exc); Don Quixote (exc); Cyrus the Great (exc); Way of the World (exc); *Weldon*: Reason, what art thou?; *Finger*: While I with wounding grief; *D. Purcell*: Achilles (exc); *Anon*: Mad Maudlin; Tom of Bedlam. (C. Bott, D. Robiou, M. Levy, A. Pleeth, P. Chateauneuf, T. Finucane)

Ⓛ **433 328-2OH** (5/92)
Mozart—Keyboard Works
Mozart: Piano Sonata, K545; Piano Sonata, K570; Rondo, K511; Rondo, K485; Minuet, K355; Fantasia, K475; Gigue, K574; Andante, K616. (A. Schiff)

Ⓛ **433 661-2OH3** (6/93)
Haydn—Symphonies, Vol 3
Haydn: Symphony 6; Symphony 7; Symphony 8; Symphony 9; Symphony 12; Symphony 13; Symphony 16; Symphony 40; Symphony 72. (AAM/C. Hogwood)

Ⓛ **433 674-2OH** (7/93)
Vivaldi—Oboe Concertos
Vivaldi: Concerto, RV457; Concerto, RV461; Concerto, RV535; Concerto, RV463; Concerto, RV447; Concerto, RV559. (S. Hammer, F. de Bruine, E. Hoeprich, A. Pay, AAM, C. Hogwood (hpd/dir))

Ⓛ **433 848-2OH** (7/93)
Schubert—Chamber and Vocal Works
Schubert: Trout Quintet, D667; Forelle, D550; Am Strome, D539; Auf dem See, D543; Erlafsee, D586; An eine Quelle, D530; Jüngling am Bache, D192; Schiffer, D536. (J. M. Ainsley, S. Lubin, AAM Chbr Ens)

Ⓛ **436 132-2OH** (7/93)
Emma Kirkby sings Mrs Arne
Arne: Comus (exc); Rosamond (exc); Tempest (exc); *Lampe*: Britannia (exc); Dione (exc); *Handel*: Ariodante (exc); Alcina (exc); Alexander's Feast (exc); Allegro, il penseroso ed il moderato (exc); Saul (exc); Overture, HWV Anh13; Hornpipe, HWV356; March, HWV345. (E. Kirkby, AAM/C. Hogwood)

Ⓛ **436 155-2OH** (2/94)
A Concorde of Sweete Sounde
Parsons: Ut re me fa sol; *Tallis*: In nomine a 4 No. 2; *Taverner*: In nomine a 4; *Carver*: Missa L'homme armé (exc); *Aston*: Hugh Ashton's Maske; *Byrd*: Fantasia a 4, BE17/4; *R. White*: Fantasias a 4 (exc); *Harding*: Fancy; *Henry VIII*: En vray amoure; *Baldwin*: Upon salva nos; 4 vocum; Upon in nomine; *Anon*: Prince Edward's Paven; Queine of Ingland's Paven; Ovet mundus letabundus; O homo considera; Tu crium primas; Inter chorus paradiscolarum. (Amsterdam Loeki Stardust Qt)

Ⓛ **436 194-2OH2** (9/93)
Ockeghem—Complete Secular Music
Ockeghem: Ma bouche rit; Despourveue; D'un aultre amer; Quant ce viendra; Il ne m'en chault plus; Presque transi; Ma maistresse; Desléaux ont la saison; Mort tu as navre; Quant de vous seul; Au travail suis; Prenez sur moi; Fors seulement l'attente; Autre Venus estes; S'elle m'amera; O rosa bella; Tant fuz gentement; Je n'ay dueil; Malheur me bat; Se vostre cuer eslongne; Ce n'est pas jeu; Resjois toy; Departés vous; D'un aultre la; Aultre Venus estés; Comago: Qu'es mi vida. (London Medieval Ens)

Ⓛ **436 428-2OH3** (4/94)
Haydn—Symphonies, Volume 1
Haydn: Symphony 1; Symphony 2; Symphony 4; Symphony 5; Symphony 10; Symphony 11; Symphony 18; Symphony 27; Symphony 32; Symphony 37; Symphony 107. (AAM/C. Hogwood)

Ⓛ **436 460-2OH** (6/94)
Biber—Requiem; Chamber Works
Biber: Requiem in F minor; Ballettae a 4 violettae; Battalia a 10; Nachtwächter; Pauern Kirchfahrt Sonata. (C. Bott, T. Bonner, C. Robson, J. M. Ainsley, M. George, S. Grant, New London Consort/P. Pickett)

① **436 585-2OH** (4/93)
Mozart—Sacred Choral Works
Mozart: Mass, K317; Church Sonatas (exc); Vespers, K339. (E. Kirkby, C. Robbin, J.M. Ainsley, M. George, Winchester Cath Ch, Winchester Quiristers, AAM/C. Hogwood)

① **436 867-2OH** (4/95)
Vivaldi—Bassoon Concertos
Vivaldi: Concerto, RV576; Concerto, RV474; Concerto, RV571; Concerto, RV498; Concerto, RV489; Concerto, RV577. (D. Bond, AAM, C. Hogwood (hpd/dir))

① **436 905-2OH** (7/94)
Recorder Concertos
Heinichen: Concerto, S211; *Schickhardt:* Concerts, Op. 19 (exc); *Telemann:* 2-Recorder Concerto in A minor; 2-Recorder Concerto in B flat; A. *Marcello:* 4-Flute Concerto in G; *Vivaldi:* Concerto, RV585. (Amsterdam Loeki Stardust Qt, AAM/C. Hogwood)

① **436 993-2OH** (2/95)
Boccherini—Symphonies
Boccherini: Symphonies, G503-8 (exc); Symphonies, G509-14 (exc); Symphony, G519. (AAM/C. Hogwood)

① **440 207-2OM** (10/94)
Capriccio di Flauti
Merula: Lusignuola; R. *Johnson II:* Temporiser; *Byrd:* Sermone blando; *Anon:* Istanpitta Gaetta; *Bach:* Art of Fugue (exc); *Sweelinck:* Mein junges Leben; *Bach:* Prelude and Fugue, BWV550 (exc); Brandenburg Concertos (exc); *Frescobaldi:* Primo libro di Capricci (exc); Primo libro di Ricercari et Canzoni francese (exc); *Conforti:* Primo libro de Ricercari; *Palestrina:* Lamentationum Hieremiae; *Trabaci:* Canzone francese (exc); *Aston:* Hugh Ashton's Maske; *Taverner:* In Nomine; *Anon:* Prince Edward's Paven; Queine of Ingland's Paven; *Shott:* Aan de Amsterdamse Grachten. (Amsterdam Loeki Stardust Qt)

① **440 222-2OH3** (11/94)
Haydn—Symphonies, Volume 6
Haydn: Symphony 26; Symphony 42; Symphony 43; Symphony 44; Symphony 48; Symphony 49. (AAM/C. Hogwood)

① **440 637-2OH** (6/95)
Monteverdi—Ballets
Monteverdi: Combattimento di Tancredi e Clorinda; Ballo delle ingrate (Cpte); Tirsi e Clori (Cpte). (C. Bott, A. King, J. M. Ainsley, C. Bott, T. Bonner, M. George, C. Bott, A. King, Chor, New London Consort/P. Pickett)

① **443 196-2OM** (9/94)
Schubert/Mendelssohn—Violin Sonatas
Schubert: Violin Sonata, D384; Violin Sonata, D385; Violin Sonata, D408; *Mendelssohn:* Violin Sonata, Op. 4. (J. Schröder, C. Hogwood)

① **443 216-2OH** (8/95)
Mozart—Horn Concertos
Mozart: Horn Concerti; Rondo, K514; Rondo, K371. (A. Halstead, AAM/C. Hogwood)

① **443 326-2OH** (10/95)
Bach—Harpsichord Concertos
Bach: Harpsichord Concerto, BWV1053; Harpsichord Concerto, BWV1055; Harpsichord Concerto, BWV1058; Violin Concerto, BWV1041. (C. Rousset, J. Schröder, AAM/C. Hogwood)

① **444 571-2OH** (9/95)
Mozart—Piano Concertos Nos 11 and 13;Rondo, K386
Mozart: Piano Concerto 11; Piano Concerto 13; Rondo, K386. (R. Levin, AAM/C. Hogwood)

Olympia

① **OCD124** (6/89)
Glinka: Piano Works
Glinka: Cotillon; Bellini Variations; Greeting to my Native Land (exc); Contredanse in G; Monastryka; Farewell Waltz; Grand Waltz in G; New Contredanses; Galopade; Chao-Kang Variations; Polonaise; Bellini Rondo; Tarantella; Mazurka in F; Mollares; Alabiev Variations. (V. Kamishov)

① **OCD129** (7/89)
Lyapunov: Orchestral Works
Lyapunov: Overture, Op.7; Zhelyazova Volya; Hashish; Polonaise; *Balakirev:* Islamey. (USSR Academy SO/E. Svetlanov)

① **OCD130** (8/88)
Glazunov: Orchestral Works
Glazunov: Symphony 8; Ballade, Op.78; Slav Holiday. (USSR Ministry of Culture SO, USSR RSO/G. Rozhdestvensky/O. Dimitriedi)

① **OCD165** (2/90)
Glazunov: Concertos
Glazunov: Violin Concerto; Piano Concerto 2; Saxophone Concerto, Op.109. (S. Stadler, D. Alexeev, L. Mikhailov, Leningrad PO/V. Ponkin, USSR RSO/Y. Nikolaevsky, USSR RSO Sols Ens/A. Korneiev)

① **OCD186** (10/87)
Chopin—Piano Works
Chopin: Piano Sonata 3; Ballades (exc); Mazurkas (exc); Barcarolle; Polonaises (exc). (P. Katin)

① **OCD190** (3/88)
The Lympany Legend, Vol. 1
Rachmaninov: Piano Concerto 1; Piano Concerto 2; *Prokofiev:* Piano Concerto 1. (M. Lympany, Philh/N. Malko/W. Susskind)

① **OCD193** (5/88)
Peter Katin plays Chopin, Vol.2
Chopin: Introduction and Variations, Op. 12; Mazurkas (exc); Piano Sonata 2; Ballades (exc); Andante Spianato and Grande Polonaise. (P. Katin)

① **OCD194** (6/88)
Shostakovich: Vocal & Orchestral Works
Shostakovich: Scherzo, Op.1; Theme and Variations, Op.3; Scherzo, Op.7; Spanish Songs, Op.100; Adventures of Korzinkina; Alone; Human Comedy. (A. Eisen, A. Bogdanova, USSR Ministry of Culture Chor, USSR Ministry of Culture SO, USSR Academy SO Sols Ens/G. Rozhdestvensky, Leningrad CO/E. Serov)

① **OCD196** (8/89)
Tchaikovsky & Shostakovich Orchestral Works
Tchaikovsky: Serenade, Op.48; *Shostakovich:* Pieces, Op.11; String Quartet 8. (Soviet Emigré Orch/L. Gozman)

① **OCD197** (7/88)
Grieg: Piano Works
Grieg: Ballade, Op.24; Song transcriptions, Op.41 (exc); Song transcriptions, Op.52 (exc); Piano Sonata, Op. 7; Lyric Pieces, Op.54 (exc); Lyric Pieces, Op.65 (exc); Lyric Pieces, Op.71 (exc). (P. Katin)

① **OCD198** (7/88)
Nikolai Petrov plays Fantasies
C. P. E. *Bach:* Fantasia, H284; *Mozart:* Fantasia, K475; *Mendelssohn:* Fantasy, Op.28; *Brahms:* Piano Pieces, Op.116; *Liszt:* Don Juan réminiscences, S418. (N. Petrov)

① **OCD199** (11/88)
Liszt: Piano Works
Liszt: Consolations, S172; Années de pèlerinage 2 (exc); Liebesträume, S541; Polonaises, S223. (P. Katin)

① **OCD212** (10/88)
Honegger: Orchestral Works
Honegger: Symphony 2; Phoedre; Napoléon (exc). (USSR Ministry of Culture Chbr Ch, USSR Ministry of Culture SO/G. Rozhdestvensky)

① **OCD214** (12/88)
Miaskovsky—Piano Sonatas
Miaskovsky: Piano Sonata 1; Piano Sonata 2; Piano Sonata 3; Piano Sonata 6. (M. McLachlan)

① **OCD217** (3/89)
Miaskovsky—Piano Works
Miaskovsky: Piano Sonata 4; Piano Sonata 5; Piano Sonatina; Prelude. (M. McLachlan)

① **OCD218** (5/89)
Schumann: Piano Works
Schumann: Kinderszenen; Piano Sonata 2; Carnaval. (P. Katin)

① **OCD230** (7/89)
Mozart—Piano Sonatas, Vol.1
Mozart: Piano Sonata, K330; Piano Sonata, K457; Piano Sonata, K331; Fantasia, K475. (P. Katin)

① **OCD231** (7/89)
Mozart—Piano Sonatas, Vol.2
Mozart: Piano Sonata, K310; Piano Sonata, K311; Piano Sonata, K332; Piano Sonata, K545. (P. Katin)

① **OCD232** (5/90)
Mozart—Piano Sonatas, Vol.3
Mozart: Piano Sonata, K279; Piano Sonata, K280; Piano Sonata, K282; Piano Sonata, K309. (P. Katin)

① **OCD233** (5/90)
Mozart—Piano Sonatas, Vol.4
Mozart: Piano Sonata, K284; Piano Sonata, K570; Piano Sonata, K533. (P. Katin)

① **OCD234** (5/90)
Mozart: Piano Sonatas, Vol.5
Mozart: Piano Sonata, K281; Piano Sonata, K283; Piano Sonata, K333; Piano Sonata, K576. (P. Katin)

① **OCD254** (12/89)
Chopin: Nocturnes & Impromptus
Chopin: Nocturnes; Impromptus; Fantaisie-impromptu. (P. Katin)

① **OCD255** (3/90)
Prokofiev: Piano Sonatas, Vol.1
Prokofiev: Piano Sonatas Vol.1; Piano Sonata 4; Piano Sonata 5; Piano Sonata 10. (M. McLachlan)

① **OCD256** (3/90)
Prokofiev: Piano Sonatas, Vol.2
Prokofiev: Piano Sonata 2; Piano Sonata 7; Piano Sonata 8. (M. McLachlan)

① **OCD257** (3/90)
Prokofiev—Piano Sonatas, Volume 3
Prokofiev: Piano Sonata 3; Piano Sonata 5; Piano Sonata 6; Piano Sonatinas, Op.54 (exc); Pieces, Op.4. (M. McLachlan)

① **OCD263** (5/91)
Brahms—Piano Works
Brahms: Piano Pieces, Op. 116; Piano Pieces, Op. 117; Rhapsodies, Op. 79; Handel Variations. (P. Katin)

① **OCD266** (4/93)
Kabalevsky—Piano Works, Vol.1
Kabalevsky: Piano Sonata 3; Preludes, Op. 38; Piano Sonatina 1. (M. McLachlan)

① **OCD267** (5/93)
Kabalevsky—Piano Works, Vol.2
Kabalevsky: Rondo, Op.59; Preludes, Op.5; Piano Sonata 1; Piano Sonatina 2; Piano Sonata 2. (M. McLachlan)

① **OCD269** (12/92)
Kabalevsky—Volume 4
Kabalevsky: Piano Concerto 2; Piano Concerto 3; Piano Concerto 4. (N. Petrov, Emil Gilels, Y. Popov, Moscow PO/D. Kitaienko, USSR TV & Rad Orch/D. Kabalevsky)

① **OCD286** (10/92)
Sviatoslav Richter, Vol.1 - Schubert
Schubert: Piano Sonata, D575; Piano Sonata, D625; Moments musicaux, D780. (S. Richter)

① **OCD287** (10/92)
Sviatoslav Richter - Vol.2
Chopin: Preludes (exc); *Schumann:* Novelletten (exc); Fantasiestücke, Op. 12 (exc). (S. Richter)

① **OCD288** (10/92)
Schubert—Piano Works
Schubert: Piano Sonata, D664; Piano Sonata, D784; Impromptus (exc). (S. Richter)

① **OCD292** (6/94)
Kabalevsky—Cello Concertos; Violin and Piano Works
Kabalevsky: Cello Concerto 1; Cello Concerto 2; Rondo, Op. 69; Improvisation, Op 21 (exc). (M. Tarasova, N. Likhopoi, L. Kuritskaya, Russia SO/V. Dudarova)

① **OCD296** (9/93)
Moscow Contemporary Music Ensemble - Volume 5
Kasparov: Linkos; Ave Maria; Genesis; Stabat Mater; Oboe Concerto; Invention. (Anon, S. Velikanov, Tamara Pilipchuk Voc Ens, Moscow Contemp Music Ens, USSR Cinema SO/E. Khachaturian/V. Ponkin)

① **OCD313** (4/93)
Gorecki—Orchestral and Vocal Works
Górecki: Olden Style Pieces; Symphony 3; Amen. (Warsaw Nat PCO/K. Teutsch, S. Woytowicz, Polish Nat RSO/J. Katlewicz, Poznan Boys' Ch/J. Kurczewski)

① **OCD328** (6/89)
Polish String Quartets
Lutosławski: String Quartet (1964); *Penderecki:* String Quartet 2; *Szymanowski:* String Quartet 1; String Quartet 2. (Varsovia Qt)

① **OCD334** (1/94)
Richter, Vol.4—Tchaikovsky Piano Works
Tchaikovsky: Morceaux, Op.10; Valse-Scherzo, Op.7; Morceaux, Op.19 (exc); Morceaux, Op.40 (exc); Romance, Op.5; Morceaux, Op. 51 (exc); Morceaux, Op.72 (exc); Seasons (exc). (S. Richter)

① **OCD336** (1/94)
Richter, Vol.6—Beethoven Piano Sonatas
Beethoven: Piano Sonata 3; Piano Sonata 4; Piano Sonata 27. (S. Richter)

ⓘ **OCD543** (10/95)
Taneyev—String Quartets
A. Taneyev: String Quartet 1; String Quartet 2; String Quartet 3. (Talan Qt)

ⓘ **OCD552** (10/92)
Belorussian Series, Vol.2 - Yevgeni Glebov
Glebov: Symphony 5; Fantastic Dances; Little Prince Suite. (Belorussian St Rad & TV Orch/B. Raisky)

ⓘ **OCD561** (1/95)
Beethoven—Piano Sonatas, Vol.1
Beethoven: Piano Sonata 1; Piano Sonata 2; Piano Sonata 3. (T. Nikolaieva)

ⓘ **OCD562** (1/95)
Beethoven—Piano Sonatas, Vol.2
Beethoven: Piano Sonata 4; Piano Sonata 5; Piano Sonata 6. (T. Nikolaieva)

ⓘ **OCD563** (1/95)
Beethoven—Piano Sonatas, Vol.3
Beethoven: Piano Sonata 7; Piano Sonata 8; Piano Sonata 9; Piano Sonata 10. (T. Nikolaieva)

ⓘ **OCD564** (1/95)
Beethoven—Piano Sonatas, Vol.4
Beethoven: Piano Sonata 11; Piano Sonata 12; Piano Sonata 13; Piano Sonata 14. (T. Nikolaieva)

ⓘ **OCD565** (6/95)
Beethoven—Piano Sonatas Nos 15-17
Beethoven: Piano Sonata 15; Piano Sonata 16; Piano Sonata 17. (T. Nikolaieva)

ⓘ **OCD566** (6/95)
Beethoven—Piano Sonatas Nos 18-22
Beethoven: Piano Sonata 18; Piano Sonata 19; Piano Sonata 20; Piano Sonata 21; Piano Sonata 22. (T. Nikolaieva)

ⓘ **OCD567** (6/95)
Beethoven—Piano Sonatas, Volume 7
Beethoven: Piano Sonata 23; Piano Sonata 24; Piano Sonata 25; Piano Sonata 26; Piano Sonata 27. (T. Nikolaieva)

ⓘ **OCD569** (6/95)
Beethoven—Piano Sonatas, Volume 9
Beethoven: Piano Sonata 30; Piano Sonata 31; Piano Sonata 32; Variations, WoO80. (T. Nikolaieva)

ⓘ **OCD601** (8/94)
Andrzej Korzyński—Music to the films of Andrzej Wajda
Korzyński: Man of Iron (exc); Man of Marble (exc); Birchwood (exc); Hunting Flies (exc). (OST/A. Korzyński)

ⓘ **OCD602** (8/94)
Wojciech Kilar—Film Music
Kilar: Land of Promise (exc); Balance (exc); Hypothesis (exc); Polaniecki Family (exc); Silence (exc); Taste of the Black Earth (exc); Pearl in the Crown (exc); Salto (exc); Jealousy and Medicine (exc); Leper (exc). (OST, Polish SO/W. Kilar)

Ondine

ⓘ **ODE727-2** (12/89)
Crusell: Clarinet Quartets
Crusell: Clarinet Quartet 1; Clarinet Quartet 2; Clarinet Quartet 3. (K. Kriikku, Avanti Qt)

ⓘ **ODE729-2** (5/90)
Prokofiev: Piano Works
Prokofiev: Piano Sonata 1; Piano Sonata 2; Piano Sonata 3; Visions fugitives. (M. Raekallio)

ⓘ **ODE730-2** (8/90)
Twentieth Century Guitar Works
Brouwer: Espiral Eterna; Tarantos; Paisaje Cubano; Donatoni: Algo; Koskelin: Tutte le corde; Ginastera: Guitar sonata, op 47. (T. Korhonen)

ⓘ **ODE731-2** (4/90)
Jorma Hynninen sings Opera Arias
Leoncavallo: Pagliacci (exc); Verdi: Traviata (exc); Trovatore (exc); Ballo in maschera (exc); Forza del destino (exc); Rigoletto (exc); Don Carlo (exc); Tchaikovsky: Eugene Onegin (exc); Queen of Spades (exc); Mozart: Nozze di Figaro (exc); Don Giovanni (exc). (J. Hynninen, Estonian SO/E. Klas)

ⓘ **ODE746-2** (7/91)
Schubert—Violin & Piano Works
Schubert: Sonata, D574; Violin Sonata, D384; Violin Sonata, D385; Violin Sonata, D408. (A. Chumachenco, R. Gothóni)

ⓘ **ODE761-2** (2/92)
Prokofiev—Piano Sonatas
Prokofiev: Piano Sonata 4; Piano Sonata 5; Piano Sonata 6. (M. Raekallio)

ⓘ **ODE767-2** (4/92)
Homage to Sibelius
Sibelius: En Saga; Musgrave: Song of the Enchanter; Englund: Ciacona; Yuasa: Midnight Sun; Tüür: Searching for Roots; Picker: Séance; Josephs: In the North; Constant: Hämeenlinna; Ruders: Tundra. (Helsinki PO/S. Comissiona)

ⓘ **ODE768-2** (9/92)
Dilbèr sings Coloratura Arias
Bellini: Puritani (exc); Sonnambula (exc); Verdi: Rigoletto (exc); Meyerbeer: Dinorah (exc); Delibes: Lakmé (exc); Donizetti: Lucia di Lammermoor (exc); R. Strauss: Ariadne auf Naxos (exc); J. Strauss II: Frühlingsstimmen, Op. 410. (Dilbèr, Estonia Op Orch/E. Klas)

ⓘ **ODE770-2** (7/92)
Ponce—Guitar Works
Ponce: Sonatina meridional; Tema variado y final; Guitar Sonata 3; La Folia Variations. (T. Korhonen)

ⓘ **ODE771-2** (8/92)
Weill—Orchestral and Vocal Works
Weill: Kleine Dreigroschenmusik; Violin Concerto; Vom Tod im Wald. (W. Wächter, T. Möwes, Leipzig RSO/M. Pommer)

ⓘ **ODE772-2** (11/92)
Kilpinen—Songs
Kilpinen: Minstrel's Songs; Lieder um den Tod, Op. 62; Lakeus; Lieder, Op. 79. (J. Hynninen, R. Gothóni)

ⓘ **ODE777-2** (8/92)
Paganini Studies
Liszt: Paganini Studies, S140; Friedman: Paganini Study; Brahms: Paganini Variations. (M. Raekallio)

ⓘ **ODE778-2** (10/92)
Works for Clarinet and Orchestra
Debussy: Première rapsodie; Tiensuu: Clarinet Concerto; Kaipainen: Clarinet Concerto. (K. Kriikku, Finnish RSO, Avanti CO/J-P. Saraste)

ⓘ **ODE779-2** (1/93)
Britten/Berkeley—Works for Tenor and Guitar
L. Berkeley: Theme and Variations, Op. 77; Sonatina, Op. 52/1; Songs of the Half-light; Britten: Chinese Songs; Nocturnal; Folk Songs (exc). (I. Partridge, J. Savijoki)

ⓘ **ODE781-2** (2/93)
Piazzolla—Works for Flute and Guitar
Piazzolla: Histoire du Tango; Guitar Pieces; Etudes tanguistiques. (M. Helasvuo, J. Savijoki)

ⓘ **ODE792-2** (8/93)
Vocal and Chamber Works
Kaipainen: Starlit Night; Klami: Rag-Time and Blues; Nielsen: Serenata in vano; Meriläinen: Metamorfora per 7; R. Strauss: Till Eulenspiegel. (K. Mattila, Lahti Chbr Ens/O. Vänskä)

ⓘ **ODE800-2** (4/94)
Schnittke—Works for Violin and Piano
Schnittke: Suite in Old Style; Violin Sonata 1; Violin Sonata 2; Suite in the old style. (M. Lubotsky, R. Gothóni)

ⓘ **ODE802-2** (11/93)
Ibert/Jolivet/Nielsen—Flute Concertos
Ibert: Flute Concerto; Jolivet: Flute Concerto; Suite en concert; Nielsen: Flute Concerto. (P. Alanko, T. Ferchen, A. Takalo, O-P. Martikainen, M. Sandström, Finnish RSO, Avanti CO/J-P. Saraste/T. Pulakka)

ⓘ **ODE804-2** (10/93)
Saariaho—Orchestral and Chamber Works
Saariaho: Du cristal; ... à la fumée; Nymphéa. (P. Alanko, A. Karttunen, Kronos Qt, Los Angeles PO/E-P. Salonen)

ⓘ **ODE825-2** (1/95)
Britten—Orchestral Works
Britten: Piano Concerto; Soirées Musicales; Matinées Musicales. (R. Gothóni, Helsingborg SO/O. Kamu)

ⓘ **ODE826-2** (6/95)
Sibelius—Early Chamber Music, Vol. 1
Sibelius: Piano Quartet; Violin Sonata; String Trio; Suite for String Trio. (E. Kovacic, J. Söderblom, M. Quarta, I. Miori, I. Angervo, J-E. Gustafsson, M. Rousi, J. Lagerspetz, V. Novikov)

ⓘ **ODE831-2** (12/95)
Sallinen—String Quartets
Sallinen: String Quartet 1; String Quartet 2; String Quartet 3; String Quartet 4; String Quartet 5. (J. Sibelius Qt)

Ongaku Records

ⓘ **024-101** (11/94)
Cohler on Clarinet
Brahms: Clarinet Sonata 1; Weber: Duo concertant, J204; H. J. Baërmann: Clarinet Quintet, Op. 23 (exc); Sargon: Deep Ellum Nights. (J. Cohler, J. Gordon)

ⓘ **024-102** (11/94)
More Cohler on Clarinet
Brahms: Clarinet Sonata 2; Poulenc: Clarinet Sonata; Schumann: Fantasiestücke, Op. 73; Milhaud: Clarinet Sonatina, Op. 100; Stravinsky: Pieces for clarinet. (J. Cohler, R. Hodgkinson)

Opal

ⓘ **OPALCDS9843** (4/90)
Karl Muck conducts Wagner
Wagner: Siegfried Idyll; Parsifal (exc); Parsifal (exc); Parsifal (exc). (G. Pistor, C. Bronsgeest, L. Hofmann, Bayreuth Fest Chor, Berlin St Op Chor, Berlin St Op Orch, Bayreuth Fest Orch/K. Muck)

ⓘ **OPALCD9839** (4/89)
Pupils of Theodore Leschetizky
Schubert: Impromptus, Op. 90; Liszt: Hungarian Rhapsodies, S244 (exc); Weber: Piano Sonata 1 (exc); Leschetizky: Arabesque in A flat; D. Scarlatti: Keyboard Sonatas (exc); Gluck: Orfeo ed Euridice (exc); Beethoven: Piano Sonata 3 (exc); J. Strauss II: Kuss-Walzer, Op. 400; Arensky: Suite, Op.15 (exc); Schütt: Impromptu-Rococo; Chopin: Nocturnes (exc); Liszt: Chants polonais, S480 (exc); Chopin: Nocturnes (exc); Nocturnes (exc); Rameau: Pièces de clavecin (exc); Leschetizky: Toccata; Chopin: Nocturnes (exc). (E. Leginska, B. Moiseiwitsch, M. Hambourg, O. Gabrilowitsch, H. Bauer, I. Paderewski, I. Friedman, F. la Forge, M. Novello, T. Leschetizky)

ⓘ **OPALCD9846** (2/92)
Francesco Tamagno—Complete Recordings
Verdi: Otello (exc); Trovatore (exc); Giordano: Andrea Chénier (exc); Meyerbeer: Prophète (exc); Massenet: Hérodiade (exc); Rossini: Guillaume Tell (exc); Saint-Saëns: Samson et Dalila (exc). (F. Tamagno, Anon)

Opera Rara

ⓘ **ORCH103** (10/90)
Italian Opera—1810-20
Pucitta: Vestale (exc); Generali: Adelina (exc); Rossini: Ah! per pietà l'arresta; Mosca: Bestie in uomini (exc); Manfroce: Ecuba (exc); Mayr: Rosa bianca (exc); García: Califfo di Bagdad (exc); Pacini: Annetta e Lucindo (exc); Mayr: Medea (exc); Elena (exc); Pavesi: Agatina (exc); Mayr: Cora (exc); Coccia: Clotilde (exc); Weber: Non paventar mia vita; Rossini: Torvaldo e Dorliska (exc); Morlacchi: Barbiere di Siviglia (exc); Winter: Maometto II (exc); Meyerbeer: Romilda (exc); Pacini: Adelaide (exc); Donizetti: Enrico (exc); Rossini: Ricciardo e Zoriade (exc); Meyerbeer: Semiramide (exc); Emma (exc); Mercadante: Apoteosi d'Ercole (exc); Mayr: Alfredo il Grande (exc); Donizetti: Falegname di Livonia (exc); Carafa: Gabriella (exc). (A. Bolton, M. Bovino, E. Harrhy, M. Hill Smith, Y. Kenny, B. Mills, S. Bickley, D. Jones, A. Mason, D. Montague, M. Moreno, P. Walker, P. Doghan, K. John, R. Leggate, C. Merritt, H. Nichol, P. Nilon, J. Best, P. Guy-Bromley, J. Cashmore, G. Dolton, C. du Plessis, R. Smythe, G. Mitchell Ch, Philh/D. Parry, S. Drake)

ⓘ **ORCH104** (8/95)
A Hundred Years of Italian Opera: 1820-1830
Balducci: Tazia (exc); Bellini: Adelson e Salvini (exc); Zaira (exc); Carafa: Nozze di Lammermoor (exc); Coccia: Maria Stuart (exc); Rosmonda (exc); C. Conti: Giovanna Shore (exc); Cordella: Sposo di provincia (exc); Donizetti: Alfredo il Grande (exc); Chiara e Serafina (exc); Nozze in villa (exc); Paria (exc); Zingara (exc); L. Ricci: Diavolo condannato (exc); Mayr: Fedra (exc); Mercadante: Amleto (exc); Gabriella di Vergy (exc); Nitocri (exc); Testa di bronzo (exc); Meyerbeer: Esule di Granata (exc); Margherita d'Anjou (exc); Pacini: Contestabile di Chesner (exc); Rossini: Ugo re d'Italia (exc); Zelmira (exc). (C. Daniels, L. Davies, N. Focile, E. Harrhy, M. Hill Smith, Y. Kenny, L. Kitchen, S. McCulloch, B. Mills, J. Rhys-Davies, T. Goble, D. Jones, F. Kimm, A. Mason, D. Montague, P. Spence, P. Walker, B. Ford, B. McBride, P. Nilon, I. Sharpe, I. Thompson, D. Ashman, K. M. Daymond, G. Dolton, I. Platt, J. Rawnsley, R. Smythe, J. Viera, C. Bayley, M. Glanville, A. Miles, A. Thorburn, G. Mitchell Ch, Philh, RPO/D. Parry)

ⓘ **ORC003** (9/94)
Donizetti—Gabriella di Vergy
Donizetti: Gabriella di Vergy (Opte); Gabriella di Vergy (1826) (exc); Gabriella di Vergy (1826) (exc); Gabriella di Vergy (1826) (exc). (L. Andrew, C. du Plessis, M. Arthur, J.

Tomlinson, J. Davies, J. Winfield, E. Harrhy, D. Jones, G. Mitchell Ch, RPO/A. Francis)

① **ORC004** (9/94)
Donizetti—Ne m'oubliez pas; Arias
Donizetti: Ne m'oubliez pas (Cpte); Imelda (exc); Dom Sébastien (exc); Gianni di Parigi (exc); Roberto Devereux (exc); Diluvio universale (exc). (M. Elkins, A. Oliver, C. du Plessis, M. Elkins, G. Mitchell Ch, Philh/J. Judd)

Opus

① **9150 1473** (9/90)
L.Mozart & Telemann: Orchestral Works
L. Mozart: 2-Horn Concerto in E flat; Sinfonia da caccia in G; *Telemann:* Musique de Table (exc); 2-Horn Overture-Suite. (B. Tylšar, Z. Tylšar, R. Beránek, Z. Divoký, Slovak CO/B. Warchal)

① **9150 1996/7** (11/89)
Dvořák: Tone Poems
Dvořák: Water Goblin; Noon Witch; Golden Spinning-Wheel; Wild Dove; Heroic Song; Symphonic Variations. (Slovak PO/Z. Košler)

① **9156 1824** (10/89)
Dvorský sings Operatic Arias
Puccini: Tosca (exc); Madama Butterfly (exc); Bohème (exc); *Massenet:* Werther (exc); *Cilea:* Arlesiana (exc); *Gounod:* Faust (exc); *Donizetti:* Favorita (exc); *Verdi:* Rigoletto (exc); *Mascagni:* Cavalleria Rusticana (exc). (P. Dvorský, V. Kincses, S. Haljáková, I. Konsulov, M. Hajóssyová, S. Kopčák, M. Nitranová, Bratislava RSO, Czech RSO/O. Lenárd)

① **9350 1710** (9/91)
Concertos For Trumpet and Orchestra
Albinoni: Concerti, Op. 9 (exc); *Baldassare:* Sonata in F; *Torelli:* Concerto con trombe, G18; *Molter:* Trumpet Concerto 1. (G. Touvron, Slovak CO/B. Warchal)

① **9350 1773** (10/89)
20th Century Works for String Orchestra
Britten: Simple Symphony; *Janáček:* Suite; *Suchoň:* Serenade, Op. 5. (Slovak CO/B. Warchal)

① **9350 1812** (11/89)
Mannheim Symphonies
F. Benda: Symphony in C; *Richter:* Symphony in G; *J. Stamitz:* Symphony in G; Symphony in A; Symphony in B flat. (Slovak CO/B. Warchal)

① **9350 1851/4** (2/88)
Schmidt: Symphonies
Schmidt: Symphony 1; Symphony 2; Symphony 3; Symphony 4. (Bratislava RSO/L. Rajter)

① **9350 2012** (4/91)
Cikker—Orchestral Works
Cikker: Slovak Suite; Reminiscences; Slovak Folksong Variations. (Bratislava RSO/O. Lenárd)

① **9351 1894** (9/89)
French Chamber Works
Debussy: Sonata for Flute, Viola and Harp; *Ravel:* Introduction and Allegro; *Roussel:* Sérénade. (K. Nováková, M. Telecký, M. Jurkovič, J. Luptáčik, Phil Qt)

① **9351 2020** (6/89)
Messiaen: Organ Works
Messiaen: Apparition de l'église éternelle; Ascension (exc); Nativité du Seigneur (exc); Corps glorieux (exc); Messe de la Pentecôte (exc); Livre d'orgue (exc); Méditations (exc). (F. Klinda)

① **9351 2130** (6/90)
Franck: Organ Works
Franck: Chorales (exc); Pastorale (exc); Pièces (1878) (exc); Prélude, Fugue et Variation (exc). (J.V. Michalko)

① **9352 1887** (8/90)
Gustav and Alma Mahler—Lieder
Mahler: Rückert Lieder (exc); Lieder und Gesänge (exc); *A. Mahler:* Lieder (1910) (exc); Lieder (1915) (exc); Lieder (1924). (M. Hajóssyová, M. Lapšanský)

Opus 111

① **OPS30-100** (1/95)
Hasse—Motets
Hasse: Gentes barbarae; Alta nubes illustrata; Salve Regina in A; Salve Regina in G. (M. Zanetti, J. Lane, Parlement de Musique, M. Gester (org/dir))

① **OPS30-101** (9/94)
Ciconia—Vocal Works
Ciconia: Merçé o morte; Panthera; Gli atti col dançar frances; O Padua; Ben che da vui donna; Sus un' fontayne; Caçando un giorno; Quod jactatur; Poy che morir mi convien; Venecie mundi splendor; O rosa bella; Chi vole amar; O felix templum jubila; Che nel servir anticho;

Deduto sey; Aler m'en veus; O virum omnimoda; Gloria; Regina gloriosa. (Alla Francesca, Alta)

① **OPS30-102** (7/95)
Campus Stellae - 12th Century Pilgrims' Songs
Anon: Discant Tropes; Conductus motets; Prosae; Versi; Rex immense; Cunctipotens genitor Deus. (Discantus/B. Lesne)

① **OPS30-116** (2/95)
Cherubini—Choral Works
Cherubini: Marches (exc); Requiem 1; In Paradisium. (Cologne Chorus Musicus, Neue Orch/C. Spering)

① **OPS30-118** (4/95)
150 Years of Italian Music, Volume 1
A. Valente: Tenore del passo e mezzo; *Facoli:* Pass'e mezzo Moderno; *Giovanni de Maque:* Keyboard works; *A. Mayone:* Primo libro di diversi (exc); *Trabaci:* Partite sopra Rugiero; *Picchi:* Intavolatura di Balli (exc); *Buono:* Sonata quinta; *Frescobaldi:* Unidentified Toccata; *Lambardi:* Gagliarda; Partite sopra Fidele; *Merula:* Capriccio cromatico; *M. Rossi:* Toccata settima; *Salvatore:* Toccata 1; Canzon Francese 3; Correnti; *B. Storace:* Toccata and Canzon; *G. Strozzi:* Corrente 3; *Stradella:* Toccata; *A. Scarlatti:* Keyboard Toccata. (R. Alessandrini)

① **OPS30-121** (5/95)
Haydn—English and Scottish Songs
Haydn: Canzonettas I; Canzonettas II; Looking glass; John Anderson; Ash grove; Roslin Castle; Shepherd's wife; O tuneful voice; White Cockade. (M. Lawson, R. Podger, O. Kogan, O. Tverskaya)

① **OPS30-126** (10/95)
Schubert—Violin Sonatas
Schubert: Sonata, D574; Violin Sonata, D384; Violin Sonata, D385; Violin Sonata, D408. (F. Biondi, O. Tverskaya)

① **OPS30-131** (12/95)
Llibre vermell de Montserrat
Anon: Llibre Vermell; Las Huelgas; Cantigas de Santa Maria. (Alla Francesca)

① **OPS30-88** (4/94)
Leo/Pergolesi—Salve Reginas
Pergolesi: Salve regina; Salve regina in C minor; *Leo:* Salve regina in F; *Gallo:* Trio Sonatas (exc). (B. Schlick, Europa Galante, F. Biondi (vn/dir))

① **OPS30-9004** (9/91)
Vivaldi—String Concertos
Vivaldi: Concerto, RV761; Concerto, RV129; Concerto, RV517; Concerto, RV547; Concerti, Op. 11 (exc); Concerto, RV130; Sinfonia, RV169. (F. Biondi (vn/dir), A. Chamorro, M. Naddeo, Europa Galante)

① **OPS30-9005** (9/91)
M.A.Charpentier—Vocal Works
M-A. Charpentier: Quatuor anni tempestatis; Quemadmodum desiderat cervus; Nisi Dominus, H231; Notus in Judea, H179. (Parlement de Musique/M. Gester)

① **OPS30-94** (10/95)
Lassus—Libro de villanelle,moresche,et altre canzoni
Lassus: Libro de Villanelle (1581) (Cpte); Tutto 'l di piango; Saccio 'na cosa; Sol'e pensoso; O Lucia miau; Madonna mia pietà. (Concerto Italiano/R. Alessandrini)

① **OPS39-9103** (10/91)
Clérambault—Secular Cantatas
Clérambault: Léandre et Héro; Isle de Délos; Pirâme et Tisbé; Apollon et Doris. (I. Poulenard, G. Ragon, Amalia Ens)

① **OPS50-9114** (4/92)
Classics of the Americas, Vol. 4
Gottschalk: Manchega; Ghirlanda; Souvenir de la Havane; Mazurka; Minuit à Seville; O ma charmante; El Cocoyé; Danse Ossianique; Deuxième banjo; Mancenillier; Suismoi; Grand Scherzo; Berceuse; Apothéose. (G. Rabol)

① **OPS55-9119** (9/92)
M-A. Charpentier—Office de Ténèbres
M-A. Charpentier: Tenebrae Lesson, H92; Tenebrae Lesson, H95; Autre leçon de ténèbres, H92; Tenebrae Responsories, H111-19 (exc); Tenebrae Responsories, H126-34 (exc); Miserere, H157. (Parlement de Musique, M. Gester (hpd/dir))

① **OPS56-9120** (4/94)
Vivaldi—The Four Seasons (Manchester Version)
Vivaldi: Concerti, Op.8 (exc); Concerto, RV163; Concerto, RV171. (Europa Galante, F. Biondi (vn/dir))

Orfeo

① **C003812H** (8/88)
Danzi: Flute Concertos
Danzi: Flute Concerto 1; Flute Concerto 2; Flute Concerto

3; Flute Concerto 4. (A. Adorján, Munich CO/H. Stadlmair)

① **C015821A** (8/87)
Stravinsky: Choral and Vocal Works
Stravinsky: Symphony of Psalms; Verlaine Poems; Babel; Abraham and Isaac; Elegy for JFK. (D. Fischer-Dieskau, Stuttgart Rad Chor, Stuttgart RSO/G. Bertini, H. Gruber, K.T. Adler, K. Berger)

① **C021821A** (9/87)
Schubert: Lieder
Schubert: Prometheus, D674; Wie Ulfru fischt, D525; Fahrt zum Hades, D526; Zürnende Barde, D785; Sehnsucht, D636; Totengräberlied, D44; Selige Welt, D743; Grenzen der Menschheit, D716; Aus 'Heliopolis' II, D754; Sieg, D805; Gruppe aus dem Tartarus, D583; Abendrot, D627; Dithyrambe, D801; Auf der Donau, D553; Schiffer, D536; Strom, D565; An den Tod, D518; Tod und das Mädchen, D531. (K. Moll, C. Garben)

① **C025821A** (4/84)
Brahms Choral Songs
Brahms: Alto Rhapsody, Op. 53; Begräbnisgesang, Op. 13; Gesang der Parzen, Op. 89; Nänie, Op. 82. (A. Hodgson, Bavarian Rad Chor, BRSO/B. Haitink)

① **C031821A** (11/86)
Schumann: Lieder
Schumann: Frauenliebe und -leben, Op. 42 (Cpte); Liederkreis, Op. 39 (exc); Myrthen, Op. 25 (exc); Gedichte, Op. 35 (exc); Gesänge, Op. 31 (exc); Romanzen und Balladen, Op. 64 (exc). (M. Price, J. Lockhart)

① **C043831A** (1/89)
Schubert: Piano Works
Schubert: Fantasy, D760; Piano Sonata, D784; Allegretto, D900; Andantino, D348. (O. Maisenberg)

① **C047831A** (6/88)
Grieg—Violin Sonatas
Grieg: Violin Sonata 1; Violin Sonata 2; Violin Sonata 3. (D. Sitkovetsky, B. Davidovich)

① **C053851A** (2/87)
Tchaikovsky: Songs
Tchaikovsky: I should like in a single word; Songs, Op. 6 (exc); Songs, Op. 28 (exc); Songs, Op. 47 (exc); Songs, Op.65; Songs, Op.73. (J. Varady, A. Reimann)

① **C058831A** (2/87)
Brahms—Lieder
Brahms: Lieder, Op. 3 (exc); Lieder, Op. 14 (exc); Lieder, Op. 19 (exc); Lieder, Op. 43 (exc); Lieder, Op. 59 (exc); Lieder, Op. 63 (exc); Lieder, Op. 69 (exc); Lieder, Op. 70 (exc); Lieder, Op. 72 (exc); Lieder, Op. 85 (exc); Lieder, Op. 86 (exc); Lieder, Op. 95 (exc); Lieder, Op. 96 (exc); Lieder, Op. 105 (exc); Lieder, Op. 107 (exc). (M. Price, J. Lockhart)

① **C060831A** (2/87)
Milhaud: Works for wind and piano
Milhaud: Flute Sonatina; Oboe Sonatina; Clarinet Sonatina, Op. 100; Sonata, Op. 47. (A. Nicolet, H. Holliger, E. Brunner, O. Maisenberg)

① **C067831A** (4/84)
Weber: Music for Clarinet and Orchestra
Weber: Clarinet Concerto 1; Clarinet Concerto 2; Clarinet Concertino. (E. Brunner, Bamberg SO/O. Caetani)

① **C081841A** (11/86)
Grace Bumbry: Famous Opera Arias
Verdi: Forza del destino (exc); Trovatore (exc); *Cilea:* Adriana Lecouvreur (exc); *Catalani:* Wally (exc); *Massenet:* Cid (exc); *Ponchielli:* Gioconda (exc); *G. Charpentier:* Louise (exc); *Cherubini:* Medea (exc); *Gounod:* Sapho (exc); *Gluck:* Alceste (1776) (exc). (G. Bumbry, Stuttgart RSO/S. Soltesz)

① **C093201A** (9/87)
Glazunov: Orchestral works
Glazunov: Symphony 8; Ouverture solennelle; Wedding Procession. (BRSO/N. Järvi)

① **C096841A** (11/86)
Famous Opera Arias
Handel: Giulio Cesare (exc); *Gluck:* Orfeo ed Euridice (exc); *Mozart:* Clemenza di Tito (exc); *Bellini:* Capuleti (exc); *Tchaikovsky:* Maid of Orleans (exc); *Bizet:* Carmen (exc); *Saint-Saëns:* Samson et Dalila (exc); *Massenet:* Werther (exc); *Wagner:* Götterdämmerung (exc). (B. Fassbaender, Stuttgart RSO/H. Graf)

① **C097841A** (3/88)
Zelter: Lieder
Zelter: Gesang der Vorwelt; Wand'rers Nachtlied; Wo geht's Liebchen; Ruhe (Wand'rers Nachtlied); Uber allen Gipfeln; Erster Verlust; Rastlose Liebe; An die Entfernte; Wonne der Wehmut; Um Mitternacht; Einsamkeit; Harfenspieler II; Klage; Berglied; Selige Sehnsucht;

Mozart: Oiseaux, si tous les ans, K307; *Rachmaninov:* Songs, Op.21 (exc); *Puccini:* Gianni Schicchi (exc); *Dvořák:* Rusalka (exc); *Lehár:* Lustige Witwe (exc). (L. Popp, G. Parsons)

Ottavo

Ⓓ **OTRC109033** (9/92)
Fauré—Late Piano Works
Fauré: Nocturnes (exc); Barcarolles (exc); Impromptus (exc); Préludes. (J. Röling)

Ⓓ **OTRC29134** (11/92)
Brahms—Piano Trios
Brahms: Piano Trio 1; Piano Trio 2; Piano Trio 3; Clarinet Trio; Horn Trio. (G. Pieterson, J. Slagter, Guarneri Trio)

Ⓓ **OTRC38611** (1/89)
Liszt—Piano Works
Liszt: Piano Sonata, S178; Harmonies poétiques, S173 (exc); Hungarian Rhapsodies, S244 (exc). (N. Grubert)

Ⓓ **OTRC39027** (5/92)
Schumann/Brahms—Piano Works
Schumann: Abegg Variations; Davidsbündlertänze; *Brahms:* Piano Pieces, Op. 116. (I. Cooper)

Ⓓ **OTRC58714** (12/88)
Schubert—Piano Works Volume 2
Schubert: Piano Sonata, D959; Piano Sonata, D840; Ecossaises, D781 (exc). (I. Cooper)

Ⓓ **OTRC68608** (4/88)
Schubert—Piano Works
Schubert: Piano Sonata, D894; Piano Sonata, D784; Ländler, D790. (I. Cooper)

Ⓓ **OTRC78923** (2/92)
Schubert—Piano Works, Vol.6
Schubert: Piano Sonata, D958; Impromptus (exc); Deutsche Tänze, D783. (I. Cooper)

Ⓓ **OTRC88821** (10/90)
Schubert—Piano Works
Schubert: Piano Sonata, D960; Impromptus (exc); Allegretto, D915. (I. Cooper)

Ⓓ **OTRC98402** (7/87)
Works by Brahms and Mahler
Brahms: Ernste Gesänge, Op. 121 (Cpte); Chorale Preludes, Op. 122 (exc); *Mahler:* Blumine; Rückert Lieder. (J. van Nes, R. Holl, Golders Orkest/Y. Talmi)

Panton

Ⓓ **81 1264-2** (2/95)
Kubelík conducts Kubelík
R. Kubelík: Orphikon; Cantata without Words; Inventions and Interludes. (Kühn Children's Chor, Bavarian Rad Chor, BRSO, Inst Ens/R. Kubelík)

Partridge

Ⓓ **Part9293-2** (1/93)
Clara Schumann—Works for Piano
C. Schumann: Piano Sonata in G minor; Romance in B minor; Impromptu in E; Romance in A minor; Scherzo, Op. 10; Scherzo, Op. 14; Präludium in F minor; Soirées musicales, Op. 6; Etude in A flat; Geburtstagmarsch; Preludes and Fugues, Op. 16; R. Schumann Variations; Romances, Op. 11; Caprices, Op. 2; Souvenir de Vienne, Op. 9; Valses romantiques, Op. 4; Variations, Op. 8; Polonaises, Op. 1; Pièces, Op. 5; Pièces, Op. 15; Fugues; Romances, Op. 21. (J. de Beenhouwer)

Past Times

Ⓓ **3589** (12/93)
Music for a Tudor Christmas
Browne: Jhesu mercy; *Byrd:* Lullaby my sweet little baby; This day Christ was born; *Pygott:* Quid petis, o fili; *Sheppard:* Verbum caro factum est; *Tallis:* Mass a 7 (exc); Videte miraculum; *Traditional:* Coventry carol; Nowell: Dieu vous garde; Sweet was the song. (Cambridge Taverner Ch/O. Rees)

Paula

Ⓓ **PACD46** (10/88)
Rachmaninov: Complete Works for Two Pianos and Piano Four and Six
Rachmaninov: Suite 1; Suite 2; Russian Rhapsody; Romance in G; Pieces; Morceaux, Op. 11; Prelude, Op.3/2; Polka Italienne; Symphonic Dances, Op. 45. (I. Thorson, J. Thurber, D. Gardiner)

Ⓓ **PACD51** (10/88)
Ravel: Works for Two Pianos and Piano Duet
Ravel: Introduction and Allegro; Rapsodie espagnole; Sites auriculaires (exc); Boléro; Ma mère l'Oye; Fanfare; Shéhérazade (exc); Frontispice; La Valse. (I. Thorson, J. Thurber, D. Gardiner)

Ⓓ **PACD55** (9/90)
Nielsen: Organ Works
Nielsen: Commotio; Little Preludes; Preludes. (U. Spang-Hanssen)

Ⓓ **PACD56** (12/90)
Nielsen: Songs
Nielsen: Songs, FS12; Songs, FS18 (exc); Strophic Songs, FS42 (exc); Ballad of the Bear, FS109; Springtime in Funen (exc); Maskarade (exc); Tove (exc); Danish Songs (exc); Songs and Verses, FS14 (exc); Songbook, FS125 (exc); Little Danish Songs, FS114 (exc); Merchant's Committee Cantata (exc); Hymns and sacred songs (exc). (J. Klint, R. Bevan)

Pavane

Ⓓ **ADW7244/5** (1/93)
Mozart—Works for 2 Pianos & Piano 4 hands
Mozart: Piano Duet Sonata, K19d; Sonata Movement, K357; Piano Sonata, K448; Andante and Variations, K501; Adagio and Allegro, K594; Larghetto and Allegro, Kdeest; Piano Duet Sonata, K381; Piano Duet Sonata, K358; Fugue, K426; Piano Duet Sonata, K497; Piano Duet Sonata, K521. (O. Ouziel, D. Ouziel)

Ⓓ **ADW7275** (7/93)
Liszt—Paraphrases & Transcriptions
Liszt: Fantasia and Fugue, S463; Meistersinger paraphrase, S448; Idée fixe, S395; Ernani—paraphrase, S432; Miserere du Trovatore, S433; Rigoletto—paraphrase, S434; Norma Réminiscences, S394. (H. du Plessis)

Ⓓ **ADW7332** (10/95)
Liszt/Debussy—Piano Works
Liszt: Années de pèlerinage 1 (exc); Nuages gris, S199; Études d'exécution, S139 (exc); Concert Studies, S145; *Debussy:* Children's Corner (exc); Préludes (exc); Suite bergamasque (exc); Images (exc); Estampes (exc). (O. De Spiegeleir)

Pearl

Ⓓ **EVC1(1)** (12/90)
The Caruso Edition, Vol.1 (pt 1)
Franchetti: Germania (exc); *Verdi:* Rigoletto (exc); Aida (exc); *Massenet:* Manon (exc); *Donizetti:* Elisir d'amore (exc); *Boito:* Mefistofele (exc); *Puccini:* Tosca (exc); *Mascagni:* Iris (exc); *Giordano:* Fedora (exc); *Ponchielli:* Gioconda (exc); *Leoncavallo:* Pagliacci (exc); *Mascagni:* Cavalleria rusticana (exc); *Denza:* Non t'amo più; *Tosti:* Mia canzone; *Cilea:* Adriana Lecouvreur (exc); *Zardo:* Luna fedel; *Trimarchi:* Bacio ancora; *Zardo:* Luna fedel; *Donizetti:* Elisir d'amore (exc); *Puccini:* Tosca (exc); *Franchetti:* Germania (exc); *Verdi:* Rigoletto (exc); *Mascagni:* Cavalleria rusticana (exc); *Pini-Corsi:* Tu non mi vuoi più ben; *Puccini:* Tosca (exc); *Meyerbeer:* Huguenots (exc); *Verdi:* Rigoletto (exc); *Donizetti:* Elisir d'amore (exc); *Verdi:* Aida (exc); *Puccini:* Tosca (exc); *Mascagni:* Cavalleria rusticana (exc); *Leoncavallo:* Pagliacci (exc); *Massenet:* Manon (exc); *Leoncavallo:* Mattinata; *Bizet:* Pêcheurs de perles (exc); *Donizetti:* Don Pasquale (exc); *Bizet:* Carmen (exc); *Meyerbeer:* Huguenots (exc); *Ponchielli:* Gioconda (exc); *Mascagni:* Cavalleria rusticana (exc). (E. Caruso, anon, S. Cottone, U. Giordano, F. Cilea, R. Leoncavallo)

Ⓓ **EVC1(2)** (12/90)
The Caruso Edition, Vol.1 (pt 2)
Flotow: Martha (exc); *Puccini:* Bohème (exc); *Gounod:* Faust (exc); *Verdi:* Trovatore (exc); *Donizetti:* Favorita (exc); *Verdi:* Forza del destino (exc); Aida (exc); *Barthélemy:* Triste ritorno; *Tosti:* Ideale; *Meyerbeer:* Africaine (exc); *Verdi:* Rigoletto (exc); *Puccini:* Bohème (exc); *Giordano:* Andrea Chénier (exc); *Leoncavallo:* Pagliacci (exc); *Puccini:* Bohème (exc); *Bizet:* Pêcheurs de perles (exc); *Donizetti:* Dom Sébastien (exc); *Barthélemy:* Adorables tourments; *Donizetti:* Lucia di Lammermoor (exc); *Verdi:* Rigoletto (exc); *Puccini:* Bohème (exc); Madama Butterfly (exc). (E. Caruso, A. Scotti, B. Abott, L. Homer, N. Melba, M. Ancona, M. Sembrich, G. Severina, F. Daddi, M. Journet, G. Farrar, G. Ciaparelli-Viafora, orch/W.B. Rogers)

Ⓓ **EVC2** (3/91)
The Caruso Edition, Vol.2—1908-12
Buzzi-Peccia: Lolita; *Verdi:* Rigoletto (exc); Trovatore (exc); Aida (exc); *Tosti:* Pour un baiser; *Nutile:* Mamma mia, che vo' sapè; *Verdi:* Forza del destino (exc); Aida (exc); Trovatore (exc); *Puccini:* Tosca (exc); *Goldmark:* Königin von Saba (exc); *Bizet:* Carmen (exc); Carmen (exc); *Meyerbeer:* Huguenots (exc); *Verdi:* Trovatore (exc); Trovatore (exc); Aida (exc); Otello (exc); *Flotow:* Martha (exc); *Gounod:* Faust (exc); Faust (exc); Faust (exc); Faust (exc); *Franchetti:* Germania (exc); *Puccini:* Madama Butterfly (exc); *Ponchielli:* Gioconda (exc); *Leoncavallo:* Pagliacci (exc); *Mascagni:* Cavalleria rusticana (exc); *Tosti:* Addio; *Geehl:* For you alone; *Verdi:* Ballo in maschera (exc); Forza del destino (exc); Aida (exc); *Leoncavallo:* Bohème (exc); *Donizetti:* Elisir d'amore (exc); *Massenet:* Manon (exc); *Gomes:* Schiavo (exc); *A. Mascheroni:* Eternamente; *Cardillo:* Core 'ngrato; *De Curtis:* Canta pe'me; *C. G. Gardner:* Love is mine; *Flotow:* Martha (exc). (E. Caruso, L. Homer, J. Gadski, F. Alda, M. Journet, G. Farrar, G. Gilibert, A. Scotti, P. Amato, J. Jacoby, NY Met Op Chor, orch)

Ⓓ **EVC3(1)** (10/91)
The Caruso Edition, Vol.3 (pt 1)
Faure: Crucifix; *Verdi:* Lombardi (exc); *Crescenzo:* Tarantella sincera; *Donizetti:* Lucia di Lammermoor (exc); *Rossini:* Soirées musicales (exc); *Verdi:* Rigoletto (exc); *Caruso:* Dreams of Long Ago; *Sullivan:* Lost Chord; *Hardelot:* Because; *Granier:* Hosanna; *Massenet:* Manon (exc); *Puccini:* Bohème (exc); *Verdi:* Don Carlo (exc); Trovatore (exc); *Tchaikovsky:* Songs, Op. 38 (exc); *Verdi:* Rigoletto (exc); *Bizet:* Agnus Dei; *Puccini:* Manon Lescaut (exc); *Kahn:* Ave Maria; *Massenet:* Élégie; *Leoncavallo:* Lasciati amar; *Crescenzo:* Guardanno 'a luna; *O'Hara:* Your eyes have told me; *Cottrau:* Fenesta che lucive; *Rossini:* Stabat Mater (exc); *Faure:* Rameaux; *Mascagni:* Cavalleria rusticana (exc); *Verdi:* Otello (exc); *Tchaikovsky:* Songs, Op. 38 (exc); *Ricciardi:* Amor mio; *V. Valente:* Manella mia; *C. G. Gardner:* Trusting Eyes; *Ronald:* Sérénade espagnole; *Tosti:* Parted!; *Verdi:* Ballo in maschera (exc); *Alvarez:* Partida; *Chapí:* Milagro de la Virgen (exc); *Verdi:* Traviata (exc); *Gomes:* Guarany (exc); *Szulc:* Hantise d'amour; *Bizet:* Carmen (exc). (E. Caruso, M. Journet, F. Alda, L. Tetrazzini, J. Jacoby, A. Bada, P. Amato, G. Farrar, A. Scotti, E. Schumann-Heink, T. Ruffo, F. Hempel, L. Rothier, A. de Segurola, M. Duchêne, A. Gluck, E. Destinn, NY Met Op Chor, NY Met Op Orch, orch/W.B. Rogers, G. Scognamiglio/G. Scognamiglio, M. Elman, P. Kahn)

Ⓓ **EVC3(2)** (10/91)
The Caruso Edition, Vol.3 (pt 2)
Tosti: Mia Canzone; *Ciociano:* Cielo turchino; *Pennino:* Pecchè; *Verdi:* Requiem (exc); *Donizetti:* Duca d'Alba (exc); *Denza:* Si vous l'aviez compris; *Leoncavallo:* Sérénade française; *Franck:* Procession; *Massenet:* Cid (exc); *Tosti:* Luna d'estate; *Di Capua:* 'O sole mio; *Gounod:* Reine de Saba (exc); *Rotoli:* Mia sposa sarà la mia bandiera; *Verdi:* Macbeth (exc); *Puccini:* Bohème (exc); *Adam:* Minuit, chrétiens (exc). (E. Caruso, M. Elman, orch/W.B. Rogers, G. Scognamiglio)

Ⓓ **EVC4(1)** (10/91)
The Caruso Edition, Vol.4 (pt 1)
Faure: Sancta Maria; *Caruso:* Tiempo antico; *Cottrau:* Santa Lucia; *Tchaikovsky:* Songs, Op.6 (exc); Eugene Onegin (exc); *Godard:* Chanson de juin; *Giordano:* Andrea Chénier (exc); *Saint-Saëns:* Samson et Dalila (exc); *Bizet:* Pêcheurs de perles (exc); *Verdi:* Rigoletto (exc); Rigoletto (exc); *Donizetti:* Lucia di Lammermoor (exc); *Flotow:* Martha (exc); *Gastaldon:* Musica proibita; *Crescenzo:* Uocchie celeste; *Tosti:* Alba separa; *Rubinstein:* Nero (exc); *Anton y Michelena:* A la luz de la luna; *P.M. Costa:* Sei morta nella vita mia; *Alvarez:* Partida; *Verdi:* Forza del destino (exc); *Cohan:* Over there; *Niedermeyer:* Pietà, Signore; *Alvarez:* A Granada; *Billi:* Campane a sera; *Olivieri:* Inno di Garibaldi. (E. Caruso, A. Galli-Curci, F. Perini, G. De Luca, M. Egener, A. Bada, M. Journet, E. de Gogorza, F. Lapitino, orch/W.B. Rogers, NY Met Op Chor/J. Pasternack, V. Bellezza)

Ⓓ **EVC4(2)** (10/91)
The Caruso Edition, Vol.4 (pt 2)
Arona: Campana di San Giusto; *Planquette:* Régiment de Sambre et Meuse; *Fucito:* Sultano a Tte; *Saint-Saëns:* Samson et Dalila (exc); *Donizetti:* Elisir d'amore (exc); *Tosti:* 'A Vucchella; *Califona:* Vieni sul mar; *De Curtis:* Tu ca nun chiagne; *Cottrau:* Addio a Napoli; *Pergolesi:* Tre giorni son che Nina; *Crescenzo:* Première caresse; *De Curtis:* Senza nisciuno; *Gomes:* Salvator Rosa (exc); *Bracco:* Serenata; *Fucito:* Scordame; *Secchi:* Love me or not; *Handel:* Serse (exc); *Posadas:* Noche feliz; *Halévy:* Juive (exc); *Gioè:* I' m'arricordo 'e Napule; *Donaudy:* Vaghissima sembianza; *Meyerbeer:* Africaine (exc); *Lully:* Amadis (exc); *Bartlett:* Dream; *Rossini:* Petite messe solennelle (exc). (E. Caruso, L. Homer, M. Journet, G. De Luca, orch/J. Pasternack)

Ⓓ **GEMMCDS9001/3(1)** (6/93)
Singers of Imperial Russia, Vol.2 (pt 1)
Glinka: Ruslan and Lyudmila (exc); *Borodin:* Prince Igor (exc); *Tchaikovsky:* Queen of Spades (exc); Songs, Op.63 (exc); *Glinka:* Fire of longing; *Nápravník:* Dubrovsky (exc); *Tchaikovsky:* Eugene Onegin (exc); Eugene Onegin (exc); *Meyerbeer:* Robert le Diable (exc); *Rubinstein:* Voyevode; *Schumann:* Romanzen und Balladen, Op.49 (exc); *Glinka:*

Life for the Tsar (exc); *Serov:* Judith (exc); *Lishin:* She laughed; *Rimsky-Korsakov:* Tsar's bride (exc); *Wagner:* Walküre (exc); *Rimsky-Korsakov:* Sadko (exc); *Borodin:* Prince Igor (exc); *Rubinstein:* Asra; *Denza:* Vieni a me; Occhi di fata; *Rubinstein:* Demon (exc); *Glinka:* Ruslan and Lyudmila (exc); *Auber:* Fra Diavolo (exc); *Verdi:* Rigoletto (exc); *Leoncavallo:* Pagliacci (exc); *Moniuszko:* Halka (exc); *Meyerbeer:* Prophète (exc); Huguenots (exc); *Tchaikovsky:* Eugene Onegin (exc); *Verdi:* Trovatore (exc); *Plotnikov:* With the sweet scent of lilacs; *Borodin:* Prince Igor (exc); *Rimsky-Korsakov:* May Night (exc); *Verdi:* Aida (exc); *Ponchielli:* Gioconda (exc). (V. Kastorsky, A. Labinsky, D. Bukhtoyarov, V. Sharonov, G. Morskoi, O. Kamionsky, P. Orlov, D. Yuzhin, A. Zaniboni, orch, anon/B. Seidler-Winkler, chor)

⦶ **GEMMCDS9001/3(2)** (6/93)
Singers of Imperial Russia, Vol.2 (pt 2)
Verdi: Aida (exc); *Serov:* Judith (exc); *Bellini:* Norma (exc); *Tchaikovsky:* Enchantress (exc); *Puccini:* Madama Butterfly (exc); *Wagner:* Fliegende Holländer (exc); *Tchaikovsky:* Oprichnik (exc); Queen of Spades (exc); Queen of Spades (exc); *Delibes:* Lakmé (exc); *Rimsky-Korsakov:* Sadko (exc); Tsar's Bride (exc); *Delibes:* Lakmé (exc); *Massenet:* Élégie; *Slonov:* Word of farewell; *A.J. Romberg:* Black clouds; *Meyerbeer:* Temptation; *Villamov:* Pray; *Tchaikovsky:* Eugene Onegin (exc); *Halévy:* Juive (exc); *Tchaikovsky:* Iolanta (exc); *Rossini:* Barbiere di Siviglia (exc); *Tchaikovsky:* Cherevichki (exc); *A.D. Davidov:* Leave me!; *Bleichman:* My lips are silent; *Dargomïzhsky:* Rusalka (exc); *Borodin:* Prince Igor (exc); *Meyerbeer:* Robert le Diable (exc); *Boito:* Mefistofele (exc); *Halévy:* Juive (exc); *Meyerbeer:* Huguenots (exc); *Glinka:* Life for the Tsar (exc); *Gounod:* Faust (exc); Faust (exc). (N. Ermolenko-Yuzhina, D. Yuzhin, A. Panina, M. Michailova, L. Sibiriakov, Moscow Imperial Op Chor, M.T. Manasevich, orch, anon)

⦶ **GEMMCDS9004/6(1)** (6/93)
Singers of Imperial Russia, Vol.3 (pt 1)
Niewiadomski: Sophia; *Zeleński:* Black skirt; *Verdi:* Traviata (exc); *Gall:* I love men; *Puccini:* Bohème (exc); *Nevhauser:* For good night; *Zarzycki:* Sad song; *Moniuszko:* Halka (exc); *Komorowski:* Guelder-rose; *Puccini:* Tosca (exc); *Halévy:* Juive (exc); *Rachmaninov:* Songs, Op.8 (exc); *Rubinstein:* Persian Songs, Op.34 (exc); *Rimsky-Korsakov:* By the sea, Op.46 (exc); Songs, Op.8 (exc); Sadko (exc); *Glinka:* Ruslan and Lyudmila (exc); Life for the Tsar (exc); *Verdi:* Traviata (exc); *Samuel-Rousseau:* Tarass Boulba (exc); *Rimsky-Korsakov:* Snow Maiden (exc); *Rossini:* Barbiere di Siviglia (exc); *Rimsky-Korsakov:* Tsar's Bride (exc); *Tchaikovsky:* Eugene Onegin (exc); Eugene Onegin (exc); Eugene Onegin (exc); *Nápravník:* Dubrovsky (exc); *Glinka:* Ruslan and Lyudmila (exc); *Dargomïzhsky:* Rusalka (exc); *Borodin:* Prince Igor (exc). (I. Bohuss, J. Korolewicz-Wayda, A. El-Tour, N. Zabela-Vrubel, M. Kuznetsova, L. Lipkowska, D. Smirnov, anon, orch/O.I. Arkadiev/J. Harrison)

⦶ **GEMMCDS9004/6(2)** (6/93)
Singers of Imperial Russia, Vol.3 (pt 2)
Grechaninov: Dobrinya Nikitich (exc); *Tchaikovsky:* Queen of Spades (exc); *Rimsky-Korsakov:* Snow Maiden (exc); *Mussorgsky:* Boris Godunov (exc); Fair at Sorochintsï (exc); *Kashevarov:* Tranquillity; *Grechaninov:* She was yours; *Rachmaninov:* Songs, Op.26 (exc); *Grechaninov:* Lullaby, Op.1/5; I wish I were with you; *Rimsky-Korsakov:* Songs, Op. 2 (exc); *Amani:* Cool summer evening; *Glinka:* Life for the Tsar (exc); *Rimsky-Korsakov:* Snow Maiden (exc); *Arensky:* Dream on the Volga (exc); *Gounod:* Faust (exc); *Sokolovsky:* By the blue sea; *Glinka:* Ruslan and Lyudmila (exc); *Schubert:* Erlkönig, D328; *Tchaikovsky:* Queen of Spades (exc); *Glinka:* Doubt; *Dargomïzhsky:* Rusalka (exc); *Borodin:* Prince Igor (exc); *Rubinstein:* Nero (exc); *Bizet:* Carmen (exc); *Glinka:* Life for the Tsar (exc); *Bemberg:* Chant hindou. (D. Smirnov, K.E. Kaidanov, E. Zbrueva, E. Witting, orch/P. Pitt/J. Harrison, anon, R.O. Von Beke, chor, anon)

⦶ **GEMMCDS9007/9(1)** (6/93)
Singers of Imperial Russia, Vol.4 (pt 1)
Tchaikovsky: Queen of Spades (exc); *Halévy:* Juive (exc); *Tosti:* Segreto; *Rubinstein:* Donkey and the Nightingale; *Meyerbeer:* Africaine (exc); *Tchaikovsky:* Songs, Op.60 (exc); *Verdi:* Aida (exc); *Bizet:* Pêcheurs de Perles (exc); *Mascagni:* Cavalleria Rusticana (exc); *A.D. Davidov:* Leave me!; *Nápravník:* Dubrovsky (exc); *Tchaikovsky:* Queen of Spades (exc); *Bizet:* Carmen (exc); *Dimitriev:* In the wild north; *Grechaninov:* She was yours; *Bleichman:* Far off; *Rubinstein:* Demon (exc); *Dargomïzhsky:* Rusalka (exc); *Tchaikovsky:* Eugene Onegin (exc); *Glinka:* Ruslan and Lyudmila (exc); *Bleichman:* Princesse lointaine (exc); *Tchaikovsky:* Cherevichki (exc); *A.D. Davidov:* What happiness!; *Gounod:* Faust (exc); *Verdi:* Traviata (exc); Traviata (exc); *Bizet:* Pêcheurs de perles (exc); *Grechaninov:* Dobrinya Nikitich (exc); *Gounod:* Roméo et Juliette (exc); *F. David:* Perle du Brésil (exc); *Nápravník:* Harold (exc); *Glinka:* Ruslan and Lyudmila (exc); *Gounod:* Sérénade; *Rimsky-Korsakov:* Sadko (exc); *Glinka:* Life for the Tsar (exc); *Bizet:* Pêcheurs de perles (exc); *Cui:* Bolero. (A. Davidov, E. Zbrueva, M. Michailova, V. Kastorsky, A. Bogdanovich, A. Nezhdanova, anon, chor, U. Masetti, anon, orch)

⦶ **GEMMCDS9007/9(2)** (6/93)
Singers of Imperial Russia, Vol.4 (pt 2)
Rimsky-Korsakov: Snow Maiden (exc); *Meyerbeer:* Huguenots (exc); *Gounod:* Mireille (exc); *Auber:* Fra Diavolo (exc); *Rimsky-Korsakov:* Golden Cockerel (exc); Tsar's Bride (exc); *Rossini:* Barbiere di Siviglia (exc); *Tosti:* Serenata; *Verdi:* Vespri siciliani (exc); *Rachmaninov:* Songs, Op.21 (exc); *Rimsky-Korsakov:* Songs, Op.2 (exc); *Glinka:* Life for the Tsar (exc); *Dimitriev:* Night; *Mussorgsky:* Boris Godunov (exc); *Glinka:* Life for the Tsar (exc); *Cui:* Oh, if Mother Volga; *Traditional:* Convict's song; *Verstovsky:* Askold's Grave (exc); *Bellini:* Sonnambula (exc); *Glinka:* Night Review; *Rubinstein:* Demon (exc); *Vil'boa:* Seafarers; *Glinka:* Elegy; *Cui:* Aeolian Harps; *Rubinstein:* Kalashnikov the Merchant (exc); *Moniuszko:* Halka (exc); *Tchaikovsky:* Enchantress (exc); Songs, Op.6 (exc); Queen of Spades (exc); *Rimsky-Korsakov:* In spring, Op.43 (exc); *Rubinstein:* Demon (exc); *Verstovsky:* Askold's Grave (exc); *A. Simon:* Song of love triumphant (exc); *Tchaikovsky:* Eugene Onegin (exc); *Cui:* Feast in time of plague (exc); Prisoner in the Caucasus (exc). (A. Nezhdanova, L. Sibiriakov, M. Michailova, G. Nikitina, A. Labinsky, E. Witting, A. Aleksandrovich, N. Shevelev, orch, anon, chor)

⦶ **GEMMCDS9044** (1/94)
Stokowski conducts Shostakovich
Shostakovich: Symphony 1; Symphony 5; Symphony 7; Preludes, Op.34 (exc). (Philadelphia, NBC SO/L. Stokowski)

⦶ **GEMMCDS9050/2(1)** (5/94)
Music from the New York Stage, Vol. 1 (part 1)
Mason: Nearer, My God, to Thee; *Kiallmark:* Old Oaken Bucket; *Kerker:* Castles in the Air (exc); *Various:* Ship Ahoy (exc); *De Koven:* Robin Hood (exc); Robin Hood (exc); *Scanlan:* Mavourneen (exc); *Various:* 1492 (exc); *Olcott:* Irish Artist (exc); *Various:* Grand Vizier (exc); *Irwin:* Bully Song; *Sidney Jones:* Artist's Model (exc); Geisha (exc); *Stanford:* Shamus O'Brien (exc); *Olcott:* Sweet Inniscarra (exc); *Herbert:* Serenade (exc); *Kerker:* Belle of New York (exc); *Irwin:* Frog Song; *Stromberg:* Pousse Café (exc); *Kerker:* Yankee Doodle Dandy (exc); *Caryll:* Runaway Girl (exc); *Stromberg:* Hurly Burly (exc); *Herbert:* Fortune Teller (exc); Fortune Teller (exc); *Sloane:* Kate Kip, Buyer (exc); *Olcott:* Romance of Athlone (exc); *Englander:* Rounders (exc); *Stromberg:* Whirl-i-Gig (exc); *Various:* Rogers Brothers in Central Park (exc); *Stuart:* Florodora (exc); *Cole:* Maiden With the Dreamy Eyes; *Caryll:* Toreador (exc); *B. Williams:* Sons of Ham (exc); *Talbot:* Chinese Honeymoon (exc); *Witmark:* Chaperons (exc); *J. W. Johnson:* Under the Bamboo Tree; *Stromberg:* Twirly-Whirly (exc); *A. H. Wilson:* Prince of Tatters (exc); *J. Edwards:* When Johnny Comes Marching Home (exc); *Rubens:* Three Little Maids (exc); *Cohan:* Mother Goose (exc); *G. Edwards:* In Zanzibar; *J. Schwartz:* Piff! Paff! Pouf (exc). (H. C. Barnabee, K. Barry, M. Cahill, G. Cameron, G. Carroll, E. Carus, G. M. Cohan, E. Cowles, M. Crichton, J. B. Davis, M. Farkoa, E. M. Favor, L. Fields, H. Fredricks, G. Frothingham, L. Gunning, D. Hopper, G. P. Huntley, M. Irwin, E. Jackson, R. Jose, W. H. MacDonald, A. Nielsen, C. Olcott, Old Homestead Double Qt, J. O'Mara, E. May, J. T. Powers, Gus Rogers, M. Rogers, L. Russell, T. Q. Seabrooke, W. H. Thompson, J. Weber, Bert Williams, A. H. Wilson, Broadway Cast)

⦶ **GEMMCDS9050/2(2)** (5/94)
Music from the New York Stage, Vol. 1 (part 2)
Robyn: Yankee Consul (exc); *Bratton:* Man From China (exc); *J. Edwards:* Love's Lottery (exc); *Cohan:* Little Johnny Jones (exc); *A. H. Wilson:* In Tyrol; *Sutton:* And the World Goes On; *J. Schwartz:* Ham Tree (exc); Fritz in Tammany Hall (exc); *Cohan:* George Washington Jnr (exc); *B. Williams:* In Abyssinia (exc); *Various:* Mrs Wilson, That's All (exc); *Rubens:* I Love You, Ma Chérie; *Kerker:* White Hen (exc); *Various:* Yankee Tourist (exc); *Hortiz:* Sing Me a Song, Fritz; *Hirsch:* That Wasn't All. (G. M. Cohan, R. C. Herz, R. Hitchcock, J. Hortiz, M. Irwin, H. Leoni, E. Levey, S. Mayhew, E. Schumann-Heink, H. Tally, G. Walker, Bert Williams, A. H. Wilson, Broadway Cast)

⦶ **GEMMCDS9053/5** (5/94)
Music from the New York Stage, Vol. 2: 1908—1913
B. Williams: I'm Tired of Eating in the Restaurants; *Cohan:* Fifty Miles from Boston (exc); *Hoschna:* Three Twins (exc); *M. Klein:* Pied Piper (exc); *Various:* Mr Hamlet of Broadway (exc); *Flynn:* Yip-I-Addy-I-Ay; *Various:* Midnight Sons (exc); *Sutton:* I Don't Care; *Butterfield:* When You and I Were Young, Maggie; *Snyder:* Oh, How that German Could Love; *Norworth:* Jolly Bachelors (exc); *Hubbell:* Jolly Bachelors (exc); *Snyder:* That Beautiful Rag; *Pryor:* Travel, Travel, Little Star; *B. Williams:* Moriah; *Various:* Ragged Robin (exc); Yankee Girl (exc); *J. Edwards:* Molly May (exc); *Various:* Summer Widowers (exc); Ziegfeld Follies of 1910 (exc); *A. Philipp:* Alma, Where Do You Live (exc); *Reinhardt:* Spring Maid (exc); *Janis:* Slim Princess (exc); *C. King:* Slim Princess (exc); *E. Ball:* Barry of Ballymore (exc); *Various:* Belle Paree (exc); Belle Paree (exc); *Norworth:* Little Miss Fix-It (exc); *Berlin:* Woodman, Spare that Tree; *M. Klein:* Around the World; *Lehár:* Gypsy Love (exc); *Various:* Vera Violetta (exc); *Tully:* Bird of Paradise (exc); *E. Ball:* Macushla (exc); *Various:* Whirl of Society (exc); Passing Show of 1912 (exc); Ziegfeld Follies of 1912 (exc); *Friml:* Firefly (exc); *E. Ball:* Isle O' Dreams (exc). (A. Albro, N. Bayes, I. Berlin, E. Brice, G. Cameron, C. Campbell, G. M. Cohan, C. Crawford, M. Ellis, I. Franklin, Hawaiian Qnt, C. Hayden, E. Janis, A. Jolson, S. Kellogg, C. King, G. LaRue, C. McDonald, T. McNaughton, S. Mayhew, Montgomery & Stone, J. Norworth, W. Oakland, C. Olcott, M. Raymond, B. Ring, H. Santrey, T. Shattuck, M. Sylva, E. Tanguay, B. Taylor, Bert Williams, Orig Broadway Cast)

⦶ **GEMMCDS9056/8** (5/94)
Music from the New York Stage, Vol. 3: 1913-17
Golden: You Can't Play Every Instrument in the Band; *Various:* Honeymoon Express (exc); Ziegfeld Follies of 1913 (exc); *Kern:* Look in Her Eyes; *Herbert:* Sweethearts (exc); *De Koven:* Rob Roy (exc); *Various:* Girl on the Film (exc); *Berlin:* Follow the Crowd; *Various:* Shameen Dhu (exc); *A. Philipp:* Midnight Girl (exc); *S. Hein:* When You're All Dressed Up and No Place to Go; *Various:* Ziegfeld Follies of 1914 (exc); *Darewski:* Sister Susie's sewing; *Various:* Dancing Around (exc); *Van Alstyne:* Pretty Baby; *Caryll:* Chin-Chin (exc); *Cuvillier:* Lilac Domino (exc); *Berlin:* Watch Your Step (exc); *Rubens:* Tonight's the Night (exc); *E. Ball:* Trilby (exc); *Various:* Ziegfeld Follies of 1915 (exc); *Herbert:* Princess Pat (exc); *Sousa:* New York Hippodrome March; *Hubbell:* Ladder of Roses; *Lehár:* Alone at Last (exc); *Friml:* Katinka (exc); *Golden:* Sybil (exc); *Jolson:* Robinson Crusoe, Jr (exc); *Various:* Heart O' Th' Heather (exc); *Kern:* My Castle in the Air; *Various:* Betty (exc); *E. Carroll:* So Long, Letty (exc); *Various:* Century Girl (exc); Follow Me (exc); *Kern:* Have a Heart (exc); *Berlin:* Dance and Grow Thin; *Felix:* Pom-Pom (exc); *B. Grant:* Step This Way (exc). (S. Ash, R. Atwell, I. Berlin, E. Brice, J. Cawthorn, J. Collins, M. Farrell, G. Grossmith, M. Hajos, L. Henson, R. Hitchcock, A. Jolson, C. King, H. Lewis, B. Linn, C. McDonald, G. MacFarlane, M. Naudain, C. Olcott, E. Painter, F. Pollock, M. Romaine, Six Brown Brothers, Sousa's Band, J. C. Thomas, B. B. Van, Van & Schenck, Bert Williams, N. M. Wills, Orig Broadway Cast)

⦶ **GEMMCDS9059/61** (5/94)
Music from the New York Stage, Vol. 4: 1917-20
Kern: Oh Boy! (exc); Oh Boy! (exc); *Herbert:* Eileen (exc); *Various:* Passing Show of 1917 (exc); Hitchy-Koo (exc); Ziegfeld Follies of 1917 (exc); *Romberg:* Maytime (exc); *Various:* Doing Our Bit (exc); *Valverde:* Land of Joy (exc); *Various:* Odds and Ends of 1917 (exc); *Von Tilzer:* If You Only Knew; *Various:* Ziegfeld Midnight Frolic (exc); Cohan Revue of 1918 (exc); *Jolson:* Sinbad (exc); *Snyder:* How'd You Like to be My Daddy?; *H. Carroll:* Oh, Look! (exc); *Various:* Why Worry? (exc); Why Worry? (exc); *Bayes:* Ladies First (exc); *Balfe:* Bohemian Girl (exc); *Kern:* She's a Good Fellow (exc); *Various:* Monte Christo, Jr (exc); Ziegfeld Follies of 1919 (exc); *Berlin:* Ziegfeld Follies of 1919 (exc); *Various:* Greenwich Village Follies of 1919 (exc); Oh, What a Girl! (exc); *Jacobi:* Apple Blossoms (exc); *Tierney:* Irene (exc); *Various:* My Lady Friends (exc). (S. Ash, Avon Comedy Four, N. Bayes, F. Brice, E. Cantor, E. Day, Duncan Sisters, G. Evans, Farber Sisters, H. Fox, I. Franklin, A. Jolson, LaCalle's Spanish Orch, H. Lewis, T. Lewis & His Orch, J. Norworth, T. Powers, H. Scott, J. Steel, V. Stiles, J. C. Thomas, Van & Schenck, E. Walker, F. Watson, Watson Sisters, S. Welsh, A. Wheaton, F. White, Bert Williams, Orig Broadway Cast/V. Herbert)

⦶ **GEMMCDS9073(1)** (5/94)
Giovanni Zenatello, Vol.1 (pt 1)
Giordano: Andrea Chénier (exc); *Puccini:* Manon Lescaut (exc); *Gounod:* Faust (exc); *Berlioz:* Damnation de Faust (exc); *Verdi:* Traviata (exc); *Wagner:* Meistersinger (exc); *Giordano:* Siberia (exc); Siberia (exc); *Leoncavallo:* Pagliacci (exc); *Giordano:* Andrea Chénier (exc); *Verdi:* Ballo in maschera (exc); Aida (exc); *Boito:* Mefistofele (exc); *Donizetti:* Lucia di Lammermoor (exc); *Boito:* Mefistofele (exc); *Verdi:* Aida (exc); Traviata (exc); Trovatore (exc); Ballo in maschera (exc); *Franchetti:* Figlia di Iorio (exc); *Bizet:* Carmen (exc); *Ponchielli:* Gioconda (exc); *Verdi:* Otello (exc); *Leoncavallo:* Pagliacci (exc); *Ponchielli:* Gioconda (exc); *Puccini:* Manon Lescaut (exc); *Denza:* Vieni a me; *Verdi:* Ballo in maschera (exc); Otello (exc); *Giordano:* Andrea Chénier (exc); *Saint-Saëns:* Samson et Dalila (exc); *Verdi:* Traviata (exc); *Bizet:* Carmen (exc); *Ponchielli:* Gioconda (exc); *Boito:* Mefistofele (exc); *Puccini:* Bohème (exc). (G. Zenatello, R. Storchio, N. Frascani, A. Parsi-Pettinella, A. Didur, M.

Hérodiade (exc); *Puccini:* Tosca (exc); *Verdi:* Ballo in maschera (exc); *Cilea:* Adriana Lecouvreur (exc); *Verdi:* Rigoletto (exc); *Gounod:* Faust (exc); *Puccini:* Manon Lescaut (exc); *Verdi:* Rigoletto (exc); Ballo in maschera (exc); *Meyerbeer:* Huguenots (exc); *Puccini:* Madama Butterfly (exc); *Gluck:* Orfeo ed Euridice (exc); *Giordano:* Andrea Chénier (exc); *Puccini:* Manon Lescaut (exc); *Verdi:* Traviata (exc); Trovatore (exc); Rigoletto (exc); Aida (exc); *Mozart:* Don Giovanni (exc); *Gounod:* Faust (exc); *Giordano:* Andrea Chénier (exc); *Puccini:* Bohème (exc); *Wagner:* Meistersinger (exc). (F. Viñas, E. Destinn, N. Melba, E. Caruso, C. Dalmores, E. Calvé, G. Anselmi, C. Boninsegna, M. Sammarco, V. Arimondi, P. Amato, S. Kurz, L. Kirkby-Lunn, G. Zenatello, R. Stracciari, M. Battistini, C. Whitehill, anon, orch, NY Met Op Chor, E. Corsi/B. Seidler-Winkler/C. Sabajno/G. Setti/P. Pitt)

Ⓓ **GEMMCDS9924(2)** (7/92)
Covent Garden on Record, Vol.2 (pt 2)
Bizet: Carmen (exc); *Wagner:* Fliegende Holländer (exc); *Donizetti:* Lucia di Lammermoor (exc); *Wagner:* Tannhäuser (exc); *Ponchielli:* Gioconda (exc); *Mozart:* Don Giovanni (exc); *Verdi:* Rigoletto (exc); *Franchetti:* Germania (exc); *Verdi:* Traviata (exc); Rigoletto (exc); *Mozart:* Don Giovanni (exc); *Bizet:* Pêcheurs de Perles (exc); *Meyerbeer:* Huguenots (exc); *Giordano:* Fedora (exc); *Puccini:* Tosca (exc); *Verdi:* Otello (exc); *Saint-Saëns:* Samson et Dalila (exc); *Wagner:* Götterdämmerung (exc); *Puccini:* Bohème (exc); *Debussy:* Pelléas et Mélisande (exc); *Verdi:* Aida (exc); *Puccini:* Tosca (exc); *Wagner:* Walküre (exc); *Puccini:* Bohème (exc); *Delibes:* Lakmé (exc); *Verdi:* Otello (exc); *Wagner:* Walküre (exc); Walküre (exc). (M. Gay, E. Destinn, M. Journet, K. Fleischer-Edel, G. De Luca, J. McCormack, M. Sammarco, L. Tetrazzini, O. Luppi, A. Bonci, J. Nivette, E. Garbin, A. Scotti, G. Zenatello, L. Kirkby-Lunn, A. Talexis, G. Russ, M. Saltzmann-Stevens, M. Kousnietzoff, Vanni-Marcoux, L. Slezak, W. Hyde, S. Sedlmair, G. Anselmi, M. Kurt, P. Cornelius, orch, anon/B. Seidler-Winkler/P. Pitt/P. Coppola/G.W. Byng)

Ⓓ **GEMMCDS9925(1)** (7/92)
Covent Garden on Record—Vol.3 (pt 1)
Mozart: Don Giovanni (exc); *Gounod:* Faust (exc); *Verdi:* Rigoletto (exc); *Meyerbeer:* Huguenots (exc); *G. Charpentier:* Louise (exc); *Verdi:* Rigoletto (exc); *Puccini:* Manon Lescaut (exc); *R. Strauss:* Rosenkavalier (exc); *Wagner:* Walküre (exc); *Puccini:* Bohème (exc); *Verdi:* Falstaff (exc); *Boito:* Mefistofele (exc); *Saint-Saëns:* Samson et Dalila (exc); *Verdi:* Aida (exc); *Mozart:* Zauberflöte (exc); *Puccini:* Madama Butterfly (exc); Madama Butterfly (exc); *Donizetti:* Don Pasquale (exc); *Gluck:* Orfeo ed Euridice (exc); *Verdi:* Trovatore (exc); *Mozart:* Zauberflöte (exc); *Verdi:* Aida (exc); *Saint-Saëns:* Samson et Dalila (exc); *Leoncavallo:* Pagliacci (exc); *Wagner:* Götterdämmerung (exc); *Puccini:* Bohème (exc). (G. De Luca, L. Sibiriakov, L. Edvina, L. Lipkowska, G. Martinelli, M. Siems, M. Kurt, J. Urlus, C. Muzio, A. Scotti, A. Didur, P. Franz, M. Licette, J. Hislop, D. Gilly, G. dalla Rizza, G. Pareto, C. Butt, E. Turner, N. Allin, F. Austral, M. Fleta, E. Thornton, D. Noble, W. Widdop, chor, orch, Sadlers Wells Op Orch, LSO, anon/P. Pitt/Henry Wood/T. Beecham/C. Sabajno/W. Braithwaite/A. Coates)

Ⓓ **GEMMCDS9925(2)** (7/92)
Covent Garden on Record—Vol.3 (pt 2)
R. Strauss: Ariadne auf Naxos (exc); *Wagner:* Walküre (exc); Walküre (exc); Walküre (exc); Walküre (exc); *Verdi:* Rigoletto (exc); *R. Strauss:* Ariadne auf Naxos (exc); Rosenkavalier (exc); *Verdi:* Aida (exc); Aida (exc); *Puccini:* Madama Butterfly (exc); *Giordano:* Andrea Chénier (exc); *Donizetti:* Lucia di Lammermoor (exc); *Rossini:* Barbiere di Siviglia (exc); *Puccini:* Tosca (exc); *Wagner:* Fliegende Holländer (exc); *Mozart:* Nozze di Figaro (exc); Nozze di Figaro (exc); *Boito:* Mefistofele (exc); *Verdi:* Otello (exc); *Puccini:* Bohème (exc); *Verdi:* Otello (exc). (Lotte Lehmann, L. Melchior, G. Ljungberg, F. Leider, F. Schorr, A. Piccaver, M. Ivogün, R. Mayr, A. Andrassy, E. Rethberg, B. Franci, M. Sheridan, A. Pertile, G. Lauri-Volpi, T. dal Monte, D. Borgioli, M. Jeritza, E. Schumann, F. Chaliapin, N. Melba, J. Brownlee, G. Zenatello, Berlin St Op Orch, orch, La Scala Orch/F. Weissmann/L. Blech/L. Collingwood/B. Walter/C. Sabajno/F. Ghione/R. Bourdon/V. Bellezza)

Ⓓ **GEMMCDS9926(1)** (7/92)
Covent Garden on Record—Vol.4 (pt 1)
Verdi: Otello (exc); *Massenet:* Manon (exc); *Verdi:* Falstaff (exc); *Mozart:* Entführung (exc); *Verdi:* Trovatore (exc); Trovatore (exc); *Puccini:* Turandot (exc); *Gluck:* Armide (exc); *Wagner:* Tannhäuser (exc); Tannhäuser (exc); *Puccini:* Bohème (exc); *Saint-Saëns:* Samson et Dalila (exc); *Verdi:* Otello (exc); Otello (exc); Aida (exc); *Gounod:* Faust (exc); Faust (exc); *Mussorgsky:* Boris Godunov (exc); *Wagner:* Meistersinger (exc); *Puccini:* Manon Lescaut (exc); *Wagner:* Walküre (exc); *Mozart:* Don Giovanni (exc); *Ponchielli:* Gioconda (exc); *Puccini:* Tosca (exc). (G. Zenatello, L. Cilla, E. Cotreil, M. Sampieri, F. Heldy, F. Ansseau, M. Stabile, M. Ivogün, A. Pertile, F. Leider, L. Schöne, H. Janssen, L. Melchior, D. Borgioli, G. Thill, G. Inghilleri, O. Dua, R. Zanelli, I. Minghini-Cattaneo, J. Hislop, F. Chaliapin, A. Kipnis, R. Pampanini, W. Widdop, H. Nash, R. Ponselle, C. Melis, chor, La Scala Chor, orch, Berlin St Op Orch, Bayreuth Fest Orch, LSO, La Scala Orch/V. Bellezza/P. Coppola/F. Zweig/K. Elmendorff/J. Barbirolli/A. Coates/P. Gaubert/C. Sabajno/E. Goossens/E. Orthmann)

Ⓓ **GEMMCDS9926(2)** (7/92)
Covent Garden on Record—Vol.4 (pt 2)
J. Strauss II: Fledermaus (exc); Fledermaus (exc); *Bellini:* Norma (exc); *Giordano:* Andrea Chénier (exc); *Mozart:* Zauberflöte (exc); *Verdi:* Forza del destino (exc); *Puccini:* Turandot (exc); Turandot (exc); Bohème (exc); *Wagner:* Meistersinger (exc); *Rossini:* Cenerentola (exc); *Puccini:* Bohème (exc); Bohème (exc); *Verdi:* Aida (exc); *Wagner:* Tristan und Isolde (exc); *Verdi:* Otello (exc); *Mozart:* Zauberflöte (exc); *Wagner:* Lohengrin (exc); *Beethoven:* Fidelio (exc); *Verdi:* Rigoletto (exc); *Mozart:* Don Giovanni (exc); *Verdi:* Traviata (exc). (Lotte Lehmann, E. Schumann, E. Pinza, B. Gigli, I. Andrésen, R. Ponselle, M. Németh, A. Cortis, J. Cross, R. Bockelmann, C. Supervia, G. Moore, D. Labbette, H. Nash, E. Rethberg, G. Lauri-Volpi, K. Flagstad, L. Tibbett, G. Martinelli, N. Massue, R. Tauber, T. Lemnitz, T. Ralf, H. Roswaenge, L. Pagliughi, M. Caniglia, J. Brownlee, S. Andreva, R. Alva, R. Easton, NY Met Op Chor, ROH Chor, orch, NY Met Op Orch, La Scala Orch, Berlin St Op Orch, Vienna St Op Orch, Berlin Staatskapelle/F. Weissmann/K. Alwin/G. Setti/U. Berrettoni/F. Zweig/R. Bourdon/C. Sabajno/C. Schmalstich/A. Albergoni/T. Beecham/H. Lange/W. Pelletier/L. Blech/B. Seidler-Winkler/B. Walter, LPO/P. Cimara)

Ⓓ **GEMMCDS9951/5** (9/92)
The Elgar Edition—Acoustic Recordings 1914-25
Elgar: Carissima; Pomp and Circumstance Marches (exc); Salut d'amour; Carillon (exc); Starlight Express (exc); Violin Concerto (exc); Bavarian Dances; Cockaigne (exc); Dream of Gerontius (exc); Fringes of the Fleet; Wand of Youth Suite 1 (exc); Wand of Youth Suite 2 (exc); Polonia; Chanson de nuit; Cello Concerto (exc); Sanguine Fan (exc); Enigma Variations; King Olaf (exc); Sea Pictures; In the South (exc); Symphony 2; *Bach:* Fantasia and Fugue, BWV537; *Handel:* Overture in D minor; *Elgar:* Light of Life (exc). (A. Nicholls, L. Megane, C. Mott, F. Henry, F. Stewart, H. Barratt, H. Ainley, M. Hall, B. Harrison, RAHO, SO/E. Elgar)

Ⓓ **GEMMCDS9979** (12/93)
Horszowski—A Centenary Celebration
C.P.E. Bach: Fantasia, H291; *Mozart:* Variations, K455; *Schubert:* Piano Sonata, D958; *Chopin:* Fantasie, Op.49; Polonaises (exc); Etudes (exc); *Beethoven:* Piano Sonata 31; Diabelli Variations; *Bach:* Partitas, BWV825-30 (exc). (M. Horszowski)

Ⓓ **GEMMCDS9996** (9/93)
Kreisler - Violin Concertos
Brahms: Violin Concerto; *Mendelssohn:* Violin Concerto, Op.64; *Bach:* 2-Violin Concerto; *Beethoven:* Violin Concerto; *Mozart:* Violin Concerto, K218. (F. Kreisler, E. Zimbalist, Berlin St Op Orch/L. Blech, Stg Qt, LSO/L. Ronald)

Ⓓ **GEMMCDS9997/9(1)** (6/93)
Singers of Imperial Russia, Vol.1 (pt 1)
Meyerbeer: Huguenots (exc); Prophète (exc); *Wagner:* Siegfried (exc); *Mussorgsky:* Songs and Dances of Death (exc); *Tchaikovsky:* Songs, Op.63 (exc); *Vilboa:* Seafarers; *Tosti:* Penso!; *Rubinstein:* Nacht; *Puccini:* Tosca (exc); *Tchaikovsky:* Queen of Spades (exc); *Nápravník:* Harold (exc); *A.D. Davidov:* Night, love and the moon; *Bizet:* Carmen (exc); *Tchaikovsky:* Oprichnik (exc); *Cui:* I remember the evening; *Vrangel:* In my soul winter reigns; *Auber:* Fra Diavolo (exc); *Tchaikovsky:* Queen of Spades (exc); *Nápravník:* Dubrovsky (exc); *Rubinstein:* We three; Demon (exc); Asra; *Ippolitov-Ivanov:* In the long grey twilight; *Rossini:* Barbiere di Siviglia (exc); *Tchaikovsky:* Songs, Op.38 (exc); *Dargomïzhsky:* Rusalka (exc); *Cui:* Angelo (exc); *Moniuszko:* Halka (exc); *Tchaikovsky:* Eugene Onegin (exc); *Borodin:* Prince Igor (exc); *Verdi:* Rigoletto (exc); *Rimsky-Korsakov:* Snow Maiden (exc); *Ivanov:* Zabava Putyatishna (exc); *Rimsky-Korsakov:* May Night (exc); *Gounod:* Où voulez-vous aller?; *Grechaninov:* Dobrinya Nikitich (exc); *Nikolayev:* I cannot banish grief; *Tchaikovsky:* Songs, Op.60 (exc). (I. Ershov, V. Sharonov, M. Mei-Figner, N. Figner, I. Tartakov, L. Sobinov, anon)

Ⓓ **GEMMCDS9997/9(2)** (6/93)
Singers of Imperial Russia, Vol.1 (pt 2)
Gounod: Faust (exc); *Flotow:* Martha (exc); *Nikolayev:* Rest; *Wagner:* Lohengrin (exc); *Massenet:* Werther (exc); Manon (exc); *Bizet:* Pêcheurs de perles (exc); *A. Thomas:* Mignon (exc); *Rimsky-Korsakov:* Snow Maiden (exc); *Arensky:* Raphael (exc); *Meyerbeer:* Huguenots (exc); *Tosti:* Si tu le voulais; *Gall:* Hidden love; *Meyerbeer:* Robert le Diable (exc); *Boito:* Mefistofele (exc); *Verdi:* Don Carlo (exc); *Moniuszko:* O, mother; *Gounod:* Faust (exc); *Verdi:* Ernani (exc); *Moniuszko:* Quack's prophecy; Haunted Manor (exc); O, mother; Quack's prophecy; *Noskowski:* Our mountaineers; *Hertz:* Old King; *Gall:* Hidden love; *Moniuszko:* Verbum Nobile (exc); Old age; *Maszynski:* Bagpiper's Song; *Moniuszko:* Phantoms (exc); Halka (exc); *Gall:* Enchanted princess; *Moniuszko:* Rokiczana (exc); Sail! young raftsmen; *Boito:* Mefistofele (exc); *Halévy:* Juive (exc); *Meyerbeer:* Robert le Diable (exc); *Gounod:* Faust (exc); *Boito:* Mefistofele (exc); *Meyerbeer:* Huguenots (exc). (L. Sobinov, A. Didur, anon, orch, D.G. Kornilov, S. Cottone)

Ⓓ **GEMMCD9020** (6/93)
Koussevitzky conducts Stravinsky and Mussorgsky
Stravinsky: Petrushka (exc); Apollon Musagète (exc); *Traditional:* Song of the Volga Boatmen; *Stravinsky:* Capriccio; *Mussorgsky:* Pictures. (J-M. Sanromá, Boston SO/S. Koussevitzky)

Ⓓ **GEMMCD9022** (2/94)
Eileen Joyce
Bach: Prelude and Fugue, BWV543; *Mozart:* Piano Sonata, K332; *Chopin:* Berceuse; Fantaisie-Impromptu; *Schumann:* Novelletten (exc); *Liszt:* Concert Studies, S144 (exc); *Brahms:* Piano Pieces, Op.76 (exc); Piano Pieces, Op.117 (exc); *Grieg:* Lyric Pieces, Op.47 (exc); *Debussy:* Pour le piano (exc); *R. Strauss:* Lieder, Op.17 (exc); *Albert:* Scherzo, Op.16/2; *Rachmaninov:* Preludes (exc); *Shostakovich:* Fantastic Dances; *C. Scott:* Danse nègre. (E. Joyce)

Ⓓ **GEMMCD9037** (7/95)
Koussevitzky conducts
Mendelssohn: Symphony 4; *Schubert:* Symphony 8; *Schumann:* Symphony 1. (Boston SO/S. Koussevitzky)

Ⓓ **GEMMCD9038** (3/94)
Walter Gieseking, Vol.3
Mozart: Piano Concerto 9; *Brahms:* Piano Pieces, Op.118 (exc); Rhapsodies, Op.79 (exc); *Chopin:* Polonaises (exc); Etudes (exc); Nocturnes (exc); Nocturnes (exc); Ballades (exc); *Casella:* Sonatina, Op.28; *Ravel:* Jeux d'eau. (W. Gieseking, Paris Nat Orch/I. Markevitch)

Ⓓ **GEMMCD9045** (9/94)
William Primrose and Albert Spalding
Brahms: Viola Sonata 2; *H. Casadesus:* Viola Concerto; *Mozart:* Sinfonia Concertante, K364. (A. Spalding, W. Primrose, G. Moore, CO/W. Goehr, New Friends of Music Orch/F. Stiedry)

Ⓓ **GEMMCD9065** (7/94)
Beecham conducts French Works
Berlioz: Damnation de Faust (exc); *Franck:* Symphony; *Debussy:* Après-midi; *Offenbach:* Contes d'Hoffmann (exc). (LPO/T. Beecham)

Ⓓ **GEMMCD9092** (12/95)
Kirsten Flagstad - Songs
Schubert: Forelle, D550; Lachen und Weinen, D777; *Beethoven:* Lieder, Op.48 (exc); Zärtliche Liebe, WoO123; *Grieg:* Melodies of the Heart, Op.5 (exc); Melodies of the Heart, Op.5 (exc); Songs, Op.25 (exc); Songs, Op.26 (exc); Songs, Op.26 (exc); Songs, Op.48 (exc); Songs, Op.60 (exc); Songs, Op.60 (exc); Songs, Op.69 (exc); Songs, Op.70 (exc); *A. Grøndahl:* Eventide; *Alnaes:* Happiness; *Hurum:* Pale Nights; *Brahms:* Lieder, Op.63 (exc); *R. Strauss:* Lieder, Op.10 (exc); *Dvořák:* Gipsy Melodies (exc); *C. Scott:* Lullaby; *Ronald:* Summertime (exc); *Charles:* When I have sung my songs. (K. Flagstad, E. McArthur)

Ⓓ **GEMMCD9119** (11/94)
Schumann—Legendary Song Cycles
Schumann: Dichterliebe, Op.48 (Cpte); Frauenliebe und -leben, Op.42 (Cpte); Liederkreis, Op.39 (Cpte). (G. Hüsch, H.U. Müller, Lotte Lehmann, Inst Ens/F. Weissmann, F. Schorr, F. Kitzinger)

Ⓓ **GEMMCD9131** (2/95)
Bruno Walter live
Bruckner: Symphony 4; *Weber:* Oberon (exc); *Smetana:* Bartered Bride (exc). (NBC SO/B. Walter)

Ⓓ **GEMMCD9132** (2/95)
Alexander Brailowsky
D. Scarlatti: Keyboard Sonatas (exc); *Weber:* Piano Sonata 1 (exc); *Schubert:* Marches Militaires, D733 (exc); *Mendelssohn:* Fantaisies, Op.16 (exc); *Chopin:* Fantaisie-Impromptu; Etudes (exc); Ballades (exc); Barcarolle; *Schumann:* Fantasiestücke, Op.12 (exc); *Liszt:* Hungarian Rhapsodies, S244 (exc); *Debussy:* Pour le piano (exc); *Scriabin:* Preludes, Op.11 (exc); Etudes, Op.8 (exc); *Liszt:* Tannhäuser—paraphrase, S442. (A. Brailowsky)

de l'adieu; *Liszt:* Es muss ein Wunderbares sein, S314. (R. Tauber, V. Schwarz, B. Ziegler, orch/E. Hauke)

ⓘ **GEMMCD9330** (9/90)
Beethoven: Violin Sonatas, Vol.1
Beethoven: Violin Sonata 1; Violin Sonata 2; Violin Sonata 3. (F. Kreisler, F. Rupp)

ⓘ **GEMMCD9331** (11/89)
Frida Leider sings Wagner
Wagner: Götterdämmerung (exc); Götterdämmerung (exc); Tristan und Isolde (exc); Tristan und Isolde (exc); Parsifal (exc). (F. Leider, A. von Stosch, E. Marherr-Wagner, L. Melchior, H. Janssen, W. Schirp, ROH Chor, ROHO/W. Furtwängler, Berlin St Op Orch/L. Blech, LSO/J. Barbirolli)

ⓘ **GEMMCD9339** (4/89)
Moriz Rosenthal—Piano Recital
Chopin: Piano Concerto 1; *Liszt:* Chants polonais, S480 (exc); *Chopin:* Etudes (exc); Mazurkas (exc); Mazurkas (exc); Berceuse; Waltzes (exc); *J. Strauss II:* Blauen Donau, Op. 314; *M. Rosenthal:* Vienna Carnival. (M. Rosenthal, Orch/F. Weissmann)

ⓘ **GEMMCD9341** (8/89)
Bach & Mozart: Violin Concertos
Bach: Violin Concerto, BWV1041; Violin Concerto, BWV1042; *Mozart:* Violin Concerto, K216. (B. Huberman, VPO/I. Dobroven)

ⓘ **GEMMCD9342** (12/89)
Vaughan Williams: Vocal Works
Vaughan Williams: Festival Te Deum; Serenade to Music; Dona nobis pacem. (L. Stiles-Allen, I. Baillie, E. Suddaby, E. Turner, R. Flynn, M. Balfour, M. Brunskill, A. Desmond, M. Jarred, Parry Jones, H. Nash, F. Titterton, W. Widdop, Roy Henderson, N. Allin, R. Easton, H. Williams, Coronation Ch, Coronation Orch, BBC Chor, BBC SO/Henry Wood/R. Vaughan Williams/E. Bullock)

ⓘ **GEMMCD9347** (4/90)
Ferruccio Busoni & Egon Petri
Chopin: Etudes (exc); Etudes (exc); Preludes (exc); Nocturnes (exc); *Bach:* Wohltemperierte Klavier (exc); Nun freut euch, BWV734; *Beethoven:* Ecossaises, WoO83 (exc); *Liszt:* Hungarian Rhapsodies, S244 (exc); *Busoni:* Sonatina 6; Indianisches Tagebuch; Bach Fantasia; Elegien (exc); Sonatina 3; *Mozart:* Don Giovanni (exc); *Liszt:* Rhapsodie espagnole, S254. (F. Busoni, E. Petri, Minneapolis SO/D. Mitropoulos)

ⓘ **GEMMCD9348** (9/90)
Debussy: Orchestral & Chamber Works
Debussy: Sonata for flute, viola and harp; Cello Sonata; Violin Sonata; Danse sacrée et danse profane; Rapsodie. (M. Moyse, E. Ginot, L. Laskine, M. Maréchal, R. Casadesus, J. Thibaud, A. Cortot, M. Viard, SO/P. Coppola)

ⓘ **GEMMCD9349** (5/89)
Casals plays Works for Cello and Orchestra
Dvořák: Cello Concerto; *Bruch:* Kol Nidrei; *Boccherini:* Cello Concerto, G482. (P. Casals, LSO, Czech PO/L. Ronald/G. Szell)

ⓘ **GEMMCD9354** (8/90)
Beethoven: Violin Sonatas, Vol.2
Beethoven: Violin Sonata 4; Violin Sonata 5; Violin Sonata 6. (F. Kreisler, F. Rupp)

ⓘ **GEMMCD9366** (5/90)
Strauss conducts Strauss
R. Strauss: Don Juan; Till Eulenspiegel; Bourgeois gentilhomme suite. (Berlin St Op Orch/R. Strauss)

ⓘ **GEMMCD9367** (5/90)
Gigli—Arias and Duets
Bizet: Pêcheurs de Perles (exc); *Buzzi-Peccia:* Torna amore; *De Curtis:* Carmela; Voce 'e notte; *Denza:* Se; *Donizetti:* Elisir d'amore (exc); Elisir d'amore (exc); Lucia di Lammermoor (exc); Lucia di Lammermoor (exc); Lucia di Lammermoor (exc); Lucia di Lammermoor (exc); *Nutile:* Mamma mia, che vo' sapè; *Ponchielli:* Gioconda (exc); Gioconda (exc); *Rimsky-Korsakov:* Sadko (exc); *Seismit-Doda:* Notte lunare; *Verdi:* Lombardi (exc). (B. Gigli, M. Talley, orch, H. Heller, A. Galli-Curci, L. Homer, A. Bada, G. De Luca, E. Pinza, NY Met Op Orch/G. Setti, NY Met Op Chor/R. Bourdon, E. Rethberg, T. Ruffo/H. Shilkret/M. Reibold, Vitaphone Orch)

ⓘ **GEMMCD9370** (9/90)
Richard Tauber sings Lieder
Schubert: Winterreise (exc); *Schumann:* Liederkreis, Op.39 (exc); Myrthen, Op. 25 (exc); *Traditional:* Ach wie ist's möglich dann; Du, du liegst mir im Herzen; Gute Kamerad; Jägerlieben; Zerbrochene Ringlein; Lebewohl; *Anon:* Frohe Botschaft; *Traditional:* Burschenlust; In der Ferne; Treue Liebe; Heidenröslein; Jäger Abschied. (R. Tauber, M. Spoliansky, P. Kahn)

ⓘ **GEMMCD9381** (4/90)
Richard Tauber sings Lieder
J. Martini: Plaisir d'amour; *Schubert:* Winterreise (exc); Ständchen, D889; Frühlingsglaube, D686; Frühlingsglaube, D686; Heidenröslein, D257; Schwanengesang, D957 (exc); Wanderer, D489; Schwanengesang, D957 (exc); Schöne Müllerin (exc); Schöne Müllerin (exc); *Schumann:* Romanzen und Balladen, Op. 49 (exc); Gedichte, Op. 35 (exc); Myrthen, Op. 25 (exc); *Mendelssohn:* Duets, Op. 63 (exc); Im Grünen, Op. 59 (exc); Lieder, Op. 57 (exc); *Loewe:* Tom der Reimer, Op. 135a; *Wolf:* Mörike Lieder (exc); Über Nacht; *Rubinstein:* Nacht; *Grieg:* Songs, Op.33 (exc); Melodies of the Heart, Op. 5 (exc); *Liszt:* Es muss ein Wunderbares sein, S314. (R. Tauber, Berlin Staatskapelle, Orch, Odeon CO, Berlin Künstlertheater Orch, Berlin Schauspielhaus Orch, Dajos Bela Orch/E. Hauke/A. Paulik/F. Weissmann)

ⓘ **GEMMCD9383** (3/90)
Julius Patzak—Opera & Operetta Recital
Donizetti: Elisir d'amore (exc); *Verdi:* Ballo in maschera (exc); Traviata (exc); Trovatore (exc); *Puccini:* Fanciulla del West (exc); Bohème (exc); *A. Thomas:* Mignon (exc); *Massenet:* Manon (exc); Manon (exc); Werther (exc); *Tchaikovsky:* Eugene Onegin (exc); *Offenbach:* Contes d'Hoffmann (exc); Goldschmied von Toledo (exc); *Flotow:* Martha (exc); *Nicolai:* Lustigen Weiber von Windsor (exc); *Smetana:* Bartered Bride (exc); *Suppé:* Boccaccio (exc); *J. Strauss II:* Lustige Krieg (exc); Nacht in Venedig (exc); *Millöcker:* Bettelstudent (exc); Gasparone (exc); *Traditional:* Ich hab' amal a Räuscherl g'habt. (J. Patzak, G. Rünger, Berlin St Op Orch, orch, Vienna Schrammel Qt/M. Gurlitt/H. Weigert/J. Prüwer/A. Melichar, Berlin St Op Chor, F. Völker)

ⓘ **GEMMCD9385** (3/90)
Wilhelm Backhaus plays Brahms
Brahms: Ballades (exc); Piano Pieces, Op.118; Piano Pieces, Op.76 (exc); Piano Pieces, Op.117 (exc); Rhapsodies, Op.79; Scherzo, Op.4; Hungarian Dances (exc); Variations, Op.21/1; Waltzes, Op.39 (exc). (W. Backhaus)

ⓘ **GEMMCD9394** (5/90)
Helge Roswaenge—Operatic Recital
Boïeldieu: Dame blanche (exc); *Mozart:* Cosi fan tutte (exc); Don Giovanni (exc); *Puccini:* Madama Butterfly (exc); Bohème (exc); Bohème (exc); Tosca (exc); *Weber:* Freischütz (exc); *Bizet:* Carmen (exc); *Verdi:* Forza del destino (exc); *Beethoven:* Fidelio (exc); *Verdi:* Trovatore (exc). (H. Roswaenge, H. von Debička, G. Hüsch, M. Perras, Berlin St Op Orch/F. Weissmann/M. Gurlitt/B. Seidler-Winkler)

ⓘ **GEMMCD9398** (9/91)
Friedrich Schorr
Haydn: Jahreszeiten (exc); *Mozart:* Zauberflöte (exc); *Weber:* Euryanthe (exc); *Beethoven:* Fidelio (exc); *Mendelssohn:* Elias (exc); Elias (exc); *Wagner:* Tannhäuser (exc); Tannhäuser (exc); Tannhäuser (exc); Meistersinger (exc); *Schubert:* Schwanengesang, D957 (exc); *Wolf:* Goethe Lieder (exc); Sechs Gedichte (exc); *R. Strauss:* Lieder, Op.29 (exc). (F. Schorr, New SO, Berlin St Op Orch, LSO/A. Coates/L. Blech/J. Barbirolli/R. Heger, anon, E. Bettendorf, orch)

ⓘ **GEMMCD9403** (1/91)
Emil von Sauer plays Liszt
Liszt: Piano Concerto 1; Piano Concerto 2; Études, d'exécution, S139 (exc); Consolations, S172 (exc); Valses oubliées, S215 (exc); Concert Studies, S145 (exc); Paganini Studies, S140 (exc). (E. von Sauer, Paris Cons/F. Weingartner)

ⓘ **GEMMCD9417** (4/91)
Holst conducts Holst
Holst: Planets; St Paul's Suite; Beni Mora; Songs without words. (LSO, orch/G. Holst)

ⓘ **GEMMCD9419** (3/92)
Herbert Ernst Groh—Opera Recital
Mozart: Entführung (exc); Zauberflöte (exc); *Wagner:* Fliegende Holländer (exc); Meistersinger (exc); *Verdi:* Forza del destino (exc); *Leoncavallo:* Pagliacci (exc); *Bizet:* Pêcheurs de Perles (exc); *A. Thomas:* Mignon (exc); *Offenbach:* Contes d'Hoffmann (exc); *Adam:* Postillon de Lonjumeau (exc); *Nicolai:* Lustigen Weiber von Windsor (exc); *Cornelius:* Barbier von Bagdad (exc); Barbier von Bagdad (exc); *Nessler:* Trompeter von Säckingen (exc); *Zeller:* Vogelhändler (exc); *J. Strauss II:* Zigeunerbaron (exc); Nacht in Venedig (exc); *Heuberger:* Opernball (exc); *Zeller:* Vogelhändler (exc); *Fall:* Rose von Stambul (exc). (H.E. Groh, G. Hüsch, E. Bettendorf, orch/F. Weissmann/O. Dobrindt)

ⓘ **GEMMCD9443** (10/91)
Feuermann—The Columbia Records, Vol.2
Brahms: Cello Sonata 1; *Beethoven:* Serenade, Op.8; *Reger:* Suites, Op.131c (exc); *Mendelssohn:* Songs without words (exc); *Schumann:* Kinderszenen (exc); *Gounod:* Ave Maria; *Drigo:* Arlekinda (exc); *Cui:* Kaleidoscope (exc); *Rimsky-Korsakov:* Sadko (exc). (E. Feuermann, T. van der Pas, S. Goldberg, P. Hindemith, W. Rebner, M. Taube, G. Moore)

ⓘ **GEMMCD9446** (10/91)
Feuermann—The Columbia Records, Vol.3
Hindemith: Solo Cello Sonata, Op.25/3; Duet; String Trio 2; *Beethoven:* Cello Sonata 3; *Weber:* Konzertstück (exc); *Albéniz:* España, Op.165 (exc); *Saint-Saëns:* Carnaval des Animaux (exc). (E. Feuermann, P. Hindemith, S. Goldberg, M. Hess, G. Moore, M. Taube)

ⓘ **GEMMCD9447** (10/91)
Gregor Piatigorsky plays Schumann, Beethoven, Weber & Brahms
Schumann: Cello Concerto; *Weber:* Violin Sonatas, J99-104 (exc); *Beethoven:* Cello Sonata 2; *Brahms:* Cello Sonata 1. (G. Piatigorsky, I. Newton, A. Schnabel, A. Rubinstein, LPO/J. Barbirolli)

ⓘ **GEMMCD9448** (2/91)
Stokowski conducts Wagner
Wagner: Tannhäuser (exc); Tannhäuser (exc); Parsifal (exc); Parsifal (exc). (Philadelphia/L. Stokowski)

ⓘ **GEMMCD9449** (4/91)
Walter Gieseking—Debussy & Ravel
Ravel: Gaspard de la nuit; Miroirs (exc); *Debussy:* Préludes (exc); Estampes (exc); Isle Joyeuse. (W. Gieseking)

ⓘ **GEMMCD9451** (10/91)
Alexander Kipnis
Gounod: Faust (exc); *Mozart:* Nozze di Figaro (exc); *Wagner:* Tristan und Isolde (exc); *Brahms:* Lieder, Op. 32 (exc); *Verdi:* Don Carlo (exc); *Meyerbeer:* Huguenots (exc); *Halévy:* Juive (exc); *Wagner:* Walküre (exc); Meistersinger (exc); *Gounod:* Faust (exc); *Mozart:* Zauberflöte (exc); Nozze di Figaro (exc); *Traditional:* Kalinka; Soldier's Song; *Verdi:* Simon Boccanegra (exc); *Wolf:* Vier Gedichte (exc); *Brahms:* Lieder, Op. 43 (exc); Lieder, Op. 58 (exc). (A. Kipnis, E. Ruziczka, anon, G. Moore, orch, Berlin Charlottenburg Op Orch, Berlin St Op Orch/J. Heidenreich/L. Blech/E. Orthmann)

ⓘ **GEMMCD9453** (10/91)
William Primrose—Viola Recital
Bax: Viola Sonata; *Bloch:* Viola Suite; *Paganini:* Caprices, Op.1 (exc); Caprices, Op.1 (exc); *Viotti:* Violin Concerto 2 (exc); *Kreisler:* Liebesfreud. (W. Primrose, H. Cohen, F. Kitzinger, Anon, H. Isaacs)

ⓘ **GEMMCD9462** (10/91)
Dame Myra Hess—Vol.1
Bach: French Suites, BWV812-17 (exc); *Schubert:* Piano Sonata, D664; Rosamunde (exc); *Beethoven:* Cello Sonata 3; *Chopin:* Nocturnes (exc); *Mendelssohn:* Songs without words (exc); *Brahms:* Piano Pieces, Op.76 (exc); *Dvořák:* Slavonic Dances (exc); *Debussy:* Images (exc); Préludes (exc); *Bach:* Cantata 147 (exc). (M. Hess, E. Feuermann, H. Harty)

ⓘ **GEMMCD9470** (11/91)
Prokofiev plays Prokofiev
Prokofiev: Piano Concerto 3; Visions Fugitives (exc); Pieces, Op.4 (exc); Tales of an old Grandmother (exc); Pieces, Op.59 (exc); Symphony 1 (exc); Pieces, Op.52 (exc); Piano Sonata 4 (exc); Pieces, Op.32 (exc). (S. Prokofiev, LSO/P. Coppola)

ⓘ **GEMMCD9473** (9/91)
Heddle Nash—Vol.2
Puccini: Bohème (exc); Bohème (exc); *Gounod:* Faust (exc); *Massenet:* Manon (exc); *Offenbach:* Belle Hélène (exc); *Millöcker:* Dubarry (exc); *Bishop:* My pretty Jane; *M.V. White:* To Mary; *Lehár:* Friederike (exc). (H. Nash, M. Licette, R. Easton, BBC Chor, SO/T. Beecham, J. Brownlee, D. Labbette, S. Andreva, LPO, orch, G. Moore, anon, R. Alva)

ⓘ **GEMMCD9488** (2/92)
A Stokowski Fantasia
Bach: Toccata and Fugue, BWV565; *Tchaikovsky:* Nutcracker Suite; *Dukas:* Apprenti sorcier; *Stravinsky:* Rite of Spring (Cpte); *Mussorgsky:* Night on the Bare Mountain. (Philadelphia/L. Stokowski)

ⓘ **GEMMCD9492** (12/91)
Koussevitzky conducts American Music
Foote: Suite in E; *McDonald:* San Juan Capistrano; *Copland:* Salón México; *R. Harris:* Symphony 1933; Symphony 3. (Boston SO/S. Koussevitzky)

Philips

Op. 41 (exc); Lieder, Op. 37 (exc); Lieder, Op. 10 (exc). (J. Norman, Leipzig Gewandhaus/K. Masur)

ⓘ **411 123-2PH** (8/84)
Popular works for piano and orchestra
Gershwin: Rhapsody in Blue; *Addinsell:* Warsaw Concerto; *Litolff:* Concerto Symphonique, Op. 102 (exc); *Chopin:* Fantasia on Polish Airs; *Liszt:* Polonaise brillante. (M. Dichter, Philh/N. Marriner)

ⓘ **411 148-2PH** (3/84)
Mozart: Opera Arias
Mozart: Zaïde (exc); Finta Giardiniera (exc); Clemenza di Tito (exc); Così fan tutte (exc); Rè pastore (exc); Lucio Silla (exc); Idomeneo (exc); Zauberflöte (exc). (K. Te Kanawa, LSO/Colin Davis)

ⓘ **412 118-2PH** (4/85)
Debussy: Piano works
Debussy: Suite bergamasque; Images oubliées; Pour le piano; Estampes. (Z. Kocsis)

ⓘ **412 122-2PH** (2/85)
Mozart—Piano Works
Mozart: Piano Sonata, K545; Rondo, K511; Piano Sonata, K533. (M. Uchida)

ⓘ **412 123-2PH** (9/84)
Mozart Piano Works
Mozart: Piano Sonata, K331; Piano Sonata, K332; Fantasia, K397. (M. Uchida)

ⓘ **412 176-2PH6** (3/85)
Schubert: Complete Symphonies
Schubert: Symphony 1; Symphony 2; Symphony 3; Symphony 4; Symphony 5; Symphony 6; Symphony 7; Symphony 8; Symphony 9; Symphony 10; Symphonic Fragment, D615; Symphonic Fragment, D708a. (ASMF/N. Marriner)

ⓘ **412 226-2PH** (6/85)
Telemann Horn Concertos
Telemann: 3-Horn & Violin Concerto; Musique de Table (exc); Horn Concerto; 2-Horn Overture-Suite; 2-Horn & 2-Oboe Concerto 1. (H. Baumann, T. Brown, N. Hill, I. Brown (vn/dir), ASMF/I. Brown)

ⓘ **412 227-2PH** (8/85)
Beethoven: Piano works
Beethoven: Variations, Op. 35; Bagatelles (exc); Ecossaises, WoO83. (A. Brendel)

ⓘ **412 228-2PH** (11/85)
Haydn: Keyboard sonatas
Haydn: Keyboard Sonata 47; Keyboard Sonata 53; Keyboard Sonata 56; Fantasia, HobXVII/4; Adagio, HobXVII/9. (A. Brendel)

ⓘ **412 230-2PH** (1/85)
Works for Cello and Piano
Schubert: Arpeggione Sonata, D821; *Schumann:* Fantasiestücke, Op. 73; Stücke, Op. 102. (M. Maisky, M. Argerich)

ⓘ **412 231-2PH** (3/85)
Travels with my Cello
Rimsky-Korsakov: Tale of Tsar Saltan (exc); *Lehár:* Lustige Witwe (exc); *Debussy:* Children's Corner (exc); *Schumann:* Kinderszenen (exc); *Albéniz:* Recuerdos de viaje (exc); *Saint-Saëns:* Carnaval des animaux (exc); *Gounod:* Ave Maria; *W. Lloyd Webber:* Andante affettuoso; *J. Strauss II:* Pizzicato Polka; *Albinoni:* Adagio; *Grainger:* Irish Tune from County Derry; *Khachaturian:* Gayaneh (exc). (J. Lloyd Webber, ECO/N. Cleobury)

ⓘ **412 237-2PH** (6/85)
Horn Concertos
R. Strauss: Horn Concerto 1; Horn Concerto 2; *Weber:* Horn Concertino. (H. Baumann, Leipzig Gewandhaus/K. Masur)

ⓘ **412 570-2PH4** (7/85)
Beethoven Violin Sonatas
Beethoven: Violin Sonata 1; Violin Sonata 2; Violin Sonata 3; Violin Sonata 4; Violin Sonata 5; Violin Sonata 6; Violin Sonata 7; Violin Sonata 8; Violin Sonata 9; Violin Sonata 10. (D. Oistrakh, L. Oborin)

ⓘ **412 575-2PH11** (1/85)
Beethoven—Complete Piano Sonatas
Beethoven: Piano Sonata 1; Piano Sonata 2; Piano Sonata 3; Piano Sonata 4; Piano Sonata 5; Piano Sonata 6; Piano Sonata 7; Piano Sonata 8; Piano Sonata 9; Piano Sonata 10; Piano Sonata 11; Piano Sonata 12; Piano Sonata 13; Piano Sonata 14; Piano Sonata 15; Piano Sonata 16; Piano Sonata 17; Piano Sonata 18; Piano Sonata 19; Piano Sonata 20; Piano Sonata 21; Piano Sonata 22; Piano Sonata 23; Piano Sonata 24; Piano Sonata 25; Piano Sonata 26; Piano Sonata 27; Piano Sonata 28; Piano Sonata 29; Piano Sonata 30; Piano Sonata 31; Piano Sonata 32; Andante favori, WoO57. (A. Brendel)

ⓘ **412 611-2PH** (11/85)
Gershwin—Orchestral Works
Gershwin: American in Paris; Piano Concerto; Rhapsody in Blue. (A. Previn (pf/dir), Pittsburgh SO/A. Previn)

ⓘ **412 616-2PH** (7/85)
Mozart—Piano Sonatas, Vol.1
Mozart: Piano Sonata, K330; Piano Sonata, K333; Adagio, K540; Gigue, K574. (M. Uchida)

ⓘ **412 617-2PH** (1/86)
Mozart: Piano Sonatas, Vol.2
Mozart: Fantasia, K475; Piano Sonata, K457; Piano Sonata, K279; Piano Sonata, K576. (M. Uchida)

ⓘ **412 620-2PH2** (7/86)
Schubert: Music for piano trio
Schubert: Piano Trio 1; Piano Trio 2; Notturno, D897; Piano Trio, D28. (Beaux Arts Trio)

ⓘ **412 623-2PH** (1/86)
Schubert: Lieder
Schubert: Musensohn, D764; Ganymed, D544; Allmacht, D852; Tod und das Mädchen, D531; Erlkönig, D328; Gretchen am Spinnrade, D118; An die Natur, D372; Zwerg, D771; Rastlose Liebe, D138; Auf dem See, D543; Auflösung, D807; Suleika I, D720. (J. Norman, P. Moll)

ⓘ **412 624-2PH** (1/86)
Vivaldi: Guitar Concertos
Vivaldi: Concerti grossi, Op. 3 (exc); Concerto, RV532; Concerti Grossi, Op. 3 (exc); Concerto, RV425; Concerto, RV93. (A. Romero, P. Romero, Celin Romero, Celedonio Romero, ASMF/I. Brown)

ⓘ **412 629-2PH** (5/85)
Sacred Evergreens
Gounod: St Cecilia Mass (exc); Repentir; *Mozart:* Vespers, K339 (exc); Ave verum corpus, K618; *Bach:* Anna Magdalena Notenbuch (1725) (exc); Cantata 147 (exc); *Mendelssohn:* Lieder, Op. 34 (exc); *Franck:* Panis angelicus; *Schubert:* Ave Maria, D839; *Purcell:* Choice Collection of Lessons (exc); *Handel:* Samson (exc). (K. Te Kanawa, St Paul's Cath Ch, ECO/Barry Rose)

ⓘ **412 632-2PH** (10/86)
Recorder Sonatas
Vivaldi: Sonatas, Op. 13 (exc); *Corelli:* Sonatas, Op. 5 (exc); *Bigaglia:* Recorder Sonata in A minor; *Bononcini:* Divertimenti da camera (exc); *Sammartini:* Solos, Op. 13 (exc); *B. Marcello:* Sonatas, Op. 2 (exc). (M. Petri, G. Malcolm)

ⓘ **412 727-2PH** (1/86)
Grieg and Sibelius: Orchestral works
Grieg: Holberg Suite; Lyric Pieces, Op. 68; *Sibelius:* Karelia Suite; Legends (exc). (ASMF/N. Marriner)

ⓘ **412 741-2PH** (7/86)
Mozart: Piano Sonatas, Vol.3
Mozart: Piano Sonata, K309; Piano Sonata, K310; Piano Sonata, K311. (M. Uchida)

ⓘ **412 851-2PH** (1/86)
Bach—Oboe Concertos
Bach: Oboe Concerto, BWV1053; Oboe Concerto, BWV1055; Oboe Concerto, BWV1059. (H. Holliger, ASMF/I. Brown)

ⓘ **412 873-2PH** (3/86)
Mozart—Sacred Music
Mozart: Vespers, K339; Kyrie, K341; Ave verum corpus, K618; Exsultate jubilate, K165. (K. Te Kanawa, E. Bainbridge, R. Davies, G. Howell, LSC, LSO/Colin Davis)

ⓘ **412 879-2PH** (4/86)
Telemann: Oboe Concertos
Telemann: Oboe Concerto 6; Oboe Concerto 4; Oboe Concerto 2; Oboe Concerto 8; Oboe Concerto 3. (H. Holliger, ASMF, I. Brown (vn/dir))

ⓘ **412 892-2PH** (7/86)
Vivaldi: Double Concertos
Vivaldi: Concerto, RV563; Concerto, RV539; Concerto, RV532; Concerto, RV533; Concerto, RV536; Concerto, RV545. (M. Laird, W. Houghton, I. Brown, T. Brown, N. Hill/J. Tyler, D. Wootton, W. Bennett, L. Smith, C. Nicklin, B. Davis, G. Sheen, ASMF/N. Marriner)

ⓘ **416 249-2PB** (12/89)
A Festival of Christmas Carols
Traditional: Hark the herald angels sing; Coventry Carol; Joy to the world; In dulci jubilo; Stille nacht; God rest you merry, gentlemen; Holly and the Ivy; Greensleeves (What Child is this?); First Nowell; Good King Wenceslas; Deck the hall; O Tannenbaum; Patapan; We three kings; Away in a manger; I saw three ships; I wonder as I wander; O come, all ye faithful. (John Aldis Ch, LSO/Colin Davis)

ⓘ **416 298-2PH** (8/86)
Richard Strauss: Lieder
R. Strauss: Lieder, Op. 17 (exc); Lieder, Op. 56 (exc); Lieder, Op. 32 (exc); Lieder, Op. 48 (exc); Lieder, Op. 10 (exc); Lieder, Op. 15 (exc); Lieder, Op. 39 (exc); Lieder, Op. 21 (exc); Lieder, Op. 69 (exc); Lieder, Op. 19 (exc); Lieder, Op. 31 (exc); Lieder, Op. 27 (exc); Malven; Lieder, Op. 29 (exc). (J. Norman, C. Erdélyi, G. Parsons)

ⓘ **416 365-2PH** (12/86)
Haydn: Piano Sonatas
Haydn: Keyboard Sonata 50; Keyboard Sonata 54; Keyboard Sonata 62; Variations, HobXVII/6. (A. Brendel)

ⓘ **416 386-2PH** (11/87)
Classical Academy
L. Mozart: Cassation in G; *Mozart:* Serenade, K525; Adagio and Fugue, K546; *Pachelbel:* Canon and Gigue. (ASMF/N. Marriner)

ⓘ **416 430-2PH** (9/86)
Berlioz: Overtures
Berlioz: King Lear; Francs-juges; Carnaval romain; Waverley; Corsaire. (LSO/Colin Davis)

ⓘ **416 431-2PH** (12/86)
Works by Berlioz
Berlioz: Harold in Italy; Tristia; Troyens (exc). (N. Imai, John Alldis Ch, LSO/Colin Davis)

ⓘ **416 437-2PH** (10/86)
French orchestral works
Bizet: Symphony; Jeux d'enfants; *Debussy:* Danse sacrée et danse profane. (V. Badings, Concertgebouw/B. Haitink)

ⓘ **416 445-2PH** (12/86)
French songs
Duparc: Vie antérieure; Phidylé; Chanson triste; Invitation au voyage; *Ravel:* Mélodies hébraïques; *Poulenc:* Banalités (exc); Montparnasse; Grenouillère; Chemins de l'amour; *Satie:* Mélodies (1916); Je te veux. (J. Norman, D. Baldwin)

ⓘ **416 460-2PH** (1/87)
Barbara Hendricks sings Gershwin
Gershwin: Strike Up The Band I (exc); Shall we dance? (exc); Goldwyn Follies (exc); Girl Crazy (exc); Damsel in Distress (exc); Porgy and Bess (exc); Blue Monday (exc). (B. Hendricks, K. Labèque, M. Labèque)

ⓘ **416 600-2PH4** (11/86)
Sibelius—Symphonies & Tone Poems
Sibelius: Symphony 1; Symphony 2; Symphony 3; Symphony 4; Symphony 5; Symphony 6; Symphony 7; Finlandia; Tapiola; Legends (exc). (Boston SO/Colin Davis)

ⓘ **416 643-2PH4** (3/87)
Haydn—Complete Piano Sonatas
Haydn: Keyboard Sonata 47; Keyboard Sonata 50; Keyboard Sonata 33; Keyboard Sonata 53; Keyboard Sonata 54; Keyboard Sonata 56; Keyboard Sonata 58; Keyboard Sonata 59; Keyboard Sonata 60; Keyboard Sonata 61; Fantasia, HobXVII/4; Adagio, HobXVII/9; Variations, HobXVII/6. (A. Brendel)

ⓘ **416 698-2PH** (3/87)
Encore! Travels with my cello, Vol. 2
Gershwin: Porgy and Bess (exc); *Tchaik:* Nocturne; *Mozart:* Piano Sonata, K331 (exc); *Debussy:* Suite bergamasque (exc); *Traditional:* Skye Boat Song; *Bizet:* Carmen (exc); *Vangelis:* Après-midi; *Narita:* Song of the seashore; *Lennon & McCartney:* When I'm 64; *Bernstein:* West Side Story (exc); *Bach:* Cantata 147 (exc); *Rimsky-Korsakov:* Sadko (exc); *Lehár:* Land des Lächelns (exc). (J. Lloyd Webber, S-B. Taube, Vangelis, RPO/N. Cleobury)

ⓘ **416 831-2PH3** (1/88)
Bartok: Works for Piano & Orchestra
Bartók: Piano Concerto 1; Music for Strings, Percussion and Celesta; Piano Concerto 2; Rhapsody, Sz27; Piano Concerto 3; Scherzo, Op.2. (Z. Kocsis, Budapest Fest Orch/I. Fischer)

ⓘ **416 838-2PH2** (1/88)
Brahms: Piano Trios
Brahms: Piano Trio 1; Piano Trio 2; Piano Trio 3; Piano Trio, Op.posth. (Beaux Arts Trio)

ⓘ **420 159-2PH** (11/87)
French piano music for four hands
Bizet: Jeux d'enfants; *Fauré:* Dolly; *Ravel:* Ma mère l'oye. (K. Labèque, M. Labèque)

ⓘ **420 168-2PH** (11/87)
Violin Works
Beethoven: Romances; *Schubert:* Polonaise, D580;

Concertstück, D345; Rondo, D438; *Dvořák*: Romance, Op.11. (St. Paul CO, P.Zukerman (vn/dir))

① **420 185-2PH** (7/87)
Mozart: Piano Sonatas, Vol.4
Mozart: Piano Sonata, K284; Piano Sonata, K570; Rondo, K485. (M. Uchida)

① **420 186-2PH** (4/88)
Mozart: Piano Sonatas, Vol.5
Mozart: Piano Sonata, K280; Piano Sonata, K281; Piano Sonata, K282; Piano Sonata, K283. (M. Uchida)

① **420 189-2PH** (4/88)
Baroque Oboe Concertos
A. Marcello: Oboe Concerto in D minor; *Sammartini*: Oboe Concerto in D; *Albinoni*: Concerti, Op.9 (exc); *Lotti*: Oboe d'amore Concerto in A; *Cimarosa*: Oboe Concerto. (H. Holliger, H. Holliger, I Musici)

① **420 203-2PH** (12/87)
Classical Trumpet Concertos
Hummel: Trumpet Concerto; *Hertel*: Trumpet Concerto in D; *J. Stamitz*: Trumpet Concerto in D; *Haydn*: Trumpet Concerto. (H. Hardenberger, ASMF/N. Marriner)

① **420 648-2PM** (5/88)
Vivaldi: Sacred Choral Music, Vol.1
Vivaldi: Lauda Jerusalem, RV609; Introduzione al Gloria, RV642; Gloria, RV589; Laudate pueri, RV602; Laudate Dominum, RV606. (M. Marshall, F. Lott, A. Murray, B. Finnilä, John Alldis Ch, ECO/V. Negri)

① **420 649-2PM** (2/89)
Vivaldi: Sacred Choral Music, Vol.2
Vivaldi: Introduzione al Dixit, RV636; Dixit Dominus, RV594; Magnificat, RV611; Beatus vir, RV598. (M. Marshall, F. Lott, S. Burgess, A. Murray, S. Daniel, L. Finnie, A. Collins, A. Rolfe Johnson, R. Holl, John Alldis Ch, ECO/V. Negri)

① **420 700-2PSL** (5/88)
Bach: Violin Concertos
Bach: Violin Concerto, BWV1041; Violin Concerto, BWV1042; Violin and Oboe Concerto, BWV1060; 2-Violin Concerto. (A. Grumiaux, H. Krebbers, H. Holliger, Solistes Romands, New Philh/A. Gerecz/E. de Waart)

① **420 750-2PH** (4/88)
Brahms: Piano Works
Brahms: Rhapsodies, Op. 79; Waltzes, Op. 39; Piano Pieces, Op. 118. (S. Kovacevich)

① **420 790-2PH** (5/88)
Haydn: Piano Trios
Haydn: Keyboard Trio 28; Keyboard Trio 29; Keyboard Trio 30; Keyboard Trio 31. (Beaux Arts Trio)

① **420 797-2PM3** (2/90)
Beethoven: Middle Period String Quartets
Beethoven: String Quartet 7; String Quartet 8; String Quartet 9; String Quartet 10; String Quartet 11. (Quartetto Italiano)

① **420 876-2PSL** (3/89)
Schubert, Dvořák & Borodin—String Quartets
Schubert: String Quartet, D810; *Dvořák*: String Quartet 12; *Borodin*: String Quartet 2 (exc). (Quartetto Italiano)

① **420 932-2PH2** (3/89)
Bruch—Orchestral Works
Bruch: Symphony 1; Symphony 2; Symphony 3; Swedish Dances. (Leipzig Gewandhaus/K. Masur)

① **420 950-2PH** (10/88)
Kiri te Kanawa sings Mozart arias
Mozart: Entführung (exc); Mitridate (exc); Don Giovanni (exc); Ch'io mi scordi di te, K505; Misera, dove son, K369. (K. Te Kanawa, M. Uchida, ECO/J. Tate)

① **420 954-2PH** (8/88)
Telemann—Trumpet Concertos
Telemann: 3-Trumpet Concerto 2; Trumpet Concerto; Musique de Table (exc); 2-Oboe & Trumpet Concerto 2; 2-Oboe & Trumpet Concerto 1. (H. Hardenberger, M. Laird, W. Houghton, C. Nicklin, T. Miller, ASMF/I. Brown)

① **420 955-2PH** (11/88)
Ramirez: Choral Works
Ramirez: Misa Criolla; Navidad en Verano; Navidad nuestra. (J. Carreras, A. Ramirez, Laredo Choral Salvé, Bilbao Choral Soc, Inst Ens/J.L. Ocejo/D. Sanchez)

① **422 048-2PH** (4/88)
Jessye Norman—Song Recital
Ochs: Dank sei dir, Herr; *Handel*: Rinaldo (exc); *Schumann*: Myrthen, Op. 25 (exc); Liederkreis, Op.39 (exc); *Schubert*: Musensohn, D764; Auf dem See, D543; Meeres Stille, D216; Ave Maria, D839; An die Natur, D372; Rastlose Liebe, D138; Gretchen am Spinnrade, D118; Liebe hat gelogen, D751; Tod und das Mädchen, D531; Erlkönig, D328; *Brahms*: Lieder, Op. 63 (exc); *R.Strauss*:

Wir beide wollen springen; *Traditional*: He's got the whole world in His hands; Great day. (J. Norman, G. Parsons)

① **422 065-2PH** (12/88)
Vivaldi: Violin Concertos
Vivaldi: Concerti, Op.8 (exc); Concerto, RV551; Concerti grossi, Op.3 (exc). (S. Accardo (vn/dir), Naples Soloists)

① **422 079-2PH3** (11/88)
Mozart: Piano Trios
Mozart: Divertimento, K254; Piano Trio Movements, K442; Piano Trio, K496; Piano Trio, K502; Piano Trio, K542; Piano Trio, K548; Piano Trio, K564. (Beaux Arts Trio)

① **422 115-2PH6** (2/89)
Mozart—Complete Piano Sonatas
Mozart: Piano Sonata, K279; Piano Sonata, K280; Piano Sonata, K281; Piano Sonata, K282; Piano Sonata, K283; Piano Sonata, K284; Piano Sonata, K309; Piano Sonata, K310; Piano Sonata, K311; Piano Sonata, K330; Piano Sonata, K331; Piano Sonata, K332; Piano Sonata, K333; Piano Sonata, K457; Piano Sonata, K545; Piano Sonata, K570; Piano Sonata, K576; Piano Sonata, K533; Fantasia, K475; Fantasia, K397; Rondo, K485; Rondo, K511; Adagio, K540; Gigue, K574. (M. Uchida)

① **422 140-2PLC3** (1/89)
Beethoven: Complete Violin Sonatas
Beethoven: Violin Sonata 1; Violin Sonata 2; Violin Sonata 3; Violin Sonata 4; Violin Sonata 5; Violin Sonata 6; Violin Sonata 7; Violin Sonata 8; Violin Sonata 9; Violin Sonata 10. (A. Grumiaux, C. Haskil)

① **422 149-2PH3** (1/89)
Beethoven: Complete Piano Concertos
Beethoven: Piano Concerto 1; Piano Concerto 2; Piano Concerto 3; Piano Concerto 4; Piano Concerto 5. (C. Arrau, Staatskapelle Dresden/Colin Davis)

① **422 229-2PH** (2/89)
Schubert—Piano Works
Schubert: Piano Works, D959; Ungarische Melodie, D817; Deutsche Tänze, D783; Allegretto, D915. (A. Brendel)

① **422 387-2PH** (5/89)
Dvořák—Orchestral Works
Dvořák: Cello Concerto; Rusalka (exc); Carnival. (J. Lloyd Webber, Czech PO/V. Neumann)

① **422 401-2PH** (4/92)
Jessye Norman - Lucky To Be Me
Rodgers: Love me Tonight (exc); Boys from Syracuse (exc); *Legrand*: Parapluies de Cherbourg (exc); Yentl (exc); *Weill*: Knickerbocker Holiday (exc); Lady in the dark (exc); One touch of Venus (exc); *Gershwin*: Girl Crazy (exc); *Bernstein*: On the Town (exc); *F. Loewe*: My Fair Lady (exc); *Joel*: Just the way you are. (J. Norman, J.T. Williams)

① **422 404-2PH** (2/90)
Debussy: Piano Works
Debussy: Images; D'un cahier d'esquisses; Isle joyeuse; Arabesques; Hommage à Haydn; Rêverie; Page d'album; Berceuse héroïque. (Z. Kocsis)

① **422 501-2PME6** (12/90)
The Complete Mozart Edition Vol 1
Mozart: Symphony 1; Symphony 4; Symphony 5; Symphony 6; Symphony 7; Symphony in G; Symphony, K45a; Symphony, K45b; Symphony 8; Symphony 9; Symphony 10; Symphony, K75; Symphony, K76; Symphony, K81; Symphony 11; Symphony, K95; Symphony, K96; Symphony, K97; Symphony 12; Symphony 13; Symphony 14; Symphony 15; Symphony 16; Symphony 17; Symphony 18; Symphony 19; Symphony 20; Symphony, K141a; Symphony, K120; Symphony, K121; Symphony 52; Symphony, K19a; Minuet, K61g/1. (ASMF/N. Marriner)

① **422 502-2PME6** (12/90)
The Complete Mozart Edition Vol 2
Mozart: Symphony 21; Symphony 22; Symphony 23; Symphony 24; Symphony 25; Symphony 26; Symphony 27; Symphony 28; Symphony 29; Symphony 30; Symphony 31; Andante, K297; Symphony 32; Symphony 33; Symphony 34; Symphony 35; Symphony 36; Symphony 37; Symphony 38; Symphony 39; Symphony 40; Symphony 41; Minuet, K409. (ASMF/N. Marriner)

① **422 503-2PME7** (12/90)
The Complete Mozart Edition Vol 3
Mozart: Symphony, K32; Divertimento, K131; Cassation, K99; March, K62; Cassation, K100; Cassation, K63; March, K215; Serenade, K204; Notturno, K286; Serenade, K203; Serenade, K239; Serenade, K525; March, K189; Marches, K335; Serenade, K185; March, K249; Serenade, K250; Serenade, K320; March, K237. (I. Brown, K. Sillito, Ambrosian Sngrs, ASMF/N. Marriner)

① **422 504-2PME5** (12/90)
The Complete Mozart Edition Vol 4
Mozart: Divertimento, K113; Divertimenti, K136-8; Divertimento, K251; Serenade, K525; Musikalischer Spass; Divertimento, K287; March, K248; Divertimento, K247; March, K290; Divertimento, K205; March, K445; Divertimento, K334. (ASMF Chbr Ens)

① **422 507-2PME12** (5/91)
The Complete Mozart Edition Vol 7
Mozart: Piano Concerto 1; Piano Concerto 2; Piano Concerto 3; Piano Concerto 4; Piano Concertos, K107; Piano Concerto 5; 3-Piano Concerto, K242; 2-Piano Concerto, K242; Piano Concerto 6; Piano Concerto 8; Piano Concerto 9; 2-Piano Concerto, K365; Piano Concerto 11; Piano Concerto 12; Piano Concerto 13; Piano Concerto 14; Piano Concerto 15; Piano Concerto 16; Piano Concerto 17; Piano Concerto 18; Piano Concerto 19; Piano Concerto 20; Piano Concerto 21; Piano Concerto 22; Piano Concerto 23; Piano Concerto 24; Piano Concerto 25; Piano Concerto 26; Rondo, K382; Rondo, K386. (I. Haebler, VCA/E. Melkus, T. Koopman (hpd/dir), Amsterdam Baroque Orch, K. Labèque, M. Labèque, BPO, S. Bychkov (pf/dir), A. Brendel, I. Cooper, ASMF/N. Marriner)

① **422 508-2PME4** (6/91)
The Complete Mozart Edition Vol 8
Mozart: Violin Concerto, K207; Violin Concerto, K211; Violin Concerto, K216; Violin Concerto, K218; Violin Concerto, K219; Violin Concerto, K271a; Adagio, K261; Concertone, K190; Rondo, K269; Rondo, K373; Sinfonia Concertante, K364; Sinfonia Concertante, K Anh104; Violin and Keyboard Concerto, K Anh56. (H. Szeryng, New Philh/A. Gibson, G. Poulet, I. Brown (vn/dir), N. Imai, S. Orton, H. Shelley, ASMF)

① **422 509-2PME5** (7/91)
The Complete Mozart Edition Vol 9
Mozart: Flute and Harp Concerto, K299; Flute Concerto, K313; Andante, K315; Clarinet Concerto, K622; Bassoon Concerto, K191; Horn Concerti; Rondo, K371; Sinfonia Concertante, K297b; Oboe Concerto, K314; Flute Concerto, K314; Sinfonia Concertante, K297b. (I. Grafenauer, M. Graf, K. Leister, K. Thunemann, P. Damm, A. Nicolet, H. Holliger, N. Black, J. Brymer, A. Civil, M. Chapman, H. Holliger (ob/dir), ASMF/N. Marriner)

① **422 510-2PME3** (8/91)
The Complete Mozart Edition Vol 10
Mozart: Clarinet Quintet, K581; Horn Quintet, K407; Oboe Quartet, K370; Duo, K292; Flute Quartets; String Quintet, K174 (exc); Minuet, K168a; Allegro, K288; String Quartet Minuet, KAnh68; Clarinet Quintet Movement, KAnh90; String Trio Movement, KAnh66; Clarinet Quintet Movement, KAnh91; String Quintet Movement, KAnh79. (ASMF Chbr Ens, K. Thunemann, S. Orton, W. Bennett, Grumiaux Trio)

① **422 511-2PME3** (9/91)
The Complete Mozart Edition Vol 11
Mozart: String Quintet, K174; String Quintet, K406; String Quintet, K515; String Quintet, K516; String Quintet, K593; String Quintet, K614. (Grumiaux Ens)

① **422 512-2PME8** (8/91)
The Complete Mozart Edition Vol 12
Mozart: String Quartet, K80; String Quartet, K155; String Quartet, K156; String Quartet, K157; String Quartet, K158; String Quartet, K159; String Quartet, K160; String Quartet, K168; String Quartet, K169; String Quartet, K170; String Quartet, K171; String Quartet, K172; String Quartet, K173; String Quartet, K387; String Quartet, K421; String Quartet, K428; String Quartet, K458; String Quartet, K464; String Quartet, K465; String Quartet, K499; String Quartet, K575; String Quartet, K589; String Quartet, K590. (Quartetto Italiano)

① **422 514-2PME5** (9/91)
The Complete Mozart Edition Vol 14
Mozart: Piano and Wind Quintet, K452; Piano Trio, K498; Adagio and Rondo, K617; Adagio, K356; Piano Quartet, K478; Piano Quartet, K493; Divertimento, K254; Piano Trio, K496; Piano Trio, K502; Piano Trio, K542; Piano Trio, K548; Piano Trio, K564; Piano Trio Movements, K442. (A. Brendel, H. Holliger, E. Brunner, H. Baumann, K. Thunemann, S. Kovacevich, J. Brymer, P. Ireland, B. Hoffmann, A. Nicolet, K. Schouten, J. Decroos, Beaux Arts Trio, B. Giuranna)

① **422 515-2PME7** (9/91)
The Complete Mozart Edition Vol 15
Mozart: Violin Sonata, K454; Variations, K360; Violin Sonata, K304; Violin Sonata, K376; Violin Sonata, K302; Violin Sonata, K526; Violin Sonata, K305; Violin Sonata, K379; Violin Sonata, K301; Violin Sonata, K380; Violin

Sonata, K377; Violin Sonata, K296; Violin Sonata, K303;
Violin Sonata, K481; Violin Sonata, K378; Violin Sonata,
K306; Violin Sonata, K31; Violin Sonata, K30; Violin
Sonata, K29; Violin Sonata, K28; Violin Sonata, K27; Violin
Sonata, K26; Violin Sonata, K15; Violin Sonata, K14; Violin
Sonata, K13; Violin Sonata, K12; Violin Sonata, K11; Violin
Sonata, K10; Violin Sonata, K9; Violin Sonata, K8; Violin
Sonata, K7; Violin Sonata, K6; Violin Sonata, K547; Violin
Sonata, K403; Violin Sonata, K404; Violin Sonata, K402;
Variations, K359; Sonata, K46d; Sonata, K46e; Sonata
Movement, K396; Sonata Movement, K372. (A. Grumiaux,
W. Klien/G. Poulet, B. Verlet, I. van Keulen, R. Brautigam,
R. Brautigam)

ⓘ **422 516-2PME2** (11/91)
The Complete Mozart Edition Vol 16
Mozart: Piano Duet Sonata, K19d; Piano Duet Sonata,
K381; Piano Duet Sonata, K358; Piano Sonata, K448;
Piano Duet Sonata, K497; Sonata Movement, K357; Piano
Duet Sonata, K521; Andante and Variations, K501; Fugue,
K426; Larghetto and Allegro, Kdeest. (I. Haebler, L.
Hoffmann, J. Demus, P. Badura-Skoda)

ⓘ **422 517-2PME5** (9/91)
The Complete Mozart Edition Vol 17
Mozart: Piano Sonata, K279; Piano Sonata, K280; Piano
Sonata, K281; Piano Sonata, K282; Piano Sonata, K283;
Piano Sonata, K284; Piano Sonata, K309; Piano Sonata,
K310; Piano Sonata, K311; Piano Sonata, K330; Piano
Sonata, K331; Piano Sonata, K332; Piano Sonata, K333;
Piano Sonata, K457; Piano Sonata, K533; Piano Sonata,
K545; Piano Sonata, K570; Piano Sonata, K576; Fantasia,
K475. (M. Uchida)

ⓘ **422 518-2PME5** (10/91)
The Complete Mozart Edition Vol 18
Mozart: Variations, K24; Variations, K25; Variations, K180;
Variations, K264; Variations, K265; Variations, K352;
Variations, K353; Variations, K354; Variations, K398;
Variations, K455; Variations, K500; Variations, K573;
Variations, K613; Minuet, K355; Fantasia, K397; Rondo,
K485; Rondo, K511; Adagio, K540; Gigue, K574;
Klavierstück, K33b; Capriccio, K395; March, K408/1;
Fantasia and Fugue, K394; Allegro, K312; Suite, K399;
Allegro, K400; Variations, K460; Variations, K179; Allegro,
K9a; Funeral March, K453a; Minuet, K4; Minuet, K94;
Andante, K1a; Allegro, K1b; Allegro, K1c; Minuet, K1d;
Minuet, K2; Allegro, K3; Minuet, K5; Minuet, K1; Fugue,
K401. (I. Haebler, M. Uchida, T. Koopman, T. Mathot)

ⓘ **422 521-2PME2** (12/91)
The Complete Mozart Edition Vol 21
Mozart: Church Sonatas; Adagio and Allegro, K594;
Fantasia, K608; Andante, K616. (D. Chorzempa, German
Bach Sols/H. Winschermann)

ⓘ **422 522-2PME6** (4/92)
The Complete Mozart Edition Vol 22
Mozart: Schuldigkeit des ersten Gebots, K35; Kommt her,
ihr frechen Sünder, K146; Grabmusik, K42; Betulia
liberata; Davidde penitente, K469; Adagio and Fugue,
K546; Lied zur Gesellenreise, K468; Lobesgesang auf die
feierliche Johannisloge, K148; Dir, Seele des Weltalls,
K429; Maurerische Trauermusik, K477; Zerfliesset heut',
K483; Ihr unsre neuen Leiter, K484; Maurerfreude, K471;
Kleine deutsche Kantate, K619; Lasst uns mit geschlungen
Händen, K623a; Kleine Freimaurer-Kantate, K623. (M.
Marshall, A. Murray, I. Nielsen, H.-P. Blochwitz, A. Baldin,
Stuttgart RSO/N. Marriner, S. Varcoe, South German Rad
Chor, P. Schreier, H. Schwarz, I. Cotrubas, W. Berry, G.
Fuchs, M. Zimmermann, Salzburg Chbr Ch, Salzburg
Mozarteum Orch/L. Hager, I. Vermillion, A. Schmidt,
Leipzig Rad Chor, Staatskapelle Dresden, P. Schreier
(ten/dir)/P. Schreier, R. Alpermann, R. Jansen)

ⓘ **422 527-2PME** (5/92)
The Complete Mozart Edition Vol 27
Mozart: Bastien und Bastienne (Cpte); Zufriedenheit,
K349; Komm, liebe Zither, K351. (G. Nigl, D. Orieschnig,
D. Busch, Vienna SO/U.C. Harrer, D. Orieschnig, W.
Würdinger)

ⓘ **422 545-2PME3** (12/91)
The Complete Mozart Edition Vol.45
Mozart: Londoner Notenskizzenbuch; Don Giovanni (excs);
Entführung (exc); Rondo, K371; Piano and Wind Quintet,
K452a; Contredanse, K535b; Contredanse, K565a;
Tantum ergo, K197; Tantum ergo, K142; Modulierendes
Präludium; Idomeneo (exc); March, Kdeest; Musical Dice
Game. (ASMF/N. Marriner, Netherlands Wind Ens, T.
Brown, K. Sillito, M. Uchida, N. Black, T. King, J. Farrell, R.
O'Neill, Leipzig Rad Chor, Leipzig RSO, P. Schreier, M.
Frimmer, E. Smith, B. Hendricks, S. Mentzer, A. Röhn,
BRSO/Colin Davis)

ⓘ **422 833-2PC** (10/89)
Mozart—Chamber Works
Mozart: Clarinet Quintet, K581; Horn Quintet, K407; Oboe

Quartet, K370. (A. Pay, T. Brown, N. Black, ASMF Chbr
Ens)

ⓘ **422 838-2PC** (10/89)
Schubert: Chamber Works
Schubert: Trout Quintet, D667; String Trio, D581; String
Trio, D471. (I. Haebler, Grumiaux Trio, J. Cazauran)

ⓘ **426 046-2PM3** (2/90)
Beethoven: Early String Quartets
Beethoven: String Quartet 1; String Quartet 2; String
Quartet 3; String Quartet 4; String Quartet 5; String
Quartet 6. (Quartetto Italiano)

ⓘ **426 050-2PM4** (2/90)
Beethoven: Late String Quartets
Beethoven: String Quartet 12; String Quartet 13; Grosse
Fuge; String Quartet 14; String Quartet 15; String Quartet
16. (Quartetto Italiano)

ⓘ **426 075-2PCC** (11/91)
Bach: Concertos
Bach: Violin Concerto, BWV1042; Violin Concerto,
BWV1041; 2-Violin Concerto; Violin and Oboe Concerto,
BWV1060. (R. Michelucci, F. Ayo, L. Driehuys, I Musici)

ⓘ **426 076-2PCC** (3/90)
Vivaldi: Concertos
Vivaldi: Concerto, RV93; Trio, RV82; Concerti grossi, Op.3
(exc); Concerto, RV532; Concerto, RV425. (A. Romero,
Celedonio Romero, Celin Romero, P. Romero, J.
Corigliano, D. Saltarelli, M. Bella, San Antonio SO/V.
Alessandro)

ⓘ **426 082-2PBQ** (3/90)
Handel—Orchestral Works
Handel: Oboe Concertos; Concerti grossi, Op. 3 (exc);
Sonata a 5; Concerto grosso: Alexander's Feast (exc);
Overture, HWV337/8 (exc); Hornpipe, HWV356 (exc). (H.
Holliger, K. Sillito, ECO/R. Leppard)

ⓘ **426 086-2PBQ** (3/90)
Vivaldi—Double Concertos
Vivaldi: Concerto, RV523; Concerto, RV533; Concerto,
RV532; Concerto, RV535; Concerto, RV531; Concerto,
RV537. (F. Ayo, R. Michelucci, S. Gazzelloni, G. Gatti, G.
del Vescovo, T. Ruta, L. Driehuys, A. Mater, M.
Centurione, F. Strano, H. Adelbrecht, J-P. Mathez, M.T.
Garatti, M.T. Garatti, I Musici)

ⓘ **426 097-2PC** (6/90)
Haydn: String Quartets
Haydn: String Quartets, Op.64 (excs); Hoffstetter: String
Quartets, Op. 3 (exc); *Haydn*: String Quartets, Op.76 (exc).
(Quartetto Italiano)

ⓘ **426 275-2PH** (2/94)
Mozart—Sacred Choral Works
Mozart: Mass, K317; Vespers, K339; Ave verum corpus,
K618. (E. Mathis, J. Rappé, H-P. Blochwitz, T. Quasthoff,
Leipzig Rad Chor, Staatskapelle Dresden/P. Schreier)

ⓘ **426 284-2PH** (8/91)
French Works for Two Pianos
Poulenc: 2-piano Concerto; Capriccio; Embarquement
pour Cythère; Sonata for four hands; Élégie (1959);
Milhaud: Scaramouche. (K. Labèque, M. Labèque, Boston
SO/S. Ozawa)

ⓘ **426 290-2PH5** (5/93)
Beethoven—Complete Symphonies
Beethoven: Symphony 1; Symphony 2; Symphony 3;
Symphony 4; Symphony 5; Symphony 6; Symphony 7;
Symphony 8; Symphony 9. (S. McNair, U. Heilmann, J.
van Nes, B. Weikl, Leipzig Rad Chor, Leipzig
Gewandhaus/K. Masur)

ⓘ **426 307-2PH** (12/91)
Vienna Boys' Choir - Recital
Handel: Samson (exc); *Mozart*: Exsultate
jubilate, K165; Ave verum corpus, K618; Vespers, K321
(exc); Sub tuum praesidium, K198; *Schubert*: Hirt auf dem
Felsen, D965; *Herbeck*: Pueri concinite; *J. Strauss II*:
Frühlingsstimmen, op. 410. (Vienna Boys' Ch/U.C.
Harrer)

ⓘ **426 311-2PH** (3/91)
Trumpet Concertos
Richter: Trumpet Concerto in D; *L. Mozart*: Trumpet
Concerto; *Molter*: Trumpet Concerto 1; *Hertel*: Trumpet
Concerto in E flat; *M. Haydn*: Trumpet Concerto, MH60.
(H. Hardenberger, LPO/E. Howarth)

ⓘ **426 384-2PC** (7/90)
Fauré & Franck—Violin Sonatas
Fauré: Violin Sonata 1; Violin Sonata 2; *Franck*: Violin
Sonata. (A. Grumiaux, P. Crossley, G. Sebok)

ⓘ **426 386-2PC** (6/90)
Schumann—Oboe Works
Schumann: Romanzen, Op. 94; Adagio and Allegro, Op.

70; Fantasiestücke, Op. 73; Stücke, Op. 102;
Klavierstücke, Op. 85 (exc); Stücke, Op. 102. (H. Holliger,
A. Brendel, H. Holliger)

ⓘ **426 462-2PBQ2** (11/91)
Bach—Orchestral Works
Bach: Suites, BWV1066-9; 2-Violin Concerto; Violin and
Oboe Concerto, BWV1060. (ASMF/N. Marriner, H.
Szeryng, M. Hasson, G. Kremer, H. Holliger (ob/dir))

ⓘ **426 637-2PSL** (11/90)
Liszt—Works for Piano and Orchestra
Liszt: Piano Concerto 2; Piano Concerto 1; Danse
Macabre, S555. (A. Brendel, LPO/B. Haitink)

ⓘ **426 640-2PSL** (11/90)
Prokofiev—Orchestral Works
Prokofiev: Love for 3 Oranges Suite; Lt. Kijé Suite;
Symphony 1. (LSO/N. Marriner)

ⓘ **426 660-2PSL** (5/91)
Bartók—Piano Concertos
Bartók: Piano Concerto 1; Piano Concerto 3; Piano
Concerto 2. (S. Kovacevich, LSO, BBC SO/Colin Davis)

ⓘ **426 714-2PH** (4/91)
Rameau & Purcell: Orchestral Works
Purcell: Fantasia, Z731; Chaconne, Z730; *Rameau*: Castor
et Pollux (exc); *Purcell*: Viola da gamba fantasia, Z745.
(Eighteenth Century Orch/F. Brüggen)

ⓘ **426 740-2PH** (7/90)
Dmitri Hvorostovsky sings Tchaikovsky & Verdi Arias
Tchaikovsky: Eugene Onegin (exc); Queen of Spades
(exc); Enchantress (exc); Iolanta (exc); Mazeppa (exc);
Verdi: Traviata (exc); Macbeth (exc); Luisa Miller (exc);
Trovatore (exc); Don Carlo (exc). (D. Hvorostovsky,
Rotterdam PO/V. Gergiev)

ⓘ **426 848-2PB4** (3/91)
Tchaikovsky: Symphonies
Tchaikovsky: Symphony 1; Symphony 2; Symphony 3;
Symphony 4; Symphony 5; Symphony 6. (LSO/I.
Markevitch)

ⓘ **426 860-2PH** (12/91)
Christmas in Vienna
Traditional: Gegrüsst seist du, Maria; Als Maria übers
Gebirge ging; Maria durch ein' Dornwald ging; Teut eilands
erwachen; Kommet ihr Hirten; Gehts, Buama; Süsser die
Glocken nie klingen; O Tannenbaum; Still, still, still; O du
fröhliche; Stille Nacht; Es wird schon glei dumpa; Ihr
Kinderlein kommet; Auf, auf ihr Hirten; Es hat sich eröffnet;
O Jubel, O Freud; Kind ward geboren gar wunderschön;
Hitsche hei; Heissa, Buama; Es ist ein Ros' entsprungen;
Heiligste Nacht. (Vienna Boys' Ch, Teufel Family/U.C.
Harrer)

ⓘ **426 925-2PM19** (7/91)
The Complete Vivaldi Edition
Vivaldi: Sonatas, Op. 1; Sonatas, Op. 2; Concerti Grossi,
Op. 3; Concerti, Op. 4; Sonata, RV18; Sonata, RV30;
Sonata, RV35; Trio Sonata, RV72; Trio Sonata, RV76;
Concerti, Op.6; Concerti, Op.7 (exc); Concerti, Op.7 (exc);
Concerti, Op. 8; Concerti, Op. 9; Concerti, Op. 10;
Concerti, Op.11; Concerti, Op. 12. (S. Accardo, F. Gulli, B.
Canino, R. de Saram, R. Michelucci, I. Musici, F. Ayo, S.
Gazeau, P. Carmirelli, H. Holliger, S. Gazzelloni)

ⓘ **426 977-2PCC** (4/91)
Works for Violin and Orchestra
Haydn: Violin Concerto, HobVlla/1; Violin Concerto,
HobVlla/4; *Mozart*: Adagio, K261; Rondo, K373; *Schubert*:
Rondo, D438. (A. Grumiaux, ECO, New Philh/R.
Leppard)

ⓘ **432 061-2PM9** (7/92)
Haydn—The 43 Piano Trios
Haydn: Keyboard Trio 39; Sonata, HobXIV/6; Keyboard
Trio 1; Keyboard Trio 37; Divertimento, HobXIV/C1;
Keyboard Trio 41; Keyboard Trio 7; Hob deest; Partita,
HobXVI/1; Divertimento, HobXIV/C1; Keyboard Trio 36;
Keyboard Trio 34; Keyboard Trio 35; Keyboard Trio 38;
Keyboard Trio 40; Keyboard Trio 2; Keyboard Trio 8;
Keyboard Trio 6; Keyboard Trio 7; Keyboard Trio 9;
Keyboard Trio 12; Keyboard Trio 5; Keyboard Trio 10;
Keyboard Trio 11; Keyboard Trio 15; Keyboard Trio 14;
Keyboard Trio 13; Keyboard Trio 16; Keyboard Trio 17;
Keyboard Trio 18; Keyboard Trio 19; Keyboard Trio 22;
Keyboard Trio 20; Keyboard Trio 24; Keyboard Trio 32;
Keyboard Trio 21; Keyboard Trio 28; Keyboard Trio 23;
Keyboard Trio 25; Keyboard Trio 16; Keyboard Trio 33;
Keyboard Trio 30; Keyboard Trio 29; Keyboard Trio 31.
(Beaux Arts Trio)

ⓘ **432 075-2PH** (6/91)
Contemporary English Trumpet Concertos
Maxwell Davies: Trumpet Concerto; *Birtwistle*: Endless
Parade; *Blake Watkins*: Trumpet Concerto. (H.
Hardenberger, P. Patrick, BBC PO/E. Howarth)

Op.102 (exc); *Shostakovich*: Preludes and Fugues, Op. 87 (exc). (S Richter)

438 685-2PH (6/94)
The Great Waltz
Tiomkin: Great Waltz (exc); *R. R. Bennett*: Murder on the Orient Express (exc); *R. Strauss*: Rosenkavalier (exc); *Herrmann*: Snows of Kilimanjaro (exc); *F. Loewe*: Gigi (exc); *Prokofiev*: Cinderella (exc); *Sondheim*: Little Night Music (exc); *Bernstein*: Candide (1956) (exc); *Rózsa*: Madame Bovary (exc); *Waxman*: Hotel Berlin (exc); *Steiner*: Jezebel (exc); *Korngold*: Prince and the Pauper (exc); *Ravel*: La Valse. (Hollywood Bowl SO/J. Mauceri)

438 700-2PM2 (4/94)
Schubert—Complete Trios
Schubert: String Trio, D471; String Trio, D581; Piano Trio 1; Piano Trio 2; Piano Trio, D28; Notturno, D897. (Grumiaux Trio, Beaux Arts Trio)

438 703-2PM2 (5/94)
Schubert—Piano Works
Schubert: Piano Sonata, D958; Piano Sonata, D959; Piano Sonata, D960; Impromptus (exc). (A. Brendel)

438 706-2PM2 (5/94)
Beethoven—Overtures; Minuets; Dances
Beethoven: Coriolan; Egmont (exc); König Stefan (exc); Prometheus (exc); Fidelio (exc); Leonore (exc); Consecration of the House Ov; Namensfeier; Ruinen von Athen (exc); Menuets, WoO7; German D nces, WoO8; Contredanses, WoO14. (Leipzig Gewandhaus/K. Masur, ASMF/N. Marriner)

438 718-2PM2 (4/94)
Debussy—Complete Piano Music, Vol.1
Debussy: Préludes; Images: Isle Joyeuse; Estampes; Children's Corner; Pour le Piano; Arabesques; Mazurka. (W. Haas)

438 721-2PM2 (4/94)
Debussy—Complete Piano Music, Vol.2
Debussy: Etudes; D'un cahier d'esquisses; Plus que lente; Suite bergamasque; Tarantelle styrienne; Valse romantique; Hommage à Haydn; Rêverie; Nocturne; Ballade; Masques; Danse; Petit nègre; Berceuse héroïque; En blanc et noir; Petite Suite; Lindaraja; Epigraphes antiques; Marche écossaise. (W. Haas, N. Lee)

438 730-2PM2 (4/94)
Beethoven—Favourite Piano Sonatas
Beethoven: Piano Sonata 8; Piano Sonata 14; Piano Sonata 15; Piano Sonata 17; Piano Sonata 21; Piano Sonata 23; Piano Sonata 26. (A. Brendel)

438 733-2PM2 (7/94)
R. Strauss—Music for Wind
R. Strauss: Serenade, Op.7; Suite, Op.4; Sonatina 1; Sonatina 2; Oboe Concerto. (H. Holliger, Netherlands Wind Ens, New Philh/E. de Waart)

438 742-2PM2 (3/94)
Debussy—Orchestral Music
Debussy: Berceuse héroïque; Images; Jeux; Marche écossaise; Après-midi; Nocturnes; La Mer; Première rapsodie; Danse sacrée et danse profane. (G. Pieterson, V. Badings, Concertgebouw/B. Haitink)

438 751-2PM2 (10/94)
Liszt—Tone Poems, Vol.1
Liszt: Ce qu'on entend sur la montagne; Tasso; Préludes; Orpheus; Prometheus; Mazeppa; Festklänge. (LPO/B. Haitink)

438 754-2PM2 (10/94)
Liszt—Tone Poems, Vol.2
Liszt: Héroïde-funèbre; Ideale; Faust Episodes, S110 (exc); Hungaria; Hamlet; Hunnenschlacht; Von der Wiege bis zum Grabe. (LPO/B. Haitink)

438 760-2PM2 (5/94)
Brahms—Choral Works and Overtures
Brahms: Deutsches Requiem, Op.45 (Cpte); Alto Rhapsody, Op.53; Schicksalslied, Op.54; Academic Festival Overture; Tragic Overture; Haydn Variations. (W. Lipp, A. Heynis, F. Crass, Vienna Singverein, Vienna SO/W. Sawallisch)

438 797-2PM2 (4/94)
Haydn—Concertos
Haydn: Violin Concerto, HobVIIa/1; Violin Concerto, HobVIIa/3; Violin Concerto, HobVIIa/4; Violin and Keyboard Concerto, HobXVIII/6; Cello Concerto in C; Cello Concerto in D. (S. Accardo (vn/dir), C. Walevska, B. Canino, ECO/E. de Waart)

438 800-2PM2 (4/94)
Mozart—Choral Works
Mozart: Mass, K427; Mass, K317; Requiem. (H. Donath, H. Harper, G. Knight, Y. Minton, R. Davies, S. Dean, G.

Nienstedt, John Alldis Ch, LSC, LSO, BBC SO/Colin Davis)

438 803-2PM2 (4/94)
Mozart—Violin Sonatas
Mozart: Violin Sonata, K6; Violin Sonata, K7; Violin Sonata, K8; Violin Sonata, K9; Violin Sonata, K10; Violin Sonata, K11; Violin Sonata, K12; Violin Sonata, K13; Violin Sonata, K14; Violin Sonata, K15; Violin Sonata, K26; Violin Sonata, K27; Violin Sonata, K28; Violin Sonata, K29; Violin Sonata, K30; Violin Sonata, K31. (G. Poulet, B. Verlet)

438 812-2PM2 (2/94)
Bartók—Orchestral Works
Bartók: Piano Concerto 1; Piano Concerto 2; Piano Concerto 3; Violin Concerto 2; Concerto for Orchestra. (H. Szeryng, K. Kovacevich, LSO, BBC SO/Colin Davis, Concertgebouw/B. Haitink)

438 863-2PH (12/94)
Beethoven—Piano Sonatas
Beethoven: Piano Sonata 12; Piano Sonata 13; Piano Sonata 14; Piano Sonata 19. (A. Brendel)

438 868-2PH (6/94)
Mozart/Weber/Spohr—Clarinet Concertos
Mozart: Clarinet Concerto, K622; *Spohr*: Clarinet Concerto 1; *Weber*: Clarinet Concerto 2. (E. Ottensamer, VPO/Colin Davis)

438 872-2PH (5/94)
Songs and Dances of Death
Rimsky-Korsakov: Sadko (exc); Kashchey (exc); Snow Maiden (exc); Tsar's Bride (exc); *Borodin*: Prince Igor (exc); *Rubinstein*: Demon (exc); Nero (exc); *Rachmaninov*: Aleko (exc); *Mussorgsky*: Songs and Dances of Death. (D. Hvorostovsky, Kirov Th Orch/V. Gergiev)

438 873-2PH2 (2/95)
Bach—Magnificat and Masses
Bach: Magnificat, BWV243; Mass, BWV233; Mass, BWV234; Mass, BWV235; Mass, BWV236. (B. Bonney, B. Remmert, R. Trost, O. Bär, Berlin RIAS Chbr Ch, CPE Bach CO/P. Schreier)

438 876-2PH (5/94)
Vivaldi—Concertos for Strings
Vivaldi: Concerto, RV163; Concerto, RV136; Concerto, RV118; Concerto, RV123; Concerto, RV160; Concerto, RV128; Concerto, RV159; Sinfonia, RV146; Concerto, RV143; Concerto, RV117. (I Musici)

438 932-2PH (3/95)
Schubert—Lieder
Schubert: Musensohn, D764; Schwanengesang, D957 (exc); Schiffer, D536; Forelle, D550; An eine Quelle, D530; Auf der Bruck, D853; Rosenband, D280; Rastlose Liebe, D138; Winterreise (exc); Auf dem Wasser zu singen, D774; Im Freien, D880; Im Abendrot, D799; Wandrers Nachtlied II, D768; Im Frühling, D882; An den Mond, D296; Auf dem Strom, D943. (H-P. Blochwitz, R. Jansen, M-L. Neunecker)

438 933-2PH (9/95)
R. Strauss—Wind Music
R. Strauss: Serenade, Op. 7; Suite, Op. 4; Sonatina 2. (COE Wind Sols/H. Holliger)

438 938-2PH (9/94)
España
Falla: Vida breve (exc); Amor brujo (exc); *Lecuona*: Malagueña; *Albéniz*: Suite española 1; Pavana capricho; Iberia (exc); Navarra; *Infante*: Danses Andalouses. (K. Labèque, M. Labèque)

438 953-2PM2 (11/94)
Alarie/Simoneau - Arias & Duets
Mozart: Idomeneo (exc); Idomeneo (exc); Don Giovanni (exc); Così fan tutte (exc); Clemenza di Tito (exc); *Verdi*: Traviata (exc); *Gounod*: Roméo et Juliette (exc); Mireille (exc); *A. Thomas*: Mignon (exc); *Bizet*: Pêcheurs de Perles (exc); *Offenbach*: Contes d'Hoffmann (exc); *Bizet*: Carmen (exc); *Delibes*: Lakmé (exc); Lakmé (exc). (P. Alarie, M. Moralès, L. Simoneau, Vienna SO/B. Paumgartner, Lamoureux Orch/P. Dervaux/A. Jouve)

438 964-2PM4(1) (3/95)
Souzay sings French Songs (pt 1)
Fauré: Songs, Op.4 (exc); Poèmes d'un jour; Songs, Op.23 (exc); Songs, Op.39 (exc); Songs, Op.51 (exc); Shylock Suite (exc); Songs, Op.58; Bonne chanson, Op.61; Songs, Op.76 (exc); Songs, Op.76 (exc); Songs, Op.83 (exc); Songs, Op.85 (exc); Don silencieux; Chanson d'Eve, Op.95 (exc); Jardin clos (exc); Mirages; Horizon chimérique; *Poulenc*: Chansons villageoises; Calligrammes; Travail du peintre; Fraîcheur et le feu; Airs chantés (exc); Grenouillère; Métamorphoses (exc); Priez pour paix; *Ravel*: Mélodies populaires grecques; Epigrammes; Histoires naturelles; Chansons madécasses; Mélodies hébraïques; Don Quichotte à

Dulcinée. (G. Souzay, D. Baldwin, M. Larrieu, P. Degenne)

438 964-2PM4(2) (3/95)
Souzay sings French Songs (pt 2)
Ravel: Grands vents venus d'outre-mer; Sainte; Sur l'herbe; *Leguerney*: Ma douce jouvence; A son page; *Hahn*: Heure exquise; *Duparc*: Invitation au voyage; Sérénade florentine; Vague et la cloche; Extase; Manoir de Rosemonde; Lamento; Vie antérieure; Testament; Phidylé; Chanson triste; Elégie; Soupir; *Gounod*: Absent; Sérénade; *Chabrier*: Cigales; Chanson pour Jeanne; *Bizet*: Chanson d'avril; *Franck*: Nocturne; *Roussel*: Poèmes, Op.3 (exc); Mélodies, Op.20 (exc). (G. Souzay, D. Baldwin)

438 970-2PM2 (12/95)
Camille Maurane
Fauré: Requiem (Cpte); Bonne Chanson, Op.61; *Duparc*: Invitation au Voyage; Soupir; Testament; Sérénade florentine; Vague et la Cloche; Lamento; Vie antérieure; Phidylé; Extase; Elégie; Manoir de Rosemonde; Chanson triste; *Britten*: Illuminations; *Ravel*: Don Quichotte à Dulcinée; Shéhérazade; *Debussy*: Ballades de François Villon. (P. Alarie, J. Micheau, C. Maurane, L. Bienvenu, E. Brasseur Ch, Lamoureux Orch/J. Fournet/P. Sacher)

438 973-2PM2 (2/95)
Igor Markevitch conducts Stravinsky
Stravinsky: Apollon musagète; Suites; Norwegian Moods; Circus Polka; Histoire du soldat; Symphony of Psalms. (J. Cocteau, P. Ustinov, J-M. Fertey, A. Tonietti, Russian St Acad Ch, Russian St Acad Orch, LSO, inst ens/I. Markevitch)

442 011-2PH (4/94)
Russian Orchestral Works
Glinka: Ruslan and Lyudmila (exc); *Khachaturian*: Gayaneh (exc); Spartacus (exc); *Borodin*: Prince Igor (exc); *Liadov*: Baba-Yaga, Op. 56; Kikimora, Op. 63; *Tchaikovsky*: 1812. (Dutch Royal Marine Band, Kirov Th Chor, Kirov Th Orch/V. Gergiev)

442 012-2PH (12/94)
20th Century Wind Music
Honegger: Petite Suite; *Denisov*: Flute and Viola Duo; *Takemitsu*: Toward the Sea III; And then I knew 'twas Wind; *Britten*: Lachrymae; *Debussy*: Sonata for Flute, Viola and Harp. (A. Nicolet, N. Imai, N. Yoshino)

442 013-2PH (6/94)
Tchaikovsky—Romances
Tchaikovsky: My genius; Take my heart away; Songs, Op. 6 (exc); Songs, Op. 16 (exc); Songs, Op. 25 (exc); Songs, Op. 28 (exc); Songs, Op. 38 (exc); Songs, Op. 60 (exc); Songs, Op. 63 (exc); Songs, Op. 65 (exc); Songs, Op. 73 (exc). (O. Borodina, L. Gergieva)

442 015-2PH (9/94)
Maderna—Oboe Concertos
Maderna: Oboe Concerto 1; Oboe Concerto 2; Oboe Concerto 3. (H. Holliger, Cologne RSO/G. Bertini)

442 016-2PH (11/94)
Bartók—Piano Works, Vol.2
Bartók: Romanian Dances, Sz43; Hungarian folksongs, Sz35a; Allegro barbaro, Sz49; Dirges, Sz45; Suite, Sz62; Romanian Carols, Sz57; Studies, Sz72; Rondos on Folktunes, Sz84; First term at the piano, Sz53. (Z. Kocsis)

442 040-2PB9 (8/94)
Bruckner—Complete Symphonies
Bruckner: Symphony 0; Symphony 1; Symphony 2; Symphony 3; Symphony 4; Symphony 5; Symphony 6; Symphony 7; Symphony 8; Symphony 9. (Concertgebouw/B. Haitink)

442 050-2PB10 (11/94)
Mahler—Complete Symphonies
Mahler: Symphony 1; Symphony 2; Symphony 3; Symphony 4; Symphony 5; Symphony 6; Symphony 7; Symphony 8; Symphony 9; Symphony 10 (exc). (E. Ameling, I. Cotrubas, H. Harper, H. van Bork, B. Finnilä, A. Heynis, M. Forrester, M. Dieleman, W. Cochran, H. Prey, H. Sotin, Netherlands Rad Chor, St Willibrord's Boys' Ch, Collegium Musicum Amsteldamense, Amsterdam Toonkunst Ch, Amsterdam Stem des Volks Ch, St Willibrord and Pius X Children's Ch, Concertgebouw/B. Haitink)

442 061-2PB6 (10/94)
Tchaikovsky—Complete Symphonies, etc
Tchaikovsky: Symphony 1; Symphony 2; Symphony 3; Symphony 4; Symphony 5; Symphony 6; Manfred Symphony; Romeo and Juliet; 1812; Capriccio italien; Marche slave; Francesca da Rimini; Storm. (Concertgebouw/B. Haitink)

ⓘ **442 068-2PB4** (9/94)
Brahms—Complete Symphonies, etc
Brahms: Symphony 1; Symphony 2; Symphony 3;
Symphony 4; Haydn Variations; Tragic Overture; Academic
Festival Overture; Hungarian Dances (exc); Serenade 1;
Serenade 2. (Concertgebouw/B. Haitink)

ⓘ **442 073-2PB5** (9/94)
Beethoven—Complete Symphonies, etc
Beethoven: Symphony 1; Symphony 2; Symphony 3;
Symphony 4; Symphony 5; Symphony 6; Symphony 7;
Symphony 8; Symphony 9; Egmont (exc). (L. Popp, C.
Watkinson, P. Schreier, R. Holl, Netherlands Rad Chor,
Concertgebouw/B. Haitink)

ⓘ **442 079-2PB2** (7/94)
Schumann—Complete Symphonies, etc
Schumann: Symphony 1; Symphony 2; Symphony 3;
Symphony 4; Genoveva (exc); Manfred (exc).
(Concertgebouw/B. Haitink)

ⓘ **442 124-2PH** (7/95)
Beethoven—Piano Sonatas
Beethoven: Piano Sonata 1; Piano Sonata 2; Piano Sonata
3. (A. Brendel)

ⓘ **442 129-2PH** (12/94)
Sure Thing—The Jerome Kern Songbook
Kern: Land Where the Good Songs Go; Roberta (exc);
Show Boat (exc); High, Wide and Handsome (exc); Swing
Time (exc); One Night In the Tropics (exc); Joy of Living
(exc); Sweet Adeline (exc); You Were Never Lovelier (exc);
Very Warm for May (exc); Can't Help Singing (exc); Girl
from Utah (exc); Oh Boy! (exc); Sally (exc); Cover Girl
(exc); Music In the Air (exc); Miss 1917 (exc). (S. McNair,
A. Previn, D. Finck)

ⓘ **442 131-2PH** (5/95)
Baroque Trumpet Concertos
Vivaldi: Concerto, RV537; *Corelli:* Trumpet Sonata in D;
Albinoni: Concerti, Op. 7 (exc); *Torelli:* Sonata, G7; A.
Marcello: Oboe Concerto in D minor; *Viviani:* Capricci, Op.
4 (exc); *Franceschini:* 2-Trumpet Sonata in D; *Baldassare:*
Sonata in F. (H. Hardenberger, I Musici)

ⓘ **442 145-2PH** (7/95)
Vivaldi—Violin Concertos
Vivaldi: Concerti, Op. 11 (exc); Concerto, RV271;
Concerto, RV581; Concerto, RV270; Concerto, RV199;
Concerto, RV234. (M. Sirbu, I Musici)

ⓘ **442 150-2PH** (4/95)
Noches de España
Tárrega: Gran jota; *Sor:* Fantasia in D minor; *Albéniz:*
Piezás características (exc); *Granados:* Tonadillas (exc);
Mudarra: Tres Libros (1546) (exc); *Guerau:* Poema
harmónico (exc); *Milán:* El Maestro: Fantasias (exc);
Turina: Guitar Sonata, Op. 61; *Falla:* Homenaje Debussy;
Rodrigo: Por tierras de Jerez; *Moreno Torroba:* Aires de la
Mancha; *Romero:* Maestros. (P. Romero)

ⓘ **442 154-2PH** (11/95)
Rolla—Viola Concertos
Rolla: Viola Concerto, Op. 3; Divertimento in F; Viola
Concertino; Rondo in G. (M. Paris, I Musici)

ⓘ **442 269-2PM2** (10/94)
Mozart—The Great Piano Concertos, Volume 1
Mozart: Piano Concerto 19; Piano Concerto 20; Rondo,
K382; Piano Concerto 23; Piano Concerto 21; Piano
Concerto 24; Rondo, K386. (A. Brendel, ASMF/N.
Marriner)

ⓘ **442 272-2PM2** (10/94)
The Best of Bizet
Bizet: Carmen Suites (exc); Arlésienne Suites; Chanson
d'avril; Pêcheurs de perles (exc); Jeux d'enfants;
Symphony; Carmen (exc); Variations chromatiques; Agnus
Dei; Jolie Fille de Perth Suite. (J. Rhodes, L Simoneau, A.
Lance, J. Carreras, G. Souzay, R. Bianco, D. Baldwin, M-
F. Bucquet, Vienna Boys' Ch, Lamoureux Concerts Orch,
LSO, Paris Op Orch, Vienna SO/A. Dorati/J. Fournet/R.
Benzi/U. C. Harrer)

ⓘ **442 275-2PM2** (10/94)
J. C. Bach—Sinfonias
J. C. Bach: Symphonies, Op. 6; Symphonies, Op. 9; Grand
Overtures, Op. 18; Favourite Overtures (exc). (Netherlands
CO/D. Zinman)

ⓘ **442 284-2PM2** (10/94)
Bartók—String Quartets
Bartók: String Quartet 1; String Quartet 2; String Quartet 3;
String Quartet 4; String Quartet 5; String Quartet 6. (Novák
Qt)

ⓘ **442 287-2PM2** (9/94)
Favourite Violin Concertos
Beethoven: Violin Concerto; *Tchaikovsky:* Violin Concerto;
Mendelssohn: Violin Concerto, Op. 64; *Brahms:* Violin

Concerto; *Beethoven:* Romances (exc). (A. Grumiaux,
Concertgebouw, New Philh/Colin Davis/J. Krenz/B.
Haitink)

ⓘ **442 290-2PM2** (10/94)
Berlioz—Great Orchestral Works
Berlioz: Symphonie fantastique; Carnaval romain;
Corsaire; Harold in Italy; Symphonie funèbre et triomphale.
(N. Imai, John Alldis Ch, LSO/Colin Davis)

ⓘ **442 299-2PM2** (10/94)
Mozart—Complete Flute Works
Mozart: Flute Concerto, K313; Flute Concerto, K314;
Andante, K315; Flute and Harp Concerto, K299; Flute
Quartets. (A. Nicolet, Concertgebouw/D. Zinman, H.
Barwahser, O. Ellis, LSO/Colin Davis, W. Bennett,
Grumiaux Trio)

ⓘ **442 302-2PM2** (10/94)
The Best of Mendelssohn
Mendelssohn: Ruy Blas; Symphony 4; Rondo capriccioso;
Midsummer Night's Dream (exc); Variations sérieuses, Op.
54; Songs without Words (exc); Hebrides; Violin Concerto,
Op. 64. (S. Accardo, W. Haas, New Philh/W. Sawallisch,
Boston SO, BBC SO/Colin Davis, LPO/C. Dutoit)

ⓘ **442 386-2PM** (12/94)
Bach—Brandenburg Concertos Nos 1-3
Bach: Brandenburg Concertos (exc); Violin Concerto,
BWV1041; Violin Concerto, BWV1042. (A. Grumiaux,
ECO/R. Leppard)

ⓘ **442 389-2PM** (9/94)
Sibelius—Orchestral Works
Sibelius: Symphony 2; Finlandia; Valse triste; Legends
(exc). (Boston SO/Colin Davis)

ⓘ **442 396-2PM** (9/94)
Baroque Favourites
Albinoni: Adagio; *Handel:* Organ Concertos (exc); *Corelli:*
Concerti Grossi, Op. 6 (exc); *Pachelbel:* Canon and Gigue;
Bach: Suites, BWV1066-9 (exc). (I Musici)

ⓘ **442 405-2PM** (9/94)
Kocsis plays Beethoven
Beethoven: Piano Sonata 1; Piano Sonata 5; Piano Sonata
8; Piano Sonata 17. (Z. Kocsis)

ⓘ **442 410-2PM** (9/94)
Queen of the Night—Cheryl Studer sings Mozart
Mozart: Entführung (exc); Zauberflöte (exc); Idomeneo
(exc); Nozze di Figaro (exc); Don Giovanni (exc);
Clemenza di Tito (exc); Così fan tutte (exc). (C. Studer,
ASMF/N. Marriner)

ⓘ **442 425-2PM** (1/95)
Hollywood Nightmares
Savino/Perry: Phantom of the Opera (exc); *Steiner:* King
Kong (exc); *Stravinsky:* Rite of Spring (exc); *J. T. Williams:*
Jurassic Park (exc); *Rózsa:* Spellbound Concerto; *Barry:* Body Heat
(exc); *Waxman:* Sunset Boulevard (exc); Dr Jekyll and Mr
Hyde (exc); *Goldsmith:* Omen (exc). (S. Hough, Los
Angeles Master Chorale, Hollywood Bowl SO/J. Mauceri)

ⓘ **442 427-2PH** (6/95)
Vaughan Williams—Orch Works
Vaughan Williams: Wasps (exc); Tallis Fantasia; In the Fen
Country; Variations for brass band; Norfolk Rhapsody 1;
Dives and Lazarus Variants. (ASMF/N. Marriner)

ⓘ **442 460-2PH** (11/94)
Schubert—Lieder
Schubert: Schwanengesang, D957 (Cpte); Wanderer an
den Mond, D870; Sehnsucht, D879; Irdisches Glück,
D866/4; Widerspruch, D865; Lebensmut, D937; Herbst,
D945; Wiegenlied, D867. (W. Holzmair, I. Cooper)

ⓘ **442 530-2PM** (12/94)
English Idylls
Vaughan Williams: Tuba Concerto; *Elgar:* Romance,
Op. 62; Idylle, Op. 4/1; *Delius:* Caprice and Elegy;
Grainger: Youthful rapture; *Dyson:* Prelude, Fantasy and
Chaconne (exc); *Ireland:* Holy Boy; W. Davies: Solemn
Melody; *Grainger:* Brigg Fair; *Holst:* Invocation; C. Scott:
Pastoral and Reel. (J. Lloyd Webber, J. Lenehan, J. Birch,
ASMF/N. Marriner)

ⓘ **442 532-2PH** (4/95)
Ustvolskaya—Compositions, I, II, III
Ustvol'skaya: Composition 1; Composition 2; Composition
3. (Schoenberg Ens/R. de Leeuw)

ⓘ **442 534-2PH** (12/95)
Janáček—Choral Works
Janáček: Wild Jack; Male-voice Choruses (1888) (exc);
Male-voice Choruses (1885-1922) (exc); Elegy on the
death of his daughter Olga; Wolf's trail; Songs of
Hradčany; Nursery Rhymes. (T. Willemstijn, B. Borden, A.
Gold, H. Vels, B. Sellers, J. Bremer, R. Coupe, D. Barrick,

E. Pameijer, E. Stoop, M. Bon, Netherlands Chbr Ch,
Schoenberg Ens/R. de Leeuw)

ⓘ **442 536-2PM** (2/95)
My Restless Soul
Tchaikovsky: Songs, Op. 6 (exc); Songs, Op. 38 (exc);
Songs, Op. 47 (exc); Songs, Op. 57 (exc); Songs, Op. 73
(exc); I should like in a single word; My genius; *Borodin:*
For the shores; *Rimsky-Korsakov:* Songs, Op. 42 (exc); To
the poet, Op. 45 (exc); By the sea, Op. 46 (exc);
Rachmaninov: Songs, Op. 4 (exc); Songs, Op. 8 (exc);
Songs, Op. 14 (exc); Songs, Op. 21 (exc). (D.
Hvorostovsky, M. Arkadiov)

ⓘ **442 544-2PM5** (12/94)
Pierre Monteux
Beethoven: Symphony 3; *Schubert:* Symphony 8;
Tchaikovsky: Swan Lake (exc); *Brahms:* Symphony 2;
Tragic Overture; Academic Festival Overture; *Ravel:*
Boléro; La Valse; Ma mère l'Oye; *Debussy:* Images;
Martyre de St Sébastien. (Concertgebouw, LSO/P.
Monteux)

ⓘ **442 571-2PM2** (4/95)
Mozart—The Great Piano Concertos, Volume II
Mozart: Piano Concerto 15; Piano Concerto 14; Piano
Concerto 22; Piano Concerto 25; Piano Concerto 27. (A.
Brendel, ASMF/N. Marriner)

ⓘ **442 577-2PM2** (8/95)
Beethoven—Concertos, Volume 1
Beethoven: Piano Concerto 1; Piano Concerto 2; Piano
Concerto 3; Piano Concerto 4; Romances. (A. Grumiaux,
S. Kovacevich, BBC SO/Colin Davis, Concertgebouw/B.
Haitink)

ⓘ **442 580-2PM2** (8/95)
Beethoven—Concertos, Volume 2
Beethoven: Piano Concerto 5; Triple Concerto; Violin
Concerto; Piano Concerto, WoO4. (H. Szeryng, H.
Krebbers, J. Starker, S. Kovacevich, C. Arrau, L.
Grychtolowna, LSO/Colin Davis, New Philh/E. Inbal,
Concertgebouw, Haitink, Folkwang CO/H. Dressel)

ⓘ **442 586-2PM2** (5/95)
Tchaikovsky—Complete Tone Poems
Tchaikovsky: Fate; Storm; Tempest; Voyevoda; Francesca
da Rimini; Hamlet; Romeo and Juliet; 1812. (Frankfurt
RSO, New Philh, Concertgebouw/E. Inbal/I. Markevitch/B.
Haitink)

ⓘ **442 592-2PM2** (5/95)
C P E Bach—Concertos
C. P. E. Bach: Flute Concerto, H431; Flute Concerto,
H435; Flute Concerto, H438; Flute Concerto, H445; Oboe
Concerto, H468; Oboe Concerto, H466; Oboe Concerto,
H549; Harp Sonata, H563. (A. Nicolet, H. Holliger, U.
Holliger, R. Jucker, Netherlands CO/D. Zinman, ECO/R.
Leppard)

ⓘ **442 603-2PH** (1/95)
Julie Andrews sings Richard Rodgers
Rodgers: Sound of Music (exc); King and I (exc); Babes in
Arms (exc); No Strings (exc); Boys from Syracuse (exc);
Connecticut Yankee (exc); Higher and Higher (exc); Spring
is Here (exc); Pal Joey (exc); Carousel (exc); South Pacific
(exc); Carousel (exc); Do I Hear a Waltz? (exc); State Fair
(exc); South Pacific (exc); Oklahoma! (exc). (J. Andrews,
London Musicians Orch/I. Fraser)

ⓘ **442 604-2PH5** (3/95)
Mozart—The Great Symphonies
Mozart: Symphony 29; Symphony 31; Symphony 32;
Symphony 33; Symphony 34; Symphony 35; Symphony
36; Symphony 38; Symphony 39; Symphony 40;
Symphony 41. (EBS/J. E. Gardiner)

ⓘ **442 625-2PM5** (11/95)
Clara Haskil—The Legacy Volume 1: Chamber Music
Beethoven: Violin Sonata 1; Violin Sonata 2; Violin Sonata
3; Violin Sonata 4; Violin Sonata 5; Violin Sonata 6; Violin
Sonata 7; Violin Sonata 8; Violin Sonata 9; Violin Sonata
10; *Mozart:* Violin Sonata, K301; Violin Sonata, K304;
Violin Sonata, K376; Violin Sonata, K378; Violin Sonata,
K454; Violin Sonata, K526. (A. Grumiaux, C. Haskil)

ⓘ **442 631-2PM4** (11/95)
Clara Haskil—The Legacy Volume 2: Concertos
Mozart: Piano Concerto 9; Piano Concerto 20; Rondo,
K386; Piano Concerto 23; Piano Concerto 24; *Beethoven:*
Piano Concerto 3; Piano Concerto 4; *Schumann:*
Piano Concerto; *Falla:* Nights in the Gardens of Spain;
Chopin: Piano Concerto 2. (C. Haskil, Vienna SO/P.
Sacher/B. Paumgartner, Lamoureux Concerts Orch/I.
Markevitch, Hague PO/W. van Otterloo)

ⓘ **442 635-2PM3** (11/95)
Clara Haskil—The Legacy Volume 3: Solo Repertoire
D. Scarlatti: Keyboard Sonatas (exc); *Mozart:* Variations,
K573; Piano Sonata, K330; *Ravel:* Sonatine; *Schumann:*

Bunte Blätter; Abegg Variations; Kinderszenen;
Waldszenen; *Beethoven:* Piano Sonata 17; Piano Sonata
18; *Schubert:* Piano Sonata, D960; *Beethoven:* Piano
Sonata 17; Piano Sonata 18. (C. Haskil)

① **442 643-2PM** (6/95)
Rimsky-Korsakov—Orchestral Works
Rimsky-Korsakov: Scheherazade; Capriccio espagnol;
Russian Easter Festival Ov. (Concertgebouw, LSO/I.
Markevitch/K. Kondrashin)

① **442 685-2PM12** (11/95)
Clara Haskil - The Legacy
Beethoven: Violin Sonata 1; Violin Sonata 2; Violin Sonata
3; Violin Sonata 4; Violin Sonata 5; Violin Sonata 6; Violin
Sonata 7; Violin Sonata 8; Violin Sonata 9; Violin Sonata
10; *Mozart:* Violin Sonata, K301; Violin Sonata, K304;
Violin Sonata, K376; Violin Sonata, K378; Violin Sonata,
K454; Violin Sonata, K526; Piano Concerto 9; Piano
Concerto 20; Rondo, K386; Piano Concerto 20; Piano
Concerto 24; *Beethoven:* Piano Concerto 3; *Mozart:* Piano
Concerto 23; *Schumann:* Piano Concerto; *Falla:* Nights in
the Gardens of Spain; *Chopin:* Piano Concerto 2; *D.
Scarlatti:* Keyboard Sonatas (exc); *Mozart:* Variations,
K573; Piano Sonata, K330; *Ravel:* Sonatine; *Schumann:*
Bunte Blätter; Abegg Variations; Kinderszenen;
Waldszenen; *Beethoven:* Piano Sonata 17; Piano Sonata
18; *Schubert:* Piano Sonata, D960; *Beethoven:* Piano
Sonata 17; Piano Sonata 18. (C. Haskil, A. Grumiaux,
Vienna SO/P. Sacher/B. Paumgartner, Lamoureux
Concerts Orch/I. Markevitch, Hague PO/W. van Otterloo)

① **442 727-2PM2** (11/95)
George Szell - The Early Years
Beethoven: Symphony 5; *Mendelssohn:* Midsummer
Night's Dream (exc); *Mozart:* Symphony 34; *Schubert:*
Rosamunde (exc); *Sibelius:* Symphony 2.
(Concertgebouw/G. Szell)

① **442 744-2PM2** (10/95)
Wolf/R.Strauss—Lieder
Wolf: Italienisches Liederbuch (Cpte); *R. Strauss:* Lieder,
Op. 21 (exc); Lieder, Op. 10 (exc); Lieder, Op. 19 (exc);
Lieder, Op. 29 (exc); Lieder, Op. 27 (exc); Lieder, Op. 17
(exc); Lieder, Op. 48 (exc); Lieder, Op. 37 (exc). (E.
Ameling, G. Souzay, D. Baldwin)

① **442 775-2PH** (7/95)
Russian Spectacular
Mussorgsky: Boris Godunov (exc); *Tchaikovsky:* Marche
slave; Capriccio italien; Eugene Onegin (exc); *Liadov:*
Enchanted Lake, Op. 62. (Kirov Th Chor, Kirov Th Orch/V.
Gergiev)

① **442 778-2PH** (12/95)
Tchaikovsky Fantasy
Tchaikovsky: Capriccio italien; *Scriabin:* Fantasy in A
minor; *Tchaikovsky:* Swan Lake; Sleeping Beauty (exc);
Marche slave. (K. Labèque, M. Labèque)

① **442 780-2PH** (8/95)
Songs of Desire
Rimsky-Korsakov: To the poet, Op. 45 (exc); Songs, Op.
42 (exc); Songs, Op. 40 (exc); Songs, Op. 2 (exc); In
Spring, Op. 43 (exc); *Borodin:* False note; Sea Princess;
Mussorgsky: What are words of love to you; Night;
Balakirev: Songs (1858-64) (exc); Forgotten songs (exc);
Songs (1895-6) (exc); *Cui:* I remember the evening;
Songs, Op. 57 (exc); Songs, Op. 54 (exc); Songs, Op. 49
(exc); It's over. (O. Borodina, L. Gergieva)

① **442 785-2PH** (8/95)
The Incomparable Alfredo Kraus
Offenbach: Contes d'Hoffmann (exc); *Cilea:* Arlesiana
(exc); *Donizetti:* Lucrezia Borgia (exc); Fille du régiment
(exc); Dom Sébastien (exc); Favorita (exc); *Gounod:* Faust
(exc); *Lalo:* Roi d'Ys (exc); *Meyerbeer:* Crociato in Egitto
(exc); *Delibes:* Lakmé (exc); *R. Strauss:* Rosenkavalier
(exc). (Alfredo Kraus, P. Gyton, WNO Chor, WNO Orch/C.
Rizzi)

① **442 787-2PH** (11/95)
Beethoven—Piano Sonatas
Beethoven: Piano Sonata 23; Piano Sonata 24; Piano
Sonata 25; Piano Sonata 27. (A. Brendel)

① **442 795-2PH** (10/95)
Skalkottas—Cycle Concert
Skalkottas: Piano and Wind Quartet 1; Piano and Wind
Quartet 2; Oboe Concertino; Sonata Concertante; Trumpet
Concertino. (H. Holliger, K. Thunemann, H. Hardenberger,
B. Canino)

① **446 057-2PB14** (10/94)
Wagner—The Ring Cycle - Bayreuth Festival 1967
Wagner: Rheingold (Cpte); Walküre (Cpte); Siegfried
(Cpte); Götterdämmerung (Cpte). (T. Adam, A. Burmeister,
W. Windgassen, E. Wohlfahrt, G. Neidlinger, A. Silja, H.
Esser, G. Nienstedt, V. Soukupová, M. Talvela, K. Böhme,
D. Siebert, H. Dernesch, R. Hesse, J. King; Leonie

Rysanek, B. Nilsson, A. Burmeister, G. Nienstedt, D.
Mastilovic, L. Synek, H. Dernesch, G. Hopf, Š. Červená, E.
Schärtel, S. Wagner, W. Windgassen, T. Adam, E. Köth, J.
Greindl, T. Stewart, L. Dvořáková, M. Mödl, S. Wagner, M.
Höffgen, A. Burmeister, A. Silja, Bayreuth Fest Chor,
Bayreuth Fest Orch/K. Böhm)

① **446 067-2PH6** (12/95)
Beethoven—Complete Symphonies
Beethoven: Symphony 1; Symphony 2; Symphony 3;
Symphony 4; Symphony 5; Symphony 6; Symphony 7;
Symphony 8; Symphony 9; Egmont (exc); Leonore (exc).
(S. Sweet, J. Rappé, P. Frey, F. Grundheber, Dresden St
Op Chor, Staatskapelle Dresden/Colin Davis)

① **446 081-2PH** (9/95)
The Echoing Air—The Music of Henry Purcell
Purcell: Staircase Overture; Hogwood Suite; Chaconne,
Z730; If music be the food of love, Z379/3; Libertine, Z600
(exc); Blessed Virgin's Expostulation, Z196; Bonduca,
Z574 (exc); O Solitude, Z406; Fairy Queen, Z629 (exc);
Pausanias, Z585 (exc); King Arthur, Z628 (exc); She that
would gain a faithful lover, Z414; Cupid, the slyest rogue
alive, Z367; Indian Queen, Z630 (exc); Oedipus, Z583
(exc); Fatal hour comes on apace, Z421. (S. McNair, C.
Steele-Perkins, S. Standage, AAM/C. Hogwood)

① **446 086-2PH** (9/95)
Schumann—Lieder
Schumann: Liederkreis, Op. 24 (Cpte); Dichterliebe, Op.
48 (Cpte); Gesänge , Op. 142 (exc); Myrthen, Op. 25 (exc);
Romanzen und Balladen, Op. 53 (exc); Romanzen und
Balladen, Op. 64 (exc). (W. Holzmair, I. Cooper)

① **446 154-2PM2** (8/95)
Mozart—The Complete Piano Trios
Mozart: Piano Trio, K542; Piano Trio, K502; Piano Trio,
K564; Piano Trio, K548; Divertimento, K254; Piano Trio,
K496; Piano trio, K498. (Beaux Arts Trio, J. Brymer, P.
Ireland, S. Kovacevich)

① **446 163-2PM2** (8/95)
Schubert—Last Four Quartets
Schubert: String Quartet, D810; String Quartet, D804;
String Quartet, D887; String Quartet, D703. (Quartetto
Italiano)

① **446 172-2PM2** (8/95)
Brahms—Complete Quintets
Brahms: Piano Quintet; String Quintet 1; String Quintet 2;
Clarinet Quintet. (W. Haas, Berlin Phil Octet)

① **446 196-2PM** (12/95)
Rossini—Overtures
Rossini: Barbiere di Siviglia (exc); Guillaume Tell (exc);
Cenerentola (exc); Italiana in Algeri (exc); Scala di seta
(exc); Gazza ladra (exc); Semiramide (exc); Signor
Bruschino (exc); Turco in Italia (exc). (ASMF/N. Marriner)

① **446 200-2PM** (11/95)
Liszt—Piano Concertos; Piano Sonata
Liszt: Piano Concerto 1; Piano Concerto 2; Piano Sonata,
S178. (S. Richter, LSO/K. Kondrashin)

① **446 366-2PH** (12/95)
Bartók—Piano Concertos
Bartók: Piano Concerto 1; Piano Concerto 2; Piano
Concerto 3. (Z. Kocsis, Budapest Fest Orch/I. Fischer)

① **446 406-2PH** (11/95)
Berlin—Heat Wave
Berlin: Annie Get Your Gun (exc); Berlin Goes to
Hollywood; As Thousands Cheer (exc); As Thousands
Cheer (exc); Top Hat (exc); Follow the Fleet (exc); Easter
Parade (exc); Call Me Madam (exc); Call Me Madam (exc);
Always; Follow the Fleet (exc); Patriotic Overture; White
Christmas (exc). (P. LuPone, B. Motley, J. Powell, G. Van
Buren, J. West, Hollywood Bowl Orch/J. Mauceri)

Pianissimo

① **PP10393** (5/93)
Works for Two Pianos/Piano Duet
Saint-Saëns: Danse macabre; *Debussy:* Petite Suite;
Tchaikovsky: Nutcracker Suite (exc); *Brahms:* Haydn
Variations; *MacDowell:* Fantasiestücke, Op.17 (exc);
Brahms: Waltzes, Op.39 (exc); *Liszt:* Hungarian
Rhapsodies, S244 (exc). (C. Cann, A. Cann)

① **PP10394** (6/94)
Scriabin—Piano Works
Scriabin: Piano Sonata 3; Piano Sonata 4; Piano Sonata 5;
Etudes, Op.8. (Y. Matsuzawa)

① **PP10792** (8/92)
Chabrier—Piano Works
Chabrier: Bourrée fantasque; Impromptu; Pièces
pittoresques. (R. McMahon)

Pierre Verany

① **PV783041** (4/84)
Liszt—Organ Works
Liszt: Prelude and Fugue, S260; Variations, S673;
Fantasia and Fugue, S259. (C. de Zeeuw)

① **PV784011** (5/84)
Organists of the Sun King
Dandrieu: Premier livre d'orgue (exc); *Clérambault:*
Premier Livre d'orgue (exc); *Marchand:* Deuxième livre
d'orgue (exc); *Raison:* Premier livre d'orgue (exc). (P.
Bardon)

① **PV784041** (3/86)
Vierne/Houbart—Organ Works
Vierne: Symphony 3; Suite 3 (exc); *Houbart:* Gaudens,
gaudebo/Laetare Jerusalem improvisation. (F-H.
Houbart)

① **PV784061** (3/86)
Bach—Organ Works
Bach: Prelude and Fugue, BWV547; Prelude and Fugue,
BWV546; Prelude and Fugue, BWV548; Orgel-Büchlein,
BWV599-644 (exc); Clavier-Übung III, BWV669-689 (exc).
(F-H. Houbart)

① **PV785031** (3/87)
Franck—Organ Works
Franck: Pièces (1878) (exc); Fantaisie idylle; Chorales. (F-
H. Houbart)

① **PV785051/2** (3/87)
French 17th and 18th Century Organ Works
Couperin: Messe à l'usage ordinaire des paroisses; Messe
pour les couvents; *Dandrieu:* Premier livre d'orgue (exc);
Guilain: Pièces d'orgue (exc); *Jullien:* Premier livre d'orgue
(exc); *Raison:* Premier livre d'orgue (exc). (P. Bardon)

① **PV786091** (5/94)
Le Groupe des Six: Piano Duets
Milhaud: Boeuf sur le toit; Scaramouche; *Poulenc:*
Embarquement pour Cythère; Capriccio; *Tailleferre:*
Premières Prouesses; Suite Burlesque; Waltzes; *Auric:*
Bagatelles; *Durey:* Neige; *Honegger:* Contrepoints. (P.
Corre, E. Exerjean)

① **PV786101** (5/87)
Campra—French Cantatas
Campra: Didon; Arion; Hébé; Achille oisif; Daphné. (J.
Nicolas, D. Cuiller, P. Allain-Dupré, J. Bernfeld, M.
Chapuis)

① **PV786102** (3/87)
French String Quartets
Debussy: String Quartet; *Ravel:* String Quartet; *Fauré:*
String Quartet. (Viotti Qt)

① **PV787092** (9/93)
Airs and Dances of Shakespeare's Time
A. Holborne: Almain, 'The Honiesuckle'; Night Watch;
Coranto 'Heigh ho Holiday'; Various Consort Pieces (exc);
R. Johnson II: Almans (Lute) (exc); Naglein Blumen;
Brade: Paduana and Galliard; *Morley:* Ayres (1600) (exc);
Campion: Ayres, Bk.3 (exc); *Rosseter:* If she forsake me;
Sweet, come again; *Pilkington:* Rest, sweet nymphs; Go
from my window. (J. Elwes, S. Stubbs, Toulon Musica
Antiqua/C. Mendoze)

① **PV788011** (1/89)
Trumpet Concertos
Harut'unyan: Trumpet Concerto; *Hummel:* Trumpet
Concerto; *Jolivet:* Trumpet Concerto 2. (B. Soustrot, Loire
PO/M. Soustrot)

① **PV788012** (9/88)
French Viola da gamba and Harpsichord Works
Marais: Pièces de viole III/I (exc); *Couperin:* Art de toucher
le clavecin (exc); Livre de clavecin II (exc); *Boismortier:*
Diverses pièces, op.31. (B. Re, R. Kohnen)

① **PV788111** (12/89)
Poulenc—Choral Works
Poulenc: Figure humaine; Motets pour le temps de Noël;
Salve Regina; Petites prières de Saint François d'Assise.
(Provence Voc Ens/H. Guy)

① **PV789104** (3/90)
Bach—Organ Works
Bach: Toccata and Fugue, BWV565; Schübler Chorales,
BWV645-650 (exc); Chorales, BWV651-668 (exc); Orgel-
Büchlein, BWV599-644 (exc); Fantasia, BWV572; Erbarm'
dich, BWV721; Herzlich tut mich verlangen, BWV727;
Clavier-Übung III, BWV669-689 (exc); Pastorale, BWV590;
Nun freut euch, BWV734; Passacaglia and Fugue,
BWV582. (J-P. Brosse)

① **PV790013** (9/90)
A. Scarlatti—Cantatas
A. Scarlatti: Diana ed Endimione; Ero ed Leandro; Correa

nel seno amato. (J. Nicolas, A. Aubin, S. Deeks, X. Julien-Laferriere, H. Williams, A. Verzier, M. Bothwell, P. Ramin)

ⓓ **PV792051** (6/94)
Chausson/Fauré—Orchestral Works
Chausson: Symphony, Op. 20; *Fauré:* Pelléas et Mélisande Suite; Pénélope (exc). (Loire PO/M. Soustrot)

ⓓ **PV794031** (8/94)
Lalo—Piano Trios
Lalo: Piano Trio 1; Piano Trio 2; Piano Trio 3. (Henry Trio)

ⓓ **PV794033** (10/94)
Vivaldi—Vocal and Wind Music
Vivaldi: Stabat Mater; Concerti, Op. 8 (exc); Nisi Dominus; Concerti, Op. 10 (exc). (C. Brett, Toulon Musica Antiqua, C. Mendoze (rec/dir))

ⓓ **PV794034** (6/95)
Dandrieu—Mass and Vespers for Easter Sunday
Dandrieu: Premier livre d'orgue (exc); *Anon:* Easter Sunday (exc); Easter Sunday (exc). (Paris Gregorian Ch/J-E. Tulve, J-P. Brosse)

ⓓ **PV794041** (9/94)
Palestrina—Motets and Madrigals
Palestrina: Salve regina (8vv); Ave mundi spes (8vv); Motets, Bk 2 (1581) (exc); Motets, Bk 3 (1575) (exc); Madrigals, Bk 1 (1581) (exc); Alma Redemptoris mater (8vv); Regina coeli (8vv); Magnificat a 8. (Akademia/F. Lasserre, L. Stewart)

ⓓ **PV794052** (2/95)
G. Morlaye—Pieces for Lute & Guitar
Morlaye: Lute Works, Bk 1 (exc); Lute Works, Bk 2 (exc); Lute Works, Bk 3 (exc); Lute Pieces (Uppsala MS) (exc); Guitar Works, Bk 1 (exc); Guitar Works, Bk 2 (exc); Guitar Works, Bk 4 (exc). (F. Marincola, F. Marincola)

ⓓ **PV794114** (4/95)
Graupner—Overtures for Chalumeaux and Orchestra
Graupner: 3-Chalumeaux Overture-Suite in D minor; Chalumeau Overture-Suite in B flat; 2-Chalumeaux Overture-Suite in F. (J-C. Veilhan, Y. Tetsu, F. Jacquemart, Mensa Sonora Ens, J. Maillet (vn/dir))

ⓓ **PV79801** (5/84)
Vivaldi—Organ Concertos
Bach/Vivaldi: Organ Concerto in D; Organ Concerto in A minor; Organ Concerto in C; Organ Concerto in G minor. (P. Bardon, Munich Pro Arte/K. Redel)

Point Music

ⓓ **434 873-2PTH** (6/93)
Jon Gibson—In Good Company
Gibson: Waltz; Song 3; Extensions II; *J. Adams:* Nixon in China (exc); *Reich:* Reed Phase; *Jennings:* Terry's G Dorian Blues; *Glass:* Einstein on the Beach (exc); *Riley:* Tread on the Trail. (J. Gibson, M. Goldray, M. Riesman, L.M. Young, B. Ruyle, J. Snyder)

Polskie Nagrania

ⓓ **PNCD020** (6/90)
Penderecki: Orchestral Works
Penderecki: Cello concerto 2; Viola concerto; Dream of Jacob; Paradise Lost. (I. Monighetti, S. Kamasa, Polish Nat RO/A. Wit)

ⓓ **PNCD040** (9/90)
Lutosławski: Vocal and Orchestral Works
Lutosławski: Concerto for orchestra (1954); Funeral Music (1958); Symphony 1; Lacrimosa. (S. Woytowicz, Silesian Phil Ch, Katowice RSO/W. Lutosławski/J. Krenz, Warsaw Nat PO/W. Rowicki)

ⓓ **PNCD041** (9/90)
Lutosławski: Choral & Orchestral Works
Lutosławski: Venetian Games (1961); Henri Michaux poems; Symphony 2. (Warsaw Nat PO/W. Rowicki/W. Lutosławski, Polish Rad Chor, Katowice RSO/J. Krenz)

ⓓ **PNCD042** (9/90)
Lutosławski: Vocal and Orchestral Works
Lutosławski: Paroles tissées; Cello concerto; Postlude 1; Livre pour orchestre. (Katowice RSO, Warsaw Nat PO, L. Devos, R. Jabłoński/J. Krenz/W. Lutosławski)

ⓓ **PNCD043** (9/90)
Lutosławski: Orchestral Works
Lutosławski: Preludes and Fugues; Mi-parti; Novelette. (Polish CO, Polish Nat RSO/W. Lutosławski, Junge Deutsche Phil/H. Holliger)

ⓓ **PNCD044** (9/90)
Lutosławski: Chamber and Orchestral Works
Lutosławski: Symphony 3; Chain 1; Chain 2; Chain 3. (Katowice RSO/A. Wit/W. Lutosławski, Junge Deutsche Phil/H. Holliger, K. Jakowicz, Warsaw Nat PO/K. Kord)

ⓓ **PNCD045** (9/90)
Lutosławski: Selected Works
Lutosławski: Studies; Paganini Variations; Songs; String Quartet (1964); Epitaph; Grave; Partita. (M. Drewnowski, J. Łukaszczyk, M. Łukaszczyk, H. Lukomska, Warsaw Nat PO/A. Markowski, LaSalle Qt, H. Holliger, S. Esztényi, R. Jabłoński, K. Kulka, E. Knapnik)

ⓓ **PNCD050** (3/91)
R. Strauss: Orchestral Works
R. Strauss: Don Juan; Tod und Verklärung; Till Eulenspiegel. (Polish Nat RSO/A. Wit)

ⓓ **PNCD065** (7/90)
Szymanowski: Chamber Works
Szymanowski: Myths, Op. 30; Romance; Harnasie (exc); Lullaby; Kurpian Song; Nocturne and Tarantella; String Quartet 2. (K. Kulka, J. Marchwinski, W. Wilkomirska, T. Chmielewski, Wilanów Qt)

ⓓ **PNCD066** (7/90)
Szymanowski: Piano Works
Szymanowski: Etudes, Op.4 (exc); Masques, Op.34; Piano Sonata 2; Mazurkas, Op.50 (exc). (W. Małcużyński, A. Stefanski, B. Hesse-Bukowska)

ⓓ **PNCD067** (7/90)
Szymanowski: Songs
Szymanowski: Songs, Op.5; Songs, Op.54; Songs, Op.31; Songs, Op.24; Songs, Op.13 (exc). (T. Zylis-Gara, A. Bachlada, J. Gadulanka, H. Lukomska, J. Marchwinski, J. Sulikowski)

Polyphonic

ⓓ **QPRL007D** (8/92)
Howard Snell Brass - The Four Seasons etc.
Handel: Water Music (exc); *Bach:* Brandenburg Concertos (exc); *Vivaldi:* Concerti, Op. 8 (exc). (H. Snell Brass/H. Snell)

ⓓ **QPRL049D** (8/92)
Boosey & Hawkes National Brass Band Gala Concert 1991
Arne: Rule Britannia; *H. Clarke:* Showers of Gold; *Geldard:* Tribute to Ted Heath; *Bizet:* Pêcheurs de perles (exc); *Vinter:* Triumphant Rhapsody; *Simpson:* Energy; *Delius:* Village Romeo and Juliet (exc); *Frackenpohl:* Pop Suite (exc); *Traditional:* David of the White Rock; *Tchaikovsky:* 1812. (R. Webster, R. Childs, N. Childs, British Tuba Qt, Britannia Building Soc Band, Desford Colliery Caterpillar Band, CWS, IMI Yorkshire Imperial Band/G. Brand/J. Watson)

ⓓ **QPRL053D** (9/93)
Slavonic Brass
Smetana: Bartered Bride (exc); *Borodin:* Prince Igor (exc); *Liszt:* Préludes; *Dvořák:* Slavonic Dances (exc); *Tchaikovsky:* Symphony 6 (exc); *Dvořák:* Symphony 9 (exc); *Rimsky-Korsakov:* Capriccio espagnol; *Dvořák:* Rusalka (exc); *Ippolitov-Ivanov:* Caucasian Sketches (exc); *Tchaikovsky:* Symphony 4 (exc); *Mussorgsky:* Pictures (exc). (Black Dyke Mills Band/J. Watson)

ⓓ **QPRL062D** (5/94)
Masterworks for Brass Band -Volume 2 - Partita
D. Bray: Salford Sinfonietta; *A. Butterworth:* Sinfonia, Op. 85; *Steadman-Allen:* Journeymen; *Bulla:* Chorale and Toccata; *Sparke:* Partita. (BNFL Band/R. Evans)

ⓓ **QPRZ005D** (9/91)
Premiere
Berlin: Suite; *Boyce:* Symphonies (exc); *Debussy:* Syrinx; *Ravel:* Ma mère l'oye (exc); *Rossini:* Soirées musicales (exc); *Sparke:* Divertimento. (H. Snell Brass/H. Snell)

Praga

ⓓ **PR250 038** (10/93)
Bartók—Violin and Piano Works
Bartók: For Children (1908/09) (exc); Violin Sonata 1; Violin Sonata 2. (D. Oistrakh, G. Kremer, F. Bauer, O. Maisenberg)

ⓓ **PR250 039** (9/93)
Brahms/Weber—Piano Works
Brahms: Ballades; Piano Pieces, Op.116; *Weber:* Piano Sonata 2. (Emil Gilels)

ⓓ **PR254 002/3** (5/93)
Ančerl Edition. Vol.2 - Shostakovich
Shostakovich: Symphony 5; Symphony 7; Symphony 9. (Czech PO/K. Ančerl)

ⓓ **PR254 009/15** (4/93)
Beethoven—Complete String Quartets
Beethoven: String Quartet 1; String Quartet 2; String Quartet 3; String Quartet 4; String Quartet 5; String Quartet 6; String Quartet 7; String Quartet 8; String

Quartet 9; String Quartet 10; String Quartet 11; String Quartet 12; String Quartet 13; String Quartet 14; String Quartet 15; String Quartet 16; Grosse Fuge. (Vlach Qt, Janáček Qt)

Preamble

ⓓ **PRCD1776** (1/89)
American Piano Music
Gershwin: Preludes; *Waxman:* Charm Bracelet; *Antheil:* Piano Sonata 4; *Copland:* Our Town; Piano Pieces; *H.Stevens:* Intrada; Inventions; *Barber:* Excursions. (E. Parkin)

Preiser

ⓓ **89001** (2/90)
Toti dal Monte (1898-1975)
Bellini: Sonnambula (exc); *Donizetti:* Lucia di Lammermoor (exc); Fille du Régiment (exc); Fille du Régiment (exc); Linda di Chamounix (exc); *A. Thomas:* Mignon (exc); *Bizet:* Pêcheurs de Perles (exc); Pêcheurs de Perles (exc); *Verdi:* Falstaff (exc); *Bishop:* Lo, here the gentle lark; *Traditional:* Carnevale di Venezia. (T. dal Monte, La Scala Orch, Orch/C. Sabajno/J. Pasternack/G. Santini/G. Nastrucci/R. Bourdon, La Scala Chor)

ⓓ **89002** (2/90)
Miguel Fleta (1893-1938)
Bellini: Puritani (exc); *Donizetti:* Favorita (exc); *Verdi:* Rigoletto (exc); *Meyerbeer:* Africaine (exc); *Verdi:* Aida (exc); Aida (exc); *Bizet:* Carmen (exc); Carmen (exc); Pêcheurs de perles (exc); *Leoncavallo:* Pagliacci (exc); *Puccini:* Bohème (exc); Tosca (exc); Tosca (exc); *Mascagni:* Amico Fritz (exc); *Zandonai:* Giulietta e Romeo (exc). (M. Fleta, F. Austral, E. Thornton, L. Bori, orch)

ⓓ **89003** (2/90)
Riccardo Stracciari (1875-1955)
Rossini: Barbiere di Siviglia (exc); *Donizetti:* Lucia di Lammermoor (exc); *Verdi:* Nabucco (exc); *Wagner:* Tannhäuser (exc); *Berlioz:* Damnation de Faust (exc); *Meyerbeer:* Dinorah (exc); Africaine (exc); *Massenet:* Roi de Lahore (exc); *Ponchielli:* Gioconda (exc); *Verdi:* Otello (exc); *Leoncavallo:* Pagliacci (exc); *Puccini:* Tosca (exc); *Di Capua:* O sole mio. (R. Stracciari, orch)

ⓓ **89004** (2/90)
Frida Leider (1888-1975) - I
Gluck: Armide (exc); *Mozart:* Don Giovanni (exc); *Beethoven:* Fidelio (exc); *Wagner:* Siegfried (exc); Tristan und Isolde (exc); Tristan und Isolde (exc); Parsifal (exc); Wesendonk Lieder (exc); Wesendonk Lieder (exc). (F. Leider, orch, Berlin St Op Orch, LSO/J. Barbirolli/L. Blech/A. Coates, R. Laubenthal, L. Melchior)

ⓓ **89005** (9/90)
Franz Völker (1899-1965) - I
Wagner: Rienzi (exc); Rienzi (exc); Fliegende Holländer (exc); Lohengrin (exc); Lohengrin (exc); Meistersinger (exc); Meistersinger (exc); *Halévy:* Juive (exc); *Meyerbeer:* Africaine (exc); *Verdi:* Trovatore (exc); Aida (exc); Aida (exc); *Leoncavallo:* Pagliacci (exc). (F. Völker, Berlin St Op Orch/A. Melichar/H. Weigert/J. Prüwer/M. Gurlitt/J. Heidenreich)

ⓓ **89006** (9/90)
Heinrich Schlusnus (1888-1952) - I
Marschner: Hans Heiling (exc); *Lortzing:* Zar und Zimmermann (exc); *Wagner:* Tannhäuser (exc); *Verdi:* Trovatore (exc); Traviata (exc); Rigoletto (exc); Ballo in maschera (exc); Vespri siciliani (exc); Simon Boccanegra (exc); *Bizet:* Carmen (exc); *Borodin:* Prince Igor (exc); *Tchaikovsky:* Eugene Onegin (exc); Queen of Spades (exc); *Leoncavallo:* Pagliacci (exc). (H. Schlusnus, Berlin St Op Orch/L. Blech/J. Schüler/G. Steeger/A. Melichar)

ⓓ **89007** (9/90)
Aureliano Pertile (1885-1952) - I
Donizetti: Lucia di Lammermoor (exc); Favorita (exc); Favorita (exc); *Rossini:* Guillaume Tell (exc); *Verdi:* Luisa Miller (exc); Trovatore (exc); Trovatore (exc); Forza del destino (exc); Otello (exc); *Bizet:* Carmen (exc); *Ponchielli:* Gioconda (exc); *Puccini:* Manon Lescaut (exc); Manon Lescaut (exc). (A. Pertile, A. Rozsa, B. Franci, E. Lattuada, G. Nessi, A. Buades, La Scala Orch/C. Sabajno/G. Nastrucci/L. Molajoli)

ⓓ **89008** (6/90)
Irene Minghini-Cattaneo (1892-1944)
Bellini: Norma (exc); *Donizetti:* Favorita (exc); *Verdi:* Trovatore (exc); Ballo in maschera (exc); Aida (exc); *Ponchielli:* Gioconda (exc); *Bizet:* Carmen (exc); *Saint-Saëns:* Samson et Dalila (exc). (I. Minghini-Cattaneo, L. Cecil, A. Pertile, A. Gelli, D. de Martis, A. Granforte, La Scala Orch/C. Sabajno, orch/J. Barbirolli)

Ⓓ **89009** (2/90)
Gino Bechi (b. 1913)
Verdi: Rigoletto (exc); Rigoletto (exc); Rigoletto (exc); Trovatore (exc); Ballo in maschera (exc); Forza del destino (exc); Otello (exc); Don Carlo (exc); Falstaff (exc); *Leoncavallo:* Pagliacci (exc); *Catalani:* Wally (exc). (G. Bechi, T. Pasero, G. Bernelli, G. Lauri-Volpi, Rome Op Orch, La Scala Orch, Orch, Santa Cecilia Academy Orch, Milan SO/L. Ricci/U. Berrettoni/R. Arduini/A. Votto/V. Bellezza/A. Quadri)

Ⓓ **89010** (6/90)
Tancredi Pasero (1893-1983) - I
Rossini: Barbiere di Siviglia (exc); *Bellini:* Sonnambula (exc); Norma (exc); *Verdi:* Ernani (exc); Trovatore (exc); Don Carlo (exc); Forza del destino (exc); *Meyerbeer:* Huguenots (exc); *Gounod:* Faust (exc); Faust (exc); Faust (exc); *A. Thomas:* Mignon (exc); *Ponchielli:* Gioconda (exc); *Boito:* Mefistofele (exc). (T. Pasero, B. Scacciati, F. Merli, G. Cigna, P. Civil, G. Zinetti, orch/L. Molajoli)

Ⓓ **89011** (5/90)
Marjorie Lawrence (1909-1979)
Reyer: Sigurd (exc); *Wagner:* Lohengrin (exc); Lohengrin (exc); Walküre (exc); Walküre (exc); Götterdämmerung (exc); *R. Strauss:* Salome (exc). (M. Lawrence, M. Singher, Y. Brothier, J. Claverie, Pasdeloup Orch/P. Coppola)

Ⓓ **89012** (9/90)
Giacomo Lauri-Volpi (1894-1979)
Bellini: Norma (exc); Puritani (exc); *Verdi:* Rigoletto (exc); Aida (exc); *Gounod:* Faust (exc); *Bizet:* Carmen (exc); *Offenbach:* Contes d'Hoffmann (exc); *Ponchielli:* Gioconda (exc); *Gomes:* Schiavo (exc); *Meyerbeer:* Africaine (exc); *Giordano:* Andrea Chénier (exc); *Puccini:* Manon Lescaut (exc); Madama Butterfly (exc); Tosca (exc). (G. Lauri-Volpi, E. Rethberg, G. De Luca, L. Borgonovo, orch/R. Bourdon, NY Met Op Chor, NY Met Op Orch/G. Setti, La Scala Orch/F. Ghione)

Ⓓ **89013** (10/90)
Giannina Arangi-Lombardi (1890-1951)
Donizetti: Lucrezia Borgia (exc); *Verdi:* Lombardi (exc); Ernani (exc); Trovatore (exc); Ballo in maschera (exc); Aida (exc); *Ponchielli:* Gioconda (exc); Gioconda (exc); *Mascagni:* Cavalleria rusticana (exc); *Puccini:* Bohème (exc); Tosca (exc). (G. Arangi-Lombardi, E. Molinari, G. Zinetti, La Scala Orch/L. Molajoli, Milan SO)

Ⓓ **89014** (1/91)
Ebe Stignani (1903-1974)
Gluck: Alceste (1776) (exc); Orfeo ed Euridice (exc); *Rossini:* Semiramide (exc); *Bellini:* Norma (exc); *Donizetti:* Favorita (exc); Linda di Chamounix (exc); *Verdi:* Trovatore (exc); Don Carlo (exc); Ballo in maschera (exc); Forza del destino (exc); *Mascagni:* Amico Fritz (exc); *A. Thomas:* Mignon (exc); *Saint-Saëns:* Samson et Dalila (exc). (E. Stignani, G. Cigna, EIAR Orch/U. Tansini/V. Gui/A. la Rosa Parodi/G. Marinuzzi)

Ⓓ **89015** (11/90)
Carlo Tagliabue (1898-1978)
Rossini: Barbiere di Siviglia (exc); *Bellini:* Puritani (exc); *Wagner:* Tannhäuser (exc); *Verdi:* Ernani (exc); Rigoletto (exc); Trovatore (exc); Ballo in maschera (exc); Forza del destino (exc); Otello (exc); *Bizet:* Carmen (exc); Pêcheurs de perles (exc); *Leoncavallo:* Pagliacci (exc). (C. Tagliabue, orch, Turin EIAR Orch, La Scala Orch/U. Berrettoni/G. Marinuzzi/A. la Rosa Parodi/U. Tansini)

Ⓓ **89016** (11/90)
Gina Cigna (b. 1900)
Bellini: Norma (exc); *Verdi:* Ballo in maschera (exc); Forza del destino (exc); *Gounod:* Faust (exc); Faust (exc); *Boito:* Mefistofele (exc); *Catalani:* Wally (exc); *Ponchielli:* Gioconda (exc); *Cilea:* Adriana Lecouvreur (exc); Adriana Lecouvreur (exc); *Puccini:* Fanciulla del West (exc). (G. Cigna, P. Civil, T. Pasero, I. Mannarini, C. Elmo, orch/L. Molajoli, EIAR Orch/U. Tansini)

Ⓓ **89017** (10/90)
Gerhard Hüsch (1901-1984) sings Schubert
Schubert: Musensohn, D764; Schwanengesang, D957 (exc); An die Musik, D547; Lied eines Schiffers an die Dioskuren, D360; Widerschein, D639; Wer sich der Einsamkeit ergibt, D478; Wer nie sein Brot mit Tränen ass, D480; An die Türen, D479; Dass sie hier gewesen, D775; Liebeslauschen, D698; Ständchen, D889; Erlkönig, D328; Schwanengesang, D957 (exc); Schwanengesang, D957 (exc). (G. Hüsch, H.U. Müller, G. Moore)

Ⓓ **89018** (5/90)
Helge Rosvaenge (1897-1972)
Auber: Fra Diavolo (exc); *Adam:* Postillon de Lonjumeau (exc); *Weber:* Oberon (exc); *Beethoven:* Fidelio (exc); *Bizet:* Carmen (exc); *Verdi:* Trovatore (exc); Aida (exc); *Leoncavallo:* Pagliacci (exc); *Puccini:* Tosca (exc); *Glinka:* Life for the Tsar (exc); *R. Strauss:* Rosenkavalier (exc); *Wille:* Königsballade (exc). (H. Roswaenge, Berlin St Op Orch/B. Seidler-Winkler, VPO/R. Moralt)

Ⓓ **89019** (12/90)
Alexander Kipnis (1891-1978)
Mozart: Entführung (exc); Nozze di Figaro (exc); Don Giovanni (exc); Zauberflöte (exc); *Rossini:* Barbiere di Siviglia (exc); *Weber:* Freischütz (exc); *Flotow:* Martha (exc); *Lortzing:* Wildschütz (exc); *Nicolai:* Lustigen Weiber von Windsor (exc); *Gounod:* Faust (exc); *Verdi:* Simon Boccanegra (exc); Don Carlo (exc); *Wagner:* Meistersinger (exc); *R. Strauss:* Rosenkavalier (exc); *Traditional:* Kalinka; Soldier's Song. (A. Kipnis, E. Ruziczka, chor, Berlin St Op Orch/C. Schmalstich/E. Orthmann)

Ⓓ **89020** (2/91)
Leo Slezak (1873-1946)
Weber: Euryanthe (exc); *Auber:* Muette de Portici (exc); *Rossini:* Guillaume Tell (exc); *Halévy:* Juive (exc); Juive (exc); *Meyerbeer:* Huguenots (exc); Huguenots (exc); Prophète (exc); *Wagner:* Lohengrin (exc); *Verdi:* Ernani (exc); Rigoletto (exc); Trovatore (exc); Ballo in maschera (exc); *Gounod:* Roméo et Juliette (exc); *Goldmark:* Königin von Saba (exc); Königin von Saba (exc). (L. Slezak, L. Demuth, W. Hesch, E. Bland, orch)

Ⓓ **89022** (1/91)
Fernand Ansseau (1890-1972)
Berlioz: Damnation de Faust (exc); *Wagner:* Lohengrin (exc); *Meyerbeer:* Africaine (exc); *Gounod:* Roméo et Juliette (exc); *Bizet:* Carmen (exc); Carmen (exc); *Février:* Monna Vanna (exc); *Massenet:* Werther (exc); *Leoncavallo:* Pagliacci (exc); *Puccini:* Tosca (exc). (F. Ansseau, F. Heldy, orch/P. Coppola)

Ⓓ **89023** (9/90)
Conchita Supervia (1895-1936)
Mozart: Nozze di Figaro (exc); *Rossini:* Barbiere di Siviglia (exc); Barbiere di Siviglia (exc); Cenerentola (exc); *Bizet:* Carmen (exc); Carmen (exc); *Saint-Saëns:* Samson et Dalila (exc); *Humperdinck:* Hänsel und Gretel (exc); *R. Strauss:* Rosenkavalier (exc). (C. Supervia, G. Manuritta, A. Apolloni, I. Mannarini, G. Nessi, A. Baracchi, I.M. Ferraris, orch/A. Albergoni)

Ⓓ **89025** (10/90)
Tiana Lemnitz (b. 1897)
Mozart: Nozze di Figaro (exc); Zauberflöte (exc); *Weber:* Freischütz (exc); Freischütz (exc); *Wagner:* Tannhäuser (exc); Lohengrin (exc); *Verdi:* Aida (exc); Otello (exc). (T. Lemnitz, BPO, Berlin St Op Orch/B. Seidler-Winkler/T. Beecham/J. Schüler/F.A. Schmidt/L. Blech)

Ⓓ **89026** (1/91)
Francesco Merli (1887-1976) - I
Verdi: Forza del destino (exc); Forza del destino (exc); Aida (exc); Aida (exc); Aida (exc); Otello (exc); *Wagner:* Lohengrin (exc); *Meyerbeer:* Africaine (exc); *Mascagni:* Cavalleria Rusticana (exc); *Ponchielli:* Gioconda (exc); *Giordano:* Andrea Chénier (exc); *Leoncavallo:* Pagliacci (exc). (F. Merli, G. Vanelli, G. Arangi-Lombardi, orch/L. Molajoli)

Ⓓ **89027** (2/91)
Sigrid Onegin (1889-1943)
Gluck: Orfeo ed Euridice (exc); *Donizetti:* Lucrezia Borgia (exc); Favorita (exc); *Meyerbeer:* Huguenots (exc); Prophète (exc); Prophète (exc); *Verdi:* Don Carlo (exc); *Bizet:* Carmen (exc); *Saint-Saëns:* Samson et Dalila (exc); *Brahms:* Alto Rhapsody, Op. 53. (S. Onegin, Berlin Doctors' Ch, Berlin St Op Orch, orch/R. Bourdon/L. Blech/K. Singer)

Ⓓ **89028** (10/90)
Ivar Andresen (1896-1940)
Mozart: Zauberflöte (exc); *Halévy:* Juive (exc); *Meyerbeer:* Huguenots (exc); *Verdi:* Macbeth (exc); Forza del destino (exc); *Wagner:* Lohengrin (exc); Tannhäuser (exc); Tannhäuser (exc); Meistersinger (exc); Götterdämmerung (exc); Parsifal (exc). (I. Andrésen, E. Habich, Berlin St Op Orch/F. Zweig/F. Weissmann/L. Blech, chor, orch)

Ⓓ **89029** (11/90)
Meta Seinemeyer (1895-1929)
Verdi: Ballo in maschera (exc); Don Carlo (exc); Aida (exc); Otello (exc); *Giordano:* Andrea Chénier (exc); *Puccini:* Manon Lescaut (exc); Bohème (exc); Bohème (exc); Madama Butterfly (exc); *Rimsky-Korsakov:* Tsar's Bride (exc); *Rubinstein:* Nacht. (M. Seinemeyer, T. Pattiera, H. Jung, Berlin St Op Orch/F. Weissmann)

Ⓓ **89031** (6/91)
Elisabeth Schumann (1885-1952)
Mozart: Nozze di Figaro (exc); Don Giovanni (exc); Rè pastore (exc); Exsultate, jubilate, K165 (exc); *Bach:* St Matthew Passion, BWV244 (exc); Cantata 159 (exc); *Handel:* Joshua (exc); *R. Strauss:* Lieder, Op. 27 (exc); Lieder, Op. 43 (exc); *Marx:* Lieder und Gesänge (exc); *Flies:* Wiegenlied; *Mozart:* Warnung, K433; *Mahler:* Knaben Wunderhorn (exc); *Schumann:* Jugend Lieder, Op. 79 (exc); Lieder und Gesänge, Op. 77 (exc); Myrthen, Op. 25 (exc). (E. Schumann, orch, Vienna St Op Orch/G.W. Byng/K. Alwin/L. Collingwood, G. Reeves)

Ⓓ **89034** (2/92)
Giuseppe Lugo (1900-1980)
Verdi: Luisa Miller (exc); *Bizet:* Pêcheurs de Perles (exc); *Massenet:* Hérodiade (exc); Manon (exc); Werther (exc); *Mascagni:* Cavalleria rusticana (exc); *Leoncavallo:* Pagliacci (exc); *Puccini:* Bohème (exc); Bohème (exc); Tosca (exc); Tosca (exc); *Leoncavallo:* Mattinata; *Di Capua:* O sole mio; *Bixio:* Mia canzone al vento; Cuore diglielo anche tu. (G. Lugo, orch/A. Wolff/E. Cohen, F. Weiss/D. Olivieri)

Ⓓ **89035** (12/91)
Erna Berger (1900-1990) - I
Mozart: Nozze di Figaro (exc); Don Giovanni (exc); *Rossini:* Barbiere di Siviglia (exc); *Verdi:* Rigoletto (exc); Traviata (exc); *Nicolai:* Lustigen Weiber von Windsor (exc); *Auber:* Fra Diavolo (exc); *Bizet:* Pêcheurs de perles (exc); *J. Strauss II:* Fledermaus (exc); *Puccini:* Bohème (exc); Madama Butterfly (exc); *Grieg:* Peer Gynt (exc); *R. Strauss:* Rosenkavalier (exc); *Weber:* Non paventar mia vita. (E. Berger, V. Ursuleac, H. Schlusnus, C. Müller, Berlin St Op Orch, Berlin City Op Orch/C. Krauss/F. Zweig/C. Schmalstich/L. Blech/W. Schütze/A. Melichar/J. Schüler/W.F. Reuss, T. Lemnitz)

Ⓓ **89036** (1/92)
Giuseppe de Luca (1876-1950) - I
Mozart: Nozze di Figaro (exc); *Rossini:* Barbiere di Siviglia (exc); Guillaume Tell (exc); *Bellini:* Puritani (exc); *Donizetti:* Favorita (exc); Don Pasquale (exc); *Verdi:* Trovatore (exc); Ballo in maschera (exc); Rigoletto (exc); Don Carlo (exc); *Gounod:* Faust (exc); *Meyerbeer:* Dinorah (exc); *Diaz:* Benvenuto Cellini (exc); *Massenet:* Hérodiade (exc). (G. De Luca, L. Bori, A. Galli-Curci, orch)

Ⓓ **89037** (12/92)
Hina Spani (1896-1969)
Verdi: Ballo in maschera (exc); Trovatore (exc); Trovatore (exc); *Wagner:* Lohengrin (exc); Lohengrin (exc); *Gounod:* Faust (exc); *Massenet:* Manon (exc); *Leoncavallo:* Pagliacci (exc); *Puccini:* Manon Lescaut (exc); Bohème (exc); Tosca (exc); Madama Butterfly (exc); *Catalani:* Wally (exc); *López Buchardo:* Canción del carretero; *Ugarte:* Dia del fiesta. (H. Spani, A. Granforte, La Scala Orch/C. Sabajno, Inst Ens/G. Nastrucci)

Ⓓ **89038** (11/91)
Giovanni Zenatello (1876-1949)
Verdi: Ballo in maschera (exc); Otello (exc); Otello (exc); *Giordano:* Andrea Chénier (exc); *Leoncavallo:* Pagliacci (exc); *Puccini:* Manon Lescaut (exc); Tosca (exc); *Bizet:* Carmen (exc); Carmen (exc). (G. Zenatello, G. Marion, A. Boemi, H. Spani, A. Granforte, M. Gay, Apollo Chor, orch, La Scala Orch/R. Bourdon/C. Sabajno)

Ⓓ **89039** (8/92)
Karin Branzell (1891-1974)
Gluck: Orfeo ed Euridice (exc); *Donizetti:* Favorita (exc); *Verdi:* Trovatore (exc); Trovatore (exc); Ballo in maschera (exc); *Meyerbeer:* Prophète (exc); Prophète (exc); *A. Thomas:* Mignon (exc); *Gounod:* Faust (exc); *Bizet:* Carmen (exc); *Saint-Saëns:* Samson et Dalila (exc); Samson et Dalila (exc); *Ponchielli:* Gioconda (exc); *Wagner:* Rheingold (exc); *Kienzl:* Evangelimann (exc). (K. Branzell, orch)

Ⓓ **89040** (2/92)
Carlo Galeffi (1884-1961)
Rossini: Barbiere di Siviglia (exc); *Gounod:* Faust (exc); *Verdi:* Ernani (exc); Trovatore (exc); Trovatore (exc); Rigoletto (exc); Rigoletto (exc); Rigoletto (exc); Rigoletto (exc); Ballo in maschera (exc); Aida (exc); Aida (exc); *Mascagni:* Guglielmo Ratcliff (exc); *Leoncavallo:* Pagliacci (exc); *Giordano:* Andrea Chénier (exc). (C. Galeffi, G. Arangi-Lombardi, E. Dominici, M. Gentile, L.B. Rasa, La Scala Orch/L. Molajoli)

Ⓓ **89041** (3/91)
Eidé Norena (1884-1968)
Handel: Atalanta (exc); *Haydn:* Schöpfung (exc); *Mozart:* Zauberflöte (exc); *Rossini:* Guillaume Tell (exc); *Meyerbeer:* Huguenots (exc); *Verdi:* Rigoletto (exc); *A. Thomas:* Hamlet (exc); Hamlet (exc); *Bizet:* Carmen (exc); *Verdi:* Otello (exc); *Puccini:* Turandot (exc). (E. Norena, orch/J. Messner/P. Coppola/H. Defosse/G. Cloëz/F. Ruhlmann)

Ⓓ **89042** (7/92)
Nazzareno de Angelis (1881-1962)
Rossini: Mosè in Egitto (exc); Barbiere di Siviglia (exc); *Weber:* Freischütz (exc); *Meyerbeer:* Robert le Diable (exc); *Halévy:* Juive (exc); *Verdi:* Nabucco (exc); Don Carlo (exc); *Wagner:* Walküre (exc); *Gounod:* Faust (exc); Faust (exc); *Boito:* Mefistofele (exc); Mefistofele (exc). (N. de

Angelis, E. Cheni, I. Mannarini, E. Venturini, G. Cigna, orch/L. Molajoli)

Ⓓ **89043** (10/91)
Antonio Cortis (1891-1952)
Verdi: Rigoletto (exc); Trovatore (exc); *Meyerbeer:* Africaine (exc); *Gounod:* Faust (exc); *Bizet:* Carmen (exc); Carmen (exc); *Massenet:* Manon (exc); Werther (exc); *Mascagni:* Cavalleria rusticana (exc); Iris (exc); *Giordano:* Andrea Chénier (exc); *Puccini:* Bohème (exc); Tosca (exc); Turandot (exc). (A. Cortis, A. Rozsa, La Scala Orch/C. Sabajno)

Ⓓ **89044** (4/93)
Dusolina Giannini (1902-1986)
Bellini: Norma (exc); *Verdi:* Forza del destino (exc); Forza del destino (exc); Aida (exc); Otello (exc); *Bizet:* Carmen (exc); *Puccini:* Manon Lescaut (exc); Madama Butterfly (exc); *Di Capua:* 'O sole mio; *V. Valente:* Manella mia; *Traditional:* Luisé; Ohie Meneche. (D. Giannini, La Scala Orch/C. Sabajno, Berlin St Op Orch/C. Schmalstich, orch/J. Barbirolli/G.W. Byng)

Ⓓ **89045** (2/92)
Mattia Battistini (1856-1928)
Mozart: Don Giovanni (exc); *Flotow:* Martha (exc); *Donizetti:* Favorita (exc); Dom Sébastien (exc); *Hérold:* Zampa (exc); *Berlioz:* Damnation de Faust (exc); *Verdi:* Ernani (exc); Ballo in maschera (exc); Traviata (exc); *A. Thomas:* Hamlet (exc); *Cocchi:* Per la patria. (M. Battistini, E. Corsi, A. Sillich, L. Colazza, orch)

Ⓓ **89046** (5/92)
Rosette Anday (1903-1977)
Donizetti: Favorita (exc); *Verdi:* Trovatore (exc); *Wagner:* Götterdämmerung (exc); *Saint-Saëns:* Samson et Dalila (exc); Samson et Dalila (exc); *Bizet:* Carmen (exc); *Bach:* St Matthew Passion, BWV244 (exc); *Ochs:* Dank sei dir, Herr; *Mendelssohn:* Elias (exc); *Hummel:* Hallelujah; *Gluck:* Orphée (exc); *Verdi:* Trovatore (exc); *Wagner:* Tristan und Isolde (exc); *Kienzl:* Evangelimann (exc). (R. Anday, Vienna St Op Orch/K. Alwin, Berlin St Op Orch/J. Prüwer, LSO/R. Heger, orch, H. Dawson)

Ⓓ **89047** (10/92)
Xenia Belmas (1890-1981)
Meyerbeer: Huguenots (exc); *Verdi:* Ernani (exc); Aida (exc); *A. Thomas:* Mignon (exc); *Rimsky-Korsakov:* Snow Maiden (exc); *Tchaikovsky:* Queen of Spades (exc); *Mascagni:* Cavalleria rusticana (exc); Cavalleria rusticana (exc); *Leoncavallo:* Pagliacci (exc); *Puccini:* Bohème (exc). (X. Belmas, W. Domgraf-Fassbaender, orch/A. Kitschin)

Ⓓ **89048** (12/91)
Apollo Granforte (1886-1975) - I
Rossini: Barbiere di Siviglia (exc); *Wagner:* Tannhäuser (exc); *Verdi:* Trovatore (exc); Rigoletto (exc); Rigoletto (exc); Rigoletto (exc); Rigoletto (exc); Rigoletto (exc); Rigoletto (exc); Traviata (exc); Otello (exc); *Leoncavallo:* Pagliacci (exc); Zazà (exc). (A. Granforte, F. Zaccarini, A. Saraceni, I. Mannarini, G. Menni, N. Palai, Ottavi, N. Sanchioni/G-F. Masini, A. Rozsa, P. Girardi, La Scala Orch/C. Sabajno/G. Nastrucci)

Ⓓ **89049** (11/92)
Margarete Teschemacher (1903-1959)
Mozart: Nozze di Figaro (exc); *Weber:* Oberon (exc); Freischütz (exc); *Lortzing:* Waffenschmied (exc); *Wagner:* Wesendonk Lieder (exc); Lohengrin (exc); *Verdi:* Don Carlo (exc); *R. Strauss:* Arabella (exc); Daphne (exc). (M. Teschemacher, I. Beilke, M. Wittrisch, Berlin St Op Orch/B. Seidler-Winkler/F. Zaun, Berlin City Op Orch/H.U. Müller, Saxon St Orch/K. Böhm)

Ⓓ **89050** (3/92)
Ezio Pinza (1892-1957)
Mozart: Don Giovanni (exc); *Bellini:* Norma (exc); Norma (exc); *Donizetti:* Favorita (exc); *Verdi:* Ernani (exc); Vespri siciliani (exc); Don Carlo (exc); Trovatore (exc); Requiem (exc); *Meyerbeer:* Robert le Diable (exc); *Halévy:* Juive (exc); *A. Thomas:* Caïd (exc); Mignon (exc); *Gounod:* Faust (exc); *Puccini:* Bohème (exc); *Tosti:* Ultima canzone. (E. Pinza, orch/R. Bourdon, NY Met Op Chor, NY Met Op Orch/G. Setti)

Ⓓ **89051** (7/94)
Elisabeth Rethberg (1894-1976)
Mozart: Nozze di Figaro (exc); Zauberflöte (exc); Ridente la calma, K152; *Meyerbeer:* Africaine (exc); *Bizet:* Carmen (exc); Carmen (exc); Pastorale; *Smetana:* Bartered Bride (exc); *J. Strauss II:* Zigeunerbaron (exc); *Puccini:* Madama Butterfly (exc); *R. Strauss:* Lieder, Op.48 (exc); Lieder, Op.17 (exc); *Paták y:* Einsame; *Giordano:* Andrea Chénier (exc); *Puccini:* Bohème (exc); Tosca (exc); Madama Butterfly (exc). (E. Rethberg, R. Tauber, anon, orch)

Ⓓ **89054** (10/93)
Miliza Korjus (1912-1980)
Mozart: Zauberflöte (exc); *Adam:* Toréador (exc); *Donizetti:* Zingara (exc); Lucia di Lammermoor (exc); *Verdi:* Ernani (exc); Rigoletto (exc); Vespri Siciliani (exc); *Gounod:* Mireille (exc); *Meyerbeer:* Dinorah (exc); *Offenbach:* Contes d'Hoffmann (exc); *Delibes:* Lakmé (exc); *Rimsky-Korsakov:* Tsar's Bride (exc); Sadko (exc); Golden Cockerel (exc); *Proch:* Air and Variations. (M. Korjus, Berlin RO/J. Müller, Berlin St Op Orch/B. Seidler-Winkler/E. Nick/F. Schönbaumsfeld)

Ⓓ **89055** (11/94)
Cesare Formichi (1883-1949)
Verdi: Rigoletto (exc); Rigoletto (exc); Rigoletto (exc); Traviata (exc); Otello (exc); *Wagner:* Walküre (exc); *Saint-Saëns:* Samson et Dalila (exc); *Massenet:* Jongleur de Notre Dame (exc); Thaïs (exc); Thaïs (exc); *Giordano:* Andrea Chénier (exc); *Puccini:* Tosca (exc); Tosca (exc); *Hahn:* D'une prison; *Fontenailles:* Obstination; *Brogi:* Volontario; Fior di Campo. (C. Formichi, I.M. Ferraris, G. Holst, orch/A. Ketèlbey/H. Harty)

Ⓓ **89057** (11/93)
Charles Kullmann (1903-1982)
Wagner: Lohengrin (exc); Meistersinger (exc); *Verdi:* Forza del destino (exc); Aida (exc); *Gounod:* Faust (exc); *Offenbach:* Contes d'Hoffmann (exc); *Tchaikovsky:* Eugene Onegin (exc); *Borodin:* Prince Igor (exc); *Smetana:* Bartered Bride (exc); *R. Strauss:* Rosenkavalier (exc); *Puccini:* Turandot (exc); *J. Strauss II:* Zigeunerbaron (exc); Nacht in Venedig (exc); Indigo und die vierzig Räuber (exc); *Meyer-Helmund:* Zauberlied (exc). (C. Kullman, W. Grossmann, E. Fuchs, E. Berger, orch/W. Goehr/E. Hauke, Berlin St Op Orch/E. Orthmann/O. Dobrindt/C. Schmalstich, Berlin City Op Orch/A. von Zemlinsky/F. Zweig)

Ⓓ **89059** (12/92)
Mark Reizen (1895-1992) - I
Glinka: Life for the Tsar (exc); Ruslan and Lyudmila (exc); Ruslan and Lyudmila (exc); *Dargomïzhsky:* Rusalka (exc); *Mussorgsky:* Boris Godunov (exc); Khovanshchina (exc); *Rubinstein:* Demon (exc); *Borodin:* Prince Igor (exc); *Tchaikovsky:* Eugene Onegin (exc); *Rimsky-Korsakov:* Sadko (exc); *Rachmaninov:* Aleko (exc). (M. Reizen, Bolshoi Th Orch/V. Nebolsin/A. Melik-Pashayev/S. Samosud/N. Golovanov)

Ⓓ **89060** (8/93)
Alfred Piccaver (1884-1958)
Donizetti: Favorita (exc); Dom Sébastien (exc); *Verdi:* Rigoletto (exc); *Weber:* Silvana (exc); *Cornelius:* Barbier von Bagdad (exc); *A. Thomas:* Mignon (exc); *Gounod:* Roméo et Juliette (exc); *Offenbach:* Contes d'Hoffmann (exc); *Massenet:* Werther (exc); *Tchaikovsky:* Eugene Onegin (exc); *Puccini:* Manon Lescaut (exc); Bohème (exc); Tosca (exc); Fanciulla del West (exc). (A. Piccaver, orch)

Ⓓ **89061** (8/93)
Pavel Lisitian (born 1911)
Verdi: Trovatore (exc); Ballo in maschera (exc); Traviata (exc); *Gounod:* Faust (exc); *Leoncavallo:* Pagliacci (exc); Zazà (exc); *Rubinstein:* Nero (exc); *Tchaikovsky:* Eugene Onegin (exc); Mazeppa (exc); Enchantress (exc); Queen of Spades (exc); *Rimsky-Korsakov:* Sadko (exc); *Chukhadjian:* Arshak II (exc). (P. Lisitsian, E. Shumskaya, Bolshoi Th Orch/V. Piradov/O. Bron/A. Orlov/V. Nebolsin/S. Samosud/A. Melik-Pashayev/N. Golovanov)

Ⓓ **89062** (3/93)
Giovanni Martinelli (1885-1969)
Verdi: Rigoletto (exc); Trovatore (exc); Forza del destino (exc); Aida (exc); Aida (exc); *Giordano:* Andrea Chénier (exc); Andrea Chénier (exc); Fedora (exc); *Mascagni:* Cavalleria Rusticana (exc); Cavalleria Rusticana (exc); *Leoncavallo:* Pagliacci (exc); Pagliacci (exc); Zazà (exc); *Puccini:* Bohème (exc); Tosca (exc). (G. Martinelli, G. Anthony, G. De Luca, E. Pinza, NY Met Op Chor, NY Met Op Orch/G. Setti, orch/J. Pasternack/R. Bourdon)

Ⓓ **89063** (8/93)
Rosetta Pampanini (1896-1973)
Gounod: Faust (exc); *Catalani:* Wally (exc); *Giordano:* Andrea Chénier (exc); *Puccini:* Manon Lescaut (exc); Bohème (exc); Madama Butterfly (exc); Madama Butterfly (exc); Turandot (exc); *Mascagni:* Amico Fritz (exc); *Zandonai:* Giuliano (exc); *Pietri:* Maristella (exc); *Wagner:* Lohengrin (exc); *Verdi:* Aida (exc); *Mascagni:* Iris (exc); *Puccini:* Manon Lescaut (exc). (R. Pampanini, F. Ciniselli, D. Borgioli, orch, EIAR Orch/A. Albergoni/E. Panizza/L. Molajoli/U. Tansini)

Ⓓ **89065** (9/94)
Maria Reining (1903-1991)
Mozart: Nozze di Figaro (exc); *Wagner:* Tannhäuser (exc); Tannhäuser (exc); *Giordano:* Andrea Chénier (exc); *Puccini:* Manon Lescaut (exc); Bohème (exc); Madama Butterfly (exc); *Albert:* Toten Augen (exc); *R. Strauss:* Lieder, Op.41 (exc); Lieder, Op.27 (exc); Lieder, Op.37 (exc); *Lehár:* Eva (exc); Friederike (exc). (M. Reining, M. Lorenz, Prussian St Orch/H.U. Müller, VPO/R. Moralt/F. Lehár, Berlin RSO/A. Rother, Vienna St Op Orch)

Ⓓ **89070** (8/94)
Franz Völker (1899-1965) - II
Mozart: Zauberflöte (exc); *Weber:* Freischütz (exc); *Beethoven:* Fidelio (exc); *Halévy:* Juive (exc); *Wagner:* Rienzi (exc); Fliegende Holländer (exc); Tannhäuser (exc); Walküre (exc); *Verdi:* Otello (exc); *Leoncavallo:* Pagliacci (exc); *Smetana:* Dalibor (exc); *Albert:* Tiefland (exc). (F. Völker, I. Langhammer, Berlin Staatskapelle/F.A. Schmidt/G. Steeger/A. Melichar/J. Schüler, chor)

Ⓓ **89071** (3/94)
Gerhard Hüsch (1901-1984) - II
Mozart: Nozze di Figaro (exc); Così fan tutte (exc); *Gumbert:* An des Rheines grünen Ufern; *Lortzing:* Undine (exc); Zar und Zimmermann (exc); *Nicolai:* Lustigen Weiber von Windsor (exc); *Wagner:* Tannhäuser (exc); *Humperdinck:* Hänsel und Gretel (exc); Königskinder (exc); *Verdi:* Trovatore (exc); Ballo in maschera (exc); *Gounod:* Faust (exc); *A. Thomas:* Mignon (exc); *Giordano:* Andrea Chénier (exc); *Puccini:* Tosca (exc). (G. Hüsch, Berlin St Op Orch/H.U. Müller, Berlin City Op Orch/A. von Zemlinsky, E. Fuchs, W. Strienz)

Ⓓ **89072** (10/94)
Aureliano Pertile (1885-1952) - II
Donizetti: Elisir d'amore (exc); Lucia di Lammermoor (exc); *Bellini:* Puritani (exc); *Flotow:* Martha (exc); *Wagner:* Lohengrin (exc); Lohengrin (exc); *Leoncavallo:* Pagliacci (exc); *Giordano:* Andrea Chénier (exc); Andrea Chénier (exc); Andrea Chénier (exc); *Puccini:* Manon Lescaut (exc); Manon Lescaut (exc); Manon Lescaut (exc); Bohème (exc); *Cilea:* Adriana Lecouvreur (exc). (A. Pertile, I.A. Tellini, M.L. Fanelli, M. Sheridan, A. Granforte, La Scala Orch/C. Sabajno/G. Nastrucci)

Ⓓ **89073** (10/94)
Giuseppe de Luca (1876-1950) - II
Verdi: Ernani (exc); Rigoletto (exc); Rigoletto (exc); Trovatore (exc); Trovatore (exc); Traviata (exc); Traviata (exc); Forza del destino (exc); Don Carlo (exc); Aida (exc); *Gounod:* Faust (exc); *Bizet:* Pêcheurs de perles (exc); *Ponchielli:* Gioconda (exc); Gioconda (exc); *Puccini:* Bohème (exc); *Wolf-Ferrari:* Gioielli della Madonna (exc). (G. De Luca, G. Anthony, A. Tedesco, A. Galli-Curci, B. Gigli, E. Rethberg, NY Met Op Chor, NY Met Op Orch/G. Setti, orch/R. Bourdon)

Ⓓ **89074** (4/95)
Tancredi Pasero (1893-1983) - II
Mozart: Nozze di Figaro (exc); Don Giovanni (exc); Zauberflöte (exc); *Rossini:* Barbiere di Siviglia (exc); Semiramide (exc); *Bellini:* Sonnambula (exc); Sonnambula (exc); *Verdi:* Nabucco (exc); Luisa Miller (exc); Rigoletto (exc); Simon Boccanegra (exc); Requiem (exc); *Mussorgsky:* Boris Godunov (exc); *Gounod:* Faust (exc); *Boito:* Mefistofele (exc); *Porrino:* Orazi (exc); *Beethoven:* In questa tomba oscura, WoO133; *Niedermeyer:* Pietà Signore. (T. Pasero, G. Bernelli, G. Bechi, orch, La Scala Orch, EIAR Orch, Rome Teatro Reale Orch, SO/A. Sabino/U. Tansini/L. Ricci/D. Marzollo)

Ⓓ **89077** (10/94)
Torsten Ralf (1901-1954)
Wagner: Lohengrin (exc); Meistersinger (exc); Walküre (exc); *Bizet:* Carmen (exc); *Verdi:* Otello (exc); Otello (exc); Otello (exc); *Puccini:* Fanciulla del West (exc); *Albert:* Tiefland (exc); *R. Strauss:* Daphne (exc); Frau ohne Schatten (exc). (T. Ralf, T. Lemnitz, F. Beckmann, J. Herrmann, Berlin St Op Orch, Saxon St Orch/B. Seidler-Winkler/H.U. Müller/K. Böhm)

Ⓓ **89079** (4/94)
Maria Jeritza (1887-1982)
Weber: Freischütz (exc); *Wagner:* Fliegende Holländer (exc); Lohengrin (exc); Walküre (exc); Wesendonk Lieder (exc); Tristan und Isolde (exc); *Tchaikovsky:* Maid of Orleans (exc); *Massenet:* Hérodiade (exc); Thaïs (exc); Cid (exc); *Delibes:* O mer, ouvre-toi; *Ponchielli:* Gioconda (exc); *Mascagni:* Cavalleria Rusticana (exc); *Giordano:* Fedora (exc); *Puccini:* Tosca (exc); *Goldmark:* Heimchen am Herd (exc); *Korngold:* Tote Stadt (exc). (M. Jeritza, orch)

Ⓓ **89080** (2/95)
Mark Reizen (1895-1992) - II
Dargomïzhsky: Rusalka (exc); *Gounod:* Faust (exc); *Rossini:* Barbiere di Siviglia (exc); *Verdi:* Vespri Siciliani (exc); Don Carlo (exc); Simon Boccanegra (exc); *Wagner:* Walküre (exc); *Mussorgsky:* Boris Godunov (exc). (M. Reizen, G. Nelepp, B. Zlatogorova, Bolshoi Th Orch/V. Nebolsin/S. Samosud/N. Golovanov)

Ⓓ **89082** (7/95)
Margarete Klose (1902-1968)
Gluck: Orfeo ed Euridice (exc); Alceste (1776) (exc); Paride ed Elena (exc); *Verdi:* Trovatore (exc); Trovatore

(exc); Ballo in maschera (exc); Don Carlo (exc); Aida (exc); *Wagner:* Walküre (exc); *Bizet:* Carmen (exc); Carmen (exc); *Saint-Saëns:* Samson et Dalila (exc). (M. Klose, M. Wittrisch, M. Perras, W. Grossmann, T. Gerson, S. Fischer, Berlin St Op Orch/B. Seidler-Winkler/F. Zweig/F.A. Schmidt, Berlin Deutsche Op Orch/G. Steeger)

Ⓒ **89084** (4/95)
Kerstin Thorborg (1896-1970)
Gluck: Orfeo ed Euridice (exc); *Bizet:* Carmen (exc); *Saint-Saëns:* Samson et Dalila (exc); *Wagner:* Lohengrin (exc); Rheingold (exc); Walküre (exc); Götterdämmerung (exc); Tristan und Isolde (exc); Parsifal (exc); *Schubert:* Allmacht, D852; Ständchen D889; *Brahms:* Lieder, Op.94 (exc); *Wolf:* Mörike Lieder (exc); Goethe Lieder (exc). (K. Thorborg, E. Rethberg, J. Huehn, L. Rosenek, Berlin St Op Orch/F. Weissmann, NY Met Op Orch/E. Leinsdorf, RCA SO/K. Riedel)

Ⓒ **89088** (7/95)
Walther Ludwig (1902-1981)
Mozart: Così fan tutte (exc); Entführung (exc); Entführung (exc); Don Giovanni (exc); Zauberflöte (exc); *Nicolai:* Lustigen Weiber von Windsor (exc); *Flotow:* Alessandro Stradella (exc); *A. Thomas:* Mignon (exc); *Bizet:* Carmen (exc); *Puccini:* Madama Butterfly (exc); *Kienzl:* Kuhreigen (exc); Evangelimann (exc); *Graener:* Friedemann Bach (exc); Lieder, Op.71 (exc). (W. Ludwig, M. Perras, G. Hüsch, F. Leitner, Berlin St Op Orch, Berlin City Op Orch, orch/B. Seidler-Winkler/F. Zaun/G. Steeger/H. von Benda/W. Ladwig)

Ⓒ **89090** (12/95)
Hans Hermann Nissen (1893-1980)
Marschner: Hans Heiling (exc); *Gounod:* Faust (exc); *Meyerbeer:* Africaine (exc); *Wagner:* Fliegende Holländer (exc); Meistersinger (exc); Meistersinger (exc); Walküre (exc); Parsifal (exc); *Loewe:* Odins Meeresritt, Op.118; Gedichte, Op.61 (exc); *Schumann:* Romanzen und Balladen, Op.45 (exc); *Wolf:* Eichendorff Lieder (exc); Mörike Lieder (exc); *Pfitzner:* Lieder, Op.9 (exc). (H. Hermann Nissen, B. Seidler-Winkler, Berlin SO/F. Zweig)

Ⓒ **89110** (12/95)
Heinrich Schlusnus (1888-1952) - II
Mozart: Don Giovanni (exc); Zauberflöte (exc); *Abt:* Wenn man beim Wein; *Rossini:* Barbiere di Siviglia (exc); Guillaume Tell (exc); *Verdi:* Rigoletto (exc); Traviata (exc); Trovatore (exc); Don Carlo (exc); Forza del destino (exc); Otello (exc); Otello (exc); Otello (exc); *Meyerbeer:* Africaine (exc); Africaine (exc); *Bizet:* Pêcheurs de perles (exc); *Offenbach:* Contes d'Hoffmann (exc); *Tchaikovsky:* Eugene Onegin (exc); *Puccini:* Bohème (exc). (H. Schlusnus, S. Kurz, R. Hutt, orch)

Ⓒ **89201** (2/92)
Helge Roswaenge (1897-1972) - I
Puccini: Bohème (exc); Tosca (exc); *Verdi:* Trovatore (exc); Traviata (exc); *Bizet:* Carmen (exc); *Mascagni:* Cavalleria Rusticana (exc); *Mozart:* Così fan tutte (exc); Don Giovanni (exc); *Adam:* Postillon de Lonjumeau (exc); *Boïeldieu:* Dame blanche (exc); *Flotow:* Martha (exc); *Verdi:* Trovatore (exc); *Puccini:* Bohème (exc); *Verdi:* Rigoletto (exc); Aida (exc); *Gounod:* Faust (exc); *Bizet:* Carmen (exc); *Verdi:* Rigoletto (exc); Aida (exc); *Massenet:* Manon (exc); *Puccini:* Bohème (exc); Madama Butterfly (exc). (H. Roswaenge, H. von Debička, E. Leisner, R. Watzke, F. Hüni-Mihacsek, T. de Garmo, T. Scheidl, orch)

Ⓒ **89202** (12/92)
Gerhard Hüsch Sings
Beethoven: An die ferne Geliebte, Op.98 (Cpte); *Schubert:* Schöne Müllerin (Cpte); Winterreise (Cpte). (G. Hüsch, H.U. Müller)

Ⓒ **89205** (1/94)
Heinrich Schlusnus Lieder Album, Vol.1
Beethoven: Adelaide, Op.46; Zärtliche Liebe, WoO123; In questa tomba oscura, WoO133; *Schubert:* Am See, D746; Jüngling an der Quelle, D300; Musensohn, D764; Wanderer an den Mond, D870; Zürnende Barde, D785; Geheimes, D719; Schöne Müllerin (exc); Erlkönig, D328; *Schumann:* Spanische Liebeslieder, Op.138 (exc); Gedichte, Op.30 (exc); Romanzen und Balladen, Op.49 (exc); Sängers Fluch, Op.139 (exc); Myrthen, Op.25 (exc); *Mendelssohn:* Lieder, Op.34 (exc); Lieder, Op.57 (exc); *Brahms:* Lieder, Op.71 (exc); Lieder, Op.106 (exc); *Wolf:* Mörike Lieder (exc); Italienisches Liederbuch (exc); Goethe Lieder (exc); Eichendorff Lieder (exc); *Brahms:* Lieder, Op.63 (exc); Lieder, Op.57 (exc); Lieder, Op.69 (exc); *R. Strauss:* Lieder, Op.29 (exc); Lieder, Op.48 (exc); Lieder, Op.27 (exc); Lieder, Op.10 (exc); *Wetzel:* In Danzig; *Graener:* Lieder, Op.71 (exc); Vale carissima; *T. Giordani:* Caro mio ben; *Ochs:* Dank sei dir, Herr; *Beethoven:* Lieder, Op.48 (exc); *Schubert:* Dem Unendlichen, D291; Du bist die Ruh', D776; *Liszt:* Es muss ein Wunderbares sein, S314; Am Rhein, S272; *Mussorgsky:* Song of the Flea; *Mahler:* Knaben Wunderhorn (exc); *Weingartner:* Liebesfeier, Op. 16/2; *H. Hermann:* Mahnung; Drei Wandrer. (H. Schlusnus, F. Rupp, F. Rupp, Berlin St Op Orch/H. Weigert/A. Melichar)

Ⓒ **89207** (6/93)
Feodor Chaliapin Song Book—Electrical Recordings
Beethoven: In questa tomba oscura, WoO133; *Schubert:* Tod und das Mädchen, D531; Schwanengesang, D957 (exc); *Schumann:* Romanzen und Balladen, Op.49 (exc); *Glinka:* Night Review; *Rimsky-Korsakov:* Songs, Op.49 (exc); *Koenemann:* When the King went forth to war; *Mussorgsky:* Songs and Dances of Death (exc); *Dargomïzhsky:* Old Corporal; *Flégier:* Cor; *Mussorgsky:* Song of the Flea; *Coningsby Clarke:* Blind Ploughman; *Malashkin:* Oh could I but express in song; *Rubinstein:* Persian Songs, Op.34 (exc); *Koenemann:* Song of the Volga boatmen; *Traditional:* Dark Eyes; Mashenka; Down the Peterskaya road; *Karatïgin:* Farewell to thee; *Lishin:* She laughed; *Rubinstein:* Prisoner; *Traditional:* Stenka Razin; Night; *Glinka:* Doubt; *Massenet:* Élégie; *Dargomïzhsky:* Bolero; *Strokine:* Now let us depart; *Vedel:* Open the gates of repentance; *Grechaninov:* Liturgy, Op. 79 (exc); *Archangelsky:* Creed; *Traditional:* Down the Volga; Twelve Robbers; *Manykin-Nevstruev:* Song of the needy pilgrim; *Traditional:* Arise, red sun; *Ibert:* Chansons de Don Quichotte. (F. Chaliapin, orch/A. Coates/E. Goossens/L. Collingwood/G.W. Byng/R. Bourdon, Aristov Ch, Balalaika Orch/A.A. Scriabin, I. Newton, J. Bazilevsky, C. Sharpe, P. Coppola, Paris Russian Met Church Ch/N. Afonsky, Anon, Afonsky Ch/J. Ibert)

Ⓒ **89208** (6/94)
Karl Erb Lieder Album
Bach: Sacred Songs, BWV489-507 (exc); *Schubert:* Litanei, D343; Du bist die Ruh', D776; Ave Maria, D839; An Silvia, D891; Nacht und Träume, D827; Wandrers Nachtlied II, D768; Fischers Liebesglück, D933; Vor meiner Wiege, D927; Winterreise (exc); Einsame, D800; Ihr Grab, D736; Wanderer an den Mond, D870; Schwanengesang, D957 (exc); An die Laute, D905; Am See, D746; Dass sie hier gewesen, D775; Liebe hat gelogen, D751; Jüngling und der Tod, D545; Lied im Grünen, D917; Im Abendrot, D799; Winterreise (exc); *Loewe:* Legends, Op.33 (exc); *Beethoven:* Adelaide, Op.46; Wachtelschlag, WoO129; Zärtliche Liebe, WoO123; Geheimnis, WoO145; *Schumann:* Gedichte, Op.90 (exc); Myrthen, Op.25 (exc); Liederkreis, Op.39 (exc); Lieder und Gesänge, Op.27 (exc); Gedichte, Op.35 (exc); Klavierstücke, Op.85 (exc); *Liszt:* Es muss ein Wunderbares sein, S314; *Brahms:* Lieder, Op.72 (exc); Lieder, Op.63 (exc); Lieder, Op.70 (exc); *Zilcher:* Ein gar alt fröhlich; *Wolf:* Mörike Lieder (exc); Spanisches Liederbuch (exc); Andenken; Mörike Lieder (exc); Frohe Botschaft; *Schoeck:* Lieder, Op.20 (exc); *Adam:* Minuit, Chrétiens (exc). (K. Erb, B. Seidler-Winkler, W. Lutz, orch/B. Seidler-Winkler)

Ⓒ **89209** (4/95)
Helge Roswaenge (1897-1972) - II
Meyerbeer: Huguenots (exc); *Verdi:* Rigoletto (exc); Traviata (exc); Vespri Siciliani (exc); Vespri Siciliani (exc); Aida (exc); Otello (exc); *Wagner:* Meistersinger (exc); Meistersinger (exc); *Flotow:* Martha (exc); *A. Thomas:* Mignon (exc); *Meyerbeer:* Africaine (exc); *Bizet:* Carmen (exc); *Offenbach:* Contes d'Hoffmann (exc); *Massenet:* Manon (exc); *Puccini:* Madama Butterfly (exc); Turandot (exc); *Mozart:* Entführung (exc); *Weber:* Freischütz (exc); Oberon (exc); *Cornelius:* Barbier von Bagdad (exc); *Auber:* Fra Diavolo (exc); *Adam:* Postillon de Lonjumeau (exc); *Verdi:* Rigoletto (exc); Ballo in maschera (exc); Ballo in maschera (exc); Traviata (exc); Traviata (exc); Forza del destino (exc); *Puccini:* Tosca (exc); *Künneke:* Grosse Sünderin (exc); Grosse Sünderin (exc). (H. Roswaenge, P. Yoder, L. Kindermann, H. Reinmar, H. Schlusnus, M. Kuttner, H. von Debička, I. Roswaenge, M. Korjus, M. Perras, T. Lemnitz, Berlin St Op Orch/F.A. Schmidt/S. Meyrowitz/A. Melichar/H. Weigert, BPO/E. Orthmann/B. Seidler-Winkler/E. Künneke, orch)

Ⓒ **89301** (5/91)
The Art of Frida Leider
Mozart: Nozze di Figaro (exc); *Beethoven:* Fidelio (exc); Ah! perfido, Op.65; *Weber:* Oberon (exc); *Wagner:* Rienzi (exc); Tannhäuser (exc); Tristan und Isolde (exc); Wesendonk Lieder (exc); *Verdi:* Aida (exc); Aida (exc); *Puccini:* Tosca (exc); *Mozart:* Nozze di Figaro (exc); Don Giovanni (exc); *Verdi:* Trovatore (exc); Trovatore (exc); Trovatore (exc); Trovatore (exc); Ballo in maschera (exc); Don Carlo (exc); Aida (exc); *Wagner:* Walküre (exc); *Puccini:* Tosca (exc); *R. Strauss:* Ariadne auf Naxos (exc); *Wagner:* Fliegende Holländer (exc); Fliegende Holländer (exc); Tannhäuser (exc); Tristan und Isolde (exc); Walküre (exc); Walküre (exc); Siegfried (exc); Siegfried (exc); Götterdämmerung (exc); Parsifal (exc); Wesendonk Lieder (exc). (F. Leider, R. Hutt, H. Schlusnus, O. Helgers, M. Abendroth, C. Günther, L. Melchior, F. Soot, orch)

Ⓒ **89302** (6/92)
The Young Lotte Lehmann
Weber: Freischütz (exc); Freischütz (exc); Freischütz (exc); *Wagner:* Tannhäuser (exc); Lohengrin (exc); Lohengrin (exc); *Gounod:* Faust (exc); *Wagner:* Meistersinger (exc); Meistersinger (exc); Walküre (exc); Walküre (exc); *Albert:* Toten Augen (exc); *R. Strauss:* Lieder, Op.27 (exc); *Mozart:* Nozze di Figaro (exc); *Weber:* Oberon (exc); *Lortzing:* Undine (exc); *Halévy:* Juive (exc); *Bizet:* Carmen (exc); *Offenbach:* Contes d'Hoffmann (exc); *Goetz:* Widerspenstigen Zähmung (exc); *Tchaikovsky:* Eugene Onegin (exc); *Verdi:* Otello (exc); *Massenet:* Manon (exc); *R. Strauss:* Rosenkavalier (exc); *Korngold:* Tote Stadt (exc); *Mozart:* Nozze di Figaro (exc); Nozze di Figaro (exc); Don Giovanni (exc); Zauberflöte (exc); *Nicolai:* Lustigen Weiber von Windsor (exc); *A. Thomas:* Mignon (exc); Mignon (exc); *Massenet:* Manon (exc); *Puccini:* Bohème (exc); Madama Butterfly (exc); Suor Angelica (exc); Manon Lescaut (exc); Tosca (exc); *Hildach:* Spielmann. (Lotte Lehmann, R. Hutt, M. Bohnen, H. Schlusnus, orch, Berlin St Op Orch/G. Szell/K. Besl/H. Weigert)

Ⓒ **89303(1)** (2/93)
Titta Ruffo Edition (pt 1)
Mozart: Don Giovanni (exc); *Leoncavallo:* Zazà (exc); *Verdi:* Ballo in maschera (exc); *Ferradini:* Non penso a lei; *Capolongo:* Suonno è fantasia; *Brogi:* Visione veneziana; *Massenet:* Thaïs (exc); *Titta:* E suonan le campane; *Mozart:* Don Giovanni (exc); *Soriano:* Guitarrico (exc); *Meyerbeer:* Dinorah (exc); *Verdi:* Otello (exc); *Franchetti:* Cristoforo Colombo (exc); *Verdi:* Nabucco (exc); *Titta:* Oh che m'importa?; *Schumann:* Romanzen und Balladen, Op.49 (exc); *Gounod:* Faust (exc); *Puccini:* Tosca (exc); *Verdi:* Forza del Destino (exc); *Meyerbeer:* Africaine (exc); *Verdi:* Ballo in maschera (exc); *Mozart:* Don Giovanni (exc); *Rossini:* Barbiere di Siviglia (exc); *Verdi:* Rigoletto (exc); *Meyerbeer:* Africaine (exc); *Verdi:* Otello (exc); *A. Thomas:* Hamlet (exc); *P.M. Costa:* Sei morta nella vita mia; Munasterio; *Trémisot:* Novembre; *Paladilhe:* Patrie (exc). (T. Ruffo, E. Caruso, orch)

Ⓒ **89303(2)** (2/93)
Titta Ruffo Edition (pt 2)
Giordano: Andrea Chénier (exc); *Massenet:* Roi de Lahore (exc); *Verdi:* Ernani (exc); *Franchetti:* Cristoforo Colombo (exc); *Seismit-Doda:* Querida; *Verdi:* Falstaff (exc); *Padilla:* Relicario; *Rubinstein:* Demon (exc); *Flotow:* Martha (exc); *Verdi:* Falstaff (exc); *De Tejada:* Perjura!; *Berlioz:* Damnation de Faust (exc); *Gounod:* Faust (exc); *Delibes:* Lakmé (exc); *Goublier:* Credo du Paysan; *Buzzi-Peccia:* Lolita; *Cottrau:* Santa Lucia; *Tosti:* Marechiare; *Schipa-Hua:* Cubanita; *Rotoli:* Mia sposa sarà la mia bandiera; *Tosti:* Chitarrata abruzzese; *Verdi:* Forza del destino (exc); *Ponchielli:* Gioconda (exc); *Puccini:* Bohème (exc); *Capolongo:* Suonno è fantasia; *Brogi:* Visione veneziana; *Billi:* Tizianello (exc); *Pugnacci:* Gitano Re; *P. M. Costa:* Sei morta nella vita mia; *Giordano:* Andrea Chénier (exc); *Meyerbeer:* Africaine (exc); *De Curtis:* Torna a Surriento. (T. Ruffo, B. Gigli, orch)

Ⓒ **89996** (6/95)
Kyra Vayne (b.1916)
Borodin: Prince Igor (exc); *Verdi:* Ernani (exc); *Gluck:* Paride ed Elena (exc); *Boito:* Mefistofele (exc); *Tchaikovsky:* Queen of Spades (exc); *Spontini:* Vestale (exc); *Puccini:* Tosca (exc); *Verdi:* Forza del destino (exc); *Schubert:* Im Frühling, D882; *Tchaikovsky:* Songs, Op.54 (exc); To forget; Songs, Op.6 (exc); *Mussorgsky:* Lullaby; But if I could meet thee again; Garden by the Don; *Glière:* Lark; *Grechaninov:* Epicedium; *Rachmaninov:* Songs, Op.21 (exc); Songs, Op.4 (exc); Songs, Op.14 (exc). (K. Vayne, anon, orch, C. Tilney)

Ⓒ **90029** (7/91)
Hans Pfitzner Accompanies & Conducts
Pfitzner: Lieder, Op. 7 (exc); Lieder, Op. 10 (exc); Lieder, Op. 9 (exc); Lieder, Op. 29 (exc); Lieder, Op. 22 (exc); Lieder, Op. 26 (exc); Lieder, Op. 19 (exc); Lieder, Op. 32 (exc); Lieder, Op. 40 (exc); Duo, Op.43; Symphony, Op.46. (G. Hüsch, H. Pfitzner, M. Strub, L. Hoelscher, Berlin St Op Orch, BPO/H. Pfitzner)

Ⓒ **90034** (12/90)
Maria Cebotari (1910-49)
Mozart: Nozze di Figaro (exc); Don Giovanni (exc); *Nicolai:* Lustigen Weiber von Windsor (exc); *J. Strauss II:* Zigeunerbaron (exc); *Gounod:* Faust (exc); *Puccini:* Bohème (exc); Madama Butterfly (exc); *R. Strauss:* Ariadne auf Naxos (exc). (M. Cebotari, M. Wittrisch, Philh, VPO, Berlin St Op Orch/J. Krips/H. von Karajan/F. Prohaska/F. Zweig)

Ⓒ **90078** (1/95)
Hilde Konetzni
Mozart: Don Giovanni (exc); *Wagner:* Tannhäuser (exc); *Beethoven:* Fidelio (exc); *Weber:* Freischütz (exc); *Puccini:* Tosca (exc); Madama Butterfly (exc); *Smetana:* Bartered

Bride (exc); *R. Strauss:* Rosenkavalier (exc); Lieder, Op.69 (exc); Lieder, Op.88 (exc); Lieder, Op.21 (exc). (H. Konetzni, Vienna SO, Berlin Deutsche Op Orch, Berlin St Op Orch, VPO, R. Strauss/H. Swarowsky/H. Schmidt-Isserstedt/H. von Karajan, M-L. Schilp)

ⓘ **90083** (9/92)
Maria Reining
Mozart: Nozze di Figaro (exc); *Wagner:* Lohengrin (exc); Tannhäuser (exc); Meistersinger (exc); *R. Strauss:* Rosenkavalier (exc); Lieder, Op. 41 (exc); *J. Strauss II:* Fledermaus (exc); *Suppé:* Boccaccio (exc); *Lehár:* Zarewitsch (exc); Paganini (exc). (M. Reining, P. Schoeffler, VPO/J. Krips, Berlin Deutsche Op Orch/W. Lutze, Zurich Tonhalle Orch/H. Knappertsbusch, R. Strauss)

ⓘ **90112** (11/92)
Clemens Krauss conducts the VPO
Haydn: Symphony 88; *J. Strauss II:* Perpetuum mobile; Annen-Polka, Op. 117; Morgenblätter, Op. 279; Fledermaus (exc); Zigeunerbaron (exc); Leichtes Blut, Op. 319; Tausend und eine Nacht; *Ziehrer:* Weana Mad'ln, Op.388; *Jos Strauss:* Sphärenklänge; *J. Strauss II:* Liebeslieder, Op. 114. (VPO/C. Krauss)

ⓘ **90114** (11/92)
Bruno Walter conducts the Vienna Philharmonic
Haydn: Symphony 96; *Brahms:* Symphony 1; *Mahler:* Symphony 5 (exc). (VPO/B. Walter)

ⓘ **90141** (3/94)
Walter directs the VPO
Haydn: Symphony 100; *Mozart:* Piano Concerto 20; Symphony 41. (B. Walter (pf/dir), VPO/B. Walter)

ⓘ **90150** (1/94)
Lehár conducts Lehár
Lehár: Lustige Witwe Overture (exc); Eva (exc); Paganini (exc); Giuditta (exc); Musikalische Memoiren; Friederike (exc); Schön ist die Welt (exc); Zarewitsch (exc); Zigeunerliebe (exc); Wien, du bist das Herz der Welt; Giuditta (exc). (E. Réthy, M. Reining, R. Tauber, VPO, Vienna SO/F. Lehár, J. Novotná)

ⓘ **90157** (8/94)
Beethoven/Wagner—Orchestral Works
Beethoven: Symphony 6; Leonore (exc); *Wagner:* Siegfried Idyll. (VPO/B. Walter)

ⓘ **90168** (5/94)
Wagner—Die Meistersinger, Act 2, etc
Wagner: Meistersinger (exc); Fliegende Holländer (exc); Lohengrin (exc); Walküre (exc). (G. Hann, H. Noort, T. Kempf, W. Schirp, E. Kunz, K. Wessely, M-L. Schilp, H. Heinz Nissen, A. Fügel, L. Windisch, H. Florian, W. Ulbricht, E. Schneider, E. Heyer, W. Lang, A. Will, Berlin Rad Chor, Berlin RO/A. Rother, Berlin Deutsche Op Orch/H. Steinkopf)

ⓘ **90172** (11/93)
Beethoven—String Quartets
Beethoven: String Quartet 9; String Quartet 11; String Quartet 14; String Quartet 15. (Busch Qt)

ⓘ **90190** (1/95)
Paul Schoeffler—Recital
Mozart: Nozze di Figaro (exc); Don Giovanni (exc); Zauberflöte (exc); *Wagner:* Meistersinger (exc); Meistersinger (exc); Meistersinger (exc); Walküre (exc); *Verdi:* Otello (exc); *Schumann:* Liederkreis, Op.39 (exc); *Brahms:* Lieder, Op.86 (exc); Lieder, Op.32 (exc); Lieder, Op.43 (exc). (P. Schoeffler, M. Reining, E. Lush, LPO, Zurich Tonhalle Orch, LSO, National SO/K. Rankl/H. Knappertsbusch/C. Krauss)

ⓘ **90205** (8/95)
Strauss conducts Strauss, Vol.1
R. Strauss: Don Quixote; Heldenleben; Alpensinfonie; Japanische Festmusik; Rosenkavalier (exc). (O. Uhl, P. Haass, Bavarian St Orch/R. Strauss)

ⓘ **90216** (8/95)
Strauss conducts Strauss, Vol.2
R. Strauss: Don Juan; Till Eulenspiegel; Also sprach Zarathustra; Heldenleben; Bourgeois gentilhomme suite; Tod und Verklärung; Sinfonia domestica. (VPO/R. Strauss)

ⓘ **90222** (8/95)
Maria Cebotari sings Richard Strauss
R. Strauss: Salome (exc); Feuersnot (exc); Rosenkavalier (exc); Daphne (exc); Taillefer. (M. Cebotari, P. Buchner, T. Lemnitz, W. Ludwig, K. Schmitt-Walter, H. Hotter, R. Lamy Sngrs, Berlin RSO/A. Rother)

ⓘ **90237** (11/95)
R Strauss—Daphne
R. Strauss: Daphne (Cpte); An den Baum Daphne; Daphne (exc). (M. Reining, K. Friedrich, H. Alsen, A. Dermota, M. Frutschnigg, G. Monthy, R. Sallaba, H.

Schweiger, H. Baier, E. Loose, M. Schober, Vienna St Op Chor, VPO/K. Böhm/W. Hagen-Groll, M. Teschemacher, T. Ralf, Dresden St Op Orch)

ⓘ **90951** (5/94)
Mozart—Symphonies
Mozart: Symphony 39; Symphony 40; Symphony 41. (Berlin St Op Orch, VPO/H. Knappertsbusch)

ⓘ **93145** (7/88)
Hans Hotter sings Schubert and Schumann Lieder
Schubert: An eine Quelle, D530; Fischers Liebesglück, D933; Du bist die Ruh, D776; Dem Unendlichen, D291; Wanderer, D649; Auf der Donau, D553; Wanderer an den Mond, D870; Greisengesang, D778; Prometheus, D674; Gruppe aus dem Tartarus, D583; Schumann: Dichterliebe, Op. 48 (Cpte). (H. Hotter, H. Altmann)

ⓘ **93261** (6/90)
Richard Strauss accompanies
R. Strauss: Lieder, Op. 15 (exc); Lieder, Op. 17 (exc); Lieder, Op. 21 (exc); Lieder, Op. 37 (exc); Lieder, Op. 49 (exc); Lieder, Op. 32 (exc); Lieder, Op. 69 (exc); Lieder, Op. 88; Lieder, Op. 19 (exc); Lieder, Op. 36 (exc); Lieder, Op. 48 (exc); Lieder, Op. 27 (exc). (A. Dermota, H. Konetzni, A. Poell, R. Strauss)

ⓘ **93262** (10/92)
R.Strauss accompanies Reining,Dermota and Piltti
R. Strauss: Lieder, Op.10 (exc); Lieder, Op.29 (exc); Lieder, Op.37 (exc); Lieder, Op. 41 (exc); Lieder, Op. 48 (exc); Lieder, Op.27 (exc); Lieder, Op.21 (exc); Lieder, Op.32 (exc); Lieder, Op.10 (exc); Lieder, Op.17 (exc); Lieder, Op.19 (exc); Lieder, Op.37 (exc); Lieder, Op.27 (exc); Lieder, Op.15 (exc); Lieder, Op.21 (exc); Lieder, Op.17 (exc); Lieder, Op.29 (exc); Lieder, Op. 49 (exc). (M. Reining, A. Dermota, L. Piltti, R. Strauss)

ⓘ **93331** (2/90)
Pfitzner: Lieder
Pfitzner: Lieder, Op. 26 (exc); Lieder, Op. 11 (exc); Lieder, Op. 22 (exc); Lieder, Op. 29; Lieder, Op. 32; Lieder, Op. 40; Sonnets, Op. 41. (R. Holl, Konrad Richter)

ⓘ **93368** (7/91)
Mendelssohn—Lieder
Mendelssohn: Lieder, Op. 19a (exc); Lieder, Op. 86 (exc); Lieder, Op. 47 (exc); Lieder, Op. 34 (exc); Waldschloss, Op. posth; Lieder, Op. 99 (exc); Pagenlied, Op. posth; Lieder, Op. 9 (exc); Lieder, Op. 71 (exc); Lieder, Op. 84 (exc); Lieder, Op. 57 (exc). (W. Holzmair, A. Wagner)

ⓘ **93390** (8/89)
Hans Hotter Lieder recital
Loewe: Archibald Douglas, Op.128; Balladen, Op. 129 (exc); Lieder, Gesänge, Romanzen und Balladen, Op. 9 (exc); *Beethoven:* Zärtliche Liebe, WoO123; In questa tomba oscura, WoO133; Lieder, Op. 48 (exc); *Schubert:* Kreuzzug, D932; Greisengesang, D778; Wandrers Nachtlied II, D768; *Schumann:* Myrthen, Op. 25 (exc); *Cornelius:* Lieder, Op. 4 (exc); *Franz:* Lieder, Op. 42 (exc); Lieder, Op. 10 (exc); Lieder, Op. 5 (exc); Lieder, Op. 20 (exc); *Wolf:* Mörike Lieder (exc); Eichendorff Lieder (exc). (H. Hotter, H. Dokoupil)

Preludio

ⓘ **PRL2153/4** (3/92)
Alain—Piano Works
Alain: Piano Works I; Piano Works II; Piano Works III. (D. Fuchs)

ⓘ **PROUCD129** (4/92)
20th Century Sacred Music
Martin: Mass; *Duruflé:* Motets, Op. 10; *Stanford:* Motets, Op. 38; *Górecki:* Totus tuus, Op. 60; *Byron:* Verba. (Oxford Schola Cantorum/J. Summerly)

Priory

ⓘ **PRCD185** (3/87)
Organ recital by Stephen Cleobury
Reger: Pieces, Op. 145 (exc); *Mendelssohn:* Organ Sonatas (exc); *Mozart:* Fantasia, K608; *Karg-Elert:* Choral-Improvisationen, Op. 65 (exc); *Hindemith:* Organ Sonatas (exc); *Liszt:* Variations, S673. (S. Cleobury)

ⓘ **PRCD228** (8/88)
Great European Organs No. 5
Reger: Introduction and Passacaglia; *Rheinberger:* Organ Sonata 11 (exc); *Howells:* Psalm-Preludes, Op. 32 (exc); *Mathias:* Berceuse, Op. 95/3; *Mendelssohn:* Organ Sonatas (exc); *Martin:* Passacaglia; *Alain:* Postlude; *Langlais:* Paraphrases grégoriennes (exc). (J. Lancelot)

ⓘ **PRCD235** (5/89)
Great European Organs No. 6
Bach: Prelude and Fugue, BWV553; Prelude and Fugue, BWV554; Prelude and Fugue, BWV555; Prelude and Fugue, BWV556; Prelude and Fugue, BWV557; Prelude

and Fugue, BWV558; Prelude and Fugue, BWV559; Prelude and Fugue, BWV560; *Handel:* Water Music (exc); *Mozart:* Adagio and Allegro, K594; Fantasia, K608. (K. John)

ⓘ **PRCD237** (10/89)
Great European Organs No. 7
Guilmant: Sonata 1; March, Op. 15; *Karg-Elert:* Passacaglia and Fugue on BACH; *Dupré:* Cortège et Litanie; Variations sur un vieux Noël; Pieces, Op. 27 (exc). (J. Watts)

ⓘ **PRCD257** (5/89)
Great Cathedral Anthems
Elgar: Give unto the Lord; *E. Walker:* I will lift up mine eyes; *Stanford:* Psalm 23, Op. 38; *Bullock:* Give us the wings of faith; *Bairstow:* Blessed city, heavenly Salem; *S.S. Wesley:* Ascribe unto the Lord; *Bairstow:* Let all mortal flesh keep silence; *Bainton:* And I saw a new heaven; *Ireland:* Greater love hath no man; *S.S. Wesley:* Thou wilt keep him; *Wood:* O thou, the central orb. (Guildford Cath Ch/A. Millington, P. Wright)

ⓘ **PRCD264** (4/90)
Bach & Reubke: Organ Works
Bach: Toccata, Adagio and Fugue, BWV564; Clavier-Übung III, BWV669-689 (exc); Trio Sonatas, BWV525-530 (exc); Concertos, BWV592-7 (exc); *Reubke:* Organ Sonata. (K. John)

ⓘ **PRCD269** (6/90)
Great European Organs, No. 13
Rheinberger: Organ Sonata 11; Organ Sonata 10; Organ Sonata 3. (G. Barber)

ⓘ **PRCD281** (3/90)
Great European Organs No. 15
Gigout: Ten Organ Pieces; *Franck:* Chorales (exc); Andantino in G minor (exc); *Guilmant:* Cantilène pastorale (exc); Grand choeur triomphale (exc); *Saint-Saëns:* Fantaisie in E flat (exc); Fantaisie, Op. 101 (exc); *Widor:* Symphony 6 (exc). (C. Walsh)

ⓘ **PRCD284** (9/90)
Great European Organs, No. 16
Vierne: Pièces en stile libre (exc); *Dupré:* Symphonie-Passion (exc); *Cochereau:* Alouette, gentille Alouette Improvisations (exc). (D. Briggs)

ⓘ **PRCD286** (9/90)
Great European Organs No. 18
Dupré: Preludes and Fugues, Op. 7; *Franck:* Prélude, Fugue et Variation; Fantaisie in A; *Alain:* Intermezzo (1935); Litanies; *Tournemire:* Petite rapsodie improvisée; Cantilène improvisée; Te Deum Improvisation. (J. Watts)

ⓘ **PRCD294** (1/92)
Great European Organs No.19
Tournemire: Triple Choral, Op. 41; Choral-Improvisation sur le Victimae Paschali; Ave maris stella Fantaisie-Improvisation; Symphonie-Choral, Op. 69. (J. Watts)

ⓘ **PRCD296** (7/91)
Evensong For St Cuthbert's Day
Langlais: Suite médiévale (exc); *R. Lloyd:* Windows; *Grier:* Preces; *Lockhart:* For all thy Saints, O Lord; *Walmisley:* Bless the Lord; *Leighton:* Second Service; *Grier:* Lesser Litany; *Tavener:* Ikon of St Cuthbert; *Baelz:* Ring Christ; *Mulet:* Carillon-Sortie. (Durham Cath Ch/J. Lancelot, I. Shaw)

ⓘ **PRCD297** (5/91)
Great European Organs, Vol.20
Rheinberger: Organ Sonata 13; *Reger:* Organ Sonata, Op. 60; *Hoyer:* Jerusalem, du hochgebaute Stadt; *Karg-Elert:* Pieces, Op. 154. (G. Barber)

ⓘ **PRCD298** (5/91)
Great European Organs, Vol.21
Ireland: Meditation; Capriccio; Holy Boy (organ); Miniature Suite; Elegiac Romance; Sursum corda; Alla marcia; *Stanford:* Preludes and Postludes, Op. 105 (exc); *Bridge:* Organ Pieces, H63 (exc); *Dyson:* Voluntary of Praise; *Darke:* Meditation; *W.H. Harris:* Flourish for an Occasion; *C.S. Lang:* Tuba tune. (J. Bielby)

ⓘ **PRCD312** (4/91)
Stanford: Choral Works
Stanford: Anthems, Op. 113; Services, Op. 115 (exc); Benedictus and Agnus Dei. (Chichester Cath Ch/A. Thurlow, J. Suter)

ⓘ **PRCD314** (7/91)
Great European Organs No 23
Parry: Wanderer Toccata; *Jackson:* English Hymn Tune Preludes; *Karg-Elert:* Impressions, Op. 108; *Fleury:* Prelude, Andante and Toccata. (G. Barber)

ⓘ **PRCD315** (11/93)
Great European Organs No 30
Reger: Chorale Fantasias, Op. 40 (exc); *Karg-Elert:*

① **PRCD494** (4/95)
Magnificat and Nunc Dimittis
Brewer: Evening Canticles in D; *Sumsion:* Evening Service in G (boys'); *S.S. Wesley:* Evening Service in E; *Sumsion:* Evening Service in G (full); *Howells:* Gloucester Service; *C. Lloyd:* Evening Service in A; *P.G. Aston:* Evening Service in F; *Sumsion:* Evening Service in G (men's); *B. Kelly:* Evening Service in C. (Gloucester Cath Ch/J. Sanders, M. Lee)

① **PRCD505** (10/95)
Magnificat and Nunc Dimittis, Volume 3
Stanford: Services, Op. 12 (exc); *S. Watson:* Evening Service; *G. Ives:* Edington Service; *Gibbons:* Short Service (exc); *Leighton:* Magdalen Service; *Howells:* Magnificat and Nunc Dimittis in G; *Dyson:* Evening Service in D. (Lichfield Cath Ch/A. Lumsden, M. Shepherd, N. Potts)

① **PRCD507** (2/95)
Te Deum and Jubilate, Volume 3
Stanford: Services, Op. 10 (exc); *Darke:* Morning Service in F (exc); *R. Lloyd:* Jubilate; *Sumsion:* Te Deum; *Ley:* Morning Service (exc); *Harwood:* Morning Service (exc); *Britten:* Festival Te Deum; *W. H. Harris:* Te Deum; *Stanford:* Services, Op. 12 (exc); *Vaughan Williams:* Te Deum in G. (Hereford Cath Ch/R. Massey, G. Bowen)

① **PRCD510** (10/95)
Great Cathedral Anthems, Volume VI
Weelkes: O Lord, arise; *Battishill:* O Lord, look down from heaven; *Walmisley:* Remember, O Lord; *Stainer:* I saw the Lord; *Mansel Thomas:* Blest are the pure in heart; For thy servant David; *Stanton:* Jesu, lover of my soul; *Howells:* Coventry Antiphon; *W. H. Harris:* Strengthen ye; R. *Shephard:* Ye choirs of new Jerusalem; And when the builders; *Rubbra:* And when the builders, Op. 125. (Llandaff Cath Ch/M. Smith, M. Hoeg)

① **PRCD511** (5/95)
Magnificat and Nunc Dimittis, Volume 2
Ayleward: Short Service; *Hawes:* Evening Service in D; *Holst:* Nunc Dimittis; *Kelway:* Evening Service in B minor; *Naylor:* Evening Service in A; *D. Purcell:* Evening Service in E minor; *H.T. Smart:* Evening Service in G; *Sumsion:* Evening Service in A; *Vann:* Chichester Service; *Weelkes:* 1st Service; 6th Service. (Chichester Cath Ch/A. Thurlow, J. Thomas)

Pro Arte

① **CDS524** (11/91)
Hitchcock—Master of Mayhem
Herrmann: North by Northwest (exc); Vertigo (exc); Marnie (exc); Psycho (exc); *Waxman:* Rebecca Suite; Rear Window (exc); *Schifrin:* Schifrin Suite (exc). (San Diego SO/L. Schifrin)

Proprius

① **PRCD9008** (10/91)
Anne Sofie Von Otter — Recital
Handel: Hercules (exc); Giulio Cesare (exc); *Monteverdi:* Scherzi musicali (1607) (exc); Lamento d'Arianna a 1; *Roman:* Swedish Mass (exc); *Telemann:* Kanarienvogel Kantate (exc); *Handel:* Semele (exc). (A.S. von Otter, Drottningholm Baroque Ens/A. Öhrwall)

① **PRCD9010** (3/92)
Messiaen—Complete Organ Works II
Messiaen: Ascension; Verset pour la fête de la dédicace; Messe de la Pentecôte. (E. Boström)

Proud Sound

① **PROUCD114** (3/87)
Sacred choral music
Vaughan Williams: O clap your hands; *Stanford:* Services, Op. 81 (exc); *Tavener:* Mater Christi; *Bainton:* And I saw a new heaven; *Britten:* Missa brevis; *Monteverdi:* Selva morale e spirituale (exc); *J. Harvey:* I love the Lord. (New College Ch/E. Higginbottom)

① **PROUCD125** (3/90)*
Rejoice in the Lamb
Bairstow: Blessed city, heavenly Salem; *Duruflé:* Motets, Op. 10; *Britten:* Rejoice in the Lamb; *Wise:* Ways of Zion do mourn; *Byrd:* Ave verum corpus; *Gibbons:* O clap your hands; *Handel:* Chandos Anthem 6. (O. Johnston, W. Missin, P. Cave, J. Bernays, New College Ch, Fiori Musicali/E. Higginbottom)

① **PROUCD126** (5/90)
Tye & Sheppard: Sacred Choral Works
Tye: Euge Bone Mass; Peccavimus cum patribus; *Sheppard:* In manus tuas II a 4; Gaude virgo Christiphera; Reges Tharsis; Libera nos, salva nos I; Libera nos, salva nos II. (Clerkes of Oxenford/D. Wulstan)

① **PROUCD133** (10/93)
Ockeghem—Missa Ecce ancilla etc
Ockeghem: Intemerata Dei mater; Ave Maria; Missa Ecce ancilla Domini; *Obrecht:* Salve regina a 6; *Josquin Desprez:* Déploration de Johannes Ockeghem. (Clerks' Group/E. Wickham)

① **PROUCD134** (12/93)
Follow that Star
Traditional: Have yourself a merry little Christmas; Winter Wonderland; Follow that star; Olde Rhyme; Santa Claus is coming to town; Mary's Boy Child; Just another star; Christmas Song; Deck the hall; Ding Dong! merrily on high; Stille Nacht; Gabriel fram heven-king; Spotless rose; I wonder as I wander; *Tavener:* Lamb; Nativity; Today the Virgin; *Traditional:* Gaudete; Riu, riu chiu; Coventry Carol; Könige; In dulci jubilo; De Virgin Mary had a baby-boy; Mary had a Baby; Jingle Bells. (Oxford Pro Musica Sngrs/M. Smedley)

① **PROUCD135** (5/94)
Music for Trumpet and Organ
Albinoni: Trumpet Sonata in C; Trio Sonatas, Op. 1 (exc); *Trattenimenti,* Op. 6 (exc); *Frescobaldi:* Canzoni with Titles (exc); *Fasch:* Concerto in D; *Georg Muffat:* Indissolubilis Amicitia Suite; *Viviani:* Capricci, Op. 4 (exc); *Telemann:* Oboe Concerto 2; *Mouret:* Symphonies de Fanfares (exc). (J. Freeman-Attwood, I. Simcock)

① **PROUCD136** (12/94)
Tavener/Pärt/Górecki—Sacred Choral Music
Tavener: Annunciation; Ikon of the Nativity; Lamb; Nativity; Today the Virgin; Lord's Prayer; Many Years; Wedding Prayer; He Hath Entered the Heven; Acclamation; *Pärt:* Magnificat; Summa; *Górecki:* Euntes Ibant, Op. 32; Totus tuus, Op. 60; Amen. (Oxford Pro Musica Sngrs/M. Smedley)

Pyramid (USA)

① **PYR13485** (6/87)
Beethoven: Violin Sonatas
Beethoven: Violin Sonata 5; Violin Sonata 8; Violin Sonata 9. (N. Gotkovsky, I. Gotkovsky)

① **PYR13487** (4/87)
Brahms: Violin Sonatas
Brahms: Violin Sonata 1; Violin Sonata 2; Violin Sonata 3. (N. Gotkovsky, I. Gotkovsky)

① **PYR13496** (9/91)
Works for Violin and Piano
Stravinsky: Duo concertant; *Webern:* Pieces, Op. 7; *Prokofiev:* Violin Sonata 1; Sonata, Op. 115; *Schoenberg:* Phantasy. (N. Gotkovsky, I. Gotkovsky)

① **PYR13500/1** (3/91)
Sviatoslav Richter at Pleyel
Beethoven: Piano Sonata 6; Piano Sonata 7; Piano Sonata 17; Piano Sonata 18; *Chopin:* Etudes (exc); Preludes (exc). (S. Richter)

① **PYR13503** (10/92)
Sviatoslav Richter - Piano Recital
Miaskovsky: Piano Sonata 3; *Shostakovich:* Preludes and Fugues, Op. 87 (exc); *Prokofiev:* Piano Sonata 8. (S. Richter)

Quintana

① **QUI90 3010** (7/91)
Bach—Wedding Cantatas
Bach: Cantata 202; Cantata 209; Cantata 210. (M. Zádori, Capella Savaria, P. Németh (fl/dir))

Radio Nacional de Espana

① **M3/03** (4/93)
Piano Works by Spanish Women Composers
Boulanger: Cortège; Vieux jardin; Jardin clair; *Prieto:* Variaciones seriales; Variaciones tonales; *Cruz:* Quasar; *Escribano Sanchez:* Quejio; Ozaita: Tema con variaciones; *Catalán:* Iruñeako Taldea (exc); *Diez:* Sad; *Bacewicz:* Piano Sonata 2. (S. Marin)

RCA Victor

① **GD60075** (2/90)
Bruckner: Symphonies
Bruckner: Symphony 1; Symphony 2; Symphony 3; Symphony 4; Symphony 5; Symphony 7; Symphony 8; Symphony 9. (Cologne RSO/G. Wand)

① **GD60096** (2/89)
Schubert: Complete Symphonies
Schubert: Symphony 1; Symphony 2; Symphony 3; Symphony 4; Symphony 5; Symphony 6; Symphony 8;

Symphony 9; Rosamunde (exc). (Cologne RSO/G. Wand)

① **GD60176** (1/90)
Prokofiev: Vocal & Orchestral Works
Prokofiev: Alexander Nevsky; Lt. Kijé Suite; *Glinka:* Ruslan and Lyudmila (exc). (R. Elias, Chicago Sym Chor, Chicago SO/F. Reiner)

① **GD60177** (1/90)
Strauss Family: Waltzes
J. Strauss II: Künstlerleben, Op. 316; Wiener Blut; Schatz; Rosen aus dem Süden; Blauen Donau, Op. 314; Kaiser, Op. 437; Morgenblätter, Op. 279; Unter Donner und Blitz; *Jos Strauss:* Mein Lebenslauf ist Lieb' und Lust; Dorfschwalben aus Österreich. (Chicago SO/F. Reiner)

① **GD60179** (1/90)
Debussy & Ravel: Orchestral Works
Ravel: Rapsodie espagnole; Valses nobles et sentimentales; Alborada del gracioso; Pavane; *Debussy:* Images (exc). (Chicago SO/F. Reiner)

① **GD60262** (1/91)
Toscanini Collection, Vol.32
Respighi: Pines of Rome; Fountains of Rome; Roman Festivals. (NBC SO/A. Toscanini)

① **GD60264** (1/91)
Wagner—Opera excerpts
Wagner: Walküre (exc); Walküre (exc); Siegfried Idyll; Tristan and Isolde (exc). (H. Traubel, L. Melchior, NBC SO/A. Toscanini)

① **GD60265** (2/92)
Debussy—Orchestral Works
Debussy: La mer; Après-midi; Images (exc); Nocturnes (exc); Nocturnes (exc). (NBC SO/A. Toscanini)

① **GD60267** (11/92)
Toscanini Collection, Vol.45
Beethoven: Leonore (exc); Consecration of the House Ov; Coriolan; Egmont (exc); Prometheus (exc); Leonore (exc); String Quartet 16 (exc). (NBC SO/A. Toscanini)

① **GD60270** (11/92)
Beethoven—Symphony No 5 etc
Beethoven: Symphony 5; Septet, Op.20; Egmont (exc). (NBC SO/A. Toscanini)

① **GD60276** (6/91)
Toscanini conducts Boito & Verdi
Boito: Mefistofele (exc); *Verdi:* Rigoletto (exc); Lombardi (exc). (N. Moscona, Z. Milanov, N. Merriman, J. Peerce, L. Warren, Columbus Boychoir, R. Shaw Chorale, V. della Chiesa, NBC SO/A. Toscanini)

① **GD60279** (1/91)
Toscanini Collection, Vol.24
Dvořák: Symphony 9; *Kodály:* Háry János Suite; *Smetana:* Má Vlast (exc). (NBC SO/A. Toscanini)

① **GD60282** (11/92)
Haydn—Orchestral Works
Haydn: Symphony 99; Symphony 101; Sinfonia concertante. (M. Mischakoff, F. Miller, P. Renzi, L. Sharrow, NBC SO/A. Toscanini)

① **GD60284** (6/92)
Mendelssohn—Symphonies, etc
Mendelssohn: Symphony 4; Symphony 5; Midsummer Night's Dream (exc); Octet, Op.20 (exc). (NBC SO/A. Toscanini)

① **GD60285** (11/92)
Mozart—Symphonies
Mozart: Symphony 39; Symphony 40; Symphony 41. (NBC SO/A. Toscanini)

① **GD60289** (11/92)
Toscanini Collection - Rossini Overtures
Rossini: Italiana in Algeri (exc); Signor Bruschino (exc); Barbiere di Siviglia (exc); Cenerentola (exc); Gazza ladra (exc); Siège de Corinthe (exc); Semiramide (exc); Guillaume Tell (exc). (NBC SO/A. Toscanini)

① **GD60294** (11/92)
Toscanini Collection - Sibelius
Sibelius: Symphony 2; Pohjola's Daughter; Finlandia; Legends (exc). (NBC SO/A. Toscanini)

① **GD60296** (11/92)
Toscanini Collection, Vol.31
R. Strauss: Don Juan; Till Eulenspiegel; Salome (exc); Wagner: Götterdämmerung (exc); Siegfried Idyll. (NBC SO/A. Toscanini)

① **GD60305** (11/92)
Toscanini Collection - Wagner
Wagner: Lohengrin (exc); Meistersinger (exc); Meistersinger (exc); Parsifal (exc); Faust Overture. (NBC SO/A. Toscanini)

M. Journet, E. de Gogorza, L. Homer, orch, V. Bellezza/J. Pasternack)

① **GD60522** (9/92)
Alexander Kipnis—Opera & Song Recital
Mussorgsky: Boris Godunov (exc); Song of the flea; *Borodin:* Prince Igor (exc); *Rimsky-Korsakov:* Sadko (exc); *Tchaikovsky:* Eugene Onegin (exc); *Dargomïzhsky:* Rusalka (exc); *Grechaninov:* Lullaby, Op.1/5; My native land; *Rachmaninov:* Songs, Op.4 (exc); *Stravinsky:* Stories for Children (exc). (A. Kipnis, C. Dougherty, A. Leskaya, I. Tamarin, Victor Chorale, Victor SO/N. Berezowski)

① **GD60523** (7/92)
Horowitz plays Brahms, Liszt & Schubert
Brahms: Piano Concerto 2; Piano Pieces, Op.117 (exc); *Schubert:* Impromptus (exc); *Liszt:* Années de pèlerinage 1 (exc); Années de pèlerinage 2 (exc); Hungarian Rhapsodies, S244 (exc). (V. Horowitz, NBC SO/A. Toscanini)

① **GD60526** (1/93)
Russian Favourites - Horowitz
Mussorgsky: Pictures; *Scriabin:* Pieces, Op.2 (exc); Preludes, Op.11 (exc); Preludes, Op.22 (exc); *Horowitz:* Moment exotique; *Scriabin:* Piano Sonata 9; *Tchaikovsky:* Dumka, Op.59; *Horowitz:* Carmen Variations; *Prokofiev:* Piano Sonata 7 (exc); *Rachmaninov:* Morceaux de salon, Op.10 (exc); *Debussy:* Children's Corner (exc); *Sousa:* Stars and Stripes Forever. (V. Horowitz)

① **GD60818** (5/92)
Great Operatic Duets
Rossini: Semiramide (exc); *Donizetti:* Anna Bolena (exc); *Bellini:* Norma (exc); *Offenbach:* Contes d'Hoffmann (exc); *Verdi:* Aida (exc); *Puccini:* Madama Butterfly (exc); *Ponchielli:* Gioconda (exc). (M. Caballé, S. Verrett, Ambrosian Op Chor, New Philh/A. Guadagno)

① **GD60874** (5/93)
R. Strauss—Scenes from Elektra & Salome
R. Strauss: Elektra (exc); Salome (exc); Salome (exc). (I. Borkh, P. Schoeffler, F. Yeend, Chicago Lyric Op Chor, Chicago SO/F. Reiner)

① **GD60919** (3/93)
Bach—Harpsichord Works
Bach: Goldberg Variations; Concertos, BWV972-987 (exc); Fantasia, BWV906; Fantasia, BWV919; Prelude, Fugue and Allegro, BWV998; 2-Part Inventions, BWV772-86; 3-Part Inventions, BWV787-801 (exc); Capriccio, BWV992; Partitas, BWV825-30 (exc). (W. Landowska)

① **GD60921** (5/95)
Legendary Performers - William Kapell
Khachaturian: Piano Concerto; *Prokofiev:* Piano Concerto 3; *Liszt:* Mephisto Waltz 1, S514. (W. Kapell, Boston SO/S. Koussevitzky, Dallas SO/A. Dorati)

① **GD60923** (3/93)
Legendary Performers - Paderewski
Beethoven: Piano Sonata 14; *Chopin:* Etudes (exc); Etudes (exc); Piano Sonata 2 (exc); *Schumann:* Nachtstücke (exc); *Liszt:* Paganini Studies, S140 (exc); *Chopin:* Nocturnes (exc); *Wagner:* Tristan und Isolde (exc); *Chopin:* Polonaises (exc); *Liszt:* Hungarian Rhapsodies, S244 (exc); *Rachmaninov:* Preludes (exc); *J. Strauss II:* Man lebt nur einmal, Op. 167; *Paderewski:* Humoresques de Concert, Op.14 (exc). (I. Paderewski)

① **GD60941** (11/92)
Rarities - Montserrat Caballé
Rossini: Donna del Lago (exc); Otello (exc); Stabat mater (exc); Armida (exc); Tancredi (exc); Siège de Corinthe (exc); *Donizetti:* Belisario (exc); Parisina d'Este (exc); Torquato Tasso (exc); Gemma di Vergy (exc); *Verdi:* Giorno di regno (exc); Lombardi (exc); Due Foscari (exc); Alzira (exc); Attila (exc); Corsaro (exc); Aroldo (exc). (M. Caballé, M. Elkins, C. Vozza, M. Sunara, E. Mauro, L. Kozma, T. McDonnell, RCA Italiana Op Chor, Ambrosian Op Chor, RCA Italiana Op Orch, LSO/C.F. Cillario/A. Guadagno)

① **GD71952** (10/89)
Bach—Keyboard Works
Bach: Italian Concerto, BWV971; Toccatas, BWV910-16 (exc); Fugue, BWV944; Fantasia, BWV906. (G. Leonhardt)

① **GD71953** (10/89)
Sequentia - Gregorian Chant
Anon: Christmas (exc); Christmas (exc); Special Sunday Services (exc); Corpus Christi (exc); Easter Sunday (exc); Easter Sunday (exc); Ascension Day (exc); Ascension Day (exc); Pentecost (exc); Requiem (exc); Feast Days (exc); Rex caeli. (MCA/K. Ruhland)

① **GD71958** (10/89)
The Baroque Lute
Bach: Suite, BWV995; Prelude, Fugue and Allegro, BWV998; *Weiss:* Infidele Sonata. (E.M. Dombois)

① **GD71964** (5/90)
Bach: Flute Works
Bach: Flute Sonatas, BWV1030-5 (exc); Partita, BWV1013; Partita, BWV1013 (exc); Partita, BWV1013 (exc); Partita, BWV1013 (exc); Partita, BWV1013 (exc); Partita, BWV1013 (exc); Flute Sonatas, BWV1030-5 (exc). (F. Brüggen, F. Brüggen, G. Leonhardt, A. Bylsma, A. Bylsma, L. Van Dael, L. Van Dael, S. Kuijken, W. Kuijken, A. Glatt, A. Woodrow)

① **GD71966** (10/90)
Josquin Desprez: Sacred Choral Works
Josquin Desprez: Missa La sol fa re mi; Miserere mei, Deus; Tu solus qui facis mirabilia; Sanctus de Passione; Qui velatus facie fuisti (exc); Absalon fili mi; Planxit autem David. (MCA/K. Ruhland)

① **GD80136** (10/90)
Now Voyager—Classic Film Scores of Max Steiner
Steiner: Warner Bros Fanfare; King Kong (exc); Saratoga Trunk (exc); Charge of the Light Brigade (exc); Four Wives (exc); Big Sleep (exc); Johnny Belinda (exc); Since You Went Away (exc); Informer (exc); Fountainhead (exc). (E. Wild, National PO/C. Gerhardt, Ambrosian Sngrs)

① **GD80183** (3/90)
Classic Film Scores for Bette Davis
Steiner: Warner Bros Fanfare; Now Voyager (exc); Stolen Life (exc); In This Our Life (exc); Jezebel (exc); Beyond the Forest (exc); Letter (exc); All, This, and Heaven Too (exc); *Korngold:* Elizabeth and Essex (exc); Juarez (exc); *Waxman:* Mr Skeffington (exc); *Alf Newman:* All about Eve (exc). (National PO/C. Gerhardt)

① **GD80185** (11/91)
Classic Film Scores of Korngold
Korngold: Anthony Adverse (exc); Cello Concerto, Op. 37; Prince and the Pauper (exc); Elizabeth and Essex Overture; Sea Wolf (exc); Another Dawn (exc); Of Human Bondage (exc). (F. Gabarro, National PO/C. Gerhardt)

① **GD80422** (11/91)
Casablanca—Classic Film Scores for Humphrey Bogart
Steiner: Casablanca (exc); Passage to Marseille (exc); Treasure of the Sierra Madre (exc); Big Sleep (exc); Caine Mutiny (exc); Virginia City (exc); *Waxman:* To Have and Have Not (exc); Two Mrs. Carrolls (exc); *Hollander:* Sabrina (exc); *V. Young:* Left Hand of God (exc); *Rózsa:* Sahara (exc). (National PO/C. Gerhardt)

① **GD80707** (11/91)
Citizen Kane—Classic Film Scores of Bernard Herrmann
Herrmann: On Dangerous Ground (exc); Citizen Kane (exc); Beneath the 12-Mile Reef (exc); Hangover Square (exc); White-Witch Doctor (exc). (K. Te Kanawa, J. Achucarro, National PO/C. Gerhardt)

① **GD80708** (11/91)
Sunset Boulevard—Classic Film Scores of Franz Waxman
Waxman: Prince Valiant (exc); Place in the Sun Suite (exc); Bride of Frankenstein (exc); Sunset Boulevard (exc); Old Acquaintance (exc); Rebecca Suite; MGM Fanfare; Philadelphia Story (exc); Taras Bulba (exc). (National PO/C. Gerhardt)

① **GD80911** (5/91)
Spellbound—Classic Film Scores of Miklos Rozsa
Rózsa: Red House (exc); Thief of Bagdad (exc); Lost Weekend (exc); Four Feathers (exc); Double Indemnity (exc); Knights of the Round Table (exc); Jungle Book (exc); Spellbound (exc); Ivanhoe (exc). (Ambrosian Sngrs, National PO/C. Gerhardt)

① **GD80912** (11/91)
Captain Blood—Classic Film Scores for Errol Flynn
Steiner: Don Juan (exc); *Korngold:* Sea Hawk (exc); Captain Blood (exc); *Steiner:* They Died with Their Boots On (exc); Warner Bros Fanfare; Dodge City (exc); *Waxman:* Objective, Burma! (exc); *Friedhofer:* Sun Also Rises (exc); *Korngold:* Adventures of Robin Hood (exc). (National PO/C. Gerhardt)

① **GD82792** (10/92)
The Spectacular World of Classic Film Scores
McHugh: Universal Pictures Fanfare; *Waxman:* MGM Fanfare; *Alf Newman:* Selznick International Pictures Fanfare; 20th Century Fox Fanfare; *Steiner:* Warner Bros Fanfare; *J. T. Williams:* Star Wars (exc); *Korngold:* Captain Blood (exc); *Steiner:* Now Voyager (exc); Gone with the Wind (exc); *Korngold:* Elizabeth and Essex (exc); *Steiner:* Caine Mutiny (exc); *Herrmann:* Citizen Kane (exc); *Rózsa:* Knights of the Round Table (exc); *Waxman:* Objective

Burma (exc); *Tiomkin:* Guns of Navarone (exc); *Rózsa:* Julius Caesar (exc); *Waxman:* Peyton Place (exc); *Tiomkin:* Thing from Another World (exc). (K. Te Kanawa, National PO/C. Gerhardt)

① **GD86215** (1/90)
Scriabin—Piano Works
Scriabin: Preludes, Op. 11 (exc); Preludes, Op. 15 (exc); Preludes, Op. 16 (exc); Preludes, Op. 13 (exc); Preludes, Op. 27 (exc); Pieces, Op. 51 (exc); Preludes, Op. 48 (exc); Preludes, Op. 67 (exc); Pieces, Op. 59 (exc); Piano Sonata 5; Piano Sonata 3; Etudes, Op. 8 (exc); Etudes, Op. 42 (exc); Etudes, Op. 8 (exc). (V. Horowitz)

① **GD86264** (4/89)
Beethoven & Brahms: Violin Sonatas
Brahms: Violin Sonata 1; Violin Sonata 3; *Beethoven:* Violin Sonata 8. (H. Szeryng, A. Rubinstein)

① **GD86517** (11/87)
Galway plays Bach
Bach: Flute Concerto, BWV1059/BWV35; Trio Sonatas, BWV1036-9 (exc); Musikalisches Opfer, BWV1079 (exc); Suites, BWV1066-9 (exc). (J. Galway, K-W. Chung, P. Moll, M. Welsh, Zagreb Sols, J. Galway (fl/dir))

① **GD86519** (11/87)
Gershwin—Orchestral Works
Gershwin: Rhapsody in Blue; Piano Concerto; American in Paris; I Got Rhythm Variations. (E. Wild, Boston Pops/A. Fiedler)

① **GD86534** (12/87)
Verdi Arias and Duets
Verdi: Giovanna d'Arco (exc); Masnadieri (exc); Jérusalem (exc); Corsaro (exc); Trovatore (exc); Vespri Siciliani (exc); Ballo in maschera (exc); Don Carlo (exc); Otello (exc). (K. Ricciarelli, P. Domingo, R. Truffelli, Rome Polyphonic Chor, Rome PO, Santa Cecilia Academy Orch/G. Gavazzeni)

① **GD86535** (11/87)
Mozart: Requiem, etc
Mozart: Requiem; Ave verum Corpus, K618; *Haydn:* Te Deum, HobXXIIIc/1. (K. Equiluz, G. Eder, Vienna Boys' Ch, Vienna Hofmusikkapelle Ch, Chorus Viennensis, Vienna St Op Chor, Vienna Hofmusikkapelle Orch, Vienna SO, Vienna CO/H. Gillesberger/H. Froschauer)

① **GD86680** (7/94)
Horowitz plays Schumann
Schumann: Piano Sonata 3; Humoreske; Fantasiestücke, Op. 111; Nachtstücke. (V. Horowitz)

① **GD86719** (7/88)
Debussy: Orchestral Works
Debussy: La Mer; Après-midi; Nocturnes; Printemps. (Boston SO/C. Munch)

① **GD86722** (7/88)
R.Strauss: Orchestral and Vocal Works
R.Strauss: Also sprach Zarathustra; *R. Strauss:* Vier letzte Lieder; *R.Strauss:* Frau ohne Schatten (exc). (L. Price, P. Clark, Ambrosian Op Chor, Chicago SO, New Philh/F. Reiner/E. Leinsdorf)

① **GD86805** (3/89)
Orchestral Works
Berlioz: Béatrice et Bénédict (exc); *Franck:* Symphony; *Indy:* Symphonie, Op. 25. (N. Henriot-Schweitzer, Boston SO, Chicago SO/P. Monteux/C. Munch)

① **GD87704** (11/88)
Beethoven: Violin Sonatas, Vol.1
Beethoven: Violin Sonata 1; Violin Sonata 2; Violin Sonata 3; Violin Sonata 4. (J. Heifetz, E. Bay)

① **GD87705** (11/88)
Beethoven: Violin Sonatas, Vol.2
Beethoven: Violin Sonata 5; Violin Sonata 6; Violin Sonata 7. (J. Heifetz, E. Bay)

① **GD87706** (11/88)
Beethoven: Violin Sonatas, Vol.3
Beethoven: Violin Sonata 8; Violin Sonata 9; Violin Sonata 10. (J. Heifetz, E. Bay, B. Smith)

① **GD87752** (9/90)
Horowitz plays Chopin, Vol.1
Chopin: Polonaises (exc); Ballades (exc); Barcarolle; Etudes (exc); Ballades (exc); Waltzes (exc); Andante spianato and Grande Polonaise. (V. Horowitz)

① **GD87753** (12/89)
Horowitz plays Clementi
Clementi: Keyboard Sonatas, Op.33 (exc); Keyboard Sonatas, Op.34 (exc); Keyboard Sonatas, Op.13 (exc); Keyboard Sonatas, Op.25 (exc); Keyboard Sonatas, Op.24 (exc). (V. Horowitz)

Feuermann, J-M. Sanromá, E. Bay, Musical Art Qt, NBC SO/A. Toscanini, Philadelphia/E. Ormandy, Cincinnati SO/E. Goossens)

Ⓓ **09026 61778-2(06)** (11/94)
The Heifetz Collection, Vol. 6
Arensky: Violin Concerto (exc); *Bach:* 2-Violin Concerto; English Suites, BWV806-811 (exc); *Bax:* Mediterranean; *Beethoven:* German Dances, WoO8 (exc); *Bruch:* Scottish Fantasy; *Castelnuovo-Tedesco:* Sea murmurs, Op. 24a; Tango, Op. 24b; *Chopin:* Nocturnes (exc); *Debussy:* Ariettes oubliées (exc); Chansons de Bilitis (exc); Préludes (exc); *Falla:* Canciones populares españolas (exc); Amor Brujo (exc); *Halffter:* Danzas (exc); *Korngold:* Much Ado About Nothing Suite (exc); Much Ado About Nothing Suite (exc); *Medtner:* Fairy tales, Op. 20 (exc); *Mendelssohn:* Piano Trio 1 (exc); Songs without words (exc); *Milhaud:* Saudades do brasil (exc); *Mozart:* Divertimento, K334 (exc); *Nin:* Cantos de España (exc); *Poldowski:* Tango; *Ravel:* Valses nobles et sentimentales (exc); *Rimsky-Korsakov:* Tale of Tsar Saltan (exc); *Sarasate:* Danzas españolas (exc); *Schubert:* Piano Sonata, D850 (exc); *Tansman:* Pieces (exc); *Vieuxtemps:* Violin Concerto 5. (J. Heifetz, E. Bay, RCA Victor CO/F. Waxman, RCA Victor SO/W. Steinberg, LSO/M. Sargent)

Ⓓ **09026 61778-2(07)** (11/94)
The Heifetz Collection, Vol. 7
Beethoven: Violin Sonata 9; *Elgar:* Violin Concerto; *Saint-Saëns:* Violin Sonata 1; *Tchaikovsky:* Violin Concerto. (J. Heifetz, B. Moiseiwitsch, E. Bay, LSO/M. Sargent, Philh/W. Susskind)

Ⓓ **09026 61778-2(08)** (11/94)
The Heifetz Collection, Vol. 8
Beethoven: Romances; *Bloch:* Violin Sonata 1; Violin Sonata 2; *Brahms:* Violin Sonata 3; *Bruch:* Violin Concerto 1; *Handel:* Violin Sonatas (exc); *Ravel:* Tzigane; *Schubert:* Violin Sonata, D408; *Wieniawski:* Polonaise, Op. 4. (J. Heifetz, E. Bay, B. Smith, W. Kapell, RCA Victor SO/W. Steinberg, LSO/M. Sargent, Los Angeles PO/A. Wallenstein)

Ⓓ **09026 61778-2(09)** (11/94)
The Heifetz Collection, Vol. 9
Grieg: Violin Sonata 2; *Handel:* Keyboard Suites Set I (exc); Violin Sonatas (exc); *Mozart:* Trio, K563; Duo, K424; Violin Sonata, K378; Violin Sonata, K454; *Sinding:* Suite, Op. 10. (J. Heifetz, W. Primrose, E. Feuermann, B. Smith, E. Bay, Los Angeles PO/A. Wallenstein)

Ⓓ **09026 61778-2(10)** (11/94)
The Heifetz Collection, Vol. 10
Beethoven: Violin Sonata 3; Violin Sonata 8; String Trio, Op. 3; String Trios, Op. 9 (exc); *Mozart:* Violin Concerto, K219; Violin Sonata, K296. (J. Heifetz, W. Primrose, G. Piatigorsky, E. Bay, LSO/M. Sargent)

Ⓓ **09026 61778-2(11-15)** (11/94)
The Heifetz Collection, Vols. 11-15
Bach: 2-Violin Concerto; *Beethoven:* Violin Concerto; *Brahms:* Violin Concerto; Double Concerto; *Bruch:* Violin Concerto 1; Scottish Fantasy; *Glazunov:* Violin Concerto; *Mendelssohn:* Violin Concerto, Op. 64; *Mozart:* Sinfonia concertante, K364; *Prokofiev:* Violin Concerto 2; *Sibelius:* Violin Concerto; *Tchaikovsky:* Violin Concerto; Sérénade mélancolique; Serenade, Op. 48 (exc); *Vieuxtemps:* Violin Concerto 5 (exc). (J. Heifetz, E. Friedman, W. Primrose, G. Piatigorsky, New SO/M. Sargent, Boston SO/C. Munch, Chicago SO/F. Reiner, RCA Victor SO/A. Wallenstein/W. Hendl/I. Solomon, CO)

Ⓓ **09026 61778-2(16)** (11/94)
The Heifetz Collection, Vol. 16
Beethoven: Violin Sonata 1; Violin Sonata 2; Violin Sonata 3; Violin Sonata 4; Violin Sonata 5; Violin Sonata 6; Violin Sonata 7; Violin Sonata 8; Violin Sonata 9; Violin Sonata 10. (J. Heifetz, E. Bay, B. Smith)

Ⓓ **09026 61778-2(18)** (11/94)
The Heifetz Collection, Vol. 18
Bach: Solo Violin Partitas and Sonatas (exc); *Franck:* Violin Sonata; *Mendelssohn:* Violin Concerto, Op. 64; *Mozart:* Violin Concerto, K218; *Sibelius:* Violin Concerto; *Tchaikovsky:* Violin Concerto. (J. Heifetz, A. Rubinstein, RPO, LPO/T. Beecham)

Ⓓ **09026 61778-2(19)** (11/94)
The Heifetz Collection, Vol. 19
Aguirre: Huella, Op. 49; *Benjamin:* Jamaican Rumba; *Rob Bennett:* Hexapoda; *Traditional:* White Christmas; *Brahms:* Hungarian Dances (exc); *C. Burleigh:* Pictures, Op. 30 (exc); Small Concert Pieces, Op. 21 (exc); *Chopin:* Nocturnes (exc); *Debussy:* Beau soir; Suite bergamasque (exc); Children's Corner (exc); *Dvořák:* Humoresques, Op. 101 (exc); *Dyer:* Outlandish Suite (exc); *Foster:* Jeanie with the light brown hair; Old folks at home; *S. Gardner:* Pieces, Op. 5 (exc); *Gershwin:* Porgy and Bess (exc); Preludes; *Gluck:* Orfeo ed Euridice (exc); *Godard:* Jocelyn (exc); *Godowsky:* Impressions (exc); *Grasse:* Wellenspiel; *Herbert:* A la valse; *Krein:* Dance 4; *Löhr:* Where my caravan has rested; *Prokofiev:* Love for 3 Oranges Suite (exc); Romeo and Juliet Pieces (exc); *Ravel:* Pièce en forme de habanera; *Rimsky-Korsakov:* Golden Cockerel (exc); *Rossini:* Barbiere di Siviglia (exc); *Saint-Saëns:* Carnaval des animaux (exc); *Schumann:* Waldszenen (exc); *Shostakovich:* Preludes, Op. 34 (exc); *Tchaikovsky:* Souvenir d'un lieu cher, Op. 42 (exc); *Traditional:* Deep River; Gweedore Brae; *F. Valle:* Prelude XV; *Weill:* Dreigroschenoper (exc); *C. C. White:* Levee Dance, Op. 27/2. (J. Heifetz, B. Crosby, E. Bay, M. Kaye, orch/S. Camarata/V. Young)

Ⓓ **09026 61778-2(20)** (11/94)
The Heifetz Collection, Vol. 20
Bruch: Violin Concerto 2; *Conus:* Violin Concerto; *Tchaikovsky:* Sérénade mélancolique; *Wieniawski:* Violin Concerto 2. (J. Heifetz, RCA Victor SO/I. Solomon, Los Angeles PO/A. Wallenstein)

Ⓓ **09026 61778-2(21)** (11/94)
The Heifetz Collection, Vol. 21
Korngold: Violin Concerto; *Rózsa:* Violin Concerto; Tema con variazioni; *Waxman:* Carmen Fantasia. (J. Heifetz, G. Piatigorsky, Los Angeles PO/A. Wallenstein, Dallas SO/W. Hendl, CO, RCA Victor SO/D. Voorhees)

Ⓓ **09026 61778-2(22)** (11/94)
The Heifetz Collection, Vol. 22
Chausson: Poème; *Lalo:* Symphonie espagnole; *Saint-Saëns:* Havanaise; Introduction and rondo capriccioso; *Sarasate:* Zigeunerweisen. (J. Heifetz, RCA Victor SO/I. Solomon/W. Steinberg)

Ⓓ **09026 61778-2(24)** (11/94)
The Heifetz Collection, Vol. 24
Bach: Violin Concerto, BWV1041; Violin Concerto, BWV1042; *Mozart:* Violin Sonata, K454; *Paganini:* Caprices, Op. 1 (exc); *Vitali:* Ciacona (exc). (J. Heifetz, B. Smith, R. Ellsasser, Los Angeles PO/A. Wallenstein)

Ⓓ **09026 61778-2(25)** (11/94)
The Heifetz Collection, Vol. 25
Beethoven: Serenade, Op. 8; *Spohr:* Violin Concerto 8; Double Quartet 1. (J. Heifetz, P. Amoyal, I. Baker, P. Rosenthal, M. Thomas, A. Harshman, W. Primrose, G. Piatigorsky, L. Lesser, RCA Victor SO/I. Solomon)

Ⓓ **09026 61778-2(26)** (11/94)
The Heifetz Collection, Vol. 26
Mozart: Violin Concerto, K219; String Quintet, K516; Violin Sonata, K378. (J. Heifetz, I. Baker, W. Primrose, V. Majewski, G. Piatigorsky, B. Smith, CO)

Ⓓ **09026 61778-2(27)** (11/94)
The Heifetz Collection, Vol. 27
Arensky: Piano Trio 1; *Kodály:* Duo, Op. 7; *Turina:* Piano Trio 1. (J. Heifetz, G. Piatigorsky, L. Pennario)

Ⓓ **09026 61778-2(28)** (11/94)
The Heifetz Collection, Vol. 28
Beethoven: Piano Trios (exc); *Boccherini:* Unidentified Sonata in D; *Brahms:* String Quintet 2; *Mozart:* Serenade, K250 (exc). (J. Heifetz, I. Baker, M. Thomas, P. Rosenthal, G. Piatigorsky, L. Pennario, B. Smith)

Ⓓ **09026 61778-2(30)** (11/94)
The Heifetz Collection, Vol. 30
Beethoven: Piano Trios (exc); *Handel:* Keyboard Suites Set I (exc); *Mozart:* Violin Concerto, K218; *Vivaldi:* Concerto, RV547. (J. Heifetz, G. Piatigorsky, J. Lateiner, New SO/M. Sargent, CO)

Ⓓ **09026 61778-2(31)** (11/94)
The Heifetz Collection, Vol. 31
Benjamin: Romantic Fantasy; *Brahms:* Hungarian Dances (exc); *Castelnuovo-Tedesco:* Lark, Op. 64; *Falla:* Canciones populares españolas (exc); *Glière:* Pieces, Op. 39 (exc); *Sgambati:* Serenata napoletana, Op. 24/2; *Stravinsky:* Suite italienne (cello); *Wieniawski:* Capriccio-Valse, Op. 7. (J. Heifetz, W. Primrose, G. Piatigorsky, E. Bay, B. Smith, RCA Victor SO/I. Solomon, Los Angeles PO/A. Wallenstein)

Ⓓ **09026 61778-2(32)** (11/94)
The Heifetz Collection, Vol. 32
Brahms: Piano Trio 1; *Dohnányi:* Serenade, Op. 10; *R. Strauss:* Violin Sonata. (J. Heifetz, W. Primrose, E. Feuermann, A. Rubinstein, B. Smith)

Ⓓ **09026 61778-2(33)** (11/94)
The Heifetz Collection, Vol. 33
Dvořák: Piano Trio 4; *Franck:* Piano Quintet; *Sibelius:* Belshazzar's Feast (exc). (J. Heifetz, I. Baker, W. Primrose, G. Piatigorsky, L. Pennario, B. Smith)

Ⓓ **09026 61778-2(34)** (11/94)
The Heifetz Collection, Vol. 34
Bach: Solo Violin Partitas and Sonatas (exc); *Mendelssohn:* Piano Trio 2; *Mozart:* String Quintet, K515. (J. Heifetz, I. Baker, W. Primrose, V. Majewski, G. Piatigorsky, L. Pennario)

Ⓓ **09026 61778-2(35)** (11/94)
The Heifetz Collection, Vol. 35
Rob Bennett: Song Sonata; *Gershwin:* Porgy and Bess (exc); *Mendelssohn:* Octet, Op. 20; *Rachmaninov:* Songs, Op. 38 (exc); *Shostakovich:* Fantastic dances (exc); *Shulman:* American Folksongs Suite (exc); *Stravinsky:* Berceuse; *Toch:* Divertimenti, Op. 37 (exc); *Heifetz:* Heifetz on Music. (J. Heifetz, I. Baker, A. Belnick, J. Stepansky, W. Primrose, V. Majewski, G. Piatigorsky, G. Rejto, B. Smith, E. Bay)

Ⓓ **09026 61778-2(37)** (11/94)
The Heifetz Collection, Vol. 37
Bach: 3-Part Inventions, BWV787-801 (exc); *Schubert:* String Quintet; String Trio, D581. (J. Heifetz, I. Baker, W. Primrose, G. Piatigorsky, G. Rejto)

Ⓓ **09026 61778-2(40)** (11/94)
The Heifetz Collection, Vol. 40
Achron: Hebrew Melody; *Debussy:* Plus que lente; *Dinicu:* Hora Staccato; *Drigo:* Airs de Ballet (exc); *Gershwin:* Porgy and Bess (exc); Preludes; *Godowsky:* Triakontameron (exc); *Khachaturian:* Gayaneh (exc); *Korngold:* Much Ado About Nothing Suite (exc); *Kroll:* Banjo and Fiddle; *Mendelssohn:* Lieder, Op. 34 (exc); *Ponce:* Estrellita; *Poulenc:* Presto; *Prokofiev:* Love for 3 Oranges Suite (exc); *Rachmaninov:* Songs, Op. 38 (exc); Cello Pieces, Op. 2 (exc); Songs, Op. 34 (exc); *Sarasate:* Danzas españolas (exc); *Schubert:* Ave Maria, D839; *Wieniawski:* Scherzo-tarantelle, Op. 16. (J. Heifetz, E. Bay, B. Smith)

Ⓓ **09026 61778-2(41)** (11/94)
The Heifetz Collection, Vol. 41
Brahms: String Sextet 2; Hungarian Dances (exc); *Dvořák:* Piano Quintet, Op. 81. (J. Heifetz, I. Baker, W. Primrose, V. Majewski, J. de Pasquale, G. Piatigorsky, G. Rejto, B. Smith, J. Lateiner)

Ⓓ **09026 61778-2(42)** (11/94)
The Heifetz Collection, Vol. 42
Beethoven: String Trios, Op. 9 (exc); *Brahms:* Piano Quartet 3; *Schubert:* Fantasie, D934. (J. Heifetz, W. Primrose, S. Schonbach, G. Piatigorsky, J. Lateiner, B. Smith)

Ⓓ **09026 61778-2(43)** (11/94)
The Heifetz Collection, Vol. 43
Castelnuovo-Tedesco: Violin Concerto 2; *H. Ferguson:* Violin Sonata 1; *Françaix:* Piano Trio; *K. Khachaturian:* Violin Sonata, Op. 1. (J. Heifetz, J. de Pasquale, G. Piatigorsky, L. Steuber, Los Angeles PO/A. Wallenstein)

Ⓓ **09026 61778-2(44)** (11/94)
The Heifetz Collection, Vol. 44
Debussy: Préludes (exc); Violin Sonata; *Martinů:* Duo, H157; *Ravel:* Sonatine (exc); Piano Trio; *Respighi:* Violin Sonata. (J. Heifetz, G. Piatigorsky, E. Bay, A. Rubinstein)

Ⓓ **09026 61778-2(45)** (11/94)
The Heifetz Collection, Vol. 45
Debussy: Beau soir; Children's Corner (exc); Chansons de Bilitis (exc); Préludes (exc); *Fauré:* Violin Sonata 1; *Ibert:* Histoires (exc); *Poulenc:* Mouvements perpétuels (exc); *Ravel:* Valses nobles et sentimentales (exc); *Saint-Saëns:* Carnaval des animaux (exc); Violin Sonata 1. (J. Heifetz, B. Smith)

Ⓓ **09026 61778-2(46)** (11/94)
The Heifetz Collection, Vol.46 - The final recital
Bach: Solo Violin Partitas and Sonatas (exc); *Bloch:* Baal shem (exc); *Castelnuovo-Tedesco:* Sea murmurs, Op. 24a; *Debussy:* Plus que lente; *Falla:* Canciones populares españolas (exc); *Franck:* Violin Sonata; *Kreisler:* Cartier Chasse; *Rachmaninov:* Etudes-tableaux, Op. 33 (exc); *Ravel:* Tzigane; *R. Strauss:* Violin Sonata. (J. Heifetz, B. Smith)

Ⓓ **09026 61789-2** (12/93)
Concerto! Galway & Robles play Mozart
Mozart: Flute and Harp Concerto, K299; Violin Sonata, K296; Violin Sonata, K376. (J. Galway, M. Robles, P. Moll, LSO/M. Tilson Thomas)

Ⓓ **09026 61790-2** (12/93)
Concerto! Stoltzman plays Copland etc.
Copland: Clarinet Concerto; *G. Jenkins:* Goodbye; *Bernstein:* West Side Story (exc); Clarinet Sonata; *Gershwin:* Shall We Dance (exc); Porgy and Bess (exc); Short Story; Preludes. (R. Stoltzman, LSO/M. Tilson Thomas/E. Stern)

Ⓓ **09026 61792-2** (8/94)
Reiner conducts Wagner & Humperdinck
Wagner: Meistersinger (exc); Götterdämmerung (exc); Lohengrin (exc); Tannhäuser (exc); *Humperdinck:* Hänsel und Gretel (exc). (Chicago SO, RCA Victor Orch/F. Reiner)

① **09026 62652-2** (3/95)
Christa Ludwig—Tribute to Vienna
Beethoven: Zärtliche Liebe, WoO123; In questa tomba oscura, WoO133; Egmont (exc); *Schubert:* Geheimnis, D491; Im Abendrot, D799; Tod und das Mädchen, D531; Frühlingsglaube, D686; Heidenröslein, D257; Winterreise (exc); Sehnsucht, D636; Musensohn, D764; *Mahler:* Lieder und gesänge (exc); *Wolf:* Italienisches Liederbuch (exc); Spanisches Liederbuch (exc); Mörike Lieder (exc); Goethe Lieder (exc); Eichendorff Lieder (exc); *Bernstein:* I hate music (exc); *R. Strauss:* Lieder, Op. 27 (exc); *Brahms:* Lieder, Op. 49 (exc). (C. Ludwig, C. Spencer)

① **09026 62681-2** (12/95)
Mr Jerry Hadley—Golden Days
Friml: Vagabond King (exc); Firefly (exc); *Herbert:* Naughty Marietta (exc); Red Mill (exc); Princess Pat (exc); Only Girl (exc); Fortune Teller (exc); Angel Face (exc); Indian Summer; *Romberg:* New Moon (exc); Desert Song (exc); Student Prince (exc); Student Prince (exc); Night is Young (exc); I love to go swimmin'. (J. Hadley, M. Lanza, T. Randall, Harvard Glee Club, American Th Orch/P. Gemignani)

① **09026 62684-2** (10/95)
Rimsky-Korsakov—Symphony No 3, etc
Rimsky-Korsakov: Symphony 3; Sadko; Mlada (exc); Maid of Pskov (exc); Tale of Tsar Saltan (exc); Tsar's Bride (exc). (Russian St SO/E. Svetlanov)

① **09026 62697-2** (5/95)
Franck/Debussy/Fauré—Violin Sonatas
Fauré: Violin Sonata 1; *Debussy:* Violin Sonata; *Franck:* Violin Sonata. (P. Zukerman, M. Neikrug)

① **09026 62710-2** (4/95)
Rachmaninov—Orchestral Works
Rachmaninov: Paganini Rhapsody; Symphonic Dances; Aleko (exc). (D. Alexeev, St Petersburg PO/Y. Temirkanov)

① **09026 62712-2** (11/95)
Weber—Symphonies, etc
Weber: Symphony 1; Symphony 2; Freischütz (exc). (Philh/C. P. Flor)

① **09026 68008-2** (9/95)
Kasarova sings Berlioz, Ravel and Chausson
Berlioz: Nuits d'été; *Chausson:* Poème de l'amour et de la mer; *Ravel:* Shéhérazade. (V. Kasarova, Austrian RSO/P. Steinberg)

① **09026 68014-2** (10/95)
Pavarotti - The Early Years, Vol.2
Bellini: Capuleti (exc); Puritani (exc); *Donizetti:* Lucia di Lammermoor (exc); *Puccini:* Turandot (exc); *Verdi:* Luisa Miller (exc); Rigoletto (exc); Traviata (exc); Lombardi (exc). (M. Freni, S. Mazzetti, L. Pavarotti, B. Giaiotti, G. Ferrin, A. Giacomotti, chor, La Scala Chor, Grudgionz Fest Chor, Rome SO, Turin SO, Modena Teatro Comunale Orch, Rome Op Orch, La Scala Orch, Grudgionz Fest Orch/N. Bonavolontà/R. Muti/F. Molinari-Pradelli/M. Rossi/L. Magiera/G. Gavazzeni/C. Abbado/G-F. Masini)

① **09026 68045-2** (11/95)
Tchaikovsky—Orchestral Works
Tchaikovsky: Symphony 2; Romeo and Juliet; 1812. (Culver Girls' Acad Ch, St Louis SO/L. Slatkin)

① **09026 68049-2** (8/95)
Fauré—Complete Works for Cello
Fauré: Romance, Op. 69; Elégie; Cello Sonata 1; Cello Sonata 2; Allegro moderato; Sérénade; Sicilienne; Papillon; Cello and Organ Andante. (S. Isserlis, D. Waterman, P. Grier)

① **09026 68052-2** (11/95)
Schumann—Violin and Piano Works
Schumann: Violin Sonata 1; Violin Sonata 2; Fantasiestücke, Op. 73; Romanzen, Op. 94; Märchenbilder. (P. Zukerman, P. Zukerman, M. Neikrug)

① **09026 68061-2** (12/95)
Stalin Cocktail
Shostakovich: Chamber Symphony 2; *Pärt:* Collage; Cantus in memory of Benjamin Britten; *Denisov:* Variations on Haydn's Canon; *Shchedrin:* Stalin Cocktail. (Moscow Virtuosi/V. Spivakov)

① **09026 68079-2** (9/95)
Respighi/Debussy—Orchestral Works
Debussy: La Mer; *Respighi:* Pines of Rome; Fountains of Rome. (Chicago SO/F. Reiner)

① **09026 68131-2** (12/95)
Classics for Children—Boston Pops
Saint-Saëns: Carnaval des animaux; *Britten:* Young Person's Guide; *Grieg:* Peer Gynt Suites (exc); *Gounod:* Marche funèbre d'une marionette; *F. Loesser:* Hans

Christian Anderson (exc); *Hayman:* Kid Stuff. (E. Farrell, H. Downs, L. Litwin, S. Lipman, Boston Pops/A. Fiedler)

① **09026 68132-2** (12/95)
Pops Caviar—Russian Orchestral Fireworks
Borodin: In the Steppes of Central Asia; Prince Igor (exc); *Rimsky-Korsakov:* Russian Easter Festival Ov; Tale of Tsar Saltan (exc); *Khachaturian:* Gayaneh (exc); *Masquerade* (exc); *Tchaikovsky:* Eugene Onegin (exc); Sleeping Beauty (exc). (Boston Pops/A. Fiedler)

① **09026 68181-2** (11/95)
French Chamber Works
Poulenc: Sextet; *Milhaud:* Création du monde; *Saint-Saëns:* Septet, Op. 65. (E. Mann, S. Taylor, D. Shifrin, D. Godburn, R. Todd, T. Stevens, A. Kavafian, J. Rosenfeld, T. Hoffman, C. Brey, J. Kulowitsch, A. Previn)

① **09026 68225-2** (10/95)
R. Strauss—Orchestral Works
R. Strauss: Also sprach Zarathustra; Rosenkavalier (exc); Don Juan. (BRSO/L. Maazel)

① **74321 17888-2** (1/95)
Mozart—Orchestral Works
Mozart: Piano Concerto 20; Piano Concerto 21; Serenade, K525. (G. Anda (pf/dir), Vienna SO, Bamberg SO/E. Jochum)

① **74321 20277-2** (5/95)
Beethoven—Complete Symphonies
Beethoven: Symphony 1; Symphony 2; Symphony 3; Symphony 4; Symphony 5; Symphony 6; Symphony 7; Symphony 8; Symphony 9. (E. Wiens, H. Hartwig, K. Lewis, R. Hermann, Hamburg St Op Chor, N. German Rad Chor, N. German RSO/G. Wand)

① **74321 20283-2** (5/95)
Brahms—Complete Symphonies
Brahms: Symphony 1; Symphony 2; Symphony 3; Symphony 4. (N. German RSO/G. Wand)

① **74321 20286-2** (8/95)
Mendelssohn—Symphonies 1-5
Mendelssohn: Symphony 1; Symphony 2; Symphony 3; Symphony 4; Symphony 5. (C. Casapietra, A. Stolte, P. Schreier, Leipzig Rad Chor, Leipzig Gewandhaus/K. Masur)

① **74321 20290-2** (8/95)
Nielsen—Symphonies 1-6
Nielsen: Symphony 1; Symphony 2; Symphony 3; Symphony 4; Symphony 5; Symphony 6. (Royal Danish Orch/P. Berglund)

① **74321 20294-2** (9/95)
Schumann—Symphonies 1-4
Schumann: Symphony 1; Symphony 2; Symphony 3; Symphony 4. (Philadelphia/James Levine)

① **74321 20297-2** (12/95)
Scriabin—Symphonies, etc
Scriabin: Symphony 1; Symphony 2; Symphony 3; Poème de l'extase; Piano Concerto; Prometheus; Rêverie, Op. 24. (T. Siniawskaia, A. Fedin, V. Krainev, G. Oppitz, Figuralchor, Frankfurt RSO/D. Kitaienko)

① **74321 21277-2** (1/95)
Mozart—Violin Concertos, etc
Mozart: Violin Concerto, K207; Violin Concerto, K211; Violin Concerto, K216; Rondo, K373. (J. Suk, Prague CO/L. Hlaváček)

① **74321 21278-2** (1/95)
Mozart—Violin Concertos, etc
Mozart: Violin Concerto, K218; Violin Concerto, K219; Adagio, K261; Rondo, K269. (J. Suk, Prague CO/L. Hlaváček)

① **74321 24894-2** (5/95)
Homage to Schnittke
Schnittke: Concerto Grosso 1; Viola Concerto; Piano Concerto; Monologue; Praeludium; Suite in the Old Style. (G. Kremer, T. Grindenko, V. Spivakov, S. Rozhdestvensky, Y. Bashmet, Y. Bashmet (va/dir), V. Krainev, S. Bezrodny, LSO/G. Rozhdestvensky/M. Rostropovich, Moscow Virtuosi/V. Spivakov, Moscow Sols Ens)

Record Collector

① **TRC3** (4/95)
The Art of Aristodemo Giorgini
Meyerbeer: Africaine (exc); *Puccini:* Tosca (exc); *Mascagni:* Stornelli marini; *Giordano:* Fedora (exc); *Bellini:* Puritani (exc); Puritani (exc); *Sonnambula* (exc); *Bizet:* Pêcheurs de perles (exc); Pêcheurs de perles (exc); *Verdi:* Luisa Miller (exc); *Cilea:* Adriana Lecouvreur (exc); *Massenet:* Werther (exc); *Rossini:* Barbiere di Siviglia (exc); *Donizetti:* Don Pasquale (exc); Lucia di Lammermoor (exc); *Leoncavallo:* Pagliacci (exc); *Boito:*

Mefistofele (exc); *Puccini:* Bohème (exc); Tosca (exc); Fanciulla del West (exc); *De Curtis:* Tu parte. (A. Giorgini, F. Federici, anon, orch)

Red Sky Records

① **RSKCD111** (12/91)
Songs and Carols for a West Country Christmas
Traditional: Lord of all this revelling; Gloucestershire Wassail; Song for Loders; Tomorrow shall be my dancing day; Come all you worthy Christian friends; Sailor's carol; Sans day carol; *Coppin:* Glastonbury Thorn; *Traditional:* Oxen; Innocent's song; O little town of Bethlehem; Wiltshire carol; Virgin most pure; Birth; Campden carol; Flowering of the thorn. (Coppin ens)

Redcliffe

① **RR006** (11/92)
British Chamber Music for Oboe & Strings
Lutyens: Driving out the Death; *Rawsthorne:* Oboe Quartet; Theme and Variations; *Routh:* Oboe Quartet; Tragic Interludes. (Redcliffe Ens)

① **RR007** (11/92)
Music by Priaulx Rainier
Rainier: String Quartet; Quanta; String Trio; Ploërmel. (Edinburgh Qt, Redcliffe Ens, RNCM Wind Ens)

① **RR008** (4/95)
Music by Alan Bush
A. Bush: Nocturne, Op. 46; Relinquishment, Op. 11; Lyric Interlude, Op. 26; Voices of the Prophets, Op. 41; English Suite, Op. 28. (P. Lane, C. Gould, S. Rahman, P. Langridge, L. Friend, Northern CO/N. Ward)

Reference Recordings

① **RRCD-29** (8/89)
20th Century Orchestral Works
Weill: Kleine Dreigroschenmusik; *Varèse:* Octandre; *Bowles:* Music for a Farce; *Martinů:* Rêvue de Cuisine (1927). (Chicago Pro Musica)

① **RRCD-47** (9/92)
Robert Farnon—Concert Works
Farnon: Captain Hornblower Suite (exc); A la claire fontaine; State Occasion; Lake of the Woods; Promise of Spring; Intermezzo; Rhapsody. (R. Cohen, A. Brewer, RPO/R. Farnon/D. Gamley)

① **RRCD-48** (6/92)
Arnold—Overtures
Arnold: Sussex Overture; Beckus the Dandipratt; Smoke; Fair Field; Commonwealth Christmas. (LPO/M. Arnold)

Regent

① **REGCD101** (10/88)
Langlais and Poulenc: Sacred Choral Works
Langlais: Messe solennelle; *Poulenc:* Mass in G; Motets pour le temps de Noël. (Regent Chbr Ch, Adrian Lucas/G. Cole)

① **REGCD103** (5/89)
Kodály: Choral Music
Kodály: Missa Brevis; Pange lingua; Laudes organi. (Regent Chbr Ch, John Scott/G. Cole)

① **REGCD104** (5/89)
The Bel Canto Bassoon
Saint-Saëns: Bassoon Sonata; *Donizetti:* Elisir d'amore (exc); *Tamplini:* Donizetti's Don Pasquale Fantasia; *Rachmaninov:* Songs, Op. 34 (exc); *Rimsky-Korsakov:* Tale of Tsar Saltan (exc); *Cokken:* William Tell Fantasia; *Elgar:* Romance, Op. 62; *Orselli:* Traviata Reminiscenze; *Kreisler:* Liebesleid; *Orselli:* Ballo in Maschera Fantasia; *Ibert:* Carignane; *Berr:* Una voce poco fa Fantasia. (K. Walker, J. Drake)

① **REGCD105** (4/91)
From Chamber to Chantry
Buxtehude: Prelude and Fugue, BuxWV146; Komm, heiliger Geist, BuxWV199; Ciacona, BuxWV160; *Bach:* Fantasia and Fugue, BWV542; *Guilain:* Pièces d'orgue (exc); *Buxtehude:* Nun freut euch, BWV734; Valet will ich dir geben, BWV735; *Buxtehude:* Canzona, BuxWV166; Fugue, BuxWV174; *Sweelinck:* Pavana Lachrimae; *Scheidt:* Dowland Galliarda; *Walther:* Meck Concerto in B minor. (John Scott, P. Hurford, Margaret Phillips)

① **REGCD106** (12/91)
Carols in Advent
Anon: Advent Antiphons; *Traditional:* This is the truth sent from above; Adam lay y-bounden; Angel Gabriel; Echo Carol; First good joy that Mary had; Jesus Christ the Apple tree; In the bleak midwinter; O come, o come Emmanuel; Hark! a herald voice is calling; *Weelkes:* Gloria in excelsis

Deo; *Bairstow*: Let all mortal flesh keep silence; *Traditional*: In the ending of the year; Outside, how hard it bloweth; 'Twas in the year that King Uzziah died; *P. Wishart*: Jesu, dulcis memoria; *F. Guerrero*: Virgen sancta. (King's College Sngrs/E.H. Warrell)

ⓘ **REGCD107** (3/94)
Lole—Choral Works
Lole: This is the Day; St David's Service; Angels; Vesper Responsary; *Traditional*: Mary's Child; Morning Star; Child of the Manger; Journey; *Lole*: St Nicholas Service; *Traditional*: Jesus, good above all other; *Lole*: Evening Hymn; I will lift up mine eyes; O God the Holy Spirit; Father's Love; Shall we not love thee; I got me flowers; St Mary's Service; Love eternal. (St Mary Collegiate Church Ch, K. Bowyer/S. Lole)

ⓘ **REGSB701CD** (2/91)
I saw the Lord
Stainer: I waited for the Lord; *Walton*: Set me as a seal; *Mozart*: Vespers, K339 (exc); *Bainton*: And I saw a new heaven; *Anon*: Ye holy angels bright; Dear Lord and Father; *Traditional*: In the bleak midwinter; *Howells*: Collegium Regale (exc); *Brahms*: Deutsches Requiem, Op. 45 (exc); *Rutter*: Candlelight Carol; *Parry*: Songs of Farewell (exc); Hear my words, ye people (exc); W. H. *Harris*: Bring us, O Lord. (St Bride's Ch, Fleet St/R. Jones/A. Watts, C. Etherington, Ghislaine Morgan)

Relief

ⓘ **CR911022** (12/93)
Beethoven—Piano Sonatas
Beethoven: Piano Sonata 30; Piano Sonata 31; Piano Sonata 32. (M. Horszowski)

ⓘ **CR911023** (12/93)
Horszowski plays Chopin
Chopin: Piano Concerto 1; Impromptus; Fantaisie-Impromptu; Polonaises (exc); Fantasie, Op.49. (M. Horszowski, Vienna St Op Orch/H. Swarowsky)

REM Editions

ⓘ **REM311049** (9/89)
Duparc Mélodies
Duparc: Invitation au voyage; Sérénade florentine; Extase; Chanson triste; Manoir de Rosemonde; Au pays où se fait la guerre; Fuite; Vague et la cloche; Sérénade; Testament; Phidylé; Romance de Mignon; Élégie; Lamento; Galop; Soupir; Vie antérieure. (F. Le Roux, D. Borst, J. Cohen)

ⓘ **REM311053** (7/89)
Boëllmann: Organ Works
Boëllmann: Suite gothique; Deuxième Suite; Douze Pièces. (P. Caire)

ⓘ **REM311068** (8/91)
Reger—Organ Works
Reger: Chorale Fantasias, Op. 52 (exc); Introduction, Passacaglia and Fugue, Op. 127 (exc); Fantasia and Fugue, Op. 135b (exc). (D. Matrone)

ⓘ **REM311069** (11/91)
Hahn—Mélodies
Hahn: Chansons grises; D'une prison; Incrédule; Offrande; Fêtes galantes; Si mes vers; Rêverie; Quand la nuit n'est pas étoilée; À Chloris; Quand je fus pris; Nocturne; Séraphine; Mai; Cygnes; Fumée; Sur l'eau; Infidélité; Seule; Paysage; Nuit; Printemps; Dans la nuit; Trois jours. (F. le Roux, J. Cohen)

ⓘ **REM311078** (8/91)
Musiques Symphoniques pour Grand Orgue
Liszt: Prelude and Fugue, S260; Consolations, S172 (exc); *Franck*: Chorales (exc); *Duruflé*: Prelude, Adagio et Choral varié, Op. 4; *Langlais*: Poèmes évangéliques (exc); Paraphrases grégoriennes (exc); *Widor*: Symphony 5 (exc); *Landry*: Orah; *Reboulot*: Pater Noster Chorale. (J-G. Proulx)

ⓘ **REM311086** (4/91)
French Duets
Fauré: Tarentelle, Op. 10/2; Pleurs d'or, Op. 72; Puisqu'ici-bas; *Duparc*: Fuite; *Massenet*: Fleurs; Poète et le fantôme; Rêvons c'est l'heure; Horace et Lydie; *Debussy*: Chanson espagnole; *Gounod*: Barcarola; Par une belle nuit; *Lalo*: Au fond des halliers; *Satie*: Je te veux; *Poulenc*: Colloque; *Chausson*: Duos, Op. 11; *Bizet*: Fuite. (C. Alliot-Lugaz, F. Le Roux, J. Cohen)

ⓘ **REM311105** (10/91)
Poulenc—Mélodies
Poulenc: Calligrammes; Poèmes de Ronsard; Tel jour, telle nuit; Bestiaire; Cocardes; Bal masqué. (D. Henry, A. Pondepeyre, Stamitz Ens)

ⓘ **REM311175** (11/92)
Fauré—Mélodies, Vol.1
Fauré: Horizon chimérique; Bonne chanson, op.61; Songs,

op.58; Songs, op.4 (exc); Songs, op.18 (exc); Songs, op.39 (exc); Songs, op.51 (exc); Songs, op.76 (exc); Songs, op.5 (exc); Songs, op.7 (exc); Songs, op.8 (exc); Songs, op.46 (exc). (F. le Roux, J. Cohen, J. Estournet, M. Ostalczyk, N. Takami, P. Gabard, P. Noharet)

Ricercar

ⓘ **RIC008029** (4/89)
Palestrina—Sacred Choral Works
Palestrina: Missa Assumpta est Maria; Motets, Bk 3 (1575) (exc); Peccantem me quotidie; Motets, Bk 2 (1581) (exc); O beata et benedicta. (Paris Chapelle Royale Chor/P. Herreweghe)

ⓘ **RIC014024** (10/89)
Boesmans—Concertos
Boesmans: Conversions; Violin Concerto (1979); Piano Concerto (1978). (R. Pieta, M. Mercenier, Liège PO/P. Bartholomée)

ⓘ **RIC037011** (10/88)
Charpentier—Cantatas and Airs
M-A. Charpentier: Orphée descendant aux enfers, H471; Quid audio, quid murmur, H474; Le Cid Airs, H457-9; Tristes déserts, H469; Ah, qu'on est malheureux, H443; Amour, vous avez beau redoubler mes alarmes, H445; Rendez-moi mes plaisirs, H463; Auprès du feu, H446; Bavolet, H499a; Sonate a 8, H548. (H. Ledroit, G. de Reyghere, M. Ledroit, G. de Mey, J. Bona, Ricercar Consort)

ⓘ **RIC041016** (1/90)
German Baroque Cantatas, Vol.2 - Buxtehude
Buxtehude: Herr, ich lasse dich nicht, BuxWV36; Wo ist doch mein Freund gebleiben, BuxWV111; Nichts soll uns scheiden, BuxWV77; Ich halte es dafür, BuxWV48; Ich suchte des Nachts, BuxWV50; Neugeborne Kindelein, BuxWV13. (G. de Reyghere, H. Ledroit, G. de Mey, M. van Egmond, Ricercar Consort)

ⓘ **RIC046023** (1/90)
German Baroque Cantatas, Vol.3
Schein: Christ unser Herr zum Jordan kam; O Jesu Christe, Gottes Sohn; *Tunder*: An Wasserflüssen Babylon; Ach Herr, lass deine liebe Engelein; Wachet auf!; *Anon*: Es ist g'nug; *Buxtehude*: Laudate pueri, BuxWV69; Fried- und Freudenreiche, BuxWV76 (exc); Gen Himmel zu dem Vater mein, BuxWV32; Singet dem Herrn, BuxWV98. (G. de Reyghere, M. Mellon, Ricercar Consort)

ⓘ **RIC048035/7** (1/90)
German Baroque Cantatas, Vol.4 - Bruhns
Bruhns: Hemmt eure Trähnenfluht; Jauchzet dem Herren alle Welt; Woll dem, die der Herren fürchtet; De profundis clamavi; Alleluja, Paratum cor meum; O werber heil' ger Geist; Zeit meines Abscheids; Erstanden ist der heilige Christ; Herr hat seinen Stuhl; Ich liege und schlafe; Mein Herz ist bereit; Muss nicht der Mensch; Prelude and Fugue in E minor I; Prelude and Fugue in G minor; Nun komm der Heiden Heiland; Prelude and Fugue in G; Prelude and Fugue in E minor II. (G. de Reyghere, J. Feldman, J. Bowman, G. de Mey, I. Honeyman, M. van Egmond, B. Foccroulle, Ricercar Consort)

ⓘ **RIC052034** (1/89)
Charpentier—Sacred Choral Works
M-A. Charpentier: Magnificat, H81; Messe pour le Port Royal, H81; O clementissime Domine Jesu, H256; Dixit Dominus, H226; Laudate Dominum, H227; Stabat Mater, H15; *Raison*: Second livre d'orgue (exc). (G. de Reyghere, I. Poulenard, J. Feldman, L. Van Gijsegem, B. Foccroulle, B. Mernier, Capella Ricercar/J. Léjeune)

ⓘ **RIC054032** (1/90)
Italian Motets and Arias
Monteverdi: Selva morale e spirituale (exc); *Carissimi*: O vulnera doloris; *Frescobaldi*: Arie musicali Bk 1 (exc); *F. Caccini*: O che nuovo stupor; *Bassani*: Nascere, dive puellule; *Cazzati*: Factum est praelium magnum; *Brevi*: Catenae terrenae; *Cazzati*: In Calvaria ruppe; *B. Marcello*: Dai tribunal 'augusto. (M. van Egmond, Ricercar Consort)

ⓘ **RIC060048** (5/90)
German Baroque Cantatas, Vol. 5
Hammerschmidt: Sonata super Nun lob, mein Seel, den Herren; Wonist der neugeborne König; *Selle*: Es begab sich aber zu der Zeit; *Schein*: Nun komm, der Heiden Heiland; Gelobet seist du, Jesu Christ; Uns ist ein Kind geboren; O Jesulein, mein Jesulein; Maria, gegrüsset seist du; *Schütz*: Kleiner geistlichen Concerten, SWV306-37 (exc); Geistliche Chormusik, SWV369-97 (exc); *Tunder*: Kleines Kindelein; *Weckmann*: Singet dem Herrn; Holdselige; *Lübeck*: Willkommen, süsser Bräutigam. (G. de Reyghere, A. Mellon, D. Visse, G. de Mey, V. Demaiffe, Capella Ricercar, Ricercar Consort)

ⓘ **RIC061041** (1/90)
Bach—Cantatas
Bach: Cantata 82; Cantata 152; Cantata 202. (G. de Reyghere, M. van Egmond, Ricercar Consort)

ⓘ **RIC062026** (11/89)
Concerto in forma di una messa
Frescobaldi: Messa sopra l'aria della Monica; Fiori musicali (exc); Canzoni with Titles (exc); *Marenzio*: Laudate Dominum I a 8; Lamentabataur Jacob; Jubilate Deo a 8; *Frescobaldi*: Secondo libro di Toccate (exc). (Capella Sancti Michaelis Voc Ens, Capella Sancti Michaelis Instr Ens, J. Laleman/E. van Nevel)

ⓘ **RIC064042** (3/90)
Bach—Organ Works, Vol.5
Bach: Toccata, Adagio and Fugue, BWV564; Wo soll ich fliehen hin, BWV694; Ein feste Burg, BWV720; Prelude and Fugue, BWV551; Wer nur den lieben, BWV690; Nun freut euch, BWV734; Prelude and Fugue, BWV545; Wir Christenleut, BWV710; Herr Jesu Christ, BWV709; Prelude and Fugue, BWV541; Chorales, BWV651-668 (exc); Toccata and Fugue, BWV538. (B. Foccroulle)

ⓘ **RIC069049** (9/90)
W.F. Bach—Keyboard Concertos
W.F. Bach: Keyboard Concerto, F43; Keyboard Concerto, F44; Sinfonia, F65. (G. Penson, Ricercar Consort/A. Chamorro)

ⓘ **RIC079061** (7/91)
German Baroque Cantatas, Vol.6 - Funeral Cantatas
Bach: Cantata 106; *Boxberg*: Bestelle dein haus; *Riedel*: Harmonische Freude; *Telemann*: Du aber Daniel. (G. de Reyghere, J. Bowman, G. de Mey, M. van Egmond, Ricercar Consort)

ⓘ **RIC085068** (10/91)
Bach—Organ Works, Vol.6
Bach: Prelude and Fugue, BWV543; Allein Gott, BWV717; Prelude and Fugue, BWV550; Jesu, meine Freude, BWV713; Prelude and Fugue, BWV536; Canzona, BWV588; Prelude and Fugue, BWV534; Fugue, BWV578; Toccata and Fugue, BWV540. (B. Foccroulle)

ⓘ **RIC086069** (10/91)
Bach—Organ Works, Vol.7
Bach: Concertos, BWV592-7 (exc); Erbarm dich, BWV721 (exc); Prelude and Fugue, BWV539 (exc). (B. Foccroulle)

ⓘ **RIC098112** (8/94)
German Baroque Chamber Music, Vol.5
Scheidt: Canzon super O Nachbar Roland; *Hentzschel*: Canzon a 8; *Posch*: Musicalische Tafelfreudt (exc); *J.M. Nicolai*: 3-Va da gamba Sonata; *Kühnel*: Sonate ò partite (exc); *Schenck*: Scherzi musicali (exc); *Funck*: Stricturae (exc). (Ricercar Consort, P. Pierlot (va da gamba/dir))

ⓘ **RIC105081** (12/92)
Mozart—Keyboard Works
Mozart: Andante, K15ii; Piano Piece, K33b; Allegro, K72a; Andante, K1a; Allegro, K1b; Allegro, K1c; Minuet, K1d; Minuet, K1; Minuet, K1f; Minuet, K2; Allegro, K3; Minuet, K4; Minuet, K5; Minuet, K9a; Londoner Notenskizzenbuch (exc); Minuet, K61g/2; Minuet, K94; Minuets, K315a; Allegro, K312; Capriccio, K395; Fugue, K401; Prelude and Fugue, K394; Minuet, K401/8; Fantasia, K396; Fantasia, K397; Suite, K399; Allegro, K400; Funeral March, K453a; Fantasia, K475; Rondo, K485; German Dances, K509; Rondo, K511; Adagio, K540; Allegro and Andante, KAnh135; Minuet, K355; Andantino, K236; Gigue, K574; Andante, K616; Adagio, K356. (B. Foccroulle, L. Devos, D. James, G. Penson, G. Penson, G. Penson)

ⓘ **RIC109097/8** (4/93)
German Baroque Cantatas, Vol.9 - Weckmann
Weckmann: Weine nicht; Zion spricht; Herr, wenn ich nur dich habe; Wie liegt die Stadt so wuste; Dialogo von Tobias und Raguel; Kommet her zu mir alle; Wenn der Herr; Angelicus coeli chorus; Gegrüsset seist du, Holdselige; Rex virtutum; Tod ist verschlungen; Es erhub sich ein Streit. (G. de Reyghere, J. Feldman, J. Bowman, I. Honeyman, G. de Mey, M. van Egmond, Capella Sancti Michaelis Voc Ens/E. van Nevel, Ricercar Consort)

ⓘ **RIC118100** (2/94)
Le Tombeau de M. de Sainte-Colombe
Marais: Pièces de viole II/2 (exc); *Du Buisson III*: Troisième Suite in A minor; *Machy*: Pièces de viole (exc); *Sainte-Colombe le fils*: Tombeau; Fantaisie en Rondeau; Concerts à deux violes esgales (exc). (P. Pierlot, S. Watillon, R. Zipperling, R. Lislevand)

Romantic Robot

ⓘ **RR1941** (8/92)
Terezin - The Music 1941-44
G. Klein: Piano Sonata; Trio; *Ullmann*: String Quartet 3; Piano Sonata 6; Abendphantasie; Immer Inmitten;

ⓘ **82001-2** (12/94)
Pol Plançon—Complete Victor Recordings
Bellini: Sonnambula (exc); *Adam:* Minuit, Chrétiens (exc);
Faure: Rameaux; *A. Thomas:* Caïd (exc); *Berlioz:*
Damnation de Faust (exc); *Gounod:* Roméo et Juliette
(exc); *Rossini:* Stabat Mater (exc); *Gounod:* Faust (exc);
Niedermeyer: Lac; *Schumann:* Romanzen und Balladen,
Op.49 (exc); *Adam:* Chalet (exc); *Gounod:* Faust (exc);
Godard: Embarquez-vous; *Gounod:* Philémon et Baucis
(exc); *Mozart:* Zauberflöte (exc); *Gounod:* Vallon;
Massenet: Si tu veux, Mignonne; *Haydn:* Jahreszeiten
(exc); *Gounod:* Jésus de Nazareth; *Ferrari:* Lazzarone;
Georges: Filibustier; *Bemberg:* Soupir; *Flégier:* Cor;
Meyerbeer: Dinorah (exc); *Faure:* Credo; *Gounod:* Faust
(exc); *Berlioz:* Damnation de Faust (exc); *Adam:* Minuit,
Chrétiens (exc); *Gounod:* Faust (exc); *A. Thomas:* Caïd
(exc); *Faure:* Rameaux; *Schumann:* Romanzen und
Balladen, Op.49 (exc); *Gounod:* Faust (exc); *Verdi:* Don
Carlos (exc); *Berlioz:* Damnation de Faust (exc); *Flotow:*
Martha (exc); *Meyerbeer:* Etoile du Nord (exc); *Robert le
Diable* (exc); *A. Thomas:* Mignon (exc); *Rossini:* Stabat
Mater (exc). (P. Plançon, E. Eames, C. Dalmores, anon,
orch)

ⓘ **82002-2** (8/95)
Edmond Clément (1867-1928)
Rossini: Barbiere di Siviglia (exc); *Gounod:* Roméo et
Juliette (exc); *Massenet:* Manon (exc); *Boïeldieu:* Dame
Blanche (exc); *Massenet:* Manon (exc); *Weckerlin:*
Romances et Chansons (exc); *Pessard:* Adieu du matin;
Arcadet: Chanson lorraine; *Massenet:* Poème d'Avril (exc);
Bemberg: Neige; Ça fait peur aux oiseaux; *Lalo:* Roi d'ys
(exc); *Godard:* Jocelyn (exc); *Massenet:* Werther (exc);
Faure: Rameaux; *Meyerbeer:* Robert le Diable (exc); *Bizet:*
Pêcheurs de perles (exc); *Gounod:* Roméo et Juliette
(exc); *Godard:* Danté et Béatrice (exc); *Boito:* Mefistofele
(exc); *Schumann:* Duette, Op.34 (exc); *Lully:* Au clair de la
lune. (E. Clément, M. Journet, G. Farrar, anon, F. La
Forge, orch/R. Bourdon)

Rondo

ⓘ **RCD8319** (1/91)
Nielsen—Songs, Vol.1
Nielsen: Study from Nature; Ariel's song, FS80; Strophic
Songs, FS42 (exc); Songs and Verses, FS14; Land of the
Future; Jutish songs, FS115; Golden River, FS127;
Denmark now sleeps, FS146; Reunion, FS151; Ballad of
the Bear, FS109; Danish Weather; Danish Songs (exc). (P.
Severin, D. Kirkeskov)

ⓘ **RCD8323** (1/91)
Nielsen—Songs, Vol.2
Nielsen: Christmas Carol; Danish Songs (exc); It is
Autumn; Songs, FS18; Strophic Songs, FS42 (exc); His
words; Flower song; In the Land of Dreams; Songs, FS3.
(P. Severin, E. Rehling, D. Kirkeskov)

ⓘ **RCD8325** (1/91)
Nielsen: Songs, Vol.3
Nielsen: O Danish Man; Son of Wolf (exc); Hagbarth and
Signe (exc); Danish Songs (exc); Merchant's Committee
Cantata; Liar (exc); Popular Melodies, FS95 (exc); Popular
Melodies, FS101 (exc); Songbook, FS125 (exc); Christmas
Song; Denmark Songbook, FS111 (exc); Songs, FS143
(exc); There is a lovely Land. (L.T. Bertelsen, T. Lønskov)

ⓘ **RCD8327** (1/91)
Nielsen: Songs, Vol.4
Nielsen: Songs, FS12; Hymns and sacred songs (exc);
Strophic Songs, FS42 (exc); Willemoes (exc); Tove (exc);
Aladdin (exc); Little Danish Songs, FS114 (Cpte). (E.
Rehling, P. Severin, D. Kirkeskov/J.E. Hansen)

ⓘ **RCD8329** (1/91)
Nielsen: Songs, Vol.5
Nielsen: May Song; Master Oluf Rides (exc); Dawn (exc);
Mother (exc); Hymns and sacred songs (exc); Cosmus
(exc); Popular Melodies, FS95 (exc); Popular Melodies,
FS101 (exc); Amor and the Poet (exc); Vocalise, FS124;
Power that gave me. (E.H. Thaysen, M. Ejsing, J. Laursen,
L.T. Bertelsen, T. Lønskov, F. Stengaard)

Rose Collection

ⓘ **3209** (7/93)
Strauss—Waltzes and Polkas
J. Strauss II: Frühlingsstimmen, Op. 410; Annen-Polka,
Op. 117; Wo die Zitronen blüh'n; Perpetuum Mobile;
Persischer Marsch; Künstlerleben, Op. 316;
Vergnügungszug; Wein, Weib und Gesang; Tritsch-
Tratsch; G'schichten aus dem Wienerwald, Op. 325; *Jos
Strauss:* Dorfschwalben aus Österreich. (Vienna Op
Orch/C. Michalski)

ⓘ **3221** (6/93)
Schumann—Miscellaneous Works
Schumann: Piano Concerto; Pedal Studies, Op. 56;

Requiem für Mignon, Op. 98b. (M. Bergerich, Berlin Fest
Orch/V. Petroschoff, H. C. Becker-Foss, E. Mathis, C.
Lehnert, M. Moreira, M. Witte-Waldbauer, R. Titze,
Meutlberg Chbr Ch, Innsbruck Cons Ch/Robert Wagner)

RPO

ⓘ **CDRPO7014** (5/90)
Ashkenazy Live in Moscow
Mussorgsky: Khovanshchina (exc); *Beethoven:* Piano
Concerto 3; *Ravel:* Daphnis et Chloé Suites (exc);
Tchaikovsky: Nutcracker Suite (exc). (RPO, Vladimir
Ashkenazy (pf/dir)/Vladimir Ashkenazy)

ⓘ **CDRPO7015** (1/91)
Ashkenazy in Moscow and London
Walton: Symphony 2; *Knussen:* Symphony 3; *Britten:*
Serenade. (M. Hill, J. Bryant, RPO/Vladimir Ashkenazy)

ⓘ **CDRPO7023** (7/94)
French Orchestral Works
Ravel: Piano Concerto; *Fauré:* Ballade, Op. 19; *Franck:*
Djinns; Symphonic Variations. (L. Parham, RPO/J-C.
Casadesus)

RSR

ⓘ **RSRD1002** (9/93)
Black Dyke Mills Band, Vol.2 - Sovereign Heritage
Berlioz: Corsaire; *Benvenuto Cellini* (exc); *Lucas:* Chorale
and Variations; *Howells:* Pageantry; *Yorke:* Shipbuilders;
Famon: Vie de Matelot; *Beaver:* Sovereign Heritage.
(Black Dyke Mills Band/G. Brand/R. Newsome/P. Parkes)

Russian Disc

ⓘ **RDCD10021** (5/94)
Liszt—Piano Works
Liszt: Don Juan réminiscences, S418; Études d'exécution,
S139 (exc); Concert Studies, S145 (exc); Paganini
Studies, S140 (exc); Années de pèlerinage 2 (exc);
Hungarian Rhapsodies, S244 (exc). (L. Kuzmin)

ⓘ **RDCD11087** (10/93)
Shostakovich/Beethoven—Works for String Quartet
Shostakovich: String Quartet 8; String Quartet Pieces
(1931) (exc); *Beethoven:* Grosse Fuge. (Borodin Qt)

ⓘ **RDCD11104** (7/94)
Elgar/Milhaud/Respighi—Works for Cello & Orchestra
Elgar: Cello Concerto; *Respighi:* Adagio con variazioni;
Milhaud: Cello Concerto 1. (M. Rostropovich, Moscow PO,
USSR TV & Rad Orch/G. Rozhdestvensky)

ⓘ **RDCD11166** (3/94)
Wagner—Orchestral excerpts from Operas
Wagner: Tannhäuser (exc); Tristan und Isolde (exc);
Lohengrin (exc); Meistersinger (exc); Siegfried (exc);
Götterdämmerung (exc); Walküre (exc). (Leningrad PO/E.
Mravinsky)

ⓘ **RDCD11208** (5/94)
Vladimir Ashkenazy Piano Recital - 1963
Beethoven: Piano Sonata 18; *Chopin:* Ballades; *Debussy:*
Isle joyeuse; Préludes (exc); Suite bergamasque (exc).
(Vladimir Ashkenazy)

ⓘ **RDCD15004** (8/94)
Neuhaus plays Scriabin
Scriabin: Piano Concerto; Poèmes, Op.32; Pieces, Op.59
(exc); Poèmes, Op.63; Pieces, Op.9; Preludes, Op.11
(exc); Preludes, Op.13; Fantasie, Op.28. (H. Neuhaus,
Moscow All-Union RSO/N. Golovanov)

ⓘ **RDCD15005** (2/95)
Shostakovich plays Shostakovich
Shostakovich: Cello Sonata, Op. 40; Piano Concerto 2;
Piano Concerto 1. (M. Rostropovich, D. Shostakovich,
Moscow RSO/A. Gauk, Moscow PO/S. Samosud)

Saga Classics

ⓘ **EC3361-2** (3/92)
Janet Baker—Lieder Recital
Schumann: Frauenliebe und -Leben, Op.42 (Cpte);
Schubert: Heimliches Lieben, D922; Minnelied, D429;
Abgeblühte Linde, D514; Musensohn, D764; *Brahms:*
Lieder, Op.43 (exc); Lieder, Op.107 (exc); Lieder, Op.97
(exc). (J. Baker, M. Isepp)

ⓘ **EC3376-2** (4/92)
Debussy—Piano Works, Vol.2
Debussy: Images; Images oubliées (exc); Pour le piano;
Danse; Arabesques; Ballade; Nocturne; Mazurka. (L.
Rév)

ⓘ **EC3377-2** (4/92)
Debussy—Piano Works, Vol.1
Debussy: Préludes (exc); Tarantelle styrienne; Hommage

à Haydn; Children's Corner; Page d'album; Plus que lente;
Elégie. (L. Rév)

ⓘ **EC3379-2** (4/92)
Boyce—Anthems and Voluntaries
Boyce: Voluntaries (exc); Turn thee unto me; By the waters
of Babylon; I have surely built thee an house. (A. Wills, Ely
Cath Ch/A. Wills)

ⓘ **EC3383-2** (4/92)
Debussy—Piano Works, Vol.3
Debussy: Etudes; Berceuse héroïque; Morceau de
concours; D'un cahier d'esquisses; Suite bergamasque. (L.
Rév)

ⓘ **EC3391-2** (3/94)
Stravinsky—Piano Works
Stravinsky: Studies, Op. 7; Serenade in A; Piano-Rag
Music; Piano Sonata (1924); Tango; Circus polka. (T.
Rajna)

ⓘ **EC3393-2** (3/94)
Satie—Piano Works
Satie: Chapitres tournés en tous sens; Gnossiennes (exc);
Valses du précieux dégoûté; Avant-dernières pensées;
Première pensée Rose & Croix; Rêveries nocturnes; Je te
veux; Pièces froides; Prélude de la porte héroïque du ciel;
Piège de Méduse; Nocturnes (exc); Préludes du fils des
étoiles; Valse-ballet; Rêverie du pauvre; Pantins dansent;
Grimaces. (J. McCabe)

ⓘ **EC3397-2** (3/94)
Fauré—Piano Works, Vol.2
Fauré: Thème et Variations, Op. 73; Pièces brèves, Op. 84
(exc); Barcarolles (exc); Préludes. (A. Ferber)

Sain

ⓘ **SCDC2013** (8/93)
Meirion Williams—Songs
M. Williams: Aros Mae'r Mynyddau Mawr; Gwynfyd;
Awelon y Mynydd; O Fab y Dyn; Y Llyn; Cloch y Llan;
Rhosyn yr Haf; Ora Pro Nobis; Ffarwel iti; Pan Ddaw'r Nos;
Adlewych (Cpte). (B. Terfel, A. Bryn Parri)

ⓘ **SCDC2070** (11/95)
Susan Bullock
Dvořák: Rusalka (exc); *Traditional:* Suo Gan; *Bernstein:*
West Side Story (exc); *Puccini:* Madama Butterfly (exc); *E.
T. Davies:* Ynys y Plant; *Bizet:* Carmen (exc); *Britten:* Folk
Songs (exc); *Sondheim:* Follies (exc); *Traditional:*
Bugeilio'r Gwenith Gwyn; *Mozart:* Nozze di Figaro (exc);
Glyn: Gwynt y haf. (S. Bullock, A. Davies, A. Bryn Parri)

ⓘ **SCDC2085** (11/95)
Arthur Davies
Puccini: Madama Butterfly (exc); *R. S. Hughes:* Arafa Don;
Verdi: Traviata (exc); *Hardelot:* Because; *William Davies:*
O! Na byddai'n haf o hyd; *Lehár:* Land des Lächelns (exc);
Bizet: Carmen (exc); *I. Lewis:* Bugail Aberdyfi; *Giordano:*
Fedora (exc); *J. Henry:* Galwad y Tywysog; *Puccini:*
Bohème (exc); *Elwyn-Edwards:* Mae hiraeth yn y môr;
Gounod: Roméo et Juliette (exc); *Glyn:* Gwynt yr haf. (A.
Davies, S. Bullock, A. Bryn Parri)

Salabert Actuels

ⓘ **SCD8904/5** (9/90)
Scelsi—Chamber Works
Scelsi: String Quartet 1; String Trio; String Quartet 2;
Khoom; String Quartet 3; String Quartet 4; String Quartet
5. (M. Hirayama, F. Lloyd, M. Ben Omar, Arditti Qt/A.
Brizzi)

Saydisc

ⓘ **CD-SDL379** (10/90)
Romantic Guitar Quartets
Mendelssohn: Songs without words (exc); *Chopin:*
Mazurkas (exc); *Borodin:* String Quartet 2 (exc); *Schubert:*
Arpeggione Sonata, D821. (English Gtr Qt)

ⓘ **CD-SDL386** (11/91)
Baroque Guitar Quartets
Handel: Concerti grossi, Op. 3 (exc); *Bach:* Passacaglia
and Fugue, BWV582; *Corelli:* Trio Sonatas, Op. 2 (exc);
Trio Sonatas, Op. 3 (exc); *Purcell:* Fairy Queen, Z629
(exc); *Vivaldi:* Concerto, RV532. (English Gtr Qt)

ⓘ **CD-SDL400** (6/93)
English National Songs
Traditional: Greensleeves (Alas! my love); When the king
enjoys; Northern Lass; Vicar of Bray; Nancy Dawson; A-
hunting we will go; Drink to me only; Begone dull care;
Early one morning; *W. Lawes:* Gather ye rosebuds a 1;
Purcell: King Arthur, Z628 (exc); *Carey:* Sally in our alley;
Leveridge: Roast Beef of Old England; *Arne:* Rule
Britannia; Love in a Village (exc); British Grenadiers;
Various: National Anthems (exc); *Mr. Collins:* Chapter of

Kings; *Hook*: Lass of Richmond Hill; *Dibdin*: Tom Bowling; *Bishop*: Home, sweet home. (L. Skeaping, J. Potter, Broadside Band/J. Barlow)

Scalen'Disc

① **ARI139** (9/89)
Bach & Busoni: Organ Works
Bach: Prelude and Fugue, BWV898; Allein Gott, BWV260; Clavier-Übung III, BWV669-689 (exc); *Busoni*: Fantasia contrappuntistica. (P. Guillot)

① **ARI142** (7/89)
Deodat de Séverac: Mélodies et Chansons, Vol 1
Séverac: Ciel est, par-dessus le toit; Temps de neige; Rêve; À l'aube dans la montagne; Phillis; Chanson de Jacques; Chanson de la nuit durable; Hiboux; Chanson pour le petit cheval; Ma poupée chérie; Aubade; Chant de Noël; Infidèle; Chanson de Blaisine; Éveil de Pâques. (M. Command, G. Bacquier, J. Bernier)

① **ARI143** (7/89)
Séverac: Songs
Séverac: Chevrier; Paysages tristes; Ritournelle; Mort y la donzella; Chansons du XVIII Cent I; Jean des Grignottes; Dans les prisons de Nantes; Huns. (M. Command, G. Bacquier, J. Bernier)

Sheffield Lab

① **CD-7/8** (8/87)
Prokofiev & Wagner: Orchestral Works
Wagner: Walküre (exc); Tristan und Isolde (exc); Götterdämmerung (exc); Siegfried (exc); *Prokofiev*: Romeo and Juliet (exc). (Los Angeles PO/E. Leinsdorf)

① **CD25** (2/88)
The Moscow Sessions - I
Tchaikovsky: Symphony 5; *Glinka*: Ruslan and Lyudmila (exc); *Mussorgsky*: Khovanshchina (exc). (Moscow PO/L. Leighton Smith)

① **CD26** (2/88)
The Moscow Sessions - II
Shostakovich: Symphony 1; *Piston*: Incredible Flutist Suite; *Barber*: Essay for Orchestra. (Moscow PO/L. Leighton Smith/D. Kitaienko)

① **CD27** (2/88)
The Moscow Sessions - III
Shostakovich: Festive Overture; *Copland*: Appalachian Spring Suite; *Gershwin*: Lullaby; *Griffes*: White Peacock; *Glazunov*: Concert Waltz 1; *Ives*: Unanswered Question. (Moscow PO/L. Leighton Smith/D. Kitaienko)

Silva Screen

① **FILMCD042** (3/90)
The Prisoner, Vol.1
Various: Prisoner: Arrival (exc); Prisoner: A, B & C (exc); Prisoner: Free For All (exc); Prisoner: The General (exc); Prisoner: Fall Out (exc); Prisoner: Many Happy Returns (exc); Prisoner: Dance of the Dead (exc); Prisoner: Checkmate (exc); Prisoner: Hammer Into Anvil (exc); Prisoner: The Girl Who Was Death (exc); Prisoner: Once Upon A Time (exc). (OST)

① **FILMCD117** (5/93)
The Television Scores of Geoffrey Burgon
Burgon: Brideshead Revisited (exc); Testament of Youth (exc); Bleak House (exc); Nunc dimittis; Tinker, Tailor (exc); Chronicles of Narnia (exc). (L. Garrett, Philh/G. Burgon)

① **FILMCD127** (10/93)
Vampire Circus—The Essential Vampire Theme Collection
Delibes: Lakmé (exc); *Whitaker*: Vampire Circus (exc); *Gerald Fried*: Return of Dracula (exc); *Fiedel*: Fright Night (exc); *Cirino*: Transylvania Twist (exc); *J. Elias*: Vamp (exc); *Licht*: Children of the Night (exc); *B. May*: Thirst (exc); *Holdridge*: Transylvania 6-5000 (exc); *Mollin*: Forever Knight (exc); *Eidelman*: To Die For (exc); *McKenzie*: Son of Darkness (exc); *Cobert*: Dracula (exc); *Richard Stone*: Sundown (exc). (L. Garrett, L. Christian, Philh/A. Greenwood/N. Richardson, OST/G. Fried/B. Fiedel/C. Cirino/J. Elias/D. Licht/B. May/L. Holdridge/F. Mollin/K. Eidelman/M. McKenzie/R. Cobert/R. Stone)

① **FILMCD129** (10/93)
Rota—The Symphonic Fellini/Rota
Rota: Sceicco Bianco (exc); Vitelloni (exc); Strada (exc); Bidone (exc); Notte di Cabiria (exc); Dolce Vita (exc); Boccaccio (exc); 8 1/2 (exc); Giulietta degli Spiriti (exc); Fellini Satyricon (exc); Clowns (exc); Roma (exc); Amarcord (exc); Casanova (exc); Prova d'Orchestra (exc). (Czech SO/D. Wadsworth)

① **FILMCD137** (3/94)
Dial M for Murder—A History of Hitchcock
Gounod: Marche funèbre d'une marionette; *Waxman*: Rebecca Suite; Suspicion (exc); *Rózsa*: Spellbound Concerto; *Addinsell*: Under Capricorn (exc); *Tiomkin*: Dial M for Murder (exc); *Herrmann*: Marnie (exc); North by Northwest (exc); Psycho (exc); Vertigo (exc); *Jarre*: Topaz (exc); *Goodwin*: Frenzy (exc). (Prague City PO/P. Bateman)

① **FILMCD141** (8/94)
The Classic John Barry
Barry: Zulu (exc); Out of Africa (exc); Midnight Cowboy (exc); Last Valley (exc); Eleanor and Franklin (exc); Hanover Street (exc); Born Free (exc); Chaplin (exc); Dances With Wolves (exc); Raise the Titanic (exc); Indecent Proposal (exc); Persuaders (exc); Robin and Marian (exc); Body Heat (exc); Somewhere in Time (exc); Lion in Winter (exc). (Prague City PO/N. Raine)

① **FILMCD144** (8/94)
Gone With the Wind—The Classic Max Steiner
Steiner: Adventures of Mark Twain (exc); Distant Trumpet (exc); Casablanca (exc); Summer Place (exc); Treasure of the Sierra Madre (exc); Helen of Troy (exc); Caine Mutiny (exc); Gone With the Wind (exc). (Westminster PO/K. Alwyn)

① **FILMCD146** (8/94)
Fantastic Voyage—A Journey Through Classic Fantasy Film Music
Goldsmith: Alien (exc); *Fiedel*: Terminator (exc); *Silvestri*: My Stepmother Is An Alien (exc); *Kamen*: Dead Zone (exc); *Goldsmith*: Gremlins 2 (exc); *Rosenman*: Countdown (exc); *Shire*: 2010 (exc); *Goldsmith*: Seconds (exc); *E. Bernstein*: Ghostbusters (exc); *H. Blake*: Flash Gordon (exc); *Harnell*: V for Victory (exc); *B. May*: Mad Max 2 (exc); *Rosenman*: Fantastic Voyage (exc); *Goldsmith*: Explorers (exc); *Talgorn*: Fortress (exc); *Wannberg*: Philadelphia Experiment (exc); *Goldsmith*: Illustrated Man (exc); *Rosenman*: Battle for the Planet of the Apes (exc); *Goldsmith*: Total Recall (exc); *Elfman*: Batman (exc). (Prague City PO/W. Motzing)

① **FILMCD151** (11/94)
The Longest Day—Music from the Classic War Films
Anka: Longest Day; *Goodwin*: 633 Squadron (exc); *Tiomkin*: Guns of Navarone (exc); *Coates*: Dam Busters (exc); *Patton* (exc); *Jarre*: Night of the Generals (exc); *Alford*: Colonel Bogey; *Goodwin*: Where Eagles Dare (exc); *Doldinger*: Boot (exc); *E. Bernstein*: Great Escape (exc); *J. T. Williams*: Midway (exc); *Frankel*: Battle of the Bulge (exc); *Goodwin*: Force 10 from Navarone (exc); *Goldsmith*: In Harm's Way (exc); *C. Parker*: Sink the Bismarck (exc); *E. Bernstein*: Bridge at Remagen (exc); *J. Addison II*: Bridge too Far (exc); *J. T. Williams*: 1941 (exc); *Jarre*: Is Paris Burning (exc). (Prague City PO/P. Bateman, M. Ayres)

① **FILMCD153** (11/94)
True Grit—Music from the Classic Films of John Wayne
Hageman: Stagecoach (exc); She Wore a Yellow Ribbon (exc); *V. Young*: Quiet Man Suite (exc); *Tiomkin*: High and the Mighty (exc); *Steiner*: Searchers (exc); *Tiomkin*: Alamo (exc); *Alf Newman*: How the West Was Won (exc); *Anka*: Longest Day; *Goldsmith*: In Harm's Way (exc); *E. Bernstein*: True Grit (exc); *J. T. Williams*: Cowboys Suite. (Prague City PO/P. Bateman)

① **FILMCD159** (9/95)
To Catch A Thief—A History of Hitchcock II
N. Van Cleve: Paramount Vista Vision Fanfare; *L. Murray*: To Catch a Thief (exc); *Beaver*: Thirty Nine Steps (exc); *C. Williams*: Lady Vanishes (exc); *Alf Newman*: 20th Century Fox Fanfare; *Friedhofer*: Lifeboat (exc); *Buttolph*: Rope (exc); *Lucas*: Stage Fright (exc); *Tiomkin*: Strangers On a Train (exc); *Waxman*: Rear Window (exc); *Herrmann*: Vertigo (exc); North by Northwest (exc); *J. Addison II*: Torn Curtain (exc); *J. T. Williams*: Family Plot (exc). (Prague City PO/P. Bateman)

① **FILMCD160** (9/95)
Schindler's List—Classic Film Music of John Williams
J. T. Williams: Born on the Fourth of July (exc); Cowboys Suite; Empire Strikes Back (exc); Far and Away (exc); Family Plot (exc); Jaws (exc); Jurassic Park (exc); Last Crusade (exc); Presumed Innocent (exc); Return of the Jedi (exc); Schindler's List (exc); Star Wars (exc); Temple of Doom (exc); 1941 (exc). (Prague City PO/P. Bateman)

① **FILMCD713** (2/91)
Classic British Film Music
Bliss: Conquest of the Air; *Easdale*: Red Shoes (exc); *Vaughan Williams*: Coastal Command; *Schumann*: Attack and Celebration. (Philh/K. Alwyn)

① **SILKD6001** (10/94)
Lament—The Brodsky Quartet
Stravinsky: Pieces (1914); *J. Alvarez*: Metro chabacano; *H. Hughes*: She moved through the fair; *D. Matthews*: Adagio; *Szymanski*: Pieces; *Massenet*: Élégie; *M. Thomas*: Harold In Islington; Waltzing Matilda Variations; *Sculthorpe*: Lament. (W. Fernandez, E. Costello, Brodsky Qt, S. Monks, M. Scully)

① **SILKD6004** (4/95)
Simple Gifts—Lesley Garrett
Handel: Messiah (exc); *Delibes*: Filles de Cadiz; *Rimsky-Korsakov*: Sadko (exc); *Boyce*: Solomon (exc); *Massenet*: Manon (exc); *Cilea*: Adriana Lecouvreur (exc); *Gounod*: Roméo et Juliette (exc); *Grieg*: Peer Gynt (exc); *Puccini*: Madama Butterfly (exc); *Sullivan*: Mikado (exc); *Tchaikovsky*: Songs, Op. 6 (exc); *Canteloube*: Chants d'Auvergne (exc); *Bach*: Cantata 202 (exc); *Lehár*: Giuditta (exc); *Traditional*: Shaker Chants and Spirituals (exc). (L. Garrett, RPO/P. Robinson)

① **SILVAD3001** (5/93)
At the Movies 1: Heroes & Tough Guys
Schifrin: Schifrin Suite (exc); *Poledouris*: Hunt for Red October (exc); *Rota*: Godfather II (exc); *John Carpenter*: Big Trouble in Little China (exc); *Schifrin*: Cool Hand Luke (exc); *Faltermeyer*: Running Man (exc); *Burgon*: Robin Hood (exc); *Best*: Heroes (exc); *J. Nitzsche*: Revenge (exc); *Mancini*: Great Waldo Pepper (exc); *M. Isham*: Hitcher (exc); *Barry*: High Road to China (exc); *Best*: Crocodile Dundee (exc); *B. May*: Missing in Action II (exc); *Monkman*: Long Good Friday (exc); *Kempel*: Double Impact (exc); *J. T. Williams*: Raiders of the Lost Ark (exc). (OST, San Diego SO/L. Schifrin, Milan Philh/C. Coppola, D. Caine, Rochester Pops, Hollywood Sound Orch)

① **SILVAD3002** (5/93)
At the Movies 2: Classic Symphonic Film Music
Jarre: Lawrence of Arabia (exc); *Steiner*: Gone With the Wind (exc); *Various*: 2001 (exc); *J. T. Williams*: Star Wars (exc); *Friedhofer*: Best Years of Our Lives (exc); *Herrmann*: Vertigo (exc); *Moross*: Big Country (exc); *Rózsa*: Time after Time (exc); *Bax*: Oliver Twist (exc); *Vaughan Williams*: Coastal Command (exc); *Bliss*: Conquest of the Air (exc); *Bax*: Malta GC (exc). (Philh/T. Bremner, Rochester Pops, San Diego SO/L. Schifrin, LPO/F. Collura, RPO/M. Rózsa/K. Alwyn)

① **SILVAD3003** (5/93)
At the Movies 3: Horror & Fantasy
Homer: Krull (exc); *Herrmann*: It's Alive 2 (exc); *Band*: Bride of the Re-Animator (exc); *Joel Goldsmith*: Moon 44 (exc); *Tangerine Dream*: Near Dark (exc); *J. T. Williams*: Empire Strikes Back (exc); *John Carpenter*: Halloween (exc); *Segal*: Phantom of the Opera (exc); *Richard Stone*: Sundown (exc); *Herrmann*: Psycho (exc); *John Carpenter*: Dark Star (exc); *Conti*: Masters of the Universe (exc); *C. Young*: Hellraiser (exc); *John Carpenter*: They Live (exc); *A. North*: Dragonslayer (exc); *J. Bernard*: Dracula Has Risen from the Grave (exc); *J. T. Williams*: Superman (exc). (OST, San Diego SO/L. Schifrin, Philh/N. Richardson, D. Caine, Tangerine Dream)

① **SILVAD3006** (5/93)
The Jerome Kern Collection
Kern: Swing Time (exc); *Roberta* (exc); High, Wide and Handsome (exc); Show Boat (exc); Music in the Air (exc); Cover Girl (exc); I Dream Too Much (exc); Can't Help Singing (exc); Cabaret Girl (exc); Cat and the Fiddle (exc); Night Boat (exc); Miss 1917 (exc); Very Warm for May (exc); Leave it to Jane (exc); Oh Boy! (exc); Girl from Utah (exc). (E. Parkin)

① **SONGCD903** (11/91)
Diva! A Soprano at the Movies
Catalani: Wally (exc); *Delibes*: Lakmé (exc); *Mozart*: Nozze di Figaro (exc); *Gounod*: Faust (exc); *Puccini*: Bohème (exc); *Dvořák*: Rusalka (exc); *Puccini*: Gianni Schicchi (exc); *Canteloube*: Chants d'Auvergne (exc); *Rossini*: Barbiere di Siviglia (exc); *Hammerstein*: Carmen Jones (exc); *Offenbach*: Contes d'Hoffmann (exc); *Forrest/Wright*: Kismet (exc). (L. Garrett, Philh/A. Greenwood)

① **SONGCD906** (8/93)
Copland—Music for Piano
Copland: Cat and the mouse; Passacaglia; Midsummer Nocturne; Down a country lane; In evening air; Variations; Our Town; Piano Blues; Piano Sonata. (E. Parkin)

Simax

① **PSC1014** (10/88)
Shostakovich—Chamber Works
Shostakovich: Piano Trio 1; Piano Trio 2; Fantastic Dances. (Oslo Trio, J.H. Bratlie)

Ⓓ **PSC1021** (4/88)
Brahms—Piano Works
Brahms: Piano Sonata 1; Piano Pieces, Op.116; Piano Pieces, Op.117. (E. Knardahl)

Ⓓ **PSC1022** (11/88)
Chamber Works for Oboe
Mozart: Oboe Quartet, K370; *Carlstedt:* Divertimento; *Britten:* Oboe Phantasy; Metamorphoses. (G. Zubicky, T. Tønnesen, L.A. Tomter, T. Mørk)

Ⓓ **PSC1029** (8/89)
Brahms—Works for Cello & Piano
Brahms: Cello Sonata 1; Cello Sonata 2; Lieder, Op. 3 (exc); Lieder, Op. 49 (exc); Lieder, Op. 71 (exc); Lieder, Op. 86 (exc); Lieder, Op. 94 (exc); Lieder, Op. 105 (exc). (T. Mørk, J. Lagerspetz)

Ⓓ **PSC1031** (9/88)
Guitar Recital
Duarte: Nuages passantes, Op.102; *Kvandal:* Guitar Sonata, Op.65; *Bibalo:* Study in blue; *Britten:* Nocturnal. (S-E. Olsen)

Ⓓ **PSC1032** (9/88)
Bach—Keyboard Works
Bach: Italian Concerto, BWV971; French Overture, BWV831; Sonata, BWV964; Adagio, BWV968. (K. Haugsand)

Ⓓ **PSC1035** (1/89)
Works for String Orchestra
Mozart: Divertimenti, K136-8 (exc); *Britten:* Frank Bridge Variations; *Tchaikovsky:* Serenade, Op. 48. (Norwegian CO/I. Brown)

Ⓓ **PSC1037** (7/89)
Mozart/Kvandal—Music for Wind Ensemble
Mozart: Serenade, K388; *Kvandal:* Nonet, Op.54; Nonet, Op.57. (Norwegian Wind Ens)

Ⓓ **PSC1049** (2/90)
Italian Oboe Concertos
A. Marcello: Oboe Concerto in D minor; *D. Scarlatti:* Oboe Concerto; *Albinoni:* Concerti, Op.7 (exc); Concerti, Op.9 (exc); *Corelli:* Oboe Concerto. (B. Hoff, ECO/I. Watson)

Ⓓ **PSC1051** (11/89)
Schumann & Wolf—Lieder Recital
Schumann: Liederkreis, Op.24 (Cpte); Myrthen, Op. 25 (exc); *Wolf:* Italienisches Liederbuch (exc); Mörike Lieder (exc). (P. Vollestad, S. Hjelset)

Ⓓ **PSC1055** (5/90)
Scriabin—Piano Sonatas, Vol. 1
Scriabin: Piano Sonata 1; Piano Sonata 4; Piano Sonata 5; Piano Sonata 7; Piano Sonata 9. (H. Austbø)

Ⓓ **PSC1059** (9/90)
Brahms—Piano Works, Vol. 2
Brahms: Rhapsodies, op 79; Handel Variations; Piano Pieces, op 118. (E. Knardahl)

Ⓓ **PSC1063** (11/90)
Chopin/Schumann—Cello and Piano Works
Chopin: Cello Sonata; *Schumann:* Adagio and Allegro, Op. 70; Stücke, Op. 102; Fantasiestücke, Op. 73. (T. Mørk, L.O. Andsnes)

Ⓓ **PSC1067** (7/93)
Children's Corner - Katin
Grovlez: Almanach aux Images; *Séverac:* En vacances; *Ibert:* Histoires; *Debussy:* Children's Corner. (P. Katin)

Ⓓ **PSC1071** (9/92)
Schubert—Lieder
Schubert: Einsame, D800; Kreuzzug, D932; Pilgrim, D794; Abendstern, D806; Wanderer an den Mond, D870; Sei mir gegrüsst, D741; Im Frühling, D882; Blumenbrief, D622; Wie Ulfru fischt, D525; Fischerweise, D881; Fischers Liebesglück, D933; Im Walde, D834; Weinen, D926; DU bist die Ruh, D776; An den Mond, D193; An die Laute, D905; Hoffnung, D637; Wiedersehn, D855; Lied des gefangenen Jägers, D843; Normans Gesang, D846. (P. Vollestad, S. Hjelset)

Ⓓ **PSC1809(1)** (6/93)
Grieg—Historical Piano Recordings (pt 1)
Grieg: Pictures, Op.19 (exc); Lyric Pieces, Op.43 (exc); Lyric Pieces, Op.71 (exc); Piano Sonata, Op. 7 (exc); Lyric Pieces, Op.54 (exc); Lyric Pieces, Op.65 (exc); Humoresques, Op.6 (exc); Pictures, Op.19 (exc); Pictures, Op.19 (exc); Lyric Pieces, Op.43 (exc); Piano Concerto (exc); Lyric Pieces, Op.43 (exc); Pictures, Op.19 (exc); Lyric Pieces, Op.65 (exc); Folksongs and Dances, Op.17 (exc); Piano Concerto (exc); Lyric Pieces, Op.54 (exc); Piano Concerto (exc); Humoresques, Op.6 (exc); Lyric Pieces, Op.71 (exc); Pictures, Op.19 (exc); Lyric Pieces, Op.65 (exc); Album Leaves, Op.28 (exc); Lyric Pieces, Op.43 (exc); Lyric Pieces, Op.12 (exc); Pictures, Op.19 (exc); Lyric Pieces, Op.43 (exc); Lyric Pieces, Op.65 (exc); Lyric Pieces, Op.54 (exc); Pictures, Op.19 (exc); Pictures, Op.19 (exc); Lyric Pieces, Op.43 (exc). (L. Ronald, E. Grieg, P. Grainger, A. de Greef, J. Stockmarr, F. Backer-Grøndahl, W. Backhaus, J. Hofmann)

Ⓓ **PSC1809(2)** (6/93)
Grieg—Historical Piano Recordings (pt 2)
Grieg: Lyric Pieces, Op.54 (exc); Lyric Pieces, Op.12 (exc); Lyric Pieces, Op.43 (exc); Lyric Pieces, Op.43 (exc); Lyric Pieces, Op.12 (exc); Pictures, Op.19 (exc); Lyric Pieces, Op.38 (exc); Lyric Pieces, Op.54 (exc); Piano Sonata, Op. 7 (exc); Lyric Pieces, Op.12 (exc); Album Leaves, Op.28 (exc); Lyric Pieces, Op.38 (exc); Lyric Pieces, Op.54 (exc); Lyric Pieces, Op.43 (exc); Lyric Pieces, Op.65 (exc); Lyric Pieces, Op.68 (exc); Lyric Pieces, Op.62 (exc); Lyric Pieces, Op.43 (exc); Lyric Pieces, Op.71 (exc); Lyric Pieces, Op.68 (exc); Peasant Dances, Op.72 (exc); Lyric Pieces, Op.43 (exc); Lyric Pieces, Op.47 (exc); Lyric Pieces, Op.62 (exc); Lyric Pieces, Op.71 (exc); Stimmungen, Op.73 (exc); Piano Concerto (exc); Lyric Pieces, Op.43 (exc); Lyric Pieces, Op.71 (exc); Piano Concerto (exc); Lyric Pieces, Op.43 (exc); Lyric Pieces, Op.47 (exc); Lyric Pieces, Op.68 (exc); Lyric Pieces, Op.65 (exc); Pictures, Op.19 (exc); Lyric Pieces, Op.12 (exc); Humoresques, Op.6 (exc). (R. Ganz, S. Rachmaninov, M. Meyer-Mahr, O. Samaroff, U. Bourne, H. Bauer, M. Barratt Due, W. Gieseking, R. Riefling, E. Joyce, I. Johnsen, A.B. Michelangeli, E. Knardahl, K. Baekkelund)

Ⓓ **PSC1810(1)** (4/94)
Grieg—Songs (historical recordings, pt 1)
Grieg: Songs, Op.21 (exc); Peer Gynt (exc); Melodies of the Heart, Op.5 (exc); Melodies of the Heart, Op.5 (exc); Melodies of the Heart, Op.5 (exc); Peer Gynt (exc); Songs, Op.25 (exc); Melodies of the Heart, Op.5 (exc); Album for Male Voices, Op.30 (exc); Songs, Op.9 (exc); Songs, Op.60 (exc); Haugtussa, Op.67 (exc); Songs, Op.26 (exc); Peer Gynt (exc); Peer Gynt (exc); Peer Gynt (exc); Melodies of the Heart, Op.5 (exc); Songs, Op.21 (exc); Songs, Op.15 (exc); Songs, Op.25 (exc); Songs, Op.33 (exc); Peer Gynt (exc); Songs, Op.25 (exc); Songs, Op.60 (exc); Peer Gynt (exc); Melodies of the Heart, Op.5 (exc); Songs, Op.25 (exc); Peer Gynt (exc); Reminiscences, Op.44 (exc); Songs, Op.26 (exc); Songs, Op.39 (exc); Songs, Op.33 (exc); Songs, Op.60 (exc); Songs, Op.60 (exc); Sigurd Jorsalfar (exc); Songs, Op.21 (exc); Songs, Op.60 (exc). (A. Lütken, N.H. Grieg, O. Brønnum, K. Scheidemantel, A. Ackté, S. Kruszelnicka, J. Forsell, E. Destinn, C. Hultgren, E. Elizza, B. Kernic, M. Lykseth-Schjerven, C. Monrad, Lilli Lehmann, M. Barrientos, G. Anselmi, K. Eide, B. Bryhn, L. Slezak, H. Hedemark, V. Herold, anon, orch, E. Alnaes)

Ⓓ **PSC1810(2)** (4/94)
Grieg—Songs (historical recordings, pt 2)
Grieg: Melodies of the Heart, Op.5 (exc); Melodies of the Heart, Op.5 (exc); Peer Gynt (exc); Peer Gynt (exc); Songs, Op.60 (exc); Songs, Op.60 (exc); Peer Gynt (exc); Songs, Op.25 (exc); Songs, Op.49 (exc); Songs, Op.60 (exc); Songs, Op.25 (exc); Songs, Op.4 (exc); Songs, Op.25 (exc); Songs, Op.21 (exc); Songs, Op.60 (exc); Songs, Op.25 (exc); Songs, Op.70 (exc); Peer Gynt (exc); Peer Gynt (exc); Peer Gynt (exc); Songs, Op.25 (exc); Songs, Op.33 (exc); Sigurd Jorsalfar (exc); Songs, Op.39 (exc); Songs, Op.48 (exc); Princess; Melodies of the Heart, Op.5 (exc); Melodies of the Heart, Op.5 (exc); Melodies of the Heart, Op.5 (exc); Peer Gynt (exc); Songs, Op.48 (exc); Songs, Op.60 (exc); Songs, Op.48 (exc); Peer Gynt (exc); Songs, Op.60 (exc); Songs, Op.48 (exc); Songs, Op.60 (exc); Songs, Op.70 (exc). (R. Olitzka, G. Elwes, F. Hempel, E. Burzio, E. Schumann-Heink, L. Tetrazzini, E. Gulbranson, F. Chaliapin, O. Kline, J. Schwarz, M. Heim, A. Galli-Curci, L. Gates, R. Burg, P. Cornelius, E. Bye, R. Tauber, E. Clément, G. Stückgold, E. Rethberg, C.M. Ohman, E. Gerhardt, G. Farrar, K. Flagstad, G. Graarud, H. Jadlowker, anon, orch)

Ⓓ **PSC1821(1)** (12/95)
Kirsten Flagstad, Vol.1 (pt 1)
Traditional: Aa Ola Ola, min eigen Onge; *Thrane:* Aagots Fjeldsang; *Grieg:* Songs, Op.33 (exc); *Rosenfeldt:* Ingalill; *Bishop:* Home, sweet home; *A. Grøndahl:* Endnu et streif kun af sol; Eventide; *Grieg:* Peer Gynt (exc); *O. Bull:* Saeterjentens Søndag; *Sinding:* Songs, Op.22 (exc); *Lie:* Snow; *Alnaes:* Happiness; *O. Bull:* Saeterjentens Søndag; *Grieg:* Peer Gynt (exc); Songs, Op.39 (exc); Songs, Op.15 (exc); *Alnaes:* Sidste reis; *Palenz:* A.B.C.-Viser; *Thommesen:* Lille-Barnet; *Nordraak:* Ingrid Sletten; *Wagner:* Tannhäuser (exc); Tristan und Isolde (exc); Walküre (exc); Lohengrin (exc). (K. Flagstad, M. Flagstad, E. Alnaes, orch/H. Lange)

Ⓓ **PSC1821(2)** (12/95)
Kirsten Flagstad, Vol.1 (pt 2)
R. Strauss: Lieder, Op.10 (exc); *Beethoven:* Lieder, Op.48 (exc); Zärtliche Liebe, WoO123; *Grieg:* Songs, Op.25 (exc); Songs, Op.60 (exc); Melodies of the heart, Op.5 (exc); Songs, Op.48 (exc); Songs, Op.70 (exc); Songs, Op.69 (exc); *Alnaes:* Happiness; *Grieg:* Songs, Op.26 (exc); *Schubert:* Im Abendrot, D799; *Franz:* Lieder, Op.17 (exc); *Brahms:* Lieder, Op.63 (exc); *Schubert:* Lachen und Weinen, D777; Forelle, D550; *Grieg:* Songs, Op.26 (exc); Songs, Op.60 (exc); *Hurum:* Pale nights; *R. Strauss:* Lieder, Op.17 (exc); Lieder, Op.27 (exc); *Wagner:* Walküre (exc); Lohengrin (exc); *Beethoven:* Fidelio (exc); *Weber:* Oberon (exc); *Beethoven:* Ah, perfido, Op.65; *Wagner:* Tristan und Isolde (exc); Götterdämmerung (exc); Parsifal (exc). (K. Flagstad, L. Melchior, E. McArthur, Philadelphia/E. Ormandy, San Francisco SO, RCA Victor SO/E. McArthur)

Ⓓ **PSC3101** (8/93)
Valen—Complete Symphonies
Valen: Symphony 1; Symphony 2; Symphony 3; Symphony 4. (Bergen PO/A. Ceccato)

Ⓓ **PSC3108** (12/94)
Geirr Tveitt—Works for harp and orchestra
Tveitt: Hardanger Suite 1; Harp Concerto 2; Water Sprite. (T. Kniejski, RPO/P. Dreier)

Ⓓ **PSC3115** (6/93)
Valen—Symphonic Poems and Orchestral Songs
Valen: Pastorale, Op. 11; Cimitière marin, Op. 20; Sonette di Michelangelo, Op. 17/1; Cantico, Op. 17/2; Nenia, Op. 18/1; Isla de las calmas, Op. 21; Ode to Solitude, Op. 35; Ave Maria, Op. 4; Chinesische Gedichte, Op. 8; Darest Thou, Op. 9; Dunkle Nacht die Seele, Op. 32. (D. Dorow, Oslo PO/M. Caridis)

Ⓓ **PSC3118** (12/94)
Jensen—Choral and Orchestral Works
L.I. Jensen: Tema con variazioni; Sinfonia in D; Japanese Spring. (K. Langebo, Oslo PO/O. Grüner-Hegge/Ø. Fjeldstad)

Sir Thomas Beecham Trust

Ⓓ **BEECHAM2** (6/89)
Beecham conducts Delius
Delius: Paris; Eventyr; Over the hills and far away; Irmelin Prelude; Fennimore and Gerda Intermezzo. (LPO/T. Beecham)

Ⓓ **BEECHAM3** (11/90)
Delius—Vocal & Orchestral Works
Delius: Sea Drift; Summer Night on the River; In a Summer Garden; Brigg Fair; First cuckoo; Village Romeo and Juliet (exc); Koanga (exc). (J. Brownlee, London Select Ch, LPO, RPS Orch, SO/T. Beecham)

Ⓓ **BEECHAM6** (11/95)
Sibelius/Mendelssohn/ Tchaikovsky—Orchestral Works
Mendelssohn: Symphony 4; *Sibelius:* Symphony 7; Pelleas and Melisande (exc); *Tchaikovsky:* Capriccio italien. (NYPO/T. Beecham)

Sony Classical

Ⓓ **CD44921** (3/90)
Poulenc: Complete Piano Works
Poulenc: Soirées de Nazelles; Pièces (1928); Mouvements perpétuels; Mélancolie; Napoli; Feuillets d'album; Pastourelle; Bourrée; Valse; Pièce brève; Improvisations; Thème varié; Intermezzi; Impromptus; Presto; Badinage; Humoresque; Valse-improvisation; Nocturnes; Suite française; Novelettes; Suite in C; Villageoises; Française; Promenades. (P. Crossley)

Ⓓ **MK34508** (7/87)
Duos by Paganini and Giuliani
Paganini: Centone di sonate (exc); Sonatas, Op. 3 (exc); Sonata concertata in A; Cantabile, Op. 17; *Giuliani:* Violin and Guitar Sonata. (J. Williams, I. Perlman)

Ⓓ **MK37228** (6/87)
Pavarotti sings Verdi
Verdi: Simon Boccanegra (exc); Ernani (exc); Attila (exc); Due Foscari (exc); Vespri siciliani (exc); Aida (exc); Opera fragment - Io la vidi. (L. Pavarotti, G. Morresi, A. Giacomotti, A. Savastano, La Scala Orch/C. Abbado)

Ⓓ **MK37298** (5/85)
Puccini and Verdi Arias
Puccini: Villi (exc); Tosca (exc); Rondine (exc); Bohème (exc); Manon Lescaut (exc); Gianni Schicchi (exc); Madama Butterfly (exc); *Verdi:* Don Carlo (exc); Trovatore (exc); Traviata (exc). (K. Te Kanawa, LPO/J. Pritchard)

Ⓓ **MK39061** (1/86)
Let the bright Seraphim
Fasch: Trumpet and 2-Oboe Concerto; *Handel:* Samson (exc); Birthday Ode for Queen Anne (exc); *Torelli:* Sonata, G3; Sonata, G7; *Purcell:* Birthday Ode, Z323 (exc); Indian Queen, Z630 (exc); King Arthur, Z628 (exc); *Molter:* Trumpet Concerto 2. (W. Marsalis, ECO/R. Leppard, E. Gruberová, C. Tunnell)

Piano Sonata 2; Preludes (exc); Etudes-tableaux, Op. 33 (exc); Etudes-tableaux, Op. 39 (exc); Moments musicaux, Op. 16 (exc). (V. Horowitz)

⊕ **SK53635** (7/95)
Haydn—Keyboard Sonatas
Haydn: Keyboard Sonata 47; Keyboard Sonata 53; Keyboard Sonata 32; Keyboard Sonata 59. (E. Ax)

⊕ **SK53960** (5/95)
Gubaidulina—Piano Works
Gubaidulina: Chaconne; Piano Sonata (1965); Musical Toys (1969); Introitus (1978). (A. Haefliger, N German Rad PO/B. Klee)

⊕ **SK53965** (3/94)
Harmoniemusik after Mozart and Rossini
Sartorius: Nozze di Figaro Harmoniemusik; *Rossini:* Quintet in F; *Sedlak:* Barbiere di Siviglia Harmoniemusik. (Mozzafiato)

⊕ **SK53969** (3/95)
Prokofiev/Stravinsky—Violin Concertos
Prokofiev: Violin Concerto 1; Violin Concerto 2; *Stravinsky:* Violin Concerto. (C-L. Lin, Los Angeles PO/E-P. Salonen)

⊕ **SK53972** (9/94)
Mozart—Keyboard and Violin Sonatas
Mozart: Violin Sonata, K454; Violin Sonata, K296; Violin Sonata, K526. (I. Stern, Y. Bronfman)

⊕ **SK53973** (6/94)
Debussy—Piano Works, Volume 4
Debussy: Suite bergamasque; Images oubliées; Pour le piano; Arabesques; Ballade; Rêverie; Valse romantique; Nocturne; Danse; Morceau de concours. (P. Crossley)

⊕ **SK53974** (5/94)
Beethoven—Orchestral Works
Beethoven: Symphony 6; Egmont (exc); Coriolan. (Milan La Scala PO/C. M. Giulini)

⊕ **SK53975** (3/95)
Composers Inspired by the Poet Friedrich Hölderlin
Brahms: Schicksalslied, Op. 54; *Reger:* An die Hoffnung; *Rihm:* Hölderlin-Fragmente; *R. Strauss:* Hymnen, Op. 71. (K. Mattila, J. M. Kösters, Leipzig Rad Chor, BPO/C. Abbado)

⊕ **SK53976** (11/94)
Music from the Court of King Janus at Nicosia (1374-1432)
Anon: Sanctus in eternis/Sanctus et ingenitus; Si doucement mon cuer; Je sui trestout d'amour raimpli; Je prens d'amour noriture; Gloria; Certes mout fu; Je prens plaisir en une dame; Credo; Personet armonia; Si doucement me fait amours. (Huelgas Ens/P. van Nevel)

⊕ **SK53978** (1/95)
Prometheus
Beethoven: Prometheus (exc); *Liszt:* Prometheus; *Scriabin:* Prometheus; *Nono:* Prometeo Suite (exc). (I. Ade-Jesemann, M. Bair-Ivenz, S. Otto, P. Hall, U. Krumbiegel, M. Schadock, M. Hasel, M. Preis, C. Gössling, Berlin Singakademie, Freiburg Sols Ch, BPO/C. Abbado)

⊕ **SK53980** (4/95)
Franchomme/Chopin—Grand Duo Concertante
Chopin: Grand Duo Concertante; *Franchomme:* Air auvergnat varié, Op. 26; Caprices, Op. 7 (exc); Nocturne; Grande valse, Op. 34; Nocturnes, Op. 15 (exc); Air russe varié, Op. 32. (A. Bylsma, K. Slowik, L. Orkis, Archibudelli, Smithsonian Chbr Plyrs)

⊕ **SK53981** (11/95)
Purcell—Anthems and Hymns
Purcell: Bell Anthem, Z49; Praise the Lord, O Jerusalem, Z46; Awake and with attention hear, Z181; O praise God in His holiness, Z42; Morning Hymn, Z198; Evening Hymn, Z193; My beloved spake, Z28; In Thee, O Lord, Z16; *Locke:* Voluntaries (exc); *Anon:* Verses. (D. Cordier, J. Elwes, P. Kooy, H. van der Kamp, Tolz Boys' Ch, Chbr Ens, G. Leonhardt, G. Leonhardt (org/dir))

⊕ **SK53985** (11/94)
Haydn—Symphonies
Haydn: Symphony 50; Symphony 64; Symphony 65. (Tafelmusik/B. Weil)

⊕ **SK53986** (11/94)
Haydn—Symphonies
Haydn: Symphony 45; Symphony 46; Symphony 47. (Tafelmusik/B. Weil)

⊕ **SK53987** (8/94)
Michael Haydn—String Quintets
M. Haydn: Divertimento, MH412; Notturno, MH187; Notturno, MH189. (Archibudelli)

⊕ **SK57487** (10/94)
Bach—Organ Works
Bach: Toccata, Adagio and Fugue, BWV564; Prelude and Fugue, BWV548; Toccata and Fugue, BWV538; Chorales, BWV651-668 (exc). (L. Antonini)

⊕ **SK57488** (7/94)
Duruflé—Organ Works
Duruflé: Fugue sur le carillon de Soissons; Prélude, Adagio et Choral varié, Op. 4; Prélude et Fugue sur le nom d'Alain, Op. 7; Prélude sur l'Introït de l'Epiphanie; Scherzo, Op. 2; Suite, Op. 5. (J-P. Lecaudey)

⊕ **SK57490** (10/94)
Schumann—Organ Works
Schumann: Pedal Studies, Op. 56; Sketches, Op. 58; B-A-C-H Fugues, Op. 60. (O. Latry)

⊕ **SK57497** (5/95)
Wynton Marsalis—The London Concert
Haydn: Trumpet Concerto; *L. Mozart:* Trumpet Concerto; *Fasch:* Trumpet and 2-Oboe Concerto; *Hummel:* Trumpet Concerto. (W. Marsalis, ECO/R. Leppard)

⊕ **SK57960** (6/95)
Zemlinsky—Posthumous Songs
Zemlinsky: Lieder (1889/90); Lieder (1890); Preislieder; Wandl' ich im Wald; Lieder (1895/96); Brettl-Lieder; Lieder (1903/05); Balladen (1907); Dehmel Lieder (exc); Lieder (1916); Und einmal gehst du. (R. Ziesak, I. Vermillion, H-P. Blochwitz, A. Schmidt, C. Garben)

⊕ **SK57961** (3/95)
The New York Album
S. Albert: Cello Concerto; *Bartók:* Viola Concerto; *Bloch:* Schelomo. (Y-Y. Ma, Baltimore SO/D. Zinman)

⊕ **SK57968** (9/95)
Weber/Hummel/Reicha—Works for Clarinet
Weber: Clarinet Quintet, J182; *Hummel:* Clarinet Quintet in E flat; *Reicha:* Clarinet Quintet. (C. Neidich, Archibudelli)

⊕ **SK57969** (1/95)
Wolf/Korngold—Eichendorff Lieder
Korngold: Einfache Lieder, Op. 9 (exc); Lieder, Op. 38 (exc); *Wolf:* Eichendorff Lieder (exc); In der Fremde I; In der Fremde II; In der Fremde VI; Rückkehr; Nachruf. (B. Skovhus, H. Deutsch)

⊕ **SK57972** (4/95)
Schumann—Lieder
Schumann: Liederkreis, Op. 39 (Cpte); Frauenliebe und -leben, Op. 42 (Cpte); Myrthen, Op. 25 (exc); Lieder, Op. 40 (exc); Jugend Lieder, Op. 79 (exc). (M. Lipovšek, G. Johnson)

⊕ **SK58914** (2/95)
Franck—Piano Works
Franck: Prélude, fugue et variation; Prélude, choral et fugue; Danse lente; Prélude, aria et final; Chorales (exc). (P. Crossley)

⊕ **SK58919** (10/95)
Romantic Harp Concertos
Boïeldieu: Harp Concerto; *Parish Alvars:* Harp Concerto, Op. 81; *Viotti:* Harp Concerto in C minor (exc). (M. Nordmann, F. Liszt CO/J-P. Rampal)

⊕ **SK58945** (6/94)
Ligeti—Concertos
Ligeti: Cello Concerto; Piano Concerto; Chamber Concerto. (U. Wiget, M. Perényi, Modern Ens/P. Eötvös)

⊕ **SK58952** (12/94)
Debussy—Orchestral and Vocal Works
Debussy: Nocturnes; Damoiselle élue; Martyre de St Sébastien (exc). (D. Upshaw, P. Rasmussen, Los Angeles Master Chorale, Los Angeles PO/E-P. Salonen)

⊕ **SK58966** (5/95)
Prokofiev—Piano Concertos, etc
Prokofiev: Piano Concerto 3; Piano Concerto 4; Overture, Op. 34. (Y. Bronfman, G. Feidman, Juilliard Qt, Israel PO/Z. Mehta)

⊕ **SK62036** (12/95)
Virtuoso Piano Transcriptions
Saint-Saëns: Rouet d'Omphale; *Handel:* Keyboard Suites Set I (exc); *Chopin:* Piano Concerto 2 (exc); *Rachmaninov:* Songs, Op. 14 (exc); *Pabst:* Paraphrase on Sleeping Beauty (Tchaikovsky); *Wild:* Improvisation on Après un rêve (Fauré); Hommage à Poulenc; *Mozart:* Don Giovanni (exc); *Wild:* Reminiscences of Snow White (Churchill); *Tchaikovsky:* Songs, Op. 38 (exc); Swan Lake (exc); *Tausig:* Nouvelles soirées de Vienne (exc); *Kreisler:* Liebesleid. (E. Wild)

⊕ **SK64133** (1/94)
The Essential Philip Glass
Glass: Lightning; Changing Opinion; Façades; Gentleman's Honor; Satyagraha (exc); Akhnaten (exc);

Einstein on the Beach (exc); Dance 8; Metamorphosis Four; Closing. (Philip Glass Ens, J. Pendarvis, B. Fowler, P. Dunkel, D. Perry, P. Esswood, M. Riesman, P. Glass, NYC Op Orch, NYC Op Chor, Stuttgart St Orch, Stuttgart St Orch, Stuttgart State Chor)

⊕ **SK64301** (12/95)
Beethoven—Songs from the British Isles
Beethoven: Scottish Songs, Op. 108 (exc); Scottish Songs, WoO156 (exc); Irish Songs, WoO152 (exc); Irish Songs, WoO153 (exc); Irish Songs, WoO154 (exc); Welsh Songs, WoO155 (exc); Songs, WoO157 (exc). (E. Woods, C. Watkinson, J. Protschka, R. Salter, C. Altenburger, J. Berger, H. Deutsch)

⊕ **SK64302** (9/95)
Clarinet & Piano Sonatas
Danzi: Clarinet Sonata in B flat; *Mendelssohn:* Clarinet Sonata; *Weber:* Duo concertant, J204. (C. Neidich, R. Levin)

⊕ **SK64306** (9/95)
Mozart/Pleyel—Wind Music
Mozart: Serenade, K375; Sextet, KAnh183; *Pleyel:* Sextet in E flat. (Mozzafiato, C. Neidich (cl/dir))

⊕ **SK64307** (3/95)
Dotzauer—Chamber Works
Dotzauer: String Quintet, Op. 134; 2-Violin Canon; Pieces, Op. 104; String Quartet, Op. 64; Allegro, Op. 155/2; Allegro non troppo, Op. 54/2; Presto, Op. 158/2. (V. Beths, J. Gatwood, L. Rautenberg, L. Rautenberg, A. Bylsma, K. Slowik, S. Doane)

⊕ **SK64309** (11/95)
Mozart—Violin Sonatas
Mozart: Violin Sonata, K380; Violin Sonata, K305; Violin Sonata, K303; Violin Sonata, K302; Violin Sonata, K376. (I. Stern, Y. Bronfman)

⊕ **SK64396** (9/95)
The Great Paraguayan
Barrios: Abejas; Aconquija; Aire de Zamba; Catedral; Choro da saudade; Cueca; Julia florida; Limosna; Maxixa; Mazurka appassionata; Medallon antiguo; Preludio in C minor; Prelude in G minor; Sueno in la Floresta; Villancico de Navidad; Waltzes, Op. 8 (exc). (J. Williams)

⊕ **SK64397** (8/95)
Beethoven—Piano Sonatas
Beethoven: Piano Sonata 1; Piano Sonata 2; Piano Sonata 3. (M. Perahia)

⊕ **SK64399** (12/94)
Chopin—Piano Works
Chopin: Ballades; Mazurkas (exc); Waltzes (exc); Etudes (exc); Nocturnes (exc). (M. Perahia)

⊕ **SK64538** (5/95)
Haydn/Schubert—Piano Sonatas
Haydn: Keyboard Sonata 45; Keyboard Sonata 62; *Schubert:* Piano Sonata, D784; Marches Militaires, D733 (exc). (E. Kissin)

⊕ **SK66243** (3/95)
Music for Queen Mary
Purcell: I was glad, Z19; Praise the Lord, O Jerusalem, Z46; Birthday Ode, Z332; Stript of their queer our groves appear, Z444; O dive custos Auriacae domus, Z504; Queen's Epicedium, Z383; Funeral Sentences (exc); March and Canzona, Z860; Blow: Whilst he strowd roses like the sun; Sullen years are past; *Morley:* I am the resurrection; I know that my Redeemer liveth; We brought nothing into this world; Man that is born of a woman; In the midst of life; I heard a voice from heaven; *Tollett:* Queen's Farewell; Paisible: Queen's Farewell. (E. Kirkby, E. Tubb, M. Chance, I. Bostridge, S. Richardson, S. Birchall, Westminster Abbey Ch, New London Consort/M. Neary)

⊕ **SK66251** (9/95)
Bruckner—Chamber Works
Bruckner: String Quintet; Intermezzo and Trio; Rondo in C minor; String Quartet in C minor. (Archibudelli)

⊕ **SK66253** (10/95)
Haydn—Symphonies
Haydn: Symphony 88; Symphony 89; Symphony 90. (Tafelmusik/B. Weil)

⊕ **SK66279** (8/95)
Nino Rota—Orchestral Works
Rota: Strada Suite; Gattopardo (exc); Concerto for strings. (Milan La Scala PO/R. Muti)

⊕ **SK66280** (11/94)
Lutosławski—Orchestral Works
Lutosławski: Symphony 3; Symphony 4; Espaces du sommeil. (J. Shirley-Quirk, Los Angeles PO/E-P. Salonen)

Campo, P. Orecchia, J. Kalendocsky, M. Podskalský, Prague Phil Chor, Prague PO/E. Brizio)

Supraphon

① **CO-2047** (11/89)
Scriabin: Orchestral Works
Scriabin: Poème de l'extase; Rêverie, Op.24; Piano Concerto. (G. Ohlsson, Czech PO/L. Pešek)

① **CO-72646** (1/90)
Dvořák: Moravian Duets
Dvořák: Moravian Duets, B50 (Cpte); Moravian Duets, B60 (Cpte); Moravian Duets, B62 (Cpte); Moravian Duets, B69 (Cpte); There on our roof, B118. (Kühn Chor, S. Bogunia/P. Kühn)

① **C37-7230** (11/85)
Dvořák: Choral works
Dvořák: Te Deum; Psalm 149; Heirs of the White Mountain. (G. Beňačková, J. Souček, Prague Phil Chor, Czech PO/V. Neumann)

① **C37-7303** (11/85)
Janáček: Operatic Orchestral Suites
Janáček: Cunning Little Vixen (exc); Fate (exc); From the House of the Dead (exc). (Czech PO/F. Jílek)

① **10 1481-2** (3/92)
Janáček—Piano Works
Janáček: In the mists; Piano Sonata (1905); Along an overgrown path (exc). (J. Páleníček)

① **10 4140-2** (6/91)
Martinů—Orchestral works
Martinů: Parables; Estampes; Overture (1953); Rhapsodie (1928). (Czech PO/J. Bělohlávek)

① **11 0098-2** (12/89)
Martinů: Serenades
Martinů: Serenade 1; Serenade 2; Serenade 3; Serenade 4; Serenade 5. (Prague CO)

① **11 0099-2** (8/90)
Martinů: Works for Violin and Piano
Martinů: Madrigal Stanzas; Violin Sonata 2; Violin Sonata 3. (J. Suk, J. Hála)

① **11 0111-2** (4/92)
Čeněk Pavlík—Violin Recital
Chausson: Poème; Sarasate: Danzas españolas (exc); Zigeunerweisen; Rimsky-Korsakov: Russian Fantasia; Tchaikovsky: Souvenir d'un lieu cher, Op. 42 (exc); Saint-Saëns: Havanaise; Introduction and Rondo Capriccioso. (C. Pavlík, Dvořák CO/V. Válek)

① **11 0282-2** (8/90)
Janáček: Orchestral Works
Janáček: Sinfonietta; Taras Bulba; Lachian Dances. (Brno St PO/F. Jílek)

① **11 0378-2** (12/91)
Dvořák—Orchestral Works
Dvořák: Slavonic Rhapsodies; My Home; Symphonic Variations; Heroic Song; Scherzo capriccioso. (Czech PO/B. Gregor)

① **11 0382-2** (1/92)
Martinů—Complete Symphonies
Martinů: Symphony 1; Symphony 2; Symphony 3; Symphony 4; Symphony 5; Symphony 6. (Czech PO/V. Neumann)

① **11 0388-2** (10/91)
Berlioz—Overtures
Berlioz: Benvenuto Cellini (exc); Rob Roy; King Lear; Corsaire. (Brno St PO/P. Vronský)

① **11 0526-2** (10/91)
Dvořák—Symphonic Poems and Concert Overtures
Dvořák: In Nature's Realm; Carnival; Othello; Water Goblin; Noon Witch; Golden Spinning-wheel; Wild Dove. (Czech PO/B. Gregor)

① **11 0559-2** (12/91)
Dvořák—Symphonies
Dvořák: Symphony 7; Symphony 8; Symphony 9. (Czech PO/V. Neumann)

① **11 0582-2** (12/91)
David Oistrakh plays Beethoven & Mozart
Mozart: Violin Concerto, K216; Beethoven: Romances (exc); Violin Sonata 1 (exc). (D. Oistrakh, V. Yampolsky, Czech PO/K. Ančerl)

① **11 0681-2** (5/93)
Roussel—Orchestral Works
Roussel: Symphony 3; Bacchus et Ariane Suites (exc); Festin de l'araignée ballet. (Brno St PO/V. Neumann, Prague SO/V. Smetáček)

① **11 0682-2** (6/93)
Novak—Orchestral Works
V. Novák: Eternal Longing, Op. 33; In the Tatra Mountains, Op. 26; Slovak Suite. (Czech PO, Brno St PO/K. Sejna)

① **11 0684-2** (8/93)
Ravel/Poulenc—Works for Piano and Orchestra
Ravel: Piano Concerto; Left-Hand Concerto; Poulenc: Aubade. (B. Krajný, Prague SO/J. Bělohlávek, Prague CO)

① **11 0703-2** (5/90)
Dvořák: Violin & Piano Works
Dvořák: Violin Sonata, Op.57; Violin Sonatina; Romantic Pieces. (J. Suk, A. Holeček)

① **11 0705-2** (5/90)
Slavonic Works for Violin & Piano
Janáček: Violin Sonata; Foerster: Violin Sonata, Op.177; Novák: Violin Sonata. (J. Suk, J. Panenka)

① **11 0710-2** (5/90)
Violin Sonatas
Franck: Violin Sonata; Respighi: Violin Sonata; Poulenc: Violin Sonata. (J. Suk, J. Panenka, J. Hála)

① **11 0714-2** (12/91)
Dvořák—Orchestral Works
Dvořák: Symphony 9; In Nature's Realm; Carnival. (Czech PO/V. Neumann)

① **11 0717-2** (6/91)
Janáček—Orchestral Works
Janáček: Violin Concerto; Sinfonietta; Taras Bulba. (J. Suk, Czech PO/V. Neumann)

① **11 0751-2** (12/92)
Martinů—Choral Works
Martinů: Mount of three lights; Prophecy of Isaiah; Hymn to St James. (N. Romanová, D. Drobková, V. Doležal, R. Novák, P. Haničinec, V. Kozderka, J. Pěruška, S. Bogunia, I. Kiezlich, Prague Rad Chor, Kühn Chor, Prague SO/P. Kühn, J. Hora)

① **11 0752-2** (4/93)
Martinů—Špalíček, etc
Martinů: Špalíček (Cpte); Romance of the Dandelions; Primrose. (A. Kratochvílová, M. Čejková, M. Kopp, R. Novák, P. Messierour, S. Bogunia, Kantiléna Children's Chor, Kühn Chor, Brno St PO/F. Jílek)

① **11 0767-2** (5/94)
Martinů—Cantatas
Martinů: Opening of the Wells; Legend of the smoke; Mikeš of the mountains. (M. Čejková, A. Čakrtová, M. Mrázová, V. Doležal, I. Kusnjer, P. Haničinec, J. Stivin, V. Mareš, P. Duda, M. Bláha, P. Messiereur, J. Kvapil, J. Talich, S. Bogunia, Kühn Chor/P. Kühn)

① **11 0768-2** (3/92)
Janáček—Chamber and Vocal Works with Piano
Janáček: Capriccio; Concertino; Nursery rhymes (Cpte). (J. Páleníček, Czech Phil Wind Ens, Kühn Phil Chbr Ens, Czech Phil Chor/J. Veselka)

① **11 0816-2** (5/92)
Zelenka—Choral Works
Zelenka: Missa Promissae gloriae; Responsoria pro Hebdomada Sancta; Sub tuum praesidium III. (J. Jonášová, M. Mrázová, V. Doležal, P. Mikuláš, Czech Phil Chor, Czech PO/J. Bělohlávek/L. Mátl)

① **11 0994-2** (5/92)
Martinů—String Quartets
Martinů: String Quartet 1; String Quartet 2; String Quartet 3; String Quartet 4; String Quartet 5; String Quartet 6; String Quartet 7. (Panocha Qt)

① **11 0999-2** (1/92)
Mozart—Wind Quintets & Quartet
Mozart: Clarinet Quintet, K581; Oboe Quartet, K370; Horn Quintet, K407. (B. Zahradník, J. Krejčí, F. Langweil, Panocha Qt)

① **11 1005-2** (3/92)
Dvořák—Symphonies
Dvořák: Symphony 4; Symphony 5; Symphony 6. (Czech PO/V. Neumann)

① **11 1105-2** (12/91)
Gershwin & Milhaud—orchestral works
Gershwin: Piano Concerto; Cuban Overture; Milhaud: Création du monde. (S. Knor, Prague SO/V. Neumann)

① **11 1114-2** (10/91)
Schubert & Schumann: Works for Violin & Orchestra
Schumann: Violin Concerto; Fantasie, Op.131; Schubert: Concertstück, D345; Polonaise, D580. (V. Snítil, Prague SO/L. Hlaváček/J. Hrnčíř)

① **11 1119-2** (11/90)
Haydn: Violin Concertos
Haydn: Violin Concerto, HobVIIa/1; Violin Concerto, HobVIIa/4; Violin Concerto, HobVIIa/B2. (B. Matoušek, Prague CO/L. Hlaváček)

① **11 1337-2** (5/94)
Emmy Destinn (1878-1930)
Mozart: Nozze di Figaro (exc); Zauberflöte (exc); Weber: Freischütz (exc); Wagner: Fliegende Holländer (exc); Tannhäuser (exc); Lohengrin (exc); Gounod: Faust (exc); Bizet: Carmen (exc); A. Thomas: Mignon (exc); Smetana: Bartered Bride (exc); Dalibor (exc); Tchaikovsky: Queen of Spades (exc); Verdi: Trovatore (exc); Aida (exc); Ponchielli: Gioconda (exc); Leoncavallo: Pagliacci (exc); Mascagni: Cavalleria Rusticana (exc); Puccini: Tosca (exc); Madama Butterfly (exc); R. Strauss: Salome (exc). (E. Destinn, orch/B. Seidler-Winkler/W.B. Rogers/F. Kark/A. Pilz)

① **11 1445-2** (3/93)
Reicha/Beethoven—Compositions for Wind
Beethoven: Sextet, Op.71; Quintet, Hess19; Reicha: Trios, Op.93. (Z. Tylšar, B. Tylšar, R. Beránek, J. Mihule, V. Kyzivát, Z. Tesař, F. Herman, V. Horák)

① **11 1461-2** (5/94)
Dvořák—Chamber Works - Volume 11
Dvořák: String Quintet, Op. 77; Intermezzo, B49; String Sextet. (J. Klusoň, M. Kaňka, P. Nejtek, Panocha Qt)

① **11 1491-2** (4/93)
Jarmila Novotna sings Czech Songs and Arias
Kovařovic: Dogs' Heads (exc); Smetana: Kiss (exc); Dvořák: Rusalka (exc); Humoresques, Op.101 (exc); Fibich: At twilight (exc); Masaryk: Songs of Lidice; Traditional: I saw my country dear; I saw my country die; Song of the Slavs; Stolibský: In the skies over Prague; Traditional: May the Lord love us; Smetana: Choruses, T119 (exc); Dvořák: Gipsy Melodies (exc); Smetana: Bartered Bride (exc); Kiss (exc); Dvořák: Rusalka (exc). (J. Novotná, orch, A. Sándor/A. von Zemlinsky, J. Masaryk, chor/W. Pelletier, J. Stolibský/R. Blum, chbr ens, RCA Victor Orch/F. Weissmann/A. Wallenstein, G. King)

① **11 1522-2** (9/93)
Janáček—Orchestral Works, Vol. 3
Janáček: Sinfonietta; Danube; Violin Concerto; Schluk und Jau. (K. Dvořáková, I. Ženatý, Brno St PO/F. Jílek)

① **11 1531-2** (2/94)
Suk—Chamber Works, Volume 1
Suk: String Quartet 1; String Quartet 2; Quartet movement; Tempo di menuetto; Meditation, Op.35a. (Suk Qt)

① **11 1532-2** (2/94)
Suk—Chamber Works, Volume 2
Suk: Piano Trio, Op.2; Elegie, Op.23; Piano Quartet; Piano Quintet, Op.8. (J. Suk, J. Talich, M. Fukačová, J. Panenka, P. Štěpán, Suk Trio, Suk Qt)

① **11 1533-2** (2/94)
Suk—Chamber Works, Volume 3
Suk: Melodie; Minuet; Violin Balada; Pieces, Op.17; Ballade, Op.3/1; Serenade, Op.3/2; Bagatelle; Barcarolle; String Quartet Balada; Elegie, Op.23; Sousedská. (J. Válek, J. Suk, J. Nováková, L. Vybíralová, M. Kosina, J. Krištůfek, Z. Mann, M. Jerie, F. Host, I. Laniar, T. Josífko, R. Kodadová, J. Hála, J. Hála, J. Panenka, I. Klánský, J. Fousek, L. Kubánek, Suk Qt)

① **11 1830-2** (6/93)
Brahms/Dvořák—Orchestral Works
Brahms: Symphony 1; Dvořák: In Nature's Realm; Carnival; Othello. (Czech PO/G. Albrecht)

① **11 1878-2** (3/95)
The Unknown Janáček
Janáček: I'm waiting for you!; War Song 1; War Song 2; Fanfare in A; Fanfare in D minor; Festival Chorus; Along an overgrown path (exc); Jealousy; Jenufa (exc); Taras Bulba (exc); Excursions of Mr Brouček (exc); Living Corpse; March of the Blue Boys; I'm waiting for you!. (A. Bárta, Prague Phil Chor, J. Holeňa, L. Kozderka, K. Kohout, K. Kučera, M. Brázda, M. Gajdošová, L. Zavadilík, A. Formáček, D. Kellerová, J. Bělor, R. Firkušný, I. Ardašev, J. Pavlová, Y. Tannenbergerova, Brno St PO/F. Jílek, K. Dvořáková, M. Kopp, A. Barová, J. Janská, V. Doležal, M. Ungrová, J. Jiskrová, P. Šumplík, E. Podhálová, F. Kantor, M. Opršal)

① **11 1905-2** (1/94)
Czech Orchestral Works
Janáček: Taras Bulba; Cunning Little Vixen (exc); V. Novák: Slovak Suite. (Czech PO/V. Talich)

① **11 1930-2** (12/94)
Janáček/Kabeláč—Choral and Orchestral Works
Janáček: Glagolitic Mass (Cpte); Kabeláč: Hamlet Improvisation; Mystery of Time. (L. Domanínská, V.

Soukupová, B. Blachut, E. Haken, J. Vodrážka, Czech Phil Chor, Czech PO/K. Ančerl)

Ⓓ **11 1931-2** (3/93)
Martinů—Orchestral Works
Martinů: Symphony 5; Lidice; Fresques de Piero della Francesca; Parables. (Czech PO/K. Ančerl)

Ⓓ **11 1945-2** (3/93)
Orchestral Works
Stravinsky: Petrushka (Cpte); *Prokofiev:* Peter and the Wolf; *Britten:* Young Person's Guide. (E. Shilling, Czech PO/K. Ančerl)

Ⓓ **11 1969-2** (11/95)
Martinů—Violin and Viola Concertos
Martinů: Violin Concerto 1; Violin Concerto 2; Viola Rhapsody. (J. Suk, J. Suk, Czech PO/V. Neumann)

Ⓓ **11 2136-2(1)** (12/94)
Emmy Destinn—Complete Edition, Discs 1 & 2
Bizet: Carmen (exc); Carmen (exc); *A. Thomas:* Mignon (exc); *Grieg:* Songs, Op.60 (exc); *Leoncavallo:* Roland von Berlin (exc); *Traditional:* Už mou milou; *Verdi:* Aida (exc); *Traditional:* Měla jsem chlapce; *A. Thomas:* Mignon (exc); *Mendelssohn:* Hohelied; *Schubert:* Schwanengesang, D957 (exc); *Smetana:* Bartered Bride (exc); *Schubert:* Schöne Müllerin (exc); *Wagner:* Tannhäuser (exc); *Mozart:* Nozze di Figaro (exc); *Wagner:* Fliegende Holländer (exc); Lohengrin (exc); *A. Thomas:* Mignon (exc); *Wagner:* Tannhäuser (exc); Lohengrin (exc); *Bizet:* Carmen (exc); *Wagner:* Fliegende Holländer (exc); Lohengrin (exc); *Bizet:* Carmen (exc); *Smetana:* Evening Songs (exc); *Traditional:* Pršívalo, jen se lilo; Andulko šafářova; Marjánko, Marjánko; Když jsem přišel včera večer k ní; *R. Strauss:* Salome (exc); *A. Thomas:* Mignon (exc); *Mascagni:* Cavalleria Rusticana (exc); *Verdi:* Aida (exc); *Puccini:* Madama Butterfly (exc); *Wagner:* Tannhäuser (exc); *Smetana:* Dalibor (exc); *Kovařovic:* Dogs' Heads (exc). (E. Destinn, E. Kraus, anon, R. Leoncavallo, orch/F. Kark/B. Seidler-Winkler, F. Kark)

Ⓓ **11 2136-2(2)** (12/94)
Emmy Destinn—Complete Edition, Discs 3 & 4
Meyerbeer: Huguenots (exc); *Puccini:* Madama Butterfly (exc); *Wagner:* Tannhäuser (exc); *Leoncavallo:* Pagliacci (exc); *Mascagni:* Cavalleria rusticana (exc); *Verdi:* Aida (exc); *Mozart:* Nozze di Figaro (exc); *Smetana:* Bartered Bride (exc); Kiss (exc); *Gounod:* Ave Maria; *Meyerbeer:* Huguenots (exc); *Hummel:* Hallelujah; *Mozart:* Zauberflöte (exc); *Mascagni:* Cavalleria rusticana (exc); *Bizet:* Carmen (exc); *Weber:* Freischütz (exc); *Mozart:* Nozze di Figaro (exc); *Meyerbeer:* Robert le Diable (exc); Africaine (exc); *Wagner:* Lohengrin (exc); *Gounod:* Faust (exc); *Mozart:* Zauberflöte (exc); *Verdi:* Trovatore (exc); *Puccini:* Madama Butterfly (exc); *Gounod:* Ave Maria; *Puccini:* Tosca (exc); *Wagner:* Tannhäuser (exc); *Smetana:* Dalibor (exc); *Tchaikovsky:* Queen of Spades (exc); *Smetana:* Bartered Bride (exc); *Jindřich:* Jen kdybych věděl; Je teskno dnes. (E. Destinn, K. Jörn, O. Mařák, anon, orch, Odeon Orch/A. Pilz/F. Kark/B. Seidler-Winkler)

Ⓓ **11 2136-2(3)** (12/94)
Emmy Destinn—Complete Edition, Discs 5 to 8
Gounod: Faust (Cpte); *Wagner:* Lohengrin (exc); *Bizet:* Carmen (Cpte). (K. Jörn, E. Destinn, P. Knüpfer, D. Zádor, M. Götze, I. von Scheele-Müller, A. Neudahm, R. Berger, E. Destinn, E. Destinn, O. Metzger, K. Jörn, M. Nast, H. Bachmann, M. Dietrich, G. Parbs, J. Lieban, R. Krasa, F. Dahn, Berlin Court Op Chor, orch, Odeon Orch/B. Seidler-Winkler/A. Pilz)

Ⓓ **11 2136-2(4)** (12/94)
Emmy Destinn—Complete Edition, Discs 9 & 10
Wagner: Tannhäuser (exc); *Weber:* Freischütz (exc); *Wagner:* Tristan und Isolde (exc); *Puccini:* Madama Butterfly (exc); Tosca (exc); *Ponchielli:* Gioconda (exc); *Verdi:* Aida (exc); *Rossini:* Soirées musicales (exc); *Wagner:* Lohengrin (exc); *A. Thomas:* Mignon (exc); *Saint-Saëns:* Samson et Dalila (exc); *Hummel:* Hallelujah; *Wagner:* Fliegende Holländer (exc); *Verdi:* Aida (exc); *Halévy:* Juive (exc); *Wagner:* Tristan und Isolde (exc); *Gounod:* Ave Maria; *Mascagni:* Cavalleria Rusticana (exc); *Ponchielli:* Gioconda (exc); *Puccini:* Madama Butterfly (exc); Tosca (exc); Tosca (exc); *Mascagni:* Cavalleria Rusticana (exc); *Verdi:* Aida (exc); *Weber:* Freischütz (exc). (E. Destinn, L. Kirkby-Lunn, J. McCormack, D. Gilly, orch/P. Pitt)

Ⓓ **11 2136-2(5)** (12/94)
Emmy Destinn—Complete Edition, Discs 11 & 12
Puccini: Bohème (exc); *Leoncavallo:* Pagliacci (exc); *Verdi:* Aida (exc); Trovatore (exc); Forza del destino (exc); *A. Thomas:* Mignon (exc); *Puccini:* Madama Butterfly (exc); *Verdi:* Aida (exc); *Ponchielli:* Gioconda (exc); *Wagner:* Tannhäuser (exc); *Gomes:* Guarany (exc); *Puccini:* Tosca (exc); *Traditional:* Wedding; Goodnight; My Homeland; *Schubert:* Wiegenlied, D498; *Mozart:* Zauberflöte (exc); *Dvořák:* Rusalka (exc); *Kovařovic:* Nazarene (exc); *Tchaikovsky:* Queen of Spades (exc); *Verdi:* Trovatore (exc); *Tosti:* Ultima canzone; *Verdi:* Trovatore (exc); *Gounod:* Ave Maria; *Flies:* Wiegenlied; *Gounod:* Sérénade; *Stange:* Bekehrte; *Liszt:* Oh quand je dors, S282; *Jindřich:* My sweetheart; *Destinn:* Wooing; Maiden's song; *Jindřich:* O Mountains; Ostroh Castle; *Destinn:* Last tears; *Hess:* Home; *Štěpán:* On my way; *Destinn:* Romance; *Smetana:* Kiss (exc); *Verdi:* Ballo in maschera (exc); *Dvořák:* In Folk Tone, B146 (exc). (E. Destinn, G. Zenatello, E. Caruso, D. Gilly, M. Duchêne, F. Lapitino, R. Bourdon, W.B. Rogers, C. Barone, chor, orch/W.B Rogers/J. Pasternack, G. Martinelli)

Ⓓ **11 2166-2** (8/95)
Schulhoff—Chamber Works, Volume 1
Schulhoff: Pieces for String Quartet; String Quartet, Op. 25; String Quartet 1; String Quartet 2. (Kocian Qt)

Ⓓ **11 2214-2** (11/95)
Janáček—Moravian, Hukvaldy & Silesian Songs
Janáček: Moravian folk poetry in songs; Hukvaldy folk poetry in songs; Silesian Songs (H Salichová Coll). (D. Pecková, I. Kusnjer, M. Lapšanský)

Ⓓ **11 2225-2** (11/95)
Janáček—26 Folk Ballads
Janáček: Folksongs which Eva Gabel sang; Folk Nocturnes; Detvan brigand songs; Folksongs (1916-7); Ballads (1908-12). (D. Pecková, I. Kusnjer, M. Lapšanský)

Ⓓ **2SUP0016** (12/87)
Haydn: Symphonies
Haydn: Symphony 93; Symphony 94; Symphony 95. (Prague CO)

Ⓓ **2SUP0023** (12/87)
Debussy: Orchestral Works
Debussy: Après-midi; Première rapsodie; Jeux (Cpte); Images. (A. Boutard, Czech PO/S. Baudo)

Ⓓ **2SUP0025** (11/88)
Orff: Choral Works
Orff: Carmina Burana; Veni Creator Spiritus; Gute Mensch. (M. Šubrtová, J. Tománek, T. Šrubař, Czech Phil Chor, Czech PO, Inst. Ens/V. Smetáček)

Ⓓ **2SUP0027** (12/88)
Mozart: Orchestral Works
Mozart: Serenade, K525; Piano Concerto 23; Piano Concerto 24. (I. Moravec, P. Badura-Skoda (pf/dir), Czech CO, Prague CO/J. Vlach)

Ⓓ **2SUP0034** (2/89)
Haydn: Symphonies
Haydn: Symphony 96; Symphony 97; Symphony 98. (Prague CO)

Symposium

Ⓓ **SYMCD1037** (4/89)
Virtuoso Variations for Piano Duet
Alkan: Don Giovanni Fantasy; *Beethoven:* Variations, WoO74; *Franck:* God save the King duet; *Schubert:* Variations, D908; *Herzogenberg:* Brahms Variations, Op.23; *Mendelssohn:* Weber Variations. (A. Goldstone, C. Clemmow)

Ⓓ **SYMCD1042** (2/89)
Otto Klemperer and the Kroll Years
Beethoven: Coriolan; *Wagner:* Siegfried Idyll; *Ravel:* Alborada del gracioso; *Debussy:* Nocturnes (exc); *Auber:* Fra Diavolo (exc); *Offenbach:* Belle Hélène (exc); *Weill:* Kleine Dreigroschenmusik. (Berlin St Op Orch/O. Klemperer)

Ⓓ **SYMCD1064** (1/90)
Schubert & Wolf—Lieder
Schubert: Fischerweise, D881; Am Bach im Frühling, D361; Schiffer, D536; Liebeslauschen, D698; Schwanengesang, D957 (exc); Geheimes, D719; Widerschein, D639; Lied im Grünen, D917; Musensohn, D764; Abendstern, D806; Auf der Bruck, D853; Jüngling an der Quelle, D300; *Wolf:* Italienisches Liederbuch (exc); Mörike Lieder (exc). (D. Hammond-Stroud, G. Kirkwood)

Ⓓ **SYMCD1065** (12/89)
The Harold Wayne Collection, Vol.1
Meyerbeer: Robert le Diable (exc); *Verdi:* Simon Boccanegra (exc); *Ponchielli:* Gioconda (exc); *Rossini:* Italiana in Algeri (exc); *Bellini:* Capuleti (exc); *Vaccai:* Giulietta e Romeo (exc); *Donizetti:* Lucrezia Borgia (exc); *Rossini:* Semiramide (exc); *Meyerbeer:* Prophète (exc); *Rossini:* Barbiere di Siviglia (exc); *Verdi:* Otello (exc); *Rubinstein:* Asra; *Bellini:* Norma (exc); *Verdi:* Don Carlo (exc); Ernani (exc); *A. Thomas:* Hamlet (exc); *Leoncavallo:* Medici (exc); *Verdi:* Otello (exc); *Bellini:* Puritani (exc); *Malibran:* Prendi, per me sei libero; *Donizetti:* Lucia di Lammermoor (exc); *Verdi:* Luisa Miller (exc); *Donizetti:* Favorita (exc); *Verdi:* Ernani (exc). (G. Gravina, G. Fabbri, G.B. de Negri, G. Kaschmann, F. Toresella, L. Signoretti, anon, S. Cottone)

Ⓓ **SYMCD1067** (12/89)
Russian & Polish Songs
Tchaikovsky: Songs, Op. 16 (exc); Songs, Op. 25 (exc); Songs, Op. 47 (exc); Songs, Op. 38 (exc); *Arensky:* I did not tell you; *Glière:* Merry I'll be; Blacksmith; *Mussorgsky:* Sunless (Cpte); *Rachmaninov:* Songs, Op. 21 (exc); Songs, Op. 26 (exc); Songs, Op. 4 (exc); Songs, Op. 14 (exc); *Chopin:* Polish Songs (exc); *Dargomïzhsky:* Garden; Miller; Sierra Nevada. (A. Orda, J. Lee, E. Lush)

Ⓓ **SYMCD1068** (1/90)
Schubert: Works for Violin and Piano
Schubert: Violin Sonata, D384; Violin Sonata, D385; Violin Sonata, D408; Sonata, D574; Rondo brillant, D895. (M. Rostal, C. Horsley)

Ⓓ **SYMCD1069** (10/90)
The Harold Wayne Collection, Vol.2
Tchaikovsky: Eugene Onegin (exc); *Meyerbeer:* Africaine (exc); *Verdi:* Requiem (exc); Rigoletto (exc); *Boito:* Mefistofele (exc); *Rubinstein:* Nero (exc); *Gounod:* Roméo et Juliette (exc); *Flotow:* Martha (exc); *Donizetti:* Lucrezia Borgia (exc); Lucrezia Borgia (exc); *Gomes:* Guarany (exc); *Rubinstein:* Nero (exc); *Verdi:* Rigoletto (exc); *Boito:* Mefistofele (exc); *Marchetti:* Ruy Blas (exc); *Meyerbeer:* Africaine (exc); *Donizetti:* Lucia di Lammermoor (exc); *Verdi:* Forza del destino (exc); *Donizetti:* Favorita (exc); *Bellini:* Puritani (exc); *Masini:* Mulattieri. (F. Marconi, B. Mililotti, M. Galvany, N. della Torre, A. Cotogni, S. Cottone, C. Sabajno, anon, orch)

Ⓓ **SYMCD1071** (8/90)
Great Violinists, Vol.1
Bach: Solo Violin Partitas and Sonatas (exc); Solo Violin Partitas and Sonatas (exc); *Ernst:* Nocturne; *Sarasate:* Miramar; Danzas españolas (exc); Caprice basque; *Tchaikovsky:* Souvenir d'un lieu cher, Op.42 (exc); *Brahms:* Hungarian Dances (exc); *Fauré:* Berceuse, Op.16; *Wieniawski:* Mazurkas, Op.19 (exc); *Hubay:* Scènes de la Csárda (exc); *Schumann:* Kinderszenen (exc); *Sarasate:* Danzas españolas (exc); *Wieniawski:* Mazurkas, Op.19 (exc); *Bach:* Solo Violin Partitas and Sonatas (exc); Suites, BWV1066-9 (exc); *Beethoven:* Violin Concerto (exc); *Sarasate:* Carmen Fantasy; *F. Schubert II:* Bagatelles, Op. 13 (exc); *Sulzer:* Sarabande, Op.8; *Bach:* Solo Violin Partitas and Sonatas (exc). (J. Joachim, H. Heermann, P. de Sarasate, L. Auer, E. Ysaÿe, J. Hubay, T. Nachez, J. Dunn, K. Gregorowicz, W. Burmester, C. Flesch, H. Marteau, F. Kreisler, anon, orch, Budapest Cons Orch, C. DeCreus/F. Kark/Mr Zsolt, P. Vladigerov)

Ⓓ **SYMCD1073** (6/90)
The Harold Wayne Collection, Vol.3
Ponchielli: Gioconda (exc); *Paloni:* Non guardarmi così; *Mascagni:* Bella cantiam l'amore; *Sidney Jones:* Geisha (exc); *Denza:* In questa sera; *Godard:* Chanson de Florian; *Cilea:* Adriana Lecouvreur (exc); *Mozart:* Nozze di Figaro (exc); *Scuderi:* Dormi pure; *Mascagni:* Cavalleria rusticana (exc); *Franchetti:* Cristoforo Colombo (exc); *Rubinstein:* Demon (exc); *Wagner:* Tannhäuser (exc); *Verdi:* Don Carlo (exc); *Massenet:* Hérodiade (exc); *Verdi:* Aida (exc); *Giordano:* Andrea Chénier (exc); *Gounod:* Faust (exc); *Berlioz:* Damnation de Faust (exc); *Verdi:* Traviata (exc); *Wagner:* Meistersinger (exc); *Giordano:* Fedora (exc); *Boito:* Mefistofele (exc); *Mascagni:* Cavalleria rusticana (exc); *Verdi:* Traviata (exc); *Giordano:* Andrea Chénier (exc). (F. Marconi, A. Pandolfini, F. Valero, E. Giraldoni, G. Zenatello, G. Bellincioni, F. Giraud, S. Cottone, anon, C. Sabajno, P. Mascagni, B. Mililotti)

Ⓓ **SYMCD1075** (12/90)
May Harrison—Vioinist and Composer
Delius: Violin Concerto; Violin Sonata 3; *Warlock:* Ha'nacker Mill; Away to Twiver; *Bax:* Violin Sonata 3; *Moeran:* Violin Sonata in E minor; *M. Harrison:* May Song. (May Harrison, Bournemouth Municipal Orch/R. Austin, A. Bax, S. Austin, H. Gaskell, C. Lynch, P. Allanson, S. Betteridge)

Ⓓ **SYMCD1076** (6/90)
Violin & Piano Works
Schubert: Fantasie, D934; *Schumann:* Violin Sonata 1; *Debussy:* Violin Sonata; *Stravinsky:* Duo Concertant. (M. Rostal, C. Horsley)

Ⓓ **SYMCD1077** (5/91)
The Harold Wayne Collection, Vol.4
Wagner: Tannhäuser (exc); Meistersinger (exc); *Tosti:* Oblio; Ancora; *Bizet:* Carmen (exc); *Verdi:* Luisa Miller (exc); *Bizet:* Carmen (exc); *Donizetti:* Lucrezia Borgia (exc); *Ponchielli:* Gioconda (exc); *Arditi:* Parla Waltz; *Westerhout:* Ovunque tu; *Anon:* Serenata; *L. Giordigiani:* Ogni Sabato; *Tosti:* Ideale; *Massenet:* Manon (exc); *Gounod:* Mireille (exc); *Leoncavallo:* Pagliacci (exc); *Puccini:* Bohème (exc); Manon Lescaut (exc); *Boito:*

Mefistofele (exc); *Parisotti:* Se tu m'ami; *Wagner:* Lohengrin (exc); *Gounod:* Faust (exc); Faust (exc); *Donizetti:* Lucrezia Borgia (exc). (F. Giraud, E. Teodorini, A. Garulli, E. Bendazzi-Garulli, C. Ferrani, G. Rossi, E. Ceresoli, G. Apostolu, anon, orch)

Ⓓ **SYMCD1078** (7/90)
Willem Mengelberg conducts
Gluck: Alceste (1776) (exc); *Beethoven:* Leonore (exc); Egmont (exc); *Schubert:* Rosamunde (exc); *Weber:* Oberon (exc); *Berlioz:* Carnaval Romain; *Wagner:* Lohengrin (exc); *Mahler:* Symphony 5 (exc); *Tchaikovsky:* Marche Slave. (Concertgebouw, NYPO, NYPSO/W. Mengelberg)

Ⓓ **SYMCD1081** (7/91)
The Harold Wayne Collection, Vol.5
Meyerbeer: Prophète (exc); *Wagner:* Meistersinger (exc); *Smetana:* Dalibor (exc); *Wagner:* Tannhäuser (exc); *Verdi:* Trovatore (exc); *Wagner:* Lohengrin (exc); Rheingold (exc); Rheingold (exc); Rheingold (exc); Walküre (exc); Siegfried (exc); Siegfried (exc); Tannhäuser (exc); Walküre (exc); Götterdämmerung (exc); Tannhäuser (exc); Tannhäuser (exc); Fliegende Holländer (exc); Lohengrin (exc); Lohengrin (exc); Tristan und Isolde (exc); *Verdi:* Aida (exc). (H. Winkelmann, O. Briesemeister, H. Breuer, T. Bertram, A. von Bary, E. Feuge, C. Whitehill, S. Sedlmair, L. Slezak, E. Schmedes, anon)

Ⓓ **SYMCD1089** (9/91)
Historic Baritones of the French School
Donizetti: Favorita (exc); *Adam:* Minuit, chrétiens (exc); *Gounod:* Roméo et Juliette (exc); Faust (exc); *Meyerbeer:* Africaine (exc); *Saint-Saëns:* Ascanio (exc); *Massenet:* Roi de Lahore (exc); Si tu veux, mignonne; Pensée d'automne; *Berlioz:* Damnation de Faust (exc); *Massé:* Paul et Virginie (exc); *Mozart:* Don Giovanni (exc); *Fontenailles:* Deux coeurs; *Paladilhe:* Mandolinata; *De Lara:* Rondel de l'adieu; *Chabrier:* Roi malgré lui (exc); *Grétry:* Richard Coeur-de-Lion (exc); *Adam:* Si j'étais Roi (exc); *Paer:* Maître de chapelle (exc); *Messager:* Basoche (exc); *Massenet:* Jongleur de Notre Dame (exc); *Isouard:* Joconde (exc); *Halévy:* Charles VI (exc); *Gounod:* Soir; *Reyer:* Sigurd (exc); *Poise:* Joli Gilles (exc); *De Lara:* Méssaline (exc); *Périer:* Dors, mon enfant. (J.B. Faure, L. Melchissédec, J. Lassalle, V. Maurel, L. Fugère, G. Soulacroix, M-N. Bouvet, J. Noté, M. Renaud, A. Ghasne, J. Périer, anon, orch)

Ⓓ **SYMCD1093** (10/92)
The Harold Wayne Collection, Vol.7
Verdi: Falstaff (exc); *Traditional:* Drink to me only; *Schubert:* Ständchen, D889; *Traditional:* My love Nell; *Wagner:* Tannhäuser (exc); *Debussy:* Pelléas et Mélisande (exc); *Mozart:* Nozze di Figaro (exc); *Sullivan:* Thou'rt passing hence; *Handel:* Theodora (exc); Serse (exc); *Bishop:* Home, sweet home; *Traditional:* Robin Adair; *Stanford:* Shamus O'Brien (exc); *Meyer-Helmund:* Ich hätte nicht daran gedacht; *Massenet:* Manon (exc); *Meyer-Helmund:* Morgen send'ich dir die Veilchen; *Offenbach:* Contes d'Hoffmann (exc); *Wagner:* Lohengrin (exc); *Tosti:* Ninon; *Traditional:* Maman, dites-moi; *Flotow:* Martha (exc); *Tchaikovsky:* Maid of Orleans (exc); *Hawley:* Sweetest flower that blows; *Marchesi:* Folletta. (D. Bispham, M. Garden, C. Santley, E. Albani, J. O'Mara, F. Saville, O. Ouroussov, E. Palliser, anon, C. Debussy, Henry Wood)

Ⓓ **SYMCD1096/7** (11/91)
Sir Thomas Beecham, Bart conducts Beecham SO & LPO
Dvořák: Symphony 5; *Gounod:* Faust (exc); *Brahms:* Hungarian Dances (exc); *Tchaikovsky:* Nutcracker (exc); *Schubert:* Marches militaires, D733 (exc); *Massenet:* Thaïs (exc); *Mendelssohn:* Midsummer Night's Dream (exc); *Wagner:* Tannhäuser (exc); *J. Strauss II:* Fledermaus (exc); *Rossini:* Guillaume Tell (exc); *Missa:* Muguette (exc); *Mascagni:* Cavalleria Rusticana (exc); *Mendelssohn:* Songs without Words (exc); *Weber:* Oberon (exc); *Mozart:* Nozze di Figaro (exc); *Massenet:* Manon (exc); *R. Strauss:* Rosenkavalier (exc); *Tchaikovsky:* Symphony 6 (exc); *Stravinsky:* Firebird Suite (1911) (exc); *Rossini:* Barbiere di Siviglia (exc); *Gounod:* Roméo et Juliette (exc); *Lully:* Amants magnifiques (exc); *Debussy:* Petite Suite (exc); *Beethoven:* Symphony 7 (exc). (LPO, SO/T. Beecham)

Ⓓ **SYMCD1098/9** (11/91)
Marko Rothmüller—Lieder Recital
Schubert: Winterreise (Cpte); Schwanengesang, D957 (exc); Rastlose Liebe, D138; Sei mir gegrüsst, D741; An die Leier, D737; Du bist die Ruh', D776; Erlkönig, D328; *Mussorgsky:* Songs and Dances of Death. (M. Rothmüller, S. Gyr)

Ⓓ **SYMCD1100** (3/93)
Harold Wayne Collection, Vol.8
Gounod: Philémon et Baucis (exc); *Faure:* Rameaux; *A. Thomas:* Caïd (exc); *Meyerbeer:* Huguenots (exc); *Gounod:* Roméo et Juliette (exc); *Godard:* Embarquez-vous; *Wagner:* Walküre (exc); Meistersinger (exc); Tannhäuser (exc); Rheingold (exc); *Traditional:* Mühlrad; *De Lara:* Méssaline (exc); *Mozart:* Don Giovanni (exc); *Rotoli:* Serenata; *Gounod:* Faust (exc); *Tosti:* Invano; *Bizet:* Carmen (exc); *Verdi:* Falstaff (exc); *Gounod:* Faust (exc); *Stern:* Coquette; *Gounod:* Roméo et Juliette (exc); *Bishop:* Home, sweet home; *P.A. Vidal:* Printemps nouveau; *Bizet:* Carmen (exc); *Traditional:* Magali; *Mascagni:* Cavalleria rusticana (exc); *Wagner:* Tannhäuser (exc); *Holmès:* Chemin du ciel. (P. Plançon, A. Van Rooy, A. Scotti, S. Adams, E. Calvé, M. Renaud, anon)

Ⓓ **SYMCD1101** (10/92)
The Harold Wayne Collection, Vol.9
Gounod: Chanson de printemps; *Gluck:* Iphigénie en Tauride (exc); *Massenet:* Marquise; *Hahn:* Heure exquise; *De Lara:* Rondel de l'adieu; *C. Erlanger:* Fédia; *Verdi:* Otello (exc); *Fauré:* Songs, Op. 23 (exc); Songs, Op. 23 (exc); *Saint-Saëns:* Samson et Dalila (exc); Samson et Dalila (exc); *Nápravník:* Harold (exc); *Wagner:* Tristan und Isolde (exc); Tristan und Isolde (exc); Walküre (exc); Walküre (exc); *Schumann:* Dichterliebe, Op.48 (exc); Dichterliebe, Op.48 (exc); *Gounod:* Sapho (exc); Faust (exc); *Massenet:* Cid (exc). (V. Maurel, F. Litvinne, anon, A. Cortot)

Ⓓ **SYMCD1105** (7/93)
The Harold Wayne Collection, Vol.10
Koenemann: When the king went forth to war; *Slonov:* Arise, red sun; *Tchaikovsky:* Songs, Op.60 (exc); *Traditional:* Night; *Glinka:* Life for the Tsar (exc); *Tchaikovsky:* Songs, Op.65 (exc); *Rimsky-Korsakov:* Sadko (exc); *Gounod:* Roméo et Juliette (exc); *Tchaikovsky:* Eugene Onegin (exc); *Wagner:* Walküre (exc); *Grechaninov:* Over the Steppe; *Verdi:* Traviata (exc); *Glinka:* Ruslan and Lyudmila (exc); *Meyerbeer:* Huguenots (exc); *Rubinstein:* Demon (exc); *Verstovsky:* Askold's Grave (exc); *Gounod:* Faust (exc); Faust (exc); *Donizetti:* Zingara (exc); *Verdi:* Traviata (exc); *Bizet:* Pastorale; *Glinka:* Ruslan and Lyudmila (exc); Life for the Tsar (exc); *Rimsky-Korsakov:* Snow Maiden (exc); *Mascagni:* M'ama, non m'ama. (F. Chaliapin, I. Alchevsky, V. Sharonov, M. Kuznetsova, A. Labinsky, E. Orel, anon)

Ⓓ **SYMCD1107** (10/92)
Schoenberg—Piano Works
Schoenberg: Klavierstücke, Op. 11; Klavierstücke, Op. 19; Klavierstücke, Op. 23; Suite, Op. 25; Klavierstück, Op. 33a; Klavierstück, Op. 33b. (K. Wolpe)

Ⓓ **SYMCD1109** (6/93)
Great Violinists, Vol.5 - Adolf Busch
Corelli: Sonatas, Op.5 (exc); *Bach:* Solo Violin Partitas and Sonatas (exc); Solo Violin Partitas and Sonatas (exc); *Tartini:* Violin Sonatas (1745) (exc); *Gossec:* Rosine (exc); *Hoffstetter:* String Quartets, Op.3 (exc); *Mozart:* String Quartet, K575 (exc); *Schubert:* String Quartet, D887 (exc); *Verdi:* String Quartet (exc); *Brahms:* Hungarian Dances (exc); Hungarian Dances (exc); *Kreisler:* Pugnani Praeludium and Allegro; Dittersdorf Scherzo; *Bach:* Solo Violin Partitas and Sonatas (exc); Violin Sonatas, BWV1020-25 (exc); *Brahms:* Violin Concerto (exc). (A. Busch, B. Seidler-Winkler, Busch Qt, anon, NBC SO/F. Black, R. Serkin)

Ⓓ **SYMCD1111** (8/93)
The Harold Wayne Collection, Vol.11
E. Mascheroni: Lorenza (exc); *Mascagni:* Cavalleria rusticana (exc); *Puccini:* Bohème (exc); *Giordano:* Fedora (exc); *Massenet:* Manon (exc); *Mascagni:* Iris (exc); *Giordano:* Andrea Chénier (exc); *Tosti:* Dopo; *Puccini:* Tosca (exc); Tosca (exc); *Cilea:* Adriana Lecouvreur (exc); *Massenet:* Roi de Lahore (exc); *Donizetti:* Favorita (exc); *Verdi:* Ballo in maschera (exc); *A. Thomas:* Hamlet (exc); *Mozart:* Don Giovanni (exc); *Donizetti:* Favorita (exc); Don Pasquale (exc); *Franchetti:* Germania (exc); *Mascagni:* Cavalleria rusticana (exc); *Bottesini:* Ero e Leandro (exc); *Ponchielli:* Gioconda (exc); *Puccini:* Tosca (exc). (E. Carelli, G. De Luca, A. Pinto, E. Ventura, M. Sammarco, E. Ceresoli, F. Cilea, anon, E. Mascheroni, S. Cottone)

Ⓓ **SYMCD1113** (12/93)
The Harold Wayne Collection, Vol.13
Verdi: Trovatore (exc); *Meyerbeer:* Dinorah (exc); *Verdi:* Ballo in maschera (exc); *Saint-Saëns:* Samson et Dalila (exc); *A. Thomas:* Mignon (exc); *Mozart:* Don Giovanni (exc); *Puccini:* Bohème (exc); *Verdi:* Aida (exc); Forza del destino (exc); *Parisotti:* Se tu m'ami; *Ponchielli:* Gioconda (exc); *Verdi:* Rigoletto (exc); *Gounod:* Faust (exc); *Ponchielli:* Gioconda (exc); *Verdi:* Aida (exc); *Wagner:* Rheingold (exc). (E. Scaramberg, A. Stehle, R. Stracciari, G. Bréjean-Silver, I. Calleja, M. Camporelli, F. Corradetti, N. de Angelis, E. Feinhals, E. Mazzoleni, G. Pacini, A. Parsi-Pettinella, L. Pasini-Vitale, E. Garbin, L. Longobardi, G. Lukacewska, O. Luppi, A. Magini-Coletti, R. Pinkert, G. Russ, M. Sammarco, G. Armanini, M. Barrientos, A. Bonci, La Scala Chor, anon, orch)

Ⓓ **SYMCD1125** (6/93)
Lucien Fugère—Opera & Song Recital
Messager: Basoche (exc); *Massenet:* Jongleur de Notre Dame (exc); *Flotow:* Ombre (exc); *Mozart:* Zauberflöte (exc); Don Giovanni (exc); *Chabrier:* Roi malgré lui (exc); *Meyerbeer:* Dinorah (exc); *Halévy:* Val d'Andorre (exc); *G. Charpentier:* Louise (exc); *Massé:* Saisons (exc); *Gounod:* Médecin malgré lui (exc); *Gluck:* Rencontre imprévue (exc); *Paer:* Maître de Chapelle (exc); *Chaminade:* Ronde d'amour; *P. Henrion:* Vieux ruban; *Levadé:* Vieilles de chez-nous; *Chaminade:* Anneau d'argent; *Widor:* Mélodies, Op. 43 (exc); *Couperin:* Livre de clavecin IV (exc). (L. Fugère, orch, anon)

Ⓓ **SYMCD1126** (12/93)
The Harold Wayne Collection, Vol.14
Granier: Hosanna; *Verdi:* Otello (exc); *Rossini:* Guillaume Tell (exc); *Massenet:* Mage (exc); *Halévy:* Juive (exc); *Flégier:* Stances; *Saint-Saëns:* Samson et Dalila (exc); *Meyerbeer:* Huguenots (exc); *Rossini:* Guillaume Tell (exc); *Meyerbeer:* Africaine (exc); Prophète (exc); Robert le Diable (exc); *Reyer:* Sigurd (exc); *Verdi:* Lombardi (exc); *Rupès:* Pastorale Languedoçienne; *Verdi:* Aida (exc); Jérusalem (exc); *Massenet:* Cid (exc); *Granier:* Pierre l'ermite (exc); *Verdi:* Otello (exc). (L. Escalais, O. Luppi, A. Magini-Coletti, A. Talexis, A. Algos, F. Corradetti, G. Masotti, G. Sala, anon)

Ⓓ **SYMCD1128** (12/94)
The Harold Wayne Collection, Vol.15
Verdi: Trovatore (exc); Otello (exc); *Gounod:* Polyeucte (exc); *Massenet:* Hérodiade (exc); *Boito:* Mefistofele (exc); *Mascagni:* Cavalleria Rusticana (exc); *Wagner:* Lohengrin (exc); *Verdi:* Aida (exc); *Meyerbeer:* Africaine (exc); *Saint-Saëns:* Samson et Dalila (exc); *Donizetti:* Favorita (exc); *Verdi:* Trovatore (exc); *Bizet:* Carmen (exc); *Meyerbeer:* Africaine (exc); *Massenet:* Cid (exc); *Verdi:* Otello (exc); *Tosti:* Marechiare; *Mozart:* Don Giovanni (exc); *De Lara:* Rondel de l'adieu; *Paladilhe:* Mandolinata; *Tosti:* Ninon; *Verdi:* Falstaff (exc); *Hardelot:* Year ago; *Tosti:* Au temps du grand roi. (L. Escalais, F. Litvinne, V. Maurel, anon, orch)

Ⓓ **SYMCD1130** (4/93)
Joseph Holbrooke—Historic Recordings
Holbrooke: Children of Don (exc); Children of Don (exc); Dylan (exc); Dylan (exc); Bronwen (exc); Piano Quartet 1 (exc); Enchanter (exc); Piano Pieces, Op. 101 (exc); Piano Pieces, Op. 105 (exc); Symphony 3 (exc). (D. Vane, J. Coates, N. Walker, J. Holbrooke, Phil Qt, orch, SO/C. Powell/A. Hammond/C. Raybould/J. Holbrooke)

Ⓓ **SYMCD1136** (8/93)
Opera in Chicago, Vol.1
Mendelssohn: Hear my prayer (exc); *Flotow:* Martha (exc); *Gounod:* Faust (exc); *Puccini:* Madama Butterfly (exc); Madama Butterfly (exc); *Cadman:* American Indian Songs, Op.45 (exc); *Del Riego:* O dry those tears; *Cadman:* American Indian Songs, Op.45 (exc); *Woodforde-Finden:* Indian Love Lyrics (exc); *Strickland:* Dreamin' time; *Tosti:* Serenata; Addio; *Debussy:* Ariettes oubliées (exc); *Verdi:* Traviata (exc); *Massenet:* Jongleur de Notre Dame (exc); Hérodiade (exc); *G. Charpentier:* Louise (exc); *Massenet:* Thaïs (exc); *Alfano:* Risurrezione (exc); *G. Charpentier:* Louise (exc); *Grechaninov:* Over the Steppe; *Bizet:* Carmen (exc); *Traditional:* John Anderson, my Jo. (E. Mason, M. Garden, orch, C. Debussy, J. Dansereau)

Ⓓ **SYMCD1138** (12/93)
The Harold Wayne Collection, Vol.16
Verdi: Trovatore (exc); Trovatore (exc); Trovatore (exc); Trovatore (exc); Trovatore (exc); Traviata (exc); Traviata (exc); Traviata (exc); Ballo in maschera (exc); Ballo in maschera (exc); Ballo in maschera (exc); Ballo in maschera (exc); Forza del destino (exc); Aida (exc); Aida (exc). (G. Zenatello, A. Parsi-Pettinella, P. Amato, E. Bruno, E. Mazzoleni, L. Cannetti, E. Burzio, N. Frascani, anon, orch, chor)

Ⓓ **SYMCD1140** (3/93)
The Harrison Sisters
Brahms: Cello Sonata 1; *Delius:* Violin Sonata 1; Cello Sonata; *C. Burleigh:* Plantation (Southland) Sketches; *Smetana:* From the Homeland (exc); *Delius:* Hassan (exc); *Popper:* Gavotte 2; Vito, Op.54/5; *Bach:* Solo Cello Suites (exc); Solo Cello Suites (exc). (B. Harrison, May Harrison, Margaret Harrison, Margaret Harrison, G. Moore, A. Bax, H. Craxton, R. Paul, May Harrison)

Ⓓ **SYMCD1145** (8/94)
Busoni, Grainger & Petri
Bach: Wohltemperierte Klavier (exc); Nun freut euch, BWV734; *Beethoven:* Ecossaises, WoO83 (exc); *Chopin:* Nocturnes (exc); Preludes (exc); Etudes (exc); *Liszt:* Hungarian Rhapsodies, S244 (exc); *Chopin:* Piano Sonata 3; *Alkan:* Études, Op.39 (exc). (F. Busoni, P. Grainger, E. Petri)

① **SYMCD1148** (12/93)
The Harold Wayne Collection, Vol.17
Verdi: Aida (exc); Aida (exc); Aida (exc); Aida (exc); Otello (exc); Otello (exc); Otello (exc); Otello (exc); Otello (exc); Otello (exc); *Marchetti:* Ruy Blas (exc); *Ponchielli:* Gioconda (exc); Gioconda (exc); Gioconda (exc). (G. Zenatello, E. Mazzoleni, E. Bruno, L. Pasini-Vitale, P. Amato, anon, orch)

① **SYMCD1149** (1/95)
Fernando De Lucia
Rossini: Barbiere di Siviglia (exc); Barbiere di Siviglia (exc); Barbiere di Siviglia (exc); Barbiere di Siviglia (exc); *Bellini:* Sonnambula (exc); Sonnambula (exc); *Donizetti:* Elisir d'amore (exc); Favorita (exc); *Verdi:* Luisa Miller (exc); Rigoletto (exc); Rigoletto (exc); Traviata (exc); Traviata (exc); Traviata (exc); *Gounod:* Faust (exc); Faust (exc); *Bizet:* Carmen (exc); Carmen (exc); *Mascagni:* Cavalleria rusticana (exc); *Massenet:* Werther (exc); *Puccini:* Tosca (exc); *Giordano:* Fedora (exc). (F. de Lucia, A. Pini-Corsi, M. Galvany, J. Huguet, E. Badini, C. Boninsegna, anon, orch)

① **SYMCD1157** (12/93)
Five Centuries of Festive Fayre
Arbeau: Orchésographie (exc); *Brade:* Newe ausserlesene liebliche Branden (exc); *Clemens non Papa:* War war es; Ich stund an einem Morgen; *Othmayr:* Es ist ein Schnee gefallen; *Vento:* Weiber mit den Flohen; *Henry VIII:* Pastyme with good companye; *Nola:* Fuggit Amore; *Traditional:* Wassail Song; Bring us good ale; *Attaingnant:* Dance Collection (1530) (exc); *Alfonso el Sabio:* Cantiga 5; Cantiga 10; *Traditional:* Leaping and dancing; Slavonic Folktunes; *Anon:* Polish Dances (17th Cent); *Traditional:* Czech Tydlidom; Bohemian Carol; Birds; Drummer Boy; Furiant; Walachian Tydlidom; As I rode out; Tomorrow shall be my dancing day; Little Jesu sweetly sleep; Sussex carol; *Gervaise:* Est il conclud; *Du Tertre:* Pavane et Galliarde I; *Traditional:* O Bethlehem; Coventry Carol; *M. Praetorius:* Puer natus in Bethlehem; *Traditional:* Joseph lieber, Joseph mein; Walk ye in all the ways; Tempus Adest Floridum; As I sat on a Sunny Bank; *Widmann:* Musicalischer Tugendtspiegel (exc); *Scheidt:* Vom Himmel hoch; *Dowland:* Whole Booke of Psalmes (exc). (London Musica Antiqua/M. Uridge)

① **SYMCD1158** (5/94)
The Harold Wayne Collection, Vol.18
Puccini: Manon Lescaut (exc); Manon Lescaut (exc); Bohème (exc); Bohème (exc); Bohème (exc); Tosca (exc); Tosca (exc); Madama Butterfly (exc); Fanciulla del West (exc); *Mascagni:* Cavalleria Rusticana (exc); Cavalleria Rusticana (exc); *Leoncavallo:* Pagliacci (exc); Pagliacci (exc); Pagliacci (exc); Pagliacci (exc); Pagliacci (exc). (G. Zenatello, M. Sammarco, L. Cannetti, E. Mazzoleni, anon, orch)

① **SYMCD1168** (5/94)
The Harold Wayne Collection, Vol.19
Rosa: Star vicino; *Donizetti:* Lucia di Lammermoor (exc); *Bellini:* Norma (exc); *Boito:* Mefistofele (exc); Mefistofele (exc); Mefistofele (exc); *Franchetti:* Germania (exc); Figlia di Iorio (exc); *Giordano:* Andrea Chénier (exc); Andrea Chénier (exc); Andrea Chénier (exc); *Wagner:* Meistersinger (exc); Meistersinger (exc); *Meyerbeer:* Huguenots (exc); *Gounod:* Faust (exc); Faust (exc); *Saint-Saëns:* Samson et Dalila (exc); *Bizet:* Carmen (exc); Carmen (exc); *Gomes:* Guarany (exc); *Denza:* Vieni a me; *Rotoli:* Mia sposa sarà la mia bandiera. (G. Zenatello, M. Barrientos, E. Mazzoleni, A. Didur, E. Giraldoni, E. Cervi-Caroli, A. Nelson, anon, orch)

① **SYMCD1170** (7/95)
The Harold Wayne Collection, Vol.20
Donizetti: Don Pasquale (exc); Duca d'Alba (exc); *Verdi:* Luisa Miller (exc); Traviata (exc); *Bizet:* Pêcheurs de Perles (exc); *A. Thomas:* Mignon (exc); *Massenet:* Manon (exc); *Mascagni:* Cavalleria Rusticana (exc); *Massenet:* Werther (exc); *Leoncavallo:* Pagliacci (exc); *Giordano:* Fedora (exc); *Mascagni:* Iris (exc); *Paderewski:* Manru (exc); *D. Scarlatti:* Consolati e spera; *Handel:* Serse (exc); *Mendelssohn:* Lieder, Op.8 (exc); *R. Strauss:* Lieder, Op.27 (exc); Lieder, Op.10 (exc); *Mugnone:* Mattinata; Spes ultima Dea; *Alagna:* Canzuna Siciliana; *Tosti:* Non t'amo piu; Vorrei morire. (G. Anselmi, G. Bellincini, L. Mugnone, anon)

① **SYMCD1172** (12/94)
The Harold Wayne Collection, Vol.21
Schumann: Romanzen und Balladen, Op.49 (exc); *Meyerbeer:* Huguenots (exc); *Paladilhe:* Patrie (exc); *Yradier:* Paloma; *Meyerbeer:* Africaine (exc); *Gounod:* Soir; Prière; *V.A. Duvernoy:* Hellé (exc); *Reyer:* Sigurd (exc); *Schumann:* Dichterliebe, Op.48 (exc); *Wagner:* Walküre (exc); *Massenet:* Werther (exc); *Schumann:* Myrthen, Op.25 (exc); *Nicolai:* Blümchen; *Schumann:* Liederkreis, Op.39 (exc); *A. Thomas:* Mignon (exc); *E. Bourgeois:* Véritable Manola; *Bizet:* Carmen (exc); *Berlioz:* Damnation

de Faust (exc); *Wagner:* Walküre (exc); *Godard:* Jocelyn (exc); *Gounod:* Au Rossignol; *G. Braga:* Melodies (exc); *Massenet:* Hérodiade (exc); *Tosti:* T'amo ancora; *Massenet:* Âme des fleurs; *De Lara:* Champs de pavots; *Gounod:* Faust (exc); *Verdi:* Traviata (exc). (J.-F. Delmas, P. Gailhard, R. Caron, E. Van Dyck, L. David, V. Capoul, M. de Reszke, A. Adini, P. Aramis, G. Bréjean-Silver, J. de Reszke, anon, orch)

Tahra

① **FURT1004/7** (3/95)
Furtwängler conducts the Berlin Philharmonic
Beethoven: Symphony 9; Coriolan; Symphony 6; *Wagner:* Tristan und Isolde (exc); *Brahms:* Piano Concerto 2; Symphony 1 (exc); *Bruckner:* Symphony 6 (exc); Symphony 7 (exc). (T. Briem, E. Höngen, P. Anders, R. Watzke, A. Aeschbacher, Bruno Kittel Ch, BPO/W. Furtwängler)

① **FURT1008/11** (3/95)
A Tribute to Wilhelm Furtwängler
Beethoven: Symphony 3; Symphony 5; Symphony 6; *Schubert:* Symphony 9; *Dvořák:* Slavonic Dances (exc); *Mendelssohn:* Hebrides (exc); *Schumann:* Cello Concerto (exc); *Schubert:* Symphony 8 (exc); *Brahms:* Symphony 2 (exc); *R. Strauss:* Till Eulenspiegel. (P. Fournier, BPO/W. Furtwängler)

① **TAH102** (9/94)
Hermann Abendroth - 1927-1941 Recordings
Brahms: Symphony 4; *Mozart:* Serenade, K239; *Vivaldi:* Concerti Grossi, Op.3 (exc); *Handel:* Concerti Grossi, Op.6 (exc); *Beethoven:* Symphony 4 (exc); Symphony 5; *Brahms:* Symphony 1. (LSO, Cologne CO, Leipzig RSO, BPO/H. Abendroth)

① **TAH106/7** (9/94)
Hermann Abendroth-Historic Recordings
Bach: Suites, BWV1066-9 (exc); *Haydn:* Symphony 88; *Mozart:* Symphony 29; *Handel:* Concerti Grossi, Op.6 (exc); *Schumann:* Manfred (exc); *Haydn:* Symphony 96; *Schubert:* Symphony 3; *Brahms:* Tragic Overture. (Leipzig Gewandhaus/H. Abendroth)

Tall Poppies

① **TP001** (12/92)
Piano Works for Children
Bach: Anna Magdalena Notenbuch (1725) (exc); *Tchaikovsky:* Album for the Young (exc); *Mozart:* Minuet, K1; Minuet, K2; Allegro, K3; Minuet, K4; Minuet, K61g/2; Piano Piece, K33b; *Schubert:* Scherzi, D593 (exc); *Prokofiev:* Music for Children (exc); *Bartók:* Mikrokosmos, Bk 5 (exc); For Children (1945) (exc); *Schumann:* Album für die Jugend (exc). (G. Tozer)

① **TP002** (7/92)
Café Concertino
Vine: Café Concertino; *Wesley-Smith:* White Knight; *Westlake:* Refractions; *Whitehead:* Manutaki; *Isaacs:* So it does. (Australia Ens)

① **TP003** (9/92)
Works for Flute and Guitar
Ibert: Entr'acte (1937); *Fauré:* Sicilienne; *Ravel:* Pièce en forme de habanera; *Gossec:* Tambourin; *Coste:* Montagnard; *Debussy:* Syrinx; *Honegger:* Danse de la chèvre; *Rodrigo:* Serenata al Alba; *Traditional:* Condor pasa; *Morel:* Danza Braziliana; *Desportes:* Pastourelle; *Ronde;* Pastorale mélancolique; Pastorale joyeuse; *Castelnuovo-Tedesco:* Sonata, Op.205. (V. Taylor, T. Kain)

① **TP025** (10/94)
Cage—Vocal & Prepared Piano works
Cage: Music for Marcel Duchamp (1947); Wonderful widow of eighteen springs; Sonatas and Interludes (1946-48). (G. English, N. Butterley)

Telarc

① **CD80038** (12/83)
Music for Wind Band
Holst: Suite 1; Suite 2; *Handel:* Fireworks Music; *Bach:* Fantasia, BWV572. (Cleveland Winds/F. Fennell)

① **CD80041** (12/83)
Tchaikovsky: Orchestral Works
Tchaikovsky: 1812; Capriccio Italien; Mazeppa (exc). (Cincinnati SO/E. Kunzel)

① **CD80049** (1/84)
Bach: Organ Works
Bach: Fantasia and Fugue, BWV542; Toccata and Fugue, BWV540; Passacaglia and Fugue, BWV582; Vater unser im Himmelreich, BWV737; Orgel-Büchlein, BWV599-644 (exc). (M. Murray)

① **CD80059** (12/83)
Popular Orchestral Works
Vaughan Williams: Tallis Fantasia; *Satie:* Gymnopédies; *Barber:* Adagio for Strings; *Fauré:* Pavane; *Grainger:* Irish Tune from County Derry. (J. Korman, B. Schiebler, T. Dumm, J. Sant'Ambrogio, St Louis SO/L. Slatkin)

① **CD80061** (5/85)
Beethoven: Piano Concertos
Beethoven: Piano Concerto 1; Piano Concerto 2; Piano Concerto 3; Piano Concerto 4; Piano Concerto 5. (R. Serkin, Boston SO/S. Ozawa)

① **CD80071** (9/85)
Debussy: Orchestral works
Debussy: La Mer; Après-midi; Danse sacrée et danse profane. (F. Fietov, St. Louis SO/L. Slatkin)

① **CD80072** (12/83)
Russian Orchestral Works
Rimsky-Korsakov: Russian Easter Festival Ov.; *Glinka:* Ruslan and Lyudmila (exc); *Borodin:* In the Steppes of Central Asia; *Glière:* Red Poppy Suite (exc); *Tchaikovsky:* Marche slave. (St. Louis SO/L. Slatkin)

① **CD80078** (12/83)
Copland: Orchestral Works
Copland: Fanfare for the Common Man; Rodeo; Appalachian Spring Suite. (Atlanta SO/L. Lane)

① **CD80080** (1/84)
Music for Strings
Pachelbel: Canon and Gigue (exc); *Borodin:* String Quartet 2 (exc); *Vaughan Williams:* Greensleeves Fantasia; *Tchaikovsky:* Serenade, Op. 48. (St Louis SO/L. Slatkin)

① **CD80085** (5/85)
Respighi: Tone poems
Respighi: Pines of Rome; Fountains of Rome; Birds. (Atlanta SO/L. Lane)

① **CD80088** (10/84)
Bach in Los Angeles
Bach: Toccata and Fugue, BWV565; Concertos, BWV592-7 (exc); Prelude and Fugue, BWV544; Prelude and Fugue, BWV532. (M. Murray)

① **CD80096** (3/85)
French Organ Music
Jongen: Symphonie Concertante; *Franck:* Fantaisie in A; Pastorale. (M. Murray, San Francisco SO/E. de Waart)

① **CD80098** (3/86)
Straussfest!
J. Strauss II: Explosionen, Op. 43; Im Krapfenwald'l, Op. 336; Champagner, Op. 211; Banditen-Galopp, Op. 378; Blauen Donau, Op. 314; Auf der Jagd, Op. 373; G'schichten aus dem Wienerwald, Op. 325; Unter Donner und Blitz; Pizzicato Polka; *Jos Strauss:* Feuerfest!; *E. Strauss:* Bahn frei. (Cincinnati Pops/E. Kunzel)

① **CD80099** (10/84)
Stars and Stripes Forever
Arnaud: Olympic Theme; Chasse; Olympiad; *Vaughan Williams:* English Folk Song Suite; Sea Songs; *Grainger:* Lincolnshire Posy; Shepherd's Hey, BFMS31; *Sousa:* Stars and Stripes Forever; *Barber:* Commando March; *Leemans:* Belgian Paratroopers; *Fučík:* Florentiner, Op. 214; *King:* Barnum and Bailey's Favorite; *Zimmerman:* Anchors Aweigh; *J. Strauss I:* Radetzky March. (Cleveland Winds/F. Fennell)

① **CD80109** (9/85)
Berlioz: Requiem, etc
Berlioz: Grande messe des morts (Cpte); *Verdi:* Pezzi sacri (exc); *Boito:* Mefistofele (exc). (J. Aler, Atlanta Sym Chor, Atlanta SO/Robert Shaw, J. Cheek, Morehouse-Spelman Chor, Callanwolde Young Sngrs)

① **CD80115** (9/86)
Orchestral Spectaculars
Rimsky-Korsakov: Mlada (exc); Snow Maiden (exc); *Dukas:* Apprenti sorcier; *Weinberger:* Schwanda the Bagpiper (exc); *Saint-Saëns:* Samson et Dalila (exc); *Liszt:* Préludes. (Cincinnati Pops/E. Kunzel)

① **CD80117** (10/87)
Copland-Orchestral Works
Copland: John Henry; Lincoln Portrait; Tender Land (exc); Old American Songs 1; Jubilee Variation; Ceremonial Fanfare; Outdoor Ov. (K. Hepburn, S. Milnes, Cincinnati Pops/E. Kunzel)

① **CD80118** (7/87)
Beethoven: Piano Sonatas
Beethoven: Piano Sonata 8; Piano Sonata 14; Piano sonata 23. (J. O'Conor)

Teldec

① **4509-90422-2** (1/94)
Tchaikovsky—Chamber Works
Tchaikovsky: String Quartet 1; String Quartet 2; String Quartet 3; String Quartet (1865); Souvenir de Florence. (Y. Yurov, M. Milman, Borodin Qt)

① **4509-90494-2** (8/93)
Mozart—Sacred Choral Works
Mozart: Mass, K337; Litanies, K125; Regina coeli, K276. (B. Bonney, E. von Magnus, U. Heilmann, G. Cachemaille, A. Schoenberg Ch, VCM/N. Harnoncourt)

① **4509-90674-2** (4/95)
Mozart—Piano Concertos, etc
Mozart: Piano Concerto 18; Piano Concerto 19; Rondo, K382. (D. Barenboim (pf/dir), BPO)

① **4509-90798-2** (10/93)
Monteverdi—Il Ballo delle ingrate
Monteverdi: Madrigals, Bk 7 (exc); Ballo delle ingrate; Tirsi e Clori; Combattimento di Tancredi e Clorinda. (B. Borden, S. Le Blanc, P. Järviö, J. Potter, D. Nasrawi, C. Righetti, H. van der Kamp, Tragicomedia, S. Stubbs)

① **4509-90799-2** (10/93)
Rossi—Le Canterine Romane
Rossi: Disperate speranza a 3; Piango, prego a 3; Infelice pensier a 2; Luigi Passacaille; Palazzo incantato (exc); Occhi belli a 2; Sarabanda; Balletto; Noi siam tre donzellette a 3; Ai sospiri a 2; Arie di passacaglia; Speranza al tuo pallore a 2; Poi che mancò speranza; Fan battaglia a 3. (Tragicomedia)

① **4509-90841-2** (5/94)
A Gift of Nature - 17th Century English Chamber Music
Baltzar: Prelude; John Come Kiss Me Now Divisions; *Schop:* Lachrime Pavaen; *N. Matteis I:* Ayres for the Violin, Bk 4 (exc); Ayres for the Violin, Bk 4 (exc); *Brade:* Coral; *W. Lawes:* Fantasia-Suites a 3 (exc); *C. Simpson:* Prelude; Divisions on a Ground; *Jenkins:* Fantasia in D minor; *Byrd:* John Come Kiss Me Now, BK81; *Farinel:* Faronell's Ground; *Anon:* Trible Violl Division; Paul's Steeple. (M. Huggett, S. Cunningham, Sonnerie Trio, S. Stubbs, S. Stubbs, A. Lawrence-King, G. Cooper)

① **4509-90842-2** (10/94)
Mozart—Orchestral Works
Mozart: March, K237; Serenade, K203; Symphony 23. (VCM/N. Harnoncourt)

① **4509-90843-2** (4/95)
Haydn—Symphonies
Haydn: Symphony 31; Symphony 59; Symphony 73. (VCM/N. Harnoncourt)

① **4509-90845-2** (1/94)
Delius—Orchestral Works
Delius: Brigg Fair; In a Summer Garden; Paris; First cuckoo; Summer Night on the River; Village Romeo and Juliet (exc). (BBC SO/A. Davis)

① **4509-90846-2** (10/93)
Trumpet Concertos
Jolivet: Trumpet Concertino; *Hummel:* Trumpet Concerto; *Tomasi:* Trumpet Concerto; *Haydn:* Trumpet Concerto. (S. Nakarjakov, A. Markovich, Lausanne CO/J. López-Cobos)

① **4509-90873-2** (3/95)
Schubert—Lieder
Schubert: Ave Maria, D839; Ganymed, D544; Kennst du das Land, D321; Heiss mich nicht reden, D877/2; So lasst mich scheinen, D877/3; Nur wer die Sehnsucht kennt, D877/4; Liebhaber in allen Gestalten, D558; Heidenröslein, D257; Nähe des Geliebten, D162; Forelle, D550; Auf dem Wasser zu singen, D774; Im Abendrot, D799; Ständchen, D889; Du bist die Ruh, D776; Gretchen am Spinnrade, D118; Gretchens Bitte, D564; Hirt auf dem Felsen, D965. (B. Bonney, G. Parsons, S. Kam)

① **4509-91002-2** (7/93)
Music at the Court of Mannheim
J.C. Bach: Quintets, Op. 11 (exc); *Holzbauer:* Quintet; *J. Stamitz:* Trio Sonatas, Op. 1 (exc); *Richter:* String Quartet, Op. 5/2. (VCM/N. Harnoncourt)

① **4509-91184-2** (12/93)
Schubert—Symphonies
Schubert: Symphony 1; Symphony 2; Symphony 3; Symphony 4; Symphony 5; Symphony 6; Symphony 8; Symphony 9. (Concertgebouw/N. Harnoncourt)

① **4509-91187-2** (7/93)
Mozart—Symphonies
Mozart: Symphony 29; Symphony 30; Symphony 31. (Concertgebouw/N. Harnoncourt)

① **4509-91189-2** (7/93)
Mozart—Symphonies
Mozart: Symphony 25; Symphony 26; Symphony 28. (Concertgebouw/N. Harnoncourt)

① **4509-91190-2** (7/93)
Mozart—Symphonies
Mozart: Symphony 32; Symphony 33; Symphony 34. (Concertgebouw/N. Harnoncourt)

① **4509-91192-2** (9/93)
Baroque Music of Bologna
Franceschini: 2-Trumpet Sonata in D; *D. Gabrielli:* Sonata à 6; *Jacchini:* Trattenimenti, Op.5 (exc); *Torelli:* Etienne Roger Concerto; Concerti grossi, Op.8 (exc); Concerto con due trombe, G24; Sinfonie e Concerti, Op.5 (exc); Sinfonia, G23; Concerti musicali, Op.6 (exc). (St James's Baroque Plyrs/I. Bolton)

① **4509-91378-2** (1/95)
Mozart—Sonatas for 2 pianos & for piano 4 hands
Mozart: Piano Sonata, K448; Andante and Variations, K501; Piano Duet Sonata, K521; Piano Duet Sonata, K381. (M. Argerich, A. Rabinovitch)

① **4509-91444-2** (7/93)
Dvořák/Schumann—Violin Concertos, etc
Dvořák: Violin Concerto; Romance, Op.11; *Schumann:* Violin Concerto. (T. Zehetmair, Philh/E. Inbal/C. Eschenbach)

① **4509-91449-2** (7/93)
Stravinsky—Orchestral Works
Stravinsky: Rite of Spring (Cpte); Etudes; Scherzo à la russe. (Philh/E. Inbal)

① **4509-91729-2** (1/95)
Respighi—Orchestral Works
Respighi: Botticelli Pictures; Birds; Ancient Airs and Dances. (St Paul CO/H. Wolff)

① **4509-91755-2** (2/95)
Bach—Cantatas, Vol.1
Bach: Cantata 1; Cantata 2; Cantata 3; Cantata 4; Cantata 5; Cantata 6; Cantata 7; Cantata 8; Cantata 9; Cantata 10; Cantata 11; Cantata 12; Cantata 13; Cantata 14; Cantata 16; Cantata 17; Cantata 18; Cantata 19. (P. Esswood, K. Equiluz, M. van Egmond, W. Gampert, P. Hinterreiter, M. van Altena, Vienna Boys' Ch, King's College Ch, VCM, Leonhardt Consort/N. Harnoncourt/G. Leonhardt, Tolz Boys' Ch, Chorus Viennensis, anon)

① **4509-91756-2** (2/95)
Bach—Cantatas, Vol.2
Bach: Cantata 20; Cantata 21; Cantata 22; Cantata 23; Cantata 24; Cantata 25; Cantata 26; Cantata 27; Cantata 28; Cantata 29; Cantata 30; Cantata 31; Cantata 32; Cantata 33; Cantata 34; Cantata 35; Cantata 36. (P. Esswood, K. Equiluz, M. van Egmond, K. Equiluz, M. van Altena, W. Gampert, W. Wyatt, S. Nimsgern, R. Jacobs, R. van der Meer, Vienna Boys' Ch, Tolz Boys' Ch, Hanover Boys' Ch, Chorus Viennensis, Kings College Ch, VCM/N. Harnoncourt, Leonhardt Consort/G. Leonhardt, anon, anon)

① **4509-91757-2** (2/95)
Bach—Cantatas, Vol.3
Bach: Cantata 37; Cantata 38; Cantata 39; Cantata 40; Cantata 41; Cantata 42; Cantata 43; Cantata 44; Cantata 45; Cantata 46; Cantata 47; Cantata 48; Cantata 49; Cantata 50; Cantata 51; Cantata 52; Cantata 54; Cantata 55; Cantata 56; Cantata 57; Cantata 58; Cantata 59; Cantata 60. (P. Esswood, K. Equiluz, R. van der Meer, R. Jacobs, M. van Altena, M. van Egmond, P. Jelosits, M. Kweksilber, S. Kronwitter, M. Schopper, H-F. Kunz, Vienna Boys' Ch, Hanover Boys' Ch, Tolz Boys' Ch, Chorus Viennensis, VCM/N. Harnoncourt, Leonhardt Consort/G. Leonhardt, anon)

① **4509-91758-2** (2/95)
Bach—Cantatas, Vol.4
Bach: Cantata 61; Cantata 62; Cantata 63; Cantata 64; Cantata 65; Cantata 66; Cantata 67; Cantata 68; Cantata 69; Cantata 69a; Cantata 70; Cantata 71; Cantata 72; Cantata 73; Cantata 74; Cantata 75; Cantata 76; Cantata 77; Cantata 78. (P. Jelosits, S. Kronwitter, P. Esswood, K. Equiluz, R. van der Meer, M. van Egmond, W. Wiedl, J. Erler, L. Visser, M. Klein, H. Adalbert Kraus, D. Bratschke, Tolz Boys' Ch, Hanover Boys' Ch, Ghent Collegium Vocale, VCM/N. Harnoncourt, Leonhardt Consort/G. Leonhardt)

① **4509-91759-2** (2/95)
Bach—Cantatas, Vol.5
Bach: Cantata 79; Cantata 80; Cantata 81; Cantata 82; Cantata 83; Cantata 84; Cantata 85; Cantata 86; Cantata 87; Cantata 88; Cantata 89; Cantata 90; Cantata 91; Cantata 92; Cantata 93; Cantata 94; Cantata 95; Cantata 96; Cantata 97; Cantata 98; Cantata 99. (D. Bratschke, P.

Esswood, M. van Egmond, W. Wiedl, K. Equiluz, R. van der Meer, P. Huttenlocher, M. Klein, C. Lengert, Hanover Boys' Ch, Ghent Collegium Vocale, Leonhardt Consort/G. Leonhardt, Tolz Boys' Ch, Vienna Boys' Ch, Chorus Viennensis, VCM/N. Harnoncourt, anon)

① **4509-91760-2** (2/95)
Bach—Cantatas, Vol.6
Bach: Cantata 100; Cantata 101; Cantata 102; Cantata 103; Cantata 104; Cantata 105; Cantata 106; Cantata 107; Cantata 108; Cantata 109; Cantata 110; Cantata 111; Cantata 112; Cantata 113; Cantata 114; Cantata 115; Cantata 116; Cantata 117. (D. Bratschke, P. Esswood, K. Equiluz, M. van Egmond, W. Wiedl, P. Huttenlocher, M. Klein, R. Harten, M. van Altena, R. van der Meer, S. Frangoulis, M. Stumpf, S. Lorenz, M. Huber, S. Hennig, R. Jacobs, Hanover Boys' Ch, Ghent Collegium Vocale, Leonhardt Consort/G. Leonhardt, Tolz Boys' Ch, VCM/N. Harnoncourt)

① **4509-91761-2** (2/95)
Bach—Cantatas, Vol.7
Bach: Cantata 119; Cantata 120; Cantata 121; Cantata 122; Cantata 123; Cantata 124; Cantata 125; Cantata 126; Cantata 127; Cantata 128; Cantata 129; Cantata 130; Cantata 131; Cantata 132; Cantata 133; Cantata 134; Cantata 135; Cantata 136; Cantata 137. (M. Huber, P. Esswood, K. Equiluz, R. Holl, P. Huttenlocher, T. Schilling, S. Rampf, A. Bergius, T. Thomaschke, M. van Egmond, R. Jacobs, S. Hennig, W. Heldwein, M. van Altena, A. Hartinger, Tolz Boys' Ch, VCM/N. Harnoncourt, Hanover Boys' Ch, Ghent Collegium Vocale, Leonhardt Consort/G. Leonhardt)

① **4509-91762-2** (2/95)
Bach—Cantatas, Vol.8
Bach: Cantata 138; Cantata 139; Cantata 140; Cantata 143; Cantata 144; Cantata 145; Cantata 146; Cantata 147; Cantata 148; Cantata 149; Cantata 150; Cantata 151; Cantata 152; Cantata 153; Cantata 154; Cantata 155; Cantata 156; Cantata 157; Cantata 158; Cantata 159; Cantata 161; Cantata 162. (A. Bergius, S. Rampf, K. Equiluz, R. Holl, P. Esswood, T. Hampson, R. Cericius, M. van Egmond, A. Pfeiffer, S. Hennig, C. Wegmann, T. Eiwanger, Tolz Boys' Ch, VCM/N. Harnoncourt, Hanover Boys' Ch, Ghent Collegium Vocale, Leonhardt Consort/G. Leonhardt)

① **4509-91763-2** (2/95)
Bach—Cantatas, Vol.9
Bach: Cantata 163; Cantata 164; Cantata 165; Cantata 166; Cantata 167; Cantata 168; Cantata 169; Cantata 170; Cantata 171; Cantata 172; Cantata 173; Cantata 174; Cantata 175; Cantata 176; Cantata 177; Cantata 178; Cantata 179; Cantata 180; Cantata 181; Cantata 182. (T. Eiwanger, P. Iconomou, K. Equiluz, R. Holl, C. Wegmann, P. Esswood, M. van Altena, A. Bergius, S. Gienger, J.P. O'Farrell, A. Raymann, Tolz Boys' Ch, VCM/N. Harnoncourt, Hanover Boys' Ch, Ghent Collegium Vocale, Leonhardt Consort/G. Leonhardt)

① **4509-91764-2** (2/95)
Bach—Cantatas, Vol.10
Bach: Cantata 183; Cantata 184; Cantata 185; Cantata 186; Cantata 187; Cantata 188; Cantata 192; Cantata 194; Cantata 195; Cantata 196; Cantata 197; Cantata 198; Cantata 199. (H. Wittek, P. Esswood, K. Equiluz, T. Hampson, A. Raymann, M. van Egmond, W. Wiedl, M. Emmermann, H. Stricker, S. Gienger, J.P. O'Farrell, R. Jacobs, J. Elwes, H. van der Kamp, B. Bonney, Tolz Boys' Ch, VCM/N. Harnoncourt, Hanover Boys' Ch, Ghent Collegium Vocale, Leonhardt Consort/G. Leonhardt)

① **4509-91852-2** (7/94)
Vivaldi—Concertos
Vivaldi: Concerti, Op. 10 (exc); Concerto, RV93; Concerto, RV94; Concerto, RV107; Concerto, RV108; Concerto, RV442; Sonatas, Op. 1 (exc). (Giardino Armonico Ens)

① **4509-91971-2** (1/94)
Monteverdi—Madrigali concertati
Monteverdi: Madrigals, Bk.8 (exc); Madrigals, Bk 7 (exc); Scherzi musicali (1632) (exc). (Tragicomedia/S. Stubbs)

① **4509-92147-2** (2/95)
Grieg—Piano Works
Grieg: Holberg Suite; Lyric Pieces, Op. 38 (exc); Lyric Pieces, Op. 43 (exc); Lyric Pieces, Op. 47 (exc); Lyric Pieces, Op. 54 (exc); Lyric Pieces, Op. 65 (exc); Lyric Pieces, Op. 68 (exc); Lyric Pieces, Op. 71 (exc); Norwegian Dances, Op. 35 (exc); Peer Gynt Suite 1 (exc); Lyric Pieces, Op. 12 (exc). (C. Katsaris)

① **4509-92176-2** (1/95)
Bach Family—Organ Works
Bach: Toccata and Fugue, BWV565; Fantasia and Fugue, BWV904; Prelude and Fugue, BWV547; Fantasia and Fugue, BWV542; *J.L. Bach:* Prelude and Fugue in D; J. M.

Bach I: Allein Gott in der Höh sei Ehr; Wenn wir in höchsten Nöten sein; *Bach:* Wenn wir in höchsten Nöten sein, BWV Anh78; Capriccio, BWV993; *J. Christoph Bach:* Prelude and Fugue in E flat; Warum betrübst du dich, mein Herz; Wach auf, mein Herz, und singe; Aus meines Herzens Grunde; *J.B. bach:* Passacaglia in B flat; Du Friedefürst, Herr Jesu Christ; *J.E. Bach:* Fantasie and Fugue in F. (W. Krumbach)

Ⓓ **4509-92177-2** (10/95)
Telemann—Paris Quartets; Suites
Telemann: Paris Quartets (Nouveaux quatuors); Suite in F; Overture-Suite, TWV55: Es 3. (J. Schröder, Amsterdam Qt, Concerto Amsterdam/F. Brüggen)

Ⓓ **4509-92180-2** (2/94)
Leclair/Naudot—Concertos
Leclair: Concertos, Op. 7 (exc); Concertos, Op. 10 (exc); *Naudot:* Recorder Concertos, Op. 17 (exc). (F. Brüggen, Concerto Amsterdam, J. Schröder (vn/dir), VCM/N. Harnoncourt)

Ⓓ **4509-92257-2** (1/95)
Brahms—Piano Works
Brahms: Haydn Variations; 2-Piano Sonata, Op. 34b; Waltzes, Op. 39. (M. Argerich, A. Rabinovitch)

Ⓓ **4509-92374-2** (2/95)
Elgar—The Music Makers; String Pieces
Elgar: Music Makers; Dream Children; Elegy; Sursum Corda; Sospiri; Chanson de matin; Chanson de nuit; Salut d'amour. (J. Rigby, BBC Sym Chor, BBC SO/A. Davis)

Ⓓ **4509-92628-2** (4/94)
Haydn—'London' Symphonies, etc
Haydn: Symphony 68; Symphony 93; Symphony 94; Symphony 95; Symphony 96; Symphony 97; Symphony 98; Symphony 99; Symphony 100; Symphony 101; Symphony 102; Symphony 103; Symphony 104. (Concertgebouw/N. Harnoncourt)

Ⓓ **4509-93157-2** (11/94)
Musica da Camera a Napoli
Sarri: Recorder Concerto in A minor; *D. Scarlatti:* Keyboard Sonatas (exc); *Durante:* Concerti per quartetto (exc); *A. Scarlatti:* Recorder Sonata in A minor; *F. Mancini:* Recorder Sonata in D minor. (Giardino Armonico Ens, G. Antonini (rec/dir))

Ⓓ **4509-93333-2** (12/94)
Mexican Baroque
Jerúsalem: Responsorio Segundo de S. S. José; Dixit Dominus; Mass in D; *Zumaya:* Sol-fa de Pedro; Lamentations of Jeremiah; Celebren, publiquen. (Chanticleer, Chanticleer Sinfonia/J. Jennings)

Ⓓ **4509-93669-2** (7/94)
Brüggen Edition Vol.2 —Italian Recorder Sonatas
Corelli: Sonatas, op. 5 (exc); *Barsanti:* Sonatas (exc); *Veracini:* Sonatas (exc); *Bigaglia:* Recorder Sonata in A minor; *Vivaldi:* Sonatas, Op. 13 (exc); *B. Marcello:* Sonatas, Op. 2 (exc). (F. Brüggen, A. Bylsma, G. Leonhardt)

Ⓓ **4509-93687-2** (10/94)
Bach—Cantatas
Bach: Cantata 198; Cantata 158; Cantata 27. (R. Hansmann, H. Watts, K. Equiluz, M. van Egmond, Monteverdi Ch, Concerto Amsterdam/J. Jürgens)

Ⓓ **4509-93688-2** (10/95)
Brüggen Edition Vol.1-Telemann Recorder Sonatas
Telemann: Getreue Music-Meister (exc); Essercizii Musici (exc); Fantaisies, TWV40: 2-13 (exc). (F. Brüggen, A. Bylsma, G. Leonhardt)

Ⓓ **4509-93772-2** (12/94)
Telemann—Darmstadt Overtures
Telemann: Overture-Suite, TWV55: g min 4; Overture-Suite, TWV55: a min 2; Overture-Suite, TWV55: C 6; Overture-Suite, TWV55: D 15; Overture-Suite, TWV55: d min 3; Overture-Suite, TWV55: f min 1. (VCM/N. Harnoncourt)

Ⓓ **4509-93856-2** (4/95)
Bortnyansky—Choral Concertos
Bortnyansky: Make a joyful noise; Cherubim Hymn 7; Let God arise; Lord, make me know mine end; Glory be to God; I cried unto God; Come o ye people; Te Deum. (St Petersburg Glinka Acad Ch/V. Chernushenko)

Ⓓ **4509-94458-2** (8/95)
Bach—Organ Works, Volume 1
Bach: Fantasia and Fugue, BWV542; Fugue, BWV578; Canzona, BWV588; Prelude and Fugue, BWV531; Prelude and Fugue, BWV543; Prelude and Fugue, BWV544; Fantasia, BWV562; Fantasia, BWV570; Fantasia, BWV572; Passacaglia and Fugue, BWV582. (T. Koopman)

Ⓓ **4509-94539-2** (3/95)
Ravel—Piano Works
Ravel: Gaspard de la nuit; Sonatine; Valses nobles et sentimentales; La Valse. (B. Berezovsky)

Ⓓ **4509-94540-2** (2/95)
Schnittke—Violin Works
Schnittke: Violin Concerto 2; Stille Nacht; Gratulations rondo; Violin Concerto 3. (G. Kremer, COE/C. Eschenbach, C. Eschenbach)

Ⓓ **4509-94551-2** (2/95)
Locatelli—Concerti grossi
Locatelli: Concerti grossi, Op. 1 (exc); Concerti, Op. 4 (exc); Concerti Grossi, Op. 7 (exc). (Cologne Concerto)

Ⓓ **4509-94552-2** (8/95)
Vivaldi—Double and Triple Concertos
Vivaldi: Concerto, RV531; Concerto, RV544; Concerto, RV551; Concerto, RV552; Concerto, RV561; Concerto, RV564. (C. Coin, Giardino Armonico Ens/G. Antonini)

Ⓓ **4509-94554-2** (6/95)
Carmen Fantasy—Virtuoso Music for Trumpet
Waxman: Carmen Fantasia; *Arban:* Norma Variations; Tyrolean Variations; *Falla:* Vida breve (exc); *Saint-Saëns:* Carnaval des animaux (exc); *Paganini:* Caprices, Op. 1 (exc); Zigeunerweisen; *Paganini:* Moto perpetuo, Op. 11; *Fauré:* Réveil; W. Brandt: Concert Piece 2. (S. Nakarjakov, A. Markovich)

Ⓓ **4509-94561-2** (2/95)
Palestrina—Vocal Works
Palestrina: Motets, Bk. 5 (1584) (exc); Missa pro defunctis; Motets, Bk. 5 (1584) (exc); Pange lingua; Motets, Bk. 3 (1575) (exc); Motets, Bk. 4 (1584) (exc); Gaude, Barbara a 5. (Chanticleer)

Ⓓ **4509-94565-2** (12/94)
Mendelssohn—String Symphonies
Mendelssohn: String Symphony 8; String Symphony 9; String Symphony 10. (Cologne Concerto)

Ⓓ **4509-94569-2** (11/95)
Salieri/Steffan—Concertos for Fortepiano
Salieri: Keyboard Concerto in C; Keyboard Concerto in B flat; *J. A. Štěpán:* Keyboard Concerto in B flat. (A. Staier, Cologne Concerto)

Ⓓ **4509-95068-2** (7/95)
Purcell—Songs of Welcome & Farewell
Purcell: Welcome song, Z340; O dive custos Auriacae domus, Z504; St Cecilia's Day Ode, Z334; Fairy Queen, Z629 (exc); Queen's Epicedium, Z383; Welcome Song, Z343; Young Thirsis' fate, Z473. (Suzie Le Blanc, B. Borden, S. Dugardin, D. Nasrawi, H. van der Kamp, S. Grant, Tragicomedia)

Ⓓ **4509-95497-2** (1/95)
Dvořák—Symphonies, etc
Dvořák: Symphony 7; Symphony 8; Symphony 9; Wild Dove. (Philh/E. Inbal)

Ⓓ **4509-95499-2** (1/95)
Chopin—Piano Works
Chopin: Waltzes; Ballades; Scherzos. (C. Katsaris)

Ⓓ **4509-95501-2** (1/95)
Schumann—Symphonies Nos 1-4
Schumann: Symphony 1; Symphony 2; Symphony 3; Symphony 4. (LPO/K. Masur)

Ⓓ **4509-95523-2** (2/95)
Brahms/Dvořák—String Quartets
Brahms: String Quartet 1; String Quartet 2; String Quartet 3; *Dvořák:* String Quartet 13. (Alban Berg Qt)

Ⓓ **4509-95518-2** (5/95)
Bach—Violin Concertos
Bach: 2-Violin Concerto; Violin Concerto, BWV1042; Violin Concerto, BWV1041; Violin Concerto, BWV1056; Violin and Oboe Concerto, BWV1060. (A. Harnoncourt, W. Pfeiffer, J. Schaeftlein, VCM/N. Harnoncourt)

Ⓓ **4509-95532-2** (2/95)
Bull—Harpsichord Music
J. Bull: In Nomines (exc); King's Hunt; Pavans and Galliards (exc); Dutch Dance; Almans (exc); Fantasias (exc); Canon in subdiapente; Gigge. (B. van Asperen)

Ⓓ **4509-95981-2** (1/95)
Tchaikovsky—Symphonies
Tchaikovsky: Symphony 4; Symphony 5; Symphony 6. (Leipzig Gewandhaus/K. Masur)

Ⓓ **4509-95998-2** (12/95)
Nathan Milstein - The Last Recital
Bach: Solo Violin Partitas and Sonatas (exc); *Beethoven:* Violin Sonata 4; *Handel:* Violin Sonatas (exc); *Liszt:* Consolations, S172 (exc); *Paganini:* Caprices, Op. 1 (exc);

Prokofiev: Tales of an old grandmother (exc); *Sarasate:* Introduction and Tarantella, Op. 43; *Tchaikovsky:* Mazeppa (exc). (N. Milstein, G. Pludermacher)

Ⓓ **4509-96200-2** (12/94)
The Three Tenors 1994
Massenet: Cid (exc); *Moreno Torroba:* Maravilla (exc); *Massenet:* Werther (exc); *Rodgers:* Spring is Here (exc); *Lara:* Granada; *De Curtis:* Non ti scordar di me; Tu, ca nun chiagne!; *Leoncavallo:* Pagliacci (exc); *Puccini:* Turandot (exc); *Verdi:* Rigoletto (exc); Traviata (exc); *Schifrin:* Tribute to Hollywood; Around the World. (J. Carreras, P. Domingo, L. Pavarotti, Los Angeles Music Center Op Chor, Los Angeles PO/Z. Mehta)

Ⓓ **4509-96800-2** (12/95)
Jennifer Larmore—Where Shall I Fly?
Mozart: Clemenza di Tito (exc); Così fan tutte (exc); *Finta giardiniera* (exc); Finta semplice (exc); Mitridate (exc); Nozze di Figaro (exc); *Handel:* Ariodante (exc); Rinaldo (exc); Serse (exc); Semele (exc); Hercules (exc). (J. Larmore, Lausanne CO/J. López-Cobos)

Ⓓ **4509-97449-2** (6/95)
Berg/Hartmann/Janáček—Violin Concertos
Berg: Violin Concerto; *Janáček:* Violin Concerto; *K. A. Hartmann:* Concerto funèbre. (T. Zehetmair, Philh/H. Holliger, Deutsche Kammerphilharmonie, T. Zehetmair (vn/dir))

Ⓓ **4509-97452-2** (11/95)
Bach—Harpsichord Concertos
Bach: Harpsichord Concerto, BWV1052; Harpsichord Concerto, BWV1053; Harpsichord Concerto, BWV1054; Harpsichord Concerto, BWV1055; Harpsichord Concerto, BWV1056; Harpsichord Concerto, BWV1057; Harpsichord Concerto, BWV1058; Harpsichord Concerto, BWV1059; 2-Harpsichord Concerti (exc); 2-Harpsichord Concerti (exc); 3-Harpsichord Concerti; 4-Harpsichord Concerto. (H. Tachezi, VCM/N. Harnoncourt, A. Uittenbosch, A. Curtis, E. Müller, J. van Wering, Leonhardt Consort, G. Leonhardt (hpd/dir))

Ⓓ **4509-97457-2** (12/95)
French Romantic Songs
Gounod: Solitude; *Franck:* Mariage des roses; Nocturne; Roses et papillons; *Saint-Saëns:* Attente; Clair de lune; Cloche; Pas d'armes; *Bizet:* Chanson du fou; *Chabrier:* Cigales; Île heureuse; Villanelle des petits canards; *Massenet:* Poème d'Avril (exc); *Fauré:* Songs, Op. 4 (exc); Songs, Op. 46 (exc); Songs, Op. 51 (exc); *Indy:* Lied maritime; Madrigal; *Chausson:* Poème de l'amour et de la mer (exc); Mélodies, Op. 2 (exc); *Pierné:* Sérénade; *Hahn:* Chansons grises (exc); Si mes vers. (D. Fischer-Dieskau, H. Höll)

Ⓓ **4509-97458-2** (12/95)
Loewe—Lieder and Balladen
Loewe: Asra, Op. 133; Balladen, Op. 1 (exc); Balladen, op. 94 (exc); Seltne Beter, Op. 141; Lieder, Gesänge, Romanzen und Balladen, Op. 9 (exc); Gedichte, Op. 61 (exc); Gefangene Admiral, Op. 115; Lieder, Op. 103 (exc); Hebräische Gesänge, Op. 4 (exc); Hebräische Gesänge, Op. 13 (exc); Legends, Op. 75 (exc); Ich bin ein guter Hirte; Dunkle Auge. (D. Fischer-Dieskau, H. Höll)

Ⓓ **4509-97459-2** (12/95)
Eisler—Hollywood Songbook
Eisler: An den kleinen Radioapparat; An den Schlaf; Auf der Flucht; Elegie 1939; Elegien; Frühling; Aus der Heimat; Gedenktafel für 4000 Soldaten; Hollywood-Elegien; Hölderlin-Fragmente (exc); Horatios Monolog; Hotelzimmer 1942; In den Weiden; In der Frühe; Landschaft des Exils; Letzte Elegie; Maske des Bösen; Pascal Lieder; Spruch; Spruch 1939; Über den Selbstmord; Über die Dauer des Exils; Verfehlte Liebe; Zufluchtsstätte. (D. Fischer-Dieskau, A. Reimann)

Ⓓ **4509-97465-2** (10/95)
Franz Brüggen Edition Vol. 3—English Ensemble Music
A. Holborne: Almain The Honiesuckle'; Various consort pieces (exc); Night watch; Sighes; Heigh Ho Holiday; *Taverner:* In Nomine a 4; *Tye:* In Nomines a 5 (exc); *Byrd:* In Nomines a 5; Browning a 5, BE17/10; *T. Simpson:* Ricercar 'Bonny Sweet Robin'; *Morley:* Fantasie (exc); *Jeffreys:* Fantasia a 3; *Parcham:* Solo in G; *R. Carr:* Divisions upon an Italian ground; *Babell:* Recorder Concerto a 7 in D; *Pepusch:* Recorder Sonata 4 in F; *Purcell:* Chaconne in F. (F. Brüggen, K. Boeke, W. van Hauwe, M. Leonhardt, A. Stuurop, A. van den Hombergh, L. van Dael, A. Bylsma, W. Möller, F. Nijenhuis, N. Harnoncourt, G. Leonhardt, B. van Asperen, Brüggen Consort)

Ⓓ **4509-97466-2** (10/95)
Frans Brüggen Edition Vol. 4—Early Baroque Recorder Music
Eyck: Fluyten Lust-hof (exc); *Frescobaldi:* Canzoni with Titles (exc); *Cima:* Recorder Sonata in D; Recorder Sonata

Campanas del Alba; Segovia: Estudio sin luz; Remembranza; Moreno Torroba: Nocturno; Madroños. (W. Lendle)

ⓘ **9031-76036-2** (11/92)
Brahms—Piano Trios
Brahms: Piano Trio 1; Piano Trio 2; Piano Trio 3; Piano Trio, Op. posth. (Fontenay Trio)

ⓘ **9031-76139-2** (10/92)
Bartók—Piano Works
Bartók: For Children (1908/09); Mikrokosmos, Bk 1; Mikrokosmos, Bk 2; Mikrokosmos, Bk 3; Mikrokosmos, Bk 4; Mikrokosmos, Bk 5; Mikrokosmos, Bk 6. (D. Ránki)

ⓘ **9031-76349-2** (3/93)
Classical Violin Sonatas
Beethoven: Violin Sonata 5; Mozart: Violin Sonata, K378; Mendelssohn: Violin Sonata (1838). (M. Vengerov, I. Golan, A. Markovich)

ⓘ **9031-76350-2** (9/94)
Bartók—Orchestral Works
Bartók: Miraculous mandarin (exc); Pictures, Sz46; Concerto for Orchestra. (Philh/H. Wolff)

ⓘ **9031-76442-2** (8/93)
Wagner—Excerpts from the 1936 Bayreuth Festival
Wagner: Lohengrin (exc); Walküre (exc); Siegfried (exc). (M. Müller, M. Klose, F. Völker, M. Lorenz, E. Zimmermann, J. Prohaska, J. von Manowarda, Bayreuth Fest Chor, Bayreuth Fest Orch/H. Tietjen)

ⓘ **9031-76456-2** (5/93)
Tchaikovsky—Orchestral Works
Tchaikovsky: Romeo and Juliet; Francesca da Rimini; Mazeppa (exc); Festival Coronation March. (Leipzig Gewandhaus/K. Masur)

ⓘ **9031-76460-2** (6/93)
Haydn—Symphonies
Haydn: Symphony 30; Symphony 53; Symphony 69. (VCM/N. Harnoncourt)

ⓘ **9031-76997-2** (1/93)
Symphonic Tango
Piazzolla: Adios Nonino; Oblivion; Filiberto: Caminito; Dames: Fuimos; Stratta: Astoreando; Villoldo: Choclo; Gardel: Día que me quieras; Rodríguez: Cumparsita; Ziegler: Milonga en el viento; Discepolo: Cafetin de Buenos Aires; Uno; Paulos: Inspiracion. (Buenos Aires Qnt, RPO/E. Stratta)

ⓘ **9031-77309-2** (2/94)
Bizet/Prokofiev/Haydn—Symphonies
Bizet: Symphony; Haydn: Symphony 1; Prokofiev: Symphony 1. (St Paul CO/H. Wolff)

ⓘ **9031-77311-2** (1/94)
CPE Bach/Vivaldi/Tartini—Cello Concertos
C.P.E. Bach: Cello Concerto, H436; Tartini: Cello Concerto in D; Vivaldi: Concerto, RV406. (M. Rostropovich, St Paul CO/H. Wolff)

ⓘ **9031-77314-2** (10/94)
Schoenberg—Orchestral Works
Schoenberg: Verklärte Nacht; Begleitungsmusik, Op. 34; Chamber Symphony 1. (COE/H. Holliger)

ⓘ **9031-77351-2** (4/94)
Virtuoso Works for Violin
Wieniawski: Polonaise, Op. 4; Paganini: Palpiti, Op. 13; Wieniawski: Légende, Op. 17; Kreisler: Schön Rosmarin; Bloch: Baal shem (exc); Tchaikovsky: Souvenir d'un lieu cher, Op. 42 (exc); Kreisler: Tambourin chinois; Messiaen: Thème et Variations; Kreisler: Caprice viennois; Sarasate: Caprice basque; Bazzini: Ronde des Lutins. (M. Vengerov, I. Golan)

ⓘ **9031-77476-2** (8/93)
Schumann—Piano Works
Schumann: Davidsbündlertänze; Piano Sonata 2; Toccata. (B. Berezovsky)

ⓘ **9031-77603-2** (12/92)
Works by Leopold and Wolfgang Amadeus Mozart
L. Mozart: Trumpet Concerto; Mozart: Bassoon Concerto, K191; Notturno, K286; Serenade, K239. (M. Turkovic, B. Immer, VCM/N. Harnoncourt)

ⓘ **9031-77608-2** (2/93)
Purcell—Anthems,Instrumental Music & Songs
Purcell: Bell Anthem, Z49; Blow up the trumpet in Sion, Z10; O God, thou art my God, Z35; O God, thou hast cast us out, Z36; My heart is inditing, Z30; Remember not, Lord, our offences, Z50; Chaconne, Z730; Overture, Z771; Overture, Z770; Overture, Z772; Pavans, Z748-51 (exc); Pavan, Z752; Sonatas, Z802-11 (exc); Grounds (exc); Choice Collection of Lessons (exc); Musick's Hand-maid, Part 2 (exc); Viola da gamba Fantasies, Z735-43 (exc); Fly swift, ye hours, Z369; Birthday Ode, Z342; Timon of

Athens, Z632 (exc). (J. Bowman, N. Rogers, M. van Egmond, King's College Ch/D. Willcocks, Leonhardt Consort/G. Leonhardt, G. Leonhardt, Baroque Instr Ens/F. Brüggen)

ⓘ **9031-77614-2** (5/93)
Bach—Cantatas
Bach: Cantata 67; Cantata 108; Cantata 127. (A. Fahberg, L. Benningsen, P. Pears, K. Engen, Munich Bach Ch, Munich St Op Orch/K. Richter)

ⓘ **9031-77620-2** (7/93)
Telemann—Orchestral Works
Telemann: Overture-Suite, TWV55: a min 2; Recorder and Flute Concerto; Viola Concerto in G; Overture des Nations, TWV55: G 4. (F. Brüggen, F. Vester, P. Doctor, South-West German Orch/F. Tilegant, Concerto Amsterdam/F. Brüggen, Amsterdam CO/A. Rieu)

ⓘ **9031-77623-2** (7/93)
C.P.E. Bach—Keyboard Sonatas
C.P.E. Bach: Keyboard Sonatas, H24-9; Württemberg Sonatas; Solo Harpsichord Concerto, H190. (B. van Asperen)

ⓘ **9031-77624-2** (7/93)
Boccherini—Cello Concertos
Boccherini: Cello Concerto, G477; Cello Concerto, G479; Cello Concerto, G480; Cello Concerto, G481. (A. Bylsma, Concerto Amsterdam/J. Schröder)

ⓘ **9031-77705-2** (5/93)
Works for Trumpet & Piano
Gershwin: Rhapsody in Blue; Arensky: Concert Waltz; Arban: Carnaval de Venise; Ravel: Pavane; Bernstein: Rondo for Lifey; Glazunov: Album leaf; Fibich: At twilight (exc); Rimsky-Korsakov: Tale of Tsar Saltan (exc); Dinicu: Hora staccato; Glière: Waltz, Op. 48/2; Rueff: Trumpet Sonatina; Stolte: Burleske; J.P.E. Hartmann: Arbucklenian Polka. (S. Nakarjakov, A. Markovich)

TER Classics

ⓘ **CDVIR8307** (1/89)
Josephine Barstow sings Verdi Arias
Verdi: Forza del destino (exc); Otello (exc); Macbeth (exc); Aida (exc); Don Carlo (exc). (J. Barstow, ENO Orch/M. Elder, S. Burgess, J. Connell)

ⓘ **CDVIR8314** (10/91)
Is it really me?
H. Schmidt: 110 in the Shade (exc); Romberg: Desert Song (exc); F. Loewe: My Fair Lady (exc); Novello: Dancing Years (exc); Lehár: Zigeunerliebe (exc); Grainer: Robert and Elizabeth (exc); Coward: Conversation Piece (exc); F. Loesser: Most Happy Fella (exc); Bernstein: Candide (1956) (exc); Kálmán: Csárdásfürstin (exc); Rodgers: Oklahoma! (exc); Lehár: Graf von Luxemburg (exc); Kálmán: Gräfin Mariza (exc); Romberg: Student Prince (exc). (M. Hill Smith, Philh, National SO/J.O. Edwards, Scottish Op Orch/J. Brown, New Sadler's Wells Op Chor, New Sadler's Wells Op Orch/B. Wordsworth)

ⓘ **CDVIR8316** (5/93)
Sullivan—Overtures
Sullivan: HMS Pinafore (exc); Pirates of Penzance (exc); Patience (exc); Iolanthe (exc); Princess Ida (exc); Mikado (exc); Gondoliers (exc); Yeomen of the Guard (exc); Ruddigore (exc); Di Ballo. (New Sadler's Wells Op Orch, D'Oyly Carte Op Orch/J. Pryce-Jones/S. Phipps/J.O. Edwards)

ⓘ **CDVIR8317** (5/94)
If I Loved You - Love Duets from the Musicals
A. Lloyd Webber: Phantom of the Opera (exc); F. Loewe: Brigadoon (exc); Berlin: Annie Get Your Gun (exc); M. Willson: Music Man (exc); F. Loesser: Guys and Dolls (exc); Bernstein: West Side Story (exc); Kern: Show Boat (exc); Friml: Rose Marie (exc); Rodgers: Oklahoma (exc); King and I (exc); King and I (exc); Carousel (exc); South Pacific (exc). (V. Masterson, T. Allen, Philh/J.O. Edwards)

Testament

ⓘ **SBT1002** (6/91)
Reginald Kell—Clarinet Works
Weber: Clarinet Concertino; Brahms: Clarinet Trio; Holbrooke: Clarinet Quintet 1. (R. Kell, A. Pini, L. Kentner, Willoughby Qt, orch/W. Goehr)

ⓘ **SBT1003** (9/91)
The Young Menuhin—Encores, Vol.1
F. Ries: Tchaikovsky: Paganini: Violin Concerto 2 (exc); Nováček: Concert caprices, Op.5 (exc); Rimsky-Korsakov: Tsar's Bride (exc); Ravel: Tzigane; Paganini: Caprices, Op.1 (exc); Falla: Vida breve (exc); Rimsky-Korsakov: Tale of Tsar Saltan (exc); Bazzini: Ronde des lutins; Paganini: Moto perpetuo, Op.11; Wieniawski: Souvenir de Moscou, Op.6; Kreisler: Tambourin chinois; Debussy: Préludes

(exc); Sarasate: Danzas españolas (exc); Brahms: Hungarian Dances (exc); Paganini: Caprices, Op.1 (exc); Dvořák: Slavonic Dances (exc); Brahms: Hungarian Dances (exc). (Y. Menuhin, L. Persinger, H. Giesen, A. Balsam, M. Gazelle, F. Webster)

ⓘ **SBT1005** (10/92)
Ten Top Tenors
Leoncavallo: Pagliacci (exc); Cardillo: Core 'ngrato; Adam: Postillon de Lonjumeau (exc); Auber: Fra Diavolo (exc); Gounod: Faust (exc); Puccini: Tosca (exc); Korngold: Tote Stadt (exc); J. Strauss II: Zigeunerbaron (exc); Bizet: Carmen (exc); Massenet: Werther (exc); Donizetti: Elisir d'amore (exc); Rachmaninov: Songs, Op.26 (exc); Ponchielli: Gioconda (exc); Verdi: Rigoletto (exc); Wagner: Lohengrin (exc); Meistersinger (exc); Verdi: Trovatore (exc); Mario: Leggenda di Rhone; Donizetti: Favorita (exc); Tosti: 'A Vucchella. (E. Caruso, H. Roswaenge, B. Gigli, R. Tauber, G. Thill, J. McCormack, J. Björling, L. Melchior, G. Martinelli, T. Schipa, orch/W.B. Rogers, Berlin St Op Chor, Berlin St Op Orch/B. Seidler-Winkler/E. Goossens, La Scala Orch/F. Ghione/G. Szell, Vienna Th Orch/A. Paulik/P. Gaubert/F. Heurteur, F. Kreisler, E. Schneider/N. Grevillius, Philadelphia/E. Ormandy, LSO/L. Collingwood/R. Bourdon)

ⓘ **SBT1007** (8/92)
Kell plays Mozart Clarinet Works
Mozart: Clarinet Concerto, K622; Clarinet Quintet, K581; Piano Trio, K498. (R. Kell, LPO/M. Sargent, Philh Qt, F. Riddle, L. Kentner)

ⓘ **SBT1008** (12/92)
Viva Rossini
Rossini: Barbiere di Siviglia (exc); Barbiere di Siviglia (exc); Barbiere di Siviglia (exc); Barbiere di Siviglia (exc); Barbiere di Siviglia (exc); Barbiere di Siviglia (exc); Barbiere di Siviglia (exc); Barbiere di Siviglia (exc); Cenerentola (exc); Cenerentola (exc); Guillaume Tell (exc); Guillaume Tell (exc); Guillaume Tell (exc); Guillaume Tell (exc); Mosè in Egitto (exc); Semiramide (exc); Semiramide (exc); Stabat Mater (exc); Stabat Mater (exc). (T. Ruffo, D. Borgioli, J. McCormack, M. Sammarco, L. Tetrazzini, A. Didur, A. Bonci, R. Stracciari, G. Huguet, F. de Lucia, A. Pini-Corsi, A. Rossi, C. Supervia, L. Pagliughi, G. Martinelli, G. De Luca, J. Mardones, A. Sved, A. d'Arkor, F. Tamagno, E. Pinza, A.M. Turchetti, E. Stignani, C. Boninsegna, E. Caruso, F. Austral, orch, anon, anon, chor, ROH Chor/J. Barbirolli/A. Albergoni)

ⓘ **SBT1009** (10/92)
R. Strauss/Weber—Wind Concertos
R. Strauss: Horn Concerto 1; Oboe Concerto; Weber: Bassoon Concerto. (L. Goossens, D. Brain, G. Brooke, Philh/A. Galliera, RLPO/M. Sargent)

ⓘ **SBT1010** (10/92)
Ginette Neveu & Josef Hassid
Kreisler: W.F.Bach Grave; Suk: Pieces, Op.17 (exc); Chopin: Nocturnes (exc); Gluck: Orfeo ed Euridice (exc); Paradies: Sicilienne; Kreisler: Tartini's Corelli Variations; Elgar: Capricieuse; Tchaikovsky: Souvenir d'un lieu cher, Op.42 (exc); Massenet: Thaïs (exc); Dvořák: Humoresques, Op.101 (exc); Sarasate: Danzas españolas (exc); Achron: Hebrew Melody; Kreisler: Caprice viennois; Elgar: Capricieuse. (G. Neveu, J. Hassid, B. Seidler-Winkler, G. Beck, G. Moore, I. Newton)

ⓘ **SBT1011** (10/92)
Debussy—Orchestral Works
Debussy: Nocturnes (exc); Après-midi; Martyre de St Sébastien (exc); La Mer. (Philh/G. Cantelli)

ⓘ **SBT1012** (2/93)
Cantelli conducts Wagner & Brahms
Brahms: Symphony 1; Wagner: Siegfried Idyll; Siegfried (exc). (D. Brain, Philh/G. Cantelli)

ⓘ **SBT1013** (12/92)
Dame Joan Hammond—A Celebration
Puccini: Gianni Schicchi (exc); Tosca (exc); Bohème (exc); Madama Butterfly (exc); Manon Lescaut (exc); Massenet: Thaïs (exc); Offenbach: Contes d'Hoffmann (exc); Saint-Saëns: Etienne Marcel (exc); Cilea: Adriana Lecouvreur (exc); Giordano: Andrea Chénier (exc); Catalani: Wally (exc); Verdi: Don Carlo (exc); Aida (exc); Tchaikovsky: Eugene Onegin (exc); Dvořák: Rusalka (exc). (J. Hammond, Hallé/L. Heward, CBO, Philh/L. Collingwood/S. Robinson/V. Tausky/W. Susskind/G. Curiel, RLPO/C. Lambert)

ⓘ **SBT1014** (5/93)
Delius—Orchestral Works
Delius: First cuckoo; Violin Concerto; Hassan (exc); Koanga (exc); Piano Concerto; Caprice and Elegy; Légende. (A. Sammons, H. Holst, B. Harrison, B. Moiseiwitsch, G. Moore, RLPO/M. Sargent, Hallé, Philh/C. Lambert, CO/E. Fenby)

① **SBT1015** (4/93)
Toscanini—Unpublished HMV Recordings, 1935/38
Brahms: Symphony 2; *Mendelssohn:* Midsummer Night's
Dream (exc); *Rossini:* Semiramide (exc). (BBC SO/A.
Toscanini)

① **SBT1016** (7/93)
Pierre Flagstad - recital
Dvořák: Cello Concerto; *Saint-Saëns:* Cello Concerto 1;
Fauré: Elégie; Berceuse, Op.16; *Ravel:* Pièce en forme de
Habanera; *Debussy:* Rêverie; *Saint-Saëns:* Carnaval des
animaux (exc). (P. Fournier, E. Lush, G. Moore, Philh/R.
Kubelik/W. Susskind)

① **SBT1017** (7/93)
Orchestral Works - Cantelli
Dukas: Apprenti Sorcier; *Ravel:* Pavane; *Falla:* Sombrero
de tres picos Suites (exc); *Ravel:* Daphnis et Chloé Suites
(exc); *Rossini:* Siège de Corinthe (exc); *Casella:*
Paganiniana, Op.65. (Philh, Santa Cecilia Academy
Orch/G. Cantelli)

① **SBT1018** (7/93)
Kirsten Flagstad
Ochs: Dank sei dir, Herr; *Handel:* Serse (exc); Messiah
(exc); *Bach:* St Matthew Passion, BWV244 (exc); *Purcell:*
Dido (exc); *Gluck:* Orfeo ed Euridice (exc); *Wagner:*
Walküre (exc); Tristan und Isolde (exc). (K. Flagstad, C.
Shacklock, S. Svanholm, Philh/W. Braithwaite/A.
Fistoulari/W. Susskind/K. Böhm)

① **SBT1019** (8/93)
Tito Gobbi - Opera Arias & Songs
Mozart: Don Giovanni (exc); *Verdi:* Don Carlo (exc);
Puccini: Fanciulla del West (exc); *Rossini:* Barbiere di
Siviglia (exc); *Leoncavallo:* Pagliacci (exc); *Verdi:* Otello
(exc); *Mozart:* Nozze di Figaro (exc); *Verdi:* Traviata (exc);
Rigoletto (exc); Macbeth (exc); *N. Valente:* Tornal; *Tosti:* 'A
Vucchella; *Denza:* Occhi di fata; *Falvo:* Dicitencello vuie;
Pigarelli: Montanara; *Sadero:* Gondoliera Veneziana;
Cottrau: Santa Lucia; *Di Capua:* 'O sole mio; *Tosti:*
Marechiare; *Anon:* Fenesta che lucive. (T. Gobbi, La Scala
Orch/U. Berrettoni, RPO/A. Erede, Philh/J. Robertson/W.
Susskind, LSO/W. Braithwaite, Orch/A. La Rosa Parodi/P.
Green, Inst Ens)

① **SBT1022** (12/93)
Brain,Kell & Goossens play Schumann & Beethoven
Beethoven: Piano Trios (exc); Horn Sonata; *Dukas:*
Villanelle; *Schumann:* Adagio and Allegro, Op.70;
Fantasiestücke, Op.73; Romanzen, Op.94. (L. Goossens,
R. Kell, D. Brain, A. Pini, G. Moore, D. Matthews)

① **SBT1023** (1/94)
Moiseiwitsch plays Schumann and Brahms
Brahms: Handel Variations; *Schumann:* Fantasie;
Fantasiestücke, Op.12. (B. Moiseiwitsch)

① **SBT1024** (12/93)
Brahms—Violin Sonatas
Brahms: Violin Sonata 1; Violin Sonata 2; Violin Sonata 3.
(G. de Vito, Edwin Fischer, T. Aprea)

① **SBT1026** (4/94)
Irmgard Seefried
Mozart: Vado, ma dove?, K583; Chi sà, K582; Zaïde (exc);
Kleine Spinnerin, K531; Kinderspiel, K598; Sehnsucht
nach dem Frühling, K596; An Chloe, K524; Warnung,
K433; Zauberer, K472; Ridente la calma, K152; Als Luise
die Briefe, K520; Veilchen, K476; Dans un bois solitaire,
K308; Traumbild, K530; Zufriedenheit, K349;
Abendempfindung, K523; *Flies:* Wiegenlied; *Brahms:*
Lieder, Op.49 (exc); *Schubert:* Wiegenlied, D498; Nacht
und Träume, D827; Heidenröslein, D257; Auf dem Wasser
zu singen, D774; Du bist die Ruh, D776; *Wolf:* Mörike
Lieder (exc); Mörike Lieder (exc); Songs for a Woman's
Voice (exc). (I. Seefried, G. Moore, H. von Nordberg, W.
Schmidt, LMP/H. Blech)

① **SBT1027** (4/94)
Medtner—Piano Concertos, etc
Medtner: Piano Concerto 2; Piano Concerto 3;
Arabesques, Op.7 (exc); Fairy Tales, Op.26 (exc). (N.
Medtner, Philh/I. Dobroven)

① **SBT1028** (4/94)
Mozart—Violin Concertos
Mozart: Violin Concerto, K216; Violin Concerto, K218;
Violin Concerto, K219. (S. Goldberg, Philh/W. Susskind)

① **SBT1029** (2/94)
Gilels plays Saint-Saëns and Rachmaninov
Rachmaninov: Piano Concerto 3; *Saint-Saëns:* Piano
Concerto 2; *Shostakovich:* Preludes and Fugues, Op.87
(exc). (Emil Gilels, Paris Cons/A. Cluytens)

① **SBT1033** (9/94)
Cherkassky plays Liszt, Saint-Saëns & Liadov
Liszt: Piano Concerto 1; Liebesträume, S541 (exc);
Hungarian Rhapsodies, S244 (exc); *Faust*—Paraphrase,

S407; Don Juan réminiscences, S418; *Saint-Saëns:*
Carnaval des Animaux (exc); *Liadov:* Musical Snuffbox,
Op.32. (S. Cherkassky, Philh/A. Fistoulari)

① **SBT1034** (11/94)
Guido Cantelli conducts Rossini, Mendelssohn &
Beethoven
Beethoven: Symphony 5 (exc); *Mendelssohn:* Symphony
4; *Rossini:* Gazza ladra (exc). (Philh/G. Cantelli)

① **SBT1036** (11/94)
Lisa Della Casa sings Richard Strauss
R. Strauss: Ariadne auf Naxos (exc); Lieder, Op.27 (exc);
Lieder, Op.69 (exc); Lieder, Op.49 (exc); Lieder, Op.36
(exc); Lieder, Op.17 (exc); Lieder, Op.39 (exc). (L. Della
Casa, L. Otto, N. Puttar, L. Kirschstein, R. Schock, S.
Peschko, BPO/A. Erede)

① **SBT1042** (10/94)
Brahms—Piano Concerto No.2, etc
Brahms: Piano Concerto 2; Piano Pieces, Op. 117 (exc);
Piano Pieces, Op. 119 (exc); Rhapsodies, Op. 79 (exc).
(Solomon, Philh/I. Dobroven)

① **SBT1052** (3/95)
Prokofiev/Hindemith/Walton—String Quartets
Hindemith: String Quartet, Op.22; *Prokofiev:* String Quartet
2; *Walton:* String Quartet. (Hollywood Qt)

① **SBT1053** (3/95)
Chamber Works
Ravel: Introduction and Allegro; *Debussy:* Danse sacrée et
danse profane; *Turina:* Oración del Torero; *Villa-Lobos:*
String Quartet 6; *Creston:* String Quartet. (A. Gleghorn, M.
Lurie, A.M. Stockton, Hollywood Qt, Concert Arts Stgs/F.
Slatkin)

① **SBT1057** (10/95)
Beethoven—Lieder
Beethoven: Lieder, Op.52 (exc); Lieder, Op.75 (exc);
Lieder, Op.83 (Cpte); Lieder, Op.48 (Cpte); Adelaide,
Op.46; Andenken, WoO136; Lied aus der Ferne, WoO137;
Sehnsucht, WoO146; Wachtelschlag, WoO129; An die
Hoffnung, Op.94; Kuss, Op.128; Abendlied, WoO150;
Resignation, WoO149; Zärtliche Liebe, WoO123; In questa
tomba oscura, WoO133. (D. Fischer-Dieskau, H. Klust)

① **SBT1058** (4/95)
James Johnston - Opera Arias and Songs
Verdi: Aida (exc); Trovatore (exc); Simon Boccanegra
(exc); *Gounod:* Faust (exc); *Bizet:* Carmen (exc); *Wagner:*
Meistersinger (exc); *Puccini:* Bohème (exc); Madama
Butterfly (exc); *Leoncavallo:* Pagliacci (exc); *Mascagni:*
Cavalleria Rusticana (exc); Cavalleria Rusticana (exc);
Vaughan Williams: Hugh the Drover (exc); *German:* Merrie
England (exc); *Leoncavallo:* Mattinata; *Traditional:* Dark-
eyed sailor; Bonny labouring boy; Star of the County
Down; Ireland, mother Ireland. (J. Johnston, J. Gartside, A.
Shuard, O. Price, Philh, orch, ROHO, W. Reynold Orch/M.
Mudie/L. Collingwood/J. Robertson/E. Robinson/F.
Collinson)

① **SBT1059** (9/95)
Erich Kunz—Opera and Song Recital
Mozart: Nozze di Figaro (exc); Don Giovanni (exc); Don
Giovanni (exc); Zauberflöte (exc); *Lortzing:* Waffenschmied
(exc); Zar und Zimmermann (exc); Wildschütz (exc); *Zeller:*
Vogelhändler (exc); *J. Strauss II:* Lustige Krieg (exc);
Nacht in Venedig (exc); Nacht in Venedig (exc);
Zigeunerbaron (exc); *E. Arnold:* Wenn der Herrgott net will;
Pick: Wiener Fiakerlied; *Zillner:* Es steht ein alter
Nussbaum; *E. Arnold:* Da draussen in der Wachau;
Krakauer: Du guater Himmelvater; *L. Gruber:* Mei Muaterl
war a Weanerin; *Kratzl:* Glück is' a Vogerl; *Fellner:* Ewiges
Wien. (E. Kunz, I. Seefried, VPO/H. von Karajan/O.
Ackermann/R. Moralt, Vienna Volksoper Orch/A. Paulik,
Kemmeter-Faltl Schrammel Ens, Philh)

① **SBT1061** (8/95)
Borodin/Glazunov/Tchaikovsky—Chamber Works
Borodin: String Quartet 2; *Glazunov:* Novelettes, Op.15;
Tchaikovsky: String Quartet 1. (Hollywood Qt)

① **SBT1064** (10/95)
Géza Anda plays Tchaikovsky & Rachmaninov
Rachmaninov: Piano Concerto 2; Preludes (exc);
Tchaikovsky: Piano Concerto 1. (G. Anda, Philh/A.
Galliera)

① **SBT1066** (10/95)
Chopin—Piano Works
Chopin: Piano Concerto 1; Etudes (exc); Ballades (exc).
(G. Anda, Philh/A. Galliera)

① **SBT1067** (10/95)
Géza Anda plays Liszt, Bartók & Dohnányi
Liszt: Piano Sonata, S178; Mephisto Waltz 1, S514;
Concert Studies, S144 (exc); Paganini Studies, S140
(exc); *Bartók:* Sonatina; *Dohnányi:* Coppélia Waltz. (G.
Anda)

① **SBT3054** (4/95)
Brahms—Symphonies, etc
Brahms: Symphony 1; Symphony 2; Symphony 3;
Symphony 4; Tragic Overture; Haydn Variations. (BPO/R.
Kempe)

① **SBT3055** (6/95)
Haydn—String Quartets, Volume 1
Haydn: String Quartets, Op.1 (exc); String Quartets, Op.20
(exc); String Quartets, Op.20 (exc); String Quartets, Op.50
(exc); String Quartets, Op.54 (exc); String Quartets, Op.54
(exc); String Quartets, Op.64 (exc); String Quartets, Op.64
(exc); String Quartets, Op.74 (exc); String Quartets, Op.76
(exc); String Quartets, Op.76 (exc); String Quartets, Op.77
(exc). (Pro Arte Qt)

① **SBT4056** (6/95)
Haydn—String Quartets, Volume 2
Haydn: String Quartets, Op.1 (exc); String Quartets, Op.20
(exc); String Quartets, Op.20 (exc); String Quartets, Op.33
(exc); String Quartets, Op.33 (exc); String Quartets, Op.33
(exc); String Quartets, Op.50 (exc); String Quartets, Op.55
(exc); String Quartets, Op.55 (exc); String Quartets, Op.64
(exc); String Quartets, Op.71 (exc); String Quartets, Op.74
(exc); String Quartets, Op.74 (exc); String Quartets, Op.77
(exc); *Hoffstetter:* String Quartets, Op.3 (exc); String
Quartets, Op.3 (exc). (Pro Arte Qt)

Thorofon

① **CTH2002** (7/88)
Piano Trios
Bruch: Piano Trio, Op. 5; *F. Hiller:* Piano Trio 4; *Widor:*
Pièces en Trio. (Göbel Trio, Berlin)

① **CTH2005** (10/89)
Smetana—Piano Works
Smetana: Souvenirs de Bohème (exc); Polkas, B94 (exc);
Czech Dances, T112 (exc); Rêves; Am Seegestade;
Sketches, B102 (exc); Macbeth and the Witches;
Characteristic Pieces, B57 (exc). (P. Schmalfuss)

① **CTH2012** (4/88)
Copland—Chamber Works
Copland: Vitebsk; Sextet; Violin Sonata; Flute Duo. (M-U.
Senn, BPO Academy, Göbel Trio, Berlin, H. Göbel, H.
Maile)

① **CTH2013** (5/88)
Martinů—Orchestral Works
Martinů: Concertino 1 (1924); Concertino 2 (1933);
Bagarre. (Berlin Göbel Trio, Pomeranian PO/T. Ukigaya)

① **CTH2035** (10/89)
Scheidemann/Scheidt—Organ Works
Scheidt: Toccata in G minor; Ach du feiner Reiter; Dowland
Galliarda; Modus ludendi; Alamanda; Est-ce Mars;
Benedicamus Domino; *Scheidemann:* Dic nobis Maria;
Benedicam. (K. Eichhorn)

① **CTH2041** (11/89)
Lutosławski—Orchestral Works
Lutosławski: Chain 2; Little Suite; Funeral music (1958);
Venetian games (1961). (K. Jakowicz, Pomeranian PO/T.
Ukigaya)

Timpani

① **1C1008** (9/93)
Honegger—Chamber Works, Vol.1
Honegger: Violin Sonata 1; Solo Violin Sonata; Violin
Sonata 2; Morceau de concours; Violin Sonata, H3; Arioso.
(D-S. Kang, P. Devoyon)

① **1C1009** (9/93)
Honegger—Chamber Works, Vol.2
Honegger: 2-Violin Sonatina; Violin and Cello Sonatina;
Paduana; Cello Sonata; Prélude, H79; Viola Sonata; Piano
Trio. (D-S. Kang, J-P. Audoli, R. Wallfisch, P. Devoyon, J.
Rossi, P-H. Xuereb)

① **1C1010** (9/93)
Honegger—Chamber Works, Vol.3
Honegger: Clarinet Sonatina; Rapsodie; Danse de la
Chèvre; Romance; Petite suite; Contrepoints; Colloque;
Introduction et Danse; Intrada; Hommage du trombone;
J'avais un fidèle amant; Chanson de Ronsard; Chansons
de la petite Sirène. (A. Marion, A. Haraldsdottir, C.
Moreaux, M. Arrignon, T. Caens, M. Becquet, P.
Zanlonghi, P. Devoyon, P-H. Xuereb, D-S. Kang, R.
Wallfisch, F. Kondo, Ludwig Qt, P. Devoyon)

① **1C1011** (9/93)
Honegger—Chamber Works, Vol.4
Honegger: String Quartet 1; String Quartet 2; String
Quartet 3; Pâques à New York. (F. Kondo, Ludwig Qt)

① **1C1013** (12/93)
Alkan—Chamber Music
Alkan: Grand duo concertant; Sonate de concert; Trio, Op. 30. (D-S. Kang, Y. Chiffoleau, O. Gardon)

① **4C1012** (9/93)
Honegger—Chamber Works
Honegger: Violin Sonata, H3; Violin Sonata 1; Violin Sonata 2; Solo Violin Sonata; Morceau de concours; Arioso; 2-Violin Sonatina; Violin and Cello Sonatina; Paduana; Cello Sonata; Prélude, H79; Viola Sonata; Piano Trio; Clarinet Sonatina; Rapsodie; Danse de la Chèvre; Romance; Petite Suite; Contrepoints; Colloque; Introduction et Danse; Intrada; Hommage du trombone; J'avais un fidèle amant; Chanson de Ronsard; Chansons de la petite Sirène; String Quartet 1; String Quartet 2; String Quartet 3; Pâques à New York. (A. Marion, A. Haraldsdottir, C. Moreaux, M. Arrignon, T. Caens, M. Becquet, D-S. Kang, J-P. Audoli, P-H. Xuereb, R. Wallfisch, J. Rossi, P. Zanlonghi, P. Devoyon, F. Kondo, Ludwig Qt, P. Devoyon)

Tremula

① **TREM101-2** (9/92)
Walter Leigh—Piano Music and Songs
Leigh: Klavieralbum; Eclogue; Polka; Music for 3 Pianos; How sweet I roamed; Echo's Lament for Narcissus; Cradle Song; Mocking Fairy; Down by the Salley Gardens; Come away Death; Bells; We don't care; Violets; Playtime Pieces; Piano Album; Waltzes. (P. Hewitt, R. Douglas, P. Mountford, E. Nash, S. Down)

① **TREM102-2** (12/93)
String Quartets
Rubbra: String Quartet 2; P. Tate: String Quartet in F; P. Wishart: String Quartet 3. (English Qt)

Tring International

① **TRP010** (3/95)
Dvořák—Orchestral Works
Dvořák: Symphony 9; Carnival; Scherzo capriccioso. (RPO/P. Järvi)

① **TRP024** (6/95)
Grieg—Piano Concerto, Op 16; Lyric Pieces
Grieg: Piano Concerto; Lyric Pieces, Op. 12 (exc); Lyric Pieces, Op. 43 (exc); Lyric Pieces, Op. 54 (exc); Lyric Pieces, Op. 57 (exc); Lyric Pieces, Op. 62 (exc); Lyric Pieces, Op. 65 (exc); Lyric Pieces, Op. 71 (exc). (R. O'Hora, RPO/J. Judd)

① **TRP027** (10/95)
Beethoven—Piano Sonatas
Beethoven: Piano Sonata 8; Piano Sonata 14; Piano Sonata 17. (C. Ortiz)

① **TRP036** (9/95)
Delius—Orchestral Works
Delius: Brigg Fair; Koanga (exc); Hassan (exc); Song before sunrise; Fennimore (exc); Village Romeo and Juliet (exc); Irmelin Prelude; Over the hills and far away. (RPO/C. Seaman)

① **TRP040** (12/95)
Copland—Orchestral Works
Copland: Fanfare for the Common Man; Billy the Kid Suite; Salón México; Rodeo (exc); Appalachian Spring Suite. (RPO/P. Ellis)

① **TRP046** (11/95)
Prokofiev—Peter and the Wolf etc
Prokofiev: Peter and the Wolf; Bizet: Jeux d'enfants; Saint-Saëns: Carnaval des animaux. (J. Gielgud, RPO/A. Licata)

Troubadisc

① **TRO-CD01405** (7/94)
Ethel Smyth—Chamber Works & Songs, Vol.3
Smyth: Songs (1907); Songs (1913); Trio in A. (M. Paulsen, U. Siebler, F. Draxinger, R. Eggebrecht-Kupsa, G. Georgiev, F. Kupsa, C. Zirkelbach, A. Gotowtschikow, A. Gassenhuber, C. Dutilly/J. Schmeller)

① **TRO-CD01409** (5/95)
Milhaud—Early Works, Vol. 1
Milhaud: String Quartet 1; String Quartet 2; Poèmes de Léo Latil; Poèmes de Jean Cocteau. (F. Mendelssohn Qt, U. Sonntag, R. Jansen)

① **TRO-CD03** (7/94)
Ethel Smyth—Chamber Works, Vols.1 & 2
Smyth: Violin Sonata, Op. 7; String Quintet, Op. 1; Cello Sonata, Op. 5; String Quartet. (R. Eggebrecht-Kupsa, J. Varner, F. Kupsa, C. Dutilly, Fanny Mendelssohn Qt)

Tudor

① **Tudor 767** (12/93)
Christmas Music
Traditional: Wiegenlied für den Christmonat; Eberlin: Piezas a Psalterio (exc); Traditional: Pastorellen vor die Weynacht-Zeit; Corelli: Concerti grossi, Op. 6 (exc); Vivaldi: Concerto, RV270 (exc); Concerti grossi, Op. 3 (exc); Traditional: Pastorella Sonata; Noëlli Weihnachtslieder; Stille Nacht. (Pantaleon Ens, K-H. Schickhaus (dulcimer/dir))

Unicorn-Kanchana

① **DKPCD9014** (4/85)
Franck—Organ Works Vol. II
Franck: Chorales (exc); Fantaisie in A; Grande pièce symphonique. (J. Bate)

① **DKPCD9024/5** (5/89)
Messiaen—Organ Works
Messiaen: Méditations; Ascension; Messe de la Pentecôte. (J. Bate)

① **DKPCD9028** (8/89)
Messiaen—Organ Works
Messiaen: Livre d'orgue; Apparition de l'église éternelle; Verset pour la fête de la dédicace. (J. Bate)

① **DKPCD9030** (9/85)
Franck—Organ Works Vol. III
Franck: Chorales (exc); Pastorale; Prière; Final, Op. 21. (J. Bate)

① **DKPCD9040** (9/85)
Delius—Works for Violin & Orchestra
Delius: Violin Concerto; Suite; Légende. (R. Holmes, RPO/V. Handley)

① **DKPCD9046** (3/86)
Holst—Choral Works
Holst: Hymn to Dionysus, H116; Rig Veda - Group 1 (exc); Rig Veda - Group 2 (exc); Rig Veda - Group 3; Rig Veda - Group 4 (exc); Eastern Pictures, H112. (O. Ellis, RCM Chbr Ch, RPO/D. Willcocks)

① **DKPCD9047** (2/86)
Dimitri Tiomkin Film Music
Tiomkin: Fall of the Roman Empire (exc); President's Country; Guns of Navarone (exc); Wild is the Wind (exc); Rhapsody of Steel (exc). (RCM Orch/D. Willcocks)

① **DKPCD9050** (6/87)
Vivaldi—Concertos
Vivaldi: Concerto, RV554; Concerto, RV767; Concerto, RV541; Concerto, RV548; Concerto, RV766. (R. Studt (vn/dir), S. Francis, J. Bate, Tate Music Group)

① **DKPCD9055** (6/88)
Cabaret Classics
Weill: Marie Galante (exc); Zemlinsky: Lieder, Op.27 (exc); Schoenberg: Cabaret Songs (exc); Satie: Diva de l'Empire; Allons-y Chochotte; Weill: Lady in the Dark (exc); Street Scene (exc); Knickerbocker Holiday (exc). (J. Gomez, J. Constable)

① **DKPCD9057** (12/86)
A Christmas Garland
G. Bush: In Praise of Mary; Ireland: Holy Boy; Traditional: Christmas Garland; Statham: Bells of St Chad's. (V. Hill, J. Watts, RCM Chbr Ch, RPO/D. Willcocks)

① **DKPCD9063** (1/88)
Delius—Choral & Orchestral Works
Delius: Songs of Sunset; Dance Rhapsody 2; Fennimore and Gerda Intermezzo; Arabesque. (Sarah Walker, T. Allen, Ambrosian Sngrs, RPO/E. Fenby)

① **DKPCD9070** (12/88)
A Celebration of Scotland
Maxwell Davies: Orkney Wedding; Kinloche his Fantassie; Seven Songs Home; Yesnaby Ground; Two Fiddlers (exc); Jimmack the Postie; Farewell to Stromness; Lullaby for Lucy; Renaissance Scottish Dances. (G. McIlwham, St Mary's Edinburgh Ch, Scottish CO/P. Maxwell Davies, P. Maxwell Davies)

① **DKPCD9071** (3/89)
Vivaldi—Chamber Concertos
Vivaldi: Concerto, RV99; Concerto, RV107; Concerto, RV88; Concerto, RV94; Concerto, RV106; Concerto, RV90. (London Hpd Ens, S. Francis (dir))

① **DKPCD9076** (9/89)
Vaughan Williams—Chamber Music
Vaughan Williams: String Quartet 1; String Quartet 2; Phantasy Quintet. (English Qt, N. Blume)

① **DKPCD9078** (9/89)
Messiaen—Piano Works
Messiaen: Préludes; Etudes de rythme; Cantéyodjayâ. (P. Hill)

① **DKPCD9080** (11/89)
Maconchy—String Quartets Vol. I
Maconchy: String Quartet 1; String Quartet 2; String Quartet 3; String Quartet 4. (Hanson Qt)

① **DKPCD9081** (6/90)
Maconchy—String Quartets Vol. II
Maconchy: String Quartet 5; String Quartet 6; String Quartet 7; String Quartet 8. (Bingham Qt)

① **DKPCD9082** (2/91)
Maconchy—String Quartets Vol. III
Maconchy: String Quartet 9; String Quartet 10; String Quartet 11; String Quartet 12; String Quartet 13. (Mistry Qt)

① **DKPCD9089** (2/90)
Lumbye—Polkas, Mazurkas & Waltzes
Lumbye: Salute to August Bournonville; Amelie Waltz; Columbine Polka Mazurka; Sandman Galop Fantastique; Queen Louise's Waltz; Lilie Polka; Copenhagen Steam Railway Galop; Salute to our Friends; Guard of Amager (exc); Napoli (exc); Helga Polka Mazurka; Pictures from a Dream; Hesperus Waltz; Amager Polka; Champagne Galop. (Odense SO, P. Guth (vn/dir))

① **DKPCD9095** (11/90)
D.Scarlatti—Cantatas
D. Scarlatti: Pur nel sonno almen tal'ora; Se fedele tu m'adori; Piangete, occhi dolenti; Che vidi, o ciel. (K. Eckersley, Fiori Musicali, P. Rapson)

① **DKPCD9096** (2/91)
From Stanley to Wesley, Vol. 1
Reading II: French Horns and Flutes; Stanley: Organ Voluntaries, Book 1 (exc); Organ Voluntaries, Book 2 (exc); Organ Voluntaries, Book 3 (exc); Handel: Fugues, HWV605-10 (exc); Roseingrave: Voluntarys and Fugues (exc); Travers: Voluntary in D minor and major; Walond: Organ Voluntaries, Op. 1 (exc); Russell: Voluntaries, Set 1 (exc); S. Wesley: Voluntaries, Op. 6 (exc); Short Pieces (exc). (J. Bate)

① **DKPCD9097** (6/91)
Bernard Stevens—Chamber Works
Stevens: Theme and Variations, Op.11; String Quartet 2; Lyric Suite, Op.30. (Delmé Qt)

① **DKPCD9098** (10/91)
S. Wesley—Symphonies
S. Wesley: Symphony in A; Symphony in D; Symphony in E flat; Symphony in B flat. (Milton Keynes CO/H.D. Wetton)

① **DKPCD9099** (5/91)
From Stanley to Wesley Vol 2
Greene: Voluntaries (exc); Stanley: Organ Voluntaries, Book 1 (exc); Organ Voluntaries, Book 2 (exc); Organ Voluntaries, Book 3 (exc); Handel: Fugues, HWV605-10 (exc); Long: Voluntary in D minor; Walond: Organ Voluntaries, Op. 2 (exc); Nares: Introduction and Fugue in F; Russell: Voluntaries, Set 1 (exc); S. Wesley: Voluntaries, Op. 6 (exc); Short Pieces (exc). (J. Bate)

① **DKPCD9101** (5/91)
From Stanley to Wesley Vol 3
Greene: Voluntarys (exc); Stanley: Organ Voluntaries, Book 2 (exc); Organ Voluntaries, Book 3 (exc); Walond: Organ Voluntaries, Op. 1 (exc); Handel: Fugues, HWV605-10 (exc); Voluntary in C minor; Burney: Cornet Pieces and Fugue (exc); Russell: Voluntaries, Set 2 (exc); S. Wesley: Voluntaries, Op. 6 (exc); Short Pieces (exc). (J. Bate)

① **DKPCD9102** (11/91)
Goehr—Orchestral and Vocal Works
Goehr: Musical Offering, Op. 46; Lyric Pieces, Op. 35; Sinfonia, Op. 42; Behold the Sun, Op. 44a. (J. Thames, J. Holland, London Sinfonietta/O. Knussen)

① **DKPCD9104** (7/91)
From Stanley to Wesley Vol 4
Greene: Voluntarys (exc); Stanley: Organ Voluntaries, Book 1 (exc); Organ Voluntaries, Book 2 (exc); Organ Voluntaries, Book 3 (exc); Handel: Fugues, HWV605-10 (exc); Fugues and Voluntaries (exc); Roseingrave: Voluntarys and Fugues (exc); S. Wesley: Voluntaries, Op. 6 (exc); Dupuis: Voluntary in B flat. (J. Bate)

① **DKPCD9105** (7/91)
From Stanley to Wesley Vol 5
Croft: Voluntary in D; Stanley: Organ Voluntaries, Book 2 (exc); Organ Voluntaries, Book 1 (exc); Organ Voluntaries, Book 3 (exc); Walond: Organ Voluntaries, Op. 1 (exc); Handel: Fugues, HWV605-10 (exc); Fugues and Voluntaries (exc); Burney: Cornet Pieces and Fugue (exc);

minor; Alla Marcia; Divertimenti; Oboe Phantasy. (D. Wickens, J. Constable, Gabrieli Qt, K. Essex)

① **UKCD2065** (11/94)
Herrmann—Film Music Suites
Herrmann: Welles Raises Kane; Devil and Daniel Webster Suite; Obsession (exc). (OST, LPO, National PO/B. Herrmann)

① **UKCD2066** (2/95)
Russian Orchestral Music
Shostakovich: Hamlet Suite, Op. 116a (exc); *Kabalevsky:* Symphony 2; *Miaskovsky:* Symphony 21. (New Philh/D. Measham, National PO/B. Herrmann)

① **UKCD2067** (10/94)
Bach—Violin Concertos
Bach: Violin Concerto, BWV1041; Violin Concerto, BWV1042; Violin Concerto, BWV1052. (R. Ricci (vn/dir), City of London Ens)

① **UKCD2068** (2/95)
Maxwell Davies—Orchestral and Chamber Works
Maxwell Davies: Vesalii icones; Bairns of Brugh; Runes from a holy island. (Fires of London/P. Maxwell Davies)

① **UKCD2071** (8/95)
The Delius Collection, Volume 1
Delius: Fantastic Dance; Dance Rhapsody 1; Dance Rhapsody 2; Song of the High Hills; Preludes; Zum Carnival. (M. Midgley, V. Midgley, E. Parkin, Ambrosian Sngrs, RPO/E. Fenby/N. del Mar)

① **UKCD2072** (8/95)
The Delius Collection, Volume 2
Delius: Irmelin Prelude; Song of Summer; Late Lark; Piano Concerto; Violin Concerto. (A. Rolfe Johnson, R. Holmes, P. Fowke, RPO/E. Fenby/V. Handley/N. del Mar)

① **UKCD2073** (8/95)
The Delius Collection, Volume 3
Delius: Koanga (exc); Idyll; Songs of Sunset; Village Romeo and Juliet (exc). (F. Lott, Sarah Walker, T. Allen, Ambrosian Sngrs, RPO/E. Fenby/N. del Mar)

① **UKCD2074** (8/95)
The Delius Collection, Volume 4
Delius: Violin Sonata 1; Violin Sonata 2; Violin Sonata 3; Cello Sonata. (R. Holmes, J. Lloyd Webber, E. Fenby)

United Recordings

① **88001-2** (1/94)
Shostakovich—Orchestral Works & Songs
Shostakovich: Hypothetically Murdered Suite; Fragments, Op.42; Jazz Suite 1; Pushkin Songs, Op.46. (D. Kharitonov, CBSO/M. Elder)

① **88002-2** (12/93)
My Beloved Spake
Handel: Coronation Anthems (exc); Theodora (exc); *Purcell:* O sing unto the Lord, Z44; My beloved spake, Z28; *Blow:* Sing unto the Lord; *Humfrey:* Hymne to God the Father; *Arne:* As You Like It (exc); Tempest (exc); Twelfth Night (exc). (J. Bowman, J.M. Ainsley, M. George, Winchester Quiristers, King's Consort Ch, Orch/R. King)

① **88005-2** (8/94)
D. Scarlatti/Soler—Music from the Courts of Europe: Madrid
D. Scarlatti: Keyboard Sonatas (exc); *Soler:* Keyboard Sonatas I (exc); Keyboard Sonatas II (exc); Fandango. (V. Black)

① **88006-2** (1/94)
Russian Cello Sonatas
Prokofiev: Cello Sonata, Op. 119; *Schnittke:* Cello Sonata; *Shostakovich:* Cello Sonata, Op.40. (P. Marleyn, S. Morley)

① **88016-2** (3/95)
Dweller in my Deathless Dreams
Warlock: Singer; Consider; I held Love's head; Thou gav'st me leave to kiss; Sad Song; Rutterkin; *Ireland:* Songs Sacred and Profane (exc); Trellis; Hardy Songs (exc); My true love; *Howells:* Gavotte; Come sing and dance; King David; Songs, Op. 22 (exc); *Bridge:* Day after day; Speak to me my love; Dweller in my deathless dreams; Journey's End; *Holst:* Songs, H174 (exc). (S. Leonard, M. Martineau)

① **88019-2** (12/94)
Messiaen—Piano Works
Messiaen: Préludes (exc); Etudes de rythme (exc); Cantéyodjayâ; Catalogue d'oiseaux (exc); Vingt regards (exc). (R. Hind)

① **88023-2** (4/95)
Tavener—Ikons
Tavener: Thunder Entered Her; Lamb; Tiger; Hymn to the Mother of God; Dormition Hymn; Responsorium; Song for

Athene; Eonia; God is with us. (BBC Sngrs/S. Joly, C. Bowers-Broadbent)

① **88033-2** (12/94)
Howells/F. Martin—Choral Works
Howells: Requiem; Take him, earth; *Martin:* Mass. (S. Barber, J. Field, M. Johnstone, A. Angus, Vasari/J. Backhouse)

Vanguard Classics

① **08.2003.72** (9/93)
Purcell—Celebrated Songs,Sacred Airs and Concert Pieces
Purcell: Oedipus, Z583 (exc); If music be the food of love, Z379/1; Not all my torments, Z400; King Arthur, Z628 (exc); Pausanias, Z585 (exc); Fatal hour comes on apace, Z421; Birthday Ode, Z321 (exc); Indian Queen, Z630 (exc); Bonduca, Z574 (exc); Dioclesian, Z627 (exc); Don Quixote, Z578 (exc); I love and I must, Z382; Don Quixote, Z578 (exc); Fairy Queen, Z629 (exc); Blessed Virgin's Expostulation, Z196; Close thine eyes, Z184; Fantasia, Z731; Sonatas, Z802-11 (exc); Pavan, Z752; Sonata, Z780; Viola da gamba Fantasia, Z745; Hornpipes (exc); Choice Collection of Lessons (exc); Musick's Hand-maid, Part 2 (exc). (A. Cantelo, A. Deller, M. Bevan, N. Marriner, P. Gibbs, G. Jones, D. Dupré, G. Malcolm, W. Bergmann, Baroque Plyrs)

① **08.2010.71** (9/93)
Bach—Choral Works
Bach: Magnificat, BWV243; Cantata 50; Cantata 70. (M. Coertse, M. Sjöstedt, A. Felbermayer, H. Rössl-Majdan, E. Wien, A. Dermota, H. Meyer-Welfing, F. Guthrie, N. Foster, Vienna St Op Chor, Vienna St Op Orch/F. Prohaska)

① **08.2028.71** (10/94)
Bach—Cantatas
Bach: Cantata 51; Cantata 209; Cantata 202. (T. Stich-Randall, Vienna St Op Orch/A. Heiller, A. Felbermayer, H. Rössl-Majdan, W. Kmentt, Vienna Bach Guild Ch, Vienna Bach Guild Orch/F. Prohaska)

① **08.4016.71** (8/92)
Music of Samuel Barber
Barber: Essay for Orchestra 2; Music for a scene from Shelley; Stopwatch; Virgin Martyrs, Op. 8/1 (exc); Hand of Bridge; Serenade, Op. 1; Adagio for Strings. (Sym of the Air/V. Golschmann, R. DeCormier Chorale, Washington Cath Ch/P. Callaway, P. Neway, E. Alberts, W. Lewis, P. Maero, Zagreb Sols/A. Janigro)

① **08.4025.71** (2/92)
Mozart—Piano Works
Mozart: Piano Sonata, K310; Fantasia, K396; Rondo, K511; Variations, K573. (A. Brendel)

① **08.4026.71** (2/92)
Schubert—Piano Works
Schubert: Piano Sonata, D958; Piano Sonata, D840; Deutsche Tänze, D783. (A. Brendel)

① **08.4030.71** (5/93)
Satie—Ballet and Orchestral Music
Satie: Parade (Cpte); Aventures de Mercure (Cpte); Relâche (Cpte); Gymnopédies (exc); Belle excentrique; Grimaces; Jack-in-the-box; Morceaux en forme de poire. (Utah SO/M. Abravanel)

① **08.4033.71** (8/92)
Earl Wild - The Virtuoso Piano
Herz: Cenerentola Variations; *Godowsky:* Künstlerleben Paraphrase; *Rubinstein:* Studies, Op. 23 (exc); *Thalberg:* Don Pasquale Fantasy; *Hummel:* Rondo, Op. 11; *Paderewski:* Miscellanea, Op. 16 (exc). (E. Wild)

① **08.4035.71** (2/92)
Earl Wild - The Demonic Liszt
Liszt: Robert le diable réminiscences, S413; Etudes Studies, S145 (exc); Mephisto polka, S217; Mephisto Waltz 1, S514; Don Juan réminiscences, S418; Faust—paraphrase, S407. (E. Wild)

① **08.4050.71** (5/93)
Gottschalk—Piano Works, Vol.1
Gottschalk: Banjo; Dying Poet; Souvenir de Porto Rico; Bananier; Ojos Criollos; Bamboula RO20; Maiden's BLush; Last Hope; Suis-moi; Pasquinade; Savane; Tournament Galop. (E. List)

① **08.4051.71** (5/93)
Gottschalk—Piano Works, Vol.2
Gottschalk: Jota aragonesa; Souvenir d'Andalousie; Gallina; Orfa; Marche de nuit; Printemps d'amour; Radieuse; Réponds-moi; Tremolo; Étincelle; Ses yeux; Union; Grande tarantelle; Symphony 1. (E. List, C. Lewis, J. Werner, R. Nibley, Utah SO/M. Abravanel)

① **08.5060.71** (7/95)
Purcell—Odes
Purcell: Birthday Ode, Z323; Bell Anthem, Z49; My beloved spake, Z28; St Cecilia's Day Ode, Z339. (A. Deller (alto/dir), Deller Consort, Oriana Concert Ch, Oriana Concert Orch, Kalmar CO, W. Bergmann)

① **08.5068.71** (4/95)
William Byrd and his Age
Anon: Come tread the paths; Ah, silly poor Joas; O death, rock me asleep; *Byrd:* Psalmes, Sonets and Songs (1588) (exc); Ye sacred muse; Lullaby my sweet little baby; Come, pretty babe; Fantasia a 4, BE17/4; *Corkine:* What booteth love?; *A. Ferrabosco II:* Fantasia a 4; Fantasia a 6; *R. Nicholson:* In a merry May morn; *Parsons:* Pour down, you pow'rs divine; *Whythorne:* Buy new broom. (A. Deller, SCB/A. Wenzinger)

① **08.5069.71** (1/95)
Bach—Cantatas; Handel—Airs
Bach: Cantata 54; Cantata 170; Mass in B minor, BWV232 (exc); *Handel:* Orlando (exc); Jephtha (exc); Theodora (exc). (A. Deller, Leonhardt Baroque Ens, G. Leonhardt (org/dir), Handel Fest Orch/A. Lewis)

① **08.7001.71** (6/91)
Mozart: Concertante Works
Mozart: Sinfonia Concertante, K364; Violin Concerto, K211; Violin Concerto, K216. (J. Suk (vn/dir), T. Kakuska, Suk CO)

① **08.8002.72** (10/91)
Canteloube: Songs of the Auvergne
Canteloube: Chants d'Auvergne (Cpte); Chants du Languedoc (exc); Chants des Pays Basques (exc); Chants paysans (exc). (N. Davrath, orch/P. de la Roche/G. Kingsley)

① **08.8032.72** (3/95)
Monteux conducts Tchaikovsky at the Vienna Festival
Tchaikovsky: Romeo and Juliet; Piano Concerto 1; Symphony 5. (J. Ogdon, LSO/P. Monteux)

① **08.99009** (1/95)
Rachmaninov—Piano Works
Rachmaninov: Piano Sonata 2; Moments musicaux, Op.16 (exc); Lilacs; Morceaux de Fantaisie, Op.3 (exc); *Tchaikovsky:* Songs, Op.16 (exc); *Mendelssohn:* Midsummer Night's Dream (exc); *Rachmaninov:* Corelli Variations. (N. Lugansky)

Varèse-Sarabande

① **VSD5207** (6/90)
The Prince and the Pauper and other film music
J. T. Williams: Reivers (exc); Jane Eyre (exc); *Rózsa:* Lost Weekend (exc); *Korngold:* Between Two Worlds (exc); Constant Nymph (exc); Prince and the Pauper (exc); Escape Me Never (exc); *Antheil:* Spectre of the Rose (exc); *M.J. Lewis:* Madwoman of Chaillot (exc); *A. North:* Cleopatra (exc); *Pennario:* Julie (exc); *A. North:* Who's Afraid of Virginia Woolf (exc); *Delerue:* Anne of the 1000 Days (exc); *Walton:* Henry V (exc); Henry V Suite. (National PO/C. Gerhardt)

① **VSD5241** (10/90)
Delerue—The London Sessions, Vol.1
Delerue: Platoon (exc); Rich and Famous (exc); Her Alibi (exc); Beaches (exc); Exposed (exc); Biloxi Blues (exc); Little Romance (exc); Crimes of the Heart (exc). (Orch/G. Delerue/F. Fitzpatrick)

① **VSD5242** (10/90)
Waxman—The Legends of Hollywood, Vol.1
Waxman: Task Force (exc); Objective, Burma! (exc); Reminiscences; Peyton Place (exc); Athaneal the Trumpeter; Paradine Case (exc); Sorry, Wrong Number (exc); Demetrius and the Gladiators (exc). (Queensland SO/R. Mills)

① **VSD5480** (11/94)
Waxman—Legends of Hollywood, Vol. 3
Waxman: Elephant Walk (exc); Nightride; Dusk; Furies Suite (exc); Hotel Berlin (exc); Destination Tokyo (exc); Mr Skeffington (exc); Silver Chalice (exc). (Queensland SO/R. Mills)

Victoria

① **VCD19006** (10/91)
Norwegian Chamber Works
Brustad: Eventyr; Capricci; *Grieg:* Violin Sonata 3; *Handel:* Keyboard Suites Set I (exc); Keyboard Suites Set II (exc). (T. Tennesen, L.A. Tomter, R. Askeland)

① **VCD19007** (11/91)
Anne Gjevang in Recital
Sibelius: Songs, Op.36 (exc); Songs, Op.17 (exc); Songs, Op.13 (exc); Songs, Op.37 (exc); *Wolf:* Mörike Lieder

(exc); *Liszt:* S'il est un charmant gazon, S284; Tombe et la rose, S285; Enfant, si j'étais roi, S283; *Grieg:* Songs, Op.25 (exc); Melodies of the Heart, Op. 5 (exc); Songs, Op.9 (exc); Songs, Op.60 (exc); *Falla:* Canciones populares españolas. (A. Gjevang, E.S. Nökleberg)

ⓘ **VCD19013** (10/92)
The Harpsichord 1689-1789
Handel: Keyboard Suites, Set II (exc); *Purcell:* Choice Collection of Lessons (exc); *Bach:* English Suites, BWV806-811 (exc); *Couperin:* Livre de clavecin IV (exc); *D. Scarlatti:* Keyboard Sonatas (exc); *Anglebert:* Harpsichord works (exc); *Duphly:* Pièces de clavecin (exc); *Balbastre:* Air Gay. (J. Henry)

ⓘ **VCD19014** (10/91)
Hallgrømsson & Nordheim—Chamber Orchestral Works
Hallgrimsson: Poemi; *Nordheim:* Rendezvous for strings; Boomerang. (E. Larsen, T. Tønnesen, Norwegian CO, T. Tønnesen (vn/dir)/C. Eggen)

ⓘ **VCD19018** (4/92)
Grieg—Songs with Orchestra
Grieg: Peer Gynt (exc); Songs, Op. 39 (exc); Songs, Op. 25 (exc); Songs, Op. 33 (exc); Norway, Op. 58 (exc); Songs, Op. 33 (exc); Mountain thrall, Op. 32. (M. Hirsti, H. Bjørkey, Trondheim SO/O.K. Ruud)

ⓘ **VCD19025** (6/93)
Grieg—Piano Works, Vol.1
Grieg: Piano Pieces, Op.1; Tone-pictures, Op.3; Humoresques, Op.6; Piano Sonata, Op. 7; Lyric Pieces, Op.12. (G.H. Braaten)

ⓘ **VCD19026** (6/93)
Grieg—Piano Works, Vol.2
Grieg: Folksongs and Dances, Op. 17; Pictures, Op. 19; Sigurd Jorsalfar; Peer Gynt Suite 1 (exc); Peer Gynt Suite 2 (exc). (G.H. Braaten)

ⓘ **VCD19027** (6/93)
Grieg—Piano Works, Vol.3
Grieg: Ballade, Op.24; Album Leaves, Op. 28; Improvisations, Op. 29; Elegiac Melodies, Op. 34; Norwegian Dances, Op. 35. (G.H. Braaten)

ⓘ **VCD19028** (6/93)
Grieg—Piano Works, Vol.4
Grieg: Waltz Caprices, Op. 37; Lyric Pieces, Op. 38; Holberg Suite; Song transcriptions, Op. 41. (G.H. Braaten)

ⓘ **VCD19031** (4/94)
Grieg—Complete Piano Music - Volume VII
Grieg: Lyric Pieces, Op. 57; Lyric Pieces, Op. 62; Nordic Melodies, Op. 63. (G.H. Braaten)

ⓘ **VCD19032** (4/94)
Grieg—Complete Piano Music - Volume VIII
Grieg: Lyric Pieces, Op. 65; Folksongs, Op. 66; Lyric Pieces, Op. 68. (G.H. Braaten)

ⓘ **VCD19035** (12/94)
Grieg—Complete Piano Music, Volume XI
Grieg: Piano Pieces, CW107; Agitato; Funeral March; Album Leaf, CW136b; Norwegian Mountain Melodies, CW134; Dance of the Mountain King's Daughter; Piano Pieces, CW154; At the Halfdan Kjerulf Statue, CW132; Bergljot, Op. 42. (G.H. Braaten, A. Folstad)

ⓘ **VCD19039** (6/93)
Grieg—Songs, Vol.2
Grieg: Melodies of the Heart, Op. 5 (Cpte); Songs, Op. 33 (Cpte); Songs, Op. 59 (Cpte); Mountain thrall, Op. 32. (K. Skram, R. Jansen)

ⓘ **VCD19040** (2/94)
Grieg—Complete Songs - Volume III
Grieg: Songs, Op. 61; Garborg Songs (1895) (exc); Haugtussa, Op. 67; Clara's Song; Posthumous Songs I (exc); Princess; Posthumous Songs II (exc); Occasional Songs, CW129 (exc). (M. Hirsti, K. Skram, R. Jansen)

ⓘ **VCD19041** (8/93)
Grieg—Songs, Vol.4
Grieg: Songs, Op. 4 (Cpte); Songs, Op. 21 (Cpte); Reminiscences, Op. 44 (Cpte); Songs, Op. 48 (Cpte); Norway, Op. 58 (Cpte). (M. Hirsti, C. Pfeiler, K.M. Sandve, K. Skram, R. Jansen)

ⓘ **VCD19048** (8/92)
Grieg—Complete String Quartets
Grieg: String Quartet, Op.27; String Quartet in F; Fugue in F minor. (Norwegian Qt)

ⓘ **VCD19066** (3/93)
Grieg—Music for Strings
Grieg: Nordic Melodies, Op. 63 (exc); Elegiac Melodies; Peer Gynt (exc); String Quartet, Op. 27. (Trondheim Sols/B. Fiskum)

ⓘ **VCD19070** (12/94)
Grieg—Complete Violin Sonatas
Grieg: Violin Sonata 1; Violin Sonata 2; Violin Sonata 3. (T. Tønnesen, E.H. Smebye)

ⓘ **VCD19071** (11/93)
Grieg—Chamber Works, Vol.1
Grieg: Intermezzo; Andante con moto (1878); Cello Sonata; Holberg Suite. (A. Kvalbein, R. Askeland, Oslo Trio, Trondheim Sols/B. Fiskum)

ⓘ **VCD19079** (10/93)
Grieg/Martin/Tchaikovsky—Piano Trios
Grieg: Andante con moto (1878); *Martin:* Trio populaires irlandaises; *Tchaikovsky:* Piano Trio, Op.50. (Oslo Trio)

ⓘ **VCD19084** (12/94)
Saeverud—Complete Piano Music, Volume I
Saeverud: Capricci, Op. 1; Easy Pieces, Op. 14; Easy Pieces, Op. 18; Siljuslåtten. (E. H. Smebye)

ⓘ **VCD19085** (12/94)
Saeverud—Complete Piano Music, Volume 2
Saeverud: Siljustøl, Op. 21; Siljustøl, Op. 22; Siljustøl, Op. 24; Siljustøl, Op. 25. (E. H. Smebye)

ⓘ **VCD19086** (12/94)
Saeverud—Complete Piano Music, Volume 3
Saeverud: Peer Gynt, Op. 28; Piano Sonatinas, Op. 30; Birdcall variations, Op. 38; Grazietta, Op. 42. (E. H. Smebye)

Video Artists International

ⓘ **VAIA1003** (12/93)
Nyiregyhazi at the Opera
Nyiregyházi: Rienzi and Lohengrin—paraphrase; Ballo in Maschera—paraphrase; Trovatore—paraphrase; Otello—paraphrase; Eugene Onegin—paraphrase; Pagliacci—paraphrase. (E. Nyiregyházi)

ⓘ **VAIA1013** (12/93)
Christmas with Renata Scotto
Traditional: Angels, from the realms of glory; *Handel:* Messiah (exc); *Traditional:* Tu scendi dalle stelle; Joy to the world; Stille Nacht; *Gounod:* Ave Maria; *Traditional:* Christmas at the Cloisters; O come, all ye faithful; *Franck:* Panis angelicus; *Schubert:* Ave Maria, D839; *Traditional:* Greensleeves (What child is this?); Coventry Carol; Maria Wiegenlied; *Adam:* Minuit, Chrétiens (exc). (R. Scotto, St Patrick's Cath Ch, St Patrick's Cath Orch/L. Anselmi)

ⓘ **VAIA1017** (8/93)
Leonard Warren—Early Recordings
Leoncavallo: Pagliacci (exc); *Verdi:* Traviata (exc); Rigoletto (exc); Aida (exc); *Bizet:* Carmen (exc); L. Warren, E. Steber, A. Tokatyan, J. Dickenson, L. Alvary, L. Browning, R. Rampton, chor, orch/W. Pelletier, A. Carron, L. Summers, N. Cordon)

ⓘ **VAIA1020** (5/93)
Josef Hofmann, Vol.2
Brahms: Academic Festival Overture; *Rubinstein:* Piano Concerto 4; *Chopin:* Ballades (exc); Nocturnes (exc); Waltzes (exc); Andante spianato and Grande Polonaise; Etudes (exc); Berceuse; *Hofmann:* Chromaticon; *Mendelssohn:* Songs without Words (exc); *Rachmaninov:* Preludes (exc); *Beethoven:* Ruinen von Athen (exc); *Moszkowski:* Caprice espagnole, Op.37; *Chopin:* Nocturnes (exc); Mazurkas (exc); Waltzes (exc); Andante spianato and Grande Polonaise; *Hofmann:* Chromaticon. (J. Hofmann, Curtis Inst Student Orch/F. Reiner/I. Hilsberg)

ⓘ **VAIA1024** (8/93)
Rosalyn Tureck recital, Teatro Colón, BA
Bach: Adagio, BWV968; Chromatic Fantasia and Fugue, BWV903; *Mendelssohn:* Songs without Words (exc); *Schubert:* Moments musicaux, D780 (exc); *Bach:* Solo Violin Partitas and Sonatas (exc); *Brahms:* Handel Variations; *Bach:* Partitas, BWV825-30 (exc); Goldberg Variations (exc); Musette, BWV Anh126. (R. Tureck)

ⓘ **VAIA1045** (6/94)
Beecham conducts Handel
Handel: Solomon (exc); Gods go a'Begging (exc); Gods go a'Begging (exc); Gods go a'Begging (exc); Origin of Design (exc); Origin of Design (exc); Israel in Egypt (exc); Concerti Grossi, Op.6 (exc); Messiah (exc); Faithful Shepherd. (Leeds Fest Chor, LPO, SO/T. Beecham)

ⓘ **VAIA1048** (11/94)
William Kapell broadcasts, Vol.2
Bach: Partitas, BWV825-30 (exc); *Mozart:* Piano Sonata, K570; *Debussy:* Children's Corner; *Liszt:* Hungarian Rhapsodies, S244 (exc); Hungarian Rhapsodies, S244 (exc); *Mussorgsky:* Pictures. (W. Kapell)

ⓘ **VAIA1072** (11/95)
Eleanor Steber Collection, Volume 1
Debussy: Enfant prodigue (exc); *Verdi:* Ernani (exc); Traviata (exc); *Leoncavallo:* Pagliacci (exc); *Rossini:* Barbiere di Siviglia (exc); *A. Thomas:* Mignon (exc); *Massenet:* Hérodiade (exc); *Flotow:* Martha (exc); *Puccini:* Bohème (exc); Turandot (exc); Gianni Schicchi (exc); *Traditional:* Danny Boy; *J.A. Bland:* Carry me back; *Rossini:* Stabat Mater (exc). (E. Steber, A. Tokatyan, G. Cehanovsky, L. Warren, anon, orch/W. Pelletier/E. Goossens/H. Barlow)

Virgin Classics

ⓘ **CUV5 61118-2** (11/94)
Ravel/Respighi—Vocal Works
Berlioz: Nuits d'été; Mélodies, Op. 2 (exc); Captive; Zaïde; *Respighi:* Sensitiva. (J. Baker, CLS/R. Hickox)

ⓘ **CUV5 61119-2** (11/94)
Bernstein—Orchestral Works
Bernstein: Candide Overture; Symphony 2; Fancy Free. (J. Kahane, Bournemouth SO/A. Litton)

ⓘ **CUV5 61126-2** (11/94)
Elgar/Vaughan Williams—String Music
Elgar: Introduction and Allegro; *Vaughan Williams:* Lark ascending; *Elgar:* Serenade; *Vaughan Williams:* Greensleeves Fantasia; Tallis Fantasia. (London CO, C. Warren-Green (vn/dir))

ⓘ **CUV5 61128-2** (11/94)
Humperdinck—Fairy-tale Music
Humperdinck: Hänsel und Gretel (exc); Blaue Vogel (exc); Königskinder Overture; Königskinder (exc); Dornröschen (exc). (Bamberg SO/K.A. Rickenbacher)

ⓘ **CUV5 61129-2** (11/94)
Liszt—Piano Works
Liszt: Mephisto Waltz 1, S514; Venezia e Napoli, S162 (exc); Rhapsodie espagnole, S254; Harmonies poétiques, S173 (exc); Légendes, S175 (exc). (S. Hough)

ⓘ **CUV5 61139-2** (11/94)
Rossini—Arias
Rossini: Siège de Corinthe (exc); Tancredi (exc); Bianca e Falliero (exc); Elisabetta (exc); Otello (exc); Guillaume Tell (exc); Semiramide (exc). (K. Ricciarelli, Lyon Op Chor, Lyon Op Orch/G. Ferro)

ⓘ **CUV5 61141-2** (11/94)
French Oboe Sonatas
Saint-Saëns: Oboe Sonata; *Bozza:* Oboe Sonata; *Dutilleux:* Oboe Sonata; *Koechlin:* Oboe Sonata; *Poulenc:* Oboe Sonata. (N. Daniel, J. Drake)

ⓘ **CUV5 61145-2** (11/94)
Vivaldi—Four Seasons
Vivaldi: Concerti, Op. 8 (exc); *Albinoni:* Adagio; *Pachelbel:* Canon and Gigue (exc). (London CO, C. Warren-Green (vn/dir))

ⓘ **CUV5 61203-2** (10/95)
Mendelssohn—Piano Quartets
Mendelssohn: Piano Quartet 1; Piano Quartet 2; Piano Quartet 3. (Domus)

ⓘ **CUV5 61204-2** (10/95)
Mozart—Orchestral Works
Mozart: Symphony 35; Symphony 36; Divertimenti, K136-8 (exc); Serenade, K239. (Sinfonia Varsovia, Lausanne CO/Y. Menuhin)

ⓘ **CUV5 61206-2** (10/95)
Prokofiev/Debussy/Milhaud—Orchestral Works
Prokofiev: Symphony 1; Sinfonietta; *Debussy:* Pour le piano (exc); Tarantelle styrienne; *Milhaud:* Création du monde. (Lausanne CO/A. Zedda)

ⓘ **VCD7 59011-2** (4/91)
Bach—French Suites etc
Bach: French Suites, BWV812-17; Suite, BWV818a; Suite, BWV819; Allemande, BWV819a. (D. Moroney)

ⓘ **VCD7 59289-2** (5/94)
Rachmaninov—Piano Works
Rachmaninov: Preludes (exc); Prelude (1917); Morceaux de fantaisie, Op.3; Lilacs; Daisies; Pièces (1887) (exc); Oriental Sketch (1917); Moments Musicaux, Op.16. (D. Alexeev)

ⓘ **VCK7 59072-2** (6/92)
Chopin—Piano Works
Chopin: Piano Sonata 1; Piano Sonata 2; Piano Sonata 3; Mazurkas (exc); Etudes (exc). (L.O. Andsnes)

ⓘ **VC5 45000-2** (12/94)
Bononcini—Vocal & Chamber Works
Bononcini: Cantate e duetti (exc); Cello Sonata in A minor;

2-Violin Sonata in D minor. (G. Lesne, Seminario Musicale)

① **VC5 45002-2** (9/89)
20th Century Violin Sonatas
R. Strauss: Violin Sonata; *Janáček*: Violin Sonata; *Debussy*: Violin Sonata. (D. Sitkovetsky, P. Gililov)

① **VC5 45003-2** (4/94)
Contemporary Trumpet Music
Maxwell Davies: Trumpet Sonata; *Jolivet*: Heptade; *Nyman*: Flugal and Piano; *Henze*: Trumpet Sonatina; *Berio*: Sequenza X; *Fenton*: Parts of the dance. (G. Ashton, J. Lenehan, G. Knowles)

① **VC5 45007-2** (7/94)
A Play of Passion
Anon: In Paradise; *A. Holborne*: Infernum; *Anon*: Dark is my delight; *Albarti*: Pavan and Galliard; *Anon*: What meat eats the Spaniard; *A. Holborne*: Pavan and Galliard 39/40; *Farrant*: Ah, alas, you salt-sea gods; *A. Holborne*: Pavan and Galliard 37/38; *Anon*: Come, tread the paths; *A. Ferrabosco II*: Almayne; *E. Johnson*: Eliza is the fayrest quene; *Anon*: Allemande and Galliard; *E. Johnson*: Come again; *A. Holborne*: Pavan and Galliard 41/42; *Anon*: Ah, silly poor Joas; *A. Ferrabosco II*: Pavan and Alman a 5; *Cobbold*: Ye mortal wights; *Byrd*: Fair Britain Isle; *Gibbons*: Silver swan; Pavan and Galliard a 6; What is our life?. (J. Budd, M. Chance, Fretwork)

① **VC5 45010-2** (9/94)
Mozart—Violin Concertos, Volume 1
Mozart: Violin Concerto, K207; Violin Concerto, K211; Violin Concerto, K219. (M. Huggett (vn/dir), OAE)

① **VC5 45016-2** (6/94)
Ravel—Chamber & Vocal Works
Ravel: Violin and Cello Sonata; Mallarmé Poems; Chansons madécasses; Piano Trio. (Sarah Walker, M. Crayford, C. van Kampen, Nash Ens/L. Friend)

① **VC5 45018-2** (4/94)
Debussy—Orchestral Works
Debussy: Khamma; Jeux; Printemps; Après-midi. (Finnish RSO/J-P. Saraste)

① **VC5 45023-2** (5/94)
Pärt/Tavener—Works for String Quartet
Tavener: Last Sleep of the Virgin; *Pärt*: Summa; Fratres; *Tavener*: Hidden Treasure. (Chilingirian Qt)

① **VC5 45024-2** (7/94)
Nightshade Rounds
Walton: Bagatelles; *MacCombie*: Nightshade Rounds; *Gershwin*: Preludes; *Tower*: Clocks; *Duarte*: English Suite, Op.31 (exc); *Britten*: Nocturnal. (S. Isbin)

① **VC5 45033-2** (10/94)
Barber—Vocal and Chamber Works
Barber: Dover Beach, Op.3; Serenade, Op.1; Songs, Op.2; Songs, Op.10; Songs, Op.13 (exc); Despite and Still, Op.41 (exc); Songs, Op.45; String Quartet, Op.11. (T. Allen, Endellion Qt, R. Vignoles)

① **VC5 45034-2** (10/94)
Grieg/Sibelius—Cello Works
Grieg: Cello Sonata; Intermezzo; *Sibelius*: Malinconia; Pieces, Op.78; Pieces, Op.77. (T. Mørk, J-Y. Thibaudet)

① **VC5 45035-2** (8/94)
Tavener—Thunder entered Her
Tavener: Angels; Annunciation; Lament of the Mother of God; Thunder entered Her; Hymns of Paradise; God is with us. (S. Kringelborn, W. Kendall, D. Sweeney, vn ens, I. Simcock, D. Dunnett, Winchester Cath Ch/D. Hill)

① **VC5 45036-2** (7/95)
Psalms, Vol. 2
Anon: Psalm 84; Psalm 85; Psalm 90; Psalm 91; Psalm 96; Psalm 104; Psalm 111; Psalm 114; Psalm 115; Psalm 118; Psalm 121; Psalm 122; Psalm 123; Psalm 130; Psalm 137; Psalm 139; Psalm 147; Psalm 148; Psalm 149; Psalm 150. (Westminster Abbey Ch/M. Neary, A. Lumsden)

① **VC5 45038-2** (12/94)
Bach—Cantatas
Bach: Cantata 51; Cantata 82; Cantata 199. (N. Argenta, Sonnerie Ens/M. Huggett)

① **VC5 45051-2** (4/95)
Grieg—Choral Works
Grieg: Bergliot, Op.42; Olav Trygvason; Funeral March. (L. Fjeldstad, S. Kringelborn, R. Stene, P. Vollestad, Trondheim Sym Chor, Trondheim SO/O.K. Ruud)

① **VC5 45053-2** (5/95)
Fauré/Ravel/Poulenc—Mélodies
Fauré: Songs, Op. 18 (exc); Songs, Op. 23 (exc); Songs, Op. 27 (exc); Songs, Op. 39 (exc); Songs, Op. 46 (exc); Songs, Op. 51 (exc); Songs, Op. 58; Songs, Op. 83 (exc); *Poulenc*: Travail du peintre; *Ravel*: Mélodies populaires

grecques; Don Quichotte à Dulcinée. (T. Allen, R. Vignoles)

① **VC5 45056-2** (7/95)
Weill/Hindemith/Toch—Chamber Works
Weill: Violin Concerto; *Hindemith*: Wind Septet; *Toch*: Wind and Percussion pieces. (C. Tetzlaff, Deutsche Kammerphilharmonie)

① **VC5 45059-2** (6/95)
Bach—Cantatas
Bach: Cantata 84; Cantata 202; Cantata 209. (N. Argenta, Sonnerie Ens/M. Huggett)

① **VC5 45060-2** (3/95)
Mozart—Violin Concertos, Volume 2
Mozart: Violin Concerto, K216; Violin Concerto, K218; Adagio, K261; Rondo, K269. (M. Huggett (vn/dir), OAE)

① **VC5 45061-2** (6/95)
Purcell—Choral and Chamber Works
Purcell: Te Deum and Jubilate, Z232; In Guilty Night, Z134; Pavans, Z748-51; Jehova quam multi sunt, Z135; When on my sick bed, Z144; Beati omnes, Z131; My beloved spake, Z28. (Taverner Consort, Taverner Plyrs/A. Parrott)

① **VC5 45062-2** (5/95)
Purcell—Fantasias
Purcell: Viola da gamba Fantasies, Z735-43; Viola da gamba Fantasias, Z732-4; Fantasia in A minor; Viola da gamba Fantasia, Z745; In Nomine, Z746; In Nomine, Z747. (Fretwork)

① **VC5 45066-2** (8/95)
Lescurel—Fontaine de grace
Jehannot de Lescurel: A vous douce debonnaire; Fi, mesdisans; Dame, vo regars; Bontés, sen, valours et pris; Amours, trop vous doi cherir; Bonnement m'agrée; Abundance de felonnie; Dis tans plus; Biétris est mes delis; Dame, par vo dous regart; D'amour qui n'est bien celée; Douce Amour, confortez moi; Belle, com loiaus amans; A vous douce debonnaire a 1; Bonne amour me rent; De gracieuse dame amer; Amours, que vous ai meffait; Comment que, pour l'eloignance; Amours, trop vous doi cherir; Gracieusette. (G. Binchois Ens/D. Vellard)

① **VC5 45074-2** (11/71)
Prokofiev—Violin Sonatas
Prokofiev: Violin Sonata 1; Violin Sonata 2; Melodies, Op. 35b; Sonata, Op. 115. (D. Sitkovetsky, P. Gililov)

① **VC5 45075-2** (9/95)
Charpentier—Leçons de ténèbres, Vol. 2
M-A. Charpentier: Prélude, H528; Prélude, H510; Prélude, H521; Leçon, H131; Répons, H144; Leçon, H139; Répons, H128; Leçon, H136; Répons, H129; *Anon*: Holy Week (exc); Holy Week (exc). (S. Piau, G. Lesne, I. Honeyman, P. Harvey, Seminario Musicale)

① **VC5 45076-2** (3/95)
Chopin—Piano Works
Chopin: Piano Sonata 2; Nocturnes (exc); Barcarolle; Scherzos (exc). (M. Pletnev)

① **VC5 45095-2** (11/94)
Bach—Concertos
Bach: Violin Concerto, BWV1056; Violin and Oboe Concerto, BWV1060; Violin Concerto, BWV1052; Oboe d'amore Concerto, BWV1055. (Elizabeth Wallfisch (vn/dir), A. Robson, A. Robson (ob/dir), OAE)

① **VC5 45103-2** (6/95)
Alessandro Scarlatti—Motets
A. Scarlatti: Infirmata, vulnerata; De tenebroso lacu; Salve Regina; Totus amore languens. (V. Gens, G. Lesne, Seminario Musicale)

① **VC5 45107-2** (9/95)
Charpentier—Leçons de ténèbres, Vol. 3
Anon: Holy Week (exc); Holy Week (exc); *M-A. Charpentier*: Leçon, H120; Leçon, H138; Leçon, H141; Répons, H117; Répons, H126; Répons, H131; Miserere, H173. (C. Greuillet, C. Pelon, G. Lesne, C. Purves, Seminario Musicale)

① **VC5 45121-2** (10/95)
Britten—Orchestral Works
Britten: Prelude and Fugue, Op. 29; Lachrymae; Elegy; Simple Symphony; Frank Bridge Variations. (L. A. Tomter, Norwegian CO/I. Brown)

① **VC5 45122-2** (11/95)
20th Century Violin Sonatas
Janáček: Violin Sonata; *Debussy*: Violin Sonata; *Ravel*: Violin Sonata (1923-27); *Nielsen*: Violin Sonata 2. (C. Tetzlaff, L. O. Andsnes)

① **VC5 45125-2** (9/95)
Zemlinsky—Piano Works
Zemlinsky: Ländliche Tänze; Balladen; Fantasien über

Gedichte von Richard Dehmel; Albumblatt; Skizze; Fuge in G minor. (S. Mauser)

① **VC5 45147-2** (10/95)
Lawes—Concord is Conquer'd
W. Lawes: Consort Setta a 6 in G minor; Consort Setta a 5 in A minor; Dances, VdGS421-2; Ah cruel love; Gather ye rosebuds a 1; I'm sick of love; White though eyes be; Consort Setta a 6 in C; Dances, VdGS430-2; Consort Setta a 5 in G minor; Aires, VdGS462-3; Consort Setta a 6 in B flat. (C. Bott, R. Boothby, P. Nicholson, Fretwork)

① **VC5 45159-2** (12/95)
Purcell—Come ye sons of art
Purcell: St Cecilia's Day Ode, Z339; Funeral Sentences; Birthday Ode, Z323; March and Canzona, Z860; Funeral Sentences (exc). (J.M. Ainsley, C. Daniels, E. Van Evera, T. Wilson, D. Thomas, Taverner Consort, Taverner Ch, Taverner Plyrs/A. Parrott)

① **VC5 45166-2** (5/95)
The Purcell Manuscript
Purcell: Choice Collection of Lessons (exc); Keyboard Pieces; Musick's Hand-maid, Part 2 (exc); *Gibbons*: Prelude in G; *Draghi*: Suite in A; Suite in G minor; Suite in C minor; Suite in G. (D. Moroney, D. Moroney)

① **VC7 59002-2** (10/88)
Weber—Works for Clarinet & Orchestra
Weber: Clarinet Concerto 1; Clarinet Concerto 2; Clarinet Concertino. (A. Pay (cl/dir), OAE)

① **VC7 59006-2** (5/90)
Gabrieli—A Venetian Coronation,1595
G. Gabrieli: Intonationi d'organo (exc); *A. Gabrieli*: Intonationi d'organo (exc); *G. Gabrieli*: Sacrae symphoniae (1597) (exc); Symphoniae sacrae (1597) (exc); *A. Gabrieli*: Missa (1587); O sacrum convivium; Benedictus Dominus Deus; *Bendinelli*: Sonata 333; Sarasinetta Fanfare; *Thomsen*: Toccata I. (J. O'Donnell, T. Roberts, Gabrieli Consort, Gabrieli Players/P. McCreesh)

① **VC7 59007-2** (7/91)
Picker—Orchestral Works
Picker: Old and Lost Rivers; Encantadas; Romances and Interludes; Old and Lost Rivers. (J. Gielgud, R. Atherholt, C. Eschenbach, Houston SO/C. Eschenbach)

① **VC7 59008-2** (7/91)
American Piano Sonatas
Copland: Piano Sonata; *Ives*: Three Page Sonata; *Carter*: Piano Sonata; *Barber*: Piano Sonata, Op. 26. (P. Lawson)

① **VC7 59015-2** (7/92)
Boccherini—Cello Concertos and Sonatas
Boccherini: Cello Concerto, G480; Cello Concerto, G482; Cello Sonata, G6; Cello Sonata, G2b; Cello Sonata, G5. (S. Isserlis, M. Cole, Ostrobothnian CO/J. Kangas)

① **VC7 59017-2** (8/91)
K.A.Hartmann—Piano Works
K.A. Hartmann: Piano Sonata (1945); Jazz-Toccata; Piano Sonatine; Kleine Suiten. (S. Mauser)

① **VC7 59020-2** (9/91)
Takemitsu—Miscellaneous Works
Takemitsu: Riverrun; Rain Coming; Tree Line; Water-ways; Rain Spell. (P. Crossley, London Sinfonietta/O. Knussen)

① **VC7 59021-2** (8/91)
Lawes—Five for Violls
W. Lawes: Consort Setta a 6 in F; Divisions in G minor; Consort Setta a 5 in C minor; Consort Setta a 5 in F; Airs; Consort Setta a 6 in C minor. (Fretwork, P. Nicholson)

① **VC7 59022-2** (8/91)
Smyth—Vocal and Orchestral Works
Smyth: Boatswain's Mate (exc); Mass; March of the Women. (E. Harrhy, J. Hardy, D. Dressen, J. Bohn, Plymouth Music Series Chor, Plymouth Music Series Orch/P. Brunelle)

① **VC7 59024-2** (11/91)
Works for Guitar and Orchestra
Rodrigo: Concierto de Aranjuez; Fantasía; *Vivaldi*: Concerto, RV93. (S. Isbin, Lausanne CO/L. Foster)

① **VC7 59034-2** (11/91)
Elizabethan Lute Music
Anon: Romanesca; Galliard; Ground; Lord Deliem's Lamentation; Conde Claros; Prelude; *Philips*: Pavan in G; *J. Johnson*: Delight Galliard; *Taverner*: In nomine; *P. Wilder*: Arthur's Dump; *A. Ferrabosco I*: Pavan; Galliard; Fantasia; *Danyel*: Rosa; *Cutting*: Galliard; Almain; *Robinson*: Spanish pavan; *A. Holborne*: Countess of Pembroke's Funeral; Pavan; Holy Eve; Countess of Pembroke's Paradise; *Dowland*: Almains (exc); Pavans (exc); Fantasies (exc). (C. Wilson)

Gnossiennes (exc); Ogives (exc); Descriptions automatiques (exc); Chapitres tournés en tous sens (exc); Croquis et agaceries (exc); Embryons desséchés (exc). (K.W. Paik)

Ⓒ **VJ7 59654-2** (12/91)
Fanfare for the Common Man
Carl Davis: Philharmonic Fanfare; *J. Strauss II:* Fledermaus (exc); Fledermaus Polka, Op. 362; Tik-Tak; Fledermaus Csárdás; Du und Du, Op. 367; *Brahms:* String Sextet 2 (exc); *Copland:* Fanfare for the Common Man; *Delius:* Village Romeo and Juliet (exc). (LPO/Carl Davis)

Ⓒ **VJ7 59655-2** (12/91)
French Impressions
Debussy: Petite Suite; *Fauré:* Ballade, Op. 19; Masques et bergamasques; *Ravel:* Pavane; Ma Mère l'oye (exc). (Northern Sinfonia, J-B. Pommier (pt/dir)/J-B. Pommier)

Ⓒ **VJ7 59656-2** (12/91)
Italian Baroque Concertos
Corelli: Concerti Grossi, Op. 6 (exc); *Pergolesi:* Flute Concerto in G; *Albinoni:* Adagio; Concerti, Op. 9 (exc); *Vivaldi:* Concerti grossi, Op. 3 (exc); Concerto, RV541. (J-L. Garcia, W. Bennett, N. Black, ECO, I. Watson (hpd/dir), I. Watson (org/dir), M. Eade)

Ⓒ **VJ7 59657-2** (12/91)
Mother Goose
Bizet: Symphony; *Ravel:* Ma Mère l'oye (Cpte); Pavane. (Scottish CO/J-P. Saraste)

Ⓒ **VJ7 59659-2** (12/91)
The Sorcerer's Apprentice
Dukas: Apprenti sorcier; *Debussy:* Après-midi; *Mussorgsky:* Night on the bare mountain; *Ravel:* Boléro; Ma mère l'oye (exc). (Bergen PO/D. Kitaienko)

Ⓒ **VMT7 59279-2** (10/93)
Rachmaninov—Orchestral Works
Rachmaninov: Symphony 1; Symphony 2; Symphony 3; Isle of the Dead; Vocalise; Symphonic Dances. (RPO/A. Litton)

Virgin Records

Ⓒ **CDV2774** (9/95)
Cinema Moods
Nyman: Piano (exc); *Sakamoto:* Sheltering Sky (exc); *Fenton:* Dangerous Liaisons (exc); *Morricone:* Mission (exc); *Fenton:* Shadowlands (exc); *J-C. Petit:* Jean de Florette (exc); *Robbins:* Remains of the Day (exc); *J-L. Roques:* Germinal (exc); *Yared:* Betty et Zorg (exc); *Byrne:* Last Emperor (exc); *Oldfield:* Killing Fields (exc); *Nyman:* Draughtsman's Contract (exc); *E. Bernstein:* Age of Innocence (exc); *Morricone:* Hamlet (exc); *Robbins:* Room With a View (exc); *Morricone:* Cinema Paradiso (exc); *Barber:* Adagio for Strings; *Serra:* Big Blue (exc). (OST)

Vox

Ⓒ **CDX2 5500** (11/93)
Beethoven—Piano Sonatas
Beethoven: Piano Sonata 29; Piano Sonata 30; Piano Sonata 32. (M. Horszowski)

Ⓒ **CDX2 5502** (11/93)
Cassadó performs Cello Masterpieces
Schubert: Arpeggione Sonata, D821; *Schumann:* Cello Concerto; *Tchaikovsky:* Rococo Variations; *Dvořák:* Cello Concerto; Rondo, B181; Silent Woods; *Respighi:* Adagio con variazioni. (G. Cassadó, Bamberg SO, Vienna Pro Musica Orch/J. Perlea)

Ⓒ **CDX2 5503** (11/93)
Liszt—Piano Works
Liszt: Harmonies poétiques, S154; Apparitions, S155 (exc); Harmonies poétiques, S173 (exc); Hungarian Folksongs, S245; Valse à capriccio, S401; Kleine Klavierstücke, S192; Elegie, S197; Nuages gris, S199; Lugubre gondola, S200; Ballade 2; Don Juan réminiscences, S418; Fliegende Holländer—paraphrase, S440; Midsummer Night's Dream—paraphrase, S410; Faust—paraphrase, S407. (L. Kentner)

Ⓒ **CDX2 5504** (11/93)
Bruckner/Liszt/Wagner—Orchestral Works
Liszt: Faust Symphony; *Wagner:* Faust Overture; *Bruckner:* Symphony 8. (F. Koch, South-West German Rad Chor, South-West German RSO, Vienna Pro Musica Orch/J. Horenstein)

Ⓒ **CDX2 5505** (11/93)
The Art of Ivry Gitlis
Tchaikovsky: Violin Concerto; *Mendelssohn:* Violin Concerto, Op. 64; *Bruch:* Violin Concerto 1; *Sibelius:* Violin Concerto; *Bartók:* Violin Concerto 2; Solo Violin Sonata. (I. Gitlis, Vienna Pro Musica orch/H. Swarowsky/J. Horenstein)

Ⓒ **CDX2 5506** (11/93)
György Sándor plays Bartók
Bartók: Piano Concerto 1; Piano Concerto 2; Piano Concerto 3; Rhapsody 1, Sz87; Sonata for 2 pianos and percussion; Scherzo, Op.2. (G. Sándor, R. Reinhardt, O. Schad, R. Sohm, South-West German RSO/R. Reinhardt, Vienna Pro Musica Orch/M. Gielen, Luxembourg RSO/P. Cao)

Ⓒ **115708-2** (5/93)
Mosonyi/Raff/Stavenhaegn—Piano Concertos
Raff: Piano Concerto; *Mosonyi:* Piano Concerto in E minor; *Stavenhagen:* Piano Concerto. (M. Ponti, J. Rose, R. Keller, Hamburg SO/R. Kapp, Luxembourg RSO, P. Cao, Berlin SO/J. Faerber)

Ⓒ **115709-2** (5/93)
D'Albert/Bronsart/Liszt—Piano Concertos
Liszt: Malédiction; *Albert:* Piano Concerto 2; *Bronsart:* Piano Concerto, Op.10. (M. Ponti, South-West German CO/P. Angerer, Luxembourg RSO, P. Cao, Westphalian SO/R. Kapp)

Ⓒ **115712-2** (5/93)
Hiller/Litolff/Moscheles—Piano Concertos
Moscheles: Piano Concerto, Op.60; *F. Hiller:* Piano Concerto, Op.69; *Litolff:* Concerto symphonique 3. (M. Ponti, Philh Hungarica/O. Maga, Luxembourg RSO/L. de Froment, Berlin SO/V. Schmidt-Gertenbach)

Ⓒ **115713-2** (5/93)
Mendelssohn/Reinecke/Rheinberger—Piano Concertos
Reinecke: Piano Concerto 1; *Mendelssohn:* Capriccio brillant, Op.22; *Rheinberger:* Piano Concerto. (M. Ponti, Luxembourg RSO, P. Cao, Berlin SO/V. Schmidt-Gertenbach)

Ⓒ **115714-2** (5/93)
Balakirev/Lyapunov/Medtner—Piano Concertos
Medtner: Piano Concerto 3; *Balakirev:* Piano Concerto in E flat; *Lyapunov:* Rhapsody, Op.28. (M. Ponti, Luxembourg RSO, P. Cao, Westphalian SO/S. Landau)

Ⓒ **115717-2** (5/93)
Chopin/Henselt/Hiller—Piano Concertos
Henselt: Piano Concerto; *F. Hiller:* Konzertstück, Op. 113; *Chopin:* Allegro de concert. (M. Ponti, J. Rose, Philh Hungarica/O. Maga, Luxembourg RSO, P. Cao, Berlin SO/V. Schmidt-Gertenbach)

Ⓒ **115772-2** (5/93)
Beethoven—Piano Sonatas, Vol.3
Beethoven: Piano Sonata 1; Piano Sonata 5; Piano Sonata 6; Piano Sonata 9; Piano Sonata 10; Piano Sonata 13; Piano Sonata 14; Piano Sonata 15; Piano Sonata 25. (A. Brendel)

Ⓒ **115775-2** (10/93)
Unknown String Quartets, Vol.2
A. Tcherepnin: String Quartet 2; *Bloch:* String Quartet 3; *Hindemith:* String Quartet (1945); *Korngold:* String Quartet 2; *Rózsa:* String Quartet, Op. 22; *Stravinsky:* Pieces (1914); *Surinach:* String Quartet (1975). (New World Qt)

Ⓒ **115845-2** (10/94)
Chamber Works by Women Composers
C. Schumann: Piano Trio; *Beach:* Piano Trio, Op. 150; *Tailleferre:* Violin Sonata 2; *Boulanger:* Violin Pieces (exc); *Mendelssohn-Hensel:* Piano Trio; *Carreño:* String Quartet; *Chaminade:* Piano Trio 1. (J. Roche, P. Freed, R. Zelnick, T. Strasser, C. Heller, D. Betts, Macalester Trio)

Wergo

Ⓒ **WER60054-50** (7/89)
Magnifically—the many voices of Cathy Berberian
Monteverdi: Madrigals, Bk 7 (exc); *Debussy:* Chansons de Bilitis; *Cage:* Flower; Wonderful widow of eighteen springs; *Bussotti:* Passion selon Sade (exc); *Weill:* Happy End (exc); *Lennon & McCartney:* Ticket to ride; *Gershwin:* Porgy and Bess (exc); *Berberian:* Stripsody. (C. Berberian, B. Canino, B. Canino)

Ⓒ **WER60114-50** (3/90)
Henze String Quartets
Henze: String Quartet 1; String Quartet 2; String Quartet 3; String Quartet 4; String Quartet 5. (Arditti Qt)

Ⓒ **WER60131-50** (3/89)
Ligeti—Piano Works
Ligeti: Musica Ricercata; Capriccio 1; Invention; Capriccio 2; Pieces for 2 pianos. (B. Uriarte, K-H. Mrongovius)

Ⓒ **WER60143-50** (9/89)
Françaix—Music for Wind Ensemble
Françaix: Haydn Variations; Mozart new-look; Musique pour une faire anglait; Hommage à l'ami Papageno; Quasi improvisando; Danses exotiques. (J. Françaix, Mainz Wind Ens)

Ⓒ **WER60145-50** (9/90)
Hindemith: Cello & Piano Works, Vol.2
Hindemith: Cello Sonata (1948); Leichte Stücke; Frog Variations; Kleine Sonate. (J. Berger, S. Mauser)

Ⓒ **WER60161-50** (11/89)
Ligeti: Instrumental Works
Ligeti: Continuum; Pieces, 1968; Organ Study 1; Organ Study 2; Volumina; Artikulation; Glissandi. (A. Vischer, South-West German Rad Wind Qnt, G. Ligeti, G.M. Koenig, C. Cardew, Z. Szathmáry, K-E. Welin)

Ⓒ **WER60162-50** (10/89)
Ligeti: Choral and Orchestral Works
Ligeti: Lux aeterna; Atmosphères; Chamber Concerto; Ramifications; Ramifications. (Reihe Ens/F. Cerha, South-West German RSO/E. Bour, Saarbrücken Rad CO/A. Janigro, Stuttgart Schola Cantorum/C. Gottwald)

Ⓒ **WER60172-50** (9/90)
Penderecki: Orchestral and Vocal Works
Penderecki: Capriccio (ob); Viola Concerto; Intermezzo; Antique Style pieces; Strophes. (T. Zimmermann, M. Pedziałek, O. Szwajgier, Poznan Amadeus CO/A. Duczmal)

Ⓒ **WER60179-50** (9/91)
Egk/Mozart—Wind Music
Egk: Divertissement; Zaubergeige Overture; *Mozart:* Sinfonia Concertante, K297b. (Mainz Wind Ens/K.R. Schöll)

Ⓒ **WER60183-50** (9/90)
Reimann—Vocal Works
Reimann: Kinderlieder; Louis Labé Sonnets; Nacht-Räume. (C. Schäfer, L. Himmelheber, A. Bauni, A. Reimann)

Ⓒ **WER60185-50** (10/90)
Schoenberg: Choral & Orchestral Works
Schoenberg: Orchestral Pieces, op 16; Variations, op 31; Cello Concerto; Moderner Psalm, Op. 50c. (H. Schiff, G. Reich, Bratislava Phil Ch, South-West German RSO/M. Gielen)

Ⓒ **WER60187-50** (5/90)
Hartmann: Symphonies
K.A. Hartmann: Symphony 1; Symphony 3; Symphony 2; Symphony 4; Symphony 5; Symphony 6; Symphony 7; Symphony 8; *K. A. Hartmann:* Gesangsszene zu Giraudoux' 'Sodom und Gomorrha'. (D. Soffel, BRSO/F. Rieger/F. Leitner/R. Kubelik, D. Fischer-Dieskau/Z. Macal)

Ⓒ **WER6074-2** (9/92)
Cage—Miscellaneous Works
Cage: Sonatas and Interludes (1946-48) (exc); Song Books I-II; Empty Words III; Music for Marcel Duchamp (1947). (P. Roggenkamp, Stuttgart Schola Cantorum/C. Gottwald)

Ⓒ **WER6087-2** (1/92)
Françaix plays Françaix
Françaix: 2-Piano Concerto; Plaisant variations; Portraits de jeunes filles. (J. Françaix, South-West German RSO/P. Stoll, Mainz Wind Ens/K.R. Schöll, C. Françaix)

Ⓒ **WER6168-2** (3/92)
Nancarrow—Studies for Player Piano
Nancarrow: Studies for Player Piano (exc); Studies for Player Piano (exc); Tango?. (C. Nancarrow)

Ⓒ **WER6173-2** (6/91)
T.W.Adorno—Chamber & Choral Works
Adorno: Pieces, Op.2; Short Orchestral Pieces; Däubler Gedichte; Schatz des Indianer-Joe; Kinderjahr. (Buchberger Qt, Frankfurt Op Orch/G. Bertini, Frankfurt Chbr Ch/H.M. Beuerle, M. Kiener, H. Neiser)

Ⓒ **WER6199-2** (3/92)
Messiaen—Organ Works
Messiaen: Ascension; Apparition de l'église éternelle; Banquet céleste; *Duruflé:* Suite, Op. 5. (E. Krapp)

Ⓒ **WER6203-2** (9/92)
Cage—Chamber Works
Cage: Second Construction; Imaginary Landscape 2; Amores; Double Music; Third Construction; She is Asleep; First Construction. (Hêlios Qt)

Ⓒ **WER6275-2** (8/95)
Orff—Trionfi
Orff: Carmina Burana (Cpte); Catulli Carmina (Cpte); Trionfo di Afrodite (Cpte). (L. Griffith, U. Ress, T. Mohr, Frankfurt Singakademie, Figuralchor, Goethegymnasiums Children's Ch, Frankfurt Children's Ch, Royal Flanders PO/M. Tang, T. Dewald, Frankfurt Kantorei, A. Ickstadt, E. Krämer, K. Rarichs, F. Walther-Lindqvist, Royal Flanders Phil Perc Ens/W. Schäfer, S. Roberts, Caecilia Chorale)

Woodmansterne

ⓘ **WOODM001-2** (12/91)
Born is the Babe—Renaissance Music
T. Ravenscroft: Remember, o thou man; *Byrd:* Christe qui lux es I, BE17/24; From Virgin's womb (exc); In Nomine a 4, BE17/17; *Traditional:* Born is the babe. (A. Tysall, Rose Consort)

ⓘ **WOODM002-2** (10/93)
Ah, Dear Heart
Byrd: Virginella; Though Amaryllis dance in green; Ye sacred muse; Come to me grief for ever; In fields abroad; O that most rare breast; Fantasia a 3, BE17/1; Fantasia a 3, BE17/2; In Nomine a 4, BE17/17; *Gibbons:* Madrigals, First Set (exc); Double Bass Fantasias a 4 (exc); Fantasias a 3 (exc); *A. Holborne:* Image of Melancholy; Ecce quam bonum; Pavan 'The Funerals'; Fruit of Love; Coranto 'The Fairie Round'; Various consort pieces (exc). (A. Tysall, Rose Consort)

York Ambisonic

ⓘ **CD101** (7/87)
Great Romantic Organ Music
Tournemire: Te Deum Improvisation; *Jongen:* Organ Pieces, Op. 53 (exc); *Mulet:* Esquisses byzantines (exc); *Dupré:* Preludes and Fugues, Op. 7 (exc); *R. Strauss:*

Hochzeitspräludium; *Karg-Elert:* Pastels, Op. 96 (exc); *Brahms:* Chorale Preludes, Op. 122 (exc); *Liszt:* Prelude and Fugue, S260. (J.S. Whiteley)

ⓘ **CD108** (4/91)
Organ of Canterbury Cathedral
Vierne: Suite 3 (exc); *Bach:* Schübler Chorales, BWV645-650 (exc); Chorales, BWV651-668 (exc); *Purcell:* Choice Collection of Lessons (exc); *Franck:* Pièces (1878) (exc); *Pachelbel:* Canon and Gigue (exc); *Eben:* Sunday Music (exc); *Saint-Saëns:* Fantaisie in E flat (exc); *Jongen:* Organ Pieces, Op. 53 (exc); *Mulet:* Esquisses byzantines (exc). (D. Flood)

ⓘ **CD109** (12/90)
Canterbury Carols
Traditional: O come, all ye faithful; Sussex Carol; Stille Nacht; Once in royal David's city; Ding dong merrily on high; *Rutter:* Candlelight Carol; *Traditional:* God rest you merry, gentlemen; *König:* O little town of Bethlehem; Good King Wenceslas; Little road to Bethlehem; Gaudete; In the bleak midwinter; While shepherds watched; Away in a manger; Hark the herald angels sing; *T. Dubois:* Pièces nouvelles (exc). (Canterbury Cath Ch, M. Harris/D. Flood)

ⓘ **CD110** (5/91)
Saint-Saëns—Music for organ
Saint-Saëns: Rhapsodies, Op. 7; Fantaisie, Op. 101; Préludes et fugues, Op. 109; Fantaisie in E flat; Fantaisie, Op. 157. (Margaret Phillips)

ⓘ **CD112** (3/92)
The Widor Tradition
Widor: Symphony 1 (exc); *Dupré:* Suite bretonne, Op. 21 (exc); *Langlais:* Suite française (exc); *Vierne:* Suite 2 (exc); *Litaize:* Variations sur un Noël angevin (exc); *Alain:* Janequin Variations (exc); *Litaize:* Prélude et Danse fuguée (exc). (M. Harris)

ⓘ **CD846** (12/91)
Christmas at York Minster
Traditional: We've been awhile a-wandering; Away in a manger; *Mulet:* Noël; *Traditional:* See amid the winter's snow; I saw three ships; I sing of a maiden; *Commette:* Offertoire sur des Noëls; *Traditional:* O come, o come Emmanuel; *Mathias:* Babe is born; *Ireland:* Preludes (exc); *Traditional:* Tomorrow shall be my dancing day; I sing the birth; Benedicamus Domino; *M. Praetorius:* Es ist ein Ros'; *Traditional:* Child is born in Bethlehem; O little town of Bethlehem; *Könige:* Unto us is born a son; *Vierne:* Pièces en stile libre (exc). (York Minster Ch, J.S. Whiteley)

3D Classics

ⓘ **(3DCL) 3D8012** (12/95)
York Bowen—Piano Works
Bowen: Preludes, Op. 102; Nocturne, Op. 78; Rêverie, Op. 86; Berceuse, Op. 93; Partita, Op. 156.